2025

LexisNexis®
Corporate Affiliations™

LexisNexis®

Content Operations:
Director-News & Business Content Operations & Metadata: Tammy Bair
Manager-Corporate Affiliations & Entity Management: Elizabeth A. Powers
Lead Content Analysts: Eric Eelman, Kevin Gaven

Production:
Senior Production Specialist: Joseph C. Stewart

Reed Elsevier Philippines-Corporate Affiliations Iloilo Team:
Operations Manager: Timothy J. Vilches
Operations Supervisor: Kristel Faye B. De la Cruz
Product Lead: Raquel G. Gajardo

2025

LexisNexis®
Corporate Affiliations™
U.S. Private Companies

Volume IV
A-J

LexisNexis®

QUESTIONS ABOUT THIS PUBLICATION?

For CONTENT questions concerning this publication, please call:

Content Operations Department at 800-340-3244
FAX 908-790-5405

For CUSTOMER SERVICE ASSISTANCE concerning shipments, billing or other matters, please call:
Customer Service at 800-340-3244, press 3

For SALES ASSISTANCE, please call:
The Sales Department at 800-340-3244, press 2

Library of Congress Catalog Card Number: 67-22770

U.S. Private Companies Volume 4, ISBN: 979-8-3417-0462-6

Corporate Affiliations 8-Volume Library, ISBN: 979-8-3417-0458-9

Corporate Affiliations

Content Operations
9443 Springboro Pike
Miamisburg, OH 45342

www.lexisnexis.com

ISBN 979-8-3417-0462-6

CONTENTS

CONTENTS

PREFACE

CORPORATE AFFILIATIONS

Corporate Affiliations is a logically organized business reference tool that covers major public and private businesses in the United States and throughout the world. The set consists of eight volumes:

Volume I   Master Index I
Volume II   Master Index II
Volume III   U.S. Public Companies
Volume IV   U.S. Private Companies I
Volume V   U.S. Private Companies II
Volume VI   International Public & Private Companies I
Volume VII   International Public & Private Companies II
Volume VIII   International Public & Private Companies III

The principle of organization for the set is geographical (by parent company) and hierarchical (by company reportage). Subsidiaries of a parent company, no matter where they are located, will be found in the same volume as the ultimate parent.

Please note that guidelines on the organization of the entire set for this edition can be found in the *Master Index* Volume I.

Entry criteria for the set are flexible. Generally speaking, U.S. based companies must demonstrate revenue in excess of $10 million, substantial assets, a work force in excess of 100 persons, or be traded on a major stock exchange. Non-U.S. based companies must demonstrate revenues in excess of $10 million.

THE *U.S. PRIVATE COMPANIES* VOLUME

Corporate Affiliations: U.S. Private Companies contains listings for privately held companies with U.S. located headquarters or holding companies. Subsidiaries for these parent companies are included, whether or not they are located in the United States. Also included are outside service firms attached to the parent companies. These are firms that perform specialized services such as accounting, legal, pension management, etc.

Content and Coverage in Corporate Affiliations-U.S. Private Companies

Listing statistics for this edition of U.S. Private are as follows:

Ultimate parent companies 67,177
U.S. located sub companies 32,903
Non-U.S. located sub companies 17,374
Total entry units listed 117,454

Outside service firms: 4,318

Companies are arranged alphabetically by the name of the parent company. Subsidiary companies follow the parent in order of reporting hierarchy. The bold number in parentheses shows the level of corporate reportage. Each listing can contain an extensive number of informational items. Please refer to the helpful 'How to Use' section for a guide to referencing methods and comprehensive listing samples.

The *U.S. Private* volume also contains several useful features in the frontmatter including 'New Listings' for this edition and 'Mergers and Acquisitions.'

COMPILATION

Corporate Affiliations is compiled and updated from information supplied by the companies themselves, business publications, internet research and annual reports.

RELATED SERVICES

For information on the corporateaffiliations.com web site, please call (800) 340-3244.

Mailing lists compiled from information contained in *Corporate Affiliations* may be ordered from:
R. Michael Patterson, Inside Sales Representative
DM2 Decision Maker
2000 Clearwater Drive, Oak Brook, IL
Tel: (630) 288-8348
E-mail: robert.patterson@dm2decisionmaker.com

Electronic database tapes of the directory in raw data format are available for licensing. For electronic database tapes or alliance opportunities, please contact:
LexisNexis, Corporate Affiliations
9443 Springboro Pike, Miamisburg, OH 45342
Tel: (800) 285-3947
E-mail: information@lexisnexis.com

Companies who wish to add or correct their listings can send information to:
LexisNexis, Corporate Affiliations Content Operations
9443 Springboro Pike
Miamisburg, OH 45342
Tel: (937) 865-6800

In addition to keeping the information in our directories as up to date as possible, we are constantly trying to improve their design, and add useful new features. Any comments or suggestions in this regard can be directed to the Managers of Operations at the above address.

HOW TO USE CORPORATE AFFILIATIONS: *U.S. PRIVATE COMPANIES*

Corporate Affiliations, *U.S. Private Companies*, contains a vast amount of useful information about firms that are not generally in the public eye. Included in *U.S. Private* are privately owned parent companies located in the United States.

This user guide is divided into three parts.

— **Part A**, 'How to Locate a Company' gives referencing instructions and samples of indexes. It demonstrates many useful methods for getting the information you need from this volume and from the *Corporate Affiliations* set at large.

— **Part B**, 'Sample Entries' shows the various data elements and listing style of companies in *Corporate Affiliations*.

— **Part C**, 'Understanding Levels of Reportage' demonstrates how company reportage structures are simply and clearly presented throughout *Corporate Affiliations*.

PART A: HOW TO LOCATE A COMPANY

1.   If you know the name of the company, but do not know its nationality or ownership status:

Look in the 'Master Index of Company Names' in volume I. This index will direct you to the correct volume of the set (i.e. Public, Private or International) and the correct page listing therein.

> **KOMAG, INCORPORATED**; *U.S. Public*, pg. 1023
> KOMAG MATERIAL TECHNOLOGY INC.—See
>   Komag, Incorporated; *U.S. Public*, pg. 1023
> KOMAGANE ELECTRONICS, INC.—See Kenwood
>   Corporation; *Int'l*, pg. 638

2.   If you know the company is a privately held parent company:

You can turn directly to the company listings in volumes IV and V, all of which are alphabetized by the name of the parent company.

3. If you cannot find the company's name in the master index:

It may mean that the company has been acquired or changed its name. To confirm this, try looking in the 'Mergers and Acquisitions' section at the front of this volume.

Sample of Mergers and Acquisitions Section

Alloway Industries–acquired by Code, Hennessy & Simmons, Inc.
Alpha Wire Company–acquired by Belden Inc.
Ambassador Steel Co.–ceased operations (no longer in business)

4. To locate companies in a given line of business:

Use the N.A.I.C.S. (North American Industrial Classification System) Master Index in volume II. This index interfiles data from all six volumes of *Corporate Affiliations*, arranging companies by particular products and services according to their primary N.A.I.C.S. code. The index is preceded by two helpful compendia: one sorts the codes alphabetically by the name of the product or service, the other numerically by the code itself.

Sample of Alpha Compendium of N.A.I.C.S. Codes

Description	*N.A.I.C.S.*
Administration of Conservation Programs	924120
Administration of Education Programs	923110

Sample of Numeric Compendium of N.A.I.C.S. Codes

Code	*Description*
523120	**SECURITIES BROKERAGE**
523210	Securities and Commodity Exchanges
523910	Miscellaneous Intermediation

Both parent and sub companies are covered in this index; parent companies are printed in bold type, sub companies in regular typeface followed by the name of its ultimate parent. A sample of the N.A.I.C.S. Master Index is shown here:

337211 — WOOD OFFICE FURNITURE MANUFACTURING

ABCO—Jami, Inc.; *Int'l*, pg. 586
ANDERSON HICKEY, INC.—Haworth, Inc.; *U.S. Public*, pg. 516
BELVEDERE COMPANY—Smith Investment Company; *Int'l*, pg. 1019
BRAYTON INTERNATIONAL INC.—Steelcase Inc.; *U.S. Public*, pg. 1048
BRODART COMPANY; *U.S. Private*, pg. 172
COMMUNITY—Jasper Seating Co., Inc.; *U.S. Private*, pg. 589
CRAMER INC.; *U.S. Public*, pg. 288
EAC CORPORATION; *Int'l*, pg. 357

PART B: BASIC COMPONENTS OF A PRIVATE COMPANY LISTING

Following is an example of a typical parent company listing with tags to some of its basic components.

SOUTHWEST PASSAGES, INC. —————————— Company Name
528 S Sandia Dr —————————————— Company Address
Denver, CO 86052
Tel: (303) 555-2156 ——————— **DE** ——— Telecommunications Data & State of Incorporation
Web Site: www.spi.com ——————————— Electronic Address
Year Founded: 1965
Assets: $18,000,000 ————————————— Financial Data
Liabilities: $10,000,000
Net Worth: $8,000,000
Earnings: $2,500,000
Emp.: 398 ——————————————————— Number of Employees; Including Subsidiaries
Fiscal Year End: 12/31/24
Retail Book Stores
N.A.I.C.S.: 424920 —————————————— North American Industry Classification
No. of U.S. Offices: 8   System Code
No. of Foreign Offices: 3
Nelly LaGuardia (*Pres*)
John Davidson (*COO*)
Gregory James (*CFO & VP-Fin*)

Following each parent company listing are the entries for each of that company's divisions, subsidiaries, affiliates, joint ventures, units, etc. Though companies vary widely in their usage of these terms, some of the more common company designations can be defined as follows:

Affiliate   A chartered business owned by the company at less than 50%.

Division   An internal unit of a company, not incorporated.

Joint Venture   A business in which two or more companies share responsibility and ownership.

Subsidiary   A chartered business owned by the company at 50% or more.

PART C: UNDERSTANDING LEVELS OF REPORTAGE

Each sub-unit of the company will have a number in parentheses to the right of the company name. This number represents the level of reportage for that particular company. Any company with a level (1) reports directly to the parent company. Level (2) companies report to the level (1) company immediately above them. Level (3) companies report to the level (2) company immediately above them, etc.

In the example below, Maine Passages, Mass Books, and Western Passages all report directly to the parent company, Southwest Passages, Inc. R.I. Books is a subsidiary of, and reports directly to, Mass Books, and B.C. Books Etc. is a subsidiary of, and reports directly to, R.I. Books.

Subsidiaries:

Maine Passages ———————— (1) ———————— **Reports to the Parent Company**
US 1 RR 32   **(Southwest Passages, Inc. from**
Bangor, ME 04402 ———————— ME ———————— **previous example)**
Tel: (207) 555-1235   (70%) ———————— **Percentage of Ownership**
Sales Range: $20-24.9 Million
Emp: 7
Mail Order Books
N.A.I.C.S.: 454113
Kurt King, Jr. (*CEO*)

Mass Books   (1) ———————— **Reports Direct to the**
1 Olympia Dr   **Parent Company**
Boston, MA 02101   MA ———————— **State of Incorporation**
Tel: (508) 555-1011
Retail Book Stores
N.A.I.C.S.: 424920
Dan Lagattuta (*Pres*)

Subsidiary:

R.I. Books ———————— (2) ———————— **Reports Direct to Level 1**
100 W 57th St   **Company Above (Mass Books)**
Newport, RI 06001   CT
Tel: (401) 555-4000
Retail Book Stores
N.A.I.C.S.: 424920
Craig Russell (*Pres*)

BC Books Etc. —————— (3) —————— **Non-U.S. Based Holding that Reports**
2 Victoria Avenue **Direct to the Level 2 Company on**
Vancouver, BC, L5T 2N5, Canada **Bottom of Previous Page (R.I. Books)**
Tel: (604) 555-8912
Emp.: 11
Retail Book Stores
N.A.I.C.S.: 424920
Jeffery Gilbert *(Pres)*

Western Passages —————— (1) —————— **Reports to Parent Company**
1200 Agua Fria Blvd **(Southwest Passages, Inc.)**
Santa Fe, NM 87501
Tel.: (505) 555-7373
Emp.: 46
Retail Book Stores
N.A.I.C.S.: 424920
Laura Maggio *(CEO)*

In addition to keeping the information in our directories as up-to-date as possible, we are constantly trying to improve their design and organization, and to add useful new features. Any comments or suggestions in this regard can be directed to: The LexisNexis Group, Corporate Affiliations Content Operations, 630 Central Avenue, New Providence, NJ 07974.

ABBREVIATIONS

Acct	Account	Matl	Material
Acctg	Accounting	Matls	Materials
Accts	Accounts	Mdse	Merchandise
Acq	Acquisition(s)	Mdsg	Merchandising
Admin	Administration	Mfg	Manufacturing
Admin	Administrative	Mfr	Manufacturer
Adv	Advertising	Mgmt	Management
Assoc	Associate	Mgr	Manager
Asst	Assistant	Mktg	Marketing
Brdcst	Broadcast	Mng	Managing
Bus	Business	Natl	National
CEO	Chief Executive Officer	Ops	Operations
CFO	Chief Financial Officer	Org	Organization
Chm	Chairman of the Board	Pkg	Packaging
CIO	Chief Information Officer	Plng	Planning
CMO	Chief Marketing Officer	Pres	President
Comm	Communication(s)	Prof	Professional
Comml	Commercial	Promo	Promotion
COO	Chief Operating Officer	Promos	Promotions
Coord	Coordinator	Pub	Public
Corp	Corporate/Corporation	Pub Rel	Public Relations
CTO	Chief Technology Officer	Publ	Publishing
Dept	Department	Publr	Publisher
Dev	Development	Pur	Purchasing
Dir	Director	R&D	Research & Development
Distr	Distribution	Reg	Regional
Div	Division	Rep	Representative
DP	Data Processing	Res	Research
Engr	Engineer	Sec	Secretary
Engrg	Engineering	Sls	Sales
Environ	Environmental	Sr	Senior
Exec	Executive	Supvr	Supervisor
Fin	Finance/Financial	Svc	Service
Gen	General	Svcs	Services
Govt	Government	Sys	Systems
Grp	Group	Tech	Technology
HR	Human Resources	Tech	Technical
Indus	Industry/Industrial	Telecom	Telecommunication(s)
Info	Information	Treas	Treasurer
Intl	International	Trng	Training
IR	Investor Relations	Vice Chm	Vice Chairman
IT	Information Technology	VP	Vice President
Jr	Junior		

COMPANY DESIGNATIONS

The following designations indicate the forms of business enterprise in various countries; these forms usually represent the organizations for large enterprises.

AB	Aktiebolag	Finland, Sweden
AG	Aktiengesellschaft	Austria, Germany, Switzerland, Liechtenstein
A/S	Aksjeselskap	Norway
	Aktieselskab	Denmark
B.V.	Besloten Vennootschap	Holland
C.V.	Commanditaire Vennootschap	Holland
Cie.	Compagnie	France, Luxembourg
Co.	Company	United States, France, South Africa, Luxembourg
Ets.	Etablissement(s)	France, Luxembourg
GmbH	Gesellschaft mit beschrankter Haftung	Austria, Germany, Switzerland
I/S	Interessantelskap	Denmark, Norway
KG	Kommanditgesellschaft	Austria, Germany, Switzerland
KK	Kabushiki Kaisha	Japan
K/S	Kommanditselskab	Denmark
Lda.	Limitada	Portugal
Ltd.	Limited	United Kingdom, United States, South Africa
Ltda.	Limitada	Brazil, Portugal
Ltee.	Limitee	Canada
Mij.	Maatschappij	Holland
N.V.	Naamloze Vennootschap	Belgium, Holland
OHG	Offene Handelsgesellschaft	Austria
Oy	Osakeyhtiot	Finland
PLC	Public Limited Company	United Kingdom
P.T.	Perusahaan Terbatas	Indonesia
Pte.	Private	Singapore
Pty.	Proprietary	Australia, South Africa
Pvt.	Private	India, Rhodesia
S.A.	Societe Anonyme	Belgium, France, Luxembourg, Switzerland
Sociedad	Anonima	Spain, Latin America
S.A.C.I.	Sociedad Anonima Comercial e Industrial	Latin America
S.A. de C.V.	Sociedad Anonima de Capital Variable	Mexico
S.A.E.	Sociedad Anonima Espanola	Spain
S.A.I.C.	Sociedad Anonima Industrial y Comercial	Latin America
S.A.R.L.	Sociedad Anonima de Responsabilidade Limitada	Brazil
	Sociedade a Responsabilitie Limitee	France, Luxembourg
S.A.S.	Societa in Accomandita Semplice	Italy
S.C.	Societe en Commandite	France
S.p.A.	Societa per Azioni	Italy
S.P.R.L.	Societe de Personnes a Responsabilitie Limitee	Belgium
S.R.L.	Societa a Responsabilita Limitata	Italy
Sdn. Bhd.	Sendirian Berhad	Malaysia
Ste.	Societe	France, Switzerland
Ste. Cve.	Societe Cooperative	Belgium
V.o.F.	Vennootschap onder firma	Holland

NEW LISTINGS 2025
Appearing for the first time in this publication

2

26NORTH BDC, INC.; NEW YORK, NY

A

AFM CAPITAL PARTNERS, INC.; INDIANAPOLIS, IN

AGITAL HOLDINGS, LLC; BURLINGTON, MA

AGNO PHARMA; NEW YORK, NY

ALGER ASSOCIATES, INC.; NEW YORK, NY

APEX SERVICE PARTNERS LLC; TAMPA, FL

APG POLYTECH, LLC; APPLE GROVE, WV

APOLLO REALTY INCOME SOLUTIONS, INC.; NEW YORK, NY

APPLIED VALUE LLC; ANDOVER,MD

ARBOL INC.; NEW YORK, NY

ARMADA GROUP, LTD.; PITTSBURGH, PA

ARMADA MATERIALS, LLC; TAMPA, FL

ASC GLOBAL INC.; BRADENTON, FL

ASCEND PLASTIC SURGERY PARTNERS; ATLANTA, GA

ASCENSION ST JOHN FOUNDATION; TULSA, OK

ATSIGN, INC.; SAN JOSE, CA

AUA PRIVATE EQUITY PARTNERS LLC; WEST PALM BEACH, FL

AUSTERLITZ ACQUISITION CORP I; LAS VEGAS, NV

AVION SOLUTIONS, INC.; HUNTSVILLE, AL

B

B&M INDUSTRIAL, INC.; EL PASO, TX

BANSK GROUP LLC; NEW YORK, NY

BARINGS PRIVATE CREDIT CORPORATION; CHARLOTTE, NC

BAY RIDGE PREP; BROOKLYN, NY

BEACON CREDIT UNION; WABASH, IN

BEAN'S BEST LLC; ANN ARBOR, MI

BENDITO RESOURCES INC.; RENO, NV

BHARCAP PARTNERS, LLC; GREENWICH, CT

BIG TREE GROUP, INC.; ROSEVILLE, MI

BINDTECH LLC; NASHVILLE, TN

BIOME MAKERS INC.; DAVIS, CA

BIP VENTURES EVERGREEN BDC; ATLANTA, GA

BLOOM EQUITY PARTNERS MANAGEMENT, LLC; NEW YORK, NY

BLOOM HOLDCO LLC; MIAMI, FL

BLOOMERANG, LLC; INDIANAPOLIS, IN

BLUE CHIP CAPITAL GROUP, INC.; BEVERLY HILLS, CA

BLUE DELTA CAPITAL PARTNERS LLC; MCLEAN, VA

BLUE WATER SHIELD LLC; HOLLYWOOD, CA

BODINE AND COMPANY, LLC; POLAND, OH

BP ENERGY PARTNERS, LLC; DALLAS, TX

BRADDOCKMATTHEWSBARRETT, LLC; NEW YORK, NY

BRAEMONT CAPITAL MANAGEMENT LLC; DALLAS, TX

BRIGHT SHEET METAL COMPANY, INC.; INDIANAPOLIS, IN

BRIGHTWORKS SUSTAINABILITY LLC; PORTLAND, OR

BROADVIEW GROUP HOLDINGS, LLC; ST. LOUIS, MO

C

C2DESIGN; CLEVELAND, OH

CACTUS COMMUNICATIONS, INC.; PRINCETON, NJ

CALIFORNIA NURSES ASSOCIATION; OAKLAND, CA

CALLAWAY CAPITAL MANAGEMENT, LLC; NASHVILLE, TN

CAPITAL MACHINE TECHNOLOGIES, INC.; TAMPA, FL

CAPITAL ONE AUTO RECEIVABLES LLC; MCLEAN, VA

CAPITAL PARTNERS LLC; EDINA, MN

CAPITAL RIVERS COMMERCIAL LLC; SACRAMENTO, CA

CES POWER LLC; MEMPHIS, TN

CHAYAH CONSULTING GROUP LLC; LOVELAND, CO

CHRISTIAN HOSPITAL FOUNDATION; SAINT LOUIS, MO

CITICORP TRUST SOUTH DAKOTA; SIOUX FALLS, SD

CONTAINER SERVICES LLC; CHICAGO, IL

CORK DISTRIBUTORS, LLC; LAS VEGAS, NV

CORPORATE PROPERTY ASSOCIATES 18 GLOBAL INC; NEW YORK, NY

CORROHEALTH, INC.; PLANO, TX

CREDITECH, INC.; BANGOR, ME

CRESCENT PRIVATE CREDIT INCOME CORP.; LOS ANGELES, CA

CROWE LLP; CHICAGO, IL

CRUX CAPITAL LTD; DALLAS, TX

CURATORS OF THE UNIVERSITY OF MISSOURI; COLUMBIA, MO

D

DARK HORSE CONSULTING; WALNUT CREEK, CA

DELCAM HOLDINGS, LLC; HOPEDALE, MA

DEMAND SCIENCE GROUP, LLC; DANVERS, MA

DERMTECH, LLC; SAN DIEGO, CA

DINI SPHERIS; HOUSTON, TX

DIRECT EDGE CAMPAIGNS, LLC; NASHVILLE, TN

DOMINION EQUITY LLC; CHICAGO, IL

DRY FLY CAPITAL LLC; LITTLETON, CO

DUNAWAY ASSOCIATES, LLC; FORT WORTH, TX

E

EBC HR & PAYROLL SOLUTIONS, INC.; BUFFALO, NY

EBERLESTOCK USA LLC; BOISE, ID

ELEMENTS HEALTH INVESTORS, LLC; NEW YORK, NY

ELEVATE ORAL CARE, LLC; WEST PALM BEACH, FL

EMED, LLC; MIAMI, FL

EMPEOPLE CREDIT UNION; MOLINE, IL

ENGINEERS WITHOUT BORDERS-USA, INC.; DENVER, CO

ENKO CHEM, INC.; MYSTIC, CT

ENVIROTROL PEST MANAGEMENT SYSTEMS INC.; GRAND PRAIRIE, TX

ERGO-FLEX TECHNOLOGIES, LLC; CONROE, TX

EVANGELICAL LUTHERAN CHURCH IN AMERICA; CHICAGO, IL

F

F&I SENTINEL, LLC; TALLAHASSEE, FL

FACTOR 89 PARTNERS, LLC; CHICAGO, IL

FIDELITY PRIVATE CREDIT COMPANY LLC; BOSTON, MA

FIRELIGHT CAPITAL PARTNERS LLC; FORT LAUDERDALE, FL

FLAG PUBLICATION, INC; OCEAN CITY, MD

FLAGLER BANCSHARES CORPORATION; NORTH PALM BEACH, FL

FLEET TEAM, INC.; INDEPENDENCE, OH

FOREST ROAD SECURITIES, LLC; SANTA MONICA, CA

G

GELLERT GLOBAL GROUP; ELIZABETH, NJ

GEORGE WASHINGTON'S MOUNT VERNON; MOUNT VERNON, VA

GLOBAL REDEMPTION INC.; LANCASTER, PA

GMSS HOLDINGS, LLC; WOBURN, MA

GOLDMAN SACHS PRIVATE CREDIT CORP.; NEW YORK, NY

GOLUB CAPITAL DIRECT LENDING UNLEVERED CORPORATION; NEW YORK, NY

GORHAM BANCORP, MHC; GORHAM, ME

GRADE EIGHT CORP; PLANO, TX

GRANITE BANK; COLD SPRING, MN

GREENOAKS CAPITAL PARTNERS LLC; SAN FRANCISCO, CA

GUARDIAR USA LLC; ENNIS, TX

GUTTMAN HOLDINGS, INC.; BELLE VERNON, PA

H

HALFF ASSOCIATES, INC.; RICHARDSON, TX

HEARTLAND DERMATOLOGY AND SKIN CANCER CENTER, P.A.; SALINA, KS

HIRSCHBACH MOTOR LINES, INC.; DUBUQUE, IA

HOAG HOSPITAL FOUNDATION; NEWPORT BEACH, CA

HOLLEWAY CAPITAL PARTNERS LLC; SAINT LOUIS, MO

HOOD CONTAINER CORPORATION; ATLANTA, GA

HOSPECO BRANDS GROUP; CLEVELAND, OH

I

ICONECTIV, LLC; BRIDGEWATER, NJ

ILION CAPITAL PARTNERS; NEW YORK, NY

ILLUMINATE OPERATIONS LLC; HERNDON, VA

INCODE TECHNOLOGIES, INC.; SAN FRANCISCO, CA

INDIVIDUAL CENTRICITY CORPORATION; SAN RAMON, CA

INFINITY HOME SERVICES; BROOKFIELD, WI

INOVA HEALTH SYSTEM FOUNDATION; FAIRFAX, VA

INTELETRAVEL.COM; DELRAY BEACH, CA

INTERNATIONAL BROTHERHOOD OF TEAMSTERS; WASHINGTON, DC

INTERNATIONAL UNION OF PAINTERS AND ALLIED TRADES; HANOVER, MD

INTERPLAY LEARNING INC.; AUSTIN, TX

IUPAT DISTRICT COUNCIL 21; PHILADELPHIA, PA

IUPAT DISTRICT COUNCIL 9; NEW YORK, NY

J

J RUSSELL & ASSOCIATES LLC; ATHENS, GA

JACMEL GROWTH PARTNERS MANAGEMENT LLC; NEW YORK, NY

JADE STEEL GROUP, LTD.; BEDFORD HEIGHTS, OH

JETS MRO, LLC; DALLAS, TX

JHM FINANCIAL GROUP, LLC; STAMFORD, CT

JOAN PEARCE RESEARCH ASSOCIATES; LOS ANGELES, CA

JUST PLAY PRODUCTS, LLC; BOCA RATON, FL

K

KAYNE DL 2021, INC.; HOUSTON, TX

KFM ENTERPRISES, LLC; TULSA, OK

KIMMERIDGE ENERGY MANAGEMENT COMPANY, LLC; NEW YORK, NY

KIND, INC.; WASHINGTON, DC

KKR PRIVATE EQUITY CONGLOMERATE LLC; NEW YORK, NY

L

LARKIN INGRASSIA, PLLC; NEWBURGH, NY

LARRY MATHIS FINANCIAL PLANNING, LLC; PHOENIX, AZ

LEGACY COMMUNITY HEALTH; HOUSTON, TX

LEPERCQ, DE NEUFLIZE & CO. INC; NEW YORK, NY

LEXAGENE HOLDINGS INC.; BEVERLY, MA

LGAM PRIVATE CREDIT LLC; NEW YORK, NY

LIBERTY 77 CAPITAL, L.P.; WASHINGTON, DC

LIUNA MIDWEST REGION; SPRINGFIELD, IL

LOS ANGELES PUBLIC LIBRARY DOCENTS; LOS ANGELES, CA

LOTUS INFRASTRUCTURE PARTNERS LLC; GREENWICH, CT

LOWER HOLDING COMPANY; COLUMBIA, MD

LUCERNE CAPITAL MANAGEMENT, LP.; GREENWICH, CT

M

MAINE COMMUNITY BANCORP, MHC; WESTBROOK, ME

MALLOY AUTOMOTIVE OF WINCHESTER LLC; ALEXANDRIA, VA

MAPR.AGENCY, INC.; BOULDER, CO

MARCUM WEALTH LLC; CLEVELAND, OH

MARILLAC ST. VINCENT FAMILY SERVICES; CHICAGO, IL

MARKQUART INC.; CHIPPEWA FALLS, WI

MASS GENERAL BRIGHAM INCORPORATED; BOSTON, MA

MATTHEWS REAL ESTATE INVESTMENT SERVICES; NASHVILLE, TN

MAURY, DONNELLY & PARR, INC.; BALTIMORE, MD

MAVIK CAPITAL MANAGEMENT, LP; NEW YORK, NY

MAX SOLUTIONS INC.; BRISTOL, CT

MBE CPAS LLP; BARABOO, WI

MD ESTHETICS, LLC; WINDHAM, NH

METEORA CAPITAL LLC; BOCA RATON, FL

METHODIST HOSPITAL FOUNDATION; OMAHA, NE

MHR MANAGEMENT LLC; PORTLAND, ME

MIDWEST BANCORPORATION, INC.; EDEN PRAIRIE, MN

MISSION CRITICAL GROUP; SPICEWOOD, TX

MOCKLER BEVERAGE CO. LP; BATON ROUGE, LA

MODE GLOBAL, LLC; DALLAS, TX

MODIGENT LLC; PHOENIX, AZ

MON SPACE NET INC.; LAS VEGAS, NV

MORRIS COUNTY LIBRARY; WHIPPANY, NJ

MOUNT NITTANY MEDICAL CENTER; STATE COLLEGE, PA

MUNA FEDERAL CREDIT UNION; MERIDIAN, MS

MUSEUM OF NEW MEXICO FOUNDATION; SANTA FE, NM

MUSICTODAY II, LLC; CROZET, VA

MUTUAL BANCORP; HYANNIS, MA

MUTUAL CAPITAL GROUP, INC.; WYALUSING, PA

MYONEX, LLC; HORSHAM, PA

N

NATIONAL FFA FOUNDATION; INDIANAPOLIS, IN

NEW RITE AID, LLC; PHILADELPHIA, PA

NEXT LEVEL BURGER COMPANY, INC.; BEND, OR

NEXTTRIP HOLDINGS, INC.; SUNRISE, FL

NORTH ATLANTIC STATES REGIONAL COUNCIL OF CARPENTERS; BOSTON, MA

NORTH BAY JOBS WITH JUSTICE; SANTA ROSA, CA

NORTH HAVEN PRIVATE INCOME FUND LLC; NEW YORK, NY

NORTH TEXAS FOOD BANK; PLANO, TX

NORTHEAST GROCERY, INC.; SCHENECTADY, NY

NXTLVL MARINE, LLC; AUSTIN, TX

O

O'DONNELL'S TERMITE & PEST CONTROL, INC.; QUINCY, MA

OAKTREE GARDENS OLP, LLC; LOS ANGELES, CA

OBRA CAPITAL, INC.; AUSTIN, TX

ONEMAIN FINANCE CORPORATION; EVANSVILLE, IN

ORCUS TECHNOLOGIES, INC; LUBBOCK, TX

OUTSIDE INTERACTIVE, INC.; BOULDER, CO

P

PALMER JOHNSON ENTERPRISES, INC.; MADISON, WI

PARADIGM CAPITAL PARTNERS; LOS ANGELES, CA

PARIC HOLDINGS, INC.; SAINT LOUIS, MO

PARMAN HOLDING CORPORATION; NASHVILLE, TN

PATHOS AI, INC.; CHICAGO, IL

PCB FINANCLAL, INC; COSTA MESA, CA

PEACH STATE FEDERAL CREDIT UNION.; LAWRENCEVILLE, GA

PERIGON WEALTH MANAGEMENT LLC; SAN FRANCISCO, CA

PERSHING SQUARE SPARC HOLDINGS, LTD.; NEW YORK, NY

PHOENIX CHILDREN'S FOUNDATION; PHOENIX, AZ

PIEZO MOTION CORP.; SARASOTA, FL

PKDW EQUITY PARTNERS, LLC; PITTSBURGH, PA

POLYVENTIVE LLC; CALHOUN, GA

POPS MART FUELS, LLC; COLUMBIA, SC

PRAGER UNIVERSITY FOUNDATION; SHERMAN OAKS, CA

PRESBYTERIAN HEALTHCARE FOUNDATION; ALBUQUERQUE, NM

PSG EQUITY L.L.C.; BOSTON, MA

PULASKI-WHITE RURAL TELEPHONE COOPERATIVE, INC.; BUFFALO, NY

Q

QUAD VIDEO HOLDINGS CORPORATION; HOUSTON, TX

QUANTUM CAPITAL GROUP LLC; HOUSTON, TX

R

RAINFOREST DISTRIBUTION CORP; BAYONNE, NJ

REDYREF INTERACTIVE KIOSKS; RIVERDALE, CA

REEDER-TRAUSCH MARINE; ROCKVILLE, MD

RESULTSCX; FORT LAUDERDALE, FL

REVOLENT CAPITAL SOLUTIONS; TAMPA, FL

RIVAL HOLDINGS, LLC.; FORT WAYNE, IN

RIVER FALLS MUTUAL INSURANCE COMPANY; RIVER FALLS, WI

ROCK SOLID UK LTD.; BENTONVILLE, AR

ROOTS EQUITY GROUP LLC; BEVERLY HILLS, CA

S

SAG-AFTRA HEALTH PLAN; BURBANK, CA

SAINT JAMES HOLDING & INVESTMENT COMPANY TRUST; DOVER, NJ

SALLYPORT COMMERCIAL FINANCE, LLC; SUGAR LAND, TX

SALT BLOCKCHAIN INC.; DENVER, CO

SANDERSON BELLECCI, INC.; CONCORD, CA

SCIENS CAPITAL MANAGEMENT LLC; NEW YORK, NY

SECURITY STATE CORPORATION; CENTRALIA, WA

SEMAFOR, INC.; NEW YORK, NY

SENDAYCO, LLC; DAYTON, OH

SENIOR CREDIT INVESTMENTS, LLC; NEW YORK, NY

SG ENTERPRISES II, LLC; BELLEVUE, WA

SIXTH STREET LENDING PARTNERS; DALLAS, TX

SKAN, INC.; MENLO PARK, CA

SMK IMAGING, LLC; ELMSFORD, NY

SOCIAL CAPITAL HEDOSOPHIA HOLDINGS CORP. IV; MENLO PARK, CA

SOCIETY BRANDS, INC.; CANTON, OH

SOUTHEAST ALASKA REGIONAL HEALTH CONSORTIUM; JUNEAU, AK

STIRLING HOTELS & RESORTS, INC.; DALLAS, TX

STO BUILDING GROUP INC.; NEW YORK, NY

STONE POINTE, LLC; NAPERVILLE, IL

STRATEGIC GOVERNMENT RESOURCES INC.; KELLER, TX

STRUCTURA, INC.; BETHESDA, MD

SUBSPLIT SERVICES GROUP, L.P.; MEMPHIS, TN

SUN POWERSPORTS INVESTMENTS, LLC; DENVER, CO

SURGE VENTURES, LLC; MENLO PARK, CA

SURVEYING AND MAPPING, LLC; AUSTIN, TX

SWELL ENERGY INC; SANTA MONICA, CA

SYNAGEX, INC; PITTSFIELD, MA

SYSTM BRANDS, LLC; NEWPORT BEACH, CA

T

TAYLOR ENERGY, LLC; WINDSOR, CT

TEAM SOLUTIONS GROUP, INC.; VAN NUYS, CA

THE BLACK PHOENIX GROUP; CHICAGO, IL

THE CHILDREN'S HOSPITAL OF PHILADELPHIA FOUNDATION; PHILADELPHIA, PA

THE CHOSEN, INC.; HURRICANE, UT

THE INTERNATIONAL SPY MUSEUM; WASHINGTON, DC

THE KENT COMPANIES; MIDLAND, TX

THE LONGHORN COUNCIL, BOY SCOUTS OF AMERICA; HURST, TX

THE METROHEALTH FOUNDATION, INC.; CLEVELAND, OH

THE STEVENS & LEE COMPANIES, LLC; READING, PA

THE UNITED SERVICE ORGANIZATIONS, INC.; WASHINGTON, DC

THOMPSON DISTRIBUTION, LLC; NASHVILLE, TN

TIMONEER STRATEGIC PARTNERS, LLC; NEWPORT BEACH, CA

TOTAL LENDER SOLUTIONS, INC.; SAN DIEGO, CA

TRANSTEX LLC; INDIANAPOLIS, IN

TREND HEALTH PARTNERS LLC; HUNT VALLEY, MD

TROUT UNLIMITED INC.; ARLINGTON, VA

TROUTMAN PEPPER HAMILTON SANDERS LLP; ATLANTA, GA

TTCP MANAGEMENT SERVICES, LLC.; BLOOMINGTON, IN

TXEX ENERGY INVESTMENTS, LLC; HOUSTON, TX

U

UC SAN DIEGO HEALTH; SAN DIEGO, CA

UCI HEALTH; ORANGE, CA

UHY LLP; ALBANY, NY

UKG INC.; WESTON, FL

UNICOIN INC.; NEW YORK, NY

UNITED FOR RESPECT EDUCATION FUND; SACRAMENTO, CA

V

VANGEO TECHNOLOGY GROUP, LLC; SCOTTSDALE, AZ

VARAGON CAPITAL CORPORATION; NEW YORK, NY

VEGAS BRAZIL LLC; LAS VEGAS, NV

VERSE INNOVATION PRIVATE LIMITED; KARNATAKA, IN

VILLAGE HEALTH WORKS; NEW YORK, NY

VIRGIN ORBIT HOLDINGS, INC.; LONG BEACH, CA

VIRGINIA LEAGUE FOR PLANNED PARENTHOOD INC.; RICHMOND, VA

VISTA CREDIT STRATEGIC LENDING CORP.; NEW YORK, NY

VIVENT HEALTH, INC.; MILWAUKEE, WI

VOYAGER INTERESTS, LLC; HOUSTON, TX

W

WALLEYE CAPITAL, LLC; NEW YORK, NY

WAYNE-SANDERSON FARMS; OAKWOOD, CA

WEILL CORNELL MEDICINE; NEW YORK, NY

WEST MAUI CONSTRUCTION, INC.; KAHULUI, HI

WHANAU INTERESTS LLC.; AUSTIN, TX

WILLIAM MACKLOWE COMPANY LLC; NEW YORK, NY

WINDY CITY NOVELTIES, INC.; VERNON HILLS, IL

WOODSON EQUITY LLC; CHICAGO, IL

WORKERS UNITED; PHILADELPHIA, PA

Y

YOUNG & ASSOCIATES; NASHVILLE, TN

Mergers and Acquisitions
January 2024—December 2024
(Parent Companies Only)

Applied Felts, Inc.—acquired by Vortex Company, LLC

Applied Thermal Systems—acquired by Gryphon Investors, LLC

Aqua Blasting Corp.—acquired by Battle Investment Group LLC

Arbor-Nomics Turf, Inc.—acquired by Senske Lawn & Tree Care, Inc.

Archerpoint, L.L.C.—acquired by Cherry Bekaert LLP

Arcoplast Inc.—acquired by Germfree Laboratories Inc.

Arnott, Inc.—acquired by MidOcean Partners, LLP

Ascend Clinical LLC—acquired by Eurofins Scientific S.E.

Ascentek, Inc.—acquired by Synagex, Inc

Ascolta, LLC—acquired by Management Science & Innovation LLC

Associated Buyers, LLC—acquired by Rainforest Distribution Corp

Association Headquarters, LLC—acquired by Corridor Capital, LLC

Astrape Consulting LLC—acquired by TA Associates, Inc.

ATEC Systems, Ltd.—acquired by Armada Group, Ltd.

Atlantis Travel & Tours—acquired by The Appointment Group Limited

Atlass Hardware Corporation—acquired by Frontenac Company LLC

Aul Brothers Tool & Die Inc.—acquired by Mursix Corporation

Auroralight, Inc.—acquired by Kuzco Lighting, Inc.

Automatic Entrances of Wisconsin, Inc.—acquired by Alpine Investors

Avian Mobile Ltd.—acquired by Nationwide Fleet Installations Ltd.

Award Solutions, Inc.—acquired by Accenture plc

Aysling LLC—acquired by Valsef Group

Azure Summit Technology, Inc.—acquired by CACI International Inc.

B

Bacon & Graham, Inc.—acquired by Wellspring Capital Management LLC

Bairstow Lifting Products Co., Inc.—acquired by Altamont Capital Partners

Baptist Memorial Health Care Corporation—acquired by Anderson Regional Health System

Barclay Water Management, Inc.—acquired by Ecolab Inc.

Bates Security, LLC—acquired by Pye-Barker Fire & Safety, LLC

Battea - Class Action Services, LLC—acquired by SS&C Technologies Holdings, Inc.

Battlefield Farms Inc.—acquired by Costa Farms, LLC

BC Cannon Co. Inc.—acquired by Investcorp Holdings B.S.C. and Trilantic Capital Management L.P.

BCC Engineering, Inc.—acquired by Parsons Corporation

Bee Equipment Sales, Ltd.—acquired by SMT Belgium NV

BelFlex Staffing Network, LLC—acquired by Elwood Staffing Services, Inc.

Beltz Ianni & Associates—acquired by Crestview Partners, L.P.

Bend Construction Supply, Inc.—acquired by Clayton, Dubilier & Rice, LLC

Benoure Plumbing & Heating Inc—acquired by Empowered Ventures, Inc.

Berliss Bearing Co.—acquired by FICODIS Inc.

Besse Forest Products Group, Co.—acquired by The Hoffmann Family of Companies

Big Tree Organic Farms, Inc.—acquired by Once Again Nut Butter Collective Inc.

Bill Brown Ford Inc.—acquired by Penske Automotive Group, Inc.

Bio-Vet, Inc.—acquired by Anpario plc

BioMatrix Specialty Pharmacy, LLC—acquired by Frazier Management, LLC

BioResource International, Inc.—acquired by Mitsui & Co., Ltd.

BioTechLogic, Inc.—acquired by Dark Horse Consulting

Biscayne Engineering Company, Inc.—acquired by Atwell, LLC

Black Eagle Consulting, Inc.—acquired by OceanSound Partners, LP

Blazer Electric Supply Company of Colorado Springs—acquired by Graybar Electric Company, Inc.

Bloomberg Consulting, Inc.—acquired by YOUNG & Associates

BMC Enterprises, Inc—acquired by Breedon Group plc

Bobby Taylor Oil Co. Inc.—acquired by Parker Holding Company, Inc.

Boston Brace International, Inc.—acquired by OrthoPediatrics Corp.

Boyd's Tire & Service—acquired by Greenbriar Equity Group, LLC

BPatt LLC—acquired by Agital Holdings, LLC

Bradford Machine Co—acquired by HC Private Investments LLC

Bradshaw, Fowler, Proctor & Fairgrave, PC—acquired by Dickinson, Mackaman, Tyler & Hagen, P.C.

Brandmark Creative Inc.—acquired by Brandmark Creative Inc.

Braner USA, Inc.—acquired by Holleway Capital Partners LLC

Brayton & Hughes Design Studio—acquired by DLR Holding, LLC

BreathableBaby, LLC—acquired by Transom Capital Group, LLC

Britt Metal Processing, Inc.—acquired by Jets MRO, LLC

Brown Wood Preserving Company Inc.—acquired by Koppers Holdings Inc.

Buddy Moore Trucking, Inc.—acquired by OEP Capital Advisors, L.P.

Bullen Midwest Inc.—acquired by Hospeco Brands Group

Bunting Door & Hardware Co., Inc.—acquired by Platinum Equity, LLC

Burklund Distributors Inc.—acquired by AMCON Distributing Company

C

C J Hensch & Associates, Inc.—acquired by Miovision Technologies, Inc.

C-D Electric, Inc.—acquired by B&M Industrial, Inc.

Cabrera Services, Inc.—acquired by The Toronto-Dominion Bank

Cad Technology Center—acquired by Addnode Group AB

Cal Tec Labs, Inc.—acquired by Medical Technology Associates, LLC

Callaway Jones Funeral Home—acquired by Homesteaders Life Co. Inc.

Campion Insurance Inc.—acquired by Maury, Donnelly & Parr, Inc.

Cannon Fabrication, Inc.—acquired by Vibration Mountings & Controls, Inc.

Capital Region Medical Center Inc.—acquired by Curators of the University of Missouri

Capital Steel Service, LLC.—acquired by Hill & Smith PLC

Capitol Vending & Coffee—acquired by Sodexo S.A.

Cargo-Link International, Inc.—acquired by Gebruder Weiss Gesellschaft m.b.H.

CargoBarn Inc.—acquired by SheerTrans Solutions, LLC

Carpenters Roofing & Sheet Metal, Inc.—acquired by Infinity Home Services

Cascade Insurance Center LLC—acquired by Inszone Insurance Services, LLC

Cascade Transportation, Inc.—acquired by Radiant Logistics, Inc.

Cashco, Inc.—acquired by May River Capital, LLC

Cassidy & Company, LLC—acquired by Galiot Insurance Services, Inc.

Cast-Rite International Inc.—acquired by Perella Weinberg Partners LP

CCRO, LLC—acquired by Susquehanna International Group, LLP

Ceatus Media Group LLC—acquired by Advice Media LLC

Cendrowski Corporate Advisors, LLC—acquired by Unity Partners LP

Central Business Systems Inc.—acquired by Advanced Business Methods Inc.

Central Steel Fabricators Inc.—acquired by Live Ventures Incorporated

Cerimele, Meyer & Wray, LLC—acquired by Bodine and Company, LLC

CF Global Trading, LLC—acquired by State Street Corporation

CFV Solar Test Laboratory, Inc.—acquired by Groundwork Renewables, Inc.

Charles E. Gillman Company—acquired by Behrman Brothers Management Corp.

Chastain-Skillman, Inc.—acquired by White Wolf Capital LLC

Chelsea Green Publishing Company—acquired by Fininvest S.p.A.

Chem Arrow Corp.—acquired by Motul S.A.

CHEMFLOW Products, LLC—acquired by Relevant Industrial LLC

Chicago Switchboard Co., Inc.—acquired by Greenbriar Equity Group, L.P.

Childhaven—acquired by Children'S Home Society Of Washington

ChlorKing, LLC—acquired by Hayward Holdings, Inc.

Churchill Linen Service Inc.—acquired by Alsco Inc.

Cimquest Inc.—acquired by Sandvik AB

Cincom Systems, Inc.—acquired by Partner One Capital, Inc.

Circle City Heat Treating, Inc.—acquired by Incertec Plating Corp.

Citiscape Property Management Group, LLC.—acquired by FirstService Corporation

CitySquare—acquired by The Stewpot

Civitas Public Affairs Group LLC—acquired by O2 Investment Partners, LLC

Classic Protection Systems, Inc.—acquired by The Carlyle Group Inc.

Cleveland Scene Publishing LLC—acquired by Great Lakes Publishing Company

CMS Processing LLC—acquired by Alvarez & Marsal, Inc.

Coast International Services, Inc.—acquired by Olympus Partners

Coastal Engineering Co. Inc.—acquired by Tighe & Bond, Inc.

Cognosante LLC—acquired by Accenture plc

Coker Group Holdings, LLC—acquired by Trinity Hunt Management, L.P.

Cokeva, Inc.—acquired by TD Synnex Corp

Colagio The Painter—acquired by Davis Painting

E

E&H Certified Public Accountants & Management Consultants P.C.—acquired by Mbe Cpas LLP

E&M International, Inc.—acquired by Chenega Corporation

Eagan Insurance Agency, Inc.—acquired by Galiot Insurance Services, Inc.

Eagle Cornice Co. Inc.—acquired by Altas Partners LP

Earl W. Johnston Roofing Inc.—acquired by Dunes Point Capital, LLC

East Coast Air & Heat, LLC—acquired by Del-Air Heating, Air Conditioning & Refrigeration Corp.

Eastern Sierra Propane—acquired by Ferrellgas Partners, L.P.

Eckhart & Company, Inc.—acquired by BindTech LLC

Eclipse Engineering, P.C.—acquired by Cushing Terrell

Ecs, Inc.—acquired by Coffman Engineers, Inc.

Ed Brown Distributors—acquired by EVI Industries, Inc.

eDot LLC—acquired by CyberAdvisors, Inc.

Electronic Warfare Associates, Inc.—acquired by Sagewind Capital LLC

Elliott Machine Works, Inc.—acquired by Stellar Industries Inc.

Emery Thompson Machine Supply Co.—acquired by The Middleby Corporation

Emily Corporation—acquired by GMSS Holdings, LLC

Engineering World Health—acquired by Engineers Without Borders-USA, Inc.

Envirosafe Services Of Ohio, Inc.—acquired by J.F. Lehman & Company, Inc.

EnviroTech Services Inc.—acquired by Monomoy Capital Partners LLC

Envoi, LLC—acquired by AlTi Global, Inc.

EpiPhotonics Corp.—acquired by Kohoku Kogyo Co., Ltd.

Ericson Insurance Services, LLC—acquired by Arthur J. Gallagher & Co.

Execupay, Inc.—acquired by Vensure Employer Services, Inc.

Executive Business Services, Inc.—acquired by Roper Technologies, Inc.

Exler & Company, Inc.—acquired by Horovitz, Rudoy & Roteman, LLC

Expand, LLC—acquired by DYN365, Inc.

Export-Import Services Inc.—acquired by Share Logistics BV

Exusia Inc.—acquired by Globant S.A.

F

Farmacia De Leo S.r.l.—acquired by Farmacosmo S.p.A.

Farris Bobango PLC—acquired by Phelps Dunbar LLP

Fastfetch Corp.—acquired by ABCO Systems LLC

Federman, Lally & Remis LLC—acquired by Marcum LLP

Ferencik Libanoff Brandt Bustamante & Goldstein, P.A.—acquired by Hinckley, Allen & Snyder LLP

Fidelity Mutual Holding Company—acquired by Mutual Bancorp

Fidelity Roof Company—acquired by HCI Equity Management, L.P.

Fillauer Companies, Inc.—acquired by Patient Square Capital, L.P.

Finance 500, Inc.—acquired by Stifel Financial Corp.

Financial Arts Inc.—acquired by Inszone Insurance Services, LLC

Fire Systems Professionals, LLC—acquired by The Riverside Company

Fiscalsoft Corp.—acquired by Black Mountain Software, LLC

Fishman Center For Total Eye Care—acquired by Ophthalmic Consultants of Long Island and Blue Sea Capital Management LLC

Fitzpatrick Engineering Group, PLLC—acquired by Structura, Inc.

Flavor Producers, LLC—acquired by Glanbia Co-Operative Society Limited

Fleet Equipment LLC.—acquired by Stonepeak Partners L.P.

Fleet Parts & Service, Inc.—acquired by Boyne Capital Management, LLC

Flex-Tec Inc.—acquired by Cerberus Capital Management, L.P.

Flint Hills Music, Inc.—acquired by Ernie Williamson, Inc.

FLOW-TRONIC S.A.—acquired by Sophora Unternehmerkapital GmbH

Folkerson Communications, Ltd.—acquired by Renaissance Systems, Inc.

Force Communications, LLC—acquired by Keystone Group, L.P.

Forensic Resolutions, Inc.—acquired by Kelso & Company, L.P.

Forklift Training Systems, Inc—acquired by Fleet Team, Inc.

Fox Valley Metal Tech, LLC—acquired by Littlejohn & Co., LLC

Frame USA, Inc.—acquired by Craig Frames, Inc.

Fran Corp.—acquired by 302 Rockwell Intellectual Property LLC

Frank Vitale Insurance Agency—acquired by Inszone Insurance Services, LLC

Freeland & Kauffman, Inc.—acquired by LJA Engineering, Inc.

Fromm International, Inc.—acquired by Firelight Capital Partners LLC [et al]

Frontier Community Bank—acquired & absorbed by

National Bankshares, Inc.

Frontier Fastener Inc.—acquired by Great Lakes Fasteners, Inc.

Frontier Roofing, Inc—acquired by EMP Management, LLC

Future Tech Consultants of New York, Inc.—acquired by Cobepa S.A.

G

Garden Supply Hardscapes—acquired by Trilantic Capital Management L.P.

GCT Semiconductor, Inc.—merged with Concord Acquisition Corp III, to form GCT Semiconductor Holding, Inc.

Gehrki Commercial Real Estate, LLC—acquired by Colliers International Group Inc.

Geiger Excavating, Inc.—acquired by Zemba Bros Inc

Geiger Pump & Equipment Company—acquired by AEA Investors LP

Gemsa Enterprises, LLC—acquired by Marubeni Corporation

General Aviation Flying Services, Inc.—acquired by Blackstone Inc., Cascade Investment LLC and Global Infrastructure Management, LLC

General Body Manufacturing Company—acquired by J.B. Poindexter & Co., Inc.

Genetics & IVF Institute, Inc.—acquired by Amulet Capital Partners, L.P.

George Lay Signs, Inc.—acquired by Miracle Signs, Inc.

Geothermal Supply Co., Inc.—acquired by Core & Main, Inc.

Gerome Technologies, Inc.—acquired by Eis Inc.

Glenn Harris & Associates, Inc.—acquired by Galiot Insurance Services, Inc.

Global Infrastructure Management, LLC—acquired by BlackRock, Inc.

Global Systems Technologies, Inc.—acquired by Broadtree Partners, LLC

Go2 Communications, Inc.—acquired by Gemspring Capital Management, LLC

Golden Harvest, Inc.—acquired by XPV Water Partners

Golden Organics—acquired by Innovative Food Holdings, Inc.

Grand Basket, Inc—acquired by Z Capital Group, LLC

Graphics East, Inc.—acquired by Detroit Legal News Company

Gray Consulting Inc.—acquired by Thoma Bravo, L.P.

Green Equipment Company—acquired by Core & Main, Inc.

Greenery of Charleston, LLC—acquired by Ruppert Landscape, LLC

Greenfield Beverage Company Inc—acquired by Zink Distributing Inc

Greensfelder, Hemker & Gale, P.C.—merged with Ulmer & Berne LLP, to form UB Greensfelder LLP

Gregg Communications Systems, Inc.—acquired by APLJ Capital Management LLC

Greiner Industries, Inc.—acquired by IES Holdings, Inc.

Grette Associates, LLC—acquired by Farallon Consulting, LLC

Gryphon Scientific, LLC—acquired by Deloitte LLP

H

Haedrich & Co., Inc.—acquired by Capital Rivers Commercial LLC

Hall Capital Partners LLC—acquired by Lovell Minnick Partners LLC

Halstead Insurance Agency, Inc.—acquired by GTCR LLC

Harbour Results Inc.—acquired by Wipfli LLP

Harger Inc.—acquired by TE Connectivity Ltd.

Harrick Scientific Products, Inc.—acquired by Ampersand Management LLC

Harris Fire Protection Co Inc.—acquired by Knox Lane LP

Hartwell Environmental Corp.—acquired by DXP Enterprises, Inc.

Healthwise, Incorporated—acquired by KKR & Co. Inc.

Heany Industries, Inc.—acquired by Crawford United Corporation

Hearron Sales, Inc.—acquired by Platinum Equity, LLC

Hearsay Social, Inc.—acquired by Yext, Inc.

Heat-Flo, Inc.—acquired by Bradford-White Corporation

Heath & Associates Inc.—acquired by Warren Equity Partners, LLC

Helgesen Industries Inc.—acquired by Standard Iron & Wire Works Inc.

Hennesy Mechanical Sales, LLC—acquired by DXP Enterprises, Inc.

Heritage Environmental Services, LLC—acquired by EQT AB

Hi-Line Industries Ii, Inc.—acquired by Sciens Capital Management LLC

Highfield Communications LLC—acquired by Kearney O'Doherty Public Affairs, LLC

Hofmann Sausage Co., Inc.—acquired by Trivest Partners, LP

Holmes Landscape Company—acquired by Landscape Developmental Inc.

Homeland Safety Systems Inc.—acquired by Alpine Investors

Homerun Electronics, Inc.—merged with iWired, Inc.,

to form Vangeo Technology Group, LLC

Homestead Building Systems Inc.—acquired by Bain Capital, LP

Horak Insurance, Inc—acquired by Arthur J. Gallagher & Co.

Horizon Services Corporation—acquired by O2 Investment Partners, LLC

Houska Insurance Services Inc.—acquired by New Mountain Capital, LLC

Hugh Wood, Inc.—acquired by Kelso & Company, L.P.

Human Resource Specialties Inc.—acquired by DCI Consulting Group, Inc.

Humm Kombucha, LLC—acquired by SYSTM Brands, LLC

Huntington Pacific Insurance Agency, Inc.—acquired by Inszone Insurance Services, LLC

Hydradyne, LLC—acquired by Applied Industrial Technologies, Inc.

Hydro Consultants Inc.—acquired by Atwell, LLC

Hydromax USA, LLC—acquired by Gallant Capital Partners, LLC

I

I.C. Thomasson Associates, Inc.—acquired by Salas O'Brien Engineers, Inc.

IB Roof Systems, Inc.—acquired by Kingspan Group PLC

Idaho Package Company—acquired by Warburg Pincus LLC and Kelso & Company, L.P.

Ideal Wood Products, Inc.—acquired by Prophet Equity L.P.

iLearningEngines Inc.—merged with Arrowroot Acquisition Corp., to form iLearningEngines, Inc.

Impact 21 Group LLC—acquired by W. Capra Consulting Group, Inc.

Independence RV Sales & Services, Inc—acquired by General RV Center Inc.

Industrial Coil Inc.—acquired by Jay Industrial Repair, Inc.

Industrial Training International, Inc.—acquired by Interplay Learning Inc.

Infinity Laboratories Inc.—acquired by Eurofins Scientific S.E.

Inland Forest Management, Inc.—acquired by F&W Forestry Services Inc.

Innovative Packaging Solutions—acquired by Welch Packaging Group, Inc.

Insight Distributing, Inc.—acquired by Bain Capital, LP

Insurance Management Company—acquired by Hellman & Friedman LLC

Integrated Computer Systems, Inc.—acquired by Banneker Partners, LLC

Inter-Pacific Motors Inc.—acquired by Steve Marshall Group Ltd.

International Cellulose Corp.—acquired by Compagnie de Saint-Gobain SA

International Parking Management, Inc.—acquired by LAZ Parking Ltd, LLC

Internetwork Engineering—acquired by BC Partners LLP

Intricity, LLC—acquired by KKR & Co. Inc.

Irwin Engineers Inc.—acquired by Pennoni Associates Inc.

Isograph Ltd.—acquired by Main Capital Partners B.V.

Italiano Insurance Services, Inc.—acquired by GTCR LLC

Iteam Consulting, LLC—acquired by Netsurit (Pty) Ltd

Ives Equipment Corporation—acquired by Frontenac Company LLC

J

J & J Calibration Services, Inc—acquired by Aldinger Company

JA Kirsch Corporation—acquired by Gellert Global Group

Jacks Tire & Oil Management Co.—acquired by Purcell Tire & Rubber Company Inc.

JAD Corporation—acquired by Bain Capital, LP

Jamco International Inc.—acquired by Littlejohn & Co., LLC

Jamesbeck Global Partners, LLC—acquired by RFE Investment Partners

Janicki Environmental, Inc.—acquired by Environmental Science Associates

JJR Solutions, LLC.—acquired by Logistics Management Institute

JLM Wholesale Inc.—acquired by Dominus Capital, L.P.

Joe & Ross Inc.—acquired by Guggenheim Partners, LLC

Johansen & Anderson, Inc.—acquired by Partners Group Holding AG

Johnson County Bank—acquired by SKYLINE BANKSHARES, INC.

Johnson Engineering, Inc.—acquired by Apex Companies, LLC

Jorgensen Conveyors, Inc.—acquired by Innovance, Inc.

Josam Company—acquired by Watts Water Technologies, Inc.

Judith Heft Associates, LLC—acquired by Aon plc

Juneau Physical Therapy, A Professional Corporation—acquired by SouthEast Alaska Regional Health Consortium

Juno Technologies, Inc.—acquired by Sagewind Capital LLC

Master Magnetics Inc.—acquired by Factor 89 Partners, LLC

Mat-Pac Inc.—acquired by HCI Equity Management, L.P.

Maxwell-Reddick & Associates, Inc.—acquired by Palm Beach Capital Partners LLC

Mazars USA LLP—acquired by FORVIS, LLP, to form Forvis Mazar, LLP

Mcbride Door & Hardware, Inc.—acquired by Platinum Equity, LLC

McCrary Daniels Insurance Agency—acquired by PointeNorth Insurance Group LLC

McGee Storage & Handling, Inc.—acquired by Atlanta Forklifts, Inc.

Mclean Engineering Company, Inc.—acquired by EQT AB

McMahon Architects—acquired by RODE Architects Inc

Mcnamara, Co.—acquired by Brown & Brown, Inc.

McVeigh Global Meetings & Events, LLC—acquired by InteleTravel.com

MD Connect, Inc.—acquired by Intellibright Corporation

Mechanical Engineering & Construction Corporation—acquired by Ares Management Corporation

Medata Inc.—acquired by The Carlyle Group Inc.

Megatran Industries Inc.—acquired by American Superconductor Corporation

Metal Trades, LLC—acquired by Arlington Capital Partners LLC

Metamap, Inc.—acquired by Incode Technologies, Inc.

Metcalf Archaeological Consultants, Inc.—acquired by Terracon Consultants, Inc.

Meyer Laboratory, Inc.—acquired by TruArc Partners, L.P.

Michigan Brush Manufacturing Company, Inc.—acquired by Gordon Brush Mfg Co, Inc.

Micron Industries Corp.—acquired by Hammond Power Solutions, Inc.

Microtel LLC—acquired by Arlington Capital Partners LLC

Midwest Box Company, Inc.—acquired by Jamestown Container Corporation

Midwest Glass Fabricators, Inc.—acquired by KPS Capital Partners, LP

Miinc, LP—acquired by SubSplit Services Group, L.P.

Miller Paint Company, Inc.—acquired by Cloverdale Paint Inc.

Millican Nurseries, Inc.—acquired by SiteOne Landscape Supply, Inc.

Mills & Associates, Inc.—acquired by Pennoni Associates Inc.

MIM Software Inc.—acquired by GE HealthCare Technologies Inc.

Mississippi River Bank—acquired by Merchants & Marine Bancorp, Inc.

Mobile Steam Boiler Rental Corp.—acquired by Miller Proctor Nickolas Inc.

Mobotrex, Inc.—acquired by Warren Equity Partners, LLC

Modern Classic Motors Inc.—acquired by Group 1 Automotive, Inc.

Modern Machinery Company—acquired by Capital Machine Technologies, Inc.

MOGAS Industries, Inc.—acquired by Flowserve Corporation

Mohawk Fine Papers, Inc.—acquired by Fedrigoni SpA

Morgan & Myers, Inc.—acquired by Gibbs & Soell, Inc.

Mortgage Lender Services, Inc.—acquired by Total Lender Solutions, Inc.

Morton Photonics, Inc.—acquired by Coldquanta, Inc.

Mott Corp.—acquired by IDEX Corp

Mountain Air Compressor Inc.—acquired by Hitachi, Ltd.

Mullins Building Products, Inc.—acquired by Platinum Equity, LLC

Municipay, LLC—acquired by Stella Point Capital, LP

Mutual Savings Bank—acquired by Oconee Federal Financial Corp.

N

Nacarato Trucks, Inc.—acquired by SF Holding Corp.

National Safety Apparel, Inc.—acquired by Blue Point Capital Partners, LLC

Nations Roof LLC—acquired by AEA Investors LP

ND Industries Inc.—acquired by H.B. Fuller Company

Nda Distributors, LLC.—acquired by Elbi S.P.A.

Netranom Communications, Inc.—acquired by Alpine Investors

Network People, Inc.—acquired by Frontenac Company LLC

Neuro-ID, Inc.—acquired by Experian plc

New Technology Investments, Inc.—acquired by RMS Omega Technologies Group, Inc.

NewBold Corporation—acquired by Fort Point Capital, LLC

Newbrook Solutions, Inc.—acquired by Edgesource Corporation

Newman Lawn Care Inc.—acquired by Crux Capital Ltd

Nextera Communications LLC—acquired by Trive Capital Inc.

Nion, Co.—acquired by Bruker Corporation

Norflex, Inc.—acquired by Arsenal Capital Management LP

North Point Geographic Solutions—acquired by Avineon, Inc.

Northeast Air Solutions Inc—acquired by Daikin Industries, Ltd.

Northern California Fertility Medical Center, A Professional, Corp.—acquired by Ivy Fertility

Northern Dry-Bulk, Inc.—acquired by Ontario Municipal Employees Retirement System

Northgate Ready Mix, LLC—acquired by CRH plc

Northtown Motor Homes, Inc.—acquired by Fun Town RV LP

Northwest Pump & Equipment Co.—acquired by H.I.G. Capital, LLC

NuAire Inc.—acquired by Kewaunee Scientific Corporation

NuMSP LLC—acquired by Tonka Bay Equity Partners LLC

O

OCR Services Inc.—acquired by The Descartes Systems Group Inc.

Octopi Brewing, LLC—acquired by Asahi Group Holdings Ltd.

ODC Construction, LLC—acquired by Asahi Kasei Corporation

Oldham Collision Center—acquired by Glaser's Collision Center

Omnica Corp.—acquired by StarFish Product Engineering Inc.

Omnyon LLC—acquired by Alpine Investors

On Time Trucking, Inc.—acquired by The RK Logistics Group, Inc.

One Beat CPR Learning Center, Inc.—acquired by Investor AB

OnKure, Inc.—merged with Reneo Pharmaceuticals, Inc., to form OnKure Therapeutics, Inc.

Open Systems Integrators, Inc.—acquired by The Carlyle Group Inc.

OpenGov, Inc.—acquired by Cox Enterprises, Inc.

Opticolor, Inc.—acquired by Techmer PM, LLC

Optimum Design Associates, Inc.—acquired by Crestview Partners, L.P.

Orange Tree Employment Screening LLC—acquired by Boathouse Capital Management, LLC

P

P2S Inc.—acquired by Blackstone Inc.

Pace Professional Services, Ltd.—acquired by Kelso & Company, L.P.

Pacesetter Steel Service, Inc.—acquired by Flack Steel LLC

Pacific Fire And Security, Inc.—acquired by Pye-Barker Fire & Safety, LLC

Pacific Magnetics Inc.—acquired by Careen, Inc.

Pacific Medical Management Services, Inc—acquired by Constellation Software Inc.

Pacific Paper Tube, Inc.—acquired by Sky Island Capital LLC

Paramount Centre, Inc.—acquired by Susquehanna International Group, LLP

Paresky Flitt & Company, LLP—acquired by UHY LLP

Park 100 Foods Inc.—acquired by OSI Group, LLC

PaymentCloud Inc.—acquired by NCR Voyix Corporation.

Paytronix Systems, Inc.—acquired by Access Technology Group Limited

Peerless Aerospace Fastener Corp.—acquired by Diploma PLC

Personal Strengths Publishing, Inc.—acquired by Leeds Equity Partners, LLC

Peterson Brustad Inc.—acquired by Round Table Capital Management, LP

PG Calc, Inc.—acquired by GTCR LLC

Pharmasite Research Inc.—acquired by KKR & Co. Inc.

Phoenix Fire Systems, Inc.—acquired by Pye-Barker Fire & Safety, LLC

Piermont Wealth Management, Inc.—acquired by TA Associates, Inc.

Pilgrim Screw Corporation—acquired by MEIDOH Co., Ltd

Pinnacle Central Company, Inc.—acquired by Source Capital, LLC

Planbox, Inc.—acquired by Main Capital Partners B.V.

Planned & Engineered Construction, Inc.—acquired by Vortex Company, LLC

Plastiform, Inc.—acquired by Nefab AB

Plutora, Inc.—acquired by TPG Capital, L.P. and TA Associates, Inc.

Plx, Inc.—acquired by SK Capital Partners, LP and Edgewater Capital Partners, L.P.

Point Eight Power Inc.—acquired by Mission Critical Group

Ponte Vedra Plastic Surgery—acquired by Ascend Plastic Surgery Partners

Pontiff & Associates, P.C.—acquired by Aprio, LLP

Port Milford LLC—acquired by Sun Communities, Inc.

Portage Lumber Company, Inc.—acquired by Bliffert Lumber & Fuel Co. Inc.

Potter Equipment Co—acquired by Machine Maintenance, Inc.

POWER Engineers, Inc.—acquired by WSP Global, Inc.

Powers & Sullivan, LLC—acquired by Marcum Wealth LLC

Precision Kidd Steel Co. Inc.—acquired by Jade Steel Group, Ltd. and Standard Horse Nail Company, LLC

S

Saint Luke's Health System, Inc.—acquired by BJC Health System

Sale Insurance Agency, Inc.—acquired by Hellman & Friedman LLC

Salm Partners, LLC.—acquired by Johnsonville, LLC

Sam Asher Computing Services Inc.—acquired by Valsef Group

San Fernando Valley Alarm, Inc.—acquired by Armet Alarm & Electronics Inc.

Sandy Hill Kennels, Inc.—acquired by General Atlantic Service Company, L.P.

SaveWay Compounding Pharmacy, LLC—acquired by Myonex, LLC

Scale Finance LLC—acquired by Belay, Inc.

Scientific Boiler Water Conditioning Co, Inc.—acquired by Nolan Capital, Inc.

Scienture, Inc.—merged with TRxADE HEALTH, Inc., to form Scienture Holdings, Inc.

Scout Bio, Inc.—acquired by Ceva Sante Animale SA

SCS Software, Inc.—acquired by CrossCountry Consulting LLC

Seaford Consulting, LLC—acquired by Godspeed Capital Management LP

Securicon, LLC.—acquired by Risk Mitigation Consulting Inc.

SecuriGence LLC—acquired by Chenega Corporation

Serina Therapeutics, Inc.—merged with AgeX Therapeutics, Inc., to form Serina Therapeutics, Inc.

Shapiro, Lifschitz and Schram, P.C.—acquired by Barclay Damon, LLP

Shearman & Sterling LLP—merged with Allen & Overy LLP, to form Allen Overy Shearman Sterling LLP

Sherex Fastening Solutions, LLC—acquired by Tinicum Enterprises, Inc.

Sierra Auction Management, Inc.—acquired by Liquidity Services, Inc.

Signallamp Health Inc.—acquired by Sunstone Partners Management LLC

Silvertip Associates, Inc.—acquired by Vance Street Capital LLC

Singhofen & Associates, Inc.—acquired by Halff Associates, Inc.

Sitex Corporation—acquired by Cintas Corporation

Skin, A Medical Spa—acquired by MD Esthetics, LLC

Skuid, Inc.—acquired by TPG Capital, L.P.

Skyline Steel, Inc.—acquired by Endres Manufacturing Co, Inc.

Skytap, Inc.—acquired by Kyndryl Holdings Inc.

SL Investment Corp.—acquired by North Haven Private Income Fund LLC

Smart Software, Inc.—acquired by Clayton, Dubilier & Rice, LLC

Smart Source, LLC—acquired by Guggenheim Partners, LLC

Smith Consulting Architects—acquired by Godspeed Capital Management LP

SNC Manufacturing Company, Inc.—acquired by Allient Inc.

Snow, Christensen & Martineau, P.C.—acquired by Spencer Fane LLP

Snugg Home LLC—acquired by ABRY Partners, LLC

Softrams LLC—acquired by Sagewind Capital LLC

Softtech Solutions, Inc.—acquired by Falfurrias Capital Partners, LP

Soil-Away Cleaning & Restoration Services—acquired by Insurcomm Construction, Inc.

Solid Restoration Inc.—acquired by Timoneer Strategic Partners, LLC and Grays Peak Capital LP [et al]

Somers Oil Service, Inc.—acquired by Taylor Energy, LLC

Southeast Mower & Saw Shop—acquired by Ag-Pro, LLC

Southern Anchor Bolt Co.—acquired by Portland Bolt & Manufacturing Co., LLC

Southern California Fleet Services, Inc.—acquired by Velocity Vehicle Group

Southern Tooling, Inc.—acquired by LFM Capital LLC

Southern Tractor & Outdoors—acquired by Sumitomo Corporation

Southwest Beverage Co. Inc.—acquired by Mockler Beverage Co. LP

Southwest Heater & Controls, Inc.—acquired by Gryphon Investors, LLC

Space Age Electronics, Inc.—acquired by DelCam Holdings, LLC

Spalding Consulting Inc.—acquired by Saalex Corp.

Spartan Tool Supply Company, Inc.—acquired by Foundation Investment Partners, LLC

Spectra Color, Inc.—acquired by Arsenal Capital Management LP

Speece Lewis Engineers, Inc.—acquired by Bowman Consulting Group Ltd.

Speechcenter Inc.—acquired by Sidekick Therapy Partners

SpinDance, Inc.—acquired by Century Technology Group

SproutLoud Media Networks, LLC—acquired by Ansira Partners, Inc.

Stan's Heating & Air Conditioning, Inc.—acquired by Catterton Management Company, LLC

Stanley M. Proctor Company, LLC—acquired by Applied Industrial Technologies, Inc.

State Alarm, Inc.—acquired by Redwire LLC

Storage Systems Unlimited, Inc.—acquired by Cme Corporation

Strausser Insurance Agency, Inc.—acquired by Key-

stone Agency Partners, LLC

Strong Systems International, Inc.—acquired by RAF Industries, Inc.

Structural Engineering Associates, Inc.—acquired by Johnson, Mirmiran & Thompson, Inc.

Studio Four Design Inc.—acquired by Michael Graves & Associates, Inc.

Sumter Packaging Corporation—acquired by Hood Container Corporation

Sun Enterprises Incorporated—acquired by Sun Powersports Investments, LLC

Sunbelt Asphalt Surfaces, Inc—acquired by Construction Partners, Inc.

Sunbelt Modular, Inc.—acquired by Littlejohn & Co., LLC

Suncoast Bakeries, Inc.—acquired by Shoreline Equity Partners, LLC

Sunshine Answering Service, Inc.—acquired by ECI Partners LLP

Sunstar Insurance Group, LLC—acquired by Reverence Capital Partners LLC

Superior Controls, Inc.—acquired by Lincoln Electric Holdings, Inc.

Superior Iron Works Inc.—acquired by Extreme Steel, Inc

Superior Systems & Technologies, Llp.—acquired by Mission Critical Group

Surdex Corp.—acquired by Bowman Consulting Group Ltd.

Surgical Product Solutions LLC—acquired by Shore Capital Partners, LLC

Surveyconnect Inc.—acquired by Orcus Technologies, Inc

Sw Resources, Inc.—acquired by Goodwill Industries of Kanawha Valley, Inc.

Swafford Warehousing, Inc.—acquired by Peoples Services Inc.

Sydell Group Ltd.—acquired by Hilton Worldwide Holdings Inc.

Synectic Research & Analysis, Inc.—acquired by Avion Solutions, Inc.

SyQwest, Inc.—acquired by CTS Corporation, and name changed to SyQwest, LLC

Systems Design Group LLC—acquired by Pye-Barker Fire & Safety, LLC

T

Takenaka Partners, LLC—acquired by YAMADA Consulting Group Co., Ltd.

Tampa Bay Steel Corporation—acquired by Russel Metals Inc.

Tara Toy Corp.—acquired by Just Play Products, LLC

Target Marketing Group—acquired by Banyan Technologies Group, LLC

Team Epiphany—acquired by Stagwell, Inc.

Tec Laboratories, Inc.—acquired by Promus Holdings, LLC

Technifab Products, Inc.—acquired by Crane Company

Technology Solutions Provider Inc.—acquired by Abt Associates Inc.

Tekmasters LLC—acquired by Godspeed Capital Management LP

Terminus Software, Inc.—acquired by Demand Science Group, LLC

Texplor of Dallas, Inc.—acquired by Terracon Consultants, Inc

The A.G. Mauro Company—acquired by Dunes Point Capital, LLC

The Connable Office, Inc.—acquired by Cresset Asset Management, LLC

The Durbin Group, LLC—acquired by The Goldman Sachs Group, Inc.

The Expo Group, Inc.—acquired by New State Capital Partners LLC

The Horton Group Inc.—acquired by Marsh & McLennan Companies, Inc.

The Patterson Capital Corporation—acquired by Estancia Capital Management, LLC

THEDACARE INC.—acquired by Froedtert Memorial Lutheran Hospital, Inc.

Theoris Inc.—acquired by Asseco Poland S.A.

Thermal Devices, Inc.—acquired by Gryphon Investors, LLC

Times Publishing Newspapers Inc.—acquired by O'Rourke Media Group, LLC

Tlc Ingredients, Inc.—acquired by Gemspring Capital Management, LLC

Toepfer Security Corp.—acquired by Alpine Investors

Tomar Computer Integration, Inc.—acquired by Trinity Hunt Management, L.P.

Total Machine Solutions, Inc.—acquired by Applied Industrial Technologies, Inc.

TPG Software, Inc.—acquired by The Carlyle Group Inc.

TR3 Solutions, Inc.—acquired by Rock Solid UK Ltd.

TraceGains, Inc.—acquired by Veralto Corporation

Trade Lake Mutual Insurance Co, Inc.—acquired by River Falls Mutual Insurance Company

Transitions Wealth Management LLC—acquired by Keystone Group, L.P. and Genstar Capital, LLC

Treasure Valley Fire Protection, Inc.—acquired by Pye-Barker Fire & Safety, LLC

Trew Auto Body, Inc.—acquired by Susquehanna International Group, LLP

Tri City Supply, Inc.—acquired by Freeman Spogli & Co. Incorporated

Tri-County Mental Health Services—acquired by Spurwink Services Incorporated

Tri-Excellence, Inc.—acquired by Gulfside Supply Inc.

Triad RF Systems Inc.—acquired by Comrod Inc.

Trinisys, LLC—acquired by Novacap Management Inc.

Trinity Supply & Installation, LLC—acquired by Lezzer Lumber, Inc.

Triumph Geo-Synthetics, Inc.—acquired by Clayton, Dubilier & Rice, LLC

Trudell Consulting Engineers, Inc.—acquired by Bowman Consulting Group Ltd.

Truss-T Structures, Inc.—acquired by Roots Equity Group LLC

Tulkoff Food Products, Inc.—acquired by The Graham Group, Inc.

Turbine Controls, Inc.—acquired by VSE Corporation

Tuttle, Inc.—acquired by LFM Capital LLC

Twin City Crane & Hoist Inc.—acquired by Balance Point Capital Advisors, LLC

U

U.S. Toy Co., Inc.—acquired by Windy City Novelties, Inc.

Ultra Pet Company, Inc.—acquired by Oil-Dri Corporation of America

Unified Life Insurance Company—acquired by Obra Capital, Inc.

United Language Group, Inc.—acquired by Leonard Green & Partners, L.P. and TTCP Management Services, LLC.

United Medco, LLC—acquired by Medline Industries, LP

Utility Coatings & Fabrication, Inc.—acquired by Victaulic Company

V

V.A. Anderson Enterprises, Inc.—acquired by Apax Partners LLP

Valley Solvent Company, Inc.—acquired by Apollo Global Management, Inc.

Valley Supply, Inc.—acquired by Clayton, Dubilier & Rice, LLC

Valley Transformer Co—acquired by Trilantic Capital Management L.P.

Value Logic, Inc.—acquired by MPAC Group PLC

Vanner, Inc.—acquired by Havis, Inc.

Varni Brothers Corporation—acquired by KKR & Co. Inc.

Veggie Grill, Inc.—acquired by Next Level Burger Company, Inc.

Velocity Dynamics, LLC—acquired by Baird Financial Group, Inc.

Ventera Corporation—acquired by CI Capital Partners LLC

Veritas Total Solutions, LLC—acquired by Marsh & McLennan Companies, Inc.

Vertos Medical Inc.—acquired by Stryker Corporation

Veth Research Associates LLC—acquired by AEVEX Aerospace

VIA Technical, LLC—acquired by Stone Point Capital LLC

Vian Enterprises, Inc.—acquired by Crane Company

Vigilanz Corporation—acquired by Inovalon Holdings, Inc.

Vistacom, Inc.—acquired by Conference Technologies, Inc.

Visual Lease, LLC—acquired by CoStar Group, Inc.

VonLehman & Co. Inc.—acquired by Dean Dorton Allen Ford, PLLC

VSee Lab, Inc.—acquired by Digital Health Acquisition Corp., to form VSee Health, Inc.

W

W C P, Inc.—acquired by AGNORA Ltd

Wallace Welch & Willingham, Inc.—acquired by IMA Financial Group, Inc.

WealthSource Partners, LLC—acquired by New Mountain Capital, LLC

Webster Industries Inc.—acquired by MPE Partners, LLC [et al]

West Virginia National Auto Insurance Co, Inc.—acquired by Warrior Insurance Network, Inc

Western Heritage Bank—acquired by Nusenda Credit Union

Wharton Lyon & Lyon—acquired by GCP Capital Partners Holdings LLC

Whitco Supply, LLC—acquired by DNOW Inc.

White Crane Co, Inc.—acquired by Barnhart Crane & Rigging Co.

Wholesale Supply Inc.—acquired by Freeman Spogli & Co. Incorporated

Wilbanks, Smith & Thomas Asset Management, LLC.—acquired by Edwards Capital, LLC

Willbrook Solutions, Inc.—acquired by Godspeed Capital Management LP

Wisconsin Title Service Company, Inc.—acquired by First American Financial Corporation

Woodbridge International LLC—acquired by Mariner Wealth Advisors, LLC

Woodhill Supply Inc.—acquired by The Macomb Group, Inc.

Work & Co—acquired by Accenture plc

WR Sims Agency Incorporated—acquired by Bain Capital, LP and Keystone Insurers Group, Inc.

Wright Paving Contractors Inc—acquired by Armada Materials, LLC

WTW Architect, Inc.—acquired by AE Works Ltd.

Wyatt Insurance Services, Inc.—acquired by Hellman & Friedman LLC

Wyoming Millwork Co.—acquired by Builders First-Source, Inc.

Y

Yellowstone Tree Surgeons, Inc.—acquired by Apax Partners LLP

Z

Zahroof Valves, Inc.—acquired by Atlas Copco AB

Zavda Technologies, LLC—acquired by Acacia Capital NL LLC

Zepnick Solutions, Inc.—acquired by Salas O'Brien Engineers, Inc.

Zubatkin Owner Representation, LLC—acquired by Cumming Construction Management, Inc.

U.S. PRIVATE COMPANIES

"B"ING THE BEST, INC.
1351 S Killian Dr Ste 1, Lake Park, FL 33403
Tel.: (561) 863-3456
Year Founded: 2001
Sales Range: $25-49.9 Million
Emp.: 1,000
Franchise Fast Food Restaurant Owner & Operator
N.A.I.C.S.: 722513
Carlton A.R. Wade (Co-Owner & Pres)
Lissette Wade (Co-Owner & VP)
Michele Wonyetye (Dir-Ops)

#1 COCHRAN, INC.
4520 William Penn Hwy, Monroeville, PA 15146
Tel.: (412) 245-3656   PA
Web Site: https://www.cochran.com
Year Founded: 1965
Sales Range: $25-49.9 Million
Emp.: 540
Sales of Motor Vehicles
N.A.I.C.S.: 441110
R. E. Cochran (Pres)
Sue Gross (Mgr-HR)
Aaron Herbick (Dir-HR)

&BARR
600 E Washington St, Orlando, FL 32801
Tel.: (407) 849-0100
Web Site: https://andbarr.co
Year Founded: 1957
Advetising Agency
N.A.I.C.S.: 541810
Guy Stephens (VP-Acct Svc)
Nancy Allen (VP)
Janette Estep (VP & Controller)
Dennis Nikles (VP-Media & Analytics)
Katherine Smith (Dir-Grp Media)
Heather Castillo (Mgr-Broadcast Traffic)
Brandy Gill (VP & Dir-Creative)
Charles Caldwell (Dir-Art)
Cristina Howard (Dir-Digital Media & Analytics)
Giles Partington (Dir-Art)
Lorena Bergan (Mgr-Distr)
Mark Robertson (Assoc Dir-Creative)
Mark Sunderland (Assoc Creative Dir)
Douglas White (VP-Innovation & Growth)
Morgan Shepard (Dir-PR)
Adam Liszewski (Grp Acct Dir)
Pete Barr Jr. (Pres & CEO)

'47 BRAND, LLC
15 SW Park, Westwood, MA 02090
Tel.: (781) 320-1384   MA
Web Site: http://www.47brand.com
Year Founded: 1947
Emp.: 250

Sporting Apparel & Accessories Distr
N.A.I.C.S.: 423910
Dominic Farrell (Pres)

Subsidiaries:

Old Time Sports, Inc.   (1)
10 Fanaras Dr, Salisbury, MA 01952-1443
Tel.: (978) 499-1844
Web Site: http://www.oldtimesports.com
Sales Range: $1-9.9 Million
Emp.: 30
Sports Apparel Distr
N.A.I.C.S.: 423910
Robert C. Magnuson (Pres)
Eric B. Magnuson (Treas)
Christopher D. Magnuson (Sec)

(ADD)VENTURES
117 Chapman St, Providence, RI 02905
Tel.: (401) 453-4748
Web Site:
    http://www.addventures.com
Year Founded: 1989
Sales Range: $50-74.9 Million
Emp.: 40
Advetising Agency
N.A.I.C.S.: 541810
Steve Rosa (Pres & CEO)
Mary Sadlier (Chief Strategy Officer & Exec VP)
Joe Miech (COO)
Wayne Vieira (Sr VP-Design & Branding)
Tracy Silva (Sr VP-Quality & Production)
Andrea Reed (VP-Mktg)
Dominic Green (Mgr-Content)
Sue Tremblay (VP-Insights & Analytics)
Lauren Roche (Mgr-Digital)
Camila Moller (Dir-Mktg)
Lisa Reefe (Mgr-Strategy & Mktg)
Dayna Bianco (VP-Digital & Strategy)
Scott Maiocchi (VP-Video & Animation)
Richard Davia (Mng Dir-Creative & Branding)
Grace Bevilacqua (Mgr-Design & Banding)
Maria Eugenia Gines (Dir-Strategy & Branding)
Jenn Snively (Dir-Content & Media)
Teresina Francis (Dir-Digital Mktg & Strategy)

.COM MARKETING
400 N Wymore Rd, Winter Park, FL 32789
Tel.: (407) 774-4606
Year Founded: 1997
Sales Range: $10-24.9 Million
Emp.: 10
Advetising Agency
N.A.I.C.S.: 541810

Hillary Bressler (Founder & CEO)
Kathy Moore (Mgr-Acctg)
Kathleen Peters (Sr Acct Exec)
Dakota Bressler (VP-Sleep Res)

.DECIMAL, INC
121 Central Park Pl, Sanford, FL 32771
Tel.: (407) 330-3300
Web Site:
    https://www.dotdecimal.com
Year Founded: 1986
Rev.: $11,800,000
Emp.: 60
Surgical Appliance & Supplies Mfr
N.A.I.C.S.: 339113
Richard Sweat (Pres & CEO)
John Roman (Mgr-Facilities)

024 PHARMA, INC.
224 Datura St, West Palm Beach, FL 33401
Tel.: (732) 696-9333   NJ
Year Founded: 2004
BGNN—(OTCIQ)
Rev.: $64,708
Assets: $175,831
Net Worth: $1,955,272
Earnings: ($853,492)
Emp.: 1
Fiscal Year-end: 12/31/15
Vitamin & Nutritional Supplement Mfr & Distr
N.A.I.C.S.: 325412

1 SOURCE CONSULTING, INC.
1250 H St NW Ste 310, Washington, DC 20005
Tel.: (202) 850-0073
Web Site: https://go-bti.com
Year Founded: 1999
Sales Range: $125-149.9 Million
Emp.: 550
IT Consulting & Services
N.A.I.C.S.: 541690
William R. Teel Jr. (CEO)
Matt Collins (Pres & CFO)

Subsidiaries:

Energy Enterprise Solutions, LLC   (1)
20440 Century Blvd Ste 150, Germantown, MD 20874
Tel.: (301) 916-0050
Web Site: http://www.eesllc.net
Sales Range: $25-49.9 Million
Emp.: 200
Government & Corporate IT Consulting
N.A.I.C.S.: 541618
William R. Teel Jr. (CEO)
Matt Collins (COO & Sr VP)

1-800 WE ANSWER, INC.
131 W.35th St 8th Floor, New York, NY 10018
Web Site: http://www.weanswer.com

Year Founded: 1979
Sales Range: $10-24.9 Million
Emp.: 700
Business Call Center Service
N.A.I.C.S.: 561421
Robert Porter (Pres & Owner)

Subsidiaries:

TMR Inc.   (1)
450 Pkwy Ste 106, Broomall, PA 19008
Tel.: (610) 359-1190
Web Site: http://www.tmrinfo.com
Sales Range: $10-24.9 Million
Emp.: 120
Market Analysis & Research Services
N.A.I.C.S.: 541910
Tom Ramsburg (Pres)
Youssef Zerkani (VP-Bus Dev)

1-800-PACK-RAT, LLC
6400 Goldsboro Rd Ste 300, Bethesda, MD 20817
Tel.: (800) 722-5728
Web Site:
    http://www.1800packrat.com
Sales Range: $10-24.9 Million
Emp.: 200
General Freight Trucking
N.A.I.C.S.: 484110
Jeff Shay (VP-Finance)

1-888-OHIOCOMP, INC.
2900 Carnegie Ave, Cleveland, OH 44115
Tel.: (216) 426-2164   OH
Web Site: http://www.1-888-ohiocomp.com
Year Founded: 1997
Emp.: 174
Insurance Services
N.A.I.C.S.: 524298
Cherie Strach (Dir-Support Svcs)
Matthew Levy (Dir-Medical)
Deanna L. Kazamek (Dir-Compliance & Projects)
Anthony Kafiti (Dir-IT)
Dan Neubert (COO)

1-CALL STAFFING LLC
802 E Beale St, Kingman, AZ 86401
Tel.: (928) 753-0001
Web Site: http://www.1-callstaffing.com
Year Founded: 2013
Sales Range: $1-9.9 Million
Emp.: 1,716
Human Resource Consulting Services
N.A.I.C.S.: 541612
Tom Beller (CEO)

1-STOP TRANSLATION USA, LLC.
3700 Wilshire Blvd Ste 630, Los Angeles, CA 90010
Tel.: (213) 480-0011

1-Stop Translation USA, LLC.—(Continued)
Web Site: http://www.1stoptr.com
Sales Range: $1-9.9 Million
Emp.: 10
Translation & Interpretation Services
N.A.I.C.S.: 541930
Don Shin *(CEO)*
Rescy de Guzman *(Mgr-Retention & Quality Control)*
Catherine Ann *(Mgr-Acct)*
Gina Lee *(Mgr-Vendor)*

1.800.VENDING, INC.
498 N Kays Dr Ste 200, Kaysville, UT 84037
Tel.: (801) 593-0084
Web Site:
http://www.1800vending.com
Sales Range: $1-9.9 Million
Emp.: 12
Vending Machine Mfr, Operator & Franchisor
N.A.I.C.S.: 445132
Michael Burnett *(Pres)*
Jeffrey Marsh *(VP)*

10/13 COMMUNICATIONS LLC
601 S Arlington Ave, Reno, NV 89509
Tel.: (775) 533-3000   **NV**
Web Site:
http://www.1013communication.com
Emp.: 500
Newspaper Publishers
N.A.I.C.S.: 513110
Randy Miller *(Pres)*
Steve Pope *(Gen Mgr-ahwatukee.com)*

Subsidiaries:

Daily News-Sun - Surprise Today - Glendale/Peoria Today   **(1)**
17220 N Boswell Blvd Ste 101, Sun City, AZ 85373
Tel.: (623) 977-8351
Web Site: http://www.yourwestvalley.com
Newspaper Publishers
N.A.I.C.S.: 513110

Star Local Media   **(1)**
624 Krona Dr Ste 170, Plano, TX 75074
Tel.: (972) 398-4200
Web Site: http://starlocalmedia.com
Newspaper Publishers
N.A.I.C.S.: 513110
Kay Carter *(Sls Mgr)*
Chris Beattie *(Mng Editor)*
Deb Hummel *(Sr Mgr-Bus)*
Melissa Rougeot *(Mgr-Circulation)*
Jeff Trevino *(District Mgr)*
Scott Wright *(Publr & Gen Mgr)*
Nick Souders *(Sls Mgr)*
Liz McGathey *(Exec Editor)*
Chris Roark *(Editor)*

Tucson Explorer   **(1)**
7225 N Mona Lisa Rd Ste 125, Tucson, AZ 85741
Tel.: (520) 797-4384
Web Site: http://www.explorernews.com
Sales Range: $10-24.9 Million
Emp.: 28
Newspaper Publishers
N.A.I.C.S.: 513110
David Rupkalvis *(Exec Editor)*
Louie Armendariz *(Mgr-Production)*
Laura Horvath *(Mgr-Circulation)*
Kate Long *(Gen Mgr)*
Jim Nintzel *(Exec Editor)*
Steve Pope *(Publr)*

101 LIVESTOCK MARKET INC.
4400 Hwy 101, Aromas, CA 95004
Tel.: (831) 726-3303
Web Site:
https://www.101livestock.com
Sales Range: $10-24.9 Million
Emp.: 5
Auctioning Livestock
N.A.I.C.S.: 424520
Jim Warren *(Pres)*

101 MOBILITY, LLC
5221 Oleander Dr, Wilmington, NC 28403
Tel.: (910) 350-2755
Web Site:
https://www.101mobility.com
Year Founded: 2008
Sales Range: $10-24.9 Million
Emp.: 30
Sales, Rentals & Installation of Mobility Equipment such as Wheelchair Ramps, Stairlifts & Patient Lifts to Health Professionals
N.A.I.C.S.: 621999
Dave Pazgan *(Co-Founder & CEO)*

101 PIPE & CASING INC.
30101 Agoura Ct Ste 201, Agoura, CA 91301
Tel.: (818) 707-9101
Web Site: http://www.101pipe.com
Sales Range: $10-24.9 Million
Emp.: 50
Mfr of Steel Pipe & Tubing
N.A.I.C.S.: 423510
Fidel J. Nabor *(Pres & CEO)*
Dusty J. Nabor *(Exec VP)*
April Ford *(Controller)*

Subsidiaries:

101 Vertical Fabrication Inc.   **(1)**
10255 Beech Ave, Fontana, CA 92335
Tel.: (909) 428-6000
Web Site: http://www.101pipe.com
Rev.: $3,000,000
Emp.: 30
Fabricated Structural Metal
N.A.I.C.S.: 332312
April Ford *(Controller)*
Marcos Cano *(Plant Mgr)*
Richard Berg *(VP)*
Dusty J. Nabor *(Exec VP)*

Branch (Domestic):

101 Vertical Fabrication, Inc.   **(2)**
5609 Alameda Pl NE, Albuquerque, NM 87113
Tel.: (505) 343-1101
Steel Piping
N.A.I.C.S.: 331210

101 Vertical Fabrication, Manufacturing Facility   **(2)**
10255 Beech Ave, Fontana, CA 92335
Tel.: (909) 428-6000
Web Site: http://www.101pipe.com
Mfr of Steel Piping
N.A.I.C.S.: 332312
Dusty Nabor *(Pres)*

101 VERMONT AUTO GROUP, INC.
200 N Vermont Ave, Los Angeles, CA 90004
Tel.: (213) 387-9999
Web Site:
http://www.101vermonthyundai.com
Sales Range: $10-24.9 Million
Emp.: 58
Car Whslr
N.A.I.C.S.: 441110
Rafeh Talas *(Gen Mgr)*

10PEARLS LLC
8614 W Wood Ctr Dr Ste 540, Vienna, VA 22182
Tel.: (703) 935-1919
Web Site: http://www.10pearls.com
IT Services
N.A.I.C.S.: 541512
Imran Aftab *(Co-Founder & CEO)*
Ghazanfar Ghori *(CTO)*
Zeeshan Aftab *(Co-Founder & Mng Dir-Offshore Ops)*
Peter Hesse *(Chief Security Officer)*
Joshua Konowe *(VP-Digital Innovation Practice)*

Subsidiaries:

TCT Computing Group, Inc.   **(1)**
9520 Berger Rd Ste 101, Columbia, MD 21046-1554
Tel.: (410) 893-5800
Web Site: http://www.tctcomputing.com
Computer Related Services
N.A.I.C.S.: 541519
Sarah Roderus *(CEO)*

110 CONSULTING
275 108th Ave SE Ste 110, Bellevue, WA 98005
Tel.: (425) 440-6230
Web Site:
http://www.110consulting.com
Year Founded: 2007
Sales Range: $1-9.9 Million
Emp.: 200
Business & Technology Consulting Services
N.A.I.C.S.: 541618
Heinrich Montana *(Dir-Ops)*
Dan Kearney *(Partner-Bus & Mgmt Ops)*
Kyle Katt *(Partner-IT)*

1100 HOLDINGS LLC
1100 Airport Access Rd, Traverse City, MI 49686
Holding Company; Business Aviation & Air Transportaion Services
N.A.I.C.S.: 551112
Omer ErSelcuk *(CEO)*

Subsidiaries:

Air Services Inc.   **(1)**
1100 Airport Access Rd, Traverse City, MI 49686
Tel.: (231) 922-0406
Web Site: http://www.flyasi.com
Aviation Operatior
N.A.I.C.S.: 488119
Omer ErSelcuk *(CEO)*
David Ziemer *(Pres)*
Michael Hannon *(Dir-Maintenance)*

1185 DESIGN
941 Emerson St, Palo Alto, CA 94301
Tel.: (650) 325-4804   **CA**
Year Founded: 1985
Sales Range: $1-9.9 Million
Emp.: 25
Fiscal Year-end: 12/31/06
Advetising Agency
N.A.I.C.S.: 541810
Peggy Burke *(Pres)*
Ann Sison *(Recruiter)*

11:24 DESIGN ADVERTISING, INC.
322 Culver Blvd, Playa Del Rey, CA 90293-7703
Tel.: (310) 821-1775   **CA**
Web Site:
http://www.1124design.com
Year Founded: 1981
Sales Range: $10-24.9 Million
Emp.: 25
N.A.I.C.S.: 541810
Art Sims *(CEO)*
Francisca Sims *(Gen Mgr)*
Steve Kelly *(VP-Creative)*
Russell Robinson *(Dir-Creative)*
Robert Matsesca *(VP-Acct Svcs)*
Tom Scott *(Sr Acct Exec)*
Mark Warlick *(VP-Strategic Plng)*
Edna Bruce *(VP-Promos & Special Events)*
Keith Fisher *(VP-Media Planning & New Media)*
Steve Miller *(VP-Production)*

11TH HOUR BUSINESS CENTERS, LLC
6300 Hazeltine National Dr Ste 100, Orlando, FL 32822

Tel.: (407) 438-4033   **FL**
Web Site:
http://www.11thhourbiz.com
Year Founded: 1998
Sales Range: $1-9.9 Million
Emp.: 100
Facilities Management & Business Support Services
N.A.I.C.S.: 561210
Brannon Wright *(CEO & Owner)*

12 INTERACTIVE, LLC
320 W Ohio St Ste 1W, Chicago, IL 60654
Web Site: http://www.perkspot.com
Year Founded: 2006
Sales Range: $10-24.9 Million
Emp.: 44
Human Resource Requirement Services
N.A.I.C.S.: 541612
Chris Hill *(Founder & Chm)*
Jared Antonyzyn *(Dir-Product Mgmt)*
Araceli Arroyo *(Dir-Product Mgmt)*
Dan Bannister *(Dir-Partnership Mktg)*
Thomas Braaksma *(Acct Mgr)*

121 FINANCIAL CREDIT UNION (Acquired by VyStar Credit Union)

1220 EXHIBITS, INC.
3801 Vulcan Dr, Nashville, TN 37211
Tel.: (615) 333-1220
Web Site: http://www.1220.com
Year Founded: 1972
Sales Range: $1-9.9 Million
Emp.: 80
Trade Show & Other Exhibit Services
N.A.I.C.S.: 541890
Matt Carden *(CEO)*
Craig Dunn *(Sr VP)*
Erma Clement *(CFO & Sr VP)*
Kacie Carrico *(VP-Client Svcs)*
Barry Owen *(Mgr-Estimating)*
Jason Cherry *(Project Mgr)*
Tammy Hicks *(Mgr-Graphic)*
Robert Williams *(VP)*

123 EXTERIORS, INC.
2200 Western Ct Ste 400, Lisle, IL 60532-1855
Tel.: (630) 517-4771
Web Site:
http://www.123exteriors.com
Year Founded: 2005
Sales Range: $1-9.9 Million
Emp.: 12
Home Remodeling Contractors
N.A.I.C.S.: 236118
Mike Braun *(Owner & Co-Partner)*

123 HOME CARE SERVICES, LLC
3407 W 6th St Ste 709, Los Angeles, CA 90020
Tel.: (310) 361-8558   **CA**
Web Site:
http://www.123homecares.co
Year Founded: 2013
Sales Range: $10-24.9 Million
Emp.: 75
Health Care Srvices
N.A.I.C.S.: 621610
Gray Freeman *(CEO)*

128 AUTO GROUP
618 N Ave, Wakefield, MA 01880
Tel.: (781) 944-7760
Web Site: http://www.128volvo.com
Rev.: $54,300,000
Emp.: 75
New & Used Automobiles
N.A.I.C.S.: 441110

128 FORD, INC.
88 Walkers Brook Dr Ste 98, Reading, MA 01867
Tel.: (781) 944-7760
Year Founded: 1960
Sales Range: $25-49.9 Million
Emp.: 75
Car Whslr
N.A.I.C.S.: 441110
C. J. Patti (Gen Mgr)

1315 CAPITAL LLC
2929 Walnut St Ste 1240, Philadelphia, PA 19104
Tel.: (215) 662-1315   DE
Web Site:
   http://www.1315capital.com
Year Founded: 2014
Venture Capital & Private Equity Firm
N.A.I.C.S.: 523999
Adele Cirone Oliva (Partner)
Michael Koby (Co-Founder & Partner)

Subsidiaries:

SciSafe, Inc.   (1)
7 Corporate Dr, Cranbury, NJ 08512
Tel.: (866) 980-8555
Web Site: http://www.scisafe.com
Sales Range: $1-9.9 Million
Emp.: 18
Pharmaceutical Product Storage Services
N.A.I.C.S.: 493110
Teresa Thorne (Mgr-Biorepository & Stability)
Graham Young (Controller)
Anthony Lago (Mgr-Facilities)
Tiffany Maliar (Mgr-Biorepository)
Garrie Richardson (Founder)

miraDry, Inc.   (1)
2790 Walsh Ave, Santa Clara, CA 95051
Tel.: (408) 579-8700
Web Site: http://miradryhcp.com
Medical Aesthetics Mfr
N.A.I.C.S.: 334510
Arash Khazei (CEO)

13I CAPITAL CORPORATION
2021 Midwest Rd Ste 200, Oak Brook, IL 60523-1370
Tel.: (630) 620-2255   IL
Web Site: https://www.13icapital.com
Year Founded: 1993
Sales Range: $10-24.9 Million
Emp.: 246
Holding Companies
N.A.I.C.S.: 541611
Ram P. Thukkaram (Founder, Mng Dir & Principal)

Subsidiaries:

RBM Precision Metal Products Inc.   (1)
3755 Mark Dabling Blvd, Colorado Springs, CO 80907-9018
Tel.: (719) 633-5596
Web Site: http://www.rbmprecision.com
Sales Range: $10-24.9 Million
Emp.: 120
Design & Prototyping, Fabrication, Metal Finishing & Electromechanical Services
N.A.I.C.S.: 332322

Stalcop L.P   (1)
1217 W Main St, Thorntown, IN 46071-8986   (100%)
Tel.: (765) 436-7926
Web Site: http://www.stalcop.com
Sales Range: $10-24.9 Million
Emp.: 67
Mfr of Copper Electrical Components & Precision Plastic Injection Molding
N.A.I.C.S.: 334419
Rick Miles (Mgr-Production)

1800ENDOSCOPE.COM, LLC
6220 Manatee Ave W, Bradenton, FL 34209-2376
Tel.: (941) 792-7138
Web Site:
   http://www.1800endoscope.com

Year Founded: 2001
Sales Range: $1-9.9 Million
Emp.: 9
Hospital Equipment & Supply Whslr
N.A.I.C.S.: 423450
Jennifer L. Whitehead (Mgr-Ops)
Wayne R. Natt (Mgr)

180S, LLC
700 S Caroline St, Baltimore, MD 21231-3309
Tel.: (410) 534-6320
Web Site: https://www.180s.com
Year Founded: 1994
Sales Range: $25-49.9 Million
Emp.: 40
Athletic Performance Wear Mfr
N.A.I.C.S.: 519290
Susan Shafton (CEO)
Bo Ballard (Mgr-Natl Sls)
Kelly Stekmack (Mgr-Mktg)
Steve Reutelhuber (VP-Sls)

1855 CAPITAL PARTNERS, LLC
200 Innovation Blvd Ste 201C, State College, PA 16803
Tel.: (814) 826-4740
Web Site: https://1855capital.com
Emp.: 100
Investment Services
N.A.I.C.S.: 523999

1864 BANCORP, INC
20 Eastman St, South Easton, MA 02375
Tel.: (508) 238-2007   MA
Web Site:
   https://www.northeastonbank.com
Year Founded: 2024
Bank Holding Company
N.A.I.C.S.: 551111
Richard B. Spencer (Pres & CEO)
Aileen Zec (VP)
Charles P. Berkeley (CFO & Treas)

Subsidiaries:

North Easton Savings Bank   (1)
20 Eastman St, South Easton, MA 02375
Tel.: (508) 238-2007
Web Site:
   https://www.northeastonsavingsbank.com
Rev.: $61,734,000
Assets: $1,566,414,000
Liabilities: $1,426,637,000
Net Worth: $139,777,000
Earnings: $7,279,000
Emp.: 175
Fiscal Year-end: 12/31/2023
State Savings Bank
N.A.I.C.S.: 522180
Richard B. Spencer (Pres & CEO)
Aileen Zec (COO & Exec VP)
Charles P. Berkeley (CFO & Sr VP)
Marilyn M. Lewis (CIO & Sr VP)
Patricia L. Polio (Officer-Loan & Sr Branch Mgr)
Kelly Pasquarose (Officer-Loan & Branch Mgr)
Tara Leal (Officer-Loan)
Courtney N. Palm (Officer-Mktg & Asst VP)
Diane L. Shannon (Officer-Loan & VP)
Donna K. Bonia (Officer-Loan Servicing & VP)
Glenn R. Breese (Officer-Loan & VP)
Janet Brown (Officer-Loan & Branch Mgr)
Jo-Anne C. Brooks (Officer-HR & Sr VP)
Marilyn J. Cyr (VP)
Michael J. Carriero (Officer-Loan & Bus Dev & VP)
Michael J. Asack (Officer-Loan & Branch Mgr)
Nicholas Mollo (Officer-Comm Loan & VP)
Robert J. Berg (Pres & CEO)
Stephen T. Pike (Chief Lending Officer & Sr VP)
Thomas A. Deubler (Exec VP)
Thomas M. Caron (VP-Bus Dev)
Thomas D. Kelly (Officer-Loan & Mgr-Sls)
Thomas E. Wooster (Officer-Loan & Branch Mgr)

Wendy L. Reynolds (Officer-Compliance & Mgr-Internal Audit)
Brian McCowan (CFO & Sr VP)
Marilyn M. Lewis (Chief Risk Officer & Sr VP)
Marilyn J. Cyr (VP-Branch Admin)
Ralph L. Letner (Chief Lending Officer & Sr VP)
Gabrielle Rito (VP-Ops)

1888 MILLS, LLC
1520 Kensington Rd Ste 115, Oakbrook Terrace, IL 60523
Tel.: (630) 620-5222
Web Site: http://www.1888mills.com
Sales Range: $10-24.9 Million
Emp.: 300
Linen & Towel Mfr
N.A.I.C.S.: 314120
Abdul Rehman Yaqub (Chm)

Subsidiaries:

1888 Mills, LLC - Distribution Facility   (1)
904 N Hightower St, Thomaston, GA 30286
Tel.: (706) 647-6800
Textile Products Distr
N.A.I.C.S.: 424990

1888 Mills, LLC - Griffin Mill   (1)
1581 Southern Dr, Griffin, GA 30224
Tel.: (770) 229-2361
Textile Products Mfr
N.A.I.C.S.: 314999

Feroze1888 Mills Limited   (1)
Plot C-3 SITE, Karachi, Pakistan
Tel.: (92) 132567890
Web Site: https://www.feroze1888.com
Rev.: $205,676,289
Assets: $276,693,070
Liabilities: $144,715,461
Net Worth: $131,977,609
Earnings: $32,267,661
Emp.: 6,623
Fiscal Year-end: 06/30/2023
Terry Towels & Other Textile Products Mfr
N.A.I.C.S.: 313210
Rehan Rahman (CEO)
Javeria Siddiqui (CFO)

1901 PARTNERS MANAGEMENT, LP
350 Park Ave 13th Fl, New York, NY 10022
Tel.: (212) 292-5836   DE
Year Founded: 2014
Investment Advisory & Management Services
N.A.I.C.S.: 523940
Neil A. Wallack (Mng Dir)
Bryan R. Begley (Mng Dir)
Robert E. Hougie (Mng Dir)
Daniel B. Penrod (Mng Dir)
Brian Cohen (CFO)
Patricia M. Perez (Chief Compliance Officer & Gen Counsel)

1BG LLC
405 Urban St Ste 120, Lakewood, CO 80228
Tel.: (855) 793-7855
Web Site: https://www.1bg.com
Content Marketing, Advertising & Marketing Services
N.A.I.C.S.: 541890
Ori Staub (Dir-Technical)
John Gadeken (Mng Partner)

Subsidiaries:

ServiceCore, LLC   (1)
405 Urban St Ste 120, Lakewood, CO 80228
Tel.: (844) 336-0611
Web Site: https://servicecore.com
Septic & Portable Software Services
N.A.I.C.S.: 513210

1LINK TECHNOLOGY, LLC
2130 West St, Germantown, TN 38138

Tel.: (901) 609-5520
Web Site:
   http://www.1linktechnology.com
Year Founded: 2014
Sales Range: $1-9.9 Million
Emp.: 55
Recruitment Consulting Services
N.A.I.C.S.: 541612
Gassia Gerges (Partner)
Zach Dasher (Partner)

1SHARPE ACQUISITION CORP.
370 Highland Ave, Piedmont, CA 94611
Tel.: (415) 515-7154   DE
Year Founded: 2021
Investment Services
N.A.I.C.S.: 523999
Gregor Watson (CEO)
Rob Bloemker (CFO & Sec)
Charles E. Haldeman (Chm)

1ST AMERICAN CARD SERVICE
25060 Hancock Ave Ste 103-230, Murrieta, CA 92562
Tel.: (951) 676-0085
Web Site:
   http://www.1stamericancard.com
Year Founded: 1986
Sales Range: $10-24.9 Million
Emp.: 200
Credit Card Processing Services
N.A.I.C.S.: 561499
Brian Roemmele (CEO)

1ST AMERICAN SYSTEMS AND SERVICES, LLC
7609 Leonard Dr, Falls Church, VA 22043
Tel.: (202) 999-4545
Web Site: http://www.1asas.com
Year Founded: 2007
Sales Range: $1-9.9 Million
Emp.: 35
Healthcare, IT, R&D, Project & Records Management & Staffing Services to Federal & State Government Businesses
N.A.I.C.S.: 921190
Alpa Shah (Pres & CEO)
Sanjay Shah (VP & COO)
Mark S. Creasap (VP-Learning & Trng Dev)
Roger A. Mandeville (VP-NAS Ops & Trng)

Subsidiaries:

1st American Systems And Services   (1)
901 D St SW Suite 1040, Washington, DC 20024   (100%)
Tel.: (202) 999-4545
Web Site: http://www.1asas.com
Wide Range of Business Services to Federal & State Government Clients
N.A.I.C.S.: 921190
Alpa Shah (Pres & CEO)
Alayna Rowlett (Mgr-HR)
Nina Esoda (Mgr-Administration)

1ST C.O.R.P. SERVICES
895 S High St, Columbus, OH 43206
Tel.: (614) 297-6420   OH
Web Site:
   https://www.paycopayee.org
Year Founded: 1998
Sales Range: $10-24.9 Million
Emp.: 12
Investment Management Service
N.A.I.C.S.: 523940
Misty Foster (Mgr-Acct)
Lynn Nichols (CEO)
Brittany McCoy (Dir-Ops)

1ST CAPITAL BANK

1st Capital Bank—(Continued)

300 Bonifacio Pl, Monterey, CA 93940
Tel.: (831) 264-4070
Web Site:
http://www.1stcapitalbank.com
Year Founded: 2007
Emp.: 97
Commericial Banking
N.A.I.C.S.: 522110
Kurt J. Gollnick (Chm)
Clayton C. Larson (Dir-Client Rels)
Jon D. Ditlevsen (Pres & Chief Lending Officer)
Daniel R. Hightower (Vice Chm)
Samuel D. Jimenez (CEO)
Vida Villanueva (COO & Exec VP)
D. Vernon Horton (Dir-Client Rels)
Danelle Thomsen (CFO & Exec VP)
Jeff Mercer (Chief Credit Officer)
Glenna Datta (Chief Banking Officer & Exec VP)

1ST CHOICE FACILITIES SERVICES CORP.
1941 Whitfield Park Loop, Sarasota, FL 34243
Tel.: (941) 758-1915
Web Site:
http://www.1stchoicecorp.com
Year Founded: 2006
Sales Range: $10-24.9 Million
Emp.: 75
Construction & Facilities Management Services
N.A.I.C.S.: 236220
Gary A. Simone (CEO)
Darrin Simone (VP-Facility Svcs)
George Rutigliano (VP-Construction)
Eileen Simone (Dir-Admin Svcs)
Chuck Knoppel (Mgr-Field Ops)

Subsidiaries:

1st Choice Property Management & Development Company, LLC **(1)**
1914 Whitfield Park Loop, Sarasota, FL 34243
Tel.: (941) 758-1915
Web Site:
http://www.1stchoicemanagement.net
Commercial & Residential Real Estate Management Services
N.A.I.C.S.: 531312
Darrin Simone (Partner)
George Rutigliano (Partner)
Wayne Jones (Dir-Ops)
Eileen Simone (Mgr-HR)
Chuck Knoppel (Mgr-Svc Delivery)
Gary SimoneSr. (Partner)

1ST CLASS REAL ESTATE LLC
831 Seahawk Cir Ste 101, Virginia Beach, VA 23452
Tel.: (757) 504-4636
Web Site:
http://www.1stclassrealestate.com
Year Founded: 2012
Sales Range: $1-9.9 Million
Emp.: 25
Real Estate Agency Services
N.A.I.C.S.: 531210
Rhyan Finch (Co-Owner & CEO)
Rhendi Crisanti (Co-Owner & COO)
Alexis Gentry (Mktg Dir)
Robin Chase (Mgr-HR)
Angie Kennedy (Branch Mgr-Ops)

1ST FARM CREDIT SERVICES, ACA
2000 Jacobssen Dr, Normal, IL 61761
Tel.: (309) 268-0100
Web Site:
http://www.usfarmcredit.com
Year Founded: 1916
Sales Range: $150-199.9 Million

Agricultural Lending Services
N.A.I.C.S.: 522299
Gary J. Ash (Pres & CEO)
Matt Ginder (Exec VP-Marketplace Delivery)
Ron Homann (Chief Risk Officer)
Terry L. Hinds (Chief Lending Officer-Diversified Markets)
Jeffrey Austman (Chm)
Roger Schrodt (Vice Chm)
Greg Carter (Chief Credit Officer)
Shannon Ganschow (Sr VP-Comml Markets)
Doug Kridner (Sr VP-Fin)

1ST FEDERAL SAVINGS BANK OF SC, INC.
300 Robertson Blvd, Walterboro, SC 29488
Tel.: (843) 549-2526
Web Site:
http://www.1stfederalofsc.com
Year Founded: 1962
Sales Range: $1-9.9 Million
Emp.: 26
Federal Savings Bank
N.A.I.C.S.: 522180
Keith M. Kinard (Chm)

1ST FINANCIAL BANK USA
101 Main St, Dupree, SD 57623
Tel.: (605) 365-5191
Web Site: http://www.1fbusa.com
Year Founded: 1910
Sales Range: $10-24.9 Million
Emp.: 406
Provider of Banking Services
N.A.I.C.S.: 522110
Al Hegyi (Chm)
Scott Scheinost (CFO & Sr VP)

1ST FRANKLIN FINANCIAL CORPORATION
135 E Tugalo St, Toccoa, GA 30577
Tel.: (706) 886-7571
Web Site: https://www.1ffc.com
Year Founded: 1941
Rev.: $275,141,672
Assets: $1,162,924,256
Liabilities: $903,631,232
Net Worth: $259,293,024
Earnings: $16,159,627
Emp.: 1,575
Fiscal Year-end: 12/31/22
Consumer Financial Services
N.A.I.C.S.: 522291
Virginia K. Herring (Pres & CEO)
Lynn E. Cox (Treas, Sec & VP)
Joseph A. Shaw (CIO & Exec VP)
Brian Gyomory (CFO & Exec VP)
Ben F. Cheek IV (Chm)
Daniel E. Clevenger II (Exec VP-Compliance)
A. Roger Guimond (Chief Acctg Officer & Exec VP-Fin & IR)

Subsidiaries:

Frandisco Property & Casualty Insurance **(1)**
135 E Tugalo St, Toccoa, GA 30577-2127 **(100%)**
Tel.: (706) 886-7571
Web Site: http://www.firstfranklin.com
Sales Range: $10-24.9 Million
Emp.: 70
Providers of Property & Casualty Insurance Services
N.A.I.C.S.: 524126

1ST IN VIDEO-MUSIC WORLD, INC.
2828 Broadway St, Quincy, IL 62301
Tel.: (217) 224-6171
Web Site:
http://www.1stinvideomusic.com
Year Founded: 1975
Rev.: $12,500,000

Emp.: 24
Electronic Appliance, Television & Radio Set Merchant Whslr
N.A.I.C.S.: 423620
Dennis Boudreau (Founder, Pres & CEO)
Jennifer Boudreau (Treas)
Suzanne Boudreau (Sec)

1ST KNIGHT REALTY, LLC
7320 State Rd 52, Hudson, FL 34667-6711
Tel.: (727) 863-0032
Year Founded: 2003
Sales Range: $10-24.9 Million
Emp.: 15
Real Estate Manangement Services
N.A.I.C.S.: 531210
Andy Linihan (CFO)
Melanie Rowley (Pres)

1ST MERCHANT FUNDING, LLC
12000 Biscayne Blvd Ste 609, Miami, FL 33181
Tel.: (305) 398-4270
Web Site:
http://www.1stmerchantfunding.com
Year Founded: 1999
Sales Range: $1-9.9 Million
Emp.: 9
Consumer Lending Services
N.A.I.C.S.: 522291
Stephen Wagman (CEO)
Levi Rosenblum (Founder & Chm)
Dylan Edwards (Dir-Credit Risk Mgmt)
Abie Blacher (VP-Fin)

1ST MIDAMERICA CREDIT UNION
731 E Bethalto Dr, Bethalto, IL 62010
Tel.: (618) 258-3168
Web Site:
http://www.1stmidamerica.org
Year Founded: 1934
Rev.: $43,709,488
Assets: $751,703,026
Liabilities: $671,901,321
Net Worth: $79,801,705
Earnings: $3,408,887
Fiscal Year-end: 12/31/18
Credit Union Operator
N.A.I.C.S.: 522130

1ST NORTHERN CALIFORNIA CREDIT UNION
1111 Pine St, Martinez, CA 94553
Tel.: (925) 228-7550
Web Site:
https://www.1stnorcalcu.org
Year Founded: 1949
Sales Range: $10-24.9 Million
Consumer Lending Services
N.A.I.C.S.: 522130
Stephen J. Ybarra (Chm)
David M. Green (Pres & CEO)
Diana Malicoat (CEO & Sr VP)

1ST SOURCE SERVALL INC.
2371 George Urban Blvd, Depew, NY 14043
Tel.: (800) 856-9874
Web Site:
http://www.1stsourceservall.com
Home Appliance Parts Distr
N.A.I.C.S.: 423620
Kevin Sullivan (COO)

1ST STOP INC.
18856 State Rte 136, Winchester, OH 45697
Tel.: (937) 695-0318
Web Site: http://www.1ststopinc.com
Rev.: $54,000,000
Emp.: 30

Convenience Store & Motel
N.A.I.C.S.: 445131
Robert Cantrell (Pres)

1SYNC INC.
Princeton Pike Corporate Ctr 1009 Lenox Dr Ste 115, Lawrenceville, NJ 08648
Tel.: (609) 620-4614
Web Site: http://www.1sync.org
Year Founded: 2005
Rev.: $16,400,000
Emp.: 159
Software Solutions
N.A.I.C.S.: 513210
Dan Wilkinson (VP-Indus Dev)

1TOUCH MARKETING
123 NW 13th St Ste 300, Boca Raton, FL 33432
Tel.: (561) 368-5067
Web Site:
http://www.1touchmarketing.com
Sales Range: $10-24.9 Million
Emp.: 50
Advetising Agency
N.A.I.C.S.: 541810
Dan Lansmen (Exec VP)

2-10 HOME BUYERS WARRANTY CORP.
10375 E Harvard Ave, Aurora, CO 80014
Tel.: (720) 747-6000
Web Site: http://www.2-10.com
Year Founded: 1980
Sales Range: $75-99.9 Million
Emp.: 310
Home Repair Warranties
N.A.I.C.S.: 524128
Jeanine Jones (VP-New Home Bus Dev)
Sue Sichler (VP-Sls-New Home Div-Natl)
Jennifer Pingrey (VP-Mktg-Natl)
Scott Zinn (Exec VP-Sls)

2-20 RECORDS MANAGEMENT, LLC (Acquired by Windjammer Capital Investors, LLC)

2.GC, INC.
1818 N Fremont St, Chicago, IL 60614
Tel.: (312) 943-6800
Web Site: http://www.2gcinc.com
Year Founded: 1996
Sales Range: $10-24.9 Million
Emp.: 5
N.A.I.C.S.: 541810
Robin Duggan (Owner)

2/90 SIGN SYSTEMS INC.
5350 Corporate Grove Blvd SE, Grand Rapids, MI 49512
Tel.: (616) 656-4310
Web Site: https://www.290signs.com
Sales Range: $10-24.9 Million
Emp.: 130
Signs & Advertising Specialties
N.A.I.C.S.: 339950
Kathy Zwiers (Project Mgr)
Theresa Wheeler (Mgr-Graphics)
Derek Benedict (Product Mgr)

20/20 FORESIGHT EXECUTIVE SEARCH LLC
300 Park Ave, New York, NY 10022
Tel.: (646) 873-6890
Web Site: http://www.2020-4.com
Year Founded: 1994
Recruitment & Staffing Services
N.A.I.C.S.: 561311

Bob Cavoto (Founder & Mng Principal)
Robert D. Peck (Mng Principal)
Stephanie Cook (Mng Principal)

Subsidiaries:

Saenger Associates (1)
28494 Westinghouse Pl Ste 315, Santa Clarita, CA 91355-0936
Tel.: (661) 284-3818
Web Site:
http://www.saengerassociates.com
Executive Search Service
N.A.I.C.S.: 561312
Gary L. Saenger (Pres)

2020 EXHIBITS, INC.
10550 S Sam Huston Pkwy W, Houston, TX 77071
Tel.: (713) 489-8556
Web Site:
https://www.2020exhibits.com
Year Founded: 1987
Sales Range: $10-24.9 Million
Emp.: 125
Management Consulting Services
N.A.I.C.S.: 541618
Robert Babine (Pres)
Lindsay Larsen (Acct Exec)
Mike Skaff (VP-Bus Dev)
Jeannette Sanders (Dir-Mktg)
Rick Terry (Dir-Environments)
Pete Babine (VP-Global Events)

2020 EXHIBITS, INC.
10550 S Sam Huston Pkwy W, Houston, TX 77071
Tel.: (713) 354-0900   TX
Web Site:
http://www.2020exhibits.com
Year Founded: 1990
Sales Range: $10-24.9 Million
Emp.: 70
Design & Installation of Custom Tradeshow Exhibits
N.A.I.C.S.: 541850
Bob Babine (Pres)
Michael Wriston (Dir-Intl Sls)

20230930-DK-BUTTERFLY-1, INC.
650 Liberty Ave, Union, NJ 07083
Tel.: (908) 688-0888   NY
Year Founded: 1971
BBBYQ—(OTCIQ)
Rev.: $9,233,028,000
Assets: $6,456,930,000
Liabilities: $5,179,994,000
Net Worth: $1,276,936,000
Earnings: ($150,773,000)
Emp.: 37,600
Fiscal Year-end: 02/27/21
Domestic Merchandise & Home Furnishings Retailer
N.A.I.C.S.: 449129
Warren Eisenberg (Co-Founder)

Subsidiaries:

Bed Bath & Beyond Canada L.P. (1)
2975 Argentia Road, Mississauga, L5N 0A2, ON, Canada
Tel.: (905) 812-1233
Web Site: http://www.bedbathandbeyond.ca
Emp.: 30
Home Furnishings Stores
N.A.I.C.S.: 449129

Buy Buy Baby, Inc. (1)
650 Liberty Ave, Union, NJ 07083
Tel.: (908) 688-0888
Web Site: http://www.buybuybaby.com
Sales Range: $10-24.9 Million
Emp.: 100
Children's & Infants' Wear Stores
N.A.I.C.S.: 458110
Patty Wu (Pres & Exec VP)

Harmon Stores, Inc. (1)
650 Liberty Ave, Union, NJ 07083
Tel.: (908) 688-7023

Web Site: http://www.facevaluesonline.com
Sales Range: $75-99.9 Million
Emp.: 1,000
Sales of Drugs & Pharmaceuticals
N.A.I.C.S.: 456110

Liberty Procurement Co. Inc. (1)
110 Bi County Blvd Ste 114, Farmingdale, NY 11735-3941
Tel.: (631) 420-7050
Home Furnishings Products Whslr
N.A.I.C.S.: 449129

One Kings Lane, Inc. (1)
8491 Sunset Blvd Ste 2500, Los Angeles, CA 90069
Tel.: (310) 550-0527
Web Site: http://www.onekingslane.com
Emp.: 201
Furniture Merchants
N.A.I.C.S.: 423210
Alison Pincus (Founder)

206INC.
1505 Western Ave Ste 500, Seattle, WA 98101
Tel.: (206) 388-1440
Web Site: http://www.206inc.com
Year Founded: 2005
Sales Range: $1-9.9 Million
Emp.: 40
Marketing, Design, Event Production, PR & Partnership Strategy Services
N.A.I.C.S.: 541613
Michael Salvadore (Partner & Sr VP-Consumer Engagement Strategy)
Mark Dyce (Partner & Sr VP)
Kerry Murphy (Partner & Sr VP-Consumer Engagement Strategy)
Tad Harmon (Partner & Exec Dir-Creative)
Rachel Roebuck (Dir-Art)
Noelle Firth (Dir-Consumer Engagement)
Kat Bryant Flaherty (Dir-Consumer Engagement)
Joe Mattson (Dir-Consumer Engagement)
Natalie Nystrom (Dir-Consumer Engagement)
Lauren Keckley (Dir-Event Production)
Kyle Lane (Dir-Fin)
Elle Galvez (Mgr-Fin)

215 HOLDING CO.
215 S 11th St, Minneapolis, MN 55403
Tel.: (612) 332-4732
Sales Range: $25-49.9 Million
Bank Holding Company
N.A.I.C.S.: 551111
M. D. Short (Pres)
Dawn Gast (Chief Credit Officer)

Subsidiaries:

First Farmers & Merchants National Bank (1)
112 S Main St, Le Sueur, MN 56058
Tel.: (507) 665-2265
Web Site: http://www.ffmbank.com
Emp.: 15
Retail & Commercial Banking
N.A.I.C.S.: 522110
Brian Pfarr (Pres)

First Farmers & Merchants National Bank (1)
303 E Main St, Luverne, MN 56156
Tel.: (507) 283-4463
Web Site: http://www.ffmbank.com
Emp.: 25
Retail & Commercial Banking
N.A.I.C.S.: 522110

First Farmers & Merchants National Bank (1)
114 S Park St, Fairmont, MN 56031
Tel.: (507) 235-5556
Web Site: http://www.ffmbank.com
Emp.: 13
Retail & Commercial Banking

N.A.I.C.S.: 522110
Andrew Noll (Pres)
Dan Hilgerndorf (Exec VP)

First Farmers & Merchants State Bank (1)
106 W Main St, Brownsdale, MN 55918
Tel.: (507) 567-2219
Web Site: http://www.ffmbank.com
Emp.: 10
Retail & Commercial Banking
N.A.I.C.S.: 522110
Dale Larson (Pres)

First Farmers & Merchants State Bank of Grand Meadow (1)
105 N Main St, Grand Meadow, MN 55936-1109
Tel.: (507) 754-5123
Web Site: http://www.ffmbank.com
Emp.: 15
Retail & Commercial Banking
N.A.I.C.S.: 522110
David Feddersen (Pres & CEO)

White Rock Bank (1)
31377 County 24 Blvd, Cannon Falls, MN 55009
Tel.: (507) 263-3030
Web Site: http://www.ffmbank.com
Rev.: $9,244,000
Emp.: 106
Retail & Commercial Banking
N.A.I.C.S.: 522110
Joseph Tapp (Pres)

21ST AMENDMENT INC.
1158 W 86th St, Indianapolis, IN 46260
Tel.: (317) 846-1678
Web Site:
https://www.21stamendment.com
Year Founded: 1971
Sales Range: $10-24.9 Million
Emp.: 50
Alcohol Distr
N.A.I.C.S.: 445320
Lou Anne Brennan (CFO)

21ST CENTURY BIOCHEMICALS
260 Cedar Hill St, Marlborough, MA 01752
Tel.: (508) 303-8222
Web Site:
https://www.21stcenturybio.com
Pharmaceutical & Bio Medical Component Developer & Mfr
N.A.I.C.S.: 325412
Eric Berg (VP-Ops & Dir-Mass Spectrometry & Analytical Svcs)

21ST CENTURY COOPERATIVE CO.
222 W 2nd St, Cumberland, IA 50843
Tel.: (712) 774-5412
Web Site:
http://www.21stcenturycoop.com
Sales Range: $10-24.9 Million
Emp.: 40
Agricultural Cooperative
N.A.I.C.S.: 424510
Randy Daugherty (Gen Mgr)

21ST CENTURY PARKS INC.
471 W Main St Ste 202, Louisville, KY 40202
Tel.: (502) 584-0350   KY
Web Site:
http://www.theparklands.org
Year Founded: 2004
Sales Range: $10-24.9 Million
Emp.: 16
Parkland Preservation Services
N.A.I.C.S.: 712190
Scott Martin (Dir-Park)
Kevin Beck (Project Mgr)
Sam Stewart (Dir-Facility & Programs)

Laura Mattingly (Coord-Dev)
Anna Rosales-Crone (Coord-Comm)
Michael Nielsen (VP-Fin)

21ST CENTURY SYSTEMS, INC.
6500 Prairie Ave, Omaha, NB 68132
Tel.: (402) 505-7881   NY
Year Founded: 1996
Sales Range: $10-24.9 Million
Emp.: 20
Decision-Making Software & Systems Developer
N.A.I.C.S.: 541512
Jeffrey Hicks (CEO)
Jeffrey Hicks (CEO)
Charles Hopkins (VP-Svcs)
Victor H. Bevilaqua (VP-Sls)
John Bevilaqua (Pres)

21ST MORTGAGE CORPORATION
620 Market St, Knoxville, TN 37902
Tel.: (865) 523-2120
Web Site:
https://www.21stmortgage.com
Rev.: $12,631,421
Emp.: 600
Mortgage Bankers & Loan Correspondents
N.A.I.C.S.: 522310
Tim Williams (Pres)
Rich Ray (CFO)
Troy Fussell (VP)
Bart Mize (Dir-Mktg)

225 UNLIMITED INCORPORATED
317 Northlake Blvd Ste 1016, Altamonte Springs, FL 32701
Tel.: (407) 894-6675
Web Site:
http://www.225unlimited.com
Rev.: $30,000,000
Emp.: 10
Toys & Hobby Goods & Supplies
N.A.I.C.S.: 541618
Kim A. Higgins (Pres)

22ND CENTURY TECHNOLOGIES, INC.
220 Davidson Ave Ste 118, Somerset, NJ 08873
Tel.: (732) 537-9191   NJ
Web Site: http://www.tscti.com
Year Founded: 1997
Rev.: $10,000,000
Emp.: 40
Computer Software Systems Analysis & Design
N.A.I.C.S.: 541511
Satvinder Singh (Pres)

22SQUARED, INC.
1170 Peachtree St NE 15th Fl, Atlanta, GA 30309-7649
Tel.: (404) 347-8700   DE
Web Site: http://www.22squared.com
Year Founded: 1922
Sales Range: $600-649.9 Million
Emp.: 248
Advertising Agencies
N.A.I.C.S.: 541810
Ben West (Founder & Chm)
Scott Stuart (Exec VP & Grp Exec Dir)
John Stapleton (Chief Creative Officer)
Brandon Murphy (Chief Client Officer)
Andrew Jones (Exec VP-Bus Dev)
Signe Garnitz (Exec VP & Exec Dir-HR)
Chris Tuff (Exec VP & Dir-Bus Dev & Partnerships)
Amanda Ferber (Exec VP & Grp Exec Dir)

22squared, Inc.—(Continued)

Mike Grindell *(Chief Admin Officer & Exec VP)*
Genna Franconi *(Sr VP)*
Krista Lang *(Sr VP & Exec Dir-Media)*
Saya Heathco *(Sr VP & Dir-Strategy)*
Meg Jokinen *(Sr VP & Acct Dir-Grp)*
Albert Patton *(Exec Dir-Creative)*
Christy Cross *(Sr VP)*
Matt Silliman *(Sr VP & Dir-Integrated Production)*
Dan Brown *(VP & Dir-Digital Experience)*
Cheryl Davis *(CFO)*
Katie Davis *(Dir-Art)*
Lindsay Baldwin *(Sr VP)*
Ashley Keetle *(Sr VP)*
Annette Sally *(Exec VP & Exec Dir-Acct Mgmt)*
Ryan Stafford *(Sr VP & Creative Dir)*
Doreen Fox *(VP & Grp Creative Dir)*
Matt O'Rourke *(Chief Creative Officer)*
Jamie Rubin *(Exec Dir-Media)*
Erica Hoholick *(Pres)*

Subsidiaries:

22squared - Tampa   (1)
401 E Jackson St 36th Fl, Tampa, FL 33602-5225
Tel.: (813) 202-1200
Web Site: http://www.22squared.com
Sales Range: $10-24.9 Million
Emp.: 110
Internet/Web Design, Newspaper, Print, Radio, T.V.
N.A.I.C.S.: 541810
Ben West *(Founder & Chm)*
Scott Sheinberg *(Exec VP & Gen Mgr-Tampa)*
Kevin Botfeld *(Exec Dir-Creative)*
Christy Cross *(VP & Dir-Bus Dev)*
Matt Silliman *(Sr VP & Dir-Integrated Production)*

23RD GROUP LLC
4944 Parkway Plaza Blvd Ste 400, Charlotte, NC 28217
Tel.: (704) 909-4423
Web Site: http://www.23rdgroup.com
Year Founded: 2014
Sales Range: $10-24.9 Million
Emp.: 80
Property Management Services
N.A.I.C.S.: 531312
Gregg Ross *(Co-Founder)*
Carl J. Paparella *(Co-Founder)*

24 HOUR COMPANY
6521 Arlington Blvd Ste 501, Falls Church, VA 22042
Tel.: (703) 533-7209
Web Site: https://www.24hrco.com
Year Founded: 1992
Sales Range: $1-9.9 Million
Emp.: 20
Graphic Design Services
N.A.I.C.S.: 541430
Dennis Fitzgerald *(Mng Partner)*
Mike Parkinson *(Principal)*

24 SEVEN, LLC
41 Madison Ave 37th fl, New York, NY 10010
Tel.: (516) 927-0500   DE
Web Site:
   http://www.24seventalent.com
Recruitment Agency
N.A.I.C.S.: 561311
Celeste Gudas *(Founder & CEO)*
Tammy Chatkin-Newman *(Exec VP-Global Search)*
Lisa Marie Ringus *(Exec VP-Global Client Strategy)*
Tracy O'Connor *(Sr VP-Bus Dev)*

Jennifer Cano *(VP & Gen Mgr-San Francisco)*
Amanda O'Sullivan *(VP-Recruiting-Fashion,Beauty,Wellness)*

Subsidiaries:

Filter LLC   (1)
1425 4th Ave Ste 1000, Seattle, WA 98101
Tel.: (425) 688-0094
Web Site: http://www.filterdigital.com
Digital Media Staffing Agency
N.A.I.C.S.: 561311
Kristin Knight *(Founder & Chm)*
Joe Melanson *(CEO)*
Terry Terry *(CFO)*
Eric Adams *(Gen Mgr & Sr VP)*
Dan Holmes *(Sr VP-Growth)*
David Hensel *(Dir-Mktg)*
Don Olson *(Dir-Mktg Practice)*
Michael Hinnant *(Dir-User Experience)*
Michele Kretzer *(Dir-Talent Solutions)*

Mckinley Marketing Partners, Inc.   (1)
3401 Lee Pkwy Apt 808, Dallas, TX 75219
Tel.: (214) 382-0737
Web Site:
   http://www.mckinleymarketing.com
Sales Range: $1-9.9 Million
Emp.: 15
Management Consulting Services
N.A.I.C.S.: 541613

SketchDeck Inc.   (1)
340 S Lemon Ave Ste 2206, Walnut, CA 91789
Web Site: http://www.sketchdeck.com
Graphic Design Services
N.A.I.C.S.: 541490
Chris Finneral *(Founder & CEO)*
Nicole Conley *(Project Mgr-Quality)*

The Cydio Group   (1)
591 Camino de la Reina Ste 1150, San Diego, CA 92108
Tel.: (619) 573-4848
Web Site: http://www.cydio.com
Sales Range: $1-9.9 Million
Emp.: 41
Information Technology Consulting Services
N.A.I.C.S.: 541511
Kimberly Sitz *(Partner)*
Curt Sterling *(Mng Dir)*

24/7 CUSTOMER INC.
910 E Hamilton Ave Ste 240, Campbell, CA 95008
Tel.: (650) 385-2247
Web Site:
   http://www.247customerinc.com
Year Founded: 2000
Sales Range: $500-549.9 Million
Emp.: 8,000
Outsourcing
N.A.I.C.S.: 541611
P. V. Kannan *(Co-Founder & CEO)*
Shanmugam Nagarajan *(Co-Founder & Chief People Officer)*
Steve Skalski *(Chief Bus Dev Officer)*
Sally Grisedale *(Chief Design Officer)*
John Mejia *(Chief Revenue Officer)*
Prashant Cherukuri *(CIO)*
Patrick Nguyen *(CTO)*
David Lloyd *(Mng Dir & Sr VP-Global Svc Delivery-Canada)*
Rohan Ganeson *(COO)*

Subsidiaries:

24/7 Customer Philippines Inc.   (1)
MJ Plaza Building #106 Valero St Salcedo Village, Makati, Philippines
Tel.: (63) 2 792 4809
Web Site: http://www.247customer.com
Outsourcing Services
N.A.I.C.S.: 541611

24/7 Customer Pvt. Ltd.   (1)
Embassy Golf Link Business Park, Off Intermediate Ring Road, Bengaluru, 560071, India
Tel.: (91) 8039890247
Web Site: http://www.247customer.com
Outsourcing
N.A.I.C.S.: 541611

24/7 EXPRESS LOGISTICS, INC.
1610 Vernon St, Kansas City, MO 64116
Tel.: (816) 471-1004
Web Site:
   http://www.247expresslogistics.com
Year Founded: 2001
Sales Range: $10-24.9 Million
Emp.: 46
General Freight, Courier & Trucking Services
N.A.I.C.S.: 488510
Steve Johns *(VP-Bus Dev & Sls)*

24HOLDINGS INC.
131 Columbia Tpke Ste 1, Florham Park, NJ 07932
Tel.: (973) 635-4047   DE
Investment Services
N.A.I.C.S.: 523999
Arnold P. Kling *(Pres & Treas)*
Kirk M. Warshaw *(CFO & Sec)*

24HR HOMECARE
21311 Hawthorne Blvd Ste 101, Torrance, CA 90503
Tel.: (310) 375-5353
Web Site: https://www.24hrcares.com
Year Founded: 2008
Sales Range: $25-49.9 Million
Emp.: 49
Women Healthcare Services
N.A.I.C.S.: 621610
David Allerby *(Co-Founder & CEO)*
Tyner Brenneman-Slay *(Co-Founder & COO)*
Ryan Iwamoto *(Co-Founder & CMO)*
Stacy Shimizu *(Dir-HR)*

26 CALIFORNIA BAZAR INC.
2652 E 45th St, Vernon, CA 90058
Tel.: (323) 588-3026
Web Site: http://www.26cb.com
Sales Range: $10-24.9 Million
Emp.: 25
General Merchandise, Non-Durable
N.A.I.C.S.: 424990
Bijan Navidbakhsh *(Pres)*

26NORTH BDC, INC.
600 Madison Ave 26th Fl, New York, NY 10022
Tel.: (917) 885-5563   MD
Year Founded: 2022
Asset Management Services
N.A.I.C.S.: 523999
Brendan McGovern *(Chm, Pres, CEO, Sr Partner & Head-Direct Lending)*

29 PRIME
2967 Michelson Dr Ste G467, Irvine, CA 92612
Tel.: (949) 777-6616
Web Site: http://www.29prime.com
Year Founded: 2008
Sales Range: $1-9.9 Million
Emp.: 149
Search Engine Marketing
N.A.I.C.S.: 541810
Tony Redman *(Co-Founder & COO)*
Russell Wallace *(Co-Founder & CEO)*
Jason Martin *(Co-Founder & CTO)*
Ashkan Yekrangi *(Gen Counsel)*
Kaylee Larkins *(Mgr-HR)*
Michelle Nguyen *(Controller)*
Christina Hart *(VP-Sls)*

2929 ENTERTAINMENT LP
2222 S Barrington Ave, Los Angeles, CA 90064
Tel.: (310) 309-5726   DE
Web Site:
   http://www.2929entertainment.com
Year Founded: 2003

Entertainment & Media Holding Company
N.A.I.C.S.: 551112
Todd Wagner *(Co-Owner & CEO)*
Mark Cuban *(Co-Owner)*
Kamruz Mohager *(Controller)*

Subsidiaries:

2929 Productions LLC   (1)
11601 Wilshire Blvd Ste 210, Los Angeles, CA 90025
Tel.: (310) 309-5200
Web Site: http://www.2929productions.com
Motion Picture & Video Production Services
N.A.I.C.S.: 512110
Marc Butan *(Pres)*

2ADVANCED STUDIOS, LLC.
32 Journey Ste 200, Aliso Viejo, CA 92656-5343
Tel.: (949) 521-7000
Web Site: http://www.2advanced.com
Year Founded: 1999
Sales Range: $10-24.9 Million
Emp.: 25
Advetising Agency
N.A.I.C.S.: 541810
Eric Jordan *(Pres & Chief Creative Officer)*
Tony Novak *(CFO & COO)*
John Carroll *(CIO & CTO)*
Shane Mielke *(Dir-Creative)*
Elijah Shepard *(Dir-Bus Dev)*

2E CREATIVE, INC.
411 N 10th St Ste 600, Saint Louis, MO 63101
Tel.: (314) 436-2323
Web Site: http://www.2ecreative.com
Year Founded: 1999
Biotechnology & Life Sciences Marketing
N.A.I.C.S.: 541714
Lynda McClure *(VP-Creative)*
Brandon Chuang *(VP-Strategic Dev)*
Steve Roseman *(Pres)*

Subsidiaries:

Fire & Rain, LLC   (1)
1 N 3rd Ave, Evansville, IN 47710-1213
Tel.: (812) 464-5244
Web Site: http://www.2ecreative.com
Healthcare Marketing
N.A.I.C.S.: 541810

2GM CORPORATION
10501 Valley Blvd, El Monte, CA 91731
Tel.: (626) 618-0777
Search Engine & Web Hosting
N.A.I.C.S.: 513140
Barry R. Su *(Pres)*
Grace Su *(CEO)*

Subsidiaries:

Tyloon, Inc.   (1)
15713 Valley Blvd, City of Industry, CA 91744
Tel.: (626) 389-0223
Web Site: http://www.tyloon.com
Sales Range: $1-9.9 Million
Search Engine & Web Hosting
N.A.I.C.S.: 513140
Barry R. Su *(Pres)*
Grace Su *(CEO)*
Ruiyi Ma *(CTO & VP)*
Juan Yanez Carrera *(VP-Mktg)*
Kiarash Jahangiri *(Chief Network Officer)*

2HB SOFTWARE DESIGNS, INC.
10480 Little Patuxent Pkwy Ste 400, Columbia, MD 21044-3568
Tel.: (240) 232-9527
Web Site: http://www.2hb.com
Sales Range: $1-9.9 Million
Emp.: 22
Software Development Services
N.A.I.C.S.: 541511

David M. Doggette *(Pres & CEO)*
Reginald T. Hay *(VP-Engrg)*
Shaun A. Burwell *(CFO & VP-Fin)*
Christopher Bulleri *(CTO)*

2IS INC.

75 W St, Walpole, MA 02081
Tel.: (508) 850-7520
Web Site: http://www.2is-inc.com
Year Founded: 2002
Sales Range: $1-9.9 Million
Emp.: 20
Engineeering Services
N.A.I.C.S.: 541330
Gary Burchill *(Co-Founder & CEO)*
Glenn D. House Sr *(Co-Founder & Pres)*
Adam Terrell *(Mgr-IT)*
Donna Zukowski *(VP-Fin & Admin)*

2J SUPPLY INC.

872 Valley St, Dayton, OH 45404
Tel.: (937) 223-0811
Web Site: http://www.2-jsupply.com
Sales Range: $10-24.9 Million
Emp.: 95
Energy Power Systems Supplier
N.A.I.C.S.: 423730
Jeff Runyon *(Chm & CEO)*
Greg Trimbach *(Pres)*
Larry Trimbach *(VP)*

2JR PIZZA ENTERPRISES, LLC

305 Townepark Cir Ste 101, Louisville, KY 40243
Tel.: (502) 254-0422
Sales Range: $10-24.9 Million
Emp.: 850
Pizza Restaurant
N.A.I.C.S.: 722513
Jeff Reetz *(Owner)*
Tony Mastropaolo *(COO)*
Brian Reetz *(VP & Gen Mgr)*

2M TOOL COMPANY, INC.

6530 W Dakin St, Chicago, IL 60634-2412
Tel.: (773) 282-0722   IL
Web Site:
   http://www.mincemaster.com
Sales Range: $10-24.9 Million
Emp.: 10
Mfr of Food Processing Equipment
N.A.I.C.S.: 332710
Vesna Doyle *(Gen Mgr)*
Vladan Mihailovic *(VP)*

Subsidiaries:

Mince Master   **(1)**
6530 W Dakin St, Chicago, IL 60634-2412   **(100%)**
Tel.: (773) 282-0722
Web Site: http://www.mincemaster.com
Sales Range: $10-24.9 Million
Mfr of Food Processing Equipment
N.A.I.C.S.: 332710
Vesna Doyle *(Gen Mgr)*
Vladan Mihailovic *(VP-Product Dev)*
Mike Mihailovic *(Pres)*

2ND SWING

2412 E Hennepin Ave, Minneapolis, MN 55413
Tel.: (612) 331-9303
Web Site: https://www.2ndswing.com
Rev.: $26,400,000
Emp.: 146
Golf Equipment Retailer
N.A.I.C.S.: 423910
Russ Higgins *(Owner)*
Tyler Bauman *(Gen Mgr)*

2ND WIND EXERCISE EQUIPMENT

7585 Equitable Dr, Eden Prairie, MN 55344

Tel.: (952) 544-5249
Web Site:
   http://www.2ndwindexercise.com
Year Founded: 1992
Sales Range: $10-24.9 Million
Emp.: 8
Sales of Exercise Equipment
N.A.I.C.S.: 459110
Angie Perrin *(Mgr-Accts Payable)*
Chris Ball *(Mgr-Store)*
David Wollschlager *(Mgr)*
Robert Brumbaugh *(Mgr-Ops)*
Tom Kelly *(CFO & CIO)*

2PI SOLUTIONS

1090 Vermont Ave Ste 800, Washington, DC 20005
Tel.: (202) 326-5250
Year Founded: 2003
Sales Range: $1-9.9 Million
Emp.: 35
Document Shredding, Business Intelligence Solutions & Waste Services for Businesses & Government Agencies
N.A.I.C.S.: 562998
Anshu Bhatnagar *(CEO)*

2TRG INC

11093 Kenwood Rd, Cincinnati, OH 45242
Tel.: (513) 761-5333
Web Site: http://www.2trg.com
Year Founded: 2003
Sales Range: $1-9.9 Million
Emp.: 250
Technology Recycling
N.A.I.C.S.: 562219
Carol Weinstein *(CEO)*

2WHEELBIKES.COM

3809 Durbin St, Irwindale, CA 91706
Tel.: (626) 539-3939
Web Site:
   http://www.2wheelbikes.com
Year Founded: 2005
Sales Range: $1-9.9 Million
Emp.: 50
Online Retailer of Bicycles
N.A.I.C.S.: 336991
May Chu *(Pres)*

3 BOYS ENTERPRISES LLC.

818 N Broadway, Portland, TN 37148-2023
Tel.: (615) 325-2700
Web Site:
   https://www.nationalbarn.com
Sales Range: $10-24.9 Million
Emp.: 12
Commercial & Institutional Building Construction
N.A.I.C.S.: 236220
Jennifer Eastman *(Mgr)*

3 BRIDGE SOLUTIONS LLC

100 S 5th St Ste 300, Minneapolis, MN 55402
Tel.: (651) 321-4080   MN
Web Site:
   http://www.threebridge.com
Management Cnsulting Services; Business Transformation & IT Consulting Solutions
N.A.I.C.S.: 541618
Jim Kelly *(Founder & CEO)*

Subsidiaries:

Keyot, LLC   **(1)**
625 Hayward Ave, Oakdale, MN 55128
Tel.: (651) 288-9990
Web Site: http://www.keyot.net
Management Consulting Services
N.A.I.C.S.: 541618
Cindy Rockwell *(CIO & Co-Partner)*
Robin Lorang *(Project Mgr)*

Anjie Cayot *(Co-Founder, CFO & Co-Partner)*
Jess LaValle *(Office Mgr)*

3 D BODY WORKS, INC.

300 W Boot Rd, West Chester, PA 19380
Tel.: (610) 692-7776
Web Site:
   http://www.3dbodyworks.com
Automotive Body, Paint & Interior Repair & Maintenance
N.A.I.C.S.: 811121
David Neistroy *(Owner & Pres)*

3 DAY BLINDS LLC

167 Technology Dr, Irvine, CA 92618-2381
Tel.: (714) 634-4600   CA
Web Site:
   https://www.3dayblinds.com
Year Founded: 1978
Sales Range: $150-199.9 Million
Emp.: 500
Mfr of Window Coverings
N.A.I.C.S.: 337920
Frank Gutierrez *(VP-Mfg)*
Joyce Glick *(Coord-Local Market)*
Phuong Nguyen *(Mgr-Production)*
Feri Khosrowpour *(Controller)*

3 FEET MEDIA

99 Weatherstone Dr, Woodstock, GA 30188
Tel.: (678) 445-3646
Web Site: http://www.3feetmedia.net
Sales Range: Less than $1 Million
Emp.: 10
N.A.I.C.S.:
Susan Dent *(Dir-Mktg)*
Chris Esposito *(Pres & CEO)*
John Bevilaqua *(Exec VP-Retail)*
Becky Repic *(Dir-Creative)*

3 INTERACTIVE

906 Rain Forest Pkwy, Columbia, MO 65202
Tel.: (573) 445-3083
Web Site: http://www.3interactive.net
Year Founded: 2003
Sales Range: $10-24.9 Million
Emp.: 32
Online Advertising Services
N.A.I.C.S.: 541810
Bobby Campbell *(CEO)*
Scott Braudis *(CFO)*
Lori Ritchie *(Dir-Sls)*
Patricia Summers *(Dir-Campaign Ops)*
Jingjing Sha *(Dir-Bus Ops)*
Katelyn Jones *(Dir-Strategic Dev)*

3 RIVERS CAPITAL, LLC

437 Grant St Ste 500, Pittsburgh, PA 15222
Tel.: (412) 765-2491
Web Site: http://www.3riverscap.com
Financial Investment Activities
N.A.I.C.S.: 523999
Robert McGuire *(Co-Founder)*
Gregory Martin *(VP)*
Dale Buckwater *(Co-Founder)*
Rob Carskadden *(Co-Founder)*
Michael Zhong *(VP)*
Josh Nanci *(Dir)*

Subsidiaries:

AGS Automotive Solutions LLC   **(1)**
PO Box 729, Muskegon, MI 49443
Tel.: (231) 733-2101
Web Site: http://www.agscompany.com
Specialized Lubricants Mfr
N.A.I.C.S.: 324191
Logan Pitts *(Pres & CEO)*

Subsidiary (Domestic):

Bludot Inc.   **(2)**

4335 Meghan Beeler Ct, South Bend, IN 46628
Tel.: (574) 277-2306
Web Site: http://www.bludotinc.com
All Other Motor Vehicle Parts Mfr
N.A.I.C.S.: 336390
Scott Blue *(Pres)*

Gaven Industries, Inc.   **(1)**
6655 North Noah Dr, Saxonburg, PA 16056
Tel.: (724) 352-8100
Web Site: http://www.gavenindustries.com
Rev.: $5,333,333
Emp.: 25
Sheet Metal Work Mfg
N.A.I.C.S.: 332322
Terri Masters *(Office Mgr)*
Jason Rivera *(Office Mgr)*

3 RIVERS TELEPHONE COOPERATIVE

202 5th St S, Fairfield, MT 59436
Tel.: (406) 467-2535
Web Site: http://www.3rivers.net
Sales Range: $25-49.9 Million
Emp.: 140
Local Telephone Communications
N.A.I.C.S.: 517121
Brad Veis *(Dir-Fin)*
David H. Gibson *(CEO-3 Rivers Comm & Gen Mgr)*

3-D ENVIRONMENTAL SERVICES CORP.

3257 Lochness Dr, Lexington, KY 40517
Tel.: (859) 272-6618
Sales Range: $10-24.9 Million
Emp.: 100
Industrial Building Construction Services
N.A.I.C.S.: 236210
Donnie Breeding *(Principal)*

3030 PARK HEALTH SYSTEMS INC.

3030 Park Ave, Bridgeport, CT 06604
Tel.: (203) 374-5611
Web Site:
   https://www.watermark.com
Sales Range: $25-49.9 Million
Emp.: 1,000
Retirement Hotel Operation
N.A.I.C.S.: 623110

305 DEGREES LLC

4230 Nautilus Dr, Miami Beach, FL 33140
Tel.: (305) 668-5764
Web Site:
   http://www.305degrees.com
Year Founded: 2007
Sales Range: $10-24.9 Million
Emp.: 5
Luxury Concierge Services
N.A.I.C.S.: 721199
Evan Weiss *(Pres & CEO)*

30DC, INC.

80 Broad St 5th Fl, New York, NY 10004
Tel.: (212) 962-4400   MD
Web Site: http://www.30dcinc.com
Year Founded: 2003
Rev.: $738,174
Assets: $1,460,539
Liabilities: $2,326,000
Net Worth: ($865,461)
Earnings: ($1,599,297)
Emp.: 11
Fiscal Year-end: 06/30/15
Internet Marketing Training Program Services
N.A.I.C.S.: 611430
Theodore A. Greenberg *(CFO & Sec)*
Henry Pinskier *(Chm & CEO-Interim)*

31-W INSULATION CO. INC.

31-W Insulation Co. Inc.—(Continued)

7434 Cycle Ln, Goodlettsville, TN
37072-9359
Tel.: (615) 859-0991
Web Site: http://www.31w.com
Year Founded: 1972
Rev.: $59,000,000
Emp.: 800
Insulation, Buildings
N.A.I.C.S.: 238310
Wayne Day *(Owner)*

32ND STREET 99 CENTS CORP.
110 W 32nd St, New York, NY 10001
Tel.: (212) 268-9962
Web Site: http://jacks99world.com
Rev.: $21,000,000
Emp.: 150
Variety Stores
N.A.I.C.S.: 455219
Jack Franco *(Pres)*

33ACROSS INC.
229 W 28th St 12th Fl, New York, NY 10001
Tel.: (646) 606-2174
Web Site: http://www.33across.com
Year Founded: 2008
Sales Range: $25-49.9 Million
Emp.: 75
Internet Publishing & Broadcasting Services
N.A.I.C.S.: 516210
Eric Wheeler *(Founder & CEO)*
Orchid Burnside *(VP-Media Ops)*
Shyam Kuttikkad *(CTO)*
Paul Bell *(Gen Mgr-Global Data Solutions)*
David Jacobs *(COO)*
Yuri Burka *(Mng Dir-Europe)*
Anita Pollert *(Sr VP-Publisher Sls & Monetization Partnerships)*
Miles Dennison *(Chief Revenue Officer)*

360 ENTERPRISES LLC
30251 Golden Lantern Ste E-261, Laguna Niguel, CA 92677
Tel.: (949) 218-6668
Web Site: http://www.noradarealestate.com
Year Founded: 2004
Sales Range: $1-9.9 Million
Emp.: 10
Real Estate Investment Services
N.A.I.C.S.: 531390
Marco Santarelli *(Founder & CEO)*

360 GROUP
36 S Pennsylvania St Ste 190, Indianapolis, IN 46204
Tel.: (317) 633-1456
Web Site: http://www.360grouponline.com
Year Founded: 1960
Sales Range: $10-24.9 Million
Emp.: 14
Full Service
N.A.I.C.S.: 541810
David V. Cranfill *(Co-Founder & Pres)*
Scott Willy *(Co-Founder & VP-Creative Svcs)*
David Bray *(Sr Art Dir)*
Dan Myers *(Media Dir)*

360 INC.
14380 Industrial Cir, La Mirada, CA 90638
Tel.: (714) 232-7236
Web Site: http://www.360-inc.com
Sales Range: $10-24.9 Million
Emp.: 70
Surfboards & Bodyboards Mfr & Sales
N.A.I.C.S.: 423910

Mike Maslowski *(Pres)*

360 MORTGAGE GROUP, LLC
11305 Four Points Dr 1-200, Austin, TX 78726
Tel.: (512) 418-6000   DE
Web Site: http://www.360mtg.com
Year Founded: 2007
Sales Range: $25-49.9 Million
Emp.: 72
Mortgage Banking Services
N.A.I.C.S.: 522292
Marie Cordova *(Acct Exec-Albuquerque)*
Trevor Pettennude *(CEO)*

360 PSG, INC.
4242 Ridge Lea Rd., Buffalo, NY 14226
Tel.: (716) 226-1349
Web Site: https://www.360psg.com
Year Founded: 2005
Advertising Marketing Services
N.A.I.C.S.: 541810
Joel Colombo *(Pres)*

Subsidiaries:

Manzella Marketing Group, Inc   (1)
5360 Genesee St Ste 203, Bowmansville, NY 14026
Tel.: (716) 681-6565
Web Site: https://manzellamarketing.com
Administrative & General Management Consulting Services
N.A.I.C.S.: 541611
Luana Davis *(Mgr)*
Scott Fierle *(VP-Bus Dev)*
Kathleen Weaver *(Coord-Traffic)*
Jillian Ahrens *(Coord-SEO & Content)*
Jenny Streams *(Dir-Mktg & Creative Svcs)*

360 PUBLIC RELATIONS LLC
200 State St, Boston, MA 02109
Tel.: (617) 585-5770
Web Site: https://www.360pr.plus
Year Founded: 2001
Emp.: 20
Public Relations & Communications Services
N.A.I.C.S.: 541820
Vince Powers *(Exec VP)*
Laura Tomasetti *(Founder & CEO)*
Caroline Hardy Pierce *(Acct Dir)*
Stacey Clement *(Sr VP)*
Caitlin Melnick *(VP)*
Michael Rush *(Sr VP)*
Victoria Renwick *(Sr VP)*
Brett Weliever *(Supvr-Acct)*
Caitlin Chalke *(VP)*
Celia Alviti *(Acct Coord)*
Emily Bennett *(Acct Coord)*
Jenny Krupski *(Supvr-Acct)*
Kalley Jolly *(Sr VP)*
Logan Breslow *(Acct Coord)*
Olivia Claparols *(Acct Coord)*
Sandra Yee *(VP)*
Sheila Tayebi *(Supvr-Acct)*

Subsidiaries:

Powers Brand Communications LLC   (1)
675 Lancaster Ave, Berwyn, PA 19312-1686
Tel.: (610) 644-1022
Web Site: http://www.powersbc.com
Public Relations Agencies
N.A.I.C.S.: 541820
Vince Powers *(Mng Dir-Philadelphia)*
Mackenzi Hockensmith *(Asst Acct Exec)*
Natalie Snyder *(Asst Acct Exec)*

360PARTNERS, LP
5926 Balcones Dr Ste 130, Austin, TX 78731
Tel.: (512) 342-8800
Web Site: http://www.360partners.com
Sales Range: $1-9.9 Million
Emp.: 35

Search Engine Marketing, Search Engine Optimization & Lead Generation Services
N.A.I.C.S.: 541810
Jim McKinley *(Principal)*
Jeff Hoogendam *(Principal)*
Barbara Preston *(CEO)*
Chris Cottam *(Controller)*

360SCIENCE LTD. (Acquired by Bridge Growth Partners, LLC)

360TRAINING.COM, INC.
6801 N Capital of Texas Hwy Bldg 1 Ste 250, Austin, TX 78731
Tel.: (512) 539-2950
Web Site: http://www.360training.com
Year Founded: 1997
Sales Range: $10-24.9 Million
Emp.: 100
Career Management Services
N.A.I.C.S.: 541618
Michael Mariano *(CFO)*
Greg Driscoll *(VP-Enterprise Sls)*
Thomas Anderson *(CEO)*
Samantha Montalbano *(COO)*
Venkat Gaddipati *(CTO)*
Andrew Stross *(Chief People Officer)*
Ryan Linders *(CMO)*

Subsidiaries:

AdvanceOnline Solutions, Inc.   (1)
1811 Bering Dr Ste 430, Houston, TX 77057
Tel.: (713) 621-1100
Web Site: https://www.advanceonline.com
Human Resources & Executive Search Consulting Services
N.A.I.C.S.: 541612
Gerald Allen *(CEO)*
Joseph M. Teeples *(Dir-Safety)*
Wayne Grotheer *(COO)*

Quickstart Intelligence, Corp.   (1)
11451 Katy Freeway Ste 360, Houston, TX 77079
Web Site: http://www.quickstart.com
Software Training Center
N.A.I.C.S.: 611420

TSS Redmond LLC   (1)
8443 154th Ave NE Bldg H, Redmond, WA 98052-3863
Tel.: (425) 213-6957
Web Site: http://www.tssredmond.com
Computer System Design Services
N.A.I.C.S.: 541512
Anna Wilson *(Acct Exec)*

365 OPERATING COMPANY LLC
200 Connecticut Ave Ste 5A, Norwalk, CT 06854
Tel.: (415) 901-5700
Web Site: http://www.365datacenters.com
Year Founded: 2002
Information Technology Consulting Services
N.A.I.C.S.: 541512
Bob DeSantis *(CEO)*
Steven Amelio *(CFO)*
Sam Zurzolo *(VP-Data Center Ops)*
Soraya Moreno *(VP-Provisioning & Procurement)*
Karen Passaro *(VP & Controller)*
Jeff Slapp *(VP-Cloud & Managed Svcs)*
James Ashton *(VP-Network Ops)*

37 BAKING HOLDINGS, LLC
3700 S Kidzie Ave, Chicago, IL 60632
Tel.: (847) 295-4244
Investment Services
N.A.I.C.S.: 523999
Haq Chaudary *(Pres & CEO)*

Subsidiaries:

Gold Standard Baking, Inc.   (1)
3700 S Kedzie Ave, Chicago, IL 60632
Tel.: (773) 523-2333
Web Site: http://www.gsbaking.com
Sales Range: $1-9.9 Million
Bakery Products Mfr
N.A.I.C.S.: 311812
Michael Ware *(Dir-Pur)*
George Caparos *(VP-Sls)*
David M. Shanholtz *(Pres & CEO)*

3D EXHIBITS, INC. (Acquired by Sparks Marketing Group LLC)

3ALITY TECHNICA
55 E Orange Grove Ave, Burbank, CA 91502
Tel.: (818) 333-3000
Web Site: https://www.3alitytechnica.com
Year Founded: 2000
Sales Range: $10-24.9 Million
Emp.: 55
Developer of Image Processing Software & Camera Rig Systems
N.A.I.C.S.: 512110
Steve Schklair *(Founder & CEO)*
Hector Ortega *(Sr VP-Mfg, Design & Product Dev)*
Sharon Martin *(Sr VP-Bus Dev)*

3B MEDICAL, INC.
203 Avenue A NW Ste 300, Winter Haven, FL 33881
Tel.: (863) 226-6285
Web Site: http://www.3bproducts.com
Year Founded: 2011
Sales Range: $10-24.9 Million
Emp.: 30
Pharmaceuticals Product Mfr
N.A.I.C.S.: 334510
Tom Thayer *(Founder & Pres)*
Alex Lucio *(CEO)*
Jose Llana *(Natl Dir-Sls)*
James A. Lucio *(Dir-Medical)*
Desiree Thomas-Greenidge *(Mgr-Fin)*

3BL MEDIA LLC
136 W St Ste 104, Northampton, MA 01060
Tel.: (802) 535-3215
Web Site: https://www.3blmedia.com
Year Founded: 2009
Emp.: 40
News Distribution & Content Marketing
N.A.I.C.S.: 541890
Dave Armon *(CMO)*
Katie Buckland *(Sr VP-Bus Dev)*
Lynne Filderman *(Sr VP-Bus Integration & Strategic Partnerships)*

Subsidiaries:

CSRwire, LLC   (1)
250 Albany St, Springfield, MA 01105
Tel.: (802) 251-0110
Web Site: http://www.csrwire.com
Franchised & Partnership, Drive-through Restaurants
N.A.I.C.S.: 722513
Emilio J. Sibilia Jr. *(CEO)*

3C SOFTWARE INC.
1300 Parkwood Cir Ste 300, Atlanta, GA 30339
Tel.: (770) 956-7744
Web Site: http://www.3csoftware.com
Year Founded: 1988
Sales Range: $1-9.9 Million
Emp.: 27
Software Publisher
N.A.I.C.S.: 513210
Joan Hayden *(VP-Fin)*
Matthew Smith *(Pres & CEO)*

Peter Tezza *(Founder & Chm)*
Scott Adams *(Dir-Sls)*
Stacey Adams *(Mgr-Mktg)*
Rich LaSalle *(Dir-Bus Analytics)*

3CINTERACTIVE CORP.

750 Park of Commerce Blvd Ste 400,
Boca Raton, FL 33487
Tel.: (561) 443-5505   DE
Web Site:
http://www.3cinteractive.com
Year Founded: 2005
Sales Range: $25-49.9 Million
Emp.: 85
CRM Software
N.A.I.C.S.: 513210
John Duffy *(Founder & CEO)*
Michael FitzGibbon *(Co-Founder & Pres)*
Mark Smith *(Founder & COO)*
Jeremy Martin *(Sr VP-Bus Dev)*
Jeff Michaud *(VP-Sls)*
Ellen Roberson *(VP-Strategic Partnerships & Carrier Rels)*
John Sculley *(Chm)*
Stephen Murphy *(CIO)*
Margie Kupfer *(VP-Mktg)*
Alejandro Guerrieri *(VP-Engrg)*
Sue Marmion *(VP-Enterprise PMO)*
Brian Heikes *(VP-Product)*
Ralph Wasner *(VP-Tech)*
Brian Kilpatrick *(VP-Fin)*
Duke Tunstall *(VP-Tech)*

3D CORPORATE SOLUTIONS, LLC

601 13th St, Monett, MO 65708
Tel.: (417) 236-9602   MO
Web Site: http://www.3dcorpsol.com
Year Founded: 2002
Sales Range: $125-149.9 Million
Emp.: 240
Food Ingredient Services; Production,
Flexible Logistics & Creative Sourcing
N.A.I.C.S.: 115210
Greg Drollinger *(VP-Sls & Mktg)*
Becky Eggelston *(Mgr-Logistics)*
Scott Clawson *(VP-Ops)*
Rusty Bowsher *(Dir-Ops)*
Hank Cotney *(Dir-Quality Assurance)*

3D FUTURE VISION II, INC.

2005 Tree Fork Ln Ste 109, Longwood, FL 32750
Tel.: (407) 310-4522
Year Founded: 2011
Sales Range: $25-49.9 Million
Telecommunication Servicesb
N.A.I.C.S.: 517112
Bernadette DiFrancesco *(Owner)*
Joseph DiFrancesco *(Chm)*

3D SOLAR LLC

11548 Pyramid Dr, Odessa, FL 33556
Tel.: (727) 868-0110
Web Site: http://www.3-dsolar.com
Year Founded: 2013
Sales Range: $1-9.9 Million
Emp.: 43
Solar Electric Power Generation Services
N.A.I.C.S.: 221114
David Ringo *(Founder)*

3DCART SHOPPING CARTS

7515 Oakland Park Blvd Ste 100,
Tamarac, FL 33319
Tel.: (800) 828-6650
Web Site: http://www.3dcart.com
Year Founded: 1997
Sales Range: $1-9.9 Million
Emp.: 25
Shopping Cart Software
N.A.I.C.S.: 513210
Gonzalo Gil *(Founder & CEO)*
Jimmy Rodriguez *(CTO)*

3DEGREES GROUP, INC.

2 Embarcadero Ctr Ste 2950, San
Francisco, CA 94111
Tel.: (415) 449-0500
Web Site:
http://www.3degreesinc.com
Year Founded: 2002
Sales Range: $10-24.9 Million
Emp.: 56
Energy Conservation Products & Services
N.A.I.C.S.: 541690
Dan Kalafatas *(CEO)*
Steve McDougal *(VP-Mktg & Bus Dev)*
Adam Capage *(VP-Utility Partnerships)*

3FORCES INC.

7702 E Doubletree Ranch Rd Unit
300, Scottsdale, AZ 85258
Tel.: (480) 289-9019   CA
Year Founded: 2016
Rev.: $3,256
Assets: $383,441
Liabilities: $1,952,034
Net Worth: ($1,568,593)
Earnings: ($367,419)
Fiscal Year-end: 12/31/21
Online Information Services
N.A.I.C.S.: 519290

3G CAPITAL INC.

600 3rd Ave 37th Fl, New York, NY
10016
Tel.: (212) 893-6727   DE
Web Site: http://www.3g-capital.com
Privater Equity Firm
N.A.I.C.S.: 523999
Paulo Luiz Araujo Basilio *(Partner)*
Alexandre Behring *(Co-Founder & Co-Mng Partner)*
Bernardo Piquet *(Partner)*
Roberto Thompson Motta *(Co-Founder)*
Carlos Alberto Sicupira *(Co-Founder)*
Marcel Herrmann Telles *(Co-Founder)*
Pedro Drevon *(Partner)*
Daniel Dreyfus *(Partner)*
Munir Javeri *(Partner)*
Marcos Romaneiro *(Partner)*
Daniel S. Schwartz *(Co-Mng Partner)*
Daniel S. Schwartz *(Co-Mng Partner)*

Subsidiaries:

The Kraft Heinz Company   **(1)**
200 E Randolph St, Chicago, IL
60601   **(24%)**
Tel.: (412) 456-5700
Web Site: https://www.kraftheinz.com
Rev.: $26,640,000,000
Assets: $90,339,000,000
Liabilities: $40,813,000,000
Net Worth: $49,526,000,000
Earnings: $2,855,000,000
Emp.: 36,000
Fiscal Year-end: 12/30/2023
Holding Company; Food Products Mfr &
Whslr
N.A.I.C.S.: 551112
John Tobin Cahill *(Vice Chm)*
Carlos Abrams-Rivera *(CEO)*
Vince Garlati *(Chief Acctg Officer, VP & Controller-Global)*
Carlos Abrams-Rivera *(Pres/Exec VP-North America)*
Marcos Eloi Lima *(Chief Procurement Officer & Exec VP)*
Sam Greenwood *(CMO/Comml Dir-Northern Europe)*
Alex Abraham *(VP-Corp Comm & Reputation Mgmt-Global)*
Yang Xu *(Treas-Global, Sr VP & Head-Corp Dev-Global)*
Diana Frost *(Chief Growth Officer-North America)*
Janelle Orozco *(Chief Procurement Officer-North America)*
Andre Maciel *(CFO-Global & Exec VP)*

Subsidiary (Domestic):

Kraft Heinz Foods Company   **(2)**
1 PPG Pl Ste 34, Pittsburgh, PA 15222
Tel.: (412) 456-5700
Web Site:
http://www.kraftheinzcompany.com
Sales Range: $5-14.9 Billion
Emp.: 31,900
Ketchup, Condiments & Sauces, Frozen
Foods, Baby Foods, Beans & Pasta Meals,
Soups & Other Processed Foods Mfr
N.A.I.C.S.: 311941
Leandro Balbinot *(CIO & Sr VP-IT-Global)*
Michael Mullen *(Sr VP-Corp & Govt Affairs)*
Emin Mammadov *(Pres-Russia, Turkey, Middle East & Africa)*
Eduardo Machado de Carvalho Pelleissone *(Exec VP-Ops)*
Andy Keatings *(Chief Quality Officer)*
Lisa West *(Mgr-Reward-UK & Ireland)*
Shirley Weinstein *(Head-Rewards-Global)*
Jose Parolin *(CIO-North America)*

Subsidiary (Non-US):

Delimex de Mexico S.A. de C.V.   **(3)**
Av Periferico Sur No 7980, Jalisco, 45600,
Mexico
Tel.: (52) 33 3001 3800
Specialty Foods Mfr
N.A.I.C.S.: 311999

Subsidiary (Domestic):

H.J. Heinz Company, L.P.   **(3)**
357 6th Ave, Pittsburgh, PA 15222-2530
Tel.: (412) 237-5757
Web Site:
http://www.kraftheinzcompany.com
Convenience Foods Mfr
N.A.I.C.S.: 311999
Priyank Jasani *(Mgr)*

Subsidiary (Non-US):

Alimentos Heinz C.A.   **(4)**
Calle Orinoco Torre 1 Piso 1, Las Mercedes, Caracas, 1060, Venezuela
Tel.: (58) 2129091999
Emp.: 200
Canned Fruits & Vegetables, Pickles,
Sauces & Dressings; Grocery Store Operations
N.A.I.C.S.: 311422
Ana Urquia *(Dir-HR)*
William Gonzalez *(Mgr-Acctg)*

Alimentos Heinz de Costa Rica
S.A.   **(4)**
1km al Este y 200m, San Jose, Costa Rica
Tel.: (506) 2549 9800
Condiments Mfr
N.A.I.C.S.: 311999

Cairo Foods Industries SAE   **(4)**
6 October City 2nd Ind Zone Location No
36, Cairo, 12581, Egypt
Tel.: (20) 238330474
Web Site: http://www.heinz-ame.com
Sales Range: $100-124.9 Million
Emp.: 400
Ketchup, Condiments & Sauces Mfr
N.A.I.C.S.: 311941
Osman Serag Eldin *(Mng Dir)*

H.J. Heinz CR/SR a.s.   **(4)**
Pocernicka 272/96, 108 00, Prague, Czech
Republic
Tel.: (420) 267 021 333
Specialty Foods Mfr
N.A.I.C.S.: 311999

H.J. Heinz Company Australia
Ltd.   **(4)**
Locked Bag 2, South Melbourne, 3205,
VIC, Australia
Tel.: (61) 398615757
Web Site: http://www.heinz.com.au
Sales Range: $250-299.9 Million
Emp.: 600
Food Products Mfr & Distr
N.A.I.C.S.: 311423
Rafael Oliveira *(CEO-Australia, New Zealand, and Papua New Guinea)*
Sarah Bryant *(Mgr-Outsourcing Procurement)*

Unit (Non-US):

Heinz Wattie's Limited   **(5)**

513 King Street North, Hastings, 4122, New
Zealand
Tel.: (64) 68731600
Web Site: http://www.watties.co.nz
Sales Range: $450-499.9 Million
Soups, Frozen & Packaged Fruit & Vegetables, Sauces & Other Foods Mfr
N.A.I.C.S.: 311421
Mike Pretty *(Mng Dir)*
Mike Butcher *(Mgr-Trade Fin)*

Subsidiary (Non-US):

H.J. Heinz Company of Canada
Ltd.   **(4)**
90 Sheppard Avenue East Suite 400, North
York, M2N 7K5, ON, Canada
Tel.: (416) 226-5757
Web Site:
http://www.kraftheinzcompany.com
Sales Range: $600-649.9 Million
Emp.: 255
Convenience Meals, Pet Foods & Treats,
Infant Feeding Products & Specialty Condiments Mfr
N.A.I.C.S.: 311421
Don Holdsworth *(Head-Condiments 7 Spreads)*
Amanda Dingman *(Head-Talent Mgmt)*
Shawn Jones *(Dir-Fin)*

Subsidiary (Domestic):

Renee's Gourmet Foods, Inc.   **(5)**
90 Sheppard Ave E Ste 400, North York,
M2N 7K5, ON, Canada
Web Site: http://www.kraftcanada.com
Sales Range: $25-49.9 Million
Emp.: 100
Salad Dressings, Sauces, Dips, Marinades
& Mayonnaise Mfr & Distr
N.A.I.C.S.: 311941

Subsidiary (Non-US):

Heinz European Holding B.V.   **(4)**
Arnhemse Bovenweg 160-178, Zeist, 3708
AH, Utrecht, Netherlands
Tel.: (31) 306973700
Web Site: http://www.heinz.nl
Emp.: 400
Holding Company
N.A.I.C.S.: 551112
Matt Hill *(Pres)*

Subsidiary (Domestic):

H.J. Heinz B.V.   **(5)**
Kantorenpark de Breul Arnhemse
Bovenweg 160-178, Zeist, 3708 AH, Netherlands
Tel.: (31) 306973700
Web Site: http://www.heinz.nl
Sales Range: $75-99.9 Million
Emp.: 400
Processed Food Products Mfr & Distr
N.A.I.C.S.: 311999
Micha Medendorp *(Dir-Mktg-Belgium, Netherlands & Luxembourg)*

Unit (Domestic):

Honig Merkartikelen   **(6)**
Arnhemse Bovenweg 160-178, 3708 AH,
Zeist, Netherlands
Tel.: (31) 30 697 3700
Web Site: http://www.honig.nl
Emp.: 300
Packaged & Dried Foods, Pasta, Sauce
Mixes, Cereals, Cake, Pudding & Pancake
Mixes, Dehydrated Soups
N.A.I.C.S.: 311999
Peter Boterman *(Dir-Mktg Ops-Europe)*

Subsidiary (Domestic):

Koninklijke De Ruijter BV   **(6)**
Postbus 397, 3700 AJ, Zeist, Netherlands
Tel.: (31) 306973700
Web Site: http://www.deruijter.nl
Emp.: 75
Confectionery Sprinkles Mfr
N.A.I.C.S.: 311352

Subsidiary (Non-US):

H.J. Heinz Belgium N.V.   **(5)**
Bleukenlaan 12, 2300, Turnhout, Belgium
Tel.: (32) 14 42 16 01
Web Site: http://www.heinz.be
Emp.: 135

3G Capital Inc.—(Continued)

Sauces & Sandwich Spreads Mfr & Distr
N.A.I.C.S.: 311941
Vets Luc *(Mgr)*

H.J. Heinz Company (Ireland) Limited (5)
Stradbrook House Stradbrook Road, Black-rock, Dublin, Ireland
Tel.: (353) 12805757
Web Site: http://www.heinz.ie
Sales Range: $10-24.9 Million
Emp.: 14
Distribution of Groceries & Canned Foods
N.A.I.C.S.: 424490
Anne Sewell *(Dir-HR-Europe)*
Jan Kruise *(Mng Dir-UK & Ireland)*

H.J. Heinz Company Limited (5)
Shard 32 London Bridge Street, London, SE1 9SG, Mddx, United Kingdom
Tel.: (44) 2085737757
Web Site: http://www.heinz.co.uk
Sales Range: $150-199.9 Million
Emp.: 300
Canned Food Products; Fresh & Processed Dairy Products Mfr
N.A.I.C.S.: 311421
Matt Hill *(Pres-Europe)*
Ross Longton *(Mgr-Sauces Mktg)*

Unit (Domestic):

H.J. Heinz Foodservice (6)
London Bridge Street, SE19SG, London, Middlesex, United Kingdom
Tel.: (44) 2085737757
Web Site: http://www.heinz.co.uk
Sales Range: $150-199.9 Million
Emp.: 350
Food Products Distr
N.A.I.C.S.: 722310
Jane Hyde *(Brand Mgr)*

Subsidiary (Domestic):

H.J. Heinz Frozen & Chilled Foods Limited (6)
The Shard, London Bridge Street, London, SE1 9SJ, Middlesex, United Kingdom
Tel.: (44) 2085737757
Emp.: 75
Frozen Food Mfr
N.A.I.C.S.: 311412

Subsidiary (Non-US):

H.J. Heinz France S.A.S. (5)
1 Place de la Pyramide Tour Atlantique, 92911, Paris, Cedex, La Defense, France
Tel.: (33) 1 41 96 70 01
Web Site: http://www.heinz.fr
Sales Range: $25-49.9 Million
Emp.: 50
Condiments Mfr
N.A.I.C.S.: 311941
Pradéls Jacques *(Mng Dir)*

H.J. Heinz GmbH (5)
Erkrather Strasse 228b, 40233, Dusseldorf, Germany
Tel.: (49) 211 960766 00
Web Site: http://www.hjheinz.de
Sales Range: $25-49.9 Million
Emp.: 75
Sales & Administration of Food & Condi-ments
N.A.I.C.S.: 424410
Heiko Gerling *(Mng Dir-Central, North & East Europe)*

HJ Heinz Polska Sp. z o.o. (5)
Budynek Orion ul Postepu 18B, Warsaw, 02 676, Poland
Tel.: (48) 22 567 21 11
Web Site: http://www.heinz.pl
Emp.: 75
Canned Foods, Pickles, Sauces & Ready Meals Mfr
N.A.I.C.S.: 311421
Emilia Zlotnicka *(Head-HR-Central, North & Eastern Europe)*
Dorota Marciniak-Lewandowska *(Head-Fin)*
Robert Krzyzewski *(Dir-Sls)*
Grzegorz Lis *(Head-Mktg-Central, North & East Europe)*

Heinz Iberica, S.A. (5)
Plaza glai corpes, Madrid, 28014, Spain

Tel.: (34) 902 94 51 84
Web Site: http://www.heinz.es
Sales Range: $25-49.9 Million
Emp.: 75
Canned Foods Mfr
N.A.I.C.S.: 311421
Ilari Gaztelumendi *(Dir-Fin)*

Heinz Italia S.p.A. (5)
Via Cascina Belcasule 7, Milan, 20141, Italy
Tel.: (39) 0252561
Web Site: http://www.heinz.it
Emp.: 750
Convenience Foods Mfr & Distr
N.A.I.C.S.: 311999
Marco Bozzini *(Mgr-Fin Statements)*

Division (Domestic):

Heinz North America (4)
1 PPG Pl # 3200, Pittsburgh, PA 15222-2500
Tel.: (412) 237-5757
Web Site: http://www.kraftheinzcompany.com
Sales Range: $550-599.9 Million
Emp.: 2,500
Canned Tuna & Pet Food Products Mfr
N.A.I.C.S.: 311111
Eduardo Luz *(Pres)*

Unit (Domestic):

Boca Foods Company (5)
910 Mayer Ave, Madison, WI 53708
Tel.: (608) 285-6950
Web Site: http://www.bocaburger.com
Sales Range: $250-299.9 Million
Meat Alternative Food Products
N.A.I.C.S.: 311412

Churny Company Inc. (5)
3 Lakes Dr, Glenview, IL 60025
Tel.: (847) 646-5500
Web Site: http://www.churny.com
Sales Range: $150-199.9 Million
Specialty Cheeses Mfr & Distr
N.A.I.C.S.: 424430
Howard Friedman *(Pres-Cheese & Dairy & Exec VP)*

Claussen Pickle Co. (5)
1300 Claussen Dr, Woodstock, IL 60098-2155
Tel.: (815) 338-7000
Web Site: http://www.kraftbrands.com
Sales Range: $150-199.9 Million
Emp.: 400
Pickle, Sauerkraut & Relish Mfr
N.A.I.C.S.: 311421

Escalon Premier Brands (5)
1905 McHenry Ave, Escalon, CA 95320
Tel.: (209) 838-7341
Web Site: http://www.escalon.net
Sales Range: $25-49.9 Million
Emp.: 75
Tomato Sauce Mfr
N.A.I.C.S.: 311941
Scott Adrian *(Plant Mgr)*
Dan Milazzo *(Sr Mgr-Sls & Mktg)*

Portion Pac (5)
7325 Snider Rd, Mason, OH 45040-9601
Tel.: (513) 398-0400
Sales Range: $200-249.9 Million
Emp.: 400
Carry-Out & Fast-Food Condiments, Sauces & Dressings Mfr
N.A.I.C.S.: 311941
Jacque Pelfrey *(Coord-Sanitation)*

Quality Chef Foods (5)
5005 C St SW, Cedar Rapids, IA 52404
Tel.: (319) 362-9633
Sales Range: $125-149.9 Million
Emp.: 275
Frozen Food Mfr
N.A.I.C.S.: 311412
Steve Maddocks *(Plant Mgr)*

Todds (5)
2450 White Rd, Irvine, CA 92614-6250
Tel.: (949) 930-2062
Emp.: 300
Salad Dressings, Sauces & Soups Mfr for Restaurants
N.A.I.C.S.: 311422
Dan Milazzo *(Sr Mgr-Sls & Mktg)*

Plant (Domestic):

Todds Foods (6)

610 S 56th Ave, Phoenix, AZ 85043-4622
Tel.: (602) 282-6101
Emp.: 200
Soups & Salad Dressings Mfr
N.A.I.C.S.: 311422
Dan Milazzo *(Sr Mgr-Sls & Mktg)*

Subsidiary (Non-US):

Heinz-UFE Ltd. (4)
Yan Tang Sha He, Guangzhou, 510507, Guangdong, China
Tel.: (86) 87706218
Web Site: http://www.heinz.com.cn
Emp.: 200
Instant Baby Food Mfr & Distr
N.A.I.C.S.: 311421
Alice Wang *(VP-Corp Affairs)*

Subsidiary (Non-US):

H.J. Heinz Finance UK PLC (3)
The Shard 32 London Bridge Street, Lon-don, SE1 9SG, United Kingdom
Tel.: (44) 7723549818
Web Site: https://heinz-finance.com
Insurance Services
N.A.I.C.S.: 524298

Kraft Canada Inc. (3)
95 Moatfield Drive, Toronto, M3B 3L6, ON, Canada
Tel.: (416) 441-5000
Web Site: http://www.kraftsciencecompany.com
Sales Range: $1-4.9 Billion
Emp.: 4,500
Food Products Mfr & Distr
N.A.I.C.S.: 311999
Tony Matta *(Chief Mktg Officer)*
Bernardo Heez *(CEO)*

Plant (Domestic):

Kraft Canada, Inc.-Ingleside (4)
70 Dickinson Dr, Ingleside, K0C 1M0, ON, Canada
Tel.: (613) 537-2226
Web Site: http://www.kraftcanada.com
Sales Range: $150-199.9 Million
Emp.: 400
Natural & Processed Cheese Mfr
N.A.I.C.S.: 311513

Kraft Canada, Inc.-Mount-Royal (4)
8600 Devonshire Rd, Mount-Royal, H4P 2K9, QC, Canada
Tel.: (514) 343-3300
Web Site: http://www.kraftcanada.com
Sales Range: $550-599.9 Million
Emp.: 1,300
Natural & Processed Cheese Mfr
N.A.I.C.S.: 311513

Affiliate (Domestic):

Kraft Food Ingredients Corp. (3)
8000 Horizon Ctr Blvd, Memphis, TN 38133
Tel.: (901) 381-6500
Web Site: http://www.kraftfoodingredients.com
Sales Range: $25-49.9 Million
Emp.: 100
Food Products, Seasonings & Flavorings Mfr
N.A.I.C.S.: 424430
Peter Losee *(Dir-Mktg)*
Stephen Williams *(Dir-Tech)*
Jill Thrasher *(Assoc Dir-Ops)*
Erica Lamar *(Sr Mgr-Quality)*
Jennifer Davidson *(Reg Sls Mgr)*

Subsidiary (Domestic):

Kraft Foods Group Puerto Rico, LLC (3)
9615 Ave Los Romeros, Guaynabo, PR 00968-8033
Tel.: (787) 620-2525
Web Site: http://www.kraftpr.com
Food & Beverage Products Mfr
N.A.I.C.S.: 722330

Plant (Domestic):

Kraft Heinz Company - Addison (3)
2250 W Pinehurst Blvd Ste 150, Addison, IL 60101-6103
Tel.: (630) 547-6000

Sales Range: $100-124.9 Million
Food Product Whslr
N.A.I.C.S.: 424490

Kraft Heinz Company - Charlotte (3)
1338 Hunter Oaks Ln Ste A, Charlotte, NC 28217-3995
Tel.: (704) 565-5500
Sales Range: $75-99.9 Million
Food Products Mfr
N.A.I.C.S.: 311999

Kraft Heinz Company - Columbia (3)
4600 Waco Rd, Columbia, MO 65202-9335
Tel.: (573) 474-9477
Web Site: http://www.kraftfoods.com
Sales Range: $250-299.9 Million
Food Production Services
N.A.I.C.S.: 311999

Kraft Heinz Company - Coshocton (3)
1660 S 2nd St, Coshocton, OH 43812-1950
Tel.: (740) 622-6433
Sales Range: $200-249.9 Million
Bacon Mfr
N.A.I.C.S.: 311999

Kraft Heinz Company - Dover (3)
1250 W N St, Dover, DE 19904
Tel.: (302) 734-6100
Sales Range: $400-449.9 Million
Food Products Mfr
N.A.I.C.S.: 311999

Kraft Heinz Company - Fullerton (3)
1500 E Walnut Ave, Fullerton, CA 92831-4731
Tel.: (714) 870-8235
Sales Range: $200-249.9 Million
Food Products Mfr
N.A.I.C.S.: 311999

Kraft Heinz Company - Garland (3)
2340 Forest Ln, Garland, TX 75042-7924
Tel.: (972) 272-7511
Sales Range: $250-299.9 Million
Food Products Mfr
N.A.I.C.S.: 311421

Kraft Heinz Company - Granite City (3)
200 E Randolph St, Chicago, IL 60601
Tel.: (618) 451-4820
Web Site: http://www.kraftrecipes.com
Sales Range: $350-399.9 Million
Fruit Drink Mfr
N.A.I.C.S.: 311411

Kraft Heinz Company - Irvine (3)
185 Technology Dr, Irvine, CA 92618
Tel.: (949) 453-3500
Web Site: http://www.kraftfoodscompany.com
Sales Range: $75-99.9 Million
Food Products Mfr
N.A.I.C.S.: 311999

Kraft Heinz Company - Lehigh Valley (3)
7352 Industrial Blvd, Allentown, PA 18106-9344
Tel.: (610) 997-6200
Sales Range: $500-549.9 Million
Emp.: 100
Natural & Processed Cheese Mfr
N.A.I.C.S.: 311513

Kraft Heinz Company - Livermore (3)
477 N Canyon Pkwy Ste D, Livermore, CA 94550-9990
Tel.: (925) 454-4500
Sales Range: $75-99.9 Million
Food Products Mfr
N.A.I.C.S.: 311999

Unit (Domestic):

Kraft Heinz Company - Louis Rich (3)
3704 Louis Rich Rd, Newberry, SC 29108-1413
Tel.: (803) 276-5015
Web Site: http://www.kraftfoods.com
Sales Range: $500-549.9 Million
Emp.: 2,400
Poultry Processing
N.A.I.C.S.: 311615
Paul Wright *(Plant Mgr)*

Plant (Domestic):

Kraft Heinz Company - Lowville (3)
7388 Utica Blvd, Lowville, NY 13367-9503
Tel.: (315) 376-6575
Web Site: http://www.kraftfoods.com
Sales Range: $150-199.9 Million
Emp.: 300
Food Products Mfr
N.A.I.C.S.: 311999
Marc Page *(Plant Mgr)*

Kraft Heinz Company - Mason City (3)
1022 12th St NW, Mason City, IA 50401-1802
Tel.: (641) 421-2900
Web Site: http://www.kraftfoods.com
Sales Range: $200-249.9 Million
Emp.: 274
Food Products Mfr
N.A.I.C.S.: 311999

Unit (Domestic):

Kraft Heinz Company - Maxwell House Coffee (3)
735 E Bay St, Jacksonville, FL 32202-2303
Tel.: (904) 632-3400
Web Site:
   http://www.maxwellhousecoffee.com
Sales Range: $200-249.9 Million
Emp.: 425
Coffee Mfr
N.A.I.C.S.: 311920
Joe Waryold *(Plant Mgr)*

Plant (Domestic):

Kraft Heinz Company - New Ulm (3)
2525 S Bridge St, New Ulm, MN 56073-3955
Tel.: (507) 354-4131
Web Site: http://www.kraftfoods.com
Sales Range: $250-299.9 Million
Emp.: 600
Food Production Services
N.A.I.C.S.: 311999

Unit (Domestic):

Kraft Heinz Company - Oscar Mayer (3)
910 Mayer Ave, Madison, WI 53704-4256
Tel.: (608) 241-3311
Web Site: http://www.oscarmayer.com
Sales Range: $300-349.9 Million
Emp.: 1,250
Lunch Meat, Hot Dog & Bacon Mfr
N.A.I.C.S.: 311612

Kraft Heinz Company - Planters (3)
4020 Planters Rd, Fort Smith, AR 72908-8438
Tel.: (479) 648-0100
Web Site: http://www.planters.com
Sales Range: $150-199.9 Million
Emp.: 300
Salted & Roasted Nuts & Seeds Producer
N.A.I.C.S.: 311423

Plant (Domestic):

Kraft Heinz Company - Richmond (3)
6002 S Laburnum Ave, Richmond, VA 23231-5002
Tel.: (804) 222-8802
Sales Range: $300-349.9 Million
Emp.: 750
Crackers, Cookies & Bakery Products Mfr
N.A.I.C.S.: 311812

Kraft Heinz Company - San Leandro (3)
100 Halcyon Dr, San Leandro, CA 94578
Tel.: (510) 639-5000
Sales Range: $150-199.9 Million
Food Products Mfr
N.A.I.C.S.: 311999

Kraft Heinz Company - Springfield (3)
2035 E Bennett St, Springfield, MO 65804-1731
Tel.: (417) 881-2701
Sales Range: $50-74.9 Million
Food Products Mfr
N.A.I.C.S.: 311999

Kraft Heinz Company - Tulare (3)

10800 Avenue 184, Tulare, CA 93274-9514
Tel.: (559) 685-0790
Sales Range: $50-74.9 Million
Food Products Mfr
N.A.I.C.S.: 311999

Kraft Heinz Company - Wausau (3)
1077 Town Line Rd, Wausau, WI 54403-6561
Tel.: (715) 842-2077
Sales Range: $50-74.9 Million
Food Products Mfr
N.A.I.C.S.: 311999

Kraft Heinz Company - Wilkes Barre (3)
50 New Commerce Blvd, Wilkes Barre, PA 18762
Tel.: (570) 820-1200
Sales Range: $100-124.9 Million
Food Mfr
N.A.I.C.S.: 311999

3G CAPITAL MANAGEMENT LLC

1750 S Brentwood Blvd 113, Saint Louis, MO 63144-1337
Tel.: (314) 918-7180   DE
Web Site: http://www.3gcapital.com
Investment Management Service
N.A.I.C.S.: 523999
Pavel Begun *(Co-Founder)*
Cory Bailey *(Co-Founder)*

3G CAPITAL PARTNERS L.P.

600 Third Ave, New York, NY 10016
Tel.: (212) 893-6727
Web Site: https://3gcapital.com
Emp.: 100
Privater Equity Firm
N.A.I.C.S.: 523999

Subsidiaries:

Hunter Douglas N.V. (1)
2 Piekstraat, PO Box 5072, 3071 EL, Rotterdam, Netherlands (75%)
Tel.: (31) 104869911
Web Site:
   http://www.hunterdouglasgroup.com
Rev.: $4,607,000,000
Assets: $3,992,000,000
Liabilities: $1,434,000,000
Net Worth: $2,558,000,000
Earnings: $633,000,000
Emp.: 23,398
Fiscal Year-end: 12/31/2021
Window Coverings & Architectural Products Mfr
N.A.I.C.S.: 423220
Joao Castro Neves *(CEO)*
Michael Jones *(Dir-Investor Relations)*

Subsidiary (Domestic):

HCI Holland Coatings Industries (2)
Marconestraat 12, PO Box 202, 7900 AE, Hoogeveen, Netherlands (100%)
Tel.: (31) 528266231
Sales Range: $25-49.9 Million
Emp.: 50
Mfr of Coil Coatings
N.A.I.C.S.: 325510

Subsidiary (Non-US):

Hunter Douglas (Malaysia) Sdn. Bhd. (2)
Lot 493 Persiaran Kuala Selangor Section 26, 40400, Shah Alam, Selangor Darul Ehsan, Malaysia
Tel.: (60) 3 5191 2020
Web Site: http://ap.hunterdouglas.asia
Window Covering & Architectural Products Mf
N.A.I.C.S.: 337212
G. Cneoh *(Mng Dir)*

Hunter Douglas (Schweiz) GmbH (2)
Langenbold 3, Root, 6037, Switzerland
Tel.: (41) 41 455 5050
Sales Range: $25-49.9 Million
Emp.: 8
Blind & Shade Mfr
N.A.I.C.S.: 337920

Hunter Douglas (Thailand) Co Ltd. (2)
124 Krungthep Kreetha Road, Saphan Sung, Bangkok, 10250, Thailand
Tel.: (66) 2 368 4141
Window Covering & Architectural Products Mfr
N.A.I.C.S.: 337212

Subsidiary (Domestic):

Hunter Douglas Alu - Coil Operations (2)
Piekstraat 2, 3071 EL, Rotterdam, Netherlands
Tel.: (31) 10 486 9911
Web Site:
   http://www.hunterdouglasgroup.com
Sales Range: $200-249.9 Million
Window Covering & Architectural Products Mfr
N.A.I.C.S.: 337212

Subsidiary (Non-US):

Hunter Douglas Architectural Products (Beijing) Co., Ltd. (2)
No 15 South Yongchang Rd, Economic & Technological Development Zone, Beijing, 100176, China
Tel.: (86) 1067889900
Web Site: http://www.nbk.cn
Architectural Product Mfr
N.A.I.C.S.: 337212

Hunter Douglas Architectural Products (China) Co., Ltd. (2)
2805 Zhongchun Road, Minhang District, Shanghai, 201108, China
Tel.: (86) 21 6442 9999
Web Site: http://www.hunterdouglas.cn
Architectural Product Mfr
N.A.I.C.S.: 337212

Hunter Douglas Architectural Products (Shenzhen) Co., Ltd. (2)
3014 East Area 30F Great China International Exchange Square, No 1 Fuhua 1 Road Futian District, Shenzhen, 518026, China
Tel.: (86) 755 6186 8600
Web Site: http://www.hunterdouglas.cn
Sales Range: $25-49.9 Million
Architectural Product Mfr
N.A.I.C.S.: 337212

Hunter Douglas Architectural Products Xiamen (2)
81 Xiafei Road Xinyang Industrial Area, Haicang, Xiamen, 361026, China
Tel.: (86) 592 6512 811
Web Site:
   http://www.hunterdouglasgroup.com
Architectural Products Distr
N.A.I.C.S.: 337212

Subsidiary (Domestic):

Hunter Douglas Architectural Projects NL (2)
Piekstraat 2, 3071 EL, Rotterdam, Netherlands
Tel.: (31) 10 496 2222
Web Site:
   http://www.hunterdouglasgroup.com
Sales Range: $200-249.9 Million
Window Covering & Architectural Products Mfr
N.A.I.C.S.: 337212

Subsidiary (Non-US):

Hunter Douglas Architektur-Systeme GmbH (2)
Erich Ollenhauer-Stasse 7, Dusseldorf-Garath, 40595, Dusseldorf, Germany
Tel.: (49) 211 97 08 60
Web Site:
   http://www.hunterdouglasarchitectural.eu
Window Covering & Architectural Products Mfr
N.A.I.C.S.: 337212

Hunter Douglas Argentina SA (2)
4755 1603 Vila Marteli, Laprida, 1603, Buenos Aires, Argentina
Tel.: (54) 11 47098700
Window Covering & Architectural Products Mfr

N.A.I.C.S.: 337212

Hunter Douglas Assembly Automation AB (2)
Handverkargatan 28, 444 32, Stenungsund, Sweden
Tel.: (46) 303 79 8000
Web Site:
   http://www.hunterdouglasgroup.com
Metal Forming Machinery Mfr
N.A.I.C.S.: 333517

Hunter Douglas Belgium Architectural Products (2)
Industriezone E17/1080 Dijkstraat 26, 9160, Lokeren, Belgium
Tel.: (32) 93489000
Emp.: 80
Window Covering & Architectural Products Mfr
N.A.I.C.S.: 337212
Luuc Ganvier *(Gen Mgr)*
Luc Janvier *(Gen Mgr)*

Hunter Douglas Belgium N.V. (2)
Industriezone E17/1080 Dijkstraat 26, Lokeren, 9160, Belgium
Tel.: (32) 9 348 9000
Web Site:
   http://www.hunterdouglasgroup.com
Sales Range: $25-49.9 Million
Emp.: 80
Window Covering & Architectural Products Mfr
N.A.I.C.S.: 337212

Division (Domestic):

Hunter Douglas Belgium - Helioscreen Projects Division (3)
Industriezone E17/1080 Dijkstraat 26, 9160, Lokeren, Belgium
Tel.: (32) 9 348 9000
Web Site:
   http://www.hunterdouglasgroup.com
Window Covering & Ceiling Material Distr
N.A.I.C.S.: 423330
Luc Janvier *(Mng Dir)*

Hunter Douglas Belgium N.V. - Helioscreen Fabrics Division (3)
Industriezone E17/1080 Dijkstraat 27, 9161, Lokeren, Belgium
Tel.: (32) 9 348 9000
Web Site: http://www.helioscreen.com
Emp.: 70
Fabric Materials Mfr
N.A.I.C.S.: 313310

Subsidiary (Domestic):

Hunter Douglas Benelux (2)
Piekstraat 2, 3071 EL, Rotterdam, Netherlands
Tel.: (31) 10 2974 373
Web Site:
   http://www.hunterdouglasgroup.com
Window Covering & Architectural Products Mfr
N.A.I.C.S.: 337212

Subsidiary (Non-US):

Hunter Douglas Bulgaria Ltd (2)
120 James Boucher Blvd Floor 1 Office 20, 1407, Sofia, Bulgaria
Tel.: (359) 2 979 03 03
Emp.: 9
Window Covering & Architectural Products Mfr
N.A.I.C.S.: 337212
Iancho Hadjistefanov *(Gen Mgr)*

Hunter Douglas C.I.S. (2)
Nizhnyaya Syromyatnicheskaya St 11/1 2nd floor room 12, 105120, Moscow, Russia
Tel.: (7) 4951327332
Web Site:
   http://www.hunterdouglasarchitectural.eu
Sales Range: $25-49.9 Million
Blind & Shade Mfr
N.A.I.C.S.: 337920

Hunter Douglas Canada, Inc. (2)
132 First Golf Blvd, Brampton, L6W 4T7, ON, Canada (100%)
Tel.: (905) 796-7883
Web Site: http://www.hunterdouglas.ca
Sales Range: $50-74.9 Million
Mfr & Distribution of Window Covering Products

3G Capital Partners L.P.—(Continued)
N.A.I.C.S.: 337920

Subsidiary (Domestic):

Shade-O-Matic Ltd. **(3)**
2908 Portland Drive, Oakville, L6H 5W8,
ON, Canada **(100%)**
Tel.: (416) 742-1524
Web Site: http://www.shadeomatic.com
Sales Range: $50-74.9 Million
Retail of Hardware & Window Blinds &
Shades
N.A.I.C.S.: 337920

Subsidiary (Non-US):

Hunter Douglas Cataluna SL **(2)**
C/ Famadas 72, 8907, L'Hospitalet de Llo-
bregat, Barcelona, Spain
Tel.: (34) 93 338 8888
Blind & Shade Mfr
N.A.I.C.S.: 337920

Hunter Douglas China/Hong Kong
Limited **(2)**
Unit 8-12 6/F Topsail Plaza No 11 On Sum
Street, Sha Tin, China (Hong Kong)
Tel.: (852) 26378111
Web Site: http://www.hunterdouglas.com.hk
Sales Range: $25-49.9 Million
Window Fashion & Architectural Products
Distr
N.A.I.C.S.: 423330

Hunter Douglas Components **(2)**
Druseltalstrasse 25, 34131, Kassel, Ger-
many
Tel.: (49) 561409980
Window Covering & Architectural Products
Mfr
N.A.I.C.S.: 337212

Hunter Douglas Components **(2)**
66 Rue Marceau, 93107, Montreuil, France
Tel.: (33) 1 4851 9825
Sales Range: $50-74.9 Million
Emp.: 3
Window Coverings Distr
N.A.I.C.S.: 423220
Frank Cabannes (Gen Mgr)

Hunter Douglas Croatia **(2)**
Hektoroviceva ulica 2, 10000, Zagreb,
Croatia
Tel.: (385) 1 6187 355
Web Site: http://www.hunterdouglas.hr
Window Covering & Architectural Products
Mfr
N.A.I.C.S.: 337212

Hunter Douglas Czechia (Slovakia)
s.r.o. **(2)**
Tomasikova 19, 821 05, Bratislava, Slovakia
Tel.: (421) 248 269 599
Web Site:
http://www.hunterdouglascontract.com
Window Covering & Architectural Products
Mfr
N.A.I.C.S.: 337212

Hunter Douglas Czechia NA **(2)**
Na Brevnovske Plani 25, 169 00, Prague,
Czech Republic
Tel.: (420) 241 727 704
Web Site: http://www.hunterdouglas.cz
Window Covering & Architectural Products
Mfr
N.A.I.C.S.: 337212

Hunter Douglas Entwicklungsgesell-
schaft mbH **(2)**
Nordenhamer Strasse 9, 27572, Bremer-
haven, Germany
Tel.: (49) 471 972 500
Window Shade Mfr
N.A.I.C.S.: 337920

Hunter Douglas Espana S.A **(2)**
La Granja 15 P I Edif B PI 1, Alcobendas,
28108, Madrid, Spain
Tel.: (34) 916618900
Web Site:
http://www.hunterdouglasgroup.com
Window Covering & Architectural Products
Mfr
N.A.I.C.S.: 337212

Subsidiary (Domestic):

Hunter Douglas Europe B.V. **(2)**

Piekstraat 2, Rotterdam, 3071 EL,
Netherlands **(100%)**
Tel.: (31) 104869911
Web Site: http://www.hunterdouglas.nl
Sales Range: $200-249.9 Million
Emp.: 600
Window Coverings & Architectural Products
Mfr & Distr
N.A.I.C.S.: 423220
Ralph Sonnenberg (CEO)
Aad Kuiper (Pres/CEO-Ops-Europe)

Branch (Domestic):

Hunter Douglas Europe **(3)**
Piekstraat 2, PO Box 5072, 3071 EL, Rot-
terdam, Netherlands **(100%)**
Tel.: (31) 104869911
Web Site: http://www.hunterdouglas.nl
Sales Range: $50-74.9 Million
Window Covering & Architectural Product
Mfr
N.A.I.C.S.: 337212

Subsidiary (Non-US):

Hunter Douglas Fabrication Sp.
Z.o.o. **(2)**
ul Poznanska 31, 62-001, Chludowo, Po-
land
Tel.: (48) 616477400
Web Site:
http://www.jestesmyhunterdouglas.pl
Decorative Windows Covering Product Mfr
N.A.I.C.S.: 326199

Hunter Douglas Hungary Ltd **(2)**
Bokor utca 9-11, 1039, Budapest, Hungary
Tel.: (36) 1 391 4590
Web Site:
http://www.hunterdouglasarchitectural.eu
Window Covering & Architectural Products
Mfr
N.A.I.C.S.: 337212

Hunter Douglas India Pvt Ltd. **(2)**
C-102 Mangalya Marol Maroshi Road, And-
heri E, Mumbai, 400 059, India
Tel.: (91) 22 6761 7500
Web Site: http://in.hunterdouglas.asia
Sales Range: $50-74.9 Million
Window Covering & Architectural Products
Distr
N.A.I.C.S.: 423330

Hunter Douglas Italy **(2)**
Via Paracelso 26, Palazzo Cassiopea 3,
20864, Agrate Brianza, Monza and Brianza,
Italy
Tel.: (39) 0398901520
Web Site: http://www.hunterdouglas.it
Window Covering & Architectural Products
Mfr
N.A.I.C.S.: 337212

Hunter Douglas Kadan s.r.o. **(2)**
Tusimice 15, 432 01, Kadan, Czech Repub-
lic
Tel.: (420) 474 319 211
Web Site: http://www.hunterdouglas-
kadan.cz
Emp.: 450
Solar Shading Products Mfr
N.A.I.C.S.: 335131

Hunter Douglas Korea Limited **(2)**
6F DongYang Bldg 216 Dongjak-daero,
Seocho-gu, Seoul, 06554, Korea (South)
Tel.: (82) 2 518 3663
Web Site: http://ap.hunterdouglas.asia
Window Fashion & Architectural Products
Distr
N.A.I.C.S.: 423220

Hunter Douglas Latina America **(2)**
Rua Gal Furtado do Nascimento 740/54
Alto de Pinheiros, Sao Paulo, 05465-070,
Brazil
Tel.: (55) 11 21351025
Sales Range: $100-124.9 Million
Emp.: 40
Window Covering & Architectural Products
Mfr
N.A.I.C.S.: 337212
Renato Rocha (Pres & CEO)

Hunter Douglas Limited **(2)**
338 Victoria Road, Rydalmere, 2116, NSW,
Australia **(100%)**
Tel.: (61) 2 9638 8000

Web Site: http://www.hunterdouglas.com.au
Sales Range: $50-74.9 Million
Mfr of Venetian & Vertical Blinds
N.A.I.C.S.: 337920

Subsidiary (Domestic):

Hunter Douglas Holdings Ltd. **(3)**
338 Victoria Rd, Rydalmere, 2116, NSW,
Australia **(100%)**
Tel.: (61) 296388000
Web Site: http://www.hunterdouglas.com.au
Holding Company
N.A.I.C.S.: 551112

Subsidiary (Domestic):

Australian Window Furnishings
(NSW) Pty. Ltd. **(4)**
338 Victoria Road, 338 Victoria Rydalmare,
Rydalmere, 2116, NSW, Australia
Tel.: (61) 296388000
Web Site: http://www.luxaflex.com.au
Sales Range: $100-124.9 Million
Emp.: 300
Mfr of Window Furnishings
N.A.I.C.S.: 337920
Tony Politis (Mng Dir)

Dural Leeds Pty. Ltd. **(4)**
100 Spring St, Port Melbourne, 3207, VIC,
Australia **(75%)**
Tel.: (61) 394999018
Mfr of Blinds & Window Coverings
N.A.I.C.S.: 337920

Subsidiary (Non-US):

Hunter Douglas Management AG **(2)**
Adligenswiler Strasse 37, 6006, Lucerne,
Switzerland **(100%)**
Tel.: (41) 414192727
Web Site: http://www.hunterdouglas.com
Sales Range: $25-49.9 Million
Emp.: 20
N.A.I.C.S.: 332323

Hunter Douglas Mexico S.A. De
C.V. **(2)**
Av Dr Gustavo Baz No 166-A Col La Es-
cuela, 54090, Tlalnepantla, Mexico
Tel.: (52) 55 2169 0010
Web Site: http://www.hunterdouglas.com.mx
Building Curtain & Blind Mfr
N.A.I.C.S.: 337212

Hunter Douglas Middle East FZE **(2)**
Jebel Ali Free Zone South Near Volvo
Showroom, PO Box 17283, Jebel Ali,
Dubai, 17283, United Arab Emirates
Tel.: (971) 4 813 1800
Web Site:
http://www.hunterdouglasarchitectural.eu
Sales Range: $25-49.9 Million
Window Shade Mfr
N.A.I.C.S.: 337212

Hunter Douglas Panama SA **(2)**
Calle tercera Galera Romani 1 Parque In-
dustrial, PO Box 0830-01313, Costa del
Este Parque Lefebre, Panama, 1313,
Panama
Tel.: (507) 66 786869
Web Site:
http://www.hunterdouglasgroup.com
Window Shade Mfr
N.A.I.C.S.: 337920

Hunter Douglas Peru S.A.C **(2)**
Jr Galdeano y mendoza 750, Lima, 01,
Peru
Tel.: (51) 1 708 4000
Web Site: http://www.hunterdouglas.com.pe
Window Curtain & Blinds Mfr
N.A.I.C.S.: 337920

Hunter Douglas Philippines Inc **(2)**
517 5/F Gateway Tower Gen Roxas Avenue
cor Gen Aguinaldo Avenue, Araneta Center
Cubao, Quezon City, 1109, Philippines
Tel.: (63) 9175540220
Web Site: http://www.hunterdouglas.com.ph
Window Fashion & Architectural Products
Distr
N.A.I.C.S.: 423220

Hunter Douglas Polska SP.
Z.o.o. **(2)**
ul Marywilska 34 B, 03-228, Warsaw, Poland
Tel.: (48) 22 614 1671

Web Site:
http://www.hunterdouglasarchitectural.eu
Window Covering & Architectural Products
Mfr
N.A.I.C.S.: 337212
Jacek Szelag (Gen Mgr)

Hunter Douglas Produktion
GmbH **(2)**
Meeraner Strasse 25, 8371, Glauchau, Ger-
many
Tel.: (49) 3763 796 0
Web Site: http://www.hdprod.de
Window Covering & Architectural Products
Mfr
N.A.I.C.S.: 337212

Hunter Douglas Romania SRL **(2)**
Bd Basarabia nr 80 et 1 sect 2, Bucharest,
28911, Romania
Tel.: (40) 2 1321 2745
Web Site:
http://www.hunterdouglasarchitectural.eu
Window Covering & Architectural Products
Mfr
N.A.I.C.S.: 337212

Hunter Douglas Scandinavia AB **(2)**
Kristineholmsvagen 14 A, 441 39, Alingsas,
Sweden
Tel.: (46) 31 93 9460
Sales Range: $50-74.9 Million
Emp.: 5
Window Covering & Architectural Products
Distr
N.A.I.C.S.: 423330
Per Stenberg (Gen Mgr)

Hunter Douglas Serbia **(2)**
Blok VI Izletnicki put 4a, 11070, Belgrade,
Serbia
Tel.: (381) 11 2608538
Web Site: http://www.hunterdouglas.co.rs
Window Covering & Architectural Products
Mfr
N.A.I.C.S.: 337212

Hunter Douglas Singapore Pte.
Ltd. **(2)**
60 Benoi Road 02-02, Singapore, 629906,
Singapore
Tel.: (65) 68624466
Web Site: http://sg.hunterdouglas.asia
Sales Range: $25-49.9 Million
Mfr of Blinds
N.A.I.C.S.: 337920

Hunter Douglas South Africa Pty
Ltd **(2)**
Northlands Commercial Park Unit 7 Aintree
Avenue, Northriding, Johannesburg, 2194,
South Africa
Tel.: (27) 112517000
Web Site:
http://www.hunterdouglasarchitectural.eu
Fabricated Aluminium Cladding Mfr
N.A.I.C.S.: 331315

Hunter Douglas Taiwan Ltd. **(2)**
10F No 172 Sec 2 Nanjing E Rd, Zhong-
shan District, Taipei, 10489, Taiwan
Tel.: (886) 225048777
Web Site: http://www.hunterdouglas.com.tw
Window Covering & Architectural Products
Distr
N.A.I.C.S.: 423220

Hunter Douglas Turkey **(2)**
Icerenkoy Mh Topcu Ibrahim Sk 8-10D 5
and Plaza, Atasehir, Istanbul, 34752, Tur-
kiye
Tel.: (90) 5332054869
Web Site:
http://www.hunterdouglasarchitectural.eu
Sales Range: $25-49.9 Million
Window Covering & Architectural Products
Mfr
N.A.I.C.S.: 337212

Hunter Douglas Venezuela SA **(2)**
La Estancia Edificio General piso 4 office
4B Chuao, Caracas, Venezuela
Tel.: (58) 212 959 5121
Web Site: http://www.hunterdouglas.com.ve
Window Shade Mfr
N.A.I.C.S.: 337212

Hunter Douglas Vietnam Ltd **(2)**
Lot A1 Street No 1 Binh Chieu Industrial
Zone, Thu Duc District, Ho Chi Minh City,
Vietnam

Tel.: (84) 8 3897 5556
Window Covering & Architectural Products Distr
N.A.I.C.S.: 423220

Hunter Douglas Window Covering Products (Beijing) Co., Ltd. (2)
501-503 Block 3 No 105 Yao Jia Yuan Road, Chaoyang District, Beijing, 100004, China
Tel.: (86) 10 5962 3311
Sales Range: $25-49.9 Million
Emp.: 49
Window Covering Products Distr
N.A.I.C.S.: 423220
Jacob Liu (Gen Mgr)

Hunter Douglas Window Covering Products (China) Co., Ltd. (2)
No 161 Yaotianhe Street Yongshun Avenue Yonghe Zone, Guangzhou, 511356, Guangdong, China
Tel.: (86) 20 3222 2888
Emp.: 80
Window Covering Products Distr
N.A.I.C.S.: 423220
Amanda Li (Mgr)

Hunter Douglas Window Covering Products (Shanghai) Co., Ltd. (2)
2805 Zhong Chun Road, Minhang District, Shanghai, 201108, China
Tel.: (86) 21 3471 7777
Window Covering Products Distr
N.A.I.C.S.: 423220

Hunter Douglas Window Covering Products (Shenzhen) Co., Ltd. (2)
1/F No 19 Industrial Building Shatoujiao Bonding Zone, Shenzhen, 518081, China
Tel.: (86) 755 2526 1068
Web Site: http://wf.hunterdouglas.asia
Window Blind & Shade Distr
N.A.I.C.S.: 423220

Hunter Douglas do Brazil Ltda. (2)
Industria R Estacio de Sa 1860 Jd Sta Genebra, Campinas, SP, Brazil (100%)
Tel.: (55) 1937084000
Web Site: http://www.hunterdouglas.com.br
Sales Range: $25-49.9 Million
Mfr of Venetian & Vertical Blinds
N.A.I.C.S.: 337920

Subsidiary (US):

Hunter Douglas, Inc. (2)
1 Blue Hill Plz, Pearl River, NY 10965 (100%)
Tel.: (845) 664-7000
Web Site: http://www.hunterdouglas.com
Sales Range: $900-999.9 Million
Mfr of Venetian Blinds, Shutters, Vertical Blinds, Pleated Shades, Honeycomb Shades, Window Shadings, Privacy Sheers, Wood Blinds & Roman Shades
N.A.I.C.S.: 337920
Ronald R. Kass (Pres & CEO)

Subsidiary (Domestic):

Carole Fabrics Corp. (3)
633 NW Frotnage Rd, Augusta, GA 30907-2406 (100%)
Tel.: (706) 863-4742
Web Site: http://www.carolefabrics.com
Sales Range: $25-49.9 Million
Mfr of Fabrics
N.A.I.C.S.: 313210

Comfortex Corporation (3)
21 Elm St, Watervliet, NY 12189-1740
Tel.: (518) 273-3333
Web Site: http://www.comfortex.com
Sales Range: $75-99.9 Million
Window Blinds
N.A.I.C.S.: 337920
John Fitzgerald (Exec VP)
Thomas J. Marusak (Founder & Pres)
Jim Barss (VP-Fabrication Ops)

Division (Domestic):

Hunter Douglas - Custom Shutter Division (3)
1805 W Drake Dr, Tempe, AZ 85283
Tel.: (877) 553-4426
Web Site:
http://www.hunterdouglasgroup.com

Window Covering & Architectural Products Mfr
N.A.I.C.S.: 337212

Hunter Douglas - Horizontal Blinds Division (3)
1171 N Fiesta Blvd Ste 1, Gilbert, AZ 85233
Tel.: (480) 558-7677
Architectural Product Mfr
N.A.I.C.S.: 337212

Hunter Douglas - Window Designs Division (3)
201 Southridge Pkwy, Bessemer City, NC 28016
Tel.: (704) 629-6500
Web Site:
http://www.hunterdouglasgroup.com
Window Covering & Architectural Products Mfr
N.A.I.C.S.: 337212

Subsidiary (Domestic):

Hunter Douglas Architectural Products Inc. (3)
5015 Oakbrook Pkwy Ste 100, Norcross, GA 30093-2265 (100%)
Tel.: (770) 806-9557
Web Site: http://www.hdceilings.com
Sales Range: $25-49.9 Million
Emp.: 30
Mfr of Metal Ceilings
N.A.I.C.S.: 332323

Hunter Douglas Fabrication (3)
1870 Milmont Dr, Milpitas, CA 95035-2512
Tel.: (408) 435-8844
Web Site: http://www.hdfab.com
Sales Range: $25-49.9 Million
Emp.: 15
Mfr of Drapery Window Blinds & Shades
N.A.I.C.S.: 337920

Hunter Douglas Fabrication Co. (3)
12250 Pkwy Ctr Dr, Poway, CA 92064-6850 (100%)
Tel.: (858) 679-7500
Web Site: http://www.hunterdouglas.com
Mfr of Venetian Blinds & Window Coverings
N.A.I.C.S.: 561990
Ronald R. Kass (Pres & CEO)
Gordon Khan (Treas)
Geoffrey Parnass (Sec)

Hunter Douglas Fashions Inc. (3)
17100 Pioneer Blvd, Artesia, CA 90701 (100%)
Tel.: (213) 749-6333
Mini Blinds
N.A.I.C.S.: 337920

Hunter Douglas Hospitality, Inc (3)
12975 Brookprinter Pl Ste 210, Poway, CA 92064
Web Site:
http://www.hunterdouglashospitality.com
Window Curtains Mfr & Distr
N.A.I.C.S.: 314120

Division (Domestic):

Hunter Douglas Metals (3)
915 175th St, Homewood, IL 60430-2058 (100%)
Tel.: (708) 799-0800
Sales Range: $25-49.9 Million
Emp.: 35
Metals Trading Company
N.A.I.C.S.: 423510
R. Sfura (CFO)
George Ribet (Pres)
John Fife (VP)

Subsidiary (Domestic):

Hunter Douglas Verticals (3)
201 Southridge Pkwy, Bessemer City, NC 28016 (100%)
Tel.: (704) 629-6500
Web Site:
http://www.hunterdouglasgroup.com
Sales Range: $25-49.9 Million
Emp.: 180
Mfr of Knitted & Insert Fabrics for Vertical Blinds
N.A.I.C.S.: 337920

Hunter Douglas Window Fashions, Inc. (3)

1 Duette Way, Broomfield, CO 80020-1090
Tel.: (303) 466-1848
Web Site: http://www.hunterdouglas.com
Sales Range: $150-199.9 Million
Drapery Hardware & Window Blinds & Shades
N.A.I.C.S.: 337920

Phoenix Trading Corp. (3)
152 Waters Edge Dr, Jupiter, FL 33477-4031
Tel.: (561) 845-8388
Sales Range: $50-74.9 Million
Emp.: 10
Distr of Fish & Seafoods
N.A.I.C.S.: 424460

Subsidiary (Non-US):

Levolor Inc. (2)
101-435 North Service Road W, Oakville, L6M 4X8, ON, Canada
Window Covering Mfr
N.A.I.C.S.: 321918

Division (US):

Levolor, Inc. (2)
5775 Glenridge Dr, Building A, Atlanta, GA 30328
Tel.: (800) 752-9677
Web Site: http://www.levolor.com
Mfr of Vertical Blinds
N.A.I.C.S.: 337920

Subsidiary (Non-US):

Levolor Kirsch Window Fashions (3)
53 Jutland Rd, Toronto, M8Z 2G6, ON, Canada (100%)
Tel.: (416) 252-3751
Web Site: http://www.levolor.ca
Sales Range: $25-49.9 Million
Emp.: 100
Drapery Window Blinds & Shades
N.A.I.C.S.: 337920

Subsidiary (Domestic):

Newell Puerto Rico, Ltd. (3)
Carr 190 Km 8.8, Carolina, PR 00984 (100%)
Tel.: (787) 769-8885
Glass Tableware Products Distributor
N.A.I.C.S.: 423220

Subsidiary (Domestic):

Multisol Raambekleding B.V. (2)
St Hubertusstraat 4, 6531 LB, Nijmegen, Netherlands
Tel.: (31) 243597777
Web Site: http://www.multisol.nl
Sales Range: $25-49.9 Million
Mfr of Window Covering Products
N.A.I.C.S.: 321911

Nedal (2)
Groenewoudsedijk 1, 3528 BG, Utrecht, Netherlands
Tel.: (31) 302925711
Web Site: http://www.nedal.com
Sales Range: $50-74.9 Million
Operator of Aluminum Extrusion Facilities
N.A.I.C.S.: 331318

Subsidiary (Non-US):

PT Hunter Douglas Indonesia (2)
WISMA 77 16th floor tower 2 Jl Letjend S Parman Kav 77 Slipi, Kebon Jeruk, Jakarta, 11420, Indonesia
Tel.: (62) 2129676001
Web Site: http://www.ap.hunterdouglas.asia
Window Fashion & Architectural Products Distr
N.A.I.C.S.: 423220

Subsidiary (Domestic):

Sunway (Benelux) B.V. (2)
Overijsselhaven 30, 3433 PH, Nieuwegein, Netherlands
Tel.: (31) 306083100
Web Site: http://www.sunway.nl
Sales Range: $25-49.9 Million
Furniture Mfr
N.A.I.C.S.: 449110

3G GRAPHIC SOLUTIONS

581 W Leffel Ln, Springfield, OH 45506
Tel.: (937) 325-5503
Sales Range: $10-24.9 Million
Gravure Printing Services
N.A.I.C.S.: 323111
Jeanne Lampe (Pres)

3I PEOPLE, INC.
5755 N Point Pkwy Ste 9, Alpharetta, GA 30022
Tel.: (404) 636-2397
Web Site: https://www.3ipeople.com
Year Founded: 2002
Sales Range: $1-9.9 Million
Emp.: 80
Full-Service Global Information Technology Systems
N.A.I.C.S.: 519290
Raj Swami (Founder & Pres)
Buvi Raj (VP-Mktg & HR)

3MV BANCORP, INC.
8712 W Dodge Rd, Omaha, NE 68114
Tel.: (402) 763-6008   NE
Web Site:
https://www.accessbank.com
Year Founded: 2007
Sales Range: $10-24.9 Million
Bank Holding Company
N.A.I.C.S.: 551111
Patrick J. Corrigan (Pres & CEO)
Dana Henricksen (CFO, Treas, Sec & Exec VP)

Subsidiaries:

Access Bank (1)
8712 W Dodge Rd, Omaha, NE 68114
Tel.: (402) 763-6000
Web Site: http://www.accessbank.com
Sales Range: $10-24.9 Million
Emp.: 61
Commercial Banking
N.A.I.C.S.: 522110
Dana Henricksen (CFO & Exec VP)
Kevin Albertsen (Chief Lending Officer & Exec VP)
Patrick J. Corrigan (Pres & CEO)

3NORTH
201 W 7th St, Richmond, VA 23224
Tel.: (804) 232-8900
Web Site: http://www.3north.com
Year Founded: 1998
Sales Range: $25-49.9 Million
Emp.: 24
Construction, Interior Design & Graphic Design Services
N.A.I.C.S.: 541430
Jay Hugo (Mng Principal)
Sanford Bond (Owner)

3PHASE ELEVATOR CORP
60 Shawmut Rd Ste 1, Canton, MA 02021
Tel.: (508) 350-9900
Web Site:
http://www.3phaseelevator.com
Year Founded: 1996
Sales Range: $1-9.9 Million
Vertical Transportation Maintenance & Repair
N.A.I.C.S.: 811310
Jeff Hannon (Pres)
Keith A. Galizio (VP)
Mike Strachan (CEO)

Subsidiaries:

Eagle Elevator Co., Inc. (1)
176 Norfolk Ave, Boston, MA 02119
Tel.: (617) 283-0613
Web Site: http://www.eagleelevator.net
Rev.: $8,050,000
Emp.: 50
Plumbing, Heating & Air-Conditioning Contractors
N.A.I.C.S.: 238220

3Phase Elevator Corp—(Continued)

Dan Wrenn *(Pres)*
Ken Murphy *(Dir-Sls-Reg)*
Michael Pierce *(Mgr-Sls-Reg)*

Hadfield Elevator (1)
2413 W Carson St, Pittsburgh,. PA 15204
Tel.: (412) 771-3277
Web Site: http://www.hadfieldelevator.com
Plumbing, Heating & Air-Conditioning Contractors
N.A.I.C.S.: 238220
Bob Hadfield Jr. *(VP)*

Halley Elevator Company, Inc. (1)
11 Tyng St, Newburyport, MA 01950-2115
Tel.: (978) 463-0020
Web Site: http://www.halleyelevator.com
Elevator & Moving Stairway Mfr
N.A.I.C.S.: 333921
Jeffrey J. Halley *(Pres)*

TEC Elevator, Inc. (1)
35C S Shore Rd, Marmora, NJ 08223-1215
Tel.: (609) 432-9237
Web Site: http://www.tecelevatorinc.com
Specialty Trade Contractors
N.A.I.C.S.: 238990
Robert Shaw *(Owner)*

3PILLAR GLOBAL, INC.
3975 Fair Ridge Dr Ste 250N, Fairfax, VA 22033
Tel.: (703) 435-6365
Web Site:
  http://www.threepillarglobal.com
Year Founded: 2003
Sales Range: $25-49.9 Million
Emp.: 600
Design, Develops & Implements IT
Products & Services for the Federal
Government, Commercial & Independent Software Enterprises
N.A.I.C.S.: 334610
Maria Izurieta *(CFO)*
David H. DeWolf *(Founder & CEO)*
Michael Dering *(Chm)*
Tony Orlando *(Exec VP-Market & Client Svcs)*
Kevin Golden *(Gen Counsel)*
Jeff Nielsen *(Sr VP-Engrg)*
Heather Combs *(COO)*
Paul Doman *(VP-Media & Info Svcs Industries)*
Jennifer Ives *(Sr VP-Tech Indus)*
Elisabeth Beller *(VP-Health & Wellness Indus)*
John Bernardi *(Co-CFO)*
Adam Hahn *(VP-Engrg)*
Jennifer Stanford *(VP-Talent)*
Casey Craig *(Sr VP-Retail)*
Chris Hansen *(Sr VP-Media & Info Svcs Client Svc Vertical)*

Subsidiaries:

Software Development Europe, Inc. (1)
8354 Six Forks Rd Ste 204, Raleigh, NC 27615
Tel.: (919) 806-4453
Web Site: http://www.sdeusa.com
Computer System Design Services
N.A.I.C.S.: 541512
Jeff Smith *(CEO)*
Donnie Goins *(Chief Engrg Officer)*
David DeWolf *(CEO)*

Tiempo Development LLC (1)
1050 W Washington St Ste 201, Tempe, AZ 85281
Tel.: (602) 910-4646
Web Site:
  http://www.tiempodevelopment.com
Outsourced Software Development & Testing Services
N.A.I.C.S.: 513210
Bruce Steele *(COO)*
Cliff Schertz *(Founder & CEO)*
James Walborm *(CFO)*
Maria Gotes *(VP-Talent & Org Dev)*
Hector Vega *(VP-Engrg & Client Solutions)*
David Sawatzky *(Chief Delivery Officer)*

Subsidiary (Non-US):

Tiempo Development Center (2)
Parque Tecnologico CIT2 Pabellon TEC
Eugenio Garza Sada, 427 Local 38 Interior
27A Col Altavista, Monterrey, Nuevo Leon, Mexico (100%)
Tel.: (52) 811 234 2192
Web Site: http://www.tiempodev.com
Software Development Services
N.A.I.C.S.: 513210
Bruce Steele *(Chief Strategy Officer)*
James Walbom *(CFO)*
Mike Hahn *(COO)*

Tiempo Development Center (2)
Blvd Garcia Morales no 545 Blvd Antonio
Quiroga Col La Manga, Hermosillo, 83210,
Sonora, Mexico (100%)
Tel.: (52) 662 260 9675
Web Site:
  http://www.tiempodevelopment.com
Emp.: 100
Software Devolopment
N.A.I.C.S.: 513210
Bruce Steele *(COO)*

3Q DIGITAL, INC.
155 Bovet Rd Ste 480, San Mateo, CA 94402
Tel.: (650) 539-4124   DE
Web Site: http://www.3qdigital.com
Sales Range: $10-24.9 Million
Emp.: 100
Media Services
N.A.I.C.S.: 541830
David Rodnitzky *(Founder & CEO)*
Scott Rayden *(CMO & Chief Revenue Officer)*
Brian Grabowski *(Chief Client Officer)*
Mason Garrity *(VP-Strategy)*
Aaron Bart *(VP-Creative Svcs)*
Feliks Malts *(VP-Decision Sciences)*
Ellen Corrigan *(VP-Bus Dev)*
Diego Rovira *(Sr VP-Client Svcs)*
Laura Rodnitzky *(VP-People)*
Christine Baker *(VP-Client Svcs)*
Bob Sturges *(VP-Client Svcs)*
Hillary Read *(VP-Mktg)*
Carl Paradiso *(VP-Tech)*
Eric Smith *(VP-Client Svcs)*
Joseph Kerschbaum *(VP-Client Svcs)*
Brad O'Brien *(VP-Social)*
Alex Funk *(VP-Strategic Dev)*
Rob Murray *(Pres)*

3RIVERS FEDERAL CREDIT UNION
1615 Northland Blvd, Fort Wayne, IN 46825
Tel.: (260) 490-8328
Web Site: http://www.3riversfcu.org
Privater Equity Firm
N.A.I.C.S.: 523999
Don Greer *(Chm)*

Subsidiaries:

West End Bank, S.B. (1)
34 S 7th St, Richmond, IN 47374-5424
Tel.: (765) 962-9587
Web Site: http://www.westendbank.com
Sales Range: $50-74.9 Million
Emp.: 73
Federal Savings Institutions
N.A.I.C.S.: 522180
John P. McBride *(Chm)*
Timothy R. Frame *(Pres & CEO)*

3S NETWORK INC.
30398 Esperanza, Rancho Santa Margarita, CA 92688
Tel.: (949) 916-4561
Web Site: http://www.3snetwork.com
Year Founded: 2001
Sales Range: $10-24.9 Million
Emp.: 228
Telecommunications
N.A.I.C.S.: 517810
Tim Burton *(VP)*

3SIXTY GROUP LLC
1827 N Squirrel Rd, Auburn Hills, MI 48326
Tel.: (248) 844-2601
Web Site:
  http://www.3sixtygroup.com
Components Mfr
N.A.I.C.S.: 335999
Roger Anderson *(Mgr-Ops)*

3T SYSTEMS, INC.
5990 Greenwood Plaza Blvd Bldg 2
Ste 350, Greenwood Village, CO 80111
Tel.: (303) 858-8800
Web Site: http://www.3tsystems.com
Sales Range: $10-24.9 Million
Emp.: 180
IT Consulting Services
N.A.I.C.S.: 541512
Ciaran Dwyer *(Chm)*
Jan Rutherford *(CEO)*
Jimmy Wang *(Sr Mgr-Client)*
Doug Kulesa *(Acct Mgr)*

3TAILER, LLC
505 S Cedar St Ste B, Charlotte, NC 28202
Web Site: http://www.3tailer.com
Year Founded: 2005
Sales Range: $1-9.9 Million
Emp.: 15
Online Health & Medical Products
Retailers
N.A.I.C.S.: 456199

3V COMPANY
17105 Groschke Rd Ste 100, Houston, TX 77084
Tel.: (281) 717-1280   TX
Web Site:
  http://www.3vcompany.com
Year Founded: 1982
Sales Range: $1-9.9 Million
Emp.: 50
Designer, Builder & Installer of Store
Fixtures & Architectural Woodwork
N.A.I.C.S.: 321918
Ruben Villarreal *(Co-Owner & Pres)*
Daniel Villarreal *(Co-Owner & Mgr-Bus Dev)*

4 CORNERS CUSTOM HOMES
6180 Boucher Dr, Edmond, OK 73034
Tel.: (405) 330-0005
Web Site:
  http://www.4cornershomes.com
Sales Range: $10-24.9 Million
Emp.: 24
General Contractors
N.A.I.C.S.: 236115
Dusty Boren *(Owner & CEO)*

4 FORCES GROUP LLC
1177 Summer St, Stamford, CT 06905-5572
Tel.: (203) 658-8880
Web Site:
  http://www.4forcesgroup.com
Emp.: 100
Marketing Consulting Services
N.A.I.C.S.: 541613

4 RIVERS EQUIPMENT LLC
924 11th St, Greeley, CO 80631
Tel.: (970) 356-3666
Web Site:
  https://www.4riversequipment.com
Year Founded: 1968
Sales Range: $25-49.9 Million
Emp.: 400
Industrial Machinery & Equipment
N.A.I.C.S.: 423830
Keith Olson *(Gen Mgr)*
Sylvia Salway *(Mgr-HR)*

Subsidiaries:

Honnen Equipment Co. (1)
5055 E 72nd Ave, Commerce City, CO 80022
Tel.: (303) 287-7506
Web Site: https://www.honnen.com
Rev.: $20,600,000
Emp.: 100
Construction & Mining Equipment Whslr
N.A.I.C.S.: 423810
Stephanie Beazley *(Mgr-Mktg)*
Judy Conn *(Mgr-Asset)*
Jim Oller *(Mgr-Parts)*
Matt Murphy *(Dir-John Deere Sls)*
Dean Hirt *(Dir-Product Support)*
Mark Honnen *(Pres)*
Jonathan Asbury *(Mgr-Sls-Wirtgen Grp)*
Mike De Martin *(CFO)*
Marty Hlawati *(Sr Mgr-Sls)*
Jardie Lauinger *(Mgr-Sls-John Deere CWP)*
Brad Parker *(Mgr-Parts)*
Daniel Russell *(Mgr-Parts)*
Doug Sharp *(Mgr-Parts)*
Erin Bower *(Dir-HR)*
Mindy Reddon *(Mgr-Parts)*
Ron Metzger *(Mgr-Parts)*
Shaun Vunder *(Mgr-Parts)*
Kevin Krausch *(Mgr-Front Range Sls-Colorado)*

4 STAR ELECTRONICS, INC.
930 Calle Negocio Ste C, San Clemente, CA 92673
Tel.: (949) 276-5225   CA
Web Site:
  https://www.4starelectronics.com
Year Founded: 2001
Sales Range: $10-24.9 Million
Emp.: 50
Electrical Apparatus & Equipment,
Wiring Supplies & Related Equipment
Merchant Whslr
N.A.I.C.S.: 423610
Mike Coon *(Sr Acct Mgr-OEM)*
Robert McBride *(Dir-Bus Dev)*
Karisa Burgess *(Mgr-Acctg)*
Jeff Storhoff *(Sr Acct Mgr-OEM)*

4 VILLY INC.
1644 S Washington St, Du Quoin, IL 62832
Tel.: (618) 542-3244
Rev.: $18,648,169
Emp.: 50
Petroleum Bulk Stations
N.A.I.C.S.: 424710

4 WALLS, INC.
PO Box 248, Narberth, PA 19072
Web Site: http://www.respage.com
Year Founded: 2002
Sales Range: $1-9.9 Million
Advertising Agency Services
N.A.I.C.S.: 541810
Jackie Koehler *(CEO)*

4-H TRANSPORTATION CO. INC.
Saratoga Rd RR 9, Fort Edward, NY 12828
Tel.: (518) 792-6571
Year Founded: 1917
Sales Range: $10-24.9 Million
Emp.: 140
Trucking
N.A.I.C.S.: 484121
Lance Hillman *(Pres)*

401KEXCHANGE.COM INC.
2230 Jog Rd, Greenacres City, FL 33415
Tel.: (561) 439-5252   FL
Year Founded: 1998
Sales Range: $25-49.9 Million
Emp.: 65
401K & Pension Administration Information & Services
N.A.I.C.S.: 525110
Randy Mysel *(Pres & COO)*

424 CAPITAL, LLC
301 Edgewater Pl Ste 425, Wakefield, MA 01880
Tel.: (781) 295-4000   MA
Web Site: https://424capital.com
Year Founded: 1995
Privater Equity Firm
N.A.I.C.S.: 523999
Walter Beinecke (Mng Partner)
Jonathan Green (Mng Dir)
Brennan Mulcahey (Mng Partner)
Kyle Stanbro (Mng Partner)
Nichole Guerrette (Controller)
Steven Williamson (VP-IR)
Jennifer Mosto (Chief Compliance Officer & Dir-Fin & Ops)
Amit Nagdev (Partner)
Edward C. Williams III (Partner)

Subsidiaries:

Cole Information Services, Inc.   (1)
17041 Lakeside Hills Plz Ste 2, Omaha, NE 68130-4677
Tel.: (402) 323-3505
Web Site: http://www.coleinformation.com
Insurance, Small Business, Real Estate & Home Services Directory Publisher & Information Services
N.A.I.C.S.: 513140
James Eggleston (Pres & CEO)

Practis Inc.   (1)
8720 Red Oak Blvd #220, Charlotte, NC 28217
Tel.: (704) 887-5300
Web Site: http://www.practisinc.com
Landscape Architectural Services
N.A.I.C.S.: 541320
Elizabeth Pettrone (Founder & Mng Partner)

itrac LLC   (1)
1160 Johnson Ferry Rd Ste 400, Sandy Springs, GA 30342
Tel.: (541) 342-2958
Web Site: https://www.alatussolutions.com
Dental Practice Management Software Developer & Publisher
N.A.I.C.S.: 513210
Steve Karasick (CEO)
Trent Arkema (COO)
Becky Meek (CMO)
Darrell Swope (CTO)

Subsidiary (Domestic):

Belvedere Marketing Group LLC   (2)
611 S Congress Ste 310, Austin, TX 78704
Tel.: (512) 628-9509
Web Site:
    http://www.localsearchfordentists.com
Sales Range: $1-9.9 Million
Dental Marketing Software & Services
N.A.I.C.S.: 513210
Graig Presti (Founder & CEO)

Dental Post, Inc.   (2)
3522 Ashford Dunwoody Rd NE Ste 152, Atlanta, GA 30319-2002
Tel.: (678) 805-7820
Web Site: http://www.dentalpost.net
Sales Range: $1-9.9 Million
Emp.: 3
Recruitment Consulting Services
N.A.I.C.S.: 541612
Christopher Wilkenloh (Co-Founder & CTO)
Tonya Lanthier (Founder & CEO)

SmartBox, LLC   (2)
819 Mount Tabor Rd No 8, New Albany, IN 47150
Tel.: (888) 741-1413
Web Site:
    http://www.smartboxwebmarketing.com
Sales Range: $1-9.9 Million
Digital Marketing Services
N.A.I.C.S.: 541613
Colin Receveur (Founder & CEO)
Seth Grundhoefer (Mgr-PR)
Jason Hahn (Mgr-Client Success)
Sean Bailey (Supvr-Video Team)
Rebekah Carroll (Supvr-Content Team)
Amanda Dalton (Mgr-Client Success)
Candice Graves (Mgr-Client Success)
Alex Hall (Dir-Digital Storytelling)
Kristina Huber (Supvr-Call Quality Analyst)
Stacey Iseler (Dir-Client Success)
Clinton Kelley (Mgr-Client Success)
Keri Langner (Mgr-Client Success)
Christina Roth (Editor-Digital Content)
Julie Gable (Controller)
Robin Hendrich (Mgr-Client Success)
Tim Horst (Mgr-Web Dev)
Ed Post (VP-Ops)
Rachel Reeves (Dir-Sls)
Sam Smock (Mgr-Digital Mktg)
Teresa G. Stephenson (Coord-Office)
Matt Tungate (Dir-Production)
Gary Wilson (Mgr-Compliance)
Lori Woody (Dir-Digital Mktg)
Darrell Rhodes III (Mgr-Client Success)

451 GROUP, LLC
20 W 37th St 6th Fl, New York, NY 10018
Tel.: (212) 505-3030   DE
Web Site:
    http://www.the451group.com
Sales Range: $125-149.9 Million
Emp.: 350
Holding Company; Information Technology Research & Advisory Services
N.A.I.C.S.: 551112
John Lindsay (CFO)
Martin McCarthy (Chm & CEO)

Subsidiaries:

Uptime Institute, LLC   (1)
5470 Shilshole Ave NW Ste 500, Seattle, WA 98107
Tel.: (206) 783-0511
Web Site: http://www.uptimeinstitute.com
Emp.: 4
Data Center Research & Consulting Services
N.A.I.C.S.: 541690
Fred Dickerman (Sr VP-Mgmt Svcs)
John Duffin (Mng Dir-South Asia)
Martin McCarthy (CEO)
Alexey Solodovnikov (Mng Dir-Russia)
Todd Traver (VP-IT Optimization & Strategy)
Madeleine Kudritzki (Sr Dir-Bus Support Svcs)
Mozart Mello (Mng Dir-Brazil)
Matt Stansberry (VP-North America)
Sarah Lee Thomas (Dir-Technical Comm)
Chris Brown (CTO)
Phil Collerton (Chief Revenue Officer)
Mark Harris (Sr VP-Mktg)

YGI, Inc.   (1)
1 Liberty Sq 7th Fl, Boston, MA 02109-4868
Tel.: (617) 598-7200
Web Site: http://www.yankeegroup.com
Sales Range: $50-74.9 Million
Emp.: 150
Information Technology Market Research & Analytical Report Services
N.A.I.C.S.: 541910
Carl D. Howe (VP-Res & Data Sciences)

49ER COMMUNICATIONS
361 RailRd Ave, Nevada City, CA 95959
Tel.: (530) 477-2590
Web Site: http://www.49ercom.com
Year Founded: 1997
Electronic Parts & Equipment Merchant Whlslr
N.A.I.C.S.: 423690
Jessica Coen (Supvr)

4C FOODS CORPORATION
580 Fountain Ave, Brooklyn, NY 11208-6002
Tel.: (718) 272-4242   NY
Web Site: https://www.4c.com
Year Founded: 1935
Sales Range: $100-124.9 Million
Emp.: 150
Mfr of Bread Crumbs, Grated Cheese, Baking Crumbs, Coating Mixes, Rib Sauce, Iced Tea Mixes, Dehydrated Soup Mixes & Lemonade Drink Mixes
N.A.I.C.S.: 311999
John Celauro (Pres)
Dan Swartz (VP-Private Label Pkg)
Herb McGarrell (Dir-Sanitation)
Dave Minassian (Dir-Traffic)

4CORNERS HOMES
PO Box 30057, Edmond, OK 73003
Web Site:
    http://www.4cornershomes.com
Year Founded: 2005
Sales Range: $25-49.9 Million
Emp.: 60
Single-Family Home Builder & Realtor
N.A.I.C.S.: 531210
Dusty Boren (Co-Owner)
Tracy Boren (Co-Owner)
Jeff Johnson (CFO)

4FRONT CREDIT UNION
101 N Park St, Traverse City, MI 49696
Tel.: (231) 929-2000
Web Site: https://www.4frontcu.com
Year Founded: 2015
Banking Services
N.A.I.C.S.: 522110
Andy Kempf (CEO)

Subsidiaries:

Old Mission Bank   (1)
2701 I 75 Business Spur, Sault Sainte Marie, MI 49783
Tel.: (906) 635-9910
Web Site: http://www.oldmissionbank.com
Sales Range: $1-9.9 Million
Emp.: 30
Commericial Banking
N.A.I.C.S.: 522110

4G ENTERPRISES, INC.
800 Town and Country Blvd Ste 300, Houston, TX 77024
Tel.: (832) 431-3123   WY
Year Founded: 2012
Solar Desalination System Mfr
N.A.I.C.S.: 221310
Anton Aleksandrov (Chm)
Valarie Grant (CFO & Sec)

4KIDZ INC.
62 Southfield Ave Ste 126, Stamford, CT 06902
Tel.: (203) 327-7949
Web Site: http://www.4kidzinc.com
Year Founded: 1994
Rev: $10,000,000
Emp.: 4
Toys & Games
N.A.I.C.S.: 423920
Jeffrey Lewis (Pres)

4LIFE RESEARCH LC
9850 S 300 W, Sandy, UT 84070
Tel.: (801) 562-3698
Web Site: https://www.4life.com
Year Founded: 1996
Sales Range: $50-74.9 Million
Emp.: 230
Nutritional Supplements & Vitamins for Humans & Animals
N.A.I.C.S.: 325411
David Lisonbee (Co-Founder & Chm)
Steve Tew (Vice Chm)
Mark Ostler (CFO)
Calvin Jolley (VP-Comm)
Bianca Lisonbee (Co-Founder)
Andrew Weeks (CIO)
Danny Lee (Pres & CEO)
Jeffrey Kalinin (Sr VP-Intl)
Trent Tenney (Sr VP-Mktg)
Tony Lee (VP-Northern Asia)
Dustin Rose (VP-Software Dev)
Rick Eastman (VP-IT Infrastructure)
Kelly Bellerose (VP-Mktg)
Catherine Larsen (VP-Svc)

4M
8130 Baymeadows Cir W Ste 111, Jacksonville, FL 32256
Tel.: (904) 355-2741
Web Site: http://www.4-m.com
Sales Range: $10-24.9 Million
Emp.: 460
Janitorial Services
N.A.I.C.S.: 561720
Mark Dimarzo (Reg Mgr)

4OVER, INC.
5900 San Fernando Rd, Glendale, CA 91202
Web Site: https://www.4over.com
Printing Services
N.A.I.C.S.: 323111
Zarik Megerdichian (CEO)

Subsidiaries:

Asap Printing Corp   (1)
643 W Billinis Rd, Salt Lake City, UT 84119
Tel.: (888) 727-2863
Web Site: http://www.asapprintingcorp.com
Sales Range: $10-24.9 Million
Commercial Printing
N.A.I.C.S.: 323111
Patricia L. Aharonov (Pres)
Amir Aharonov (CEO)

4WALL ENTERTAINMENT, INC.
3165 W Sunset Rd Ste 100, Las Vegas, NV 89118
Tel.: (702) 263-3858   NV
Web Site: http://www.4wall.com
Year Founded: 1999
Entertainment Lighting Systems
N.A.I.C.S.: 238210
Kathy Torjman (CEO)
Larry Mikalishen (Gen Mgr-West Coast)
Mike Mancuso (Dir-Used Sls)
Sheila Rivera (VP-Acctg)
Erin Leone (Mgr-Credit)
Wes Bailey (VP-M&A & Product Strategy)
Bill Groener (VP-Bus Dev-Natl)
Marc Morris (CFO)
Dan Abdalla (VP-Mktg & Sls)
Lindsay Meyers (VP-HR)
Scott Church (VP-Bus Dev-Natl)
Elliot Krowe (VP-Bus Dev)
Kitty Charde (Controller-Ops)
Luke Lytle (Dir-Mktg)
Michael Dedic (VP-Fin Plng & Analysis)
Clint Zaayer (Dir-Trng)
Dan Adams (Dir-IT)

Subsidiaries:

4Wall Entertainment, Inc. - Orange County   (1)
400 N Berry St, Brea, CA 92821
Tel.: (714) 674-0148
Web Site: http://www.4wall.com
Entertainment Lighting Systems
N.A.I.C.S.: 423610
Todd Roberts (Dir-Live Events)
Nathan Jones (Mgr-Production)
Colin Johnson (Mgr-Production)
Larry Mikalishin (Gen Mgr-West Reg)
Tommy Green (Reg Mgr-Asset-West)
Collin Barnes (Reg Mgr-Cross Rental-West)

5 B'S INC.
1000 5 B's Dr, Zanesville, OH 43701-7630
Tel.: (740) 454-8453   OH
Web Site: http://www.5bs.com
Year Founded: 1969
Sales Range: $25-49.9 Million
Emp.: 550
Provider of Pleating & Stitching Services
N.A.I.C.S.: 313310
Paula Moore (VP-Sls)
Vicci Biles (Owner)

5 DEVELOPMENT CORP.
11769 Pkwy Dr, Irwin, PA 15642
Tel.: (724) 864-6920
Year Founded: 1992

5 Development Corp.—(Continued)

Sales Range: $10-24.9 Million
Emp.: 300
Fast-Food Restaurant, Chain
N.A.I.C.S.: 722513
Timothy J. Auvil (Pres)

5 STAR HOTEL LAUNDRY, INC
1060 W Division St, Chicago, IL
60642
Tel.: (312) 944-7827
Web Site:
　http://www.5starlaundry.com
Year Founded: 1999
Rev.: $25,800,000
Emp.: 300
Industrial Launderers
N.A.I.C.S.: 812332

**5 STAR ROOFING & RESTO-
RATION LLC**
230 Oxmoor Cir Ste 1104, Birming-
ham, AL 35209
Tel.: (205) 518-8433
Web Site: http://www.5starroofer.com
Year Founded: 2015
Sales Range: $1-9.9 Million
Emp.: 40
Roofing Contractor Services
N.A.I.C.S.: 238160
Bill Cooper (Founder)

**5-STAR REFRIGERATION &
AIR CONDITIONING, INC.**
23091 Cortez Blvd, Brooksville, FL
34601
Tel.: (352) 345-4813
Web Site: http://www.5-
starrefrigeration.com
Sales Range: $1-9.9 Million
Emp.: 100
Refrigeration & Air-Conditioning Con-
tractor
N.A.I.C.S.: 238220
Gwen Lahera (VP)
Gary Read (Mgr-Sls & Mktg)
Ed Kelly (Project Mgr-Installation)
Joseph E. Matthews III (Pres & CEO)

525 MADE IN AMERICA INC.
525 7th Ave 10th Fl, New York, NY
10018
Tel.: (212) 921-5688
Web Site:
　http://www.525america.com
Sales Range: $10-24.9 Million
Emp.: 15
Women'S & Children'S Clothing
N.A.I.C.S.: 424350
Robert Bock (Pres)
Marty Sack (CFO)

5AM SOLUTIONS INC.
11710 Plaza America Dr Ste 2000,
Reston, VA 20190
Web Site:
　http://www.5amsolutions.com
Year Founded: 2003
Sales Range: $10-24.9 Million
Emp.: 48
Software Publisher
N.A.I.C.S.: 513210
Susan Mason (COO)
William FitzHugh (Chief Scientific Of-
ficer)
Brent Gendleman (Founder)
Shilpa Gorfine (Sr VP-Ops & Fin)

**5AM VENTURE MANAGE-
MENT, LLC**
2200 Sand Hill Rd Ste 110, Menlo
Park, CA 94025
Tel.: (650) 233-8600
Web Site:
　http://www.5amventures.com

Year Founded: 2002
Rev.: $435,000,000
Emp.: 25
Venture Capital
N.A.I.C.S.: 523999
James W. Young (Partner-Venture)
John D. Diekman (Mng Partner)
Andrew J. Schwab (Mng Partner)
Mason W. Freeman (Venture Partner)
Richard Ulevitch (Partner-Venture)
Mark Samuel Colella (Principal)
Jenny M. Lee (VP-Fin)
Paul A. Stone (COO & Gen Counsel)
Peter S. Kim (Partner-Venture)
Brian F. Daniels (Partner-Venture)
Scott M. Rocklage (Mng Partner)
Jon Congleton (CEO)
Kush M. Parmar (Mng Partner)

5B INVESTMENTS, INC.
111 Main St Ste 302, Ketchum, ID
83340
Tel.: (208) 726-4300
Web Site:
　http://www.5binvestments.com
Sales Range: $10-24.9 Million
Emp.: 77
Commercial & Institutional Building
Construction Services
N.A.I.C.S.: 236220
Chris R. Stephens (CEO)

5BARZ INTERNATIONAL INC.
9670 Gateway Dr 2nd Fl, Reno, NV
89521　　　　　　　　　　　　NV
Web Site: http://www.5barz.com
Year Founded: 2008
Mobile Device Mfr
N.A.I.C.S.: 334220
Daniel S. Bland (Founder & CEO)
Orlando Cueter (VP-Bus Dev)
Naresh H. Soni (Chm-Supervisory
Bd)
Mark Geohegan (Dir-Fin)

5BY5, LLC
5210 Maryland Way Ste 200, Brent-
wood, TN 37027　　　　　　　TN
Web Site:
　http://www.5by5agency.com
Year Founded: 2014
Sales Range: $1-9.9 Million
Emp.: 37
Advertising Agency Services
N.A.I.C.S.: 541810
Shannon Litton (Pres & CEO)
Mike Schatz (Partner & Chief Rela-
tionship Officer)
Josh Miller (Chief Product Officer)
Aaron Crum (COO)
Derrick Hoog (VP-Strategy)

5LINX ENTERPRISES, INC.
275 Kenneth Dr Ste 100, Rochester,
NY 14623
Tel.: (585) 334-2600
Web Site: http://www.5linx.com
Year Founded: 2001
Sales Range: $10-24.9 Million
Emp.: 70
Telecommunications Services & Prod-
ucts
N.A.I.C.S.: 517810
Jason Guck (Exec VP-Sls)
Larry Harper (Chief Sls Officer)
William Faucette Jr. (CEO)

5METACOM
630 W Carmel Dr Ste 180, Carmel,
IN 46032
Tel.: (317) 580-7540
Web Site: http://www.5metacom.com
Year Founded: 1977
Rev.: $29,002,828
Emp.: 30
N.A.I.C.S.: 541810

Chris Wirthwein (CEO)
Mark Duffin (Dir-Client Svcs)
Jennifer McPhail (Acct Exec)
Jason Williams (Acct Exec)

5TH GEAR ADVERTISING
3611 Motor Ave Ste 205, Los Ange-
les, CA 90034-5772
Tel.: (310) 567-3234
Year Founded: 1998
Rev.: $20,000,000
Emp.: 25
Advetising Agency
N.A.I.C.S.: 541810
Sharon Dyer (Owner)

**5TH GEAR TECHNOLOGIES
CONCEPTS, INC.**
640 Spence Ln Ste 100, Nashville,
TN 37217
Tel.: (615) 606-3121
Web Site:
　https://5thgearconcepts.com
Emp.: 100
Computer Support & Services
N.A.I.C.S.: 541519

Subsidiaries:

Tri-Tech Solutions, Inc.　　　　(1)
106 Wind Chime Ct, Raleigh, NC 27615-
6433
Tel.: (919) 676-2244
Web Site: http://www.etemplatesystem.com
Measuring & Controlling Device Mfr
N.A.I.C.S.: 334519
Paul W. Hansen (Founder)

5W PUBLIC RELATIONS
The Helmsley Bldg 230 Park Ave
32nd Fl, New York, NY 10169
Tel.: (212) 999-5585　　　　NY
Web Site: http://www.5wpr.com
Year Founded: 2002
Sales Range: $10-24.9 Million
Emp.: 175
Public Relations Agency
N.A.I.C.S.: 541820
Ronn D. Torossian (Founder, Pres &
CEO)
Erika Kauffman (Partner, Exec VP &
Gen Mgr)
Ilisa Wirgin (Sr VP & Grp Dir-Beauty,
Health & Wellness)
Dara A. Busch (Exec VP)
Matthew Caiola (Exec VP)
Annette Banca (Sr VP-Health & Well-
ness)
John Ferrari (Sr VP-Fin)
Nina Morrison (VP)
Angela Sposato (Chief HR Officer &
Sr VP)
Shane Russell (Sr VP-Tech)
Robert Ford (Sr VP)
Suejin Kim (Sr VP-Consumer Pack-
aged Goods)
Jonathan Mark (Sr VP)
Leslie Bishop (Sr VP-Travel, Enter-
tainment & Lifestyle)
Carolina Lopez Herz (Sr VP & Gen
Mgr-Miami)

Subsidiaries:

5W Public Relations　　　　　　(1)
11111 Santa Monica Blvd 16th Fl, Los An-
geles, CA 90025
Tel.: (424) 270-2347
Web Site: http://www.5wpr.com
Emp.: 5
Public Relations Agency
N.A.I.C.S.: 541820
Ronn Torossian (Pres & CEO)
Annette Banca (VP-Health & Wellness)
Dara A. Busch (Exec VP-Consumer Prac-
tice)
Matthew Caiola (Exec VP-Corp & Tech
Practices)
Kristin Connor (VP-Food & Beverage)

Juda Engelmayer (Sr VP-Crisis Mgmt &
Special Assignments)
Chloe Gallo (Sr VP & Dir-Lifestyle Grp)
Jason Geller (VP-Consumer Products &
Brands)
Jocelyn Kahn (Sr VP-Consumer Products &
Brands)
Shane Russell (Sr VP-Tech)
Angela Sposato (Sr VP-HR)

60 PLUS ASSOCIATION
515 King St Ste 315, Alexandria, VA
22314
Tel.: (703) 807-2070　　　　VA
Web Site: http://www.60plus.org
Year Founded: 1992
Sales Range: $10-24.9 Million
Emp.: 5
Senior Citizen Support Services
N.A.I.C.S.: 813410

600 LB GORILLAS INC
PO Box 343, Duxbury, MA 02331
Tel.: (781) 452-7274
Web Site:
　http://www.600lbgorillas.com
Year Founded: 1999
Sales Range: $1-9.9 Million
Emp.: 5
Frozen Cookie Dough & Ice Cream
Sandwiches
N.A.I.C.S.: 311520
Paula White (Founder)

6FUSION USA, INC.
107 Fayetteville St Ste 400, Raleigh,
NC 27601-2916
Tel.: (888) 492-4408
Web Site: http://www.6fusion.com
Year Founded: 2010
Information Technology Services
N.A.I.C.S.: 541519
John D. Cowan (Co-Founder & CEO)
Delano Seymour (Co-Founder &
CTO)
Richard Martin (COO)
Richard Donaldson (Head-Platform
Strategy)

6K SYSTEMS, INC.
11710 Plaza America Dr Ste 810,
Reston, VA 20190
Tel.: (703) 724-1320
Web Site:
　https://www.6ksystems.com
Year Founded: 2001
Rev.: $7,500,000
Emp.: 100
Custom Computer Programming Ser-
vices
N.A.I.C.S.: 541511
Bryan Crittenton (Pres & CEO)

6TH & K LTD. PARTNERSHIP
10951 Sorrento Vly Rd Ste 2h, San
Diego, CA 92121
Tel.: (858) 453-0020
Year Founded: 1986
Sales Range: $10-24.9 Million
Emp.: 4
Investors, Nec
N.A.I.C.S.: 523999
Steve Higgins (Partner)

7 C'S MANUFACTURING, INC.
3895-D Corsair, Reno, NV 89502
Tel.: (775) 829-1717
Web Site: http://www.7c-s.com
Sales Range: $10-24.9 Million
Emp.: 80
Sheet Metal Work Mfg
N.A.I.C.S.: 332322
Jim Clewett (VP)
Stacy Ojers (Pres)
Mark Clewett (Gen Mgr)
Will Florence (Dir-Machining Ops &
Mgr-Sls)

Chuck Curran *(Mgr-Shipping & Receiving)*
Dino Cecchi *(Mgr-Quality Control)*

777 PARTNERS LLC
600 Brickell Ave 9th Fl, Miami, FL 33131
Tel.: (305) 921-2801
Web Site: https://www.777part.com
Year Founded: 2015
Emp.: 100
Investment Services
N.A.I.C.S.: 522320
Steven W. Pasko *(Founder & Mng Partner)*

7DIGITAL GROUP PLC (Acquired by Songtradr, Inc.)

7G DISTRIBUTING, LLC
9925 Sixth St SW, Cedar Rapids, IA 52404
Tel.: (319) 848-2337   IA
Web Site:
    http://www.7gdistributing.com
Year Founded: 2010
Emp.: 150
Beer Distr
N.A.I.C.S.: 424810
Tod Wolter *(Gen Mgr)*
Nick Whisler *(CFO)*
Marty Hayes *(VP-Sls & Mktg)*
Kevin Wedo *(Mgr-Sls-West)*
Mason Lee *(VP-Ops)*

80/20 INC.
1701 S 400 E, Columbia City, IN 46725
Tel.: (260) 248-8030
Web Site: https://www.8020.net
Year Founded: 1989
Emp.: 296
Aluminum Frame Mfr
N.A.I.C.S.: 332312
Don Wood *(Founder, Pres & CEO)*

80STEES.COM INC.
230 Westec Dr, Mount Pleasant, PA 15666
Tel.: (724) 696-5121
Web Site: http://www.80stees.com
Year Founded: 1999
Sales Range: $1-9.9 Million
Emp.: 15
Online T-shirt Retailer
N.A.I.C.S.: 424350
Kevin Stecko *(Pres)*

84 LUMBER COMPANY
1019 Route 519, Eighty Four, PA 15330-2813
Tel.: (724) 222-8600   PA
Web Site: https://www.84lumber.com
Year Founded: 1956
Sales Range: $1-4.9 Billion
Emp.: 6,700
Home Center Operator
N.A.I.C.S.: 444110
Joseph A. Hardy III *(Founder)*
Maggie Hardy-Magerko *(Owner & Pres)*
Frank Cicero *(COO)*
Mike McCrobie *(Chief Procurement Officer)*
Paul Yater *(CIO)*
Amy Smiley *(Dir-Mktg)*
David Cochran *(VP-Store Ops)*
Jim Barbes *(VP-Natl Sls)*
Billy Ball *(VP-Southeast)*
Rob Woodrow *(VP-Southwest)*
Dave Dahl *(VP-Mid Atlantic)*
John Hay *(VP-Mid Atlantic)*
Ken Kucera *(VP-Installed Sls & Mfg)*
James Abbott *(VP-Engineered Wood Products)*

Michelle Buczkowski *(VP-Talent Mgmt)*
Maggie Hardy *(Owner)*

Subsidiaries:

84 Components Company   **(1)**
1019 Rte 519, Eighty Four, PA 15330
Tel.: (724) 228-8820
Sales Range: $1-4.9 Billion
Emp.: 10,000
Provider of Structural Wood Services
N.A.I.C.S.: 321215
Paul Lenz *(VP-Fin)*

84 Financial L.P.   **(1)**
12627 San Jose Blvd Ste 305, Jacksonville, FL 32223
Tel.: (904) 260-0059
Sales Range: $1-9.9 Million
Emp.: 8
Construction-Related & Other Loans
N.A.I.C.S.: 522310

84 Lumber Company - Charolette Truss Plant
420 Dixon Dairy Rd, Kings Mountain, NC 28086
Tel.: (704) 937-3712
Web Site: http://www.84lumber.com
Emp.: 100
Timber Product Mfr
N.A.I.C.S.: 321113
Scott Remick *(Gen Mgr)*

84 Lumber Company - Coal Center Truss Plant   **(1)**
151 Trusty Truss Dr, Coal-Center, PA 15423
Tel.: (724) 938-6000
Timber Product Mfr
N.A.I.C.S.: 321113

84 Lumber Company - Mt Airy Truss Plant   **(1)**
4488 Quad Counties Ct, Mount Airy, MD 21771
Tel.: (301) 829-2845
Web Site: http://www.84lumber.com
Timber Product Mfr
N.A.I.C.S.: 321113

8TH LIGHT, INC.
1232 American Way, Libertyville, IL 60048
Tel.: (847) 407-4154
Web Site: http://www.8thlight.com
Year Founded: 2006
Sales Range: $1-9.9 Million
Emp.: 26
Software Developer
N.A.I.C.S.: 513210
Paul Pagel *(Co-Founder)*
Angelique Martin *(CFO)*
Margaret Pagel *(Dir-Sls)*
Susan Rosso *(Dir-Administration)*

9&10 NEWS
PO Box 627, Cadillac, MI 49601
Tel.: (231) 775-3478
Web Site:
    http://www.9and10news.com
Sales Range: $10-24.9 Million
Emp.: 105
Television Broadcasting Station
N.A.I.C.S.: 516120
Mario F. Iacobelli *(Pres)*
Leah Tabacsko *(Coord-Creative)*
Kevin Dunaway *(Gen Mgr)*

9008 GROUP INC.
1999 W 190th St, Torrance, CA 90504
Tel.: (310) 750-3400   NC
Web Site: http://www.act1group.com
Year Founded: 1978
Sales Range: $200-249.9 Million,
Emp.: 400
Full Sevice Employment Agencies
N.A.I.C.S.: 561311
Janice Bryant Howroyd *(Founder, Chm & CEO)*

908 DEVELOPMENT GROUP

2209 E 7th Ave Ste C, Tampa, FL 33605
Tel.: (813) 445-7101
Web Site:
    http://www.908development.com
Year Founded: 2006
Sales Range: $1-9.9 Million
Real Estate Development Services
N.A.I.C.S.: 236116
Alex English *(Principal)*
Justin Wilson *(Principal)*
Mark Levey *(Principal)*
Ken Pierce *(Principal)*

90OCTANE, LLC
518 17th St Ste 1400, Denver, CO 80202
Tel.: (720) 904-8169
Web Site: http://www.90octane.com
Year Founded: 2000
Sales Range: $1-9.9 Million
Emp.: 40
Advertising, Information Technology, Integrated Marketing, Media Planning & Search Engine Optimization
N.A.I.C.S.: 541810
Sam Eidson *(Partner)*
Jim Grinney *(Partner)*
Kelly Snyder *(Mng Dir)*
Rosemary Dempsey *(Dir-Creative)*
Leslie Norgren *(Dir-Audience Engagement)*
Allie Winters *(Acct Mgr)*
Becky Shortell *(Controller)*
Christie Declements *(Accountant)*
Jenny Bridges *(Acct Supvr)*
Mike Aus *(Acct Supvr)*

919 MARKETING COMPANY
(See Under Landon Capital Partners, LLC)

93 OCTANE
23 W Broad St Ste 302, Richmond, VA 23220
Tel.: (804) 643-8800
Web Site: http://www.93-octane.com
Sales Range: Less than $1 Million
Emp.: 8
N.A.I.C.S.: 541810
Linda Bott *(Dir-Acct)*
John Lindner *(Dir-Creative & Owner)*
Adam Smith *(Dir-Art)*

944 MEDIA, LLC
627 N La Peer Dr, West Hollywood, CA 90069
Tel.: (310) 652-2944   NV
Web Site: http://www.944.com
Year Founded: 2000
Sales Range: $10-24.9 Million
Emp.: 78
Social Networking Websites
N.A.I.C.S.: 813319
Brian Dommer *(CFO)*
Jennifer Marnach *(Mgr-Pub Rel)*

@PROPERTIES
618 W Fulton, Chicago, IL 60661-1144
Tel.: (312) 491-0200
Web Site:
    http://www.atproperties.com
Year Founded: 2000
Sales Range: $25-49.9 Million
Emp.: 300
Real Estate Broker
N.A.I.C.S.: 531210
Michael Golden *(Co-Founder)*
Thaddeus Wong *(Co-Founder)*
Wayne Kouf *(VP-Brokerage Svcs-Gold Coast & Streeterville)*
Don Shea *(VP-Brokerage Svcs-Evanston)*

Kevin Van Eck *(VP-Brokerage Svcs-Chicago)*
Anne Brahin *(VP-Brokerage Svcs-Winnetka)*
Natasha O'Connor *(VP-Brokerage Svcs-Glenview)*
Rick Sobin *(VP-Brokerage Svcs-Lincoln Park)*
Amy Corr *(Mng Partner & VP-Brokerage Svcs-Highland Park)*
John D'Ambrogio *(Exec VP-Relocation & Corp Svcs)*
Stephanie Szigetvari *(VP-Brokerage Svcs-Arlington Heights)*
Jim Barcelona *(VP-Brokerage Svcs)*

@RADICAL MEDIA
435 Hudson St, New York, NY 10014
Tel.: (212) 462-1500
Web Site:
    http://www.radicalmedia.com
Emp.: 120
N.A.I.C.S.: 541810
Jon Kamen *(Co-Founder, Chm & CEO)*
Cathy Shannon *(Exec VP)*
Michael Fiore *(CFO & COO)*
Dana Locatell *(Exec Producer-Content Grp)*
Rich Kronengold *(CMO)*
James Spindler *(Chief Creative Officer)*
Frank Scherma *(Co-Founder & Pres)*
Joan Aceste *(Gen Counsel)*
Evan Schechtman *(CTO)*
Chris Kim *(Dir-Comml-Mktg)*
India Hammer *(Head-Ops & HR)*
Candice Cook Simmons *(Chief Strategy Officer)*

@XI COMPUTER CORPORATION
980 Calle Negocio, San Clemente, CA 92673
Tel.: (949) 498-0858
Web Site:
    https://www.xicomputer.com
Year Founded: 1987
Sales Range: $50-74.9 Million
Emp.: 30
Computer Systems Whslr
N.A.I.C.S.: 449210
Robert Bragaglia *(Pres & CEO)*

A & A JEWELRY TOOLS FINDINGS
319 W 6th St, Los Angeles, CA 90014-1703
Tel.: (213) 627-8004
Web Site: https://www.aajewelry.com
Year Founded: 2009
Sales Range: $10-24.9 Million
Emp.: 23
Jewelry Tool, Precious Metal Finding, Jewelry Display & Box Distr
N.A.I.C.S.: 423710
Danny Farah *(Dir-Mktg)*

A & D FIRE PROTECTION INC.
11465 Woodside Ave Fl 1, Santee, CA 92071
Tel.: (619) 258-7697
Web Site: http://www.adgcinc.com
Sales Range: $10-24.9 Million
Emp.: 80
Plumbing, Heating & Air-Conditioning Contractors
N.A.I.C.S.: 238220
Andrew R. Otero *(Pres)*

A & G MACHINE, INC.
1231 37th St NW, Auburn, WA 98001
Tel.: (253) 887-8433
Web Site: https://www.agmach.com
Year Founded: 1984
Sales Range: $25-49.9 Million

A & G Machine, Inc.—(Continued)

Emp.: 70
Hardware Mfr
N.A.I.C.S.: 332510
Jim Bakken (Gen Mgr)
Dan Burns (Mgr-Quality)

A & I CORPORATION
1004 8th Ave N, Myrtle Beach, SC
29577-3848
Tel.: (843) 448-8485   SC
Web Site: http://www.ai-
restoration.com
Year Founded: 1974
Sales Range: $10-24.9 Million
Emp.: 12
Residential Remodeling Services
N.A.I.C.S.: 236118
Daniel H. Isaac (Pres)
Billy Alford (VP)
Danny Isaac (Pres)
J. Stuart Newton (CFO)
Mark Goldspink (CEO)
Matthew Attwell (Dir-Svcs)
Robin Whitehead (CTO)
David Gilhespy (COO)
Natasha Westover (Dir-Fin)

A & I TRAVEL SERVICE
5124 Poplar Ave Ste 101, Memphis,
TN 38117
Tel.: (901) 291-1400
Web Site: http://www.aitvl.com
Year Founded: 1953
Rev.: $3,200,000
Emp.: 33
Travel Agencies & Services
N.A.I.C.S.: 561510
Keith Stevens (CFO)
Linda O'Donnell (Mgr-Acctg)
Bruce Kidwell (Dir-Tech)
Barbara Melton (Mgr-Client Svcs)
Rebecca Martin (Pres)
Vicki Rush (CEO)
Tanya McKnight (Mgr-Client Svcs)

A & M MOTORS INC.
2225 E 5th Ave, Anchorage, AK
99501-2924
Tel.: (907) 279-5508
Year Founded: 1954
Sales Range: $10-24.9 Million
Emp.: 60
Recreational Vehicle Whslr
N.A.I.C.S.: 441210
Ted Palmer (Dir-Ops)
Butch Phillips (Owner)

A & R PLUMBING, INC.
1720 Contra Costa St, Sand City, CA
93955
Tel.: (831) 394-7221   CA
Web Site:
https://www.aandrplumbinginc.com
Year Founded: 1974
Sales Range: $1-9.9 Million
Emp.: 20
Plumbing, Heating, Air-Conditioning
Services
N.A.I.C.S.: 238220
Merrill Roper (Pres)

A & T CHEVROLET, INCORPO-RATED
801 Bethlehem Pike, Sellersville, PA
18960
Tel.: (215) 257-8022
Web Site:
https://www.atchevrolet.com
Year Founded: 1984
Sales Range: $25-49.9 Million
Emp.: 100
Car Whslr
N.A.I.C.S.: 441110
Bruce C. Allen (Pres)

A & T HEALTH CARE LLC.
339 N Main St Ste 11, New City, NY
10956
Tel.: (845) 638-4342
Web Site: https://www.at-
healthcare.com
Rev.: $13,800,000
Emp.: 850
Women Healthcare Services
N.A.I.C.S.: 621610
Toni Babington (Pres)
Margret Onody (CFO)

A + MORTGAGE SERVICES, INC.
W188 S7820 Ste100 Racine Ave,
Muskego, WI 53150
Tel.: (262) 679-8500
Web Site: https://www.trustaplus.com
Year Founded: 2000
Rev.: $219,300,000
Emp.: 19
Mortgage & Nonmortgage Loan Bro-
kers
N.A.I.C.S.: 522310
Alex Leykin (Owner)
Pete Bethke (Pres)

A AMERICA INC.
18255 Segale Pk Dr B, Tukwila, WA
98188
Tel.: (206) 575-3044
Web Site: http://www.a-america.com
Rev.: $35,000,000
Emp.: 40
Furniture Producer
N.A.I.C.S.: 423210
Fred G. Rohrbach (Pres)
Dean Banks (Sr VP-Sls, Mktg &
Mdsg)
Cindy Hartzer (Mgr-Acctg & HR)
Marcia Tolstad (Supvr-Credit Svcs)

A BETTERWAY RENT-A-CAR INC.
1110 Northchase Pkwy SE, Marietta,
GA 30067-6420
Tel.: (770) 240-3305   GA
Web Site: http://www.budgetatl.com
Year Founded: 1977
Rev.: $32,000,000
Emp.: 500
Car Rental Services
N.A.I.C.S.: 532111
Roger G. Gelder (Pres)

Subsidiaries:

Adamson Car & Truck Rental
Inc.   (1)
2301 3rd Ave S, Birmingham, AL 35233-
2401
Tel.: (205) 322-3596
Rev.: $3,600,000
Emp.: 45
Passenger Car Rental & Truck
N.A.I.C.S.: 532111
Patric Siniscalchi (Exec VP-Intl Ops)
Mark J. Servodidio (Exec VP-HR)

A BRITE COMPANY
3217 Wood Dr, Garland, TX 75041
Tel.: (214) 291-0400
Web Site: https://www.abrite.com
Year Founded: 1982
Mfr & Marketer of Chemicals for
Metal Finishing & Environmental In-
dustries
N.A.I.C.S.: 325998
Scott Dunigan (Pres Emeritus)
Les Winkler (COO)
Dan Dunigan (Pres)
Pat Vonasek (Exec VP)
Tom Hyman (VP & Dir-Tech)

A C CENTER, INC.
259 Monroe Ave, Rochester, NY
14607

Tel.: (585) 545-7200   NY
Web Site:
http://www.trilliumhealthny.org
Year Founded: 1989
Sales Range: Less than $1 Million
Emp.: 26
Specialty Health Care Services Orga-
nization
N.A.I.C.S.: 813910
Samuel Antonio Brett Sanchez (Vice
Chm)
Robert Scanlon (Sec)
William M. Valenti (Co-Founder & Sr
VP-Org Advancement)
Andrea DeMeo (Pres & CEO)
Robert Biernbaum (Chief Medical Of-
ficer)
Stuart Mitchell (Chm)
Jason Barnecut-Kearns (CFO)
Gregory Ewing (Chief Compliance
Officer & VP-Compliance & Regula-
tory Affairs)

Subsidiaries:

Pleasant Street Apothecary   (1)
259 Monroe Ave, Rochester, NY 14607
Tel.: (585) 241-9000
Web Site: http://www.pleasantstreetrx.com
Emp.: 10
Pharmacy Operator
N.A.I.C.S.: 456110
Mark J. Malahosky (VP-Pharmacy Svcs)

A CLASSIC TIME WATCH COMPANY INC.
10 W 33rd St, New York, NY 10001
Tel.: (212) 947-7600
Web Site: http://www.classictime.com
Rev.: $28,000,000
Emp.: 18
Watches & Parts
N.A.I.C.S.: 423940

A CLEAN ENVIRONMENT CO., INC.
2071 Cimmaron Rd, Wilson, OK
73463
Tel.: (580) 668-2347
Web Site:
https://www.acleanenvironment.net
Sales Range: $10-24.9 Million
Emp.: 20
Environmental Cleanup Services
N.A.I.C.S.: 562219
Lonnie Edwards (Pres & CEO)

A CLOUD GURU LTD.
Ste 340 800 Brazos St, Austin, TX
78701   TX
Web Site: https://acloudguru.com
Year Founded: 2015
Online Cloud School
N.A.I.C.S.: 611699
Ryan Kroonenburg (Founder)

A KID'S PLACE OF TAMPA BAY, INC.
1715 Lithia Pinecrest Rd, Brandon,
FL 33511
Tel.: (813) 381-3839
Web Site:
https://www.akidsplacetb.org
Sales Range: $1-9.9 Million
Emp.: 75
Family Services
N.A.I.C.S.: 624190
Susan Stagon (Program Dir)

A LA CARTE CHARTS COR-PORATION
42211 N 41st Dr A105, Phoenix, AZ
85086
Tel.: (425) 949-9196   DE
Year Founded: 2016
Emp.: 1

Secured Software Application Devel-
opment Services
N.A.I.C.S.: 541511
David Meyers (Pres & Treas)

A LAMP CONCRETE CON-TRACTORS, INC.
1900 Wright Blvd, Schaumburg, IL
60193
Tel.: (847) 891-6000
Web Site:
https://www.alampconcrete.com
Year Founded: 1965
Sales Range: $10-24.9 Million
Emp.: 200
Poured Concrete Foundation & Struc-
ture Contractor Services
N.A.I.C.S.: 238110
Adele Lampignano (Pres)

A MACFRUGEL COMPANY INC.
1701 East 79th St, Minneapolis, MN
55425
Tel.: (952) 851-0010
Rev.: $10,000,000
Emp.: 35
Rent-A-Car Service
N.A.I.C.S.: 532111

A MESSAGE CENTER INC.
89 Pearl St N, Bridgeton, NJ 08302
Tel.: (856) 451-6300
Rev.: $18,668,238
Emp.: 10
Telephone Answering Services
N.A.I.C.S.: 561421
Bill Grubert (Owner)

A MONTEVERDI INC.
30 N Day St, Orange, NJ 07050
Tel.: (973) 672-8800   NJ
Sales Range: $10-24.9 Million
Emp.: 14
Provider of Tobacco & Tobacco Prod-
ucts
N.A.I.C.S.: 424940
John Monteverdi (Pres)
Brian Monteverdi (CFO & VP)
Peter Monteverdi (VP)
Annie Monteverdi (VP)

A NEW LEAF
868 E University Dr, Mesa, AZ
85203-8033
Tel.: (480) 969-4024   AZ
Web Site:
https://www.turnanewleaf.org
Year Founded: 1971
Sales Range: $10-24.9 Million
Emp.: 494
Behavioral Healthcare Services
N.A.I.C.S.: 623220
Michael T. Hughes (Co-CEO)
Connie Orr (COO)
Deanna Villanueva-Saucedo (Chm)
Catherine Dyciewski (CFO)
Joe Dulin (Chief Philanthropy Officer)
Barbara Bennett (Pres)
Kathy Di Nolfi (Chief Program Officer)
Mark Schnepf (Owner)

A PASS EDUCATIONAL GROUP LLC
7650 Cooley Lake Rd, Union Lake,
MI 48387
Tel.: (248) 742-5124
Web Site: http://www.apasseducation.com
Educational Support Services
N.A.I.C.S.: 513199
Andrew Pass (Founder & CEO)

Subsidiaries:

Victory Productions, Inc.   (1)
7650 Cooley Lake Rd, Union Lake, MI
48387

Tel.: (248) 742-5124
Web Site: http://www.victoryprd.com
Publisher
N.A.I.C.S.: 513199
Victoria Porras *(Pres)*

A PLUS INTERNATIONAL INC.
5138 Eucalyptus Ave, Chino, CA 91710
Tel.: (909) 591-5168
Web Site: https://www.aplusgroup.net
Rev.: $45,000,000
Emp.: 100
Mfr & Sales of Medical Equipment & Supplies
N.A.I.C.S.: 423450
Wayne Lin *(Pres)*

A PLUS TREE, LLC
985 Walnut Ave, Vallejo, CA 94592
Tel.: (866) 815-2525
Web Site: https://aplustree.com
Tree Care Services
N.A.I.C.S.: 111421
Cyrus DeVere *(CEO)*
Subsidiaries:

Tree Men Inc.   (1)
PO Box 364, Pacific Palisades, CA 90272-0364
Tel.: (310) 454-6871
Web Site: http://www.treemeninc.com
Landscaping Services
N.A.I.C.S.: 561730

A SQUARED PRODUC-TIONS GROUP, INC. (Ac-quired by Duncan Channon)

A SERVIDONE INC
1364 Rte 9, Castleton on Hudson, NY 12033
Tel.: (518) 732-2040
Web Site: http://www.asibacc.com
Year Founded: 1985
Rev.: $20,928,826
Emp.: 60
Land Reclamation
N.A.I.C.S.: 236210
Mark Servidone *(Pres)*
Vince Mazzone *(Project Mgr)*

A SOUTHERN SEASON INC.
201 S Estes Blvd, Chapel Hill, NC 27514
Tel.: (919) 929-7133
Web Site:
  http://www.southernseason.com
Year Founded: 1975
Sales Range: $10-24.9 Million
Emp.: 200
Owner & Operator of Gourmet Food Store & Restaurant; Catalog Sales of Specialty Foods & Gifts
N.A.I.C.S.: 445298
Linwood Bradley *(Mgr)*
W. Clay Hamner *(CEO)*

A STAR ELECTRIC COMPANY
200 Seegers Ave, Elk Grove Village, IL 60007
Tel.: (847) 439-4122
Web Site: https://www.astareg.com
Year Founded: 1982
Sales Range: $10-24.9 Million
Emp.: 7
High Voltage Electrical Product Mfr & Distr
N.A.I.C.S.: 335999
Joseph G. Cane *(Owner)*
Frank P. McGovern *(Pres)*

A TO Z TIRE & BATTERY INC.
PO Box 9138, Amarillo, TX 79105-9138
Tel.: (806) 373-2592   TX
Web Site: http://www.atoztire.com

Year Founded: 1926
Sales Range: $25-49.9 Million
Emp.: 220
Auto & Home Supply Stores
N.A.I.C.S.: 441340
Philip Nussbaum *(Pres)*
Don Dodson *(CFO)*
Beth Candelaria *(Dir-Mktg)*

A TO ZMEDIA
650 Broadway 4th Fl, New York, NY 10012
Tel.: (212) 260-0237
Web Site: http://www.atozmedia.com
Year Founded: 1994
Sales Range: $1-9.9 Million
Emp.: 20
Personalized CD, DVD & Vinyl Manu-facturing Services
N.A.I.C.S.: 532490
Sarah Robertson *(Founder & CEO)*

A TOOL SHED INC.
3700 Soquel Ave, Santa Cruz, CA 95062-1774
Tel.: (831) 477-7133
Web Site: https://www.atoolshed.com
Rev.: $11,000,000
Emp.: 8
Equipment Rental & Leasing
N.A.I.C.S.: 532412
Robert Pedersen *(VP & Gen Mgr)*
Bruce Harmon *(Mgr)*

A WORK OF ART INC.
1621 NW 102nd Way, Coral Springs, FL 33071
Tel.: (954) 341-4151
Web Site: http://www.awoa.com
Sales Range: $10-24.9 Million
Emp.: 13
Advertising Agencies, Collateral, Full Service, Graphic Design, Health Care, Internet/Web Design, Media Buying Services, Public Relations, Recruitment
N.A.I.C.S.: 541810
David Nagle *(Pres & Dir-Creative)*

A WORLD OF TILE LLC
2899 S Santa Fe Dr, Englewood, CO 80110
Tel.: (303) 761-0272
Web Site: http://www.worldoftile.net
Rev.: $11,664,862
Emp.: 150
Ceramic Tile
N.A.I.C.S.: 444180
Shawn Kerns *(Pres)*

A YARD & A HALF LAND-SCAPING LLC
26 Thayer Rd, Waltham, MA 02453
Tel.: (781) 788-8855   MA
Web Site:
  https://www.ayardandahalf.com
Year Founded: 1988
Rev.: $1,400,000
Emp.: 18
Landscape Designer & Builder
N.A.I.C.S.: 541320
Eileen T. Michaels *(Founder & Gen Mgr)*
Geovani Aguilar *(Mgr-Construction Projects)*
Eulalio Guevara *(Mgr-Property Main-tenance Projects)*
Laurel Halpin *(Office Mgr)*

A&A GLOBAL INDUSTRIES INC.
17 Stenersen Ln, Cockeysville, MD 21030
Tel.: (410) 252-1020   MD
Web Site:
  http://www.aaglobalind.com

Year Founded: 1939
Sales Range: $10-24.9 Million
Emp.: 200
Toys, Gifts & Novelties; Coin Oper-ated Vending Machines
N.A.I.C.S.: 331110
Edward B. Kovens *(Pres)*
Steven A. Kovens *(Exec VP)*
Brian S. Kovens *(Exec VP)*
Phillip A. Brilliant *(VP-Licensing & Mktg)*
Stacy Johnson *(Mgr-Acct)*
Joe McCormack *(Mgr-Acct)*
Ann Krull *(Mgr-Redemption Sls)*
Ben Graham *(Mgr-Sls-Bulk Vending)*
Lawrence Saad *(Mgr-Powder Coating Div)*
Garry Popkin *(Mgr-Reg Sls)*
Steve Easterday *(Mgr-Sls-Powder Coating)*
Eugene Lipman *(VP-Fin & Admin)*
David Cramer *(VP-Ops)*
Gerry Clothier *(VP-Sls)*

A&A MACHINE & FABRICA-TION, LLC
3101 Texas Ave, La Marque, TX 77568
Tel.: (409) 938-4274
Web Site: https://www.aagroup.com
Year Founded: 1957
Sales Range: $10-24.9 Million
Emp.: 83
Fabricated Metal Products Mfr
N.A.I.C.S.: 332999
C. Alan Hutchins *(Pres & CEO)*
David E. Vasichko *(VP & Mgr-Machining)*
Steve Jones *(Mgr-IT & Sys)*
Jon Jenkins *(Coord-Warehouse)*
Andy Kallinger *(Supvr-Fabrication)*
Dan A. O'Meara *(Mgr-Operation Sys)*
Gerald Trahan *(Supvr-Machine Dept)*
Taylor Nyquist *(Engr-Mechanical)*
Merari Medina *(Project Mgr)*
Johnny May *(Mgr-Quality Control)*
Kraig Warren *(Mgr-Fabrication)*
Rodney Stanley *(Coord-Svc)*
Shane Washburn *(Mgr-Bus Dev)*
Tim Newman *(Project Mgr)*

A&A READY MIXED CON-CRETE INC.
4621 Teller Ave Ste 130, Newport Beach, CA 92660
Tel.: (949) 253-2800
Web Site:
  http://www.aareadymix.com
Year Founded: 1949
Sales Range: $100-124.9 Million
Emp.: 750
Mfr of Ready-Mixed Concrete
N.A.I.C.S.: 327320
Kurt Caillier *(Pres)*
Randy Caillier *(VP)*
Kevin Brown *(Controller)*

A&A WINDOW PRODUCTS INC.
15 Joseph St, Malden, MA 02148
Tel.: (781) 322-9282
Web Site:
  https://www.aawindowproducts.com
Sales Range: $10-24.9 Million
Emp.: 15
Installer of Windows & Doors
N.A.I.C.S.: 238130
Paul Giggey *(VP-Ops)*
Heather Wicken *(Office Mgr)*

A&B ENTERPRISES INC.
10102 N Mcalister Rd, La Grande, OR 97850-8701
Tel.: (541) 963-8461   OR

Web Site:
  http://www.waldropoilco.com
Year Founded: 1966
Sales Range: $25-49.9 Million
Emp.: 190
Gasoline Service Stations
N.A.I.C.S.: 722513
Donald Waldrop *(Owner)*
Nikki Robertson *(Dir-Mktg)*

A&B INGREDIENTS, INC.
24 Spielman Rd, Fairfield, NJ 07004
Tel.: (973) 227-1390
Web Site:
  https://www.abingredients.com
Sales Range: $10-24.9 Million
Emp.: 20
Food Ingredients Distr & Juice Ex-tract Supply Services
N.A.I.C.S.: 311423
Leonard Mackowiak *(VP)*
Gil Bakal *(Mng Dir)*
Joe O'Neill *(VP-Sls & Bus Dev)*

A&B PROCESS SYSTEM CORP.
201 S Wisconsin Ave, Stratford, WI 54484
Tel.: (715) 687-4332
Web Site: http://www.abprocess.com
Sales Range: $25-49.9 Million
Emp.: 400
Food Service Equipment Installation
N.A.I.C.S.: 238990
Anthony Hilgemann *(Owner)*
Glen Lensmeyer *(Pres)*

A&B VALVE & PIPING SYS-TEMS, LLC
212 Thruway Park Rd, Broussard, LA 70518
Web Site: http://www.abvalve.com
Year Founded: 1972
Sales Range: $10-24.9 Million
Industrial Supplies Merchant Whslr
N.A.I.C.S.: 423840
Don Poarch *(Co-Owner)*
Joe Swinbank *(Co-Owner)*

A&B WIPER SUPPLY INC.
5601 Paschall Ave, Philadelphia, PA 19143
Tel.: (215) 482-6100   PA
Web Site: http://www.bestrags.com
Year Founded: 1950
Sales Range: $10-24.9 Million
Emp.: 50
Mfr & Distr of Wiping Cloths
N.A.I.C.S.: 449210
Joel Kanefsky *(Pres & CEO)*
Michael Klausman *(Head-Sls)*
Donna Foti *(Mgr-Import)*

A&C PLASTIC PRODUCTS INC.
6135 Northdale, Houston, TX 77087-5095
Tel.: (713) 645-4915
Web Site:
  https://www.acplasticsinc.com
Sales Range: $10-24.9 Million
Emp.: 45
Plastics Products, Nec
N.A.I.C.S.: 424610
Carolyn Faulk *(Pres)*
Katie Clapp *(VP-Pur)*

A&C PLASTICS, INC.
6135 Northdale St, Houston, TX 77087
Tel.: (713) 645-4915
Web Site:
  https://www.acplasticsinc.com
Year Founded: 1973
Rev.: $21,600,000
Emp.: 40

A&C Plastics, Inc.—(Continued)
Metals Mfr
N.A.I.C.S.: 423510
Fernando Garcia (Asst Mgr-Warehouse)
Nicole Vega (Mgr-Accts Receivable)
Don Snyder (Mgr-Warehouse-Illinois)
Jose Perez (Mgr-Warehouse)
Jessica Calderon (Office Mgr)
Carolyn Faulk (Pres)
Katie Clapp (VP-Pur)
Keith Gaddis (VP-Special Projects)

A&D AUTOMATIC GATE & ACCESS
810 Warrington Ave, Redwood City, CA 94063
Tel.: (650) 365-8828
Web Site: http://www.adautogate.com
Rev.: $13,000,000
Emp.: 65
Vehicle & Pedestrian Gate Mfr & Installer; Contractor Services
N.A.I.C.S.: 238130
Linda Hird (CEO, Sec & VP)
Skip Lang (Branch Mgr)
Arthur D. Hird Jr. (Pres & Treas)

A&E MANUFACTURING COMPANY
5501 21st St, Racine, WI 53406
Tel.: (262) 554-2300
Web Site: http://www.aetools.com
Year Founded: 1932
Rev.: $12,100,000
Emp.: 120
Hand & Edge Tools
N.A.I.C.S.: 423710
John R. Lang (Chm)

A&E STORES, INC.
1000 Huyler St, Teterboro, NJ 07608-1142
Tel.: (201) 393-0600   NY
Web Site: http://www.aestores.com
Year Founded: 1973
Sales Range: $450-499.9 Million
Emp.: 1,800
Retailer of Women's Apparel
N.A.I.C.S.: 458110
Dennis Erani (Exec VP & Gen Mgr)
Jim Hamlin (VP-Store Opers)
Philip Harrison (VP-Fin)
Bruce Kleiman (VP)
Susan Leventhal (Dir-Mktg)
Alan A. Ades (CFO, Founder, Principal, Owner, Chm & Pres)

A&H SPORTSWEAR CO. INC
500 William St, Pen Argyl, PA 18072
Tel.: (610) 863-4176
Rev.: $20,000,000
Emp.: 400
Swimwear Mfr & Sales
N.A.I.C.S.: 424350
Mark Waldman (Pres)
Bruce Waldman (VP)
Mark Greenberg (CEO)

A&H STORES INC.
610 W Meeker St Ste 201, Kent, WA 98032
Tel.: (253) 520-0333
Web Site: http://www.ahstores.com
Year Founded: 1946
Sales Range: $10-24.9 Million
Emp.: 18
Owner & Operator of Greeting Card Stores
N.A.I.C.S.: 459420
Charlie Sizemore (VP)

A&I BROADWAY REALTY
170 Broadway Ste 411, New York, NY 10038
Tel.: (212) 577-2270

Web Site:
http://www.broadwayrealty.com
Year Founded: 1996
Rev.: $2,500,000
Emp.: 12
Offices of Real Estate Agents & Brokers
N.A.I.C.S.: 531210
Elliot Bogod (Pres & Mng Dir)
Gennady Perepada (Head-Intl Mktg)
Greg Litman (Dir-Sls)
Dimitri Semakov (Dir-Creative)

A&J ELECTRIC CABLE CORP.
1932 W Winton Ave Ste 9, Hayward, CA 94545
Tel.: (510) 786-2700
Web Site: http://www.aandjcable.com
Year Founded: 1976
Sales Range: $100-124.9 Million
Emp.: 12
Industrial Wire, Cable & Telecommunications Equipment Whslr & Distr
N.A.I.C.S.: 423610
Gerald Reilly (Pres)

A&J SEABRA SUPERMARKET INC.
574 Ferry St, Newark, NJ 07105-2124
Tel.: (973) 491-0399   NJ
Year Founded: 1985
Sales Range: $10-24.9 Million
Emp.: 127
Grocery Stores
N.A.I.C.S.: 445110
Antonio Seabra (Owner)
John Martins (Dir-Mktg)

A&K EARTH MOVERS INC.
515 Wind Mill Dr, Fallon, NV 89406
Tel.: (775) 423-6085   NV
Web Site:
https://www.akearthmovers.com
Year Founded: 1957
Sales Range: $25-49.9 Million
Emp.: 250
Underground Utilities & Highway Construction Services
N.A.I.C.S.: 237110
Michael Hiatt (VP)
Scott R. Hiatt (VP)
Sharon J. Ream (Treas)

A&K RAILROAD MATERIALS INC.
1505 S Redwood Rd, Salt Lake City, UT 84104
Tel.: (801) 974-5484   CA
Web Site: https://www.akrailroad.com
Year Founded: 1959
Sales Range: $25-49.9 Million
Emp.: 550
Railroad Equipment Mfr & Sales
N.A.I.C.S.: 423860
Allen Vickers (Mgr-Credit)
Dan Britten (VP & Gen Mgr-Fastener Div-Kansas City)
Alfredo Sansores (VP-Intl Sls)
Doug Davis (Gen Counsel)
Jeff Galyean (CFO)
Robert Rolf (VP & Gen Mgr)
Rocky Smith (VP-Field Ops)

Subsidiaries:

A&K Railroad Materials Inc. - Kansas City Mfg Facility   (1)
2131 S 74th St, Kansas City, KS 66106
Tel.: (913) 375-1810
Railroad Rolling Stock Mfr
N.A.I.C.S.: 336510
Phil Poce (COO & Exec VP)
Pat Reeves (VP & Gen Mgr-Ops)
Greg Cornett (VP & Gen Mgr-Trackwork Div)

Dan Britten (VP & Gen Mgr-Fastener Div)
Jim Sharp (Mgr-Quality Assurance)
Rick Gasser (Mgr-Ops)

A&L HOLDING COMPANY INC.
9200 NW Prairie View Rd, Kansas City, MO 64153-1856
Tel.: (816) 452-7000
Year Founded: 1984
Sales Range: $10-24.9 Million
Emp.: 125
Retailer of New & Used Cars
N.A.I.C.S.: 441110
John Chezik (Pres)
Joe McNair (Controller)

Subsidiaries:

Honda of Tiffany Springs   (1)
9200 NW Prairie View Rd, Kansas City, MO 64153-2645
Tel.: (816) 452-7000
Web Site:
http://www.hondaoftiffanysprings.com
Retailer of New & Used Cars
N.A.I.C.S.: 441110
Deana Tasoulas (Mgr-Internet Sls)
Jesse Mora (Mgr-Fin)
Anthony Cecena (Mgr-Fin)
Jim Eary (Mgr-Parts)
Bobby Hennessey (Pres)

A&L IRON AND METAL COMPANY
2000 Milbocker Rd, Gaylord, MI 49735
Tel.: (989) 732-5900
Web Site:
https://www.alironandmetal.com
Sales Range: $25-49.9 Million
Emp.: 108
Ferrous Metal Scrap & Waste
N.A.I.C.S.: 423930
Arnold Higley (Pres)

A&M SUPPLY CORP.
6701 90th Ave N, Pinellas Park, FL 33782
Tel.: (727) 541-6631
Web Site: http://www.marketing.a-msupply.com
Year Founded: 1951
Plywood & Related Products
N.A.I.C.S.: 423310
Raymond Prozzillo (Pres & CEO)

A&M WHOLESALE HARDWARE SUPPLY COMPANY
37 W Cherry St, Rahway, NJ 07065
Tel.: (732) 574-1111
Web Site: https://www.am-ind.com
Sales Range: $10-24.9 Million
Emp.: 100
Mill Supplies
N.A.I.C.S.: 423840
Arnold Young (Pres)

A&P AG STRUCTURES INC.
11266 Ave 264, Visalia, CA 93277
Tel.: (559) 685-8700   CA
Web Site: https://www.aandpag.com
Year Founded: 1982
Sales Range: $10-24.9 Million
Emp.: 27
Producer of Grapes
N.A.I.C.S.: 238130
David E. Parrish (Owner)

A&P CONSULTING TRANSPORTATION ENGINEERS CORP. (Acquired by First Reserve Management, L.P.)

A&P COAT, APRON & LINEN SUPPLY
161 S Macquesten Pkwy, Mount Vernon, NY 10550

Tel.: (914) 840-3200   NY
Web Site: http://www.unitex.com
Year Founded: 1966
Sales Range: $125-149.9 Million
Emp.: 1,500
Linen Supply
N.A.I.C.S.: 812331
Michael R. Potack (Owner & Pres)
Steve Gottlied (CFO)
Robert Potack (Owner & Pres)

A&R FOODS INC.
6320 Augusta Dr Ste 1500, Springfield, VA 22150
Tel.: (703) 912-9000
Rev.: $24,080,928
Emp.: 12
Fast-Food Restaurant, Chain
N.A.I.C.S.: 722513
Denise Bannin-Webb (Asst Controller)

A&R KATZ MANAGEMENT INC.
3175 Commercial Ave Ste 100, Northbrook, IL 60062
Tel.: (847) 205-1200
Web Site: http://www.arkatz.com
Rev.: $25,000,000
Emp.: 16
Real Estate Brokers & Agents
N.A.I.C.S.: 531210

A&R PACKING CO.
34165 Autry St, Livonia, MI 48150-1333
Tel.: (734) 422-2060
Sales Range: $10-24.9 Million
Emp.: 25
Cured Meats & Smoked Meats
N.A.I.C.S.: 311611
Larry Kornacki (Pres)

A&R TRANSPORT, INC.
8440 S Tabler Rd, Morris, IL 60450
Tel.: (815) 941-5200
Web Site: http://www.artransport.com
Sales Range: $100-124.9 Million
Ground Transport of Dry & Liquid Bulk Commodities
N.A.I.C.S.: 484121
Bob Dotson (COO-A&R Pkg & Distr Svcs)
Mike Bedeker (Sr VP-Fleet)
James E. Bedeker (Pres & CEO)
Andrew J. Mantey (COO)
Paul D. Sweeden (Exec VP-Bus Dev & Logistics Ops)
Paul Garber (VP-Sls & Mktg)
Jeremy Lohrens (Controller)
Ken Pate (VP-Safety & Compliance)
Brian Reichert (CFO)
Ed Oppenlander (Mgr-Ops)

Subsidiaries:

A&R Packaging & Distribution Services, Inc.   (1)
8440 S Tabler Rd, Morris, IL 60450
Tel.: (815) 729-1308
Web Site: http://www.arpdsi.com
Sales Range: $75-99.9 Million
Emp.: 600
Packaging & Redistribution of Bulk Commodities; Warehousing Services
N.A.I.C.S.: 493110
Brenda Barnhart (Dir-HR)
Ken Pate (VP)

A&R Packaging & Distribution Services, Inc.   (1)
8440 S Tabler Rd, Morris, IL 60450
Tel.: (815) 941-5200
Web Site: http://www.artransport.com
Sales Range: $100-124.9 Million
Emp.: 300
Packaging & Redistribution of Bulk Commodities, Warehousing Service & Sea-Bulk Containers
N.A.I.C.S.: 541614

Bob Dotson *(COO-A&R Pkg & Distr Svcs)*

A&S BMW MOTORCYCLES
1125 Orlando Ave, Roseville, CA 95661
Tel.: (916) 726-7334
Web Site: https://www.ascycles.com
Sales Range: $10-24.9 Million
Emp.: 45
Motorcycle Sales
N.A.I.C.S.: 441227
Randy Felice *(Pres)*

A&S PAVING, INC.
4755 S 12th Ave, Tucson, AZ 85714
Tel.: (520) 434-9223
Year Founded: 1986
Sales Range: $10-24.9 Million
Emp.: 6
Provider of Highway & Street Paving Services
N.A.I.C.S.: 237310
Sal Pedregon *(Pres)*

A&S, INC.
443 N Frederick Ave, Gaithersburg, MD 20877
Tel.: (301) 670-4140
Web Site:
  http://www.bannershallmark.com
Year Founded: 1975
Sales Range: $25-49.9 Million
Greeting Cards & Gifts Stores Owner & Operator
N.A.I.C.S.: 459420
Leonard Banner *(Pres & CEO)*

Subsidiaries:

Banner Management Company Inc.   (1)
443 N Frederick Ave, Gaithersburg, MD 20877
Tel.: (301) 670-4140
Sales Range: $25-49.9 Million
Emp.: 200
Greeting Cards
N.A.I.C.S.: 424120
Leonard Banner *(Pres)*

A&T SYSTEMS INC.
12200 Tech Rd Ste 200, Silver Spring, MD 20904
Tel.: (301) 384-1425
Web Site: https://www.ats.com
Year Founded: 1984
Sales Range: $50-74.9 Million
Emp.: 18
Telecommunication Servicesb
N.A.I.C.S.: 517121
Ashok K. Thareja *(Founder, Pres & CEO)*
Mureed Nazir *(CIO & CTO)*

Subsidiaries:

A&T Systems   (1)
12200 Tech Rd Ste 100, Silver Spring, MD 20904
Tel.: (301) 384-1425
Web Site: http://www.ats.com
Computers, Peripherals & Software
N.A.I.C.S.: 423430
Ashok K. Thareja *(Founder, Pres & CEO)*
Adam Nouravarsani *(VP-Telecommunications & Infrastructure Svcs)*
Kimberly Thareja *(Officer-Facility Security)*

A&W BEARINGS & SUPPLY CO.
4935 Sharp St, Dallas, TX 75247
Tel.: (214) 630-6509
Web Site:
  http://www.awbearings.com
Year Founded: 1977
Sales Range: $10-24.9 Million
Emp.: 50
Bearing Distr
N.A.I.C.S.: 423840
George Yarborough *(Pres)*

A&W RESTAURANTS, INC.
1648 McGrathiana Pkwy Ste 380, Lexington, KY 40511
Tel.: (502) 874-3000   MI
Web Site:
  http://www.awrestaurants.com
Year Founded: 1919
Sales Range: $150-199.9 Million
Emp.: 2,000
Quick-Service Restaurants Operator & Franchiser
N.A.I.C.S.: 722513
Martin R. Brown *(Mng Gen Partner)*
Kevin Bazner *(CEO)*
Paul Martino *(Pres & COO)*
Janice Pratt *(Office Mgr)*
Dave Crowley *(Dir-Franchise Recruitment)*

A+ DERR HEATING & AIR CONDITIONING, LLC
7545 Peachwood Dr, Newburgh, IN 47630
Tel.: (812) 490-4328
Web Site: http://www.aplusderr.com
Year Founded: 2002
Sales Range: $10-24.9 Million
Emp.: 66
Air Conditioning Repair & Installation Services
N.A.I.C.S.: 238220
Christian Andersen *(VP)*

A-1 A-LECTRICIAN INC.
2849 Kaihikapu St, Honolulu, HI 96819
Tel.: (808) 839-2771
Sales Range: $10-24.9 Million
Emp.: 150
General Electrical Contractor
N.A.I.C.S.: 238210
Kent Fukuhara *(Engr-Svcs)*
Wes Enokawa *(Project Mgr)*
James T. Yamada Jr. *(CEO)*

A-1 CONTRACT STAFFING, LLC
3829 Coconut Palm Dr, Tampa, FL 33619
Tel.: (813) 620-1661   GA
Web Site: http://www.a-1contractstaffing.com
Year Founded: 1989
Sales Range: $350-399.9 Million
Emp.: 60
Human Resouce Services
N.A.I.C.S.: 561330
Mel Klinghoffer *(Founder & Pres)*
Ana B. Alfonso *(Sec)*
Paul Bernier *(Dir-Sls & Mktg)*
Larissa Colvin *(Dir-Client Svcs)*
Scott A. Johnson *(Dir-Risk & Safety)*
Cindy Fowler *(Dir-HR)*
Tammy A. Martin *(Dir-Workers' Compensation Claims)*
Mick Murshell *(Dir-IT)*
Linda Patterson *(Dir-Payroll)*
Michael Smiling *(Dir-Payroll)*
Thomas D. Harrington Jr. *(Gen Counsel & VP)*

A-1 DOOR AND BUILDING SOLUTIONS INC.
4300 Jetway Ct, North Highlands, CA 95660-5702
Tel.: (916) 481-5030
Web Site: http://www.a1door.com
Year Founded: 1949
Sales Range: $25-49.9 Million
Emp.: 97
Doors, Windows, Hardware & Millwork
N.A.I.C.S.: 321911
Jeff Wilson *(CEO)*

A-1 EXCAVATING, INC.

408 26th Ave, Bloomer, WI 54724
Tel.: (715) 568-4141
Web Site:
  http://www.a1excavating.com
Year Founded: 1972
Sales Range: $10-24.9 Million
Emp.: 142
Water & Sewer Utilities Services
N.A.I.C.S.: 237110
Terry Pecha *(Pres)*
Todd Pecha *(VP)*
Sandy Schmidt *(Sec & Treas)*
Richard Crusing *(Controller)*
Charlie Storing *(Project Mgr)*
Al Gingras *(Project Mgr)*
Brad Nielsen *(Project Mgr)*

A-1 EXPRESS DELIVERY SERVICE, INC.
1450 W Peachtree St Ste 200, Atlanta, GA 30309
Tel.: (404) 888-9999
Web Site: https://www.1-800courier.com
Year Founded: 1997
Sales Range: $1-9.9 Million
Emp.: 30
Freight Transportation Arrangement
N.A.I.C.S.: 492110
Cathy Ford *(Mgr-Customer Svc)*
Mark J. McCurry *(Owner)*
Donald Jones *(Dir-Sls)*

A-1 FIBER GLASS, INC.
4495 S Gunpower Cir, Hastings, NE 68901
Tel.: (402) 463-0180
Web Site:
  http://www.a1fiberglass.com
Sales Range: $10-24.9 Million
Emp.: 150
Industrial Mold Mfr
N.A.I.C.S.: 333511
Randy Skalka *(VP-Admin)*

A-1 FLORIDA SOD, INC.
450 Deen Still Rd, Davenport, FL 33897
Tel.: (863) 424-6222
Web Site:
  http://www.a1floridasod.com
Year Founded: 1969
Sales Range: $50-74.9 Million
Emp.: 49
Floriculture Production Services
N.A.I.C.S.: 111422
Ray Swart *(Pres)*
Marsha Watkins *(Controller)*
Tammy Jones *(Mgr-Accts Receivable)*
Carlton Pomeroy *(Mgr-Environmental Health & Safety)*
Sam Cordar *(Mgr-District)*
Joseph Locrasto *(Gen Mgr)*
Jessie Crisostomo *(Mgr-Ops)*
Melissa Kingan *(Mgr-Payroll & Officer-EEO)*

A-1 FREEMAN MOVING & STORAGE INC.
11517 Broadway Ext, Oklahoma City, OK 73114-6607
Tel.: (405) 751-7561   OK
Web Site: http://www.a-1freeman.com
Year Founded: 1974
Sales Range: $1-9.9 Million
Emp.: 400
Provider of Trucking Services
N.A.I.C.S.: 484210
James W. Freeman *(Founder)*
Dennis Lovett *(Pres & Gen Mgr)*

A-1 HEATING & AIR CONDITIONING, INC.
327 N Linder Rd, Meridian, ID 83642
Tel.: (208) 343-4445

Web Site: https://www.a1heating.com
Year Founded: 1956
Sales Range: $10-24.9 Million
Emp.: 80
Plumbing, Heating & Air-Conditioning Services
N.A.I.C.S.: 238220
Pat Minegar *(Co-Owner)*
Scott Privette *(Co-Owner)*
Carol Clark *(Gen Mgr)*
Joel Biagi *(Mgr-Production)*
Randy Thomas *(Mgr)*

A-1 HOSPITALITY PRODUCTS INC.
12386 Osborne Pl, Pacoima, CA 91331
Tel.: (818) 890-6744   CA
Web Site:
  http://www.a1dormroom.com
Year Founded: 1981
Sales Range: $10-24.9 Million
Emp.: 24
Whslr of Linens & Towels
N.A.I.C.S.: 423320
Corey McCarthy *(VP-Mktg)*

A-1 INTERNATIONAL, INC.
2226 Morris Ave, Union, NJ 07083
Tel.: (908) 851-2288
Web Site:
  https://www.aoneonline.com
Year Founded: 1979
Sales Range: $10-24.9 Million
Emp.: 300
Courier Service
N.A.I.C.S.: 492110
Ronald DeSena *(Pres)*
Michael Pollack *(VP-Sls)*
John V. Rutigliano *(VP-Ops)*
Barbara Knapp *(VP-Fin)*

A-1 LIMOUSINE INC.
2 Emmons Dr, Princeton, NJ 08540
Tel.: (609) 951-0070
Web Site: https://www.a1limo.com
Year Founded: 1970
Sales Range: $25-49.9 Million
Emp.: 423
Limousine Rental Services
N.A.I.C.S.: 485320
Eric Dove *(Mgr-Ops)*
Claudia Rutt *(Asst Mgr-Fleet)*
Frank Foy *(CFO)*
Lenore Brown *(Office Mgr-Acctg)*

A-1 PLATING INC.
2655 Lafayette St, Santa Clara, CA 95050
Tel.: (408) 727-6111
Sales Range: $10-24.9 Million
Emp.: 45
Plating Of Metals Or Formed Products
N.A.I.C.S.: 332813
Bob Thomas *(Pres)*
David Crowe *(Chm)*

A-1 TEMPS INC.
9202 Florida Palm Dr, Tampa, FL 33619-4352
Tel.: (813) 623-5777
Web Site: http://www.a1temps.com
Sales Range: $10-24.9 Million
Emp.: 45
Temporary Help Service
N.A.I.C.S.: 561320
Melvin Klinghoffer *(Founder, Pres & CEO)*
James A. Landay *(Controller)*
Tim McPherson *(Pres-Nesco)*

A-1 TOYOTA
50 Amity Rd, New Haven, CT 06515
Tel.: (203) 389-1531
Web Site: https://www.a1toyota.com

A-1 Toyota—(Continued)

Sales Range: $10-24.9 Million
Emp.: 50
New Car Retailer
N.A.I.C.S.: 441110
Annalynn Wheeler (VP & Gen Mgr)
Anthony Galardi (Pres)
Stephen Wheeler (Mgr-Ops)
Alicia Laudano (Office Mgr)
Gary Dos Reis (Mgr-Sls)
John Alberta (Mgr-Inventory)
Ralph Doyon (Coord-Body Shop)
Evan Jones (Mgr-Parts)
Carlos Orozco (Bus Mgr)
Mike Querfeld (Dir-Parts & Svc)
Rebecca Santiago (Coord-Rental)
Michelle Tortora (Mgr-Body Shop)
Paul Wright (Bus Mgr)
Hatim Yousef (Mgr-Sls)
Jeffrey Rodrigue (Controller)
Stephen Wheeler Jr. (Mgr-Used Car)

A-ACTIVE TERMITE & PEST CONTROL COMPANY

2500 Encounter Ct, Virginia Beach, VA 23453
Tel.: (757) 425-0855
Web Site:
http://www.123bugfree.com
Year Founded: 1967
Sales Range: $1-9.9 Million
Emp.: 37
Pest Control Services
N.A.I.C.S.: 561710
Kevin J. Kordek (Pres)
Becky Weil (Mgr-Comml Sls)
Keith McCormick (Gen Mgr)
Jeff Johnson (VP-Ops)

A-BOY PLUMBING & ELECTRICAL SUPPLY

4010 NE Broadway St, Portland, OR 97232
Tel.: (503) 287-0776
Web Site:
https://www.aboysupply.com
Sales Range: $10-24.9 Million
Emp.: 50
Plumbing & Electrical Supplies
N.A.I.C.S.: 423720
Daniel Dolan (Pres)

A-C ELECTRIC COMPANY

2921 Hangar Way, Bakersfield, CA 93308
Tel.: (661) 327-0973
Web Site: http://www.a-celectric.com
Sales Range: $10-24.9 Million
Emp.: 110
General Electrical Contractor
N.A.I.C.S.: 238210
Thomas J. Alexander (Pres)
Tom Zauber (Controller)
Daren Alexander (Gen Mgr)

A-DEC, INC.

2601 Crestview Dr, Newberg, OR 97132-9529
Tel.: (503) 538-9471   OR
Web Site: https://www.a-dec.com
Year Founded: 1964
Sales Range: $150-199.9 Million
Emp.: 30,100
Mfr of Dental Equipment
N.A.I.C.S.: 339114
Joan D. Austin (Co-Founder)
G. Kenneth Austin (Co-Founder)
Eileen Kunze (VP-HR)
Scott Parrish (Pres & CEO)
Phil Westover (Sr Mgr-Product)
Larry Martin (VP-Mfg)
Lindsey Kantawee (Gen Counsel & VP)

A-DEL CONSTRUCTION COMPANY, INC.

351 Salem Church Rd, Newark, DE 19702
Tel.: (302) 453-8286
Web Site: http://www.a-del.com
Sales Range: $10-24.9 Million
Emp.: 100
Highway & Street Construction Services
N.A.I.C.S.: 237310
Audra Morgan (Principal)

A-E DOOR SALES AND SERVICE, INC.

1260 W Sharon Rd, Cincinnati, OH 45240
Tel.: (513) 742-1984
Web Site:
https://www.aedoorsales.com
Sales Range: $10-24.9 Million
Emp.: 50
Installation of Garage Doors
N.A.I.C.S.: 238130
William C. Weber (Pres & CEO)
Lori Bridgers (Controller)
Greg W. Zinser (VP)
Debbie Rais (Mgr-Credit)
Rosemary H. Weber (Treas)

A-HEAD FOR PROFITS LLC

240 Great Cir Rd Ste 344-346, Nashville, TN 37228
Tel.: (615) 499-4197
Web Site:
http://www.aheadforprofits.com
Year Founded: 2011
Sales Range: $1-9.9 Million
Draft Beer System Installation Services
N.A.I.C.S.: 722410
Mark Rubenstein (COO)
Mark Davis (Pres & CFO)
Rick Autery (VP-Ops)
Bill Hardin (VP-Sls)
Brad Pitts (Ops Mgr)

A-L COMPRESSED GASES, INC.

4230 E Trent Ave, Spokane, WA 99202
Tel.: (509) 534-1595
Web Site: https://www.a-lcompressedgases.com
Rev.: $10,023,196
Emp.: 48
Gas & Welding Supply Distr
N.A.I.C.S.: 333992
Keith Keck (Mgr-Pur)
Craig Burkhart (Mgr-Acct)
Steve Balmes (Mgr-Acct)
Bert Batchelder (Mgr-Acct)
Steve McKee (Mgr-Acct-Beverage Div)
Barb Bush (Controller)
Ken Wilson (VP-Sls)
Shan Bush (Pres)
Rob Matherly (Plant Mgr)

A-L FINANCIAL CORPORATION

1551 N Tustin Ave Ste 400, Santa Ana, CA 92705
Tel.: (714) 479-1300
Rev.: $24,900,000
Emp.: 20
Buying Of Installment Notes
N.A.I.C.S.: 522299
Claudia Ahumada (VP-Ops)

A-P-T RESEARCH, INC.

4950 Research Dr NW, Huntsville, AL 35805-5906
Tel.: (256) 327-3373   AL
Web Site: https://www.apt-research.com

Year Founded: 1990
Sales Range: $10-24.9 Million
Emp.: 95
Systems Engineering Services & Software Development
N.A.I.C.S.: 541519
Tom Pfitzer (Pres)
W. Pete Yutmeyer (COO & Sr VP)
John Hall (Dir-Tech)
Saralyn Dwyer (VP)
Rhonda Barnes (VP & Dir-Software)
Meredith Hardwick (CFO)
John R. Fellows (CEO)
Myra Nickson (Dir-HR)
Clark Kilgore (VP & Dir-Missiles & Tech Div)
Jeanette Colvert (VP & Comptroller)
John Tatom (VP & Dir-Explosives Safety & Test Div)
Jimmy Rudolph (VP & Dir-Space Div)
Jerry Rufe (VP & Dir-Test Support Div)
Alex Adams (VP-Bus Dev)
Rebecca Merrill (VP-Contracts)

A-T TRADE INC.

8383 Wilshire Blvd Ste 339, Beverly Hills, CA 90211-2434
Tel.: (323) 951-9114
Rev.: $16,929,109
Emp.: 45
General Merchandise, Non-Durable
N.A.I.C.S.: 424990
Alexei Kourotchkine (Pres)

A-TECH

14 McFadden Rd, Palmer, PA 18045
Tel.: (610) 515-1655
Web Site:
http://www.atechdelivers.com
Sales Range: $10-24.9 Million
Emp.: 57
Lumber, Plywood, Millwork & Wood Panel Whslr
N.A.I.C.S.: 423310
F. Scott Schmidt (COO)

A-TECH CORP.

1300 Britt St SE, Albuquerque, NM 87123
Tel.: (505) 767-1200
Web Site: http://www.aptec.com
Year Founded: 1975
Sales Range: $25-49.9 Million
Emp.: 65
Precision Sensing, Measurement & Controls Mfr
N.A.I.C.S.: 334513
Robert Pierson (Program Mgr)
Dan Gillings (Pres)
Tony Tenorio (Owner)
Neil McCasland (Dir-Tech)

A-Z BUS SALES, INC.

1900 S Riverside Ave, Colton, CA 92324
Tel.: (951) 781-7188
Web Site: https://www.a-zbus.com
Sales Range: $75-99.9 Million
Emp.: 85
Buy, Sell, Repair Busses
N.A.I.C.S.: 423110
Brandon Bluhm (Dir-New School Bus Sls)
Leo Lovato (VP-Sls & Mktg-Emissions Solutions)
Karl Esguerra (Dir-Comml & Transit Bus Sls)

Subsidiaries:

Blue Star Bus Sales, Ltd.   (1)
5907 63rd St, Lubbock, TX 79424
Tel.: (806) 794-1959
Web Site: http://www.bluestarbussales.com
School Buses
N.A.I.C.S.: 485410

Brandon Bluhm (VP-Sls)
Carolyn Degenhart (Founder & CEO)
Wayne Dever (Dir-Sls)

A-Z OFFICE RESOURCE, INC.

3014 Owen Dr, Antioch, TN 37013
Tel.: (615) 831-0600
Web Site: https://www.azorinc.com
Rev.: $25,000,000
Emp.: 14
Office Forms & Supplies
N.A.I.C.S.: 459410
Kenneth Crouch (Dir-Mktg)
Malcolm G. West Jr. (Pres & CEO)

A. ARNOLD MOVING COMPANY, INC.

5200 Interchange Way, Louisville, KY 40229
Tel.: (502) 426-7050
Rev.: $26,648,200
Emp.: 70
Household Goods Transport
N.A.I.C.S.: 484210
Richard L. Russell (Pres)
Gary Robbins (CFO)
Steve Yacko (VP-Fleet Dev)

Subsidiaries:

A. Arnold Moving Company, Inc. Indianapolis Division   (1)
8161 Zionsville Rd, Indianapolis, IN 46268
Tel.: (317) 537-9888
Web Site: http://www.aarnold.com
Household Goods Moving Services
N.A.I.C.S.: 484210

A. Arnold of Kansas City, LLC   (1)
15761 S Keeler St, Olathe, KS 66062
Tel.: (913) 800-9100
Household Goods Moving Services
N.A.I.C.S.: 484210

Sterling International, Inc.   (1)
5200 Interchange Way, Louisville, KY 40229
Tel.: (502) 810-0625
Web Site:
http://www.sterlinginternational.com
Sales Range: $25-49.9 Million
Moving & Relocation Services
N.A.I.C.S.: 484210

A. BRIGHT IDEA

210 Archer St, Bel Air, MD 21014
Tel.: (410) 836-7180
Web Site:
https://www.abrighteaonline.com
Year Founded: 1996
Sales Range: $10-24.9 Million
Emp.: 40
Full-Service Creative Advertising, Marketing, Public Relations, Graphic & Web Design
N.A.I.C.S.: 541820
Anita Brightman (Founder & CEO)
T. J. Brightman (Pres)
Cobey Dietrich (Exec VP-Verbal & Visual Comm)
Lisa Condon (Sr Dir-Graphic Svcs)
Chad Schwartz-Mitchell (CFO)
Melissa Mauldin (VP-Verbal Comm)
Teri O'Neal (Dir-PR)
Katie MacNichol (Dir-Adv)

Subsidiaries:

A. Bright Idea   (1)
13750 Arnold Dr, Glen Ellen, CA 95442   (100%)
Tel.: (707) 935-1377
Web Site: http://www.abrighteaonline.com
Public Relations
N.A.I.C.S.: 541820

A. BROWN-OLMSTEAD ASSOCIATES

274 W Paces Ferry Rd, Atlanta, GA 30305
Tel.: (404) 659-0919
Web Site: http://www.newaboa.com

Year Founded: 1972
Sales Range: Less than $1 Million
Emp.: 10
Advertising, Content, Crisis Communications, Graphic Design, Investor Relations, Public Relations, Sales Promotion, Strategic Planning/Research
N.A.I.C.S.: 541810
Amanda Brown-Olmstead *(Pres & CEO)*

A. DAIGGER & COMPANY INC.
620 Lakeview Pkwy, Vernon Hills, IL 60061
Tel.: (847) 816-5060
Web Site: http://www.daigger.com
Rev.: $13,500,000
Emp.: 56
Laboratory Equipment
N.A.I.C.S.: 423490
Armando Cardenas *(Mgr-Intl Sls)*
John Halpin *(Dir-Mktg)*
Karen Sahm *(Mgr-Pur)*
Paul Gauger *(Product Dir-Supply)*

A. DUCHINI INCORPORATED
2550 McKinley Ave, Erie, PA 16503-2322
Tel.: (814) 456-7027
Web Site: https://www.duchini.com
Sales Range: $10-24.9 Million
Emp.: 40
Concrete Block & Brick
N.A.I.C.S.: 327331
James A. Duchini *(Pres)*

A. DUDA & SONS INC.
1200 Duda Trl, Oviedo, FL 32765-4504
Tel.: (407) 365-2111   FL
Web Site: http://www.duda.com
Year Founded: 1926
Sales Range: $450-499.9 Million
Emp.: 550
Agribusiness & Real Estate; Vegetable, Citrus & Sod Growers; Cattle; Crop Preparation
N.A.I.C.S.: 444240
Susan Howard *(Dir-Corp Comm)*
Tommy Duda *(Sr VP-Land)*
David J. Duda *(CEO)*
Bart Weeks *(COO)*

Subsidiaries:

Duda Farm Fresh Food   (1)
PO Box 620257, Oviedo, FL 32762
Tel.: (407) 365-2111
Web Site: http://www.dudafresh.com
Sales Range: $10-24.9 Million
Emp.: 50
Agricultural Supplies
N.A.I.C.S.: 445230
Manuel Alcala *(Mgr-Ops)*

Duda Ranches - Duda Sod Division   (1)
1200 Duda Trl, Oviedo, FL 32765
Tel.: (407) 365-2111
Web Site: http://www.duda-sod.com
Sod Farming Services
N.A.I.C.S.: 111421

The Viera Company   (1)
7380 Murrell Rd Ste 201, Melbourne, FL 32940-8130
Tel.: (321) 242-1200
Web Site: http://www.viera.com
Sales Range: $10-24.9 Million
Emp.: 30
Real Estate Company
N.A.I.C.S.: 237210
Todd J. Pokrywa *(Pres)*
Scott Miller *(Sr VP-Sls & Community Dev)*
Eva Rey *(Dir-Community Mgmt Amenities & Comm)*
Tyler Duda *(Mgr-Land Dev)*
Jason Carter *(Mgr-Land Dev Construction)*
R. Lee Ward Jr. *(VP-Comml Properties)*

A. DUIE PYLE INC.
650 Westtown Rd, West Chester, PA 19381-0564
Tel.: (610) 696-5800   PA
Web Site: https://www.aduiepyle.com
Year Founded: 1924
Sales Range: $150-199.9 Million
Emp.: 2,095
Integrated Logistics Resources & Truckload Transportation
N.A.I.C.S.: 484110
Russ Miceli *(Dir-Sls)*

Subsidiaries:

Pyle Transport Services Inc.   (1)
650 Westtown Rd, West Chester, PA 19382
Tel.: (610) 696-5800
Web Site: http://www.pyleco.com
Rev.: $12,534,900
Emp.: 30
Local Trucking without Storage
N.A.I.C.S.: 484110

A. EPSTEIN & SONS INTERNATIONAL, INC.
600 W Fulton St, Chicago, IL 60661-1199
Tel.: (312) 454-9100   IL
Web Site: https://www.epsteinglobal.com
Year Founded: 1921
Sales Range: $100-124.9 Million
Emp.: 350
Architecture, Interiors, Engineering & Construction Services
N.A.I.C.S.: 541330
James Jirsa *(Mng Dir-Chicago & CFO)*
Christine Paccione-Anderson *(Sr VP & Dir-Corp Svcs-Chicago)*
Andrew L. Metter *(Dir-Design-Chicago)*
Michael Damore *(Exec Mng Dir-Chicago)*
Thomas E. Smiles *(Sr VP & Dir-Engrg-Chicago)*
Jason Chandler *(VP & Dir-Project Mgmt-Chicago)*
Janusz Lichocki *(Mng Principal-Warsaw)*
Noel Abbott *(VP & Dir-Mktg & PR-Chicago)*
Dan Boland *(VP & Dir-Construction)*
Darrin McCormies *(Sr VP & Dir-Industrial Process Engrg)*
Greg Osborne *(VP & Dir-Civil Engrg)*
Kevin Christensen *(VP & Dir-MEP & FP Engrg)*
L. Randall Buescher *(Sr VP & Dir-Architecture)*
Larry Dalziel *(VP & Sr Dir-Technical-New York)*
Michael J. Kaufman *(VP-Bus Dev)*
Stuart White *(Sr VP & Dir-Industrial Projects)*
Tom Suarez *(VP & Dir-Structural Engrg)*
Steve Marx *(Dir-Client Svcs)*

Subsidiaries:

Epstein Architecture & Engineering SRL   (1)
Premium Plaza 63-69 Dr Iacob Felix Street Floor 7 & 8 Sector 1, Bucharest, Romania
Tel.: (40) 213116122
Web Site: http://www.epsteinglobal.com
Architecture, Interiors, Engineering & Construction Services
N.A.I.C.S.: 541330

Epstein Civil Engineering, Inc.   (1)
600 W Fulton St, Chicago, IL 60661-1259   (100%)
Tel.: (312) 454-9100
Web Site: http://www.epsteinglobal.com
Emp.: 200
Municipal Engineering; Highway & Bridge Construction; Pollution Control; Land Development; Sitework for Buildings

N.A.I.C.S.: 541330

Epstein Construction Inc.   (1)
600 W Fulton, Chicago, IL 60661-1259   (100%)
Tel.: (312) 454-9100
Web Site: http://www.epsteinglobal.com
Sales Range: $10-24.9 Million
Emp.: 120
Construction; Construction Management & Design Build
N.A.I.C.S.: 236220
James Jirsa *(Exec Mng Dir & CFO)*
Greg Osborne *(VP & Dir-Civil Engrg-Chicago)*
Noel Abbott *(VP & Dir-Bus Dev & Mktg-Chicago)*
Criss Paccione-Anderson *(Sr VP & Dir-Corp Svcs-Chicago)*
Tom Smiles *(Sr VP & Dir-Engrg-Chicago)*
Tom Suarez *(VP & Dir-Structural Engrg-Chicago)*

Epstein Sp. z.o.o.   (1)
ul Woloska 9A, 02-583, Warsaw, Poland   (100%)
Tel.: (48) 225250300
Web Site: http://www.epsteinglobal.com
Rev.: $10,000,000
Emp.: 100
Architecture, Interiors, Engineering & Construction Services
N.A.I.C.S.: 541330
Janusz Lichocki *(Dir-Intl Ops)*

A. HAROLD & ASSOCIATES, LLC
7595 Baymeadows Way, Jacksonville, FL 32256
Tel.: (904) 265-1940
Web Site: http://www.aha-llc.com
Year Founded: 2003
Sales Range: $1-9.9 Million
Emp.: 92
Technology, Engineering, Training, Management, Educational & Manufacturing Services to Federal Government
N.A.I.C.S.: 921190
Michael Van Jaarsveld *(Mgr-Contract)*
Stephanie M. Landing *(Exec VP & COO)*
Angie Harper *(VP)*
Greg Partney *(VP)*
Scott Wolfe *(VP)*
Andy E. Harold Jr. *(Pres & CEO)*

A. LAVIN COMMUNICATIONS
8 Haven Ave Ste 223, New York, NY 10001
Tel.: (212) 290-9540
Web Site: http://www.alavin.com
Sales Range: Less than $1 Million
Emp.: 4
Brand Development & Integration, Broadcast, Communications, Event Planning & Marketing, Exhibit/Trade Shows, Financial, Health Care, Information Technology, Media Relations, Media Training
N.A.I.C.S.: 541810
Andrew R. Lavin *(Pres)*

A. MORTON THOMAS & ASSOCIATES INC.
800 King Farm Blvd 4th Fl, Rockville, MD 20850
Tel.: (301) 881-2545
Web Site: https://www.amtengineering.com
Year Founded: 1955
Sales Range: $10-24.9 Million
Emp.: 550
Public Works, Land Use & Environmental Services
N.A.I.C.S.: 924110
Janice Gary *(Dir-HR)*
Michael J. Wiercinski *(Pres & CEO)*
Marques Jacobs *(Engr-Transportation Project)*

Nick Ramirez *(Mgr-Transportation Design Project)*
John Boryschuk *(Dir-Wastewater & Wastewater Engrg)*
Stephen E. Roberts *(Dir-Transportation Engrg-Southeast)*

A. P. O'HORO COMPANY
3130 Belmont Ave, Youngstown, OH 44504-0228
Tel.: (330) 759-9317
Web Site: https://www.apohoro.com
Year Founded: 1947
Sales Range: $25-49.9 Million
Emp.: 60
Sewer Line & Related Structure Construction Services
N.A.I.C.S.: 237110
Daniel P. O'Horo *(Pres)*
Daniel J. O'Horo *(Chm)*

A. PERIN ROOFING & SIDING, INC.
259 Main St, Chester, NJ 07930
Tel.: (908) 879-4729
Web Site: https://www.aproofingandsiding.com
Year Founded: 1986
Sales Range: $10-24.9 Million
Emp.: 2
Roofing Installation Services
N.A.I.C.S.: 238390
Adelino Perin *(Pres)*

A. POMERANTZ & COMPANY
123 S Broad Ste 1260, Philadelphia, PA 19109
Tel.: (215) 408-2100   PA
Web Site: https://www.pomerantz.com
Year Founded: 1888
Sales Range: $75-99.9 Million
Emp.: 40
Provider of Commercial Office Furniture & Related Services
N.A.I.C.S.: 449110
Garry Maddox *(Owner, Chm & CEO)*
Linda F. Rudi *(COO)*
Gordon Pfeil *(VP-Bus Dev)*
Donna Leis *(Project Mgr)*
Tom Smith *(Project Mgr)*
Holly Gack *(Mgr-Govt Sls)*
Kelly Gordon *(Mgr-Ops)*
Bob Martin *(Dir-Svcs)*

A. SCHONBEK & CO.
61 Industrial Blvd, Plattsburgh, NY 12901-1908
Tel.: (518) 563-7500
Web Site: https://www.schonbek.com
Year Founded: 1870
Sales Range: $50-74.9 Million
Emp.: 480
Mfr of Crystal Chandelier & Lighting Fixtures
N.A.I.C.S.: 335131
Mike Dupuis *(Dir-Fin)*

A. SHEFTEL AND SONS, INC.
2121 31st St SW, Allentown, PA 18103
Tel.: (610) 797-9420   DE
Web Site: http://www.sheftel.com
Year Founded: 1917
Sales Range: $200-249.9 Million
Emp.: 100
Textile Waste Services
N.A.I.C.S.: 423930
Michael Sheftel *(Pres)*

A. W. TROUTMAN CO.
640 State St, Millersburg, PA 17061-1462
Tel.: (717) 692-2137
Web Site: https://www.troutmansauto.com

A. W. Troutman Co.—(Continued)

Sales Range: $10-24.9 Million
Emp.: 52
Car Whslr
N.A.I.C.S.: 441110
David A. Troutman (Owner & Pres)

A. W. ZENGELER CLEANERS, INC.

770 Skokie Blvd, Northbrook, IL 60062
Tel.: (847) 272-8472
Web Site:
http://www.zengelercleaners.com
Year Founded: 1857
Emp.: 125
Dry Cleaning Services
N.A.I.C.S.: 812320
Oscar Gonzalez (Mgr)
Tom Zengeler (Pres)

A. WATTS, INC.

120 Club Oak Ct, Winston Salem, NC 27104-4680
Tel.: (336) 765-9300   NC
Year Founded: 1991
Sales Range: $10-24.9 Million
Emp.: 90
Nonresidential Construction Services
N.A.I.C.S.: 236220
Anthony H. Watts (Pres & Treas)

A. WILBERT'S SONS, LLC

58020 Bayou Rd, Plaquemine, LA 70764
Tel.: (225) 687-3591   LA
Year Founded: 1997
Real Estate Investment, Development & Property Management; Golf Course Operator; Bank Operator
N.A.I.C.S.: 531390
John M. Higdon (Chm)
Klein W. Kirby (Pres)

Subsidiaries:

A. Wilbert's Sons Island, LLC   (1)
23550 Myrtle Grove Rd, Plaquemine, LA 70764
Tel.: (225) 685-0808
Web Site: http://www.theislandgolf.com
Golf Course Operator
N.A.I.C.S.: 713910
Klein W. Kirby (Pres)

A. WIMPFHEIMER & BROS., INC.

300 Church St, Blackstone, VA 23824
Tel.: (434) 292-7211
Web Site: http://www.wimpvel.com
Year Founded: 1845
Sales Range: $10-24.9 Million
Emp.: 35
Fabric Mill
N.A.I.C.S.: 313210
Norman Nitschke (Pres & CEO)

A. ZEREGA'S SONS, INC.

20-01 Broadway, Fair Lawn, NJ 07410-2058
Tel.: (201) 797-1400   NJ
Web Site: http://www.zerega.com
Year Founded: 1848
Sales Range: $400-449.9 Million
Emp.: 1,500
Mfr of Macaroni Products, Spaghetti & Egg Noodle Products
N.A.I.C.S.: 311824
John B. Vermylen (Pres & CEO)
Mark E. Vermylen (Sec & VP)
Robert A. Vermylen (VP-Sls & Mktg)
Nicholas Pugliese (Treas)

A.A. ANDERSON COMPANY INCORPORATED

21365 Gateway Ct, Brookfield, WI 53045-5110

Tel.: (262) 784-3340
Web Site: http://www.aaaco.com
Year Founded: 1958
Sales Range: $10-24.9 Million
Emp.: 60
Pumps & Pumping Equipment Mfr
N.A.I.C.S.: 423830
Greg Domino (Pres)

A.A. CASEY CO.

5124 Nebraska Ave, Tampa, FL 33603
Tel.: (813) 234-8831
Web Site: https://www.aacasey.com
Year Founded: 1959
Sales Range: $1-9.9 Million
Emp.: 15
Tools, Construction Equipment & Fasteners Distr
N.A.I.C.S.: 423710
Richard Casey (Pres)

A.B. CLOSING CORPORATION

12001 Research Pkwy Ste 344, Orlando, FL 32826
Tel.: (407) 243-6006
Web Site: http://www.kavaliro.com
Sales Range: $10-24.9 Million
Emp.: 250
Staffing Services
N.A.I.C.S.: 561311
Mark Moore (Pres)
Diane Mahony (CEO)
John Mahony (COO)
Bill Peppler (Mng Partner)
Jennifer Miller (CFO)
Timothy Harrington (Mng Dir)
Amy Simpson (Dir-Tampa)

A.B. DATA, LTD.

600 AB Data Dr, Milwaukee, WI 53217-2645
Tel.: (414) 961-6400   WI
Web Site: https://www.abdata.com
Year Founded: 1980
Sales Range: $25-49.9 Million
Emp.: 100
Direct Marketing Services
N.A.I.C.S.: 541860
Lizabeth Ludowissi (VP-Production)
Mary Getz (VP-Digital Mktg-Washington)
Meredith Feldman (VP-Milwaukee)
Cathy Grams (VP-Strategy & Dev-Washington)

Subsidiaries:

A.B. Data, Ltd. - Washington, D.C.   (1)
1808 Swann St NW, Washington, DC 20009-5505
Tel.: (202) 462-2040
Web Site: http://www.abdata.com
Emp.: 5
Direct Marketing Services
N.A.I.C.S.: 541810

A.C. DELLOVADE INC.

108 Cavasina Dr, Canonsburg, PA 15317-1767
Tel.: (724) 873-8190   PA
Web Site:
http://www.acdellovade.com
Year Founded: 1973
Sales Range: $25-49.9 Million
Emp.: 200
Commercial Metal Siding & Roofing Contractor
N.A.I.C.S.: 238160
Armand C. Dellovade (Pres)
Pat Riley (VP)
Jim Grosjen (Controller)

A.C. HORN & COMPANY

1269 Majesty Dr, Dallas, TX 75247-3917
Tel.: (214) 630-3311   TX

Web Site: http://www.achornco.com
Year Founded: 1907
Rev.: $170,000,000
Emp.: 100
Metal Fabricator
N.A.I.C.S.: 332322
Doug Horn (Pres & CEO)
Mark Ritter (VP)
Paul Lima (Mgr-Ops)
Harold Herrick (Project Mgr)
Bobby Howell (VP)
Michael Horn Jr. (Mgr-Sls)

Subsidiaries:

Cantrell International   (1)
1269 Majesty Dr, Dallas, TX 75247
Tel.: (214) 630-3311
Web Site: http://www.achornco.com
Sales Range: $10-24.9 Million
Emp.: 58
Sheet Metal Work Mfg
N.A.I.C.S.: 332322

A.C. HOUSTON LUMBER COMPANY

2912 E La Madre Way, North Las Vegas, NV 89081
Tel.: (702) 633-5100
Web Site:
http://www.houstonlumber.com
Rev.: $130,381,012
Emp.: 250
Lumber & Other Building Materials
N.A.I.C.S.: 423310
Robert Houston (Chm & CEO)
Ron Mason (Pres & COO)
Donna Arais (Controller)

A.C. ISRAEL ENTERPRISES, INC.

12 E 49th St 27th Fl, New York, NY 10017
Tel.: (212) 634-3366   DE
Web Site:
http://www.inglesideinvestors.com
Sales Range: $10-24.9 Million
Emp.: 25
Investment Holding Company
N.A.I.C.S.: 551112
Thomas C. Israel (Chm & CEO)
Barry W. Gray (Vice Chm)
Jody Phillips (VP)
Kenneth A. Glennon (Mgr-Acctg)
Lawrence E. Kraus (VP & Dir-Tax)
Ona Lee (Mgr-Fin Acctg & Investment Reporting)
Mayer Rosenzweig (Mng Dir-Investments)
Jim Israel (VP)

Subsidiaries:

Ingleside Capital Co., Inc.   (1)
12 E 49th St 41th Fl, New York, NY 10017
Tel.: (212) 634-3366
Web Site: http://www.inglesidellc.com
Emp.: 22
Privater Equity Firm
N.A.I.C.S.: 523999
Thomas C. Israel (Chm & CEO)
Greg Warner (Pres)
Jody Phillips (VP)

A.C. KISSLING, INC.

161 E Allen St, Philadelphia, PA 19125-4144
Tel.: (215) 423-4700   PA
Sales Range: $10-24.9 Million
Emp.: 10
Sauerkraut & Meats
N.A.I.C.S.: 424470
Mark Kissling (Treas & Sec)
Richard W. Kissling Jr. (Pres)

A.C. LEGG PACKING COMPANY, INC.

6330 Hwy 31 S, Calera, AL 35040
Tel.: (205) 324-3451   AL

Web Site: https://www.aclegg.com
Year Founded: 1923
Sales Range: $100-124.9 Million
Emp.: 140
Mfr of Dry Mixes & Seasonings for the Food Industry
N.A.I.C.S.: 311942
James E. Purvis (Pres, CEO & Treas)

A.C. MILLER CONCRETE PRODUCTS INC.

31 E Bridge St, Spring City, PA 19475
Tel.: (610) 948-4600
Web Site: https://www.acmiller.com
Year Founded: 1965
Sales Range: $10-24.9 Million
Emp.: 141
Concrete Products, Precast
N.A.I.C.S.: 327390
Brian Jackson (Dir-Ops)
Kevin Eddy (Plant Mgr)
Leo Middlemiss (Mgr-Engrg & QC)

A.C. NELSEN ENTERPRISES INC.

11818 L St, Omaha, NE 68137
Tel.: (402) 333-1122
Web Site: https://www.acnrv.com
Sales Range: $10-24.9 Million
Emp.: 22
Automotive Supplies & Parts
N.A.I.C.S.: 423120
Andrew C. Nelsen (Owner, Pres & CEO)

A.C. SCHULTES, INC.

664 S Evergreen Ave, Woodbury Heights, NJ 08097
Tel.: (856) 845-5656   NJ
Web Site:
https://www.acschultes.com
Year Founded: 1921
Sales Range: $10-24.9 Million
Emp.: 60
Water & Wastewater Well Drilling & Equipment Repair Services
N.A.I.C.S.: 237110
Gus Schultes IV (Pres & Mgr-Drilling Div Project)

Subsidiaries:

A.C. Schultes of Carolina, Inc.   (1)
3887 S NC Hwy 41, Wallace, NC 28466
Tel.: (910) 285-7465
Web Site: http://www.acschultes.com
Sales Range: $1-9.9 Million
Water & Wastewater Well Drilling & Equipment Repair Services
N.A.I.C.S.: 237110
William Jefferys (Pres)
Melissa Littlefield-Young (Office Mgr)

A.C. Schultes of Delaware, Inc.   (1)
16289 Sussex Hwy Rte 13 N, Bridgeville, DE 19933
Tel.: (302) 337-8254
Web Site: http://www.acschultes.com
Sales Range: $1-9.9 Million
Emp.: 12
Water & Wastewater Well Drilling & Equipment Repair Services
N.A.I.C.S.: 237110
R. Michael Collison (Pres & Gen Mgr)

A.C. Schultes of Florida, Inc.   (1)
11865 US Hwy 41 S, Gibsonton, FL 33534
Tel.: (813) 741-3010
Web Site: http://www.acschultesfl.com
Sales Range: $1-9.9 Million
Emp.: 15
Water & Wastewater Well Drilling & Equipment Repair Services
N.A.I.C.S.: 237110
Gregory Schultes (VP)

Division (Domestic):

Jaffer Well Drilling   (2)
1451 SE 9th Ct, Hialeah, FL 33010
Tel.: (305) 576-7363

Web Site: http://www.jafferwells.com
Sales Range: $1-9.9 Million
Emp.: 40
Water Well Drilling Services
N.A.I.C.S.: 237110
Caroline Urtiaga *(Principal)*

A.C. Schultes of Maryland, Inc.   **(1)**
8221 Cloverleaf Dr, Millersville, MD 21108
Tel.: (410) 841-6710
Web Site: http://www.acschultes.com
Sales Range: $1-9.9 Million
Water & Wastewater Well Drilling & Equipment Repair Services
N.A.I.C.S.: 237110

A.C. WHITE TRANSFER & STORAGE CO.
1775 Founders Pkwy, Alpharetta, GA 30009
Tel.: (404) 688-1888
Web Site:
  http://www.acwhitemovers.com
Rev.: $13,504,524
Emp.: 50
Local Trucking with Storage
N.A.I.C.S.: 484121
Thomas Sterling White *(Chm)*

A.C.&T. CO. INC.
11535 Hopewell Rd, Hagerstown, MD 21740
Tel.: (301) 582-2700   **MD**
Web Site: https://www.acandt.com
Year Founded: 1959
Sales Range: $250-299.9 Million
Emp.: 300
Wholesale & Retail of Petroleum Products
N.A.I.C.S.: 424720
Adna Fulton *(Pres)*

A.C.K. DEVELOPMENT, INC.
1702 S Bumby Ave, Orlando, FL 32806
Tel.: (407) 898-1055
Web Site:
  http://www.ackdevelopment.com
Sales Range: $10-24.9 Million
Emp.: 4
Independent Stores & Gas Stations
N.A.I.C.S.: 445131
Jaime Rodriguez *(Owner & Pres)*

A.D. ADAMS ADVERTISING, INC.
560 Sylvan Ave, Englewood Cliffs, NJ 07632
Tel.: (201) 541-3111
Web Site: http://www.ad-adams.com
Year Founded: 1949
Sales Range: $10-24.9 Million
Emp.: 9
Advertising Agencies, Business Publications, Business-To-Business, Commercial Photography, Engineering, High Technology, Magazines, Public Relations, Publicity/Promotions, Technical Advertising
N.A.I.C.S.: 541820
Connie Adams *(Owner)*
D. Graham Jemmett *(Art Dir)*

A.D. HEMBROUGH ADVERTISING & MARKETING SERVICES
581 Mountain Ave Ste 110, Washington, NJ 07676
Tel.: (201) 664-2449   **NJ**
Year Founded: 1971
Sales Range: $10-24.9 Million
Emp.: 4
N.A.I.C.S.: 541810
Alan D. Hembrough *(Owner)*
Linda Del Guercio *(Creative Svcs Dir)*

A.D. LUBOW, LLC
1 Penn Plz Ste 5312, New York, NY 10119-5312

Tel.: (212) 564-3250   **NY**
Web Site: http://www.adlubow.com
Year Founded: 1968
Rev.: $12,000,000
Emp.: 10
N.A.I.C.S.: 541810
Anne Van Der Does *(Principal Photographer & VP)*
Mildred Lalica *(Sr Dir-Art)*
Nico Marcellino *(Dir-Multimedia)*
Cynthia Lugo *(Production Editor)*
Vincent Iaropoli *(Supvr-Media & Billing)*

A.D. MORGAN CORPORATION
716 N Renellie Dr, Tampa, FL 33609
Tel.: (813) 832-3033
Web Site: https://www.admorgan.com
Year Founded: 1989
Sales Range: $10-24.9 Million
Emp.: 30
Commercial & Office Building Construction
N.A.I.C.S.: 236220
Rebecca Smith *(Founder & Pres)*
S. Glenn Hodges *(Comptroller)*
John Kalaf *(VP-Ops)*

A.D. SUTTON & SONS
20 W 33rd St 2nd Fl, New York, NY 10001
Tel.: (212) 695-7070
Web Site: http://www.adsutton.com
Rev.: $24,200,000
Emp.: 40
Handbags Mfr
N.A.I.C.S.: 424350
Ronald Shalom *(CEO)*
Albert Shalom *(VP)*
Pamela Sinishtaj *(Pres-Baby Div)*

A.D. WILLIS COMPANY, INC.
4266 Felter Ln, Austin, TX 78744
Tel.: (512) 385-3993
Year Founded: 1962
Sales Range: $10-24.9 Million
Emp.: 85
Roofing Installation Services
N.A.I.C.S.: 238390
Charlie Glaze *(Mgr)*

A.D. WINSTON CORPORATION
4315 36th St, Long Island City, NY 11101
Tel.: (718) 786-7848
Web Site:
  https://www.adwinstoncorp.com
Year Founded: 1958
Sales Range: $10-24.9 Million
Emp.: 40
Plumbing, Heating & Air-Conditioning Contracting Services
N.A.I.C.S.: 238220
Salvatore Barbera *(Principal)*
Mark Condon *(Exec VP & Principal)*
Peter O'Connell *(Principal)*
Andrew Benazzi *(Project Mgr)*
Joe Casale *(Project Mgr)*
Matthew Cebulski *(VP & Principal)*
Jeremy Welch *(Project Mgr)*

A.E. FINLEY & ASSOCIATES OF TENNESSEE, INC.
9724 Parkside Dr, Knoxville, TN 37922
Tel.: (865) 693-9440   **TN**
Web Site: http://www.aefinley.com
Year Founded: 1966
Sales Range: $10-24.9 Million
Emp.: 35
Distribution of Construction & Mining Machinery
N.A.I.C.S.: 423810
Gene Wilson *(Treas & Sec)*
Everett D. Meador *(Pres)*

A.E. NATHAN COMPANY INC.
49 W 34th St Fl 14, New York, NY 10018
Tel.: (212) 686-5194
Web Site: http://www.aenathan.com
Rev.: $10,000,000
Emp.: 25
Whslr of Textiles
N.A.I.C.S.: 424310
Robert Fortunoff *(Pres)*
Joel Preefer *(Mgr-Sls)*

A.E. NEW, JR., INC.
460 Van Pelt Ln, Pensacola, FL 32505
Tel.: (850) 472-1001
Sales Range: $10-24.9 Million
Emp.: 85
Commercial & Institutional Building Construction Services
N.A.I.C.S.: 236220
A. E. New Jr. *(Pres)*

A.E. ROBINSON OIL CO. INC.
1020 W Main St, Dover Foxcroft, ME 04426
Tel.: (207) 564-8131   **ME**
Web Site:
  https://www.aerobinson.com
Year Founded: 1950
Sales Range: $75-99.9 Million
Emp.: 20
Provider of Fuel Oil, Kerosene, Diesel, Gasoline, LP Gas & Motor Oil
N.A.I.C.S.: 457210
Jim Robinson *(Pres)*

A.E. WEASE INC.
1000 N Main St, De Soto, MO 63020
Tel.: (636) 586-3955
Web Site:
  http://www.weasedistributing.com
Sales Range: $75-99.9 Million
Emp.: 80
Tobacco & Tobacco Products
N.A.I.C.S.: 424940
Perry Hoffman *(Mgr-Sls)*

A.E.P. ENVIRONMENTAL, L.L.C.
1030 Victory Dr, Westwego, LA 70094
Tel.: (504) 328-9877
Web Site:
  https://www.ambarenvironment.com
Oil Skimmers Mfr
N.A.I.C.S.: 541690

A.F. STERLING HOME BUILDERS LTD. INC.
6340 N Campbell St 100 Ste 240, Tucson, AZ 85718-3206
Tel.: (520) 577-3600   **AZ**
Web Site: http://www.afsterling.com
Year Founded: 1986
Sales Range: $10-24.9 Million
Emp.: 13
Single-Family Housing Construction
N.A.I.C.S.: 236115
Jon Fenton *(Pres)*

A.G. DAVIS/AA GAGE
6533 Sims Dr, Sterling Heights, MI 48313
Tel.: (586) 977-9000
Web Site: https://www.agdavis-aagage.com
Sales Range: $10-24.9 Million
Emp.: 40
Gage Components, Custom Gaging Equipment & Automatic Gaging Systems Mfr
N.A.I.C.S.: 333515

Edwin G. Chapman *(Pres)*
Greg Chapman *(VP)*
Ray Verdoodt *(Engr-Sls)*
Ryan Bissett *(Engr-Electrical)*

A.G. FERRARI FOODS
2000 N Loop Rd, Alameda, CA 94502
Tel.: (510) 346-2100
Web Site: http://www.agferrari.com
Year Founded: 1919
Sales Range: $75-99.9 Million
Emp.: 70
Purveyor & Importer of Specialty & Italian Foods, Catering, e-Commerce & Wholesale Services
N.A.I.C.S.: 445298
Paul Ferrari *(Pres)*
Jarret Peppard *(Pres)*

A.G. LAYNE INC.
4578 Brazil St, Los Angeles, CA 90039
Tel.: (323) 245-2345
Web Site: https://www.aglayne.com
Rev.: $11,435,042
Emp.: 17
Chemicals & Allied Products
N.A.I.C.S.: 424690
Mike Lee *(CEO)*
Steve Cooper *(VP & Gen Mgr)*

A.G. LEE OIL COMPANY INC.
110 Roxy Dr, Selma, NC 27576
Tel.: (919) 934-6013   **NC**
Web Site: https://www.agleeoil.com
Year Founded: 1965
Sales Range: $25-49.9 Million
Emp.: 10
Distr of Oil & Petroleum Products
N.A.I.C.S.: 457120
Albert G. Lee Jr. *(Pres)*

A.G. RHODES HEALTH & REHAB
2801 Buford Hwy NE Ste 500, Atlanta, GA 30329
Tel.: (404) 636-3512   **GA**
Web Site: http://www.agrhodes.org
Year Founded: 1904
Sales Range: $25-49.9 Million
Emp.: 189
Elder Care Services
N.A.I.C.S.: 624120
Tammy Luther-Chalker *(Dir-Rehabilitation & Therapy Svcs)*
Jackie H. Summerlin *(Dir-Clinical Svcs)*
Kim Beasley *(Dir-Volunteer Svcs & Community Engagement)*
David L. Perdue *(Chm)*
Ann S. Barrett *(Sec)*
Rhett Austin *(CFO)*
John W. Wilcox III *(Treas)*

A.G. SPANOS COMPANIES
10100 Trinity Pkwy 5th Fl, Stockton, CA 95219
Tel.: (209) 478-7954   **CA**
Web Site: https://www.agspanos.com
Year Founded: 1960
Sales Range: $1-4.9 Billion
Emp.: 600
Multifamily Housing & Commercial Building Construction & Management Services
N.A.I.C.S.: 236116
Michael A. Spanos *(Pres)*
Dean A. Spanos *(Chm & CEO)*
Michael A. Spanos *(Pres)*
Dea Spanos Berberian *(Sec & Exec VP)*

Subsidiaries:

A.G. Spanos Construction   **(1)**
10100 Trinity Pkwy, Stockton, CA 95219
Tel.: (209) 478-7954

A.G. Spanos Companies—(Continued)

Web Site: http://www.agspanos.com
Sales Range: $10-24.9 Million
Emp.: 40
Construction Services
N.A.I.C.S.: 236116

A.G. Spanos Development (1)
10100 Trinity Pkwy 5th Fl, Stockton, CA 95210
Tel.: (209) 478-7954
Sales Range: $10-24.9 Million
Emp.: 40
Developer of Residential Real Estate
N.A.I.C.S.: 237210
Jerry Murphy (VP-Fin)

A.G. Spanos Enterprises (1)
10100 Trinity Pkwy, Stockton, CA 95219
Tel.: (209) 478-7954
Web Site: http://www.agspanos.com
Sales Range: $10-24.9 Million
Emp.: 40
Manager of Residential Real Estate Property
N.A.I.C.S.: 237210

A.G. Spanos Management (1)
10100 Trinity Pkwy, Stockton, CA 95219
Tel.: (209) 478-7954
Web Site: http://www.agspanos.com
Emp.: 50
Management Services
N.A.I.C.S.: 531120
Jeremiah Murphy (CEO)
Natalia Orfanos (Dir-PR)
Nick Faklis (VP-Dispositions)
Tom Allen (VP-Land Acq)

A.G. Spanos Realty (1)
10100 Trinity Pkwy 5th Fl, Stockton, CA 95219
Tel.: (209) 478-7954
Sales Range: $10-24.9 Million
Emp.: 50
Real Estate Sales
N.A.I.C.S.: 236117
Michael A. Spanos (VP)
Michael Spanos (VP)
Steven Cohen (CFO)

A.G. Spanos Securities (1)
10100 Trinity Pkwy 5th Fl, Stockton, CA 95219
Tel.: (209) 478-7954
Web Site: http://www.agspanos.com
Sales Range: $10-24.9 Million
Emp.: 50
Securities Brokerage
N.A.I.C.S.: 236117
Jane Pop (Mgr)

AGS Financial Corporation (1)
10100 Trinity Pkwy 5th Fl, Stockton, CA 95219
Tel.: (209) 478-7954
Sales Range: $10-24.9 Million
Emp.: 40
Financial Services
N.A.I.C.S.: 531120
Jane Pope (Mgr)

The Spanos Corporation (1)
10100 Trinity Pkwy Fl 5, Stockton, CA 95219
Tel.: (209) 478-7954
Web Site: http://www.agspanos.com
Rev.: $11,200,000
Emp.: 65
Management of Real Estate Properties
N.A.I.C.S.: 236117
Alexandros Economou (Reg VP)
Steve Cohen (CFO)

A.H. BECK FOUNDATION CO. INC.
5123 Blanco Rd, San Antonio, TX 78216
Tel.: (210) 342-5261
Web Site: http://www.ahbeck.com
Rev.: $10,800,000
Emp.: 15
Erection & Dismantling Of Forms For Poured Concrete
N.A.I.C.S.: 238990
Greg Korn (Controller)
Keith Anderson (VP-Ops)

Ian Kolda (Project Mgr)
August H, Beck III (Pres)
August H. Beck IV (VP)

A.H. ENTERTAINERS INC.
1151 Rohlwing Rd, Rolling Meadows, IL 60008
Tel.: (847) 253-2070
Web Site: https://www.ah-inc.com
Year Founded: 1939
Sales Range: $25-49.9 Million
Emp.: 350
Provider of Merchandising Machine Operations & Food Service Management
N.A.I.C.S.: 445132
Donald Hesch (Pres)
Tim Sherwood (VP-Sls)
Brad Hamma (Mgr-Chicago)

A.H. HERMEL CANDY & TO-BACCO CO. INC.
PO Box 447, Mankato, MN 56002-0447
Tel.: (507) 387-5634
Web Site: http://www.ahhermel.com
Year Founded: 1935
Sales Range: $25-49.9 Million
Emp.: 150
Confectionery
N.A.I.C.S.: 424450
David Hermel (Owner)
Jerry Underwood (Pres & CEO)

A.H. RIISE STORES
37 Main St, Saint Thomas, VI 00802
Tel.: (340) 772-2222
Web Site: https://www.ahriise.com
Year Founded: 1834
Jewelry Stores
N.A.I.C.S.: 458310
Bjorn Jensen (Dir-Sls)
Greg Ebenholtz (Gen Mgr)
James Eilen (Dir)

A.H. SCHADE INC.
1331 11th Ave N, Nampa, ID 83687-6708
Tel.: (208) 466-2475
Rev.: $23,500,000
Emp.: 110
Petroleum Bulk Stations
N.A.I.C.S.: 424710
Craig Lunt (VP & Gen Mgr)

A.H.I. INVESTMENT INC.
675 Glenoaks Blvd, San Fernando, CA 91340
Tel.: (818) 979-0030
Web Site: http://www.linzerproducts.com
Year Founded: 1988
Sales Range: Less than $1 Million
Emp.: 350
Holding Company
N.A.I.C.S.: 339994
Mark Saji (Treas)
Hisatoshi Ohtsuka (Pres)

Subsidiaries:

American Brush Company Inc. (1)
112 Industrial Blvd, Claremont, NH 03743
Tel.: (603) 542-9951
Rev.: $10,000,000
Emp.: 30
Mfr of Brooms & Brushes
N.A.I.C.S.: 339994
Randy Russell (Mgr-Production)

A.I. FRIEDMAN LP
44 W 18th St, New York, NY 10011-4611
Tel.: (212) 243-9000
Web Site: http://www.aifriedman.com
Year Founded: 1989
Sales Range: $25-49.9 Million
Emp.: 150

Mfr & Sales of Nondurable Goods
N.A.I.C.S.: 424990
Jim White (Pres)
George Morales (CFO)
Robert Levy (Dir-IT)
Christine Starito (Gen Mgr)

A.I. ROOT CO.
623 W Liberty St, Medina, OH 44256-2225
Tel.: (330) 723-4359
Web Site:
    https://www.rootcandles.com
Year Founded: 1869
Sales Range: $25-49.9 Million
Emp.: 280
Ecclesiastical & Decorative Candles; Periodical & Book Publishing
N.A.I.C.S.: 339999
Dawn Feagan (Coord-Subscription)

Subsidiaries:

A.I. Root Co. - San Antonio   (1)
Factory
918 S Laredo St, San Antonio, TX   (100%)
78204-1218
Tel.: (210) 223-2948
Web Site: http://www.rootcandles.com
Decorative Candles & Church Candles Mfr
N.A.I.C.S.: 339999

A.J. DANBOISE SON INC.
31015 Grand River Ave, Farmington Hills, MI 48336
Tel.: (248) 477-3626
Web Site: http://www.ajdanboise.com
Year Founded: 1925
Sales Range: $10-24.9 Million
Emp.: 85
Heating Oil
N.A.I.C.S.: 238220
Carol D. Gatewood (Pres)

A.J. DAW PRINTING INK CO.
3559 Greenwood Ave, Los Angeles, CA 90040
Tel.: (323) 723-3253
Sales Range: $10-24.9 Million
Emp.: 8
Printing Ink
N.A.I.C.S.: 325910
Mark Daw (Pres & CEO)

A.J. FUNK & CO. INC.
1471 Timber Dr, Elgin, IL 60123-1827
Tel.: (847) 741-6760
Web Site:
    http://www.glasscleaner.com
Year Founded: 1946
Sales Range: $50-74.9 Million
Emp.: 5
Glass Cleaner Mfr
N.A.I.C.S.: 325612

A.J. JERSEY INC.
125 St Nicholas Ave, South Plainfield, NJ 07080
Tel.: (908) 754-7333
Web Site: https://www.ajjersey.net
Year Founded: 1970
Rev.: $18,000,000
Emp.: 125
Material Handling Equipment Mfr
N.A.I.C.S.: 423830
David Rizzo (Pres)
Nancy Willan (Controller)
Steven Rizzo (VP)
Susan Janisch (Supvr-Sls & Mktg)

A.J. JOHNS, INC.
3225 Anniston Rd, Jacksonville, FL 32246-3696
Tel.: (904) 641-2055
Web Site: https://www.ajjohns.com
Year Founded: 1970
Sales Range: $10-24.9 Million
Emp.: 150

Civil Engineering Services
N.A.I.C.S.: 237310
A. J. Johns (Pres)
Elliot Jones (Project Mgr)

A.J. O'NEAL & ASSOCIATES, INC.
109 Falkenburg Rd N, Tampa, FL 33619
Tel.: (813) 654-4199
Web Site: http://www.ajoneal.com
Year Founded: 1984
Sales Range: $1-9.9 Million
Emp.: 5
Staffing Services
N.A.I.C.S.: 561311
Denise R. Sutton (Pres)
Cheri Colon (Mgr-Ops)

A.J. ROSE MANUFACTURING CO. INC.
38000 Chester Rd, Avon, OH 44011-1086
Tel.: (440) 934-7700
Web Site: https://www.ajrose.com
Year Founded: 1922
Sales Range: $25-49.9 Million
Emp.: 400
Automotive Equipment
N.A.I.C.S.: 336370
Michael Cox (Project Engr & Sys Engr-Electrical)

A.J. WELLER CORP.
9901 Drag Strip Rd, Keithville, LA 71047
Tel.: (318) 925-1010
Web Site: https://www.ajweller.com
Year Founded: 1981
Rev.: $14,000,000
Emp.: 25
Fabricated Structural Metal
N.A.I.C.S.: 332312
Linda Choate (Dir-Fin)
Robin Rambin (Dir-Mktg)

A.K. DURNIN CHRYSLER JEEP INC
11955 Airline Hwy, Baton Rouge, LA 70817-4406
Tel.: (225) 927-3900
Year Founded: 1971
Sales Range: $100-124.9 Million
Emp.: 65
Retailer of New & Used Automobiles
N.A.I.C.S.: 441110
Douglas K. Durnin (Pres)
Terry L. Durnin (VP)
Jerry L. Durnin (Treas & Sec)

A.L. EASTMOND & SONS INC.
1175 Leggett Ave, Bronx, NY 10474
Tel.: (718) 378-3000
Web Site: https://www.easco.com
Sales Range: $10-24.9 Million
Emp.: 80
Boiler Mfr
N.A.I.C.S.: 332410
Neil Tomasetti (Project Mgr)
Arlington L. Eastmond Jr. (Pres)

A.L. GEORGE INC.
1 Link Dr, Binghamton, NY 13904
Tel.: (607) 722-2300
Sales Range: $10-24.9 Million
Emp.: 60
Beer & Other Fermented Malt Liquors
N.A.I.C.S.: 424810
Debbie Herbert (Controller)

A.L. GILBERT COMPANY
304 N Yosemite Ave, Oakdale, CA 95361-3140
Tel.: (209) 847-1721
Year Founded: 1892
Sales Range: $25-49.9 Million

Emp.: 300
Mfr of Cattle & Dairy Feed
N.A.I.C.S.: 424910
David Gilbert (Pres & CEO)
Mark Villines (Mgr-Fleet)

Subsidiaries:

Farmers Warehouse   (1)
4367 Jessup Rd, Keyes, CA 95328
Tel.: (209) 632-2333
Web Site:
    http://www.farmerswarehouse.com
Emp.: 30
Farming Supplies Warehousing & Whslr
N.A.I.C.S.: 424910
Jay Gilbert (Gen Mgr)
Joseph Walker (Plant Mgr-Logistics)
Norma Sandlin (Office Mgr)

A.L. HANSEN MANUFACTUR-ING CO.
701 Pershing Rd, Waukegan, IL
60085-4079
Tel.: (847) 244-8900   IL
Web Site: https://www.alhansen.com
Year Founded: 1920
Sales Range: $75-99.9 Million
Emp.: 100
Mfr of Commercial Body & Industrial
Hardware
N.A.I.C.S.: 332510
William Hansen II (Pres)

A.L. SCHUTZMAN COMPANY INC.
N21 W23560 Ridgeview Pkwy W,
Waukesha, WI 53188
Tel.: (262) 832-8200
Web Site:
    http://www.ashdonfarms.com
Rev.: $37,000,000
Emp.: 65
Salted & Roasted Nuts & Seeds
N.A.I.C.S.: 311911
Gordon J. Liebl (Pres)
Mark Beveridge (VP)
Tim Angers (Controller)

A.L. WILSON CHEMICAL CO.
1050 Harrison Ave, Kearny, NJ
07032-5941
Tel.: (201) 997-3300
Web Site: https://www.alwilson.com
Year Founded: 1928
Sales Range: $50-74.9 Million
Emp.: 15
Mfr of Laundry & Dry Cleaning Stain
Removal Specialty Chemicals
N.A.I.C.S.: 325612
Bob Edwards (Reg VP)
Randy Schwarzmann (Dir-Special
Projects)

Subsidiaries:

Novel Technology Laboratories   (1)
1050 Harrison Ave, Kearny, NJ 07032
Tel.: (201) 997-3300
Stain Removal Products Mfr
N.A.I.C.S.: 424690

A.L.T. ADVERTISING & PRO-MOTION
12000 Lincoln Dr W Ste 408, Marlton,
NJ 08053
Tel.: (856) 810-0400
Web Site:
    http://www.altadvertising.com
Sales Range: $10-24.9 Million
Emp.: 5
N.A.I.C.S.: 541810
Jean Arlene (VP)
Les Altenberg (Pres)
William C. Heron (Sr Dir-Art)

A.M. ANDREWS CO.
4621 SW Beaverton-Hillsdale Hwy,
Portland, OR 97221

Tel.: (503) 244-1163
Web Site:
    https://www.amandrews.com
Year Founded: 1945
Sales Range: Less than $1 Million
Emp.: 4
Sprinkler Hoses & Repair Kits Mfr
N.A.I.C.S.: 326220
Dean Anderson (Pres)

A.M. COHRON & SON, INC.
62180 Great River Rd, Atlantic, IA
50022
Tel.: (712) 243-2448   IA
Web Site: https://www.amcohron-son.com
Year Founded: 1928
Sales Range: $10-24.9 Million
Emp.: 80
Bridge Construction Services
N.A.I.C.S.: 237310
Keith Harlan (Chm)
Doug Williams (VP)

A.M. LOGISTICS, INC.
101 Skinner Industrial Dr, Saint
Charles, MO 63301
Tel.: (636) 949-3992   MO
Web Site:
    http://www.mcairfreight.com
Year Founded: 2004
Sales Range: $1-9.9 Million
Emp.: 30
Logistical Services Offering Truck-
loads, Air Freight, Warehousing &
Shipping Services
N.A.I.C.S.: 488510
Michael McLaughlin (Co-Owner &
Co-Founder)
William B. McLaughlin Jr. (Co-Owner
& Co-Founder)

A.M. ORTEGA CONSTRUC-TION INC.
10125 Channel Rd, Lakeside, CA
92040
Tel.: (619) 390-1988
Web Site: https://www.amortega.com
Year Founded: 1985
Sales Range: $25-49.9 Million
Emp.: 240
Electrical Wiring Services
N.A.I.C.S.: 238210
Archie Maurice Ortega (Pres & CEO)

A.M. TODD COMPANY
1717 Douglas Ave, Kalamazoo, MI
49007-1600
Tel.: (269) 343-2603   MI
Web Site: http://www.amtodd.com
Year Founded: 1869
Sales Range: $75-99.9 Million
Emp.: 60
Mfr of Essential Oils
N.A.I.C.S.: 311942
Robert Wheeler (VP-Ops)
Robert A. King (Pres-
Botanical/Therapeutics)

Subsidiaries:

A.M. Todd - Ingredients &
Flavors   (1)
1717 Douglas Ave, Kalamazoo, MI 49007
Tel.: (269) 343-2603
Web Site: http://www.amtodd.com
Sales Range: $25-49.9 Million
Emp.: 57
Supplier of Specialty Mint Oils & Flavors
N.A.I.C.S.: 311942
Timothy Chambers (Dir-Mint Innovation)

A.M. Todd Botanical
Therapeutics   (1)
PO Box 415, Smithfield, UT 84335-0415
Tel.: (435) 713-4888
Web Site: http://www.amtodd.com
Sales Range: $10-24.9 Million
Emp.: 11

Supplier of Ingredients for Enhancing
Health & Wellness
N.A.I.C.S.: 325411

A.M.E. SERVICES, INC.
23 Barreca St, Norco, LA 70079
Tel.: (504) 712-3220
Sales Range: $10-24.9 Million
Emp.: 825
Building Maintenance Services
N.A.I.C.S.: 561720
Edward Chatman (Pres)
Charles Hamilton (CFO)
Glenn Aikin (Dir-Mktg)

A.M.E.'S UNIFORMS, INC.
700 NW 57th Pl, Fort Lauderdale, FL
33309
Tel.: (954) 739-7507
Web Site:
    http://www.amesuniforms.com
Sales Range: $10-24.9 Million
Emp.: 25
Uniforms Mfr
N.A.I.C.S.: 315250
Mark Forst (Pres)

A.N. DERINGER, INC.
64 N Main St, Saint Albans, VT
05478
Tel.: (802) 524-8110   VT
Web Site:
    https://www.anderinger.com
Sales Range: $150-199.9 Million
Emp.: 500
Provider of Custom House Broker-
age, Freight Transportation Arrange-
ments & International Logistics Ser-
vices
N.A.I.C.S.: 488510
Sandy Mayotte (Sec & Sr VP)
Gary Smith (District Mgr)
Jake Holzscheiter (Pres & CEO)
Amy Magnus (Dir-Customs Affairs &
Compliance)
Erica Rawson (District Mgr)
Kris Rocheleau (Dir-IT)
Linda Mydland (District Mgr)
Mark Mills (District Mgr)
Matt Parrott (Dir-Transportation)
Jack Bender (Dir-Sls & Mktg)

A.N. WEBBER INC.
2150 State Route 45-52, Kankakee,
IL 60901
Tel.: (815) 939-2235
Web Site: http://www.anwebber.com
Sales Range: $10-24.9 Million
Emp.: 250
Trucking Service
N.A.I.C.S.: 484121
Kae Webber (Sr VP-Bus Dev)
Matt Magiera (Supvr-Ops)
Pat Gillespie (Mgr-Logistics Procure-
ment)
Todd Perzee (Pres)
Adam Beherns (Mgr-Warehouse)

A.O. CONSTRUCTION COM-PANY, INC.
3535 Gate Alfred Rd, Winter Haven,
FL 33881
Tel.: (863) 299-4444   FL
Web Site:
    https://aoconstructionco.com
Year Founded: 1960
Rev.: $3,500,000
Emp.: 27
Fiscal Year-end: 12/31/06
Industrial Building Construction Ser-
vices
N.A.I.C.S.: 236220
Gannon Olmert (Pres)

Subsidiaries:

Wagner Construction Company,
LLC   (1)

1903 Greenleaf Ln, Leesburg, FL 34748
Tel.: (352) 728-2221
Web Site: http://www.wagner-florida.com
Sales Range: $1-9.9 Million
Emp.: 12
Construction Services
N.A.I.C.S.: 236220
James A. Wagner (Principal)

A.O. HARDEE & SON, INC.
55 Park St, Little River, SC 29566
Tel.: (843) 249-1264
Web Site: https://www.aohardee-son.com
Year Founded: 1955
Sales Range: $25-49.9 Million
Emp.: 210
Industrial Building Construction Ser-
vices
N.A.I.C.S.: 236210
Benjy Hardee (Pres)

A.P. HUBBARD WHOLESALE LUMBER
1027 Arnold St, Greensboro, NC
27405
Tel.: (336) 275-1343
Web Site:
    http://www.hubbardlumber.com
Sales Range: $10-24.9 Million
Emp.: 5
Lumber: Rough, Dressed & Finished
N.A.I.C.S.: 423310
Marion Hubbard (Pres)

A.P. WAGNER INC.
307 Cayuga Rd Ste 100, Buffalo, NY
14225-1953
Tel.: (716) 856-5005
Web Site: http://www.apwagner.com
Year Founded: 1953
Sales Range: $25-49.9 Million
Emp.: 300
Household Appliance Sales
N.A.I.C.S.: 423620
Rick Essex (CEO)
Jim Bochenski (Dir-Pur)
Mark Creighton (Mgr-Sls)

A.R. LOCKHART DEVELOP-MENT CO.
800 W Waterloo Rd, Akron, OH
44314
Tel.: (330) 745-6520
Sales Range: $10-24.9 Million
Emp.: 20
Subdividers & Developers
N.A.I.C.S.: 237210
Amy McDougal (Office Mgr)

A.R. SAVAGE & SON, LLC
202 S Rome Ave Ste 200, Tampa, FL
33606-1800
Tel.: (813) 247-4550
Web Site: https://www.arsavage.com
Year Founded: 1945
Sales Range: $1-9.9 Million
Emp.: 12
Freight Transportation Arrangement
N.A.I.C.S.: 488510
Arthur R. Savage (Pres & CEO)

A.R.E. ACCESSORIES, LLC
400 Nave Rd, Massillon, OH 44646
Tel.: (330) 830-7800
Web Site: https://www.4are.com
Year Founded: 1969
Sales Range: $25-49.9 Million
Emp.: 550
Manufactured Truck Caps, Tonneau
Covers & Accessories
N.A.I.C.S.: 336390
Jason Warren (Plant Mgr)
Andrew Rohr (VP-Engrg & Quality)

A.R.K. CONTRACTING SER-VICES LLC.

A.R.K. Contracting Services LLC.—(Continued)
420 S Dick Price Rd, Kennedale, TX 76060
Tel.: (817) 478-7400
Web Site:
http://www.arkcontracting.com
Sales Range: $10-24.9 Million
Emp.: 100
Nonresidential Construction Services
N.A.I.C.S.: 236220
Mary Beth Shipka (Owner)

A.R.M. SOLUTIONS, INC.
PO Box 2929, Camarillo, CA 93011-2929
Tel.: (888) 772-6468   CA
Web Site:
http://www.armsolutions.net
Year Founded: 2005
Sales Range: $1-9.9 Million
Emp.: 46
Custom Debt Recovery Services
N.A.I.C.S.: 561440
Richard Finkle (CIO)

A.S. MANAGEMENT CORPORATION
888 Park Ave, New York, NY 10021-0235
Tel.: (203) 967-4003   CA
Year Founded: 1990
Sales Range: $150-199.9 Million
Emp.: 650
Operator of Restaurant Chain
N.A.I.C.S.: 541618

Subsidiaries:

Victoria Station Inc.   (1)
Pickering Wharf 86 Wharf St, Salem, MA 01970   (100%)
Tel.: (978) 745-3400
Web Site:
http://www.victoriastationsalem.com
Sales Range: $10-24.9 Million
Emp.: 70
Restaurant
N.A.I.C.S.: 722511
Elizabeth Collett (Gen Mgr)

A.S.R. ELECTRICAL CONTRACTING
39 Cain Dr, Plainview, NY 11803
Tel.: (516) 420-0101
Web Site: http://www.asrelectric.com
Sales Range: $10-24.9 Million
Emp.: 65
General Electrical Contractor
N.A.I.C.S.: 238210
Robert Chaikin (Pres)
Jodi Casciano (Owner)
Rudy Weissberg (VP)

A.S.W. SERVICES INC.
3375 Gilchirst Rd, Mogadore, OH 44260
Tel.: (330) 733-6291
Web Site: https://www.aswglobal.com
Year Founded: 2000
Sales Range: $75-99.9 Million
Emp.: 200
Civil Engineering Services
N.A.I.C.S.: 237310
Nick J. Mihiylov (Pres)

A.T. CLAYTON & COMPANY, INC.
300 Atlantic St, Stamford, CT 06902
Tel.: (203) 658-1200   CT
Web Site: http://www.atclayton.com
Year Founded: 1949
Sales Range: $50-74.9 Million
Emp.: 50
Paper Mfr
N.A.I.C.S.: 541611

A.T. FERRELL COMPANY, INC.

1440 S Adams St, Bluffton, IN 46714-9793
Tel.: (260) 824-3400   DE
Web Site: https://www.atferrell.com
Year Founded: 1869
Sales Range: $10-24.9 Million
Emp.: 50
Process Equipment Mfr of Products for Agricultural & Industrial Use
N.A.I.C.S.: 333111
Steve Stuller (Pres)
Dale Zeigler (Controller)

Subsidiaries:

A.T. Ferrell Company, Inc. - Clipper Separation Division   (1)
1440 S Adams St, Bluffton, IN 46714
Tel.: (260) 824-3400
Farming Equipments Mfr
N.A.I.C.S.: 333111
Phil Teeple (Mgr-Sls)
Mike Lehman (Mgr-Sls)

A.T. KEARNEY, INC.
227 West Monroe St, Chicago, IL 60606
Tel.: (312) 648-0111   DE
Web Site: http://www.atkearney.com
Year Founded: 1926
Sales Range: $750-799.9 Million
Emp.: 2,500
Global Strategic Management Consultancy Services
N.A.I.C.S.: 541611
David A. Asper (Partner)
Johan Aurik (Chm & Mng Partner)
Dietrich Neumann (Partner)
Sieghart Scheiter (Partner)
Jeffrey C. Ward (Partner & VP)
Christine Laurens (CFO)
Isaac Krakovsky (Partner-Consumer Products & Retail Practice-New York)
David Hanfland (Sr Partner & Head-Americas)
Andrew Stewart (Mng Partner-UK & Ireland)
Simon Kent (Head-Fin Svcs-Global)
Abhinav Agrawal (Partner)
John Gomes (Partner-Comm, Media & Tech Practice)
Bronwyn Tinker-Kelly (Head-Learning-Global)

Subsidiaries:

Cervello Inc.   (1)
155 Seaport Boulevard, Fl 2, Boston, MA 02210
Tel.: (617) 307-4131
Web Site: http://www.mycervello.com
Information Technology Support Services
N.A.I.C.S.: 541512
Glyn Heatley (Pres)

A.T. WALL COMPANY
55 Service Ave, Warwick, RI 02886-1020
Tel.: (401) 739-0740   RI
Web Site:
http://www.atwcompanies.com
Year Founded: 1886
Rev.: $30,000,000
Emp.: 66
Fabricated Metal Tubing Drawing & Metal Stampings
N.A.I.C.S.: 332999
Jacquelyn Miranda (Mgr-Matls)
Donna M. Parker (Dir-Sls & Mktg)
Lee Becton (Mgr-Sls & Mktg)

Subsidiaries:

Judson A. Smith Company   (1)
857-863 Sweinhart Rd, Boyertown, PA 19512   (100%)
Tel.: (610) 367-2021
Web Site: http://www.judsonsmith.com
Emp.: 100
Fabricated Metal Tube Drawing Services
N.A.I.C.S.: 332618

John Shields (Mgr-Sls & Mktg)

A.T. WILLIAMS OIL COMPANY
5446 University Pkwy, Winston Salem, NC 27105-1366
Tel.: (336) 767-6280   NC
Web Site: http://www.wilcohess.com
Year Founded: 1963
Sales Range: $10-24.9 Million
Emp.: 2,000
Gasoline Service Stations
N.A.I.C.S.: 551112
Arthur T. Williams Jr. (Founder)

Subsidiaries:

Wilco   (1)
3610 W Wendover Ave, Greensboro, NC 27407-1521   (100%)
Tel.: (336) 292-6643
Sales Range: $10-24.9 Million
Emp.: 9
Gasoline Service Stations
N.A.I.C.S.: 457120

A.V. OLSSON TRADING CO. INC.
2001 W Main St Ste 215, Stamford, CT 06902-4542
Tel.: (203) 969-2090
Web Site: http://www.avolsson.com
Year Founded: 1920
Rev.: $5,000,000
Emp.: 40
Scandinavian Food Importer
N.A.I.C.S.: 424490
Kenneth Olsson (Pres)
Heather Langer (Dir-Customer Rels Ops)

A.W. CHESTERTON COMPANY
860 Salem St, Groveland, MA 01834
Tel.: (978) 469-6810   MA
Web Site:
https://www.chesterton.com
Year Founded: 1884
Sales Range: $150-199.9 Million
Emp.: 1,250
Mechanical Packing Seals, Pumps & Special Technical Products
N.A.I.C.S.: 339991
Andrew W. Chesterton (Pres & CEO)

Subsidiaries:

A.W. Chesterton Co. Ltd.   (1)
889 Fraser Drive Unit 105, Burlington, L7L 4X8, ON, Canada
Tel.: (905) 335-5055
Web Site: http://www.chesterton.com
Gasket, Packing & Sealing Device Mfr
N.A.I.C.S.: 339991

CHESTERTON CR s.r.o.   (1)
Masarykova 56, Telc, 588 56, Czech Republic
Tel.: (420) 567 213 095
Web Site: http://www.chesterton.com
Emp.: 12
Gasket, Packing & Sealing Device Mfr
N.A.I.C.S.: 339991
Peter Podsednik (Mng Dir)

Chesterton Hungary KFT   (1)
Godolloi Ut 115, Mogyorod, 2146, Hungary
Tel.: (36) 28 540 450
Gasket, Packing & Sealing Device Mfr
N.A.I.C.S.: 339991

Chesterton International GmbH   (1)
Am Lenzenfleck 23, Ismaning, 85737, Germany
Tel.: (49) 89 9965 46 0
Web Site: http://www.chesterton.com
Emp.: 45
Gasket, Packing & Sealing Device Mfr
N.A.I.C.S.: 339991
Didier Thalinger (Mng Dir)

Chesterton Mexicana S.A. de C.V.   (1)
Av Olmecas No 1 Parque Industrial Naucalpan, 53470, Naucalpan, Mexico
Tel.: (52) 55 50891350

Gasket, Packing & Sealing Device Mfr
N.A.I.C.S.: 339991

Chesterton Ningbo Sealing Technology Co. Ltd   (1)
Xinmo Village Xiaogang Township, Ningbo, Zhejiang, China
Tel.: (86) 574 8617 9166
Gasket, Packing & Sealing Device Mfr
N.A.I.C.S.: 339991

Chesterton Polska SP.ZO.O   (1)
Al W Korfantego 191, Katowice, 40 153, Poland
Tel.: (48) 32 249 5290
Web Site: http://www.chesterton.com.pl
Emp.: 18
Gasket, Packing & Sealing Device Mfr
N.A.I.C.S.: 339991
Kazemear Gubas (Gen Mgr)

Chesterton Roma Srl   (1)
Via Amatrice 15, Rome, 199, Italy
Tel.: (39) 068 620 3721
Web Site: http://www.chestetron.com
Gasket, Packing & Sealing Device Mfr
N.A.I.C.S.: 339991

Chesterton Slovakia s.r.o.   (1)
Strojnicka 103, Bratislava, 821 05, Slovakia
Tel.: (421) 2 4363 2151
Web Site: http://www.chesterton.com
Emp.: 10
Gasket, Packing & Sealing Device Mfr
N.A.I.C.S.: 339991
Dusan Bobek (Gen Mgr)

A.W. HASTINGS & CO. INC.
Two Pearson Way, Enfield, CT 06082-2654
Tel.: (860) 745-2424   DE
Web Site: http://www.awhastings.com
Year Founded: 1854
Rev.: $39,000,000
Emp.: 62
Lumber, Plywood & Millwork
N.A.I.C.S.: 423310
Dusty Hoyt (Pres)
J. Keenan Burns (COO & Exec VP)
Jody Hoyt (Treas)
Miana Hoyt Dawson (Mgr-Mktg Brand)

A.W. HERNDON OIL CO. INC.
104 N Ct Sq, Abbeville, AL 36310
Tel.: (334) 585-6424   AL
Year Founded: 1957
Sales Range: $25-49.9 Million
Emp.: 90
Operator of Gasoline Service Stations
N.A.I.C.S.: 457120
Sherri Herndon (Pres)
Sandy Jones (Office Mgr)

A.W. MILLER TECHNICAL SALES INC.
7661 Seneca St, East Aurora, NY 14052-9457
Tel.: (716) 652-8282   NY
Web Site: https://www.awmiller.com
Year Founded: 1970
Sales Range: $50-74.9 Million
Emp.: 50
Retail Distributors of Industrial Machinery & Equipment
N.A.I.C.S.: 423830
Dave Augustyniak (VP-Finance)
Albert LeBlanc (VP-Operations)

Subsidiaries:

A.W. Miller   (1)
3 Tara Dr, Harmony, PA 16037
Tel.: (724) 453-1690
Web Site: http://www.awmiller.com
Rev.: $20,000,000
Emp.: 20
Retail Distributors of Industrial Machinery & Equipment
N.A.I.C.S.: 423830
Russ Weis (Gen Mgr)

A.W. Miller Technical Sales, Inc.   (1)
5590 McAdam Rd, Mississauga, L4Z 1P1,

ON, Canada **(100%)**
Tel.: (905) 890-8686
Web Site: http://www.awmiller.com
Sales Range: $10-24.9 Million
Emp.: 9
Retail Distributors of Industrial Machinery & Equipment
N.A.I.C.S.: 333248

A.W. PERRY INC.
20 Winthrop Sq, Boston, MA 02110
Tel.: (617) 542-3164
Web Site: https://www.awperry.com
Sales Range: $10-24.9 Million
Emp.: 25
Commercial & Industrial Building Operation
N.A.I.C.S.: 531120
Mark Flaherty (CFO & Controller)
Richard Beal (CEO)
Susan Perry O'Day (Pres)

A.Y. MCDONALD MANUFAC-TURING CO.
4800 Chavenelle Rd, Dubuque, IA 52002
Tel.: (563) 583-7311   IA
Web Site:
http://www.aymcdonald.com
Year Founded: 1856
Sales Range: $150-199.9 Million
Emp.: 320
Plumbing Fixture & Valve Mfr
N.A.I.C.S.: 332913
Rob McDonald (Pres & CEO)

Subsidiaries:

A.Y.M. Inc. **(1)**
1701 Hwy 5 S, Albia, IA 52531-8802
Tel.: (641) 932-7841
Sales Range: $10-24.9 Million
Emp.: 100
Gas Valves & Meter Devices Mfr
N.A.I.C.S.: 334514
Rob Mcdonald (CEO)

Brock-McVey Company **(1)**
1100 Brock McVey Dr, Lexington, KY 40509-4116
Tel.: (859) 255-1412
Web Site: http://www.brockmcvey.com
Sales Range: $50-74.9 Million
Emp.: 100
Wholesale Distr of Plumbing, Heating, Cooling, Light Fixtures, Kitchen Cabinets, Industrial & Electrical Products
N.A.I.C.S.: 423730
Reggie Hickman (Pres & COO)
Brenda Holdren (VP-Fin)
Stephen Jones (Mgr-IT)

Cambridge Brass **(1)**
140 Orion Pl, PO Box 249, Cambridge, N1T 1R9, ON, Canada
Tel.: (519) 621-5520
Web Site: http://www.cambridgebrass.com
Sales Range: $25-49.9 Million
Emp.: 200
Underground Pipes & Waterworks Brass Products
N.A.I.C.S.: 237990
Byron Murrin (Gen Mgr)

A1 GARAGE DOOR SERVICES LLC
3254 E Broadway Rd, Phoenix, AZ 85040
Tel.: (480) 757-3550
Web Site: http://www.a1garage.com
Year Founded: 2007
Sales Range: $25-49.9 Million
Emp.: 140
Garage Door Services
N.A.I.C.S.: 238290
Tommy Mello (Owner)
Angela Johnson (Mgr-Call Center)

A1 GROUP, INC.
7040 Avenida Encinas Ste 104-159, Carlsbad, CA 92011
Tel.: (760) 487-7772   NV

Web Site: http://www.freebutton.com
Year Founded: 2006
Sales Range: Less than $1 Million
Emp.: 4
Investment Services
N.A.I.C.S.: 523999
Bruce Storrs (Chm, Pres, CEO, Sec & Treas)
Andy Diaz (COO)
Timothy S. Hart (CFO)

A1 POOL PARTS
1507 W Alton Ave, Santa Ana, CA 92704
Web Site:
http://www.a1poolparts.com
Year Founded: 2005
Sales Range: $1-9.9 Million
Emp.: 6
Swimming Pool Contractor
N.A.I.C.S.: 238990
Scott Miller (Co-Owner)
Raymond Danfield (Co-Owner)

A10 CLINICAL SOLUTIONS, INC.
2000 Regency Pkwy Ste 675, Cary, NC 27518
Tel.: (919) 465-3366
Web Site: http://www.a10clinical.com
Year Founded: 2005
Sales Range: $1-9.9 Million
Emp.: 220
Clinical Research & Occupational Health Care Services
N.A.I.C.S.: 923120
Leah Brown (Owner & Pres)

A1A AIRPORT & LIMOUSINE SERVICE
1990 NW Boca Raton Blvd, Boca Raton, FL 33432
Tel.: (561) 622-2222
Web Site: https://www.a1alimo.com
Year Founded: 1987
Sales Range: $1-9.9 Million
Emp.: 12
Limousine Service
N.A.I.C.S.: 485320
James Parkes (Gen Mgr)

A1C PARTNERS, LLC
917 Elsie Barber Ct, Davidsonville, MD 21035
Tel.: (410) 703-2897
Web Site:
http://www.a1cpartners.com
Year Founded: 2004
Sales Range: $1-9.9 Million
Emp.: 25
Advertising Agency Services
N.A.I.C.S.: 541810
Chris Turner (Founder & Mng Principal)
Ted Langhoff (VP)

A24 FILMS LLC
31 W 27th St 11th Fl, New York, NY 10001
Tel.: (646) 568-6015
Web Site: https://a24films.com
Emp.: 100
Film & Television Production
N.A.I.C.S.: 512110

Subsidiaries:

Cherrylane Theatre **(1)**
38 Commerce St, New York, NY 10014-3755
Tel.: (212) 989-2020
Web Site: http://www.cherrylanetheatre.org
Motion Picture Theaters (except Drive-Ins)
N.A.I.C.S.: 512131

A2L TECHNOLOGIES, INC.
10220 Harney Rd, Thonotosassa, FL 33592

Tel.: (813) 248-8558
Web Site:
http://www.a2ltechnologies.com
Sales Range: $1-9.9 Million
Environmental Consulting, Engineering & Remediation Services
N.A.I.C.S.: 541620
Kent R. Ward (VP & Dir-Environ Svcs)
Jeff Borgmeyer (Sr Engr)

A2Z ENVIRONMENTAL GROUP, LLC
250 S Kresson St, Baltimore, MD 21224-2533
Tel.: (410) 327-8674
Web Site: http://www.a2zgroup.com
Year Founded: 1996
Sales Range: $10-24.9 Million
Emp.: 55
Specialty Trade Contractors
N.A.I.C.S.: 238990
Rita Holderby (Owner & Pres)
Bob Holderby (Officer-Procurement)
Michael Cardinale (Project Mgr)
Yvonne Bennit (Office Mgr)
Richard Cope (Project Mgr)
Brian Lewis (Supvr-Demolition)

A2Z FIELD SERVICES
7450 Industrial Pkwy Ste 105, Plain City, OH 43064-8789
Tel.: (614) 873-0211
Web Site:
https://www.a2zfieldservices.com
Year Founded: 2001
Sales Range: $10-24.9 Million
Emp.: 104
Property Maintenance & Home Inspection Service
N.A.I.C.S.: 541350
Jennifer Sells (COO & Sr VP)
Amie Sparks-Beebe (CEO)
Todd Arena (Dir-Ops)
Felicia Ketteman (Mgr-Bus Project)
Allen Markarian (Controller)
Julie Blankenship (Mgr-HR)
Ed Becker (Mgr-IT)
Lori Ashcraft (Mgr-Sls)
Chris Slaughenhoupt (Sr Project Mgr-Client)
Tony D'Aurelio (Dir-Sls)

A2Z, INC.
10320 Little Patuxent Pkwy Ste 400, Columbia, MD 21044
Tel.: (410) 740-9200
Web Site: http://www.a2zinc.net
Sales Range: $1-9.9 Million
Emp.: 54
Software Development Services
N.A.I.C.S.: 541511
Rajiv Jain (Pres & CEO)
Angela Carr (COO)

A3 GLOBAL, LLC
300 Schell LN Ste 309-310, Phoenixville, PA 19460
Tel.: (445) 345-6225
Web Site: http://www.a3global.com
Year Founded: 2021
Commercial & Military Vehicles Parts Mfr & Integrated Systems
N.A.I.C.S.: 336320
Eugene Smotkin (Sr VP-R&D)
Michael Cardone III (CEO)

Subsidiaries:

NuVant Systems Inc. **(1)**
130 N W St, Crown Point, IN 46307-3916
Tel.: (219) 644-3231
Web Site: http://www.nuvant.com
Electrical Equipment & Component Manufacturing
N.A.I.C.S.: 335999
Linda Smotkin (Sec)
Eugene Smotkin (Pres)

AA ADVANCE AIR, INC.
1920 NW 32nd St, Pompano Beach, FL 33064
Tel.: (954) 971-5801
Web Site:
https://www.aaadvanceair.com
Year Founded: 1976
Sales Range: $10-24.9 Million
Emp.: 108
Air-Conditioning, Plumbing & Heating Services
N.A.I.C.S.: 238220
Doug Cady (VP)
Robert Burrow (Pres)
Christine Giardino (Supvr-Customer Svc)

AA CATER TRUCK MANUFAC-TURING COMPANY, INC.
750 E Slauson Ave, Los Angeles, CA 90011-5236
Tel.: (323) 235-6650   CA
Web Site:
https://www.aacatertruck.com
Year Founded: 1946
Sales Range: $50-74.9 Million
Emp.: 40
Mfr & Repairer of Catering Trucks
N.A.I.C.S.: 336211
Vahe Karapetian (Owner & Pres)

AA ELECTRIC INC.
1665 Lakes Pkwy Ste 108, Lawrenceville, GA 30043-5879
Tel.: (770) 822-6262
Web Site: https://www.a-aelectric.com
Year Founded: 1961
Sales Range: $10-24.9 Million
Emp.: 25
Electrical Apparatus & Equipment Distr
N.A.I.C.S.: 423610
Gerald T. Wisniewski (VP)

Subsidiaries:

AA Electric SE Inc. **(1)**
2011 S Combee Rd, Lakeland, FL 33801
Tel.: (863) 665-6941
Web Site: http://www.aaelectric.com
Sales Range: $10-24.9 Million
Emp.: 20
Electric Apparatus & Equipment
N.A.I.C.S.: 423610

AA IMPORTING
7700 Hall St, Saint Louis, MO 63147
Tel.: (314) 383-8800
Web Site:
https://www.aaimporting.com
Rev.: $20,000,000
Emp.: 50
Antiques Reproduction
N.A.I.C.S.: 423990
Richard Tallin (Pres)
Robert Tallin (VP)

AA METALS, INC
11616 Landstar Blvd, Orlando, FL 32824
Tel.: (407) 377-0246
Web Site: https://www.aametals.com
Year Founded: 2003
Sales Range: $50-74.9 Million
Emp.: 23
Aluminium Product Distr
N.A.I.C.S.: 331313
Jack Cheng (Pres & CEO)
Bruce Ferguson (VP-Product Dev)
Agnes Fazekas (Sr Acct Mgr)
Siji Shan (Mgr-Shipping & Receiving)
Bob Frascella (VP-Strategic Acct Dev)
Robert Rogers (Mgr-Inside Sls)
Edwin Vega (Mgr-Warehouse)
Robert Closs (CFO)
Dawn McFarlane (Mgr-Acctg)

AA Metals, Inc—(Continued)

Gary Doscher (Mgr-Inside Sls)
Daniel Day (Mgr-Ops)
Geoff Moncher (Project Mgr)
Julie Ashburn (Supvr-Acct)
Stanley Mielach (Supvr-Acct)

AA TRUCK RENTING CORPORATION
575 Underhill Blvd Ste 223, Syosset, NY 11791
Tel.: (718) 937-8611
Web Site: http://www.aatruck.com
Rev.: $11,100,000
Emp.: 100
Truck Leasing, Without Drivers
N.A.I.C.S.: 532120
Eric W. Roberts (Pres)
Paul Lanciotti (Controller)

AA WHEEL & TRUCK SUPPLY INC.
717 E 16th Ave, Kansas City, MO 64116
Tel.: (816) 221-9556
Web Site: https://www.aawheel.com
Sales Range: $10-24.9 Million
Emp.: 25
Truck Parts & Accessories
N.A.I.C.S.: 423120
Nancy Ringel (CEO)

AA WORLD CLASS CORP.
65 Railroad Ave Unit 3, Ridgefield, NJ 07657
Tel.: (201) 313-0022
Web Site: http://www.aaworld.com
Year Founded: 1982
Sales Range: $10-24.9 Million
Emp.: 30
Mfr of Emblems, Embroidery Lapel Pins
N.A.I.C.S.: 313310
Benjamin Amoruso (Pres & Principal)

AAA BUSINESS SUPPLIES LIMITED PARTNERSHIP
325 Mendell St, San Francisco, CA 94124
Tel.: (415) 821-4430   CA
Web Site: https://www.aaasolutions.com
Year Founded: 1980
Sales Range: $10-24.9 Million
Emp.: 60
Office Supplies & Furniture Retailer
N.A.I.C.S.: 459410
Stephen Danziger (Owner)

AAA FLAG & BANNER MANUFACTURING CO., INC.
8955 National Blvd, Los Angeles, CA 90034
Tel.: (310) 276-1178
Web Site: http://www.aaaflag.com
Year Founded: 1973
Rev.: $15,000,000
Emp.: 200
Banners, Flags, Decals & Posters
N.A.I.C.S.: 459999

AAA REFRIGERATION SERVICE INC
1804 Nereid Ave, Bronx, NY 10466
Tel.: (718) 324-2231
Web Site: https://www.aaarefrig.com
Sales Range: $10-24.9 Million
Emp.: 80
Commercial Refrigeration Contractor
N.A.I.C.S.: 238220
Ron Sarison (VP-CT Div)

AAA SUNDRIES INC.
134 NE 1st St, Miami, FL 33132
Tel.: (305) 372-1766

Sales Range: $10-24.9 Million
Emp.: 9
Watches & Watch Parts
N.A.I.C.S.: 423690
Madatali Panjwani (Pres)

AAA TRANSPORTATION GROUP LTD.
3333 New Hyde Park Rd, New Hyde Park, NY 11042
Tel.: (516) 365-2000
Web Site: http://www.aaagroup.net
Rev.: $61,000,000
Emp.: 10
Freight Transportation Arrangement
N.A.I.C.S.: 488510
Jack Meehan (CEO)
Robert Vecchione (Gen Counsel & VP)
Kristine Lee (Dir-Svcs)

AAAA WORLD IMPORT EXPORT
7800 NW 29th St, Miami, FL 33122-2901
Tel.: (305) 688-1000
Web Site: http://www.aaaaworld.com
Sales Range: $10-24.9 Million
Emp.: 20
Electrical Appliances, Television & Radio
N.A.I.C.S.: 423620
Karin Patel (VP)

AABBITT ADHESIVES INC.
2403 N Oakley Ave, Chicago, IL 60647
Tel.: (773) 227-2700
Web Site: https://www.aabbitt.com
Rev.: $30,000,000
Emp.: 60
Mfr & Distr of Adhesives
N.A.I.C.S.: 325520
Benjamin B. Sarmas (Pres)

AABR
1508 College Point Blvd, College Point, NY 11356
Tel.: (718) 321-3800   NY
Web Site: https://www.aabr.org
Year Founded: 1956
Sales Range: $25-49.9 Million
Emp.: 853
Developmental Disability Assistance Services
N.A.I.C.S.: 624120
Mary Bosnack (CFO)
Luis Reynoso (Dir-Maintenance)
Kathryn Flood (Dir-Quality Assurance)
Hezikeigh Elliott (Dir-Residential)

AAC CONTRACTING INC.
175 Humboldt St, Rochester, NY 14610
Tel.: (585) 527-8000
Web Site: https://www.aac-contracting.com
Rev.: $10,761,040
Emp.: 95
Environmental Contracting
N.A.I.C.S.: 562910
Kevin Cannan (Pres)
Craig Everhart (VP & Mgr-Ops)
Peter DeLucia (Dir-Safety)
Julie Redden (Controller)

AAC ENTERPRISES LLC
4401 Division St, Metairie, LA 70002
Tel.: (504) 835-0055
Web Site: http://www.aacstyle.com
Year Founded: 2004
Sales Range: $1-9.9 Million
Emp.: 11
Custom Lighting for Automobiles
N.A.I.C.S.: 336320
Justin Hartenstien (Owner)

AAC HOLDINGS, INC.
200 Powell Pl, Brentwood, TN 37027
Tel.: (615) 732-1231   NV
Web Site: http://www.americanaddiction.org
Rev.: $295,763,000
Assets: $452,277,000
Liabilities: $410,004,000
Net Worth: $42,273,000
Earnings: ($59,404,000)
Emp.: 1,900
Fiscal Year-end: 12/31/18
Holding Company; Specialty Outpatient Centers
N.A.I.C.S.: 551112
Michael T. Cartwright (Chm)
Kathryn Sevier Phillips (Chief Legal Officer, Gen Counsel & Sec)
Andrew W. McWilliams (CEO)
Karen Abbott (Chief Compliance Officer)
Stephen Ebbett (Chief Digital & Mktg Officer)
Lawrence Weinstein (Chief Medical Officer)
Mark Calarco (Dir-Medical-Clinical Diagnostics-Natl)
Joy Sutton (Dir-Corp Comm)

Subsidiaries:

AdCare Criminal Justice Services, Inc. (1)
4 Ct St Ste 110, Taunton, MA 02780
Tel.: (508) 821-7883
Addiction Recovery Services
N.A.I.C.S.: 621420

AdCare Hospital of Worcester, Inc. (1)
107 Lincoln St, Worcester, MA 01605-2401
Tel.: (508) 799-9000
Drug Addiction Rehabilitation Services
N.A.I.C.S.: 623220
Susan B. Hillis (VP-Clinical Svcs)
Patrice M. Muchowski (Sr VP-Clinical Svcs)
Marcella Rivard (CFO & Treas)
Joan L. Bertrand (VP-HR)
Andrea M. Tirocchi (Program Mgr)
Leslie Goncalves (Dir-Nursing)
Brian Stoesz (CEO)

AdCare Rhode Island, Inc. (1)
1950 Tower Hill Rd, North Kingstown, RI 02852
Addiction Recovery Services
N.A.I.C.S.: 621420

American Addiction Centers, Inc. (1)
200 Powell Pl, Brentwood, TN 37027
Tel.: (615) 732-1616
Web Site: http://www.americanaddictioncenters.org
Mental Health Care Services
N.A.I.C.S.: 622210
Michael T. Cartwright (Chm & CEO)
Joy Sutton (Mgr-PR)
Mark Calarco (Natl Dir-Medical-Clinical Diagnostics)
Lawrence M. Weinstein (Chief Medical Officer)
Michael Nanko (Pres & COO)
Chris Chi (Gen Counsel & Sec)

Subsidiary (Domestic):

AAC Dallas Outpatient Center, LLC (2)
2301 Ave J, Arlington, TX 76006
Tel.: (817) 649-3780
Substance Abuse Treatment Services
N.A.I.C.S.: 621111

AAC Las Vegas Outpatient Center, LLC (2)
3441 S Eastern Ave, Las Vegas, NV 89169-3314
Tel.: (702) 545-6444
Substance Abuse Treatment Services
N.A.I.C.S.: 621111

Addiction Labs of America, LLC (2)
500 Wilson Pike Cir Ste 360, Brentwood, TN 37027-5252
Tel.: (615) 678-5973
Web Site: http://www.addictionlabs.com

Medical Laboratory Services
N.A.I.C.S.: 621511

Canyon Vista Recovery Center (2)
860 N Center St, Mesa, AZ 85201
Tel.: (480) 464-5764
Web Site: http://www.canyonvista.com
Rehabilitation Services
N.A.I.C.S.: 622210
Stan Frank (CEO)
Richard Miller (Dir-Bus Dev)
Andrea Vaughan (Dir-Nursing)

Clinical Services of Rhode Island - Greenville (2)
600 Putnam Pike Ste 7, Greenville, RI 02828
Tel.: (401) 567-1103
Web Site: http://www.clinicalservicesri.com
Health Care Srvices
N.A.I.C.S.: 621111

Concorde Treatment Center, LLC (2)
2465 E Twain Ave Ofc, Las Vegas, NV 89121
Tel.: (702) 789-6197
Substance Abuse Treatment Services
N.A.I.C.S.: 621111

Forterus Health Care Services, Inc. (2)
41655 Date St Ste 101, Murrieta, CA 92562
Tel.: (951) 894-8654
Substance Abuse Treatment Services
N.A.I.C.S.: 621111

Greenhouse Treatment Center, LLC (2)
1171 107th St, Grand Prairie, TX 75050
Tel.: (972) 848-0221
Web Site: http://www.greenhousetreatment.com
Mental Health Care Services
N.A.I.C.S.: 622210
Anthony Walters (CEO)
Tyler Harrell (COO)
Casey Green (Dir-Medical)

Laguna Treatment Hospital, LLC (2)
24552 Pacific Park Dr, Aliso Viejo, CA 92656
Tel.: (949) 565-2377
Web Site: http://www.lagunatreatment.com
Substance Abuse Rehabilitation
N.A.I.C.S.: 621330
Susan McNally (Mgr-Health Info)
Barbara Kennedy (CEO)

New Jersey Addiction Treatment Center, LLC (2)
37 Sunset Inn Rd, Lafayette, NJ 07848
Tel.: (973) 862-4820
Web Site: http://www.sunrisehouse.com
Rehabilitation Services
N.A.I.C.S.: 622210
Mack Roth (COO)

Oxford Treatment Center, LLC (2)
297 Cr 244, Etta, MS 38627
Tel.: (662) 281-9992
Web Site: http://www.oxfordtreatment.com
Mental Health Care Services
N.A.I.C.S.: 621330
Billy Young (Co-CEO)
Dee Meux (Coord-Family Program)
Tori Ossenheimer (Dir-Experiential Svcs)
Mary L. Smith (Dir-Admissions)
Jerri Avery (Dir-Clinical)
Mark Sawyer (Co-CEO)
Mark Stovall (COO)
Barry Doughty (Coord-Direct Care)
Reggie Watkins (Coord-Young Adult Program)
Vernon Robinson (Dir-Ops)
Mary Bragg (Dir-HR)

Parallax Center, LLC (2)
145 E 32nd St, New York, NY 10016
Tel.: (212) 779-9207
Web Site: http://www.parallaxcenter.com
Health Care Srvices
N.A.I.C.S.: 621111
Armin Baier (Dir-Special Projects & Dev)

Recovery First of Florida, LLC (2)
4110 Davie Rd Ext Ste 203, Hollywood, FL 33024
Tel.: (954) 526-5776
Web Site: http://www.recoveryfirst.org

Substance Abuse Treatment & Rehabilitation Services
N.A.I.C.S.: 621420

Sagenex Diagnostics Laboratory, LLC (2)
1379 Corporate Square Dr, Slidell, LA 70458
Tel.: (985) 718-1692
Web Site: www.sagenexlabs.com
Medical Laboratory Services
N.A.I.C.S.: 621511
David Lirette (Dir-Technical)

San Diego Addiction Treatment Center, Inc. (2)
995 Gateway Center Way Ste 108, San Diego, CA 92102
Tel.: (619) 577-4483
Web Site: http://www.sdtreatmentcenter.com
Mental Health Care Services
N.A.I.C.S.: 622210
Julie Brunetto (Dir-Program Svcs)

Solutions Recovery Inc. (2)
2975 S Rainbow Blvd, Las Vegas, NV 89146
Tel.: (702) 800-2682
Web Site: http://www.solutions-recovery.com
Social Advocacy Services
N.A.I.C.S.: 813319

Solutions Treatment Center, LLC (2)
2209 Miguel Chavez Rd, Santa Fe, NM 87505
Tel.: (505) 424-3170
Web Site: http://www.treatmentsolutions.org
Mental Health Care Services
N.A.I.C.S.: 622310
Amy Lashway (Founder & Exec Dir)
Becca Schwilling (Dir-Ops)
Carol Parker (Dir-Clinical)

Townsend Recovery Center New Orleans, LLC (2)
5620 Read Blvd, New Orleans, LA 70127-3106
Tel.: (504) 513-4200
Drug Addiction Recovery Services
N.A.I.C.S.: 623220

Behavioral Healthcare Realty, LLC (1)
115 E Park Dr 2nd Fl, Brentwood, TN 37027
Tel.: (615) 732-1499
Substance Abuse Treatment Services
N.A.I.C.S.: 531390

Subsidiary (Domestic):

Greenhouse Real Estate, LLC (2)
1171 107 th St, Grand Prairie, TX 76011
Tel.: (615) 491-4274
Substance Abuse Treatment Services
N.A.I.C.S.: 531390
Michael Cartwright (Exec Dir)

Clinical Revenue Management Services, LLC (1)
115 Eastpark Dr Ste 125, Brentwood, TN 37027-2313
Tel.: (615) 727-8405
Substance Abuse Treatment Services
N.A.I.C.S.: 561440

Hamilton Medically Assisted Treatment Associates, LLC (1)
1799 Klockner Rd Ste 1, Hamilton, NJ 08619
Tel.: (800) 990-0340
Health Care Srvices
N.A.I.C.S.: 621111

Singer Island Recovery Center LLC (1)
4460 Medical Ctr Way, West Palm Beach, FL 33407
Tel.: (800) 848-0776
Substance Abuse Treatment Services
N.A.I.C.S.: 621111
Alexandria Witte (Dir-Nursing)

Taj Media, LLC (1)
926 Colorado Ave, Santa Monica, CA 90401
Tel.: (310) 359-8666
Web Site: http://www.ranklab.com
Substance Abuse Treatment Services
N.A.I.C.S.: 541613

Abhilash Patel (CEO)
Andrew O'Connor (Dir-Strategy)
Cynthia Johnson (Dir-Mktg & Social Media)
Tim Winter (Sr Mgr-SEO)
Zach Binder (COO)

AACER FLOORING LLC
970 Ogden Rd, Peshtigo, WI 54157
Tel.: (715) 582-1181
Web Site:
http://www.aacerflooring.com
Sales Range: $75-99.9 Million
Emp.: 140
Floor Systems Mfr & Distr
N.A.I.C.S.: 321918
Steven Gutsch (Mgr-Sls)
Ray Webb (VP & Gen Mgr)
Greg Arnold (Reg Mgr-Sls)
Whit Lovinggood (Sls Mgr-Western)

AACTION MOVERS
3403 E Rosser Ave, Bismarck, ND 58501
Tel.: (701) 223-5535
Web Site:
https://www.aactionmovers.com
Year Founded: 1932
Rev.: $12,200,000
Emp.: 40
Household Goods Transport
N.A.I.C.S.: 484210
Steven A. Herman (Pres)
Steven Herman (CEO)

AADLEN BROTHERS AUTO WRECKING
11590 Tuxford St, Sun Valley, CA 91352
Tel.: (818) 504-1091
Web Site:
https://www.aadlenbros.com
Rev.: $16,400,000
Emp.: 80
Metal Scrap & Waste Materials
N.A.I.C.S.: 423930

AAFCPAS, INC.
50 Washington St, Westborough, MA 01581
Tel.: (508) 366-9100
Web Site:
http://www.staging.aafcpa.com
Accounting Firm & Services
N.A.I.C.S.: 541211
Carla McCall (Co-Mng Partner)
David McManus (Co-Mng Partner)
Herb Alexander (Chm & Partner)

Subsidiaries:

Scott A. Goffstein & Associates, LLP (1)
411 Waverly Oaks Rd Ste 331, Waltham, MA 02452-8422
Tel.: (781) 398-1770
Web Site: http://www.sagacpa.com
Offices of Certified Public Accountants
N.A.I.C.S.: 541211
Scott A. Goffstein (Partner)

AAIC, INC.
1 Design Mesa, Collinsville, IL 62234
Tel.: (618) 345-1270
Web Site: https://www.aaicinc.com
Architectural Services
N.A.I.C.S.: 541310
Cal Morris (Principal)

AAJ TECHNOLOGIES
6301 NW 5th Way Ste 1700, Fort Lauderdale, FL 33309
Tel.: (954) 689-3984
Web Site: http://www.aajtech.com
Year Founded: 1997
Sales Range: $1-9.9 Million
Emp.: 60
Information Technology System Integration Services
N.A.I.C.S.: 541512

Amjad Shamim (CEO)
Ed Kirchmier (VP-Managed Svcs & BI)
Colleen Taylor (VP-Ops)
Jeremy Ecenbarger (Chief Acctg Officer & VP-Fin)
Mark Demeo (Sr VP-Consulting)
Nadeem Akhter (VP-Integration)
Alex Barenboim (VP-Mobility & Enterprise Solutions)
Nizar Lavji (VP-Portals & Collaboration)
Ric Cavieres (Exec VP-Markets & Consulting)
Linda Haury (Chief Mktg Officer & VP)
Sal Cardozo (VP-Analytics)

AALCO FORWARDING INC.
10965 Granada Ln, Overland Park, KS 66211
Tel.: (913) 345-0234
Web Site:
http://www.aalcoforwarding.com
Year Founded: 1982
Rev.: $11,862,021
Emp.: 9
Freight Forwarding Services
N.A.I.C.S.: 488510
Anthony Dimarco (Mgr-Acctg)

AALP, INC.
55 Cambridge Pkwy Ste 200, Boston, MA 02142
Tel.: (617) 859-4800   MA
Web Site:
http://www.alliedmarketing.com
Year Founded: 1946
Sales Range: $600-649.9 Million
Emp.: 1,000
Advertising & Public Relation Agency Services
N.A.I.C.S.: 541810
Adam Cinque (CFO)
Clint Kendall (CEO)
Kymn Goldstein (COO)
Adam Cunningham (Chief Digital Officer)

Subsidiaries:

AALP, Inc. - Atlanta (1)
Piedmont Ctr N 3565 Piedmont Rd Bldg 2 Ste 700, Atlanta, GA 30305-4657
Tel.: (404) 812-7000
Web Site: http://www.alliedim.com
Sales Range: $10-24.9 Million
Emp.: 16
Advertising & Public Relations Agency
N.A.I.C.S.: 541810

AALP, Inc. - Chicago (1)
500 N Michigan Ave Ste 400, Chicago, IL 60611
Tel.: (312) 755-0888
Web Site: http://www.alliedim.com
Sales Range: $10-24.9 Million
Emp.: 20
Advertising & Public Relations Agency
N.A.I.C.S.: 541810
Barry Newmark (Sr VP-Publicity & Promos)
Morgan Johnson (Dir-Publicity & Promos)
Jill Wheeler (Dir-Publicity & Promos)

AALP, Inc. - Cleveland (1)
3601 Green Rd Ste316, Cleveland, OH 44112
Tel.: (216) 932-7151
Web Site: http://www.alliedim.com
Sales Range: $10-24.9 Million
Emp.: 7
Advertising & Public Relations Agency
N.A.I.C.S.: 541810
Jennifer Vinson (VP-Ops-Publicity & Promos)

AALP, Inc. - Denver (1)
11990 Grant St Ste 216, Northglenn, CO 80233
Tel.: (303) 451-4440
Web Site: http://www.alliedim.com

Sales Range: $10-24.9 Million
Advertising & Public Relations Agency
N.A.I.C.S.: 541810
Kellie Barnes (VP-Allied Faith & Family)
Los Angeles (VP-Integrated Mktg & Media)
Elisabeth Baker (Sr VP-Allied Creative)
Erin Corbett (Sr VP-Natl Promos & Branded Entertainment)
Kelly Estrella (Sr VP-Integrated Mktg & Media)
Gary Faber (Partner-Entertainment Res & Mktg-New York)
Sandi Isaacs (Sr VP-Bus Dev)
Barbara King (Sr VP-Strategic Mktg)
Barry Newmark (Sr VP-Publicity & Promos)

AALP, Inc. - Detroit (1)
1301 W Long Lake Rd Ste 130, Troy, MI 48098
Tel.: (248) 593-7821
Web Site:
http://www.alliedglobalmarketing.com
Sales Range: $10-24.9 Million
Emp.: 11
Advertising & Public Relations Agency
N.A.I.C.S.: 541810
Nick Thomas (VP-Mktg)
Dawn Kelley (Dir-Publicity & Promos)

AALP, Inc. - Kansas City (1)
1656 Washington St Ste 150, Kansas City, MO 64108
Tel.: (816) 474-9995
Web Site: http://www.alliedim.com
Advertising & Public Relations Agency
N.A.I.C.S.: 541810

AALP, Inc. - Los Angeles (1)
6908 Hollywood Blvd 3rd Fl, Hollywood, CA 90028-6104
Tel.: (323) 954-7644
Web Site: http://www.alliedim.com
Sales Range: $10-24.9 Million
Emp.: 35
Advertising & Public Relations Agency
N.A.I.C.S.: 541810

AALP, Inc. - Miami (1)
6400 N Andrews Ave Ste 470, Fort Lauderdale, FL 33309
Tel.: (954) 229-9030
Web Site: http://www.alliedim.com
Sales Range: $10-24.9 Million
Emp.: 11
Advertising & Public Relations Agency
N.A.I.C.S.: 541810
Christina Swanno (Dir-Publicity & Promos)
Lisa Giannakopulos (Sr VP-Publicity & Promos)
Adam Cinque (CFO)
Sandi Isaacs (Sr VP-Bus Dev)
Carolyn Sloss (VP-Publicity & Promos)
Billy Zimmer (VP-Strategic Mktg)

AALP, Inc. - New York (1)
5 Penn Plz 21st Fl, New York, NY 10001
Tel.: (212) 819-8120
Web Site: http://www.alliedim.com
Sales Range: $25-49.9 Million
Emp.: 50
Advertising & Public Relations Agency
N.A.I.C.S.: 541810
Adam Cinque (Grp CFO)
Peter Kindlon (Dir-Publicity & Promos)
Erin Corbett (Sr VP-Natl Promos & Branded Entertainment)
Kelly Estrella (Sr VP-Integrated Mktg & Media)
Gary Faber (Partner-Entertainment Res & Mktg)
Kymn Goldstein (Exec VP-Acct Mgmt & Bus Dev)
Sandi Isaacs (Sr VP-Bus Dev)
Barbara King (Sr VP-Strategic Mktg)
Jane Lanouette (Sr VP-Publicity & Promos)
Jo Manley (VP-Integrated Mktg & Media)
Barry Newmark (Sr VP-Publicity & Promos)
Sara Taylor (Sr VP-Publicity & Promos)

AALP, Inc. - Philadelphia (1)
2001 Market St Ste 510, Philadelphia, PA 19103-7051
Tel.: (215) 496-0675
Web Site: http://www.alliedim.com
Sales Range: $10-24.9 Million
Emp.: 15
Advertising & Public Relations Agency
N.A.I.C.S.: 541810
Jesse Cute (VP)

AALP, Inc.—(Continued)

AALP, Inc. - Phoenix (1)
11333 N Scottsdale Rd Ste 190, Scottsdale, AZ 85254
Tel.: (602) 544-5710
Web Site: http://www.alliedim.com
Sales Range: $10-24.9 Million
Emp.: 4
Advertising & Public Relations Agency
N.A.I.C.S.: 541810

AALP, Inc. - San Diego (1)
Cabrillo Plza 3990 Old Town Ave Ste B206, San Diego, CA 92110-2968
Tel.: (619) 688-1818
Web Site: http://www.alliedim.com
Advertising & Public Relation Agency Services
N.A.I.C.S.: 541810

AALP, Inc. - San Francisco (1)
180 Sansome St Ste 200, San Francisco, CA 94104
Tel.: (415) 824-1111
Web Site: http://www.alliedim.com
Sales Range: $10-24.9 Million
Emp.: 15
Advertising & Public Relations Agency
N.A.I.C.S.: 541810

AALP, Inc. - Seattle (1)
1300 Dexter Ave N Ste 255, Seattle, WA 98109
Tel.: (206) 297-7064
Web Site: http://www.alliedim.com
Sales Range: $10-24.9 Million
Emp.: 5
Advertising & Public Relations Agency
N.A.I.C.S.: 541810

AALP, Inc. - St. Louis (1)
103 W Lockwood Ste 204, Saint Louis, MO 63119
Tel.: (314) 918-7788
Web Site: http://www.alliedim.com
Sales Range: $10-24.9 Million
Emp.: 7
Advertising & Public Relations Agency
N.A.I.C.S.: 541810
Pete Maniscalco (Dir-Publicity & Promos)

AALP, Inc. - Washington, D.C. (1)
1726 M St NW Ste 400, Washington, DC 20036-4650
Tel.: (202) 223-3660
Web Site: http://www.alliedim.com
Sales Range: $10-24.9 Million
Emp.: 15
Advertising & Public Relations Agency
N.A.I.C.S.: 541810

Allied Advertising Public Relations of Canada, Inc. (1)
21 Saint Clair Avenue East Suite 1410, Toronto, M4T 1L9, ON, Canada
Tel.: (416) 413-0557
Web Site: http://www.alliedim.com
Sales Range: $10-24.9 Million
Emp.: 20
Advertising & Public Relations Agency
N.A.I.C.S.: 541810

Allied Experiential (1)
111 E 12 St 2nd Fl, New York, NY 10003
Tel.: (212) 253-8777
Web Site:
http://www.grandcentralmarketing.com
Sales Range: $1-9.9 Million
Advetising Agency
N.A.I.C.S.: 541810
Matthew Glass (Sr VP)
Jennifer Granozio (Sr VP)
SeeLun Mak (VP-Experiential Mktg)
Jennifer Guillette (VP-Experiential Mktg)

Branch (Domestic):

Allied Experiential - Los Angeles (2)
333 S Beverly Dr Ste 208, Beverly Hills, CA 90212
Tel.: (310) 843-9855
Web Site:
http://www.grandcentralmarketing.com
Sales Range: $1-9.9 Million
Advertising & Public Relations Agency
N.A.I.C.S.: 541810

Allied Live (1)
500 N Michigan Ave Ste 700, Chicago, IL 60611

Tel.: (312) 475-0327
Web Site: http://www.alliedlive.com
Sales Range: $1-9.9 Million
Emp.: 10
Publicity, Advertising & Marketing Strategy Development Services
N.A.I.C.S.: 541810
Laura Matalon (Pres)
Marya Peters (VP-Touring)

AAMP OF FLORIDA, INC.
15500 Lightwave Dr Ste 202, Clearwater, FL 33760
Tel.: (727) 572-9255   FL
Web Site:
http://www.aampglobal.com
Year Founded: 1987
Sales Range: $25-49.9 Million
Emp.: 75
Automobile Audio & Video Electronics Mfr & Distr
N.A.I.C.S.: 334310
Marie Still (CMO)
John Bell (Mng Dir-Europe)
Herb Brown (Sr VP-Sls)
Scott Forst (Pres-Americas)
Brett Riggs (Exec VP & Gen Mgr-Infotainment & Installation)
Don Tolson (Dir-Fin-AAMP Europe)
Steve Verano (CFO)
Jamie Fraser (CEO)
Brad Chapple (Exec VP & Gen Mgr-Safety)
Lisa Gibbings (Mktg Dir)
Randall Schwartz (Dir-Bus Dev)

Subsidiaries:

Armour Automotive Group Limited (1)
Woolmer Way, Bordon, GU35 9QE, Hants, United Kingdom
Tel.: (44) 1420 476 767
Web Site: http://www.armourauto.com
Emp.: 30
Holding Company; Motor Vehicle Entertainment & Communications Electronics Mfr & Distr
N.A.I.C.S.: 551112
Mike Smith (Dir)

Subsidiary (Domestic):

Armour Automotive Limited (2)
Woolmer Way, Bordon, GU35 9QE, Hants, United Kingdom
Tel.: (44) 1420 476 767
Web Site: http://www.armourauto.com
Motor Vehicle Entertainment & Communications Electronics Mfr & Distr
N.A.I.C.S.: 334310
Barry Davies (Mng Dir)

Subsidiary (Non-US):

Armour Nordic AB (2)
Brödalsvägen 1 B, Partille, 433 38, Sweden
Tel.: (46) 31444412
Motor Vehicle Entertainment & Communications Electronics Distr
N.A.I.C.S.: 423620

Armour Nordic AS (2)
Tuneveien 97, Gralum, Sarpsborg, Norway
Tel.: (47) 21424121
Motor Vehicle Entertainment & Communications Electronics Distr
N.A.I.C.S.: 423620

AAR OF NORTH CAROLINA INC.
655 Peddycord Rd, Kernersville, NC 27284-8351
Tel.: (336) 727-4534
Web Site: http://www.aarnc.com
Sales Range: $10-24.9 Million
Emp.: 140
Provider of Roofing, Siding & Sheetmetal Services
N.A.I.C.S.: 238160
Michelle Strickland (Controller)
Brad Kurth (Sr VP)
Tim Hyde (Project Mgr)

AARDVARK EVENT LOGISTICS, INC.
1957 Pioneer Rd, Huntingdon Valley, PA 19006
Tel.: (215) 441-0690
Web Site: http://www.aardvarkel.com
Year Founded: 2008
Sales Range: $1-9.9 Million
Emp.: 213
Event Logistics & Marketing Services
N.A.I.C.S.: 541614
Rachel Konar (VP-Client Svcs)
Chris Makos (Acct Dir)

AARDVARK SWIM & SPORT, INC.
14221-A Willard Rd Ste 1050, Chantilly, VA 20151
Tel.: (703) 631-6045
Web Site:
http://www.aardvarkswim.com
Year Founded: 1985
Sales Range: $25-49.9 Million
Emp.: 30
Swim Wear, Swim Equipment & Related Accessories Mail Order
N.A.I.C.S.: 424350
Robert York (Pres)

AARON & COMPANY INC.
30 Turner Pl, Piscataway, NJ 08854-3839
Tel.: (732) 752-8200   NJ
Web Site: http://www.aaronco.com
Year Founded: 1977
Sales Range: $50-74.9 Million
Emp.: 150
Retailer of Plumbing, Fixtures, Equipment & Supplies
N.A.I.C.S.: 423720
Barry Portnoy (Pres)
Kevin Manning (VP-Sls & Mktg)
Anthony Panko (VP-Ops)
John Provenzano (VP-HVAC Div)
Bruce Sax (Mgr-Kitchen Div)
Mike Kelco (Mgr-Somerville)
Harry Opdyke (Mgr-Flemington)
Chet Wohltman (Dir-Branch Ops)
Victoria Choi (Controller)
Mathew Lease (Mgr-Acct)
Ted Garrigana (Mgr-Acct-HVAC)
Glenn Reger (Mgr-Acct-HVAC)
Mary Aure (Mgr-Credit)
Lindsey Portnoy Rodner (Mgr-Mktg)
Alan Mandel (Mgr-New Construction)
Scott Bennett (Mgr-Piscataway Plumbing)
Diane Bradley (Mgr-Showrooms)
Tom Gasper (Mgr-Trenton)
Anthony Conte (CFO)
Douglass Noe (Principal Acctg Officer)

Subsidiaries:

Aaron Kitchen & Bath Design Gallery (1)
10 Industrial Dr, New Brunswick, NJ 08901
Tel.: (877) 602-2766
Web Site: http://www.aaronkbdgallery.com
Kitchen Appliance & Bathroom Accessory Whslr
N.A.I.C.S.: 423620
Bruce Sax (Mgr-Kitchen Div)

AARON CARLSON CORPORATION
1505 Central Ave NE, Minneapolis, MN 55413
Tel.: (612) 789-8885
Web Site:
http://www.aaroncarlson.com
Rev.: $11,000,000
Emp.: 120
Door Trim, Wood
N.A.I.C.S.: 321911
Jason Horner (Pres)

AARON EQUIPMENT COMPANY
735 E Green St, Bensenville, IL 60106
Tel.: (630) 350-2200
Web Site:
http://www.aaronequipment.com
Sales Range: $10-24.9 Million
Emp.: 60
Industrial Machinery & Equipment
N.A.I.C.S.: 423830

AARON FERER & SONS CO.
155 Ida St, Omaha, NE 68110
Tel.: (402) 342-2436
Rev.: $18,200,000
Emp.: 11
Ferrous Metals
N.A.I.C.S.: 423510
Matthew Ferer (Pres & Treas)

AARON GROUP OF COMPANIES
161 Washington St 10th Fl, Conshohocken, PA 19428-2087
Tel.: (610) 940-0800
Web Site:
http://www.aaronpaper.com
Sales Range: $10-24.9 Million
Emp.: 25
Holding Company; Pulp & Paper
N.A.I.C.S.: 424110
Drew Aaron (CEO)
Gene Aaron (Chm)
Mark Speiser (Sr VP & Dir-Fin)
Mindy Aaron (Treas)
Franco D'Orazio (Sr VP & Dir-Credit)

Subsidiaries:

E. Aaron Enterprises Inc. (1)
161 Washington St Ste 1150, Conshohocken, PA 19428-2087   (100%)
Tel.: (610) 940-0800
Rev.: $23,000,000
Emp.: 20
Printing Paper
N.A.I.C.S.: 424110
Brent Aaron (Exec VP)
Gene Aaron (Pres)
Eugene Aaron (Chm)
Ivy Frimer (Sr VP)

Priority Papers, Inc. (1)
704 Ginesi Dr Ste 25, Morganville, NJ 07751
Tel.: (732) 972-8190
Fine Paper Merchant Whslr
N.A.I.C.S.: 424110

AARON INVESTMENTS INC.
100 Robin Rd, Acworth, GA 30102
Tel.: (678) 255-1000
Web Site:
http://www.woodstockoutlet.com
Sales Range: $10-24.9 Million
Emp.: 110
Owner & Operator of Furniture Stores
N.A.I.C.S.: 449110
Pam McCrary (CFO)
Irvin W. Aaron Jr. (Chm)

AARON THOMAS CO. INC.
7421 Chapman Ave, Garden Grove, CA 92841-2115
Tel.: (714) 894-4468
Web Site:
https://www.packaging.com
Sales Range: $10-24.9 Million
Emp.: 100
Packaging & Labeling Services
N.A.I.C.S.: 561910
James T. Chang (CEO)

AARP
601 E St NW, Washington, DC 20049
Tel.: (202) 434-2277
Web Site: https://www.aarp.org
Year Founded: 1958

Sales Range: $100-124.9 Million
Emp.: 1,800
Retirement Association Services
N.A.I.C.S.: 813410
Nancy A. LeaMond (*Chief Advocacy & Engagement Officer & Exec VP*)
Joan R. Ruff (*Chm*)
Eric J. Schneidewind (*Pres*)
Martha Boudreau (*Chief Comm & Mktg Officer & Exec VP*)
Debra Tyler-Horton (*Dir-Georgia*)
Joanne Grossi (*Pres-Pennsylvania*)
Bill Johnston-Walsh (*Dir-Pennsylvania*)
Wayne Detzler (*Pres-Connecticut*)
Bobbie G. Savoie (*Pres-Louisiana*)
Denise Bottcher (*Dir-Louisiana*)
Lloyd E. Johnson (*Vice Chm*)
Jewell D. Hoover (*Treas & Co-Sec*)
Scott Frisch (*COO & Exec VP*)
Nancy M. Smith (*Co-Sec & Exec VP*)
Cindy Lewin (*Exec VP*)
Victoria Brown (*Assoc Dir-Comm-Little Rock*)
Jo Ann C. Jenkins (*CEO*)
Hillary A. Johnson (*Mgr-Outreach & Volunteer Engagement*)
Ashley McBride (*Dir-Arkansas*)
Sam Wilson (*VP-Central Reg*)
Stella Montano (*Pres-Wyoming*)

Subsidiaries:

AARP Publications   **(1)**
99 Park Ave, New York, NY 10016 **(100%)**
Tel.: (646) 521-2500
Web Site: http://www.aarpmedia.org
Sales Range: $10-24.9 Million
Emp.: 35
Magazine Publisher
N.A.I.C.S.: 813212
Shelagh Daly Miller (*VP-Adv*)
Laurie Levitt (*Assoc Dir-Integrated Mktg*)

AARROW, INC.
4312 Valeta St, San Diego, CA 92107
Tel.: (619) 222-3770
Web Site: http://www.aarrowads.com
Year Founded: 2002
Rev.: $3,800,000
Emp.: 2,000
Advertising Agencies
N.A.I.C.S.: 541810
Max Durovic (*CEO*)
Mike Kenny (*COO*)
Joe Ambert (*VP-Bus Ops*)

AARSAND & COMPANY, INC.
11019 McCormick Rd Ste 320, Hunt Valley, MD 21031-8670
Tel.: (410) 771-1880
Web Site: http://www.aarsand.com
Year Founded: 1983
Sales Range: $100-124.9 Million
Emp.: 1,300
Franchise Owner of Fast-Food Restaurants
N.A.I.C.S.: 722513
Kurt Aarsand (*Pres*)
Torben Aarsand (*Dir-Mktg*)

AASKI TECHNOLOGY, INC.
804 C W Park Ave, Ocean, NJ 07712
Tel.: (732) 493-1700
Web Site: http://www.aaski.com
Sales Range: $10-24.9 Million
Emp.: 88
Engineeering Services
N.A.I.C.S.: 541330
Bharat Parikh (*COO & Sr Engr-IT*)
Rina Parikh (*Pres & CEO*)
Neil Manheimer (*VP-Fin & Contracts*)

AASYS GROUP, INC.
11301 N US Hwy 301 Ste 106, Thonotosassa, FL 33592
Tel.: (813) 246-4757   FL

Web Site: https://www.aasysgroup.com
Year Founded: 1992
Sales Range: $1-9.9 Million
Emp.: 38
Computer System Design Services
N.A.I.C.S.: 541512
Tony Coleman (*Pres & CEO*)
Cheryl Buntin (*Sr VP-Mktg & Sls*)
Linda Hoydic (*VP-Fin Ops Solutions*)
Roxanne Laveau (*VP-Admin*)

AAVALAR CONSULTING, INC.
649 Swedesford Rd, Malvern, PA 19355
Tel.: (610) 889-9990
Web Site: http://www.aavalar.com
Year Founded: 1999
Rev.: $4,000,000
Emp.: 30
Human Resource Consulting Services
N.A.I.C.S.: 541612
Tommy Ross (*Gen Mgr*)
Joseph Yesulaitis (*Pres & CEO*)

AAVIN, LLC
1245 1st Ave SE, Cedar Rapids, IA 52402
Tel.: (319) 247-1072   IA
Web Site: https://www.aavin.com
Private Equity & Venture Capital Firm
N.A.I.C.S.: 523999
James Thorp (*Mng Partner*)
Eric Hender (*Sr Partner*)
Paul Rhines (*Sr Partner*)
David Schroder (*Sr Partner*)
Thies Kolln (*Partner*)
Kevin Mullane (*Partner*)
Gina Milroy (*CFO*)

Subsidiaries:

Green Diamond Sand Products Inc.   **(1)**
Cnr 6th & E St, Riddle, OR 97469-7469
Tel.: (541) 874-3111
Web Site: http://www.greendiamondsand.com
Construction & Industrial Sand Mining, Processing & Sales
N.A.I.C.S.: 212321
Brian Rebuck Jr. (*Gen Mgr-Ops*)

AB BEVERAGE CO., INC.
665 Industrial Park Rd, Evans, GA 30809-3683
Tel.: (706) 855-8555   GA
Year Founded: 1978
Sales Range: $10-24.9 Million
Emp.: 150
Beer & Ale Distr
N.A.I.C.S.: 424810
Catherine Barnadore (*Pres*)
Doug Barnadore (*Branch Mgr*)
Julie Brentnell (*Mgr-HR*)

AB CARTER INC.
4801 York Hwy, Gastonia, NC 28052
Tel.: (704) 865-1201
Web Site: https://www.abcarter.com
Sales Range: $10-24.9 Million
Emp.: 150
Textile Machinery
N.A.I.C.S.: 333248
J. Bynum Carter (*Chm & CEO*)
Richard K. Craig (*Pres & COO*)
Al Abedi (*Gen Mgr*)

AB PRIVATE CREDIT INVESTORS CORPORATION
1345 Avenue of the Americas, New York, NY 10105
Tel.: (212) 969-1000   MD
Year Founded: 2015
Rev.: $93,359,262
Assets: $1,191,734,099
Liabilities: $734,855,606

Net Worth: $456,878,493
Earnings: $34,797,252
Fiscal Year-end: 12/31/22
Investment Services
N.A.I.C.S.: 523940
J. Brent Humphries (*Pres & CEO*)

AB STAFFING SOLUTIONS, LLC
2680 S Val Vista Dr Bldg 10 Ste 152, Gilbert, AZ 85295
Tel.: (480) 345-6668
Web Site: http://www.abstaffing.com
Year Founded: 2002
Sales Range: $10-24.9 Million
Emp.: 322
Healthcare Professional Staffing Services
N.A.I.C.S.: 561330
Stanley Rashkin (*CEO*)
Evan Burks (*Pres*)
Travis Schugg (*Dir-Govt Svcs*)
Shannon Crane (*Dir-Recruitment*)
Lance Burgeson (*Mgr-Physician*)
Marlea Dadisman (*Controller*)

AB&I
7825 San Leandro St, Oakland, CA 94621
Tel.: (510) 632-3467
Web Site: http://www.abifoundry.com
Sales Range: $50-74.9 Million
Emp.: 195
Soil Pipe & Fittings: Cast Iron
N.A.I.C.S.: 331511
Gary Wickham (*VP-Sls*)
Michael Lowe (*VP-Mktg*)

ABA MORIAH CORPORATION
6585 Merchant Pl Ste 100, Warrenton, VA 20187   TX
Web Site: https://www.abamoriah.com
Year Founded: 1962
Office Printing Equipment Sales & Services
N.A.I.C.S.: 423420
Gregory A. Rayburn (*Pres*)

ABA-PGT INC.
10 Gear Dr, Manchester, CT 06042
Tel.: (860) 649-4591
Web Site: http://www.abapgt.com
Sales Range: $10-24.9 Million
Emp.: 100
Dies, Plastics Forming
N.A.I.C.S.: 333514
Samuel D. Pierson (*CEO*)
Ray Paquet (*Controller*)
Nancy Russo (*Pres*)

ABABA BOLT
1466-1 Pioneer Way, El Cajon, CA 92020-1634
Tel.: (619) 440-1781
Web Site: http://www.ababaqa.com
Sales Range: $10-24.9 Million
Emp.: 50
Hardware Product Whslr
N.A.I.C.S.: 423710
Darlene Peer (*Controller*)

ABACAST, INC.
13115 NE 4th St Ste 140, Vancouver, WA 98684
Tel.: (360) 326-4798   WA
Web Site: http://www.abacast.com
Year Founded: 2000
Sales Range: $1-9.9 Million
Emp.: 12
Custom Computer Programming Services
N.A.I.C.S.: 541511
Dan Huntington (*Chm*)
Jim Kott (*Sr VP-Products & Mktg*)

Rob Green (*CEO*)
John Morris (*CTO*)
Michael Dalfonzo (*Dir-Sls & Revenue*)

ABACO MOBILE INC.
5 Concourse Pkwy Ne Ste 3000, Atlanta, GA 30328-7106
Tel.: (678) 319-0105
Web Site: http://www.abacomobile.com
Rev.: $17,000,000
Emp.: 15
System Software Development Services
N.A.I.C.S.: 449210
Rene Lorenzo (*CFO*)
Enrique Capo (*VP-Pro Svcs & Quality*)
Fernando M. Alvarez III (*Founder & Chm*)

ABACUS 24-7 LLC
2990 E Northern Ave Ste C 103, Phoenix, AZ 85028
Tel.: (602) 787-1223
Web Site: http://www.abacus24-7.com
Year Founded: 2001
Rev.: $3,800,000
Emp.: 13
Printer Accessory Retailer
N.A.I.C.S.: 423430
Robert Wilkinson (*Founder*)

ABACUS CORPORATION
610 Gusryan St, Baltimore, MD 21224
Tel.: (410) 633-1900   MD
Web Site: https://www.abacuscorporation.com
Year Founded: 1944
Sales Range: $50-74.9 Million
Emp.: 3,000
Providers of Employee Leasing Service
N.A.I.C.S.: 561330
Michael Brady (*COO*)
David M. Hausner (*CFO & Gen Counsel*)
Devin McGee (*Exec VP*)
John Wunder (*Pres-Div*)
Cecilia Dubon (*VP-Building Svcs*)
Adam Hendrickson (*VP-Security Ops*)
Bill Lund (*VP-Staffing Ops*)
Richard P. McGee Sr. (*Chm*)

ABACUS GROUP LLC
14 Penn Plz 14th Fl, New York, NY 10122
Tel.: (212) 812-8444   NY
Web Site: https://abacusgrpllc.com
Year Founded: 1997
Permanent & Temporary Placement Services
N.A.I.C.S.: 561311
Adam Haworth (*Partner-Acctg & Fin Div*)
Charles Amato (*Partner-Acctg & Fin Div*)
Gennaro Vitale (*Partner-Acctg & Fin Div*)
Robert B. Pickus (*Dir-Acctg & Fin Div*)
Laurie F. Kotton (*Partner-Acctg & Fin Div*)
Brain Ruina (*Partner-Acctg & Fin Div*)
Brian Bereck (*Partner*)
Len Frankel (*Partner*)
Jason Fleischer (*Partner-Acctg & Fin Div*)

Subsidiaries:

GoVanguard, LLC   **(1)**
315 W 36th St, New York, NY 10018
Tel.: (212) 696-0500

Abacus Group LLC—(Continued)

Web Site: http://www.govanguard.com
Cyber Security Services
N.A.I.C.S.: 561621
Mahdi Hedhli (CEO)
Blake Shalem (Chief Customer Officer)

Subsidiary (Domestic):

Gotham Security, Inc. (2)
33 Irving Pl 3rd Fl, New York, NY 10003
Tel.: (631) 421-4950
Web Site: http://www.gotham-security.com
Cyber Security Services
N.A.I.C.S.: 561621

ABACUS PLANNING GROUP, INC.

2500 Devine St, Columbia, SC 29205
Tel.: (803) 933-0054
Web Site:
https://www.abacusplanning.com
Year Founded: 1998
Sales Range: $10-24.9 Million
Emp.: 25
Marketing Consulting Services
N.A.I.C.S.: 541613
Charlie Hammer (COO)

ABACUS PLUMBING COMPANY

11437 Todd St, Houston, TX 77055
Tel.: (713) 812-7070
Web Site:
http://www.abacusplumbing.net
Sales Range: $1-9.9 Million
Emp.: 75
Plumbing Services
N.A.I.C.S.: 238220
Alan O'Neill (Pres & CEO)

ABACUS SOLUTIONS GROUP, LLC (ASG)

400 N Loop 1604 E Suite 107, San Antonio, TX 78232
Tel.: (210) 293-6400
Web Site: http://www.abacussg.com
Year Founded: 2005
Sales Range: $1-9.9 Million
Emp.: 67
Technology & Medical Services Solutions
N.A.I.C.S.: 519290
Buffy Koehn (CEO)

ABACUS TECHNOLOGY CORP.

5404 Wisconsin Ave Ste 1100, Chevy Chase, MD 20815-6925
Tel.: (301) 907-8500
Web Site:
https://www.abacustech.com
Year Founded: 1983
Sales Range: $25-49.9 Million
Emp.: 400
Provider of Management Consulting Services
N.A.I.C.S.: 541611
Dennis J. Yee (Pres)
William R. Magro (Sr VP)
Alice A. Solomon (VP-Ops-Middle East)
Susan N. Suskin (Sr VP-Washington Client Svcs)
Archie Riviera (VP-Info Assurance)
David Lee (Mgr-Cost Center-New Mexico)
Michael Wang (Mgr-Cost Center-Oklahoma)
Patty Stratton (VP & Mgr-KSC Program)
Randy Vieira (Mgr-Colorado & Texas Cost Center)
Raymond E. Zdancewicz (VP-Corp Svcs)
Sharon Church (CFO & VP)
David Provancha (Mgr-Alabama Cost Center)

ABACUS WEALTH PARTNERS, LLC

429 Santa Monica Blvd Ste 500, Santa Monica, CA 90401
Tel.: (310) 566-1888
Web Site:
http://www.abacuswealth.com
Year Founded: 1987
Sales Range: $1-9.9 Million
Emp.: 22
Financial Advisory Services
N.A.I.C.S.: 523940
Brent Kessel (Co-Founder & Co-CEO)
Spencer Sherman (Co-Founder & Co-CEO)
Darius Gagne (CIO & Partner)
David DeWolf (CFO)
Jason Cole (Partner)
J. D. Bruce (Pres)
Rachel Robasciotti (Dir-Advocacy Engagement)

Subsidiaries:

Robasciotti & Associates, Inc. (1)
870 Market St Ste 580, San Francisco, CA 94102-3017
Tel.: (415) 986-5502
Web Site: http://www.robasciotti.com
Investment Advice
N.A.I.C.S.: 523940

ABAJIAN MOTOR SALES

606 N Wilbur Ave, Walla Walla, WA 99362
Tel.: (509) 525-1920
Web Site:
http://www.mccurleytoyota.com
Sales Range: $10-24.9 Million
Emp.: 40
Car Whslr
N.A.I.C.S.: 441110
Mason McCurley (Pres)

ABAKAN INC.

2665 S Bayshore Dr Ste 450, Miami, FL 33133
Tel.: (786) 206-5368
Web Site: http://www.abakaninc.com
Year Founded: 2006
Rev.: $1,040,069
Assets: $14,220,770
Liabilities: $11,411,239
Net Worth: $2,809,531
Earnings: ($7,452,239)
Emp.: 25
Fiscal Year-end: 05/31/15
Holding Company; Designs, Develops, Manufactures & Markets Nanocomposite Materials, Fabricated Metal Products, Engineered Metal Composites & Engineered Reactive Materials
N.A.I.C.S.: 551112
Stephen C. Goss (COO)

Subsidiaries:

MesoCoat Inc. (1)
24112 Rockwell Dr, Euclid, OH 44117-1252 (100%)
Tel.: (216) 453-0866
Web Site: http://www.mesocoat.com
Nanocomposite Materials & Fabricated Metal Products Developer, Mfr & Marketer
N.A.I.C.S.: 332812
Stephen C. Goss (CEO)
Andrew J. Sherman (Pres)
Richard Burns (COO)
James Chew (VP-Bus Dev)

Powdermet, Inc. (1)
24112 Rockwell Dr, Euclid, OH 44117 (41%)
Tel.: (216) 404-0053
Web Site: http://www.powdermetinc.com
Sales Range: $1-9.9 Million
Emp.: 24
Wear & Corrosion Resistant Coatings Mfr
N.A.I.C.S.: 325510

Andrew Sherman (Founder & Pres)
Brian Doud (Gen Mgr)

ABANDONED CHILDREN'S FUND

2360 Mendocino Ave Ste A2-220, Santa Rosa, CA 95403-3154
Tel.: (888) 884-0567
Web Site:
http://www.abandonedchildren.org
Year Founded: 2006
Sales Range: $10-24.9 Million
Community Action Services
N.A.I.C.S.: 624190
Ken McGrath (Dir-Admin)
Colonel Doner (Pres & Exec Dir)

ABARTA INC.

200 Alpha Dr, Pittsburgh, PA 15238
Tel.: (412) 963-6226
Web Site: https://www.abarta.com
Sales Range: $150-199.9 Million
Emp.: 22
Mfr of Nonalcoholic Carbonated Beverages
N.A.I.C.S.: 312111
Charles W. Bitzer (Pres)
John Bitzer III (Pres & CEO)

ABATIX CORP.

2400 Skyline Dr Ste 400, Mesquite, TX 75149
Tel.: (214) 381-0322
Web Site: https://www.abatix.com
Year Founded: 1983
Sales Range: $75-99.9 Million
Supplier of Safety, Construction & Industrial Products
N.A.I.C.S.: 423830
Terry W. Shaver (Pres & CEO)
Gary L. Cox (COO & Exec VP)
Frank J. Cinatl IV (CFO & Exec VP)

ABB/CON-CISE OPTICAL GROUP LLC

1230 NW 39th St, Coral Springs, FL 33065
Tel.: (954) 733-2300
Web Site:
https://www.abboptical.com
Year Founded: 2013
Soft Contact Lens Distr
N.A.I.C.S.: 423460
Emily Ashworth (CTO)
Aaron See (VP-Mktg)
Steve Heft (Sr VP-Ops)
Jonathan Mish (CIO)
Tom Burke (Grp CEO)
Brad Weinbrum (Pres)
Paul Sherman (Chief Dev Officer)

Subsidiaries:

ABB Concise Inc. (1)
12301 NW 39th St, Coral Springs, FL 33065
Tel.: (954) 733-2300
Web Site: http://www.abboptical.com
Emp.: 500
Contact Lense Distr
N.A.I.C.S.: 423460
Angel Alvarez (CEO)
Brad Weinbrum (Pres)

Optical Distributor Group, LLC (1)
4 Skyline Dr, Hawthorne, NY 10532
Tel.: (914) 347-7400
Web Site: http://www.opticaldg.com
Sales Range: $1-9.9 Million
Emp.: 86
Optical Goods Distr
N.A.I.C.S.: 456130

ABBA STAFFING & CONSULTING SERVICES

2350 Airport Fwy Ste 130, Bedford, TX 76022-6783
Tel.: (817) 354-2800

Web Site:
https://www.abbastaffing.com
Year Founded: 2001
Sales Range: $10-24.9 Million
Emp.: 500
Human Resource Consulting Services
N.A.I.C.S.: 541612
Darla Beggs (Owner)

ABBA TECHNOLOGIES INC.

1501 San Pedro Dr NE, Albuquerque, NM 87110
Tel.: (505) 889-3337
Web Site: http://www.abbatech.com
Sales Range: $25-49.9 Million
Emp.: 40
IT Consulting Services
N.A.I.C.S.: 541690
Andrew L. Baca (Pres & CEO)

ABBELL ASSOCIATES, LLC

30 N Lasalle St Ste 2120, Chicago, IL 60602
Tel.: (312) 341-9000
Web Site: https://www.abbell.com
Year Founded: 1971
Sales Range: $75-99.9 Million
Emp.: 7
Real Estate Development Services
N.A.I.C.S.: 541611
Elizabeth I. Holland (CEO-Abbell Credit Corporation)

ABBEY CARPET CO., INC.

3471 Bonita Bay Blvd, Bonita Springs, FL 34134
Tel.: (239) 948-0900
Web Site:
http://www.abbeycarpet.com
Year Founded: 1958
Sales Range: $1-4.9 Billion
Floor Covering Stores Owner & Franchisor
N.A.I.C.S.: 449121
Philip Gutierrez (Chm & CEO)
Stephen Silverman (Pres & COO)
Chad Gillen (Mgr-Acctg)
Christina Freedman (Mgr-Mdsg)
Glenn Phillips (Mgr-Meetings & Convention)
Barbara Wells (Dir-Adv)
Colleen Bucher- McCarty (Mgr-Cash Back Incentive)

ABBEY ROAD GROUP LLC

2102 E Main Ave Ste 109, Puyallup, WA 98372
Tel.: (253) 435-3699
Web Site:
http://www.abbeyroadgroup.com
Year Founded: 2000
Sales Range: $1-9.9 Million
Holding Company; Land Development Services
N.A.I.C.S.: 551112
Giles F. Hulsmann III (Owner & CEO)

Subsidiaries:

Abbey Road Group Land Development Services Company (1)
2102 E Main Ave Ste 109, Puyallup, WA 98372
Tel.: (253) 435-3699
Web Site: http://www.abbeyroadgroup.com
Land Development Services
N.A.I.C.S.: 237210
Giles F. Hulsmann III (CEO)

ABBOTT & MILLS INC.

238 Gardnertown Rd, Newburgh, NY 12550
Tel.: (845) 561-0462
Web Site:
http://www.abbottandmills.com
Rev.: $10,783,304
Emp.: 45

Fuel Oil Dealers
N.A.I.C.S.: 457210
Ralph Mills (Pres)

ABBOTT INDUSTRIES INC.
9525 149th St, Jamaica, NY 11435-4511
Tel.: (718) 291-0800   NY
Year Founded: 1958
Sales Range: $25-49.9 Million
Emp.: 350
Miscellaneous Fabricated Wire Products Mfr
N.A.I.C.S.: 332618
Leonard Grossman (Pres & Treas)
Ronald J. Stone (Sec)
Cindy Ackerman (Controller)
Jeffrey Grossman (VP)

Subsidiaries:

Loroman Co. Inc.   (1)
9525 149th St, Jamaica, NY 11435-4511
Tel.: (718) 291-0800
Rev.: $5,400,000
Emp.: 24
Furniture
N.A.I.C.S.: 423210

ABBOTT LABORATORIES EMPLOYEES CREDIT UNION
401 N Riverside Dr Ste 1-A, Gurnee, IL 60031-5915
Tel.: (847) 688-8000   IL
Web Site: http://www.alecu.org
Year Founded: 1990
Sales Range: $10-24.9 Million
Emp.: 87
Credit Union
N.A.I.C.S.: 522130
Bruce Van Schaack (VP)

ABBOTT LABORATORIES INC
100 Abbott Pk Rd, Abbott Park, IL 60064
Tel.: (224) 667-6100
Web Site: http://www.abbott.com
Rev.: $732,756,654
Assets: $624,151,551
Liabilities: $179,620,430
Net Worth: $444,531,121
Earnings: $144,362,139
Emp.: 3,814
Fiscal Year-end: 03/31/24
Health Care Srvices
N.A.I.C.S.: 621610

ABBOTT RUBBER COMPANY, INC.
1700 Nicholas Blvd, Elk Grove Village, IL 60007
Tel.: (847) 952-1800
Web Site: http://www.abbottrubber.com
Sales Range: $10-24.9 Million
Emp.: 50
Industrial Hose & Rubber Product Whslr
N.A.I.C.S.: 423840
Melody Santos (Mgr-Pur)

ABBYLAND FOODS, INC.
502 E Linden St, Abbotsford, WI 54405-9699
Tel.: (715) 223-6386   WI
Web Site: https://www.abbyland.com
Year Founded: 1977
Sales Range: $200-249.9 Million
Emp.: 607
Whslr of Fresh Meats & Butchering Services
N.A.I.C.S.: 311611
Jane Langman (Office Mgr)
Harland Schraufnagel (Pres)
Paul Hess (CFO)

Subsidiaries:

Abbyland Pork Pack   (1)

539 Meridian St, Curtiss, WI 54422-8814   **(100%)**
Tel.: (715) 223-4676
Web Site: http://www.abbyland.com
Sales Range: $50-74.9 Million
Emp.: 200
Whslr of Fresh Meats & Provider of Butchering Services
N.A.I.C.S.: 311611
Harland Schraufnagel (Pres & CEO)

Abbyland Trucking, Inc.   (1)
330 Plaza Dr PO Box 69, Curtiss, WI 54422-8856
Tel.: (715) 223-3402
Truck Repair & Maintenance Services
N.A.I.C.S.: 811111

ABBYS INC.
1960 River Rd, Eugene, OR 97404
Tel.: (541) 689-0019
Web Site: http://www.abbys.com
Year Founded: 1964
Sales Range: $1-9.9 Million
Emp.: 1,200
Pizzeria Chain
N.A.I.C.S.: 722513
B. Mills Sinclair (Owner)
Rich Olson (CFO)
Doug Phillips (Dir-Mktg)

ABBYSON LIVING
26500 Agoura Rd Ste 102-875, Calabasas, CA 91302
Web Site: https://www.abbyson.com
Year Founded: 1989
Sales Range: $25-49.9 Million
Emp.: 60
Exclusive Luxury Designer & Mfr of Home Furnishings
N.A.I.C.S.: 449110
Yavar Rafieha (Pres)
Doddy Rafieha (Exec VP)
Rodd Rafieha (Sr VP)
Bill Ashton (VP-Ops)
Naeem Arastu (Principal)
Taran Kaur (VP-HR Strategy & Legal)
Abby Rafieha (Founder)
Steve Segvich (CFO)

ABC APPLIANCE INC.
1 W Silverdome Industrial Park, Pontiac, MI 48343-6001
Tel.: (248) 335-4222   MI
Web Site: https://www.abcwarehouse.com
Year Founded: 1963
Sales Range: $500-549.9 Million
Emp.: 1,200
Whslr of Retail Household Appliances, Electronics & Car Radios
N.A.I.C.S.: 449210
Gordon Hartunian (Pres)
Don Behrendt (Controller)
Lisa Palmer (Coord-Payroll)

ABC AUTO PARTS LTD.
920 W Marshall Ave, Longview, TX 75604
Tel.: (903) 232-3060
Web Site: http://www.abcauto.com
Year Founded: 1968
Sales Range: $25-49.9 Million
Emp.: 350
Whslr & Retailer of Automotive Supplies & Parts
N.A.I.C.S.: 423120
Karen Maddox (VP)
David Wilkins (Exec VP)
Amanda Dolson (Mgr-Acctg)
Eric Dyess (Mgr-Warehouse)

ABC AUTOMOTIVE, INC.
8005 W Weddington Rd, Fayetteville, AR 72704
Tel.: (479) 521-6100
Sales Range: $1-9.9 Million
Emp.: 8

Home Supply Whslr
N.A.I.C.S.: 441330
Bill Bartholowmew (Owner)

ABC AUTOS, INC.
6112 N Florida Ave, Tampa, FL 33604-6624
Tel.: (813) 237-3934
Web Site: http://www.abcautostar.com
Year Founded: 1973
Sales Range: $10-24.9 Million
Emp.: 32
Used Car Whslr
N.A.I.C.S.: 441120
David B. Fernandez (Pres)
Douglas B. Fernandez (VP)
Miranda Jones (Treas)
Kim Kernon (Controller)

ABC BAKERY SUPPLIES & EQUIPMENT, INC.
7200 NW 1st Ave, Miami, FL 33150
Tel.: (305) 757-3885
Web Site: https://www.abcbakerysupply.com
Sales Range: $10-24.9 Million
Emp.: 17
Other Grocery & Related Product Whslr
N.A.I.C.S.: 424490
Israel A. Aguilar (Pres)
Ana T. Tambini (Controller)
Jose M. Gispert (VP)
America Gispert (Treas)

ABC BUS COMPANIES, INC.
1506 30th St NW, Faribault, MN 55021-1800
Tel.: (507) 333-5200   MN
Web Site: http://www.abc-companies.com
Year Founded: 1986
Sales Range: $250-299.9 Million
Emp.: 410
Supplier of Automobiles & Other Motor Vehicles
N.A.I.C.S.: 423110

Subsidiaries:

ABC Companies Inc.   (1)
17469 W Colonial Dr, Winter Garden, FL 34787-9710   **(100%)**
Tel.: (407) 656-7977
Web Site: http://www.abc-companies.com
Sales Range: $25-49.9 Million
Emp.: 100
Motor Coach Distr
N.A.I.C.S.: 423110
Dane C. Cornell (Chm & CEO)
Shari Sanders (Reg Mgr-Fin)
Bryan O'Connell (Sr VP-Sls-West)
Roman Cornell (Chief Comml Officer)
Ashley Cornell (VP-Strategic Accts)
Thom Peebles (VP-Mktg)
Jon Savitz (Sr VP-Svc Ops)
Mike Laffan (Sr VP-Sls-East Coast)

ABC Financial Services   (1)
1506 30th St NW, Faribault, MN 55021-5120
Tel.: (507) 334-1871
Web Site: http://www.abc-companies.com
Sales Range: $25-49.9 Million
Emp.: 100
Provider of Financial Services for Auto Purchase
N.A.I.C.S.: 532120
Tim Wayland (COO)
Dan Axelson (Controller)

Ameritrans Bus, Inc.   (1)
2503 Ada Dr, Elkhart, IN 46514
Tel.: (574) 262-8935
Web Site: http://www.ameritransbus.com
Emp.: 90
Passenger Vehicles Mfr
N.A.I.C.S.: 336110
Dana Lenhart (Mgr-Pur)
Troy Snyder (Gen Mgr)

ABC CARPET & HOME INC.
888 Broadway Fl 6, New York, NY 10003
Tel.: (212) 473-3000
Web Site: https://www.abchome.com
Rev.: $39,437,724
Emp.: 400
Homefurnishings
N.A.I.C.S.: 449110
Karen Konas (Controller)
Paulette Cole (Chm & Creative Dir)
Dave Lauber (CFO)
Stacey Spielman (Dir-Brand & Mktg)
Aaron Rose (CEO)
Eileen Applebaum (Sr VP & Gen Mgr)
Haynes Robinson (Sr VP-Product Design & Dev)

ABC COMPOUNDING COMPANY, INC.
6970 Jonesboro Rd, Morrow, GA 30260
Tel.: (770) 968-9222   GA
Web Site: http://www.abccompounding.com
Year Founded: 1949
Rev.: $19,000,000
Emp.: 150
Aersols, Liquids & Powders Mfr
N.A.I.C.S.: 325612
Steve R. Walker (Pres)
Destry Holmes (Mgr-Network)
Diane Stewart (Dir-Pur)
Myra Hager (CIO)

ABC DISPOSAL SERVICE, INC.
1245 Shawmut Ave, New Bedford, MA 02746
Tel.: (508) 995-0544   MA
Web Site: http://www.abcdisposal.com
Year Founded: 1967
Sales Range: $10-24.9 Million
Emp.: 19
Solid Waste Landfill Services
N.A.I.C.S.: 562212
Laurinda Camara (Pres)

ABC FINE WINES & SPIRITS
8989 S Orange Ave, Orlando, FL 32824-7904
Tel.: (407) 851-0000   FL
Web Site: https://www.abcfws.com
Year Founded: 1936
Sales Range: $150-199.9 Million
Emp.: 1,400
Liquor Stores
N.A.I.C.S.: 445320
Charles Zales Jr. (CEO)

ABC HOME & COMMERCIAL SERVICES
9475 US 290, Austin, TX 78724
Tel.: (512) 837-9500
Web Site: http://www.abcpest.com
Year Founded: 1949
Emp.: 900
Pest Control Services
N.A.I.C.S.: 561710
Raleigh Jenkins (Pres)
Derek Salazar (Gen Mgr-HVAC, Security, Lawn Care, Lawn & Pool Maintenance)
Terry Cooper (COO)
Norman S. Nelms (VP)
Steven Martin (Gen Mgr-Comml & Residential Pest Control)
Kevin King (Sr Acct Mgr)
Ben Jalomo (Mgr-Comml Sls-South)
Tiffani Johnson (Dir-Mktg)
Dennis Jenkins (Pres-Dallas)
Derrick Henderson (VP-Ops)
Dylan Jenkins (Gen Mgr)
Todd Boggs (Mgr-Svc)

ABC Home Medical Supply, Inc.—(Continued)

ABC HOME MEDICAL SUPPLY, INC.
900 E Prima Vista Blvd Ste 300, Port Saint Lucie, FL 34952-2363
Web Site: https://www.abc-med.com
Year Founded: 2003
Medical & Hospital Equipment & Supplies Distr & Whslr
N.A.I.C.S.: 423450
Andrew J. Junikiewicz (VP-Fin & Admin)
Martina D'Antonio (VP-Sls)
Michael J. Breslin (COO)
Keith W. Jones (CEO)
Patrricia Dimarcello (VP-Reimbursement)

ABC IMAGING LLC
1919 M St, Washington, DC 20036
Tel.: (202) 429-8870
Web Site:
http://www.spectrumcreative.com
Rev.: $12,400,000
Emp.: 3
Blueprinting Service
N.A.I.C.S.: 323111
Medi Falsafi (Pres)
Bruce Wiener (Sr VP-Corp Dev)
Blain Topel (VP)
Kim Yong (Mgr-Acctg)
Timothy Sachs (Sr VP)

ABC INC.
3001 Fiechtner Dr, Fargo, ND 58103
Tel.: (701) 293-5952
Web Site:
http://www.abcseamless.com
Year Founded: 1973
Sales Range: $10-24.9 Million
Emp.: 50
Siding Contractors
N.A.I.C.S.: 238170
Susann Lenzmeier (Mgr-HR)

ABC MOVING & STORAGE INC.
12 Bockes Rd, Hudson, NH 03051
Tel.: (603) 881-9444
Web Site: http://www.abcmoving.com
Rev.: $10,182,860
Emp.: 200
Household Goods Transport
N.A.I.C.S.: 484210
Frank Fisher (Pres)
Don Olbakwski (Dir-Mktg & Sls)

ABC NURSERY INC
424 E Gardena Blvd, Gardena, CA 90248
Tel.: (310) 327-9212
Web Site:
https://www.abcnursery.com
Sales Range: $10-24.9 Million
Emp.: 100
Flowers & Florists Supplies Whslr
N.A.I.C.S.: 424930
Harry Yonemura (Pres)
Barbara Deguire (Office Mgr)

ABC PACKAGING MACHINE CORPORATION
811 Live Oak St, Tarpon Springs, FL 34689-4137
Tel.: (727) 937-5144
Web Site:
https://www.abcpackaging.com
Year Founded: 1940
Sales Range: $50-74.9 Million
Emp.: 80
Mfr of Case Sealing, Packing, Traymaker & Unscrambler/Unloading Equipment & Erectors
N.A.I.C.S.: 333993

Mark Reichert (Pres)
Bryan Sinicrope (VP-Sls & Mktg)
Michael Jurgensen (Treas)

ABC PAVING COMPANY
2650 Van Horn Rd, Trenton, MI 48183
Tel.: (734) 671-2120
Web Site:
https://www.abcpaving.com
Sales Range: $25-49.9 Million
Emp.: 50
Highway & Street Paving Contractor
N.A.I.C.S.: 237310
Thomas G. Morrison (Pres)

ABC PHONES OF NORTH CAROLINA, INC.
1290-B E Arlington Blvd, Greenville, NC 27858
Tel.: (252) 317-0388
Web Site: http://www.awireless.net
Year Founded: 1996
Sales Range: $300-349.9 Million
Emp.: 1,500
Mobile Phone Equipment Distr
N.A.I.C.S.: 423690

Subsidiaries:

GoWireless, Inc.   (1)
9970 W Cheyenne Ave, Las Vegas, NV 89129
Tel.: (702) 853-6200
Web Site: http://www.gowireless.com
Sales Range: $100-124.9 Million
Emp.: 800
Sales of Verizon Wireless Services
N.A.I.C.S.: 517112
Kevin Elder (Founder, Pres & CEO)
John Salisbury (COO)
Paul Huether (CFO)
Dan Wilkins (Pres-Desert Mountain Reg)

ABC POLYMER INDUSTRIES, LLC
545 Elm St Helena Industrial Park, Helena, AL 35080
Tel.: (205) 620-9889   **AL**
Web Site:
https://www.abcpolymerindustry.com
Year Founded: 1964
Sales Range: $25-49.9 Million
Emp.: 50
Specialty Plastic Fibers & Products Mfr
N.A.I.C.S.: 326199
Dean Leader (VP-Ops)
Randy Reed (Pres & CEO)
Trip Summersell (CFO)
Leslee Quiggle (Mgr-Customer Svc & Logistics)
Denzil Schmitz (Sr VP-Sls & Mktg-FiberForce)
Robert Charles Zellers (Chief Engr)
Brian Bacon (VP-Sls & Quality Control-Bulk Bag)
Tim Hartsell (VP-FiberForce-Nationwide)
Angela Slone (Mgr-Sls-Southwest Reg-FiberForce)
Sean Owen (Mgr-Technical Sls-Pacific Northwest)
Hunter Wallace (Mgr-Concrete Fibers Technical Sls-Southeast)
Gavin Bailey (Mng Dir-FiberForce)

ABC SECURITY SERVICE, INC.
1840 Embarcadero, Oakland, CA 94606
Tel.: (510) 436-0666   **CA**
Web Site:
http://www.abcsecurityservice.com
Year Founded: 1968
Sales Range: $1-9.9 Million
Emp.: 250
Security Guards & Patrols
N.A.I.C.S.: 561612

Ray Thrower (Gen Mgr)

ABC STONE, INC.
234 Banker St, Brooklyn, NY 11222-2873
Tel.: (718) 389-8360
Web Site:
https://www.abcworldwidestone.com
Sales Range: $1-9.9 Million
Emp.: 12
Stone Distr
N.A.I.C.S.: 423390
Ken Saretsky (Gen Mgr)

ABC STORES
766 Pohukaina St, Honolulu, HI 96813-5391
Tel.: (808) 591-2550
Web Site: http://www.abcstores.com
Year Founded: 1965
Sales Range: $50-74.9 Million
Emp.: 804
Convenience Store Services
N.A.I.C.S.: 445131
Neil Ishida (Dir-PR)
Durwin Tanimoto (Dir-Ops Dev)
Dayne Yoshioka (Mgr-Tech Support)
Miles Oda (VP)
Paul J. Kosasa (Pres & CEO)

ABC SUPPLY CO. INC.
1 ABC Pkwy, Beloit, WI 53511
Tel.: (608) 362-7777   **CA**
Web Site: https://www.abcsupply.com
Year Founded: 1982
Sales Range: $10-24.9 Million
Emp.: 18,000
Other Building Equipment Contractors
N.A.I.C.S.: 238290

Subsidiaries:

Thermal Tech, Inc.   (1)
2301 US Highway 2 E, Kalispell, MT 59901
Tel.: (406) 755-3388
Sales Range: $1-9.9 Million
Emp.: 10
Siding Contractors
N.A.I.C.S.: 238170
Jay Nordwall (VP)

ABC TARGET, LLC
180 Flushing Ave, Brooklyn, NY 11205-1115
Tel.: (516) 670-9119
Web Site: http://www.abctarget.com
Rev.: $15,000,000
Emp.: 100
Store Fixtures & Display Equipment
N.A.I.C.S.: 423440
Howard Schulman (Pres)

ABC TELEVISION & APPLIANCE RENTAL
2117 Williamson Rd, Roanoke, VA 24012
Tel.: (540) 265-2555
Sales Range: $10-24.9 Million
Emp.: 140
Computer, TV & Appliance Rental
N.A.I.C.S.: 532210
Norman D. Mason (Pres)

ABC-CLIO
130 Cremona Dr Ste C, Santa Barbara, CA 93117
Tel.: (805) 968-1911
Web Site: https://www.abc-clio.com
Sales Range: $10-24.9 Million
Emp.: 115
Books, Publishing Only
N.A.I.C.S.: 513130
Becky Snyder (Pres)
Judy Fay (Dir-Editorial-Electronic)

ABCO AUTOMATION, INC.
6202 Technology Dr, Browns Summit, NC 27214

Tel.: (336) 375-6400
Web Site: https://www.goabco.com
Year Founded: 1977
Sales Range: $25-49.9 Million
Emp.: 150
Industrial Automation Machinery Mfr
N.A.I.C.S.: 333998
Brad Kemmerer (Pres)
Graham Ricks (Founder)

ABCO FIRE PROTECTION, INC.
14202 Hwy 87, Lubbock, TX 79423
Tel.: (806) 745-3398   **TX**
Web Site: http://www.abcofire.com
Sales Range: $1-9.9 Million
Emp.: 60
Fire Sprinkler System Installation
N.A.I.C.S.: 238220
Bob Titmas (Pres & CEO)

ABCO REFRIGERATION SUPPLY CORP.
49-70 31st St, Long Island City, NY 11101
Tel.: (718) 937-9000
Web Site: http://www.abcorefrig.com
Rev.: $27,000,000
Emp.: 100
A/C & Refrigeration Equipment & Supplies
N.A.I.C.S.: 423740
Michael Center (Pres)

ABCO SYSTEMS LLC
326 19th St, Carlstadt, NJ 07072
Tel.: (201) 507-0999   **NJ**
Web Site:
http://www.abcosystems.net
Year Founded: 1975
Sales Range: $1-9.9 Million
Emp.: 10
Industrial Machinery And Equipment
N.A.I.C.S.: 423830
Michael Weisberg (Pres)
Thomas Hoff (VP-Sls)
Andrew Noble (Dir-Ops)
Seth Weisberg (CEO)

Subsidiaries:

Fastfetch Corp.   (1)
708 Topaz Ct, Seneca, SC 29672-6858
Tel.: (864) 498-1019
Web Site: http://www.fastfetch.biz
General Warehousing & Storage
N.A.I.C.S.: 493110

ABCO WELDING & INDUSTRIAL SUPPLIES INC.
130 Cross Rd, Waterford, CT 06385
Tel.: (860) 442-0363
Web Site: http://www.airgas.com
Sales Range: $10-24.9 Million
Emp.: 72
Welding Machinery & Equipment
N.A.I.C.S.: 423830
William R. McCourt (Co-Owner)
David McCourt (Co-Owner)
Mike Ross (Pres)
Peter Marzano (VP-Sls & Mktg)
Phil Kruse (VP-Distr & Plant Ops)
Cindy Busch (Mgr-HR)
Bill McCourt Jr. (VP-Retail Sls)

ABCOM COMPUTER RENTAL, INC.
1680 Carolina Dr, Elk Grove Village, IL 60007-2926
Tel.: (630) 894-9393   **IL**
Web Site:
http://www.abcomrents.com
Year Founded: 1994
Rev.: $1,300,000
Emp.: 10
Office Machinery & Equipment Rental & Leasing
N.A.I.C.S.: 532420

Shiv Goyal *(Pres)*
Marc Nielsen *(Dir-Ops)*
Vishal Goyal *(Dir-Bus Dev)*
Sonny Goyal *(CEO)*

Subsidiaries:

Rent-A-PC, Inc.   (1)
265 Oser Ave, Hauppauge, NY 11788
Tel.: (631) 273-8888
Web Site:
    http://www.smartsourcerentals.com
Computer Rental & Leasing Services
N.A.I.C.S.: 532420
Timothy M. Barry *(Acct Exec-Sls-Washington)*
Lauren Cushing *(Acct Exec)*
Stephen Rupolo *(VP-Product Strategy)*
Mary Caldiero *(Mgr-Digital Mktg)*
Martin Tessler *(Dir-Fin)*
Sanjay Kapur *(CEO)*
Anne Marie Russell *(Controller)*
Craig Sukenic *(VP-Sls)*

Branch (Domestic):

SmartSource Computer & Audio Visual Rentals   (2)
490 S Dean St, Englewood, NJ 07631
Tel.: (201) 568-6555
Web Site:
    http://www.smartsourcerentals.com
Audio-Visual Equipment & Supplies
N.A.I.C.S.: 532210
Kevin McPherson *(Acct Mgr-Technical-Orange County)*
Robert Edwards *(Mgr-Event Mgmt Solutions)*

ABD INSURANCE & FINAN-CIAL SERVICES, INC.
3 Waters Park Dr Ste 100, San Mateo, CA 94403
Tel.: (650) 488-8565
Web Site:
    http://www.theabdteam.com
Sales Range: $25-49.9 Million
Emp.: 110
Insurance Services
N.A.I.C.S.: 524210
Kurt M. de Grosz *(Pres)*
Brian M. Hetherington *(Chm)*
Michael F. McCloskey *(CFO)*
Brent Rineck *(CIO)*
Rod Sockolov *(Exec VP-Property & Casualty)*
Renee H. Polk *(Exec VP-Employee Benefits)*
Chris J. Call *(Pres-Retirement Svcs)*
Amy R. Steadman *(Sr VP-HR)*
Jane Paolucci *(Sr VP-Mktg)*
Michael Hennessey *(Asst VP)*
Abiy Fisseha *(Acct Exec)*
Liz Braun *(Dir-IT)*
Maggie Tang *(Acct Exec)*
Steven Ichihara *(Acct Exec)*
John Haskell *(Exec VP)*
Darren Brown *(Exec VP-Employee Benefits)*
Dereick Wood *(Sr VP-Natl Claims Svcs & Client Engagement-ERS Natl Practice)*

Subsidiaries:

ABD Insurance & Financial Services Inc. - Walnut Creek   (1)
1550 Park Side Dr Ste 120, Walnut Creek, CA 94598
Tel.: (925) 934-0505
Web Site: http://www.theabdteam.com
Sales Range: $50-74.9 Million
Emp.: 15
Property & Casualty Insurance Agent
N.A.I.C.S.: 524210
Kurt de Grosz *(Gen Mgr)*

SharedHR   (1)
1000 4th St Ste 300, San Rafael, CA 94901
Tel.: (415) 459-4400
Web Site: http://www.sharedhr.com
Human Resource Support Services
N.A.I.C.S.: 541612

Malcolm Whyte *(Exec VP & Principal)*
Saul Macias *(VP-Pro Svcs)*
Cathy Cushing *(Office Mgr)*
Paul Finkle *(Founder, Pres & CEO)*

ABDALLAH INCORPORATED
3501 County Rd 42 W, Burnsville, MN 55306
Tel.: (952) 890-4770
Web Site:
    http://www.adballahcandies.com
Rev.: $15,400,000
Emp.: 75
Confectionery
N.A.I.C.S.: 424450
Steven R. Hegedus Jr. *(Pres)*

ABDO INVESTMENTS, INC.
5201 Eden Ave Ste 250, Edina, MN 55436
Tel.: (320) 257-1600   MN
Year Founded: 2005
Bank Holding Company
N.A.I.C.S.: 551111
Jay Abdo *(CEO)*

Subsidiaries:

BankVista   (1)
125 Twin Rivers Ct, Sartell, MN 56377
Tel.: (320) 257-1600
Web Site: http://www.bankvista.com
Sales Range: $1-9.9 Million
Emp.: 24
Commericial Banking
N.A.I.C.S.: 522110
Robyn Holthaus *(CFO & VP)*
Saasha Peterson *(Coord-Mktg)*
Mary Shottenkirk *(VP-Ops & Compliance)*
Daniel Nygaard *(VP & Mgr-Small Bus Div)*
Stefan Freeman *(Pres & CEO)*
LouAnn Peterson *(VP-Mortgage Lending)*
Michael Phillips *(Officer-Lending & VP)*
Thomas Templin *(VP-Mortgage Lending)*
Robert Klefsaas *(Chm)*
Sheila Christiansen *(Mgr-Client Svcs)*
Jan Cook *(Officer-Personal Banking)*
Christina Froehlich *(Pres-Market-Mankato)*

ABEL CHEVROLET PONTIAC BUICK
280 N Front St, Rio Vista, CA 94571-1420
Tel.: (707) 374-6317
Web Site: https://www.abelgm.com
Year Founded: 1935
Sales Range: $10-24.9 Million
Emp.: 39
New Car Whslr
N.A.I.C.S.: 441110
John Abel *(Pres)*

ABEL CONSTRUCTION CO. INC.
3925 Columbia Ave, Mountville, PA 17554
Tel.: (717) 285-3103
Web Site: https://www.abelconst.com
Sales Range: $10-24.9 Million
Emp.: 15
Pipeline Construction
N.A.I.C.S.: 237110
Troy E. Abel *(Pres)*
Christopher Bennett *(Project Mgr)*
Hap Witmer *(Project Mgr)*

ABEL CONSTRUCTION COMPANY
3401 Bashford Ave CT, Louisville, KY 40218
Tel.: (502) 451-2235
Web Site:
    http://www.abelconstruct.com
Sales Range: $25-49.9 Million
Emp.: 250
Industrial Buildings Construction Company
N.A.I.C.S.: 236210
Tonii Rizzo *(Sr VP)*

ABEL OIL CO. INC.
10406 Hwy 79, Louisiana, MO 63353
Tel.: (573) 754-5595   MO
Web Site: https://www.abeloil.com
Year Founded: 1940
Sales Range: $25-49.9 Million
Emp.: 120
Gasoline & Convenience Store Services
N.A.I.C.S.: 457120
Mark Abel *(Pres)*

ABEL SOLUTIONS, INC.
3820 Mansell Rd Ste 260, Alpharetta, GA 30022
Tel.: (678) 393-1704
Web Site:
    http://www.abelsolutions.com
Year Founded: 1995
Rev.: $2,800,000
Emp.: 21
Custom Computer Programming Services
N.A.I.C.S.: 541511
David J. Hammond *(Pres)*
Shannon Webster *(Dir-Solutions Delivery)*
Pedro Speed *(Dir-Consulting)*
Glen Feucht *(Dir-Consulting)*

ABEL UNLIMITED INC.
2020 Seabirg Way, Riviera Beach, FL 33404
Tel.: (561) 688-2175
Web Site: http://www.ironwear.com
Industrial Workwear Mfr & Distr
N.A.I.C.S.: 423840
Marvin Maltz *(Pres)*

ABEL WOMACK INTEGRATED HANDLING SOLUTIONS
1 International Way, Lawrence, MA 01843-1065
Tel.: (978) 989-9400   MA
Web Site:
    https://www.abelwomack.com
Year Founded: 1922
Sales Range: $10-24.9 Million
Emp.: 110
Industrial Equipment & Material Handling Services
N.A.I.C.S.: 423430
John L. Croce *(Pres & CEO)*
Gary Mell *(Controller)*
Darrel Barlow *(Mgr-Parts)*
Tony Fedele *(VP-Ops)*

ABELCONN LLC
9210 Science Center Dr, New Hope, MN 55428-3621
Tel.: (763) 533-3533   MN
Web Site: http://www.abelconn.com
Year Founded: 1997
Sales Range: $10-24.9 Million
Emp.: 140
Electric Connectors & Assembler Printer Circuit Boards Mfr
N.A.I.C.S.: 334417
Donna Sauter *(VP-HR-Atrenne Integrated Solutions)*

Subsidiaries:

CBT Technology Inc.   (1)
358 N St, Randolph, MA 02368-4171
Tel.: (781) 963-7200
Web Site: http://www.cbttechnology.com
Aluminum Rolling, Drawing & Extruding Svcs
N.A.I.C.S.: 331318
Jeff Snyder *(Dir-Global Sls & Customer Rels)*

SIE Computing Solutions, Inc.   (1)
10 Mupac Dr, Brockton, MA 02301
Tel.: (508) 588-6110
Web Site: http://www.sie-cs.com
Emp.: 83
Electric Equipment Mfr

N.A.I.C.S.: 334419
James Tierney *(VP-Sls)*
Chris Boutilier *(Pres)*
Mike Pieniazek *(CFO)*

ABELL CORPORATION
2500 Sterlington Rd, Monroe, LA 71203-3047
Tel.: (318) 343-7565   LA
Web Site:
    http://www.ouachitafertilizer.com
Year Founded: 1955
Sales Range: $50-74.9 Million
Emp.: 20
Mfr of Fertilizers
N.A.I.C.S.: 424910
Dixon W. Abell *(Pres)*

ABELSONTAYLOR, INC.
33 W Monroe St Ste 600, Chicago, IL 60603
Tel.: (312) 894-5500   IL
Web Site:
    http://www.abelsontaylor.com
Year Founded: 1981
Sales Range: $75-99.9 Million
Emp.: 450
Advetising Agency
N.A.I.C.S.: 541810
Dale Taylor *(Founder, Chm & CEO)*
Jay Carter *(Exec VP)*
Stephen Neale *(Sr VP & Exec Dir-Creative)*
Jeff Berg *(Pres)*
Scott Hansen *(VP & Exec Dir-Digital Creative)*
Kristen McGirk *(VP & Dir-Acct)*
Tristen George *(VP & Creative Dir-UK)*
Keith Stenlund *(CFO & Exec VP)*
Noah Lowenthal *(VP & Dir-Creative)*
Donald Dowd *(VP-Fin)*
Bradley Graetz *(VP & Grp Dir-Creative)*
Katerina Steele *(Assoc Dir-Bus Dev & Analysis)*
Amanda Hartzmark *(Sr Dir-Mktg & Intelligence)*
Scott Moers *(Sr Dir-Bus Dev)*

Subsidiaries:

Abelson-Taylor, Inc.   (1)
55 Monument Cir Ste 700, Indianapolis, IN 46204
Tel.: (317) 261-9230
Sales Range: $10-24.9 Million
Emp.: 5
Advertising Agencies
N.A.I.C.S.: 541810

ABERCROMBIE & KENT USA, LLC
1411 Opus Place Executive Towers West II Ste 300, Chicago, IL 60515-1098
Tel.: (630) 725-3400   DE
Web Site:
    http://www.abercrombiekent.com
Year Founded: 1962
Sales Range: $50-74.9 Million
Emp.: 140
Tour & Travel Services
N.A.I.C.S.: 561510
Geoffrey Kent *(Founder)*
Michael Fleetwood *(Mgr-Programme-Escorted Tours-London)*
Ross Pakes *(Dir-Product-UK)*
Kerry Golds *(Mng Dir-UK)*
Martin Froggatt *(Exec VP-Destination Mgmt)*
Michael Wale *(Pres & CEO)*

ABERCROMBIE OIL COMPANY INCORPORATED
2930 W Main St, Danville, VA 24541-6251
Tel.: (434) 792-8022   VA

Abercrombie Oil Company
Incorporated—(Continued)

Web Site:
http://www.abercrombieoil.com
Year Founded: 1956
Sales Range: $25-49.9 Million
Emp.: 80
Petroleum Product Whslr
N.A.I.C.S.: 424720
Milo B. Abercrombie *(Pres & CEO)*
Terry Smith *(Controller & Office Mgr)*

Subsidiaries:

Motor Oils Inc.   (1)
201 Cahill Ct, Danville, VA 24541-2329
Tel.: (434) 799-1741
Web Site: http://www.abercrombieoil.com
Sales Range: $1-9.9 Million
Emp.: 18
Petroleum Product Whslr
N.A.I.C.S.: 424720
Tommy Ritchie *(Gen Mgr)*

ABERDEEN ADVISORS INC.
146 2nd St N Ste 310, Saint Peters-
burg, FL 33701
Tel.: (727) 639-4716
Web Site:
http://www.aberdeenadvisors.com
Sales Range: $1-9.9 Million
Emp.: 10
Business Broker
N.A.I.C.S.: 561499
Emery Ellinger *(CEO)*
Wendy Andrews-Fine *(VP-Client Svs)*

**ABERDEEN CHRYSLER CEN-
TER INC.**
901 Auto Plaza Dr, Aberdeen, SD
57402-0076
Tel.: (605) 225-1656   SD
Web Site:
http://www.aberdeenchrysler.com
Year Founded: 1988
Sales Range: $10-24.9 Million
Emp.: 120
Sales of New & Used Cars
N.A.I.C.S.: 441110
Toby Doeden *(Gen Mgr-Sales)*

**ABERDEEN DYNAMICS SUP-
PLY INC.**
17717 E Admiral Pl, Tulsa, OK 74158
Tel.: (918) 437-8000
Web Site:
https://www.aberdeendynamics.com
Year Founded: 1974
Sales Range: $10-24.9 Million
Emp.: 49
Hydraulic Systems Equipment & Sup-
plies
N.A.I.C.S.: 423830
Dominic White *(Pres)*
Mike Stratton *(VP-Sls)*

Subsidiaries:

Industrial Specialties, LLC   (1)
3500 S MacArthur Blvd, Oklahoma City, OK
73179
Tel.: (405) 672-1221
Web Site: https://isfluidpower.com
Rev.: $5,700,000
Emp.: 10
Industrial Supplies Merchant Whslr
N.A.I.C.S.: 423840

**ABERDEEN HOTEL LTD.
PARTNERSHIP**
980 Hospitality Way, Aberdeen, MD
21001
Tel.: (410) 273-6300
Rev.: $10,000,000
Emp.: 10
Motel, Franchised
N.A.I.C.S.: 721110
Robert Lewam *(Gen Mgr)*

ABERDEEN ROAD COMPANY
105 Sinking Springs Ln, Emigsville,
PA 17318-0435
Tel.: (717) 764-1192   DE
Web Site: http://www.herculite.com
Year Founded: 1999
Sales Range: $25-49.9 Million
Emp.: 100
Holding Company
N.A.I.C.S.: 313320
Peter Mckernan *(Pres)*

Subsidiaries:

Hercon Environmental
Corporation   (1)
105 E Sinking Springs Ln, Emigsville, PA
17318-0435   (100%)
Tel.: (717) 764-1192
Web Site: http://www.herconenviron.com
Sales Range: $10-24.9 Million
Emp.: 30
Mfr of Controlled Release Dispensers &
Pheromone Products for Insect Control &
Household Use
N.A.I.C.S.: 313320
Dan Kaussman *(Plant Mgr)*

Herculite Products, Inc.   (1)
PO Box 435 105 E Sinking Spring Ln,
Emigsville, PA 17318-0435   (100%)
Tel.: (717) 764-1192
Web Site: http://www.herculite.com
Sales Range: $10-24.9 Million
Industrial & Safety Fabrics
N.A.I.C.S.: 313320
Deena J. Davis *(Coord-Marketing)*

ABERS GARAGE INC.
1729 Claremont Ave, Ashland, OH
44805
Tel.: (419) 281-5500   OH
Web Site:
https://www.aberstrucks.com
Year Founded: 1950
Sales Range: $10-24.9 Million
Emp.: 44
Sales of New & Used Trucks, Trac-
tors & Trailers
N.A.I.C.S.: 441110
Dan Aber *(Pres)*

ABETECH, INC.
12560 Fletcher Ln Ste 100, Rogers,
MN 55374
Tel.: (763) 428-3170
Web Site: https://www.abetech.com
Year Founded: 1992
Sales Range: $10-24.9 Million
Emp.: 70
Magnetic Ink & Optical Scanning De-
vices
N.A.I.C.S.: 334118
Steve Schmidt *(Founder & CEO)*
Becky Stumpf *(CFO)*
Todd Jacobs *(CTO & VP-Sls)*
Brent Pollard *(VP-Sls)*
Rick Segal *(VP-Svcs)*

ABEX DISPLAY SYSTEMS
7101 Fair Ave, North Hollywood, CA
91605
Tel.: (818) 503-0999
Web Site: http://www.abex.com
Rev.: $28,700,000
Emp.: 140
Mfr of Solid Fiber Display Items
N.A.I.C.S.: 322211
Robbie Blumenfeld *(Pres)*

ABF DATA SYSTEMS INC.
9020 Kenamar Dr Ste 201, San Di-
ego, CA 92121
Tel.: (858) 547-8307
Sales Range: $50-74.9 Million
Emp.: 100
Computers, Nec
N.A.I.C.S.: 423430
Jimmy Herbst *(Pres)*
Amy Thompson *(Controller)*

ABFB INC.
128 Main St, Lyndonville, VT 05851
Tel.: (802) 626-5339
Web Site:
http://www.whitemarketvt.com
Rev.: $11,000,000
Emp.: 100
Grocery Stores, Independent
N.A.I.C.S.: 445110
Bryan Bona *(Owner)*

**ABG CAULKING CONTRAC-
TORS INC.**
861 Springfield Hwy, Goodlettsville,
TN 37072
Tel.: (615) 859-4935
Web Site:
https://www.abgcaulking.com
Year Founded: 1970
Rev.: $18,000,000
Emp.: 270
Caulking, Waterproofing & Sealants
N.A.I.C.S.: 238990
Arles B. Greene *(Pres & CEO)*
Shannon Greene *(Treas & Sec)*

ABHE & SVOBODA, INC.
18100 Dairy Ln, Jordan, MN 55352
Tel.: (952) 447-6025   MN
Web Site:
https://www.abheonline.com
Year Founded: 1968
Sales Range: $50-74.9 Million
Emp.: 200
Industrial Painting Contractor
N.A.I.C.S.: 236220
Gail S. Svoboda *(Pres)*
Norman Van Haaften *(Controller)*
Roxane Svoboda *(Sec)*
James Svoboda *(VP-Ops)*
Don Holle *(VP)*

ABI COMPANIES, INC.
5425 Beaumont Center Blvd Ste 900,
Tampa, FL 33634
Tel.: (813) 289-8808
Web Site: https://www.abiinc.com
Sales Range: $25-49.9 Million
Emp.: 40
Industrial Building Construction
N.A.I.C.S.: 236210
Hank Booth *(Pres)*

ABILENE AERO INC.
2850 Airport Blvd, Abilene, TX 79602
Tel.: (325) 677-2601
Web Site:
https://www.abileneaero.com
Year Founded: 1968
Sales Range: $10-24.9 Million
Emp.: 40
Fuel Oil Dealers
N.A.I.C.S.: 457210
Joe Crawford *(Pres)*

ABILENE MACHINE INC.
2150 Daisy Rd, Solomon, KS 67480
Tel.: (785) 655-9455
Web Site:
http://www.abilenemachine.com
Year Founded: 1982
Sales Range: $10-24.9 Million
Emp.: 107
Agricultural Machinery
N.A.I.C.S.: 423820
Randy Roelofsen *(Pres)*
Doug Swanson *(Mgr-Sls-Wholesale)*

ABILIS, INC.
50 Glenville St, Greenwich, CT 06831
Tel.: (203) 531-1880   CT
Web Site: https://www.abilis.us
Year Founded: 1951
Sales Range: $10-24.9 Million
Emp.: 405

Developmental Disability Assistance
Services
N.A.I.C.S.: 624120
Karen Feder *(Dir-Youth Svcs)*

ABILITY BEYOND DISABILITY
4 Berkshire Blvd, Bethel, CT 06801-
1001
Tel.: (203) 775-4700   CT
Web Site:
https://www.abilitybeyond.org
Year Founded: 1954
Sales Range: $75-99.9 Million
Emp.: 1,000
Rehabilitation Services
N.A.I.C.S.: 624190
Fred L. Baker *(Gen Counsel & Sec)*
Lori I. Pasqualini *(Chief Fin & Admin
Officer & Treas)*
Gregory Smith *(Chm)*
Anne Marie Russo *(Vice Chm)*
Jane Davis *(Pres & CEO)*

ABILITY COMMERCE, INC.
1300 NW 17th Ave Ste 200, Delray
Beach, FL 33445
Tel.: (561) 330-3151
Web Site:
http://www.abilitycommerce.com
Year Founded: 1986
Sales Range: $25-49.9 Million
Emp.: 120
E-Commerce Software; Marketing
Consulting
N.A.I.C.S.: 513210
Diane Buzzeo *(Founder & Pres)*
Debbie Longo *(VP)*
Patrick Reineke *(VP-Dev & IT)*
David Faidley *(VP-Fin)*
Gary Moen *(Mgr-Info Sys)*
Shawn Ellen *(Dir-Sls Ops & Profes-
sional Svcs)*
Christopher Sullivan *(Pres)*

ABILITY CONNECTION TEXAS
8802 Harry Hines Blvd, Dallas, TX
75235
Tel.: (214) 351-2500   TX
Web Site:
https://www.abilityconnection.org
Year Founded: 1953
Sales Range: $10-24.9 Million
Emp.: 253
Disability Assistance Services
N.A.I.C.S.: 624120
Troy Greisen *(Pres & CEO)*
David McKeever *(CFO)*
Justin Banta *(Chief Dev Officer)*

ABILITYFIRST
1300 E Green St, Pasadena, CA
91106
Tel.: (626) 396-1010   CA
Web Site: https://www.abilityfirst.org
Year Founded: 1926
Sales Range: $10-24.9 Million
Emp.: 677
Child & Youth Care Services
N.A.I.C.S.: 624110
Lori Gangemi *(Pres & CEO)*
Keri Castaneda *(Chief Program Offi-
cer)*

ABINGTON GROUP INC.
195 West Rd, Portsmouth, NH 03801
Tel.: (603) 436-5800
Web Site:
http://www.abingtongroup.com
Sales Range: $10-24.9 Million
Emp.: 130
Industrial Buildings, New Construction
N.A.I.C.S.: 236210
Michael Carr *(Pres)*
Patrisha Bartelt *(Sec)*

ABIP, PC

1717 Saint James Pl Ste 500, Houston, TX 77056
Tel.: (713) 954-2002   TX
Web Site: https://www.abipcpa.com
Accounting, Tax & Advisory Services
N.A.I.C.S.: 541211
Scott L. Irvine *(Mng Partner)*
Michael A. Palmer *(Partner)*
Michael Del Toro *(Partner)*
Janet Pitman *(Partner)*
Dean Blount *(Partner)*
Manish Seth *(Partner)*
Richard Dyo *(Partner)*
Andrew T. Barbe *(Partner)*
Joe Gubic *(Partner)*
Fernando J. Rocha *(Partner)*
Lee Schwartzman *(Principal)*
Caroline Lochte *(Principal)*
David Schmidt *(Principal)*
David Zurbriggen *(Principal)*
Anthony DeBenedictis *(Principal)*

ABITA BREWING CO.
21084 Hwy 36, Covington, LA 70433
Tel.: (985) 893-3143
Web Site: https://www.abita.com
Year Founded: 1986
Sales Range: $10-24.9 Million
Emp.: 45
Brewery
N.A.I.C.S.: 312120
David Blossman *(Pres)*
Leo Basile *(VP-Sls)*

ABL MANAGEMENT INC.
11224 Boardwalk Dr, Baton Rouge, LA 70816
Tel.: (225) 272-6063
Web Site:
    http://www.ablmanagement.com
Rev.: $34,343,296
Emp.: 15
Food Services Direct Sales
N.A.I.C.S.: 722330
Sandee Scott *(Treas, Sec & VP)*
Roshon Cody *(VP)*
John Appleton *(Chm, Pres & CEO)*

ABLAK HOLDINGS, LLC
1005 S Bee St, Pittsburgh, PA 15220
Tel.: (412) 919-2111   PA
Web Site:
    https://www.ablakholdings.com
Investment Holding Company
N.A.I.C.S.: 551112
Varol Ablak *(Chm & CEO)*
Jim Powers *(Exec VP)*

Subsidiaries:

Sincerely Yogurt Franchising
LLC   (1)
1005 S Bee St, Pittsburgh, PA 15220
Tel.: (412) 919-2111
Web Site: http://www.sincerelyyogurt.com
Frozen Yogurt Shops Franchisor
N.A.I.C.S.: 533110
Varol Ablak *(Chm & CEO)*

ABLE EQUIPMENT RENTAL, INC.
21 Dixon Ave, Copiague, NY 11726
Tel.: (631) 841-3333   NY
Web Site:
    http://www.ableequipment.com
Year Founded: 1996
Sales Range: $10-24.9 Million
Emp.: 52
Equipment Rental/Leasing
N.A.I.C.S.: 532490
Delores Laganas *(Pres)*
Steven Laganas *(CEO)*
Thomas Caldaroni *(CFO)*
Philippe Bisson *(Dir-Bus Dev-Rotator & Telehandler)*
Neil Goldstein *(Mgr-Mktg)*

Chris Pera *(COO)*
Stacy Irons *(VP-Sls Ops)*
Patrick Farley *(CIO)*

ABLE FREIGHT SERVICES INC.
5510 W 102nd St, Los Angeles, CA 90045-6010
Tel.: (310) 568-8883   CA
Web Site: http://www.ablefreight.com
Year Founded: 1993
Sales Range: $10-24.9 Million
Emp.: 300
Freight Transportation Services
N.A.I.C.S.: 488510
Orlando Wong *(Exec VP)*

Subsidiaries:

Able Transporte de Carga S. de R.L.
de C.V.   (1)
Avenida Solidaridad Iberoamericana No 9880 Col Aeropuerto, Internacional Miguel Hidalgo, 45659, Tlajomulco de Zuniga, Jalisco, Mexico
Tel.: (52) 33 3688 63 57
Web Site: http://www.ablefreight.com
Emp.: 7
Logistics Consulting Servies
N.A.I.C.S.: 541614
Sdijay Nallamilli *(Gen Mgr)*

ABLE INFORMATION TECHNOLOGIES, INC.
2915 W Fairview St, Chandler, AZ 85224
Tel.: (480) 477-0139   AZ
Year Founded: 1993
Sales Range: $1-9.9 Million
Emp.: 10
IT Solutions, Products & Services
N.A.I.C.S.: 519290
Brandon Ames *(Pres & CEO)*
Duke Merhavy *(Dir-Mktg)*
Tricia Brooks *(Dir-Fin)*
Jessica Soqui *(Dir-HR)*

Subsidiaries:

Able Information Technologies,
Inc.   (1)
220 E 3rd Ave, Corsicana, TX 75110   (100%)
Tel.: (903) 872-0300
IT Solutions, Products & Services
N.A.I.C.S.: 519290

ABLE MACHINERY MOVERS, INC.
600 Westport Pkwy, Grapevine, TX 76051
Tel.: (817) 410-8881
Web Site:
    https://www.ablemachinery.com
Year Founded: 1957
Sales Range: $10-24.9 Million
Emp.: 70
Transporter of Heavy Machinery
N.A.I.C.S.: 484220
David G. Krieger *(Pres)*

ABLE MANUFACTURING AND ASSEMBLY LLC
1000 S Chifferdecker Ave, Joplin, MO 64801
Tel.: (417) 623-3060
Web Site: http://www.ablemfg.com
Year Founded: 1954
Sales Range: $25-49.9 Million
Emp.: 286
Truck Cabs, For Motor Vehicles
N.A.I.C.S.: 336211
Gary Huffaker *(Acct Mgr)*

ABLE SALES COMPANY, INC.
Centro Distribucion del Norte Edificio 1 Carretera 869 Bo Palmas, Catano, PR 00962
Tel.: (787) 620-4141   PR

Web Site: http://www.ablesales.com
Year Founded: 1967
Food & Pharmaceutical Ingredients Warehousing & Distribution Services
N.A.I.C.S.: 493190
Luis Silva *(Pres)*
Gabriela Soler *(Specialist-Pur)*

Subsidiaries:

Alimentos Liquidos Industriales   (1)
Km 17 Los Cedros Park, Los Alcarrizos, Santo Domingo, Dominican Republic
Tel.: (809) 3721259
Web Site: http://www.alindus.com
Food & Pharmaceutical Ingredients Mfr & Distr
N.A.I.C.S.: 325412
Ernesto Arostequi *(Gen Mgr)*
Ingrid Paulino *(Sls Mgr)*

Envasadora de Azucar, Inc.   (1)
Carretera 896 Bo Palmas, Catano, PR 00962
Tel.: (787) 620-4141
Web Site: http://www.ablesales.com
Refined Sugar Packaging
N.A.I.C.S.: 311314

Ponce Caribbean Distributors   (1)
Carretera 896 Bo Palmas, Catano, PR 00962
Tel.: (787) 620-4141
Web Site: http://www.ablesales.com
Sales Range: $10-24.9 Million
Emp.: 125
Grocery Product Distr
N.A.I.C.S.: 424490

ABLE2 ENHANCING POTENTIAL
1118 Charles St, Elmira, NY 14904
Tel.: (607) 734-7107   NY
Web Site: https://www.able-2.org
Year Founded: 1950
Sales Range: $10-24.9 Million
Emp.: 423
Developmental Disability Assistance Services
N.A.I.C.S.: 623210
Michaleen Lehman *(Dir-Community Svcs & Staff Dev)*
Carole Berg *(Dir-HR)*

ABLENET, INC.
2625 Patton Rd, Roseville, MN 55113-1137
Tel.: (651) 294-2200   MN
Web Site:
    https://www.ablenetinc.com
Year Founded: 1985
Sales Range: $10-24.9 Million
Emp.: 45
Educational & Technical Solutions
N.A.I.C.S.: 513210
Jennifer Thalhuber *(CEO)*

Subsidiaries:

TeleConcepts, Inc.   (1)
7100 Northland Cir Ste 117, Minneapolis, MN 55428
Tel.: (763) 566-5360
Sales Range: $10-24.9 Million
Emp.: 25
Telemarketing Bureaus
N.A.I.C.S.: 561422
Marcia Walker *(VP)*

ABOFFS INC.
33 Gerard St Ste 204, Huntington, NY 11743-2742
Tel.: (631) 427-2008
Web Site: http://www.aboffs.com
Rev.: $18,500,000
Emp.: 6
Distribute Paints, Varnishes & Supplies
N.A.I.C.S.: 424950
Michael Aboff *(Pres)*

ABOUT TIME INC.

7220 Bob Bullock Loop Ste 4A, Laredo, TX 78041-2058
Tel.: (956) 723-1198
Web Site: https://www.about-time.com
Sales Range: $50-74.9 Million
Emp.: 31
Video Games
N.A.I.C.S.: 423920
Shashi Vaswani *(Pres)*
Hosea Vela *(Controller)*

ABOUTGOLF LTD.
352 Tomahawk Dr, Maumee, OH 43537
Tel.: (419) 482-9095
Web Site: http://www.aboutgolf.com
Sales Range: $1-9.9 Million
Emp.: 21
Indoor Golf Simulator Mfr
N.A.I.C.S.: 423910
Joe Young *(CEO)*
Mike Boylan *(Mgr-Warehouse)*

Subsidiaries:

AboutGolf Europe Ltd.   (1)
Unit 8 Hollybush Business Centre, Shipley Bridge Lane, Horley, RH6 9TL, United Kingdom
Tel.: (44) 1273727250
Web Site: http://www.aboutgolfeurope.com
Indoor Golf Simulator Mfr
N.A.I.C.S.: 611620

ABP INDUCTION LLC
21905 Gateway Rd, Brookfield, WI 53045
Tel.: (262) 317-5300
Web Site:
    http://www.abpinduction.com
Sales Range: $10-24.9 Million
Emp.: 6
Industrial Furnaces & Ovens
N.A.I.C.S.: 551112
Don Wiseman *(VP)*
Frank Possinger *(Treas)*

ABR WHOLESALERS INC.
510 N Goodman St, Rochester, NY 14609
Tel.: (585) 482-3601
Web Site:
    http://www.abrwholersalers.com
Sales Range: $50-74.9 Million
Emp.: 30
Warm Air Heating Equipment & Supplies
N.A.I.C.S.: 423730
Jody Monaco Mc Garry *(CEO)*
Brian Hodges *(Branch Mgr-Inside Sls-HVAC)*

ABRAKADOODLE INC.
46030 Manekin Plz Ste 110, Sterling, VA 20166
Tel.: (703) 860-6570
Web Site:
    http://www.abrakadoodleinc.com
Year Founded: 2002
Sales Range: $1-9.9 Million
Emp.: 20
Creativity & Art Education Classes, Camps, Parties & Events for Children
N.A.I.C.S.: 611699
Mary Rogers *(Co-Founder)*
Rosemarie Hartnett *(Co-Founder)*
Gina Bennette *(Dir-Education)*
Ceneetra Anderson *(Dir-Education)*

ABRAMS AIRBORNE MANUFACTURING, INC.
3735 N Romero Rd, Tucson, AZ 85705
Tel.: (520) 887-1727
Web Site: https://www.abrams.com
Rev.: $24,000,000
Emp.: 205

Abrams Airborne Manufacturing, Inc.—(Continued)

Electroplating, Plating, Polishing, Anodizing & Coloring
N.A.I.C.S.: 332813
Christopher R. Abrams (VP & Plant Mgr)
Barbara Abrams (Chm & Treas)
Gary Abrams (Pres)
Jenny A. Wilson (VP)

ABRAMS CAPITAL, LLC
222 Berkeley St 21st Fl, Boston, MA 02116
Tel.: (617) 646-6100   **DE**
Web Site:
      http://www.abramscapital.com
Year Founded: 1999
Real Estate & Private Equity Investment Services
N.A.I.C.S.: 531390
David Charles Abrams (Mng Partner)
Alison Bomberg (Mng Dir & Gen Counsel)
Drew Pluhar (Mng Dir)
Frederic Leif (Mng Dir & CFO)
James Cafferty (Mng Dir)
Michael Josephson (Mng Dir & COO)
Travis Rhodes (Mng Dir)

Subsidiaries:

Abrams Capital Management, LLC   (1)
222 Berkeley St 21st Fl, Boston, MA 02116
Tel.: (617) 646-6100
Web Site: http://www.abramscapital.com
Emp.: 5
Private Equity Investment Management
N.A.I.C.S.: 523940
David Charles Abrams (Mng Dir)
Kate Rowe (Dir-Ops)

Hudson's Bay Company   (1)
8925 Torbram Road, Brampton, L6T 4G1, ON, Canada
Tel.: (905) 792-4400
Web Site: http://www3.hbc.com
Rev.: $6,872,326,720
Assets: $7,165,514,720
Liabilities: $5,709,836,300
Net Worth: $1,455,678,420
Earnings: ($397,269,740)
Emp.: 40,000
Fiscal Year-end: 02/02/2019
Specialty Retail & Department Stores Operator
N.A.I.C.S.: 455110
Richard A. Baker (Exec Chm)
Marc J. Metrick (Pres-Saks Fifth Avenue)
Kerry Mader (Chief Customer Officer & Exec VP)
Todd Zator (Chief Acctg Officer)
Ian Putnam (Chief Corp Dev Officer & Pres-Real Estate)
David J. Schwartz (Gen Counsel, Sec & Exec VP)
Andrew Blecher (Chief Comm Officer)
Edward Record (CFO)
Janis Leigh (Chief HR Officer)
Stephen J. Gold (Chief Tech & Digital Ops Officer)
Vanessa LeFebvre (Pres-Lord & Taylor)
Anu Penmetcha (VP-Digital Mdsg & Ops)
Meghan Nameth (Sr VP-Mktg)
Paige Thomas (Pres-Saks OFF 5TH)
Alexander Meyer (Chief Customer Officer)

Division (Domestic):

Home Outfitters   (2)
401 Bay Street, Toronto, M5H 2Y4, ON, Canada
Tel.: (416) 861-6404
Web Site: http://www.homeoutfitters.com
Kitchen, Bed & Bath Products Retailer
N.A.I.C.S.: 449129

Subsidiary (US):

Saks Incorporated   (2)
611 5th Ave, New York, NY 10022
Tel.: (212) 940-5305
Web Site: http://www.saks.com
Rev.: $3,147,554,000
Assets: $2,090,247,000

Liabilities: $940,398,000
Net Worth: $1,149,849,000
Earnings: $62,882,000
Emp.: 13,900
Fiscal Year-end: 02/02/2013
Holding Company: Department Store Operator & Online Retailer
N.A.I.C.S.: 551112
Richard A. Baker (Chm)
Lucas Evans (Treas & Sr VP)

Subsidiary (Domestic):

Saks Fifth Avenue, Inc.   (3)
611 5th Ave, New York, NY 10022
Tel.: (212) 753-4000
Web Site: http://www.saksfifthavenue.com
Sales Range: $1-4.9 Billion
Emp.: 500
Department Store Operator & Online Retailer
N.A.I.C.S.: 455110
Eric Jennings (VP & Dir-Mktg-Fashion-Mens & Home Gifts)
Marta Nowakowski (Mgr-Mdsg-Jewelry & Watches)
Romina Nabhen (Dir-New Fashion & Fifth Avenue Club)
Kate Oldham (Sr VP & Gen Mgr-Mdse-Beauty, Fragrance, Lingerie & Swimwear)
Marc J. Metrick (Pres)
Roopal Patel (Dir-Fashion)
Shelley Tadaki Cramer (Gen Mgr-Waikiki)
Jennifer Welch (Mgr-District Asset Protection)
Deb McGinnis (VP & Gen Mgr-Palm Beach Gardens)
Ramona Messore (VP & Gen Mgr-Brickell City Centre)
Alicia Williams (VP-Diversity, Equity & Inclusion)
Cara Chacon (Sr VP-ESG)
Kathleen Shea (VP-Travel & Tourism Strategy)
John Antonini (Sr VP & Dir-Stores)

Division (Domestic):

The Bay   (2)
401 Bay Street Suite 700, Toronto, M5H 2Y4, ON, Canada
Tel.: (416) 861-6437
Web Site: http://www.thebay.ca
Sales Range: $100-124.9 Million
Departmental Store Operator
N.A.I.C.S.: 455110
Bonnie R. Brooks (Pres & CEO)

ABRAMS INTERNATIONAL LLP
5811 Trade Center Dr Bldg 1, Austin, TX 78744
Tel.: (512) 322-4000
Web Site: http://www.jdabrams.com
Sales Range: $75-99.9 Million
Emp.: 800
General Contractor Highway & Street Construction Services
N.A.I.C.S.: 237310

Subsidiaries:

Austin PreStress Co   (1)
7300 US 183 S, Austin, TX 78744-7830
Tel.: (512) 243-1090
Web Site: http://www.austinprestress.com
Concrete Products Mfr
N.A.I.C.S.: 327390
Bryan Villas (Mgr-Quality Assurance & Quality Control)
Nick Lujan (Mgr-Production)
Jim Abrams Jr. (Pres)

J.D. Abrams LP   (1)
111 Congress Ave Ste 2400, Austin, TX 78701
Tel.: (512) 322-4000
Web Site: http://www.jdabrams.com
Rev.: $3,900,000
Emp.: 1
General Contractor, Highway & Street Construction
N.A.I.C.S.: 237310
Jon Abrams (Chm)

McRae Aviation Services Inc   (1)
4309 General Aviativic common Ave, Austin, TX 78719

Tel.: (512) 385-9615
Web Site: http://www.mcraeaviation.com
Sales Range: Less than $1 Million
Emp.: 3
Aircraft Rental
N.A.I.C.S.: 532411
Mark Richard (Gen Mgr)

ABRASIVE TECHNOLOGY INCORPORATED
8400 Green Meadows Dr N, Lewis Center, OH 43035
Tel.: (740) 548-4100
Web Site: https://www.abrasive-tech.com
Year Founded: 1971
Sales Range: $25-49.9 Million
Emp.: 200
Abrasive Stones, Except Grinding Stones
N.A.I.C.S.: 327910
Loyal M. Peterman (Pres & CEO)

ABRASIVE-TOOL CORPORATION
1555 Emerson St, Rochester, NY 14606
Tel.: (585) 254-4500
Web Site:
      https://www.abrasivetool.com
Year Founded: 1968
Rev.: $30,000,000
Emp.: 60
Whslr of Abrasives & Cutting Tools
N.A.I.C.S.: 423840
Michael T. Hanna (Pres)
Jerry Hanford (Mgr-Inside Sls)
Mark Hanna (VP)
Gerald B. Hanna (Treas & Sec)

ABREOS BIOSCIENCES, INC.
2223 Avenida de la Playa Ste 206, La Jolla, CA 92037
Tel.: (858) 203-1169
Web Site: http://www.abreos.com
Precision Medicine Research & Development
N.A.I.C.S.: 541714
Bradley Messmer (CEO)

Subsidiaries:

AegirBio AB   (1)
c/o LifeAssays AB Solvegatan 43A, 22371, Lund, Sweden
Tel.: (46) 462865400
Web Site: http://www.aegirbio.com
Therapeutic Drug Mfr
N.A.I.C.S.: 541714
Martin Linde (CEO)
Mohamad Takwa (COO)
Gunnar Telhammar (CFO)
Bradley Messmer (Chief Sls Officer)
Anders Ingvarsson (Chm)

ABRI CREDIT UNION
1350 W Renwick Rd, Romeoville, IL 60446
Tel.: (815) 267-7700   **IL**
Web Site: http://www.abricu.com
Year Founded: 1949
Sales Range: $10-24.9 Million
Emp.: 133
Financial Support Services
N.A.I.C.S.: 523999
James Miller (Chm)
Marty McGinnis (Treas)

ABRO INDUSTRIES, INC.
3580 Blackthorn Ct, South Bend, IN 46628
Tel.: (574) 232-8289
Web Site: https://www.abro.com
Year Founded: 1979
Sales Range: $50-74.9 Million
Emp.: 25
Automotive, Industrial & Consumer Products Distr
N.A.I.C.S.: 423840

Peter F. Baranay (Pres)
Tim Demarais (VP-Sls-Intl)

Subsidiaries:

Abro Distribution Service LLC   (1)
2509 Dean Forest Dr Ste 100, Savannah, GA 31408
Tel.: (843) 761-0084
Automobile Component Distr
N.A.I.C.S.: 423120

ABRY PARTNERS, LLC
888 Boylston Ste 1600, Boston, MA 02199
Tel.: (617) 859-2959   **DE**
Web Site: http://www.abry.com
Year Founded: 1989
Privater Equity Firm
N.A.I.C.S.: 523999
Jay M. Grossman (Co-CEO & Mng Partner)
Andrew Banks (Co-Founder)
Peggy Koenig (Chm)
Brian St. Jean (Partner)
Brent Stone (Partner)
Azra Kanji (Partner)
C. J. Brucato (Co-CEO & Mng Partner)
John Connor (Partner)
Rob MacInnis (Partner)
Michael Ashton (Partner)
Matt Lapides (Partner)
Debbie Johnson (CFO)
Eric Cooper (VP-Fin)
Tomer Yosef-Or (Partner)
Tyler Wick (Partner)
Austin Heiman (Principal)
Chris Anzivino (Sr VP)
Steve Zammit (Partner)
Garrett Blank (Principal)
Ralph Choufani (Partner)
Akshay Mahajan (Sr VP)
Rob Nicewicz (Partner)
Nathan Ott (Partner)
T. J. Rose (Partner)
Mike Yirilli (Partner)
Kostas Sofronas (Chief Compliance Officer & Gen Counsel)
Tapiwa Mutomba (Controller)
Lori Stachelski (Chief Talent Officer)
Anders Bjork (Partner)
Medhini Srinivasan (Principal)
James Scola (Partner)
Nicolas Massard (Partner)
Nicolas Massard (Partner)
John Hunt (Mng Partner)

Subsidiaries:

Aegis Toxicology Sciences Corporation   (1)
515 Great Cir Rd, Nashville, TN 37228
Tel.: (615) 255-2400
Web Site: http://www.aegislabs.com
Toxicology Testing Services
N.A.I.C.S.: 541380
Rebecca Heltsley (Sr VP-R&D)
Frank Basile (CEO)
Joel Galanter (Chief Legal Officer & Gen Counsel)
Matthew Hardison (Sr VP-Lab Ops)
Michael Patrick (Chief Bus Dev Officer)
David Priestley (CFO)
Tim Ryan (CIO)
Lisa Wooten (Sr VP-Organizational Effectiveness)
Mike Ziegler (Chief Sls Officer)

Aftermath Services LLC   (1)
75 Executive Dr Ste 200, Aurora, IL 60504
Tel.: (877) 872-4339
Web Site: http://www.aftermath.com
Biohazard Removal Services
N.A.I.C.S.: 562211

Anju Software, Inc.   (1)
4500 S Lakeshore Dr, Tempe, AZ 85282
Tel.: (630) 246-2527
Web Site: http://www.anjusoftware.com
Comprehensive Software Services
N.A.I.C.S.: 513210

Marc Eigner *(CEO)*

Subsidiary (Domestic):

OmniComm Systems, Inc. (2)
2101 W Commercial Blvd Ste 3500, Fort
Lauderdale, FL 33309
Tel.: (954) 473-1254
Web Site: http://www.omnicomm.com
Rev.: $27,104,480
Assets: $10,228,214
Liabilities: $21,912,118
Net Worth: ($11,683,904)
Earnings: $3,687,965
Emp.: 164
Fiscal Year-end: 12/31/2018
Web-Based Electronic Data Capture &
eClinical Software & Services
N.A.I.C.S.: 513210
Cornelis F. Wit *(Chm)*

Subsidiary (Non-US):

OmniComm Europe GmbH. (3)
Kaiserstrasse 139-141, 53113, Bonn, Germany
Tel.: (49) 228227440
Healthcare Software Development Services
N.A.I.C.S.: 541511
Yvonne Rollinger *(Mng Dir)*

OmniComm Spain S.L. (3)
Ctra Fuencarral Km 3800-Arbea Campus
Empresa, 28108, Alcobendas, Spain
Tel.: (34) 902111868
Advertising Services
N.A.I.C.S.: 541810

OmniComm Systems B.V (3)
Zernikedreef 8, 2333 CL, Leiden, Netherlands
Tel.: (31) 715246460
Software Development Services
N.A.I.C.S.: 541511

Archonix Systems, LLC (1)
30 Lake Ctr Executive Pk 401 Rt 73 N Ste
105, Marlton, NJ 08053
Tel.: (856) 787-0020
Web Site: http://www.archonixsystems.com
Sales Range: $1-9.9 Million
Emp.: 21
Custom Computer Programming Services
N.A.I.C.S.: 541511
Anthony Graham *(Pres & COO)*
Sanjay Singhvi *(CEO)*
Joe Heaney *(Dir-Programming)*
Les Grovatt *(Dir-Product Dev)*
Reginald McDaniel *(Mgr-Support)*
Denise Straub *(Mgr-Ops)*

Centauri Health Solutions, Inc. (1)
16260 N 71st St Ste 350, Scottsdale, AZ
85254
Tel.: (888) 447-8908
Web Site: http://www.centaurihs.com
Data Management Services
N.A.I.C.S.: 518210
Adam Miller *(CEO)*
Michelle Miller *(CTO)*
Judy Smythe *(Chief Revenue Officer)*
Robert Armknecht *(CFO)*
Mike McNelis *(Chief Dev Officer)*
Bob Glaser *(COO)*

Subsidiary (Domestic):

HCFS, Inc. (2)
3011 Internet Blvd Ste 100, Frisco, TX
75034
Tel.: (800) 394-4237
Web Site: http://www.hcfsinc.com
Management Consulting Services
N.A.I.C.S.: 541618
Brett Floyd *(Dir-IT)*
Adell Brown *(Dir-Trng & Dev)*

Human Arc Corporation (2)
1457 E 40th St, Cleveland, OH 44103
Tel.: (216) 431-5200
Web Site: http://www.humanarc.com
Individual & Family Services
N.A.I.C.S.: 624190
Adam Miller *(CEO)*
Michelle Miller *(CTO)*
Mark Fabiano *(Chief Revenue Officer)*
Robert Armknecht *(CFO)*
Mike McNelis *(Chief Dev Officer)*
Robert W. Glaser *(COO)*
Jimmy Griffin *(VP-HR)*
Jenny Roman *(Mgr-Compliance & Legal
Svcs)*

Integration Management, Inc. (2)
205 Powell Pl Ste 318, Brentwood, TN
37027
Tel.: (615) 538-7068
Web Site: http://www.imihealth.com
Sales Range: $1-9.9 Million
Emp.: 22
Custom Computer Programming Services
N.A.I.C.S.: 541511

Ivy Ventures, LLC (2)
7231 Forest Ave # 306, Richmond, VA
23226
Tel.: (804) 864-1880
Web Site: http://www.ivyventures.com
Rev.: $2,010,000
Emp.: 5
Healthcare Solutions
N.A.I.C.S.: 621999
Roger Johnson *(Partner)*
Barrett Clark *(Dir-Strategy & Analytics)*
Milan DiPierro *(COO)*
Douglas Wetmore *(Partner)*
Robert W. Oldfield *(Partner-Bus Dev)*

Chambers & Partners Media Ltd. (1)
No 3 Waterhouse Square 138 Holborn, Holborn, London, EC1N 2SW, United Kingdom
Tel.: (44) 2076068844
Web Site:
    http://www.chambersandpartners.com
Legal Guides Publisher & Researcher
N.A.I.C.S.: 513140
Chris Thomas *(Chief Comml Officer)*
James Lee *(CTO)*
Laura Alexander *(CFO)*
Rick Jakubowski *(Chief Product Officer)*

Cygnus Business Media Inc. (1)
1233 Janesville Ave, Fort Atkinson, WI
53538-2738
Tel.: (920) 563-6388
Web Site: http://www.cygnusb2b.com
Sales Range: $150-199.9 Million
Business-To-Business Communications
N.A.I.C.S.: 513120
John French *(CEO)*
Ed Nichols *(Dir-Events & Pub Safety)*
Scott Bieda *(VP-Sls-Fire, EMS & Security)*
Larry Greenberger *(Publr-Transportation
Grp)*
Brett Ryden *(Assoc Publr-Aircraft Maintenance Tech & Airport Bus Magazine)*
Ed Tearman *(Dir-PR)*

Direct Travel, Inc. (1)
95 N State Rte 17 Ste 105, Paramus, NJ
07652
Tel.: (201) 847-9000
Web Site: http://www.dt.com
Emp.: 900
Holding Company; Travel Services
N.A.I.C.S.: 551112
Ed Adams *(CEO)*
John Coffman *(CFO)*

Subsidiary (Domestic):

Georgia International Travel, Inc. (2)
6285 Barfield Rd Ste 150, Atlanta, GA
30328
Tel.: (404) 851-9166
Web Site: http://www.gitravel.com
Travel Agencies & Services
N.A.I.C.S.: 561510
Vela McClam Mitchell *(Pres & COO)*

Peak Travel Group, Inc. (2)
1221 Lincoln Ave, San Jose, CA 95125
Tel.: (800) 831-1366
Web Site: http://www.peaktravelgroup.com
Sales Range: $150-199.9 Million
Travel Agency
N.A.I.C.S.: 561510
R. Tyler Peak *(Founder & Pres)*
Helen Leon *(Exec VP)*
Tom Walker *(Sr VP-Sls & Mktg)*

Professional Travel Inc. (2)
25000 Country Club Blvd, Cleveland, OH
44070-5344
Tel.: (440) 734-8800
Web Site: http://www.protrav.com
Travel Agencies
N.A.I.C.S.: 561510
Robert A. Sturm *(Chm & CEO)*
Robert Turk *(Pres)*
Nigel Adams *(Chief Talent Officer)*
Patrick Tierney *(Controller)*
Michael Benz *(Dir-Leisure Travel Ops)*
Lynn Pfeiffer *(Sr VP-Ops)*

Subsidiary (Domestic):

Action Travel Center, Inc. (3)
5900 Harper Rd, Solon, OH 44139-1866
Tel.: (440) 248-4949
Web Site: http://www.actiontravelnow.com
Rev.: $4,000,000
Emp.: 20
Travel Agency Services
N.A.I.C.S.: 561510
Arlene Goldburg *(Founder & Pres)*

Crossroads Travel, Inc. (3)
15294 Pearl Rd, Strongsville, OH 44136-
5021
Tel.: (440) 238-7015
Sales Range: $25-49.9 Million
Emp.: 3
Travel Agency
N.A.I.C.S.: 561510

VIP Travel of Wooster, Inc. (3)
2200 Benden Dr Ste 1, Wooster, OH
44691-2569
Tel.: (330) 264-5554
Web Site: http://www.viptrvl.com
Sales Range: $10-24.9 Million
Emp.: 20
Travel Agency Services
N.A.I.C.S.: 561510
Linda Phillips *(VP-Ops)*

Subsidiary (Domestic):

**Travel Destinations Management
Group, Inc.** (2)
110 Painters Mill Rd, Owings Mills, MD
21117
Tel.: (410) 363-3111
Web Site: http://www.traveldest.com
Sales Range: $25-49.9 Million
Emp.: 80
Travel & Meeting Management Services
N.A.I.C.S.: 561510
Bill Sanborn *(VP-Ops)*
Ira S. Weiner *(Pres & CEO)*
Wendy Acevedo Kilroy *(Dir-Corp & Meetings Ops)*

FLS Transportation Services, Ltd (1)
180 N La Salle St Ste 29950, Chicago, IL
60601
Tel.: (877) 744-7357
Web Site: http://www.flstransport.com
Logistics Solutions Services
N.A.I.C.S.: 541614
John Leach *(CEO)*
Nichole Thompson *(Chief People Officer)*

Subsidiary (Domestic):

AMAC Logistics, LLC. (2)
4365 E Pecos Rd Ste 128, Gilbert, AZ
85295
Tel.: (480) 279-3200
Web Site: http://www.amaclogistics.com
Sales Range: $1-9.9 Million
Emp.: 18
Freight Transportation Arrangement Services
N.A.I.C.S.: 488510
Doug Hazen *(CEO)*

Scott Logistics Corp. (2)
375 Technology Pkwy, Rome, GA 30165
Tel.: (706) 234-1184
Web Site: http://www.scottlogistics.com
Emp.: 160
Intermodal, Full Service Logistics & Transportation Services
N.A.I.C.S.: 488510
Diane L. Manis *(Owner & CEO)*
Jay Matthews *(Pres)*
Chad Green *(COO)*
Missy Deems *(CFO)*
Doug Bush *(CIO)*

Subsidiary (Domestic):

Apex Freight Services, Inc. (3)
300 Mecca St, Lafayette, LA 70508
Tel.: (337) 981-9212
Web Site: http://www.apexfrt.com
Transportation & Logistics Services
N.A.I.C.S.: 488510
Tracy Pellerin *(CEO & Branch Mgr)*
Casey Foreman *(Ops Mgr)*

FastMed Urgent Care (1)

935 Shotwell Rd Ste 108, Clayton, NC
27520
Tel.: (919) 550-0821
Web Site: http://www.fastmed.com
Sales Range: $25-49.9 Million
Emp.: 470
Health Care Srvices
N.A.I.C.S.: 621999
Kyle A. Bohannon *(Pres)*
Jason A. Williams *(CEO-Eastern Reg)*
Michael P. Dunn *(Chief Medical Officer-
Western Reg)*
Melvin G. Lee *(Chief Medical Officer-North
Carolina)*
Brittany R. Loisel *(Exec VP-Strategy)*
Carrie A. Demery *(Sr VP-Ops)*
Jan G. Pickett *(Sr VP-Ops-North Carolina)*
Jessica D. Pendola *(Chief Admin & Compliance Officer)*
Sekhar Kommu *(Chief Medical Officer-Natl)*
Robert W. Hutchison *(CFO)*
Webster F. Golinkin *(CEO)*

Franklin Energy Services LLC (1)
102 N Franklin St, Port Washington, WI
53074
Tel.: (262) 284-3838
Web Site: http://www.franklinenergy.com
Energy Consulting Services
N.A.I.C.S.: 541690
Paul Schueller *(Founder)*
Dan Tarrence *(Exec VP)*
Ed Carroll *(Sr VP)*
Tina Semotan *(Chief Admin Officer)*
Kevin McDonough *(Pres)*
Ed McGlynn *(VP-Large C&I Strategy)*
Steve Malloy *(Chief Innovation Officer)*
Nicole Willette *(Corp Counsel)*
Marisa Uchin *(Chief Comml Officer)*
Eileen Cavanaugh *(CFO)*
Jim Gould *(Dir-Corp Affairs)*
Terry Sobolewski *(CEO)*

Subsidiary (Domestic):

Snugg Home LLC (2)
PO Box 82, Boulder, CO 80302-5672
Tel.: (720) 663-7836
Web Site: http://www.snugghome.com
Software Publisher
N.A.I.C.S.: 513210
Adam Stenftenagel *(Co-Founder & CEO)*

**High Street Insurance Partners,
Inc.** (1)
Harbour View Ctr 333 West Grandview
Pkwy Ste 201, Traverse City, MI 49684
Tel.: (531) 922-7220
Web Site: https://www.hsip.com
Insurance Provider
N.A.I.C.S.: 524298
James E. Hutchinson *(CMO & Pres-
Northeast Region)*
Emma Riza *(Chief Dev Officer)*
Scott M. Wick *(Founder & CEO)*
Scott Goodreau *(Pres & COO)*
Kevin R. Smith *(CIO)*

Subsidiary (Domestic):

Badge Agency, Inc. (2)
1000 Woodbury Rd Ste 207, Woodbury, NY
11797
Tel.: (516) 676-0070
Web Site: http://www.badgeagency.com
Sales Range: $1-9.9 Million
Emp.: 17
Insurance Agencies & Brokerages
N.A.I.C.S.: 524210
Arthur Ventura *(Pres)*

Berkshire Agency, Inc. (2)
1263 W Sq Lk Rd, Bloomfield Hills, MI
48302
Tel.: (248) 333-2500
Web Site:
    http://www.capitalinsuranceagent.com
Sales Range: $1-9.9 Million
Emp.: 20
Insurance Agencies & Brokerages
N.A.I.C.S.: 524210
Robert Moglia *(Partner)*
Edmund George *(Partner)*
Tom Moglia *(Partner)*
Donn Johnson *(Partner)*

Clarke & Sampson, Inc. (2)
228 S Washington St, Alexandria, VA 22314
Tel.: (703) 683-6601

ABRY Partners, LLC—(Continued)

Web Site:
http://www.clarkeandsampson.com
Rev.: $1,500,000
Emp.: 16
Insurance Agencies & Brokerages
N.A.I.C.S.: 524210
Timothy Geary (Pres)
Bill Howard (Acct Exec)
Jim Hebert (Acct Exec)
Scott Jefferson (Acct Exec)

Curley Associates, Inc. (2)
1087 Main St, Sanford, ME 04073
Tel.: (352) 669-8001
Web Site: http://www.curleyassociates.com
Sales Range: $1-9.9 Million
Emp.: 16
Insurance Agencies & Brokerages
N.A.I.C.S.: 524210
Timothy Curley (Pres)

Dudek Insurance Agency Group (2)
36120 Gree St, New Baltimore, MI 48047
Tel.: (586) 725-0030
Web Site: http://www.insurewithdave.com
Insurance Related Activities
N.A.I.C.S.: 524298
Dave Dudek (Pres)

Elliott-Hartman Agency (2)
611 Ansborough Ave, Waterloo, IA 50701-5841
Tel.: (319) 233-8459
Web Site: http://www.elliotthartman.com
Insurance Related Activities
N.A.I.C.S.: 524298
Richard Arenholz (Owner)

First Security Company, Inc. (2)
212 3rd Ave NW, Hickory, NC 28601
Tel.: (828) 322-4171
Web Site:
http://www.firstsecuritycompany.com
Insurance Agencies & Brokerages
N.A.I.C.S.: 524210
Charles F. Conner (Pres)
David Rockett (Treas & Controller)
Kay Bowman (Sec)
Karl Sherrill (CEO)
Joab Cotton III (Exec VP)

Hanasab Insurance Services, Inc. (2)
8600 Utica Ave Ste 100, Rancho Cucamonga, CA 91730-4875
Tel.: (323) 782-8454
Web Site:
http://www.hanasabinsurance.com
Insurance Agencies & Brokerages
N.A.I.C.S.: 524210
Farhad Hanasab (Pres)

Hartzell Insurance Associates, Inc. (2)
2501 Bethlehem Pike, Hatfield, PA 19440
Tel.: (215) 997-5800
Web Site: http://www.hartzellinsurance.com
Insurance Related Activities
N.A.I.C.S.: 524298
Scott Hartzell (Owner)

InPro Insurance Group, LLC (2)
2095 E Big Beaver Rd Ste 100, Troy, MI 48083
Tel.: (248) 526-3260
Web Site: http://www.inproagent.com
Insurance & Brokerage Services
N.A.I.C.S.: 524210
David W. Goodman (Pres & Principal)

Milestone Insurance Brokers, LLC (2)
8 Corporate Park Ste 130, Irvine, CA 92606
Tel.: (949) 852-0909
Web Site: http://www.milestonepromise.com
Sales Range: $1-9.9 Million
Insurance Agencies & Brokerages
N.A.I.C.S.: 524210

Ottawa-Kent Insurance Agency, Inc. (2)
7472 Main St, Jenison, MI 49429-0349
Tel.: (616) 797-3400
Web Site: http://www.ottawakent.com
Insurance Agencies & Brokerages
N.A.I.C.S.: 524210
Janice Chapin (Mgr-Personal Lines)
Delora Mills (Office Mgr)

Paragon Underwriters, Inc. (2)
7115 Orchard Lake Rd Ste 500, 48322, West Bloomfield, MI
Tel.: (248) 851-3066
Web Site:
http://www.paragonunderwriters.com
Insurance Agents, Brokers, And Service, N
N.A.I.C.S.: 524210
Kenneth M. Lipson (Pres & CEO)
Brenda Hendrickson (Sr Acct Exec-Professional Liability Div)
David M. Lipson (VP)
Gary Rosenberg (Dir-Life, Health & Disability Div)
Lori Kuehn (VP-Admin)

Stratton Agency (2)
10 Bennett Rd, Redwood City, CA 94062
Tel.: (650) 508-0124
Web Site: http://www.strattonagency.com
Insurance Agencies & Brokerages
N.A.I.C.S.: 524210

The Elite Group LLC (2)
5 Great Vly Pkwy Ste 355, Malvern, PA 19355-1251
Tel.: (610) 280-4350
Web Site: http://www.elitegrp.com
Janitorial Services
N.A.I.C.S.: 561720
William Naylor (Pres)

The Yorke Agency Inc. (2)
1231 Pennsylvania Ave, Monaca, PA 15061-1836
Tel.: (724) 774-2580
Web Site:
http://www.yorkeinsuranceagency.com
Insurance Agencies & Brokerages
N.A.I.C.S.: 524210
Bonnie Diamond (Mgr)

Tracy-Driscoll & Co., Inc. (2)
126 Main St, Bristol, CT 06010-6306
Tel.: (860) 589-3434
Web Site: http://www.tracy-driscoll.com
Insurance Services
N.A.I.C.S.: 524210
Elizabeth Sikorski (Office Mgr)
Cheryl Hayden (Asst Comptroller-Acctg)
Diana DeLeo (Comptroller-Acctg)
Lisa Rhodes (Mgr-Personal Lines)
Janice Mauriello (Mgr-Comml Lines)
Bob McFadden (Partner)
Cynthia Jackson (Asst Comptroller)
Mike Rivers (Sr VP)

Wall Street Insurance Inc. (2)
105 Edwards Vlg Blvd Ste C20, Edwards, CO 81632
Tel.: (970) 926-4900
Web Site:
http://www.wallstreetinsurance.com
Insurance Agencies & Brokerages
N.A.I.C.S.: 524210
Noel Harris (Owner)

Highwinds Network Group Inc. (1)
941 W Morse Blvd Ste 350, Winter Park, FL 32789
Tel.: (469) 929-2795
Web Site: http://www.highwinds.com
Content Delivery, Network & IP Services
N.A.I.C.S.: 513210
Chance Brannen (Pres-Hosted IP Solutions)
Gabe Miller (CFO)

LanguageLine Solutions, Inc. (1)
1 Lower Ragsdale Dr Bldg 2, Monterey, CA 93940
Tel.: (800) 752-6096
Web Site: http://www.languageline.com
Translation & Interpretation Services
N.A.I.C.S.: 541930
Dennis G. Dracup (Chm)
Scott W. Klein (Pres & CEO)
Dave Bethea (VP-Mktg & Sls Ops)
Vanessa Eke (Mng Dir & VP)
Frank A. Perry (VP-HR)
Michael Schmidt (CFO & Sr VP)
Simon Yoxon-Grant (VP-Sls)
Jeff Cordell (CIO & VP-Tech)
Scott Merritt (VP-Ops)

Long Term Care Group, Inc. (1)
11000 Prairie Lakes Dr Ste 600, Eden Prairie, MN 55344
Tel.: (925) 516-6777
Web Site: http://www.ltcg.com
Insurance Industry Business Process Outsourcing Services

N.A.I.C.S.: 524292

Subsidiary (Domestic):

LifePlans LLC (2)
51 Sawyer Rd Ste 340, Waltham, MA 02453
Tel.: (781) 893-7600
Web Site: http://www.lifeplansinc.com
Emp.: 170
General Insurance Services
N.A.I.C.S.: 524210
Denise Liston (VP-Long-Term Care Svcs)

Millennium Trust Company, LLC (1)
2001 Spring Rd Ste 700, Oak Brook, IL 60523
Tel.: (630) 368-5600
Web Site: http://www.mtrustcompany.com
Rev.: $23,900,000,000
Emp.: 1,200
Financial Custodian & Trust Services
N.A.I.C.S.: 523940
Gary Anetsberger (Chm)
Dan Laszlo (CEO)
Bob Kunimura (CTO)
Tom Daley (Mng Dir-Custody Svcs)
Terry Dunne (Mng Dir)
Mary Hackbarth (Sr VP & Mktg Dir)
Mary Johnson (Sr VP & Dir-Strategic Initiatives)
John Perugini (Gen Counsel)
John Samaan (Sr VP & Head-HR)
Meg O'Connor Zwick (Sr VP & Dir-Client Svcs)
John Ryan (VP & Sr Mgr-Comm)
Maribel Gerstner (Sr VP & Dir-Ops)
Jason Lomax (Chief Compliance Officer)
Erik Beck (Chief Growth Officer)
Pete Welsh (Head-Retirement Svcs)
Sirisha Gorjala (Chief Product Officer)
Michelle Spellerberg (CMO)

Subsidiary (Domestic):

Accruit Holdings LLC (2)
1514 Curtis St, Denver, CO 80202
Tel.: (720) 963-5000
Web Site: http://www.accruit.com
Rev.: $2,600,000
Emp.: 32
Industrial Building Construction
N.A.I.C.S.: 236210

Benefit Resource, Inc. (2)
245 Kenneth Dr, Rochester, NY 14623-4277
Tel.: (585) 424-5200
Web Site: http://www.benefitresource.com
Sales Range: $10-24.9 Million
Emp.: 100
Third-Party Administrator of Pre-Tax Medical & Transportation Benefits for US Clients
N.A.I.C.S.: 524292
Anthony J. DiBarnaba (Co-Founder & Pres)
Thomas A. Guiler (Co-Founder & VP)
Mary Fleming (Mgr-Product Dev)
Ben Meyers (Mgr-IT)
Becky Seefeldt (Dir-Mktg)
Mike Griffith (Dir-Sls)
Rachel Kielon (CFO)
Andrew J. Musolino (Partner)
Jason Hall (COO)

Subsidiary (Domestic):

Pacific Benefits Consultants, Inc. (3)
3090 Fite Cir Ste 101, Sacramento, CA 95827
Tel.: (916) 363-2101
Web Site: http://www.pacificbenefits.com
Emp.: 10
Administration Services for Insurance & Health Accounts
N.A.I.C.S.: 524292
Joe Gaither (Pres & CEO)
Sharol Gaither (CFO & VP)
Mimi Lyon (VP-Ops)

Subsidiary (Domestic):

InspiraFS, Inc. (2)
8 Penn Center W Ste 101, Pittsburgh, PA 15276
Web Site: http://www.inspirafs.com
Sales Range: $10-24.9 Million
Emp.: 53
IRA Record-Keeping Platform Developer & Data Services
N.A.I.C.S.: 518210

Joe Golubski (Sr Mgr-Relationship)
Mark Fleckenstein (Product Mgr)
Ron Eggert (Pres)
Terri Sams (Ops Mgr)
Collin Ballantine (Mgr-Platform)

Payflex Holdings, Inc. (2)
10802 Farnam Dr. Ste 100, Omaha, NE 68154
Tel.: (402) 345-0666
Holding Company
N.A.I.C.S.: 551111

Subsidiary (Domestic):

PayFlex Systems USA, Inc. (3)
10802 Farnam Dr Ste 100, Omaha, NE 68154
Tel.: (402) 345-0666
Web Site: https://www.payflex.com
Sales Range: $50-74.9 Million
Emp.: 423
Third Party Health Plan Administration Services
N.A.I.C.S.: 524292
Jenn Plasse-Puzey (Head-Strategy & Product Dev)
Jeff Protextor (Head-Oversight & Control)
Michael Wolfe (Head-Member Svcs & Claim Ops)
Carolyn Arabolos (Head-Core Ops)
Jack Gehrke (Head-Client Svcs)
Stephanie Christino (Dir-Bus Initiatives)
Michael Herman (CTO)
Susan Bambara (CMO)
Carla Pollard (Chief People Officer)
Paul Sari (Chief Comml Officer)
Morgan Hunt (CFO)

NexusTek, Inc. (1)
5889 S Greenwood Plz Blvd Ste 201, Greenwood Village, CO 80111
Tel.: (877) 470-0401
Web Site: http://www.nexustek.com
Managed IT & Consulting Services
N.A.I.C.S.: 541690
J Michael Jenner (CEO)

Oliver Street Dermatology Holdings LLC (1)
5310 Harvest Hill Rd Ste 290, Dallas, TX 75230
Tel.: (214) 420-0650
Web Site:
http://www.usdermatologypartners.com
Sales Range: $1-9.9 Million
Dermatological Health Services Organization
N.A.I.C.S.: 813920
Billy Parsons (VP-HR)
Glenn Goldstein (Chief Medical Officer)
Paul Singh (CEO)
Mark Fleishman (Pres-Midwest)
Howard Luber (Pres-Southwest)
Alexandra Theriault (Pres-Mountain West)
Jennifer Holman (Pres-East & South Texas & Oklahoma)
Aubrey Chad Hartmann (Pres-Central Texas)
Jay Wofford (Pres-Northeast Texas)
Kathryn Durham (Pres-Northwest Texas)

Subsidiary (Domestic):

Dermatology & Laser Center of Fort Worth (2)
4201 Camp Bowie Blvd Ste A, Fort Worth, TX 76107-3928
Tel.: (817) 377-1243
Web Site: http://www.skinlasercare.com
Dermatological Health Service Center Operator
N.A.I.C.S.: 621111
Virginia Foley (Mgr)

Dermatology Associates of Central Texas (2)
1300 E 6th Ave, Belton, TX 76513-2810
Tel.: (254) 778-5400
Web Site:
http://www.usdermatologypartners.com
Dermatology Services
N.A.I.C.S.: 621111
Leo A. Conger Jr. (Principal)

Options Information Technology LLC (1)
28 Liberty St Ste 930, New York, NY 10005
Tel.: (646) 205-2500

Web Site: http://www.options-it.com
Custom Computer Programming Services
N.A.I.C.S.: 541511
Danny Moore (Pres & CEO)

Subsidiary (Domestic):

ACTIV Financial Systems, Inc (2)
120 E Liberty St Ste 200, Wheaton, IL
60187
Tel.: (630) 682-5700
Web Site: http://www.activfinancial.com
Sales Range: $10-24.9 Million
Emp.: 100
Stock Market Data Services
N.A.I.C.S.: 519290
Steve McNeany (CEO)
Ben Collins (Dir-Sls-EMEA)

Psychological Services, Inc. (1)
2950 N Hollywood Way Ste 200, Burbank,
CA 91505
Tel.: (818) 847-6180
Sales Range: $1-9.9 Million
Information Technology Consulting Services
N.A.I.C.S.: 541512

SAMBA Holdings, Inc. (1)
5619 DTC Pkwy 1000, Greenwood Village,
CO 80111
Web Site: http://www.sambasafety.com
Sales Range: $25-49.9 Million
Driver Record Monitoring Services
N.A.I.C.S.: 551112
Richard Lacey (Exec VP-Product Mgmt)
Chris Stites (Exec VP-Sls & Mktg)
Allison Guidette (CEO)
Patrick Kemble (CTO)
John Diana (Chief Compliance Officer &
Gen Counsel)
Steve Bryan (Exec VP-Transportation)
Bill Bakken (Sr VP-Ops)

Subsidiary (Domestic):

American Driving Records, Inc. (2)
2860 Gold Tailings Ct, Rancho Cordova, CA
95670 (100%)
Tel.: (916) 456-3200
Motor Vehicle Record Information & Ser-
vices
N.A.I.C.S.: 519290
Richard Crawford (CEO)
Chris McKay (Sec)

Vigillo LLC (2)
630 NW 10th Ave, Portland, OR 97209
Tel.: (503) 688-5100
Web Site: http://www.vigillo.com
Software Development Services
N.A.I.C.S.: 513210
Steve Bryan (Founder & Pres)
Peter Rowe (CTO)

Screenvision Cinema Network
LLC (1)
1411 Broadway 33rd Fl, New York, NY
10018
Tel.: (212) 497-0400
Web Site: http://screenvisionmedia.com
Cinema Advertising Services
N.A.I.C.S.: 541890
Darryl Schaffer (Exec VP-Ops & Exhibitor
Rels)
Kevin J. Neary (CFO)
John McCauley (CMO & Exec VP-Strategic
Alliances)
Matt Arden (VP & Dir-Creative)
Cheryl Magiros (Exec VP-Direct Sls)
Matt Friedland (Sr VP-Campaign Mgmt &
Ops)
Michael Henry (Sr VP-IT)
Kim Youngberg (Sr VP & Gen Counsel)
Kristen Edge (Sr VP-Sls Plng)
Bernadette McCabe (Sr VP-Bus Strategy)
Andrew Gyves (VP-Sls)
Michael Golden (VP-Strategic Sls Alliances)
John Partilla (CEO)
Gina Bucciero (VP-Sls-Northeast)
Laura Griffith (Acct Exec-Sls-Natl)
Shelly Howard (Dir-Sls-North Central Reg)
Scott Johnson (VP-Sls-West)
Janice Myers (VP-Reg Sls)
Scott Patrick (Dir-Sls-Southwest Reg)
Jaishree Ramakrishnan (VP-Sls-Midwest)
Pete Snyder (VP-Sls-Southeast)

The Hilb Group, LLC (1)
6802 Paragon Pl Ste 200, 23230, Richmond, VA

Tel.: (804) 414-6501
Web Site: http://www.hilbgroup.com
Insurance Brokerage & Benefits Manage-
ment Services
N.A.I.C.S.: 524210
Bob Hilb (Founder)
Jason S. Angus (COO)
Robert Blanton (CFO)
Anne Nicoll (VP-Legal & Compliance)
Richard G. Spiro (CEO)
Darren Cohen (Sr VP-Carrier Rels & Insur-
ance Strategy)
Bert Hardy (CIO)

Subsidiary (Domestic):

Clark-Mortenson Agency, Inc. (2)
102 Main St, Keene, NH 03431
Tel.: (603) 352-2121
Web Site: http://www.clarkmortenson.com
Sales Range: $1-9.9 Million
Emp.: 48
Insurance Brokerage & Financial Services
N.A.I.C.S.: 524210
Thomas J. Minkler (Pres)

Dowling & O'Neil Insurance Agency,
Inc. (2)
973 Iyannough Rd 2nd Fl, Hyannis, MA
02601
Tel.: (508) 775-1620
Web Site: http://www.doins.com
Insurance Related Activities
N.A.I.C.S.: 524298
Mark S. McCartin (Principal-Agency-CIC)
Robert W. Miller (Principal-Agency-CIC-AAI)

Endeavor Insurance Services,
Inc. (2)
218 Trade St Ste G, Greer, SC 29651-3446
Tel.: (864) 877-6644
Web Site: http://www.endeavorsc.com
Insurance Agencies & Brokerages
N.A.I.C.S.: 524210
John M. Adair (Pres)
Rod W. Fountain (CFO)

Engle, Paxson & Hawthorne Insur-
ance Services, LLC (2)
114 Edwards Ferry Rd NE, Leesburg, VA
20176-2301
Tel.: (703) 737-6565
Web Site: http://www.ephinsurance.com
Insurance Agents
N.A.I.C.S.: 524210
Prescott Engle (Pres)

Gencorp Insurance Group Inc. (2)
16 Main St, East Greenwich, RI 02818
Tel.: (401) 884-7800
Web Site: http://www.gencorp-ins.com
Emp.: 56
Insurance Brokerage
N.A.I.C.S.: 524210
Robert Padula (CEO)
Chad Bjorklund (VP)
Christopher Iannotti (Asst VP)
Joseph Padula (Exec VP)
Richard Padula (Pres-Retail Div)
Robert Bikash (Dir-Fin & Admin)
Elisa Cardone (Dir-Client Svcs)
Anne R. Nicoll (Gen Counsel & Dir-Ops)

Gentry Insurance Agency, Inc. (2)
175 E Main St Ste 200, Apopka, FL 32703-
3213
Tel.: (407) 886-3301
Web Site: http://www.gentryins.com
Emp.: 12
Insurance Agencies & Brokerages
N.A.I.C.S.: 524210
Fawn P. Clark (Treas & Sec)

German American Insurance,
Inc. (2)
711 Main St, Jasper, IN 47546
Tel.: (812) 482-2866
Emp.: 15
Commercial Banking Services
N.A.I.C.S.: 522110

Hockman Insurance Agency, Inc. (2)
3438 Colwell Ave, Tampa, FL 33614
Tel.: (813) 636-4000
Web Site:
   http://www.hockmaninsurance.com
Sales Range: $10-24.9 Million
Emp.: 11
Insurance Services
N.A.I.C.S.: 524210

Janice Johnson (Mgr-Ops)

Lake Norman Benefits, Inc. (2)
109 Professional Park Dr Ste 103, Moores-
ville, NC 28117
Tel.: (704) 663-4236
Web Site:
   http://www.lakenormanbenefits.com
Insurance Benefits Management Services
N.A.I.C.S.: 524292
David Contorno (Pres)

NPB Insurance Services, Inc. (2)
75 Commonwealth Ave, Bristol, VA 24201-
3824
Tel.: (276) 666-1044
Web Site: http://www.npbins.com
Fire Insurance Services
N.A.I.C.S.: 524113
Sharon Duckett (Mgr-Site)

Newman Crane & Associates Insur-
ance, Inc. (2)
5639 Hansel Ave, Orlando, FL 32809-4215
Tel.: (407) 859-3691
Web Site: http://www.newmancraneins.com
Emp.: 20
Insurance Agencies & Brokerages
N.A.I.C.S.: 524210
Steven Buckner (Pres)

P.A. Post Agency, LLC (2)
401 Hackensack Ave Fl 7, Hackensack, NJ
07601
Tel.: (201) 342-2180
Web Site: http://www.papost.com
Sales Range: $1-9.9 Million
Emp.: 43
Insurance Agents
N.A.I.C.S.: 524210
Bradley Post (Pres)

Summit Insurance Services, LLC (2)
310 N Main St, Moorefield, WV 26836
Tel.: (800) 832-6896
Web Site:
   http://www.summitinsuranceservices.com
Insurance Brokerage Services
N.A.I.C.S.: 524210
Kirstin Gervia (Acct Mgr)
Elizabeth LaTorre (Acct Mgr)
Wantae Seong (Acct Mgr)
Tracy Teague (Acct Mgr)

The Hilb Group of Indiana, LLC (2)
501 Lincoln Ave, Bedford, IN 47421
Tel.: (317) 215-4179
Web Site: http://www.hilbgroup.com
Insurance Services
N.A.I.C.S.: 524126

The Hilb Group of Virginia, LLC (2)
263 W Main St, Abingdon, VA 24210
Tel.: (276) 628-4121
Web Site: http://www.cseagency.com
Sales Range: $1-9.9 Million
Insurance Brokerage & Financial Services
N.A.I.C.S.: 524210
John Henderson (Pres)
Pam Coleburn (Mgr-Comml Dept)

The Keane Insurance Group,
Inc. (2)
10777 Sunset Office Dr, Saint Louis, MO
63127
Tel.: (314) 966-7733
Sales Range: $1-9.9 Million
Emp.: 11
Insurance Agent/Broker
N.A.I.C.S.: 524210
C. Keane (Pres)
Tammy Bristoe (Mgr-Fin & HR)
Nonie Whitesell (Acct Mgr)

The Martin Agency Inc. (2)
430 W Walnut St, Danville, KY 40422
Tel.: (859) 236-6782
Web Site: http://www.themartinagency.net
Insurance Agents
N.A.I.C.S.: 524210
Angela Martin (Pres)

The Pennoyer Group, Inc. (2)
2135 Defense Hwy, Crofton, MD 21114-
2430
Tel.: (301) 261-6940
Web Site: http://www.pennoyer.com
Emp.: 500
Insurance Agents
N.A.I.C.S.: 524210

Robert Hilb (Pres)

Xexec Limited (1)
Mountcliff House 154 Brent Street, London,
NW4 2DR, United Kingdom
Tel.: (44) 2082016483
Web Site: http://www.xexec.com
Sales Range: $25-49.9 Million
Emp.: 45
Platform & Interface Development Services
N.A.I.C.S.: 541511
Dipika Parmar (Coord-Accts)

Subsidiary (US):

Xexec Inc. (2)
195 Plymouth St 3rd Fl, Brooklyn, NY
11201
Tel.: (844) 576-2457
Software Development Services
N.A.I.C.S.: 541511

ABS CAPITAL PARTNERS, L.P.
400 E Pratt St Ste 910, Baltimore,
MD 21202-3116
Tel.: (410) 246-5600   DE
Web Site: http://www.abscapital.com
Year Founded: 1990
Private Equity Investments
N.A.I.C.S.: 523999
Bobby Goswami (Gen Partner)
Don Hebb (Co-Founder, Chm & Part-
ner)
Phillip A. Clough (Chm & Gen Part-
ner)
Timothy T. Weglicki (Co-Founder &
Partner)
Stephanie Carter (Gen Partner)
James Stevenson (CFO)
Paul Mariani (Gen Partner)
Robyn Lehman (Principal)
Andrew Boyd (Principal)
Kimberly Kile (Principal)
Michael Avon (Venture Partner)
John Stobo (Mng Gen Partner)

Subsidiaries:

Alarm.com Holdings, Inc. (1)
8281 Greensboro Dr Ste 100, Tysons, VA
22102
Web Site: https://www.alarm.com
Rev.: $842,559,000
Assets: $1,329,375,000
Liabilities: $730,516,000
Net Worth: $598,859,000
Earnings: $56,338,000
Emp.: 1,733
Fiscal Year-end: 12/31/2022
Holding Company: Alarm Systems Software
N.A.I.C.S.: 551112
Daniel Ramos (Chief Legal Officer, Chief
Compliance Officer & Sr VP-Corp Ops)
Stephen Trundle (CEO)
Jeffrey Bedell (Pres-Ventures Bus & Corp
Strategy)
Daniel Kerzner (Pres-Platforms Bus)
Reed Grothe (Sr VP-Bus Dev)
Donald Natale (Sr VP-Sls)
Alison Slavin (Sr VP-Creation Lab)
Steve Valenzuela (CFO)
Michelle Cipolla-Feinstein (VP-Human Re-
sources)

Subsidiary (Domestic):

Alarm.com Inc. (2)
8281 Greensboro Dr Ste 100, Tysons, VA
22102
Tel.: (703) 286-2620
Web Site: http://www.alarm.com
Sales Range: $1-9.9 Million
Wireless Home Security System Alert Ser-
vices
N.A.I.C.S.: 561621
Daniel Ramos (Chief Legal Officer, Chief
Compliance Officer & Sr VP-Corp Ops)
Timothy McAdam (Chm)
Stephen Trundle (Pres, Pres & CEO)
Jeffrey Bedell (Pres-Ventures Bus & Corp
Strategy)
Daniel Kerzner (Pres-Platforms Bus)
Steve Valenzuela (CFO)
Jeffrey Bedell (Chief Strategy & Innovation
Officer)
Jean-Paul Martin (Co-Founder & CTO)

ABS Capital Partners, L.P.—(Continued)

Daniel Ramos (Sr VP-Corp Dev)
Reed Grothe (Sr VP-Bus Dev)
Donald Natale (Sr VP-Sls)
Alison Slavin (Co-Founder & Sr VP-Creation Lab)

ObjectVideo Labs, LLC (2)
8281 Greensboro Dr Ste 100, Tysons, VA 22102
Tel.: (571) 327-3673
Web Site: http://www.objectvideolabs.com
Computer Software Development Services
N.A.I.C.S.: 541511
Raul J. Fernandez (Chm)

ClearObject, Inc. (1)
8626 E 116th St, Fishers, IN 46038
Tel.: (888) 850-2568
Web Site: http://www.oncloudone.com
Software Development Services
N.A.I.C.S.: 541511
John McDonald (CEO)
John Annakin (Chief Revenue Officer)
Tom Kilcoyne (COO)
Mike Reffeitt (Pres)

ConnectYourCare LLC (1)
307 International Cir, Hunt Valley, MD 21030
Tel.: (410) 891-1000
Web Site: http://www.connectyourcare.com
Health Savings Account Management
N.A.I.C.S.: 522320
Allan Pease (Chief Bus Dev Officer)
Reese Feuerman (CFO)
Julie M. Linn (Chief Compliance Officer)
Tim Sand (COO)
Jennifer Hervy (VP-HR)
Steve Grieco (CEO)
Heather Barnes (Sr VP-Sls)
Barbara Boudreau (VP-Strategic Initiatives)
Raj Bhavsar (CTO)
Nicole Williams (VP-Sls)
E. Harrison Stone Jr. (Gen Counsel)

Fluxx Labs, Inc. (1)
2261 Market St #4060, San Francisco, CA 94114
Tel.: (855) 358-9946
Web Site: http://www.fluxx.io
Management Software Development Services
N.A.I.C.S.: 541511
Jason Ricci (Founder & CEO)
Kerrin Mitchell (Chief Dev Officer)
Eric Hansen (CTO)
Irene White (CMO)
Jen Lau (Mgr-Bus)
Kristy Gannon (CFO)
Sam Remeika (Sr Dir-Client Svcs)
Erin Colling (Engr-Sls)
David Goodman (Dir-Impact)
Chloe Rowshani (Mgr-Product Mktg)
Aaron Lester (Mgr-Content Mktg)
Fintan Kelly (Mgr-Client Svcs)
Kris Tan (Mgr-Client Svcs)
Janele Aldana (Mgr-Technical Project)
Maggie Son (Project Mgr)
Tom Snider (Mgr-Technical Project)
Jess McNinch (Mgr-Learning & Dev)
Karen West (Project Mgr)
Allison Bengston (Project Mgr)
Kazumi Taniguchi (Sr Project Mgr)
Travis McDermott (Mgr-Client Success)
Sonia Sarao (Dir-Product Mgmt)
Ben Lambillotte (Mgr-Product)
Justin Sung (Mgr-Product)

ABSCO LTD. CORP.
119 Littleton Rd, Parsippany, NJ 07054
Tel.: (973) 402-1200
Web Site: http://www.fiagroup.com
Rev.: $64,800,000
Emp.: 130
Surety Insurance
N.A.I.C.S.: 524126
Patrick J. Lynch (Pres)

ABSHER CONSTRUCTION COMPANY
1001 Shaw Rd, Puyallup, WA 98372-7437
Tel.: (253) 845-9544
Web Site: https://www.absherco.com

Sales Range: $150-199.9 Million
Emp.: 250
Nonresidential Construction Services
N.A.I.C.S.: 236220
Daniel Absher (Pres)
Jeff Richards (COO)

ABSOCOLD CORPORATION
1122 NW T St, Richmond, IN 47374
Tel.: (765) 935-7501
Web Site: http://www.absocold.com
Year Founded: 1969
Rev.: $28,000,000
Emp.: 7
Refrigerators & Freezers
N.A.I.C.S.: 423620
Sue Jackson (Controller)
Tim McCullum (VP)

ABSOLUTDATA RESEARCH & ANALYTICS (P) LTD.
1320 Harbor Bay Pkwy Ste 175, Alameda, CA 94502
Tel.: (510) 748-9922   CA
Web Site: http://www.absolutdata.com
Year Founded: 2000
Sales Range: $1-9.9 Million
Emp.: 170
Marketing Data & Analysis
N.A.I.C.S.: 541613
Anil Kaul (Founder & CEO)
Sudeshna Datta (Founder & Exec VP)
Suhale Kapoor (Founder & Exec VP)
Sudeep Haldar (Sr VP-Growth Analytics & AI Solutions)

ABSOLUTE CAPITAL MANAGEMENT LLC
101 Pennsylvania Blvd, Pittsburgh, PA 15228
Tel.: (412) 388-1600
Web Site: https://www.abscap.com
Year Founded: 2002
Sales Range: $1-9.9 Million
Emp.: 10
Investment Advisor & Money Management Programs
N.A.I.C.S.: 523940
Brenden Gebben (Mng Dir)
Matthew Hardin (Chief Compliance Officer)
Vikash Banka (Dir-Back Office Ops)
Venera Petrova (Dir-Info Sys)
Tom Kapfer (Mgr-Data Ops)
Bob Mallon (COO)

ABSOLUTE CONCRETE, INC.
505 1st Ave N, Slater, IA 50244-9503
Tel.: (515) 228-3030
Web Site: http://www.absoluteconcrete.com
Year Founded: 1999
Sales Range: $10-24.9 Million
Emp.: 86
Agricultural, Commercial & Residential Concrete Construction
N.A.I.C.S.: 238110
Sonny Hall (Pres)
Kraig Kriegel (VP)
Amber Funk (Office Mgr)

ABSOLUTE DENTAL GROUP, LLC
2250 S Rancho Dr STE 205, Las Vegas, NV 89102
Tel.: (702) 291-2031
Web Site: http://www.absoluedental.com
Dental Services
N.A.I.C.S.: 621210
David Drzewiecki (CEO)

Subsidiaries:

Aces Dental   (1)

3674 E Sunset Rd Ste 120, Las Vegas, NV 89120
Tel.: (702) 998-2237
Web Site: http://www.acesdental.com
Sales Range: $1-9.9 Million
Dental & Orthodontic Service Provider
N.A.I.C.S.: 621210
Vilas Sastry (CEO)

ABSOLUTE IT SOLUTIONS, LLC
4017 W Dr Martin Luther King Jr Blvd, Tampa, FL 33614
Tel.: (813) 908-6862
Web Site: http://www.absoluteitsolutions.com
Year Founded: 2000
Mobile Applications
N.A.I.C.S.: 513210
Alfred Goldberg (Pres)
Mine Salkin (Mgr-Digital Mktg)
Amy Fabian (Acct Mgr)

Subsidiaries:

Absolute IT Solutions, SRL   (1)
IT Park 23 Port Str Suite 302-305, 800025, Galati, Romania
Tel.: (40) 236 407 068
Mobile Applications
N.A.I.C.S.: 513210

ABSOLUTE MACHINE TOOL INC.
7420 Industrial Pkwy D, Lorain, OH 44053
Tel.: (440) 960-6911
Web Site: https://www.absolutemachine.com
Sales Range: $25-49.9 Million
Emp.: 50
Machine Tools & Accessories
N.A.I.C.S.: 423830
Steve Ortner (Owner & Pres)

ABSOLUTE MEDIA INC.
1150 Summer St, Stamford, CT 06905
Tel.: (203) 327-9090
Web Site: http://www.absolutemediainc.com
Year Founded: 1994
Sales Range: $10-24.9 Million
Emp.: 16
Business-To-Business, Consumer Marketing & Media Buying Services
N.A.I.C.S.: 541810
Gene Willhoft (Pres & Founder)
Mary Ozkan (Assoc Dir-Media)

ABSOLUTE WINDOW & SHUTTER, INC.
171 Center Rd, Venice, FL 34285
Tel.: (941) 485-7774   FL
Web Site: http://www.absolutewindows.net
Year Founded: 1999
Sales Range: $1-9.9 Million
Emp.: 30
Window & Door Mfr
N.A.I.C.S.: 332321
Dale DesJardins (Pres)
Sean Gerathy (VP)

ABSOLUTELY OUTDOORS
6046 Fm 2920 Rd Ste 306, Spring, TX 77379
Tel.: (281) 686-5296
Web Site: http://www.absolutelyoutdoors.net
Year Founded: 1996
Rev.: $4,600,000
Emp.: 60
Landscaping Services
N.A.I.C.S.: 561730
Josh Milne (Owner)

ABSOPURE WATER COMPANY INC.
8835 General Dr, Plymouth, MI 48170-4623
Tel.: (734) 459-8000   MI
Web Site: http://www.absopure.com
Year Founded: 1908
Sales Range: $25-49.9 Million
Emp.: 200
Mfr & Purification of Water
N.A.I.C.S.: 312112
William C. Young (Owner)

ABSORBENT, INK.
2401 Oxford Rd, Lawrence, KS 66049-2870
Tel.: (785) 842-9164   KS
Web Site: http://www.absorbentprinting.com
Year Founded: 1991
Sales Range: $1-9.9 Million
Emp.: 35
Custom Corporate & Consumer Promotional Materials Printing
N.A.I.C.S.: 323111
Lee Elridge (Founder & CEO)

ABSTRACT DISPLAYS, INC.
6465 Creek Rd, Cincinnati, OH 45242
Tel.: (513) 985-9700
Web Site: https://www.abstractdisplays.com
Year Founded: 2000
Rev.: $3,900,000
Emp.: 22
Commercial Equipment Merchant Whslr
N.A.I.C.S.: 423440
Carla Eng (Pres)
Michael Eng (VP)
Brett Eng (Mgr-Production)

ABT ASSOCIATES INC.
55 Wheeler St, Cambridge, MA 02138-1168
Tel.: (617) 492-7100   MA
Web Site: http://www.abtassociates.com
Year Founded: 1965
Sales Range: $200-249.9 Million
Emp.: 1,000
Business Consulting & Research Services
N.A.I.C.S.: 541618
Kathleen L. Flanagan (Pres & CEO)
Mark Spranca (VP-Reputational Capital & Technical Leadership)
Terry Moore (VP-Health Policy)
Margarita P. Fernandez (VP-Intl Health)
Anne C. Hudzik (VP-Health-US)
Brian Roemer (Chief Compliance Officer, Gen Counsel & VP)
Christopher Spera (VP-Health & Environment)
Marvin Chambers (VP)
Mauricio Poodta (VP-IT Dept)
Thierry Van Bastelaer (VP-Intl Health)
Melinda S. Williams (VP-Strategic Comm)
Selena Ramkeesoon (VP-Health-US)
Mario Bazan (VP)
Paul Jay Anninos (VP)
Noel N. Samuel (CFO)
Jorge Elguera (CIO)
Dan Gunther (VP-Enterprise Platforms)
Lisa Ashcraft (VP)
Stephen Bell (VP)
Rodolfo Camacho (VP)
Carlos Cuellar (VP)
Bradford Lucas (VP)
Mary F. Maguire (Chief Comm Officer)
Tiernan Mennen (VP)

Susan Mitchell *(VP)*
Kevin O'Reilly *(VP)*
Patricia Shifflett *(VP)*
Cindy Taylor *(VP)*
Garett Presson *(VP-Enterprise Platforms)*
Gisela Abbam *(Dir-Strategic Partnerships)*
Jay Knott *(Chief Bus Officer & Exec VP)*
Paul Faeth *(Dir-Technical-Climate & Energy-Global)*

Subsidiaries:

Abt Associates Inc.   **(1)**
6130 Executive Blvd, Rockville, MD
20852   **(100%)**
Tel.: (301) 347-5000
Web Site: http://www.abtassociates.com
Sales Range: $25-49.9 Million
Emp.: 350
Provider of Business Consulting & Research Services
N.A.I.C.S.: 541910
Stephen Pelliccia *(VP-Economic Growth Div-Intl)*
Marvin Chambers *(VP-HR)*
Noel Samuel *(CFO)*
Kathleen Flanagan *(Pres & CEO)*
Gary L. Perlin *(Chm)*
Carol Adoum *(VP-Intl Economic Growth)*
Mary Joel Holin *(VP-Social & Economic Policy)*
Joshua Lipton *(VP-Environment & Natural Resources)*
Brian Roemer *(Chief Ethics & Compliance Officer, Gen Counsel & VP)*
Melinda S. Williams *(VP-Brand & Mktg-Global)*
Scott Hefter *(Chief Mktg & Bus Dev Officer)*
Diana Silimperi *(Sr VP-Health-Global)*
Jessen Carroll *(VP-HR)*
John St. Clair *(VP-Project Delivery & Ops)*
Lisa Simeon *(COO)*
Danielle Rentz Hunt *(VP-Client Acct Mgmt)*
Christen Smith *(Sr VP-Domestic)*
Andrew Keck *(Reg VP-West Africa, Middle East & North Africa)*
Lauren Pittenger *(VP-Human Svcs Portfolio)*

Abt Global Inc.   **(1)**
6130 Executive Blvd, Rockville, MD 20852
Tel.: (301) 347-5000
Consulting & Research Services
N.A.I.C.S.: 541690

Division (Domestic):

Technology Solutions Provider
Inc.   **(2)**
1801 Robert Fulton Dr Ste 320, Reston, VA
20191
Tel.: (571) 252-5151
Web Site: http://www.tspi.net
Sales Range: $10-24.9 Million
Emp.: 17
It Consulting
N.A.I.C.S.: 541690
Vishal Suri *(Pres & CEO)*

Abt JTA Pty Ltd.   **(1)**
Level 2 5 Gardner Close, PO Box 1874,
Milton, Brisbane, 4064, QLD, Australia
Tel.: (61) 7 3114 4600
Web Site: http://www.abtjta.com.au
Emp.: 300
Health Consulting Services
N.A.I.C.S.: 541690
Jane Thomason *(CEO)*
Dan Drewe *(COO)*
Luke Elich *(Gen Counsel & Sec)*
Clare Woolsey *(Mktg & Comm)*
Scott Mills *(Controller-Fin)*

Abt SRBI, Inc.   **(1)**
180 Maiden Ln Ste 802, New York, NY
10038
Tel.: (212) 779-7700
Web Site: http://www.srbi.com
Market Analysis, Research & Consulting
Services
N.A.I.C.S.: 541910
Mark A. Schulman *(Founder & Chief Res Officer)*
Michael Link *(Pres & CEO)*
Elizabeth Teehan *(COO)*
Alisha Creel *(VP-Health Policy)*

Kelly Daley *(VP-Family Workforce & Nutrition Grp)*
Charles DiSogra *(Sr VP-Advanced Methods Grp)*
Ken Gaalswyk *(VP-Intl Res)*
Heather Hammer *(VP-Health Behaviors & Policy Grp)*
Ricki Jarmon *(VP-Family, Workforce & Nutrition Grp)*
Mark Morgan *(Sr VP-Community Health)*
Benjamin Phillips *(VP-Social Policy & Polling Grp)*
Mindy Rhindress *(Sr VP & VP-Transportation, Recreation, Plng & Preservation Grp)*
Paul Schroeder *(VP-Transportation Safety Grp)*
Chintan Turakhia *(Sr VP & VP-Social Policy & Polling Grp)*

Stratus Consulting, Inc.   **(1)**
1881 9th St Ste 201, Boulder, CO 80302
Tel.: (303) 381-8000
Web Site: http://www.stratusconsulting.com
Sales Range: $1-9.9 Million
Emp.: 60
Environmental & Energy Research Consultants
N.A.I.C.S.: 541690
Joshua Lipton *(CEO)*
Chuck Herrick *(Exec VP)*
Jamie Holmes *(VP)*
Joel Smith *(Principal)*
Connie Travers *(VP)*
David Chapman *(VP)*
Nimmi Damodaran *(VP)*
Bob Raucher *(VP)*

ABT ELECTRONICS, INC.
1200 N Milwaukee Ave, Glenview, IL
60025
Tel.: (847) 967-8830
Web Site: https://www.abt.com
Year Founded: 1936
Sales Range: $400-449.9 Million
Emp.: 1,300
Electronics Retailer
N.A.I.C.S.: 449210
Ken Au *(Dir-e-Commerce)*

ABTECH HOLDINGS, INC.
4110 N Scottsdale Rd Ste 235,
Scottsdale, AZ 85251
Tel.: (480) 874-4000   NV
Web Site:
http://www.abtechindustries.com
Year Founded: 2007
Water Clean-Up Technology Products
& Services
N.A.I.C.S.: 924110
Glenn R. Rink *(Pres & CEO)*
Lane J. Castleton *(CFO, Chief Acctg Officer, VP & Treas)*
Robert Backman *(COO)*
Shawn M. Lolling *(Dir-Engrg)*

Subsidiaries:

AbTech Industries, Inc.   **(1)**
4110 N Scottsdale Rd Ste 235, Scottsdale,
AZ 85251
Tel.: (480) 874-4000
Web Site: http://www.abtechindustries.com
Water Treatment Product Mfr
N.A.I.C.S.: 325998
Glenn R. Rink *(Pres & CEO)*

ABTECH TECHNOLOGIES, INC.
2042 Corte De Nogal, Carlsbad, CA
92011
Tel.: (760) 827-5100   CA
Web Site:
http://www.abtechtechnologies.com
Year Founded: 1989
Sales Range: $10-24.9 Million
Information Technology Services
N.A.I.C.S.: 541519
Jill Twombly *(Controller)*

Subsidiaries:

Abtech Systems, Inc.   **(1)**

2042 Corte del Nogal St D, Carlsbad, CA
92011
Tel.: (760) 827-5100
Web Site: http://www.abtechsystems.com
Sales Range: $10-24.9 Million
Emp.: 50
Information Technology Whslr & Integration
Services
N.A.I.C.S.: 423430
Robert M. Russell *(Pres)*
Mark Zender *(Sr Acct Mgr)*

ABTEX BEVERAGE LTD
650 Colonial Dr, Abilene, TX 79603
Tel.: (325) 673-7171
Rev.: $70,000,000
Emp.: 250
Soft Drinks: Packaged In Cans,
Bottles
N.A.I.C.S.: 312111

ABYSS GROUP INC
1200 Summer St Ste 204, Stamford,
CT 06905
Tel.: (203) 517-9690
Year Founded: 2005
Sales Range: $1-9.9 Million
Emp.: 16
Data Integrity Solutions Software
N.A.I.C.S.: 423430
Smita Gawande *(Pres)*

AC ADVERTISING
1023 Bethany St, North Charleston,
SC 29405
Tel.: (843) 747-8761
Year Founded: 2004
Sales Range: Less than $1 Million
Emp.: 1
Media Buying Services
N.A.I.C.S.: 541830
Alan Coker *(Owner)*

AC COIN & SLOT SERVICE COMPANY
201 W Decatur Ave, Pleasantville, NJ
08232
Tel.: (609) 641-7811
Web Site: http://www.ac-coin.com
Year Founded: 1978
Sales Range: $75-99.9 Million
Emp.: 250
Game Machines, Coin-Operated
N.A.I.C.S.: 423990
Mac Seelig *(Pres)*
Jerald C. Seelig *(Exec VP & Gen Mgr)*
Robert Chorba *(Controller)*

AC CORPORATION
301 Creek Ridge Rd, Greensboro,
NC 27406-4421
Tel.: (336) 273-4472   NC
Web Site:
https://www.accorporation.com
Year Founded: 1935
Sales Range: $200-249.9 Million
Emp.: 600
Provider of HVAC, Plumbing & Electrical Components & Equipment; Control Panels; Fabricated Metal Products
N.A.I.C.S.: 238220
G. T. Nickell *(Chm)*
David Nickell *(Pres)*
Brett Wagner *(Gen Mgr-Svc)*

Subsidiaries:

Hasten Systems   **(1)**
301 Creek Rdg Rd, Greensboro, NC
27406-4421   **(100%)**
Tel.: (336) 271-6395
Sales Range: $25-49.9 Million
Emp.: 300
Hospital Staff Locator Systems & Emergency Communication Systems
N.A.I.C.S.: 423610

AC FURNITURE CO. INC.
3872 Martin Dr, Axton, VA 24054
Tel.: (276) 650-3356
Web Site: http://www.acfurniture.com
Sales Range: $100-124.9 Million
Emp.: 500
Office Chair Mfr
N.A.I.C.S.: 337211
George Hodge *(Supvr-Shipping)*
Ronnie Montgomery *(Supvr-Fabric)*
Sharon Wolfe *(Dir & Office Administrator)*

AC HOLDING CO.
7015 Krick Rd, Cleveland, OH 44146
Tel.: (440) 439-4404
Web Site: http://www.ac-holding.net
Sales Range: $10-24.9 Million
Emp.: 4
Holding Company
N.A.I.C.S.: 238160
Curtis Cost *(Pres)*

Subsidiaries:

Cost Enterprises Inc.   **(1)**
7015 Krick Rd, Cleveland, OH 44146
Tel.: (440) 439-2095
Web Site: http://www.warrenroofing.com
Sales Range: $10-24.9 Million
Roofing & Siding Materials
N.A.I.C.S.: 423330
Curtis Cost *(Pres)*
Michael Loparo *(CFO)*
Michael Puleo *(Dir-Svcs)*
Lexie Musgrave *(Controller)*
John Vetrovsky *(VP)*

Warren Roofing & Insulating Co.   **(1)**
7015 Krick Rd, Cleveland, OH 44146
Tel.: (440) 439-0473
Web Site: http://www.warrenroofing.com
Sales Range: $10-24.9 Million
Roofing Contractors
N.A.I.C.S.: 238160
Curtis Cost *(Pres)*
Alexis J. Musgrave *(Treasurer)*

AC INC.
1085 Jordan Rd, Huntsville, AL 35811
Tel.: (256) 851-9020
Web Site: https://www.acincorp.com
Sales Range: $10-24.9 Million
Emp.: 100
Containers, Shipping (Bombs, Etc,):
Metal Plate
N.A.I.C.S.: 332313
George A. Smith *(Pres)*
Dan Bobrowski *(VP-Ops)*

AC MARTIN PARTNERS, INC.
444 S Flower St Ste 1200, Los Angeles, CA 90071
Tel.: (213) 683-1900   CA
Web Site: https://www.acmartin.com
Year Founded: 1906
Sales Range: $10-24.9 Million
Emp.: 100
Provider of Architectural, Engineering
& Planning Services
N.A.I.C.S.: 541310
Oliver Santos *(CFO)*
Ken Lewis *(Pres)*
Gail Bouvrie *(Dir-Design)*

AC PRO
11700 Industry Ave, Fontana, CA
92337-6939
Tel.: (951) 360-0630
Web Site: http://www.acpro.com
Sales Range: $50-74.9 Million
Emp.: 170
Warm Air Heating & Air Conditioning
Products Supplier & Contractor
N.A.I.C.S.: 423730
Dion Quinn *(Pres & CEO)*
Blake Quinn *(Dir-Mktg)*
Robert Hascall *(VP-IT)*
John Dautrich *(VP-Pur)*
David Tatum *(Controller)*

AC Pro—(Continued)

AC SUPPLY COMPANY
100 Page Ave, Fort Worth, TX 76110
Tel.: (817) 922-0544
Web Site:
　https://www.acsupplytexas.com
Year Founded: 1959
Sales Range: $10-24.9 Million
Emp.: 37
Air Conditioning, Refrigeration & Ventilation Part Distr
N.A.I.C.S.: 423730
Bob Henry *(Mgr-Store)*
Randy Boyd *(Pres)*
Peggy Osburn *(Mgr-Territory)*
James Fulton *(Mgr-Sls)*
Kristin Jordan *(Mgr-Mktg)*
Bryan Boyd *(Mgr-Pur)*
Berkley Reagan *(Mgr-NRH Store)*
Diane Moody *(Mgr-Credit)*
Matt Holt *(Mgr-West Side Store)*
Mike Lucas *(Mgr-Arlington Store)*

AC TECHNOLOGY, INC.
2300 Wilson Blvd 7th Fl, Arlington, VA 22201
Tel.: (703) 481-6500
Web Site:
　http://www.actechnology.com
Year Founded: 1991
Sales Range: $10-24.9 Million
IT Services
N.A.I.C.S.: 541512
Katherine Smith *(Dir-Mktg)*

ACA CORP.
394 Boston Tpke, Shrewsbury, MA 01545
Tel.: (508) 842-2700
Web Site:
　http://www.acacorporation.com
Rev.: $2,590,000
Emp.: 5
Hardware Stores
N.A.I.C.S.: 444140
Abbas Chipty *(Owner)*

ACACIA CAPITAL NL LLC
2465 Centreville Rd PMB 809 Ste J17, Herndon, VA 20171-3026
Tel.: (301) 280-1000
Web Site:
　http://www.acaciagroup.com
Privater Equity Firm
N.A.I.C.S.: 523999
Frederic Cassis *(Co-Founder & Partner)*
Craig Dawson *(Co-Founder & Partner)*
Gavin Long *(Co-Founder & Partner)*
Matt Milstead *(Co-Founder & Partner)*
Tim Matthews *(Partner)*
Michael Heywood *(Partner)*
Dede Dascalu *(Partner-Tech)*
Josh Tambor *(Partner)*
Chris Figueredo *(VP)*

Subsidiaries:

ID Technologies, LLC　**(1)**
21445 Beaumeade Cir, Ashburn, VA 20147
Tel.: (703) 554-1600
Web Site: http://www.intelligent.net
Sales Range: $400-449.9 Million
Emp.: 350
Information Technology Consulting & Support Services
N.A.I.C.S.: 541519
Erin Driscoll *(VP-Mktg)*
Michael Hippchen *(Dir-Contracts)*
Theresa Pond *(VP-HR & Corp Dev)*
Rhett Butler *(VP-Sls)*
Andrew T. Sullivan *(Dir-Dept of Defence Sls)*
Marty Fischer *(Dir-Federal Enterprise Solutions)*
Clarence Pape *(VP-Trng & Simulation)*
Chris Oliver *(Pres)*

ACACIA FINANCIAL GROUP, INC.
6000 Midlantic Dr Ste 410 N, Mount Laurel, NJ 08054
Tel.: (856) 234-2266
Web Site: http://www.acaciafin.com
Year Founded: 2006
Emp.: 60
Financial Advisory Services
N.A.I.C.S.: 523940
Kim M. Whelan *(Co-Pres)*
Noreen P. White *(Co-Pres)*
Jennifer G. Edwards *(Mng Dir)*
Peter D. Nissen *(Mng Dir)*
Joshua C. Nyikita *(Mng Dir)*
Dara I. Melchionni *(Asst VP & Officer-Ops)*
Richard Lopatin *(Asst VP & Officer-Ops)*
Siamac Y. Afshar *(Asst VP & Officer-Ops)*

ACACIA PARTNERS LLC
901 S MoPac Expy Bldg 1 Ste 300, Austin, TX 78746
Tel.: (512) 329-1925
Web Site:
　http://www.acaciapartnersllc.com
Privater Equity Firm
N.A.I.C.S.: 523999
Brad Johl *(Founder & Partner)*
Jeff Sokol *(Partner)*
Greg Maletsky *(Partner)*

ACADEMIC TRAVEL ABROAD, INC.
1155 Connecticut Ave NW Ste 300, Washington, DC 20036
Tel.: (202) 785-9000
Web Site: https://www.academic-travel.com
Rev.: $14,000,000
Emp.: 50
Travel & Touring Services
N.A.I.C.S.: 561520
David Parry *(Chm)*
Sarah Saleh *(VP-Fin & Admin)*
Chase Poffenberger *(Exec VP)*
Chris Roper *(Dir-Supplier Mgmt & Program Mgr-Fin)*
Emma Impavido *(Dir-Program Mgmt)*

ACADEMIXDIRECT INC.
4000 Belhnnan Ste Mont, Menlo Park, CA 94025
Tel.: (650) 265-1500
Web Site:
　http://www.academixdirect.com
Year Founded: 2004
Sales Range: $10-24.9 Million
Emp.: 25
Performance Based Marketing
N.A.I.C.S.: 541613
Bruce Onder *(CTO)*

ACADEMY BUS LLC
111 Paterson Ave, Hoboken, NJ 07030-6012
Tel.: (201) 420-7000
Web Site:
　http://www.academybus.com
Year Founded: 1968
Sales Range: $75-99.9 Million
Emp.: 1,000
Tour & Commuter Bus Services
N.A.I.C.S.: 561520
Robert Keller *(Dir-Safety)*
Violet Penyacsek *(Mgr-HR)*
Craig Sterk *(Reg Mgr-Maintenance)*
Gregory Rhodes *(Mgr-Mktg)*
Joe Porcelli *(Mgr)*
Steve Marek *(Mgr-Ops)*
Monika Harmulowicz *(Asst Mgr-Sls)*

ACADEMY COMMUNICATIONS INC.

677-C Alpha Dr Ste C, Cleveland, OH 44143
Tel.: (440) 646-9900
Year Founded: 1996
Rev.: $12,000,000
Emp.: 20
N.A.I.C.S.: 541810
Blair Mooney *(Pres)*
Michael Mooney *(Gen Mgr)*
Beth Szczesniak *(Office Mgr)*

ACADEMY FOR URBAN SCHOOL LEADERSHIP
3400 N Austin Ave, Chicago, IL 60634-0990
Tel.: (773) 943-7810　　　IL
Web Site:
　https://www.auslchicago.org
Year Founded: 2001
Sales Range: $25-49.9 Million
Emp.: 473
Educational Support Services
N.A.I.C.S.: 611710
Michael Whitmore *(Mng Dir-Teaching & Learning)*
Shana Hayes *(Mng Dir-External Affairs)*
Jarvis Sanford *(Mng Dir-AUSL Network Schools)*
Scott MacDonald *(Mng Dir-Strategy & Ops)*
Donald Feinstein *(Exec Dir)*
Gary E. McCullough *(Chm)*
Martin J. Koldyke *(Founder)*
Mike Zafirovski *(Vice Chm)*

ACADEMY MORTGAGE CORPORATION
339 W 13490 S, Draper, UT 84020
Tel.: (801) 233-3700
Web Site:
　https://www.academymortgage.com
Year Founded: 1988
Rev.: $21,069,798
Emp.: 300
Mortgage Services
N.A.I.C.S.: 522292
Adam Kessler *(Chm)*
Brian Boyles *(Mgr-North Central)*
Barry Abt *(Officer-Loan)*
Brandon Aiello *(Officer-Loan)*
Brandy Afuvai *(Officer-Loan)*
Chris Alexander *(Officer-Loan)*
Jim Abrecht *(Officer-Loan)*
Mike Adams *(Officer-Loan)*
Rebecca Adams *(Officer-Loan)*
Roger Ahumada *(Officer-Loan)*
Sonny Aguilera *(Officer-Loan)*
Steve Adams *(Officer-Loan)*
Eric Zeier *(Reg Mgr-Southeast)*
Jerry Devlin *(Mgr-East)*
Jorge Valencia *(Mgr-Upper Midwest)*
Rob Shockley *(Sr VP-HR)*
John Norman *(VP-Risk Mgmt)*
Abby Hawkins *(VP-Learning, Trng & Dev)*
James MacPherson *(Pres)*
James Mac Pherson *(CEO)*
Kristi Pickering *(COO)*
Mike Jensen *(Exec VP-Mktg & Corp Dev)*

ACADEMY OF GENERAL DENTISTRY
560 W Lake St 6th Fl, Chicago, IL 60661-6600
Tel.: (312) 440-4300　　　IL
Web Site: https://www.agd.org
Year Founded: 1952
Sales Range: $10-24.9 Million
Emp.: 82
Medical Professional Association
N.A.I.C.S.: 813920
John Thorner *(Exec Dir & CEO)*

ACADEMY OF MOTION PIC-

TURE ARTS & SCIENCES
8949 Wilshire Blvd, Beverly Hills, CA 90211-1907
Tel.: (310) 247-3000
Web Site: https://www.oscars.org
Year Founded: 1927
Sales Range: $25-49.9 Million
Emp.: 325
Organization for the Promotion of Motion Pictures
N.A.I.C.S.: 512199
Andrew Horn *(CFO)*
Randy Haberkamp *(Mng Dir-Preservation & Foundation Programs)*
Christina Kounelias *(CMO)*
Bev Kite *(CIO)*
Kim Congdon *(Mng Dir-HR)*
Michael Pogorzelski *(Dir-Academy Film Archive)*
Fernando Garcia *(Exec VP-Member Relations & Awards)*
Christine Simmons *(COO)*
Jennifer Davidson *(Chief Comm Officer)*
Bill Kramer *(CEO)*
Jeanell English *(Exec VP-Impact & Inclusion)*
Janet Yang *(Pres)*

ACADEMY SOLUTIONS GROUP, LLC.
6700 Alexander Bell Dr Ste 195, Columbia, MD 21046
Tel.: (410) 290-0871
Web Site: https://www.asg-llc.com
Sales Range: $1-9.9 Million
Emp.: 35
Engineeering Services
N.A.I.C.S.: 541330
Greg Whaley *(Owner & Pres)*
Joe Mudd *(VP-Western Ops)*
Mike Sonnefeld *(Program Mgr)*
Steve Hubbard *(Program Mgr)*

ACADEMYHEALTH
1666 K St NW Ste 1100, Washington, DC 20006
Tel.: (202) 292-6700　　　DC
Web Site:
　https://www.academyhealth.org
Year Founded: 1981
Sales Range: $10-24.9 Million
Emp.: 77
Medical Research Services
N.A.I.C.S.: 813212
Bonnie Austin Cluxton *(VP)*
Deborah L. Edwards *(CFO & VP-Ops)*
Stacy L. Halbert *(Dir-IT)*
Teasha Powell *(Dir-HR)*
Kristin Rosengren *(VP-Strategic Comm & Dir-Translation & Dissemination Institute)*
Robin Weinick *(VP)*

ACADIA AUTO GROUP INC.
8 Murray Rd, Carmel, ME 04419
Tel.: (207) 941-2345
Web Site: http://www.acadia-auctions.com
Rev.: $19,100,000
Emp.: 60
Automobile Auction Services
N.A.I.C.S.: 423110
E. David Wescott *(Pres)*

ACADIA MALIBU, INC.
28955 Pacific Coast Hwy Ste 200, Malibu, CA 90265
Web Site:
　http://www.alorecovery.com
Year Founded: 2013
Sales Range: $10-24.9 Million
Emp.: 90
Health Care Srvices
N.A.I.C.S.: 621610

Jared Valentine (Co-Founder)
Evan Haines (Co-Founder)
Rachel Corbett (Chief Bus Dev Officer)
David Cisneros (Dir-Clinical)
Jodi Wagner (Dir-Case Mgmt)

ACADIA TECHNOLOGY GROUP
168 Park St Ste 300, Montclair, NJ 07042
Tel.: (973) 233-1260
Web Site: http://www.acadiatech.com
Sales Range: $1-9.9 Million
Emp.: 14
Information Technology Services
N.A.I.C.S.: 541512
Kevin Hynes (Founder)
Jon Kadis (Pres)

ACADIA WHOLESALE & TOBACCO COMPANY, INC.
9684 Church Point Hwy, Church Point, LA 70525
Tel.: (337) 684-5411
Web Site:
    http://www.churchpointsales.com
Rev.: $38,502,317
Emp.: 83
Groceries, General Line
N.A.I.C.S.: 424940
George Casanova (Gen Mgr)

ACADIAN AMBULANCE SERVICE INC.
130 E Kaliste Saloom Rd, Lafayette, LA 70508
Tel.: (337) 291-3399
Web Site: http://www.acadian.com
Year Founded: 1971
Sales Range: $75-99.9 Million
Emp.: 2,000
Ambulance Service
N.A.I.C.S.: 621910
Richard Zuschlag (Chm & CEO)
David L. Kelly (CFO & Exec VP)
Gregory Hill (VP & Controller)
John R. Zuschlag (Chief Admin Officer & Exec VP)
Daniel J. Lennie (Sr VP)
Tim Burke (Reg VP)
Mike Sonnier (Dir-Air Svcs Program)
Justin Back (Pres)

ACADIAN ENERGY, LLC
16475 Dallas Pkwy Ste 400, Addison, TX 75001
Tel.: (281) 751-7720   ON
Web Site:
    http://www.acadianenergy.com
Year Founded: 2007
Sales Range: Less than $1 Million
Oil & Natural Gas Exploration Services
N.A.I.C.S.: 211120
John E. McDevitt (Chm & CEO)
Timothy C. Williams (CFO, Sec & VP)

ACADIANA BOTTLING CO. INC.
700 Kaliste Saloom Rd, Lafayette, LA 70508
Tel.: (337) 237-3935
Rev.: $42,000,000
Emp.: 110
Soft Drinks: Packaged In Cans, Bottles, Etc.
N.A.I.C.S.: 312111
Dennis Smith (Pres)

ACADIANA COMPUTER SYSTEMS INC.
324 Dulles Dr, Lafayette, LA 70506
Tel.: (337) 981-2494
Web Site: http://www.acsmd.net

Year Founded: 1969
Sales Range: $10-24.9 Million
Emp.: 100
Value-Added Resellers, Computer Systems
N.A.I.C.S.: 541512
Bryan Dupre (VP-Software Dev)
Michelle Hanks (Exec VP)

ACADIANA DODGE, INC.
1700 SE Evangeline Trwy, Lafayette, LA 70508
Tel.: (337) 232-7361
Web Site:
    http://www.acadianadodge.net
Sales Range: $25-49.9 Million
Emp.: 140
Car Whslr
N.A.I.C.S.: 441110
Tim Barbier (Principal)

ACADIANA SYMPHONY ASSOCIATION
412 Travis St Ste A, Lafayette, LA 70503
Tel.: (337) 232-4277
Web Site:
    https://www.acadianasymphony.org
Sales Range: Less than $1 Million
Emp.: 5
Symphony Orchestra
N.A.I.C.S.: 711130
Tonio Cutrera (Mgr-Ops)
Emil D. Ivanov (Mgr-Personnel & Librarian)

ACADIASOFT, INC.
93 Longwater Cir, Norwell, MA 02061
Tel.: (617) 459-4080
Web Site: http://www.acadiasoft.com
Software Publisher
N.A.I.C.S.: 513210
Chris Walsh (CEO)
Mark Demo (Dir-Product)
Fred Dassori (Head-Risk Products & Corp Dev-New York)
Scott Fitzpatrick (Dir-Collateral Bus & Client Ops)
John Pucciarelli (Dir-Strategic Initiatives)

Subsidiaries:

AcadiaSoft (UK) Ltd.   (1)
Ropemaker Place 25 Ropemaker Street, London, EC24 9LY, United Kingdom
Tel.: (44) 20 3004 8226
Software Publisher
N.A.I.C.S.: 513210
David Radley (Dir-Sls & Mktg)
Lee McCormack (Head-Collateral Product Mgmt & Pro Svcs)

ACAI ASSOCIATES
2937 W Cypress Creek Rd Ste 200, Fort Lauderdale, FL 33309
Tel.: (954) 484-4000
Web Site: http://www.acaiworld.com
Year Founded: 1985
Sales Range: $1-9.9 Million
Emp.: 37
Architectural Services
N.A.I.C.S.: 541310
Adolfo Cotilla (Pres)
Birgitta Foster (Dir-Facilities Integration)
David Thirlwell (Mgr-BIM)
Robert Voelker (Dir-Interiors & Visualization)

ACB AMERICAN INC.
4351 Winston Ave, Covington, KY 41015
Tel.: (859) 261-8745
Web Site:
    http://www.acbrecovery.com
Rev.: $12,000,000
Emp.: 80

Collection Agency, Except Real Estate
N.A.I.C.S.: 561440
Susan N. Faeth (CEO)
Randall Dunn (CIO & VP)
Anthony Faeth (Pres)

ACC CONSTRUCTION COMPANY, INC.
635-A NW Frontage Rd, Augusta, GA 30917
Tel.: (706) 868-1037
Web Site:
    http://www.accconstructionco.com
Year Founded: 1987
Sales Range: $10-24.9 Million
Emp.: 100
Industrial Building Construction Services
N.A.I.C.S.: 236210
Matthew M. McKnight (VP)
Mason H. McKnight III (Pres)
Mason H. McKnight IV (VP)

ACC DISTRIBUTORS, INC.
300 Oakland Ct Oakland Meadows Business Park Hwy 82 W, Leesburg, GA 31763
Tel.: (229) 432-9141
Web Site:
    https://www.accdistributors.com
Rev.: $27,700,000
Emp.: 40
Packaged Frozen Food Merchant Whslr
N.A.I.C.S.: 424420
Megan Rogers (Office Mgr)
Bennie Waters (Dir-Sls)

ACC HOLDING, INC.
6135 S Jasper Ave, Milwaukee, WI 53207
Tel.: (414) 482-1711
Web Site: http://www.telfordgroup.biz
Year Founded: 2009
Emp.: 200
Holding Company
N.A.I.C.S.: 551112
James M. Germek (Owner & CEO)

Subsidiaries:

Air Cargo Carriers, LLC   (1)
4940 S Howell Ave, Milwaukee, WI 53207
Tel.: (414) 482-1711
Web Site: http://www.aircar.com
Rev.: $13,591,988
Emp.: 150
Air Cargo Carrier Services
N.A.I.C.S.: 481212

ACC INDUSTRIES INCORPORATED
2550 Braga Dr, Broadview, IL 60155
Tel.: (708) 345-1900
Web Site: https://www.aircomfort.com
Sales Range: $10-24.9 Million
Emp.: 75
Warm Air Heating & Air Conditioning Contractor
N.A.I.C.S.: 238220
Jim Bartolotta (Exec VP)
Tim Smerz (Pres)
Lynette Mantey (CFO)

ACCEL LIQUID GELS, INC.
5308 W Cygnus Hill Cv, West Jordan, UT 84081
Tel.: (801) 946-6125   WY
Web Site:
    https://www.accelliquidgels.com
Year Founded: 2016
Rev.: $5,754
Assets: $213,620
Liabilities: $246,558
Net Worth: ($32,938)
Earnings: ($444,475)
Fiscal Year-end: 05/31/22

Health Supplement Product Distr
N.A.I.C.S.: 456191
Pauline Carson (Pres, CEO, Founder, CFO & Sec)

ACCEL PARTNERS L.P.
500 University Ave, Palo Alto, CA 94301
Tel.: (650) 614-4800   DE
Web Site: http://www.accel.com
Year Founded: 1984
Venture Capital Firm
N.A.I.C.S.: 523999
James W. Breyer (Mng Partner)
Richard P. Wong (Partner)
Abhinav Chaturvedi (Principal)
Subrata Mitra (Founder)
Kevin Comolli (Partner-London)

Subsidiaries:

Accel-KKR Company LLC   (1)
2500 Sand Hill Rd Ste 300, Menlo Park, CA 94025
Tel.: (650) 289-2460
Web Site: https://www.accel-kkr.com
Privater Equity Firm
N.A.I.C.S.: 523999
Gregory Williams (Mng Dir-Growth Capital Investments)
Patrick J. Fallon (Mng Dir & COO)
David Cusimano (Principal)
Kristy Curtis (Office Mgr)
Park Durrett (Mng Dir)
Maurice Hernandez (VP-London office)
Dean Jacobson (Mng Dir)
Matt Marinaro (VP)
Joe Porten (VP)
Joe Savig (Principal)
Clara Yee (Sr VP-Fin)
Phil Cunningham (Mng Dir)
Roy Kelvin (CFO)
Samantha Shows (Mng Dir)
Weston Ahlswede (VP)
Eric Armagost (VP)
Scotty Lu (VP)
Dave Moore (VP)
Adam Malinowski (VP)
Gordon MacNeill (VP)
Alissa Palatiello (VP)
Nishant Patel (Principal)
Andy Rich (Principal)
Christian Stewart (VP)
Johnny Van Siclen (VP)
Andrew Zbella (Principal)
Jason Klein (Mng Dir)
Adam Malinowski (VP)
Paul Hazen (Chm)
Paul Hazen (Chm)

Holding (Domestic):

Accertify, Inc.   (2)
2 Pierce Pl Ste 900, Itasca, IL 60143
Tel.: (630) 735-4400
Web Site: https://www.accertify.com
Software Development Services
N.A.I.C.S.: 541511

Joint Venture (Non-US):

Basware Oyj   (2)
Linnoitustie 2 Cello-rakennus, PL 97, 02601, Espoo, Finland
Tel.: (358) 9879171
Web Site: https://www.basware.com
Rev.: $188,111,097
Assets: $271,097,133
Liabilities: $181,481,058
Net Worth: $89,616,075
Earnings: ($17,481,540)
Emp.: 1,347
Fiscal Year-end: 12/31/2021
Software Publisher
N.A.I.C.S.: 513210
Jane Broberg (Chief HR Officer)
Lars Madsen (CMO)
Klaus Andersen (CEO)
Martti Nurminen (CFO)
Alwin Schauer (Chief Revenue Officer)
Jason Kurtz (CEO-Basware)
Barrett Schiwitz (CIO)
Sam Pathmasiri (Gen Counsel)

Subsidiary (Non-US):

Basware A/S   (3)

Accel Partners L.P.—(Continued)

Kirkebjerg Alle 84 1 Sal, 2605, Brondby, Denmark
Tel.: (45) 7 022 9955
Web Site: https://www.basware.com
Emp.: 25
Software Development Services
N.A.I.C.S.: 541511

Basware AB (3)
Gustavslundsv 151 C, 167 51, Bromma, Stockholm, Sweden
Tel.: (46) 85 057 4400
Web Site: https://www.basware.com
Sales Range: $25-49.9 Million
Emp.: 35
Software Development Services
N.A.I.C.S.: 541511
Jukka Virkkunen (Sr VP)

Basware AS (3)
Vollsveien 6, PO Box 241, Lilleaker, 1366, Lysaker, Norway
Tel.: (47) 2 337 0300
Web Site: http://www.basware.com
Financial Software Development Services
N.A.I.C.S.: 541511

Basware B.V. (3)
Krijn Taconiskade 436, Duivendrecht, 1087 HW, Amsterdam, Netherlands
Tel.: (31) 20 850 8020
Web Site: http://www.basware.com
Software Development Services
N.A.I.C.S.: 541511

Basware Belgium NV (3)
Clinton Park Ninovesteenweg 196, Erembodegem, 9320, Belgium
Tel.: (32) 53 60 11 11
Web Site: http://www.basware.be
Emp.: 50
Software Development Services
N.A.I.C.S.: 541511
Pieter Geeraerts (Gen Mgr)

Basware Corporation (3)
Ocean Financial Centre Level 40 10 Collyer, Quay, Singapore, 49315, Singapore
Tel.: (65) 6808 6494
Software Development Services
N.A.I.C.S.: 541511
Ben Selby (Head-IR)
Jukka Janonen (Dir-Comm)

Basware GmbH (3)
Rossstr 96, 40476, Dusseldorf, Germany
Tel.: (49) 211 41 55 95 50
Sales Range: $25-49.9 Million
Emp.: 70
Software Development Services
N.A.I.C.S.: 541511
Frank Wuschech (Mng Dir)

Basware Holdings Ltd. (3)
4th Floor 120 Old Broad Street, London, EC2N 1AR, United Kingdom
Tel.: (44) 845 603 2885
Software Services
N.A.I.C.S.: 541511

Basware India Private Limited (3)
Rajiv Gandhi IT Park DLF Building Tower A Ground Floor, Chandigarh, 160 001, India
Tel.: (91) 172 301 2020
Web Site: http://www.basware.com
Software Development Services
N.A.I.C.S.: 541511

Basware Pty Ltd (3)
Level 15 67 Albert Ave, PO Box 148, Chatswood, 2067, NSW, Australia
Tel.: (61) 2 8622 5850
Software Development Services
N.A.I.C.S.: 541511
Niclas Hill (Dir-Consulting)

Basware Russia (3)
Helsinki House 4 Rostovsky per 1/2, Moscow, 119121, Russia
Tel.: (7) 499 248 16 73
Web Site: http://www.basware.ru
Software Development Services
N.A.I.C.S.: 541511

Basware SAS (3)
20 Rue Caumartin, 75009, Paris, France
Tel.: (33) 14 008 1820
Web Site: https://www.basware.com
Software Development Services

Basware UK Ltd. (3)
1-3 Berkeley Court Borough Road, Newcastle, ST5 1TT, Staffordshire, United Kingdom
Tel.: (44) 845 6711953
Software Development Services
N.A.I.C.S.: 541511

Subsidiary (US):

Basware, Inc. (3)
1245 Rosemont Dr Ste 200, Fort Mill, SC 29707
Tel.: (203) 487-7900
Web Site: https://www.basware.com
Sales Range: $25-49.9 Million
Emp.: 50
Software Development Services
N.A.I.C.S.: 541511
Tehseen Dahya (Gen Mgr-North America)

Subsidiary (Domestic):

Verian Technologies, Inc. (4)
8701 Mallard Creek Rd, Charlotte, NC 28262
Tel.: (704) 547-7301
Web Site: http://www.verian.com
Sales Range: $10-24.9 Million
Emp.: 75
Procurement Technology Solutions
N.A.I.C.S.: 541511
Tehseen Ali Dahya (Pres & CEO)
Lindsay Munn (Mgr-Mktg Comm)
Bilal Soylu (CTO)
Tommy Benston (VP-Customer Svc)
Dana Saylors (VP-Mktg & Product Strategy)
Jerry Ellis (VP-Sls)
Steve Ayala (VP-Tech)
Bhavin Shah (Dir-Product Strategy)

Subsidiary (Non-US):

Glantus Holdings Plc (3)
Marina House Block V Eastpoint Business Park, Dublin, D03 AX24, Ireland
Tel.: (353) 18895300
Rev.: $12,925,013
Assets: $32,981,867
Liabilities: $20,630,120
Net Worth: $12,351,748
Earnings: ($2,806,273)
Emp.: 124
Fiscal Year-end: 12/31/2021
Holding Company
N.A.I.C.S.: 551112

Holding (Domestic):

GPS Insight LLC (2)
7201 E Henkel Way Ste 400, Scottsdale, AZ 85255
Tel.: (480) 663-9454
Web Site: http://www.gpsinsight.com
Sales Range: $1-9.9 Million
Emp.: 65
GPS Tracking, Navigation & Messaging Technologies
N.A.I.C.S.: 334511
Rob Donat (Founder)
Tyler Mortensen (Sr Acct Mgr)
Elliot Batcheller (Dir-Ops)
Gary Fitzgerald (CEO)
Wayne Holder (CFO)
Jason Walker (Chief Revenue Officer)
Geoffrey Garrett (Chief Revenue Officer)

National Electronic Attachment, Inc. (2)
3577 Pkwy Ln Ste 250, Norcross, GA 30092
Tel.: (770) 441-3203
Web Site: http://www.nea-fast.com
Sales Range: $1-9.9 Million
Internet Based Solutions for Health Information Exchange
N.A.I.C.S.: 541519
Melinda H. Benton (CEO)
Claudia Stein-Martin (CFO)
Kent McAllister (Chief Dev Officer & Chief Ops Officer)
Nicole Smith (VP-Govt Svcs)
Scott Hefner (VP-Sls)

Subsidiary (Domestic):

The White Stone Group Inc. (3)

6422 E Main St Ste 100, Reynoldsburg, OH 43068
Tel.: (614) 501-7007
Web Site: https://www.whitestonegroup.us
Sales Range: $1-9.9 Million
Emp.: 65
Healthcare Management Consulting
N.A.I.C.S.: 541618
Randy Smith (CFO)
Jeff Peters (Pres & CEO)
Dave Stridde (COO)
Phillip McClure (VP-Bus Dev)
Jo Norris (VP-Strategic Acct Dev)
Blair Wright (Exec VP-Bus Dev)
Jerry Thomas (Exec VP-Accts Dev)
Scott Overholt (CMO & Exec VP-Market Dev)
Matt Jernigan (Dir-Product Mgmt)

Joint Venture (Non-US):

Reapit Ltd (2)
67 - 74 Saffron Hill 3rd Floor London, Greater, London , EC1N 8QX, United Kingdom
Tel.: (44) 8453302965
Web Site: https://www.reapit.com
Software Publisher
N.A.I.C.S.: 513210
Mark Armstrong (CEO)

Subsidiary (Non-US):

Console Australia Pty Ltd (3)
Level 8 Elizabeth Plaza North Sydney, Sydney, 2060, NSW, Australia
Tel.: (61) 1300131311
Web Site: http://www.console.com.au
Real Estate Software Development Services
N.A.I.C.S.: 541511

Subsidiary (Non-US):

Console New Zealand Limited (4)
Level 7 203 Queen Street, Auckland, 1010, New Zealand
Tel.: (64) 508 641 199
Web Site: http://www.console.co.nz
Emp.: 10
Real Estate Software Development Services
N.A.I.C.S.: 541511
Jose Antonio Cadarso (Office Mgr)

Holding (Domestic):

Salary.com, LLC (2)
610 Lincoln St North Ste 200, Waltham, MA 02451
Tel.: (617) 631-8000
Web Site: http://www.salary.com
On-Demand Compensation & Performance Management Services
N.A.I.C.S.: 518210
G. Kent Plunkett (Founder, Pres & CEO)
Yong Zhang (COO, CTO & Pres-Global Ops)
Robert Merklinger (Sr VP-Sls)
Anne Huemme (CFO)
ALys Reynders Scott (CMO)
Brian Davis (Head-People)

SciQuest, Inc. (2)
3020 Carrington Mill Blvd Ste 100, Morrisville, NC 27560
Tel.: (919) 659-2100
Web Site: https://www.jaggaer.com
Technology & Services to Optimize Procurement & Materials Management
N.A.I.C.S.: 513210
Zia Zahiri (CTO)

Subsidiary (Non-US):

BravoSolution S.p.A. (3)
Via Rombon 11, 20134, Milan, Italy
Tel.: (39) 022105121
Web Site: http://www.jaggaer.com
Electronic Sourcing Software & Services Developer
N.A.I.C.S.: 513210

Subsidiary (Domestic):

BravoBus S.r.l. (4)
Via Rombon 11, Milan, 20134, Italy
Tel.: (39) 022105121
Web Site: http://www.jaggaer.com
Software Development Services
N.A.I.C.S.: 541511

Subsidiary (Non-US):

BravoSolution Benelux B.V. (4)
Nieuwezijds Voorburgwal 162, Amsterdam, 1012 SJ, Netherlands
Tel.: (31) 0208203825
Web Site: http://www.jaggaer.com
Supply Management Software Development Services
N.A.I.C.S.: 541511

BravoSolution China Co. Ltd (4)
Room C06 No 13 Lane 345 Danshui Road, Huangpu District, Shanghai, 200003, China
Tel.: (86) 21 6145 8500
Web Site: http://www.jaggaer.com
Software Development & Management Services
N.A.I.C.S.: 541511

BravoSolution Espana S.A. (4)
Avenida Manoteras 42 Calle 3 Edificio Esindus 1 Planta, 28050, Madrid, Spain
Tel.: (34) 917870200
Web Site: http://www.jaggaer.com
Supply Management Software Development Services
N.A.I.C.S.: 541511

BravoSolution France S.a.s. (4)
81 83 Le Quintet Batiment E 81 Avenue Edouard Vaillant, 92100, Boulogne-Billancourt, France
Tel.: (33) 146095678
Web Site: http://www.jaggaer.com
Software Development Services
N.A.I.C.S.: 541511

BravoSolution GmbH (4)
Ottobrunner Str 41, 82008, Munich, Germany
Tel.: (49) 89 121 93 35 0
Software Development & Management Services
N.A.I.C.S.: 541511

BravoSolution Mexico S.r.l. de C.V. (4)
Av Homero 1933-301 Col Los Morales, 11510, Mexico, Mexico
Tel.: (52) 55 5395 8936
Supply Chain Software Development Services
N.A.I.C.S.: 541511

Subsidiary (US):

BravoSolution Software, Inc. (4)
120 Plaza Dr Ste F, Vestal, NY 13850
Tel.: (607) 231-6000
Web Site: http://www.jaggaer.com
Software Development & Management Services
N.A.I.C.S.: 541511

Subsidiary (Non-US):

BravoSolution Technologies Ltd (4)
103 St John Street, London, EC1M 4AS, United Kingdom
Tel.: (44) 20 7796 4170
Web Site: http://www.jaggaer.com
Software Development Services
N.A.I.C.S.: 541511

BravoSolution UK Ltd (4)
103 St John Street, London, EC1M 4AS, United Kingdom
Tel.: (44) 2077964170
Web Site: http://www.jaggaer.com
Software Development Services
N.A.I.C.S.: 541511

Holding (Domestic):

SugarCRM Inc. (2)
10050 N Wolfe Rd Ste SW2-130, Cupertino, CA 95014
Tel.: (408) 454-6900
Web Site: http://www.sugarcrm.com
Sales Range: $10-24.9 Million
Emp.: 150
Open Source Customer Relationship Management (CRM) Software
N.A.I.C.S.: 541511
Chuck Coulson (VP-Bus Dev)
Clint Oram (Co-Founder & VP-Product Mgmt)
Larry Augustin (Chm)
Majed Itani (VP-Dev)
Jennifer Stagnaro (CMO)

Sherry Pulvers *(VP-People & Places)*
Remy Malan *(Chief Customer Officer)*
Fred Gewant *(Exec VP-Worldwide Sls)*
Rich Green *(Chief Product Officer)*
Juan Herrera *(Exec VP-Sls-Worldwide)*
Mark Liu *(Gen Counsel, Sec & VP)*
Craig Charlton *(CEO)*
John Donaldson *(CFO)*
Shana Sweeney *(Chief HR Officer)*
Jason Rushforth *(Gen Mgr-Americas)*
Clare Dorrian *(CMO)*

Subsidiary (Domestic):

Salesfusion Inc. **(3)**
3565 Piedmont Rd NE Building 2, Atlanta,
GA 30305
Tel.: (770) 217-1228
Web Site: http://www.salesfusion.com
Holding Company
N.A.I.C.S.: 551112
Malinda Wilkinson *(CMO)*
Matt Barman *(Exec VP-Client Svcs)*
Gavin Harris *(VP-Sls)*
Logan Henderson *(CEO)*

Subsidiary (Non-US):

SugarCRM Deutschland GmbH **(3)**
Luise-Ullrich-Strasse 20, 80636, Munich,
Germany
Tel.: (49) 89189172000
Web Site: http://www.sugarcrm.com
Emp.: 55
Open Source Customer Relationship Man-
agement (CRM) Software
N.A.I.C.S.: 513210
Kevan Baker *(Gen Mgr)*

Division (Non-US):

SugarCRM Sweden **(4)**
Master Samuelsgatan 60 8th Floor, 111 21,
Stockholm, Sweden
Tel.: (46) 8 44 68 02 56
Open Source Customer Relationship Man-
agement (CRM) Software
N.A.I.C.S.: 513210

SugarCRM UK **(4)**
Work Life 20 Red Lion St, Holborn, London,
WC1R 4PS, Cambridge, United Kingdom
Tel.: (44) 2038088507
Web Site: http://www.sugarcrm.com
Open Source Customer Relationship Man-
agement (CRM) Software
N.A.I.C.S.: 513210

Holding (Domestic):

Team Software, Inc. **(2)**
407 S 27th Ave, Omaha, NE 68131
Tel.: (402) 345-5660
Web Site: https://teamsoftware.com
Sales Range: $1-9.9 Million
Emp.: 25
Computer Related Services
N.A.I.C.S.: 541519
Colleen Slepicka *(Accountant)*

Subsidiary (Non-US):

Innovise Ltd. **(3)**
Keypoint 17-23 High Street, Slough, SL1
1DY, Berks, United Kingdom
Tel.: (44) 370 626 0400
Web Site: http://www.innovise.com
Sales Range: $25-49.9 Million
Information Technology Management Ser-
vices
N.A.I.C.S.: 541513
Mike Taylor *(CEO)*
Graeme Hughes *(Mng Dir)*

Holding (Non-US):

TimeTarget Pty Ltd **(2)**
Level 14 90 Arthur St, North Sydney, 2060,
NSW, Australia
Tel.: (61) 300886698
Web Site: https://humanforce.com
Payroll Solutions Provider
N.A.I.C.S.: 513210
Clayton Pyne *(CEO)*
Alex Panich *(CFO)*
Sylvia Vasas *(CMO)*

Subsidiary (Domestic):

IntelliHR Limited **(3)**
Level 28 345 Queen Street, Brisbane,

4000, QLD, Australia
Tel.: (61) 300993803
Web Site: http://www.intellihr.com.au
Rev.: $2,151,780
Assets: $7,523,029
Liabilities: $3,702,803
Net Worth: $3,820,226
Earnings: ($5,847,812)
Emp.: 45
Fiscal Year-end: 06/30/2021
Software Management Services
N.A.I.C.S.: 541512
Robert Bromage *(Founder & CEO)*
Suzanne M. Yeates *(CFO & Sec)*
Paul Trappett *(COO)*
Kelly Harvey *(Head-Mktg)*
Andrew Smith *(CTO)*
Laura Butler *(Head)*
Gemma Murdoch *(Head)*
Kate Charge *(Head)*
Tony Lehner *(Head)*

Subsidiary (Domestic):

VisiQuate, Inc. **(2)**
500 Bicentennial Way Ste 300, Santa Rosa,
CA 95403
Tel.: (707) 546-4377
Web Site: http://www.visiquate.com
Web Based Content Management Services
N.A.I.C.S.: 541511
Rich Waller *(CTO)*
Keith Eggert *(Exec VP & Gen Mgr-
Healthcare)*
Leonid Nekhymchuk *(Sr VP-Engrg)*
Brian Robertson *(Co-Founder & CEO)*
Jim Kolmansberger *(Co-Founder & Pres)*
Andrii Svydlo *(Sr Engr-Data)*
Greg Karraker *(CMO & Sr VP)*
Lurii Mekesha *(Sr Engr-Data)*
Mykola Kryvenchuk *(Engr-R&D)*
Nataliya Vasyutyn *(Project Mgr)*
Sven P. Zabka *(Chief Legal Officer & Exec
VP)*
Svitlana Sharypina *(Project Mgr)*
Valerie R. Gallo-Pompa *(Sr Project Mgr)*
Vitaliy Gontovoi *(Sr Engr-Data)*
Melissa Ross *(COO)*
Chuck Rackley *(Exec VP-Velocity Consult-
ing & HealthMobile.D Ecosystem)*
Terry Blessing III *(Sr VP-Client Dev)*

ACCELA INC.
2633 Camino Ramon Ste 500, San
Ramon, CA 94583
Tel.: (925) 659-3200
Web Site: https://www.accela.com
Emp.: 30
Software Publisher
N.A.I.C.S.: 513210
Brian Wienke *(Principal & Product
Mgr)*
Jeffrey C. Tung *(COO)*
Jerald Lo *(CTO)*
Mark Watts *(Mng Dir)*
Maury Blackman *(Pres)*
Mitch Bradley *(VP-Sls & Bus Dev)*
Khaled Jaouni *(Mng Dir)*
Lee Ann Slinkard *(Sr VP-Svcs)*
Max Schnoedl *(Pres/Gen Mgr-
Portland-Springbrook)*
Rob Cassetti *(Sr VP-Sls & Mktg)*
Kris Trujillo *(VP-Products)*
Colin Sameuls *(Gen Counsel)*
Dani Chehak *(Sr VP-People & Cul-
ture)*
Jay Colfer *(Chief Revenue Officer)*
Troy Coggiola *(Chief Product Officer)*
Srini Kakkera *(Sr VP-Engrg)*
Jonathon Knight *(Chief Customer Of-
ficer)*
Edward Whelan *(Chm)*
Gary Kovacs *(CEO)*

Subsidiaries:

PublicStuff, LLC **(1)**
447 Broadway 2nd Fl, New York, NY 10013
Tel.: (347) 284-6136
Web Site: http://www.publicstuff.com
Software Publisher
N.A.I.C.S.: 513210
Vincent Polidoro *(Founder & CTO)*

ACCELERA SOLUTIONS, INC.
12150 Monument Dr Ste 800, Fairfax,
VA 22033
Tel.: (800) 506-0182
Web Site:
    http://www.accelerasolutions.com
Sales Range: $10-24.9 Million
Virtualization Solutions
N.A.I.C.S.: 541512
Chong Yi *(CEO)*
Greg Farias *(Controller)*
Terrill Andrews *(Exec VP)*
Steve Daly *(Exec VP)*
Steve Weiss *(Pres & COO)*
Jason March *(VP-Growth & Dev)*
Andrea J. Goldsmith *(Founder)*
Andrew Schreiner *(Mgr-Principal
Mktg)*
Dennis Groh *(Exec Dir-Corp Rels)*

ACCELERATE SOLAR LLC
10345 Nations Ford Rd Ste W, Char-
lotte, NC 28273
Web Site: http://www.accelerate-
    solar.com
Year Founded: 2012
Sales Range: $1-9.9 Million
Emp.: 28
Solar Panels Installation Services
N.A.I.C.S.: 238210
Xavier Veille *(CEO)*
Chris Verner *(COO)*
Mathew King *(CFO)*
David Verner *(CTO)*
Patrick Wylie *(VP-Sls)*

ACCELERATED CHRISTIAN
EDUCATION INC.
2600 Ace Ln, Lewisville, TX 75067
Tel.: (615) 612-5200
Web Site:
    https://www.aceministries.com
Year Founded: 1970
Rev.: $37,700,000
Emp.: 100
Book Publishing & Printing Services
N.A.I.C.S.: 513130
Scott Spencer *(Controller)*

ACCELERATED CLAIMS INC.
PO Box 2315, Kennesaw, GA 30156
Web Site:
    https://www.accelclaims.com
Year Founded: 2006
Sales Range: $1-9.9 Million
Emp.: 48
Medical Claims Adjusters of Motor
Vehicle Accident Victims
N.A.I.C.S.: 524292
Phil Wofford *(CFO)*

ACCELERATED INTERNA-
TIONAL FORWARDERS LLC.
3726 Lake Ave, Fort Wayne, IN
46805
Tel.: (260) 490-7473
Web Site: http://www.accelerated-
international.com
Year Founded: 1999
Sales Range: $25-49.9 Million
Emp.: 30
Freight Transportation Arrangement
Services
N.A.I.C.S.: 488510
Jackie Dennis *(Pres)*

ACCELERATED PHARMA, INC.
15w 155 81st St, Burr Ridge, IL
60527
Tel.: (847) 960-5630   DE
Web Site:
    http://www.apipharmaceuticals.com
Year Founded: 2014
Emp.: 7
Biopharmaceutical Research & De-
velopment

N.A.I.C.S.: 541715
Randy S. Saluck *(CFO)*
Daniel Perez *(Chm)*
Michael Fonsteix *(Pres & CEO)*
Ekaterina Nikolaevskaya *(COO)*
Dmitry Prudnikov *(Chief Medical
Officer)*

ACCELERATED WASTE SOLU-
TIONS, LLC
8710 W Hillsborough Ave, Tampa, FL
33615
Tel.: (813) 321-7333
Web Site:
    http://www.acceleratedwaste.com
Sales Range: $1-9.9 Million
Waste Removal Services
N.A.I.C.S.: 562111
Fred Tomlin *(Dir-Bus Dev)*
Sherrod Hunter *(Dir-Ops)*

ACCELERATION COMMUNITY
OF COMPANIES
1875 Century Park E Ste 1200, Los
Angeles, CA 90067
Tel.: (424) 224-9226
Web Site: https://accelerationcc.com
Marketing & Advertising
N.A.I.C.S.: 541810
Michael Nyman *(Founder & CEO)*

Subsidiaries:

MKG Productions, LLC **(1)**
599 Broadway 4th Floor, New York, NY
10012
Tel.: (212) 620-7770
Web Site: http://www.thisismkg.com
Creative Digital & Interactive Marketing Ser-
vices, Live Events & Social Media Services
N.A.I.C.S.: 541820
Maneesh K. Goyal *(Founder & Chm)*
Tracy Bussan *(Pres)*
Lauren Austin *(Dir-Creative)*
Christine Capone *(Dir-Mktg & Strategic
Partnerships)*
Jake Brooks-Harris *(Pres-MKG West)*

Division (Domestic):

MKG Chicago **(2)**
1017 W Washington Unit 2J, Chicago, IL
60607   **(100%)**
Tel.: (312) 620-7000
Web Site: http://www.thisismkg.com
Brand Strategy, Social Media Marketing &
Web & Digital Design
N.A.I.C.S.: 541820
Sean Callahan *(Mng Dir)*

MKG West **(2)**
8314 Beverly Blvd Ste 204, Los Angeles,
CA 90048   **(100%)**
Tel.: (323) 656-7770
Web Site: http://www.thisismkg.com
Brand Strategy, Event Production & Digital
Integration
N.A.I.C.S.: 541820
Jake Brooks-Harris *(Mng Dir)*

ACCELLION, INC.
1804 Embarcadero Rd Ste 200, Palo
Alto, CA 94303
Tel.: (650) 485-4300
Web Site: http://www.accellion.com
Year Founded: 1997
Sales Range: $50-74.9 Million
Emp.: 200
Enterprise-Class Mobile File Sharing
Solutions
N.A.I.C.S.: 513210
Yorgen H. Edholm *(Pres)*
Paula Skokowski *(CMO)*
Glen Segal *(CFO & VP-Bus Dev)*
Rebecca Soler *(VP-HR)*
Kieran O'Shaughnessy *(Dir-Sls-Asia-
Pacific)*
Rajeev Gupta *(VP-Tech)*
Vijay Rao *(VP-Sys Engrg)*
Jonathan Yaron *(Chm & CEO)*

Accellion, Inc.—(Continued)

ACCELLOS, INC.
90 S Cascade Ave Ste 1200, Colorado Springs, CO 80903
Tel.: (719) 433-7000   DE
Web Site: http://www.accellos.com
Supply Chain Software & Services
N.A.I.C.S.: 513210
Michael J. Cornell *(Co-Founder & CEO)*
Ross Elliott *(Co-Founder, Chief Strategy Officer & Exec VP)*
E. Flint Seaton *(Co-Founder & CFO)*

Subsidiaries:

HighJump Software Inc.   (1)
5600 W 83rd St Ste 600, Minneapolis, MN 55437
Tel.: (952) 947-4088
Web Site: http://www.highjump.com
Supply Chain Software Publisher
N.A.I.C.S.: 513210
Sean Elliott *(CTO)*
Hans-Georg Reichl *(CFO)*
Bill Ryan *(COO-North America)*

Subsidiary (Domestic):

Nexternal Solutions Inc.   (2)
560 Carlsbad Village Dr Ste 204, Carlsbad, CA 92008
Tel.: (760) 730-9015
Web Site: http://www.nexternal.com
Sales Range: $1-9.9 Million
Emp.: 30
Software Solutions for Supply Chain Management
N.A.I.C.S.: 513210
Taryn Reynolds *(Mgr-Acct)*
Alex Gile *(Founder)*

Prophesy Transportation Solutions, Inc.   (2)
204C W Newberry Rd, Bloomfield, CT 06002-1308
Tel.: (860) 243-0533
Web Site: http://www.mile.com
Sales Range: $10-24.9 Million
Emp.: 30
Transportation Software & Solutions
N.A.I.C.S.: 513210
William Ashburn *(Sr VP & Gen Mgr)*

Redtail Solutions Inc   (2)
112 Turnpike Rd Suite 201, Westborough, MA 01581
Tel.: (508) 983-1900
Web Site: http://www.redtailsolutions.com
Sales Range: $1-9.9 Million
Data Processing, Hosting & Related Services
N.A.I.C.S.: 518210

Subsidiary (Non-US):

Wesupply Limited   (2)
9 & 10 Rowan House Westwood Way, Westwood Business Park, Coventry, CV4 8LE, United Kingdom
Tel.: (44) 8456436600
Web Site: http://www.wesupply.com
Business Administration Software Development Services
N.A.I.C.S.: 541511
David Grosvenor *(CEO)*
Donna Lane *(Dir-Fin & Implementation Svcs)*
Nigel Kibble *(Dir-Dev)*
Nick Fernihough *(Dir-Managed Svcs)*
Neil Phillips *(Chief Architect-Sys)*

ACCELMED PARTNERS II MANAGEMENT, LLC
400 Madison Ave Ste 9B, New York, NY 10017
Tel.: (212) 554-4601
Web Site: http://www.accelmed.com
Holding Company; Commercial Stage HealthTech Companies
N.A.I.C.S.: 551112
Uri Geiger *(Founder & Mng Partner)*

Subsidiaries:

TearLab Corp.   (1)

---

150 LaTerraza Blvd Ste 101, Escondido, CA 92025
Tel.: (858) 455-6006
Web Site: http://www.tearlab.com
Rev.: $22,655,000
Assets: $14,293,000
Liabilities: $40,314,000
Net Worth: ($26,021,000)
Earnings: ($5,416,000)
Emp.: 39
Fiscal Year-end: 12/31/2019
Ophthalmic Therapeutic Products Researcher & Mfr
N.A.I.C.S.: 325413
Benjamin Sullivan *(Founder & Chief Scientific Officer)*
Michael A. Lemp *(Chief Medical Officer)*
Michael Berg *(VP-Regulatory)*
Steve Zmina *(VP-Mfg & Engrg)*
Michael Marquez *(CFO)*
Sam Fakhoury *(VP-Quality, Compliance & Supply Chain)*
Adam Szaronos *(Pres & CEO)*
Jim Mazzo *(Chm)*

ACCELON CAPITAL LLC
2470 El Camino Real Ste 210, Palo Alto, CA 94306
Tel.: (650) 213-8353
Web Site:
        http://www.acceloncapital.com
Privater Equity Firm
N.A.I.C.S.: 523999
Abhijit Phanse *(Mng Partner)*

Subsidiaries:

UnitedLayer, Inc.   (1)
200 Paul Ave Ste 110, San Francisco, CA 94124
Tel.: (415) 349-2102
Web Site: http://www.unitedlayer.com
Sales Range: $1-9.9 Million
Emp.: 20
Colocation & Managed Hosting Services
N.A.I.C.S.: 518210
Abhijit Phanse *(CEO)*

ACCENT ANNEX ENTERPRISES INC.
1009 McDermott Rd, Metairie, LA 70001
Tel.: (504) 733-4700
Rev.: $12,916,641
Emp.: 25
Carnival Supplies
N.A.I.C.S.: 424990

ACCENT MEDIA PRODUCTIONS, INC.
1937 Reprise Ct, Vienna, VA 22182
Tel.: (703) 356-9427   VA
Web Site:
        https://www.accentmediainc.com
Year Founded: 1988
Sales Range: $1-9.9 Million
Emp.: 10
Public Relations Agency
N.A.I.C.S.: 541820
Cecilia Domeyco *(Pres, Dir & Producer)*
Jack Jorgens *(VP & Producer)*

ACCENT WINDOWS INC.
14175 E 42nd Ave, Denver, CO 80241
Tel.: (303) 295-1170
Web Site:
        http://www.accentwindows.com
Rev.: $13,864,000
Emp.: 110
Mfr of Metal Sash, Doors & Windows
N.A.I.C.S.: 332321
Anthony Rodriguez *(Mgr-Matls)*
Cindi Tetley *(Office Mgr-HR)*

ACCENT WIRE
10131 FM 2920, Tomball, TX 77375
Tel.: (281) 251-0700
Web Site: http://www.accentwire.com
Year Founded: 1986

Emp.: 200
Wire Product Distr
N.A.I.C.S.: 423510
Bill Sims *(Pres)*

ACCESS
701 Patterson Ave, Roanoke, VA 24016
Tel.: (540) 344-8499   VA
Web Site: http://www.visitaccess.com
Year Founded: 1996
Sales Range: $10-24.9 Million
Emp.: 14
Advetising Agency
N.A.I.C.S.: 541810
Alex Blavatnik *(Vice Chm & Exec VP)*
Todd Marcum *(Pres & Sr Partner)*
Tony Pearman *(Sr Partner & Chief Creative Officer)*
Kris Bailey *(Assoc Dir-Creative)*
Laura Wood *(Sr Acct Mgr & Assoc)*
Gary Gilmore *(Assoc Dir-Creative)*
Terri Jones *(Principal-PR)*
Rachel Spencer *(Acct Mgr)*

ACCESS ADVERTISING, LLC
1100 Main St Ste 206, Kansas City, MO 64105
Tel.: (816) 471-1577
Web Site:
        http://www.accessadvertising.com
Year Founded: 2001
Advetising Agency
N.A.I.C.S.: 541810
Trae Nunnink *(CEO)*

ACCESS CAPITAL SERVICES, INC.
18377 Beach Blvd Ste 214, Huntington Beach, CA 92648
Tel.: (714) 415-7820   CA
Web Site:
        https://www.accesscapitalcorp.com
Year Founded: 2002
Sales Range: $1-9.9 Million
Emp.: 15
Financial Services
N.A.I.C.S.: 525990
Anthony Monti *(Pres)*

ACCESS CAPITAL, INC.
405 Park Ave Fl 16, New York, NY 10022
Tel.: (212) 644-9300
Web Site:
        http://www.accesscapital.com
Sales Range: $50-74.9 Million
Emp.: 37
Financial Services
N.A.I.C.S.: 522299
Miles M. Stuchin *(Co-Founder & Chm)*
Paul Mehring *(Co-Pres)*
Marc Postiglione *(VP & Acct Mgr)*
Angela Santi *(Co-Pres)*
Terry M. Keating *(CEO)*
Marcie Stuchin *(Co-Founder)*
Brian Richardson *(Sr VP-Bus Dev)*
Raphael Torres *(Exec VP & Head-Bus Dev)*
Brian Sheehy *(Officer-Bus Dev & VP)*
John Belling *(Chief Credit Officer & Exec VP)*

ACCESS DESTINATION SERVICES
3515 Hancock St Ste 200, San Diego, CA 92110
Tel.: (619) 299-2200
Web Site: http://www.accessdmc.com
Year Founded: 1970
Sales Range: $25-49.9 Million
Emp.: 857
Destination Management Services & Event Production Services
N.A.I.C.S.: 561599

Jennifer Miller *(CEO)*
Christopher H. Lee *(Partner)*
Jim Cavanagh *(Sr VP-Sls)*

Subsidiaries:

ACCESS Destination Services   (1)
7525 E Camelback Rd, Scottsdale, AZ 85251   (100%)
Tel.: (480) 664-1500
Web Site: http://www.accessdmc.com
Destination Management Services
N.A.I.C.S.: 561599
Christopher H. Lee *(CEO)*

ACCESS Destination Services   (1)
3363 Sheridan St Ste 205, Hollywood, FL 33021   (100%)
Tel.: (954) 927-0507
Web Site: http://www.accessdmc.com
Emp.: 8
Destination Management & Event Services
N.A.I.C.S.: 561599
Jeff Nelke *(Partner)*

ACCESS Destination Services   (1)
1050 E Flamingo Rd, Las Vegas, NV 89119   (100%)
Tel.: (702) 489-4477
Web Site: http://www.accessdmc.com
Emp.: 5
Destination Management Services
N.A.I.C.S.: 561599

ACCESS Destination Services   (1)
6881 Kingspointe Pkwy Ste 2, Orlando, FL 32819   (100%)
Tel.: (407) 839-4752
Web Site: http://www.accessdmc.com
Emp.: 20
Destination Management & Event Services
N.A.I.C.S.: 561599
J. B. Ryan *(Partner)*

ACCESS Destination Services   (1)
7 Bendix Ste A, Irvine, CA 92618-2031   (100%)
Tel.: (949) 454-2111
Web Site: http://www.accessdmc.com
Emp.: 13
Destination Management & Event Services
N.A.I.C.S.: 561599
Candace Bisconte *(Partner)*
Greg Bisconte *(Partner)*

ACCESS Destination Services   (1)
4004 Ck St Ste 1, Palm Desert, CA 92211   (100%)
Tel.: (760) 200-0112
Web Site: http://www.accessdmc.com
Destination Management Services
N.A.I.C.S.: 561599
Barbara Smith *(Partner)*
Ken Smith *(Partner)*

ACCESS Destination Services   (1)
8888 Governors Row, Dallas, TX 75247   (100%)
Tel.: (214) 350-6282
Web Site: http://www.accessdmc.com
Destination Management Services
N.A.I.C.S.: 561599
Jeff Davis *(Partner)*

ACCESS Destination Services - Chicago   (1)
27 E Monroe St, Chicago, IL 60603
Tel.: (312) 807-3700
Web Site: http://www.accessdmc.com
Destination Management Services
N.A.I.C.S.: 561599
Gary W. Marr *(Mng Partner)*

ACCESS Destination Services - Lafayette   (1)
242 Lafayette Cir Ste 2A, Lafayette, CA 94549
Tel.: (925) 283-0111
Web Site: http://www.accessdmc.com
Destination Management Services
N.A.I.C.S.: 561599

ACCESS DIRECT SYSTEMS, INC.
91 Executive Blvd, Farmingdale, NY 11735
Tel.: (631) 420-0770

Web Site:
http://www.accessresponsesite.com
Rev.: $49,300,000
Emp.: 468
Data Processing Hosting & Related Services
N.A.I.C.S.: 518210
Lori Messina *(Exec VP)*
John Dinozzi *(Pres)*
Robert Ingenito *(VP)*

ACCESS DISPLAY GROUP INC.
151 S Main St, Freeport, NY 11520
Web Site:
http://www.swingframe.com
Year Founded: 1992
Sales Range: $1-9.9 Million
Emp.: 22
Poster Frames & Display Cases
N.A.I.C.S.: 337215
Charles Abrams *(Pres & Founder)*

ACCESS EAST INC
2100 Stantonsburg Rd, Greenville, NC 27834
Tel.: (252) 847-5129   NC
Year Founded: 1995
Sales Range: $10-24.9 Million
Grantmaking Services
N.A.I.C.S.: 813219
Michelle Brooks *(VP)*
David Hughes *(Treas & Sec)*
Thomas Irons *(Chm)*
Joel Butler *(Pres)*

ACCESS GENETICS, LLC
7400 Flying Cloud Dr Ste 150, Eden Prairie, MN 55344
Tel.: (952) 942-0671   MN
Web Site: https://www.access-genetics.com
Year Founded: 2001
Sales Range: $10-24.9 Million
Molecular Testing Software, Laboratory Materials & Technical Services
N.A.I.C.S.: 541380
Elizabeth Skinner *(VP-Legal, Quality & Regulatory)*
Scott W. Kelley *(VP-Sls & Mktg)*

Subsidiaries:

OralDNA Labs, Inc.   (1)
7400 Flying Cloud Dr Ste 100, Eden Prairie, MN 55344
Tel.: (615) 577-9055
Web Site: http://www.oraldna.com
Medical Laboratory Services
N.A.I.C.S.: 621511
George Hoedeman *(CEO)*

ACCESS GROUP INC.
5500 Brandywine Pkwy, Wilmington, DE 19803
Tel.: (302) 477-4000
Web Site:
http://www.accessgroup.org
Sales Range: $600-649.9 Million
Emp.: 318
Consumer Lending
N.A.I.C.S.: 522291
Richard A. Matasar *(Chm)*
Christopher P. Chapman *(Pres & CEO)*
Mary S. Chan *(VP-IT)*
Elise S. Miller *(Exec Dir-Center Res & Policy Analysis)*
Cynthia Cassity *(VP-Mktg & Strategic Engagement)*
Libby Rosenberg *(Dir-Mktg)*
Hannah R. Arterian *(Chm)*
Lyssa Thaden *(Dir-Fin Education)*

ACCESS HEALTH CARE, LLC
5350 Spring Hill Dr, Spring Hill, FL 34606
Tel.: (352) 688-8116

Web Site:
http://www.accesshealthcarellc.net
Year Founded: 2001
Sales Range: $1-9.9 Million
Emp.: 500
Medical Practice
N.A.I.C.S.: 621111
Pariksith Singh *(Dir-Medical)*
Maria Scunziano-Singh *(Dir-Medical)*
Karen Hayes *(CFO)*
Dalton Benson *(Dir-Medical)*
Manjusri Vennamaneni *(Dir-Medical)*

ACCESS INDUSTRIES, INC.
730 5th Ave 20th Fl, New York, NY 10019
Tel.: (212) 247-6400   NY
Web Site:
http://www.accessindustries.com
Year Founded: 1986
Investment Holding Company
N.A.I.C.S.: 551112
Lincoln E. Benet *(CEO)*
Leonard Blavatnik *(Founder & Chm)*
Donald A. Wagner *(Sr Mng Dir)*
Barry Dinaburg *(Sr VP-Global Tax)*
Alejandro Moreno *(Sr VP & Gen Counsel)*
Peter Thoren *(Exec VP)*
Liam Ratcliffe *(Head-Biotechnology)*
Christine Borowski *(VP)*
Pueo Keffer *(Executives)*

Subsidiaries:

Clal Industries Ltd.   (1)
3 Azrieli Center 45 floor, Tel Aviv, 67023, Israel   (49.9%)
Tel.: (972) 36075777
Web Site: http://www.cii.co.il
Holding Company; Industrial & Technological Products & Services
N.A.I.C.S.: 551112
Avi Fischer *(Chm & CEO)*
Gonen Biber *(VP-Fin)*
Yehuda Ben-Ezra *(VP & Comptroller)*
Daniel Shinar *(CEO-ClalTech & Head-Tech Investments)*
Nufar Malovani *(Gen Counsel, Sec & VP)*
Menashe Sagiv *(CFO)*

Subsidiary (Domestic):

Clal Biotechnology Industries Ltd.   (2)
Azrieli Center Triangle Building 45th Flr, Tel Aviv, 67023, Israel   (62.93%)
Tel.: (972) 36121616
Web Site: https://www.cbi.co.il
Rev.: $10,813,924
Assets: $43,759,082
Liabilities: $10,216,328
Net Worth: $33,542,754
Earnings: ($7,761,569)
Fiscal Year-end: 12/31/2023
Miscellaneous Financial Investment Activities
N.A.I.C.S.: 523999
Ofer Gonen *(CEO)*
Avi Fischer *(Chm)*
Arnon Aharon *(Dir)*

Subsidiary (Domestic):

MediWound Ltd.   (3)
42 Hayarkon Street, Yavne, 8122745, Israel   (55.5%)
Tel.: (972) 779714100
Web Site: https://www.mediwound.com
Rev.: $18,686,000
Assets: $66,459,000
Liabilities: $31,595,000
Net Worth: $34,864,000
Earnings: ($6,716,000)
Emp.: 88
Fiscal Year-end: 12/31/2023
Wound Treatment Product Mfr
N.A.I.C.S.: 325412
Nachum Shamir *(Chm)*
Lior Rosenberg *(Founder & Chief Medical Officer)*
Ofer Gonen *(CEO)*
Andrey Kon *(VP & Plant Mgr)*
Eilon Asculai *(VP-R&D)*

Yaron Meyer *(Gen Counsel, Sec & Exec VP)*
Keren David-Zarbiv *(VP-Clinical Affairs)*
Ety Klinger *(Chief R&D Officer)*
Nachum Shamir *(Chm)*
Robert J. Snyder *(Chief Medical Officer)*
Barry Wolfenson *(Exec VP)*
Alicia Torrenova *(VP)*
Aya Ben-Yakov *(Dir)*
Shmulik Hess *(COO & Chief Comml Officer)*
Hani Luxenburg *(CFO)*
Roni Solomon *(VP-Fin)*
Alexandra Teplitsky *(Exec Dir-Quality Assurance)*

Subsidiary (Domestic):

Clal Electronic Industries Ltd.   (2)
45 Fl 3 Azrieli Ctr Triangle Power, Tel Aviv, 67023, Israel   (100%)
Tel.: (972) 36075777
Web Site: http://www.cii.co.il
Sales Range: $75-99.9 Million
Emp.: 65
Investment Company
N.A.I.C.S.: 523940
Avraham Fischer *(CEO & Chm)*

Unit (Domestic):

Clal Information Technology   (3)
Clal Tower Bldg 4, Kiryat Atidim, Tel Aviv, 61581, Israel
Tel.: (972) 3 7650215
Data Communications & Content Services
N.A.I.C.S.: 334290

Subsidiary (Domestic):

Clal Energy   (2)
3 Azrieli Ctr 45 fl, Tel Aviv, 67023, Israel
Tel.: (972) 36075777
Web Site: http://www.cii.co.il
Sales Range: $50-74.9 Million
Emp.: 10
Private Power Generation, Renewable Energy & Natural Energy Resources
N.A.I.C.S.: 221122
Nochi Dankner *(Chm)*
Avraham Fischer *(Co-CEO)*
Daniel Shinar *(CEO)*

Golf & Co. Ltd.   (2)
Pinchas Rosen 57, Tel Aviv, 69512, Israel   (62.82%)
Tel.: (972) 36451515
Web Site: http://www.golfco.co.il
Rev.: $258,614,229
Assets: $272,868,879
Liabilities: $218,656,797
Net Worth: $54,212,082
Earnings: ($4,776,314)
Emp.: 2,700
Fiscal Year-end: 12/31/2022
Clothing & Accessories Retailer
N.A.I.C.S.: 458110
Raviv Brookmayer *(CEO)*

Holding (Non-US):

Ice Group ASA   (2)
Nydalsveien 18B, 0484, Oslo, Norway
Tel.: (47) 21000000
Web Site: http://www.icegroup.com
Rev.: $244,348,860
Assets: $743,898,750
Liabilities: $953,123,920
Net Worth: ($209,225,170)
Earnings: ($113,656,060)
Emp.: 226
Fiscal Year-end: 12/31/2020
Telecommunication Servicesb
N.A.I.C.S.: 517810
Eivind Helgaker *(CEO)*
Henning Karlsrud *(CFO)*
Shiraz Abid *(Chief Comml Officer)*
Hans Heggenhaugen *(Chief Product Officer)*
Jan-Erik Hvidsten *(CTO)*

Subsidiary (Domestic):

Kitan Industries Ltd.   (2)
3 Azrieli Center, 45 floor, Tel Aviv, 67023, Israel
Tel.: (972) 06075777
Web Site: http://www.kitan.com
Textiles
N.A.I.C.S.: 313310

Nesher Israel Cement Enterprises Ltd.   (2)
5 Druyanov St, Tel Aviv, 63143, Israel   (75%)
Tel.: (972) 36075777
Web Site: http://www.nesher.co.il
Sales Range: $50-74.9 Million
Cement Production; Owned 75% by Clal Industries & Investments & 25% by CRH, plc
N.A.I.C.S.: 327310

Subsidiary (Domestic):

MP Mineral Ltd.   (3)
5 Druyanov St., Tel Aviv, 63143, Israel
Tel.: (972) 3 6075 777
White Chalk Quarrying
N.A.I.C.S.: 212390

EP Energy Corporation   (1)
601 Travis St Ste 1400, Houston, TX 77002   (13.9%)
Tel.: (713) 997-1000
Web Site: http://www.epenergy.com
Sales Range: $1-4.9 Billion
Emp.: 372
Holding Company; Oil & Natural Gas Exploration, Development & Production Services
N.A.I.C.S.: 551112
Jace D. Locke *(Gen Counsel, Sec & VP)*
Kyle A. McCuen *(CFO, Chief Acctg Officer, Treas & Sr VP)*
Raymond J. Ambrose *(Sr VP-Engrg & Subsurface)*
Chad D. England *(Sr VP-Ops)*
Peter D. Addison *(VP-Land & Land Admin)*
Mark E. Hargis *(VP-Geoscience)*
Dennis M. Price *(VP-Mktg)*
Alan R. Crain Jr. *(VP)*

Subsidiary (Domestic):

EP Energy LLC   (2)
1001 Louisiana St, Houston, TX 77002
Tel.: (713) 997-1200
Web Site: http://www.epenergy.com
Rev.: $1,323,999,999
Assets: $4,180,999,999
Liabilities: $4,779,999,999
Net Worth: ($599,000,000)
Earnings: ($1,002,999,999)
Emp.: 991
Fiscal Year-end: 12/31/2018
Oil & Natural Gas Exploration & Production
N.A.I.C.S.: 211120
Kyle McCuen *(CFO, Treas & Sr VP)*

Warner Music Group Corp.   (1)
1633 Broadway, New York, NY 10019
Tel.: (212) 275-2000
Web Site: https://www.wmg.com
Rev.: $6,426,000,000
Assets: $9,155,000,000
Liabilities: $8,480,000,000
Net Worth: $675,000,000
Earnings: $478,000,000
Emp.: 5,800
Fiscal Year-end: 09/30/2024
Recorded Music Publisher
N.A.I.C.S.: 512230
Leonard Blavatnik *(Vice Chm)*
Paul M. Robinson *(Gen Counsel & Exec VP)*
Maria Osherova *(Chief People Officer & Exec VP)*
Max Lousada *(CEO-Recorded Music)*
James Steven *(Chief Comm Officer & Exec VP)*
Robert Kyncl *(CEO)*
Oana Ruxandra *(Chief Digital Officer & Exec VP-Bus Dev)*
Maurice Stinnett *(Head-Diversity, Inclusion & Equity-Global)*
Danielle M. Lee *(Pres-Warner Music Artist-Fan Experiences)*
Louis Dickler *(Sr VP & Controller)*
Leila Oliveira *(Pres-Brazil)*
Alejandro Duque *(Pres-Latin America)*
Simon Robson *(Pres-Intl-Recorded Music)*
Charlotte Saxe *(Sr VP-Legal & Bus Affairs-UK)*
Shawnae Corbett-Rice *(Sr VP-Mktg)*
Dionnee Harper *(Exec VP-Mktg & Artist Dev)*
Bernadette Rotolo *(Sr VP)*
Charlie Cohen *(Pres)*
Janelle Curtis *(Chief Enterprise Transformation Officer)*
Moin Haque *(Chief Data Officer)*
Michael M. Lynton *(Chm)*

Access Industries, Inc.—(Continued)

Subsidiary (Domestic):

Asylum Records LLC (2)
1290 Ave of the Americas, New York, NY 10104
Tel.: (212) 707-3020
Web Site: http://www.asylumrecords.com
Sales Range: $10-24.9 Million
Emp.: 50
Records, Tapes & Music Publisher
N.A.I.C.S.: 512230

Atlantic Records Group (2)
1290 Ave of the Americas, New York, NY 10104-0101
Tel.: (212) 707-2978
Web Site: http://www.atlanticrecords.com
Sales Range: $50-74.9 Million
Music Based Content Company
N.A.I.C.S.: 449210
Julie Greenwald (Co-Chm & COO)
Craig Kallman (Co-Chm & CEO)
Pete Ganbarg (Pres-A&R)
Sheila Richman (Exec VP-Press & Media)
Dionnee Harper (Sr VP-Urban Mktg)
Marsha St. Hubert (Sr VP-Urban Mktg)
John Mcmann (Sr VP-Pop & Rhythm)
Jessica Hiromoto (Sr Dir-Rhythm-Los Angeles)
Randy Reyes (Natl Dir-Pop & Rhythm Mixshow)
Austin Daboh (Exec VP-UK)
Liz Goodwin (Gen Mgr-UK)
Rich Castillo (Dir-A&R-UK)
Ed Howard (Co-Pres)
Briony Turner (Co-Pres)
Keith Parker (VP-A&R)
Dallas Martin (Sr VP-A&R)

Subsidiary (Domestic):

Elektra Records (3)
1290 Avenue of the Americas, New York, NY 10104
Tel.: (212) 707-3300
Web Site: http://www.elektra.com
Records, Tapes & Music Publisher
N.A.I.C.S.: 334610
Craig Kallman (Chm & COO)
Gregg Nadel (Co-Pres)
Suzy Yoder (Head-Digital Mktg-Elektra Music Grp)
Katie Robinson (VP-Mktg-Elektra Music Grp-Los Angeles)
Mike Easterlin (Co-Pres)
Greg Dorfman (Exec VP-Promotion)

Joint Venture (Domestic):

Bad Boy Records (2)
1710 Broadway, New York, NY 10019
Tel.: (212) 381-1540
Web Site: http://www.badboyonline.com
Sales Range: $1-9.9 Million
Music Record Producer; Owned 50% by Bad Boy Worldwide Entertainment Group & 50% by Warner Music Group, Inc.
N.A.I.C.S.: 711130

Subsidiary (Non-US):

Parlophone Records Limited (2)
27 Wrights Lane, London, W8 5SW, United Kingdom
Tel.: (44) 2077957000
Web Site: http://www.parlophone.co.uk
Sales Range: $400-449.9 Million
Music Publisher & Distr
N.A.I.C.S.: 512230
Miles Leonard (Chm)
Nick Burgess (Co-Pres)
Mark Mitchell (Co-Pres)

Subsidiary (Domestic):

Warner Bros. Records, Inc. (2)
3300 Warner Blvd, Burbank, CA 91505
Tel.: (818) 846-9090
Web Site:
 http://www.warnerbrosrecords.com
Sales Range: $75-99.9 Million
Records, Tapes & Music Publisher
N.A.I.C.S.: 512290
Lori Feldman (Exec VP-Strategic Mktg)
Lee L'Heureux (Sr VP-Rhythm & Urban Promotion)
Monti Olson (Sr VP-Artist & Repertoire)

Allyson Cherny-Weston (VP-Brand Partnerships)
P. J. Bloom (Sr VP-Film, Television Music & Soundtracks)
Aaron Bay-Schuck (Co-Chm & CEO)
Tom Corson (Co-Chm & COO)
Laura Swanson (Exec VP-Media & Strategic Dev)
Phil Christie (Pres)
Jennifer Ivory (Gen Mgr-UK)
Sebastian Simone (Head-Digital Strategy-UK)
Wilt Wallace (VP-Urban & Rhythm Promotion-Atlanta)
Larry Mattera (Exec VP/Gen Mgr-Commerce & Mktg)
Mike Sherwood (Sr VP-Revenue & Comml Accts)
Yashar Zadeh (VP)
Aishah White (Sr VP)
Claudia Butzky (Sr VP-Brand Partnerships, Strategic Mktg & Comml Sync Licensing)
Dalia Ganz (Sr VP-Digital Mktg)
Sean Stevens (VP-A&R & Head-Res & Analytics)

Subsidiary (Domestic):

Reprise Records, Inc. (3)
1290 6th Ave, New York, NY 10019
Tel.: (212) 707-3200
Web Site: http://www.repriserec.com
Sales Range: $25-49.9 Million
Records, Tapes & Music Publisher
N.A.I.C.S.: 459510
Howie Klein (Pres)

Sire Records (3)
1290 6th Ave, New York, NY 10019
Tel.: (212) 707-3200
Web Site: http://www.sirerecords.com
Sales Range: $10-24.9 Million
Emp.: 40
Records, Tapes & Music Publisher
N.A.I.C.S.: 512290
Seymour Stein (Gen Mgr)

Subsidiary (Non-US):

Warner Music Australia Pty Ltd (2)
39-47 Albany St, Crows Nest, Sydney, 2065, NSW, Australia
Tel.: (61) 299501500
Web Site: http://www.warnermusic.com.au
Sales Range: $25-49.9 Million
Emp.: 85
Music Producer & Distr
N.A.I.C.S.: 334610

Warner Music Benelux N.V. (2)
Romeinse Steenweg 468, Grimbergen, 1853, Belgium
Tel.: (32) 22630300
Web Site: http://www.warnermusic.be
Sales Range: $25-49.9 Million
Emp.: 20
Music Publisher & Distr
N.A.I.C.S.: 512250
Oligi Sam Primtont (Mgr)

Warner Music Denmark (2)
Falkoner Alle 7 3 Fl, Frederiksberg, 2000, Denmark
Tel.: (45) 36935400
Web Site: http://www.warnermusic.dk
Sales Range: $25-49.9 Million
Emp.: 22
Music Publisher & Distr
N.A.I.C.S.: 512230
Yan Erik Stig (Mgr-Mktg)

Warner Music France (2)
118 Rue du Mont Cenis, 75018, Paris, France
Tel.: (33) 156557777
Sales Range: $25-49.9 Million
Emp.: 200
Music Publisher & Distr
N.A.I.C.S.: 512230

Warner Music Norway (2)
Karl Johans Gate 12J, PO Box 492, Sentrum, 0154, Oslo, Norway
Tel.: (47) 23407700
Web Site: http://www.warnermusic.no
Sales Range: $25-49.9 Million
Emp.: 25
Music Publishing Services
N.A.I.C.S.: 512250
Mike Herbrik (Gen Mgr)

Warner Music Sweden (2)
Limmegatan 89 B, Box 240 58, 104 50, Stockholm, Sweden
Tel.: (46) 852715000
Web Site: http://www.emi.se
Sales Range: $25-49.9 Million
Emp.: 40
Music Publisher & Distr
N.A.I.C.S.: 512250
Helen McLaughlin (Mng Dir)

Division (Domestic):

Warner Special Products (2)
3400 W Olive Ave 5th Fl, Burbank, CA 91505-4253
Tel.: (818) 238-6200
Web Site:
 http://www.warnerspecialproducts.com
Sales Range: $10-24.9 Million
Emp.: 70
Records, Tapes & Music Marketer
N.A.I.C.S.: 512290

Subsidiary (Domestic):

Warner/Chappell Music, Inc. (2)
10585 Santa Monica Blvd, Los Angeles, CA 90025-4921
Tel.: (310) 441-8600
Web Site: http://www.warnerchappell.com
Sales Range: $50-74.9 Million
Records, Tapes & Music Publisher
N.A.I.C.S.: 512230
Valentin Blavatnik (Sr Dir-Bus Dev)
Dave Pettigrew (Sr VP-Strategic Mktg)
Ben Vaughn (CEO-Nashville)
Ron Broitman (Exec VP & Head-Synchronization)
Sean Condon (VP-Strategic Mktg)
David Costa (Mgr-Licensing & Sync Bus Dev)
Jessica Cutri (Mgr-Film & Television)
Devin Penzella (Mgr-Licensing)
Pat Woods (Sr VP-Licensing)
Monica Lee (Pres-Asia Pacific)
Kate Alderton (VP-Ops & Fin-UK)
Mike Lavin (Dir-Fin-Europe)
Rob Owen (VP-Creative, Catalogue & Mktg)
Katie Jelen (Mgr-Creative-Synchronization)
Eric Mackay (Exec VP-Digital Strategy-Global)
Javier Dean (Dir-A&R-Spain)
Santiago Menendez-Pidal (Mng Dir-Latin America)
Carianne Marshall (Co-Chm & COO)
Travis Carter (VP-A&R)
Rich Robinson (Exec VP-Sync & Creative Svcs-London)
Carlos Ruiz Diaz (Mng Dir-Mexico)
Menendez Menendez (Pres-Latin America)
Mary Nunez (VP-Sync-Latin)
Guy Moot (Co-Chm & CEO)
Alec Sharpe (VP-Bus Dev & Ops-Production Music Div)
Pat Weaver (Head-Production-Production Music Div)
Ashley Winton (Sr VP-Creative Svcs)
Shani Gonzales (Mng Dir-UK & Head-A&R-Intl)
Amber Davis (Head-A&R)
June Gao (Gen Mgr-China)
Jenni Pfaff (Sr VP & Head-Global Strategic Integration & Ops)
Jesse Dang (Sr VP-People)
Nathalie Monnet (Dir-Legal-France)
Lucie Sort (Dir-Fin & Admin-France)
Matthieu Tessier (Mng Dir)

ACCESS INSURANCE COMPANY

3 Ravinia Dr Ste 400, Atlanta, GA 30346
Tel.: (770) 234-3600
Web Site: http://www.access.com
Year Founded: 1994
Sales Range: $300-349.9 Million
Emp.: 536
Auto, Property & Casualty Insurance Services
N.A.I.C.S.: 524210
Michael McMenamin (Chm, Pres & CEO)
Daniel Gerard Lazarek (Treas & Sec)

ACCESS MAIL PROCESSING

SERVICES, INC.
14240 62nd St N, Clearwater, FL 33760
Tel.: (727) 539-6245   FL
Web Site: http://www.accessmail.biz
Year Founded: 1985
Sales Range: $1-9.9 Million
Emp.: 30
Mail Processing Services
N.A.I.C.S.: 561431
Elizabeth A. Bell (Pres)
Frank Stofel (Mgr-Transportation)
John Sanford (Mgr-IT)

ACCESS MEDIA 3, INC.

900 Commerce Dr, Oak Brook, IL 60537
Tel.: (630) 230-0555
Web Site: http://www.am3inc.com
Year Founded: 2006
Sales Range: $10-24.9 Million
Emp.: 75
Digital Media Solutions
N.A.I.C.S.: 541990
Eric Welles (VP-Bus Dev)
Mark McMaster (VP-Customer Experience)
Alan Rosenberg (CEO)

ACCESS OVERHEAD DOOR, INC.

4555 Forest Hill Cir, Fort Worth, TX 76140
Tel.: (817) 478-2808   TX
Web Site:
 https://accessoverheaddoor.com
Year Founded: 1984
Sales Range: $10-24.9 Million
Emp.: 10
Fiscal Year-end: 03/31/14
Lumber, Plywood, Millwork & Wood Panel Merchant Whslr
N.A.I.C.S.: 423310

ACCESS SYSTEMS, INC.

11710 Plz America Dr Ste 900, Reston, VA 20190
Tel.: (703) 464-6900
Web Site: http://www.accsys-inc.com
Sales Range: $25-49.9 Million
Emp.: 350
Network Management & Website Development Services for the Federal Government
N.A.I.C.S.: 519290
Julie S. Lee (Pres & CEO)
David E. Gardner (COO)

ACCESS TCA INC.

1 Main St, Whitinsville, MA 01588
Tel.: (508) 234-9791
Web Site: https://www.accesstca.com
Year Founded: 1985
Rev.: $40,000,000
Emp.: 125
Market Analysis & Research
N.A.I.C.S.: 541910
Michael C. Yag (Chm & CEO)
Jon Ellms (Principal & VP)
Stephen Ross (VP-Creative)
Jerry Grady (VP-Bus Dev)
Doug Liston (Dir-Production)
Corinna Chan (Dir-Client Svcs)
Danielle DelVecchio (Mgr-Client Svcs)
Scott Williams (Dir-Client Svcs-Boston)
Amy Yag-Sondrup (Pres)
Dean Cerrati (Dir-Production)
Ken Konicki (VP-Fin)
Bill Smith (Exec Creative Dir-San Francisco)
Wendi Sabo (VP-Mktg & Comm-Dallas)

ACCESS TECHNOLOGY SO-LUTIONS, LC
5252 N Edgewood Dr Ste 275, Provo, UT 84604
Web Site:
　http://www.corporate.accessts.com
Year Founded: 2002
Sales Range: $10-24.9 Million
Emp.: 53
Logistics & Transportation Service
N.A.I.C.S.: 541614
Chris Boyle (Pres & CEO)

ACCESS TELEVISION NET-WORK
2710 Alton Pkwy Ste 109, Irvine, CA 92606-2195
Tel.: (949) 263-9900
Web Site: http://www.accesstv.com
Year Founded: 1993
Sales Range: $10-24.9 Million
Emp.: 15
Distr of Infomercials & Other Paid Programming
N.A.I.C.S.: 516210
Robert T. Tyler (CFO & VP-Fin)

Subsidiaries:

Product Information Network　　(1)
2710 Alton Pkwy Ste 109, Irvine, CA 92606-2195　　(100%)
Tel.: (949) 263-9900
Web Site: http://www.pinnet.com
Sales Range: $10-24.9 Million
Emp.: 13
Cable Television Advertising Services
N.A.I.C.S.: 516120

ACCESS US OIL AND GAS INC.
673 Woodland Sq Lp SE, Lacey, WA 98503
Tel.: (206) 792-7578　　DE
Web Site: http://www.ausog.com
Year Founded: 2012
Sales Range: Less than $1 Million
Oil & Gas Exploration
N.A.I.C.S.: 211120
Michael Mattox (CEO)
Charles McSwain (CFO)
Yu Li (VP)

ACCESS VALUE INVESTORS LLC
200 West Madison St Ste 410, Chicago, IL 60606
Tel.: (312) 948-5615
Sales Range: $25-49.9 Million
Emp.: 8
Privater Equity Firm
N.A.I.C.S.: 523999
Charles T. Price (Principal)

Subsidiaries:

Avi Lion Holdings LLC　　(1)
3033 E 1st Ave Ste 501, Denver, CO 80206
Tel.: (303) 847-4100
Privater Equity Firm
N.A.I.C.S.: 523999

ACCESS-POWER, INC.
17164 Dune View Dr Apt 106, Grand Haven, MI 49417
Tel.: (616) 312-5390　　FL
Web Site: http://www.myaccess-power.com
Year Founded: 1996
Wireless Telecommunication Services
N.A.I.C.S.: 517112
Patrick J. Jensen (Pres & CEO)

ACCESSIBLE SPACE INC.
2550 University Ave W Ste 330 N, Saint Paul, MN 55114
Tel.: (651) 645-7271

Web Site:
　https://www.accessiblespace.org
Rev.: $24,357,715
Emp.: 50
Real Estate Managers
N.A.I.C.S.: 531210
Dan Billmark (Dir-Real Estate Dev)
Deborah Hellerud (Reg Mgr-Housing)
Judith Lemke-Kline (Dir-Fin)

ACCESSIBLE SYSTEMS, INC.
3025 W Jefferson Ave, Englewood, CO 80110
Tel.: (303) 816-3430
Web Site:
　https://www.accessiblemed.com
Year Founded: 1999
Emp.: 100
Medical, Dental & Hospital Equipment Whslr
N.A.I.C.S.: 423450

ACCESSORY EXPORT, LLC
4105 Indus Way, Riverside, CA 92503
Tel.: (951) 687-1140
Web Site:
　http://www.empirecase.com
Year Founded: 2005
Sales Range: $1-9.9 Million
Emp.: 24
Cellular Telephone Equipment Whslr
N.A.I.C.S.: 517112
William Land (Partner)
Zack Sawyer (Mgr-Customer Svc)

ACCESSORY NETWORK GROUP INC.
350 5th Ave Fl 4, New York, NY 10118-0219
Tel.: (212) 842-3000　　NY
Web Site:
　http://www.accessorynetwork.com
Year Founded: 1983
Sales Range: $25-49.9 Million
Emp.: 200
Womens, Childrens & Infants Clothing Mfr
N.A.I.C.S.: 424350
Karyn Weiss (Sr VP-Bus Dev & Licensing)

ACCESSORY PLACE INC.
12850 Memorial Dr Ste 1500, Houston, TX 77024-4975
Tel.: (713) 467-2106
Web Site:
　http://www.theaccessoryplace.com
Sales Range: $10-24.9 Million
Emp.: 40
Distr Of Bath Accessories
N.A.I.C.S.: 449129
Andrew McKemie (Pres)
Jeff Pennington (VP)

ACCESSORYGEEKS.COM
18430 San Jose Ave Unit B, City of Industry, CA 91748
Tel.: (626) 363-8500
Web Site:
　https://www.accessorygeeks.com
Year Founded: 2004
Sales Range: $1-9.9 Million
Emp.: 40
Supplier of Branded Cell Phone & Other Electronic Device Accessories
N.A.I.C.S.: 517121
David Byun (Pres)

ACCIDENT FUND INSURANCE COMPANY OF AMERICA
200 N Grand Ave, Lansing, MI 48933
Tel.: (517) 342-4200　　MI
Web Site:
　http://www.accidentfund.com
Year Founded: 1912

Sales Range: $600-649.9 Million
Emp.: 600
Workers Compensation Insurance Benefits
N.A.I.C.S.: 524298
Michael K. Britt (Pres)
Al Gileczek (VP-Bus Dev-Reg Ops)
Paul Kauffman (Dir-Medical Programs)
Lisa Riddle (VP-Claims & Medical Ops)
Linda Barnes (VP-Svc Center)
Dan Hassenzahl (Dir-South)
Mike Seling (VP-Bus Dev & Reg Ops)
Dean Holland (VP-Claims)

Subsidiaries:

United Wisconsin Insurance Company　　(1)
15200 W Small Rd, New Berlin, WI 53151
Tel.: (262) 787-7400
Web Site: http://www.unitedheartland.biz
Sales Range: $25-49.9 Million
Emp.: 350
Workers Compensation Specialist Services
N.A.I.C.S.: 524298
Stephan Cooper (Pres)
Rick Hobbs (VP-Claims & Managed Care)
Justin Bealhen (VP-Field Ops)

ACCION SOCIAL DE PUERTO RICO, INC.
PO Box 3930, Guaynabo, PR 00970-3930
Tel.: (787) 273-1878　　PR
Web Site: http://www.aspri-pr.org
Year Founded: 1982
Sales Range: $10-24.9 Million
Emp.: 555
Individual & Family Support Services
N.A.I.C.S.: 624190
Alicia Ramirez Suarez (CEO & Exec Dir)

ACCO ENGINEERED SYS-TEMS
6265 San Fernando Rd, Glendale, CA 91201-2214
Tel.: (818) 244-6571　　CA
Web Site: http://www.accoes.com
Year Founded: 1934
Sales Range: $450-499.9 Million
Emp.: 2,500
Heating, Ventilating & Air Conditioning Systems Designer & Mfr
N.A.I.C.S.: 238220
John Aversano (Chm)
Steven J. Smith (Sr VP-Building Svcs)
Jeffrey R. Marrs (CEO)

Subsidiaries:

All Area Plumbing, Inc.　　(1)
6446 E Washington Blvd, Commerce, CA 90040
Tel.: (626) 966-2026
Web Site: http://www.allareaplumbing.com
Sales Range: $1-9.9 Million
Emp.: 235
Plumbing & Mechanical Piping Contractor
N.A.I.C.S.: 238220
Robert Felix (VP-Plumbing Grp)
Steve Felix (Sr Project Mgr)
Bryan Felix (Mgr-BIM & Engrg)
Steve Clark (Mgr-Sls & Construction)
Kate Tunnicliffe (Mgr-Bus Ops-Plumbing)

ACCOLO, INC.
900 Larkspur Landing Cir Ste 160, Larkspur, CA 94939
Tel.: (415) 785-7833
Web Site: http://www.accolo.com
Year Founded: 2000
Sales Range: $50-74.9 Million
Emp.: 36
Employment Placement Services
N.A.I.C.S.: 561311

John Younger (Founder & Chm)
Luis Rivera (Pres)
Victoria Rose (Dir-Customer Success)
Mike Tastle (Sr VP)

ACCORD FINANCIAL GROUP INC.
19 N Pearl St Ste 2, Covington, OH 45318
Tel.: (937) 473-5991
Web Site:
　http://www.accordlease.com
Year Founded: 1992
Sales Range: $10-24.9 Million
Emp.: 20
Loan Broker
N.A.I.C.S.: 522220
Doug Ritchters (CEO)

Subsidiaries:

Accord Leasing LLC　　(1)
7577 Central Park Blvd, Mason, OH 45040
Tel.: (513) 229-0333
Web Site: http://www.accordlease.com
Rev.: $6,000,000
Emp.: 2
Loan Broker
N.A.I.C.S.: 522310
Ian Liddell (VP & Gen Mgr)

ACCORD INC.
3300 Maple Valley Hwy, Renton, WA 98058
Tel.: (425) 226-6656
Web Site: http://www.tacotimenw.com
Sales Range: $10-24.9 Million
Emp.: 20
Franchiser of Restaurants
N.A.I.C.S.: 533110
Jim Tonkin (CEO)
Mathew Tonkin (Pres)
Gretchen Everett (Dir-Mktg & Adv)

ACCORD INDUSTRIES LLC
4001 Forsyth Rd, Winter Park, FL 32792
Tel.: (407) 671-5200
Sales Range: $10-24.9 Million
Emp.: 137
Commercial Lighting Fixtures
N.A.I.C.S.: 335132
James Goulden (CEO)

ACCORDION PARTNERS LLC
One Vanderbilt Ave 24th Fl, New York, NY 10017
Tel.: (646) 485-8000
Web Site: https://www.accordion.com
Year Founded: 2009
Emp.: 274
Financial Services
N.A.I.C.S.: 523999
Nick Leopard (Founder & CEO)
Atul Aggarwal (Pres)
Mark Copeland (Chief Comml Officer)
John Bittner (Sr Mng Dir)

Subsidiaries:

Platform Specialists, LLC　　(1)
28 Valley Rd Ste 1 125, Montclair, NJ 07042
Tel.: (888) 857-1585
Web Site: http://platformspecialists.com
Sales Range: $1-9.9 Million
Emp.: 8
Financial Management Consulting Services
N.A.I.C.S.: 541611
Jim Moore (Specialist-EPM)

ACCOUNT RECOVERY SPE-CIALISTS, INC. (ARSI)
3505 N Topeka St, Wichita, KS 67219
Tel.: (316) 267-5400
Web Site: https://www.arsico.com
Year Founded: 1992

Account Recovery Specialists, Inc.
(ARSI)—(Continued)

Sales Range: $1-9.9 Million
Emp.: 85
Debt Collection Agencies
N.A.I.C.S.: 561440
Nikki Esquibel (VP-Client Svcs)
Irene Hoheusle (VP-Collections &
Education)
Candye Daughhetee (VP-Ops &
Quality Assurance)
Josh Shea (Atty)

**ACCOUNTABILITY OUT-
SOURCING, INC.**
2 Newton Executive Pk, Newton
Lower Falls, MA 02462
Tel.: (781) 431-0420
Web Site: http://www.accountab.com
Year Founded: 2003
Sales Range: $1-9.9 Million
Emp.: 20
Corporate Financial Management
Services
N.A.I.C.S.: 561499
Ann M. Vickers (CEO)
Elaine Banks (Mng Dir-Bay Area)

**ACCOUNTANTS IN TRANSI-
TION, INC.**
10509 Vista Sorrento Pky Ste 300,
San Diego, CA 92121
Tel.: (858) 404-9900
Web Site: http://www.aitransition.com
Year Founded: 2005
Rev.: $2,200,000
Emp.: 7
Accounting & Finance
N.A.I.C.S.: 541219
Steve Boegly (Founder & Mng Part-
ner)
Genia Bellaconis (Founder & Mng
Partner)
Shaun Enders (Founder & Mng Part-
ner)

ACCOUNTFULLY LLC
1567 Meeting St Ste 100, Charleston,
SC 29405
Tel.: (843) 501-2774
Web Site:
　　http://www.accountfully.com
Year Founded: 2012
Sales Range: $1-9.9 Million
Emp.: 23
Financial Investment Services
N.A.I.C.S.: 523940
Brad Ebenhoeh (Mng Partner)
Meredith Ebenhoeh (Partner)
Chris Simon (Dir-Acctg)
Heather B. Schultz (Dir-HR)

**ACCOUNTING EQUIPMENT
CORP.**
2310 Crossroads Dr Ste 2800, Madi-
son, WI 53718
Tel.: (608) 395-2900
Web Site: http://www.aebs.com
Sales Range: $50-74.9 Million
Emp.: 75
Networking & Consulting
N.A.I.C.S.: 423430
Rick Gordon (CEO)

**ACCOUNTING MANAGEMENT
SOLUTIONS, INC.**
800 S St Ste 195, Waltham, MA
02453
Tel.: (781) 419-9200
Web Site: http://www.amsolutions.net
Year Founded: 1998
Sales Range: $50-74.9 Million
Emp.: 30
Accounting Services
N.A.I.C.S.: 541219

James Bourdon (Founder & CEO)
Leigh Tucker (Mng Dir-Nonprofit
Practice)
Edward Blum (Dir-Pro Search)
Laura Willis (Dir-Bus Dev)
Susan Lentini (Dir-Ops & Client Svcs-
New York)
Tony Boschetto (Dir-Bus Advisory
Svcs)

ACCOUNTNOW, INC.
2603 Camino Ramon Ste 485, San
Ramon, CA 94583
Tel.: (925) 498-1800
Web Site:
　　http://www.accountnow.com
Year Founded: 2004
Sales Range: $25-49.9 Million
Emp.: 96
Prepaid Debit Card Services
N.A.I.C.S.: 522320
James R. Jones (CEO)

Subsidiaries:

nFinanSe Inc.　　　　　　　　　(1)
Tel.: (813) 367-4400
Web Site: http://www.nfinanse.com
Sales Range: $1-9.9 Million
Emp.: 71
Prepaid Credit Cards
N.A.I.C.S.: 522210
Jerry A. Welch (CEO)

ACCRA CARE
1011 1st St S Ste 315, Hopkins, MN
55343
Tel.: (952) 935-3515　　　MN
Web Site: http://www.accracare.org
Year Founded: 1998
Sales Range: $25-49.9 Million
Emp.: 2,358
Disability Assistance Services
N.A.I.C.S.: 624120

ACCRA-FAB INC.
23201 E Apple Way Dr, Liberty Lake,
WA 99019
Tel.: (509) 922-3300
Web Site: https://www.accrafab.com
Rev.: $40,000,000
Emp.: 175
Sheet Metalwork
N.A.I.C.S.: 332322
Greg Konkol (Pres)
Barry Stewart (Dir-HR)
Don Bolling (Mgr-Quality)
Arnold Powell (Supvr)
Jon Coker (Mgr-Engrg & Innovation)
Randi Brown (Supvr-Estimating)

ACCRAM INC.
2901 W Clarendon Ave, Phoenix, AZ
85017
Tel.: (602) 264-0288
Web Site: http://www.accram.com
Year Founded: 1981
Sales Range: $10-24.9 Million
Emp.: 40
Computer & Data Processing Equip-
ment Repair
N.A.I.C.S.: 811210
Robert A. Daquilante (Pres)
Traci Aldano (VP)
Carrie Roethler (Mgr-Bus Dev & Acct
Mgr)

**ACCREDITING COUNCIL FOR
INDEPENDENT COLLEGES
AND SCHOOLS**
750 1st St NE Ste 980, Washington,
DC 20002-4223
Tel.: (202) 336-6780　　　　　VA
Web Site: http://www.acics.org
Year Founded: 1912
Sales Range: $10-24.9 Million
Emp.: 46
Educational Support Services

N.A.I.C.S.: 611710

ACCROTOOL, INC.
401 Hunt Valley Rd, New Kensington,
PA 15068
Tel.: (724) 339-3560
Web Site: https://www.accrotool.com
Year Founded: 1972
Sales Range: $10-24.9 Million
Emp.: 150
Fabricated Pipe & Pipe Fitting Mfr
N.A.I.C.S.: 332996
Bill Phillips (Chm & CEO)
Paul Landi (Mgr-Facilities & Mainte-
nance)

ACCRUEPARTNERS, INC.
1000 W Morehead St Ste 200, Char-
lotte, NC 28208
Tel.: (704) 632-9955
Web Site:
　　https://www.accruepartners.com
Year Founded: 2002
Sales Range: $10-24.9 Million
Emp.: 30
Help Supply Services
N.A.I.C.S.: 561320
Amy Noland (Partner)
Patty Comer (Partner)
Matt Donato (VP)

**ACCTTWO SHARED SER-
VICES, LLC**
1111 N Loop W Ste 250, Houston, TX
77008
Tel.: (713) 744-8400　　　　TX
Web Site: http://www.accttwo.com
Year Founded: 2010
Cloud-Based Accounting & Consult-
ing Firm
N.A.I.C.S.: 541512
Marcus Wagner (Founder & CEO)
Brett Michalson (CTO)
John Silver (VP-Sls)
Rauli Garcia (Chief Revenue Officer)
Ken West Jr. (COO)

ACCU TECH PLASTICS, INC.
1353 International Dr, Eau Claire, WI
54701
Tel.: (715) 833-1677　　　　MO
Web Site: http://www.atpamerica.com
Year Founded: 1997
Plastic Tapes, Reel Bands & Data
Sheets Mfr
N.A.I.C.S.: 326121
Ronald Pribyl (Owner)
Jason Skrtic (Mgr-Sls & Mktg)
Chris Stoddard (Plant Mgr)

ACCU-TEC INC.
1735 W Burnett Ave, Louisville, KY
40210-1739
Tel.: (502) 339-7511
Web Site: https://www.accu-tec.com
Sales Range: $10-24.9 Million
Emp.: 100
Packaging & Labeling Services
N.A.I.C.S.: 561910
Susan Browning (Dir-Customer Svc)
Gary Klass (Mgr-Pur)
Roy Kraemer (VP & Gen Mgr)
Jeff Nash (VP-Fin)
Rebecca Schulte (Mgr-Acctg)

**ACCUBUILT ACQUISITION
HOLDINGS INC.**
2550 Central Point Pkwy, Lima, OH
45804
Tel.: (419) 222-1501
Web Site: http://www.accubuilt.com
Sales Range: $200-249.9 Million
Emp.: 130
Motor Vehicle Assembly
N.A.I.C.S.: 336110
Larry Doyle (Pres)

Subsidiaries:

Accubuilt Inc.　　　　　　　　　(1)
2550 Central Point Pkwy, Lima, OH 45804
Tel.: (419) 222-1501
Web Site: http://www.accubuilt.com
Sales Range: $25-49.9 Million
Emp.: 112
Specialty Vehicle Mfr
N.A.I.C.S.: 336110
Brad Smith (Pres)

Division (Domestic):

Dabryan Coach Builders Inc.　　　(2)
2550 Central Point Pkwy, Lima, OH 45804
Tel.: (419) 222-1501
Web Site: http://www.dabryancoach.com
Sales Range: $10-24.9 Million
Emp.: 110
Automobile Bodies & Passenger Cars Mfr
N.A.I.C.S.: 336110
Rob Hubbard (CEO)

ACCUCODE, INC.
6886 S Yosemite St Ste 100, Centen-
nial, CO 80112
Tel.: (303) 639-6111
Web Site: http://www.accucode.com
Year Founded: 1996
Sales Range: $10-24.9 Million
Emp.: 120
Computer Software Services
N.A.I.C.S.: 541511
Wyatt Love (Dir-Software Dev)
Kevin Price (Founder & CEO)
Chad Haynes (VP-VAR Svcs)
Don Everett (Sr Acct Exec-Retail)
Sandy Deskin (Acct Exec-
Transportation)
Morgan Deppe (Dir-Mktg)

ACCUCOMP, LLC
7030 Pointe Inverness Way Ste 270,
Fort Wayne, IN 46804
Tel.: (260) 755-5092
Web Site:
　　http://www.accucompllc.com
Year Founded: 2011
Sales Range: $1-9.9 Million
Emp.: 6
Real Estate Manangement Services
N.A.I.C.S.: 531390
Mark Music (Founder & Owner)

ACCUDATA TECHNOLOGIES
800 N Watters Dr Ste 130, Allen, TX
75013
Tel.: (972) 390-2610
Web Site:
　　http://www.accudatatech.com
Year Founded: 1989
Sales Range: $1-9.9 Million
Emp.: 10
Technology & Database Storage Ser-
vices
N.A.I.C.S.: 541519
M. Gregory Smith (Pres & CEO)
Monica Martino (CTO)
James White (Dir-Sls)

**ACCUDUCT MANUFACTURING
INC.**
316 Ellingson Rd, Algona, WA 98001
Tel.: (253) 939-7741
Web Site: https://www.accuduct.com
Year Founded: 1987
Sales Range: $10-24.9 Million
Sheet Metal Duct Pipe Mfr
N.A.I.C.S.: 332322
Jeff Hermanson (Pres)
Kirk Mansanarez (Mgr-Estimation,
Project Mgmt & Customer Svc)

**ACCUFORM MANUFACTUR-
ING, INC.**
16228 Flight Path Dr, Brooksville, FL
34604
Tel.: (352) 799-5434

Web Site: https://www.accuform.com
Sales Range: $10-24.9 Million
Emp.: 300
Sign Mfr
N.A.I.C.S.: 339950
David Johnson *(COO)*
Wayne Johnson *(CEO)*
John Murphy *(VP-HR)*
Kevin Bosman *(Dir-Brand Strategy)*
Matt Johnson *(Dir-Product Dev)*
Erin DeCoste *(Supvr-Acct)*
Rob Ogilbee *(Pres)*
Mitch Fein *(VP-Sls-Global)*
Stephanie Adams *(Dir-Plant Ops)*

ACCUMA CORPORATION

133 Fanjoy Rd, Statesville, NC 28625
Tel.: (704) 873-1488
Web Site:
   http://www.accumacorp.com
Year Founded: 1985
Sales Range: $10-24.9 Million
Emp.: 130
Mfr of Battery Cases, Plastics & Injection Molding
N.A.I.C.S.: 326199
Mark Chambers *(COO)*
Francesca Invernizzi *(Chm)*
Paolo Invernizzi *(Pres)*

ACCUQUOTE

1400 S Wolf Rd Bldg 500, Wheeling, IL 60090-6588
Tel.: (847) 850-2000
Web Site:
   https://www.accuquote.com
Year Founded: 1986
Rev.: $23,100,000
Emp.: 150
Insurance Agencies
N.A.I.C.S.: 524210
Byron J. Udell *(Founder & CEO)*
Glenn Garbowicz *(Exec VP-Fin, Mktg, IT & HR)*
Jeremy Hewett *(Exec VP-Sls & Fulfillment)*
John Schroeder *(VP-CRS & Admin Svcs)*

ACCURATE BOX COMPANY, INC.

86 5th Ave, Paterson, NJ 07524-1172
Tel.: (973) 345-2000   NJ
Web Site:
   https://www.accuratebox.com
Year Founded: 1945
Sales Range: $100-124.9 Million
Emp.: 140
Mfr of Paperboard Boxes, Folding Displays & Food Carton Specialties
N.A.I.C.S.: 322130
Lisa Hirsh *(Pres & CEO)*
Mark Schlossman *(VP-Sls)*

ACCURATE BUSHING COMPANY, INC.

443 N Ave, Garwood, NJ 07027-1014
Tel.: (908) 789-1121   NJ
Web Site:
   http://www.accuratebushing.com
Year Founded: 1942
Sales Range: $50-74.9 Million
Emp.: 50
Mfr of Aircraft Parts, Bushings, Needle Rollers, Bearings & Track Rollers
N.A.I.C.S.: 331513
John Palumbo *(Mgr-Sls)*

ACCURATE CHEMICAL & SCIENTIFIC CORPORATION

300 Shames Dr, Westbury, NY 11590-1736
Tel.: (516) 333-2221   NY
Web Site:
   http://www.accuratechemical.com

Year Founded: 1974
Rev.: $5,000,000
Emp.: 22
Organic & Inorganic Chemicals & Biochemicals
N.A.I.C.S.: 424690
Rudy Rosenberg *(Pres)*

Subsidiaries:

Accurate Surgical & Scientific Instruments Corporation   (1)
300 Shames Dr, Westbury, NY 11590
Tel.: (516) 333-2570
Web Site: http://www.accuratesurgical.com
Sales of Surgical & Scientific Instruments
N.A.I.C.S.: 423450

Leeches U.S.A. Ltd.   (1)
300 Shames Dr, Westbury, NY 11590
Tel.: (516) 333-2570
Web Site: http://www.leechesusa.com
Sales Range: $10-24.9 Million
Emp.: 5
Leech Therapy Services
N.A.I.C.S.: 424210
Marie Bonazinga *(Pres)*

ACCURATE ELASTOMER PRODUCTS

1112 Swenson Blvd, Elgin, TX 78621
Tel.: (512) 285-4585
Web Site:
   http://www.accurateelastomer.com
Sales Range: $10-24.9 Million
Emp.: 100
Mfr of Molded Rubber Products
N.A.I.C.S.: 326299
Jose Martinez *(Mgr-Product Dev)*
Marcel Smith *(Acct Mgr)*
Tony Miller *(Owner)*

ACCURATE FORMING LLC

24 Ames Blvd, Hamburg, NJ 07419-1502
Tel.: (973) 827-7155
Web Site:
   https://www.accurateforming.com
Year Founded: 1955
Deep-Drawn Metal Parts Mfr for Pens & Cosmetic Packaging
N.A.I.C.S.: 332119
Chuck Segar *(Pres)*

ACCURATE GROUP

6000 Freedom Sq Ste 300, Independence, OH 44131
Web Site:
   https://www.accurategroup.com
Year Founded: 2003
Sales Range: $50-74.9 Million
Emp.: 187
Appraisal & Title Services
N.A.I.C.S.: 531320
Paul M. Doman *(Pres & CEO)*
Michael S. Cullen *(CIO)*
Scott Vilseck *(Mgr-Sls-Natl)*
Richard L. Heltzel III *(VP & Acct Mgr-Natl)*

ACCURATE HOME CARE, LLC

9000 Quantrelle Ave NE Ste 200, Otsego, MN 55330
Tel.: (763) 633-3800
Web Site:
   https://www.accuratehomecare.com
Year Founded: 2002
Sales Range: $25-49.9 Million
Emp.: 2,248
Women Healthcare Services
N.A.I.C.S.: 621610
Rick Bourne *(Pres & CEO)*
Bill English *(COO)*

ACCURATE LUBRICANTS & METALWORKING FLUIDS, INC.

403 Homestead Ave, Dayton, OH 45408
Tel.: (937) 461-9906

Web Site: http://www.acculube.com
Year Founded: 1990
Sales Range: $10-24.9 Million
Emp.: 38
Petroleum Product Whslr
N.A.I.C.S.: 424720
Jay Webb *(VP)*

ACCURATE METAL FABRICATORS, LLC.

2100 E Orangewood Ave, Anaheim, CA 92806
Tel.: (714) 363-9206
Web Site: http://www.amf1.com
Year Founded: 1976
Sales Range: $25-49.9 Million
Emp.: 400
Sheet Metal Work Mfr
N.A.I.C.S.: 332322
Gary Sawyer *(VP-Bus Dev & Mktg)*

ACCURATE MOLDED PLASTICS INC.

3910 Industrial Ave S, Coeur D'Alene, ID 83815
Tel.: (208) 765-3000
Web Site:
   http://www.accurateplastics.com
Rev.: $10,000,000
Emp.: 150
Injection Molded Finished Plastics Products, Nec
N.A.I.C.S.: 326199
Dale A. Meyer *(CEO)*
Julie McMurdie *(Controller)*

ACCURATE PERFORATING COMPANY, INC.

3636 S Kedzie Ave, Chicago, IL 60632-2727
Tel.: (773) 254-3232   IL
Web Site:
   https://www.accurateperforating.com
Sales Range: $10-24.9 Million
Perforated Metal Stampings Mfr
N.A.I.C.S.: 332119
Larry H. Cohen *(Chm)*
Aaron Kamins *(Pres)*

Subsidiaries:

Accurate Metal Fabricating   (1)
1657 N Kostner Ave, Chicago, IL 60639
Tel.: (773) 382-8563
Web Site: http://www.accuratemetalfab.com
Fabricated Structural Metal Mfr
N.A.I.C.S.: 332312
Brian Fricano *(Engr-Mfg)*

ACCURATE PLASTICS INC.

18 Morris Pl, Yonkers, NY 10705
Tel.: (914) 476-0700
Web Site: https://www.acculam.com
Rev.: $15,000,000
Emp.: 40
Mfr of Plastics, Materials & Resins
N.A.I.C.S.: 325211
Michael Stacey *(Pres)*

ACCUREC LLC

2880 N Berkeley Lake Rd Ste 7, Duluth, GA 30096
Tel.: (770) 449-5280
Web Site: http://www.accurec.com
Year Founded: 1997
Sales Range: $10-24.9 Million
Emp.: 8
Miscellaneous Durable Goods Merchant Whslr
N.A.I.C.S.: 423990
Larry Lyu *(Mktg Dir)*

ACCURIDE INTERNATIONAL INC.

12311 Shoemaker Ave, Santa Fe Springs, CA 90670
Tel.: (562) 903-0200

Web Site: http://www.accuride.com
Sales Range: $150-199.9 Million
Emp.: 100
Ball Bearing Slides Mfr & Designer
N.A.I.C.S.: 332510
Scott Jordan *(Pres)*
Jeffrey Dunlap *(VP-Fin)*
Pablo Mares *(Mgr-Tooling)*
Sandra Dischinger *(Project Mgr-IT)*
Steve Helms *(Dir-IS)*
Claudia Tuttle *(Mgr-Mktg)*

ACCURO SOLUTIONS, LLC

12505 Whitewater Pl, Lakewood Ranch, FL 34202
Tel.: (877) 222-8616   DE
Web Site:
   https://www.accurosolutions.com
Bill Review & Payment Processing Services
N.A.I.C.S.: 522320

ACCUTECH DATA SUPPLIES INC.

4284 Transport St, Ventura, CA 93006
Tel.: (805) 644-7100
Web Site:
   https://www.accutechdata.com
Year Founded: 1992
Rev.: $65,000,000
Emp.: 45
Computers & Accessories, Personal & Home Entertainment
N.A.I.C.S.: 423430
Mark Dirado *(Pres)*
Brian Ross *(VP)*
Pat Fairly *(Dir-Sls)*
Paul Grenier *(Mgr-Sls)*
Wade Runestad *(VP)*
Scott Cadenhead *(Sr Mgr-Sls)*
Lawrence O'Neil *(Dir-Sls)*

ACCUTITLE LLC

1518 Long Beach Township, Ship Bottom, NJ 08008
Tel.: (877) 354-1170
Web Site: http://www.accutitle.com
Title Abstract & Settlement Offices
N.A.I.C.S.: 541191
Bill Bartzak *(CEO)*

Subsidiaries:

Landtech Data Corp.   (1)
1460 Royal Palm Beach Blvd, Royal Palm Beach, FL 33411
Tel.: (561) 790-1265
Web Site: http://www.landtechdata.com
Software Publisher
N.A.I.C.S.: 513210
Alice Bell *(CEO)*

Millennium Software Developers, Inc.   (1)
12276 San Jose Blvd Ste 214, Jacksonville, FL 32257
Tel.: (904) 256-0053
Web Site: http://www.closerschoice.com
Sales Range: $1-9.9 Million
Emp.: 20
Custom Computer Programming Services
N.A.I.C.S.: 541511
Sriram Vemuri *(Pres)*

ACCUTREX PRODUCTS INC.

112 Southpointe Blvd, Canonsburg, PA 15317
Tel.: (724) 746-4300
Web Site: https://www.accutrex.com
Sales Range: $10-24.9 Million
Emp.: 150
Mfr of Metal Stampings
N.A.I.C.S.: 332119
Denise Dudik *(Mgr-Quality Assurance)*
Darlene Horvath *(Mgr-Credit)*
Marty Howsare *(Mgr-Laminating Dept)*

Accutrex Products Inc.—(Continued)

Chris Kraynak (Acct Exec)
Lauren Popp (Mgr-Mktg)
Jim Stark (Mgr-Production-Lamination & Waterjet)

ACCUTRUST MORTGAGE INC.
1107 Pleasant St, Fall River, MA 02723
Tel.: (508) 646-6650
Web Site:
http://www.accutrustmortgage.com
Year Founded: 2004
Sales Range: $1-9.9 Million
Emp.: 112
Mortages Advisory Services
N.A.I.C.S.: 524210
Donald Lambert (Pres & CEO)

ACCUWEATHER, INC.
385 Science Park Rd, State College, PA 16803-2215
Tel.: (814) 237-0309
Web Site:
http://www.accuweather.com
Year Founded: 1962
Sales Range: $25-49.9 Million
Emp.: 325
Weather Information Supplier
N.A.I.C.S.: 516210
Joel N. Myers (Founder & Chm)
Evan Myers (COO)
Scott Homan (Exec Dir-Newspaper Svcs)
Marie Svet (Chief Revenue Officer-Global)
Steven R. Smith (CEO)
Helen Swenson (Chief Content Officer)
Chris Patti (CTO)
Bill Boss (Dir-Product Dev, Display Sys & Svcs)
Elliot Abrams (Sr VP)
Joe Sobel (Sr VP)
Bill McGarry (VP-Sls)
Eric Danetz (Chief Revenue Officer)
Deirdre Daly-Markowski (Dir-Adv Sls)
Brian Baker (VP-Product Experience)
Kurt Fulepp (Chief Product Officer)
Scott Mackaro (VP-Science, Innovation & Dev)
Jennifer Chung (Chief Legal Officer & Gen Counsel)
Stephen Mummey (Sr VP-Digital Ad Revenue & Tech)

Subsidiaries:

WeatherBank, Inc.   (1)
1015 Waterwood Pkwy Ste J, Edmond, OK 73034
Tel.: (405) 359-0773
Web Site: http://www.weatherbank.com
Sales Range: $1-9.9 Million
Emp.: 41
Meteorological Consulting
N.A.I.C.S.: 541690
Mary Sullaway (Mgr-Acctg)

ACCUWORX, LLC
7156 Sulier Dr, Temperance, MI 48182-9510
Tel.: (734) 847-6115
Web Site: https://www.accuworx.net
Sales Range: $1-9.9 Million
Industrial Assembly Automation & Testing Equipment Mfr
N.A.I.C.S.: 333248
Larry Carter (Owner)

ACE ADVENTURE RESORT
1 Concho Rd, Oak Hill, WV 25901
Tel.: (877) 787-3982
Web Site: http://www.aceraft.com
Whitewater Rafting & Adventure Vacation Destination
N.A.I.C.S.: 713990

Haynes Mansfield (Mktg Dir)

ACE BATTERY SALES, INC.
2166 Bluff Rd, Indianapolis, IN 46225
Tel.: (317) 786-2717   IN
Web Site:
http://www.acebatteryinc.com
Year Founded: 1945
Sales Range: $75-99.9 Million
Emp.: 4
Battery Wholesaler
N.A.I.C.S.: 423930
James Kirkham (Owner & Pres)
Matt Bailey (COO)

ACE CLEARWATER ENTERPRISES
19815 Magellan Dr, Torrance, CA 90502
Tel.: (310) 538-5380
Web Site:
https://www.aceclearwater.com
Sales Range: $10-24.9 Million
Emp.: 98
Aircraft Parts & Equipment
N.A.I.C.S.: 336413
Gary Johnson (VP)
Gen Perez (Mgr-HR)

ACE COFFEE BAR, INC.
601 E Lake St, Streamwood, IL 60107
Tel.: (630) 233-2800   DE
Web Site:
http://www.acecoffeebar.com
Year Founded: 1949
Sales Range: $25-49.9 Million
Emp.: 350
Merchandising Machine Operators
N.A.I.C.S.: 445132
Jill Cavitt-Lorenzen (Pres)
Mary Fioretti (VP)
Robert Kranig (Mgr-Ops)
Greg Gallas (Supvr-OCS)
Mara Nieto (Mgr)
Roger Sweeney (VP-Sls)

ACE DORAN HAULING & RIGGING COMPANY
1601 Blue Rock St, Cincinnati, OH 45223-2502
Tel.: (513) 681-7900   OH
Web Site: http://www.acedoran.com
Year Founded: 1913
Sales Range: $25-49.9 Million
Emp.: 81
Transportation of General Commodities
N.A.I.C.S.: 484121
Cathy Newman (Controller)
Paul Molnar (Dir-Safety)
Jim Collins (Pres)
Janet Wagers (Mgr-Traffic)

Subsidiaries:

Ace Doran Brokerage Co.   (1)
1601 Blue Rock St, Cincinnati, OH 45223-2502   (100%)
Tel.: (513) 681-7900
Web Site: http://www.acedoran.com
Sales Range: $25-49.9 Million
Emp.: 60
Trucking Mfr
N.A.I.C.S.: 484122
Anastasia M. Comes (VP)
Terry G. Sexton (Mgr-Acctg)
Lee Gentry (Exec VP-Bennett Intl Grp)
Chad Liter (Mgr)

ACE ENDICO CORP.
80 International Blvd, Brewster, NY 10509
Tel.: (914) 347-3131
Web Site:
https://www.aceendico.com
Sales Range: $50-74.9 Million
Emp.: 100

Groceries, General Line
N.A.I.C.S.: 424410
William A. Endico (CEO)
Matthew Hertzberg (VP-Operations)
Michael Endico (VP)

ACE ENGINEERING INC.
1880 Wright Ave, La Verne, CA 91750
Tel.: (909) 392-4600
Web Site:
http://www.aceengineeringinc.com
Sales Range: $25-49.9 Million
Emp.: 30
Grading Services
N.A.I.C.S.: 237310
John Lee (Founder)

ACE ETHANOL LLC
815 W Maple St, Stanley, WI 54768
Tel.: (715) 644-2909
Web Site:
https://www.aceethanol.com
Year Founded: 2001
Petroleum & Coal Product Mfr
N.A.I.C.S.: 324199
Joe Fischer (Plant Mgr)
LaMae Drier (Controller)
Matt Smith (Mgr-Ops)
Neal Kemmet (Pres & Gen Mgr)
Joe Wild (Mgr-Maintenance)
Colton Walz (Mgr-Technical Svcs)

ACE EXHIBITS, INC.
440 Seaton St Suite 201, Los Angeles, CA 90013
Tel.: (309) 422-2840
Web Site: http://www.aceexhibits.com
Year Founded: 2006
Sales Range: $1-9.9 Million
Emp.: 31
Mfr & Discount Retailer of Various Products for Tradeshows & Exhibitions
N.A.I.C.S.: 561920
Tom Hand (CEO)
Nelson Sabater (Dir-IT)
James Beare (Acct Mgr)

ACE GLASS INCORPORATED
1430 NW Blvd, Vineland, NJ 08360
Tel.: (856) 692-3333   NJ
Web Site: https://www.aceglass.com
Year Founded: 1936
Chemical & Laboratory Glassware & Supplies
N.A.I.C.S.: 327215
Kristi Donoflio (Coord-Admin Sls)

ACE HARDWARE BLUE RIDGE LLC
4344 Old Hwy 76 E, Blue Ridge, GA 30513
Tel.: (706) 632-8002
Web Site:
https://acehardwareblueridge.com
Sales Range: $10-24.9 Million
Emp.: 100
Hardware Stores
N.A.I.C.S.: 444140
Lamar Lance (Pres)

ACE HARDWARE CORPORATION
2200 Kensington Ct, Oak Brook, IL 60523-2100
Tel.: (630) 990-6600   IL
Web Site:
http://www.acehardware.com
Year Founded: 1924
Sales Range: $1-4.9 Billion
Hardware Products Distr
N.A.I.C.S.: 423710

Lori L. Bossmann (Chief Supply Chain Officer & Exec VP)
John Venhuizen (Pres & CEO)
Kane Calamari (Chief HR Officer & Sr VP)

Subsidiaries:

Ace Handyman Services   (1)
12567 W Cedar Dr Ste 200, Lakewood, CO 80228
Tel.: (866) 808-8401
Web Site:
https://www.acehandymanservices.com
Miscellaneous Personal Services
N.A.I.C.S.: 812990
Stacy Huston (Pres)

Ace Hardware Corporation - Paint Division   (1)
21901 S Central Ave, Matteson, IL 60443-2801
Tel.: (708) 720-0600
Web Site: http://www.acehardware-vendors.com
Sales Range: $25-49.9 Million
Emp.: 170
Distr Of Paints
N.A.I.C.S.: 325510
Bill Wachter (Mgr-Facilities & EHS)

Ace Home Center De Michoacan S.A. De C V   (1)
Acueducto 3175-A, 58240, Morelia, Michoacan, Mexico
Tel.: (52) 443 315 8161
Hardware Retailer
N.A.I.C.S.: 444140

Emery-Waterhouse Company   (1)
7 Rand Rd, Portland, ME 04104
Tel.: (207) 775-2371
Web Site: http://www.emeryonline.com
Sales Range: $100-124.9 Million
Emp.: 300
Home Improvement & Building Products Distr
N.A.I.C.S.: 423710
Stephen M. Frawley (Pres & CEO)
Lori Grenier (Dir-Customer Rels)
Don Dickson (COO & Sr VP)
Dean Frost (VP-Ops)
Dan Pendergast (VP-Mdsg)
Jason Hanegan (VP-Sls)
John Mathieu (Dir-Retail Svcs)
Kathy Nason (Dir-HR)
Levi Robbins (Dir-Bus Dev)

Giant Ace Sdn. Bhd.   (1)
245a 1st Floor Jalan Bandar 13, Kuala Lumpur, 53100, Malaysia
Tel.: (60) 341057231
Sales Range: $25-49.9 Million
Emp.: 300
Hardware Product Whslr
N.A.I.C.S.: 423710
Kok Soon Chen (Gen Mgr)

Jensen Distribution Services   (1)
10110 W Aero Rd, Spokane, WA 99224
Tel.: (509) 624-1321
Web Site: http://www.jensenonline.com
Hardware Distr
N.A.I.C.S.: 423710
Micah Jensen Dunlap (Pres & COO)

Mount Dora Ace Hardware, Inc.   (1)
18691 US Highway 441, Mount Dora, FL 32757
Tel.: (352) 383-2101
Web Site: http://www.acehardware.com
Hardware Stores
N.A.I.C.S.: 444140

Mutual Ace Hardware   (1)
1393 Half Day Rd, Highland Park, IL 60035
Tel.: (847) 432-0026
Web Site:
http://www.mutualspartyrentals.com
Hardware Stores
N.A.I.C.S.: 444140
Dane E. Sheahen (Pres)

Proctor Ace Hardware Neptune Beach   (1)
580 Atlantic Blvd, Neptune Beach, FL 32266
Tel.: (904) 249-5622
Web Site: http://www.proctorace.com

Hardware Merchant Whslr
N.A.I.C.S.: 423710
Thomas Proctor (Mgr-IT)

Ryan Supply, Inc. (1)
117 N Fabens St, Fabens, TX 79838
Tel.: (915) 764-2239
Hardware Stores
N.A.I.C.S.: 444140

Westlake Hardware, Inc. (1)
14000 Marshall Dr, Lenexa, KS 66215
Tel.: (913) 888-0808
Web Site: http://www.westlakehardware.com
Hardware Store Operator
N.A.I.C.S.: 444140
Timothy Benesch (Gen Mgr-Red Oak)
Bryan Allen (Gen Mgr-Council Bluffs)
Bryan Chester (Gen Mgr-Topeka)
Mike Walker (Gen Mgr-Arkansas City)
Brian Gramlich (Gen Mgr-Hays)
Joe Jeffries (Pres & CEO)

ACE HARDWARE OF OAK FOREST
15541 S Cicero Ave, Oak Forest, IL 60452
Tel.: (708) 687-2730
Rev.: $12,000,000
Emp.: 48
Hardware Stores
N.A.I.C.S.: 444140
Kevin Ebel (Pres)

ACE INDUSTRIES INC.
6295 McDonough Dr, Norcross, GA 30093
Tel.: (770) 441-0898
Web Site:
  https://www.aceindustries.com
Rev.: $24,775,876
Emp.: 35
Cranes, Industrial
N.A.I.C.S.: 423830
Dan Carmichael (VP-Sls & Bus Dev)
Paul Fleming (Plant Mgr)
Lance White (Mgr-Sls-Natl)
Bryan Scott (Mgr-Svc-Natl)
Claude Owens (VP-Ops)

ACE LITHOGRAPHERS OF MORRIS COUNTY, INC.
22 Russo Pl, Berkeley Heights, NJ 07922-1606
Tel.: (973) 428-4911
Web Site: http://www.acelitho.com
Year Founded: 1992
Sales Range: $10-24.9 Million
Emp.: 17
Commercial Printing Services
N.A.I.C.S.: 323111
Brett Cooper (Treas & Sec)

Subsidiaries:

Twill, Inc. (1)
22 Russo Pl, Berkeley Heights, NJ 07922
Tel.: (908) 665-1700
Web Site: http://www.twill.com
Sales Range: $10-24.9 Million
Emp.: 15
Commercial Printing Services
N.A.I.C.S.: 323111

ACE MART RESTAURANT SUPPLY COMPANY INC.
2653 Austin Hwy, San Antonio, TX 78218-2049
Tel.: (210) 323-4400
Web Site: http://www.acemart.com
Year Founded: 1975
Sales Range: $25-49.9 Million
Emp.: 250
Provides Commercial Restaurant Equipment
N.A.I.C.S.: 423440
Paul Gustafson (Pres)

Subsidiaries:

Wichita Restaurant Supply Co, Inc. (1)

1122 Scott Ave, Wichita Falls, TX 76301
Tel.: (940) 766-4389
Web Site: http://www.wichitasupply.com
Sales Range: $1-9.9 Million
Emp.: 12
Commercial Equipment Merchant Whslr
N.A.I.C.S.: 423440

ACE MINERS HARDWARE, INC.
1056 W Grand Ave, Grover Beach, CA 93433
Tel.: (805) 489-2931
Web Site:
  https://www.minershardware.com
Year Founded: 1964
Sales Range: $10-24.9 Million
Emp.: 150
Hardware Stores
N.A.I.C.S.: 444140

ACE PARKING MANAGEMENT INC.
645 Ash St, San Diego, CA 92101-3211
Tel.: (619) 233-6624
Web Site:
  https://www.aceparking.com
Year Founded: 1950
Sales Range: $125-149.9 Million
Emp.: 400
Automobile Parking
N.A.I.C.S.: 812930
Scott Jones (Owner & Chm)
John Baumgardner (CEO & Vice Chm)
Steve Burton (Pres)
Brian Gansert (Pres-Operations)
Ross Seibert (CFO)
Jon Gjerset (CIO)
Clay Adams (Dir-Audit & Revenue Control)
Sasha Lally (VP-Hospitality Div)
Michelle Dente (VP-Member Svcs)

ACE PAVING CO. INC.
4795 Wilkinson Rd W, Bremerton, WA 98312
Tel.: (360) 479-4200
Web Site: http://www.acepaving.com
Rev.: $31,400,000
Emp.: 20
Highway & Street Paving Contractor
N.A.I.C.S.: 237310
Bruce R. Christopherson (Exec VP)
Richard N. Christopherson (Pres)

ACE PRECISION MACHINING CORP.
977 Blue Ribbon Cir N, Oconomowoc, WI 53066
Tel.: (262) 252-4003
Web Site:
  https://www.aceprecision.com
Rev.: $19,100,000
Emp.: 250
Machine Shops
N.A.I.C.S.: 332710
Kathleen Erdmann (Treas)
Paul Erdmann (Pres)
Jeffrey Luedeke (Engr-Mfg)
Terry Briggs (Engr-Quality)
Theresa Clark (Engr-Mfg)
Brian Sellung (Engr-Mfg)
Brenda Peiffer (Mgr-HR)
Doug Bittl (Mgr-Quality)
Jason Glocka (Mgr-Quality-R&O)
Cris Ostrand (VP-Sls)

ACE RELOCATION SYSTEMS INC.
5608 Eastgate Dr, San Diego, CA 92121
Tel.: (858) 677-5500
Web Site:
  http://www.acerelocation.com
Sales Range: $25-49.9 Million

Emp.: 70
Transportation of Household Goods
N.A.I.C.S.: 484210
Richard Clarke (VP)
Dan Lammers (VP-Ops & Govt Sls)

ACE STAMPING & MACHINE CO, INC.
2801 S Memorial Dr, Racine, WI 53403
Tel.: (262) 637-7946
Web Site:
  https://www.acestamping.com
Year Founded: 1955
Sales Range: $1-9.9 Million
Emp.: 35
Metal Stamping
N.A.I.C.S.: 332119
Deanna Larrabee (Mgr-Pur)
Rebecca Leclair (Accountant)

Subsidiaries:

Heinrich Co. (1)
2707 S Memorial Dr, Racine, WI 53403-3212
Tel.: (262) 634-7365
Web Site: http://www.heinrichco.com
Cutting Tool & Machine Tool Accessory Mfr
N.A.I.C.S.: 333515
Bob Hayssen (CEO)

ACE SUPPLY CO. INC.
3825 Edgewood Ave S, Minneapolis, MN 55426
Tel.: (952) 929-1618
Web Site:
  http://www.acesupplyco.com
Year Founded: 1958
Emp.: 50
Air Conditioning & Ventilation Products & Accessories Whslr & Distr
N.A.I.C.S.: 423730
Greg Vogel (Dir-Technical-Info Svcs & CIO)

ACE TANK & EQUIPMENT CO.
19111 Des Moines Memorial Dr Ste 8, Seatac, WA 98148
Tel.: (206) 281-5000
Web Site: http://www.acetank.com
Year Founded: 1937
Sales Range: $1-9.9 Million
Emp.: 90
Mfr of Fabricated Steel Plate Work Including Storage Tanks; Distributor Industrial Petroleum Handling Equipment
N.A.I.C.S.: 423830
Bill Durkin (Mgr-Sls)
Glen Corkill (Pres)

ACE TECHNOLOGIES INC.
2375 Zanker Rd Ste 250, San Jose, CA 95131
Tel.: (408) 521-1139
Web Site:
  http://www.acetechnologies.com
Year Founded: 1993
Sales Range: $25-49.9 Million
Emp.: 26
Provider of Custom Software Services
N.A.I.C.S.: 541511

ACE TELEPHONE ASSOCIATION
207 E Cedar St, Houston, MN 55943
Tel.: (507) 896-3192
Web Site: http://www.acegroup.cc
Sales Range: $10-24.9 Million
Emp.: 86
Local & Long Distance Telephone Communications
N.A.I.C.S.: 517121
Cynthia Sweet (Controller)

ACE TOOL REPAIR, INC.

2201 Wantagh Ave, Wantagh, NY 11793
Tel.: (516) 783-8899
Web Site:
  http://www.acetoolonline.com
Year Founded: 1983
Sales Range: $10-24.9 Million
Emp.: 25
Power Tools Distr & Service Center
N.A.I.C.S.: 423710
Maria Polidoro (Owner & Pres)

ACE UNDERWRITING GROUP
5305 W Broward Blvd, Plantation, FL 33317
Tel.: (954) 581-0202
Web Site:
  http://www.underwriting.com
Sales Range: $1-9.9 Million
Emp.: 16
Insurance Underwriting Services
N.A.I.C.S.: 524298
Ralph Francis (Pres & CEO)

ACE WIRE & CABLE CO. INC.
72-01 51st Ave, Woodside, NY 11377
Tel.: (718) 458-9200
Web Site: https://www.acewireco.com
Rev.: $11,100,000
Emp.: 45
Wiring Devices
N.A.I.C.S.: 423610
Jerry Firestone (Pres)
Lynn Pruden (Asst Controller)
Harris Firestone (Owner)

ACE WORLD WIDE MOVING & STORAGE CO. INC.
1900 E College Ave, Cudahy, WI 53110-2801
Tel.: (414) 764-1000
Web Site:
  http://www.aceworldwide.com
Year Founded: 1956
Sales Range: $10-24.9 Million
Emp.: 130
Trucking Service
N.A.I.C.S.: 484210
John W. Steiner (Owner)

ACECO PRECISION MANUFACTURING
4419 S Federal Way, Boise, ID 83716
Tel.: (208) 343-7712
Web Site: http://www.aceco.com
Sales Range: $10-24.9 Million
Emp.: 75
Knife Blades & Blanks
N.A.I.C.S.: 332215
Raleigh J. Jensen (Pres)

ACELITY L.P. INC.
12930 W Interstate 10, San Antonio, TX 78249-2248
Tel.: (210) 524-9000
Web Site: http://www.acelity.com
Sales Range: $1-4.9 Billion
Emp.: 5,800
Medical Product Mfr & Distr
N.A.I.C.S.: 339112
Gaurav Agarwal (Grp Pres-Bus & Innovation)
David E. Ball (Sr VP-Ops)
Gregory Kayata (Sr VP-HR)
Dennis Crowley (Sr VP-Strategy, Bus Dev & Licensing)
William J. Gumina (Chm)
Ron Silverman (Chief Medical Officer & Sr VP)
Ramesh Subrahmanian (Pres-Intl)
John McAuley (Sr VP-Europe)
William F. Hulse IV (Chief Compliance Officer & Sr VP-Enterprise Risk Mgmt, Quality)

Acelity L.P. Inc.—(Continued)

ACEMCO INCORPORATED
7297 Enterprise Dr, Spring Lake, MI 49456
Tel.: (231) 799-6500   MI
Web Site: http://www.acemco.com
Year Founded: 1968
Sales Range: $10-24.9 Million
Emp.: 150
Provider of Automotive Stampings
N.A.I.C.S.: 336370
Erik Rasmussen (Pres)

ACENDA INTEGRATED HEALTH
42 Delsea Dr S, Glassboro, NJ 08028
Tel.: (844) 422-3632
Web Site:
   http://www.acendahealth.org
Non-profit Organization Management
N.A.I.C.S.: 541618
Lisa Haya (VP-Child & Family Services)

ACENTO ADVERTISING, INC.
2254 S Sepulveda Blvd, Los Angeles, CA 90064
Tel.: (310) 943-8300   CA
Web Site: http://www.acento.com
Year Founded: 1983
Rev.: $38,500,000
Emp.: 40
N.A.I.C.S.: 541810
Marco Cassese (Head-Creative Dept)
Tony Aguilar-Arellano (Partner & Chief Integration Officer)
Roberto Orci (CEO)
Jacqueline Hauser (Dir-Pub Rel-Bus Mktg)
Genesis Capunitan (Dir-Interactive)
Luz Marina Lopez (Dir-Fin & Ops)
Steve Roth (Dir-Agency Dev)
Joe Kutchera (Dir-Digital Mktg)

Subsidiaries:

Acento Advertising (1)
900 W Jackson Ste 3 E, Chicago, IL 60607
Tel.: (312) 850-4130
Web Site: http://www.acento.com
Emp.: 5
N.A.I.C.S.: 541810
Elizabeth Vargas (Acct Supvr)
Roberto Orci (CEO)
Marco Cassese (Partner & VP-Creative Svcs)
Tony Aguilar (Partner & Chief Integration Officer)

DPZ Argentina (1)
Av del Libertador 15 082 1 Piso, Acassuso, San Isidro, B1641ANT, Prov de Buenos Aires, Argentina
Tel.: (54) 11 4575 4300
N.A.I.C.S.: 541810
Nelo Pimentel (Pres & Creative Dir)

DPZ-Duailibi, Petit, Zaragoza, Propaganda S.A. (1)
Cidade Jardim Ave 280, Sao Paulo, 01454-900, SP, Brazil
Tel.: (55) 11 3068 4000
Web Site: http://www.dpz.com.br
N.A.I.C.S.: 541810
Roberto Duailibi (Partner)
Francesc Petit (Partner & Dir)
Jose Zaragoza (Partner & Dir-Creative)
Flavio Conti (Dir-Support Svcs)
Angelica Armentano (Gen Planner & Dir-Convergence)
Fernando Rodrguez (Dir-Creative)
Diego Zaragoza (Dir-Creative)
Daniel Poletto (Dir-Art)

Branch (Domestic):

DPZ-Rio de Janeiro (2)
R Visconde de Priaja 351 14 andar, IPANEMA, Rio de Janeiro, 22410-003, Brazil
Tel.: (55) 21 2227 8484
Web Site: http://www.dpz.com.br
Rev.: $82,000,000

Emp.: 55
N.A.I.C.S.: 541810
Sergio Prazeres (Dir-Media)

ACES A/C SUPPLY INC.
5801 S Loop E, Houston, TX 77033
Tel.: (713) 738-3800
Web Site:
   https://www.acessupply.com
Rev.: $18,100,000
Emp.: 30
Air Conditioning Equipment
N.A.I.C.S.: 423730
Daniel Davenport (VP)
Michael Davenport (Pres)
David Collins (VP & Mgr-Sls)

ACETO CORPORATION
4 Tri Harbor Ct, Port Washington, NY 11050
Tel.: (516) 627-6000   NY
Web Site: http://www.aceto.com
Year Founded: 1947
Rev.: $711,359,000
Assets: $767,024,000
Liabilities: $671,739,000
Net Worth: $95,285,000
Earnings: ($316,121,000)
Emp.: 315
Fiscal Year-end: 06/30/18
Health & Industrial Chemical Distr
N.A.I.C.S.: 424690
Raymond Bartone (Sr VP-Nutritionals)
Keith Wilkinson (Sr VP-Performance Chemicals)
Charles J. Alaimo (Sr VP-HR)
Steven S. Rogers (Pres)
Terry Kippley (Sr VP-Agricultural Protection Products)
Guillaume Saint-Clair (VP-Pharmaceutical Intermediates)
Carrianne J. M. Basler (CFO)
Gilles Cottier (CEO)

Subsidiaries:

Aceto (Holding) B.V. (1)
Jan Ligthartstraat 75/II, Heemskerk, 1964 HA, Netherlands
Tel.: (31) 251252322
Web Site: http://www.aceto.com
Sales Range: $25-49.9 Million
Emp.: 8
Investment Management Service
N.A.I.C.S.: 523999
Jan van Eis (VP)

Aceto (Shanghai) Ltd. (1)
1701 Beijing Road West Jingan China Tower 9th Floor, Shanghai, 200040, China
Tel.: (86) 2162880099
Web Site: http://www.aceto.com
Emp.: 26
Chemical & Pharmaceutical Product Whslr
N.A.I.C.S.: 424210
William Ku (Gen Mgr)

Aceto Agricultural Chemicals Corp. (1)
4 Tri Harbor Ct, Port Washington, NY 11050 (100%)
Tel.: (516) 627-6000
Web Site: http://www.aceto.com
Sales Range: $300-349.9 Million
Emp.: 100
Wholesale & Distribution of Agricultural Chemicals
N.A.I.C.S.: 424910
Douglas Roth (Sr VP & CFO)

Aceto B.V. (1)
Jan Ligdstraat 75, Heemskerk, 1964, Netherlands (100%)
Tel.: (31) 251252322
Web Site: http://www.acetobv.com
Sales Range: $50-74.9 Million
Emp.: 7
Specialty Chemicals Mfr
N.A.I.C.S.: 424690
Janvanis Van Eis (Mng Dir)

Aceto FineChem GmbH (1)

Winterhuder Weg 27, D-22085, Hamburg, Germany
Tel.: (49) 4022702666
Web Site: http://www.de.aceto.com
Sales Range: $25-49.9 Million
Emp.: 6
Specialty Chemicals Mfr
N.A.I.C.S.: 424690
Gunter Schenkel (Mng Dir)

Aceto France S.A.S. (1)
3-5 Rue Scheffer, 75016, Paris, France
Tel.: (33) 144146940
Web Site: http://www.aceto.com
Distr of Human Health Products, Pharmaceutical Ingredients & Performance Chemicals
N.A.I.C.S.: 424690
Guillaume Saint-Clair (Mng Dir)

Aceto Pharma GmbH (1)
Winterhuder Weg 27, Hamburg, D 22085, Germany (100%)
Tel.: (49) 402270260
Web Site: http://www.aceto-europe.com
Sales Range: $50-74.9 Million
Emp.: 40
Distribute, Market & Sell Specialty Chemicals
N.A.I.C.S.: 424690
Gunto Shenko (Mng Dir)

Aceto Pharma India Pvt. Ltd. (1)
W-116/117 MIDC Phase II, Dombivali East, Kalyan, 421203, India
Tel.: (91) 2512870605
Web Site: http://www.aceto.com
Sales Range: $25-49.9 Million
Emp.: 12
Pharmaceutical & Chemical Products Mfr
N.A.I.C.S.: 325412
Pradeep Thakur (Mng Dir)

Aceto Pte Ltd. (1)
300 Beach Road, 40th Floor, Singapore, 199555, Singapore (100%)
Tel.: (65) 62960800
Web Site: http://www.aceto.com
Sales Range: $50-74.9 Million
Emp.: 13
Distribute, Market & Sell Specialty Chemicals
N.A.I.C.S.: 424690
Pauling Sng (Mng Dir)

IsleChem, LLC (1)
2801 Long Rd, Grand Island, NY 14072
Tel.: (716) 773-8401
Web Site: http://www.islechem.com
Sales Range: $1-9.9 Million
Emp.: 25
Chemicals Mfr
N.A.I.C.S.: 325199
John Dahl (Mgr)
Murray Mike (Engr-Maintenance)
Pat Canavan (Pres)

Pharma Waldhof GmbH (1)
Hansaallee 159, D 40549, Dusseldorf, Germany (100%)
Tel.: (49) 211 52 60 20
Web Site: http://www.pharmawaldhof.de
Sales Range: $25-49.9 Million
Emp.: 12
Bio-Chemicals Mfr
N.A.I.C.S.: 424690
Lukas von Hippel (Mng Dir)
Salvatore Guccione (Mng Dir)

ACF COMPONENTS & FASTENERS
31014 Huntwood Ave, Hayward, CA 94544
Tel.: (510) 487-2100
Web Site: http://www.acfcom.com
Rev.: $14,000,000
Emp.: 55
Miscellaneous Fasteners
N.A.I.C.S.: 423710
John Y. Mizutani (Chm)
Gerry Reese (Pres)
Robert Mandler (CFO, COO & Exec VP)
Tsuyoshi Arakaki (Coord-Mktg)

ACF ENVIRONMENTAL

2831 Cardwell Rd, Richmond, VA 23234
Tel.: (804) 271-2363
Web Site:
   https://www.acfenvironmental.com
Year Founded: 1984
Sales Range: $10-24.9 Million
Emp.: 200
Distributed Geosynthetic
N.A.I.C.S.: 423320

ACF INDUSTRIES LLC
101 Clark St, Saint Charles, MO 63301
Tel.: (636) 949-2399   NJ
Web Site:
   http://www.acfindustries.com
Year Founded: 1899
Rev.: $600,000,000
Emp.: 20
Railroad Replacement Parts Mfr
N.A.I.C.S.: 336510
Michael Farmakis (Pres & CEO)

ACHA TRADING CO. INC.
PO Box 9020150, San Juan, PR 00902-0150
Tel.: (787) 275-6095
Web Site:
   https://www.achatrading.com
Sales Range: $10-24.9 Million
Emp.: 53
Accoustical Ceiling; Vinyl Floors; Partitions
N.A.I.C.S.: 444140
Esaer Mora (Pres)

ACHEN-GARDNER CONSTRUCTION, LLC
550 S 79th St, Chandler, AZ 85226-4706
Tel.: (480) 940-1300   AZ
Web Site: https://www.achen.com
Year Founded: 1989
Sales Range: $25-49.9 Million
Emp.: 150
Highway, Street & Underground Utilities Construction
N.A.I.C.S.: 237310
Dennis Troggio (Co-Owner & CEO)
John Walstrom (Co-Owner & Pres)
Dah Spitza (VP & Dir-Bus Dev, Project Mgr & Design Svcs)
Kevin Nunez (VP)

Subsidiaries:

Achen-Gardner Inc. - GDC Homes (1)
550 S 79th St, Chandler, AZ 85226-4706
Tel.: (480) 940-1300
Sales Range: $10-24.9 Million
Emp.: 70
Residential Construction
N.A.I.C.S.: 236115
Dennis Troggio (Pres)

ACHIEVA CREDIT UNION
1150 Virginia St, Dunedin, FL 34698
Tel.: (727) 431-7680
Web Site: http://www.achievacu.com
Year Founded: 1937
Credit Union
N.A.I.C.S.: 522130
Gary Regoli (Pres & CEO)
Janice Hollar (CFO)
Jeff Blake (Chief People Officer)

Subsidiaries:

Achieva Insurance Agency, LLC (1)
1659 Achieva Wy, Dunedin, FL 34698
Tel.: (813) 258-8084
Insurance Agents
N.A.I.C.S.: 524210
Joseph Cannella (Dir)

Subsidiary (Domestic):

Cannella Insurance Services Inc. (2)

1220 S Dale Mabry Hwy, Tampa, FL 33629-5019
Tel.: (813) 258-8084
Web Site: http://www.cannellainsurance.com
Insurance Agencies & Brokerages
N.A.I.C.S.: 524210

ACHIEVE 3000, INC.
1985 Cedar Bridge Ave Ste 3, Lakewood, NJ 08701
Tel.: (732) 367-5505
Web Site:
    http://www.achieve3000.com
Year Founded: 2000
Sales Range: $10-24.9 Million
Emp.: 110
Web-Based Educational Programs
N.A.I.C.S.: 611710
Saki Dodelson (Co-Founder, Pres & CEO)
Susan Gertler (Co-Founder & Chief Academic Officer)
Jim O'Neill (Chief Product & Strategy Officer)
Rivki Locker (COO)
Joel Jeselsohn (CFO)

ACHIEVE PARTNERS MANAGEMENT, LLC
530 7th Ave Ste 1909, New York, NY 10018
Tel.: (917) 821-9194
Web Site:
    http://www.achievepartners.com
Venture Capital & Private Equity
N.A.I.C.S.: 523999
Daniel S. Pianko (Co-Founder & Mng Dir)
Aanand Randia (Mng Partner)
Ryan Craig (Co-Founder)
Daniel Pianko (Co-Founder)

Subsidiaries:

Optimum Healthcare IT, LLC   (1)
1300 Marsh Landing Pkwy Ste 105, Jacksonville Beach, FL 32250
Tel.: (904) 373-0831
Web Site: http://www.optimumhit.com
Healthcare Staffing Services
N.A.I.C.S.: 561311
Gene Scheurer (Chm)
Jason Mabry (CEO)
Jason Jarrett (CEO)
Lydia Veal (CFO & COO)
Steve Glomski (VP-Client Svcs)
Susie Morgan (VP-HR)
Leah Kromar (VP-Consulting Svcs)
Sheryl Bushman (Chief Medical Info Officer)
Larry Kaiser (VP-Mktg)

ACHIEVEMENT CENTER, INC.
4950 W 23rd St, Erie, PA 16506
Tel.: (814) 459-2755   PA
Web Site:
    https://www.achievementctr.org
Year Founded: 1923
Sales Range: $10-24.9 Million
Emp.: 523
Behavioral Healthcare Services
N.A.I.C.S.: 623220
Rebecca N. Brumagin (Exec Dir)
Adam Bratton (Dir-Dev)

ACHIEVENEXT, LLC
4 Glenhardie Corporate Ctr 1255 Drummers Ln Ste 103, Wayne, PA 19087-1565
Tel.: (610) 316-1660
Web Site:
    http://www.achievenext.com
Executive Coaching & Career Management Services
N.A.I.C.S.: 611430
Nick Araco Jr. (CEO)

Subsidiaries:

Kelleher Associates, LLC   (1)
4 Glenhardie Corporate Ctr 1255 Drummers

Ln Ste 103, Wayne, PA 19087-1565
Tel.: (610) 293-1115
Web Site: http://www.kelleherllc.com
Executive Coaching & Career Management Services
N.A.I.C.S.: 611430
James W. Miller (Principal & Sr VP)
Sandra D. Ford (Exec VP)
Richard H. Hartzell (Principal)
Mitch Wienick (Pres & CEO)
Dean M. Becker (VP-Corp Bus Dev)
Jill Aquino (Coord-Office)
Marcia M. Wilf (Partner)

ACHIM IMPORTING COMPANY INC.
58 2nd Ave, Brooklyn, NY 11215
Tel.: (718) 369-2200
Web Site:
    http://www.achimonline.com
Rev.: $10,200,000
Emp.: 15
Window Furnishings
N.A.I.C.S.: 423220
Marton Grossman (Founder & Pres)
Howard Siegal (Gen Mgr)

ACI CAPITAL CO. LLC
299 Park Ave 34th Fl, New York, NY 10071
Tel.: (212) 634-3333   DE
Web Site: http://www.acicapital.com
Year Founded: 1950
Privater Equity Firm
N.A.I.C.S.: 523999
Kevin S. Penn (Founder & Mng Dir)
James E. Mattutat (Co-CFO)
Matthew Bronfman (Mng Dir)
Mira Muhtadie (VP)
Gregory Nolff (Co-CFO)

Subsidiaries:

Accent Energy Group, LLC   (1)
6100 Emerald Pkwy, Dublin, OH 43016
Tel.: (614) 408-1050
Web Site: http://www.accentenergy.com
Sales Range: $10-24.9 Million
Natural Gas & Electricity Distr
N.A.I.C.S.: 221210
Ray Hamman (COO)

Cornhusker Energy Lexington, LLC   (1)
1111 E Industry Dr, Lexington, NE 68850
Tel.: (308) 324-6800
Web Site: http://www.cornhuskerenergy.com
Sales Range: $1-9.9 Million
Ethanol Mfr & Distr
N.A.I.C.S.: 325199

Unified Logistics Holdings LLC   (1)
4800 Hampden Ln Ste 200, Bethesda, MD 20814
Tel.: (240) 482-4861
Web Site: http://www.unifiedlogistics.com
Sales Range: $10-24.9 Million
Holding Company; Specialized Freight Transportation & Logistics Services
N.A.I.C.S.: 551112
Kevin S. Penn (Executives)
Geoffrey B. Davis (CEO)
John G. Flick (CFO)

Subsidiary (Domestic):

Benchmark Logistics, Inc.   (2)
6942 Satsuma Dr, Houston, TX 77041
Tel.: (281) 412-6400
Web Site: http://www.benchmark-logistics.com
Sales Range: $1-9.9 Million
Specialized Freight Transportation Services
N.A.I.C.S.: 484230

McTyre Trucking Company, Inc.   (2)
501 4th St, Orlando, FL 32824
Tel.: (407) 859-5171
Web Site: http://www.mctyretrucking.com
Sales Range: $1-9.9 Million
Emp.: 60
Specialized Freight Transportation Services
N.A.I.C.S.: 484230
John H. McTyre Sr. (COO)

Silk Road Transport, Inc.   (2)
8781 State Rte 36, Arkport, NY 14807
Tel.: (607) 295-7406
Web Site: http://www.silkroadtrans.com
Sales Range: $1-9.9 Million
Emp.: 50
Specialized Freight Transportation Services
N.A.I.C.S.: 484230
Todd Haraty (COO)

ACI CONTROLS INC.
295 Main St, West Seneca, NY 14224
Tel.: (716) 675-9450
Web Site: http://www.aci-controls.com
Sales Range: $10-24.9 Million
Emp.: 40
Whslr of Industrial Machinery & Equipment
N.A.I.C.S.: 423830
John Wischerath (VP)
Thomas Wischerath (VP)
Robert D. Wischerath Sr. (Chm)
Robert Wischerath Jr. (Pres)

ACI GROUP
828 New Meister Ln Ste 300, Pflugerville, TX 78660
Tel.: (972) 233-0203
Sales Range: $10-24.9 Million
Emp.: 300
Holding Company
N.A.I.C.S.: 551112
Tim Peddecord (Pres & CEO)
Ken Bandy (VP-Ops)

Subsidiaries:

Avant North America   (1)
828 New Meister Ln Bldg 10 Ste 300, Pflugerville, TX 78660
Tel.: (800) 779-0257
Web Site: http://www.avantmemory.com
Rev.: $150,000,000
Emp.: 110
Computer Memory & Processor Solutions
N.A.I.C.S.: 541512

ACI INFOTECH
3 Executive Dr Suite 303, Somerset, NJ 08873
Tel.: (732) 824-8161
Web Site: http://www.aciinfotech.com
Year Founded: 2007
Sales Range: $1-9.9 Million
Emp.: 24
Consulting, Application Integration & Enterprise-Level IT Services
N.A.I.C.S.: 541690

ACI INTERNATIONAL
844 Moragh Dr, Los Angeles, CA 90049
Tel.: (310) 889-3400   CA
Web Site: http://www.aciint.com
Year Founded: 1952
Sales Range: $10-24.9 Million
Emp.: 70
Whslr of Footwear
N.A.I.C.S.: 424340
Steve Jackson (Pres & CEO)
Muriel Jackson (Treas)
Rudy Melo (Controller)

Subsidiaries:

L.A. Gear, Inc.   (1)
844 Moraga Dr, Los Angeles, CA 90049
Tel.: (310) 889-3499
Web Site: http://www.lagear.com
Sales Range: $10-24.9 Million
Athletic & Lifestyle Footwear, Apparel & Accessories Mfr
N.A.I.C.S.: 316210
David Mankowitz (CFO)
Sean Mitcheol (Sr VP-Mktg)
Sarah McAdams (Office Mgr)

Subsidiary (Domestic):

L.A. Gear California, Inc.   (2)

844 Moraga Dr, Los Angeles, CA 90049   (100%)
Tel.: (310) 889-3499
Web Site: http://www.lagear.com
Footwear, Except Rubber
N.A.I.C.S.: 316210
Ana Chazoya (Gen Mgr)

ACI LAST MILE NETWORK LLC
330 Golden Shore Ste 410, Long Beach, CA 90802
Tel.: (310) 233-2750
Web Site: http://www.acilastmile.com
Distribution Services
N.A.I.C.S.: 541614
Keith Somers (CEO)

ACI MECHANICAL & HVAC SALES
6100 6th Ave S, Seattle, WA 98108
Tel.: (206) 767-2600
Web Site:
    http://www.acimechsales.com
Year Founded: 1985
Emp.: 30
Warm Air Heating & Air Conditioning
N.A.I.C.S.: 423730
Jim Sinclair (Pres)
Diane Martorana (Controller)
Mike Otani (VP)
Judy Rabe (Mgr-Credit)
Brian Wolford (VP-Engrg)
Anthony Mazzola (Engr-Sls)

ACI NORTHWEST, INC.
6600 N Government Way, Dalton Gardens, ID 83815
Tel.: (208) 772-9571
Web Site: https://www.acinw.com
Year Founded: 1992
Sales Range: $10-24.9 Million
Emp.: 50
Plumbing, Heating & Air-Conditioning Services
N.A.I.C.S.: 238220
Jason Roop (Gen Mgr)

ACKER MERRALL & CONDIT COMPANY, INC.
160 W 72nd St, New York, NY 10023
Tel.: (212) 787-1700
Web Site: http://www.ackerwines.com
Year Founded: 1820
Sales Range: $100-124.9 Million
Emp.: 25
Retailer of Wine
N.A.I.C.S.: 445320
John Kapon (Chm)
David Hamburger (Dir-Special Events)
Mark Gray (Gen Mgr)
Irfan Mughal (CFO)
Jamie Pollack (Mng Dir-Bus Dev & Sls-Global)
Irv Goldman (CEO)
Alicia Martell (Head-Authentication & Quality Control-Global)
Stacey Chervin Sigda (Gen Counsel)

ACKERMAN & CO.
10 Glenlake Pkwy S Tower Ste 1000, Atlanta, GA 30328
Tel.: (770) 913-3900
Web Site:
    https://www.ackermanco.com
Year Founded: 1967
Rev.: $61,500,000
Emp.: 105
Cemeteries & Crematories
N.A.I.C.S.: 812220
Vivian Barnes (CFO & Exec VP)
Fara Wilson (VP & Dir-Mktg & Comm)
Leo Wiener (Pres-Ackerman Retail)
Jimmy Stevens (Sr VP-Brokerage)
Weber Jodesty (Dir-Acctg)

Ackerman & Co.—(Continued)

Brandon Cramer (Mng Dir-Retail Svcs)
Andrew Murphy (Sr VP-Healthcare Investment Sls)
Angela Chapman (Mgr-Property)
Brett Buckner (Sr VP-Brokerage)
Charles Ackerman (Founder & Chm)
Frank Farrell (Sr VP-Leasing)
John Willig (Principal)
Larry Wood (Sr VP-Brokerage)
Michael Anderson (VP-Brokerage)
Walt Boden (Sr VP-Brokerage)
Kim Dworkin (Dir-Property Mgmt)
Brian Lefkoff (Sr VP-Retail)
Kris Miller (Pres)
Jonathan DiGiovanni (VP-Retail Svcs-Ackerman Retail)
Roosevelt Brown (VP-Medical Retail Practice-Ackerman Retail)

ACKERMAN INVESTMENT COMPANY

1625 5th Ave S, Fort Dodge, IA 50501
Tel.: (515) 576-8181
Sales Range: $10-24.9 Million
Emp.: 150
Owning & Operating Franchised Hotels
N.A.I.C.S.: 721110
James Bocken (Pres)

ACKERMAN MCQUEEN, INC.

1100 The Tower 1601 NW Expy, Oklahoma City, OK 73118
Tel.: (405) 843-7777   OK
Web Site: http://www.am.com
Year Founded: 1939
Sales Range: $250-299.9 Million
Emp.: 150
Advetising Agency
N.A.I.C.S.: 541810
Angus McQueen (Co-CEO)

Subsidiaries:

Ackerman McQueen, Inc.   (1)
320 S Boston Ste 100, Tulsa, OK 74103-3706
Tel.: (918) 582-6200
Web Site: http://www.am.com
Sales Range: $10-24.9 Million
Emp.: 20
Full Service
N.A.I.C.S.: 541810
Bruce Parks (Sr VP & Dir-Creative)
Tom Twomey (Sr VP & Sr Producer)
Alan Turner (Mgr-Traffic)
Alyssa Lair (Sr VP)
Amy Hearn (VP)
Ande Courtney (Supvr-Acct)
Angus McQueen (CEO)
Ashley Ball (Exec VP & Dir-Creative)
Ashley Hackler (VP)
Ashley Root (Mgr-Online Content)

Ackerman McQueen, Inc.   (1)
1717 McKinney Ave Ste 1800, Dallas, TX 75202
Tel.: (214) 217-2500
Web Site: http://www.am.com
Sales Range: $10-24.9 Million
Emp.: 15
Advertising Agency Services
N.A.I.C.S.: 541810

Ackerman McQueen, Inc. - Colorado Springs   (1)
517 S Cascade Ave Ste 150, Colorado Springs, CO 80903
Tel.: (719) 630-7000
Web Site: http://www.am.com
Emp.: 4
Advetising Agency
N.A.I.C.S.: 541810
Clay Turner (Exec VP & Dir-Creative)

The Mercury Group   (1)
201 N Union St Ste 510, Alexandria, VA 22314
Tel.: (703) 299-9470

Sales Range: $10-24.9 Million
Emp.: 10
Communications, Government/Political/Public Affairs, Public Relations
N.A.I.C.S.: 541810
Anthony Makris (Pres)
Bill Powers (Exec VP)
Ginny Simone (Sr VP)
Jon Carter (Acct Exec)
Nadar Tavangar (Exec VP & Mng Dir)
Garrett Johnson (Acct Exec)
Lacey Duffy (VP & Acct Supvr)

ACKERMANN PR

1111 Northshore Dr Ste N-400, Knoxville, TN 37919
Tel.: (865) 584-0550
Web Site: http://www.ackermannpr.com
Year Founded: 1981
Sales Range: $50-74.9 Million
Emp.: 15
Public Relations Agency
N.A.I.C.S.: 541820
Cathy G. Ackermann (Pres & CEO)
Crystal Cardwell (COO)
Rick Laney (VP)
Christi McIlwain (Designer)
Erin Burns Freeman (Acct Exec)
Pat Staats (Controller)
Tommy Smith (VP-Mktg Strategy)

ACKLEY BEVERAGE GROUP, LLC

600 University St Ste 902, Seattle, WA 98101
Tel.: (206) 812-9404   WA
Web Site: https://www.ackleybrands.com
Year Founded: 2014
Investment Services
N.A.I.C.S.: 523999
Brandon Ackley (Pres)

Subsidiaries:

Mac & Jack's Brewery, Inc.   (1)
17825 NE 65th St, Redmond, WA 98052
Tel.: (425) 558-9697
Web Site: http://www.macandjacks.com
Sales Range: $1-9.9 Million
Emp.: 17
Beverages Mfr
N.A.I.C.S.: 312120

ACKLEY STATE BANK

650 Main St, Ackley, IA 50601
Tel.: (641) 847-2651
Web Site: http://www.ackleystatebank.com
Sales Range: $1-9.9 Million
Emp.: 25
Provider of Banking Services
N.A.I.C.S.: 522110
Kathy Eichmeier (VP)

ACKLEY SWEENEY ADVERTISING

9 N 4th St, Emmaus, PA 18049
Tel.: (610) 841-7855
Web Site: https://www.ackleysweeneyads.com
Year Founded: 1979
Sales Range: $1-9.9 Million
Emp.: 8
Full-Service Advertising & Marketing
N.A.I.C.S.: 541810
Tom Sweeney (Sr Art Dir)

ACLIVITI LLC

135 S LaSalle St Ste 2450, Chicago, IL 60603
Tel.: (312) 281-2677
Web Site: http://www.acliviti.com
Year Founded: 2015
Sales Range: $1-9.9 Million
Emp.: 10
Telecommunication Servicesb

N.A.I.C.S.: 517810
Ryan Young (Co-Founder & Mng Dir)
Joe Rice (Co-Founder & Mng Dir)

ACLOCHE

1800 Watermark Dr Ste 430, Columbus, OH 43215
Tel.: (614) 824-3790   OH
Web Site: https://www.acloche.com
Year Founded: 1968
Sales Range: $50-74.9 Million
Emp.: 98
Help Supply Services
N.A.I.C.S.: 561320
Kimberly Shoemaker (CEO)

Subsidiaries:

Acloche - Executive Search Division   (1)
1800 Watermark Dr Ste 430, Columbus, OH 43215
Tel.: (614) 824-3700
Human Resource Consulting Services
N.A.I.C.S.: 541612

ACM TECHNOLOGIES INC.

2535 Research Dr, Corona, CA 92882
Tel.: (951) 738-9898
Web Site: https://www.acmtech.com
Sales Range: $10-24.9 Million
Emp.: 50
Office Equipment
N.A.I.C.S.: 423420
Lynn Lee (Product Mgr)
Sharon Lee (Mgr-Acctg)

ACMA COMPUTERS INC.

1565 Reliance Way, Fremont, CA 94539
Tel.: (510) 257-6800   CA
Web Site: http://www.acma.com
Year Founded: 1989
Sales Range: $10-24.9 Million
Emp.: 38
Retailer of Computers & Software
N.A.I.C.S.: 449210
Matt Thauberger (Dir-Sls)

ACME ARCHITECTURAL PRODUCTS INC.

251 Lombardy St, Brooklyn, NY 11222
Tel.: (718) 384-7800   NY
Year Founded: 1995
Sales Range: $25-49.9 Million
Emp.: 500
Metal Doors, Sash & Trim
N.A.I.C.S.: 332321
Jack Teich (Pres & CEO)

Subsidiaries:

Acme Steel Door Corp.   (1)
513 Porter Ave, Brooklyn, NY 11222-5312
Tel.: (718) 384-7800
Web Site: http://www.acmesteel.com
Sales Range: $10-24.9 Million
Emp.: 100
Mfr of Steel Door
N.A.I.C.S.: 332321

ACME BUILDING MAINTENANCE COMPANY

941 Catherine St, Alviso, CA 95002
Tel.: (408) 263-5911
Web Site: http://www.gcaservices.com
Sales Range: $25-49.9 Million
Emp.: 600
Building & Office Cleaning Services
N.A.I.C.S.: 561720
Richard Sanchez (Pres)

ACME CONCRETE PAVING INC.

4124 E Broadway Ave, Spokane, WA 99202

Tel.: (509) 242-1234
Web Site: https://www.acmecpi.com
Year Founded: 2002
Sales Range: $25-49.9 Million
Emp.: 30
Highway & Street Construction Services
N.A.I.C.S.: 237310
Steven Clark (Owner)
Robert Seghetti (VP)
James Welsh (Owner)

ACME CONSTRUCTION SUPPLY CO. INC.

330 SE Salmon St, Portland, OR 97214-3357
Tel.: (503) 872-9805   OR
Web Site: https://www.acmetool.com
Year Founded: 1979
Sales Range: $25-49.9 Million
Emp.: 135
Distr of Hardware
N.A.I.C.S.: 423710
Jordan Bader (Pres)

ACME DELIVERY SERVICE INC.

18101 E Colfax Ave, Aurora, CO 80011
Tel.: (303) 340-2100
Web Site: https://www.acmedistribution.com
Sales Range: $250-299.9 Million
Emp.: 200
General Warehousing
N.A.I.C.S.: 493110
Nancy Manilla (CFO)
Jeff Goldfogel (Pres)

ACME DIE CASTING CORPORATION

3610 Commercial Ave, Northbrook, IL 60062
Tel.: (847) 272-9520   WI
Web Site: https://www.acmealliance.com
Year Founded: 1946
Sales Range: $25-49.9 Million
Emp.: 100
Aluminum Die-Castings
N.A.I.C.S.: 331523
Matt Lovejoy (Pres)

ACME ELECTRIC MOTOR INC.

1705 13th Ave N, Grand Forks, ND 58203-2321
Tel.: (701) 746-6481   ND
Web Site: http://www.acme1948.com
Year Founded: 1948
Sales Range: $50-74.9 Million
Emp.: 275
Industrial Machinery & Equipment
N.A.I.C.S.: 423830
Daniel A. Kuhlman (Pres)

ACME ENGINEERING AND MANUFACTURING CORP.

1820 N York St, Muskogee, OK 74403
Tel.: (918) 682-7791
Web Site: http://www.acmefan.com
Rev.: $40,000,000
Emp.: 350
Blowers & Fans Mfr
N.A.I.C.S.: 333413
Lee Buddris (Pres)

ACME FARMS, INC.

1024 S King St, Seattle, WA 98104-3021
Tel.: (206) 323-4300   WA
Year Founded: 1928
Sales Range: $10-24.9 Million
Emp.: 6
Sales & Distributor of Poultry Items
N.A.I.C.S.: 424440

Tom Terry *(Mgr)*

ACME FOOD SALES, INC.
5940 1st Ave S, Seattle, WA 98108
Tel.: (206) 762-5150   WA
Web Site: http://www.acmefood.com
Year Founded: 1973
Sales Range: $10-24.9 Million
Emp.: 35
Groceries & Related Products
N.A.I.C.S.: 424490
Dean Polik *(Pres)*
Rob Polik *(Exec VP)*

ACME FOUNDRY, INC.
1502 Spruce St, Coffeyville, KS
67337
Tel.: (620) 251-6800   KS
Web Site:
  https://www.acmefoundry.net
Year Founded: 1914
Sales Range: $75-99.9 Million
Emp.: 270
Gray Iron Foundry
N.A.I.C.S.: 331511
Richard M. Tatman *(Chm & CEO)*
Thomas A. Tatman *(Pres)*
Robert L. Shepard *(CFO, Treas & Sec)*
Richard J. Tatman *(Owner)*

Subsidiaries:

Magic Circle Manufacturing
Division   (1)
1209 Buckeye St, Coffeyville, KS 67337-
3711
Tel.: (620) 251-4920
Rev.: $2,700,000
Emp.: 45
Machine Shops
N.A.I.C.S.: 332710
Richard J. Tatman *(VP)*
Phil Mashburn *(Dir-Pur)*
Dick Yates *(Gen Mgr)*

ACME HOLDINGS, INC.
14400 N Brook Dr Ste 220, San Antonio, TX 78232
Tel.: (210) 798-3460
Sales Range: $25-49.9 Million
Emp.: 25
Holding Company
N.A.I.C.S.: 551112
Jeffrey E. Garvens *(Pres)*
Dan Beigel *(Mgr-Compliance)*

Subsidiaries:

Electro-Coatings of California
Inc.   (1)
893 Carleton St, Berkeley, CA 94710-2609
Tel.: (510) 849-4075
Web Site: http://www.electro-coatings.com
Emp.: 15
Industrial Metal Coating & Plating Services
N.A.I.C.S.: 332813
Brian Carney *(Gen Mgr)*

Electro-Coatings of Iowa, Inc. (1)
911 Shaver Rd NE, Cedar Rapids, IA 52402
Tel.: (319) 363-9602
Web Site: http://www.electro-coatings.com
Sales Range: $10-24.9 Million
Emp.: 15
Industrial Metal Coating & Plating Services
N.A.I.C.S.: 332813
Shannon Kelty *(Gen Mgr)*
Mike Smith *(Mgr-Ops)*

Electro-Coatings of Texas, Inc. (1)
216 Baywood St, Houston, TX 77011
Tel.: (713) 923-5935
Web Site: http://www.electro-coatings.com
Emp.: 20
Industrial Metal Coating & Plating Services
N.A.I.C.S.: 332813
Dan Johnson *(Plant Mgr)*

ACME LIFT COMPANY, LLC
4751 E Indigo St, Mesa, AZ 85205
Tel.: (602) 254-0650   AZ

Web Site: https://www.acmelift.com
Year Founded: 1997
Aerial Equipment Rentals; Telescopic
Boom Lifts, Telehandlers & Air Compressors Mfr
N.A.I.C.S.: 334511
Woody Weld *(Chm & CEO)*
Richard Jewell *(Chief Admin Officer)*
Yuko Nagura *(CFO)*
JP Patterson *(Exec VP-Sls & Ops)*

ACME MANUFACTURING COMPANY INC.
4661 Monaco St, Denver, CO 80216
Tel.: (303) 355-2344
Web Site:
  https://www.acmemfgco.com
Year Founded: 1992
Sales Range: $10-24.9 Million
Emp.: 150
Hardware Mfr
N.A.I.C.S.: 332510
L. G. Broderick *(Pres)*

Subsidiaries:

The Steelworks Corporation   (1)
4661 Monaco St, Denver, CO 80216
Tel.: (303) 355-2344
Web Site: http://www.steelworks.com
Rev.: $340,000
Emp.: 100
Packaging & Labeling Services
N.A.I.C.S.: 332510
Larry Broderick *(Owner)*

ACME METAL CAP CO., INC.
3353 62nd St, Woodside, NY 11377-
2235
Tel.: (718) 335-3000   NY
Web Site: http://www.acmepans.com
Year Founded: 1935
Sales Range: Less than $1 Million
Emp.: 50
Metal & Non-Metallic Stamping Services
N.A.I.C.S.: 332119
Mike Roughton *(Pres)*

ACME MILLS CO. INC.
33 Bloomfield Hills Pkwy Ste 120,
Bloomfield Hills, MI 48304
Tel.: (248) 203-2000   MI
Web Site: https://acmemills.com
Year Founded: 1917
Sales Range: $75-99.9 Million
Emp.: 100
Automotive Industrial Textiles
N.A.I.C.S.: 314999
James A. Colman *(Chm & CEO)*
Neil G. Gross *(Pres)*
Ray Lambert *(CFO)*
Matt Utley *(Grp Dir-Sls)*

Subsidiaries:

Ervins Group, LLC   (1)
301 Arch Ave, Hillsdale, MI 49242
Tel.: (517) 437-8940
Web Site: http://www.ervinsgroup.com
Design & Mfr of Automotive, Office Furniture & General Industrial Products
N.A.I.C.S.: 313310
Steve Firavich *(Pres)*

Fairway Products   (1)
301 Arch Ave, Hillsdale, MI 49242 **(100%)**
Tel.: (517) 437-8940
Web Site: http://www.fairway-products.com
Sales Range: $10-24.9 Million
Emp.: 120
Automotive Interior Soft Trim, Seating Components & Safety Restraint Assemblies
N.A.I.C.S.: 313210
Darrell Derr *(Inventory & Lean)*

Great Lakes Filters   (1)
301 Arch Ave, Hillsdale, MI 49242
Tel.: (517) 437-8940
Web Site: http://www.greatlakesfilters.com
Sales Range: $10-24.9 Million
Emp.: 25
Mfr Of Filters

N.A.I.C.S.: 423840

ACME NISSAN
2050 R130 N, Monmouth Junction,
NJ 08852-0200
Tel.: (732) 821-9300   NJ
Web Site:
  https://www.acmenissan.com
Year Founded: 1951
Sales Range: $10-24.9 Million
Emp.: 50
New & Used Car Dealers
N.A.I.C.S.: 441110
Darrel Grady *(Controller & Office Mgr)*
Paul Jaskowski III *(Bus Mgr)*
Paul Jaskowski II *(Principal)*

ACME PAPER & SUPPLY CO. INC.
8229 Sandy CT, Savage, MD 20763
Tel.: (410) 792-2333   MD
Web Site: http://www.acmepaper.com
Year Founded: 1946
Sales Range: $50-74.9 Million
Emp.: 100
Industrial & Personal Service Paper &
Janitorial Supplies Distr
N.A.I.C.S.: 424130
Edward Attman *(Founder & Pres)*
Ronald Attman *(VP)*
Keith Attman *(Dir-Pur)*
Phil Carrizales *(Dir-Field Sls)*
Joe Theis *(Mgr-Janitorial Equipment Sls)*
Kevin Krown *(Mgr-Svc-Restaurant Equipment Div)*

Subsidiaries:

Acme Paper & Supply Co., Inc.   (1)
2100 Jefferson Davis Hwy, Richmond, VA
23224
Tel.: (804) 233-8336
Web Site: http://www.acmepaper.com
Sales Range: $10-24.9 Million
Emp.: 12
Packaging Product Distr
N.A.I.C.S.: 561910

ACME PLASTICS, INC.
220 Browertown Rd, Woodland Park,
NJ 07424-2670
Tel.: (973) 256-6666
Web Site:
  http://www.acmeplastics.com
Year Founded: 1943
Plastics Product Mfr
N.A.I.C.S.: 339999
Angela Travezano *(Mgr-Accts Payables)*
Vijay Bahl *(Dir-Mfg)*
Marisa Andreottola *(Dir-IT)*

ACME REFINING SCRAP IRON & METAL COMPANY
3357 S Justine St, Chicago, IL
60608-6351
Tel.: (773) 523-4500   IL
Web Site: http://www.acmescrap.com
Year Founded: 1970
Sales Range: $50-74.9 Million
Emp.: 85
Scrap & Waste Materials
N.A.I.C.S.: 423930
Larry Baron *(Pres & CEO)*

ACME SMOKED FISH CORPORATION
30 Gem St, Brooklyn, NY 11222
Tel.: (718) 383-8585
Web Site:
  https://www.acmesmokedfish.com
Year Founded: 1954
Emp.: 55
Seafood Whslr
N.A.I.C.S.: 424460

Buzz Billik *(Dir-Sls)*
Eduardo Carbajosa *(CFO)*
Adam Caslow *(VP)*
David Caslow *(VP-Ops)*
Richard Schiff *(Gen Mgr)*

ACME TRADING CORPORATION
18895 E Arenth Ave, City of Industry,
CA 91748-1304
Tel.: (626) 964-3456   CA
Web Site: https://www.acmecorp.com
Year Founded: 1985
Sales Range: $10-24.9 Million
Emp.: 80
Nondurable Goods
N.A.I.C.S.: 424990
George Chen *(Founder & Owner)*

ACME TRUCK LINE, INC.
200 Westbank Expy, Gretna, LA
70053
Tel.: (504) 368-2510   LA
Web Site: http://www.acmetruck.com
Year Founded: 1960
Sales Range: $400-449.9 Million
Emp.: 5,000
Provider of Oilfield Hauling & Truckloading
N.A.I.C.S.: 484121
Michael Coatney *(Pres)*
Kimberly Foster *(CFO)*
Keith Cheramie *(VP & Mgr-Sls & Natl Accounts)*
Ray Broussard *(Acct Mgr-Natl)*
Tommy Woodard *(Acct Mgr-Natl)*
Mike Dohrman *(VP-Natl Accounts)*
Kellye Storm *(VP-Natl Accounts & Employee Dev)*
Jimmie Vicknair *(VP & Dir-Trng)*
Rusty Weigl *(VP-Natl Accounts)*

ACME-MCCRARY CORPORATION
159 North St, Asheboro, NC 27204-
1287
Tel.: (336) 625-2161
Web Site: https://www.acme-mccrary.com
Year Founded: 1909
Rev.: $48,800,000
Emp.: 900
Hosiery & Seamless Apparel Mfr
N.A.I.C.S.: 313110
Rod Spruill *(VP-Sales)*

Subsidiaries:

Sapona Manufacturing Company,
Inc.   (1)
2478 Cedar Falls Rd PO Box 128, Cedar
Falls, NC 27230-0128
Tel.: (336) 625-2727
Web Site: http://www.saponamfg.com
Sales Range: $50-74.9 Million
Emp.: 200
Yarn & Textile Mfr
N.A.I.C.S.: 313110
S. Steele Redding *(Pres & CEO)*
Pete McMichael *(Gen Mgr)*
Larry Marley *(Controller)*
Henry Needham *(Mgr-Pur)*
Gene Simpson *(Mgr-Credit)*
Joe Kearns *(Mgr-Plng)*
Marilyn Allred *(Supvr-Quality)*

ACME-MONACO CORPORATION
75 Winchell Rd, New Britain, CT
06052
Tel.: (860) 224-1349
Web Site:
  https://www.acmemonaco.com
Rev.: $10,407,482
Emp.: 140
Steel Springs, Except Wire
N.A.I.C.S.: 332613

Acme-Monaco Corporation—(Continued)

Michael Karabin *(CEO)*
Jerry Blais *(Dir-IT)*
Michael Fasci *(Sr VP-Mfg & Tech)*

ACMG, INC.
2570 Technical Dr, Miamisburg, OH 45342
Tel.: (937) 866-6660
Sales Range: $25-49.9 Million
Emp.: 32
Medical Insurance Claim Processing Services
N.A.I.C.S.: 524292
Paul W. Mcvay *(Pres & CEO)*
Charles P. Duncan *(CFO & Exec VP)*

ACN, INC.
1000 Progress Pl, Concord, NC 28025-2449
Tel.: (704) 260-3000
Web Site: https://www.acn.com
Year Founded: 1993
Sales Range: $75-99.9 Million
Emp.: 600
Local & Long Distance Telephone Communications
N.A.I.C.S.: 517111

ACO HARDWARE, INC.
23333 Commerce Dr, Farmington Hills, MI 48335-2727
Tel.: (248) 471-0100　　　MI
Web Site:
　http://www.acohardware.com
Year Founded: 1946
Sales Range: $500-549.9 Million
Emp.: 1,400
Retail Hardware Stores
N.A.I.C.S.: 444140
Misty Carpus *(Coord-Import)*
Daniel Kull *(Asst Mgr)*
Deanna Hanner *(Asst Mgr)*
Michael Dunne *(Mgr-Store)*

ACOM SOLUTIONS INC.
2850 E 29th St, Long Beach, CA 90806-2313
Tel.: (562) 424-7899
Web Site: https://www.acom.com
Year Founded: 1983
Sales Range: $10-24.9 Million
Emp.: 80
Document Management Solutions
N.A.I.C.S.: 518210
Patrick McMahon *(Pres & CEO)*
Steven R. Snider *(CFO)*
James J. Scott *(Sr VP-Core Bus Div)*
Sam Mikhail *(Sr VP-Sls)*
Mark Firmin *(Sr VP & Gen Mgr)*
Hoang Nguyen *(VP-Tech & Dev)*
Tony Chavez *(VP-Ops-e-Business Div)*

Subsidiaries:

ACOM Medical Billing　　　　　(1)
1094 S Gilbert Rd Ste 203, Gilbert, AZ 85296
Tel.: (480) 545-2610
Web Site:
　http://www.acommedicalbilling.com
Sales Range: $10-24.9 Million
Emp.: 23
Medical Billing Services
N.A.I.C.S.: 541219

ACOM Solutions Inc. -iSeries AS/400 Division　　　　　(1)
2455 Meadowbrook Pkwy NW, Duluth, GA 30096
Tel.: (770) 279-8955
Web Site: http://www.acom.com
Sales Range: $10-24.9 Million
Emp.: 30
System Software Development Services
N.A.I.C.S.: 541512

ACOMA ENERGY, LLC

4100 E Mississippi Ave Ste 400, Denver, CO 80246
Tel.: (720) 420-4700
Web Site:
　http://www.acomaenergy.com
Year Founded: 2006
Sales Range: $1-9.9 Million
Emp.: 14
Acquires & Develops Mineral Assets Within the Oil & Gas Industry
N.A.I.C.S.: 213112
Matthew Anderson *(Owner)*
Gary Beggs *(Bus Mgr)*

ACON INVESTMENTS, LLC
1133 Connecticut Ave NW Ste 700, Washington, DC 20036
Tel.: (202) 454-1100　　　DE
Web Site:
　http://www.aconinvestments.com
Year Founded: 1996
Rev.: $5,600,000,000
Privater Equity Firm
N.A.I.C.S.: 523999
Aron I. Schwartz *(Mng Partner)*
Jonathan Ginns *(Co-Founder & Mng Partner)*
Daniel Jinich *(Mng Partner)*
Kenneth Ross Brotman *(Co-Founder & Mng Partner)*
Alberto Hernandez *(Mng Dir)*
Andre Bhatia *(Mng Partner)*
Anjali Jolly *(Partner)*
Diogo Yano *(Principal)*
Jared Rubenstein *(Principal)*
Jorge Dickens *(Mng Partner)*
Jose Miguel Knoell *(Mng Partner)*
Mauricio Cortes *(Partner)*
Mo Bawa *(Partner)*
Rodrigo Galvao *(Partner)*
Santiago Delgado *(Principal-Ops)*
Suma Kulkarni *(Partner)*
Teresa Y. Bernstein *(COO, Chief Compliance Officer & Gen Counsel)*
Bernard W. Aronson *(Mng Partner)*

Subsidiaries:

APR Energy plc　　　　　(1)
3600 Port Jacksonville Pkwy, Jacksonville, FL 32226
Tel.: (904) 223-8488
Web Site: http://www.aprenergy.com
Sales Range: $450-499.9 Million
Emp.: 270
Holding Company; Temporary & Mobile Electric Power Generation & Transmission Services
N.A.I.C.S.: 551112

Subsidiary (Domestic):

APR Energy, LLC　　　　　(2)
3600 Port Jacksonville Pkwy, Jacksonville, FL 32226
Tel.: (904) 223-8488
Web Site: http://www.aprenergy.com
Temporary & Mobile Electric Power Generation & Transmission Services
N.A.I.C.S.: 221121
Charles P. Ferry *(Pres)*
Joseph DiCamillo *(Gen Counsel)*

Diverzify　　　　　(1)
865 W Irving Park Rd, Itasca, IL 60143
Tel.: (847) 250-4600
Web Site: http://www.diverzify.com
Flooring Services
N.A.I.C.S.: 238330
Bill Graves *(Pres)*

Subsidiary (Domestic):

Spectra Holdings, Inc.　　　　　(2)
865 W Irving Park Rd, Itasca, IL 60143
Tel.: (770) 729-2700
Web Site: http://www.spectracf.com
Flooring Installation Services
N.A.I.C.S.: 238330

Subsidiary (Domestic):

Re:Source Colorado, Inc.　　　　　(3)

700 W Mississippi Ave Ste C4, Denver, CO 80223
Tel.: (303) 756-7100
Web Site: http://www.resourcecolorado.com
Sales Range: $10-24.9 Million
Emp.: 55
Flooring Contractors
N.A.I.C.S.: 238330
John Stanfield *(Pres)*
Lisa VanGilder *(Mgr-HR)*

Subsidiary (Domestic):

Wholesale Floors, Inc.　　　　　(2)
1938 E Osborn Rd, Phoenix, AZ 85016-7234
Tel.: (602) 248-7878
Web Site: http://www.wholesalefloors.com
Rev.: $5,800,000
Emp.: 35
Home Furnishing Merchant Whslr
N.A.I.C.S.: 423220
Scott Wolf *(Pres)*
Josh Sugidono *(Owner)*
Mike Watson *(Gen Mgr)*

Fleetwash, Inc.　　　　　(1)
26 E Law Dr, Fairfield, NJ 07004
Tel.: (877) 513-1593
Web Site: http://www.fleetwash.com
Sales Range: $10-24.9 Million
Truck Wash
N.A.I.C.S.: 811192
Vito DiGiovanni *(Owner)*
Anthony DiGiovanni *(COO)*

Subsidiary (Domestic):

Krystal Klean Inc.　　　　　(2)
13679 Atlantic Blvd, Jacksonville, FL 32225
Tel.: (904) 220-3337
Web Site: http://www.krystalklean.com
Janitorial Services
N.A.I.C.S.: 561720
Ruth Wade *(Owner)*
Jeremy Morgan *(CEO)*

Subsidiary (Domestic):

Krystal Klean USA Inc.　　　　　(3)
13679 Atlantic Blvd, Jacksonville, FL 32225
Tel.: (904) 220-3337
Web Site: https://www.krystalklean.com
Pressure Washing Services
N.A.I.C.S.: 811192

Subsidiary (Domestic):

Under Pressure Washing, LLC　　　　　(4)
1820 Kirkwood Ln, Sarasota, FL 34232-3331
Tel.: (941) 256-7218
Web Site:
　https://www.pressurewashnow.com
Home & Garden Equipment Repair & Maintenance
N.A.I.C.S.: 811411

Subsidiary (Domestic):

Reflections Window and Pressure Washing　　　　　(3)
11246 Distribution Ave E Ste 18, Jacksonville, FL 32256
Tel.: (904) 322-8900
Web Site: http://www.reflectionsjax.com
Specialty Trade Contractors
N.A.I.C.S.: 238990

Window Doctors, Inc.　　　　　(3)
125 Crispen Blvd, Brunswick, GA 31525-1227
Tel.: (912) 226-8001
Web Site: http://www.windowdoctors.net
Specialty Trade Contractors
N.A.I.C.S.: 238990

Goody Products, Inc.　　　　　(1)
3 Glenlake Pkwy, Atlanta, GA 30328
Tel.: (770) 418-7300
Web Site: http://www.goody.com
Sales Range: $800-899.9 Million
Emp.: 800
Hair Rollers, Barrettes, Headbands, Combs, Brushes, Clips, Pins, Shower Caps & Mirrors Mfr
N.A.I.C.S.: 456191
Zoe Garey *(Associate Brand Mgr)*

Subsidiary (Domestic):

JD Beauty Co., LLC　　　　　(2)

5 Adams Ave, Hauppauge, NY 11788
Tel.: (631) 273-2800
Web Site: http://www.jdbeauty.com
Sales Range: $1-9.9 Million
Emp.: 21
Service Establishment Equipment & Supplies Merchant Whslr
N.A.I.C.S.: 423850
Jeff Rosenzweig *(Founder)*
Jeffrey Davidson *(CEO)*

International Imaging Materials, Inc.　　　　　(1)
310 Commerce Dr, Amherst, NY 14228　　　　　(92.5%)
Tel.: (716) 691-6333
Web Site: http://www.iimak.com
Sales Range: $100-124.9 Million
Emp.: 350
Thermal Transfer Ribbons Mfr
N.A.I.C.S.: 339940
Tom Noonan *(VP-IT)*

New Era Cap LLC　　　　　(1)
160 Delaware Ave, Buffalo, NY 14202-2404
Tel.: (716) 604-9000
Web Site: https://www.neweracap.com
Sales Range: $600-649.9 Million
Emp.: 400
Sports-Licensed Headwear Mfr & Distr
N.A.I.C.S.: 315990
Christopher H. Koch *(CEO)*
Kelsey McArthur *(Coord-Category-Arena Sports)*
Jack Merren *(Mgr-PR-Europe, Middle East & Africa)*

Subsidiary (Non-US):

New Era Asia Pacific Limited　　　　　(2)
1611B Exchange Tower 33 Wang Chiu Road Kowloon Bay, Kowloon, China (Hong Kong)
Tel.: (852) 35808845
Apparel Store Retailer
N.A.I.C.S.: 458110

New Era Cap Company Ltd.　　　　　(2)
Building H3 Westcott Venture Park, Westcott, Aylesbury, HP18 0XB, Bucks, United Kingdom
Tel.: (44) 1296655166
Web Site: https://www.neweracap.co.uk
Apparel Store Retailer
N.A.I.C.S.: 458110

New Era Cap S.r.l.　　　　　(2)
Via Postumia 2, 00198, Rome, Italy
Tel.: (39) 068417779
Apparel Store Retailer
N.A.I.C.S.: 458110

Pine Environmental Services, LLC　　　　　(1)
Windsor Industrial Park 92 N Main St Bldg 20, Windsor, NJ 08561
Tel.: (609) 371-9663
Web Site: http://www.pine-environmental.com
Sales Range: $10-24.9 Million
Environmental Testing Equipment Sales, Leasing & Repair Services
N.A.I.C.S.: 423490
Roger Pinheiro *(Co-Founder)*
Angelo Pinheiro *(Co-Founder)*

Spencer Gifts LLC　　　　　(1)
6826 Black Horse Pike, Egg Harbor Township, NJ 08234-4197
Tel.: (609) 645-3300
Web Site: http://www.spencersonline.com
Sales Range: $500-549.9 Million
Novelty Store Operator
N.A.I.C.S.: 459420
Steven B. Silverstein *(Pres & CEO)*

Suzo-Happ Group　　　　　(1)
1743 Linneman Rd, Mount Prospect, IL 60056
Tel.: (847) 593-6130
Web Site: http://www.suzohapp.com
Sales Range: $75-99.9 Million
Amusement, Gaming & Vending Parts Mfr & Distr
N.A.I.C.S.: 334419
Dave Pallotto *(VP-Engrg)*
Laura Sadowski *(Mgr-Inside Sls & Mktg)*
Frank Koelk *(Dir-OEM Supply Chain Mgmt)*
Matt Brown *(CFO)*
Marcel Oelen *(Mng Dir)*

Subsidiary (Non-US):

SCAN COIN AB **(2)**
Jagershillgatan 26, SE-213 75, Malmo,
Sweden
Tel.: (46) 40 6000 600
Web Site: http://www.scancoin.se
Cash Processing Equipment Mfr
N.A.I.C.S.: 334118

Subsidiary (US):

Scan Coin, Inc. **(3)**
1743 Linneman Rd, Mount Prospect, IL
60056
Tel.: (703) 729-8600
Web Site: http://www.scancoin-usa.com
Cash Processing Equipment Mfr
N.A.I.C.S.: 334118

Subsidiary (Non-US):

Suzo-Happ Group (NL) BV **(2)**
Antonie Van Leeuwenhoekstraat 9, Oud-
Beijerland, 3261 LT, Netherlands
Tel.: (31) 186643333
Web Site: http://www.suzohapp.com
Sales Range: $25-49.9 Million
Systems & Components Mfr for Amuse-
ment, Gaming, Casino & Vending Industries
N.A.I.C.S.: 423690
Peter Robyn (Gen Mgr)

Suzo-Happ Group (UK) Ltd. **(2)**
Units 1 & 2 King Georges Trading Estate,
Davis Road, Chessington, KT9 1TT, Surrey,
United Kingdom
Tel.: (44) 208 391 7700
Web Site: http://www.suzohapp.co.uk
Sales Range: $25-49.9 Million
Systems & Components Mfr for Amuse-
ment, Gaming, Casino & Vending Industries
N.A.I.C.S.: 423690
John Vallis (Dir-Sls)

Suzo-Happ Group Americas (AR)
S.R.L. **(2)**
Ruta 8 Km 60 Calle 11 #853 Esq 12,
Parque Industrial Pilar, 1629, Buenos Aires,
Argentina
Tel.: (54) 223 466 190
Web Site: http://www.suzohapp.com
Systems & Components Mfr for Amuse-
ment, Gaming, Casino & Vending Industries
N.A.I.C.S.: 423690

Suzo-Happ Group Do Brasil Ltda **(2)**
Av Santos Dumont 6760, Joinville, 89226
470, SC, Brazil
Tel.: (55) 47 4674871
Web Site: http://www.suzohapp.com
Systems & Components Mfr for Amuse-
ment, Gaming, Casino & Vending Industries
N.A.I.C.S.: 423690

Suzo-Happ Group GmbH **(2)**
Aachener Strasse 122, Alsdorf, 52477, Ho-
engen, Germany
Tel.: (49) 240498680
Web Site: http://www.suzohapp.com
Sales Range: $25-49.9 Million
Emp.: 12
Systems & Components Mfr for Amuse-
ment, Gaming, Casino & Vending Industries
N.A.I.C.S.: 423690
Marcel Oelen (Mng Dir)

Suzo-Happ Group Sp. zo.o **(2)**
ul Brzozowa 5, 64 320, Niepruszewo, Po-
land
Tel.: (48) 618948682
Web Site: http://www.suzohapp.eu
Emp.: 8
Systems & Components Mfr for Amuse-
ment, Gaming, Casino & Vending Industries
N.A.I.C.S.: 423690
Tomasz Andrzejewski (Gen Mgr)

Suzo-Happ Group Technical Compo-
nents Espana, SAU
C/ Diez No2, Pinoso, 03650, Alicante, Spain
Tel.: (34) 966187240
Web Site: http://www.na.suzohapp.com
Sales Range: $25-49.9 Million
Emp.: 4
Amusement & Gaming Component System
Distr
N.A.I.C.S.: 423440
Juan Gomez (Gen Mgr)

True Value Company, L.L.C. **(1)**
8600 W Bryn Mawr Ave, Chicago, IL
60631-3505 **(70%)**
Tel.: (773) 695-5000
Web Site:
    http://www.truevaluecompany.com
Hardware, Lumber, Building Materials & Re-
lated Merchandise Distr; Paint & Paint Ap-
plicators Mfr
N.A.I.C.S.: 444140
Jean Niemi (VP-Comm)
Deborah O'Connor (CFO & Sr VP)
David Elliott (Sr VP-Mktg)
Chris Kempa (Chief Comml Officer)
William Donahue (VP-HR)
Avynash Gersappe (VP-Pricing & Sls Ops)
Paul Green (Sr VP-Mdsg)
Tim Mills (Sr VP-Growth)
Lyndsi Lee (Sr VP-Supply Chain)

Unit (Domestic):

Home & Garden Showplace **(2)**
8600 W Bryn Mawr Ave, Chicago, IL 60631-
3505
Tel.: (773) 695-5000
Garden Decorative Articles & Equipment
Whslr
N.A.I.C.S.: 423710

Division (Domestic):

Taylor Rental **(2)**
201 Jandus Rd, Cary, IL 60013-2889
Tel.: (847) 639-2058
Consumer Goods Rental Services
N.A.I.C.S.: 532289

Truvalue Manufacturing Co. **(2)**
201 Jandus Rd, Cary, IL 60013-2889
Tel.: (847) 639-2058
Paint Mfr & Distr
N.A.I.C.S.: 424950

U.S. Vision, Inc. **(1)**
1 Harmon Dr Glen Oaks Industrial Park,
Glendora, NJ 08029 **(100%)**
Tel.: (856) 228-1000
Web Site: http://www.usvision.com
Optical Products & Services Retailer
N.A.I.C.S.: 456130
Mike McPhillips (VP-Vision Care & Contact
Lenses)
John Fryers (VP-Canada)
Lynn Romano (VP-Dept Stores Div)
William A. Schwartz Jr. (Vice Chm)

ACOPIAN TECHNICAL COM-
PANY

131 Loomis St, Easton, PA 18045
Tel.: (610) 258-5441
Web Site: https://www.acopian.com
Year Founded: 1960
Sales Range: $50-74.9 Million
Emp.: 130
Electronic Power Supply Mfr
N.A.I.C.S.: 334419
G. Acopian (Pres)
G. Hariton (Treas)

ACORIO LLC

260 Franklin St 3rd Fl, Boston, MA
02110
Web Site: http://www.acorio.com
Year Founded: 2013
Sales Range: $25-49.9 Million
Emp.: 178
Information Technology Management
Services
N.A.I.C.S.: 541513
Ellen Daley (CEO)
Sven Ingard (COO)
Brian Murphy (Chief Sls Officer)
Christine Dostal (VP-Fin)
Mike Hanrahan (VP-Ops)

ACORN ENGINEERING COM-
PANY, INC.

15125 Proctor Ave, City of Industry,
CA 91746-3327
Tel.: (626) 336-4561   CA
Web Site: https://www.acorneng.com
Year Founded: 1955
Sales Range: $50-74.9 Million

Emp.: 1,500
Metal Products Mfr
N.A.I.C.S.: 332999
Kirk Kleinen (Pres & Gen Mgr)
Ron Stewart (VP & Gen Mgr)

Subsidiaries:

Acorn-Gencon Plastics **(1)**
13818 Oaks Ave, Chino, CA
91710-7008 **(100%)**
Tel.: (909) 591-8461
Web Site: http://www.acorn-gencon.com
Sales Range: $25-49.9 Million
Emp.: 60
Custom Plastic Injection Moulding
N.A.I.C.S.: 326199

Chronomite Laboratories, Inc. **(1)**
17451 Hurley St, City of Industry, CA 91744
Tel.: (626) 937-4270
Web Site: http://www.chronomite.com
Sales Range: $25-49.9 Million
Emp.: 30
Mfr of Energy Conservation Commercial &
Industrial Tankless Plumbing Applications
N.A.I.C.S.: 238220
Donald F Morris (Chm, Pres & CEO)

Elmco Sales Inc. **(1)**
15070 Proctor Ave, City of Industry, CA
91746
Tel.: (626) 333-9942
Web Site: http://www.elmcosales.com
Rev.: $17,000,000
Emp.: 30
Plumbing & Hydronic Heating Supplies
N.A.I.C.S.: 423720
Tom Duddy (CEO)

Murdock-Super Secur **(1)**
15125 Proctor Ave, City of Industry, CA
91746
Tel.: (626) 333-2543
Web Site: http://www.murdock-
supersecur.com
Sales Range: $25-49.9 Million
Emp.: 20
Designer, Mfr & Supplier of Outdoor Drink-
ing Fountains, Hydrants, Pre-Engineered
Park & Recreation Buildings & Bicycle Se-
curity Lockers
N.A.I.C.S.: 332999
Robert A. Murdock (Pres)

Whitehall Manufacturing, Inc. **(1)**
15125 Proctor Ave, City of Industry, CA
91746 **(100%)**
Tel.: (626) 968-6681
Web Site: http://www.whitehallmfg.com
Sales Range: $10-24.9 Million
Emp.: 40
Stainless Steel Whirlpools & Hot Pac Units
for Hydrotherapy
N.A.I.C.S.: 332999
Don Morris (Pres)

ACORN GROWTH COMPA-
NIES, LC

621 N Robinson Ste 550, Oklahoma
City, OK 73102
Tel.: (405) 737-2676   OK
Web Site:
    http://www.acorngrowthcos.com
Year Founded: 2005
Privater Equity Firm
N.A.I.C.S.: 551112
Jeff Morton (Sr Partner & CFO)
Jeff Davis (Founding Partner)
Brandon Bradford (Partner)
Rick Nagel (Mng Partner)
Robert Hinaman (Sr Partner)
Craig Woodruff (VP-Fin)
Peter Greenthal (CEO)
Matthew Ritchie (Mng Dir-Mergers &
Acq-Washington)
Greg Agnew (Partner)
Henry Gregson (Partner)

Subsidiaries:

Aerospares 2000 Limited **(1)**
3 Caxton Way Watford Business Park, Watford, WD18 8UA, Herts, United Kingdom
Tel.: (44) 1923 244 277
Web Site: https://www.aerospares2000.com

Aircraft Spare Parts Distr
N.A.I.C.S.: 336413
Adam Nemenyi (CEO)

Subsidiary (US):

Sentry Aerospace Corp. **(2)**
708 Ginesi Dr, Morganville, NJ 07751-1216
Tel.: (732) 617-8225
Web Site: http://www.sentryaerospace.com
Aircraft Spare Parts Distr
N.A.I.C.S.: 336413
Anthony Disimone (Pres)

Berry Aviation Inc. **(1)**
1807 Airport Dr, San Marcos, TX 78666
Tel.: (512) 353-2379
Web Site: http://www.berryaviation.com
Airport Operations
N.A.I.C.S.: 488119
Sonny Berry (Founder)
David Boxley (Mgr-Travel)
Dan Miller (Dir-Ops)
Tom Ballenger (VP-Unmanned Aerial Sys-
tems)
Stan Finch (Pres)

Dimo Corp. **(1)**
46 Industrial Blvd, New Castle, DE 19720-
2091
Tel.: (302) 324-8100
Web Site: http://www.dimo.com
Military Equipment Mfr & Services
N.A.I.C.S.: 336992
Sohrab Naghshineh (Pres)
Omid Naghshineh (COO)

Hill Aerosystems Inc. **(1)**
911 Battersby Ave, Enumclaw, WA 98022
Tel.: (360) 802-8300
Web Site: http://www.hillaerosystems.com
Sales Range: $10-24.9 Million
Metal Stamping
N.A.I.C.S.: 332119
Steve Hill (Pres)
Randy Haworth (Gen Mgr)

Raisbeck Engineering, Inc. **(1)**
4411 S Ryan Way, Seattle, WA
98178 **(100%)**
Tel.: (206) 723-2000
Web Site: http://www.raisbeck.com
Sales Range: $1-9.9 Million
Emp.: 50
Advanced Aircraft Technology Services
N.A.I.C.S.: 336413
James D. Raisbeck (Chm)
Tony Armstrong (CEO)
Bill Cadow (Dir-Sls)
Robert D. Richardson (Dir-Dealer Support)
David Sylvester (Dir-Sls)
Tim Morgan (VP-Engrg)
Hal Chrisman (Pres)
Don Graves (CFO)
Lisa Wood (Dir-Mktg)

Telecommunication Support Services,
Inc. **(1)**
720 N Dr, Melbourne, FL 32934-9286
Tel.: (321) 242-0000
Web Site: http://www.tssincorp.com
Professional, Scientific & Technical Services
N.A.I.C.S.: 541990
Mark Wolfe (Pres)

ACORN PETROLEUM

76 S Sierra Madre St Ste 200, Colo-
rado Springs, CO 80903
Tel.: (719) 635-3551
Web Site:
    https://www.acornpetroleuminc.com
Sales Range: $100-124.9 Million
Emp.: 180
Petroleum Bulk Stations
N.A.I.C.S.: 424710
Charles Ochs (Pres)

ACORN PRODUCTS CO. INC.

2 Cedar St, Lewiston, ME 04240
Tel.: (207) 786-3526
Web Site: http://www.acornearth.com
Year Founded: 1978
Sales Range: $10-24.9 Million
Emp.: 30
House Slippers Mfr
N.A.I.C.S.: 424340

Acorn Products Co. Inc.—(Continued)

David K. Quinn (CEO)
Sonya Purington (Mgr-Mktg)

ACORN SERVICES INC.
3553 W Chester Pike 401, Newtown
Square, PA 19073
Tel.: (610) 664-2291
Web Site: https://www.acornfood.com
Sales Range: $10-24.9 Million
Emp.: 50
Contract Food Services
N.A.I.C.S.: 722310
Deborah Lepera (Pres)

ACORNS GROW INCORPORATED
5300 California Ave, Irvine, CA 92617
Tel.: (949) 251-0095   **DE**
Web Site: http://www.acorns.com
Year Founded: 2012
Online Investment, Wealth Management & Financial Advisory Data Services
N.A.I.C.S.: 522320
Noah Kerner (CEO)
Jasmine Lee (CFO & COO)
Manning Field (Chief Bus Officer)
Hugh Tamassia (CTO)
James Moorhead (CMO)
Ashley Good (Chief Legal Officer)
Jessica Schaefer (Chief Comm Officer)
Katie Makstenieks (Chief Compliance Officer)
Kennedy Reynolds (Chief Brand Officer & Head-Creative Mktg)
Imad Banna (Chief Info Security Officer)
Jennifer Barrett (Chief Education Officer)
Pete Johnson (Chief Data Officer)
Patricia Gonzales (VP-HR)
Hasrat Godil (VP-Engrg)

Subsidiaries:

Acorns Advisers, LLC   **(1)**
5300 California Ave, Irvine, CA 92617
Tel.: (949) 438-4245
Web Site: http://www.acorns.com
Financial Advisory, Investment & Wealth Management Services
N.A.I.C.S.: 523940
Colin Lam (Controller)

Acorns Securities, LLC   **(1)**
5300 California Ave, Irvine, CA
92617   **(100%)**
Tel.: (949) 438-4245
Web Site: http://www.acorns.com
Securities Brokerage & Trading Services
N.A.I.C.S.: 523150
Colin Lam (Principal-Fin & Ops)

ACOSTA, INC.
6600 Corporate Center Pkwy, Jacksonville, FL 32216
Tel.: (904) 281-9800   **DE**
Web Site: http://www.acosta.com
Year Founded: 1927
Sales Range: $1-4.9 Billion
Emp.: 19,800
Outsourced Sales, Marketing & Retail Merchandising Services
N.A.I.C.S.: 425120
Robert E. Hill (Vice Chm)
Todd Johnson (Chief Legal Officer & Sec)
Claudia Saenz Amlie (Chief HR Officer)
Kathy Caldwell (Exec VP-Client Dev)
Richard Hall (CTO)
Steve Kremser (Chief Strategy & Transformation Officer)
Ashley Taylor (Chief Customer Officer)
Alejandro Rodriguez Bas (Pres)

Taylor Crown (Pres-Foodservice)
Colin Stewart (Exec VP-Bus Intelligence)
Sharon Hart (CIO)
Mike Anderson (Sr VP-Natural Specialty Sls)
David Johnston (Exec VP/Gen Mgr-Canada)
Mark Stovin (Exec VP-Diversified Channels)
John Carroll (Chief Growth Officer)
Brian Wynne (CEO)
Chandra McCormack (CFO)
Kelly Socia (Exec VP-Bus Dev-North America)
Derek Bowen (Pres-Mktg Svcs-North America)

Subsidiaries:

ADW Acosta, LLC   **(1)**
1180 NW Maple St Ste 330, Issaquah, WA 98027
Tel.: (425) 507-3100
Web Site: http://www.adww.com
Emp.: 200
Sales & Marketing Agency
N.A.I.C.S.: 541613
Sean Lewis (Exec VP)
Steve Dichter (Bus Mgr-Non-Food)
Tom Garvey (Exec VP-Non-Food-Intl)
Mark Mobilia (Pres)
Jeff Tater (Sr VP)
Mark Stovin (Sr VP)
Karl Bissen (Sr VP)

Acosta Foodservice   **(1)**
1328 S Loop W, Houston, TX 77054
Tel.: (713) 799-9394
Web Site: http://www.acosta.com
Sales Range: $10-24.9 Million
Emp.: 30
Outsourced Sales, Marketing & Retail Merchandising Services
N.A.I.C.S.: 425120

Acosta Military Sales, LLC   **(1)**
2551 Eltham Ave Ste P, Norfolk, VA 23513
Tel.: (757) 423-2832
Web Site: http://www.military.acosta.com
Sales Range: $100-124.9 Million
Outsourced Military-Based Retail Sales, Marketing & Merchandising Services
N.A.I.C.S.: 425120
David Johnson (Pres)

Acosta Sales & Marketing Co. - Boston/Marlborough Office   **(1)**
130 Lizotte Dr, Marlborough, MA 01752
Tel.: (508) 486-8200
Web Site: http://www.acosta.com
Sales Range: $75-99.9 Million
Outsourced Sales, Marketing & Retail Merchandising Services
N.A.I.C.S.: 425120

Acosta Sales & Marketing Co. - Pleasanton Office   **(1)**
6870 Koll Ctr Pkwy, Pleasanton, CA 94566
Tel.: (925) 600-3500
Web Site: http://www.acosta.com
Sales Range: $200-249.9 Million
Outsourced Sales, Marketing & Retail Merchandising Services
N.A.I.C.S.: 425120
Sandy Ramsey (Exec VP-Operational Fin)

Acosta Sales & Marketing Company   **(1)**
2800 Westoak Dr, Charlotte, NC 28217
Tel.: (704) 227-7575
Web Site: http://www.acosta.com
Sales Range: $50-74.9 Million
Outsourced Sales, Marketing & Retail Merchandising Services
N.A.I.C.S.: 541613
John Morris (Dir-Bus Insights)
Marty Mace (Gen Mgr)

CORE Foodservice   **(1)**
14544 Central Ave, Chino, CA 91710
Tel.: (909) 438-2626
Sales & Marketing Services
N.A.I.C.S.: 541613
John Goodman (CEO)

CROSSMARK, Inc.   **(1)**

5100 Legacy Dr, Plano, TX 75024-3104
Tel.: (469) 814-1000
Web Site: http://www.crossmark.com
Sales Range: $1-4.9 Billion
Emp.: 20,000
Consumer Packaged Goods Sales & Marketing Services
N.A.I.C.S.: 541613
Todd Mitchell (Exec VP-Client & Customer Dev)
J. Johnette Oden-Brunson (Gen Counsel & Exec VP)
Ben Fischer (Chm)
Lance Andersen (Exec VP-Strategic Initiatives, Products & Svcs)
Alex Yakulis (Exec VP-Bus Dev)
Sheila Gamble (Sr VP-Client Svcs)
Mike Anderson (CIO)
Holly Meloy (Sr VP & Mng Dir-Mktg Werks)
Brendon Walker (Dir-Client Experience-ShopperXP)
Katherine Fuller (Mgr-Field Intelligence)
Jami McDermid (Pres-Sls Agency)
Mark Ayer (Sr VP-Customer Dev-Canada)
Melissa Martin (Sr Acct Mgr-Bus-Canada)
Chris Moye (CEO)

Subsidiary (Non-US):

CROSSMARK Australia Pty. Ltd.   **(2)**
Units 1 & 2 - 39 Herbert Street, Saint Leonards, 2065, NSW, Australia
Tel.: (61) 294391233
Web Site: http://www.crossmark.com.au
Sales Range: $300-349.9 Million
Consumer Packaged Goods Sales & Marketing Services
N.A.I.C.S.: 541613
Kevin Moore (Chm-Asia Pacific)
Andy Kirk (CEO-Australia & New Zealand)
David Murray (COO-Australia & New Zealand)
Polly Yule (Mng Dir-Australia)
Hilary Lamb (Dir-HR & Host Svcs)
Brendon Walker (Dir-Client Svcs)

Branch (Domestic):

CROSSMARK Australia Pty. Ltd. - Melbourne   **(3)**
Level 1 582 Swan Street Burnley, Melbourne, 3121, VIC, Australia
Tel.: (61) 388472800
Web Site: http://www.crossmark.com.au
Sales Range: $50-74.9 Million
Emp.: 50
Consumer Packaged Good Sale & Marketing Services
N.A.I.C.S.: 541613
Charles Stevens (Dir-Client Svcs)

Subsidiary (Domestic):

Marketing Werks, Inc.   **(2)**
130 E Randolph St Ste 2400, Chicago, IL 60601
Tel.: (312) 228-0800
Web Site: http://www.marketingwerks.com
Sales Range: $100-124.9 Million
Marketing Consulting Services
N.A.I.C.S.: 541613
Scott Moller (Founder)
Holly Meloy (Mng Dir & Sr VP)
Dan Miller (Sr VP-Ops)
David Rothkopf (Sr VP & Dir-Creative)
Lisa Fasana (Sr VP & Dir-Acct)

Promo Works, LLC   **(2)**
300 N Martingale Rd, Schaumburg, IL 60173
Tel.: (847) 585-1392
Web Site: http://www.promoworks.com
Sales Range: $10-24.9 Million
Emp.: 75
Administrative Management & General Management Consulting Service
N.A.I.C.S.: 541611
Mark J. Wagner (CFO)
Julie Beck (Exec VP-Sls & Mktg)
Dan Lyman (VP-Shopper Insights & Strategy)
Dan Miller (VP-In-Store Ops)

Kirkpatrick Brokerage Co.   **(1)**
2534 18th St Ste 200, Denver, CO 80211
Tel.: (303) 458-7281
Web Site: http://www.kbcfoods.com
Sales Range: $1-9.9 Million
Emp.: 22

Outsourced Sales, Marketing & Retail Merchandising Services
N.A.I.C.S.: 425120
Michael T. Kirkpatrick (Gen Mgr)

ACOUSTI INCORPORATED
1491 Trae Ln, Lithia Springs, GA 30312
Tel.: (404) 355-1331
Web Site: http://www.acoustiatlanta.com
Sales Range: $10-24.9 Million
Emp.: 75
Acoustical Doors & Specialty Products
N.A.I.C.S.: 238310
Kristin Roskaft (Pres)

ACOUSTIBLOK INC.
6900 Interbay Blvd, Tampa, FL 33616
Tel.: (813) 980-1400
Web Site: https://www.acoustiblok.com
Sales Range: $1-9.9 Million
Soundproofing Materials
N.A.I.C.S.: 332311
Lahnie Johnson (Founder & Pres)

ACOUSTIC INNOVATIONS INC.
1377 Clint Moore Rd, Boca Raton, FL 33487
Tel.: (561) 995-0090
Web Site: http://www.acousticinnovations.com
Sales Range: $10-24.9 Million
Emp.: 35
Acoustic Panels & Custom Theater Seating Mfr
N.A.I.C.S.: 327993
Jay Miller (Owner)

ACOUSTICAL SHEETMETAL INCORPORATED
2600 Production Rd, Virginia Beach, VA 23454
Tel.: (757) 456-9720
Web Site: https://www.acousticalmetals.com
Year Founded: 1994
Sales Range: $10-24.9 Million
Emp.: 76
Sheet Metal Work Mfg
N.A.I.C.S.: 332322

ACOUSTICAL SPECIALTIES & SUPPLY, INC.
12433 S Choctaw Dr, Baton Rouge, LA 70815
Tel.: (225) 275-3440   **LA**
Web Site: http://www.acousticalspecialties.com
Year Founded: 1963
Sales Range: $10-24.9 Million
Emp.: 200
Resilient Floor Coverings; Tile or Sheet
N.A.I.C.S.: 423220
Nathan Selders (Product Mgr)
Albert S. Greene Jr. (Pres)

ACOUSTICS BY DESIGN, INC.
124 Fulton St E Ste 200, Grand Rapids, MI 49503-3232
Tel.: (616) 241-5810
Web Site: http://www.acousticsbydesign.com
Year Founded: 1962
Emp.: 15
Acoustical Consulting Services
N.A.I.C.S.: 541690
Marci Boks (COO & Dir-Ops)

ACQUIRENT, LLC
1603 Orrington Ave Ste #305, Evanston, IL 60201
Tel.: (847) 440-1600

Web Site: http://www.acquirent.com
Year Founded: 2003
Sales Range: $1-9.9 Million
Emp.: 90
Business Process Outsourcing Services
N.A.I.C.S.: 561439
Geoff Winthrop *(Pres)*
Jeffrey Purtell *(COO)*
Sharon Murphy *(Controller)*
John Gutierrez *(Mgr-Recruiting)*

Subsidiaries:

Vorsight LLC   **(1)**
1901 N Fort Myer Dr Ste 902, Arlington, VA 22209
Tel.: (571) 259-3613
Web Site: http://www.vorsight.com
Business Consultancy Services
N.A.I.C.S.: 561499
David Stillman *(Co-Founder & CEO)*
Steve Richard *(Co-Founder)*

ACQUIS CONSULTING GROUP, LLC

299 Broadway 12th Fl, New York, NY 10007
Tel.: (212) 609-2700
Web Site:
http://www.acquisconsulting.com
Year Founded: 1998
Management Consulting Services
N.A.I.C.S.: 541611
David Kaufman *(Founder & Mng Partner)*
Douglas Locke *(Partner)*
Adam Schwartz *(Mng Dir)*
Debra Moss *(Mng Dir)*
Jeff Berk *(Mng Dir)*
Joanna Sears *(Mng Dir)*
Kerby Houff *(Mng Dir)*
Madhav Gurijala *(Mng Dir)*

Subsidiaries:

SSI Strategy   **(1)**
9 Campus Dr 1st Fl, Parsippany, NJ 07054
Tel.: (973) 500-6686
Web Site: http://ssistrategy.com
Management Consulting & Medical Planning Services
N.A.I.C.S.: 541611
Doug Locke *(CEO)*
Adam Schwartz *(Pres)*
Madhav Gurijala *(Sr VP)*
Cathryn Clary *(Sr VP-Medical)*
Jen Seda *(Sr VP-Medical)*

Subsidiary (Domestic):

Scientific Advantage LLC   **(2)**
80 Morristown Rd, Bernardsville, NJ 07924
Tel.: (908) 204-0995
Medical Communication Management & Consulting Services
N.A.I.C.S.: 541611
Robin Winter-Sperry *(Pres & CEO)*

ACQUISITIONS RESEARCH & LOGISTICS LLC

120 Waterfront St Ste 225, Oxon Hill, MD 20745
Tel.: (301) 749-1410
Web Site: http://www.ar-dc.com
Year Founded: 2003
Sales Range: $1-9.9 Million
Emp.: 35
Scientific & Engineering Support
N.A.I.C.S.: 541690
Greg Yette *(Pres)*

ACRE, LLC

10161 Park Run Dr Ste 150, Las Vegas, NV 89145
Tel.: (949) 637-0423
Web Site: http://www.acre-co.com
Year Founded: 1997
Holding Company; Electronic Security Mfr
N.A.I.C.S.: 551112

Donald Joos *(CEO)*
Coreen Sawdon *(CFO)*
Kim Loy *(Chief Product Officer)*
Steve Wagner *(Grp Pres-Americas)*
Will O'Donnell *(CIO)*

Subsidiaries:

Communication Networks, LLC   **(1)**
3 Corporate Dr, Danbury, CT 06810
Tel.: (203) 796-5300
Web Site: http://www.comnet.net
Sales Range: $1-9.9 Million
Emp.: 40
Video & Data Communication Transmission Equipment Mfr
N.A.I.C.S.: 334419
Bruce Berman *(VP-Bus Dev)*
Bruce Miller *(Reg Mgr)*
Dave Sinise *(Mgr-Sls)*
Jeff Vogt *(Acct Mgr-Sls)*
Jens-Uwe Ludwig *(Mgr-Sls-Reg)*

Open Options L.P.   **(1)**
16650 Westgrove Ste 150, Addison, TX 75001
Tel.: (972) 818-7003
Web Site: https://www.ooaccess.com
Software Publisher
N.A.I.C.S.: 513210

RS2 Technologies, LLC   **(1)**
400 Fisher St Ste G, Munster, IN 46321
Tel.: (219) 836-9002
Web Site: http://www.rs2tech.com
Electrical Apparatus & Equipment, Wiring Supplies & Related Equipment Merchant Whslr
N.A.I.C.S.: 423610

Security Identification Systems Corporation   **(1)**
3595 Fiscal Ct, West Palm Beach, FL 33404
Tel.: (561) 691-0050
Web Site: http://www.siscocorp.com
Sales Range: $1-9.9 Million
Emp.: 28
Security Systems Services (except Locksmiths)
N.A.I.C.S.: 561621
David Seltzer *(Dir-Mktg)*
Greg Ruhl *(VP & Gen Mgr)*

ACREE OIL COMPANY

272 W Currahee St, Toccoa, GA 30577
Tel.: (706) 886-2838
Web Site: https://www.acreeoil.com
Year Founded: 1959
Petroleum Bulk Station & Terminal Services
N.A.I.C.S.: 424710
John Davis *(Controller)*

ACRES REAL ESTATE SERVICES INC.

2045 Jefferson St Ste B, Napa, CA 94559
Tel.: (707) 254-8000   **CA**
Web Site: http://www.acresinfo.com
Sales Range: $10-24.9 Million
Real Estate Agency
N.A.I.C.S.: 531210
Burt Marlen Polson *(Owner & CEO)*

ACRILEX INC.

230 Culver Ave, Jersey City, NJ 07305
Tel.: (201) 333-1500
Web Site: https://www.acrilex.com
Sales Range: $10-24.9 Million
Emp.: 51
Plastics Materials
N.A.I.C.S.: 424610
Steve Sullivan *(Pres)*
Domenic Procopio *(Supvr-Fabrication)*

ACRISON, INC.

20 Empire Blvd, Moonachie, NJ 07074-1303
Tel.: (201) 440-8300   **NJ**

Web Site: https://www.acrison.com
Year Founded: 1963
Sales Range: $75-99.9 Million
Emp.: 225
Metering, Mixing & Blending Equipment Mfr
N.A.I.C.S.: 334513
Ronald Ricciardi *(VP & Gen Mgr)*
Terry Shaw *(Mng Dir)*

Subsidiaries:

Acrison, Inc. - Acrison International Division   **(1)**
20 Empire Blvd, Moonachie, NJ 07074
Tel.: (201) 440-8300
Web Site: http://www.acrison.com
Industrial Equipment Mfr
N.A.I.C.S.: 333310

Sapplicator Ltd   **(1)**
Unit 6 Littlers Point Second Avenue Trafford Park, Manchester, M17 1LT, United Kingdom
Tel.: (44) 161 877 9955
Web Site: http://www.sapplicator.co.uk
Industrial Equipment Mfr
N.A.I.C.S.: 333310

ACRISURE, LLC

5664 Prairie Creek Dr SE, Caledonia, MI 49316   **MI**
Web Site: http://www.acrisure.com
Year Founded: 2005
General Insurance Services
N.A.I.C.S.: 524210
Gregory L. Williams *(Founder, Pres & CEO)*
Ricky L. Norris *(Exec VP)*
Andrew Schutt *(Exec VP-Midwest)*
Lisa Smoker *(Controller)*
Trish Partin *(Sr Mgr-Corp Affairs)*
Dave Palmisano *(Dir-Mktg & Carrier Rels)*
Kyle Miller *(VP-Bus Dev)*
Matt Schweinzger *(Chief Acq Officer)*
Adam Reed *(Gen Counsel)*
Bill Parker *(Exec VP-South)*
Tim Johnson *(Exec VP-Northeast)*
Sozon Vatikiotis *(Exec VP-Employee Benefits)*
William Malloy *(Pres-Specialty Div)*
Nick Jemas *(Exec VP-Personal Lines)*
Grahame Millwater *(Head-Insurance-Global)*
Tye Elliott *(Exec VP-Voluntary Benefits)*
Colleen O'Hara *(Exec VP-Mktg & Comm)*
Shawn Ferguson *(Sr VP-Voluntary Benefits)*
Matthew Marolda *(Chief Innovation Officer)*
Alex Orloff *(Mng Dir-Acrisure Re Corp Advisory & Solutions-North America)*
Ben Canagaretna *(Mng Dir-Acrisure Re Corp Advisory & Solutions)*
Norman L. Brown Jr. *(CFO)*

Subsidiaries:

ManhattanTechSupport.com LLC   **(1)**
55 W 39th St 12th Fl, New York, NY 10018
Tel.: (212) 710-2338
Web Site: https://www.homefieldit.com
Sales Range: $1-9.9 Million
Emp.: 24
Software Development Services
N.A.I.C.S.: 541511
James Refino *(Co-Founder)*
Christian Ugolini *(Co-Founder)*
Joseph Rabinowitz *(Co-Founder)*

ACRO AUTOMATION SYSTEMS INC.

2900 W Green Tree Rd, Milwaukee, WI 53209
Tel.: (414) 352-4540

Web Site: https://www.acro.com
Rev.: $16,688,044
Emp.: 100
Welding & Cutting Apparatus
N.A.I.C.S.: 333992
Clifford R. Loomis *(Pres)*
Jeff Weinberger *(CFO)*
Jack Tagliava *(Controller)*

ACRO ENERGY TECHNOLOGIES CORP.

10700 Richmond Ave Ste 275, Houston, TX 77042
Tel.: (713) 715-1000   **BC**
Year Founded: 2007
Sales Range: $10-24.9 Million
Emp.: 71
Investment Services
N.A.I.C.S.: 523999
Darren Rawson *(Exec VP & Gen Mgr-Bus-California)*
Martin C. Spake *(CFO)*
Brad Kovnat *(VP-Ops)*

ACRO INDUSTRIES INC.

554 Colfax St, Rochester, NY 14606-3112
Tel.: (585) 254-3661   **NY**
Web Site: https://www.acroind.com
Year Founded: 1974
Sales Range: $25-49.9 Million
Emp.: 145
Mfr of Metal Stampings
N.A.I.C.S.: 333514
Joseph Noto *(Pres)*
John Gefeoo *(Exec VP)*
David Nicoletti *(Engr-Electrical & Customer Support)*
Allen V. Caruso *(Mgr-Engrg & Quality)*
Paul Kast *(Mgr-Bus Dev)*
Robert Coyne *(Gen Mgr)*

ACRO SERVICE CORP.

39209 6 Mile Rd Ste 250, Livonia, MI 48152
Tel.: (734) 591-1100
Web Site: https://www.acrocorp.com
Year Founded: 1982
Rev.: $56,135,930
Emp.: 900
Temporary Help Service
N.A.I.C.S.: 561320
Rick Faber *(Exec VP)*
Shirley Jones *(Coord-Accts Receivable)*
Valerie Thomas *(Office Mgr)*
Barbara Carpenter *(Controller-Accts Payable)*
Terri Smith *(Supvr-Payroll)*

ACROBATANT, LLC

1336 E 15th St, Tulsa, OK 74120
Tel.: (918) 938-7901
Web Site: http://www.acrobatant.com
Sales Range: $1-9.9 Million
Emp.: 20
Strategic Planning, Brand Development, Advertising, Digital & Media Marketing Services
N.A.I.C.S.: 541613
Angela Lawrence *(Mng Partner)*
David Downing *(Head-Acct Svc)*
Diane Davis *(Mng Dir & Dir-Creative Svcs)*
Hal Collins *(Mgr-Digital Svcs)*
Tamara Green *(Dir-Media)*
Great Dane *(Owner)*

ACRONIS INC.

300 TradeCenter Ste 6700 Elm St, Woburn, MA 01801
Tel.: (781) 782-9000
Web Site: http://www.acronis.com
Sales Range: $100-124.9 Million
Emp.: 500

Acronis Inc.—(Continued)
Data Storage Management & Disaster Recovery Software & Services
N.A.I.C.S.: 513210
Serguei Beloussov (Founder & Chief Res Officer)
Stanislav Protassov (Sr VP-Engrg)
Yury Larichev (Pres-Global Ops)
Ezequiel Steiner (Sr VP-Bus Dev & Corp Dev)
Chris Hilderbrand (VP-Global Channel Sls)
John Zanni (Pres)
Jim Herman (Chief Revenue Officer)
Kevin Baillie (CFO)
Tony Drewitt (Gen Mgr-Australia & New Zealand)
Mike Chadwick (VP-Engrg & Cloud Ops)
Sussie Thorenfeldt (Mgr-Distr Sls-Northern Europe)
Dmitry Martynov (VP-Product Mgmt)
Mark Shmulevich (Chief Strategy Officer)
Kirill Tatarinov (Vice Chm)
Patrick Pulvermueller (CEO)
Rene Bonvanie (Chm)
Michael Callahan (CMO)

Subsidiaries:

DeviceLock, Inc.   (1)
3130 Crow Canyon Pl Ste 215, San Ramon, CA 94583-1344
Web Site: http://www.devicelock.com
Software Publisher
N.A.I.C.S.: 513210
Vitaly Shipitsin (Founder & CTO)

ACRONYM MEDIA INC.
Empire State Bldg 350 5th Ave Ste 6520, New York, NY 10118
Tel.: (212) 691-7051
Web Site: https://www.acronym.com
Year Founded: 1995
Sales Range: $1-9.9 Million
Emp.: 40
Email Marketing Services
N.A.I.C.S.: 541890
Anton E. Konikoff (Founder)
Michael Bruh (Pres)
Stephanie Hart (VP-Client Dev)
Erin Gentry (COO)
Dave Rollo (CEO)

Subsidiaries:

Acronym Asia Pte. Ltd.   (1)
8 Eu Tong Sen St 13-85 The Central Singapore, 02-03 Far East Square, Singapore, 59818, Singapore
Tel.: (65) 6224 0619
Web Site: http://www.acronym.com
Emp.: 7
Email Marketing Services
N.A.I.C.S.: 541890
Janice Tan (Gen Mgr)

Acronym Europe   (1)
Berkeley Square House Berkeley Square Mayfair, London, W1J 6BD, Middlesex, United Kingdom
Tel.: (44) 7786253854
Web Site: http://www.acronym.com
Email Marketing Services
N.A.I.C.S.: 541890
Angela Lawrence (Gen Mgr)
Farah Sadiq (Gen Mgr)

Acronym Media   (1)
Suite 320 34 Eglinton Avenue West, Toronto, M4R 2H4, ON, Canada
Tel.: (416) 994-4375
Email Marketing Services
N.A.I.C.S.: 541890

ACS CARSTAR
3945 Tollhouse Dr Ste 913, Naples, FL 34114-0103
Tel.: (239) 732-9206
Web Site: http://www.acscarstar.com
Sales Range: $1-9.9 Million

Emp.: 4
Auto Body Repair Services
N.A.I.C.S.: 811121
Vicky Tracy (Office Mgr)

ACS INDUSTRIES INC.
2151 Mogadore Rd, Kent, OH 44240-0810
Tel.: (330) 678-2511
Web Site: https://www.acs-coupler.com
Sales Range: $10-24.9 Million
Emp.: 100
Construction Machinery Attachments
N.A.I.C.S.: 333120
Joseph R. Zeno (CEO)
Bob Willoughby (VP)
John Purdon (CFO)
Mel Schindler (Mgr-Inside Sls & Sls-Intl)
Jeremy McDonald (Coord-Parts)
Bill T. Donohue (Mgr-Sls-Natl)
Justin Lilly (Mgr-Territory-Sls)

ACS INDUSTRIES, INC.
1 New England Way, Lincoln, RI 02865
Tel.: (401) 769-4700   RI
Web Site:
  https://www.acsindustries.com
Year Founded: 1939
Sales Range: $150-199.9 Million
Emp.: 2,000
Automotive & Industrial Wire Mesh Products Mfr
N.A.I.C.S.: 332618
Steven Buckler (Pres)

Subsidiaries:

ACS Industries (Shanghai) Co.   (1)
No 30 Fu Te Dong San Road, Shanghai, 200131, China
Tel.: (86) 2150481338
Knitted Wire Product Mfr
N.A.I.C.S.: 331420

ACS Industries, Inc. - Scrubble Products Division   (1)
1 New England Way, Lincoln, RI 02865
Tel.: (800) 222-2880
Web Site: http://www.scrubble.com
Sales Range: $25-49.9 Million
Emp.: 100
Copper Sponge Mfr
N.A.I.C.S.: 325612
Rory Beaudette (Mng Dir)

ACS Internacional S. de R.L. de C.V.   (1)
Av Las Americas No 601, Valle del Mezquital, 66632, Guadalupe, Nuevo Leon, Mexico
Tel.: (52) 8146244956
Automotive & Industrial Product Mfr
N.A.I.C.S.: 331491

ACS Internacional S.A. de C.V.   (1)
Ave Ruiz Cortines 1855, Monterrey, 64400, Nuevo Leon, Mexico   (100%)
Tel.: (52) 8183512622
Mfr of Telephone (Coil & Line) Cords; Computer Cords; Pot Scourers
N.A.I.C.S.: 331318

ACS INTEGRATED SYSTEMS, INC.
9210 Science Center Dr, New Hope, MN 55428
Tel.: (763) 533-3533
Web Site: https://www.atrenne.com
Sales Range: $1-9.9 Million
Emp.: 50
Electro-Mechanical Services
N.A.I.C.S.: 541330
Jane Kipp (Gen Mgr)
Jan Mathiesen (Sr VP-New Bus Dev)

Subsidiaries:

Hybricon Corporation   (1)
12 Willow Rd, Ayer, MA 01432

Tel.: (978) 487-3219
Rev.: $5,000,000
Emp.: 33
Other Computer Peripheral Equipment Mfr
N.A.I.C.S.: 334118
C. M. Hayward (CEO)

ACS INTERNATIONAL RESOURCES INC.
1290 Baltimore Pike Ste 118, Chadds Ford, PA 19317
Tel.: (610) 387-6005
Web Site: http://www.acs-intl.com
Year Founded: 1992
Sales Range: $10-24.9 Million
Emp.: 100
Software Integration & Development Services
N.A.I.C.S.: 541512
Milan Patel (CEO)
S. J. Patel (Founder & Pres)
Amit Rao (CFO)

Subsidiaries:

Advance Computer Services Ltd.   (1)
Millennium Business Park Units 201-204 Sector 2 Bldg 5 2nd Floor, Mumbai, 400701, Mahape, India   (100%)
Tel.: (91) 22 2778 2805
Web Site: http://www.acs-intl.com
Emp.: 85
Cost-Effective, Technology-Based Solutions
N.A.I.C.S.: 541618
Milan Patel (CEO)

ACS SERVICES, INC.
160 Manley St, Brockton, MA 02301
Tel.: (508) 238-6334
Web Site: http://www.acs.com
Year Founded: 1985
Sales Range: $1-9.9 Million
Emp.: 50
Information Technology Consulting Services
N.A.I.C.S.: 541512
Stephen McGann (Dir-Svcs & Client Success)
David Laurent (Project Mgr)
Sergio Pires (Mgr-MSP)
William J. Adams Jr. (Pres)

ACT 1 PERSONNEL SERVICES
1999 W 190th St, Torrance, CA 90504
Tel.: (310) 750-3400
Web Site: http://www.act-1.com
Sales Range: $800-899.9 Million
Emp.: 1,300
Employment Placement Agencies
N.A.I.C.S.: 561311
Janice Bryant Howroyd (Founder, Chm & CEO)
Jeff Kornreich (VP)
Carlton Bryant (Exec VP)
Chuck Pearson (Dir-Mktg)

ACT APPRAISAL MANAGEMENT
1141 E Main St Ste 102, East Dundee, IL 60118
Tel.: (630) 377-8900
Web Site:
  https://www.actappraisal.com
Year Founded: 1998
Sales Range: $1-9.9 Million
Emp.: 30
Real Estate Appraisal Management Services
N.A.I.C.S.: 531320
Bryan Franks (Pres & CEO)

ACT INC.
500 A Court Dr, Iowa City, IA 52243-0168
Tel.: (319) 337-1270   IA
Web Site: http://www.act.org
Year Founded: 1960
Sales Range: $150-199.9 Million

Emp.: 1,500
College Admissions Testing Program & Other Educational Services
N.A.I.C.S.: 611710
Thomas J. Goedken (CFO)
Daniel A. Domenech (Chm)
Wayne Camara (Sr VP-Res)
Suzana Delanghe (Chief Comml Officer)
Brad Lindaas (VP-Strategy)
Donna Matovinovic (Sr VP-Test Dev)
Alina Von Davier (VP)
Angie McAllister (Sr VP-Res)
Jennifer Yi Boyer (Chief Talent Officer)
Janet E. Godwin (CEO)
Mehul Doshi (Chief Product & Tech Officer)

Subsidiaries:

ACT Education Solutions (Australia) Pty. Limited   (1)
Suite 1201 Level 12 275 Alfred Street, North Sydney, 2060, NSW, Australia
Tel.: (61) 2 8912 5103
Web Site:
  http://www.actinternationalservices.com
Educational Support Services
N.A.I.C.S.: 611710
Gaye Pullyn (Gen Mgr)

ACT Information Consulting (Shanghai) Co., Ltd.   (1)
Room 1405 Tian An Center No 338 Nan Jing West Road, Shanghai, 200003, China
Tel.: (86) 21 6359 1100
Educational Support Services
N.A.I.C.S.: 611710
Pier He (Mgr-Bus Dev)

ACT PIPE & SUPPLY INC.
6950 W Sam Houston Pkwy N, Houston, TX 77041-4023
Tel.: (713) 937-0600   TX
Web Site: http://www.actpipe.com
Year Founded: 1976
Waterworks Supplies Distr
N.A.I.C.S.: 423510
Harry Kirk (CEO)
Andy Zizinia (Pres)

ACT-ON SOFTWARE, INC.
121 SW Morrison St Ste 1600, Portland, OR 97204
Tel.: (503) 530-1555
Web Site: https://www.act-on.com
Sales Range: $25-49.9 Million
Emp.: 260
Marketing Automation Software
N.A.I.C.S.: 513210
Raghu Raghavan (Founder & Co-CTO)
Kate Johnson (CEO)
Kevin Bobowski (VP-Demand Generation)
Matt Zelen (Chief Customer Officer)
Bill Pierznik (COO)
Michelle Huff (CMO)
Nina Church-Adams (Sr VP-Mktg)
Roger Rowe (CFO)
Christopher Masino (Chief Revenue Officer)
Philip Sims (Co-CTO)
Kevin Williams (Sr VP-Customer Success)
Jennifer Schoof (Gen Counsel)
Jeffrey Coleman (Chief Customer Officer)

Subsidiaries:

Act-On Software India Private Limited   (1)
1201-1204 12th Floor Prestige Meridian I, 29 MG Road, Bengaluru, 560-001, India
Tel.: (91) 80 409 5338
Marketing Automation Software
N.A.I.C.S.: 513210
Leo Thomas (Head-Ops)

ACTION AIR SYSTEMS, INC.
131 Adams St, Manchester, CT 06042
Tel.: (860) 645-8838
Web Site:
https://www.actionairsystems.com
Year Founded: 1987
Sales Range: $10-24.9 Million
Emp.: 62
Plumbing Services
N.A.I.C.S.: 238220
Vincent J. Savino *(Pres)*

ACTION AMBULANCE SERVICE INC.
844 Woburn St, Wilmington, MA 01887
Tel.: (978) 694-8550
Web Site:
http://www.actionambulance.com
Rev.: $10,000,000
Emp.: 150
Ambulance Service
N.A.I.C.S.: 621910
Michael Woronka *(CEO)*

ACTION BAG COMPANY
1001 Entry Dr, Bensenville, IL 60106
Tel.: (630) 496-6200
Web Site:
https://www.actionbags.com
Rev.: $7,100,000
Emp.: 30
Industrial & Personal Service Paper Merchant Whslr
N.A.I.C.S.: 424130
Nancy Cwynar *(Pres)*
Haley Cwynar *(CEO)*

Subsidiaries:

The J. J. Elemer Corp. (1)
1895 Craig Rd, Saint Louis, MO 63146
Tel.: (314) 542-9988
Web Site: http://www.jjelemer.com
Rev.: $1,400,000
Emp.: 12
All Other Specialty Trade Contractors
N.A.I.C.S.: 238990
Edward Ebsworth *(Pres)*

ACTION BOLT & TOOL COMPANY
2051 W Blue Heron Blvd, West Palm Beach, FL 33404
Tel.: (561) 845-8800
Web Site:
http://www.actionboltandtool.com
Rev.: $17,800,000
Emp.: 100
Bolts, Nuts & Screws
N.A.I.C.S.: 423710
Chris Wilcox *(Mgr-Mgmt Info Sys)*

ACTION BOX COMPANY INC.
6207 N Houston Rosslyn Rd, Houston, TX 77091
Tel.: (713) 869-7701
Web Site:
http://www.actionboxinc.com
Rev.: $12,800,000
Emp.: 100
Manufactures Corrugated & Solid Fiber Boxes
N.A.I.C.S.: 322211
Terry Malloy *(CEO)*
Ken Dean *(VP-Sls)*

ACTION CARRIER
PO Box 85530, Sioux Falls, SD 57118
Tel.: (605) 335-5500 SD
Year Founded: 1978
Sales Range: $10-24.9 Million
Emp.: 6
Transporting Services
N.A.I.C.S.: 484121

Mike Walsh *(Pres, Controller & Mgr-Safety Dept)*

ACTION COMPANY
1425 N Tennessee St, McKinney, TX 75069-1833
Tel.: (972) 542-1543
Web Site:
http://www.actioncompany.com
Year Founded: 1968
Sales Range: $200-249.9 Million
Emp.: 350
Leather Tanning & Finishing Services
N.A.I.C.S.: 316110

Subsidiaries:

Tex Tan Western Leather
Company (1)
601 Hickey St, Yoakum, TX 77995-1212
Tel.: (361) 293-2314
Web Site: http://www.textan.com
Sales Range: $10-24.9 Million
Emp.: 31
Supplier of Leather Goods
N.A.I.C.S.: 316990
Jay Cassell *(Pres)*

ACTION ELECTRIC SALES CO. INC.
3900 N Rockwell St, Chicago, IL 60618
Tel.: (773) 539-1800
Web Site: https://www.basicwire.com
Rev.: $11,900,000
Emp.: 60
Electrical Apparatus & Equipment
N.A.I.C.S.: 423610
Lisa Garoon *(Controller)*

ACTION ENVELOPE & PRINTING CO., INC.
5300 New Horizons Blvd, Amityville, NY 11701
Tel.: (631) 225-3900 NY
Web Site:
http://www.actionenvelope.com
Year Founded: 1971
Sales Range: $10-24.9 Million
Emp.: 35
Stationery & Office Supplies Sales
N.A.I.C.S.: 424120
Sharon Newman *(Pres)*

ACTION EQUIPMENT & SCAFFOLD CO. INC.
2229 S 16th St, Phoenix, AZ 85034
Tel.: (602) 252-3417
Web Site:
https://www.actionscaffold.com
Sales Range: $10-24.9 Million
Emp.: 75
Scaffolds, Mobile Or Stationary: Metal
N.A.I.C.S.: 332323
Howard Schapira *(CEO)*
R. David Schroder *(Pres)*

ACTION FOOD SALES INC.
8401 University Executive Park Dr Ste 129, Charlotte, NC 28262
Tel.: (704) 549-8500
Web Site:
http://www.actionfoodsales.com
Sales Range: $10-24.9 Million
Emp.: 15
Bond Brokers
N.A.I.C.S.: 424410
John Nilsson *(Pres)*
Lori Snave *(Coord-Sls & Mktg)*

ACTION FOR BOSTON COMMUNITY DEVELOPMENT, INC.
178 Tremont St, Boston, MA 02111
Tel.: (617) 348-6000 MA
Web Site:
https://www.bostonabcd.org
Year Founded: 1962
Sales Range: $150-199.9 Million

Emp.: 1,793
Community Development Services
N.A.I.C.S.: 624190
Andres Molina *(Vice Chm)*
John J. Drew *(Pres & CEO)*
Sharon Scott-Chandler *(COO & Exec VP)*

ACTION FOR BRIDGEPORT COMMUNITY DEVELOPMENT, INC.
1070 Park Ave, Bridgeport, CT 06604
Tel.: (203) 366-8241 CT
Web Site: http://www.abcd.org
Year Founded: 1964
Sales Range: $25-49.9 Million
Emp.: 816
Community Welfare Services
N.A.I.C.S.: 624190
Charles B. Tisdale *(Exec Dir)*
Rodney Dennis *(Comptroller)*
Carmen Rodriguez *(Dir-HR)*
Cora Wright *(Treas)*
Irena Kandybowicz *(Chm)*
Laurel Gross *(Sec)*
Ralph Jowers *(Vice Chm)*

ACTION INC.
180 Main St, Gloucester, MA 01930
Tel.: (978) 282-1000 MA
Web Site: https://www.actioninc.org
Year Founded: 1967
Sales Range: $50-74.9 Million
Emp.: 203
Welfare Services
N.A.I.C.S.: 525120
Dennis Acker *(Treas)*
Linda Murphy *(Sec)*
Tone Kenney *(Vice Chm)*

ACTION INTERNATIONAL MARKETING, INC.
1521 Gehman Rd, Harleysville, PA 19438-2930
Tel.: (267) 421-5328
Web Site:
http://www.actionmarketplace.com
Year Founded: 1997
Computers, Peripherals & Software
N.A.I.C.S.: 423430
Robert S. Beckett *(Pres)*

ACTION INVESTMENT GROUP, INC.
1633 Westwood Blvd, Los Angeles, CA 90024
Tel.: (213) 387-2974 CA
Year Founded: 1990
Sales Range: $1-9.9 Million
Emp.: 20
Property Management
N.A.I.C.S.: 531312
Mayer Separzadeh *(Pres & CEO)*
Mayer Separzadeh *(Pres)*

ACTION LABOR MANAGEMENT, LLC
900 Osceola Dr Ste 222, West Palm Beach, FL 33409
Tel.: (561) 683-1211 NV
Web Site: http://www.actionlabor.com
Sales Range: $25-49.9 Million
Emp.: 18
Temporary Employment Agencies
N.A.I.C.S.: 561311
Karen Hoover *(Pres)*
Paul Chase *(Mgr-Mgmt Info Sys)*

ACTION LIFT, INC.
1 Memco Dr, Pittston, PA 18640
Tel.: (570) 655-2100 PA
Web Site:
https://www.actionliftinc.com
Sales Range: $10-24.9 Million
Emp.: 40

Sales & Servicer of Material Handling Equipment
N.A.I.C.S.: 423830
William F. Medico *(Pres)*
Bernie Thoma *(Mgr-Rental)*
Chet Williams *(Gen Mgr-Parts & Svc)*
Joseph Mikiewicz *(Gen Mgr)*

ACTION MANUFACTURING CO.
100 E Erie Ave, Philadelphia, PA 19134-1009
Tel.: (215) 739-6400 DE
Web Site: http://www.action-mfg.com
Year Founded: 1946
Sales Range: $100-124.9 Million
Emp.: 300
Mfr of Precision Ordnance Products
N.A.I.C.S.: 332993
Arthur Mattia *(Chm & Pres)*
Lorraine Prostoss *(Treas & Controller)*

ACTION MEDIA, INC.
101 The Embarcadero Ste 130, San Francisco, CA 94105-1215
Tel.: (415) 392-6411 CA
Year Founded: 1977
Sales Range: Less than $1 Million
Emp.: 5
Advertising, Government/Political/Public Affairs, Health Care, Retail
N.A.I.C.S.: 541830
Richard R. Rojas *(Pres)*
Ron E. Rojas *(VP)*
Jim Spellman *(Creative Dir)*

ACTION PARTY RENTALS
620 Union Blvd, Allentown, PA 18109
Tel.: (610) 435-8900
Web Site:
https://www.actionpartyrentals.com
Year Founded: 1967
Sales Range: $1-9.9 Million
Emp.: 10
Party Equipment Rental
N.A.I.C.S.: 532289
Sue Horn *(Pres)*

ACTION PETROLEUM COMPANY LTD.
10 Baldwin St, Prestonsburg, KY 41653-1103
Tel.: (606) 886-2368 KY
Year Founded: 1981
Sales Range: $10-24.9 Million
Emp.: 25
Operator of Petroleum Bulk Stations And Terminals
N.A.I.C.S.: 445131
Tim McDonald *(Gen Mgr)*
Curt Tackett *(Mgr-Fin)*

ACTION PLUMBING SUPPLY CO.
5411 NW 15th St, Margate, FL 33063
Tel.: (954) 971-7782
Web Site:
http://www.actionsupply.com
Year Founded: 1978
Sales Range: $10-24.9 Million
Emp.: 50
Wholesale Distributors For Plumbing & Air Conditioners
N.A.I.C.S.: 423720
Stuart Berke *(Pres)*

ACTION RESOURCES INC.
40 County Rd 517, Hanceville, AL 35077
Tel.: (256) 352-2689
Web Site: http://www.action-resources.com
Sales Range: $10-24.9 Million
Emp.: 90

Action Resources Inc.—(Continued)

Local Trucking without Storage
N.A.I.C.S.: 484110
Steve Sherbert (Dir-Ops)
Kathy Anderson (Mgr-IT Svc)
Philip Desimone (COO)
Steve Talley (Mgr-Sls-Natl)
Charles Corpening (Chm)
Steve Royce (Exec VP-HR)
Jeff Cowart (VP-IT)

ACTION SPORTS MEDIA, INC.
6613 Corte Real, Carlsbad, CA
92009
Tel.: (858) 900-8989   NV
Year Founded: 2013
Sports Marketing Consulting, Branding & Public Relations
N.A.I.C.S.: 541613
Jason Fierro (Pres, CEO & CFO)

ACTION TARGET, INC.
3411 S Mountain Vista Pkwy, Provo,
UT 84606
Tel.: (801) 377-8033
Web Site:
   https://www.actiontarget.com
Year Founded: 1986
Sales Range: $50-74.9 Million
Emp.: 300
Shooting Range Products Mfr
N.A.I.C.S.: 339920
Tom Wright (Pres)
Addison Sovine (Co-Founder)
Kyle Bateman (Co-Founder)
Kyle Burdette (VP-Quality)
Shayne Gibbons (CFO)
Michael T. Birch (CEO)

ACTION, INC.
1308 Church St, Barling, AR 72923
Tel.: (479) 452-5723   AR
Web Site: https://www.action-
   mechanical.com
Year Founded: 1981
Sales Range: $10-24.9 Million
Emp.: 75
Mechanical & Sheet Metal Contractor
N.A.I.C.S.: 238220
Allen P. Wright (Pres)
Clinton V. Elliott (Treas & Sec)

ACTION-HOUSING, INC.
425 6th Ave Ste 950, Pittsburgh, PA
15219
Tel.: (412) 281-2102   PA
Web Site:
   http://www.actionhousing.org
Year Founded: 1957
Sales Range: $10-24.9 Million
Housing Assistance Services
N.A.I.C.S.: 624229
Larry Swanson (Exec Dir)

ACTIONET, INC.
2600 Park Tower Dr Ste 1000, Vienna, VA 22180
Tel.: (703) 204-0090   DE
Web Site: http://www.actionet.com
Year Founded: 1998
Sales Range: $25-49.9 Million
Emp.: 33
Information Technology Services
N.A.I.C.S.: 519290
Ashley W. Chen (Pres & CEO)
Jeffrey D. Abish (CIO & Exec VP)
Janice Raleigh (Sr Dir-HR)
Purshina Patel (Dir-Corp Fin)
David K. Collignon (VP-Health Svcs)
Ramon P. De Guzman (VP-Science & Res)
Michael L. Genebach (COO & Exec VP)
Julie Sharps (VP-Civilian Programs)
David Fink (VP-Defense Programs)
R. Dennis Gibbs (VP)

Joseph Kobsar (CTO-Defense Programs)
Reuben Maher (Chief Innovation Officer & Sr VP)

ACTIONTEC ELECTRONICS, INC.
760 N Mary Ave, Sunnyvale, CA
94085-2908
Tel.: (408) 752-7700   CA
Web Site: http://www.actiontec.com
Year Founded: 1993
Rev.: $70,000,000
Emp.: 200
Developers of Broadband-Powered Solutions
N.A.I.C.S.: 334412
Brian Henrichs (Chief Bus Dev Officer)

Subsidiaries:

ATP Electronics, Inc.   (1)
750 N Mary Ave, Sunnyvale, CA 94085-
2908
Tel.: (408) 732-5000
Web Site: http://www.atpinc.com
Sales Range: $25-49.9 Million
Emp.: 32
Computer Digital Flash Media Products Mfr
N.A.I.C.S.: 334112
Tim Hsieh (Pres)
Jay Wang (Acct Mgr-Enterprise Mobility)

ACTIVAR, INC.
7808 Creekridge Cir, Minneapolis,
MN 55439-2611
Tel.: (952) 944-3533   MN
Web Site: http://www.activar.com
Year Founded: 1968
Sales Range: $25-49.9 Million
Emp.: 400
Investment Holding Company
N.A.I.C.S.: 551112
Jon L. Reissner (Pres & CEO)

Subsidiaries:

Activar Construction Products Group, Inc.   (1)
4450 W 78th St Cir, Bloomington, MN
55435   (100%)
Tel.: (952) 835-6850
Web Site: http://www.activarcpg.com
Sales Range: $300-349.9 Million
Emp.: 65
Holding Company; Metal Safety Panel, Louver & Industrial Hardware Mfr & Distr
N.A.I.C.S.: 551112
Jon L. Reissner (Pres & CEO)

Subsidiary (Domestic):

Air Louvers, Inc.   (2)
6285 Randolph St, Commerce, CA 90040-
3514
Tel.: (323) 726-8814
Web Site: http://www.airlouvers.com
Sales Range: $25-49.9 Million
Metal Doors, Sash & Trim
N.A.I.C.S.: 332321

Hiawatha, Inc.   (2)
4450 W 78th St Cir, Bloomington, MN
55435
Tel.: (952) 835-6850
Web Site: http://www.activarcpg.com
Sales Range: Less than $1 Million
Emp.: 25
Hardware
N.A.I.C.S.: 332510
Kirby Bayerle (Pres)

JL Industries, Inc.   (2)
4450 W 78th St Cir, Bloomington, MN
55435
Tel.: (952) 835-6850
Web Site: http://www.activarcpg.com
Construction Materials Distr
N.A.I.C.S.: 423390

Samson Products Inc.   (2)
6285 Randolph St, Los Angeles, CA 90040-
3514
Tel.: (323) 726-9070
Web Site: http://www.samsonproducts.com

Sales Range: $1-9.9 Million
Provider Of Partitions & Fixtures
N.A.I.C.S.: 337126

Activar Industrial Products Group, Inc.   (1)
7808 Creekridge Cir, Minneapolis, MN
55439   (100%)
Tel.: (952) 944-3533
Web Site: http://www.activar.com
Sales Range: $250-299.9 Million
Emp.: 4
Holding Company; Industrial Tube, Spring, Wire, Plastisol Coating & Molding Products Mfr
N.A.I.C.S.: 551112

Subsidiary (Domestic):

Bending Technologies, Inc.   (2)
522 SW 19th St, Forest Lake, MN 55025
Tel.: (952) 946-1018
Web Site: http://www.bendingtech.com
Sales Range: $1-9.9 Million
Emp.: 65
Metal Tube Bending & Fabrication Services
N.A.I.C.S.: 332996
Duane Bryngelson (Gen Mgr)

Springs Inc.   (2)
522 19th St SW, Forest Lake, MN
55025-1355   (100%)
Tel.: (651) 982-6100
Web Site: http://www.springsinc.com
Sales Range: $1-9.9 Million
Provider of Steel Springs
N.A.I.C.S.: 332613
Jon L. Reissner (CEO)

Activar Plastic Products Group, Inc.   (1)
7808 Creekridge Cir Ste 200, Minneapolis,
MN 55439   (100%)
Tel.: (952) 944-3533
Web Site: http://www.activar.com
Sales Range: $125-149.9 Million
Emp.: 4
Holding Company; Plastic Products Mfr
N.A.I.C.S.: 551112
Jon L. Reissner (Pres)

Subsidiary (Domestic):

LabAire Systems Co   (2)
9650 Newton Ave S, Bloomington, MN
55431
Web Site: http://www.labairesystems.com
Laboratory Construction Services
N.A.I.C.S.: 238390

Mid-America Plastics   (2)
700 Industrial Cir S, Shakopee, MN 55379
Tel.: (952) 445-7667
Web Site:
   http://www.midamericaplastics.com
Sales Range: $50-74.9 Million
Custom Fabricated Plastic & Metal Products Mfr
N.A.I.C.S.: 326199

Seelye-Eiler Industrial Plastic Products   (2)
9700 Newton Ave S, Bloomington, MN
55431
Tel.: (952) 881-2658
Web Site: http://www.seelyeplastics.com
Sales Range: $10-24.9 Million
Custom Fabricated & Engineered Industrial Plastic Products Mfr & Distr
N.A.I.C.S.: 326191
Molly Meyer (Mgr-Sls-Global)

Unit (Domestic):

Circuit Chemistry Equipment   (3)
9700 Newton Ave S, Bloomington, MN
55431
Tel.: (952) 392-8450
Web Site: http://www.circuitchem.com
Emp.: 65
Printed Circuit Industry Wet Processing Equipment Mfr & Distr
N.A.I.C.S.: 333248
Molly Meyer (Mgr-Sls)

Activar Technical Products Group, Inc.   (1)
9650 Newton Ave S, Bloomington, MN
55431   (100%)
Tel.: (952) 935-6921

Web Site: http://www.activartpg.com
Sales Range: $350-399.9 Million
Emp.: 50
Holding Company; Material Handling Equipment, Motion Control Systems & Magnetic Assemblies Mfr
N.A.I.C.S.: 551112
Jon L. Reissner (Pres & CEO)

Aztec, Inc.   (1)
21455 Hamburg Ave, Lakeville, MN 55044
Tel.: (952) 469-4407
Web Site: http://www.azinc.com
Emp.: 15
Metal Plating Services
N.A.I.C.S.: 332812
Dave Sersen (Mgr-Ops)

ACTIVATE INC.
9520 SW Nimbus Ave, Beaverton,
OR 97008
Tel.: (503) 641-6545
Web Site:
   http://www.activateonline.com
Year Founded: 1995
Sales Range: $10-24.9 Million
Emp.: 100
Telephone Equipment & Systems
N.A.I.C.S.: 449210
Jason Chambers (Pres)
Christopher W. Walters (Executives)
Chris Walters (Sr Partner)

ACTIVATE PERMANENT CAPITAL CORP.
50 California St Ste 680, San Francisco, CA 94111
Tel.: (610) 574-9069   DE
Year Founded: 2021
Emp.: 2
Investment Services
N.A.I.C.S.: 523999
Christopher Roberts (CFO)
David Lincoln (Chm)
Tim Healy (CEO)

ACTIVATED HOLDINGS LLC
767 5th Ave 50th Fl, New York, NY
10153
Tel.: (212) 605-0844
Holding Company; Private Equity Firm
N.A.I.C.S.: 551112

Subsidiaries:

Shaklee Corporation   (1)
4747 Willow Rd, Pleasanton, CA
94588   (40.5%)
Tel.: (925) 924-2000
Web Site: http://www.shaklee.com
Sales Range: $100-124.9 Million
Emp.: 300
Vitamins & Nutritional Products Distr
N.A.I.C.S.: 424210
Roger Barnett (Chm & CEO)
Marjorie Fine (Gen Counsel, Sec & Exec VP)
Jamie McManus (Chm-Medical Affairs, Health Sciences & Education)
Mike Batesole (CFO)
Rich Libby (CIO)
Enlie Widjaja (Gen Mgr)
Philip Wong (Gen Mgr)
Rong Xue (Chief Supply Officer)
Laura Evans (Sr VP-Sls & Field Dev)
Emanuel Fakoukakis (Chief Innovation Officer)
Jon Fieldman (Chief Supply Officer)
Brad Harrington (CMO)

Subsidiary (Non-US):

Shaklee Canada, Inc.
529 Michigan Drive Unit 700, Oakville, L6L
0C4, ON, Canada
Tel.: (905) 681-1422
Web Site: http://www.shaklee.com

Sales Range: $25-49.9 Million
Emp.: 32
Industrial Products Mfr
N.A.I.C.S.: 541420
Roger L. Barnett (CEO)
Jeff Hill (Pres)
Shobhna Asthana (CFO)
Franci Kursh (CIO)
Melina Baxter (CMO)
Matt Town (Gen Counsel)
Kelley Moran (VP)
James R. Brooks (Exec VP)

Shaklee Mexico, S.A. de C.V. (2)
Juan de la Fontaine 23, Col Chapultepec
Polanco, CP 11560, Mexico, Mexico
Tel.: (52) 5591387000
Web Site: http://www.shaklee.com.mx
Sales Range: $25-49.9 Million
Emp.: 23
Nutritional Product Mfr
N.A.I.C.S.: 456191
Julio P. Cepeda (Gen Mgr)

Shaklee Products (Malaysia) Sdn.
Bhd. (2)
Level 9 The Pinnacle Persiaran Lagoon
Bandar Sunway, 47500, Subang Jaya, Se-
langor Darul Ehsan, Malaysia
Tel.: (60) 3 5622 3188
Web Site: http://www.shaklee.com.my
Sales Range: $25-49.9 Million
Emp.: 120
Nutritional Products
N.A.I.C.S.: 456191
Helen Lam (Pres)
Mike Batesole (CFO)
Tony Tucker (Gen Counsel, Sec & Sr VP)
Bruce Daggy (Chief Science Officer & Sr
VP-R&D)

Subsidiary (Domestic):

Shaklee Research Center (2)
1992 Alpine Way, Hayward, CA 94545-1702
Tel.: (510) 781-0713
Web Site: http://www.shaklee.com
Sales Range: $25-49.9 Million
Emp.: 114
Provider of Nutritional Research Services
N.A.I.C.S.: 624190
Roger Barnett (Pres & CEO)
Bruce Daggy (Chief Innovation Officer)
Rich Libby (Chief Supply Officer)
Jennifer Steeves-Kiss (CFO)
Todd Tucker (CIO)
Enlie Widjaja (Gen Mgr)
Philip Wong (Gen Mgr)
Laura Evans (Sr VP-Sls & Field Dev)
Jon Fieldman (Chief Supply Officer)
Brad Harrington (CMO)
Cindy Latham (Sr VP-Global Mktg)

Shaklee U.S. (2)
4747 Willow Rd, Pleasanton, CA 94588-
2763
Tel.: (925) 924-2000
Web Site: http://www.us.shaklee.com
Provider of Nutritional Product Distr
N.A.I.C.S.: 424210

ACTIVE ELECTRICAL SUPPLY COMPANY
4240 W Lawrence Ave, Chicago, IL
60630-2730
Tel.: (773) 282-6300
Web Site: https://www.active-
elec.com
Year Founded: 1953
Sales Range: $75-99.9 Million
Emp.: 120
Wholesale Electrical Distr
N.A.I.C.S.: 423610
James Swan (VP & Gen Mgr)
Linda Fox (VP & Mgr-Credit)

ACTIVE HEALTHCARE, INC.
9104 Falls of Neuse Rd Ste 100, Ra-
leigh, NC 27615
Tel.: (919) 870-8600
Web Site:
https://www.activehealthcare.com
Year Founded: 1990
Sales Range: $1-9.9 Million
Emp.: 26

CPAP & Respiratory Specialists
N.A.I.C.S.: 621511
Lisa Feierstein (Co-Founder & Pres)
Steve Feierstein (Co-Founder &
CEO)
Elaine Ellison (Office Mgr)

ACTIVE INTEREST MEDIA, INC.
5720 Flatiron Pkwy, Boulder, CO
80301
Tel.: (310) 356-4100
Web Site: http://www.aimmedia.com
Year Founded: 2003
Sales Range: $10-24.9 Million
Emp.: 3
Periodical Publishers
N.A.I.C.S.: 513120
Andrew W. Clurman (Pres & CEO)
Brian J. Sellstrom (Sr VP)
Jonathan Dorn (Chief Innovation Offi-
cer)
Sharon Houghton (Mng Dir-Outdoor
Grp)
Michael Henry (CFO)
Eric Henderson (Dir-Sls-Outdoor
Trade Grp-Natl)
Allen Crolius (VP-Sls-Outdoor Grp)
Kristin Hostetter (Editor-in-Chief-
SNEWS)
Joe Cohen (VP & Controller)
Tom Winsor (Sr VP-Bus Dev &
Equine)
Andy Hawk (Mng Dir-Mountain Grp)
Brian Van Heuverswyn (COO)
Efrem Zimbalist III (Founder)

Subsidiaries:

Bahamas Billfish Championship,
Inc. (1)
4828 NE 12th Ave, Oakland Park, FL 33334
Tel.: (954) 562-0503
Web Site: http://www.bahamasbillfish.com
Deep Sea Fishing Tournament Promoter
N.A.I.C.S.: 711320
Jennifer Dudas (Gen Mgr)

The Equine Network (1)
656 Quince Orchard Rd Ste 600, Gaithers-
burg, MD 20878
Tel.: (301) 977-3900
Web Site: http://www.equisearch.com
Sales Range: $10-24.9 Million
Periodical Publishers
N.A.I.C.S.: 513120

Unit (Domestic):

Horse & Rider (2)
2520 55th St Ste 210, Boulder, CO 80301-
5736
Tel.: (940) 497-4600
Web Site: http://www.equisearch.com
Periodical Publishers
N.A.I.C.S.: 513120
Debbie Moors (Editor)

The Taunton Press, Inc. (1)
63 S Main St, Newtown, CT 06470-2355
Tel.: (203) 426-8171
Web Site: http://www.taunton.com
Sales Range: $25-49.9 Million
Emp.: 243
Publisher of Periodicals & Books
N.A.I.C.S.: 513120
Paul Roman (Founder)
Rick Straface (VP-Adv Sls & Mktg)
Renee Jordan (CEO)
Michael Pekovich (Editor/Creative Dir-Fine
Woodworking)
Tom McKenna (Grp Dir-Editorial)

Vegetarian Times (1)
300 N Continental Blvd Ste 650, El Se-
gundo, CA 90245
Tel.: (310) 356-4100
Web Site: http://www.vegetariantimes.com
Sales Range: $10-24.9 Million
Periodicals
N.A.I.C.S.: 513120
Elizabeth Turner (Editor-in-Chief)
Jeff Tkach (Grp Publr)
Haley Brockmeier (Assoc Publr)

Scott Hyers (Assoc Dir-Art)
Cynthia Lyons (Dir-Production)
Daphna Shalev (Dir-Creative)

Yoga Journal (1)
475 Samson St Ste 850, San Francisco, CA
94111
Tel.: (415) 591-0555
Web Site: http://www.yogajournal.com
Publisher of Yoga Health Magazine
N.A.I.C.S.: 513120
Dayna Macy (Dir-Comm)
Melissa Strome (Publr)
Kino MacGregor (Co-Founder)
Tim Miller (Dir-Ashtanga Yoga Center)
Robin Rothenberg (Dir-Essential Yoga
Therapy)
Tasha Eichenseher (Co-Dir-Brand)
Jonathan Dorn (Chief Innovation
Officer/Gen Mgr-Healthy Living Grp)
Greg Brenton (Co-Dir-Brand)

ACTIVE MEDIA SERVICES, INC.
1 Blue Hill Plz, Pearl River, NY
10965-1705
Tel.: (845) 735-1700   FL
Web Site:
http://www.activeinternational.com
Year Founded: 1984
Sales Range: $800-899.9 Million
Emp.: 600
Corporate Trade Services
N.A.I.C.S.: 541611
Alan S. Elkin (Co-Founder, Chm &
CEO)
Arthur Wagner (Co-Founder & Pres)
Gary Steinbeck (CFO)
Dominic Bencivenga (Pres-Travel
Div)
Dennis Quinn (Chief Revenue Offi-
cer)
Tom Turner (Sr VP-Direct Response
Media)
Liz Margolis (Exec VP-Ops & Plng)
Bill Georges (COO-Global)
Dayna Frank (Gen Counsel)
Dean Wilson (CEO-Div-Intl)
Elizabeth Topazio (Pres & Chief Le-
gal Officer)
Hector Rodriguez (Pres-Active
Freight & Logistics)
Lisa Brown (Chief Strategy Officer &
Chief Bus Dev Officer)
Anat Gilad (Exec VP-Retail & Shop-
per Mktg)
Andrew Frank (Exec VP-Sls & Mdsg
Sls)
Bethany Harris (Exec VP-Strategic
Partnerships)
Bob O'Neill (Exec VP & Dir-Media)
Robert Pankuck (Exec VP-Client
Mgmt)
Catherine Boera (Sr VP & Dir-Comm
Plng & Media Planning)
Fran Baric (Sr VP & Dir-Client Mgmt)

Subsidiaries:

Active International (Europe)
S.A.R.L. (1)
21 rue Godot de Mauroy, 75009, Paris,
France
Tel.: (33) 145043290
Web Site: http://www.activeinternational.com
Corporate Trade Services
N.A.I.C.S.: 541611
Alan S. Elkin (Co-Founder & CEO)
Naveen Raj (CIO)

Active International (Mexico) S.A. de
C.V. (1)
Blvd Miguel de Cervantes Saavedra 169
Piso 12-129 Colonia Granada, Col San
Jose Insurgentes, Mexico, DF, Mexico
Tel.: (52) 55 8503 6300
Web Site: http://www.activeinternational.mx
Corporate Trade Services
N.A.I.C.S.: 541611

Active International Australia Pty
Ltd. (1)

Level 3 140 Arthur Street, North Sydney,
2060, NSW, Australia
Tel.: (61) 294669166
Web Site:
http://www.activeinternational.com.au
Emp.: 20
Corporate Trade Services
N.A.I.C.S.: 541611
Tom Bernardin (Chm & CEO)
Cameron Swan (Mng Dir)
Andrew Rogers (Head-Media)

Active International Corporate Trading
Spain S.L. (1)
Avenida de los Toreror 24, Edificio Grundig,
28028, Madrid, Spain
Tel.: (34) 91 356 84 05
Web Site: http://www.activeinternational.com
Corporate Trade Services
N.A.I.C.S.: 541830

Active International GmbH (1)
Burggrafenstrasse 5, 40545, Dusseldorf,
Germany
Tel.: (49) 211 367 080
Web Site: http://www.activeinternational.de
Corporate Trade Services
N.A.I.C.S.: 541611
Yvonne Hill (Office Mgr)

Active International Inc. (1)
City Air Tower Suite 2507 159-9 Samsung-
dong, Gangnam-Gu, Seoul, 135-190, Korea
(South)
Tel.: (82) 220166091
Web Site:
http://www.activeinternational.co.kr
Emp.: 15
Marketing Consulting Services
N.A.I.C.S.: 541613

Active International LLC. (1)
Around Tokyo Bldg 6/F No 3-15-8 Nishi-
Gotanda, Shinagawa-ku, Tokyo, 141-0031,
Japan
Tel.: (81) 364200695
Business Support Services
N.A.I.C.S.: 561499

Active International Ltd. (1)
103 New Oxford St, London, WC1A 1DD,
United Kingdom
Tel.: (44) 207 520 6666
Web Site:
http://www.activeinternational.co.uk
Emp.: 35
Corporate Trade Services
N.A.I.C.S.: 541611
Alan S. Elkin (Co-Founder & CEO)
Alan Brown (Pres-Global Media & Strategic
Dev)

Active International Northern
Europe (1)
Patrijzenlaan 7, 3080, Tervuren, Belgium
Tel.: (32) 2 782 2088
Web Site: http://www.activeinternational.com
Emp.: 10
Corporate Trade Services
N.A.I.C.S.: 541611

Active International Poland Sp. Z
o.o. (1)
Al Ujazdowskie 26/8, 00478, Warsaw, Po-
land
Tel.: (48) 22 502 3355
Corporate Trade Services
N.A.I.C.S.: 541830

Active International do Brasil
S.A. (1)
Rua Florida 1703 10 andar cj 102, Itaim
Bibi, Sao Paulo, CEP 04565-909, Brazil
Tel.: (55) 1148900101
Web Site: http://www.activeinternational.com
Corporate Trade Services
N.A.I.C.S.: 541611

Active Media Services Canada,
Inc. (1)
55 Commerce Valley Drive W Suite 601,
Markham, L3T 7V9, ON, Canada
Tel.: (905) 273-8040
Web Site: http://www.activeinternational.com
Emp.: 10
Corporate Trade Services
N.A.I.C.S.: 541611

Active Media Services- Central Europe Group (1)

Active Media Services, Inc.—(Continued)

Karinthy Frigyes Ut 9 Fl 4/1, H1117, Budapest, Hungary
Tel.: (36) 13614030
Sales Range: $10-24.9 Million
Emp.: 4
Corporate Trade Services
N.A.I.C.S.: 541611
Javor Ivan (Gen Mgr)

ACTIVE MOTIF, INC.
1914 Palomar Oaks Way Ste 150, Carlsbad, CA 92008
Tel.: (760) 431-1263
Web Site: http://www.activemotif.com
Year Founded: 1999
Sales Range: $1-9.9 Million
Emp.: 39
Biology Research Tools Developer & Distr
N.A.I.C.S.: 325414
Joe Fernandez (CEO)
Seth Rubin (Mgr-Sls-United States)
Terry Kelly (Mgr-R&D)
Ted DeFrank (Pres & CEO)
Fritz Eibel (Chief Comml Officer)

Subsidiaries:

Active Motif-Europe   (1)
Office Park Nysdam Avenue Reine Astrid 92, Box 25, 1310, La Hulpe, Belgium
Tel.: (32) 26530001
Emp.: 10
Biology Research Product Distr
N.A.I.C.S.: 424210
Joe Fernandez (CEO)

Active Motif-Japan   (1)
Azuma Building 7th Floor, 2-21 Ageba-Cho Shinjuku-Ku, Tokyo, 162-0824, Japan
Tel.: (81) 352253638
Emp.: 4
Biology Research Tools Developer & Distr
N.A.I.C.S.: 325414
Joseph Fernandez (Pres)

ACTIVE PLUMBING SUPPLY CO
216 Richmond St, Painesville, OH 44077
Tel.: (440) 352-4411
Web Site: https://www.activeplumbing.com
Sales Range: $10-24.9 Million
Emp.: 50
Plumbing Fittings & Supplies
N.A.I.C.S.: 423720
Chuck Rathburn (Pres)
Cliff Holroyd (Mgr-Logistics)

ACTIVE RETIREMENT COMMUNITY INC.
1 Jefferson Ferry Dr, Setauket, NY 11720
Tel.: (631) 650-2600   NY
Web Site: https://www.jeffersonsferry.org
Year Founded: 1997
Sales Range: $10-24.9 Million
Emp.: 411
Lifecare Retirement Community Services
N.A.I.C.S.: 623311
Brian Amtmann (CFO)
Robert E. Caulfield (CEO)
Cathy DeAngelo (Dir-Mktg & Sls)
Don Jacobowitz (Exec VP-Health Svcs)
Jane Willsey (Dir-HR)
George Rice (Chm)
John Sini (Treas)
Wayne Shattes (Sec)
Linda Kolakowski (VP-Independent Living Ops)
Chris Adamo (VP-Hospitality Svcs)

ACTIVE SALES CO. INC.

8743 Sorensen Ave, Santa Fe Springs, CA 90670
Tel.: (562) 945-4414
Web Site: http://www.activesalesco.com
Sales Range: $10-24.9 Million
Emp.: 60
Staplers & Tackers
N.A.I.C.S.: 423840
Robert Myers (VP-Sls)
Shaun Wang (Mgr-Pur)

ACTIVE SCREW & FASTENER
5215 Old Orchard Rd Ste 700, Skokie, IL 60077-1045
Tel.: (847) 967-0800
Web Site: http://www.activescrew.com
Sales Range: $10-24.9 Million
Emp.: 37
Bolts, Nuts & Screws
N.A.I.C.S.: 423710
Barbara Sullivan (Mgr-Admin & Fin)
Ed Esparza (Mgr-Sourcing & Quality)
Raymond Mormann (Mgr-Warehouse-Countryside)
Tom Anderson (Mgr-Sls-Infrastructure)
Andre Williams (Mgr-Bridgeport)
Simon Blattner Buddy (Owner & Pres)
Kevin Miller (Pres-Charlotte)

ACTIVE SPORTS LIFESTYLE USA, LLC
12178 4th St, Rancho Cucamonga, CA 91730
Tel.: (951) 934-4200   FL
Web Site: http://www.activerideshop.com
Year Founded: 2009
Sales Range: $25-49.9 Million
Skateboarding & Snowboarding Equipment, Accessories & Apparel Retailer
N.A.I.C.S.: 459110
Jenner Heller (Pres)

ACTIVENGAGE, INC.
2701 Maitland Ctr Pkwy Ste 200, Orlando, FL 32751
Tel.: (321) 441-7722
Web Site: http://www.activengage.com
Year Founded: 2007
Sales Range: $1-9.9 Million
Emp.: 77
Chat Solutions for the Automotive Industry
N.A.I.C.S.: 541613
Todd Smith (Co-Founder & CEO)
Ted Rubin (Co-Founder & Pres)
Eric Schlesinger (Dir-Natl Sls)
Andrew Shansky (CTO)
Michael Third (Dir-Software Architecture)
Carol Marshall (Dir-Trng & Virtual Sls)
Amy Wheeler (Dir-HR)
Joe Vraneza (Dir-Outside Sls)

ACTIVEWORLDS, INC.
95 Parker St, Newburyport, MA 01950
Tel.: (978) 499-0222
Web Site: http://www.activeworlds.com
Year Founded: 1997
Sales Range: $25-49.9 Million
Emp.: 20
3D Interaction Software Products & Online Services
N.A.I.C.S.: 541512
Rick Noll (Founder, Pres & CEO)
J. P. McCormick (CFO)

ACTIVITYREZ, LLC

725 Klapiolani Blvd Ste C205, Honolulu, HI 96813
Tel.: (888) 450-2002
Web Site: http://www.activityrez.com
Year Founded: 2000
Sales Range: $1-9.9 Million
Emp.: 15
Activity Booking Engine Used by Expedia & Others Connecting Agents/Suppliers with Rate Management & Real-Time Inventory Systems
N.A.I.C.S.: 425120
Lubuw Falanruw (Founder & CEO)

ACTIVU CORPORATION
301 Roundhill Dr, Rockaway, NJ 07866
Tel.: (973) 366-5550
Web Site: https://www.activu.com
Year Founded: 1983
Sales Range: $10-24.9 Million
Emp.: 70
Software & Information Technology Services for Mission-Critical Command & Control Environments
N.A.I.C.S.: 513210
Paul Noble (Founder & CEO)
Hesha Patel (Dir-Mktg)
John Desmond (VP-Sls)
John Stark (VP-Product Mgmt)
Chris Bryczkowski (CTO)
David Opitz (Dir-Installation Svcs)
John Alfieri (COO)
Michael Sansone (Controller-US & Global)

ACTON FORD, INC.
76 Powdermill Rd, Acton, MA 01720
Tel.: (978) 897-7000
Web Site: https://www.actonford.com
Year Founded: 1993
Sales Range: $10-24.9 Million
Emp.: 42
Car Whslr
N.A.I.C.S.: 441110
David Abatsis (VP)

ACTON INTERNATIONAL LTD.
5760 Cornhusker Hwy Ste 1, Lincoln, NE 68507
Tel.: (402) 694-2586   NE
Web Site: https://www.acton.com
Year Founded: 1968
Sales Range: $10-24.9 Million
Emp.: 20
Direct Marketing
N.A.I.C.S.: 541810
Bruce Wilson (Dir-HR)
Kraig Prange (Pres)
Debb Bovett (Sr Mgr-Data Products)
Frank Lambert (Chm)
Joni Kenney (Dir-Creative)

Subsidiaries:

Acton AWKK (Osaka)   (1)
Shinmachi 3-8-18, Nishi-ku, 550-0013, Osaka, Japan
Tel.: (81) 6 6366 0761
Web Site: http://www.awkk.co.jp
Sales Range: $10-24.9 Million
Asian Market, Direct Marketing, Financial, Information Technology, Internet/Web Design, Production
N.A.I.C.S.: 541810

Acton Direkt-Marketing GmbH   (1)
Postfach 510228, D-30632, Hannover, Germany
Tel.: (49) 175 7 89 18 74
Web Site: http://www.acton.com
Sales Range: $10-24.9 Million
Emp.: 3
Solutions for Global Marketing
N.A.I.C.S.: 541613

Acton Wins Co. Ltd.   (1)
Nihonbashi hisamacho 9-8, Shinjuku-Ku, Tokyo, 103-0002, Chuo-Ku, Japan
Tel.: (81) 3 3341 1691
Web Site: http://www.awkk.co.jp

Emp.: 96
N.A.I.C.S.: 541810

ACTON TECHNOLOGIES, INC.
100 Thompson St, Pittston, PA 18640
Tel.: (570) 654-0612   PA
Web Site: https://www.actontech.com
Year Founded: 1985
Sales Range: $10-24.9 Million
Emp.: 50
Specialty Chemicals Processor & Mfr
N.A.I.C.S.: 326113
Kevin G. Nelson (Chm)

ACTRON ENGINEERING, INC.
13089 60th St N, Clearwater, FL 33760
Tel.: (727) 531-5871   FL
Web Site: https://www.actronengineering.com
Year Founded: 1963
Sales Range: $1-9.9 Million
Emp.: 50
Precision Fabricated & Machined Components & Assemblies to the Security, Defense, Aerospace & Medical Industries
N.A.I.C.S.: 332322
Doug Hermann (Owner, Pres & Gen Mgr)

ACTRON MANUFACTURING, INC.
1841 Railroad St, Corona, CA 92878
Tel.: (951) 371-0885
Web Site: https://www.actronmfginc.com
Year Founded: 1971
Sales Range: $10-24.9 Million
Emp.: 87
Aircraft Hardware Mfr.
N.A.I.C.S.: 332510
Frank Rechberg (Pres)
Robert Rechberg (Founder)
Dale Richards (Dir-Sls & Mktg)
Laura Castera (Mgr-HR)
Ben Swanson (Mgr-Quality Assurance)
Dawn Stratton (Supvr-Customer Svc)

ACTS RETIREMENT-LIFE COMMUNITIES, INC.
375 Morris Rd, West Point, PA 19486-0090
Tel.: (215) 661-2156
Web Site: http://www.actsretirement.com
Year Founded: 1972
Emp.: 402
Elder Care Services
N.A.I.C.S.: 623312
Glenn D. Fox (Gen Counsel & Sr VP)
Gerald T. Grant (Pres & CEO)
Howard C. Braxton II (VP-Sls)

ACTS-AVIATION SECURITY, INC.
1669 Phoenix Pkwy Ste 104, College Park, GA 30349
Tel.: (770) 991-4512
Web Site: http://www.acts-sec.com
Year Founded: 2001
Security Solutions & Services
N.A.I.C.S.: 561621

ACTSOFT, INC.
10006 N Dale Mabry Hwy Ste 100, Tampa, FL 33618
Tel.: (813) 367-8854   FL
Web Site: https://www.actsoft.com
Year Founded: 1999
Sales Range: $10-24.9 Million
Emp.: 100
Software Solutions
N.A.I.C.S.: 513210

Dmitri Korotkevitch *(Dir-Dev)*
Kevin Thigpen *(Exec VP)*
Michael Courter *(VP-Product Mgmt)*
Trent Cherin *(VP-Tech)*
Andrew Velker *(VP-Sls)*

ACTUA CORPORATION
555 E Lancaster Ave Ste 640, Radnor, PA 19087
Tel.: (610) 727-6900   DE
Web Site: http://www.actua.com
Year Founded: 1996
Sales Range: $100-124.9 Million
Emp.: 717
Internet & Software Investment Holding Company
N.A.I.C.S.: 551112
Walter W. Buckley III *(Chm & CEO)*

Subsidiaries:

FDX Advisors Inc.   (1)
2399 Gateway Oaks Dr Ste 200, Sacramento, CA 95833
Tel.: (916) 288-6400
Web Site: http://www.fdxadvisors.com
Investment Advisory Services
N.A.I.C.S.: 523940
Shari Hensrud-Ellingson *(Pres & Chief Investment Officer)*
Bob Mehringer *(Exec VP-Advisory Svcs)*

Subsidiary (Domestic):

AP Institutional Advisors LLC.   (2)
25 NW Riverside Dr Ste 202, Evansville, IN 47708
Tel.: (812) 402-8040
Investment Advisory Services
N.A.I.C.S.: 523940

Jamcracker, Inc.   (1)
4677 Old Ironside Dr St 450, Santa Clara, CA 95054
Tel.: (408) 496-5500
Web Site: http://www.jamcracker.com
Sales Range: $100-124.9 Million
Enabling Technologies, Strategic Consulting & Systems Integration
N.A.I.C.S.: 513210
K. B. Chandrasekhar *(Founder, Chm & CEO)*

NuCivic, Inc.   (1)
156 5th Ave Ste 502, New York, NY 10010
Tel.: (917) 426-9136
Web Site: http://www.nucivic.com
Data Processing, Hosting & Related Services
N.A.I.C.S.: 518210
Andrew Hoppin *(Pres)*
Sheldon Rampton *(CTO)*

ACUATIVE CORP.
30 2 Bridges Rd Ste 240, Fairfield, NJ 07004
Tel.: (973) 227-8040
Web Site: http://www.acuative.com
Year Founded: 1984
Sales Range: $75-99.9 Million
Emp.: 450
System Integration Services
N.A.I.C.S.: 541519
Vincent Sciarra *(Co-Founder & CEO)*
Rich Ackerman *(Co-Founder & Gen Mgr)*
Patrick Danna *(CFO)*
Robert Foley Jr. *(Pres)*

Subsidiaries:

Acuative - Research & Development   (1)
2830 Market Loop Ste 104, Southlake, TX 76092
Tel.: (817) 251-1180
Emp.: 9
Intercommunication Systems Research & Development
N.A.I.C.S.: 517810
Susan Pirzchalski *(VP-Product Dev)*

Acuative - Service Contract Administration   (1)

570 Lake Cook Rd #405, Deerfield, IL 60015
Tel.: (847) 580-4050
Web Site: http://www.acuative.com
Emp.: 10
Hardware Maintenance Contract Manager
N.A.I.C.S.: 561499
Sandra L. Ford *(Dir-Contract Admin Svcs)*

ACUITY
2800 S Taylor Dr, Sheboygan, WI 53082-0058
Tel.: (920) 458-9131   WI
Web Site: http://www.acuity.com
Year Founded: 1925
Sales Range: $800-899.9 Million
Emp.: 4,000
Property & Casualty Insurance Products & Services
N.A.I.C.S.: 524126
Ben Salzmann *(Pres & CEO)*
Wendy Schuler *(VP-Fin)*
Wally Waldhart *(VP-Sls & Comm)*
Sheri Murphy *(VP-Svcs & Admin)*
Gen Mervyn *(Mgr-Svcs)*
Joan Ravanelli Miller *(Gen Counsel & VP-HR)*

ACUITY INC.
12930 Worldgate Dr Ste 100, Herndon, VA 20170
Tel.: (703) 766-0977
Web Site: http://www.myacuity.com
Year Founded: 2002
Sales Range: $10-24.9 Million
Emp.: 146
Management & IT Consulting
N.A.I.C.S.: 541618
Rui Garcia *(Pres & CEO)*
Karen Garcia *(VP-Bus Dev)*
Michael Sledge *(COO)*
Dave Riggs *(VP-Homeland Security & Law Enforcement)*
Gregg Melanson *(Chief Growth Officer)*

ACUITY SURGICAL DEVICES, LLC
8710 N Royal Ln, Irving, TX 75063TX
Web Site:
  http://www.acuitysurgical.com
Year Founded: 2014
Sales Range: $1-9.9 Million
Emp.: 13
Surgical Implant Product Mfr
N.A.I.C.S.: 339113
Bryan Cowan *(Co-Founder & Co-CEO)*
John Davidson *(Co-Founder & Co-CEO)*
John Copeland *(CFO)*
Shawn Thomas *(VP-Bus Dev)*
Charlie Forton *(Dir-Engrg & Regulatory Affairs)*

ACUITYCFO, LLC
3423 Piedmont Rd NE, Atlanta, GA 30305
Tel.: (888) 418-8410   GA
Web Site: http://www.acuity.co
Year Founded: 2004
Bookkeeping, Tax & Accounting Services
N.A.I.C.S.: 541219
Kenji Kuramoto *(CEO)*

Subsidiaries:

Counting House Associates, LLC   (1)
524 Portsmouth Ave, Greenland, NH 03840
Tel.: (603) 766-1099
Web Site: http://www.countinghousebiz.com
Accounting Services
N.A.I.C.S.: 541211
Marc Michaud *(Mgr)*

ACUMEN BUILDING ENTERPRISE, INC.

7770 Pardee Waine Ste 200, Oakland, CA 94621-1490
Tel.: (510) 530-3029   CA
Web Site:
  https://www.acumentransit.com
Year Founded: 1994
Sales Range: Less than $1 Million
Emp.: 40
Management Consulting Services
N.A.I.C.S.: 541611
Walter E. Allen *(Pres & CEO)*
Marlene Barrett *(Mgr-HR)*
Lydia Y. Chan *(Mgr-Acctg)*

ACUMEN LEARNING, LLC
226 N Orem Blvd, Orem, UT 84057
Web Site:
  http://www.acumenlearning.com
Sales Range: $1-9.9 Million
Emp.: 18
Business Training Center
N.A.I.C.S.: 611430
Kevin Cope *(Pres & CEO)*

ACUMENTRICS CORPORATION
20 SW Park, Westwood, MA 02090-1548
Tel.: (781) 461-8251   MA
Web Site:
  http://www.acumentrics.com
Year Founded: 1994
Emp.: 80
Power Conversion Units, A/C to D/C: Static-Electric Fuel Cells
N.A.I.C.S.: 335999
Norman Bessette *(CTO & Sr VP-Engrg)*
John C. Cerulli *(CFO)*
Paul Buzzotta *(VP-Admin)*
Ersson Zapata *(Sr VP-Ops)*
James H. Rosenfield *(Chm)*
Michael J. Gagnon *(VP-Sls & Mktg)*

ACURA OF AUGUSTA
1760 Gordon Hwy, Augusta, GA 30904
Tel.: (706) 737-5200
Web Site:
  http://www.acuraofaugusta.com
Year Founded: 1989
Sales Range: $10-24.9 Million
Emp.: 50
New Car Whslr
N.A.I.C.S.: 441110
Greg Hodges *(Gen Mgr)*
W. E. Stokes Sr. *(Pres)*

ACURA OF OCEAN
909 Route 35, Ocean, NJ 07712
Tel.: (732) 776-5200
Web Site:
  https://www.acuraofocean.com
Sales Range: $10-24.9 Million
Emp.: 50
Car Whslr
N.A.I.C.S.: 441110
Robert Buys *(Controller-Inventory)*
Lori Marchak *(Mgr-Inventory)*

ACURA OF WAPPINGERS FALLS
1271 Route 9, Wappingers Falls, NY 12590
Tel.: (845) 298-0400
Web Site:
  https://www.acuraofwappingers.com
New & Used Car Dealer
N.A.I.C.S.: 441110
Joseph Cifalino *(Gen Mgr)*

ACUSPORT CORPORATION
1 Hunter Pl, Bellefontaine, OH 43311-3002
Tel.: (937) 593-7010
Web Site: http://www.acusport.com

Year Founded: 1986
Sales Range: $100-124.9 Million
Emp.: 234
Sporting & Recreational Goods Distr
N.A.I.C.S.: 423910
Mary Grim *(VP-Ops)*

ACW CORP.
406 Larch Cir, Newport, DE 19804
Tel.: (302) 427-1776
Sales Range: $10-24.9 Million
Emp.: 500
Franchise Owner of Fast-Food Restaurants
N.A.I.C.S.: 722513
Charles Crawford *(Pres)*
Maria Hilger *(Controller)*
Christian Gilligan *(VP)*

ACW MANAGEMENT CORPORATION
2019 Eastchester Dr, High Point, NC 27265
Tel.: (336) 841-4188
Web Site:
  https://www.acleanerworld.com
Year Founded: 1969
Rev.: $11,000,000
Emp.: 325
Provider of Dry Cleaning Services
N.A.I.C.S.: 812320
Ray W. Edwards *(Chm)*
Christoper Edwards *(Pres)*
Sallie Edwards *(VP)*
Diane Black *(CFO)*

ACXIOM DIGITAL
1051 Hillsdale Blvd Ste 400, Foster City, CA 94404
Tel.: (650) 356-3400
Web Site: http://www.acxiom.com
Emp.: 200
Digital/Interactive
N.A.I.C.S.: 541810
John A. Meyer *(Pres & CEO)*
John A. Adams *(COO & Exec VP)*
Cindy Childers *(Sr VP-HR)*

AD BEL LTD.
700 Sam Newell Rd, Matthews, NC 28105-4515
Tel.: (704) 844-1100   NC
Web Site: http://www.carotek.com
Year Founded: 1964
Sales Range: $50-74.9 Million
Emp.: 100
Real Estate Holding Company
N.A.I.C.S.: 551112
J. Addison Bell *(Chm & CEO)*

Subsidiaries:

Carotek Inc.   (1)
700 Sam Newell Rd, Matthews, NC 28105-4515   (100%)
Tel.: (704) 847-4406
Web Site: http://www.carotek.com
Industrial Machinery & Equipment Distr
N.A.I.C.S.: 423830
Tara Snyder *(VP & Controller)*
Stephen Bell *(VP-Pumps, Seal Pots, Process Skids & Mechanical Sys)*
Carl Eibl *(VP-Georgia)*
Rod Holland *(VP-Ops)*

AD CLUB
1304 W Roseburg Ave, Modesto, CA 95350-4855
Tel.: (209) 343-1900   CA
Web Site: https://www.adclub.com
Year Founded: 1987
Sales Range: $10-24.9 Million
Emp.: 15
Advetising Agency
N.A.I.C.S.: 541810
Dan Walsh *(Pres & Sec)*

Ad Club—(Continued)

Subsidiaries:

Ad Club 2-Sales Office   **(1)**
1304 W Roseburg Ave, Modesto, CA 95350
Tel.: (209) 343-1810
Web Site: http://www.adclub.com
Sales Range: $10-24.9 Million
Emp.: 10
Advertising Agencies
N.A.I.C.S.: 541810

AD CONSULTANT GROUP INC.
7541 Black Olive Way, Tamarac, FL
33321
Tel.: (954) 234-3101   **FL**
Year Founded: 1981
Rev.: $19,000,000
Emp.: 2
N.A.I.C.S.: 541810
Bernard Weisblum *(Pres)*
Thierry Degombert *(VP-Intl)*
Michael Cadieux *(Creative Dir)*

AD EXCELLENCE
2450 Hollywood Blvd Ste 300, Holly-
wood, FL 33020
Tel.: (954) 522-8772
Web Site: http://www.ad-
excellence.com
Year Founded: 2003
Rev.: $12,000,000
Emp.: 6
Advetising Agency
N.A.I.C.S.: 541810
Rick Goldman *(Pres)*
Al Tomasetti *(Specialist-Video Pro-
duction)*
Nicole Hennessey *(Rep-Customer
Svc)*
Ryan Nolan *(Graphic Artist & Web
Devel)*
Ben Davenport *(Graphic Artist & Web
Devel)*

AD PARTNERS INC.
4631 Woodland Corporate Blvd Ste
109, Tampa, FL 33614-2416
Tel.: (813) 418-4645
Web Site:
http://www.adpartnersagency.com
Year Founded: 2004
Sales Range: $10-24.9 Million
Emp.: 12
Advetising Agency
N.A.I.C.S.: 541810
Darlene Levi *(Mng Dir & Exec VP)*
Dennis Garcia *(Assoc Dir-Creative)*
Becky Tanner *(Dir-Media)*
Tony Ceresoli II *(Founder & Pres)*

AD RESULTS
320 Westcott St Ste 101, Houston,
TX 77007
Tel.: (713) 783-1800
Web Site:
http://www.adresultsinc.com
Year Founded: 1998
Rev.: $70,000,000
Emp.: 70
Advertising Agencies, Advertising
Specialties, Bilingual Marketing, Con-
sumer Marketing, Direct Marketing,
Hispanic Marketing, Radio
N.A.I.C.S.: 541810
Marshall Williams *(Co-Founder, Co-
Owner & Partner)*
Russell Lindley *(Co-Founder, Co-
Owner & Partner)*
Jennifer Christman *(VP-Media & Cli-
ent Svcs)*
Jenni Skaug *(VP-Bus Dev)*

AD VENTURES, INC.
620 Colonial Park Dr, Roswell, GA
30075-3746
Tel.: (770) 640-5225   **GA**

Web Site:
http://www.adventuresinc.net
Year Founded: 1992
Rev.: $15,000,000
Emp.: 13
Advertising, Business Publications,
Consumer Marketing, Local Market-
ing, Mobile Marketing, Newspaper,
Newspapers & Magazines, Print, Yel-
low Pages Advertising
N.A.I.C.S.: 541810
David Cogdell *(Pres)*
Dave Miglin *(Dir-Interactive Svcs)*
David Federico *(VP)*

AD WORKSHOP
44 Hadjis Way, Lake Placid, NY
12946
Tel.: (518) 523-3359   **NY**
Web Site:
http://www.adworkshop.com
Year Founded: 1977
Sales Range: $10-24.9 Million
Emp.: 30
N.A.I.C.S.: 541810
H. Thomas Connors *(Principal)*
Adele Pierce *(VP & New Bus Con-
tact)*
Kathleen Ford *(Supvr-Production &
Sr Designer)*
Jon Bouman *(Dir-Client Svcs & Strat-
egist)*
Wendy Poole *(Acct Supvr)*
Sandra Gagnon *(Dir-Fin)*
Ben Hamelin *(Web Programmer)*
Jim Duhaime *(Dir-Internet Svcs)*

AD-BASE GROUP, INC.
8 Penn Ctr W Ste 101, Pittsburgh, PA
15276
Tel.: (412) 440-2000   **PA**
Web Site: http://www.abgcapital.com
Year Founded: 1992
Sales Range: $50-74.9 Million
Emp.: 50
Information Technology Investment
Holding Company & Business Sup-
port Services
N.A.I.C.S.: 551112
Jeff Tapolci *(CEO)*
Erica Penrod *(Controller)*
Nick Jenkner *(Coord-Acctg)*
Adam Scott *(Dir-IT)*
Natalie DeCario *(Mgr-Mktg)*
Cherie Steffen *(Coord-Mktg Comm)*

Subsidiaries:

End User Services, Inc.   **(1)**
8 Penn Ctr W Ste 101, Pittsburgh, PA
15276
Web Site: http://www.enduserservices.net
Holding Company; Dial-Up Internet Services
N.A.I.C.S.: 551112

Subsidiary (Domestic):

PGH Connect, Inc.   **(2)**
8 Penn Ctr W Ste 101, Pittsburgh, PA
15276
Tel.: (412) 440-2070
Web Site: http://www.pghconnect.com
Dial-Up Internet Services
N.A.I.C.S.: 517810

GlobalPOPs, Inc.   **(1)**
8 Penn Ctr W Ste 101, Pittsburgh, PA
15276
Tel.: (412) 440-2070
Web Site: http://www.abgcapital.com
Sales Range: $10-24.9 Million
Emp.: 45
Wholesale Dialup & Managed Modem Ports
Mfr
N.A.I.C.S.: 517810
Ron Eggert *(CFO)*
Nick Medina *(VP-Mktg)*
Ari Sigalov *(Product Mgr)*
Sebastian Kiely *(Pres)*

AD-SUCCESS MARKETING

501 Darby Creek Rd Ste 61, Lexing-
ton, KY 40509-1800
Tel.: (859) 263-1822
Web Site: http://www.adsuccess.com
Year Founded: 1985
Sales Range: $10-24.9 Million
Emp.: 12
Advetising Agency
N.A.I.C.S.: 541810
Sharalee Scanlon *(Owner)*
Lauren Sellers *(Art Dir)*
Leah Pear *(Creative Dir)*

AD-VANCE TALENT SOLU-
TIONS, INC.
3911 Golf Park Loop Ste 103,
Bradenton, FL 34203
Tel.: (941) 739-8883
Web Site: https://www.ad-vance.com
Sales Range: $1-9.9 Million
Emp.: 10
Staffing Services
N.A.I.C.S.: 561311
Brion Sunseri *(Owner & Pres)*

AD-VANTAGE ADVERTISING
236 Liberty Trace, Macon, GA 31216
Tel.: (478) 788-1002
Year Founded: 1996
Sales Range: $25-49.9 Million
Emp.: 4
Real Estate
N.A.I.C.S.: 541810
Karen White *(Owner)*

AD-VANTAGENET, INC.
1960 Stickney Point Rd Ste 210,
Sarasota, FL 34231
Tel.: (941) 927-7674   **FL**
Web Site: http://www.gravityfree.com
Year Founded: 1997
Sales Range: $1-9.9 Million
Emp.: 17
Web & Interactive Marketing & Adver-
tising Services
N.A.I.C.S.: 541890
Scott Heaps *(Founder)*
John Barron *(Dir-Managed Svcs)*
Ken Sons *(Gen Mgr)*
Sean Lamberger *(Dir-Creative)*
Vivia Martin *(Office Mgr)*
Eric Price *(Dir-Platform Architecture)*
Rob Kuhn *(Dir-Software Engrg)*

ADA BELTRAMI COOP
PO Box 202, Ada, MN 56510
Tel.: (218) 784-2481
Web Site:
http://www.westcentralag.com
Sales Range: $10-24.9 Million
Emp.: 30
Petroleum Bulk Stations
N.A.I.C.S.: 424710
Jesse McCollum *(Mgr)*

ADA COCA-COLA BOTTLING
COMPANY
1205 Cradduck Rd, Ada, OK 74821
Tel.: (580) 332-0257
Web Site:
http://www.adacocacola.com
Year Founded: 1905
Sales Range: $10-24.9 Million
Emp.: 100
Bottled Water & Softdrink Mfr
N.A.I.C.S.: 312112
Tom Crabtree *(Pres)*

ADA FORD LINCOLN MOTORS
1600 Lonnie Abbott Blvd, Ada, OK
74820
Tel.: (580) 332-6161
Web Site:
http://www.adafordcars.com
Year Founded: 1994
Sales Range: $10-24.9 Million

Emp.: 38
New Car Retailer
N.A.I.C.S.: 441110
Brian Cowart *(Mgr-Gen Sls)*
Eugene Weber *(Mgr-Parts)*
Adam Flanagan *(Mgr-Internet)*

ADA S. MCKINLEY COMMU-
NITY SERVICES, INC.
1359 W Washington Blvd, Chicago,
IL 60607-1905
Tel.: (312) 554-0600
Web Site:
https://www.adasmckinley.org
Sales Range: $25-49.9 Million
Emp.: 500
Child Day Care Services
N.A.I.C.S.: 624410
Brent Hawkins *(First VP)*
Jamal K. Malone *(CEO)*
Beth E. Gallagher *(Second VP)*
Carol E. Bell *(Treas)*
Damita P. Wilson *(Sec)*
Ezekiel Morris *(Pres)*
Crystal Officer *(VP-Ops)*
Margo Roethlisberger *(VP-Program
Ops)*
Sandor Szajkovics *(CFO & Chief Ad-
min Officer)*
Curt Holderfield *(VP-Child Dev &
Youth Svcs)*

ADAC PLASTICS INC.
5920 Tahoe Dr SE, Grand Rapids, MI
49588-8375
Tel.: (616) 957-0311
Web Site:
http://www.adacplastics.com
Year Founded: 1975
Sales Range: $75-99.9 Million
Emp.: 1,000
Mfr of Engineered Products
N.A.I.C.S.: 326199
Gene Hawkins *(VP-Engrg)*
Peter Hungerford *(COO)*

ADAFRUIT INDUSTRIES, LLC
150 Varick St, New York, NY 10013
Tel.: (646) 248-7822
Web Site: https://www.adafruit.com
Year Founded: 2005
Sales Range: $1-9.9 Million
Emp.: 50
Online Sales of DIY Electronics,
Tools & Kits
N.A.I.C.S.: 449210
Limor Fried *(Founder)*

ADAGE TECHNOLOGIES
10 S Riverside Plz Ste 1500, Chi-
cago, IL 60606
Tel.: (312) 258-1200
Web Site:
https://www.adagetechnologies.com
Year Founded: 2001
Sales Range: $1-9.9 Million
Emp.: 30
Software & Web Development Ser-
vices
N.A.I.C.S.: 541511
Patrick Emmons *(Dir-Pro Svcs)*
Roy Chomko *(Pres)*
Mathieu Agee *(Dir-Tech)*
Russ Klitchman *(Dir-Ops)*

ADAGIO HEALTH
960 Penn Ave Ste 600, Pittsburgh,
PA 15222
Tel.: (412) 288-2130   **PA**
Web Site:
http://www.adagiohealth.org
Year Founded: 1971
Sales Range: $25-49.9 Million
Emp.: 274
Health Care Srvices
N.A.I.C.S.: 622110

B. J. Leber *(Pres & CEO)*

ADAIR COUNTY HOSPITAL DISTRICT
901 Westlake Dr, Columbia, KY 42728
Tel.: (270) 384-4753   KY
Web Site:
   http://www.westlakehospital.org
Year Founded: 1980
Sales Range: $10-24.9 Million
Emp.: 100
Healtcare Services
N.A.I.C.S.: 622110
James Evans *(Chm)*
Russell Perkins *(Sec)*
Bruce White *(Treas)*
John Nall *(Vice Chm)*
Neal Gold *(CEO)*

ADAIR FEED & GRAIN COM-PANY
1200 Broad St, Adair, IA 50002-3855
Tel.: (641) 742-3855   IA
Web Site:
   http://www.adairfeedandgrain.com
Year Founded: 1961
Sales Range: $75-99.9 Million
Emp.: 7
Livestock Feed Farm Equipment Sales
N.A.I.C.S.: 423820
Randy Crawford *(Pres)*

Subsidiaries:

Crawford & Crawford, Inc.   (1)
1200 Broad St, Adair, IA 50002   **(100%)**
Tel.: (641) 742-3855
Sales Range: $10-24.9 Million
Farming Entity & Seed Sales
N.A.I.C.S.: 423820
Randy Vrawford *(Pres)*

ADAIR GREENE-MCCANN
1575 Northside Dr NW Bldg 200 Atlanta Technology Dr, Atlanta, GA 30318
Tel.: (404) 351-8424   GA
Year Founded: 1966
Sales Range: $10-24.9 Million
Emp.: 13
Advetising Agency
N.A.I.C.S.: 541810
Mark Perlotto *(Exec VP & Mng Dir)*

ADAIR PRINTING COMPANY
7850 2nd St, Dexter, MI 48130
Tel.: (734) 426-2822
Web Site:
   http://www.adairprinting.com
Sales Range: $10-24.9 Million
Emp.: 64
Catalog Printing
N.A.I.C.S.: 323113
Dennis Adair *(Pres)*

ADAM COMMUNICATIONS
2 Roxbury Ln, Pittsford, NY 14534-4201
Tel.: (585) 271-4010
Web Site:
   http://www.adamcomm.com
Year Founded: 1984
Sales Range: Less than $1 Million
Emp.: 12
Advetising Agency
N.A.I.C.S.: 541810
Ken Frank *(Pres)*
Marty Kiesel *(VP)*

ADAM FRIEDMAN ASSOCI-ATES
28 W 44th St Ste 1111, New York, NY 10036
Tel.: (212) 981-2529

Web Site: http://www.adam-friedman.com
Sales Range: $10-24.9 Million
Emp.: 11
Public Relations Agency
N.A.I.C.S.: 541820
Adam Friedman *(Owner & Principal)*

ADAM HOUSE
605 Ridgefield Rd, Wilton, CT 06897
Tel.: (203) 761-0555
Web Site:
   http://www.adamhouse.com
Year Founded: 1992
Sales Range: Less than $1 Million
Emp.: 4
N.A.I.C.S.: 541810
Anthony Esposito *(Pres)*
Julie Nightingale *(Partner & Dir-Photography)*
Kirsten Long *(Dir-Art)*
Cynthia Montero *(Web Producer)*

ADAM&CO.
80 Dartmouth St, Boston, MA 02116
Tel.: (617) 875-2075
Web Site:
   http://www.adamncompany.com
Sales Range: $1-9.9 Million
Advetising Agency
N.A.I.C.S.: 541810
Adam Larson *(Founder & Principal)*

ADAMA TECHNOLOGIES CORP.
110 Directors Row Ste B, Jackson, TN 38301
Tel.: (702) 896-1009   DE
Year Founded: 2007
ADAC—(OTCBB)
Investment Holding Company
N.A.I.C.S.: 551112

Subsidiaries:

Alpine Industries, Inc.   (1)
898 S State St, Richmond, UT 84333
Tel.: (435) 258-0606
Web Site:
   http://www.alpineindustriesusa.com
Emp.: 8
Precision Machined & Aerospace Components Mfr
N.A.I.C.S.: 332721
Eric Durrant *(Gen Mgr)*

ADAMBA IMPORTS INTERNA-TIONAL
585 Meserole St, Brooklyn, NY 11237
Tel.: (718) 628-9700
Web Site: http://www.adamba.com
Year Founded: 1978
Sales Range: $75-99.9 Million
Emp.: 11
Liqueur Importer
N.A.I.C.S.: 424820
Adam M. Bak *(Pres)*
Robert Bak *(Treas)*

ADAMECS CYCLE SALES CO. INC.
1520 Wells Rd, Orange Park, FL 32073
Tel.: (904) 215-1931
Web Site:
   https://www.adamecharley.com
Rev.: $10,000,000
Emp.: 75
Motorcycle Dealers
N.A.I.C.S.: 441227
Mark A. Adamec *(Owner)*
Chris Adamec *(Owner)*
Joe Key *(VP)*

ADAMS & KNIGHT ADVERTISING/PUBLIC RELA-TIONS

80 Avon Meadow Ln, Avon, CT 06001
Tel.: (860) 676-2300
Web Site:
   http://www.adamsknight.com
Year Founded: 1988
Rev.: $32,000,000
Emp.: 35
Advetising Agency
N.A.I.C.S.: 541810
Bill Knight *(CMO)*
Jill Adams *(Pres & Agency Principal)*
Don Carter *(Dir-Creative)*
Herb Emanuelson *(Acct Supvr)*
Gary Griffin *(Dir-PR)*
Donna Logan-Gabel *(COO)*
Tony Berry *(Sr Acct Exec)*
Amy Naeser *(Acct Exec)*
Marc McFarland *(VP-Acct Svc)*
Brian McClear *(VP-Interactive Svcs)*
Tom Morgan *(Dir-Media)*
Patrick Dugan *(Assoc Dir-Creative)*
Reem Nouh *(Sr VP-Strategic Svcs)*
Meghan Burns *(Dir-Social Media)*
Jim Kieffer *(VP-Interactive Strategy)*
Felicia Lindau *(Chief Bus Dev Officer)*

ADAMS & SMITH INC.
1380 W Ctr St, Lindon, UT 84042
Tel.: (801) 785-6900
Web Site:
   http://www.adamsmithinc.com
Rev.: $24,753,614
Emp.: 75
Bridge Construction
N.A.I.C.S.: 237310

ADAMS AND REESE LLP
One Shell Square 701 Poydras St Ste 4500, New Orleans, LA 70139
Tel.: (504) 581-3234   LA
Web Site:
   http://www.adamsandreese.com
Year Founded: 1951
Sales Range: $125-149.9 Million
Emp.: 267
General Practice Law Services
N.A.I.C.S.: 541110
Ann M. Wallace *(CMO)*
Martin S. Brown Jr. *(Atty)*
E. Paige Sensenbrenner *(Sr Partner)*
A. Kirk Gasperecz *(Partner)*
Lisa Weeks *(Reg Mgr)*
Linda Soileau *(Dir-HR)*
Raymond R. Ferrera *(Partner)*
Adam Massey *(Partner)*
Melissa Rizzo *(Partner)*
Matt Paxton *(Partner-Washington)*
Gif Thornton *(Mng Partner-St. Petersburg)*
Charles N. Parrott *(Partner)*
Eric J. Partlow *(Partner)*
Lucian T. Pera *(Partner)*
Giles Perkins *(Partner)*
Andrew A. Pidgirsky *(Partner)*
Glen M. Pilie *(Partner)*
Charles C. Pinckney *(Partner)*
Edward H. L. Playfair *(Partner)*
James J. Porter *(Partner)*
Kyle L. Potts *(Partner)*
Matt Jackson *(Partner)*
David E. Bender *(CIO)*
Matthew B. Norton *(Partner)*
Bryan E. Busch *(Partner)*
Mike Bednarek *(Partner)*
David F. Katz *(Partner)*
Stephen C. Wolf *(COO)*
Ryan W. Owen *(Partner-Sarasota)*
Dana F. Bird *(CFO)*
Edmund S. Whitson III *(Partner)*

ADAMS AUTOMOTIVE INC.
1797 W St, Annapolis, MD 21401
Tel.: (410) 263-2341   MD
Web Site:
   http://www.adamsautomotive.com

Sales Range: $25-49.9 Million
Emp.: 75
Sales of New & Used Automobiles
N.A.I.C.S.: 441110
Robert J. Adams *(Owner)*
Bob Adams *(Gen Mgr)*

ADAMS BEVERAGES, INC.
3116 John D Odom Rd, Dothan, AL 36303-0936
Tel.: (334) 983-5161   AL
Web Site:
   http://www.adamsbeverages.net
Year Founded: 1950
Rev.: $4,800,000
Emp.: 100
Beer & Ale Merchant Whslr
N.A.I.C.S.: 424810
Billy J. Adams *(Chm)*
Irene Chen *(Controller)*
Terry Andrews *(Mgr-Natl Chain Acct)*
Chris Buck *(Mgr-Sls-Opelika)*
Jeff Camp *(Mgr-Sls-Tuscaloosa)*
Glen Cleveland *(Dir-Sls-Tuscaloosa)*
Fred Davis *(Coord-Sls Execution)*
Caroline Lasseter *(Mgr-Key Accts)*
Billy Norwalk *(Mgr-Sls-Dothan)*
Julia Phifer *(Mgr-Sls-Tuscaloosa)*
Chuck Tucker *(Dir-Ops-Tuscaloosa)*

Subsidiaries:

Adams Beverages of North Carolina, LLC   (1)
7505 Statesville Rd, Charlotte, NC 28269
Tel.: (704) 509-3000
Beer Distr
N.A.I.C.S.: 424810
Donnie Bobbitt *(CFO)*

Subsidiary (Domestic):

Birmingham Beverage Company Inc.   (2)
201 Citation Ct, Birmingham, AL 35209
Tel.: (205) 942-9403
Web Site: http://www.alabev.com
Sales Range: $25-49.9 Million
Emp.: 105
Beverage Importer & Distr
N.A.I.C.S.: 424810
Harry Kampakis *(Owner)*

ADAMS BOOK CO. INC.
140 58th St Ste 6g, Brooklyn, NY 11220
Tel.: (718) 875-5464
Web Site:
   http://www.adamsbook.com
Rev.: $11,200,000
Emp.: 55
Books Sales
N.A.I.C.S.: 424920
Gail Higgins *(Pres)*

ADAMS BROS. CABINETRY, INC.
2221 Murphy Ct, North Port, FL 34289
Tel.: (941) 639-7188
Web Site:
   https://www.discoveradams.com
Year Founded: 1978
Sales Range: $10-24.9 Million
Emp.: 80
Cabinetry Mfr
N.A.I.C.S.: 321918
Ethan Adams *(Pres & CEO)*

ADAMS BROWN, LLC
358 N Main Ste 100, Wichita, KS 67202
Tel.: (316) 262-6578
Web Site:
   https://www.adamsbrowncpa.com
Emp.: 100
Accounting Services
N.A.I.C.S.: 541211
Ben Wilson *(CEO & Mng Partner)*

Adams Brown, LLC—(Continued)

Subsidiaries:

Vonfeldt, Bauer, & Vonfeldt
Chartered   **(1)**
2505 Anderson Ave Ste 103, Manhattan,
KS 66502-2853
Tel.: (785) 320-2555
Web Site: http://www.cpavbv.com
Offices of Certified Public Accountants
N.A.I.C.S.: 541211

ADAMS BUICK-GMC TRUCK, INC.

1017 Berea Rd, Richmond, KY
40475-3554
Tel.: (859) 623-8131
Web Site:
   https://www.adamsgmctruck.com
Year Founded: 1993
Sales Range: $10-24.9 Million
Emp.: 100
Car Whslr
N.A.I.C.S.: 441110
Margaret Adams (Pres)
Sid Adams (VP)
Bix Brown (Gen Mgr)
Tim Sizemore (Mgr-Svc)
Pat Spicer (Office Mgr)

ADAMS CAMPBELL COMPANY LTD.

15343 Proctor Ave, City of Industry,
CA 91745
Tel.: (626) 330-3425
Web Site:
   https://www.adamscampbell.com
Rev.: $18,000,000
Emp.: 100
Sheet Metalwork
N.A.I.C.S.: 332322
Victoria Hobbs (Owner)

ADAMS CONSTRUCTION COMPANY

523 Rutherford Ave NE, Roanoke, VA
24016
Tel.: (540) 982-2366
Web Site:
   https://www.adamspaving.com
Year Founded: 1946
Sales Range: $25-49.9 Million
Emp.: 290
Contractor of Highway & Street Paving
N.A.I.C.S.: 237310
Jack Lanford (Chm)
Gary Wright (Pres)
Rick James (Exec VP)
Gregg Shultz (VP)

ADAMS ELECTRIC COOPERATIVE

700 E Wood St, Camp Point, IL
62320
Tel.: (217) 593-7701
Web Site:
   https://www.adamselectric.coop
Rev.: $11,756,394
Emp.: 35
Electronic Services
N.A.I.C.S.: 221118
Bill Stalder (Mgr-Mktg)
Steven R. Rasmussen (CEO & Gen
Mgr)
Mike Feathers (Coord-Ops)
Brooke Balek (Coord-HR)
Sarah Frank (Coord-Digital Comm-
Comm & Community Svcs Dept)

ADAMS EXTRACT & SPICE LLC

3217 Johnston Rd, Gonzales, TX
78629
Tel.: (512) 359-3050   **TX**

Web Site:
   https://www.adamsextract.com
Year Founded: 1888
Sales Range: $75-99.9 Million
Emp.: 105
Vanilla, Butter Flavoring, Spices &
Food Colors Mfr
N.A.I.C.S.: 424490
Clay Ruple (Pres & CFO)
Jennifer Hawkes (Dir-HR)
Beth Henderschott (Mgr-Mktg)

ADAMS FAIRACRE FARMS INC.

765 Dutchess Tpke, Poughkeepsie,
NY 12603
Tel.: (845) 454-4330
Web Site:
   https://www.adamsfarms.com
Rev.: $66,454,596
Emp.: 225
Independent Grocery Store
N.A.I.C.S.: 445110
Donald Adams (Co-Owner)
Patrick Adams (Co-Owner)
William Lessner (Dir-Mktg)
Eric Foose (Mgr-Garden Center &
Greenhouse)
Phil Burley (Mgr-Garden Center)
Ken Fredericks (Gen Mgr)
Barbara Johnson (Mgr-Store)
Patrick Paulson (Asst Mgr-Store)
Margaret Waz (Asst Mgr-Store)
Greg White (Controller)
Gaye Mallet (Dir-HR)
Michael DeCiutiis (Dir-IT)
June Embler (Mgr-Front End)
Carol Armstrong (Mgr-Greenhouse)
Phil Jacovino (Mgr-Grocery)
Marianne McFadden (Mgr-
Landscaping Bulk Yard)
Timothy Bellamy (Mgr-Nursery)
Darren Albelli (Mgr-Seafood)

ADAMS HOMES OF NORTH-WEST FLORIDA INC.

3000 Gulf Breeze Pkwy, Gulf Breeze,
FL 32563
Tel.: (850) 934-0470
Web Site:
   http://www.adamshomes.com
Rev.: $137,961,364
Emp.: 75
New Construction, Single-Family
Houses
N.A.I.C.S.: 236115
Wayne Adams (Founder)
Duncan Hudnall (Reg Mgr)
Mike Ginn (Gen Mgr)

ADAMS INVESTMENT COMPANY

4100 SE Adams Rd Ste E103,
Bartlesville, OK 74006-8409
Tel.: (918) 335-1010   **OK**
Sales Range: $25-49.9 Million
Emp.: 100
Investment Holding Company
N.A.I.C.S.: 551112
Kenneth G. Adams (Pres)

Subsidiaries:

Central States Business Forms   **(1)**
2500 Industrial Pkwy, Dewey, OK 74029
Tel.: (918) 534-1280
Web Site: http://www.centralstates.net
Sales Range: $25-49.9 Million
Mfr of Business Forms
N.A.I.C.S.: 323111
Gwen Nichols (Mgr-Sls)

Plant (Domestic):

Central States Business Forms - Su-
wanee Plant   **(2)**
70 Buford Hwy, Suwanee, GA 30024
Tel.: (770) 945-2131
Web Site: http://www.centralstates.net

Sales Range: $10-24.9 Million
Emp.: 45
Business Forms
N.A.I.C.S.: 323111
Kenneth Adams (Owner)

ADAMS JEEP OF MARYLAND

3485 Churchville Rd, Aberdeen, MD
21001
Tel.: (410) 734-3604
Web Site:
   https://www.adamsjeep.com
Year Founded: 2002
Sales Range: $10-24.9 Million
Emp.: 31
New Car Retailer
N.A.I.C.S.: 441110
Ron Adams (Owner)
Steve Michaels (Gen Mgr)
Galen Fleming (Mgr-Fixed Ops)
John Loucks (Mgr-Svc)
Keith Cook (Mgr-Internet)
Mike Davidson (Mgr-Fin)
Kim Mumpower (Office Mgr)
Chuck Racine (Mgr-Adams Xtreme)
David Budnick (Mgr-Parts-Columbus)

ADAMS KEEGAN, INC.

6055 Primacy Pkwy Ste 300, Mem-
phis, TN 38119-5773
Tel.: (901) 683-5353   **TN**
Web Site:
   http://www.adamskeegan.com
Year Founded: 1987
Sales Range: $300-349.9 Million
Emp.: 74
Human Resources Management &
Administrative Services
N.A.I.C.S.: 541611
Marty B. Barton (Chief HR Officer,
Gen Counsel & Sr VP)
Courtney Allen (Dir-Sls-Natl Accts)
Kristin Lockhart (VP-Recruiting)
Trevor Benitone (VP-Bus Dev)
Jeff Young (Mgr-Bus Dev)
Brian Evans (Dir-Bus Dev)
James F. Keegan Jr. (Pres & CEO)
George G. Early III (CFO & Sr VP)
Eugene L. Fidell Jr. (Pres-Atlanta)

ADAMS LAND & CATTLE CO.

327 S 1st Ave, Broken Bow, NE
68822
Tel.: (308) 872-6494
Web Site:
   https://www.adamslandcattle.com
Sales Range: $10-24.9 Million
Emp.: 180
Cattle Feedlot Services
N.A.I.C.S.: 112112
Barry Fox (Pres)

ADAMS MFG. CO.

9790 Midwest Ave, Cleveland, OH
44125-2425
Tel.: (216) 587-6801
Web Site:
   http://www.adamsmanufacture.com
Year Founded: 1945
Sales Range: $75-99.9 Million
Emp.: 30
Humidifiers Mfr
N.A.I.C.S.: 333415
Marty L. Schonberger (Pres)
R. Schonberger (VP-HR)

ADAMS PUBLISHING GROUP, LLC

4095 Coon Rapids Blvd, Minneapolis,
MN 55433
Tel.: (423) 359-3113
Web Site: http://www.adamspg.com
Year Founded: 2013
Newspaper Publishers
N.A.I.C.S.: 513110
Jeff Patterson (Pres-Central)
Mark Adams (Pres & CEO)

Michael Beatty (Pres-Florida)
Bob Wallace (CFO)
Chris Knight (Reg Pres-Northern Min-
nesota)
Heather Hernandez (Reg Pres-
Washington)
Matt Davison (Reg Pres-Western
Idaho)
Mark Dobie (Reg Pres-Montana &
Oregon)
Travis Quast (Reg Pres-Eastern
Idaho - Utah)
Robin L. Quillon (Reg VP-Eastern
North Carolina)
Nick Monico (COO)

Subsidiaries:

Antigo Daily Journal   **(1)**
612 Superior St, Antigo, WI 54409
Tel.: (715) 623-4191
Web Site: http://www.antigodailyjournal.com
Internet Publishing & Broadcasting & Web
Search Portals
N.A.I.C.S.: 516210

Bliss Communications, Inc.   **(1)**
1 S Parker Dr, Janesville, WI 53545-3928
Tel.: (608) 755-8220
Web Site: http://www.blissnet.net
Sales Range: $25-49.9 Million
Emp.: 150
Holding Company; Radio Broadcast Sta-
tions, Newspaper & Internet Publisher
N.A.I.C.S.: 551112
Mary Jo Villa (VP)
Tim Bremel (Dir-WCLO Program)

Subsidiary (Domestic):

Eagle Herald Publishing LLC   **(2)**
1809 Dunlap Ave, Marinette, WI 54143-
1706
Tel.: (715) 735-6611
Web Site: http://www.ehextra.com
Rev.: $5,000,000
Emp.: 60
Newspapers Publication
N.A.I.C.S.: 513110
Dan Kitkowski (Editor)
Kathy Springberg (Gen Mgr)

Monroe Publishing Company
LLC   **(2)**
1065 4th Ave W, Monroe, WI 53566-1318
Tel.: (608) 328-4202
Web Site: http://www.themonroetimes.com
Rev.: $2,500,000
Emp.: 70
Publishing Newspapers
N.A.I.C.S.: 513110
Carl Herring (Gen Mgr)
Connie Flint (Bus Mgr)
Laura Hughes (Mgr-Adv)

Racine Broadcasting LLC   **(2)**
4201 Victory Ave, Racine, WI
53405-3277   **(100%)**
Tel.: (262) 634-3311
Web Site: http://www.wrjn.com
Sales Range: $10-24.9 Million
Emp.: 11
Radio Broadcasting Stations
N.A.I.C.S.: 531120

Southern Wisconsin Broadcasting
LLC   **(2)**
1 S Parker Dr PO Box 5001 53547, Janes-
ville, WI 53545-3928
Tel.: (608) 752-7895
Web Site: http://www.wclo.com
Sales Range: $10-24.9 Million
Emp.: 35
Radio Broadcasting Stations
N.A.I.C.S.: 516110
Sidney H. Bliss (Pres)
Mike O'Brien (VP & Gen Mgr)
Tim Bremel (Mgr-Ops)
Chet Daniels (Coord-Promos)
Shar Hermanson (Mgr-Adv Sls)

West Bend Broadcasting Co.,
Inc.   **(2)**
2410 S Main St Ste A, West Bend, WI
53095-5270   **(100%)**
Tel.: (262) 334-2344
Web Site: http://www.wbwifm.com
Rev.: $700,000

Emp.: 17
Radio Broadcasting Stations
N.A.I.C.S.: 516110
Ken Scott (Gen Mgr)

Defiance Publishing Company, LLC **(1)**
624 W Second St, Defiance, OH 43512
Tel.: (419) 784-5441
Web Site: http://www.crescent-news.com
Sales Range: $1-9.9 Million
Emp.: 56
Newspaper Publishers
N.A.I.C.S.: 513110
Dennis Van Scoder (Editor-Newsroom)
Mark Ryan (Publr)
Chris Van Scoder (Dir-Adv)
Greg Meyers (Mgr-Circulation)
Adam Breckler (Mgr-IT & Prepress)
Greg Gobrogge (Mgr-Acctg)

ECM Publishers, Inc. **(1)**
4095 Coon Rapids Blvd, Coon Rapids, MN 55433
Tel.: (763) 712-2400
Web Site: http://ecmpublishers.com
Newspaper Publisher, Distr & Commercial Printing Services
N.A.I.C.S.: 513110
Marge Winkelman (Pres & COO)
John McGraw (CFO)

Unit (Domestic):

ECM Printing **(2)**
4101 Coon Rapids Blvd, Coon Rapids, MN 55433
Tel.: (763) 712-3595
Web Site: http://www.ecmprinting.com
Sales Range: $1-9.9 Million
Emp.: 35
Commercial Printing Services
N.A.I.C.S.: 323111
Marge Winkelman (Pres)

Subsidiary (Domestic):

ECM-Sun Group, LLC **(2)**
10917 Valley View Rd, Eden Prairie, MN 55344
Tel.: (952) 392-6800
Web Site: http://www.mnsun.com
Sales Range: $10-24.9 Million
Emp.: 175
Newspaper Publishers
N.A.I.C.S.: 513110
Julian Anderson (Owner)

Unit (Domestic):

Sun Current/Sun Newspapers **(3)**
10917 Valley View Rd, Eden Prairie, MN 55344
Tel.: (952) 392-6800
Web Site: http://www.hometownsource.com
Newspaper Publishers
N.A.I.C.S.: 513110
Matthew Hankey (Mng Editor)

Eau Claire Press Company **(1)**
701 S Farwell St, Eau Claire, WI 54701
Tel.: (715) 833-9200
Web Site: http://www.leadertelegram.com
Newspapers, Publishing & Printing
N.A.I.C.S.: 513110
Dan Graaskamp (VP-Sls)
Mike Carlson (Dir-Circulation & Mktg)

Greater Beloit Publishing Co. **(1)**
444 E Grand Ave Ste 102, Beloit, WI 53511
Tel.: (608) 365-8811
Newspaper & Magazine Publisher
N.A.I.C.S.: 513110

Jones Media, Inc. **(1)**
103 W Summer St, Greeneville, TN 37743
Tel.: (423) 638-4181
Web Site: http://www.jonesmedia.biz
Newspaper Publisher; Print & Digital Travel Guides Publisher; Marketing Services
N.A.I.C.S.: 513110
Gregg K. Jones (Pres & CEO)
Jo Ann Hopson (Dir-HR)

Unit (Domestic):

Avery Journal-Times **(2)**
335 Linville St, Newland, NC 28657
Tel.: (828) 733-2448
Web Site: http://www.averyjournal.com
Newspaper Publishers

N.A.I.C.S.: 513110
Jamie Shell (Editor)

Subsidiary (Domestic):

Post-Athenian Company LLC **(2)**
320 S Jackson St, Athens, TN 37303
Tel.: (423) 745-5664
Web Site: http://www.dailypostathenian.com
Newspaper Publishers
N.A.I.C.S.: 513110
Douglas Headrick (Editor)
Brittany Freeman (Bus Mgr)
Leanne Malloy (Mgr-Web)
Rhonda Whaley (Publr)
Jeff Schumacher (Dir-Adv)
Pat Helms (Mgr-Circulation)
Scott Wall (Mgr-IT)
Shannon Sayne (Mgr-Special Projects)

Unit (Domestic):

The Greeneville Sun **(2)**
121 W Summer St, Greeneville, TN 37743
Tel.: (423) 638-4181
Web Site: http://www.greenevillesun.com
Newspaper Publishers
N.A.I.C.S.: 513110
Gregg K. Jones (Publr)
Michael S. Reneau (Editor)
Brian Cutshall (Dir-Online)
Artie Wehenkel (Dir-Adv & Mgr-Accts-Natl)
Dale Long (Dir-Circulation & Printing)

Subsidiary (Domestic):

Watauga Democrat Newspapers, Inc. **(2)**
474 Industrial Park Dr, Boone, NC 28607
Tel.: (828) 264-6397
Web Site: http://www.wataugademocrat.com
Emp.: 50
Newspaper Publishers
N.A.I.C.S.: 513110
Tom Mayer (Exec Editor)
Anna Oakes (Editor)

Unit (Domestic):

The Blowing Rocket **(3)**
474 Industrial Park Dr, Boone, NC 28607
Tel.: (828) 264-6397
Web Site: http://www.blowingrocket.com
Newspaper Publishers
N.A.I.C.S.: 513110
Jeff Eason (Editor)

The Mountain Times **(3)**
474 Industrial Park Dr, Boone, NC 28607
Tel.: (828) 264-6397
Web Site: http://www.mountaintimes.com
Newspaper Publishers
N.A.I.C.S.: 513110
Gene Fowler (Publr)
Andy Gainey (Mgr-Circulation)
Charlie Price (Dir-Adv)

Wyoming Business Report **(1)**
702 W Lincolnway, Cheyenne, WY 82001-4560
Tel.: (307) 638-3200
Web Site: http://www.wyomingbusinessreport.com
Trade Journal Publisher
N.A.I.C.S.: 513120
Belinda Nelson (Publr)
M.J. Clark (Editor)

ADAMS RANCH INC.
26003 Orange Ave, Fort Pierce, FL 34945
Tel.: (772) 461-6321
Web Site: https://www.adamsranch.com
Year Founded: 1937
Sales Range: $1-9.9 Million
Emp.: 22
Cattle Ranching & Farming
N.A.I.C.S.: 112111
Mike Adams (Pres)

ADAMS REMCO INC.
2612 Foundation Dr, South Bend, IN 46628-4331
Tel.: (574) 288-2113   **IN**
Web Site: https://www.adamsremco.com

Year Founded: 1945
Sales Range: $25-49.9 Million
Emp.: 260
Office Equipment
N.A.I.C.S.: 513110
Donald M. Carlile (Pres)
Rex Carlile (Founder)

Subsidiaries:

Max Davis Associates Inc. **(1)**
1101 Northpoint Pkwy Ste B, West Palm Beach, FL 33407
Tel.: (561) 640-4444
Web Site: http://adamsremco.com
Office Equipment Retail Dealers
N.A.I.C.S.: 459999

Pixelcreek Technology Inc. **(1)**
2750 Foundation Dr, South Bend, IN 46628
Tel.: (574) 968-1442
Web Site: http://www.pixelcreek.com
Emp.: 150
Information Technology Consulting Services
N.A.I.C.S.: 541512
Dave Riggs (Gen Mgr)
Paul Sykes (Mgr-Lab)
Phil Fletcher (Dir-Customer Solutions)

ADAMS ROBINSON ENTERPRISES
2735 Needmore Rd, Dayton, OH 45414
Tel.: (937) 274-5318
Web Site:
https://www.adamsrobinson.com
Year Founded: 1983
Rev.: $37,173,000
Emp.: 150
Waste Water & Sewage Treatment Plant Construction
N.A.I.C.S.: 237110
Michael Adams (Owner)

ADAMS RURAL ELECTRIC COOPERATIVE INC.
4800 State Route 125, West Union, OH 45693
Tel.: (937) 544-2305
Web Site: http://www.adamsrec.com
Year Founded: 1940
Sales Range: $10-24.9 Million
Emp.: 33
Electric Power Distribution Services
N.A.I.C.S.: 221122
Bill Swango (Gen Mgr)

ADAMS THERMAL SYSTEMS, INC.
47920 5th St, Canton, SD 57013
Tel.: (605) 764-2347
Web Site:
https://www.adamsthermals.com
Year Founded: 2004
Rev.: $23,200,000
Emp.: 1,100
Engine Cooling Systems Mfr
N.A.I.C.S.: 333415
Ronda Thompson (Coord-Document Control)
Todd Hirschkorn (Program Dir-Mgmt)

ADAMS TOYOTA
501 NE Colbern Rd, Lees Summit, MO 64086-4718
Tel.: (816) 358-7600
Web Site:
https://www.adamstoyota.com
Year Founded: 1970
Sales Range: $10-24.9 Million
Emp.: 85
New Car Retailer
N.A.I.C.S.: 441110
Shawn Sweeney (Mgr-Svc)

ADAMS TOYOTA LEES SUMMIT
501 NE Colbern Rd, Lees Summit, MO 64086

Tel.: (816) 358-7600
Web Site:
http://www.adamsscionlees.com
Sales Range: $25-49.9 Million
Emp.: 85
New & Used Car Dealers Service & Parts
N.A.I.C.S.: 441110
E. Ray Adams (Pres)
Teresa Bohen (Controller)

ADAMS TRI CITIES ENTERPRISES
6515 W Clearwater Ave Ste 214, Kennewick, WA 99336
Tel.: (509) 735-9311
Rev.: $10,900,000
Emp.: 16
Franchiser of Fast-Food Restaurants
N.A.I.C.S.: 722513
Lee Adams (Pres)

ADAMS UNLIMITED
80 Broad St Ste 3202, New York, NY 10004
Tel.: (212) 956-5900   **NY**
Web Site: http://www.adams-pr.com
Year Founded: 1985
Sales Range: $1-9.9 Million
Emp.: 5
Public Relations Agency
N.A.I.C.S.: 541820
Candice Adams Kimmel (Owner & Pres)
Marie Rosa (VP)
Yenny Lim (Office Mgr)

ADAMS USA ATHLETICS INC.
610 South Jefferson Ave, Cookeville, TN 38501
Tel.: (931) 526-2109
Web Site: http://www.adamsusa.com
Year Founded: 1947
Sales Range: $10-24.9 Million
Emp.: 140
Sales of Athletic Equipment
N.A.I.C.S.: 339920
Debi Carlcion (Controller)
Ray Abel Jr. (Pres)

ADAMS WHOLESALE COMPANY
101 Nashville Rd, Rocky Mount, NC 27803
Tel.: (252) 977-2185
Web Site:
http://www.adamswholesalesco.com
Sales Range: $10-24.9 Million
Emp.: 85
Groceries, General Line
N.A.I.C.S.: 424410
Adam Fred Adams (Pres & CEO)
Mike Labounty (Gen Mgr)
Roger Boles (Exec VP)
Heather Ray (Controller)
James Holland (Mgr-Distr Center)
Heather Horn (Office Mgr)

ADAMS WINE GROUP, LLC
822 Hampshire Rd Ste C, Westlake Village, CA 91361
Web Site:
http://www.adamswinegroup.com
Wineries
N.A.I.C.S.: 312130
Lawrence Dutra (Pres & CEO)

Subsidiaries:

Michel-Schlumberger Wines **(1)**
4155 Wine Creek Rd, Healdsburg, CA 95448
Tel.: (707) 433-7427
Web Site: http://www.michelschlumberger.com
Sales Range: $10-24.9 Million
Emp.: 20
Wineries

Adams Wine Group, LLC—(Continued)
N.A.I.C.S.: 312130
Bryan Davison (Dir-Winemaking)

ADAMS-COLUMBIA ELECTRIC COOPERATIVE
401 E Lake St, Friendship, WI 53934
Tel.: (608) 339-3346
Web Site: https://www.acecwi.com
Sales Range: $25-49.9 Million
Emp.: 130
Electronic Services
N.A.I.C.S.: 221118
Lawrence Becker (Sec)
Kendal Nichols (Chm)
Scott Parr (Treas)
Martin A. Hillert Jr. (CEO & Gen Mgr)

ADAMSON FORD INC.
1922 2nd Ave S, Birmingham, AL 35233-2002
Tel.: (205) 324-2553   AL
Web Site:
  http://www.adamsonford.com
Year Founded: 1958
Sales Range: $25-49.9 Million
Emp.: 120
New & Used Car Dealers
N.A.I.C.S.: 441110
Bill Israel (Pres)
Chris Charles (Mgr-Comml)
Melissa Shaw (Controller)

ADAPT SOFTWARE APPLICATIONS, INC.
959 South Coast Dr Ste 100, Costa Mesa, CA 92626
Tel.: (714) 389-1584
Web Site: http://www.adaptcrm.com
Year Founded: 1993
Rev.: $2,314,502
Emp.: 10
Enterprise Software Reproducing Solutions
N.A.I.C.S.: 513210
Zeke Wildflower (Pres)
Dave Teper (Mgr-Bus Dev)

ADAPTIVE CORP.
118 W Streetsboro St, Hudson, OH 44236
Tel.: (440) 257-7460
Web Site:
  https://www.adaptivecorp.com
Software Mfr
N.A.I.C.S.: 513210
Eric Doubell (CEO)

Subsidiaries:

Leading Edge Engineering, PC   (1)
222 S Morgan St Ste 4D, Chicago, IL 60607-3093
Tel.: (312) 256-9401
Web Site: http://www.leadedge.com
Rev.: $1,000,000
Emp.: 8
Engineeering Services
N.A.I.C.S.: 541330
Ed Walsh (VP)

ADAPTIVE NURSING & HEALTHCARE SERVICES, INC.
702 N Shore Dr Ste 103, Jeffersonville, IN 47130
Web Site: http://adaptiveindiana.com
Year Founded: 2011
Sales Range: $25-49.9 Million
Emp.: 5,000
Nursing & Healthcare Services
N.A.I.C.S.: 623110
Jenny Miller (Dir-Clinical Ops)
Beth Tourney-Shelton (Dir-HR)
Coumba Kebe (Officer-Corp Compliance & Trng)

ADAPTIVE SPORTS USA, INC.
PO Box 621023, Littleton, CO 80162

Tel.: (720) 412-7979
Web Site:
  http://www.adaptivesportsusa.org
Year Founded: 1956
Disability Assistance Services
N.A.I.C.S.: 624120
Susan B. Rossi (Dir-Competition)

Subsidiaries:

Disabled Sports USA, Inc.   (1)
451 Hungerford Dr Ste 100, Rockville, MD 20850
Tel.: (301) 217-0960
Web Site: http://www.disabledsportsusa.org
Rev.: $3,540,855
Assets: $4,558,024
Liabilities: $751,209
Net Worth: $3,806,815
Earnings: $292,673
Emp.: 16
Fiscal Year-end: 09/30/2014
Disabled People Assistance Services
N.A.I.C.S.: 624120
Karalyn Stott (Program Mgr & Mgr-Comm)
Cheryl Collins (Dir-Insurance & Risk)
Bill Snyder (CFO & COO)
Kirk Bauer (Exec Dir)
Julia Ray (Program Dir)
Huayra Gomez-Garcia (Program Mgr)
Robert Meserve (Pres)
Todd Sajauskas (Treas & Sec)
Steven Goodwin (VP)
Rob Mueller (Program Mgr-Trng & Education)
Dave Simonson (Dir-Dev)
Glenn Merry (Exec Dir)

ADAQUEST, INC.
CW Title Bldg 14450 NE 29th Pl Ste 220, Bellevue, WA 98007
Tel.: (425) 284-7800
Web Site: http://www.adaquest.com
Sales Range: $1-9.9 Million
Emp.: 46
Project Management Software Development Services
N.A.I.C.S.: 541511
Hiram Machado (Pres & CEO)
Nany Aguado (VP-Fin & HR)
David Ducolon (Dir-Consulting Svcs)

ADASIA COMMUNICATIONS, INC.
85 Fifth Ave 7th Fl, New York, NY 10003
Tel.: (212) 871-6886   NY
Web Site: http://www.adasia-us.com
Year Founded: 1997
Sales Range: $75-99.9 Million
Emp.: 25
Advetising Agency
N.A.I.C.S.: 541810
Kevin Lee (Owner)
Young Kim (Exec VP & Chief Dir-Creative)
Harrie Kim (Sr VP & Acct Dir)
Annie Shih (Exec VP & Grp Acct Dir)

ADB INTERESTS, LLC
5205 Broadway St Ste 139, Pearland, TX 77581
Tel.: (917) 942-9420
Web Site:
  http://www.fasciablaster.com
Year Founded: 2014
Sales Range: $10-24.9 Million
Emp.: 11
Massage Product Retailer
N.A.I.C.S.: 423850
Ashley Black (Owner)

ADBANC, INC.
202 N Spruce St, Ogallala, NE 69153
Tel.: (308) 284-8401
Web Site: http://www.abtbank.com
Sales Range: $10-24.9 Million
Emp.: 300
Bank Holding Company
N.A.I.C.S.: 522110

Chad S. Adams (Pres)
Todd S. Adams (Chm & CEO)

Subsidiaries:

Adams Bank & Trust, Corporate Office   (1)
202 N Spruce St, Ogallala, NE 69153
Tel.: (308) 284-8401
Web Site: http://www.abtbank.com
Sales Range: $25-49.9 Million
Emp.: 5
Provider of Banking Services
N.A.I.C.S.: 522110
Chad S. Adams (Pres)
Amanda Adams Hoover (CFO)

ADBIT'S ADVERTISING & PR
757 SE 17th St 358, Fort Lauderdale, FL 33316
Tel.: (954) 467-8420
Web Site: http://www.adbits.com
Year Founded: 1994
Sales Range: Less than $1 Million
Emp.: 2
Advetising Agency
N.A.I.C.S.: 541810
Bit Grubbstrom (Founder)

ADC L.P.
1720 S Wolf Rd, Wheeling, IL 60090-6517
Tel.: (847) 541-3030   IL
Web Site: http://www.adclp.com
Year Founded: 1926
Sales Range: $10-24.9 Million
Emp.: 200
Provider of Zinc & Aluminum Die Castings
N.A.I.C.S.: 331523
Patrick Tang (Pres)
Joseph Rodarte (Mgr-Quality)

ADC LTD. NM
909 Virginia St NE Ste 104, Albuquerque, NM 87108
Tel.: (505) 265-5800
Web Site: http://www.adcltdnm.com
Sales Range: $10-24.9 Million
Emp.: 400
Physical Security, Pre-Employment Screening, Security Clearance Background Investigations
N.A.I.C.S.: 561612
Brenda Cordova-Busick (Pres)
A. Jerome Cordova (Exec VP-Mktg & Security)
Arthur D. Cordova Jr. (CEO)

ADCAP NETWORK SYSTEMS, INC.
10400 Old Alabama Rd Conn Ste 100, Alpharetta, GA 30022
Tel.: (678) 456-6986
Web Site: http://www.adcapnet.com
Year Founded: 2002
Sales Range: $25-49.9 Million
Emp.: 62
Computer Software Technology Services
N.A.I.C.S.: 541511
Rolf Versluis (CTO)
Tina McGeehen (Controller)
Joshua Cain (Dir-Engrg)
Bradford Wilkins (Dir-Talent Mgmt & HR Svcs)
Meghan Brown (Mgr-Pur)
Steve Norton (Dir-Solutions & Sys)
Matthew Merriman (VP-Ops)

ADCELLERANT, LLC
900 Bannock St, Denver, CO 80204
Tel.: (303) 656-1355
Web Site: http://www.adcellerant.com
Year Founded: 2013
Sales Range: $10-24.9 Million
Emp.: 43
Digital Marketing Services

N.A.I.C.S.: 541810
Brock Berry (Co-Founder & CEO)
Shelby Carlson (Co-Founder & COO)
John Chamberlin (Co-Founder & CIO)
Christopher Christopulos (CFO)
Jonathan Muzio (Chief Bus Dev Officer)

ADCETERA GROUP
3000 Louisiana St, Houston, TX 77006
Tel.: (713) 522-8006
Web Site: http://www.adcetera.com
Year Founded: 1982
Sales Range: $10-24.9 Million
Emp.: 60
Advetising Agency
N.A.I.C.S.: 541810
Kristy Sexton (Pres & Chief Creative Officer)
John Sexton (CFO)
Misty Saha (VP-Client Svcs)
Schott Schafer (VP-Digital Strategy)

ADCO ELECTRICAL CORP.
201 Edward Curry Ave, Staten Island, NY 10314
Tel.: (718) 494-4400
Web Site: http://www.adcoonline.com
Year Founded: 1977
Sales Range: $50-74.9 Million
Emp.: 800
Electronic Services
N.A.I.C.S.: 238210
Gina M. Addeo (Pres & CEO)
Lisa Addeo (Owner & Exec VP)
Brian E. O'Sullivan (VP)
John Celiberti (VP-Pur)
Thomas Delfino (VP & Mgr-Westchester Office)
Daniel Leiter (Sr VP-Estimating & Bus Dev)
Erwin Moskowitz (CFO)
Bradley M. Sussman (Chief Compliance Officer & Gen Counsel)

ADCOCK FINANCIAL GROUP
311 W Fletcher Ave, Tampa, FL 33612
Tel.: (813) 935-4091
Web Site:
  https://www.adcockfinancial.com
Sales Range: $25-49.9 Million
Emp.: 20
Investment Management & Advisory Services
N.A.I.C.S.: 523940
Johnny Adcock (CEO)
Brian Adcock (Pres)
Deborah Bradnick (VP-Employee Benefits)
Jenni Smith (Mgr-Client Relationship)
Jennifer Miley (Mgr-Underwriting)
Kristin Hayes (Dir-Retirement Benefits)
Christian Taulbee (Mgr-Case Design & Coord-Sls Intl)
Doris Smith (Coord-Front Office)

ADCOMM GROUP, INC.
202 Stephen Rd, Lemont, IL 60439
Tel.: (630) 243-1630
Web Site:
  http://www.adcommgrp.com
Sales Range: $1-9.9 Million
Emp.: 3
Advetising Agency
N.A.I.C.S.: 541810
Tracy L. Napier (Pres & CEO)

ADCOMM, INC
131 W Hamilton St, Allentown, PA 18101
Tel.: (610) 820-8565
Web Site: http://www.adcomm.tv

Year Founded: 1970
Sales Range: $1-9.9 Million
Emp.: 13
Creative Development, Design, Direct
Marketing & Media Planning
N.A.I.C.S.: 541830
Richard D. Mikitz (Pres)

ADD3, LLC.
500 E Pike St Ste 200A, Seattle, WA
98122
Tel.: (206) 568-3772
Web Site: http://www.add3.com
Year Founded: 2007
Sales Range: $1-9.9 Million
Emp.: 18
Marketing Consulting Services
N.A.I.C.S.: 541613
Paul K. Uhlir (CEO)
Tim Wisner (COO)

Subsidiaries:

Point It Inc.   (1)
3131 Western Ave Ste 428, Seattle, WA
98121
Tel.: (206) 525-3000
Web Site: http://www.pointit.com
Sales Range: $1-9.9 Million
Emp.: 20
Direct Mail Advertising Services
N.A.I.C.S.: 541860
Frank Coyle (Pres)
Jon Lisbin (Chm)
Sarah Dahlin (VP-Client Svcs)
Meredith Walker (Controller)

ADDED VALUE, INC.
6600 France Ave S Ste 490, Minne-
apolis, MN 55435
Tel.: (952) 925-9566
Web Site:
    http://www.addedvalueinc.com
Sales Range: Less than $1 Million
Emp.: 5
Advetising Agency
N.A.I.C.S.: 541810
Scott Anderson (Mng Partner)
Jack Klobucar (Mng Partner)
Izzy Pugh (Assoc Dir-Cultural Insight)
Paul McGowan (CEO-Global Clients)

ADDEN FURNITURE INC.
710 Chelmsford St, Lowell, MA 01851
Tel.: (978) 454-7848
Web Site:
    http://www.addenfurniture.com
Year Founded: 1997
Sales Range: $10-24.9 Million
Emp.: 80
Public Building & Related Furniture
N.A.I.C.S.: 337127
Jessica Hardy (Mgr-Customer Svc)
Patrick Furnari (Pres)

ADDEPAR, INC.
1215 Terra Bella Ave, Mountain View,
CA 94043
Tel.: (855) 464-6268   DE
Web Site: http://www.addepar.com
Year Founded: 2011
Emp.: 98
N.A.I.C.S.:
Eric Poirier (CEO)

ADDIS CRESON
2515 9th St, Berkeley, CA 94710
Tel.: (510) 704-7500
Web Site:
    http://www.addiscreson.com
Year Founded: 1984
Rev.: $7,000,000
Emp.: 28
Advertising & Marketing Services
N.A.I.C.S.: 541810
Steven Addis (CEO)
Susan Kodani (CFO)
Joanne Hom (Dir-Creative)
Stephanie Rose (Dir-Client Svcs)

Jeni Rogers (Dir-Strategy)
Tom Parrette (Dir-Verbal Branding)
Paul Costanza (Dir-Mktg)
Rodney Williams (Principal)
Jonathan Fisher (Production Mgr)
Mark Galbraith (VP-Client Svcs)

ADDISON
48 Wall St, New York, NY 10005
Tel.: (212) 229-5000
Web Site: https://www.addison.com
Year Founded: 1962
Brand Strategy & Design Firm
N.A.I.C.S.: 541613
Jessica Hitchen (Mng Dir-Advisor
Custom Branding)

**ADDISON CAPITAL PART-
NERS**
319 Clematis St Ste 211, West Palm
Beach, FL 33401-4616
Tel.: (561) 835-4041
Web Site:
    https://www.addisoncapital.com
Privater Equity Firm
N.A.I.C.S.: 523999
Brian Miller (Mgr)

ADDISON FOODS INC.
16415 Addison Rd Ste 135, Addison,
TX 75001-5331
Tel.: (972) 381-1209   TX
Web Site: https://www.addtrans.com
Year Founded: 1981
Sales Range: $25-49.9 Million
Emp.: 40
Packaged Frozen Goods
N.A.I.C.S.: 424420
Randy C. Burwell (Pres)
Kevin Kokjohn (VP-Ops)
Brian Evans (Mgr-Branch)
Jason Moore (Mgr-Ops)
Kevin Kokjohn (VP-Ops)
Wayne Bookout (Sr VP)
Greg Setter (Mgr)

ADDITECH, INC.
10925 Kinghurst Ste 500, Houston,
TX 77099
Tel.: (281) 498-5954   TX
Web Site: http://www.additech.com
Year Founded: 1995
Sales Range: $10-24.9 Million
Emp.: 35
Develops & Operates Digital Mer-
chandising Systems for Fuel Retailers
N.A.I.C.S.: 457210
Ralph Koehrer (Chm)
Bolling H. Sasnett III (Pres & CEO)

ADDLOGIX, INC.
459 Wald, Irvine, CA 92618
Tel.: (949) 341-0888
Web Site: http://www.addlogix.com
Year Founded: 1979
Sales Range: $10-24.9 Million
Emp.: 30
Interface Cable Mfr
N.A.I.C.S.: 332618
Alex Chen (Acct Mgr)

**ADDRESSABLE NETWORKS,
INC.**
248 Rickenbacker Cir, Livermore, CA
94551
Tel.: (408) 868-8150   CA
Web Site:
    http://www.addressablenetwork.com
Custom Computer Programming Ser-
vices
N.A.I.C.S.: 541511

ADDX CORPORATION
4900 Seminary Rd Ste 570, Alexandria, VA 22311
Tel.: (703) 933-7637

Web Site: http://www.addxcorp.com
Year Founded: 2002
Sales Range: $1-9.9 Million
Emp.: 27
Technology Consulting for Govern-
ment & Military Agencies
N.A.I.C.S.: 541690
William Millward (Pres & CEO)
Emily Elks (Dir-Proposal Dev)

ADEC INC.
19670 State Rd 120, Bristol, IN
46507
Tel.: (574) 848-7451   IN
Web Site: https://www.adecinc.com
Year Founded: 1952
Sales Range: $10-24.9 Million
Emp.: 400
Developmental Disability Assistance
Services
N.A.I.C.S.: 623210
Donna Belusar (VP-Fin)
Mitch Walorski (CFO)
Sally Russell (VP)
Cindie L. McPhie (Vice Chm)
Don Anderson (Treas & Sec)
Kevin R. Boyer (Chm)
Jessica Koscher (Chief Dev Officer)

ADEL WHOLESALERS, INC.
1101 State St, Bettendorf, IA 52722
Tel.: (563) 355-4734
Web Site:
    https://www.adelwholesalers.com
Sales Range: $10-24.9 Million
Emp.: 50
Plumbing Heating & Air Conditioning
Whlsr
N.A.I.C.S.: 423720
Ralph Gibson (Owner)
Daryl Pearson (Branch Mgr)
Scott Forbes (Mgr-Ops)

ADELANTE LIVE INC.
202 S 22nd St Ste 110, Tampa, FL
33605
Tel.: (813) 248-2735
Web Site:
    http://www.adelantelive.com
Sales Range: $1-9.9 Million
Experiential Marketing & Promotional
Talent Agency
N.A.I.C.S.: 561311
Kristen Brown (Mgr-Client Svcs)
Jonathan P. Drago (Acct Mgr)

ADELBROOK, INC.
60 Hicksville Rd, Cromwell, CT
06416
Tel.: (860) 635-6010   CT
Web Site: http://www.adelbrook.org
Year Founded: 1907
Sales Range: $10-24.9 Million
Emp.: 600
Disabled Child Care Services
N.A.I.C.S.: 624110
Amy Guay-Macfarlane (VP-
Education)
David Maibaum (CFO)
Sabrina Cameron (COO-Residential
& Community Svcs)
Tricia Sobraske (Dir-Education)

ADELL PLASTICS INC.
4530 Annapolis Rd, Baltimore, MD
21227
Tel.: (410) 789-7780
Web Site: http://www.adellplas.com
Year Founded: 1957
Rev.: $12,000,000
Emp.: 120
Resin Or Plastic Coated Fabrics
N.A.I.C.S.: 313320
Arthur F. Dellheim (Pres)
James Lochary (Dir-Ops)
Jim Waterfield (Mgr-Warehouse)
Roger Mason (Plant Mgr)

**ADELMAN ENTERPRISES,
INC.**
798 Moorpark Ave, Moorpark, CA
93021
Tel.: (818) 436-0410   DE
Year Founded: 2006
Sales Range: $10-24.9 Million
Emp.: 3
Online Social Community & Broad-
cast Television Network
N.A.I.C.S.: 516120
Charles N. Adelman (Pres & CEO)
Douglas Ridley (COO & Sec)
Robert L. Denton (CFO)

ADELPHI ENTERPRISES L.P.
2000 Waukegan Rd, Glenview, IL
60025
Tel.: (847) 729-6000
Web Site:
    http://www.lexus.bredemann.com
Year Founded: 1988
Sales Range: $10-24.9 Million
Emp.: 100
New & Used Car Dealers
N.A.I.C.S.: 441110
Martin Bredemann (Gen Mgr)
Pete Livingston (Controller)
Joseph Bredemann Jr. (Pres)

**ADELPHI PAPER HANGINGS
LLC**
PO Box 135, Sharon Springs, NY
13459
Tel.: (518) 284-9066
Web Site:
    http://www.adelphihangings.com
Sales Range: Less than $1 Million
Emp.: 4
Historically-Accurate Wallpaper Re-
production
N.A.I.C.S.: 337127
Chris Ohrstrom (Co-Owner)
Steve Larson (Co-Owner)

**ADELPHIA LAMP & SHADE
INC.**
2500 Gettysburg Rd Ste 101, Camp
Hill, PA 17011
Tel.: (717) 737-7120   PA
Web Site:
    http://www.remingtonlamp.com
Year Founded: 1935
Sales Range: $50-74.9 Million
Emp.: 50
Table Lamps & Shades Mfr
N.A.I.C.S.: 335131
Doug Scott (Owner)

ADELPHIA SEAFOOD INC.
3024 Penn Ave, Reading, PA 19609-
1421
Tel.: (610) 670-2500
Web Site:
    https://www.adelphiaseafood.com
Sales Range: $10-24.9 Million
Emp.: 70
Provider of Fresh & Frozen Seafood
Products
N.A.I.C.S.: 424460
John Flannery (Dir-Ops)
Robert Laughlin (Dir-Sls & Mktg)
Steve Jarrell (Coord-Retail)

ADENA CORPORATION
1310 W 4th St, Mansfield, OH 44906
Tel.: (419) 529-4456
Web Site:
    https://www.adenacorporation.com
Sales Range: $50-74.9 Million
Emp.: 140
Civil Engineering Services
N.A.I.C.S.: 237310
Randy Payne (Pres)
Liska Liska (VP-Bus Dev)

Adena Corporation—(Continued)

ADENA HEALTH SYSTEM
272 Hospital Rd, Chillicothe, OH 45601
Tel.: (740) 779-7500   **OH**
Web Site: https://www.adena.org
Year Founded: 1895
Sales Range: $400-449.9 Million
Emp.: 2,937
Health Care Srvices
N.A.I.C.S.: 622110
John Fortney (Pres-Interim & CEO)
Martha Livingston (Chief Strategy Officer)
Patricia Roam (Chief Compliance Officer)
Jeffrey J. Graham (Pres & CEO)
Steve Burkhardt (Chm)
Katherine Edrington (COO)
Lisa Carlson (CFO)

ADENNA
11932 Baker Pl, Ontario, CA 91761
Tel.: (562) 777-8026
Web Site: http://www.adenna.com
Year Founded: 1997
Sales Range: $10-24.9 Million
Emp.: 15
Hand Protection Gloves & Other Healthcare Products
N.A.I.C.S.: 456199
Maxwell Lee (Pres & CEO)
Steven Sanborn (Mgr-Shipping)

ADEPTPROS INC.
14301 87th St Ste 110, Scottsdale, AZ 85260
Tel.: (877) 664-2777   **NV**
Web Site: http://www.adeptpros.com
Year Founded: 2011
Sales Range: $1-9.9 Million
Emp.: 55
Application Development, Training & Consulting
N.A.I.C.S.: 541690
Venkat Nallapati (Pres & CEO)
Elise Porter (CMO)
Chris Damron (CIO)
Scott R. Chichester (CFO)

ADEPTUS HEALTH INC.
220 E Las Colinas Blvd Ste 1000, Irving, TX 75039
Tel.: (972) 899-6666   **DE**
Web Site: http://www.adpt.com
Sales Range: $400-449.9 Million
Emp.: 3,202
Holding Company; Emergency Medical Centers Operator
N.A.I.C.S.: 551112
Traci Bowen (VP-HR)
Gregory W. Scott (Chm)
Michael R. Corey (Chief Dev Officer & Exec VP)
Jason Worley (CIO)
Heather Weimer (Sr VP-Operational Svcs)
Timothy M. Mueller (VP-Legal Affairs)
Ricardo Martinez (Chief Medical Officer)
James Hopwood (CFO & Exec VP)
Frank R. Williams Jr. (CEO)

Subsidiaries:

AJNH Medical Center LLC   (1)
10407 Jollyville Rd, Austin, TX 78759
Tel.: (512) 628-0470
Emergency Medical Care Service
N.A.I.C.S.: 621493

Adeptus Health LLC   (1)
220 E Las Colinas Blvd Ste 1000, Irving, TX 75039
Tel.: (972) 899-6666
Web Site: http://www.adpt.com
Emergency Medical Centers Operator
N.A.I.C.S.: 621493

James Hopwood (CFO & Exec VP)

Subsidiary (Domestic):

First Choice ER, LLC   (2)
2941 S Lake Vista Ste 200, Lewisville, TX 75067
Tel.: (972) 899-6666
Web Site: http://www.fcer.com
Sales Range: $100-124.9 Million
Emergency Medical Centers Operator
N.A.I.C.S.: 621493
Kenneth Alan Totz (Dir-Facility Medical-Houston & Fallbrook)
Michael Caraway (Dir-Medical-North Houston)
Douglas J. Harrison (Dir-Medical-Sienna Plantation Facility)
Stephen Van Roekel (Dir-Medical-Austin-Riverside)
Ricardo Martinez (Chief Medical Officer)
Howard Ng (Dir-Medical-FM 685 Facility-Pflugerville)

Allen Bethany Medical Center LLC   (1)
1836 E Bethany Dr, Allen, TX 75002
Tel.: (972) 912-1130
Emergency Medical Care Service
N.A.I.C.S.: 621493

Alvin Medical Center LLC   (1)
2860 S Gordon St, Alvin, TX 77511-4731
Tel.: (281) 968-7500
Emergency Medical Care Service
N.A.I.C.S.: 621493

Briar Forest-Eldridge Medical Center LLC   (1)
1717 Eldridge Pkwy, Houston, TX 77077
Tel.: (832) 672-4010
Web Site: http://www.fcer.com
Emergency Medical Care Service
N.A.I.C.S.: 621493

Center Street DP Medical Center LLC   (1)
3701 Center St, Deer Park, TX 77536
Tel.: (281) 884-8700
Web Site: http://www.fcer.com
Emergency Medical Care Service
N.A.I.C.S.: 621493

Converse Medical Center LLC   (1)
7898 Kitty Hawk Rd, Converse, TX 78109-0000
Tel.: (210) 462-1210
Health Care Srvices
N.A.I.C.S.: 622110

Copperwood Medical Center LLC   (1)
9740 Barker Cypress Rd Ste 108, Cypress, TX 77433
Tel.: (281) 463-5200
Emergency Medical Care Service
N.A.I.C.S.: 621493

East Pflugerville Medical Center LLC   (1)
1501 Fm 685, Pflugerville, TX 78660
Tel.: (512) 614-2810
Web Site: http://www.ster.com
Emp.: 30
Emergency Medical Care Service
N.A.I.C.S.: 621493
Ester Jimenez (Controller)

FCER Management LLC   (1)
2217 Blue Sage Dr, Flower Mound, TX 75028
Tel.: (972) 874-9391
Emp.: 2
Administrative Management Services
N.A.I.C.S.: 561110

First Texas Hospital Carrollton LLC   (1)
1401 E Trinity Mills Rd, Carrollton, TX 75006
Tel.: (972) 810-0700
Web Site: http://www.texashealthhospital.com
Health Care Srvices
N.A.I.C.S.: 622110
Joanna Hailey (Dir-Quality Mgmt)

Gilbert Medical Center LLC   (1)
7530 NW 23rd St, Bethany, OK 73008
Tel.: (405) 787-8550

Web Site: http://www.gilbertmedicalcenter.net
Ambulatory Health Care Services
N.A.I.C.S.: 621493

Katy ER Center LLC   (1)
1510 S Mason Rd, Katy, TX 77450
Tel.: (281) 371-8300
Web Site: http://www.scer.com
Emp.: 14
Emergency Medical Care Service
N.A.I.C.S.: 621493

Kuykendahl Medical Center LLC   (1)
21301 Kuykendahl Rd Ste A, Spring, TX 77379
Tel.: (281) 803-1000
Web Site: http://www.fcer.com
Emp.: 3
Mental Health Care Services
N.A.I.C.S.: 621112
Jacob Novak (CEO)

La Porte Medical Center LLC   (1)
1220 W Fairmont Pkwy, La Porte, TX 77571-6105
Tel.: (281) 941-4820
Emergency Medical Care Service
N.A.I.C.S.: 621493

Lewisville Medical Center LLC   (1)
500 West Main St, Lewisville, TX 75057
Tel.: (972) 420-1000
Web Site: http://www.lewisvillemedical.com
General Hospital Services
N.A.I.C.S.: 622110
Sharn Barbarin (CEO)
Jim Russell (COO)
Brandy Farrer (Chief Nursing Officer)
Sue Cobb (VP-Quality)
Dara Biegert (VP-HR)
Gary Fullerton (Asst VP-Ops)
Kyle Bryan (Chief Nursing Officer)

Louetta Medical Center LLC   (1)
13105 Louetta Rd, Houston, TX 77429
Tel.: (972) 899-6666
General Hospital Services
N.A.I.C.S.: 622110

Matlock Medical Center LLC   (1)
8020 Matlock Rd, Arlington, TX 76002-4779
Tel.: (682) 222-7670
Emergency Medical Care Service
N.A.I.C.S.: 621493

North Aurora Medical Center LLC   (1)
2941 Lake Vista Dr, Lewisville, TX 75067
Tel.: (972) 899-6666
Web Site: http://www.uchealthemergencyroom.com
Health Care Srvices
N.A.I.C.S.: 622110

North Dallas Tollway Medical Center LLC   (1)
4535 Frankford Rd, Dallas, TX 75287-6824
Tel.: (972) 707-9860
Emergency Medical Care Service
N.A.I.C.S.: 621493

Pearland Sunrise Medical Center LLC   (1)
2752 Sunrise Blvd, Pearland, TX 77584
Tel.: (832) 672-8040
Web Site: http://www.fcer.com
Emergency Medical Care Service
N.A.I.C.S.: 621493

Plano ER Care Center LLC   (1)
1905 Preston Rd, Plano, TX 75093-2338
Tel.: (972) 384-4600
Emergency Medical Care Service
N.A.I.C.S.: 621493

Potranco Medical Center LLC   (1)
738 W Loop 1604 N, San Antonio, TX 78251
Tel.: (210) 462-9870
Health Care Srvices
N.A.I.C.S.: 622110

SSH Medical Center LLC   (1)
3033 Marina Bay Dr Ste 100, League City, TX 77573
Tel.: (281) 549-9400
Ambulatory Surgical Center
N.A.I.C.S.: 621493

San Antonio Nacogdoches Medical Center LLC   (1)

7898 Kitty Hawk Rd, Converse, TX 78109
Tel.: (210) 462-1210
Emergency Medical Care Service
N.A.I.C.S.: 621493

Sterling Ridge Medical Center LLC   (1)
10333 Kuykendahl Rd Ste B, Spring, TX 77382
Tel.: (281) 419-6510
General Hospital Services
N.A.I.C.S.: 622110

Summerwood Medical Center LLC   (1)
13665 W Lake Houston Pkwy, Houston, TX 77044
Tel.: (281) 406-8320
Emergency Medical Care Service
N.A.I.C.S.: 621493

UCHealth Broomfield Hospital LLC   (1)
11820 Destination Dr, Broomfield, CO 80021
Tel.: (303) 460-6000
Health Care Srvices
N.A.I.C.S.: 622110
Derek Rushing (CEO)

WCB Medical Center LLC   (1)
4551 Western Ctr Blvd, Fort Worth, TX 76137-2628
Tel.: (817) 644-3340
Emergency Medical Care Service
N.A.I.C.S.: 621493

Waterside Medical Center LLC   (1)
8111 W Grand Pkwy, Richmond, TX 77407
Tel.: (832) 759-5000
Emergency Medical Care Service
N.A.I.C.S.: 621493

ADERAS, INC.
11911 Freedom Dr Ste 650, Reston, VA 20190
Tel.: (703) 230-0646
Web Site: https://www.aderas.com
Year Founded: 2004
Sales Range: $10-24.9 Million
Emp.: 58
Computer System Design Services
N.A.I.C.S.: 541512
Jimmy Nguyen (CEO)
Jason DeLano (CFO)
Brad Rendell (Pres & COO)
Matt Symons (VP-Bus Dev)
Lynda Taskett (VP-Enterprise Applications)

ADESSO, INC.
160 Commerce Way, Walnut, CA 91789
Tel.: (909) 839-2929
Web Site: http://www.adesso.com
Year Founded: 2002
Sales Range: $10-24.9 Million
Emp.: 200
Computer Hardware Services
N.A.I.C.S.: 444140
Allen Ku (CEO)
Sarah Chi (Dir-Sls)

ADEX MACHINING TECHNOLOGIES, LLC
260 Feaster Rd, Greenville, SC 29615
Tel.: (864) 416-3100
Web Site: http://www.adexmt.com
Year Founded: 1987
Sales Range: $1-9.9 Million
Emp.: 42
Mechanical Engineering Services
N.A.I.C.S.: 541330
Jason Premo (Co-Owner)
Sean Witty (Co-Owner)

ADEXA INC.
5777 West Century Blvd Ste 1100, Los Angeles, CA 90045
Tel.: (310) 642-2100
Web Site: https://www.adexa.com

Sales Range: $10-24.9 Million
Emp.: 100
Computer Related Consulting Services; Developmers Of Supply Chain Management
N.A.I.C.S.: 541512
Kameron Hadavi (VP-Sls)
K. Cyrus Hadavi (Pres & CEO)
William Green (VP-Customer Satisfaction & Solution Strategy)
Mario A. DiSandro (VP-Fin & Controller)
Tim Field (CTO)
Marcos Meirelles (VP-Supply Base)

ADFERO GROUP
1666 K St NW Ste 250, Washington, DC 20006
Tel.: (202) 333-4444
Web Site: http://www.adfero.com
Year Founded: 2001
Sales Range: $1-9.9 Million
Emp.: 35
Advertising & Public Relations
N.A.I.C.S.: 541810
Jeff Mascott (CEO)
Darren Scher (COO)
Kara Frank (Supvr-Acct)
Misty Fuller (Sr Acct Supvr)
Dianne Harris (Sr Engr-Quality Assurance)
Amanda Markmann (Dir-Creative)
Meghan Moran (VP)
Emily Pravlis (Sr Project Mgr)
Molly Wannen (Dir-Fin)
Philip Perry (Sr Acct Supvr)
Gina Savory (Exec Dir-Digital Mktg)
Aimee Manjarres (Acct Coord)
Dawn Whitehead (Project Mgr)

ADH HEALTH PRODUCTS, INC.
215 N Route 303, Congers, NY 10920-1726
Tel.: (845) 268-0027   NY
Web Site: https://www.adhhealth.com
Year Founded: 1976
Sales Range: $75-99.9 Million
Emp.: 65
Vitamin & Dietary Supplements Mfr
N.A.I.C.S.: 325412
Ashwin Advani (COO)
Carmen Ortiz (Mgr-Customer Svc)

ADHESIVE APPLICATIONS, INC.
41 O'Neill St, Easthampton, MA 01027
Tel.: (413) 527-7120
Web Site:
https://www.adhesiveapps.com
Holding Company; Adhesive Products Mfr
N.A.I.C.S.: 551112
H. Michael Schaefer (CEO)

ADHESIVE PACKAGING SPECIALTIES, INC.
103 Foster St, Peabody, MA 01960
Tel.: (978) 531-3300   MA
Web Site:
https://www.adhesivepackaging.com
Year Founded: 1977
Resinous Impregnated Paper Packaging
N.A.I.C.S.: 322220
Stephen J. Buchanan (Pres)

ADHESIVE RESEARCH, INC.
400 Seaks Run Rd, Glen Rock, PA 17327-0100
Tel.: (717) 235-7979
Web Site:
https://www.adhesivesresearch.com
Sales Range: $125-149.9 Million

Emp.: 400
Mfr of Adhesives
N.A.I.C.S.: 325520
Jackson Tan (Mng Dir-Asia Pacific)
George Stolakis (Chm)
Gray Messersmith (Dir-Fin)
Richard Widden (Pres)
William Schultz (VP-Strategic Dev)

Subsidiaries:

ARx, LLC   (1)
400 Seaks Run Rd, Glen Rock, PA 17327
Tel.: (717) 227-3326
Pharmaceutical Product Mfr & Distr
N.A.I.C.S.: 325412
Megan Greth (Bus Mgr)

Adhesives Research PTE Ltd.   (1)
20 Maxwell Road Ste 10-06 Maxwell House, Singapore, 069113, Singapore
Tel.: (65) 6774 9580
Adhesive Tape Distr
N.A.I.C.S.: 424690
Mark Mapp (Gen Counsel)

ADHESIVE TECHNOLOGIES INC.
3 Merrill Industrial Dr, Hampton, NH 03842
Tel.: (603) 926-1616
Web Site:
https://www.adhesivetech.com
Sales Range: $1-9.9 Million
Emp.: 30
Glue Guns, Glue Sticks & Other Adhesive Products Mfr
N.A.I.C.S.: 325520
Peter Melendy (Founder)

ADHESO-GRAPHICS, INC.
1 Selina Dr, Albany, NY 12205-6741
Tel.: (518) 869-6929
Web Site: http://www.adheso-graphics.com
Printing Machinery & Equipment Mfr
N.A.I.C.S.: 333248
Don Scanlon (Pres)

ADINC/J. KAPLAN ADVERTISING
639 Teaneck Rd, Teaneck, NJ 07666
Tel.: (201) 833-9020
Web Site: http://www.printmyad.com
Year Founded: 1987
Sales Range: $10-24.9 Million
Emp.: 15
N.A.I.C.S.: 541810
Joanne Pannuzo (Controller)
Laurie Jacober (Mgr-Adv & PR)
Dari Izhaky (Dir-Creative)

ADINO ENERGY CORPORATION
2500 City W Blvd Ste 300, Houston, TX 77042
Tel.: (281) 209-9800   MT
Web Site:
http://www.adinoenergycorp.com
Oil & Gas Exploration Services
N.A.I.C.S.: 211120
B. J. Burney (VP-Ops)
Nancy K. Finney (Controller)
Sonny Wooley (Chm)
Timothy G. Byrd Sr. (Pres, CEO & CFO)

ADIR INTERNATIONAL EXPORT LTD.
1605 W Olympic Blvd Ste 700, Los Angeles, CA 90015-3861
Tel.: (213) 386-4412
Web Site: http://www.lacuracao.com
Year Founded: 1980
Sales Range: $25-49.9 Million
Emp.: 300
Department Stores
N.A.I.C.S.: 455110

Ron Azarkman (Pres)
Gus Ponce (VP)

ADIRONDACK BANKCORP, INC.
185 Genesee St, Utica, NY 13501
Tel.: (315) 272-2500
Web Site:
https://www.adirondackbank.com
Sales Range: $25-49.9 Million
Emp.: 142
Bank Holding Company
N.A.I.C.S.: 551111
Anthony Zammiello (Asst VP & Branch Mgr)
Steve Hartnett (Chief Credit Officer & Sr VP)
Harold T. Clark Jr. (Chm)
Rocco Arcuri Sr. (Pres & CEO)

Subsidiaries:

Adirondack Bank   (1)
185 Genesee St, Utica, NY 13501
Tel.: (315) 798-4039
Web Site: http://www.adirondackbank.com
Sales Range: $10-24.9 Million
Emp.: 100
Banking Services
N.A.I.C.S.: 522110
Kenneth J. Finegan (Chief Loan Officer & Sr VP)
Thomas P. Grasso (Sr VP-Risk Mgmt)
J. Daniel Mohr (CFO & Sr VP)
Deborah L. Cotton (Sr VP-Retail Banking)
Rocco F. Arcuri Sr. (Pres & CEO)
Harold T. Clark Jr. (Chm)

ADIRONDACK SCENIC, INC.
439 County Rte 45, Argyle, NY 12809
Tel.: (518) 638-8000
Web Site:
https://www.adkstudios.com
Year Founded: 1975
Sales Range: $10-24.9 Million
Emp.: 100
Theatrical Scenery
N.A.I.C.S.: 339999
Christopher Detmer (Co-Owner & CFO)
David Thomas Lloyd (Co-Owner & Pres)
Louis C. Allen (VP-Creative)
Joel Krasnove (COO)
Ken Crosby (VP-Production)
Michael Blau (VP-Bus Dev)

ADITI CONSULTING LLC
11820 Northup Way STE 305, Bellevue, WA 98005
Tel.: (425) 305-5091   WA
Web Site:
https://www.aditiconsulting.com
Year Founded: 2009
IT Consulting & Services
N.A.I.C.S.: 541690

Subsidiaries:

Resolvit Resources, LLC   (1)
2525 Meridian Pkwy 280, Durham, NC 27713
Tel.: (919) 544-9422
Web Site: http://www.resolvit.com
Rev.: $1,099,000
Emp.: 7
Custom Computer Programming Services
N.A.I.C.S.: 541511
Craig S. Scates (Partner)

Subsidiary (Domestic):

Resolvit, LLC   (2)
8000 Towers Crescent Dr Ste 1100, Vienna, VA 22182
Tel.: (703) 564-2100
Web Site: http://www.resolvit.com
Sales Range: $10-24.9 Million
Emp.: 200
Information Technology Consulting Services
N.A.I.C.S.: 541512

Craig S. Scates (Partner-Raleigh)
Lowell Lehmann (Mng Dir-Midwest Reg & Partner)

ADJMI APPAREL GROUP, INC.
463 7th Ave, New York, NY 10018
Tel.: (212) 594-5511
Web Site: https://www.adjmi.com
Year Founded: 1976
Sales Range: $10-24.9 Million
Emp.: 40
Provider of Children's Clothing
N.A.I.C.S.: 315250
Eric Adjmi (Pres)

Subsidiaries:

Beluga Inc.   (1)
100 W 33rd St, New York, NY 10001
Tel.: (212) 629-9600
Rev.: $30,000,000
Emp.: 5
Men's & Boys' Sportswear & Athletic Clothing
N.A.I.C.S.: 315250
Eric Adjmi (Pres)

Sister Sister, Inc.   (1)
463 7th Ave 4 Fl, New York, NY 10018
Tel.: (212) 629-9600
Web Site: http://www.adjmi.com
Sales Range: $1-9.9 Million
Mens & Boys Clothing Mfr
N.A.I.C.S.: 315250
Eric Adjmi (Treas)

ADJUSTABLE CLAMP COMPANY
404 N Armour St, Chicago, IL 60622
Tel.: (312) 666-0640
Web Site: http://www.ponytools.com
Sales Range: $10-24.9 Million
Emp.: 75
Metal Clamps
N.A.I.C.S.: 332510
Daniel V. Holman (Chm)

ADJUSTERS INTERNATIONAL INC.
126 Business Park Dr, Utica, NY 13502
Tel.: (315) 797-3035
Web Site:
http://www.adjustersinternational.com
Sales Range: $10-24.9 Million
Emp.: 230
Insurance Claim Adjusters, Not Employed By Insurance Company
N.A.I.C.S.: 524291
Steve Surace (Controller)
Thomas W. Aro (Exec VP)
John W. Marini (COO & VP)
Ronald A. Cuccaro (Pres & CEO)
Daniel Craig (Sr VP)

ADKINS DESIGN VISUAL COMMUNICATIONS LLC
35 Corporate Dr Ste 1090, Trumbull, CT 06611
Tel.: (203) 880-9517
Web Site: http://www.sabinc.com
Year Founded: 1985
Rev.: $35,000,000
Emp.: 20
N.A.I.C.S.: 541810
Thomas C. Adkins (Exec VP & Dir-Creative)

ADKINS ENERGY LLC
Tel.: (815) 369-9173
Web Site:
https://www.adkinsenergy.com
Year Founded: 1996
Petroleum & Coal Product Mfr
N.A.I.C.S.: 324199
Ray Baker (Gen Mgr)
Jason Townsend (Plant Mgr)
Bill Howell (Gen Mgr)

Adkins Energy LLC—(Continued)

Mary Wernicke (Mgr-Human Resources & Training)
Dean Vander Zanden (Controller)
Lee Clark (Dir-HSE)
Eric Lockart (Mgr-Risk & Commodity)

ADKM, INC.
78 Irving Pl Ste 7A, New York, NY 10003
Web Site: http://www.harrys.com
Mens Razors Whlsr
N.A.I.C.S.: 812199
Andy Katz-Mayfield (Co-Founder)
Jeff Raider (Co-Founder)

Subsidiaries:

Feintechnik GmbH (1)
Seeweg 4, 98673, Eisfeld, Thuringen, Germany
Tel.: (49) 36863620
Web Site: http://www.feintechnik.com
Sales Range: $25-49.9 Million
Emp.: 500
Shaving Systems, Razors & Blades Mfr & Supplier
N.A.I.C.S.: 332216
Heinz Dieter Becker (Co-CEO)

ADKNOWLEDGE, INC.
4600 Madison Ave 10th Fl, Kansas City, MO 64112
Tel.: (816) 931-1771
Web Site:
  http://www.adknowledge.com
Sales Range: $10-24.9 Million
Emp.: 220
Advertising Network
N.A.I.C.S.: 541890
Brett C. Brewer (Vice Chm & Sr VP-Corp Dev)
Ben Legg (CEO)
Matt Sutton (CEO-Asia)
Ted Kim (Dir-Korea)
Damien Lavin (Chief Revenue Officer-Asia)
Neeraj Bansal (Head-India)

Subsidiaries:

Adknowledge UK Limited (1)
Stanford House 4th Fl 27 A Floral St, Covent Garden, London, WC2E 9EZ, United Kingdom
Tel.: (44) 2072129030
Web Site: http://www.adknowledge.com
Online Marketing Services
N.A.I.C.S.: 541810
Brett C. Brewer (Vice Chm & Sr VP-Corp Dev)
Scott Lynn (CEO)

Hydra Group, Inc. (1)
8800 Wilshire Blvd 2nd Fl, Beverly Hills, CA 90211
Tel.: (310) 659-5755
Rev.: $108,000,000
Emp.: 82
Direct Response Marketing & Advertising
N.A.I.C.S.: 541810

ADKORE STAFFING GROUP
6441 Bonny Oaks Dr Ste G, Chattanooga, TN 37416
Tel.: (423) 468-3003
Web Site: http://www.adkore.com
Sales Range: $10-24.9 Million
Emp.: 400
Office Administrative Services
N.A.I.C.S.: 561110
Mick Frederes (Gen Mgr)

ADL DELIVERY
11471 N US Hwy 301 Ste 114, Thonotosassa, FL 33592
Tel.: (877) 423-3741
Web Site: http://www.adldelivery.com
Year Founded: 1999
Sales Range: $10-24.9 Million
Emp.: 70

Parcel Delivery, Fleet Replacement, Customized Logistics, Warehousing & Distribution Services
N.A.I.C.S.: 493110
Jeff Gambill (Mgr-Operations)

ADLER GROUP, INC.
1400 NW 107th Ave, Miami, FL 33172
Tel.: (305) 392-4000 FL
Web Site: http://www.adlergroup.com
Year Founded: 1996
Sales Range: $1-9.9 Million
Emp.: 100
Commercial & Institutional Building Construction
N.A.I.C.S.: 236220
Michael M. Adler (Chm & CEO)
Matthew L. Adler (Pres & CEO)
Joel Levy (Vice Chm)
Van Antle (Dir-Ops)
Tina Spano (CFO)
Steven R. Brownstein (Exec VP)

ADLETA CORPORATION
1645 Diplomat Dr Ste 200, Carrollton, TX 75006-8393
Tel.: (972) 620-5600 TX
Web Site: https://www.adleta.com
Year Founded: 1922
Sales Range: $10-24.9 Million
Emp.: 103
Homefurnishings
N.A.I.C.S.: 423220
John B. Sher (Pres)

ADLINK CABLE ADVERTISING, LLC.
11150 Santa Monica Blvd, Los Angeles, CA 90025
Tel.: (310) 477-3994
Web Site: http://www.twcmedia.com
Year Founded: 1988
Sales Range: $10-24.9 Million
Emp.: 120
Advertising Agency Services
N.A.I.C.S.: 541810
Stacia Burke (Dir-Mktg)
Debbie Lynn (Dir-Sls)
Dereck Messana (Dir-Sls)
Hans Fischmann (Gen Mgr)

ADLUCENT, LLC
508 E 53rd St #101, Austin, TX 78751
Web Site: http://www.adlucent.com
Year Founded: 2004
Sales Range: $1-9.9 Million
Emp.: 20
Internet Retail SEO & Online Marketing Services
N.A.I.C.S.: 541613
Michael Griffin (Founder & CTO)
Ashwani Dhar (CEO)
Tim Ozor (VP-Engrg)
Matt Zeiger (VP-Tech)
Ryan Gibson (VP-Strategy)

ADM VENTURES INC.
2230 N US Hwy 301, Tampa, FL 33619-2690
Tel.: (813) 621-4671 FL
Web Site: http://www.yaleflorida.com
Year Founded: 1982
Sales Range: $10-24.9 Million
Emp.: 110
Industrial Forklifts Machinery & Equipment
N.A.I.C.S.: 333248
Sandy MacKinnon (Founder, Co-Owner & CEO)
John Christiansen (Co-Owner & Pres)
Alex MacKinnon (VP & Co-Owner)

ADMAN ELECTRIC, INC.

2311 E 28th St, Chattanooga, TN 37407
Tel.: (423) 622-5103
Web Site:
  https://www.admanelectric.com
Sales Range: $25-49.9 Million
Emp.: 275
Electrical Wiring Services
N.A.I.C.S.: 238210
Ricky Etherton (CFO)
Todd Moreland (CEO)
Joe Gibson (Pres)
Paula O'Rear (Office Mgr)

ADMAR SUPPLY CO. INC.
1950 Brighton Henrietta Town Line Rd, Rochester, NY 14623
Tel.: (585) 272-9390
Web Site:
  http://www.admarsupply.com
Year Founded: 1972
Sales Range: $25-49.9 Million
Emp.: 175
Heavy Construction Equipment Rental
N.A.I.C.S.: 532412
Joel DiMarco (VP & Gen Mgr)
Larry Keeley (CFO)
Jeffrey Gillette (Controller)
Jeff Roberts (Branch Mgr)
Evan Brumm (VP-Ops)

ADMARKETPLACE, INC.
3 Park Ave 27th Fl, New York, NY 10004
Tel.: (212) 925-2022 DE
Web Site:
  http://www.admarketplace.com
Year Founded: 2000
Emp.: 133
Search Network Advertising Solutions
N.A.I.C.S.: 541890
Adam J. Epstein (Pres & COO)
James W. Hill (Chm & CEO)
Michael E. Yudin (CTO & Chief Product Officer)
Chris Osborn (Sr VP-Engrg)
Scott Ellentuch (VP-Infrastructure)
Edward Caminiti (Sr VP-Fin & Ops)
Rebecca Engle (VP-Marketplace Ops)
Ariff Quli (Chief Revenue Officer)
Mary Young (VP-Bus Dev)
Todd Adest (VP-Advertiser Sls)

ADMARSH, INC.
7451 Warner Ave Ste E, Huntington Beach, CA 92647-5485
Tel.: (714) 241-4600 CA
Web Site: http://www.admarsh.com
Year Founded: 1981
Sales Range: Less than $1 Million
Emp.: 5
Advetising Agency
N.A.I.C.S.: 541810
Charlotte T. Marsh (Pres & Chief Creative Officer)
August J. Marsh (Gen Mgr)

ADMERA HEALTH, LLC
126 Corporate Blvd, South Plainfield, NJ 07080
Tel.: (908) 222-0533
Web Site:
  http://www.admerahealth.com
Year Founded: 2014
Sales Range: $10-24.9 Million
Emp.: 80
Health Care Srvices
N.A.I.C.S.: 621999
Guanghui Hu (CEO)
Ruben Bonilla-Guerrero (Dir-Medical)
Min Wei (Head-Clinical Ops)
Brady Millican (Chief Bus Officer)
Omar Karame (CFO)

ADMERASIA, INC.
159 W 25th St 6th Fl, New York, NY 10001-7203
Tel.: (212) 686-3333
Web Site: http://www.admerasia.com
Year Founded: 1993
Rev.: $15,000,000
Emp.: 60
Advetising Agency
N.A.I.C.S.: 541810
Zan Ng (Founder & Pres)
Hsin Ling Chuang (Dir-Media)
Tommy Ng (Gen Mgr)
Tuan Pu Wang (Creative Dir)
Vivian Lau Guerriero (Dir-Production)
Yiping Lee (Dir-Bus Dev)

Subsidiaries:

AAAZA, Inc. (1)
3250 Wilshire Blvd Ste 1901, Los Angeles, CA 90010
Tel.: (213) 380-8333
Web Site: http://www.aaaza.com
Emp.: 30
N.A.I.C.S.: 541810
Kevin Vu (Mng Dir)
Peter Huang (CEO & Exec Dir-Creative)
Ann Lu (Dir-Client Svcs)
Meg Terada Choi (Interim Acct Dir & Dir-Media)
Kellie Chen (Acct Mgr)

ADMET, INC.
51 Morgan Dr, Norwood, MA 02062
Tel.: (781) 769-0850
Web Site: https://www.admet.com
Year Founded: 1989
Sales Range: $1-9.9 Million
Emp.: 14
Material Testing System Mfr
N.A.I.C.S.: 334519
Richard Gedney (Founder & CEO)

ADMINISTRATIVE CONCEPT CORP.
406 43rd St W, Bradenton, FL 34209-2952
Tel.: (941) 744-1317
Year Founded: 1995
Sales Range: $100-124.9 Million
Emp.: 7,500
Employer Organization Services
N.A.I.C.S.: 561330
George Bushon (Owner & Pres)

ADMINISTRATIVE RESOURCE OPTIONS, INC.
200 W Adams St, Chicago, IL 60606
Tel.: (312) 634-0300
Web Site: http://www.aroptions.us
Rev.: $17,300,000
Emp.: 275
Management Consulting Services
N.A.I.C.S.: 541618
Dan Stikkers (Dir-Natl Sls)
Jeff Moe (VP-Sls)
William McClung (CEO)
John Western (VP-Ops)
Allecia McClung (CEO)

ADMINISTRATIVE RESOURCES, INC.
801 Sunset Dr Ste 1, Johnson City, TN 37604
Tel.: (423) 283-0296
Web Site:
  http://www.adminresources.net
Year Founded: 1984
Sales Range: $50-74.9 Million
HR Administrative Processing & Payroll Accounting Services
N.A.I.C.S.: 923130
Leann Morris (Gen Mgr)
John LaFevre (Reg Mgr)
Glenda Carter (Mgr-Acctg)

Trisha Renfro *(Coord-Benefits)*
Jay Thomason *(Coord-Payroll)*
Katie Branham *(Coord-Payroll)*

ADMINISTRATORS FOR THE PROFESSIONS, INC.
1800 Northern Blvd, Roslyn, NY 11576
Tel.: (516) 365-6690
Web Site: http://www.pri.com
Sales Range: $400-449.9 Million
Emp.: 300
Medical Malpractice Insurance
N.A.I.C.S.: 524298
Anthony J. Bonomo *(CEO-Admin)*
Carl Bonomo *(Exec VP)*
Gerald Dolman *(Pres)*
Marjorie O. Thomas *(Sr VP-Risk Mgmt & Underwriting)*
Mark Paykin *(Sr VP-Actuarial Svcs)*
Bernard McArthur *(Chief Technical Officer)*

Subsidiaries:

Physicians Reciprocal Insurers   **(1)**
1800 Northern Blvd, Roslyn, NY 11576
Tel.: (516) 365-6690
Web Site: http://www.pri.com
Sales Range: $75-99.9 Million
Emp.: 260
Medical Malpractice Insurance Services
N.A.I.C.S.: 524298
Christine Quinn *(Head-Risk Mgmt)*
Barry F. Schwartz *(Vice Chm)*
Jeanne H. Braun *(Exec VP-Hospitals & Special Program)*
Mehmet Cetin *(Chm)*
Sanford R. Goldberg *(Sec-Gastroenterology)*
Howard D. Kolodny *(Treas-Internal Medicine)*
Chris Curcio *(Head-Mktg)*
Brian Dalton *(Head-Dental)*
Esi Stuart *(Head-HR)*

ADMIRAL BEVERAGE CORPORATION
821 Pulliam Ave, Worland, WY 82401
Tel.: (307) 347-4205   WY
Web Site:
http://www.admiralbeverage.com
Year Founded: 1947
Sales Range: $50-74.9 Million
Emp.: 1,000
Soft Drink Bottler & Distr
N.A.I.C.S.: 312111
Forrest L. Clay *(Pres)*

ADMIRAL BUILDING PRODUCTS, INC.
3 Wheeling Ave, Woburn, MA 01801-2008
Tel.: (978) 988-1166
Web Site: http://www.abcsupply.com
Sales Range: $25-49.9 Million
Emp.: 35
Distr of Roofing Materials
N.A.I.C.S.: 423330

ADMIRAL FINANCIAL CORP.
7101 SW 67 Ave, South Miami, FL 33143
Tel.: (305) 904-4400   FL
Year Founded: 1987
Financial Investment Services
N.A.I.C.S.: 523940
William Lee Popham *(Chm, Pres, CEO & CFO)*

ADMIRAL LINEN SERVICE INC.
2030 Kipling St, Houston, TX 77098-1532
Tel.: (713) 630-0303   TX
Web Site:
http://www.admiralservices.com
Year Founded: 1961
Sales Range: $25-49.9 Million

Emp.: 500
Linen Supply
N.A.I.C.S.: 812331
Les Craft *(Pres)*
Joe Wootton *(VP)*

ADMIRAL NISSAN INC.
6021 Black Horse Pike, Egg Harbor Township, NJ 08234-4801
Tel.: (609) 646-1104   NJ
Web Site:
http://www.admiralnissan.com
Year Founded: 1977
Sales Range: $10-24.9 Million
Emp.: 75
New & Used Car Dealers
N.A.I.C.S.: 441110
Brad Pogachefsky *(Pres)*

ADMIRAL PACKAGING, INC.
10 Admiral St, Providence, RI 02908-3203
Tel.: (407) 274-7000   RI
Web Site:
https://www.admiralpkg.com
Year Founded: 1898
Printers & Converters of Flexible Packaging
N.A.I.C.S.: 322220
Harley Frank *(Pres)*
John Wilbur *(VP)*
Mike Kauffman *(VP-Sls)*

ADMIRAL TOOL & MANUFACTURING COMPANY INC.
38010 Amrhein Rd, Livonia, MI 48150
Tel.: (734) 462-0222   IL
Web Site: http://www.admiraltool.com
Year Founded: 1945
Sales Range: $10-24.9 Million
Emp.: 180
Metal Stamping
N.A.I.C.S.: 332119
Wayne Avers *(VP)*
Steve Waldie *(Dir-Engrg)*

ADMIRAL TRAVEL INTERNATIONAL, INC.
1284 N Palm Ave, Sarasota, FL 34236
Tel.: (941) 951-1801
Web Site:
http://www.admiraltravel.com
Year Founded: 1997
Sales Range: $1-9.9 Million
Emp.: 15
Luxury Travel Services
N.A.I.C.S.: 561599
Ryan Hilton *(Co-Owner)*
Malaka Hilton *(Co-Owner & CEO)*

ADMIRAL WINE & LIQUOR CO.
74 Sand Pk Rd, Cedar Grove, NJ 07009
Tel.: (973) 857-2100
Web Site:
http://www.admiralwine.com
Year Founded: 1961
Sales Range: $75-99.9 Million
Emp.: 65
Wine Buying & Selling
N.A.I.C.S.: 424820
Michael Zieger *(Owner & Pres)*

ADMIRALS COVE ASSOCIATES LTD.
3535 Military Trl Ste 101, Jupiter, FL 33458
Tel.: (561) 744-1033
Rev.: $65,900,000
Emp.: 12
Operative Builders
N.A.I.C.S.: 236117

Tom Frankel *(VP)*
Ben Frankel *(CEO)*
Matt King *(Asst Dir-Golf)*

ADMIRALTY ISLAND FISHERIES INC.
2025 1st Ave, Seattle, WA 98121
Tel.: (206) 448-5400
Web Site: https://www.aquastar.com
Year Founded: 1990
Sales Range: $25-49.9 Million
Emp.: 145
Whslr of Fish & Seafoods
N.A.I.C.S.: 424460
Robert Hooey *(Exec VP)*
Andrew Pickering *(CFO)*
Dennis Spomer *(Controller)*

ADMIRALTY PARTNERS, INC.
1170 Somera Rd, Los Angeles, CA 90077
Tel.: (310) 471-3772
Web Site:
http://www.admiraltypartners.com
Year Founded: 1992
Privater Equity Firm
N.A.I.C.S.: 523999
Jon B. Kutler *(Chm & CEO)*

ADMO, INC.
1714 Deer Tracks Trl Ste 205, Saint Louis, MO 63131
Tel.: (314) 993-9300
Web Site: http://www.admo.com
Year Founded: 1986
Rev.: $25,000,000
Emp.: 9
Advetising Agency
N.A.I.C.S.: 541810
Dan Shroyer *(Pres)*
Matt Kinsell *(Acct Mgr)*
Dan Ford *(Creative Dir)*

ADMY TECHNOLOGY GROUP, INC.
1180 N Town Ctr Dr Ste 100, Las Vegas, NV 89144
Tel.: (669) 244-9698   DE
Web Site:
http://www.admytechnology.com
Year Founded: 2021
Investment Services
N.A.I.C.S.: 523999
Shekar G. Ayyar *(CEO)*
Niccolo M. de Masi *(Co-Chm)*
Niccolo de Masi *(Co-Chm)*
Harry L. You *(Co-Chm)*

ADNET ADVERTISING AGENCY, INC.
116 John St 35th Fl, New York, NY 10038-3709
Tel.: (212) 587-3164   NY
Web Site: http://www.adnet-nyc.com
Year Founded: 1992
Rev.: $20,000,000
Emp.: 25
Advetising Agency
N.A.I.C.S.: 541810
Fahd Mumtaz *(Pres)*
Kiran Vairale *(CEO)*

ADNET SYSTEMS, INC.
164 Rollins Ave Ste 303, Rockville, MD 20852
Tel.: (301) 770-4850
Web Site: http://www.adnet-sys.com
Sales Range: $100-124.9 Million
Emp.: 300
Custom Computer Programming Services
N.A.I.C.S.: 541511
David Humayun *(VP)*
Ashok Jha *(Pres)*
James Blurton *(CFO)*

ADOLFSON & PETERSON, INC.
5500 Wayzata Blvd Ste 600, Minneapolis, MN 55416
Tel.: (952) 544-1561   MN
Web Site: http://www.a-p.com
Year Founded: 1946
Emp.: 600
General Contractors & Construction Managers; Designers & Builders of Commercial, Industrial & Apartment Buildings
N.A.I.C.S.: 236220
Jeffrey Hansen *(CEO)*
Cesar Diaz *(CFO)*
Frank Sarno *(VP-Construction Processes & Technologies-Exec & Strategic)*
Brenna Mann *(Gen Counsel & Sr VP)*
Corbett Nichter *(Pres-Gulf States & Sr VP)*
Tom Horsting *(Pres-Mountain States & Sr VP)*
Mark Liska *(Pres-Midwest & Sr VP)*
Mike Bontrager *(Pres-Southwest & Sr VP)*
Brantley Barrow *(Chm)*
Eric Churchill *(Dir-Bus Dev-Central Texas-Austin)*
Melisa Baune *(Dir-Bus Dev-North Texas-Dallas)*

Subsidiaries:

Adolfson & Peterson, Arizona   **(1)**
5002 S Ash Ave, Tempe, AZ 85282
Tel.: (480) 345-8700
Web Site: http://www.a-p.com
Sales Range: $10-24.9 Million
Emp.: 45
Building Construction Services
N.A.I.C.S.: 236220
Christian Green *(Dir-Bus Dev)*
Brian Kinney *(VP-Ops)*

Adolfson & Peterson, Colorado   **(1)**
797 Ventura St, Aurora, CO 80011
Tel.: (303) 363-7101
Web Site: http://www.a-p.com
Sales Range: $10-24.9 Million
Emp.: 40
General Contractors & Construction Managers
N.A.I.C.S.: 236220

Adolfson & Peterson, Texas   **(1)**
1600 N Collins Blvd Ste 2000, Richardson, TX 75080   **(100%)**
Tel.: (972) 387-1700
Web Site: http://www.a-p.com
Sales Range: $10-24.9 Million
Emp.: 57
General Contractor & Construction Manager Designer & Builder of Commercial Industrial & Apartment Building Services
N.A.I.C.S.: 236220
Corbett Nichter *(Pres)*

ADOLPH GASSER INC.
181 2nd St, San Francisco, CA 94105
Tel.: (415) 495-3852
Web Site:
http://www.adolphgasser.com
Rev.: $225,000,000
Emp.: 42
Photographic Cameras, Projectors, Equipment & Supp
N.A.I.C.S.: 423410
John Gasser *(CEO)*

ADOLPH KIEFER & ASSOCIATES, INC.
1700 Kiefer Dr, Zion, IL 60099
Tel.: (847) 872-8866   IL
Web Site: http://www.kiefer.com
Year Founded: 1947
Sales Range: $25-49.9 Million
Emp.: 100
Swimming Apparel, Supplies & Equipment Mfr & Retailer

Adolph Kiefer & Associates, Inc.—(Continued)
N.A.I.C.S.: 339920
Greg Kadens (Pres)

ADONEL CONCRETE
2101 NW 110th Ave, Miami, FL 33172
Tel.: (305) 669-0611
Web Site:
  https://www.adonelconcrete.com
Rev.: $11,500,000
Emp.: 150
Concrete Work
N.A.I.C.S.: 238110
Luis Garcia (Chm & CEO)
Augusto Estrada (Acct Mgr)
Chris Gregory (Acct Mgr)
Elizabeth Picado (Mgr-Billing)
Fatima Dominguez (Mgr-Credit)
Frank Mier (Dir-Ops)
Karen Vargas (Mgr-HR)
Ray Sparkes (CFO)
Tomas Rodriguez (Mgr-Safety)
Willy Izquierdo (Acct Mgr)
Xavier Vazquez (Dir-Quality Control)
Bob Cardonne (Pres)

ADORAMA CAMERA INC.
42 W 18th St, New York, NY 10011
Tel.: (212) 741-0052
Web Site: http://www.adorama.com
Rev.: $20,900,000
Emp.: 45
Mail Order of Cameras & Photography Supplies
N.A.I.C.S.: 449210
Shloma Zenwirth (Dir-Mgmt Info Sys)
Yoel Weisz (Mgr-Product & Pur)
Ben Mandelbaum (Mgr-IT)
Jerry Greenbaum (Mgr)

ADORN FASHIONS INC.
1407 Broadway Rm 1402, New York, NY 10018
Tel.: (212) 764-9595
Web Site:
  http://www.adornfashions.com
Sales Range: $10-24.9 Million
Emp.: 18
Mfr of Women's & Children's Sportwear
N.A.I.C.S.: 424350
Morrris Zinn (CEO)
Ricky Zinn (VP-Sls)
Christine Chiu (Mgr-Import)
Lorrie Markman (Mgr-Acctg)
Steven Bach (Mgr-Shipping)

ADPERIO
2000 S Colorado Blvd Tower 1 Ste 7000, Denver, CO 80222
Tel.: (303) 985-2700   NY
Web Site: http://www.adperio.com
Year Founded: 1994
Sales Range: $25-49.9 Million
Emp.: 50
Advertising Agencies
N.A.I.C.S.: 541810
David Asseoff (CEO)
Jill Fletcher (Pres)
Brian Fox (Sr Dir-Bus Dev)
Bryan Tyler (Sr Dir-IT)
Audrey Eng (VP-Acct Mgmt)

ADPLEX INC.
650 Century Plaza Dr Ste 120, Houston, TX 77073
Tel.: (281) 443-4301
Web Site: http://www.adplex.com
Sales Range: $25-49.9 Million
Emp.: 25
Advertising Services
N.A.I.C.S.: 541810
Edward Raine (CEO)
Allen Ruch (Sr VP-Ops)

ADR GROUP
3207 Mercer St, Houston, TX 77027
Tel.: (713) 621-2200
Web Site:
  http://www.adrservicesintl.com
Sales Range: $10-24.9 Million
Emp.: 3
Personal Service Agents; Offers Mediation Services
N.A.I.C.S.: 541990
Joe Tita (Pres & CEO)

ADREKA ADVERTISING
4485 Tench Rd, Suwanee, GA 30024
Tel.: (678) 951-1300
Web Site: http://www.adreka.com
Sales Range: $1-9.9 Million
Emp.: 10
Advertising Agencies
N.A.I.C.S.: 541810
Lisa Graham (Owner)

ADRENALINA
5726 La Jolla Blvd Ste 105, La Jolla, CA 92037
Tel.: (858) 456-2061   NV
Web Site:
  http://www.adrenalinastore.com
Year Founded: 2001
Outdoor Adventure & Extreme Sports Equipment & Products Retailer; Magazine Publisher; Television Broadcasting Services
N.A.I.C.S.: 459110
Pablo Lanatta (Pres)

ADRIAN STEEL COMPANY INC.
906 James St, Adrian, MI 49221-3996
Tel.: (517) 265-6194   MI
Web Site:
  https://www.adriansteel.com
Year Founded: 1953
Emp.: 300
Truck Equipment Mfr
N.A.I.C.S.: 332999
Carol McMillan (Controller)

Subsidiaries:

Adrian Equipment Company Inc. (1)
906 James St, Adrian, MI 49221-3914
Tel.: (517) 265-6194
Web Site: http://www.adriansteel.com
Sales Range: $25-49.9 Million
Emp.: 20
Mfr of Miscellaneous Fabricated Wire Products
N.A.I.C.S.: 332618
Carol Mcmillan (Controller)

Adrian Upfitting Company Inc. (1)
906 James St, Adrian, MI 49221-3914
Tel.: (517) 265-6194
Web Site: http://www.adrianco.com
Sales Range: $50-74.9 Million
Provider of Employment Services
N.A.I.C.S.: 561311
Harley Westfall (Chm)

Adscom Corporation (1)
7364 Baltimore Annapolis Blvd # A, Glen Burnie, MD 21061-3242
Tel.: (410) 768-8505
Web Site: http://www.adscom1.com
Sales Range: $25-49.9 Million
Emp.: 40
Van & Truck Equipment Distr, Installer & Sales
N.A.I.C.S.: 423120

Carter Industries Inc. (1)
950 Whipple Rd, Union City, CA 94587-1347   (100%)
Tel.: (510) 324-6700
Sales Range: $25-49.9 Million
Emp.: 25
Distr of Motor Vehicle Parts & Accessories
N.A.I.C.S.: 336390

Commercial Truck & Van Equipment Inc. (1)

4800 Buford Hwy, Norcross, GA 30071-2405   (100%)
Tel.: (800) 937-9229
Web Site: http://www.comtruckequip.com
Sales Range: $25-49.9 Million
Emp.: 24
Provider of Truck Bodies
N.A.I.C.S.: 332618
Ed Hooker (Gen Mgr)

ADRIANNA PAPELL, LLC
500 7th Ave Fl 10, New York, NY 10018
Tel.: (212) 695-5244   DE
Web Site:
  http://www.adriannapapell.com
Year Founded: 1980
Sales Range: $50-74.9 Million
Emp.: 140
Provider of Womens, Childrens & Infant Clothing
N.A.I.C.S.: 424350
Jean Berkman (Pres)

ADRIATIC MEDIA INVESTORS LLC
5440 Harvest Hill Rd Ste 253, Dallas, TX 75230
Tel.: (214) 904-8001
Private Investment Firm
N.A.I.C.S.: 523999
Gavin Susman (CEO)

Subsidiaries:

Lagardere Services Distribution SAS   (1)
2 Rue Lord Byron, 75008, Paris, France
Tel.: (33) 142990700
Duty Free Product Retailer
N.A.I.C.S.: 445320

ADRIENNE DESIGNS INC.
17150 Newhope St Ste 514, Fountain Valley, CA 92708-4253
Tel.: (714) 558-1209
Web Site:
  http://www.adgoldchain.com
Rev.: $50,000,000
Emp.: 27
Necklaces, Precious Metal
N.A.I.C.S.: 339910
Clifford E. Johnston (Pres)
Patrick Turner (Owner)

ADROIT ASSOCIATES INC.
100 Wood Ave S Ste 108, Iselin, NJ 08830
Tel.: (732) 516-9600
Web Site:
  https://www.adroitassociates.com
Year Founded: 2004
Sales Range: $10-24.9 Million
Emp.: 100
IT Staffing & Consulting
N.A.I.C.S.: 541690
Ravi Mudunuri (Acct Mgr)

ADROLL, INC.
972 Mission St 3rd Fl, San Francisco, CA 94103
Tel.: (877) 723-7655
Web Site: http://www.adroll.com
Year Founded: 2007
Sales Range: $100-124.9 Million
Online Advertising Services
N.A.I.C.S.: 541890
Jared Kopf (Co-Founder & Chm)
Aaron Bell (Co-Founder & Chief Product Officer)
Peter Krivkovich (COO & CFO)
Valentino Volonghi (CTO)
Suresh Khanna (Chief Revenue Officer)
Stacey Manes (VP-HR & Recruiting)
Greg Fulton (VP-Product)
Scott Gifis (Pres)
Patrick Mee (VP-Engrg)
Robin Bordoli (CEO)

ADRONICS/ELROB MANUFAC-TURING
9 Sand Park Rd, Cedar Grove, NJ 07009
Tel.: (973) 239-3800
Sales Range: $10-24.9 Million
Emp.: 120
Mfrs. of Antennas & Receiving Units
N.A.I.C.S.: 334220
Richard C. Robinson (Pres)

ADS DIRECT MEDIA INC.
11780 US Highway 1 Suite 202, Palm Beach Gardens, FL 33408
Tel.: (800) 615-8845
Web Site: http://www.adsdirect.com
Year Founded: 2009
Sales Range: $25-49.9 Million
Emp.: 25
Performance Marketing Services
N.A.I.C.S.: 541890
Jesse Lo Re (COO & Sr VP-Bus Dev)
Nate Poupko (Pres & CEO)
Noy Elimeleh (Gen Mgr)
Brian Pirocchi (Dir-Creative)
Cynthia Gomez (Controller)
Ken Narvios (Dir-Optimization)

ADS R US
4781 Cedar Dr, Loganville, GA 30052-7210
Tel.: (770) 876-7588
Sales Range: Less than $1 Million
Emp.: 2
N.A.I.C.S.: 541810
Wayne Dillard (Owner)

ADS VENTURES, INC.
3 Post Office Sq 8th Fl, Boston, MA 02110
Tel.: (617) 236-5830   MA
Web Site: http://www.adsventures.net
Strategic Business Consulting Services
N.A.I.C.S.: 541611
Chest Atkins (CEO)
Leah Conley (COO)
Bill Cortese (Assoc VP)
Savannah Kelleher (Assoc VP)
Liesl Grebenstein (VP-Federal Affairs)
George Gomes (Assoc VP-Res & Policy)
Emily Kowtoniuk (VP-State Affairs)

ADS, INC.
621 Lynnhaven Pkwy Ste 160, Virginia Beach, VA 23452
Tel.: (757) 481-7758   DE
Web Site: https://www.adsinc.com
Year Founded: 1997
Sales Range: $900-999.9 Million
Emp.: 400
Body Armor, Helmets & Ballistic Goggles for Military Combat Units & Federal Agents
N.A.I.C.S.: 315250
Jason S. Wallace (CEO)
Chris Philbrick (VP-Mktg)
Thomas Hazelbaker (VP-Program Mgmt)
Lushana Offutt (VP-Programs & Bus Dev)
Kevin Hickey (VP-Product Mgmt)
Jennifer Edwards (VP-HR)
Brad Anderson (VP-Contracts)
Brant Feldman (VP-Sls)
Karan Rai (Pres & CFO)

ADSOUTH PARTNERS, INC.
375 N Stephanie St Ste 1411, Henderson, NV 89014
Tel.: (647) 426-1640
Advertising Services
N.A.I.C.S.: 541810
Sandra Palmer (Pres, Treas & Sec)

ADSPACE NETWORKS, INC.
99 Park Ave Rm 320, New York, NY 10016-1601
Tel.: (646) 367-5300
Web Site:
http://www.adspacenetworks.com
Year Founded: 2001
Sales Range: $10-24.9 Million
Emp.: 34
Owner & Operator of In-Mall Digital Billboards
N.A.I.C.S.: 541890
William Ketcham (CMO & Exec VP)
Peter Krieger (CFO, COO & Exec VP)
John Moran (VP-Natl Sls-Adspace Digital Mall Network-Detroit)
Eric Steinert (Chief Revenue Officer & Exec VP)
Jonny Hamilton (Sr VP-Creative & Content Dev)
Amanda E. Sheplee (VP-Dev & Strategic Partnerships)
Ye Ling Chen (VP-Fin)
Ian Mirmelstein (Sr VP-Digital Engagement)
Subhash Durga (VP-Network Ops)
Kelly McGuier (VP-Media Ops)
Pete Miles (Sr VP-Ad Platform & Ops)

ADSTAFFING.COM
24806 61st St, Salem, WI 53168
Tel.: (847) 408-7326   IL
Year Founded: 1992
Sales Range: Less than $1 Million
Emp.: 3
Electronic Media, Print, Real Estate, Recruitment, Telemarketing
N.A.I.C.S.: 541810
Mel Zwirn (CEO & Media Dir)
Mary Zwirn (Chief Admin Officer & Creative Dir)

ADTEC ELECTROPLATING INC.
125 Glenn St, Lawrence, MA 01843
Tel.: (978) 683-2082
Web Site:
http://www.adtecelectroplating.com
Sales Range: $1-9.9 Million
Emp.: 50
Electroplating of Metals & Formed Products
N.A.I.C.S.: 332813
John Hoegen (Mgr-Production)
Dennis Reidy (Dir-Tech)

ADTECH SYSTEMS INC.
490 Boston Post Rd, Sudbury, MA 01776
Tel.: (978) 261-1077
Web Site:
http://www.adtechsystems.com
Rev.: $34,795,478
Emp.: 50
Mfr of Multimedia Projectors & Audio Visual Equipment
N.A.I.C.S.: 424610
Stephan Kolpinski (Acct Mgr)
Taki Fragopoulos (Project Mgr)

ADTEGRITY.COM
38 Commerce SW Ste 200, Grand Rapids, MI 49546
Tel.: (616) 285-5429
Web Site: http://www.adtegrity.com
Sales Range: $10-24.9 Million
Emp.: 25
N.A.I.C.S.: 541810
Scott Brew (Pres & CEO)
Kurt Filla (Chief Revenue Officer)
Jason A. Balk (CFO)
Dustin Turner (VP-Tech)
Chad Jansen (VP-Agency Sls)

Michael Struyk (COO)
Todd Morris (VP-Mktg-Adv Ops)
Tom Simpson (VP-Sls-West Coast)

ADULT & PEDIATRIC DERMA-TOLOGY, PC
526 Main St Ste 302, Acton, MA 01720
Tel.: (978) 371-7010
Web Site: https://www.apderm.com
Year Founded: 1992
Cosmetic Dermatology Services
N.A.I.C.S.: 622110
Samuel D. Goos (Founder & Mng Partner)
Matt Griffith (Chief Development Officer)

Subsidiaries:

Dermatology Professionals, Inc.   (1)
1672 S County Trl Ste 101, East Greenwich, RI 02818-5099
Tel.: (401) 885-7546
Web Site: http://www.dermri.com
Dermatology Services
N.A.I.C.S.: 812112
Michele Crudale (Office Mgr)
Lynn E. Iler (Co-Founder)

ADULT AND CHILD
222 E Ohio St, Indianapolis, IN 46204-2144
Tel.: (317) 275-8800   IN
Web Site:
http://www.adultandchild.com
Year Founded: 1982
Sales Range: $25-49.9 Million
Emp.: 462
Behavioral Healthcare Services
N.A.I.C.S.: 623220
Dawn Shimp (Sec)
Dustin Huddleston (Treas)
Steve Wohlford (VP)
Sue Collins (Pres)

ADVANCE BAG & PACKAGING CO.
5720 Williams Lake Rd, Waterford, MI 48329
Tel.: (248) 674-3126
Web Site:
https://www.advancepac.com
Sales Range: $10-24.9 Million
Emp.: 50
Packaging Materials
N.A.I.C.S.: 424990
Robert I. Cohen (Pres)

ADVANCE BOILER & TANK CO.
6600 W Washington St Ste 700, West Allis, WI 53214-5646
Tel.: (414) 475-3120
Web Site:
http://www.advanceboiler.com
Year Founded: 1919
Sales Range: $25-49.9 Million
Emp.: 50
Vessels, Process & Storage
N.A.I.C.S.: 332313
Randy Bauer (Project Mgr)
Ken Griffioen (Pres)

ADVANCE DISPLAY TECH-NOLOGIES, INC.
42230 Zevo Dr, Temecula, CA 92590-3732
Tel.: (303) 267-0111   CO
Year Founded: 1983
Sales Range: Less than $1 Million
Emp.: 27
Digital Video Display Technology
N.A.I.C.S.: 334310
James P. Martindale (Pres & CEO)
Gregory L. Heacock (CTO & VP-R & D)

Robert Ridgeway (VP-Global Bus Dev & Plng)
Robert Ridgeway (VP-Global Bus Dev & Plng)

ADVANCE DRUM SERVICE, INC.
1835 Dickerson Dr, Mableton, GA 30126
Tel.: (404) 699-7048
Web Site:
https://www.advancedrum.com
Year Founded: 1994
Sales Range: $1-9.9 Million
Emp.: 36
Mfr & Recycler of Quality Containers & Drums
N.A.I.C.S.: 332439
Brent Bernath (VP)
Eric Bernath (COO)
Joe Bernath (VP-Ops & Logistics)

ADVANCE ELECTRICAL SUP-PLY CO.
263 N Oakley Blvd, Chicago, IL 60612
Tel.: (312) 421-2300
Web Site:
https://www.advanceelectrical.com
Sales Range: $25-49.9 Million
Emp.: 70
Electrical Supplies
N.A.I.C.S.: 423610
Steven Anixter (Pres)
Scott Eubanks (Mgr-Mgmt Info Sys)
Dave Neubauer (Exec VP)
Tim Schlesser (Mgr-Corp Ops)
Joe Colasuono (Mgr-Credit)
Mike Harrold (Branch Mgr)
Donna Thickpenny (Office Mgr)

ADVANCE ENGINEERING COMPANY
12025 Dixie Ave, Redford, MI 48239
Tel.: (313) 537-3500
Web Site: http://www.adveng.net
Sales Range: $10-24.9 Million
Emp.: 100
Mfr of Automotive Stampings
N.A.I.C.S.: 336370
George Helms (Pres)
Kevin Jordan (Sr VP-Fin)

Subsidiaries:

Advance Engineering Company   (1)
6185 Wales Rd, Northwood, OH 43619-1435   (100%)
Tel.: (419) 693-6591
Web Site: http://www.adveng.net
Automotive Stampings
N.A.I.C.S.: 336370
Goerge Helms (Pres)

ADVANCE FINANCIAL
100 Oceanside Dr, Nashville, TN 37204
Tel.: (615) 341-5900
Web Site: https://www.af247.com
Year Founded: 1996
Sales Range: $25-49.9 Million
Emp.: 293
Financial Services
N.A.I.C.S.: 523940
Shantrelle Edmondson (VP-Community Outreach)
Chris Manner (Branch Mgr)

ADVANCE LATEX PRODUCTS, INC.
126 N Ash Ave, Inglewood, CA 90301
Tel.: (310) 559-8300   CA
Year Founded: 1946
Sales Range: $1-9.9 Million
Emp.: 19
Women's Foundation Undergarments Mfr

N.A.I.C.S.: 315250
Michael Wellman (Pres)

ADVANCE LOCAL LLC
4 Times Square 11th Fl, New York, NY 10036
Tel.: (201) 459-2888
Web Site:
http://www.advancelocal.net
Media Services
N.A.I.C.S.: 541830
Peter Weinberge (PRes)

Subsidiaries:

Advance Digital, Inc.   (1)
Plaza, Jersey City, NJ 07311
Tel.: (201) 459-2888
Digital News & Information Products Mfr
N.A.I.C.S.: 334419
Peter Weinberge (Pres)

Subsidiary (Domestic):

Matchcraft, Inc.   (2)
2701 Ocean Park Blvd Ste 220, Santa Monica, CA 90405
Tel.: (310) 314-3320
Web Site: http://www.matchcraft.com
Digital Marketing Services
N.A.I.C.S.: 541810
Sean Greene (Co-CEO)
Alex Dionysian (CTO)
Chris Brake (Head-Product)
Jim Clemens (VP-Ops)
Tero Fagerstrom (Mgr-Campaign)
Anne Lafree (Sr Mgr-Campaign)
Sandy Lohr (Co-CEO)
Marc Zaks (Chief Revenue Officer)
Jeff Chew (Gen Mgr-EMEA)

ADVANCE MECHANICAL CON-TRACTORS
1301 E Burnett St, Signal Hill, CA 90755-3511
Tel.: (562) 426-1729   CA
Web Site:
https://www.advancecontractors.com
Year Founded: 1990
Sales Range: $10-24.9 Million
Emp.: 40
Mechanical Contractor
N.A.I.C.S.: 238220
Taylor Davis (Mgr-Svcs)

ADVANCE MECHANICAL SYS-TEMS, INC.
425 E Algonquin Rd, Arlington Heights, IL 60005-5750
Tel.: (847) 593-2510   IL
Web Site: https://www.advmech.com
Year Founded: 1912
Sales Range: $125-149.9 Million
Emp.: 250
Heating & Air Conditioning Contracting Services
N.A.I.C.S.: 238220
David M. Weiner (Pres)
Daniel Krebsbach (VP)
Richard Morris (VP)
Dave Cederberg (Controller)
Chris Brown (Exec VP)

ADVANCE NOTICE, INC.
24 Winter St, Peabody, MA 01960-7593
Tel.: (978) 531-6722   MA
Web Site:
http://www.advancenotice.com
Year Founded: 1984
Rev.: $32,000,000
Emp.: 27
Financial, Health Care, Medical, Outdoor, Print, Recruitment, Strategic Planning/Research
N.A.I.C.S.: 541810
John Ivester (Pres)
Theresa Lanxner (Treas & VP)
David Stowell (Dir-Creative)
Dean Asadorian (VP-Client Svcs)

Advance Notice, Inc.—(Continued)

ADVANCE PACKAGING COR-PORATION

4459 40th St SE, Grand Rapids, MI
49512-1917
Tel.: (616) 949-6610   MI
Web Site:
   https://www.advancepkg.com
Year Founded: 1966
Corrugated Shipping Containers Mfr
N.A.I.C.S.: 322211
Donald W. Crossley (Pres)
David L. Straten (Dir-Graphic Pkg)
R. Scott Wilcox (VP-Sls & Mktg)
Steve Philp (CIO)
Sue Albrecht (VP-Admin)
Dan Boucher (CFO)

ADVANCE PAPER BOX COM-PANY

6100 S Gramercy Pl, Los Angeles,
CA 90047
Tel.: (323) 750-2550
Web Site:
   https://www.advancepaperbox.com
Rev.: $30,000,000
Emp.: 150
Paper Bag Mfr
N.A.I.C.S.: 322211
Martin Gardner (Pres)

ADVANCE PETROLEUM DIS-TRIBUTING CO.

2451 Great SW Pkwy, Fort Worth, TX
76106
Tel.: (817) 626-5458
Web Site:
   https://www.advancefuel.com
Sales Range: $10-24.9 Million
Emp.: 17
Distr of Petroleum Products
N.A.I.C.S.: 424720
Kyle W. Kirby (Pres)
Gary Hawkins (VP)

ADVANCE POLYBAG INC.

1470 1st Colony Blvd, Sugar Land,
TX 77479
Tel.: (713) 580-4800
Web Site: http://www.apicorp.com
Sales Range: $25-49.9 Million
Emp.: 550
Mfr of Plastic Bags
N.A.I.C.S.: 326111
Janak Sheth (CFO & Exec VP)
Robert Gary (Controller)
Amy Manuel (Mgr-HR)

ADVANCE PUBLICATIONS, INC.

950 Fingerboard Rd, Staten Island,
NY 10305
Tel.: (718) 981-1234   NY
Sales Range: Less than $1 Million
Newspaper, Magazine, Book & Inter-net Publisher
N.A.I.C.S.: 513120
Donald E. Newhouse (Co-Pres)
Peter D. Weinberger (Chief Innova-tion Officer-Advance Local)
Michael Fricklas (Chief Legal Officer)
Steve Newhouse (Co-Pres)
Oren Klein (CFO)

Subsidiaries:

Advance Communication Corp. **(1)**
5000 Campus Wood Dr, East Syracuse, NY
13057
Tel.: (315) 438-4100
Sales Range: $75-99.9 Million
Emp.: 80
Holding Company; Cable Network Operator;
Voice & Internet Telecommunication Ser-vices
N.A.I.C.S.: 551112
Steven A. Miron (CEO)

Advance Publications **(1)**
6300 Wilshire Blvd 11th Fl, Los Angeles,
CA 90048 **(100%)**
Tel.: (323) 965-3466
Sales Range: $25-49.9 Million
Emp.: 100
Printing & Distribution of Periodicals
N.A.I.C.S.: 513110

American City Business Journals,
Inc. **(1)**
120 W Morehead St Ste 400, Charlotte, NC
28202-1844 **(100%)**
Tel.: (704) 973-1000
Web Site: http://www.acbj.com
Sales Range: $125-149.9 Million
Emp.: 200
Local Business Weekly Newspapers Pub-lisher
N.A.I.C.S.: 513110
Whitney Shaw (Chm, Pres & CEO)
Alex Orfinger (Exec VP)
Mike Olivieri (Exec VP)
Lori Michaels (CTO)
Jenn McGuigan (CMO)
Ashley Ganci (VP-HR)
Michelle Vargo (VP-Product Dev-The Busi-ness Journals)
A. T. Castillo (VP-Circulation Ops)
Leigh Rogers (VP-Digital Revenue)
Don Baker (Publr)
Bridgette Bello (Publr)
Kourtney Geers (Mng Editor)
Jon Wile (VP-Design)

Branch (Domestic):

American City Business Journals **(2)**
233 N Michigan Ave, Chicago, IL 60601
Tel.: (312) 337-3981
Web Site: http://www.bizjournals.com
Sales Range: $25-49.9 Million
Emp.: 5
Publishing of Trade Journals
N.A.I.C.S.: 513120
Filomena Volpe (Coord-Adv)
Laurie Lyga (Controller)

Unit (Domestic):

Atlanta Business Chronicle **(2)**
3384 Peachtree Rd NE Ste 900, Atlanta,
GA 30326-2828 **(100%)**
Tel.: (404) 249-1000
Web Site: http://www.atlanta.bizjournals.com
Sales Range: $10-24.9 Million
Emp.: 75
Publisher of Business Newspaper
N.A.I.C.S.: 513120
Ed Baker (Publr)
Crystal Edmonson (Editor-Brdcst)
Emily Boyle (Dir-Adv)
Eric Mandel (Mng Editor)

Baltimore Business Journal **(2)**
1 E Pratt St Ste 205, Baltimore, MD
21202 **(100%)**
Tel.: (410) 576-1161
Web Site:
   http://www.baltimore.bizjournals.com
Sales Range: $10-24.9 Million
Emp.: 30
Publisher of Local Business Weekly
N.A.I.C.S.: 513110
Jennifer White (Dir-Adv)

Bizjournals.com **(2)**
120 W Morehead St Ste 400, Charlotte, NC
28202-1844 **(100%)**
Tel.: (704) 973-1000
Web Site: http://www.bizjournals.com
Sales Range: $10-24.9 Million
Emp.: 50
Business Journal Website Operator
N.A.I.C.S.: 513110
Ryan Whittington (Gen Mgr)

Boston Business Journal **(2)**
160 Federal St 12th Fl, Boston, MA 02110-
3036
Tel.: (617) 330-1000
Web Site: http://www.bizjournals.com
Sales Range: $10-24.9 Million
Emp.: 40
Newspaper Publishers
N.A.I.C.S.: 513110
Steph Solis (Editor-Digital)

Buffalo Law Journal **(2)**

465 Main St, Buffalo, NY
14203-1716 **(100%)**
Tel.: (716) 854-2480
Web Site: http://www.lawjournalbuffalo.com
Sales Range: $10-24.9 Million
Emp.: 6
Publisher of Law Journal
N.A.I.C.S.: 513110
Jennifer Lyons Greco (Bus Mgr)
Sean Connors (Coord-Web-Production)
Kim Schaus (Gen Mgr)
Jack Connors (Pres & Publr)

Business First of Columbus **(2)**
300 Marconi Blvd, Columbus, OH
43215 **(100%)**
Tel.: (614) 461-4040
Web Site: http://www.bizjournals.com
Sales Range: $10-24.9 Million
Emp.: 30
Publisher of Local Business Weekly
N.A.I.C.S.: 513110
Nick Fortini (Publr)

Business First of Louisville **(2)**
455 4th St Ste 278, Louisville, KY
40202 **(100%)**
Tel.: (502) 583-1731
Web Site:
   http://www.businessfirstoflouisville.com
Sales Range: $10-24.9 Million
Emp.: 32
Publishing
N.A.I.C.S.: 513110
Krysteen Cissell (Asst Dir-Adv & Sr Acct
Exec)
Rachel McMahan (Dir-Audience Dev)

Charlotte Business Journal **(2)**
1100 S Tryon St Ste 100, Charlotte, NC
28203 **(100%)**
Tel.: (704) 973-1100
Web Site:
   http://www.charlotte.bizjournals.com
Sales Range: $10-24.9 Million
Emp.: 35
Publisher Of Local Business Weekly
N.A.I.C.S.: 513110
Maggie Lynn (Dir-Production)
Jen Wilson (Assoc Editor-Online)
Cat Francis (Dir-Audience Dev)
Rob Tallman (Acct Exec-Multimedia)

Cincinnati Business Courier **(2)**
101 W 7th St, Cincinnati, OH
45202-2411 **(100%)**
Tel.: (513) 621-6665
Web Site:
   http://www.cincinnati.bizjournals.com
Sales Range: $10-24.9 Million
Emp.: 40
Weekly Newspaper Publisher
N.A.I.C.S.: 513110
Kelly Tassos (Assoc Dir-Adv)
Jamie Smith (Publr)
Gigi Verna (Editor-Daily News)
Meg Garner (Editor-Digital)
Tom Demeropolis (Mng Editor)

Dallas Business Journal **(2)**
2515 Mckinney Ave, Dallas, TX
75201 **(100%)**
Tel.: (214) 696-5959
Sales Range: $10-24.9 Million
Emp.: 25
Publisher of Local Business Weekly
N.A.I.C.S.: 513120
Suzy Parker (Mgr-Bus Dev)
Allie Gatlin (Dir-Events)

Dayton Business Journal **(2)**
40 N Main St Ste 810, Dayton, OH 45423
Tel.: (937) 528-4400
Web Site: http://www.bizjournals.com
Sales Range: $10-24.9 Million
Emp.: 18
Newspaper Publishers
N.A.I.C.S.: 513110
Caleb Stephens (Editor)
Don Baker (CEO)

Denver Business Journal **(2)**
1660 Lincoln St Ste 2300, Denver, CO
80264 **(100%)**
Tel.: (303) 837-3500
Web Site: http://www.denver.bizjournals.com
Sales Range: $10-24.9 Million
Emp.: 32
Publisher
N.A.I.C.S.: 513110

Jan Wambolt (Mgr-Circulation)
Pete Casillas (Publr)
Rebecca Troyer (Editor)
Jonathan Rose (Assoc Editor)
Jim Carr (Dir-Creative)

Subsidiary (Domestic):

Houston Business Journal, Inc. **(2)**
1233 W Loop S Ste 1300, Houston, TX
77027-9025 **(100%)**
Tel.: (713) 688-8811
Web Site: http://www.bizjournals.com
Sales Range: $25-49.9 Million
Emp.: 50
Publisher of Local Business Weekly
N.A.I.C.S.: 513110
Sherri Bell (Bus Mgr)
John C. Beddow (Publr)
Madison Henry (Dir-Res)
B. Candace Beeke (Editor-in-Chief)

Unit (Domestic):

Jacksonville Business Journal **(2)**
200 W Forsyth St Ste 1350, Jacksonville,
FL 32202 **(100%)**
Tel.: (904) 396-3502
Web Site: http://www.bizjournals.com
Sales Range: $10-24.9 Million
Emp.: 30
Local Business Newspaper Publisher
N.A.I.C.S.: 513110
Timothy Gibbons (Editor-in-Chief)
Jackie Geary (Mgr-Event)

Kansas City Business Journal **(2)**
1100 Main St Ste 210, Kansas City, MO
64105-5123 **(100%)**
Tel.: (816) 421-5900
Web Site: http://www.bizjournals.com
Sales Range: $10-24.9 Million
Emp.: 27
Local Business Journals Publisher
N.A.I.C.S.: 513120

Orlando Business Journal **(2)**
255 S Orange Ave Ste 650, Orlando, FL
32801-1949 **(100%)**
Tel.: (407) 649-8470
Web Site:
   http://www.orlandobusinessjournals.com
Sales Range: $10-24.9 Million
Emp.: 19
Publisher of Local Business Weekly
N.A.I.C.S.: 541840
Dena Sandy (Acct Exec-Multimedia)

Subsidiary (Domestic):

Pacific Business News Inc. **(2)**
737 Bishop St Ste 1590, Honolulu, HI
96813 **(100%)**
Tel.: (808) 955-8100
Web Site: http://www.pacific.bizjournals.com
Sales Range: $25-49.9 Million
Emp.: 35
Publisher of Local Business Weekly
N.A.I.C.S.: 516210
A. Kam Napier (Editor-in-Chief)

Unit (Domestic):

Phoenix Business Journal **(2)**
101 N 1st Ave Ste 2300, Phoenix, AZ
85003 **(100%)**
Tel.: (602) 230-8400
Web Site:
   http://www.phoenix.bizjournals.com
Sales Range: $10-24.9 Million
Emp.: 50
Publisher of Local Business Weekly
N.A.I.C.S.: 513110
Diane McCarthy (Dir-Bus Partnerships &
Legislative Affairs)
Karen Fullenwider (Editor-Projects)
Jim Poulin (Editor-Photo)
Ray Schey (Publr)

Pittsburgh Business Times **(2)**
45 S 23rd St, Pittsburgh, PA 15203
Tel.: (412) 481-6397
Web Site:
   http://www.pittsburgh.bizjournals.com
Sales Range: $10-24.9 Million
Emp.: 24
Publisher of Newspapers
N.A.I.C.S.: 513110
Mary Ann Fabian (Controller)
Whitney Shaw (Chm)
Evan Rosenberg (Publr)

San Antonio Business Journal (2)
200 E Grayson Ste 110, San Antonio, TX 78215
Tel.: (210) 341-3202
Web Site: http://www.bizjournals.com
Emp.: 50
Newspaper Publishers
N.A.I.C.S.: 513110
Jimmy Holmes (Pres-Market & Publr)
Tony Quesada (Editor-in-Chief)
Liz English (Dir-Adv)
Ed Arnold (Editor-in-Chief)
Tricia Schwennesen (Assoc Editor)
Kim Hernandez (Dir-Res)
Stephanie Schillaci (Acct Mgr)
Victoria Rich (Acct Mgr)
Keith Dennis (Dir-Audience Dev)
Jaime Hernandez (Creative Designer)
Giselle Vazquez (Coord-Event Design)
Summer West (Dir-Events)
Debi Slowik (Sr Acct Mgr)

San Francisco Business Times (2)
275 Battery St Ste 600, San Francisco, CA 94111
Tel.: (415) 989-2522
Web Site: http://www.bizjournals.com
Emp.: 50
Newspaper Publisher Services
N.A.I.C.S.: 513110
Kathy Biddick (Office Mgr)
Mary Huss (Pres & Publr)
Michael S. Fernald (Dir-Adv)
Siggi Reavis (Acct Exec)
Kierstyn Moore (Acct Exec)
Lacey Patterson (Mgr-Bus Dev)
Isela Velasco (Mgr-Events)
Jim Gardner (Mng Editor)
Mitch Green (Mgr-Production)

San Jose Business Journal (2)
125 S Market St Ste 1100, San Jose, CA 95113-2286
Tel.: (408) 295-3800
Web Site:
　http://www.sanjose.bizjournals.com
Sales Range: $10-24.9 Million
Emp.: 40
Newspaper Publishers
N.A.I.C.S.: 513110

South Florida Business Journal (2)
1000 E Hillsboro Blvd Ste 103, Deerfield Beach, FL 33441
Tel.: (954) 949-7501
Web Site:
　http://www.southflorida.bizjournals.com
Sales Range: $10-24.9 Million
Emp.: 40
Publishing And Printing Of Trade Journals
N.A.I.C.S.: 513120
Melanie Dickinson (Pres & Publr)
Brian Bandell (Editor-Real Estate)

Sporting News Radio (2)
2800 28th St Ste 308, Santa Monica, CA 90405
Tel.: (310) 452-7100
Sales Range: $10-24.9 Million
Emp.: 75
Sports Radio Network
N.A.I.C.S.: 516110

Subsidiary (Domestic):

St. Louis Business Journal Corporation (2)
815 Olive St Ste 100, Saint Louis, MO 63101 **(100%)**
Tel.: (314) 421-6200
Web Site: http://www.stlouis.bizjournals.com
Sales Range: $25-49.9 Million
Emp.: 38
Local Business Weekly Publisher
N.A.I.C.S.: 513110
Patricia Miller (CEO)

Street & Smith Sports Group (2)
120 W Morehead St Ste 320, Charlotte, NC 28202-1844 **(100%)**
Tel.: (704) 973-1300
Web Site: http://www.streetandsmiths.com
Sales Range: $25-49.9 Million
Emp.: 100
Publisher of NASCAR Motorsports Publication
N.A.I.C.S.: 513110
Jim Penegar (Pres)

Unit (Domestic):

Tampa Bay Business Journal (2)

4890 W Kennedy Blvd Ste 850, Tampa, FL 33609-1880 **(100%)**
Tel.: (813) 873-8225
Web Site:
　http://www.tampabaybusinessjournal.com
Sales Range: $10-24.9 Million
Emp.: 23
Local Business Weekly Publisher
N.A.I.C.S.: 513110
Alexis Muellner (Editor)
Ian Anderson (Publr)
Ashley Gurbal Kritzer (Editor-Real Estate)

Subsidiary (Domestic):

The Business Journal of Portland, Inc. (2)
851 SW 6th Ave Ste 500, Portland, OR 97204-1342 **(100%)**
Tel.: (503) 274-8733
Web Site: http://www.bizjournals.com
Sales Range: $25-49.9 Million
Emp.: 31
Local Business Weekly Publisher
N.A.I.C.S.: 513120
Craig Wessel (Publr)
Rob Smith (Editor)

Unit (Domestic):

The Business Review (2)
40 British American Blvd, Latham, NY 12210 **(100%)**
Tel.: (518) 640-6800
Web Site: http://www.albany.bizjournals.com
Sales Range: $10-24.9 Million
Emp.: 30
Publisher of Local Business Weekly
N.A.I.C.S.: 513110

The Puget Sound Business Journal (2)
801 2nd Ave Ste 210, Seattle, WA 98104-1528 **(100%)**
Tel.: (206) 583-0701
Web Site: http://www.seattle.bizjournals.com
Sales Range: $10-24.9 Million
Emp.: 40
Publisher of Local Business Weekly
N.A.I.C.S.: 513110
Jim Hammerand (Mng Dir)
Jon Silver (Mng Editor)

The Sporting News (2)
750 3rd Ave Fl 7, New York, NY 10017-2700
Tel.: (212) 500-0650
Web Site: http://www.sportingnews.com
Sales Range: $10-24.9 Million
Emp.: 122
Magazine Publisher
N.A.I.C.S.: 513110
Jeff Price (Pres & Publr)

Subsidiary (Domestic):

Triangle Business Journals of North Carolina, LLC (2)
3600 Glenwood Ave Ste 100, Raleigh, NC 27612-4951 **(100%)**
Tel.: (919) 878-0010
Web Site:
　http://www.trianglebusinessjournals.com
Sales Range: $25-49.9 Million
Emp.: 20
Publisher of Local Business Weekly
N.A.I.C.S.: 513120
Sougata Mukherjee (Editor)
Jason Christie (Publr)

Washington Business Journal, Inc. (2)
1555 Wilson Blvd Ste 400, Arlington, VA 22209-2405 **(100%)**
Tel.: (703) 875-2200
Web Site:
　http://www.washington.bizjournals.com
Sales Range: $25-49.9 Million
Emp.: 49
Publisher of Local Business Weekly
N.A.I.C.S.: 513120
Doug Fruehling (Editor)
James MacGregor (Publr)
Michael Neibauer (Mng Editor)
Drew Hansen (Asst Mng Editor)
Rebecca Cooper (Editor-Digital)

Wichita Business Journal, Inc. (2)
121 N Mead Ste 100, Wichita, KS 67202-3700 **(100%)**

Tel.: (316) 267-6406
Web Site:
　http://www.wichitabusinessjournal.com
Sales Range: $25-49.9 Million
Emp.: 17
Publisher of Local Business Weekly
N.A.I.C.S.: 513110
John Ek (Publr)
Stacie Myers (Acct Exec-Adv)
Brittany Schowalter (Editor-Digital)

Birmingham News (1)
2201 4th Ave N, Birmingham, AL 35203-3802 **(100%)**
Tel.: (205) 325-2222
Web Site: http://www.bhamnews.com
Newspaper Sales
N.A.I.C.S.: 513110

Booth Newspapers, Inc. (1)
St 155 Michigan NW, Grand Rapids, MI 49503
Tel.: (616) 222-5825
Web Site: http://www.boothmichigan.com
Sales Range: $10-24.9 Million
Emp.: 25
Newspaper Publishers
N.A.I.C.S.: 513110

Branch (Domestic):

Booth Newspapers (2)
100 S Michigan Ave Ste 3, Saginaw, MI 48602
Tel.: (989) 752-7171
Web Site: http://www.mlive.com
Publisher & Printer of Newspapers
N.A.I.C.S.: 513110

Booth Newspapers (2)
217 N Sycamore St, Lansing, MI 48933-1033 **(100%)**
Tel.: (517) 487-8888
Provider of News Reporting Services for Newspapers & Periodicals
N.A.I.C.S.: 513110
Chad Griewahn (Engr-Infrastructure)

Conde Nast, Inc. (1)
1 World Trade Ctr, New York, NY 10007 **(100%)**
Tel.: (212) 286-2860
Web Site: http://www.condenast.com
Sales Range: $1-4.9 Billion
Emp.: 3,000
Magazine & Digital Media Publisher; Entertainment Production & Distribution Services
N.A.I.C.S.: 513120
Scott McDonald (Sr VP-Market Res)
Jonathan Newhouse (Chm)
Roger J. Lynch (CEO)
Anna Wintour (Dir-Artistic)
Lisa Valentino (Chief Revenue Officer-Industry & Agency)
John Kulhawik (VP-Consumer Bus Dev)
Edward Menicheschi (Pres-Media Grp)
Wolfgang Blau (Pres)
Brooke Ellis (Exec Dir-Digital Design & UX)
Matthew Starker (Gen Mgr-Digital Strategy & Initiatives)
Jim Norton (Chief Bus Officer & Pres-Revenue)
Michel Ballard (Gen Mgr-Conde Nast Pharma)
Joe Libonati (Chief Comm Officer)
Karthic Bala (Head-Data Strategy)
Jen Mormile (Chief Indus Officer-Conde Nast Pharma)
Jonathan Schaaf (Chief Agency Officer)
Vikki Chowney (Dir-Brand Partnerships-Britain)
Simon Gresham Jones Chowney (Chief Digital Officer-UK)
Roger J. Lynch (CEO)
John Deschner (Dir-CNX Grp)
Whembley Sewell (Exec Editor)
Stan Duncan (Chief People Officer)
Danielle Carrig (Chief Comm Officer-Global)
Yashica Olden (Chief Diversity & Inclusion Officer-Global)
Jackie Marks (CFO)
David B. Chemidlin (Sr VP & Controller)

Unit (Domestic):

Architectural Digest (2)
1 World Trade Ctr, New York, NY 10007
Tel.: (212) 286-2479
Web Site:
　http://www.architecturaldigest.com

Sales Range: $10-24.9 Million
Emp.: 50
Architecture Magazine
N.A.I.C.S.: 513120
Paige Rense (Editor-in-Chief)
Giulio Capua (Publr)
Sam Cochran (Editor-Features)
Amy Astley (Editor-in-Chief)
David Kaufman (Dir-Digital)

Bon Appetit Magazine (2)
6300 Wilshire Blvd, Los Angeles, CA 90048
Tel.: (323) 965-3600
Web Site: http://www.bonappetit.com
Sales Range: $100-124.9 Million
Emp.: 1,500
Food & Entertaining Magazine
N.A.I.C.S.: 513120
Bobby Flay (Editor-in-Chief)
Jill Baughman (Editor-Digital Recipe)
Liesel Davis (Editor-Recipe)
Julia Duquette (Editor-Photo)
Kristin Eddington (Dir-Art)
Alex Grossman (Dir-Creative)
Cristina Martinez (Dir-Production)
Carla Lalli Music (Dir-Food)
Chris Penberthy (Dir-Res)
Alex Pollack (Dir-Photo)

Subsidiary (Domestic):

CitizenNet, Inc. (2)
8548 W Washington Blvd, Culver City, CA 90232-7464
Tel.: (877) 303-5795
Web Site: http://www.citizennet.com
Social Media Advertising Services
N.A.I.C.S.: 541810
Dan Benyamin (Founder & CEO)

Joint Venture (Non-US):

Conde Nast & National Magazine Distributors Limited (2)
Tavistock Road, West Drayton, UB7 7QE, Middlesex, United Kingdom
Tel.: (44) 1895 433600
Web Site: http://www.comag.co.uk
Sales Range: $10-24.9 Million
Emp.: 170
Magazine Publisher
N.A.I.C.S.: 424920
Charlotee Macleod (Mng Dir)

Subsidiary (Domestic):

COMAG Forward (3)
Forward House Toledo Close Coventry Business Park, Coventry, CV5 6UN, United Kingdom
Tel.: (44) 2476 854 750
Web Site: http://www.comagforward.co.uk
Magazine Publisher
N.A.I.C.S.: 424920
Rob Everett (Head-Client Svcs)
Dominic Byrne (Mng Dir)
Shaun Callaghan (Dir-Ops)

COMAG Specialist (3)
Tavistock Works Tavistock Road, West Drayton, UB7 7QX, Middlesex, United Kingdom
Tel.: (44) 1895 433800
Web Site: http://www.comagspecialist.co.uk
Magazine Publisher
N.A.I.C.S.: 424920
Pete Lewis (Gen Mgr)
Neil Selby (Acct Mgr)
Jenna Spearing (Acct Mgr)
Santosh Jairajh (Acct Mgr)
Pippa Boothroyd (Acct Mgr)
Mark Foker (Acct Mgr)

Gold Key Media (3)
3rd Floor Josaron House 5-7 John Princes Street Oxford Circus, Mayfair, London, W1G 0JN, United Kingdom
Tel.: (44) 20 7491 4065
Web Site: http://www.gkml.co.uk
Magazine Publishing Services
N.A.I.C.S.: 513120
Chris Horn (Mng Dir)
Duncan MacGillivray (Deputy Mng Dir)
Oliver Morgan (Dir-Bus Dev)
Ruth Atkinson (Publr & Acct Mgr)
Duncan McIntosh (Head-Publr Svcs)
Sally Ingram (Dir-Sls-Venue)
Natalie Gibson (Mgr-Bus Dev)
Clare Scott (Head-New Bus)

Advance Publications, Inc.—(Continued)

Katie Stevens *(Publr & Acct Mgr)*
Alex Nicholls *(Publr & Acct Mgr)*
Charlotte Turton *(Publr & Acct Mgr)*

Division (Domestic):

Conde Nast Entertainment (2)
4 Times Sq, New York, NY 10036
Tel.: (212) 286-2860
Web Site: http://www.condenast.com
Television Program, Motion Picture & Digital
Video Production & Distribution
N.A.I.C.S.: 512110
Joanna D. Massey *(Head-Comm)*
Jeremy Steckler *(Exec VP-Motion Pictures)*
Joe LaBracio *(Exec VP-Alternative Pro-
gramming)*
Lisa Valentino *(Sr VP-Digital Sls)*
Joy Marcus *(Exec VP & Gen Mgr-Digital
Video)*
Tatiana Gonzalez Rama *(Head-Video Data
& Growth)*
Jonathan Koa *(Sr VP-Scripted Program-
ming)*
Nathan Guetta *(VP-Product & Tech)*
Lauren Lumsden *(Dir-Digital-The Scene)*
Edward Menicheschi *(CMO)*
Charles H. Townsend *(Chm)*
Anna Wintour *(Dir-Artistic)*
Geneva Wasserman *(Sr VP-Motion Pic-
tures)*
Roger Lynch *(CEO)*
Agnes Chu *(Pres)*
Jessica Rach *(Mgr-Global Content)*
Dawn Tarnofsky Ostroff *(Co-Founder)*

Subsidiary (Non-US):

Conde Nast Johansens Ltd. (2)
13 Hanover Square, London, W1S 1HN,
United Kingdom
Tel.: (44) 2074999080
Web Site: http://www.johansens.com
Sales Range: $25-49.9 Million
Emp.: 20
Publisher of Accomodation, Business Meet-
ing & Travel Information Guides in Print &
Electronic Formats
N.A.I.C.S.: 513120
Laura Kerry *(Editor-Production)*

Unit (Domestic):

Conde Nast Traveler (2)
1 World Trade Ctr, New York, NY 10007
Tel.: (212) 286-2860
Web Site: http://www.cntraveler.com
Sales Range: $10-24.9 Million
Emp.: 80
Trade Magazine Publisher
N.A.I.C.S.: 513120
John Hillock *(Exec Dir)*
Wendy Perrin *(Dir-Consumer News & Digi-
tal Community)*
Mark Connolly *(Dir-Style)*
Susan Harrington *(Assoc Publr-Mktg)*
Pilar Guzman *(Editor-in-Chief)*
Hanya Yanagihara *(Exec Editor)*
Jennifer Hicks *(Assoc Publr)*
Giulio Capua *(Publr)*

Branch (Domestic):

Conde Nast, Inc. - Detroit (2)
2600 W Big Beaver Rd Ste 440, Troy, MI
48084-3319
Tel.: (248) 458-3100
Web Site: http://www.condenast.com
Magazine Distr
N.A.I.C.S.: 424920

Conde Nast, Inc. - Los Angeles (2)
6300 Wilshire Blvd, Los Angeles, CA 90048-
5204
Tel.: (323) 965-3400
Web Site: http://www.condenast.com
Emp.: 210
Publisher of Magazines
N.A.I.C.S.: 513120
Carri Oosterbaan *(Dir-Editorial Production)*

**Conde Nast, Inc. - San
Francisco** (2)
50 Francisco St Ste 115, San Francisco,
CA 94133-2108
Tel.: (415) 955-8200
Web Site: http://www.condenast.com
Magazine Publisher

N.A.I.C.S.: 513120

Unit (Domestic):

Details Magazine (2)
4 Times Sq, New York, NY 10036
Tel.: (212) 630-4000
Web Site: http://www.condenast.com
Sales Range: $10-24.9 Million
Emp.: 120
Magazine Publisher
N.A.I.C.S.: 513120
Daniel Peres *(Editor-in-Chief)*

Glamour (2)
1 world trade centre, New York, NY 10007
Tel.: (212) 286-2860
Web Site: http://www.glamour.com
Emp.: 145
Women's Magazine Publisher
N.A.I.C.S.: 513120
David Posegay *(Dir-Midwest)*
Grace Wasyluk *(Assoc Publr)*
Florence Kane *(Dir-Digital Fashion)*
Jaime Marsanico *(Mgr-PR)*
Samantha Rosenthal *(Exec Dir-PR)*
Jen Weinberg *(Assoc Dir-PR)*
Alessandra Steinherr *(Assoc Dir-Creative &
Beauty)*
Deborah Joseph *(Chief Content Officer)*

Golf Digest Publications (2)
20 W Port RD PO Box 850, Wilton, CT
06897-0850
Tel.: (203) 761-5100
Web Site: http://www.golfdigest.com
Sales Range: $25-49.9 Million
Emp.: 175
Golf Magazine Publisher
N.A.I.C.S.: 513120

Division (Domestic):

Golf World Business (3)
PO Box 850, Wilton, CT 06897-0850
Tel.: (203) 761-5100
Sales Range: $25-49.9 Million
Emp.: 175
Golf Equipment Retailer Trade Magazine
N.A.I.C.S.: 513120

Unit (Domestic):

Self Magazine (2)
4 Times Sq 5th Fl, New York, NY 10036-
6518
Tel.: (212) 286-2860
Web Site: http://www.self.com
Sales Range: $10-24.9 Million
Emp.: 100
Beauty & Health Magazine
N.A.I.C.S.: 513120
Lauren Theodore *(Dir-PR)*
Zahra Barnes *(Editor-Lifestyle)*
Claire Hannum *(Editor-Lifestyle)*
Liz Plosser *(Dir-Fitness)*

Subsidiary (Domestic):

The New Yorker Magazine, Inc. (2)
1 World Trade Ctr, New York, NY 10007
Tel.: (212) 286-5400
Web Site: http://www.newyorker.com
Sales Range: $75-99.9 Million
Emp.: 225
Magazine Publisher
N.A.I.C.S.: 513120
David Remnick *(Editor-in-Chief)*
Lisa Hughes *(Publr & VP)*
Leily Kleinbard *(Mng Editor)*

Unit (Domestic):

The New Yorker Magazine (3)
6300 Wilshire Blvd 12th Fl, Los Angeles,
CA 90048
Tel.: (323) 965-3466
Web Site: http://www.newyorker.com
Sales Range: $25-49.9 Million
Emp.: 10
Magazine Publisher
N.A.I.C.S.: 513120

Unit (Domestic):

Vanity Fair (2)
4 Times Sq Fl 22, New York, NY 10036
Tel.: (212) 286-2860
Web Site: http://www.vanityfair.com

Sales Range: $10-24.9 Million
Emp.: 40
Magazine
N.A.I.C.S.: 513120
Sara Marks *(Dir-Special Projects)*
Sunhee C. Grinnell *(Dir-Beauty)*
Chris Mitchell *(Chief Bus Officer)*
Stephanie Mehta *(Deputy Editor)*
Jim Craemer *(Exec Acct Dir)*
Alana Segars *(Dir-Brand Mktg & Strategy)*
Radhika Jones *(Editor-in-Chief)*
Miriam Elder *(Exec Editor-The Hive)*

Vogue Magazine (2)
4 Times Sq Fl 12, New York, NY 10036-
6518
Tel.: (212) 286-2860
Web Site: http://www.vogue.com
Sales Range: $10-24.9 Million
Emp.: 120
Publisher of Women's Magazine
N.A.I.C.S.: 513120
Anna Wintour *(Editor-in-Chief)*
Susan Plagemann *(VP & Publr)*
Megan Salt *(Dir-Pub Rel)*
Carlos Nazario *(Editor-Contributing)*

WIRED (2)
520 3rd St Ste 305, San Francisco, CA
94107-1815
Tel.: (515) 243-3273
Web Site: http://www.wired.com
Sales Range: $10-24.9 Million
Trade Magazine Publisher
N.A.I.C.S.: 513120
Gaia Filicori *(Dir-Comm)*
Jahna Berry *(Head-Content Ops)*
Maria Streshinsky *(Exec Editor)*
Vera Titunik *(Editor-Features-New York)*
Ivylise Simones *(Dir-Design-Platforms)*
Scott Rosenfield *(Dir-Site-New York)*
Meghann Farnsworth *(Dir-Social Media)*
Anthony Lydgate *(Sr Editor)*
Caitlin Kelly *(Sr Editor-New York)*

Easton Publishing Co. (1)
6 Market St, Belvidere, NJ 07823
Tel.: (908) 475-8184
Web Site: http://www.express-times.com
Sales Range: $10-24.9 Million
Emp.: 4
Newspaper Publication
N.A.I.C.S.: 513110

Branch (Domestic):

Easton Publishing Co. (2)
30 N 4th St, Easton, PA 18042-3528
Tel.: (610) 258-7171
Web Site: http://www.lehighvalleylive.com
Newspapers
N.A.I.C.S.: 513110
Martin Till *(Pres & Publr)*

Express Times (1)
35 Elizabeth Ave, Bethlehem, PA 18018-
5837
Tel.: (610) 867-5000
Web Site: http://www.express-times.com
Sales Range: $10-24.9 Million
Emp.: 30
Newspapers
N.A.I.C.S.: 513110

Hillsboro Argus (1)
150 SE 3rd Ave, Hillsboro, OR
97123-4019 (100%)
Tel.: (503) 648-1131
Web Site: http://www.hillsboroargus.com
Sales Range: $10-24.9 Million
Emp.: 45
Provider of Newspaper Publishing Services
N.A.I.C.S.: 323111
Voni Martinez *(Acct Mgr)*

Huntsville Times (1)
2317 Memorial Pkwy SW, Huntsville, AL
35801-5623
Tel.: (256) 532-4000
Web Site: http://www.htimes.com
Sales Range: $25-49.9 Million
Emp.: 200
Newspaper Publishers
N.A.I.C.S.: 513110

Jersey Journal Newspaper (1)
30 Journal Sq, Jersey City, NJ 07306-4101
Tel.: (201) 653-1000
Web Site: http://www.thejerseyjournal.com
Sales Range: $25-49.9 Million
Emp.: 150
Job Printing & Newspaper Publishing

N.A.I.C.S.: 513110
Margaret Schmidt *(Editor)*
Ron Zeitlinger *(Mng Editor)*

**Newark Morning Ledger
Company** (1)
1 Star Ledger Plz, Newark, NJ 07102-1200
Tel.: (973) 877-4141
Web Site: http://www.nj.com
Sales Range: $100-124.9 Million
Emp.: 1,000
Newspapers Publishing & Printing
N.A.I.C.S.: 513110
Donald Newhouse *(Pres)*

Newhouse News Service (1)
618 A St Se Apt 27, Washington, DC
20003-1228 (100%)
Tel.: (202) 383-7800
Web Site: http://www.newhousenews.com
Sales Range: $10-24.9 Million
Emp.: 40
Provider of News Reporting Services for
Newspapers & Periodicals
N.A.I.C.S.: 513110

Oregonian Publishing Co. (1)
1320 SW Broadway, Portland, OR 97201-
3411
Tel.: (503) 221-8327
Web Site: http://www.oregonlive.com
Sales Range: $25-49.9 Million
Emp.: 900
Newspaper Publishers
N.A.I.C.S.: 513110
Therese Bottomly *(Mng Editor-Readership
& Standards)*
JoLene Krawczak *(Mng Editor-Features)*
Denice Williams *(Mgr-Adv)*
Brad Harmon *(Dir-Sls & Mktg)*
Kevin Fuller *(Owner & Mgr)*
Ryan Courtney *(Dir-Classified Adv)*

Affiliate (Domestic):

Oregonian V 5 (2)
5601 E 18th St, Vancouver, WA 98661-
6885
Tel.: (360) 896-5701
Sales Range: $50-74.9 Million
Emp.: 2
Newspaper Distr For Local Area
N.A.I.C.S.: 513110

Parade Publications Inc. (1)
711 3rd Ave, New York, NY 10017-4014
Tel.: (212) 450-7000
Web Site: http://www.parade.com
Sales Range: $25-49.9 Million
Emp.: 180
Magazine Publisher
N.A.I.C.S.: 513120
Heather Faust *(VP)*
David Barber *(Exec VP-Newspaper Rels)*
Melinda Carson *(Acct Mgr)*
Jack Haire *(CEO)*
Wayne Powers *(Pres & Grp Publr)*

Division (Domestic):

Parade Magazine (2)
711 3rd Ave, New York, NY 10017 (100%)
Tel.: (212) 450-7000
Web Site: http://www.parade.com
Sales Range: $25-49.9 Million
Emp.: 5
Magazine
N.A.I.C.S.: 513120

Patriot-News Co (1)
2020 Technology Pkwy Ste 300, Mechan-
icsburg, PA 17050
Tel.: (717) 255-8100
Web Site: http://www.patriot-news.com
Sales Range: $10-24.9 Million
Emp.: 12
Newspaper Publishing Services
N.A.I.C.S.: 513110
Janet Krajcsik *(Editor-Calendar)*
Shelly Stallsmith *(Mgr-Online Content)*

Branch (Domestic):

Patriot-News Co. Inc. (2)
2020 Technology Pkwy Ste 300, Mechan-
icsburg, PA 17050-9412
Tel.: (717) 255-8100
Web Site: http://www.patriot-news.com
Newspapers Publishing & Printing
N.A.I.C.S.: 513110

Plain Dealer Publishing Co. (1)
1801 Superior Ave Plain Dealer Plz, Cleveland, OH 44114
Tel.: (216) 999-4800
Web Site: http://www.plaindealer.com
Sales Range: $100-124.9 Million
Emp.: 1,800
Newspaper Publishing
N.A.I.C.S.: 513110
Joseph J. Bowman (VP-Ops)
William V. Mickey (VP-Info Sys)
Bryan Schneider (Dir-Circulation Distr & Transportation)
George Rodrigue (Pres)
Howard Patterson (Controller)

Branch (Domestic):

Plain Dealer Publishing Co. (2)
1801 Superior Ave, Cleveland, OH 44114
Tel.: (216) 999-4005
Web Site: http://www.cleveland.com
Newspapers
N.A.I.C.S.: 513110

Plain Dealer Publishing Co. (2)
Fl 23A 155 E Broad St, Columbus, OH 43215-3609 (100%)
Tel.: (614) 228-8200
Web Site: http://www.cleveland.com
Sales Range: $25-49.9 Million
Emp.: 3
Newspaper Publishing
N.A.I.C.S.: 513110
Mark Rollenhagen (Gen Mgr)

Reddit Inc. (1)
303 2nd St Ste 500, San Francisco, CA 94107
Tel.: (707) 733-3484
Web Site: http://www.reddit.com
Sales Range: $10-24.9 Million
Emp.: 20
Social Media Website Operator
N.A.I.C.S.: 516210
Steve Huffman (Co-Founder & CEO)

Republican Company Inc. (1)
210 High St, Holyoke, MA 01040-6517
Tel.: (413) 534-3700
Web Site: http://www.masslive.com
Sales Range: $25-49.9 Million
Emp.: 700
Newspapers
N.A.I.C.S.: 513110
David Evans (Controller)

Branch (Domestic):

Republican Company Inc. (2)
1860 Main St, Springfield, MA 01103-1000
Tel.: (413) 788-1000
Web Site: http://www.masslive.com
Sales Range: $75-99.9 Million
Emp.: 350
Publisher & Printer of Newspapers
N.A.I.C.S.: 513110
David Starr (Pres)
David B. Evans (Treas)
Norman Newhouse (VP)
George Arwady (Publr)

Republican Company Inc. (2)
210 Exchange St, Chicopee, MA 01013-1241
Tel.: (413) 592-2377
Web Site: http://www.masslive.com
Sales Range: $25-49.9 Million
Emp.: 4
Newspapers
N.A.I.C.S.: 516210

Staten Island Advance (1)
950 W Fingerboard Rd, Staten Island, NY 10305
Tel.: (718) 981-1234
Web Site: http://www.statenislandmediagroup.com
Digitally-focused News, Information & Advertising Company
N.A.I.C.S.: 513110
Brian J. Laline (Exec Editor)
Steve Alessi (Reg Pres)

The Star-Ledger (1)
1 Star Ledger Plz, Newark, NJ 07102-1200
Tel.: (973) 392-4141
Web Site: http://www.starledger.com
Sales Range: $100-124.9 Million
Emp.: 2,000
Publisher of Newspapers

N.A.I.C.S.: 513110
John Dennan (Gen Mgr)

The Times of Trenton (1)
413 River View Plz, Trenton, NJ 08611
Tel.: (609) 989-5739
Web Site: http://www.nj.com
Newspaper Publishers
N.A.I.C.S.: 513115
Kevin Shea (Editor-Community)

The Times-Picayune Publishing Corp. (1)
3800 Howard Ave, New Orleans, LA 70125-1429
Tel.: (504) 822-6660
Web Site: http://www.timespicayune.com
Sales Range: $25-49.9 Million
Emp.: 900
Newspaper Publishers
N.A.I.C.S.: 513110
Jim Amoss (Editor)

Turnitin, LLC (1)
2101 Webster St Ste 1800, Oakland, CA 94612
Tel.: (510) 764-7600
Web Site: http://www.turnitin.com
Education Technology Services
N.A.I.C.S.: 611710
Chris Caren (CEO)

Subsidiary (Domestic):

ExamSoft Worldwide, Inc. (2)
6400 Congress Ave Ste 1050, Boca Raton, FL 33487
Tel.: (954) 429-8889
Web Site: http://examsoft.com
Sales Range: $25-49.9 Million
Educational Software
N.A.I.C.S.: 513210
Mark Haney (CTO)
Ken Knotts (VP-Mktg)
Jason Gad (VP-Bus Dev)
Mike Patterson (Controller)
Sherrod Seeharack (Sr Acct Mgr)
Sebastian Vos (CEO)

Lightside Labs, LLC (2)
160 N Craig St, Pittsburgh, PA 15213
Tel.: (724) 272-7250
Web Site: http://www.lightsidelabs.com
Software Publisher
N.A.I.C.S.: 513210
Rajiv Enand (Co-Founder)
Mayfield Elijahl (Founder & CEO)
David Adamson (Co-Founder & VP)

ADVANCE REALTY GROUP, LLC
1041 US Hwy 202-206, Bridgewater, NJ 08807
Tel.: (908) 719-3000
Web Site:
 http://www.advancerealtygroup.com
Year Founded: 1979
Sales Range: $10-24.9 Million
Emp.: 100
Commercial Real Estate Services
N.A.I.C.S.: 531210
Peter J. Cocoziello (Pres & CEO)
Nadine Golis (Sr Mgr-Mktg)
Michael Sommer (Mng Dir-Dev)
Barry Quiner (Dir-Asset Mgmt)
Rick Zack (Mng Dir-Property Mgmt)
Jennifer Mercer (Dir-Corp & Property Acctg)
Dave C. Surti (Dir-Fin & Acq)
Christopher M. Bellapianta (Mng Dir & Principal)

ADVANCE SALES & MARKETING INC.
1801 Royal Ln Ste 1012, Dallas, TX 75229
Tel.: (972) 620-7212
Web Site:
 http://www.advancesales.com
Sales Range: $25-49.9 Million
Emp.: 40
Bond Brokers
N.A.I.C.S.: 424410

Sharon Foster (CFO)
Brian Lehr (Acct Exec)
Jess Culwell (Pres)

ADVANCE STEEL CO.
Ste 325 16250 Northland Dr, Southfield, MI 48075-5219
Tel.: (313) 571-6700 MI
Year Founded: 1955
Sales Range: $10-24.9 Million
Emp.: 30
Distr of Flat Rolled Steel Products
N.A.I.C.S.: 423510
Robert A. Stewart (CEO)
Patrick Porte (Mgr-Credit)

ADVANCE TANK & CONSTRUCTION CO. INC.
3700 E County Rd 64, Wellington, CO 80549-1533
Tel.: (970) 568-3444 WY
Web Site:
 http://www.advancetank.com
Year Founded: 1982
Sales Range: $25-49.9 Million
Emp.: 220
Mfr Erect Welded Steel Tanks & Plate Steel Products
N.A.I.C.S.: 238120
Mark Wrobel (Mgr-Acct)
John Burke (Mgr-Construction)
Rodney Dotson (Mgr-Construction)
Dan Callison (Mgr-Drafting)
Jim Noren (Mgr-Engrg)
Lanny Fievet (Mgr-Hydro Construction Div)
Ted Webber (Mgr-Maintenance & Repair Div)
John Clark (Mgr-Ops & Mfg Div)
Rob Burke (Mgr-Safety)
Scott Roark (Mgr-Acct)
Jim Clay (Pres)
Geoff Van Alsburg (Sr Project Mgr)

ADVANCE TRADING INC.
1619 Commerce Pkwy, Bloomington, IL 61704
Tel.: (309) 663-9021
Web Site: http://www.advance-trading.com
Year Founded: 1982
Sales Range: $25-49.9 Million
Emp.: 75
Commodity Contracts Brokers, Dealers
N.A.I.C.S.: 523160
Mike Bohl (Controller)

ADVANCE TURNING & MANUFACTURING, INC.
4901 James McDivitt St, Jackson, MI 49201-8958
Tel.: (517) 783-2713
Web Site:
 https://www.advanceturning.com
Year Founded: 1968
Industrial Machinery Mfr
N.A.I.C.S.: 332710
John Rappleye (Pres)
Joe Sorenson (VP)
John Macchia Jr. (CEO)

ADVANCE YOUR REACH LLC
PO Box 64112, Colorado Springs, CO 80962
Tel.: (719) 203-5712
Web Site:
 http://www.advanceyourreach.com
Year Founded: 2006
Sales Range: $1-9.9 Million
Consumer Product Services
N.A.I.C.S.: 532289
Jess Andrews (Dir-Ops)
Daniel Moskowitz (Dir-Sls & Strategy)

Josh Langston (Fin Dir)
Erin Wahl (Mgr-HR)
Leif Olson (Project Mgr)

ADVANCED
3745 Cherokee St NW Ste 704, Kennesaw, GA 30144
Tel.: (770) 429-0040 GA
Web Site: http://www.advanc-ed.org
Year Founded: 2006
Sales Range: $25-49.9 Million
Emp.: 194
Educational Support Services
N.A.I.C.S.: 611710
Kenneth I. Bergman (Chief Legal Officer)
Ludy van Broekhuizen (Chief Innovation Officer)
Annette Bohling (COO)
Mark Elgart (Pres & CEO)
Albert Mayo (CIO)
Claudia Carter (VP-Specialized Svcs)
Sherif El Taweel (VP)
Al Grade (Principal-Pacific Area)
Kem Hussain (VP)

ADVANCED AMERICAN CONSTRUCTION, INC.
8444 NW St Helens Rd, Portland, OR 97231
Tel.: (503) 445-9000
Web Site: https://www.advanced-american.com
Sales Range: $25-49.9 Million
Emp.: 200
Marine Construction
N.A.I.C.S.: 236210
Mike Johns (VP)
Tim Nelson (Project Mgr)

ADVANCED APPLICATIONS INSTITUTE, INC.
305 Patton Dr, Atlanta, GA 30336
Tel.: (404) 699-2121
Web Site:
 https://www.nationaldiagnostics.com
Year Founded: 1975
Sales Range: $10-24.9 Million
Emp.: 35
Mfr & Development of Chemicals & Related Products for Scientific Research
N.A.I.C.S.: 325199
L. Mirsky (Pres)

ADVANCED ARCHITECTURAL PRODUCTS, LLC
959 Industrial Dr, Allegan, MI 49010
Tel.: (269) 355-1818
Web Site:
 http://www.smartcisystems.com
Year Founded: 2014
Sales Range: $10-24.9 Million
Emp.: 51
Commercial Building Construction Services
N.A.I.C.S.: 236220
Matt Krause (Founder & CEO)

ADVANCED ASPHALT COMPANY
308 W Railroad Ave, Princeton, IL 61356
Tel.: (815) 872-9911
Web Site: http://www.advasphalt.biz
Sales Range: $10-24.9 Million
Emp.: 100
Highway & Street Construction
N.A.I.C.S.: 237310
Steve Kelly (Controller)
Steve Harmon (Gen Mgr)

ADVANCED AUTOMATION GROUP, LLC

Advanced Automation Group, LLC—(Continued)

1685 W Hamlin Rd, Rochester Hills,
MI 48309
Tel.: (248) 299-8100
Web Site:
http://www.advancedautomate.com
Year Founded: 2007
Sales Range: $25-49.9 Million
Emp.: 6
Industrial Automation Controllers Mfr
N.A.I.C.S.: 335314
Shaotang Chen (Gen Mgr)

ADVANCED AV, LLC
208 Carter Dr Ste 7, West Chester,
PA 19382
Tel.: (610) 692-7348
Web Site:
http://www.advancedav.com
Sales Range: $1-9.9 Million
Emp.: 80
Computer Related Services
N.A.I.C.S.: 541519
John P. Greene (VP-Sls & Mktg)
Eric Bixler (Acct Exec)
Travis A. Lisk (VP-Technical Ops)
Michael Boettcher (CEO)
Joe Ewart (Chm)

Subsidiaries:

Promedia Technology Services
Inc.   (1)
535 Route 46 E, Little Falls, NJ 07424
Tel.: (973) 253-7600
Web Site: http://www.promedianj.com
Sales Range: $1-9.9 Million
Emp.: 55
Computer System Design Services
N.A.I.C.S.: 541512
Gene Murphy (Pres)
William Paul Nolan (COO)

ADVANCED BATTERY TECH-
NOLOGIES, INC.
15 W 39th St Ste 14A, New York, NY
10018-0618
Tel.: (212) 391-2752   **DE**
Year Founded: 1984
Sales Range: $75-99.9 Million
Emp.: 850
Holding Company; Polymer Lithium
Ion Battery Designer, Marketer & Mfr
N.A.I.C.S.: 551112
Zhiguo Fu (Chm & CEO)

Subsidiaries:

Harbin ZhongQiang Power-Tech Co.,
Ltd.   (1)
1 Weiyou Road Economy & Technology De-
velopment Zone, Shuangcheng, 150100,
Heilongjiang, China   (100%)
Tel.: (86) 45153118471
Web Site: http://www.zqpt.com
Polymer Lithium Ion Battery Mfr
N.A.I.C.S.: 335910

ADVANCED BEAUTY, INC.
5501 LBJ Fwy Ste 900, Dallas, TX
75240
Tel.: (972) 934-9888   **TX**
Web Site: http://www.bodycology.com
Sales Range: $10-24.9 Million
Emp.: 2
Marketer & Distr of Skin, Hair & Bath
Products
N.A.I.C.S.: 456199
Chris McClain (Owner)

ADVANCED BRAIN MONITOR-
ING, INC.
2237 Faraday Ave Ste 100, Carlsbad,
CA 92008
Tel.: (760) 720-0099   **CA**
Web Site:
https://www.advancemonitoring.com
Year Founded: 1997
Sales Range: $1-9.9 Million

Emp.: 40
Developer & Mfr of Products for
Sleep Apnea Diagnosis, Memory
Dysfunction Measurement & Alert-
ness Monitoring
N.A.I.C.S.: 541715
Chris Berka (Co-Founder & CEO)
Dan Levendowski (Co-Founder &
Pres)
Philip Westbrook (Chief Medical Offi-
cer)
Sandy Crow (VP-Govt Contracts)

ADVANCED BUSINESS METH-
ODS INC.
1515 13th Ave E, West Fargo, ND
58078
Tel.: (701) 282-3151
Web Site: http://abmnow.com
Sales Range: $10-24.9 Million
Emp.: 34
Office Supplies & Stationery Stores
N.A.I.C.S.: 459410
Kenneth Retzer (Pres)

Subsidiaries:

Central Business Systems Inc.   (1)
2514 Highway 281 South, Jamestown, ND
58401
Tel.: (701) 252-7474
Web Site: http://www.cbsi-online.com
Rev.: $4,000,000
Emp.: 12
Office Equipment Merchant Whslr
N.A.I.C.S.: 423420
Lloyd Kuhlmann (Pres)

ADVANCED CABLE CONNEC-
TION, INC.
13654 N 12th St Ste 1, Tampa, FL
33613
Tel.: (813) 978-0101   **FL**
Web Site: http://www.accicable.com
Year Founded: 1987
Sales Range: $1-9.9 Million
Emp.: 24
Low Voltage Wiring Contractor
N.A.I.C.S.: 238210
Richard Schemitsch (Pres)

ADVANCED CALL CENTER
TECHNOLOGIES, LLC
1235 Westlakes Dr Ste 160, Berwyn,
PA 19312
Tel.: (610) 695-0500
Web Site: https://www.acttoday.com
Year Founded: 1996
Sales Range: $75-99.9 Million
Emp.: 2,300
Wired Telecommunication Services
N.A.I.C.S.: 517111
Joseph Lembo (Pres)
Tammy McEwen (Office Mgr)

ADVANCED CARE PARTNERS,
LLC
3525 Piedmont Rd NE Bldg 5 Ste
415, Atlanta, GA 30305
Tel.: (404) 835-3512
Web Site:
http://www.advancedpartners.com
Year Founded: 2010
Sales Range: $10-24.9 Million
Health Care Srvices
N.A.I.C.S.: 621610
Greice Murphy (Founder & CEO)
Rob Monn (Dir-Client Svcs)
Karen Woronick (Dir-Nursing)
Anthony Moore (Dir-IT)
Nick Hijonosa (Dir-Ops)

ADVANCED CHEMICAL COM-
PANY
105 Bellows St, Warwick, RI 02888
Tel.: (401) 785-3434
Web Site: http://www.advchem.com
Year Founded: 1972

Sales Range: $25-49.9 Million
Emp.: 40
Plating Compounds
N.A.I.C.S.: 325998
David Farnum (Pres & COO)
Michael Fioskis (CFO)
Jonathan Crowell (VP-New Bus Dev)
Daniel Seminaro (Sr Mgr-Bus Dev)
Gerald A. Smith III (CEO)

ADVANCED CHEMICAL CON-
CEPTS, INC.
7050 Engle Rd Ste 103, Middleburg
Heights, OH 44130
Tel.: (216) 221-3952
Web Site:
http://www.advancedchemicals.com
Year Founded: 2006
Sales Range: $1-9.9 Million
Emp.: 8
Mfr & Distributes Specialty Chemical
Products for the Home, Industrial &
Institutional Companies
N.A.I.C.S.: 325998
Craig Tungate (Pres)
Peter Zaccari (VP)
Elise Kachinski (Mgr-Procurement)

ADVANCED CHEMICAL
TRANSPORT, INC.
1210 Elko Dr, Sunnyvale, CA 94089
Tel.: (408) 548-5050   **CA**
Web Site:
http://www.advancedchemical.net
Year Founded: 2000
Sales Range: $10-24.9 Million
Emp.: 82
Waste Management Services
N.A.I.C.S.: 562998
Walter Singer (Pres)
Vince Cavaliere (Dir-Sls-Southern
California)
Douglas Downey (Branch Mgr)
Adam Brandin (Dir-Sls-Northern Cali-
fornia)
Larry Moore (Branch Mgr)
Brian Trefault (Mgr-Merced)
Krista Wood Harsono (Dir-
Compliance)
Pasquale M. Paduano (VP-Ops)
Harold DeGuzman (CFO)
Russ Cowperthwaite (Mgr-
Transportation)
Chris Dean (Mgr-Contract)
John Smrdeli (Gen Mgr-Sunnyvale)
Tobi Moore (Gen Mgr-Denver)
Daniel Busbee (Gen Mgr)

ADVANCED CLEANUP TECH-
NOLOGIES
18414 S Santa Fe Ave, Rancho
Dominguez, CA 90221
Tel.: (310) 763-1423
Web Site: http://www.actird.com
Rev.: $10,600,000
Emp.: 55
Hazardous Waste Transport
N.A.I.C.S.: 562112
Ruben Garcia (Pres)

ADVANCED COMMUNICA-
TIONS SERVICE INC.
4635 W Lawrence Ave, Chicago, IL
60630
Tel.: (773) 427-6633
Web Site: http://www.advanced-
comm.com
Sales Range: $10-24.9 Million
Emp.: 20
Telephone & Communication Equip-
ment
N.A.I.C.S.: 449210
Woong Y. Uhm (Pres)

ADVANCED COMPUTER CON-
CEPTS

7927 Jones Branch Dr 600 N,
McLean, VA 22102
Tel.: (703) 276-7800   **NJ**
Web Site: http://www.acconline.com
Year Founded: 1983
Sales Range: $75-99.9 Million
Emp.: 48
Computer Distr
N.A.I.C.S.: 423430
Reza Zarafshar (Pres)
Mary Zarafshar (CEO)

ADVANCED CONCEPTS &
TECHNOLOGIES INTERNA-
TIONAL, LLC
1105 Wooded Acres Ste 500, Waco,
TX 76710
Tel.: (254) 776-9511
Web Site: http://www.act-i.com
Year Founded: 1998
Sales Range: $10-24.9 Million
Emp.: 50
Computer System Design Services
N.A.I.C.S.: 541512
Michael A. Niggel (CEO)
Jeffrey R. Earley (Exec VP-Military
Sys)
Miklos Kiss (Dir-Intl Programs)
Corey Gomez (Sr Project Mgr-
Contract)
Claudio Monticelli (COO)
Bill Ward (VP-Fin & Acctg)
Neil Albert (Pres)
Mark Hughes (CFO)
Shawn Boykin (VP & Mgr-Ops)
Christopher Devens (Exec VP-Bus
Dev)
Michael Zembrzuski (Chief Growth
Officer)
Nedim Kirimca (Exec VP-Ops)

Subsidiaries:

Advanced Concepts & Technologies
International, LLC - Arlington   (1)
200 12th St S Ste 1101, Arlington, VA
22202
Tel.: (703) 418-0636
Technical & Professional Services
N.A.I.C.S.: 541990
Chris Devens (Dir-Bus Dev)

ADVANCED COOLING TECH-
NOLOGIES, INC.
1046 New Holland Ave, Lancaster,
PA 17601-5606
Tel.: (717) 295-6061
Web Site: http://www.1-act.com
Research & Development in the
Physical, Engineering & Life Sciences
N.A.I.C.S.: 541715
Jon Zuo (Pres)

Subsidiaries:

Tekgard, Inc.   (1)
3390 Farmtrail Rd, York, PA 17406-5614
Tel.: (717) 854-0005
Web Site: http://www.tekgard.com
Air-Conditioning, Warm Air Heating Equip-
ment & Commercial & Industrial Refrigera-
tion Equipment Mfr
N.A.I.C.S.: 333415
Mika Bahn (VP)
Matt Keller (Gen Mgr)
Mike Grothey (Dir-Ops)
Matt Meyer (Mgr-Engrg)

ADVANCED CORE CON-
CEPTS, LLC
3715 Northside Pkwy NW, Atlanta,
GA 30327
Tel.: (478) 923-9995
Web Site:
http://www.advancedconcepts.com

Engineering & Technical Support Services
N.A.I.C.S.: 541330
Trase Travers (CEO)
Linda Damm (CFO)
Jim Hudson (Pres-ACTA - ACC Space Sys)
Ed Rios (Pres-ACC Cyberspace Ops)
Bryant Walker (Pres-ACC Advanced Materials)
Darren Bergan (VP-Tech Svcs)
Lorene Avendano (VP-Space Sys)
Steve Tidwell (VP-ACC Advanced Materials)
Ray Walker (VP-Keystone-ACC Advanced Materials)
Kevin Dailey (VP-ACC Cyberspace Ops)
Miles Maye (Dir-Contracts)
Sydni Wassel (Dir-Bus Dev)
Trina Cohenour (Dir-HR)

Subsidiaries:

ACTA, LLC   (1)
2790 Skypark Dr Ste 310, Torrance, CA 90505
Tel.: (310) 530-1008
Web Site: http://www.actainc.com
Engineeering Services
N.A.I.C.S.: 541330
James Hudson (Pres)
Elliot Porterfield (Engr-Risk)

ADVANCED CORRECTIONAL HEALTHCARE

3922 W Baring Trace, Peoria, IL 61615
Tel.: (309) 692-8100
Web Site:
    http://www.advancedch.com
Year Founded: 2002
Sales Range: $25-49.9 Million
Emp.: 497
Health Care Srvices
N.A.I.C.S.: 621491
Norman R. Johnson (CEO & Principal)
Neil Leuthold (Pres)
Karen Stocke (VP-Quality Assurance & Risk Mgmt)
Deborah Ash (Dir-Medical Ops)

ADVANCED DATA SYSTEMS CORP.

15 Prospect St, Paramus, NJ 07652
Tel.: (201) 368-9393
Web Site: https://www.adsc.com
Rev.: $19,300,000
Emp.: 69
Computers, Peripherals & Software
N.A.I.C.S.: 423430
David Barzillai (Pres)
Adam Andrew (Dir-EMR Div)
Carol McCormick (Reg Mgr-Ops)
Serge Zenou (Dir-IT)
Mike Christie (Controller)
Lucy Allen (Dir-Clinical)
Lisa Boyd (Founder & Pres)
Joann Corbisiere-Ashley (Mgr-Practice)
Gary Roth (Pres & CEO-East Meadow Mgmt Grp)

ADVANCED DATACOMM SOLUTIONS, INC.

213 Bellagio Dr, Austin, TX 78734
Tel.: (720) 479-9402
Web Site:
    http://www.advanceddatacomm.com
Year Founded: 1993
Sales Range: $1-9.9 Million
Emp.: 10
Sells Voice & Data Communications Products & Services
N.A.I.C.S.: 423610
Michael Schmidlen (Pres)

ADVANCED DIGITAL DATA INC.

6 Laurel Dr, Flanders, NJ 07836
Tel.: (973) 584-4026
Web Site: https://www.addsys.com
Sales Range: $10-24.9 Million
Emp.: 150
Custom Computer Programming Services
N.A.I.C.S.: 541511
Bruce C. Bott (Pres)

ADVANCED DIGITAL SERVICES

948 N Cahuanga, Hollywood, CA 90038
Tel.: (323) 468-2200
Web Site:
    http://www.adshollywood.com
Rev.: $19,100,000
Emp.: 85
Video Tape Production
N.A.I.C.S.: 512110
Brad Weyl (COO)

ADVANCED DIGITAL SOLUTIONS INTERNATIONAL, INC.

4255 Business Ctr Dr, Fremont, CA 94538
Tel.: (510) 490-6667
Web Site: http://www.adsii.com
Rev.: $33,000,000
Emp.: 30
Computer & Software Stores
N.A.I.C.S.: 449210
Mike Minhas (VP-Sls)
Roya Sheikh (CFO)
Shahid Sheikh (Pres)

ADVANCED DOCUMENT SOLUTIONS, INC.

653 W Michigan St, Orlando, FL 32805
Tel.: (407) 412-6929
Web Site: http://www.myadsusa.com
Year Founded: 2007
Sales Range: $1-9.9 Million
Emp.: 25
Industrial Machinery Maintenance Services
N.A.I.C.S.: 811310
Lynda N. Lizarazo (Pres)
Daniel Guzman (VP-Mktg & Ops)
Moody Hamdan (CEO)

Subsidiaries:

Velox Systems, Inc.   (1)
4270 Dow Rd Ste 213, Melbourne, FL 32934
Tel.: (386) 274-1840
Web Site: http://www.veloxsystems.com
Sales Range: $1-9.9 Million
Emp.: 72
Office Equipment Distr
N.A.I.C.S.: 423420

ADVANCED DUPLICATION SERVICES INC.

2155 Niagara Ln N Ste 120, Minneapolis, MN 55447
Tel.: (763) 449-5500
Web Site: http://www.ads-cd.com
Sales Range: $25-49.9 Million
Emp.: 150
Computer Related Maintenance Services
N.A.I.C.S.: 541519
Scott Bartsch (CFO)
Michael Hardwick (CEO)

ADVANCED EDUCATIONAL PRODUCTS, INC.

2495 Main St Ste 230, Buffalo, NY 14214
Tel.: (716) 446-0739   NY
Web Site: http://www.aepbooks.com

Year Founded: 2000
Sales Range: $10-24.9 Million
Emp.: 45
Multimedia & Book Services
N.A.I.C.S.: 424920
Kenneth A. Pronti (CEO)

ADVANCED ELECTRONIC SERVICES, INC.

101 Technology Ln, Mount Airy, NC 27030
Tel.: (336) 386-1000
Web Site: http://www.aesintl.com
Rev.: $1,100,000
Emp.: 33
Other Electronic & Precision Equipment Repair & Maintenance
N.A.I.C.S.: 811210
Steve Cooke (Pres)
James Boyd (VP-Bus Dev)

Subsidiaries:

MSB Group, Inc.   (1)
2885 N Berkeley Lk Rd NW Ste 1, Duluth, GA 30096-4343
Tel.: (678) 417-5825
Web Site: http://www.woltersmotors.com
Electrical Apparatus & Equipment, Wiring Supplies & Related Equipment Merchant Whslr
N.A.I.C.S.: 423610
Scott Blake (Owner)

ADVANCED ELECTRONIC SYSTEMS INTEGRATORS, LLC

2400 Trade Center Way, Naples, FL 34109
Tel.: (239) 596-8500
Web Site: http://www.advanced-esi.com
Year Founded: 1999
Sales Range: $10-24.9 Million
Emp.: 110
Home Theaters & Other Electronics Installation Services
N.A.I.C.S.: 238210
Daniel Robbins (Co-Owner & Pres)

ADVANCED ENERGY ECONOMY

1000 Vermont Ave NW 3rd Fl, Washington, DC 20009
Tel.: (202) 380-1950   DC
Web Site: http://www.aee.net
Year Founded: 2011
Sales Range: $10-24.9 Million
Emp.: 48
Business Associations
N.A.I.C.S.: 813910
Matt Stanberry (VP-Market Dev)

ADVANCED ENGINEERING CONSULTANTS

1405 Dublin Rd, Columbus, OH 43215
Tel.: (614) 486-4778
Web Site: https://www.aecmep.com
Year Founded: 1998
Sales Range: $1-9.9 Million
Emp.: 29
Engineeering Services
N.A.I.C.S.: 541330
Lisa Huang (Pres)
Sam Reed (VP)
Jeremy Hatfield (Mgr-Indianapolis)

ADVANCED ENTERPRISES INC.

2183 Hwy 98, Mary Esther, FL 32569
Tel.: (850) 398-4338
Web Site:
    http://www.advancedenterprise.com
Year Founded: 2005
Sales Range: $50-74.9 Million
Emp.: 346
Marketing Consulting Services
N.A.I.C.S.: 541613

Jeff Davis (CEO)

ADVANCED EQUIPMENT COMPANY

1408 Central Park Dr, Charlotte, NC 28217
Web Site: https://www.aec-carolina.com
Sales Range: $10-24.9 Million
Emp.: 15
Materials Handling Machinery
N.A.I.C.S.: 423830
Larry Abernathy (CEO)
Daryle Ogburn (Pres)
Tony Stewart (VP)
Derek Helton (Mgr-Ops)

ADVANCED FEDERAL SERVICES

250 Sun Temple Dr, Madison, AL 35758
Tel.: (256) 772-7795
Year Founded: 1996
Rev.: $25,500,000
Emp.: 355
Facilities Support Services
N.A.I.C.S.: 561210
Al Bonilla (Pres & CEO)
Elea Hanks (COO & VP-Admin)
Courtney Carter (CFO)
Eric Sanders (VP-Bus Dev)
Julia Stiles (Bus Mgr)

ADVANCED FLUID SYSTEMS INC.

3rd & Green Sts, Royersford, PA 19468
Tel.: (610) 948-1000
Web Site:
    http://www.advancedsystems.com
Rev.: $11,195,538
Emp.: 45
Pneumatic Tools & Equipment
N.A.I.C.S.: 423830
Joshua Hubler (Mgr-Mfg)
John White (Engr-Sls)
Matt Anderson (Engr-Sls)
James V. Vaughn Sr. (Pres)

ADVANCED FOOD SYSTEMS, INC.

21 Roosevelt Ave, Somerset, NJ 08873
Tel.: (732) 873-6776
Web Site: https://www.afsnj.com
Year Founded: 1982
Sales Range: $25-49.9 Million
Emp.: 37
Sauces, Meat & Poultry & Frozen Food Mfr
N.A.I.C.S.: 311941
Sunny Joh (VP)
Chris Kelly (Dir-Tech Svcs & Sls)
Jessyca Susanto (Product Mgr-Commercialization)

ADVANCED FRAUD SOLUTIONS

1231 Shields Rd Ste 5, Kernersville, NC 27284
Web Site:
    http://www.advancedfraud.com
Year Founded: 2007
Sales Range: $1-9.9 Million
Emp.: 12
Fraud Prevention Software
N.A.I.C.S.: 513210
Lawrence Reaves (CEO)

ADVANCED GLASSFIBER YARNS LLC

2556 Wagener Rd, Aiken, SC 29801
Tel.: (803) 648-8351
Web Site: https://www.agy.com

Advanced Glassfiber Yarns LLC—(Continued)

Year Founded: 1988
Rev.: $206,302,000
Emp.: 550
Fiberglass Fabrics
N.A.I.C.S.: 524210
Iain Montgomery (Dir-NBD)
Thierry Philibert (Dir-Sls-EMEA)
Victor Gu (Dir-Sls-Asia Pacific)
Winn Cannon (Dir-Sls-Americas)

ADVANCED GOVERNMENT SOLUTIONS, INC.
16901 Melford Blvd Ste 101, Bowie, MD 20715
Tel.: (240) 260-4040
Web Site: http://www.agsi.net
Year Founded: 1999
Sales Range: $1-9.9 Million
Emp.: 63
Engineering & Technical Services
N.A.I.C.S.: 541330
Patricia Cresta-Savage (Pres & CEO)
Jack Savage (Co-Founder & Exec VP)

ADVANCED HEALTH EDUCATION CENTER, LTD.
8502 Tybor Dr, Houston, TX 77074-0157
Tel.: (713) 772-0157
Web Site:
  https://www.aheconline.com
Year Founded: 1988
Sales Range: $10-24.9 Million
Provider of Education in the use of MRIs, CT Scans & Ultrasounds
N.A.I.C.S.: 611699
Peggy Hoosier (VP)
T. J. Zwakenberg (Dir-Cardiovascular Svcs)

ADVANCED HI-TECH CORPORATION
2426 W 237th St, Torrance, CA 90501-5911
Tel.: (310) 214-8600
Web Site: http://www.aht.com
Rev.: $25,000,000
Emp.: 30
Computer Integrated Systems Design
N.A.I.C.S.: 541512
Fou-Sen Chang (Pres & CEO)
Jed DeYoung (VP-Mktg Sls)
Mark Ekstrand (VP)
Arthur Jen (Dir-Software Devel)

ADVANCED HORIZONS INC.
185 Fairfield Ave Ste 4C, West Caldwell, NJ 07006
Tel.: (973) 226-8007
Web Site:
  http://www.advancedhorizons.com
Rev.: $12,195,995
Emp.: 2
Electrical Heating Equipment
N.A.I.C.S.: 423730
William Murphy (Pres)
Kathy Ryan (Mgr-Acctg)

Subsidiaries:

PCI Inc. (1)
185 Fairfield Ave Ste 4c, Caldwell, NJ 07006
Tel.: (973) 226-8007
Web Site:
  http://www.advancedhorizons.com
Rev.: $11,200,000
Rental Agent, Real Estate
N.A.I.C.S.: 531210

ADVANCED IMAGING SOLUTIONS INC.
4070 Meghan Beeler Ct, South Bend, IN 46628
Tel.: (574) 243-1096

Web Site:
  http://www.advancedimaging.net
Rev.: $10,000,000
Emp.: 80
All Other Miscellaneous Store Retailers
N.A.I.C.S.: 459999
James Lauer (Sec & VP)
Stephen E. Klatt (Pres & Treas)
Jackie Hein (Controller)

ADVANCED IMAGING SOLUTIONS, INC.
3865 W Cheyenne Ave Ste 505, North Las Vegas, NV 89032
Tel.: (702) 951-4247
Web Site: https://www.ais-now.com
Year Founded: 2002
Office Equipment Merchant Wholesalers
N.A.I.C.S.: 423420
Gary Harouff (Founder & Pres)

Subsidiaries:

Comworx Inc. (1)
5160 S Vly View Blvd Ste 100, Las Vegas, NV 89118-1778
Tel.: (702) 791-3224
Web Site: http://www.comworxinc.com
Electronics Stores
N.A.I.C.S.: 449210

ADVANCED INDUSTRIAL COMPUTER INC.
21808 Garcia Ln, City of Industry, CA 91789
Tel.: (909) 895-8989
Web Site: https://www.aicipc.com
Sales Range: $50-74.9 Million
Emp.: 53
Computer Peripheral Equipment & Software
N.A.I.C.S.: 423430
C. T. Sun (VP-Engrg)

ADVANCED INDUSTRIAL DEVICES, INC.
4323 S Elwood Ave, Tulsa, OK 74107
Tel.: (918) 445-1254
Web Site: https://www.aidusa.com
Rev.: $12,000,000
Emp.: 33
Electrical Equipment Whslr
N.A.I.C.S.: 423610
Heather Embry (Branch Mgr-Kansas City)
Jerry Hopper (Branch Mgr-Oklahoma City)
Jerry Clavin (VP-Sls)

ADVANCED INTEGRATION TECHNOLOGY, LP
2805 E Plano Pkwy Ste 100, Plano, TX 75074
Tel.: (972) 423-8354
Web Site: http://www.aint.com
Year Founded: 1992
Computer System Design Services
N.A.I.C.S.: 541512
Edward J. Chalupa (Pres)

Subsidiaries:

Nova-Tech Engineering, LP (1)
2805 E Plano Pkwy Ste 300, Plano, TX 75069
Tel.: (425) 245-7000
Web Site: http://www.ntew.com
Engineering Services
N.A.I.C.S.: 541330

ADVANCED INTERACTIVE SYSTEMS
665 Andover Park W, Tukwila, WA 98188
Tel.: (206) 575-9797
Rev.: $19,600,000
Emp.: 42

Service Establishment Equipment
N.A.I.C.S.: 541612
Ron Enneking (Exec VP & Gen Mgr-Simulation Trng Products)
Scott Martin (VP-Eng)
Keith Taylor (Mng Dir)

Subsidiaries:

Advanced Interactive Solutions Ltd. (1)
Unit 3 Bridge Court River Lane, Wrecclesham, GU10 4QE, Surrey, United Kingdom
Tel.: (44) 1252725500
Web Site: http://www.ais-solutions.com
Sales Range: $10-24.9 Million
Emp.: 10
Provider of Interactive Simulation Systems
N.A.I.C.S.: 541512

FSS Inc. (1)
7760 Technology Dr, Melbourne, FL 32904-1575
Tel.: (206) 575-9797
Web Site: http://www.rbd.com
Sales Range: $10-24.9 Million
Emp.: 9
Teaching Machines & Aids, Electronic
N.A.I.C.S.: 333310

Firearms Simulation Systems Inc. (1)
7760 Technology Dr, Melbourne, FL 32904
Tel.: (206) 575-9797
Web Site: http://www.rbd.com
Sales Range: $10-24.9 Million
Emp.: 10
Electronic Training Devices
N.A.I.C.S.: 333310

Reality By Design Inc. (1)
665 Andover Park W, Tukwila, WA 98188
Tel.: (206) 575-9797
Web Site: http://www.rbd.com
Rev.: $2,600,000
Emp.: 15
Computer Software Development & Applications
N.A.I.C.S.: 541511

ADVANCED INTERNET TECHNOLOGIES INC.
421 Maiden Ln, Fayetteville, NC 28301
Tel.: (910) 321-1201
Web Site: http://www.ait.com
Year Founded: 1996
Rev.: $30,000,000
Emp.: 200
E-Commerce & Web Hosting Services
N.A.I.C.S.: 517810
Clarence Briggs (CEO)

ADVANCED LABELWORX, INC.
1006 Larson Dr, Oak Ridge, TN 37830
Tel.: (865) 966-8711
Web Site:
  http://www.advancedlabelworx.com
Sales Range: $10-24.9 Million
Emp.: 130
Mfr of Pressure Sensitive Tapes, Labels & Medical Adhesives
N.A.I.C.S.: 323111
Lana Sellers (Pres)
Eric Hjelmquist (Plant Mgr)

Subsidiaries:

Advanced Labelworx, Inc. - Anderson (1)
2800 W Whitner St, Anderson, SC 29626
Tel.: (864) 224-2122
Web Site:
  http://www.advancedlabelworx.com
Sales Range: $10-24.9 Million
Label & Sticker Printing Services
N.A.I.C.S.: 323111
Kamal Giroti (Controller)

ADVANCED LEARNING CENTERS, INC.

5619 Dtc Pkwy, Englewood, CO 80111
Tel.: (303) 504-9312
Web Site:
  http://www.leadandlearn.com
Year Founded: 1992
Rev.: $11,800,000
Emp.: 42
Professional Development Services
N.A.I.C.S.: 611430
Liz Monsma (Dir-Client Rels)
Herb Miller (Dir-Client Solutions)
Brooke Little (Dir-Conference Sls)
Peggy Morales (Dir-Fin)
Cindy Wasinger (Mgr-Acctg)
Robin Hoey (Mgr-Fin & Admin)
Adam Stevens (Mgr-Online Dev & Production)
Katie Schellhorn (Mgr-Publ)
Greg Atkins (Mgr-Tech)
Peggy Lush (Pres)
Nan Caldwell (Sr Dir-Conferences)
Peter Juergens (Sr Dir-Mktg)
Bob Burgess (Sr Dir-Ops)
Donna Anderson-Davis (Sr Dir-Prof Certification)
Kristin Anderson (Sr Dir-Prof Dev)
Sandy Schaeffer (Dir-Client Rels)

ADVANCED LIQUID LOGIC, INC.
615 Davis Dr, Morrisville, NC 27560
Tel.: (919) 287-9010
Web Site: http://www.liquid-logic.com
Sales Range: $10-24.9 Million
Emp.: 15
Surgical & Medical Instrument Mfr
N.A.I.C.S.: 339112
Michael Pollack (Co-Founder)
Richard West (CEO)
Vamsee Pamula (Co-Founder)

ADVANCED LOGISTICS, LLC.
2014 W Pinhook Rd Ste 310, Lafayette, LA 70508
Tel.: (337) 232-4699
Web Site: https://www.al-llc.com
Year Founded: 2004
Rev.: $4,100,000
Emp.: 23
Management Consulting Services
N.A.I.C.S.: 541618
Jeffery M. Svendson Sr. (Pres & CEO)
Frank Creaghan (CFO)

ADVANCED M & D SALES INC.
2335 N Clark Ave, Portland, OR 97227
Tel.: (503) 284-7601
Web Site:
  http://www.advancedmdsales.com
Sales Range: $10-24.9 Million
Emp.: 50
Whslr of Floor Coverings
N.A.I.C.S.: 423220
Stanley Herman (Pres & CEO)
Jim Rozos (Mgr-Sls & Svc)

ADVANCED MACHINE & ENGINEERING CO.
2500 Latham St, Rockford, IL 61103
Tel.: (815) 962-6076
Web Site: https://www.ame.com
Year Founded: 1966
Sales Range: $10-24.9 Million
Emp.: 140
Machine Shop, Jobbing & Repair
N.A.I.C.S.: 332710
Dietmar Goellner (Pres & CEO)
Harold Goellner (Product Mgr)
Shane Hatfield (Mgr-Acctg)
Scott Johnson (Mgr-Svcs)

ADVANCED MACHINE & TOOL CORP.

3706 Transportation Dr, Fort Wayne, IN 46818
Tel.: (260) 489-3572
Web Site: https://www.amt-corp.com
Year Founded: 1970
Rev.: $24,000,000
Emp.: 155
Custom Machinery
N.A.I.C.S.: 333998

ADVANCED MACHINERY COMPANIES
4530 Wadsworth Rd, Dayton, OH 45414
Tel.: (937) 278-7337
Web Site:
  https://www.advancedmachine.com
Sales Range: $10-24.9 Million
Emp.: 20
Industrial Supplies
N.A.I.C.S.: 423830
Pete Schinaman *(VP)*

ADVANCED MAINTENANCE
2820 N Kerr Ave, Wilmington, NC 28405
Tel.: (910) 251-0008
Web Site:
  https://www.admaintenance.com
Sales Range: $10-24.9 Million
Emp.: 52
Vehicle Dealers
N.A.I.C.S.: 441227
Lee Smoot *(Mgr-Ops)*
Fred Collins *(Mgr-Ops-Raleigh)*
Robert Overton *(Mgr-Sls & Svc-Fayetteville)*
Mike Di Ruscio *(Mgr-Ops-Durham)*
Chris Sheraden *(Mgr-Ops & Sls)*
Bobby Godwin *(Mgr-Ops-Greenville)*
Dale Kratovil *(Mgr-Svc-Jacksonville)*
Jim Larson *(Mgr-Svc-Kenly)*
Christopher P. Holman II *(Mgr-Svc-Wilmington)*

ADVANCED MARKETING GROUP, INC.
820 Pennsylvania Blvd, Feasterville-Trevose, PA 19053
Tel.: (215) 809-1000
Web Site:
  http://www.advancedmerchant.com
Sales Range: $1-9.9 Million
Emp.: 10
Financial Services
N.A.I.C.S.: 523999
Kevin Wiener *(Co-Pres)*
Errick Wiener *(Co-Pres)*
Mike Wiener *(CEO)*

ADVANCED MARKETING STRATEGIES
4010 Morena Blvd Ste 210, San Diego, CA 92117-4547
Tel.: (858) 490-6910   CA
Web Site: http://www.am-strategies.com
Year Founded: 1987
Sales Range: $10-24.9 Million
Emp.: 20
N.A.I.C.S.: 541810
Jim Tindaro *(CEO)*
Kathy Cunningham *(Owner & Pres)*
Bonnie Carlson *(Gen Mgr)*

Subsidiaries:

Advanced Marketing Strategies   (1)
901 Dover Dr Ste 104, Newport Beach, CA 92660
Tel.: (949) 548-8411
Web Site: http://www.am-strategies.com
Emp.: 15
N.A.I.C.S.: 541810
David Ripley *(Dir-MIS)*

ADVANCED MARKETPLACE INC.
3018 N US Hwy 301 Ste 800, Tampa, FL 33619
Tel.: (813) 655-7173
Web Site:
  http://www.advancedmarkets.com
Year Founded: 1995
Sales Range: $10-24.9 Million
Emp.: 52
Technology Consulting & Professional Services
N.A.I.C.S.: 541690
Angela Peeples *(Treas)*
William Sheridan *(VP-Sls & Mktg)*
Matthew Peeples *(Pres)*

ADVANCED MASONRY SYSTEMS LLC
5403 Ashton Ct, Sarasota, FL 34233
Tel.: (941) 926-3155
Sales Range: $10-24.9 Million
Emp.: 220
Masonry, Drywall & Framing Contractor
N.A.I.C.S.: 238140
Richard Karp *(Pres)*

ADVANCED MEDICAL SPECIALTIES
9350 SW 72nd St Ste 200, Miami, FL 33173
Tel.: (786) 594-4210
Web Site:
  http://www.miamicancer.com
Sales Range: $1-9.9 Million
Emp.: 41
Medical & Radiation Oncology Services
N.A.I.C.S.: 621111
Alina Camero *(Asst Controller)*
Angelica Martinez *(Supvr-Charge Posting)*
Leonard Kalman *(Chm)*
Eduardo Zambrano *(Dir-IT)*

ADVANCED MEDICAL TRANSPORT OF CENTRAL ILLINOIS
1718 N Sterling Ave, Peoria, IL 61655
Tel.: (309) 494-6200   IL
Web Site:
  http://www.advancedmedical.org
Year Founded: 1975
Sales Range: $10-24.9 Million
Emp.: 352
Ambulance & Paramedical Services
N.A.I.C.S.: 621910
Andrew Rand *(CEO)*

ADVANCED METALS GROUP, LLC
18 Mystic Ln, Malvern, PA 19355
Tel.: (610) 408-8006   DE
Web Site:
  http://www.advancedmetalsllc.com
Sales Range: $25-49.9 Million
Holding Company; Aluminum & Iron Foundries
N.A.I.C.S.: 551112

Subsidiaries:

Mabry Iron Castings, LLC   (1)
6531 Industrial Rd, Beaumont, TX 77705
Tel.: (409) 842-2223
Web Site: http://www.mabrycastings.com
Iron Cast Mfr
N.A.I.C.S.: 331511

Oberdorfer, LLC   (1)
6259 Thompson Rd, Syracuse, NY 13206-1405
Tel.: (315) 437-7588
Sales Range: $10-24.9 Million
Emp.: 75
Mfr of Aluminum Products
N.A.I.C.S.: 331524

Ross Aluminum Castings, LLC   (1)

815 N Oak Ave, Sidney, OH 45365
Tel.: (937) 498-2828
Web Site: http://www.rossal.com
Sales Range: $25-49.9 Million
Emp.: 180
Aluminum Die-Castings Mfr
N.A.I.C.S.: 331523
Robert Clement *(CFO)*
John Barga *(Coord-Safety & Environmental)*

U.S. Castings, LLC   (1)
14351 Shamel St, Entiat, WA 98822
Tel.: (509) 784-1001
Web Site: http://www.us-castings.com
Sales Range: $10-24.9 Million
Emp.: 95
Aluminum Casting & Foundry Mfr
N.A.I.C.S.: 331524
John Kepler *(CEO)*

ADVANCED MICRO - ELECTRONICS, INC.
6001 E Old Hwy 50, Vincennes, IN 47591-9652
Tel.: (812) 726-4500   IN
Web Site:
  https://www.theamegroup.com
Year Founded: 1986
Sales Range: $10-24.9 Million
Emp.: 160
Computer Consulting Services
N.A.I.C.S.: 541519
Renee Beck *(Dir-Call Mgmt)*
Brent Williams *(Pres)*

ADVANCED MICROELECTRONICS, INC.
6001 E Old Hwy 50, Vincennes, IN 47591
Tel.: (812) 726-4500
Web Site:
  https://www.theamegroup.com
Year Founded: 1985
Sales Range: $10-24.9 Million
Emp.: 100
Programmer of Computer Software; Data Processing, Web Developing & Equipment Repair
N.A.I.C.S.: 811210
Mark Gerkin *(Pres & CEO)*
Chris Caldwell *(Mgr-Svc-Fort Wayne)*

ADVANCED NETWORK MANAGEMENT, INC.
4601 Columbine Ave NE, Albuquerque, NM 87113
Tel.: (505) 888-8822
Web Site: http://www.anm.com
Year Founded: 1994
Sales Range: $1-9.9 Million
Emp.: 22
Computer System Design Services
N.A.I.C.S.: 541512
Maninder Mann *(Pres)*
Raminder Mann *(CEO)*
Vance Krier *(CTO)*
Aman Arora *(VP-Ops)*
Goran Velickovski *(VP-Sls)*

Subsidiaries:

Digital Roads, Inc.   (1)
304 Inverness Way S Ste 400, Englewood, CO 80112
Tel.: (303) 832-4500
Web Site: http://www.digitalroads.com
Sales Range: $1-9.9 Million
Emp.: 15
Digital Applications Design
N.A.I.C.S.: 561499
Mary Hood *(CEO)*
Shelby Hood *(Pres)*

ADVANCED NETWORK MARKETING, INC.
5252 Orange Ave Ste 109, Cypress, CA 90630
Tel.: (714) 226-0585   CA
Web Site:
  http://www.smpprinting.com

Year Founded: 1999
Sales Range: $1-9.9 Million
Emp.: 10
Commercial Printing Services & Magazine Publishing
N.A.I.C.S.: 323111
Robert Pittman *(Pres & CEO)*
Nicole Pittman *(Exec VP)*
Craig Vaughan *(Mgr-Customer Svc)*
Dan Harkey *(Gen Mgr)*

ADVANCED NETWORK SOLUTIONS
820 Palmer Pl, Nashville, TN 37203
Tel.: (615) 277-0500
Web Site:
  http://www.ansolutions.com
Year Founded: 1997
Sales Range: $1-9.9 Million
Emp.: 50
Computer Network Support Services
N.A.I.C.S.: 423430
Greg Summey *(CTO)*
Bryan Crawford *(Mgr-Svc Delivery)*
Jennifer Boyer *(VP-Fin)*
Matt Hamilton *(VP-Sls)*
Jeff Prouse *(VP-Engrg)*
Ryan Thornberg *(Mgr-Client IT)*
Taylor Siegrist *(Mgr-Client IT)*
Andrew Scott *(Mgr-Client IT)*
Trey Chowning *(Mgr-Client IT)*
John Cook *(Mgr-Client IT)*
Michael Curatolo *(CIO-Virtual)*
Devin Davenport *(Mgr-Acctg)*
Jake Swartz *(Dir-Mktg)*
Patty Clark *(Dir-Client IT Ops)*
David Greene *(Mgr-Client IT)*
Nikki Shea *(Coord-Sls & Mktg)*
Corey Bryant *(Mgr-Client IT)*
Matt Feirn *(Mgr-Client IT)*
Nathan White *(VP-Client Svcs)*

ADVANCED OFFICE ENVIRONMENTS, INC.
160 Quaker Ln, Malvern, PA 19355
Tel.: (610) 993-3450
Web Site:
  http://www.advancedofficeenv.com
Year Founded: 1959
Sales Range: $25-49.9 Million
Emp.: 80
Whslr of Office Furniture
N.A.I.C.S.: 423210
Frank D. Kuch *(Pres)*
Steve Kuch *(VP)*
Patricia Taylor *(Owner)*
Lee Mumber *(Controller)*
Michael Raspanti *(Dir-Interior Construction)*

ADVANCED OFFICE SYSTEMS INC.
296 E Main St, Branford, CT 06405
Tel.: (203) 481-5349
Web Site: https://www.aosinc.com
Year Founded: 1977
Rev.: $12,014,236
Emp.: 26
Personal Computers Printers
N.A.I.C.S.: 449210
Rich Sgueglia *(VP)*

ADVANCED PAVEMENT GROUP CORP.
1499 Jersey St, South Plainfield, NJ 07080
Tel.: (631) 277-8400   DE
Year Founded: 1963
Asphalt, Concrete, Drainage & Maintenance Services
N.A.I.C.S.: 423390
Michael Kmiec *(CFO)*

Subsidiaries:

Bureski Holdings, Inc.   (1)
1060 Boot Rd, Downingtown, PA 19335

Advanced Pavement Group Corp.—(Continued)

Tel.: (610) 296-0816
Commercial Paving Services
N.A.I.C.S.: 237310
Robert Bureski *(Pres)*

Easmunt Paving, Inc.   **(1)**
2103 E Main St, Millville, NJ 08332
Tel.: (856) 825-4247
Web Site: http://www.easmuntpaving.com
Specialty Trade Contractors
N.A.I.C.S.: 238990

ADVANCED PLANNING SERVICES, INC.
2888 Loker Ave E Ste 109, Carlsbad, CA 92010
Tel.: (619) 220-8116
Web Site: http://www.apshome.com
Year Founded: 1999
Sales Range: $10-24.9 Million
Emp.: 46
Financial & Business Consulting Services
N.A.I.C.S.: 541611
Tifani Brakke *(Dir-Brokerage)*

ADVANCED PLASTICS INCORPORATED
7360 Cockrill Bend Blvd, Nashville, TN 37209
Tel.: (615) 350-6500
Web Site: https://www.advanced-plastics.com
Sales Range: $10-24.9 Million
Emp.: 70
Plastics Products, Nec
N.A.I.C.S.: 424610
Roy Abner *(Pres)*
Keith Abner *(Sec)*
Tom Arnold *(Mgr-Sls)*

ADVANCED POLYMER TECHNOLOGY CORPORATION
109 Conica Ln, Harmony, PA 16037
Tel.: (724) 452-1330
Web Site: https://www.advpolytech.com
Rev.: $40,000,000
Emp.: 45
Paints & Allied Products
N.A.I.C.S.: 424690
Bob Roxbury *(Plant Mgr)*
Gary Wilson *(Dir-Sls Track Div-America)*

ADVANCED POWER CONTROL INCORPORATED
126 Sandy Dr, Newark, DE 19713
Tel.: (302) 368-0443
Web Site: http://www.adv-power.com
Sales Range: $200-249.9 Million
Emp.: 100
Electronic Controls Installation
N.A.I.C.S.: 238210
Paul E. Czerwin *(Pres)*
John Magness *(CFO)*
J. D. Smith *(Mgr-Quality Control)*
Don Theobald *(Engr-Sls)*
Louis Nickles *(Mgr-Quality Control)*
Scott Dight *(Dir-Sls)*
Park Beaudett *(VP)*

ADVANCED POWER SOLUTIONS
5936 Las Positas Rd, Livermore, CA 94551-7804
Tel.: (925) 456-9890
Web Site: https://www.advpower.com
Rev.: $423,610
Emp.: 8
Electrical Apparatus & Equipment Wiring Supplies & Related Equipment Merchant Whslr
N.A.I.C.S.: 423610
Linda Szulborski *(Pres)*

ADVANCED PROGRAMMING RESOURCES
2715 Tuller Pkwy, Dublin, OH 43017
Tel.: (614) 761-9994   OH
Web Site: http://www.aprnet.com
Year Founded: 1996
Sales Range: $10-24.9 Million
Emp.: 100
Computer Related Consulting Services
N.A.I.C.S.: 541512

ADVANCED PROTECTION TECHNOLOGIES, INC.
14550 58th St N, Clearwater, FL 33760
Tel.: (727) 535-6339
Web Site: http://www.apttvss.com
Year Founded: 1985
Sales Range: $10-24.9 Million
Emp.: 120
Surge Protector Mfr & Distr
N.A.I.C.S.: 335999
Bill Green *(Mgr-Ops)*
Holly Arbogast *(Acct Mgr-Siemens)*
Jill A. Cole *(Mgr-Sls-Intl)*
Michelle Damiano *(Mgr-HR)*
Vincent Lampert *(VP-Ops)*
Jon Conrad *(Engr-Sls)*
Eiborys Lounders *(Mgr-Sls-Latin America)*

ADVANCED PROTECTIVE COATINGS INC.
1862 Sparkman Dr NW, Huntsville, AL 35816
Tel.: (256) 721-1331
Web Site: http://www.2.line-x.com
Rev.: $15,000,000
Emp.: 16
Plastics Material & Resin Mfg
N.A.I.C.S.: 325211
David Garnett *(Mgr)*
Kevin Heronimus *(CEO)*

ADVANCED RESOURCE TECHNOLOGIES, INC.
1555 King St Ste 200, Alexandria, VA 22314
Tel.: (703) 682-4740
Web Site: https://www.team-arti.com
Year Founded: 1986
Rev.: $35,766,878
Emp.: 122
Computer Integrated Systems Design
N.A.I.C.S.: 541512
Horace F. Jones *(Founder & CEO)*
Lawrence E. Beavers *(CFO)*
Charles Anderson *(Pres & Chief Mktg Officer)*

ADVANCED ROOFING INC.
1950 NW 22nd St, Fort Lauderdale, FL 33311
Tel.: (954) 522-6868
Web Site: https://www.advancedroofing.com
Year Founded: 1983
Sales Range: $75-99.9 Million
Emp.: 350
Roofing Contractors
N.A.I.C.S.: 238160
Robert P. Kornahrens *(Pres & CEO)*
David Baytosh *(Mgr-Construction)*
Matt Ladd *(VP-Ops)*
Clint Sockman *(VP-Sls & Bus Dev)*
Kevin Kornahrens *(Exec VP)*
Michael Kornahrens *(Exec VP)*

ADVANCED SOFTWARE SYSTEMS, INC.
22866 Shaw Rd, Sterling, VA 20166
Tel.: (703) 230-3100
Web Site: https://www.assyst.net
Year Founded: 1993
Sales Range: $10-24.9 Million

Emp.: 413
Computer Related Services
N.A.I.C.S.: 541512
Shyama P. Mandal *(CEO)*
Joseph A. Anderson *(COO)*
Vinay Shirke *(CIO)*

ADVANCED SOFTWARE TALENT, LLC
308 Lang Rd, Burlingame, CA 94010
Tel.: (650) 596-2800
Web Site: https://www.advancedtalent.com
Sales Range: $10-24.9 Million
Emp.: 20
Employment Agencies
N.A.I.C.S.: 541511
Patti Black *(Acct Mgr)*

ADVANCED SOLUTIONS INTERNATIONAL INC.
901 N Pitt St, Alexandria, VA 22314
Tel.: (703) 739-3100
Web Site: http://www.advsol.com
Year Founded: 1991
Computer Software Services
N.A.I.C.S.: 541511
Don Robertson *(Pres & CTO)*
Robert Alves *(Chm & CEO)*
Paul Ramsbottom *(Mng Dir-ASI Asia-Pacific)*
John Benda *(VP-Sls)*
Andrew Sherwin *(Mng Dir-ASI Canada)*
Donna Benz *(VP-Ops)*
Jocelyn Dyer *(VP, Gen & Sec)*
Gary Kinman *(CFO)*

Subsidiaries:

Innovative Software Solutions, Inc.   **(1)**
3000 South Lenola Rd, Maple Shade, NJ 08052
Tel.: (856) 910-9190
Web Site: http://www.issisystems.com
Software Publisher
N.A.I.C.S.: 513210

Subsidiary (Domestic):

Zenith American Solutions Inc.   **(2)**
9555 W Sam Ho Pkwy S Ste 400, Houston, TX 77099-2145
Tel.: (713) 219-1200
Web Site: http://www.zenith-american.com
Pension Funds
N.A.I.C.S.: 525110
Bill Rhodes *(VP)*
Art Schultz *(Pres)*
Chris Johnson *(COO)*

ADVANCED SOLUTIONS INTERNATIONAL, INC.
4030 W Braker Ln, Austin, TX 78759
Tel.: (512) 491-0550
Web Site: http://www.advsol.com
Sales Range: $10-24.9 Million
Emp.: 195
Prepackaged Software
N.A.I.C.S.: 513210
Don Robertson *(Pres)*
Bob Alves *(Chm & CEO)*
Fred Lawrence *(CFO)*
John Benda *(VP-Customer/Channel Sls & Mktg-Global)*
Niroo Rad *(Mng Dir-Europe)*
Andrew Sherwin *(Mng Dir-ASI Canada)*
Jocelyn Dyer *(Gen Counsel & VP-HR)*
Paul Ramsbottom *(Mng Dir-ASI Asia-Pacific)*
Donna Benz *(VP-Ops)*
Gary Kinman *(Co-CFO)*

ADVANCED SPORTS, INC.
10940 Dutton Rd, Philadelphia, PA 19154

Tel.: (215) 824-3854   NC
Web Site: https://www.bikecollc.com
Year Founded: 1998
Holding Company; Bicycle Mfr & Whslr
N.A.I.C.S.: 551112
Patrick Cunnane *(CEO)*
Donna Steiner *(Mgr-Credit)*

ADVANCED STIMULATION TECHNOLOGIES INC.
2903 E Interstate 20, Midland, TX 79706
Tel.: (432) 617-3250
Web Site: http://www.advstimtech.com
Year Founded: 2007
Sales Range: $75-99.9 Million
Emp.: 157
Oil & Gas Extraction Services
N.A.I.C.S.: 213112
Robert Booth *(Co-Pres)*
Tito Betancur *(Mgr-Ops)*

ADVANCED SYSTEM DESIGN INC.
2915 Kerry Forest Pkwy Ste 104, Tallahassee, FL 32309-7803
Tel.: (850) 385-5129
Web Site: http://www.asd-web.com
Sales Range: $10-24.9 Million
Emp.: 77
Computer Software Systems Analysis & Design
N.A.I.C.S.: 541511
John A. DuBard *(Pres)*
John Adams *(Sr VP)*

ADVANCED SYSTEMS GROUP INC.
12405 Grant St, Thornton, CO 80241
Tel.: (303) 301-3000
Web Site: http://www.virtual.com
Sales Range: $75-99.9 Million
Emp.: 100
Computer Integrated Systems Design Services
N.A.I.C.S.: 541512
John Murphy *(Exec VP)*
Dan Park *(CIO)*
Patrick Smith *(VP-Sls-Central Reg)*
Kent Kellough *(VP-Sls-Western Reg)*
Doug Darnell *(Dir-Acctg Ops)*
Elizabeth Stuart *(Dir-Sls Ops)*
Rich Williams *(VP-Engrg Svcs)*
Brett Dibkey *(Pres)*

ADVANCED SYSTEMS GROUP, LLC
1226 Powell St, Emeryville, CA 94608-2618
Tel.: (510) 654-8300
Web Site: https://www.asgllc.com
Emp.: 100
Media & Entertainment Technology & Engineering Services
N.A.I.C.S.: 541618
Dave Van Hoy *(Founder & Pres)*

Subsidiaries:

Audio Intervisual Design, Inc.   **(1)**
1155 N La Brea Ave, West Hollywood, CA 90038
Tel.: (323) 845-1155
Web Site: http://www.aidinc.com
Sales Range: $1-9.9 Million
Emp.: 15
Industrial Machinery & Equipment Merchant Whslr
N.A.I.C.S.: 423830
James Pace *(Founder & Pres)*

ADVANCED SYSTEMS TECHNOLOGY, INC.
4111 W Gore Blvd, Lawton, OK 73505
Tel.: (580) 248-0321

Web Site: https://www.astcorp.com
Sales Range: $25-49.9 Million
Emp.: 340
Computer Systems Analysts & Design
N.A.I.C.S.: 541512
Steve Webley (Pres)
Debbie Webley (Dir-HR)

ADVANCED TECHNICAL RESOURCES INC.
1230 Oakmead Pkwy Ste 110, Sunnyvale, CA 94085-4026
Tel.: (408) 328-8000   CA
Web Site:
   http://www.atrinternational.com
Year Founded: 1988
Sales Range: $10-24.9 Million
Emp.: 70
Employment Services
N.A.I.C.S.: 561311
Jerry Brenholz (Co-Founder & CEO)
Theresa Siegfried (VP-Fin)
Wendy Sun (VP-Recruiting)
Jeff Monaghan (Dir-Mktg)
Maria Novoa (Founder)
Maggie Morelle (CIO)

ADVANCED TECHNICAL SOLUTIONS, INC.
36 Nason St, Maynard, MA 01754
Tel.: (978) 849-0533
Web Site: http://www.atsusa.com
Year Founded: 1987
Sales Range: $10-24.9 Million
Emp.: 24
Computer Maintenance & Repair Services
N.A.I.C.S.: 811210
Bill Miller (Sls Mgr)
Alden Edwards (Pres)
Max Coebergh (Pres-mWave Media)

ADVANCED TECHNICAL SOLUTIONS, LLC
152 Erskine Ln, Scott Depot, WV 25560
Tel.: (304) 757-6542
Web Site:
   http://www.atsnetworking.com
Sales Range: $1-9.9 Million
Emp.: 30
Information Technology Services
N.A.I.C.S.: 541512
Bob Marchi (Mgr-Svc & Mgr-Implementation)
Josh Stepp (Mgr-Sls)
Jason Lambert (Mgr-Svc Delivery)
Brian Sims (Co-Owner & VP-Network Ops)
Gary Sims Jr. (Co-Owner, Pres & CEO)
Gary Sims Sr. (CFO)

ADVANCED TECHNOLOGY INTERNATIONAL, LLC
2733 W Carmen Ave, Milwaukee, WI 53209-4228
Tel.: (414) 466-8352
Web Site:
   http://www.atigunstocks.com
Sales Range: $1-9.9 Million
Emp.: 20
Rifle & Related Product Accessory Mfr
N.A.I.C.S.: 332992
John Chvala (Owner)

ADVANCED TECHNOLOGY SOLUTIONS, INC.
802 W Park Ave Ste 223, Ocean, NJ 07712
Tel.: (732) 918-4664
Web Site: http://www.atsolutions.com
Sales Range: $10-24.9 Million
Emp.: 85

System Integration Services
N.A.I.C.S.: 541512
Joann Wean (Founder & Pres)
Autumn Ortenzi (Mgr-Tech Recruiting)

ADVANCED TELECOM SERVICES
1150 First Ave Ste 105, King of Prussia, PA 19406
Tel.: (610) 688-6000
Web Site: http://www.atsmobile.com
Year Founded: 1989
Sales Range: $10-24.9 Million
Emp.: 65
Interactive Mobile Marketing
N.A.I.C.S.: 541810
Robert Bentz (Pres)
Bret J. Dunlap (Co-Founder & Dir)
Eric Deininger (Product Mgr)
Frank Butler (VP-Engrg)

ADVANCED TEMPORARIES INC.
1221 W Southwest Loop 323, Tyler, TX 75701-9344
Tel.: (903) 561-8204
Web Site: https://www.advtemp.com
Rev.: $11,100,000
Emp.: 983
Temporary Help Service
N.A.I.C.S.: 561320
Hammond Scott Gibson (Pres & Owner)
Gilda Richardson (Project Mgr-HR)

ADVANCED TEMPORARIES, INC.
820 Church St, Norfolk, VA 23510
Tel.: (757) 533-9188
Web Site:
   http://www.advancedtemporary.com
Rev.: $3,300,000
Emp.: 200
Temporary Help Service
N.A.I.C.S.: 561320
Trish Luchau (Mgr)

ADVANCED VISUAL SYSTEMS INC.
2 Burlington Woods Dr Ste 100, Burlington, MA 01803
Tel.: (781) 890-4300
Web Site: https://www.avs.com
Year Founded: 1991
Sales Range: $1-9.9 Million
Emp.: 8
Data Visualization Software Developer & Distr
N.A.I.C.S.: 513210
Steve Sukman (Exec VP)
Anoop Chatterjee (CTO)
Brian Selle (VP-Pro Svcs)

ADVANCED WEB TECHNOLOGIES, INC.
600 Hoover St NE Ste 500, Minneapolis, MN 55413
Tel.: (612) 706-3700   MN
Web Site:
   http://www.awtlabelpack.com
Year Founded: 1976
Flexographic Label Printing Services
N.A.I.C.S.: 323111
Jim Lundquist (CEO)

ADVANCED WEIGHT LOSS CLINICS
1063 Narrows Way Ste D, Birmingham, AL 35242
Tel.: (205) 670-5355
Web Site: http://www.letslose.com
Year Founded: 2003
Sales Range: $1-9.9 Million
Emp.: 50
Diet & Weight Loss Clinic
N.A.I.C.S.: 812191

Anita Gibson (Founder & Pres)
Awl Greystone (Office Mgr)
Keri Parker (Mgr)

ADVANCED WIRELESS COMMUNICATIONS
20809 Kensington Blvd, Lakeville, MN 55044-8353
Tel.: (952) 469-5400
Web Site:
   https://www.advancedwireless.com
Sales Range: $10-24.9 Million
Emp.: 50
Telephone & Communication Equipment
N.A.I.C.S.: 449210
Kenneth Coons (VP)
John Kenney (VP-Sls)

ADVANCED WORKPLACE STRATEGIES, INC.
17542 E 17th St Ste 330, Tustin, CA 92780
Tel.: (714) 731-3084
Web Site: http://www.awsi.com
Year Founded: 1990
Rev.: $7,400,000
Emp.: 35
Administrative Management & General Management Consulting Services
N.A.I.C.S.: 541611
Joseph R. Gonzalez (Pres)
David B. Cory (VP-Sls & Mktg)
Steven L. Ferris (VP-Ops)
Michael J. Gonzalez (VP-Fin & Admin)
Randy J. Gonzalez (VP-IT)

ADVANCEMENT PROJECT
1910 W Sunset Blvd Ste 500, Los Angeles, CA 90026
Tel.: (213) 989-1300   CA
Web Site:
   https://www.advanceprojectca.org
Year Founded: 2001
Sales Range: $10-24.9 Million
Emp.: 116
Law firm
N.A.I.C.S.: 541199
John Kim (Exec Dir)
Constance L. Rice (Co-Founder)
Molly Munger (Co-Founder)
Stephen R. English (Co-Founder, Treas & Sec)

ADVANCETEC INDUSTRIES INC.
1150 NW 163rd Dr, Miami, FL 33169
Tel.: (305) 623-3939
Web Site:
   https://www.advancetec.com
Rev.: $10,000,000
Emp.: 65
Telephone & Telegraph Apparatus
N.A.I.C.S.: 334210
Gil Ron (Pres)

ADVANCIA CORPORATION
655 Research Pkwy Ste 400, Oklahoma City, OK 73104
Tel.: (405) 996-3000
Web Site: http://www.advancia.com
Sales Range: $10-24.9 Million
Emp.: 170
Commercial Physical Research
N.A.I.C.S.: 541715
Jim Burns (VP-Bus Dev)
Ron Gott (Program Mgr)

ADVANCIAL FEDERAL CREDIT UNION
1845 Woodall Rodgers Fwy Ste 1300, Dallas, TX 75201-2240
Tel.: (972) 201-1881
Web Site: https://www.advancial.org

Year Founded: 1937
Sales Range: $900-999.9 Million
Emp.: 100
Federal Credit Union & Mortgage Services
N.A.I.C.S.: 522130
Paul Graff (Asst VP-Dev)
Brent Sheffield (Pres & CEO)
Lacey Maynor (Mgr-Community Dev-Bus Rels-Lafayette)

ADVANCING NATIVE MISSIONS
PO Box 5303, Charlottesville, VA 22905
Tel.: (540) 456-7111   VA
Web Site:
   http://www.advancingmissions.com
Year Founded: 1990
Sales Range: $10-24.9 Million
Emp.: 58
Community Action Services
N.A.I.C.S.: 624190
Andrew Needham (VP-Media & Mktg)
Autumn Nims (Exec Dir-Intl Women's Ministry)
Bo Barredo (Co-Founder & Pres)
Bud Voight (Dir-Buildings & Grounds)
Danny McAllister (VP-Projects Admin)
Arlin Martin (Treas)
Carl A. Gordon (Co-Founder & Exec VP-Intl Ministry Dev)
Philip Zodhiates (Chm)
Oliver Asher (CEO)
P. R. Misra (Exec VP-Strategic Partnerships)
Dick Prins (Sr VP-Ops & Stewardship)
Dan Reichard (VP-Spiritual Dev & Dir-Far East Desk)

ADVANSOFT INTERNATIONAL INC.
415 W Golf Rd, Arlington Heights, IL 60005
Tel.: (847) 952-0000
Web Site: http://www.adso.com
Sales Range: $25-49.9 Million
Emp.: 500
Computer System Design Services
N.A.I.C.S.: 541512
Anil K. Sunkara (CEO)
Shilpa Boppana (CFO)
Murali Sajja (Coord-Resource)

ADVANTA INSURANCE PARTNERS
1121 Judson Rd Ste 142, Longview, TX 75601
Tel.: (903) 230-7601
Web Site: http://www.advantaas.com
Insurance Agents
N.A.I.C.S.: 524210
Dana Parr (Pres)

Subsidiaries:

John Traylor Insurance   (1)
816 Linda Dr, Daingerfield, TX 75638-2120
Tel.: (903) 645-7375
Web Site:
   http://www.johntraylorinsurance.com
Insurance Agents
N.A.I.C.S.: 524210

ADVANTAGE ACADEMY OF MIAMI INC.
11575 SW 243rd St, Miami, FL 33032
Tel.: (305) 253-2123   FL
Year Founded: 2005
Sales Range: $10-24.9 Million
Educational Support Services
N.A.I.C.S.: 611710
Nathaniel Grasch (Chm)

ADVANTAGE AVIATION TECHNOLOGIES, INC.

Advantage Aviation Technologies, Inc.—(Continued)

201 Regal Row, Dallas, TX 75247
Tel.: (972) 647-7300
Web Site: http://www.aatinc.net
Aerospace Components & Systems Mfr
N.A.I.C.S.: 336330
David MacDonald (CEO)
Glenn Mayberry (Pres & Gen Mgr)

ADVANTAGE BENEFIT SOLUTIONS

4635 SW Fwy Ste 750, Houston, TX 77027
Tel.: (713) 665-8066
Web Site: http://www.abs-insurance.com
Emp.: 12
Insurance Agencies & Brokerages
N.A.I.C.S.: 524210
Mark Stefanick (Pres & CEO)
Jeff Hildreth (VP)
Dennis McDowell (VP-Client Solutions)
Greg Faldyn (VP-Client Svcs)

Subsidiaries:

Collins Benefits Solutions Inc.   (1)
8014 Oceanside Dr, Houston, TX 77095
Tel.: (281) 345-1235
Web Site: http://www.collinsbenefits.com
Insurance Agencies & Brokerages
N.A.I.C.S.: 524210
Mary K. Collins (Pres)

ADVANTAGE CAPITAL CORPORATION

909 Poydras St Ste 2230, New Orleans, LA 70112
Tel.: (504) 522-4850   LA
Web Site:
   https://www.advantagecap.com
Year Founded: 1992
Privater Equity Firm
N.A.I.C.S.: 523999
M. Scott Murphy (Mng Dir)
James O'Rourke (Mng Dir-New York)
Maurice E. Doyle (Mng Dir)
Louis T. Dubuque (Mng Dir)
Jonathan I. Goldstein (Mng Dir)
Timothy W. Hassler (Mng Dir-Ag Fund)
Reid C. Hutchins (Mng Dir)
Michael T. Johnson (Mng Dir & Chief Compliance Officer)
Sandra M. Moore (Mng Dir & Chief Impact Officer)
Damon L. Rawie (Mng Dir)
Thomas Bitting (Sr VP)
Troy Blaine (VP-Bus Dev)
Charles Booker (Principal)
Sandra Bradford (VP-Bus Dev)
Kathy Cornell (Tax Manager)
Jeffrey W. Craver (Principal)
John Daniels (VP-Bus Dev)
Jeremy R. Degenhart (Principal)
Ryan C. Dressler (Principal)
Eric Dunham (VP-Bus Dev)
Michele Fleher (Asst VP)
Keith Freeman (Principal)
Christopher C. Harris (Sr VP)
Sherry Hartnett (Office Manager)
Tasha Harvey (VP-Bus Dev)
Leah T. Hendricks (VP)
Donya Hengehold (Dir-Comm)
Kira Hess (Mgr-Credit Ops)
Stephanie Hiatt (Sr VP)
Richard Hummell (Principal)
Mark Lange (VP-Bus Dev)
Franchesca B. Lorio (Sr VP & Controller)
Tyler Mayoras (Principal)
Fong Wa C. Mui (VP)
Brian Muller (Asst Acctg Mgr)
Stuart S. Noel (Sr VP)
Justin N. Obletz (CFO)

Paul Olsen (VP)
Allison Regis (Asst Acctg Mgr)
Jim Rieker (VP-Syndication)
Rachel Robards (Project Mgr-Syndication)
Valentino Rovere (VP)
Philip J. Ruppel (VP)
Cara M. Schiffman (VP-Regulatory Affairs)
Greg Schwarztrauber (Sr VP)
Talmadge Singer (Principal)
Craig Smidt (Sr VP)
Ruth Sorrell (Principal)
Daniel L. Stoute (Dir-IT)
Renee Struckel (Coord-Investment)
Adam M. Suberi (Sr VP)
Sara H. Talbot (Mgr-Loan Ops & Scving)
Thomas Titus (VP-Bus Dev)
Anthony Toups (Principal)
Brittany Walker (Asst VP)
Thomas C. Willsey (Sr VP & Treas)
Ryan Brennan (Mng Dir-Napa)
Steven T. Stull (Founder & Pres)

ADVANTAGE CAPITAL FUNDS LLC

13263 Ventura Blvd, Studio City, CA 91604
Web Site:
   http://www.advantagecapital.com
Year Founded: 2008
Sales Range: $1-9.9 Million
Emp.: 8
Working Capital
N.A.I.C.S.: 523999
David Castro (CEO)

ADVANTAGE COMMUNICATIONS GROUP, LLC

125 Mineola Ave Ste 306, Roslyn Heights, NY 11577
Tel.: (516) 821-1700
Web Site:
   http://www.advantagecg.com
Year Founded: 2003
Sales Range: $1-9.9 Million
Emp.: 10
Telecommunication Servicesb
N.A.I.C.S.: 517810
David Gardner (Pres & CEO)
David Bass (Dir-Bus Dev-East Windsor)
Stephen B. Johnson (Co-Founder)
Steve Rome (Sr VP-Sls)
Eric Wansong (COO-Global)
Diane Miller (COO)

ADVANTAGE COMP, INC.

23 Mays Landing Rd Ste 1, Somers Point, NJ 08244
Tel.: (609) 365-8990
Web Site:
   http://www.sciadvantage.com
Workers Compensation Coverage Provider
N.A.I.C.S.: 524126

ADVANTAGE COMPUTING SYSTEMS INC.

3850 Ranchero Dr, Ann Arbor, MI 48108
Tel.: (734) 327-3600
Web Site:
   https://www.advantagecs.com
Year Founded: 1979
Rev.: $10,000,000
Emp.: 100
Marketing & Fulfillment Software
N.A.I.C.S.: 513210
Glenda Stegenga (Mgr-HR)
Rebecca Sharp (Controller & Office Mgr)
Philippe Van Mastrigt (Dir-Ops-Europe)

ADVANTAGE DISPOSAL SOLUTIONS, INC.

42583 N Coyote Rd, Queen Creek, AZ 85140
Tel.: (602) 421-4464   WY
Year Founded: 2011
Sales Range: $10-24.9 Million
Emp.: 2
Waste Water Treatment & Disposal
N.A.I.C.S.: 562211
Griffin Scarlett (CEO & Owner)

ADVANTAGE ENGINEERING INCORPORATED

525 E Stop 18 Rd, Greenwood, IN 46143
Tel.: (317) 887-0729   IN
Web Site:
   https://www.advantageengineer.com
Year Founded: 1977
Rev.: $23,000,000
Emp.: 120
Temperature Controls, Automatic
N.A.I.C.S.: 334512
Randy Goode (VP-Mfg)
Susan Schaub (VP)
Shawn Tuell (Reg Mgr)
Glen Oswalt (Reg Mgr)
Ron Wolfe (VP-Engrg)
Jon Gunderson (Pres)
Terry Fellers (Mgr-Svc)
Jon Gunerson (Pres)
Randy Goode (VP-Mfg)
Ron Wolfe (VP-Engrg)
Susan Schaub (VP)
Jeff Manifold (Mgr-O.E.M. Markets)
Sharon Todd (Mgr-Parts)
Terry Fellers (Mgr-Svc)

ADVANTAGE FUNDING CORPORATION

1000 Parkwood Cir SE Ste 300, Atlanta, GA 30339
Tel.: (770) 955-2274
Web Site:
   http://www.advantagefunding.com
Sales Range: $10-24.9 Million
Emp.: 4
Financial Services
N.A.I.C.S.: 522299
Jeff Farkas (Owner)
Mark Bonanno (CFO)

ADVANTAGE HOUSING INC.

13078 Helmer Rd S, Battle Creek, MI 49015
Tel.: (269) 979-8818
Sales Range: $10-24.9 Million
Emp.: 7
Mobile Home Dealers
N.A.I.C.S.: 459930
Michael Mead (Pres)
Denise Mead (Mgr)

ADVANTAGE INSURANCE INC.

American International Plz 250 Munoz Rivera Ave Ste 710, San Juan, PR 00918
Tel.: (787) 705-2900   PR
Web Site:
   http://www.advantagelife.com
Year Founded: 2015
Sales Range: $10-24.9 Million
Emp.: 19
Fire Insurance Services
N.A.I.C.S.: 524113
Walter C. Keenan (Pres & CEO)
Mark Moffat (Chief Investment Officer)
Leslie C. Boughner (Chm-Bus Insurance)
Eduardo Colon (Chief Banking Officer)
Stuart N. Jessop (Chief Underwriting Officer-Life Insurance)
Tamara K. Kravec (CFO)

Matthew I. Lawson (Chief Acctg Officer)
Eric A. Miller (CIO)
Liam Fleming (Sr Mgr-Bus Insurance)
Paul Fordham (Sr Mgr-Client Svcs-Life Insurance-Cayman)
Simon Kilpatrick (Sr VP-Bus Insurance)
William Pare (Controller-Financial)
Charla Smyser (VP-Bus Insurance-US)

ADVANTAGE L.P.

328 Desiard St, Monroe, LA 71201-7429
Tel.: (203) 352-5900
Year Founded: 1983
Sales Range: $10-24.9 Million
Emp.: 150
Help Supply Services
N.A.I.C.S.: 541611
Wendy Mascowitz (Dir-HR)

ADVANTAGE MARKETING, INC.

915 W Douglas Ave, Wichita, KS 67213
Tel.: (316) 729-0500
Web Site: https://admarkict.com
Year Founded: 2013
Traditional Media Buying & Digital Marketing Services
N.A.I.C.S.: 541830
Cori K. Kohlmeier (Pres & Founder)
Amy Hoefer (VP)

Subsidiaries:

Media Partners Inc.   (1)
4020 Barrett Dr #104, Raleigh, NC 27609-6625
Tel.: (919) 781-0433
Web Site: http://www.mediapartners-inc.com
Media Marketing Agencies
N.A.I.C.S.: 541810
Nancy Bono (Partner)
Tim McKay (Dir-Client Svcs)
Sal Conino (Partner)
Betty Zaring (Dir-Acct Svc)

ADVANTAGE MEDIA GROUP, INC.

65 Gadsden St, Charleston, SC 29401
Tel.: (843) 414-5600
Web Site:
   http://www.advantagefamily.com
Year Founded: 2005
Sales Range: $1-9.9 Million
Emp.: 15
Business & Professional Development Book Publishing Services
N.A.I.C.S.: 513130
Adam Witty (CEO & Founder)
John Witty (Chief Compliance Officer & Treas)

Subsidiaries:

Shelton Interactive   (1)
3006 Bee Caves Rd Ste A300, Austin, TX 78746-5541
Tel.: (512) 206-0229
Web Site: http://www.sheltoninteractive.com
Sales Range: $1-9.9 Million
Emp.: 16
Advertising Agencies
N.A.I.C.S.: 541810
Rusty Shelton (Owner)

ADVANTAGE NURSING SERVICES, INC.

3340 Severn Ave Ste 320, Metairie, LA 70002
Tel.: (504) 456-0073
Web Site:
   http://www.advantagenursing.com
Year Founded: 1984
Rev.: $12,800,000
Emp.: 800

Provider of Nurses' Registry Services
N.A.I.C.S.: 561311
Bill Mcnary (Controller)

ADVANTAGE PERSONNEL CONSULTANTS, INC.
PO Box 9878, Chattanooga, TN 37412-0878
Tel.: (423) 499-9397
Year Founded: 1993
Sales Range: $10-24.9 Million
Emp.: 1,500
Employment Services
N.A.I.C.S.: 541612
Ann Fowler (Owner)

ADVANTAGE SALES & MARKETING, LLC
18100 Von Karman Ave Ste 1000, Irvine, CA 92612
Tel.: (949) 797-2900   CA
Web Site:
http://www.advantagesolutions.net
Year Founded: 1987
Sales Range: $1-9.9 Million
Business Consulting Services
N.A.I.C.S.: 541611
Tanya L. Domier (CEO)
Brian G. Stevens (CFO & COO)
David Cortese (Pres-Digital Tech Solutions & Svcs)
Jill Griffin (Pres-Mktg)
Michael O'Keefe (Pres-Sls)
Melissa Oesterreich (Chief People Officer)
Bryce Robinson (Gen Counsel & Sec)
Rekha Ramesh (CIO)

Subsidiaries:

Brand Connections, LLC   (1)
360 Lexington Ave 19th Fl, New York, NY 10017
Tel.: (917) 909-7060
Web Site: http://www.brandconnections.com
Marketing & Media Advertising Services
N.A.I.C.S.: 541613
Dave Chatoff (VP-Strategy & Insights)
Victoria Drechsler (Sr VP & Gen Mgr)
John Fagan (VP-Retail Ops)
Emily Ryan (Sr Dir-Count Svcs)
Lindsay Pinchuk (Founder-Bump Club & Beyond)

Quantum Networks, LLC   (1)
1120 Ave of the Americas 13th Fl, New York, NY 10036
Tel.: (212) 993-5898
Web Site: http://www.quantum-co.com
Wireless Communication Services
N.A.I.C.S.: 517111
Ari Zoldan (CEO)
Eytan Wiener (COO)

ADVANTAGE SCI
222 N Sepulveda Blvd, El Segundo, CA 90245
Tel.: (310) 536-9876
Web Site:
http://www.advantagesci.com
Year Founded: 2000
Sales Range: $10-24.9 Million
Emp.: 60
Management Consulting Services
N.A.I.C.S.: 541618
Elsa Lee (Pres)
Pete Lee (COO)

ADVANTAGE STAFFING
14655 NW Freeway Ste 104, Houston, TX 77040
Tel.: (713) 690-4610
Web Site:
http://www.hirethinking.com
Year Founded: 1987
Sales Range: $25-49.9 Million
Emp.: 100
Provider of Temporary Help Services
N.A.I.C.S.: 561320

David Lamoine (VP)

ADVANTAGE TECHNOLOGIES CONSULTING, INC.
34350 23 Mile Rd Ste C, Chesterfield, MI 48047
Web Site: https://www.adv-tech.com
Year Founded: 2000
Sales Range: $1-9.9 Million
Emp.: 45
Software & Network Technology Specifically for Dental & Orthodontic Offices
N.A.I.C.S.: 513210
Bryan Currier (Pres & Founder)

ADVANTAGE TRAVEL LLC
4259 S Florida Ave, Lakeland, FL 33813
Tel.: (863) 686-1400
Web Site:
http://www.greatescapesonline.com
Sales Range: $10-24.9 Million
Emp.: 88
Membership Sports & Recreation Clubs
N.A.I.C.S.: 713940
Joseph P. St John (Pres)
Linda Mayhugh (COO)

ADVANTEDGE HEALTHCARE SOLUTIONS, INC.
30 Technology Dr, Warren, NJ 07059
Tel.: (908) 279-8111   NY
Web Site: https://www.ahsrcm.com
Year Founded: 1999
Medical Billing Software Developer
N.A.I.C.S.: 513210
David H. Langsam (Pres & CEO)
Jeanne A. Gilreath (Sr VP)
J. Paul O'Haro (COO)
Terence Halloran (CFO & Chief Admin Officer)
Kevin McDonald (Sr VP-Sls & Mktg)

ADVANTEGO CORPORATION
3801 East Florida Ave Ste 400, Denver, CO 80210
Tel.: (949) 627-8977   CO
Web Site: http://www.advantego.com
Year Founded: 1988
ADGO—(OTCBB)
Sales Range: Less than $1 Million
Emp.: 4
Gold Mining Services
N.A.I.C.S.: 212220
Fred Popke (COO)
Robert W. Ferguson (Chm & CEO)
Tracy Alan Madsen (CFO & Chief Acctg Officer)

ADVANTEX
5720 Brdwy Ste 104, Pearland, TX 77581
Tel.: (866) 780-5651
Web Site:
https://www.goadvantex.com
Emp.: 200
IT Support Services
N.A.I.C.S.: 561499
Eliot Vancil (Pres)

Subsidiaries:

Round Rock Solutions, Inc.   (1)
2150 W 18th St Ste 209, Houston, TX 77008
Tel.: (713) 622-4001
Web Site:
http://www.roundrocksolutions.com
Sales Range: $1-9.9 Million
Emp.: 12
Computer Related Services, Nec, Nsk
N.A.I.C.S.: 541512
John Avritt (Pres)

ADVANTICA

19321 US Hwy 19 N Bldg C Ste 320, Clearwater, FL 33764
Tel.: (727) 538-7719
Web Site: http://www.advantica.com
Sales Range: $50-74.9 Million
Emp.: 150
Vision & Dental Insurance Carrier
N.A.I.C.S.: 524114
Timothy Olsen (Sr Acct Exec)

ADVANTICOM, INC.
191 Wyngate Dr, Monroeville, PA 15146
Tel.: (412) 385-5000
Web Site:
https://www.advanticom.com
Year Founded: 1996
Sales Range: $10-24.9 Million
Emp.: 40
IT Services
N.A.I.C.S.: 541990
Julie Spear (Acct Exec)
Brian Conboy (Pres & CEO)
Chris Conboy (VP)
Heather Viszlay (Project Mgr)

ADVANTIS CREDIT UNION
10501 SE Main St, Milwaukie, OR 97222
Tel.: (503) 785-2528   OR
Web Site: https://www.advantiscu.org
Year Founded: 1928
Sales Range: $25-49.9 Million
Emp.: 207
Credit Union
N.A.I.C.S.: 522130
Amanda Owings (Chm)
Christopher Groshko (Chief Retail Officer & Sr VP)

ADVANTIS GLOBAL, INC.
301 Howard St Ste 1400, San Francisco, CA 94105
Tel.: (415) 395-4444
Web Site:
http://www.advantisglobal.com
Year Founded: 2007
Sales Range: $25-49.9 Million
Emp.: 482
IT Staff Augmentation & Contingent Workforce Management Services
N.A.I.C.S.: 561311
Bryan Barber (CEO)
Jeff Taylor (Sr VP-Ops)
Scott Bruman (Dir-Recruiting & Bus Dev)

ADVANTIVE LLC
4221 W Boy Scout Blvd Ste 390, Tampa, FL 33607
Tel.: (656) 444-9844   DE
Web Site: https://www.advantive.com
Year Founded: 2022
Emp.: 100
Software Publr
N.A.I.C.S.: 513210
Benoit de la Tour (CEO)

Subsidiaries:

Productivity Quality Systems, Inc.   (1)
210 B E Spring Valley Rd, Dayton, OH 45458
Tel.: (937) 813-4700
Web Site: http://www.pqsystems.com
Sales Range: $10-24.9 Million
Emp.: 50
Quality Control Software Publisher & Training Services
N.A.I.C.S.: 513210
Beth Savage (Pres)

Proplanner, Inc   (1)
2321 N Loop Dr, Ames, IA 50010
Tel.: (515) 296-9914
Web Site: http://www.proplanner.net
Rev.: $1,000,000
Emp.: 13
Custom Computer Programming Services

N.A.I.C.S.: 541511

ADVANTIX SYSTEMS
13800 NW 2nd St Ste 100, Sunrise, FL 33325
Tel.: (305) 503-0446
Web Site:
http://www.advantixsystems.com
Sales Range: $1-9.9 Million
Emp.: 200
Dehumidifiers & Cooling Systems Mfr
N.A.I.C.S.: 333415
Hannah Granade (Pres)
Niv Cousins (VP-Global Support)
Phil Farese (VP-R&D)
Trevor Wende (VP-Engrg)
Mooki Talby (VP-Sls & Bus Dev-Europe & Asia)
Gil Simoes (CFO & Chief Strategy Officer)
Tommy Forkosh (CTO)
Dan Forkosh (Chm)

ADVANTOR HOLDING CORPORATION
424 N Washington St, Alexandria, VA 22314
Tel.: (703) 549-3900
Rev.: $20,700,000
Emp.: 6
Burglar Alarm Apparatus Mfr
N.A.I.C.S.: 541618

ADVANTUS CORPORATION
12276 San Jose Blvd Ste 618, Jacksonville, FL 32223-8672
Tel.: (904) 482-0091   FL
Web Site: https://www.advantus.com
Rev.: $5,000,000
Emp.: 90
Mfr & Provider of Office Products
N.A.I.C.S.: 332510
Kevin Carpenter (Pres)
Charles Frohman (VP)
Pete Levy (COO)

ADVECOR, INC.
7428 Trade St, San Diego, CA 92121
Tel.: (858) 397-1400   CA
Web Site: http://www.advecor.com
Year Founded: 2003
Sales Range: $10-24.9 Million
Emp.: 25
Advetising Agency
N.A.I.C.S.: 541810
Greg Dowd (Pres & CEO)
Todd Armstrong (Dir-Tech)

ADVENT ELECTRIC, INC.
301 E 4th St, Bridgeport, PA 19405
Tel.: (610) 277-6610   PA
Web Site: http://adventelect.com
Year Founded: 1978
Industrial Control Products Mfr
N.A.I.C.S.: 423830
Carl S. Hanski (Treas)

ADVENT GLOBAL SOLUTIONS, INC.
12777 Jones Rd Ste 445, Houston, TX 77070
Tel.: (281) 970-3000
Web Site:
https://www.adventglobal.com
Year Founded: 1997
Information Technology Services & Solutions
N.A.I.C.S.: 541512

ADVENT INTERNATIONAL CORPORATION
Prudential Tower 800 Boylston St, Boston, MA 02199-8069
Tel.: (617) 951-9400   DE
Web Site:
https://www.adventinternational.com

Advent International Corporation—(Continued)

Year Founded: 1984
Privater Equity Firm
N.A.I.C.S.: 523999
Susan Gentile *(Mng Dir)*
Tricia Glynn *(Mng Partner)*
Tricia Glynn *(Mng Dir)*
Neha Mathur *(VP)*
Morgan McKee *(VP)*
Tricia Glynn *(Mng Partner)*
James Mullen *(Operating Partner)*
John P. Bilbrey *(Operating Partner)*
Chris Egan *(Mng Partner)*
John Maldonado *(Mng Partner)*

Subsidiaries:

ATI Physical Therapy, Inc. (1)
790 Remington Blvd, Bolingbrook, IL 60440
Tel.: (219) 791-9021
Web Site: http://www.atipt.com
Vocational Rehabilitation Services
N.A.I.C.S.: 624310
Samuel Allen Hamood *(Pres)*
Eric Meadors *(Mgr-Bus Dev)*
Samuel Allen Hamood *(Pres)*
Brent Mack *(COO)*
Labeed Diab *(CEO)*
David Swift *(Chm)*
Joseph Jordan *(CFO)*
Todd Powers *(Sr VP-Real Estate)*
John Sanford *(VP-Design, Construction & Facilities)*

Subsidiary (Domestic):

Rush-Copley Medical Center (2)
2000 Ogden Ave, Aurora, IL 60504
Tel.: (630) 978-6200
Web Site: http://www.rushcopley.com
Emp.: 2,000
General Medical & Surgical Hospitals
N.A.I.C.S.: 622110
Bruce Dienst *(Chm)*
William Skoglund *(Vice Chm)*

U.S. Therapy, Inc. (2)
#5 W State & 8th Plz, Quincy, IL 62301
Tel.: (217) 224-1750
Web Site: http://www.firstchoicetherapy.net
Outpatient Rehabilitation Services
N.A.I.C.S.: 621498
Dennis E. Venvertloh *(Pres & CEO)*

Aareal Bank AG (1)
Paulinenstrasse 15, D-65189, Wiesbaden,
Germany (37%)
Tel.: (49) 6113480
Web Site: https://www.aareal-bank.com
Rev.: $2,634,362,184
Assets: $50,542,844,809
Liabilities: $46,981,437,513
Net Worth: $3,561,407,295
Earnings: $76,624,218
Emp.: 3,463
Fiscal Year-end: 12/31/2023
Commercial Banking Services
N.A.I.C.S.: 522110
Jurgen Junginger *(Head-IR)*
Jean Pierre Mustier *(Chm-Supervisory Bd)*
Christof Winkelmann *(Chief Market Officer & Member-Mgmt Bd)*
Sebastian Gotzken *(Dir-IR)*
Hans-Hermann Lotter *(Deputy Chm-Supervisory Bd)*
Barbara Antonia Knoflach *(Deputy Chm-Supervisory Bd)*
Christian Klaus Ricken *(CEO)*
Karin Desczka *(Mgr-IR)*
Carsten Schafer *(Dir-IR)*
Marc Oliver Hess *(CFO & Member-Mgmt Bd)*
Klaus Novatius *(Deputy Chm-Supervisory Bd)*
Nina Babic *(Chief Risk Officer & Member-Mgmt Bd)*
Frank Finger *(Head-Treasury)*
Andy Halford *(CFO)*

Subsidiary (Non-US):

Aareal Bank AG (2)
29 bis rue d'Astorg, 75008, Paris,
France (100%)
Tel.: (33) 14 451 6630
Web Site: http://www.aareal-bank.com
Sales Range: $50-74.9 Million
Emp.: 25
International Real Estate Financing

N.A.I.C.S.: 522292

Aareal Bank Asia Limited (2)
3 Church Street, Singapore, 49483, Singapore
Web Site: http://www.aareal-bank.com
Tel.: (65) 63729750
Web Site: http://www.aareal-bank.com
Emp.: 10
Real Estate Investment Services
N.A.I.C.S.: 522292

Subsidiary (US):

Aareal Bank Capital Funding Trust (2)
250 Park Ave Ste 820, New York, NY 10177
Tel.: (646) 465-8601
Web Site: http://www.aareal-capital-funding.com
Investment Banking Services
N.A.I.C.S.: 523150

Aareal Capital Corporation (2)
360 Madison Ave - 18th Fl, New York, NY 10017
Tel.: (212) 508-4080
Web Site: http://www.aareal-bank.com
Sales Range: $50-74.9 Million
Property Financing
N.A.I.C.S.: 522292

Subsidiary (Domestic):

Aareal Estate AG (2)
Paulinenstrasse 15, D 65189, Wiesbaden,
Germany (100%)
Tel.: (49) 6113480
Web Site: http://www.aareal-bank.com
Sales Range: $50-74.9 Million
Emp.: 21
Development, Management & Marketing of
Commercial Properties
N.A.I.C.S.: 531390

Aareal First Financial Solutions AG (2)
Isaac-Fulda-Allee 6, 55124, Mainz, Germany
Tel.: (49) 61314864500
Web Site: http://www.first-financial.biz
Software Development Services
N.A.I.C.S.: 541511

Aareal Gesellschaft fur Beteiligungen und Grundbesitz Dritte mbH & Co. KG (2)
Paulinenstr 15, 65189, Wiesbaden, Germany
Tel.: (49) 6113482950
Property Management Services
N.A.I.C.S.: 531312

Aareal Gesellschaft fur Beteiligungen und Grundbesitz Erste mbH & Co. KG (2)
Paulinenstr 15, 65189, Wiesbaden, Germany
Tel.: (49) 6113480
Web Site: http://www.aareal-bank.com
Emp.: 800
Real Estate Management Services
N.A.I.C.S.: 531390

Aareal IT Beteiligungen GmbH (2)
Paulinenstr 15, 65189, Wiesbaden, Germany
Tel.: (49) 6113480
Web Site: http://www.aareal-bank.com
Emp.: 2,200
Investment Management Consulting Services
N.A.I.C.S.: 523999

Aareal Valuation GmbH (2)
Paulinenstrasse 15, 65189, Wiesbaden,
Germany (100%)
Tel.: (49) 6113480
Web Site: http://www.aareal-valuation.com
Sales Range: $25-49.9 Million
Property Valuation & Consulting Services
N.A.I.C.S.: 541618

Subsidiary (Non-US):

Aareal-Financial Service, spol. s r.o. (2)
Vaclavske Namesti 19, 11000, Prague,
Czech Republic
Tel.: (420) 234656006

Web Site: http://www.aareal-bank.com
Financial Management Consulting Services
N.A.I.C.S.: 541611

Subsidiary (Domestic):

Aareon AG (2)
Isaac-Fulda-Allee 6, 55124, Mainz, Germany
Tel.: (49) 6 131 3010
Web Site: https://www.aareon.de
Sales Range: $400-449.9 Million
Emp.: 1,200
Software & IT Services for the Management
of Residential & Commercial Properties
N.A.I.C.S.: 449210
Manfred Alflen *(CEO & Member-Mgmt Bd)*
Sabine Fischer *(CMO & Member-Mgmt Bd)*
Andre Rasquin *(COO & Member-Mgmt Bd)*
Christian M. Schmahl *(CFO & Member-Mgmt Bd)*
Imad Abdallah *(Chief Digital & Ventures Officer & Member-Mgmt Bd)*

Subsidiary (Non-US):

Aareon France S.A.S. (3)
Parc Tertiaire De Meudon Batiment Le
Newton 9-11 Rue Jeanne Braconnier, Meudon La Foret, 92366, Meudon, Cedex,
France
Tel.: (33) 145379230
Web Site: http://www.aareon.fr
Sales Range: $75-99.9 Million
Property Management Consulting Services
N.A.I.C.S.: 531312

Aareon UK Ltd. (3)
Building 500 Abbey Park, Stareton, Kenilworth, CV8 2LY, United Kingdom
Tel.: (44) 2476323723
Web Site: http://www.aareon.co.uk
Sales Range: $10-24.9 Million
Business Management Software Development Services
N.A.I.C.S.: 541511
Rob Griffiths *(Mng Dir)*

Subsidiary (Domestic):

Aareon Deutschland GmbH (2)
Im Muenchfeld 1-5, 55122, Mainz, Germany
Tel.: (49) 6131 301 295
Investment Banking Services
N.A.I.C.S.: 523150

Subsidiary (Non-US):

Aareon Finland Oy (2)
Pohjoisesplanadi 39, 00100, Helsinki, Finland
Tel.: (358) 317254380
Web Site: http://www.aareon.fi
Software Development Services
N.A.I.C.S.: 541511

Aareon Nederland B.V. (2)
Cornelis Houtmanstraat 36, 7825 VG, Emmen, Netherlands
Tel.: (31) 882420242
Web Site: http://www.aareon.nl
Software Development Services
N.A.I.C.S.: 541511

Aareon Norge AS (2)
Calmeyers Gate 5, 0183, Oslo, Norway
Tel.: (47) 90825054
Web Site: http://www.aareon.no
Software Development Services
N.A.I.C.S.: 541511

Subsidiary (Domestic):

Aareon Software Handelsgesellschaft mbH (2)
Isaac Fulda Allee 6, Mainz, 55124, Germany
Tel.: (49) 61313010
Web Site: http://www.aareon.com
Computer Peripheral Equipment Distr
N.A.I.C.S.: 423430

Subsidiary (Non-US):

Aareon Sverige AB (2)
Flojelbergsgatan 10, 431.37, Molndal, Sweden
Tel.: (46) 317254300
Web Site: http://www.aareon.se
Software Development Services
N.A.I.C.S.: 541511

Subsidiary (Domestic):

Aareon Wodis GmbH (2)
Rheinlanddamm 199, Dortmund, 44139,
Germany
Tel.: (49) 23177510
Web Site: http://www.aareon.com
Sales Range: $50-74.9 Million
Emp.: 100
Real Estate Manangement Services
N.A.I.C.S.: 531390

COREALCREDIT Bank AG (2)
Gruneburgweg 58-62, D-60322, Frankfurt
am Main, Germany (99.9%)
Tel.: (49) 6971790
Web Site: http://www.corealcredit.de
Sales Range: $5-14.9 Billion
Emp.: 175
Mortgage Banking Services
N.A.I.C.S.: 522310

CalCon Deutschland GmbH (2)
Beethovenplatz 4, 80336, Munich, Germany
Tel.: (49) 895526980
Real Estate Services
N.A.I.C.S.: 531390

Capital Funding GmbH & Co. KG (2)
Steinweg 3-5, 60313, Frankfurt am Main,
60313, Germany
Tel.: (49) 6929925385
Web Site: http://www.capital-funding.de
Financial Management Consulting Services
N.A.I.C.S.: 523999
Florian Schluter *(Gen Mgr)*

Collect Artificial Intelligence GmbH (2)
Am Sandtorkai 50, 20457, Hamburg, Germany
Tel.: (49) 40609412950
Web Site: http://www.collect.ai
Emp.: 50
Ecommerce Services
N.A.I.C.S.: 541512
Thomas V. Hake *(Mng Dir)*
Frederik Werner *(Co-Owner-Product)*
Adeline Paasch *(Head-People & Culture)*
Wiebke Tschorn *(Co-Owner-Product)*
Nina Walz *(Mgr-Corp Dev)*

Deutsche Structured Finance GmbH (2)
Feuerbachstrasse 26-32, 60325, Frankfurt,
Germany
Tel.: (49) 699714970
Web Site: http://www.dsf-fra.de
Financial Management Consulting Services
N.A.I.C.S.: 541611

Deutsche Structured Finance GmbH & Co. Alphard KG (2)
Feuerbachstrasse 26-32, Frankfurt am
Main, Germany
Tel.: (49) 699714970
Web Site: http://www.dsf-fra.de
Sales Range: $25-49.9 Million
Emp.: 17
Financial Management Consulting Services
N.A.I.C.S.: 541611

Deutsche Structured Finance GmbH & Co. Deneb KG (2)
Feuerbachstr 26- 32, 60325, Frankfurt am
Main, Germany
Tel.: (49) 699714970
Financial Management Consulting Services
N.A.I.C.S.: 541611

Deutsche Structured Finance GmbH & Co. Titan KG (2)
Westendstr 24, Frankfurt am Main, 60325,
Germany
Tel.: (49) 699714970
Financial Management Consulting Services
N.A.I.C.S.: 541611

GEV GmbH (2)
Gadastr 4, Bergkirchen, 85232, Dachau,
Germany
Tel.: (49) 8142652250
Web Site: http://www.gev-online.com
Catering Equipment Mfr & Whslr
N.A.I.C.S.: 333310

Subsidiary (Non-US):

IMMO Consulting S.p.A. (2)

Via Mercadante 12/14, 198, Rome, Italy
Tel.: (39) 0683004400
Financial Management Consulting Services
N.A.I.C.S.: 541611

Kalshoven Automation B.V. (2)
Kabelweg 37, 1014 BA, Amsterdam, Netherlands
Tel.: (31) 206068606
Web Site: http://www.kalshoven.nl
Software Development Services
N.A.I.C.S.: 541511

Subsidiary (Domestic):

Real Verwaltungsgesellschaft mbH (2)
Elisabeth-Schwarzkopf-Weg, 65510, Idstein, Germany
Tel.: (49) 6113480
Web Site: http://www.aareal-bank.com
Real Estate Management Services
N.A.I.C.S.: 531390

Rehabilitationsklinik Barby Besitzgesellschaft mbH (2)
Paulinenstr 15, 65189, Wiesbaden, Hessen, Germany
Tel.: (49) 39298 61600
Health Insurance Services
N.A.I.C.S.: 524298

Subsidiary (Non-US):

SG Automatisering B.V. (2)
Cornelis Houtmanstraat 36, Postbus 2036, 7825 VG, Emmen, Netherlands
Tel.: (31) 591630111
Web Site: http://www.sg.nl
Software Development Services
N.A.I.C.S.: 541512

SG Detachering B.V. (2)
Cornelis Houtmanstraat 36, Emmen, 7825 VG, Drenthe, Netherlands
Tel.: (31) 591630111
General Management Consulting Services
N.A.I.C.S.: 541618

SG Facilitor B.V. (2)
Gronausestraat 710, 7534 AM, Enschede, Netherlands
Tel.: (31) 534800710
Web Site: http://facilitor.nl
Sales Range: $25-49.9 Million
Software Development Services
N.A.I.C.S.: 541512

SG Professional Services B.V. (2)
Cornelis Houtmanstraat 36, Emmen, 7825 VG, Drenthe, Netherlands
Tel.: (31) 591666833
Software Development Services
N.A.I.C.S.: 541511

Tactile Limited (2)
International House 24 Holborn Viaduct, London, EC1A 2BN, United Kingdom
Tel.: (44) 2071831222
Web Site: https://www.fixflo.com
Computer System Integration Services
N.A.I.C.S.: 541512

Subsidiary (Domestic):

Terrain-Aktiengesellschaft Herzogpark (2)
Paulinenstr 15, 65189, Wiesbaden, Hessen, Germany
Tel.: (49) 6113480
Web Site: http://www.aareal-bank.com
Real Estate Management Services
N.A.I.C.S.: 531390

Westdeutsche Immobilien Servicing AG (2)
Kantstrasse 1, 55122, Mainz, Germany
Tel.: (49) 61313029890
Web Site: https://www.westimmo.com
Sales Range: $600-649.9 Million
Emp.: 274
Real Estate Financing & Investment Banking Services
N.A.I.C.S.: 522292

Westdeutsche Immobilien Servicing AG (2)
Grosse Bleiche 54, 55116, Mainz, Germany
Tel.: (49) 61313029890
Web Site: http://www.westimmo.com
Software Development Services

N.A.I.C.S.: 541511

mse Augsburg GmbH (2)
Kurzes Geland 12, 86156, Augsburg, Germany
Tel.: (49) 821710040
Web Site: http://www.relion.business.site
Software Development Services
N.A.I.C.S.: 541511

mse Immobiliensoftware GmbH (2)
Jarrestrasse 2, 22303, Hamburg, Germany
Tel.: (49) 405343510
Web Site: http://www.mse-immo.com
Software Development Services
N.A.I.C.S.: 541511

plusForta GmbH (2)
Dusseldorf Talstr 24, 40217, Dusseldorf, Germany
Tel.: (49) 2115426830
Web Site: http://kautionsfrei.de
Software Development Services
N.A.I.C.S.: 541511

AccentCare, Inc. (1)
17855 N Dallas Pkwy, Dallas, TX 75287
Tel.: (626) 395-7256
Web Site: http://www.accentcare.com
Sales Range: $1-9.9 Million
Continuing Care Retirement Communities
N.A.I.C.S.: 623311
Stephan S. Rodgers *(CEO)*
Steve Jakubcanin *(COO)*

Subsidiary (Domestic):

Sta-Home Health & Hospice, Inc. (2)
406 Briarwood Dr #200, Jackson, MS 39206
Tel.: (601) 956-5100
Web Site: http://accentcare.com
Women Healthcare Services
N.A.I.C.S.: 621610
Vincent Caracci *(CEO)*

Advent India PE Advisors Pvt. Ltd. (1)
Unit 1702 17th FloorOne India Bulls Centre Tower 2 Wing A 841, Senapati Bapat Marg, Mumbai, 400 013, India
Tel.: (91) 22 4057 3000
Private Equity Fund Management Services
N.A.I.C.S.: 523940
Shweta Jalan *(Mng Dir)*

Advent International (Shanghai) Co Ltd. (1)
STE 3207-3208 Park Place No 1601 Nanjing Road W, Jingan District, Shanghai, 200040, China
Tel.: (86) 21 6032 0788
Web Site:
 http://www.adventinternational.com
Private Equity Fund Management Services
N.A.I.C.S.: 523940
David Chen *(VP)*
Filippo de Vecchi *(Mng Dir)*
Andrew Li *(Principal)*

Advent International Advisory S.L. (1)
Serrano n 57 2, 28006, Madrid, Spain
Tel.: (34) 91 745 48 60
Web Site:
 http://www.adventinternational.com
Sales Range: $25-49.9 Million
Emp.: 12
Private Equity Fund Management Services
N.A.I.C.S.: 523940

Advent International Colombia S.A.S. (1)
Avenida Calle 82 10-33 Oficina 902, Bogota, 110221, Colombia
Tel.: (57) 1 254 4747
Web Site:
 http://www.adventinternational.com
Emp.: 15
Financial Management Services
N.A.I.C.S.: 523940
Mauricio Salgar *(Mng Dir)*

Advent International GmbH (1)
Westhafenplatz 1, 60327, Frankfurt am Main, Germany
Tel.: (49) 69 955 2700
Web Site: http://www.adventinternational.de
Private Equity Fund Management Services
N.A.I.C.S.: 523940

Advent International PE Advisors S.C (1)
Edificio Omega Campos Eliseos 345 7 Piso Col Polanco, Polanco, 11560, Mexico
Tel.: (52) 55 5281 0303
Web Site:
 http://www.adventinternational.com
Private Equity Fund Management Services
N.A.I.C.S.: 523940
Santiago Castillo *(Mng Dir)*
Juan Carlos Torres *(Mng Partner)*

Advent International Romania S.R.L. (1)
89-97 Grigore Alexandrescu Street 3rd floor, Bucharest, 010624, Romania
Tel.: (40) 21 211 1602
Sales Range: $25-49.9 Million
Emp.: 7
Financial Management Services
N.A.I.C.S.: 523940

Advent International S.R.O (1)
Palladium Na Porici 3a, 110 00, Prague, Czech Republic
Tel.: (420) 234 749 750
Sales Range: $25-49.9 Million
Emp.: 7
Private Equity Fund Management Services
N.A.I.C.S.: 523940

Advent International SAS (1)
8-10 rue Lamennais, 75008, Paris, France
Tel.: (33) 1 55 37 29 00
Web Site:
 http://www.adventinternational.com
Sales Range: $25-49.9 Million
Emp.: 13
Financial Management Services
N.A.I.C.S.: 523940
Cedric Chateau *(Mng Dir & Pres)*

Advent International SP. Z.O.O. SP.K (1)
Marszalkowska 89, 00-693, Warsaw, Poland
Tel.: (48) 226275141
Sales Range: $25-49.9 Million
Emp.: 10
Financial Management Services
N.A.I.C.S.: 523940

Advent International plc (1)
111 Buckingham Palace Road, London, SW1W 0SR, United Kingdom
Tel.: (44) 20 7333 0800
Web Site:
 http://www.adventinternational.com
Sales Range: $50-74.9 Million
Emp.: 100
Private Equity Fund Management Services
N.A.I.C.S.: 523940
Chris Mruck *(Mng Partner)*
Werner Geissler *(Operating Partner)*
James Brocklebank *(Mng Partner)*

Advent do Brasil Consultoria e Participacoes Ltda. (1)
Av Brig Faria Lima 3311, 04538-133, Sao Paulo, SP, Brazil
Tel.: (55) 11 3014 6800
Web Site:
 http://www.adventinternational.com
Sales Range: $25-49.9 Million
Emp.: 23
Financial Management Services
N.A.I.C.S.: 523940
Patrice Etlin *(Mng Partner)*
Marco Mendes *(Sr Dir-Portfolio Support)*
Rafael Patury *(Mgr)*
Juan Pablo Zucchini *(Mng Dir)*

Aimbridge Hospitality, LLC (1)
5301 Headquarters Dr, Plano, TX 75024
Tel.: (972) 952-0200
Web Site:
 http://www.aimbridgehospitality.com
Sales Range: $1-9.9 Million
Emp.: 99
Management Services
N.A.I.C.S.: 561110
Lynne Roberts *(Exec VP-Capital Markets)*
Robert Burg *(COO)*
Tom Kenney *(VP)*
Vince Cuce *(VP)*
Michael Johnson *(Treas & Sr VP-Fin)*
Rich Cortese *(Sr VP-Caribbean Ops & Dev)*
Greg Moundas *(Gen Counsel & Exec VP)*
Judy Hendrick *(CFO)*

Gerard Forster *(CIO & Sr VP)*
Bill Stadler *(Controller)*
Kevin Dingle *(Sr VP)*
Don Ayres *(VP-Dev)*
Brad Frazier *(Sr VP-Sls & Mktg)*
David W. Johnson *(Co-Founder)*
T. Seth Williams *(Head-Asian Capital Markets)*
Les Bentley *(Co-Founder)*
Jamie Grittman *(Sr VP-Sls, Strategy & Innovation)*
Wade Fischer *(Sr VP-Project Mgmt)*
Natalie White *(Exec VP-Mktg)*
Simon Mendy *(Sr VP-Ops)*
Ian McAuley *(Pres-Canada)*
Mark M. Chloupek *(Chief Legal Officer)*
Michael J. Deitemeyer *(Pres & CEO)*
John P. Caparella *(Pres-Evolution Hospitality)*
Joe Isaac *(Sr VP-Mergers & Acq)*
Mark Tamis *(Pres-Global Ops)*
David W. Johnson *(Co-Founder)*

Subsidiary (Domestic):

Interstate Hotels & Resorts, Inc. (2)
4501 N Fairfax Dr Ste 500, Arlington, VA 22203
Tel.: (703) 387-3100
Web Site: http://www.interstatehotels.com
Emp.: 30,000
Hotel & Resort Property Management Services
N.A.I.C.S.: 531312
George J. Brennan *(Exec VP-Sls & Mktg)*
Leslie Ng *(Chief Investment Officer)*
Samuel Knighton *(COO)*
Edward J. Blum *(Exec VP-Dev & Acq)*
Carrie McIntyre *(CFO)*
Aaron Greenman *(Exec VP-Acq & Dev-EMEA)*
Jim Abrahamson *(Chm)*
Emily Boling Lynn *(Sr VP-Global & Strategic Accts)*
Jenny Zhan *(Chief Acct Officer & Exec VP)*
Erica H. Hageman *(Gen Counsel & Exec VP)*
Patrick Beron *(Sr VP-Sls & Mktg)*
Sherry Serio *(Sr VP-Sls & Mktg)*
Brett Stewart *(Sr VP-Dev & Acq-Capital Markets)*
James Lamb *(CIO)*
Russ Cox *(Exec VP-Ops-Rim Hospital Div)*
Bill Deller *(Exec VP-Hotel Finance-North America)*
Mark LeBlanc *(Exec VP-Dev & Acq)*
Darren Brennen *(Exec VP-Intl Fin)*
John A. Rubino *(Exec VP-Crossroads Hospitality-Select Svc Div)*
Andrew Jordan *(CMO)*
Carrie David *(Chief HR Officer)*
Rogier Hurkmans *(VP-Ops-Continental Europe)*
Greg O'Stean *(Chief Dev Officer-North America)*
Fernando Salazar *(Sr VP-Food & Beverage)*
Mike Wylie *(Head-ECommerce-Dallas)*
Andrew J. Arthurs *(CIO)*
Nicole Turnhout-Ammerlaan *(VP-Ops-Western Europe)*

Prism Hotel Company, Inc. (2)
13760 Noel Rd Ste 610, Dallas, TX 75240
Tel.: (214) 987-9300
Web Site: http://www.prismhotels.com
Sales Range: $1-9.9 Million
Emp.: 43
Home Management Services
N.A.I.C.S.: 721110
John Bailey *(CFO)*
Mark Van Amerongen *(Sr VP-Ops)*
Allison Handy *(Sr VP-Mktg)*
Beth Mahony *(Reg Dir-Sls)*
Chris Charbonnet *(Reg VP-Ops)*
Kristi Griffith *(Dir-Sls Performance Support)*
Moses Qidwai *(Sr VP-Ops)*
Steve Van *(Pres & CEO)*
Will Traywick *(VP-ECommerce & Digital Mktg)*

Subsidiary (Domestic):

Prism Hospitality, LP (3)
3131 West Loop S, Houston, TX 77027
Tel.: (713) 961-1640
Sales Range: $1-9.9 Million
Emp.: 40
Hotels (except Casino Hotels) & Motels

Advent International Corporation—(Continued)
N.A.I.C.S.: 721110
Steve Van (Pres & CEO)

Allnex Holding S.a.r.l. (1)
78 Grand Rue, 1660, Luxembourg, Luxembourg
Tel.: (352) 2822 9121
Web Site: http://www.allnex.com
Sales Range: $1-4.9 Billion
Emp.: 4,000
Holding Company; Coatings & Resins Mfr
N.A.I.C.S.: 551112
Miguel Mantas (CEO)
Markus Aschauer (Chief Integration Officer)
Jean-Marc Durbuis (Exec VP-Performance Resins)
Ruben Mannien (Exec VP-Liquid Resins & Additives)
Duncan Taylor (CFO)
Francois L. Thys (COO)
Petra Zimmer (Head-HR)

Subsidiary (Non-US):

Allnex Austria GmbH (2)
Leechgasse 21, 8010, Graz, Austria
Tel.: (43) 50 399 0
Web Site: http://www.allnex.com
Sales Range: $25-49.9 Million
Emp.: 200
Chemical Products Mfr
N.A.I.C.S.: 325998
Muller Intrie (Gen Mgr)
Miguel Mantas (Gen Mgr)

Allnex Belgium SA/NV (2)
Square Marie Curie 11, 1070, Brussels, Belgium
Tel.: (32) 2.5604511
Web Site: http://www.allnex.com
Sales Range: $1-4.9 Billion
Coating Resins Developer, Mfr & Distr
N.A.I.C.S.: 325510
Jean-Marc Durbuis (Grp Exec VP-Performance Resins)
Duncan Taylor (Grp CFO)

Plant (Domestic):

Allnex Belgium SA/NV - Drogenbos (3)
Anderlechtstraat 33, 1620, Drogenbos, Belgium
Tel.: (32) 2334 5111
Web Site: http://www.allnex.com
Coating Resins Research & Development, Mfr, Technical Services & Whslr
N.A.I.C.S.: 325510

Allnex Belgium SA/NV - Schoonaarde (3)
Steenweg naar Wetteren 20, Schoonaarde, Dendermonde, 9200, Belgium
Tel.: (32) 2334 5050
Web Site: http://www.allnex.com
Coating Resins Mfr
N.A.I.C.S.: 325510

Subsidiary (Non-US):

Allnex Holding II Germany GmbH (2)
Kasteler Strasse 45, 65203, Wiesbaden, Germany
Tel.: (49) 611 962 02
Web Site: http://www.allnex.com
Holding Company; Coating Resins Mfr
N.A.I.C.S.: 551112

Subsidiary (Domestic):

Allnex Germany GmbH (3)
Kasteler Strasse 45, 65203, Wiesbaden, Germany
Tel.: (49) 611 962 02
Web Site: http://www.allnex.com
Coating Resins Mfr
N.A.I.C.S.: 325510

Plant (Domestic):

Allnex Germany GmbH - Hamburg Plant (4)
Helbingstrasse 46, 22047, Hamburg, Germany
Tel.: (49) 40 6943 0
Web Site: http://www.allnex.com
Coating Resins Mfr

N.A.I.C.S.: 325510

Subsidiary (Non-US):

Allnex Norge KS (2)
Svelleveien 33, 2004, Lillestrom, Norway
Tel.: (47) 63 89 72 00
Web Site: http://www.allnex.com
Sales Range: $75-99.9 Million
Emp.: 100
Specialty Chemicals & Materials Developer, Marketer & Mfr
N.A.I.C.S.: 325998

Allnex Resins Australia Pty. Ltd. (2)
49-61 Stephen Road, Botany, 2019, NSW, Australia (100%)
Tel.: (61) 296660331
Resin Mfr
N.A.I.C.S.: 325211
Mike Law (Gen Mgr)

Subsidiary (US):

Allnex USA, Inc. (2)
9005 Westside Pkwy, Alpharetta, GA 30009
Tel.: (770) 280-8300
Web Site: http://www.allnex.com
Coatings & Resins Mfr & Whslr
N.A.I.C.S.: 325510
Tom Kelly (VP-Americas & Bus Dir-Crosslinking Resins-Global)
Ramesh Subramanian (Sls Dir-Liquid Resins & Additives-Americas)

Plant (Domestic):

Allnex USA, Inc. - Kalamazoo Plant (3)
2715 Miller Rd, Kalamazoo, MI 49001
Tel.: (269) 385-1255
Web Site: http://www.allnex.com
Sales Range: $50-74.9 Million
Emp.: 75
Coating Resins Mfr
N.A.I.C.S.: 325510

Unit (Domestic):

Allnex USA, Inc. - Stamford R&D Facility (3)
1937 W Main St, Stamford, CT 06904
Tel.: (203) 321-2467
Web Site: http://www.allnex.com
Specialty Coating Resins Research & Development
N.A.I.C.S.: 541715

Plant (Domestic):

Allnex USA, Inc. - Wallingford Plant (3)
528 S Cherry St, Wallingford, CT 06492
Tel.: (203) 294-5512
Web Site: http://www.allnex.com
Coating Resins Mfr
N.A.I.C.S.: 325510

Allnex USA, Inc. - Willow Island Plant (3)
252 Heilman Ave Willow Island, Belmont, WV 26134
Tel.: (304) 665-1600
Web Site: http://www.allnex.com
Emp.: 37
Coating Resins Mfr
N.A.I.C.S.: 325510
Gus Barbarito (Plant Mgr)

Ammeraal Beltech Holding BV (1)
Comeniusstraat 8, 1817 MS, Alkmaar, Netherlands
Tel.: (31) 725751212
Web Site: http://www.ammeraalbeltech.com
Emp.: 200
Conveyor Belts, Flat Belts, Modular Belts, Endless Woven Belts, Engineered Belts & Timing Belts Mfr
N.A.I.C.S.: 326220
Prakash K. Iyengar (CEO)

Subsidiary (Domestic):

AMMEGA (2)
Comeniusstraat 8, Alkmaar, 1817 MS, North Holland, Netherlands
Tel.: (31) 725751212
Conveying & Power Transmission
N.A.I.C.S.: 221118
Ralph Schuck (CEO)

Subsidiary (US):

Midwest Industrial Rubber Inc. (3)
10431 Midwest Industrial Dr, Saint Louis, MO 63132
Tel.: (314) 890-0016
Web Site: http://www.mir-belting.com
Hose, Belting & Packing
N.A.I.C.S.: 423840
Brian McSharry (CEO)

Subsidiary (US):

Ammeraal Beltech Inc. (2)
7501 N St Louis Ave, Skokie, IL 60076
Tel.: (847) 673-6720
Web Site: http://www.ammeraalbeltech.com
Conveyor Belts, Flat Belts, Modular Belts, Endless Woven Belts, Engineered Belts & Timing Belts Mfr
N.A.I.C.S.: 326220
Kerry Baskins (Pres)
Stijn Vriends (CEO)

Subsidiary (Non-US):

Ammeraal Beltech SA (2)
Plaza dels Avellaners 15, Pol Ind Santiga, Barbera del Valles, 8210, Barcelona, Spain
Tel.: (34) 937183305
Web Site: http://www.ammeraalbeltech.es
Conveyor Belts, Flat Belts, Modular Belts, Endless Woven Belts, Engineered Belts & Timing Belts Mfr
N.A.I.C.S.: 326220
Jarvey Causafon (Gen Mgr)

BOS Solutions Ltd. (1)
Suite 1200 635 8th Avenue SW, Calgary, T2P 3M3, AB, Canada
Tel.: (403) 234-8103
Web Site: http://www.bos-solutions.com
Sales Range: $25-49.9 Million
Emp.: 25
Oil & Gas Field Engineering Services
N.A.I.C.S.: 541330
Len Cornez (CFO)
Ryan Pilsner (VP-Ops)
Susan Gallivan (VP-HR)
Brad Whitaker (Safety & Equipment)
Lizely Abita (Dir-Quality Assurance)
Shyla Stinson (Controller)

BioDuro LLC (1)
11011 Torreyana Rd, San Diego, CA 92121
Tel.: (858) 529-6600
Web Site: http://bioduro.com
Pharmaceuticals Mfr
N.A.I.C.S.: 325412
Cyrus K. Mirsaidi (Pres & CEO)
David Preston (Co-Chm)
Masood Tayebi (Founder & Co-Chm)
Magdalena Mejillano (Exec VP & Gen Mgr-Global CMC Solutions)
David Hedden (Chief Scientific Officer-Global CMC Solutions)
TJ Deng (Gen Mgr-China & BioDuro Discovery)
Jeffery Blazevich (CFO)

Subsidiary (Domestic):

Molecular Response LLC (2)
11011 Torreyana Rd, San Diego, CA 92121-1154
Tel.: (858) 529-6600
Research & Development in Biotechnology
N.A.I.C.S.: 541714

Bottom Line Food Processors, Inc. (1)
200 Michael Angelo Way, Austin, TX 78728
Tel.: (512) 218-3500
Web Site: http://www.michaelangelos.com
Sales Range: $100-124.9 Million
Frozen Specialty Food Mfr
N.A.I.C.S.: 311412
Michael Angelo (Chm & CEO)

Brammer plc (1)
St Ann's House 1 Old Market Place, Knutsford, WA16 6PD, Cheshire, United Kingdom
Tel.: (44) 1565756800
Web Site: http://www.brammer.biz
Bearings, Power Transmission Products & Motion Control Equipment, Equipment Management, Calibration & Rental Services for Instruments, Test Equipment & Computer Products Distr

N.A.I.C.S.: 423830
Duncan J. Magrath (Fin Dir-Grp)
Alison Gould (Treas)

Subsidiary (Non-US):

Brammer France (2)
5 Pauling Street, 91240, Saint-Michel-sur-Orge, France
Tel.: (33) 180376700
Web Site: http://www.fr.brammer.biz
Bearing Sprocket & Various Mechanical Part Mfr
N.A.I.C.S.: 333517
Carrier Bruno (Head-Growth & Mktg)

CCC Information Services, Inc. (1)
222 Merchandise Mart Plz Ste 900, Chicago, IL 60654
Tel.: (312) 222-4636
Web Site: http://www.cccis.com
Cloud, Mobile, Telematics, Hyperscale Technologies & Apps (for Automotive, Insurance & Collision Repair Industries)
N.A.I.C.S.: 541511
Githesh Ramamurthy (Chm & CEO)
Mary Jo Prigge (Pres-Svc Ops)
James A. Dickens (Exec VP & Gen Mgr-Supply Chain)
Andrew G. Balbirer (CFO & Exec VP)
Peter Morowski (Exec VP-Products & Tech)
Joe Allen (Sr VP & Gen Mgr-Automotive Svcs Grp)
Barrett Callaghan (Sr VP & Gen Mgr-Insurance Svcs Grp)
Kevin Ho (Sr VP & Gen Mgr-China)
Gary Newman (Chief HR Officer & Sr VP)
David Merritt (Gen Counsel, Sec & Sr VP)
Marc Fredman (Sr VP-Corp Strategy & Dev)
Andreas Hecht (Sr VP/Gen Mgr-Original Equipment Manufacturers)
Shivani Govil (Chief Product Officer)
Michael Silva (Chief Comml & Customer Success Officer)

Subsidiary (Domestic):

Auto Injury Solutions, Inc. (2)
1900 W Littleton Blvd,, Littleton, CO 80120
Tel.: (732) 636-3259
Web Site: https://aisreview.com
Direct Health & Medical Insurance Carriers
N.A.I.C.S.: 524114

Cobham plc (1)
Brook Road, Wimborne, BH21 2BJ, Dorset, United Kingdom
Tel.: (44) 1202882121
Web Site: http://www.cobham.com
Rev.: $2,364,564,966
Assets: $3,296,787,058
Liabilities: $1,784,495,924
Net Worth: $1,512,291,134
Earnings: $93,526,774
Emp.: 10,069
Fiscal Year-end: 12/31/2018
Holding Company; Aerospace & Defense Systems Designer & Mfr
N.A.I.C.S.: 551112
David Mellors (CFO & Exec Dir)
David Lockwood (CEO & Exec Dir)
Gillian Duggan (Exec VP-HR & Comm)
Chris Shaw (COO)

Subsidiary (Non-US):

AFI Flight Inspection GmbH (2)
Hermann Blenk Strasse 34, Braunschweig, 38108, Germany
Tel.: (49) 531 235 27 0
Web Site: http://www.cobham.com
Sales Range: $25-49.9 Million
Emp.: 2
Flight Inspection Services
N.A.I.C.S.: 926150

Subsidiary (US):

Aeroflex Holding Corp. (2)
35 S Service Rd, Plainview, NY 11803
Tel.: (516) 694-6700
Web Site: http://www.ams.aeroflex.com
Sales Range: $650-699.9 Million
Emp.: 2,600
Holding Company; RF & Microwave Component Mfr
N.A.I.C.S.: 551112
Rafi Albarian (VP & COO)

Subsidiary (Domestic):

Aeroflex Incorporated (3)
35 S Service Rd, Plainview, NY 11803
Tel.: (516) 694-6700
Web Site: http://www.aeroflex.com
Sales Range: $650-699.9 Million
Microelectronics, Test & Measurement
Equipment Mfr
N.A.I.C.S.: 334413
Leonard Borow (Pres & CEO)

Subsidiary (Domestic):

Aeroflex AVComm-Research & Development Center (4)
383 N Liberty St, Powell, OH 43065
Tel.: (614) 888-2700
Web Site: http://www.ats.aeroflex.com
Emp.: 30
Produces Synthetic High Speed Test &
Measurement Systems for RF & Microwave
Applications
N.A.I.C.S.: 541380

Aeroflex AvComm (4)
14408 W 105th St, Lenexa, KS 66215
Tel.: (913) 693-1700
Web Site: http://www.aeroflex.com
Sales Range: $25-49.9 Million
Emp.: 200
Specialized Electronic Test Equipment for
Military Aviation & Commercial Industries
N.A.I.C.S.: 334515
Guy Hill (Dir)

Division (Domestic):

Cobham Microwave Filter Components (4)
350 Kennedy Dr, Hauppauge, NY 11788
Tel.: (719) 594-8000
Web Site: http://www.ams.aeroflex.com
Sales Range: $25-49.9 Million
Emp.: 200
Mfr of Filters for Space & Military Applications
N.A.I.C.S.: 927110
James Barber (Sr VP)

Subsidiary (Non-US):

Aeroflex Nanjing (5)
1st Floor Westside Factory B 1706 Shuang
Long Da Dao, Jiangning Econo, Nanjing,
211100, Jiangsu, China
Tel.: (86) 2552122735
Web Site: http://www.aeroflex.com
Emp.: 200
Supplies High Power Cable Terminations,
SMA Terminations, Attentuators,
Isolators/Circulators & Adapters
N.A.I.C.S.: 333995

Division (Domestic):

Cobham Motion Control (4)
350 Kennedy Dr, Hauppauge, NY 11788
Tel.: (631) 231-9100
Web Site: http://www.ams.aeroflex.com
Sales Range: $450-499.9 Million
Emp.: 2,800
Products for Space, Military, Avionics, Industrial & Commercial Markets
N.A.I.C.S.: 334511

Subsidiary (Domestic):

Cobham Semiconductor Solutions (4)
35 S Service Rd, Plainview, NY 11803
Tel.: (516) 694-6700
Web Site: http://ams.aeroflex.com
Sales Range: $50-74.9 Million
Emp.: 450
Manufactures Advanced Microelectronic
Multi-chip Modules for Airborne, Space,
Shipboard, Ground Based & Commercial
Avionics & Telecom Systems
N.A.I.C.S.: 517410

Cobham Signal & Control Solutions (4)
40 Industrial Way East, Eatontown, NJ
07724
Tel.: (732) 460-2120
Web Site: http://www.aeroflex.com
Emp.: 100

Supplier of High-Performance RF & Microwave Frequency Synthesizers & Signal
Generation Sources, Integrated Microwave
Assemblies (IMA) & Multi-Function Modules
(MFM)
N.A.I.C.S.: 334515

Subsidiary (Non-US):

Air Precision SAS (2)
5 Avenue Denis Papin, PO Box 36, 92350,
Le Plessis-Robinson, France
Tel.: (33) 1 46 01 2124
Web Site: http://www.cobham.com
Emp.: 100
Aircraft Equipment Mfr
N.A.I.C.S.: 336413

Subsidiary (US):

Chelton Inc. (2)
1955 Lakeway Dr Ste 200, Lewisville, TX
75057-6448
Tel.: (972) 221-1783
Sales Range: $25-49.9 Million
Emp.: 50
Holding Company
N.A.I.C.S.: 551112

Subsidiary (Non-US):

Chelton Antennas SA (3)
7 Chemin de Vaubesnard, 91410, Dourdan,
France
Tel.: (33) 1 60 81 5555
Web Site: http://www.chelton-antennas.com
Sales Range: $25-49.9 Million
Aerospace Communication Equipment Mfr
N.A.I.C.S.: 336413
Jean-Marc Billaud (Gen Mgr)

Team SA (3)
Silic 36 rue de Montlhery, BP 20191,
94563, Rungis, Cedex, France
Tel.: (33) 149786600
Communication Equipment Mfr
N.A.I.C.S.: 334220
Eiji Kawaishi (Chm & CEO)

Subsidiary (Non-US):

Cobham (India) Pvt Limited (2)
Cobham India Liaison Office 4th Floor Birla
Tower 25 Barakhamba Road, New Delhi,
110001, India
Tel.: (91) 11 451 72300
Web Site: http://www.cobham.com
Aircraft Part Mfr
N.A.I.C.S.: 336413

Subsidiary (US):

Cobham Advanced Electronic Solutions Inc. (2)
305 Richardson Rd, Lansdale, PA 19446
Tel.: (215) 996-2000
Web Site: http://www.cobham.com
Aircraft Part Mfr
N.A.I.C.S.: 336413
Robert Hitt (Vice Chm)
Mike Kahn (Pres & CEO)
Stephen Sartwell (Sr VP-Program & Ops
Excellence)
Sean Daily (CFO)
Mike Elias (Sr VP/Gen Mgr-Space Sys Div)

Subsidiary (Domestic):

Cobham Electronic Systems Inc. (3)
1011 Pawtucket Blvd, Lowell, MA 01853
Tel.: (978) 442-4000
Web Site: http://www.cobham.com
Sales Range: $200-249.9 Million
Emp.: 600
Microwave & Radio Communications Systems Developer & Mfr
N.A.I.C.S.: 334290

Unit (Domestic):

Cobham Electronic Systems, Inc. - San Jose (4)
5300 Hellyer Ave, San Jose, CA 95138-1003
Tel.: (408) 624-3000
Sales Range: $150-199.9 Million
Emp.: 345
Microwave & Radio Communications Systems Developer & Mfr
N.A.I.C.S.: 423690

Subsidiary (Domestic):

Cobham MAL Limited (2)

Subsidiary (Domestic):

Colorado Engineering Inc. (3)
1310 United Hts, Colorado Springs, CO
80921
Tel.: (719) 388-8582
Web Site:
http://www.coloradoengineeringinc.com
Rev.: $1,100,000
Emp.: 11
Engineeering Services
N.A.I.C.S.: 541330
Lawrence Scally (Pres)
Lance Brown (Dir-Bus Dev)
Nancy Scally (CEO)

Continental Microwave & Tool Co, Inc (3)
11 Continental Dr, Exeter, NH 03833
Tel.: (603) 775-5200
Web Site: http://www.cobham.com
Electronic Components Mfr
N.A.I.C.S.: 334419

REMEC Defense & Space, Inc (3)
9404 Chesapeake Dr, San Diego, CA
92123
Tel.: (858) 560-1301
Aircraft Part Mfr
N.A.I.C.S.: 336413

Subsidiary (Non-US):

Cobham Antenna Systems (2)
Torshamnsgatan 30 F, 16422, Kista, Sweden
Tel.: (46) 8 477 68 00
Microwave Component Mfr
N.A.I.C.S.: 334413
Hans Wallgren (Gen Mgr)

Cobham Aviation Services Pty Limited (2)
National Drive Adelaide Airport, Adelaide,
5950, SA, Australia
Tel.: (61) 8 8154 7000
Emp.: 400
Contract Aviation Services
N.A.I.C.S.: 488119
Peter Nottage (CEO)

Subsidiary (Domestic):

Cobham Defence Communications Ltd. (2)
The Innovation Centre Haslingden Road,
Blackburn, BB1 2FD, Lancashire, United
Kingdom (100%)
Tel.: (44) 1254292010
Web Site: http://www.cobham.com
Emp.: 27
Military Command, Control & Tactical Communication Systems Designer & Mfr
N.A.I.C.S.: 334290

Cobham Flight Inspection Limited (2)
Building 360 Durham Tees Valley Airport,
Darlington, DL2 1NJ, Co Durham, United
Kingdom
Tel.: (44) 1325 331360
Sales Range: $25-49.9 Million
Emp.: 40
Flight Inspection Services
N.A.I.C.S.: 926150

Subsidiary (Non-US):

Cobham Gaisler AB (2)
Kungsgatan 12, SE 411 19, Gothenburg,
Sweden (100%)
Tel.: (46) 31 7758650
Web Site: http://www.gaisler.com
Emp.: 1,000
IP Cores & Supporting Development Tools
for Embedded Processors
N.A.I.C.S.: 513210
Sandi Habinc (Gen Mgr)
Jan Andersson (Dir-Engrg)

Subsidiary (US):

Cobham Long Island Inc. (2)
350 Kennedy Dr, Hauppauge, NY 11788
Tel.: (631) 231-9100
Electronic Parts & Communication Equipment Distr
N.A.I.C.S.: 423690

Subsidiary (Domestic):

Featherstone Road Wolverton Mill, Milton
Keynes, MK12 5EW, Buckinghamshire,
United Kingdom
Tel.: (44) 1908 574200
Sales Range: $25-49.9 Million
Emp.: 6
Microwave Semiconductor Mfr
N.A.I.C.S.: 334413
Karen Oddey (CEO)

Subsidiary (US):

Cobham New Jersey Inc. (2)
40 Industrial Way E, Eatontown, NJ 07724
Tel.: (732) 460-0212
Electronic Parts & Communication Equipment Distr
N.A.I.C.S.: 423690

Subsidiary (Domestic):

Cobham RAD Europe Limited (2)
168 Maxwell Avenue, Didcot, Harwell, OX11
0QT, Oxfordshire, United Kingdom
Tel.: (44) 1235436620
Electronic Parts & Communication Equipment Distr
N.A.I.C.S.: 423690

Subsidiary (Non-US):

Cobham Tracking and Locating Limited (2)
120 Eileen Stubbs Ave Ste 200, Dartmouth,
B3B 1Y1, NS, Canada
Tel.: (902) 468-3007
Web Site: http://www.cobhamtl.com
Sales Range: $25-49.9 Million
Emp.: 10
Electronic Tracking Machinery Mfr
N.A.I.C.S.: 334419

Subsidiary (US):

Comant Industries, Inc (2)
577 Burning Tree Rd, Fullerton, CA 92833
Tel.: (714) 870-2420
Aircraft Communication Equipment Mfr
N.A.I.C.S.: 334220
Walt Stierhoff (Gen Mgr)

Conax Florida Corporation (2)
2801 75th St N, Saint Petersburg, FL 33710
Tel.: (727) 345-8000
Web Site: http://www.conaxfl.com
Aircraft Part Mfr
N.A.I.C.S.: 336413

DTC Communications, Inc. (2)
486 Amherst St, Nashua, NH
03063-1224 (100%)
Tel.: (603) 880-4411
Sales Range: $10-24.9 Million
Emp.: 110
Miniature Wireless Audio & Video Communication Products Designer & Mfr
N.A.I.C.S.: 334220

Subsidiary (Domestic):

FB Heliservices Limited (2)
Bournemouth International Airport,
Christchurch, BH23 6NE, Dorset, United
Kingdom
Tel.: (44) 1202409000
Electronic Parts & Communication Equipment Distr
N.A.I.C.S.: 423690

FR Aviation Limited (2)
Bournemouth International Airport,
Christchurch, BH23 6NE, Dorsetshire,
United Kingdom
Tel.: (44) 1202 409 000
Sales Range: $75-99.9 Million
Emp.: 300
Aircraft Surveillance Maintenance Services
N.A.I.C.S.: 811210
Paul Armstrong (Mng Dir)

Flight Refuelling Limited (2)
Brook Road, Wimborne, Dorset, BH21 2BJ,
United Kingdom
Tel.: (44) 1202 882121
Aircraft Machinery Mfr
N.A.I.C.S.: 336413

Subsidiary (Non-US):

Hyper-Technologies SAS (2)
28 Rue des Dames, 78340, Les Clayes-

Advent International Corporation—(Continued)
sous-Bois, France
Tel.: (33) 130550705
Sales Range: $50-74.9 Million
Emp.: 115
Aircraft Equipment Mfr
N.A.I.C.S.: 336413
Jean-luc Rodet (CEO)

Subsidiary (US):

Kevlin Corporation (2)
596 Lowell St, Methuen, MA
01844 (100%)
Tel.: (978) 557-2400
Web Site: http://www.kevlin.com
Sales Range: $25-49.9 Million
Emp.: 75
Microwave Devices for Uses in Military
Commercial Radar Systems Design & Mfr
N.A.I.C.S.: 334419

Unit (Domestic):

MAST Microwave (3)
5 Cornell Pl, Wilmington, MA
01887-2129 (100%)
Tel.: (978) 694-9595
Sales Range: $25-49.9 Million
Emp.: 10
Mfr of Low Cost Rotary Couplers & Special
Connectors
N.A.I.C.S.: 334419

Subsidiary (Non-US):

Label SAS (2)
18 Rue de Montreal, BP 439, Ville la
Grand, Annemasse, 74108, France
Tel.: (33) 450 87 7250
Web Site: http://www.label.fr
Sales Range: $25-49.9 Million
Emp.: 85
Aircraft Equipment Mfr
N.A.I.C.S.: 336413

Subsidiary (Domestic):

**Lockman Electronic Holdings
Limited** (2)
4th Ave Globe Park, Marlow, SL7 1YD,
Buckinghamshire, United Kingdom
Tel.: (44) 1628472072
Investment Management Service
N.A.I.C.S.: 523999

Subsidiary (Non-US):

Mastsystem International Oy (2)
Muovilaaksontie 8, 82110, Heinavaara, Fin-
land
Tel.: (358) 207750810
Web Site: https://www.mastsystem.com
Automobile Parts Mfr
N.A.I.C.S.: 336390
Markku Vuorinen (Dir-Sls & Mktg)
Riitta Sorsa (Mgr-Sls & Mktg)
Heikki Miettinen (Gen Mgr)
Seppo Saerkiniemi (Mgr-Production)

Subsidiary (Domestic):

Micromill Electronics Limited (2)
Leydene House Waterberry Drive, Water-
looville, PO7 7XX, Hampshire, United King-
dom
Tel.: (44) 2392 366600
Electronic Equipment Research & Develop-
ment Services
N.A.I.C.S.: 541715

Subsidiary (US):

S-TEC Corporation (2)
1 S-Tec Way Municipal Airport, Mineral
Wells, TX 76067
Tel.: (817) 215-7600
Web Site: http://www.s-tec.com
Aircraft Part Mfr
N.A.I.C.S.: 336413

Subsidiary (Non-US):

SMS S.A.S. (2)
174-178 Quai De Jemmapes, Paris, France
Tel.: (33) 153389898
Web Site: http://www.cobham.com
Aircraft Components Mfr
N.A.I.C.S.: 336413

Spectronic Denmark A/S (2)

Skindbjergvej 44, Grena, 8500, Denmark
Tel.: (45) 8791 8100
Web Site: http://www.spectronic.com
Sales Range: $25-49.9 Million
Emp.: 70
Surveillance Equipment Mfr
N.A.I.C.S.: 334511

**Surveillance Australia Pty
Limited** (2)
National Drive Adelaide Airport, Adelaide,
5950, SA, Australia
Tel.: (61) 8 81545670
Aircraft Surveillance System Mfr
N.A.I.C.S.: 334511

TEAM SA (2)
35 Rue de Montlhery, Silic, 94563, France
Tel.: (33) 1 49 78 66 00
Web Site: http://www.team-avionics.com
Sales Range: $25-49.9 Million
Emp.: 70
Aircraft Machinery Mfr
N.A.I.C.S.: 336413

Thrane & Thrane A/S (2)
Lundtoftegaardsvej 93 D, 2800, Lyngby,
Denmark
Tel.: (45) 39558800
Web Site: http://www.cobham.com
Cockpit & Cabin Communication,
Navigation-at-Sea & Land Mobile Satcom
Systems
N.A.I.C.S.: 517410

Subsidiary (Non-US):

Naval Electronics AB (3)
Hojdrodergatan 18, 212 39, Malmo, Scania,
Sweden
Tel.: (46) 40292045
Web Site: http://www.naval.se
Sales Range: $25-49.9 Million
Emp.: 15
Marine Communication Equipments Mfr
N.A.I.C.S.: 334220

**Omnipless Manufacturing (Propri-
etary) Limited** (3)
Westlake Business Park 2 Westlake Drive,
Westlake, Cape Town, 7945, South Africa
Tel.: (27) 21 700 7000
Web Site: http://www.omnipless.com
Sales Range: $50-74.9 Million
Emp.: 200
Electronic Equipment Mfr & Distr
N.A.I.C.S.: 334419

Subsidiary (US):

SeaTel, Inc. (3)
4030 Nelson Ave, Concord, CA
94520 (100%)
Tel.: (925) 798-7979
Web Site: http://www.cobham.com
Sales Range: $25-49.9 Million
Emp.: 150
Marine Satellite Communication Antenna
Systems Mfr
N.A.I.C.S.: 334220

Tracstar Systems, Inc. (3)
2100 N Alafaya Trl Ste 300, Orlando, FL
32826
Tel.: (407) 650-9054
Web Site: http://www.cobham.com
Satellite Tracking System Mfr
N.A.I.C.S.: 334290

Subsidiary (US):

Trivec-Avant Corporation (2)
17831 Jamestown Ln, Huntington Beach,
CA 92647
Tel.: (714) 841-4976
Web Site: http://www.trivec.com
Sales Range: $50-74.9 Million
Emp.: 50
Antenna Systems Mfr
N.A.I.C.S.: 334220

Subsidiary (Domestic):

**Ultra Electronics Holdings
Limited** (2)
35 Portman Square, London, W1H 6LR,
United Kingdom
Tel.: (44) 2088134321
Web Site: https://www.ultra.group
Rev.: $1,167,367,656
Assets: $1,351,067,172

Liabilities: $720,134,688
Net Worth: $630,932,484
Earnings: $113,776,936
Emp.: 4,253
Fiscal Year-end: 12/31/2020
Electronic & Electromechanical Products
Mfr for Aerospace & Defense Industries
N.A.I.C.S.: 334511
Simon Pryce (CEO)
Martin Lee Barrow (Dir)

Subsidiary (US):

3 Phoenix, Inc. (3)
14585 Avion Pkwy Ste 200, Chantilly, VA
20151
Tel.: (703) 956-6480
Web Site: http://www.ultra-3pi.com
Emp.: 182
Technology Products & Services
N.A.I.C.S.: 541512
James B. Gallemore (Co-Founder)
Joseph Murray (Co-Founder)
Joseph A. Liverman (Co-Founder)
Russell Jeffers (Co-Founder)
John M. Jamieson III (Co-Founder)

**3E Technologies International
Inc.** (3)
12410 Milestone Center Dr Ste 225, Ger-
mantown, MD 20876
Tel.: (301) 670-6779
Web Site: http://www.ultra-3eti.com
Secure Wireless Network & Security Ser-
vices
N.A.I.C.S.: 517112
Dirk Van Der Vaart (Pres)
Edward Murphy (VP-Fin)
Brian Garcia (VP-Contracts & Gen Counsel)
Steven Schaller (Dir-Ops)
Ana Maria Montalvo (Dir-Engrg)

EMS Development Corporation (3)
95 Horseblock Rd Unit 2, Yaphank, NY
11980-9710 (100%)
Tel.: (631) 345-6200
Web Site: http://www.ultra-ems.com
Sales Range: $25-49.9 Million
Emp.: 50
Mfr of Military Electronic Systems & Indus-
trial & Commercial Components
N.A.I.C.S.: 334419

Subsidiary (Domestic):

RFI Corporation (4)
100 Pine Aire Dr, Bay Shore, NY
11706-1107 (100%)
Tel.: (631) 231-6400
Web Site: http://www.rficorp.com
Design & Manufacture of RF Interference
Filters & Power Conditioning Devices
N.A.I.C.S.: 334416

Subsidiary (Non-US):

**Forensic Technology (Europe)
Limited** (3)
9 The Courtyard Kilcarbery Business Park
Nangor Road, Dublin, Ireland
Tel.: (353) 16909100
Secure Wireless Network & Security Ser-
vices
N.A.I.C.S.: 517112

**Forensic Technology AEC Thailand
Limited** (3)
1-7 Zuellig House Unit 303-304 3rd Floor
Silom Road, Bangrak, Bangkok, 10500,
Thailand
Tel.: (66) 26362898
Secure Wireless Network & Security Ser-
vices
N.A.I.C.S.: 517112

Projectina AG (3)
Dammstrasse 2, PO Box 9435, Heerbrugg,
Switzerland
Tel.: (41) 717272800
Secure Wireless Network & Security Ser-
vices
N.A.I.C.S.: 517112
Wolfgang Stefanelli (Gen Mgr)

Subsidiary (US):

**Ultra Electronics Advanced Tactical
Systems, Inc.** (3)
4101 Smith School Rd Bldg IV Ste 100,
Austin, TX 78744-3204

Tel.: (512) 327-6795
Web Site: http://www.ultra-ats.com
Sales Range: $10-24.9 Million
Emp.: 150
Tactical Command, Control Systems &
Products Designer & Mfr
N.A.I.C.S.: 513210

Subsidiary (Domestic):

**Ultra Electronics, Nuclear Sensors &
Process Instrumentation** (4)
707 Jeffrey Way, Round Rock, TX 78665-
2408
Tel.: (512) 434-2900
Web Site: http://www.ultra-nspi.com
Sales Range: $10-24.9 Million
Emp.: 100
Temperature Gauge, Pressure & Fiber Optic
Instruments Mfr
N.A.I.C.S.: 334513

Subsidiary (Domestic):

Furnace Parts, LLC (5)
6133 Rockside Rd Ste 300, Cleveland, OH
44135
Tel.: (216) 676-5005
Web Site: http://www.ultra-furnaceparts.com
Sales Range: $1-9.9 Million
Emp.: 28
Industrial Supplies, Nsk
N.A.I.C.S.: 423840
Debby Nieman (Mgr-Sls)
John Popovich (Dir-Admin & HR)

Subsidiary (Domestic):

Ultra Electronics Airport Systems (3)
The Oaks Business Park Crew Rd, Wythen-
shawe, Manchester, M23 9SS, United
Kingdom (100%)
Tel.: (44) 1619463600
Web Site: http://www.ultra-as.com
Sales Range: $50-74.9 Million
Emp.: 150
IT Solutions
N.A.I.C.S.: 334610

Subsidiary (Non-US):

**Ultra Electronics Australia Pty
Limited** (3)
12 Douglas Drive Mawson Lakes, Adelaide,
5095, SA, Australia
Tel.: (61) 881691200
Secure Wireless Network & Security Ser-
vices
N.A.I.C.S.: 517112

Ultra Electronics Canada Inc. (3)
40 Atlantic Street, Dartmouth, B2Y 4N2,
NS, Canada
Tel.: (902) 466-7491
Web Site: http://www.ultra-electronics.com
Sales Range: $200-249.9 Million
Emp.: 375
Builder of Tactical & Sonar Systems, Aircraft
& Vehicle Systems & Information & Power
Systems
N.A.I.C.S.: 334511

Subsidiary (Domestic):

**Ultra Electronics Maritime
Systems** (4)
40 Atlantic Street, Dartmouth, B2Y 4N2,
NS, Canada (100%)
Tel.: (902) 466-7491
Web Site: http://www.ultra-ms.com
Sales Range: $50-74.9 Million
Emp.: 180
Developer & Mfr of Advanced Communica-
tion, Surveillance, Command & Control &
Security Systems
N.A.I.C.S.: 334290

Subsidiary (Domestic):

**Ultra Electronics Card Systems
Ltd** (3)
Waverley House Hampshire Road, Granby
Est, Weymouth, DT4 9XD, Porset, United
Kingdom (100%)
Tel.: (44) 305784738
Web Site: http://www.ultramagicard.com
Sales Range: $50-74.9 Million
Emp.: 200
ID Badge & Card Printing Machines Mfr
N.A.I.C.S.: 333248

Ray Coles (Mng Dir)

Branch (US):

Ultra Electronics Card Systems Inc (4)
6711 176th Ave NE, Redmond, WA 98052 **(100%)**
Tel.: (425) 556-9708
Web Site: http://www.ultramagicard.com
Sales Range: $25-49.9 Million
Emp.: 10
ID Badge & Card Printing Machines Mfr
N.A.I.C.S.: 333248

Subsidiary (Domestic):

Ultra Electronics Command & Control Systems (3)
Knaves Beech Business Ctr, Loudwater, High Wycombe, HP10 9UT, United Kingdom **(100%)**
Tel.: (44) 1628530000
Web Site: http://www.ultra-ccs.com
Sales Range: $100-124.9 Million
Emp.: 300
Submarine Torpedo Fire Control Systems & Data Handling; Data Processing Cards
N.A.I.C.S.: 334519

Ultra Electronics Controls Division (3)
417 Bridport Road, Greenford, UB6 8UE, Middlesex, United Kingdom **(100%)**
Tel.: (44) 2088134444
Sales Range: $25-49.9 Million
Emp.: 100
Aircraft Control Systems Mfr
N.A.I.C.S.: 334519

Subsidiary (US):

Ultra Electronics DNE Technologies, Inc. (3)
50 Barnes Industrial Park N, Wallingford, CT 06492-5912
Tel.: (203) 265-7151
Web Site: http://www.ultra-dne.com
Sales Range: $10-24.9 Million
Emp.: 72
Defense & Commercial Electronics
N.A.I.C.S.: 334210
William Gill (Pres & CEO)

Unit (US):

Ultra Electronics Flightline Systems (3)
7625 Omnitech Pl, Victor, NY 14564-9795 **(100%)**
Tel.: (585) 924-4000
Web Site: http://www.ultra-fei.com
Sales Range: $50-74.9 Million
Emp.: 120
Sonobuoy Receivers & Telemetry Systems Mfr
N.A.I.C.S.: 334511
Paul Fardellone (Pres)
Kevin Ames (Engr-Software)

Subsidiary (Non-US):

Ultra Electronics Forensic Technology Inc. (3)
800 Hymus Blvd, Saint-Luc, H4S 0B5, QC, Canada
Tel.: (514) 489-4247
Web Site: https://www.ultra-forensictechnology.com
Secure Wireless Network & Security Services
N.A.I.C.S.: 517112

Subsidiary (US):

Ultra Electronics Herley (3)
10 Sonar Dr, Woburn, MA 01801
Tel.: (781) 729-9450
Web Site: http://www.ultra-herley.com
Flight Instrumentation Products, Range Safety Transponders & Microwave Components Design & Mfr
N.A.I.C.S.: 334511

Division (Domestic):

Herley CTI (4)
9 Whippany Rd Bldg A 1, Whippany, NJ 07981
Tel.: (973) 884-2580

Web Site: http://www.ultra-herley.com
Emp.: 35
Integrated Frequency Converter Assemblies, Microwave & RF Components Mfr
N.A.I.C.S.: 334411

Herley Lancaster (4)
3061 Industry Dr, Lancaster, PA 17603
Tel.: (717) 397-2777
Web Site: http://www.ultra-herley.com
Flight Instrumentation Systems Design & Mfr

Herley New England (4)
10 Sonar Dr, Woburn, MA 01801
Tel.: (781) 729-9450
Web Site: http://www.ultra-herley.com
Microwave Switching Devices Mfr
N.A.I.C.S.: 334419

Subsidiary (US):

Ultra Electronics ICE, Inc. (3)
2700 Amherst Ave, Manhattan, KS 66502
Tel.: (785) 776-6423
Electronic System Mfr
N.A.I.C.S.: 334417
Randy O'Boyle (Pres)
Mike Casey (VP)
Ben Ketley (Dir-Ops)

Subsidiary (Domestic):

Ultra Electronics Limited (3)
417-419 Bridport Road, Greenford, UB6 8UA, Middlesex, United Kingdom
Tel.: (44) 20 8813 4321
Web Site: http://www.ultra-electronics.com
Electric Equipment Mfr
N.A.I.C.S.: 335999

Subsidiary (US):

Ultra Electronics Measurement Systems, Inc. (3)
50 Barnes Park N, Wallingford, CT 06492 **(100%)**
Tel.: (203) 949-3500
Web Site: http://www.ultra-msi.com
Sales Range: $25-49.9 Million
Emp.: 80
Control Handles Switches Mfr
N.A.I.C.S.: 335314

Ultra Electronics Ocean Systems Inc. (3)
115 Bay State Dr, Braintree, MA 02184
Tel.: (781) 848-3400
Web Site: http://www.ultra-os.com
Sales Range: $10-24.9 Million
Emp.: 100
Aircraft, Submarine & Surface Ship Special Purpose Acoustic & Radio Frequency Device & System Mfr; Open Water Acoustic Research & Production Test Site Operator
N.A.I.C.S.: 334511
Thomas P. Bourgault (VP-Mktg)
Richard Speer (VP-Fin & Contracts)
Barabara O'Leary (Mgr-HR)

Subsidiary (Domestic):

Ultra Electronics PMES (3)
Towers Business Park Wheelhouse Road, Rugeley, WS15 1UZ, Staffordshire, United Kingdom **(100%)**
Tel.: (44) 1889503300
Web Site: http://www.ultra-pmes.com
Sales Range: $50-74.9 Million
Emp.: 250
Advanced Electronic System Services
N.A.I.C.S.: 336320

Ultra Electronics Precision Air Systems Ltd (3)
Anson Bus Pk, Cheltenham Rd E, Gloucester, GL2 9QN, United Kingdom **(100%)**
Tel.: (44) 01452714382
Web Site: http://www.ultra-pas.com
Sales Range: $25-49.9 Million
Emp.: 70
Gas Compressors Mfr
N.A.I.C.S.: 333912

Subsidiary (US):

Ultra Electronics Precision Air Systems Inc (4)

5751 General Washington Dr, Alexandria, VA 22312 **(100%)**
Tel.: (703) 914-8881
Sales Range: $25-49.9 Million
Emp.: 8
Gas Compressors Mfr
N.A.I.C.S.: 335999
George Straubs (Dir-Mktg)

Subsidiary (Domestic):

Ultra Electronics SML Technologies Ltd. (3)
316 Botley Rd, Burridge, Southampton, SO31 1BQ, S Hampshire, United Kingdom **(100%)**
Tel.: (44) 489557373
Web Site: http://www.smltechnologies.com
Sales Range: $25-49.9 Million
Emp.: 50
Radar & Transponder Systems
N.A.I.C.S.: 334511

Ultra Electronics Sonar & Communications Systems (3)
The Metropolitan Center 417 Bridport Road, Greenford, UB6 8UA, Middlesex, United Kingdom **(100%)**
Tel.: (44) 2088134567
Web Site: http://www.ultrascs.com
Sales Range: $100-124.9 Million
Emp.: 450
Sonobouys & Receivers Mfr
N.A.I.C.S.: 334310
Graham French (Dir-Fin)

Subsidiary (US):

UnderSea Sensor Systems Inc. (3)
4868 Park 30 Dr, Columbia City, IN 46725-8869 **(100%)**
Tel.: (260) 248-3500
Web Site: http://www.ultra-ussi.com
Sales Range: $50-74.9 Million
Emp.: 250
Submarine Detection Equipment Mfr
N.A.I.C.S.: 334511

Faerch A/S (1)
Rasmus Faerchs Vej 1, 7500, Holstebro, Denmark
Tel.: (45) 9910 1010
Web Site: http://www.faerch.com
Plastic Food Packaging Products Mfr & Whslr
N.A.I.C.S.: 326112

Subsidiary (Non-US):

Faerch France SAS (2)
ZI des Iles 200 routes des Sarves, 74370, Metz-Tessy, France
Tel.: (33) 450273450
Web Site: http://www.faerch.com
Custom Food Packaging Mfr & Whslr
N.A.I.C.S.: 326199

Subsidiary (Domestic):

CGL Pack Annecy (3)
ZI des Iles 200 Routes des Sarves, 74370, Metz-Tessy, France
Tel.: (33) 450273450
Web Site: http://www.cglpack.com
Custom Food Packaging Mfr
N.A.I.C.S.: 326199

CGL Pack Lorient (3)
450 rue d'Arvor, 56530, Gestel, France
Tel.: (33) 2 97 80 12 80
Web Site: http://www.cglpack.com
Custom Food Packaging Mfr
N.A.I.C.S.: 326199

Subsidiary (Non-US):

Faerch Plast Bunol S.L.U. (2)
El Rincon sector 5 Correos 166, 46360, Bunol, Valencia, Spain
Tel.: (34) 962502775
Web Site: http://www.faerchplast.com
Packaging Products Mfr
N.A.I.C.S.: 322220

First Watch Restaurants, Inc. (1)
8027 Cooper Creek Blvd Ste 103, Bradenton, FL 34201
Tel.: (941) 907-9800
Web Site: http://www.firstwatch.com
Restaurant Owner & Franchiser
N.A.I.C.S.: 722511

Christopher A. Tomasso (CEO & Pres)
Shane Schaibly (VP-Culinary Strategy)
Jay Wolszczak (Chief Legal Officer & Gen Counsel)
Mel Hope (CFO)
Laura Sorensen (Chief People Officer)
Eric Hartman (Chief Dev Officer & Exec VP)
Christopher A. Tomasso (Pres & CEO)
Kenneth L. Pendery Jr. (Chm)

Forescout Technologies, Inc. (1)
190 W Tasman Dr, San Jose, CA 95134
Tel.: (408) 213-3191
Web Site: http://www.forescout.com
Rev.: $336,801,000
Assets: $416,227,000
Liabilities: $318,682,000
Net Worth: $97,545,000
Earnings: ($118,535,000)
Emp.: 1,206
Fiscal Year-end: 12/31/2019
Custom Computer Programming Services
N.A.I.C.S.: 541511
David G. DeWalt (Vice Chm)
Barry Mainz (CEO)
Dror Comay (Co-Founder)
Darren J. Milliken (Gen Counsel & Sr VP)
Ori Naishtein (Sr VP-R&D)
Jason Pishotti (Chief Customer Officer)
Michelle Spolver (Chief Comm Officer)
Steve Redman (Chief Revenue Officer)
Neville Letzerich (CMO)
Rob McNutt (Co-CTO)
Rohan Langdon (Dir-Australia & New Zealand)
Wahab Yusoff (VP-Asia Pacific)
Greg Clark (Chm)
Wael Mohamed (CEO)

Subsidiary (Non-US):

Forescout Technologies Israel Ltd. (2)
24 Raoul Wallenberg St Entrance D 6th floor, Tel Aviv, 6971924, Israel
Tel.: (972) 36449987
Software Development Services
N.A.I.C.S.: 541511

Fort Dearborn Company (1)
1530 Morse Ave, Elk Grove Village, IL 60007
Tel.: (847) 357-9500
Web Site: http://www.fortdearborn.com
Packaging & Labeling Services
N.A.I.C.S.: 561910
Mike Anderson (Owner)

Unit (Domestic):

Fort Dearborn - Bowling Green (2)
350 Southwood Ct, Bowling Green, KY 42101
Tel.: (270) 745-0700
Web Site: http://www.fortdearborn.com
Sales Range: $25-49.9 Million
Food & Beverage Label Mfr
N.A.I.C.S.: 323111

Fort Dearborn - Fort Worth (2)
4601 Pylon St, Fort Worth, TX 76106-1918
Tel.: (817) 625-1116
Web Site: http://www.fortdearborn.com
Sales Range: $25-49.9 Million
Labeling & Packaging Services
N.A.I.C.S.: 561910
Louis Belliveau (Gen Mgr)

Subsidiary (Domestic):

Hammer Packaging Corp. (2)
200 Lucius Gordon Dr, West Henrietta, NY 14586
Tel.: (585) 424-3880
Web Site: http://www.hammerpackaging.com
Sales Range: $100-124.9 Million
Emp.: 400
Commercial Printing & Lithographic Services
N.A.I.C.S.: 323111
James E. Hammer (Pres & CEO)
Christopher Bartlett (Coord-Flexo Tech)
Gary Kellerson (Supvr-Ops-Roll Finishing)
Neil Kendrick (Mgr-IT)
Tom Mason (VP-Sls)
Peggi Mort (Mgr-Net Svc)
Stephen Brown (Mgr-Strategic Bus)
Chris Wieser (CFO)
Marty Karpie (VP-Ops)

Advent International Corporation—(Continued)

Lou Iovoli *(VP-Strategic Partnerships & Mktg)*
Trevor Esten *(Coord-Second Shift Press)*
Blaine Heaman *(Mgr-Maintenance-Lucius Gordon Drive Facility)*
Lynda Lundstrom *(Mgr-Sls)*
Marijke Squire *(Asst Coord-Flexo Technical)*
Peter Swanson *(Coord-Flex Technical)*
Melvin Terrell *(Mgr-Maintenance-Rochester Tech Park Facility)*
Karl Wilcox *(Dir-Engrg & Maintenance)*

Grupo Farmaceutico Somar   **(1)**
Adolfo Prieto 1427 Benito Juarez, Benito Juarez Federal District, 03100, Mexico, Mexico
Tel.: (52) 55 5340 2355
Web Site: http://www.gruposomar.com
Pharmaceutical Mfr & Distr
N.A.I.C.S.: 325412
Daniel Del Conde *(CEO)*

H.C. Starck GmbH & Co. KG   **(1)**
Im Schleeke 78 91, 38642, Goslar, Germany
Tel.: (49) 53217510
Web Site: http://www.hcstarck.com
Sales Range: $1-4.9 Billion
Ceramics & Refractory Metals Mfr
N.A.I.C.S.: 325180
Jan Losch *(Member-Exec Bd)*
Jens Knoll *(Member-Exec Bd)*

Subsidiary (US):

H.C. Starck Inc   **(2)**
45 Industrial Pl, Newton, MA 02461-1951
Tel.: (617) 630-5800
Web Site: http://www.hcstarck.com
Sales Range: $25-49.9 Million
Emp.: 175
Mfr of Capacitor Grade Tantalum Powder, Tantalum & Niobium Mill Products for Electronic, Chemical Processing, Aerospace & Nuclear Industries
N.A.I.C.S.: 331410
Jacques Gagnon *(Mgr-Facility Maintenance & Ops Support)*

Branch (Domestic):

H.C. Starck Inc   **(3)**
21801 Tungsten Rd, Euclid, OH 44117
Tel.: (216) 692-3990
Web Site: http://www.hcstarck.com
Sales Range: $50-74.9 Million
Mfr of Alloys & Molybdenum Products
N.A.I.C.S.: 541330
Craig W. Butchello *(Coord-EDM)*

H.C. Starck, Inc.   **(3)**
1250 E 222 St, Euclid, OH 44117
Tel.: (201) 438-9000
Web Site: http://www.hcstarck.com
Sales Range: $25-49.9 Million
Emp.: 110
Mfr of Nonferrous Rolling & Drawing
N.A.I.C.S.: 331491
Craig W. Butchello *(Coord-EDM)*
Chip Urban *(Engr-Inside Sls)*
Gerald Stavlas *(Mgr-Maintenance & Facilities)*
Ray Blasko *(Supvr-Machine Shop)*
Melody Randolph *(Supvr-Outside Svcs)*

Subsidiary (Non-US):

H.C. Starck, Inc.   **(2)**
Portemarsh Industrial Estate 1 Harris Road, Calne, SN11 9PT, Wiltshire, United Kingdom
Tel.: (44) 1249823832
Web Site: http://www.hcstarck.com
Sales Range: $25-49.9 Million
Emp.: 44
Production & Distribution of Metallurgical Product Mfr
N.A.I.C.S.: 332812

IDEMIA France SAS   **(1)**
2 Place Samuel de Champlan, 92400, Courbevoie, France   **(90%)**
Tel.: (33) 1 7360 2020
Web Site: http://www.idemia.com
Emp.: 10,000
Smart Cards, Secure Printing Services & Cash Protection Technologies
N.A.I.C.S.: 561621

Pierre Barrial *(Pres & CEO)*
Astrid Warren *(Chief People Officer)*
Yann Delabriere *(Chm)*
Matt Cole *(Grp Exec VP-Pub Security & Identity Bus)*

Subsidiary (Domestic):

IDEMIA Identity & Security France SAS   **(2)**
11 Boulevard Gallienii, 92130, Issy-les-Moulineaux, France
Tel.: (33) 1 73 60 20 20
Web Site: http://www.idemia.com
Security Technology Mfr; Biometric Identifications Systems, Smartcards, Access Control, Road Safety Systems & Border Control Solutions
N.A.I.C.S.: 561621
Donnie Scott *(CEO-North America)*

Subsidiary (Non-US):

IDEMIA Australasia Pty. Ltd.   **(3)**
Building A Level 3 Ste 5 11 Talavera Road, Macquarie Park, Sydney, 2113, NSW, Australia
Tel.: (61) 2 9424 35 00
Web Site: http://www.idemia.com
Biometric Device Mfr
N.A.I.C.S.: 334118

IDEMIA Germany GmbH   **(3)**
Konrad Zuse Ring 1, 124220, Schleswig, Germany
Tel.: (49) 43477150
Web Site: http://www.idemia.com
Electronic Identification, Financial & Security Cards Mfr
N.A.I.C.S.: 334419

IDEMIA Identity & Security Canada, Inc.   **(3)**
2872 Bristol Circle Suite 100, Oakville, L6H 6G4, ON, Canada
Tel.: (905) 829-9988
Biometric Device Mfr
N.A.I.C.S.: 334118

IDEMIA Identity & Security Sucursal Colombia   **(3)**
Transversal 18 No 96-41 Piso 13, Bogota, Colombia
Tel.: (57) 1 646 86 00
Biometric Device Mfr
N.A.I.C.S.: 334118

IDEMIA Identity & Security UK Limited   **(3)**
255 Wharfedale Road, Winnersh, RG41 5TP, United Kingdom
Tel.: (44) 118 377 43 00
Biometric System Mfr
N.A.I.C.S.: 334118

Subsidiary (US):

IDEMIA Identity & Security USA, LLC   **(3)**
296 Concord Rd Ste 300, Billerica, MA 01821
Tel.: (978) 215-2400
Web Site: http://www.idemia.com
Personal Identity & Asset Security Services, Technologies Developer & Mfr
N.A.I.C.S.: 561621
Bonnie Webber *(Sr Mgr-HR, Ops & Compensation)*

Subsidiary (Non-US):

IDEMIA Identity & Security Germany AG   **(4)**
Universitatstrasse 160, 44801, Bochum, Germany
Tel.: (49) 23497870
Identity Verification Software Mfr
N.A.I.C.S.: 513210

Subsidiary (Domestic):

IDEMIA Identity & Security USA, LLC   **(4)**
5705 W Old Shakopee Rd Ste 100, Bloomington, MN 55437-3107
Tel.: (952) 932-0888
Web Site: http://www.idemia.com
Mfr, Developer, Designer & Marketer of Comprehensive Security Solutions for Open Wired & Wireless Networks

N.A.I.C.S.: 541512

IdentoGO   **(4)**
625 Bakers Bridge Ave Ste 105, Franklin, TN 37067
Tel.: (615) 871-0522
Web Site: http://www.identogo.com
Biometric Identification & Authentication Security Technologies Developer & Mfr
N.A.I.C.S.: 335999

Subsidiary (Non-US):

IDEMIA Singapore Pte Ltd   **(3)**
21 Media Circle Infinite Studio #06-08, 138562, Singapore, Singapore
Tel.: (65) 65114360
Web Site: http://www.idemia.com
Electronic Identification, Financial & Security Cards Mfr
N.A.I.C.S.: 326199

IDEMIA The Netherlands B.V.   **(3)**
Oudeweg 32, PO Box 5300, 2000 GH, Haarlem, Netherlands
Tel.: (31) 23 799 51 11
Web Site: http://www.idemia.com
Biometric Device Mfr
N.A.I.C.S.: 334118

NiD SA   **(3)**
Le Cret-du-Locle 10, PO Box 1161, 2301, La Chaux-de-Fonds, Switzerland
Tel.: (41) 32 924 0404
Web Site: http://www.nagraid.com
Security & Identification Smart Card Mfr
N.A.I.C.S.: 326199
Frederic Clauss *(CEO)*

Subsidiary (US):

More Magic Solutions, Inc.   **(2)**
221 Crescent St Ste 402, Waltham, MA 02453-3436
Tel.: (617) 244-1598
Web Site: http://www.moremagic.com
Sales Range: $25-49.9 Million
Emp.: 40
Carrier-Class Transaction Solutions for Mobile Payments
N.A.I.C.S.: 541511

Unit (Domestic):

Oberthur Card Systems   **(2)**
71-73 rue des Hautes-Patures, F-92726, Nanterre, Cedex, France   **(100%)**
Tel.: (33) 147855400
Web Site: http://www.oberthurcs.com
Security Card Systems Developer & Mfr
N.A.I.C.S.: 551112

Subsidiary (Non-US):

Oberthur Card Systems KK   **(2)**
3rd Floor Toranomon MT Building, 3-10-3 Toranomon Minato-ku, 105-0001, Tokyo, Japan
Tel.: (81) 354051880
Web Site: http://www.oberthurcs.com
Sales Range: $50-74.9 Million
Emp.: 5
Financial Transactions Processing Reserve & Clearinghouse Activities
N.A.I.C.S.: 522320
Nobuyoshi Nezu *(Mgr-Sls)*

Oberthur Card Systems Kart Sistemleri. Sanayi ve Ticaret Limited Sirketi   **(2)**
BJK Plaza suleyman Seba caddesi, N 92 Blok Kat 7 Daire 71-72 34, Istanbul, Türkiye
Tel.: (90) 2122361853
Sales Range: $50-74.9 Million
Emp.: 4
Credit Card Issuing
N.A.I.C.S.: 522210

Oberthur Card Systems Kft.   **(2)**
To Park Plot N 3301-21, 2045, Torokbalint, Hungary
Tel.: (36) 23531800
Web Site: http://www.oberthurcs.com
Sales Range: $10-24.9 Million
Emp.: 30
Plastics Product Mfr
N.A.I.C.S.: 326199

Oberthur Card Systems OOO   **(2)**
5 Naryshkinskaya Alley, 125167, Moscow, Russia

Tel.: (7) 04957487771
Sales Range: $50-74.9 Million
Emp.: 7
Credit Card Issuing
N.A.I.C.S.: 522210

Oberthur Card Systems Pvt. Ltd.   **(2)**
A-201 Sector 63, Noida, 201303, Delhi, Uttar Pradesh, India
Tel.: (91) 1203911700
Web Site: http://www.oberthurcs.com
Sales Range: $50-74.9 Million
Emp.: 100
Credit Card Issuing
N.A.I.C.S.: 522210

Oberthur Card Systems Romania S.R.L   **(2)**
Str Marasesti N 15, Secteur 4, 040251, Bucharest, Romania
Tel.: (40) 213301120
Web Site: http://www.oberthurcs.com
Sales Range: $10-24.9 Million
Emp.: 25
Computer System Design Services
N.A.I.C.S.: 541512

Oberthur Card Systems Science & Technology (Shenzhen) Co. Ltd   **(2)**
East of 3rd Floor Great Wall Technology Building # 1 No 2 Kefa Rd, Science & Technology Pk, Shenzhen, 518057, Nanshan, China
Tel.: (86) 75526717318
Web Site: http://www.oberthurcs.com.cn
Credit Card Issuing
N.A.I.C.S.: 522210

Oberthur Card Systems Sp. z o.o.   **(2)**
ul Napoleona 4C, Kobylka, 05-230, Poland
Tel.: (48) 227634800
Web Site: http://www.oberthurcs.com
Sales Range: $10-24.9 Million
Emp.: 8
Computer Related Services
N.A.I.C.S.: 541519

Oberthur Cash Protection UK Limited   **(2)**
The Broadgate Tower 3rd Floor 20 Primrose Street, London, EC2A 2RS, United Kingdom
Tel.: (44) 20 3116 3000
Web Site: http://www.reedsmith.com
Cash Protection Services
N.A.I.C.S.: 522390

Oberthur Technologies (Beijing) Co Ltd   **(2)**
B 709 Winterless Center No1 West Dawang Road, Chaoyang District, Beijing, 100026, China
Tel.: (86) 10 6538 8338
Sales Range: $10-24.9 Million
Emp.: 20
Smartcard Mfr
N.A.I.C.S.: 339999

Oberthur Technologies Colombia   **(2)**
Carrera 23 94-33 Office 701, Barrio Chico, Bogota, Colombia   **(100%)**
Tel.: (57) 1 691 4100
Smartcard Mfr
N.A.I.C.S.: 339999

Oberthur Technologies Denmark A/S   **(2)**
Rugardsvej 10, 5000, Odense, Denmark
Tel.: (45) 63 14 27 70
Smartcard Mfr
N.A.I.C.S.: 339999

Oberthur Technologies Finland Segenmark OY   **(2)**
Vallikallionkatu 7, 02650, Espoo, Finland
Tel.: (358) 9 5915 900
Sales Range: $10-24.9 Million
Emp.: 25
Smartcard Mfr
N.A.I.C.S.: 339999
Satu Seppanen *(Mng Dir)*

Oberthur Technologies Iberica   **(2)**
Calle Metano 4 Torrejon de Ardoz, Madrid, 28850, Spain
Tel.: (34) 917355466
Emp.: 100
Credit Card Issuing
N.A.I.C.S.: 522210

Oberthur Technologies Inc. (2)
25th FL Etron Mega Plz Bldg 358 Senator
Gil Puyat Ave, Makati, 1200, Philippines
Tel.: (63) 2 811 0460
Smartcard Mfr
N.A.I.C.S.: 339999

Oberthur Technologies Italia SRL (2)
Via Monte Spluga 58, 20021, Milan, Baranzate, Italy
Tel.: (39) 02382171
Technology Systems & Services
N.A.I.C.S.: 561499

Oberthur Technologies KK (2)
3/F Toranomon MT Building 3-10-3 Toranomon, Minato-ku, Tokyo, 105-0001, Japan
Tel.: (81) 3 5405 1880
Smartcard Mfr
N.A.I.C.S.: 339999

Oberthur Technologies Kft (2)
2045 Torokbalint To Park West Gate Business Park Plot n 3301/21, Oberthur Building, Budapest, Hungary
Tel.: (36) 23 531 800
Smartcard Mfr
N.A.I.C.S.: 339999

Oberthur Technologies Korea Inc. (2)
HC Haus Bldg 38-7 Nonhyeon-Dong, Gangmam-gu, Seoul, 135-010, Korea (South)
Tel.: (82) 2 3446 6277
Smartcard Mfr
N.A.I.C.S.: 339999

Oberthur Technologies Latvia SIA (2)
Varkalu Iela 13, 1067, Riga, Latvia
Tel.: (371) 6789 2678
Web Site:
    http://www.oberthurtechnologies.com
Emp.: 35
Smartcard Mfr
N.A.I.C.S.: 339999

Oberthur Technologies Ltd (2)
23 Tarlington Place, Smithfield, 2164, NSW, Australia
Tel.: (61) 2 8786 6500
Sales Range: $10-24.9 Million
Emp.: 50
Smartcard Mfr
N.A.I.C.S.: 339999

Oberthur Technologies Ltda (2)
Alicia Moreau de Justo 846 2nd Floor Suite 13, Buenos Aires, Argentina
Tel.: (54) 11 4331 2445
Smartcard Mfr
N.A.I.C.S.: 339999

Oberthur Technologies Norway A/S (2)
Sandakerveien 116, 0172, Oslo, Norway
Tel.: (47) 23327800
Emp.: 50
Smartcard Mfr
N.A.I.C.S.: 339999

Oberthur Technologies Romania S.R.L. (2)
Str Soseaua Iancului nr 46 secteur 2, 021726, Bucharest, Romania
Tel.: (40) 37 420 0010
Smartcard Mfr
N.A.I.C.S.: 335999

Oberthur Technologies South Africa (PTY) Ltd (2)
10 Cleveland Road, Cleveland, Johannesburg, 2000, South Africa
Tel.: (27) 11 622 0400
Emp.: 70
Smartcard Mfr
N.A.I.C.S.: 339999
Hennie Du Plessis (Country Mgr)

Oberthur Technologies Sucursal EM Portugal (2)
Edifico Monumental av Praia de Vitoria 71 A 11, 1069-006, Lisbon, Portugal
Tel.: (351) 91 735 5450
Smartcard Mfr
N.A.I.C.S.: 339999

Oberthur Technologies Sweden ACSC AB (2)

Farogatan 7, 164 40, Kista, Sweden
Tel.: (46) 8 658 75 00
Smartcard Mfr
N.A.I.C.S.: 339999

Oberthur Technologies Teknoloji Sanayi ve Ticaret Ltd.
Ataturk Mahallesi Atasehir Bulvari 38 Ada Ata 3 3 Plaza Kat 2 Daire 24, Atasehir, 34758, Istanbul, Turkiye
Tel.: (90) 216 580 98 90
Sales Range: $10-24.9 Million
Emp.: 4
Smartcard Mfr
N.A.I.C.S.: 339999
David Lisal (Mgr-Sls)

Oberthur Technologies The Netherlands BV (2)
Fischerpad 100, 6135 KS, Sittard, Netherlands
Tel.: (31) 464202400
Web Site: http://www.oberthurcs.com
Sales Range: $50-74.9 Million
Emp.: 11
Credit Card Issuing Services
N.A.I.C.S.: 522210

Oberthur Technologies UK Ltd. (2)
Alexandra Way, Ashchurch Business Centre, Tewkesbury, GL20 8GA, Gloucestershire, United Kingdom
Tel.: (44) 1684290290
Web Site: http://www.oberthur.com
Sales Range: $125-149.9 Million
Emp.: 330
Credit Card Issuing
N.A.I.C.S.: 522210
Eric Quinlan (Dir-Fin)

Oberthur Technologies de Mexico, S. de R.L. de C.V. (2)
Anahuac No 150 B Col El Mirador, Coyoacan, 4950, Mexico
Tel.: (52) 55 5483 0953
Smartcard Mfr
N.A.I.C.S.: 339999

Subsidiary (US):

Oberthur Technologies of America Corp. (2)
4250 Pleasant Valley Rd, Chantilly, VA 20151
Tel.: (703) 263-0100
Smartcard Mfr
N.A.I.C.S.: 339999
Jim Sanchez (Dir-Tech & Payment-North America)

Integer.pl S.A. (1)
ul Malborska 130, 30-624, Krakow, Poland
Tel.: (48) 12 619 98 00
Web Site: http://www.inpost.pl
Logistic Services
N.A.I.C.S.: 541614
Miroslaw Nowacki (Head-Intl Ops)

LaborMed Pharma S.A. (1)
Phadolpallav No 44 B, Bucharest, Romania
Tel.: (40) 213180377
Web Site: http://www.labormedpharma.ro
Sales Range: $25-49.9 Million
Pharmaceuticals Mfr
N.A.I.C.S.: 325412

Laboratorio LKM SA (1)
Artilleros 2436, C1428APH, Buenos Aires, Argentina
Tel.: (54) 11 4896 6100
Web Site: http://www.lkmsa.com.ar
Pharmaceutical Product Mfr & Distr
N.A.I.C.S.: 325412

Subsidiary (Non-US):

LKM Peru S.A. (2)
Rep De Panama 6543, Dist De Surco, Lima, Peru
Tel.: (51) 1 44 58780
Pharmaceutical Product Mfr & Distr
N.A.I.C.S.: 325412

Making Memories Wholesale Inc. (1)
1168 W 500 N, Centerville, UT 84014
Tel.: (801) 294-0430
Web Site: http://www.makingmemories.com
Sales Range: $10-24.9 Million
Emp.: 76
Stationery Stores

N.A.I.C.S.: 424120

Manjushree Technopack Limited (1)
60E F Hosur Rd Bommasandra Industrial Area, Hosur Road, Bengaluru, 560099, Karnataka, India
Tel.: (91) 8043436200
Web Site: http://www.manjushreeindia.com
Rev.: $201,173,727
Assets: $272,410,880
Liabilities: $149,461,344
Net Worth: $122,949,536
Earnings: $9,666,220
Fiscal Year-end: 03/31/2022
Plastic Packaging Products Mfr
N.A.I.C.S.: 322220
Vimal Kedia (Mng Dir)
Surendra Kedia (Exec Dir)
Basant Kumar Mohata (CFO)
Rasmi Ranjan Naik (Sec)
Sanjay Kupote (CEO)

Maxar Technologies Inc. (1)
1300 W 120th Ave, Westminster, CO 80234
Tel.: (303) 684-7660
Web Site: https://www.maxar.com
Rev.: $1,605,000,000
Assets: $4,606,000,000
Liabilities: $3,218,000,000
Net Worth: $1,388,000,000
Earnings: ($150,000,000)
Emp.: 4,600
Fiscal Year-end: 12/31/2022
Satellites, Earth imagery, Geospatial Data & Analytics
N.A.I.C.S.: 541370
Tony Frazier (Exec VP & Gen Mgr-Public Sector Earth Intelligence)
Jeff Robertson (COO & Sr VP)
Dan Smoot (CEO)
Susanne Hake (Gen Mgr-Government)
Anders Linder (Gen Mgr-International Government)
Paul Granito (Gen Mgr-Enterprise)
Randy Rehovich (Gen Mgr-Svcs)
Peter Wilczynski (Chief Product Officer)
Arvind Srinivasan (CTO)
Anat Gan Eden (Chief HR Officer)
Will Cocos (Chief Transformation Officer)
Laurie Korneffel (Gen Counsel)

Subsidiary (Domestic):

DigitalGlobe, Inc. (2)
1300 W 120th Ave, Westminster, CO 80234
Tel.: (303) 684-4000
Commercial High Resolution Earth Imagery Solutions
N.A.I.C.S.: 541360
Jeffrey S. Kerridge (Sr VP & Gen Mgr)
Jeff Culwell (COO & Sr VP-Operations)
Jeff Robertson (CIO & Sr VP)
Randy Lynch (CFO, Treas & Sr VP)
William Arras (Sr VP, VP & Gen Mgr)
Megan Wood (Sr Dir-Corporate Strategy)
Michael J. Edwards (VP)
Laurie Korneffel (VP)

Subsidiary (Domestic):

DigitalGlobe Intelligence Solutions, Inc. (3)
2325 Dulles C Fl 10, Herndon, VA 20171
Tel.: (703) 480-7500
Software Design Services
N.A.I.C.S.: 541511
David Grason (Mgr-Analytics Tech)

Subsidiary (Non-US):

DigitalGlobe International Asia Pacific Pte. Ltd. (3)
1 Kim Seng Promenade 09-01 Great World City East Tower, Singapore, 237994, Singapore
Tel.: (65) 63894851
Web Site: http://www.digitalglobe.com
Geospatial Information & Cloud Solutions
N.A.I.C.S.: 541370

Subsidiary (Domestic):

DigitalGlobe International, Inc. (3)
1601 Dry Creek Dr Ste 260, Longmont, CO 80503
Tel.: (303) 684-4000
Satellite Surveying & Mapping Services
N.A.I.C.S.: 541370

Spatial Energy, LLC (3)

1881 9th St Ste 303, Boulder, CO 80302
Tel.: (303) 625-1048
Energy-specific Imagery, Imagery Analysis & Online Enterprise Imagery & Data Management Services
N.A.I.C.S.: 333310
Sherry Madison (CFO)

The Radiant Group, LLC (3)
4501 Singer Ct Ste 220, Chantilly, VA 20151
Tel.: (571) 521-8024
Web Site: http://www.theradiantgroup.com
Technology & Analytics Software & Services
N.A.I.C.S.: 541519

Subsidiary (Domestic):

Radiant Mission Solutions Inc. (4)
1975 Research Pkwy Ste 315, Colorado Springs, CO 80920
Tel.: (719) 387-1250
Web Site: http://www.radiantblue.com
Software & Data Analytics
N.A.I.C.S.: 518210
Theresa Klimiuk (COO)

Subsidiary (Non-US):

MDA Hub Limited (2)
25 Hosier Lane, London, EC1A 9LQ, United Kingdom
Tel.: (44) 1732877778
Data Processing Services
N.A.I.C.S.: 518210

MDA Information Products Ltd. (2)
Ground Fl Richland House Langley Bus Ctr, Station Rd, Langley, SL3 8DS, Berkshire, United Kingdom
Tel.: (44) 1753214550
Web Site: http://www.mda-hips.co.uk
Sales Range: $50-74.9 Million
Emp.: 60
Home Information Pack Producer
N.A.I.C.S.: 531390

MDA Space & Robotics Limited (2)
Bepo Building Harwell Campus, Didcot, OX11 0RL, Oxfordshire, United Kingdom
Tel.: (44) 1235841591
Web Site: http://is.mdacorporation.com
Sales Range: $50-74.9 Million
Emp.: 4
Space Optical Cameras Sales
N.A.I.C.S.: 423410

Subsidiary (Domestic):

MDA Systems Inc. (2)
1300 Hercules Dr Ste 210, Houston, TX 77058-2770
Tel.: (281) 226-5200
Space-Qualified Software & Hardware Systems Mfr
N.A.I.C.S.: 541330

Subsidiary (Non-US):

MDA Systems Ltd. (2)
13800 Commerce Parkway, Richmond, V6V 2J3, BC, Canada
Tel.: (604) 278-3411
Web Site: https://www.mda.space
Satellite Systems
N.A.I.C.S.: 517410

MacDonald, Dettwiler & Associates Inc. (2)
9445 Airport Rd, Brampton, L6S 4J3, ON, Canada
Tel.: (905) 790-2800
Web Site: http://www.mdacorporation.com
Satellite Payload Systems & Robotics Equipment Developer & Mfr
N.A.I.C.S.: 927110
Luigi Pozzebon (VP-Satellite Sys)
Mike Greenley (CEO)

MacDonald, Dettwiler and Associates Corp. (2)
Suite 60 - 1000 Windmill Road, Dartmouth, B3B 1L7, NS, Canada
Tel.: (902) 468-3356
Web Site: http://www.mdacorporation.com
Emp.: 30
Monitoring & Surveillance Systems
N.A.I.C.S.: 334511

Subsidiary (US):

MDA Informations Systems LLC (3)

Advent International Corporation—(Continued)

820 W Diamond Ave Ste 300, Gaithersburg, MD 20878 **(100%)**
Tel.: (240) 833-8200
Web Site: http://www.mdaus.com
Emp.: 400
Geospatial Solutions Services
N.A.I.C.S.: 541370
David J. Cunningham (Sr VP-Govt Solutions)
Jeanine Melican (Dir-Comml Products)
Gregory T. Koeln (CTO)
Jim Friedel (VP-ISR Systems)

Subsidiary (Domestic):

Spacea Systems/Loral, LLC **(2)**
3825 Fabian Way, Palo Alto, CA 94303-4604 **(100%)**
Tel.: (650) 852-4000
Web Site: http://www.sslmda.com
Sales Range: $1-4.9 Billion
Emp.: 2,400
Satellite & Satellite Systems Mfr
N.A.I.C.S.: 927110
Michael B. Targoff (Vice Chm & CEO)

The Human Geo Group LLC **(2)**
4350 N Fairfax Dr Ste 950, Arlington, VA 22203
Tel.: (703) 888-1247
Data Management Services
N.A.I.C.S.: 518210

Wovenware Inc. **(2)**
601 Del Parque St Ste 506 Pesquera Bldg, San Juan, PR 00909
Tel.: (787) 946-7412
Web Site: http://www.wovenware.com
Software Development Services
N.A.I.C.S.: 541511
Christian G. Gonzalez (Co-Founder & CEO)
Carlos M. Melendez (Co-Founder & COO)
Miguel Moreda (CFO)

McAfee, LLC **(1)**
2821 Mission College Blvd, Santa Clara, CA 95054
Tel.: (408) 970-5151
Web Site: http://www.mcafee.com
Emp.: 7,330
Computer Security Software, Products & Services
N.A.I.C.S.: 513210
Steve Grobman (CTO & Sr VP)
Gagan Singh (Exec VP & Chief Product & Revenue Officer)
Dawn Smith (Chief Legal Officer & Exec VP)
Allison Cerra (CMO & Sr VP)
Rajiv Gupta (Sr VP-Cloud Security Bus Unit)
Aneel Jaeel (Sr VP-Customer Success Grp)
Chatelle Lynch (Chief HR Officer & Sr VP)
Gregory N. Johnson (Pres & CEO)
Bruce Chizen (Chm)

Subsidiary (Non-US):

McAfee Co., Ltd. **(2)**
Shibuya Mark City West 16/20th Fl 1-12-1 Dougenzaka, Shibuya-ku, Tokyo, 150 0043, Japan
Tel.: (81) 3 5428 1100
Web Site: http://www.mcafee.com
Computer Security Software, Products & Services
N.A.I.C.S.: 513210
Sanjay Manohar (Mng Dir-India)
Craig Nielsen (VP-Asia Pacific)

McAfee International BV **(2)**
Boeingavenue 30, 1119 PE, Schiphol-Rijk, Netherlands
Tel.: (31) 205863800
Web Site: http://www.mcafee.com
Data Security, Protection & Encryption Software Services
N.A.I.C.S.: 513210

Mediq B.V. **(1)**
Rijnzathe 10, 3454 PV, Demeern, Netherlands
Tel.: (31) 30 282 1911
Web Site: http://www.mediq.com
Sales Range: $1-4.9 Billion
Emp.: 3,000
Holding Company; Pharmaceuticals, Medical Devices & Supplies Distr & Online/Mail-Order Retailer

N.A.I.C.S.: 551112
C. De Jong (Chm-Supervisory Bd)
Christian Wojczewski (CEO)
Paul Hitchin (CFO)
Alex Jonker (Exec VP-Supply Chain)
Leah Bayer (Exec VP-Sourcing)
Stefaan Kindekens (CIO)

Subsidiary (US):

Byram Healthcare, Inc. **(2)**
120 Bloomingdale Rd, White Plains, NY 10605
Tel.: (914) 286-2000
Web Site: http://www.byramhealthcare.com
Sales Range: $25-49.9 Million
Medical Product Distr
N.A.I.C.S.: 423450
Perry Bernocchi (CEO)
Marcel Overweel (CFO)
Nicholas Piecora (CIO)
Marianne Hines (Exec VP-Sls & Mktg)
Jeffrey Mignone (Sr VP-Ops)
John W. Ras (Chief Compliance Officer)
Michelle L. Knowles (Gen Counsel & Sec)

Subsidiary (Domestic):

Diabetes Specialty Center, LLC **(3)**
645 E 4500 S Ste 200, Salt Lake City, UT 84107
Tel.: (801) 268-9699
Web Site: https://www.diabetesspecialty.com
Emp.: 200
Diabetic Testing & Treatment Equipment Distr & Retailer
N.A.I.C.S.: 423450
Doug Corpuz (Sr Dir-Field Sls & Mktg)

Subsidiary (Domestic):

CombiCare B.V. **(2)**
Coenecoop 375, 2741 PN, Waddinxveen, Netherlands
Tel.: (31) 182622444
Web Site: http://www.mediqcombicare.nl
Sales Range: $25-49.9 Million
Emp.: 120
Ostomy, Incontinence & Wound Care Medical Products Distr
N.A.I.C.S.: 423450
Arnoud van Dorth (Mgr-Mktg)

Subsidiary (Domestic):

CombiCare Vastgoed B.V. **(3)**
Hengelderweg 24, 6942 NB, Didam, Netherlands
Tel.: (31) 316582658
Web Site: http://www.zorgservice.nl
Medical Supplies Distr
N.A.I.C.S.: 423450

Subsidiary (Domestic):

Dispomed Diabetes Service Nederland **(2)**
Lorentzpark 10-12, 9351 VJ, Leek, Netherlands
Tel.: (31) 594 58 7730
Web Site: http://www.dsntrade.com
Sales Range: $25-49.9 Million
Emp.: 13
Medical Equipment & Supplies Whslr
N.A.I.C.S.: 423450
Jan Eisen (Gen Mgr)

Subsidiary (Non-US):

Mediq Danmark A/S **(2)**
Kornmarksvej 15-19, 2605, Brondby, Denmark
Tel.: (45) 36379200
Web Site: http://www.mediqdanmark.dk
Sales Range: $25-49.9 Million
Emp.: 120
Medical Equipment & Supplies Distr
N.A.I.C.S.: 423450
Jesper Boysen (Grp Exec VP-Direct & Institutional Sls)
Jan Kolbye Jensen (Mng Dir)
Nicolene Hulten (Mgr-HR)
Jacob Mark Sorensen (Mgr-Hospital Market)
Marianne Verbes (Mgr-Market)
Bent Jensen (Mgr-Institutions, Indus & Retail Markets)
Cindy Nijs (Dir-Direct Market)

Subsidiary (Domestic):

Mediq Direct Diabetes B.V. **(2)**
Hengelderweg 24, 6942 NB, Didam, Netherlands
Tel.: (31) 316582690
Web Site: http://www.mediqdirectdiabetes.nl
Diabetes Testing & Treatment Supplies Distr
N.A.I.C.S.: 423450
Doeschka Motmans (Mgr-Bus Dev)

Subsidiary (Non-US):

Mediq Direkt Diabetes GmbH **(2)**
Barensteiner Strasse 27-29, 1277, Dresden, Germany
Tel.: (49) 800 342 7325
Web Site: http://www.mediqdirekt.de
Diabetic Testing & Treatment Equipment Distr & Retailer
N.A.I.C.S.: 423450
Michael Spreth (Mng Dir)

Mediq Eesti OU **(2)**
Kungla 2, 76505, Saue, Harjumaa, Estonia
Tel.: (372) 6 515 151
Web Site: http://www.mediq.ee
Emp.: 42
Medical Equipment & Supplies Distr
N.A.I.C.S.: 423450
Aare Jarvelaid (CEO)
Maare Kapper (Sec)

Subsidiary (Non-US):

SIA Mediq Latvija **(3)**
Raunas iela 41C, 1084, Riga, Latvia
Tel.: (371) 6780 2463
Web Site: http://www.mediq.lv
Medical Equipment & Supplies Distr
N.A.I.C.S.: 423450

Subsidiary (Non-US):

Mediq Lietuva UAB **(2)**
Laisves pr 75, Vilnius, LT006144, Lithuania
Tel.: (370) 5 268 8451
Web Site: http://www.mediq.lt
Emp.: 11
Medical Equipment & Supplies Distr
N.A.I.C.S.: 423450
Giedrius Marcinkonis (Mng Dir)

Subsidiary (Domestic):

Mediq Medeco **(2)**
Alexander Flemingstraat 2, 3261 MA, Oud-Beijerland, Netherlands
Tel.: (31) 186 63 4400
Web Site: http://www.mediqmedeco.nl
Emp.: 175
Medical Equipment & Supplies Whslr
N.A.I.C.S.: 423450
Ronald Hoozemans (Mng Dir)
Arjan van Driel (Mgr-HR)
Nienke Smolders-de Jong (Product Mgr-E-Commerce & Digital Mktg)
Arthur de Bok (CEO)

Subsidiary (Non-US):

Medeco SA/NV **(3)**
Ikaroslaan 19, 1930, Zaventem, Belgium
Tel.: (32) 2 725 1880
Web Site: http://www.medeco.be
Medical Equipment & Supplies Whslr
N.A.I.C.S.: 423450
Rudivanr David (Gen Mgr)

Mediq Direkt Kft. **(3)**
Vasut ut 11, 2040, Budaors, Hungary
Tel.: (36) 23 802 881
Web Site: http://www.mediqdirekt.hu
Medical Equipment & Supplies Distr
N.A.I.C.S.: 423450
Rising Karolyne (Dir-Education & Client Rels)
Simko Tamas (Mgr-Logistics)

Subsidiary (Domestic):

Mediq Medisource B.V. **(2)**
Hertogswetering 159, 3543 AS, Utrecht, Netherlands
Tel.: (31) 302821240
Web Site: http://www.medisource.nl
Emp.: 150
Health Care Professional Referral Services
N.A.I.C.S.: 624190
Anneke Nummerdor Resowidjojo (Mgr-Ops)

Subsidiary (Non-US):

Mediq Norge AS **(2)**
Dyrskueveien 13, PO Box 113, 2041, Klofta, Norway
Tel.: (47) 6702 4300
Web Site: http://www.mediqnorge.no
Sales Range: $50-74.9 Million
Emp.: 170
Medical Equipment & Supplies Whslr
N.A.I.C.S.: 423450
Lars Magnus Mikkelsen (CEO)
Kjell Paulsrud (Dir-Logistics)

Unit (Domestic):

Mediq Pharma Services **(2)**
Archimedesbaan 26A, 3439 ME, Nieuwegein, Netherlands
Tel.: (31) 30 753 2700
Web Site: http://www.mediq.com
Emp.: 10
Pharmaceutical & Medical Supplies Distr
N.A.I.C.S.: 424210
Christian Wojczewski (CEO)

Subsidiary (Non-US):

Mediq Suisse AG **(2)**
Gewerbestrasse 12, 8132, Frauenfeld, Switzerland
Tel.: (41) 52 720 2526
Web Site: http://www.mediqsuisse.ch
Medical Equipment & Supplies Distr
N.A.I.C.S.: 423450
Rene Vete (Mng Dir)
Ralph Schonbachler (CEO)

Mediq Suomi Oy **(2)**
Luomanportti 3, 02200, Espoo, Finland
Tel.: (358) 2011 21500
Web Site: http://www.mediq.fi
Emp.: 165
Medical Equipment & Supplies Distr
N.A.I.C.S.: 423450
Ilari Vaalavirta (CEO)

Mediq Sverige AB **(2)**
Hallabacksvagen 1, 434 37, Kungsbacka, Sweden
Tel.: (46) 313889000
Web Site: http://www.mediqsverige.se
Emp.: 160
Medical Equipment & Supplies Distr
N.A.I.C.S.: 423450
Eva Weigert (Mgr-HR)
Malin Loften (Mgr-Customer Svc)
Patrik Vilhjalmsson (Mgr-Pur)
Tomas Borgenstam (Mgr-Warehouse)
Johan Malm (Mgr-Mktg)

Subsidiary (Domestic):

Mediq Tefa B.V. **(2)**
Hertogswetering 159, 3543 AS, Utrecht, Netherlands
Tel.: (31) 30 282 1300
Web Site: http://www.mediqtefa.nl
Emp.: 100
Infusion Therapy, Respiratory Care & Medical Nutrition Equipment & Supplies Distr
N.A.I.C.S.: 423450
Xander Schrage (Gen Mgr)

Romedic B.V. **(2)**
Weerterveld 49, 6231 NC, Meerssen, Netherlands
Tel.: (31) 433650256
Web Site: http://www.mediqromedic.nl
Emp.: 15
Inhalation & Nebulizer Medical Equipment Distr
N.A.I.C.S.: 423450
Rosalie Crombag (Mgr-Quality)

Systemfarma B.V. **(2)**
Stationspark 410, 3364 DA, Sliedrecht, Netherlands
Tel.: (31) 184 493838
Web Site: http://www.mediqsystemfarma.nl
Emp.: 160
Specialty Pharmacies Operator
N.A.I.C.S.: 456110

Subsidiary (Non-US):

assist GmbH **(2)**
In der Bruchwies 10, 66663, Merzig, Germany
Tel.: (49) 800 33 44 800
Web Site: http://www.assist.de

Emp.: 350
Medical Equipment & Pharmaceutical Distr
N.A.I.C.S.: 423450
Jorn Oldigs *(Mng Dir)*
Jurgen Waldraff *(Head-Mktg & Customer Svc)*

Mercury Payment Services S.p.A. (1)
Via Giulio Richard 7, 20143, Milan, Italy
Tel.: (39) 02 891371
Web Site: http://www.mercurypayments.it
Payment Processing Services
N.A.I.C.S.: 522320

Mercury Processing Services International LLC (1)
Radnicka cesta 50, 10000, Zagreb, Croatia
Tel.: (385) 1 645 60 41
Web Site: http://www.mercury-processing.com
Credit Card Payment Processing Services
N.A.I.C.S.: 522320
Zdenek Houser *(Chm-Mgmt Bd & Gen Dir)*
Stuart James Ashley Gent *(Chm-Supervisory Bd)*
Bernardo Mingrone *(Vice Chm-Supervisory Bd)*
Alberto Barroero *(Member-Mgmt Bd & Dir)*
Irina Brucic *(Member-Mgmt Bd & Dir)*
Giovanni Cetrangolo *(Member-Mgmt Bd & Dir)*
Tatjana Novak *(Member-Mgmt Bd & Dir)*

Subsidiary (Non-US):

Mercury Processing Services International Payment Card Processing & Development Ltd. (2)
Slovenceva Ulica 24, 1000, Ljubljana, Slovenia
Tel.: (386) 1 568 03 00
Web Site: http://www.mercury-processing.com
Credit Card Payment Processing Services
N.A.I.C.S.: 522320

Nets A/S (1)
Klausdalsbrovej 601, DK-2750, Ballerup, Denmark
Tel.: (45) 44684468
Web Site: http://www.nets.eu
Rev.: $1,264,993,856
Assets: $4,521,658,722
Liabilities: $2,816,559,886
Net Worth: $1,705,098,836
Earnings: $36,059,492
Emp.: 2,460
Fiscal Year-end: 12/31/2019
Holding Company; Payment Solutions, Information Services & Digital Security Solutions
N.A.I.C.S.: 551112
Soren Winge *(Head-Media)*
Bo Nilsson *(CEO)*
Pia Jorgensen *(CIO)*
Klaus Pedersen *(CFO)*
Robert Hoffmann *(CEO-Merchant Svcs)*
Gianluca Ventura *(Chief HR Officer)*
Christian Lintner *(Sr Mgr-Treasury)*

Subsidiary (Domestic):

Nets Denmark A/S (2)
Lautrupbjerg 10, DK-2750, Ballerup, Denmark
Tel.: (45) 4468 4468
Web Site: http://www.nets.eu
Payment, Card & Information Services
N.A.I.C.S.: 522320
Nevena Duric *(Officer-Press)*
Mads Allingstrup *(Officer-Press)*

Subsidiary (Non-US):

Nets Norway AS (2)
Haavard Martinsensvei 54, 0978, Oslo, Norway
Tel.: (47) 22898989
Web Site: http://www.nets.eu
Payment Solutions
N.A.I.C.S.: 522320
Stein-Arne Tjore *(Mgr-Press)*

Nets Sweden AB (2)
Lumaparksvagen 11, 120 31, Stockholm, Sweden
Tel.: (46) 8609 9400
Web Site: http://www.nets.eu
Electronic Payment Systems

N.A.I.C.S.: 522320
Soren Winge *(Mgr-Press)*

Nielsen Consumer LLC (1)
200 W Jackson Blvd, Chicago, IL 60606
Tel.: (312) 385-6768
Web Site: http://www.nielseniq.com
Market Research Services
N.A.I.C.S.: 541910
Tracey Massey *(COO)*
Jim Peck *(Chm & CEO)*

Subsidiary (Non-US):

CGA Strategy Limited (2)
Strawberry Studios Stockport, Manchester, SK1 3AZ, United Kingdom
Tel.: (44) 1614768330
Web Site: http://www.cga.co.uk
Market Management Consulting Services
N.A.I.C.S.: 541618
Scott Elliott *(Mng Dir-Americas)*
Jonathan Jones *(Mng Dir-UK & Ireland)*
Graeme Loudon *(Mng Dir-EMEA & APAC)*
Kate Willett *(Mgr-HR)*
Declan Sullivan *(Dir-Global Bus Solutions)*
Alex Eyre *(Dir-Product Leadership)*
Alison Powell *(Dir-Ops)*
Rachel Weller *(Dir-Consumer Res & Mktg)*
Phil Tate *(CEO-Grp)*

GfK SE (2)
Nordwestring 101, 90419, Nuremberg, Germany
Tel.: (49) 9113950
Web Site: http://www.gfk.com
Sales Range: $1-9.9 Million
Emp.: 13,069
Market Research Services
N.A.I.C.S.: 541910
Christian Diedrich *(CFO & Member-Mgmt Bd)*
Alessandra Cama *(COO & Member-Mgmt Bd)*
Ralf Klein-Bolting *(Chm-Supervisory Bd)*
Peter Feld *(CEO)*
Christian Bigata Joseph *(CFO)*
David Krajicek *(Chief Comml Officer & Member-Mgmt Bd)*

Subsidiary (US):

GfK Custom Research, LLC (3)
200 Liberty St 4th Fl, New York, NY 10281
Tel.: (212) 240-5300
Web Site: http://www.gfk.com
Sales Range: $25-49.9 Million
Emp.: 52
Custom Market Research
N.A.I.C.S.: 541910

Branch (Domestic):

GfK Custom Research, LLC - Minneapolis (4)
8401 Golden Valley Rd Ste 100, Minneapolis, MN 55427-4486
Tel.: (763) 542-0800
Web Site: http://www.gfk.com
Sales Range: $25-49.9 Million
Commercial Market Research
N.A.I.C.S.: 541910

GfK Custom Research, LLC - Princeton (4)
1060 State Rd, Princeton, NJ 08540-1423
Tel.: (609) 683-6100
Web Site: http://www.gfk.com
Sales Range: $25-49.9 Million
Market Research
N.A.I.C.S.: 541910

Subsidiary (Domestic):

GfK Mediamark Research & Intelligence, LLC (4)
75 9th Ave Fl 5, New York, NY 10011-4756
Tel.: (212) 884-9200
Web Site: http://www.gfkmri.com
Sales Range: $25-49.9 Million
Emp.: 45
Media & Marketing Databases Distr
N.A.I.C.S.: 513140
Alain Tessier *(Chm)*
Ian Jack *(COO & Exec VP)*
George Kronheimer *(VP-Sls)*
Chris Schlagheck *(Sr VP-Sls)*
Paul Gold *(VP-Market Solutions)*
Andy Arthur *(Sr VP)*
Julian Baim *(Exec VP & Chief Res Officer)*

David Napior *(Sr VP-Res)*
Risa Becker *(VP-Res Ops)*
Jay Mattlin *(Sr VP-Ventures)*
Jana Slaten *(VP-Market Res)*
Jim Collins *(Sr VP-Res)*
Steve Goodreds *(Exec VP-Fin & HR & CFO)*
Chetan Shah *(VP-West Coast Sls)*
Karen Ring *(VP-Res-MRI Starch Adv Res)*
Florian Kahlert *(Mng Dir)*
Christie Kawada *(Exec VP-Product Mgmt & Innovation)*

Knowledge Networks, Inc. (4)
2100 Geng Rd Ste 210, Palo Alto, CA 94303
Tel.: (650) 289-2000
Sales Range: $75-99.9 Million
Emp.: 400
Consumer Market Research & Opinion Polling Services
N.A.I.C.S.: 541910
Ellen Veccia *(Chief Res Officer)*
Patricia Graham *(Chief Strategy Officer)*
Audrey Rosen *(Exec VP-CPG Retail)*
J. Michael Dennis *(Exec VP-Govt & Academic Res)*
Carlos E. Garcia *(Sr VP)*
Neal Heffernan *(Sr VP & Gen Mgr)*
Wendy Wallner *(Sr VP-CPG Retail)*

Subsidiary (Non-US):

GfK NOP Ltd. (3)
Level-18 25 Canada Square Canary Wharf, London, E14 5LQ, United Kingdom
Tel.: (44) 2078909000
Web Site: http://www.gfknop.com
Sales Range: $25-49.9 Million
Emp.: 500
Market Research
N.A.I.C.S.: 541910
Amanda Wheeler *(Mgr-Comm & PR)*
Nick Moon *(Mng Dir-Social Res Sector)*
Richard Morland *(Dir-Bus Dev-Tech Sector)*

Subsidiary (Domestic):

Rakuten Intelligence, Inc. (2)
900 Concar Dr Fl 5, San Mateo, CA 94402
Tel.: (650) 323-9100
Web Site: http://www.rakutenintelligence.com
E-Commerce Online Services
N.A.I.C.S.: 519290
Paul Brody *(CTO)*

P2 Energy Solutions, Inc. (1)
1670 Broadway Ste 2800, Denver, CO 80202
Tel.: (303) 292-0990
Web Site: http://www.p2energysolutions.com
Sales Range: $100-124.9 Million
Emp.: 700
Energy Industry Software, Geospatial Data, Land Management Tools & Outsourcing Services
N.A.I.C.S.: 513210
Brandon Elam *(VP-Customer Success)*
Chris Lenig *(Sr VP-Production)*
Liz Nguyen *(Sr VP-Product Dev)*
J. Scott Lockhart *(CEO)*
Mark Kilpatrick *(Sr VP-Operational Excellence)*
Scott Key *(Chm)*
Ben Farquharson *(Sr VP-APAC)*
Dale McMullin *(CTO)*
Derrick Barker *(CFO)*
Mary Lyke *(Sr VP-Sls)*
Michael Danielewicz *(Sr VP-Canada)*
Shelley Pettet *(Chief HR Officer)*
Steven Ferrigno *(Sr VP-EMEA)*
Tony Sperduti *(Sr VP-Tobin Data Solutions)*

Subsidiary (Non-US):

P2 Energy Solutions Pty Ltd (2)
Australia Level 1 1195 Hay Street, West Perth, 6005, WA, Australia
Tel.: (61) 8 9241 0300
Web Site: http://www.issgroup.com.au
Sales Range: $10-24.9 Million
Emp.: 130
Infrastructure Software Developer
N.A.I.C.S.: 513210
Richard Pang *(Sr VP-Asia Pacific)*

Subsidiary (Non-US):

ISS Group (Asia) Pte. Ltd. (3)

20 Anson Road Unit 12-03, Singapore, 79912, Singapore
Tel.: (65) 65340091
Web Site: http://www.p2energysolutions.com
Sales Range: $10-24.9 Million
Emp.: 15
Packaged Software Publishers
N.A.I.C.S.: 513210
Ben Farquharson *(Sr VP)*

ISS Group Europe Limited (3)
26 Compass House Ensign Way, Hamble, Southampton, SO31 4RA, Hants, United Kingdom
Tel.: (44) 2380605920
Web Site: http://www.issgroup.com.au
Sales Range: $10-24.9 Million
Emp.: 15
Packaged Software Publishers
N.A.I.C.S.: 513210

Branch (Domestic):

P2 Energy Solutions, Inc. - Livingston (2)
220 S Orange Ave Ste 105, Livingston, NJ 07039
Tel.: (973) 992-8000
Web Site: http://www.p2energysolutions.com
Emp.: 75
Oil & Gas Industry Software Developer
N.A.I.C.S.: 513210

P2 Energy Solutions, Inc. - San Antonio (2)
1355 Central Pkwy S Ste 500, San Antonio, TX 78232
Tel.: (210) 402-5900
Custom Map Printing Services
N.A.I.C.S.: 323111
Mary Kimball *(Dir-HR)*

RatePAY GmbH (1)
Franklinstrabe 28-29, 101587, Berlin, Germany
Tel.: (49) 3033988560
Web Site: http://www.ratepay.com
Electronic Payment Services
N.A.I.C.S.: 522320
Miriam Wohlfarth *(Founder & Mng Dir)*
Jesper Wahrendorf *(CEO)*
Urs Bader *(COO & Mng Dir)*
Luise Linden *(CTO)*

SC Ceramica SA (1)
Calea Chisinaului nr 176, Iasi, 700180, Romania
Tel.: (40) 232 200 200
Web Site: http://www.ceramica-iasi.ro
Sales Range: $25-49.9 Million
Emp.: 200
Ceramic Brick Mfr
N.A.I.C.S.: 327331
Lulian Mangalagiu *(Mng Dir)*

Sovos Brands Intermediate, Inc. (1)
1901 4th St Ste 200, Berkeley, CA 94710
Tel.: (510) 646-8013
Web Site: http://sovosbrands.com
Food & Beverage Company
N.A.I.C.S.: 311991
Todd Lachman *(Founder, Pres & CEO)*
Chris Hall *(CFO)*
Wendy Behr *(Chief R&D Officer)*
Larry E. Bodner *(Co-Founder)*

Subsidiary (Domestic):

Noosa Yoghurt LLC (2)
4120 N County Rd 25E, Bellvue, CO 80512
Tel.: (970) 493-0949
Web Site: http://www.noosayoghurt.com
Ice Cream & Frozen Dessert Mfr
N.A.I.C.S.: 311520
Koel Thomae *(Co-Founder)*

Suven Pharmaceuticals Limited (1)
202 A-Wing Galaxy Towers Plot No-1 Hyderabad Knowledge City, TSIIC Raidurg Serilingampally Rangareddy District, Hyderabad, 500081, Telangana, India (50.1%)
Tel.: (91) 4023549414
Web Site: https://www.suvenpharm.com
Rev.: $139,769,926
Assets: $201,264,486
Liabilities: $40,084,153
Net Worth: $161,180,333

Advent International Corporation—(Continued)

Earnings: $49,459,656
Emp.: 1,114
Fiscal Year-end: 03/31/2021
Pharmaceuticals Mfr
N.A.I.C.S.: 325412
Sudhir Kumar Singh *(CEO)*
Vaidheesh Annaswamy *(Exec Chm)*
Vetukuri Venkata Naga Kali Vara Prasada Raju *(Mng Dir)*
Subba Raju Komaravolu *(Chief Strategy Officer)*
Gaurav Narain Bahadur *(Chief HR Officer)*
Brian Shaughnessy *(Chief Comml Officer)*

TK Elevator GmbH **(1)**
thyssenkrupp Allee 1, 45143, Essen, Germany
Tel.: (49) 2018440
Web Site: http://www.thyssenkrupp-elevator.com
Sales Range: $5-14.9 Billion
Emp.: 39,501
Holding Company; Elevator & Lift Developr, Mfr & Distr
N.A.I.C.S.: 551112
Uday Yadav *(CEO)*

Subsidiary (US):

Braun Thyssenkrupp Elevator, LLC **(2)**
2829 Royal Ave, Madison, WI 53713
Tel.: (608) 221-4400
Web Site: http://www.braun-corp.com
Sales Range: $1-9.9 Million
Emp.: 100
Building Equipment Contractors
N.A.I.C.S.: 238290
Darrell Braun *(CEO)*

O'Keefe Elevator Company Inc. **(2)**
1402 Jones St, Omaha, NE 68102
Tel.: (402) 345-4056
Web Site: http://www.okeefe-elevator.com
Sales Range: $10-24.9 Million
Elevators
N.A.I.C.S.: 423830
Denny B. Wychulis *(CEO)*

Subsidiary (Non-US):

Sun Rhine Enterprises Ltd. **(2)**
10F-1 No 18 Sec 1 Chang-An E Road, Taipei, 104, Taiwan
Tel.: (886) 2 25618310
Web Site: http://www.thyssenkrupp-elevator.com.tw
Sales Range: $25-49.9 Million
Emp.: 100
Lift Repair & Installation Services
N.A.I.C.S.: 238290

TK Elevator **(2)**
Andropov Ave 18 bldg 7, 115432, Moscow, Russia
Tel.: (7) 4959358517
Web Site: http://tkelevator.ru
Sales Range: $50-74.9 Million
Emp.: 150
Elevator Mfr
N.A.I.C.S.: 333921

ThyssenKrupp Accessibility B.V. **(2)**
Van Utrechtweg 99, 2921 LN, Krimpen aan de ijssel, Netherlands
Tel.: (31) 180 530 900
Web Site: http://www.tkacc.nl
Elevator & Stair Lift Mfr
N.A.I.C.S.: 333921

Subsidiary (Domestic):

ThyssenKrupp Accessibility Holding GmbH **(2)**
Hatzper Strasse 36, 45149, Essen, Germany
Tel.: (49) 2017995911
Web Site: http://www.tk-access4all.com
Sales Range: $25-49.9 Million
Emp.: 11
Holding Company; Wheel Chair Lift Mfr
N.A.I.C.S.: 551112

ThyssenKrupp Aufzuge GmbH **(2)**
Bernhaeuser Strasse 45, PO Box 280370, 73765, Neuhausen, Germany
Tel.: (49) 711652220

Web Site: http://www.thyssenkrupp-elevator.com
Sales Range: $1-4.9 Billion
Emp.: 3,000
Elevator Mfr
N.A.I.C.S.: 331513

Subsidiary (Non-US):

ThyssenKrupp Elevadores S.A. **(2)**
Fonrouge 1561, C1440CYO, Buenos Aires, Argentina
Tel.: (54) 1146301600
Web Site: http://www.thyssenkrupp.com
Elevator Mfr
N.A.I.C.S.: 333921

ThyssenKrupp Elevadores S.A. **(2)**
Carrera 85K 46 A 66 Torre 2 of 401, Centro Logistico San Cayetano 666 Santa Fe, Bogota, Colombia
Tel.: (57) 16700070
Web Site: http://www.thyssenkrupp.com
Sales Range: $100-124.9 Million
Emp.: 270
Elevator Mfr
N.A.I.C.S.: 333921

ThyssenKrupp Elevadores S.A. **(2)**
Via Porras San Francisco Local 65, Panama, Panama
Tel.: (507) 3881111
Web Site: http://www.thyssenkrupp.com
Elevator Mfr
N.A.I.C.S.: 333921

ThyssenKrupp Elevadores S.A. **(2)**
Alcantara 200 Piso 6, Las Condes, Santiago, Chile
Tel.: (56) 2 370 2932
Elevator Mfr
N.A.I.C.S.: 333921

ThyssenKrupp Elevadores S.A.C. **(2)**
Av San Borja Sur 1180 - 1182, San Borja, Lima, Peru
Tel.: (51) 16250400
Web Site: http://www.thyssenkrupp.com
Elevator Mfr
N.A.I.C.S.: 333921

ThyssenKrupp Elevadores, S.A. **(2)**
4th avenue 17-09 - zone 14, Guatemala, Guatemala
Tel.: (502) 2 368 2020
Web Site: http://www.thyssenkrupp.com
Sales Range: $25-49.9 Million
Emp.: 40
Elevator Mfr
N.A.I.C.S.: 333921

ThyssenKrupp Elevadores, S.A. **(2)**
Rua Santa Maria 1000, 92500-000, Guaiba, Portoalegre, Brazil
Tel.: (55) 51 2129 7241
Elevator Mfr
N.A.I.C.S.: 333921

ThyssenKrupp Elevadores, S.A. **(2)**
Sintra Business Park Building 4 2B, 2710-089, Sintra, Portugal
Tel.: (351) 21 430 81 00
Sales Range: $100-124.9 Million
Emp.: 500
Elevator & Escalator Installation Services
N.A.I.C.S.: 238290
Ricardo Malheiro *(CEO)*

ThyssenKrupp Elevadores, S.A. de C.V. **(2)**
General Mendez 19 Col Daniel Garza Extension, 11840, Mexico, Mexico
Tel.: (52) 55 5344 4571
Web Site: http://www.thyssenkrupp.com
Sales Range: $25-49.9 Million
Emp.: 100
Elevator Mfr
N.A.I.C.S.: 333921

ThyssenKrupp Elevadores, S.L. **(2)**
Calle Cifuentes s / n, 28021, Madrid, Spain
Tel.: (34) 901020909
Web Site: http://www.thyssenkrupp-elevator.com
Installation, Modernization & Maintenance of Elevators, Escalators, Moving Walks, Platform & Scenic Equipment
N.A.I.C.S.: 333921

ThyssenKrupp Elevadores, S.R.L. **(2)**

Democracia N 1893, 11800, Montevideo, Uruguay
Tel.: (598) 51 48 07 206
Elevator Mfr
N.A.I.C.S.: 333921

ThyssenKrupp Elevator & Escalator (Shanghai) Co.Ltd. **(2)**
Room 2603 Wisdom Plaza 518 Wuning South Road, Shanghai, 200042, China
Tel.: (86) 21 5298 8958
Web Site: http://www.thyssenkrupp-elevator.com.cn
Elevator Mfr
N.A.I.C.S.: 333921

ThyssenKrupp Elevator (BD) Pvt. Ltd. **(2)**
AncAnchor Tower 7th Floor 108 Bir Uttam C R Dutta Road, 1205, Dhaka, Bangladesh
Tel.: (880) 2448620013
Web Site: http://www.thyssenkrupp-elevator.com.bd
Sales Range: $25-49.9 Million
Emp.: 70
Elevator Mfr
N.A.I.C.S.: 333921

ThyssenKrupp Elevator (HK) Ltd. **(2)**
31st Floor Enterprise Plaza 3 39 Wang Chiu Road, Kowloon Bay, Kowloon, China (Hong Kong)
Tel.: (852) 2766 0218
Web Site: http://www.thyssenkrupp-elevator.com.hk
Emp.: 250
Elevator Mfr
N.A.I.C.S.: 333921

ThyssenKrupp Elevator (India) Private Limited **(2)**
A-4 Vardhan House Street no 3 MIDC, Andheri East, Mumbai, 400 093, Maharashtra, India
Tel.: (91) 2266902300
Web Site: http://www.thyssenkrupp-elevator.com
Sales Range: $100-124.9 Million
Emp.: 500
Elevator Mfr
N.A.I.C.S.: 333921

ThyssenKrupp Elevator (Korea) Ltd. **(2)**
201 Mokdongseo-ro, Yangcheon-gu, Seoul, 158-719, Korea (South)
Tel.: (82) 2 2610 7777
Web Site: http://www.thyssenkrupp-elevator.co.kr
Elevator Mfr
N.A.I.C.S.: 333921

Plant (Domestic):

ThyssenKrupp Elevator (Korea) Ltd. - Cheonan Plant **(3)**
115-24 Sindu-ri Ipjang-myeon, Seobuk-gu, Cheonan, 330-826, Chungcheongnam-do, Korea (South)
Tel.: (82) 41 589 4000
Web Site: http://www.thyssenkrupp-elevator.co.kr
Emp.: 1,000
Elevator Mfr
N.A.I.C.S.: 333921

Subsidiary (Non-US):

ThyssenKrupp Elevator (Singapore) Pte.Ltd. **(2)**
3 International Business Park 06-01 Nordic European Centre, Singapore, 609927, Singapore
Tel.: (65) 68901640
Web Site: http://www.thyssenkrupp-elevator.com.sg
Emp.: 70
Elevator & Escalator Installation Services
N.A.I.C.S.: 238290

ThyssenKrupp Elevator A/S **(2)**
Erhvervsvej 4, 2600, Glostrup, Denmark
Tel.: (45) 70130808
Web Site: http://www.thyssenkrupp-elevator.dk
Sales Range: $25-49.9 Million
Emp.: 231
Elevator Mfr
N.A.I.C.S.: 333921

ThyssenKrupp Elevator A/S **(2)**
Brobekkveien 38, PO Box 6877, Rodelokka, 504, Oslo, Norway
Tel.: (47) 23173700
Sales Range: $25-49.9 Million
Emp.: 30
Elevator Mfr
N.A.I.C.S.: 333921

ThyssenKrupp Elevator Almoayyed W.L.L. **(2)**
Suite 2703 Almoayyed Tower Building 2504 Road 2832, PO Box 60059, Al Seef District, 428, Manama, Bahrain
Tel.: (973) 17311515
Web Site: http://www.thyssenkrupp-elevator-seame.com
Elevator Installation & Maintenance Services
N.A.I.C.S.: 811310

Subsidiary (US):

ThyssenKrupp Elevator Americas Corp. **(2)**
2500 Northwinds Pkwy, Alpharetta, GA 30004
Tel.: (678) 319-3245
Web Site: http://www.thyssenkruppelevator.com
Elevator & Lift Product Mfr & Maintenance
N.A.I.C.S.: 333921

Subsidiary (Domestic):

Computerized Elevator Control Corp. **(3)**
24 Empire Blvd, Moonachie, NJ 07074-1303
Tel.: (201) 508-2300
Web Site: http://www.swiftcec.com
Sales Range: $25-49.9 Million
Emp.: 85
Elevators & Equipment Mfr
N.A.I.C.S.: 333921

National Wheel-O-Vator Co. Inc. **(3)**
509 W Font St, Roanoke, IL 61561
Tel.: (309) 923-7803
Web Site: http://www.wheelovator.com
Sales Range: $25-49.9 Million
Emp.: 150
Wheelchair Lift & Home Elevator Mfr & Distr
N.A.I.C.S.: 333921

Plant (Domestic):

ThyssenKrupp Elevator **(3)**
1650 Shelby Oaks Dr N Ste 6, Memphis, TN 38134
Tel.: (901) 377-1993
Web Site: http://www.thyssenkruppelevator.com
Sales Range: $25-49.9 Million
Emp.: 100
Passenger & Freight Elevators & Stage Lifts Mfr
N.A.I.C.S.: 333921

ThyssenKrupp Elevator **(3)**
700 Hicksville Rd, Bethpage, NY 11714
Tel.: (631) 491-3111
Web Site: http://www.thyssenkruppelevator.com
Sales Range: $50-74.9 Million
Emp.: 215
Elevator Installation & Conversion
N.A.I.C.S.: 238290

Subsidiary (Domestic):

ThyssenKrupp Elevator Capital Corp. **(3)**
3965 Mendenhall Rd Ste 10, Memphis, TN 38115
Tel.: (901) 365-5100
Web Site: http://www.thyssenkrupp.com
Elevator Mfr
N.A.I.C.S.: 333921

ThyssenKrupp Elevator Corp. **(3)**
15141 E Whittier Blvd Ste 505, Whittier, CA 90603
Tel.: (901) 365-5600
Web Site: http://www.thyssenkrupp.com
Elevator Mfr
N.A.I.C.S.: 333921

ThyssenKrupp Elevator Inc. **(3)**

1650 Shelby Oaks Dr Ste 6, Memphis, TN
38134
Tel.: (901) 377-1993
Web Site: http://www.thyssenkrupp.com
Emp.: 260
Elevator Mfr
N.A.I.C.S.: 333921

ThyssenKrupp Elevator Manufacturing Inc. (3)
9280 Crestwyn Hills Dr, Collierville, TN
38125
Tel.: (901) 261-1800
Elevator Mfr
N.A.I.C.S.: 333921

Subsidiary (Non-US):

ThyssenKrupp Elevator Asia Pacific Ltd. (2)
7/F Sun Hung Kai Center 30 Habour Road,
Wanchai, China (Hong Kong)
Tel.: (852) 3511 0688
Web Site: http://www.thyssenkrupp-elevator-ap.com
Sales Range: $25-49.9 Million
Emp.: 40
Elevator Installation & Maintenance Services
N.A.I.C.S.: 811310

ThyssenKrupp Elevator B.V. (2)
Fascinatio Boulevard 806-808, 2909 VA,
Capelle aan den IJssel, Netherlands
Tel.: (31) 88 4479 200
Web Site: http://www.thyssenkruppliften.nl
Sales Range: $25-49.9 Million
Emp.: 60
Elevator Installation Services
N.A.I.C.S.: 238290

ThyssenKrupp Elevator Canada Ltd. (2)
2075 Kennedy Rd Suite 600, Scarborough,
M1T 3V3, ON, Canada
Tel.: (416) 291-2000
Sales Range: $25-49.9 Million
Emp.: 1,800
Elevator & Lift Mfr & Distr
N.A.I.C.S.: 333921

ThyssenKrupp Elevator Holding France S.A.S. (2)
8 Rue Parmentier, 92816, Puteaux, France
Tel.: (33) 1 573265 58
Web Site: http://www.thyssenkrupp.com
Elevator Installation & Maintenance Services
N.A.I.C.S.: 811310

ThyssenKrupp Elevator Innovation Center, S.A. (2)
La Laboral Ciudad de la Cultura, '33203,
Gijon, Asturias, Spain
Tel.: (34) 98 519 67 92
Elevator Mfr
N.A.I.C.S.: 333921

ThyssenKrupp Elevator Ireland, Ltd. (2)
Unit 11 Seatown Business Campus
Seatown Road, Swords, Dublin, Ireland
Tel.: (353) 1 8956903
Web Site: http://www.thyssenkrupp.com
Sales Range: $25-49.9 Million
Emp.: 20
Elevator Installation Services
N.A.I.C.S.: 238290

ThyssenKrupp Elevator Italia S.p.A. (2)
Via A Volta 16, 20093, Cologno Monzese,
Italy
Tel.: (39) 02 89 69 63 00
Web Site: http://www.thyssenkrupp-elevator.com
Elevator Installation Services
N.A.I.C.S.: 238290

ThyssenKrupp Elevator Malaysia Sdn. Bhd. (2)
Level 18 The Pinnacle Persiaran Lagoon
Bandar Sunway, 46150, Petaling Jaya, Selangor Darul Ehsen, Malaysia
Tel.: (60) 356229988
Web Site: http://www.thyssenkrupp-elevator.com.my
Emp.: 200
Elevator Installation & Maintenance Services

N.A.I.C.S.: 811310

ThyssenKrupp Elevator Manufacturing France S.A.S. (2)
Rue de Champfleur Z I Saint-Barthelemy,
BP 10746, 49007, Angers, France
Tel.: (33) 2 41 33 36 75
Web Site: http://www.thyssenkrupp-ascenseurs.fr
Elevator & Escalator Mfr
N.A.I.C.S.: 333921

ThyssenKrupp Elevator Manufacturing Spain S.L. (2)
C/ Federico Cantero Villamil 4 Parque
Tecnologico, 28935, Mostoles, Madrid,
Spain
Tel.: (34) 91 481 7700
Web Site: http://www.thyssenkrupp-elevator-manufacturing-spain.com
Elevator Mfr
N.A.I.C.S.: 333921
Elena Mozo (Mgr-Comm)

ThyssenKrupp Elevator Queensland Pty. Ltd. (2)
303 Cleveland Street, PO Box 16, Surry
Hills, 2010, NSW, Australia
Tel.: (61) 2 8303 9000
Web Site: http://www.thyssenkrupp.com
Elevator Installation Services
N.A.I.C.S.: 238290

ThyssenKrupp Elevator SRL (2)
Preciziei no 11 floor 3 sector 6, 6th District,
Bucharest, 62202, Romania
Tel.: (40) 21 3180879
Web Site: http://www.thyssenkrupp-elevator-romania.com
Sales Range: $25-49.9 Million
Emp.: 32
Elevator Installation Services
N.A.I.C.S.: 238290

ThyssenKrupp Elevator Saudi Co. Ltd. (2)
Salah Eddin Al-Ayoubi Street, PO Box
9812, Jarir District Al Bawani Tower 6th
Floor, 11423, Riyadh, Saudi Arabia
Tel.: (966) 114868900
Web Site: http://www.thyssenkrupp.com
Elevator Installation & Maintenance Services
N.A.I.C.S.: 811310

ThyssenKrupp Elevator Southern Europe, Africa & Middle East, S.L.U. (2)
Paseo de la Castellana 259C Floor 23, Madrid, 28046, Spain
Tel.: (34) 912028000
Web Site: http://www.thyssenkrupp-elevator-seame.com
Elevator Mfr
N.A.I.C.S.: 333921

ThyssenKrupp Elevator Sp. z o.o. (2)
Aleje Jerozolimskie 179, 02-222, Warsaw,
Poland
Tel.: (48) 22 530 99 00
Web Site:
http://www.thyssenkruppelevator.pl
Emp.: 50
Elevator Installation & Maintenance Services
N.A.I.C.S.: 811310

ThyssenKrupp Elevator Sverige AB (2)
Storsatragrand 12, 127 39, Skarholmen,
Sweden
Tel.: (46) 8 449 2250
Web Site: http://www.thyssenkrupp.com
Sales Range: $25-49.9 Million
Emp.: 100
Elevator Installation Services
N.A.I.C.S.: 238290

ThyssenKrupp Elevator UK Ltd. (2)
4 Bull Close Road, Nottingham, NG7 2UL,
United Kingdom
Tel.: (44) 115 986 8213
Web Site: http://www.thyssenkrupp-elevator.com
Elevator Installation Services
N.A.I.C.S.: 238290

ThyssenKrupp Elevator Vietnam Co., Ltd. (2)

198 Truong Chinh, Khuong Thuong Ward
Dong Da District, 10200, Hanoi, Vietnam
Tel.: (84) 437282116
Web Site: http://www.thyssenkrupp.com.vn
Elevator Installation Services
N.A.I.C.S.: 238290

ThyssenKrupp Elevatori d.o.o. (2)
Bulevar Mihaila Pupina 10z/1, Belgrade,
11000, Serbia
Tel.: (381) 11 21 29 612
Web Site: http://www.thyssenkrupp-elevator.rs
Sales Range: $25-49.9 Million
Emp.: 20
Elevator Installation & Maintenance Services
N.A.I.C.S.: 811310
Igor Tanaskovic (Mng Dir)

ThyssenKrupp Elevators (Shanghai) Co., Ltd. (2)
No 2 Xunye Rd Sheshan Subarea Songjiang Industrial Area, Shanghai, 201602,
China
Tel.: (86) 2157076888
Web Site: http://www.thyssenkrupp-elevator.com.cn
Elevator Mfr
N.A.I.C.S.: 333921

ThyssenKrupp Elevators Hellas S.A. (2)
37 Sepolion Str, 104 45, Athens, Greece
Tel.: (30) 210 825 2766
Web Site: http://www.thyssenkrupp.com
Sales Range: $25-49.9 Million
Emp.: 52
Elevator Installation Services
N.A.I.C.S.: 238290

ThyssenKrupp Northern Elevator Ltd. (2)
410 Passmore Avenue Unit 1, Scarborough,
M1V 5C3, ON, Canada
Tel.: (416) 291-2000
Sales Range: $75-99.9 Million
Emp.: 300
Elevator Mfr
N.A.I.C.S.: 333921

Subsidiary (Domestic):

Thyssen Dover Elevator (Canada) Ltd. (3)
410 Passmore Ave, Scarborough, M1V
5C3, ON, Canada
Tel.: (416) 291-2000
Web Site: http://www.thyssenkrupp.com
Elevator Mfr
N.A.I.C.S.: 333921

Subsidiary (Non-US):

ThyssenKrupp Tailored Blanks (Wuhan) Ltd. (2)
Yinguang Av Guannan Industry Park,
430074, Wuhan, China
Tel.: (86) 27 8756 1616
Web Site: http://www.thyssenkrupp.com
Automotive Tailored Blank Mfr
N.A.I.C.S.: 336390

Tinsa (1)
Jose Echegaray 9 Parque Empresarial,
28232, Las Rozas, Spain
Tel.: (34) 91 372 75 00
Web Site: http://www.tinsa.es
Real Estate Valuation, Analysis & Advisory
Services
N.A.I.C.S.: 531320
Juan Jose Hernandez-Chanclon (Mgr-Ops
& HR)
Juan Guerra Julia (CFO)

UNIT4 NV (1)
Stationspark 1000, 3364, Sliedrecht, Netherlands
Tel.: (31) 88 247 17 77
Accounting Software Mfr
N.A.I.C.S.: 513210

Subsidiary (US):

Three Rivers Systems, Inc. (2)
174 Clarkson Rd Ste 200, Ellisville, MO
63011-2258
Tel.: (636) 386-8616
Web Site:
http://www.threeriverssystems.com

Software Publisher
N.A.I.C.S.: 513210
Jami Morshed (VP-Global Sls & Mktg)

Williams Lea Limited (1)
55 Wells Street, London, W1A 3AE, United
Kingdom (100%)
Tel.: (44) 02072514571
Web Site: http://www.williamslea.com
Corporate Information Management Services
N.A.I.C.S.: 541611

Subsidiary (Domestic):

The Stationery Office Limited (2)
St Crispins Duke Street, Norwich, NR3
1PD, United Kingdom
Tel.: (44) 1603 622211
Web Site: http://www.tso.co.uk
Online Book Publishing Services
N.A.I.C.S.: 513130

Subsidiary (Non-US):

Williams Lea (Beijing) Limited (2)
Room 1201I 12/F Excel Centre No 6 Wudinghou Street, Xicheng District, Beijing,
100140, China
Tel.: (86) 10 8800 3796
Business Process Outsourcing Services
N.A.I.C.S.: 561499

Williams Lea (Brazil) Assessoria Em Solucoes Empresariais Ltda. (2)
Rua Wisard 305 Conjunto 52, Sao Paulo,
05434 080, Vila Madalena, Brazil
Tel.: (55) 1130938040
Business Process Outsourcing Services
N.A.I.C.S.: 561499

Subsidiary (Domestic):

Williams Lea (US Acquisitions) Limited (2)
55 Well Street, London, W1A 3AE, United
Kingdom
Tel.: (44) 20 7772 4200
Web Site: http://www.williamslea.com
Business Process Outsourcing Services
N.A.I.C.S.: 561499

Subsidiary (Non-US):

Williams Lea France SAS (2)
1 Place Boieldieu, 91400, Paris, France
Tel.: (33) 1 42 61 64 41
Business Process Outsourcing Services
N.A.I.C.S.: 561499

Williams Lea GmbH (2)
Ganghofer Str 70, 80339, Munich, Germany
Tel.: (49) 8930907570
Business Process Outsourcing Services
N.A.I.C.S.: 561499
Christine Elgey (Mng Dir)

Subsidiary (Domestic):

Williams Lea Holdings PLC (2)
1 5 Poland Street, London, W1F 8PR,
United Kingdom
Tel.: (44) 20 7394 4200
Business Process Outsourcing Services
N.A.I.C.S.: 561499
Clare Hart (CEO)

Subsidiary (US):

Williams Lea Inc. (2)
30 S Wacker Dr 22nd Fl, Chicago, IL 60606
Tel.: (312) 681-6400
Web Site: http://www.williamslea.com
Document & Facilities Management
N.A.I.C.S.: 541618
Lynn Breakey (Dir-Mktg)

Subsidiary (Non-US):

Williams Lea India Private Limited (2)
Module 0308 D Block Third Floor Tidel Park
Taramani, Chennai, 600113, India
Tel.: (91) 44 3068 5000
Business Process Outsourcing Services
N.A.I.C.S.: 561499

Williams Lea Ireland Limited (2)
Block 10-3 Blanchardstown Corporate Park,
Dublin, 15, Ballycoolin, Ireland
Tel.: (353) 1 866 5015

Advent International Corporation—(Continued)

Business Process Outsourcing Services
N.A.I.C.S.: 561499

Williams Lea Japan Limited (2)
Gotenyama Trust Tower 9th Fl 4 7 35
Kitashinagawa, Shingawa-ku, Tokyo, 140-0001, Japan
Tel.: (81) 357925050
Business Process Outsourcing Services
N.A.I.C.S.: 561499

Subsidiary (Domestic):

Williams Lea Limited (2)
1-5 Poland street, London, W1F 8PR,
United Kingdom
Tel.: (44) 2074681000
Web Site: http://www.williamslea.com
Business Process Outsourcing Services
N.A.I.C.S.: 561499

Subsidiary (Non-US):

Williams Lea Private Limited (2)
90 EU Tong Sen Street 03-01 Level 3 Block
A Creative Innovation Centre, Singapore,
059811, Singapore
Tel.: (65) 62279177
Business Process Outsourcing Services
N.A.I.C.S.: 561499

Williams Lea Pty Limited (2)
Level 2 60 62 Clarence Street, Sydney,
2000, NSW, Australia
Tel.: (61) 2 9641 2300
Business Process Outsourcing Services
N.A.I.C.S.: 561499

WorldPay Ltd. (1)
The Science Park Milton Road Units 270-289, Cambridge, CB4 0WE, United Kingdom
Tel.: (44) 1223 258493
Web Site: http://www.worldpay.com
Online Payment Processing Services
N.A.I.C.S.: 522320
James Frost *(CMO)*
Ron M. Kalifa *(Deputy Chm)*
Mark Edwards *(Grp Gen Counsel)*
Michael Rake *(Chm)*
Asif Ramji *(Chief Product Officer)*

Subsidiary (US):

WorldPay US, Inc. (2)
600 Morgan Falls Rd Ste 260, Atlanta, GA
30350
Tel.: (770) 396-1616
Web Site: http://www.worldpay.us
Online Payment Processing Services
N.A.I.C.S.: 522320
Andy Doyle *(Chief HR Officer)*
Dave Hobday *(Mng Dir-Worldpay UK)*
Ron Kalifa *(Vice Chm & Exec Dir)*
Mark Kimber *(CIO)*
Rick Medlock *(CFO)*

Subsidiary (Domestic):

Century Payments, Inc. (3)
2601 Network Blvd Ste 200, Frisco, TX
75034
Tel.: (469) 252-0074
Web Site: http://www.centurypayments.com
Sales Range: $10-24.9 Million
Electronic Payment Processing Services
N.A.I.C.S.: 522320
Robert Wechsler *(Co-Founder & CEO)*
Patricia Keller *(CFO & Chief Revenue Officer)*
Thomas W. Bannon *(COO)*
Eric Frazier *(Co-Founder & Chief Vision Officer)*
Kristen Scott *(Chief People Officer)*
Irina Haydon *(Chief Sls Officer)*
Hila Shpigelman *(CMO)*
Lauren Harris *(Sr VP-Sls-Inside, Trng & Customer Svc)*

Zentiva N.V. (1)
Fred Roeskestraat 123, 1076 EE, Amsterdam, Netherlands
Tel.: (31) 206739753
Web Site: http://www.zentiva.cz
Sales Range: $900-999.9 Million
Holding Company
N.A.I.C.S.: 551112

Subsidiary (Non-US):

Zentiva Group, a.s. (2)
U Kabelovny 130, Dolni Mecholupy,
Prague, 102 37, Czech Republic
Tel.: (420) 267241111
Web Site: http://www.zentiva.cz
Sales Range: $800-899.9 Million
Emp.: 1,400
Pharmaceuticals Product Mfr
N.A.I.C.S.: 325412

Subsidiary (Non-US):

Apontis Pharma AG (3)
Alfred-Nobel-Str 10, 40789, Monheim,
Germany (83.57%)
Tel.: (49) 217389554949
Web Site: https://www.apontis-pharma.de
Rev.: $39,891,858
Assets: $62,011,264
Liabilities: $29,350,801
Net Worth: $32,660,463
Earnings: ($12,198,310)
Emp.: 177
Fiscal Year-end: 12/31/2023
Pharmaceutical Product Mfr & Distr
N.A.I.C.S.: 325412
Thomas Milz *(Chief Product Officer)*

Subsidiary (Domestic):

**APONTIS PHARMA Deutschland
GmbH & Co. KG** (4)
Alfred-Nobel-Str 10, 40789, Monheim, Germany
Tel.: (49) 217389554949
Web Site: https://apontis-pharma.de
Pharmaceutical Consulting Services
N.A.I.C.S.: 541618

Subsidiary (Non-US):

**Zentiva Inhalationsprodukte
GmbH** (3)
Staffelseestr 4, Munich, 81477, Bavaria,
Germany
Tel.: (49) 897874760
Web Site: http://www.zentiva.com
Medicinal Product Mfr
N.A.I.C.S.: 325411

Zentiva International a.s. (3)
Einsteinova 24, 851 01, Bratislava, Slovakia
Tel.: (421) 239183010
Web Site: http://www.zentiva.sk
Pharmaceutical Products Mfr & Whslr
N.A.I.C.S.: 325412

Zentiva S.A. (3)
Blvd Theodore Pallady no 50 Sector 3, Bucharest, Romania
Tel.: (40) 213047200
Web Site: https://www.zentiva.ro
Rev.: $218,358,531
Assets: $322,230,273
Liabilities: $65,763,508
Net Worth: $256,466,765
Earnings: $41,468,241
Emp.: 956
Fiscal Year-end: 12/31/2023
Pharmaceutical Product Mfr & Distr
N.A.I.C.S.: 325412
Nicholas Robert Haggar *(Chm)*
Simona Cocos *(Gen Mgr)*
Francisc Koos *(CFO)*

**Zentiva Saglik Urunleri San.Ve
Tic.A.S.** (3)
Buyukdere Cad No 193 Kat 3-10, Levent,
34394, Istanbul, Turkiye
Tel.: (90) 212 339 39 00
Web Site: http://www.zentiva.com.tr
Pharmaceuticals Product Mfr
N.A.I.C.S.: 325412

ADVENT, LLC
2316 Cruzen St, Nashville, TN 37211
Tel.: (615) 742-3355   TN
Web Site:
    http://www.adventresults.com
Year Founded: 2000
Sales Range: $1-9.9 Million
Emp.: 50
Targeted Messaging & Graphics for
Clients
N.A.I.C.S.: 541890

John Roberson *(Founder & CEO)*
Todd Austin *(Pres)*
Todd Cyphers *(VP-Implementation)*
Brad Jones *(VP-Design)*
Rick Myers *(Dir-Brand & Mktg)*
Tracy McGlocklin *(VP-Mktg & Community Rels)*
Brock Warner *(VP-Client Strategies)*

ADVENTECH, INC.
2957 Wyandot St, Denver, CO 80211
Tel.: (303) 777-3519
Web Site: http://www.adven-tech.com
Sales Range: $1-9.9 Million
Emp.: 40
Data Processing, Hosting & Related
Services
N.A.I.C.S.: 518210
Tami Young *(Founder, Pres & CEO)*
Stacy Olson *(VP)*
Lily Pool *(Dir-Ops)*

ADVENTIST HEALTH SYSTEM
2100 Douglas Blvd, Roseville, CA
95661-9002
Tel.: (916) 406-0000   CA
Web Site:
    http://www.adventisthealth.org
Year Founded: 1980
Emp.: 20,500
Health Care Services Association
N.A.I.C.S.: 813910
Wayne Ferch *(Pres/CEO-Central
California)*
Bill Wing *(Pres)*
JoAline Olson *(Chief HR Officer,
Chief Innovation Officer & Sr VP)*
Jeff Eller *(Pres/CEO-Northern California)*
Joyce Newmyer *(Pres-Northwest)*
Mark Ashlock *(Sr VP-Physician Strategy)*
Scott Reiner *(CEO)*
Hoda Asmar *(Chief Clinical Officer &
Sr VP)*
Joe Reppert *(CFO)*
Ben Leedle *(Pres-Well-Being Div)*

Subsidiaries:

**Adventist Health Central Valley
Network** (1)
115 Mall Dr, Hanford, CA 93230-3230
Tel.: (559) 582-9000
Web Site: http://www.adventisthealthcv.com
Emp.: 2,800
Hospitals & Medical Centers Network Operator
N.A.I.C.S.: 561110
Wayne Ferch *(Pres & CEO)*
Venton Gruvenfky *(VP-HR)*

**Adventist Health/Home Care & Hospice Services - Mendocino
County** (1)
100 San Hedrin Cir, Willits, CA 95490
Tel.: (707) 459-1818
Sales Range: $1-9.9 Million
Emp.: 30
Women Healthcare Services
N.A.I.C.S.: 621610
Trudy Miller *(Office Mgr)*
Charles Hott *(Dir-Hospice)*

Blue Zones, LLC (1)
724 N 1st St, Minneapolis, MN 55401
Tel.: (612) 596-3000
Web Site: http://www.bluezones.com
Professional, Scientific & Technical Services
N.A.I.C.S.: 541690
Amelia Clabots *(Mgr-Ops)*
Ben Leedle *(CEO)*
Lynn Richards *(Sr VP-Policy & Implementation)*

Sierra Vista Hospital, Inc. (1)
1010 Murray Ave, San Luis Obispo, CA
93405
Tel.: (805) 546-7600
Web Site:
    http://www.sierravistaregional.com
Emp.: 800

Hospital
N.A.I.C.S.: 622110

**Twin Cities Community Hospital,
Inc.** (1)
1100 Las Tablas Rd, Templeton, CA 93465
Tel.: (805) 434-3500
Web Site:
    https://www.tenethealthcentralcoast.com
Sales Range: $75-99.9 Million
Hospital
N.A.I.C.S.: 622110
Mark Lisa *(CEO)*
Michael Lane *(COO)*
Diane McCluskey *(Chief HR Officer)*
Scott Wartelle *(CFO)*
Robert Cook *(Chief Nursing Officer)*
Michael Keleman *(Chief Strategy Officer)*
Debra Leonard Albert *(Chm)*
Patricia Wilmore *(Vice Chm)*

Subsidiary (Domestic):

Templeton Imaging, Inc. (2)
262 Posada Ln Ste B and C, Templeton,
CA 93465
Tel.: (805) 434-1491
Web Site: http://www.templetonimaging.net
Sales Range: $1-9.9 Million
Diagnostic Imaging Centers
N.A.I.C.S.: 621512
Linda Cosgrove *(Office Mgr)*

ADVENTIST HEALTH SYSTEM
SUNBELT HEALTHCARE CORPORATION
900 Hope Way, Altamonte Springs,
FL 32714
Tel.: (407) 357-1000   FL
Web Site:
    http://www.adventhealth.com
Health Care Services Association
N.A.I.C.S.: 813910
Brent G. Snyder *(CIO & Exec VP)*
Sandra K. Johnson *(Chief Admin Officer & Exec VP)*
Paul C. Rathbun *(CFO & Sr Exec
VP)*
Terry D. Shaw *(Pres & CEO)*
Daryl Tol *(Sr Exec V, Pres/CEO, Central Florida & South)*
Randy Haffner *(Sr Exec VP,
Pres/CEO & Multi-State Div)*
Michael H. Schultz *(Sr Exec VP,
Pres/CEO & West Florida Div)*
Jeffrey S. Bromme *(Chief Legal Officer & Exec VP)*
David Banks *(Chief Strategy Officer &
Exec VP)*
David Moorhead *(Chief Clinical Officer & Exec VP)*
Eddie Soler *(Exec VP-Fin)*
Olesea Azevedo *(Chief HR Officer &
Sr VP)*

Subsidiaries:

Adventhealth Heart of Florida (1)
40100 US Hwy 27, Davenport, FL 33837
Tel.: (863) 422-4971
Web Site: http://www.heartofflorida.com
Sales Range: $25-49.9 Million
Emp.: 1,500
Hospital Services
N.A.I.C.S.: 622110
Ann Barnhart *(CEO)*
Nicole Hendricks *(COO)*
Danny Warren *(CFO)*

Subsidiary (Domestic):

**Heart of Florida Surgery Center,
LLC** (2)
410 Lionel Way Ste 100, Davenport, FL
33837-7809
Tel.: (863) 866-9950
Web Site: http://www.hofsurgerycenter.com
Health Care Srvices
N.A.I.C.S.: 622110

Adventist Midwest Health (1)
120 N Oak St, Hinsdale, IL 60521
Tel.: (630) 856-7525

Web Site: http://www.keepingyouwell.com
Health Care Services Association
N.A.I.C.S.: 813910
David L. Crane (Pres & CEO)

Unit (Domestic):

Adventist GlenOaks Hospital (2)
701 Winthrop Ave, Glendale Heights, IL
60139-1405
Tel.: (630) 545-8000
Web Site: http://www.keepingyouwell.com
Rev.: $24,900,000
Emp.: 550
General Medical & Surgical Hospital
N.A.I.C.S.: 622110
Bruce Christian (CEO)

Adventist Hinsdale Hospital (2)
120 N Oak St, Hinsdale, IL 60521
Tel.: (630) 856-9000
Web Site: http://www.keepingyouwell.com
General Medical & Surgical Hospital
N.A.I.C.S.: 622110
Michael Goebel (CEO)

Florida Hospital Dade City, Inc. (1)
13100 Fort King Rd, Dade City, FL 33525
Tel.: (352) 521-1100
Web Site: http://www.adventhealth.com
Medical Programs & Health Care Services
N.A.I.C.S.: 622110
Terry D. Shaw (Pres & CEO)

Florida Hospital Medical Group,
Inc. (1)
601 E Rollins St, Orlando, FL 32803-1248
Tel.: (407) 303-2800
Web Site: http://www.floridahospital.com
Health Care Services Association
N.A.I.C.S.: 813910
David Banks (Pres)
Michael Wiederhold (Dir-Medical-Clinical
Informatics)
Howard Drenth (CEO)
Shannon Gravitte (VP-Pub Affairs)
Robin McGuinness (Chief Clinical Officer-
West, Chief Nursing Officer)
Mike Schultz (Pres/CEO-West)

Subsidiary (Domestic):

Florida Hospital Credit Union (2)
601 E Rollins St, Orlando, FL 32803
Tel.: (407) 303-1527
Web Site:
    http://www.floridahospitalcreditunion.org
Credit Union
N.A.I.C.S.: 522130
Susan Green (COO)

Florida Hospital Foundation (2)
550 E Rollins St 6th Fl, Orlando, FL 32803
Tel.: (407) 303-2784
Web Site: http://www.floridahospital.org
Emp.: 50
Grantmaking Foundations
N.A.I.C.S.: 813211
Des Cummins (Pres)
Leilani Jacobs (CFO)
Roel Yambao (COO)
David Collis (Chief Dev Officer & VP)
Rebecca Becker (Dir-Donor Rels)
Diana Boyce (VP)
Carolyn Saliba (VP)
Tom Kapusta (Exec Dir)

Florida Hospital Healthcare System,
Inc. (2)
602 Courtland St Ste 162, Orlando, FL
32804
Tel.: (407) 741-4808
Web Site: http://www.fhhsonline.com
Integrated Delivery System Healthcare Net-
work Management Services
N.A.I.C.S.: 524292
David Banks (Chm)

Unit (Domestic):

Florida Hospital Heartland Medical
Center (2)
4200 Sunn Lk Blvd, Sebring, FL 33871
Tel.: (863) 314-4466
Web Site: http://www.fhhd.org
General Medical & Surgical Hospitals
N.A.I.C.S.: 622110
Michelle Myers (Dir-HR)
Randy Surber (CEO)

Subsidiary (Domestic):

Florida Hospital Waterman, Inc. (2)
1000 Waterman Way, Tavares, FL 32778
Tel.: (352) 253-3333
Web Site: http://www.fhwat.org
Hospital
N.A.I.C.S.: 622110
Anita Young (COO)
Abel Biri (CEO)
Michael Stimson (Chief Nursing Officer)
Terri Warren (CFO)

Lake Wales Hospital Corporation (1)
410 S 11th St, Lake Wales, FL 33853
Web Site: http://www.adventhealth.com
Hospital Services
N.A.I.C.S.: 621999

ADVENTIST HEALTHCARE
820 W Diamond Ave Ste 600, Gaith-
ersburg, MD 20878
Tel.: (301) 315-3030   **MD**
Web Site:
    https://www.adventisthealthcare.com
Year Founded: 1983
Sales Range: $550-599.9 Million
Emp.: 6,327
Christian Ministry Services
N.A.I.C.S.: 813910
Keith Ballenger (VP)
James Damron (Chief Dev Officer &
VP)
Thomas Grant (VP-PR & Mktg)
Marta Brito Perez (Chief HR Officer &
Sr VP)
James G. Lee (CFO & Exec VP)
David E. Weigley (Chm)
Robert T. Vandeman (Vice Chm)
Terry Forde (Pres, CEO & Sec)
Kenneth B. DeStefano (Gen Counsel
& VP)
Christopher Ghion (CIO & VP)
Dwayne Leslie (Chief Compliance
Officer & VP)

ADVENTIST RISK MANAGE-
MENT INC.
12501 Old Columbia Pike, Silver
Spring, MD 20904
Tel.: (301) 680-6800   **MD**
Web Site:
    https://www.adventistrisk.org
Year Founded: 1995
Sales Range: $25-49.9 Million
Emp.: 110
Provider of Risk Management Ser-
vices & Solutions
N.A.I.C.S.: 524210
Derick White (Pres)

ADVENTIVE MARKETING, INC.
415 E Golf Rd Ste 111, Arlington
Heights, IL 60005-1932
Tel.: (847) 590-1110   **IL**
Web Site:
    http://www.adventivemarketing.com
Year Founded: 1995
Sales Range: $10-24.9 Million
Emp.: 12
Advetising Agency
N.A.I.C.S.: 541810
Steven E. Bork (Pres)
Brian Kahle (Dir-Creative Svcs)

ADVENTURE 16 INC.
4620 Alvarado Cyn Rd, San Diego,
CA 92120
Tel.: (619) 283-2362
Web Site:
    http://www.adventure16.com
Sales Range: $300-349.9 Million
Emp.: 100
Mfr of Backpacking Equipment
N.A.I.C.S.: 459110
John D. Mead (Pres)
Ben Reade (Mgr-Retail Store)
Terri Embrey (Mgr-Adv)

ADVENTURE BOUND ALASKA
76 Eagan Dr Ste 110, Juneau, AK
99801-1775
Tel.: (907) 463-2509
Web Site:
    https://www.adventurealaska.com
Year Founded: 1994
Sales Range: $1-9.9 Million
Emp.: 6
Custom Charter Tours
N.A.I.C.S.: 561520
Winona Weber (Co-Owner & Pres)
Steven Weber (Owner)

ADVENTURE CREDIT UNION
630 32nd St SE, Grand Rapids, MI
49548
Tel.: (616) 243-0125   **MI**
Web Site: http://www.option1cu.org
Year Founded: 1936
Sales Range: $10-24.9 Million
Emp.: 126
Credit Union Operator
N.A.I.C.S.: 522130
David Ferguson (Chm)
Dave Kidd (Treas)
Ann Marie Nelson (Interim CEO)

ADVENTURE LANDS OF
AMERICA, INC.
305 34th Ave NW, Altoona, IA 50009
Tel.: (515) 266-2121   **IA**
Web Site:
    http://www.adventurelandpark.com
Year Founded: 1972
Sales Range: $10-24.9 Million
Emp.: 1,000
Amusement Park
N.A.I.C.S.: 713110
John F. Krantz (Pres)
Doug Cornwell (COO)
Dan A. Bohner (CFO)

ADVENTURE LIFE
712 W Spruce St Ste 1, Missoula,
MT 59802
Tel.: (406) 541-2677
Web Site: https://www.adventure-
life.com
Year Founded: 1999
Sales Range: $10-24.9 Million
Emp.: 23
Travel Agency Services
N.A.I.C.S.: 561510
Brian Morgan (CEO)
Jonathan Brunger (Gen Mgr)
Julia Kocubinski (Controller-Fin)
Aaron Conway (Dir-IT & Web)
Mary Curry (Dir-Voyage Product)
Lynessa Nelson (Office Mgr)
Fabio Salas (Coord-Costa Rica)
Jenny Johnston (Coord-Content)
Betty Lorena Jaramillo Zurita (Coord-
Ecuador)

ADVENTURE PROPERTIES
INC.
8524 Hospital Dr, Douglasville, GA
30134
Tel.: (770) 920-9292
Sales Range: $10-24.9 Million
Emp.: 3
Real Estate Brokers & Agents
N.A.I.C.S.: 531210
James Ponder (Pres)

ADVENTURES UNLIMITED CA-
NOE RENTAL & SALES, INC.
8974 Tomahawk Landing Rd, Milton,
FL 32570
Tel.: (850) 626-1669
Web Site:
    http://www.adventuresunlimited.com
Year Founded: 1980
Sales Range: $1-9.9 Million
Emp.: 25

Outdoor Recreation; Canoe Rental &
Sales
N.A.I.C.S.: 713990
Jack Sanborn (Pres)
Marc Vallianos (Mgr-Ops)
Wayne Stansfield (Mgr-Resort)
Martha Szymoniak (Mgr-Zip Adven-
tures)
Suzanne Roberts (Bus Mgr)

ADVERTISE PURPLE, INC.
2200 Michigan Ave Ste A, Santa
Monica, CA 90404
Web Site:
    http://www.advertisepurple.com
Year Founded: 2012
Sales Range: $1-9.9 Million
Emp.: 38
Digital Marketing Services
N.A.I.C.S.: 541810
Kyle Mitnick (Founder, Pres & CEO)

ADVERTISERS PRESS INCOR-
PORATED
2222 Parview Rd, Middleton, WI
53562
Tel.: (608) 831-1222
Web Site: https://www.adpress.com
Sales Range: $10-24.9 Million
Emp.: 150
Manifold Business Forms
N.A.I.C.S.: 323111
William Wild (Pres)
Doug Bollig (Branch Dir)

ADVERTISING ASSOCIATES
INTERNATIONAL
90 Canal St 4th Fl, Boston, MA
02114
Tel.: (508) 544-1250
Web Site: http://www.aai-agency.com
Year Founded: 1965
Emp.: 12
Advetising Agency
N.A.I.C.S.: 541810
A. Richard Hersum (Chm, CEO, Acct
Supvr & New Bus Contact)
Rob Allen (Pres, Acct Supvr & Acct
Exec)
Mark Hersum (Treas, Exec VP, Acct
Supvr & Acct Exec)
Patrick Murphy (Dir-Creative)
Julie Medjanis (Controller)
Janet Smith (VP & Dir-Art)

ADVERTISING ASSOCIATES,
INC.
110 Bass Rd SW, Eatonton, GA
31024-7131
Tel.: (478) 968-5047
Year Founded: 1997
Sales Range: Less than $1 Million
Emp.: 3
Advertising Agencies, Newspaper,
Real Estate
N.A.I.C.S.: 541810
Larry Lane (Pres)
Sue Ellen Lane (Acct Exec)
Maranda Vice (Creative Dir)

ADVERTISING CHECKING BU-
REAU INCORPORATED
675 3rd Ave, New York, NY 10017
Tel.: (212) 684-3377   **DE**
Web Site: http://www.acbcoop.com
Year Founded: 1917
Sales Range: $100-124.9 Million
Emp.: 300
Management Consulting Services
N.A.I.C.S.: 541618
Brian McShane (Pres)
John Portelli (VP-Sls)
Charles Janson (Controller)

Advertising Connection Inc.—(Continued)

ADVERTISING CONNECTION INC.
273 W Point Rd, Ava, IL 62907-2318
Tel.: (618) 426-3384
Web Site:
    http://www.advertisingconnect.com
Year Founded: 1994
Sales Range: $1-9.9 Million
Emp.: 4
Media Buying Solutions
N.A.I.C.S.: 541810
Joyce Bartens (Partner)
Larry Dierks (Co-Owner)
Pam Dierks (Co-Owner)
Marvin Bartens (Partner)

ADVERTISING DISTRIBUTORS OF AMERICA INC.
80 Orville Dr Ste 102, Bohemia, NY 11716-2505
Tel.: (631) 231-5700   NY
Web Site: http://www.go-ada.com
Year Founded: 1921
Sales Range: $100-124.9 Million
Emp.: 300
Direct Mail Services
N.A.I.C.S.: 541860
John Baratelli (Exec VP)
Debra Aji (VP-Sls & Client Svcs)
Barbara Kay (Controller)

ADVERTISING SAVANTS, INC.
2100 Locust St 3rd Fl N, Saint Louis, MO 63103
Tel.: (314) 231-7900
Web Site: http://www.adsavants.com
Year Founded: 1991
Sales Range: $10-24.9 Million
Emp.: 10
Advertising Agencies, Brand Development, Education, Financial, Health Care, Travel & Tourism
N.A.I.C.S.: 541810
Kevin Reardon (Principal & Dir-Acct)
Tia Liston (Dir-Creative)
Karen Boes-Decampi (Project Mgr)
Ray McAnallen (Dir-Creative)
Amanda Kinder (Dir-Digital Strategy)
Ashley Harrison (Acct Dir)
Courtney Turner (Acct Coord)
Lizzy Hinrichs (Dir-Art)
Mark Guttropf (Coord-Digital)
David Smith (Sr Creative Dir)

ADVERTISING WORKS & PRODUCTION
7352 Winward Dr, Meridian, ID 83642-1733
Tel.: (208) 888-4800   ID
Year Founded: 1976
Sales Range: Less than $1 Million
Emp.: 8
N.A.I.C.S.: 541810
Terry Porter (Pres)
Darwin Porter (Dir-Mktg & PR)
Joe Callahan (Acct Dir, Acct Supvr, Acct Exec & Media Buyer)
Sue Long (Acct Exec)
Kate Place (Graphic Artist)

ADVIA CREDIT UNION
550 S Riverview Dr, Parchment, MI 49004
Web Site: https://www.adviacu.org
Year Founded: 1938
Credit Union
N.A.I.C.S.: 522130
Cheryl A. DeBoer (Pres & CEO)
Ray Black (Exec VP-Sls & Mktg)
Jeff Fielder (CFO & Exec VP-Fin)
Marty Doorn (Chm)
Nicole Kalmbach (Vice Chm)
Danielle Streed (Treas)
Donna Kalmeta (Sec)

ADVICE INTERACTIVE GROUP LLC
7850 Collin McKinney Pkwy Ste 300, McKinney, TX 75070
Tel.: (214) 214-4540
Web Site:
    http://www.adviceinteractive.com
Year Founded: 2008
Sales Range: $1-9.9 Million
Emp.: 33
Online Marketing Services
N.A.I.C.S.: 541810
Tom Coleman (CFO)
Bernadette Coleman (CEO)
Todd Bryson (Dir-Local Search)
Randall Turner (COO)
Justin Liles (Sr VP-Local Search)
Lissa Duty (VP-Community Mgmt)
Sarah Smith (Dir-Mktg)
Diem Huynh (Mgr-Delivery)
William Cosey (Mgr-Fulfillment Ops)
Nate Henry Luedtke (Pres-SMB Div)
Rachel Morgan (Sr Mgr-SEO)
Ryan Nielsen (Sr VP-Dev)
Brad Petty (Sr VP-Fin)
Cassondra Nelson (Supvr-Acct)
Alison Toyne (VP-Ops)
Chris Jamieson (Pres)

ADVICE MEDIA LLC
1389 Center Dr Ste 230, Park City, UT 84098
Tel.: (435) 575-7470
Web Site:
    http://www.advicemedia.com
Year Founded: 1998
Emp.: 50
Web Development Services
N.A.I.C.S.: 541519
Shawn Miele (Founder & CEO)
Chad Erickson (VP-Sls & Bus Dev)

Subsidiaries:

Ceatus Media Group LLC   (1)
960 Grand Ave 2, San Diego, CA 92109
Tel.: (858) 454-5505
Web Site: http://www.ceatus.com
Rev.: $1,100,000
Emp.: 16
Wired Telecommunications Carriers
N.A.I.C.S.: 517111
Jack Barrient (VP-Sls)
David Evans (CEO)
Tamara Evans (VP-Mktg)

MedNet Technologies, Inc.   (1)
115 Broadhollow Rd, Melville, NY 11747
Tel.: (516) 285-2200
Web Site: http://www.mednet-tech.com
Sales Range: $1-9.9 Million
Emp.: 38
Web Development Services for Healthcare Industry
N.A.I.C.S.: 513210
Christian Pellman (VP)
Brian Hancock (Sr Dir-Client Svcs)
Steven Ruhs (Sr Dir-Creative Svcs)
Barbara Boylan Wen (Dir-Content Dev)
Reginald Quintyne (Dir-Compliance & Ops)
April Jimenez (Assoc Dir-Internet Mktg Svcs)
Ivanka J. Kostial (Assoc Dir-Creative Svcs)

ADVICE, INC.
7365-4 Merchant Ct, Sarasota, FL 34240
Tel.: (941) 907-9507
Web Site: http://www.advice-inc.com
Sales Range: $1-9.9 Million
Emp.: 10
Advertising Agency
N.A.I.C.S.: 541810
Linda Gross (Owner)
Gail Dipsiner (Mgr-Admin)

ADVILLE/USA
44 S Mentor Ave, Pasadena, CA 91106-2902
Tel.: (626) 397-9911

Web Site: http://www.adville-usa.com
Year Founded: 1995
Sales Range: $1-9.9 Million
Emp.: 11
Sales Promotion
N.A.I.C.S.: 541810
Vicki Walls (Pres)
Mark Shiozaki (VP)

ADVISER INVESTMENT MANAGEMENT INC
85 Wells Ave Ste 109, Newton, MA 02459
Tel.: (617) 321-2200
Web Site:
    https://www.adviserinvestments.com
Year Founded: 1994
Portfolio Management
N.A.I.C.S.: 523940
Daniel P. Wiener (Chm & CEO)
Dan Silver (Co-Founder & Pres)
David Thorne (Co-Founder)
David D'Amico (Exec VP)
Jeffrey DeMaso (Dir-Res)
Chris Keith (Sr VP-Fixed Income)
Richard Veidenheimer (Mng Dir)
James H. Lowell III (CIO & Partner)

ADVISERS CAPITAL MANAGEMENT INC.
60 E 42nd St Rm 1420, New York, NY 10165-1444
Tel.: (212) 286-9116   DE
Year Founded: 1978
Sales Range: $150-199.9 Million
Emp.: 7
Provider of Portfolio Management Services to Domestic & Global Institutional Investors in Fixed Income Securities
N.A.I.C.S.: 523940
Patricia DeBlank Klink (Pres & CEO)
Andy Barrad (Mgr)

ADVISORS MORTGAGE GROUP, LLC.
5114 Route 33, Wall, NJ 07727
Tel.: (732) 292-3133
Web Site:
    http://www.advisorsmortgage.com
Year Founded: 1999
Sales Range: $10-24.9 Million
Emp.: 200
Loan Broker
N.A.I.C.S.: 522310
Steven Meyer (Pres & CEO)
Sean Clark (VP)
Rick Bottino (Branch Mgr)
Christopher Keelin (Branch Mgr)
Michael Murphy (Branch Mgr)
Chris Stanziale (Branch Mgr)
Ethan Baumholtz (Branch Mgr)
Edward Walz (Branch Mgr)
John Marchione (Branch Mgr)
Robert Willis (Branch Mgr)
William Hendricks (Branch Mgr)
Luke McCann (Branch Mgr-Dev)
Dan Kim (Branch Mgr)
Mark Narcisi (Branch Mgr)
Mike Cruz (Branch Mgr)
Sherry Geck (Owner)
David Wicki Jr. (Branch Mgr)

ADVISORY RESEARCH, INC.
Two Prudential Plz 180 N Stetson Ave Ste 5500, Chicago, IL 60601
Tel.: (312) 565-1414
Web Site:
    http://www.advisoryresearch.com
Year Founded: 1974
Sales Range: $25-49.9 Million
Emp.: 50
Investment Management Service
N.A.I.C.S.: 523940
Matthew K. Swaim (Exec Chm & Mng Dir)

Paul Graffy (Mng Dir-Bus Dev, Mktg & Client Svcs)
Susan Steiner (Mng Dir & Chief Compliance Officer)
Ellen Freeman (Mng Dir & Head-Ops)

ADVISORYCLOUD, INC.
Hangar 7 Hamilton Landing Ste 100, Novato, CA 94949
Tel.: (415) 289-7115
Web Site:
    http://www.advisorycloud.com
Year Founded: 2012
Sales Range: $25-49.9 Million
Emp.: 156
Business Management Consulting Services
N.A.I.C.S.: 541611
Jonathan Aspatore (Co-Founder & CEO)
Dallas Bond (Co-Founder & COO)
Chris Beaver (Co-Founder & CMO)
Lehua Stuart (Chief People Officer)
John Green (CFO)

ADVIZEX TECHNOLOGIES LLC
6480 Rockside Woods Blvd S Ste 190, Independence, OH 44131
Tel.: (216) 901-1818
Web Site: https://www.advizex.com
Sales Range: $75-99.9 Million
Emp.: 330
Value-Added Resellers, Computer Systems
N.A.I.C.S.: 517810
Alfred A. Traversi (CEO)

ADVOC8, LLC
1250 4th St NE, Washington, DC 20002
Tel.: (202) 796-7995
Web Site: http://www.advoc8.com
Year Founded: 2015
Sales Range: $10-24.9 Million
Emp.: 50
Creative Agency Services
N.A.I.C.S.: 541890
John Legittino (CEO)

ADVOCATE BILLING LLC.
10567 Sawmill Pkwy Ste 100, Powell, OH 43065
Tel.: (614) 210-1885
Web Site:
    http://www.radadvocate.com
Year Founded: 1971
Sales Range: $10-24.9 Million
Emp.: 200
Business Consulting Services
N.A.I.C.S.: 541618
Kirk Reinitz (Pres & CEO)
Mike Nicholas (Exec VP)
Paulo Santos (Dir-Bus Dev)
Julia Leo (Chief Compliance Officer)

ADVOCATE HEALTH CARE NETWORK
3075 Highland Pkwy, Downers Grove, IL 60515
Tel.: (630) 572-9393   IL
Web Site:
    http://www.advocatehealth.com
Year Founded: 1995
Health Care Services Organization
N.A.I.C.S.: 813920
James H. Skogsbergh (Pres & CEO)
William P. Santulli (COO)
Kevin R. Brady (Chief HR Officer)
Kelly Jo Golson (CMO)
Scott Powder (Chief Strategy Officer)

Subsidiaries:

Advocate Aurora Enterprises, Inc. (1)
750 W Virginia St., Milwaukee, WI 53204-1539
Tel.: (833) 528-7672
Web Site:
https://www.advocateaurorahealth.org
Health Care Srvices
N.A.I.C.S.: 621610

Advocate Charitable Foundation (1)
3075 Highland Pkwy Ste 600, Downers Grove, IL 60515
Tel.: (630) 929-6900
Web Site: http://www.advocategiving.org
Sales Range: $50-74.9 Million
Emp.: 200
Health Care Srvices
N.A.I.C.S.: 561110
Ed Malysiak (Chm)

Advocate Medical Group (1)
1775 Dempster St, Park Ridge, IL 60068
Tel.: (847) 723-6080
Web Site: http://www.advocatehealth.com
Accident Prevention Services
N.A.I.C.S.: 813319
Kevin C. McCune (Chief Medical Officer)
Vincent Bufalino (Pres)

Aurora Health Care, Inc. (1)
750 W Virginia St, Milwaukee, WI 53204
Tel.: (414) 647-3000
Web Site: http://www.aurorahealthcare.org
Hospital Owner & Operator
N.A.I.C.S.: 622110
Leslie Lenzo (CIO)
Cristina A. Garcia-Thomas (Chief External Affairs Officer)

Dreyer Medical Group, Ltd. (1)
1870 W Galena blvd, Aurora, IL 60506-7334
Tel.: (630) 906-5151
Web Site: http://www.dreyermed.com
N.A.I.C.S.: 813319

ADVOCATE HOME CARE SERVICES
7866 W Commercial Blvd, Lauderhill, FL 33351
Tel.: (954) 788-4555
Web Site:
http://www.advocatehcs.com
Year Founded: 2007
Sales Range: $1-9.9 Million
Emp.: 450
Women Healthcare Services
N.A.I.C.S.: 621610
David Maymon (Owner)

ADVOCATE MEDIA
6301 Gaston Ave Ste 820, Dallas, TX 75214
Tel.: (214) 560-4204
Web Site:
https://www.advocatemag.com
Year Founded: 1991
Sales Range: $1-9.9 Million
Emp.: 23
Magazine Publisher
N.A.I.C.S.: 513120
Rick Wamre (Pres)
Judy Liles (Office Mgr)
Jynnette Neal (Dir-Art)
Mitchell Meals (Dir-Mktg)

ADWORKS, INC.
1225 19th St NW Ste 500, Washington, DC 20036
Tel.: (202) 342-5585   MD
Web Site: http://www.adworks.com
Year Founded: 1979
Rev.: $75,000,000
Emp.: 20
N.A.I.C.S.: 541810
Bruce Levin (CFO & Controller)
Mark Greenspun (Dir-Creative)
Nancy Karpinski (Dir-Acct Svcs)
Dan Johnson (Dir-IT)

Katherine Pastre (Dir-Client Svcs)
Lakeeta Brunk (Office Mgr)
Mat Sachs (Dir-Interactive)

ADX FIRE PROTECTION, INC.
10475 Irma Dr, Northglenn, CO 80233
Tel.: (303) 761-2000
Web Site:
http://www.adxfireprotection.com
Year Founded: 1931
Sales Range: $1-9.9 Million
Emp.: 12
Fire Extinguisher Mfr
N.A.I.C.S.: 332999
Dave Walker (Gen Mgr)

ADZAM INC.
22130 Hwy 99, Edmonds, WA 98026
Tel.: (425) 774-3551
Web Site: http://www.dougs.com
Year Founded: 1974
Sales Range: $10-24.9 Million
Emp.: 100
Automobiles, New & Used
N.A.I.C.S.: 441110
F. Douglas Ikegami (Pres)

AE INDUSTRIAL PARTNERS, LP
6700 Broken Sound Pkwy NW, Boca Raton, FL 33487
Tel.: (561) 372-7820   DE
Web Site:
https://www.aeroequity.com
Year Founded: 1998
Privater Equity Firm
N.A.I.C.S.: 523999
Thomas K. Churbuck (Operating Partner)
Michael Greene (Mng Partner)
Wayne P. Garrett (Operating Partner)
Charlie Santos-Buch (Partner)
Shawn Vick (Partner)
Charles Compton (Mng Partner)
David H. Rowe (Mng Partner)
Jon Nemo (Mng Partner)
Peter Schumacher (Partner)
Kelly A. Romano (Operating Partner)
Paul McElhinney (Senior Operating Partner & Co-Head-AEI Portoflio Strategy & Optimization Grp)
Jeffrey Hart (Principal)
Charlie Compton (Mng Partner)
Trey Bivins (Principal)
Katie Folmar (VP)
Nathan Dickstein (Mng Dir & Head-AEI Aerospace Leasing)
Tyler Rowe (Principal)
Austen Dixon (VP)
Graham Kantor (VP)
Eugene Kim (VP)
Kevin McAllister (Senior Operating Partner & Co-Head-AEI Portfolio Strategy & Optimization Grp)
Jim McConville (Operating Partner)
Kirk Konert (Mng Partner)
Louis Reggie Brothers (Operating Partner)

Subsidiaries:

AC&A Enterprises LLC (1)
25692 Atlantic Ocean Dr, Lake Forest, CA 92630
Tel.: (949) 716-3511
Web Site: http://www.acamfg.com
Automotive, Space & Aerospace Metallic Components & Tooling Services
N.A.I.C.S.: 336412
David Horner (CEO)

Subsidiary (Domestic):

Applied Composites Engineering, Inc. (2)
705 S Girls School Rd, Indianapolis, IN 46231
Tel.: (317) 243-4225

Web Site:
http://www.appliedcomposites.com
Special Die & Tool, Die Set, Jig & Fixture Mfr
N.A.I.C.S.: 333514
Garret Mertz (Gen Mgr)

Subsidiary (Domestic):

Alliance Spacesystems, LLC (3)
4398 Corporate Ctr Dr, Los Alamitos, CA 90720
Tel.: (714) 226-1400
Web Site:
http://www.alliancespacesystems.com
Mechanical System Engineering Services
N.A.I.C.S.: 541330
Rick Byrens (Sr VP & Gen Mgr)
Allan Ark (VP-Ops)
Dave Kwan (Dir-Contracts & Supply Chain)
Mike Mastroianni (Dir-Ops)
Dale Neverman (Dir-Programs)
Joe Ramos (Dir-Bus Dev)
Joe Colombo (Dir-Quality & Reliability)
Teri Morales (Mgr-HR)

Subsidiary (Domestic):

San Diego Composites, Inc. (2)
9220 Activity Rd, San Diego, CA 92126
Tel.: (858) 751-0450
Web Site: http://www.sdcomposites.com
Engineeering Services
N.A.I.C.S.: 541330
Jameson Schultz (Project Engr)

AE Group Materials Inc. (1)
450 Medinah Rd, Roselle, IL 60172
Tel.: (847) 233-5800
Web Site: http://www.kellstrommaterials.com
Aircraft Part Mfr & Distr
N.A.I.C.S.: 336413
Paul Fulchino (Chm)
Oscar E. Torres (Pres & CEO)
Oscar E. Torres (Pres & CEO)

Subsidiary (Domestic):

AE Materials Group, Inc. - Florida (2)
14400 NW 77th Ct Ste 306, Miami Lakes, FL 33016
Tel.: (305) 818-5400
Web Site: http://www.kellstrommaterials.com
Aircraft Components Whslr
N.A.I.C.S.: 423860

Tag One, Inc. (2)
Airport Office Park 2538 E University Dr Ste 165, Phoenix, AZ 85034-6917
Tel.: (602) 244-1500
Web Site: http://www.theaircraftgroup.com
Sales Range: $1-9.9 Million
Emp.: 20
Aircraft Asset Management & Streamlining of Aircraft Data
N.A.I.C.S.: 518210
Wade C. Walker (Pres)
James Palacios (VP-Bus Dev & Technical Sls)

Aerostructures Acquisition, LLC (1)
4425 W May St Bldg A, Wichita, KS 67209-2841
Tel.: (316) 942-7931
Web Site: https://atlasgroupaero.com
Search, Detection, Navigation, Guidance, Aeronautical & Nautical System & Instrument Mfr
N.A.I.C.S.: 334511
Keith Kranzow (Pres & CFO)
Jim McMullen (CEO)
Jaysa Stuhlsatz (Gen Mgr-PMC)
Scott Goforth (Gen Mgr-WASI)
Mike Porter (Gen Mgr-Brenner)

Alpine Air Express, Inc. (1)
1177 Alpine Air Way, Provo, UT 84601
Tel.: (801) 373-1508
Web Site: http://www.alpine-air.com
All Cargo Services
N.A.I.C.S.: 481211
Robert Frisch (COO)
Michael Dancy (CEO)

Subsidiary (Domestic):

Alpine Aviation Inc (2)
1177 Alpine Air Way, Provo, UT 84601
Tel.: (801) 373-1508

Web Site: http://www.alpine-air.com
Sales Range: $10-24.9 Million
Emp.: 33
Air Cargo Services
N.A.I.C.S.: 481112
Rick C. Wood (CFO)

Suburban Air Freight Inc. (2)
4010 Amelia Earhart Plz, Omaha, NE 68110-2697
Tel.: (402) 234-4100
Web Site: http://www.subair.com
Scheduled Freight Air Transportation
N.A.I.C.S.: 481112
Julie Ludlow (Mgr)

Belcan LLC (1)
10200 Anderson Way, Cincinnati, OH 45242
Tel.: (513) 891-0972
Web Site: http://www.belcan.com
Emp.: 7,000
Technical Staffing Solutions & Engineering Consultancy Services
N.A.I.C.S.: 541330
Lance H. Kwasniewski (CEO)
Andy Melton (VP-Engrg Sls)
Terry Williams (CIO)
Donavan McDonald (Pres-Technical Staffing & Recruiting)
Steve Houghtaling (Sr VP-Engrg)
Neal Montour (Sr VP-Global Ops)
Lee Shabe (Pres-Belcan Govt Svcs Segment)
Joe Triompo (Pres-Engrg Svcs)
Scott Briggs (Sr VP)
Spencer Rogers (VP-Ops)
Jas Powell (CTO-Enterprise IT-Govt Svcs)
Rodney Hite (VP-Growth & Strategy)
Clint Green (VP-Tech & Innovation)
Mark Brown (CTO-Advanced Engrg-Belcan Govt Svcs Segment)

Subsidiary (Domestic):

AVISTA Incorporated (2)
1575 E Business Hwy 151, Platteville, WI 53818-0636
Tel.: (608) 348-8815
Web Site: http://www.avistainc.com
Sales Range: $25-49.9 Million
Emp.: 200
Embedded Software Developer
N.A.I.C.S.: 513210

Intercom Consulting & Federal Systems Corporation (2)
44084 Riverside Pkwy Ste 150, Lansdowne, VA 20176
Tel.: (703) 729-1007
Web Site: http://www.intercomfed.com
Technical & Management Consulting Services
N.A.I.C.S.: 541618
Michael Strich (Pres)
Joan Beitel (VP-Fin & Controller)
Eric Emilio (Dir-Ops)

RTM Consulting, Inc. (2)
3221 Ivy Hills Blvd, Cincinnati, OH 45244-2574
Web Site: http://www.rtmconsulting.net
Computer System Design Services
N.A.I.C.S.: 541512
Randy T. Mysliviec (Pres & CEO)

Tandel Systems, Inc. (2)
3982 Tampa Rd, Oldsmar, FL 34677
Tel.: (727) 530-1110
Web Site: http://www.tandelsystems.com
Engineeering Services
N.A.I.C.S.: 541330
Kim Vogel (Co-Founder & VP-Engrg)
Mike Varga (Co-Founder & CEO)
Vince Poole (VP-Technical Svcs)
Jim Hanna (Mgr-Production)
Steve Wurst (Dir-Engrg)
Paul Mahorney (Dir-Talent Acq)
Bert White (Mgr-Procurement)

The Kemtah Group Inc. (2)
7601 Jefferson St NE Ste 120, Albuquerque, NM 87109
Tel.: (505) 346-4900
Web Site: http://www.kemtah.com
Personal Service Agents, Brokers & Bureaus
N.A.I.C.S.: 541519
Lance Kwasniewski (Pres & CEO)

AE Industrial Partners, LP—(Continued)

BigBear.ai Holdings LLC (1)
6811 Benjamin Franklin Dr Ste 200, Columbia, MD 21046 (83.5%)
Tel.: (410) 312-0885
Web Site: https://bigbear.ai
Emp.: 480
IT Consulting & Services
N.A.I.C.S.: 541690
Norm Laudermilch (COO)
Julie Peffer (CFO)
Dan Jones (Chief Product Officer)
Sean Ricker (Chief Acctg Officer)
Andre Hentz (Chief Transformation Officer)
Tony Barrett (Pres-Federal Market & Gen Mgr-Federal Market)
Amanda Long (CEO)
Greg Goldwater (Chief Growth Officer)

Subsidiary (Domestic):

Promodel Corporation (2)
7540 Windsor Dr, Allentown, PA 18195
Tel.: (610) 391-9700
Web Site: http://www.promodel.com
Rev.: $4,500,000
Emp.: 54
Custom Computer Programming Services
N.A.I.C.S.: 541511
Keith Vadas (Pres)
Bruce Gladwin (VP)
Carl Napoletano (VP & Gen Mgr)
Kurtis E. Shampine (VP & Gen Mgr)
Charles Harrell (Founder & Dir-ProModel)
Jim Tilney (CFO)

CDI Corporation (1)
11200 Richmond Ave Ste 500, Houston, TX 77082
Tel.: (215) 569-2200
Web Site: http://www.cdicorp.com
Rev.: $864,367,000
Assets: $289,292,000
Liabilities: $100,316,000
Net Worth: $188,976,000
Earnings: ($31,573,000)
Emp.: 6,300
Fiscal Year-end: 12/31/2016
Engineering & Information Technology Outsourcing & Professional Staffing Services
N.A.I.C.S.: 541690

Subsidiary (Domestic):

CDI Engineering Solutions, LLC (2)
100 N 18th St Ste 300, Philadelphia, PA 19103 (100%)
Tel.: (215) 569-2200
Web Site:
　https://www.cdiengineeringsolutions.com
Engineering & Technical Services
N.A.I.C.S.: 541330

Columbia Helicopters, Inc. (1)
14452 Arndt Rd NE, Aurora, OR 97002-9525
Tel.: (503) 678-1222
Web Site: http://www.colheli.com
Helicopter Charter Services
N.A.I.C.S.: 113310
David Mlodinoff (Gen Counsel)
Matt Long (CFO)
Steve Bandy (Co-Pres)
Mark Johnson (VP-HR)
Kurt Koehnke (VP-Maintenance)

Cross Fire & Security Co., Inc. (1)
1756 86th St, Brooklyn, NY 11214
Tel.: (718) 234-8600
Web Site: http://www.cfsnyc.com
Security System Services
N.A.I.C.S.: 561621
Chris Neil (Engr-Fire Alarm Sls)
Jason Springard (Project Mgr)
Kelly Romano (Chm)

Edge Autonomy SLO, LLC (1)
831 Buckley Rd, San Luis, CA 93401
Tel.: (805) 544-0932
Web Site: https://edgeautonomy.io
Emp.: 100
Aviation & Aerospace Component Mfr
N.A.I.C.S.: 334511
John Purvis (CEO)

Subsidiary (Domestic):

Adaptive Energy LLC (2)
5500 S State Rd, Ann Arbor, MI 48108
Tel.: (734) 302-7632

Web Site:
　https://www.adaptiveenergyllc.com
Emp.: 100
Engineering Services
N.A.I.C.S.: 541330
Ranvir Gujral (Chm)
Mike Edison (CEO)
Tom Westrich (CTO)
Jennifer Kay (CMO)

FMI, Inc. (1)
5615 N Broadway St, Wichita, KS 67219
Tel.: (316) 838-3970
Web Site: http://www.atlasgroupaero.com
Forming & Machining Services
N.A.I.C.S.: 336413

G.S. Precision, Inc. (1)
101 John Seitz Dr, Brattleboro, VT 05301
Tel.: (802) 257-5200
Web Site: http://www.gsprecision.com
Sales Range: $25-49.9 Million
Emp.: 300
Aircraft Assemblies, Subassemblies & Parts Mfr
N.A.I.C.S.: 336413
Norman Schneeberger (CEO)

Subsidiary (Domestic):

G.S. Precision, Inc. - Keene Division (2)
18 Bradco St, Keene, NH 03431
Tel.: (603) 355-1166
Web Site: http://www.gsprecision.com
Machine Shops
N.A.I.C.S.: 332710
Cathy Mayrand (Mgr-Quality Assurance)

Gryphon Technologies, LC (1)
80 M St SE Ste 600, Washington, DC 20003
Tel.: (202) 621-1100
Web Site: http://www.gryphonlc.com
Provider of Services in Support of System Acquisition Programs for the Navy & Marine Corps
N.A.I.C.S.: 541511
P. J. Braden (Founder & CEO)
Jerry Punderson (COO)
Claire Grady (Exec VP)
Joe Donohue (CFO)

Subsidiary (Domestic):

Gryphon Marine, LLC (2)
9550 Regency Sq Blvd Ste 400, Jacksonville, FL 32225-8149
Tel.: (904) 805-0700
Sales Range: $25-49.9 Million
Emp.: 50
Naval Architecture, Marine & Ocean Engineering Services
N.A.I.C.S.: 541310

Omnitec Solutions, Inc. (2)
6701 Democracy Blvd, Bethesda, MD 20817
Tel.: (301) 896-9704
Web Site: http://www.omnitecinc.com
Engineering Services
N.A.I.C.S.: 541330
Morris L. Brown (Pres & CEO)
Joan Phillips Holland (Dir-Strategic Support & Comm)
Peter Carlson (Exec VP-Media, Engrg & Technical Svcs)
David Cornwell (VP-IT & Info Security)
John Goodwin (CFO)
Suzy Lang (Exec VP-Bus Mgmt Svcs)
Micheal Kitchens (VP-Strategic Plng & Ops)
Dan Hall (VP-Health Svcs)
Jim Greeley (VP-Web Enterprise Solutions)

Schafer Corporation (2)
3811 North Fairfax Dr Ste 400, Arlington, VA 22203
Tel.: (703) 516-6000
Laboratory Research, Development & Testing Services
N.A.I.C.S.: 541715
Ron Ford (VP-Critical Programs Infrastructure)
Rodney Hite (VP-Growth & Strategy)
Clint Green (VP-Tech & Innovation)
Scott Briggs (Sr VP-Public Govt)

Healthway Home Products, Inc. (1)
3420 Maple Ave, Pulaski, NY 13142
Tel.: (315) 298-2904

Web Site: http://www.healthway.com
Air & Gas Filter Mfr
N.A.I.C.S.: 333413
Vincent G. Lobdell (Co-Founder)
Karen Hurd (Dir-Ops)
Chet Chase (Mgr-Quality Assurance)
Vincent Lobdell (Co-Founder)

Moeller Mfg. Company, LLC. (1)
30100 Beck Rd, Wixom, MI 48393
Tel.: (248) 960-3999
Web Site: http://www.moeller-aerospace.com
Aircraft Parts & Equipment
N.A.I.C.S.: 336413
Bob Longuski (Dir-Sls)

NuWave Solutions LLC (1)
2010 Corp Ridge Ste 450, McLean, VA 22102
Tel.: (703) 790-1122
Web Site: http://www.nuwavesolutions.com
Software Publisher
N.A.I.C.S.: 513210
Ryan Legge (VP-Pub Sector)
Jim McHugh (VP)
Reggie Brothers (CEO)
Keith Conner (CTO)
Andre Hentz (COO)

Subsidiary (Domestic):

Open Solutions Group, Inc. (2)
31 Greenridge Dr, Stafford, VA 22554-5122
Tel.: (703) 752-6135
Web Site: http://www.opensgi.com
Custom Computer Programming Services
N.A.I.C.S.: 541511
Brian Levy (Pres & CEO)

Redlattice, Inc. (1)
14399 Penrose Pl Ste 420, Chantilly, VA 20151-1791
Tel.: (703) 829-0733
Web Site: http://www.redlattice.com
Research & Development in the Physical, Engineering & Life Sciences
N.A.I.C.S.: 541715
John Ayers (Founder & CEO)
Don DeSanto (VP-Ops)

Seanair Machine Co., Inc. (1)
95 Verdi St, Farmingdale, NY 11735
Tel.: (631) 694-2820
Web Site: http://www.seanairmachine.com
Sales Range: $1-9.9 Million
Emp.: 18
Machine Shops
N.A.I.C.S.: 332710
Avi Das (CEO)

Triman Industries, Inc. (1)
1042 Industrial Dr, West Berlin, NJ 08091
Tel.: (856) 767-7945
Web Site: http://www.trimanindustries.com
Military, Aerospace & Aftermarket Components Distr
N.A.I.C.S.: 423840
Jon Nemo (Chm)
Glenn Van Etten (CIO)
Ryan LeBon (CFO)
Paul Elefonte (Chief Growth Officer)
Ann Marie Sheer (Sr VP-Mktg)
Mike Boyd (Chief Strategic Sls Officer)
Hilary Bily (VP-HR)
Patti Picone (Sr VP-Sls Ops)
Cathy Murphy (Exec VP-Corp Compliance & Risk Mgmt)
Tim Driscoll (CEO)

Subsidiary (Domestic):

Brighton Cromwell, LLC (2)
1500 Mt Kemble Ave Ste 102-202, Morristown, NJ 07960
Tel.: (973) 252-4100
Web Site: http://www.brightoncromwell.com
Supply Services & Logistics To The Department Of Defense
N.A.I.C.S.: 921190
Glenn Van Etten (CFO)
Robert Van Etten (Pres & CEO)
Terence Cusick (Exec VP-Bus Dev)
Gabe Albanito (Chief Quality Officer)

UAV Factory Ltd. (1)
1 Jaunbridagi, 2167, Marupes, Latvia
Tel.: (371) 2026 2126
Web Site: http://www.uavfactory.com
Aircraft Systems Mfr

N.A.I.C.S.: 336413

Subsidiary (US):

UAV Factory USA LLC (2)
2777 Lolo Dr Ste 130, Bend, OR 97703
Tel.: (541) 678-0515
Aircraft Systems Mfr
N.A.I.C.S.: 336413

Subsidiary (Domestic):

Jennings Aeronautics Inc. (3)
831 Buckley Rd, San Luis Obispo, CA 93401
Tel.: (805) 544-0942
Web Site: http://www.jenaero.com
Engineering Services
N.A.I.C.S.: 541330
Elias Sullwold (Engr-Mechanical)

Yingling Aircraft, LLC (1)
2299 S Airport Rd 2010, Wichita, KS 67209
Tel.: (316) 943-3246
Web Site: http://www.yinglingaviation.com
Rev.: $5,500,000
Emp.: 75
All Other Motor Vehicle Dealers
N.A.I.C.S.: 441227
Lynn Nichols (Chm & CEO)
Andrew Nichols (Pres)

AE WORKS LTD.
418 Beaver St, Pittsburgh, PA 15143
Tel.: (412) 287-7333
Web Site: https://aeworks.com
Year Founded: 2007
Sales Range: $1-9.9 Million
Emp.: 22
Engineering Services
N.A.I.C.S.: 541330
Michael A. Cherock (Owner & Pres)
Renee Schoop (Coord-Mktg)

Subsidiaries:

WTW Architect, Inc. (1)
127 Anderson St, Pittsburgh, PA 15212
Tel.: (412) 321-0550
Web Site: https://www.wtwarchitects.com
Rev.: $5,700,000
Emp.: 73
Architectural Services
N.A.I.C.S.: 541310
Paul Whitehead (Principal)

AEA FEDERAL CREDIT UNION
1780 S 1st Ave, Yuma, AZ 85364
Tel.: (928) 783-8881
Web Site: https://www.aeafcu.org
Year Founded: 1942
Sales Range: $10-24.9 Million
Emp.: 134
Online Banking & Loan Broker
N.A.I.C.S.: 522310
Athena Godwin (Dir-Fin Svcs)

AEA INVESTORS LP
520 Madison Ave 40th Fl, New York, NY 10022
Tel.: (212) 644-5900　　DE
Web Site:
　https://www.aeainvestors.com
Year Founded: 1968
Private Equity & Debt Investment Firm
N.A.I.C.S.: 523999
Vinay Kumar (Partner)
John L. Garcia (Chm, CEO & Partner)
Timothy Whelan (Partner)
Thomas Groves (Partner & COO-Private Debt Funds)
Thomas Pryma (Partner & COO)
Alan Wilkinson (Partner & Head-Small Bus Funds)
Scott Zoellner (Partner & Head-Capital Markets)
Rahul Goyal (Partner & Head-Strategic Rels)
James Ho (Partner)
Christian Johnson (Partner)
John Smith (Partner)

Nannette McNally *(Partner)*
J. Louis Sharpe *(Partner)*
Jeffrey Nagel *(Operating Partner)*
Alexandra A. Jung *(Partner & Head-Private Debt)*
James Powers *(Principal & Mng Dir-Portfolio Solutions)*
Daniel Schorr *(Partner & Principal)*
Benjamin Althaus *(Partner & VP)*
Benjamin Fischer *(Principal & VP)*
Sandra Grinker *(Principal, VP & Head-Human Resources)*
Haroon Ismail *(Principal & VP)*
Anneka Kamel *(Partner & VP)*
Cindy Li *(Principal & VP)*
Jeffrey Schmidt *(Principal & VP)*
Kathryn Alberti *(VP)*
Nick Alers *(VP)*
Keith Alexander *(Partner)*
John Almeida *(Partner)*
Chandler Anthony *(Principal)*
Patrick Arbeznik *(VP)*
Alex Bales *(VP)*
Kaitlin Bilby *(Head-Communications)*
Steven Botnick *(Dir-Tax)*
Christopher Brown *(VP)*
Sean Chan *(Dir-Information Technology)*
Riz Chand *(Operating Partner & Chief Talent Officer)*

Subsidiaries:

1-800 CONTACTS, Inc. (1)
66 E Wadsworth Park Dr 3rd Fl, Draper, UT 84020-7942
Tel.: (801) 924-9800
Web Site: http://www.1800contacts.com
Sales Range: $200-249.9 Million
Contact Lens Retailer
N.A.I.C.S.: 456130
Brian W. Bethers *(CEO)*
John R. Murray *(CIO)*
Rod Lacey *(VP-HR)*
John Graham *(COO)*
Amy Larson *(CTO)*

24 Hour Fitness USA, Inc. (1)
12647 Alcosta Blvd 5th Fl, San Ramon, CA 94583
Tel.: (925) 543-3100
Web Site: http://www.24hourfitness.com
Fitness Centers Owner & Operator
N.A.I.C.S.: 713940
Patrick Flanagan *(CFO)*
Tim Segneri *(Mgr-Area Loss Prevention)*
Jason Parker *(Mgr-Area Loss Prevention)*
Oscar Mejia *(Mgr-Area Loss Prevention)*
Beth Taska *(Exec VP-HR)*
Roland C. Smith *(Chm)*
Karl Sanft *(Pres & CEO)*

Subsidiary (Domestic):

Lady Fitness Inc. (2)
2231 Rutherford Rd, Carlsbad, CA 92008-8815
Tel.: (760) 931-0880
Sales Range: $10-24.9 Million
Emp.: 5
Provider of Physical Fitness Services
N.A.I.C.S.: 713940

AEA Investors (Asia) Limited (1)
Suite 3001 30F Gloucester Tower The Landmark, 15 Queen's Road Central, Hong Kong, China (Hong Kong)
Tel.: (852) 35568888
Web Site: http://www.aeainvestors.com
Sales Range: $25-49.9 Million
Emp.: 10
Private Equity Group
N.A.I.C.S.: 523999

AEA Investors (Germany) GmbH (1)
Widenmayerstr 3, 80538, Munich, Germany
Tel.: (49) 89 244 173 0
Web Site: http://www.aeainvestors.com
Emp.: 5
Privater Equity Firm
N.A.I.C.S.: 523999

AEA Investors (UK) Limited (1)
78 Brook Street, London, W1K 5EF, United Kingdom

Tel.: (44) 2076597800
Web Site: http://www.aeainvestors.com
Sales Range: $25-49.9 Million
Emp.: 9
Private Equity Group
N.A.I.C.S.: 523999
Alexander Hoffman *(Partner)*
Ramzi Gedeon *(Partner)*

API Technologies Corp. (1)
400 Nickerson Rd, Marlborough, MA 01752
Tel.: (508) 251-6400
Electronic Components & Microelectronic Circuits Mfr
N.A.I.C.S.: 334419
Michael Schwarm *(VP-Worldwide Sls & Mktg)*
Ed Fuhr *(VP)*
Richard Farrington *(Sr VP & Mng Dir)*
Craig Lindberg *(VP& Gen Mgr)*
Lawrence Howanitz *(Sr VP)*
Laura Reeder *(VP)*
Krystian Michnicki *(VP)*
Eric F. Seeton *(CFO & Sr VP)*
Robert J. McKenna *(Sr VP-Strategy)*
Robert J. McKenna *(Sr VP-Strategy)*

Subsidiary (Domestic):

API / Inmet, Inc. (2)
300 Dino Dr, Ann Arbor, MI 48103
Tel.: (734) 426-5553
Microwave Components Supplier
N.A.I.C.S.: 334419

API / Weinschel, Inc. (2)
5305 Spectrum Dr, Frederick, MD 21703
Tel.: (301) 846-9222
Web Site: http://weinschel.apitech.com
Microwave Components Supplier
N.A.I.C.S.: 334419

Subsidiary (Non-US):

API Microelectronics Limited (2)
Fenner Road South Denes, Great Yarmouth, NR30 3PX, Norfolk, United Kingdom
Tel.: (44) 1493743100
Electronic Components Mfr
N.A.I.C.S.: 334419

Emcon Emanation Control Ltd. (2)
360 Terry Fox Drive, Kanata, K2K 2P5, ON, Canada
Tel.: (613) 270-9009
Electronic Components Mfr
N.A.I.C.S.: 334419

Subsidiary (Domestic):

ION Networks, Inc. (2)
120 Corporate Blvd Ste A, South Plainfield, NJ 07080
Tel.: (908) 546-3900
Remote Device Management & Secure Access Technology Developer
N.A.I.C.S.: 334118

Subsidiary (Non-US):

RF2M Ltd. (2)
Fenner Road South Denes, Great Yarmouth, Norfolk, NR30 3PX, United Kingdom
Tel.: (44) 1493 743 100
Web Site: http://www.apitech.com
Emp.: 150
Holding Company; Radio Frequency & Microwave Electronics & Systems Mfr
N.A.I.C.S.: 551112
Richard Farrington *(Mng Dir)*

Secure Systems & Technologies Ltd
Brunel Court, Waterwells, Gloucester, GL2 2AL, United Kingdom
Tel.: (44) 1452557237
Electronic Components Mfr
N.A.I.C.S.: 334419
Richard Mundy *(Dir-Technical)*

Subsidiary (Domestic):

Spectrum SEI Microwave, Inc. (2)
38166 Old Stage Rd, Delmar, DE 19940
Tel.: (302) 462-3500
High Performance Filter Products Military & Space Filters, Multiplexers, Switched Filter Banks, Filter-Based IMAs & Filtered GPS/LNAs
N.A.I.C.S.: 333998

BWG Holdings I Corp (1)
1382 Bell Ave, Tustin, CA 92780
Tel.: (714) 384-0384
Web Site: http://www.balboawatergroup.com
Portable Spa Product Whslr
N.A.I.C.S.: 423910
Bob Spillar *(VP-Mktg)*

Subsidiary (Non-US):

HydroAir International A/S (2)
Roustvej 50, 6800, Varde, Denmark
Tel.: (45) 75 22 46 88
Emp.: 16
Portable Spa Product Whslr
N.A.I.C.S.: 423910
Helene Foght *(Mgr-Ops)*

Crane Engineering Sales, LLC (1)
707 Ford St, Kimberly, WI 54136
Tel.: (920) 733-4425
Web Site: https://www.craneengineering.net
Sales Range: $25-49.9 Million
Emp.: 80
Industrial Machinery & Equipment
N.A.I.C.S.: 423830
Bryan Hendricks *(Acct Mgr)*
Ed Steinbrecher *(Acct Mgr)*
Eric Finnila *(Acct Mgr)*
John Witek *(Engr-Application)*
Keith DenRuyter *(Acct Mgr)*
Kurt Schwei *(Mgr-Field Sls)*
Mike Baxter *(Mgr-Field Sls)*
Nathan Worzalla *(Engr-Controls)*
Peggy Campbell *(Controller)*

Subsidiary (Domestic):

Geiger Pump & Equipment Company (2)
8924 Yellow Brick Rd, Baltimore, MD 21237-2304
Tel.: (410) 682-2660
Web Site: http://www.geigerinc.com
Pump & Pumping Equipment Mfr
N.A.I.C.S.: 333914
Henry Peck *(Pres)*

Excelitas Technologies Corp. (1)
200 West St, Waltham, MA 02451
Tel.: (781) 996-5941
Web Site: http://www.excelitas.com
Optoelectronics & Advanced Electronic Systems Developer & Mfr
N.A.I.C.S.: 333310
David Nislick *(CEO)*
Jim Rao *(CFO & Exec VP)*
Joel Falcone *(COO & Exec VP)*
Michael Ersoni *(Exec VP-Comml)*
Doug Benner *(Exec VP-Defense & Aerospace)*
Stephanie Pittman *(Chief HR Officer & Exec VP)*

Subsidiary (Domestic):

Axsun Technologies, Inc. (2)
1 Fortune Dr, Billerica, MA 01821
Tel.: (978) 262-0049
Web Site: http://www.axsun.com
Emp.: 100
Optical Channel Monitors Mfr
N.A.I.C.S.: 334413
Jonathan Hartmann *(CEO)*
Peter Whitney *(Chief Science Officer & VP-Engrg)*

Subsidiary (Non-US):

Excelitas Canada, Inc. (2)
2600 Alfred Nobel Suite 401, Vaudreuil-Dorion, H4S0A9, QC, Canada
Tel.: (450) 424-3300
Web Site: https://www.excelitas.com
Developer & Mfr of Photonic Detectors, Thermal Infrared Detectors, Solid State Emitters & Imaging Solutions
N.A.I.C.S.: 334419

Excelitas Noblelight GmbH (2)
Heraeusstrasse 12-14, 63450, Hanau, Germany
Tel.: (49) 6181358492
Sales Range: $100-124.9 Million
Emp.: 700
Specialty Lamp & Lighting Product Mfr
N.A.I.C.S.: 335132
Wolfgang Stang *(Pres & CEO)*

Subsidiary (Non-US):

Excelitas Noblelight Limited (3)

Cambridge Science Park Milton Road, Cambridge, CB4 0GQ, United Kingdom
Tel.: (44) 1223429857
Chemical Products Mfr
N.A.I.C.S.: 325998

Subsidiary (US):

Heraeus Noblelight America LLC (3)
910 Clopper Rd, Gaithersburg, MD 20878-1357
Tel.: (301) 527-2660
Web Site: http://www.fusionuv.com
Ultraviolet Light Equipment & Systems Mfr
N.A.I.C.S.: 334419
James Elliott *(VP-Ops)*
Christopher Brandl *(Reg Mgr-Sls)*
David Harbourne *(Pres)*
Sarah Mather *(VP-HR & Quality Mgmt)*
Kevin Joesel *(Dir-Sls-Americas)*
Lonnie Murphy *(Dir-Sls-Western North America)*
Michael West *(Dir-Engrg)*
Gina Gonzalez *(Mgr-Mktg Comm)*

Subsidiary (Non-US):

Heraeus Noblelight Analytics Ltd. (3)
Unit 3-4 Nuffield Close, Cambridge, CB4 1SS, United Kingdom
Tel.: (44) 1223424100
Emp.: 15
Ultraviolet Lamp Mfr
N.A.I.C.S.: 335139

Subsidiary (Non-US):

Excelitas Technologies GmbH & Co. KG (2)
Wenzel-Jaksch-Strasse 31, D 65199, Wiesbaden, Germany
Tel.: (49) 611 492 430
Web Site: https://www.excelitas.com
Infrared Detectors & Sensors Developer & Mfr
N.A.I.C.S.: 334419

Excelitas Technologies Philippines, Inc. (2)
3 Ampere Street Light Industry & Science Park 1 Barangay Diezmo, Cabuyao, 4025, Laguna, Philippines
Tel.: (63) 27796599
Web Site: https://www.excelitas.com
Detection Products, Including Photodiodes & Photodiode Arrays Mfr
N.A.I.C.S.: 334419

Excelitas Technologies Shenzhen Co., Ltd. (2)
Longchang Road Block 68 Bao'an District, Nanshan District, Shenzhen, 518133, Guangdong, China
Tel.: (86) 755 2523 366
Web Site: https://www.excelitas.com
Lighting & Detection Products Developer & Mfr
N.A.I.C.S.: 335139

Excelitas Technologies Singapore Pte. Ltd. (2)
8 Tractor Road, Singapore, 627969, Singapore
Tel.: (65) 64997777
Web Site: https://www.excelitas.com
Optical Product Mfr
N.A.I.C.S.: 333310

PT. Excelitas Technologies Batam (2)
Block 207 Jalan Beringin Batamindo Industrial Park, Muka Kuning, Batam, 29433, Indonesia
Tel.: (62) 770 613 450
Web Site: http://www.excelitas.com
Infrared Detectors, Emitters, Power Supplies, Xenon-Based Lighting & LED Lighting Mfr
N.A.I.C.S.: 335139

Subsidiary (Domestic):

Phoseon Technology, Inc. (2)
7425 Nw Evergreen Pkwy, Hillsboro, OR 97124
Tel.: (503) 439-6446
Web Site: http://www.phoseon.com
Optical Instrument & Lens Mfr
N.A.I.C.S.: 333310

AEA Investors LP—(Continued)

Karey Holland (CTO)
John North (VP-Worldwide Sls)
Bill Cortelyou (Pres & CEO)
David Richards (Mgr-Sls-Europe)
Rob Karsten (Dir-Sls & Mktg-EMEA)
Chris O'Leary (Founder & CFO)
Scott Igl (VP-Engrg)
Michael Beck (VP-Worldwide Sls)
Craig Baldwin (VP-Ops)
Chad Taggard (VP & Gen Mgr-Life Sciences)
Keate Despain (VP-Mktg)

Subsidiary (Non-US):

Qioptiq Ltd. (2)
Glascoed Road, Saint Asaph, LL17 0LL,
Denbighshire, United Kingdom
Tel.: (44) 1745588000
Web Site: https://www.excelitas.com
Optical Product Mfr
N.A.I.C.S.: 333310

**Qioptiq Photonics GmbH & Co.
KG** (2)
Konigsallee 23, 37081, Gottingen, Germany
Tel.: (49) 55169350
Web Site: https://www.excelitas.com
Optical Product Mfr
N.A.I.C.S.: 333310

Qioptiq Photonics Limited (2)
Mitchell Point Ensign Way, Hamble, SO31
4RF, United Kingdom
Tel.: (44) 2380 744500
Web Site: https://www.excelitas.com
Emp.: 70
Optical Product Mfr
N.A.I.C.S.: 333310
Jim Coombs (Dir-Ops)
Emma Wood (Mgr-HR)

Subsidiary (Domestic):

Research Electro-Optics Inc. (2)
5505 Airport Blvd, Boulder, CO 80301
Tel.: (303) 938-1960
Web Site: http://www.reoinc.com
Optical Instruments & Lenses
N.A.I.C.S.: 333310
Susan J. Anway (CFO & VP-Fin)
Trey Turner (Chief Competitive Officer &
VP-Engrg)
Paul Kelly (Pres & CEO)
Ed Yousse (VP-Sls)

Generation Brands LLC (1)
7400 Linder Ave, Skokie, IL 60077
Web Site: http://www.generation-
brands.com
Emp.: 1,000
Lighting Equipment Whslr
N.A.I.C.S.: 335132
Matt Vollmer (Pres & Chief Sls Officer)
Greg Vandia (VP-Sls)
Stacey Rosenstein (VP-Builder Sls-East)
Mark Gorog (Dir-Customer Svc)
Josh Weiss (CEO)
Michael Incardone (VP-Builder Sls-West)
Mark Horning (Dir-Mdsg & Events & Mgr-
Natl Showroom)
Corbin Philhower (Mgr-Mdsg)
Amanda Foust (Dir-Natl Accts)
Sherry L. Bale (Mgr-PR)

Subsidiary (Domestic):

LBL Lighting LLC (2)
7400 Linder Ave, Skokie, IL 60077
Tel.: (847) 626-6300
Emp.: 300
Lighting Equipment Whslr
N.A.I.C.S.: 335132

**Monte Carlo Ceiling Fan
Company** (2)
7400 Linder Ave, Skokie, IL 60077
Web Site: http://www.montecarlofans.com
Ceiling Fan & Lighting Products Mfr &
Whslr
N.A.I.C.S.: 423620
Gary Biarsky (Sls Mgr-Central Reg)
Greg Vandia (VP-Sls)
Sherry L. Bale (Mgr-PR)

Sea Gull Lighting Products, LLC (2)
7400 Linder Ave, Skokie, IL 60077
Web Site: http://www.seagulllighting.com

Lighting Equipment Mfr & Distr
N.A.I.C.S.: 335139
Jody De Vine (Dir-Brand & Channel Mktg)
Ace H. Rosenstein (VP-Mktg & Corp Dev)
Sherry L. Bale (Mgr-PR)

Tech Lighting L.L.C. (2)
7400 Linder Ave, Skokie, IL 60077
Tel.: (847) 410-4400
Web Site: http://www.techlighting.com
Emp.: 300
Lighting Equipment Whslr
N.A.I.C.S.: 423610
Holly Graves (Sls Mgr-West Reg)
Jose Bizzaro (Mgr)

Hero Digital LLC (1)
555 Montgomery Street Suite 1250, San
Francisco, CA 94111
Tel.: (415) 230-0724
Web Site: https://herodigital.com
Digital Consultancy Services
N.A.I.C.S.: 541690
Danielle Rossi (Mng Dir)
Iser Cukierman (CFO)
David Kilimnik (Founder)
Kenneth Parks (CMO)
Kelli Trujillo (Chief People Officer)
Patrick Frend (Pres)
Erin Lynch (Chief Creative Officer)
Katie Comerford (Exec VP-Mktg)
Jay Dettling (CEO)

Subsidiary (Domestic):

Avionos, LLC (2)
33 N LaSalle St Ste 1350, Chicago, IL
60602
Tel.: (312) 572-8000
Web Site: http://www.avionos.com
Sales Range: $10-24.9 Million
Emp.: 47
Digital Marketing Services
N.A.I.C.S.: 541810
Craig Traxler (Co-Founder & Principal)
Dan Neiweem (Co-Founder & Principal)
Gibson Smith (Co-Founder, Principal & Dir-
Talent Acquisition & Mgmt)
Scott Webb (CEO)
Jim Sherman (CFO)
Chris Hauca (Mng Dir)

Subsidiary (Domestic):

Objectwave Corporation (3)
225 W Washington St Ste 1000, Chicago,
IL 60606-1255
Tel.: (312) 269-0111
Web Site: http://www.objectwave.com
Rev.: $4,200,000
Emp.: 35
Computer System Design Services
N.A.I.C.S.: 541512
Sam Cinquegrani (CEO)

Subsidiary (Domestic):

Bulldog Solutions, Inc. (2)
7600 N Capital of texas Hwy Bldg C Ste
250, Austin, TX 78731
Tel.: (512) 402-9199
Web Site: http://www.bulldogsolutions.com
Sales Range: $1-9.9 Million
Emp.: 33
Sales Lead Generation & Marketing Ser-
vices
N.A.I.C.S.: 541613
Rob Solomon (Co-Founder & Chief Strategy
Officer)
Naylor Gray (VP)
Randy Watson (CEO & COO)
Brian Maschler (Chief Creative Officer)
Chris Parisi (COO)

Division (Non-US):

Bulldog Solutions Europe (3)
Oude Keerbergsebaan 22, 2820, Bonhe-
iden, Belgium
Tel.: (32) 495270200
Sales Lead Generation & Marketing Ser-
vices
N.A.I.C.S.: 541613

**Industrial Acoustics Company,
Ltd.** (1)
IAC House Moorside Rd, Winchester, SO23
7US, Hampshire, United Kingdom
Tel.: (44) 1962873000
Web Site: http://www.iacl.co.uk

Sales Range: $25-49.9 Million
Emp.: 150
Acoustical Treatment & Noise Control Prod-
ucts
N.A.I.C.S.: 339999
Mike Jackson (Mgr-Sls)
Jason Saunders (Bus Mgr-Sls & Mktg-
Architectural Products & Svcs)

Subsidiary (Non-US):

IAC Acoustics Australia (2)
Unit 3/2-4 Dupas Street, Smithfield, 2164,
NSW, Australia
Tel.: (61) 287810400
Web Site: http://www.iac-australia.com.au
Sales Range: $50-74.9 Million
Emp.: 40
Noise & Acoustic Control Products Mfr
N.A.I.C.S.: 334513
Paul Godbold (Gen Mgr)
Mike Walsh (Dir-Engrg)
Mark Rubino (Pres-IAC Acoustics)

IAC Acoustics Italiana SpA (2)
Via Leonardo da Vinci 43, Trezzano Sul
Naviglio, Milan, 20090, Italy
Tel.: (39) 02 48 44 22 1
Web Site: http://www.gastechinsights.com
Sales & Services of Noise Control Products
N.A.I.C.S.: 423990
Giorgio Pelagatti (Dir-Technical)

IAC Boet Stopson SAS (2)
26 Rue Paul Doumer, PO Box 704, 59493,
Villeneuve d'Ascq, Cedex, France
Tel.: (33) 320058888
Sales Range: $25-49.9 Million
Noise & Acoustic Control Product Distr
N.A.I.C.S.: 423690

IAC Nordic A/S (2)
Jernholmen 44, 2650, Hvidovre, Denmark
Tel.: (45) 36778800
Web Site: http://www.iac-nordic.dk
Noise Control Product Mfr
N.A.I.C.S.: 334513

IAC Sim Engineering (2)
26 Rue du President Paul Doumer, 59650,
Villeneuve d'Ascq, France
Tel.: (33) 320058855
Web Site: http://www.sim-engineering.com
Sales Range: $25-49.9 Million
Emp.: 20
Noise & Acoustic Control Product Distr
N.A.I.C.S.: 423690
David Berrier (Dir-Dev)
Guillaume VandenBossche (Bus Mgr)
Philippe Lefebvre (Mgr-Bus & Legal)
Adrien Vandenbussche (Mgr-Acoustician &
Monitoring)
Jean-Francois Papin (Project Engr)
Francois Mores (Project Engr)
Gregory Caudron (Project Engr)
Baptiste Herbaux (Project Engr)
Isabelle Dubart (Mgr-Acctg & Admin)

IAC Stopson Espanoloa, SA (2)
Deu Y Mata 104-110, 08029, Barcelona,
Spain
Tel.: (34) 933216684
Sales Range: $25-49.9 Million
Emp.: 17
Noise & Acoustic Control Product Distr
N.A.I.C.S.: 423690

**Industrial Acoustics Company
GmbH** (2)
Sohlweg 17, 41372, Niederkruchten,
Germany (100%)
Tel.: (49) 2163 9991 0
Web Site: http://www.iac-acoustics.com
Sales Range: $25-49.9 Million
Emp.: 21
Sales & Service of Noise Control Products
N.A.I.C.S.: 423990
Hoerchens Voaker (Mgr-Sls)

Subsidiary (US):

**Industrial Acoustics Company,
Inc.** (2)
1160 Commerce Ave, Bronx, NY 10462-
5599
Tel.: (718) 931-8000
Web Site:
http://www.industrialacoustics.com
Sales Range: $75-99.9 Million
Noise Control Equipment
N.A.I.C.S.: 339999

Inovar Packaging Group, LLC (1)
10470 Miller Rd, Dallas, TX 75238
Tel.: (817) 277-6666
Web Site: https://inovarpackaging.com
Sales Range: $10-24.9 Million
Emp.: 90
Custom Packaging Products Designer, Mfr
& Labeling Services
N.A.I.C.S.: 326112
Zack Hall (COO)
Jeff Brezek (Chm & CEO)
Brent Steineman (CFO)
Jordan Destiche (VP-Acq, Corp Dev &
Merger)
Steve Zisler (VP-Sls)
Bob Bruno (VP-Corp Accts)
Bob Bruno (VP-Corp Accts)
Michelle Hawkins (Dir-HR Mgmt)

Subsidiary (Domestic):

Flexo-Graphics, LLC (2)
12820 W Glendale Ave, Butler, WI 53007
Tel.: (262) 790-2740
Web Site: http://www.flexo-graphics.com
Commercial Flexographic Printing
N.A.I.C.S.: 323111
Michael Albers (Acct Mgr)
Tim McDonough (Pres)

Safeprints LLC (2)
9590 NW 25th St, Doral, FL 33172-1402
Tel.: (305) 640-5991
Web Site: http://www.safeprints.com
Commercial Printing Services
N.A.I.C.S.: 323111
Luis A. Rojas (Mgr)

Jack's Family Restaurants Inc. (1)
124 W Oxmoor Rd Ste 21, Birmingham, AL
35209
Tel.: (205) 945-8167
Web Site: http://www.eatatjacks.com
Sales Range: $25-49.9 Million
Emp.: 25
Fast-Food Restaurant, Chain
N.A.I.C.S.: 722513
Guy Kirk (Dir-HR)
Betty Hamrick (Reg Dir)
Faye Riley (Mgr)
Jena Barnett (Asst Dir-Trng)
Britt Swenson (Coord-Mktg)
Brandon Weaver (CTO)
Pam Measel (Dir-Mktg)
Roland Smith (Chm)

Monroe Engineering, LLC (1)
2990 Technology Dr, Rochester Hills, MI
48309
Tel.: (877) 392-4573
Web Site:
http://www.monroeengineering.com
Industrial Component Distr
N.A.I.C.S.: 423830
Kevin Budzynski (CMO)

Subsidiary (Domestic):

Northwest Fastener Sales Inc. (2)
10764 SW Manhasset Dr, Tualatin, OR
97062
Tel.: (503) 691-6040
Web Site:
http://www.northwestfastenersales.com
Rev.: $4,662,000
Emp.: 9
Hardware Stores
N.A.I.C.S.: 444140
Len Odegaard (Pres & CEO)

NES Fircroft Limited (1)
Station House Stamford New Road, Altrin-
cham, WA14 1EP, Cheshire, United King-
dom
Tel.: (44) 161 942 4000
Web Site: http://www.nesfircroft.com
Oil & Gas Distr
N.A.I.C.S.: 333132
Theron I. Gilliam Jr. (CEO)
Tig Gilliam (CEO)

Subsidiary (Domestic):

**Fircroft Engineering Services
Ltd.** (2)
Lingley House 120 Birchwood Point Birch-
wood Boulevard, Warrington, WA3 7QH,
Cheshire, United Kingdom
Tel.: (44) 192 528 1555
Web Site: http://www.fircroft.com

Sales Range: $350-399.9 Million
Technical Recruitment Services
N.A.I.C.S.: 561311
John Johnson *(Founder)*
Johnathan Johnson *(CEO)*
Stuart Hall *(CFO)*

Subsidiary (Non-US):

Fircroft (Vietnam) Company Ltd (3)
Unit 3 Floor 12 Green Power Building 35
Ton Duc Thang, Ben Nghe Ward District 1,
Ho Chi Minh City, Vietnam
Tel.: (84) 839117292
Employee Recruitment Services
N.A.I.C.S.: 561311
Andrei Lucaciu *(Mgr-Recruitment)*

Fircroft Australia Pty Ltd (3)
Level 11 116 Adelaide Street, Brisbane,
4000, QLD, Australia
Tel.: (61) 732332300
Web Site: http://www.fircroft.com
Employee Recruitment Services
N.A.I.C.S.: 561311
Craig McTamney *(Dir-Strategic Sls-
Brisbane)*

Fircroft Canada Inc (3)
500 Panarctic Plaza 815 - 8 Avenue SW,
Calgary, T2P 3P2, AB, Canada
Tel.: (403) 705-2170
Web Site: http://www.fircroft.com
Employee Recruitment Services
N.A.I.C.S.: 561311

Subsidiary (US):

Fircroft Inc (3)
3 Riverway Ste 825, Houston, TX 77056
Tel.: (713) 235-8100
Web Site: http://www.fircroft.com
Employee Recruitment Services
N.A.I.C.S.: 561311
Mike Johnson *(Mgr-Recruitment)*

Subsidiary (Non-US):

Fircroft Norge AS (3)
Professor Olav Hanssens vei 7A, 4021,
Stavanger, Norway
Tel.: (47) 51555800
Employee Recruitment Services
N.A.I.C.S.: 561311

Fircroft Pte Ltd (3)
6 Battery Road 16-03, Singapore, 49909,
Singapore
Tel.: (65) 63955750
Employee Recruitment Services
N.A.I.C.S.: 561311
Mia Lyons *(Country Mgr)*

Fircroft Qatar LLC (3)
Building 40 Office 305 Ibin Sina Stree, PO
Box 200183, Muntazah, Doha, Qatar
Tel.: (974) 44911930
Employee Recruitment Services
N.A.I.C.S.: 561311
Toni Piedipalumbo *(Country Mgr)*

Fircroft Russia, LLC. (3)
Bolshaya Sukharevskaya Square 16/18 Bld
1 2nd Floor Office 37, Moscow, 107045,
Russia
Tel.: (7) 4996492829
Web Site: http://www.fircroft.com
Employee Recruitment Services
N.A.I.C.S.: 561311
Marc Prager *(Country Mgr)*

Fircroft Thailand Limited (3)
22nd Floor 2202 Pacific Place II Building
142 Sukhumvit Road, Bangkok, Thailand
Tel.: (66) 26532947
Employee Recruitment Services
N.A.I.C.S.: 561311
Damien Lee *(Country Mgr)*

PT. Fircroft Indonesia (3)
Sampoerna Strategic Square South Tower
18th Floor, Jl Jend Sudirman Kav 45-46,
Jakarta, 12930, Indonesia
Tel.: (62) 215750831
Employee Recruitment Services
N.A.I.C.S.: 561311
Thomas Damecour *(Country Mgr)*

Subsidiary (Domestic):

NES Global Talent Limited (2)

Station House Stamford New Road, Altrin-
cham, WA14 1EP, Cheshire, United King-
dom
Tel.: (44) 161 942 4000
Web Site: http://www.nesfircroft.com
Engineering Recruitment Services
N.A.I.C.S.: 541330
Tim Gilliam *(CEO)*

Nations Roof LLC (1)
1400 Honeyspot Rd Ext, Stratford, CT
06615
Tel.: (203) 335-8949
Web Site: http://www.nationsroof.com
Sales Range: $75-99.9 Million
Emp.: 675
Roofing Services
N.A.I.C.S.: 238160
Richard M. Nugent *(CEO)*
James L. Nugent *(VP)*
Gabriella Gross-Bogran *(Mgr-CAD & Coord-
PM)*
Kyle DiSanto *(Project Mgr)*
Claude Carnahan *(Controller)*
Jake Hyatt *(Pres)*

Division (Domestic):

Nations Roof East (2)
255 Lake Ave, Yonkers, NY 10701
Tel.: (718) 618-6243
Web Site: http://www.nationsroof.com
Rev.: $5,308,000
Emp.: 16
Roof Repair
N.A.I.C.S.: 238160
Michael Johannes *(Pres)*

Redwood Logistics LLC (1)
1765 N Elston Ave Ste 216, Chicago, IL
60642
Tel.: (844) 467-3396
Web Site: http://www.redwoodlogistics.com
Logistic Services
N.A.I.C.S.: 541614
Todd Colin *(Chief Integration Officer)*
John Centers *(Chief Sls Officer)*
Mark Yeager *(CEO)*
Michael Reed *(Chief Product Officer)*
James Liakos *(CFO)*
Andrea Alaimo *(Sr VP-HR)*

Subsidiary (Domestic):

Rockfarm Supply Chain Solutions
Inc. (2)
300 Data Ct, Dubuque, IA 52003
Tel.: (815) 573-0155
Web Site: http://www.rockfarm.com
Supply Chain Management, Technology &
Consulting Services
N.A.I.C.S.: 541690
Brad Stewart *(Pres)*
Drew Burken *(Dir-Solutions Svcs)*
Matthew Randecker *(VP-Solutions)*
Pete Recker *(VP-Ops)*
Angie Landsman *(Controller)*
Seth Pacha *(Dir-Product Dev)*

Subsidiary (Domestic):

Supply Chain Coach, Inc. (3)
300 Data Ct, Dubuque, IA 52003
Tel.: (815) 573-0155
Web Site: http://www.supplychaincoach.com
Process, Physical Distribution & Logistics
Consulting Services
N.A.I.C.S.: 541614
Tom French *(Founder)*

Subsidiary (Domestic):

Strive Logistics, LLC (2)
3008 N Lincoln Ave, Chicago, IL 60657
Tel.: (773) 524-3630
Web Site: http://www.strivelogistics.com
Sales Range: $1-9.9 Million
Freight Transportation Arrangement
N.A.I.C.S.: 488510
Ben Greene *(CEO)*

SBP Holdings Inc. (1)
899 Airport Park Rd Ste D, Glen Burnie,
MD 21061
Tel.: (443) 831-6357
Web Site: http://www.sbpholdings.com
Sales Range: $200-249.9 Million
Emp.: 650
Holding Company
N.A.I.C.S.: 551112

Otis Dufrene *(CEO)*

Representative Office (Domestic):

Ray Lewis & Co. (2)
205 S Main St, Harrisville, PA 16038-1705
Tel.: (724) 735-4231
Web Site:
    http://www.raylewisandcompany.com
Industrial Machinery & Equipment Merchant
Whslr
N.A.I.C.S.: 423830

Subsidiary (Domestic):

Singer Equities Inc. (2)
899 Airport Park Rd Ste D, Glen Burnie,
MD 21061
Tel.: (410) 553-9192
Industrial Rubber Products Mfr & Distr
N.A.I.C.S.: 326291
Otis Dufrene *(CEO)*
Don Fritzinger *(Pres)*
Pete Haberbosch *(Grp VP)*

Subsidiary (Domestic):

Hampton Rubber Company Inc. (3)
1669 W Pembroke Ave, Hampton, VA
23661-1901
Tel.: (757) 722-9818
Web Site: http://www.hamptonrubber.com
Retailer of Industrial Supplies
N.A.I.C.S.: 423840

Hanna Rubber Co., Inc. (3)
908 W 25th St, Kansas City, MO 64108
Tel.: (816) 221-9600
Web Site:
    http://www.hannarubbercompany.com
Emp.: 50
Industrial Rubber & Plastics Product Mfr &
Distr
N.A.I.C.S.: 326291
Scott Assyia *(VP & Gen Mgr)*

Industrial & Marine Equipment Co.,
Inc. (3)
525 Elmwood Park Blvd, New Orleans, LA
70123
Tel.: (504) 733-5030
Web Site: http://www.industrial-marine-
    eq.com
Hydraulic & Pneumatic Components Distr
N.A.I.C.S.: 423840
Paul Haworth *(Pres)*
Daniel Haworth *(Gen Mgr)*
Courtney Gravois *(Mgr-Acctg Dept)*

National Hose & Accessory, Inc. (3)
1831 Richey St, Pasadena, TX 77502
Tel.: (713) 920-2030
Web Site: http://www.nationalhose.com
Industrial Hose, Couplings & Gasketing
Product Distr
N.A.I.C.S.: 423840
Michael Johnson *(VP & Gen Mgr)*

PRC Industrial Supply, Inc. (3)
21 W Commercial St, Portland, ME 04112
Tel.: (207) 774-3993
Web Site: http://www.prcindustrial.com
Emp.: 35
Industrial Rubber Products Distr
N.A.I.C.S.: 423840
Kevin Easler *(VP & Gen Mgr)*

R/W Connection, Inc. (3)
936 Links Ave, Landisville, PA 17538
Tel.: (717) 898-5257
Web Site: http://www.rwconnection.com
Hose, Belt & Gasket Distr
N.A.I.C.S.: 423840

Subsidiary (Domestic):

Allied Rubber & Rigging Supply (4)
140 Hindman Ln, Butler, PA 16001
Tel.: (724) 482-2965
Web Site: http://www.alliedrubber.com
Hose, Fittings, Gaskets, Rubber Tubing &
Conveyor Belting Retailer
N.A.I.C.S.: 423840
David Marki *(VP & Gen Mgr)*

Virginia-Carolina Belting, Inc. (4)
475 Electric Rd, Salem, VA 24153
Tel.: (540) 389-3220
Web Site: http://www.vcbelting.com

Sales Range: $1-9.9 Million
Emp.: 19
Industrial Rubber Supplies Distr
N.A.I.C.S.: 423840
Alan Brinkley *(Mgr-Ops)*

Subsidiary (Domestic):

Stewart-Hunt Inc. (3)
8 Garfield Cir, Burlington, MA 01803
Tel.: (781) 272-4411
Web Site: http://www.stewarthunt.com
Hydraulic Equipment Distr
N.A.I.C.S.: 423840
Nelson Smith *(Pres)*

Summers Rubber Co. Inc. (3)
12555 Berea Rd, Cleveland, OH 44111
Tel.: (216) 941-7700
Web Site: http://www.summersrubber.com
Industrial Hose Mfr & Distr
N.A.I.C.S.: 326220
Dennis Owens *(Dir-Procurement)*
Norm Fye *(Mgr-Ops)*
Roger Weiss *(Mgr-Ops)*

Texas Rubber Supply, Inc. (3)
2436 Irving Blvd, Dallas, TX 75207
Tel.: (214) 631-3143
Web Site:
    http://www.texasrubbersupply.com
Industrial Supplies Merchant Whslr
N.A.I.C.S.: 423840
Larry Redd *(Mgr-Ops & Pur)*

Unisource Manufacturing, Inc. (3)
8040 NE 33rd Dr, Portland, OR 97211
Tel.: (503) 281-4673
Web Site: http://www.unisource-mfg.com
Sales Range: $10-24.9 Million
Hose Mfr
N.A.I.C.S.: 332912
Ron Bateman *(Mgr-Ops & Pur)*
Ken Jockers *(Mgr-Cryogenic, Sanitary Prod-
ucts & HVAC)*
Joseph Thompson *(Pres & Mgr-Sls &
Hydraulics-Natl)*
Dan Christiansen *(Gen Mgr-HR)*
Geoff Zagelow *(Sls Mgr-Inside)*
Blu Matsell *(Mgr-Quality)*

Soho Studio, LLC (1)
15 Hoover St, Inwood, NY 11096
Tel.: (718) 677-8453
Web Site: http://www.sohostudiocorp.com
Tile & Specialty Interior Products Mfr
N.A.I.C.S.: 238340

Springs Window Fashions LLC (1)
7549 Graber Rd, Middleton, WI 53562-1001
Tel.: (608) 836-1011
Web Site:
    http://www.springswindowfashions.com
Drapery Rods, Window Shades, Pleated
Shades, Horizontal & Vertical Blinds Mfr
N.A.I.C.S.: 337920
Frank A. Natoli Jr. *(Exec VP-Integrated
Supply Chain)*
Eric Jungbluth *(Pres & CEO)*
John Weinstock *(Exec VP-Mktg)*
James Gross *(VP-Field Sls)*
Kent Owens *(Sr VP & Gen Mgr-Retail)*
Tim Oswald *(Sr VP-HR)*
John Comerford *(Sr VP-Corp Admin)*
Jason Grommon *(Exec VP & Pres-Comml
Bus Unit)*
Grant Gustafson *(Sr VP-New Bus Dev)*
Sean Martin *(Gen Mgr & Sr VP)*
Frank Natoli Jr. *(Exec VP-Integrated Supply
Chain)*

Subsidiary (Domestic):

Mariak Industries, Inc. (2)
575 W Manville St, Rancho Dominguez, CA
90220
Tel.: (310) 661-4400
Web Site: http://www.mariak.com
Window Coverings Mfr
N.A.I.C.S.: 326199
Leo Elinson *(Co-Founder)*
Patty Elinson *(Co-Founder)*

Sunsetter Products, LP (2)
184 Charles St, Malden, MA 02148
Tel.: (800) 876-2340
Web Site: http://www.sunsetter.com
Retractable Awnings Mfr
N.A.I.C.S.: 332323
Jonathan Hershberg *(Pres)*

AEA Investors LP—(Continued)

ThreeSixty Group Limited (1)
8 Lam Chak Street, Kwun Tong, China
(Hong Kong)
Tel.: (852) 34082200
Web Site:
http://www.thethreesixtygroup.com
Holding Company; Branded Merchandising
Services
N.A.I.C.S.: 551112
Johann Clapp (Founder & Mng Partner)

Subsidiary (US):

MerchSource, LLC (2)
15 Cushing, Irvine, CA 92618
Tel.: (949) 587-9207
Web Site: http://www.merchsource.com
Sales Range: $1-9.9 Million
Consumer Products Designer & Distr
N.A.I.C.S.: 423990
Carrie Blodgett (Mgr-Licensing & Acct Exec)

Vornado Air, LLC (2)
415 E 13th St, Andover, KS 67002
Tel.: (800) 234-0604
Web Site: http://www.vornado.com
Room Comfort Appliances, Including Fans,
Heaters, Humidifiers & Purifiers Design &
Mfr
N.A.I.C.S.: 333413

Troxell Communications, Inc. (1)
4830 S 38th St, Phoenix, AZ 85040
Tel.: (602) 437-7240
Web Site: http://www.trox.com
Audio Visual Products Retailer
N.A.I.C.S.: 423620
Dorri Carpenter (Dir-HR)

Division (Domestic):

Integrated A/V Systems LLC (2)
5440 Brittmoore, Houston, TX 77041
Tel.: (713) 468-8699
Sales Range: $50-74.9 Million
Audio-Visual Solutions for Educational Insti-
tutions & Corporations
N.A.I.C.S.: 423690

Division (Domestic):

CCS Louisiana (3)
4500 York St Ste 200, Metairie, LA 70001
Tel.: (504) 454-2749
Web Site: http://www.summit-sys.com
Rev.: $11,200,000
Emp.: 32
Computer Industry & Sales Representative
N.A.I.C.S.: 541519
Randy Duet Champagne (Mgr-Sls & Ops)

United Seating & Mobility LLC (2)
13300 Lakefront Dr, Earth City, MO 63045
Tel.: (314) 699-9500
Web Site: http://www.numotion.com
Sales Range: $200-249.9 Million
Surgical Appliances & Supplies Mfr
N.A.I.C.S.: 339113
Mike Swinford (CEO)
Warren Degraff (Co-COO)
Tamas Feitel (CFO)
Tim Casey (Co-COO & Gen Counsel)
Dan Prestegaard (CIO)
Bret Barczak (CMO)
Melissa Georgeoff (Exec VP-Payer Rels)
Gary J. Gilberti (Exec VP-East Div)
James Hartman (Exec VP-West Div)
John Pryles (Exec VP-Sls)
Neill Rowland (Sr VP-Svcs)
Adam Holton (Chief HR Officer)

Subsidiary (Domestic):

Monroe Wheelchair, Inc. (2)
724 Watervliet Shaker Rd, Latham, NY
12110
Tel.: (518) 783-1653
Web Site:
http://www.monroewheelchair.com
Surgical & Medical Instrument Mfr
N.A.I.C.S.: 339112
Doug Westerdahl (Pres & CEO)

Wheeler's Medical Supply LLC (2)
14603 Beach Blvd Ste 750-B, Jacksonville,
FL 32250-2113
Tel.: (904) 412-5181
Web Site:
http://www.wheelersmedicalsupply.com

Catheters & Incontinence Supplies Distr
N.A.I.C.S.: 423450
Donald Moran III (Founder)

Verdesian Life Sciences, LLC (1)
1001 Winstead Dr Ste 480, Cary, NC 27513
Tel.: (919) 825-1901
Web Site: http://www.vlsci.com
Emp.: 32
Nutritional & Plant Health Technologies
N.A.I.C.S.: 311999
J. J. Grow (Chm)
Greg Thompson (Founder)
Francis X. Pirozzi (CFO)
Mike King (VP-Ops)
C. Ryan Bond (VP-Product & Tech Dev)
Joe Olesko (Acct Mgr-Western Canada)
Charles Broughton (VP-Sls-Seed Treat-
ments & Inoculants-US & Canada)
Martin Brown (Gen Mgr-Europe)
John Haywood (Mgr-Technical & Product
Dev)
Kenneth M. Avery (Pres & CEO)

Subsidiary (Domestic):

Cytozyme Laboratories, Inc. (2)
134 S 700 W, Salt Lake City, UT 84104-
1018
Tel.: (801) 533-9208
Web Site: http://www.cytozyme.com
Sales Range: $1-9.9 Million
Emp.: 25
Phosphatic Fertilizer Mfr
N.A.I.C.S.: 325312
Eric Baughman (CEO)
Karla Webb (Controller)

**Northwest Agricultural Products,
Inc.** (2)
821 S Chestnut Ave, Pasco, WA 99301
Tel.: (509) 547-8234
Web Site: http://www.nap-chem.com
Nutritionals & Crop Protection Products Mfr
N.A.I.C.S.: 325320

QC Corp. (2)
One Reservoir Circle Ste 100, Baltimore,
MD 21208
Tel.: (410) 486-0010
Web Site: http://www.qccorporation.com
Ferrous Sulfate Mfr
N.A.I.C.S.: 327999
Tom Kiser (Plant Mgr)
Jason Gordon (Pres)
Brian Barrett (VP-Quality Assurance)
Eric Hyatt (COO)
Lisa Long (Mgr-Customer Svc & Logistics)
John Guglielmi (Sr VP-Sls & Mktg)
Jake Socherman (Mgr-Sls-Natl)

**Specialty Fertilizer Products,
LLC** (2)
11550 Ash St Ste 220, Leawood, KS 66211
Tel.: (913) 956-7500
Web Site: http://www.sfp.com
Fertilizer Mfr
N.A.I.C.S.: 325320
J. Larry Sanders (Pres & CEO)
John Hardy (COO & Gen Counsel)
Dave Schwartz (Exec VP-Sls)
C. Ryan Bond (VP-Mktg)
J. J. Grow (CEO)
Mike King (VP-Ops)
Francis X. Pirozzi (CFO)
Greg Thompson (COO)

Window Nation, LLC (1)
2288 E Aurora Rd, Twinsburg, OH 44087-
1926
Tel.: (216) 464-4141
Web Site: http://www.windownation.com
Emp.: 500
Residential Remodeler
N.A.I.C.S.: 236118
Joe Tripi (Dir-Ops)
Yang H. Chang (CFO)

Worldwide Electric Corp. (1)
1 Grove St Ste 201B, Pittsford, NY 14534
Tel.: (585) 389-8531
Sales Range: $1-9.9 Million
Emp.: 17
Electrical Apparatus & Equipment, Wiring
Supplies & Related Equipment Merchant
Whslr
N.A.I.C.S.: 423610
Rick Simmonds (Pres)

AEB INTERNATIONAL INC.

654 Madison Ave Ste 1809, New
York, NY 10065-6526
Tel.: (212) 752-4647
Web Site:
https://www.aebinternational.com
Year Founded: 1979
Sales Range: $10-24.9 Million
Emp.: 70
Metal Center Services
N.A.I.C.S.: 423510
A. Erkan Buyuksoy (Pres & CEO)

Subsidiaries:

Atlantic Specialty Wire Inc. (1)
529 Chucks Dr, Duncan, SC (100%)
29334-9292
Tel.: (864) 877-6947
Web Site: http://www.aebint.com
Sales Range: $10-24.9 Million
Emp.: 50
Copper Rolling & Specialty Wire Products
N.A.I.C.S.: 331420

AEC GROUP, INC.

1735 5th Ave, McKeesport, PA 15132
Tel.: (800) 552-1440
Web Site: http://www.aecgroup.com
Year Founded: 1992
Sales Range: $25-49.9 Million
Emp.: 50
Consulting & Installation Services for
IT Systems & Electrical Infrastructure
N.A.I.C.S.: 541690
Joe Falba (Engr-Network)
Kennith Rindt (Sr VP-Sls & Strategic
Alliances)
Marty Connelly (Mng Partner & Exec
VP)
Brendan Surma (Mgr-Bus Dev)

AEDAN FINANCIAL CORP.

1390 Market St Ste 200, San Fran-
cisco, CA 94102 DE
Web Site: https://www.aedan.io
Assets: $1,468
Liabilities: $11,880
Net Worth: ($10,412)
Earnings: ($98,902)
Emp.: 1
Fiscal Year-end: 12/31/18
Investment Services
N.A.I.C.S.: 523999
Eric Fitzgerald (Founder & Chm)

AEEC LLC

11710 Plaza America Dr Ste 125,
Reston, VA 20190-4737
Tel.: (703) 766-4300
Web Site:
https://www.americanconsult.com
Sales Range: $10-24.9 Million
Emp.: 100
Information Technology, Engineering,
Environmental & Project Management
Services
N.A.I.C.S.: 541990
Raj Patil (CEO)
Chris Gray (Office Mgr)
Ambika Kakar (Exec VP)
Brian Rivett (Exec VP)
Darwin Layog (CTO)
Greg Erdman (Dir-Enterprise Solu-
tions)
Robert S. Poulin (Chief Revenue
Officer)

**AEG HOLDING COMPANY,
INC.**

77 Monroe Ctr Ste B, Grand Rapids,
MI 49503
Tel.: (616) 301-1221 DE
Web Site:
https://www.fusionacademy.com
Year Founded: 2007
One-to-One Teaching Model & Men-
toring Services
N.A.I.C.S.: 611710

Peter G. Ruppert (Pres & CEO)

**AEGIS ASSISTED LIVING
PROPERTIES LLC**

415 118th Ave SE, Bellevue, WA
98005
Tel.: (425) 861-9993
Web Site:
https://www.aegisliving.com
Year Founded: 1997
Sales Range: $50-74.9 Million
Emp.: 2,000
Provider of Assisted Living Services
N.A.I.C.S.: 623110
Dwayne Clark (Chm & CEO)

**AEGIS FIRE PROTECTION
SYSTEMS, LLC.**

156 Industrial Loop S, Orange Park,
FL 32073-2858
Tel.: (904) 215-9669
Web Site: http://www.aegisfps.com
Sales Range: $1-9.9 Million
Emp.: 27
Fire Protection Equipment Whslr
N.A.I.C.S.: 423850
Doug Kirk (Pres)

**AEGIS HEDGING SOLUTIONS,
LLC**

2829 Technology Forest Blvd #440,
The Woodlands, TX 77381
Tel.: (713) 322-9798
Web Site: http://www.aegis-
hedging.com
Year Founded: 2013
Hedge Portfolio Advisory Services
N.A.I.C.S.: 523940
Bryan Christopher Sansbury
(Founder, Chm, CEO & Partner)
Bryan Sansbury (Founder, Chm, CEO
& Partner)
Steve Resnick (Chief Customer Offi-
cer)
Dave McLellan (Dir-Canada)

Subsidiaries:

Emission Advisors, Inc. (1)
1235 N Loop W Ste 920, Houston, TX
77008
Tel.: (713) 385-3321
Web Site: http://www.emissionadvisors.com
Environmental Services
N.A.I.C.S.: 541620
Mike Taylor (Founder & CEO)
Chris Pepper (Gen Counsel)

AEGIS LIGHTWAVE, INC.

78A Olympia Ave, Woburn, MA 01801
Tel.: (781) 904-4000
Web Site:
http://www.aegislightwave.com
Year Founded: 2000
Optical Channel Monitors Mfr
N.A.I.C.S.: 334413
Chris Koeppen (Gen Mgr)

Subsidiaries:

AOFR Pty. Ltd. (1)
2 Faulding Street, Symonston, Canberra,
2609, ACT, Australia
Tel.: (61) 262062220
Web Site: http://www.aofr.com
Sales Range: $10-24.9 Million
Emp.: 100
Fibber Optic Components Mfr
N.A.I.C.S.: 335921

**AEGIS POWER SYSTEMS,
INC.**

805 Greenlawn Cemetery Rd, Mur-
phy, NC 28906
Tel.: (828) 837-4029 DE
Web Site:
https://www.aegispower.com
Year Founded: 1995

Rapid Response Custom Power Systems Designer, Mfr & Whslr
N.A.I.C.S.: 335999
William H. Dockery (Pres)
Jeff Martin (Mgr-Mfg)

AEI CORE PROPERTY INCOME TRUST, INC.
1300 Wells Fargo Pl, Saint Paul, MN 55101　　　　　MN
Year Founded: 2011
Real Estate Investment Services
N.A.I.C.S.: 525990
Robert P. Johnson (Chm, Pres & CEO)
Patrick W. Keene (CFO, Exec VP & Treas)

AEM, INC.
6610 Cobra Way, San Diego, CA 92121-4107
Tel.: (858) 481-0210
Web Site: https://www.aem-usa.com
Year Founded: 1986
Sales Range: $10-24.9 Million
Emp.: 70
Mfr of Electronic Inductors
N.A.I.C.S.: 334416
Daniel H. Chang (Pres)
Frank Covalt (Controller)
Gary Miscikowski (Mgr-Engrg Sls)
Liwu Wang (Mgr-Engrg)

AEMS SERVICE COMPANY
395 Main St, Tennent, NJ 07763
Tel.: (888) 230-0149　　　　　NJ
Web Site:
　　http://www.aemsserviceco.com
Year Founded: 1979
Plumbing Services
N.A.I.C.S.: 238220
Sudeep Das (Pres & CEO)
Mike Roberto (Gen Mgr)
Roger Pilkington (Mgr-Svc & Installation)

Subsidiaries:

Ram Services Inc.　　　　　(1)
PO Box 1403, Woodstock, GA 30188-1681
Tel.: (770) 928-2067
Web Site: http://www.crushedcore.com
Plumbing Services
N.A.I.C.S.: 238220
Michael Morawic (Pres)

AENEAS COMMUNICATIONS, LLC
300 N Cumberland St Ste 200, Jackson, TN 38301
Tel.: (731) 554-9200
Web Site: https://aeneas.com
Year Founded: 1995
Sales Range: $1-9.9 Million
Emp.: 28
Telephone Cables Distr
N.A.I.C.S.: 518210
Jonathan V. Harlan (Founder & CEO)
Sally Harlan (Sec)

AEON
901 N 3rd St Ste 150, Minneapolis, MN 55401
Tel.: (612) 341-3148　　　　　MN
Web Site: http://www.aeonmn.org
Year Founded: 1986
Sales Range: $10-24.9 Million
Emp.: 130
Housing Assistance Services
N.A.I.C.S.: 624229
Eric Schnell (COO)
Caroline Horton (CFO)
Lori Huinker-Wollner (Controller)
Angie Emmrich (Dir-HR & Admin)
Alan Arthur (Pres & CEO)
Lynette Dumalag (Chm)
Scott Anderson (Vice Chm & Sec)

Debra Behrens (Chief Advancement Officer-Resource Dev)
Barb Halverson (VP-Property Ops)
Scott Redd (VP-Supportive Svcs & Resident Connections)

AEON ACQUISITION CORP.
1715 Hwy 35 Ste 101, Middletown, NJ 07748　　　　　DE
Year Founded: 2020
Investment Services
N.A.I.C.S.: 523999
Demetrios Mallios (Chm & CEO)
Valentino La Rosa (CFO & Treas)
Alan D. Lewis (Chief Strategy Officer)
Pete Petino (COO & Sec)

AEON GLOBAL HEALTH CORP.
2225 Centennial Dr, Gainesville, GA 30504
Tel.: (678) 276-8412　　　　　DE
Web Site:
　　https://www.aeonglobalhealth.com
Year Founded: 1985
AGHC—(OTCBB)
Rev.: $12,932,305
Assets: $3,911,096
Liabilities: $9,892,935
Net Worth: ($5,981,839)
Earnings: ($8,318,201)
Emp.: 52
Fiscal Year-end: 06/30/19
Holding Company; Web-Based Authentication Services for Digital Documents
N.A.I.C.S.: 551112

Subsidiaries:

Authentidate, Inc.　　　　　(1)
Connell Corporate Center 300 Connell Dr 5th Fl, Berkeley Heights, NJ 07922
Tel.: (908) 787-1700
Web Site: http://www.authentidate.com
Sales Range: $100-124.9 Million
Web-Based Authentication Services for Digital Documents
N.A.I.C.S.: 561499

AEON LAW PLLC
1718 E Olive Way, Seattle, WA 98102
Tel.: (206) 466-0073
Web Site: https://www.aeonlaw.com
Emp.: 100
Law firm
N.A.I.C.S.: 541110
Adam L.K. Philipp (Founder)

Subsidiaries:

DWC Law Firm PS　　　　　(1)
219 1st Ave S Ste 400, Seattle, WA 98104-2551
Tel.: (206) 583-2609
Web Site: http://www.dwcattorney.com
Law firm
N.A.I.C.S.: 541110

AEPS CORPORATION
7700 Chevy Chase Dr Ste 230, Austin, TX 78752
Tel.: (512) 380-9700
Web Site: http://www.aeps.us
Year Founded: 2002
Sales Range: $1-9.9 Million
Emp.: 102
Security & Facilities Services for Government & Commercial Customers
N.A.I.C.S.: 561612
Dwight Scales (Mgr-Bus Dev)
Craig Overmyer (CFO)

AEQUITAS CAPITAL MANAGEMENT
5300 Meadows Rd Ste 400, Lake Oswego, OR 97035
Tel.: (503) 419-3500

Web Site:
　　http://www.aequitascapital.com
Rev.: $15,000,000
Emp.: 50
Computer Integrated Systems Design
N.A.I.C.S.: 541611
Robert Jesenik (CEO)
Brian A. Oliver (Exec VP)
Olaf Janke (CFO)
Brett Brown (Sr VP-Bus Ops)
R. Scott Wood (Gen Counsel)
Keith E. Gregg (Pres-Partners)
Thomas Goila (Sr Mng Dir-Private Credit & Private Equity)
Brian Rice (Pres-Wealth Mgmt, Partner & Exec VP)

AEQUOR TECHNOLOGIES, LLC
377 Hoes Ln, Piscataway, NJ 08854-4138
Tel.: (732) 494-4999
Web Site: http://www.aequor.com
Custom Computer Programming Services
N.A.I.C.S.: 541511
Andy Bakshi (Mgr-Bus Dev)

Subsidiaries:

HireLifeScience LLC　　　　　(1)
62 Pine Dr, Roosevelt, NJ 08555
Tel.: (609) 308-2658
Web Site: http://www.hirelifescience.com
Pharmacies & Drug Stores
N.A.I.C.S.: 456110
Robert Masterson (Founder)

AER MANUFACTURING, INC.
1605 Surveyor Blvd, Carrollton, TX 75006-5103
Tel.: (972) 417-2582　　　　　TX
Web Site:
　　https://www.aermanufacturing.com
Year Founded: 1973
Sales Range: $400-449.9 Million
Emp.: 500
Motor Vehicle Parts & Accessories
N.A.I.C.S.: 336390
Robert G. McGraw (Chm & CEO)
Robert P. McGraw (COO & VP-Ops)
Nolan J. Skaggs (Pres-Mfg & Sls)

AER TECHNOLOGIES, INC.
650 Columbia St, Brea, CA 92821
Tel.: (714) 446-8125
Web Site: https://www.aertech.com
Year Founded: 1984
Sales Range: $10-24.9 Million
Emp.: 320
Electronic & Precision Equipment Services
N.A.I.C.S.: 811210
Michael McGroarty (Pres)
Kim Quick (Chm)
Ingrid Faro (VP-Fin & Admin)

AERA ENERGY LLC
10000 Ming Ave, Bakersfield, CA 93311-1302
Tel.: (661) 665-5000　　　　　CA
Web Site:
　　https://www.aeraenergy.com
Year Founded: 1997
Sales Range: $150-199.9 Million
Emp.: 1,000
Producer of Oil & Gas Products
N.A.I.C.S.: 213111
Lynne J. Carrithers (Gen Counsel & Sr VP)
Ronald H. John (Sr VP-Production)
Theresa Bush (Sr VP-HR)
Randy Hoyle (Chief Carbon Solutions Officer)
Brent D. Carnahan (Sr VP)
Sergio V. DeCastro (CFO & Sr VP)
Christina S. Sistrunk (Pres)
Allan Skov (CIO & Sr VP)

Aimee Blaine (Sr VP-Technical)
Andy Anderson (Sr VP-Ops)
Scott Corby (Sr VP-Environment, Health & Safety)
Erik Bartsch (CEO)
Kimberly Ellis (Comm Mgr-External Affairs)

Subsidiaries:

Aera Energy LLC　　　　　(1)
29235 Hwy 33, Maricopa, CA 93252-9793
Tel.: (661) 769-8454
Web Site: http://www.aeraenergy.com
Sales Range: $25-49.9 Million
Emp.: 60
Crude Petroleum & Natural Gas Production
N.A.I.C.S.: 211120

AERIAL ADVERTISING SERVICES
333 W Jack London Blvd Hangar 241, Livermore, CA 94551
Tel.: (925) 449-0210
Web Site:
　　http://www.aerialservices.org
Year Founded: 1992
Sales Range: $1-9.9 Million
Emp.: 5
Advetising Agency
N.A.I.C.S.: 541830
Robert Franklin (Pres)

AERIAL BOUQUETS
1258 E Main St, Piggott, AR 72454
Tel.: (870) 598-2583
Web Site:
　　https://www.aerialbouquets.com
Sales Range: $10-24.9 Million
Emp.: 200
Sales of Balloons & Novelty Products
N.A.I.C.S.: 423920
Teresa Roberts (Mgr-HR & Payroll)

AERIES ENTERPRISES, LLC
1100 Carillon Point, Kirkland, WA 98033
Tel.: (425) 739-9997
Sales Range: $10-24.9 Million
Emp.: 6
Aviation Holding Company
N.A.I.C.S.: 336310
William R. Monkman (Pres)
Mehboob Samani (Mgr-IT)

Subsidiaries:

Lamar Technologies Corporation　　(1)
14900 40th Ave NE, Marysville, WA 98271
Tel.: (360) 651-6666
Web Site: http://www.lamartech.com
Sales Range: $10-24.9 Million
Emp.: 11
Aircraft Engines & Engine Parts Company
N.A.I.C.S.: 811310
Scott Grafenauer (Pres)
Jim Errington (Mgr-Sls & Mktg)

Precision Airmotive LLC　　　　(1)
14800 40th Ave NE Bldg D, Marysville, WA 98271
Tel.: (360) 651-8282
Web Site: http://www.precisionairmotive.com
Sales Range: $10-24.9 Million
Aircraft Engines & Engine Parts Company
N.A.I.C.S.: 336412
Mike Allen (Owner)

Precision Engines, LLC　　　　(1)
3220 100th St SW Bldg E, Everett, WA 98204
Tel.: (425) 347-2800
Web Site: http://www.precisionengines.com
Sales Range: $10-24.9 Million
Aircraft Engines & Engine Parts Company
N.A.I.C.S.: 336412
Dave Cort (Pres)
Bob Dalton (Mgr-Sls)

Zenith Fuel Systems LLC　　　　(1)
14570 Industrial Park Rd, Bristol, VA 24202-3706
Tel.: (276) 669-5555
Web Site: http://www.zenithfuelsystems.com

Aeries Enterprises, LLC—(Continued)
Sales Range: $10-24.9 Million
Mfr of Carburetors & Fuel Valves & Pumps
N.A.I.C.S.: 336310
Darcio Giovanetti (Pres)
Chet Zinnanti (Mgr-Ops)
Debra Thompson (Controller)

AERO CONTROLS INC.
1610 20th St NW, Auburn, WA 98001
Tel.: (253) 269-3000
Web Site:
  https://www.aerocontrols.com
Year Founded: 1957
Sales Range: $25-49.9 Million
Emp.: 230
Aircraft & Heavy Equipment Repair Services
N.A.I.C.S.: 811310
John Titus (Pres)
Richard Hickson (Dir-Customer Support)
Brian Thomas (VP-Maintenance Ops)
Al Vinson (Mgr-Hydraulic Shop)
Scot Felkins (Mgr-Pur)
Toms John (Mgr)
Mike Olesik (CEO)

AERO DESIGN & MANUFAC-TURING, INC.
3409 E Wood St, Phoenix, AZ 85040
Tel.: (602) 437-8080
Web Site:
  http://www.aerodesignmfg.com
Year Founded: 1966
Sales Range: $10-24.9 Million
Emp.: 100
Machine Shop, Jobbing & Repair
N.A.I.C.S.: 332710
Parker Hannifin (Dir-Ops)
Richard Martinez (Dir-Mfg-Global)
Michael Holmes (Pres-Admin Ops)
Curt Schroeder (Pres-Giddens Ops)
Ken Kelley (Pres-PMW Ops)
Bob Zubaty (Pres-QFI Ops)
David Smith (Pres-Tell Tool Ops)
John Seguin (VP-Bus Dev-Cadence Aerospace)
Joyce Pae (VP-Fin-Cadence Aerospace Mgmt)
Don Devore (CFO & Exec VP-Cadence Aerospace Mgmt)

AERO FASTENER CO., INC.
76 Servistar Industrial Way, Westfield, MA 01085
Tel.: (413) 562-5851
Web Site:
  https://www.aerofastener.com
Year Founded: 1982
Rev.: $14,000,000
Emp.: 25
Original Equipment Mfr, Supplier & Distr for Aerospace Industries
N.A.I.C.S.: 336999
James M. Avery (Pres & CEO)

AERO FULFILLMENT SER-VICES CORPORATION
3900 Aero Dr, Mason, OH 45040
Tel.: (513) 459-3945
Web Site:
  https://www.aerofulfillment.com
Year Founded: 1986
Emp.: 109
Mailing Service
N.A.I.C.S.: 561431
Brenda Conaway (VP-Fin)
Charlotte Eynon (VP-Ops)
Jon T. Gimpel (Founder)

AERO INDUSTRIAL TOOL CO., INC.
799 Bell Rd, Sarasota, FL 34240
Tel.: (941) 379-5444
Web Site: https://www.aerotools.com

Emp.: 6
Industrial Machinery & Equipment Merchant Whslr
N.A.I.C.S.: 423830
Frank Mosca (VP)
Ina Mosca (Pres)
Mike Mallon (Gen Mgr)

AERO METALS INC.
1201 E LincolnWay, La Porte, IN 46350-2510
Tel.: (219) 326-1976   IN
Web Site:
  https://www.aerometals.com
Year Founded: 1961
Sales Range: $25-49.9 Million
Emp.: 400
Steel Investment Foundries
N.A.I.C.S.: 331512
Robert Stowell (Pres)

Subsidiaries:

American Metal Testing Inc.   (1)
1201 E Lincoln Way, La Porte, IN 46350-2510
Tel.: (219) 324-2381
Rev.: $250,000
Emp.: 5
Testing Laboratories
N.A.I.C.S.: 541380   (1)

AERO SHADE TECHNOLO-GIES, INC.
3104 Industrial Ave 3, Fort Pierce, FL 34946-8662
Tel.: (772) 562-2243
Web Site: https://www.aero-shade.com
Aircraft Cabin Interiors Products Designer & Mfr
N.A.I.C.S.: 336413
John M. Manchec (Pres)

Subsidiaries:

MSA Aircraft Products, Inc.   (1)
3106 Industrial Ave 3, Fort Pierce, FL 34946
Tel.: (772) 562-2243
Web Site: http://www.msaaircraft.com
Other Aircraft Parts & Auxiliary Equipment Mfr
N.A.I.C.S.: 336413
Robert Barefoot (Mgr-Mfg Composite)
Joe Pedrotti (Mgr-Ops)

AERO SIMULATION, INC.
4450 E Adamo Dr Ste 501, Tampa, FL 33605-5941
Tel.: (813) 628-4447   FL
Web Site:
  http://www.aerosimulation.com
Year Founded: 1983
Sales Range: $10-24.9 Million
Emp.: 80
Commercial & Military Flight Simulator Mfr
N.A.I.C.S.: 336413
Mike McCarthy (Pres & CEO)
Robert Rodriguez (CFO & Dir-HR)
Russ Shepard (Dir-Sls & Mktg)

AERO TECH DESIGNS CY-CLING APPAREL
1132 4th Ave, Coraopolis, PA 15108
Tel.: (412) 262-3255
Web Site:
  https://www.aerotechdesigns.com
Sales Range: $1-9.9 Million
Emp.: 23
Sportswear Mfr
N.A.I.C.S.: 459110
Cathy Schnaubelt Rogers (Founder)

AERO TECH MANUFACTUR-ING INC.
395 W 1100 N, North Salt Lake, UT 84054-2621

Tel.: (801) 292-0493
Web Site:
  https://www.aerotechmfg.com
Year Founded: 1967
Sales Range: $10-24.9 Million
Emp.: 115
Sheet Metal Mfr
N.A.I.C.S.: 332322

AERO-DATA METAL CRAFT-ERS, INC.
2085 5th Ave, Ronkonkoma, NY 11779-6903
Tel.: (631) 471-7788   NY
Web Site: http://www.metal-crafters.com
Year Founded: 1978
Sales Range: $75-99.9 Million
Emp.: 95
Precision Sheet Metal Parts
N.A.I.C.S.: 332322
William Mabanta (Sec)

AERO-ELECTRIC CONNEC-TOR INC.
2280 208th St, Torrance, CA 90501-1452
Tel.: (310) 618-3737   CA
Web Site: https://www.aero-electric.com
Year Founded: 1986
Sales Range: $25-49.9 Million
Emp.: 375
Current-Carrying Wiring Devices
N.A.I.C.S.: 335931

AEROBOTIX, INC.
125 Jetplex Cir, Madison, AL 35758
Tel.: (256) 772-9035   AL
Web Site: http://www.aerobotix.net
Year Founded: 2005
Emp.: 42
Aluminum Foundries
N.A.I.C.S.: 331524
Kirk McLaughlin (Pres & CEO)
Austin Jones (Engr-Controls)

Subsidiaries:

Shape Fidelity, Inc.   (1)
5021 Bradford Dr Ste A, Huntsville, AL 35801-4665
Tel.: (256) 469-8333
Web Site: http://www.shapefidelity.com
Emp.: 23
Engineering Services
N.A.I.C.S.: 541330
Gil Handley (Engr-Quality)
Rob Black (Pres)

AEROCAST, INC.
1736 S Nevada Way, Mesa, AZ 85204
Tel.: (480) 830-0848   Ca
Web Site:
  http://www.aerocastinc.com
Year Founded: 2006
Sales Range: $1-9.9 Million
Emp.: 50
Aluminum & Magnesium Castings Mfr
N.A.I.C.S.: 331523
Robert L. Jamieson Sr. (Pres & CEO)

AERODYN ENGINEERING, INC.
1919 S Girls School Rd, Indianapolis, IN 46241
Tel.: (317) 334-1523
Web Site:
  http://www.aerodyneng.com
Year Founded: 2002
Rev.: $6,700,000
Emp.: 84
Engineeering Services
N.A.I.C.S.: 541330

Dave Lawrence (Pres)
Keith Yeager (VP)
Richard Mckinney (Mgr-Quality Assurance)

AERODYNAMICS, INCORPO-RATED
1690 Stone Vlg Ln Bldg 100 Ste 121, Kennesaw, GA 30152
Tel.: (404) 410-7612
Web Site: http://www.flyadi.com
Sales Range: $450-499.9 Million
Emp.: 165
Flying Charter & Shuttle Service, Aircraft Records Management & Operational Preparedness
N.A.I.C.S.: 481219
Steve Antuna (Mgr)
Bob Looney (Dir-Safety & Security)
F. Darrell Richardson (Chm, Pres & CEO)

AEROEQUITY PARTNERS, LLC
15 Lake St Ste 235, Savannah, GA 31411
Tel.: (912) 598-3102   GA
Web Site: http://www.aeroequity.com
Year Founded: 1998
Aerospace Industry Private Equity Firm
N.A.I.C.S.: 523999
David H. Rowe (Mng Dir)
Thomas K. Churbuck (Mng Partner)
Michael Greene (Mng Partner)
Wayne P. Garrett (Partner)
Dennis Walsh (Partner-Operating)
Charles Compton (Principal)
Charlie Santos-Buch (Partner)
Kirk Konert (Principal)
Peter Schumacher (Principal)
Shawn Vick (Partner)
Thomas E. Brew Jr. (Partner)

Subsidiaries:

Dynamic Precision Group   (1)
3651 SE Commerce Ave, Stuart, FL 34997
Tel.: (772) 287-7770
Web Site: http://www.gotodpg.com
Gas Turbine Engine Parts Mfr
N.A.I.C.S.: 336412

Holding (Domestic):

Paradigm Precision Holdings, LLC   (2)
404 W Guadalupe Rd, Tempe, AZ 85283
Tel.: (480) 839-0501
Web Site:
  http://www.paradigmprecision.com
Holding Company; Aerospace & Industrial Gas Turbine Engine Complex Machined Components Mfr
N.A.I.C.S.: 551112
Ronojoy Ghosh (VP-Bus Dev-Manchester)
Steve Croke (Pres & CEO)

Plant (Domestic):

Paradigm Precision - Berlin   (3)
134 Commerce St, East Berlin, CT 06023
Tel.: (860) 828-0344
Web Site:
  http://www.paradigmprecision.com
Sales Range: $1-9.9 Million
Emp.: 75
Machine Shops
N.A.I.C.S.: 332710
Don Balducci (VP-Ops)

Paradigm Precision - Malden   (3)
243 Medford St, Malden, MA 02148-7301
Tel.: (781) 321-0480
Web Site:
  http://www.paradigmprecision.com
Sales Range: $25-49.9 Million
Emp.: 185
Aircraft Engine Components Mfr
N.A.I.C.S.: 336412
Tom Mitchell (VP)

Paradigm Precision - Tempe   (3)

404 W Guadalupe Rd, Tempe, AZ 85283
Tel.: (480) 839-0501
Web Site:
    http://www.paradigmprecision.com
Sales Range: $25-49.9 Million
Emp.: 100
Aircraft Engines & Engine Parts Mfr
N.A.I.C.S.: 336412
Eric Hall *(Dir-IT)*

Plant (Non-US):

Paradigm Precision - Tunis   (3)
Route De Sousse GP 1 KM7, 2033, Me-
grine, Tunisia
Tel.: (216) 71 429 605
Web Site:
    http://www.paradigmprecision.com
Sales Range: $25-49.9 Million
Emp.: 300
Aerospace & Aircraft Engine Parts Mfr
N.A.I.C.S.: 336412

Holding (Domestic):

TurboCombustor Technology,
Inc.   (2)
3651 SE Commerce Ave, Stuart, FL 34997
Tel.: (772) 287-7770
Web Site: http://www.tct-inc.com
Sales Range: $100-124.9 Million
Emp.: 490
Turbo Combustor Mfr
N.A.I.C.S.: 336412
Steve Croke *(Pres & CEO)*
Ray Grochowski *(Gen Counsel & VP)*
Brenda M. Thulen *(VP-HR)*
Rita Lei *(CFO)*
Alec Searle *(COO)*

Subsidiary (Non-US):

TurboCombustor Kft.   (3)
Grassalkovich ut 294, 1239, Budapest,
Hungary
Tel.: (36) 12878270
Turbo Combustor Mfr
N.A.I.C.S.: 336412

AEROFLOW, INC.
3165 Sweeten Creek Rd, Asheville,
NC 28803-2115
Tel.: (828) 277-1400
Web Site:
    https://www.aeroflowinc.com
Home Respiratory & Mobility Equip-
ment Services
N.A.I.C.S.: 423450
Casey Hite *(CEO)*
Scott Sonnone *(CFO)*
Mica Phillips *(VP-Aeroflow Urology)*

AEROLITE EXTRUSION COM-
PANY, INC.
4605 Lk Park Rd, Youngstown, OH
44512
Tel.: (330) 782-1127
Web Site: http://www.aeroext.com
Year Founded: 1953
Sales Range: $10-24.9 Million
Emp.: 90
Aluminum Extruded Product Mfr
N.A.I.C.S.: 331315
Thomas E. Hutch Jr. *(Pres)*

AEROMEDICAL COLLECTION
SERVICES, INC.
401 Market St Ste 200, Shreveport,
LA 71101
Tel.: (318) 747-9977
Web Site: http://www.acs-ems.com
Sales Range: $50-74.9 Million
Emp.: 80
Collection Agency, Except Real Es-
tate
N.A.I.C.S.: 561440
Scott Shurley *(CIO & VP-Info Svcs)*
Earl Tonjes *(Chief Admin Officer &
VP-Admin)*
Mary Tyler-Newman *(Sec & Exec VP)*
Amy McMullen *(Pres)*

AEROMETALS INC.
3920 Sandstone Dr, El Dorado Hills,
CA 95762
Tel.: (916) 939-6888
Web Site:
    http://www.aerometals.aero
Sales Range: $10-24.9 Million
Emp.: 125
Aircraft Mfr
N.A.I.C.S.: 336411
Rex Kamphefner *(Pres)*
Eric Martin *(Project Coord)*
Bob Peake *(Dir-Quality)*
Lorie Symon *(Mgr-Acctg)*
Terry Harrison *(Mgr-IT)*
George Azzam *(Dir-Tech Engrg)*
Alan Haynes *(Engr-Production)*

AERONET WORLDWIDE INC.
42 Corporate Park Ste 150, Irvine,
CA 92606
Tel.: (949) 474-9292
Web Site: http://www.aeronet.com
Sales Range: $50-74.9 Million
Emp.: 114
Domestic Freight Forwarding
N.A.I.C.S.: 488510
Anthony N. Pereira *(Chm & CEO)*
Malcolm Hurcombe *(Pres & Chief Sls
Officer)*
Larry W. Coyle *(Dir-Sls-Los Angeles)*
Michael J. Mackowiak *(Mgr-Bus Dev-
Global)*
Michael Crowley *(Mgr-Bus Dev-Los
Angeles)*
Andrew Hurcombe *(Gen Mgr-
Chicago)*
Christine Miller *(Dir-Ocean Product-
Chicago)*
Jeff Borgese *(Mgr-Bus Dev-San
Jose)*
Lisley Davenport *(Dir-Comml Svcs)*
Patrick Mulstay *(Gen Mgr-Aeronet
Denver)*

AEROPRES CORPORATION
1324 N Hearne Ave Ste 200, Shreve-
port, LA 71107
Tel.: (318) 221-6282
Web Site: https://www.aeropres.com
Year Founded: 1964
Sales Range: $25-49.9 Million
Emp.: 150
Aerosol Mfr
N.A.I.C.S.: 325120
Mark Rivers *(Dir-Tech)*
Harry McCain *(VP-Tech Svcs)*
Joe Bowen *(VP-Sls & Mktg)*

Subsidiaries:

Aeropres Corporation-Sibley
Plant   (1)
773 North Main St., Sibley, LA 71073
Tel.: (318) 377-7284
Web Site: http://www.aeropres.com
Sales Range: $25-49.9 Million
Emp.: 40
Aerosol Mfr
N.A.I.C.S.: 325120

AEROSCOUT, INC.
1300 Island Dr Ste 202, Redwood
City, CA 94065
Tel.: (650) 596-2994
Web Site: http://www.aeroscout.com
Year Founded: 2004
Sales Range: $10-24.9 Million
Emp.: 150
Wireless Asset Tracking & Monitoring
Solutions
N.A.I.C.S.: 334220
Beni Tzur *(VP-Ops)*
Yuval Bar-Gil *(Pres & CEO)*

AEROSEAL, LLC
7989 S Suburban Rd, Centerville, OH
45458

Tel.: (937) 428-9300
Web Site: http://www.aeroseal.com
Emp.: 5
Fabricated Structural Metal Mfr
N.A.I.C.S.: 332312
Robert Hageman *(Mgr)*

Subsidiaries:

Comfort Institute, Inc.   (1)
3926 Irongate Rd, Suite D, Bellingham, WA
98226
Tel.: (360) 671-7773
Web Site: http://www.comfortinstitute.org
Emp.: 10
Heating, Ventilation & Air Conditioning
Equipment Mfr
N.A.I.C.S.: 333415
Brendan Reid *(Founder)*
Ken Summers *(VP-Trng)*

AEROSHARES CHARTER, LLC
Pease International Tradeport 1 New
Hampshire Ave Ste 125, Portsmouth,
NH 03801
Tel.: (603) 610-8889
Web Site: http://www.aeroshares.com
Emp.: 7
Chartered Aircraft Services
N.A.I.C.S.: 481211
Donald W. S. Bishop *(CEO)*

Subsidiaries:

CharterAuction.com   (1)
1 New Hampshire Ave, Portsmouth, NH
03801
Tel.: (603) 610-4491
Web Site: http://www.charterauction.com
Sales Range: $10-24.9 Million
Emp.: 50
Jet Charter Services
N.A.I.C.S.: 481211

AEROSOLUTIONS, LLC
5500 Flatiron Pkwy Ste 100, Boulder,
CO 80301
Tel.: (720) 304-6882
Web Site:
    http://www.aerosolutionsllc.com
Year Founded: 2002
Sales Range: $10-24.9 Million
Emp.: 20
Designs, Engineers & Installs Tele-
communications Towers
N.A.I.C.S.: 517810
James Lockwood *(CEO)*
Amit Singhal *(Engr-CAD Tech)*

AEROSPACE ASSET TRAD-
ING, LLC
1800 NW 129th Ave, Miami, FL
33126
Web Site:
    http://www.aerospaceasset.com
Year Founded: 2013
Sales Range: $25-49.9 Million
Emp.: 50
Aircraft Part Services
N.A.I.C.S.: 488190
Steve Polederos *(CEO)*
Konstantinos Constant *(COO)*
Frank Cordero *(VP-Ops)*

AEROSPACE DISTRIBUTORS
INC.
34110 9th Ave S, Federal Way, WA
98003
Tel.: (253) 661-9600
Web Site: http://www.aerod.com
Rev.: $13,000,000
Emp.: 20
Aircraft & Parts, Nec
N.A.I.C.S.: 423860
Pierre Pinsonnault *(Pres)*
Rob Littleton *(Dir-Fin)*

Subsidiaries:

Aerospace Distributors Pte Ltd   (1)
57 UBI Avenue 1 07-07 UBI Centre, Singa-

pore, 408936, Singapore
Tel.: (65) 6844 4593
Web Site: http://www.aerod.com
Aerospace Equipment Distr
N.A.I.C.S.: 423860
Pierre Pinsonnault *(Pres)*

Aerospace Precision Inc.   (1)
2851 Evans St, Hollywood, FL 33020-1119
Tel.: (954) 923-3213
Web Site: http://www.aerod.com
Sales Range: $10-24.9 Million
Emp.: 12
Aircraft & Heavy Equipment Repair Ser-
vices
N.A.I.C.S.: 811310

AEROSPACE TECHNOLOGIES
GROUP, INC.
620 NW 35th St, Boca Raton, FL
33431
Tel.: (561) 244-7400
Web Site:
    https://www.atgshades.com
Year Founded: 1998
Sales Range: $10-24.9 Million
Emp.: 130
Blind & Shade Mfr
N.A.I.C.S.: 337920
Raymond P. Caldiero *(Chm)*
Jack Leonard *(COO & VP)*
Jean Freitas *(Dir-Ops & Gen Mgr)*
Linna Falzone *(Exec VP-Sls & Mktg)*
Simon R. Kay *(CEO)*
Bill Goings *(VP-Engrg & Design)*
Tim Gwinnell *(CFO & VP)*
Matt Isley *(Pres)*
Matthew Duntz *(VP-New Bus Dev)*

AEROTECH INC.
101 Zeta Dr, Pittsburgh, PA 15238-
2811
Tel.: (412) 963-7470   PA
Web Site: https://www.aerotech.com
Year Founded: 1970
Sales Range: $10-24.9 Million
Emp.: 375
Precision Positioning & Motion Con-
trol Component Mfr
N.A.I.C.S.: 334419
Jeff Wisyanski *(Controller)*
Mark Botos *(Pres & CEO)*

Subsidiaries:

Aerotech China   (1)
Room 101 No 28 Building Tianlin Road 140,
Xuhui District, Shanghai, 200234, China
Tel.: (86) 21 3319 7715
Web Site: http://www.aerotech.com
Electrical Equipment Distr
N.A.I.C.S.: 423610

Aerotech KK   (1)
17-25 1-chome Kitahoncho, Funabashi,
273-0864, Chiba, Japan
Tel.: (81) 47 489 1741
Web Site: http://www.aerotechkk.co.jp
Electrical Equipment Distr
N.A.I.C.S.: 423610
Tadashi Imai *(Mgr-Site)*

Aerotech Ltd   (1)
Jupiter House Calleva Park, Aldermaston,
RG7 8NN, Berks, United Kingdom **(100%)**
Tel.: (44) 001189409400
Web Site: http://www.aerotech.com
Sales Range: $10-24.9 Million
Emp.: 9
Mfr of Precision Positioning & Motion Con-
trol Components
N.A.I.C.S.: 334513

Aerotech Taiwan   (1)
5F No 32 Aly 18 Lane 478 Ruiguang Rd,
Neihu District, Taipei, Taiwan
Tel.: (886) 2 8751 6690
Electrical Equipment Distr
N.A.I.C.S.: 423610
Kao Chi Chuan *(Product Mgr)*

Germany Aerotech GmbH   (1)
Gustav Weibkopf Str 18, Furth, 90768,
Germany   **(100%)**
Tel.: (49) 9119679370

Aerotech Inc.—(Continued)

Web Site: http://www.aerotech.com
Sales Range: $10-24.9 Million
Emp.: 15
Mfr of Precision Positioning & Motion Control Components
N.A.I.C.S.: 334513
Norbert Ludwit (Gen Mgr)

AEROTECH WORLD TRADE CORP.
11 New King St, White Plains, NY 10604
Tel.: (914) 681-3000   NY
Year Founded: 1975
Sales Range: $10-24.9 Million
Emp.: 48
Aircraft & Space Vehicle Supplies & Parts
N.A.I.C.S.: 423860
Jan R. Endresen (Pres & CEO)

Subsidiaries:

Aerotech GmbH   (1)
Kopernikusstrasse 9, D 81679, Munich, Germany
Tel.: (49) 89471073
Web Site: http://www.aerotechworld.com
Provider of Aircraft & Space Vehicle Supplies & Parts
N.A.I.C.S.: 336412

Aerotech Holland B.V.   (1)
Hoofweg 67A, 2131 BV, Hoofddorp, Netherlands
Tel.: (31) 35440900
Web Site: http://www.aerotechworld.com
Sales Range: $10-24.9 Million
Provider of Aircraft & Space Vehicle Supplies & Parts
N.A.I.C.S.: 336412

Aerotech World Trade Co., Ltd.   (1)
1204 Totoo Barrey Building, Hang Ang Ru 2 GA, Yon San Gu, Seoul, 140-735, Korea (South)   (100%)
Tel.: (82) 27972789
Aircraft & Space Vehicle Supplies & Parts
N.A.I.C.S.: 336412

Aerotech World Trade Ltd.   (1)
31316 Via Colinas Unit 118, Westlake Village, CA 91362
Tel.: (818) 991-2972
Web Site: http://www.aerotechusa.com
Provider of Aircraft & Space Vehicle Supplies & Parts
N.A.I.C.S.: 423860

Aerotech World Trade Ltd.   (1)
St Peters Rd, Maidenhead, SL6 7QU, Berks, United Kingdom
Tel.: (44) 628760100
Sales Range: $10-24.9 Million
Emp.: 10
Provider of Aircraft & Space Vehicle Supplies & Parts
N.A.I.C.S.: 336412

Aviquipo de Portugal, Ltda   (1)
Rua Alvaro Antonio Dos Santos 16, 2780 182, Oeiras, Portugal
Tel.: (351) 214460620
Web Site: http://www.aviquipo.com
Sales Range: $10-24.9 Million
Emp.: 20
Provider of Aircraft & Space Vehicle Supplies & Parts
N.A.I.C.S.: 336412

AERUS LLC
300 E Vly Dr, Bristol, VA 24201
Tel.: (214) 378-4000   DE
Web Site: http://www.aerushome.com
Year Founded: 1924
Sales Range: $100-124.9 Million
Emp.: 2,500
Commercial & Retail Vacuum Cleaners & Floor Polishers Mfr & Direct Sales
N.A.I.C.S.: 335210
Michael Young (Dir-Cash Mgmt)

Subsidiaries:

Aerus Electrolux Canada   (1)
44 Dundas Street West, Mississauga, L5B 1H3, ON, Canada   (100%)
Tel.: (905) 270-6432
Web Site: http://www.aeruselectroluxcanada.com
Sales Range: $25-49.9 Million
Emp.: 45
Marketing & Sales of Vacuum Cleaners & Water Purification Services
N.A.I.C.S.: 423620

AERVOE INDUSTRIES INCORPORATED
1100 Mark Cir, Gardnerville, NV 89410
Tel.: (775) 783-3100   NV
Web Site: https://www.aervoe.com
Year Founded: 1979
Sales Range: $25-49.9 Million
Emp.: 125
Paints, Coatings, Cleaners & Lubricants Mfr
N.A.I.C.S.: 325510
David A. Williams (Co-Pres & CEO)
Mark Williams (Co-Pres)
Randall Perry (Engr-Safety & Regulatory)
Carma Schramm (Mgr-Mktg)

AES CLEAN TECHNOLOGY INC.
422 Stump Rd, Montgomeryville, PA 18936
Tel.: (215) 393-6810
Web Site: https://www.aesclean.com
Foundation, Structure & Building Exterior Contractors
N.A.I.C.S.: 238190
Cliff Satterfield (Pres)

AES ELECTRICAL, INC.
13335 Mid Atlantic Blvd, Laurel, MD 20708
Tel.: (301) 595-0665
Web Site: http://www.aeselectrical.com
Year Founded: 1989
Sales Range: $100-124.9 Million
Emp.: 700
Electronic Services
N.A.I.C.S.: 238210
Michael Dugan (Pres)
Gregg Kaderabek (VP)
Tim Miller (Sec)
Charley Wooldridge (Treas)

AES LOGISTICS, INC.
140 SW 153rd St, Burien, WA 98166
Tel.: (206) 214-0341
Web Site: http://www.globalcargomanager.com
Year Founded: 2000
Sales Range: $1-9.9 Million
Emp.: 15
Freight Transportation Arrangement
N.A.I.C.S.: 488510
Anne Schwieger (Owner & Pres)
Bob Schwieger (VP-Mktg & Coord-Logistics)
Jessi Bach (Coord-Logistics)

AESP, INC.
999 NW 159th Dr, Miami, FL 33169
Tel.: (305) 944-7710   FL
Web Site: http://www.aesp.com
Year Founded: 1983
Sales Range: $10-24.9 Million
Emp.: 20
Computer Connectivity & Networking Devices Designer, Mfr & Marketer
N.A.I.C.S.: 334210
Slav Stein (Pres & CEO)
Stephen Daily (VP)
Roman Briskin (Exec VP)

Subsidiaries:

Signamax Connectivity Systems Canada, Inc.   (1)
975 Bleams Rd Unit 2, Kitchener, N2E 3Z5, ON, Canada
Tel.: (519) 570-3911
Web Site: http://www.psidata.ca
Network Connectivity Cable Installation Services
N.A.I.C.S.: 238210

AESYS TECHNOLOGIES, LLC
693 N Hills Rd, York, PA 17402-2212
Tel.: (717) 755-1081
Web Site: http://www.aesystech.com
Sales Range: $10-24.9 Million
Emp.: 100
Mfr of Boilers, HVAC & Pressure Vessel Technology
N.A.I.C.S.: 332410
Kevin J. Hoey (Pres & CEO)
Fred Shufane (COO & VP)
Winnie McDonagh (Controller)

Subsidiaries:

Jackson & Church HVAC Global   (1)
693 N Hills Rd, York, PA 17402-2212
Tel.: (717) 755-1081
Web Site: http://www.jchvacglobal.com
Emp.: 50
Mfr of Heating, Ventilation & Air Conditioning Equipment
N.A.I.C.S.: 332410
Winnie Mcdonagh (Mgr-HR)

York Shipley Global   (1)
693 N Hills Rd, York, PA 17402-2212
Tel.: (717) 755-1081
Web Site: http://www.aesystech.com
Sales Range: $10-24.9 Million
Dryback & Wetback Packaged Boilers & HVAC Equipment Mfr
N.A.I.C.S.: 332410
Winnie McDonagh (Mgr-HR)
Jeff Conrad (Mgr-Intl Sls)

AET HOLDINGS, LLC
2415 W Northwest Hwy Ste 105, Dallas, TX 75220-4446
Tel.: (972) 480-6326
Holding Company
N.A.I.C.S.: 551112
Shanali Bhagat (Pres & CEO)

Subsidiaries:

American Energy Transport, LLC   (1)
2415 W Northwest Hwy Ste 105, Dallas, TX 75220
Tel.: (972) 480-6326
Web Site: http://www.ae-transport.com
Oil & Gas Transportation & Logistics Services
N.A.I.C.S.: 213112
Scott Dickess (Reg Mgr-Ops)
Alykhan Bhagat (Mgr)
Shanali Bhagat (Pres & CEO)

Subsidiary (Domestic):

Stampede Transportation, LLC   (2)
2301 W 60th St, Little Rock, AR 72209
Tel.: (501) 569-9999
Web Site: http://www.stampede-trans.com
Emp.: 10
Fuel Transportation & Logistics Services
N.A.I.C.S.: 484121
Donnie Lydick (Mgr)

AETNA BEARING COMPANY
1081 Sesame St, Franklin Park, IL 60131
Tel.: (630) 694-0024   DE
Web Site: https://www.aetnabearing.com
Year Founded: 1917
Sales Range: $75-99.9 Million
Emp.: 125
Mfr of Bearings & Related Products
N.A.I.C.S.: 332991
Mark Boozell (VP-Fin & HR)

AETNA BRIDGE COMPANY
30 Lockbridge St, Pawtucket, RI 02860
Tel.: (401) 728-0400
Web Site: http://www.aetnabridge.com
Sales Range: $25-49.9 Million
Emp.: 15
Bridge Construction
N.A.I.C.S.: 237310
Chip Mainelli (VP)
Chris Jameson (Controller)
Hugo R. Mainelli Jr. (Pres)

Subsidiaries:

Aetna Construction Co. Inc.   (1)
100 Jefferson Blvd Ste 100, Warwick, RI 02888
Tel.: (401) 728-0400
Web Site: http://www.aetnabridge.com
Sales Range: $10-24.9 Million
Bridge Construction
N.A.I.C.S.: 237310
Chris Jameson (Mgr-HR)

AETNA BUILDING MAINTENANCE, INC.
646 Parsons Ave, Columbus, OH 43206
Tel.: (614) 476-1818
Web Site: http://www.aetnabuilding.com
Sales Range: $75-99.9 Million
Emp.: 1,000
Facilities Management Services
N.A.I.C.S.: 561720

AETNA PLYWOOD, INC.
1401 St Charles Rd, Maywood, IL 60153-1208
Tel.: (708) 343-1515   DE
Web Site: https://www.aetnaplywood.com
Year Founded: 1937
Sales Range: $25-49.9 Million
Emp.: 120
Wholesale Distr of Wood & Wood Related Products & Laminates
N.A.I.C.S.: 423310

AETOS CAPITAL REAL ESTATE, LP
680 5th Ave 24th Fl, New York, NY 10019
Tel.: (212) 710-3200   DE
Web Site: http://www.aetoscapitalasia.com
Year Founded: 2001
Real Estate Investment Management Services
N.A.I.C.S.: 531390
Scott M. Kelley (CEO & Founder)
Yanting Wang (Dir)

AEVEX AEROSPACE
380 Stevens Ave Ste 150, Solana Beach, CA 92075
Tel.: (858) 704-4125
Web Site: http://www.aevex.com
Year Founded: 2017
Emp.: 500
Aviation & Aerospace Solutions
N.A.I.C.S.: 334511
Brian Raduenz (CEO)
Dan Talati (COO)
Manan Patel (Chief Strategy Officer)
Edward Lake (CFO)
Gretchen Larsen Idsinga (Chief Growth Officer)
Skip Arny (VP-Tech Solutions)

Subsidiaries:

Geodetics Incorporated   (1)
2649 Ariane Dr, San Diego, CA 92117
Tel.: (858) 729-0872
Web Site: http://www.geodetics.com

Sales Range: $1-9.9 Million
Emp.: 25
Develops & Markets Real-Time, High-
Precision Positioning & Navigation Hard-
ware & Software Solutions for Military &
Civilian Applications
N.A.I.C.S.: 334511
Lydia Bock *(Pres & CEO)*
Jeffrey Fayman *(CTO)*

Veth Research Associates LLC   (1)
1148 Troon Dr W, Niceville, FL 32578-4063
Tel.: (937) 529-8384
Web Site: http://www.vethresearch.com
Engineering Services
N.A.I.C.S.: 541330
Michael J. Veth *(Mgr)*

AEXCEL CORP.
7373 Production Dr, Mentor, OH
44060-4858
Tel.: (440) 974-3800   OH
Web Site:
    https://www.aexcelcorp.com
Year Founded: 1974
Sales Range: $25-49.9 Million
Emp.: 30
Mfr of Industrial & Traffic Codings
N.A.I.C.S.: 325510
John S. Milgram *(Pres)*
Jerrie Rispoli *(Controller)*
Mike Orlando *(Plant Mgr)*
Lorie Webb *(Mgr-Pur)*

AF HOLDING COMPANY
303 W Raymond St, Sullivan, IL
61951
Tel.: (217) 728-8388
Web Site: http://www.agri-fab.com
Sales Range: $25-49.9 Million
Emp.: 400
Holding Company
N.A.I.C.S.: 332119
Mike Cohan *(Pres)*

Subsidiaries:

Agri-Fab Inc.   (1)
809 S Hamilton S, Sullivan, IL 61951-1823
Tel.: (217) 728-8388
Web Site: http://www.agri-fab.com
Sales Range: $75-99.9 Million
Emp.: 250
Metal Stamping Mfr
N.A.I.C.S.: 332119
Mike Cohan *(Pres)*

Subsidiary (Domestic):

Clark Pulley Industries Inc.   (2)
120 Clark Dr, Russellville, AL 35654
Tel.: (256) 332-4981
Web Site: http://www.clarkpulley.com
Sales Range: $25-49.9 Million
Emp.: 90
Outdoor Power Pulley Mfr
N.A.I.C.S.: 332510
Steven Smith *(Mgr-Sls)*
Terry Moore *(Pres)*
Bruce Lieder *(Mgr-Engrg)*
Angie Skidmore *(Mgr-Acctg)*
Tim Skidmore *(Mgr-Quality)*

AF INTERNATIONAL CORPO-
RATION
2200 Woodale Ave, Green Bay, WI
54313-8910
Tel.: (920) 434-0230
Year Founded: 1989
Rev.: $38,700,000
Emp.: 300
Industrial Construction
N.A.I.C.S.: 236210
Michael Meyer *(Pres)*
Dennis Rabe *(CFO)*

Subsidiaries:

The Selmer Company   (1)
2200 Woodale Ave, Green Bay, WI 54313
Tel.: (920) 434-0230
Web Site: http://www.selmer.com

Sales Range: $50-74.9 Million
Emp.: 200
Industrial Buildings & Warehouses Mfr
N.A.I.C.S.: 236210

AF MUTUAL HOLDING CO.,
INC.
500 E 10th St, Alamogordo, NM
88310
Tel.: (505) 437-9334
Year Founded: 1997
Sales Range: $10-24.9 Million
Emp.: 63
Mutual Holding Company
N.A.I.C.S.: 551112
Jill Gutierrez *(Pres/CEO-Alamogordo
Fin & BANK34)*

Subsidiaries:

Alamogordo Financial Corp.   (1)
500 E 10th St, Alamogordo, NM 88310
Tel.: (575) 437-9334
Web Site: http://www.bank34online.com
Rev.: $17,126,638
Assets: $270,984,407
Liabilities: $241,340,683
Net Worth: $29,643,724
Earnings: $320,614
Fiscal Year-end: 12/31/2015
Bank Holding Company
N.A.I.C.S.: 551112

AF SUPPLY CORP.
942 Lafayette Ave, Brooklyn, NY
11221
Tel.: (718) 443-6900
Web Site: https://www.afsupply.com
Sales Range: $10-24.9 Million
Emp.: 40
Plumbing Fittings & Supplies
N.A.I.C.S.: 423720

AFBA - THE 5 STAR ASSOCIA-
TION
909 N Washington St, Alexandria, VA
22314
Tel.: (703) 549-4455
Web Site: http://www.afba.com
Year Founded: 1947
Sales Range: $125-149.9 Million
Emp.: 245
Commercial & Industrial Building Op-
eration
N.A.I.C.S.: 531120
Ralph Edward Eberhart *(Bd of Dirs,
Executives)*
John N. Abrams *(Vice Chm)*
Larry O. Spencer *(Pres)*
Craig R. McKinley *(Chm)*

AFC AQUISITION CORP.
801 Comanche NE, Albuquerque, NM
87107
Tel.: (505) 816-6500   NM
Web Site:
    http://www.americanhome.com
Year Founded: 1936
Sales Range: $500-549.9 Million
Emp.: 1,000
Furniture Retailer
N.A.I.C.S.: 449110
Jerome Martinez *(VP-Mktg)*
Ted Leveque *(COO)*
Kenton V. Harten *(Pres)*

AFC-HOLCROFT LLC
49630 Pontiac Trl, Wixom, MI 48393-
2042
Tel.: (248) 624-8191   MI
Web Site: https://www.afc-
holcroft.com
Year Founded: 1963
Sales Range: $1-9.9 Million
Emp.: 120
Heat Tracing Equipment Mfr
N.A.I.C.S.: 333994

Subsidiaries:

Atmosphere Heat Treating Inc.   (1)
30760 Century Dr, Wixom, MI 48393-2063
Tel.: (248) 960-4700
Web Site:
    http://www.atmosphereheattreat.com
Emp.: 46
Provider of Metal Heat Treating Services
N.A.I.C.S.: 332811
Jim Haase *(Plant Mgr)*

Austemper Inc.   (1)
30760 Century Dr, Wixom, MI 48393-2063
Tel.: (586) 293-4554
Provider of Metal Heat Treating Services
N.A.I.C.S.: 332811

AFCO INDUSTRIES, INC.
3400 Roy St, Alexandria, LA 71302-
4449
Tel.: (318) 448-1651
Web Site: https://www.afco-ind.com
Year Founded: 1946
Sales Range: $25-49.9 Million
Emp.: 355
Mfr of Custom Extrusion & Fabrica-
tion Products
N.A.I.C.S.: 326199
Eli Cooper *(Mgr-HR)*

AFCO STEEL INC.
1423 E 6th St, Little Rock, AR 72202
Tel.: (501) 340-6200
Web Site: http://www.afcosteel.com
Sales Range: $125-149.9 Million
Emp.: 400
Fabricated Structural Metal
N.A.I.C.S.: 332312
Grady Harvell *(Pres)*

AFD CONTRACT FURNITURE,
INC.
810 7th Ave, New York, NY 10019-
5851
Tel.: (212) 721-7100   NY
Web Site: https://www.afd-inc.com
Year Founded: 1980
Sales Range: $125-149.9 Million
Emp.: 150
Office Furniture Sales
N.A.I.C.S.: 449110
Richard Aarons *(Pres)*
Ted Cohen *(COO)*
David Aarons *(Exec VP)*
Salvador de la Rosa *(Exec VP & Gen
Mgr)*
Todd Basile *(CFO)*

AFE INDUSTRIES, INC.
13233 Barton Cir, Whittier, CA 90670-
1303
Tel.: (562) 944-6889
Web Site:
    https://www.afeindustries.com
Sales Range: $10-24.9 Million
Emp.: 25
Letterpress & Screen Printing
N.A.I.C.S.: 323111
Fred Elhami *(Pres)*
Ruth Elhami *(Controller)*

Subsidiaries:

Calico Tag & Label Inc   (1)
10300 Calico Crossing Ln, Charlotte, NC
28273
Tel.: (704) 522-1295
Web Site: http://www.calicotag.com
Rev.: $1,417,057
Emp.: 13
Tag & Label Printing
N.A.I.C.S.: 323111
Fred Elhami *(Pres)*

Coastal Tag & Label Inc.   (1)
13233 Barton Cir, Santa Fe Springs, CA
90670-1303
Tel.: (562) 946-4318
Web Site: http://www.coastaltag.com
Label Printing Services
N.A.I.C.S.: 323111

Fred Elhami *(Pres)*

US1com Inc.   (1)
715 Southpoint Blvd Ste D, Petaluma, CA
94954
Tel.: (707) 781-2560
Web Site: http://www.us1com.com
Rev.: $3,852,893
Emp.: 12
Printing Services
N.A.I.C.S.: 323111
Fred Elhami *(Pres)*

Western Yankee, Inc.   (1)
13233 Barton Cir, Santa Fe Springs, CA
90670
Tel.: (562) 944-6889
Web Site: http://www.afeindustries.com
Sales Range: $10-24.9 Million
Letterpress & Screen Printing
N.A.I.C.S.: 323111

AFFCO LLC
208 Gunther Ln, Belle Chasse, LA
70037-3156
Tel.: (504) 394-2900
Year Founded: 1988
Sales Range: $10-24.9 Million
Emp.: 20
Provider of Oil Field Products & Ser-
vices
N.A.I.C.S.: 213112
John Powers *(Pres)*

AFFILIATED DISTRIBUTORS
INC.
500 E. Swedesford Rd, Wayne, PA
19087
Tel.: (610) 977-3100
Web Site: https://www.adhq.com
Year Founded: 1981
Rev.: $10,000,000
Emp.: 47
All Other Miscellaneous Electrical
Equipment & Component Mfr
N.A.I.C.S.: 335999
William Weisberg *(CEO)*
Neil Cohen *(VP-HR)*
Scott Renninger *(Chief Investment
Officer)*

Subsidiaries:

Independent Distributors, Inc.   (1)
6581 Kitimat Rd Unit 12, Mississauga, L5N
3T5, ON, Canada
Tel.: (905) 858-0988
Retailer of Electrical Appliances, Television
& Radio
N.A.I.C.S.: 449210
John Morrison *(VP-Supplier Rels)*

AFFILIATED ENGINEERS, INC.
5802 Research Park Blvd, Madison,
WI 53719
Tel.: (608) 238-2616
Web Site: https://www.aeieng.com
Rev.: $50,000,000
Emp.: 400
Engineeering Services
N.A.I.C.S.: 541330
David S. Odegard *(Pres & CEO)*
Nancy Yu *(Mgr-Personnel & Asst
Mgr)*
Michael Click *(Mng Principal-Natl
Commissioning Practice)*

AFFILIATED FOOD STORES,
INC.
4109 Vine St, Abilene, TX 79602
Tel.: (325) 692-1440   OK
Sales Range: $150-199.9 Million
Emp.: 150
Holding Company; Grocery Stores
Owner & Operator
N.A.I.C.S.: 551112
Darrell Earnest *(Pres & CEO)*
Jimmy Doan *(VP)*
Samon Beard *(Mgr)*

AFFILIATED FOODS, INC.

Affiliated Foods, Inc.—(Continued)

1401 W Farmers Ave, Amarillo, TX 79118
Tel.: (806) 372-3851   **TX**
Web Site: http://www.afiama.com
Year Founded: 1946
Sales Range: $900-999.9 Million
Emp.: 1,200
Wholesale Food Cooperative
N.A.I.C.S.: 424410
Roger Lowe (Chm)
Gene Blackburn (Dir-HR)
Tammie Coffee (CFO)
Dale Thomson (Dir-New Accts)
Randy Arceneaux (Pres, CEO & COO)

Subsidiaries:

Affiliated Finance Inc.   **(1)**
1401 W Farmers Ave, Amarillo, TX 79118-6134   **(100%)**
Tel.: (806) 345-7708
Web Site: http://www.affiliatedfoods.com
Sales Range: $25-49.9 Million
Emp.: 20
Financing for Member Grocery Stores & Employee Loans
N.A.I.C.S.: 522299

Plains Dairy   **(1)**
300 N Taylor St, Amarillo, TX 79107-5238   **(100%)**
Tel.: (806) 374-0385
Web Site: http://www.plainsdairy.com
Sales Range: $10-24.9 Million
Emp.: 80
Dairy Products Mfr
N.A.I.C.S.: 311511
Dub Garlington (Pres)

Tri-State Baking Co.   **(1)**
6800 S Washington St, Amarillo, TX 79118
Tel.: (806) 373-6696
Sales Range: $125-149.9 Million
Bakery Product Mfr & Distr
N.A.I.C.S.: 424490
Randy Arceneaux (Pres)

AFFILIATED PUBLISHERS, INC.
1508 South St, Nashville, TN 37212-2302
Tel.: (615) 291-5007   **TN**
Year Founded: 1987
Sales Range: $50-74.9 Million
Emp.: 4
Music Publishing & Management Services
N.A.I.C.S.: 512230

AFFILIATED STEAM EQUIP-MENT COMPANY
12424 S Lombard Ln, Alsip, IL 60803
Tel.: (708) 371-0600
Web Site:
  https://www.affiliatedsteam.com
Year Founded: 1958
Sales Range: $10-24.9 Million
Emp.: 40
Heating Equipment (Hydronic) Steam Specialty Products
N.A.I.C.S.: 423720
Richard K. Lee (Founder)

Subsidiaries:

Affiliated Steam Equipment Co. - Indianapolis   **(1)**
690 W Northfield Dr Ste 400, Brownsburg, IN 46112
Tel.: (708) 371-0600
Web Site: http://www.affiliatedsteam.com
Heating Equipment
N.A.I.C.S.: 444180

Affiliated Steam Equipment Co. - Wisconsin   **(1)**
W 140 N 5979 Lilly Rd, Menomonee Falls, WI 53051
Tel.: (262) 252-9945
Web Site: http://www.affiliatedsteam.com

Heating Equipment (Hydronic) Steam Specialty Products
N.A.I.C.S.: 423720

AFFINIA HOSPITALITY
551 5th Ave, New York, NY 10176
Tel.: (212) 465-3700
Web Site: http://www.denihen.com
Rev.: $20,600,000
Emp.: 250
Real Estate Managers
N.A.I.C.S.: 531210
Sherry Kaufman (Grp Acct Dir-Natl)
Aisha Umar (Coord-Exec Svcs)
Louis DiNapoli (Mgr-Corp Credit)
Marymelia Perez (Mgr-Grp Svcs)
Elise Bennett (Dir-Sls)
Eleanor Carter (Mgr-Benefits)
Anne Meade (Mgr-Acctg)
Tulsi Drepaul (Dir-Pur)
Matt Humphrey (Office Mgr)
Jahira Isabel (Coord-Front Desk)
Benjamin J. Denihan Jr. (CEO)

AFFINIA THERAPEUTICS INC.
43 Foundry Ave Ste 120, Waltham, MA 02453
Tel.: (617) 430-7817   **DE**
Web Site: https://www.affiniatx.com
Year Founded: 2019
Rev.: $250,000
Assets: $50,728,000
Liabilities: $74,300,000
Net Worth: ($23,572,000)
Earnings: ($21,753,000)
Emp.: 63
Fiscal Year-end: 12/31/20
Biotechnology Research & Development Services
N.A.I.C.S.: 541714
Paula K. Cobb (Chief Bus Officer)
Sean P. Nolan (Chm)
Rick Modi (CEO)
Thomas Leggett (CFO)
Charles Albright (Chief Scientific Officer)

AFFINIPAY, LLC
6200 Bridge Point Pkwy Bldg 4 Ste 250, Austin, TX 78730
Web Site: http://www.affinipay.com
Year Founded: 2005
Sales Range: $1-9.9 Million
Emp.: 30
Credit Card & Payment Processing Services
N.A.I.C.S.: 522320
Amy Porter (Founder & Chm)
Carrie Fisher (VP-Mktg)
Greg Haney (VP-Ops)
Dru Armstrong (CEO)
Keely Leonard (Mgr-PR)
Bryan D. Thompson (CTO)
Catherine Dawson (Gen Counsel)

AFFINITAS CORPORATION
1015 N 98th St Ste 100, Omaha, NE 68114-2357
Tel.: (402) 505-5000   **NE**
Web Site: https://www.affinitas.net
Year Founded: 1993
Sales Range: $25-49.9 Million
Emp.: 900
Direct Marketing Services for Various Industries
N.A.I.C.S.: 541613

Subsidiaries:

Affinitas Marketing, Inc.   **(1)**
1015 N 98 St Ste 100, Omaha, NE 68114-2357
Tel.: (402) 505-5000
Web Site: http://www.affinitas.net
Marketing Services
N.A.I.C.S.: 541890
Lee Ann Young (Mgr-HR, Actcg & Admin)

AFFINITECH, INC.
1264 Park Rd, Chanhassen, MN 55317
Tel.: (952) 443-9810
Web Site:
  http://www.affinitechinc.com
Technological Security Services
N.A.I.C.S.: 561621
Todd Brown (Pres)

Subsidiaries:

National Communications Services, Inc.   **(1)**
1100 Lund Blvd, Anoka, MN 55303-1091
Tel.: (763) 576-9977
Web Site: http://www.natcomm.com
Sales Range: $1-9.9 Million
Emp.: 28
Computer & Office Machine Repair Services
N.A.I.C.S.: 811210
Gary Hegarty (CEO)
Joe Delarco (Sr Acct Mgr-Natl)
Archie Smith (Gen Mgr)

AFFINITI LLC
9208 Waterford Center Blvd Ste 150, Austin, TX 78758
Tel.: (512) 334-4100
Web Site: http://www.affiniti.com
WAN, VoIP, Dedicated Internet Access & Managed Broadband Services
N.A.I.C.S.: 517121
Cynthia Schultz (Chief Compliance Officer & Gen Counsel)
David T. Jolly (VP-Mktg)
Andy Perlmutter (Pres & CEO)

Subsidiaries:

Affinity LLC - Pennsylvania Office   **(1)**
120 S 16th St, Lebanon, PA 17042
Tel.: (717) 270-1979
Web Site: http://www.affinity.com
WAN, VoIP, Dedicated Internet Access & Managed Broadband Services
N.A.I.C.S.: 517121
John Negley (VP-Network Ops)
Carl Heininger (VP-Sls)
Darryl Loose (VP-Fin)
Hanjoo Lee (Vice Chm & Exec Dir)
Vijay Mehta (VP-Engrg)
Sunil Merchant (Exec Dir)
Lucas Roh (Chm)
Nikunj Soni (VP-Tech)

AFFINITIV, INC.
300 S Wacker Ste 900, Chicago, IL 60606
Tel.: (847) 955-9740
Web Site: http://www.affinitiv.com
Digital Marketing & Advertising Services
N.A.I.C.S.: 541613
Adam C. Meier (CEO)
Kevin D. Winter (Chief Strategy Officer & Chief Product Officer)
Jillian Slagter (Chief People Officer)
Jennifer Lee (Chief Software Officer)
Hans Bodine (Exec VP-Sls)
Marvin Grimm (Exec VP-Bus Dev)
Kevin McShane (Chief Revenue Officer)
Steve Anderson (Chm)
Lisa Shaw (VP-Mktg)
Adam Pavkov (Chief Product Officer)

Subsidiaries:

Dealer Product Services, Inc.   **(1)**
3 Corporate Dr Ste 160, Long Grove, IL 60047
Tel.: (847) 955-9740
Web Site: http://www.dpscrm.com
Sales Range: $10-24.9 Million
Emp.: 150
New Car Dealers
N.A.I.C.S.: 441110
Prabhakar Sonparote (COO)
Timothy O'Neill (Founder & CEO)

Gunnar Winckler (VP-Bus Dev)
Leigh Koulouras (VP-Mktg & Digital Media)
Mike Wines (Dir-Sls-Central Reg)
Kirk Cave (VP-Sls)

OneCommand, Inc.   **(1)**
4680 Pkwy Dr Ste 202, Mason, OH 45040-8173
Tel.: (877) 607-2471
Web Site: http://www.onecommand.com
Emp.: 500
Customer Loyalty Marketing & Communication Solutions
N.A.I.C.S.: 561422
Leonard Traficanti (Compliance Officer & VP-Ops)
Mary Angela Braunstein (CIO & VP-IT)
Andrew Smith (CTO-Highgear CRM)

AFFINITY BEAUTY BRANDS
160 Meister Ave Ste 20, North Branch, NJ 08876
Tel.: (908) 231-8888   **NJ**
Web Site:
  http://affinitybeautybrands.com
Year Founded: 1955
Sales Range: $50-74.9 Million
Emp.: 10
Skin Care Product Mfr
N.A.I.C.S.: 325620
Douglas Siegel (Founder, Pres & CEO)
Richard Keller (VP-Mktg)

AFFINITY DISPLAY & EXPOSITION
1301 Glendale Milford Rd, Cincinnati, OH 45215
Tel.: (513) 771-2339
Web Site: https://www.adex-intl.com
Year Founded: 1978
Sales Range: $25-49.9 Million
Emp.: 150
Signs & Advertising Specialties
N.A.I.C.S.: 339950
Timothy Murphy (Pres)
Mike Murphy (VP-HR)

AFFINITY FEDERAL CREDIT UNION
73 Mountainview Blvd Bldg 200, Basking Ridge, NJ 07920
Tel.: (908) 860-3991
Web Site: http://www.affinityfcu.org
Year Founded: 1935
Rev.: $59,677,020
Emp.: 300
Credit Union Services
N.A.I.C.S.: 522130
Irena Kaler (Sec)
Robert L. Birkhahn (Exec VP)
John T. Fenton (Pres & CEO)
Michael L. Rose (VP-Payment & Tech Solutions)
Kevin Brauer (CFO)
John R. McGovern (Chm)
Michael Rec (Treas)
Gregory T. Simpson (Vice Chm)
Jacquelyn Kearns (Chief Brand Officer)
Scott O. Witherspoon (Chief Credit Officer)
Joseph P. Herbst (Chief Strategic Officer)
Frank Madeira (Sr VP-Fin)
Catherine M. Ricker (Sr VP-HR & External Affairs)
Kathleen Metz (VP-Comml Lending)
Theresa Williams-Barrett (VP-Consumer Lending & Loan Admin)
Pamela Cohen (VP-HR)
Nancy Eiden (VP-Investments & Insurance)
Elizabeth Miller (VP-Member Experience)
Anne Colucci (VP-Risk & Compliance)

Heather Direnzo (*VP-Contact Center Ops*)
Michael Oualid (*Dir-Product Mgmt*)
Odalis Tejada (*Dir-Infrastructure*)
Charles W. White Jr. (*VP-Project Mgmt Office*)

AFFINITY GOLD CORP.
7950 Main St Ste 217, Maple Grove, MN 55369
Tel.: (763) 515-1462   NV
Year Founded: 2007
Sales Range: Less than $1 Million
Minerals Exploration
N.A.I.C.S.: 212220
Antonio Rotundo (*CFO*)
Corey J. Sandberg (*Pres & CEO*)
Craig S. Laughlin (*Sec*)

AFFINITY HEALTH SYSTEM
1570 Midway Pl, Menasha, WI 54952
Tel.: (920) 720-1700   IL
Web Site:
    http://www.affinityhealth.org
Sales Range: $1-9.9 Million
Emp.: 4,100
Regional Health Network; Management Services
N.A.I.C.S.: 561110
Daniel E. Neufelder (*Pres & CEO*)
Trevor Nebel (*Mgr-Rehab Svcs*)
Mark Kehrberg (*Chief Medical Officer*)
Roxana Huebscher (*Dir-Graduate Program*)
Karin Derenne (*Dir-Spiritual Svcs*)

Subsidiaries:

Network Health Plan   (1)
1550 Midway Pl, Menasha, WI 54952-1165
Tel.: (920) 720-1300
Web Site: http://www.networkhealth.com
Rev.: $93,249,890
Emp.: 200
Medical Service Plans
N.A.I.C.S.: 621491
Ed Scanlan (*Dir-Medical*)
Stacie Gunderson (*Acct Exec-Small Grp*)
Josh Weisbrod (*Dir-Risk Adjustment*)
Michael Muchnicki (*Interim Pres & Interim CEO*)
Brian Brenner (*Dir-Ops Support*)
Keith Bell (*VP-Sls & Underwriting*)
Ami Prag (*VP-Medical Affairs*)
Terry Dent (*Dir-Internal Controls*)
Rema Momberg (*VP-HR*)
Colleen Singh (*VP-Ops*)
Scott Wille (*VP-Network Dev*)
Kate Finerty (*Gen Counsel*)
Tom Hitchcock (*VP-Sls*)

AFFINITY, INC.
10850 W Park Pl Ste 470, Milwaukee, WI 53224
Tel.: (414) 258-0200   WI
Web Site: https://www.affinityit.com
Year Founded: 2003
Sales Range: $10-24.9 Million
Emp.: 50
IT Services & Solutions
N.A.I.C.S.: 541618
Steve Schmidt (*Pres & CEO*)
Thomas Keyes (*Chief Delivery Officer*)

AFFIRMA CONSULTING
3380 146th Pl SE Ste 420, Bellevue, WA 98007
Tel.: (425) 880-9984
Web Site: https://www.affirma.com
Year Founded: 2001
Sales Range: $1-9.9 Million
Emp.: 52
Business & Technology Consulting Services, including Branding, Visual Design, Business Analysis, Technological Services & Temporary/Permanent Staffing

N.A.I.C.S.: 541618
Michael Brown (*CEO & Founder*)
Mark Mason (*Principal*)
Ryan Hoffman (*Dir-Project Svcs*)

AFFIRMED NETWORKS, INC.
35 Nagog Park, Acton, MA 01720
Tel.: (978) 268-0800
Web Site:
    http://www.affirmednetworks.com
Year Founded: 2010
Sales Range: $10-24.9 Million
Emp.: 100
Mobile Network Solutions
N.A.I.C.S.: 513210
Terry Durand (*VP-Carrier Rels & Bus Dev*)
Harris Fishman (*Treas*)
George Hale (*VP-Fin & Admin*)
Anand Krishnamurthy (*Pres & CEO*)
Mohammed Shanableh (*VP-Sls & Ops*)
Paul Sherer (*VP-Tech*)
Amit Tiwari (*VP-Product Mgmt*)

AFFLUENT INSIGHTS
1825 Ponce de Leon Blvd #187, Coral Gables, FL 33134
Tel.: (561) 876-8077
Web Site:
    http://www.affluentinsights.com
Sales Range: $1-9.9 Million
Luxury Sales Consulting Services
N.A.I.C.S.: 541611
Christopher P. Ramey (*CEO*)

AFFORDABLE ALARM & MONITORING, INC. (AAMI)
4427 Mercantile Ave, Naples, FL 34104
Tel.: (239) 353-1000   FL
Web Site: https://www.aami-online.com
Year Founded: 1994
Sales Range: $1-9.9 Million
Emp.: 23
Consultation, Installation & Maintenance of Security Systems
N.A.I.C.S.: 561621
John Toscano (*Owner*)

AFFORDABLE CARS & FINANCE
27932 Lorain Rd, North Olmsted, OH 44070
Tel.: (440) 777-7600
Year Founded: 1992
Sales Range: $10-24.9 Million
Emp.: 50
Car Whslr
N.A.I.C.S.: 441110
Carl Halleen (*Pres*)

AFFORDABLE CONCEPTS, INC.
2975 W Lake Mead Blvd, North Las Vegas, NV 89032
Tel.: (702) 399-3330
Web Site:
    https://www.affordableconcepts.com
Year Founded: 1985
Rev.: $59,200,000
Emp.: 45
Commercial & Institutional Building Construction
N.A.I.C.S.: 236220
Robert W. Potter (*Pres & CEO*)
Julie Schoffer (*Office Mgr*)
Scott Weisheim (*Treas & VP*)
Irl Potter (*Principal*)
Travis Broughton (*Dir-Bus Dev*)

AFFORDABLE GREAT LOCATIONS
4305 Rte 5, Caledonia, NY 14423
Tel.: (585) 226-2727

Web Site: http://www.aglhomes.com
Rev.: $10,200,000
Emp.: 35
Manufactured & Mobile Home Dealers
N.A.I.C.S.: 459930
Jeffrey N. Cohen (*Pres*)
Lou Giorgione (*Dir-Mktg*)

AFFORDABLE RENT TO OWN LLC
3118 W Pinhook Rd, Lafayette, LA 70508
Tel.: (337) 264-0407
Web Site:
    http://www.affordablerto.net
Rev.: $12,153,514
Emp.: 16
Furniture & Appliance Rental Services
N.A.I.C.S.: 449110
Chris L. Overton (*Pres*)

AFFORDABLEBUTTONS.COM
3269 19th St NW, Rochester, MN 55901
Web Site:
    https://www.affordablebuttons.com
Year Founded: 1994
Sales Range: $1-9.9 Million
Emp.: 29
Custom Designs & Manufactures Pin-On Buttons in Various Shapes & Sizes
N.A.I.C.S.: 339993
Linda Christopherson (*Founder & Pres*)

AFG BIOSOLUTIONS, INC.
9119 Gaither Rd, Gaithersburg, MD 20877
Tel.: (240) 361-1700
Sales Range: $10-24.9 Million
Emp.: 6
Vaccines & Immunotherapeutics Developer for Infectious Diseases & Biochemical Agents
N.A.I.C.S.: 541714

AFG HOLDINGS, INC.
19450 State Hwy 249 Ste 500, Houston, TX 77070
Tel.: (713) 393-4200
Web Site: http://afgholdings.com
Holding Company
N.A.I.C.S.: 551112
Joe Jenkins (*Pres*)
Michael Walter (*CEO*)
Christine Mathers (*VP-Mktg & Comm*)

Subsidiaries:

Maass Flange Corporation   (1)
6202 Lumberdale, Houston, TX 77092
Tel.: (713) 329-5500
Web Site: http://www.maassflange.com
Industrial Valve Mfr
N.A.I.C.S.: 332911
Jorge Lerma (*Plant Mgr*)

AFG-UPL II LLC.
Stone Quarry Crossing 811 Camp Horne Rd Ste 100, Pittsburgh, PA 15237
Tel.: (412) 367-3880
Year Founded: 2007
Sales Range: $10-24.9 Million
Energy Conservation Services
N.A.I.C.S.: 924120
James J. Browne (*Exec Dir*)

AFI PARTNERS LLC
158 Mercer St 2nd Fl, New York, NY 10012
Tel.: (212) 938-0016   DE
Web Site:
    https://www.afipartners.com
Privater Equity Firm

N.A.I.C.S.: 523999
Joseph Lapinsky (*Operating Partner*)
Rick Stephenson (*Operating Partner*)
E.J. Antonio III (*Mng Partner*)

Subsidiaries:

Garsite Progress LLC   (1)
539 S 10th St, Kansas City, KS 66105-1201
Tel.: (913) 342-5600
Web Site: http://www.garsite.com
Sales Range: $25-49.9 Million
Emp.: 70
Aviation Refueling Equipment Mfr
N.A.I.C.S.: 336120

AFLAC - LEHIGH VALLEY
1600 Lehigh Pkwy E, Allentown, PA 18105
Tel.: (610) 433-5297
Web Site: http://www.ez2elect.com
Year Founded: 1974
Sales Range: $1-9.9 Million
Emp.: 5
Insurance Agency & Brokerage
N.A.I.C.S.: 524210
Bethany Anderson (*Principal*)
Quentin C. Kent (*Principal*)

AFM CAPITAL PARTNERS, INC.
250 E 96th St Ste 150, Indianapolis, IN 46240
Tel.: (317) 418-4527
Web Site: https://www.afmcap.com
Emp.: 100
Privater Equity Firm
N.A.I.C.S.: 523999
Mark McTigue (*Pres & Founding Partner*)

Subsidiaries:

Pro Products, Inc.   (1)
918 S Lansing Ave, Sturgeon Bay, WI 54235-2860
Tel.: (920) 743-1575
Web Site: http://www.proproducts-inc.com
Sales Range: $1-9.9 Million
Emp.: 16
General Purpose Machinery Mfr
N.A.I.C.S.: 333998
Sandy Hurley (*CFO*)
Jon Hurley (*Mgr-Sls & Pur*)
Lee Ann B. (*Coord-ISO & Quality Assurance*)
Steven Hurley (*Pres*)
Dick Clark (*Plant Mgr*)

AFMS LOGISTICS MANAGEMENT GROUP
10260 SW Greenburg Rd Ste 1020, Portland, OR 97223
Tel.: (503) 246-3521
Web Site: https://www.afms.com
Year Founded: 1992
Sales Range: $25-49.9 Million
Emp.: 23
Domestic & International Shipping Services
N.A.I.C.S.: 488999
Mike Erickson (*Pres & CEO*)
Jerry Bishop (*Controller*)

AFOGNAK NATIVE CORPORATION
300 Alimaq Dr, Kodiak, AK 99615
Tel.: (907) 486-6014
Web Site: https://www.afognak.com
Year Founded: 1971
Business Support Services
N.A.I.C.S.: 561499
Kristy Clement (*Chm*)

Subsidiaries:

Alutiiq, LLC   (1)
3909 Arctic Blvd, Ste. 500, Anchorage, AK 99503
Tel.: (907) 222-9500
Web Site: http://www.alutiiq.com

Afognak Native Corporation—(Continued)

Diversified Commercial Services
N.A.I.C.S.: 561499

Subsidiary (Domestic):

McCallie Associates Inc. (2)
3906 Raynor Pkwy Ste 200, Bellevue, NE
68123
Tel.: (402) 291-2203
Web Site: https://www.alutiiq.com
Custom Computer Programming Services
N.A.I.C.S.: 541511
Jennifer Maassen (CEO)

AFP INDUSTRIES, INC.
7900 Whitepine Rd, Richmond, VA
23237
Tel.: (804) 275-1436
Web Site: https://www.afpind.com
Year Founded: 1971
Sales Range: $10-24.9 Million
Emp.: 50
Industrial Machinery & Equipment
Whslr
N.A.I.C.S.: 423830
Wayne Kish (Pres)
Dick Kish (Co-Founder)
Frank Kish (Co-Founder)

AFR INSURANCE
800 N Harvey Ave, Oklahoma City,
OK 73102-2813
Tel.: (405) 218-5400
Web Site:
    http://www.americanfarmers.com
Year Founded: 1982
Sales Range: $50-74.9 Million
Emp.: 235
Fire, Marine & Casualty Insurance
N.A.I.C.S.: 524126
Terry Detrick (Pres)
Chris Blevins (CEO)

AFRICA GROWTH CORPORATION
3773 Howard Hughes Pkwy Ste 500,
Las Vegas, NV 89169
Tel.: (281) 334-9479   NV
Web Site:
    https://www.africagrowthcorp.com
Year Founded: 2010
AFGC—(OTCQB)
Sales Range: Less than $1 Million
Residential & Commercial Real Estate Investment, Management &
Leasing Services
N.A.I.C.S.: 531110

AFRICAN WILDLIFE FOUNDATION
1100 New Jersey Ave SE Ste 900,
Washington, DC 20003
Tel.: (202) 939-3333   DC
Web Site: https://www.awf.org
Year Founded: 1961
Rev.: $26,401,695
Assets: $56,142,993
Liabilities: $14,104,878
Net Worth: $42,038,115
Emp.: 48
Fiscal Year-end: 06/30/18
Wildlife Preservation Services
N.A.I.C.S.: 813312
Craig Sholley (VP-Philanthropy &
Mktg)

AFRICARE
440 R St NW, Washington, DC
20001
Tel.: (202) 462-3614   DC
Web Site: http://www.africare.org
Year Founded: 1971
Sales Range: $50-74.9 Million
Emp.: 83
Community Development Services
N.A.I.C.S.: 624190

Jean E. Denis (Dir-Mgmt Info Sys)
Peter Francis (Treas)
Darius Mans (Pres)
Joseph C. Kennedy (Sec)
Stephen D. Cashin (Chm)

AFS JANITORIAL LLC
1212 N 39th St Ste 400, Tampa, FL
33605
Tel.: (813) 886-7236
Web Site:
    http://www.afsjanitorial.com
Janitorial & Facility Services
N.A.I.C.S.: 561720
Bryson Raver (Mng Partner)
Carolyn Closson (Office Mgr)

Subsidiaries:

AFS Healthcare Support
Services (1)
1213 N 39th St Ste 323, Tampa, FL 33605
Tel.: (813) 886-7236
Web Site: http://www.afsjanitorial.com
Emp.: 50
Janitorial & Facility Services
N.A.I.C.S.: 561720
Bryson Raver (Owner)

AFS LOGISTICS, LLC
670 Emberwood Dr, Shreveport, LA
71106
Tel.: (318) 798-2111   LA
Web Site: https://www.afs.net
Sales Range: $50-74.9 Million
Emp.: 250
Logistics & Freight Transportation
Services
N.A.I.C.S.: 488510
Brian J. Barker (Founder & Chm)
Scott Matthews (VP-Freight Audit &
Payment Svcs)
Ben Townsend (CFO)
David Proctor (CEO)
Warren R. Patterson (CIO)
Jeff Hoban (COO)
Scott Boyer (Chief Comml Officer)

AFSCO INC.
1101 N Central Ave, Marshfield, WI
54449
Tel.: (715) 359-7794
Rev.: $15,600,000
Emp.: 400
Fast-Food Restaurant, Chain
N.A.I.C.S.: 722513
Ron Fish (Owner)

AFTER SCHOOL MATTERS, INC.
66 E Randolph St, Chicago, IL 60601
Tel.: (312) 768-5200   IL
Web Site:
    https://www.afterschoolmatters.org
Year Founded: 2000
Rev.: $17,291,348
Assets: $6,966,328
Liabilities: $1,190,402
Net Worth: $5,775,926
Earnings: $354,713
Emp.: 953
Fiscal Year-end: 06/30/12
After School Services
N.A.I.C.S.: 611710
Mary Ellen Caron (CEO)
Adrienne Scherenzel-Curry (Chief
Program Officer)
Anedra Kerr (Chief Dev Officer)
Jocelyn Guzman-Moralde (Project
Mgr)
Lindrea Ross (Mgr-Mktg)
Michael Reinsdorf (Pres & COO)
Sergio Roca (Mgr-Facilities)
Michael Bradley (CFO)

AFTERMARKET AUTO PARTS ALLIANCE, INC.

2706 Treble Creek Ste 100, San Antonio, TX 78258-4496
Tel.: (210) 492-4868   TX
Web Site: http://www.apwusa.com
Year Founded: 1963
Sales Range: $25-49.9 Million
Emp.: 20
Distr Of Auto Parts
N.A.I.C.S.: 813920
John R. Washbish (Pres & CEO)

AFTON ALPS INC.
6600 Peller Ave S, Hastings, MN
55033
Tel.: (651) 436-5245
Web Site: https://www.aftonalps.com
Year Founded: 1963
Sales Range: $10-24.9 Million
Emp.: 850
Skiing, Golf & Mountain Biking Recreational Facilities Owner & Operator
N.A.I.C.S.: 721214
Rob Katz (Pres & CEO)

AFX INC.
2345 N Ernie Krueger Cir, Waukegan, IL 60087-3225
Tel.: (847) 249-5970   IL
Web Site: http://www.afxinc.com
Year Founded: 1938
Sales Range: $25-49.9 Million
Emp.: 160
Fluorescent Lighting Products Mfr
N.A.I.C.S.: 335131
William R. Solomon (Owner)
Mark Dugan (Dir-HR)
David Shore (Mgr-Mktg Comm)
Tim Tevyaw (Pres)
Charles Morley (VP-Ops)
Paul Cuitino (CFO)
James Serra (VP-Bus Dev)

AG ACQUISITION GROUP, INC.
330 Clematis St Ste 217, West Palm
Beach, FL 33401
Tel.: (800) 341-2684   DE
Year Founded: 2017
Financial Services
N.A.I.C.S.: 523999
Laura Anthony (CFO)

Subsidiaries:

Zivaro, Inc. (1)
990 S Broadway Ste 400, Denver, CO
80209
Tel.: (303) 455-8800
Web Site: http://www.gtri.com
Sales Range: $10-24.9 Million
Emp.: 110
Technology Consulting Services
N.A.I.C.S.: 541519
Glenn Smith (CFO)
Greg Byles (Founder & CEO)
Matt Lederle (Sr Acct Exec)
Stephen Foster (CEO)
Sean Mares (VP-Enterprise Sls & Ops)
Patricia Moscarelli (Exec VP-Ops)
Eric Toler (CFO)
Sarah Sample-Reif (Chief Strategy Officer)

AG CREDIT, ACA
610 W Lytle St, Fostoria, OH 44830
Tel.: (419) 435-7758
Web Site: https://www.agcredit.net
Sales Range: $10-24.9 Million
Emp.: 100
Production Credit Association, Agricultural
N.A.I.C.S.: 522299
Brian Ricker (CEO)

AG EXPRESS, INC.
22 S 200 W, Burley, ID 83318
Tel.: (208) 678-4625
Year Founded: 2007
Sales Range: $10-24.9 Million
Emp.: 143
Freight Trucking Services

N.A.I.C.S.: 484220
Kirk Woodland (Owner)

AG FINANCIAL INVESTMENT TRUST, INC.
245 Park Ave 26th Fl, New York, NY
10167
Tel.: (212) 692-2000   MD
Real Estate Investment Trust
N.A.I.C.S.: 525990
Jonathan Lieberman (Pres & Chief
Investment Officer)

AG FIRST FARMERS COOPERATIVE
204 1st St S, Brookings, SD 57006
Tel.: (605) 692-6216
Web Site:
    http://www.agfirstfarmers.com
Sales Range: $10-24.9 Million
Emp.: 30
Grain Distr
N.A.I.C.S.: 424510
Terry Knudsen (Gen Mgr)
Kevin Gross (Asst Mgr-Feed Dept)

AG HILL PARTNERS LLC
1601 Elm St, Dallas, TX 75201
Tel.: (214) 922-1112
Private Equity Firm
N.A.I.C.S.: 523999
Keith Benedict (COO & Gen Counsel)
Al Hill (Chm)

Subsidiaries:

Vspeed Capital LLC (1)
PO Box 941611, Plano, TX 75094
Tel.: (214) 363-4641
Private Equity Firm
N.A.I.C.S.: 523999
Brian Alton (Mng Partner)
Brendon Mills (Mng Partner)

AG LAND CO-OP INC.
364 Lisbon St, Canfield, OH 44406
Tel.: (330) 533-5551
Web Site: http://www.agland.coop
Sales Range: $10-24.9 Million
Emp.: 100
Grain Elevators
N.A.I.C.S.: 424510
Jeff Osentoski (Pres)
Doug Marti (Chm)

AG PARTNERS CO-OP
1st and Broadway, Cannon Falls, MN
55027
Tel.: (651) 923-4496
Web Site: http://www.agpartners.net
Sales Range: $50-74.9 Million
Emp.: 150
Grain Elevators
N.A.I.C.S.: 424910
Greg Schwanbeck (Gen Mgr)

AG PARTNERS COOPERATIVE INC.
708 S 10th St, Hiawatha, KS 66434
Tel.: (785) 742-2196
Web Site:
    https://www.agpartnerscoop.com
Sales Range: $25-49.9 Million
Emp.: 30
Distribution Of Grains
N.A.I.C.S.: 424510

AG PLUS INC.
401 N Main St, South Whitley, IN
46787
Tel.: (260) 723-5141
Web Site: https://www.agplusinc.com
Sales Range: $10-24.9 Million
Emp.: 17
Grain Elevators
N.A.I.C.S.: 424510
Jeff Mize (Gen Mgr)

AG POWER ENTERPRISE INC.
3555 18th St SW, Owatonna, MN 55060
Tel.: (507) 451-4054
Web Site: http://www.agpowerjd.com
Sales Range: $25-49.9 Million
Emp.: 25
Farm Implements
N.A.I.C.S.: 423820
Mike Milstead *(Gen Mgr)*

AG PROCESSING INC.
12700 W Dodge Rd, Omaha, NE 68154-2154
Tel.: (402) 496-7809   IA
Web Site: https://www.agp.com
Year Founded: 1983
Sales Range: $1-4.9 Billion
Emp.: 250
Agricultural Services
N.A.I.C.S.: 424510
J. Keith Spackler *(CEO & Gen Mgr)*
Chris Schaffer *(Sr VP-Ag Products)*
Dave Wilwerding *(Gen Counsel & Sr VP)*
Ernie Kiley *(Sr VP-Ops)*
Greg Twist *(Sr VP-Transportation)*
Mark Sandeen *(Sr VP-Soybean Processing)*
Scott Simmelink *(CFO & Grp VP)*
Troy Alberts *(Sr VP-Refined Oils)*

Subsidiaries:

Ag Environmental Products, LLC   (1)
12700 W Dodge Rd, Omaha, NE 68154-2154
Tel.: (402) 496-7809
Soybean Distr
N.A.I.C.S.: 424510
Keith Spackler *(CEO)*

AG PRODUCERS CO-OP
PO BOX 430, Sunray, TX 79086
Tel.: (806) 349-1031
Web Site:
    http://www.agproducerscoop.com
Grain & Cotton Supply & Marketing Operations & Agronomy Services, Fuel & Retail Stores
N.A.I.C.S.: 926140
Gregg Allen *(CEO)*
Bret Brown *(CFO)*

Subsidiaries:

Olton Co-Op Gin   (1)
106 E Highway 70, Olton, TX 79064
Tel.: (806) 285-2525
Web Site: http://www.agproducerscoop.com
Cotton Crop & Ginning Mfr
N.A.I.C.S.: 115111
Chris Williams *(Mgr-Gin)*
Deanna Swart *(Office Mgr)*

AG RESERVES INC
139 ES Temple Ste 110, Salt Lake City, UT 84111-1175
Tel.: (801) 715-9100
Web Site: http://www.fmc-slc.com
Year Founded: 1991
Sales Range: $25-49.9 Million
Emp.: 600
Farm Management
N.A.I.C.S.: 115116
Paul Genho *(Pres)*
Jeff Whitesides *(Mgr-Application Support)*
Levi Shaw *(Mgr-Bus Intelligence)*
Lynn Giles *(Dir-HR)*

Subsidiaries:

AgReserves, Inc.   (1)
79 S Main St, Salt Lake City, UT 84111-1175
Tel.: (801) 359-1600
Web Site: http://www.fmc-slc.com
Sales Range: $10-24.9 Million
Emp.: 55
Farm Products

N.A.I.C.S.: 115116
Rick Hansen *(Dir-IS & IT)*
Patrick Osborn *(Mgr-Internal Audit)*
Teressa Fuller *(Mgr-Payroll-HRIS)*
Jason Baker *(Mgr-Tax)*
Zella Jeanne Jensen *(Sec)*
David Secrist *(VP)*

Division (Domestic):

Agri Northwest   (2)
6716 W Rio Grande, Kennewick, WA 99336
Tel.: (509) 734-1195
Web Site: http://www.agrinorthwest.com
Raw Farm Products Producer & Distr
N.A.I.C.S.: 424510
Matthew Funk *(Mgr-Farm Unit)*

AG RX, INC.
751 S Rose Ave, Oxnard, CA 93030
Tel.: (805) 487-0696
Web Site: https://www.agrx.com
Year Founded: 1993
Sales Range: $10-24.9 Million
Emp.: 122
Nitrogenous Fertilizer Mfr
N.A.I.C.S.: 325311
Chris Oliva *(Dir-Sls)*
Kenneth Burdullis *(Pres & CEO)*
Kimberly Eisel *(Corp Sec & CFO)*
Walt Johnson *(Chm)*

AG SHIP MAINTENANCE CORP.
99 Chapel St, Newark, NJ 07105
Tel.: (973) 589-4400
Rev.: $23,100,000
Emp.: 15
Marine Cargo Handling
N.A.I.C.S.: 488320
Susan Ruiz *(Treas)*
Umberto Guido III *(Pres)*

AG SOLUTIONS L.L.C.
405 W Pikes Peak Rd, Chickasha, OK 73018
Tel.: (405) 224-1194
Web Site:
    http://www.agsolutionsok.com
Year Founded: 2005
Sales Range: $10-24.9 Million
Emp.: 13
Soil Preparation, Planting & Cultivating Services
N.A.I.C.S.: 115112
Dan Amme *(Mgr-Parts)*
Bill Snider *(Reg Mgr)*
Dale Hoff *(Reg Mgr)*
Rick Hill *(Reg Mgr)*
Mark Morris *(Gen Mgr)*
Greg Hardin *(Mgr-Parts)*

AG TWIN BROOK BDC, INC.
245 Park Ave 26th Fl, New York, NY 10167
Tel.: (212) 692-2000   DE
Year Founded: 2016
Rev.: $15,752,000
Assets: $203,069,000
Liabilities: $7,482,000
Net Worth: $195,587,000
Earnings: $9,928,000
Fiscal Year-end: 12/31/22
Financial Services
N.A.I.C.S.: 522291
Trevor Clark *(Chm & CEO)*
Christopher D. Moore *(Acting Gen Counsel & Acting Sec)*
Terrence Walters *(CFO & Treas)*
Richa Gulati *(Chief Compliance Officer)*

AG VALLEY COOPERATIVE NON-STOCK
72133 N Hwy 136, Edison, NE 68936
Tel.: (308) 927-3681   NE
Web Site: https://www.agvalley.com
Year Founded: 1953

Sales Range: $25-49.9 Million
Emp.: 160
Grain & Field Beans
N.A.I.C.S.: 424510
Ron Hunter *(Gen Mgr)*
Tim Goding *(Dir-Grain Div)*
Tom Hansen *(Pres)*
Elden Hall *(Dir-Feed Div)*
Ken Moore *(Dir-Safety)*
Don Masten *(Dir-Water Resources Div)*
Eldon Kroemer *(Mgr-Agronomy Location)*
Kevin Farner *(Mgr-Location)*
Todd Johnson *(Mgr-Location)*
Gordy Lange *(Mgr-Northern Reg)*
Lavern Banzhaf *(Sec)*
Leon Ehrke *(VP)*

AG VIEW FS, INC.
22069 US Hwy 34, Princeton, IL 61356
Tel.: (815) 875-2800
Web Site: https://www.agviewfs.com
Rev.: $50,200,000
Emp.: 60
Agricultural Chemical Distr
N.A.I.C.S.: 424910
James Burke *(Treas)*
Ron Pierson *(Pres)*
Tim Green *(VP)*
Jim Chase *(Sec)*

AG-BOX CO
1930 Railroad St, Oceano, CA 93445
Tel.: (805) 489-0377
Web Site:
    https://www.agboxcompany.com
Sales Range: $10-24.9 Million
Emp.: 12
Mfr of Corrugated & Solid Fiber Boxes
N.A.I.C.S.: 322211
Leroy Facciani *(Gen Mgr)*

AG-LAND FS, INC.
1505 Valle Vista, Pekin, IL 61554
Tel.: (309) 346-4145
Web Site: https://www.aglandfs.com
Rev.: $28,455,636
Emp.: 9
Animal Feed
N.A.I.C.S.: 424910
Floyd Heller *(Gen Mgr)*
Randy Brim *(Treas & Sec)*

AG-MEIER INDUSTRIES LLC
920 E 6th Ave, Belton, TX 76513-2712
Tel.: (254) 939-3731   TX
Web Site: https://www.ag-meier.net
Year Founded: 1947
Sales Range: $1-9.9 Million
Emp.: 30
Farm Implements Mfr
N.A.I.C.S.: 423820
Lyle Meier *(Owner & Pres)*

AG-POWER INC.
3501 N Central Expy, McKinney, TX 75071-7817
Tel.: (214) 544-2900
Web Site: http://www.ag-power.com
Year Founded: 1988
Sales Range: $10-24.9 Million
Emp.: 100
Farm & Garden Machinery
N.A.I.C.S.: 423820
Jack M. Radke *(Owner)*
Jason Moseley *(Mgr-Store)*
Jeff Conway *(Mgr-Svc-Columbus)*

AG-PRO, LLC
P.O. Box 95, Boston, GA 31626
Tel.: (866) 835-9766

Web Site:
    https://www.agprocompanies.com
Year Founded: 1958
Farm Machinery Retailer
N.A.I.C.S.: 459999
James Groover *(CEO)*

Subsidiaries:

South Daytona Tractor & Mower, Inc.   (1)
3000 S Ridgewood Ave A, Daytona Beach, FL 32119
Tel.: (386) 760-5067
Web Site:
    http://www.southdaytonatractor.com
Sales Range: $1-9.9 Million
Emp.: 11
Garden Supplies Distr & Repair Services
N.A.I.C.S.: 444230
Max Berger *(Pres)*

Southeast Mower & Saw Shop   (1)
2294 Brunswick Hwy, Waycross, GA 31503-6511
Tel.: (912) 285-4222
Web Site: http://www.semower.com
Outdoor Power Equipment Stores
N.A.I.C.S.: 444230

AG-WEST DISTRIBUTING COMPANY
199 W 2nd N, Burley, ID 83318
Tel.: (208) 678-3589
Web Site: http://www.agwestdist.com
Sales Range: $10-24.9 Million
Emp.: 11
Sales of Agricultural Machinery & Equipment
N.A.I.C.S.: 423820
Don Allen Knopp *(Founder & Pres)*

AG/GRO FERTILIZER COMPANY
2111 Waterworks Rd, Winchester, KY 40391-9798
Tel.: (859) 744-3759
Sales Range: $10-24.9 Million
Emp.: 20
Farm Supplies
N.A.I.C.S.: 424910
William L. Quisenberry *(Pres)*
Everett Cury *(Owner)*

AGA JOHN ORIENTAL RUGS
8687 Melrose Ave Ste B538, West Hollywood, CA 90069-5789
Tel.: (310) 657-0890
Web Site:
    http://www.agajohnrugsss.com
Rev.: $22,000,000
Emp.: 45
Rugs
N.A.I.C.S.: 423220
Parviz Illoulian *(VP)*
Jerry Illoulian *(Pres)*

AGAIN FASTER LLC
1 Design Center Pl Ste 848, Boston, MA 02210
Tel.: (617) 460-5999
Web Site: http://www.againfaster.com
Year Founded: 2006
Sales Range: $1-9.9 Million
Emp.: 25
Retails Fitness Equipment & Training & Health Media to CrossFit Customers
N.A.I.C.S.: 713940
Mary Brown *(Mgr-Mktg)*

AGAMYA CAPITAL LLC
550 W Washington Blvd Ste 201, Chicago, IL 60661
Tel.: (312) 612-2219   IL
Web Site:
    https://www.agamyacapital.com
Year Founded: 2013
Private Equity Investment Firm
N.A.I.C.S.: 523999

Agamya Capital LLC—(Continued)

Praful Mittal *(Pres)*

Subsidiaries:

World Inspection Network International, Inc. **(1)**
3326 Aspen Grove Dr Ste 160, Franklin, TN 37067
Tel.: (206) 728-8100
Web Site: http://www.wini.com
Professional, Scientific & Technical Services
N.A.I.C.S.: 541990

AGAPE LUXURY CORP.
560 Southern Blvd, Bronx, NY 10455
Tel.: (718) 585-2222
Web Site:
   http://www.agapeluxurycars.com
Year Founded: 2012
Sales Range: $25-49.9 Million
Emp.: 60
Medical Transportation Services
N.A.I.C.S.: 621910
Mario Sena *(Pres & CEO)*

AGBAYANI CONSTRUCTION CORP.
88 Dixon Ct, Daly City, CA 94014
Tel.: (415) 221-2065
Web Site: http://www.agbayani.com
Sales Range: $25-49.9 Million
Emp.: 150
General Remodeling, Single-Family Houses
N.A.I.C.S.: 236118
Vincent D. Agbayani *(Pres)*
Jenny Yang *(Controller & CFO)*
Alfonso Garcia *(VP)*
Maria Agbayani *(Sec)*

AGBEST LLC
2101 N Granville Ave, Muncie, IN 47303
Tel.: (765) 288-5001
Web Site: https://www.agbest.com
Sales Range: $10-24.9 Million
Emp.: 50
Farm Supplies
N.A.I.C.S.: 424910
James Swigart *(Mgr-Safety)*

AGCAROLINA FINANCIAL
4000 Poole Rd, Raleigh, NC 27610-2923
Tel.: (919) 250-9500
Web Site:
   https://www.agcarolina.com
Year Founded: 1933
Sales Range: $25-49.9 Million
Emp.: 100
Miscellaneous Business Credit Institution
N.A.I.C.S.: 522299
David W. Corum *(Pres & CEO)*
Roy P. Robertson Jr. *(Sr VP-Corp Lending)*

AGCHOICE FARM CREDIT
300 Winding Creek Blvd, Mechanicsburg, PA 17050-1860
Tel.: (717) 796-9372
Web Site: https://www.agchoice.com
Sales Range: $50-74.9 Million
Emp.: 127
Provider fo Agricultural Credit Institutions
N.A.I.C.S.: 522299
Richard Stup *(Branch Mgr-Sls)*
Keith Walker *(Officer-Loan)*

AGCO INC.
10th Fossil St, Russell, KS 67665
Tel.: (785) 483-2128
Web Site: http://www.agcoinc.coop
Rev.: $15,000,000
Emp.: 25

Fuel, Feed, Fertilizer, Seed, Pesticides, Convenience Store Merchandise, Custom Application & Grain Storage Handling
N.A.I.C.S.: 424510
Dan Bernard *(Gen Mgr)*

AGCO INC.
2782 Simpson Cir, Norcross, GA 30071
Tel.: (770) 447-6990   GA
Web Site:
   https://www.agcomarble.com
Year Founded: 1979
Rev.: $31,400,000
Emp.: 135
Mfr of Cultured Marble for Counter Tops
N.A.I.C.S.: 326191
Larry J. Pulliam *(CEO)*

Subsidiaries:

Atlanta Whirlpool **(1)**
2762 Simpson Cir, Norcross, GA 30071-2819 **(100%)**
Tel.: (770) 447-6990
Sales Range: $10-24.9 Million
Emp.: 100
Mfr of Whirlpool Baths
N.A.I.C.S.: 459999
Larry Pulliam *(Pres)*
Melinda Pulliam *(Dir-Fin)*
Paula Wedding *(Sec)*

Kraft Mart **(1)**
2772 Simpson Cir, Norcross, GA 30071-2819 **(100%)**
Tel.: (770) 447-6990
Web Site: http://www.agcomarble.com
Sales Range: $10-24.9 Million
Emp.: 50
Mfr of Counter Tops
N.A.I.C.S.: 311821
Gary Pulliam *(CEO)*

AGCO OF SPEARMAN INC.
821 S Hwy 207, Spearman, TX 79081
Tel.: (806) 659-3751
Year Founded: 1981
Sales Range: $10-24.9 Million
Emp.: 9
Grain Distr
N.A.I.C.S.: 424510
Haley Shields *(Pres)*

AGCOUNTRY FARM CREDIT SERVICES, ACA
1900 44th St S, Fargo, ND 58108
Tel.: (701) 282-9494
Web Site: https://www.agcountry.com
Rev.: $279,942,000
Assets: $12,239,535,000
Liabilities: $9,742,097,000
Net Worth: $2,497,438,000
Earnings: $210,440,000
Emp.: 700
Fiscal Year-end: 12/31/22
Agricultural Lending & Credit Services
N.A.I.C.S.: 522299
Randy Aberle *(Exec VP-Agribusiness & Capital Markets)*
Howard Olson *(Sr VP-Pub Affairs & Govt)*
Jeni Strand *(Exec VP-HR)*
Greg Sabolik *(Chm)*
Becky Thibert *(CFO)*
Marc L. Knisely *(Pres & CEO)*
Lynn Pietig *(Vice Chm)*
Kim Zeltinger *(Chief Credit Officer)*
Jessica Fyer *(COO & Gen Counsel)*
Jeff Schmidt *(Chief Risk Officer)*
Troy Andreasen *(Chief Marketplace Officer)*
Jessica Fyre *(COO & Gen Counsel)*
Gordon Hanson *(Chief Strategy Officer)*

AGE GROUP LTD
2 Park Ave Fl 18, New York, NY 10016
Tel.: (212) 213-9500
Web Site: http://www.agegroup.com
Year Founded: 1985
Sales Range: $10-24.9 Million
Emp.: 100
Mfr of Women's & Children's Lingerie & Undergarments
N.A.I.C.S.: 424350
Karen Bleistern *(Mgr-Sls)*
Richard Adjmi *(CEO)*

AGE REVERSAL, INC.
2324 Colony Plz, Newport Beach, CA 92660
Tel.: (949) 706-2468   MD
Web Site:
   http://www.agereversalinc.com
Year Founded: 2010
Sales Range: $10-24.9 Million
Emp.: 2
Pharmaceutical Mfr, Researcher & Developer
N.A.I.C.S.: 325412
David A. Kekich *(Dir-Mktg)*

AGEATIA TECHNOLOGY CONSULTANCY SERVICES INC.
850 E Higgins Rd Ste 125 P, Schaumburg, IL 60173
Tel.: (847) 517-8415
Web Site: https://www.ageatia.com
Year Founded: 2005
Sales Range: $1-9.9 Million
Emp.: 35
IT Staffing & Project Consulting
N.A.I.C.S.: 541618
Chandra Srinivasan *(Pres)*

AGENCY 33
455 Sherman St Ste 205, Denver, CO 80203
Tel.: (303) 894-3130
Web Site: http://www.agency33.com
Sales Range: Less than $1 Million
Emp.: 3
Creative Services, Social Media Consulting, Media Relations & Crisis Communications
N.A.I.C.S.: 541820
James Wall *(Pres, CEO & Partner)*
Andrew Laing *(Partner)*
Gwen Kawashima *(Office Mgr)*

AGENCY EA, LLC
311 W Walton St, Chicago, IL 60610
Tel.: (312) 879-0186
Web Site: https://www.agencyea.com
Sales Range: $10-24.9 Million
Emp.: 40
Advetising Agency
N.A.I.C.S.: 541810
Fergus Rooney *(CEO)*
Sarah Ruer *(Coord-Production)*
Kerry Roach *(Sr Acct Exec)*
Lauren Vissat *(Sr Mgr-Bus Dev)*
Elise Farrington *(Acct Exec)*
Jon Kirsch *(VP-Building Ops)*
Hunter Haas *(Acct Dir)*
Kate Mcgivney *(Acct Coord)*
Becca Lyon *(Mgr-Mktg Comm)*
Claire Holland *(Dir-Mktg Comm)*
Brittany McCullars *(Assoc Dir-Digital)*
Kelley Gripp *(Dir-Strategic Initiatives)*
Gabrielle Martinez *(Mng Partner)*
Susan Gooding *(VP-Client Svcs)*
Ellie Meyer *(VP-Client Svcs)*
Rick Cosgrove *(Pres)*

AGENCY FOR COMMUNITY TREATMENT SERVICES, INC.
4612 N 56th St, Tampa, FL 33610
Tel.: (813) 246-4899   FL
Web Site: https://www.actsfl.org

Year Founded: 1978
Sales Range: $10-24.9 Million
Emp.: 460
Health Care Srvices
N.A.I.C.S.: 622110
Catherine Batsche *(Sec)*
James C. Jacob *(VP)*
Larry Gilley *(CFO)*
Asha Terminello *(COO)*
James D. Previtera *(Pres)*
Richard E. Brown *(CEO)*

AGENCY HOLDING COMPANY OF MARYLAND INC.
7450 Coca Cola Dr, Hanover, MD 21076
Tel.: (410) 691-9100
Web Site: http://www.asionline.com
Year Founded: 1994
Sales Range: $25-49.9 Million
Emp.: 76
Personal Credit Institution Services
N.A.I.C.S.: 522291
Henry H. Stansbury *(Pres)*

Subsidiaries:

Agency Insurance Company of Maryland, Inc. **(1)**
7450 Coca Cola Dr, Hanover, MD 21076
Tel.: (410) 684-3399
Web Site:
   http://www.agencyinsurancecompany.com
Sales Range: $25-49.9 Million
Emp.: 45
Insurance Services
N.A.I.C.S.: 524210

Agency Services Inc. **(1)**
7450 Coca Cola Dr, Hanover, MD 21076 **(100%)**
Tel.: (410) 691-9100
Web Site: http://www.agencyservices.com
Sales Range: $25-49.9 Million
Emp.: 15
Provider of Personal Credit Institution Services
N.A.I.C.S.: 522291
Cliff Myers *(Mgr-Ops)*

Agency Services, Inc. **(1)**
PO Box 8959, Elkridge, MD 21075-8959
Tel.: (410) 691-9100
Web Site: http://www.asionline.com
Sales Range: $50-74.9 Million
Emp.: 70
Personal Credit Institution Services
N.A.I.C.S.: 522291

AGENCY212, LLC
276 Fifth Ave Ste 801, New York, NY 10001
Tel.: (212) 994-6700   NY
Web Site: http://www.agency212.com
Year Founded: 1995
Sales Range: $125-149.9 Million
Emp.: 75
Advetising Agency
N.A.I.C.S.: 541810
William W. Tucker *(CEO)*
Tracy Brennan *(Exec Dir-Creative)*
Kristina Tucker *(Exec VP-Acct Mgmt)*
Tom Di Domenico *(Mng Partner-iFuel Interactive)*

AGENDA
400 Gold Ave SW Ste 1200, Albuquerque, NM 87102
Tel.: (505) 888-5877   NM
Web Site: http://www.agenda-global.com
Sales Range: $10-24.9 Million
Emp.: 28
Fiscal Year-end: 12/31/14
Public Relations, Corporate Communications, Digital & Creative Services & Bilingual/Multicultural Programs
N.A.I.C.S.: 541820
Douglas W. Turner *(Founder & Partner)*
Craig Pattee *(Partner)*

Max Hamel (Partner)
Chris Taylor (COO)
Gerges Scott (Sr VP)
Lorenne Gavish (Acct Exec-Agenda Global)

Subsidiaries:

Agenda   (1)
2630 Exposition Blvd Suite G4, Austin, TX 78703   (100%)
Tel.: (505) 888-5877
Web Site: http://www.agenda-global.com
Public Relations
N.A.I.C.S.: 541820

AGENT ELITE, INC.
7220 Trade St, San Diego, CA 92121
Web Site: http://www.agentelite.com
Year Founded: 2011
Sales Range: $1-9.9 Million
Emp.: 46
Real Estate Manangement Services
N.A.I.C.S.: 531390
Justin Hancy (Co-Founder & CEO)
Nick Reis (Co-Founder & COO)
Nick Ossey (Dir-Mktg & Media)

AGENT LINK
1130 Cleveland St Ste 120, Clearwater, FL 33755
Tel.: (727) 214-0016
Web Site:
     https://www.agentlinkmarketing.com
Year Founded: 2009
Sales Range: $10-24.9 Million
Emp.: 15
Marketing & Public Relations
N.A.I.C.S.: 541613
Senia Gramajo (Co-Founder & Pres)
Stu Gramajo (Co-Founder & CEO)

AGENT SUPPORT SERVICES INC.
39 Park Ave 11th Fl, New York, NY 10016
Tel.: (212) 697-2025
Web Site: http://www.asglife.com
Rev.: $10,000,000
Emp.: 7
Insurance Agents & Brokers
N.A.I.C.S.: 524210
Samuel J. Kaufman (CEO)
Jennifer Cannella (Mgr)
Marion Olthoff (Mgr)
Eileen LaVigne (Mgr)
Cynthia Lucci (Mgr)
Louise Lombardi (Dir-Mktg Direct Line)
Maggie Arambarry (Dir-Underwriting)
Michael Inserra (Mgr-New Jersey Internal Sls)
Gary Bleetstein (Principal)
Mark Milbrod (Principal)
Jay L. Scheiner (Principal)

AGENT X
38 Commerce Ave SW, Grand Rapids, MI 49503
Tel.: (616) 855-6368
Web Site: http://www.agent-x.com
Year Founded: 2007
Sales Range: $1-9.9 Million
Emp.: 11
Advetising Agency
N.A.I.C.S.: 541810

AGENT16
228 E 45th St 6th Fl, New York, NY 10017
Tel.: (212) 367-3800   NY
Web Site: http://www.agent16.com
Year Founded: 1991
Rev.: $45,500,000
Emp.: 30

Advertising, Brand Development & Integration, Business-To-Business, Electronic Media, Planning & Consultation, Sales Promotion, Strategic Planning/Research
N.A.I.C.S.: 541810
Bill Brown (Chm)
Robert Manni (Pres)
William Walters (Dir-Graphic Svcs)
Alexandra Bissett (Dir-Project Mngmt)
Daniel Rootenberg (CFO)

AGENTEK, INC.
5900 Windward Pkwy Ste 400, Alpharetta, GA 30005
Tel.: (678) 393-1808
Web Site: http://www.agentek.com
Year Founded: 1995
Sales Range: $10-24.9 Million
Emp.: 30
Mobile Computing Solutions
N.A.I.C.S.: 517112
Dick Cook (Chm)

AGEOPTIONS
1048 Lake St Ste 300, Oak Park, IL 60301
Tel.: (708) 383-0258   IL
Web Site: https://www.ageoptions.org
Year Founded: 1974
Sales Range: $10-24.9 Million
Emp.: 128
Elder Care Services
N.A.I.C.S.: 623312
Robert Mapes (Dir-Program & Community Support)
Mike Giuntoli (Dir-Fin & Admin)
Kim Bauer Blechschmidt (Dir-Plng, Grants & Program Dev)
Diane Slezak (Pres & CEO)

AGESPAN, INC.
280 Merrimack St Ste 400, Lawrence, MA 01843
Tel.: (978) 683-7747   MA
Web Site: https://agespan.org
Year Founded: 1974
Sales Range: $25-49.9 Million
Emp.: 258
Elder Care Services
N.A.I.C.S.: 623312
Roseann Robillard (Pres)
William Chrisemer (Dir-Fin & Admin)
Rosanne DiStefano (Exec Dir)
Anne Proli Cataldo (Assoc Exec Dir)
Joan Hatem-Roy (Assoc Exec Dir)
Alicia Ritter (Dir-Home Care)
Marie Kissel (Dir-Home Care)
Ron Bourque (Dir-Quality & Facilities)
Christine Tardiff (Dir-Home Care)
Kim Flowers (Dir-Clinical)
Mark Batchelder (Dir-HR)
Meredith Fisher (Dir-Home Care)
Pati Fernandez (Dir-Dev & Community Programs)

AGETEC INC.
14567 Big Basin Way Ste A3, Saratoga, CA 95070-6039
Tel.: (408) 736-0800
Web Site: http://www.agetec.com
Sales Range: $10-24.9 Million
Emp.: 10
Video Games
N.A.I.C.S.: 423920
Hide Irie (Pres)

AGFINITY, INC.
260 Factory Rd, Eaton, CO 80615
Tel.: (970) 454-4000   CO
Web Site: https://www.agfinityinc.com
Year Founded: 1905
Sales Range: $250-299.9 Million
Agricultural Farm Supply Co-Op
N.A.I.C.S.: 424590

AGFM HOLDING CORPORATION
1200 Cavalier Blvd, Chesapeake, VA 23323
Tel.: (757) 487-2442
Web Site: http://www.agfm.com
Sales Range: $10-24.9 Million
Emp.: 180
Machine Tools, Metal Forming Type
N.A.I.C.S.: 333517
Robert Kralowitz (Pres)
Jeff Hall (Controller)

AGGEORGIA FARM CREDIT, ACA
468 Perry Pkwy, Perry, GA 31069
Tel.: (478) 987-8300
Web Site: http://www.aggeorgia.com
Rev.: $65,330,000
Assets: $950,840,000
Liabilities: $713,258,000
Net Worth: $237,582,000
Earnings: $21,738,000
Fiscal Year-end: 12/31/18
Farm Mortgage Services
N.A.I.C.S.: 522292
Richard David Neff (Chm)
Vikki J. Wooley (Sec)
Stephen G. Connelly (Dir-IT)
Corey W. Cottle (Mktg Dir)
Zachary T. Purvis (Chief Lending Officer)
Brandie L. Thompson (Mgr-Risk)
T. Royal (Co-Chief Credit Officer)
Jack C. Drew Jr. (CEO)
Jack W. Bentley Jr. (Vice Chm)

AGGREGATE INTELLIGENCE, INC.
615 Griswold St Ste 520, Detroit, MI 48226
Tel.: (800) 234-1340
Web Site:
     http://www.aggregateintel.com
Year Founded: 2015
Data Mining, Artificial & Business Intelligence Services
N.A.I.C.S.: 518210
John Tilly (CEO)

AGGRENE CORPORATION
925 Tower Ave, Superior, WI 54880-1527
Tel.: (715) 392-3011
Rev.: $44,500,000
Emp.: 150
Nitrogenous Fertilizer Mfr
N.A.I.C.S.: 325311
Dean Alexander (VP)
Allen Amatuzion (VP)
Albert J. Amatuzio (Pres & Treas)

AGGRESSOR ADVENTURES, LLC
209 Hudson Trace, Augusta, GA 30907
Tel.: (706) 993-2531
Web Site: http://www.aggressor.com
Year Founded: 2007
Sales Range: $25-49.9 Million
Emp.: 32
Adventure Vacation Services
N.A.I.C.S.: 561520
Wayne Brown (Chm & CEO)
Larry Speaker (VP-Ops)
Anne Hasson (VP-Reservations, Adv & Mktg)
Jay Roberts (Ops Mgr)
Jeff McNutt (Ops Mgr)

AGI GENERAL CONTRACTING
8210 Katella Ave Ste I, Stanton, CA 90680-3271
Tel.: (714) 934-8066
Web Site: https://www.agigc.com
Year Founded: 1979

Sales Range: $25-49.9 Million
Emp.: 40
Civil Engineering Services
N.A.I.C.S.: 237310
James McCullough (Principal)
Barbara Barkley (Office Mgr)

AGI INDUSTRIES, INC.
2110 SW Evangeline Trwy, Lafayette, LA 70508
Tel.: (337) 233-0626   LA
Web Site:
     https://www.agiindustries.com
Sales Range: $10-24.9 Million
Emp.: 134
Packager & Distributor of Pumps, Pump Systems, Hydraulics & Related Fluid Power Equipment
N.A.I.C.S.: 423830
David B. George (Owner)
Pat Sabolyk (VP)
Dan Theriot (CFO)

AGI PUBLISHING, INC
1850 N Gateway Blvd, Fresno, CA 93727-1600
Tel.: (559) 251-8888
Web Site:
     http://www.valleyyellowpages.com
Year Founded: 1985
Sales Range: $125-149.9 Million
Emp.: 650
Telephone Directory Publisher
N.A.I.C.S.: 513199
Siegfried Fischer (Pres)
Doris Engelmann (VP)
Mike Schilling (VP-Ops)

AGILAIRE LLC
2904B Tazewell Pike Ste A, Knoxville, TN 37918-1896
Tel.: (865) 927-9440
Web Site:
     http://www.agilairecorp.com
Software Publisher
N.A.I.C.S.: 513210
Debra Grey (Dir-Projects)
Rena Dykes (Dir-Support)
Paul Yankey (VP-Ops & Dir-Hosted Sys)
Ric Maples (Engr-Project)
Victoria DeFreese (Dir-Info Science)

AGILE DECISIONPOINT CORPORATION
702 Russell Ave Ste 312, Gaithersburg, MD 20877
Tel.: (301) 527-0330
Web Site:
     https://www.decisionpointcorp.com
Computer System Design Services
N.A.I.C.S.: 541512
Brian Flood (Founder & CEO)

AGILE GLOBAL SOLUTIONS INC.
13405 Folsom Blvd Ste 515, Folsom, CA 95630
Tel.: (916) 655-7745
Web Site:
     http://www.agileglobalsolutions.com
Year Founded: 2003
Sales Range: $1-9.9 Million
Emp.: 58
Global Business & IT Solutions
N.A.I.C.S.: 519290
Raja Krishnan (Pres)
Pranav Damle (Mgr-HR)
Vasudha Krishnan (COO)

AGILE SPORTS TECHNOLOGIES, INC.
151 N 8th St Ste 250, Lincoln, NE 68508
Tel.: (402) 817-0060
Web Site: http://www.hudl.com

Agile Sports Technologies, Inc.—(Continued)
Year Founded: 2006
Software Development Services
N.A.I.C.S.: 513210
Matt Mueller (VP-Ops)
Bryant Bone (VP-Bus Dev)
Andrew Brinkman (Project Mgr)
Brian Fleissner (VP-Fin)
David S. Graff (Co-Founder & CEO)

Subsidiaries:

Krossover Intelligence Inc.   (1)
148 W 24th St Fl 8, New York, NY 10011
Tel.: (347) 875-7677
Sports Analytics Company
N.A.I.C.S.: 512199

AGILEASSETS, INC.
3001 Bee Caves Rd Ste 200, Austin,
TX 78746
Tel.: (512) 327-4200   TX
Web Site: http://www.agileassets.com
Year Founded: 1994
Sales Range: $10-24.9 Million
Emp.: 68
Software Solutions for Infrastructure
Asset Management
N.A.I.C.S.: 541511
Stuart Hudson (Pres)
David Armstrong (Sr VP-Worldwide
Svcs)
Pascal Laumet (Dir-Ops-EMEA)
James Robertson (Dir-Bus Dev-
EMEA)
Michael Smallcombe (Sr Acct Exec)
Joe Garvey (Chief Growth Officer)
Sai Machavarapu (VP-Engrg)
John Perreault (VP-Sls)
Jim Edgerton (VP-Natl Partner Pro-
gram)
Greg Earp (Dir-Sls)
Michael Lester (COO)

AGILENCE, INC.
1020 Briggs Rd Ste 110, Mount Lau-
rel, NJ 08054
Tel.: (856) 366-1200
Web Site: http://www.agilenceinc.com
Year Founded: 2006
Computer Software Product Services
N.A.I.C.S.: 541511
Catherine Penizotto (VP-Customer
Success)
Pedro Ramos (VP-Sls)
Russ Hawkins (Pres & CEO)
Derek M. Rodner (VP-Product Strat-
egy)
Brian Harvel (CTO)
Bruce Katz (CFO)
Brian Brinkman (CMO & Chief Pro-
curement Officer)

AGILEPATH CORPORATION
4 Middle St Ste 208, Newburyport,
MA 01950
Tel.: (978) 462-5737
Web Site: http://www.agile-path.com
IT Management & Consulting Ser-
vices
N.A.I.C.S.: 541512
Eric Marks (Founder, Pres & CEO)
Paul Dube (CFO)

**AGILIS HOLDING COMPANY
LLC**
130 Turner St Bldg 3 Ste 510,
Waltham, MA 02453
Tel.: (781) 373-6900   DE
Web Site: https://agilis.llc
Year Founded: 2022
Emp.: 100
Investment, Actuarial & Risk Manage-
ment Services
N.A.I.C.S.: 523999
Tom Cassara (CEO)
Bill Mischell (Mng Dir)

Subsidiaries:

River & Mercantile LLC   (1)
130 Turner St Bldg 3 Ste 510, Waltham,
MA 02453
Tel.: (781) 373-6900
Financial Consulting Services
N.A.I.C.S.: 541611

AGILITY MFG, INC.
279 Locust St, Dover, NH 03820
Tel.: (603) 742-8977
Web Site: http://www.agilitymfg.com
Year Founded: 1987
Sales Range: $1-9.9 Million
Emp.: 45
Electro-Mechanical Assemblies Mfr
N.A.I.C.S.: 334412
Michael McGreevy (Pres)
Shawn Housley (Mgr-Tech Bus)
Reggie Michaud (Mgr-Ops)

AGILTRON, INC.
15 Presidential Way, Woburn, MA
01801
Tel.: (781) 935-1200
Web Site: https://www.agiltron.com
Year Founded: 2001
Sales Range: $25-49.9 Million
Emp.: 85
Optic Components & Systems Devel-
oper & Producer
N.A.I.C.S.: 517810
Ge Rong (Engr-Optical Application)

AGINGCARE, LLC
720 Goodlette Rd N 4th Fl, Naples,
FL 34102
Tel.: (239) 676-6671
Web Site: http://www.agingcare.com
Year Founded: 2007
Sales Range: $1-9.9 Million
Senior Care Information Website
N.A.I.C.S.: 519290
Joe Buckheit (Founder & Pres)
Gina Paddock (VP-Sls)

AGITAL HOLDINGS, LLC
1 Wall Street 5th Fl., Burlington, MA
01803
Tel.: (339) 215-8124
Web Site: https://agital.com
Marketing Services
N.A.I.C.S.: 513210

Subsidiaries:

BPatt LLC   (1)
2221 S Clark St, Arlington, VA 22202
Tel.: (703) 596-1353
Web Site: http://www.gofishdigital.com
Sales Range: $1-9.9 Million
Emp.: 17
Digital Marketing Services
N.A.I.C.S.: 541613
Brian Patterson (Co-Founder & Partner)
Dan Hinckley (Co-Founder & Partner)
Gretchen Garrett (Office Mgr)
Mike Moriarty (Partner)

Dialogconcepts, Inc.   (1)
209 Strand St, Alexandria, VA 22314-2643
Tel.: (202) 997-2678
Web Site:
    http://www.webdevelopmentgroup.com
Graphic Design Services
N.A.I.C.S.: 541430
Deirdre Bagley (Exec Dir)

**AGL WELDING SUPPLY CO.
INC.**
600 US-46, Clifton, NJ 07013
Tel.: (973) 478-5000
Web Site:
    https://www.aglweldingsupply.com
Rev.: $13,500,000
Emp.: 83
Welding Machinery & Equipment
N.A.I.C.S.: 423830
Patrick M. Fenelon (Pres)
Maureen Darcy (Owner & Sec)

Dave Malin (CFO)
Vince Murray (Mgr-Sls)
William Brancato (Mgr-Pur)

AGLAND CO-OP
115 S 1st St, Parkston, SD 57366
Tel.: (605) 928-3381
Sales Range: $10-24.9 Million
Emp.: 27
Fertilizer & Fertilizer Materials
N.A.I.C.S.: 424910
Bill Tape (Gen Mgr)

**AGM CONTAINER CONTROLS,
INC.**
3526 E Fort Lowell Rd, Tucson, AZ
85716
Tel.: (520) 881-2130
Web Site:
    https://www.agmcontainer.com
Year Founded: 1970
Sales Range: $10-24.9 Million
Emp.: 113
Environmental Control Hardware Mfr
N.A.I.C.S.: 334512
Howard N. Stewart (Pres & CEO)
Ron Corbin (Mgr-Ops)
Gabriela Cervantes (Mgr-Mktg)
Tom Christie (Mgr-IT)
Blake Koomar (Mgr-Sls)
Pat Lane (Mgr-Design Engrg)
Eric Zuercher (VP-Engrg)

**AGMARK INTERMODAL SYS-
TEMS, INC.**
222 2nd Ave N Ste 311, Nashville,
TN 37201
Tel.: (615) 313-6590
Web Site:
    https://www.agmarkintermodal.com
Year Founded: 1977
Rev.: $88,392,674
Emp.: 90
Provider of Bulk Agricultural Products
& Transportation Services
N.A.I.C.S.: 424510
Richard Hagemeyer (Pres)
Duncan Hagemeyer (VP)

AGMET METALS INC
7800 Medusa St, Oakwood Village,
OH 44146
Tel.: (440) 439-7400
Web Site: https://www.agmet1.com
Rev.: $18,135,106
Emp.: 60
Ferrous Metal Scrap & Waste
N.A.I.C.S.: 423930
Michael Agin (Chm)
Tim Andel (Controller)

**AGNES HUFF COMMUNICA-
TIONS GROUP, LLC.**
Marina Towers PO Box 91194, Los
Angeles, CA 90009
Tel.: (310) 641-2525
Web Site: http://www.ahuffgroup.com
Year Founded: 1995
Sales Range: $1-9.9 Million
Emp.: 12
Advetising Agency
N.A.I.C.S.: 541810
Agnes Huff (Pres & CEO)

AGNO PHARMA
752 56th St 1st Fl, New York, NY
11220
Tel.: (212) 574-4825
Web Site:
    http://www.agnopharma.com
Emp.: 100
Pharmaceutical Preparation Mfr
N.A.I.C.S.: 325412
James J. Chen (Pres-Global Ops)

Subsidiaries:

Particle Sciences Inc.   (1)
3894 Courtney St, Bethlehem, PA 18017-
8920
Tel.: (610) 861-4701
Web Site: http://www.particlesciences.com
Rev.: $5,005,000
Emp.: 5
Other Chemical & Allied Products Merchant
Whslr
N.A.I.C.S.: 424690
Garry Gwozdz (Dir-Formulation Sciences)
Mark Mitchnick (Founder & CEO)
Judith Cohen (VP-Quality Assurance)
Barbara Morgan (Gen Mgr)
Robert W. Lee (Pres)
Laurie Ann Goldman (Dir-Analytic Svcs)

**AGORA DIGITAL HOLDINGS,
INC.**
145 King St Ste 410, Charleston, SC
29401   NV
Web Site:
    https://www.agoradigital.com
Year Founded: 2021
Emp.: 10
Holding Company
N.A.I.C.S.: 551112
William B. Hoagland (CEO)
Randy May (Chm)
Jay Puchir (CFO)
Britt Swann (Pres & Principal Exec
Officer)
Daniel Koehler (Pres & Principal
Exec Officer)
Daniel Koehler (Pres & Principal
Exec Officer)

AGOSTO, INC.
901 N 3rd St Ste 115, Minneapolis,
MN 55401
Tel.: (612) 605-3500
Web Site: http://www.agostoinc.com
Year Founded: 2001
Rev.: $4,500,000
Emp.: 15
Computer System Design Services
N.A.I.C.S.: 541512
Aric Bandy (Pres)
Irfan Khan (CEO)
Mark Erlandson (Dir-Cloud Svcs)
Mike Majerus (VP-Fin & HR)
Paul Lundberg (CTO)
Linda Hofflander (VP-Global Chan-
nels & Alliances-Skykit)

AGRA INDUSTRIES, INC.
1211 W Water St, Merrill, WI 54452
Tel.: (715) 536-9584
Web Site: https://www.agraind.com
Rev.: $188,800,000
Emp.: 226
Engineeering Services
N.A.I.C.S.: 541330
Robert Klessig (VP)
David Marcott (Treas & VP)
Kathy McKenize (Mgr-HR)

AGRACE HOSPICECARE, INC.
5395 E Cheryl Pkwy, Madison, WI
53711
Tel.: (608) 276-4660   WI
Web Site: https://www.agrace.org
Year Founded: 1978
Sales Range: $25-49.9 Million
Emp.: 641
Community Care Services
N.A.I.C.S.: 624190
Brian Tennant (CIO)
Julia Houck (Chief Admin Officer)
Dena Green (Sr Dir-Medical)
Jennifer Maurer (CFO)
Marcia Whittington (Chief Dev Offi-
cer)
Michael Fitzpatrick (Chm)
Chris Queram (Sec)
Ann Sheehy (Vice Chm)

William Albright *(Treas)*
Steve Ditullio *(Chm)*
Pamela Edwards *(Chief Clinical Officer)*
G. Linn Roth *(Sec)*
Patrick Ryan *(Vice Chm)*
Lynne Sexten *(Pres & CEO)*
Ken Thompson *(Treas)*

AGRECOL, LLC
10101 N Casey Rd, Evansville, WI
53536
Tel.: (608) 223-3571   WI
Web Site: https://www.agrecol.com
Year Founded: 1991
Sales Range: $10-24.9 Million
Commercial Nursery & Garden Supplies Retailer; Specialty Erosion Control Systems Mfr & Whslr
N.A.I.C.S.: 111421
William T. Graham *(Founder & Chm)*

Subsidiaries:

Envirolok, LLC   (1)
10101 N Casey Rd, Evansville, WI
53536   **(100%)**
Tel.: (608) 223-3571
Web Site: http://www.envirolok.com
Emp.: 30
Vegetated Retaining Wall Systems Mfr & Installation
N.A.I.C.S.: 541320
William N. Isermann *(Pres & CEO)*

AGREEYA SOLUTIONS LLC
110 Woodmere Rd Ste 100, Folsom,
CA 95630
Tel.: (916) 294-0075
Web Site: http://www.agreeya.com
Year Founded: 1999
Sales Range: $25-49.9 Million
Emp.: 100
Business & IT Consulting Services
N.A.I.C.S.: 541611
Ajay Kaul *(Mng Partner)*
Sanjay Khosla *(VP)*
David Price *(Exec VP-Solutions)*
Niki Hirst *(Mgr-Bus Dev)*
Rakesh K. Jain *(Head-Global Delivery)*
Arindam Ray Chaudhuri *(COO)*
Kamal Deep Singh *(Dir-Recruitment & Intl Resourcing)*

AGRESTA STORMS & O'LEARY P.C.
1459 E Brunswick Ave, Indianapolis,
IN 46227
Tel.: (317) 780-9850
Web Site: http://www.asocpa.com
Offices of Certified Public Accountants
N.A.I.C.S.: 541211
S. Shawn Storms *(VP)*

AGRI BEEF CO., INC.
1555 Shoreline Dr Ste 320, Boise, ID
83702
Tel.: (208) 338-2500   ID
Web Site: https://www.agribeef.com
Year Founded: 1978
Sales Range: $25-49.9 Million
Emp.: 550
Provider of Beef Cattle Feedlot Services
N.A.I.C.S.: 112112
Garrett Tschida *(Dir-Wagyu Genetics)*
J. W. Wood *(Gen Mgr)*

AGRI MARKETING INC.
1403 Hwy 67, Hoxie, AR 72433
Tel.: (870) 886-7011
Rev.: $15,000,000
Emp.: 4
Grain Elevator, Storage Only
N.A.I.C.S.: 493130
Wilson Crisler *(Pres)*

AGRI PRODUCERS INC.
205 Main St, Tampa, KS 67483
Tel.: (785) 965-2221
Web Site: http://www.api.coop
Sales Range: $10-24.9 Million
Emp.: 13
Grains
N.A.I.C.S.: 424510
Stan Utting *(Pres & Gen Mgr)*

AGRI SERVICE INCORPORATED
3204 Kimberly Rd, Twin Falls, ID
83301
Tel.: (208) 734-7772
Web Site: http://www.agri-service.com
Year Founded: 1990
Emp.: 150
Agricultural Equipment Repair Services
N.A.I.C.S.: 811310
Doug Ottersberg *(Reg Mgr-Sls)*
Dennis Nipper *(Mgr-Inventory)*
Cleve Buttars *(Owner, Pres & CEO)*
Nate Harmon *(Mgr-Parts)*

AGRI SERVICES BRUNSWICK LLC
Hwy 24 W, Brunswick, MO 65236
Tel.: (660) 549-3351
Web Site: http://www.agriservices.com
Rev.: $50,050,597
Emp.: 50
Grains
N.A.I.C.S.: 424510
William P. Jackson *(Gen Mgr)*

AGRI-CHEM INC.
1106 W 15th St, Hopkinsville, KY
42240
Tel.: (270) 886-0141   KY
Web Site: http://www.agrichemky.aghost.net
Year Founded: 1947
Sales Range: $10-24.9 Million
Emp.: 130
Whslr of Agricultural Farm Supplies
N.A.I.C.S.: 459999
Wayne Hunt *(Pres)*
Steve Hunt *(VP)*

AGRI-COVER, INC.
3000 Hwy 281 SE, Jamestown, ND
58401
Tel.: (701) 251-1427
Web Site: https://www.agricover.com
Year Founded: 1981
Emp.: 110
Apparel Accessories Mfr
N.A.I.C.S.: 315990
Amy Wobbema *(Mgr-Mktg)*

AGRI-EMPRESA INC.
6001 W Industrial Ave, Midland, TX
79706
Tel.: (432) 694-1994
Rev.: $20,000,000
Emp.: 35
Drilling Mud Distr
N.A.I.C.S.: 325998
Steve Goree *(Pres)*
Kent Carlisle *(Mgr-Traffic)*

AGRI-KING INC.
18246 Waller Rd, Fulton, IL 61252
Tel.: (815) 589-2525
Web Site: https://www.agriking.com
Year Founded: 1968
Sales Range: $10-24.9 Million
Emp.: 200
Livestock Nutrition Products
N.A.I.C.S.: 424910
Clark W. Curley *(Chm)*

AGRI-MARK, INC.
100 Milk St, Methuen, MA 01844-
4600
Tel.: (978) 552-5541   DE
Web Site: http://www.agrimark.net
Year Founded: 1980
Sales Range: $200-249.9 Million
Emp.: 700
Dairy Marketing Cooperative
N.A.I.C.S.: 311511
Richard Stammer *(Sr Exec VP)*
Robert Wellington *(Sr VP-Economics, Comm & Legislative Affairs)*
Neal Rea *(Chm)*
Ed Townley *(CEO)*

Subsidiaries:

Cabot Creamery Co-Operative
Inc.   (1)
193 Home Farm Way, Waitsfield, VT 05673
Tel.: (802) 229-9361
Web Site: http://www.cabotcheese.coop
Sales Range: $100-124.9 Million
Emp.: 350
Natural & Processed Cheese Fluid Milk & Creamery Butter Distr
N.A.I.C.S.: 424430
Jed Davis *(Dir-Sustainability)*

AGRI-SYSTEMS
1300 Minnesota Ave, Billings, MT
59101
Tel.: (406) 245-6231
Web Site: http://www.agrisystems.net
Sales Range: $10-24.9 Million
Emp.: 70
Agricultural Building Contractors
N.A.I.C.S.: 236220
Robert H. Hamlin *(Pres)*

AGRI-WEST INTERNATIONAL INC.
199 W Rhapsody, San Antonio, TX
78216
Tel.: (210) 525-1101
Rev.: $11,000,000
Emp.: 12
Bond Brokers
N.A.I.C.S.: 424410
John Bellinger *(Chm)*

AGRICO SALES INC.
15100 Intracoastal Dr, New Orleans,
LA 70129
Tel.: (504) 436-6546
Web Site: http://www.agricosales.com
Sales Range: $10-24.9 Million
Emp.: 25
Provider of Grain Elevator Construction Services
N.A.I.C.S.: 236220
Frank Kelly *(Founder & Pres)*
Bob Rieck *(VP-Sls)*
Gary Handbury *(Project Mgr)*

AGRICULTURAL COMMODITIES INC.
2224 Oxford Rd, New Oxford, PA
17350-9643
Tel.: (717) 624-8249   PA
Year Founded: 1983
Sales Range: $10-24.9 Million
Emp.: 70
Producers of Prepared Feeds
N.A.I.C.S.: 424910
Richard Sharrer *(Pres)*
Rob Simmons *(Controller)*

AGRICULTURAL SERVICE INC.
2777 N Broadwell Ave, Grand Island,
NE 68803
Tel.: (308) 382-0160
Web Site: https://www.asihiyield.com
Sales Range: $10-24.9 Million
Emp.: 70

Fertilizer & Fertilizer Materials
N.A.I.C.S.: 424910

AGRIFARM INDUSTRIES LLC
510 E Bedford St, Dimmitt, TX
79027-2120
Tel.: (806) 647-2141   TX
Year Founded: 1998
Sales Range: $10-24.9 Million
Emp.: 48
Sales Of Grain & Field Beans
N.A.I.C.S.: 424510

AGRIHOLDING INC.
1227 Silver Ct, Pebble Beach, CA
93953-3221
Tel.: (831) 626-3932
Sales Range: $10-24.9 Million
Emp.: 5
Holding Company
N.A.I.C.S.: 488510
Robert Ingleheart *(Pres)*

AGRILAND FS, INC.
421 N 10th St, Winterset, IA 50273
Tel.: (515) 462-5353   IA
Web Site: https://www.agrilandfs.com
Year Founded: 1931
Sales Range: $250-299.9 Million
Agricultural Services
N.A.I.C.S.: 115112
John Knobloch *(Gen Mgr)*
Brian Dickinson *(Mgr)*

AGRITECH WORLWIDE, INC.
1011 Campus Dr, Mundelein, IL
60060
Tel.: (847) 549-6002   NV
Web Site: http://www.ztrim.com
Year Founded: 1994
Sales Range: $1-9.9 Million
Emp.: 14
All-Natural Agricultural-Based Fat Replacement Product Mfr
N.A.I.C.S.: 325414
Steven J. Cohen *(Mng Dir-Comm & Plng)*
Craig R. Jalbert *(Interim CEO & Interim CFO)*
Therese Malundo *(VP-Science & Tech)*
Craig R. Jalbert *(Interim CEO & Interim CFO)*

Subsidiaries:

FiberGel Technologies, Inc.   (1)
1011 Campus Dr, Mundelein, IL 60060
Tel.: (847) 549-6002
Web Site: http://www.ztrim.com
Sales Range: $10-24.9 Million
All-Natural Agricultural-Based Fat Replacement Product Mfr & Licensor
N.A.I.C.S.: 325414

AGRITEK HOLDINGS, INC.
777 Brickell Ave Ste 500, Miami, FL
33131
Tel.: (305) 721-2727   DE
Web Site: http://www.agritekholdings.com
Year Founded: 1997
AGTK—(OTCBB)
Sales Range: Less than $1 Million
Emp.: 1
Holding Company; Marijuana Brand & Cultivation Real Estate Assets Investment, Development & Leasing Services
N.A.I.C.S.: 551112

AGRIVEST INC.
650 W U S 136, Waynetown, IN
47990
Tel.: (765) 234-2252
Web Site: http://www.agrivestinc.com
Rev.: $13,000,000
Emp.: 70

Agrivest Inc.—(Continued)

Producer of Hogs
N.A.I.C.S.: 311119
Fritz Holzgrefe *(Pres)*
Erich Wesjohann *(Sec & VP)*

AGRIVISION GROUP, LLC
58668 190th St, Pacific Junction, IA 51561
Tel.: (712) 622-8223
Web Site: http://www.agrivision.us
Sales Range: $10-24.9 Million
Emp.: 150
Farming Equipment Distr
N.A.I.C.S.: 423820
Donald Athen *(Principal)*
Todd Barker *(Principal)*

AGRO-IRON, INC.
201 W Christina Blvd Ste 3, Lakeland, FL 33813
Tel.: (863) 648-9555   DE
Year Founded: 1994
Sales Range: $10-24.9 Million
Holding Company; Lawn & Garden Products Retailer & Landscaping Services
N.A.I.C.S.: 551112
Lawrence Hjersted *(Chm & CEO)*
Evin Netzer *(Pres)*
Robert Livengood *(CFO & Sec)*

Subsidiaries:

Bay Breeze Farms, Inc.   (1)
4331 Cockroach Bay Rd, Ruskin, FL 33570
Tel.: (813) 645-6911
Sod Nursery, Fertilizer Mfr & Vegetated Retaining Wall Systems Installation
N.A.I.C.S.: 111421
Lawrence Hjersted *(Chm & CEO)*
Evin Netzer *(Pres)*

Subsidiary (Domestic):

Dieter's Sod Service, Inc.   (2)
2315 Zipperer Rd, Bradenton, FL 34212   (75%)
Tel.: (941) 745-2334
Web Site: http://www.dieterssod.com
Sales Range: $1-9.9 Million
Emp.: 22
Sod Sales & Landscaping Services
N.A.I.C.S.: 561730
Mike Lacombe *(Coord-Logistics)*

AGROMIN INC.
201 Kinetic Dr, Oxnard, CA 93030
Tel.: (805) 485-9200
Web Site: https://www.agromin.com
Year Founded: 2005
Sales Range: $10-24.9 Million
Emp.: 86
Pulp Mill
N.A.I.C.S.: 322110
Dave Green *(VP-Mktg & Sls)*

AGSI
201 17th St Nw Ste 300, Atlanta, GA 30363
Tel.: (404) 816-7577   GA
Web Site: http://www.agsi.com
Year Founded: 1981
Sales Range: $10-24.9 Million
Emp.: 110
Provider of Computer Integrated Systems Design & Services
N.A.I.C.S.: 541512
Gregg Fellows *(Mng Partner)*
Terrie Jones *(Founder)*

AGSTEN CONSTRUCTION COMPANY
209 Washington St W Ste 100, Charleston, WV 25302
Tel.: (304) 343-5400
Web Site:
   http://www.agstenconstruction.com
Sales Range: $25-49.9 Million

Emp.: 50
Commercial & Institutional Building Construction
N.A.I.C.S.: 236220
Mary B. Agsten *(Sec & VP)*
Carl Agsten *(Pres & Treas)*

AGTEGRA COOPERATIVE
811 3rd Ave SE, Aberdeen, SD 57401
Tel.: (605) 225-5500
Web Site: https://www.agtegra.com
Year Founded: 2018
Agronomy Cooperative
N.A.I.C.S.: 813990
Chris Pearson *(CEO)*
Tracy Limbo *(Sr Vp-Agronomy, Comm & Mktg)*

AGUDATH ISREAL OF AMERICA COMMUNITY SERVICES INC
42 Broadway, New York, NY 10004
Tel.: (212) 797-9000   NY
Year Founded: 1997
Sales Range: $1-9.9 Million
Community Care Services
N.A.I.C.S.: 624190
David Tannenbaum *(Sec)*

AGVANTAGE FS, INC.
1600 8th St SW, Waverly, IA 50677
Tel.: (319) 483-4900   IA
Web Site:
   https://www.agvantagefs.com
Year Founded: 1931
Sales Range: $10-24.9 Million
Emp.: 105
Farm Supplies & Petroleum Distr
N.A.I.C.S.: 423820

AGVENTURE FEEDS & SEED INC.
209 2nd St, Watkins, MN 55389
Tel.: (320) 764-9910
Web Site:
   http://www.agventurefeeds.com
Year Founded: 1970
Sales Range: $1-9.9 Million
Emp.: 8
Feed Products
N.A.I.C.S.: 112112
Sandy Hansen-Wolff *(Owner & Pres)*

AGVENTURES, LLC.
720 N Main St, Shawano, WI 54154
Tel.: (920) 846-4770
Web Site: http://agventuresllc.com
Rev.: $12,900,000
Emp.: 50
Seed, Fertilizer & Chemical Merchant Whslr
N.A.I.C.S.: 424910
Tom Heimke *(Mgr-Sls)*
Randy Heise *(Mgr-Sls)*
Steve Wery *(CFO)*

AGW CAPITAL ADVISORS
511 W Bay St Ste 310, Tampa, FL 33606
Tel.: (813) 254-4700
Web Site:
   https://www.agwcapital.com
Rev.: $548,000,000
Investment Banking & Advisory Services
N.A.I.C.S.: 523150
Jay Annis *(Co-Founder)*
P. J. Gardner *(Co-Founder)*
Kathy Bryant *(Dir-Client Rels)*
Paul Whiting Jr. *(Co-Founder)*

AGWAY SYSTEMS
12959 Ronaldson Rd, Baton Rouge, LA 70807
Tel.: (225) 778-1440

Web Site:
   https://www.agwaysystems.com
Year Founded: 1970
Sales Range: $25-49.9 Million
Emp.: 113
Trucking Service
N.A.I.C.S.: 484121
Leonard F. Aguillard *(Pres)*

AHA!
415 W 6th St Ste 605, Vancouver, WA 98660
Tel.: (360) 750-1680
Web Site: http://www.ahainc.com
Year Founded: 1994
Sales Range: $1-9.9 Million
Emp.: 32
Online Advertising Services
N.A.I.C.S.: 541810
Angela Matthews *(Project Mgr)*
Betsy Henning *(Founder & CEO)*
Brett Thacher *(Acct Dir)*
Bridget Berquist *(Project Mgr)*
Christian Hicks *(Dir-Creative)*
Eric Smith *(Dir-Creative)*
Corey Shields *(Dir-Art)*
Eileen Wong *(Dir-Mktg & Bus Dev)*
Jim Schwenke *(Sr Dir-Creative)*
Pamela Fiehn *(Sr Dir-Creative)*
Steve Shields *(Mng Partner)*

AHC INC.
2230 N Fairfax Dr Ste100, Arlington, VA 22201
Tel.: (703) 486-0626   VA
Web Site: https://www.ahcinc.org
Year Founded: 1975
Sales Range: $10-24.9 Million
Emp.: 92
Affordable Housing Services
N.A.I.C.S.: 624229
Arno L. Harris *(Mng Partner)*
James Ponder *(CEO)*
Steve Yeatman *(CFO)*
Stania Romain *(Dir-HR)*
Catherine Bucknam *(Dir-Community Rels)*
Stephen E. Smith *(Sr VP)*
Walter D. Webdale *(Pres)*
Justin Oliver *(Chm)*
Carleton Jenkins *(Treas)*
Michael Werner *(Sr VP-Property Mgmt)*
Arno L. Harris *(Mng Partner)*

AHD ASSOCIATES INC.
27470 Gloede Dr, Warren, MI 48088
Tel.: (586) 552-1414
Web Site:
   https://www.ahdvintners.com
Rev.: $10,300,000
Emp.: 10
Winery
N.A.I.C.S.: 424820
Anthony C. Delsener *(Pres)*

AHEAD MAGNETICS, INC.
6410 Via Del Oro, San Jose, CA 95119
Tel.: (408) 226-9991   CA
Web Site: http://www.aheadtek.com
Year Founded: 2002
Sales Range: $1-9.9 Million
Emp.: 100
Electronic Components Mfr
N.A.I.C.S.: 334419
Tim Higgins *(Pres)*
Patrick Johnston *(Exec VP-Bus Dev)*
Hristo Mishkov *(Dir-Mfg)*
Yolanda Verdugo *(Dir-HR)*
Ed Soldani *(CFO)*

AHEARINGAID.COM LLC
1141 Mall Dr Ste E, Las Cruces, NM 88011-1009
Tel.: (575) 522-7610   NM

Year Founded: 1997
Sales Range: Less than $1 Million
Emp.: 8
Online Hearing Aids & Related Products Retailer
N.A.I.C.S.: 423450
Steve McAfee *(Owner & CEO)*

AHERN & ASSOCIATES INC.
5725 Kanawha Tpke, South Charleston, WV 25309
Tel.: (304) 766-8062
Rev.: $24,376,000
Emp.: 20
Dam Construction
N.A.I.C.S.: 236210
Brian Burgett *(Pres)*

AHF INDUSTRIES, INC.
8647 W State Rd 56, French Lick, IN 47432
Tel.: (812) 936-9988
Web Site: https://www.plutocorp.com
Year Founded: 1913
Sales Range: $10-24.9 Million
Emp.: 150
Bottle Mfr & Packaging & Labeling Services
N.A.I.C.S.: 326160
Bernice Friedman *(Corp Sec)*
Steve Tow *(Mgr-Engrg)*
Dave Mathers *(Mgr-Ops)*

AHI SUPPLY INC.
2800 N Gordon, Alvin, TX 77511
Tel.: (281) 331-0088
Web Site: https://www.ahi-supply.com
Rev.: $20,700,000
Emp.: 85
Brick, Stone & Related Material
N.A.I.C.S.: 423320
Bob Allen *(Owner)*
Micheal Hill *(Pres)*

AHMC & AHMC HEALTHCARE INC.
1000 S Fremont Ave Bldg A-9 E Unit 6, Alhambra, CA 91803
Tel.: (626) 457-7400
Web Site:
   https://www.ahmchealth.com
Year Founded: 2004
Sales Range: $50-74.9 Million
Emp.: 5,500
Hospital Services
N.A.I.C.S.: 622110
Philip A. Cohen *(COO)*
Pacita Diaz *(Mgr-Acctg)*
Nicole Chorvat *(Project Mgr)*
Linda Marsh *(Sr Exec VP)*

Subsidiaries:

Anaheim Regional Medical Center   (1)
1111 W La Palma Ave, Anaheim, CA 92801   (100%)
Tel.: (714) 774-1450
Web Site:
   http://www.anaheimregionalmc.com
Sales Range: $75-99.9 Million
Emp.: 1,200
Health Services
N.A.I.C.S.: 622110
Margaret Martin *(Dir-Quality Svcs)*
Rick Castro *(CEO)*
Mary Anne Monje *(CFO & COO)*
Lisa Hahn *(Chief Nursing Officer)*

San Gabriel Valley Medical Center   (1)
438 W Las Tunas Dr, San Gabriel, CA 91776-1216
Tel.: (626) 289-5454
Web Site: http://www.sgvmc.com
Sales Range: $25-49.9 Million
Emp.: 800
Healthcare Facilities
N.A.I.C.S.: 621112

Jon Aquino *(CEO-Interim)*
Andrew Grim *(CFO)*
Edgar Solis *(Chief Nursing Officer)*
Eileen Diamond *(Chief Bus Dev Officer)*

AHN INTERNATIONAL LLC
8521 Six Forks Rd Ste 105, Raleigh, NC 27615
Tel.: (919) 846-8641
Veterinary Supplies Wholesaler
N.A.I.C.S.: 423450
Kathleen Lopiano *(CFO)*
Cathy Matarese *(Office Mgr)*

AHNTECH, INC.
3333 Camino del Rio St Ste 120, San Diego, CA 92108
Tel.: (619) 516-5900
Web Site: http://www.ahntech.com
Sales Range: $25-49.9 Million
Emp.: 375
Engineeering Services
N.A.I.C.S.: 541330
Sam Ahn *(Founder & Pres)*

AHTNA INCORPORATED
115 Richardson Hwy, Glennallen, AK 99588
Tel.: (907) 822-3476   AK
Web Site: http://www.ahtna-inc.com
Year Founded: 1972
Emp.: 2,000
Heavy Construction
N.A.I.C.S.: 236210
Ken Johns *(Pres & CEO)*
Kathryn Martin *(Sr VP)*
Gloria Stickwan *(Coord-Customary, Traditional & Environmental)*
Tom Maloney *(Co-CEO)*
Mitchelle Anderson *(Pres)*
Joe Bovee *(VP-Land Resources)*
Douglas Miller *(VP-HR)*
Eleanor Dementi *(Vice Chm)*
Jason B. Hart *(Treas)*
Linda Pete *(Sec)*
Roy J. Tansy Jr. *(Exec VP)*

Subsidiaries:

Ahtna Construction & Primary Products Corporation   (1)
110 W 38th Ave Ste 100, Anchorage, AK 99503
Tel.: (907) 929-5612
Web Site: http://www.ahtnaconstruction.com
Sales Range: $10-24.9 Million
Emp.: 4
Pipeline Maintenance Contractor
N.A.I.C.S.: 237120
David O'Donnell *(Pres)*

Ahtna Development Corporation   (1)
PO Box 649, Glennallen, AK 99588   (100%)
Tel.: (907) 868-8250
Web Site: http://www.ahtna-inc.com
Sales Range: $10-24.9 Million
Emp.: 2
Property Management & Site Development Services
N.A.I.C.S.: 531110

Ahtna Enterprises Corporation   (1)
406 W Fireweed Ln Ste 101, Anchorage, AK 99503   (100%)
Tel.: (907) 868-8209
Web Site: http://www.ahtna-inc.com
Sales Range: $1-9.9 Million
Emp.: 40
Nonresidential Construction
N.A.I.C.S.: 236220
Brenda Rebne *(Pres)*

Ahtna Netiye', Inc.   (1)
110 W 38th Ave Ste 100B, Anchorage, AK 99503
Tel.: (907) 868-8250
Web Site: http://www.ahtna.net
Emp.: 5
Investment Management Service
N.A.I.C.S.: 523940
Roy Jake Tansy Jr. *(Exec VP)*

Subsidiary (Domestic):

Ahtna Contractors, LLC   (2)
3680 Industrial Blvd Ste 600H, West Sacramento, CA 95691
Tel.: (916) 329-1591
Web Site: http://www.ahtnacontractors.com
Sales Range: $1-9.9 Million
Construction Engineering Services
N.A.I.C.S.: 541330

Ahtna Design-Build, Inc.   (2)
3200 El Camino Real Ste 240, Irvine, CA 92602
Tel.: (714) 824-3471
Web Site: http://www.ahtnadb.com
Emp.: 250
Construction Engineering Services
N.A.I.C.S.: 541330
Craig O'Rourke *(Pres)*
David Fehrenbach *(CFO)*
Gregory Grabowski *(Dir-Engrg Svcs)*

Ahtna Engineering Services, LLC   (2)
110 W 38th Ave Ste 100, Anchorage, AK 99503
Tel.: (907) 646-2969
Web Site: http://www.ahtnaes.com
Emp.: 40
Construction Engineering Services
N.A.I.C.S.: 541330
Tim Finnigan *(Dir-Programs & Project Mgmt)*
Ken Gould *(Pres & CEO)*

Ahtna Environmental, Inc.   (2)
110 W 38th Ave Ste 200B, Anchorage, AK 99503
Tel.: (907) 644-0760
Web Site: http://www.ahtna-inc.com
Environmental Engineering Services
N.A.I.C.S.: 541330
Tim Finnigan *(Pres)*

Ahtna Government Services Corporation   (2)
3100 Beacon Blvd, West Sacramento, CA 95691
Tel.: (916) 372-2000
Web Site: http://www.ahtnagov.com
Emp.: 40
Engineering Consulting Services
N.A.I.C.S.: 541330
Craig O'Rourke *(Pres)*
David Frenzel *(Dir-Construction Ops)*
Randy Rogers *(Sr Mgr-Program)*

Ahtna Professional Services, Inc. (2)
110 W 38th Ave Ste 200F, Anchorage, AK 99503
Tel.: (907) 868-8285
Engineering Consulting Services
N.A.I.C.S.: 541330

Ahtna Support and Training Services, LLC   (2)
110 W 38th Ave Ste 200D, Anchorage, AK 99503
Tel.: (907) 334-6477
Web Site: http://www.ahtnasts.com
Emp.: 5
Business Support Services
N.A.I.C.S.: 561499
Vicky Dunlap *(Pres)*

Ahtna Technical Services Inc.   (2)
110 W 38th Ave Ste 200C, Anchorage, AK 99503
Tel.: (907) 334-9664
Web Site: http://www.atsiak.com
Sales Range: $1-9.9 Million
Emp.: 30
Facilities Support Services
N.A.I.C.S.: 561210
Sue Taylor *(Pres & CEO)*

Ahtna Technologies, Inc.   (2)
110 W 38th Ave Ste 100C, Anchorage, AK 99503
Tel.: (907) 865-3841
Engineering Consulting Services
N.A.I.C.S.: 541330

Koht'aene Enterprises Company, LLC   (2)
110 W 38th Ste 200 G, Anchorage, AK 99503
Tel.: (907) 334-9255
Web Site: http://www.kohtaene.com
Construction Engineering Services

N.A.I.C.S.: 541330
Susan Taylor *(Pres)*

AHTNA, INC.
115 Richardson Hwy, Glennallen, AK 99588
Tel.: (907) 822-3476   AK
Web Site: http://www.ahtna-inc.com
Year Founded: 1971
Civil Engineering & Business Management Services
N.A.I.C.S.: 541330
Michelle Anderson *(Pres)*
Nicholas Jackson *(Chm)*
Linda Pete *(Treas)*
Karen Linnell *(Vice Chm)*
Genevieve John *(Sec)*
Kathryn Martin *(Sr VP)*
Joe Bovee *(VP-Land & Resources)*
Douglas Miller *(VP-HR)*
Matt Tisher *(CFO & VP-Fin)*
Nicholas Ostrovsky *(Gen Counsel)*
Eric Mclaurin *(VP-Bus Dev)*
Brian Robbins *(VP-IT)*
Roy J. Tansy Jr. *(CEO)*

Subsidiaries:

AAA Valley Gravel, LLC   (1)
1100 Little Brook Ln, Palmer, AK 99645
Tel.: (907) 745-8199
Web Site:
    http://www.alaskavalleygravel.com
Sales Range: $1-9.9 Million
Highway, Street & Bridge Construction
N.A.I.C.S.: 237310
Dave O'Donnell *(Pres)*

Cavache, Inc.   (1)
2125 E Atlantic Blvd, Pompano Beach, FL 33062
Tel.: (954) 933-7863
Web Site: http://www.cavache.com
Heavy & Civil Engineering Construction
N.A.I.C.S.: 237990

AI COLLABORATIVE, INC.
1907 E 7th Ave, Tampa, FL 33605
Tel.: (813) 247-3332
Web Site: https://www.aicoll.com
Year Founded: 1990
Sales Range: $1-9.9 Million
Emp.: 15
Architectural & Interior Design Services
N.A.I.C.S.: 541310
Leigh M. Young *(Pres & Partner)*
Donald E. Whallen *(Partner & VP)*
Michael M. Puckett *(Mng Partner)*

AI INTERNATIONAL CORP.
414 E 75th St Fl 2, New York, NY 10021
Tel.: (212) 737-3000
Sales Range: $10-24.9 Million
Emp.: 28
Automotive Supplies & Parts
N.A.I.C.S.: 523940
Kalman Maduro *(Controller)*
Les Christosseo *(Gen Mgr)*

AIA CORPORATION
222 College Ave Fl 9, Appleton, WI 54911
Tel.: (800) 460-7836
Web Site:
    http://www.aiacommunity.com
Year Founded: 1981
Services Related to Advertising
N.A.I.C.S.: 541890
Billie Jo Mathusek *(Dir-Mktg)*

AIB FINANCIAL GROUP
3020 NW 79th Ave, Doral, FL 33122-1010
Tel.: (305) 554-0800
Year Founded: 1973
Rev.: $26,300,000
Emp.: 115

Insurance Services
N.A.I.C.S.: 524210

AIC VENTURES, LP
4131 N Central Expwy Ste 820, Dallas, TX 75204
Tel.: (214) 363-5620   TX
Web Site:
    http://www.aicventures.com
Year Founded: 1990
Sales Range: $25-49.9 Million
Emp.: 40
Real Estate Investment Fund Manager
N.A.I.C.S.: 525910
Paul Robshaw *(Chm & Mng Partner)*
Peter S. Carlsen *(Pres & Mng Partner)*
Michael J. Baucus *(Mng Partner-Portfolio Ops)*
David Robshaw *(Mng Partner-Capital & Mktg)*
Luis Medina *(Mng partner-Acq)*
Matthew W. Albracht *(Partner-Acq)*
Tom E. Cramer *(Dir-Asset Mgmt)*
Heath Esterak *(Mng Dir-Legal)*
David Gimbel *(Dir-Capital Markets)*
R. L. Stowe Mills *(CFO)*

AIDAN INDUSTRIES, INC.
275 W 39th St, New York, NY 10018
Tel.: (212) 840-0106
Web Site:
    http://www.catherinemalandrino.com
Sales Range: $10-24.9 Million
Emp.: 30
Designer & Whslr of Women's Apparel
N.A.I.C.S.: 424350
Bernard Aidan *(CEO)*

AIDS ACTION COMMITTEE OF MA, INC.
75 Amory St, Boston, MA 02119
Tel.: (617) 437-6200   MA
Web Site: https://www.aac.org
Year Founded: 1986
Sales Range: $10-24.9 Million
Emp.: 293
Disease Prevention Services
N.A.I.C.S.: 923120
Susan Kelley *(VP-Ops)*

AIDS HEALTHCARE FOUNDATION
6255 W Sunset Blvd 21st Fl, Los Angeles, CA 90028
Tel.: (323) 860-5200
Web Site: https://www.aidshealth.org
Sales Range: $10-24.9 Million
Medicine & Advocacy Services
N.A.I.C.S.: 327910
Michael Weinstein *(Pres)*
Peter Reis *(Sr VP)*
Lyle Honig *(CFO)*
Rodney L. Wright *(Sec)*
Cynthia Davis *(Chm)*
Diana Hoorzuk *(Vice Chm)*
Steve L. Carlton *(Treas)*
Samantha Granberry *(Sr Dir-Mktg & Sls)*
Whitney Engeran-Cordova *(Sr Dir-Pub Health)*
Scott Carruthers *(Chief Pharmacy Officer)*
Donna Tempesta *(VP-Fin-Northern Reg)*
Anita Castille *(VP-HR)*

Subsidiaries:

MOMS Pharmacy, Inc.   (1)
45 Melville Park Rd, Melville, NY 11747
Tel.: (631) 547-6520
Web Site: http://www.momspharmacy.com
Rev.: $3,000,000
Emp.: 50

AIDS Healthcare Foundation—(Continued)

Prescription Medication Ditsr
N.A.I.C.S.: 456110

Subsidiary (Domestic):

AHF Pharmacy - San Diego   (2)
3940 4th Ave, San Diego, CA 92103
Tel.: (619) 574-9700
Web Site: http://ahfpharmacy.org
Emp.: 10
Prescription Medications Distr
N.A.I.C.S.: 456110
Christine Turner (Mgr-Pharmacy)

AIDS RESOURCE CENTER OF WISCONSIN
820 N Plankinton Ave, Milwaukee, WI 53203
Tel.: (414) 273-1991   WI
Web Site: http://www.arcw.org
Year Founded: 1986
Sales Range: $10-24.9 Million
Emp.: 183
HIV Prevention Services
N.A.I.C.S.: 622110
Mike Gifford (Pres & CEO)
Debra J. Endean (COO & VP)
Dan Bitenc (Dir-Govt Revenue Procurement-Milwaukee)
Dan Mueller (Chief Dev Officer-Milwaukee & VP)
Roma Hanson (VP-Organizational Dev-Milwaukee)
Anne Daugherty-Leiter (Dir-HR-Madison)
Laura Johnson (Dir-Case Mgmt-Madison)
Rebekah Kopec-Farrell (Dir-Legal Svcs-Milwaukee)
Winsome Panton (Dir-Clinic Ops-Green Bay)
Scott Stokes (Dir-Prevention Svcs-Green Bay)
Mary Hartwig (Dir-Special Events-Milwaukee)
Nick Olson (Dir-Clinical Pharmacy Svcs-Milwaukee)
Karin Sabey (VP-Ops)
Freda Russell (VP-Cultural & Organizational Dev)

AIDS UNITED
1101 14st, Washington, DC 20005
Tel.: (202) 408-4848   OH
Web Site: http://www.aidsunited.org
Year Founded: 1990
Sales Range: $10-24.9 Million
Emp.: 84
Grantmaking Services
N.A.I.C.S.: 813211
Jesse Milan Jr. (Pres & CEO)

AIG DIRECT INSURANCE SERVICES, INC.
9640 Granite Ridge Dr Ste 200, San Diego, CA 92123
Tel.: (858) 309-3000   CA
Web Site: https://www.aigdirect.com
Year Founded: 1995
Insurance Services
N.A.I.C.S.: 524113
Ron Harris (Founder)
Brad Johnson (Dir-Software Dev)
Patty Karstein (Sr VP-Media)
Kevin Wilshusen (Sr VP-Sls)
Terre Remington (Dir-Admin)

AIGLON CAPITAL MANAGEMENT LLC
3102 Surrey Rd, Durham, NC 27707
Tel.: (919) 973-5555
Web Site: http://www.aigloncapital.com
Privater Equity Firm
N.A.I.C.S.: 523999
Richard Griffin (Mng Partner)

AIGNER PRENSKY MARKETING GROUP
214 Lincoln St Ste 300, Allston, MA 02134
Tel.: (617) 254-9500   MA
Web Site: http://www.aignerprenskymktg.com
Year Founded: 1984
Sales Range: $10-24.9 Million
Emp.: 10
Public Relations Agency
N.A.I.C.S.: 541820
Anne-Marie Aigner (Pres & Principal)
Janet Prensky (Principal & Sr VP)

AIIR CONSULTING, LLC
50 Monument Rd Ste 205, Bala Cynwyd, PA 19004
Tel.: (215) 337-4939
Web Site: http://www.aiirconsulting.com
Year Founded: 2009
Sales Range: $25-49.9 Million
Emp.: 12
Business Consulting Services
N.A.I.C.S.: 541613
Jonathan Kirschner (Founder & CEO)
Megan Marshall (VP-Client Svcs)
Robyn Garrett (VP-Mktg)
Christopher Cotteta (Dir-Res & Innovation)
Derek Smith (Dir-IT)

AIJJ ENTERPRISES INC.
1000 Pennsylvania Ave, Brooklyn, NY 11207-8417
Tel.: (718) 485-3000
Web Site: http://www.rainbowshops.com
Year Founded: 1981
Sales Range: $450-499.9 Million
Emp.: 500
Sales of Women's Clothing
N.A.I.C.S.: 458110
Albert Chehebar (Pres)

Subsidiaries:

Rainbow Apparel Companies Inc.   (1)
1000 Pennsylvania Ave, Brooklyn, NY 11207-8417
Tel.: (718) 485-3000
Web Site: http://www.rainbowshops.com
Apparel Sales
N.A.I.C.S.: 458110
David Cost (Dir-ECommerce)

AIKEN ELECTRIC COOPERATIVE INC.
2790 Wagner Rd, Aiken, SC 29801
Tel.: (803) 649-6245   SC
Web Site: https://www.aikenco-op.org
Year Founded: 1938
Sales Range: $75-99.9 Million
Emp.: 130
Distr of Electric Power
N.A.I.C.S.: 221118
Gary L. Stooksbury (CEO)
Annelle Stone (VP-Fin & Tech)
Linda Bramlett (Co-Treas & Sec)
Robert Curry (VP)
Frank Dorn (Co-Treas)
April Collins (VP-Fin & Tech)

AILERON CAPITAL MANAGEMENT, LLC
5510 W La Salle St 3rd Fl, Tampa, FL 33607
Tel.: (813) 341-3654
Web Site: http://www.aileroncap.com
Sales Range: $1-9.9 Million
Emp.: 6
Real Estate Lending Services
N.A.I.C.S.: 522310
Joseph R. Bonora (Mng Dir)

AIM AGENCY
10679 Westview Pkwy 2nd Fl, San Diego, CA 92126
Tel.: (619) 821-8218
Web Site: http://www.aimagency.rcbeta.info
Sales Range: $10-24.9 Million
Emp.: 32
Event Marketing & Outdoor Advertising
N.A.I.C.S.: 541810
Annette Monagas (CEO & Gen Counsel)
Jeff Symon (Pres & Chief Creative Officer)
Scott Cone (Sr VP-Mktg Strategy)

AIM CONSULTING GROUP, LLC
8430 W Bryn Mawr Ave Ste 1150, Chicago, IL 60631
Tel.: (773) 243-7732
Web Site: http://www.aimconsulting.com
Emp.: 282
Information Technology Services
N.A.I.C.S.: 519290
Bill VanSickle (Co-Founder & CEO)
Josh Bowser (Co-Founder & Partner)
Ron Rother (Co-Founder & Pres-Central)
Kyle Guilford (Co-Founder & Pres-West)
Areos Ledesma (Dir-Solutions)
Vinesh Kapadia (Mng Dir)
Katie Merkle (Mgr-Talent Strategy & Recruiting)
Taylor Hadley (VP-Natl Recruiting)

AIM ELECTRONICS
2080 Hartel St, Levittown, PA 19057
Tel.: (215) 946-3900
Web Site: http://www.aimelectronics.com
Year Founded: 1982
Sales Range: $10-24.9 Million
Emp.: 22
Industrial Electronic Components Distr
N.A.I.C.S.: 423610
Jim Dunn (Pres & CEO)
Allan Kolbes (VP)
Ronnie Gale (Mgr-Production)

AIM ENGINEERING & SURVEYING INC.
5300 Lee Blvd, Lehigh Acres, FL 33971
Tel.: (239) 332-4569
Web Site: http://www.aimengineering.com
Year Founded: 1980
Sales Range: $25-49.9 Million
Emp.: 140
Engineering & Surveying Services
N.A.I.C.S.: 541330
James D. Hull (Pres & CEO)
Jerron K. Hull (COO)
Ron Kerfoot (Engr-Civil)

AIM INTERNATIONAL, INC.
3923 E Flamingo Ave, Nampa, ID 83687-3102
Tel.: (208) 465-5116   ID
Web Site: http://www.theaimcompanies.com
Year Founded: 1982
Sales Range: $10-24.9 Million
Emp.: 50
Medicinal Products
N.A.I.C.S.: 325411
Ron Wright (Co-Owner & Co-Pres)

Subsidiaries:

AIM Canada Inc   (1)
390 - 2025 W 42nd Ave, Vancouver, V6M

2B5, BC, Canada
Tel.: (888) 343-9977
Herbal Supplement Distr
N.A.I.C.S.: 424210

Aim U.S.A. Inc.   (1)
3923 E Flamingo Ave, Nampa, ID 83687-3102   (100%)
Tel.: (208) 465-5116
Web Site: http://www.theaimcompanies.com
Drugs, Proprietaries & Sundries
N.A.I.C.S.: 424210
Dennis J. Itami (Co-Owner)
Shirley McAllister (Dir-HR)

AIM LEASING CO.
1500 Trumbull Ave, Girard, OH 44420-3453
Tel.: (330) 759-0438   OH
Web Site: http://www.aimntls.com
Year Founded: 1982
Sales Range: $200-249.9 Million
Emp.: 800
Provider of Truck Leasing Services
N.A.I.C.S.: 532120
Thomas Fleming (Chm, Pres & CEO)
Rick Fox (VP-Fin)
Terry DiMascio (Sr VP-Ops)
Jeff Manion (VP-Sls)
Dan Fleming (VP-Sls Ops)

Subsidiaries:

Estes Leasing LLC   (1)
701 Commerce Rd, Richmond, VA 23224
Tel.: (877) 378-3753
Equipment Finance Leasing Services
N.A.I.C.S.: 522220

AIM MEDIA TEXAS, LLC
1400 E Nolana Ave, McAllen, TX 78504
Tel.: (214) 697-9779   DE
Web Site: http://www.aimmediatx.com
Year Founded: 2012
Emp.: 500
Holding Company; Newspaper Publisher
N.A.I.C.S.: 551112
Jeremy L. Halbreich (Chm & CEO)
William R. Starks (Pres & COO)
Patrick S. Canty (Reg VP)

Subsidiaries:

The Brownsville Herald   (1)
1135 E Van Buren St, Brownsville, TX 78520
Tel.: (956) 542-4301
Web Site: http://www.brownsvilleherald.com
Sales Range: $10-24.9 Million
Emp.: 63
Newspapers
N.A.I.C.S.: 513110
Sandy McGehee (Dir-Educational Svcs)
Odie Carden (Dir-IT & Internet Svcs)
Frank Escobedo (Publr)
Abe Gonzalez (Dir-Circulation)

The Mid Valley Town Crier   (1)
401 S Iowa, Weslaco, TX 78596
Tel.: (956) 969-2543
Web Site: http://www.midvalleytowncrier.com
Sales Range: $10-24.9 Million
Emp.: 15
Newspapers
N.A.I.C.S.: 513110
John Drieder (Gen Mgr)

The Monitor   (1)
1400 E Nolana, McAllen, TX 78504   (100%)
Tel.: (956) 683-4000
Web Site: http://www.themonitor.com
Sales Range: $10-24.9 Million
Emp.: 250
Newspapers
N.A.I.C.S.: 513110
Benita Mendell (Gen Mgr)
Armando Martinez (Dir-HR)
Doug Fullerton (Dir-IT)
Robert Levrier (Dir-Circulation)
Stephan Wingert (Publr, Reg VP & Editor)

The Odessa American (1)
222 E 4th St, Odessa, TX 79760
Tel.: (432) 337-4661
Web Site: http://www.oaoa.com
Sales Range: $10-24.9 Million
Emp.: 70
Newspapers
N.A.I.C.S.: 513110
Patrick S. Canty *(Publr)*
Stacey Ream *(Dir-Adv & Mktg)*
Coye S. Kerley *(Mgr-Adv Sls)*
Stacy Reeves *(Coord-Natl Adv)*
Laura Denn *(Dir-Adv)*
Jim King *(Dir-Ops)*

Valley Morning Star (1)
1310 S Commerce, Harlingen, TX 78550
Tel.: (956) 430-6200
Web Site: http://www.valleystar.com
Sales Range: $10-24.9 Million
Emp.: 85
Newspapers
N.A.I.C.S.: 513110
Chris Castillo *(Dir-Adv)*
Diana Eva Maldonado *(Editor-Digital)*
Frank Escobedo *(Publr)*

AIM SERVICES, INC.
4227 Route 50, Saratoga Springs,
NY 12866
Tel.: (518) 587-3208   NY
Web Site:
  https://www.aimservicesinc.org
Year Founded: 1978
Sales Range: $10-24.9 Million
Emp.: 343
Developmental Disability Assistance
Services
N.A.I.C.S.: 624120
Renee Hebert *(Officer-Compliance &
Dir-Quality Metrics)*
June MacClelland *(Exec Dir)*
Janine Gennett *(Dir-Pro Clinical
Svcs)*
Scott Hartung *(Dir-Fin)*
Martin Glastetter *(Pres)*
Robert Ricketts *(VP)*
John Fleming *(Treas)*
John Paolucci *(Sec)*
Danielle Wiltsie *(Dir-Independent
Svcs)*
Gerard LaBarge *(Dir-Ops)*
Josh Phelps *(Officer-Safety & Dir-
Quality Metrics)*
Katie Carson *(Dir-HR)*
Katie Page *(Program Dir-Employment
Svcs)*
Nick Miner *(Dir-Behavioral Svcs Pro-
gram)*
Derek Taylor *(Program Dir-
Residential)*
Walt Adams *(Dir-PR)*
Marissa Wendolovske *(Program Dir-
Dev & Media)*
Carrie Wood *(Dir-Svc Coordination
Program)*

AIMCLEAR BLOG
9 W Superior St Ste 200, Duluth, MN
55802
Tel.: (218) 727-4325
Web Site:
  http://www.aimclearblog.com
Year Founded: 2007
Sales Range: $1-9.9 Million
Emp.: 16
Online Marketing Services
N.A.I.C.S.: 541613
Marty Weintraub *(Founder)*
Manny Rivas *(CMO)*
Lindsay Schleisman *(Sr Acct Mgr)*
Molly Ryan *(Sr Acct Mgr)*

AIME BELLAVANCE & SONS INCORPORATED
5 S Vine St, Barre, VT 05641
Tel.: (802) 479-9311
Web Site:
  http://www.bellavancetrucking.com

Sales Range: $10-24.9 Million
Emp.: 160
Trucking Service
N.A.I.C.S.: 484121
Roland Bellavance *(Pres)*
Chris White *(Mgr-Acctg)*

AIMEE LYNN ACCESSORIES INC.
366 5th Ave, New York, NY 10001
Tel.: (212) 268-4747
Web Site: https://amieelynn.com
Sales Range: $10-24.9 Million
Emp.: 30
Women's & Children's Accessories
N.A.I.C.S.: 424350
Steven Spolansky *(Pres)*

AIMI INC.
2606 Hwy 80 W, Garden City, GA
31408
Tel.: (912) 964-4055
Web Site: http://www.chusmart.com
Sales Range: $10-24.9 Million
Emp.: 10
Convenience Store
N.A.I.C.S.: 445131
Bobby Chu *(CEO)*
Jim Soles *(CFO)*

AINA LE'A, INC.
69-201 Waikoloa Beach Dr 2617,
Waikoloa, HI 96738
Tel.: (808) 238-0649   DE
Web Site: https://ainaleahi.com
Emp.: 6
Real Estate Development, Syndica-
tion, Asset Management & Services
N.A.I.C.S.: 531390
Robert J. Wessels *(Chm, Pres &
CEO)*
Mark E. Jackson *(CFO)*
Richard P. Bernstein *(Sec)*
Joe Bennett *(Mgr-Infrastructure)*

AIO ACQUISITIONS INC.
3200 Guasti Rd Ste 300, Ontario, CA
91761-8642
Tel.: (800) 333-3795
Web Site:
  http://www.personnelconcepts.com
Rev.: $15,000,000
Emp.: 180
Publish Safety Products & Human
Resources Solutions
N.A.I.C.S.: 513199
Robert Leland *(Dir-Res)*
Donn Dufford *(Dir-Sls & Mktg)*

AIP, LLC
450 Lexington Ave 40th Fl, New York,
NY 10017
Tel.: (212) 627-2360   DE
Web Site:
  http://www.americanindustrial.com
Year Founded: 1989
Equity Investment Firm
N.A.I.C.S.: 523999
John Becker *(Sr Mng Partner)*
Ryan Hodgson *(Partner)*
Eric Baroyan *(Partner)*
Ben DeRosa *(Partner-Bus Dev)*
Derek Leck *(Partner)*
Pete Lee *(Dir-Acctg)*
Katharine Dailey *(Mgr-Ops)*
Jen Pountain *(Office Mgr)*
Jorge Amador *(Partner)*
Daniel Davis *(Partner)*
Rich Dennis *(Partner)*
Paul J. Bamatter *(Partner & CFO)*
Dino M. Cusumano *(Sr Mng Partner
& Gen Partner)*
Joel M. Rotroff *(Partner)*
Neil D. Snyder *(Partner)*
Joel Rotroff *(Partner)*

Lee E. Evangelakos *(Partner)*
Abbas O. Elegba *(Partner)*
Kim A. Marvin *(Gen Partner)*

Subsidiaries:

AC Products, Inc. (1)
5465 Legacy Dr, Plano, TX 75024-3106
Tel.: (214) 887-2100
Web Site: http://www.armstrong.com
Sales Range: $125-149.9 Million
Emp.: 750
Kitchen & Bathroom Wood Cabinets Mfr &
Distr
N.A.I.C.S.: 337110

Subsidiary (Domestic):

Masco Cabinetry, LLC (2)
4600 Arrowhead Dr, Ann Arbor, MI 48105
Tel.: (517) 263-0771
Web Site: http://www.mascocabinetry.com
Kitchen Cabinets
N.A.I.C.S.: 337110
Joe Durham *(CFO)*
Michael Gulbernat *(VP-Builder Channel)*
Jessica Joffe *(VP-Mktg)*
Rich Wiese *(VP-HR & Customer Care)*
Chris Winans *(VP-Ops)*

Subsidiary (Domestic):

KraftMaid Cabinetry, Inc. (3)
15535 S State Ave, Middlefield, OH
44062   (100%)
Tel.: (440) 632-5333
Web Site: http://www.kraftmaid.com
Sales Range: $25-49.9 Million
Wood Cabinet Mfr
N.A.I.C.S.: 337110
Jamison Benner *(Brand Mgr)*

Division (Domestic):

Kraftmaid Cabinetry (4)
15535 S State Ave, Middlefield, OH 44062
Tel.: (877) 765-4783
Web Site: http://www.kraftmaid.com
Kitchen Cabinet Mfr
N.A.I.C.S.: 337110

Plant (Domestic):

**Masco Builder Cabinet Group-
Merillat, Atkins Panel Plant** (3)
249 Mulberry Ln, Atkins, VA 24311
Tel.: (276) 783-8550
Web Site: http://www.mascocabinetry.com
Emp.: 110
Wood Kitchen Cabinets
N.A.I.C.S.: 337110

**Masco Builder Cabinet Group-
Merillat, Jackson Plant** (3)
960 E Main St, Jackson, OH 45640
Tel.: (740) 286-5033
Web Site: http://www.merillat.com
Sales Range: $100-124.9 Million
Emp.: 176
Cabinets
N.A.I.C.S.: 337110

**Masco Builder Cabinet Group-
Merillat, Las Vegas Plant** (3)
6405 Ensworth St, Las Vegas, NV 89119-
3211
Tel.: (702) 361-4353
Cabinets
N.A.I.C.S.: 337110

**Masco Builder Cabinet Group-
Merillat, Mount Jackson Plant** (3)
1325 Industrial Park Rd, Mount Jackson,
VA 22842
Tel.: (540) 477-2961
Web Site: http://www.merillatindustries.com
Sales Range: $25-49.9 Million
Emp.: 140
Wood Kitchen Cabinets
N.A.I.C.S.: 337110

AIP, LLC - San Francisco (1)
1 Maritime Plz Ste 1925, San Francisco,
CA 94111
Tel.: (415) 788-7354
Web Site:
  http://www.americanindustrial.com

Sales Range: $125-149.9 Million
Emp.: 5
Privater Equity Firm
N.A.I.C.S.: 523999

AIP/Aerospace Holdings, LLC (1)
1395 S Lyon St, Santa Ana, CA 92705
Tel.: (877) 936-4906
Emp.: 1,300
Holding Company
N.A.I.C.S.: 551112
Jonathon Levine *(CFO & Exec VP)*
Brian Williams *(CEO)*

Subsidiary (Domestic):

Ascent Aerospace (2)
1395 S Lyon St, Santa Ana, CA 92705
Tel.: (877) 936-4906
Aircraft Tooling Systems, Composite As-
semblies & Components Mfr
N.A.I.C.S.: 336413
Brian Williams *(CEO)*
Michael Mahfet *(Pres-Integration & Automa-
tion Grp)*
Courtney Sturniolo *(Mgr-Mktg)*

Subsidiary (Domestic):

**Brown Aerospace Mfg. Systems,
LLC** (3)
65 Gaffield Dr, Kimball, MI 48074-4533
Tel.: (810) 966-9166
Web Site: http://www.aipaerospace.com
Sales Range: $1-9.9 Million
Emp.: 27
Mfr of Automated Drilling & Fastening Sys-
tems for Aerospace Industry
N.A.I.C.S.: 336413
Mark Brown *(Pres)*

Coast Composites, Inc. (3)
1395 S Lyon St, Santa Ana, CA 92705-
4608
Tel.: (949) 455-0665
Web Site: http://www.coastcomposites.com
Sales Range: $25-49.9 Million
Emp.: 300
Special Die & Tool Die Set Jig & Fixture Mfr
N.A.I.C.S.: 333514
Jerry Anthony *(Pres)*

Flow Aerospace (3)
1635 Production Dr, Jeffersonville, IN
47130-9624
Tel.: (812) 283-7888
Web Site: http://aipaerospace.com
Sales Range: $25-49.9 Million
Emp.: 65
Aerospace Products Mfr
N.A.I.C.S.: 336412

Gemcor II, LLC (3)
100 Gemcor Dr, West Seneca, NY 14224
Tel.: (716) 674-9300
Web Site: http://www.gemcor.com
Sales Range: $1-9.9 Million
Emp.: 50
Mfr of Automated Fastening, Riveting &
Workpiece Positioning Systems for Aero-
space Industry
N.A.I.C.S.: 336413
William Mangus *(Pres)*
Tony S. Goddard *(COO & Exec VP)*

Global Tooling Systems Inc. (3)
16445 23 Mile Rd, Macomb, MI 48042
Tel.: (586) 726-0500
Web Site: http://www.global-tooling-
  systems.com
Aerospace Component Mfr
N.A.I.C.S.: 334511
Tim Bellestr *(Dir-Program Mgmt)*

Odyssey Industries, LLC (3)
3020 Indianwood Rd, Lake Orion, MI 48362
Tel.: (248) 814-8800
Web Site: http://www.aipaerospace.com
Aerospace Component Mfr
N.A.I.C.S.: 334511
Josh Wood *(Project Mgr)*

Subsidiary (Domestic):

L-3 Crestview Aerospace (2)
5486 Fairchild Rd, Crestview, FL 32539
Tel.: (850) 331-4308
Web Site: http://www.l-3crestview.com
Aircraft Structures, Major Airframe Assem-
blies & Military Aircraft Modifications
N.A.I.C.S.: 336413

AIP, LLC—(Continued)

Jeff Barger *(VP & Gen Mgr)*
Brian Anderson *(VP & Gen Mgr)*
Jeff Kingsmore *(CFO & Sr Dir-Fin)*

Armstrong Wood Products, Inc.   **(1)**
5465 Legacy Dr, Plano, TX 75024
Tel.: (972) 378-4023
Web Site: http://www.armstrong.com
Sales Range: $50-74.9 Million
Emp.: 500
Hardwood Flooring, Kitchen & Bathroom
Wood Cabinets Mfr & Distr
N.A.I.C.S.: 321918

Brock Enterprises, LLC   **(1)**
10343 Sam Houston Park Dr Ste 200,
Houston, TX 77064
Tel.: (281) 807-8200
Web Site: http://www.brockgroup.com
Holding Company; Industrial Construction
Services
N.A.I.C.S.: 551112
Randall Swift *(COO)*
Michael E. McGinnis *(Chm)*
Ricardo Iglesias *(CFO)*
Drew Ashcraft *(VP & Dir-HSE)*
Krystal Hunter *(Gen Counsel)*
Alexander J. Buehler *(Pres & CEO)*

Subsidiary (Non-US):

Brock Canada Inc.   **(2)**
3735-8 Street, Nisku, T9E 8J8, AB, Canada
Tel.: (780) 465-9016
Web Site: http://www.brockgroup.com
Industrial Scaffolding, Industrial Insulation &
General Plant Maintenance Services
N.A.I.C.S.: 236210
W. C. Gary *(Pres)*
Mark Margavio *(CFO)*
Ron Lang *(Pres)*
Lee Gros *(Pres)*
Jim Dreyer *(Pres)*
Brian Narramore *(Sr VP)*
Gustav Backman *(Sr VP)*
Drew Ashcraft *(VP)*

Subsidiary (Domestic):

Brock Services, LLC   **(2)**
1670 E Cardinal Dr, Beaumont, TX 77705
Tel.: (409) 833-6226
Web Site: http://www.brockgroup.com
Industrial Painting Services
N.A.I.C.S.: 238320

Custom Blast Services, Inc.   **(2)**
2550 Genoa Red Bluff Rd, Houston, TX
77034
Tel.: (281) 487-6353
Web Site: http://www.brockgroup.com
Specialty Trade Contractors
N.A.I.C.S.: 238990

Branch (Domestic):

Custom Blast Services, Inc.   **(3)**
4835 Bourque Rd, Nederland, TX 77627
Tel.: (409) 729-6353
Web Site: http://www.brockgroup.com
Specialty Engineering Contractors
N.A.I.C.S.: 238990

Subsidiary (Domestic):

Custom Pipe Coating, Inc.   **(2)**
7177 Cavalcade St, Houston, TX 77028
Tel.: (713) 675-2324
Web Site: http://www.brockgroup.com
Specialty Trade Contractors
N.A.I.C.S.: 238990

Canam Group Inc.   **(1)**
11505 1re Avenue Bureau 500, Saint-
Georges, G5Y 7X3, QC, Canada
Tel.: (418) 228-8031
Web Site: http://www.groupecanam.com
Fabricated Steel Mfr
N.A.I.C.S.: 332312
Marcel C. M. Dutil *(Chm)*
Rene Guizzetti *(CFO & VP)*
Jean-Francois Blouin *(Sr VP)*
Matthieu Delorme *(Sr VP)*
Larry Doyon *(Sr VP)*
Frederic Gendron *(VP)*
Karine Hubert *(VP)*
Pooya Roohi *(Pres)*

Annie Vezina *(Sec)*
Tony Begin *(VP)*
George Poumbouras *(VP)*

Subsidiary (US):

Canam Steel Corporation   **(2)**
4010 Clay St, Point of Rocks, MD 21777
Tel.: (301) 874-5141
Web Site: http://www.groupecanam.com
Steel Products Mfr
N.A.I.C.S.: 331110
Randy Leonard *(Ops Mgr)*

Plant (US):

Canam-Bridge   **(2)**
386 River Rd, Claremont, NH 03743
Tel.: (603) 542-5202
Web Site: http://www.canambridges.com
Bridge Construction Services
N.A.I.C.S.: 237310

Subsidiary (Non-US):

Steel Plus Limited   **(2)**
Gn 37 B Sector 5 Salt Lake, Kolkata,
700091, West Bengal, India
Tel.: (91) 3323575865
Web Site: http://www.groupecanam.com
Steel Joists Mfr
N.A.I.C.S.: 332312
Partha Pratim Ghosh *(Gen Mgr)*

Subsidiary (US):

Stonebridge Inc.   **(2)**
165 Ryan St, South Plainfield, NJ 07080
Tel.: (908) 753-1100
Web Site:
     http://www.stonebridgesteelerection.com
Structural Steel & Precast Concrete Con-
tractors
N.A.I.C.S.: 238120
Jack Falcone *(VP-Bus Dev)*

Subsidiary (Non-US):

Technyx Euro Services S.R.L.   **(2)**
9 Ionescu Crum Street, 500446, Brasov,
Romania
Tel.: (40) 268318057
Web Site: http://www.groupecanam.com
Construction Product Mfr
N.A.I.C.S.: 332312
Mihu Anghelescu *(Deputy Mgr)*

Current Lighting Solutions, LLC   **(1)**
1975 Noble Rd, Cleveland, OH 44112
Web Site: http://www.gecurrent.com
Sales Range: $650-699.9 Million
Emp.: 1,900
Lighting Products Mfr & Whslr
N.A.I.C.S.: 335132
Manish Bhandari *(Pres & CEO)*
Courtney Abraham *(Chief People Officer)*
Jason Scott Fokens *(Gen Counsel & VP)*

Subsidiary (Domestic):

Forum, Inc.   **(2)**
100 Chapel Harbor Dr, Pittsburgh, PA
15238
Tel.: (412) 781-5970
Web Site: http://www.forumlighting.com
Rev.: $6,700,000
Emp.: 64
Commercial, Industrial & Institutional Elec-
tric Lighting Fixture Mfr
N.A.I.C.S.: 335132
Julie McElhattan *(Controller)*
Steve Seligman *(VP-Sls)*
Roger Ziegler *(Mgr-Inside Sls)*
Jonathan Garret *(Pres)*

HLI Solutions, Inc.   **(2)**
701 Millennium Blvd, Greenville, SC 29607
Tel.: (864) 678-1000
Web Site: https://www.currentlighting.com
Electric Equipment Mfr
N.A.I.C.S.: 335999

Subsidiary (Domestic):

Hubbell Electrical Products   **(3)**
40 Waterview Dr, Shelton, CT 06484
Tel.: (203) 882-4800
Web Site: http://www.hubbelllighting.com
Sales Range: $100-124.9 Million
Residential & Commercial Fluorescent &
Incandescent Lighting Products

N.A.I.C.S.: 335931

Gerber Technology LLC   **(1)**
24 Industrial Park Rd W, Tolland, CT
06084-1624   **(100%)**
Tel.: (860) 871-8082
Web Site: http://www.gerbertechnology.com
Computer Software Services & Hardware
Systems Mfr
N.A.I.C.S.: 541511
Patricia Burmahl *(Sr VP-HR)*
Bud McCann *(VP & Gen Mgr-Aftermarkets)*
Peter Morrissey *(VP-Global Sls)*
Karsten Newbury *(VP & Gen Mgr-Software
Solutions)*
Todd Rhodes *(VP & Gen Mgr-Virtek Vision
Systems)*
Bill Brewster *(Vp & Gen Mgr-Enterprise
Software Solutions)*
Peter Doscas *(VP & Gen Mgr-Americas)*
James Martin *(Corp VP-Strategy Mgmt &
Analysis)*
Theo Ostendorf *(VP & Gen Mgr-Europe,
Middle East & Africa)*
Samuel Simpson *(VP-Global Stategic
Accts)*
Mohit Uberoi *(Pres & CEO)*
Ketty Pillet *(VP-Global Mktg)*

Goss International Americas,
LLC   **(1)**
121 Technology Dr, Durham, NH 03824
Tel.: (603) 749-6600
Web Site: http://www.gossinternational.com
Sales Range: $200-249.9 Million
Emp.: 700
Web Offset Printing Presses Mfr
N.A.I.C.S.: 333248
Stan Blakney *(COO)*
Ken Litman *(Sr VP-IT)*
Sven Doerge *(CFO)*

Subsidiary (Non-US):

Goss Graphic Systems Japan Corpo-
ration - Sayama   **(2)**
3-7-4 Hirosedai, Sayama, 350-1328, Sai-
tama, Japan   **(100%)**
Tel.: (81) 429541141
Web Site: http://www.gossinternational.com
Emp.: 55
Printing Press Mfr
N.A.I.C.S.: 333248
Nakamura Hideyuki *(Mgr-Sls)*

Goss International Europe UK
Ltd.   **(2)**
The Oak Business Park Longridge Road,
Preston, PR2 5BQ, Lancashire, United
Kingdom
Tel.: (44) 772257571
Web Site: http://www.gossinternational.com
Printing Presses & Auxiliary Equipment Mfr
N.A.I.C.S.: 333248
Mark John Weston *(Sec)*

manroland Goss web systems
GmbH   **(2)**
Alois-Senefelder-Allee 1, 86153, Augsburg,
Germany
Tel.: (49) 821 424 0
Web Site: http://www.manrolandgoss.com
Commercial Printing Services
N.A.I.C.S.: 323111
Franz Kriechbaum *(CEO)*
Dirk Rauh *(CFO & Chief Sls officer)*
Daniel Raffler *(Chief Corp Officer)*

Subsidiary (Domestic):

grapho metronic Mess- und
Regeltechnik GmbH   **(3)**
Lilienstrasse 60, 81669, Munich, Germany
Tel.: (49) 894809040
Web Site: http://www.grapho-metronic.com
Measuring Device Mfr
N.A.I.C.S.: 334519
Manuel Kosok *(Mng Dir)*

Subsidiary (Non-US):

manroland web systems (UK)
Ltd.   **(2)**
Unit 7 Kings Grove Industrial Estate Kings,
Grove, Maidenhead, SL6 4DP, Berkshire,
United Kingdom
Tel.: (44) 7831110012
Web Site: http://www.manroland-web.com
Commercial Printing Services

N.A.I.C.S.: 323111
John Ellis *(Mng Dir)*

Heil Trailer International, Co.   **(1)**
1125 Congress Pkwy, Athens, TN
37303   **(100%)**
Tel.: (423) 745-5830
Web Site: http://www.heiltrailer.com
Sales Range: $100-124.9 Million
Emp.: 350
Trailer Mfr
N.A.I.C.S.: 336212
Bill Harris *(Dir-Military Sls & Bus Dev)*
Oscar Vargas *(Mgr-Mexico)*
Salauddin Mohammed *(Mgr-Middle East &
Africa Sls)*
David Morrow *(VP-Bus Dev-Intl)*

Plant (Domestic):

Heil Trailer International, Co. - Heil
Athens Manufacturing Facility   **(2)**
1125 Congress Pkwy, Athens, TN 37303
Tel.: (423) 745-5830
Web Site: http://www.heiltrailer.us
Industrial Truck & Trailer Mfr
N.A.I.C.S.: 333924

Heil Trailer International, Co. - Heil
Tank Service - Manufacturing
Facility   **(2)**
3808 Bells Ln, Louisville, KY 40211
Tel.: (800) 428-7101
Industrial Truck & Tractor Mfr
N.A.I.C.S.: 333924

Heil Trailer International, Co. -
Texas   **(2)**
500 Randall St, Rhome, TX 76078-0247
Tel.: (817) 430-1472
Web Site: http://www.heiltrailer.com
Sales Range: $100-124.9 Million
Emp.: 140
Trailer Mfr
N.A.I.C.S.: 336212

Optimas OE Solutions, LLC   **(1)**
2651 Compass Rd, Glenview, IL 60026
Tel.: (224) 999-1000
Web Site: http://www.optimas.com
Sales Range: $900-999.9 Million
Emp.: 1,900
Fasteners Mfr & Distr
N.A.I.C.S.: 339993
Marc Strandquist *(Pres-Americas)*
Mike Tuffy *(COO)*
Kate Daly *(Sr VP-Global HR)*
Nicole Winokur *(VP-Mktg-Global)*

Subsidiary (Non-US):

Optimas OE Solutions GmbH   **(2)**
Robert-Bosch Strasse 3, 66773, Schwal-
bach, Germany
Tel.: (49) 683170020
Web Site: http://www.optimas.com
Emp.: 120
Fastener Distr
N.A.I.C.S.: 423710
David Kessler *(Gen Mgr)*

Optimas OE Solutions Ltd.   **(2)**
Unit A Acorn Office Park Ling Road Poole,
Dorset, BH12 4NZ, United Kingdom
Tel.: (44) 1202 865 222
Web Site:
     http://www.optimascomponents.com
Fastener Distr
N.A.I.C.S.: 423710
Andrew Fletcher *(Mng Dir)*

Potomac Supply, LLC   **(1)**
1398 Kinsale Rd, Kinsale, VA 22488
Tel.: (804) 472-2527
Web Site: http://www.potomacsupply.com
Wood Container & Pallet Mfr
N.A.I.C.S.: 321920
Ann Swann *(Mgr-HR)*

REV Group, Inc.   **(1)**
245 S Executive Dr Ste 100, Brookfield, WI
53005
Tel.: (414) 290-0190
Web Site: https://www.revgroup.com
Rev.: $2,380,200,000
Assets: $1,213,000,000
Liabilities: $777,900,000
Net Worth: $435,100,000
Earnings: $257,600,000
Emp.: 5,700

Fiscal Year-end: 10/31/2024
Designer, Mfr & Distr of Specialty Vehicles
& Related Aftermarket Parts & Services
N.A.I.C.S.: 336211
Paul J. Bamatter *(Co-Chm)*
Amy A. Campbell *(CFO & Sr VP)*
Mark A. Skonieczny *(Pres & CEO)*
Drew Konop *(VP-IR & Corp Dev)*
Mark A. Skonieczny *(Pres, CEO & Interim CFO)*
Julie Nuernberg *(Sr Dir-Mktg & Comm)*
Mark Van Arnam *(Pres)*
Michael Lanciotti *(Pres-Recreation Segment)*
Sagar Murthy *(CIO & Sr VP)*
Dan DesRochers *(Pres-REV Fire Grp)*
Stephen Zamansky *(Gen Counsel, Sec & Sr VP)*
John Dreasher *(Chief HR Officer & Sr VP)*

Subsidiary (Domestic):

Capacity of Texas, Inc.   **(2)**
401 Capacity Dr, Longview, TX 75604-5341
Tel.: (903) 759-0610
Web Site: http://www.capacitytrucks.com
Sales Range: $25-49.9 Million
Emp.: 250
Heavy Duty Freight Terminal Tractors Mfr
N.A.I.C.S.: 333924

Division (Domestic):

Capacity of Texas, Inc. - LayMor Division   **(3)**
401 Capacity Dr, Longview, TX 75604
Tel.: (903) 759-0610
Web Site: http://www.laymor.com
Sales Range: $1-9.9 Million
Emp.: 200
Rental & Paving Industry Sweeper Vehicles Mfr
N.A.I.C.S.: 333924
Philip Ford *(Pres)*
Steven Ramo *(Dir-Sls)*

Subsidiary (Domestic):

Champion Bus, Inc.   **(2)**
331 Graham Rd, Imlay City, MI 48444-9738
Tel.: (810) 724-6474
Web Site: http://www.championbus.com
Sales Range: $125-149.9 Million
Emp.: 300
Bus Mfr
N.A.I.C.S.: 336120
Theresa Smith *(VP-Fin)*

E-ONE, Inc.   **(2)**
1601 SW 37th Ave, Ocala, FL 34474-2827
Tel.: (352) 237-1122   **(100%)**
Web Site: http://www.e-one.com
Sales Range: $125-149.9 Million
Emp.: 800
Fire Emergency Rescue Vehicle & Aluminum-Bodied Firefighting Apparatus Designer, Mfr & Marketer
N.A.I.C.S.: 336211
Jimbo Thompson *(Supvr-Customer Svc)*
Kevin Kearns *(Mgr-Customer Svc)*

Subsidiary (Domestic):

Hall-Mark Fire Apparatus, Inc.   **(3)**
725 SW 46th Ave, Ocala, FL 34474
Tel.: (352) 629-6305
Web Site: http://www.hall-markfire.com
Sales Range: $1-9.9 Million
Emp.: 30
Fire Apparatus Sales & Service
N.A.I.C.S.: 423850
Dee Daniels *(Mgr-Sls)*
Chance Seiler *(Mgr-Fin)*
William Alm *(VP & Gen Mgr)*

Subsidiary (Domestic):

Hall-Mark Fire Apparatus - Texas, LLC   **(4)**
10315 Veterans Memorial, Houston, TX 77038-1727
Tel.: (800) 922-4142
Web Site: http://www.hall-markfire.com
Fire Apparatus Sales & Service
N.A.I.C.S.: 423850
William Alm *(VP & Gen Mgr)*

Subsidiary (Domestic):

Kovatch Mobile Equipment Corp.   **(3)**

1 Industrial Complex, Nesquehoning, PA 18240-1420
Tel.: (570) 669-9461
Web Site: http://www.kmefire.com
Sales Range: $50-74.9 Million
Emp.: 850
Mfr of Specialty Vehicles, Including Fire Apparatus, Rescue Vehicles & Fuel Trucks
N.A.I.C.S.: 336120
Ryan Slane *(Product Mgr-Pumpers & Tankers)*
Jennifer Davis *(Dir-HR)*
Bob Beck *(VP & Gen Mgr)*

Subsidiary (Domestic):

ElDorado National (California), Inc.   **(2)**
9670 Galena St, Riverside, CA 92509   **(100%)**
Tel.: (909) 591-9557
Web Site: http://www.eldorado-ca.com
Sales Range: $75-99.9 Million
Emp.: 200
Commercial Bus Mfr
N.A.I.C.S.: 336120
Andrew Imanse *(Pres)*

ElDorado National (Kansas), Inc.   **(2)**
1655 Wall St, Salina, KS 67401-8923   **(100%)**
Tel.: (785) 827-1033
Web Site: http://www.eldorado-bus.com
Sales Range: $125-149.9 Million
Emp.: 300
Buses & Handicapped Vans Mfr
N.A.I.C.S.: 336120

Ferrara Fire Apparatus Inc.   **(2)**
27855 James Chapel Rd, Holden, LA 70744
Tel.: (225) 567-7100
Web Site: http://www.ferrarafire.com
Firefighting Equipment Mfr
N.A.I.C.S.: 336120
Bert McCutcheon *(VP & Gen Mgr)*
Aaron Blackwell *(Mgr-Refurb & Svc Center)*
Jason Louque *(Dir-Sls)*

Goshen Coach, Inc.   **(2)**
25161 Leer Dr, Elkhart, IN 46514
Tel.: (574) 970-6300
Web Site: http://www.goshencoach.com
Sales Range: $25-49.9 Million
Emp.: 150
Commercial Bus Mfr
N.A.I.C.S.: 336120
Troy Snyder *(Pres)*

Halcore Group, Inc.   **(2)**
3800 McDowell Rd, Grove City, OH 43123
Tel.: (614) 539-8181
Web Site: http://www.hortonambulance.com
Sales Range: $25-49.9 Million
Emp.: 400
Ambulance & Rescue Vehicles Mfr
N.A.I.C.S.: 336211
John Slawson *(Pres)*

Unit (Domestic):

AEV - American Emergency Vehicles   **(3)**
165 American Way, Jefferson, NC 28640
Tel.: (336) 982-9824
Web Site: http://www.aev.com
Sales Range: $10-24.9 Million
Emp.: 300
Ambulance Mfr
N.A.I.C.S.: 336211

Leader Emergency Vehicles   **(3)**
10941 Weaver Ave, South El Monte, CA 91733
Tel.: (626) 575-0880
Web Site: http://www.leaderambulance.com
Sales Range: $25-49.9 Million
Emp.: 160
Ambulance Mfr
N.A.I.C.S.: 336211

Subsidiary (Domestic):

Lance Camper Manufacturing Corporation   **(2)**
43120 Venture St, Lancaster, CA 93535-4510
Tel.: (661) 949-3322
Web Site: http://www.lancecamper.com
Travel Trailers & Truck Campers Mfr

N.A.I.C.S.: 336214

REV Ambulance Group Orlando, Inc.   **(2)**
2737 N Forsyth Rd, Winter Park, FL 32792-6672
Tel.: (407) 677-7777
Web Site: http://www.wheeledcoach.com
Sales Range: $25-49.9 Million
Emp.: 275
Medical, Rescue & Fire Emergency Vehicles Mfr
N.A.I.C.S.: 336211
Scott Barnes *(VP)*
Jere Riggs *(Controller)*
Lynn Whalen *(Mgr-Ops)*
Tara Houchins *(Mgr-Pur)*
Mark Van Arnam *(Pres)*
Randy Hanson *(COO, VP-American Emergency Vehicles & Gen Mgr-American Emergency Vehicles)*

Subsidiary (Domestic):

Road Rescue USA, Inc.   **(3)**
725 SW 46th Ave, Ocala, FL 34474
Tel.: (407) 677-7777
Web Site: http://www.roadrescue.com
Sales Range: $25-49.9 Million
Emp.: 200
Ambulances & Other Rescue Vehicles Mfr
N.A.I.C.S.: 336110
Greg Gleason *(Mgr-Sls)*

Subsidiary (Domestic):

REV Recreation Group, Inc.   **(2)**
1031 US 224 E, Decatur, IN 46733
Web Site: http://www.revgroup.com
Recreational Vehicle Mfr
N.A.I.C.S.: 336213
Jim Jacobs *(Pres)*
Matt Buckman *(VP-Sls-Monaco Coach & Holiday Rambler)*
Jamie Buckmeier *(Dir-Product Dev & Engrg)*

Subsidiary (Domestic):

Goldshield Fiberglass, Inc.   **(3)**
2004 Patterson St, Decatur, IN 46733
Tel.: (260) 728-2476
Web Site: http://www.goldshield.com
Sales Range: $10-24.9 Million
Emp.: 280
Fiber Glass Products Mfr
N.A.I.C.S.: 326199
Bryan Smith *(Dir-Sls)*
Jeff Condon *(Mgr-Production)*

Kibbi, LLC   **(3)**
52216 State Rd 15, Bristol, IN 46507
Tel.: (574) 848-1126
Web Site: http://www.renegaderv.com
Emp.: 175
Recreational Vehicles & Trailers Mfr
N.A.I.C.S.: 441210
Danny Lagunas *(Mgr-Sls-Motorsports)*
Kevin Erdman *(Dir-Sls & Mktg)*
Matt Maskill *(Mgr-Sls-Specialty Vehicles)*
Daryle Lambright *(Product Mgr-Trailers)*

Subsidiary (Domestic):

Spartan Motors USA, Inc.   **(2)**
907 7th Ave N, Brandon, SD 57005
Tel.: (605) 582-4000
Web Site: http://www.spartanerv.com
Fire Apparatus Mfr
N.A.I.C.S.: 922160

Subsidiary (Domestic):

Detroit Truck Manufacturing, LLC   **(3)**
111 E 12 Mile, Madison Heights, MI 48071
Tel.: (248) 268-6681
Web Site: http://www.detroittruckmanufacturing.com
Trucks Mfr
N.A.I.C.S.: 336110

Division (Domestic):

Smeal SFA, LLC   **(3)**
610 W 4th St, Snyder, NE 68664
Tel.: (402) 568-2224
Web Site: http://www.smeal.com
Fire Apparatus Mfr
N.A.I.C.S.: 336390

Rand Logistics, Inc.   **(1)**

333 Washington St Ste 201, Jersey City, NJ 07302
Tel.: (212) 863-9403
Web Site: http://www.randlog.com
Transportation Investment Services
N.A.I.C.S.: 523999
Paul J. Joaquin *(VP-Ops-Grand River Navigation Company)*
Gerald J. Ray *(VP-Ops-Lower Lakes Towing Ltd.)*
Peter Coxon *(CEO)*
Phillip Carr *(VP-Comml)*

Subsidiary (Domestic):

American Steamship Company   **(2)**
500 Essjay Rd, Williamsville, NY 14221   **(100%)**
Tel.: (716) 635-0222
Web Site: http://www.americansteamship.com
Sales Range: $200-249.9 Million
Emp.: 334
Freight Transportation Services
N.A.I.C.S.: 483113
David W. Foster *(Pres)*

Grand River Navigation Company, Inc.   **(2)**
1026 Hannah Ave Ste D, Traverse City, MI 49684
Tel.: (231) 922-1023
Web Site: http://www.randlog.com
Lakes Freight Transportation Services
N.A.I.C.S.: 483113
Paul Joaquin *(VP-Ops-Grand River Navigation Company)*

Subsidiary (Non-US):

Lower Lakes Towing (17) Ltd.   **(2)**
517 Main Street, PO Box 1149, Port Dover, N0A1N0, ON, Canada
Tel.: (519) 583-0982
Web Site: http://www.randlog.com
Inland Water Freight Transportation Services
N.A.I.C.S.: 483211

Lower Lakes Towing Ltd.   **(2)**
517 Main Street, PO Box 1149, Port Dover, N0A 1N0, ON, Canada
Tel.: (519) 583-0982
Web Site: http://www.randlog.com
Great Lakes Freight Transportation Services
N.A.I.C.S.: 483113
David W. Foster *(CEO)*
Peter Coxon *(CEO)*
Ray Capote *(CFO)*
Paul Joaquin *(Pres)*
Phillip Carr *(VP)*

RelaDyne LLC   **(1)**
8280 Montgomery Rd Ste 101, Cincinnati, OH 45236
Tel.: (513) 489-6000
Web Site: http://www.reladyne.com
Oil & Lubrication Distr
N.A.I.C.S.: 811191
Larry J. Stoddard *(Pres & CEO)*
Jess Brown *(CIO)*
Paul Helton *(CFO)*
Jeff Hart *(Chief Strategy Officer)*
Dan Oehler *(VP-Sls & Mktg)*
Doug Oehler *(Exec VP-Branch Distr & Reg Mgr-North)*
Glenn Pumpelly *(Exec VP & Reg Mgr-South)*
Scott Hill *(VP-Reliability Svcs)*
David Schumacher *(Chief Strategy & Operating Officer)*
Jennifer Graft *(VP-HR)*

Subsidiary (Domestic):

Allied Oil & Tire Company, LLC   **(2)**
2209 S 24th St, Omaha, NE 68108-3815
Tel.: (402) 344-4343
Web Site: https://www.alliedoil.com
Sales Range: $75-99.9 Million
Emp.: 185
Lubricants & Tires Distr
N.A.I.C.S.: 423130
Steve Phillips *(Pres)*

Subsidiary (Non-US):

Canadian Chemical Cleaning Services Inc.   **(2)**
1099 Highway 6 RR 2, Hamilton, L8N 2Z7,

AIP, LLC—(Continued)
ON, Canada
Tel.: (905) 689-2266
Chemical Cleaning Services
N.A.I.C.S.: 238220

Subsidiary (Domestic):

Cardwell Distributing, Inc. **(2)**
8137 State St, Midvale, UT 84047-3244
Tel.: (801) 561-4251
Web Site: http://www.cardwelldist.com
Petroleum Bulk Stations & Terminals
N.A.I.C.S.: 424710
Bill Rawson *(Pres & CEO)*

Circle Lubricants Inc. **(2)**
35 Drexel Dr, Bay Shore, NY 11706
Tel.: (631) 234-8900
Web Site: https://reladyne.com
Petroleum & Petroleum Products Merchant
Whslr
N.A.I.C.S.: 424720
Ronald Birmbaum *(Founder & Pres)*

Dal Chem, Inc. **(2)**
219 Glider Cir, Corona, CA 92880
Tel.: (951) 279-9830
Web Site: http://www.alexisoil.com
Sales Range: $1-9.9 Million
Emp.: 20
Petroleum Bulk Stations & Terminals
N.A.I.C.S.: 424710
Angelo Leara *(Pres)*

Enterprise Oil Co. **(2)**
3200 S Western Ave, Chicago, IL 60608
Tel.: (773) 847-6700
Web Site: http://www.entoilusa.com
Petroleum Bulk Stations
N.A.I.C.S.: 424710
Linda Chance *(Controller)*
Kyle Kruke *(VP)*

Hager Oil Company Inc. **(2)**
1002 Old Birmingham Hwy, Jasper, AL 35501
Tel.: (205) 384-3422
Web Site: http://www.hageroil.com
Convenience Store
N.A.I.C.S.: 424710
Russell S. Hager *(Owner & Pres)*

Jasper Oil, Inc. **(2)**
PO Box 10246, Birmingham, AL 35502
Tel.: (205) 945-6300
Web Site: http://www.drummondco.com
Petroleum Product Mfr
N.A.I.C.S.: 324110
Dennis Evy *(Gen Mgr)*

Michigan Petroleum Technologies, Inc. **(2)**
3030 Moak St, Port Huron, MI 48060
Tel.: (810) 982-2811
Web Site:
    http://www.michiganpetroleum.com
Sales Range: $1-9.9 Million
Emp.: 29
Petroleum Products, Nec
N.A.I.C.S.: 424720
Kim White *(VP-Ops)*

Nick Barbieri Trucking, LLC **(2)**
50 W Lk Mendocino Dr, Ukiah, CA 95482
Tel.: (707) 442-5823
Web Site: http://www.barbieritrucking.com
General Freight Trucking, Long-Distance,
Less than Truckload
N.A.I.C.S.: 484122
David Ringstrom *(Mgr-Transportation)*

Orange Line Oil Company, Inc. **(2)**
404 E Commercial St, Pomona, CA 91767
Tel.: (909) 623-0533
Web Site: http://www.orangelineoil.com
Sales Range: $25-49.9 Million
Bulk Motor Oil, Synthetics & Specialty Lubricants Distr
N.A.I.C.S.: 424720
Scott Tredinnick *(Pres)*

PPC Lubricants, Inc. **(2)**
305 Micro Dr, Jonestown, PA 17038
Web Site: http://www.ppclubricants.com
Petroleum & Petroleum Products Merchant
Whslr
N.A.I.C.S.: 424720
Geoff Vinton *(Mgr)*
Dave Klinger *(Pres)*

Parker Oil Company, Inc. **(2)**
4343 S W St, Wichita, KS 67217-0383
Tel.: (316) 529-4343
Web Site: http://parkeroilco.com
Petroleum Bulk Stations
N.A.I.C.S.: 424710

Richard Oil and Fuel LLC **(2)**
2330 Hwy 70, Donaldsonville, LA 70346
Tel.: (225) 473-8389
Web Site: http://www.richardoil.com
Distr of Fuels & Lubricants
N.A.I.C.S.: 424710
Carol Savoie *(VP)*
Slade Klack *(VP-Ops)*
Tony Savoie *(Pres)*

Sun Coast Resources Inc. **(2)**
6405 Cavalcade St Bldg 1, Houston, TX 77026
Tel.: (713) 844-9600
Web Site:
    http://www.suncoastresources.com
Sales Range: $500-549.9 Million
Emp.: 300
Petroleum Brokers
N.A.I.C.S.: 424720
Kathy Lehne *(Founder & CEO)*

Turbo Filtration, LLC **(2)**
1490 Telegraph Rd, Mobile, AL 36610
Tel.: (251) 457-8807
Web Site: http://www.tfcglobal.com
Emp.: 40
Turbine & Industrial Cleaning Services
N.A.I.C.S.: 238210
Dhuck Davis *(Mgr)*

Western Marketing Inc. **(2)**
1010 S Access Rd, Tye, TX 79563
Tel.: (325) 692-4662
Web Site: http://www.westmktg.com
Petroleum Product Distr
N.A.I.C.S.: 424720
Jason Hancock *(Gen Mgr)*
Kurt Ackerman *(Gen Mgr)*
Gene Bowden *(Gen Mgr)*
Matt Conley *(Gen Mgr)*
Mike Henry *(Gen Mgr)*
Ken Skidmore *(Gen Mgr)*

SEACOR Holdings Inc. **(1)**
2200 Eller Dr, Fort Lauderdale, FL 33316
Tel.: (954) 523-2200
Web Site: http://www.seacorholdings.com
Rev.: $753,826,000
Assets: $1,532,104,000
Liabilities: $686,687,000
Net Worth: $845,417,000
Earnings: $23,311,000
Emp.: 2,195
Fiscal Year-end: 12/31/2020
Marine Services for Offshore Oil Operations
N.A.I.C.S.: 483111
Eric Fabrikant *(COO)*
Bruce Weins *(CFO & Sr VP)*
William C. Long *(Chief Legal Officer, Sec & Exec VP)*
Lisa Manekin *(Treas)*
Scott Weber *(Sr VP-Corp Dev & Fin)*
Oivind Lorentzen III *(Vice Chm)*

Subsidiary (Domestic):

Arctic Leasing LLC **(2)**
17223 Lakewood Blvd, Bellflower, CA 90706
Tel.: (562) 212-1440
Deep Sea Freight Transportation Services
N.A.I.C.S.: 483111

C-Lift LLC **(2)**
16201 E Main St, Galliano, LA 70354
Tel.: (985) 601-4444
Marine Transportation Services
N.A.I.C.S.: 483111

Joint Venture (Domestic):

CG Railway, LLC **(2)**
601 Poydras St Ste 1625, New Orleans, LA 70130 **(60%)**
Tel.: (251) 266-5239
Web Site: http://www.cgrailway.com
Short Line Railroad
N.A.I.C.S.: 482112

Subsidiary (Domestic):

CLEANCOR Energy Solutions LLC **(2)**

460 Park Ave 12th Fl, New York, NY 10022
Tel.: (212) 307-6633
Web Site: http://www.cleancorenergy.com
Energy Merchant Platform
N.A.I.C.S.: 213112
Jeff Woods *(CEO)*
Mark Kimberlin *(COO)*
Brain Fowkes *(VP-Sls & Bus Dev)*
Scott Johns *(Pres-CLEANCOR LNG)*

International Shipholding Corporation **(2)**
11 N Water St 18 Fl, Mobile, AL 36602
Tel.: (251) 243-9100
Worldwide Waterborne Freight Transportation
N.A.I.C.S.: 483111
Erik L. Johnsen *(Pres & CEO)*
David B. Drake *(Treas & VP)*
Manuel G. Estrada *(CFO & VP)*

Subsidiary (Domestic):

Coastal Carriers, LLC **(3)**
120 Hammer Ln, Troy, MO 63379
Tel.: (636) 528-8988
Web Site: http://www.coastalcarriers.com
Freight Transportation Services
N.A.I.C.S.: 484230
John Harrell *(Controller)*
Devon R. Harris *(Dir-Safety)*
John Dunard *(Pres)*
Greg Vaccaro *(Dir-Ops)*

Waterman Steamship Corporation **(3)**
460 Park Ave Fl 12, New York, NY 10022
Tel.: (212) 747-8550
Web Site: http://seacorholdings.com
Deep Sea ocean Carrier Operators
N.A.I.C.S.: 483111

Subsidiary (Domestic):

Sulphur Carriers, Inc. **(4)**
11 N Water St 18th Fl, Mobile, AL 36602-5018
Tel.: (251) 243-9120
Maritime Transportation Services
N.A.I.C.S.: 483211

Subsidiary (Domestic):

NRC Environmental Services Inc. **(2)**
9520 10th Ave S Ste 150, Seattle, WA 98108
Tel.: (206) 607-3000
Web Site: http://www.nrces.com
Hazardous & Nonhazardous Waste Management Services
N.A.I.C.S.: 562112

Nationall Response Corporation of Puerto Rico **(2)**
359 San Claudio Avenue Box 16 Suite 309-B, San Juan, PR 00926
Tel.: (787) 789-2000
Web Site: http://nrcc.com
Oil Spill Response, Site Remediation, Vessel Services, Training & Consultancy Company
N.A.I.C.S.: 541611

O'Brien's Response Management Inc. **(2)**
2000 Old Spanish Trl Ste 210, Slidell, LA 70458
Tel.: (985) 781-0804
Web Site: http://www.obriensrm.com
Emp.: 450
Emergency Response Management Services
N.A.I.C.S.: 541618

SCF Marine Inc. **(2)**
727 N 1st St Ste 600, Saint Louis, MO 63102
Tel.: (314) 436-7559
Web Site: http://www.scfmarine.com
Emp.: 35
River Freight Transportation Services
N.A.I.C.S.: 483211
Ken Gillum *(Controller)*
Tim Power *(Pres & CEO)*
Tim Robinson *(Mgr-Safety & Compliance)*
Rick Barbee *(VP-Mktg)*
David Esper *(Mgr-Ops)*
Paul Wellhausen *(Sr VP-Fleeting & Dry Terminal Ops)*

Brice Power *(Gen Mgr-Terminals)*
Ryan Shores *(Coord-Terminal Ops)*
Scott Keehner *(Mgr-Terminals Ops)*
Marshall Bockman *(VP)*
Kenny Inman *(Gen Mgr-Fleeting)*
Larry Marse *(Mgr-Traffic)*
Myron McDonough *(VP)*
Lance Boverie *(Mgr-Maintenance)*
Cory Knight *(Mgr-Machine Shop)*
Keith McDonough *(Engr-Structural Design)*
Jeremy Ward *(Gen Mgr-Shipyard)*
Rich Teubner *(VP)*
Phillip Christian *(Mgr-Terminal)*
Allison Soileau *(Mgr-Intermodal)*
Chris Pierre *(Supvr-Ops)*

SEACOR AMH LLC **(2)**
2200 Eller Dr, Fort Lauderdale, FL 33316
Tel.: (954) 523-2200
Web Site: http://www.seacoramh.com
Marine Transportation Services
N.A.I.C.S.: 483111

Subsidiary (Non-US):

SEACOR Energy Canada Limited **(2)**
633 6th Avenue SW Suite 200, Calgary, T2P 2Y5, AB, Canada
Tel.: (403) 206-3220
Sales Range: $25-49.9 Million
Emp.: 3
Crude Oil & Petroleum Product Distr
N.A.I.C.S.: 424720
Herbert Hamilton *(Pres)*
Erin Jones *(VP)*

Subsidiary (Domestic):

SEACOR Island Lines LLC **(2)**
1300 Eller Dr, Fort Lauderdale, FL 33316
Tel.: (954) 920-9292
Web Site: http://www.seacorislandlines.com
Logistics Consulting Servies
N.A.I.C.S.: 541614

SEACOR Liftboats LLC **(2)**
7910 Main St 2nd Fl, Houma, LA 70360
Tel.: (985) 876-5400
Web Site: http://www.seacorliftboats.com
Logistics Consulting Servies
N.A.I.C.S.: 541614

Subsidiary (Non-US):

SEACOR Marine (Asia) Pte. Ltd. **(2)**
20 Harbour Dr 05 01A PSA Vista, Singapore, 117612, Singapore **(100%)**
Tel.: (65) 68721123
Web Site: http://www.seacormarine.com
Sales Range: $25-49.9 Million
Emp.: 6
Operator of Marine Vessels for Shipping Industries
N.A.I.C.S.: 488320

SEACOR Marine (International) Ltd. **(2)**
Columbus Buildings Waveney Road, Lowestoft, NR32 1BN, Suffolk, United Kingdom **(100%)**
Tel.: (44) 1502 573366
Web Site: http://www.seacormarine.com
Sales Range: $100-124.9 Million
Emp.: 40
Shipping & Marine Services
N.A.I.C.S.: 488320

Subsidiary (Domestic):

SEACOR Marine LLC **(2)**
7910 Main St 2nd Fl, Houma, LA 70360
Tel.: (985) 876-5400
Web Site: http://www.seacormarine.com
Marine Offshore & Transportation Services
N.A.I.C.S.: 483112

Subsidiary (Non-US):

SEACOR Offshore Dubai (L.L.C.) **(2)**
Gulf Towers Bldg Nr K M Trdg, PO Box 32387, Dubai, United Arab Emirates
Tel.: (971) 43344533
Marine Offshore Operators
N.A.I.C.S.: 488320

Subsidiary (Domestic):

Seabulk International, Inc. **(2)**
2200 Eller Dr, Fort Lauderdale, FL 33316

Tel.: (954) 523-2200
Web Site: http://www.seabulktankers.com
Sales Range: $350-399.9 Million
Emp.: 2,600
Offshore Energy Support Services for Oil & Gas Industry, Harbor Towing, Marine Transportation
N.A.I.C.S.: 483111

Subsidiary (Domestic):

Seabulk Tankers, Inc. (3)
2200 Eller Dr,, Fort Lauderdale, FL 33316-0100
Tel.: (954) 523-2200
Web Site: http://www.seabulktankers.com
Emp.: 100
Marine Transportation for Petroleum & Chemicals
N.A.I.C.S.: 483111

Seabulk Towing (3)
1305 Shoreline Dr, Tampa, FL 33605
Tel.: (813) 248-1123
Web Site: http://www.seabulktowing.com
Rev.: $45,000,000
Emp.: 70
Harbor & Offshore Towing & Escort Services
N.A.I.C.S.: 488330
Dwayne Wheeler (Mgr-Ops)

Subsidiary (Domestic):

Seabulk Towing Holdings Inc. (2)
2200 Eller Dr,, Fort Lauderdale, FL 33316
Tel.: (954) 523-2200
Marine Services
N.A.I.C.S.: 713930

Subsidiary (Domestic):

Seabulk Towing Services, Inc. (3)
2200 Eller Dr,, Fort Lauderdale, FL 33316
Tel.: (409) 962-0201
Web Site: http://www.seabulktowing.com
Sales Range: $1-9.9 Million
Emp.: 58
Support Activities for Transportation
N.A.I.C.S.: 488999
Jeffrey A. William (VP-Bus Dev)
Bill Osmer (Chief Comml Officer)

Subsidiary (Non-US):

Seassurance Limited (2)
Sea Meadow House Blackburne Highway Road Town, PO Box 116, Tortola, Virgin Islands (British)
Tel.: (284) 2844942137
Logistics Consulting Servies
N.A.I.C.S.: 541614

Sociedad Portuaria Puerto Wilches Mutiproposito SA (2)
Calle 94 11 20 Ap 301, Bogota, Colombia
Tel.: (57) 12184672
Logistics Consulting Servies
N.A.I.C.S.: 541614

Subsidiary (Domestic):

Strategic Crisis Advisors LLC (2)
PO Box 17823, Atlanta, GA 30316
Tel.: (404) 596-5300
Web Site:
  http://www.strategiccrisisadvisors.com
Crisis Management Services
N.A.I.C.S.: 624190
Charlie McDonald (VP-Corp Crisis Mgmt)
Grace Burley (Mng Partner)
Brent H. Law (VP-Client Svcs)

U.S. Shipping Corp. (2)
399 Thornall St 8th Fl, Edison, NJ 08837
Tel.: (732) 635-1500
Web Site: http://www.usslp.com
Sales Range: $150-199.9 Million
Emp.: 454
Domestic Marine Shipping of Petroleum
N.A.I.C.S.: 488320
Jeffrey M. Miller (Sr VP-Chartering Ops)
Sam Cermack (COO & Sr VP)
Paul J. McDade (CFO & Sr VP)

Waterman Logistics, Inc. (2)
1201 15th St NW Ste 600, Washington, DC 20005
Tel.: (202) 379-9692
Web Site: http://www.watermanlogistics.com
Logistic Services

N.A.I.C.S.: 541614
Sean Murphy (Dir-Comml Ops)

Subsidiary (Non-US):

Windcat Workboats B.V. (2)
Trawlerkade 106, 1976 CC, IJmuiden, Netherlands
Tel.: (31) 255520336
Web Site: http://www.windcatworkboats.com
Sales Range: $25-49.9 Million
Emp.: 8
Inland Water Passenger Transportation Services
N.A.I.C.S.: 483211

Windcat Workboats International Limited (2)
Elizabeth House, PO Box 191, Saint Martin's, Guernsey
Tel.: (44) 1481816433
Logistics Consulting Servies
N.A.I.C.S.: 541614

Witt O'Brien's Ltd (2)
Trent House RTC Business Park London Road, Derby, DE24 8UP, United Kingdom
Tel.: (44) 1332222299
Web Site: http://www.wittobriens.co.uk
Logistics Consulting Servies
N.A.I.C.S.: 541614

Strike LLC (1)
1800 Hughes Landing Blvd, The Woodlands, TX 77380
Web Site: http://www.strikeusa.com
Sales Range: $300-349.9 Million
Emp.: 1,254
Pipeline, Facilities, Fabrication, Maintenance & Integrity Services to the Oil, Gas, Utility & Power Industries
N.A.I.C.S.: 486990
A. Cole Pate (Pres & COO)
Chuck Davison Jr. (CEO)

The Carlstar Group LLC (1)
725 Cool Springs Blvd Ste 500, Franklin, TN 37067
Tel.: (615) 503-0220
Web Site: http://www.carlstargroup.com
Sales Range: $750-799.9 Million
Emp.: 4,000
Industrial Belts, Specialty Tires & Wheels Mfr & Distr
N.A.I.C.S.: 326220
Max Narancich (VP-Fin Plng & Ops Fin)
Laren Harmon (Exec VP-Sls)
Thom Clark (VP-Original Equipment Sls & Emerging Market Dev)
Jacob Thomas (CEO)
Steve Swanson (Sls Mgr-Natl)
Balazs Sztranyai (Product Mgr-Europe)

Subsidiary (Domestic):

Marastar LLC (2)
7925 S 196th St, Kent, WA 98032
Tel.: (253) 893-7014
Web Site: http://www.marathonind.com
Sales Range: $10-24.9 Million
Solid Rubber Tire Mfr & Distr
N.A.I.C.S.: 326211
Jon Foster (Pres)

Subsidiary (Non-US):

The Carlstar Group B.V. (2)
Nieuwe Stationsstraat 20, 6811 KS, Arnhem, Netherlands
Tel.: (31) 26 3527 412
Web Site:
  http://www.ctptransportationproducts.eu
Sales Range: $25-49.9 Million
Emp.: 15
Tiles Mfr
N.A.I.C.S.: 326211

Waterjet Holdings, Inc. (1)
330 Madison Ave 28th Fl, New York, NY 10017
Tel.: (800) 446-3569
Web Site: http://www.waterjetholdings.com
Holding Company
N.A.I.C.S.: 551112
David Savage (Pres & CEO)
Monique Liard (CFO)
Daric Schweikart (CIO & VP)
Theresa Treat (VP-HR)
Dick LeBlanc (Pres-Flow Waterjet)

Subsidiary (Domestic):

Flow International Corporation (2)
23500 64th Ave S, Kent, WA 98032
Tel.: (253) 850-3500
Web Site: http://www.flowcorp.com
Rev.: $259,338,000
Assets: $162,093,000
Liabilities: $65,359,000
Net Worth: $96,734,000
Earnings: $5,037,000
Emp.: 680
Fiscal Year-end: 04/30/2013
Developer & Mfr of Ultrahigh-Pressure (UHP) Waterjet & Abrasive Waterjet Cutting & Machining Technologies for Advanced Industrial & Manufacturing Applications
N.A.I.C.S.: 327910
Monique Savage (CFO)
David Savage (CEO)
Daric Schweikart (CIO & VP)
David Crewe (Sr VP-Engrg)

Subsidiary (Non-US):

Flow Asia Corporation (3)
2F -2 No 9 Zhanye 1st Road Hsinchu Science Based Industrial Park, Hsin-chu, 300, Taiwan (100%)
Tel.: (886) 35772102
Web Site: http://www.flowasia.com
Sales Range: $25-49.9 Million
Emp.: 100
Ultra-High-Pressure Waterjet & Abrasivejet Cutting Systems
N.A.I.C.S.: 333515
Simone Lo (Gen Mgr)

Subsidiary (Non-US):

Flow Bangalore Waterjet Pvt, Ltd. (4)
No 96 Peenya Industrial Area, 10th Main Rd Peenya Industrial Area III Phase, Bengaluru, India
Tel.: (91) 83768 06457
Waterjest Cutting Systems & Pumps Mfr
N.A.I.C.S.: 333998
Ajitesh Dutta (Mgr-Sks)

Flow Japan Corporation (4)
Level 18 Yebisu Garden Place Tower 4-20-3-Ebisu, Shibuya-ku, Tokyo, 150-6018, Japan
Tel.: (81) 357895920
Web Site: http://www.flowmwjs.com
Sales Range: $10-24.9 Million
Emp.: 25
Ultra-High Pressure Waterjet & Abrasivejet Cutting System Mfr
N.A.I.C.S.: 334514

Branch (Domestic):

Flow Japan Corporation - Nagoya (5)
4 129 Kamiyashiro Meito Ku, Nagoya, 465 0025, Aichi, Japan
Tel.: (81) 527017021
Web Site: http://www.flowwaterjet.com
Sales Range: $10-24.9 Million
Emp.: 25
Ultra-High Pressure Waterjet & Abrasivejet Cutting Systems for Industrial Applications
N.A.I.C.S.: 334514
Eric Lin (Mgr-Fin)

Subsidiary (Non-US):

Flow Ultra High Pressure Waterjet Technology (Shanghai) Co., Ltd. (4)
1st Floor & Room 202 Building 6 No 168 Jixing Road, Minhang District, Shanghai, 201 104, China (100%)
Tel.: (86) 2154382222
Web Site: http://www.flowcorp.com
Sales Range: $25-49.9 Million
Emp.: 90
Ultra-High Pressure Waterjet & Abrasivejet Cutting Systems for Industrial Applications
N.A.I.C.S.: 333515
Elain Wan (Dir-Mktg)

Subsidiary (Non-US):

Flow Eastern Europe, S.R.O. (3)
Holandska 2/4, Brno, 63900, Czech Republic
Tel.: (420) 511120400
Web Site: http://www.flowcorp.cz

Sales Range: $25-49.9 Million
Emp.: 4
Water Transmission Equipment Mfr
N.A.I.C.S.: 327910
William Wallace Wifler (Mng Dir)

Flow Europe GmbH (3)
Gewerbestrasse 95, Bretten, 75015, Germany (100%)
Tel.: (49) 72525380
Sales Range: $25-49.9 Million
Emp.: 60
Ultra-High Pressure Waterjet & Abrasivejet Cutting Systems
N.A.I.C.S.: 333517

Flow Italia S.r.l. (3)
Strada Per Turbigo 64, I-20010, Milan, Arluno, Italy
Tel.: (39) 0290379383
Web Site: http://www.flowwaterjet.com
Sales Range: $10-24.9 Million
Emp.: 6
Ultra-High Pressure Waterjet & Abrasivejet Cutting Systems
N.A.I.C.S.: 334514

Flow Latino Americana Industria e Comercio Ltda. (3)
Rua do Curtume 694, Lapa, 05065-001, Sao Paulo, SP, Brazil
Tel.: (55) 1136112822
Web Site: http://www.flowwaterjet.com
Sales Range: $1-9.9 Million
Emp.: 25
Ultra-High Pressure Waterjet & Abrasivejet Cutting Systems for Industrial Applications
N.A.I.C.S.: 334514

Flow UK Limited (3)
19 Wheatfield Way, Hinckley, LE10 1YG, United Kingdom (100%)
Tel.: (44) 01455895300
Sales Range: $10-24.9 Million
Emp.: 8
Ultra-High Pressure Waterjet & Abrasivejet Cutting Systems
N.A.I.C.S.: 334514
Paul Castle (Dir-Sls)

Subsidiary (Non-US):

KMT Group AB (2)
Stureplan 3, 111 45, Stockholm, Sweden
Tel.: (46) 8 59421150
Web Site: http://www.kmtgroup.com
Sales Range: $150-199.9 Million
Emp.: 400
Production Machines, Pump Technology & Industrial Equipment Mfr
N.A.I.C.S.: 333517

Subsidiary (Domestic):

Dynamic Robotic Solutions AB (3)
V Industrigatan 3B, 372 25, Ronneby, Sweden
Tel.: (46) 457 345 00
Web Site: http://www.drsrobotics.com
Automated Trimming Systems & Robotic Flexible Material Removal Systems Mfr
N.A.I.C.S.: 333248

Subsidiary (Non-US):

Dynamic Robotic Solutions GmbH (4)
Schanzenfeldstrasse 14b, D-35578, Wetzlar, Germany
Tel.: (49) 6441 44 596 0
Automated Trimming Systems & Robotic Flexible Material Removal Systems Mfr
N.A.I.C.S.: 333248
Frank Thorn (Mng Dir)

Subsidiary (US):

Dynamic Robotic Solutions, Inc. (4)
1255 Harmon Rd, Auburn Hills, MI 48326
Tel.: (248) 829-2800
Web Site: http://www.drsrobotics.com
Automated Trimming Systems & Robotic Flexible Material Removal Systems Mfr
N.A.I.C.S.: 333248
Jerry Kuhn (VP-Ops)

Subsidiary (Domestic):

KMT Precision Grinding AB (3)
Fabriksgatan 2, PO Box 910, Lidkoping, 53119, Sweden (100%)

AIP, LLC—(Continued)

Tel.: (46) 51088000
Web Site: http://www.kmtgrinding.com
Sales Range: $25-49.9 Million
Emp.: 220
Precision Grinding Machines Mfr
N.A.I.C.S.: 333248
Thomas Karlsson (Mng Dir)
Olof Hammar (Mgr-Fin)
Urban Larsson (Dir-Mktg)

Subsidiary (Non-US):

KMT Precision Grinding GmbH (4)
Roemerstraze 75, 71229, Leonberg, Germany
Tel.: (49) 7152 35 939 0
Web Site: http://www.kmtgrinding.com
Sales Range: $25-49.9 Million
Emp.: 9
Precision Grinding Machines Mfr
N.A.I.C.S.: 333248
Immanuel Grau (Mng Dir)

Subsidiary (US):

KMT Precision Grinding, Inc. (4)
Milford Industrial Plz 4 Industrial Rd Ste 3, Milford, MA 01757
Tel.: (508) 634-4301
Web Site: http://www.kmtgrinding.com
Emp.: 7
Precision Grinding Machines Mfr
N.A.I.C.S.: 333248
Brad Klar (Pres)

Subsidiary (US):

KMT Waterjet Systems, Inc. (3)
635 W 12th St, Baxter Springs, KS 66713
Tel.: (620) 856-2151
Web Site: http://www.kmtwaterjet.com
Sales Range: $25-49.9 Million
Emp.: 150
Waterjet Cutting Machinery Mfr
N.A.I.C.S.: 333515
Bob Pedrazas (Mktg Mgr)
Brendan Shackelford (Pres)

Subsidiary (Non-US):

KMT GmbH (4)
Auf der Laukert 11, 61231, Bad Nauheim, Germany
Tel.: (49) 60 32 99 70
Web Site: http://www.kmt-waterjet.de
Sales Range: $25-49.9 Million
Emp.: 50
Cutting Tool & Machine Tool Accessory Mfr
N.A.I.C.S.: 333515
Dirk Potthoff (Mng Dir)
Kirk Potthoff (Mng Dir)

AIR & HYDRAULIC EQUIPMENT, INC.
821 E 11th St, Chattanooga, TN 37403
Tel.: (423) 756-2000
Web Site: https://www.aheinfo.com
Year Founded: 1971
Sales Range: $1-9.9 Million
Emp.: 35
Distr of Fluid Power
N.A.I.C.S.: 423830
Dick La Follette (Pres)

AIR & WATER, INC.
1100 S Linwood Ave Bldg B, Santa Ana, CA 92705   CA
Web Site: http://www.air-n-water.com
Year Founded: 2002
Sales Range: $10-24.9 Million
Emp.: 32
Household Appliance Stores
N.A.I.C.S.: 449210
Luke Peters (Owner & Pres)

AIR CARGO ASSOCIATES INC.
147 W 35th St Ste 702, New York, NY 10001
Tel.: (718) 276-4400
Web Site:
http://www.aircargoassociates.com
Sales Range: $10-24.9 Million

Emp.: 10
Air Cargo Services
N.A.I.C.S.: 481212
Jim Farrell (Pres)

AIR CHARTERS, INC.
333 Industrial Ave-Hangar 3, Teterboro, NJ 07608
Tel.: (201) 288-9000   NJ
Web Site:
http://www.aircharterseb.com
Year Founded: 1986
Emp.: 150
Scheduled Air Transportation Equipment Rental/Leasing
N.A.I.C.S.: 481111
Susan Bopp (Pres & CEO)

AIR COMPONENTS & ENGINEERING
1181 58th St SW, Grand Rapids, MI 49509
Tel.: (616) 532-1181
Web Site: https://www.air-componentsinc.com
Year Founded: 1975
Sales Range: $50-74.9 Million
Emp.: 32
Distr Of Industrial Machinery & Equipment
N.A.I.C.S.: 423830

AIR COMPRESSOR ENGINEERING COMPANY
17 Meadow St, Westfield, MA 01085
Tel.: (413) 568-2884
Web Site:
https://www.aircompressoreng.com
Sales Range: $10-24.9 Million
Emp.: 50
Compressors, Except Air Conditioning
N.A.I.C.S.: 423830
Jack Klaubert (Chm)
Russell Klaubert (Pres)
Mike Maslak (Mgr-Svcs)
Richard Gardiner (Mgr-Svcs)

AIR COMPRESSOR SOLUTIONS
3001 Kermit Hwy, Odessa, TX 79764
Tel.: (432) 335-5900
Web Site: https://www.acsir.com
Rev.: $16,700,000
Emp.: 12
Dealer of Construction, Industrial Equipment & Mining Machinery
N.A.I.C.S.: 561499
Bruce Peeler (Pres)

AIR CONTACT TRANSPORT INC.
PO Box 570, Budd Lake, NJ 07828
Tel.: (973) 691-7077
Web Site:
http://www.actovernight.com
Sales Range: $10-24.9 Million
Emp.: 73
Trucking Except Local
N.A.I.C.S.: 484121
Bradford Honigsberg (Founder & CEO)
Cynthia Stocking (Dir-Fin)

AIR CONTROL PRODUCTS INC.
3800 Towpath Rd, Broadview Heights, OH 44147
Tel.: (440) 526-3020
Web Site:
https://www.aircontrolproducts.com
Year Founded: 1975
Sales Range: $10-24.9 Million
Emp.: 30
Air Ducts & Sheet Metal Products Mfr
N.A.I.C.S.: 423730

Michael Greene (Pres)
Janet Heuser (Office Mgr)
Robert Greene (CEO)
Lou Maglione (CFO)

AIR DISTRIBUTION ENTERPRISES, INC.
19 Wilbur St, Lynbrook, NY 11563-2360
Tel.: (516) 256-4800
Web Site: http://www.airdist.com
Year Founded: 1973
Sales Range: $10-24.9 Million
Emp.: 80
Air Conditioning Equipment
N.A.I.C.S.: 423730
Richard Arote (Pres)
Sandra Wolters (VP)
Nick Cotumaccio (Mgr-Mechanical Sys)
John Modzelewski (Mgr-Sls)
Luis Patino (Mgr-Warehouse)
Stephen Fenenbock (Exec VP)
Mark Agulis (VP-Engrg)

AIR ENERGY, INC.
6 Norfolk Ave, South Easton, MA 02375
Tel.: (508) 230-9445
Web Site: https://www.airenergy.com
Sales Range: $10-24.9 Million
Emp.: 35
Air Conditioning Equipment Whslr
N.A.I.C.S.: 423730
Don Mazanec (Pres)

AIR EXPERTS TODAY CORP.
1715 Independence Blvd Ste B1, Sarasota, FL 34234
Tel.: (941) 758-5000
Web Site:
https://www.airexperstoday.com
Emp.: 15
Plumbing, Heating & Air-Conditioning Contractor
N.A.I.C.S.: 238220
Ryan Diedrich (Pres)

AIR FLOW DESIGNS INC.
250 Jasmine Rd, Casselberry, FL 32707
Tel.: (407) 831-3600
Web Site:
https://www.airflowdesigns.com
Year Founded: 1958
Rev.: $23,000,000
Emp.: 100
Warm Air Heating & Air Conditioning Contractor
N.A.I.C.S.: 238220
Terry Burd (CEO)
Jesse Burd (VP)
Barry Weiss (VP-Ops)

AIR FORCE ACADEMY
3116 Academy Dr, USAF Academy, CO 80840-4475
Tel.: (719) 472-0300
Year Founded: 1965
Educational Support Services
N.A.I.C.S.: 611710

AIR FORCE AID SOCIETY, INC.
241 18th St S Ste 202, Arlington, VA 22202
Tel.: (703) 972-2650   VA
Web Site: https://www.afas.org
Year Founded: 1942
Sales Range: $10-24.9 Million
Emp.: 22
Charitable Organization
N.A.I.C.S.: 813211

AIR FORCE ONE
5800 Shier Rings Rd, Dublin, OH 43016

Tel.: (614) 889-0121
Web Site:
https://www.airforceone.com
Year Founded: 1984
Sales Range: $10-24.9 Million
Emp.: 110
Energy Efficient Building Construction
N.A.I.C.S.: 236210
Greg Guy (CEO)
Brett Horvath (VP & Gen Mgr-Southwest Region)
Michelle Lyke (CFO)
Mike Goodell (Exec VP)
Curtis Czemeres (COO)
Bob Flynn (VP-Sls-Northern Reg)
Lisa Senger (VP-Sls-Northern Reg)

AIR FORCE RETIRED OFFICERS COMMUNITY
20522 Falcons Landing Cir, Sterling, VA 20165
Tel.: (703) 404-5100   VA
Web Site:
http://www.falconslanding.org
Year Founded: 1984
Sales Range: $25-49.9 Million
Emp.: 398
Continuing Care Retirement Community Operator
N.A.I.C.S.: 623311
Fred Simpson (Dir-HR)
Donna Cassani (Dir-Resident Svcs)
Hardy Lister (CFO)
Barbara Brannon (Pres & CEO)
Leah Daily (Dir-Sls & Mktg)
William Timme (Chm)
Stephen Plummer (Vice Chm)
Robert BessererDir (Dir-Dining Svcs)
Peter Plante (Dir-Facilities Mgmt)

AIR FRAME STRAIGHTENING
15544 Minnesota Ave, Paramount, CA 90723
Tel.: (562) 663-1662
Rev.: $800,000
Emp.: 10
Commercial & Industrial Machinery & Equipment Repair & Maintenance
N.A.I.C.S.: 811310
Leland M. Holden (Owner)

AIR GENERAL INC.
403 The Hill, Portsmouth, NH 03801
Tel.: (978) 535-1304
Web Site: https://www.airgeneral.com
Year Founded: 1956
Sales Range: $10-24.9 Million
Emp.: 450
Airport Terminal Services
N.A.I.C.S.: 488119
Paul Z. Siebols (VP-Ops)
Frank J. Keller (Dir-Ops)
Jeff Lyter (Dir-Compliance)

AIR GENIE AIR CONDITIONING CO.
28731 S Cargo Ct, Bonita Springs, FL 34135
Tel.: (239) 390-0069
Web Site: http://www.brunoair.com
Sales Range: $1-9.9 Million
Emp.: 20
Air Conditioning Contractor
N.A.I.C.S.: 238220
Louis Bruno (Owner & Pres)

AIR GROUND XPRESS, INC.
55 Machette Rd, Clinton, PA 15026
Tel.: (724) 695-1110
Web Site: http://www.airground.com
Year Founded: 1981
Sales Range: $25-49.9 Million
Emp.: 200
Provider of Freight Transportation Services
N.A.I.C.S.: 484121

Richard Rubense (*VP*)
Richard Patterson (*Treas, Sec & Controller*)
Dave Londino (*Pres*)

AIR HYDRO POWER INC.
2550 Blankenbaker Pkwy, Louisville, KY 40299
Tel.: (502) 451-1000
Web Site:
    http://www.airhydropower.com
Year Founded: 1961
Pneumatic Tools & Equipment
N.A.I.C.S.: 423610
Brian Martel (*Product Mgr*)
Dan McFarland (*Mgr-Automation*)
Kevin Kuhn (*Mgr*)
Matt Ott (*VP*)
Geoff Luber (*Dir-Fin*)

Subsidiaries:

Alabama Bolt & Supply, Inc.   (1)
630 Air Base Blvd, Montgomery, AL 36108
Tel.: (334) 269-9560
Web Site: http://www.airhydropower.com
Hardware Merchant Whslr
N.A.I.C.S.: 423710
Charles Ferguson (*Pres & CEO*)

Lebanon Power & Apparatus Company, Inc.   (1)
108 Village Way, Lebanon, KY 40033-1025
Tel.: (270) 692-6091
Web Site: http://lebanonpower.com
Electrical Apparatus & Equipment, Wiring Supplies & Related Equipment Merchant Whslr
N.A.I.C.S.: 423610
Tim Clark (*Gen Mgr*)
Debbie Thompson (*VP*)
Tony Clark (*VP*)

AIR LIFT COMPANY
2727 Snow Rd, Lansing, MI 48917-9595
Tel.: (517) 322-2144   MI
Web Site:
    https://www.airliftcompany.com
Year Founded: 1950
Rev.: $7,000,000
Emp.: 50
Air Spring Suspension Products
N.A.I.C.S.: 332613
Kevin Mehigh (*Pres*)
Melanie Conran (*Mgr-Consumer Mktg*)

AIR LOGISTICS CORPORATION
146 RailRd Ave, Monrovia, CA 91016
Tel.: (626) 256-1257
Web Site: http://www.airlog.com
Sales Range: $10-24.9 Million
Emp.: 21
Reinforcing Mesh, Plastics
N.A.I.C.S.: 326199
George H. Schirtzinger (*CEO & CFO*)
David L. Buckley (*VP*)
Luis Rivera (*Mgr-Safety*)

AIR MANAGEMENT SYSTEMS INC.
11905 W Sample Rd, Coral Springs, FL 33065
Tel.: (305) 651-0440
Web Site: http://www.amsiac.com
Year Founded: 1986
Sales Range: $25-49.9 Million
Emp.: 25
Contractor of Warm Air Heating & Air Conditioning
N.A.I.C.S.: 238220
James M. Hightower (*CEO*)
Chris Hightower (*Pres & COO*)
Dave McCoy (*Project Mgr*)
Rick Moreland (*VP-Sls-Svc*)

AIR MECHANICAL & SERVICE CORP.
4311 W Ida St, Tampa, FL 33614
Tel.: (813) 875-0782
Web Site: https://www.amsco-ac.com
Rev.: $10,535,472
Emp.: 130
Warm Air Heating & Air Conditioning Contractor
N.A.I.C.S.: 238220
Warren Byers (*Pres*)
Harold Spaw (*VP*)
John Gallo (*Mgr-Svc Ops*)
Neil Connelly (*VP & Gen Mgr*)

AIR POWER, INC.
1430 Trinity Ave, High Point, NC 27260-8360
Tel.: (336) 886-5081   NC
Web Site: https://www.airpower-usa.com
Year Founded: 1967
Sales Range: $75-99.9 Million
Emp.: 67
Wholesale Distribution of Industrial Machinery & Equipment
N.A.I.C.S.: 423830
Darren Stone (*Mgr-Corp Finishing Sls*)
Jim Boyd (*Project Mgr & Engr-Design*)
Michael John (*Project Mgr*)
Robin Eanes (*Mgr-Sls*)
Randy Pennington (*Branch Mgr*)
John Jenkins (*Mgr-Pur*)

AIR PRO HOLDINGS, INC.
3918 US Hwy 80 E, Mesquite, TX 75149
Tel.: (972) 288-8888
Sales Range: $10-24.9 Million
Emp.: 45
Air Compressing Components Mfr
N.A.I.C.S.: 423740
Arnie Gartman (*Pres*)
Mel Graves (*Mgr-Installer Sls & Engr-Applications*)

AIR PROS
8609 E Golf Links Rd, Tucson, AZ 85730
Tel.: (520) 886-3164
Web Site: http://www.airprosinc.com
Rev.: $1,880,000
Emp.: 100
Site Preparation Contractor
N.A.I.C.S.: 238910
Diego Sosa (*Owner*)

Subsidiaries:

Personalized Air Conditioning, Inc.   (1)
159 NW 11th St, Boca Raton, FL 33432
Tel.: (561) 391-8190
Web Site: http://www.personalizedair.com
Sales Range: $1-9.9 Million
Emp.: 18
Plumbing, Heating, Air-Conditioning, Nsk
N.A.I.C.S.: 238220
Susan Frank (*Pres*)

AIR PROS USA
3801 SW 47th Ave Ste 504, Davie, FL 33314
Tel.: (954) 546-9111
Web Site: https://airprosusa.com
Plumbing, Heating & Air-Conditioning Services
N.A.I.C.S.: 238220
Robert DiPietro (*CEO*)
Anthony Perera (*Founder & Chief Growth Officer*)

Subsidiaries:

Universal Restoration, Inc.   (1)
3250 N Andrews Ave Ext, Pompano Beach, FL 33064

Tel.: (954) 581-7110
Web Site: https://www.uahac.com
Sales Range: $1-9.9 Million
Emp.: 10
Plumbing, Heating & Air-Conditioning Contractors
N.A.I.C.S.: 238220
Michael Forgione (*Pres*)

AIR PURCHASES INCORPORATED
24 Blanchard Rd, Burlington, MA 01803
Tel.: (781) 273-2050
Web Site:
    https://www.airpurchases.com
Year Founded: 1969
Sales Range: $10-24.9 Million
Emp.: 73
Heating Equipment (Hydronic)
N.A.I.C.S.: 423720

AIR QUALITY CONTROL, INC.
4582 28th St N, Saint Petersburg, FL 33714
Tel.: (727) 347-0202   FL
Web Site: http://www.aqcinc.biz
Year Founded: 1980
Sales Range: $1-9.9 Million
Emp.: 21
Plumbing, Heating & Air-Conditioning Contractors
N.A.I.C.S.: 238220
Joseph Hadala (*Sec*)

AIR RESCUE AIR CONDITIONING, INC.
1429 Massaro Blvd, Tampa, FL 33619
Tel.: (813) 612-5600
Web Site: http://www.4airrescue.com
Year Founded: 1946
Sales Range: $10-24.9 Million
Emp.: 100
Air Conditioning & Heating Contractor
N.A.I.C.S.: 238220
Stacey Myers (*Treas*)
Harold J. Myers (*Pres*)

AIR RIDE TECHNOLOGIES LLC
1495 13th Rd, Central City, NE 68826
Tel.: (308) 946-2420
Web Site: https://www.airridecab.com
Year Founded: 1999
Specialized Freight Trucking; Long-Distance
N.A.I.C.S.: 484230
Keith Brown (*Owner*)

AIR ROYALE INTERNATIONAL INC.
8335 Sunset Blvd Ste 231, Los Angeles, CA 90069-1555
Tel.: (310) 289-9800
Web Site: http://www.airroyale.com
Sales Range: $10-24.9 Million
Emp.: 10
Flying Charter Service
N.A.I.C.S.: 481219
Wayne J. Rizzi (*Pres & CEO*)
Tige Osbourne (*VP*)

AIR RUTTER INTERNATIONAL, LLC
4310 Donald Douglas Dr Ste 202, Long Beach, CA 90808
Tel.: (562) 425-8880
Web Site: http://www.jfijets.com
Year Founded: 1993
Sales Range: $1-9.9 Million
Emp.: 50
Chartered Passenger Air Transportation
N.A.I.C.S.: 481211

Robert Seidel (*CEO*)
Valerie Boes (*Mgr-FBO*)
Gino Jooyan (*VP-Bus Dev*)
Harold Henderson (*Dir-Ops*)

Subsidiaries:

ACP Jets, LLC   (1)
4145 Southern Blvd Ste 5-8, West Palm Beach, FL 33406
Tel.: (561) 686-5551
Web Site: http://www.acpjets.com
Charter, Management, Maintenance & Aircraft Acquisition & Consulting Services
N.A.I.C.S.: 488190
Suran Wijayawardana (*COO*)

AIR SAFETY EQUIPMENT INC.
PO Box 147, Holmdel, NJ 07733
Tel.: (732) 591-9412
Web Site:
    http://www.airsafetyequipment.com
Year Founded: 1976
Sales Range: $5-14.9 Billion
Emp.: 3,200
Aircraft Servicing & Repairing
N.A.I.C.S.: 488190
Shital Rajan (*Pres & CEO*)

AIR SERVICE HAWAII
Hilo International Airport Gate 27, Hilo, HI 96720
Tel.: (808) 961-6601
Web Site:
    https://www.airservicehawaii.com
Sales Range: $10-24.9 Million
Emp.: 5
Airline Services
N.A.I.C.S.: 488119
Shanna Sato (*Mgr-Base Ops*)

AIR SUNSHINE INC.
400 Terminal Dr, Fort Lauderdale, FL 33315
Tel.: (954) 434-8900
Web Site:
    https://www.airsunshine.com
Rev.: $10,700,000
Emp.: 5
Flying Charter Service
N.A.I.C.S.: 481219
Allen Adili (*Pres*)

AIR SYSTEMS SALES INC.
4240 Delenere Ct, Royal Oak, MI 48073
Tel.: (248) 549-1105
Web Site: https://www.airsystems-usa.com
Sales Range: $10-24.9 Million
Emp.: 80
Distributing Industrial Machinery & Equipment
N.A.I.C.S.: 423830
Bart Tinsley (*Pres*)
Doug Roehl (*VP*)

AIR TECHNIQUES, INC.
1295 Walt Whitman Rd, Melville, NY 11747
Tel.: (516) 433-7676   NY
Web Site:
    https://www.airtechniques.com
Year Founded: 1962
Sales Range: $75-99.9 Million
Emp.: 300
Equipment & Chemistry for the Medical & Dental Industry Mfr & Distr
N.A.I.C.S.: 339114
Edward Marill (*Mgr-Intl Sls*)
John Mancus (*Mgr-Sls-Central United States*)
Lou Guellnitz (*VP-Sls-North America*)
Christoph Roeer (*CEO*)
Frank Napoli (*VP-Ops*)
Martin Durrstein (*Chm*)
Axel Schramm (*Exec VP-Sls & Mktg*)
Carol Eckert (*Dir-Sls Support*)

Air Techniques, Inc.—(Continued)

Laura Walsh (Mgr-Mktg)
Patrick Strohkirch (Dir-Special Markets)
Sylvia Rochon (Mgr-Sls-Natl)
Casey Baldwin (Dir-Sls-North America)

Subsidiaries:

Air Techniques, Inc. - Western Facility **(1)**
291 Bonnie Ln Ste 101, Corona, CA 92880
Tel.: (800) 247-8324
Dental Equipment Mfr
N.A.I.C.S.: 339114
Michael Murphy (Mgr-Natl Sls)

All-Pro Imaging Corp. **(1)**
1295 Walt Whiteman Rd, Melbourn, NY 11747 **(100%)**
Tel.: (516) 433-7676
Web Site: http://www.allproimaging.com
Mfr of Medical X-Ray Film Processors
N.A.I.C.S.: 333310

DURR DENTAL AG **(1)**
Hopfigheimer Strasse 17, Bietigheim-Bissingen, 74321, Germany
Tel.: (49) 71427050
Web Site: http://www.duerrdental.com
Emp.: 400
Dental Product Marketing Services
N.A.I.C.S.: 423450
Joachim Eppinger (VP-Equipment)
Christian Pflug (VP-Hygiene)
Axel Schramm (Exec VP)
Wolfgang Blatt (Head-Customer Svc)

Jelrus International **(1)**
70 Cantiague Rock Rd, Hicksville, NY 11801-1163 **(100%)**
Tel.: (516) 942-0202
Web Site: http://www.jelrus.com
Dental Laboratory Equipment Mfr
N.A.I.C.S.: 339114

AIR TECHNOLOGY ENGINES, INC.
2884 S Horseshoe Dr, Naples, FL 34104
Tel.: (239) 643-0011 FL
Web Site:
  https://www.airtechnology.com
Year Founded: 1996
Sales Range: $10-24.9 Million
Emp.: 18
Helicopter & Engine Parts Distr; Helicopter Engine & Transmission Repair
N.A.I.C.S.: 423860
Mike Turner (Pres)

AIR TRANSPORT COMPONENTS, LLC
615 W Knox Rd, Tempe, AZ 85284
Tel.: (480) 831-1268 AZ
Web Site: http://www.atcphx.com
Year Founded: 1999
Sales Range: $1-9.9 Million
Emp.: 28
Support Activities for Air Transportation
N.A.I.C.S.: 488190
Chris Behne (Dir-Ops)
Damian Allen (Mgr-Quality)
Dieter Welle (VP-Pur)
Gary Himes (Dir-Sls & Mktg)
Josh Wilson (Gen Mgr-Ops)
Roy Hyde (Pres & CEO)
Tim Szkatulski (CFO)

AIR TREATMENT CORP.
640 N Puente St, Brea, CA 92821
Tel.: (909) 869-7975
Web Site:
  https://www.airtreatment.com
Sales Range: $10-24.9 Million
Emp.: 125
Electrical Heating Equipment
N.A.I.C.S.: 423730

Mark Hartman (Pres, Principal & Mgr-Sls)
Deborah Hudson (CFO & Mgr-Ops)
Barbara Lohman (Mgr-Acctg)
David Eisenberg (Engr-Sls)
Tim Thomas (VP)
Greg Blackfelner (VP & Engr-Sls)
Brian McCutcheon (Engr-Sls)
Samer Abu-Wishah (Engr-Sls)
Jerry Conklin (Engr-Sls)
Dan Rohrbach (Engr-Sls)
Vicki Rolofson (Engr-Sls)
Scott McCarthy (Engr-Sls)
Fred Pedersen (Engr-Sls)
Jim Thomas (Engr-Sls)
Robert Shafer (Engr-Sls)
Linda Porrett (Mgr-Credit)
Ken Mozek (Mgr-Sls-Northern CA)
Craig Domagala (VP-Sls)

AIR WISCONSIN AIRLINES CORPORATION
W 6390 Challenger Dr Ste 203, Appleton, WI 54914-9120
Tel.: (920) 739-5123 DE
Web Site: http://www.airwis.com
Year Founded: 1993
Sales Range: $400-449.9 Million
Emp.: 2,800
Passenger Airline Services
N.A.I.C.S.: 481111
Christine Deister (Pres & CEO)
Janet Huculak (VP-Maintenance, Engrg & Procurement)
Chris White (VP-Safety & Security)
Jeff Joy (VP-IT & Sys Ops Control)
Gary Pratt (VP-Engrg)
Patrick Thompson (Chm)
Stan Petersen-Gauthier (CFO, Treas & Sr VP)
Laurie Martin (VP-Inflight & Customer Svc)
Jeffrey Bethune (VP-Fin & Bus Analysis)

AIR-CONDITIONING, HEATING, AND REFRIGERATION INSTITUTE
2111 Wilson Blvd Ste 500, Arlington, VA 22201
Tel.: (703) 524-8800 VA
Web Site: http://www.ari.org
Year Founded: 2007
Sales Range: $10-24.9 Million
Emp.: 79
Trade Assocation
N.A.I.C.S.: 813910
Stephen Yurek (Pres & CEO)

AIR-RIDE INC.
11900 Sager Rd, Swanton, OH 43558-9415
Tel.: (419) 826-7777 OH
Year Founded: 1982
Sales Range: $25-49.9 Million
Emp.: 60
Ground Freight & Trucking Services
N.A.I.C.S.: 484121
Albert Mackey (CEO)
Karen Stock (Controller)

AIR-RITE HEATING & COOLING
1150 Frontenac Rd, Naperville, IL 60563
Tel.: (630) 966-8100
Web Site: http://www.airrite.com
Sales Range: $50-74.9 Million
Emp.: 100
Heating & Air Conditioning Contractors
N.A.I.C.S.: 238220
Terry Van Someren (Pres)
Tess Salek (Mgr-Sls)

AIR-SEA FORWARDERS INC.
9009 La Cienega Blvd, Inglewood, CA 90301-4403
Tel.: (310) 216-1616 CA
Web Site: https://www.airseainc.com
Year Founded: 1947
Sales Range: $10-24.9 Million
Emp.: 160
Freight Transportation Arrangement
N.A.I.C.S.: 488510
Todd Hinkley (CEO)

AIR-WAY MANUFACTURING COMPANY
586 N Main St, Olivet, MI 49076
Tel.: (269) 749-2161
Web Site: https://www.air-way.com
Sales Range: $25-49.9 Million
Emp.: 275
Hose & Tube Fittings & Assemblies, Hydraulic/Pneumatic
N.A.I.C.S.: 332912
Ronald Hamm (Chm)
Bill Blank (Pres)
Gina Fox (Coord-PPAP)
Kari Place (Supvr-Pur)
Kim DeYoung (VP-Ops)

AIRBORNE WIRELESS NETWORK
4115 Guardian St Ste C, Simi Valley, CA 93063
Tel.: (805) 583-4302 NV
Web Site:
  https://www.airbornewireless.com
Year Founded: 2011
ABWN—(OTCIQ)
Sales Range: Less than $1 Million
Emp.: 8
Investment Services
N.A.I.C.S.: 523999
Edward J. Daniels (Pres & CEO)
Marius de Mos (VP-Technical Affairs & Development)

AIRCO MECHANICAL INC.
8210 Demetre Ave, Sacramento, CA 95828-1106
Tel.: (916) 381-4523 CA
Web Site:
  https://www.aircomech.com
Year Founded: 1974
Sales Range: $50-74.9 Million
Emp.: 250
Warm Air Heating & Air Conditioning; Ventilation, Duct Work & Plumbing Contractors
N.A.I.C.S.: 238220
Brian Leighton (Project Mgr)
Christopher Barker (Project Mgr)
Joann Hillenbrand (Controller)
Rob Courtnier (Superintendent-Shop)

AIRCRAFT CABIN SYSTEMS
18080 NE 68th St Bldg B, Redmond, WA 98052
Tel.: (425) 883-8008
Web Site:
  https://www.aircraftcabins.com
Year Founded: 1999
Rev.: $6,300,000
Emp.: 10
Electronic Appliance, Television & Radio Set Merchant Whslr
N.A.I.C.S.: 423620
Yukio Sugimoto (Pres & CEO)
Richie Sugimoto (CFO)

AIRCRAFT GEAR CORPORATION
611 Beacon St, Loves Park, IL 61111-5902
Tel.: (815) 877-7473
Web Site:
  https://www.rockfordacromatic.com
Sales Range: $10-24.9 Million

Emp.: 50
Screw Machine Products; Aircraft Parts; Machinery; Driveline Components & Automotive Components
N.A.I.C.S.: 336413
James N. Olson (Pres)

Subsidiaries:

Rockford Acromatic Product Co. **(1)**
611 Beacon St, Loves Park, IL 61111
Tel.: (815) 877-7473
Web Site: http://www.rockfordacromatic.com
Sales Range: $10-24.9 Million
Automotive & Driveline Components Mfr
N.A.I.C.S.: 336330
Jim Olson (Pres)

Rockford Constant Velocity **(1)**
1500 11th Ave, Rockford, IL 61104
Tel.: (815) 962-1411
Web Site: http://www.rockfordcv.com
Mfr & Distr of C.V. & Rear Driveline Parts
N.A.I.C.S.: 423120
Jim Olson (Pres)

AIRCRAFT INSTRUMENT & RADIO CO.
1853 S Eisenhower Ct, Wichita, KS 67209
Tel.: (316) 945-0445
Web Site: http://www.airco-ict.com
Sales Range: $10-24.9 Million
Emp.: 55
Whslr of Aircraft Equipment & Supplies
N.A.I.C.S.: 423860
Martin Potash (Pres)
Melanie Combs (Founder & VP-Ops)
Marty Clem (Mgr-Domestic Sls)
Jerry Urcavich (VP-Mktg)
Marigene Bloomer (Mgr-Ops)
Michael Molina (Dir-IT)
Jerry Ward (Dir-Ops-Intl)
Adam Holstine (Gen Mgr-Svcs)
Vincent Boucher (Mgr-Sls-Intl)
Randy Staub (COO & VP-Fin)
Cor Tjalsma (Dir-Asia Pacific Reg)
Donna Crombie (Controller)
Steve Irwin (Dir-Bus Dev)
Sammie Collins (Mgr-Quality Assurance)
Trudy Stout (Office Mgr)

AIRCRAFT PRECISION PRODUCTS, INC.
185 Industrial Pkwy, Ithaca, MI 48847
Tel.: (989) 875-4186
Web Site:
  https://www.aircraftprecision.net
Rev.: $10,457,171
Emp.: 73
Aircraft Engines & Engine Parts
N.A.I.C.S.: 336412
Gary W. Henderson (Pur Mgr)
Ray Schoenborn (Mgr-Engrg)
Ron Abbott (Gen Mgr)
Dave Halfman (Mgr-Production)
William Henderson III (Pres)

AIRDEX INTERNATIONAL, INC.
8975 S Pecos Rd Ste 7A, Henderson, NV 89074
Tel.: (702) 270-6004
Web Site: http://www.airdex.com
Sales Range: $10-24.9 Million
Emp.: 23
Plastics Product Mfr
N.A.I.C.S.: 326199
Jefferey Dahl (Pres & CEO)

AIRDYNE AEROSPACE INC.
3160 Premier Dr, Spring Hill, FL 34604
Tel.: (352) 593-4163
Web Site: http://www.airdyne.org
Sales Range: $10-24.9 Million
Emp.: 20
Airplane Parts Mfr

N.A.I.C.S.: 336413
Ross Neyedly *(Pres & CEO)*
Mike Hillestad *(VP-Mktg & Sls)*
Ed Lewis *(VP-R&D)*

Subsidiaries:

Airdyne R&D Inc. (1)
25240 Township Road 254, Calgary, T3L
2P7, AB, Canada
Tel.: (403) 920-0211
Web Site: http://www.airdyne-aero.com
Airplane Parts Mfr
N.A.I.C.S.: 336413

AIRDYNE INC.
14910 Henry Rd, Houston, TX 77060
Tel.: (281) 820-0000
Web Site: http://www.airdyne.net
Sales Range: $10-24.9 Million
Emp.: 100
Industrial Machinery & Equipment
N.A.I.C.S.: 423830
Jonathan Michel *(Pres)*

AIRECO SUPPLY, INC.
8860 Gorman Rd, Laurel, MD 20723
Tel.: (301) 317-4773   MD
Web Site: https://www.aireco.com
Year Founded: 1952
Heating, Ventilating, Air Conditioning
& Refrigeration (HVACR) Whslr
N.A.I.C.S.: 423730
Matthew Kemp *(Gen Mgr-Advanced
Products Group)*
Dan Hinchman *(Pres)*

AIREHEALTH, LLC
3251 Progress Dr Ste F, Orlando, FL
32826
Web Site: http://www.aire.health
Portable Nebulizer Mfr & Dist
N.A.I.C.S.: 325412
Stacie Ruth *(Co-Founder & CEO)*
Ken Sakal *(Head-Product)*
Frank O'Neill *(Head-Tech)*
Nirinjan Yee *(Head-Innovation)*

Subsidiaries:

Breathresearch Inc. (1)
2064 Essenay Ave, Walnut Creek, CA
94597-2432
Tel.: (925) 934-8242
Web Site: http://www.breathresearch.com
Electromedical & Electrotherapeutic Apparatus Mfr
N.A.I.C.S.: 334510
Gary Yee *(Owner)*

AIREKO CONSTRUCTION CORP.
Las Casas St Lot Ste 20 Bairoa Industrial Park, Caguas, PR 00725
Tel.: (787) 653-6300   PR
Web Site: https://www.aireko.com
Year Founded: 1963
Sales Range: $50-74.9 Million
Emp.: 600
Nonresidential Construction
N.A.I.C.S.: 238220
Maria Rojas *(Mgr-Human Resources)*
Waldemar E. Toro *(Pres & Partner)*
Josen Rossi *(Chm & Mng Partner)*

AIRES
6 Penn Center W Ste 200, Pittsburgh, PA 15276
Tel.: (412) 788-0461   PA
Web Site: http://www.aires.com
Year Founded: 1981
Sales Range: $10-24.9 Million
Emp.: 85
Relocation & Freight Transportation
Services
N.A.I.C.S.: 488510
Bryan Putt *(CEO)*
Jeff Wangler *(Pres)*
Wayne Lawrence *(Acct Mgr)*

Sarah Beck *(Acct Mgr-West Coast
Reg)*
Joleen Lauffer *(VP-Ops)*
Pamela Dunleavy *(VP-Sls)*
Rob Capiola *(Acct Mgr-Central Reg)*
John Casuccio *(Gen Mgr)*
Andrew Meadowcroft *(Global Mgr-
Client Svc)*
Emma Herblot *(Global Mgr-Client
Svc)*
Richard Hooker *(Dir-Ops)*

AIREY-THOMPSON COMPANY INC.
5310 Irwindale Ave, Irwindale, CA
91706
Tel.: (626) 960-3355
Web Site: https://www.airey-
thompson.com
Year Founded: 1935
Noncurrent-Carrying Wiring Devices
N.A.I.C.S.: 335932
Ralph Seth *(Pres)*
Corey Seth *(Gen Mgr)*

AIRFOIL PUBLIC RELATIONS
1000 Town Ctr Dr Ste 600, Southfield, MI 48075
Tel.: (248) 304-1400
Web Site: http://www.airfoilgroup.com
Year Founded: 2000
Sales Range: $10-24.9 Million
Emp.: 50
Public Relations
N.A.I.C.S.: 541820
Lisa Vallee-Smith *(Pres & CEO)*
Tracey Parry *(Sr VP)*
Amy Bryson *(VP)*
Keith Donovan *(Sr VP)*
Kristen Stippich *(Sr VP)*
Steve Friedman *(Dir-Mktg Comm)*
David Bailey *(Exec VP)*
Helena Dobbins *(Mgr-Social & Digital
Media)*
Leah Haran *(Sr VP)*
Sharon Neumann *(Sr VP)*
Jennifer Akoma *(VP)*
Andy Kill *(VP)*
Joe Kilmer *(VP)*
Kevin Sangsland *(VP)*

AIRGUIDE CORPORATION
795 W 20th St, Hialeah, FL 33010-
2429
Tel.: (305) 888-1631
Web Site:
https://www.airguidemfg.com
Year Founded: 1958
Sales Range: $10-24.9 Million
Emp.: 140
Air Heating & Air Conditioning Grills,
Registers & Diffusers Mfr
N.A.I.C.S.: 331318
Chuck Robinson *(Controller)*
Douglas Marty Jr. *(VP-Ops)*

AIRLINE HYDRAULICS CORPORATION
3557 Progress Dr, Bensalem, PA
19020
Tel.: (215) 638-4700   PA
Web Site: https://www.airlinehyd.com
Year Founded: 1949
Sales Range: $100-124.9 Million
Emp.: 180
Hydraulic & Pneumatic Electronic
Component Mfr & Distr
N.A.I.C.S.: 333998
Joseph E. Loughran *(Pres & CEO)*

Subsidiaries:

Fluid Power Automation LLC (1)
376 Dry Bridge Rd Bldg B-1, North Kingstown, RI 02852
Tel.: (401) 583-0190
Industrial Automation Equipment Distr

N.A.I.C.S.: 423830
Innovative Automation And Controls,
Inc. (1)
11459 Cronhill Dr, Owings Mills, MD 21117
Tel.: (410) 581-2200
Web Site: http://www.iacitech.com
Sales Range: $1-9.9 Million
Emp.: 9
Electrical Controls & Automation Components Distr
N.A.I.C.S.: 335999
Catherine Jones *(Treas)*
Clay Rorher *(Pres)*

AIRLINE TARIFF PUBLISHING COMPANY
45005 Aviation, Dulles, VA 20166
Tel.: (703) 471-7510
Web Site: http://www.atpco.net
Year Founded: 1965
Rev.: $51,792,008
Emp.: 450
Statistical Reports (Periodicals): Publishing & Printing
N.A.I.C.S.: 513120
Bryan Kirk *(CFO)*
Shauna Koca *(Mgr-Product Trng)*
Kevin Fliess *(VP-Mktg & Sls)*
Jerry Foran *(Chm)*
Robert Albert *(Exec VP-Retailing)*
Jonathan Savitch *(Chief Comml Officer)*
Jaivin Anzalota *(Chief Product Officer)*
Tom Gregorson *(Chief Strategy Officer)*
John Murphy *(CIO)*
Priscilla O'Donnell *(Chief HR Officer)*
Alex Zoghlin *(CEO)*

AIRLINES REPORTING CORPORATION
3000 Wilson Blvd Ste 300, Arlington,
VA 22201-3862
Tel.: (703) 816-8000
Web Site: https://www.arccorp.com
Year Founded: 1964
Sales Range: $50-74.9 Million
Emp.: 455
Travel Products & Services, Ticket
Distribution & Settlement & Broker
Services
N.A.I.C.S.: 541990
Lauri Reishus *(COO & Exec VP)*
Mike Premo *(Pres & CEO)*
Bonnie S. Reitz *(Chm)*
Eric J. Barger *(Chief HR Officer &
VP)*
Dickie Oliver *(Chief Info Svcs Officer
& VP)*

Subsidiaries:

nuTravel Technology Solutions,
LLC (1)
2500 Westchester Ave Ste 108, Purchase,
NY 10577
Tel.: (914) 848-4566
Web Site: http://nutravel.com
Computer System Design Services
N.A.I.C.S.: 541512
Carmine Carpanzano *(Co-Founder, Pres &
CEO)*
Joseph J. Sternlicht *(CTO & Exec VP)*
Paul LaBate *(Dir-Software Dev)*
Joseph R. Zimmel *(Chm)*
Curtis Socha *(Dir-Software Dev)*
Damar Christopher *(VP-Product & Customer Solutions)*
Joseph Ascanio *(Dir-UX/UI Design & Brand
Mktg)*
Michael J. Materasso *(Co-Founder & COO)*
Richard Miller *(Chief Strategy Officer)*
Rob Brown *(Exec VP & Gen Mgr-Airline
Solutions)*

AIRLITE PLASTICS COMPANY
6110 Abbott Dr, Omaha, NE 68110
Tel.: (402) 341-7300

Web Site:
http://www.airliteplastics.com
Year Founded: 1946
Sales Range: $50-74.9 Million
Emp.: 900
Plastic Packaging Mfr
N.A.I.C.S.: 326199
Brad Crosby *(CEO)*
Beccy Smith *(Dir-Quality)*
Becky Hulvey *(Coord-Pur)*
Christopher Varnell *(Dir-Graphics)*
Chuck Cooper *(Sr Mgr-Project Engrg)*
Greg Sosso *(Dir-Product Dev)*
Joe Allen *(Engr-Quality)*
Marge Hoehn *(Asst Mgr-Shift)*
Rob Mankhey *(Supvr-Warehouse)*
Rich Hays *(Mgr-IML Ops)*
Sandra Armetta *(Coord-Quality Assurance Customer Support)*
Tom Belt *(Project Mgr)*
Brian Christensen *(VP-Ops)*
Steve Kane *(CFO)*

Subsidiaries:

Airlite Plastics Co. (1)
2860 Bath Pike, Nazareth, PA 18064
Tel.: (610) 759-0280
Web Site: http://www.measurexscoops.com
Sales Range: $10-24.9 Million
Emp.: 70
Plastics Product Mfr
N.A.I.C.S.: 326199
John Bungert *(VP)*

Cosmetic Specialties International
LLC (1)
550 E 3rd St, Oxnard, CA 93030
Tel.: (817) 865-6570
Web Site: http://www.csillc.com
Beauty & Skincare Products Container Mfr
N.A.I.C.S.: 561910
Christopher Gedwed *(COO & Exec VP)*

AIRMASTER FAN COMPANY
1300 Falahee Rd, Jackson, MI
49203-3554
Tel.: (517) 764-2300   MI
Web Site:
http://www.airmasterfan.com
Year Founded: 1975
Sales Range: $50-74.9 Million
Emp.: 75
Air Circulators, Exhaust Fans, Ceiling
Fans & Roof Ventilators
N.A.I.C.S.: 333413
Richard Stone *(Pres & CEO)*
Michael Pignataro *(Exec VP)*
Ed Laabs *(VP-Sls & Mktg)*
Matt Johnson *(Mgr-Pur)*
Forest Owen *(Reg Mgr-Sls)*

AIRMATE COMPANY
16280 County Road D, Bryan, OH
43506
Tel.: (419) 636-3184   OH
Web Site:
http://www.airmatecompany.com
Year Founded: 1946
Sales Range: $1-9.9 Million
Emp.: 55
Mfr of Plastic Products for Advertising
Displays
N.A.I.C.S.: 326199
Carol Schreder *(Pres & CEO)*
Ben Bucklew *(Controller)*

AIRNET GROUP, INC.
801 Broad St Ste 530, Chattanooga,
TN 37402
Tel.: (423) 664-7678
Web Site:
http://www.airnetgroup.com
Sales Range: $1-9.9 Million
Emp.: 25
Data Processing & Preparation Services
N.A.I.C.S.: 518210

AirNet Group, Inc.—(Continued)

Jeff Averbeck (Pres & CEO)
Joe McCall (CFO)

AIROLDI BROTHERS INC.
6930 S 6th St, Oak Creek, WI 53154
Tel.: (414) 856-0508
Web Site:
　https://www.airoldibrothers.com
Sales Range: $10-24.9 Million
Emp.: 70
Truck Leasing Services
N.A.I.C.S.: 532120
Jeff Sirovina (Dir-HR & Safety)
Mike Airoldi (Dir-Maintenance)
Debbie Vlaj (Mgr)
Tom A. Martino (Exec VP)
Elizabeth Stevens (Pres-Custom Express)
James C. Airoldi Jr. (Dir-Ops)

AIROOM INCORPORATED
6825 N Lincoln Ave, Lincolnwood, IL 60712
Tel.: (847) 325-5447
Web Site: https://www.airoom.com
Sales Range: $10-24.9 Million
Emp.: 50
General Remodeling, Single-Family Houses
N.A.I.C.S.: 236118
Greg Sutton (Mgr-Project Dev)
Kevin Bigos (Mgr-Construction)
Dan Carlman (Mgr-Production)
Joe LaBelle (Mgr-Project Dev)
Jack Kapala (Superintendent)
Doug Klee (Sr VP)
Marty Meadow (Sr VP)

AIRPARTS COMPANY INC.
2310 NW 55th Ct Ste 128, Fort Lauderdale, FL 33309
Tel.: (954) 739-3575
Web Site: http://www.airpartsco.com
Sales Range: $25-49.9 Million
Emp.: 40
Distribute Aircraft Parts
N.A.I.C.S.: 423860
Andy Montidoro (Mgr-Sls)

AIRPORT AUTHORITY WASHOE COUNTY
2001 E Plumb Ln, Reno, NV 89502
Tel.: (775) 328-6400
Web Site:
　https://www.renoairport.com
Sales Range: $10-24.9 Million
Emp.: 200
Airport
N.A.I.C.S.: 488119
Brian Kulpin (Dir-Mktg & Pub Affairs)

AIRPORT EQUIPMENT RENTALS INC.
1285 Van Horn Rd, Fairbanks, AK 99701
Tel.: (907) 456-2000
Web Site: http://www.aer-inc.net
Sales Range: $10-24.9 Million
Emp.: 2,500
Equipment Rental & Leasing
N.A.I.C.S.: 532490
Jerry Sadler (Pres)

AIRPORT TERMINAL SERVICES INC.
111 W Port Plz Ste 400, Saint Louis, MO 63146
Tel.: (314) 739-1900
Web Site: http://www.atsstl.com
Year Founded: 1975
Sales Range: $50-74.9 Million
Emp.: 1,300
Ground Handling Services
N.A.I.C.S.: 561720

Sally A. Leible (Pres & COO)
Vince Knipp (Controller)
Ingrid Braeuninger (VP-Sls & Bus Dev)

AIRRATTLE INC.
3643 Dill Rd, Centerburg, OH 43011
Tel.: (740) 625-0001
Web Site: https://www.airrattle.com
Year Founded: 2005
Sales Range: $1-9.9 Million
Emp.: 8
Airsoft Guns
N.A.I.C.S.: 332994
Aaron Morgan (Owner)

AIRROSTI REHAB CENTERS, LLC
911 Central Pkwy N Ste 300, San Antonio, TX 78232
Tel.: (800) 404-6050
Web Site: http://www.airrosti.com
Year Founded: 2004
Sales Range: $1-9.9 Million
Emp.: 245
Specializing in Musculoskeletal Therapy & Care Management
N.A.I.C.S.: 621399
John Cybulski (Dir-Rehab-Therapy)

AIRSPLAT, CO.
11688 Clark St A, Arcadia, CA 91006
Tel.: (626) 357-5700
Web Site: http://www.airsplat.com
Year Founded: 2005
Sales Range: $10-24.9 Million
Emp.: 35
Online Seller of Airsoft Guns & Accessories
N.A.I.C.S.: 332993
Kent Wu (Pres)
Mary Chafe (Gen Mgr)

AIRTECH INTERNATIONAL INC.
5700 Skylab Rd, Huntington Beach, CA 92647
Tel.: (714) 899-8100
Web Site: https://www.airtechintl.com
Year Founded: 1973
Sales Range: $10-24.9 Million
Emp.: 104
Aircraft Parts & Equipment
N.A.I.C.S.: 336413
William Dahlgren (Owner)

Subsidiaries:

Tygavac Advanced Materials Ltd. (1)
Kingsway West Business Park Moss Bridge Road, Rochdale, OL16 5LX, Lancashire, United Kingdom
Tel.: (44) 1706 649 222
Web Site: http://www.tygavac.co.uk
Sales Range: $10-24.9 Million
Emp.: 35
Vacuum Bag Material Mfr
N.A.I.C.S.: 325211
Kerry Lee (Gen Mgr)

AIRTIGHT NETWORKS, INC.
339 Bernardo Ave, Mountain View, CA 94043
Tel.: (650) 961-1111　　　　CA
Web Site:
　http://www.airtightnetworks.com
Year Founded: 2003
Sales Range: $25-49.9 Million
Emp.: 150
Secure Cloud Wi-Fi Solutions
N.A.I.C.S.: 513210
David King (Chm)
Pravin Bhagwat (CTO)
Kiran Deshpande (Pres-Intl)
Hemant Chaskar (VP-Tech)
Gopinath KN (VP-Engrg)
Jatin Parekh (VP-Product Mgmt)
Kaustubh Phanse (Chief Evangelist)

Rick Wilmer (CEO)
Kester Kyrie (VP-Worldwide Sls & Channels)
Freddy Mangum (CMO)

AIRTREKS
7 Spring St, San Francisco, CA 94104
Tel.: (415) 977-7100
Web Site: http://www.airtreks.com
Year Founded: 1987
Sales Range: $10-24.9 Million
Emp.: 30
Travel Agency Services
N.A.I.C.S.: 561510
Mark L. Ludwig (Principal)
Lee Marona (Pres)

AIRTROL, INC.
3960 N St, Baton Rouge, LA 70806-3318
Tel.: (225) 383-2617　　　　LA
Web Site:
　https://www.airtrolmechanical.com
Year Founded: 1946
Sales Range: $100-124.9 Million
Emp.: 19
Heating & Air Conditioning Services
N.A.I.C.S.: 238220
Stephen W. Pol (Chm & Pres)
Francis Jumonville (Controller)
Brooks Chauvin (Project Mgr)

AIRVANA, INC.
19 Alpha Rd, Chelmsford, MA 01824
Tel.: (978) 250-3000　　　　DE
Web Site: http://www.airvana.com
Year Founded: 2000
Sales Range: $50-74.9 Million
Emp.: 100
Network Infrastructure Products Mfr
N.A.I.C.S.: 334210
Vedat M. Eyuboglu (Co-Founder & CTO)
Sanjeev Verma (Co-Founder & Exec VP-Corp Dev)
Richard Lowe (Pres & CEO)
Michael Cohen (Dir-Legal)
Rayadurgam Ravikanth (VP-Engrg)
Christina Clohecy (VP-Fin & Admin)
Rod Gatehouse (VP-Mktg & Product Mgmt)
Randall S. Battat (Chm)

Subsidiaries:

Airvana Networks India Private Limited (1)
1st Fl B Wing Block A Salarpuria Softzone Survey Nos 80/1 81/1 81/2, Varthur Hobli-Outer Ring Rd, Bengaluru, 560103, India (99.99%)
Tel.: (91) 8066189300
Web Site: http://www.airvana.com
Emp.: 150
Network Infrastructure Products Mfr
N.A.I.C.S.: 334210
Sandeep Dikshit (Mng Dir)

AIRWELD INC.
94 Marine St, Farmingdale, NY 11735
Tel.: (631) 694-4343
Web Site: http://www.airweld.net
Rev.: $15,000,000
Emp.: 50
Industrial Gases
N.A.I.C.S.: 424690
John Zak (CEO)
Thomas Diedermann (VP)

AIRXPANDERS INC.
3047 Orchard Pkwy, San Jose, CA 95134
Tel.: (650) 390-9000
Year Founded: 2005
Rev.: $7,817,000
Assets: $24,004,000
Liabilities: $19,478,000

Net Worth: $4,526,000
Earnings: ($26,721,000)
Emp.: 70
Fiscal Year-end: 12/31/18
Medical Device Mfr & Distr
N.A.I.C.S.: 423450

AIS CONSTRUCTION EQUIPMENT CORP.
600 AIS Dr SW, Bridgeport, MI 48722
Tel.: (616) 538-2400
Web Site: https://www.aisequip.com
Rev.: $115,800,000
Emp.: 600
Construction & Mining Machinery
N.A.I.C.S.: 423810
Larry Behrenwald (Owner)
Bob Allison (Pres)
Laura Thelen (Mgr-Admin & Fin)
David Riccius (CFO)
Rachel Cook (Mgr-Adv)

AISLING CAPITAL LLC
888 7th Ave 12th Fl, New York, NY 10106
Tel.: (212) 651-6380　　　　DE
Web Site:
　http://www.aislingcapital.com
Sales Range: $25-49.9 Million
Emp.: 30
Private Equity Investments in Business, Healthcare & Technology
N.A.I.C.S.: 523999
Jan Hoerrner (Dir-IR & Mktg)
Robert J. Wenzel (Controller)
Josh Bilenker (Partner)
Dennis J. Purcell (Founder)
Aftab R. Kherani (Partner)
Stacey D. Seltzer (Partner)
Scott Braunstein (Operating Partner)
Eric Aguiar (Partner)
Andrew N. Schiff (Mng Partner)
Steven Arnote Elms (Mng Partner)
Eric Aguiar (Partner)
Eric Aguiar (Partner)

AIT WORLDWIDE LOGISTICS, INC.
701 N Rohlwing Rd, Itasca, IL 60143
Tel.: (630) 766-8300　　　　IL
Web Site:
　http://www.aitworldwide.com
Year Founded: 1979
Freight Forwarding
N.A.I.C.S.: 488510
Vaughn Moore (Exec Chm, Pres & CEO)
Ray Fennelly (CIO)
Keith Tholan (Pres & COO)
Ryan Carter (VP-Americas)
Greg Weigel (Chief Bus Officer)
Mike Rothacher (Exec VP-Truckload Brokerage & Perishables & Healthcare)
Matt Sanders (Mgr-PR)

Subsidiaries:

Intelligent Logistics, LLC (1)
1100 E Howard Lane, Austin, TX 78753
Tel.: (512) 238-6874
Web Site: http://www.inlogistics.com
Sales Range: $1-9.9 Million
Emp.: 17
Transportation Logistics & Supply Chain Management Services
N.A.I.C.S.: 488510
Leah Fenech (VP-Sls & Mktg)
Tim Miller (Founder & Pres)
Brandon Arnold (VP-Ops)
Ed Valle (VP-Bus Ops)

Select Express & Logistics LLC (1)
55 W 39th St, New York, NY 10018
Tel.: (212) 947-4114
Web Site: http://www.selectexp.com
Couriers
N.A.I.C.S.: 492110
Kern Weissman (CIO)
Jay Waldman (CEO)

Unitrans International Corp. **(1)**
709 Hindry Ave, Inglewood, CA 90301
Tel.: (310) 410-7676
Web Site: http://www.unitrans-us.com
Emp.: 45
Freight Transportation Arrangement
N.A.I.C.S.: 488510

AITECH RUGGED COMPUTER SYSTEMS
19756 Prairie St, Chatsworth, CA 91311
Tel.: (408) 980-6200
Web Site: http://www.rugged.com
Sales Range: $10-24.9 Million
Emp.: 105
Electronic Computer Related Products
N.A.I.C.S.: 423690
Moshe Tal *(CEO)*

Subsidiaries:

Aitech Space Systems Inc **(1)**
19756 Prairie St, Chatsworth, CA 91311
Tel.: (818) 700-2000
Web Site: http://www.rugged.com
Rev.: $5,500,000
Emp.: 32
Electronic Computers
N.A.I.C.S.: 334111
Doug Patterson *(VP-Sls & Mktg-Worldwide)*

AITKIN COMMUNITY HOSPITAL
200 Bunker Hill Dr, Aitkin, MN 56431
Tel.: (218) 927-2121   MN
Web Site:
   http://www.riverwoodhealthcare.org
Year Founded: 1948
Sales Range: $50-74.9 Million
Emp.: 394
Health Care Srvices
N.A.I.C.S.: 622110
Cindi Hills *(Dir-HR)*
Chad Cooper *(CEO)*
Daryl Kallevig *(CIO)*
Kristine Layne *(Chief Nursing Officer)*
Mark Heggem *(Chief Medical Officer)*
Christine Bright *(Sec)*

AJ BART INC.
4130 Lindbergh Dr, Addison, TX 75001
Tel.: (972) 960-8300
Web Site: http://www.ajbart.com
Year Founded: 1987
Sales Range: $10-24.9 Million
Emp.: 135
Offset Printing Services
N.A.I.C.S.: 323111
Tracey Johnson *(Acct Mgr-Print)*
Bob Stein *(Head-Ops)*
Don Meador *(VP-Sls)*
Karen Nicholson *(Mgr-Fulfillment)*
Jonathan Sumners *(VP-Sls)*
Roel Garza *(Mgr-Sls)*

AJ CATAGNUS INC.
1299 W James St, Norristown, PA 19401
Tel.: (610) 275-5328
Web Site: http://www.ajcatagnus.com
Rev.: $10,500,000
Emp.: 56
Recycling, Waste Materials
N.A.I.C.S.: 562920
Chuck Williams *(Mgr-Sls)*

AJ DEMOR & SONS INC.
2150 Eldo Rd, Monroeville, PA 15146
Tel.: (412) 242-6125
Web Site: https://www.ajdemor.com
Sales Range: $10-24.9 Million
Emp.: 35
Mechanical Contractor
N.A.I.C.S.: 238220
David A. Demor *(Founder)*

AJ DIANI CONSTRUCTION CO
351 N Blosser Rd, Santa Maria, CA 93456-0636
Tel.: (805) 925-9533
Web Site: https://www.diani.com
Rev.: $54,460,576
Emp.: 100
Specialized Public Building Contractors
N.A.I.C.S.: 236220
James A. Diani *(Pres)*

AJ MANUFACTURING INC.
1217 Oak St, Bloomer, WI 54724
Tel.: (715) 568-2204
Web Site: https://www.ajdoor.com
Sales Range: $10-24.9 Million
Emp.: 150
Metal Doors
N.A.I.C.S.: 332321
Dominick Rider *(CFO)*
Todd Carlson *(Pres)*
Tim Rogge *(Dir-Engrg)*

AJ STATIONERS INC.
6810 Deerpath Rd Ste 425, Elkridge, MD 21075-6349
Tel.: (410) 360-4900
Web Site:
   http://www.ajstationers.com
Sales Range: $10-24.9 Million
Emp.: 45
Stationery Stores
N.A.I.C.S.: 459410
Angela Jeung *(Pres)*

AJAX BUILDING CORPORATION
1080 Commerce Blvd, Midway, FL 32343-6678
Tel.: (850) 224-9571   FL
Web Site:
   https://www.ajaxbuilding.com
Year Founded: 1958
Sales Range: $100-124.9 Million
Emp.: 130
Building Services
N.A.I.C.S.: 236220
Bill Byrnejay *(Pres)*
James Marini *(Project Mgr)*
Tim Templeton *(Dir-Bus Dev & Mktg)*

AJAX BUSINESS INTERIORS, INC.
15360 US 19 N, Clearwater, FL 33764
Tel.: (727) 535-1300
Web Site:
   https://www.ajaxinteriors.com
Sales Range: $1-9.9 Million
Emp.: 10
Office Furniture Dealer
N.A.I.C.S.: 423210
Mark Skolnick *(Pres)*

AJAX CONSTRUCTION CO., INC.
2833 Victory Hwy, Harrisville, RI 02830
Tel.: (401) 765-6500
Sales Range: $10-24.9 Million
Emp.: 70
Commercial & Institutional Building Construction Services
N.A.I.C.S.: 236220
Donald A. Morel *(Pres)*

AJAX DISTRIBUTING CO. INC.
330 Warfield Blvd, Clarksville, TN 37043
Tel.: (931) 648-0645
Web Site:
   https://www.ajaxdistributing.com
Sales Range: $10-24.9 Million
Emp.: 50
Beer & Other Fermented Malt Liquors

N.A.I.C.S.: 424810
Jeff Turner *(Pres)*

AJAX ELECTRIC CO.
60 Tomlinson Rd, Huntingdon Valley, PA 19006
Tel.: (215) 947-8500
Web Site:
   https://www.ajaxelectric.com
Year Founded: 1931
Sales Range: $1-9.9 Million
Emp.: 20
Industrial Furnace & Oven Mfr
N.A.I.C.S.: 333994
Donna Stelman *(Pres)*
Joe Bauer *(Mgr-Engrg)*
Andrew Garttmeyer *(Mgr-Pur)*

Subsidiaries:

Central Panel, Inc. **(1)**
60 Tomlinson Rd, Huntingdon Valley, PA 19006 **(100%)**
Tel.: (215) 947-8500
Web Site: http://www.centralpanelinc.com
Emp.: 15
Electronic, Pneumatic & Hydraulic Control Panel Mfr
N.A.I.C.S.: 335313
Bruce Arnold *(Pres)*

AJAX PAVING INDUSTRIES, INC.
1957 Crooks Rd Ste A, Troy, MI 48084
Tel.: (248) 244-3300   MI
Web Site:
   https://www.ajaxpaving.com
Year Founded: 1951
Sales Range: $125-149.9 Million
Emp.: 200
Asphalt Paving Mixtures Mfr; Highway & Street Construction
N.A.I.C.S.: 237310
James A. Jacob *(CEO)*
James Friel *(CFO)*

Subsidiaries:

Ajax Paving Industries, Inc. - BALD MOUNTAIN PLANT **(1)**
4875 Bald Mountain Rd, Auburn Hills, MI 48326
Tel.: (248) 244-3435
Asphalt Paving Mixture Mfr
N.A.I.C.S.: 324121

Ajax Paving Industries, Inc. - INKSTER ROAD PLANT **(1)**
8744 S Inkster Rd, Romulus, MI 48174
Tel.: (248) 244-3470
Asphalt Paving Mixture Mfr
N.A.I.C.S.: 324121

Ajax Paving Industries, Inc. - LARGO PLANT **(1)**
1550 Starkey Rd, Largo, FL 33771
Tel.: (727) 499-2168
Emp.: 8
Asphalt Paving Mixture Mfr
N.A.I.C.S.: 324121
Nickey Cox *(Gen Mgr)*

Ajax Paving Industries, Inc. - NEW HAVEN PLANT **(1)**
57295 Ajax Dr, New Haven, MI 48048
Tel.: (248) 244-3425
Emp.: 4
Asphalt Paving Mixture Mfr
N.A.I.C.S.: 324121
Dave Grabowski *(Mgr)*

Ajax Paving Industries, Inc. - NOKOMIS PLANT **(1)**
510 Gene Green Rd, Nokomis, FL 34275
Tel.: (941) 486-3420
Asphalt Paving Mixture Mfr
N.A.I.C.S.: 324121

Ajax Paving Industries, Inc. - ODESSA PLANT **(1)**
11603 State Rd 54, Odessa, FL 33556
Tel.: (727) 375-5780
Asphalt Paving Mixture Mfr
N.A.I.C.S.: 324121

Scott Pittman *(Mgr)*

Ajax Paving Industries, Inc. - PLANT 5 **(1)**
8744 Inkster Rd, Romulus, MI 48174
Tel.: (248) 244-3470
Asphalt Paving Mixture Mfr
N.A.I.C.S.: 324121

Ajax Paving Industries, Inc. - PORT MANATEE PLANT **(1)**
12165 US 41 N, Palmetto, FL 34221
Tel.: (941) 845-1138
Asphalt Paving Mixture Mfr
N.A.I.C.S.: 324121

Ajax Paving Industries, Inc. - PUNTA GORDA PLANT **(1)**
40851 Cook Brown Rd, Punta Gorda, FL 33982
Tel.: (239) 543-4544
Asphalt Paving Mixture Mfr
N.A.I.C.S.: 324121

Ajax Paving Industries, Inc. - TAMPA PLANT **(1)**
6050 Jensen Rd, Tampa, FL 33619
Tel.: (813) 574-8331
Emp.: 5
Asphalt Paving Mixture Mfr
N.A.I.C.S.: 324121
Mike Horan *(Plant Mgr)*

AJAX UNION
2233 Nostrand Ave, Brooklyn, NY 11210
Tel.: (718) 569-1020
Web Site: http://www.ajaxunion.com
Year Founded: 2008
Sales Range: $1-9.9 Million
Emp.: 50
Online Marketing Services
N.A.I.C.S.: 541613
Joe Apfelbaum *(Co-Founder & CEO)*
Zevi Friedman *(Co-Founder & Pres)*

AJAY GLASS & MIRROR COMPANY INCORPORATED
101 N St, Canandaigua, NY 14424
Tel.: (585) 393-0082
Web Site: https://www.ajayglass.net
Sales Range: $10-24.9 Million
Emp.: 65
Glass & Glazing Work
N.A.I.C.S.: 238150

AJC INTERNATIONAL, INC.
1000 Abernathy Rd NE Ste 600, Atlanta, GA 30328
Tel.: (404) 252-6750   GA
Web Site: https://www.ajcfood.com
Year Founded: 1972
Sales Range: $800-899.9 Million
Emp.: 380
Importer & Exporter of Meat, Poultry, Seafood, Canned, Frozen, Dry Fruits & Vegetables
N.A.I.C.S.: 424420
Eric J. Joiner *(Co-Founder & Vice Chm)*
Gerald L. Allison *(Co-Founder & Chm)*
John D. Partington *(CFO & Sr VP)*
Evan S. Davidman *(Pres & Chief Comml Officer)*
Tina R. Sorrels *(Sec & Dir-Credit-Global)*

Subsidiaries:

AJC Food **(1)**
Buchanan Ofc Ctr 202 Rd 165 No 40, Guaynabo, PR 00920
Tel.: (787) 792-0606
Web Site: http://www.ajc.com
Sales Range: $25-49.9 Million
Emp.: 12
Distr of Food
N.A.I.C.S.: 425120

AJC International, Inc. **(1)**
Buchanan Ofc Ctr Ste 202 Rd 165 No 40, Guaynabo, PR 00968

AJC International, Inc.—(Continued)

Tel.: (787) 792-0606
Web Site: http://www.ajcfood.com
Sales Range: $10-24.9 Million
Emp.: 10
Cold Storage & Warehouse Services
N.A.I.C.S.: 493120
Brad Allison (Pres)

American Institutional Foods   (1)
605 Chestnut St Ste 1040, Chattanooga,
TN 37450
Tel.: (423) 266-7114
Web Site: http://www.amerifoods.com
Sales Range: $25-49.9 Million
Emp.: 50
Food Products
N.A.I.C.S.: 424420
Candy Judkins (Controller)

AJD HOLDING CO.

2181 Enterprise Pkwy, Twinsburg,
OH 44087
Tel.: (330) 405-4477
Web Site:
   https://www.ajdholding.com
Sales Range: $10-24.9 Million
Emp.: 60
Fabricated Wire Products
N.A.I.C.S.: 332119

Subsidiaries:

D Martone Industries Inc.   (1)
15060 Madison Rd, Middlefield, OH 44062
Tel.: (440) 632-5800
Web Site: http://www.jacoproducts.com
Rev.: $2,900,000
Emp.: 50
Injection Molded Finished Plastics Products,
Nec
N.A.I.C.S.: 326199

Wedge Products, Inc.   (1)
2181 Enterprise Pkwy, Twinsburg, OH
44087
Tel.: (330) 425-0099
Web Site: http://www.wedgeproducts.com
Rev.: $2,800,000
Emp.: 20
Metal Stampings, Nec
N.A.I.C.S.: 332119
Anthony J. Defino (Pres)

AJILLUS INC.

1411 4th Ave, Seattle, WA 98101
Tel.: (206) 652-5944
Web Site: http://www.ajillus.com
Rev.: $1,105,000
Emp.: 5
Computer System Design Services
N.A.I.C.S.: 541512
Michael Murphy (Pres)

AJJ BANCORP, INC.

102 N Main St, Elkader, IA 52043
Tel.: (563) 245-2110
Web Site:
   http://www.centralstate.bank
Bank Holding Company
N.A.I.C.S.: 551111
Kenneth Pittman (Sr VP)
Gregory A. Johnson (CEO)

Subsidiaries:

Central State Bank   (1)
102 N Main St, Elkader, IA 52043
Tel.: (563) 245-2110
Web Site: http://www.centralstate.bank
Commericial Banking
N.A.I.C.S.: 522110
Gregory A. Johnson (CEO)

AJM PACKAGING CORPORATION

E-4111 Andover Rd, Bloomfield Hills,
MI 48302
Tel.: (248) 901-0040   MI
Web Site: https://www.ajmpack.com
Year Founded: 1957
Sales Range: $150-199.9 Million
Emp.: 800

Paper Bags, Pails, Sanitary Food
Containers & Lunch Bags
N.A.I.C.S.: 322219
Robert A. Epstein (Pres)

AJS REALTY GROUP, INC.

2950 Immokalee Rd Ste 2, Naples,
FL 34110
Tel.: (239) 596-9500
Web Site:
   http://www.ajsrealtygroup.com
Sales Range: $1-9.9 Million
Emp.: 5
Real Estate Services
N.A.I.C.S.: 531210
Andrew Saluan (Owner & Mng Broker)
Lisa Paul (Dir-Property Mgmt)

AKA MEDIA INC

142 E Ontario St Ste 1600, Chicago,
IL 60611
Tel.: (312) 787-5834
Web Site:
   http://www.akamediainc.com
Year Founded: 1998
Rev.: $2,700,000
Emp.: 10
Wireless Telecommunications Carriers
N.A.I.C.S.: 517112
Myles Erick de Fonseca (Editor)
Andrew Krause (Founder & CEO)
Jason Vargas (CMO)
Scott Moller (Principal)

AKADEMA, INC.

46 Starlake Rd Steb, Bloomingdale,
NJ 07403
Tel.: (973) 304-1470
Web Site:
   http://www.akademapro.com
Year Founded: 1998
Sales Range: $1-9.9 Million
Emp.: 10
Mfr of Baseball Equipment
N.A.I.C.S.: 339920
Joe Gilligan (Co-Founder & CEO)
Lawrence Gilligan (Co-Founder &
Pres)
Kris Totten (VP)
Marcos Agramonte (Sr Dir-Sls-Latin
American Div)

AKAL SECURITY, INC.

7 Infinity Loop, Espanola, NM 87532-
6737
Tel.: (505) 753-7832   NM
Web Site:
   http://www.akalsecurity.com
Year Founded: 1980
Sales Range: $500-549.9 Million
Emp.: 10,000
Commercial & Governmental Security
& Protection Services
N.A.I.C.S.: 561612

Subsidiaries:

Coastal International Security,   (1)
Inc.
6101 Fallard Dr, Upper Marlboro, MD
20772
Tel.: (703) 339-0233
Web Site: http://www.coastal-security.com
Security Management Services
N.A.I.C.S.: 561612
Bobby Jackson (Dir-Environmental Health &
Safety)
Henry Wolfe (VP)

Saber Protection Solutions, LLC   (1)
1125 Kent Ave NW, Albuquerque, NM
87102-2908
Tel.: (505) 692-2080
Web Site:
   http://www.saberprotectionsolutions.com
Security Management Services
N.A.I.C.S.: 541690

AKASHA CRYSTALS, INC.

123 N Ashley St, Ann Arbor, MI
48104
Tel.: (734) 996-5933
Web Site:
   http://www.akashacrystals.com
Year Founded: 1996
Rev.: $9,900,000
Emp.: 17
Home Furnishing Merchant Whslr
N.A.I.C.S.: 423220
Adam S. Kasha (Pres)
Joseph C. Albrecht (VP-Fin)

AKCELERANT HOLDINGS LLC

100 Lindenwood Dr, Malvern, PA
19355
Tel.: (610) 232-2800
Web Site: http://www.akcelerant.com
Year Founded: 2000
Sales Range: $10-24.9 Million
Emp.: 84
Supplies Connected Software Applications & Advisory Services to the
Financial Industry
N.A.I.C.S.: 513210
Jim Simon (Pres-Akcelerant Advisors
LLC)
Kevin Bingham (Mng Partner-
Akcelerant Advisors LLC)
Eric Snyder (Exec VP-Bus Dev)
Kathryn Thompson (CFO)
Mark Price (CTO-Akcelerant Software
LLC)
Emily Steele (Pres-Akcelerant Software LLC)
G.A. Mossman III (CEO)

Subsidiaries:

Akcelerant Advisors LLC   (1)
100 Lindenwood Dr, Malvern, PA
19355   (100%)
Tel.: (610) 232-0157
Web Site: http://www.akcelerant.com
Business Performance Management & Analytics
N.A.I.C.S.: 541618

AKELA PHARMA, INC.

11501 Domain Dr Ste 130, Austin, TX
78758
Tel.: (512) 834-0449   Ca
Web Site:
   http://www.akelapharma.com
Sales Range: $25-49.9 Million
Emp.: 57
Holding Company; Contract Pharmaceutical Testing, Development &
Manufacturing Services
N.A.I.C.S.: 551112
W. Blair West (Chief Scientific Officer)
Berenice Brownlee (CFO)

Subsidiaries:

Formulation Technologies, LLC   (1)
11501 Domain Dr Ste 130, Austin, TX
78758   (100%)
Tel.: (512) 834-0449
Web Site: http://www.pharmaform.com
Contract Pharmaceutical Testing, Development & Manufacturing Services
N.A.I.C.S.: 541380

AKERMAN LLP

420 S Orange Ave Ste 1200, Orlando, FL 32801-3445
Tel.: (407) 423-4000
Web Site: https://www.akerman.com
Year Founded: 1920
Sales Range: $250-299.9 Million
Emp.: 700
Law firm
N.A.I.C.S.: 541110
Richard B. Brosnick (Partner-
Litigation-New York)
Carolyn V. Metnick (Co-Chm-Privacy,
Cybersecurity & Emerging Tech)

Michael L. Molinaro (Partner-
Bankruptcy & Reorganization-
Chicago)
Lansing R. Palmer (Partner-Litigation-
West Palm Beach-New York)
Carolyn M. Kershner (Partner-Tax-
Fort Lauderdale)
Michael P. Gennett (Partner-
Healthcare-Fort Lauderdale)
Esther A. McKean (Partner)
Kenneth R. Wiggins (Partner-M&A &
Private Equity-Miami)
Robert W. Bowser (Partner-
Residential Land Acquisitions & Dev-
Orlando)
Daniel W. Schwartz (Partner-Miami)
Jarrett D. Bingemann (Partner-Real
Estate Acquisitions & Sls-Orlando)
Ryan Roman (Partner-Litigation-
Miami)
Adam K. Hodges (Deputy Chm-Fraud
& Recovery Practice Grp-West Palm
Beach)
Adam G. Schwartz (Partner-
Consumer Fin Svcs-West Palm
Beach)
Stephen J. Giovinco (Partner-
Litigation-West Palm Beach)
Andrew J. Wamsley (Partner-Real
Estate Acquisitions & Sls-Fort Lauderdale)
Christian P. George (Mng Partner-
Jacksonville)
Ashley A. Sawyer (Partner-Comml
Disputes-Fort Lauderdale)
Heather L. Fesnak (Partner)
Brett Kappel (Partner-Govt Affairs &
Pub Policy Practice Grp-Washington)
Bruce Platt (Mng Partner-
Tallahassee)
Marcy Hahn-Saperstein (Partner)
Andres G. Mendoza (Partner)
Noelle P. Pankey (Partner)
Bradley S. McPherson (Partner)
Jennifer M. Kramer (Partner)
Felipe Berer (Partner)
Steven J. Wernick (Partner)
Stacy J. Rodriguez (Partner)
Julia R. Lissner (Partner)
Peter G. Hawkins (Partner)
Tyler B. Engar (Partner-Consumer
Fin Svcs-Dallas)
Thomas J. Kearney (Partner-
Consumer Fin Svcs-Washington)
James M. Miller (Partner)
John E. Mitchell (Partner-Bankruptcy
& Reorganization)
David W. Parham (Partner-
Bankruptcy & Reorganization-Dallas)
E. Paul Quinn (Partner-M&A & Private Equity)
Mason H. Drake (Partner)
David C. Blum (Partner-Tax-Chicago)
Jack I. Habert (Partner)
Lorenzo Borgogni (Partner)
Mark S. Bernstein (Partner-Comml
Disputes-Chicago)
Sarir Z. Silver (Partner-Employment &
Labor-New York)
Bran Noonan (Partner-Labor &
Employment-New York)
D. Brett Marks (Partner-Bankruptcy &
Reorganization-Fort Lauderdale)
Eyal Berger (Partner-Bankruptcy &
Reorganization Grp-Fort Lauderdale)
Jacob A. Brown (Deputy Chm-
Bankruptcy & Reorganization Practice
Grp-Jacksonville)
Jules S. Cohen (Partner-Bankruptcy
& Reorganization-Orlando)
Susan F. Balaschak (Partner-
Bankruptcy & Reorganization Grp-
New York)
Ronald S. Kornreich (Partner)

Thomas G. Pasternak *(Partner-Intellectual Property-Chicago)*
William L. Weiner *(Partner-Healthcare)*
Joshua D. Bernstein *(Partner-Real Estate Litigation-New York)*
Thomas F. Diorio *(Partner-Real Estate-New York)*
Ira B. Stechel *(Partner-Tax-New York)*
Michael R. Weiss *(Partner-Litigation-Los Angeles)*
Mark Y. Liu *(Partner-Capital Markets-Los Angeles)*
Lisa B. Kolieb *(Partner-California Land Use & Entitlements-Los Angeles)*
Preston Ascherin *(Partner-Los Angeles)*
Eric Levine *(Partner-West Palm Beach)*
Erin Maddocks *(Partner-West Palm Beach)*
Nicholas Purvis *(Partner-West Palm Beach)*
Roy Zachariah *(Partner-West Palm Beach)*
Kimberly Lopez Narbona *(Partner)*
Paul Ettori *(Partner)*
Allison Nelson *(Partner)*
Lori Albert *(Partner)*
Kathleen A. Duncan *(Partner-Chicago)*
Meg E. George *(Mng Partner-Chicago)*
John J. George *(Partner-Chicago)*
Bassel Frick *(Mng Partner-Tampa)*
Karen Buesing *(Partner)*
Brian S. Fraser *(Partner-Litigation Practice Grp)*
Caroline Mankey *(Partner-Intellectual Property-Los Angeles)*
Kanika Corley *(Partner-Comml & Litigation-Los Angeles)*
Lawrence Rochefort *(Chm-Litigation Practice Grp)*
Sue Zabloudil *(Mng Partner-Los Angeles)*
James Burns *(Partner-Washington)*
Ted Rosen *(Partner-Merger & Acq & Private Equity Practice-New York)*
Carl Roston *(Co-Chm-Corp Practice Grp)*
Jonathan Awner *(Co-Chm-Corp Practice Grp)*
Stacey Prince-Troutman *(Partner)*
Scott A. Meyers *(Mng Partner)*
David I. Spector *(Chm & CEO)*
Beth Alcalde *(Partner-Pro Dev)*
Christopher Duke *(Mng Partner-Palm Beach County)*
Francisco Rodriguez *(Deputy Partner-Recruiting)*
Michael O'Brien *(Partner-Merger & Acq & Private Practice-New York)*
Robert Stein *(Chm-Corp Fin & Lending Practice-New York)*
Todd Reed *(Mng Partner-Austin)*
Bentley Harris *(Partner-Austin)*
Robert Winner *(Partner-Chicago)*
Amy Doehring *(Partner-Litigation-Chicago)*
C. Matthew Detzel *(Partner)*
William D. Ellis *(Partner-Real Estate-Los Angeles)*
Larry W. Ross II *(Partner-Miami)*
Martin L. Monaco Jr. *(Partner-Healthcare-New York)*
Stephen K. Roddenberry *(Partner & Atty)*

Subsidiaries:

Akerman LLP - Dallas **(1)**
2001 Ross Ave Ste 2550, Dallas, TX 75201
Tel.: (214) 720-4300
Web Site: http://www.akerman.com
Emp.: 45

Law firm
N.A.I.C.S.: 541110
C. Charles Townsend *(Mng Partner)*
Andrew Thomas *(Partner)*

Akerman LLP - Fort Lauderdale **(1)**
350 E Las Olas Blvd Ste 1600, Fort Lauderdale, FL 33301
Tel.: (954) 463-2700
Web Site: http://www.akerman.com
Emp.: 200
Legal Practice
N.A.I.C.S.: 541199
Tami SEGAL *(Coord-HR)*
Michelle Romeo Keon *(Coord-Legal Recruiting)*
Victor Berwin *(Partner & Atty)*
Scott Bettridge *(Partner)*
Eric D. Rapkin *(Mng Partner-Office)*
Brian Gart *(Partner)*
Eyal Berger *(Partner)*
David F. Birke *(Partner)*
Stacy Bercun Bohm *(Partner)*
Dee Dee Fischer *(Partner)*
Michael Francis *(Partner)*
Rick J. Fucci *(Partner)*
Michael P. Gennett *(Partner)*
Andrew P. Gold *(Partner)*
Marc J. Gottlieb *(Partner)*

Akerman LLP - Houston **(1)**
1300 Post Oak Blvd Ste 2500, Houston, TX 77056
Tel.: (713) 623-0887
Web Site: http://www.akerman.com
Emp.: 50
Law firm
N.A.I.C.S.: 541110
Martin D. Beirne *(Sr Partner)*
Scott D. Marrs *(Mng Partner)*
Brit T. Brown *(Mng Partner)*

Akerman LLP - Miami **(1)**
7 St Ste 1100, Miami, FL 33131
Tel.: (305) 374-5600
Web Site: http://www.aerman.com
Emp.: 300
Law firm
N.A.I.C.S.: 541110
Alan H. Aronson *(Atty)*
Marcy Levine Aldrich *(Atty)*
Jonathan L. Awner *(Atty)*
Michael A. Berke *(Atty)*
William C. Arnhols *(Atty)*
Adam Hodges *(Atty)*
Jim Miller *(Atty)*
Kimberly Leary *(Atty)*
Steven J. Wernick *(Atty)*
Patricia M. Carlson *(Partner-West Palm Beach)*
Andres Mendoza *(Partner)*

AKERS PACKAGING SERVICE INC.
2820 Lefferson Rd, Middletown, OH 45044
Tel.: (513) 422-6312   **OH**
Web Site: https://www.akers-pkg.com
Year Founded: 1963
Sales Range: $50-74.9 Million
Emp.: 149
Design & Mfr Customized Corrugated Boxes
N.A.I.C.S.: 322211
Michael Akey *(Mng Dir)*
James F. Akers *(CEO)*
William C. Akers II *(Pres & COO)*

Subsidiaries:

Tecumseh Packaging Solutions **(1)**
707 S Evans St, Tecumseh, MI 49286-1919
Tel.: (517) 423-2126
Sales Range: $25-49.9 Million
Emp.: 100
Mfr of Corrugated Shipping Containers & Sheets
N.A.I.C.S.: 322211
Jeffrey Robideau *(Gen Mgr)*

AKERUE INDUSTRIES, LLC
90 McMillen Rd, Antioch, IL 60002-1845
Tel.: (847) 395-3300
Web Site:
    http://www.kayhomeproducts.com

Sales Range: $75-99.9 Million
Emp.: 100
Molded Plastic & Metal Products
N.A.I.C.S.: 339910
Karen Borre *(Controller)*

Subsidiaries:

Kay Home Products **(1)**
90 McMillen Rd, Antioch, IL 60002 **(100%)**
Tel.: (800) 626-5296
Web Site: http://www.kayhomeproducts.com
Sales Range: $10-24.9 Million
Emp.: 50
Mfr & Marketer of Housewares, Lawn, Garden Equipment & Hardware Goods
N.A.I.C.S.: 333112
Lori Petti *(Mgr-HR)*

AKH COMPANY, INC.
1160 N Anaheim Blvd, Anaheim, CA 92801
Tel.: (714) 861-9024   **CA**
Web Site:
    http://www.discounttirecenters.com
Year Founded: 1975
Sales Range: $450-499.9 Million
Emp.: 450
Automotive Tire Dealership & Service Centers Owner, Operator & Franchisor
N.A.I.C.S.: 441340
Andy K. Andonian *(Chm & Co-CEO)*
Hratch K. Andonian *(Vice Chm & Co-CEO)*
Michael Schaeper *(Pres)*
Rick Helton *(Sr VP-Retail Ops)*
Joseph Seitz Jr. *(COO)*

AKI, INC.
1740 Broadway Ste 14A, New York, NY 10019
Tel.: (212) 541-2600   **DE**
Web Site:
    https://www.arcadebeauty.com
Year Founded: 1992
Fragrance Sampling, Scent Sampling & Interactive Product Sampling Technologies
N.A.I.C.S.: 323111
Patrycja Wysocka *(Mgr-Marketing-Sales)*

AKIMA MANAGEMENT SERVICES LLC
1001 E Benson Blvd Ste 100, Anchorage, AK 99508
Tel.: (907) 277-2058
Web Site: http://www.akima.com
Year Founded: 1995
Sales Range: $150-199.9 Million
Emp.: 2,872
Employment Search & Application Process
N.A.I.C.S.: 561311
Ed Morris *(Pres & CEO)*
Dan Melchior *(Sr VP-Ops)*
Mary Langdon *(Interim Dir-HR)*
Marsha Gross *(CFO & VP)*

AKIN COMPLETE FURNITURE
113 Commerce Dr, Monticello, AR 71655
Tel.: (800) 395-2981   **AZ**
Web Site:
    http://www.akinindustries.com
Year Founded: 1985
Wooden Furniture Mfr
N.A.I.C.S.: 337122
John Akin *(VP)*

AKIN GUMP STRAUSS HAUER & FELD LLP
Robert S Strauss Bldg 1333 New Hampshire Ave NW, Washington, DC 20036-1564
Tel.: (202) 887-4000
Web Site: http://www.akingump.com

Year Founded: 1945
Sales Range: $750-799.9 Million
Emp.: 1,001
Legal Advisory Services
N.A.I.C.S.: 541110
Scott L. Alberino *(Partner)*
Allison C. Binney *(Partner)*
Douglas I. Brandon *(Partner)*
Paul W. Butler *(Partner)*
Cono A. Carrano *(Partner)*
Joel M. Cohn *(Partner)*
Charles Francis Connolly *(Partner)*
Sean G. D'Arcy *(Partner)*
Tom W. Davidson *(Partner)*
David S. Turetsky *(Partner)*
Leslie B. Kiernan *(Partner)*
John A. Bain *(Partner-Real Estate Fin Practice-Dallas)*
Brad M. Kahn *(Partner-Fin Restructuring Practice-New York)*
Andrew B. Lehman *(Partner-Global Energy Transactions Practice-Houston)*
Ruben H. Munoz *(Partner-Intellectual Property Practice-Philadelphia)*
Dennis P. Pereira *(Partner-Investment Funds Practice-New York)*
Elizabeth M. Scott *(Partner-Litigation Practice-Dallas)*
David N. Sewell *(Partner-Cross Border Transactions Practice-London)*
James E. Tysse *(Partner-Supreme Court & Appellate Practice)*
Michael Joyce *(Partner-Global Energy & Transactions Practice-Singapore)*
Smith W. Davis *(Partner)*
Claudius Modesti *(Partner)*
Angela Styles *(Partner-Govt Contracts)*
Haidee Schwartz *(Partner)*
Joe Donnelly *(Partner)*
George Cannon Jr. *(Partner)*

AKM LLC
17474 Old Jefferson Hwy, Prairieville, LA 70769
Tel.: (225) 673-3236
Web Site:
    https://www.volksconst.com
Sales Range: $25-49.9 Million
Emp.: 80
Industrial Buildings & Warehouses
N.A.I.C.S.: 236220
Lawson King *(Pres)*

AKORN, INC.
1925 W Field Ct Ste 300, Lake Forest, IL 60045
Tel.: (847) 279-6100   **LA**
Web Site: http://www.akorn.com
Year Founded: 1971
Rev.: $682,429,000
Assets: $1,288,639,000
Liabilities: $1,054,347,000
Net Worth: $234,292,000
Earnings: ($226,770,000)
Emp.: 2,220
Fiscal Year-end: 12/31/19
Sterile Specialty Pharmaceutical Products Mfr, Marketer & Distr
N.A.I.C.S.: 325412
Alan D. Weinstein *(Chm)*
Duane A. Portwood *(CFO & Exec VP)*
Jonathan Kafer *(Chief Comml Officer & Exec VP-Sls & Mktg)*
Douglas S. Boothe *(Pres & CEO)*
Christopher C. Young *(Exec VP-Global Ops)*
Erislandy Dorado-Boladeres *(Exec VP-Global Quality)*
Sandhya Goyal *(Chief Scientific Officer & Sr VP)*

Subsidiaries:

Advanced Vision Research, Inc. **(1)**

Akorn, Inc.—(Continued)

2929 Plymouth Rd Ste 275, Ann Arbor, MI 48105
Tel.: (800) 579-8327
Web Site: http://www.theratears.com
Sales Range: $10-24.9 Million
Pharmaceutical Preparation Mfr
N.A.I.C.S.: 325412

Akorn (New Jersey), Inc. **(1)**
72 Veronica Ave, Somerset, NJ 08873 **(100%)**
Tel.: (732) 846-8066
Sales Range: $25-49.9 Million
Emp.: 80
Mfr of Pharmaceutical Ointments, Suspensions & Sterile Liquids
N.A.I.C.S.: 325412
Robert Gasper (Mgr-Facilities)

Akorn AG
Riethofstrasse 1, 8442, Hettlingen, Switzerland
Tel.: (41) 523041011
Web Site: http://www.akorn.ch
Pharmaceuticals Product Mfr
N.A.I.C.S.: 325412
Markus Grob (Head-Production)
Nicola Natterer (Head-HR)
Jens-Uwe Rengers (Gen Mgr)
Ivan Salnikov (Head-Fin)
Hans-Herwig Bauer (Dir-Quality)
Friedrich Schmidt (Head-Engrg)

Olta Pharmaceuticals Corp. **(1)**
16477 Hwy 16 E, De Kalb, MS 39328
Tel.: (215) 441-9546
Emp.: 2
Pharmaceutical Preparation Mfr
N.A.I.C.S.: 325412

AKOYA CAPITAL LLC
401 N Michigan Avenue Ste 625, Chicago, IL 60611
Tel.: (312) 546-8302   **DE**
Web Site:
   http://www.akoyacapital.com
Equity Investment Firm
N.A.I.C.S.: 523999
Max DeZara (Founder & Partner)
Lou Nieto (Mng Dir)
Carr Preston (Chm & Mng Dir)
Don Stanutz (Mng Dir)
Liz Dominick (Mng Dir-Talent & Bus Dev)
Karen Scalise (VP-Bus Dev & Ops)
Pat Riley (Mng Dir)
Mark L. Breckheimer (Mng Dir)
Dave Burger (Mng Dir)
Greg Vas Nunes (Mng Dir)
John J. Regazzi (Operating Partner & Mng Dir)

Subsidiaries:

Adherex Group **(1)**
3100 Hamilton Ave, Cleveland, OH 44114
Tel.: (201) 440-3806
Web Site: https://adherexgroup.com
Packaging tapes & shrink wraps Mfg & Distr
N.A.I.C.S.: 339991

Subsidiary (Domestic):

Stretchtape, Inc. **(2)**
18460 Syracuse Ave, Cleveland, OH 44110
Tel.: (216) 486-9400
Web Site: http://www.stretchtape.com
Sales Range: $1-9.9 Million
Emp.: 40
Coated & Laminated Paper Mfr
N.A.I.C.S.: 322220

FabEnCo, Inc. **(1)**
2002 Karbach St, Houston, TX 77092
Tel.: (713) 686-6620
Web Site: http://www.fabenco.com
Sales Range: $10-24.9 Million
Metal Safety Gate Mfr
N.A.I.C.S.: 332323
David H. LaCook (CEO)
Donald Henderson (Exec VP)
Scott Friedman (Sls Mgr)
Donna Dennis (Controller)
Philippe Suhas (Chm)

ICM Products, Inc. **(1)**
805 Wolfe Ave, Cassopolis, MI 49031
Tel.: (269) 445-0847
Web Site: http://www.icmproducts.com
Sales Range: $1-9.9 Million
Silicone Polymers, Defoamers & Specialty Emulsion Chemicals Mfr
N.A.I.C.S.: 325998
Ken Charboneau (Founder)

Subsidiary (Non-US):

The Amber Chemical Company Ltd. **(2)**
Amber House Showground Road, Bridgwater, TA6 6AJ, United Kingdom
Tel.: (44) 278 411400
Web Site: http://www.amberchemical.com
Organic Chemical Mfr
N.A.I.C.S.: 325199

Subsidiary (Domestic):

ACC Silicones Ltd. **(3)**
Amber House Showground Road, Bridgwater, TA6 6AJ, United Kingdom
Tel.: (44) 1278411400
Web Site: http://www.acc-silicones.com
Sales Range: $25-49.9 Million
Emp.: 45
Silicone Chemicals Mfr
N.A.I.C.S.: 325998
Frank Geerdsen (Mng Dir)

Subsidiary (Non-US):

Treco s.r.l. **(4)**
Via Romagna N 8, Sesto Ulteriano, 20098, Milan, Italy
Tel.: (39) 029880913
Web Site: http://www.acc-silicones.it
Silicone Mfr
N.A.I.C.S.: 325998

Subsidiary (Non-US):

Amber Silicones (Tianjin) Co. Ltd. **(3)**
F2 Hong Tai Industrial Park, Number 9 Road TEDA, 300457, Tianjin, China
Tel.: (86) 22 2532 3808 809
Silicone Mfr
N.A.I.C.S.: 325998
David Kong (Gen Mgr)

Subsidiary (US):

Quantum Silicones, Inc. **(3)**
8021 Reycan Rd, Richmond, VA 23237
Tel.: (804) 271-9010
Web Site: http://www.quantumsilicones.com
Silicone Mfr
N.A.I.C.S.: 325998
Chris Martin (Mgr-Sls-East Coast)
Greg Wegener (Mgr-Sls-Midwest)
Matt Plimpton (Mgr-Sls-Great Lakes)
Sherry Anderson (Mgr-Sls-West Coast)

Siovation, LLC **(3)**
1270 Progress Center Ave Ste 200, Lawrenceville, GA 30043
Tel.: (770) 339-4460
Web Site: http://www.siovation.com
Specialty Silicone-based Fluids Mfr
N.A.I.C.S.: 325998
Marcelo Zocchi (Mgr-Bus Dev)

AKQURACY
800 Washington Ave N Suite 206, Minneapolis, MN 55401
Tel.: (612) 605-7556
Web Site: http://www.akquracy.com
Year Founded: 2007
Sales Range: $1-9.9 Million
Emp.: 15
Analytic Research in the Completion of Communication Campaigns & Multi-Channel Marketing Strategies
N.A.I.C.S.: 541910
Scott Petinga (Founder)

AKRAYA, INC.
840 W California Ave Ste 220, Sunnyvale, CA 94086
Tel.: (408) 907-6400
Web Site: http://www.akraya.com

Year Founded: 2001
Rev.: $32,000,000
Emp.: 85
Employment Agency Engineering Services & Custom Computer Programing
N.A.I.C.S.: 561311
Sonu Ratra (Co-Founder & Pres)
Amar Panchal (Co-Founder & CEO)
Pankaj Jindal (COO)
Keshava Kumar (Dir-HR)
Lance Lennier (VP-Acct Mgmt)

AKROCHEM CORPORATION
255 Fountain St, Akron, OH 44304-1920
Tel.: (330) 535-2108   **OH**
Web Site: https://www.akrochem.com
Year Founded: 1930
Sales Range: $75-99.9 Million
Emp.: 45
Sales of Products Used in the Manufacturing of Rubber & Plastic Products
N.A.I.C.S.: 424690
Walt Silver (CEO)

AKRON FOUNDRY CO.
2728 Wingate Ave, Akron, OH 44314
Tel.: (330) 745-3101
Web Site:
   http://www.akronfoundry.com
Sales Range: $10-24.9 Million
Emp.: 175
Castings, Except Die-Castings, Precision
N.A.I.C.S.: 331529
George Ostich (Pres)
Gerry Ostich (Owner)

AKRON HARDWARE CONSULTANTS, INC.
1100 Killian Rd, Akron, OH 44312
Tel.: (330) 644-7167
Web Site:
   http://www.akronhardware.com
Year Founded: 1960
Sales Range: $10-24.9 Million
Emp.: 60
Hardware Merchant Whslr
N.A.I.C.S.: 423710
Bill Monaghan (Mgr-Inventory Control)
Joe Schlosser (Mgr-Pur)
Kenneth Orihel (CEO)
Nancy Murray (CFO)
Roy Crute (Pres)
Tom Orihel (COO)
Dwayne Spencer (Mgr-Sls)
John Flower (Mgr-Bus Dev)
Randy Floyd (Dir-Facilities & Logistics)
Rick Buzaki (Supvr-Sls)
Don Hohman (Mgr-Accts-Natl)
Craig Hoffman (Mgr-Tennessee)
Rodney Dell (Mgr-Texas)
Bill Jubara (VP-Supply Chain Mgmt)

AKRON PORCELAIN & PLASTICS CO.
2739 Cory Ave, Akron, OH 44314-0157
Tel.: (330) 745-2159
Web Site:
   https://www.akronporcelain.com
Sales Range: $10-24.9 Million
Emp.: 120
Injection Molded Finished Plastics Products
N.A.I.C.S.: 326199
David W. Lewis (Pres)
Ken Burkins (VP-Sls & Mktg)
Michael Dunphy (Treas & VP)

AKRON REBAR CO.

809 W Waterloo Rd, Akron, OH 44314
Tel.: (330) 745-7100
Web Site:
   https://www.akronrebar.com
Year Founded: 1978
Sales Range: $10-24.9 Million
Emp.: 50
Bars, Concrete Reinforcing; Fabricated Steel
N.A.I.C.S.: 332312
Dennis Stump (Pres)

AKRON SERVICES INC.
17705 N Elevator Rd, Edelstein, IL 61526-9716
Tel.: (309) 249-2700   **IL**
Web Site:
   https://www.akronservices.com
Year Founded: 1965
Sales Range: $10-24.9 Million
Emp.: 25
Grain & Field Beans
N.A.I.C.S.: 424510

Subsidiaries:

Akron Services, Brimfield **(1)**
13625 N Bell School Rd, Brimfield, IL 61517
Tel.: (309) 446-3777
Web Site: http://www.akronservices.com
Sales Range: $10-24.9 Million
Emp.: 5
Grain & Field Beans
N.A.I.C.S.: 493110

AKROTEX, INC.
1301 Childers, Orange, TX 77630-1508
Tel.: (409) 886-0111
Web Site: http://www.akrotex.com
Year Founded: 1989
Holding Company
N.A.I.C.S.: 551112
Ross Smith (Pres)

Subsidiaries:

Akrotex Extusion & Recycling Inc. **(1)**
1804 Austin St, Orange, TX 77630
Tel.: (409) 886-0063
Web Site: http://www.akrotex.com
Custom Compounding & Pelletizing
N.A.I.C.S.: 325991
Ed McIntyre (Gen Mgr)

Akrotex Films Inc. **(1)**
1301 Childers St, Orange, TX 77630
Tel.: (409) 886-0111
Web Site: http://www.akrotex.com
Rev.: $13,500,000
Emp.: 40
Mfr of Plastics & Film Products
N.A.I.C.S.: 326113
John Sims (Gen Mgr)
Trey Smith (Plant Mgr)
D. Terry (Acct Mgr)

Akrotex Trucking Inc **(1)**
1301 Childers Rd, Orange, TX 77630
Tel.: (409) 886-0111
Web Site: http://www.akrotex.com
Rev.: $270,000
Emp.: 6
Local Trucking without Storage
N.A.I.C.S.: 484110

Akrotex Warehousing, Inc. **(1)**
1301 Childers Rd, Orange, TX 77630-1508
Tel.: (409) 886-0111
Sales Range: $1-9.9 Million
Emp.: 30
Civil Engineering Services
N.A.I.C.S.: 237310
Stan Hodge (Gen Mgr)

AKT ENTERPRISES
6424 Forest City Rd, Orlando, FL 32810
Web Site:
   https://www.aktenterprises.com
Year Founded: 2005

Sales Range: $10-24.9 Million
Emp.: 70
Design, Merchandising & Marketing
Services
N.A.I.C.S.: 541490
Alex Tchekmeian (Pres & CEO)
Jared Mendelewicz (COO & VP)
Grant Tchekmeian (COO)

AKTA WEB STUDIO
223 W Erie St Ste 4E, Chicago, IL
60654
Tel.: (312) 361-3555
Web Site: http://www.akta.com
Sales Range: $1-9.9 Million
Emp.: 15
Digital Product Research & Design
Services
N.A.I.C.S.: 541519
John Roa (CEO)
Dean DeBiase (Chm)
Drew Davidson (VP-Design)
Sara Frisk (VP-Brand Strategy)

AKTION ASSOCIATES, INC.
1687 Woodlands Dr, Maumee, OH
43537
Tel.: (419) 893-7001
Web Site: https://www.aktion.com
Year Founded: 1979
Software & Technology Development
Services
N.A.I.C.S.: 513210
Scott E. Irwin (CEO)
Christina Birmingham (Sls Mgr-Multi-
Indus Div)
Bob Black (VP-Multi-Indus Div)

Subsidiaries:

United Solutions, Inc.   (1)
28 Lord Rd, Marlborough, MA 01752
Tel.: (508) 460-0045
Web Site: http://www.u-s-i.com
Rev.: $3,100,000
Emp.: 18
Computer & Computer Peripheral Equip-
ment & Software Merchant Whslr
N.A.I.C.S.: 423430
Greg Kirshe (CEO & Principal)
Graham MacLeod (Dir-Sage CRM)
Christine Galeucia (CFO)
Nancy Gabrielli (Mgr-Sls Support)
Craig Trussell (VP-Sls & Mktg)
Scott Kirshe (Dir-Estimating Sls)
Ted O'Shea (Pres & Principal)

**AKUWA SOLUTIONS GROUP,
INC.**
6341 Porter Rd Ste 1, Sarasota, FL
34240
Tel.: (941) 343-9947
Web Site: https://www.akuwa.com
Sales Range: $1-9.9 Million
Emp.: 10
IT Consulting Services
N.A.I.C.S.: 541690
Terry Nelson (Pres)

AKWEN LLC
3743 Boettler Oaks Dr Ste A, Union-
town, OH 44685
Tel.: (330) 896-0742
Sales Range: $10-24.9 Million
Emp.: 700
Fast-Food Restaurant, Chain
N.A.I.C.S.: 722513
Bruce G. Obenour (Pres)
Chris VanRiper (Dir-Ops)
Jasna Keller (Mgr-HR)
Betty Heath (Controller)

AL & ED'S CORPORATION
3728 S Grand Ave, Los Angeles, CA
90007
Tel.: (818) 908-5700   CA
Web Site: http://www.al-eds.com
Year Founded: 1954

Retailer of Mobile Electronics; Cellu-
lar Phones, Car Radios, Stereos,
Navigation Systems, Paging, Vehicle,
Multimedia & Car Alarms
N.A.I.C.S.: 459999
Barry Hodis (Mgr-Ops)

AL ASHER & SONS, INC.
5301 Valley Blvd, Los Angeles, CA
90032
Tel.: (323) 225-2295   CA
Web Site: https://www.alasher.com
Year Founded: 1914
Sales Range: $10-24.9 Million
Emp.: 25
Used Heavy Construction Equipment
Rental & Sales
N.A.I.C.S.: 532412
James A. Asher (Pres & CEO)
Robert L. Asher (CFO)

**AL BAZZINI COMPANY INCOR-
PORATION**
240 Food Ctr Dr, Bronx, NY 10474
Tel.: (718) 842-8644
Web Site: http://www.bazzininuts.com
Sales Range: $10-24.9 Million
Emp.: 35
Confectionery
N.A.I.C.S.: 424450
Rocco Damato (Pres)

AL HENDRICKSON TOYOTA
5201 W Sample Rd, Coconut Creek,
FL 33073
Tel.: (954) 545-6528
Web Site:
     https://www.alhendrickson.com
Year Founded: 1988
Sales Range: $50-74.9 Million
Emp.: 200
New Car Retailer
N.A.I.C.S.: 441110
Erik Coxwell (Dir-Pre-Owned)
Gary Cann (VP-Svc & Parts)

**AL J. MUELLER CONSTRUC-
TION COMPANY**
1305 S 59th St, Saint Joseph, MO
64507
Tel.: (816) 233-6055
Web Site: https://www.aljmueller.com
Year Founded: 1974
Emp.: 45
Commercial & Institutional Building
Construction Services
N.A.I.C.S.: 236220
Brett Hausman (VP)
Lawrence McPhee (Owner)
Meri Markt (Controller)

AL LARSON BOAT SHOP, INC.
1046 S Seaside Ave, Terminal Island,
CA 90731-7334
Tel.: (310) 514-4100   CA
Web Site:
     https://www.larsonboat.com
Year Founded: 1903
Sales Range: $25-49.9 Million
Emp.: 80
Ship Repair & Marine Services
N.A.I.C.S.: 336611
George Wall (VP)

AL MINNERATH INC.
6325 County Rd 87 SW, Alexandria,
MN 56308
Tel.: (320) 762-7289
Web Site:
     http://www.centralspecialties.com
Year Founded: 1976
Sales Range: $25-49.9 Million
Emp.: 240
General Contractor, Highway & Street
Construction
N.A.I.C.S.: 237310

Joe Minnerath (Pres)

AL NEYER, LLC
302 W 3rd St Ste 800, Cincinnati, OH
45202
Tel.: (513) 271-6400   OH
Web Site: http://www.neyer.com
Year Founded: 1894
Sales Range: $50-74.9 Million
Emp.: 45
Corporate Environments & Facilities
Designer & Developer
N.A.I.C.S.: 237210
James T. Neyer (Exec VP-Capital &
Investments)
Robert R. Thrun (Sr VP-Architecture)
Mark Vella (Sr VP-Bus Dev)
Dan Ruh (Exec VP)
Pat Moore (VP-Architecture)
Matt Blankenship (Exec VP-Design
Build)
Rob Gage (VP-Real Estate Dev)
Ryan Reardon (Dir-Real Estate Dev)
Stephen Huff (Mgr-Acctg & Sys)
Anne Pielage (Sr Mgr-Real Estate
Transaction)
Steve Rizzo (Dir-Field Ops)
Justin Hartung (VP-Design Build)
David Okun (Mgr-Real Estate Dev)
Brandon Snyder (VP-Real Estate
Dev)
Bob Fessler (Exec VP-Bus Dev)
Lesley Schaefer Koth (Sr VP-Legal
Svcs)
Stephanie P. Gaither (CFO & Sr VP)
Molly North (Pres & CEO)

Subsidiaries:

Neyer Holdings   (1)
302 W 3rd St Ste 800, Cincinnati, OH
45202   (10%)
Tel.: (513) 271-6400
Web Site: http://www.neyer.com
Sales Range: $50-74.9 Million
Holding Company
N.A.I.C.S.: 237210
Molly North (Pres & CEO)

AL PACKER, INC.
1530 N Military Trl, West Palm
Beach, FL 33409
Tel.: (561) 689-6550   MD
Web Site:
     http://www.alpackerford.com
Year Founded: 1972
Sales Range: $100-124.9 Million
Emp.: 400
Holding Company; New & Used Car
Dealership Owner & Operator
N.A.I.C.S.: 551112
Mark Packer (Pres)

Subsidiaries:

Al Packer Ford - East   (1)
1530 N Military Trl, West Palm Beach, FL
33409
Tel.: (561) 689-6550
Web Site: http://www.alpackerford.com
Sales Range: $25-49.9 Million
New & Used Car Dealer
N.A.I.C.S.: 441110
Gary Weil (Gen Mgr-Sls)
Rick Klotz (Dir-Fixed Ops)
John Riley (Mgr-Fleet)

**AL PRIME ENERGY CONSUL-
TANT INC.**
319 Salem St, Wakefield, MA 01880-
4942
Tel.: (781) 246-7738   MA
Web Site: http://www.alprime.com
Year Founded: 1991
Sales Range: $1-9.9 Million
Emp.: 100
Whslr & Retailer of Gasoline
N.A.I.C.S.: 541990
Nasser Buiser (Pres)
Nasser Abu Eid (VP)

AL PUNTO ADVERTISING, INC.
730 El Camino Way Ste 200, Tustin,
CA 92780-7733
Tel.: (714) 544-0888   CA
Web Site: http://www.alpunto.com
Year Founded: 1994
Rev.: $87,000,000
Emp.: 25
Advetising Agency
N.A.I.C.S.: 541810
Eduardo Bottger (Pres, Principal &
Exec Dir-Creative)
Roy Zuloaga (Acct Mgr)

**AL PURMORT INSURANCE
INC.**
3340 Bee Ridge Rd, Sarasota, FL
34239
Tel.: (941) 306-1112
Web Site: http://www.alpurmort.com
Sales Range: $25-49.9 Million
Emp.: 15
Insurance Brokerage
N.A.I.C.S.: 524210
Tammy Mulrain (Mgr-Personal Lines
Acct)
Andrea Allison (Mgr-Personal Lines)
Andrea Johnson (Mgr-Comml Acct)
Angela Smith (VP-Comml Lines)
April Kincey (Mgr-Personal Acct)
Cindy Stock (Office Mgr)
Danielle Shamblin (Mgr-Personal
Acct)
Lori Warnelo (Mgr-Mktg)
Pat Chrapowicki (Mgr-Comml Acct)
Patrick Del Medico (COO)
Rosie Iemolo (Mgr-Personal Acct)
Al Purmort Jr. (Pres)

AL SERRA AUTO PLAZA
G-6167 S Saginaw, Grand Blanc, MI
48439
Tel.: (810) 694-5440
Web Site: http://www.alserra.com
Year Founded: 1974
Sales Range: $125-149.9 Million
Emp.: 300
Car Whslr
N.A.I.C.S.: 441110
Denny Dunfield (Gen Mgr)
Antony Young (Mgr-Fin)
Douglas W. Nolan (Mgr-Sls)
Dave Wenzel (Mgr-Sls)

AL SERRA CHEVROLET
1570 Auto Mall Loop, Colorado
Springs, CO 80920
Tel.: (719) 867-1000
Web Site:
     http://www.alserracolorado.com
Sales Range: $10-24.9 Million
Emp.: 50
New Car Retailer
N.A.I.C.S.: 441110
Jerry Colten (Owner & Gen Mgr)

**AL SHANKLE CONSTRUCTION
COMPANY**
3309 Grapevine St, Mira Loma, CA
91752-3503
Tel.: (951) 727-8882
Web Site:
     http://www.alshankleconstruct.com
Sales Range: $10-24.9 Million
Emp.: 30
Construction of Industrial Buildings
N.A.I.C.S.: 236220
Rita Preuss (Mgr-Office & Payroll)

**AL SWIDERSKI IMPLEMENT
INC.**
820 Old Hwy 51, Mosinee, WI 54455
Tel.: (715) 693-3015
Web Site:
     http://www.swiderskiequipment.com
Rev.: $20,000,000

Al Swiderski Implement Inc.—(Continued)
Emp.: 110
Wholesale Distributor of Agricultural
Machinery
N.A.I.C.S.: 423820
Alex Swiderski (CEO)

AL'S CORNER OIL CO.
12053 Hwy 71, Carroll, IA 51401
Tel.: (712) 673-2723
Web Site:
   https://www.sparkysonestop.com
Sales Range: $25-49.9 Million
Emp.: 275
Gasoline & Convenience Store Services
N.A.I.C.S.: 445131
Rollin Tiefenthaler (Pres)

AL'S GARDEN CENTERS & GREENHOUSES, LLC.
1220 N Pacific Hwy, Woodburn, OR 97071
Tel.: (503) 981-1245
Web Site: https://www.als-gardencenter.com
Year Founded: 1948
Sales Range: $10-24.9 Million
Emp.: 200
Nursery, Garden Center & Farm Supply Distr
N.A.I.C.S.: 444240
Darcy Ruef (CFO)

AL-AMIN BROTHERS TRANSPORTATION, LLC.
17585 Paxton Ave, Lansing, IL 60438
Tel.: (708) 895-5060
Web Site: http://www.al-aminbros.com
Year Founded: 1997
Sales Range: $10-24.9 Million
Emp.: 25
Long-Distance & Less Than Truck-load Freight Trucking Services
N.A.I.C.S.: 484122
Rafi Al-Amin (COO)

ALA SERVICES LLC
704 Goodlette Rd N, Naples, FL 34102
Tel.: (239) 330-6093
Web Site: http://www.alanaples.com
Enterprise Software Services
N.A.I.C.S.: 513210
Arthur L. Allen (Founder, Pres & CEO)
Richard Vance (Exec VP)
Charles Keen (CFO)

Subsidiaries:

Adaptive Computing Enterprises Inc.   (1)
1712 S East Bay Blvd Ste 300, Provo, UT 84606
Tel.: (801) 717-3700
Web Site:
   http://www.adaptivecomputing.com
Software Publisher
N.A.I.C.S.: 513210
Michael A. Jackson (Co-Founder)
Scott Hurst (Head-Sls-Americas, Asia Pacific & Japan)
Mark Norton (Head-Sls-EMEA)

ALABAMA BUREAU OF TOURISM & TRAVEL
401 Adams Ave Ste 126, Montgomery, AL 36104-4325
Tel.: (334) 242-4169
Web Site: http://www.alabama.travel
Year Founded: 1951
Sales Range: $75-99.9 Million
Emp.: 63
State Travel & Tourism Administration Services
N.A.I.C.S.: 561591

Grey Brennan (Dir-Mktg)
Rosemary Judkins (Mgr-Grp Travel)

ALABAMA CATFISH FEED-MILL, LLC.
PO Box 799, Uniontown, AL 36786
Tel.: (334) 628-6446
Sales Range: $25-49.9 Million
Emp.: 18
Animal Feed Mfr
N.A.I.C.S.: 311119
James Whidby (Gen Mgr)

ALABAMA CONCRETE CO., INC.
4200 Stringfield Rd NW, Huntsville, AL 35806-1426
Tel.: (256) 859-0311
Web Site:
   https://www.alabamaconcrete.com
Year Founded: 1963
Sales Range: $10-24.9 Million
Emp.: 90
Readymix Concrete Mfr
N.A.I.C.S.: 327320
Bruce Ables (Pres)

ALABAMA CREDIT UNION
Po Box 862998, Tuscaloosa, AL 35486
Tel.: (205) 348-5944
Web Site: http://www.alabamacu.com
Year Founded: 1956
Sales Range: $25-49.9 Million
Emp.: 205
Credit Union
N.A.I.C.S.: 522130
Stephen K. Swofford (Pres)

ALABAMA ELECTRIC COMPANY INC. OF DOTHAN
1728 Headland Ave, Dothan, AL 36303
Tel.: (334) 792-5164
Web Site: https://www.alaelectric.com
Sales Range: $10-24.9 Million
Emp.: 155
General Electrical Contractor
N.A.I.C.S.: 238210
Clifford E. Sloop (VP)

ALABAMA FARMERS COOP-ERATIVE, INC.
121 Somerville Rd NE, Decatur, AL 35601-2659
Tel.: (256) 353-6843
Web Site: http://www.alafarm.com
Year Founded: 1936
Sales Range: $450-499.9 Million
Emp.: 2,300
Agricultural Products & Services
N.A.I.C.S.: 424510
Al Cheatham (COO & VP)
Bill Sanders (Vice Chm)
David Womack (Chm)
Jo Ann Fuller (Chief Acctg Officer)
Thomas Hallin (CFO)
H. Rivers Myres III (Pres & CEO)

Subsidiaries:

Alabama Farmers Co-Op - South-Fresh Farms Division   (1)
1792 McFarland Blvd N, Tuscaloosa, AL 35406
Tel.: (205) 247-4490
Web Site: http://www.southfresh.com
Emp.: 6
Catfish Farming Services
N.A.I.C.S.: 112511

Bonnie Plant Farm   (1)
1727 Hwy 223, Union Springs, AL 36089
Tel.: (334) 738-3104
Web Site: http://www.bonnieplants.com
Sales Range: $50-74.9 Million
Emp.: 500
Whslr of Plants
N.A.I.C.S.: 111421

Stan Cope (Gen Mgr)
Currie Gin   (1)
43 Washington Ave, Atmore, AL 36502-8902   (100%)
Tel.: (334) 577-6411
Web Site: http://www.alafarm.com
Sales Range: $10-24.9 Million
Emp.: 13
Cotton Gin
N.A.I.C.S.: 115111

SouthFresh Farms - Indianola Processing Plant   (1)
Court House, Indianola, MS 38751
Tel.: (662) 887-1765
Web Site: http://www.southfresh.com
Sales Range: $25-49.9 Million
Emp.: 10
Catfish Farming Services
N.A.I.C.S.: 112511
George Applewhite (Plant Mgr)

ALABAMA INTER-FOREST CORP.
460 Industrial Dr, Eufaula, AL 36027
Tel.: (334) 687-8009
Web Site: https://www.panel.com
Year Founded: 1982
Sales Range: $10-24.9 Million
Emp.: 50
Sales of Furniture Component Parts
N.A.I.C.S.: 321999
Darrell Calhoun (Plant Mgr)
Renee Snell (Office Mgr)

ALABAMA MOTOR EXPRESS INC.
10720 E Hwy 84, Ashford, AL 36312-0487
Tel.: (334) 899-5136
Web Site:
   https://www.amxtrucking.com
Year Founded: 1988
Provider of Trucking Services
N.A.I.C.S.: 484121
Scott White (Pres & CEO)
Rodney Holland (Dir-Traffic)
Keith Grantham (Dir-Ops)
Collins White (Pres-Logistics)
Taylor White (VP-Ops)
Jared Moore (VP-Logistics)
Edward Berry (VP-Bus Dev)

ALABAMA ONE CREDIT UNION
1215 Veterans Memorial Pkwy, Tuscaloosa, AL 35404
Tel.: (205) 759-1595
Web Site:
   https://www.alabamaone.org
Year Founded: 1951
Sales Range: $25-49.9 Million
Emp.: 200
Credit Union
N.A.I.C.S.: 522130
John Dee Carruth (Pres)
Darlene Wallace (Sec)
Cheri Bogart (Mgr-Mortgage)
Brittany Dickey (Dir-HR & Mktg)
William C. Wells II (CEO)

ALABAMA PUBLIC TELEVI-SION
2112 11th Ave S Ste 400, Birmingham, AL 35205
Tel.: (205) 328-8756
Web Site: https://www.aptv.org
Sales Range: $10-24.9 Million
Emp.: 50
Television Broadcasting Station
N.A.I.C.S.: 516120
Roy Clem (Exec Dir)
Brian James (Asst Dir-Engrg)
Tracy Neeley (Mgr-HR)
Mary Davis (Mgr-Studio Facilities)
Despina Vodantis (Dir-Membership & Pledge)
J. Whitson (Mgr-Production)

Brian Monie (Mgr-Corp Support)
Beverly B. Phillips (Mgr-Corp Support)
Cindy Kirk (VP-Education Svcs)
Heather Daniels (Mgr-Educational Production)
Mary Gould (Designer-Multimedia)
Peggy Hair (Officer-Major Gifts)
Sandy Boyd (Asst Dir-Brdcst)
Caroline Martin (Mgr-Education Special Projects)

ALABAMA SPECIALTY PROD-UCTS, INC.
152 Metal Samples Rd, Munford, AL 36268
Tel.: (256) 358-4202
Web Site: https://www.alspi.com
Rev.: $14,800,000
Emp.: 199
Testing Equipment Mfr
N.A.I.C.S.: 334519

ALAC INTERNATIONAL, INC.
708 3rd Ave 5th Fl, New York, NY 10017
Tel.: (212) 209-3968
Web Site:
   http://www.alacinternational.com
Year Founded: 2004
Sales Range: $50-74.9 Million
Emp.: 11
Chemical Product Mfr & Distr
N.A.I.C.S.: 325998
Lily Frishman (Mng Dir-North America)
Aaron Wei (Mng Dir-Asia Pacific)
Alan Frishman (COO)

ALACRITY SOLUTIONS GROUP, INC.
9725 Windermere Blvd, Fishers, IN 46037
Tel.: (985) 345-4400
Web Site:
   https://www.alacritysolutions.com
Year Founded: 2008
Emp.: 1,000
Insurance Carrier
N.A.I.C.S.: 524210
Jim Pearl (CEO)

Subsidiaries:

Property Damage Appraisers, Inc.   (1)
6100 SW Blvd Ste 200, Fort Worth, TX 76109
Tel.: (817) 731-5555
Web Site: http://www.pdacorporation.com
Sales Range: $10-24.9 Million
Emp.: 30
Insurance Services
N.A.I.C.S.: 561499
Tom Dolfay (CEO)
Jennifer Salazar (CFO)
Grady Nance (Chief Compliance Officer)
Jeff Mucci (Chief Sls & Mktg Officer)

ALADDIN
1959 Palomar Oaks Way Ste 200, Carlsbad, CA 92011
Tel.: (760) 431-9911
Web Site:
   http://www.aladdinbailbonds.com
Sales Range: $10-24.9 Million
Emp.: 400
Bail Bonding
N.A.I.C.S.: 541990
Rob Hayes (Pres & CEO)

ALADDIN STEEL INC.
18473 Route 16, Gillespie, IL 62033
Tel.: (217) 839-2121
Web Site:
   https://www.aladdinsteel.com
Year Founded: 1976
Sales Range: $25-49.9 Million

Emp.: 140
Mfr of Carbon Steel Tubing & Pipe
N.A.I.C.S.: 423510
Kevin Gray (Mgr-Sls)
Mark Kloss (Asst Mgr-Sls)
Glen Herbeck (Asst Mgr-Sls)

ALAMANCE EXTENDED CARE, INC.
1860 Brookwood Ave, Burlington, NC 27215
Tel.: (336) 570-8400   NC
Web Site:
https://www.villageatbrookwood.org
Year Founded: 1985
Sales Range: $10-24.9 Million
Lifecare Retirement Community Operator
N.A.I.C.S.: 623311

ALAMANCE FOODS INC.
739 S Worth St, Burlington, NC 27215-3819
Tel.: (336) 226-6392
Web Site:
http://www.alamancefoods.com
Year Founded: 1959
Sales Range: $10-24.9 Million
Emp.: 100
Producer of Waters & Fruit Juices
N.A.I.C.S.: 312112
Jessica Kirkland (Mgr-Accts Receivable & Customer Svc)
Gene Smith (Mgr-Tech Svcs)
Jerry Shumate (Mgr-Sls-East)
Steve Chambers (Dir-Retail)
Dave Shearn (Mgr-Sls-Natl)
Larry Allumbaugh (Mgr-Sls-West)
Jeff Parker (VP-Sls & Mktg)

ALAMEDA COUNTY COMMUNITY FOOD BANK
7900 Edgewater Dr, Oakland, CA 94621
Tel.: (510) 635-3663   CA
Web Site: https://www.accfb.org
Year Founded: 1985
Sales Range: $50-74.9 Million
Emp.: 95
Community Food Services
N.A.I.C.S.: 624210
Barbara Darrow-Blake (Chief Dev Officer)
Amy Prescott Donovan (CFO)
Erick Lovdahl (Dir-Ops)
Ted Monk (Co-Chm)
Suzan W. Bateson (Exec Dir)
Tarang P. Amin (Chm)

ALAMEDA COUNTY WATER DISTRICT
43885 S Grimmer Blvd, Fremont, CA 94538
Tel.: (510) 668-4200
Web Site: https://www.acwd.org
Year Founded: 1913
Sales Range: $25-49.9 Million
Emp.: 200
Water Supply
N.A.I.C.S.: 221310
Ariz Naqvi (Mgr-IT)
Marta Lutsky (Coord-Quality Improvement)
Pamela Evans (Coord-Alameda County Green Bus)
Andrea Mueller (Mgr-Youth & Family Svcs Bureau)
Dave MacDonald (CIO-Registrar of Voters)
Otis Ward (Coord-Asset Dev)
Jason Perez (Deputy Dir-ITD)
Andrea Ford (Dir-Policy)
Beth Gentry (Engr-Environmental)

ALAMEDA ELECTRICAL DIS-

TRIBUTORS INC.
3875 Bay Center Pl, Hayward, CA 94545
Tel.: (510) 786-1400
Web Site:
http://www.alamedaelectric.com
Sales Range: $10-24.9 Million
Emp.: 45
Electrical Supplies
N.A.I.C.S.: 423610
Greg Berkowitz (VP-Sls & Ops)

ALAMEDA JUICE LLC
727 N Waco Ave Ste 400, Wichita, KS 67203-3900
Tel.: (316) 263-3201
Rev.: $10,800,000
Emp.: 160
Lessors of Nonfinancial Intangible Assets (except Copyrighted Works)
N.A.I.C.S.: 533110

ALAMEDA MUNICIPAL POWER
2000 Grand St, Alameda, CA 94501
Tel.: (510) 748-3900
Web Site:
https://www.alamedamp.com
Year Founded: 1887
Sales Range: $25-49.9 Million
Emp.: 120
Electric Bulk Power Transmission & Control Services
N.A.I.C.S.: 221121

ALAMEDA-CONTRA COSTA TRANSIT DISTRICT
1600 Franklin St, Oakland, CA 94612
Tel.: (510) 891-4777
Web Site: https://www.actransit.org
Year Founded: 1869
Sales Range: $50-74.9 Million
Emp.: 2,521
Operator of Bus Service
N.A.I.C.S.: 485113
Rick Fernandez (Gen Mgr)
Joe Wallace (VP)
Kenneth C. Scheidig (Gen Counsel)
Kathleen Kelly (Gen Mgr)
Elsa Ortiz (Pres)
Linda Nemeroff (Sec)
Michael A. Hursh (Gen Mgr)
Denise C. Standridge (Gen Mgr)
Alan Parello (Mgr-Internal Audit)
Claudia L. Allen (CFO)
Ahsan Baig (CIO)

ALAMO 1
10843 Gulfdale, San Antonio, TX 78216
Tel.: (210) 404-1220
Web Site: http://www.alamo1.com
Year Founded: 1999
Rev.: $29,000,000
Emp.: 185
Facilities Support Services
N.A.I.C.S.: 561210
Alex Salas (CEO)
Javier Torres (VP-A1 Armor Div)
J. Kevin Turner (Dir-Ops)

ALAMO CARIBE BAKERY DISTRIBUTORS
Centro de Distribucion del Norte No 1 Bldg, Catano, PR 00962
Tel.: (787) 620-4141
Web Site: http://www.ablesales.com
Rev.: $11,329,739
Emp.: 100
Flour & Bakery Products Distr
N.A.I.C.S.: 424490
Luis Silva (Pres)
Maria Felix (Gen Mgr-Indus Sls)

ALAMO CEMENT COMPANY
6055 W Green Mountain Rd, San Antonio, TX 78266

Tel.: (210) 208-1880
Rev.: $175,000,000
Emp.: 1,000
Portland Cement
N.A.I.C.S.: 327310
Rene Gomez (Supvr-Laboratory)
Rhett Morrow (Mgr-Sls)
Billy Gibbs (Chief Engr)
Don Winzeler (Dir-QC)

Subsidiaries:

Alamo Concrete Products Ltd.   (1)
6055 W Green Mountain Rd, San Antonio, TX 78266
Tel.: (210) 208-1500
Web Site: http://www.alamocement.com
Rev.: $50,000,000
Emp.: 650
Concrete Products, Nec
N.A.I.C.S.: 327390
Allen Walsh (Pres)
Randy Weeks (Supvr-DP)

ALAMO CITY HARLEY-DAVIDSON
11005 N Interstate Hwy 35, San Antonio, TX 78233
Tel.: (210) 646-0499
Sales Range: $10-24.9 Million
Emp.: 120
Motorcycles
N.A.I.C.S.: 441227
James Skinner (Gen Mgr)

ALAMO ENERGY CORP.
3000 Wilcrest Ste 220, Houston, TX 77024
Tel.: (832) 436-1832   NV
Web Site:
http://www.alamoenergycorp.com
Year Founded: 2006
Sales Range: Less than $1 Million
Oil & Gas Exploration Services
N.A.I.C.S.: 211120
Allan Blair Millmaker (Pres & CEO)
Philip K. Mann (Sec)
Donald J. Sebastian (CFO)

ALAMO FOREST PRODUCTS
125 Railroad Ave Ste 203, Danville, CA 94526
Tel.: (925) 838-5533
Rev.: $25,000,000
Emp.: 2
Lumber: Rough, Dressed & Finished
N.A.I.C.S.: 423310
William Broderick (Partner)

ALAMO TILE CO. INC.
848 West Rhapsody, San Antonio, TX 78216
Tel.: (210) 732-8350
Web Site:
http://www.alamotileandstone.com
Sales Range: $10-24.9 Million
Emp.: 60
Tile Installation, Ceramic
N.A.I.C.S.: 238340
Roland Martinez (Pres)

ALAMO TOYOTA INC.
2119 NE Loop 410, San Antonio, TX 78217
Tel.: (210) 657-6100
Web Site:
http://www.alamotoyota.com
Rev.: $27,900,000
Emp.: 85
Automobiles, New & Used
N.A.I.C.S.: 441110
John J. Toomey (Pres)
Monica Cole (Mgr-HR)

ALAMO WORKFORCE DEVELOPMENT, INC.
115 E Travis Ste 220, San Antonio, TX 78205
Tel.: (210) 272-3260   TX

Web Site:
http://www.workforcesolutions.org
Year Founded: 1994
Sales Range: $50-74.9 Million
Emp.: 40
Social Welfare Services
N.A.I.C.S.: 525120

ALAMON TELCO INCORPO-RATED
315 W Idaho St, Kalispell, MT 59901
Tel.: (406) 752-8838   MT
Web Site: https://www.alamon.com
Year Founded: 1975
Sales Range: $25-49.9 Million
Emp.: 200
Communications Specialization
N.A.I.C.S.: 238210
Dan Dennison (Dir-Safety & Mgr-Ops-Outside Plant Svcs)
Alex Hatfield (Gen Mgr)
Terry Mickens (VP-Wireless)
Brad Cronk (Pres)
Scott Lawrence (VP-Ops)
Dennis Gesker (Mgr-IT)
Mike Gallagher (Mgr-Engrg-DC Power & Comm Svcs)
Troy Reeves (Mgr-Ops-Comm Svcs)
Eric Shelton (Mgr-Ops-Utility Svcs)
Travis Williams (Mgr-Ops-Wireless Svcs)

ALAN BYER AUTO SALES INC.
1230 W Genesee St, Syracuse, NY 13204
Tel.: (315) 471-6107
Web Site:
http://www.alanbyervolvo.com
Rev.: $10,900,000
Emp.: 70
Automobiles, New & Used
N.A.I.C.S.: 441110
Alan I. Byer (Pres)
Paula Thurston (Controller)

ALAN GRAY LLC
88 Broad St, Boston, MA 02110
Tel.: (617) 426-6255   MA
Web Site: http://www.alangray.com
Year Founded: 1988
Emp.: 90
Insurance Claims Management & Financial Services
N.A.I.C.S.: 524292
Alan H. Gray (Founder & Exec VP)
Paul M. Roach (Pres)
Joseph F. Cascino (Exec VP-Enterprise Consulting)
Seth Patel (CEO)
Bill O'Farrell (Chm)

ALAN JAY AUTOMOTIVE MANAGEMENT, INC.
3201 US Hwy 27 S, Sebring, FL 33870
Tel.: (863) 314-5338   FL
Web Site: https://www.alanjay.com
Sales Range: $50-74.9 Million
Emp.: 200
New & Used Car Dealerships Operator
N.A.I.C.S.: 561110
Alan J. Wildstein (Founder, Pres & CEO)
David Edelson (Dir-Variable Ops)
Don Elwell (Dir-Mktg & Comm)
Joe Mullins (Dir-Used Car)
Michael Witham (COO)

Subsidiaries:

Alan Jay Chrysler Jeep, Inc.   (1)
1401 US Hwy 17 S, Wauchula, FL 33873-9403
Tel.: (863) 773-4744

Alan Jay Automotive Management, Inc.—(Continued)

Web Site:
http://www.alanjaychryslerdodgejeep.com
Sales Range: $10-24.9 Million
Emp.: 50
New & Used Car Distr
N.A.I.C.S.: 441110
Alan Jay Wildstein (Founder, Pres & CEO)

Alan Jay Ford Lincoln Mercury, Inc. (1)
3201 US Hwy 27 S, Sebring, FL 33870
Tel.: (863) 385-0144
Web Site:
http://www.alanjayfordofsebring.com
Sales Range: $25-49.9 Million
Emp.: 80
New & Used Car Dealer
N.A.I.C.S.: 441110
Santiago Hernandez (Gen Mgr-Sls)

ALAN JAY AUTOMOTIVE NETWORK
441 US Hwy 27 N, Sebring, FL 33870
Tel.: (863) 402-4250
Web Site: https://www.alanjay.com
Year Founded: 1992
Sales Range: $10-24.9 Million
Emp.: 82
Car Whslr
N.A.I.C.S.: 441110
Todd Harlib (COO)
Randall Leonard (Mgr-Ops)
Alan Wildstein (Pres)

ALAN RITCHEY INC.
Interstate 35 Frontage Rd, Valley View, TX 76272
Tel.: (940) 726-3276
Web Site: http://www.alanritchey.com
Year Founded: 1959
Sales Range: $250-299.9 Million
Emp.: 1,000
Mfr of Prepared Feeds
N.A.I.C.S.: 112120
Alan Ritchey (Pres & CEO)
Lora Hinton (VP & Mgr-Postal Contract)
Bobby Ritchey (VP-Ops)
Sheri L. Pantermuehl (CFO)

ALAN SHINTANI INC.
94 409 Akoki St, Waipahu, HI 96797
Tel.: (808) 841-7631
Web Site: https://www.alan-shintani.com
Year Founded: 1984
Sales Range: $10-24.9 Million
Emp.: 65
Commercial & Institutional Building Construction Services
N.A.I.C.S.: 236220
Alan Shintani (Pres)

ALAN WEBB AUTOMOTIVE GROUP
3712 NE 66th Ave, Vancouver, WA 98661
Tel.: (360) 450-0021
Web Site:
https://www.alanwebbauto.com
Sales Range: $10-24.9 Million
Emp.: 80
New & Used Car Dealerships Owner & Operator
N.A.I.C.S.: 441110
Michelle Dolan (Principal)

ALAN WEINKRANTZ & COMPANY
115 E Pecan St, San Antonio, TX 78205
Tel.: (210) 820-3070
Web Site: http://alanweinkrantz.com
Year Founded: 1980
Sales Range: $1-9.9 Million

Emp.: 12
Public Relations Agency
N.A.I.C.S.: 541820
Alan L. Weinkrantz (Pres)

ALAN/ANTHONY, INC.
55 Broad St 14th Fl, New York, NY 10004
Tel.: (212) 825-1582
Year Founded: 1983
Rev.: $750,000
Emp.: 4
Fiscal Year-end: 12/31/03
N.A.I.C.S.: 541810
Robert A. Bell (Sr Partner)
Louis A. Zacharilla (Sr Partner)
Tamera Bond (Dir-Ops)
Randall Barney (Program Admin)
Linda Thornburg (Editor)
Orly Konig-Lopez (Mgr-Comm)

ALANDALE INSURANCE AGENCY INC.
11022 Winners Cir Ste 100, Los Alamitos, CA 90720
Tel.: (562) 493-3521
Web Site: https://www.alandale.com
Sales Range: $10-24.9 Million
Emp.: 8
Insurance Services
N.A.I.C.S.: 524210
Robert G. Kuhn (Pres)
Gary A. Neal (Owner & CEO)

ALANT CORPORATION
1919 N Lakewood Blvd, Long Beach, CA 90815-2715
Tel.: (562) 597-3663
Web Site: https://www.circleaudi.com
Year Founded: 1988
Sales Range: $25-49.9 Million
Emp.: 100
New & Used Car Dealers
N.A.I.C.S.: 441110
Carl Maeda (CEO)

ALARM CENTER, INC.
7354 Convoy Ct, San Diego, CA 92111-1110
Tel.: (858) 244-2468
Web Site:
https://www.alarmcenter.com
Year Founded: 1979
Sales Range: $10-24.9 Million
Fire Alarm, Close-Circuit Television, Central Vacuum, Intercom, Sound Systems & Access Control Systems Distr
N.A.I.C.S.: 423610
Steve Kenville (Pres)

ALARM DETECTION SYSTEMS, INC.
1111 Church Rd, Aurora, IL 60505
Tel.: (630) 844-6300
Web Site: https://www.adsalarm.com
Year Founded: 1968
Sales Range: $10-24.9 Million
Emp.: 200
Sales of Security Systems Services
N.A.I.C.S.: 561621
Robert A. Bonifas (Pres & CEO)

ALARM NEW ENGLAND LLC
65 Inwood Rd, Rocky Hill, CT 06067
Tel.: (617) 445-4004
Web Site:
https://www.alarmnewengland.com
Year Founded: 1972
Security & Investigation Services
N.A.I.C.S.: 561621
Kevin Larche (CFO)
Doug Curtiss (CEO & Founder)

ALARM TEAM, INC.

5305 Raynor Rd Ste 100, Garner, NC 27529
Tel.: (919) 773-7802
Web Site: http://www.alarmteam.com
Sales Range: $25-49.9 Million
Emp.: 198
All Other Miscellaneous Store Retailers, Except Tobacco Stores
N.A.I.C.S.: 459999
Barry J. Simmons (Pres)

ALARMAX DISTRIBUTORS INC.
750 Holiday Dr Ste 310, Pittsburgh, PA 15220-2783
Tel.: (412) 921-8330 DE
Web Site: http://www.alarmax.com
Year Founded: 1990
Sales Range: $10-24.9 Million
Emp.: 60
Electrical Apparatus & Equipment
N.A.I.C.S.: 423610
Roger Graf (Pres)

Subsidiaries:

Cassidy Technologies (1)
2135 Energy Park Dr, Saint Paul, MN 55108
Web Site:
http://www.cassidytechnologies.com
Fiber Optic Cable Mfr
N.A.I.C.S.: 335921
Mark Hoodecheck (Sr Acct Mgr)

Northern Sound & Light, Inc (1)
3021 Liberty Ave., Pittsburgh, PA 15201
Tel.: (412) 331-1000
Web Site:
http://www.northernsoundandlight.com
Scenic & Sightseeing Transportation, Land
N.A.I.C.S.: 487110
Armand P. Biondi (Owner)

ALASKA COMMUNITY FOUNDATION
3201 C St Ste 110, Anchorage, AK 99503
Tel.: (907) 334-6700 AK
Web Site: https://www.alaskacf.org
Year Founded: 1995
Sales Range: $10-24.9 Million
Emp.: 15
Grantmaking Services
N.A.I.C.S.: 813211
Kris Norosz (Vice Chm)
Nina Kemppel (Pres & CEO)

ALASKA COMPREHENSIVE HEALTH INSURANCE ASSOCIATION
2015 16th St, Great Bend, KS 67530
Web Site: https://www.achia.com
Year Founded: 1992
Sales Range: $10-24.9 Million
Health Insurance Services
N.A.I.C.S.: 524114
J. Brian Angel (Vice Chm)

ALASKA DIGITEL WIRELESS COMMUNICATIONS LLC
PO Box 201387, Anchorage, AK 99520
Tel.: (907) 274-3114
Web Site: http://www.akdigitel.com
Sales Range: $75-99.9 Million
Emp.: 1,600
Wireless Telecommunications
N.A.I.C.S.: 517112
Jeff Roe (COO)
Thomas Studer (Dir-Mktg)
Peter Pounds (CFO, Sec & Sr VP)
Ronald Duncan (Co-Founder, Pres & CEO)

ALASKA DISPATCH PUBLISHING LLC

2301 Merrill Field Dr, Anchorage, AK 99501
Tel.: (907) 743-0744
Web Site:
http://www.alaskadispatch.com
Year Founded: 2008
Emp.: 30
Newspaper Publishers
N.A.I.C.S.: 513110
Tony Hopfinger (Exec Editor)
Alice Rogoff (Publr)
Margy Johnson (Exec VP)
Mike Campbell (Mng Editor)

ALASKA DISTRIBUTORS CO.
2000 Fairview Ave E Ste 101, Seattle, WA 98102-3555
Tel.: (206) 622-7311 WA
Year Founded: 1957
Sales Range: $100-124.9 Million
Emp.: 430
Wine & Distilled Beverages Distr
N.A.I.C.S.: 424820
Richard Loeb (Vice Chm)
Alex Shulman (Chm)
Steve Loeb (Pres)
Jerry Goldman (CFO)

ALASKA ELECTRIC LIGHT & POWER COMPANY
5601 Tonsgard Ct, Juneau, AK 99801-7201
Tel.: (907) 780-2222
Web Site: https://www.aelp.com
Eletric Power Generation Services
N.A.I.C.S.: 221118
Timothy D. McLeod (Pres)

ALASKA HOUSEWARES INC.
2125 E 79th, Anchorage, AK 99507
Tel.: (907) 561-2240
Web Site:
http://www.alaskahousewares.com
Sales Range: $10-24.9 Million
Emp.: 40
Home Furnishings Whslr
N.A.I.C.S.: 423020
Gary Bucy (Pres)
Scott Emery (VP-Ops)
Jim Kaletka (VP-Sls)
Ray King (Controller)

ALASKA HOUSING FINANCE CORPORATION
4300 Boniface Pkwy, Anchorage, AK 99504
Tel.: (907) 338-6100
Web Site: https://www.ahfc.us
Year Founded: 1971
Rev.: $246,280,000
Assets: $4,101,560,000
Liabilities: $2,562,864,000
Net Worth: $1,538,696,000
Emp.: 300
Fiscal Year-end: 06/30/18
Mortgage Banking & Loan Services
N.A.I.C.S.: 522292
Bryan Butcher (CEO & Exec Dir)
Kim Coy (Officer-Contract Compliance)
Mark Romick (Deputy Exec Dir)
Elaine Hodl (Dir-HR)
Tom Remaklus (Dir-Info Sys)
Brent Levalley (Chm)
Stacy Schubert (Dir-Govt Rels & Pub Affairs)
Les Campbell (Dir-Budget)
Catherine Stone (Dir-Pub Housing)
Michael Courtney (Dir-Housing Ops)
Gregory Rochon (Dir-Admin Svcs)
Eric Havelock (Officer-Lending & Mortgage Ops)
Alan Wilson (Vice Chm)
Jan Miyagishima (Dir-Mortgage Ops)

John Anderson *(Dir-Res & Rural Dev)*
Terry Kincaid *(Officer-Admin Svcs)*
Jim B. McCall *(Officer-Housing Rels)*

ALASKA LOGISTICS, LLC.
327 S Kenyon, Seattle, WA 98108-3460
Tel.: (206) 767-2555
Web Site: http://www.alaska-logistics.com
Year Founded: 2003
Sales Range: $10-24.9 Million
Emp.: 35
Freight Transportation Arrangement Services
N.A.I.C.S.: 488510
Allyn Long *(Pres & Gen Mgr)*
Steve Sauerbrey *(VP)*
Bill Emory *(Mgr-AK Ops-Nome & Bristol Bay)*
Eric Day *(Mgr-Seward Ops)*
Jennie Duffield *(Mgr-Documentation & Receiving)*
Eric Brown *(Controller)*

ALASKA MECHANICAL INC.
8540 Dimond D Cir, Anchorage, AK 99515
Tel.: (907) 349-8502
Web Site: https://www.ami-alaska.com
Rev.: $30,706,179
Emp.: 10
Industrial Buildings, New Construction
N.A.I.C.S.: 236210
Larry Buss *(Pres)*

ALASKA MINING & DIVING SUPPLY, INC.
3222 Commercial Dr, Anchorage, AK 99501
Tel.: (907) 277-1741
Web Site: http://www.akmining.com
Sales Range: $10-24.9 Million
Emp.: 30
Boat Dealers
N.A.I.C.S.: 441222

ALASKA NATIONAL CORPORATION
7001 Jewel Lake Rd, Anchorage, AK 99502
Tel.: (907) 248-2642   AK
Web Site:
    http://www.alaskanational.com
Year Founded: 1979
Rev.: $53,000,000
Emp.: 150
Insurance Agents Brokers & Service
N.A.I.C.S.: 551112
Rich Suddock *(Sr VP & Controller)*
Gary Oehler *(Exec VP)*
Craig Nodvedt *(Pres)*

Subsidiaries:

Alaska National Insurance
Company   (1)
7001 Jewel Lake Rd, Anchorage, AK
99502-2825   (100%)
Tel.: (907) 248-2642
Web Site: http://www.alaskanational.com
Property & Casualty Insurance Products & Services
N.A.I.C.S.: 524126
George S. Suddock *(Chm)*

ALASKA NATIVE INDUSTRIES COOP ASSOCIATION
4634 E Marginal Way S, Seattle, WA 98134
Tel.: (206) 767-0333
Web Site: http://www.anicainc.com
Rev.: $34,649,038
Emp.: 35
Cooperative Food Store
N.A.I.C.S.: 445110
Ed Tebrock III *(CEO)*

ALASKA PACIFIC TRADING COMPANY
12011 NE 1st St, Bellevue, WA 98005
Tel.: (425) 453-1031
Sales Range: $25-49.9 Million
Emp.: 4
Brokerage For Logs, Hewn Ties, Posts & Poles
N.A.I.C.S.: 423990
Takuya Hasegawa *(Pres)*

ALASKA PUBLIC MEDIA, INC.
3877 University Dr, Anchorage, AK 99508
Tel.: (907) 550-8400
Web Site: https://alaskapublic.org
Rev.: $5,600,000
Emp.: 50
Fiscal Year-end: 12/31/06
Television Broadcasting Stations, Nsk
N.A.I.C.S.: 516110

ALASKA RAILROAD CORPORATION
327 W Ship Creek Ave, Anchorage, AK 99501-7500
Tel.: (907) 265-2430   AK
Web Site: http://www.akrr.com
Year Founded: 1985
Sales Range: $25-49.9 Million
Emp.: 550
Rail System Services
N.A.I.C.S.: 482111
Phyllis C. Johnson *(Gen Counsel & VP)*
James M. Kubitz *(VP-Corp Plng & Real Estate)*
Eileen Reilly *(VP-Advanced Train Control Sys)*
William G. O'Leary *(Pres)*
Paul Farnsworth *(Mgr-Facilities Program)*
Mike Fretwell *(Mgr-Land Svcs)*
Robert Gonzalez *(Dir-Supply Mgmt)*
Ruth Rosewarne *(Mgr-Sls)*
Kevin Meier *(Mgr-Rail Marine Ops)*
Karen Morrissey *(Dir-Real Estate)*
Jeff Johnson *(Mgr-Sls)*
Patt Winslow *(Mgr-HR-Drug)*
Dale Wade *(VP-Mktg & Customer Svc)*
Andrew Donovan *(Mgr-Leasing)*
Clark Hopp *(COO)*

ALASKA ROAD BORING COMPANY
1600 A St Ste 302, Anchorage, AK 99501-5148
Tel.: (907) 344-6895
Web Site: http://www.arbcalaska.com
Sales Range: $10-24.9 Million
Emp.: 35
General Construction
N.A.I.C.S.: 237110
Earl Frawner *(Pres)*

ALASKA SALES & SERVICE, INC.
1300 E 5th Ave, Anchorage, AK 99501-2886
Tel.: (907) 279-9641   AK
Web Site:
    http://www.alaskasalesservice.com
Year Founded: 1945
Sales Range: $125-149.9 Million
Emp.: 300
Automobile Dealership
N.A.I.C.S.: 441110
Diane G. Pfeiffer *(Pres)*
Shaun Pfeiffer *(Gen Mgr)*

ALASKA TRAVEL INDUSTRY ASSOCIATION
2600 Cordova St Ste 201, Anchorage, AK 99503
Tel.: (907) 929-2842
Web Site: http://www.alaskatia.org
Year Founded: 1999
Sales Range: $10-24.9 Million
Emp.: 18
Convention & Visitors Bureaus Services
N.A.I.C.S.: 561591
Sarah Leonard *(Pres & CEO)*
Jackie Englund *(Mgr-Membership & Sls)*
Erica Hedman *(Mgr-Mktg & Travel Trade)*
Sioux-z Marshall *(CFO)*
Jillian Simpson *(VP)*
Laurie Booyse *(Mgr-Sls-Membership & Adv)*
Tanya Carlson *(Dir-Mktg & Travel Trade Rels)*
Andrea Rayt *(Mgr-Ops & Acctg)*
Jennifer Nuzzo *(VP-Ops)*

ALASKA VILLAGE ELECTRIC COOPERATIVE, INC.
4831 Eagle St, Anchorage, AK 99503
Tel.: (907) 561-1818   AK
Web Site: https://www.avec.org
Year Founded: 1968
Sales Range: $50-74.9 Million
Electric Power Distr
N.A.I.C.S.: 221122
Charlie Curtis *(Vice Chm)*
Phyllis Clough *(Sec)*
Helena R. Jones *(Treas)*
Robert L. Beans Sr. *(Chm)*

ALASKAN BREWING COMPANY
5429 Shaune Dr, Juneau, AK 99801-9540
Tel.: (907) 780-5866
Web Site:
    https://www.alaskanbeer.com
Year Founded: 1986
Sales Range: $10-24.9 Million
Emp.: 80
Brewery
N.A.I.C.S.: 312120
Geoffrey Larson *(Co-Founder, Pres & CEO)*
Curtis Holmes *(Mgr-Plant)*

ALBA MANUFACTURING INC.
8950 Seward Rd, Fairfield, OH 45011
Tel.: (513) 874-0551
Web Site: https://www.albamfg.com
Year Founded: 1972
Sales Range: $10-24.9 Million
Emp.: 60
Conveyors & Conveying Equipment
N.A.I.C.S.: 333922
Tom Inderhees *(Pres-Alba Mfg)*

ALBAN TIRE CORP.
7244 Boudinot Dr, Springfield, VA 22150
Tel.: (703) 455-9300
Web Site: https://www.albantire.com
Year Founded: 1974
Sales Range: $10-24.9 Million
Automobile Tires & Tubes Whslr
N.A.I.C.S.: 423130
Richard W. Daugherty *(Gen Mgr)*

ALBANY ADVOCACY RESOURCE CENTER, INC.
PO Box 71026, Albany, GA 31708
Tel.: (229) 888-6852
Web Site: http://www.albanyarc.org
Year Founded: 1963
Sales Range: $10-24.9 Million
Emp.: 187
Disability Assistance Services
N.A.I.C.S.: 624120

Laura C. Calhoun *(Dir-Dev)*
Yvette Adams *(Dir-Performance Improvement & Incident Mgmt)*
Ernestine Douglas *(Dir-Billing & Data Entry)*
Deanna Julian *(Deputy Dir)*
Dawn Tippins *(Dir-Education & Preschool)*
Sonja West *(Dir-Vocational Svcs / Thrift Store)*
Kathy Batson *(Dir-HR)*
Shon Houston *(Dir-ICWP)*
Eddie McCarty *(Dir-Mktg & PR)*
Gigi Wakem *(Dir-Residential Svcs)*
Grace Williams *(Dir-Adult Day & Independent Living)*

ALBANY BANCORP, INC.
200 S Washington St, Albany, KY 42602-1226
Tel.: (606) 387-6416
Web Site:
    http://www.albanybancorp.com
Year Founded: 1993
Sales Range: $10-24.9 Million
Bank Holding Company
N.A.I.C.S.: 551111
Autumn L. Upchurch *(CFO & VP)*
Pete Mahurin *(Chm)*
Lester Key *(Vice Chm)*
Kim Phelps *(Sec)*

Subsidiaries:

First & Farmers National Bank,
Inc.   (1)
100 Public Sq, Somerset, KY 42501
Tel.: (606) 679-7451
Web Site: http://www.firstandfarmers.com
Rev.: $19,719,000
Assets: $506,917,000
Liabilities: $439,148,000
Net Worth: $67,769,000
Earnings: $6,365,000
Emp.: 165
Fiscal Year-end: 12/31/2017
Commericial Banking
N.A.I.C.S.: 522110
Alan Houck *(Pres-Pulaski Market & VP)*
Vickie Wells *(Pres-Burkesville)*
Janice Harris *(VP & Branch Mgr-Downtown Albany)*
Ann Martin *(Pres-Columbia)*
Autumn L. Upchurch *(CFO & VP)*
Danielle Lowhorn *(Asst VP)*
Terry Pugh *(Pres & CEO)*
Jennifer Dalton *(Chief HR Officer & VP)*

ALBANY BANK & TRUST COMPANY, N.A.
3400 W Lawrence Ave, Chicago, IL 60625
Tel.: (773) 267-7300
Web Site:
    https://www.albanybank.com
Year Founded: 1953
Sales Range: $50-74.9 Million
Emp.: 200
Banking Services
N.A.I.C.S.: 522110
Robert D. Gecht *(Pres)*
Adam Steinback *(Sr VP-Comml Svcs)*
Stuart Rosenberg *(Sr VP-Ops)*
Brenda Helms *(Officer-Trust & Gen Counsel)*

ALBANY FORD INC.
718 San Pablo Ave, Albany, CA 94706
Tel.: (510) 528-1244
Web Site:
    http://www.albanyfordsubaru.com
Rev.: $23,000,000
Emp.: 60
Automobiles, New & Used
N.A.I.C.S.: 441110

ALBANY STEEL INC.

Albany Steel Inc.—(Continued)

566 Broadway, Albany, NY 12204-2802
Tel.: (518) 436-4851　　　　NY
Web Site:
https://www.albanysteel.net
Year Founded: 1923
Mfr of Steel
N.A.I.C.S.: 423510
Peter J. Hess (*Pres*)
Erla Miller (*Mgr-Fabrication*)
Richard DeVeau (*Gen Mgr*)

ALBANY TRAVEL UNLIMITED INC.
30 Corporate Dr, Clifton Park, NY 12065-8603
Tel.: (518) 292-9000　　　NY
Web Site:
http://www.albanytravel.com
Year Founded: 1952
Sales Range: $10-24.9 Million
Emp.: 56
Travel Agencies
N.A.I.C.S.: 561510
Thomas Child (*Owner*)

ALBAR INDUSTRIES, INC.
780 Whitney Dr, Lapeer, MI 48446-2570
Tel.: (810) 667-0150
Web Site: https://www.albar.com
Emp.: 187
Motor Vehicle Parts Mfr
N.A.I.C.S.: 336390
Andrew Woodruff (*Mgr-Plant*)
Glenn Curtis (*Pres*)
Mark Gerics (*Mgr-IT*)
Annette Lawrey (*Mgr-Quality*)

ALBARELL ELECTRIC INC.
901 W Lehigh St, Bethlehem, PA 18018
Tel.: (610) 691-8606　　　PA
Web Site: https://www.albarell.com
Year Founded: 1937
Sales Range: $10-24.9 Million
Emp.: 120
Contractor of General Electrical Services
N.A.I.C.S.: 238210
Michael M. Albarell (*Pres*)
Ernie Hahn (*Project Mgr*)
Tom Ofchus (*Mgr-Pur & Bus Dev*)
Don Keim (*Project Mgr*)

ALBAUGH INC.
1525 NE 36th St, Ankeny, IA 50021
Tel.: (515) 964-9444
Web Site: http://www.albaughinc.com
Sales Range: $50-74.9 Million
Emp.: 21
Fungicides, Herbicides
N.A.I.C.S.: 325320
Dennis Albaugh (*Chm*)
Spencer Vance (*Pres*)
Jim Kahnk (*Mgr-Ops*)
Greg Mulhall (*Coord-Project & Mgr-Acctg*)
Chad Shelton (*Mgr-Mktg*)
Craig Musselman (*Mgr-Sls-Carmel*)
David Long (*Mgr-Technical*)
Dean Ladner (*Mgr-Sls-Collierville*)
Eddie Allen (*Mgr-Sls-Sanger*)
Jerry Miller (*Mgr-Sls-Cary*)
Jim Schmidt (*Mgr-Sls-Meridian*)
Kem Cunningham (*Mgr-Sls-Fresno*)
Mark Blume (*Dir-Sls*)
Steve Williams (*Mgr-Sls-Albany*)
Justin Watts (*Natl Sls Mgr*)
Jeremy Moore (*Mgr-Southeast*)

ALBCO SALES INC.
230 Maple St, Lisbon, OH 44432
Tel.: (330) 424-7716

Web Site: https://www.albco.com
Year Founded: 1985
Sales Range: $25-49.9 Million
Emp.: 20
Metals Service Centers & Offices
N.A.I.C.S.: 423510
Tim Redovian (*VP-Sls & Mktg*)

ALBECO INC.
150 Shoreline Hwy Bldg D, Mill Valley, CA 94941
Tel.: (415) 289-5720
Year Founded: 1985
Sales Range: $10-24.9 Million
Emp.: 30
Grocery Store Services
N.A.I.C.S.: 445110
Michael Stone (*Partner*)
Steve Stamos (*COO & Gen Mgr*)
Thomas E. Wheeler (*Dir-Produce Ops*)

ALBEO TECHNOLOGIES INC.
2108 55th St, Boulder, CO 80301
Tel.: (720) 407-4960
Web Site: http://www.albeotech.com
Sales Range: $10-24.9 Million
Emp.: 37
Lighting Product Mfr & Distr
N.A.I.C.S.: 335999
Alicia Gauer (*Sr Mgr-Comm*)

ALBERIC COLON AUTO SALES INC.
2 Villa Kennedy Hm5, San Juan, PR 00936
Tel.: (787) 999-8888
Web Site:
http://www.albericcolon.com
Rev.: $45,829,087
Emp.: 200
Automobiles, New & Used
N.A.I.C.S.: 441110
Alberic Colon Jr. (*Pres*)

ALBERICI CORPORATION
8800 Page Ave, Saint Louis, MO 63114-6106
Tel.: (314) 733-2000　　　MO
Web Site: https://www.alberici.com
Year Founded: 1918
Sales Range: Less than $1 Million
Emp.: 2,500
Commercial & Institutional Building Construction
N.A.I.C.S.: 236220
Gabriel J. Alberici (*Chm*)
John S. Alberici (*Chm*)
Leroy J. Stromberg (*Chief Construction Officer*)
Gregory T. Hesser (*Pres-Construction*)
Mark Okroy (*VP*)
Joe Turner (*Exec VP-Construction*)
Ronald W. Wiese (*VP*)
Christopher J. Hermann (*Exec VP*)
Trevor L. Ladner (*Gen Counsel & VP*)
David P. Calcaterra (*Exec VP-Construction*)
Michael W. Burke (*COO*)
Donald C. Oberlies (*VP-Industrial Process Div*)
Gregory J. Kozicz (*Pres, Pres, CEO & CEO*)
James G. Klingensmith (*Sr VP-Project Acquisition*)
Michael W. Ryan (*VP-Project Costs-Tracking, Analyzing & Forcasting Project Costs*)
Mike Szymkowicz (*VP-Project Dev*)
Richard N. Jaggers (*Co-CFO*)
Timothy M. Gunn (*VP-Construction*)
Aaron Geiger (*CTO*)
Kevin Williams (*Exec VP*)
Peter Kozicz (*Pres*)

Subsidiaries:

Alberici Construcciones S.A. de C.V..　　　　　　　　　　(1)
Rio Churubusco No 276, Coyoacan, Mexico, 04230, I, Mexico
Tel.: (52) 55 5203 5180
Construction Management Services
N.A.I.C.S.: 236220

Alberici Constructors, Ltd.　　　(1)
1005 Skyview Drive, Burlington, L7P 5B1, ON, Canada　　　(100%)
Tel.: (905) 315-3000
Web Site: http://www.alberici.com
Sales Range: $25-49.9 Million
Emp.: 50
General Construction Services
N.A.I.C.S.: 236220
Greg Brokenshire (*Pres*)
Jack Scott (*Chief Admin Officer*)

Subsidiary (Domestic):

Hillsdale Structures, LP.　　　(2)
1005 Skyview Drive Ste 300, Burlington, L7P 5B1, ON, Canada
Tel.: (905) 315-3000
Web Site: http://www.alberici.com
Sales Range: $75-99.9 Million
Structural Steel Fabrication Services
N.A.I.C.S.: 238120
Sean Thibeault (*Project Dir*)

Alberici Healthcare, LLC　　　(1)
8800 Page Ave, Overland, MO 63114
Tel.: (314) 733-2000
Construction Management Services
N.A.I.C.S.: 236220

Alberici Western Constructors, Ltd.　　　　　　　　　　(1)
120 Sonnenschein Place, Saskatoon, S7M 0W2, SK, Canada
Tel.: (306) 203-0119
Construction Engineering Services
N.A.I.C.S.: 541330

CAS Constructors, LLC　　　(1)
3500 SW Fairlawn Rd Ste 200, Topeka, KS 66614
Tel.: (785) 354-9953
Web Site: http://www.casconstructors.com
Sales Range: $10-24.9 Million
Emp.: 35
Construction Services
N.A.I.C.S.: 236210
Michael Hafling (*Pres*)
Travis Stryker (*Exec VP*)

Gunther Nash Incorporated　　　(1)
2 City Pl Ste 380, Saint Louis, MO 63141　　　　　　　　　　(100%)
Tel.: (314) 692-2611
Web Site: http://www.alberici.com
Sales Range: $10-24.9 Million
Emp.: 50
Mining Contractor; Tunneling
N.A.I.C.S.: 236210

Hillsdale Fabricators　　　(1)
2150 Kienlen Ave, Saint Louis, MO 63121
Tel.: (314) 553-8205
Web Site:
http://www.hillsdalefabricators.com
Structural Steel Fabrication Services
N.A.I.C.S.: 238120
Steve Door (*Dir-Bus Dev*)

Kienlen Constructors　　　(1)
2150 Kienlen Ave, Saint Louis, MO 63121
Tel.: (314) 553-8202
Web Site: http://www.alberici.com
Emp.: 100
Construction & Engineering Management Services
N.A.I.C.S.: 236220
Rick Kayser (*Gen Mgr*)

WWPS, LLC.　　　(1)
9935 Villa Rica Hwy, Villa Rica, GA 30180
Tel.: (770) 456-9984
Web Site: http://www.wwpsinc.com
Water Facility Construction Services
N.A.I.C.S.: 236210
Leslie Brown (*Office Mgr*)

ALBERN CO.

7379 Pagedale Industrial Ct, Saint Louis, MO 63133-1305
Tel.: (314) 725-1110
Web Site: http://www.albernco.com
Year Founded: 1996
Sales Range: $10-24.9 Million
Emp.: 150
Air Conditioning System Installation Services
N.A.I.C.S.: 238220
Terry Donovan (*Pres*)

ALBERT & ASSOCIATES INC.
4741 College Pk, San Antonio, TX 78249
Tel.: (210) 226-6446
Web Site: http://www.aatran.com
Sales Range: $10-24.9 Million
Emp.: 10
Truck Transportation Brokers
N.A.I.C.S.: 488510
Bernard Jensen (*Chm*)
Joe Douglas (*Pres*)

ALBERT BROS., INC.
225 E Aurora St, Waterbury, CT 06721
Tel.: (203) 753-4146
Web Site: http://www.albertbros.com
Year Founded: 1895
Sales Range: $10-24.9 Million
Emp.: 45
Recyclable Material Whslr
N.A.I.C.S.: 423930
Eric Albert (*Pres*)

ALBERT C. KOBAYASHI INC.
94 535 Ukee St, Waipahu, HI 96797-4214
Tel.: (808) 671-6460
Web Site: https://www.ack-inc.com
Year Founded: 1944
Construction Services
N.A.I.C.S.: 236220
Russell Young (*Pres & CEO*)
Clyde Sugawa (*Sec & Treas*)
Michael Young (*VP*)
Joe Alameda (*Mgr-Ops*)

ALBERT CITY ELEVATOR, A COOPERATIVE
30 Main St, Albert City, IA 50510-1215
Tel.: (712) 843-2291
Year Founded: 1985
Sales Range: $25-49.9 Million
Emp.: 150
Grain Cooperative
N.A.I.C.S.: 424510
Troy Upah (*CEO*)

Subsidiaries:

Ag Partners L.L.C.　　　(1)
30 E Main St, Albert City, IA 50510-1215　　　　　　　(100%)
Tel.: (712) 843-2291
Web Site: http://www.agpartners.com
Sales Range: $25-49.9 Million
Emp.: 50
Products, Services & Market Access to Customers in the Areas of Grain, Feed, Petroleum & Agronomic Inputs
N.A.I.C.S.: 424510
Troy Upah (*CEO*)
Bill Lyster (*Mgr-Special Projects*)
Fran Marron (*VP-Grain*)
Steve Betts (*VP-Agronomy*)
Scott Lovin (*VP-Feed*)
Brent Low (*VP-Agronomy & Corp Mktg*)
Dan De Jong (*VP-Western Ops*)
Jared Bruggman (*VP-Ops-Eastern*)

ALBERT F. AMLING, LLC
331 N York St, Elmhurst, IL 60126
Tel.: (630) 530-5700
Web Site:
https://www.chicagoflowers.com

Flowers, Garden Products & Gifts Retailer, Landscaping Services & Commercial Plant Rentals
N.A.I.C.S.: 459310

ALBERT KAHN ASSOCIATES, INC.
Albert Kahn Bldg 7430 2nd Ave, Detroit, MI 48202-2798
Tel.: (313) 202-7000   MI
Web Site: http://www.albertkahn.com
Year Founded: 1895
Sales Range: $150-199.9 Million
Emp.: 375
Architectural & Engineering Services
N.A.I.C.S.: 541310
W. Clift Montague *(VP)*
Alan H. Cobb *(VP)*
Charles T. Robinson *(Pres)*
Gar Hoplamazian *(VP & Sec)*

Subsidiaries:

Kahn Global Services, Inc.   (1)
7430 2nd Ave, Detroit, MI 48202-2798
Tel.: (313) 202-7824
Sales Range: $10-24.9 Million
Emp.: 25
Facility Management Solutions
N.A.I.C.S.: 531312

Kahn South, Inc.   (1)
2821 2nd Ave S Ste G, Birmingham, AL 35233
Tel.: (205) 328-2827
Web Site: http://www.kahnsouth.com
Project Planning, Design & Management Services for Corporate, Educational, Industrial & Health Care Markets
N.A.I.C.S.: 541310

Kahn do Brasil Ltda.   (1)
Schilling 413 Room 401, Santana de Parnaiba, 06541-038, Sao Paulo, Brazil
Tel.: (55) 1141523500
Web Site: http://www.kahndobrasil.com.br
Sales Range: $10-24.9 Million
Emp.: 13
Architectural Services
N.A.I.C.S.: 541310
Danile Canha *(Exec Dir)*

ALBERT KEMPERLE INC.
176 New Hwy, Amityville, NY 11701-1117
Tel.: (631) 842-5300   NY
Web Site: https://www.kemperle.com
Year Founded: 1940
Sales Range: $10-24.9 Million
Emp.: 130
Motor Vehicle Supplies & New Parts
N.A.I.C.S.: 423120
Audrey Connolly *(Mgr-Sales)*

Subsidiaries:

Albert Kemperle of Florida, LLC   (1)
2698 Dardanelle Dr, Orlando, FL 32808
Tel.: (407) 445-8300
Web Site: http://www.albertkemperle.com
Emp.: 11
Automotive Part Whslr
N.A.I.C.S.: 423120
Brian Bishop *(Mgr)*

ALBERT M. GREENFIELD & CO., INC.
1500 Chestnut St Ste L-M, Philadelphia, PA 19102-2737
Tel.: (215) 569-8200   PA
Web Site:
  http://www.amgreenfield.com
Year Founded: 1905
Sales Range: $75-99.9 Million
Emp.: 4
Real Estate Brokerage & Property Management Investment Banking
N.A.I.C.S.: 531210
Susan Kelly *(Sec & Sr VP)*
Albert M. Greenfield III *(Pres & Mng Dir)*

ALBERT M. HIGLEY COMPANY
2926 Chester Ave, Cleveland, OH 44114
Tel.: (216) 861-2050
Web Site: http://www.amhigley.com
Year Founded: 1927
Sales Range: $25-49.9 Million
Emp.: 150
New Construction for Commercial & Office Buildings
N.A.I.C.S.: 236220
Bruce G. Higley *(Chm)*
Kurt L. Heinicke *(VP)*
Rex E. Lewers *(VP)*
Gareth D. Vaughan *(Pres & CEO)*
Carlo Barone *(CFO)*
Anna C. Dodson *(VP-Bus Dev)*

ALBERT MOTORS INC.
905 Brady Ave, Steubenville, OH 43952
Tel.: (740) 283-4131
Year Founded: 1985
Sales Range: $10-24.9 Million
Emp.: 100
Car Whslr
N.A.I.C.S.: 441110
Geary Teramana *(Pres)*

ALBERT MOVING & STORAGE, INC.
4401 Barnett Rd, Wichita Falls, TX 76310-2306
Tel.: (940) 696-7020   TX
Web Site:
  http://www.albertmoving.com
Year Founded: 1938
Personal & Corporate Moving & Storage Services
N.A.I.C.S.: 484210
Bobby Albert *(Pres)*

ALBERTO HERNANDEZ REAL ESTATE INC.
1603 Calle Loiza, San Juan, PR 00911
Tel.: (787) 728-6124
Web Site: http://ligiahernandez1.com
Sales Range: $10-24.9 Million
Emp.: 22
Real Estate Brokers & Agents
N.A.I.C.S.: 531210
Alberto Hernandez *(Pres)*

ALBEST METAL STAMPING, CORP.
1 Kent Ave, Brooklyn, NY 11249
Tel.: (718) 388-6000   NY
Web Site: https://www.albest.com
Year Founded: 1959
Sales Range: $10-24.9 Million
Emp.: 65
Metal Stamping Services
N.A.I.C.S.: 332119
Joseph Abraham *(VP)*

ALBINA HEAD START, INC.
3417 NE 7th Ave, Portland, OR 97212
Tel.: (503) 282-1975   OR
Web Site: http://www.albinajhs.org
Year Founded: 1993
Sales Range: $10-24.9 Million
Emp.: 286
Child Care & Development Services
N.A.I.C.S.: 624410
Richard Brown *(Pres)*

ALBION INVESTORS, LLC
501 Madison Ave Fl 701, New York, NY 10022
Tel.: (212) 277-7520
Web Site:
  https://www.albioninvestors.com
Year Founded: 1996

Emp.: 15
Investment Advisory Services
N.A.I.C.S.: 523940
Alister Tedford *(Mng Partner)*
Eugene Fouksman *(COO & Controller)*
Mark Arnold *(Mng Partner)*
Charles Gonzalez *(Mng Dir)*
Basil Livanos *(Mng Dir)*
Christine Vogt *(VP)*
Art Meehan *(Sr VP)*
Edina Leiher *(VP-Ops)*

Subsidiaries:

AddisonMckee Inc.   (1)
1637 Kingsview Dr, Lebanon, OH 45036
Tel.: (513) 228-7000
Web Site: http://www.addisonmckee.com
Sales Range: $25-49.9 Million
Emp.: 100
Tube Bending, Tube End Forming & Non-Contact Tube Measuring Machines Mfr & Distr
N.A.I.C.S.: 333517
Jim Sabine *(Pres)*
Doug DeVouge *(VP-Sls & Mktg)*
Brad Zimmerman *(Mgr-Field Svc)*
Scott Rowe *(Dir-Customer Support)*

ALBRIGHT CAPITAL MANAGEMENT LLC
601 13th St NW Ste 1000, Washington, DC 20005
Tel.: (202) 370-3500
Web Site:
  http://www.albrightcapital.com
Emp.: 17
Private Equity & Investment Management Services
N.A.I.C.S.: 523940
John Yonemoto *(Co-Founder & Chief Investment Officer)*
Gregory Bowes *(Co-Founder & Mng Principal)*
Nelson Oliveira *(Gen Counsel & Mng Dir)*
Ahmad Al-Sati *(Mng Dir)*
Lap Wai Chan *(Mng Dir)*
Milgo Galaydh *(Mng Dir)*
Neil Mahapatra *(Mng Dir)*
Peter Wernink *(Mng Dir)*

ALBRITTON FRUIT COMPANY INC.
5430 Proctor Rd, Sarasota, FL 34233
Tel.: (941) 925-7155
Web Site:
  http://www.albrittonfruit.com
Sales Range: $10-24.9 Million
Emp.: 15
Fruit Shippers
N.A.I.C.S.: 445230
John M. Albritton *(Pres)*
Gwen Watts *(Controller)*

ALBU & ASSOCIATES, INC.
2711 Fairbanks Ave, Winter Park, FL 32789
Tel.: (407) 788-1450
Web Site: https://www.albu.biz
Sales Range: $10-24.9 Million
Commercial Construction
N.A.I.C.S.: 236220
Jason D. Albu *(CEO)*
Andrew Albu *(CEO)*
Bob Dzurino *(Mgr-Construction)*
Shawn Epp *(Project Mgr)*

ALCAN ELECTRICAL & ENGINEERING
6670 Arctic Spur Rd, Anchorage, AK 99518
Tel.: (907) 563-3787
Web Site:
  https://www.alcanelectric.com
Sales Range: $300-349.9 Million
Emp.: 150

Electrical Work
N.A.I.C.S.: 238210
Scott Bringmann *(Pres)*

ALCHEMIST MEDIA, INC.
60 29th St, San Francisco, CA 94110
Tel.: (415) 777-2524
Web Site:
  http://www.alchemistmedia.com
Year Founded: 2002
Sales Range: $1-9.9 Million
Search Engine Optimization & Marketing Consulting Services
N.A.I.C.S.: 541890
Jessie Stricchiola *(Founder & Pres)*

ALCO CAD-NICKEL CORP.
1400 Long Beach Ave, Los Angeles, CA 90021
Tel.: (213) 749-7561
Web Site:
  https://www.alconickelchrome.com
Year Founded: 1932
Sales Range: $10-24.9 Million
Emp.: 60
Mfr Plating of Metals or Formed Products
N.A.I.C.S.: 332813
Emil Manzetti *(Pres)*
Dave Manzetti *(VP)*

ALCO CORPORATION
PO Box 1623, Canovanas, PR 00729-1623
Tel.: (787) 886-3551
Web Site: http://www.alcopr.com
Year Founded: 1977
Sales Range: $25-49.9 Million
Emp.: 215
Asphalt Paving Mixtures
N.A.I.C.S.: 324121
Alfonso Rodriguez *(Pres)*

ALCO HIGH-TECH PLASTICS, INC.
PO Box 679, Corozal, PR 00783
Tel.: (787) 859-6590
Web Site:
  http://www.alcohtgroup.com
Year Founded: 1997
Sales Range: $10-24.9 Million
Emp.: 100
Flexible Packaging Products Mfr
N.A.I.C.S.: 561910
Gilberto Nieves *(Pres & CEO)*
Luis Guzman *(Mgr-Ops)*
Ivan Rivera *(Comptroller)*
Gilberto Junior *(Mgr-Ops)*

ALCO INVESTMENT CO., INC.
27402 72nd Ave S, Kent, WA 98032-2105
Tel.: (206) 623-5800   WA
Web Site: http://www.alascop.com
Year Founded: 1913
Sales Range: $50-74.9 Million
Emp.: 450
Fabricated Pipe & Metal Fittings Mfr
N.A.I.C.S.: 332996
Brian Legrelli *(CFO)*

Subsidiaries:

Alaskan Copper & Brass Company   (1)
27402 72nd Ave S, Kent, WA 98032
Tel.: (206) 623-5800
Web Site: http://www.alaskancopper.com
Stainless Steel, Copper Nickel Pipe & Fittings Mfr; Corrosion-Resisting Metals Distr
N.A.I.C.S.: 423510
Douglas C. Rosen *(Pres)*

Alco Investment Co., Inc.—(Continued)

Holding (Non-US):

Alaskan Copper & Brass
Company   (2)
225 North Road, Coquitlam, V3K 3V7, BC,
Canada   **(100%)**
Tel.: (604) 937-6620
Web Site: http://www.alaskancopper.com
Sales Range: $50-74.9 Million
Emp.: 40
Metals Service Center
N.A.I.C.S.: 423510
Gord Hague (Gen Mgr)

Subsidiary (Domestic):

Alaskan Copper & Brass
Company-Portland   (2)
2440 SE Raymond St, Portland, OR 97202-
4638
Tel.: (503) 238-7171
Web Site: http://www.alaskancopper.com
Sales Range: $25-49.9 Million
Emp.: 50
Metals Service Center
N.A.I.C.S.: 423510
Jim Dunlap (Branch Mgr)

Alaskan Copper & Brass
Company-Seattle   (2)
3200 6th Ave S, Seattle, WA 98134-2106
Tel.: (206) 623-5800
Web Site: http://www.alaskancopper.com
Metal Distr
N.A.I.C.S.: 423510
Doug Rosen (Pres)

Alaskan Copper Works   (2)
3203 Sixth Ave S, Seattle, WA
98124   **(100%)**
Tel.: (206) 623-5800
Web Site: http://www.alaskancopper.com
Metals Service Center
N.A.I.C.S.: 331420

Stainless Piping Systems, Inc.   (1)
21 Steinway Blvd Unit 6, Toronto, M9W
6N4, ON, Canada
Tel.: (416) 679-2937
Web Site: http://www.stainlesspiping.com
Steel Pole Mfr
N.A.I.C.S.: 331210
Rut Damen (Pres)

ALCO IRON & METAL CO.
2140 Davis St, San Leandro, CA
94577-1062
Tel.: (510) 562-1107
Web Site: http://www.alcometals.com
Year Founded: 1953
Rev.: $24,500,000
Emp.: 200
Metal Scrap & Waste Materials
N.A.I.C.S.: 423930
Kem Kantor (Pres)
Mario Bantugan (Mgr-Fabrication)
Kari Fletcher (Gen Mgr)

ALCO PARKING CORP.
501 Martindale St DL Clark Bldg,
Pittsburgh, PA 15212-5844
Tel.: (412) 323-4455
Web Site:
     https://www.alcoparking.com
Sales Range: $10-24.9 Million
Emp.: 200
Parking Lots
N.A.I.C.S.: 812930
Michael Webb (VP)
Merrill Stabile (Pres & CEO)
Bruce Miller (Area Mgr)
Helen Vash (Coord-Payroll & Ben-
efits)

ALCO PLASTICS INC.
160 E Pond Dr, Romeo, MI 48065
Tel.: (586) 752-4527
Web Site:
     https://www.alcoplastics.com
Year Founded: 1976
Rev.: $16,500,000
Emp.: 150

Injection Molded Finished Plastics
Products
N.A.I.C.S.: 326199
Derrick Miller (Mgr-Quality)
Vickie Snyder (Mgr-Acctg)
William L. Kozyra (Chm & CEO)

ALCO SALES & SERVICE CO.
6851 High Grove Blvd, Burr Ridge, IL
60527
Tel.: (630) 655-1900
Web Site: https://www.alcosales.com
Sales Range: $10-24.9 Million
Emp.: 45
Medical, Dental & Hospital Equipment
& Supplies Merchant Whslr
N.A.I.C.S.: 423450
Mark Herman (VP)
Michael Kikos (VP-House Acct Sls)
Alvin Herman Jr. (Pres & CEO)

ALCO TRANSPORTATION INC.
36253 Michigan Ave, Wayne, MI
48184
Tel.: (734) 595-9700
Sales Range: $10-24.9 Million
Emp.: 10
Trucking Except Local
N.A.I.C.S.: 484121
Paul Russo (VP)

ALCOHOL & DRUG RECOV-
ERY CENTERS, INC.
500 Blue Hills Ave, Hartford, CT
06112
Tel.: (860) 714-3701   CT
Web Site: http://www.adrc-ct.org
Year Founded: 1972
Sales Range: $10-24.9 Million
Emp.: 239
Drug & Alcohol Addiction Rehabilita-
tion Services
N.A.I.C.S.: 624190
Hebe Kudisch (Dir-Intensive & Inter-
mediate Residential)
John Pierson (Dir-IT)
Cooley M. Buy (Dir-HR)
Natalie Cummings (CFO)
William Young (COO)
Donna Gilbert (Treas)
Ruthie Mathews (Sec)
Danilo Pangilinan (Dir-Medical)
Brian Cutino (Chm)

ALCOM PRINTING GROUP,
INC.
140 Christopher Ln, Harleysville, PA
19438-2034
Tel.: (215) 513-1600   PA
Web Site:
     http://www.alcomprinting.com
Year Founded: 1947
Sales Range: $100-124.9 Million
Emp.: 150
Commercial Lithograph & Web Print-
ing & Computerized Typesetting
N.A.I.C.S.: 323111
Don Eichman (Pres & CEO)
Sharon Tucker (Dir-Mktg)
Judy Baehrle (Dir-HR)
Chris Ambruch (VP-Sls & Mktg)
John Carrelli (Mgr-Facility, EHS &
Finishing)
Doug Yeager (COO)

Subsidiaries:

Christmas City Printing Co., Inc.   (1)
861 14th Ave, Bethlehem, PA 18018
Tel.: (610) 868-5844
Web Site: http://www.xmascity.com
Commercial Lithographic Printing
N.A.I.C.S.: 323111
Barry Paulus (Sec)
James Herr (Controller)
Christopher Sicinski (VP)
Paul Sicinski (Pres)

ALCON INDUSTRIES INC.
7990 Baker Ave, Cleveland, OH
44102-1953
Tel.: (216) 961-1100
Web Site:
     https://www.alconindustries.com
Year Founded: 1977
Sales Range: $10-24.9 Million
Emp.: 150
Steel Foundries
N.A.I.C.S.: 331513
Jim Montemagno (Gen Mgr-
Fabrication)
Kurt Shubert (Mgr-Sls)
Marco Moser (VP-Bus Dev)

Subsidiaries:

Castalloy Inc.   (1)
7990 Baker Ave, Cleveland, OH
44102-1953   **(100%)**
Tel.: (216) 961-7990
Web Site: http://www.castalloy.com
Sales Range: $10-24.9 Million
Emp.: 50
Mfr of Steel Investment Castings
N.A.I.C.S.: 331512
Jeremy Wood (Gen Mgr)

ALCON MECHANICAL, INC.
1932 Warren Ave, Niles, OH 44446
Tel.: (330) 505-1704   OH
Web Site:
     https://www.alconmechanical.com
Year Founded: 2003
Sales Range: $10-24.9 Million
Custom Pipe Fabrication & Installa-
tion Contract Services
N.A.I.C.S.: 238220
George Poschner (Pres)

ALCONEX SPECIALTY PROD-
UCTS, INC.
4204 W Ferguson Rd, Fort Wayne,
IN 46809
Tel.: (260) 744-3446
Web Site: http://www.alconex.com
Year Founded: 1987
Sales Range: $10-24.9 Million
Emp.: 50
Aluminum Rolling & Drawing Services
N.A.I.C.S.: 331318
C. D. McBane (Pres)

ALCONOX, INC.
30 Glenn St Ste 309, White Plains,
NY 10603-3252
Tel.: (914) 948-4040   NY
Web Site: https://www.alconox.com
Year Founded: 1946
Sales Range: $50-74.9 Million
Emp.: 25
Soap & Detergent Mfr
N.A.I.C.S.: 325611
Elliot M. Lebowitz (COO)
Malcolm McLaughlin (VP)
Stewart Katts (Pres)

ALCORN FENCE COMPANY
9901 Glenoaks Blvd, Sun Valley, CA
91352
Tel.: (323) 875-1342
Web Site: https://www.alcorn-
fence.com
Sales Range: $10-24.9 Million
Emp.: 150
Fence Construction
N.A.I.C.S.: 238990

ALCORN MCBRIDE, INC.
3300 S Hiawassee Rd Bldg 105, Or-
lando, FL 32835
Tel.: (407) 296-5800   FL
Web Site: http://www.alcorn.com
Year Founded: 1986
Sales Range: $1-9.9 Million
Emp.: 22

Audio, Video & Lighting Equipment
Mfr
N.A.I.C.S.: 334310
Steve Alcorn (Founder)
Jim Carstensen (Dir-Engrg)
Scott Harkless (Chief Innovation Offi-
cer)
Loren Barrows (COO)

ALCOTRADE INC.
16300 NE 19th Ave, Miami, FL 33162
Tel.: (305) 947-0790
Web Site: http://alcotrade-usa.com
Rev.: $12,500,000
Emp.: 2
Chemical & Allied Products Merchant
Whslr
N.A.I.C.S.: 424690

ALCOTT HR
71 Executive Blvd, Farmingdale, NY
11735
Tel.: (631) 420-0100
Web Site: http://www.alcotthr.com
Year Founded: 1987
Emp.: 1,000
Human Resource Outsourcing Ser-
vices
N.A.I.C.S.: 541612
John Bradley (VP-Western New York)
Barry Shorten (Exec VP)
Steven Politis (CEO)
Peter Rothman (CIO)
Dawn Davidson Drantch (Corp Coun-
sel)
Douglas P. Heuzey (Controller)
Al Anastasi (Dir-Bus Dev)
Robert Brynes (Dir-Risk Mgmt)
Robert Chanin (Dir-HR)
Pat Patane (Dir-Admin Svcs)
Athena Sherron (Dir-Ops)
James Toner (Dir-Sls-Rochester)
Cara Calvin (Mgr-Benefits)
Kimberly Hamm (Mgr-Benefits-
Western New York)
Alanna Popa (Mgr-Retirement Svcs)
David Gaffney (Dir-Sls)
Louis Basso Jr. (Founder)

ALCOVA MORTGAGE
3629 Franklin Road SW Suite 207,
Roanoke, VA 24014
Tel.: (540) 772-3877
Web Site:
     http://www.alcovamortgage.com
Year Founded: 2003
Sales Range: $10-24.9 Million
Emp.: 111
Mortgage & Refinancing Services
N.A.I.C.S.: 522310
Brandon Nicely (Branch Mgr)
Chris Maxwell (Mgr-Secondary Mktg)
Mitch Sellers (Branch Mgr)
Andrew Smith (Dir-Rooftop-India)

ALDA OFFICE PROPERTIES,
INC.
315 S Beverly Dr Ste 211, Los Ange-
les, CA 90212
Tel.: (310) 734-2300   MD
Sales Range: $1-9.9 Million
Real Estate Investment Services
N.A.I.C.S.: 525990
Alan D. Gordon (Chm)
Bennett Kim (Chief Investment Offi-
cer)
Robert Gold (Gen Counsel & Sec)
Richard S. Ackerman (CEO)

ALDAG-HONOLD MECHANI-
CAL, INC.
3509 Business Dr, Sheboygan, WI
53082-1265
Tel.: (920) 458-5558   WI
Web Site:
     https://www.aldaghonold.com

Year Founded: 1901
Sales Range: $10-24.9 Million
Emp.: 110
Complete Design & Build Capabilities for Piping, Heating, Ventilation, Air Conditioning & Metal Fabrication
N.A.I.C.S.: 238220
David J. Aldag (Pres & CEO)

ALDANA & ASSOCIATES PSC LTD.
133 Rawlings Ave Ste 1, Rockville, MD 20852
Tel.: (301) 770-4901
Web Site: https://www.aldanas.com
Sales Range: $50-74.9 Million
Emp.: 9
Accounting, Auditing & Bookkeeping
N.A.I.C.S.: 541219
Henry Aldana (Founder & Pres)

ALDELANO PACKAGING COR-PORATION
1736 Fe Wright Dr, Jackson, TN 38301
Tel.: (731) 935-7211
Web Site: http://www.aldelano.com
Year Founded: 1968
Sales Range: $10-24.9 Million
Emp.: 250
Contract Packaging Services
N.A.I.C.S.: 488991
Alfred Hollingsworth (Pres)
Joe Hollingsworth (Gen Mgr)
Marvin Chatman (Mgr-Production)
Chris Turner (Mgr-Site)

ALDEN ENTERPRISES, INC.
5900 Gulf Blvd, Saint Petersburg, FL 33706
Tel.: (727) 360-7081   FL
Web Site:
    http://www.aldenbeachresort.com
Year Founded: 1969
Sales Range: $1-9.9 Million
Emp.: 55
Hotel & Resort Owner & Operator
N.A.I.C.S.: 721110
Gennifer Renfrow (Chm)
Tony Satterfield (VP-Ops)

ALDEN GLOBAL CAPITAL LLC
885 3rd Ave 34th Fl, New York, NY 10022
Tel.: (212) 418-6865   DE
Web Site:
    http://www.aldenglobal.com
Privater Equity Firm
N.A.I.C.S.: 523999
Marc Cali (Mng Dir)
Jason Pecora (Mng Dir-Ops)

Subsidiaries:

MediaNews Group, Inc.   (1)
101 W Colfax Ave, Denver, CO 80202-5177
Tel.: (303) 954-6360
Web Site: http://www.digitalfirstmedia.com
Newspaper Publisher; Radio & Television Station Operator
N.A.I.C.S.: 513110
Michael J. Koren (CFO)
Steven B. Rossi (Pres & CEO)
Joe Sciacca (Editor-in-Chief-Northeast)

Unit (Domestic):

Advisor-Source Newspapers   (2)
48075 Van Dyke Ave, Utica, MI 48317-3258
Tel.: (586) 731-1000
Web Site:
    http://www.sourcenewspapers.com
Sales Range: $10-24.9 Million
Emp.: 25
Weekly Newspaper Publisher
N.A.I.C.S.: 513110
Jody Mcveigh (Editor)

Subsidiary (Domestic):

Boston Herald Inc.   (2)

70 Fargo St Ste 600, Boston, MA 02210
Tel.: (617) 619-6893
Web Site: http://www.bostonherald.com
Publisher & Printer of Newspapers
N.A.I.C.S.: 516210
Marc D. Grasso (CFO & Controller)

Unit (Domestic):

Brattleboro Reformer   (2)
62 Black Mountain Rd, Brattleboro, VT 05301
Tel.: (802) 254-2311
Web Site: http://www.reformer.com
Sales Range: $10-24.9 Million
Emp.: 20
Newspaper Publishers
N.A.I.C.S.: 513110
Robert Audette (Mng Editor-Day)
Jillisa Solomon (Supvr-Niche)
Melanie Winters (Editor)
Elena Newsmith (Coord-Adv)

Unit (Domestic):

Bellows Falls Town Crier   (3)
62 Black Mountain Rd, Brattleboro, VT 05301
Tel.: (802) 254-2311
Web Site: http://www.reformer.com
Sales Range: $10-24.9 Million
Newspaper Publishers
N.A.I.C.S.: 513110

The Greenfield Town Crier   (3)
393 Main St, Greenfield, MA 01301
Tel.: (413) 774-7226
Web Site: http://www.reformer.com
Sales Range: $10-24.9 Million
Emp.: 3
Newspaper Publishers
N.A.I.C.S.: 513110

Subsidiary (Domestic):

California Newspapers Partnership   (2)
4000 Executive Pkwy, San Ramon, CA 94583   (54.23%)
Tel.: (925) 302-1628
Sales Range: $50-74.9 Million
Emp.: 36
Holding Company; Newspaper Publisher
N.A.I.C.S.: 551112
Steve Rossi (Pres & CEO)
Sharon Ryan (CFO)

Group (Domestic):

Bay Area News Group   (3)
4000 Executive Pkwy Ste 200, San Ramon, CA 94583-4313
Tel.: (925) 945-4786
Web Site:
    http://www.bayareanewsgroup.com
Holding Company; Newspaper Publisher
N.A.I.C.S.: 551112
Sharon Ryan (Pres & Publr)
Neil Chase (Exec Editor)

Subsidiary (Domestic):

Contra Costa Newspapers, Inc.   (4)
2640 Shadelands Dr, Walnut Creek, CA 94598
Tel.: (925) 935-2525
Web Site: http://www.contracostatimes.com
Newspaper Publishers
N.A.I.C.S.: 513110

Unit (Domestic):

Alameda Journal   (5)
1516 Oak St, Alameda, CA 94501
Tel.: (510) 748-1666
Web Site: http://www.contracostatimes.com
Sales Range: $25-49.9 Million
Emp.: 25
Newspaper Publishers
N.A.I.C.S.: 513110
Connie Rux (Editor)

Contra Costa Times   (5)
2640 Shadelands Dr, Walnut Creek, CA 94598
Tel.: (925) 935-2525
Web Site: http://www.contracostatimes.com
Newspaper Publishers
N.A.I.C.S.: 513110

Ledger Dispatch   (5)

1700 Cavallo Rd, Antioch, CA 94509
Tel.: (925) 757-2525
Web Site: http://www.contracostatimes.com
Emp.: 35
Newspaper Publishers
N.A.I.C.S.: 513110

West County Times   (5)
050 Marina Way S, Richmond, CA 94804
Tel.: (510) 758-8400
Web Site: http://www.contracostatimes.com
Newspaper Publishers
N.A.I.C.S.: 513110

Division (Domestic):

East Bay Newspapers   (4)
7677 Oakport St Ste 950, Oakland, CA 94621
Tel.: (510) 208-6300
Web Site: http://www.insidebayarea.com
Holding Company; Newspaper Publisher
N.A.I.C.S.: 551112

Unit (Domestic):

San Mateo County Times   (5)
477 9th Ave Ste 110, San Mateo, CA 94402
Tel.: (650) 348-4321
Web Site: http://www.insidebayarea.com
Newspaper Publishers
N.A.I.C.S.: 513110
Glenn Reeves (Editor-Sports)
Glenn Rapinowitz (Editor-News)

The Argus   (5)
37468 Fremont Bvld, Fremont, CA 94536
Tel.: (510) 353-7027
Web Site: http://www.insidebayarea.com
Sales Range: $25-49.9 Million
Emp.: 8
Newspaper Publishers
N.A.I.C.S.: 513110

The Daily Review   (5)
22533 Foothill Blvd, Hayward, CA 94541
Tel.: (510) 887-7323
Web Site: http://www.insidebayarea.com
Sales Range: $25-49.9 Million
Emp.: 30
Newspaper Publishers
N.A.I.C.S.: 513110
Scott Swyres (Editor-News)
Steve Waterhouse (Editor)
Bill Decker (Mng Editor)
Tiffany Towner (Editor-in-Chief)

The Oakland Tribune   (5)
7677 Oakport St Ste 950, Oakland, CA 94621
Tel.: (510) 208-6300
Web Site: http://www.insidebayarea.com
Newspaper Publishers
N.A.I.C.S.: 513110
Pamela Lewis Turntine (Editor-Night City)

Unit (Domestic):

Alameda Times-Star   (6)
1970 Broadway Ste 100, Oakland, CA 94621
Tel.: (510) 208-6300
Web Site:
    http://www.bayareanewsgroup.com
Newspaper Publishers
N.A.I.C.S.: 513110

Unit (Domestic):

Tri-Valley Herald   (5)
127 Spring St, Pleasanton, CA 94566
Tel.: (925) 935-2525
Web Site: http://www.insidebayarea.com
Newspaper Publishers
N.A.I.C.S.: 513110
Allison Crooks (Head-HR)

Unit (Domestic):

Marin Independent Journal   (4)
150 Alameda Del Prado, Novato, CA 94949   (100%)
Tel.: (415) 883-8600
Web Site: http://www.marinij.com
Newspaper Publishers
N.A.I.C.S.: 513110
Ron Thayer (Dir-Adv)
Susan Harvey (Editor-Copy)
Rob Devincenzi (Pres & Publr)

San Jose Mercury News   (4)

750 Ridder Park Dr, San Jose, CA 95190
Tel.: (408) 920-5000
Web Site: http://www.mercurynews.com
Emp.: 200
Newspaper Publishers
N.A.I.C.S.: 513110
Bert Robinson (Mng Editor)
David J. Butler (VP & Exec Editor)

Unit (Domestic):

Milpitas Post   (5)
59 Marylinn Dr, Milpitas, CA 95035
Tel.: (408) 262-2454
Web Site: http://www.mercurynews.com
Sales Range: $25-49.9 Million
Emp.: 12
Newspaper Publishers
N.A.I.C.S.: 513110
Robert J. Devincenzi (Publr & Editor)
Gloria Guillen (Bus Mgr)

Pacifica Tribune   (5)
59 Bill Drake Way PO Box 1189, Pacifica, CA 94044
Tel.: (650) 359-6666
Web Site: http://www.pacificatribune.com
Sales Range: $25-49.9 Million
Emp.: 12
Newspaper Publishers
N.A.I.C.S.: 513110
Elaine Larsen (Publr & Editor)
Sherman Frederick (Publr)

Silicon Valley Community Newspapers   (5)
1095 The Alameda, San Jose, CA 95126
Tel.: (408) 200-1000
Web Site: http://www.mercurynews.com
Sales Range: $25-49.9 Million
Emp.: 35
Newspaper Publishers
N.A.I.C.S.: 513110
Dick Sparrer (Editor-Sports)

Unit (Domestic):

Santa Cruz Sentinel   (4)
1800 Green Hills Rd Ste 210, Scotts Valley, CA 95066
Tel.: (831) 423-4242
Web Site: http://www.santacruzsentinel.com
Newspaper Publishers
N.A.I.C.S.: 513110
Don Miller (Editor)
Mardi Browning (Mgr-Circulation & Mktg)
Mike Blaesser (Dir-Internet)
Julie Copeland (Editor-City)
Dan Krolczyk (VP-Adv)
Gary Omernick (Publr)
Steve Bennett (Dir-Adv)

The Reporter   (4)
916 Cotting Ln, Vacaville, CA 95688
Tel.: (707) 448-6401
Web Site: http://www.thereporter.com
Newspaper Publishers
N.A.I.C.S.: 513110
Jim Gleim (Publr)
Jerry Schoenberg (Mgr-Circulation)
Mark Hutt (Mgr-Classified)
Janice Alpeche (Dir-Digital)
Mary Enriquez (Mgr-HR)
Kelly Spadorcio (Mgr-Adv Sls)

Times-Herald   (4)
420 Virginia St Ste 2A, Vallejo, CA 94590
Tel.: (707) 644-1141
Web Site: http://www.timesheraldonline.com
Emp.: 21
Newspaper Publishers
N.A.I.C.S.: 513110
Jack F. K. Bungart (Editor)
Richard Freedman (Editor-Community)
Shawna Gilroy (Mgr-Adv Sls)
Lisa Lerseth (Mgr-Pre-Press)

Unit (Domestic):

Enterprise-Record   (3)
400 E Park Ave, Chico, CA 95928
Tel.: (530) 891-1234
Web Site: http://www.chicoer.com
Sales Range: $10-24.9 Million
Newspaper Publishers
N.A.I.C.S.: 513110
Fred Crosthwaite (Dir-Adv)
Dave Berman (Acct Exec)
Darren Holden (Acct Exec)
Mazi Kavoosi (VP-Circulation)
Tamora Memmer (Acct Exec)

Alden Global Capital LLC—(Continued)

LA.com (3)
21860 Burbank Blvd Ste 200, Woodland
Hills, CA 91367
Tel.: (818) 713-3000
Web Site: http://www.dailynews.com
Online City Guide for Los Angeles
N.A.I.C.S.: 519290

Lake County Record-Bee (3)
PO Box 849, Lakeport, CA 95453
Tel.: (707) 263-5636
Web Site: http://www.record-bee.com
Sales Range: $10-24.9 Million
Newspaper Publishers
N.A.I.C.S.: 513110
Carol Wilbur (Dir-Production)
Greg DeBoth (District Mgr)
Kristen Krohn (Coord-Special Sections &
Lifestyle Pages)
Dave Faries (Mng Editor)

Oroville Mercury-Register (3)
400 E Park Ave, Chico, CA 95928
Tel.: (530) 891-1234
Web Site: http://www.orovillemr.com
Sales Range: $10-24.9 Million
Emp.: 5
Newspaper Publishers
N.A.I.C.S.: 513110
Fred Crosthwaite (Dir-Adv)

Paradise Post (3)
5399 Clark Rd, Paradise, CA 95969
Tel.: (530) 877-4413
Web Site: http://www.paradisepost.com
Sales Range: $10-24.9 Million
Emp.: 30
Newspaper Publishers
N.A.I.C.S.: 513110
Jim Gleim (Publr)

Pasadena Star-News (3)
911 E Colorado Blvd, Pasadena, CA 91106
Tel.: (626) 578-6300
Web Site:
    http://www.pasadenastarnews.com
Sales Range: $10-24.9 Million
Emp.: 15
Newspaper Publishers
N.A.I.C.S.: 513110
Gloria Arango (VP-HR)
Tom Kelly (Chief Revenue Officer)
Michelle Vielma (Mgr-Digital Sls)
Mark Welches (VP-Adv)

Red Bluff Daily News (3)
728 Main St, Red Bluff, CA 96080
Tel.: (530) 527-2151
Web Site: http://www.redbluffdailynews.com
Sales Range: $10-24.9 Million
Emp.: 20
Newspaper Publishers
N.A.I.C.S.: 513110
Kathy Hogan (Mgr-Circulation)

The Daily Democrat (3)
711 Main St, Woodland, CA 95695
Tel.: (530) 662-5421
Web Site: http://www.dailydemocrat.com
Emp.: 17
Newspaper Publishers
N.A.I.C.S.: 513110
Jim Gleim (Publr)
Marc Hutt (Dir-Adv)

The Sun (3)
4030 N Georgia Blvd, San Bernardino, CA
92407
Tel.: (909) 889-9666
Web Site: http://www.sbsun.com
Sales Range: $50-74.9 Million
Newspaper Publishing
N.A.I.C.S.: 513110
Sandra Gray (Mgr-Retail Sls)
John Weeks (Editor-Features)
Daniel Tedford (Dir-Digital News)
Gloria Arango (VP-HR)
Tom Kelly (Chief Revenue Officer)
Jim Maurer (VP-Adv)

The Ukiah Daily Journal (3)
590 S School St PO Box 749, Ukiah, CA
95482
Tel.: (707) 468-3500
Web Site: http://www.ukiahdailyjournal.com
Newspaper Publishers
N.A.I.C.S.: 513110
Yvonne Bell (Mgr-Bus)
Kevin McConnell (Publr)

Gail McAlister (Dir-Digital)
Thomas Strother (Acct Exec)

Times-Standard (3)
PO Box 3580, Eureka, CA 95502
Tel.: (707) 441-0500
Web Site: http://www.times-standard.com
Newspaper Publishers
N.A.I.C.S.: 513110
Jason Kennedy (Dir-Production)
Kenny Priest (Dir-Creative Svcs)
Claudette Lemon (Controller)
Rich Somerville (Mng Editor)
Frank Callaway (Mgr-Production)
Caitlin Fowler (Designer-Graphic)
Rory Hubbard (Supvr-Creative Dept)
Michelle Kagan (Mgr-HR & Office)
Christina Nevarez (Coord-Adv)
Candace Schneider (Coord-Digital Fulfill-
ment)

Unit (Domestic):

Tri-City Weekly (4)
930 6th St, Eureka, CA 95501
Tel.: (707) 441-0500
Web Site: http://www.times-standard.com
Emp.: 65
Newspaper Publishers
N.A.I.C.S.: 513110
Michelle Kagan (Office Mgr)

Unit (Domestic):

**Capitol City Publishing Company,
Inc.** (2)
600 Perry St, Trenton, NJ 08602 (100%)
Tel.: (609) 989-7800
Web Site: http://www.trentonian.com
Sales Range: $10-24.9 Million
Emp.: 90
Newspaper Publishers
N.A.I.C.S.: 513110
Bill Murray (Publr)

Charleston Daily Mail (2)
1001 Virginia St E, Charleston, WV 25301
Tel.: (304) 348-5124
Web Site: http://www.dailymailwv.com
Newspaper Publishers
N.A.I.C.S.: 513110
Brad McElhinny (Publr & Editor)

Clear Lake Observer American (2)
PO Box 849, Lakeport, CA 95453
Tel.: (707) 263-5636
Web Site: http://www.record-bee.com
Sales Range: $10-24.9 Million
Emp.: 50
Newspaper Publishers
N.A.I.C.S.: 513110
Cynthia Parkhill (Editor)

Foothills Trader Inc. (2)
59 Field St, Torrington, CT 06790-5224
Tel.: (860) 489-3121
Web Site: http://www.foothillstrader.com
Sales Range: $10-24.9 Million
Emp.: 20
Newspaper Publishers
N.A.I.C.S.: 513110

Fort Bragg Advocate-News (2)
450 N Franklin St, Fort Bragg, CA 95437
Tel.: (707) 964-5642
Web Site: http://www.advocate-news.com
Sales Range: $10-24.9 Million
Emp.: 20
Newspaper Publishers
N.A.I.C.S.: 513110
Sharon DiMauro (Publr)
Chris Calger (Editor)

Gazette Newspapers (2)
5225 E 2nd St, Long Beach, CA 90803
Tel.: (562) 433-2000
Web Site: http://www.gazettes.com
Sales Range: $10-24.9 Million
Emp.: 20
Newspaper Publishers
N.A.I.C.S.: 513110

Subsidiary (Domestic):

Graham Newspapers, Inc. (2)
620 Oak St, Graham, TX 76450
Tel.: (940) 549-7800
Web Site: http://www.grahamleader.com
Sales Range: $50-74.9 Million
Emp.: 30

Holding Company; Newspaper Publisher &
Radio Broadcasting Stations
N.A.I.C.S.: 551112
Robert Krecklow (Publr)

Unit (Domestic):

Lake Country Radio (3)
620 Oak St, Graham, TX 76450
Tel.: (940) 549-1330
Web Site: http://www.grahamleader.com
Emp.: 25
Radio Broadcasting Stations
N.A.I.C.S.: 516110
Joe Graham (Gen Mgr-Radio Station)

Group (Domestic):

Star Group Newspapers (3)
319 N Burleson Blvd, Burleson, TX 76097-
0909
Tel.: (817) 295-0486
Web Site: http://www.thestargroup.com
Holding Company; Newspaper Publisher
N.A.I.C.S.: 551112

Unit (Domestic):

Alvarado Star (4)
319 N Burleson Blvd, Burleson, TX 76097
Tel.: (817) 295-0486
Web Site: http://www.alvaradostar.net
Sales Range: $10-24.9 Million
Emp.: 4
Newspaper Publishers
N.A.I.C.S.: 513110
Candy McMichen (Editor)

Burleson Star (4)
327 NW Renfro, Burleson, TX 76028-0909
Tel.: (817) 295-0486
Web Site: http://www.burlesonstar.net
Sales Range: $10-24.9 Million
Emp.: 22
Newspaper Publishers
N.A.I.C.S.: 513110

Crowley Star (4)
237 Nw Renfro St, Burleson, TX 76028
Tel.: (817) 295-0486
Web Site: http://www.thestargroup.com
Emp.: 10
Newspaper Publishing Services
N.A.I.C.S.: 513110
Ben Tinsley (Editor)

Joshua Star (4)
319 N Burleson Blvd, Burleson, TX 76028
Tel.: (817) 295-0486
Web Site: http://www.joshuastar.net
Sales Range: $10-24.9 Million
Emp.: 12
Newspaper Publishers
N.A.I.C.S.: 513110
Ben Tinsley (Editor)

Keene Star (4)
327 NW Renfro St, Burleson, TX 76028
Tel.: (817) 295-0486
Web Site: http://www.burlesonstar.net
Sales Range: $10-24.9 Million
Emp.: 15
Newspaper Publishers
N.A.I.C.S.: 513110
Ben Tinsley (Editor)

Unit (Domestic):

The Graham Leader (3)
620 Oak St, Graham, TX 76450
Tel.: (940) 549-7800
Web Site: http://www.grahamleader.com
Sales Range: $10-24.9 Million
Emp.: 22
Newspaper Publishers
N.A.I.C.S.: 513110
Linda McDougal (Controller)
Robb Krecklow (Publr)
Cesir Ramos (Dir-Adv)

Unit (Domestic):

Jacksboro Gazette-News (4)
212 N Church, Jacksboro, TX 76458
Tel.: (940) 567-2616
Web Site:
    http://www.jacksboronewspapers.com
Emp.: 4
Newspaper Publishers
N.A.I.C.S.: 513110
Robb Krecklow (Publr)

The Breckenridge American (4)
114 E Elm St, Breckenridge, TX 76424
Tel.: (254) 559-5412
Web Site:
    http://www.breckenridgeamerican.com
Emp.: 5
Newspaper Publishers
N.A.I.C.S.: 513110
Ashley Creager (Mgr-Adv)

The Jack County Herald (4)
212 N Church, Jacksboro, TX 76458
Tel.: (940) 567-2616
Web Site:
    http://www.jacksboronewspapers.com
Sales Range: $10-24.9 Million
Emp.: 4
Newspaper Publishers
N.A.I.C.S.: 513110
Cherry Rushin (Editor)
Sandy Argo (Mgr-Adv)

The Lake Country Sun (4)
617 N FM 2353 Ste 4, Graford, TX 76449
Tel.: (940) 779-3040
Web Site: http://www.lakecountrysun.com
Sales Range: $10-24.9 Million
Emp.: 1
Newspaper Publishers
N.A.I.C.S.: 513110
Tyler Patton (Publr)

The Olney Enterprise (4)
213 E Main St, Olney, TX 76374
Tel.: (940) 564-5558
Web Site: http://www.olneyenterprise.com
Sales Range: $10-24.9 Million
Emp.: 3
Newspaper Publishers
N.A.I.C.S.: 513110
David Miller (Editor)

Unit (Domestic):

Heritage Newspapers, Inc. (2)
1 Heritage Pl Ste 100, Southgate, MI 48195
Tel.: (734) 246-0800
Rev.: $11,700,000
Emp.: 70
Publisher of Newspapers
N.A.I.C.S.: 513110
Annette Cortiana Clark (Dir-New Media)
Jim Williams (Pres-Publr-Press)
Carol Krummer (Mgr-Adv)

Humboldt Beacon (2)
930 6th St, Eureka, CA 95501
Tel.: (707) 441-0563
Web Site: http://www.humboldtbeacon.com
Newspaper Publishers
N.A.I.C.S.: 513110

Leader & Kalkaskian (2)
318 N Cedar St, Kalkaska, MI 49646-8424
Tel.: (231) 258-4600
Web Site:
    http://www.leaderandkalkaskian.com
Sales Range: $10-24.9 Million
Emp.: 7
Weekly Newspaper Publishing
N.A.I.C.S.: 513110

Main Line Media News (2)
311 E Lancaster Ave, Ardmore, PA 19003
Tel.: (610) 642-4300
Web Site: http://www.mainlinenews.com
Sales Range: $10-24.9 Million
Emp.: 40
Newspaper Publishers
N.A.I.C.S.: 621610

Subsidiary (Domestic):

**MediaNews Group Interactive,
Inc.** (2)
101 W Colfax Ave Ste 950, Denver, CO
80202 (100%)
Tel.: (303) 954-6360
Newspaper Website Publishing, Hosting,
Advertising & Content Management Ser-
vices
N.A.I.C.S.: 518210

Monterey Newspapers, LLC (2)
8 Upper Ragsdale, Monterey, CA 93940
Tel.: (831) 372-3311
Web Site: http://www.montereyherald.com
Sales Range: $25-49.9 Million
Emp.: 185
Newspaper Publishers

N.A.I.C.S.: 513110
Mazi Kavoosi (Dir-Circulation)
Vern Fisher (Dir-Photography)
Lorraine Roque (Mgr-Adv Support)

Unit (Domestic):

Daily Camera (3)
2500 55th St Ste 210, Boulder, CO
80301 (100%)
Tel.: (303) 466-1202
Web Site: http://www.dailycamera.com
Sales Range: $75-99.9 Million
Emp.: 275
Newspaper Publishing
N.A.I.C.S.: 513110
Jill Stravolemos (VP-Mktg & Adv)
Albert J. Manzi (Publr)
Matt Flood (Dir-Digital Solutions)
Kevin Kaufman (Exec Editor)
Justin Mock (CFO)
Kathy Johnson (Mgr-Sls-Adv)

Unit (Domestic):

Nashoba Publishing (2)
78 Barnum Rd, Devens, MA 01434-3508
Tel.: (978) 772-0777
Web Site:
   http://www.nashobapublishing.com
Sales Range: $25-49.9 Million
Emp.: 6
Newspaper Publisher & Commercial Print-
ing Services
N.A.I.C.S.: 513110
King Walsh (Mng Editor)
Bill Tyers (Dir-Ops)

Unit (Domestic):

Groton Landmark (3)
78 Barnum Rd, Devens, MA 01434-3508
Tel.: (978) 772-0777
Web Site:
   http://www.nashobapublishing.com
Sales Range: $10-24.9 Million
Emp.: 5
Newspaper Publishers
N.A.I.C.S.: 513110

Harvard Hillside (3)
78 Barnum Rd, Devens, MA 01434-3508
Tel.: (978) 772-0777
Web Site:
   http://www.nashobapublishing.com
Sales Range: $10-24.9 Million
Newspaper Publishers
N.A.I.C.S.: 513110
Kate Walsh (Mng Editor)

Pepperell News (3)
78 Barnum Rd, Devens, MA 01434-3508
Tel.: (978) 772-0777
Web Site:
   http://www.nashobapublishing.com
Sales Range: $10-24.9 Million
Emp.: 40
Newspaper Publishers
N.A.I.C.S.: 513110
Kate Walsh (Mng Editor)

Public Spirit-Ayer (3)
78 Barnum Rd, Devens, MA 01434-3508
Tel.: (978) 772-0777
Web Site:
   http://www.nashobapublishing.com
Sales Range: $10-24.9 Million
Newspaper Publishers
N.A.I.C.S.: 513110

Townsend Times (3)
78 Barnum Rd, Devens, MA 01434-3508
Tel.: (978) 772-0777
Web Site:
   http://www.nashobapublishing.com
Newspaper Publishers
N.A.I.C.S.: 513110

Unit (Domestic):

New Haven Register, Inc. (2)
40 Sargent Dr, New Haven, CT 06511
Tel.: (203) 789-5200
Web Site: http://www.nhregister.com
Sales Range: $25-49.9 Million
Emp.: 400
Newspaper Publishers
N.A.I.C.S.: 513110
Helen Bennett Harvey (Exec Editor)
George Velezis (Controller)

North Adams Transcript (2)
124 American Legion Dr, North Adams, MA
01247
Tel.: (413) 663-7942
Web Site: http://www.thetranscript.com
Sales Range: $10-24.9 Million
Emp.: 20
Newspaper Publishers
N.A.I.C.S.: 513110

Unit (Domestic):

The Advocate (3)
124 American Legion Dr, North Adams, MA
01247
Tel.: (413) 664-6900
Web Site: http://www.advocateweekly.com
Sales Range: $10-24.9 Million
Emp.: 20
Newspaper Publishers
N.A.I.C.S.: 513110

Unit (Domestic):

Phoenixville Newspapers, Inc. (2)
24 N Hanover St, Pottstown, PA
19464-5410 (100%)
Tel.: (610) 933-8926
Web Site: http://www.phoenixvillenews.com
Sales Range: $10-24.9 Million
Emp.: 23
Newspaper Publishers
N.A.I.C.S.: 513110
Patricia Paul (Controller)
Tim Dietterick (Mgr-Circulation)

Subsidiary (Domestic):

Prairie Mountain Publishing Company
LLP (2)
5450 Western Ave, Boulder, CO 80301-
2709
Tel.: (303) 442-1202
Web Site:
   http://www.prairiemountainmedia.com
Newspaper Publishers
N.A.I.C.S.: 513110

Unit (Domestic):

Akron News-Reporter (3)
69 Main Ave, Akron, CO 80720
Tel.: (970) 345-2296
Web Site:
   http://www.akronnewsreporter.com
Newspaper Publishers
N.A.I.C.S.: 513110

Broomfield Enterprise (3)
3400 Industrial Ln Ste 2, Broomfield, CO
80020
Tel.: (303) 448-9898
Web Site:
   http://www.broomfieldenterprise.com
Newspaper Publishers
N.A.I.C.S.: 513110
Albert J. Manzi (Publr)
Julie Baxter (Editor)
Christine Labozan (Mgr-Adv)

Brush News Tribune (3)
216 1/2 Clayton St, Brush, CO 80723
Tel.: (970) 842-5516
Web Site: http://www.brushnewstribune.com
Emp.: 2
Newspaper Publishers
N.A.I.C.S.: 513110
Brian Porter (Publr & Editor)

Canon City Daily Record (3)
701 S Ninth St, Canon City, CO 81212
Tel.: (719) 275-7565
Web Site:
   http://www.canoncitydailyrecord.com
Newspapers
N.A.I.C.S.: 513110
Karl Wurzbach (Publr)

Colorado Daily (3)
5450 Western Ave, Boulder, CO 80301-
2709
Tel.: (303) 473-1111
Web Site: http://www.coloradodaily.com
Newspaper Publishers
N.A.I.C.S.: 513110

Colorado Hometown Weekly (3)
350 Terry St, Longmont, CO 80501
Tel.: (303) 666-6576
Web Site:
   http://www.coloradohometownweekly.com

Newspaper Publishers
N.A.I.C.S.: 513110
Dean Lehman (Publr)
Maurice Elhart (Dir-Circulation)

Daily Camera (3)
5450 Western Ave, Boulder, CO 80301-
2709
Tel.: (303) 442-1202
Web Site: http://www.dailycamera.com
Newspaper Publishers
N.A.I.C.S.: 513110
Albert J. Manzi (Publr)
Kevin Kaufman (Editor)
Jill Stravolemos (VP-Mktg & Adv)
Dave Krieger (Editor-Editorial Page)
Matt Flood (Dir-Digital Solutions)
Shellie Hoff (Co-CFO)
Kathy Johnson (Mgr-Majors-Natl)
Donna Jones (Mgr-Accts Receivable)
Nick Middlebrooks (Mgr-Accts Receivable)
Justin Mock (Co-CFO)
Melissa Najera (Mgr-Classified)
Mary Romano (Mgr-Majors-Natl)

Estes Park Trail-Gazette (3)
251 Moraine Ave, Estes Park, CO 80517
Tel.: (970) 586-3356
Web Site: http://www.eptrail.com
Newspaper Publishers
N.A.I.C.S.: 513110
Mike Romero (Publr)

Journal Advocate (3)
504 N 3rd St, Sterling, CO 80751
Tel.: (970) 522-1990
Web Site: http://www.journal-advocate.com
Emp.: 10
Newspaper Publishers
N.A.I.C.S.: 513110
Julie Tonsing (Gen Mgr)

Julesburg Advocate (3)
108 Cedar St, Julesburg, CO 80737
Tel.: (970) 474-3388
Web Site:
   http://www.julesburgadvocate.com
Newspaper Publishers
N.A.I.C.S.: 513110
Vickie Sandlin (Publr & Editor)

Lamar Ledger (3)
222 S Main St, Lamar, CO 81052
Tel.: (719) 336-2266
Web Site: http://www.lamarledger.com
Emp.: 5
Newspaper Publishers
N.A.I.C.S.: 513110
Chris Frost (Gen Mgr-Paper)

Plant (Domestic):

Lehman Printing Center (3)
801 N 2nd St, Berthoud, CO 80513
Tel.: (970) 532-3509
Web Site:
   http://www.lehmanprintingcenter.com
Commercial Printing Services
N.A.I.C.S.: 323111
Chris Klein (Head-Comml Print Sls)

Unit (Domestic):

Longmont Times-Call (3)
1860 Industrial Cir Ste E, Longmont, CO
80501
Tel.: (303) 776-2244
Web Site: http://www.timescall.com
Newspapers
N.A.I.C.S.: 513110
John Vahlenkamp (Mng Editor)

Loveland Reporter-Herald (3)
201 E 5th St, Loveland, CO 80537
Tel.: (970) 669-5050
Web Site: http://www.reporterherald.com
Emp.: 30
Newspapers
N.A.I.C.S.: 513110
Jeff Stahla (Mng Editor)

The Burlington Record (3)
202 S 14th St, Burlington, CO 80807
Tel.: (719) 346-5381
Web Site: http://www.burlington-record.com
Emp.: 14
Newspaper Publishers
N.A.I.C.S.: 513110
Rol Hudler (Gen Mgr)
Shannon Floyd (Dir-Adv)

The Fort Morgan Times (3)
230a Main St, Fort Morgan, CO 80701-
2108
Tel.: (970) 867-5651
Web Site: http://www.fortmorgantimes.com
Emp.: 8
Newspaper Publishers
N.A.I.C.S.: 513110
Josephina Monsivias (Mgr-Circulation)

Unit (Domestic):

Press & Guide (2)
1 Heritage Dr, Southgate, MI 48195
Tel.: (734) 243-2100
Web Site: http://www.pressandguide.com
Emp.: 30
Newspaper Publishers
N.A.I.C.S.: 513110
Jeanne Parent (Pres)

Redwood Times (2)
433 Melville Rd, Garberville, CA 95542
Tel.: (707) 923-1396
Web Site: http://www.redwoodtimes.com
Sales Range: $10-24.9 Million
Emp.: 3
Newspaper Publishers
N.A.I.C.S.: 513110
Susan Gardner (Editor)

Subsidiary (Domestic):

Republican & Herald (2)
111 Mahantongo St, Pottsville, PA 17901
Tel.: (570) 622-3456
Web Site: http://www.republicanherald.com
Rev.: $12,200,000
Emp.: 80
Newspaper Publishers
N.A.I.C.S.: 459420
David Sickle (Dir-Circulation)
Leslie Wagner (Mgr-Adv Sls)
Mike Joyce (Publr)

Scranton Times Tribune (2)
149 Penn Ave, Scranton, PA 18503
Tel.: (570) 348-9100
Web Site: http://www.thetimes-tribune.com
Rev.: $30,000,000
Emp.: 250
Newspapers, Publishing & Printing
N.A.I.C.S.: 513110
Edward Pikulski (Dir-Digital Audience)

Unit (Domestic):

Sentinel & Enterprise (2)
808 Main St, Fitchburg, MA 01420
Tel.: (978) 343-6911
Web Site:
   http://www.sentinelandenterprise.com
Sales Range: $10-24.9 Million
Emp.: 60
Newspaper Publishers
N.A.I.C.S.: 513110
Dennis West (Mgr-Circulation)
Tom Zuppa (Sr Editor)
Kevin Corrado (Publr)

Shore Line Newspaper (2)
40 Sargent Dr, New Haven, CT 06511
Tel.: (203) 789-5200
Web Site: http://www.shorelinetimes.com
Newspapers
N.A.I.C.S.: 513110
John Slater (Gen Mgr)

Group (Domestic):

Southern California News Group (2)
21860 Burbank Blvd Ste 200, Woodland
Hills, CA 91367
Tel.: (818) 713-3000
Web Site: http://www.socalnewsgroup.com
Emp.: 100
Newspaper Publishers
N.A.I.C.S.: 513110
Liz Hamm (Dir-Market Res & Adv Ops)
Bill Van Laningham (VP-Mktg)
Ronald C. Hasse (Publr)
Frank Pine (Exec Editor)
Scott Kaufman (Editor-Opinion)
Kyla Rodriguez (Sr VP-Adv)
Dan Scofield (CFO)

Unit (Domestic):

Inland Valley Daily Bulletin (3)
2041 E Fourth St, Ontario, CA 91764
Tel.: (909) 987-6397

Alden Global Capital LLC—(Continued)

Web Site: http://www.dailybulletin.com
Newspaper Publishers
N.A.I.C.S.: 513110
Jim Maurer *(Gen Mgr)*

Subsidiary (Domestic):

Long Beach Publishing Company   **(3)**
300 Oceangate, Long Beach, CA 90844
Tel.: (562) 435-1161
Web Site: http://www.presstelegram.com
Newspaper Publishers
N.A.I.C.S.: 513110
Daniel Tedford *(Dir-Digital News)*
Gloria Arango *(VP-HR)*
Craig Hymovitz *(Mgr-Retail Adv)*
Marilyn James *(Mgr-Classified & Real Estate)*
Tom Kelly *(Chief Revenue Officer)*
Leslie Lindemann *(VP-Adv)*
Yasmine Vatere *(Mgr-Digital Sls)*

Unit (Domestic):

Impacto USA   **(4)**
300 Oceangate 14th Fl, Long Beach, CA 90844
Tel.: (562) 499-1415
Web Site: http://www.impactousa.com
Spanish-language Newspaper Publisher
N.A.I.C.S.: 513110

Subsidiary (Domestic):

Los Angeles Daily News Publishing Company   **(3)**
PO Box 4200, Woodland Hills, CA 91365
Tel.: (818) 713-3000
Web Site: http://www.dailynews.com
Sales Range: $125-149.9 Million
Newspaper Publishing
N.A.I.C.S.: 513110
Bill Van Laningham *(Dir-Mktg)*

Unit (Domestic):

Peninsula News   **(3)**
609 Deep Valley Dr Ste 200, Rolling Hills Estates, CA 90274
Tel.: (310) 377-6877
Web Site: http://www.pvnews.com
Sales Range: $10-24.9 Million
Emp.: 10
Weekly Newspaper Publisher
N.A.I.C.S.: 513110
Ed Pilolla *(Editor-in-Chief)*

Redlands Daily Facts   **(3)**
700 Brookside Ave, Redlands, CA 92373
Tel.: (909) 793-3221
Web Site: http://www.redlandsdailyfacts.com
Sales Range: $10-24.9 Million
Emp.: 16
Newspaper Publishers
N.A.I.C.S.: 513110
Ron Hasse *(CEO)*

San Gabriel Valley Tribune   **(3)**
605 E Huntington Dr Ste 100, Monrovia, CA 91016
Tel.: (626) 962-8811
Web Site: http://www.sgvtribune.com
Emp.: 200
Newspaper Publishers
N.A.I.C.S.: 513110
Dave Williams *(VP-Circulation)*
Rose Maria Alteria *(Mgr-HR)*

Unit (Domestic):

Azusa Highlander   **(4)**
605 E Huntington Ave, Monrovia, CA 91016
Tel.: (626) 962-8811
Web Site: http://www.sgvtribune.com
Emp.: 250
Newspaper Publishers
N.A.I.C.S.: 513110
Frank Girardot *(Exec Editor)*
Frank Pine *(Exec Editor)*

Covina Press-Courier Highlander **(4)**
605 E Huntington Dr Ste 100, Monrovia, CA 91016
Tel.: (626) 962-8811
Web Site: http://www.sgvtribune.com
Emp.: 180
Weekly Newspaper
N.A.I.C.S.: 513110

Michael Anastasi *(CEO)*

Diamond Bar Highlander   **(4)**
605 E Huntington Dr Ste 209, Monrovia, CA 91016
Tel.: (626) 962-8811
Web Site: http://www.sgvtribune.com
Newspaper Publishers
N.A.I.C.S.: 513110
Randy Sieger *(CEO)*

Glendora Highlander   **(4)**
605 E Huntington Dr, Monrovia, CA 91016
Tel.: (626) 962-8811
Web Site: http://www.sgvtribune.com
Newspaper Publishers
N.A.I.C.S.: 513110
Gloria Arango *(VP-HR)*
Tom Kelly *(Chief Revenue Officer)*
Michelle Vielma *(Mgr-Digital Sls)*
Mark Welches *(VP-Adv)*

Hacienda Heights Highlander **(4)**
605 E Huntington Dr Ste 100, Monrovia, CA 91016
Tel.: (626) 962-8811
Web Site: http://www.sgvtribune.com
Sales Range: $25-49.9 Million
Newspaper Publishers
N.A.I.C.S.: 513110
Ron Hasse *(Pres)*

La Puente Highlander   **(4)**
1210 N Azusa Canyon Rd, West Covina, CA 91790
Tel.: (626) 962-8811
Web Site: http://www.sgvtribune.com
Newspaper Publishers
N.A.I.C.S.: 513110

LaVerne Highlander   **(4)**
1210 N Azusa Canyon Rd, West Covina, CA 91790
Tel.: (626) 962-8811
Web Site: http://www.sgvtribune.com
Newspaper Publishers
N.A.I.C.S.: 513110
Fredric D. Rutberg *(Pres & Publr)*
Kathy Worth *(CFO)*

Rowland Heights Highlander **(4)**
1210 N Azusa Canyon Rd, West Covina, CA 91790
Tel.: (626) 962-8811
Web Site: http://www.sgvtribune.com
Newspaper Publishers
N.A.I.C.S.: 513110

San Dimas Highlander   **(4)**
1210 N Azusa Canyon Rd, West Covina, CA 91790
Tel.: (626) 962-8811
Web Site: http://www.sgvtribune.com
Newspaper Publishers
N.A.I.C.S.: 513110

Walnut Highlander   **(4)**
605 E Huntington Dr Ste 100, Monrovia, CA 91016
Tel.: (626) 962-8811
Web Site: http://www.sgvtribune.com
Newspaper Publishers
N.A.I.C.S.: 513110
Daniel Tedford *(Editor)*

West Covina Highlander   **(4)**
1210 N Azusa Canyon Rd, West Covina, CA 91790
Tel.: (626) 962-8811
Web Site: http://www.sgvtribune.com
Emp.: 200
Newspaper Publishers
N.A.I.C.S.: 513110
Karen Haase *(Publr)*

Unit (Domestic):

The Daily Breeze   **(3)**
21250 Hawthorne Blvd Ste 170, Torrance, CA 90503
Tel.: (310) 540-5511
Web Site: http://www.dailybreeze.com
Sales Range: $25-49.9 Million
Newspaper Publishers
N.A.I.C.S.: 513110

The Press-Enterprise   **(3)**
1825 Chicago Ave Ste 100, Riverside, CA 92507
Tel.: (951) 684-1200
Web Site: http://www.pe.com
Newspaper Publishers

The San Bernardino County Sun **(3)**
290 N D St Ste 102, San Bernardino, CA 92401
Tel.: (909) 889-9666
Web Site: http://www.sbsun.com
Newspaper Publishers
N.A.I.C.S.: 513110
Ronald Hasse *(Pres & Publr)*

Whittier Daily News   **(3)**
7612 Greenleaf Ave, Whittier, CA 90602
Tel.: (562) 698-0955
Web Site: http://www.whittierdailynews.com
Newspaper Publishers
N.A.I.C.S.: 513110
Gloria Arango *(VP-HR)*
Tom Kelly *(Chief Revenue Officer)*
Michelle Vielma *(Mgr-Digital Sls)*
Mark Welches *(VP-Adv)*

Unit (Domestic):

The Beach Reporter   **(2)**
2615 Pacific Coast Hwy Ste 329, Hermosa Beach, CA 90254
Tel.: (310) 372-0388
Web Site: http://www.tbrnews.com
Sales Range: $10-24.9 Million
Emp.: 25
Newspaper Publishers
N.A.I.C.S.: 513110
Lisa Jacobs *(Gen Mgr)*

The Bennington Banner   **(2)**
425 Main St, Bennington, VT 05201
Tel.: (802) 447-7567
Web Site: http://www.benningtonbanner.com
Sales Range: $10-24.9 Million
Emp.: 60
Newspaper Publishers
N.A.I.C.S.: 513110
Fredric D. Rutberg *(Pres & Publr)*
Kathy Worth *(CFO)*

The Berkshire Eagle   **(2)**
75 S Church St, Pittsfield, MA 01201   **(100%)**
Tel.: (413) 447-7311
Web Site: http://www.berkshireeagle.com
Sales Range: $10-24.9 Million
Emp.: 200
Newspaper Publishers
N.A.I.C.S.: 513110
William MacFarlane *(Dir-Sys)*
Tony Dobrowolski *(Editor-Bus)*
Catherine Wandrei *(Mgr-HR)*
Andy Swanton *(VP-Ops & Distr)*
Eric Kern *(Mgr-Facilities)*
Frank McKenna *(CFO)*
Kevin Moran *(VP-News-New England)*
Tom Tripicco *(Mng Editor)*
Tara Whitney *(Dir-Circulation)*
Becky Grande *(Mgr-Call Center)*
Jordan Brechenser *(VP-Adv)*
Kate Teutsch *(Mgr-Adv Sls)*
Alan English *(Publr)*
Warren C. Dews Jr. *(VP-Audience Dev, Sls & Mktg)*

The Daily Local News   **(2)**
250 N Bradford Ave, West Chester, PA 19382-2800
Tel.: (610) 696-1775
Web Site: http://www.dailylocal.com
Sales Range: $10-24.9 Million
Emp.: 100
N.A.I.C.S.: 513110
E. William March *(Mng Editor)*

The Daily News   **(2)**
255 Constitution Dr, Menlo Park, CA 94025
Tel.: (650) 391-1000
Web Site: http://www.thedailynews.com
Sales Range: $10-24.9 Million
Emp.: 100
Newspaper Publishers
N.A.I.C.S.: 513110
Joe Lauletta *(Mgr-Circulation)*
Jamie Casini *(Mng Editor)*
Jason Green *(Editor-City)*
Greg Frazier *(Editor-Sports)*
Christine Eng *(Mgr-Production & Creative Svcs)*

The Daily Oakland Press   **(2)**
48 W Huron St, Pontiac, MI 48342
Tel.: (248) 332-8181
Web Site: http://www.theoaklandpress.com

Sales Range: $10-24.9 Million
Emp.: 100
Daily Newspaper
N.A.I.C.S.: 513110
Joann Powell *(Mgr-Customer Satisfaction)*
Noelle Klomp *(Dir-Classified Ad)*
Nicole Robertson *(Editor-Arts & Entertainment)*
Steve Frye *(Editor-Online)*
Jeff Kuehn *(Editor-Sports)*
Jeff Hoard *(Editor-News)*

The Daily Tribune   **(2)**
19176 Hall Rd Ste 200, Clinton Township, MI 48038
Tel.: (586) 469-4510
Web Site: http://www.dailytribune.com
Sales Range: $10-24.9 Million
Emp.: 40
Daily Newspaper Publishing
N.A.I.C.S.: 513110

Subsidiary (Domestic):

The Denver Post Corporation **(2)**
101 W Colfax Ave, Denver, CO 80202-5177
Tel.: (303) 954-1010
Web Site: http://www.denverpost.com
Sales Range: $25-49.9 Million
Emp.: 800
Newspaper Publishers
N.A.I.C.S.: 513110
Bill Reynolds *(Sr VP-Circulation)*
Missy Miller *(Sr VP-HR & Labor Rels)*
Bob Kinney *(VP-IT & Pre-Publi)*
Michael Tully *(CEO & Publr)*
Lee Ann Colacioppo *(Editor)*
Glen Barber *(Editor-Digital Photo)*
Vincent Carroll *(Editor-Editorial Page)*
Michael Henry *(CFO & Sr VP-Fin)*
Ken Lyons *(Sr Editor-Photo)*
Rebecca Risch *(Dir-Digital)*
Linda Shapley *(Dir-Ops)*
Reid Wicoff *(VP-Digital Sls)*
Katie Wood *(Editor-Digital Video)*

The Detroit News, Inc.   **(2)**
615 W Lafayette Blvd, Detroit, MI 48226-3124
Tel.: (313) 222-6400
Web Site: http://www.detroitnews.com
Sales Range: $25-49.9 Million
Emp.: 350
Newspaper Publishers
N.A.I.C.S.: 513110
Nick Assendelft *(Editor-Govt)*
Arthur Brooks *(Editor-Copy)*
Leslie Crutchfield *(Editor-Copy)*
Lawrence Davis *(Editor-Copy)*
Rick Epps *(Editor-Presentation)*
Chris Farina *(Editor-Photo Assignment)*
Robert L'Heureux *(Editor-Online Graphics)*
Kathleen Niezurawski *(Editor-Copy)*
Chris Rizk *(Editor-Night City)*
Steve Wilkinson *(Editor-Copy)*
Jonathan Wolman *(Editor & Publr)*
Marie Ann Thompson *(Mgr-Staff Support)*
Kelley Root *(Editor-Suburban)*

Plant (Domestic):

The Detroit News - Sterling Heights Printing Facility   **(3)**
6200 Metropolitan Pkwy, Sterling Heights, MI 48312-1022
Tel.: (313) 222-6400
Web Site: http://www.detnews.com
Newspaper Printing Services
N.A.I.C.S.: 323111

Unit (Domestic):

The Dolphin   **(2)**
Naval Submarine Base NLON, Groton, CT 06349-5044   **(100%)**
Tel.: (860) 694-3514
Sales Range: $10-24.9 Million
Emp.: 1
Weekly Newspaper
N.A.I.C.S.: 459420
John Slater *(Mgr-Advertising)*

The Ile Camera   **(2)**
1 Heritage Pl, South Gate, MI 48195
Tel.: (734) 676-0515
Sales Range: $10-24.9 Million
Emp.: 25
Publisher of Newspapers
N.A.I.C.S.: 513110
Jason Alley *(Editor)*

The Lorain Journal Company-The Morning Journal **(2)**
1657 Broadway, Lorain, OH 44052-3439 **(100%)**
Tel.: (440) 245-6901
Web Site: http://www.morningjournal.com
Sales Range: $10-24.9 Million
Emp.: 24
Newspaper Publishers
N.A.I.C.S.: 513110
Jeff Sudbrook *(Publr)*
Darlene Smith *(Mgr-Inside Sls)*
Dennis Mahilo *(Mgr-Single Copy)*
Ron Adams *(CFO)*
Ron Beal *(Dir-Adv & Gen Mgr)*
Tom Pottorff *(Dir-Circulation)*

The Macomb Daily **(2)**
100 Macomb Daily Dr, Mount Clemens, MI 48043-5802
Tel.: (586) 469-4510
Web Site: http://www.macombdaily.com
Sales Range: $25-49.9 Million
Emp.: 200
Daily Newspaper Publishing
N.A.I.C.S.: 513110
Don Wyatt *(Mng Editor)*

The Manchester Journal **(2)**
3624 Main St, Manchester Center, VT 05255
Tel.: (802) 362-2222
Web Site:
     http://www.manchesterjournal.com
Sales Range: $10-24.9 Million
Emp.: 2
Newspaper Publishers
N.A.I.C.S.: 513110
Greg Sukiennik *(Mng Editor)*

The Mendocino Beacon **(2)**
690 S Main St, Fort Bragg, CA 95437
Tel.: (707) 964-5642
Web Site:
     http://www.mendocinobeacon.com
Emp.: 27
Newspaper Publishers
N.A.I.C.S.: 513110

The Middletown Press **(2)**
386 Main St, Middletown, CT 06457-3443 **(100%)**
Tel.: (860) 347-3331
Web Site: http://www.middletownpress.com
Sales Range: $10-24.9 Million
Emp.: 50
N.A.I.C.S.: 513110
Victoria Sundqvist *(Editor)*

The News-Herald **(2)**
1 Heritage Pl Ste 100, Southgate, MI 48195
Tel.: (734) 246-0800
Sales Range: $10-24.9 Million
Emp.: 45
Newspaper Publishers
N.A.I.C.S.: 513110
Jason Alley *(Mgr)*

The News-Herald (Lake County) **(2)**
7085 Mentor Ave, Willoughby, OH 44094 **(100%)**
Tel.: (440) 951-7653
Web Site: http://www.news-herald.com
Sales Range: $10-24.9 Million
Emp.: 60
Newspaper Publishers
N.A.I.C.S.: 513110
Tricia Ambrose *(Editor)*

The Orange County Register **(2)**
2190 S Towne Ctr Pl, Anaheim, CA 92806
Tel.: (714) 796-7000
Web Site: http://www.ocregister.com
Emp.: 250
Daily Newspaper Publisher
N.A.I.C.S.: 513110
Chris Dahl *(CFO & VP-Fin)*

The Register Citizen **(2)**
59 Field St, Torrington, CT 06790-4942
Tel.: (860) 489-3121
Web Site: http://www.registercitizen.com
Sales Range: $10-24.9 Million
Emp.: 40
N.A.I.C.S.: 513110
John Berry *(Editor)*
Susan Good *(Mgr-Adv Traffic)*
Emily M. Olson *(Mng Editor)*

The Reporter Publishing Co. **(2)**

307 Derstine Ave, Lansdale, PA 19446-3532 **(100%)**
Tel.: (215) 855-8440
Web Site: http://www.thereporteronline.com
Rev.: $5,500,000
Emp.: 54
Newspaper Publishing
N.A.I.C.S.: 513110
Ann Cornell *(Editor-in-Chief)*
Joseph E. Forst *(Dir-Circulation)*
Edward S. Condra *(Publr)*
Beth Douglas *(Mgr-Adv)*
Brian Kuhns *(Mgr-Digital Sls)*

The Sun **(2)**
491 Dutton St, Lowell, MA 01854
Tel.: (978) 458-7100
Web Site: http://www.lowellsun.com
Sales Range: $10-24.9 Million
Emp.: 125
Newspaper Publishers
N.A.I.C.S.: 513110
Mark O'Neil *(Publr)*
Kendall Wallace *(Chm)*
Dave McArdle *(Editor-Editorial Page)*
Tom Zuppa *(Sr Editor)*

The Times Herald **(2)**
410 Markley St, Norristown, PA 19401-4617 **(100%)**
Tel.: (610) 272-2500
Web Site: http://www.timesherald.com
Sales Range: $10-24.9 Million
Emp.: 50
N.A.I.C.S.: 513110
Jennifer Schultz *(Mgr-Adv)*

The Willits News **(2)**
77 W Commercial St, Willits, CA 95490
Tel.: (707) 459-4643
Web Site: http://www.willitsnews.com
Sales Range: $10-24.9 Million
Emp.: 7
Newspaper Publishers
N.A.I.C.S.: 513110
Kevin McConnell *(Editor)*
Linda Williams *(Editor)*

Subsidiary (Domestic):

Utah Media, Inc. **(2)**
1670 Bonanza Dr Ste 202, Park City, UT 84060
Tel.: (435) 649-9014
Web Site: http://www.parkrecord.com
Sales Range: $10-24.9 Million
Emp.: 20
Newspaper Publishers
N.A.I.C.S.: 513110
Andy Bernhard *(Publr)*
Valerie Spung *(Dir-Adv)*
Jennifer Snow *(Mgr-Acctg)*
Lacy Brundy *(Mgr-Circulation)*
Tiffany Rivera *(Office Mgr)*
Jeff Dempsey *(Editor-Copy)*

Unit (Domestic):

Voice Communications Corp. **(2)**
51180 Bedford St, New Baltimore, MI 48047-2533
Tel.: (586) 716-8100
Web Site: http://www.voicenews.com
Sales Range: $10-24.9 Million
Emp.: 42
Weekly Newspaper Publishing
N.A.I.C.S.: 513110
Debbie Loggins *(Gen Mgr-ADV)*
Jess Payne *(Exec Editor)*
Rene Allard *(Mgr-Circulation)*

Unit (Domestic):

Armada Times **(3)**
23061 E Main St, Armada, MI 48005
Tel.: (586) 784-5551
Sales Range: $10-24.9 Million
Emp.: 2
Weekly Newspaper
N.A.I.C.S.: 513110

The San Diego Union-Tribune, LLC **(1)**
600 B St 1201, San Diego, CA 92101
Tel.: (619) 299-3131
Web Site:
     http://www.sandiegouniontribune.com
Newspaper Publishers
N.A.I.C.S.: 513110

ALDEN LEEDS, INC.
55 Jacobus Ave, Kearny, NJ 07032
Tel.: (973) 589-3544
Web Site: http://www.aldenleeds.com
Rev.: $17,680,874
Emp.: 80
Mfr & Distr of Water Treating Compounds
N.A.I.C.S.: 325998
Mark Epstein *(Pres)*
Mark Visconti *(Gen Mgr)*
Steve Belvin *(Plant Mgr)*

ALDEN PADFIELD INC.
1335 W 2100 S, Salt Lake City, UT 84119
Tel.: (801) 972-1944
Web Site:
     http://www.qualitytirecompany.com
Year Founded: 1983
Sales Range: $10-24.9 Million
Emp.: 67
Tire & Tube Whslr
N.A.I.C.S.: 423130
Scott Hansen *(CMO)*

ALDEN STATE BANK
13216 Broadway, Alden, NY 14004
Tel.: (716) 937-3381
Web Site:
     https://www.aldenstate.com
Year Founded: 1916
Sales Range: $1-9.9 Million
Emp.: 63
Banking Services
N.A.I.C.S.: 522110
Richard D. Koelbl *(Pres & CEO)*
Cherie Uebelhoer *(Branch Mgr)*
Stephen Schouten *(Controller)*
Katy Paul *(Mgr-Loan Ops)*

ALDEN SYSTEMS, INC.
10 Inverness Ctr Pkwy Ste 500, Birmingham, AL 35242
Tel.: (205) 978-2400
Web Site: http://www.aldensys.com
Year Founded: 1995
Sales Range: $25-49.9 Million
Emp.: 25
Consulting Services & Software for Telecommunications Industry
N.A.I.C.S.: 541511
John Sciarabba *(Pres)*
Barbara Warren *(Mgr-Fin)*
Karin Olinger *(Mgr-QA)*

ALDERFER, INC.
382 Main St, Harleysville, PA 19438-0002
Tel.: (215) 256-8818   PA
Web Site:
     http://www.alderfermeats.com
Year Founded: 1922
Sales Range: $10-24.9 Million
Emp.: 60
Smoked & Dried Meat Vendors
N.A.I.C.S.: 445240
Jim Van Stone *(Pres)*
Phil McClay *(Mgr-HR)*

ALDERMAN BUILDING COMPANY, INC.
339 Center St, Jacksonville, NC 28546
Tel.: (910) 346-9505
Web Site:
     http://www.aldermanbuilding.com
Sales Range: $10-24.9 Million
Emp.: 28
Commercial & Institutional Building Construction Services
N.A.I.C.S.: 236220
John Henderson *(Project Mgr)*
Melissa Schumaker *(Mgr-Acct)*
April Lewis *(Office Mgr)*

ALDERMAN'S CHEVROLET, INC.
65 Windcrest Rd, Rutland, VT 05701-4731
Tel.: (802) 779-0005
Web Site:
     https://www.aldermanchevrolet.com
Sales Range: $10-24.9 Million
Emp.: 60
New Car Retailer
N.A.I.C.S.: 441110
Philip E. Alderman *(Pres)*

ALDERSON ENTERPRISES INC.
1302 19th St, Lubbock, TX 79401
Tel.: (806) 763-8099
Web Site: http://www.alderson.com
Sales Range: $25-49.9 Million
Emp.: 100
Automobiles New & Used Service & Parts
N.A.I.C.S.: 441120
David Alderson *(Owner & Pres)*
Paul Scott *(Gen Mgr)*

ALDERWOOD WATER & WASTE WATER DISTRICT
3626 156th St SW, Lynnwood, WA 98087
Tel.: (425) 743-4605
Web Site:
     http://www.alderwoodwater.com
Year Founded: 1931
Sales Range: $25-49.9 Million
Emp.: 110
Water Supply
N.A.I.C.S.: 221310
Jeff Clark *(Gen Mgr)*
Joe Bolam *(Mgr-Maintenance & Ops)*
Kelli Armstrong *(Supvr-Acctg)*

ALDINE CAPITAL PARTNERS, INC.
30 W Monroe St Ste 710, Chicago, IL 60603
Tel.: (312) 346-3950
Web Site:
     http://www.aldinecapital.com
Year Founded: 2005
Sales Range: $100-124.9 Million
Privater Equity Firm
N.A.I.C.S.: 523999
Michael J. Revord *(Co-Founder & Mng Partner)*
Bert Brahm *(Co-Founder & Partner)*
Steve Groya *(Partner)*
Christopher Schmaltz *(Mng Dir)*
Brian Lamp *(VP)*

Subsidiaries:

Accredited Home Elevator, Inc. **(1)**
127 S Main St, Barnegat, NJ 08005
Tel.: (609) 660-8000
Web Site: https://www.accelevator.com
Home Elevator Mfr & Maintenance Services
N.A.I.C.S.: 333921
Michael Gurzo *(CEO)*
Scott Wallace Sr. *(Founder)*
Scott Wallace Jr. *(Principal)*

Subsidiary (Domestic):

Sunrise Elevator Co., Inc. **(2)**
433 Plaza Dr, Tarpon Springs, FL 34689
Tel.: (727) 934-8280
Web Site: https://sunriseelevatorco.com
Sales Range: $1-9.9 Million
Emp.: 15
Building Equipment Contractors
N.A.I.C.S.: 238290
Edith Slater *(Treas)*

Design Tanks LLC **(1)**
612 W Blackhawk St, Sioux Falls, SD 57104
Tel.: (605) 965-1600
Web Site: http://www.designtanks.com

Aldine Capital Partners, Inc.—(Continued)

Sales Range: $1-9.9 Million
Emp.: 45
Fiberglass-Reinforced Plastics Mfr
N.A.I.C.S.: 326199

ALDINGER COMPANY

1440 Prudential Dr, Dallas, TX
75235-4110
Tel.: (214) 638-1808
Web Site: http://www.aldingerco.com
Testing Laboratories
N.A.I.C.S.: 541380
Tim Detten (Pres)

Subsidiaries:

J & J Calibration Services, Inc   (1)
471 Main Ave, Walcott, ND 58077-4001
Tel.: (701) 469-2342
Web Site: http://www.jjcalibration.com
Veterinary Services
N.A.I.C.S.: 541940

ALDORA ALUMINUM & GLASS PRODUCTS, INC.

11500 Miramar Pkwy Ste 300, Mira-
mar, FL 33025
Tel.: (954) 784-6900
Web Site: http://www.aldora-
architectural.com
Aluminum & Glass Fabrication
N.A.I.C.S.: 327215
Leon Silverstein (CEO)
Waylon McCall (Branch Mgr)

Subsidiaries:

Louisville Plate Glass Company,
Inc.   (1)
1401 W Broadway, Louisville, KY 40201
Tel.: (502) 584-6145
Web Site:
http://www.louisvilleplateglass.com
Insulated Glass Mfr
N.A.I.C.S.: 423390
William A. Stone (Pres)
Brian Walker (Gen Mgr)
Diana Yates (Mgr-Sls)
Brian O'Connell (Project Coord)
Pam Willen (Chief Acctg Officer)
Ed Embers (Plant Mgr-Insulating Glass)

ALDRICH & ELLIOTT PC

6 Market Pl Ste 2, Essex Junction,
VT 05452-2937
Tel.: (802) 879-7733
Web Site:
https://www.aeengineers.com
Year Founded: 1995
Civil & Environmental Engineering &
Consulting
N.A.I.C.S.: 541330
Bradley Aldrich (Founder & Partner)
Wayne Elliott (Pres)
Jason Booth (VP)

ALDRICH CAPITAL PART-NERS, LLC

8614 Westwood Ctr Dr Ste 710
Westwood Metro Tower, Vienna, VA
22182
Tel.: (703) 376-3570
Web Site:
https://www.aldrichcap.com
Emp.: 100
Investment Services
N.A.I.C.S.: 523999

Subsidiaries:

Paymerang, LLC   (1)
7401 Beaufont Springs Dr Ste 300, Rich-
mond, VA 23225
Web Site: http://www.paymerang.com
Sales Range: $1-9.9 Million
Emp.: 200
Financial Consulting Services
N.A.I.C.S.: 541611
Nasser Chanda (CEO)
John Heyel (CFO)

Andy Savage (CTO)
Gloria Garber (Dir-HR)
Greg Marcel (Dir-Ops)

Subsidiary (Domestic):

ImageTag, Inc.   (2)
1400 E Southern Ave Ste 800, Tempe, AZ
85282
Tel.: (480) 753-9300
Web Site: http://www.imagetag.com
Software Publisher
N.A.I.C.S.: 513210
Danny Calhoun (VP-Support & Ops)
Darius DiTallo (CFO & VP-Fin)
Luke Detering (Dir-Product Mgmt)
Mary Miller (Dir-Mktg & Channel)
Peter Clark (VP-Pro Svcs)
Brian Curry (Pres)
Mike Fernandes (VP-Dev)
Chris Worton (Sr VP-Worldwide Sls)

ALDRICH FARMS, LLC

4782 Aldrich Road, Bellingham, WA
98226
Tel.: (360) 920-5653
Web Site:
http://www.aldrichfarms.com
Fruit & Vegetable Canning
N.A.I.C.S.: 311421
Richard Buford (Owner)

ALDRIDGE CONSTRUCTION, INC.

10625 N County Rd Ste 200, Frisco,
TX 75033
Tel.: (855) 486-1100
Web Site:
http://www.aldridgeconstruction.com
Construction Services
N.A.I.C.S.: 237990
Alex Aldridge (Pres)

Subsidiaries:

Magco Drilling, Inc.   (1)
716 N Mckeever Ave, Azusa, CA 91702
Tel.: (626) 969-1000
Web Site: http://www.magcodrilling.com
Rev.: $4,700,000
Emp.: 38
Commercial & Institutional Building Con-
struction
N.A.I.C.S.: 236220
Holly A. Maggio (Pres)
Ida Lengson (Controller)
Steve Herald (Project Mgr)
Bill Burton (Mgr-Estimating)
Don Upton (Project Mgr)
John Klein (VP)
Silvia Macias (Mgr-HR)

ALDRIDGE ELECTRIC INC.

844 E Rockland Rd, Libertyville, IL
60048-9500
Tel.: (847) 680-5200
Web Site: http://www.aldridge-
electric.com
Year Founded: 1952
Emp.: 1,500
Provider of Electrical Contracting
Services
N.A.I.C.S.: 238210
Ken Aldridge (Chm)
Tom McLinden (Pres)
Wayne Gearig (Exec VP-Power Div)
Tim Bradley (Exec VP-Transit Div)
Frank Manna (Exec VP-Airport &
Highway Div)
Steve Rivi (CEO)
Brian Mazzei (Exec VP-Power Div)
Daniel Galovich (VP-Power & Utility
Div)
Gene Huebner (CFO)
Guy Niedorkorn (VP-Power & Utility
Div)
Steve Aldridge (COO)
Alex Aldridge (Co-COO)
Mark Carani (VP)

ALE HOUSE MANAGEMENT, INC.

612 N Orange Ave Ste C6, Jupiter,
FL 33458
Tel.: (561) 743-2299
Web Site:
http://www.millersalehouse.com
Year Founded: 1988
Sales Range: $125-149.9 Million
Casual, Rustic-Themed Restaurants
N.A.I.C.S.: 722511
Jack Miller (Co-Owner)
Claire Miller (Co-Owner)

Subsidiaries:

Miller's Ale House, Inc.   (1)
612 N Orange Ave Ste C6, Jupiter, FL
33458
Tel.: (561) 743-2299
Web Site: http://www.millersalehouse.com
Emp.: 3,000
Restaurant
N.A.I.C.S.: 722511
Jack Miller (Co-Owner)
Claire Miller (Co-Owner)

ALENCO WINDOW HOLDING CORP.

615 W Carson St, Bryan, TX 77801
Tel.: (979) 779-7770
Sales Range: $100-124.9 Million
Emp.: 800
Mfr of Window & Door Frames
N.A.I.C.S.: 332321
Brian Redpath (Pres)
Chuck Gessler (CFO)

ALERION CAPITAL GROUP, LLC

7702 E Doubletree Ranch Rd Ste
350, Scottsdale, AZ 85258
Tel.: (480) 367-0900
Web Site: https://www.alerion.com
Privater Equity Firm
N.A.I.C.S.: 523999
Ricardo DeAvila (Mng Dir)
Jeff Unruh (Principal)
Jim Unruh (Founder & Principal)
Jerry Lindfelt (Principal)
Christine Wolcott (Exec Asst-Admin &
Officer Mgr)

ALERISLIFE INC.

Tel.: (617) 796-8387   MD
Web Site: https://www.alerislife.com
Year Founded: 2001
ALR—(NASDAQ)
Rev.: $934,593,000
Assets: $376,277,000
Liabilities: $194,687,000
Net Worth: $181,590,000
Earnings: ($29,925,000)
Emp.: 19,500
Fiscal Year-end: 12/31/21
Holding Company; Senior Indepen-
dent Living, Assisted Living & Skilled
Nursing Facilities Operator
N.A.I.C.S.: 551112
Jennifer Babbin Clark (Sec)
Jeffrey C. Leer (Pres & CEO)
Lisa Cooney (Gen Counsel & Sr VP)
Jeffrey C. Leer (Pres & CEO)
Heather Pereira (CFO, Treas & Sr
VP)
Philip Benjamson (COO & Sr VP)
Zehra Abid-Wood (Sr VP)
Michael Lopez (Chief HR Officer)
Vijay Moses (Corp Counsel)
Stephen Geiger (Chief Acctg Officer)
James Kotarski (CIO)
Susan Dooley (VP)
Vern Larkin (Dir)

Subsidiaries:

Dominion Village at Chesapeake   (1)
2856 Forehand Dr, Chesapeake, VA 23323
Tel.: (757) 487-9400

Web Site:
http://www.fivestarseniorliving.com
Sales Range: $10-24.9 Million
Emp.: 32
Residential Care Services
N.A.I.C.S.: 623312

Encinitas Heritage Partners, LLC   (1)
1350 S El Camino Real, Encinitas, CA
92024-4904
Tel.: (760) 479-1818
Nursing Care Facility Services
N.A.I.C.S.: 623110

FS Leisure Park Tenant Trust   (1)
1400 Rte 70, Lakewood, NJ 08701
Tel.: (732) 370-0444
Nursing Care Facilities Services
N.A.I.C.S.: 623110
Patrick Duffi (Exec Dir)

FS Lexington Tenant Trust   (1)
700 Mason Headley Rd, Lexington, KY
40504
Tel.: (859) 259-3486
Web Site:
http://www.lexingtoncountryplace.com
Nursing Care Facilities Services
N.A.I.C.S.: 623110

FSQC-AL, LLC   (1)
2184 Pkwy Lk Dr, Hoover, AL 35244-1803
Tel.: (205) 403-7400
Web Site:
http://www.fivestarseniorliving.com
Emp.: 50
Nursing Care Facilities Services
N.A.I.C.S.: 623110

FVE EC LLC   (1)
501 Laurel Oak Rd, Voorhees, NJ 08043-
4418
Tel.: (856) 566-2340
Web Site:
http://www.fivestarseniorliving.com
Nursing Care Services
N.A.I.C.S.: 623110

FVE SE Home Place New Bern
LLC   (1)
1309 McCarthy Blvd, New Bern, NC 28562
Tel.: (252) 637-7133
Web Site:
http://www.fivestarseniorliving.com
Nursing Care Services
N.A.I.C.S.: 623110

Five Star Aspenwood LLC   (1)
14400 Homecrest Rd, Silver Spring, MD
20906
Tel.: (301) 598-6424
Web Site:
http://www.fivestarseniorliving.com
Nursing Care Services
N.A.I.C.S.: 623110
P. J. Petkovic (Exec Dir)
Kathy Lavin (Sls Dir)
Katherine Luther (Dir-Lifestyle 360 Pro-
gram)
Peter J. Franklin (Dir-Food & Beverage)
Idowu Oluyomi (Dir-Resident Care-Assisted
Living)
Patrick Kincius (Dir-Rehab & Personal Fit-
ness)
Sam Agyekum (Dir-Environmental Svcs)

Five Star Cary Heartfields LLC   (1)
1050 Crescent Green Dr, Cary, NC 27518
Tel.: (919) 852-5757
Web Site:
http://www.fivestarseniorliving.com
Emp.: 60
Nursing Care Services
N.A.I.C.S.: 623110

Five Star Coral Oaks LLC   (1)
900 W Lake Rd, Palm Harbor, FL 34684
Tel.: (727) 787-3333
Web Site:
http://www.fivestarseniorliving.com
Nursing Care Services
N.A.I.C.S.: 623110

Five Star Desert Harbor LLC   (1)
13840 N Desert Harbor Dr, Peoria, AZ
85381
Tel.: (623) 972-0995
Web Site:
http://www.fivestarseniorliving.com
Nursing Care Services

N.A.I.C.S.: 623110

Five Star Easton Heartfields LLC (1)
700 Port St, Easton, MD 21601
Tel.: (410) 820-4400
Web Site:
  http://www.fivestarseniorliving.com
Nursing Care Services
N.A.I.C.S.: 623110

Five Star Ellicott City LLC (1)
3004 N Ridge Rd, Ellicott City, MD 21043-3381
Tel.: (410) 461-9494
Web Site:
  http://www.fivestarseniorliving.com
Nursing Care Services
N.A.I.C.S.: 623110

Five Star Foulk Manor North LLC (1)
1212 Foulk Rd, Wilmington, DE 19803
Tel.: (302) 478-4296
Web Site:
  http://www.fivestarseniorliving.com
Nursing Care Services
N.A.I.C.S.: 623110

Five Star Frederick Heartfields LLC (1)
20 HeartFields Ln, Fredericksburg, VA 22405
Tel.: (540) 373-8800
Web Site:
  http://www.heartfieldsfredericksburg.com
Emp.: 100
Nursing Care Services
N.A.I.C.S.: 623110

Five Star Home Health, Inc. (1)
8616 La Tijera Blvd Ste 408, Los Angeles, CA 90045
Tel.: (310) 642-0026
Web Site:
  https://www.fivestarhomehealth.com
Nursing Care Services
N.A.I.C.S.: 623110

Five Star Insurance, Inc. (1)
215 E Main St, Festus, MO 63028
Tel.: (636) 937-9383
Web Site:
  http://www.fivestarinsuranceagency.com
Nursing Care Services
N.A.I.C.S.: 623110

Five Star Knightsbridge LLC (1)
4590 Knightsbridge Blvd, Columbus, OH 43214
Tel.: (614) 451-6793
Web Site:
  http://www.fivestarseniorliving.com
Emp.: 280
Nursing Care Services
N.A.I.C.S.: 623110

Five Star Lincoln Heights LLC (1)
311 W Nottingham Pl, San Antonio, TX 78209
Tel.: (210) 824-2314
Web Site:
  http://www.fivestarseniorliving.com
Emp.: 200
Nursing Care Services
N.A.I.C.S.: 623110

Five Star Memorial Woods LLC (1)
777 N Post Oak Rd, Houston, TX 77024
Tel.: (713) 956-0870
Web Site:
  http://www.fivestarseniorliving.com
Nursing Care Services
N.A.I.C.S.: 623110

Five Star Montebello LLC (1)
10500 Academy Rd NE, Albuquerque, NM 87111
Tel.: (505) 294-9944
Web Site:
  http://www.fivestarseniorliving.com
Nursing Care Services
N.A.I.C.S.: 623110

Five Star Morningside Bellgrade LLC (1)
2800 Polo Pkwy, Midlothian, VA 23113
Tel.: (804) 379-2800
Web Site:
  http://www.fivestarseniorliving.com
Nursing Care Services

N.A.I.C.S.: 623110

Five Star Morningside Charlottesville LLC (1)
491 Crestwood Dr, Charlottesville, VA 22903
Tel.: (434) 971-8889
Web Site:
  http://www.fivestarseniorliving.com
Nursing Care Services
N.A.I.C.S.: 623110

Five Star Newport News LLC (1)
655 Denbigh Blvd, Newport News, VA 23608
Tel.: (757) 890-0905
Web Site:
  http://www.fivestarseniorliving.com
Nursing Care Services
N.A.I.C.S.: 623110

Five Star Northshore LLC (1)
10803 N Port Washington Rd, Mequon, WI 53092
Tel.: (262) 478-2200
Web Site:
  http://www.fivestarseniorliving.com
Nursing Care Services
N.A.I.C.S.: 623110

Five Star Overland Park LLC (1)
6555 W 75th St, Overland Park, KS 66204
Tel.: (913) 383-9876
Web Site:
  http://www.fivestarseniorliving.com
Nursing Care Services
N.A.I.C.S.: 623110

Five Star Quality Care-CA, LLC (1)
1642 W Ave J, Lancaster, CA 93534-2814
Tel.: (661) 942-8463
Web Site:
  http://www.fivestarseniorliving.com
Nursing Care Facilities Services
N.A.I.C.S.: 623110

Five Star Quality Care-GA, LLC (1)
606 Simmons St, Dublin, GA 31021
Tel.: (478) 272-1666
Nursing Care Services
N.A.I.C.S.: 623110

Five Star Quality Care-GHV, LLC (1)
950 Morgan Hwy, Clarks Summit, PA 18411
Tel.: (570) 586-8080
Skilled Nursing Facility Services
N.A.I.C.S.: 623110

Five Star Quality Care-IA, Inc. (1)
400 Center St Ste 200, Newton, MA 02458
Tel.: (617) 796-8387
Emp.: 3
Skilled Nursing Facility Services
N.A.I.C.S.: 623110

Five Star Quality Care-IL, LLC (1)
7130 Crimson Ridge Dr, Rockford, IL 61107
Tel.: (815) 398-7792
Web Site:
  http://www.fivestarseniorliving.com
Nursing Care Services
N.A.I.C.S.: 623110

Five Star Quality Care-IN, LLC (1)
2455 Tamarack Trl, Bloomington, IN 47408
Tel.: (812) 336-7060
Web Site:
  http://www.fivestarseniorliving.com
Emp.: 200
Nursing Care Facilities Services
N.A.I.C.S.: 623110

Five Star Quality Care-KS, LLC (1)
510 W 7th St, Ellinwood, KS 67526
Tel.: (620) 564-2337
Web Site:
  http://www.fivestarseniorliving.com
Nursing Care Services
N.A.I.C.S.: 623110

Five Star Quality Care-MS, LLC (1)
1488 Belk Blvd, Oxford, MS 38655
Tel.: (662) 234-8244
Nursing Care Facilities Services
N.A.I.C.S.: 623110

Five Star Quality Care-NJ, LLC (1)
1400 Hwy 70 Ste 1, Lakewood, NJ 08701
Tel.: (732) 370-0444
Skilled Nursing Facility Services
N.A.I.C.S.: 623110

Five Star Quality Care-Savannah, LLC (1)
7410 Skidaway Rd, Savannah, GA 31406
Tel.: (912) 354-6185
Web Site:
  http://www.fivestarseniorliving.com
Nursing Care Services
N.A.I.C.S.: 623110

Five Star Quality Care-WY, LLC (1)
503 S 18th St, Laramie, WY 82070-4391
Tel.: (307) 742-3728
Web Site:
  http://www.fivestarseniorliving.com
Emp.: 150
Nursing Care Services
N.A.I.C.S.: 623110

Five Star Rehabilitation and Wellness Services, LLC (1)
250 Faunce Corner Rd, North Dartmouth, MA 02747-1221
Tel.: (508) 984-7226
Nursing Care Facilities Services
N.A.I.C.S.: 623110

Five Star Remington Club LLC (1)
16925 Hierba Dr, San Diego, CA 92128
Tel.: (858) 673-6340
Web Site:
  http://www.fivestarseniorliving.com
Nursing Care Services
N.A.I.C.S.: 623110

Five Star Rio Las Palmas LLC (1)
877 E March Ln, Stockton, CA 95207
Tel.: (209) 957-4711
Web Site:
  http://www.fivestarseniorliving.com
Emp.: 70
Nursing Care Services
N.A.I.C.S.: 623110

Five Star Severna Park LLC (1)
715 Benfield Rd, Severna Park, MD 21146
Tel.: (410) 729-1600
Web Site:
  http://www.fivestarseniorliving.com
Nursing Care Services
N.A.I.C.S.: 623110

Five Star Tucson Forum LLC (1)
2500 N Rosemont Blvd, Tucson, AZ 85712
Tel.: (520) 325-4800
Web Site:
  http://www.fivestarseniorliving.com
Emp.: 240
Nursing Care Services
N.A.I.C.S.: 623110

Fresno Heritage Partners, a California Limited Partnership (1)
6075 N Marks Ave, Fresno, CA 93711-1600
Tel.: (559) 446-6226
Nursing Care Facilities Services
N.A.I.C.S.: 623110

HeartLands Assisted Living at Severna Park (1)
715 Benfield Rd, Severna Park, MD 21146-2210
Tel.: (410) 729-1600
Web Site:
  http://www.heartlandsassistedliving.com
Rev.: $1,750,000
Emp.: 63
Residential Care Services
N.A.I.C.S.: 623990
Anne Stewart *(Sls Dir)*
Greg Brianas *(Asst Exec Dir)*
Linda Seegmuller *(Dir-Lifestyle360)*
David Anderson *(Dir-Food & Beverage)*
Heather Plummer *(Dir-Resident Care)*
Sharon Stag *(Asst Dir-Resident Care)*
Dawn Mynes *(Dir-Rehab & Personal Fitness Ageility)*
Craig Sandusky *(Dir-Maintenance)*

Homeplace of Burlington (1)
118 Alamance Rd, Burlington, NC 27215
Tel.: (336) 227-2328
Web Site:
  http://www.homeplaceofburlington.com
Emp.: 50
Assisted Living Facility Operator
N.A.I.C.S.: 623312

Morningside of Anderson, L.P. (1)
1304 McLees Rd, Anderson, SC 29621
Tel.: (864) 964-9088

Web Site:
  http://www.fivestarseniorliving.com
Nursing Care Services
N.A.I.C.S.: 623110

Morningside of Belmont, LLC (1)
1710 Magnolia Blvd, Nashville, TN 37212
Tel.: (615) 383-2557
Web Site:
  http://www.fivestarseniorliving.com
Nursing Care Services
N.A.I.C.S.: 623110

Morningside of Bowling Green, LLC (1)
981 Campbell Ln, Bowling Green, KY 42104
Tel.: (270) 746-9600
Web Site:
  http://www.fivestarseniorliving.com
Nursing Care Services
N.A.I.C.S.: 623110

Morningside of Camden, LLC (1)
719 Kershaw Hwy, Camden, SC 29020
Tel.: (803) 713-8668
Web Site:
  http://www.fivestarseniorliving.com
Nursing Care Services
N.A.I.C.S.: 623110

Morningside of Cleveland, LLC (1)
2900 Westside Dr NW, Cleveland, TN 37312
Tel.: (423) 614-5424
Web Site:
  http://www.fivestarseniorliving.com
Nursing Care Services
N.A.I.C.S.: 623110

Morningside of Columbus, L.P. (1)
4500 S Stadium Dr, Columbus, GA 31909
Tel.: (706) 561-5560
Web Site:
  http://www.fivestarseniorliving.com
Emp.: 25
Nursing Care Services
N.A.I.C.S.: 623110

Morningside of Conyers, LLC (1)
1352 Wellbrook Cir, Conyers, GA 30012
Tel.: (770) 922-1654
Web Site:
  http://www.fivestarseniorliving.com
Nursing Care Services
N.A.I.C.S.: 623110

Morningside of Cookeville, LLC (1)
1010 E Spring St, Cookeville, TN 38501
Tel.: (931) 525-1083
Web Site:
  http://www.fivestarseniorliving.com
Emp.: 50
Nursing Care Services
N.A.I.C.S.: 623110

Morningside of Cullman, LLC (1)
2021 Dahlke Dr NE, Cullman, AL 35058
Tel.: (256) 737-1088
Web Site:
  http://www.fivestarseniorliving.com
Nursing Care Services
N.A.I.C.S.: 623110

Morningside of Decatur, L.P. (1)
2115 Point Mallard Dr SE, Decatur, AL 35601
Tel.: (256) 350-0089
Web Site:
  http://www.fivestarseniorliving.com
Emp.: 30
Nursing Care Services
N.A.I.C.S.: 623110

Morningside of Evans, Limited Partnership (1)
353 N Belair Rd, Evans, GA 30809
Tel.: (706) 228-4709
Web Site:
  http://www.fivestarseniorliving.com
Nursing Care Services
N.A.I.C.S.: 623110

Morningside of Franklin, LLC (1)
105 Sunrise Cir, Franklin, TN 37067
Tel.: (615) 591-3362
Web Site:
  http://www.fivestarseniorliving.com
Emp.: 25
Nursing Care Services
N.A.I.C.S.: 623110

AlerisLife Inc.—(Continued)

Morningside of Gainesville, LLC (1)
2435 Limestone Pkwy, Gainesville, GA 30501
Tel.: (770) 531-6100
Web Site:
http://www.fivestarseniorliving.com
Nursing Care Services
N.A.I.C.S.: 623110

Morningside of Gallatin, LLC (1)
1085 Hartsville Pike, Gallatin, TN 37066
Tel.: (615) 230-5600
Web Site:
http://www.fivestarseniorliving.com
Emp.: 28
Nursing Care Services
N.A.I.C.S.: 623110

Morningside of Gastonia, LLC (1)
2755 Union Rd, Gastonia, NC 28054
Tel.: (704) 810-0111
Web Site:
http://www.fivestarseniorliving.com
Emp.: 60
Nursing Care Services
N.A.I.C.S.: 623110

Morningside of Greenwood, L.P. (1)
116 Enterprise Ct, Greenwood, SC 29649
Tel.: (864) 388-9433
Web Site:
http://www.fivestarseniorliving.com
Emp.: 25
Nursing Care Services
N.A.I.C.S.: 623110

Morningside of Hartsville, LLC (1)
1901 W Carolina Ave, Hartsville, SC 29550
Tel.: (843) 857-0159
Web Site:
http://www.fivestarseniorliving.com
Emp.: 30
Nursing Care Services
N.A.I.C.S.: 623110
Shannon Berg (Gen Mgr)

Morningside of Hopkinsville, Limited Partnership (1)
4190 Lafayette Rd, Hopkinsville, KY 42240
Tel.: (270) 885-0220
Web Site:
http://www.fivestarseniorliving.com
Emp.: 26
Nursing Care Services
N.A.I.C.S.: 623110

Morningside of Jackson, LLC (1)
1200 N Pkwy, Jackson, TN 38305
Tel.: (731) 423-1004
Web Site:
http://www.fivestarseniorliving.com
Nursing Care Services
N.A.I.C.S.: 623110

Morningside of Lexington, LLC (1)
218 Old Chapin Rd, Lexington, SC 29072
Tel.: (803) 957-3600
Web Site:
http://www.fivestarseniorliving.com
Nursing Care Services
N.A.I.C.S.: 623110

Morningside of Orangeburg, LLC (1)
2306 Riverbank Dr, Orangeburg, SC 29118
Tel.: (803) 539-2911
Web Site:
http://www.fivestarseniorliving.com
Emp.: 30
Nursing Care Services
N.A.I.C.S.: 623110

Morningside of Paducah, LLC (1)
1700 Elmdale Rd, Paducah, KY 42003
Tel.: (270) 534-9173
Web Site:
http://www.fivestarseniorliving.com
Emp.: 40
Nursing Care Services
N.A.I.C.S.: 623110

Morningside of Paris, LLC (1)
350 Volunteer Dr, Paris, TN 38242
Tel.: (731) 644-9680
Web Site:
http://www.fivestarseniorliving.com
Nursing Care Services
N.A.I.C.S.: 623110

Morningside of Raleigh, LLC (1)

801 Dixie Trl, Raleigh, NC 27607
Tel.: (919) 828-5557
Web Site:
http://www.fivestarseniorliving.com
Nursing Care Services
N.A.I.C.S.: 623110

Morningside of Skipwith-Richmond, LLC (1)
3000 Skipwith Rd, Richmond, VA 23294
Tel.: (804) 270-3990
Web Site:
http://www.fivestarseniorliving.com
Emp.: 200
Nursing Care Services
N.A.I.C.S.: 623110

Morningside of South Carolina, L.P. (1)
1830 W Main St, Rock Hill, SC 29732
Tel.: (803) 980-4100
Emp.: 30
Skilled Nursing Facility Services
N.A.I.C.S.: 623110

Morningside of Sumter (1)
2500 Lin-Do Ct, Sumter, SC 29150
Tel.: (803) 469-4490
Web Site:
http://www.fivestarseniorliving.com
Nursing Care Facilities Services
N.A.I.C.S.: 623110

Morningside of Williamsburg, LLC (1)
440 McLaws Cir, Williamsburg, VA 23185
Tel.: (757) 221-0018
Web Site:
http://www.fivestarseniorliving.com
Emp.: 80
Nursing Care Services
N.A.I.C.S.: 623110

Newark Heritage Partners I, LLC (1)
501 S Harmony Rd, Newark, DE 19713
Tel.: (302) 283-0540
Nursing Care Facilities Services
N.A.I.C.S.: 623110

Progress Pharmacy LTD (1)
14130 Sullyfield Cir Ste B, Chantilly, VA 20151-1611
Tel.: (703) 378-4400
Nursing Care Facilities Services
N.A.I.C.S.: 623110

Somerford House Frederick (1)
2100 Whittier Dr, Frederick, MD 21702
Tel.: (301) 668-3930
Web Site:
http://www.fivestarseniorliving.com
Nursing Care Facilities Services
N.A.I.C.S.: 623110

Somerford Place LLC (1)
2717 Riva Rd, Annapolis, MD 21401
Tel.: (410) 224-7300
Web Site:
http://www.fivestarseniorliving.com
Emp.: 80
Nursing Care Services
N.A.I.C.S.: 623110
Penny Brown (Dir-Bridge to Re-Discovery)
Rodrigio Fredgoso (Dir-Food & Beverage)
Elizabeth Balderrama (Mgr-Bus Office)
Terry Sampson (Dir-Maintenance)

Sutherland Care Center (1)
333 Maple St, Sutherland, NE 69165-0307
Tel.: (308) 386-4393
Web Site:
http://www.fivestarseniorliving.com
Nursing Care Facilities Services
N.A.I.C.S.: 623110

The Forum At The Woodlands, Inc. (1)
5055 W Panther Creek Dr, Spring, TX 77381
Tel.: (281) 292-2600
Web Site:
http://www.fivestarseniorliving.com
Emp.: 175
Nursing Care Facilities Services
N.A.I.C.S.: 623110

The Montebello on Academy (1)
10500 Academy Rd NE, Albuquerque, NM 87111
Tel.: (505) 294-9944

Web Site:
http://www.themontebelloseniorliving.com
Continuing Care Retirement Community Operator
N.A.I.C.S.: 623311

The Wellstead of Rogers Diamondcrest Senior Living (1)
20600 S Diamond Lake Rd, Rogers, MN 55374
Tel.: (763) 428-1981
Web Site:
http://www.fivestarseniorliving.com
Nursing Care Services
N.A.I.C.S.: 623110

ALERT AMBULANCE SERVICE, INC.
1195 Airport Rd, Lakewood, NJ 08701
Tel.: (732) 364-2856
Web Site:
http://www.alertambulance.com
Year Founded: 1972
Rev.: $15,766,782
Emp.: 250
Medical Transportation Services
N.A.I.C.S.: 621910
Chip Berryman (Mgr-Fleet Maintenance)
John Reeve (Dir-Bus Dev)
Patricia Davis (Mgr-Billing)
Brian Stanwise (Mgr-Ops)
Dawn Polo (Dir-Compliance & Risk)
Jack Trovato (Dir-IT)
Robert Davis (Pres)
Michael Husenica (Controller)
John Iazzetta (Dir-Ops)
David Glazer (Mgr-Ops)

ALERT HOLDINGS GROUP, INC.
3210 Ualena St, Honolulu, HI 96819
Tel.: (808) 521-5000
Web Site:
https://www.alertalarmhawaii.com
Year Founded: 1962
Sales Range: $10-24.9 Million
Emp.: 150
Security & Fire Alarm System Design, Installation, Maintenance & Monitoring Services
N.A.I.C.S.: 561621
John Cannon (Pres & CEO)

Subsidiaries:

Sentinel Silent Alarm Co., Inc. (1)
99-1036 Iwaena St, Aiea, HI 96701
Tel.: (808) 487-0088
Web Site:
http://www.sentinelalarmhawaii.com
Sales Range: $1-9.9 Million
Emp.: 54
Security System Services
N.A.I.C.S.: 561621
John Cannon (CEO)

ALESSI BAKERIES, INC.
5202 Eagle Trl Dr, Tampa, FL 33634
Tel.: (813) 871-2286
Web Site:
http://www.alessibakery.com
Year Founded: 1912
Sales Range: $10-24.9 Million
Emp.: 150
Bakery
N.A.I.C.S.: 311811
Sefik Turan (COO)
Adam Kunder (Mgr-Warehouse)
Sandra Bragg (Office Mgr-Mktg)

ALEVA STORES
1840 Enterprise Dr, Rochester Hills, MI 48309
Tel.: (248) 289-1188
Web Site:
https://www.alevastores.com
Year Founded: 1957
Sales Range: $10-24.9 Million

Emp.: 20
Sales of Medical & Healthcare Products
N.A.I.C.S.: 456199
Derek Gaskins (Founder, Pres & CEO)
Larry Gaskins (CFO)
Carl LoPiccolo (VP-Bus Dev)
Scot Stier (Creative Dir)

ALEX & ANI LLC
2000 Chapel View Blvd, Cranston, RI 02920
Tel.: (401) 467-3952
Web Site: http://www.alexandani.com
Year Founded: 2004
Sales Range: $200-249.9 Million
Emp.: 1,100
Eco Friendly Jewelry
N.A.I.C.S.: 458310
Carolyn Rafaelian (Founder & Chief Creative Officer)
Tarik Chaudhary (Sr VP-IT)
Igor Bekker (VP-ECommerce)
Jeff Thomas (Sr Dir-HR)
Suzanne Turcotte (Gen Counsel & Sr VP-HR)
Mark Geragos (Atty)
Scott Burger (Chm & CEO)

ALEX C. FERGUSSON, INC.
5121 Coffey Ave, Chambersburg, PA 17201
Tel.: (717) 264-9147
Web Site: http://www.afcocare.us
Sales Range: $25-49.9 Million
Emp.: 150
Polish & Other Sanitation Good Mfr
N.A.I.C.S.: 325612
Michael Hinkle (Pres)
Kent Loew (VP-Wyandotte Pro Div)

Subsidiaries:

Pure-Chem Products Co., Inc. (1)
8371 Monroe Ave, Stanton, CA 90680
Tel.: (714) 995-4141
Sales Range: $10-24.9 Million
Emp.: 4
Mfr of Soap & other Detergents
N.A.I.C.S.: 325611

ALEX E. PARIS CONTRACTING CO., INC.
1595 Smith Township State, Atlasburg, PA 15004
Tel.: (724) 947-2235
Web Site: http://www.alexparis.com
Year Founded: 1928
Sales Range: $10-24.9 Million
Emp.: 150
Underground Utility Contracting Services
N.A.I.C.S.: 237110
Timothy A. Paris (VP)
Andy Miller (Mgr-Sls)

ALEX FOOD INC.
1050 E Main St, Bridgeport, CT 06608
Tel.: (203) 366-9060
Sales Range: $10-24.9 Million
Emp.: 62
Independent Supermarket
N.A.I.C.S.: 445110
Paulino Pena (Pres)
Tony Pena (VP)

ALEX LEE, INC.
120 4th St SW, Hickory, NC 28602
Tel.: (828) 725-4442
Web Site: https://www.alexlee.com
Year Founded: 1931
Sales Range: Less than $1 Million
Emp.: 16,000
Offices of Other Holding Companies
N.A.I.C.S.: 551112

Kimberly Davis *(Dir-HR Ops, Compensation & Benefits)*
Anita Harris *(Dir-MDI Applications)*
Chris Mundy *(Dir-Retail Applications Dev)*
Richard Sigmon *(Dir-Internal Audit)*

Subsidiaries:

Capital Resources of Virginia, Inc.   (1)
7277 Hanover Green Dr, Mechanicsville, VA 23111   (100%)
Tel.: (804) 569-9737
Finance Company
N.A.I.C.S.: 523910

Capital Resources, Inc.   (1)
120 4th St Ste, Hickory, NC 28602-3026   (100%)
Tel.: (828) 323-4424
Sales Range: $50-74.9 Million
Emp.: 120
Finance Company
N.A.I.C.S.: 523999

Lowe's Food Stores, Inc.   (1)
1381 Old Mill Cir Ste 200, Winston Salem, NC 27103   (100%)
Tel.: (336) 659-0180
Web Site: http://www.lowesfoods.com
Sales Range: $750-799.9 Million
Emp.: 9,000
Supermarket Store Operator
N.A.I.C.S.: 445110
John Sapp *(Controller & Dir-Fin)*

MDI Management Inc.   (1)
PO Box 2148, Hickory, NC 28613   (100%)
Tel.: (828) 323-4100
Web Site:
    http://www.merchantsdistributors.com
Sales Range: $10-24.9 Million
Emp.: 45
Real Estate Management
N.A.I.C.S.: 424410
Bob Mcteir *(Pres)*

Merchants Distributors, Inc.   (1)
5005 Alex Lee Blvd, Hickory, NC 28601   (100%)
Tel.: (828) 725-4100
Web Site:
    http://www.merchantsdistributors.com
Emp.: 1,250
Grocery Distr
N.A.I.C.S.: 424410
Tim Markham *(VP-Sls)*
John Dollar *(VP-HR)*
Michael Harris *(Mgr-Distr)*
Paul Miller *(Dir-Transportation)*
Tammy Wilcox *(Mgr-Adv)*
Thurman Roe *(Mgr-Safety)*

Merchants Transport of Hickory   (1)
PO Box 2148, Hickory, NC 28603   (100%)
Tel.: (828) 725-4071
Sales Range: $25-49.9 Million
Emp.: 250
Transportation Services
N.A.I.C.S.: 484230

Souto Foods LLC   (1)
1925 N Norcross Tucker Rd, Norcross, GA 30071
Tel.: (678) 528-8328
Web Site: http://www.soutofoods.com
Food Store Operator
N.A.I.C.S.: 445298
Sebastian Souto *(Pres)*

ALEX MONTGOMERY MT. WASHINGTON

9000 Hwy 44 E, Mount Washington, KY 40047
Tel.: (502) 955-6800
Web Site:
    http://www.alexmontgomery.com
Rev.: $19,000,000
Emp.: 48
New & Used Automobile Dealer
N.A.I.C.S.: 441110

ALEX R. MASSON INC.

12819 198th St, Linwood, KS 66052
Tel.: (913) 723-3712

Web Site: http://www.armasson.com
Rev.: $25,100,000
Emp.: 120
Plants, Potted
N.A.I.C.S.: 424930
Tom Franchett *(Gen Mgr)*
John Duggan *(Mgr-Processing & Ops)*
Connie Matlock *(Mgr-Pur)*
Devon McDonald *(Mgr-Sls)*
Mark Illausky *(Pres)*

ALEX'S LEMONADE STAND FOUNDATION FOR CHILDHOOD CANCER

3 Bala Plz W, Bala Cynwyd, PA 19004
Tel.: (610) 649-3034   PA
Web Site:
    https://www.alexslemonade.org
Year Founded: 2005
Sales Range: $10-24.9 Million
Emp.: 36
Fundraising Services
N.A.I.C.S.: 813211
Erin Flynn-Blair *(Treas)*
Tim Lung *(Sec)*

ALEXA ENERGY LTD.

1248 Wayne St, Reading, PA 19601
Tel.: (610) 374-3835
Web Site: https://www.pennpride.com
Rev.: $17,120,182
Emp.: 10
Petroleum Bulk Stations & Terminals
N.A.I.C.S.: 424710
John S. Vespico *(Pres)*

Subsidiaries:

Penn Pride Inc   (1)
1248 Wayne St, Reading, PA 19601
Tel.: (610) 374-3835
Web Site: http://www.pennpride.com
Gasoline Service Stations
N.A.I.C.S.: 457120
John Vespico *(Pres)*

ALEXA'S ANGELS, INC.

621 Innovation Cir, Windsor, CO 80550
Tel.: (970) 686-7247   CO
Web Site: http://www.alexas-angels.com
Year Founded: 1995
Sales Range: $1-9.9 Million
Emp.: 12
Jewelry Stores
N.A.I.C.S.: 339910
Beth Lang *(Pres & CEO)*

ALEXANDER AUTOMOTIVE

685 Hwy 431 S, Boaz, AL 35957
Tel.: (256) 593-4204
Web Site:
    http://www.alexanderautos.com
New & Used Car Dealer
N.A.I.C.S.: 441110
Steven Smith *(Mgr-Sls)*

Subsidiaries:

Alexander Chevrolet   (1)
7710 US Highway 431, Albertville, AL 35950
Tel.: (256) 878-0281
Sales Range: $1-9.9 Million
Emp.: 30
New Car Dealers
N.A.I.C.S.: 441110

Alexander Ford Co. Inc.   (1)
685 US Hwy 431, Boaz, AL 35957
Tel.: (256) 593-4204
Web Site:
    http://www.alexanderfordboaz.com
Sales Range: $25-49.9 Million
Emp.: 25
Automobiles, New & Used
N.A.I.C.S.: 441110

Jalon Alexander *(Controller)*
Max Chandler *(Gen Mgr)*
Greg Osterhage *(Mgr-Fin)*
Leon J. Alexander Jr. *(Pres)*

Chevrolet of Boaz, Inc.   (1)
1134 Hwy 431, Boaz, AL 35957
Tel.: (256) 593-4253
Web Site: http://www.chevroletofboaz.com
Sales Range: $10-24.9 Million
Emp.: 30
Automobiles, New & Used
N.A.I.C.S.: 441110
Charles Spears *(Gen Mgr)*

ALEXANDER AUTOMOTIVE GROUP

1550 NW Broad St, Murfreesboro, TN 37129
Tel.: (615) 956-0346
Web Site:
    https://www.fordofmurfreesboro.com
Emp.: 200
Holding Company; Owner of Automobile Dealerships
N.A.I.C.S.: 423120
Steven Link *(CFO)*

Subsidiaries:

Alexander Ford Lincoln-Mercury, Inc.   (1)
1550 NW Broad St, Murfreesboro, TN 37129
Tel.: (615) 893-4121
Web Site:
    http://www.fordofmurfreesboro.com
Sales Range: $25-49.9 Million
Emp.: 120
Provider of New & Used Automobiles
N.A.I.C.S.: 441110
Donald Alexander *(Pres & Gen Mgr)*
David Lee *(Owner & Gen Mgr)*
Tamara Box *(Mgr-Customer Rels)*
Joe Blevins *(Mgr-BDC & Internet Sls)*
Sandy Clanton *(Office Mgr)*
Chuck Clemens *(Mgr-Dealer Trade & Inventory)*
Chris Ecclesine *(Mgr-Fin)*
Cynthia Gandarilla *(Coord-Bus Dev)*
Art Hill *(Gen Mgr-Sls)*
Terry Kidd *(Mgr-Used Sls)*
Keith McCullough *(Mgr-Fleet Sls)*
Tess Preble *(Controller)*

Ford Lincoln of Franklin   (1)
1129 Murfreesboro Rd, Franklin, TN 37064
Tel.: (615) 794-4585
Web Site:
    http://www.fordlincolnoffranklin.com
Sales Range: $100-124.9 Million
New & Used Automobiles
N.A.I.C.S.: 441110
Buddy Victory *(Dir-Fin)*
Greg Brown *(Mng Partner)*
Jeff Pyle *(Gen Mgr-Sls)*

ALEXANDER BUICK GMC CADILLAC

1501 E Ventura Blvd, Oxnard, CA 93036-1873
Tel.: (805) 351-3005
Web Site:
    https://www.alexanderbgc.com
Sales Range: $25-49.9 Million
Emp.: 100
Car Whslr
N.A.I.C.S.: 441110

ALEXANDER BUILDING CONSTRUCTION, CO.

315 Vaughn St, Harrisburg, PA 17110
Tel.: (717) 234-7041
Web Site:
    https://www.alexanderbuilding.com
Year Founded: 1928
Sales Range: $100-124.9 Million
Emp.: 60
Commercial & Institutional Building Construction Services
N.A.I.C.S.: 236220

Rick Seitz *(Pres)*
Tina Petrie *(Office Mgr)*
Brenda Amoroso *(Dir-Acctg)*

ALEXANDER CHEMICAL CORPORATION

1901 Butterfield Rd Ste 120, Downers Grove, IL 60515
Tel.: (630) 955-6050
Web Site:
    http://www.alexanderchemical.com
Sales Range: $10-24.9 Million
Emp.: 11
Chlorine
N.A.I.C.S.: 424690
Bob Smith *(Mgr-Technical & Regulatory)*
David Kuzy *(Pres & CEO)*
Greg Thiess *(Gen Counsel, Sec & VP)*
Marie Marcenac *(VP-Sls & Mktg-Global)*
Michael Sams *(Gen Mgr-Comml)*
Scott Hoge *(VP-Global Ops)*
Susan Buchanan *(CFO, Treas & VP)*

ALEXANDER GLOBAL PROMOTIONS, INC.

12011 Bel-Red Rd Ste 101, Bellevue, WA 98005
Tel.: (425) 637-0610
Web Site:
    http://www.alexanderglobal.com
Sales Range: $10-24.9 Million
Emp.: 7
Mfr & Distr of Bobblehead Dolls & Promotional Items
N.A.I.C.S.: 541890

ALEXANDER KARTEN

309 E 94th St, New York, NY 10128
Tel.: (212) 368-3000
Web Site:
    http://www.kartenrealty.com
Sales Range: $10-24.9 Million
Emp.: 4
Dry Cleaning Services
N.A.I.C.S.: 812320
Alexander Karten *(Pres)*

ALEXANDER LUMBER CO., INC.

515 Redwood Dr, Aurora, IL 60506-3382
Tel.: (630) 844-5123   DE
Web Site: http://www.alexlbr.com
Year Founded: 1891
Sales Range: $75-99.9 Million
Emp.: 500
Lumber Products Sales
N.A.I.C.S.: 423310
Russell Kathrein *(Pres & CEO)*
Watt Alexander *(Chm)*

Subsidiaries:

Brittingham & Hixon Lumber Co.   (1)
515 Redwood Dr, Aurora, IL 60506-3382
Tel.: (630) 844-5123
Web Site: http://www.alexlbr.com
Sales Range: $10-24.9 Million
Emp.: 20
Lumber, Plywood & Millwork
N.A.I.C.S.: 423310
Russ Kathrein *(Pres & CEO)*

Nagle Lumber Co.   (1)
1201 S Gilbert St, Iowa City, IA 52240
Tel.: (319) 338-1113
Web Site: http://www.doitbest.com
Sales Range: $1-9.9 Million
Emp.: 30
Home Center & Lumber Distr
N.A.I.C.S.: 444110
Jeff Maske *(Pres)*

ALEXANDER MORTGAGE CORP.

Alexander Mortgage Corp.—(Continued)

350 Lincoln St Ste 213, Hingham, MA 02043
Tel.: (781) 740-4161
Web Site: http://www.amortgage.com
Rev.: $100,000,000
Emp.: 6
Mortgage Bankers & Loan Corre-
spondents
N.A.I.C.S.: 522310
John Habeeb (Pres)
Gary Babcock (Sr VP-Sls)
Joanne Dexter (VP-Ops)
Joe Hajjar (VP)

ALEXANDER OIL COMPANY
Hwy 290 & FM 389, Brenham, TX 77833
Tel.: (979) 836-2722
Sales Range: $450-499.9 Million
Emp.: 16
Petroleum Bulk Stations
N.A.I.C.S.: 424720
Jay Alexander (VP-Food Stores)
Jud G. Alexander Sr. (Pres & CEO)
Jud Alexander Jr. (VP-Ops)

ALEXANDER PLASTICS INC.
12750 Perimeter Dr Bldg 120, Dallas, TX 75228
Tel.: (972) 686-7836
Web Site:
   http://www.creationsatdallas.com
Sales Range: $1-9.9 Million
Emp.: 30
Advertising Display Products
N.A.I.C.S.: 339999
Ben Goldfarb (Owner & CEO)

ALEXANDER SERVICES, LLC
802 SE 199th Ave, Portland, OR 97233
Tel.: (503) 666-9491
Web Site: http://www.alexpdx.com
Rev.: $25,842,955
Emp.: 130
Architectural Interiors Fabricator & Installer
N.A.I.C.S.: 337127

ALEXANDER YOUTH NET-WORK
6220 Thermal Rd, Charlotte, NC 28211
Tel.: (704) 366-8712   NC
Web Site:
   https://www.alexanderyouthnet.org
Year Founded: 1903
Sales Range: $10-24.9 Million
Emp.: 407
Child Care Services
N.A.I.C.S.: 624110
Sandra Y. Pizarro (VP-Human Capital)
Trish Hobson (VP-Advancement)
Katy Bullock (Dir-Donor & Volunteer Engagement)

ALEXANDER'S HOLDINGS, LC
245 S 1060 W, Lindon, UT 84042-1606
Tel.: (801) 224-8666   UT
Web Site:
   https://www.alexanders.com
Sales Range: $10-24.9 Million
Emp.: 100
Commercial Printing Services
N.A.I.C.S.: 323111
Jeff Alexander (Founder)
Daniel Mortimer (CTO)
Doyle Mortimer (VP-Ops)

ALEXANDER'S MOBILITY SERVICES
2942 Dow Ave, Tustin, CA 92780
Tel.: (714) 731-1658

Web Site: https://www.alexanders.net
Year Founded: 1953
Rev.: $38,000,000
Emp.: 200
Trucking Service
N.A.I.C.S.: 484121
Donnie Hill (Pres)
Beth Myers (CFO)
Dave Cook (VP-Ops)
James Fellenz (Mgr-Natl Acct & Sls)
Bev Peabody (VP-Sls & Mktg)

Subsidiaries:

Alexander's Mobility Services   (1)
1200 Bengies Rd, Baltimore, MD 21220
Tel.: (410) 406-9200
Web Site: http://www.alexanders.net
Rev.: $18,201,624
Emp.: 65
Contract Haulers
N.A.I.C.S.: 484121
Pam Deem-Hergan (Mgr-Media)
Lisa Jolson (Mgr-Customer Svc)

ALEXANDER-PATTERSON GROUP INC.
12075 NW Blvd Ste 100, Cincinnati, OH 45246-1228
Tel.: (513) 621-9111   OH
Web Site: http://www.apgof.com
Year Founded: 1969
Sales Range: $10-24.9 Million
Emp.: 75
Retailing of Office Furniture
N.A.I.C.S.: 423210
Connie Goings (Pres & Owner)

ALEXANDER/RYAN MARINE & SAFETY CO.
2000 Wayside Dr, Houston, TX 77011
Tel.: (713) 923-1671
Web Site:
   https://www.alexanderryan.com
Year Founded: 1985
Sales Range: $50-74.9 Million
Emp.: 50
Marine Safety Supplies
N.A.I.C.S.: 423860
Tom Jelson (Exec VP & Gen Mgr)
Jamie Matte (CFO & Exec VP)
Mark Dunlap (Exec VP & Gen Mgr)
John F. Ryan III (Pres)

ALEXANDRIA AGTECH/CLIMATE INNOVA-TION ACQUISITION CORP.
26 N Euclid Ave, Pasadena, CA 91101
Tel.: (626) 578-0777   DE
Year Founded: 2021
Investment Services
N.A.I.C.S.: 523999
Joel S. Marcus (Chm & CEO)
Dean A. Shigenaga (Pres & CFO)
Jackie B. Clem (Gen Counsel, Sec & Exec VP)
Lynne Zydowsky (Chief Scientific Officer)
Monica Rivera Beam (Chief Investment Officer)
Blake L. Stevens (Chief Bus Officer)
Jeremy A. Lieberman (VP-Bus Dev)

ALEXANDRIA EXTRUSION COMPANY INC.
401 County Rd 22 NW, Alexandria, MN 56308-4974
Tel.: (320) 763-6537   DE
Web Site:
   http://www.alexandriaextrusion.com
Year Founded: 1966
Sales Range: $10-24.9 Million
Emp.: 424
Mfr of Aluminum Extruded Products
N.A.I.C.S.: 331318
Brian Bloedorn (VP-Sls)
Ritchie Burkey (Mgr-Engrg)

Lynette Kluver (Mgr-Org Dev)
Marc Illies (CFO)
Steve Schabel (Chief Sls & Mktg Officer)

ALEXANDRIA PETERSON CO. INC.
2612 S Broadway St, Alexandria, MN 56308-3415
Tel.: (320) 762-1158   MN
Web Site:
   http://www.petescountymarket.com
Year Founded: 1937
Sales Range: $25-49.9 Million
Emp.: 120
Grocery Stores
N.A.I.C.S.: 445110
Neil R. Peterson (Owner & Pres)

ALEXANDRIA TOYOTA
3750 Richmond Hwy, Alexandria, VA 22305
Tel.: (703) 684-0700
Web Site:
   https://www.alexandriatoyota.com
Sales Range: $75-99.9 Million
Emp.: 180
New Car Retailer
N.A.I.C.S.: 441110
Jeff Salton (Gen Mgr)
George Jermstad (Mgr-Sls)
Aaron Veerothai (Dir-Fin Svcs)
Mikael Holt (Mgr-Fin)
Baiko Ochir (Mgr-Fin)
Darrin Porter (Mgr-Fin)
Cindy Weygandt (Mgr-Fin)
Michael Nguyen (Mgr-Gen Sls)
Carlos Guzman (Mgr-Get Ready Dept)
Yared Manalebih (Mgr-Sls)
Joe Parsons (Mgr-Svc-Columbus)
Jack Taylor (Owner)
Rocky Sulayman Jr. (Mgr-Used Car Sls)

ALEXX, INC.
6520 Platt Ave 633, West Hills, CA 91307
Tel.: (818) 347-7295
Web Site:
   https://www.finderskeypurse.com
Year Founded: 2004
Sales Range: $1-9.9 Million
Emp.: 7
Purse Accessories Mfr
N.A.I.C.S.: 339910
Sandy Stein (Owner & Pres)
Jennifer Jenkins (Dir-Mktg & PD)

ALFA CORPORATION
2108 S Blvd Ste E, Montgomery, AL 36116
Tel.: (334) 288-3900   DE
Web Site: http://www.alfains.com
Year Founded: 1946
Sales Range: $800-899.9 Million
Emp.: 2,500
Holding Company; Insurance Services
N.A.I.C.S.: 551112
C. Lee Ellis (Exec VP-Ops)
Carol Golsan (Sr VP-Mktg Svcs)
Jerry A. Newby (Chm & Pres)
Wyman W. Cabaniss (Sr VP-Underwriting)
Stephen G. Rutledge (Exec VP-Bus Dev)
Thomas E. Bryant (Sr VP-HR)
John T. Jung (CIO & Sr VP)
Ralph C. Forsythe (CFO & Sr VP)
Herman A. Watts (Exec VP-Mktg)
W. Jerry Johnson (Sr VP-Claims)
H. Al Scott (Gen Counsel, Sec & Sr VP)

Alfred E. Schellhorn (Sr VP-Corp Dev)
Robert E. Robison (Sr VP-Life & Loan Ops)

Subsidiaries:

Alfa Agency   (1)
2108 E S Blvd, Montgomery, AL 36116
Tel.: (334) 288-3900
Web Site: http://www.alfafarmers.org
Sales Range: $250-299.9 Million
Emp.: 1,100
Insurance Services
N.A.I.C.S.: 524210

Alfa Alliance Insurance Corp.   (1)
4480 Cox Rd, Glen Allen, VA 23060-6751
Tel.: (804) 346-1900
Web Site: http://www.alfaaic.com
Sales Range: $50-74.9 Million
Emp.: 80
Fire Marine & Casualty Insurance Services
N.A.I.C.S.: 524126
Doug Joyce (Pres)
Scott Beller (VP-Mktg & Integrated Svcs)
Ken Gee (VP-Claims & Ops)
Matt Roberts (CIO)

Alfa Financial Corporation   (1)
2108 E S Blvd, Montgomery, AL 36116   (100%)
Tel.: (334) 288-3900
Sales Range: $750-799.9 Million
Lending Institution
N.A.I.C.S.: 522291
Rob Robison (Sr VP-Life Insurance)
Steve Rutledge (Exec VP-Ops)
James Parnell (Pres)

Alfa Insurance Corp.   (1)
2108 E S Blvd, Montgomery, AL 36116-0001   (100%)
Tel.: (334) 288-3900
Web Site: http://www.alfains.com
Sales Range: $250-299.9 Million
Emp.: 1,100
Property & Casualty Insurers
N.A.I.C.S.: 524126
Jimmy Parnell (Pres)
David Christenberry (Sr VP-Mktg)
Darrell McNeal (Sr VP-Mktg)
Mark Evans (Sr VP-Mktg)
Tim Timmons (Sr VP-Mktg)
Al Dees (Exec VP-Mktg)
Carol Golsan (Sr VP-Mktg Svcs)
Tommy Coshatt (Exec VP-Ops)
John Hemmings (CFO)
Beth Chancey (Sr VP-Property & Casualty Ops)

Alfa Life Insurance Corporation   (1)
2108 E S Blvd, Montgomery, AL 36116   (100%)
Tel.: (334) 288-3900
Web Site: http://www.alfains.com
Sales Range: $250-299.9 Million
Emp.: 1,100
Life Insurance
N.A.I.C.S.: 524113

Alfa Realty, Inc.   (1)
8191 Seaton Pl, Montgomery, AL 36116   (100%)
Tel.: (334) 213-2532
Web Site: http://www.alfarealty.com
Sales Range: $10-24.9 Million
Emp.: 65
Real Estate
N.A.I.C.S.: 531210
Jerry A. Newby (Chm & Pres)
C. Lee Ellis (Exec VP-Opers)
Norman Schlemmer (Gen Mgr)
Denise T. Haviland (Dir-Relocation)

ALFABET, INC.
1 Broadway, Cambridge, MA 02142
Tel.: (617) 401-2320
Web Site: http://www.alfabet.com
Sales Range: $10-24.9 Million
Emp.: 15
Custom Computer Programming Services
N.A.I.C.S.: 541511
Erik Masing (Pres)

ALFANO MOTORCARS, INC.

1423 Calle Jaoquin, San Luis Obispo, CA 93401
Tel.: (805) 543-5752
Web Site:
http://www.alfanomotorcars.com
Year Founded: 2012
Car Whslr
N.A.I.C.S.: 441110
Jeff Kimbal (Sls Mgr)
James Yates (Gen Mgr)
Charlie Alfano (Owner)
Billy Dy (Asst Mgr-Parts)

ALFONSO ARCHITECTS, INC.
1705 N 16th St, Tampa, FL 33605
Tel.: (813) 247-3333   FL
Web Site:
https://www.alfonsoarchitects.com
Year Founded: 1988
Sales Range: $1-9.9 Million
Emp.: 28
Architectural Services
N.A.I.C.S.: 541310
Carlos J. Alfonso (Co-Founder, CEO & Principal)
Alberto E. Alfonso (Co-Founder, Pres & Principal)
Angel Del Monte (Partner, Principal & VP)
Subsidiaries:
Alfonso Architects, Inc. - Italy
Office   (1)
Piazza Tricolore 2, 20129, Milan, Italy
Tel.: (39) 02 795886
Architectural Services
N.A.I.C.S.: 541310

ALFORD MOTORS INC.
Hwy 171, Leesville, LA 71446
Tel.: (337) 239-3811
Web Site:
http://www.alfordmotors.com
Sales Range: $10-24.9 Million
Emp.: 40
New & Used Car Dealers
N.A.I.C.S.: 441110
Steve Alford (Pres)
Sandra Bake (Sec & Controller)

ALFRED ANGELO, INC.
1625 S Congress Ave Ste 400, Delray Beach, FL 33445
Tel.: (215) 659-5300
Web Site:
http://www.alfredangelo.com
Sales Range: $150-199.9 Million
Emp.: 476
Mfr of Bridal, Bridesmaids, Flowergirl & Mother-of-the-Bride Gowns; Bridal Headpieces & Accessories
N.A.I.C.S.: 315250
Michele Piccione (Sec & VP)
Andrew Georgiou (VP-Mktg-Delray Beach)
Paul Quentel (Pres & CEO)

ALFRED BENESCH & COMPANY
400 1 Norwegian Plz, Pottsville, PA 17901
Tel.: (570) 622-4055
Web Site: https://www.benesch.com
Year Founded: 1946
Sales Range: $10-24.9 Million
Emp.: 500
Civil, Structural, Environmental & Geotechnical Engineering Services to Transportation & Infrastructure Development
N.A.I.C.S.: 541330
Gregory Brennan (Sr VP)
George M. Horas (Sr VP & Mgr-Allentown Div)
John F. Curran III (Sr VP-Mid Atlantic)

Subsidiaries:

Alfred Benesch & Company   (1)
840 Hamilton St Ste 400, Allentown, PA 18101   (100%)
Tel.: (610) 439-7066
Web Site: http://www.benesch.com
Emp.: 25
Civil, Structural & Environmental Engineering Services
N.A.I.C.S.: 541330
George Horas (Mgr-Div)

Alfred Benesch & Company   (1)
One S Church St Ste 300 Renaissance Ctr, Hazleton, PA 18201   (100%)
Tel.: (570) 454-2750
Web Site: http://www.benesch.com
Civil, Structural & Geotechnical Engineering Services
N.A.I.C.S.: 237990
Michael Cera (Office Mgr)

Alfred Benesch & Company   (1)
600 Blvd S SW Suite 104, Huntsville, AL 35802-2175   (100%)
Tel.: (256) 705-3575
Web Site: http://www.benesch.com
Civil, Structural, Environmental & Geotechnical Engineering Services
N.A.I.C.S.: 541330
Stephen E. Meyer (Branch Mgr)

Alfred Benesch & Company   (1)
8 Cadillac Dr Ste 250, Brentwood, TN 37027   (100%)
Tel.: (615) 370-6079
Web Site: http://www.benesch.com
Civil, Structural & Environmental Engineering Services
N.A.I.C.S.: 541620
Thomas M. Clinard (Mgr-Div)

Alfred Benesch & Company   (1)
651 E 4th St Suite 100, Chattanooga, TN 37403   (100%)
Tel.: (423) 386-5888
Web Site: http://www.benesch.com
Civil, Structural & Environmental Engineering Services
N.A.I.C.S.: 541330
Stephen E. Meyer (Branch Mgr)

Alfred Benesch & Company   (1)
90 National Dr, Glastonbury, CT 06033   (100%)
Tel.: (860) 633-8341
Web Site: http://www.benesch.com
Civil, Environmental & Geotechnical Engineering Services
N.A.I.C.S.: 237990
James L. Fuda (Mgr-Div)

Alfred Benesch & Company   (1)
50 Redfield St Ste 102, Boston, MA 02122   (100%)
Tel.: (617) 288-0900
Web Site: http://www.web.benesch.com
Emp.: 12
Civil, Structural, Environmental & Geotechnical Engineering Services
N.A.I.C.S.: 541330
Matt Card (Mgr-Div)

Alfred Benesch & Company   (1)
7825 Akron Canfield Rd Suite A, Canfield, OH 44406   (100%)
Tel.: (330) 398-8020
Web Site: http://www.benesch.com
Civil Structural & Geotechnical Engineering Services
N.A.I.C.S.: 541330
Brent W. Hall (Project Manager)

Alfred Benesch & Company   (1)
4660 S Hagadorn Rd Ste 315, East Lansing, MI 48823   (100%)
Tel.: (517) 482-1682
Web Site: http://www.web.benesch.com
Emp.: 15
Civil, Environmental & Structural Engineering Services
N.A.I.C.S.: 237990
James H. Canham (Mgr-Div)

Alfred Benesch & Company   (1)
741 Kenmoor SE Ste A, Grand Rapids, MI 49546   (100%)
Tel.: (616) 214-8117
Web Site: http://www.web.benesch.com

Civil, Engineering & Geotechnical Engineering Services
N.A.I.C.S.: 541330
Chad Rajala (Dir-Construction Svcs)

Alfred Benesch & Company   (1)
1300 W Canal St Ste 150, Milwaukee, WI 53233   (100%)
Tel.: (414) 308-1310
Web Site: http://www.benesch.com
Emp.: 20
Civil, Structural, Environmental & Geotechnical Engineering Services
N.A.I.C.S.: 237990
John Van Huis (Mgr-Div)

Alfred Benesch & Company   (1)
4614 Red Fox Rd, Oshkosh, WI 54904   (100%)
Tel.: (920) 230-6860
Web Site: http://www.benesch.com
Emp.: 3
Civil, Structural & Geotechnical Engineering Services
N.A.I.C.S.: 237990
Dan Grasser (Mgr-Div)

Alfred Benesch & Company   (1)
35 W Wacker Dr Ste 3300, Chicago, IL 60601   (100%)
Tel.: (312) 565-0450
Web Site: http://www.web.benesch.com
Civil, Structural & Environmental Engineering Services
N.A.I.C.S.: 237990
Kevin Fitzpatrick (Mgr-Div)
William H. Epp (Branch Mgr)

Alfred Benesch & Company   (1)
14W 3rd St Ste 220, Kansas City, MO 64105   (100%)
Tel.: (816) 221-4222
Web Site: http://www.benesch.com
Civil, Environmental & Structural Engineering Services
N.A.I.C.S.: 237990
Christopher Burns (Mgr-Div)

Alfred Benesch & Company   (1)
7979 E Tufts Ave Ste 800, Denver, CO 80237   (100%)
Tel.: (303) 771-6868
Web Site: http://www.benesch.com
Civil, Environmental & Geotechnical Engineering Services
N.A.I.C.S.: 237990
Steven C. Banks (Mgr-Div)

Alfred Benesch & Company   (1)
3226 Kimball Ave, Manhattan, KS 66503   (100%)
Tel.: (785) 539-2202
Web Site: http://www.benesch.com
Emp.: 15
Civil, Structural & Environmental Engineering Services
N.A.I.C.S.: 541620
Brad Waller (Branch Mgr)

Alfred Benesch & Company   (1)
913 Sheidley Ave Ste 110, Bonner Springs, KS 66012   (100%)
Tel.: (913) 441-1100
Web Site: http://www.benesch.com
Civil, Environmental & Geotechnical Engineering Services
N.A.I.C.S.: 541330
Christopher Burns (Mgr-Div)

Alfred Benesch & Company   (1)
825 M St Ste 100, Lincoln, NE 68508   (100%)
Tel.: (402) 479-2200
Web Site: http://www.web.benesch.com
Emp.: 65
Civil, Structural & Geotechnical Engineering Services
N.A.I.C.S.: 237990
Anthony Dirks (Mgr-Div)

Alfred Benesch & Company   (1)
14748 W Center Rd Ste 200, Omaha, NE 68144   (100%)
Tel.: (402) 333-5792
Web Site: http://www.web.benesch.com
Civil, Structural & Environmental Engineering Services
N.A.I.C.S.: 237990
Jeffery Sockel (Mgr-Div)

Alfred Benesch & Company - Milwaukee   (1)

1300 W Canal St Ste 150, Milwaukee, WI 53233
Tel.: (414) 308-1310
Web Site: http://www.benesch.com
Civil, Environmental & Geotechnical Engineering Services
N.A.I.C.S.: 541330

McAfee Henderson Solutions, Inc.   (1)
15323 W 95th St, Lenexa, KS 66219
Tel.: (913) 888-4647
Web Site: http://www.mhs-eng.com
Engineeering Services
N.A.I.C.S.: 541330
Aaron Norris (Project Engr)
Matt Henderson (Pres)

ALFRED CONHAGEN INCORPORATED
2025 State Rte 27, Edison, NJ 08817
Tel.: (732) 287-4565
Web Site: http://www.conhagen.com
Sales Range: $10-24.9 Million
Emp.: 29
Industrial Equipment Services
N.A.I.C.S.: 811210
Alfred Conhagen Jr. (Pres)

ALFRED MATTHEWS, INC.
PO Box 577287, Modesto, CA 95357-7287
Tel.: (209) 577-0140
Web Site:
http://www.alfredmatthews.com
Sales Range: $25-49.9 Million
Emp.: 87
Car Whslr
N.A.I.C.S.: 441110
Paul Caron (Owner)
Vince Porter (Owner)
Susan Filippi (VP)

ALFRED NICKLES BAKERY, INC.
26 N Main St, Navarre, OH 44662-1158
Tel.: (330) 879-5635   OH
Web Site:
https://www.nicklesbakery.com
Year Founded: 1909
Sales Range: $1-4.9 Billion
Emp.: 2,500
Baker of Bread, Buns, Sweet Goods (Including Sweet Rolls, Donuts, Cake) & Hard Rolls; Brown-n-Serve Rolls; English Muffins
N.A.I.C.S.: 311812

Subsidiaries:

Alfred Nickles Bakery, Inc. - Lima   (1)
1950 N Sugar St, Lima, OH 45801
Tel.: (419) 229-6012
Web Site: http://www.nicklesbakery.com
Bakery
N.A.I.C.S.: 311812

Nickles Bakery, Inc.   (1)
1000 Broadway St, Martins Ferry, OH 43935-1972   (100%)
Tel.: (740) 633-1711
Web Site: http://www.nicklesbakery.com
Rev.: $30,000,000
Emp.: 175
Mfr of Bread & Buns
N.A.I.C.S.: 311812
Mark Sponseller (Treas & VP-Fin)
David A. Gardner (Sec & Exec VP)
Philip Gardner (VP-Mktg)
Christian Gardner (VP-Admin)
Tony Slee (VP-HR)

ALFRED PUBLISHING COMPANY INC.
16320 Roscoe Blvd Ste 100, Van Nuys, CA 91406-1216
Tel.: (818) 891-5999   NY
Web Site: http://www.alfred.com
Year Founded: 1922

Alfred Publishing Company Inc.—(Continued)
Sales Range: $25-49.9 Million
Emp.: 182
Educational Music Publisher & Music Supplies Retailer
N.A.I.C.S.: 513199

Subsidiaries:

Alfred Music (S) Pte Ltd   (1)
20 Sin Ming Lane 05-54 Midview City 5th Floor, Singapore, 573968, Singapore
Tel.: (65) 6659 8919
Educational Music Publisher & Music Supplies Retailer
N.A.I.C.S.: 513199

Alfred Music Co. (UK) Ltd.   (1)
Burnt Mill Elizabeth Way, Harlow, CM20 2HX, Essex, United Kingdom
Tel.: (44) 1279 828960
Web Site: http://www.alfreduk.com
Emp.: 4
Educational Music Publisher & Music Supplies Retailer
N.A.I.C.S.: 513199
Alex Ordonez (VP-Mktg)

Alfred Music GmbH   (1)
Lutzerathstrasse 127, 51107, Cologne, Germany
Tel.: (49) 2219335390
Web Site: http://www.alfredmusic.de
Educational Music Publisher & Music Supply Services
N.A.I.C.S.: 513199

ALFRED STEIN INC.
235 S Main St, Doylestown, PA 18901
Tel.: (215) 348-9438   **PA**
Web Site:
http://www.keystonemotors.com
Year Founded: 1956
Sales Range: $50-74.9 Million
Emp.: 100
New & Used Car Dealers
N.A.I.C.S.: 441110

ALFRED WILLIAMS & COMPANY
410 S Southbury St Ste 200, Raleigh, NC 27601
Tel.: (919) 832-9570
Web Site:
https://www.alfredwilliams.com
Year Founded: 1867
Sales Range: $25-49.9 Million
Emp.: 185
Office Furniture Mfr & Distr
N.A.I.C.S.: 423210
J. Blount Williams (Chm & CEO)
Gordon Brown (Exec VP-Fin & Admin)
Katherine Thomas (VP-Bus Dev & Mktg)
John McKinney (Pres)
Kevin Wilson (Dir-Design)
Nicholas Hofer (Dir-Interior Construction)
Katherine Owens (Mgr-Design-Raleigh, Durham & Triad)
Jennifer Hickerson (Pres-Triangle & Triad)

ALFREDO'S FOREIGN CARS INC.
2030 Boston Post Rd, Larchmont, NY 10538
Tel.: (914) 834-4222
Rev.: $25,000,000
Emp.: 35
Owner & Operator of Car Dealerships
N.A.I.C.S.: 441110
Ellonor Gulla (Gen Mgr)

ALFY, INC.
391 Broadway Fl 5, New York, NY 10013
Tel.: (212) 968-0600   **DE**

Web Site: http://www.alfy.com
Year Founded: 1998
Sales Range: $10-24.9 Million
Emp.: 6
Web Portal for Children
N.A.I.C.S.: 541511

ALG ADMIRAL INC
745 Dillon Dr, Wood Dale, IL 60191
Tel.: (630) 766-3900
Web Site:
http://www.algworldwide.com
Sales Range: $10-24.9 Million
Emp.: 90
Provider of Logistics Services
N.A.I.C.S.: 488510
James Herzinger (CEO)

Subsidiaries:

Admiral Air Express Inc.   (1)
745 Dillon Dr, Wood Dale, IL 60191
Tel.: (630) 350-7000
Web Site: http://www.algworldwide.com
Sales Range: $10-24.9 Million
Freight Transportation Arrangement
N.A.I.C.S.: 488510
Eric Hezinger (Pres)

ALGENOL BIOFUELS INC.
28100 Bonita Grande Dr Ste 200, Bonita Springs, FL 34135
Tel.: (239) 498-2000
Web Site:
http://www.algenolbiofuels.com
Sales Range: $1-9.9 Million
Emp.: 160
Biofuel Production
N.A.I.C.S.: 324199
Edward J. Legere (Co-Founder & COO)
Ronald Chance (Exec VP-Engrg)
Kathleen McFadden (CFO)
Quang Ha (Gen Counsel)
Paul Roessler (Chief Scientific Officer)
Jacques Beaudry-Losique (Sr VP-Corp & Bus Dev)
Craig R. Smith (COO & Exec VP)

Subsidiaries:

Algenol Biofuels Germany GmbH (1)
Magnusstrasse 11, 12489, Berlin, Germany
Tel.: (49) 30 63 92 44 80
Web Site: http://www.algenol.com
Emp.: 30
Biofuel Production
N.A.I.C.S.: 324199
Heike Enke (Chief Scientific Officer)
Christian Mosoer (Mng Dir)

ALGER ASSOCIATES, INC.
100 Pearl St,, New York, NY 10004
Tel.: (212) 806-8800
Web Site: https://www.alger.com
Emp.: 100
Financial Services
N.A.I.C.S.: 523999

Subsidiaries:

Alger Group Holdings, LLC.   (1)
100 Pearl St,, New York, NY 10004
Tel.: (212) 806-8000
Web Site: https://www.alger.com
Financial Services
N.A.I.C.S.: 523999

Subsidiary (Domestic):

Fred Alger Management, Inc.   (2)
369 Park Ave S, New York, NY 10010
Tel.: (212) 806-8800
Web Site: http://www.alger.com
Sales Range: $25-49.9 Million
Emp.: 170
Investment Services
N.A.I.C.S.: 523940
Dan C. Chung (CEO, Chief Investment Officer & Portfolio Mgr)
Gregory S. Adams (Sr VP, Dir-Quantitative & Risk Mgmt & Mgr-Portfolio)
Ted Doyle (Sr VP)

Alex Goldman (Sr VP & Portfolio Mgr)
David B. Molnar (VP)
Pedro Marcal (Sr VP & Portfolio Mgr)
Warren Zhang (VP)
Matthew Margolis (VP)
Amy Y. Zhang (Sr VP & Portfolio Mgr)
Teresa McRoberts (Sr VP & Portfolio Mgr)
John P. Carbone (Sr VP-Institutional Sls & Svc)
Ankur Crawford (Sr VP & Portfolio Mgr)
Christopher R. Walsh (Sr VP & Portfolio Mgr)
Deborah A. Velez Medenica (Sr VP & Portfolio Mgr)
Michael J. Melnyk (Sr VP & Head-Equality Trading)
Steven Thumm (Sr VP & Head-Equality Trading)
Vikram Khullar (VP)
Tina M. Payne (Gen Counsel & Sr VP)
Scott Anderson (VP)
Joshua D. Bennett (Sr Mng Dir & Dir-Res)
Daniel J. Brazeau (Mng Dir)
Nidhi Chadda (VP)
Elizabeth Clapp-Carey (Sr VP & Head-Retail Sls)
Thomas Debourcy (VP)
Mathew Goldberg (Sr VP & Mgr-Sls-Western US)
Andrew Gustin (VP)
Dennis Hearns (Sr VP & Mgr-Sls-Eastern US)
Kirk Hotte (Sr VP & Head-Intl Sls)
Alan C. Kirby (Sr VP)
Marcus Kupferschmidt (VP)
David Lewis (VP)
Heiner Lez (VP)
Andrew Merrill (VP)
David Miele (VP & Mgr-Acct-Natl)
Edward M. B. Minn (Mng Dir)
Robert O'Dell (VP)
May Poon (Sr VP & Dir-Natl Accts)
Benjamin Reynolds (VP)
Eric Seidman (VP-Retirement Sls)
C. J. Sylvester (VP)
Siang Meng Tan (VP)
Christie Tully (Sr VP & Head-HR)
Sanjiv Talwar (Sr VP, Head-Health Care & Portfolio Mgr)
Keye S. K. Chow (Sr VP)
Brandon Geisler (Sr VP & Portfolio Mgr)
John Stergiou (Sr VP & Head-Natl Accounts)
Christoph Hofmann (Pres & Chief Distr Officer)

Subsidiary (Domestic):

Fred Alger & Company Incorporated   (3)
600 Plaza One, Jersey City, NJ 07311-4041   (100%)
Web Site: http://www.alger.com
Sales Range: $50-74.9 Million
Emp.: 125
Security Brokers & Dealers
N.A.I.C.S.: 523940
William Huang (VP-Institutional Sls & Svc)
Jim Tambone (Chief Distr Officer & Exec VP)
John Dashtara (Sr VP & Co-Head-Institutional)
Ted Doyle (Co-Head-Institutional)

ALGER MANUFACTURING, LLC
724 S Bon View Ave, Ontario, CA 91761
Tel.: (909) 986-9099
Web Site: http://www.alger1.com
Year Founded: 1957
Emp.: 111
Screw Machine Product Mfr
N.A.I.C.S.: 333517
Duane Femrite (CEO)
Jim Hemingway (Pres)
Danny Hankla (VP-Ops)
Sherri Cheline (Acct Exec)
Debbie Miller (Dir-Quality Assurance)
Cathy Peterson (Supvr-Customer Svc)

ALGIERE CONSTRUCTION SERVICES, INC.
7704 San Jacinto Pl Ste 100, Plano, TX 75024-3200

Tel.: (972) 618-1100
Web Site:
https://www.algierehospitality.com
Sales Range: $10-24.9 Million
Emp.: 35
Residential Construction Services
N.A.I.C.S.: 236118
Robert Algiere (Owner)

ALGOOD FOOD COMPANY
7401 Trade Port Dr, Louisville, KY 40258
Tel.: (502) 637-3631   **KY**
Web Site:
https://www.algoodfood.com
Year Founded: 1985
Sales Range: $100-124.9 Million
Emp.: 200
Peanut Butter, Jellies, Jams, Preserves & Salsa
N.A.I.C.S.: 311911
Cecil C. Barnett (Owner)
Nick Melhuish (Pres)
James Melmuish (Mgr-Sls)

Subsidiaries:

Windstone Farms, LLC.   (1)
3097 N Middletown Rd, Paris, KY 40361
Tel.: (859) 987-0739
Web Site: http://www.windstonefarms.com
Jam Whslr
N.A.I.C.S.: 424490
James Melhuish (Gen Mgr)

ALHAMBRA CHRYSLER JEEP DODGE
1100 W Main St, Alhambra, CA 91801
Tel.: (626) 576-5988
Web Site:
http://www.alhambracdjr.com
Year Founded: 2009
Sales Range: $10-24.9 Million
Emp.: 60
New Car Whslr
N.A.I.C.S.: 441110
R. Bridenstine (COO)

ALHAMBRA NISSAN
726 E Main St, Alhambra, CA 91801-4052
Tel.: (626) 289-6161
Web Site:
http://www.alhambranissan.com
Year Founded: 1984
Sales Range: $10-24.9 Million
Emp.: 54
New Car Whslr
N.A.I.C.S.: 441110
Ashkan Pirhadi (Dir-Sls)

ALI SPECIALTIES
1614 N 17th St, Tampa, FL 33605
Tel.: (813) 402-2759
Web Site:
http://www.alispecialties.com
Sales Range: $1-9.9 Million
Emp.: 5
Marketing Promotional Products
N.A.I.C.S.: 541890
Ali Carr (CEO)

ALIA CORP.
140 Heron Way, Merced, CA 95341
Tel.: (209) 723-3716
Sales Range: Less than $1 Million
Emp.: 10
Fast-Food Restaurant, Chain
N.A.I.C.S.: 722513
Anthony Abbate (Pres)

ALIANDA
11579 Vicolo Loop, Windermere, FL 34786

Tel.: (407) 694-5210
Sales Range: $500-549.9 Million
Emp.: 5
Advertising, Broadcast, Corporate Identity, Email, Graphic Design, Health Care, Hospitality, Internet/Web Design, Logo & Package Design, Print, Real Estate, Retail
N.A.I.C.S.: 541810
Mitchell Erick *(Principal & Dir-Creative)*
Daniel Moye *(Principal & Dir-Creative)*
Kathleen Peters *(Dir-Strategic Mktg)*

ALIANZA INC.

1064 S N County Blvd, Pleasant Grove, UT 84062
Tel.: (801) 802-6400
Web Site: http://www.alianza.com
Software Publisher
N.A.I.C.S.: 513210
Clint Peck *(CTO)*
Brian Beutler *(Founder, Pres & CEO)*

Subsidiaries:

CounterPath Corporation (1)
Suite 300 One Bentall Centre 505 Burrard Street, Vancouver, V7X 1M3, BC, Canada
Tel.: (604) 320-3344
Web Site: http://www.counterpath.com
Rev.: $12,101,326
Assets: $13,655,953
Liabilities: $11,611,636
Net Worth: $2,044,317
Earnings: ($1,096,565)
Emp.: 72
Fiscal Year-end: 04/30/2020
Multimedia Application Software Designer, Developer & Marketer
N.A.I.C.S.: 513210
Michael Doyle *(VP-Tech)*
Bruce Ford *(Sr VP-Strategic Bus Dev)*
John Wigboldus *(Sr VP-Sls)*
Nemer D. Abourizk *(Gen Counsel)*
Jim O'Brien *(VP-Server Engrg, Ops & IT)*
Rahim Rehmat *(VP-Client Dev)*
Damian Wallace *(VP-Product & Customer Success)*
Hanna Miller *(VP-Mktg)*
Brian Beutler *(CEO)*

Subsidiary (US):

BridgePort Networks, Inc. (2)
651 W Washington Blvd Ste 500, Chicago, IL 60661
Tel.: (312) 377-1345
Sales Range: $25-49.9 Million
Emp.: 5
Software Publisher
N.A.I.C.S.: 513210

Subsidiary (Domestic):

CounterPath Technologies Inc. (2)
Suite 300 One Bentall Centre 505 Burrard St, PO Box 95, Vancouver, V7X 1M3, BC, Canada
Tel.: (604) 320-3344
Web Site: https://www.counterpath.com
Telecommunication Servicesb
N.A.I.C.S.: 517111

ALICE MANUFACTURING CO. INC.

208 E 1st Ave, Easley, SC 29640-3039
Tel.: (864) 859-6323   SC
Web Site:
http://www.alicemillsinc.com
Year Founded: 1952
Sales Range: $25-49.9 Million
Emp.: 250
Provider of Broadwoven Fabric Mill Services
N.A.I.C.S.: 313210
Robert Thomas *(Controller)*
E. Smyth McKissick III *(Pres)*

ALIEN TECHNOLOGY CORPORATION

845 Embedded Way, San Jose, CA 95138
Tel.: (408) 782-3900   DE
Web Site:
http://www.alientechnology.com
Year Founded: 1994
Emp.: 241
Radio Frequency Identification Mfr
N.A.I.C.S.: 334220
David Aaron *(Chief Legal Officer & VP-Bus Dev)*
Patrick Ervin *(Pres, CMO & Chief Sls Officer)*
Duane E. Zitzner *(Chm)*
Steve Wang *(CTO)*
Glenn R. Haegele *(CFO)*

ALIGN CAPITAL PARTNERS, LLC

4001 Maple Ave Ste 20, Dallas, TX 75219
Tel.: (214) 780-0850   TX
Web Site: http://www.aligncp.com
Year Founded: 2016
Rev.: $325,000,000
Privater Equity Firm
N.A.I.C.S.: 523999
Steve P. Dyke *(Co-Founder & Mng Partner)*
Christopher K. Jones *(Co-Founder & Mng Partner)*
Kurt Smentek *(VP)*
David Tiley *(Sr Operating Partner)*
Matt Iodice *(Principal)*

Subsidiaries:

Alliance Source Testing LLC (1)
255 Grant St Ste 600, Decatur, AL 35603
Tel.: (256) 351-0121
Web Site: http://stacktest.com
Environmental Services
N.A.I.C.S.: 541620

Subsidiary (Domestic):

Almega Environmental & Technical Services, Inc. (2)
5251 McFadden Ave, Huntington Beach, CA 92649
Tel.: (714) 889-4000
Web Site:
http://www.almegaenvironmental.com
Sales Range: $1-9.9 Million
Emp.: 11
Scientific & Technical Consulting Services
N.A.I.C.S.: 541690
John Phillips *(Pres)*

Counsel Press, Inc (1)
460 W 34th St 4th Fl, New York, NY 10001
Tel.: (212) 685-9800
Web Site: http://www.counselpress.com
Legal Appellate Services
N.A.I.C.S.: 541110

E Source Companies, LLC (1)
1745 38th St, Boulder, CO 80301
Tel.: (303) 444-7788
Web Site: http://www.esource.com
Business Consulting Services
N.A.I.C.S.: 541690
Ted Schultz *(CEO)*
Matthew Burks *(Chief Strategy Officer)*
Michael Carter *(Chief Revenue Officer & Pres-Research & Advisory Div)*
Tom Martin *(VP-Commercialization & Data Science)*
Adam Stotz *(CTO)*
Jonathan Willcox *(CFO)*
Kym Wootton *(Chief Admin Officer)*
Filomena Gogel *(Sr VP-Mgmt Consulting)*
Reinhard Sturm *(Sr VP-Water Loss Consulting)*
Edwin Crow *(Sr VP-Customer Sys Consulting)*

Subsidiary (Domestic):

StrategyWise, LLC (2)
2204 1st Ave S Ste 101, Birmingham, AL 35233
Web Site: http://www.strategywise.com
Business Management Consulting Services
N.A.I.C.S.: 541611

Joshua Jones *(Mng Partner)*

Ums Group, Inc. (2)
5 Sylvan Way Ste 120, Parsippany, NJ 07054
Tel.: (973) 335-3555
Web Site: http://www.umsgroup.com
Sales Range: $1-9.9 Million
Emp.: 45
Management Consulting Services
N.A.I.C.S.: 541611
Jan Schipper *(Mng Dir)*
Jeffrey W. Cummings *(Mng Dir-Americas)*
Ennio R. Neumann Senese *(Mng Dir-Europe)*
Ed De Vroedt *(Mng Dir-Benelux & Dir-Fin-Europe)*
Diego Klappenbach *(Mng Dir-Scandinavia)*

Utiliworks Consulting, LLC (2)
2351 Energy Dr Ste 1200, Baton Rouge, LA 70808
Tel.: (225) 766-4188
Web Site: http://www.utiliworks.com
Other Electric Power Generation
N.A.I.C.S.: 221117
Todd James Barlow *(VP-Ops)*

Utilligent LLC (2)
118 E Main St, New Albany, OH 43054-9143
Web Site: http://www.utilligent.com
Management Consulting Services
N.A.I.C.S.: 541611
Helen A. Burt *(Chief Customer Officer & Exec VP)*
Mike Bassignani *(Founder & CEO)*
Maria DeChellis *(VP-Customer Engagement)*
Jay Reseigh *(VP-Data & Analytics)*

Water Systems Optimization, Inc. (2)
102 Space Park S, Nashville, TN 37211
Tel.: (615) 834-6100
Web Site: http://www.wso.us
Rev.: $1,714,000
Emp.: 7
Engineeering Services
N.A.I.C.S.: 541330
Reinhard Strom *(CEO)*

Lewellyn Technology, LLC (1)
6210 Technology Ctr Dr Ste 200, Indianapolis, IN 46278
Tel.: (812) 847-3525
Web Site: http://www.lewellyn.com
Rev.: $6,200,000
Emp.: 35
Electrical & Combustible Dust Safety Services
N.A.I.C.S.: 561499

Subsidiary (Domestic):

Predictive Service, LLC (2)
25200 Chagrin Blvd Ste 300, Cleveland, OH 44122
Tel.: (216) 378-3500
Web Site: http://www.predictiveservice.com
Sales Range: $1-9.9 Million
Emp.: 27
Inspection of Electrical & Mechanical Equipment
N.A.I.C.S.: 334515
Donald Frankel *(Pres & CEO)*
John Harman *(COO)*
Bret Bevis *(Mng Dir)*

Marco Rubber & Plastic Products, Inc. (1)
35 Woodworkers Way, Seabrook, NH 03874
Tel.: (603) 468-3600
Web Site: http://www.marcorubber.com
Rubber & Plastic Product Whslr
N.A.I.C.S.: 423840
Chad Belinsky *(Pres)*
Kal Al-Saleem *(VP)*

Subsidiary (Domestic):

American Seal & Packaging, Inc. (2)
1537 E McFadden Ave Ste A, Santa Ana, CA 92705-4317
Tel.: (714) 593-9780
Web Site: http://www.aspseal.com
Industrial Supplies Merchant Whslr
N.A.I.C.S.: 423840

Anchor Rubber Products, LLC (2)

152 Rockwell Rd, Newington, CT 06111
Tel.: (860) 667-2628
Web Site: http://www.anchorrubber.com
Sales Range: $1-9.9 Million
Emp.: 10
Hose, Belting & Packing
N.A.I.C.S.: 423840
Robert Shannon *(Pres)*

Pleatco, LLC (1)
11201 Ampere Ct, Louisville, KY 40299
Tel.: (502) 240-0443
Web Site: http://www.pleatco.com
Commercial & Service Industry Machinery Mfr
N.A.I.C.S.: 333310
Seth Soltow *(Pres)*
Battista Remati *(CMO)*
Sharon Adams *(CFO)*
Josh Saxon *(VP-Ops-IAF)*

Subsidiary (Domestic):

APEL International, LLC (2)
11201 Ampere Ct, Louisville, KY 40299
Tel.: (502) 240-0443
Air Purification Equipment Mfr
N.A.I.C.S.: 333413

Subsidiary (Non-US):

Milton Manufacturing Inc. (2)
8155 Parkhill Dr, Milton, L9T 5H5, ON, Canada
Tel.: (905) 878-1714
Filtration Products Mfr
N.A.I.C.S.: 322299

Subsidiary (Domestic):

TVS Filters (2)
3040 Dublin Cir, Bessemer, AL 35022
Tel.: (205) 426-8770
Industrial & Commercial Fan & Blower Mfr
N.A.I.C.S.: 333413

Protegis, LLC (1)
6155 Rockside Rd Ste 400, Independence, OH 44131
Tel.: (502) 694-1550
Web Site: http://www.protegis.com
Electrical Apparatus & Related Equipment Merchant Whslr
N.A.I.C.S.: 423610
Jason Hauser *(Ops Mgr-Security)*

Subsidiary (Domestic):

ABCO Fire Protection, Inc. (2)
4545 W 160th St, Cleveland, OH 44135
Tel.: (216) 433-7200
Fire Protection Products & Services
N.A.I.C.S.: 922160
Steve DeJohn *(Pres & COO)*

Fireguard LLC (2)
1516 Jabez Run, Millersville, MD 21108
Tel.: (410) 487-0500
Web Site: http://www.protegis.com
Foundation, Structure & Building Exterior Contractors
N.A.I.C.S.: 238190

StenTech, Inc. (1)
22 Manchester Rd Unite 8B, Derry, NH 03038
Tel.: (603) 505-4470
Web Site: https://www.stentech.com
Appliances, Electrical & Electronics Mfg.
N.A.I.C.S.: 334412

Subsidiary (Domestic):

Photo Etch Technology (2)
3014 Scott Blvd, Santa Clara, CA 95054-3323
Tel.: (408) 988-0220
Bare Printed Circuit Board Mfr
N.A.I.C.S.: 334412

ALIGN COMMUNICATIONS INC.

55 Broad St 6th Fl, New York, NY 10004
Tel.: (212) 207-2600
Web Site: http://www.align.com
Year Founded: 1986
Sales Range: $10-24.9 Million
Emp.: 120

Align Communications Inc.—(Continued)

Provider of Global Information Technology Solutions
N.A.I.C.S.: 541618
Bruce M. Gans (Dir-Asset Point)
James J. Dooling (Pres & CEO)
Tom Weber (Principal)
Mark Rode (VP-Sls)
Stuart McArthur (Head-AV Consultancy Workplace Tech-London)
John Sarkis (Chief Revenue Officer)

ALIGN CREDIT UNION
40 Market St, Lowell, MA 01852
Tel.: (978) 452-9961   **MA**
Web Site: https://www.aligncu.com
Year Founded: 1922
Sales Range: $10-24.9 Million
Emp.: 139
Credit Union Operator
N.A.I.C.S.: 522130
Kenneth M. Del Rossi (Pres & CEO)
Andrew Patton (Asst VP-Comml Lending)
Kelly Tahan (Mgr-Haverhill)
Megan Brady (Mgr-Danvers)

ALIGN FINANCIAL GROUP, LLC
350 10th Ave Ste 1450, San Diego, CA 92101
Tel.: (619) 333-2500
Web Site:
https://www.aligngeneral.com
Year Founded: 2005
Emp.: 30
Holding Company; Insurance Agency & Claims Services
N.A.I.C.S.: 551112
Kieran Sweeney (Pres & CEO)
Jerry Batcheller (COO)
Frank Dunne (Sr VP-Specialty Program)
Rod Eldred (Sr VP-Workers Compensation & Comml Auto Div)
Michelle Roccoforte (CFO)

Subsidiaries:

Align General Insurance Agency, LLC   (1)
350 10th Ave Ste 1450, San Diego, CA 92101
Tel.: (619) 333-2500
Web Site: http://www.aligngeneral.com
Insurance Agents
N.A.I.C.S.: 524210
Kieran A. Sweeney (Pres & CEO)
Jerry Batcheller (COO)
Frank Dunne (Sr VP-Specialty Program Div)
Rod Eldred (Sr VP-Workers Compensation & Comml Auto Div)
Mike Towell (Sr VP-Excess & Umbrella Liability)
Jack Abney (Sr VP-Environmental)

National Lloyds Corporation   (1)
510 N Vly Mills Dr, Waco, TX 76710-6075
Tel.: (254) 399-0626
Sales Range: $50-74.9 Million
Emp.: 140
Holding Company; Property & Casualty Insurance Products & Services
N.A.I.C.S.: 551112

Subsidiary (Domestic):

NLASCO National Lloyds, Inc.   (2)
325 N Saint Paul Ste 800, Dallas, TX 75201
Tel.: (800) 749-6419
Web Site:
http://www.nationalllloydsinsurance.com
Property & Casualty Insurance
N.A.I.C.S.: 524126

NationsBuilders Insurance Services, Inc.   (1)
Overlook III 2859 Paces Ferry Rd Ste 800, Atlanta, GA 30339
Tel.: (770) 257-1704
Web Site: http://www.nbis.com

Sales Range: $75-99.9 Million
Emp.: 110
Insurance Underwriter for the Construction Industry
N.A.I.C.S.: 236115
William C. Tepe (Pres)
Arthur P. Kirkner (VP-Claims)
Chris Nelson (Program Mgr-Transportation)
Joe Doerr (Asst Program Mgr-Crane & Rigging)
Lisa McAbee (Mktg Dir)
Keith Adolf (Asst VP-Risk Mgmt)
Ned N. Fleming III (Chm)

Personable General Insurance Agency, Inc.   (1)
350 10th Ave Ste 1450, San Diego, CA 92101
Tel.: (619) 702-7022
Web Site:
http://www.personableinsurance.com
Insurance Agency & Claims Services
N.A.I.C.S.: 524210
Kieran A. Sweeney (Pres & CEO)
Rick Becker (Sr VP-Ops)
Brian Jewell (VP)
Rick Lavite (Chm)
Christal LaVite (VP)
Ken Perilli (Sr VP-Fin)

Subsidiary (Domestic):

Network Holdings Inc.   (2)
2889 Elmwood Dr SE, Smyrna, GA 30080
Tel.: (770) 436-7575
Web Site: http://www.finusa.com
Sales Range: $10-24.9 Million
Emp.: 40
Insurance Agents
N.A.I.C.S.: 524210

Subsidiary (Domestic):

First Insurance Network Inc.   (3)
2889 Elmwood Dr SE, Smyrna, GA 30080
Tel.: (770) 436-7575
Web Site: http://www.finusa.com
Rev.: $10,000,000
Insurance Agents
N.A.I.C.S.: 524210

Peaches Insurance Agency Inc   (3)
2899 Elmwood Dr SE, Smyrna, GA 30080
Tel.: (770) 436-7575
Web Site: http://www.finusa.com
Sales Range: Less than $1 Million
Insurance Agents, Brokers & Service
N.A.I.C.S.: 524210

Peachtree Casualty Insurance Company   (3)
350 10th Ave Ste 1400, San Diego, CA 92101-8701
Tel.: (770) 436-7575
Property & Casualty Insurance Agent
N.A.I.C.S.: 524210
Ricardo J. Lavite (CEO)

Western Re/Managers Insurance Services, Inc.   (1)
2381 Rosecrans Ave Ste 330, El Segundo, CA 90245
Tel.: (424) 236-4300
Web Site: http://www.westernre.com
Sales Range: $150-199.9 Million
Managing General Agents for Excess Property Insurance
N.A.I.C.S.: 524210
Ian Fitt (CEO)
Jon Knouse (Pres)
Janey Hessing (Exec VP)
Melissa Forbes (Exec VP)
John Sauder (VP-Catastrophe Risk)

ALIGN TECHNICAL RESOURCES, LLC
1057 Lincoln Ave, San Jose, CA 95125
Tel.: (408) 800-4018
Web Site:
http://www.alignworkforces.com
Year Founded: 2012
Sales Range: $1-9.9 Million
Information Technology Staffing Services
N.A.I.C.S.: 561311

Jason Lammers (Founder)
Nick Lammers (Mgr-Bus Dev)
Mitch Corsini (Head-Talent)
Ayushi Thinda (Mgr-Ops)
Bettina Zivney (Dir-Mktg)

ALIMCO FINANCIAL CORPORATION
Tel.: (858) 829-6713   **DE**
Web Site:
https://www.alimcofinancial.com
Year Founded: 1985
ALMC—(OTCIQ)
Sales Range: $1-9.9 Million
Emp.: 3
Supplier of High Performance Memory & Memory Intensive Logic Products to the PC, Networking, Telecommunications, Data Communications & Instrumentation Industries
N.A.I.C.S.: 334413
Alan Bradley Howe (Interim CEO)
Chris Dougherty (CEO)
Jon Marcus (Chm)

Subsidiaries:

Alliance Semiconductor (India) Private Limited   (1)
Consulate 1 No1 Richmond Road, Bengaluru, 560 025, India
Tel.: (91) 8056604800
Sales Range: $100-124.9 Million
Mfr of Semiconductors
N.A.I.C.S.: 334413

ALIMED, INC.
297 High St, Dedham, MA 02026-2852
Tel.: (781) 329-2900   **MA**
Web Site: http://www.alimed.com
Year Founded: 1970
Sales Range: $125-149.9 Million
Emp.: 150
Rehabilitation Products, Operating Room Products, X-Ray Accessories & Other Accessories Mfr
N.A.I.C.S.: 423450
Julian Cherubini (Co-Founder)
Shrikant Rahalkar (VP-Mktg)
Adam S. Epstein (CEO)
Alexandra Cherubini (Chm & Pres)
Barbara Cherubini (Co-Founder)

ALINABAL HOLDINGS CORPORATION
28 Woodmont Rd, Milford, CT 06460-8572
Tel.: (203) 877-3241   **DE**
Web Site: https://www.alinabal.com
Year Founded: 1913
Sales Range: $25-49.9 Million
Emp.: 325
Motor Vehicle Parts & Accessories
N.A.I.C.S.: 336350
Samuel S. Bergami (Pres & CEO)
Kevin M. Conlisk (CFO)
Steve Bennett (Dir-HR)

Subsidiaries:

Alinabal Inc.   (1)
28 Woodmont Rd, Milford, CT 06460-8572
Tel.: (203) 877-3241
Web Site: http://www.alinabal.com
Sales Range: $25-49.9 Million
Emp.: 230
Metal Stamping Mfr
N.A.I.C.S.: 332119
Kevin M. Conlisk (CFO)
Steve Bennett (Dir-HR)
Cheryl Lemos (Mgr-IT)
Brian Wood (Controller)

Subsidiary (Domestic):

Alinabal Engineered Products   (2)
28 Woodmont Rd, Milford, CT 06460
Tel.: (203) 877-3241
Web Site: http://www.alinabalepg.com
Emp.: 200

Machine Tools Mfr
N.A.I.C.S.: 333517
Paul Kelly (Gen Mgr)

Alinabal Motion Transfer Devices   (2)
28 Woodmont Rd, Milford, CT 06460
Tel.: (203) 877-3241
Web Site: http://www.alinabalmtd.com
Spherical Bearing Mfr
N.A.I.C.S.: 333613

Practical Automation Inc.   (1)
45 Woodmont Rd, Milford, CT 06460-2883
Tel.: (203) 882-5640
Web Site:
http://www.practicalautomation.com
Sales Range: $10-24.9 Million
Emp.: 50
Printing Trades Machinery
N.A.I.C.S.: 333248

Subsidiary (Domestic):

Daco Instrument Company   (2)
45 Woodmont Rd, Milford, CT 06460
Tel.: (203) 874-2515
Web Site: http://www.dacoinstruments.com
Aircraft Part Mfr
N.A.I.C.S.: 336413

ALINES AUTO GROUP
412 Medford Ave, Patchogue, NY 11772
Tel.: (631) 654-5660
Web Site:
http://www.alinesautosales.com
Year Founded: 1970
Sales Range: $10-24.9 Million
Emp.: 16
Used Car Retailer
N.A.I.C.S.: 441120
Andrew Aline (Pres)
Noah Laden (Mgr-Sls)

ALIPHCOM
PO Box 391600, Mountain View, CA 94039
Tel.: (415) 230-7600   **CA**
Web Site: http://www.jawbone.com
Year Founded: 1999
Emp.: 450
Personal Audio Device, Wireless Communications & Noise-Cancelling Technologies Developer & Mfr
N.A.I.C.S.: 334310

Subsidiaries:

BodyMedia, Inc.   (1)
1 Gateway Ctr 420 Fort Duquesne Blvd, Pittsburgh, PA 15222
Tel.: (412) 288-9901
Web Site: http://www.bodymedia.com
Sales Range: $10-24.9 Million
Emp.: 60
Personal On-Body Sensory & Monitoring Technologies Developer & Mfr
N.A.I.C.S.: 334510
Ivo Stivoric (CTO & VP-New Products)
Jim Seles (VP-Sls & Customer Solutions)

ALIRM, LLC
10 New Maple Ave, Pine Brook, NJ 07058
Web Site: http://www.mellanni.com
Year Founded: 2014
Sales Range: $25-49.9 Million
Linen Product Retailer
N.A.I.C.S.: 449129
Matthew Martin (Mgr-Logistics & Pur)

ALIRON INTERNATIONAL, INC.
5231 Massachusetts Ave, Bethesda, MD 20816
Tel.: (301) 229-1900
Web Site: http://www.aliron.com
Year Founded: 1989
Sales Range: $1-9.9 Million
Emp.: 500
Health Care, Environmental & IT Services
N.A.I.C.S.: 541620

Cora Alisuag *(Pres & CEO)*
Ronald E. Grow *(COO & Exec VP)*
Victoria Emanuelson *(Coord-HR)*

ALIVE COR INC.
30 Maiden Ln Ste 6, San Francisco, CA 94108-5429
Tel.: (415) 795-9807
Web Site: http://www.alivecor.com
Electronics Stores
N.A.I.C.S.: 449210
Priya Abani *(CEO)*

Subsidiaries:

CardioLabs, Inc.   (1)
357 Riverside Dr Ste 1000, Franklin, TN 37067
Tel.: (800) 304-5549
Web Site: http://www.cardiolabs.com
Medical Laboratories
N.A.I.C.S.: 621511
Ghislain Vanderelst *(CEO)*

ALIVE HOSPICE
1718 Patterson St, Nashville, TN 37203
Tel.: (615) 327-1085   TN
Web Site:
   http://www.alivehospice.org
Year Founded: 1975
Sales Range: $25-49.9 Million
Emp.: 442
Hospice & Palliative Care Services
N.A.I.C.S.: 623110
Joseph Hampe *(CFO)*
Barbara Brennan *(COO & Chief Nursing Officer)*
Robert Berkompas *(Chief Medical Officer)*
Kathi Lindstrom *(Sr Dir-Simulation Trng & Pro Dev)*
Judy Orr *(VP-Mission Based Svcs)*
Clark Baker *(Chm)*
Kimberly Goessele *(Pres & CEO)*

ALIVI
3511 NW 91st Ave, Doral, FL 33172
Tel.: (786) 441-8500
Web Site: http://www.alivi.com
Year Founded: 2012
Sales Range: $10-24.9 Million
Emp.: 100
Health Care Srvices
N.A.I.C.S.: 621610
Magdiel Rodriguez *(CEO)*
Caleb Rojas *(Pres)*
Gabriel Rojas *(Chief Revenue Officer)*
Maikel Rodriguez *(VP)*
Manuel Leon *(VP-Bus Dev)*

ALKANO CHEMICAL, INC.
655 N Central Ave 17th Fl, Glendale, CA 91203
Tel.: (818) 649-7826
Web Site:
   http://www.alkanochemicals.com
Pharmaceutical Product Mfr & Distr
N.A.I.C.S.: 325412

ALKIT PRO-CAMERA INC.
227 E 45 St 5 Fl, New York, NY 10017
Tel.: (516) 771-2312
Web Site: http://www.alkit.com
Year Founded: 1984
Sales Range: $25-49.9 Million
Emp.: 104
Sales of Cameras & Photographic Supplies
N.A.I.C.S.: 449210
Steven Buchbinder *(Co-Pres)*
David Buchbinder *(Co-Pres)*

ALKO DISTRIBUTORS, INC.
8801 Kelso Dr, Baltimore, MD 21221
Tel.: (410) 391-4270

Web Site:
   https://www.alkodistributors.com
Year Founded: 1975
Sales Range: $10-24.9 Million
Emp.: 300
Clothing Accessories Whslr
N.A.I.C.S.: 424350
Barry Kozlowski *(VP)*
Damien Pappagallo *(Coord-Warehouse)*
Francesco Deitos *(Gen Mgr)*

ALL ABOUT GIFTS & BASKETS
13129 196th Ave Nw, Elk River, MN 55330
Tel.: (763) 274-1852
Year Founded: 2002
Rev.: $3,900,000
Emp.: 5
Gift, Novelty & Souvenir Shops
N.A.I.C.S.: 459420
William Smith *(Pres)*

ALL ABOUT PACKAGING
2200 W Everett St, Appleton, WI 54914
Tel.: (920) 830-2700
Web Site: https://www.aapack.com
Year Founded: 1997
Rev.: $5,700,000
Emp.: 17
Commercial Printing
N.A.I.C.S.: 323111
April D. Schein *(VP)*
Thomas P. Schein *(Pres)*
Craig Sickler *(Mgr-Pur)*

ALL ABOUT PEOPLE, INC.
4422 E Indian School Rd, Phoenix, AZ 85018
Tel.: (602) 955-1212
Web Site:
   https://www.allaboutpeople.net
Sales Range: $10-24.9 Million
Emp.: 1,428
Human Resources & Executive Search Consulting Services
N.A.I.C.S.: 541612
Sherri Mitchell *(Pres)*
Charles Mitchell *(CEO)*

ALL ACCESS APPAREL INC.
1515 Gage Rd, Montebello, CA 90640
Tel.: (323) 889-4300
Web Site:
   http://www.selfesteemusa.com
Sales Range: $50-74.9 Million
Emp.: 200
Apparel & Outerwear Fabrics, Cotton
N.A.I.C.S.: 313210
Richard Clareman *(Pres)*
Andrea Rankin *(Exec VP)*

ALL AMERICA-PHILLIP'S FLOWER SHOPS, INC.
524 N Cass Ave, Westmont, IL 60559-1503
Tel.: (630) 719-5200
Web Site: https://www.800florals.com
Year Founded: 1923
Sales Range: $25-49.9 Million
Emp.: 300
Online & Telephone Order Florists
N.A.I.C.S.: 459310
Baxter Phillip *(Exec VP)*
Jim Phillip *(Chm)*

ALL AMERICAN ASPHALT
400 E 6th St, Corona, CA 92879
Tel.: (951) 736-7600
Web Site:
   http://www.allamericanasphalt.net
Sales Range: $50-74.9 Million
Emp.: 60

Provider of Highway & Street Paving Contracting Services
N.A.I.C.S.: 237310
Robert Bradley *(VP)*
Michael Farkas *(Controller)*
Mark Luer *(Pres)*

ALL AMERICAN AUTO SALES GROUP
3698 US Hwy 9, Old Bridge, NJ 08857
Tel.: (732) 591-1111
Web Site:
   http://www.allamericansales.com
Sales Range: $100-124.9 Million
Emp.: 140
Holding Company; New & Used Auto Dealerships Owner & Operator
N.A.I.C.S.: 551112
Chris Savino *(Gen Mgr-Ford & Subaru Dealerships-Old Bridge)*
Steve Selman *(Co-Owner)*
Jon Selman *(Co-Owner)*

Subsidiaries:

All American Ford of Kingston, LLC   (1)
128 Rte 28, Kingston, NY 12401
Tel.: (845) 338-7800
Web Site:
   http://www.allamericanfordofkingston.com
Sales Range: $25-49.9 Million
Emp.: 100
New & Used Car Dealer
N.A.I.C.S.: 441110
Ron Mancinelli *(Gen Mgr)*
Cliff Dayton *(Sls Mgr)*
Matthew Gelsleichter *(Mktg Mgr)*
Ken Winters *(Sls Mgr)*
Vincent J. Paliotta *(Gen Sls Mgr)*
Thomas Carter *(Mgr-Internet)*
Eugene Dachenhausen *(Mgr-Svc)*
Andy Gayton *(Mgr-Body Shop)*
Ron Hoetger *(Mgr-Parts)*
Gene Dachenhausen *(Mgr-Parts)*
Bernie Fragola *(Mgr-Body Shop)*
Louis Guerra *(Mgr-Bus)*
James Kennedy *(Mgr-Bus)*
Dave Lieberman *(Mgr-Svc)*
Sherri Nolan *(Mgr-Customer Rels)*
Lann Rubin *(Gen Mgr)*
Melissa Sasso *(Controller)*

All American Ford, Inc.   (1)
3698 Route 9 S, Old Bridge, NJ 08857
Tel.: (732) 591-1111
Web Site:
   http://www.allamericanfordoldbridge.com
New & Used Car Dealer
N.A.I.C.S.: 441110
Chris Savino *(Gen Mgr)*
Joseph Pedi *(Sls Mgr)*
Randy Rudd *(Mgr-Sls-Comml)*
David Nault *(Mgr-Sls-Fleet)*
Nick Savino *(Mgr-Svc Dept)*
Greg Pfeffer *(Mgr-Used Car)*
Lori Lima *(Mgr-Internet Sls)*
Andrew Ly *(Sls Mgr)*
Nicole Pohlmeyer *(Bus Mgr)*
Jason Savino *(Dir-Digital Ops)*
George Villafane *(Bus Mgr)*
Frank Pedi *(Sls Mgr)*
Kimberly Meigh *(Sls Mgr)*
Scott Giaraffa *(Bus Mgr)*
Vince Palazzolo *(Bus Mgr)*
Dave Marino *(Dir-Parts)*

Unit (Domestic):

All American Subaru   (2)
3706 Route 9 S, Old Bridge, NJ 08857
Tel.: (732) 242-0400
Web Site:
   http://www.allamericansubaru.com
New & Used Car Dealer
N.A.I.C.S.: 441110
Chris Savino *(Gen Mgr)*
Mohammed Dada *(Mgr-Bus)*
George Villafane *(Mgr-Bus)*

ALL AMERICAN FOODS, INC.
121 Mohr Dr, Mankato, MN 56001
Tel.: (507) 387-6480   MN
Web Site: https://www.aafoods.com

Year Founded: 1987
Sales Range: $10-24.9 Million
Emp.: 50
Perfumes, Flavorings & Food Additives
N.A.I.C.S.: 561910
Jeff Thom *(CEO)*
Kevin Olson *(Dir-Fin)*
Connie Stokman *(Dir-Sls & Mfg Svcs)*
Kathy Jacobson *(Dir-Tech Svcs)*
Ann Jones *(Dir-HR)*
Crystal Anderson *(VP-Plant Ops)*

ALL AMERICAN GLAMOUR CORP.
700 N High School Rd Ste 203, Indianapolis, IN 46214
Tel.: (562) 453-7643
Year Founded: 2006
Gold Exploration Services
N.A.I.C.S.: 212220
Arlene Meza *(CEO)*

ALL AMERICAN GLASS DISTRIBUTORS INC.
6301 Indiana Ave, Lubbock, TX 79413
Tel.: (806) 799-8807
Rev.: $10,000,000
Emp.: 8
Automobile Glass
N.A.I.C.S.: 423120

ALL AMERICAN HOLDINGS LLC
4200 Northside Pkwy Bldg 5 Ste 508, Atlanta, GA 30327
Tel.: (404) 229-8368   GA
Web Site:
   http://www.allamericanholdings.com
Year Founded: 2006
Privater Equity Firm
N.A.I.C.S.: 523999
Marshall Hunt *(Co-Founder & Mng Partner)*

ALL AMERICAN LENDING GROUP, LLC
4511 North Campbell Ave Ste 205, Tucson, AZ 85718
Tel.: (520) 544-4422
Web Site:
   http://www.allamericanlending.com
Year Founded: 2004
Sales Range: $1-9.9 Million
Emp.: 200
Mortgage Banking Services
N.A.I.C.S.: 522292
David Hand *(Founder)*

ALL AMERICAN MEAT INC.
2800 N Main St, Roswell, NM 88201
Tel.: (575) 623-0042
Rev.: $29,600,000
Emp.: 247
Grocery Stores, Independent
N.A.I.C.S.: 445110
Janet Duffy *(Office Mgr)*

ALL AMERICAN MEATS INC.
11626 I St, Omaha, NE 68137
Tel.: (402) 453-0200
Web Site:
   https://www.allamericanmeats.com
Year Founded: 1966
Sales Range: $25-49.9 Million
Emp.: 30
Processes Meats & Meat Products
N.A.I.C.S.: 311611
Shawn Buchanan *(Pres)*

ALL AMERICAN POLY CORP.
40 Turner Pl, Piscataway, NJ 08854-3839
Tel.: (732) 752-3200
Web Site: http://www.allampoly.com

All American Poly Corp.—(Continued)

Year Founded: 1975
Sales Range: $25-49.9 Million
Emp.: 300
Plastic, Laminated & Coated Bags
N.A.I.C.S.: 326113
Jack Klein *(Pres & CEO)*
James Cerny *(Reg Mgr-Sls)*
Drew Schultz *(Reg Mgr-Sls)*

Subsidiaries:

All American Poly Corp. - Lawrenceville Plant   **(1)**
135 Industrial Park Cir, Lawrenceville, GA
30045
Tel.: (800) 650-1099
Plastics Product Mfr
N.A.I.C.S.: 326199

All American-Arkansas Poly
Corp.   **(1)**
309 Phillips Rd, North Little Rock, AR
72117-4105
Tel.: (501) 945-5763
Web Site: http://www.allamericanpoly.com
Sales Range: $10-24.9 Million
Emp.: 60
Mfr of Plastic, Laminated & Coated Bags
N.A.I.C.S.: 326111

**ALL AMERICAN PROPANE,
INC.**
1617 S Keys Rd, Yakima, WA 98901
Tel.: (509) 575-7682   **WA**
Year Founded: 1995
Sales Range: $10-24.9 Million
Emp.: 10
Liquefied Petroleum Gas Mfr
N.A.I.C.S.: 457210
Dick Start *(Chm & CEO)*
Steve Amdahl *(Pres)*

**ALL AMERICAN QUALITY
FOODS INC.**
125 Eagles Landing Pkwy, Stock-
bridge, GA 30281-3745
Tel.: (770) 474-5904   **GA**
Web Site:
   http://www.myfooddepot.com
Year Founded: 1976
Sales Range: $100-124.9 Million
Emp.: 1,000
Grocery Stores
N.A.I.C.S.: 445110
Raymond Johnson *(VP)*
Donald Chapman *(Mgr-HR)*
Donnie Farmer *(Mgr-Meet)*
Valerie Jean Leger *(Coord-Pricing &
Receiving)*
Sam Taylor *(Mgr-Produce)*

**ALL AMERICAN SEMICON-
DUCTOR, LLC**
3100 NW 363, Miami, FL 33014-6205
Tel.: (305) 621-8282   **DE**
Web Site:
   http://www.allamerican.com
Year Founded: 1964
Sales Range: $200-249.9 Million
Emp.: 600
Electronic Components Distr
N.A.I.C.S.: 423690
Jamil Nizan *(Pres & CEO)*

ALL AMERICAN SWIM
239 County Rd 30, Florence, AL
35634
Tel.: (256) 718-2070
Web Site:
   http://www.allamericanswim.com
Year Founded: 2006
Sales Range: $1-9.9 Million
Emp.: 20
Swimwear Mfr for Men, Women &
Children
N.A.I.C.S.: 315990

Keith Haden *(Co-Owner & Pres)*
Debbie Haden *(Co-Owner)*
Mark Oostman *(Owner)*

**ALL AREA ROOFING & WA-
TERPROOFING, INC.**
1820 N 57th St, Tampa, FL 33619
Tel.: (813) 247-7663
Web Site:
   http://www.allarearoofing.com
Year Founded: 1997
Sales Range: $10-24.9 Million
Emp.: 20
Roofing Contractors
N.A.I.C.S.: 238160
Douglas Richards *(VP-HR & IT)*
Elsa B. Richards *(Pres)*
James Garrett *(Superintendent-
Roofing)*

**ALL AROUND PROPERTY
PRESERVATION, LLC.**
701 Decatur Ave N 201, Golden Val-
ley, MN 55427
Tel.: (763) 447-3944
Web Site:
   http://www.goallaround.com
Year Founded: 2008
Sales Range: $10-24.9 Million
Emp.: 15
Residential Remodeling Services
N.A.I.C.S.: 236118
Nick Zeman *(COO)*
Jordan Muehlberg *(VP)*
Charles Thayer *(Founder & Gen Mgr)*
Eli Clendenen *(Dir-IT)*
Scott Kvigne *(Accountant)*

ALL BASES COVERED INC.
101 Redwood Shores Pkwy, Red-
wood City, CA 94065
Tel.: (650) 486-5000
Web Site: http://www.allcovered.com
Rev.: $28,419,000
Emp.: 45
Computer Related Consulting Ser-
vices
N.A.I.C.S.: 541512
David Beaver *(VP)*
Nick Pegley *(VP-Mktg)*

ALL CAMPUS LLC
30 S Wacker Dr Ste 1650, Chicago,
IL 60606
Tel.: (312) 525-3100
Web Site: http://www.allcampus.com
Year Founded: 2012
Student Recruitment Services
N.A.I.C.S.: 541870
Joe Diamond *(CEO)*
Kyle Shea *(Exec VP-Revenue)*
Heather Shulick *(Exec VP-HR & Ops)*
Andrea Maconachy *(Exec VP-Mktg)*
Pranu Bhargava *(Exec VP-Tech)*
James Wallace *(Exec VP-Enrollment
& Client Svcs)*
Chris Campbell *(VP-Fin)*
Michael Lenzen *(VP-Analytics)*
Steven Robinson *(VP-Creative De-
sign)*
Renda Lederer *(Dir-Sls)*
Josh Fauske *(Dir-Sls)*
Jack Harney *(Mgr-Sls Acct)*
Sara Nolte *(Associate VP-Enrollment
Mgmt)*
Maureen M. Scott *(Dir-Student Suc-
cess)*
Megan Lenzen *(Sr Dir-Client Svcs)*
Samantha Goldstein *(Dir-Client Svcs)*
Heather La Belle *(Dir-Client Svcs)*
Sharon Dalinis *(Dir-Client Svcs)*
Aditya Nathan *(Sr Designer)*

**ALL CHEMICAL LEASING,
INC.**

1975 Rutgers University B, Lake-
wood, NJ 08701
Tel.: (732) 730-2110
Web Site: http://www.allchemical.com
Year Founded: 1978
Sales Range: $10-24.9 Million
Emp.: 70
Shipping, Transportation & Leasing of
Chemicals
N.A.I.C.S.: 532289
Steven Quadrel *(Pres)*

Subsidiaries:

All Chemical Transport   **(1)**
1975 Rutgers Univ B, Lakewood, NJ 08701
Tel.: (732) 730-2110
Trucking Except Local
N.A.I.C.S.: 484121
Steven Quadrel *(Pres)*

**ALL CHICAGOLAND MOVING
& STORAGE CO.**
730 N York Rd, Elmhurst, IL 60126
Tel.: (630) 832-4114
Web Site:
   https://www.allchicagoland.com
Rev.: $12,626,203
Emp.: 50
Trucking Except Local
N.A.I.C.S.: 484121
Michael Illingworth *(Pres)*

**ALL CHILDREN'S HOSPITAL
INC.**
501 6th Ave S St, Saint Petersburg,
FL 33701
Tel.: (727) 898-7451
Web Site: http://www.allkids.org
Year Founded: 1926
Sales Range: $150-199.9 Million
Emp.: 2,800
Children's Hospital
N.A.I.C.S.: 622110
Amy Burton *(Dir-Mktg)*
Roberta M. Alessi *(COO)*
Kristin Maier *(Dir-Child Life Dept)*
Marcos DeLeon *(VP-HR)*
Mohamed Rehman *(Chm-Anesthesia
Dept)*
Sandra Diamond *(Chm)*
Darryl LeClair *(Sec)*
Chris Whitby *(CFO & VP)*
Jose Atilio Canas *(Dir-Endocrinology
& Diabetes)*
Giovanni Cucchiaro *(Dir-Chronic Pain
Program-Dept of Anesthesia)*
Mike Griffin *(CEO)*
Sherron Rogers *(CFO)*
William Lane Jr. *(Vice Chm)*

ALL COAST, LLC
151 Southpark 3rd Fl, Lafayette, LA
70508
Tel.: (337) 560-8000   **LA**
Web Site: https://www.allcoastllc.com
Year Founded: 2013
Liftboat Operator
N.A.I.C.S.: 213112
John Powers *(Co-CEO & Mgr)*
Byron Allemand *(COO & VP)*
John T. Nesser III *(Co-CEO & Mgr)*

**ALL COMMERCIAL FLOORS,
INC.**
2927 Armory Dr, Nashville, TN 37204
Tel.: (615) 742-7465
Web Site:
   http://www.allcommercialfloors.com
Rev.: $2,922,500
Emp.: 13
Home Furnishing Merchant Whslr
N.A.I.C.S.: 423220

**ALL CONTROL ENTERPRISES
INC.**
1644 Cambridge Dr, Elgin, IL 60123

Tel.: (847) 488-9200
Web Site: https://www.allcontrol.com
Year Founded: 1963
Sales Range: $10-24.9 Million
Emp.: 15
Electrical Apparatus & Equipment
Distr
N.A.I.C.S.: 423690
Robert Aslan *(Pres)*

ALL COPY PRODUCTS LLC
4141 Colorado Blvd, Denver, CO
80211
Tel.: (303) 295-0741
Web Site:
   http://www.allcopyproducts.com
Year Founded: 1975
Rev.: $9,000,000
Emp.: 200
Photocopy & Fax Machines Whslr
N.A.I.C.S.: 459999
Brad Knepper *(Pres)*
Donald Schoeninger *(Controller)*

Subsidiaries:

Gobins Inc.   **(1)**
615 N Santa Fe Ave, Pueblo, CO 81003
Tel.: (719) 544-2324
Web Site: http://www.gobins.com
Sales Range: $10-24.9 Million
Emp.: 100
Binoculars
N.A.I.C.S.: 459999
Robert E. Gobin *(Pres)*
Dave Barrows *(Mgr-Sls)*
Ryan Ruiz *(Mgr-Warehouse)*
Ken Spinuzzi *(Mgr-Svc)*

**ALL ERECTION & CRANE
RENTAL CORP.**
7809 Old Rockside Rd, Cleveland,
OH 44131
Tel.: (216) 524-6550
Web Site: https://www.allcrane.com
Rev.: $35,000,000
Emp.: 350
Heavy Construction Equipment
Rental Services
N.A.I.C.S.: 532412
John Sivak *(Controller)*
Michael C. Liptak Jr. *(Pres)*

ALL FASHIONS IMPORTS INC.
1407 Broadway Ste 906, New York,
NY 10018-5199
Tel.: (212) 354-8600
Year Founded: 1990
Sales Range: $10-24.9 Million
Emp.: 72
Clothing Distr
N.A.I.C.S.: 424350

**ALL FLORIDA ELECTRIC
COMPANY INC.**
2606 NE 17th Ter, Gainesville, FL
32609
Tel.: (352) 378-6014   **FL**
Web Site:
   https://www.allfloridaelectric.com
Year Founded: 1967
Sales Range: $10-24.9 Million
Emp.: 80
Electrical Contracting Services
N.A.I.C.S.: 238210
George E. Smith *(Pres)*
Mike Gentry *(VP)*
Sharon Smith *(Treas)*
Dave Sanders *(Project Mgr)*

ALL FLORIDA PAPER
9150 NW 105th Way, Medley, FL
33178
Tel.: (305) 835-6060

Web Site:
https://www.allfloridapaper.com
Sales Range: $25-49.9 Million
Emp.: 70
Printing & Writing Paper Merchant
Whslr
N.A.I.C.S.: 424110
Armando Caceres (Pres)

ALL FREIGHT SYSTEMS INC.
1134 S 12th St, Kansas City, KS
66105
Tel.: (913) 281-1203
Web Site:
http://www.allfreightsystems.com
Rev.: $19,925,435
Emp.: 265
Trucking Service
N.A.I.C.S.: 484121
Robert E. Smith (Pres)
Rich Cambell (Comptroller)
Tom Scholl (Mgr-Ops)

ALL HAPPENING LLC
2248 Meridian Blvd Ste H, Minden,
NV 89423
Web Site:
http://www.newlawbusiness.com
Year Founded: 2011
Sales Range: $1-9.9 Million
Emp.: 7
Educational Support Services
N.A.I.C.S.: 611710
Alexis Katz (Co-Founder & CEO)
Andrew Thomaides (COO)
Robert Kandell (CFO)
Scott De Stephanis (Dir-Client Svcs)
Alexis Neely (Co-Founder)

ALL INC.
185 Plato Blvd W, Saint Paul, MN
55107
Tel.: (651) 227-6331
Web Site: https://www.allinc.com
Year Founded: 1947
Sales Range: $25-49.9 Million
Emp.: 80
Electrical Appliances, Major
N.A.I.C.S.: 423620
James Rutzick (Pres)

ALL LEGAL STAFF INC.
146 2nd St N Ste 310, Saint Peters-
burg, FL 33701
Tel.: (727) 823-3800
Web Site: https://www.als-staff.com
Year Founded: 2001
Sales Range: $1-9.9 Million
Legal Staffing
N.A.I.C.S.: 561311
Theresa Stenner-Jones (Pres)

ALL MAGNETICS INC.
2831 Via Martens, Anaheim, CA
92806
Tel.: (714) 632-1754
Web Site:
https://www.allmagnetics.com
Rev.: $800,000
Emp.: 10
Miscellaneous Fabricated Metal Prod-
uct Mfr
N.A.I.C.S.: 332999
John Nellessen (Owner)

ALL MAKES OFFICE EQUIP-
MENT CO. INC.
2558 Farnam St, Omaha, NE 68131-
3628
Tel.: (402) 341-2413   NE
Web Site: https://www.allmakes.com
Year Founded: 1918
Sales Range: $10-24.9 Million
Emp.: 100
Furniture Dealers
N.A.I.C.S.: 449110

Jeff Kavich (Pres & CEO)
Amee Zetzman (CFO & Exec VP)

Subsidiaries:

All Makes Office Equipment Co.   (1)
3333 O St, Lincoln, NE
68510-1547   (100%)
Tel.: (402) 477-7131
Web Site: http://www.allmakes.com
Sales Range: $10-24.9 Million
Emp.: 35
Office Furniture
N.A.I.C.S.: 423210
Gretchen Golter (VP & Mgr-Store)

All Makes Office Interiors   (1)
500 East Court Ave Ste 150, Des Moines,
IA 50315
Tel.: (515) 282-2166
Web Site: http://www.allmakes.com
Sales Range: $10-24.9 Million
Emp.: 10
Office Furniture
N.A.I.C.S.: 449110

ALL MARINE SPARES INTER-
NATIONAL, LLC
375 Fairfield Ave Bldg 5, Stamford,
CT 06902
Tel.: (203) 487-0422
Web Site:
http://www.allmarinespares.com
Year Founded: 1999
Sales Range: $1-9.9 Million
Emp.: 8
International Trading Specializing in
Supply of Marine Parts & Equipment
N.A.I.C.S.: 425120
Theodosios Panourgias (Co-Pres)

ALL MED MEDICAL SUPPLY,
LLC
6321 Commerce Dr, Westland, MI
48185
Tel.: (734) 728-9490
Web Site: http://www.amms.net
Year Founded: 1995
Sales Range: $10-24.9 Million
Emp.: 33
Physicians & Surgeons Equipment
Whslr
N.A.I.C.S.: 423450
Darryl Franklin (Acct Mgr)
Jessica Pries (Acct Mgr)
Andrea Logan (Pres)
Tim Logan (COO)
Theresa Morris (Dir-Contracts)
Becky Randall (Dir-Corp Accounts)
Kim Schwieter (VP-Ops)

ALL METALS PROCESSING
OF ORANGE COUNTY, LLC
8401 Standustrial St, Stanton, CA
90680
Tel.: (714) 828-8238   CA
Web Site:
https://www.allmetalprocessing.com
Non-destructive Testing, Anodizing,
Plating, Paint & Coatings & Additional
Metal Finishing Services
N.A.I.C.S.: 332813
Michael Coburn (CEO)

Subsidiaries:

Embee Processing, LLC   (1)
2136 S Hathaway St, Santa Ana, CA 92705
Tel.: (714) 546-9842
Web Site: http://www.embee.com
Aircraft Equipment Mfr
N.A.I.C.S.: 336412
Jose Tapia (Mgr-Shipping)
Jaime Michel (Mgr-Receiving)
Debbie Boone (Mgr-Customer Svc)

ALL METRO HEALTH CARE
170 Earle Ave, Lynbrook, NY 11563
Tel.: (516) 887-1200
Web Site: https://www.all-metro.com
Year Founded: 1955

Home Care Services
N.A.I.C.S.: 621610

ALL MOBILE VIDEO
221 W 26th St, New York, NY 10001
Tel.: (212) 727-1234
Web Site:
https://www.allmobilevideo.com
Year Founded: 1976
Provider of Videotape Communica-
tions; Services Allied to TV Produc-
tion
N.A.I.C.S.: 532282
Todd Bivona (Mgr-Stage)
Lenny Laxer (VP)
Tom D'Angelo (Dir)
Ian Dittbrenner (VP-Production Ops &
Bus Dev)
Nova Calise (Mgr-Production)
Lee Blanco (Dir-Engrng)
Derek Purtell (Mgr-Sls Support)
Michael Carberry (VP-VP Transmis-
sion Svcs)

ALL NATION INSURANCE
COMPANY
26600 Telegraph Rd, Southfield, MI
48033-2438
Tel.: (248) 358-4010   MI
Web Site: http://www.coverx.com
Year Founded: 1961
Sales Range: $150-199.9 Million
Emp.: 36
Commercial Insurance
N.A.I.C.S.: 524210
Marcia Paulfen (VP)

ALL POINTS COOPERATIVE
120 W 8th St, Gothenburg, NE
69138-1008
Tel.: (308) 537-7141   NE
Web Site: http://www.allpoints.coop
Year Founded: 1927
Sales Range: $10-24.9 Million
Emp.: 125
Agricultural Services
N.A.I.C.S.: 424510
Mike Schroeder (CFO)
Donna Schnackenberg (Office Mgr)
Mark Ballmer (VP-Agronomy)
Britt Anderson (Sec)
Jeff Beattie (Vice Chm)
Janell Rossen (Mgr-Credit)
Seth Grube (Vice Chm)
Alan Dailey (Mgr-Agronomy)
Jeff Gibbens (Mgr-Agronomy)
Dennis Triplett (Mgr-Car Care)
Rick Esslinger (Mgr-Car Care Center)
Bill Scoville (Mgr-Car Care Center &
C-Store)
Craig Saum (VP-Petroleum)

Subsidiaries:

All Points Cooperative   (1)
707 E Pacific St, Lexington, NE 68850
Tel.: (308) 324-2000
Web Site: http://www.allpoints.coop
Sales Range: $10-24.9 Million
Emp.: 40
Fertilizer, Fertilizer Materials, Feeds & Pe-
troleum Products Wholesaler
N.A.I.C.S.: 424590

ALL PRINTING RESOURCES
INC.
140 W Lake Dr, Glendale Heights, IL
60139
Tel.: (630) 784-3115
Web Site: http://www.teamflexo.com
Sales Range: $10-24.9 Million
Emp.: 50
Printing Trades Machinery; Equip-
ment & Supplies
N.A.I.C.S.: 423830
David Nieman (CEO)
Robert Jacob (CFO)
Catherine Haynes (Dir-Trng)

ALL PRO FREIGHT SYSTEMS
INC.
1200 Chester Industrial Pkwy, Avon,
OH 44011
Tel.: (440) 934-2222
Web Site:
http://www.allprofreight.com
Rev.: $11,831,365
Emp.: 40
Local Trucking with Storage
N.A.I.C.S.: 484110
Chris Haas (Pres & CEO)

ALL PRO SALES, INC.
1108 Quaker St, Dallas, TX 75207
Tel.: (214) 905-0052
Web Site:
http://www.allprosalesinc.com
Year Founded: 1994
Emp.: 50
Electrical Apparatus & Equipment
Distr
N.A.I.C.S.: 423610
Jim Elam (Principal)
Keith Oxley (Principal)
Mal Watson (Mgr-Ops)
David Johansen (Gen Mgr-Lighting)

Subsidiaries:

All Pro Sales, Inc. - Houston   (1)
1295 N Post Oak Rd, Houston, TX 77055
Tel.: (713) 333-7000
Web Site: http://www.allprosalesinc.com
Sales Range: $10-24.9 Million
Emp.: 7
Electrical Apparatus & Equipment Distr
N.A.I.C.S.: 423610
Bobby Mitchell (Principal)
Bob Plummer (Mgr-Ops)
David Johansen (Gen Mgr-Lighting Div)
Kevin Thomas (Gen Mgr-Wire & Cable Div)

ALL PURPOSE, INC.
2625 S 600th W, Salt Lake City, UT
84115
Tel.: (801) 487-8807
Web Site:
http://www.allpurposewindows.com
Year Founded: 1982
Sales Range: $10-24.9 Million
Emp.: 100
Whslr & Retailer of Window & Door
Installation
N.A.I.C.S.: 238130

ALL QUALITY & SERVICES
INC.
401 Kato Ter, Fremont, CA 94539
Tel.: (510) 249-5800   CA
Web Site: http://www.aqs-inc.com
Year Founded: 1991
Printed Circuit Board Mfr
N.A.I.C.S.: 334412
Regina Prim (Mgr-Program)

ALL R.V. SERVICE & REPAIR
155 El Pueblo Dr, Scotts Valley, CA
95066-4229
Tel.: (831) 461-1777
Web Site:
https://www.allrvservice.com
Sales Range: $10-24.9 Million
Emp.: 40
New & Used Car Dealers
N.A.I.C.S.: 441110
Tim Jones (Pres & Owner)

ALL ROADS COMPANY
925 Merritt Blvd, Dundalk, MD 21222
Tel.: (410) 285-0600
Web Site:
http://allroadscompany.com
Year Founded: 1917
Holding Company; Commercial
Equipment, Work Trucks, Heavy Duty
Trucks & Retail Autos
N.A.I.C.S.: 336120

All Roads Company—(Continued)

Andy Franklin *(CEO)*

Subsidiaries:

Vermeer Mid Atlantic, LLC   (1)
8832 Corridor Rd, Annapolis Junction, MD 20701
Tel.: (301) 498-5200
Web Site: https://www.vermeerallroads.com
Full-service Equipment Dealer
N.A.I.C.S.: 532420
John L. Vos *(Founder)*

Unit (Domestic):

Vermeer Northeast   (2)
1235 Rte 9, Castleton on Hudson, NY 12033-9646
Tel.: (800) 333-4183
Web Site: https://www.vermeerallroads.com
Wholesale Trade Agents & Brokers
N.A.I.C.S.: 425120

ALL ROUND FOODS BAKERY PRODUCTS INC.
437 Railroad Ave, Westbury, NY 11590-4314
Tel.: (516) 338-1888
Web Site:
https://www.allroundfoods.com
Year Founded: 1997
Rev.: $25,000,000
Emp.: 12
Retail Bakery
N.A.I.C.S.: 311811
Glen Wolther *(Pres)*
Steven Finkelstein *(COO)*

ALL SAFE INDUSTRIES, INC.
11360 Bluegrass Pkwy, Louisville, KY 40299-1912
Tel.: (502) 499-7988
Web Site:
http://www.firstresponders.com
Year Founded: 1996
Sales Range: $10-24.9 Million
Emp.: 11
Safety Products & Equipment Whslr
N.A.I.C.S.: 423990
Steve Haise *(Founder)*

ALL SEASONS TRAVEL AGENCY INC.
2900 Cahaba Rd, Birmingham, AL 35223
Tel.: (205) 870-3003   AL
Web Site:
http://www.allseasonstravel.com
Year Founded: 1970
Sales Range: $10-24.9 Million
Emp.: 70
Travel Agencies
N.A.I.C.S.: 561510
Travis Tanner *(Exec VP)*
Don Hawkins *(VP)*
Meredith Price *(Mgr-Leisure)*
Ann Johnston *(Pres)*
Ellen Ray *(Sr VP)*
Jeanine Eissler *(VP-Ops)*
Borden H. Burr II *(Chm)*

ALL SENSORS, CORP.
16035 Vineyard Blvd, Morgan Hill, CA 95037
Tel.: (408) 225-4314   CA
Web Site: https://www.allsensors.com
Year Founded: 1999
Sales Range: $1-9.9 Million
Emp.: 25
Semiconductors & Related Devices
N.A.I.C.S.: 334413
Dennis Dauenhauer *(Pres)*
Katie Dauenhauer *(Mgr-Production Control)*
Mark DeJarnette *(Mgr-Sls-Eastern USA, Canada & Asia)*

ALL STAR AUTOMOTIVE GROUP
PO Box 77330, Baton Rouge, LA 70879-7330
Tel.: (225) 298-3210
Web Site:
http://www.allstarautomotive.com
Sales Range: $50-74.9 Million
Emp.: 400
Owner & Operator of Auto Dealerships
N.A.I.C.S.: 441110
Bill Lockwood *(CFO)*

Subsidiaries:

All Star Nissan   (1)
12422 Florida Blvd, Baton Rouge, LA 70815
Tel.: (225) 272-9330
Web Site: http://www.allstarautomotive.com
Sales Range: $10-24.9 Million
Emp.: 35
Retail New & Used Automobiles
N.A.I.C.S.: 441110
Matt McKay *(CEO)*

All Star Toyota   (1)
9150 Airline Hwy, Baton Rouge, LA 70816
Tel.: (225) 925-2525
Web Site: http://www.allstarautomotive.com
Sales Range: $10-24.9 Million
Emp.: 104
Retailer of New & Used Automobile Distr
N.A.I.C.S.: 441110
Matt McKay *(Owner)*
Lee Carney *(Gen Mgr)*

ALL STAR AUTOMOTIVE PRODUCTS
4150 Puente Ave, Baldwin Park, CA 91706
Tel.: (626) 337-2222
Web Site: http://www.galaxystar.com
Sales Range: Less than $1 Million
Emp.: 10
Automotive Supplies & Parts Distr
N.A.I.C.S.: 423120
Robert Ehlers *(Owner)*

ALL STAR CONSULTING INC.
1111 Oak St, San Francisco, CA 94117
Tel.: (415) 552-1400
Web Site: http://www.all-stars.com
Year Founded: 1985
Sales Range: $10-24.9 Million
Emp.: 15
Computer Consulting Services
N.A.I.C.S.: 541512
Pamela Munn *(Pres)*

ALL STAR DIRECTORIES, INC.
2200 Alaskan Way Ste 200, Seattle, WA 98121
Tel.: (206) 436-7500
Web Site:
http://www.allstardirectories.com
Year Founded: 2001
Sales Range: $25-49.9 Million
Emp.: 85
Online Marketing for Schools, Universities & Other Education Institutions
N.A.I.C.S.: 541810
Douglas W. Brown *(CEO)*
Bill Hummel *(Pres)*
Kelly Huffman *(Mgr-Content Mktg-Bus & Tech)*
Jen Jope *(Mgr-Content Mktg)*
Grant Daniels *(Mgr-Bus Dev)*
Courtney Crooks *(Sr Acct Mgr)*
Kris Reeter *(Dir-HR)*
Diana Green *(Dir-Sls)*
Marc Teale *(Engr-Sys)*
Dave Davis *(Gen Counsel & Sec)*
Lala Gusakov *(Mgr-Acct)*
Scott Harrison *(Mgr-IT Ops)*
Paula Nechak *(Mgr-Online Content)*
Serge Bondar *(Mgr-SEM Channel)*

Krystal Dupar *(Sr Acct Mgr)*
Laura Thramer *(Sr Mgr-Mktg Channel)*
Jason Gilbert *(Sr Mgr-Organic Growth)*
Carissa Jamerson *(Sr Mgr-Sls)*
Travis Wright *(VP-Products)*

ALL STAR DODGE
4600 Canyon Dr, Amarillo, TX 79109-6010
Tel.: (806) 359-2886
Web Site:
https://www.allstardodgetexas.com
Year Founded: 1975
Sales Range: $50-74.9 Million
Emp.: 239
New Car Whslr
N.A.I.C.S.: 441110
Edward Bradley *(Owner)*

ALL STAR DODGE CHRYSLER JEEP
4600 Canyon Dr, Amarillo, TX 79109-6010
Tel.: (806) 359-2886
Web Site: http://www.allstardodge.us
Sales Range: $10-24.9 Million
Emp.: 51
Car Whslr
N.A.I.C.S.: 441110
Edward Bradley *(Owner)*
Don Pedro *(Gen Mgr)*

ALL STAR FORD LLC
1925 Cooper Point, Olympia, WA 98508
Tel.: (360) 352-9300
Web Site: http://www.olyford.com
Rev.: $46,700,000
Emp.: 110
New Car Dealers
N.A.I.C.S.: 441110
Kevin Neiswanger *(Gen Mgr)*
Michael Renard *(Mgr-Parts)*
Verle Ketchum *(Dir-Fleet Svcs)*

ALL STAR GLASS CO. INC.
1845 Morena Blvd, San Diego, CA 92110-3636
Tel.: (619) 275-3343   CA
Web Site: https://www.allstarglass.net
Year Founded: 1978
Sales Range: $10-24.9 Million
Emp.: 200
Automotive Glass Replacement Shops
N.A.I.C.S.: 811122
Bob Scharaga *(Pres)*
Al Silva *(Mgr-IT)*

ALL STAR INCENTIVE MARKETING, INC.
660 Main St, Fiskdale, MA 01518
Tel.: (508) 347-7672
Web Site:
http://www.incentiveusa.com
Year Founded: 1970
Sales Range: $10-24.9 Million
Emp.: 56
Sales Promotion
N.A.I.C.S.: 541810
Mike Balcom *(VP-Corp Identity)*
Ann Galonek *(CFO)*
Gary Galonek *(Mgr-Sls-Gaming Natl)*
Brian Galonek *(Pres)*
Heidi Chatfield *(VP-Mktg & Bus Dev)*
Allison Wooten *(Mgr-Bus Dev)*
Geri Labonte *(Mgr-HR)*
Jeff Becotte *(Mgr-IT)*
Ryan Chase *(Mgr-Warehouse)*
Tom Melkus *(Dir-Ops)*
Jim Drakakis *(Mgr-Sls-Natl)*

Tara Linton *(Mgr-Sls-Incentive Div-Natl)*
Timothy Leland *(Sr Mgr-Sls)*
Glen Neary *(Sr Mgr-Sls)*

ALL STAR VACATION HOMES MANAGEMENT, INC.
7822 E Irlo Bronson Memorial Hwy, Kissimmee, FL 34747
Tel.: (321) 281-4966
Web Site:
http://www.allstarvacationhomes.com
Year Founded: 1998
Sales Range: $10-24.9 Million
Emp.: 70
Management Consulting Services
N.A.I.C.S.: 541618
Steve Trover *(CEO)*
Jose Ocasio *(Dir-IT)*
Mindy Tomko *(Dir-HR)*
Sara Moore *(CMO)*
Brooke Pfautz *(Chief Bus Dev Officer)*
Sue Trover *(Co-Owner & Pres)*
Phil Trover *(COO)*
Kent Bjorklund *(Chief Performance Officer)*
Dillon Muto *(COO-Purpose Built)*
Steve Leavens *(Dir-Guest Svcs)*
Cari Trover-Licata *(Dir-Reservations)*
John Brost *(Gen Mgr)*
Diane Napoli *(Dir-Quality Control)*
Brian Maloney *(Dir-Owner Rels)*
Mike Trover *(Dir-Property Care)*
Heather Weiermann *(COO-California)*
Chelsea Graue *(Mgr-Guest Svcs-San Diego Ops)*
Jason Wingerter *(Acct Mgr-San Diego Ops)*
Megan Rose *(Mgr-Property Care-San Diego Ops)*
Ana Skonezny *(Mgr-Quality Control)*
Karen Mulera *(Dir-Ops-Sun Valley)*
Brady Graham *(Dir-Mgmt Svcs-Sanibel & Captiva Islands Ops)*
Sarah Wackerly *(Dir-Hospitality Svcs-Sanibel & Captive Islands Ops)*
Joe Rothfuss *(Owner-Rels & Dir-Guest)*
Kelly Trover-DiGiovanni *(Dir-All Star Standards)*

ALL STATE FASTENER CORPORATION
15460 E 12 Mile Rd, Roseville, MI 48066
Tel.: (586) 773-5400
Web Site:
https://www.allstatefastener.com
Sales Range: $50-74.9 Million
Emp.: 100
Bolts
N.A.I.C.S.: 423710
Anthony Giorgio *(Chm)*
Pamela Meyer *(CFO)*
Virgil Cummings *(Vice Chm)*

ALL STATE HOMES, INC.
11300 N Central Ave, Tampa, FL 33612
Tel.: (813) 931-8952   FL
Web Site:
https://www.allstatehomes.com
Year Founded: 1955
Sales Range: $10-24.9 Million
Emp.: 8
New Single-Family Housing Construction
N.A.I.C.S.: 236115
Mary Jaworske *(Controller)*
Steve Hansen *(Pres)*

ALL STATES ASPHALT INC.
325 Amherst Rd, Sunderland, MA 01375

Tel.: (413) 665-7021   MA
Web Site:
    http://www.allstatesasphalt.com
Year Founded: 1962
Sales Range: $10-24.9 Million
Emp.: 100
Asphalt Mixture Whslr
N.A.I.C.S.: 423320
David Hankowski *(Pres)*
Richard J. Miller *(Exec VP)*
Alan Chicoine *(Div Mgr)*

ALL STEEL CONSULTANTS, INC.
714A 17th St E, Palmetto, FL 34221
Tel.: (941) 727-1444   FL
Web Site: https://www.ascifl.com
Year Founded: 1973
Sales Range: $1-9.9 Million
Emp.: 37
Structural Steel, Steel Truss Systems & Metal Roofing
N.A.I.C.S.: 238120
Ralph George *(Pres)*
Deborah George *(Treas & Sec)*

ALL STYLE APPAREL & AC-TIVEWEAR
1501 E Cerrito, Anaheim, CA 92805
Tel.: (714) 765-0415
Web Site: http://www.alstyle.com
Sales Range: $200-249.9 Million
Emp.: 1,800
Shirts (Outerwear), Knit
N.A.I.C.S.: 313310
Bill Pellegrini *(Mgr-Sls-Eastern Reg)*

ALL SYSTEMS GO, LLC
2860 N Commerce St, North Las Vegas, NV 89030
Tel.: (702) 895-9288   NV
Web Site: http://www.asglv.com
Year Founded: 2001
Sales Range: $1-9.9 Million
Emp.: 50
Integration Company
N.A.I.C.S.: 541330
David Krajniak *(Dir-Ops)*

ALL SYSTEMS INSTALLATION INC.
8300 10th Ave N Ste A, Golden Valley, MN 55427
Tel.: (763) 593-1330
Web Site: http://www.allsysinst.com
Year Founded: 1985
Sales Range: $10-24.9 Million
Emp.: 100
Provider of Computer Networking Services Including Network Design, Consulting, Analysis & Implementation
N.A.I.C.S.: 541512
Mark Broadwater *(Pres)*
Dave Skatter *(Project Mgr)*
Bret Soucy *(Project Mgr)*
Alex Dascalos *(Acct Mgr)*
Bryan Chippendale *(Controller)*
Paul Silliman *(Mgr-Bridgeport)*
Wendy Boosalis *(Sr VP-Tech)*
Chris Busch *(VP-Tech Field Ops)*

ALL TEMPS PERSONNEL SERVICE
4639 Corona Ste 99, Corpus Christi, TX 78411
Tel.: (361) 808-8367
Web Site:
    https://www.atpersonnelservice.com
Sales Range: $10-24.9 Million
Emp.: 20
Employment Agencies
N.A.I.C.S.: 561311
Rodney L. Hay *(VP)*
Ronald L. Hay *(Founder & CEO)*
Ronald L. Hay II *(Pres & CFO)*

ALL TERIORS FLOOR COVER-ING, INC.
214 S Price Rd Ste 101, Tempe, AZ 85281
Tel.: (480) 921-8419
Web Site:
    https://www.phoenixcabinets.com
Year Founded: 1994
Sales Range: $10-24.9 Million
Emp.: 10
Floor Covering, Cabinet & Counter Top Design & Installation Services
N.A.I.C.S.: 238330
Dexter Rose *(Pres)*
Tina Rose *(VP)*

ALL TERRAIN
2675 W Grand Ave, Chicago, IL 60612
Tel.: (312) 421-7672
Web Site: http://www.allterrain.net
Year Founded: 1998
Sales Range: $1-9.9 Million
Emp.: 32
Marketing Programs
N.A.I.C.S.: 541613
Brook Jay *(Co-Founder & CMO)*
Sarah Eck-Thompson *(Co-Founder)*
April Quealy *(Dir-Creative)*

ALL TILE INC.
1201 N Chase Ave, Elk Grove Village, IL 60007
Tel.: (847) 979-2500   DE
Web Site: http://www.alltile.com
Year Founded: 1975
Sales Range: $10-24.9 Million
Emp.: 110
Homefurnishings
N.A.I.C.S.: 423220
Robert Weiss *(Pres)*

ALL TRI-R INC.
1301 E Jackson St, Pana, IL 62557-6408
Tel.: (217) 562-5113
Rev.: $55,000,000
Emp.: 200
Factory Construction
N.A.I.C.S.: 236220
Roger Simpson *(Pres)*

ALL WALL CONTRACTING, INC.
723 S Lochsa St, Post Falls, ID 83854
Tel.: (208) 773-4650
Web Site: https://www.allwallinc.com
Year Founded: 1996
Sales Range: $10-24.9 Million
Emp.: 100
Drywall & Insulation Contracting Services
N.A.I.C.S.: 238310
Roy Glisson *(CEO)*
Terry Jones *(VP)*
Dan Ratza *(Sr Project Mgr-ID/WA Ops)*
Jared Greaser *(Sr Project Mgr-AK Ops)*
Jaims Greenfield *(Office Mgr)*

ALL WEATHER INC.
1065 National Dr Ste 1, Sacramento, CA 95834
Tel.: (916) 928-1000
Web Site:
    https://www.allweatherinc.com
Sales Range: $10-24.9 Million
Emp.: 35
Weather Tracking Equipment
N.A.I.C.S.: 334519
Barbara Baca *(Mgr-Sls)*
Neal Dillman *(CTO)*
Adam Thomas *(Dir-Mfg)*
Steve Glander *(Dir-Sls & Mktg-Intl)*

ALL WELD MACHINE & FAB-RICATION COMPANY
1011 Pecten Court, Milpitas, CA 95035
Tel.: (408) 946-5890   CA
Web Site: http://www.allweld.com
Year Founded: 1973
Sales Range: $10-24.9 Million
Emp.: 8
Machine & Fabrication Services
N.A.I.C.S.: 332710
Delores Owen *(Treas & Sec)*
Tim Green *(Pres)*

ALL WORLD TRAVEL INC.
314 Gilmer St, Sulphur Springs, TX 75482-2767
Tel.: (903) 885-0896
Web Site:
    https://www.allworldtravel.com
Year Founded: 1971
Sales Range: $10-24.9 Million
Emp.: 28
Travel Services
N.A.I.C.S.: 561510
Charles M. Moore *(Pres & CEO)*

ALL-AMERICAN CO-OP
113 4th St SE, Stewartville, MN 55976
Tel.: (507) 533-4222
Web Site:
    http://www.allamericancoop.com
Sales Range: $10-24.9 Million
Emp.: 45
Grains
N.A.I.C.S.: 424510
Jeff Anderson *(Controller)*

ALL-AMERICAN FIRE EQUIP-MENT, INC.
3253 US Rte 60, Ona, WV 25545
Tel.: (304) 733-3581
Web Site: http://www.aafe911.com
Sales Range: $1-9.9 Million
Emp.: 22
Safety Equipment & Supplies
N.A.I.C.S.: 423990
Jeffrey T. Vossler *(Founder & Pres)*
Jill Marcus *(Controller)*

ALL-AMERICAN MOVING GROUP LLC
4340 Hwy 51 N, Memphis, TN 38127
Tel.: (901) 353-2900
Web Site:
    http://www.allamericanmoving.com
Rev.: $34,000,000
Emp.: 65
Moving & Transportation Services
N.A.I.C.S.: 484210
Gerald Wright *(Owner)*

ALL-IN-ONE NETWORK SOLU-TIONS, INC.
1700 Pacific Ave Ste 1260, Dallas, TX 75201-4691
Tel.: (214) 613-0100
Web Site:
    http://www.aiosolutions.com
Year Founded: 1999
Sales Range: $1-9.9 Million
Emp.: 19
Information Technology Services
N.A.I.C.S.: 541512
Michael Ehrich *(Founder, Pres & CEO)*
J. Michael Cucinotta *(Mgr-Ops)*
Victor Calabrese *(VP-Client Svcs)*

ALL-LIFT OF GEORGIA INC.
175 Carnes Dr, Fayetteville, GA 30214
Tel.: (770) 460-7163
Web Site:
    http://www.allliftofgeorgia.com

Sales Range: $10-24.9 Million
Emp.: 20
Forklift Dealer
N.A.I.C.S.: 423830
Barry Naulls *(Pres)*

ALL-PRO FASTENERS INC.
1916 Peyco Dr N, Arlington, TX 76001
Tel.: (817) 467-5700
Web Site: http://www.all-profasteners.com
Year Founded: 1976
Rev.: $38,000,000
Emp.: 90
Fasteners, Industrial: Nuts, Bolts, Screws, Etc.
N.A.I.C.S.: 423840
Tom Shelton *(Owner & Pres)*
Johnny Chavez *(Acct Mgr)*
Jerry Dunsmore *(Pres-Lok-Mor Inc)*
Russell Mask *(Acct Mgr)*
Sue Taylor *(Project Mgr)*
Ruth Stiver *(Mgr-HR)*

ALL-SOUTH SUBCONTRAC-TORS INC.
2678 Queenstown Rd, Birmingham, AL 35210
Tel.: (205) 836-8111
Web Site:
    https://www.allsouthsub.com
Year Founded: 1957
Sales Range: $25-49.9 Million
Emp.: 167
Roofing Contractors
N.A.I.C.S.: 238160
Wesley Willings *(Controller)*

ALL-STAR CHEVROLET GEO, INC.
7240 Craft Goodman Rd, Olive Branch, MS 38654
Tel.: (662) 895-5536
Web Site:
    https://www.allstarautogroup.com
Rev.: $10,300,000
Emp.: 35
New & Used Automobiles & Light Trucks Dealer
N.A.I.C.S.: 441110
Lynn French *(Office Mgr)*
Drew D. Priest *(Pres)*

ALL-STATE BELTING COM-PANY
520 S 18th St, West Des Moines, IA 50322
Tel.: (515) 645-6959   DE
Web Site: http://www.all-statebelting.com
Conveyor Belting, Accessories & Field Installation Services
N.A.I.C.S.: 326220
Casey Price *(VP-Engrg)*

ALL-STATE EXPRESS, INC.
121-I Shields Park Dr, Kernersville, NC 27284
Tel.: (336) 992-6880
Web Site:
    https://www.allstateexpress.com
Year Founded: 1996
Sales Range: $10-24.9 Million
Emp.: 28
General Freight Trucking & Logistics
N.A.I.C.S.: 484110
Sherri Squier *(CEO)*
Bill Gansman *(VP)*

ALL-STATE INTERNATIONAL, INC.
1 Commerce Dr, Cranford, NJ 07016
Tel.: (908) 272-0800
Web Site: https://www.aslegal.com
Year Founded: 1956

ALL-STATE International, Inc.—(Continued)
Sales Range: $25-49.9 Million
Emp.: 200
Continuous Forms, Office & Business
N.A.I.C.S.: 323111
Robert Busch (CEO)

ALL-TECH DECORATING COMPANY
1227 Naperville Dr, Romeoville, IL 60446-1041
Tel.: (630) 378-0003
Web Site: https://www.alltechdecorating.com
Sales Range: $10-24.9 Million
Emp.: 165
Painting & Paper Hanging Services
N.A.I.C.S.: 238320
Craig Gluszek (Principal)
Don Steadman (Principal)

ALL-TEX ERECTION SYSTEMS INC.
2218 Pech Rd, Houston, TX 77055
Tel.: (713) 464-4558
Sales Range: $10-24.9 Million
Emp.: 150
Structural Steel Erection
N.A.I.C.S.: 551112
Jon Murray (Pres)

ALL-TEX INC.
14093 Balboa Blvd, Sylmar, CA 91342-1000
Tel.: (818) 768-3333   CA
Web Site: https://www.inlineco.com
Year Founded: 1978
Sales Range: $100-124.9 Million
Commercial & Industrial Safety Devices & Supplies Distr
N.A.I.C.S.: 423840
Scott D. Bader (Pres & CEO)
Valerie Day (CEO & CFO)
Bryan Miller (VP-Natl Sls)

ALL-TEX PIPE & SUPPLY, INC.
9743 Brockbank, Dallas, TX 75220
Tel.: (214) 350-5886
Web Site: https://www.alltexsupply.com
Year Founded: 1973
Emp.: 100
Pipe, Valves & Fittings Distr
N.A.I.C.S.: 423720
Jill Hurd (Owner, Pres & CEO)

ALL-TEX ROOFING INC.
5605 Creekmont Dr, Houston, TX 77091
Tel.: (713) 683-6775
Web Site: http://www.alltexroofing.com
Sales Range: $10-24.9 Million
Emp.: 20
Roofing Contractors
N.A.I.C.S.: 238160
Lynn Mobley (VP)
Ron Wubenlick (Sec)

ALL-WAYS ADVERTISING COMPANY
1442 Broad St, Bloomfield, NJ 07003
Tel.: (973) 338-0700
Web Site: https://www.awadv.com
Year Founded: 1969
Sales Range: $25-49.9 Million
Emp.: 30
Publicity & Promotional Services
N.A.I.C.S.: 541810
Robert J. Lieberman (Pres)
Diane Dellefave (VP)

ALL4 LLC
2393 Kimberton Rd, Kimberton, PA 19442

Tel.: (610) 933-5246
Web Site: http://www.all4inc.com
Year Founded: 2002
Sales Range: $1-9.9 Million
Emp.: 55
Business Consulting Services
N.A.I.C.S.: 541690
William Straub (CEO)
Nick Leone (Project Engr)
Eric M. Swisher (Mgr-Technical)
Neal Lebo (Project Mgr)
Kristin M. Gordon (Dir-Houston)
Brandie Moroskie (Mgr-Ops)
Lindsey Kroos (Project Mgr)
Sally Atkins (Project Mgr)
Renee Cheng (Project Mgr)
Dan Dix (Mgr-Tech)
Jennifer Flannery (Project Mgr)
Ron Harding (Project Mgr)
Heather Horvath (Dir-HR)
J. P. Kleinle (Project Mgr)
Robert Kuklentz (Project Mgr)
Annalise Matulewicz (Dir-Strategic Rels)
Colin McCall (Chief Technical Officer)
Sarah McCall (Dir-Mktg)
Chuck Doyno (Project Engr)
Christina Giannascoli (Engr-Consulting)
Frank Dougherty (Project Engr)
Meghan Barber (Engr-Consulting)
Matt Gallo (Project Engr)
Maggie Greene (Engr-Consulting)
Sean Cunningham (Project Engr)

Subsidiaries:

Environmental Strategy Consultants, Inc.   (1)
1528 Walnut St Ste 1812, Philadelphia, PA 19102-3612
Tel.: (215) 731-4200
Web Site: http://www.envirostrat.com
Research & Development in the Physical, Engineering & Life Sciences
N.A.I.C.S.: 541715
Lorna Velardi (Pres)

Smith Management Group, Inc.   (1)
1405 Mercer Rd, Lexington, KY 40511-1028
Tel.: (859) 231-8936
Web Site: http://www.smithmanage.com
Environmental Consulting Services
N.A.I.C.S.: 541620
Sara G. Smith (CEO)
Kyle Hagen (Mgr-Engrg Svcs)
Karen Thompson (Mgr-Environmental Svcs)
Clay Whitney (Pres)

ALLAN A. MYERS, INC.
1805 Berks Rd, Worcester, PA 19490
Tel.: (610) 222-8800
Web Site: http://www.americanstructure.com
Year Founded: 1939
Sales Range: $400-449.9 Million
Emp.: 2,000
Highway, Street & Bridge Construction Services
N.A.I.C.S.: 237310
A. Ross Myers (Chm)
Joe Prego (VP-Bus Dev)

ALLAN BLOCK CORPORATION
7424 W 78th St, Bloomington, MN 55420
Tel.: (952) 835-5309
Web Site: https://www.allanblock.com
Year Founded: 1987
Sales Range: $10-24.9 Million
Emp.: 10
Concrete Block & Brick Mfr
N.A.I.C.S.: 327331
Bob Gravier (Owner)
Kyle Huerd (Engr-Design)
Eric Roloff (Engr-Design)

ALLAN BRITEWAY ELECTRI-

CAL CONTRACTORS, INC.
360 Lexington Ave 6th F, Whippany, NJ 07981
Tel.: (646) 694-8900
Web Site: http://www.allanbriteway.com
Year Founded: 2005
Sales Range: $1-9.9 Million
Electric Power Distribution Services
N.A.I.C.S.: 221122
Bernard Nangle (COO)

ALLAN COMPANY
14620 Joanbridge St, Baldwin Park, CA 91706-1750
Tel.: (626) 962-4047   CA
Web Site: https://www.allancompany.com
Year Founded: 1963
Sales Range: $10-24.9 Million
Emp.: 100
Provider of Scrap & Waste Material Services
N.A.I.C.S.: 423930
Stephen A. Young (Chm)

Subsidiaries:

Allan Company - Roll Division   (1)
1404 W Holt Ave, Pomona, CA 91768
Tel.: (909) 622-2481
Material Recovery Services
N.A.I.C.S.: 562920

Cedarwood-Young Company, Inc.   (1)
14618 Arrow Hwy, Baldwin Park, CA 91706
Tel.: (818) 962-4047
Web Site: http://www.allancompany.com
Paper Processing Buyback Center
N.A.I.C.S.: 423930

ALLAN INDUSTRIES INC.
270 US Rte 46 E, Rockaway, NJ 07866
Tel.: (973) 586-9400
Web Site: http://www.allanindustries.com
Sales Range: $75-99.9 Million
Emp.: 1,200
Provider of Building Cleaning Services
N.A.I.C.S.: 561720
Paul Allan (Pres)
Michael Carroll (Pres)
Amber DeRidder (VP & Gen Mgr)
Kevin Ginsberg (Dir-Restoration Svcs)
Gene Herrmann (Mgr-Acct & Specialist-Ops)
John Rietzen (VP & Dir-Janitorial-Ops)
Matty Scalera (Acct Mgr-Bus Dev Specialist)
Eleanor Gracyalny (CFO & Exec VP)
Mary Kate Dodds (Coord-Office Svcs)
Brian Prescott (Dir-Southwest Reg)
Jan Lee (Mgr-Acct & Auditor)
Carlos Gonzalez (Mgr-Ops)
Vinnie Gortaire (Mgr-Ops)
Craig Utt (Mgr-Remediation Dept)
Emery Malasits (Project Mgr)
Jennifer Morgan (Reg Dir)
James Strite (Reg Dir)
Andres Pizzaro (Sr Mgr-Ops)

ALLAN MYERS, INC.
1805 Berks Rd, Worcester, PA 19490
Tel.: (610) 584-6020   PA
Web Site: https://www.allanmyers.com
Year Founded: 1939
Land Preparation Construction
N.A.I.C.S.: 236210
Shannon Moody (Mgr-PR)

ALLAN S. GOODMAN INCORPORATED

180 Goodwin St, East Hartford, CT 06108
Tel.: (860) 289-2731
Year Founded: 1933
Rev.: $23,600,000
Sales Range: -
Emp.: 65
Beer & Other Fermented Malt Liquors
N.A.I.C.S.: 424810
Roger S. Loeb (CEO)
David Heller (Pres)
Teresa Roe (Controller)

ALLAN TOOL & MACHINE CO., INC.
1822 E Maple Rd, Troy, MI 48083
Tel.: (248) 585-2910
Web Site: https://www.allantool.com
Rev.: $14,276,000
Emp.: 65
Screw Machine Products
N.A.I.C.S.: 332721
Jeffrey M. Scott (Pres)

ALLAN VIGIL'S FORD
6790 Mount Zion Blvd, Morrow, GA 30260
Tel.: (678) 364-3673   GA
Web Site: http://www.vigilford.com
Year Founded: 1982
Sales Range: $125-149.9 Million
Emp.: 400
Retailer of New & Used Automobiles
N.A.I.C.S.: 441110
Michael Vigil (VP)
Dennis Kerce (Gen Mgr)
Jeff Murrell (Dir-Parts & Svc)
Adam Hardt (Mgr-Fin)
Alan Parson (Gen Mgr-Sls)
Andrew Spinks (Mgr-Internet Sls)
Chris Daugherty (Dir-IT)
Kim Mitchell (Mgr-Sls)
Peter McCormack (Mgr-Comml Fin)
Rusty Stewart (Mgr-Parts)
Tommy Lancaster (Mgr-Inventory)
Zac Christopher (Mgr-Internet Sls)

ALLANA BUICK & BERS, INC.
990 Commercial St, Palo Alto, CA 94303
Tel.: (650) 543-5600   CA
Web Site: https://www.abbae.com
Year Founded: 1987
Sales Range: $10-24.9 Million
Emp.: 84
Engineeering Services
N.A.I.C.S.: 541330
Karim Allana (CEO)
Eugene Buick (COO & Principal)
Gerson Bers (Principal)

ALLANN BROS. COFFEE, INC.
1852 Fescue St SE, Albany, OR 97322
Tel.: (541) 812-8000
Web Site: http://www.allannbrothers.com
Year Founded: 1972
Sales Range: $10-24.9 Million
Emp.: 30
Roasted Coffee & Tea Mfr
N.A.I.C.S.: 311920
Allan Stuart (Owner)

ALLARD NAZARIAN GROUP INC.
124 Joliette St, Manchester, NH 03102-3017
Tel.: (603) 668-1900   NH
Web Site: http://www.allardventures.com
Year Founded: 1938
Sales Range: $300-349.9 Million
Emp.: 80
Asset & Investment Management
N.A.I.C.S.: 523999

Glenn Lawton *(Pres)*
Robert Blake *(Dir-Mgmt Info Sys)*
John Allard *(Chm & CEO)*
Paul Chapman *(Mgr-Contracts Program)*

Subsidiaries:

Granite State Manufacturing **(1)**
124 Joliette St, Manchester, NH
03102-3017 **(100%)**
Tel.: (603) 668-1900
Web Site: http://www.gogsmgo.com
Sales Range: $10-24.9 Million
Electrical Instruments Mfr
N.A.I.C.S.: 334511
Glen Lawton *(Pres)*
John Allard *(CEO)*

Subsidiary (Domestic):

Snow-Nabstedt Power
Transmissions **(2)**
1011 Joliette St, Manchester, NH
03102 **(100%)**
Tel.: (603) 314-0017
Web Site: http://www.snpt.biz
Sales Range: $10-24.9 Million
Emp.: 15
Transmissions Mfr
N.A.I.C.S.: 811114

ALLARI SOLUTIONS, INC.
9240 Bonita Beach Rd Ste 201, Bonita Springs, FL 34135
Tel.: (239) 949-4814   FL
Web Site: http://www.allari.com
Year Founded: 1999
Sales Range: $1-9.9 Million
Emp.: 25
Information Technology Consulting
Services
N.A.I.C.S.: 541690
John Mathieu *(Pres)*
Ravi Madhavan *(Mgr-Sls)*

ALLATA, LLC
2777 N Stemmons Fwy Ste 1240,
Dallas, TX 75207
Tel.: (972) 996-2360
Web Site: http://www.allata.com
Year Founded: 2014
Sales Range: $10-24.9 Million
Emp.: 71
Information Technology Development
Services
N.A.I.C.S.: 541511
Matt Rosen *(Founder & CEO)*
Phil Leary *(Sr VP)*
Trish Webb *(Sr VP)*
Rush Weston *(VP)*
Eric Jenson *(VP)*

ALLBRIDGE, LLC
6880 Perry Creek Rd, Raleigh, NC
27615
Tel.: (888) 918-9544
Web Site: http://www.allbridge.com
Year Founded: 2004
Sales Range: $50-74.9 Million
Emp.: 140
Wired Telecommunication Service
Provider
N.A.I.C.S.: 517111
Thomas Conley *(Pres)*
Timothy Conley *(COO)*
Emily Bradshaw *(VP-Mktg)*
Tony Calametti *(VP-Tech Svcs)*
Malcolm Clarke *(CFO)*
Mark Dixon *(VP-Ops)*
James Jessel *(VP-Sls)*
Christian Keller *(Mgr-HR)*
Mike Kelmel *(VP-Tech Svcs)*
Sarah Lawson *(Dir-Customer Care)*
Tara Morgan *(VP-Fin)*
Craig Snelgrove *(VP-Bus Dev)*
Steve Tutino *(CTO)*
Todd Johnstone *(CEO)*
John Gatti *(Chm)*

Subsidiaries:

Ipanema Solutions LLC **(1)**
830 Phoenix Dr, Ann Arbor, MI 48108-2221
Tel.: (734) 913-1101
Web Site: http://www.ipanemasolutions.com
Telecommunication Servicesb
N.A.I.C.S.: 517810
Steve Tutino *(Pres)*
Geoffrey Wahonya *(Mgr-Managed Svc)*
Tatiana Tutino *(Controller)*

**ALLCHEM INDUSTRIES
GROUP**
6010 NW 1st Pl, Gainesville, FL
32607
Tel.: (352) 378-9696
Web Site: http://www.allchem.com
Year Founded: 1982
Sales Range: $25-49.9 Million
Emp.: 180
Importer & Sales of Chemical Raw
Materials
N.A.I.C.S.: 424690
Jim Calais *(Pres)*
Josh Feldstein *(CEO)*
Brian Milan *(Mgr-Sls-North East &
Mid West)*
Alfredo T. Palmer *(Coord-Inside Sls &
Customer Svcs)*
Nate Camire *(Gen Mgr-Sls)*
Mark Sims *(VP-Mfg)*
Steve DeMoss *(VP-Shipping)*
Rebecca Prince *(CFO)*
Keith Chapman *(Area Mgr-Sls-South
East & West Coast)*
Rosalie Alfonso *(Coord-Customer
Svc)*
Aida Baez *(Coord-Customer Svc)*
Kraig Whitesel *(Coord-Customer Svc)*
Glen Heedy *(Exec VP-Bus Dev)*
Debra Lynch *(Mgr-Customer Svc)*
Betty Rippe *(Mgr-Logistics & Customer Svc)*
Mateo Altamira *(Plant Mgr)*

Subsidiaries:

AllChem Industries Industrial Chemicals Group **(1)**
6010 NW 1st Pl, Gainesville, FL 32607
Tel.: (352) 378-9696
Web Site: http://www.allchem.com
Sales Range: $10-24.9 Million
Emp.: 30
Marketer of Industrial Chemicals
N.A.I.C.S.: 424690
Tom Van der Weijde *(Pres)*
Nate Camire *(Gen Mgr-Sls)*
Brian Milan *(Mgr-Sls-North East & Mid West Area)*
Betty Rippe *(Mgr-Logistics & Customer Svc)*

AllChem Industries Performance
Products **(1)**
6010 NW 1st Pl, Gainesville, FL 32607
Tel.: (352) 378-9696
Web Site: http://www.allchem.com
Sales Range: $10-24.9 Million
Emp.: 72
Importer of Specialty Chemicals
N.A.I.C.S.: 424690
Jim Calais *(Pres)*
Glen Heedy *(Exec VP-Bus Dev)*
Debra Lynch *(Mgr-Customer Svc)*

AllChem Industries Performance
Products **(1)**
416 S Main St, Corsicana, TX 75110
Tel.: (903) 872-9997
Web Site: http://www.allchem.com
Mfr of Specialty Chemicals
N.A.I.C.S.: 424990

AllChem Industries Petroleum Chemicals Group **(1)**
6010 NW 1st Pl, Gainesville, FL 32607
Tel.: (352) 378-9696
Web Site: http://www.allchem.com
Sales Range: $10-24.9 Million
Emp.: 50
Marketer of Specialty Chemicals, Fuel Additives & Process Chemicals
N.A.I.C.S.: 424690

Alfredo Palmer *(Grp Mgr-Ops)*

ALLCO INCORPORATED
6720 College St, Beaumont, TX
77707
Tel.: (409) 860-4459
Web Site: https://www.allco.com
Rev.: $25,000,000
Emp.: 15
Commercial & Office Building, New
Construction
N.A.I.C.S.: 237110

ALLCO LTD.
6720 College St, Beaumont, TX
77707-3309
Tel.: (409) 860-4459
Web Site: https://www.allco.com
Year Founded: 1985
Sales Range: $25-49.9 Million
Emp.: 15
Construction Engineering Services
N.A.I.C.S.: 237310
T. W. Harrison *(Pres)*

ALLCOAT TECHNOLOGY, INC.
100 Eames St, Wilmington, MA
01887
Tel.: (978) 988-0880
Web Site:
    https://www.allcoattech.com
Sales Range: $10-24.9 Million
Emp.: 33
Noncorrosive Products & Materials
N.A.I.C.S.: 424690
Michael Lombard *(Pres)*
Corine Parigian *(VP-Tech)*

ALLCONNECT, INC.
4 Concourse Pkwy Ste 410, Atlanta,
GA 30328
Tel.: (404) 260-2200   DE
Web Site: http://www.allconnect.com
Year Founded: 1998
Sales Range: $50-74.9 Million
Emp.: 600
Telecommunications Resellers
N.A.I.C.S.: 517121
R. Lee Pritchard *(Founder & Vice
Chm)*
Kim Shumway *(Exec VP-Partner
Svcs & Bus Dev)*
Sam Howe *(CEO)*
Liz Pastor *(Chief Product Officer)*
Tippu Gagguturu *(CIO)*
Chris Camerieri *(Gen Counsel)*
Steve Sibley *(Co-CEO)*

Subsidiaries:

WhiteFence, Inc. **(1)**
5333 Westheimer Rd Ste 1000, Houston,
TX 77056
Tel.: (713) 663-0000
Web Site: http://www.whitefence.com
Sales Range: $10-24.9 Million
Emp.: 70
Telecommunications, Utilities & Home Security Services Reseller
N.A.I.C.S.: 517121
Kim Schram *(Sr VP-Bus Dev & Strategic
Alliances)*
Lonnie Ferrell *(Sr VP-Customer Care & Call
Center Ops)*
Francisco J. Arbide *(Chief Strategy Officer
& Sr VP-Alternative Channels)*
Leigh Stitham *(VP-Digital Call Center Ops)*

ALLCONNEX
141 Chestnut St, North Attleboro, MA
02760
Tel.: (508) 660-2688
Web Site: https://www.allconnex.com
Year Founded: 2002
Rev.: $2,300,000
Emp.: 4
Scientific & Technical Consulting Services
N.A.I.C.S.: 541690

Beth Anne Haskell *(Mgr-Pricing &
Admin)*
Michael Walton *(Mgr-Svc & Implementation)*
Steve King *(Mng Partner)*
Jamie Kuzman *(Mng Partner)*

**ALLEARTH RENEWABLES,
INC.**
94 Harvest Ln, Williston, VT 05495
Tel.: (802) 872-9600
Web Site:
    https://www.allearthrenewables.com
Year Founded: 2005
Sales Range: $1-9.9 Million
Emp.: 30
Solar Energy Renewable Equipment
Mfr
N.A.I.C.S.: 333414
David Blittersdorf *(Founder & CEO)*
Joyce Dicianna *(Dir-HR)*
Christie Hutchins *(Mgr-Acctg)*
Phil Pouech *(Dir-Ops)*

ALLEGAN GENERAL HOSPITAL
555 Linn St, Allegan, MI 49010
Tel.: (269) 673-8424   MI
Web Site: http://www.aghosp.org
Year Founded: 1944
Sales Range: $25-49.9 Million
Emp.: 386
Health Care Srvices
N.A.I.C.S.: 621610
Steve McKown *(Chm)*
John Walstrum *(Vice Chm)*
Jim Connell *(Sec)*
Jim Muenzer *(Treas)*

ALLEGANY OPTICAL LLC
703 S Antrim Way, Greencastle, PA
17225
Tel.: (717) 593-4521
Web Site:
    http://www.alleganyoptical.com
Sales Range: $10-24.9 Million
Emp.: 5
Optical Goods Stores
N.A.I.C.S.: 456130
Steven K. Kasinof *(Founder & Pres)*
Audrey Golden *(Gen Mgr)*

**ALLEGHENY BRADFORD
CORPORATION**
1522 South Ave, Lewis Run, PA
16738
Tel.: (814) 362-2590
Web Site:
    http://www.alleghenybradford.com
Year Founded: 1962
Rev.: $20,000,000
Emp.: 94
Food Products Machinery
N.A.I.C.S.: 333241
Tim Roff *(Mgr-HR)*
Dan McCune *(Pres & CEO)*

Subsidiaries:

Allegheny Surface Technology **(1)**
14 Egbert Ln, Lewis Run, PA 16738
Tel.: (814) 368-4465
Web Site: http://www.alleghenysurface.com
Sales Range: $10-24.9 Million
Emp.: 20
Stainless Steel Finishing Services to Pharmaceutical, Biotechnical, Medical, Food, Dairy & Marine Industries
N.A.I.C.S.: 423820
Thomas Hoffmann *(Gen Mgr)*

ALLEGHENY COUNTY LIBRARY ASSOCIATION
22 Wabash St Ste 202, Pittsburgh,
PA 15220
Tel.: (412) 921-1123   PA

Allegheny County Library
Association—(Continued)

Web Site:
https://www.aclalibraries.org
Year Founded: 1994
Sales Range: $10-24.9 Million
Emp.: 19
Library Management Services
N.A.I.C.S.: 519210
Marilyn Jenkins *(Exec Dir)*
Carol Morris *(Office Mgr & Mgr-Fin)*

ALLEGHENY ELECTRIC CO-OPERATIVE
212 Locust St, Harrisburg, PA 17108
Tel.: (717) 233-5704
Web Site: https://www.prea.com
Sales Range: $150-199.9 Million
Emp.: 500
Distr of Electric Power
N.A.I.C.S.: 221122
David Dulick *(Gen Counsel)*
Mauria R. Matthews *(VP-Strategic & Corp Svcs)*
J. R. Shope *(Treas)*
Leroy D. Walls *(Chm)*
Timothy D. Burkett *(Vice Chm)*
Daniel Lyzinski *(VP-Fin & Acctg)*
Stephen M. Brame *(VP-Pub Affairs & Member Svcs)*
Todd A. Sallade *(VP-Power Supply & Engrg)*

ALLEGHENY HEALTH NET-WORK
120 5th Ave Suite 2900, Pittsburgh, PA 15222
Tel.: (412) 330-2400
Web Site: http://www.ahn.org
Year Founded: 2013
Healthcare System Provider
N.A.I.C.S.: 621399
Cynthia Hundorfean *(CEO)*
Jim Benedict *(COO)*
Jeff Crudele *(CFO & Treas)*
Louise Urban *(Sr VP-Ops)*
David A. Blandino *(Chm)*
Margaret Larkins-Pettigrew *(Chief Clinical Diversity, Equity & Inclusion Officer)*
Bill Johnjulio *(Chief Population Health Officer)*
Donald Whiting *(Chief Medical Officer)*
James Benedict *(Pres)*

Subsidiaries:

Grove City Medical Center **(1)**
631 N Broad St Ext, Grove City, PA 16127
Tel.: (724) 450-7000
Web Site: http://www.gcmcpa.org
Rev.: $47,666,978
Assets: $51,768,752
Liabilities: $5,487,586
Net Worth: $46,281,166
Earnings: $844,905
Emp.: 581
Fiscal Year-end: 06/30/2014
Medical Center Operator
N.A.I.C.S.: 622110
Timothy R. Bonner *(Chm)*
Ernest D. May *(Vice Chm)*
Roger Towle *(Treas)*
Bradley Smith *(Sec)*
David A. Poland *(CFO & VP-Fin)*
Brad VanSickles *(VP-Ops & Patient Safety)*
Donald E. Henley *(VP-HR)*
JoAnne Clobus *(VP-Mktg & PR)*
Robert C. Jackson Jr. *(CEO)*

ALLEGHENY HIGH LIFT IN-CORPORATED
757 S Main St, Greensburg, PA 15601-4146
Tel.: (724) 836-1535
Web Site:
http://www.alleghenyhighlift.com
Sales Range: $10-24.9 Million

Emp.: 15
Industrial Machinery & Equipment
N.A.I.C.S.: 423830
Kim Scott *(Controller)*

ALLEGHENY INSURANCE SERVICE INC.
104 3rd St, Elkins, WV 26241
Tel.: (304) 636-1680
Web Site:
http://www.alleghenyinsurance.com
Rev.: $22,000,000
Emp.: 14
Insurance Agencies & Brokerages
N.A.I.C.S.: 524210
James Wallace *(Pres)*

ALLEGHENY LUTHERAN SO-CIAL MINISTRIES
998 Logan Blvd., Altoona, PA 16602
Tel.: (814) 696-4500   **PA**
Web Site:
http://www.alsmseniorliving.org
Year Founded: 1948
Sales Range: $25-49.9 Million
Emp.: 680
Elder Care Services
N.A.I.C.S.: 624120
Patricia W. Savage *(Pres & CEO)*
Christopher Reighard *(Sr VP-Fin & Plng)*
Rebecca Young *(VP-HR)*
Marty Jo Irvin Stellabotte *(Dir-Mission Advancement)*

ALLEGHENY MILLWORK
104 Commerce Blvd, Lawrence, PA 15055
Tel.: (724) 873-8700
Web Site:
https://www.alleghenymillwork.com
Rev.: $28,342,571
Emp.: 75
Millwork
N.A.I.C.S.: 321918
Richard A. Serdy *(CEO)*
Rick Wehan *(Controller)*

ALLEGHENY PLASTICS INC.
3A Ave A, Leetsdale, PA 15056-1304
Tel.: (412) 749-0700   **PA**
Web Site: http://www.allegheny.com
Year Founded: 1936
Sales Range: $25-49.9 Million
Emp.: 230
Supplier of Advanced Technical Solutions Worldwide
N.A.I.C.S.: 333248
Phillips Mark *(Product Mgr)*

Subsidiaries:

Allegheny Plastics, Inc. - Performance Plastics Division **(1)**
3 Ave. A, Leetsdale, PA 15056
Tel.: (412) 741-4416
Web Site: http://www.allegheny.com
Sales Range: $10-24.9 Million
Emp.: 35
Machine Shops
N.A.I.C.S.: 332710

Allegheny Printed Plastics, LLC. **(1)**
1224 Freedom Rd, Cranberry Township, PA 16066
Tel.: (724) 776-0100
Web Site: http://www.printedplastics.com
Emp.: 15
Plastics Product Mfr
N.A.I.C.S.: 326199
Don Ranalli *(Pres)*
Les Gamble *(Mgr-Ops)*
Paul Friedrich *(VP-Sls)*

ALLEGHENY WOOD PROD-UCTS INC.
Airport Rd, Petersburg, WV 26847-0867
Tel.: (304) 257-1082   **WV**

Web Site:
https://www.alleghenywood.com
Year Founded: 1972
Sales Range: $25-49.9 Million
Emp.: 500
Sawmill & Planing Mill Services
N.A.I.C.S.: 321113
John W. Crites II *(Owner, Chm, Pres & CEO)*
Yongjie Hu *(Dir-Sales-Asia)*

Subsidiaries:

Allegheny Dimension LLP **(1)**
390 Industrial Park Rd, Moorefield, WV 26836   **(100%)**
Tel.: (304) 257-9513
Web Site:
http://www.alleghenydimension.com
Sales Range: $10-24.9 Million
Emp.: 50
Producers of Hardwood Dimension Parts
N.A.I.C.S.: 321211
John W. Crites II *(Partner)*

Allegheny Wood Products
Princeton **(1)**
577 Clover Dew Dairy Rd, Princeton, WV 24740
Tel.: (304) 324-8337
Web Site: http://www.alleghenywood.com
Sales Range: $25-49.9 Million
Emp.: 70
Sawmill Mfr
N.A.I.C.S.: 321113

ALLEGIANCE CREDIT UNION
4235 N Meridian Ave, Oklahoma City, OK 73112
Tel.: (405) 789-7900   **OK**
Web Site:
https://www.allegiancecu.org
Year Founded: 1963
Sales Range: $10-24.9 Million
Emp.: 103
Credit Union
N.A.I.C.S.: 522130
Carol Gill *(Sr VP-Admin)*
Sabrina Warner *(CFO & Sr VP)*
Amy Downs *(Pres & CEO)*
Jeff Havener *(Chief Lending Officer)*

ALLEGIANCE FUNDRAISING LLC
3064 49th St. S, Fargo, ND 58104
Tel.: (800) 858-7654
Web Site: https://teamallegiance.com
Advertising Services
N.A.I.C.S.: 541810
Rich Aukland *(CEO)*

Subsidiaries:

The Pursuant Group, Inc. **(1)**
15660 Dallas Pkwy, Dallas, TX 75248
Tel.: (214) 866-7700
Web Site: http://www.pursuant.com
Sales Range: $10-24.9 Million
Emp.: 132
Fundraising Agency for Nonprofit Organizations
N.A.I.C.S.: 561439
Ross Miller *(CFO & COO)*
Curt Swindoll *(Exec VP)*
Trent Ricker *(Pres & CEO)*
Gary Kline *(Sr VP-Direct Response-North Virginia)*
Stuart Boyd *(Sr VP-Tech Products)*
Andy Goldsmith *(Sr VP & Dir-Creative)*
Mikey Centrella *(Dir-Digital Strategy)*
Taylor Shanklin *(VP-Product Mktg & Strategy)*
Matthew Mielcarek *(VP-Analytics & Insights Strategy)*
Hilary Noon *(Exec VP-Pursuant Insights)*

Subsidiary (Domestic):

ADVIZOR Solutions, Inc. **(2)**
1333 Butterfield Rd, Downers Grove, IL 60515
Tel.: (630) 971-5250
Web Site: http://www.advizorsolutions.com
Software/Services Company
N.A.I.C.S.: 513210

Douglas A. Cogswell *(Founder, Pres & CEO)*

ALLEGIANCE MOBILE HEALTH
501 S Austin Ave Ste 1310, Georgetown, TX 78626
Tel.: (855) 935-2424
Web Site: http://www.allmh.com
Emp.: 1,200
Medical Transportation & Emergency Services
N.A.I.C.S.: 621910
David M. Lee *(CEO)*

ALLEGIANCE TRUCKS, LLC
2181 Providence Hwy, Walpole, MA 02081
Tel.: (508) 668-3112   **DE**
Web Site:
https://www.allegiancetrucks.com
Year Founded: 2019
Commercial Truck Dealer
N.A.I.C.S.: 336120
Chad Schrempp *(COO)*

Subsidiaries:

Allegiance Fire & Rescue **(1)**
2181 Providence Hwy, Walpole, MA 02081
Tel.: (508) 668-3112
Web Site: https://www.allegiancefr.com
Commercial Truck Dealer
N.A.I.C.S.: 441110
Jeff Fournier *(Pres)*
Bill O'Connor *(VP-Sls & Mktg)*
Patrick Kelleher *(Dir-Svc Ops)*
Jim Yang *(Mgr-Contract)*
Beverly Barlow *(Office Mgr)*

Subsidiary (Domestic):

Minuteman Trucks, LLC **(2)**
2181 Providence Hwy, Walpole, MA 02081
Tel.: (508) 668-3112
Automotive Repair Services
N.A.I.C.S.: 811111

ALLEGIANCE, INC.
10235 S Jordan Gateway Ste 120, South Jordan, UT 84095
Tel.: (801) 617-8000
Web Site: http://www.allegiance.com
Year Founded: 2004
Sales Range: $1-9.9 Million
Emp.: 86
Real Time Survey & Feedback Collecting/Analyzing Software Solutions
N.A.I.C.S.: 541910
Greg Wiggins *(CTO)*
Chris Cottle *(VP-Mktg)*
Jason Taylor *(Exec VP-Engrg)*

ALLEGIANT PROFESSIONAL BUSINESS SERVICES, INC.
11838 Bernardo Plz Ct Ste 240, San Diego, CA 92128
Tel.: (858) 798-1644
Year Founded: 2005
Human Resource Consulting Services
N.A.I.C.S.: 561499
David Goldberg *(Pres & CEO)*

ALLEGIENT LLC
201 W 103rd St Ste 520, Indianapolis, IN 46290
Tel.: (317) 564-5700
Web Site: http://www.allegient.com
Year Founded: 2001
Sales Range: $10-24.9 Million
Emp.: 150
Business Software Consulting Services
N.A.I.C.S.: 541512
Bill Russell *(Exec VP)*
Gregg Gallant *(Co-Founder & CEO)*
Kyle Klimek *(Dir-Practice Area)*
Kevin Wyatt *(Project Mgr)*

Will Freeman *(Mgr-IT)*
Nancy Cuppy *(Sr Mgr-Enterprise Accts)*
Chelsie Hatoway *(Mgr-Delivery Ops)*
Sarah Roberts *(Mgr-Delivry Ops)*
Kevin Smith *(Program Mgr)*
Rod Hughes *(Sr Mgr-Project)*
Jenny Quinnette *(Dir-Fin & Acctg)*
Margaret Mitchell *(Dir-HR)*
Monica Corman *(Office Mgr)*
Laura Sweeney *(Dir-Mktg)*
Josh Burkhead *(Coord-Digital Mktg)*
Marcy Mattice *(Mgr-Business Dev)*
Joel Spittal *(Sr Mgr-Enterprise Accts)*
Ronda Woldmoe *(Sr Mgr-Enterprise Accts)*
Brent Warnecke *(Sr Mgr-Enterprise Accts)*
Liz Adams *(Mgr-Business Dev)*
Kim Kirtley *(Mgr-Regional Business Dev)*
David Ortiz *(Dir-Practice Area)*
Matt Jimison *(Dir-Practice Area)*
Joe Cooper *(Mgr-Program)*
Heather Bush *(Project Mgr)*
Jim Kerr *(VP-Bus Dev)*
Louise Hughes *(VP-Client Solutions & Delivery)*
John Holton *(VP-Mktg & Reg Dev)*
Robert Lescano *(VP-Solutions)*

ALLEGIS CORPORATION

8001 Central Ave NE, Minneapolis, MN 55432
Tel.: (763) 780-4333
Web Site:
   https://www.allegiscorp.com
Sales Range: $10-24.9 Million
Emp.: 100
Whslr of Hardware
N.A.I.C.S.: 423710
Duncan Woodhull *(Mgr-Bus Dev)*

ALLEGIS GROUP, INC.

7301 Parkway Dr S, Hanover, MD 21076   **MD**
Web Site:
   https://www.allegisgroup.com
Year Founded: 1983
Sales Range: $1-4.9 Billion
Emp.: 20,000
Offices of Other Holding Companies
N.A.I.C.S.: 551112
John Cashman *(Pres-Allegis Partners)*
Steve Bisciotti *(Co-Founder)*
Jim Davis *(Co-Founder)*
Steve Schumacher *(Pres-Allegis Global Solutions)*

Subsidiaries:

Aerotek, Inc.   **(1)**
7301 Pkwy Dr, Hanover, MD 21076
Tel.: (410) 694-5100
Web Site: http://www.aerotek.com
Sales Range: $750-799.9 Million
Emp.: 234
Technical, Professional & Industrial Staffing Services
N.A.I.C.S.: 561330
Todd Mohr *(Pres)*
Tony Bartolucci *(VP-West)*
Mark Cooper *(VP-Intl Bus Dev)*
John Flanigan *(Sr VP-Ops)*
Stacey Jenkins *(VP-Human Capital Solutions)*
Thomas B. Kelly *(CFO)*
Mike Kerrigan *(VP-Org Dev)*
Chad Koele *(Sr VP-Strategic Sls & Ops)*
Rick Wheaton *(Exec Dir-Reg Ops)*

Allegis Group GmbH   **(1)**
Solms Strasse 83, 60486, Frankfurt am Main, Germany
Tel.: (49) 69 22221 3800
Web Site: http://www.aerotek.de
Staffing & Recruitment Services
N.A.I.C.S.: 541612
Andrew Williams *(Mng Dir)*

Allegis Group Ltd.   **(1)**
OTV House East Wing Wokingham Road, Bracknell, RG42 1NG, Berks, United Kingdom   **(100%)**
Tel.: (44) 3333 455 500
Web Site: http://www.allegisgroup.co.uk
Sales Range: $25-49.9 Million
Emp.: 120
Holding Company; Professional Staffing Services
N.A.I.C.S.: 551112
Timothy Clements *(Mng Dir)*

Major, Lindsey & Africa, LLC **(1)**
7301 Pkwy Dr, Hanover, MD 21076
Tel.: (410) 579-3000
Web Site: http://www.mlaglobal.com
Emp.: 100
Legal Professional Recruiting & Executive Search Services
N.A.I.C.S.: 561312
John Cashman *(Pres)*
Jennifer Silver *(Global Head-Mktg & Comm & Exec Dir-Boston)*
Robert J. Brigham *(Partner-Practice Grp-San Francisco & Palo Alto)*
Joshua Emery Dull *(Partner-Practice Grp-Miami)*
Sonya Olds Som *(Partner-Practice Grp-Chicago)*
W. DeVane Tidwell *(Dir-Partner Practice Grp-Atlanta)*
George J. Hittner *(Mng Dir-Partner Practice Grp-Houston)*
Kirsten Vasquez *(Partner & VP-Law Firm Recruiting & Interim Legal Solutions)*
Ashish Raivadera *(Head-Private Practice-Partner Practice Grp-South Asia)*
Brent Harris *(Pres-Europe, Middle East & Africa & Asia Pacific)*
Richard Hsu *(Mng Dir-Partner Practice Grp-San Francisco)*
Jennifer Moss *(Mng Dir)*
Jasmine Guy *(Mgr-Diversity, Inclusion & Corp Social Responsibility Program)*
Carlos Pauling *(Exec Dir-Partner Practice Grp)*
Cynthia Barnardiston *(Mng Dir-Interim Legal Grp)*
Ron Ciardiell *(Mng Dir-Boston)*
Nancy Reiner *(Mng Dir-Boston)*
Daniel Davila *(CFO)*

MarketSource, Inc.   **(1)**
11700 Great Oaks Way Ste 500, Alpharetta, GA 30022
Tel.: (770) 674-5000
Web Site: http://www.marketsource.com
Emp.: 100
Outsourced Sales & Marketing Professional Staffing Services
N.A.I.C.S.: 561330
Rick Haviland *(Pres)*
Mike Christensen *(VP-Comml & Retail Channel Svcs)*
Bob Hunter *(VP-Pro Svcs Grp)*
Mark Mueller *(VP-Fin & Admin)*
Jeff Verhoff *(VP-Retail Sls Ops)*
Ted Grulikowski *(VP-Comml Bus)*
Elizabeth Novak *(Dir-HR)*

QuantumWork Advisory   **(1)**
7301 Pkwy S, Hanover, MD 21076
Tel.: (44) 7710484834
Web Site: https://quantumwork.com
Advisory Firm
N.A.I.C.S.: 541810

Subsidiary (Domestic):

Talent Tech Labs, LLC   **(2)**
307 W 38th St, New York, NY 10018
Tel.: (646) 300-7060
Web Site: http://www.talenttechlabs.com
Investment Funding Services
N.A.I.C.S.: 525910
Jonathan F. Kestenbaum *(Co-Founder & Mng Dir)*
Chris Hartman *(Dir)*
Brian Delle Donne *(Co-Founder & Pres)*
Irina Sapsay *(Dir-Client Delivery)*
Gabrielle Norton *(Acct Mgr)*
Adam Zec *(Dir-Bus Dev)*

Stephen James Associates, Inc. **(1)**
8140 Corporate Dr Ste 200, White Marsh, MD 21236
Tel.: (410) 657-3222
Web Site: http://www.stephenjames.com

Accounting & Finance Professional Staffing Services
N.A.I.C.S.: 561330

TEKsystems, Inc.   **(1)**
7437 Race Rd, Hanover, MD 21076
Tel.: (410) 540-7700
Web Site: http://www.teksystems.com
Sales Range: $1-4.9 Billion
Emp.: 3,476
Information Technology & Communications Staffing & Consulting Services
N.A.I.C.S.: 561330
Von Baker *(Dir-Healthcare Pactice)*
Keith Bozeman *(Pres)*
Anthony Cacioppo *(Acct Mgr)*
Jared Koon *(Acct Mgr-End User Svcs)*

Subsidiary (Domestic):

TEKsystems Global Services, LLC   **(2)**
7437 Race Rd, Hanover, MD 21076
Tel.: (410) 540-7700
Web Site: http://www.teksystems.com
Rev.: $40,300,000
Emp.: 250
Information Technology & Communications Consulting Services
N.A.I.C.S.: 541690
Keith Bozeman *(Pres)*
Kelly Cooper *(Coord-Mktg Comm)*
Sean McGraw *(Dir-Fin)*
Nicole Lagrotteria *(Mgr-Ops Support)*

Talent2 International Limited **(1)**
Level 4 77 Pacific Highway, North Sydney, 2060, NSW, Australia   **(50%)**
Tel.: (61) 290876333
Web Site: http://www.talent2.com
Sales Range: $300-349.9 Million
Emp.: 1,700
Human Resources Outsourcing Services & Solutions
N.A.I.C.S.: 541612
David Patteson *(Sec)*
Glenn Anthony *(Mgr-Natl Sls)*
Sarah Galbraith *(Gen Mgr-Ops)*
Jack Goh *(CEO-HR & Payroll Svcs-Asia)*
Greg McManus *(CEO-HR & Payroll Svcs-Australia & New Zealand)*
Andrew Banks *(Chm)*

Subsidiary (Domestic):

National Payroll Systems Pty. Ltd.   **(2)**
17-23 Station Street, Malvern, 3144, VIC, Australia
Tel.: (61) 3 9576 0077
Sales Range: $25-49.9 Million
Emp.: 30
Payroll & Human Resource Processing Services
N.A.I.C.S.: 541214

T2 Optimise Pty. Ltd.   **(2)**
Level 35 Central Plaza One 345 Queen St, Brisbane, 4000, QLD, Australia
Tel.: (61) 732957444
Web Site: http://www.talent2.com
Sales Range: $25-49.9 Million
Emp.: 40
Outsourced Learning & Development Services
N.A.I.C.S.: 561499
Andrew Banks *(Chm & Mng Dir)*

Subsidiary (Non-US):

Talent2 K.K.   **(2)**
Kojimachi Central Building 9F 2-2-4 Kojimachi, Chiyoda-ku, Tokyo, 102-0083, Japan
Tel.: (81) 3 6821 4730
Sales Range: $25-49.9 Million
Emp.: 50
Payroll Outsourcing Services
N.A.I.C.S.: 541214

Subsidiary (Domestic):

T2 Tokyo K.K.   **(3)**
Akasaka 2 14 Plaza Building 2nd Floor 2-14-32 Akasaka, Minato-ku, Tokyo, 107-0052, Japan
Tel.: (81) 345887444
Web Site: http://www.talent2.com
Sales Range: $10-24.9 Million
Emp.: 40

Human Resource Consulting & Outsourcing Services
N.A.I.C.S.: 561312
Judina Makumura *(Office Mgr)*
Yuan Yuan Chie *(Gen Mgr)*

Subsidiary (Non-US):

Talent2 NZ Limited   **(2)**
Ground Floor Montreaux Building 164-168 The Terrace, Wellington, 6011, New Zealand
Tel.: (64) 4 978 1040
Web Site: http://www.talent2.com
Sales Range: $25-49.9 Million
Emp.: 40
Human Resource Consulting & Outsourcing Services
N.A.I.C.S.: 541612

Subsidiary (Domestic):

Talent2 Pty Limited   **(2)**
Level 4 77 Pacific Highway, North Sydney, 2060, NSW, Australia
Tel.: (61) 2 9087 6333
Web Site: http://www.talent2.com
Sales Range: $25-49.9 Million
Emp.: 50
Human Resource Consulting & Outsourcing Services
N.A.I.C.S.: 541612
Nina Idle *(Office Mgr)*

Subsidiary (Non-US):

Talent Partners (Dubai) LLC **(3)**
148 Emarat Atrium Bldg, Sheikh Zayed Rd, Dubai, United Arab Emirates
Tel.: (971) 43439960
Web Site: http://www.talent2.com
Sales Range: $10-24.9 Million
Emp.: 20
Human Resource Consulting & Outsourcing Services
N.A.I.C.S.: 541612

Subsidiary (Non-US):

Talent2 Singapore Pte. Ltd. **(2)**
7 Temasek Boulevard, 33-01 Suntec Tower One, Singapore, 038987, Singapore
Tel.: (65) 65118555
Sales Range: $25-49.9 Million
Emp.: 70
Human Resource Consulting & Outsourcing Services
N.A.I.C.S.: 541612
Ellen Lee *(Office Mgr)*

Talent2 UK Executive Limited **(2)**
Level 7 South 200 Aldersgate Street, London, E1A 4HD, United Kingdom
Tel.: (44) 20 7015 3999
Web Site: http://www.talent2.com
Sales Range: $25-49.9 Million
Emp.: 20
Human Resource Consulting & Outsourcing Services
N.A.I.C.S.: 561312
Paul Dixon *(Mng Dir)*

Subsidiary (Domestic):

Talent2 Works Pty. Ltd.   **(2)**
Suite 3 6 Brodie Hall Drive, Bentley, 6102, WA, Australia
Tel.: (61) 893558300
Web Site: http://www.talent2.com
Emp.: 30
Human Resource Consulting & Outsourcing Services
N.A.I.C.S.: 541612

Subsidiary (Non-US):

Talent2 Works Limited   **(3)**
Level 59 The Center 99 Queens Road, Central, China (Hong Kong)
Tel.: (852) 34733111
Web Site: http://www.talent2.com
Sales Range: $10-24.9 Million
Emp.: 30
Human Resource Consulting & Outsourcing Services
N.A.I.C.S.: 541612
Caleb Baker *(Gen Mgr)*

ALLEGRA BRANDS

Allegra Brands—(Continued)

2444 W 16th St 2nd Fl, Chicago, IL
60608
Tel.: (312) 243-4612
Web Site: http://www.gelscrubs.com
Year Founded: 2000
Sales Range: $1-9.9 Million
Emp.: 21
Mfr of Licensed Medical Scrubs &
Apparel for Colleges & Retail Establishments
N.A.I.C.S.: 315990
David M. Hunt (Owner & CEO)

ALLEGRO CORPORATION
20048 NE San Rafel St, Portland, OR
97230
Tel.: (503) 257-8480
Web Site: http://www.allegro-music.com
Rev.: $17,000,000
Emp.: 120
Music & DVD Distr
N.A.I.C.S.: 423990
Joseph Micallef (CEO)
Bryan Huitt (Mgr-Allegro Classical
Product)
Bill Tennant (Product Mgr)
John Schman (Product Mgr-
NewSound-Allegro Media Grp)

ALLEGRO MERGER CORP.
777 3rd Ave 37th Fl, New York, NY
10017
Tel.: (212) 319-7676   DE
Year Founded: 2017
Assets: $106
Liabilities: $926,641
Net Worth: ($926,535)
Earnings: ($48,925)
Emp.: 3
Fiscal Year-end: 12/31/22
Investment Services
N.A.I.C.S.: 523999
Adam H. Jaffe (CFO)

ALLEN & ALLEN COMPANY
202 Culebra Rd, San Antonio, TX
78201
Tel.: (210) 733-9191
Web Site:
https://www.lumberhardware.com
Rev.: $19,082,140
Emp.: 77
Lumber: Rough, Dressed & Finished
N.A.I.C.S.: 423310
Bobby Joe Miller (Pres & CEO)
Christina Martin (Dir-Mktg & HR)

ALLEN & GERRITSEN, INC.
2 Seaport Ln, Boston, MA 02210
Tel.: (857) 300-2000   MA
Web Site: https://www.a-g.com
Year Founded: 1985
Sales Range: $75-99.9 Million
Emp.: 73
Advetising Agency
N.A.I.C.S.: 541810
Andrew Graff (CEO)
Gary Greenberg (Exec VP)
Scott Sneath (Mng Dir-Primal)
Monica Lorusso (Sr VP-Engagement
Strategy)
Jason Lewis (VP-Philadelphia)
Janet Freed (Sr VP-Talent)
Nina Rossello (Sr VP-Strategy)

ALLEN & HOSHALL, INC.
1661 Intl Dr Ste 100, Memphis, TN
38120-1440
Tel.: (901) 820-0820   TN
Web Site:
https://www.allenhoshall.com
Year Founded: 1915
Sales Range: $100-124.9 Million
Emp.: 150

Architectural, Engineering & Consulting Services
N.A.I.C.S.: 541330
Glen Heath (Sr VP & Engr-Civil)
Rob T. Herd (Sr VP & Engr-Electrical)
Michael Sheridan (Sr VP & Engr-
Structural)
Angie Thweatt (Engr-Civil)
Harry J. Pratt III (Pres & Engr-Civil)
James B. Caughman III (VP)

Subsidiaries:

Allen & Hoshall
8331 E Walker Springs Ln Ste 102, Knoxville, TN 37923   (100%)
Tel.: (865) 693-7881
Web Site: http://www.allenandhoshall.com
Sales Range: $25-49.9 Million
Emp.: 100
Architectural, Engineering & Consulting
Services
N.A.I.C.S.: 541330
James Crowder (Project Mgr)

Allen & Hoshall   (1)
3000 Old Canton Rd, Jackson, MS
39216-4200   (97%)
Tel.: (601) 366-3388
Architectural, Engineering & Consulting
Services
N.A.I.C.S.: 541310

Allen & Hoshall Inc - Nashville   (1)
402 BNA Dr Bldg 100 Ste 208, Nashville,
TN 37217-2552
Tel.: (615) 399-2661
Web Site: http://www.allenhoshall.com
Architectural, Engineering & Consulting
Services
N.A.I.C.S.: 541330
Joe Nims (Sr VP)

ALLEN & SHARIFF CORPORATION
7061 Deepage Dr, Columbia, MD
21045
Tel.: (410) 381-7100
Web Site:
https://www.allenshariff.com
Year Founded: 1993
Sales Range: $50-74.9 Million
Emp.: 187
Construction Engineering Services
N.A.I.C.S.: 237990
Mary Cannon (Pres)
Zack H. Shariff (Co-Founder & CEO)
David S. van der Vossen (Sr VP)
David Jackson (COO)
Gregorio Torchia (VP)
Donald Beyer (VP-Engrg-Pittsburgh)
David Price (Sr VP-Engrg-Pittsburgh)
Diane McCloskey (CFO)
John Hossick (VP-Engrg-Columbia)
Richard Bowser (VP-Engrg-Evans
City & PA)
Russ Sullivan (VP-Engrg-Evans City
& PA)
Diane Bookwalter (VP)

ALLEN & WEBB INDUSTRIAL SUPPLY
3127 Rivers Ave, North Charleston,
SC 29405-7736
Tel.: (843) 747-7321
Web Site: https://www.allenwebb.com
Year Founded: 1927
Sales Range: $10-24.9 Million
Emp.: 34
Industrial Supply Whslr
N.A.I.C.S.: 423840
Charles Swicord (Pres)
Nathan Holleman (VP)

ALLEN AIRCRAFT PRODUCTS, INC.
6168 Woodbine Rd, Ravenna, OH
44266-1211
Tel.: (330) 296-9621   OH

Web Site:
https://www.allenaircraft.com
Year Founded: 1947
Sales Range: $10-24.9 Million
Emp.: 135
Airplane Fluid Systems Component
Mfr
N.A.I.C.S.: 336413
Trey Mann (VP)
Mike Stader (Controller)
Neil W. Mann Jr. (Pres)

Subsidiaries:

Allen Aircraft Products, Inc. - Aircraft
Division   (1)
6168 Woodbine Ave, Ravenna, OH 44266
Tel.: (330) 296-9621
Web Site: http://www.allenaircraft.com
Emp.: 100
Aircraft Fluid System Component Mfr
N.A.I.C.S.: 332912
Debbie Drago (VP-Ops)

ALLEN ASSOCIATES
201 N Milpas St, Santa Barbara, CA
93103-3201
Tel.: (805) 884-8777
Web Site: https://www.buildallen.com
Sales Range: $10-24.9 Million
Emp.: 70
Residential Remodeler
N.A.I.C.S.: 236118
Dennis Allen (Pres)
Ian Cronshaw (Chief Safety Officer)

ALLEN C. EWING & CO.
7807 Baymeadows Rd E, Jacksonville, FL 32256
Tel.: (904) 354-5573   FL
Web Site: http://www.allenewing.com
Year Founded: 1939
Sales Range: $1-9.9 Million
Emp.: 16
Investment Banking
N.A.I.C.S.: 523150
Benjamin C. Bishop Jr. (Chm)
W. Allen Rogers II (Mng Dir-Mergers
& Acq)

ALLEN CHRISTIAN BUICK OLDSMOBILE PONTIAC GMC, INC.
PO Box 9, Dexter, MO 63841
Tel.: (573) 624-4505
Web Site:
http://www.allenchristian.com
Sales Range: $10-24.9 Million
Emp.: 25
Car Whslr
N.A.I.C.S.: 441110
Denny Christian (Principal)

ALLEN CORPORATION OF AMERICA, INC.
10400 Eaton Pl Ste 450, Fairfax, VA
22030
Web Site: http://www.allencorp.com
Year Founded: 1991
Sales Range: $10-24.9 Million
Emp.: 232
IT Services
N.A.I.C.S.: 541511
K. C. Vaughey (Pres)
T. S. Schimkus (CFO)
H. F. Ludwig (Sr VP-Logistics Svcs)
C. D. Hosmer (Sr VP-Cyber Security)
T. R. Pearson (VP-Trng Sys)
D. F. Delaney (VP-Integrated Networks)

ALLEN COUNTY RECYCLERS INC.
541 S Central Ave, Lima, OH 45804
Tel.: (419) 223-5010
Web Site:
https://www.allencountyrecycle.com

Year Founded: 1983
Sales Range: $10-24.9 Million
Emp.: 15
Ferrous Metal Scrap & Waste, Recycled Rubber Particles
N.A.I.C.S.: 423930
Adam Wright (Pres)

Subsidiaries:

Color Rubber Nuggets, Inc.   (1)
541 S Central, Lima, OH 45802
Tel.: (419) 223-5010
Web Site: http://www.rubbernuggets.com
Sales Range: $10-24.9 Million
Recycled Rubber Particles
N.A.I.C.S.: 326299

ALLEN DANIEL ASSOCIATES INC.
880 Main St 4th Fl, Waltham, MA
02451
Tel.: (781) 647-7722
Web Site: http://www.adacollect.com
Sales Range: $50-74.9 Million
Emp.: 30
Collection Agency, Except Real Estate
N.A.I.C.S.: 531120
Daniel B. Desatnick (Co-Founder &
Pres)
Vicki Desatnick (Controller)

ALLEN DISTRIBUTION
670 Allen Rd, Carlisle, PA 17015
Tel.: (717) 258-3040
Web Site:
http://www.allendistribution.com
Year Founded: 1988
Sales Range: $10-24.9 Million
Emp.: 150
General Warehousing
N.A.I.C.S.: 493110
Dennis Trautman (Exec VP)
Chuck McCreary (Dir-Sls & Mktg)
Jamie Pittman (Dir-IT)
Chris Matangos (VP-Ops)

ALLEN ENGINEERING CORPORATION
819 S 5th St, Paragould, AR 72450
Tel.: (870) 236-7751
Web Site: https://www.alleneng.com
Year Founded: 1962
Sales Range: $10-24.9 Million
Emp.: 85
Cement & Concrete Related Products
& Equip,
N.A.I.C.S.: 333120
J. Dewayne Allen (Chm & CEO)
Mary Ann Allen (Treas & Sec)
Jay Allen (Pres)
Roger Euliss (VP-Sls & Mktg)
Mark A. Conte (Dir-Sls-Paving Equipment)

ALLEN ENTERPRISES, INC.
2900 S 9th St, Ironton, OH 45638
Tel.: (740) 532-5913   OH
Web Site: https://tristatewilbert.com
Year Founded: 1978
Sales Range: $10-24.9 Million
Emp.: 15
Fiscal Year-end: 11/30/13
Service Establishment Equipment &
Supplies Merchant Whslr
N.A.I.C.S.: 423850

ALLEN FAMILY FOODS, INC.
126 N Shipley St, Seaford, DE
19973-3100
Tel.: (302) 629-9136   DE
Web Site:
http://www.allenfamilyfoods.com
Year Founded: 1919
Sales Range: $250-299.9 Million
Emp.: 2,400

Poultry Slaughtering & Processing Services
N.A.I.C.S.: 311615
Tracy Morris *(VP-HR)*
Gary Gladys *(Pres & CEO)*
Yong-Jae Park *(Controller-Fin)*

ALLEN GWYNN CHEVROLET
1400 S Brand Blvd, Glendale, CA 91204-2810
Tel.: (818) 240-5720
Web Site:
  https://www.lovemychevy.com
Year Founded: 1930
Sales Range: $25-49.9 Million
Emp.: 76
New Car Retailer
N.A.I.C.S.: 441110
Mark Toohey *(Mgr-Svc)*

ALLEN HOLDING INC.
711 Fifth Ave, New York, NY 10022
Tel.: (212) 832-8000
Sales Range: $25-49.9 Million
Holding Company; Investment & Brokerage Services
N.A.I.C.S.: 551112
Kim Wieland *(CFO)*
Howard M. Felson *(VP)*

Subsidiaries:

711 Air Corp.   **(1)**
233 Industrial Ave, Teterboro, NJ 07608
Tel.: (201) 288-7645
Rev.: $950,000
Emp.: 10
Air Taxis
N.A.I.C.S.: 481211

Allen & Company Incorporated   **(1)**
711 5th Ave, New York, NY 10022
Tel.: (212) 832-8000
Sales Range: $50-74.9 Million
Emp.: 160
Bond Dealers & Brokers
N.A.I.C.S.: 523150
Enrique Francisco Jose Senior Hernandez *(Mng Dir)*
Nancy B. Peretsman *(Mng Dir & Exec VP)*
Herbert A. Allen III *(Pres)*

Global Education Network   **(1)**
200 W 57th St, New York, NY 10019
Tel.: (212) 489-6300
Rev.: $990,000
Emp.: 30
Education Services
N.A.I.C.S.: 611699

ALLEN INDUSTRIES INC.
6434 Burnt Poplar Rd, Greensboro, NC 27409
Tel.: (336) 668-2791
Web Site:
  https://www.allenindustries.com
Sales Range: $10-24.9 Million
Emp.: 200
Electric Signs
N.A.I.C.S.: 339950
Thomas L. Allen *(Pres)*
Steve Haymore *(CFO)*
Heather Surratt *(Project Mgr)*
Julie Cheek *(Project Mgr)*
Lecia Neptune *(Project Mgr)*

ALLEN L. BENDER, INC.
2798 Industrial Blvd, West Sacramento, CA 95691
Tel.: (916) 372-2190
Web Site:
  http://www.allenlbender.com
Year Founded: 1971
Sales Range: $50-74.9 Million
Emp.: 120
Commercial & Institutional Building Construction Services
N.A.I.C.S.: 236220
Brian Bender *(Pres)*

ALLEN LUMBER COMPANY INC.
502 N Main St, Barre, VT 05641
Tel.: (802) 476-4156
Web Site:
  http://www.allenlumbercompany.com
Sales Range: $1-9.9 Million
Emp.: 50
Lumber & Other Building Materials
N.A.I.C.S.: 423310
Burnie Allen *(Treas & Sec)*
Debbie Lyon *(Controller)*
Lance Allen *(Mgr-Store-Windows & Doors)*
Steven Allen *(Pres)*

ALLEN LUND COMPANY, LLC
4529 Angeles Crest Hwy, La Canada, CA 91011
Tel.: (818) 790-8412
Web Site: http://www.allenlund.com
Year Founded: 1976
Sales Range: $125-149.9 Million
Emp.: 160
Transportation Brokerage Services
N.A.I.C.S.: 488510
Demetrios Bournias *(Mgr-Chicago)*
Kenny Lund *(VP)*
Leonora Winegar *(Mgr-Grand Rapids)*
Jeff Kleyn *(Mgr-Ops-Grand Rapids)*

Subsidiaries:

Des Moines Truck Brokers, Inc.   **(1)**
1505 North Ave, Norwalk, IA 50211-1568
Tel.: (515) 981-5115
Web Site: http://www.dmtb.com
Sales Range: $1-9.9 Million
Emp.: 8
Transportation Arrangement Services
N.A.I.C.S.: 488510
Eric Davis *(Sr Acct Mgr)*
Trent McIntyre *(Acct Mgr)*
Denise Shannon *(Accountant)*
Randy Eilers *(Accountant)*
Vickie Doerr *(Controller)*
Christian Ferkin *(Coord-Carrier)*
Jeff Feaker *(Coord-Carrier)*
Jimmy DeMatteis *(Pres & CEO)*

Magic Valley Truck Brokers Inc.   **(1)**
2906 S Featherly Way, Boise, ID 83709
Tel.: (208) 375-5677
Web Site:
  http://www.magicvalleytruckbrokers.com
Specialized Freight Trucking
N.A.I.C.S.: 484230
Wes Blaser *(Pres)*

Northern Freight Service, Inc.   **(1)**
8309 Greenway Blvd Ste 200, Middleton, WI 53562
Tel.: (608) 836-8688
Web Site: http://www.northernfreight.com
Emp.: 20
Freight Trucking Services
N.A.I.C.S.: 484110
Richard Barker *(Pres)*

ALLEN MATKINS LECK GAMBLE MALLORY & NATSIS LLP
515 S Figueroa St 9th Fl, Los Angeles, CA 90071-3309
Tel.: (213) 622-5555
Web Site:
  http://www.allenmatkins.com
Year Founded: 1977
Sales Range: $150-199.9 Million
Emp.: 201
Legal Advisory Services
N.A.I.C.S.: 541110
Frederick L. Allen *(Co-Partner)*
Michael L. Matkins *(Partner-Los Angeles)*
Marvin E. Garrett *(Partner)*
Brian C. Leck *(Co-Partner)*
John J. Allen *(Co-Partner)*
Patrick E. Breen *(Partner)*
Robert J. Cathcart *(Partner)*
Michael Cerrina *(Partner)*

Lorraine R. Connally *(Dir-Legal Recruiting & Diversity)*
Matthew J. Ertman *(Partner)*
Michael R. Farrell *(Partner)*
Neil N. Gluck *(Partner)*
Debra Dison Hall *(Partner)*
Benjamin Fackler *(Partner)*
Martha Bernard *(Dir-Office Admin)*
Ramona R. Whitley *(Dir-Client Svcs)*
Clark Snyder *(CTO)*
David H. Blackwell *(Partner)*
David D. Cooke *(Partner)*
David L. Osias *(Mng Partner)*
Martin L. Togni *(Partner)*
Nancy Lundeen *(Partner)*
Michelle McDermott *(Partner)*
Julie Hoffman *(Partner)*
Stephen Etheredge *(Partner)*
Frank W. Dworak *(Partner-Corp & Fin Dept & Tax Practice Grp-Orange County)*
O'Malley M. Miller *(Partner-Real Estate Dept)*
Marc D. Young *(Partner-Real Estate Fin)*
Kate Kraus *(Partner)*
Ryan W. Smith *(Partner-litigation-Orange County)*
Jeffrey R. Patterson *(Mng Partner)*
Grant Alexander *(Partner-Labor & Employment)*
Spencer Kallick *(Partner-Land use-Century City)*
Mark Nicoletti *(Partner-Real estate)*
Larry Kleinberg *(COO)*
Bennet Van De Bunt *(Executives)*

ALLEN OIL COMPANY INC.
2809 Limerick St, Savannah, GA 31404
Tel.: (912) 691-1015
Sales Range: $10-24.9 Million
Emp.: 6
Owner & Operator of Convenience Stores
N.A.I.C.S.: 445131
William H. Smith III *(Pres)*

ALLEN OIL COMPANY OF SYLACAUGA
1251 Old Birmingham Hwy, Sylacauga, AL 35150
Tel.: (256) 245-5478
Web Site: https://www.allenoil.com
Sales Range: $10-24.9 Million
Emp.: 30
Gasoline Distribution
N.A.I.C.S.: 424720
Harmon Allen *(Co-Owner)*
Tim Allen *(Co-Owner & VP)*

ALLEN ORGAN COMPANY
150 Locust St, Macungie, PA 18062-1165
Tel.: (610) 966-2202   DE
Web Site:
  https://www.allenorgan.com
Year Founded: 1945
Sales Range: $75-99.9 Million
Emp.: 200
Mfr of Electronic Keyboards, Digital Organs & Accessories for Churches
N.A.I.C.S.: 339992
Steven A. Markowitz *(Pres)*
Barry Holben *(VP)*

Subsidiaries:

Allen Audio, Inc.   **(1)**
150 Locust St, Macungie, PA
18062-0036   **(100%)**
Tel.: (610) 966-2202
Web Site: http://www.allenaudio.com
Sales Range: $25-49.9 Million
Audio System Designers
N.A.I.C.S.: 334310
Steven Markowitz *(Pres)*

Allen Integrated Assemblies   **(1)**
150 Locust St, Macungie, PA 18062-1165
Tel.: (610) 966-2200
Web Site: http://www.allen.com
Sales Range: $25-49.9 Million
N.A.I.C.S.: 339992
Henry Nibbe *(Gen Mgr)*

ALLEN PRESS INC.
810 E Tenth St, Lawrence, KS 66044-3018
Tel.: (785) 843-1235   KS
Web Site: http://www.allenpress.com
Year Founded: 1935
Sales Range: $25-49.9 Million
Emp.: 200
Scientific Periodicals Publisher
N.A.I.C.S.: 513120
Bill Tofflemire *(Dir-Bus Dev)*
Julie Rinke *(VP-Ops)*
John Aamot *(Dir-Bus Dev)*
Barbara Buzzi *(Dir-Bus Dev)*
Randy Radosevich *(Pres & CEO)*
Dan Scobee *(Dir-Mfg)*
Maria Preston *(Sr VP-Sls & Mktg)*
Maria Preston-Cargill *(Exec VP)*
Mark Kohlhase *(CEO)*

ALLEN PRINTING, INC.
415-A Spence Ln, Nashville, TN 37210
Tel.: (615) 255-2078
Web Site:
  http://www.allenprinting.com
Year Founded: 1931
Sales Range: $1-9.9 Million
Emp.: 63
Graphic Design, Printing & Mailing Services
N.A.I.C.S.: 323111
Jerry Bell *(Mgr-Tech)*
Shannon Heffington *(Owner)*

ALLEN SAMUEL CHRYSLER DODGE JEEP
8181 Memorial Blvd, Port Arthur, TX 77640
Tel.: (409) 983-5171
Web Site:
  http://www.midcountychrysler.com
Rev.: $14,677,465
Emp.: 44
Automobiles, New & Used
N.A.I.C.S.: 441110
Allen Tate *(Owner)*

ALLEN SAMUELS AUTO GROUP
301 Owen Ln, Waco, TX 76710-5579
Tel.: (254) 761-6800   TX
Web Site:
  http://www.allensamuelswaco.com
Year Founded: 1983
Sales Range: $75-99.9 Million
Emp.: 10
Holding Company for Automobile Dealerships
N.A.I.C.S.: 441110
Allen Samuels *(Chm)*
Jeff Wooley *(Pres)*
Maxine Hall *(VP)*

Subsidiaries:

Allen Samuels Chevrolet   **(1)**
1625 N Vly Mills Dr, Waco, TX 76710-2552
Tel.: (254) 772-8850
Web Site:
  http://www.allensamuelschevrolet.com
Sales Range: $25-49.9 Million
Retail New & Used Cars, Trucks & Parts
N.A.I.C.S.: 441110
Judy Schwieger *(Controller)*
Norman Ferguson *(Mgr-Body Shop)*

ALLEN SUPER SAVE MARKETS
340 S Main St, Springville, UT 84663

Allen Super Save Markets—(Continued)

Tel.: (801) 224-0999
Sales Range: $10-24.9 Million
Emp.: 100
Independent Supermarket
N.A.I.C.S.: 445110
G. Steven Allen *(Pres)*

ALLEN SYSTEMS GROUP, INC.

708 Goodlette-Frank Rd, Naples, FL
34102-6400
Tel.: (239) 435-2200
Web Site: http://www.asg.com
Year Founded: 1986
Sales Range: $250-299.9 Million
Emp.: 1,250
Software & Professional Services for
Information, Operations & Applications Management
N.A.I.C.S.: 513210
Alan Bolt *(CIO & Exec VP)*
Richard Vance *(Exec VP-Ops)*
Scott McCurdy *(Sr VP-Bus Solutions)*
Tom Romnios *(Exec VP-Global HR)*
Alex Derby *(Sr VP-Sls Ops)*
Dietmar Wendt *(Exec VP-Global Sls & Mktg)*
Charles Sansbury *(Pres & CEO)*

Subsidiaries:

ASG Software Solutions   (1)
Palazzo Galileo Via Francesco Sforza,
Basiglio, 20080, Milan, Italy
Tel.: (39) 0290450008
Web Site: http://www.asg.com
Sales Range: $10-24.9 Million
Emp.: 4
N.A.I.C.S.: 541512
Carlo Bonomi *(Mgr-Svc)*

ASG Software Solutions   (1)
Solna Strandvag 78, 171 54, Solna, Sweden
Tel.: (46) 8 5052 1098
Web Site: http://www.asg.com
Sales Range: $10-24.9 Million
Emp.: 6
Mfr of Software Products
N.A.I.C.S.: 541512

Allen Systems Group   (1)
Centurion Point Abbey View Business Park,
Saint Albans, AL1 2PS, United Kingdom
Tel.: (44) 1727736300
Sales Range: $10-24.9 Million
Emp.: 25
Mfr of Software Products
N.A.I.C.S.: 541512

Mobius Management Systems Benelux B.V.   (1)
Perkinsbaan 11, 3439 ND, Nieuwegein,
Netherlands
Tel.: (31) 306300121
Web Site: http://www.mobius.nl
Sales Range: $10-24.9 Million
Emp.: 4
Mfr of Software Products
N.A.I.C.S.: 541512

Mobius Management Systems,
Australia   (1)
Level 40 100 Miller St, Sydney, 2060, NSW,
Australia
Tel.: (61) 2 9911 7735
Sales Range: $10-24.9 Million
Emp.: 10
Software Solutions & Services
N.A.I.C.S.: 513210

ALLEN TILLERY CHEVROLET, INC.

4573 Central Ave, Hot Springs, AR
71913
Tel.: (501) 525-4343
Sales Range: $10-24.9 Million
Emp.: 70
Car Whslr
N.A.I.C.S.: 441110
Susan Sanders *(Bus Mgr)*
Chad Tillery *(Owner & Mgr)*

ALLEN TURNER HYUNDAI INC.

6000 Pensacola Blvd, Pensacola, FL
32505
Tel.: (850) 479-9667
Web Site:
http://www.allenturnerhyundai.com
Sales Range: $25-49.9 Million
Emp.: 60
Car Dealership Owner & Operator
N.A.I.C.S.: 441110
Mark Rask *(Dir-BDC)*

ALLEN, ALLEN, ALLEN & ALLEN

1809 Staples Mill Rd, Richmond, VA
23230
Tel.: (804) 353-1200
Web Site:
https://www.allenandallen.com
Sales Range: $10-24.9 Million
Emp.: 120
Law firm
N.A.I.C.S.: 541110
P. Christopher Guedri *(Atty)*
Charles L. Allen *(Atty)*
R. Clayton Allen *(Atty)*
W. Coleman Allen Jr. *(Atty)*

ALLEN-BAILEY TAG & LABEL INC.

3177 Lehigh St, Caledonia, NY
14423
Tel.: (585) 538-2324
Web Site: https://www.abtl.com
Sales Range: $10-24.9 Million
Emp.: 80
Paper Products Mfr
N.A.I.C.S.: 322299
Kim Gifaldi *(Acct Mgr)*

ALLEN-KEITH CONSTRUCTION CO., INC.

2735 Greensburg Rd, North Canton,
OH 44720
Tel.: (330) 699-5668
Web Site: https://www.allenkeith.com
Emp.: 95
Nonresidential Construction Services
N.A.I.C.S.: 236220
Daniel Keith Hanlon *(Owner)*
Bill F. McGuire *(Pres)*

ALLENS OF HASTINGS, INC.

1115 W 2nd St, Hastings, NE 68901-
4974
Tel.: (402) 463-5633
Web Site:
http://www.allensuperstore.com
Year Founded: 1958
Sales Range: $10-24.9 Million
Emp.: 155
Sales of Groceries
N.A.I.C.S.: 445110
Jennifer Obermier *(Mgr-Pharmacy)*

ALLENS STEEL PRODUCTS INC.

11475 Memphis Arlington Rd, Arlington, TN 38002
Tel.: (901) 867-0171
Web Site: http://www.allenssteel.com
Sales Range: $10-24.9 Million
Emp.: 150
Structural Steel Erection
N.A.I.C.S.: 238120
J. C. Allen *(Pres)*

ALLENSVILLE PLANING MILL INC.

108 E Main St, Allensville, PA 17002
Tel.: (717) 483-6386
Web Site: https://www.apm-inc.net
Sales Range: $10-24.9 Million

Emp.: 123
Lumber Products
N.A.I.C.S.: 444110
Wendy Snair *(Coord-HR)*

ALLENTOWN MACK SALES & SERVICE, INC.

1407 Bulldog Dr, Allentown, PA
18104
Tel.: (610) 395-6801
Web Site: http://www.allentown-
mack.com
Sales Range: $25-49.9 Million
Emp.: 65
Truck Sales & Service
N.A.I.C.S.: 423110
Robert J. Dwyer *(Pres)*
Charlie Craig *(Mgr-Parts)*
Dave Wirth *(Mgr-Svc)*
Frank Szilezy *(Mgr-Sls)*

Subsidiaries:

Pittsburgh Mack Sales & Service
Inc.   (1)
1407 Bulldog Dr, Allentown, PA 18104
Tel.: (412) 237-6000
Web Site: http://www.transedgetruck.com
Sales Range: $10-24.9 Million
Emp.: 42
Commercial Truck Sales & Service
N.A.I.C.S.: 423110
Ed Levendosky *(Mgr-Parts)*
Eric Schenck *(Mgr-Svc)*
David Stahl *(Mgr-Sls)*
Kirsten Dwyer *(Mgr-Mktg)*
Stacey Kester *(Office Mgr)*
Frank Meehan *(VP-Ops)*
Brian Umberger *(Controller)*

ALLERTON SUPPLY CO.

309 E Yates, Allerton, IL 61810
Tel.: (217) 834-3301
Web Site:
https://www.allertonsupply.com
Sales Range: $10-24.9 Million
Emp.: 50
Fertilizer & Fertilizer Materials
N.A.I.C.S.: 424910
Vickie Allan *(Controller)*
Ron Mowen *(Gen Mgr)*

ALLERVIE HEALTH PROFESSIONAL CORPORATION

4975 Preston Park Blvd Ste 800,
Plano, TX 75093
Tel.: (214) 227-8112
Web Site: https://www.allervie.com
Hospitals & Health Care Services
N.A.I.C.S.: 622110

ALLESCO INDUSTRIES INC.

15 Amflex Dr, Cranston, RI 02921
Tel.: (401) 275-9771
Web Site: http://www.allesco.net
Year Founded: 1962
Sales Range: $10-24.9 Million
Holding Company; Hardware Equipments Mfr
N.A.I.C.S.: 332722
Frank Ferretti *(Mgr-IT)*
Chris Rotondo *(VP-Ops)*
Joseph Smith Jr. *(CFO)*

ALLETE & AFFILIATED COMPANIES RETIREE HEALTH PLAN A

30 W Superior St, Duluth, MN 55802
Tel.: (218) 723-3922
Year Founded: 1994
Sales Range: $10-24.9 Million
Retiree Health Benefit Services
N.A.I.C.S.: 525110
Bonnie A. Kepper *(Pres)*

ALLEY THEATRE

615 Texas Ave, Houston, TX 77002
Tel.: (713) 228-9341

Web Site:
https://www.alleytheatre.org
Year Founded: 1947
Rev.: $13,000,000
Emp.: 135
Theatre Production
N.A.I.C.S.: 711310
James Black *(Interim Dir-Artistic)*
Kevin Rigdon *(Assoc Dir-Design)*
Dennis Draper *(Dir-Ops & Events)*
Don Poole *(Dir-Fin)*
Tom O'Dell *(Dir-Audience Svcs)*
Dean R. Gladden *(Mng Dir)*
Nancy Giles *(Dir-Dev)*
Kay Ross *(Controller)*
Kathryn Straw *(Dir-Corp Rels)*
Katie Jackman *(Dir-Mktg & Comm)*
Amy Schwab Lampi *(Assoc Dir-Dev)*
Mary Sutton *(Dir-Education & Community Engagement)*
Peter Yenne *(Dir-Foundation & Govt Rels)*
Tim Richey *(Dir-Individual Giving)*
Elizabeth Frankel *(Dir-New Work)*
Laura Woods *(Dir-Special Events)*
Patrick A. Orndorff *(Dir-Technical)*
Charlotte Weschler *(Mgr-Patron Svcs)*
Rachel Applegate *(Dir-Mktg & Comm)*

ALLEY-CASSETTY COMPANIES

2 Oldham St, Nashville, TN 37213-
1107
Tel.: (615) 244-0440
Web Site: http://www.alley-
cassetty.com
Year Founded: 1964
Sales Range: $125-149.9 Million
Emp.: 225
Coal Brokerage Services, Building
Supplies & Concrete Blocks; Truck
Sales, Repair & Trucking Services
N.A.I.C.S.: 423520
Curt Hirsch *(Gen Mgr)*
Tim Pedigo *(VP-Comml Sls)*

Subsidiaries:

Alley-Cassetty Brick Bowling Green
Division   (1)
2777 Griffin Dr, Bowling Green, KY 42101
Tel.: (270) 781-3474
Web Site: http://www.alley-cassetty.com
Sales Range: $25-49.9 Million
Emp.: 6
Construction Materials
N.A.I.C.S.: 444180
James Mc Lusky *(Reg Mgr)*

Alley-Cassetty Brick Columbia
Div.   (1)
100 Hill St, Columbia, TN 38401
Tel.: (931) 380-9124
Provider of Construction Materials
N.A.I.C.S.: 423310
Jason Anderson *(Gen Mgr)*

Alley-Cassetty Brick Gallatin Div.   (1)
PO Box 8044, Gallatin, TN 37266
Tel.: (615) 452-4620
Web Site: http://www.alley-cassetty.com
Sales Range: $10-24.9 Million
Emp.: 25
Provider of Construction Materials
N.A.I.C.S.: 327331
Keith Green *(Branch Mgr)*

Alley-Cassetty Brick Murfreesboro
Div.   (1)
415 New Salem Rd, Murfreesboro, TN
37129
Tel.: (615) 893-6280
Web Site: http://www.alley-cassetty.com
Sales Range: $25-49.9 Million
Emp.: 20
Provider of Construction Materials
N.A.I.C.S.: 423320
Randy Huffman *(Gen Mgr)*

Alley-Cassetty Brick Nashville
Div.   (1)
PO Box 23305, Nashville, TN 37202

Tel.: (615) 244-0440
Web Site: http://www.alley-cassetty.com
Sales Range: $25-49.9 Million
Emp.: 50
Provider of Construction Materials
N.A.I.C.S.: 423520
Sam Strang (Pres)

Alley-Cassetty Companies - Alley-
Cassetty Truck Center Division   (1)
727 Fesslers Ln, Nashville, TN 37210
Tel.: (615) 244-6191
Web Site: http://www.actruckcenter.com
Automotive Part Whslr
N.A.I.C.S.: 423120
James White (Mgr-Parts)

ALLEYCORP
520 Broadway 4th Fl, New york, NY
10012
Tel.: (646) 929-6710
Web Site: http://alleycorp.com
Investment Services
N.A.I.C.S.: 523940
Kevin Ryan (Founder, Chm & CEO)
Wendy tsu (Partner)
Susannah Shipton (Head-Platform)

ALLFAX SPECIALTIES INC.
130 James Dr E, Saint Rose, LA
70087
Tel.: (504) 443-0188
Web Site: https://www.allfax.com
Year Founded: 1988
Sales Range: $10-24.9 Million
Emp.: 100
Sales of Fax Machine Related Equip-
ment
N.A.I.C.S.: 423690
Brian Grosch (Owner)
Randy Dufour (CFO)
Brent Martin (VP)

ALLGEIER, MARTIN & ASSO-
CIATES, INC.
7231 E 24th St, Joplin, MO 64804
Tel.: (417) 680-7200
Web Site: http://www.amce.com
Year Founded: 1965
Emp.: 130
Engineeering Services
N.A.I.C.S.: 541330
Steven Mcnabb (Pres)

Subsidiaries:
White River Engineering Inc.   (1)
700 W Wall St, Springfield, MO 65802-4142
Tel.: (417) 862-3355
Web Site: http://www.whiterivereng.com
Engineeering Services
N.A.I.C.S.: 541330
Richard McMillian (Pres)

ALLGLASS SYSTEMS INC.
34 Noeland Ave Ste B, Langhorne,
PA 19047
Tel.: (215) 752-3224
Rev.: $24,000,000
Emp.: 50
Glass & Glazing Work
N.A.I.C.S.: 238150
Glenn Christie (Mgr-Ops)
Glenn Chrisite (Dir-Ops)
Ivonne Davis (Pres)

ALLIANCE 2020, INC.
304 Main Ave S Ste 101, Renton, WA
98057
Tel.: (425) 271-8065
Web Site:
http://www.alliance2020.com
Year Founded: 1987
Sales Range: $1-9.9 Million
Emp.: 30
Background Screening Services
N.A.I.C.S.: 561611
Kathy L. Faulkes (Co-Founder &
Pres)

Bradley J. Faulkes (Co-Founder &
CEO)
Debbie Loyning (Gen Mgr)
Joan Archie (Compliance Officer)
Kimberly Shaw (Supvr-Court Dept)

ALLIANCE ADVISORS LLC
200 Broadacres Dr Ste 3, Bloomfield,
NJ 07003-3154
Tel.: (904) 425-5005
Web Site:
http://www.allianceadvisorsllc.com
Emp.: 100
Process, Physical Distribution & Lo-
gistics Consulting Services
N.A.I.C.S.: 541614
Eileen M. Scully (Mgr)
Celine Feng (VP-Bus Dev-Greater
China)
Ted Wallace (Sr VP & Head-Asia Pa-
cific)
Joseph Caruso (CEO)
Race Chan (Head-Investor
Intelligence-Greater China)

Subsidiaries:
The Proxy Advisory Group, LLC   (1)
18 E 41st St Ste 2000, New York, NY
10017
Tel.: (212) 616-2180
Web Site: http://www.proxyadvisory.net
Sales Range: $1-9.9 Million
Emp.: 12
Securities & Commodity Exchanges
N.A.I.C.S.: 523210
Bill Poudrier (Founder & Pres)

ALLIANCE BANCORP
101 W Montgomery St, Francesville,
IN 47946
Tel.: (219) 567-9151
Web Site:
https://www.myalliancebank.com
Year Founded: 1986
Sales Range: $10-24.9 Million
Emp.: 71
Bank Holding Company
N.A.I.C.S.: 551111
Shane Pilarski (Pres & CEO)

Subsidiaries:
Alliance Bank   (1)
101 W Montgomery St, Francesville, IN
47946
Tel.: (219) 567-9151
Web Site: http://www.myalliancebank.com
Commericial Banking
N.A.I.C.S.: 522110

ALLIANCE BANK
105 E Lyon Ave, Lake City, MN
55041
Tel.: (651) 345-3311
Web Site:
https://www.alliancebanks.com
Year Founded: 1867
Sales Range: $450-499.9 Million
Emp.: 50
Commericial Banking
N.A.I.C.S.: 522110
Bill D. Otis (Bd of Dirs, Executives)
Ann Reim-Woessner (Chm)
Cindy Cole (CIO)
Josh Campbell (Asst VP-Real Estate
Lending)
Dean Anderson (Sr VP-Comml Bank-
ing)
R. Scott Johnson (VP-Comml Bank-
ing)
Carla Baier (Asst VP & Mgr-Personal
Banking)
Jonathan Chaffee (VP)
Jahn Vieve Howe (VP-Cash Mgmt)
Eileen Olsen (VP-Comml & Private
Banking)

ALLIANCE BANK INC.

100 W Jefferson St, Sulphur Springs,
TX 75482
Tel.: (903) 885-2187   TX
Web Site:
https://www.alliancebank.com
Year Founded: 1927
Rev.: $21,028,000
Emp.: 175
State Commercial Banks
N.A.I.C.S.: 522110
L. F. Bridges (Chm)
James Worsham (Exec VP)
Thomas Sellers (Pres & CEO)
James Law (Exec VP)

ALLIANCE BENEFIT GROUP,
LLC
456 Fulton St Ste 345, Peoria, IL
61602
Tel.: (309) 671-4200   IL
Web Site:
http://www.abgnational.com
Year Founded: 1992
Holding Company; Employee Benefits
Consulting & Administration Services
N.A.I.C.S.: 551112
Don Mackanos (Pres)

Subsidiaries:
Alliance Benefit Group Carolinas,
Inc.   (1)
5250 77 Ctr Dr Ste 450, Charlotte, NC
28217-0709
Tel.: (704) 452-4167
Web Site: http://www.abgpentegra.com
Employee Benefits Consulting & Administra-
tion Services
N.A.I.C.S.: 524292
Betty Caldwell (VP)

Alliance Benefit Group Midatlantic,
LLC   (1)
3501 Masons Mill Rd, Huntingdon Valley,
PA 19006
Tel.: (215) 706-4000
Rev.: $6,000,000
Emp.: 60
Employee Benefits Consulting & Administra-
tion Services
N.A.I.C.S.: 524292

Alliance Benefit Group of Houston,
Inc.   (1)
7425 Hollister St, Houston, TX 77040
Tel.: (713) 690-9898
Web Site: http://www.abghouston.com
Employee Benefits Consulting & Administra-
tion Services
N.A.I.C.S.: 524292
Michael G. Pettey (Pres & CEO)
Scott Dozier (VP-Sls & Mktg)
Parrish Pettey (Partner)
David Eudoxie (Dir-Ops & Compliance)
Rick Bruce (Exec VP)

Alliance Benefit Group of Illinois,
Inc.   (1)
456 Fulton St Ste 345, Peoria, IL 61602
Tel.: (309) 671-4200
Web Site: http://www.abgil.com
Emp.: 55
Employee Benefits Consulting & Administra-
tion Services
N.A.I.C.S.: 524292
Daphne M. Weitzel (Sr VP)

Alliance Benefit Group of Michigan,
Inc.   (1)
30100 Telegraph Rd Ste 170, Bingham
Farms, MI 48025
Web Site: http://www.abgmi.com
Sales Range: $1-9.9 Million
Emp.: 30
Employee Benefits Consulting & Administra-
tion Services
N.A.I.C.S.: 524292
Larry Raymond (Pres)

Spectrum Pension Consultants,
Inc.   (1)
6402 19th St W, Tacoma, WA 98466
Tel.: (253) 565-2100
Web Site: http://www.spectrumpension.com

Sales Range: $1-9.9 Million
Emp.: 20
Employee Benefits Consulting & Administra-
tion Services
N.A.I.C.S.: 524292
Maria Koumantaros (Mgr-Accts Receivable)
Petros P. Koumantaros (CEO & Mng Dir)
Yannis P. Koumantaros (Mng Dir-Client En-
gagements)

ALLIANCE BROKERAGE
CORP.
990 Westbury Rd 3rd Fl, Westbury,
NY 11590
Tel.: (516) 333-7300
Web Site: http://www.abc990.com
Sales Range: $25-49.9 Million
Emp.: 30
Insurance Agents
N.A.I.C.S.: 524210
Lisa Traganos (Mgr-Personal Lines)
Patricia Palk (VP)

ALLIANCE COMMUNITY HOS-
PITAL
200 E State St, Alliance, OH 44601
Tel.: (330) 596-6000   OH
Web Site: http://www.achosp.org
Year Founded: 1901
Sales Range: $75-99.9 Million
Emp.: 1,197
Health Care Srvices
N.A.I.C.S.: 622110
Ron Lyons (Treas)
Woody McCallum (Sec)
David Lundgren (VP)
Don McAlister (Pres)

ALLIANCE CONSTRUCTION
SOLUTIONS LLC
2260 Broadway, Denver, CO 80205
Tel.: (970) 663-9700   CO
Web Site:
http://www.allianceconstruction.com
Year Founded: 1982
Sales Range: $75-99.9 Million
Emp.: 30
Provider of Construction & Contract-
ing Services
N.A.I.C.S.: 236220
William Joyner (CEO)
Brian Weinmaster (Exec VP)
Martin G. Ariano (CFO & VP)
Doug Miller (Dir-Bus Dev)
Jeremy Nothdurft (VP)
Greg Conger (Mgr-Pre Construction)

ALLIANCE CREDIT UNION
3315 Almaden Expy Ste 55, San
Jose, CA 95118-1557
Tel.: (408) 265-7322   CA
Web Site:
http://www.alliancecreditunion.org
Year Founded: 1952
Sales Range: $1-9.9 Million
Emp.: 125
Credit Union
N.A.I.C.S.: 522130
James Delyea (Sr VP-Ops)
Brian Dorcy (Pres & CEO)
Surya Turaga (Chm)
Ralph Finelli (Treas & Sec)
Donna Rhody (Vice Chm)
Deborah Sunderman (Sr VP-Lending)
Kevin Alsup (Sr VP-Tech)
Tim Furlong (VP-Fin)
Taruna Bajaj (VP-Mktg)
Trish Ellingson (VP-Real Estate
Lending)
Hector Espinoza (VP-Risk Mgmt)
Richard DeCrescente (VP-Sls)

ALLIANCE DEFENDING FREE-
DOM, INC.
15100 N 90th St, Scottsdale, AZ
85260

Alliance Defending Freedom, Inc.—(Continued)

Tel.: (480) 444-0020   VA
Web Site: https://www.adflegal.org
Year Founded: 1993
Sales Range: $25-49.9 Million
Emp.: 212
Legal & Advocacy Organization
N.A.I.C.S.: 813319
Tom Minnery (Vice Chm)
Michael Farris (Pres, CEO & Gen counsel)
Kristen K. Waggoner (Gen Counsel-Arizona & Sr VP-Legal Div)
Timothy D. Chandler (Sr VP-Alliance Advancement)
Douglas H. Napier (Sr VP-Alliance Rels)
Joseph Infranco (VP-Alliance Coordination)
Brett Harvey (VP-Grants & Funding)
Jeremy Tedesco (VP-Advocacy & Admin)
David A. Cortman (VP-Litigation)

ALLIANCE DEVELOPMENT GROUP

443 Leah Dr, Fort Washington, PA 19034
Tel.: (215) 654-0440
Web Site:
   http://www.thealliancedevgroup.com
Sales Range: $1-9.9 Million
Emp.: 25
Investment Firm
N.A.I.C.S.: 523999

Subsidiaries:

Damon's International Inc.   (1)
4555 Knightsbridge Blvd, Columbus, OH 43214-4324
Tel.: (614) 442-7900
Web Site: http://www.damons.com
Sales Range: $200-249.9 Million
Owner & Franchiser of Casual Dining Restaurants
N.A.I.C.S.: 722513

ALLIANCE ENERGY GROUP, LLC

634 Main St Ste 300, East Aurora, NY 14052
Tel.: (716) 805-1469   NV
Web Site:
   http://www.allianceenergy.com
Electric Power Generation; Natural Gas Exploration, Production & Transportation
N.A.I.C.S.: 221112
Bonnie M. Philipps (VP-Fin)
Samuel G. Nappi (Chm)
J. Matthew Grubka (Dir-Acctg)
Robert W. Miller (Dir-HR)
Joseph Klimaszewski Jr. (VP-Ops & New Dev)

ALLIANCE ENERGY SERVICES, LLC

318 Armour Rd, Kansas City, MO 64116-3506
Tel.: (816) 421-5192   MN
Web Site: https://www.alliancec3.com
Emp.: 52
Petroleum & Petroleum Products Merchant Whslr
N.A.I.C.S.: 424720
Jason Doyle (Pres)
Beth Gatewood (Sr Accountant)

ALLIANCE ENGINEERING INC.

9011 Albertum Pkwy Ste 310, Richmond, VA 23236
Tel.: (804) 275-1400
Web Site:
   https://www.allianceengineering.com
Year Founded: 1989
Sales Range: $10-24.9 Million

Emp.: 60
Provider of Engineering Services
N.A.I.C.S.: 541330
James Burnette (Co-Founder)
Mark Feola (VP-Engrg)
Anthony Bream (Project Mgr)
Derek Cannon (Engr-Structural)
Kevin Kokal (Owner)
Danny Boyce (Dir-Construction Mgmt)
Tony Delgado (VP-Food & Personal Care)

Subsidiaries:

Alliance Engineering Inc.   (1)
6810 Deerpath Rd Ste 315, Elkridge, MD 21075   (100%)
Tel.: (410) 636-9555
Sales Range: $10-24.9 Million
Emp.: 10
Provider of Engineering Services
N.A.I.C.S.: 541330
Jim Burnett (Pres)
Kevin Kokal (Founder)

ALLIANCE ENVIRONMENTAL GROUP, LLC

777 N Georgia Ave, Azusa, CA 91702
Tel.: (626) 499-6665
Web Site: http://www.alliance-enviro.com
Year Founded: 1995
Sales Range: $1-9.9 Million
Emp.: 65
Specialty Trade Contractors
N.A.I.C.S.: 238990
Joseph W. McLean (Co-Founder & CEO)
Carlos Sanguinetti (Mgr-San Diego)
Craig Sawyer (Branch Mgr)
William J. Wood (Dir-Client Rels)
Edward A. Work (Branch Mgr-Bay Area)
Jeff McLean (Co-Founder & CEO)
Jimmy Nguyen (Branch Mgr)
Rick Bradley (Mgr-Demolition Ops)
Shaun Murphy (VP-Ops)
Steven K. Reaves (Controller)

Subsidiaries:

Coast Environmental, Inc.   (1)
2221 Las Palmas Dr Ste J, Carlsbad, CA 92011
Tel.: (760) 929-9570
Web Site:
   http://www.coastenvironmental.com
Medical Laboratories
N.A.I.C.S.: 621511
Dan Hughes (Pres)
Chris Heitman (Pres)

Thermatech Northwest, Inc.   (1)
10312 Sales Rd S, Lakewood, WA 98499
Tel.: (253) 984-1818
Web Site:
   http://www.thermatechnorthwestinc.com
Remediation Services
N.A.I.C.S.: 562910
James Guiley (Ops Mgr)
Bob Guiley (Co-Founder)

ALLIANCE FINANCIAL GROUP, INC.

14021 Metropolis Ave, Fort Myers, FL 33912
Tel.: (239) 561-2900   FL
Web Site: https://www.afgfl.com
Year Founded: 1982
Sales Range: $1-9.9 Million
Emp.: 30
Life Insurance Brokerage Services
N.A.I.C.S.: 524210
Douglas Gribin (Pres)

ALLIANCE FOODS INC.

605 W Chicago St Ste 1, Coldwater, MI 49036
Tel.: (517) 278-2396   MI

Web Site: https://www.alliance-foods.com
Year Founded: 1925
Sales Range: $50-74.9 Million
Emp.: 400
Owner & Operator of Grocery Stores
N.A.I.C.S.: 445110
Paul Miller (Mgr-IT)
Sal Stazzone (Pres & CEO)
Judy Rossom (CFO & Treas)

Subsidiaries:

Proactive Sales & Marketing Inc.   (1)
4580 Weaver Pkwy Ste 101, Warrenville, IL 60555
Tel.: (630) 293-5400
Web Site: http://proactivesales.net
General Line Grocery Merchant Whslr
N.A.I.C.S.: 424410
Stephen Diebold (Pres)

ALLIANCE FOR AUDITED MEDIA

48 W Seegers Rd, Arlington Heights, IL 60005-3913
Tel.: (224) 366-6939   IL
Web Site:
   http://www.auditedmedia.com
Year Founded: 1914
Sales Range: $25-49.9 Million
Digital Consulting, Cross-Media Verification & Information Services
N.A.I.C.S.: 541890
Christopher Black (Chm)
Edward W. Boyd (Dir-Adv Agency)
Phillip Crawley (Vice Chm)
Tom Drouillard (Pres, CEO & Mng Dir)
Brian Condon (Exec VP-Comml Dev)

Subsidiaries:

BPA Worldwide, Inc.   (1)
100 Beard Sawmill Rd 6th Fl, Shelton, CT 06484
Tel.: (203) 447-2800
Web Site: https://www.bpaww.com
Sales Range: $10-24.9 Million
Emp.: 120
Accounting & Auditing Services
N.A.I.C.S.: 541219
Richard J. Murphy (Pres & CEO)
David Adelman (Chm)

ALLIANCE FOR BANGLADESH WORKER SAFETY

1747 Pennsylvania Ave NW Ste 1000, Washington, DC 20006
Tel.: (336) 424-6151   DE
Web Site:
   http://www.workersafety.org
Year Founded: 2013
Sales Range: $25-49.9 Million
Emp.: 1
Safety Professional Association
N.A.I.C.S.: 813920
Belayet Hossain (Mgr-Admin)
Uttam Kumar Debnath (Sr Mgr-Accts)
Paul Rigby (Chief Safety Officer)

ALLIANCE FOUNDATION OF FLORIDA, INC.

3989 Chain Bridge Rd, Fairfax, VA 22030
Tel.: (703) 359-7200   FL
Year Founded: 1999
Sales Range: $10-24.9 Million
Emp.: 595
Nursing Care Services
N.A.I.C.S.: 623110
David M. Bushey (CFO)
Jim S. Purdum (Sec)
Robert P. Hostler (Pres)

ALLIANCE FRANCHISE BRANDS LLC

47585 Galleon Dr, Plymouth, MI 48170

Tel.: (248) 596-8600
Web Site:
   https://www.alliancefranchises.com
Franchising Services
N.A.I.C.S.: 533110
Mike Marcantonio (CEO)
Kevin Cushing (Pres-Mktg & Print Div)
Ramon L. Palmer (Pres-Sign & Graphics Div)
Laura Pierce-Marutz (VP-Fin & Admin)
Joe D'Aguanno (CTO)
Brian Tyll (VP-Corp Ops)
Greg Schwartz (Gen Mgr)

Subsidiaries:

Allegra Network LLC   (1)
47585 Galleon Dr, Plymouth, MI 48170
Tel.: (248) 596-8600
Web Site: http://www.allegranetwork.com
Sales Range: $250-299.9 Million
Emp.: 45
Quick Printing Services
N.A.I.C.S.: 541990
Kevin Cushing (Pres)
Meredith Flynn (VP-Fin Svcs & Franchise Compliance)
Mike Dye (VP-Franchise Member Support)
Jessica Eng (VP-Mktg)
Dori Bennett (VP-Sls & Trng)
Tim Wood (VP-Tech)

ALLIANCE FUNDING GROUP, INC.

17542 17th St #200, Tustin, CA 92780
Tel.: (714) 704-1440   CA
Web Site: http://alliancefunding.com
Year Founded: 1998
Commercial & Industrial Machinery & Equipment Rental & Leasing
N.A.I.C.S.: 532490
Brijesh Patel (Pres & CEO)
David Goldstein (Reg Mgr-Sls)
Adam Patel (Mgr-Sls)

Subsidiaries:

Pinnacle Capital Partners, LLC   (1)
914 A St Ste 200, Tacoma, WA 98402
Tel.: (253) 284-5600
Web Site: http://www.pinnaclecap.com
Private Equity Firm
N.A.I.C.S.: 523999
Brent Hall (CEO)
Skip Wehner (COO)
Erik Weedon (CFO)

ALLIANCE GRAIN COMPANY INC.

1306 W 8th St, Gibson City, IL 60936-1365
Tel.: (217) 784-4284   IL
Web Site: https://www.alliance-grain.com
Year Founded: 1991
Sales Range: $10-24.9 Million
Emp.: 45
Agricultural Services
N.A.I.C.S.: 424510
Gary Allen (Mgr-Ops)

ALLIANCE GROUND INTERNATIONAL, LLC

Cargo Bldg 516 & 517 O'Hare International Airport, Chicago, IL 60666
Tel.: (773) 917-2000   FL
Web Site:
   http://www.allianceground.com
Airline Cargo Handling Services
N.A.I.C.S.: 488190
Anthony Romeo (Chm & CEO)
Gerald P. Finn (Pres)
Jared Azcuy (COO)

Subsidiaries:

International Cargo Marketing Consultants, Inc.   (1)

Cargo Bldg 517 O'Hare Airport, Chicago, IL 60666
Tel.: (773) 917-2008
Sales Range: $200-249.9 Million
Emp.: 350
International Travel & Air Freight Transportation Arrangement Services
N.A.I.C.S.: 481212
Robert L. Jones *(Pres)*

ALLIANCE GROUP SERVICES, INC.
1221 Post Rd E, Westport, CT 06880
Tel.: (203) 349-4915
Web Site:
https://www.alliancegrp.com
Sales Range: $10-24.9 Million
Emp.: 20
Telecommunications Provider
N.A.I.C.S.: 517121
Jess Di Pasquale *(Pres & CEO)*
Mary O'Keeffe *(CFO)*

ALLIANCE HEALTH, INC.
134 Rumford Ave Ste 306, Newton, MA 02466
Tel.: (617) 332-3366   MA
Web Site: http://www.alliancehhs.org
Year Founded: 1999
Sales Range: $25-49.9 Million
Emp.: 608
Nursing Care Services
N.A.I.C.S.: 623110
Michael A. Dodos *(Corp Controller)*
Doris Davila *(VP-Human Svcs)*
Francis J. Grady *(CFO & Sr VP)*

ALLIANCE HOLDINGS GP, L.P.
1717 S Boulder Ave Ste 400, Tulsa, OK 74119
Tel.: (918) 295-1415
Web Site: http://www.ahgp.com
Rev.: $1,795,841,000
Assets: $2,221,251,000
Liabilities: $1,068,378,000
Net Worth: $1,152,873,000
Earnings: $185,988,000
Emp.: 3,321
Fiscal Year-end: 12/31/17
Holding Company
N.A.I.C.S.: 551112

Subsidiaries:

Alliance Resource Partners, L.P.   **(1)**
1717 S Boulder Ave Ste 400, Tulsa, OK 74119-4833
Tel.: (918) 295-7600
Web Site: https://www.arlp.com
Rev.: $2,406,511,000
Assets: $2,661,473,000
Liabilities: $1,019,995,000
Net Worth: $1,641,478,000
Earnings: $577,190,000
Emp.: 3,371
Fiscal Year-end: 12/31/2022
Coal Mining
N.A.I.C.S.: 212114
Joseph W. Craft III *(Chm, Pres & CEO)*
Megan J. Cordle *(Chief Acctg Officer, VP & Controller)*
Cary P. Marshall *(CFO)*
Timothy J. Whelan *(Sr VP)*
D. Andrew Woodward *(Sr VP)*

Subsidiary (Domestic):

Gibson County Coal, LLC   **(2)**
2579 W Gibson Coal Rd, Princeton, IN 47670
Tel.: (812) 385-1816
Web Site: http://www.arlp.com
Underground Coal Mining Services
N.A.I.C.S.: 212114

Matrix Design Group, LLC   **(2)**
3299 Tower Dr, Newburgh, IN 47630
Tel.: (812) 490-1525
Web Site: http://www.matrixteam.com
Designer, Developer & Marketer of Safety & Productivity Technology for Use in Underground Mining Industry
N.A.I.C.S.: 333131

Aric Pryor *(Pres)*
Todd Beck *(Sr Project Mgr-Controls & Automation)*
David Clardy *(Pres)*
Tracy Hayford *(Dir-Tech & Dev)*
Randy Moore *(Dir-Engrg)*
Kevin Kerr *(VP-Ops)*
Craig Money *(Mgr-Product-Proximity Detection)*

Webster County Coal, LLC   **(2)**
1758 State Route 874, Clay, KY 42404
Tel.: (270) 249-2205
Web Site: http://www.arlp.com
Underground Coal Mining Services
N.A.I.C.S.: 212114

White County Coal, LLC   **(2)**
1525 County Rd 1650 N, Carmi, IL 62821-4607
Tel.: (618) 382-4651
Web Site: http://www.arlp.com
Underground Coal Mining Services
N.A.I.C.S.: 212114

White Oak Resources LLC   **(2)**
121 S Jackson St, McLeansboro, IL 62859
Tel.: (618) 643-5500
Web Site:
http://www.whiteoakresources.com
Explores, Produces & Markets Coal
N.A.I.C.S.: 213115
Gary Halstead *(VP-Engrg)*
B. Scott Spears *(Pres)*
Beverly Parrish Reynolds *(VP-Sls)*
Chris Smith *(Gen Mgr-Ops)*

ALLIANCE HOLDINGS, INC.
1021 Old York Rd Ste 3, Abington, PA 19001-4625
Tel.: (215) 706-0873   PA
Web Site: http://allianceholdings.com
Year Founded: 1994
Investment Holding Company
N.A.I.C.S.: 551112
Eric Lynn *(Dir-Portfolio Mgmt)*
Ken Wanko *(Dir-Acq)*

Subsidiaries:

The Spencer Turbine Co.   **(1)**
600 Day Hill Rd, Windsor, CT 06095-1703
Tel.: (860) 688-8361
Web Site: http://www.spencerturbine.com
Sales Range: $25-49.9 Million
Emp.: 140
Industrial & Commercial Air Purification Equipment Mfr
N.A.I.C.S.: 333413
Dave C. Earley *(VP-Order Fulfillment)*
Janis Cayne *(Mgr-Mktg)*
John Dulak *(Gen Mgr-Engrng)*
Richard Hart *(Pres)*

Walker Magnetics Group, Inc.   **(1)**
600 Day Hill Rd, Windsor, CT 06095
Tel.: (508) 853-3232
Web Site: http://www.walkermagnet.com
Sales Range: $50-74.9 Million
Emp.: 100
Industrial Magnetic Equipment Mfr
N.A.I.C.S.: 333248
Mark Calderan *(Controller)*
Michael C. Hadjinian *(Pres & CEO)*

Division (Domestic):

O.S. Walker Co. Inc.   **(2)**
60C Solferino St, Worcester, MA 01604
Tel.: (508) 853-3232
Web Site: http://www.walkermagnet.com
Sales Range: $25-49.9 Million
Emp.: 20
Magnetic Chucks, Lift Magnets & Instruments; Ceramics; Separation Equipment Mfr
N.A.I.C.S.: 333515
Kristian Knights *(Mgr-Mktg)*

Subsidiary (Non-US):

Walker Magnetics National, Ltd.   **(2)**
901 Arvin Ave, Stoney Creek, L8E 5N9, ON, Canada
Tel.: (905) 643-3338
Scrap Lifting Magnet Mfr
N.A.I.C.S.: 339999

Subsidiary (Domestic):

Walker National, Inc.   **(2)**

2195 Wright Brothers Ave, Columbus, OH 43217
Tel.: (614) 492-1614
Scrap Lifting Magnet Mfr
N.A.I.C.S.: 339999

ALLIANCE HOME SERVICES INC
384 E 149th St Ste 600, Bronx, NY 10455
Tel.: (718) 994-6780   NY
Web Site:
http://www.allianceservices.com
Year Founded: 1979
Sales Range: $10-24.9 Million
Emp.: 655
Home Care Services
N.A.I.C.S.: 621610
Sandy Quinones *(Program Dir)*

ALLIANCE HOSPITALITY MANAGEMENT, LLC.
1001 Wade Ave Ste 215, Raleigh, NC 27605
Tel.: (919) 791-1801
Web Site:
http://www.alliancehospitality.com
Year Founded: 2003
Sales Range: $10-24.9 Million
Emp.: 1,800
Office Administrative Services
N.A.I.C.S.: 561110
Kathleen Flanders *(Dir-Fin)*
E. J. Schanfarber *(Pres & CEO)*

ALLIANCE INTERACTIVE INC.
715 6th St NW, Washington, DC 20001
Tel.: (202) 350-9020
Web Site:
http://www.allianceinteractive.com
Year Founded: 2003
Sales Range: $1-9.9 Million
Emp.: 10
Online Marketing & Advertising
N.A.I.C.S.: 541890
Erica Young *(Mgr-PR)*
Adam Aloi *(Mng Partner)*

ALLIANCE INTERNATIONAL FORWARDERS, INC.
7155 Old Katie Rd Ste 100 S, Houston, TX 77024
Tel.: (713) 428-3100
Year Founded: 1988
Rev.: $21,304,595
Emp.: 35
Domestic Freight Forwarding Services
N.A.I.C.S.: 488510
Mario Cassier *(VP)*

Subsidiaries:

LTS Shipping Corporation   **(1)**
7155 Old Katy Rd Ste 100 S, Houston, TX 77024
Tel.: (713) 428-3100
Web Site: http://www.aifi.com
Rev.: $3,913,909
Emp.: 6
Freight Transportation Arrangement
N.A.I.C.S.: 488510

ALLIANCE MANAGEMENT, INC.
1515 NW 52nd St Ste B, Seattle, WA 98107
Tel.: (206) 903-2480   WA
Web Site:
http://www.mgmt.allianceapts.com
Year Founded: 1986
Sales Range: $75-99.9 Million
Emp.: 80
Real Estate Investment & Property Management Services
N.A.I.C.S.: 531210

Michael J. Roeter *(Owner)*
Nancy Guthrie *(Gen Mgr-AR AP)*

ALLIANCE MANUFACTURERS REPRESENTATIVES INC.
4660 Pine Timbers Ste 132, Houston, TX 77041
Tel.: (281) 579-9400
Web Site:
http://www.alliancereps.com
Rev.: $22,500,000
Emp.: 5
Plumbing Fittings & Supplies
N.A.I.C.S.: 423720
Cary Ostera *(Pres)*

ALLIANCE MATERIAL HANDLING INC.
8320 Sherwick Ct, Jessup, MD 20794
Tel.: (443) 980-0358
Web Site:
https://www.alliancemat.com
Rev.: $40,000,000
Emp.: 165
Material Handling Machinery Mfr
N.A.I.C.S.: 333248
Thomas Albero *(Pres & CEO)*
David Judd *(Sr VP-Ops)*
George Whelan *(Branch Mgr-Jessup Branch)*

ALLIANCE MEDIA GROUP
1877 Catasauqua Rd Suite 390, Allentown, PA 18109
Tel.: (484) 224-1877
Web Site:
http://www.alliancemediagroup.net
Year Founded: 2008
Sales Range: $1-9.9 Million
Emp.: 9
Media Planning, Placement Strategy & Creative Design
N.A.I.C.S.: 541830
Glenn A. Geissinger *(Mng Partner)*
David A. Moore *(Specialist-Media)*
Josy Buss *(Controller)*
Rick Schoenen *(Dir-Marketing)*
Michaela Ruehlmann *(Mgr-Marketing-Media)*

ALLIANCE OF PROFESSIONALS & CONSULTANTS, INC.
8200 Brownleigh Dr, Raleigh, NC 27617
Tel.: (919) 510-9696
Web Site: http://www.apc-services.com
Year Founded: 1993
Sales Range: $100-124.9 Million
Emp.: 420
Provider of Professional Staffing & Consulting Services
N.A.I.C.S.: 541618
Roy Roberts *(CEO)*
Tom Lynch *(Controller)*
Rebecca Aslaksen *(Coord-Client)*
Don Scott *(VP-Sls)*

ALLIANCE OFFICE SYSTEMS
469 Cherry Ln, Southlake, TX 76092-5409
Tel.: (817) 481-9922
Consumer Electronics Repair & Maintenance
N.A.I.C.S.: 811210
Tammy Dayton *(Sls Mgr)*

Subsidiaries:

Farmer Business Systems   **(1)**
1880 Crown Dr Ste 1210, Farmers Branch, TX 75234
Tel.: (972) 818-4500
Web Site: http://www.farmerbusiness.com
Office Equipment Merchant Whslr
N.A.I.C.S.: 423420
Deanne Ong *(Acct Exec)*
Taylor Farmer *(Sls Mgr)*

Alliance Packaging LLC—(Continued)

ALLIANCE PACKAGING LLC
1000 SW 43rd, Renton, WA 98057
Tel.: (425) 291-3500　　　**WA**
Web Site:
　https://www.alliancepackaging.net
Year Founded: 1967
Sales Range: $150-199.9 Million
Emp.: 500
Mfr of Corrugated Containers, Fabricated Plastic Forms & Printing Papers
N.A.I.C.S.: 322211
Gordon M. Younger (Owner & Chm)
Mark Held (Pres)
Tony Boisen (CFO)

Subsidiaries:

Alliance Packaging-Beaverton
Division　　　　　　　　　　　(1)
1255 SW Burlington Dr, Beaverton, OR 97006-6098
Tel.: (503) 641-9220
Web Site: http://www.alliancepackaging.net
Sales Range: $25-49.9 Million
Emp.: 65
Mfr of Packaging
N.A.I.C.S.: 322211
John Bean (Gen Mgr)

Alliance Packaging-Seattle Corrugated Division　　　　　　　(1)
1000 SW 43rd St, Renton, WA 98057
Tel.: (425) 291-3500
Web Site: http://www.alliancepackaging.net
Sales Range: $50-74.9 Million
Custom Corrugated & Foam Packaging
N.A.I.C.S.: 322211
Scott Younger (Gen Mgr)
Mark Held (Pres)

ALLIANCE PLASTICS, LLC
2805 Commerce Dr, Rock Hill, SC 29730-8962
Tel.: (803) 802-7955
Web Site:
　http://www.allianceplastics.net
Year Founded: 2002
Sales Range: $10-24.9 Million
Emp.: 25
Stretch Film Products Mfr
N.A.I.C.S.: 326112
Ronald Grubbs (Pres)

ALLIANCE PROMOTIONS, INC.
6135 Airways Blvd, Chattanooga, TN 37421
Tel.: (423) 485-4712　　　**GA**
Web Site:
　http://www.alliancepromotions.com
Year Founded: 1987
Sales Range: $1-9.9 Million
Emp.: 4
Sales Promotion
N.A.I.C.S.: 541810
Marlene Lindsey (Office Mgr)
Earl Williams (Pres)
Harold Williams (VP)

ALLIANCE REALTY ADVISORS
3828 W Davis St Ste 314, Conroe, TX 77304-1842
Tel.: (936) 756-1717
Web Site: http://www.alliance-realty-advisors.net
Year Founded: 1997
Residential Property Managers
N.A.I.C.S.: 531311
Malcolm Willey (Owner)

ALLIANCE RUBBER COMPANY
210 Carpenter Dam Rd, Hot Springs, AR 71901
Tel.: (501) 262-2700
Web Site:
　https://www.rubberband.com
Year Founded: 1923

Sales Range: $50-74.9 Million
Emp.: 175
Rubber Bands
N.A.I.C.S.: 326299
Bonnie Swayze (Pres)
Garvis Hughes (Supvr-Shipping)
Jay Aronstan (Exec Dir)

ALLIANCE SECURITY INC.
60 Jefferson Park Rd, Warwick, RI 02888
Web Site: http://www.ahprotect.com
Year Founded: 2003
Sales Range: $25-49.9 Million
Emp.: 215
Alarm Systems
N.A.I.C.S.: 561621
Jay Gotra (CEO)

ALLIANCE SHIPPERS, INC.
516 Sylvan Ave, Englewood Cliffs, NJ 07632-3022
Tel.: (201) 227-0400　　　**NJ**
Web Site: https://www.alliance.com
Year Founded: 1977
Sales Range: $25-49.9 Million
Emp.: 550
Freight Transportation Services
N.A.I.C.S.: 488510
Mark Shustak (CFO)
Steve Golich (Exec VP)
Rick Plieninger (VP-Ohio Valley)
Gary Laporte (VP-Michigan & Canada)
Joe Nagy (VP-Ops-Michigan & Canada)
Tom Charters (Dir-Bus Dev)
Jonathan Lefcourt (Pres & CEO)

Subsidiaries:

Alliance Shippers - Transportation
Broker　　　　　　　　　　　(1)
15515 S 70th Ct, Orland Park, IL 60462-5105　　　　　　　(100%)
Tel.: (708) 802-7000
Web Site: http://www.alliance.com
Sales Range: $25-49.9 Million
Freight Transportation Services
N.A.I.C.S.: 488510
Larry Henry (VP-Logistics)
Tim De La Torre (Co-CFO)
Frank De La Torre (Exec VP-Alliance Intl)
Steve Golich (Exec VP)
Joe Nagy (Reg VP-Ops)
Mark Shustak (Co-CFO)

ALLIANCE SOLUTIONS GROUP
4500 Rockside Rd, Independence, OH 44131
Tel.: (216) 525-0100
Web Site:
　http://www.alliancesolutionsgrp.com
Year Founded: 2001
Sales Range: $25-49.9 Million
Emp.: 72
Staffing Services
N.A.I.C.S.: 561311
Aaron Grossman (Founder & Pres)
Matt Lyon (CFO)

ALLIANCE SOLUTIONS GROUP, INC.
11818 Rock Landing Dr Ste 105, Newport News, VA 23606
Tel.: (757) 223-7233
Web Site: https://www.asg-inc.org
Sales Range: $1-9.9 Million
Emp.: 16
Emergency Planning & Management Services
N.A.I.C.S.: 922190
Bob Campbell (Pres & CEO)

ALLIANCE SPORTS GROUP, L.P.

3025 N Great SW Pkwy, Grand Prairie, TX 75050-1407
Tel.: (972) 343-1000　　　**TX**
Web Site:
　http://www.alliancesportsgroup.net
Year Founded: 1974
Sales Range: $75-99.9 Million
Emp.: 100
Mfr of Sporting Goods & Accessories
N.A.I.C.S.: 334510
Glenn D. Bollinger (CEO)
Bobby D. Bollinger (Owner)
Rhonda Cox (Mgr-Credit)

ALLIANCE STORAGE TECHNOLOGIES, INC.
10045 Federal Dr, Colorado Springs, CO 80908
Tel.: (719) 593-7900
Web Site:
　http://www.alliancestoragetech.com
Sales Range: $10-24.9 Million
Emp.: 100
Data Archiving Systems Mfr
N.A.I.C.S.: 334112
Chris Carr (CEO)
Fran Rogers (Dir-Admin)

ALLIANCE TECHNOLOGIES
420 Watson Powell Jr Way Ste 100, Des Moines, IA 50309
Tel.: (515) 245-7777
Web Site:
　http://www.alliancetechnologies.net
Year Founded: 1994
Rev.: $14,900,000
Emp.: 100
Data Processing, Hosting & Related Services
N.A.I.C.S.: 518210
Steve Sikkink (COO)
John Vogelaar (CFO)
Darwin Rouw (VP)
Michael Van Well (Mgr-Client Svcs)
James Canada (CEO)
Jim Mosquera (VP-Corp Dev)
Kirk Ross (VP-Talent Solutions-Alliance Advisors Div)

ALLIANCE TECHNOLOGY GROUP, LLC
7010 Hi Tech Dr, Hanover, MD 21076
Tel.: (410) 712-0270
Web Site: https://www.alliance-it.com
Year Founded: 1987
Sales Range: $25-49.9 Million
Emp.: 75
IT Products & Services
N.A.I.C.S.: 541512
Hope Hayes (Pres)
Scott Gurganus (Mgr-Federal Sls)
Chuck DeSocio (Acct Exec-Federal)
Michael Joseph (Sr Acct Exec)
Steve Berry (Sr Acct Mgr-Federal Civilian Sls)
Briana Rossi (Coord-Mktg)

ALLIANCE TECHNOLOGY SOLUTIONS, LLC.
40 Engelwood Dr Ste H, Orion, MI 48359
Tel.: (248) 364-2195
Web Site: http://www.ats.biz
Year Founded: 2002
Sales Range: $10-24.9 Million
Emp.: 7
Information Technology Services
N.A.I.C.S.: 541511
Margie Garza-Carlson (Owner & Pres)
Donna DaSilva (Acct Mgr)

ALLIANCE TRUCK AND EQUIPMENT, LLC
8100 Alban Rd, Springfield, VA 22150
Tel.: (703) 569-5100

Year Founded: 1957
Sales Range: $10-24.9 Million
Emp.: 24
Truck Equipment, Parts & Service
N.A.I.C.S.: 423120
John Price (Pres & CEO)

ALLIANCE WORKFORCE SOLUTIONS LLC
5406 Hoover Blvd Unit 7, Tampa, FL 33634
Tel.: (813) 872-0001
Web Site: https://www.alliancewf.com
Year Founded: 2005
Sales Range: $10-24.9 Million
Employment Placement Agencies
N.A.I.C.S.: 561311
Rodney Rohrs (Pres)

ALLIANCEONE INC.
4850 St Rd Ste 300, Trevose, PA 19053
Tel.: (215) 354-5511
Web Site:
　http://www.allianceoneinc.com
Sales Range: $50-74.9 Million
Emp.: 20
Collection Agency, Except Real Estate
N.A.I.C.S.: 561440

ALLIANT COMPANY LLC
21600 Oxnard St Ste 1200, Woodland Hills, CA 91367
Tel.: (818) 668-6800
Web Site:
　http://www.thealliantcompany.com
Rev.: $9,200,000,000
Emp.: 100
Financial & Investment Services
N.A.I.C.S.: 525990
Brian Goldberg (Pres)
Shawn Horwitz (CEO)
Scott Kotick (Co-Founder & Exec VP)
Melvin Gevisser (CFO)
Monique Hastings (Principal-Alliant Newport)
Sidney Kohl (Co-Founder & Chm)
Holly Waldhoff (VP)

ALLIANT CREDIT UNION
11545 W Touhy Ave, Chicago, IL 60666
Tel.: (773) 462-2000　　　**IL**
Web Site:
　https://www.alliantcreditunion.org
Year Founded: 1935
Sales Range: $150-199.9 Million
Emp.: 399
Credit Union
N.A.I.C.S.: 522130
Harry Zhu (CFO & Sr VP-Fin)

ALLIANT HEALTH SOLUTIONS
1455 Lincoln Pkwy Ste 800, Atlanta, GA 30346
Tel.: (678) 527-3100
Web Site:
　https://www.allianthealth.org
Year Founded: 1970
Sales Range: $10-24.9 Million
Emp.: 160
Health Care Solution Provider
N.A.I.C.S.: 621491
Sherry Simmons (Dir-HR)
Gary Miller (Dir-Medical-Medical Mgmt Svcs)
Kimberly Rask (Dir-Medical)
John Slaughter (Dir-IT)

Subsidiaries:

End Stage Renal Disease Network of
Texas, Inc.　　　　　　　　(1)
4040 McEwen Rd Ste 350, Dallas, TX 75244
Tel.: (972) 503-3215
Web Site: http://www.esrdnetwork.org

Sales Range: $1-9.9 Million
Kidney Transplant Health Care Services
N.A.I.C.S.: 622310
Debbie O'Daniel (Office Mgr)
Glenda Harbert (Exec Dir)
Kelly Shipley (Dir-Quality Improvement)
Charles Orji (Co-Sec)
Devon Osborne (Co-Sec)

ALLIANT HEALTHCARE PRODUCTS
333 Bridge St NW Ste 1125, Grand Rapids, MI 49504
Tel.: (269) 629-0300
Web Site:
http://www.allianthealthcare.com
Year Founded: 2002
Sales Range: $1-9.9 Million
Emp.: 35
Designer, Developer & Mfr of Medical Device Products
N.A.I.C.S.: 339112
Robert Taylor (Owner & CEO)

ALLIANT NATIONAL TITLE INSURANCE COMPANY
1831 Lefthand Cir Ste G, Longmont, CO 80501
Tel.: (303) 682-9800
Web Site:
https://www.alliantnational.com
Year Founded: 2005
Sales Range: $50-74.9 Million
Emp.: 30
General Insurance Services
N.A.I.C.S.: 524210
Robert J. Grubb (Pres & CEO)
R. Scott Hendrickson (CFO)
Phyllis J. Mulder (Chief Legal & Compliance Officer & Exec VP)
Rodney Anderson (Sr VP)
Kyle K. Rank (Exec VP)
David Sinclair (Chief Operating & Info Officer)
Michael Rubin (VP-Bus Dev)
Nathan Marinchick (Dir-Res & Educational Programming)

ALLIANZGI DIVERSIFIED INCOME & CONVERTIBLE FUND
1633 Broadway, New York, NY 10019
Tel.: (212) 739-3222
Investment Services
N.A.I.C.S.: 523999
Angela Borreggine (Chief Legal Officer & Sec)

ALLIED ADVERTISING AGENCY, INC.
3700 Blanco Rd, San Antonio, TX 78212
Tel.: (210) 732-7874   TX
Web Site: http://www.alliedad.com
Year Founded: 1952
Sales Range: $1-9.9 Million
Emp.: 55
Commercial Screen Printing Services
N.A.I.C.S.: 323113
Lola Herbots (Pres)
John Herbots (Owner & VP)

ALLIED AEROFOAM PRODUCTS, LLC
216 Kelsey Ln, Tampa, FL 33619
Tel.: (813) 626-0090
Web Site:
http://www.alliedaerofoam.com
Year Founded: 1988
Plastic Foam Products Mfr & Supplier
N.A.I.C.S.: 326140
Richard Ruebusch (CEO)

ALLIED AMERICAN STEEL CORPORATION
600 Grant St Ste 660, Pittsburgh, PA 15219

Tel.: (412) 223-2663   NV
Web Site:
http://www.alliedamericansteel.com
Year Founded: 2007
Iron Ore & Titanium Dioxide Exploration & Production
N.A.I.C.S.: 212210
Jes Black (Chm & CEO)

ALLIED ARTIST INTERNATIONAL, INC.
15810 E Gale Ave Ste 133, Hacienda Heights, CA 91745
Tel.: (626) 330-0600
Web Site:
http://www.us.alliedartists.com
Sales Range: $50-74.9 Million
Motion Picture & Video Production
N.A.I.C.S.: 512110
Greg Hammond (CTO & VP)
Robert Fitzpatrick (Pres)
Kim Richards (Chm & CEO)
Jerry Sifuentes (CFO-Entertainment Grp)
Danny Ramos (VP-Artist Rels & Allied Artists Music Grp)

ALLIED BEVERAGE GROUP L.L.C.
600 Washington Ave, Carlstadt, NJ 07072-2902
Tel.: (201) 842-6200
Web Site:
http://www.alliedbeverage.com
Year Founded: 1996
Sales Range: $750-799.9 Million
Emp.: 840
Whslr of Wine/Spirits, Craft Beers & Distilled Beverages
N.A.I.C.S.: 424820
Angelo Ramon (Brand Mgr-Mktg)
Kevin Murray (Mgr-Transportation)
Matthew Hunter (Dir-Sls-Intl Vintners)
Arjun Dewan (VP-Wines)
Calogera Alfonso (Mgr-IT)
Johnny Pollack (Dir-Ops)
Pat Rafferty (Dir-Office Facilities & Svcs)
Philip Kirsch (Dir-Inventory)
Richard Torres (Dir-Ops)
Sean Woods (Mgr-Sls)
Rick Weinstein (Sr Mgr-Premise)
Louis Demarino (VP-Strategic Initiatives)
Tom Rose (Mgr-Mktg)

Subsidiaries:

Majestic Wine & Spirits USA, Inc.   (1)
487 Devon Park Dr Ste 216, Wayne, PA 19087
Tel.: (610) 902-9400
Web Site:
http://www.majesticwinespiritspa.com
Sales Range: $10-24.9 Million
Emp.: 100
Alcoholic Beverage Brokerage & Distributor
N.A.I.C.S.: 424820
Chris Papariello (Exec VP)
Edward Murray (Dir-Mktg)
Emily Bell (Dir-Fine Wine)
Jim Matos (Gen Sls Mgr)

ALLIED BUILDING CORP.
574 Main St Suite 200, Bethlehem, PA 18018
Tel.: (484) 898-1111
Web Site:
http://www.alliedbuildingcorp.com
Year Founded: 1998
Sales Range: $1-9.9 Million
Emp.: 50
Construction Management & General Contracting Services
N.A.I.C.S.: 236220
James F. Kostecky (Exec VP)
Anthony D. Scarcia Jr. (Pres & COO)

ALLIED BUILDING MATERIALS INC.
221 W Wyoming Ave, Las Vegas, NV 89102
Tel.: (702) 382-8704
Web Site: http://www.abmnv.com
Sales Range: $10-24.9 Million
Emp.: 8
Brick, Except Refractory
N.A.I.C.S.: 423320
Thomas Allen (Pres)

ALLIED BUSINESS INTELLIGENCE, INC.
249 South St, Oyster Bay, NY 11771
Tel.: (516) 624-2500
Web Site:
http://www.abiresearch.com
Year Founded: 1990
Sales Range: $1-9.9 Million
Marketing Research Service
N.A.I.C.S.: 541910
Jim Mielke (VP-Teardowns)
Tim Archdeacon (CEO)
Ed Rerisi (COO)
Stuart Carlaw (Chief Res Officer)
Dominque Bonte (VP-Verticals & End Markets)
Jake Saunders (Mng Dir & VP-Advisory Svcs-Asia Pacific)
Pete Rumpel (Chief Sls Officer & Mng Partner)
Nick Marshall (Dir-Res)
Michela Menting (Dir-Res)
Lance Wilson (Dir-Res)
Sam Rosen (VP-Video, OTT, Virtual Reality & Augmented Reality)
Malik Saadi (VP-Strategic Tech)

Subsidiaries:

ABI Research Singapore   (1)
Suntec Tower One 9th Floor, Singapore, 189702, Singapore
Tel.: (65) 65920290
Web Site: http://www.abiresearch.com
Market Research Services
N.A.I.C.S.: 541910

ABI Research Switzerland   (1)
56 Rue de Lausanne, 1202, Geneva, Switzerland
Tel.: (41) 227323315
Market Research
N.A.I.C.S.: 541910

ABI Research UK   (1)
4-6 Staple Inn 3rd Floor Suite B, London, WC1V 7QH, United Kingdom
Tel.: (44) 2033260140
Market Research
N.A.I.C.S.: 541910
Paul Gilbert (VP-Bus Dev)

ALLIED CAPITAL AND DEVELOPMENT OF SOUTH FLORIDA LLC
115 Front St Ste 300, Jupiter, FL 33477
Tel.: (561) 799-0050
Web Site:
https://www.alliedcapital.com
Year Founded: 2002
Emp.: 15
Real Estate Investment & Development
N.A.I.C.S.: 531390
Brian D. Friedman (CFO)
Paul Angelo (Sr Mgr-Dev)
Nicholas A. Mastroianni II (Pres)
Nicholas A. Mastroianni III (VP-Plng & Ops)

ALLIED CHUCKER & ENGINEERING COMPANY
3529 Scheele Dr, Jackson, MI 49202-1296
Tel.: (517) 787-1370   MI

Web Site:
https://www.alliedchucker.com
Year Founded: 1948
Sales Range: $75-99.9 Million
Emp.: 250
Production Machinery for Castings, Forgings & Bar Stocks Mfr
N.A.I.C.S.: 332710
Patrick McCann (Pres)
Daniel Maes (Mgr-Engrg)
Brian Schalhamer (VP-Info Sys)

ALLIED CONCRETE PRODUCTS INC.
3900 Shannon St, Chesapeake, VA 23324
Tel.: (757) 494-5200
Web Site:
http://www.alliedconcrete.com
Rev.: $15,600,000
Emp.: 34
Glass Construction Materials
N.A.I.C.S.: 423390
Kirk D. Eden (Pres)

ALLIED CONSTRUCTION CO. INC.
1000 S Grand Ave, Charles City, IA 50616
Tel.: (641) 228-4256
Web Site: http://www.allied-ia.com
Sales Range: $10-24.9 Million
Emp.: 120
Highway & Street Paving Contractor
N.A.I.C.S.: 212312
Graham Cunningham (VP-Paving Div)

ALLIED CONSTRUCTION SERVICES INC.
2122 Fleur Dr, Des Moines, IA 50321-1158
Tel.: (515) 288-4855   IA
Web Site:
https://www.alliedconst.com
Year Founded: 1950
Sales Range: $10-24.9 Million
Emp.: 30
Provider of Construction Services
N.A.I.C.S.: 238310
Chuck Follett (VP)
Mikki Killin (Supvr-Payroll)
Tug DenOtter (Project Mgr)
Robert Maddox Jr. (Pres & CEO)

ALLIED DAIRY PRODUCTS INC.
15 Bleeker St, Millburn, NJ 07041
Tel.: (973) 258-9600
Web Site: http://www.mctdairies.com
Year Founded: 1980
Sales Range: $50-74.9 Million
Emp.: 26
Dairy Products, Except Dried Or Canned
N.A.I.C.S.: 424430

ALLIED DISCOUNT TIRE & BRAKE
PO Box 80429, Lafayette, LA 70598
Tel.: (337) 232-9600
Sales Range: $10-24.9 Million
Emp.: 12
Automotive Tires
N.A.I.C.S.: 441340
Carroll Kuntz (Pres)
Adam Mach (Mgr-Ops)

ALLIED ELECTRIC INC.
2503 Waldorf Ct NW, Grand Rapids, MI 49544
Tel.: (616) 791-1164
Web Site:
https://www.alliedelectricinc.com
Year Founded: 1969
Sales Range: $25-49.9 Million

Allied Electric Inc.—(Continued)
Emp.: 150
Provider of Electrical Contracting
Services
N.A.I.C.S.: 238210
Mike Powers (VP)
Paul Hansma (Pres)
Tom Vandenbosch (Controller)

ALLIED ELECTRIC MOTOR SERVICE
4690 E Jensen Ave, Fresno, CA 93725
Tel.: (559) 486-4222
Web Site: http://www.alliedelectric.net
Rev.: $17,200,000
Emp.: 55
Electrical Supplies
N.A.I.C.S.: 423610
Salvatore Rome (Chm)
Krystle Johnson (Mgr-Motor Shop Div)

ALLIED EMPLOYER GROUP
4400 Buffalo Gap Rd Ste 4500, Abilene, TX 79606-2717
Tel.: (325) 695-5822   TX
Web Site: https://www.coemployer.com
Year Founded: 1989
Sales Range: $25-49.9 Million
Emp.: 14
Employment Agency
N.A.I.C.S.: 561311
Frank R. Caceres (CFO & VP)
Linda Eaves (Mgr-Bus Dev-Abilene & Lubbock)
Shelia Clark (Mgr-Ops)

ALLIED ENTERPRISES INC.
26021 Ctr Rdg Rd, Westlake, OH 44145
Tel.: (440) 808-8760
Web Site: http://www.alliedenterprisesinc.com
Year Founded: 1979
Sales Range: $10-24.9 Million
Emp.: 10
Electronic Parts & Equipment Mfr
N.A.I.C.S.: 423690
Eric Pfaff (Pres)

ALLIED ENVELOPE CO. INC.
33 Commerce Rd, Carlstadt, NJ 07074
Tel.: (201) 440-2000
Web Site: http://www.allied.com
Rev.: $14,400,000
Emp.: 50
Envelopes
N.A.I.C.S.: 424120
Robert James Royer (Pres)

ALLIED FASTENER & TOOL INC.
1130 NG St, Lake Worth, FL 33460
Tel.: (561) 585-2113
Web Site: http://www.aft1.com
Year Founded: 1982
Sales Range: $10-24.9 Million
Emp.: 20
Miscellaneous Fasteners Mfr
N.A.I.C.S.: 423710
Judy Makela (Mgr-Pur)

ALLIED FEEDS INC.
208 Hutcheson St, Cuero, TX 77954
Tel.: (361) 275-5711
Web Site: http://www.fulopep.com
Rev.: $14,808,528
Emp.: 67
Livestock Feeds
N.A.I.C.S.: 311119
Sara Gossett (Office Mgr)

ALLIED FIRST BANCORP, INC.

3201 Orchard Rd, Oswego, IL 60543
Tel.: (630) 554-8899
Web Site: http://www.alliedfirst.com
Year Founded: 1994
AFBA—(OTCBB)
Bank Holding Company
N.A.I.C.S.: 551111
Kenneth L. Bertrand (Pres, CEO)
Brian K. Weiss (CFO)

Subsidiaries:
Allied First Bank (1)
3201 Orchard Rd, Oswego, IL 60543
Tel.: (630) 554-8899
Web Site: http://www.alliedfirst.com
Sales Range: $25-49.9 Million
Emp.: 70
Commercial Banking Services
N.A.I.C.S.: 522110
Ken Holmstrom (Sr VP)

ALLIED FITTING LP
7200 Mykaawa Rd, Houston, TX 77033
Tel.: (713) 799-1100
Web Site: http://www.alliedfit.com
Rev.: $13,800,000
Emp.: 60
Valves, Pistons & Fittings
N.A.I.C.S.: 423830
Philip Goerner (Controller)
Jose Luis Loaeza (Coord-Receiving)
Edward Salazar (Coord-Tri-Lad)
Tracey Lytle (Mgr-Comml Div-Gulf Coast Reg)
Bill Beecher (Mgr-Inside Sls)
Alex Blanco (Mgr-Intl Shipping)
Kyle Rose (Mgr-Logistics)
Ricardo Vargas (Mgr-Ops)
Mike Sweet (Mgr-Quality Control & Machine Shop)
Juventino Rodriquez (Mgr-Shipping)
Juan Leal (Mgr-Will Call)
Jose Coronado (VP-Sls-Latin America)

Subsidiaries:
Ezeflow, Inc. (1)
985 rue Andre-Line, Granby, J2J 1J6, QC, Canada
Tel.: (450) 375-3575
Web Site: http://www.ezeflow.com
Corrosion Resistant Alloy Pipe Fittings & Flanges Mfr
N.A.I.C.S.: 332919

ALLIED HOME MEDICAL, INC.
3075 Poplar Grove Rd, Cookeville, TN 38506-7466
Tel.: (931) 528-6199   TN
Web Site: http://www.alliedhomemedical.com
Year Founded: 1995
Sales Range: $10-24.9 Million
Emp.: 80
Mobility Products Sales & Services
N.A.I.C.S.: 423450
Kirk Caskey (Pres)
Linda Caskey (Treas)

ALLIED INDUSTRIES, INC.
11333 Vanowen St, North Hollywood, CA 91605
Tel.: (818) 781-2490   NV
Web Site: http://www.alliedlead.com
Year Founded: 1997
Sales Range: $10-24.9 Million
Emp.: 200
Demolition, Environmental Remediation, Asbestos Removal & Commercial Building Renovations
N.A.I.C.S.: 541620
Ernesto Gutierrez (Pres & CEO)

ALLIED INFORMATICS INC.
1815 Satellite Blvd Ste 302, Duluth, GA 30097
Tel.: (770) 246-9800

https://www.alliedinformatics.com
Year Founded: 1991
Rev.: $13,000,000
Emp.: 13
Prepackaged Software
N.A.I.C.S.: 513210
Kris Gadde (Pres & CEO)
Vijay Akkineni (VP)

ALLIED INSULATION SUPPLY CO., INC.
315 N 12th St, Milwaukee, WI 53233
Tel.: (414) 347-1600
Web Site: https://www.alliedinsulation.com
Year Founded: 1969
Sales Range: $10-24.9 Million
Emp.: 45
Whslr of Roofing, Siding & Insulation Materials
N.A.I.C.S.: 423330
Shirley Flack (Pres)

ALLIED INTERNATIONAL CORP.
7 Hill St, Bedford Hills, NY 10507
Tel.: (914) 241-6900
Web Site: http://www.alliedinter.com
Sales Range: $10-24.9 Million
Emp.: 18
Aeronautical Equipment
N.A.I.C.S.: 423860
Lindsey Ulman (Treas & Sec)
Frank Lore (Controller)
Alex Ulman Jr. (Chm, Pres & CEO)

ALLIED LUBE INC.
959 S Coast Dr Ste 450, Costa Mesa, CA 92626-7814
Tel.: (714) 545-4558
Web Site: http://www.gclube.com
Rev.: $11,000,000
Emp.: 8
General Automotive Repair Shops
N.A.I.C.S.: 811111
Richard Paek (Pres)

ALLIED MACHINERY CORPORATION
94168 Leoole St, Waipahu, HI 96797
Tel.: (808) 671-0541
Web Site: https://www.alliedmachineryco.com
Year Founded: 1978
Sales Range: $25-49.9 Million
Emp.: 40
Construction Machinery & Equipment
N.A.I.C.S.: 423810
Patrick J. Feyerisen (Pres)
Jeff Feyerisen (VP)
Gary Feyerisen (Treas)

ALLIED MANUFACTURING INC.
3928 Oregon St, Benicia, CA 94510
Tel.: (707) 745-0506
Web Site: http://www.alliedexhaust.com
Rev.: $46,864,000
Emp.: 45
Mufflers (Exhaust), Motor Vehicle
N.A.I.C.S.: 423120

Subsidiaries:
Allied Exhaust Systems (1)
6838 S 190th, Kent, WA 98032
Tel.: (425) 251-8037
Web Site: http://www.alliedexhaust.com
Sales Range: $10-24.9 Million
Emp.: 10
Exhaust Systems
N.A.I.C.S.: 811114
Jeff Jorgensen (Mgr)

ALLIED MARBLE, INC.
5219 4th Ave S, Seattle, WA 98108

Tel.: (206) 453-2766
Web Site: https://www.alliedmarbleinc.com
Year Founded: 1982
Sales Range: $1-9.9 Million
Emp.: 25
Natural Stone Installation Services
N.A.I.C.S.: 327991
Quang Mai (Co-Owner)
Magic Mai (Co-Owner)
Jimmy Mai (Mgr)

ALLIED MARKETING GROUP, INC.
1555 Regal Row, Dallas, TX 75247
Tel.: (214) 915-7000
Web Site: http://www.alliedmarketinggroup.com
Sales Range: $10-24.9 Million
Emp.: 130
Service Bureau, Computer
N.A.I.C.S.: 518210
Steven Hammond (CEO)
John Wright (CFO)
Joe Malazzo (VP)
Karen Bradley (Coord-Mktg & Production)

ALLIED METAL COMPANY
4528 W Division St, Chicago, IL 60651-1632
Tel.: (312) 225-2800
Web Site: https://www.alliedmetalcompany.com
Sales Range: $100-124.9 Million
Emp.: 65
Aluminum Smelting & Refining (Secondary)
N.A.I.C.S.: 331314

ALLIED METAL, LLC
2902 NW 32nd Ave, Miami, FL 33142
Tel.: (305) 635-3360   DE
Web Site: https://www.alliedmetalsllc.com
Year Founded: 1963
Emp.: 48
Recyclable Material Merchant Whslr
N.A.I.C.S.: 423930
Paul Mosheim (Pres)

ALLIED METALS CORP.
1750 Stephenson Hwy, Troy, MI 48083-2147
Tel.: (248) 680-2400
Web Site: http://www.alliedmet.com
Year Founded: 1975
Sales Range: $10-24.9 Million
Emp.: 60
Metal Services
N.A.I.C.S.: 423510
Gary L. Wasserman (Owner)

ALLIED MINERAL PRODUCTS, INC.
2700 Scioto Pkwy, Columbus, OH 43221-4657
Tel.: (614) 876-0244   OH
Web Site: https://www.alliedmin.com
Year Founded: 1961
Sales Range: $150-199.9 Million
Emp.: 500
Nonclay Monolithic Refractories Mfr
N.A.I.C.S.: 327120
Douglas K. Doza (Exec VP)
Thomas E. Gibson (VP-Corp Dev)
James M. Bade (VP-Bus-Domestic Foundry)
Steven L. Roe (VP-Bus-Intl)
Paul D. Jamieson (VP-Bus-Steel Industry)

Subsidiaries:
Allied Metallurg South Africa (AMETSA) (1)
Crocker Rd Wadeville Ext 4, Germiston,

1422, Guateng, South Africa **(51%)**
Tel.: (27) 00119022900
Web Site: http://www.netline.co.za
Sales Range: $10-24.9 Million
Emp.: 20
Metal Works
N.A.I.C.S.: 423510

Allied Mineral Products (Tianjin) Co., Ltd. (AMT) **(1)**
2 Yanshan Rd Tanggu Marine High & New Tech Dev Area, Tianjin, 300459, China **(100%)**
Tel.: (86) 2225210378
Web Site: http://www.alliedchina.com
Sales Range: $10-24.9 Million
Emp.: 70
Mfr of Nonclay Monolithic Refractories
N.A.I.C.S.: 327120

Allied Mineral Products Europe BV **(1)**
Energieweg 5, 4691 SE, Tholen, Netherlands
Tel.: (31) 166 601 200
Monolithic Refractory Ceramics Mfr
N.A.I.C.S.: 327120
Koos Heijboer *(Mng Dir)*

Allied Mineral Products, Asia **(1)**
401-2002 Han-Yank Apartment, Beak Ma Ma UI, Ma Doo Dong, Ko Yang Si, Koyang, Korea (South)
Tel.: (82) 344 902 2737
Mfr of Nonclay Monolithic Refractories
N.A.I.C.S.: 327120

Allied Mineral Products, Latin America **(1)**
5316 Norte 21A Colonia Vallejo, 07750, Mexico, DF, Mexico **(100%)**
Tel.: (52) 5555670775
Web Site: http://www.alliedprodigy.com
Mfr of Nonclay Monolithic Refractories
N.A.I.C.S.: 327120

Allied Mineral Technical Services, Inc. **(1)**
9697 E Mineral Ave, Centennial, CO 80112
Tel.: (614) 876-0244
Blast Furnace & Cupola Technical Assistance Services
N.A.I.C.S.: 541690

Allied Refractory Products India Private, Ltd. **(1)**
SM-5 Bol GIDC B/H Tata Nano Sanand, Ahmedabad, 382170, Gujarat, India
Tel.: (91) 2717 616800
Web Site: http://www.alliedmin.com
Sales Range: $10-24.9 Million
Emp.: 32
Refractory Products Mfr
N.A.I.C.S.: 327120
Bhuwan Vashishtha *(Mng Dir)*

American Precast Refractories Division **(1)**
2700 Scioto Pkwy, Columbus, OH 43221-4657 **(100%)**
Tel.: (614) 876-0244
Web Site: http://www.amprecast.com
Sales Range: $10-24.9 Million
Emp.: 18
Precast Industries
N.A.I.C.S.: 423510

Matrix Refractories Division **(1)**
2700 Scioto Pkwy, Columbus, OH 43221-4657
Tel.: (614) 876-0244
Web Site: http://www.alliedmineral.com
Refractories
N.A.I.C.S.: 423510
Paul Jamieson *(Pres)*

ALLIED MORTGAGE & FINANCIAL CORP.
13680 NW 5th St Ste 100, Hollywood, FL 33325
Tel.: (954) 983-7007
Sales Range: $25-49.9 Million
Emp.: 10
Bond & Mortgage Companies
N.A.I.C.S.: 522310
Tony Chao *(VP)*
Daniel Jacobs *(Pres)*

ALLIED MOULDED PRODUCTS INC.
222 N Union St, Bryan, OH 43506
Tel.: (419) 636-4217
Web Site: https://www.alliedmoulded.com
Year Founded: 1958
Sales Range: $10-24.9 Million
Emp.: 300
Fiberglass Electrical Boxes & Enclosures
N.A.I.C.S.: 335999
Dave Gordon *(Natl Sls Mgr-Residential Products)*

Subsidiaries:

Allied Moulded Enclosure Products (India) Pvt Ltd. **(1)**
No 199 & 242 Road No 8 KIADB Industrial Area, Bommasandra Jigani Link Road, Bengaluru, 56210, Karnataka, India
Tel.: (91) 8067926666
Web Site: http://www.alliedmoulded.in
Emp.: 48
Fiberglass Electrical Boxes & Enclosures
N.A.I.C.S.: 335999
Sanjeev Gambhir *(CEO-India)*
Shubhashish Mohanty *(Mgr-Natl Sls)*

ALLIED OLD ENGLISH, INC.
100 Markley St, Port Reading, NJ 07064
Tel.: (732) 636-2060 NJ
Web Site: https://www.alliedoldenglish.com
Year Founded: 1951
Sales Range: $75-99.9 Million
Emp.: 70
Prepared Foods, Chinese Condiments, Molasses & Fruit Preserves
N.A.I.C.S.: 311999
Fred C. Ross *(CEO)*
Beverley Gould *(Dir-Pur)*
Richard Gould *(Exec VP-Sls & Mktg)*
Frank Gotti *(CFO)*
Sean Colon *(Exec VP)*

ALLIED PERSONNEL SERVICES, INC.
752 Union Blvd, Allentown, PA 18109
Tel.: (610) 821-0220
Web Site: https://www.alliedps.com
Year Founded: 1984
Emp.: 137
Human Resource Consulting Services
N.A.I.C.S.: 541612
John D. MacDonald *(Pres)*

ALLIED PLASTIC SUPPLY, INC.
1544 Valwood Pkwy Ste 110, Carrollton, TX 75006
Tel.: (972) 241-0762
Web Site: http://www.alliedplastic.org
Sales Range: $10-24.9 Million
Emp.: 80
Engineered Plastics Sheets & Rod Mfr
N.A.I.C.S.: 326199
James Gay *(Pres)*
Stanley Tanner *(Dir-Mgmt Info Sys)*

ALLIED POWER GROUP, LLC
10131 Mills Rd, Houston, TX 77070-4712
Tel.: (281) 444-3535
Web Site: http://www.alliedpg.com
Year Founded: 2005
Sales Range: $50-74.9 Million
Emp.: 70
Machine Part Refurbishing Services
N.A.I.C.S.: 541330
David Theis *(Pres & CEO)*
Austin G. David *(CFO)*

Marty Magby *(VP-Bus Dev-Bundle Svcs)*
Jeremy Clifton *(VP-Bus Dev)*

Subsidiaries:

Combustion Parts Inc. **(1)**
1770 Gillespie Way Ste 111, El Cajon, CA 92020
Tel.: (858) 759-3320
Web Site: http://www.combustionparts.com
Sales Range: $1-9.9 Million
Emp.: 5
Turbine Parts Mfr
N.A.I.C.S.: 333611
Lori Jenks *(Pres)*
Lynda Powell *(Dir-Fin)*
Pete Battaglia *(Mgr-Logistics)*

ALLIED PRINTING SERVICES, INC.
1 Allied Way, Manchester, CT 06042
Tel.: (860) 643-1101 CT
Web Site: https://www.alliedprinting.com
Year Founded: 1949
Sales Range: $100-124.9 Million
Emp.: 300
Provider of Commercial Printing Services
N.A.I.C.S.: 323111
John G. Sommers *(Pres)*

ALLIED PROPANE SERVICE INC.
5000 Seaport Ave, Richmond, CA 94804
Tel.: (510) 237-7077
Web Site: https://www.alliedpropane.com
Sales Range: $10-24.9 Million
Emp.: 40
Whslr of Propane Gas
N.A.I.C.S.: 424720
Stan Teaderman *(Pres)*
Phil Teaderman *(CEO)*

ALLIED REALTY COMPANY
20 26th St, Huntington, WV 25703
Tel.: (304) 525-9125
Web Site: http://www.alliedlogistics.com
Sales Range: $10-24.9 Million
Emp.: 100
Commercial & Industrial Building Operation
N.A.I.C.S.: 531120
Linda Ellinson *(Office Mgr)*
Rebecca Polan *(Pres)*
Lake Polan III *(CEO)*

ALLIED REFRIGERATION INC.
2300 E 28th St, Signal Hill, CA 90755
Tel.: (562) 595-5301 CA
Web Site: https://www.allied-refrig.com
Year Founded: 1946
Sales Range: $10-24.9 Million
Emp.: 120
Warm Air Heating & Air Conditioning
N.A.I.C.S.: 423730
Michael R. Luther *(Pres & COO)*
David Rivera *(Branch Mgr)*
Robert Nichols Jr. *(CEO)*

ALLIED RESOURCE CORPORATION
Bldg 200 435 Devon Park Dr, Wayne, PA 19087
Tel.: (610) 254-4100 DE
Web Site: http://www.alliedresourcecorp.com
Clean Energy Technology Equipment & Services
N.A.I.C.S.: 541620
Heinz C. Schimmelbusch *(Chm)*
Matthew Bulley *(Mng Dir)*

Subsidiaries:

BAMAG GmbH **(1)**
Wetzlarer Strasse 136, 35510, Butzbach, Germany
Tel.: (49) 6033839
Sales Range: $10-24.9 Million
Emp.: 50
Water Purification & Processing Equipment Design & Manufacturing Services
N.A.I.C.S.: 237110

ENVIROTHERM GmbH **(1)**
Ruhrallee 185, 45136, Essen, Germany
Tel.: (49) 2016346400
Web Site: http://www.envirotherm.de
Sales Range: $25-49.9 Million
Emp.: 300
Air Quality Control Equipment Design Services
N.A.I.C.S.: 333248
Georg Daradimos *(Chm, CEO, Mng Dir & Member-Mgmt Bd)*
Jorg Ladenthin *(Mng Dir, CFO & Member-Mgmt Bd)*

Subsidiary (US):

Allied Environmental Solutions, Inc. **(2)**
7110 Samuel Morse Dr Ste150, Columbia, MD 21046
Tel.: (410) 910-5100
Web Site: http://www.andrizinc.com
Sales Range: $10-24.9 Million
Emp.: 11
Air Quality Control Equipment Design Services
N.A.I.C.S.: 333248
Don Hug *(Pres)*

PURALUBE Inc. **(1)**
435 Devon Park Dr Ste 200, Wayne, PA 19087-1937
Tel.: (610) 293-5803
Web Site: http://www.puralube.com
Sales Range: $10-24.9 Million
Emp.: 10
Waste Oil Recycling Technology Design & Manufacturing Services
N.A.I.C.S.: 333248
Hwan Chung *(CEO)*

Subsidiary (Non-US):

PURALUBE GmbH **(2)**
Hauptstrasse 30 Gebaude 37, 06729, Elsteraue, Germany
Tel.: (49) 3441842214
Web Site: http://www.puralube.de
Waste Oil Recycling Technology Design & Manufacturing Services
N.A.I.C.S.: 333248

ALLIED SAFE & VAULT CO. INC.
425 W 2nd Ave, Spokane, WA 99201-4311
Tel.: (509) 624-3152 WA
Web Site: http://www.alliedfiresafety.com
Year Founded: 1949
Sales Range: $125-149.9 Million
Emp.: 150
Security Alarm Systems
N.A.I.C.S.: 444140
Jay Hunt *(Pres)*

ALLIED SEED LLC
9311 Hwy 45, Nampa, ID 83686
Tel.: (208) 466-6700
Web Site: http://www.alliedseed.com
Year Founded: 1985
Sales Range: $25-49.9 Million
Emp.: 40
Grass Seed
N.A.I.C.S.: 424910
Steve Cawood *(CEO)*

ALLIED SOFT LLC
8330 Boone Blvd Ste 200, Tysons Corner, VA 22182
Tel.: (571) 321-5350

Allied Soft LLC—(Continued)

Web Site:
http://www.nehemiahsecurity.com
Cyber Software Security
N.A.I.C.S.: 513210
Paul Farrell *(Co-Founder & CEO)*
Todd Bramblett *(Co-Founder & Pres)*
Shonda Hiers *(VP-HR)*
Richard Comish *(CTO)*

ALLIED SOLUTIONS LLC
350 Veterans Way, Carmel, IN 46032
Tel.: (317) 706-7600
Web Site:
https://www.alliedsolutions.net
Year Founded: 2001
Rev.: $115,500,000
Emp.: 600
Accident & Health Insurance
N.A.I.C.S.: 524114
Fred Caprio *(Sr VP-Sls-Northeast)*
Fran Mertens *(Sr VP-Sls-Southern)*
Jeff Wisdorf *(COO & Exec VP)*
Pete Hilger *(Pres & CEO)*
Ann D. Davidson *(VP-Risk Consulting-Bond)*
Jaime Kernus *(Mgr-Field & Client Support-Eastern)*
Kathy Zwiefelhofer *(Mgr-Field & Client Support-Western)*
Dave Underdale *(CMO & Exec VP)*
Catherine Pettygrove *(Sr VP)*
David Hilger *(CIO & Sr VP)*

Subsidiaries:

Allied Solutions LLC **(1)**
2805 N Dallas Pkwy Ste 300, Plano, TX
75093 **(100%)**
Tel.: (469) 467-3000
Web Site: http://www.alliedsolutions.net
Rev.: $12,600,000
Emp.: 75
Insurance Agents
N.A.I.C.S.: 524210
Janelle Hufnagelle *(Office Mgr)*

ALLIED STEEL BUILDINGS, INC.
101 NE 3rd Ave Ste 300, Fort Lauderdale, FL 33301
Tel.: (954) 590-4297
Web Site:
http://www.alliedbuildings.com
Year Founded: 2003
Sales Range: $25-49.9 Million
Emp.: 42
Steel Built Structures
N.A.I.C.S.: 238120
Michael Lassner *(CEO)*
Brett Ehlin *(Mgr-Tech Project)*
Channing Brodsky *(Project Coord)*
Peter Rivera *(Project Mgr)*

ALLIED SYSTEMS COMPANY
21433 SW Oregon St, Sherwood, OR
97140-9808
Tel.: (503) 625-2560
Web Site:
https://www.alliedsystems.com
Year Founded: 1976
Sales Range: $10-24.9 Million
Emp.: 350
Provider of Material Handling Equipment for the Wood Products Industry
N.A.I.C.S.: 333923
Jeff Rink *(Pres)*

Subsidiaries:

Allied Systems **(1)**
21433 SW Oregon St, Sherwood, OR
97140-9808
Tel.: (503) 625-2560
Web Site: http://www.alliedsystems.com
Emp.: 300
Mfr of Parts & Attachments for Forklifts
N.A.I.C.S.: 333923
Jeff Rink *(Pres)*
Michael Brentano *(Mgr-Sls)*

Long Reach Inc. **(1)**
21433 SW Oregon St, Sherwood, OR
97140
Tel.: (503) 625-2560
Web Site: http://www.alliedsystems.com
Emp.: 375
Material Handling Equipment Mfr
N.A.I.C.S.: 333924
Erin Bruce *(Exec VP)*

Presto Lifts Inc. **(1)**
21 Park St, Attleboro, MA 02703
Tel.: (508) 222-0177
Web Site: http://www.prestolifts.com
Mfr of Lifts
N.A.I.C.S.: 333924

ALLIED SYSTEMS INC.
2200 E Douglas Ave, Des Moines, IA
50313
Tel.: (515) 223-6642
Web Site: https://www.asidsm.com
Sales Range: $25-49.9 Million
Emp.: 14
Sales of Plumbing Fittings & Supplies
N.A.I.C.S.: 423720
Gina Beals *(Mgr-Customer Svcs)*
Heidi Peck *(Mgr-Acctg)*
Kenn Spahr *(VP)*

ALLIED TELESYN INTERNATIONAL, INC.
19800 N Creek Pkwy Ste 100, Bothell, WA 98011
Tel.: (425) 487-8880
Web Site:
http://www.alliedtelesyn.com
Sales Range: $25-49.9 Million
Emp.: 1,000
Mfr of Computer Peripheral Equipment
N.A.I.C.S.: 334118
Takayoshi Oshima *(Chm & CEO)*
Miodrag Sundic *(Mng Dir-Sls-Eastern Europe & Sr VP)*

ALLIED UNIKING CORPORATION
4750 Cromwell Ave, Memphis, TN
38118
Tel.: (901) 365-7240
Web Site:
https://www.allieduniking.com
Year Founded: 1972
Sales Range: $10-24.9 Million
Emp.: 14
Conveyors & Conveying Equipment
N.A.I.C.S.: 333922
Kenneth Anderson *(Chm & CEO)*

ALLIED UNIVERSAL HOLDING CORPORATION
3901 NW 115 Ave, Miami, FL 33178
Tel.: (305) 888-2623 **FL**
Web Site:
http://www.allieduniversal.com
Year Founded: 2003
Holding Company; Water Treatment Chemicals Mfr & Distr
N.A.I.C.S.: 551112
Robert M. Namoff *(Chm)*
James W. Palmer *(Pres)*

Subsidiaries:

Allied Universal Corp. **(1)**
3901 NW 115 Ave, Miami, FL 33178
Tel.: (305) 888-2623
Web Site: http://www.allieduniversal.com
Sales Range: $25-49.9 Million
Emp.: 300
Water Treatment Chemicals Mfr & Distr
N.A.I.C.S.: 325998
Robert M. Namoff *(Chm)*
Carlos Fernandez *(VP-Sls)*
Todd Tucker *(VP-Ops)*
Carlos Perez *(VP-Bus Dev)*

ALLIED UNIVERSAL MANAGER LLC

1551 N Tustin Avenue Ste 650, Santa
Ana, CA 92705 **DE**
Web Site: http://www.aus.com
Year Founded: 2016
Emp.: 246,000
Holding Company; Security Services
N.A.I.C.S.: 551112
Steve Jones *(Chm & CEO)*
Tim Brandt *(CFO)*
Vanessa Showalter *(Mgr-PR)*

Subsidiaries:

American Services, Inc. **(1)**
1300 Rutherford Rd, Greenville, SC 29609
Tel.: (864) 292-7450
Web Site: http://www.american-services-inc.com
Sales Range: $25-49.9 Million
Emp.: 25
Security Guard Services
N.A.I.C.S.: 561612
Henry C. Harrison *(Chm & CEO)*
Joy Rollins *(Controller)*
Mieko Fox *(Pres-Charlotte)*
Cam Keriazakos *(Pres-Sls-Greenville)*
Mike Gardner *(Dir-Hospital Security)*
Carole Ann Owens *(Dir-HR)*
Donna Bishop *(Exec VP-Action)*
Jackie Hatmaker *(District Mgr)*

G4S PLC **(1)**
6th Floor 50 Broadway, London, SW1H
0DB, United Kingdom
Tel.: (44) 2087707000
Web Site: https://www.g4s.com
Rev.: $9,532,878,240
Assets: $7,020,218,640
Liabilities: $6,026,575,980
Net Worth: $993,642,660
Earnings: $114,211,800
Emp.: 559,880
Fiscal Year-end: 12/31/2018
International Security Solution Services
N.A.I.C.S.: 561612
Jesus Rosano *(COO-Intl)*
Sanjay Verma *(CEO-Asia Pacific Reg)*
Catherine Hooper *(Chief HR Officer)*
Cobus Groenewoud *(CEO-Africa & Risk Management)*
Eddy Esquivel *(Reg Pres-Latin America & Caribbean)*
Fiona Walters *(CEO-UK & Ireland)*
James Davies *(Exec VP-Sales, Marketing, and International)*
Vinz van Es *(Reg Pres-Europe)*
Kitty George *(Dir-Corp Affairs)*
Matthew Ingham *(Gen Counsel-International)*
Paul Carter *(CIO-International)*
Ashley Almanza *(Chm-Allied Universal International)*
Ashley Almanza *(Chm-Allied Universal International)*

Subsidiary (Non-US):

AS G4S Eesti **(2)**
Paldiski Mnt 80, Tallinn, 10617, Estonia
Tel.: (372) 6511700
Web Site: http://www.g4s.ee
Rev.: $72,676,450
Emp.: 3,100
Security System Services
N.A.I.C.S.: 561621
Andrus Ossip *(Chm)*
Jaan Nappus *(Dir-Sls Div)*

Subsidiary (US):

Adesta LLC **(2)**
1200 Landmark Ctr Ste 1300, Omaha, NE
68102-1892
Communication Network & Infrastructure
Services
N.A.I.C.S.: 517810

Subsidiary (Non-US):

Alarmtec AS **(2)**
Workshop 1, Tallinn, 11313, Estonia
Tel.: (372) 6511500
Web Site: http://www.alarmtec.ee
Security Equipment Whslr
N.A.I.C.S.: 423420

Subsidiary (Domestic):

Amag Technology Ltd. **(2)**

1 International Dr, Tewkesbury, GL20 8UQ,
United Kingdom
Tel.: (44) 1684850977
Web Site: http://www.amag.com
Technical & Professional Services
N.A.I.C.S.: 541990
Mark Williams *(Dir-Sls)*

Subsidiary (Non-US):

G4S (Botswana) Ltd. **(2)**
Plot No 20584 Block 3 Industrial Western-
Bypass, Gaborone, Botswana
Tel.: (267) 3698000
Integrated Security Business Services
N.A.I.C.S.: 561621

G4S (DRC) S.A.R.L. **(2)**
Kolwezi Avenue, Gombe, 4885, Kinshasa,
Congo, Democratic Republic of
Tel.: (243) 810595259
Integrated Security Business Services
N.A.I.C.S.: 561621

G4S (Hellas), S.A. **(2)**
7 Sorou St, 144 52, Metamorfosis, Athens,
Greece
Tel.: (30) 2102896300
Web Site: http://www.g4s.gr
Sales Range: $550-599.9 Million
Emp.: 3,000
Security Services
N.A.I.C.S.: 561621

G4S (Hong Kong - Holding) Ltd. **(2)**
1st Floor Securicor Centre 481 Castle Peak
Road, Kowloon, China (Hong Kong)
Tel.: (852) 21733333
Integrated Security Business Services
N.A.I.C.S.: 561621

G4S (Mali) SARL **(2)**
Posted in Hamdallaye ACI 2000 near Radisson Hotel, PO Box 1289, Bamako, Mali
Tel.: (223) 295268
Integrated Security Business Services
N.A.I.C.S.: 561621
Bertrand Duffaut *(Country Mgr)*
Anne-Catherine Duffaut *(Mgr-Sls)*

G4S Beheer BV **(2)**
Hogehilweg 12, 1101 CD, Amsterdam,
Netherlands
Tel.: (31) 206604100
Web Site: http://www.g4s.nl
Management Services
N.A.I.C.S.: 561110

G4S Cash Solutions (Belgium)
SA/NV **(2)**
Stationsstraat 20, 1702, Groot-Bijgaarden,
Belgium
Tel.: (32) 24641115
Web Site: http://www.g4s.be
Sales Range: $25-49.9 Million
Emp.: 50
Security System Services
N.A.I.C.S.: 561621
Jean-Paul van Avermaet *(Gen Mgr)*
Andreas Coppens *(Mng Dir)*

G4S Cash Solutions (Ireland)
Limited **(2)**
51 Bracken Road Sandyford Industrial Estate, Dublin, Ireland
Tel.: (353) 12179100
Web Site: http://www.g4s.com
Sales Range: $150-199.9 Million
Emp.: 700
Cash Handling Services
N.A.I.C.S.: 561621

G4S Cash Solutions BV **(2)**
Ptolemaeuslaan 61, 3528 BR, Utrecht,
Netherlands
Tel.: (31) 900 447 22 74
Web Site: http://www.geldnet.nl
Cash Transportation & ATM Management
Services
N.A.I.C.S.: 561613

G4S Cash Solutions SRL **(2)**
Str George Constantinescu Nr 3 Sector 2,
020339, Bucharest, Romania
Tel.: (40) 212507253
Web Site: http://www.g4s.ro
Security System Services
N.A.I.C.S.: 561621

G4S Compliance & Nvestigations
(Ireland) Limited **(2)**

1st Floor Unit B Citywest Shopping Centre, Saggart, D24 P650, Ireland
Tel.: (353) 15719266
Web Site: http://www.cni-g4s.ie
Investigation Solution Services
N.A.I.C.S.: 561611
Michael J. Malone *(Pres)*
David Snow *(Dir-Bus)*

G4S Fire & Safety BV (2)
Donk 1C, 2991 LE, Barendrecht, Netherlands
Tel.: (31) 881160630
Integrated Security Business Services
N.A.I.C.S.: 561621

G4S Holdings (Hong Kong) Ltd. (2)
1st Fl Securicor Ctr 481 Castle Peak Rd, Kowloon, China (Hong Kong) **(100%)**
Tel.: (852) 21733333
Web Site: http://www.g4sht.com
Sales Range: $25-49.9 Million
Emp.: 100
Security Services
N.A.I.C.S.: 561621

G4S International Logisitics (Hong Kong) Ltd. (2)
Unit 02 7/F Beautiful Group Tower 77 Connaught Road, Central, China (Hong Kong)
Tel.: (852) 29590055
Integrated Security Business Services
N.A.I.C.S.: 561621

G4S International Logistics (Germany) GmbH (2)
Rathenaustrasse 53, Neu-Isenburg, 63263, Frankfurt, Germany
Tel.: (49) 61024393600
Integrated Security Business Services
N.A.I.C.S.: 561621

Subsidiary (US):

G4S International Logistics (USA), Inc. (2)
1 Cross Island Plaza 133-33 Brookville Blvd Ste 305, Rosedale, NY 11422
Tel.: (718) 244-6206
Security System Services
N.A.I.C.S.: 561621

Subsidiary (Non-US):

G4S Kenya Limited (2)
Witu Road Off Lusaka Road, PO Box 30242-00100, Nairobi, 00100, Kenya
Tel.: (254) 206982000
Web Site: http://www.g4s.co.ke
Sales Range: $1-4.9 Billion
Emp.: 15,000
Security Guard Services
N.A.I.C.S.: 561612
Trevor Dighton *(CFO)*

G4S Keszpenzlogisztikai Kft (2)
Rozsnyai u 21-25, 1139, Budapest, Hungary
Tel.: (36) 12373200
Web Site: http://www.g4s.com
Security Guard Services
N.A.I.C.S.: 561612

Subsidiary (Domestic):

G4S Risk Consulting Ltd. (2)
48 Gillingham Street, London, SW1V 1HU, United Kingdom
Tel.: (44) 2079633219
Security System Services
N.A.I.C.S.: 561621

G4S Risk Management Limited (2)
46 Gillingham Street, London, SW1V 1HU, United Kingdom
Tel.: (44) 2079633219
Web Site:
   http://www.g4sriskmanagement.com
Risk Management & Consulting Services
N.A.I.C.S.: 541611

Subsidiary (Non-US):

G4S Secure Solutions (CI) SA (2)
Rue J 82 Lot 2310A Ilot 23/Ilot 170 Cocody les II Plateaux vallon 20, PO Box 845, Abidjan, Cote d'Ivoire
Tel.: (225) 22480100
Integrated Security Business Services
N.A.I.C.S.: 561621

G4S Secure Solutions (Canada) Limited (2)
6375 Dixie Rd, Mississauga, L5T 2C7, ON, Canada
Tel.: (888) 717-4447
Security System Services
N.A.I.C.S.: 561621

G4S Secure Solutions (Cyprus) Limited (2)
Dilaneiras 17 2045 Strovolos, PO Box 23989, CY 1687, Nicosia, Cyprus **(100%)**
Tel.: (357) 22745300
Web Site: http://www.g4s.com.cy
Sales Range: $150-199.9 Million
Emp.: 600
Security Services
N.A.I.C.S.: 561621

G4S Secure Solutions (Egypt) LLC (2)
2nd District El Teseen St Area 6 5th Settlement, New Cairo, Egypt
Tel.: (20) 25647039
Integrated Security Business Services
N.A.I.C.S.: 561621
Mark Lipton *(Mng Dir)*
Karim Shoukry *(Dir-Fin)*
Mahmoud El Morsy *(Mgr-Training Dev)*
Ahmed Alqazzaz *(Dir-Sls & Bus Dev)*
Hesham Helmy *(Dir-HR)*

G4S Secure Solutions (Gambia) Ltd. (2)
9 Booster Station, Fajara, Gambia
Tel.: (220) 4497695
Integrated Security Business Services
N.A.I.C.S.: 561621
Fatou Max Njie *(Mgr-HR)*

G4S Secure Solutions (Macau) Ltd. (2)
Avenida Venceslau de Morais No 157 Bl 2 2 Ndar H, Ed centro Industrial Keck Seng, Macau, China (Macau)
Tel.: (853) 28718600
Emp.: 1,500
Integrated Security Business Services
N.A.I.C.S.: 561621

G4S Secure Solutions (SA) (Pty) Limited (2)
Byls Bridge Building 11 13 Candela St Highveld Extension 73, Hatfield, Centurion, 0157, South Africa
Tel.: (27) 124313700
Web Site: http://www.g4s.co.za
Security System Services
N.A.I.C.S.: 561621

G4S Secure Solutions (SL) Ltd. (2)
6 Spur Road, Freetown, Sierra Leone
Tel.: (232) 30695477
Security System Services
N.A.I.C.S.: 561621
Joseph Komba *(Ops Mgr)*

G4S Secure Solutions (Singapore) Pte. Ltd. (2)
380 Jalan Besar 10-06/12, Singapore, 209000, Singapore
Tel.: (65) 63924140
Security System Services
N.A.I.C.S.: 561621
Sam Loke *(Mgr-IT)*

G4S Secure Solutions (Trinidad) Ltd. (2)
61-63 Edward Street, Port of Spain, Trinidad & Tobago
Tel.: (868) 6245751
Security System Services
N.A.I.C.S.: 561621

Subsidiary (Domestic):

G4S Secure Solutions (UK) Limited (2)
Sutton Park House 15 Carshalton Road, Sutton, SM1 4LD, Surrey, United Kingdom
Tel.: (44) 8459000447
Security System Services
N.A.I.C.S.: 561621

Subsidiary (US):

G4S Secure Solutions (USA) Inc. (2)
1395 University Blvd, Jupiter, FL 33458

Tel.: (561) 622-5656
Web Site: http://www.g4s.us
Sales Range: $100-124.9 Million
Emp.: 400
Security Services
N.A.I.C.S.: 561612
Susanne Jorgensen *(CFO)*

Subsidiary (Domestic):

G4S Secure Integration LLC (3)
1299 Farnam St 1200 Landmark Ctr Ste 1300, Omaha, NE 68102-1892
Tel.: (402) 233-7700
Web Site: http://us.g4stechnology.com
Sales Range: $75-99.9 Million
Emp.: 250
Systems Integration & Project Management Services for Integrated Security Systems & Communication Systems
N.A.I.C.S.: 541519

Subsidiary (Non-US):

G4S Wackenhut (UK) Ltd. (3)
Sutton Pk House 15 Carshalton Rd, Surrey, Sutton, SM1 4LD, United Kingdom
Tel.: (44) 2087707000
Web Site: http://www.g4s.uk.com
Security Services
N.A.I.C.S.: 561621

GS4 Peru, S.A. (3)
Avenida el Sol 916 Urbanizacion la Campina Chorrillos, Lima, 09, Peru
Tel.: (51) 12131200
Web Site: http://www.g4s.com.pe
Security Services
N.A.I.C.S.: 561621
Carlos Chavez *(Gen Mgr)*

Grupo Wackenhut S.A. de C.V. (3)
Calzada De La Viga # 398 4 Piso Col, Jamaica, CP 15800, Mexico, DF, Mexico **(100%)**
Tel.: (52) 5557411038
Web Site: http://www.wackenhut.com.mx
Sales Range: $75-99.9 Million
Security Services
N.A.I.C.S.: 561621

Subsidiary (Domestic):

RONCO Consulting Corporation (3)
6710 Oxon Hill Rd Ste 200, Oxon Hill, MD 20745
Tel.: (240) 493-3910
Web Site: http://www.roncoconsulting.com
Environmental Consulting Services
N.A.I.C.S.: 541620

Subsidiary (Non-US):

Wackenhut Cameroon S.A. (3)
Rue Chococho, PO Box 3798, Bonaprisote, Douala, Cameroon **(100%)**
Tel.: (237) 343 3133
Security Services
N.A.I.C.S.: 561621

Wackenhut Dominicana, S.A. (3)
Paseo de los Locutores 36, Ensanche Piantini, Apartado 1677 Zona 1, Santo Domingo, Dominican Republic
Tel.: (809) 544 3333
Sales Range: $75-99.9 Million
Emp.: 400
Security Services
N.A.I.C.S.: 561621

Wackenhut El Salvador S.A. (3)
Ave Olimpica 3765 Colonia Escalon, San Salvador, El Salvador
Tel.: (503) 25006285
Web Site: http://www.sb.g4s.com
Security Services
N.A.I.C.S.: 561621

Wackenhut Paraguay S.A. (3)
Nery Quevedo 315 Esquina Hipolito Garron Barrio San Miguel, Asuncion, Paraguay **(100%)**
Tel.: (595) 21663896
Sales Range: $125-149.9 Million
Security Services
N.A.I.C.S.: 561621

Wackenhut S.A. (3)
Sabana Sur Yamuni 200 Sur Frente a Consejo, Nacional de Procuccion Ave 10, San Jose, Costa Rica

Tel.: (506) 2330654
Security Services
N.A.I.C.S.: 561621

Wackenhut Venezolana C.A. (3)
Avenida Diego Cisneros Principal De Los Ruices, Edificio Lanex Piso 3, Tranversal, Caracas, Venezuela **(100%)**
Tel.: (58) 2122386542
Security Services
N.A.I.C.S.: 561621

Wackenhut de Bolivia S.A. (3)
Ave Hector Ormachea No.4929, La Paz, Obrajes, Bolivia **(100%)**
Tel.: (591) 22789121
Web Site: http://www.g4s.com.bo
Sales Range: $25-49.9 Million
Emp.: 160
Security Services
N.A.I.C.S.: 561621

Wackenhut del Ecuador S.A. (3)
Luis Cordero E 12 114 y Toledo Ed, Lugano Esq La Floresta, Quito, 04791, Ecuador
Tel.: (593) 22945400
Web Site: http://www.g4s.com
Sales Range: $75-99.9 Million
Security Services
N.A.I.C.S.: 561621

Subsidiary (Non-US):

G4S Secure Solutions (Uruguay) S.A. (2)
Cufre 2324 Esq Cagancha, 11800, Montevideo, Uruguay
Tel.: (598) 22089824
Security System Services
N.A.I.C.S.: 561621

G4S Secure Solutions AG (2)
Dresdner Strasse 91/1, 1200, Wiener Neustadt, Austria
Tel.: (43) 1313150
Integrated Security Business Services
N.A.I.C.S.: 561621

G4S Secure Solutions France SAS (2)
9 Place de la Madeleine, 75008, Paris, France
Tel.: (33) 142612614
Integrated Security Business Services
N.A.I.C.S.: 561621

G4S Secure Solutions Japan K.K. (2)
2299-4 Fussa Musashino Hills 202, Fussa, 197-0011, Tokyo, Japan
Tel.: (81) 425199303
Integrated Security Business Services
N.A.I.C.S.: 561621

G4S Secure Solutions Mocambique Limitada (2)
African Union Organization Avenue OUA no 121, Malanga, Maputo, Mozambique
Tel.: (258) 21400810
Integrated Security Business Services
N.A.I.C.S.: 561621
Pedro Matsinhe *(Mgr-Cash Solution Sls)*
Nelmio Magunga *(Mgr-Tech Solutions Sls)*

G4S Secure Solutions Nigeria Ltd. (2)
7th Floor Etiebets Place 21-22 Mobolaji Bank Anthony Way, Ikeja, Lagos, Nigeria
Tel.: (234) 8176656010
Integrated Security Business Services
N.A.I.C.S.: 561621

G4S Secure Solutions Zambia Ltd. (2)
Plot 3144 Mukwa Road, PO Box 32914, Lusaka, 10101, Zambia
Tel.: (260) 211244832
Security System Services
N.A.I.C.S.: 561621

G4S Secure Solutions d.o.o. (2)
Viline Vode 6, 11000, Belgrade, Serbia
Tel.: (381) 112097900
Security System Services
N.A.I.C.S.: 561621

G4S Security Services (India) Pvt. Limited (2)
Tower A Fifth Floor Unitech Cyber Park

Allied Universal Manager LLC—(Continued)

Sector 39, Gurgaon, 122 001, Haryana, India
Tel.: (91) 1242398888
Web Site: http://www.g4s.in
Sales Range: $15-24.9 Billion
Emp.: 160,000
Security Guard Services
N.A.I.C.S.: 561612

G4S Security Services (Mauritania) SA (2)
Tevragh Zeina Ilot C - No 26, PO Box 4201, Nouakchott, Mauritania
Tel.: (222) 45295758
Integrated Security Business Services
N.A.I.C.S.: 561621

G4S Security Services (Thailand) Limited (2)
2019 New Petchburi Rd Huay-Kwang Bang-kopi, 10310, Bangkok, Thailand
Tel.: (66) 27138700
Web Site: http://www.g4s.com
Sales Range: $1-4.9 Billion
Emp.: 10,000
Security Services
N.A.I.C.S.: 561612

G4S Security Services A/S (2)
Roskildevej 157, 2620, Albertslund, Denmark
Tel.: (45) 43865000
Web Site: http://www.g4s.dk
Sales Range: $75-99.9 Million
Emp.: 500
Security Guard Services
N.A.I.C.S.: 561612

G4S Security Services AG (2)
Dresdner Strasse 91/1, 1200, Vienna, Austria
Tel.: (43) 1313150
Web Site: http://www.g4s.com
Emp.: 200
Security Guard Services
N.A.I.C.S.: 561612

G4S Security Services Canada Ltd. (2)
50 McIntosh Dr Ste 252, Markham, L3R 9T3, ON, Canada
Tel.: (905) 946-1884
Web Site: http://www.g4s.ca
Sales Range: $25-49.9 Million
Emp.: 20
Security Services
N.A.I.C.S.: 561621
Katie McLeod (Mgr-Natl Collections & Admin-Security Svcs)
Jean P. Taillon (Pres & CEO)
Doug Durant (Reg VP-Western Canada)
Pamela MacLellan (Dir-HR)
Rene Wells (Mgr-Fort McMurray)

G4S Security Services Nepal (P) Ltd. (2)
Ichhunadi Marg Baluwatar-4, Kathmandu, Nepal
Tel.: (977) 4435117
Integrated Security Business Services
N.A.I.C.S.: 561621
Mahesh Shrestha (Mng Dir)

G4S Security Services SA/NV (2)
Koning Boudewijnlaan 30, 1800, Vilvoorde, Belgium
Tel.: (32) 27125911
Web Site: http://www.g4s.com
Security Guard Services
N.A.I.C.S.: 561612

G4S Security Solutions AB (2)
Warfvinges Vag 39, Stockholm, 112 51, Sweden
Tel.: (46) 102222000
Web Site: http://www.g4s.se
Security Guard Services
N.A.I.C.S.: 561612

G4S Security Solutions Sarl (2)
Rue Du Pere Raphael 14, BP 1513, 2413, Luxembourg, Luxembourg
Tel.: (352) 246611
Web Site: http://www.g4s.lu
Emp.: 1,200
Security Guard Services
N.A.I.C.S.: 561612

G4S Security Systems GmbH (2)

Peilsteinerstr 5-7, 5020, Salzburg, Austria
Tel.: (43) 1313150
Integrated Security Business Services
N.A.I.C.S.: 561621

G4S Security Systems Lebanon SAL (2)
Awkar Square Saliba Bldg 2nd & 3rd Fl Awkar, Beirut, Lebanon
Tel.: (961) 4404903
Integrated Security Business Services
N.A.I.C.S.: 561621

G4S Soluciones de Seguridad S.A. (2)
Timoteo Gordillo 5697 Con Salida Por Ferre 6250, Buenos Aires, 1439, Argentina
Tel.: (54) 1146306600
Web Site: http://www.g4s.com.ar
Security Guard Services
N.A.I.C.S.: 561612
Fernando Kelly (Gen Mgr)

Subsidiary (Domestic):

G4S Technology Ltd. (2)
Challenge House International Drive, Tewkesbury, Gloucestershire, United Kingdom
Tel.: (44) 1684850977
Web Site: http://www.g4stechnology.com
Emp.: 400
Security System Software Development Services
N.A.I.C.S.: 541511

Subsidiary (Non-US):

Hill & Associates (India) Pvt. Ltd. (2)
Tower A 5th Floor Unitech Cyber Park Sector 39, 122002, Gurgaon, Haryana, India
Tel.: (91) 1242398888
Integrated Security Business Services
N.A.I.C.S.: 561621

Hill & Associates (PRC) Ltd. (2)
Room 2406 Zhongrong Hengrui International Building No 620 Zhangyang Rd, Pudong New District, Shanghai, 200122, China
Tel.: (86) 2152385599
Integrated Security Business Services
N.A.I.C.S.: 561621

Hill & Associates Limited (2)
1701 Tower 1 Times Square, Causeway Bay, Hong Kong, China (Hong Kong)
Tel.: (852) 28022123
Web Site: http://www.hill-assoc.com
Sales Range: $75-99.9 Million
Emp.: 30
Security & Risk Management Consulting Services
N.A.I.C.S.: 541618

Indo British Garments (P) Ltd. (2)
Plot No 23 Sector 24, Faridabad, 121005, Haryana, India
Tel.: (91) 1294193300
Web Site: http://www.ibgcorporate.com
Emp.: 500
Garment Mfr & Distr
N.A.I.C.S.: 315250

Instalarme Industria e Comercio Ltda (2)
Rua Joao Sierra 245, Distrito Industrial II, Araras, 13600-970, Brazil
Tel.: (55) 1935437000
Web Site: http://www.instalarme.com.br
Electronic Security System Mfr
N.A.I.C.S.: 334290

Inzetbaar BV (2)
Radonstraat 100, 2718 TA, Zoetermeer, Netherlands
Tel.: (31) 884472900
Web Site: http://www.inzetbaar.nl
Healtcare Services
N.A.I.C.S.: 621999

SSE Do Brasil Ltda (2)
Rua Almeida de Morais 86 Vila Matias, Santos, Sao Paulo, 11045-003, Brazil
Tel.: (55) 1332234543
Web Site: http://www.sse.inimagen.com.br
Power Generation Supervisory System Mfr
N.A.I.C.S.: 334519

Safeguards Securicor Sdn Bhd (2)
Lot 14 Jalan 241 Section 51A, 46100, Pet-

---

aling Jaya, Selangor, Malaysia
Tel.: (60) 378848888
Web Site: http://www.g4s.com.my
Sales Range: $1-4.9 Billion
Emp.: 2,000
Security Consulting & Guarding Services
N.A.I.C.S.: 561612

Search Organizacion de Seguridad, S.A. (2)
Timoteo Gordillo 5697, Buenos Aires, C1439GKA, Argentina
Tel.: (54) 11 4630 6600
Web Site: http://www.g4ssearch.com
Sales Range: $650-699.9 Million
Emp.: 4,194
Security Services
N.A.I.C.S.: 561621
Fernando Miguel Kelly (Country Mgr)

SecurCash B.V. (2)
Kiotoweg 221, 3047, BG, Rotterdam, Netherlands
Tel.: (31) 102383355
Information Technology Services
N.A.I.C.S.: 541511

Skycom (Pty) Ltd (2)
Umgeni Business Park 99 Intersite Ave, Durban, 4051, South Africa
Tel.: (27) 312630926
Web Site: http://www.skycom.co.za
Sales Range: $10-24.9 Million
Emp.: 40
Biometric Access Control Services
N.A.I.C.S.: 561499

International Protection Group, Inc. (1)
481 8th Ave 1570, New York, NY 10001
Tel.: (212) 947-1681
Web Site:
http://www.internationalprotection.com
Sales Range: $1-9.9 Million
Emp.: 300
Electronic Parts And Equipment, Nec, Nsk
N.A.I.C.S.: 423690
Jerry Heying (Pres & CEO)
Steffanie Lascari (Asst Dir-Ops)
John Negus (VP-Protective Ops)

Landmark Event Staffing Services, Inc. (1)
2629 Redwing Rd Ste 250, Fort Collins, CO 80526
Tel.: (510) 632-9000
Web Site:
http://www.landmarkeventstaff.com
Security Guards & Patrol Services
N.A.I.C.S.: 561612
Peter Kranske (Co-Founder)
Mike Harrison (Co-Founder)

Universal Services of America, LP (1)
1551 N Tustin Avenue Ste 650, Santa Ana, CA 92705
Web Site: http://www.aus.com
Security & Janitorial Services
N.A.I.C.S.: 561612
Steve Jones (CEO)
Steve Claton (Pres-Southwest)
Mark Olivas (Pres-Janitorial Svcs)
Jason Stapleton (Reg VP)
Rafael Sorto (Reg VP)
Devin Samaha (VP-Sls)
Michelle Bresnahan (Reg VP-Arizona Ops)
Michael Smidt (Pres-Northwest)
Eliot Hermanson (Pres-Midwest)
Caress Kennedy (Pres-Northeast)
DelMar Laury (Pres-Mid-Atlantic)
Robert Wood (Pres-Southeast)
Randy Dorn (Pres-Central)
Michael J. Martin (Pres-Canada & Sr Reg VP-Midwest)
Ty Richmond (Pres-Natl Accts & Security Sys Tech)
William C. Whitmore Jr. (Chm)

Subsidiary (Domestic):

APG Security LLC (2)
116 N Broadway Ste 2, South Amboy, NJ 08879-1671
Tel.: (401) 921-3177
Web Site: http://www.apgsecurity.com
Miscellaneous Durable Goods Merchant Whslr
N.A.I.C.S.: 423990

Dennis Kelly (Owner)

FJC Security Services, Inc. (2)
275 Jericho Tpke, Floral Park, NY 11001
Tel.: (516) 328-6000
Web Site: http://www.fjcsecurity.com
Security Guards & Patrol Services
N.A.I.C.S.: 561612
Robert Hopes (Sr VP-Client Rels & Admin Programs)
William Richard (Sr VP)
Mark D. Coffino (COO & Exec VP)
Gary O'Connor (Asst VP-HR)
Joshua Primrose (VP-Ops-Federal Svcs Div)
Robert Stabile (VP-Aviation Svcs)

Midstate Security Company LLC (2)
5975 Crossroads Commerce Pkwy SW, Wyoming, MI 49519
Tel.: (616) 257-1100
Web Site: http://www.midstatesecurity.com
Emp.: 89
Security System Services
N.A.I.C.S.: 561621
David Nemmers (CEO)

Peoplemark, Inc. (2)
3003 Airways Blvd, Memphis, TN 38131 (100%)
Tel.: (901) 332-5555
Web Site: http://www.aus.com
Emp.: 100
Temporary Help Service
N.A.I.C.S.: 561320
Jacky Patterson (Branch Mgr)

SOS Security LLC (2)
1915 Rte 46 E, Parsippany, NJ 07054
Tel.: (973) 402-6600
Web Site: http://www.sossecurity.com
Sales Range: $125-149.9 Million
Emp.: 3,000
Security Guard Services
N.A.I.C.S.: 561612
Edward B. Silverman (Chm & CEO)
Kenneth M. Fisher (Pres)
Scott B. Alswang (Exec VP)
Marc Bognar (COO & Exec VP)
Thomas Gustafson (CFO)
Christopher N. Walsh (Sr VP & Dir-Trng & Special Svcs)
Rosanne Manghisi (Sr VP)
Leslie A. Watkins (VP-HR)
Christina Duffey (Sr VP & Dir-Midwest)
J. P. Saini (CIO)
Joseph Martino (Sr Vp & Reg Dir)
John Frazer (Sr VP & Reg Dir-Mid-Atlantic)
Bob Larkin (Exec VP-Globall Retail)
Aaron Silverman (Dir-Bus Intelligence)
Andrew Silverman (Dir-Special Svcs)

Subsidiary (Domestic):

Asset Protection Associates, Inc. (3)
2305 Old Milton Pkwy, Alpharetta, GA 30005
Tel.: (678) 566-0220
Web Site:
http://www.assetprotectionassociates.net
Emp.: 100
Temporary & Permanent Security Guards, Operational & Loss Prevention Services for Retailers
N.A.I.C.S.: 561612
Bob Larkin (Sr VP-SOS Security)
Kendra Parker (Mng Dir-Custom Risk Solutions)
Sandra Saxon (Dir-Ops)

Eastern Security, Inc. (3)
303 Wyman St Ste 300, Waltham, MA 02451
Tel.: (617) 491-8181
Web Site: http://www.easternsecurityinc.com
Rev.: $4,300,000
Emp.: 50
Professional Security Guard Services & Security Personnel
N.A.I.C.S.: 561612
Joseph Frawley (CEO)

New Horizon Security Services, Inc. (3)
7820 Sudley Rd, Manassas, VA 20109
Tel.: (703) 368-6477
Web Site:
http://www.newhorizonsecurity.com
Professional Security Services
N.A.I.C.S.: 561612

Gilbert Garcia (Dir-Bus Ops)

Subsidiary (Domestic):

SecurAmerica, LLC   (2)
3399 Peachtree Rd NE Ste 1500, Atlanta,
GA 30326
Tel.: (404) 926-4222
Web Site: http://www.securamericallc.com
Contract Security Services
N.A.I.C.S.: 561612
John Garrigan (Sr VP-Org Dev)
Suzanne Fountain (VP-HR)
Thomas Givens (COO)
Tom Marano (CEO)
Adam Taylor (Pres-Aviation Svcs)
Don Ridgway (Chief Customer Officer)
Karan Ishwar (Pres)
Frank Argenbright Jr. (Chm)

Subsidiary (Domestic):

American Security Programs Inc.   (3)
22900 Shaw Rd Ste 101-4, Dulles, VA
20166
Tel.: (703) 834-8900
Web Site: http://www.securityprograms.com
Sales Range: $25-49.9 Million
Emp.: 800
Security Guards & Patrol Services
N.A.I.C.S.: 561612
Elaine Y. Bellan (CFO)
John Adams (Chm)
Frank Argenbright (Chm & CEO-
SecurAmerica)
Thomas Givens (Pres & COO-
SecurAmerica)

ERMC II, L.P.   (3)
2226 Encompass Dr Ste 116, Chattanooga,
TN 37421
Tel.: (423) 899-2753
Web Site: http://www.ermc2.com
Janitorial, Landscaping, Facilities Mainte-
nance & Security Services
N.A.I.C.S.: 561720

Subsidiary (Domestic):

Securadyne Systems LLC   (2)
14900 Landmark Blvd Ste 350, Dallas, TX
75254
Tel.: (972) 248-4949
Web Site: http://www.securadyne.com
Sales Range: $50-74.9 Million
Emp.: 300
Security Design Engineering Services
N.A.I.C.S.: 561621
Carey Boethel (Pres & CEO)
Chris Young (CFO)

Subsidiary (Domestic):

Advent Systems Inc.   (3)
15 Collins Industrial Dr Ste C, North Little
Rock, AR 72113
Tel.: (501) 537-6132
Web Site: http://www.adventsystems.com
Rev.: $2,331,000
Emp.: 7
Wired Telecommunications Carriers
N.A.I.C.S.: 517111
Michael Walsdorf (Pres)

Intelligent Access Systems of North
Carolina LLC   (3)
284 Hein Dr, Garner, NC 27529
Tel.: (919) 773-9400
Web Site: http://www.securadyne.com
Sales Range: $10-24.9 Million
Emp.: 5
Security System Services
N.A.I.C.S.: 561621
Ron Oetjen (Co-Founder & Pres)

Subsidiary (Domestic):

Service Works, Inc.   (2)
95 Megill Rd, Farmingdale, NJ 07727
Tel.: (732) 919-7900
Web Site: http://www.serviceworksinc.com
Sales Range: $1-9.9 Million
Emp.: 34
Security System Services
N.A.I.C.S.: 561621
Adele Kunyz (Sec)
Doug Amici (Project Mgr)

U.S. Security Associates, Inc.   (2)
200 Mansell Ct 5th Fl, Roswell, GA
30076-4856   (100%)

Tel.: (770) 625-1500
Web Site:
    http://www.ussecurityassociates.com
Contract Security Services
N.A.I.C.S.: 561612
Richard L. Wyckoff (Pres & CEO)
David Kahn (Chief HR Officer)

Subsidiary (Domestic):

McRoberts Protective Agency,
Inc.   (3)
87 Nassau St, New York, NY 10038
Tel.: (212) 425-6500
Web Site: http://www.mcroberts1876.com
Sales Range: $25-49.9 Million
Emp.: 350
Security Solutions; Detective & Armored
Car Services
N.A.I.C.S.: 561612
Meredith McRoberts (Pres)

Branch (Domestic):

U.S. Security Associates, Inc.   (3)
1560 Broadway 1209, New York, NY 10036
Tel.: (212) 391-6957
Web Site:
    http://www.ussecurityassociates.com
Sales Range: $150-199.9 Million
Emp.: 9
Detective & Armored Car Services
N.A.I.C.S.: 561612
Pablo Escobar (Mgr-HR)

Subsidiary (Domestic):

Universal Protection Security Sys-
tems, LP   (2)
1815 E Wilshire Ave Ste 910, Santa Ana,
CA 92705
Tel.: (714) 288-2227
Web Site: http://legacy.aus.com
Sales Range: $10-24.9 Million
Emp.: 50
Security System Services
N.A.I.C.S.: 561621
Louis Boulgarides (Pres-Western Reg)
Steve Jones (CEO)
Mark Olivas (Pres)
Bill Whitmore (Chm)

Universal Protection Service, LP   (2)
1551 N Tustin Ave Ste 650, Santa Ana, CA
92705
Tel.: (866) 877-1965
Web Site: http://www.aus.com
Security Services
N.A.I.C.S.: 561612
Geoff Craighead (VP)

Subsidiary (Domestic):

All Phase Security, Inc.   (3)
2959 Promenade St Ste 200, West Sacra-
mento, CA 95691
Tel.: (916) 375-6640
Web Site: http://www.allphasesecurity.com
Sales Range: $1-9.9 Million
Emp.: 275
Security Officers & Services
N.A.I.C.S.: 561612

Subsidiary (Domestic):

Vinson Guard Service Inc.   (2)
955 Howard Ave, New Orleans, LA 70113
Tel.: (504) 525-0591
Web Site: http://www.vinsonguard.com
Rev.: $24,264,872
Emp.: 1,300
Protective Services
N.A.I.C.S.: 561612
Christine M. Vinson (Pres)

Yale Enforcement Services, Inc.   (2)
3601 N Belt West, Belleville, IL 62226
Tel.: (888) 925-3363
Web Site: http://www.yaleenforcement.com
Security Guards & Patrol Services
N.A.I.C.S.: 561612
Barbara Yale (Pres & CEO)

ALLIED VAUGHN INC.

7600 Parklawn Ave Ste 300, Minne-
apolis, MN 55435
Tel.: (952) 832-3100
Web Site:
    https://www.alliedvaughn.com

Year Founded: 1999
Sales Range: $10-24.9 Million
Emp.: 70
Provider of Investment Holding Ser-
vices
N.A.I.C.S.: 551112
David Willette (CEO)
Doug Olzenak (Pres)

Subsidiaries:

Allied Vaughn   (1)
1616 17th St Ste 568, Denver, CO 80202
Tel.: (303) 375-8500
Web Site: http://www.alliedvaughn.com
Sales Range: $10-24.9 Million
Emp.: 30
Video Production, Post-Production, Duplica-
tion & Fulfillment Services
N.A.I.C.S.: 334610

Allied Vaughn - Chicago   (1)
901 Bilter Rd Ste 141, Aurora, IL 60502
Tel.: (630) 626-0215
Web Site: http://www.alliedvaughn.com
Video Production, Post-Production, Duplica-
tion & Fulfillment Services
N.A.I.C.S.: 334610
Rick Polizzi (Gen Mgr)

ALLIED WASTE SERVICES OF CORVALLIS

110 NE Walnut Blvd, Corvallis, OR
97330
Tel.: (541) 757-0011
Web Site: http://www.disposal.com
Rev.: $37,500,000
Emp.: 100
Refuse & Recycling Collection Sys-
tems
N.A.I.C.S.: 562219
Daniel Strandy (Controller)

ALLIED WHOLESALE ELEC-TRICAL SUPPLY INCORPO-RATED

120 N Lynhurst Dr, Indianapolis, IN
46224
Tel.: (317) 487-4100
Web Site: http://www.awesi.com
Year Founded: 1985
Sales Range: $10-24.9 Million
Emp.: 40
Whslr of Electrical Supplies
N.A.I.C.S.: 423610
Gary Lewis (VP)
Kevin Horn (Mgr-Will Call)
Rebecca Reichart (Controller)
Rich Kelly (Mgr-Sls)
Rob McCurdy (Pres)
Ryan Toole (Mgr-Counter)
Steve Elliott (Mgr-Anderson)
Steve Lyons (Mgr-Warehouse)
Jeff Roach (VP-Sls & Ops)

ALLIED WIRE & CABLE INC.

101 Kestrel Dr, Collegeville, PA
19426
Tel.: (484) 928-6700
Web Site: http://www.awcwire.com
Year Founded: 1988
Sales Range: $10-24.9 Million
Emp.: 129
Sales of Wire Mfr
N.A.I.C.S.: 423510
Tim Flynn (Owner & Co-CEO)
Dan Flynn (Co-CEO)

Subsidiaries:

Allied Wire & Cable Inc.   (1)
101 Kestrel Dr, Phoenixville, PA 19426
Tel.: (484) 928-6700
Web Site: http://www.awcwire.com
Wire
N.A.I.C.S.: 423510

Allied Wire & Cable Inc. - Midwestern
Division   (1)
W233 N2870 Roundy Cir W, Pewaukee, WI
53072

Tel.: (262) 312-2620
Web Site: http://www.awcwire.com
Wire & Cable Product Mfr
N.A.I.C.S.: 332618
Tim Flynn (Pres)

Allied Wire & Cable Inc. - New Eng-
land Division   (1)
1 Executive Park Dr, Bedford, NH 03310
Tel.: (603) 423-9390
Web Site: http://www.atawcwire.com
Emp.: 12
Wire & Cable Product Mfr
N.A.I.C.S.: 332618
Jessica Gamlin (Mgr)

Allied Wire & Cable Inc. - Southeast-
ern Division   (1)
420 S Ware Blvd Ste C, Tampa, FL 33619
Tel.: (800) 936-6405
Wire & Cable Product Mfr
N.A.I.C.S.: 332618

Allied Wire & Cable Inc. - West Coast
Division   (1)
1650 Helm Dr Ste 100 & 200, Las Vegas,
NV 89119
Tel.: (888) 991-9473
Web Site: http://www.awc.com
Wire & Cable Product Mfr
N.A.I.C.S.: 332618

ALLIED-LOCKE INDUSTRIES INCORPORATED

1088 Corregidor Green River Indus-
trial Park, Dixon, IL 61021-9378
Tel.: (815) 288-1471
Web Site:
    https://www.alliedlocke.com
Year Founded: 1964
Sales Range: $25-49.9 Million
Emp.: 350
Mfr of Chains & Sprockets
N.A.I.C.S.: 332111
William R. Crowson (Pres)

ALLIES & ROSS MANAGE-MENT AND DEVELOPMENT CORPORATION

200 Ross St 9th Fl, Pittsburgh, PA
15219
Tel.: (412) 456-5022   PA
Year Founded: 2007
Sales Range: $10-24.9 Million
Community Housing Assistance Ser-
vices
N.A.I.C.S.: 624229
Edward Mauk (Treas)

ALLIES INC.

1262 Whitehorse Hamilton Square
Rd Bldg A Ste 101, Hamilton, NJ
08690
Tel.: (609) 689-0136
Web Site: https://www.alliesnj.org
Year Founded: 1999
Rev.: $14,705,472
Emp.: 750
Nursing Care Services
N.A.I.C.S.: 623110
Phil Monetti (Dir-R&D & Quality As-
surance)
C. Doug Conkling (Dir-Housing)
Anita Bogdan (Sr VP-HR)
Beth Carey-Lopez (VP-Vocational
Svcs)
Richard Manall (CFO)

ALLIES LIMITED

12020 Shamrock Plz Ste 200,
Omaha, NE 68154
Tel.: (402) 778-4844   NV
Web Site:
    http://www.allieslimited.com
Year Founded: 2009
Sales Range: $25-49.9 Million
Emp.: 1
Investment Services
N.A.I.C.S.: 523999
Don Leath (Mng Dir)

Alligator Diesel Performance LLC—(Continued)

ALLIGATOR DIESEL PERFOR-MANCE LLC
11783 N Warren St, Hayden, ID 83835
Tel.: (208) 719-7400
Web Site:
    https://www.alligatordiesel.com
Year Founded: 2005
Sales Range: $1-9.9 Million
Emp.: 15
Diesel Parts & Accessories Retailers
N.A.I.C.S.: 336390
Jayme Hall (Founder)

ALLIKRISTE LLC
9900 18th St N Ste 102, Saint Petersburg, FL 33716-4224
Tel.: (727) 822-9213
Web Site: http://www.allikriste.com
Year Founded: 1996
Sales Range: $1-9.9 Million
Emp.: 40
Cabinetry, Kitchen Design & Remodeling
N.A.I.C.S.: 337110
Joe Houlton (CEO)

ALLINA HEALTH SYSTEM, INC.
2925 Chicago Ave, Minneapolis, MN 55407
Tel.: (612) 262-5000   MN
Web Site:
    https://www.allinahealth.org
Year Founded: 1994
Sales Range: $600-649.9 Million
Emp.: 21,500
Not-For-Profit Health Care System
N.A.I.C.S.: 622110
Timothy A. Welsh (Vice Chm)

Subsidiaries:

Abbott-Northwestern Medical Building
Pharmacy Inc.   (1)
2545 Chicago Ave Ste 120, Minneapolis, MN 55404-4541
Tel.: (612) 863-4190
Web Site: http://www.allina.com
Sales Range: $10-24.9 Million
Emp.: 30
Drug Stores & Proprietary Stores
N.A.I.C.S.: 456110
Vick Antilly (Gen Mgr)

Comprehensive Medical Care Ltd., Inc.   (1)
9055 Springbrook Dr NW, Coon Rapids, MN 55433-5841
Tel.: (763) 780-9155
Web Site: http://www.allina.com
Sales Range: $25-49.9 Million
Emp.: 500
Offices & Clinics of Medical Doctors
N.A.I.C.S.: 621111
Michael Slama (Gen Mgr)

ALLIS TOOL & MACHINE CORP.
647 S 94th Pl, Milwaukee, WI 53214
Tel.: (414) 453-5500   WI
Web Site: https://www.allistool.com
Year Founded: 1954
Sales Range: $1-9.9 Million
Emp.: 35
Designer & Mfr of Precision Progressing Dies, Jigs, Gauges & Fixtures
N.A.I.C.S.: 333998
Joseph Giuliani (Controller)

ALLISON & CHUMNEY, PC.
5050 Poplar Ave Ste 313, Memphis, TN 38157
Tel.: (901) 761-4335
Year Founded: 1990
Sales Range: $10-24.9 Million
Emp.: 6

Accounting Services
N.A.I.C.S.: 541211
Jerry Allison (Pres)

ALLISON & PARTNERS LLC
40 Gold St, San Francisco, CA 94133
Tel.: (415) 217-7500   DE
Web Site: http://www.allisonpr.com
Year Founded: 2001
Sales Range: $10-24.9 Million
Emp.: 106
Public Relations Agency
N.A.I.C.S.: 541820
Scott Allison (Chm & CEO)
Andy Hardie-Brown (Co-Founder & COO)
Scott Pansky (Co-Founder & Partner)
Aimee Grove (VP-Consumer & Hospitality Practice)
Matt Averitt (VP-Dallas)
Carlos de Leon (Sr VP-Consumer Practice)
Dawn Wilcox (Mng Dir-Social Impact Practice Grp)
Lisa Rosenberg (Chief Creative Officer)
Corey Scott (Sr VP & Head-Design)
Carline Jorgensen (Gen Mgr-Los Angeles)
Jonathan Heit (Founder & CEO)
Karyn Barr (Pres-Ops-Global)
Jordan Fischler (Pres-Global Strategy-Tech Grp)
Paddi Hurley (Mng Dir)

Subsidiaries:

Allison & Partners   (1)
8880 Rio San Diego Dr Ste 1090, San Diego, CA 92108
Tel.: (619) 533-7978
Web Site: http://www.allisonpr.com
Sales Range: $10-24.9 Million
N.A.I.C.S.: 541820

Allison & Partners   (1)
410 N 44th St Ste 1100, Phoenix, AZ 85008
Tel.: (480) 966-0100
Web Site: http://www.allisonpr.com
Emp.: 6
N.A.I.C.S.: 541820

Allison & Partners   (1)
116 East 27th St 4th Fl, New York, NY 10016-8410
Tel.: (212) 302-5460
Web Site: http://www.allisonpr.com
Emp.: 15
N.A.I.C.S.: 541820

Allison & Partners   (1)
2001 Wilshire Blvd Ste 501, Santa Monica, CA 90403-5640
Tel.: (310) 452-7540
Web Site: http://www.allisonpr.com
Emp.: 15
N.A.I.C.S.: 541820
Serina Tan (Mng Dir-Asia Pacific & Gen Mgr-Singapore)
Robin Chang (VP-Singapore)
Natashia Jaya (Dir-Singapore)

Allison & Partners-Washington D.C.   (1)
1025 Connecticut Ave NW Ste 220, Washington, DC 20036
Tel.: (202) 223-9260
N.A.I.C.S.: 541860
Scott Allison (Pres & CEO)
Scott Pansky (Co-Founder & Partner)
Lauren Selikoff (CMO)
Andy Hardie-Brown (Co-Founder & COO)
Brian Feldman (Partner)
Trudi Boyd (Gen Mgr)

Allison and Partners K.K.   (1)
5-5-1 Shimbashi, Minatu-ku, Tokyo, 105-0004, Japan
Tel.: (81) 368091300
Web Site: http://www.allisonpr.com
Advertising Services
N.A.I.C.S.: 541810
Akemi Ichise (Pres & CEO)

Focused Communications Co., Ltd.   (1)
2-9-1 Nishi Shimbashi, Minato-ku, Tokyo, 1050033, Japan
Tel.: (81) 3 5157 0033
Web Site: http://www.focused.co.jp
Rev.: $268,530
Emp.: 15
Public Relations Services
N.A.I.C.S.: 541820
Takashi Miura (Chm)
Akemi Ichise (Pres & CEO)

ALLISON CHEVROLET INC.
2152 N Wheeler St, Jasper, TX 75951
Tel.: (409) 384-4693
Web Site:
    http://www.allisonchevrolet.com
Rev.: $20,507,467
Emp.: 30
Automobiles, New & Used
N.A.I.C.S.: 441110
Robert Allison (Pres)

ALLISON CORPORATION
15 Okner Pkwy, Livingston, NJ 07039-1603
Tel.: (973) 992-3800
Web Site: http://www.allisoncorp.com
Auto Accessories, Seat Covers
N.A.I.C.S.: 313210

ALLISON JAMES ESTATES & HOMES INC.
309 Tamiami Trl, Punta Gorda, FL 33950
Tel.: (866) 463-5780
Web Site:
    http://www.allisonjamesinc.com
Sales Range: $1-4.9 Billion
Internet-Based Real Estate Brokers
N.A.I.C.S.: 531210
Matthew Crumbaugh (Pres & CEO)
Jessica Crumbaugh (VP & Dir-Natl Growth & Dev)
Jill Lemons (Mgr-Ops)

ALLISON REED GROUP, INC.
655 Waterman Ave, East Providence, RI 02914-1712
Tel.: (401) 438-0550   RI
Web Site: http://www.allisonreed.com
Year Founded: 1851
Sales Range: $10-24.9 Million
Emp.: 55
Jewelry Mfr
N.A.I.C.S.: 551112
Barry Cohen (Chm)
Lawrence Cohen (Pres)

Subsidiaries:

A&Z Hayward, Inc.   (1)
655 Waterman Ave, East Providence, RI 02914-1712
Tel.: (401) 438-0550
Web Site: http://www.azhayward.com
Jewelry Sales
N.A.I.C.S.: 339910

ALLIXO TECHNOLOGIES, LLC
1520 Parker Way, Mount Vernon, WA 98273
Tel.: (360) 848-0810
Web Site: http://www.allixo.com
Year Founded: 2009
Sales Range: $1-9.9 Million
Emp.: 21
Information Technology Services
N.A.I.C.S.: 541512
Jason Nelson (Co-Founder & CEO)
Scott Taylor (Co-Founder & COO)
Sam Riley (Co-Founder & CTO)
Dave Ellis (CFO)

ALLMEDIA, INC.
5601 Democracy Dr Ste 255, Plano, TX 75024

Tel.: (469) 467-9100   TX
Web Site: http://www.allmediainc.com
Year Founded: 1981
Sales Range: $1-9.9 Million
Emp.: 12
Direct Mail Advertising Services
N.A.I.C.S.: 541860
Laura McClendon (Pres)
Rick Becker (VP)
Mary Loeffler (VP)

ALLMETAL RECYCLING, LLC
800 E 21st St N, Wichita, KS 67214
Tel.: (316) 262-1475
Web Site:
    http://www.amrrecycles.com
Year Founded: 2009
Metal Recycling
N.A.I.C.S.: 331491
Justin Martin (Supvr-Non-Ferrous)

Subsidiaries:

Salina Iron & Metal Co.   (1)
312 N 5th St, Salina, KS 67401
Tel.: (785) 826-9838
Web Site: http://www.salinairon.com
Rev.: $4,000,000
Emp.: 19
Recyclable Material Merchant Whslr
N.A.I.C.S.: 423930
Robert Butts (Pres)

ALLMETAL SCREW PRODUCTS CORP.
94A E Jefryn Blvd, Deer Park, NY 11729
Tel.: (631) 243-5200
Web Site:
    http://www.allmetalcorp.com
Year Founded: 1929
Stainless Steel Fastener Distr
N.A.I.C.S.: 423710

ALLMETAL, INC.
1 Pierce Pl Ste 295W, Itasca, IL 60143
Tel.: (630) 250-8090
Web Site:
    https://www.allmetalinc.com
Sales Range: $10-24.9 Million
Emp.: 10
Metal Doors, Sash & Trim
N.A.I.C.S.: 332321
Philip W. Collin (Pres)
Corinne Wiegand (Dir-Pur)
Kevin Grenda (Mgr-IT)

ALLMODES TRANSPORT INC.
1 Cory Rd, Morristown, NJ 07960
Tel.: (973) 359-1144
Web Site: http://www.amslog.com
Sales Range: $1-9.9 Million
Emp.: 15
Freight Transportation Fulfillment
N.A.I.C.S.: 488510
Zadick Askinazi (Sr VP-Sls)
Carl Sambus (Sr VP-Ops)

ALLOSOURCE
6278 S Troy Cir, Centennial, CO 80111
Tel.: (720) 873-0213   IL
Web Site: https://www.allosource.org
Year Founded: 1994
Sales Range: $100-124.9 Million
Emp.: 491
Human Organ Transplantation Services
N.A.I.C.S.: 813212
Dean Elliott (Gen Counsel & VP-Corp Compliance)
Kerr Holbrook (Chief Comml Officer)
Thomas Cycyota (Pres & CEO)
Shelley Zelin (VP-HR)

Milo Metcalf *(VP-Ops)*
Peter Stevens *(VP-Strategy, Dev & Growth)*
Bob Lay *(COO)*

ALLOY & STAINLESS FAS-TENERS, INC.
11625 Charles Rd, Houston, TX 77041
Tel.: (713) 466-3031
Web Site: https://www.goasf.com
Sales Range: $10-24.9 Million,
Emp.: 150
Whslr of Industrial Fasteners
N.A.I.C.S.: 423840
David Robertson *(Controller)*
Debi McDonough *(Project Coord)*
Fernando Espino *(Mgr-Production)*
Randy Sims *(Mgr-Facility Mainte-nance)*
Surin Fernando *(Mgr-Ops)*
Krishna Chimbli *(Mgr-Quality Assur-ance & Engr-Matls)*
Chris Vitek *(Mgr-Sls)*
Garfield Edmonds III *(Pres)*

ALLOY CARBIDE COMPANY
7827 Ave H, Houston, TX 77012
Tel.: (713) 923-2700
Web Site:
   https://www.alloycarbide.com
Rev.: $10,000,000
Emp.: 52
Machine Shop, Jobbing & Repair
N.A.I.C.S.: 332710
Walter J. Mccain Jr. *(Pres & CEO)*

ALLOY ENGINEERING COM-PANY
844 Thacker St, Berea, OH 44017
Tel.: (440) 243-6800
Web Site:
   http://www.alloyengineering.com
Sales Range: $10-24.9 Million
Emp.: 70
Plate Work For The Metalworking Trade
N.A.I.C.S.: 332313
Louis D. Petonovich *(Pres & CEO)*
Donald Andrews *(Mgr-Bus Dev)*

ALLOY PRODUCTS CORP.
1045 Perkins Ave, Waukesha, WI 53187-0529
Tel.: (262) 542-6603   WI
Web Site:
   https://www.alloyproductscorp.com
Year Founded: 1929
Sales Range: $200-249.9 Million
Emp.: 150
Mfr of Food Products Machinery & Industrial Process Vessels
N.A.I.C.S.: 332313
Joseph E. Vick *(Pres)*
Ray Woo *(Dir-Engrg)*
Ron Kasprzak *(Mgr-Quality Assur-ance)*
Robert Rosenkranz *(CFO)*

ALLOY SOFTWARE, INC.
88 Park Ave Ste 2B, Nutley, NJ 07110
Tel.: (973) 661-9700
Web Site: http://www.alloy-software.com
Year Founded: 2002
Rev.: $2,400,000
Emp.: 9
Software Consultancy & Supply
N.A.I.C.S.: 513210
Fred Seltzer *(VP-Sls & Mktg)*
Vladimir Vinogradsky *(CEO)*

ALLOY, SILVERSTEIN, SHA-PIRO, ADAMS, MULFORD,

CICALESE, WILSON & COM-PANY
900 N Kings Highway, Cherry Hill, NJ 08034
Tel.: (856) 667-4100
Web Site:
   https://www.alloysilverstein.com
Year Founded: 1959
Sales Range: $10-24.9 Million
Emp.: 50
Accounting Services, Except Auditing
N.A.I.C.S.: 541219
Joseph F. Adams *(Partner)*
Bruce R. Mulford *(Partner)*
Harry W. Wilson *(Partner)*

ALLRED'S INC.
631 W Commerce Park Dr, Midvale, UT 84047
Tel.: (801) 561-8300
Web Site: https://www.allreds.net
Rev.: $16,014,352
Emp.: 48
Warm Air Heating Equipment & Sup-plies
N.A.I.C.S.: 423730
Laurie Allred *(CEO)*
Ralph Bird *(Officer-Accounts Payable)*
Walter Scott *(Officer-IT)*

ALLSALE ELECTRIC INC.
9240 Jordan Ave, Chatsworth, CA 91311
Tel.: (818) 715-0181
Web Site:
   http://www.allsaleelectric.com
Year Founded: 1985
Sales Range: $25-49.9 Million
Emp.: 45
Electrical Apparatus & Equipment
N.A.I.C.S.: 423610
Chuck Johnson *(CFO)*
Moses Gutierrez *(Mgr-Ops)*

ALLSOP, INC.
PO Box 23, Bellingham, WA 98227
Tel.: (360) 734-9090   WA
Web Site: https://www.allsop.com
Year Founded: 1964
Sales Range: $75-99.9 Million
Emp.: 100
Electronic Audio, Video & Computer Accessories; Office Care Products Mfr
N.A.I.C.S.: 334112
Tracie Cyr *(Controller)*
Karl Forsberg *(Mgr-IT)*
Johanna Zahner-Farrell *(Product Mgr)*

Subsidiaries:

Allsop Europe Limited   (1)
I D A Industrial Park, Waterford, Ireland
Tel.: (353) 51 355091
Emp.: 50
Computer Peripherals Mfr
N.A.I.C.S.: 334118
Ciaran Duffy *(Mgr-Sls & Mktg)*

Softride, Inc.   (1)
PO Box 9709, Bellingham, WA 98227
Tel.: (360) 647-7420
Web Site: http://www.softride.com
Sales Range: $1-9.9 Million
Bike Rack Mfr
N.A.I.C.S.: 336390

ALLSTAR BUILDING MATERI-ALS LTD.
1361 N Hwy US 1, Ormond Beach, FL 32174
Tel.: (386) 677-6330
Web Site:
   https://www.allstarbuilding.com
Sales Range: $25-49.9 Million
Emp.: 15
Lumber & Other Building Materials Distr & Retailer
N.A.I.C.S.: 423310

ALLSTAR FINANCIAL GROUP INC.
365 Northridge Rd Ste 400, Atlanta, GA 30350-6101
Tel.: (404) 522-3898
Web Site:
   http://www.allstarfinancialgroup.com
Emp.: 300
Security Guards & Patrol Services
N.A.I.C.S.: 561612
Andrew Heaner *(Founder, Chm & CEO)*
David Brett *(Pres)*
Tommy Duffy *(COO & Exec VP)*
Jack Glass *(Dir-Bus Dev)*

Subsidiaries:

Renova Partners, LLC   (1)
365 Northridge Rd Ste 400, Atlanta, GA 30350
Tel.: (800) 424-0132
Web Site: http://www.renovapartners.net
Financial Advisory & Investment Banking Services
N.A.I.C.S.: 522299
Tommy Duffy *(Founder)*
Russ Richards *(Mng Dir-Investment Bank-ing)*

ALLSTAR MAGNETICS INC.
6205 NE 63rd St, Vancouver, WA 98661
Tel.: (360) 693-0213
Web Site:
   http://www.allstarmagnetics.com
Rev.: $13,200,000
Emp.: 50
Sales of Electronic Parts
N.A.I.C.S.: 423690
Cathy Boyer *(Co-Pres)*

ALLSTAR PRODUCTS GROUP LLC
2 Skyline Dr, Hawthorne, NY 10532
Tel.: (914) 347-7827
Web Site: https://www.allstarmg.com
Sales Range: $500-549.9 Million
Emp.: 60
Household Products Sales
N.A.I.C.S.: 424990
Terri Schuka-Gentile *(Dir-Bus Ops)*
Teresa Sinapi *(Mgr)*
Scott Boilen *(Pres)*

ALLSTATE CONSTRUCTION INC.
5718 Tower Rd, Tallahassee, FL 32303
Tel.: (850) 514-1004
Web Site:
   http://www.allstateconstruction.com
Year Founded: 1986
Sales Range: $10-24.9 Million
Emp.: 60
Commercial & Office Building, New Construction
N.A.I.C.S.: 236220
Bill E. Weldon *(Pres)*
Mary Suber *(Office Mgr)*
Brian Orr *(Engr-Pre-Construction)*

ALLSTATE FLORAL & CRAFT, INC.
14038 Pkwy Pl, Cerritos, CA 90703-2439
Tel.: (562) 926-2302
Web Site:
   http://www.allstatefloral.com
Year Founded: 1979
Sales Range: $25-49.9 Million
Emp.: 200
Suppliers of Flowers & Florists Sup-plies
N.A.I.C.S.: 424930
Jack Wang *(Pres & Treas)*
Pam Chao *(Mgr-HR)*
Shu-Ming Chow *(Engr-Software)*

ALLSTATE G.E.S. APPLIANCE, INC.
15250 N Hayden Rd, Scottsdale, AZ 85260
Tel.: (602) 252-6507   AZ
Web Site:
   http://www.allstateappliances.com
Year Founded: 1970
Sales Range: $10-24.9 Million
Emp.: 20
Electrical Appliances
N.A.I.C.S.: 423620
Ernold R. Goodwin *(Owner & Pres)*
Ron Goodwin *(Mgr-Sls & Mktg)*

ALLSTATE IMAGING INC.
21621 Nordhoff St, Chatsworth, CA 91311
Tel.: (818) 678-4550
Rev.: $19,000,000
Emp.: 40
Office Equipment
N.A.I.C.S.: 423420

ALLSTATE MORTGAGE CORP.
1090 Broadway, West Long Branch, NJ 07764
Tel.: (732) 222-3600
Sales Range: $100-124.9 Million
Emp.: 30
Mortgage Bankers & Loan Services
N.A.I.C.S.: 522310
Don Barkkume *(Pres)*

ALLSTATE STEEL COMPANY INC.
130 S Jackson Ave, Jacksonville, FL 32220
Tel.: (904) 781-6040
Web Site:
   https://www.allstatesteel.com
Year Founded: 1963
Rev.: $10,000,000
Emp.: 60
Structural Steel Erection
N.A.I.C.S.: 238120
Sharon Suggs *(Pres)*

ALLSTATE SUGAR BOWL
1500 Sugar Bowl Dr, New Orleans, LA 70112
Tel.: (504) 828-2440   LA
Web Site:
   https://www.allstatesugarbowl.org
Year Founded: 1935
Sales Range: $25-49.9 Million
Emp.: 15
Sport Event Organizer
N.A.I.C.S.: 711310
Jeff Hundley *(COO)*
Stacey Castillo *(Dir-Ticket Ops)*
John Sudsbury *(Dir-Comm)*
Tim Shay *(Controller)*

ALLSTATES WORLDCARGO, INC.
1 Telican Dr, Bayville, NJ 08721
Tel.: (732) 831-6868   NJ
Web Site: https://www.allstates-worldcargo.com
Year Founded: 1961
Sales Range: $50-74.9 Million
Emp.: 85
Freight Forwarding
N.A.I.C.S.: 488510
Craig D. Stratton *(CFO)*
Sam Digirolamo *(Pres & CEO)*
Barton C. Theile *(COO & Exec VP)*

Subsidiaries:

Ground Freight Expeditors, LLC   (1)
8800 NE Underground Dr Stop 206, Kan-sas City, MO 64161-9746
Tel.: (502) 380-4015
Web Site: http://www.shipgfe.com
Scheduled Freight Air Transportation
N.A.I.C.S.: 481112

Allstates WorldCargo, Inc.—(Continued)

John Swendrowski (Mgr-Ops)

ALLSUP ENTERPRISES INC.
2112 Thornton St, Clovis, NM 88101
Tel.: (505) 769-2311
Sales Range: $125-149.9 Million
Emp.: 1,500
Convenience Store
N.A.I.C.S.: 445131
Lonnie Allsup (Pres)
Rogene Chaddick (Controller)
Cameron Williams (Fin Mgr)
Lisa Rodder (Office Mgr)

Subsidiaries:

Allsup Petroleum Inc.   (1)
2112 Thornton St, Clovis, NM 88101
Tel.: (575) 769-2311
Web Site: http://www.allsup.com
Rev.: $1,200,000
Emp.: 75
Petroleum Bulk Stations
N.A.I.C.S.: 424710
Lonnie Allsup (Pres)

El Cid Land & Cattle Inc.   (1)
2112 Thornton St, Clovis, NM 88101
Tel.: (575) 769-2311
Rev.: $420,000
Emp.: 11
Farm Land Leasing
N.A.I.C.S.: 531190

Zia Broadcasting Company   (1)
710 CR K, Clovis, NM 88101
Tel.: (575) 763-4401
Sales Range: Less than $1 Million
Emp.: 10
Radio Broadcasting Stations
N.A.I.C.S.: 516110

ALLTECH ENGINEERING CORP.
2515 Pilot Knob Rd, Mendota Heights, MN 55120-1135
Tel.: (651) 452-7893
Web Site:
  https://www.alltechengineering.com
Sales Range: $10-24.9 Million
Emp.: 100
Building Equipment Installation Services
N.A.I.C.S.: 238290
Kevin Points (Project Mgr)
Ryan Will (Project Mgr)
Rich Tschida (Project Mgr)

ALLTECH, INC.
3031 Catnip Hill Rd, Nicholasville, KY 40356-8700
Tel.: (859) 885-9613   **KY**
Web Site: https://www.alltech.com
Year Founded: 1980
Sales Range: $1-4.9 Billion
Emp.: 4,700
Supplier of Prepared Feeds
N.A.I.C.S.: 311119
Thomas Pearse Lyons (Co-Founder)
Patrick Charlton (VP)
Marc Larousse (VP-Business Development)
Mark Hulsebus (Dir-Sls & Portfolio-Pig Bus)
Andy Rash (Gen Mgr-Pig Bus)
Deirdre Lyons (Co-Founder & Dir-Corp Image & Design)
Mark Lyons (Pres & CEO)
Orla McAleer (CMO)
E. Michael Castle II (CEO & Exec VP)

Subsidiaries:

Masterfeeds Inc.   (1)
1020 Hargrieve Road, London, N6E 1P5, ON, Canada
Tel.: (519) 685-4300
Web Site: http://www.masterfeeds.com
Emp.: 300
Animal Feed Mfr

N.A.I.C.S.: 311119

Ridley USA Inc.   (1)
111 W Cherry St Ste 500, Mankato, MN 56001
Tel.: (507) 388-9400
Web Site: http://www.hubbardfeeds.com
Holding Company; Animal Feed Mfr & Distr
N.A.I.C.S.: 551112
Earl Witham (Mgr-Sls)
Lori Stevermer (Mgr-Swine Products)
Mark Robbins (Mgr-Res & Nutrition Svcs)

Subsidiary (Domestic):

Lakeland Animal Nutrition, Inc.   (2)
2801 S Combee Rd, Lakeland, FL 33803
Prepared Animal Feed Mfr & Whslr
N.A.I.C.S.: 311119

Ridley Block Operations, Inc.   (2)
111 W Cherry St Ste 500, Mankato, MN 56001
Tel.: (800) 869-7219
Web Site: https://www.alltech.com
Farm Animal Supplements Mfr & Distr
N.A.I.C.S.: 311119

ALLTERRA CENTRAL, INC.
116 E Huntland Dr, Austin, TX 78752
Tel.: (512) 487-7083
Web Site:
  http://www.allterracentral.com
Commercial Air, Rail & Water Transportation Equipment Rental & Leasing
N.A.I.C.S.: 532411
Martin Richardson (VP)

ALLTRADE TOOL LLC
6122 Katella Ave, Cypress, CA 90630
Tel.: (310) 522-9008
Web Site:
  https://www.alltradetools.com
Sales Range: $10-24.9 Million
Emp.: 77
Hand Tools
N.A.I.C.S.: 423710
Andy Livian (Pres)

ALLTRUST INSURANCE INC.
2965 Alt 19, Palm Harbor, FL 34683
Tel.: (727) 772-4200
Web Site:
  https://www.alltrustinsurance.com
Year Founded: 1994
Sales Range: $1-9.9 Million
Emp.: 35
Insurance Agents
N.A.I.C.S.: 524210
Joe Part (Founder & Mng Partner)
Sandy Harrington (Mgr-Client Advocacy)
Sozon Vatikiotis (Exec VP-Employee Benefits)
Adam Hertz (Exec VP)
Steve Hall (Pres)
Tim Love (CEO)
Jeremy Hertz (VP-Compliance)
Beau Morris (Dir-Worksite Solutions)
Brad Zenz (Dir-Mktg)
Austin Brooks (Dir-Pricing & Analytics)
Dan Posada (VP-HR Consulting & Trng)

ALLURE HOME CREATIONS INC.
85 Fulton St Unit 8, Boonton, NJ 07005
Tel.: (973) 402-8888
Web Site: http://www.allurehome.com
Rev.: $55,513,177
Emp.: 89
Sales of Home Furnishings & Bathroom Accessories
N.A.I.C.S.: 423220
Stanley Ho (Pres)
Edward Ho (Dir-Mktg)
Gabrielle Colquitt (VP-Design & Mktg)

ALLURED PUBLISHING CORPORATION
336 Gundersen Dr Ste A, Carol Stream, IL 60188
Tel.: (630) 653-2155
Web Site: http://www.allured.com
Sales Range: $1-9.9 Million
Emp.: 50
Periodical Publishers
N.A.I.C.S.: 513120
Janet Ludwig (Pres)
Bryan Crowe (Mgr-Production)
Marie Kuta (Acct Exec)

Subsidiaries:

Creative Age Publications, Inc.   (1)
7628 Densmore Ave, Van Nuys, CA 91406
Tel.: (818) 782-7328
Web Site: http://www.creativeage.com
Periodical Publishers
N.A.I.C.S.: 513120
Deborah Carver (Pres & CEO)
Barbara Shepherd (Dir-Circulation)
Diane Jones (Dir-Adv)
Jerry Lovell (Dir-Adv)
Lisa Fisco (Dir-Adv)
Mindy Rosiejka (COO & VP)
Nazli Santana (Dir-Adv)
Sheryl Lenzkes (Mng Editor)

ALLURESOFT, INC.
117 W 20th St Ste 202, Kansas City, MO 64108
Web Site: https://www.divvyhq.com
Sales Range: $1-9.9 Million
Emp.: 10
Content Marketing & Editorial Calendar Application
N.A.I.C.S.: 513210
Brody Dorland (Co-Founder)
Brock Stechman (Co-Founder)

ALLVUE SYSTEMS HOLDINGS, INC.
396 Alhambra Cir 11th Fl, Coral Gables, FL 33134
Tel.: (305) 901-7060   **DE**
Year Founded: 2021
Emp.: 600
Holding Company
N.A.I.C.S.: 551112
Deborah Mason (Chief Legal Officer)
Paul Wasinger (CFO)
Ryan Keough (Chief Revenue Officer)
Brandon Meeks (Chief Technical Officer)
Nadeem Syed (Chm)
Andrew Skehel (COO)
Sha Farley (Chief HR Officer)
Susan Wohleking (CMO)

ALLWIRE INC.
PO Box 1000, Chowchilla, CA 93610
Tel.: (559) 665-4893
Web Site: http://www.allwire.com
Rev.: $16,365,918
Emp.: 200
Manufacture Plastics Pipe & Custom Wires
N.A.I.C.S.: 326122
Alan R. Hopkins (Pres)

ALLWORLD PROJECT MANAGEMENT, LLC
60 N BB King Blvd, Memphis, TN 38103
Tel.: (901) 881-2985
Web Site: http://www.allworldpm.com
Year Founded: 2010
Sales Range: $1-9.9 Million
Emp.: 47
Business Management Consulting Services
N.A.I.C.S.: 541611
Brent Hooks (Chief Admin Officer)
Ron Hooks (Mgr-Field Svcs)

A. J. Robinson (Mgr-GIS & Info)
April Simmons (Coord-Project Mgmt)
Michael Hooks Jr. (Owner & CEO)

ALLY AUTO ASSETS LLC
500 Woodward Ave, Detroit, MI 48226   **DE**
Investment Services
N.A.I.C.S.: 523999
Ryan C. Farris (Pres)

ALLY LOGISTICS LLC
1090 36th St SE Ste 628, Grand Rapids, MI 49508   **MA**
Web Site:
  http://www.allylogistics.com
Year Founded: 2012
Sales Range: $25-49.9 Million
Emp.: 37
Freight Transportation Services
N.A.I.C.S.: 488510
Dan Manshaem (Founder & CEO)

ALLY WASTE SERVICES, LLC
2509 S. Power Rd. Ste 101, Mesa, AZ 85209
Tel.: (877) 689-2559
Web Site: https://allywaste.com
Waste Recycling Services
N.A.I.C.S.: 423930

Subsidiaries:

Waste Consolidators, Inc.   (1)
5869 S Kyrene Rd Ste 1, Tempe, AZ 85283   (51%)
Tel.: (480) 897-3601
Web Site:
  https://www.wasteconsolidators.com
Building Maintenance Services
N.A.I.C.S.: 561720
Jose Mercado (Ops Mgr)

ALLY WHOLESALE ENTERPRISES LLC
500 Woodward Ave, Detroit, MI 48226   **DE**
Investment Services
N.A.I.C.S.: 523999
Ryan C. Farris (Pres)

ALLYIS, INC.
10210 NE Points Dr Ste 200, Kirkland, WA 98033
Tel.: (425) 691-3000   **WA**
Web Site: https://www.allyis.com
Year Founded: 1996
Sales Range: $10-24.9 Million
Emp.: 212
System Integration & IT Consulting
N.A.I.C.S.: 541511
Rochelle Hill (Mgr-HR)

ALMA AGENCY
2601 S Bayshore Dr Fl 4, Coconut Grove, FL 33133
Tel.: (305) 428-0094   **FL**
Web Site: https://www.almaad.com
Year Founded: 1994
Sales Range: $100-124.9 Million
Emp.: 80
Advetising Agency
N.A.I.C.S.: 541810
Luis Miguel Messianu (CEO & Chm-Creative)
Angela Battistini (VP-Acct Svcs)
Leo Peet (VP-Fin)
Marta Insua (VP-Strategic Insights)
Michael Sotelo (VP-Digital)
Beatriz Del Amo (VP & Grp Acct Dir)
Alvar Sunol (Co-Pres & Chief Creative Officer)
Adrian Castagna (Dir-Production)
Genevieve Jenkins (VP-Digital)
Louis Mefsianu (Pres & COO)

ALMA TRACTOR & EQUIPMENT INC.
35 Hwy 71 N, Alma, AR 72921
Tel.: (479) 632-6300
Web Site: http://www.almatractor.com
Sales Range: $10-24.9 Million
Emp.: 35
Sells Tractors, Agricultural
N.A.I.C.S.: 423820
Jack Alexander (Owner)
Jim Barker (Pres & Gen Mgr)
Elizabeth Gunsolus (Office Mgr)

ALMACENES PITUSA INC.
PO Box 190839, San Juan, PR 00919
Tel.: (787) 641-8200
Rev.: $247,856,309
Emp.: 150
Department Stores
N.A.I.C.S.: 455110
Israel Kopel (Pres)

ALMAN ELECTRIC
7677 Hunnicut Rd, Dallas, TX 75228
Tel.: (214) 388-1800
Web Site:
  https://www.almanelec.com
Year Founded: 1979
Sales Range: $10-24.9 Million
Emp.: 140
Electrical Wiring Services
N.A.I.C.S.: 238210
Robert G. Guzman (Pres)
Linda Diane Nalon (Office Mgr)

ALMAN ELECTRIC INC.
7677 Hunnicut Rd, Dallas, TX 75228
Tel.: (214) 388-1800
Web Site: http://www.almanelec.com
Year Founded: 1979
Sales Range: $10-24.9 Million
Emp.: 140
General Electrical Contractor
N.A.I.C.S.: 238210
Steve Guzman (VP & Project Mgr)
Stephen P. Blackburn (Project Mgr)

ALMAR ASSOCIATES INC.
2393 S Congress Ave, West Palm Beach, FL 33406
Tel.: (561) 439-3253
Web Site: http://www.almarcoast.com
Sales Range: $10-24.9 Million
Emp.: 4
Industrial Machinery & Equipment Merchant Whslr
N.A.I.C.S.: 423830
Brian Strunck (Pres)

ALMAR SALES CO. INC.
320 5th Ave 3rd Fl, New York, NY 10001
Tel.: (212) 594-6920
Web Site: http://www.almarsales.com
Rev.: $25,333,374
Emp.: 50
Provider of Women's & Children's Accessories
N.A.I.C.S.: 424350
Jackie Ashkenazie (Exec VP)
Saul Hassoun (VP-Production & Sourcing)
Ahillia Ramraj (Mgr-Logistics)
Barbara McCahill (VP-Mdse-Fashion Accessories)
Ginny So (Mgr-Production)
Ken Levine (CFO)
Jeffrey Chafetz (VP & Dir-Ops)
Corey Lynch (VP-ECommerce)
Vanessa Vizcarra (VP-Mdsg-Girl's Role-Play-Novelty)

ALMEIDA & CARLSON INSURANCE AGENCY
92 Tupper Rd, Sandwich, MA 02563

Tel.: (508) 888-0207
Web Site:
  https://www.almeidacarlson.com
Rev.: $10,000,000
Emp.: 18
Insurance Agents
N.A.I.C.S.: 524210
Noel J. Almeida (Pres)

ALMON, INC.
W223 N797 Saratoga Dr, Waukesha, WI 53186-0404
Tel.: (262) 548-1360
Web Site: https://www.almoninc.com
Sales Range: $25-49.9 Million
Emp.: 175
Publisher
N.A.I.C.S.: 513199
Aaron Montoure (VP-HR)
Jim Ferguson (Gen Mgr)

ALMOST NEVER FILMS INC.
8605 Santa Monica Blvd No 98258, West Hollywood, CA 90069-4109
Tel.: (213) 296-3005   NV
Web Site:
  https://almostneverfilms.com
Year Founded: 2007
HLWD—(OTCBB)
Assets: $223,978
Liabilities: $521,000
Net Worth: ($297,022)
Earnings: ($128,149)
Fiscal Year-end: 06/30/21
Film Production
N.A.I.C.S.: 512110
Danny Chan (CEO & CFO)
Daniel Roth (COO & Chief Creative Officer)

ALMSTED ENTERPRISES INC.
2326 Louisiana Ave S, Minneapolis, MN 55426
Tel.: (952) 541-5343
Sales Range: $10-24.9 Million
Emp.: 40
Independent Supermarket
N.A.I.C.S.: 445110
James Almsted (Pres)

ALNC, INC.
2152 W FM 2105, San Angelo, TX 76902
Tel.: (325) 658-3612
Web Site: http://www.alncsteel.com
Year Founded: 2003
Sales Range: $10-24.9 Million
Emp.: 68
Fabricated Structural Metal Mfr
N.A.I.C.S.: 332312
Britney Hart (Gen Mgr)

ALO SOLUTIONS, LLC
705 University Dr Bldg 700, Durham, NC 27707-3489
Tel.: (919) 237-1337
Web Site:
  https://www.alosolutions.com
Emp.: 100
Hospitals & Health Care Services
N.A.I.C.S.: 621610
Matt Eirich (Pres & CEO)

Subsidiaries:

Davidson Family Medicine, P.A.   (1)
104 Knox Ct Ste 100, Davidson, NC 28036
Tel.: (704) 892-5454
Web Site:
  http://www.davidsonfamilymedicine.com
Offices of Physicians (except Mental Health Specialists)
N.A.I.C.S.: 621111
Craig White (Founder)

ALOETTE COSMETICS, INC.
3715 Northside Pkwy NW Bldg 200 Ste 200, Atlanta, GA 30327

Tel.: (678) 444-2563   PA
Web Site: http://www.aloette.com
Year Founded: 1978
Sales Range: $25-49.9 Million
Emp.: 180
Skin Care Products & Cosmetics Mfr & Whslr
N.A.I.C.S.: 424210
Shellie Sullivan (VP-Bus Dev & Field Innovation)
Cathy McKenna (Pres)

Subsidiaries:

Aloette Cosmetics of Canada   (1)
3455 Harvester Rd Unit 36, Burlington, L7N 3P2, ON, Canada   (100%)
Tel.: (905) 336-6590
Web Site: http://www.aloette.com
Sales Range: $25-49.9 Million
Emp.: 3
Sales of Skin Care & Cosmetic Products
N.A.I.C.S.: 456120

ALOFT GROUP, INC.
26 Parker St, Newburyport, MA 01950
Tel.: (978) 462-0002
Web Site: http://www.aloftgroup.com
Year Founded: 1996
Rev.: $13,800,000
Emp.: 15
Advetising Agency
N.A.I.C.S.: 541810
Matt Bowen (Pres & CEO)
Tracy Hartman (Dir-PR)
Mark Willingham (Partner & Chief Strategist)
David Willingham (Partner, Dir & Chief Strategist)
Chris Maynard (Dir-Fin & Talent)
Jenny Coyle (Office Mgr)
Rudy Karty (Coord-Production)
Valerie Hart (Sr Dir-Art)
Dustin Pons (Dir-Mktg-Bus Dev)

ALOHA AUTO GROUP, LTD.
2841 N Nimitz Hwy, Honolulu, HI 96819-1902
Tel.: (808) 833-9000
Web Site: https://www.alohakia.com
Year Founded: 1997
Sales Range: $25-49.9 Million
Emp.: 110
New Car Retailer
N.A.I.C.S.: 441110
Russ Wong (CFO)
Tim Rasic (COO)
William van den Hurk (Pres)
Monique van den Hurk (Exec VP)
Cindy Standeser (Office Mgr-Bus)

ALOHA FREIGHT FORWARDERS, INC.
1800 S Anderson Ave, Compton, CA 90220
Tel.: (310) 631-6116
Web Site:
  https://www.alohafreight.com
Sales Range: $10-24.9 Million
Emp.: 18
Freight Forwarding Services & Logistics
N.A.I.C.S.: 488510
Glenn Griley (Pres)

ALOHA RESTAURANTS, INC.
204 Main St 960, Newport Beach, CA 92661
Tel.: (949) 250-0331
Web Site:
  http://www.aloharestaurants.com
Rev.: $18,761,714
Emp.: 200
Eating Place
N.A.I.C.S.: 722511
Steven G. Moyer (Pres)

ALOHACARE
1357 Kapiolani Blvd Ste 1250, Honolulu, HI 96814
Tel.: (808) 973-0712   HI
Web Site: http://www.alohacare.org
Year Founded: 1994
Sales Range: $200-249.9 Million
Emp.: 213
Community Health Care Services
N.A.I.C.S.: 621498
Richard Taaffe (Treas)
Emmanuel Kintu (Pres)
Mary Oneha (Sec)

ALOI MATERIALS HANDLING INC
140 Commerce Dr, Rochester, NY 14623
Tel.: (585) 292-0920
Web Site: http://www.aloi.com
Sales Range: $10-24.9 Million
Emp.: 28
Materials Handling Machinery
N.A.I.C.S.: 423830
Jeff Gambrill (Pres)
Trish Heceen (Controller)
John McJury (Engr-Sls)

ALOPEXX, INC.
186 Alewife Brook Pkwy Ste 1068, Cambridge, MA 02138
Tel.: (617) 780-1598   DE
Web Site: https://www.alopexx.com
Year Founded: 2021
Assets: $148,816
Liabilities: $891,243
Net Worth: ($742,427)
Earnings: ($956,954)
Fiscal Year-end: 12/31/21
Biotechnology Research & Development Services
N.A.I.C.S.: 541714
Daniel R. Vlock (Pres, CEO & Co-Founder)
Thomas T. Thomas (CFO)
Gerald B. Pier (Co-Founder & Chief Scientific Officer)
Christine de los Reyes (Chief Bus & Commercialization Officer)

ALORICA INC.
5 Park Plz Ste 1100, Irvine, CA 92614
Tel.: (909) 606-3600
Web Site: http://www.alorica.com
Year Founded: 1999
Sales Range: $50-74.9 Million
Emp.: 24,000
Customer Service Management Solutions
N.A.I.C.S.: 561499
Andy Lee (CEO)
Art DiBari (Exec VP)
James Molloy (CFO)
Colleen Beers (Pres-North America & Europe)
Jeffrey Aldaz (Sr VP-Global Svcs)
Cindy Fiorillo (Co-CFO)
Miro Batista (Pres-Latin America)
Rainerio Bong Borja (Pres-Asia)
Tania King (Chief Legal Officer & Chief Compliance Officer)
Jay King (Pres-Fin Solutions)
Gregory A. Haller (COO)
Bhaskar Bhaskar (Chief Transformation Officer)
K. J. Tjon (CFO)
Shawn Stacy (Chief Client Officer)
Mike Clifton (CIO & Exec VP)

ALOYSIUS, BUTLER & CLARK ASSOCIATES, INC.
819 N Washington St, Wilmington, DE 19801-1509
Tel.: (302) 655-1552   DE

Aloysius, Butler & Clark Associates, Inc.—(Continued)

Web Site:
https://www.abccreative.com
Year Founded: 1971
Sales Range: $25-49.9 Million
Advertising & Public Relation Agency
Services
N.A.I.C.S.: 541810
John Clark Hawkins (Founder)
Tom McGivney (CEO-Wilmington)
Paul Pomeroy (Pres)
Scott Bille (Dir-Interactive)
Mike Cordrey (Acct Supvr)
Lynda Rudolph (Dir-Brand Strategy)
Linda H. Shopa (Mng Partner & CFO)
Lee Ann Qualls (Media Dir)
Alex Parkowski (Acct Supvr)
Tony Ross (Dir-Creative Svcs)
Maria Stearns (Dir-Healthcare Team)
Linda Miniscalco (Sr Supvr-Media)
Chris Marts (Dir-IT)
Alice Clark (Mgr-Accts Payable)
Ted Arnold (Sr Strategist)
Cheryl Bailey (Office Mgr)
Michael English (Dir-Motion Graphics & Animation)
Suzanne Fields (Mgr-Traffic)
John Orr (Dir-PR)
David Brond (VP & Dir-Acct Svcs)
Jason Cockerham (Designer-User Experience)
Steve Merino (Chief Creative Officer & Mng Partner)
Shawn Kessler (Mng Dir-Recruitment)
John Sammons III (Supvr-Media)

Subsidiaries:

Caspari McCormick   (1)
4 S Poplar St, Wilmington, DE 19801
Tel.: (302) 421-9080
Web Site: http://www.casparimccormick.com
Rev.: $10,000,000
Emp.: 10
Advetising Agency
N.A.I.C.S.: 541810

Central Focus, Inc.   (1)
819 N Washington St, Wilmington, DE
19801
Tel.: (302) 655-3665
Web Site: http://www.abcfocus.com
Emp.: 38
Marketing Research Service
N.A.I.C.S.: 541910
John Clark Hawkins (Pres & CEO)

ab+c Philadelphia LLC   (1)
125 S 9th St Ste 801, Philadelphia, PA
19107
Tel.: (215) 923-9600
Web Site: http://www.a-b-c.com
Rev.: $60,860,000
Emp.: 65
Advertising & Public Relations Agency
N.A.I.C.S.: 541810
David Lewandowski (Supvr-Acct-PR)
Bob Palangio (Supvr-Acct-PR)
Gabrielle Shirdan (Assoc Dir-Creative)
Steve Rosen (Mng Dir-PR)

ALP ASSOCIATES
12400 Wilshire Blvd Ste 1450, Los
Angeles, CA 90025
Tel.: (310) 826-3174
Web Site: http://www.crgpm.com
Year Founded: 1971
Sales Range: $25-49.9 Million
Emp.: 20
Investors of Real Estate, Except
Property Operators
N.A.I.C.S.: 523999
Arnold L. Porath (CEO)
Steve Levinson (Pres)

ALP INDUSTRIES, INC.
1229 W Lincoln Hwy, Coatesville, PA
19320-1858
Tel.: (610) 384-1300   PA
Web Site: http://www.alpind.com

Year Founded: 1981
Sales Range: $25-49.9 Million
Emp.: 170
Fabricated Wire Rope Slings, Chain
Slings, Metal Slings, Polyester Round
Slings & Synthetic Slings Mfr
N.A.I.C.S.: 423510
Reitzel Swaim (Pres)

Subsidiaries:

ALP Leasing Corporation   (1)
512 N Market St Ste 100, Lancaster, PA
17603
Tel.: (610) 384-1300
Web Site: http://www.alpind.com
Rev.: $220,000
Emp.: 16
Provider of Heavy Construction Equipment
Rental Services
N.A.I.C.S.: 532412
Shawn Ober (Pres)

ALP Management Corp.   (1)
1229 W Lincoln Hwy, Coatesville, PA
19320-1858
Tel.: (610) 384-1300
Web Site: http://www.alpind.com
Rev.: $880,000
Emp.: 12
Provider of Management Services
N.A.I.C.S.: 541611

American Lifting Products Inc.   (1)
1227 W Lincoln Hwy, Coatesville, PA
19320-1858
Tel.: (610) 384-1800
Web Site: http://www.alpind.com
Rev.: $4,000,000
Emp.: 26
Provider of Metals Services
N.A.I.C.S.: 423510
Ron Space (Dir-Branch Ops)

Carolina Chain & Cable Co, Inc.   (1)
2630 Yonkers Rd Ste 106, Raleigh, NC
27604-1546
Tel.: (919) 831-2333
Web Site: http://www.alpind.com
Rev.: $500,000
Emp.: 7
Supplier of Hardware
N.A.I.C.S.: 423710
Don Hamilton (Gen Mgr)

Cobb Wire Rope & Sling Company
Inc.   (1)
5580 Fulton Industrial Blvd, Atlanta, GA
30336
Tel.: (404) 494-9994
Web Site: http://www.alpind.com
Rev.: $2,700,000
Emp.: 5
Provider of Rigging Services
N.A.I.C.S.: 332618
Ed Hamilton (CEO)

Florida Rope & Supply, Inc.   (1)
13031 Ponce DeLeon Blvd, Brooksville, FL
34601
Tel.: (352) 796-8632
Industrial Supplies Whslr
N.A.I.C.S.: 423840

Harding Company Inc.   (1)
6 Industrial Park Dr, Exeter, NH
03833-4557   (100%)
Tel.: (603) 778-7070
Web Site: http://www.alpindustries.com
Sales Range: $10-24.9 Million
Emp.: 6
Provider of Metals Services
N.A.I.C.S.: 423510

Northwest Wire Rope & Sling
Company   (1)
1952 Milwaukee Way, Tacoma, WA 98421
Tel.: (253) 572-8981
Emp.: 8
Industrial Supplies Whslr
N.A.I.C.S.: 423840
Rockney Nigretto (Gen Mgr)

Pennsylvania Sling Co. Inc.   (1)
421 Amity Rd, Harrisburg, PA 17111
Tel.: (717) 657-7700
Web Site: http://www.alpind.com
Sales Range: $10-24.9 Million
Emp.: 6
Provider of Metals Services

N.A.I.C.S.: 423510
Jason Wiggins (Branch Mgr)

Wayland Inc.   (1)
4535 11th St, Long Island City, NY 11101-
5205
Tel.: (718) 472-2722
Web Site: http://www.alpind.com
Sales Range: $10-24.9 Million
Emp.: 10
Provider of Elevator Wire Rope Distribution
Services
N.A.I.C.S.: 423510
Michael Sheldon (Branch Mgr)

**ALP LIGHTING & CEILING
PRODUCTS, INC.**
6333 W Gross Point Rd, Niles, IL
60714-3915
Tel.: (773) 774-9550   IL
Web Site: http://www.alplighting.com
Year Founded: 1972
Sales Range: $75-99.9 Million
Emp.: 1,000
Lighting Components Mfr & Distr
N.A.I.C.S.: 335132
William Brown (Founder & Chm)
Steve Brown (CEO)
Jim Grady (CFO)
David Brown (COO)
Tom Barnes (VP & Bus Mgr-ALP Lex-
aLite Brand)
Jeff Benton (Pres)
Steve Dix (VP-Customer Fulfillment)
Patti Maenza (Dir-HR)
Alan Dorsky (VP & Bus Mgr)
Sal Casas (VP & Mgr-Bus, Plastics &
Metals)

ALP LIQUIDATING TRUST
900 N Michigan Ave, Chicago, IL
60611
Tel.: (312) 915-1987   DE
Year Founded: 2005
Sales Range: Less than $1 Million
Financial Management Consulting
Services
N.A.I.C.S.: 541611
Gary Nickele (Pres)
Gailen J. Hull (CFO & VP)

**ALPAC MARKETING SER-
VICES INC.**
4900 Woodway 760, Houston, TX
77056
Tel.: (713) 623-0977
Web Site: http://www.alpac-mkt.com
Year Founded: 1990
Sales Range: $10-24.9 Million
Emp.: 3
Provider of Chemical Products
N.A.I.C.S.: 424690
Lawrence Dinkelman (Pres)

ALPACA AUDIOLOGY
1525 E Republic Rd Ste B-135,
Springfield, MO 65804
Tel.: (888) 557-9203
Web Site:
http://www.alpacaaudiology.com
Hearing Health Brands & Community-
based Clinics
N.A.I.C.S.: 621340
Brian Vesely (Pres)

Subsidiaries:

Abingdon Hearing Care   (1)
612 Campus Dr, Abingdon, VA 24210-9699
Tel.: (276) 676-0001
Web Site: http://www.abingdonhearing.com
Offices of Physical, Occupational & Speech
Therapists & Audiologists
N.A.I.C.S.: 621340
Mary Hinchey (Mgr)

Main Line Audiology Consultants,
PC   (1)
916 Montgomery Ave, Penn Valley, PA
19072

Tel.: (610) 667-3277
Web Site: http://www.mainlineaudiology.com
Process, Physical Distribution & Logistics
Consulting Services
N.A.I.C.S.: 541614
Anne Eidschun (Pres)

ALPARK PETROLEUM, INC.
275 12th St, Elko, NV 89801
Tel.: (775) 738-3835   NV
Web Site:
http://www.alparkpetroleum.com
Year Founded: 1964
Sales Range: $10-24.9 Million
Emp.: 30
Lubricants & Fuels Distr
N.A.I.C.S.: 424720
Park R. Blair (Founder & Owner)
Galen Schorsch (Pres & Ops Mgr)

ALPENA POWER COMPANY
401 N 9th Ave, Alpena, MI 49707
Tel.: (989) 358-4900
Web Site:
https://www.alpenapower.com
Sales Range: $200-249.9 Million
Emp.: 37
Generation, Electric Power
N.A.I.C.S.: 532112
Stephen H. Fletcher (Chm & CEO)

ALPENA SUPERMARKET INC.
2205 US 23 Ste 144, Alpena, MI
49707
Tel.: (989) 356-4720
Web Site:
http://www.neimansfamilymarket.com
Sales Range: $10-24.9 Million
Emp.: 140
Independent Supermarket
N.A.I.C.S.: 445110
Hal Neiman (Owner & Pres)

ALPHA ASSOCIATES, INC.
145 Lehigh Ave, Lakewood, NJ
08701
Tel.: (732) 634-5700   NJ
Web Site: https://www.alphainc.com
Year Founded: 1968
Sales Range: $75-99.9 Million
Emp.: 115
Resin Coated & Laminated Fabrics
N.A.I.C.S.: 313320
A. Louis Avallone (Chm & CEO)
Christopher J. Avallone (Pres &
COO)
John T. Baxter (VP-Sls & Mktg)
Pamela Avallone (Sec)

**ALPHA BAKING COMPANY,
INC.**
5001 W Polk St, Chicago, IL 60644
Tel.: (773) 261-6000   DE
Web Site:
http://www.alphabaking.com
Year Founded: 1977
Sales Range: $200-249.9 Million
Emp.: 400
Bakery Products Mfr
N.A.I.C.S.: 424490
Lawrence L. Marcucci (Pres & CEO)

Subsidiaries:

Natural Ovens Bakery Inc.   (1)
4300 County Trunk Cr, Manitowoc, WI
54220
Tel.: (920) 758-2500
Web Site: http://www.naturalovens.com
Sales Range: $10-24.9 Million
Emp.: 200
Bread Mfr
N.A.I.C.S.: 311812
Alpha Baking (Mgr)

**ALPHA BUILDING CENTER
INC.**

855 N State Rd 5, Shipshewana, IN 46565
Tel.: (260) 768-4410
Web Site: http://www.alpha-building.com
Rev.: $11,497,643
Emp.: 28
Lumber & Other Building Materials
N.A.I.C.S.: 423310

ALPHA CAPITAL PARTNERS, LTD.
150 N Michigan Ave Ste 800, Chicago, IL 60601
Tel.: (312) 322-9800
Web Site: http://www.alphacapital.com
Year Founded: 1984
Sales Range: $10-24.9 Million
Emp.: 10
Privater Equity Firm
N.A.I.C.S.: 523999
Andrew H. Kalnow (Founder & CEO)

Subsidiaries:

NM Group Global LLC   (1)
122 S Michigan Ave Ste 1700, Chicago, IL 60603
Tel.: (312) 322-3640
Web Site: http://www.nmgroupglobal.com
Industrial Holding Company
N.A.I.C.S.: 551112
Andrew H. Kanlow (Owner & CEO)

Subsidiary (Domestic):

National Machinery LLC   (2)
161 Greenfield St, Tiffin, OH 44883-2422
Tel.: (419) 447-5211
Web Site: http://www.nationalmachinery.com
Sales Range: $25-49.9 Million
Cold Forging Machinery Mfr
N.A.I.C.S.: 333517
Jerry Bupp (VP-Sls)

Subsidiary (Domestic):

Cleaning Technologies Group, LLC   (3)
4933 Provident Dr, Cincinnati, OH 45246
Tel.: (513) 870-0100
Web Site: http://www.ctgclean.com
Sales Range: $25-49.9 Million
Industrial Parts Washers & Cleaning Systems Mfr
N.A.I.C.S.: 423830
Chris Whittaker (VP-Bus Dev & Mktg)
Kailash Chauhan (Mgr-Bus Dev-India)
Igor Pinto (Mgr-Bus Dev-Mexico)
Bernard A. Bosse Jr. (CEO)

Division (Domestic):

Blackstone Ney Ultrasonics Inc.   (4)
9 N Main St, Jamestown, NY 14703
Tel.: (716) 665-2340
Web Site: http://www.ctgclean.com
Sales Range: $50-74.9 Million
Industrial Cleaning Systems Mfr
N.A.I.C.S.: 333248
Dean Phaneuf (Pres)
Milton Svetanics (Reg Mgr-Sls)

Ransohoff   (4)
4933 Provident Dr, Cincinnati, OH 45246-1020
Tel.: (513) 870-0100
Web Site: http://www.cleaningtechnologies.com
Sales Range: $75-99.9 Million
Emp.: 200
Industrial Cleaning Machinery Mfr
N.A.I.C.S.: 333248
Ruben Chasteen (Head-Ops)
Nate Buckner (Engr-Mechanical Design)
Joe Servizzi (Mgr-Tech Svc)
Kevin Ochterski (Project Mgr)

ALPHA CARD SERVICES INC.
1210 Northbrook Dr Ste 475, Feasterville Trevose, PA 19053
Tel.: (215) 494-0200
Web Site: http://www.alphacardservices.com
Year Founded: 2000

Sales Range: $1-9.9 Million
Emp.: 19
Payment & Transaction Processor
N.A.I.C.S.: 561499
Lazaros Kalemis (CEO)
Janet Whitaker (Dir-POS Svcs)
Matt Weinsieder (Dir-Mktg)
David Headley (Dir-Ops)
Michael Connor (VP-Fin)

ALPHA DYNO NOBEL
3400 Nader Rd, Lincoln, CA 95648
Tel.: (916) 645-3377
Web Site: https://www.alphaexplosives.com
Rev.: $10,000,000
Emp.: 29
Explosives
N.A.I.C.S.: 424690
Brad P. Langner (Pres)

ALPHA ELECTRIC SUPPLY CORPORATION
343 Kea St, Kahului, HI 96732
Tel.: (808) 871-9711
Web Site: http://www.aeshawaii.com
Rev.: $18,000,000
Emp.: 38
Sales of Electrical Supplies
N.A.I.C.S.: 423610
Hank Pacheco (Exec VP & Gen Mgr)
Dano Pereida (Branch Mgr)

ALPHA FLYING, INC.
115 Flightline Rd, Portsmouth, NH 03801
Tel.: (603) 501-6035
Web Site: http://www.planesense.com
Year Founded: 1992
Emp.: 211
Transit & Passenger Transportation Services
N.A.I.C.S.: 485999
George A. Antoniadis (Pres & CEO)
Jim Paradis (CFO & Treas)
Gary Arber (Gen Counsel & VP)
Lorri Badolato (Deputy Gen Counsel & Sec)
Robyn Moses-Harney (VP-HR)

ALPHA GARMENT INC.
1385 Broadway Fl 5, New York, NY 10018
Tel.: (212) 398-9050
Web Site: http://www.zanadi.com
Rev.: $81,585,759
Emp.: 50
Sportswear, Women's & Children's
N.A.I.C.S.: 424350
Assad Jebara (Pres)
Sally Scimeca (Mgr-AR)

ALPHA GREEN ENERGY LIMITED
8040 E Morgan Trail Ste 18, Scottsdale, AZ 85258
Tel.: (602) 490-0620   AZ
Web Site: http://www.alphagreenenergy.com
Year Founded: 2009
Sales Range: $25-49.9 Million
Emp.: 2
Renewable Energy Power
N.A.I.C.S.: 221118
Donald Low (CFO & VP)
Jeffrey Tan (Dir)

ALPHA II, LLC
2074 Summit Lake Dr, Tallahassee, FL 32317
Tel.: (850) 668-3922
Web Site: https://www.alphaii.com
Sales Range: $1-9.9 Million
Emp.: 80

Custom Computer Programming Services
N.A.I.C.S.: 541511
Roy Maloy (VP)
Jan Powell (CEO)
Scott Schimpf (VP-Tech)
Shawna Singletary (Mgr-Software Release)

Subsidiaries:

Alpha II, LLC - Montgomery   (1)
4160 Carmichael Rd, Montgomery, AL 36106
Tel.: (334) 260-8150
Software Developer
N.A.I.C.S.: 513210
Rex Stanley (Pres)

ALPHA INDUSTRIES INC.
14200 Park Meadow Dr Ste 110 S Tower, Chantilly, VA 20151
Tel.: (703) 378-3023
Web Site: https://www.alphaindustries.com
Rev.: $14,600,000
Emp.: 30
Military Uniforms Mfr
N.A.I.C.S.: 315120
Michael Cirker (CEO)
Marci Lesser Shere (Sr Acct Mgr)
Ivan Saldana (Pres)
Mary Caprino (Acct Mgr)
Ying Tian (Dir-Ops)
Colin Israel (CFO & COO)
Matthew Pantoja (Chief Brand Officer)

ALPHA INDUSTRIES, INC.
Page & Schuyler Ave, Lyndhurst, NJ 07071
Tel.: (201) 933-5353   NJ
Web Site: http://www.sigmaplastics.com
Year Founded: 1978
Emp.: 5,000
Plastics Bag & Pouch Manufacturing
N.A.I.C.S.: 326111
Alan Teo (CIO & VP)

Subsidiaries:

Aargus Plastics, Inc.   (1)
540 Allendale Dr, Wheeling, IL 60090
Tel.: (847) 325-4444
Web Site: http://www.aargusplastics.com
Polyethylene Product Mfr
N.A.I.C.S.: 326199
Jerome Starr (CEO)

Allied Plastics Holdings, LLC   (1)
36-08 Review Ave, Long Island City, NY 11101
Tel.: (718) 729-5500
Polyethylene Product Mfr
N.A.I.C.S.: 326199
Michael Reiger (VP-Ops)

Beta Plastics Corporation   (1)
120 Amor Ave, Carlstadt, NJ 07072-2103
Tel.: (201) 933-1400
Web Site: http://www.alpha-industries.com
Sales Range: $25-49.9 Million
Emp.: 7
Plastics
N.A.I.C.S.: 326111
Alfred S. Teo (Pres)

Coastal Films of Florida   (1)
627 N Lane Ave, Jacksonville, FL 32254
Tel.: (904) 786-2031
Plastic Packaging Products Mfr
N.A.I.C.S.: 326199
Tom Carlton (VP-Sls)

Epsilon Plastics, Inc.   (1)
3100 E Harcourt St, Rancho Dominguez, CA 90221
Tel.: (310) 609-1320
Web Site: http://www.sigmaplasticsgroup.com
Plastic Garment Bags Mfr
N.A.I.C.S.: 326111
Lilly Lopez (Mgr-HR)

Filmtech Corp.   (1)
2121 31st St SW, Allentown, PA 18103
Tel.: (610) 709-9999
Emp.: 100
Polyethylene Product Mfr
N.A.I.C.S.: 326199
Mark Jordan (Pres)

Flexsol Packaging Corp.   (1)
1531 NW 12th Ave, Pompano Beach, FL 33069
Tel.: (800) 231-4191
Web Site: http://www.flexsolpackaging.com
Plastic Product Mfr & Distr
N.A.I.C.S.: 424130
Dave Clarke (Pres & COO)

Plant (Domestic):

Flexsol Packaging Corp. - North Carolina Facility   (2)
3610 Taylorsville Hwy, Statesville, NC 28625
Tel.: (704) 871-8880
Polyethylene Product Mfr
N.A.I.C.S.: 326199

Flexsol Packaging Corp. - Tennessee Facility   (2)
1105 Visco Dr, Nashville, TN 37210
Tel.: (888) 595-4855
Plastics Product Mfr
N.A.I.C.S.: 326199

ISO Poly Films, Inc.   (1)
101 ISO Pkwy, Gray Court, SC 29645
Tel.: (864) 876-4300
Web Site: http://www.isopoly.com
Emp.: 150
Polyethylene Product Distr
N.A.I.C.S.: 326112
Russ Joseph (VP-Sls & Mktg)
Russell P. Gehrke (VP-Tech & Product Dev)
Beth Stroble Scherpenberg (Vp-Sls Ops)
Morgan Dean (Mgr-Technical)

McNeely Plastic Products Inc.   (1)
1111 Industrial Park Dr, Clinton, MS 39056
Tel.: (601) 926-1000
Web Site: http://www.mcneelyplastics.com
Plastic Product Distr
N.A.I.C.S.: 424130
Greg McNeely (Pres)

Subsidiary (Domestic):

Tara Plastics Corporation   (2)
175 Lake Mirror Rd, Forest Park, GA 30297
Tel.: (404) 366-4464
Web Site: http://www.taraplastics.com
Plastic & Packaging Films Mfr
N.A.I.C.S.: 326111
Blaine Hale (Plant Mgr)

Omega Plastics   (1)
Page Schuyler Ave, Lyndhurst, NJ 07071-0808
Tel.: (201) 933-5353
Web Site: http://www.alpha-industries.com
Sales Range: $75-99.9 Million
Emp.: 400
N.A.I.C.S.: 425120
Alfred S. Teo (CEO)

Performance Packaging Inc.   (1)
301 Grand Blvd North, Cowansville, J2K 1A8, QC, Canada
Tel.: (450) 263-6360
Polyethylene Product Distr
N.A.I.C.S.: 326199

Poly Plastic Products Inc   (1)
21 Schultz Dr, Delano, PA 18220
Tel.: (570) 467-3000
Web Site: http://www.polyplasticproducts.com
Emp.: 100
Plastics Product Mfr
N.A.I.C.S.: 326199
Alfred S. Teo (Chm, Treas & Sec)
Steve Redlich (Pres)
Dave Eye (Mgr-Production)
John Lorah (Mgr-Traffic)
Tim McGowan (VP-Ops)
Donna Marie Petri (Mgr-Acctg)
Donna McGowan (Mgr-HR)
Vince Oberto (VP-Sls)
Janet Zemantauski (Mgr-Customer Svc)
Jenny Weaver (Asst Mgr-Customer Svc)
Lori Smith (Mgr-Traffic-Pennsylvania)

Alpha Industries, Inc.—(Continued)

Subsidiary (Domestic):

Poly Plastic Products of North Carolina, Inc (2)
1206 Traywick Rd, Marshville, NC 28103
Tel.: (704) 624-2555
Web Site: http://www.sigmaplastic.com
Plastics Product Mfr
N.A.I.C.S.: 326199

Republic Bag Inc. (1)
580 E Harrison St, Corona, CA 92879-1344
Tel.: (951) 734-9740
Web Site: http://www.republicbag.com
Polyethylene Product Mfr
N.A.I.C.S.: 326199
Steve Schroeder (Pres)
Chris Cervantes (Mgr-Sls)

Santa Fe Packaging Corp. (1)
15315 Marquardt Ave, Santa Fe Springs, CA 90670
Tel.: (800) 645-0626
Web Site: http://www.sfpkg.com
Polyethylene Product Mfr
N.A.I.C.S.: 326199
Cheryl O'Donnell (Controller)
Brick Pinckney (VP)

Sigma Stretch Film - California Plant (1)
1576 Omaha Ct, Riverside, CA 92507
Web Site: http://www.sigmastretchtools.com
Stretch Films Mfr
N.A.I.C.S.: 326199
Bruce Gustafson (Reg Mgr-Sls)

Sigma Stretch Film - Canada Plant (1)
Jamieson Bone Road, PO Box 380, Belleville, K8N 5A5, ON, Canada
Tel.: (866) 848-4400
Web Site: http://www.sigmastretchfilm.com
Stretch Films Mfr
N.A.I.C.S.: 326199
Brian Fraser (Dir-Mktg)

Sigma Stretch Film - Kentucky Plant (1)
901 Commerce Cir, Shelbyville, KY 40065
Tel.: (888) 826-2224
Web Site: http://www.sigmastretchfilm.com
Stretch Films Mfr
N.A.I.C.S.: 326199
Chuck Magee (Reg Mgr-Sls)

Sigma Stretch Film - Oklahoma Plant (1)
4035 W 49th, Tulsa, OK 74107
Tel.: (877) 330-4035
Web Site: http://www.sigmaplastics.com
Stretch Films Mfr
N.A.I.C.S.: 326199
Barry Gerber (Reg Mgr-Sls)

Southeastern Plastics Corp. (1)
15 Home News Row, New Brunswick, NJ 08901
Tel.: (732) 846-8500
Polyethylene Product Mfr
N.A.I.C.S.: 326199

ALPHA MARKETING, INC.
510 Glenwood Ave Ste 321, Raleigh, NC 27603
Tel.: (919) 836-2169
Web Site:
http://www.alphamarketing.com
Year Founded: 2000
Sales Range: $1-9.9 Million
Emp.: 17
Marketing Consulting Services
N.A.I.C.S.: 541613
Nicky Peele (Pres)
Amber Fitz (Dir-Fin)
Rob Ruchte (Dir-Dev)

ALPHA MATERIAL HANDLING CO., INC.
25496 Cornell Rd, Arcadia, IN 46030
Tel.: (317) 578-7695
Web Site: http://www.alphahoist.com
Sales Range: $1-9.9 Million
Emp.: 4

Industrial Machinery & Equipment Whslr
N.A.I.C.S.: 423830
John McNamee (Engr)

ALPHA MEDIA LLC
1211 SW 5th Ave Ste 750, Portland, OR 97204
Tel.: (503) 517-6200 DE
Web Site:
https://www.alphamediausa.com
Year Founded: 2012
Multimedia Holding Company; Radio Stations Owner & Operator
N.A.I.C.S.: 551112
Larry Wilson (Founder)
John Grossi (CFO)
Donna Heffner (Chief Strategy Officer)
Larry Bastida (CEO)
Mike Hartel (Exec VP-Mid-Atlantic)
Bill McElveen (Exec VP-East)
George Pelletier (Exec VP-Central)
Sarah Jordan (Dir-Mktg)
Phil Kukawinski (Program Dir)
David J. Drutz (VP-Market & Mgr-Market-San jose)

Subsidiaries:

KDES-FM (1)
1321 N Gene Autry Trl, Palm Springs, CA 92262
Tel.: (760) 322-7890
Web Site: http://www.985thebull.com
Radio Broadcasting Stations
N.A.I.C.S.: 516110
Cristine Constantinescu-Isabell (Dir-Promos)
Tricia Bastida (Gen Mgr)

KEEZ-FM (1)
1807 Lee Blvd N, Mankato, MN 56003
Tel.: (507) 345-4646
Web Site: http://www.myz99.com
Radio Broadcasting Stations
N.A.I.C.S.: 516110
Robert Rose (Gen Mgr-Mankato Market)
Shannon Magers (Bus Mgr)
Jeff Spence (Ops Mgr)

KEZR-FM (1)
100 Park Center Plz Ste 200, San Jose, CA 95113
Tel.: (408) 287-5775
Web Site: http://www.mymix106.com
Radio Broadcasting Stations
N.A.I.C.S.: 516110

KINK-FM (1)
1211 SW 5th Ave Ste 600, Portland, OR 97204
Tel.: (503) 517-6000
Web Site: http://www.kink.fm
Radio Broadcasting Stations
N.A.I.C.S.: 516110
Lisa Decker (Gen Mgr)

KTSA-FM/AM (1)
4050 Eisenhauer Rd, San Antonio, TX 78218
Tel.: (210) 654-5100
Web Site: http://www.ktsa.com
Radio Broadcasting Stations
N.A.I.C.S.: 516110
Greg Martin (Dir-Content)
Dennis Foley (Dir-News)
Jane Smith (Sls Mgr)

WCPR-FM (1)
9471 3 Rivers Rd Ste A, Gulfport, MS 39503
Tel.: (228) 388-2001
Web Site: http://www.979cprrocks.com
Radio Broadcasting Stations
N.A.I.C.S.: 516110
Ricky Mitchell (Gen Mgr)
Mindy Patton (Dir-Promos)
Scot Fox (Dir-Music)
Steve Price (Sls Mgr)

WDHT (1)
717 E David Rd, Dayton, OH 45429
Tel.: (937) 294-5858
Web Site: http://www.hot1029.com
Radio Stations

N.A.I.C.S.: 516110
Keith Wright (Mgr-Sls)
Ryan Drake (Dir-Content)

ALPHA MILLS CORP.
122 S Margaretta St, Schuylkill Haven, PA 17972-1694
Tel.: (570) 385-0511 PA
Web Site:
http://www.alphamillscorp.com
Year Founded: 1936
Sales Range: $100-124.9 Million
Emp.: 150
Knitwear, Underwear & Sportswear Mfr
N.A.I.C.S.: 315120
Richard D. Biever (Pres)
Tim Shabler (Controller)
Sue Jones (Supvr-Receiving)

ALPHA NATURAL RESOURCES, INC.
1989 E Stone Dr, Kingsport, TN 37660
Tel.: (423) 723-8900 DE
Web Site: http://www.alphanr.com
Year Founded: 2004
Emp.: 8,900
Coal Mining Services
N.A.I.C.S.: 212114
Jason Whitehead (COO & Sr VP)
Andrew McCallister (Gen Counsel & Sr VP)
Judy Tweed Hill (Chief Admin Officer & Sr VP)
Samuel M. Hopkins II (CFO & Sr VP)

Subsidiaries:

A.T. Massey Coal Company, Inc. (1)
4 N 4th St, Richmond, VA 23219-2230
Tel.: (804) 788-1800
Sales Range: $150-199.9 Million
Coal Mining Services
N.A.I.C.S.: 212114

Subsidiary (Domestic):

Appalachia Coal Sales Company, Inc. (2)
PO Box 26765 4th & Main St, Richmond, VA 23219-2230
Tel.: (804) 788-1800
Sales Range: $150-199.9 Million
Coal, Other Minerals & Ores Whslr
N.A.I.C.S.: 423520

Subsidiary (Domestic):

Boone East Development Co. (3)
300 Morgan Massey Dr, Madison, WV 25529
Tel.: (304) 369-8500
Sales Range: $10-24.9 Million
Emp.: 75
Land Subdividers & Developers
N.A.I.C.S.: 237210
Mark Clemens (Pres)

Lauren Land Company (3)
24406 US Rte 19, Belfry, KY 41514
Tel.: (606) 353-0928
Sales Range: $1-9.9 Million
Emp.: 12
Land Subdividers & Developers
N.A.I.C.S.: 237210

Massey Coal Services, Inc. (3)
300 Running Right Way, Julian, WV 25529
Tel.: (304) 369-8500
Sales Range: $25-49.9 Million
Emp.: 34
Mining Engineering Services
N.A.I.C.S.: 213113
Don L Blankenship (Pres)

New River Energy Corporation (3)
125 Hurricane Branch Rd, Chapmanville, WV 25508
Tel.: (304) 369-8500
Sales Range: $10-24.9 Million
Emp.: 13
Natural Gas Distr
N.A.I.C.S.: 221210

Subsidiary (Domestic):

Elk Run Coal Company, Inc. (2)
31754 Coal River Rd, Sylvester, WV 25193
Tel.: (304) 854-1890
Sales Range: $50-74.9 Million
Emp.: 467
Coal Mining
N.A.I.C.S.: 212114
Jennifer Chandler (Dir-HR)

Subsidiary (Domestic):

Aracoma Coal Company, Inc. (3)
Rt 17 Bandmill Hollow Rd, Logan, WV 25076
Tel.: (304) 752-6194
Coal Mining
N.A.I.C.S.: 212114

Independence Coal Company, Inc. (3)
782 Robinson Creek Rd, Madison, WV 25130
Tel.: (304) 369-7108
Sales Range: $50-74.9 Million
Emp.: 385
Coal Mining
N.A.I.C.S.: 212115

Marfork Coal Company, Inc. (3)
Route 3 Over 1, Whitesville, WV 25209
Tel.: (304) 854-1852
Sales Range: $75-99.9 Million
Coal Mining
N.A.I.C.S.: 212114
Charles I. Bearse III (Pres)

Subsidiary (Domestic):

Long Fork Coal Company (2)
375 Rockhouse Rd, Sidney, KY 41564
Tel.: (606) 353-9936
Sales Range: $10-24.9 Million
Emp.: 71
Coal Mining
N.A.I.C.S.: 212114

Subsidiary (Domestic):

Bandmill Coal Corporation (3)
County Rt 14 Rum Creek Rd, Yolyn, WV 25654
Tel.: (304) 792-6221
Web Site: http://www.alphanr.com
Coal Mining
N.A.I.C.S.: 212114

Coalsolv, LLC (3)
4 N 4th St, Richmond, VA 23219-2230
Tel.: (804) 788-1800
Management Consulting Services
N.A.I.C.S.: 541611

Omar Mining Company (3)
Robinson Creek Rd Route 85, Madison, WV 25130
Tel.: (304) 369-1046
Sales Range: $10-24.9 Million
Emp.: 11
Coal Mining Services
N.A.I.C.S.: 212114
Billy McCoy (Gen Mgr)

Stirrat Coal Company (3)
Route 44 S, Omar, WV 25638
Tel.: (304) 946-2639
Sales Range: $10-24.9 Million
Emp.: 8
Coal Mining
N.A.I.C.S.: 212114

Subsidiary (Domestic):

Martin County Coal Corporation (2)
3185 Middle Fork Work Creek Rd, Inez, KY 41224
Tel.: (606) 395-6881
Sales Range: $75-99.9 Million
Emp.: 500
Coal Mining
N.A.I.C.S.: 212114

Subsidiary (Domestic):

Knox Creek Coal Corporation (3)
2295 Governor G C Perry Hwy, Raven, VA 24639
Tel.: (276) 964-4333
Web Site:
http://www.alphanaturalresources.com

Sales Range: $50-74.9 Million
Emp.: 150
Coal Mining
N.A.I.C.S.: 212115

Subsidiary (Domestic):

Performance Coal Company (2)
130 Frontier St, Montcoal, WV 25140-9550
Tel.: (304) 854-1761
Sales Range: $50-74.9 Million
Emp.: 325
Coal Mining
N.A.I.C.S.: 212114
Charles I. Bearse III (Pres)

Rawl Sales & Processing Co. (2)
State Route 49 S, Lobata, WV 25691
Tel.: (304) 235-4290
Sales Range: $125-149.9 Million
Emp.: 200
Coal Mining
N.A.I.C.S.: 212114

Rum Creek Coal Sales, Inc. (2)
PO Box 1096, Holden, WV 25625
Tel.: (304) 752-7850
Sales Range: $10-24.9 Million
Emp.: 6
Coal Mining Services
N.A.I.C.S.: 213113

Sidney Coal Company, Inc. (2)
115 N Big Creek Rd, Sidney, KY 41564-8557
Tel.: (606) 353-7201
Web Site: http://www.alphanr.com
Sales Range: $200-249.9 Million
Emp.: 1,000
Coal Mining
N.A.I.C.S.: 212115
Larry Johnson (Head-Oil)
Kevin Varney (Gen Mgr)

Subsidiary (Domestic):

Alex Energy, Inc. (3)
US Rte 119, Holden, WV 25625
Tel.: (304) 239-2018
Sales Range: $10-24.9 Million
Emp.: 2
Coal Mining
N.A.I.C.S.: 212114
Steve Poe (VP)

Green Valley Coal Company (3)
Rte 20, Leivasy, WV 26676
Tel.: (304) 846-6600
Sales Range: $75-99.9 Million
Emp.: 500
Coal Mining
N.A.I.C.S.: 212114
John Brown (Gen Mgr)

Logan County Mine Services, Inc. (3)
S 2nd Rd, Holden, WV 25625
Tel.: (304) 239-2300
Web Site: http://www.alpanr.com
Sales Range: $25-49.9 Million
Emp.: 35
Coal Mining
N.A.I.C.S.: 212114
Eric Sayler (Pres)

Power Mountain Coal Company (3)
2 Jerry Fork Rd, Drennen, WV 26667
Tel.: (304) 872-5065
Sales Range: $10-24.9 Million
Emp.: 28
Coal Whslr
N.A.I.C.S.: 423520
Chris Ray (Office Mgr)

Alpha Coal Resources Company, LLC (1)
158 Portal Rd, Waynesburg, PA 15370
Tel.: (724) 627-7500
Coal Mining Services
N.A.I.C.S.: 213113

Alpha Coal Sales Company, LLC (1)
340 Martin Luther King Jr Blvd, Bristol, TN 37620
Tel.: (423) 573-0300
Web Site: http://www.alphanr.com
Sales Range: $150-199.9 Million
Coal Whslr
N.A.I.C.S.: 423520

Alpha Coal West, Inc. (1)

2273 Bishop Rd, Gillette, WY 82718
Tel.: (307) 687-3400
Coal Mining Services
N.A.I.C.S.: 213113

Alpha Midwest Holding Company (1)
3050 12th St Sw, Cedar Rapids, IA 52404-4854
Tel.: (319) 364-7143
Emp.: 12
Coal Mining Services
N.A.I.C.S.: 213113

Alpha Natural Resources, LLC (1)
1 Alpha Pl, Bristol, VA 24202
Tel.: (276) 619-4410
Web Site: http://www.alphanr.com
Emp.: 250
Coal Mining Services
N.A.I.C.S.: 213113
Harry Hull (Dir-Running Right Cultural Dev)

Black Mountain Resources LLC (1)
152 Valley St Ne, Abingdon, VA 24210-2833
Tel.: (276) 676-1151
Coal Mining Services
N.A.I.C.S.: 213113

Brooks Run Mining Company, LLC (1)
25 Little Birch Rd, Sutton, WV 26601
Tel.: (304) 765-4006
Coal Mining Services
N.A.I.C.S.: 213113

Cobra Natural Resources, LLC (1)
1000 Mingo Logan Ave, Wharncliffe, WV 25651
Tel.: (304) 929-6340
Coal Mining Services
N.A.I.C.S.: 213113

Dry Systems Technologies, Inc. (1)
10420 Rising Ct, Woodridge, IL 60517-4958
Tel.: (630) 427-2051
Web Site: http://www.drysystemstech.com
Sales Range: $50-74.9 Million
Emp.: 50
Mining & Construction Equipment Mfr
N.A.I.C.S.: 333131
Ronald D. Eberhart (Pres)
Tony Arbaney (Gen Mgr)

Freeport Mining, LLC (1)
158 Portal Rd, Waynesburg, PA 15370
Tel.: (724) 627-7500
Web Site: http://www.alphanr.com
Coal Mining Services
N.A.I.C.S.: 213113

Kingston Mining, Inc. (1)
600 Resource Dr, Scarbro, WV 25917
Tel.: (304) 469-6299
Coal Mining Services
N.A.I.C.S.: 213113
Shad West (Mgr-HR)

Kingston Processing, Inc. (1)
400 Patterson Ln, Charleston, WV 25311-1570
Tel.: (304) 345-0970
Coal Mining Services
N.A.I.C.S.: 213113

Kingwood Mining Company, LLC (1)
4615 Yorks Run Rd, Newburg, WV 26410-9231
Tel.: (304) 568-2460
Coal Mining Services
N.A.I.C.S.: 213113

Maxxim Rebuild Co., LLC (1)
12003 Virginia Blvd, Ashland, KY 41102-8641
Tel.: (606) 928-7911
Web Site: http://www.maxxim-rebuild.com
Sales Range: $50-74.9 Million
Emp.: 20
Coal Mining Services
N.A.I.C.S.: 213113
Anthony Keaton (Pres)

Mountaineer Capital, LP (1)
107 Capitol St Ste 300, Charleston, WV 25301
Tel.: (304) 347-7525
Consumer Lending Services
N.A.I.C.S.: 522291

New Market Land Company (1)
5245 S Durango Dr, Las Vegas, NV 89113

Tel.: (702) 221-2500
Web Site: http://www.newmarketadvisors.com
Emp.: 4
Coal Mining Services
N.A.I.C.S.: 213113
Charles Creigh (Pres)

Nicholas Energy Company (1)
2 Jerry Fork Rd, Drennen, WV 26667
Tel.: (304) 872-5065
Coal Mining Services
N.A.I.C.S.: 213113

Pilgrim Mining Company, Inc. (1)
3201 Ridge Top Rd, Inez, KY 41224
Tel.: (606) 395-6881
Coal Mining Services
N.A.I.C.S.: 213113

ALPHA OFFICE SUPPLIES INC.
4950 Parkside Ave Ste 502, Philadelphia, PA 19131
Tel.: (215) 226-2690
Web Site: https://www.alphaos.com
Year Founded: 1985
Sales Range: $10-24.9 Million
Emp.: 5
Office Furniture Whslr
N.A.I.C.S.: 423210
Carmine Soto (VP-Furniture)

ALPHA OMEGA INTEGRATION, LLC
8150 Leesburg Pike Ste 1010, Vienna, VA 22182
Tel.: (703) 637-7300
Web Site: http://www.alphaomegallc.com
Year Founded: 2010
Sales Range: $1-9.9 Million
Emp.: 200
Information Technology Consulting Services
N.A.I.C.S.: 541512
Gautam Ijoor (Pres & CEO)
Jean Lewis (VP-Strategic Growth)
Jocelyn Hsu (Chief Delivery Officer)
Sridhar Rajagopalan (Sr VP-Core Accts)
Tom Edson (CFO)

ALPHA PACKAGING INC.
2020 E Center St, Greenwood, AR 72936
Tel.: (479) 996-2829
Web Site: https://www.alphapackaging.com
Year Founded: 1987
Sales Range: $10-24.9 Million
Emp.: 100
Corrugated & Solid Fiber Boxes Mfr
N.A.I.C.S.: 322211
Michael Stec (Pres)
Kenny Schenk (Mgr-Foam Products)
Phil Yates (Chm)

ALPHA PLASTICS INC.
800 Woodside Blvd, Saint Louis, MI 48880
Tel.: (989) 681-5781
Web Site: http://www.alphaplastics.com
Year Founded: 1986
Sales Range: $10-24.9 Million
Emp.: 72
Plastics Bottles
N.A.I.C.S.: 326199
Larry Lipper (Pres)

ALPHA Q, INC.
87 Upton Rd, Colchester, CT 06415
Tel.: (860) 537-7340   DE
Web Site: https://www.gsgage.com
Year Founded: 1986
Sales Range: $75-99.9 Million
Emp.: 100
Machine Shop Products

N.A.I.C.S.: 332710
Stephen Prout (Pres & CEO)
Richard Hurley (CFO & Gen Mgr)
Dave Harris (Mgr-Quality Control)

Subsidiaries:

Galstonbury Southern Gage (1)
87 Upton Rd, Colchester, CT 06415-0531
Tel.: (860) 537-7340
Web Site: http://www.gsgage.com
Sales Range: $10-24.9 Million
Emp.: 90
Mfr of Fixed Limit Guages
N.A.I.C.S.: 332710
Steven Prout (Pres)

Southern Gage Inc. (1)
46 Industrial Park Rd, Erin, TN 37061 (100%)
Tel.: (931) 289-4242
Web Site: http://www.gsgage.com
Sales Range: $10-24.9 Million
Fixed Limit Gaging Manufacturer; Precision Special Machining
N.A.I.C.S.: 333515
Steven Prout (Pres)

ALPHA RAE PERSONNEL INC.
347 W Berry St Ste 7, Fort Wayne, IN 46802-2299
Tel.: (260) 426-8227
Web Site: https://www.alpha-rae.com
Year Founded: 1980
Sales Range: $50-74.9 Million
Emp.: 1,350
Human Resources & Executive Search Consulting Services
N.A.I.C.S.: 541612
Rae Pearson (Pres & CEO)

ALPHA ROOFING INDUSTRIES, LLC
15 Roundville Ln Ste 200, Round Rock, TX 78664
Tel.: (512) 677-9001
Web Site: http://www.alpharoofingtexas.com
Year Founded: 2014
Sales Range: $1-9.9 Million
Emp.: 4
Roofing Contractor Services
N.A.I.C.S.: 238160
Peter Brady (Pres & Gen Mgr)

ALPHA SOURCE, INC.
6619 W Calumet Rd, Milwaukee, WI 53223-4186
Tel.: (414) 760-2222
Web Site: http://www.alphasource.com
Year Founded: 1986
Medical Equipment & Supplies
N.A.I.C.S.: 423450
Rich Springer (Pres)
Vionnta Rivers (Chief Commercial Officer)
Karen Tichy (CFO)
Peter Strimaitis (Sr VP-Svcs & PMO Ops)
Sue Fiegel (Sr VP-HR)

Subsidiaries:

BC Technical, Inc. (1)
7172 S Airport Rd, West Jordan, UT 84084
Tel.: (801) 280-2900
Web Site: http://www.bctechnical.com
Molecular Imaging Equipment Mfr & Services
N.A.I.C.S.: 334516
Rich Springer (Pres)

ALPHA SPECIALTY PRODUCTS INC.
233b Camson Rd, Anderson, SC 29625
Tel.: (706) 377-2770
Rev.: $14,000,000
Emp.: 18

Alpha Specialty Products Inc.—(Continued)
Temperature Measurement Instruments, Industrial
N.A.I.C.S.: 334513

ALPHA SYNOPSYS INC
2140 Avon Industrial Dr, Rochester Hills, MI 48309
Tel.: (586) 439-5258
Web Site:
http://www.alphasynopsys.com
Year Founded: 2006
Sales Range: $1-9.9 Million
Emp.: 25
It Consulting
N.A.I.C.S.: 541690
Sanjib Das (Pres)

ALPHA SYSTEMS INC.
5120 Beck Dr, Elkhart, IN 46516-9512
Tel.: (574) 295-5206   IN
Web Site: http://www.alphallc.us
Year Founded: 1984
Sales Range: $25-49.9 Million
Emp.: 150
Building Materials
N.A.I.C.S.: 423330
David Smith (Pres)
Nancy Smith (VP)
Chris Kintzele (CFO)

ALPHA TELECOM INC.
1072 S De Anza Blvd, San Jose, CA 95129
Tel.: (408) 895-1800   AL
Web Site: http://www.alpha-tele.com
Year Founded: 1994
Sales Range: Less than $1 Million
Emp.: 10
Sales of ISDN Terminal Adapters for Telecommunications Equipment
N.A.I.C.S.: 423690
Wen Sung (Pres)

ALPHA VIDEO & AUDIO, INC.
7690 Golden Triangle Dr, Eden Prairie, MN 55344
Tel.: (952) 896-9898
Web Site:
https://www.alphavideo.com
Year Founded: 1970
Sales Range: $10-24.9 Million
Emp.: 100
Video & Digital Media Content Creation, Distribution & Management Products Mfr
N.A.I.C.S.: 334310
Kevin Groves (COO & Dir-Sls)
Lance Hutchinson (VP)

ALPHABET HOLDING COMPANY, INC.
2100 Smithtown Ave, Ronkonkoma, NY 11779
Tel.: (631) 567-9500   DE
Year Founded: 2010
Sales Range: $1-4.9 Billion
Emp.: 13,100
Food Supplement Mfr & Distr
N.A.I.C.S.: 456191
Sandra Horbach (Chm)
Harvey Kamil (Vice Chm)
Joseph Looney (Chief Acctg Officer & VP-Fin)
Karla Packer (Sr VP-HR)
Bernard O'Keefe (Chief Supply Chain Officer)
Dipak Golechha (CFO)
Brian Wynne (Pres-NBTY Americas)

ALPHACORE CAPITAL LLC
875 Prospect St Ste 315, La Jolla, CA 92037
Tel.: (858) 875-4100

Web Site:
https://alphacorewealth.com
Financial Services
N.A.I.C.S.: 523999

Subsidiaries:

James M. Johnston & Associates Inc.   (1)
600 S Cherry St Ste 1110, Denver, CO 80246
Tel.: (303) 831-6120
Web Site: https://www.jmjassoc.com
Insurance Related Activities
N.A.I.C.S.: 524298
James Johnston (Pres)

ALPHAEON CORPORATION
18191 Von Karman Ave Ste 500, Irvine, CA 92612
Tel.: (949) 284-4555   DE
Web Site: http://www.alphaeon.com
Healthcare Services & Nutraceuticals Retailer
N.A.I.C.S.: 621111
Rui Avelar (Chief Medical Officer)
Kris Garcia (VP-Fin)
Jeff Plumer (VP-Legal)

Subsidiaries:

Evolus, Inc.   (1)
520 Newport Ctr Dr Ste 1200, Newport Beach, CA 92660
Tel.: (949) 284-4555
Web Site: https://www.evolus.com
Rev.: $148,616,000
Assets: $177,983,000
Liabilities: $159,484,000
Net Worth: $18,499,000
Earnings: ($74,412,000)
Emp.: 215
Fiscal Year-end: 12/31/2022
Biotechnology Research & Development Services
N.A.I.C.S.: 541714
Vikram Malik (Chm)
Rui Avelar (Chief Medical Officer & Head-R&D)
Tomoko Yamagishi-Dressler (CMO)
Jeff Plumer (Gen Counsel)
David Moatazedi (Pres & CEO)
Jessica Novak (Sr VP-HR)
David K. Erickson (VP-IR)
Sandra Beaver (CFO)
Umberto La Magna (Sr VP-Evolus International)

Strathspey Crown LLC   (1)
4040 Macarthur Blvd Ste 210, Newport Beach, CA 92660
Tel.: (949) 260-1700
Web Site: http://www.strathspeycrown.com
Emp.: 20
Privater Equity Firm
N.A.I.C.S.: 525990
Vikram Malik (Mng Partner)
Robert E. Grant (Chm)

Subsidiary (Non-US):

Clarion Medical Technologies Inc.   (2)
125 Fleming Dr, Cambridge, N1T 2B8, ON, Canada
Tel.: (519) 620-3900
Web Site: http://www.clarionmedical.com
Diagnostic Equipment Mfr & Sales
N.A.I.C.S.: 334510
Dan Webb (CEO)

Subsidiary (Domestic):

Eveo Inc.   (2)
1160 Battery St Suite 275, San Francisco, CA 94111
Tel.: (415) 844-9400
Web Site: http://www.eveo.com
Sales Range: $1-9.9 Million
Emp.: 50
Full-Service Health & Wellness Agency
N.A.I.C.S.: 541840
Olivier Zitoun (CTO)

PRN Physician Recommended Nutriceuticals LLC   (2)
502 W Germantown Pike Ste 610, Plymouth Meeting, PA 19462

Web Site: http://www.prnomegahealth.com
Sales Range: $1-9.9 Million
Emp.: 50
Nutritional Supplements
N.A.I.C.S.: 456191
Kenneth A. Krieg (CEO)
Michael B. Gross (Chief Medical Officer & Exec VP)
Michael Chaiken (Pres-PRN Canada)
Drew M. Pinkin (CFO & VP)
Stefan Schoen (VP-Bus Dev)

ALPHAGILITY LLC
100 Corporate Dr Ste 304, Lebanon, NJ 08833
Tel.: (732) 962-6680   NJ
Web Site: http://www.alphagility.com
Marketing Services
N.A.I.C.S.: 541613
Charles Mertz (CEO)

Subsidiaries:

Swim & Sweat, Inc.   (1)
39 Stangl Rd, Flemington, NJ 08822   (100%)
Tel.: (888) 788-7946
Web Site: https://swimandsweat.com
Miscellaneous Apparel & Accessory Stores
N.A.I.C.S.: 458110

ALPHAMETRIX, LLC
181 W Madison 34th FL, Chicago, IL 60602
Tel.: (312) 267-8400
Web Site:
http://www.alphametrix.com
Year Founded: 2005
Sales Range: $25-49.9 Million
Emp.: 70
Hedge Fund Investments
N.A.I.C.S.: 525910
George Brown (CFO)

ALPHANUMERIC SYSTEMS INC.
3801 Wake Forest Rd, Raleigh, NC 27609-6864
Tel.: (919) 781-7575
Web Site:
http://www.alphanumeric.com
Year Founded: 1979
Sales Range: $10-24.9 Million
Emp.: 50
Mfr of Computer Integrated Systems Design
N.A.I.C.S.: 541512
Steve Chase (VP-Sls & Mktg)
Rebecca Jones (Controller)
Harvey Braswell (Pres)

ALPHAPOINTE ASSOCIATION FOR THE BLIND
7501 Prospect, Kansas City, MO 64132
Tel.: (816) 421-5848
Web Site: http://www.alphapointe.org
Sales Range: $10-24.9 Million
Emp.: 165
Plastics Bottles
N.A.I.C.S.: 326160
Reinhard Mabry (Pres & CEO)
Amy Campbell (VP-HR)
Gina Gowin (VP-Program Svcs & Dev)
Jake McCabe (VP-Sls & Mktg)
Michael Stephens (VP-Ops)
Stan Wright (Dir-IT)
Ed Marquette (Co-Chm)
David Westbrook (Co-Chm)
Stephen Mock (Treas)
Jeff McHenry (CFO & VP)
Danny Davies (VP & Gen Mgr)

ALPHASERVE TECHNOLOGIES, LLC.
104 W 40th St 19th Fl, New York, NY 10018

Tel.: (212) 763-5500
Web Site:
http://www.alphaserveit.com
Year Founded: 2003
Sales Range: $10-24.9 Million
Emp.: 80
Information Technology Consulting Services
N.A.I.C.S.: 541512
Arup Das (CEO & CTO)

ALPHASTAFF GROUP, INC.
800 Corporate Dr Ste 600, Fort Lauderdale, FL 33334
Tel.: (954) 267-1760
Web Site: http://www.alphastaff.com
Year Founded: 1997
Sales Range: $1-4.9 Billion
Emp.: 70,000
Human Resource Outsourcing Services
N.A.I.C.S.: 561499
Daniel M. Franzblau (VP-Fin & Plng)
Julio Chez (VP-Bus Dev-Southeast)
Kyle R. Kelly (Pres & CEO)
Maria Whelan (Mgr-HR)
Harry Glazer (VP-Bus Dev)
Jeniece Carter-Henson (VP-Strategic Bus Dev)
Dorothy Miraglia King (VP-Benefits)

ALPI INTERNATIONAL, LTD
1685 34th St, Oakland, CA 94608
Tel.: (510) 655-6456   CA
Web Site: http://www.alpi.net
Year Founded: 1983
Sales Range: $1-9.9 Million
Emp.: 28
Promotional Products Distr
N.A.I.C.S.: 423990
Francesco Indrio (Pres)
Steve Klein (Acct Mgr)

ALPIN HAUS SKI SHOP INC.
4850 State Hwy 30, Amsterdam, NY 12010
Tel.: (518) 843-4400   NY
Web Site: http://www.alpinhaus.com
Year Founded: 1964
Sales Range: $50-74.9 Million
Emp.: 147
Sales of New & Used Travel Trailers
N.A.I.C.S.: 441210
Chris Carmichael (Controller)
David Behuniak (Mgr-Team)
Katie Osborn (Mgr-Mktg)

ALPINE ARMORING INC.
571 Herb Dr, Herndon, VA 20170
Tel.: (703) 471-0002
Web Site: http://www.alpineco.com
Sales Range: $10-24.9 Million
Emp.: 13
Armored Cars
N.A.I.C.S.: 336110
Fred Khoroushi (Pres)
Shahid Khan (Mgr-Bus Dev-Asia)

ALPINE ASSOCIATES, L.P.
574 Sylvan Ave Ste 100, Englewood Cliffs, NJ 07632
Tel.: (201) 871-0866
Web Site:
http://www.alpineassociates.com
Year Founded: 1976
Sales Range: $200-249.9 Million
Emp.: 40
Investment Firm General Brokerage
N.A.I.C.S.: 523150
Elaine Giordano (Office Mgr)
Brian Donahue (Portfolio Mgr)
Greg Eagan (Mng Dir)
Frank Matcovich (Mgr-Ops)

ALPINE BUICK, PONTIAC, GMC

8120 W Tufts Ave, Denver, CO
80123
Tel.: (303) 932-8000
Web Site:
   http://www.alpinebuickgmc.com
Year Founded: 2005
Sales Range: $10-24.9 Million
Emp.: 50
Car Dealer
N.A.I.C.S.: 441110
Ivette Dominguez (Pres)

**ALPINE COLONY ENTER-
PRISES INC.**
1240 Knollwood Dr, Cambria, CA
93428
Tel.: (805) 927-1302
Web Site:
   https://www.cookiecrock.com
Rev.: $12,273,774
Emp.: 120
Independent Supermarket
N.A.I.C.S.: 445110
Del Clegg (Pres)

ALPINE COUNTRY CLUB
80 Anderson Ave, Demarest, NJ
07627
Tel.: (201) 768-2121   NJ
Web Site: https://www.alpinecc.org
Year Founded: 1928
Sales Range: $10-24.9 Million
Emp.: 207
Country Club
N.A.I.C.S.: 713910
Chris Hull (Gen Mgr)

**ALPINE GROVE PARTNERS
LLP**
340 Madison Ave 19th Fl, New York,
NY 10173
Tel.: (212) 710-7875   DE
Web Site:
   http://www.alpinegrovepartners.com
Year Founded: 2004
Privater Equity Firm
N.A.I.C.S.: 523999
Richard Georgi (Co-Founder, Mng
Partner & Chief Investment Officer)
Markus Hens (Mng Partner-Europe)
Xander Wassink (Partner & COO)
David Ziegler (Partner, CFO & Head-
Grove Fund Mgmt)
Michael Bidinger (Partner)
Rohit Wanchoo (Partner)

Subsidiaries:

Alpine Grove (Netherlands) B.V. (1)
Barbara Strozzilaan 101, 1083 HN, Amster-
dam, Netherlands
Tel.: (31) 20 722 0790
Web Site:
   http://www.alpinegrovepartners.com
Privater Equity Firm
N.A.I.C.S.: 523999
Markus Hens (Mng Partner)
Bodo Krug von Nidda (Principal)

Alpine Grove Partners (US) LLC (1)
340 Madison Ave 19th Fl, New York, NY
10173
Tel.: (212) 710-7875
Web Site:
   http://www.alpinegrovepartners.com
Private Equity Investment Firm
N.A.I.C.S.: 523999
Richard Georgi (Mng Partner & Chief In-
vestment Officer)
Krzysztof Augustynowicz (Principal)

Ishin Hotels Group Co., Ltd. (1)
Hulic Kamiyacho Bldg 10F 4-3-13 Tora-
nomon, Minato-ku, Tokyo, 150-0001,
Japan   (50%)
Tel.: (81) 357337733
Web Site: http://www.ishinhotels.com
Emp.: 222
Holding Company; Hotel Investment, Op-
eration & Asset Management
N.A.I.C.S.: 551112

Kenji Matsuo (VP-Tech Svcs)
Yasushi Kamei (CFO)
Lenny Kung (CEO)

Unit (Domestic):

International Garden Hotel Narita (2)
241-1 Yoshikura, Narita, 286-0133, Chiba,
Japan
Tel.: (81) 476235522
Sales Range: $25-49.9 Million
Emp.: 60
Hotel Operations
N.A.I.C.S.: 721110
Ikuya Kubo (Gen Mgr)

ALPINE HOLDING COMPANY
6775 E Highland Rd, White Lake, MI
48383
Tel.: (248) 887-2180   MI
Web Site:
   http://www.skialpinevalley.com
Year Founded: 1973
Sales Range: $10-24.9 Million
Emp.: 162
Ski Lodge Operator
N.A.I.C.S.: 721199
Willis Stoick (Pres)
Helen Stoick (Controller)

ALPINE INVESTORS
1 California St Ste 2900, San Fran-
cisco, CA 94111
Tel.: (415) 392-9100
Web Site: http://www.alpine-
   investors.com
Year Founded: 2001
Emp.: 60
Financial Investment Services
N.A.I.C.S.: 523999
Graham Weaver (Founding Partner)
Will Adams (Partner)
Billy Maguy (Partner)
Dan Sanner (Partner)
Mark Strauch (Partner)
Matt Moore (Partner)
Tim Burke (CEO-NetGain)

Subsidiaries:

Acumen, LLC (1)
3800 N Central Ave Ste 460, Phoenix, AZ
85012
Tel.: (480) 497-0343
Administrative Management & General
Management Consulting Service
N.A.I.C.S.: 541611
Gerald Nebeker (Mgr)

Architectural Computer Services,
Inc. (1)
465 S 400 E Ste 200, Salt Lake City, UT
84111-3345
Tel.: (801) 521-9162
Web Site: http://www.arcomnet.com
Rev.: $6,000,000
Emp.: 25
Engineering Related Software Developers
N.A.I.C.S.: 513210
Angelica Matinkhah (VP-Mktg & Sls)
Christopher G. Bushnell (Vice Chm)
Alan Burningham (Mgr-Info Sys)
Betty D. Scheibly (Mgr-Office & Ops)
Jim Contardi (CEO)
Paul Brosnahan (VP-Specifications)
Matthew Johnson (CTO)
Mark Bemis (CFO)
Karthik Mani (Exec VP-Products & Delivery)
Lynn Tenney (Mgr-Comm)

Cobalt Service Partners, LLC (1)
124 E 14th St 14th Fl, New York, NY 10003
Tel.: (332) 910-5678
Web Site: https://www.cobaltsp.com
Facilities Services
N.A.I.C.S.: 561210

Subsidiary (Domestic):

Automatic Entrances of Wisconsin,
Inc. (2)
1712 Paramount Ct, Waukesha, WI 53186
Tel.: (262) 549-8600
Web Site: http://www.aewinc.net

Sales Range: $1-9.9 Million
Emp.: 30
Electrical Apparatus & Equipment, Wiring
Supplies & Related Equipment Merchant
Whslr
N.A.I.C.S.: 423610
Jay J. Walt (VP)
Nick Liederbach (Dir-Field Ops)
Tim Doughman (Mgr-Direct Sls)
Cindy Leuzinger (Dir-Sls Admin)
Ed Lenz (Mgr-Svc)

Evergreen Services Group LLC (1)
1 California St Ste 2900, San Francisco, CA
94111
Tel.: (415) 591-1318
Web Site: http://www.evergreensg.com
Holding Company
N.A.I.C.S.: 551112
Jeff Totten (CEO)
Sydney Hockett (VP-M&A)

Subsidiary (Domestic):

Netgain Technologies Inc. (2)
2031 Georgetown Rd, Lexington, KY 40511
Tel.: (859) 255-0155
Web Site: http://www.netgainit.com
Emp.: 150
Managed IT Services
N.A.I.C.S.: 518210
Jim Jacobson (COO)
Robin Fischer (Mgr-Engrg)
Brendan Jacobson (Pres)
Hayder Allebban (VP-Ops)
Tim Burke (CEO)

Subsidiary (Domestic):

Experienced Office Solutions
LLC (3)
9815 Dawsons Creek Blvd, Fort Wayne, IN
46825
Tel.: (260) 490-7925
Web Site: http://www.4eos.com
Network Design & Installation, Security &
Data Center Services
N.A.I.C.S.: 518210
Jeremy Holle (Founder & CEO)

Progressive Computer Systems,
Inc. (3)
615 Eastowne Dr, Chapel Hill, NC 27514
Tel.: (919) 929-3080
Web Site: http://www.pc-net.com
Rev.: $3,600,000
Emp.: 20
Data Processing, Hosting & Related Ser-
vices
N.A.I.C.S.: 518210
Lisa Mitchell (Co-Founder)
Mark Michal (Co-Founder)

Subsidiary (Domestic):

Netranom Communications, Inc. (2)
2801 Virginia Ave Ste 200, Hurricane, WV
25526
Tel.: (304) 562-9495
Web Site: http://www.nationsguide.com
Sales Range: $1-9.9 Million
Emp.: 20
Computer System Design Services
N.A.I.C.S.: 541512
Scott Edwards (Pres)

Omnyon LLC (2)
8212 Lexington Dr, Severn, MD 21144-2713
Tel.: (443) 599-9846
Web Site: http://www.omnyon.com
Custom Computer Programming Services
N.A.I.C.S.: 541511
Timothy Gorski (Principal)

Telco Experts LLC (2)
169 Ramapo Vly Rd Upper Level, Oakland,
NJ 07436
Web Site: http://www.telcoexperts.com
Sales Range: $10-24.9 Million
Emp.: 20
Business Consulting Services
N.A.I.C.S.: 541611
Mendy Kupfer (VP-Ops)
Eric Klein (Co-Founder)
Adam Goldberg (Co-Founder)

Western Computer, LLC (2)
351 Candelaria Rd, Oxnard, CA 93030
Tel.: (805) 581-5020
Web Site: http://www.westerncomputer.com

Sales Range: $1-9.9 Million
Emp.: 100
Turnkey Consulting, Programming, Installa-
tion & Training Services
N.A.I.C.S.: 541519
Tom Bardos (CEO)
Kelly Holwagner (VP-Ops)

Homeland Safety Systems Inc. (1)
223 Clearview Ln, Benton, LA 71006
Tel.: (318) 965-3699
Web Site:
   http://www.homelandsafetysystems.com
Sales Range: $1-9.9 Million
Emp.: 6
Electrical Apparatus & Equipment, Wiring
Supplies & Related Equipment Merchant
Whslr
N.A.I.C.S.: 423610
Mike Elliott (VP)

Toepfer Security Corp. (1)
2215 Corporate Dr, Waukesha, WI 53189
Tel.: (262) 650-7233
Web Site: http://www.toepfersecurity.com
Sales Range: $1-9.9 Million
Emp.: 21
Electrical Contractor Repair Services
N.A.I.C.S.: 561621
Ronald G. Lund (Pres)

**ALPINE LUMBER COMPANY
INC.**
10170 Church Ranch Way Ste 350,
Westminster, CO 80021
Tel.: (303) 451-8001
Web Site:
   https://www.alpinelumber.com
Year Founded: 1963
Sales Range: $100-124.9 Million
Emp.: 237
Supplier of Lumber & Other Building
Materials
N.A.I.C.S.: 423310
Mark Morrison (CFO & Sec)
Dave McKinney (Mgr-Pur)
Hamid Taha (Pres & CEO)
Tammie Speth (Mgr-Credit)

ALPINE MEATS INC.
9850 Lower Sacramento Rd, Stock-
ton, CA 95210-3912
Tel.: (209) 477-2691   CA
Web Site:
   http://www.alpinemeats.com
Year Founded: 1936
Sales Range: $10-24.9 Million
Emp.: 50
Sausage Producer, Processor & Distr
N.A.I.C.S.: 311611
Rick Martin (Owner & Pres)

ALPINE PAYMENT SYSTEMS
9120 NE Vancouver Mall Loop Ste
270, Vancouver, WA 98662
Tel.: (360) 713-0690
Web Site:
   http://www.alpinepayments.com
Year Founded: 2006
Sales Range: $1-9.9 Million
Emp.: 103
Merchant Services, Credit Card Pro-
cessing, ATMs & Cash Services
N.A.I.C.S.: 522390
Robert Ensminger (Pres & CEO)
Ashley Robinson (Mgr-Customer Svc)
Brian McDevitt (VP)
Jared Crouch (Mgr-Sls)

ALPINE PRODUCTS INC.
550 3rd St SW Bldg C, Auburn, WA
98001
Tel.: (253) 351-9828
Web Site:
   https://www.alpinemarkings.com
Rev.: $14,000,000
Emp.: 11
Paint Varnish & Supplies Merchant
Whslr
N.A.I.C.S.: 424950

Alpine Products Inc.—(Continued)

Bart Farrar (Pres & CEO)
Tim Williams (Mgr-Production)

ALPINE PROPERTY MANAGE-MENT LLC
804 N Delaware St Ste A, Indianapolis, IN 46204
Tel.: (317) 924-0810
Web Site: http://www.indyapm.com
Sales Range: $10-24.9 Million
Emp.: 20
Property Management
N.A.I.C.S.: 531311
Aaron Adams (Owner)

ALPINE SALES INC.
9650 Mill Field Rd, Columbia, SC 29223
Tel.: (803) 788-9160
Web Site:
http://www.alpinesalesinc.com
Sales Range: $10-24.9 Million
Emp.: 20
Cabinet Hardware & Countertop Wholesale Distr
N.A.I.C.S.: 424610
Glenn Cox (Branch Mgr)
Michael Steck (Pres)

ALPINE WASTE & RECYCLING
7373 Washington St, Commerce City, CO 80229
Tel.: (303) 744-9881
Web Site:
http://www.alpinewaste.com
Year Founded: 1999
Sales Range: $10-24.9 Million
Emp.: 105
Refuse System
N.A.I.C.S.: 562211
Alek Orloff (CFO)
John Griffith (Pres)
Brent Hildebrand (VP)
John E. Tovado (VP)

ALPS CONSTRUCTION INC.
15745 Annico Dr, Homer Glen, IL 60441
Tel.: (708) 301-3366
Web Site:
http://www.alpsconstruction.com
Rev.: $15,139,889
Emp.: 12
Commercial & Office Building, New Construction
N.A.I.C.S.: 236220
Alfred W. Peterson (Pres)
Joel Parker (Superintendent)

ALPS CORPORATION
Florence Bldg 111 N Higgins Ste 600, Missoula, MT 59802
Tel.: (406) 728-3113
Web Site: http://www.alpsnet.com
Sales Range: $50-74.9 Million
Emp.: 60
Attorney Liability Protection Insurance & Risk Management Services
N.A.I.C.S.: 524128
Christopher L. Newbold (Exec VP)
Bradley D. Dantic (Sec & VP)
David Bell (Pres & CEO)

Subsidiaries:

Southern Title Insurance Corp. (1)
7231 Forest Ave Ste 202, Richmond, VA 23226
Tel.: (804) 648-6000
Web Site: http://www.southerntitle.com
Sales Range: $50-74.9 Million
Emp.: 30
Title Insurance Carrier & Services
N.A.I.C.S.: 524127

ALPS SOUTH LLC

2895 42nd Ave N, Saint Petersburg, FL 33714
Tel.: (727) 528-8566
Web Site: https://www.easyliner.com
Year Founded: 1988
Sales Range: $25-49.9 Million
Emp.: 130
Prosthetics, Orthotics & Silicone Gel-Based Products Mfr
N.A.I.C.S.: 339112
Kara Poe (Asst Controller)
Chantal Kelly (Mgr-Ops)

ALPS SPORTSWEAR MANU-FACTURING CO., INC.
15 Union St, Lawrence, MA 01840-1823
Tel.: (978) 683-2438   MA
Year Founded: 1934
Sales Range: Less than $1 Million
Emp.: 20
Men's & Women's Sweaters & Related Apparel Mfr
N.A.I.C.S.: 315120
Marvin Axelrod (Pres)
Jerry Stone (Dir-Sls & Mktg)

ALRO STEEL CORPORATION
3100 E High St, Jackson, MI 49204-0927
Tel.: (517) 787-6390   MI
Web Site: http://www.alro.com
Year Founded: 1948
Sales Range: $450-499.9 Million
Emp.: 1,600
Distr of Metals
N.A.I.C.S.: 423510
Alvin Glick (Chm & CEO)

Subsidiaries:

Alro Metal Service Center, Boca Raton (1)
6200 Park Of Commerce Blvd, Boca Raton, FL 33487-8201
Tel.: (561) 997-6766
Web Site: http://www.alro.com
Sales Range: $25-49.9 Million
Emp.: 75
Industrial Supplies
N.A.I.C.S.: 423510
John Sintarelli (Gen Mgr)

Alro Metals Plus, Clearwater (1)
12490 49th St N, Clearwater, FL 33762-4310
Tel.: (727) 572-4344
Web Site: http://www.alroy.com
Sales Range: $25-49.9 Million
Emp.: 12
Distr of Metals
N.A.I.C.S.: 423510

Alro Metals Plus, Kalamazoo (1)
5382 Wynn Rd, Kalamazoo, MI 49048-3336
Tel.: (269) 343-9575
Web Site: http://www.alro.com
Sales Range: $25-49.9 Million
Emp.: 14
Supplier of Metals
N.A.I.C.S.: 423840
Jim Crowell (Gen Mgr)

Alro Metals Service Center, Orlando (1)
2505 N Forsyth Rd, Orlando, FL 32807-6431
Tel.: (407) 678-2576
Web Site: http://www.alro.com
Sales Range: $25-49.9 Million
Emp.: 50
Industrial Supplies
N.A.I.C.S.: 423510

Alro Specialty Metals, Charlotte (1)
12933 Sam Neely Rd, Charlotte, NC 28273-5615
Tel.: (704) 588-5880
Web Site: http://www.alro.com
Sales Range: $25-49.9 Million
Emp.: 30
Specialty Metal Distr
N.A.I.C.S.: 423510
Al Glick (Pres & CEO)

Alro Specialty Metals, Melrose Park (1)
4501 James Pl, Melrose Park, IL 60160-1080
Tel.: (708) 343-4343
Web Site: http://www.alro.com
Sales Range: $25-49.9 Million
Emp.: 20
Specialty Metals
N.A.I.C.S.: 212290
Mark Alyea (VP)

Alro Specialty Metals, Redford (1)
34401 Schoolcraft Rd, Livonia, MI 48150   (100%)
Tel.: (734) 261-2200
Web Site: http://www.alro.com
Emp.: 20
Specialty Metals Distr
N.A.I.C.S.: 423510

Alro Steel (1)
1298 Lipsey Dr, Charlotte, MI 48813   (100%)
Tel.: (419) 720-5300
Web Site: http://www.alro.com
Sales Range: $150-199.9 Million
Distr of Steel, Metals
N.A.I.C.S.: 423510
Alvin Glick (Co-Founder)
Robert Glick (Co-Founder)

Alro Steel (1)
50 Ensminger Rd, Tonawanda, NY 14150-6718
Tel.: (716) 877-6242
Web Site: http://www.alrosteel.com
Sales Range: $25-49.9 Million
Emp.: 30
Specialty Metals
N.A.I.C.S.: 423510
Dennis Brooker (Gen Mgr)

Alro Steel Corporation - Alro Industrial Supply Division (1)
4324 Air Lane Dr SE, Grand Rapids, MI 49512-3933
Tel.: (616) 656-2800
Web Site: http://www.teamalro.com
Emp.: 7
Industrial Supplies Distr
N.A.I.C.S.: 423840
Al Glick (Pres)

Alro Steel Corporation - Alro Plastics Division (1)
2218 Enterprise, Jackson, MI 49204-0927
Tel.: (517) 787-5500
Web Site: http://www.alro.com
Emp.: 50
Plastic Material Distr
N.A.I.C.S.: 325211
Alvin Glick (Pres)

Pottinger Steel Works, Inc. (1)
2711 Mount Pleasant St, Racine, WI 53404
Tel.: (262) 637-9574
Web Site: http://www.pottingersteel.com
Sales Range: $1-9.9 Million
Emp.: 16
Metal Service Centers & Other Metal Merchant Whslr
N.A.I.C.S.: 423510

ALROD ENTERPRISES INC.
119 N Sycamore St, Petersburg, VA 23803
Tel.: (804) 732-3972
Web Site:
http://www.alrodenterprises.com
Rev.: $11,713,343
Emp.: 75
Security Guard Services
N.A.I.C.S.: 561612
Betty W. Hweatt (VP-Ops)

ALSCO INC.
505 E 200 S, Salt Lake City, UT 84102-1004
Tel.: (801) 328-8831   NV
Web Site: https://www.alsco.com
Year Founded: 1889
Sales Range: $250-299.9 Million
Emp.: 12,000

Holding Company; Commercial Laundry & Linen Supply Services & Washroom Products Mfr
N.A.I.C.S.: 551112
Kevin K. Steiner (Co-CEO)
Timothy Weiler (Dir-HR)
Larry Tomsic (CIO & Dir-IP)
Steve Larson (VP)
Robert Steiner (Co-Pres & Co-CEO)
Jim Kearns (COO)

Subsidiaries:

ALSCO Berufskleidungs-Service GmbH (1)
Radiumstrasse 26, 51069, Cologne, Germany
Tel.: (49) 221986050
Web Site: http://www.alsco.de
Leisure Clothing Mfr
N.A.I.C.S.: 315250

ALSCO Italia Srl (1)
Via Pordenone 8, 20132, Milan, Italy
Tel.: (39) 02 89400523
Web Site: http://www.alsco.it
Linen & Uniform Laundry Services
N.A.I.C.S.: 812332

Alsco Servitex, Inc. (1)
717 Summit Ave, Kinston, NC 28501-3133
Tel.: (252) 523-3191
Web Site: http://www.alsco.com
Sales Range: $10-24.9 Million
Emp.: 150
Linen Supply Services
N.A.I.C.S.: 812331
Robert Steiner (Co-CEO)
Kevin Steiner (Co-CEO)

American Linen Supply Co. (1)
3370 W 1820 S, Salt Lake City, UT 84104
Tel.: (801) 973-7771
Web Site: http://www.alsco.com
Sales Range: $50-74.9 Million
Emp.: 400
Commercial Laundry & Linen Supply Services
N.A.I.C.S.: 812331

American Uniform Co. (1)
Ocoee St N Ste 34363, Cleveland, TN 37312-4832
Tel.: (423) 476-6561
Sales Range: $25-49.9 Million
Emp.: 3
Mfr of Industrial Work Clothing & Linen Apparel; Uniform Rental
N.A.I.C.S.: 315250

Churchill Linen Service Inc. (1)
7 Evans St, Brockton, MA 02302
Tel.: (508) 586-1953
Web Site: https://www.churchill-linen.com
Rev.: $10,000,000
Emp.: 160
Apron Supply
N.A.I.C.S.: 812331
Ken DeDominici (Pres)

ALSIP HOTEL INVESTORS INC.
5000 W 127th St, Alsip, IL 60803-3245
Tel.: (708) 371-7300   IL
Web Site:
http://doubletree3.hilton.com
Hotels Investment Group
N.A.I.C.S.: 721110
Clarissa Palumbo (Sls Mgr-Wedding)

ALSO ENERGY INC.
5400 Airport Blvd Ste 100, Boulder, CO 80301   DE
Web Site: http://www.alsoenergy.com
Year Founded: 2007
Custom Computer Programming Services
N.A.I.C.S.: 541511
Robert Schaefer (CEO)
Holden Caine (CTO)
Brian Musfeldt (CFO)
Kevin Smart (VP-Global Sls & Mktg)
Bryan Noakes (Dir-Production)

Kevin Suhr *(Dir-Engrg)*
Mesa Scharf *(Dir-Global Solutions)*
Lester Hoffman *(Dir-Support)*

Subsidiaries:

Locus Energy, LLC (1)
2 Hudson Pl 6th Fl, Hoboken, NJ 07030
Tel.: (877) 562-8736
Web Site: http://www.locusenergy.com
Software Publisher
N.A.I.C.S.: 513210

ALSTIN COMMUNICATIONS, INC.
121 S Broad St 16th Fl, Philadelphia, PA 19102-3128
Tel.: (215) 568-3200
Year Founded: 1968
Rev.: $12,000,000
Emp.: 21
Collateral, Internet/Web Design, Print, Recruitment
N.A.I.C.S.: 541810
Michael V. Schluth *(Pres & Owner)*
Michael Tedesco *(Sr VP)*
Patricia Cara *(VP-Creative Svcs)*
Tony Rosato *(VP-Client Dev)*
Annette DeHaven *(VP-Ops)*
Anne Hillman *(Sr Acct Exec)*
Christy Parker *(Mgr-Creative)*
Nicole Ballinger *(Acct Exec)*
Melissa Sweeney *(Dir-Art)*

ALSTON & BIRD LLP
One Atlantic Ctr 1201 W Peachtree St, Atlanta, GA 30309-3424
Tel.: (404) 881-7000
Web Site: http://www.alston.com
Year Founded: 1893
Sales Range: $650-699.9 Million
Emp.: 1,001
Legal Advisory Services
N.A.I.C.S.: 541110
Richard R. Hays *(Mng Partner)*
Jamye Gunter *(Dir-Fin & Acctg-Litigation Support)*
Mark Steele *(Dir-Fin & Acctg-Litigation Support)*
Elizabeth A. Price *(Partner-Pro Personnel)*
Mary T. Benton *(Partner)*
Lisa R. Bugni *(Partner)*
H. Douglas Hinson *(Partner)*
Robert L. Lee *(Partner)*
Robert R. Long *(Partner)*
Jason D. Rosenberg *(Partner)*
Margaret Ward Scott *(Partner)*
Cathy A. Benton *(Chief HR Officer)*
Richard G. Levinson *(CFO)*
Robert Marburger *(CIO)*
Mark L. Thompson *(CMO)*
Jeffrey R. Allaman *(Dir-IT)*
Joan W. Gilbert *(Sr Dir-Fin)*
Linda S. Herndon *(Dir-Conference Svcs)*
Emily S. Leeson *(Dir-Atty Pro Dev)*
Ted Lucas *(Dir-Fin Plng & Analysis)*
Allison H. Lynch *(Dir-Paralegal Svcs)*
Brenda C. Martin *(Dir-Client Fin Svcs)*
Cheryl Naja *(Dir-Pro Bono & Community Svc)*
Bil W. Seymour *(Dir-Benefits & Payroll)*
Erin L. Springer *(Dir-Atty Hiring)*
Michael G. Stephens *(Dir-HR Ops)*
Tricia Bond Thomas *(Dir-Library Svcs)*
Nola M. Vanhoy *(Dir-Practice Innovation)*
Steven E. Wilson *(Dir-Admin Svcs)*
Tiffany Zeigler *(Dir-Special Projects-Bus Dev)*
T. C. Spencer Pryor *(Partner)*
Sarah Smith Ernst *(Partner)*
Derin B. Dickerson *(Partner)*

Michael Cecka *(Partner)*
Michael Park *(Partner)*
Lance Termes *(Partner)*
Bryan Skelton *(Partner)*
Andrew Allen *(Partner)*
Meaghan Boyd *(Partner)*
Kyle Healy *(Partner)*
Matthew Kent *(Partner)*
Andrew Tuck *(Partner)*
Sage Sigler *(Partner)*
Daniel Jarcho *(Partner)*
Ardeshir Tabibi *(Partner)*
Scott Harty *(Partner-Federal Income & Intl Tax Grp)*
John Snyder *(Partner-Antitrust)*
Clark Calhoun *(Partner)*
Tara Castillo *(Partner-Fin Grp)*
Matthew P. Hedstrom *(Partner-State & Local Tax Grp)*
Clifford S. Stanford *(Partner)*
W. Scott Kitchens *(Partner)*
Donald Houser *(Partner)*
Elizabeth Helmer *(Partner)*
Brian D. Harvel *(Partner)*
Lauren P. Giles *(Partner)*
David S. Frist *(Partner)*
Dane A. Baltich *(Partner)*
William Snyder *(Partner-Corp Transactions & Securities Grp)*
Jacqueline Baratian *(Partner-Health Care Grp)*
Sanford Brown *(Partner)*
Michael Tankersley *(Partner)*
Thomas G. Walker *(Partner)*
Michael Thimmig *(Partner)*
Michael Zweiback *(Partner)*
Gidon M. Caine *(Partner)*
Joe Liebeschuetz *(Partner)*
Lior O. Nuchi *(Partner)*
Romy L. Celli *(Partner)*
Ryan W. Koppelman *(Partner)*
Yitai Hu *(Partner)*
Frank E. Sheeder *(Partner-Dallas)*
Leslie Overton *(Partner)*
Dominic DeMatties *(Partner)*
Colgate Selden *(Partner-Fin Svcs & Products Grp)*
Rudy Missmar *(Partner-Health Care Grp)*
Julie Mediamolle *(Partner-Corp Transactions & Securities Grp)*
Emily Seymour Costin *(Partner-Compensation, Benefits & ERISA Litigation Grp)*
Martin Dozier *(Partner)*
Bo Griffith *(Partner)*
Russell Hilton *(Partner)*
Xavier Brandwajn *(Partner-Intellectual Property Litigation Grp)*
Robert Phillips *(Partner-San Francisco)*
Michael Agoglia *(Partner-San Francisco)*
John D. Hanover *(Partner)*
Paul Monnin *(Partner)*
Brian Frey *(Partner-Washington)*
Kevin Minoli *(Partner-Washington)*
Elinor Hiller *(Partner-Washington)*
Alex Park *(Partner-Corp Transactions & Securities Practice-Washington)*
Amy Mushahwar *(Partner-Washington)*
Brady W. Mullinax Jr. *(Dir-Fin & Acctg-Litigation Support)*
Michael A. Calandra Jr. *(Partner)*

ALSTON CAPITAL PARTNERS LLC
551 Fifth Avenue 14th fl, New York, NY 10176-0001
Tel.: (917) 542-8651
Web Site: http://alstoncapital.com
Private Capital
N.A.I.C.S.: 523999
Robert Egan *(Mng Partner)*

Subsidiaries:

Compass Systems & Sales, Inc. (1)
1643 Massillon Rd, Akron, OH 44312
Tel.: (330) 733-2111
Web Site:
http://www.compasssystemsandsales.com
Sales Range: $1-9.9 Million
Emp.: 26
Machine Tools, Metal Forming Type
N.A.I.C.S.: 333517
Brenda Pavlantos *(Mgr-Engrg)*

ALSUM FARMS & PRODUCT, INC.
N9083 County Rd EF, Cambria, WI 53923
Tel.: (920) 348-5127
Web Site: https://www.alsum.com
Rev.: $42,400,000
Emp.: 100
Organic Fresh Fruit & Vegetable Producer
N.A.I.C.S.: 424480
Larry Alsum *(Owner)*
Derrick Smit *(Coord-Safety & Trng)*
Jan Braaksma *(CFO)*
Randy Fischer *(Mgr-Production)*
Jeff Stiemsma *(Asst Mgr-Production)*
Wendy Dykstra *(COO)*
Matt Smith *(Mgr-HR)*

ALTA COMMUNICATIONS, INC.
200 Clarendon St Fl 51, Boston, MA 02116
Tel.: (617) 262-7770   MA
Year Founded: 1996
Holding Company; Media & Telecommunications Service Companies
N.A.I.C.S.: 551112
Timothy Dibble *(Partner)*
Philip Thompson *(Gen Partner)*
Eileen McCarthy Toti *(CFO & Gen Partner)*

Subsidiaries:

1105 Media, Inc. (1)
9201 Oakdale Ave Ste 101, Chatsworth, CA 91311
Tel.: (818) 814-5200
Web Site: http://www.1105media.com.
Sales Range: $50-74.9 Million
Emp.: 300
Online & Print Business-to-Business Information Product Services
N.A.I.C.S.: 513120
Michael J. Valenti *(Exec VP)*
Anne A. Armstrong *(Chief Content Officer & Chief Alliances Officer)*
Karen Cavallo *(Publr-Home Medical Equipment Editorial Grp)*
Kevin O'Grady *(Pres & Publr)*
Rajeev Kapur *(CEO)*
Irene Fincher *(Dir-Audience Dev-Enterprise Computing Grp)*
Becky Nagel *(VP-Digital Strategy)*
Brent Sutton *(VP-Events)*
Erik A. Lindgren *(CTO)*
Sanjay Tanwani *(CFO)*

Subsidiary (Domestic):

1105 Media Government Information Group (2)
3141 Fairview Park Dr Ste 777, Falls Church, VA 22042
Tel.: (703) 876-5100
Web Site: http://www.1105govinfo.com
Government Media & Publishing Services
N.A.I.C.S.: 513110
Anne Armstrong *(Pres)*

ALTA EAST, INC.
50 Industrial Pl, Middletown, NY 10940
Tel.: (845) 344-4271
Web Site: http://www.altaeast.com
Sales Range: $25-49.9 Million
Emp.: 10
Investment Holding Company
N.A.I.C.S.: 551112

Debbie Weeden *(Controller)*
Mark Dombal *(VP-Ops)*

ALTA ENVIRONMENTAL CORPORATION
121 Broadway, Colchester, CT 06415
Tel.: (860) 537-2582
Web Site:
https://www.altaenvironmental.com
Environmental Consulting Services
N.A.I.C.S.: 541620
Ryan Kerrigan *(CFO)*
Lisa Kay *(Pres)*
Nicolas Serieys *(VP)*
Ghina Yamout *(Head-Bus Dev-Water Resources)*

ALTA MESA RESOURCES, INC.
15021 Katy Fwy Ste 400, Houston, TX 77094
Tel.: (281) 530-0991   DE
Web Site: http://www.altamesa.net
Year Founded: 2016
Rev.: $413,320,000
Assets: $1,907,054,000
Liabilities: $992,160,000
Net Worth: $914,894,000
Earnings: ($610,082,000)
Emp.: 151
Fiscal Year-end: 12/31/19
Holding Company; Oil & Natural Gas Exploration, Development & Production Services
N.A.I.C.S.: 551112
Randy L. Limbacher *(Exec VP-Strategy)*
John C. Regan *(CFO, Exec VP & Asst Sec)*
Mark Castiglione *(CEO)*

Subsidiaries:

Alta Mesa Holdings, L.P. (1)
15021 Katy Fwy Ste 400, Houston, TX 77094 (46.9%)
Tel.: (281) 530-0991
Sales Range: $400-449.9 Million
Oil & Natural Gas Exploration & Production
N.A.I.C.S.: 211120
Mark Castiglione *(CEO)*

ALTA RESOURCES CORPORATION
120 N Commercial St, Neenah, WI 54956
Tel.: (920) 751-5800
Web Site:
https://www.altaresources.com
Year Founded: 1995
Sales Range: $25-49.9 Million
Emp.: 3,400
Telemarketing Services
N.A.I.C.S.: 561422
James F. Bere *(Chm & CEO)*
Paul Loebbaka *(VP-Fulfillment)*
Lisa Schulze *(VP-HR)*
Matt Nelson *(Sr VP-Ops)*
David Quandt *(Sr VP)*
Heather Owen Nigl *(CFO)*
Diana Floyd *(Chief Compliance Officer & Gen Counsel)*

Subsidiaries:

Alta Resources - Philippines (1)
34th Floor Wynsum Corporate Plaza F Ortigas Jr Avenue Ortigas Centre, Pasig, 1605, Philippines
Tel.: (63) 26382733
Call Center
N.A.I.C.S.: 561422

ALTA VISTA TECHNOLOGY LLC
26622 Woodward Ste 105, Royal Oak, MI 48067
Web Site:
http://www.altavistatech.com

Alta Vista Technology LLC—(Continued)

Year Founded: 2014
Sales Range: $1-9.9 Million
Emp.: 20
Software Development Services
N.A.I.C.S.: 541511
Scott Jackson (Pres)
David Valade (CTO)
Hollie Murray (VP-Svcs)

ALTADYN CORP.

2192 Dupont Dr Ste 108, Irvine, CA
92612
Tel.: (949) 273-0479
Web Site: http://www.3dxplorer.com
Year Founded: 2002
3D Technology
N.A.I.C.S.: 513210
Darius Lahoutifard (CEO)
Guillaume Lurenbaum (Founder &
CTO)

Subsidiaries:

Altadyn SA   (1)
2 route de la bonde Batiment 5, 91300,
Massy, France
Tel.: (33) 9 77 19 77 39
3D Technology
N.A.I.C.S.: 513210

ALTAFRESH LLC

301 E Johnson Ave, Chelan, WA
98816
Tel.: (509) 682-4252
Web Site:
https://www.chelanfresh.com
Year Founded: 2004
Fresh Fruit Marketer
N.A.I.C.S.: 424480
Daniel Gebbers (Sls Mgr)

Subsidiaries:

Borton & Son's Inc.   (1)
2550 Borton Rd, Yakima, WA 98903-9766
Tel.: (509) 966-3905
Web Site: http://www.bortonfruit.com
Fruit & Vegetable Markets
N.A.I.C.S.: 445230
Eric Borton (Dir-Bus Dev)

ALTAGHENY INC.

181 Sophira Ln, Altoona, PA 16602
Tel.: (814) 946-1845
Web Site:
http://www.reevetrucking.com
Sales Range: $25-49.9 Million
Emp.: 210
Supermarket
N.A.I.C.S.: 445110
William Mckillop (Pres)

ALTAIR GLOBAL RELOCA-
TION

7500 Dallas Pkwy Ste 300, Plano, TX
75024
Tel.: (972) 468-3000
Web Site: http://www.altairglobal.com
Sales Range: $10-24.9 Million
Emp.: 130
Relocation Services
N.A.I.C.S.: 561990
Gail Plummer (CEO)
Chad Sterling (Pres & CFO)
Mary Beth Nitz (Dir-Global Consulting
Svcs)
Kathryn Cassidy (Exec VP-Global
Client Svcs)

ALTAIR NANOTECHNOLOGIES
INC.

204 Edison Way, Reno, NV 89502-
2306
Tel.: (775) 856-2500
Web Site: http://www.altairnano.com
Year Founded: 1973
Sales Range: $50-74.9 Million

Emp.: 1,125
Titanium Dioxide Particle Producer
N.A.I.C.S.: 325130
Yincang Wei (Chm)
Guohua Wei (Gen Mgr-China)
Karen Werner (Interim CFO & Sec)

Subsidiaries:

Altair US Holdings, Inc.   (1)
204 Edison Way, Reno, NV
89502-2306   (100%)
Tel.: (775) 856-2500
Holding Company
N.A.I.C.S.: 551112

Subsidiary (Domestic):

Altairnano, Inc.   (2)
204 Edison Way, Reno, NV 89502
Tel.: (775) 856-2500
Web Site: http://www.altairnano.com
Nanomaterials & Titanium Dioxide Pigment
Technology
N.A.I.C.S.: 325130
Terry Coceland (CEO)

ALTAIR-STRICKLAND INCOR-
PORATED

1605 S Battleground Rd, La Porte,
TX 77571
Tel.: (281) 478-6200
Web Site:
https://www.altairstrickland.com
Rev.: $32,402,110
Emp.: 155
Renovation, Remodeling & Repairs:
Industrial Buildings
N.A.I.C.S.: 236220
Jeffrey Webber (Pres)
James McCauley (Dir-HR)
Mike Murphey (Project Mgr)
Robert Bellow (Project Mgr)
Scott Creasman (CFO)
Charles Johnson (Dir-Health, Safety
& Environmental Affairs)
Rick Ramirez (Dir-Sls & Mktg)
Glenn Carpenter (Mgr-Ops)
James Robinson (VP-Engrg)

ALTAK INC.

250 Covington Dr, Bloomingdale, IL
60108-3106
Tel.: (630) 622-0300
Web Site: https://www.altakinc.com
Rev.: $13,300,000
Emp.: 85
Fabricated Wire Product Mfr
N.A.I.C.S.: 332618
Miko Kabeshita (Pres)
Arata Kabeshita (Chm)
Dawn Berggren (Coord-Pur)
Hideshiro Tanaka (Asst Mgr)

ALTAMAHA ELECTRIC MEM-
BERSHIP CORPORATION

611 W Liberty Ave, Lyons, GA 30436
Tel.: (912) 526-8181
Web Site:
https://www.altamahaemc.com
Rev.: $13,800,000
Emp.: 60
Distribution, Electric Power
N.A.I.C.S.: 221122
Ramanus Dotson (Gen Mgr)

ALTAMED HEALTH SERVICES
CORPORATION

2040 Camfield Ave, Los Angeles, CA
90040
Tel.: (323) 725-8751
Web Site: http://www.altamed.org
Year Founded: 1970
Rev.: $360,363,626
Assets: $248,721,208
Liabilities: $78,552,679
Net Worth: $170,168,529
Earnings: $65,660,403
Emp.: 2,195

Fiscal Year-end: 04/30/14
Health Care Srvices
N.A.I.C.S.: 622110
Frank Meza (Chm)
Shirley Dettloff (Vice Chm)
Janice Fauchier (Treas)
Ana Fonseca (Sec)
Castulo de la Rocha (Pres & CEO)
Marie S. Torres (Sr VP-Govt Rels &
Community Res Initiative)
Zoila D. Escobar (VP-Strategic Dev &
Community Support)
Jose U. Esparza (CFO)
Martin Serota (Chief Medical Officer
& VP)
Angela D. Roberts (VP-Facilities)
Robert J. Turner (VP-HR)
Erika Sockaci (VP-Health Svcs)
Jennifer Spalding (VP-Sr Care Ops)
Martha Santana-Chin (VP-Managed
Care)
Ricardo Puertas (Dir-Medical-Quality
& Safety)
Rico Cristian (Reg Dir-Los Angeles
County)
Felix Carpio (Dir-Medical-Clinical In-
formatics)
Desmond Lew (Dir-Medical-Utilization
Mgmt)
Esiquio Casillas (Reg Dir-Medical-Sr
Svcs)
Rosa Arzu (Dir-Medical & Dental)
Robert Gomez (VP-Bus Ops)
Hector Barreto (Chm)
Alex Chen (Dir-Medical)

ALTAMIRA TECHNOLOGIES
CORPORATION

8201 Greensboro Dr Ste 800,
McLean, VA 22102
Tel.: (703) 813-2115
Web Site:
http://www.altamiracorp.com
Year Founded: 1999
Sales Range: $75-99.9 Million
Emp.: 175
Engineering & Analytic Services
N.A.I.C.S.: 541330
Jane P. Chappell (CEO)
Blaine Worthington (COO)
Adam Omar (CFO)
John Price (VP-Growth & Strategy)
Clay Sherman (Dir-Capture & Pro-
posals)
Caroline McConnell (Chief Human
Capital Officer)
Jason Siminski (VP-Bus Dev)
Craig Reed (Pres & Chief Growth
Officer)
Jane Chappell (CEO)
Richard Campos (Sr VP-Bus Dev)
Justin Shum (VP-Bus Dev)
Joseph R. Wright Jr. (Chm)

Subsidiaries:

Invertix Communications Mission
System Operations   (1)
Physical Science Laboratory NMSU Ander-
son Hall, Las Cruces, NM 88003   (100%)
Tel.: (575) 646-9100
Web Site: http://www.invertix.com
Sales Range: $25-49.9 Million.
Visualization & Integration of Security Sys-
tems
N.A.I.C.S.: 928110
Barb Trent (VP)

Prime Solutions LLC   (1)
6760 Alexander Bell Dr Ste 210, Columbia,
MD 21046
Tel.: (410) 384-4600
Web Site: http://www.primeso.com
Computer Software & Design Consulting
Services
N.A.I.C.S.: 541690
Jae Collins (COO)
Paul Barsotti (CEO)

Virginia Systems & Technology,
Inc.   (1)

6801 Kennedy Rd Ste 301, Warrenton, VA
20187-3992
Tel.: (540) 359-7550
Web Site: http://www.vast-inc.com
Engineeering Services
N.A.I.C.S.: 541330
Jay Hebert (Pres)

ALTAMONT CAPITAL MAN-
AGEMENT, LLC

100 Coxe Ave, Asheville, NC 28801-
4051
Tel.: (828) 236-0610
Web Site:
http://www.altamontcm.com
Office Administrative Services
N.A.I.C.S.: 561110
David Pheil (Owner)

ALTAMONT CAPITAL PART-
NERS

400 Hamilton Ave Ste 230, Palo Alto,
CA 94301
Tel.: (650) 264-7750   DE
Web Site:
http://www.altamontcapital.com
Year Founded: 2010
Privater Equity Firm
N.A.I.C.S.: 523999
Jesse Rogers (Mng Dir)
Randall Eason (Mng Dir)
Casey Lynch (Mng Dir)
Alex Rolfe (Mng Dir)
Kristin Johnson (Mng Dir)
Carol Pereira (CFO)
Keoni Schwartz (Mng Dir)
Steve Brownlie (Mng Dir)
Iain Bridges (Principal)
Greg Ruiz (Principal)
Sam Gaynor (Principal)
Kevin Mason (Principal)
Jason Friedrichs (Principal)
Melissa Francis (Principal)
Pete Meyerdirk (Principal)
Greg Corkran (VP)
Kai Li (VP)
Jennifer Mello (Chief Compliance Of-
ficer & Gen Counsel)
Chase Beeler (Principal)

Subsidiaries:

Bishop Lifting Products, Inc.   (1)
125 McCarty St, Houston, TX 77029
Tel.: (713) 674-2266
Web Site: http://www.lifting.com
Lifting & Rigging Equipment Mfr
N.A.I.C.S.: 333922
Harold King (Pres)
David Moseley (VP-Sls & Mktg)

Subsidiary (Domestic):

All-Lifts, Inc.   (2)
27-39 Thatcher St, Albany, NY 12207
Tel.: (518) 465-3461
Web Site: http://www.all-lifts.com
Sales Range: $1-9.9 Million
Emp.: 25
Miscellaneous Fabricated Wire Products
N.A.I.C.S.: 332618

Bairstow Lifting Products Co.,
Inc.   (2)
1785 Ellsworth Industrial Dr NW, Atlanta,
GA 30318-3747
Tel.: (404) 351-2600
Web Site: http://www.bairstow.com
Fabricated Wire Product Mfr
N.A.I.C.S.: 332618
Robert Bairstow (Pres)

General Work Products, Inc.   (2)
4912 Mehurin St, New Orleans, LA 70121
Tel.: (504) 733-1808
Rev.: $2,314,900
Emp.: 10
Industrial Supplies Merchant Whslr
N.A.I.C.S.: 423840
Gregory W. Palmer (Founder)
Mark Jeansonne (COO)

Silver State Wire Rope and Rigging, Inc. (2)
8740 S Jones Blvd, Las Vegas, NV 89139
Tel.: (702) 597-2010
Web Site: http://www.sswr.net
Rope, Cordage & Twine Mills
N.A.I.C.S.: 314994
Pete Rogers (Gen Mgr)
Andrew Rogers (Ops Mgr)

Western Sling Company (2)
5453 N Peterson Rd, Sedalia, CO 80135
Tel.: (800) 748-2651
Web Site: http://www.westernsling.com
All Other Miscellaneous Textile Product Mills
N.A.I.C.S.: 314999

Cotton Patch Cafe Inc. (1)
600 E Dallas Rd Ste 300, Grapevine, TX 76051
Tel.: (817) 865-6500
Web Site: http://www.cottonpatch.com
Sales Range: $10-24.9 Million
Emp.: 15
Family Restaurants
N.A.I.C.S.: 722511
Kathy Nelson (CEO)

Intermix (ITM) Inc. (1)
1440 Broadway 5th Fl, New York, NY 10018
Tel.: (212) 741-5075
Web Site: http://www.intermixonline.com
Rev.: $14,000,000
Emp.: 15
Women's Sportswear Mfr
N.A.I.C.S.: 458110
Taylor Bodo (Mgr-Store)
Karen Katz (Interim CEO)

J.D. Byrider Systems, LLC (1)
12802 Hamilton Crossing Blvd, Carmel, IN 46032
Tel.: (317) 249-3000
Web Site: http://www.jdbyrider.com
Sales Range: $100-124.9 Million
Patent Owners & Lessor Services
N.A.I.C.S.: 522220
Michael Maenhout (CIO)
Brad M. Malott (Treas, VP & Controller)
Jeffrey B. Higgins (Gen Counsel, Sec & VP)
Thomas L. Welter (VP-Franchising)
Steven E. Wedding (CEO)
Bryan Hohne (VP-Talent & Dev)
Jack Humbert (VP-Franchise Sls)

Subsidiary (Domestic):

Byrider Finance, LLC (2)
12802 Hamilton Crossing Blvd, Carmel, IN 46032
Tel.: (317) 249-3000
Used Cars Sales Financing Services
N.A.I.C.S.: 522220
James De Voe (Founder)
Walter Scott (CMO)

Byrider Sales of Indiana, LLC (2)
12802 Hamilton Crossing Blvd, Carmel, IN 46032
Tel.: (317) 249-3000
Web Site: http://www.jdByrider.com
Provider of Used Car Services
N.A.I.C.S.: 522220

Maxi Canada Inc. (1)
688 Rue du Parc, Saint-Lin-Laurentides, J5M 3B4, QC, Canada
Tel.: (450) 439-2500
Web Site: http://www.maxi.com
Emp.: 300
Frozen Poultry Products Mfr & Distr
N.A.I.C.S.: 311615

OMNIPLEX World Services Corporation (1)
14151 Park Meadow Dr, Chantilly, VA 20151-3805
Tel.: (703) 652-3100
Web Site: http://www.omniplex.com
Sales Range: $100-124.9 Million
Emp.: 2,500
Professional Intelligence Support, Investigative & Physical Security Services
N.A.I.C.S.: 561621
Michael S. Santelli (Pres & COO)
Philip T. Sweeney (Chm)
Jon N. Peterson (CFO, Controller & VP)
Kelly C. Grems (Sr VP)

William A. Turk (Gen Counsel & VP)
Gerry Decker (Chief Growth Officer)
Patrick Piccininno (CIO & VP)
Jamin E. Rogovoy (VP-Bus Dev)

Paramount Windows, Inc. (1)
550 W Southern Ave, Tempe, AZ 85282
Tel.: (480) 736-8988
Web Site: http://www.paramountwc.com
Residential Remodeler
N.A.I.C.S.: 236118
Sam Regina (Pres)

Tacala LLC (1)
4268 Cahaba Hts Ct, Birmingham, AL 35243
Tel.: (205) 443-9600
Web Site: http://www.tacala.com
Sales Range: $10-24.9 Million
Operates Chain of Fast Food Restaurants
N.A.I.C.S.: 722513
Don Ghareeb (Founder)
Joey Pierson (CFO)
Marjorie Perlman (VP-Mktg)
Michael Border (VP-Dev & Facilities)
Ragan Cain (Treas & VP)
Angelique DeFranco (Dir-Employee Admin)
Javier Maravi (VP-Trng & Staffing)
Tim Morrison (Pres & COO)

Tall Tree Foods, Inc. (1)
c/o ACP - 400 Hamilton Ave Ste 230, Palo Alto, CA 94301
Tel.: (650) 264-7750
Holding Company; Food Products Mfr & Whslr
N.A.I.C.S.: 551112
Tim Bruer (CEO)

Subsidiary (Domestic):

Blue Ribbon, LP (2)
2030 N Loop W Ste 100, Houston, TX 77018
Tel.: (713) 880-9766
Web Site:
   http://www.blueribbonsausage.com
Sausage, Bacon & Other Processed Meat Products Mfr & Whslr
N.A.I.C.S.: 311612
Tom Engelbert (Controller)

Carlton Foods Corp. (2)
880 Hwy 46 E, New Braunfels, TX 78130
Tel.: (830) 625-7583
Web Site: http://www.carltonfoods.com
Sausage & Other Processed Meat Products Mfr
N.A.I.C.S.: 311612
Randy Rust (Pres)

Klement Sausage Co., Inc. (2)
207 E Lincoln Ave, Milwaukee, WI 53207-1593
Tel.: (414) 744-2330
Web Site: http://www.klements.com
Sales Range: $25-49.9 Million
Emp.: 230
Sausage & Other Processed Meat Products Mfr & Whslr
N.A.I.C.S.: 311612
Mike Skodinski (Acct Mgr-Natl Sls)
Raymond D. Booth (Pres)

Richard's Cajun Foods Corp. (2)
1186 E Ebey St, Church Point, LA 70525
Tel.: (337) 684-6309
Web Site:
   http://www.richardscajunfoods.com
Sales Range: $100-124.9 Million
Cajun Spices, Sauces, Frozen Meals & Processed Meat Products Mfr & Whslr
N.A.I.C.S.: 311999
Ronnie Doucet (Pres)

The Specialized Packaging Group, Inc (1)
180 Grand Ave, Ste 900, Oakland, CA 94612
Tel.: (510) 324-3626
Web Site: https://spg-ges.com
Packaging & Containers Mfr
N.A.I.C.S.: 322219
Carlton L. Highsmith (Founder)

Subsidiary (Domestic):

Complete Packaging, Inc. (2)
633 Detroit Ave, Monroe, MI 48162
Tel.: (734) 241-2900

Web Site: http://www.completepkg.com
Sales Range: $1-9.9 Million
Emp.: 60
Custom Designed Packaging Services
N.A.I.C.S.: 561910
Robert Maul (Pres)

Pacific Pulp Molding, Inc (2)
11285 Forestview Ln, San Diego, CA 92131
Tel.: (619) 977-5617
Web Site: http://www.pacificpulp.com
Sales Range: $1-9.9 Million
Emp.: 30
Paper (except Newsprint) Mills
N.A.I.C.S.: 322120
John McNeil (Principal)

ALTAMONT PHARMA ACQUISITION CORP.
600 Congress Ave 14th Fl, Austin, TX 78702
Tel.: (512) 759-6267   DE
Year Founded: 2021
Investment Services
N.A.I.C.S.: 523999
Mark Pearson (Founder, Pres, Chm & CEO)
Rhozel Ocampo (Sr Dir-Fin)

ALTARIS CAPITAL PARTNERS, LLC
10 E 53rd St 31st Fl, New York, NY 10022
Tel.: (212) 931-0250   DE
Web Site: http://altariscap.com
Year Founded: 2003
Rev.: $775,000,000
Investment Firm
N.A.I.C.S.: 523999
Daniel G. Tully (Co-Founder & Mng Dir)
George E. Aitken-Davies (Co-Founder & Mng Dir)
Philip I. Smith (Operating Partner)
Charles T. Mullens (CFO)
James D. O'Brien (Mng Dir-Medical Devices & Diagnostics)
Daniel G. Tully (Co-Founder & Mng Dir)
Nicholas D. Fulco (Principal-Healthcare Svcs)
Garikai Nyaruwata (Mng Dir-Pharmaceuticals & Pharma Svcs)

Subsidiaries:

Analogic Corporation (1)
8 Centennial Dr, Peabody, MA 01960
Tel.: (978) 326-4000
Web Site: http://www.analogic.com
Medical & Security Imaging Systems & Subsystems Developer, Designer & Mfr
N.A.I.C.S.: 334515
Will Rousmaniere (CFO)
Tom Ripp (CEO)
Steve Urchuk (CTO)

Subsidiary (Non-US):

Analogic Canada Corporation (2)
4950 Levy Road, Saint Laurent, H2R 2P1, QC, Canada   (100%)
Tel.: (514) 856-6920
Web Site: http://www.analogic.com
Sales Range: $25-49.9 Million
Emp.: 120
Electronic Products Mfr
N.A.I.C.S.: 334419

Subsidiary (Domestic):

Ultrasonix Medical Corporation (3)
130-4311 Viking Way, Richmond, V6V2K9, BC, Canada
Tel.: (604) 279-8550
Web Site: http://www.ultrasonix.com
Sales Range: $10-24.9 Million
Emp.: 70
Medical Ultrasound Technologies & Equipment Mfr
N.A.I.C.S.: 334510

Subsidiary (Non-US):

Analogic Italia S.r.L (2)

Via Morandi 10, 20077, Melegnano, Milan, Italy
Tel.: (39) 0290781347
Medical Equipment Distr
N.A.I.C.S.: 423450
Daniele Mosconi (Mgr-Natl)

Analogic Medical Equipment (Shanghai) Co. Ltd. (2)
1377 Lan Dian Road, Pu Dong New District, Shanghai, China
Tel.: (86) 2120890333
Medical & Security Imaging Systems & Subsystems Designer & Mfr
N.A.I.C.S.: 334510

Subsidiary (Domestic):

B-K Medical Systems, Inc. (2)
8 Centennial Dr, Peabody, MA 01960
Tel.: (978) 326-1300
Web Site:
   http://www.analogicultrasound.com
Urological & Surgical Diagnostic Ultrasound Systems Supplier & Mfr
N.A.I.C.S.: 339112
Mark Miller (Gen Mgr)
Michael Brock (Pres & CEO)
Jesper L. Manigoff (VP-Ultrasound Engrg & Mng Dir)

Subsidiary (Non-US):

B-K Medical AB (3)
Vastberga Alle 26 3tr, 126 30, Hagersten, Sweden
Tel.: (46) 87440211
Web Site: http://www.bkmedical.com
Sales Range: $10-24.9 Million
Emp.: 7
Urological & Surgical Diagnostic Ultrasound System Distr
N.A.I.C.S.: 423450
Jorgen Noojd (Gen Mgr)

BK Medical ApS (3)
Mileparken 34, 2730, Herlev, Denmark
Tel.: (45) 44528100
Web Site: http://www.bkmedical.com
Urological & Surgical Diagnostic Ultrasound System Supplier & Mfr
N.A.I.C.S.: 339112
Jesper Hek Hansen (Gen Mgr & Dir-Sls)

BK Medical Medizinische Systeme GmbH (3)
Pascalkehre 13, 25451, Quickborn, Germany
Tel.: (49) 410699550
Sales Range: $25-49.9 Million
Emp.: 28
Medical Ultrasound Equipment Mfr & Supplies
N.A.I.C.S.: 339112
Peter Weedermann (Gen Mgr)

Subsidiary (Non-US):

BK Ultrasound Limited (2)
Units A20/A20a Basepoint Business & Innovation Centre 110 Butterfield, Great Marlings, Luton, LU2 8DL, Bedfordshire, United Kingdom
Tel.: (44) 1582433710
Ultrasonic Medical Equipment Distr
N.A.I.C.S.: 423450
Geoff Pick (Mng Dir)

Subsidiary (Domestic):

Sound Technology, Inc. (2)
401 Science Park Rd, State College, PA 16803
Tel.: (814) 234-4377
Web Site: http://www.bkmedical.com
Sales Range: $50-74.9 Million
Emp.: 285
Mfr of Diagnostic Medical Ultrasound Transducers & Probes
N.A.I.C.S.: 334419

Clearwater Compliance LLC (1)
40 Burton Hills Blvd Ste 200, Nashville, TN
Tel.: (800) 704-3394
Web Site: https://clearwatercompliance.com
Cyber Risk Management & Regulatory Compliance Solutions
N.A.I.C.S.: 541512
Steve Cagle (CEO)

Altaris Capital Partners, LLC—(Continued)

Subsidiary (Domestic):

CynergisTek, Inc. (2)
11940 Jollyville Rd Ste 300N, Austin, TX 78759
Tel.: (512) 402-8550
Web Site: http://www.cynergistek.com
Rev.: $16,301,905
Assets: $28,885,003
Liabilities: $4,924,503
Net Worth: $23,960,500
Earnings: ($2,246,579)
Emp.: 89
Fiscal Year-end: 12/31/2021
Holding Company; Information Technology Security Consulting Services
N.A.I.C.S.: 551112
David Finn (Exec VP-External Affairs, Information Sys & Security)
Benjamin Denkers (Exec VP-Ops)
Robert McCashin (Chm)
Rafael Lammie (VP-People & Culture)
Carrie Mulcahy (VP-Mktg)
Dave Bailey (VP-Healthcare Svcs)
Steve Rivera (Sr VP-Sls)
Tim McMullen (COO)

Subsidiary (Domestic):

CTEK Security, Inc. (3)
8303 N Mopac Expy, Austin, TX 78759
Tel.: (512) 402-8550
Web Site: http://www.cynergistek.com
Security System Services
N.A.I.C.S.: 561621
Michael H. McMillan (Pres, CEO & Chief Strategy Officer)

Division (Domestic):

Redspin (3)
4690 Carpinteria Ave Ste B, Carpinteria, CA 93013
Tel.: (805) 684-6858
Web Site: http://www.redspin.com
Security Software Development Services
N.A.I.C.S.: 541511

HealthTronics, Inc. (1)
9825 Spectrum Dr Bldg 3, Austin, TX 78717
Tel.: (512) 328-2892
Web Site: http://www.healthtronics.com
Sales Range: $150-199.9 Million
Medical & Hospital Equipment Mfr
N.A.I.C.S.: 334510
Russell Newman (Pres)
Clint B. Davis (Gen Counsel & Sr VP)
Jose E. Martinez (VP-HR)
Gary J. Kozen (VP-Ops)
Robert Whyte (Officer-Compliance)

Subsidiary (Domestic):

Laser Ventures, Inc. (2)
125 Smokehill Ln, Woodstock, GA 30188
Tel.: (770) 516-4600
Web Site: http://www.laserventures.com
Emp.: 15
Mobile Medical Laser Services
N.A.I.C.S.: 334510
Matthew McIntyre (CFO & Sec)
Robin Santana (Owner)

Meridian Medical Technologies, Inc. (1)
6350 Stevens Forest Rd Ste 301, Columbia, MD 21046
Medicinal Product Mfr
N.A.I.C.S.: 339112

Plant (Domestic):

Meridian Medical Technologies - Westport (2)
1945 Craig Rd, Saint Louis, MO 63146 (100%)
Tel.: (800) 638-8093
Automatic Injector Products for Civilian & Military Use; Syringe Components for the Pharmaceutical & Medical Device Industry
N.A.I.C.S.: 339112

Sharecare, Inc. (1)
255 E Paces Ferry Rd NE Ste 700, Atlanta, GA 30305-2233
Tel.: (404) 671-4000
Web Site: https://www.sharecare.com
Rev.: $442,415,000
Assets: $701,001,000

Liabilities: $178,401,000
Net Worth: $522,600,000
Earnings: ($118,707,000)
Emp.: 3,485
Fiscal Year-end: 12/31/2022
Investment Services
N.A.I.C.S.: 523999
Jeff Arnold (Founder, Chm & CEO)
Justin Ferrero (Co-Pres & CFO)
Dawn Whaley (Co-Pres & CMO)
Carrie Ratliff (Chief Legal Officer)
Shannon Bagley (COO)
Elizabeth Colyer (Chief Comml Officer-Enterprise)
Tim Husted (Sr VP & Gen Mgr-Provider & CareLinx)
Darragh Wright (Sr VP & Gen Mgr-Provider)
Sam De Brouwer (Chief Strategy Officer)
Harsha Panyadahundi (CTO)
Toni Pashley (Exec VP-Product)
Walter De Brouwer (Chief Scientific Officer)
Donna Hill Howes (Chief Nursing Officer)
Henry Jay (Officer-Diversity & Gen Counsel)
Jen Martin Hall (Exec VP-Corporate Communications)
Dermot Waters (Exec VP-Marketing)

Subsidiary (Domestic):

CareLinx Inc. (2)
1350 Old Bayshore Hwy, Burlingame, CA 94010
Tel.: (650) 209-7305
Web Site: http://www.carelinx.com
Software Publisher
N.A.I.C.S.: 513210
Sherwin Sheik (Founder & CEO)

Sharecare, Inc. (2)
255 East Pl Ferry Rd NE, Atlanta, GA 30305
Tel.: (404) 671-4000
Web Site: http://www.sharecare.com
Internet Medical Advice Platform
N.A.I.C.S.: 513210
Mehmet Oz (Co-Founder)
Justin Ferrero (Pres)
Howard Gruverman (Exec VP-Enterprise)
Towers Watson (Sr VP-Actuarial Consulting & Bus Dev)
Ami Patel (Chief Legal & Compliance Officer)
Jerry Mooty (Exec VP-Markets, Community & Fitness)

Subsidiary (Domestic):

Lucid Global, Inc. (3)
1680 Fruitville Rd Ste 202, Sarasota, FL 34236
Tel.: (941) 893-4400
Web Site: http://www.biolucid.com
Sales Range: $10-24.9 Million
Emp.: 15
Digital Health Care Services
N.A.I.C.S.: 541512
Jeff Hazelton (Co-Founder & CTO)
Lawrence Kiey (Co-Founder, Chm & CEO)
Dale Park (Co-Founder, Chief Scientific Officer & Treas)
Zelka Ridjosic (Exec VP-Mktg & Sls)

RealAge, Inc. (3)
5375 Mira Sorrento Pl Ste 250, San Diego, CA 92121
Tel.: (858) 200-7171
Web Site: http://www.realage.com
Sales Range: $10-24.9 Million
Emp.: 75
Consumer Health & Wellness Information Website Operator
N.A.I.C.S.: 513199
Theresa Brennan (VP-Tech)

Solesis, Inc. (1)
1000 E Walnut St Ste 521, Perkasie, PA 18944 (51%)
Tel.: (215) 453-2174
Web Site: http://www.solesis.com
Pharmaceuticals Product Mfr
N.A.I.C.S.: 325412
Karen M. West (Pres)
Christopher B. Edwards (VP-Fin)
Jeff Robertson (VP)

Subsidiary (Domestic):

Polyzen, LLC (2)
1041 Classic Rd, Apex, NC 27539
Tel.: (919) 319-9599

Web Site: http://www.polyzen.com
Rev.: $5,000,000
Emp.: 45
Surgical & Medical Instrument Mfr
N.A.I.C.S.: 339112
Tilak Shah (Founder)
Nikin Shah (CEO-Fin & Ops)
Rubin Shah (CEO-Sls & Mktg)
Tilak M. Shah (Founder)

Trean Insurance Group, Inc. (1)
150 Lake St W, Wayzata, MN 55391
Tel.: (952) 974-2200
Web Site: https://www.trean.com
Rev.: $303,242,000
Assets: $1,581,939,000
Liabilities: $1,266,920,000
Net Worth: $315,019,000
Earnings: ($65,955,000)
Emp.: 344
Fiscal Year-end: 12/31/2022
Insurance Holding Company
N.A.I.C.S.: 551112
Andrew M. O'Brien (Chm)
Julie A. Baron (CEO)
Jill K. Johnson (Gen Counsel)
Martin A. Ericson (Sr VP-Underwriting)
Matthew J. Spencer (CIO)
Elisabeth Rosandich (Sr VP-Bus Dev)

Subsidiary (Domestic):

American Liberty Insurance Company (2)
3601 N University Ave Ste 100, Provo, UT 84604
Tel.: (801) 226-8008
Web Site: http://www.american-liberty.net
Insurance Services
N.A.I.C.S.: 524210

Trean Corporation (2)
150 Lake St W, Wayzata, MN 55391
Tel.: (952) 974-2200
Web Site: https://www.treancorp.com
Insurance Services
N.A.I.C.S.: 524210
Andrew M. O'Brien (Pres & CEO)
Julie A. Baron (CFO, Treas & Sec)
Joy N. Edler (COO)
Matthew Spencer (CIO)
Elisabeth Rosandich (Sr VP-Business Development-Program Svcs)

ALTAROCK ENERGY INC.
4010 Stone Way N Ste 400, Seattle, WA 98103
Tel.: (206) 729-2400
Web Site:
  https://www.altarockenergy.com
Geothermal Technology Services
N.A.I.C.S.: 541715
Aaron Mandell (CEO)
Susan Petty (Pres & CTO)

Subsidiaries:

Bottle Rock Power, LLC. (1)
7385 High Vly Rd, Anaheim, CA 95426
Tel.: (707) 928-4578
Web Site: http://www.bottlerockpower.com
Sales Range: $1-9.9 Million
Emp.: 25
Renewable Energy Distr
N.A.I.C.S.: 221118

ALTEC INDUSTRIES INC.
210 Inverness Center Dr, Birmingham, AL 35242-4834
Tel.: (205) 991-7733 **AL**
Web Site: https://www.altec.com
Year Founded: 1929
Sales Range: $100-124.9 Million
Emp.: 200
Mobile Utility Equipment, Hydraulic Digger Derricks & Aerial Devices Mfr
N.A.I.C.S.: 333120
Lee Joseph Styslinger III (Co-Chm)

Subsidiaries:

Altec Industries Inc. (1)
210 Inverness Center Dr, Birmingham, AL 35242-4834
Tel.: (205) 991-7733
Web Site: http://www.altec.com

Sales Range: $10-24.9 Million
Emp.: 30
Arial Lift Insulated & Non-Insulated Trucks; Telecommunications; Central Office Air Driers Mfr
N.A.I.C.S.: 333413

Teupen Maschinenbau GmbH (1)
Marie-Curie-Str 13, 48599, Gronau, Germany
Tel.: (49) 2562 8161 0
Web Site: http://www.teupen.com
Holding Company
N.A.I.C.S.: 551112
Michael Scheuss (CEO)
David Kesser (Exec VP-USA)

ALTER BARGE LINE INC.
2117 State St, Bettendorf, IA 52722-5030
Tel.: (563) 344-5100 **IA**
Web Site: http://www.alterbarge.com
Year Founded: 1979
Sales Range: $10-24.9 Million
Emp.: 130
Provider of Water Transportation for Freight
N.A.I.C.S.: 483211
Jeffrey D. Goldstein (Chm & CEO)
Tom Streight (VP-Sls)
Larry R. Daily (Pres)

ALTER COMPANIES
2117 State St, Bettendorf, IA 52722
Tel.: (563) 344-5000
Sales Range: $75-99.9 Million
Emp.: 30
River Transportation Services
N.A.I.C.S.: 483211
Jeffrey D. Goldstein (Chm & Pres)

Subsidiaries:

Alter Trucking and Terminal Corp. (1)
2117 State St, Bettendorf, IA 52722
Tel.: (563) 344-5000
Sales Range: Less than $1 Million
Emp.: 4
Truck Brokering
N.A.I.C.S.: 484220
Jeffrey D. Goldstein (Pres)

River/Gulf Grain Company (1)
2117 State St, Bettendorf, IA 52722
Tel.: (563) 344-5178
Web Site: http://www.rivergulf.com
Rev.: $1,300,000
Emp.: 8
Commodity Contracts Brokers, Dealers
N.A.I.C.S.: 523160

ALTER ECO
2325 3rd St Ste 324, San Francisco, CA 94107
Tel.: (415) 701-1212
Web Site:
  http://www.alterecofoods.com
Year Founded: 2004
Sales Range: $1-9.9 Million
Emp.: 20
Food Product Fair Trade Operator
N.A.I.C.S.: 561920
Edouard Rollet (Co-Founder & COO)
Mathieu Sen (Co-Founder & CEO)
Jeanne Cloutier (Dir-Supply Chain)
Lauren Storella (Mgr-Inside Sls & Admin)
Antoine Ambert (Dir-Mktg)
Naomi Petrash (Coord-Order Entry & Inventory Control)
Ilse Keijzer (Founder)
Andrea Kuhl (Mgr-Fin & Admin)

ALTER TRADING CORPORATION
700 Office Pkwy, Saint Louis, MO 63141-6884
Tel.: (314) 872-2400 **IA**
Web Site: http://www.altertrading.com
Year Founded: 1898

Scrap & Waste Materials
N.A.I.C.S.: 423930
Robert S. Goldstein *(Chm)*
Robert G. Ellis *(Gen Counsel & Sr VP)*
Don H. Martin *(Sr VP-Ferrous Mktg & Trading)*
Jay Robinovitz *(Pres & CEO)*
Michael E. Vail *(VP-Ops)*
Jack Grundfest *(Chief Admin Officer & Sr VP)*

Subsidiaries:

Behr Iron & Steel, Inc.   (1)
1100 Seminary St, Rockford, IL 61104
Tel.: (815) 987-2700
Web Site: http://www.behrim.com
Rev.: $7,500,000
Emp.: 43
Recyclable Material Merchant Whslr
N.A.I.C.S.: 423930
William J. Bremner *(Pres & CEO)*
Jodi Behr *(VP-Mktg)*
John Menne *(Sr VP-HR-Safety)*
Lee Foecking *(CFO)*
Nancy Del Castillo *(Treas)*
Roger Little *(Sr VP-Admin)*
Wade Bigali *(Sr VP-Sls & Mktg)*

Tenenbaum Recycling Group, LLC   (1)
4500 W Bethany Rd, North Little Rock, AR 72117-3401
Tel.: (501) 945-0881
Web Site: http://www.trg.net
Wholesale Scrap Metal & Steel
N.A.I.C.S.: 423930
Jack D. Grundfest *(Pres & CEO)*
Timothy R. McGrath *(CFO)*
Harold S. Tenenbaum *(Chm)*

Subsidiary (Domestic):

TRG Berryville LLC   (2)
903 Freeman Switch Rd, Berryville, AR 72616
Tel.: (870) 423-3380
Web Site: http://www.trg.net
Scrap Metal Recycling Services
N.A.I.C.S.: 562920

TRG Harrison, LLC   (2)
316 W Industrial Park Rd, Harrison, AR 72601
Tel.: (870) 741-8080
Web Site: http://www.trg.net
Scrap Metal Recycling Services
N.A.I.C.S.: 562920

TRG Hot Springs, LLC   (2)
4400 Malvern Rd, Hot Springs, AR 71901
Tel.: (501) 262-3420
Web Site: http://www.trg.net
Scrap Metal Recycle & Retail
N.A.I.C.S.: 331314

TRG Jonesboro, LLC   (2)
130 Flint St, Jonesboro, AR 72401
Tel.: (870) 932-8361
Web Site: http://www.trg.net
Recycling Services
N.A.I.C.S.: 562920

TRG Rogers, LLC   (2)
3459 N Arkansas St, Rogers, AR 72756
Tel.: (479) 621-8800
Web Site: http://www.trg.net
Metal Recycling Services
N.A.I.C.S.: 562920

ALTERMAN, INC.
14703 Jones Maltsberger, San Antonio, TX 78247-3713
Tel.: (210) 496-6888   TX
Web Site:
   https://www.goalterman.com
Year Founded: 1923
Sales Range: $25-49.9 Million
Emp.: 300
Electrical Contractor
N.A.I.C.S.: 238210
Chris Thiel *(CFO & Exec VP)*

Subsidiaries:

Alterman Enterprises Inc.   (1)

14703 Jones Maltsberger Rd, San Antonio, TX 78247-3713
Tel.: (210) 496-6888
Web Site: http://www.goalterman.com
Emp.: 500
Electrical contractor
N.A.I.C.S.: 532412
Kristi Seibert *(Mgr-HR)*

ALTERNA CAPITAL PARTNERS LLC
15 River Rd Ste 320, Wilton, CT 06897
Tel.: (203) 210-7333
Web Site:
   https://www.alternacapital.com
Miscellaneous Financial Investment Services
N.A.I.C.S.: 523999
Roger P. Miller *(Mng Partner)*
Eric M. Press *(Mng Partner)*

ALTERNATE SOLUTIONS HOMECARE
1050 Forrer Blvd, Kettering, OH 45420
Tel.: (937) 298-1111
Web Site:
   http://www.ashomecare.com
Sales Range: $10-24.9 Million
Emp.: 400
Home & Social Care Services
N.A.I.C.S.: 621610
Sara Stump *(Coord-Patient Scheduling)*
Linda Kramer *(Dir-Org Dev)*
Judy Hayes *(Coord-Mktg & Comm)*
Holly Clemens *(Mgr-HR)*

ALTERNATE STAFFING INC.
4918 Fort Hamilton Pkwy, Brooklyn, NY 11219
Tel.: (718) 972-2500
Web Site:
   https://www.alternatestaffing.com
Rev.: $43,000,000
Emp.: 8
Medical Help Service
N.A.I.C.S.: 561320
Norma Dreyfuss *(Pres)*

ALTERNATE TRANSIT ADVERTISING
295 Bayside Rd, Greenland, NH 03840-2130
Tel.: (603) 436-0008
Web Site: http://www.atatransit.com
Year Founded: 1992
Sales Range: Less than $1 Million
Emp.: 5
Advertising, Mobile Marketing
N.A.I.C.S.: 541810
Jane M. Cutter *(Pres)*
Mary Anne Carpenter *(Dir-Sls-Mktg)*
Stephanie Bergeron *(Mgr-Production)*

ALTERNATIVE BILLING SOLUTIONS, INC.
8120 Penn Ave S Ste 500, Minneapolis, MN 55431
Tel.: (952) 881-2416
Year Founded: 1987
Sales Range: $1-9.9 Million
Emp.: 90
Medical Billing Services
N.A.I.C.S.: 541618

ALTERNATIVE ENERGY STORE, LLC
43 Broad St Ste A408, Hudson, MA 01749
Tel.: (978) 562-5858
Web Site: http://www.altestore.com
Year Founded: 1999
Rev.: $5,700,000
Emp.: 18
Energy Retailers

N.A.I.C.S.: 459999
Sascha Deri *(Co-Founder & Pres)*
Nick Albright *(Co-Founder & CTO)*
Normand Martin *(Supvr-Warehouse)*

ALTERNATIVE FAMILY SERVICES
1421 Guerneville Rd Ste 218, Santa Rosa, CA 95403
Tel.: (707) 576-7700   CA
Web Site: http://www.afs4kids.org
Year Founded: 1977
Sales Range: $10-24.9 Million
Emp.: 255
Family Support Services
N.A.I.C.S.: 624190
Martha E. Duarte *(CFO)*
Craig Barton *(Dir-Foster Care & Adoptions)*

ALTERNATIVE HOSE, INC.
20 N 48th Ave, Phoenix, AZ 85043
Tel.: (602) 269-6900   AZ
Web Site: https://www.althose.com
Year Founded: 1992
Hydraulic Industrial Hose Distr
N.A.I.C.S.: 423840
Dirk Lange *(Owner)*
Jason Fontaine *(Dir-Pur)*
Steve Ahrenberg *(Dir-Sls)*
Michael Casey *(VP)*

ALTERNATIVE INVESTMENT CORPORATION
150 E 52nd St Ste 1102, New York, NY 10022
Tel.: (917) 480-1169   NV
Web Site: http://aikocapital.com
Year Founded: 2007
AIKO—(OTCBB)
Rev.: $11,557
Assets: $3,584
Liabilities: $988,246
Net Worth: ($984,662)
Earnings: ($375,478)
Emp.: 2
Fiscal Year-end: 09/30/19
Investment Services
N.A.I.C.S.: 523999

ALTERNATIVE MARKETING SOLUTIONS, INC.
342 Nutt Rd, Phoenixville, PA 19460-3910
Tel.: (610) 783-1320
Year Founded: 1995
Sales Range: Less than $1 Million
Emp.: 20
N.A.I.C.S.: 541810
Mike Guntick *(Pres)*
Patricia Breckley-Guntick *(Exec VP)*

ALTERNATIVE REHABILITATION COMMUNITIES, INC.
2743 N Front St, Harrisburg, PA 17110
Tel.: (717) 238-7101   PA
Web Site: http://www.arcfamily.com
Year Founded: 1975
Sales Range: $10-24.9 Million
Emp.: 282
Youth Rehabilitation Services
N.A.I.C.S.: 623220
Michael Elby *(Dir-Ops)*
Daniel P. Elby *(CEO)*
Ronald E. Sharp *(Dir-Treatment)*

ALTERNATIVE RESIDENCES TWO INC.
67051 Executive Dr, Saint Clairsville, OH 43950
Tel.: (740) 695-0634   OH
Year Founded: 1979
Sales Range: $10-24.9 Million
Emp.: 318

Developmental Disability Assistance Services
N.A.I.C.S.: 623210
Shirley Johnson-Mallory *(Chm)*
Fran McAfee *(Sec)*
Linda Ross *(Treas)*

ALTERNATIVE RISK MANAGEMENT LTD.
814 W Northwest Hwy, Arlington Heights, IL 60004-5344
Tel.: (847) 394-1700
Web Site: https://www.altrisk.com
Year Founded: 1992
Rev.: $10,000,000
Emp.: 15
Insurance Information & Consulting Services
N.A.I.C.S.: 524298
John Mitchell *(Pres)*

ALTERNATIVE SCHOOLS NETWORK
1807 W Sunnyside Ave Ste 1D, Chicago, IL 60640
Tel.: (773) 728-4030   IL
Web Site:
   https://www.asnchicago.org
Year Founded: 1973
Sales Range: $10-24.9 Million
Emp.: 117
Educational Support Services
N.A.I.C.S.: 611710
Matt Rodriguez *(Sec)*
Jose Rodriguez *(Treas)*
Jack Wuest *(Exec Dir)*
Oye Kale *(Pres)*

ALTERNATIVE SERVICES INC.
32625 W 7 Mile Rd Ste 10, Livonia, MI 48152
Tel.: (248) 471-4880   MI
Web Site: https://www.asi-mi.org
Year Founded: 1978
Sales Range: $10-24.9 Million
Emp.: 820
Intellectual & Developmental Disability Assistance Services
N.A.I.C.S.: 623210
Jenny Spencer *(Exec Dir)*

ALTERNATIVE SOLUTIONS, INC.
400 Trade Ctr Ste 5900, Woburn, MA 01801
Tel.: (617) 262-4900   MA
Web Site:
   http://www.alternativesolutions.com
Year Founded: 1982
Rev.: $16,000,000
Emp.: 200
Healthcare Temporary Help & Permanent Professional Employment Placement Services
N.A.I.C.S.: 561311
Keith Alter *(Pres)*
Keith Karpowich *(Acct Mgr)*

ALTERNATIVE STAFFING INC.
1505 Remount Rd Ste A, North Charleston, SC 29406
Tel.: (843) 744-6040
Web Site:
   https://www.alternativestaffing.com
Sales Range: $10-24.9 Million
Emp.: 750
Employment Services for Temporary Employees
N.A.I.C.S.: 561320
Craig Lake *(Pres)*

ALTERNATIVE TECHNOLOGY SOLUTIONS
65 Enterprise, Aliso Viejo, CA 92656
Web Site:
   http://www.alttechsolutions.com

Alternative Technology Solutions—(Continued)

Year Founded: 2009
Sales Range: $1-9.9 Million
Emp.: 52
Software & Consulting Services
N.A.I.C.S.: 423430
Vivian Keena (CEO)
Donna Barnett (CTO)
Allan Ward (VP-Svcs)
Melissa Sarver (VP-Managed Svcs & Tech)
Nina Patnala (Dir-Product Dev)
Paul Vranas (Dir-Sls)
Aaron Korsen (Exec VP-Sls & Mktg)
Andie Dang (Sr Mgr-Ops)
Cassandra Nicholson (Dir-Product Mgmt)
Jeff Underdahl (VP-Tech Sls & Product Innovation)
Juel Hood (Dir-Practice)
Laura Monn Ginsburg (Sr Dir-Mktg)

ALTERNATIVES, INC.

600 1st Ave, Raritan, NJ 08869
Tel.: (908) 685-1444   NJ
Web Site:
     http://www.alternativesinc.org
Year Founded: 1980
Sales Range: $10-24.9 Million
Emp.: 467
Community Support Services
N.A.I.C.S.: 624190
Fresia Skoczypec (VP-Svcs)
Jorge R. Diaz (VP-Fin)
Karola Terlaje (Dir-Admin)
Stephen Kalucki (Dir-HR)
Anita Feiner (Dir-Dev & Comm)
Morris Malmstrom (Treas)
Susan Anczarki (Sec)
Nancy Good (Pres)
Linda Leparulo (Chm)
Christina Demetro (Asst Dir-Community Outreach Svcs)
Nicole Zenner (Dir-Community Outreach Svcs)
Dara Reagan (Dir-Svcs)
Lynn Omslaer (Dir-Svcs)
Glori Bine-Callagy (Dir-Svcs & Bridges to Employment)
Carolyn Suero (Sr Dir-Svcs)
Donna Clinger (VP-Quality Support Unit)

ALTERNET SYSTEMS, INC.

2665 S Bayshore Dr Ste 305, Miami, FL 33133
Tel.: (786) 265-1840   NV
Year Founded: 2010
Data Processing Services
N.A.I.C.S.: 518210

ALTES LLC

5901 Broken Sound Pkwy Ste 310, Boca Raton, FL 33487
Tel.: (561) 241-4511
Sales Range: $25-49.9 Million
Emp.: 2,400
Fast-Food Restaurant Chain Owner & Operator
N.A.I.C.S.: 722513
Robert Alrod (CEO)

ALTEVA, INC.

47 Main St, Warwick, NY 10990
Tel.: (877) 258-3722   NY
Web Site: http://www.alteva.com
Year Founded: 1902
Rev.: $30,105,000
Assets: $57,118,000
Liabilities: $16,962,000
Net Worth: $40,156,000
Earnings: $29,434,000
Emp.: 109
Fiscal Year-end: 12/31/14

Telephone Communications, Video & Internet Services
N.A.I.C.S.: 517121

Subsidiaries:

Alteva of Syracuse, Inc.   (1)
47 Main St, Warwick, NY 10990
Tel.: (845) 986-8080
Web Site: http://www.warwick.net
Communication Service
N.A.I.C.S.: 517810

ALTEX ELECTRONICS, LTD.

11342 IH 35 N, San Antonio, TX 78233
Tel.: (210) 655-8882
Web Site: https://www.altex.com
Year Founded: 1980
Rev.: $33,000,000
Emp.: 150
Whslr of Computer & Networking Equipment
N.A.I.C.S.: 423690
Mike Meyers (Pres)
Jeff Meyers (VP)
Coco Cates (Mgr-Adv Dept)
Patrick Boyer (Asst Mgr-Production)

ALTEX PACKAGING, INC.

2510 Electronics Dr, Anniston, AL 36207
Tel.: (256) 290-7225
Web Site:
     https://www.altexpackaging.com
Year Founded: 1998
Sales Range: $10-24.9 Million
Emp.: 40
Corrugated & Solid Fiber Box Mfr
N.A.I.C.S.: 322211
Randall Rigsby (Founder)

ALTEXSOFT, INC.

701 Palomar Airport Rd Ste 300, Carlsbad, CA 92011
Web Site: http://www.altexsoft.com
Year Founded: 2007
Sales Range: $1-9.9 Million
Emp.: 150
Information Technology Development Services
N.A.I.C.S.: 541511
Oleksandr Medovoi (Pres & CEO)

ALTHOFF INDUSTRIES INC.

8001 S Rte 31, Crystal Lake, IL 60014
Tel.: (815) 455-7000   IL
Web Site: https://www.althoffind.com
Year Founded: 1961
Plumbing, Heating & Air-Conditioning
N.A.I.C.S.: 238220
Chris Bennett (Exec VP)
Tom Les (CFO)
Tod W. Althoff (Pres)
Rami Nassib (VP)
Blake Wiltshire (Dir-Residential Svcs)

ALTICOR INC.

7575 Fulton St E, Ada, MI 49355-0001
Tel.: (616) 787-7833   MI
Web Site:
     http://www.amwayglobal.com
Year Founded: 2000
Sales Range: $5-14.9 Billion
Emp.: 13,000
Holding Company
N.A.I.C.S.: 551112
Doug DeVos (Pres)
Steve Van Andel (Chm)
Candace S. Matthews (Pres-Americas)
Michael Mohr (Gen Counsel, Sec & VP)
Michael J. Cazer (COO)
Gary VanderVen (Mgr-Svc)
Su Jung Bae (CMO)

George Calvert (Chief Supply Chain Officer)
Michael Nelson (Chief Admin Officer)
Nick Thole (CFO)
Alex Yeung (CIO)

Subsidiaries:

Access Business Group LLC   (1)
7575 Fulton St E, Ada, MI 49355-0001
Tel.: (616) 787-6000
Web Site:
     http://www.accessbusinessgroup.com
Sales Range: $300-349.9 Million
Emp.: 4,000
Business Services, Including Product Development, Sourcing, Manufacturing, Printing, Packaging & Distribution
N.A.I.C.S.: 561499
Jim Siewertsen (VP-Global Svc)
Joey Edwards (Dir-Contract Printing)
Paul Nadel (Dir-Global Contract Sls)
Jamie Francis (Mgr-Contract Sls)
Al McQueen (Dir-Natl Sls)

Division (Domestic):

Access Business Group   (2)
5600 Beach Blvd, Buena Park, CA 90622-6397
Tel.: (714) 562-6200
Web Site:
     http://www.accessbusinessgroup.com
Sales Range: $75-99.9 Million
Emp.: 500
Vitamin & Food Supplement Mfr
N.A.I.C.S.: 424690

Alticor Corporate Enterprises   (1)
7575 Fulton St E, Ada, MI 49355-0001
Tel.: (616) 787-1000
Web Site: http://www.alticor.com
Investment Management Service
N.A.I.C.S.: 523940
Roger C. Colman (VP-Corp Dev)

Amway Corporation   (1)
7575 Fulton St E, Ada, MI 49355-0001
Tel.: (616) 787-7833
Web Site: https://www.amway.com
Sales Range: $350-399.9 Million
Emp.: 15,000
Other Chemical & Allied Products Merchant Wholesalers
N.A.I.C.S.: 424690
Doug DeVos (Co-Chm & Pres)
Steve Van Andel (Co-Chm)
Jim Payne (Vice Chm)
Su Jung Bae (CMO)
Mark Beiderwieden (Pres-Asia Pacific)
George D. Calvert (Chief Supply Chain & R&D Officer)
Michael Cazer (COO)
Michael Mohr (Gen Counsel & Sec)
John Parker (Chief Sls Officer)
Bill Payne (Vice Chm)
Kelly Savage (Chief HR Officer)
Maxim Bobin (Dir-Legal-Russia & Kazakhstan)
Nick Thole (CFO)
Milind Pant (CEO)
Anouchah Sanei (Chief R&D Officer)

Subsidiary (Non-US):

Amway (Europe) Ltd.   (2)
Snowdon Drive, Winterhill, Milton Keynes, MK6 1AR, United Kingdom
Tel.: (44) 1908298050
Web Site: http://www.amivo.com
Sales Range: $25-49.9 Million
Emp.: 80
Distribution of Amway Products
N.A.I.C.S.: 722330

Subsidiary (Non-US):

Amway Hungaria Marketing KFT.   (3)
Szerena Ut 11, 1025, Budapest, Hungary
Tel.: (36) 13451300
Web Site: http://www.amway.hu
Sales Range: $25-49.9 Million
Emp.: 20
Home & Personal Health Beauty & Nutrition Product Distr
N.A.I.C.S.: 456199

Subsidiary (Non-US):

Amway (Japan) Limited   (2)

7 1 Udagawacho, Shibuya Ku, Tokyo, 150 0042, Japan
Tel.: (81) 354287000
Web Site: http://www.amway.co.jp
Sales Range: $100-124.9 Million
Emp.: 600
Household Product Distr
N.A.I.C.S.: 456120

Amway (Malaysia) Sdn. Bhd.   (2)
No 34 Jalan 223 Selangor, 46100, Petaling Jaya, Malaysia
Tel.: (60) 379645222
Web Site: http://www.amway2u.com
Sales Range: $50-74.9 Million
Emp.: 250
Household Product Distr
N.A.I.C.S.: 456120

Amway (Schweiz) AG   (2)
Industrie Strasse 27, 4703, Kestenholz, Switzerland
Tel.: (41) 227614124
Web Site: http://www.amway.ch
Sales Range: $25-49.9 Million
Emp.: 18
Amway Product Distribution Services
N.A.I.C.S.: 722330

Amway (Thailand) Limited   (2)
52 183 Ramkhamhaeng Rd Sukhapibal 3, Huamark Bangkapi, Bangkok, 10240, Thailand
Tel.: (66) 23748000
Web Site: http://www.amway.co.th
Sales Range: $25-49.9 Million
Emp.: 53
Household Product Distr
N.A.I.C.S.: 456120

Amway (U.K.) Limited   (2)
Snowdon Dr, Winterhill, Milton Keynes, MK6 1AR, Buckinghamshire, United Kingdom
Tel.: (44) 1908298050
Web Site: http://www.clyde-marine.com
Sales Range: $25-49.9 Million
Emp.: 130
Distribution of Amway Products
N.A.I.C.S.: 722330

Amway Argentina, Inc.   (2)
Av Cabildo 86 2A Piso, Buenos Aires, C1426AAN, Argentina
Tel.: (54) 1147794600
Web Site: http://www.amway.com.ar
Sales Range: $50-74.9 Million
Emp.: 60
Sale of Home & Personal Health, Beauty & Nutrition Products; Household Cleaning Products; Housewares; Catalog Services & Commercial Products; Auto, Realty, Communications, Travel & Legal Services
N.A.I.C.S.: 456199
Marte Galazz (Office Mgr)

Amway Belgium Co   (2)
Kunstlaan 50, Box 18, 1000, Brussels, Belgium
Tel.: (32) 2 200 89 07
Web Site: http://www.amway.be
Cosmetics Whslr
N.A.I.C.S.: 424210

Amway Canada Corporation   (2)
375 Exeter Road, PO Box 7777, London Station Main, London, N5Y 5V6, ON, Canada
Tel.: (519) 685-7700
Web Site: http://www.amway.ca
Sales Range: $50-74.9 Million
Emp.: 67
Household & Personal Products Distr
N.A.I.C.S.: 456120
Lydia Ayaora (Gen Mgr)

Amway Czech Republic   (2)
Jankovcova 1596/14A, Holesovice, 170 00, Prague, Czech Republic
Tel.: (420) 239018075
Web Site: http://www.amway.cz
Sales Range: $50-74.9 Million
Emp.: 25
Sale of Home & Personal Health Beauty & Nutrition Product Household Cleaning Product Houseware Catalog Services & Commercial Product Auto Realty Communication Travel & Legal Distr

N.A.I.C.S.: 456199
Ildiko Dikosova *(Gen Mgr)*

Amway Denmark ApS (2)
Carl Gustavs Gade 3, 2630, Taastrup, Denmark
Tel.: (45) 43313233
Web Site: http://www.amway.dk
Emp.: 40
Cosmetics Whslr
N.A.I.C.S.: 424210
Charlotte Norring *(Mgr-HR)*

Amway Dominican Republic, LLC (2)
Aut Duarte Kim 13 Esq Prolongacion 27 de Febrero, Santo Domingo, Dominican Republic
Tel.: (809) 372 5587
Web Site: http://www.amway.com.do
Cosmetics Whslr
N.A.I.C.S.: 424210

Amway France (2)
5 Rue du Bois des Nots, 91640, Vaugrigneuse, France
Tel.: (33) 0149932402
Web Site: http://www.amway.fr
Sales Range: $50-74.9 Million
Emp.: 80
Household Product Distr
N.A.I.C.S.: 456120

Amway GmbH (2)
Benzstrasse 11B-C, 82178, Puchheim, Germany
Tel.: (49) 89800940
Web Site: http://www.amway.de
Sales Range: $50-74.9 Million
Emp.: 270
Household Product Distr
N.A.I.C.S.: 456120

Subsidiary (Domestic):

Amway Grand Plaza Hotel (2)
187 Monroe Ave NW, Grand Rapids, MI 49503-2621
Tel.: (616) 774-2000
Web Site: http://www.amwaygrand.com
Sales Range: $100-124.9 Million
Emp.: 1,500
Operator of Hotel Properties
N.A.I.C.S.: 722511
Richard Winn *(Pres & CEO)*
Mark Koster *(VP-Fin)*

Subsidiary (Non-US):

Amway Hellas (2)
Kifisias 15 Marousi, Kallithea, 15124, Athens, Greece
Tel.: (30) 2109552900
Web Site: http://www.amway-gr.com
Sales Range: $50-74.9 Million
Emp.: 30
Sale of Home & Personal Health, Beauty & Nutrition Products; Household Cleaning Products; Housewares; Catalog Services & Commercial Products; Auto, Realty, Communications, Travel & Legal Services
N.A.I.C.S.: 456199

Amway Hong Kong Ltd. (2)
38 F The Lee Gardens 33 Nysan Avenue, Causeway Bay, China (Hong Kong)
Tel.: (852) 29696333
Web Site: http://www.amway.com.hk
Sales Range: $25-49.9 Million
Emp.: 100
Distribution of Amway Products
N.A.I.C.S.: 722330

Amway Indonesia (2)
Wisma 46 Kota BNI 26th Fl Ste 360 Jalan Jenderal Sudirman Kav 11, Jakarta, 10224, Indonesia
Tel.: (62) 2157980800
Web Site: http://www.amway.co.id
Sales Range: $50-74.9 Million
Emp.: 80
Sale of Home & Personal Health, Beauty & Nutrition Products; Household Cleaning Products; Housewares; Catalog Services & Commercial Products; Auto, Realty, Communications, Travel & Legal Services
N.A.I.C.S.: 456199
Kon Vetheyen *(Gen Mgr)*

Amway Italia s.r.l. (2)

Viale Liguria 24, 20143, Milan, Italy
Tel.: (39) 0287103603
Web Site: http://www.amway.it
Sales Range: $50-74.9 Million
Emp.: 50
Nutrition Beauty & Personal Care Product Distr
N.A.I.C.S.: 456199
Frazio Sutaria *(Gen Mgr)*

Amway Korea, Ltd. (2)
Textile Bldg 8th Fl, Daechi 3 Dong 944 31 Kangnam K, 135 713, Seoul, Korea (South)
Tel.: (82) 234686000
Web Site: http://www.amwaykorea.co.kr
Sales Range: $50-74.9 Million
Emp.: 300
Household Product Distr
N.A.I.C.S.: 456120
Kim Jang-hwan *(CEO)*

Amway Nederland Ltd. (2)
Karsenbooggerd 2, 4003 BW, Tiel, Netherlands
Tel.: (31) 344677200
Web Site: http://www.amway.nl
Sales Range: $25-49.9 Million
Emp.: 25
Household Product Distr
N.A.I.C.S.: 456120

Amway Philippines (2)
108 V A. Rufino St, Makati, 1229, Philippines
Tel.: (63) 2814818
Web Site: http://www.amway-ph.com
Sales Range: $50-74.9 Million
Emp.: 60
Sale of Home & Personal Health, Beauty & Nutrition Products; Household Cleaning Products; Housewares; Catalog Services & Commercial Products; Auto, Realty, Communications, Travel & Legal Services
N.A.I.C.S.: 456199

Amway Poland (2)
Pulawska St 366 A, Warsaw, 02891, Poland
Tel.: (48) 223271900
Web Site: http://www.amway.pl
Sales Range: $50-74.9 Million
Emp.: 50
Sale of Home & Personal Health, Beauty & Nutrition Products; Household Cleaning Products; Housewares; Catalog Services & Commercial Products; Auto, Realty, Communications, Travel & Legal Services
N.A.I.C.S.: 456199

Amway Romania Marketing S.R.L. (2)
Strada Barbu Vacarescu No 241A, Bucharest, 020276, Romania
Tel.: (40) 21 202 00 00
Emp.: 30
Cosmetics Whslr
N.A.I.C.S.: 424210
Ioana Enache *(Gen Mgr)*

Amway Slovenia l.l.c. (2)
Smartinska Cesta 130 Podruznica Ljubljana, 1000, Ljubljana, Slovenia
Tel.: (386) 15844104
Web Site: http://www.amway.si
Sales Range: $50-74.9 Million
Emp.: 20
Sales of Home & Personal Health, Beauty & Nutrition Products; Household Cleaning Products; Housewares; Catalog Services & Commercial Products; Auto, Realty, Communications, Travel & Legal Services
N.A.I.C.S.: 456199

Amway Slovensko, s.r.o. (2)
Letna 3, 831 03, Bratislava, Slovakia
Tel.: (421) 249204444
Web Site: http://www.amwayoffice.sk
Sales Range: $50-74.9 Million
Emp.: 8
Sales of Home & Personal Health, Beauty & Nutrition Products; Household Cleaning Products; Housewares; Catalog Services & Commercial Products; Auto, Realty, Communications, Travel & Legal Services
N.A.I.C.S.: 456199
Ildiko Dakosova *(Gen Mgr)*

Amway South Africa (2)
Amway House 71 Dock Road, Cape Town, 8001, South Africa
Tel.: (27) 214051700

Web Site: http://www.amway.co.za
Sales Range: $50-74.9 Million
Emp.: 70
Sale of Home & Household Products
N.A.I.C.S.: 423220

Amway Taiwan, Ltd. (2)
11 F No 168 Tun Hwa N Rd, Taipei, Taiwan
Tel.: (886) 225467566
Web Site: http://www.amway.com.tw
Sales Range: $25-49.9 Million
Emp.: 200
Distribution of Amway Products
N.A.I.C.S.: 722330

Amway Turkey Ltd. (2)
Sair Esref Bulvari No 6 Kat 7, 35210, Cankaya, Izmir, Turkiye
Tel.: (90) 2324454848
Web Site: http://www.amway.com.tr
Sales Range: $75-99.9 Million
Emp.: 150
Sales of Home & Household Products
N.A.I.C.S.: 423220

Amway Uruguay (2)
Pedro Berron 631, 11300, Montevideo, Uruguay
Tel.: (598) 27112818
Web Site: http://www.amway-uy.com
Sale of Home & Personal Health, Beauty & Nutrition Products; Household Cleaning Products; Housewares; Catalog Services & Commercial Products; Auto, Realty, Communications, Travel & Legal Services
N.A.I.C.S.: 456199

Amway de Espana, S.A. (2)
Parque De CI Narcis Monturiol 10-12, Sant Just Desvern, Barcelona, 08960, Spain
Tel.: (34) 934794100
Web Site: http://www.amway.es
Sales Range: $25-49.9 Million
Emp.: 31
Household Product Distr
N.A.I.C.S.: 456120

Amway de Guatemala, S.A. (2)
2 Avenida 901, Zona 10, 0110, Guatemala, Guatemala
Tel.: (502) 23313515
Web Site: http://www.latinamway.com
Sales Range: Less than $1 Million
Emp.: 15
Household Product Distr
N.A.I.C.S.: 456120

Amway de Panama S.A. (2)
Urb La Alameda, CL 63, Panama, Panama
Tel.: (507) 2364515
Web Site: http://www.amway-pa.com
Sales Range: $25-49.9 Million
Emp.: 11
Distribution of Amway Products
N.A.I.C.S.: 722330

Amway de Portugal, Inc. (2)
Av do Forte 10C, N1525, 2799-521, Carnaxide, Linda-A-Vehla, Portugal
Tel.: (351) 213041900
Web Site: http://www.amway.pt
Sale of Home & Personal Health, Beauty & Nutrition Products; Household Cleaning Products; Housewares; Catalog Services & Commercial Products; Auto, Realty, Communications, Travel & Legal Services
N.A.I.C.S.: 456199

Amway of Australia (2)
46 Carrington Road, PO Box 202, Castle Hill, 2154, NSW, Australia
Tel.: (61) 298432000
Web Site: http://www.amway.com.au
Sales Range: $50-74.9 Million
Emp.: 200
Household Product Distr
N.A.I.C.S.: 456120
Michael Coldwell *(Gen Mgr)*

Amway of New Zealand (2)
6a Pacific Rise Mt Wellington, PO Box 94401, 2013, Auckland, New Zealand
Tel.: (64) 99198840
Web Site: http://www.amway.co.nz
Sales Range: $50-74.9 Million
Emp.: 100
Household Product Distr
N.A.I.C.S.: 456120
Simon Dennett *(Mgr-Mktg & Sls)*

Metagenics Incorporated (1)

25 Enterprise Ste 200, Aliso Viejo, CA 92656
Tel.: (949) 366-0818
Web Site: http://www.metagenics.com
Sales Range: $25-49.9 Million
Emp.: 750
Provider of Drugs, Proprietaries & Sundries
N.A.I.C.S.: 424210
Jerry H. Morey *(CFO)*
Jim Weaver *(Vice Chm)*
John Troup *(Chief Science Officer & Pres-MetaProteomics-Gig Harbor)*
Jeffrey Bland *(Pres-Personalized Lifestyle Medicine Institute)*
Brent Eck *(Pres & CEO)*

ALTIG INTERNATIONAL
15440 Bel-Red Rd, Redmond, WA 98052
Tel.: (425) 885-2838
Web Site: http://www.altig.com
Rev.: $19,800,000
Emp.: 35
Insurance Agents
N.A.I.C.S.: 524210
James Hill *(COO)*
Richard Altig Jr. *(Chm & Partner)*

ALTIRA, INC.
3225 NW 112th St, Miami, FL 33167
Tel.: (305) 687-8074
Web Site: https://www.altira.com
Year Founded: 1972
Sales Range: $10-24.9 Million
Emp.: 100
Plastics Bottle Mfr
N.A.I.C.S.: 326160
Faustino Poo *(VP)*
Ramon Poo *(Pres)*

ALTITUDE DIGITAL, INC.
1037 Broadway Unit B, Denver, CO 80216
Tel.: (303) 292-1414
Web Site: http://altitudedigital.com
Year Founded: 2009
Sales Range: $1-9.9 Million
Emp.: 19
Online Display & Video Advertising Technology
N.A.I.C.S.: 541810
Jeremy Ostermiller *(Founder & CEO)*
Joe Grover *(CMO)*
Max Gideon *(VP-Mobile)*
Bradley Downes *(CFO)*

ALTITUDE MARKETING
225 Main St, Emmaus, PA 18049
Tel.: (610) 421-8601
Web Site: https://www.altitudemarketing.com
Year Founded: 2004
Sales Range: $1-9.9 Million
Emp.: 17
Integrated Digital & Traditional Marketing Services
N.A.I.C.S.: 541613
Andrew Stanten *(Co-Founder & Pres)*
Gwen Shields *(COO)*

Subsidiaries:

Altitude Marketing (1)
PO Box 2613, Chapel Hill, NC 27517 (100%)
Tel.: (919) 244-9896
Web Site: http://www.altitudemarketing.com
Technology & Integrated Marketing Services
N.A.I.C.S.: 541613
Rebecca Sipes *(Gen Mgr)*

ALTL INC.
3000 Corporate Grove Dr, Hudsonville, MI 49426
Tel.: (616) 669-6060
Web Site: http://www.altl.com
Year Founded: 1972
Sales Range: $10-24.9 Million
Emp.: 150

ALTL Inc.—(Continued)

Customized Transportation & Supply Chain Management Services
N.A.I.C.S.: 484121
Ross Luurtsema (Pres)
Carl Oosterhouse (COO)
Melissa Straub (Coord-Acctg)
Sam Williams (Mgr-Bus Dev)

ALTMAN SPECIALTY PLANTS, INC.
3742 Blue Bird Canyon Rd, Vista, CA 92084-7432
Tel.: (760) 744-8191   CA
Web Site:
https://www.altmanplants.com
Year Founded: 1975
Succulent Breeder & Grower; Nurseries
N.A.I.C.S.: 424930
Erin McCarthy (VP-Sls)
Laurie Harrison (Controller)
Frank Justice (Acct Mgr)
Kathy Nyquist (Acct Mgr-Natl)
Matthew Altman (COO)
Ken Altman (Pres)

ALTMAN-CHARTER COMPANY
315 Consort Dr, Ballwin, MO 63011
Tel.: (636) 207-8670
Web Site: https://www.altman-charter.com
Sales Range: $50-74.9 Million
Emp.: 25
Hotel/Motel & Multi-Family Home Construction
N.A.I.C.S.: 236220
Eddie Stechschulte (Project Mgr)

ALTMEYER HOME STORES INC.
6515 Rte 22, Delmont, PA 15626
Tel.: (724) 468-3434   PA
Web Site:
https://www.bedbathhome.com
Year Founded: 1941
Sales Range: $10-24.9 Million
Emp.: 35
Provider of Bed & Bath Furnishings
N.A.I.C.S.: 449129
Robert Altmeyer (Owner)
Rod H. Altmeyer Sr. (Pres)

ALTO CONSTRUCTION CO., INC.
4102 Causeway Blvd, Tampa, FL 33619
Tel.: (813) 751-3027
Web Site:
https://www.altoconstruction.com
Year Founded: 1978
Sales Range: $10-24.9 Million
Emp.: 85
Other Specialty Trade Contracting Services
N.A.I.C.S.: 238990
Stewart G. Smith (CEO)
Rich Bolesta (Pres)
Michelle Jung (Comptroller)
Kevin Stringer (Gen Mgr)

ALTO ENTERPRISES, INC.
7311 K Grove Rd, Frederick, MD 21704
Tel.: (301) 663-5111
Web Site:
https://www.elevatorshoes.com
Rev.: $1,500,000
Retailer Elevator Shoes
N.A.I.C.S.: 424340
Robert Martin (VP)
James Martin Sr. (Pres)

Subsidiaries:

Richlee Shoe Company   (1)

7311 K Grove Rd, Frederick, MD 21704-3300
Tel.: (301) 663-5111
Web Site: https://www.elevatorshoes.com
Sales Range: $10-24.9 Million
Emp.: 13
Elevator Shoes Distr
N.A.I.C.S.: 424340

ALTO PHARMACEUTICALS, INC.
PO Box 271150, Tampa, FL 33688-1150
Tel.: (813) 968-0522   FL
Web Site: http://www.altopharm.com
Year Founded: 1968
Sales Range: $10-24.9 Million
Emp.: 5
Contract Mfr & Distr of Pharmaceuticals
N.A.I.C.S.: 424210
John J. Cullaro (Pres)
Joan Chypyha (Founder & Pres)

ALTO PRODUCTS CORP.
1 Alto Way, Atmore, AL 36502
Tel.: (251) 368-7777
Web Site: https://www.altousa.com
Rev.: $22,600,000
Emp.: 150
Motor Vehicle Parts
N.A.I.C.S.: 336350
David Landa (Pres)
Kevin Farkas (VP-West Coast Div)
Randy Sowers (VP-Sls)

ALTO-SHAAM INC.
W164 N9221 Water St, Menomonee Falls, WI 53052
Tel.: (262) 251-3800
Web Site: http://www.alto-shaam.com
Year Founded: 1955
Sales Range: $10-24.9 Million
Emp.: 310
Food Service Machines Mfr
N.A.I.C.S.: 333310
Steve Maahs (Pres & COO)

ALTON BEAN TRUCKING INC.
203 S Mountain St, Amity, AR 71921
Tel.: (870) 342-9551
Rev.: $10,041,750
Emp.: 97
Trucking Except Local
N.A.I.C.S.: 484121
Gary Bean (Pres)

ALTON E. BLAKLEY COMPANY INC.
2130 US 27, Somerset, KY 42501
Tel.: (606) 678-5181
Web Site:
http://www.altonblakley.com
Year Founded: 1965
Sales Range: $25-49.9 Million
Emp.: 62
Automobiles, New & Used
N.A.I.C.S.: 441110
Lisa Greer (Controller)
Alton E. Blakley Jr. (Pres)

ALTON STEEL INC.
5 Cut St, Alton, IL 62002
Tel.: (618) 374-3271
Web Site: https://www.altonsteel.com
Year Founded: 2003
Sales Range: $25-49.9 Million
Emp.: 259
Steel Products Mfr
N.A.I.C.S.: 331110
Kasha Windmiller (Mgr-Sls & Svcs)
Mike Fitch (Pres)
James Hrusovsky (CEO)
John Goldschmidt (CFO)
Terry Laird (Gen Mgr-Ops)
Jeff Hoerr (Gen Mgr-Sls & Mktg)

ALTONA RESOURCES, INC.
3414 Pino Cir, Las Vegas, NV 89121
Tel.: (702) 738-8614   NV
Year Founded: 2011
Metal Mining
N.A.I.C.S.: 212290
Ying Nie (Pres, CEO, CFO, Chief Acctg Officer, Treas & Sec)

ALTOONA WATER AUTHORITY
900 Chestnut Ave, Altoona, PA 16603
Tel.: (814) 949-2222
Web Site:
https://www.altoonawater.com
Year Founded: 1948
Sales Range: $10-24.9 Million
Emp.: 137
Water Supply & Wastewater Treatment
N.A.I.C.S.: 221310
Maurice Lawruk (Chm)
Mark Perry (Gen Mgr)
Frank Ake (Sec)
William Schirf (Asst Treas & Asst Sec)

ALTORFER INC.
2600 6th St SW, Cedar Rapids, IA 52406
Tel.: (319) 365-0551
Web Site: http://www.altorfer.com
Rev.: $200,000,000
Emp.: 720
Construction Equipment Distr
N.A.I.C.S.: 423810
Bruce Altorfer (Pres)
Craig Robeen (VP-Construction Mktg & Sls)
Derek R. Altorfer (Pres)
Dave Hixson (VP-Construction Product Support)

ALTOUR INTERNATIONAL, INC.
1270 Avenue of the Americas, New York, NY 10020
Tel.: (212) 897-5000   DE
Web Site: https://www.altour.com
Year Founded: 1991
Sales Range: $1-4.9 Billion
Emp.: 1,300
Travel Agencies
N.A.I.C.S.: 561510
David Sefton (VP-Ops-West Coast)
Joseph Oppold (Exec VP-Ops-Global)
Alexandre H. Chemla (Founder & Pres)
Barry Noskeau (COO & Exec VP)
Sherman Snyder (CFO)
Lee Thomas (Pres-The Travel Authority & Exec VP)

Subsidiaries:

TTA, Inc.   (1)
21171 S Western Ave Ste 200, Torrance, CA 90501
Tel.: (310) 320-4722
Web Site: http://www.tta-us.com
Sales Range: $25-49.9 Million
Emp.: 500
Travel Agency Services
N.A.I.C.S.: 561510
Lee Thomas (CEO)
Alan Busse (Sr VP-Corp Ops)
Doug Payne (Sr VP-Sls)

Subsidiary (Domestic):

SwiftTrip, LLC   (2)
702 N Shore Dr Ste 300, Jeffersonville, IN 47130
Tel.: (812) 206-5200
Web Site: http://www.swifttrip.com
Sales Range: $1-9.9 Million
Emp.: 15
Travel Agency Software Platform Developer
N.A.I.C.S.: 513210
Lee Thomas (Pres)

ALTOVIDA, INC.
7582 Las Vegas Blvd S Ste 236, Las Vegas, NV 89123
Tel.: (702) 217-3964
Year Founded: 2011
Mineral Exploration Services
N.A.I.C.S.: 212290
Michael Richard Hawthorne (Pres & CEO)

ALTRAZEAL LIFE SCIENCES INC.
4410 Beltway Dr, Addison, TX 75001
Tel.: (214) 905-5145   NV
Web Site: https://altrazeal.com
Year Founded: 1987
ULUR—(OTCQB)
Sales Range: Less than $1 Million
Emp.: 2
Wound Management, Plastic Surgery & Oral Care Products Developer
N.A.I.C.S.: 325412
Vaidehi Shah (Chm & CEO)

ALTRU HEALTH SYSTEM
1200 S Columbia Rd, Grand Forks, ND 58201
Tel.: (701) 780-5000
Web Site: https://www.altru.org
Sales Range: $50-74.9 Million
Emp.: 3,702
Medical Health Network
N.A.I.C.S.: 622110
Brad Wehe (CEO)
Dwight Thompson (CFO & Treas)
Sara Dvorak (Mgr-Learning & Organizational Dev)
Shayla Solberg (Mgr-Clinic-Crookston, Erskine, Fertile & Red Lake Falls)
Kris Compton (Chm)
Kristi Hall-Jiran (Chief Philanthropy Officer & Exec VP)
Lonnie Laffen (Vice Chm)
Philip Gisi (Sec)
Dennis Reisnour (Chief Strategy Officer)
Janice Hamscher (Chief Nursing Officer)
Kellee Fisk (Chief People Officer)
Mark Waind (CIO)

ALTRUI BROTHERS TRUCK SALES, INC.
1100 Warren Ave, East Providence, RI 02914
Tel.: (401) 434-3540
Web Site: http://www.altruibros.com
Sales Range: $10-24.9 Million
Emp.: 23
New Car Retailer
N.A.I.C.S.: 441110
Tony Altrui (Pres)

ALTRUIST CORP
3030 S La Cienega, Culver City, CA 90232
Tel.: (888) 510-4660
Web Site: https://altruist.com
Emp.: 100
Financial Services
N.A.I.C.S.: 523999

Subsidiaries:

Shareholder Services Group   (1)
9845 Erma Rd, San Diego, CA 92131
Tel.: (858) 530-1031
Web Site: http://www.ssginstitutional.com
Rev.: $3,618,000
Emp.: 9
Investment Banking & Securities Dealing
N.A.I.C.S.: 523150
Peter Mangan (CEO & Founder)

ALTURA CREDIT UNION
2847 Campus Pkwy, Riverside, CA 92507

Tel.: (951) 571-5395   CA
Web Site: https://www.alturacu.com
Year Founded: 1957
Sales Range: $25-49.9 Million
Emp.: 278
Credit Union
N.A.I.C.S.: 522130
Ofelia Valdez-Yeager (Chm)

ALTURA HOMES DFW, LP.
2529 Waterstone Ln, Rockwall, TX
75032
Tel.: (214) 771-0888
Web Site:
   http://www.alturahomes.com
Sales Range: $25-49.9 Million
Emp.: 26
Construction Management Services
N.A.I.C.S.: 236115
Justin Webb (Pres)
Edward Hamilton (Pres-Div)
Kerry Ainsworth (VP)

ALTUS CAPITAL PARTNERS, INC.
10 Westport Rd Ste C204, Wilton, CT
06897
Tel.: (203) 429-2000   DE
Web Site:
   http://www.altuscapitalpartners.com
Year Founded: 2003
Private Equity Firm
N.A.I.C.S.: 523999
Russell J. Greenberg (Founder & Mng Partner)
Gregory L. Greenberg (Founder & Sr Partner)
Heidi M. Goldstein (Partner)
Peter Polimino (Partner, CFO & Chief Compliance Officer)
Denise Miller (Office Mgr)
Thomas R. Groh (Partner-Bus Dev)
Joseph A. Melo (Controller)

Subsidiaries:

Choice Spine, LLC   (1)
400 Erin Dr., Knoxville, TN 37919
Tel.: (865) 246-3333
Web Site: https://choicespine.com
Medical Equipment Manufacturing
N.A.I.C.S.: 339112
Rick Henson (Co-Pres)
Keith Clements (VP-Sls)
Ron Moore (Sr Dir-Mktg-Thoracolumbar)
Marty Altshuler (Co-Pres)
Lauren Bishop (VP-Biologics)

Nichols Portland, LLC   (1)
2400 Congress St, Portland, ME 04102-1949
Tel.: (207) 774-6121
Web Site: http://nicholsportland.com
Custom Designed Gerotor Gears & Pumps Mfr
N.A.I.C.S.: 333612
Rick Izor (Pres)

Thermal Solutions Manufacturing, Inc.   (1)
15 Century Blvd Ste 102, Nashville, TN 37214
Web Site:
   http://www.thermalsolutionsmfg.com
Temperature Control & Industrial Automotive Product Mfr & Dist
N.A.I.C.S.: 811198
Ken Robinson (Pres & CEO)

Subsidiary (Domestic):

TSM Champ, LLC   (2)
2359 Trailmate Dr, Sarasota, FL 34243-4041
Tel.: (941) 727-1900
Sales Range: $25-49.9 Million
Emp.: 103
Heat Exchanger Mfr
N.A.I.C.S.: 332410

Winsert, Inc.   (1)
2645 Industrial Pkwy S, Marinette, WI 54143
Tel.: (715) 732-1703

Web Site: http://www.winsert.com
Fabricated Metal Products Mfr
N.A.I.C.S.: 331513
Xuecheng Liang (Dir-R&D & CTO)
Trisha Dickinson Lemery (Chief Bus Dev Officer)
Mark Coduti (Pres)

Subsidiary (Domestic):

Alloy Cast Products, Inc.   (2)
700 Swenson Dr, Kenilworth, NJ 07033
Tel.: (908) 245-2255
Web Site: http://www.alloycastproducts.com
Steel Foundries, except Investment
N.A.I.C.S.: 331513
Ann Panico (VP)
Ken Fisher (Pres)

ALUCHEM INC.
1 Landy Ln, Cincinnati, OH 45215-3405
Tel.: (513) 733-8519
Web Site: https://www.aluchem.com
Year Founded: 1978
Sales Range: $10-24.9 Million
Emp.: 94
Mfr of Chemical Preparations
N.A.I.C.S.: 327992
Ronald P. Zapletal (Founder)
Myia Glenklerdaugherty (Mgr-Customer Svcs-Pur)
Edward Butera (Owner)
Jake Wieland (Mgr-Sls-Natl)

ALUF PLASTICS
2 Glenshaw St, Orangeburg, NY 10962
Tel.: (845) 365-2200
Web Site:
   https://www.alufplastics.com
Year Founded: 1977
Rev.: $95,500,000
Emp.: 250
Plastics Bag Mfr
N.A.I.C.S.: 326111
Harold Mechalzics (Mgr-IT & Internet Support)
Susan Rosenburg (Pres)
Joseph Rosenberg (VP-Sls & Mktg)

ALUMA-FORM INC.
3625 Old Getwell Rd, Memphis, TN 38118
Tel.: (901) 362-0100
Web Site:
   https://www.alumaform.com
Rev.: $39,273,975
Emp.: 150
Hardware Mfr
N.A.I.C.S.: 332510
Angela Hale (Controller)
Gwen Hubbard (Dir-IT)
Harry Orr (CFO)
Karen McDonald (Mgr-Pur)
Mike Hedrick (Mgr-Safety & Environmental)

ALUMA-GLASS INDUSTRIES, INC.
909 N Orchard St, Boise, ID 83706-2155
Tel.: (208) 375-0326
Web Site:
   http://www.architecturalglass.com
Year Founded: 1951
Sales Range: $1-9.9 Million
Emp.: 40
Window, Door & Storefront System Mfr & Distr
N.A.I.C.S.: 321911
Rick Atkinson (Pres)

Subsidiaries:

Architectural Glass & Glazing   (1)
909 North Orchard St, Boise, ID 83706
Tel.: (904) 269-3094
Web Site: http://www.architecturalglass.com
Glass Products & Commercial Glazing

N.A.I.C.S.: 236220

ALUMA-WELD INC.
199 Extrusion Pl, Hot Springs, AR 71901
Tel.: (501) 262-5300
Web Site:
   https://www.xpressboats.com
Year Founded: 1966
Small Fishing Boat Mfr
N.A.I.C.S.: 336612

ALUMAROLL SPECIALTY CO. INC.
2932 Behrens Pkwy, Sheboygan, WI 53081-7394
Tel.: (920) 451-4000
Web Site: http://www.alumaroll.com
Sales Range: $10-24.9 Million
Emp.: 150
Screen Mfr
N.A.I.C.S.: 332321
Mark Dezwarte (Pres)
Dave Nyenhuis (VP-Ops)

ALUMINUM COIL ANODIZING CORP.
501 E Lake St, Streamwood, IL 60107
Tel.: (630) 837-4000
Web Site: https://www.acacorp.com
Year Founded: 1961
Rev.: $27,000,000
Emp.: 120
Anodizing (Plating) of Metals or Formed Products
N.A.I.C.S.: 332813
Ronald L. Rusch (Pres)
Mike Emerson (Controller)
Martin Ley (Dir-Mgmt Info Sys)

ALUMINUM LINE PRODUCTS COMPANY
24460 Sperry Cir, Westlake, OH 44145
Tel.: (440) 835-8880
Web Site:
   https://www.aluminumline.com
Sales Range: $25-49.9 Million
Emp.: 90
Metals Service Centers & Offices
N.A.I.C.S.: 423510
Wendy Kieding (VP)
Richard Daniel (CFO & VP)
Jim Guerin (VP-Sls & Mktg)
Guy Martin (VP-Mfg)
Lynne Sextella (Mgr-Credit)
Greg Thompson (Mgr-Inside Sls)
Joseph McNamara (Mgr-Quality & Engrg)
Dale Jenne (Mgr-Sls)
Paul Karfomenos (Mgr-Sls-Midwest)
Dave Livingston (Mgr-Sls-Southeast)

ALUMINUM MAINTENANCE SYSTEMS OF TEXAS, INC.
7777 Parnell St, Houston, TX 77021
Tel.: (832) 255-4500
Web Site: https://www.jobs-amst.com
Sales Range: $10-24.9 Million
Emp.: 200
Window Cleaning, Pressure Washing & Building Restoration Services
N.A.I.C.S.: 332812
Dustin Mattison (Mgr-Safety)
LaRue Coleman (Pres)
Peter Buzzini (VP)
Rodney Powdrill (Mgr-Ops)
Richard Powdrill (Supvr-Night)
Frank Viscaino (Mgr-Fabrication Shop)

ALUMINUM PRECISION PRODUCTS INC.
3333 W Warner Ave, Santa Ana, CA 92704-5316

Tel.: (714) 546-8125
Web Site:
   https://www.aluminumprecision.com
Year Founded: 1965
Sales Range: $25-49.9 Million
Emp.: 500
Mfr of Nonferrous Forgings
N.A.I.C.S.: 332112
Laila Hussain (Coord-AQS)
Mary Block (Dir-HR)
Andrew Millian (Engr-Sls)
John Haroldson (Mgr-Engrg)

ALUMINUM ROOFING SPECIALISTS INC.
22982 Al Calde Dr Ste 100, Laguna Hills, CA 92653
Tel.: (714) 558-8008
Web Site:
   http://www.dialonewindows.com
Sales Range: $10-24.9 Million
Emp.: 80
Window & Door Replacement
N.A.I.C.S.: 332321
Charles H. Gindele (Owner)

ALUMINUM.IO, INC.
5940 S Rainbow Blvd Ste 400, Las Vegas, NV 89118-2507
Tel.: (507) 242-1916
Web Site: https://aluminum.io
Private Equity Firm
N.A.I.C.S.: 523999
John Cross (CEO & Mng Dir)

Subsidiaries:

TrueAbility Inc.   (1)
1150 N Loop 1604 W Suite 108-244, San Antonio, TX 78248
Web Site: http://www.trueability.com
Software Publisher
N.A.I.C.S.: 513210
Marcus Robertson (Co-Founder & CTO)
Frederick Mendler (Co-Founder & CEO)

ALUTIIQ INTERNATIONAL SOLUTIONS, LLC
3909 Arctic Blvd Ste 500, Anchorage, AK 99503
Tel.: (907) 222-9500
Web Site: https://www.alutiiq.com
Year Founded: 2001
Prefabricated Metal Buildings & Components
N.A.I.C.S.: 332311
Dusty Kaser (CEO)
Ron Hancock (Sr VP-Bus Dev)

ALVA/AMCO PHARMACAL COMPANIES, INC.
7711 N Merrimac Ave, Niles, IL 60714-3423
Tel.: (847) 663-0700   IL
Web Site: https://www.alva-amco.com
Year Founded: 1904
Sales Range: $100-124.9 Million
Emp.: 300
OTC Drugs, Dietary Supplements & Cosmetics Mfr & Distr
N.A.I.C.S.: 325412
Terry Riddel (Sr VP)
Michael Reisner (VP)

ALVARADO CONSTRUCTION, INC.
924 W Colfax Ave Ste 301, Denver, CO 80204-3546
Tel.: (303) 629-0783
Web Site:
   http://www.alvaradoconstruction.com
Year Founded: 1971
Sales Range: $10-24.9 Million
Emp.: 45

Alvarado Construction, Inc.—(Continued)

Provider of Nonresidential Construction
N.A.I.C.S.: 236220
Michelle Mayland (Controller)
Jennifer Coons (Area Mgr)
Linda G. Alvarado (Founder, Pres & CEO)

ALVARADO STREET BAKERY
2225 S McDowell Blvd Ext, Petaluma, CA 94954-5661
Tel.: (707) 789-6700
Web Site:
    https://www.alvaradostreet.com
Sales Range: $10-24.9 Million
Emp.: 115
Bakery Products
N.A.I.C.S.: 311812
Frank Vallin (Mgr-Production)
Tim Lewallen (Asst Mgr-Shipping)
Karin Anderson (Controller)
Michael Girkout (Pres)
Jim Canterbury (Mgr-Reg Sls)

ALVAREZ & MARSAL, INC.
600 Madison Ave 8th Fl, New York, NY 10022
Tel.: (212) 759-4433   DE
Web Site:
    http://www.alvarezandmarsal.com
Year Founded: 1983
Holding Company; Business Management Consulting Services
N.A.I.C.S.: 551112
Karin-Joyce Tjon (Mng Dir)
Scott Coleman (Gen Counsel-Operating Companies)
Brian J. Fox (Head--North America)
Tony Alvarez II (Co-Founder & Co-CEO)
Bryan Marsal (Co-Founder & Co-CEO)
Jeffrey Klein (Mng Dir-Private Equity Performance Improvement Practice)
Joel O'Driscoll (Mng Dir)
Manish Saigal (Mng Dir-Corp Solutions Grp-India)
Richard Jenkins (Mng Dir)
Suman Jagdev (Sr Dir-Corp Solutions Practice-India)
Kristin Kohler Burrows (Sr Dir-Private Equity Performance Improvement Practice)
Helene Willberg (Mng Dir-Stockholm)
Maria Coccaro (Chief HR Officer)
Steven Cohn (Co-CFO)
Stuart Ells (Chief Admin Officer)
Sean Farnan (Co-CFO & Co-COO)
Carlos Garcia (CIO)
Doug Sigler (Chief Info Security Officer)
John Suckow (Co-COO)
Kaustav Ganguli (Mng Dir-Corp Solutions Grp)
Dennis E. Stogsdill (Mng Dir)
Robert Campagna (Mng Dir & Head-Restructuring Practice-East)
Jeff Stegenga (Mng Dir)
Jeffrey Huddleston (Mng Dir-Houston)
Kumu Puri (Mng Dir-Telecom, Media & Tech Practice)
Tim Jellison (Mng Dir-Telecom, Media & Tech Practice)
Ben Hope (Mng Dir-Corp Performance Improvement Practice-Los Angeles)
Paulo Mota (Mng Dir-Transaction Advisory Grp-Global)
Paul Aversano (Mng Dir-Transaction Advisory Grp-Global)
Ash Mathradas (Mng Dir-Corp Performance Improvement Grp-San Francisco)
Michael Balistreri (Mng Dir-Corp Fin Practice)

Ryan Wells (Dir-Compensation & Benefits Practice)
Vance Yudell (Dir-Compensation & Benefits Tax)
Jeff Swerdlow (Sr Dir-Compensation & Benefits Practice)
Gint Baukus (Sr Dir-Human Capital Practices & Strategies)
Ken Tsai (Mng Dir-Corp Performance Improvement-Houston)
Rocco Grillo (Mng Dir-Disputes & Investigations Global Cyber Risk Svcs Practice)
Kevin Negangard (Mng Dir-Disputes & Investigations-Chicago)
Robert Decicco (Mng Dir-Disputes & Investigations-Los Angeles)
Vishal Oza (Sr Dir-Disputes & Investigations Practice-Los Angeles)
Erin Brookes (Chief Restructuring Officer & Interim Mktg Dir)
Christopher Kulp (Mng Dir-Private Equity Svcs Grp)
Markus Lahrkamp (Mng Dir-Private Equity Performance Improvement Practice)
Carlos Munoz (Mng Dir-San Francisco)
Chuck Moore (Mng Dir-Restructuring-Turnaround)
Brian Whittman (Head-North American Restructuring & Turnaround Practice-Midwest)
Vincent Walden (Mng Dir-Disputes & Investigation Practice)
Jason Clatworthy (Mng Dir-London)
Wayne Jephson (Mng Dir-London)
Lisa Price (Mng Dir-Restructuring & Turnaround Practice-Atlanta)
David Wong (Mng Dir)
Jonathan Nus (Mng Dir-Capital Markets & Acctg Advisory Group)
Anthony Caporrino (Mng Dir-Transaction Advisory Group)
Erik Kessler (Mng Dir-Chicago)
Vlad Halas (Mng Dir-London)
Ryan Orme (Sr Dir-San Francisco)
Kurt Jonske (Sr Dir- Global Transaction Analytics)
Sandra Sokoloff (Dir-Global PR)
Ron Thompson (Mng Dir-Asia & Head-Restructuring Practice-Asia)
Edward Middleton (Mng Dir)
Nick Alvarez (Mng Dir)
James Marceau (Mng Dir-Private Equity Performance Improvement Grp)
Rick Kozole (Mng Dir-Automotive & Industrials Grp)
Tom Elsenbrook (Mng Dir)
Omar Mata (Mng Dir-Private Equity Performance Improvement Grp)
Luigi Peluso (Mng Dir-Private Equity Performance Improvement Grp)
Martin McGahan (Mng Dir & Head-Healthcare Indus Grp)
Michael Niarchos (Mng Dir-Healthcare Indus Grp)
Yawar Murad (Mng Dir-Private Equity Performance Improvement Grp)
Abhinav Agarwal (Sr Dir-London)
Hunt Holsomback (Mng Dir-Private Equity Performance Improvement Practice)
Hameer Vaid (Sr Dir-Private Equity Performance Improvement Grp)
Cyndi Joiner (Mng Dir)
Eric Dustman (Mng Dir-Performance Improvement Practice)
David Evans (Mng Dir-Transaction Advisory Grp-Global)
Tamseel Butt (Mng Dir)
James McDermott (Mng Dir)
John Scerbo (Mng Dir-Private Equity Performance Improvement Grp)
Steve Hurt (Mng Dir)

Matt Campbell (Mng Dir-CPI Grp)
Mike Cremin (Mng Dir)
Sooho Choi (Mng Dir)
Rishi Chhatwal (Mng Dir-Forensic Tech Svcs)
Jerry Dent (Mng Dir-Disputes & Investigations Grp)
Jonathan Marshall (Mng Dir-Disputes & Investigations Practice-Forensic Tech Svcs)
William Kosturos (Mng Dir-Comml Restructuring-North America)
Daniel Jerneycic (Mng Dir-Restructuring & Turnaround Practice)
Nicholas Grossi (Mng Dir-North American Commercial Restructuring Practice-Chicago)
Brooke Hopkins (Mng Dir-Disputes & Investigations Practice)
Steve Spiegelhalter (Mng Dir)

Subsidiaries:

Alvarez & Marsal North America, LLC   (1)
600 Madison Ave, New York, NY 10022
Tel.: (212) 759-4433
Web Site: http://www.alvarezandmarsal.com
Sales Range: $50-74.9 Million
Regional Managing Office; Business Management Consulting Services
N.A.I.C.S.: 551114
Scott Coleman (Gen Counsel)
Brian J. Fox (Chief Restructuring Officer)
Tony Alvarez II (CEO)
Amy O'Brien-Bird (Mng Dir & Head-Revenue Enhancement practice)
Justin Schmaltz (Mng Dir-Turnaround & Restructuring-Chicago)
Adam Zalev (Mng Dir)
Mike McKenna (Mng Dir-Private Equity Svcs-New York)
Faye Wattleton (Mng Dir)
Paul Rundell (Mng Dir)

Affiliate (Non-US):

A&M Capital Advisors Europe, LLP   (2)
6 Grosvenor Street, Mayfair, London, W1K 4PZ, United Kingdom
Tel.: (44) 20 7073 0501
Web Site: http://www.a-mcapital.com
Investment Services
N.A.I.C.S.: 523999
Mark Kelly (Mng Partner)
Shepard Spink (Mng Partner)

Holding (Non-US):

Bolle Brands SAS   (3)
23 bis rue Nieuport, 92150, Suresnes, France
Tel.: (33) 1 41 44 94 80
Web Site: http://www.bolle.com
Sunglasses & Goggles Distr
N.A.I.C.S.: 423460
Peter Smith (Chm)
Francois Benaben (Pres-Sport & Luxury Div)

Subsidiary (Non-US):

Bolle (N.Z.) Limited   (4)
Unit 5 114 Sawyers Arms Road, Christchurch, 8052, New Zealand
Tel.: (64) 33751400
Sports Product Distr
N.A.I.C.S.: 459110

Bolle Australia Pty Ltd   (4)
32-40 Fairchild Street, Heatherton, 3202, VIC, Australia
Tel.: (61) 1300138098
Web Site: http://www.bolle.com
Sunglass Distr
N.A.I.C.S.: 423460

Subsidiary (US):

Spy Inc.   (4)
1896 Rutherford Rd, Carlsbad, CA 92008
Tel.: (760) 804-8420
Web Site: http://www.spyoptic.com
Sales Range: $25-49.9 Million
Action Sports Products Designer Developer & Marketer

N.A.I.C.S.: 339113
Seth W. Hamot (Chm)
Stephen Roseman (Pres)

Subsidiary (Non-US):

Spy Optic srl   (5)
Via Vajone 2, 21020, Galliate Lombardo, Varese, Italy
Tel.: (39) 0332949833
Web Site: http://www.spyoptic.com
Sales Range: $100-124.9 Million
Eyewear Mfr
N.A.I.C.S.: 333310

Affiliate (Domestic):

A&M Capital Advisors, LLC   (2)
325 Greenwich Ave 3rd Fl, Greenwich, CT 06830
Tel.: (203) 742-5880
Web Site: http://www.a-mcapital.com
Equity Investment Firm
N.A.I.C.S.: 523999
Kurtis J. Kaull (Partner & Mng Dir)
Alex Nivelle (Principal)
David Perskie (Principal)
Michael R. Bardorf (CFO)
Randall Harrigan (VP)
Rob Haisch (Principal)
Jack D. McCarthy Jr. (Sr Mng Dir)

Holding (Domestic):

BrigtPet Nutrition Group, LLC   (3)
38281 Industrial Park Rd, Lisbon, OH 44432
Tel.: (330) 424-1431
Web Site: http://www.brightpetnutrition.com
Premium Pet Foods Mfr
N.A.I.C.S.: 311111
Matthew Golladay (CEO)

Subsidiary (Domestic):

Bravo, LLC   (4)
349 Wetherell St, Manchester, CT 06040
Tel.: (860) 896-1256
Web Site: http://www.bravorawdiet.com
Sales Range: $1-9.9 Million
Emp.: 17
Animal Feed Mfr
N.A.I.C.S.: 311119
Bette Schubert (Co-Founder)
David Bogner (Co-Founder)

Miraclecorp Products   (4)
2425 W Dorothy Ln, Dayton, OH 45439
Tel.: (937) 293-9994
Web Site: http://www.miraclecorp.com
Sales Range: $10-24.9 Million
Emp.: 100
Pet Food Product Mfr
N.A.I.C.S.: 311119
Bill Sherk (CEO)
Scott Gibson (Dir-IT)

Holding (Domestic):

FPT Operating Company, LLC   (3)
12712 Park Central Dr Ste 350, Dallas, TX 75251
Tel.: (800) 787-4105
Web Site: https://taluspay.com
Business Payment Processing Services
N.A.I.C.S.: 522320
Eric Pottebaum (Gen Mgr-Clarus)
Kim Fitzsimmons (CEO)

Subsidiary (Domestic):

CMS Processing LLC   (4)
3 E Diamond Ave, Gaithersburg, MD 20877
Tel.: (888) 245-7216
Web Site: http://www.clarusdc.com
Sales Range: $1-9.9 Million
Financial Payment Processing Services
N.A.I.C.S.: 522320
Matt Holtzman (VP-Corp Strategy)
Samuel Rogers (COO)
Theresa LaRocca (Dir-Partner Rels)
Tom Gaynor (Sr Mgr-Acct)
Valerie Mefferd (Controller-Fin)
Maka Julios (Dir-Global Mktg)
Michael Rickman (Supvr-Boarding & Ops)

Joint Venture (Domestic):

Good Source Solutions, Inc. (3)
3115 Melrose Dr Ste 160, Carlsbad, CA 92010
Tel.: (858) 455-4800
Web Site: http://www.goodsource.com
Acquires & Distributes Food Products for Schools, Institutions & Non-Profit Organizations
N.A.I.C.S.: 722310
Eric Shiring (CFO)
Laurie McCluskey (VP-Tools for Schools & Northwest Distr)
Jim Worrall (VP-Client Solutions & Contract Sls)
Rich Friedlen (Pres & CEO)
Stephanie McCart (VP-Sls & Mktg)
Brandon Marvin (VP-Product Dev & Sourcing)

Subsidiary (Domestic):

Fresno Produce, Inc. (4)
1415 B St, Fresno, CA 93706
Tel.: (559) 495-0143
Web Site: http://www.fresnoproduce.com
Fresh Fruit & Vegetable Merchant Whslr
N.A.I.C.S.: 424480

Gold Star Foods Inc. (4)
3781 E Airport Dr, Ontario, CA 91761-1761
Tel.: (909) 843-9600
Web Site: http://www.goldstarfoods.com
Nutritional Food Distr
N.A.I.C.S.: 541614
Dan Madsen (CEO)
Sean Leer (Pres)

Branch (Domestic):

Good Source Solutions (4)
3115 Melrose Dr Ste 160, Carlsbad, CA 92010
Tel.: (208) 365-1445
Web Site: http://www.goodsource.com
Acquires & Distributes Food Products for Schools & Institutions in Idaho, Utah, Washington & Oregon
N.A.I.C.S.: 722310
Laurie McCluskey (VP-Tools For Schools & ID-Northwest Div)

Subsidiary (Domestic):

Hayes Distributing, Inc. (4)
4945 Industrial Way, Benicia, CA 94510
Tel.: (707) 746-1660
Web Site: http://www.hayesdist.com
Confectionery & Nut Stores
N.A.I.C.S.: 445292

Pon Food Corp (4)
101 Industrial Park Blvd, Ponchatoula, LA 70454
Tel.: (985) 386-6941
Packaged Frozen Goods
N.A.I.C.S.: 424420

School Lunch Products, Inc. (4)
558 Central Ave, Shafter, CA 93263
Tel.: (661) 746-3136
Web Site: http://www.slpdelivers.com
Sales Range: $1-9.9 Million
Emp.: 10
Packaged Frozen Food Merchant Whslr
N.A.I.C.S.: 424420
Michael Fackler (Pres)

Tools For Schools, Inc. (4)
1525 Faraday Ave Ste 200, Carlsbad, CA 92008
Tel.: (858) 455-4800
Web Site: http://tfs.goodsource.com
Foodservice for Schools
N.A.I.C.S.: 722310
Katie Silva (Mgr-Sls-San Diego)
Laurie McCluskey (VP-Idaho)

Joint Venture (Domestic):

Lamm Food Service, LLC (3)
3219 NW Evangeline Thruway, Lafayette, LA 70507-3537
Tel.: (337) 896-0331
Web Site: http://www.lammfoodservice.com
General Line Grocery Merchant Whslr
N.A.I.C.S.: 424410
Dale Lagan (Dir-Pur & IT)
Bruce Mattingly (CEO)

Holding (Domestic):

PatientCare EMS Solutions (3)
115 Jordan Plz Blvd Ste 200, Tyler, TX 75704
Tel.: (903) 705-7620
Ambulance & Other Critical Healthcare Services
N.A.I.C.S.: 621910
Herman Schwarz (CEO)

Subsidiary (Domestic):

Paramedics Plus LLC (4)
575 Marina Blvd, San Leandro, CA 94577-3521
Tel.: (510) 746-5700
Web Site: http://www.paramedicsplus.com
Ambulatory Surgical & Emergency Centers
N.A.I.C.S.: 621493
Dale Feldhauser (COO-Alameda County)
Debbie Vass (Dir-Quality Initiatives)
Kimberly Lacina (Dir-Quality & Clinical Svcs-Alameda County)
Rob Lawrence (COO)
Ron Schwartz (Pres)
Mark Postma (VP)

Subsidiary (Domestic):

VT Services, Inc. (3)
14111 Park Meadow Dr Ste 130, Chantilly, VA 20151
Tel.: (703) 650-0780
Web Site: http://www.vt-group.com
Engineering & Technical Support Services
N.A.I.C.S.: 541330
John Hassoun (Pres & CEO)
Sunil Ramchand (Chief Growth Officer)

Subsidiary (Domestic):

VT Group (US) Plc (4)
14111 Park Meadow Dr Ste 130, Chantilly, VA 20151
Tel.: (703) 658-7500
Web Site: http://www.vt-group.com
Facilities Management & Technical Support Services
N.A.I.C.S.: 561990
John Hassoun (Pres & CEO)
Alicia Townes (CFO)
Ted Timberlake (Chief Legal Officer)
Sunil Ramchand (Chief Growth Officer)
Elizabeth Alston (Chief Human Resources Officer)
Thomas Lydon (Pres-Aviation Solutions Div)
Ryan Reed (Pres-Maritime Solutions Div)
William Powell (Pres-Information Systems & Tech Div)
Maria Proestou (Pres-Delta Resources Div)
Rick Sabol (Sr VP)

Subsidiary (Domestic):

Delta Resources, Inc. (5)
3601 Eisenhower Ave Ste 220, Alexandria, VA 22304
Tel.: (703) 418-1960
Engineeering Services
N.A.I.C.S.: 541330
Tom Winckler (COO)

Division (Domestic):

VT Services, Inc. - Alpharetta Division (4)
10745 Westside Way Ste 300, Alpharetta, GA 30009
Tel.: (770) 952-1479
Engineering & Technical Support Services
N.A.I.C.S.: 541330

VT Services, Inc. - Charleston Division (4)
3185 Industry Dr, North Charleston, SC 29418
Tel.: (843) 767-1442
Engineering & Technical Support Services
N.A.I.C.S.: 541330

VT Services, Inc. - Chesapeake Division (4)
901 Professional Pl, Chesapeake, VA 23320
Tel.: (757) 547-0202
Engineering & Technical Support Services
N.A.I.C.S.: 541330

VT Services, Inc. - Groton Division (4)
32 Taugwonk Spur Rd Bldg 32 Unit 1A/1B, Stonington, CT 06378
Tel.: (860) 535-0364
Engineering & Technical Support Services
N.A.I.C.S.: 541330

VT Services, Inc. - Hawaii Division (4)
99-994 Iwaena St Bay 102, Aiea, HI 96701
Tel.: (808) 676-2322
Engineering & Technical Support Services
N.A.I.C.S.: 541330

VT Services, Inc. - Jacksonville Division (4)
7091 Davis Creek Rd, Jacksonville, FL 32256
Tel.: (904) 880-1886
Technical Support Services
N.A.I.C.S.: 541990
David Kasun (Gen Mgr)

VT Services, Inc. - Madison Division (4)
9238 Madison Blvd Bldg 2 Ste 110, Madison, AL 35758
Tel.: (256) 464-9191
Technical Support Services
N.A.I.C.S.: 541990

VT Services, Inc. - Pensacola Division (4)
8781 Paul Starr Dr, Pensacola, FL 32514-7048
Tel.: (850) 478-4836
Technical Support Services
N.A.I.C.S.: 561499

VT Services, Inc. - San Diego Division (4)
2232 Verus St Ste A, San Diego, CA 92154
Tel.: (619) 424-9024
Engineering & Technical Support Services
N.A.I.C.S.: 541330

VT Services, Inc. - Sterling Division (4)
45665 Willow Pond Plz, Sterling, VA 20164
Tel.: (703) 658-7500
Engineering & Technical Support Services
N.A.I.C.S.: 541330

VT Services, Inc. - Virginia Beach Division (4)
2700 Avenger Dr Ste 100, Virginia Beach, VA 23452
Tel.: (757) 463-2800
Engineering & Technical Support Services
N.A.I.C.S.: 541330

Holding (Domestic):

Worldwise, Inc. (3)
6 Hamilton Landing Ste 150, Novato, CA 94949
Tel.: (415) 721-7400
Web Site: http://www.worldwise.com
Sales Range: $50-74.9 Million
Environmentally Safe Pet Toys,Treats & Accessories Mfr
N.A.I.C.S.: 459910
Andy Murrer (VP-Ops)
Kevin Fick (CEO)
Jeff Leh (VP-Sls)
Petar Katurich (CFO)
John Stephens (VP-eCommerce & Digital Mktg)

Subsidiary (Domestic):

Pet Factory (4)
845 E High St, Mundelein, IL 60060-3100
Tel.: (847) 837-8900
Web Site: http://www.petfactory.com
Sales Range: $10-24.9 Million
Emp.: 70
Dog Food Mfr
N.A.I.C.S.: 311111

Subsidiary (Domestic):

Alvarez & Marsal Business Consulting, LLC (2)
700 Louisiana St Ste 900, Houston, TX 77002
Tel.: (713) 571-2400
Web Site: http://www.alvarezandmarsal.com
Business Consulting Services
N.A.I.C.S.: 541611
Thomas Elsenbrook (CEO)
Brian Harris (Mng Dir-Chicago)
Matson Blocker (Mng Dir)

Alvarez & Marsal Dispute Analysis & Forensic Services, LLC (2)
600 Madison Ave 8th Fl, New York, NY 10022
Tel.: (212) 759-4433
Web Site: http://www.alvarezandmarsal.com
Financial & Regulatory Dispute Consulting Services
N.A.I.C.S.: 541618
Suzanne Stuckwisch (Mng Dir-San Francisco)
Stephen Millington (Mng Dir-Dubai)
Jane Kidd (Mng Dir-Houston)
Aaron Stai (Mng Dir-Houston)

Alvarez & Marsal Healthcare Industry Group, LLC (2)
600 Magison Ave 8th Fl, New York, NY 10022
Tel.: (212) 759-4433
Web Site: http://www.alvarezandmarsal.com
Emp.: 300
Management Consulting Services
N.A.I.C.S.: 541611
Lars Enstrom (Mng Dir-New York)
Steve Geringer (Mng Dir)
Matthew Box (Mng Dir-Washington)
Steven Boyd (Mng Dir)
Alexander McLean (Mng Dir)
Malcolm McKenzie (Mng Dir)
Faye Wattleton (Mng Dir)
Beth Devin (Mng Dir-San Francisco)
Mark Paling (Mng Dir-Houston)
Ramin Tabibzadeh (Mng Dir)
Guy P. Sansone (Founder)

Alvarez & Marsal Public Sector Services, LLC (2)
655 15th St NW Ste 600, Washington, DC 20005
Tel.: (202) 729-2100
Web Site: http://www.alvarezandmarsal.com
Public Sector Consulting Services
N.A.I.C.S.: 541611
Lauren Hill (Mng Dir-Valuation Svcs Practice)
Jay Brown (Mng Dir)
Erin Covington (Mng Dir)
Michael Carrasco (Mng Dir-Houston)
Jay Nagy (Sr Dir-New York)

Alvarez & Marsal Real Estate Advisory Services, LLC (2)
600 Magison Ave 8th Fl, New York, NY 10022
Tel.: (212) 759-4433
Web Site: http://www.alvarezandmarsal.com
Real Estate Advisory Services
N.A.I.C.S.: 541618
Klaus Kretschmann (Mng Dir)
Gerald D. Pietroforte (Mng Dir)
John Heywood (Mng Dir-San Francisco)

Alvarez & Marsal Taxand, LLC (2)
600 madison Ave, New York, NY 10020
Tel.: (212) 759-4433
Web Site: http://www.alvarezmarsal.com
Emp.: 300
Tax Advisory Services
N.A.I.C.S.: 541618
Albert Liguori (Mng Dir)
James Bartek (Mng Dir)
Enrique MacGregor (Mng Dir-USA)
Jeffrey Olin (Mng Dir-Chicago)
Andrew Johnson (Mng Dir-USA)
Daniel F. Rahill (Mng Dir)
Tim Wach (Mng Dir-Global)
Alexander Duncan (Dir-Tax Transaction Advisory Practice)
Jason Clatworthy (Mng Dir)
Cassandra de la Fe (Dir-Miami)
Elizabeth Goodwin (Mng Dir-Federal Tax Practice)
Ernesto R. Perez (Mng Dir)
Tyler Horton (Mng Dir)
Siva Sellathurai (Sr Dir-Denver)
Robert N. Lowe Jr. (CEO)

Subsidiary (Non-US):

North American Tungsten Corporation Ltd. (2)
Suite 1680 - 400 Burrard Street, Vancouver, V6C 3A6, BC, Canada

Alvarez & Marsal, Inc.—(Continued)

Tel.: (604) 638-7440
Web Site: http://www.naturgsten.com
Tungsten Mining Services
N.A.I.C.S.: 212290

ALVAREZ HOMES, INC.
3617 Hudson Ln Ste 101, Tampa, FL
33618
Tel.: (813) 969-3033   FL
Web Site:
    https://www.alvarezhomes.com
Year Founded: 1983
Sales Range: $10-24.9 Million
Emp.: 25
Residential Home Builder
N.A.I.C.S.: 236115
Bobby Alvarez (Pres)
Fernando Socias (VP)
Alex Socias (Dir-Field Ops)

ALVAREZ TECHNOLOGY GROUP, INC.
209 Pajaro St Ste A, Salinas, CA
93901
Tel.: (831) 753-7677   CA
Web Site: https://www.alvareztg.com
Year Founded: 2001
Sales Range: $1-9.9 Million
Emp.: 50
Information Technology Services
N.A.I.C.S.: 541511
Luis M. Alvarez (Owner)
Cristel Andersen (Dir-Customer Care
& Ops)

ALVARO P. ESCANDON, INC.
130 Maple Ave Ste 6, Red Bank, NJ
07701-1729
Tel.: (973) 274-1040
Rev.: $13,000,000
Emp.: 8
Textiles Whslr
N.A.I.C.S.: 424990

ALVIMAR GLOBAL INC.
640 3 Mile Rd NW, Grand Rapids, MI
49544
Tel.: (616) 784-3803
Web Site:
    http://www.alvimarglobal.com
Year Founded: 1947
Sales Range: $10-24.9 Million
Emp.: 10
P.O.P. Displays & Promotional Prod-
ucts Mfr
N.A.I.C.S.: 339930
Glenn Bodien (VP-Sls)
Dave Vander Schaaf (Dir-Art & Mgr-
Production)
Tre Carlsen (CEO)

ALVIN EQUIPMENT COMPANY INC.
3375 E Hwy 6, Alvin, TX 77511
Tel.: (281) 331-3177
Web Site:
    https://www.alvinequipment.com
Rev.: $15,000,000
Emp.: 17
General Construction Machinery &
Equipment
N.A.I.C.S.: 423810
David C. Beaver (CEO)
Chad Beaver (Pres)
Shannon Matejka (Controller)

ALVIN HOLLIS & CO. INC.
1 Hollis St, South Weymouth, MA
02190
Tel.: (781) 335-2100   MA
Web Site: https://www.alvinhollis.com
Year Founded: 1850
Sales Range: $10-24.9 Million
Emp.: 200
Fuel Oil Dealers

N.A.I.C.S.: 457210
Gordon Williamson (Engr-Sls)

ALVIN J. COLEMAN & SON INC.
9 New Hampshire Rte 113, Conway,
NH 03818
Tel.: (603) 447-5936   NH
Web Site:
    https://www.ajcoleman.com
Year Founded: 1940
Sales Range: $25-49.9 Million
Emp.: 151
Provider of Sand & Gravel Construc-
tion
N.A.I.C.S.: 237310
Calvin Coleman (Pres)
Patrick Holland (VP-Construction
Ops)

ALVIS, INC.
2100 Stella Ct, Columbus, OH 43215
Tel.: (614) 252-8402   OH
Web Site: http://www.alvishouse.org
Year Founded: 1967
Sales Range: $10-24.9 Million
Emp.: 478
Community Action Services
N.A.I.C.S.: 624190
Joseph Geary (CFO)
Denise M. Robinson (Pres & CEO)
Phil Nunes (COO)
Heidi Riggs (Chief Admin Officer)

ALVORD-POLK INC.
125 Gearhart St, Millersburg, PA
17061
Tel.: (717) 692-2128
Web Site:
    https://www.alvordpolk.com
Sales Range: $10-24.9 Million
Emp.: 150
Reamers, Machine Tool
N.A.I.C.S.: 333515
Ronald Boyer (CEO)
Jim Kelly (Controller)
Steven T. Boyer (Pres-Cutting Tool
Div)

ALWAYS BAGELS, INC.
10 Keyland Ct, Bohemia, NY 11716
Tel.: (631) 218-6604
Web Site:
    https://www.alwaysbagels.com
Year Founded: 1985
Emp.: 151
Retail Bakery Services
N.A.I.C.S.: 311811
Anthony Pariti (VP)
Mike Yarmaloff (VP-Sls & Mktg)
Tony Pariti (Pres)
Joe Holovach (Mgr-Natl Sls)

ALWAYS SUMMER LLC
31 W 34th St 7th Fl, New York, NY
10001
Tel.: (212) 695-6878
Sales Range: $10-24.9 Million
Emp.: 100
Distr of Costume Jewelry, Women's &
Children's Clothing & Toys
N.A.I.C.S.: 812199

Subsidiaries:

Bikini.com   (1)
2001 Meridian Ave Ph 16, Miami Beach, FL
33139-1553
Tel.: (305) 932-6655
Website Promoting Beach-Related Merchandise
N.A.I.C.S.: 424610

ALYCE DESIGNS INC.
7901 N Caldwell Ave, Morton Grove,
IL 60053
Tel.: (847) 966-9200
Web Site: http://www.alyceparis.com

Sales Range: $25-49.9 Million
Emp.: 150
Dresses & Gowns for Proms, Special
Occasions, Pageants & Weddings
N.A.I.C.S.: 315250
Jean Paul Hamm (Owner)
Barbara Holmes (Mgr-Credit)

ALYESKA PIPELINE SERVICE COMPANY
3700 Centerpoint Dr, Anchorage, AK
99503
Tel.: (907) 787-8700   DE
Web Site: http://www.alyeska-
    pipeline.com
Year Founded: 1970
Sales Range: $150-199.9 Million
Emp.: 900
Provider of Petroleum Pipeline Ser-
vices
N.A.I.C.S.: 486110
Thomas J. Barrett (Pres)
Rod Hanson (Sr VP-Ops & Mainte-
nance)
Curtis Nuttall (VP-Risk & Technical
Div)
Ed Hendrickson (CFO & Sr VP)
Fred Millen (Dir-HR)
Hal Eppley (Coord-Field Matls)
Michelle Egan (Chief Comm Officer)
Sue Britt (Mgr-Compliance & Docu-
mentation)
Susan Parkes (Gen Counsel & VP)

ALZHEIMER'S ASSOCIATION
225 N Michigan Ave Fl 17, Chicago,
IL 60601
Tel.: (845) 639-6776
Web Site: https://www.alz.org
Sales Range: $1-9.9 Million
Emp.: 25
Miscellaneous Ambulatory Health
Care Services
N.A.I.C.S.: 621999
Ashley Giron (Coord-Special Events)
David Grams (Exec Dir)
Robyn McGill (Mgr-Mktg Comm)
Clayton Jacobs (Exec Dir)
Karen Ortiz (Dir-Dev-California Cen-
tral Coast Chapter)
Lindsey Leonard (Exec Dir)

ALZHEIMER'S RESOURCE CENTER OF CONNECTICUT, INC.
1261 S Main St, Plantsville, CT
06479
Tel.: (860) 628-9000   CT
Web Site:
    http://www.alzheimersresource.org
Year Founded: 1992
Sales Range: $10-24.9 Million
Emp.: 225
Behavioral Healthcare Services
N.A.I.C.S.: 623220
Harry E. Morgan (Dir-Medical)
Anne M. McCarty (Dir-HR)
Eileen O'Connor (Dir-Nursing Svcs)
Julie Thompson Robison (Sec)
Michael J. Lenkiewicz (Treas)
Waldo Klein (Co-Pres)
Michael J. Smith (Co-Pres & CEO)

ALZHEON, INC.
111 Speen St Ste 306, Framingham,
MA 01701
Tel.: (508) 861-7709   DE
Web Site: http://www.alzheon.com
Year Founded: 2013
Emp.: 6
Research & Development in Biotech-
nology
N.A.I.C.S.: 541714
Susan Abushakra (Chief Medical Offi-
cer)
Martin Tolar (Founder, Pres & CEO)

John Hey (Chief Scientific Officer)
Aidan Power (VP-Program & Portfolio
Mgmt)
Petr Kocis (VP-Preclinical Dev)
Kenneth Mace (VP-Fin)
Peter N. Laivins (Head-Comml Strat-
egy & Plng)
Neil William Flanzraich (Vice Chm)

AM COMMUNICATIONS
5707 State Route 309, Galion, OH
44833
Tel.: (419) 528-3051
Web Site: https://www.amcable.com
Sales Range: $10-24.9 Million
Emp.: 140
Other Scientific & Technical Consult-
ing Services
N.A.I.C.S.: 541690
Alan Miller (Pres & CEO)
Chris Schafer (Dir-Ops)
Jason S. Phillips (Dir-Tech Ops)
Nicia Cary (Dir-HR)

AM CONTRACTING LLC
4 Norman Dr, Albany, NY 12205
Tel.: (518) 783-0032
Web Site:
    http://www.amcontracting.com
Sales Range: $10-24.9 Million
Emp.: 60
Renovation, Remodeling & Repairs:
Industrial Buildings
N.A.I.C.S.: 236220
Angelo Muscolino (Pres & CEO)
Keith Paul (Project Mgr)

AM ENGINEERING, INC.
8340 Consumer Ct, Sarasota, FL
34240
Tel.: (941) 377-9178   FL
Web Site: http://www.amengfl.com
Year Founded: 1986
Emp.: 80
Engineering Services, Nsk
N.A.I.C.S.: 541330
Shawn Leins (Owner & Pres)

AM NETWORKS
1900 AM Dr, Quakertown, PA 18951-
2107
Tel.: (215) 538-8700   DE
Web Site: http://www.amcomm.com
Sales Range: $25-49.9 Million
Emp.: 424
Network Monitoring Products & Ser-
vices for Cable TV & Broadband Sys-
tem Operators
N.A.I.C.S.: 334220
Javad K. Hassan (Chm)
Gus Kamnitsis (COO)
Maqbool Qurashi (Grp VP-AM Train-
ing Svcs)
Joseph Rocci (VP-AM Broadband
Products)
Bret Matz (VP & Gen Mgr)

AM PIERCE & ASSOCIATES, INC.
46591 Expedition Dr, Lexington Park,
MD 20653
Tel.: (240) 718-3800
Web Site: http://www.ampierce.com
Year Founded: 2007
Sales Range: $1-9.9 Million
Emp.: 38
System Engineering & Integration
Services
N.A.I.C.S.: 541330
Adelle Pierce (Pres & CEO)
Melinda Brown (VP-HR & Ops)
Tracey Jubeck (VP-Fin & Contracts)

AM SLEEP INC.

768 E Dundee Rd, Palatine, IL 60074
Tel.: (847) 202-5200
Web Site:
   http://www.americanmattress.com
Sales Range: $25-49.9 Million
Emp.: 100
Retailer of Beds & Accessories
N.A.I.C.S.: 449110
Bruce Berman *(Mgr-Sls)*
Kristie Pechtel *(CFO)*

AM TECHNICAL SOLUTIONS, INC.

2213 RR 620 N Ste 105, Austin, TX 78734
Tel.: (512) 266-5122
Web Site: http://www.amts.com
Year Founded: 1994
Emp.: 255
Business Advisory & Technical Consulting Services
N.A.I.C.S.: 541618
Kelly McAndrew *(Chm)*
Tim Self *(Founder)*
Johannes Brinkmann *(CFO)*
Stephen Poindexter *(COO)*
Dan Codi *(CEO)*
Harry Engwer *(VP)*
Sandeep Dave *(Chief Bus Officer)*

AM TRANSPORT SERVICES, INC.

1903 Miller Dr, Olney, IL 62450
Tel.: (618) 395-4880
Web Site:
   http://www.amtransportonline.com
Year Founded: 1990
Sales Range: $10-24.9 Million
Emp.: 26
General Freight Trucking, Long-Distance, Truckload
N.A.I.C.S.: 484121
Rob McClain *(Dir-Sls)*
Michael McKinney *(Pres)*
Molly Volk *(Coord-Billing)*
Liz Strubhart *(Mgr-Billing)*
Brett Stirnaman *(Mgr-Carrier)*
Laura Matthews *(Acct Mgr)*
Dave Marquart *(Acct Mgr)*

AM&G WATERPROOFING, LLC

2120 Atlantic Ave, Brooklyn, NY 11233
Tel.: (718) 852-3330
Web Site:
   https://www.amgwaterproofing.com
Sales Range: $200-249.9 Million
Emp.: 285
Hotel/Motel & Multi-Family Home Renovation & Remodeling
N.A.I.C.S.: 236220
William Rivera *(COO)*
Eddy Philippe *(VP-Sls & Mktg)*
Thomas Hussey *(CFO)*

AM-CAN TRANSPORT SERVICE INC.

330 Webb Rd, Williamston, SC 29697
Tel.: (864) 226-3476
Web Site: http://www.am-cantransport.com
Rev.: $34,352,549
Emp.: 200
Trucking Service
N.A.I.C.S.: 484121

Subsidiaries:

A-C Logistics   (1)
330 Webb Rd, Williamston, SC 29697
Tel.: (864) 226-3476
Web Site: http://www.am-cantransport.com
Sales Range: $10-24.9 Million
Emp.: 6
Provider of Logistics Services
N.A.I.C.S.: 484121

AM-PAT INCORPORATED

15776 Laguna Canyon Rd, Irvine, CA 92618
Tel.: (714) 288-8181
Web Site: http://www.bootbarn.com
Rev.: $30,000,200
Emp.: 900
Men's & Women's Boot Mfr
N.A.I.C.S.: 458210
Patrick Meany *(CEO)*

AM/PM ADVERTISING INC.

345 Claremont Ave Ste 26, Montclair, NJ 07042
Tel.: (973) 824-8600
Year Founded: 1962
Emp.: 130
N.A.I.C.S.: 541810
Robert Saks *(Chm)*
Michael Saltz *(Pres)*
Fred Minotola *(Exec VP)*
Ann Ellis *(VP)*

AMA PLASTICS

1100 Citrus St, Riverside, CA 92507-1731
Tel.: (951) 734-5600
Web Site:
   http://www.amaplastics.com
Year Founded: 1971
Sales Range: $25-49.9 Million
Emp.: 150
Molding Primary Plastics
N.A.I.C.S.: 326199
Mark Atchison *(CEO)*
Jim Bean *(Mgr-Warehouse)*
Eddie Buehler *(Mgr-Tooling & Engrg)*
Susan Calvert *(Mgr-Acct-Sls)*
Donald Jensen *(VP-Fin)*
Laura Raney *(Mgr-Pur)*
Cheryl Buhler *(Pres)*
John Gorup *(Mgr-Quality)*
Ken Pravitz *(Gen Mgr)*

AMA TECHTEL COMMUNICATIONS

4630 50th St Ste 402, Lubbock, TX 79414-3519
Tel.: (806) 722-2222
Web Site: http://www.amatechtel.com
Rev.: $15,000,000
Emp.: 80
Data Telephone Communications
N.A.I.C.S.: 517121
Bryce Byers *(Supvr-Wireless Ops)*
Dell Purdy *(VP-Regulatory Compliance Revenue Assurance)*
Jaden Duncan *(Engr-Network)*
Chuck Howell *(VP-Field Ops)*

AMAANAH REFUGEE SERVICES

10333 Harwin Dr Ste 675, Houston, TX 77036
Tel.: (713) 370-3063   TX
Year Founded: 2008
Sales Range: Less than $1 Million
Emp.: 9
Refugee Welfare Services
N.A.I.C.S.: 624230
Ghulam Kehar *(Exec Dir)*

AMACPI CORP.

1771 Railroad St, Corona, CA 92878
Tel.: (951) 272-5858
Web Site:
   https://www.airmarkintl.com
Sales Range: $10-24.9 Million
Emp.: 20
Transportation Equipment Distr
N.A.I.C.S.: 423860
Dawn Rocky *(CFO)*

AMADAS GROUP INC.

1100 Holland Rd, Suffolk, VA 23434
Tel.: (757) 539-0231

Web Site: https://www.amadas.com
Rev.: $20,111,210
Emp.: 105
Farm Machinery & Equipment Mfr
N.A.I.C.S.: 333111
Bob Jones *(Mgr-Mid-Atlantic Agricultural Sls)*
Ted H. Williams *(VP-Sls & Mktg)*
Chris Beaty *(Mgr-Sls-AL)*
Willie Branche *(Mgr-Svc-Columbus)*
Chuck Sewell *(Mgr-Territory Sls-Western US)*

Subsidiaries:

Amadas Group Inc. - Albany Plant   (1)
1701 S Slappey Blvd, Albany, GA 31706
Tel.: (229) 439-2217
Web Site: http://www.amadas.com
Emp.: 6
Agricultural Equipment Mfr
N.A.I.C.S.: 333111
Roger Mercer *(Plant Mgr)*

Amadas Industries Inc   (1)
1100 Holland Rd, Suffolk, VA 23434
Tel.: (757) 539-0231
Web Site: http://www.amadas.com
Sales Range: $10-24.9 Million
Emp.: 100
Construction Machinery Mfr
N.A.I.C.S.: 333120

AMAG PHARMACEUTICALS, INC.

1100 Winter St, Waltham, MA 02451
Tel.: (617) 498-3300   DE
Web Site:
   http://www.amagpharma.com
Year Founded: 1981
Rev.: $327,751,000
Assets: $791,227,000
Liabilities: $505,108,000
Net Worth: $286,119,000
Earnings: ($466,456,000)
Emp.: 440
Fiscal Year-end: 12/31/19
Biopharmaceutical Mfr; Organ-Specific Contrast Agents & Therapeutic Iron Compounds for Treating Anemia
N.A.I.C.S.: 325412
Joseph D. Vittiglio *(Chief Bus Officer, Gen Counsel-Quality & Exec VP)*
Anthony Casciano *(COO, Chief Comml Officer & Exec VP)*
Kelly Schick *(Chief HR Officer & Sr VP)*
Scott Dunseth Myers *(Pres)*

Subsidiaries:

Lumara Health Inc.   (1)
110 Winter St Ste 3000, Waltham, MA 02451
Tel.: (617) 498-3303
Specialty Pharmaceutical Research & Development Services
N.A.I.C.S.: 325412

Lumara Health Services Ltd.   (1)
1100 Winter St Ste 3000, Waltham, MA 02451
Tel.: (617) 498-3300
Web Site: http://www.lumarahealth.com
Pharmaceutical Mfr & Distr
N.A.I.C.S.: 325412

AMAIN.COM, INC.

424 Otterson Dr Ste 160, Chico, CA 95928
Tel.: (530) 894-0797   CA
Web Site:
   https://www.amainhobbies.com
Year Founded: 2004
Sales Range: $10-24.9 Million
Emp.: 57
Internet Retailer of Radio-Controlled Cars, Trucks, Helicopters & Airplanes
N.A.I.C.S.: 423920
Derrick Threatt *(Mgr-Digital Mktg)*

AMALFE BROS INC.

120 Fieldcrest Ave, Edison, NJ 08837
Tel.: (732) 738-9155
Web Site: https://www.abswhse.com
Sales Range: $10-24.9 Million
Emp.: 50
Automotive Supplies & Parts
N.A.I.C.S.: 423120
John P. Amalfe *(Pres & CEO)*
Anthony Amalfe *(VP)*
Angela Camicia *(Controller)*

AMALGAMATED INSURANCE FUND

333 Westchester Ave, White Plains, NY 10604
Tel.: (212) 473-5700
Web Site:
   http://www.amalgamatedlife.com
Year Founded: 1942
Sales Range: $100-124.9 Million
Emp.: 425
Provider of Insurance & Pension Services
N.A.I.C.S.: 525120
Victoria R. Sartor *(Sr VP)*
John Dubil *(Sr VP)*
Raghubar Singh *(CIO & Sr VP)*
Ann Joo Kim *(Sr VP)*
Ellen R. Dunkin *(Gen Counsel & Sr VP)*
John Thornton *(Exec VP-Sls & Mktg)*
Leslie Bostic *(Sr VP)*
Richard Rust *(Exec VP)*

Subsidiaries:

The Amalgamated Life Insurance Co. Inc.   (1)
333 Westchester Ave, White Plains, NY 10604-2910   (100%)
Tel.: (914) 367-5000
Web Site: http://www.amalgamatedlife.com
Sales Range: $125-149.9 Million
Provider of Insurance Services
N.A.I.C.S.: 525110
Paul Mallen *(Pres & CEO)*
Timothy J. Kristof *(CFO & Sr VP)*
Jonathan Pollio *(Chief Actuary & Sr VP)*

AMALGAMATED INVESTMENTS CO.

1 W Monroe St FL 3, Chicago, IL 60603
Tel.: (312) 822-3000
Web Site: http://www.aboc.com
Sales Range: $10-24.9 Million
Emp.: 210
Bank Holding Company
N.A.I.C.S.: 551111

Subsidiaries:

Amalga Trust Inc.   (1)
1 W Monroe St, Chicago, IL 60603
Tel.: (312) 822-3000
Web Site: http://www.aboc.com
Sales Range: $50-74.9 Million
Emp.: 150
Trust Services
N.A.I.C.S.: 522110

Amalgamated Bank of Chicago   (1)
1 W Monroe St, Chicago, IL 60603
Tel.: (312) 822-3000
Web Site: http://www.aboc.com
Rev.: $53,051,000
Emp.: 45
State Commercial Banks
N.A.I.C.S.: 522110
Robert J. Majdecki *(Chief Investment Officer & Sr VP)*

AMALIE OIL COMPANY

1601 McClosky Blvd, Tampa, FL 33605
Tel.: (813) 248-1988
Web Site: https://www.amalie.com
Year Founded: 1903
Lubricating Oils & Greases Mfr & Distr

Amalie Oil Company—(Continued)

N.A.I.C.S.: 324191
Dennis J. Madden (Sr VP-Sls & Mktg-Global)
Richard Barkett (COO)
Ken Holder (Mgr-Sls-Natl)
Larry Mitchell (VP-Accts-Natl)

Subsidiaries:

Lubricating Specialties Company Inc. (1)
8015 Paramount Blvd, Pico Rivera, CA 90660-4811
Tel.: (562) 776-4000
Web Site: http://www.lsc-online.com
Lubricating Oils & Greases Mfr
N.A.I.C.S.: 324191

AMANA SOCIETY, INC.
506 39th Ave, Amana, IA 52203-8229
Tel.: (319) 622-7500 IA
Web Site: https://www.amanasociety.com
Year Founded: 1932
Sales Range: $150-199.9 Million
Emp.: 325
Commercial Farming Services
N.A.I.C.S.: 111998
Howard Hagen (Chm)
Guy Wendler (Vice Chm)
Greg Luerkens (Pres & CEO)

Subsidiaries:

Amana Coffee & Tea Co. (1)
4423 220th Trl, Amana, IA 52203
Tel.: (319) 622-6598
Coffee & Tea Retailer
N.A.I.C.S.: 445298

Amana Farms,. Inc. (1)
PO Box 189, Amana, IA 52203-0189 (100%)
Tel.: (319) 622-7551
Sales Range: $10-24.9 Million
Emp.: 30
Farming
N.A.I.C.S.: 111998
John McGrath (Mgr)

Amana Society Service Co. (1)
708 49th Ave, Amana, IA 52203-8115 (100%)
Tel.: (319) 622-3052
Sales Range: $1-9.9 Million
Emp.: 6
Electric & Water Utilities
N.A.I.C.S.: 221122
Sue Hahn (Office Mgr)
Terry Hershberger (Gen Mgr)

Amana-Nordstrom Motel Co. (1)
2211 U Ave, Williamsburg, IA 52361 (50%)
Tel.: (319) 668-1175
Web Site: http://www.amanahotel.com
Sales Range: $10-24.9 Million
Emp.: 120
Hotel Operations
N.A.I.C.S.: 721110
David Nordstrom (Pres)

AMANDO PENA INC.
776 E Grant St, Roma, TX 78584
Tel.: (956) 849-3177
Rev.: $16,425,533
Emp.: 69
Grocery Stores, Independent
N.A.I.C.S.: 445110
Amando Pena (Owner)

AMANDUS D. MOYER LUMBER INCORPORATED
1200 E Philadelphia Ave, Gilbertsville, PA 19525
Tel.: (610) 367-2036 PA
Web Site: https://www.admoyer.com
Year Founded: 1939
Sales Range: $10-24.9 Million
Emp.: 75
Provider of Building Supplies
N.A.I.C.S.: 423310

Scott Moyer (Co-Owner)
Terry Moyer (Co-Owner)
Brian Schlegel (Mgr-Sls)

AMAR OIL CO. INC.
1610 W Church St, Hammond, LA 70401
Tel.: (985) 345-1827 LA
Web Site: http://www.amaroil.com
Year Founded: 1974
Sales Range: $25-49.9 Million
Emp.: 7
Petroleum Products
N.A.I.C.S.: 424720
Edward Amar (VP)
Darrell Amar Jr. (Gen Mgr-Sls)

Subsidiaries:

Tickfaw Pit Stop Inc. (1)
14069 Hwy 442 W, Tickfaw, LA 70466-3077
Tel.: (985) 542-6511
Sales Range: $10-24.9 Million
Emp.: 2
Gasoline Service Stations
N.A.I.C.S.: 722511

AMARILLO HARDWARE COMPANY
622 S Grant St, Amarillo, TX 79101-2526
Tel.: (806) 376-4722 TX
Year Founded: 1904
Sales Range: $25-49.9 Million
Emp.: 400
Hardware, Furniture, Appliances & Industrial Supplies Distr
N.A.I.C.S.: 423710
Dave Kittley (Mgr-Catalog)
R. Joseph Wildman (Pres)
J. Charles Short (COO & Exec VP)
Jim Belcher (VP & Controller)
Patrick Perkins (VP-Sls & Mdsg)
Jim Tate (Mgr-Furniture Div)
Richard Kirkland (Mgr-Appliance Div)

Subsidiaries:

California Hardware Company (1)
3601 E Jurupa St, Ontario, CA 91761
Tel.: (909) 390-6100
Web Site: http://www.chcusa.com
Sales Range: $75-99.9 Million
Emp.: 150
Hardware, Tools, Plumbing & Ventilation Components, Electrical Components, Paint, Housewares, Industrial Supplies, Farm & Garden Supplies Distr
N.A.I.C.S.: 423710

AMARILLO NATIONAL BANCORP, INC.
410 S Taylor St, Amarillo, TX 79101-1555
Tel.: (806) 378-8000 TX
Web Site: http://www.anb.com
Year Founded: 1982
Sales Range: $300-349.9 Million
Emp.: 856
Bank Holding Company
N.A.I.C.S.: 551111
Patrick Ware (Vice Chm)
William Ware (Pres-Bank)
Richard C. Ware II (Chm & CEO)

Subsidiaries:

Amarillo National Bank (1)
410 S Taylor St, Amarillo, TX 79101-1555
Tel.: (806) 378-8000
Web Site: http://www.anb.com
Sales Range: $300-349.9 Million
Commericial Banking
N.A.I.C.S.: 522110
Patrick Ware (Vice Chm)
William Ware (Pres)
Richard C. Ware II (Chm)
Terri Boswell-Williams (Sr VP-Branch Admin)
Brenda Wilkins (VP & Mgr-Loan Review)
Adrian Meander (VP & Branch Mgr-North)
Alisha Amero (VP & Mgr-Private Banking)

Lee Bates (Asst VP & Mgr-Network)
Cliff Bickerstaff (Exec VP & Mgr-Asset Mgmt Div)
Debbie Bigelow (Sr VP & Mgr-Home Loans)
Briget Cain (VP & Sr Underwriter-Mortgage Loans)
Cynthia Donnell (VP & Branch Mgr-Bell)
Jennifer Gallardo (VP & Branch Mgr-Northeast)
Robert Glenn (VP & Mgr-Collections)
John Hunt (VP & Mgr-Direct Lending Installment Loans)
Ross Kerns (Sr VP & Controller)
Matt Ray (VP & Mgr-Consumer Card Svcs)
Patrick Stanley (Sr VP-Ops Risk Mgmt)
David Strange (VP-Bus Dev-Comml Loans)
Cory Ramsey (Sr VP-Comml Loans)
Erik Schrader (Asst VP & Mgr-Comml Teller)
Wade Porter (Exec VP-Comml Loans)
Corey Krusa (Sr VP & Dir-Personnel)

AMARO FOOD ENTERPRISES INC.
2011 8th St, North Bergen, NJ 07047
Tel.: (201) 902-9990
Web Site: http://www.amarofoods.com
Sales Range: $10-24.9 Million
Emp.: 23
Sell Beef Pork, Chicken Etc.
N.A.I.C.S.: 424470
Aose Ray (VP)

AMATEUR ELECTRONIC SUPPLY LLC
5710 W Good Hope Rd, Milwaukee, WI 53223-4736
Tel.: (414) 358-4088
Web Site: http://www.aesham.com
Year Founded: 1998
Sales Range: $10-24.9 Million
Emp.: 25
Radios & Electronic Supplies Distr
N.A.I.C.S.: 449210
Phil M. Majerus (Owner)

AMATO COLLISION CENTER, INC.
8301 N 76th St, Milwaukee, WI 53223
Tel.: (414) 357-7800
Web Site: http://www.amatoauto.com
Year Founded: 1995
Sales Range: $10-24.9 Million
Emp.: 35
Car Whslr
N.A.I.C.S.: 441110
Jim Reincke (Gen Mgr)

AMATOM ELECTRONIC HARDWARE, INC.
5 Pasco Hill Rd, Cromwell, CT 06416
Tel.: (860) 828-0847 DE
Web Site: http://www.amatom.com
Year Founded: 1989
Rev.: $15,000,000
Emp.: 125
Electronic Hardware, Time Recording Equipment & Hydraulic & Pneumatic Valves
N.A.I.C.S.: 332510
John Cary (Pres)
Laurie Cary (VP)

AMAX GLOBAL SERVICES INC.
1565 Reliance Way, Fremont, CA 94539
Tel.: (510) 651-8886
Web Site: http://www.amax.com
Year Founded: 1979
Sales Range: $100-124.9 Million
Emp.: 250
Mfr & Distr of Server, Industrial, Workstation, Storage & Clustering Systems
N.A.I.C.S.: 423430

Jerry K. Shih (Chm & CEO)
Jay Ni (VP)
Jean Shih (Founder & Chief Bus Officer)
Margaret Huang (Controller)
Paul Jensen (Pres)

AMAX INDUSTRIAL PRODUCTS
369 E Main St Ste 13, East Islip, NY 11730
Web Site: http://www.amaxindustrial.com
Sales Range: $10-24.9 Million
Emp.: 10
Industrial Organic Chemicals, Nec
N.A.I.C.S.: 325199

AMAZEUM
1009 Museum Way, Bentonville, AR 72712
Tel.: (479) 696-9280 AR
Web Site: https://www.amazeum.org
Year Founded: 2006
Sales Range: $10-24.9 Million
Emp.: 6
Museums
N.A.I.C.S.: 712110
Erik Smith (Dir-Exhibits & Facilities)
Bryce Graves (Mgr-Facilities)
Sam Dean (Exec Dir)
Amy Stockton (Mgr-Membership)

AMAZING GRACE OUTREACH MINISTRIES & US FOOD RESCUE INC
580 Woods Dr, Bear, DE 19701
Tel.: (302) 777-7791
Sales Range: $10-24.9 Million
Community Care Services
N.A.I.C.S.: 624190
Carolyn D. Ferretti-Johnson (CEO)
Ruth Taylor (Treas & Sec)

AMAZING LUXURY CARS
468 Cobb Pkwy S, Marietta, GA 30060
Tel.: (770) 425-3500
Web Site: https://www.amazingluxurycars.com
Year Founded: 1987
Sales Range: $10-24.9 Million
Emp.: 14
Used Car Retailer
N.A.I.C.S.: 441120
Deni Hodzic (Mgr-Fin)

AMAZON ADVERTISING
30 Hotaling Pl Ste 100, San Francisco, CA 94111
Tel.: (415) 433-3004
Web Site: http://www.amazonadv.com
Year Founded: 1996
Sales Range: $50-74.9 Million
Emp.: 30
Advertising Agencies
N.A.I.C.S.: 541810
Millie Olson (Founder)
Lynda Pearson (Co-Founder & Chief Creative Officer)
Connie Chen (Sr VP & Dir-Acct Mgmt)
Andy Jassy (CEO)
James Hamilton (Sr VP)
Drew Herdener (Sr VP)

AMAZULU INC.
1239 Commons Ct, Clermont, FL 34711
Tel.: (352) 243-5309
Web Site: https://www.amazuluinc.com
Sales Range: $1-9.9 Million
Emp.: 10

Natural & Synthetic Architectural Materials Distr
N.A.I.C.S.: 444180
Claire Evans (CEO)
Ginger Simpson (COO)
Chris Martins (Mgr-Bus Dev)

AMB DEVELOPMENT GROUP LLC
1243 N Tenth St, Milwaukee, WI 53205-5818
Tel.: (414) 291-4420   WI
Web Site:
   http://www.americanmedical.com
Year Founded: 1965
Sales Range: $125-149.9 Million
Emp.: 25
Designer, Developer & Constructor of Medical Office Buildings; Clinics; Ambulatory Care Centers
N.A.I.C.S.: 541310
Jack Amormino (Pres & CEO)
Gilbert J. Sass (Exec VP)
Mike Janssen (Sr VP)
Peter Lamberti (Sr VP-Dev & Fin)

AMBAC INTERNATIONAL CORPORATION
910 Spears Creek Ct, Elgin, SC 29045
Tel.: (803) 462-9600   DE
Web Site:
   http://www.ambacdiesel.net
Year Founded: 1987
Sales Range: $10-24.9 Million
Emp.: 50
Fuel Injection Equipment Mfr
N.A.I.C.S.: 336310
Ken Smith (Mgr-Mktg)

AMBASSADOR BOOK SERVICE, INC.
445 Broad Hollow Rd Ste 206, Melville, NY 11747
Tel.: (631) 770-1010   NY
Web Site: http://www.absbook.com
Year Founded: 1973
Sales Range: $100-124.9 Million
Emp.: 1,200
Print & Non-Print Materials
N.A.I.C.S.: 424920
Gary Herald (Pres & CEO)

AMBASSADOR ENTERPRISES, LLC
11020 Diebold Rd, Fort Wayne, IN 46845
Tel.: (91) 2604874000
Web Site:
   https://www.ambassadorsupply.com
Emp.: 100
Holding Company
N.A.I.C.S.: 551112

Subsidiaries:

Ambassador Supply, LLC   (1)
2817 East Dupont Rd, Fort Wayne, IN 46825
Tel.: (260) 487-4000
Web Site:
   https://www.ambassadorsupply.com
Investment Services
N.A.I.C.S.: 523999

Holding (Domestic):

Straight Line Metal Buildings, Inc.   (2)
32916 Fm 529 Rd, Brookshire, TX 77423
Tel.: (281) 375-2020
Rev.: $2,300,000
Emp.: 23
Structural Steel & Precast Concrete Contractors
N.A.I.C.S.: 238120
Steven Poorman (Pres)

AMBASSADOR FOOD SERVICES CORP.
5-30 54th Ave, Long Island City, NY 11101
Tel.: (718) 361-2512   DE
Year Founded: 1963
Sales Range: $10-24.9 Million
Emp.: 74
Provider of Contract Catering Services
N.A.I.C.S.: 711110
Authur D. Stevens (Chm)

AMBASSADOR INC.
501 Congressional Blvd Ste 250, Carmel, IN 46032
Tel.: (317) 571-6838   IN
Web Site:
   http://www.ambassadorsolution.com
Year Founded: 1984
Sales Range: $200-249.9 Million
Emp.: 50
Provider of Technology Solutions to the Marketplace
N.A.I.C.S.: 541512
Brad Lindemann (Founder, Pres & CEO)

AMBASSADOR LIMOUSINE, INC.
4419 N Hubert Ave Ste A, Tampa, FL 33614
Tel.: (727) 442-9050
Web Site:
   https://www.ambassadorlimo.com
Sales Range: $10-24.9 Million
Emp.: 50
Limousine Service
N.A.I.C.S.: 485320
Ken Lucci (Pres & CEO)

AMBASSADOR PROGRAMS, INC.
2001 S Flint Rd, Spokane, WA 99224
Tel.: (509) 568-7000
Web Site:
   http://www.peopletopeople.com
Sales Range: $900-999.9 Million
Educational Travel Program Services
N.A.I.C.S.: 923110
Gabriel Gima (Sr Dir-Creative)
Jay Sandler (Mgr-Web)

Subsidiaries:

Marketing Production Systems, LLC   (1)
2001 S Flint Rd, Spokane, WA 99224
Tel.: (509) 568-7000
Web Site: http://www.peopletopeople.com
Sales Range: $100-124.9 Million
Management & Marketing Services
N.A.I.C.S.: 561499

AMBASSADOR SERVICES, INC.
10330 S Dolfield Rd, Owings Mills, MD 21117
Tel.: (410) 833-1575
Web Site:
   https://www.ambassadorservice.net
Year Founded: 1995
Rev.: $5,600,000
Emp.: 40
Plumbing, Heating & Air-Conditioning Contractors
N.A.I.C.S.: 238220
Ken French (Pres)
Tracey French (Sec)

AMBASSADOR TRAVEL LTD.
5236 Vogel Rd, Evansville, IN 47715
Tel.: (812) 479-8687   WA
Web Site:
   http://www.ambassadortravel.com
Year Founded: 1973
Sales Range: $10-24.9 Million

Emp.: 25
Cruise & Travel Operations
N.A.I.C.S.: 561510
Connie Corbett (Pres)

AMBASSADOR VAN LINES INC.
1822 Debarry Ave, Orange Park, FL 32073
Tel.: (904) 278-0708
Sales Range: $10-24.9 Million
Emp.: 25
Household Goods Moving Services
N.A.I.C.S.: 484121
Jeff Bell (Owner)

Subsidiaries:

Eagle Moving Systems Inc.   (1)
1822 Debarry Ave, Orange Park, FL 32073
Tel.: (904) 278-0708
Rev.: $2,200,000
Emp.: 21
Domestic Freight Forwarding
N.A.I.C.S.: 488510
Jeff Bell (Pres)
Mike Richardson (VP)
Alisa Ralph (Office Mgr)

Senate Forwarding Inc   (1)
1822 Debarry Ave, Orange Park, FL 32073
Tel.: (904) 278-0708
Web Site: http://www.avlgroup.com
Rev.: $16,230,763
Emp.: 16
Freight Forwarding
N.A.I.C.S.: 488510
Mike Richardson (Gen Mgr)

AMBC INC.
424 Fort Hill Business Ctr Ste 109, Naperville, IL 60540
Tel.: (630) 369-6441
Web Site:
   https://www.ambconline.com
Year Founded: 2001
Sales Range: $1-9.9 Million
Emp.: 40
SAP Services: Project Implementation, Contingent Staffing, Training & Outsourcing
N.A.I.C.S.: 541618
Seema Chelliah (VP-Ops)
Shanta M. Balakumar (Pres)

AMBER DIAGNOSTICS, INC.
2180 Premier Row, Orlando, FL 32809
Tel.: (407) 438-7847   FL
Web Site: https://www.amberusa.com
Year Founded: 1993
Sales Range: $25-49.9 Million
Emp.: 75
Diagnostic Imaging Centers & Refurbishment of Radiology & Diagnostic Equipment
N.A.I.C.S.: 621512

Subsidiaries:

Amber Diagnostics Cameroon SARL   (1)
498 Douala Manga Bell, Quartier Bali, Douala, Cameroon
Tel.: (237) 33421819
Medical Imaging Equipment Sales & Service
N.A.I.C.S.: 423450

AMBICOM HOLDINGS, INC.
500 Alder Dr, Milpitas, CA 95035
Tel.: (408) 321-0822   NV
Web Site: http://www.ambicom.com
Year Founded: 2008
Rev.: $301,060
Assets: $5,037,633
Liabilities: $2,072,570
Net Worth: $2,965,063
Earnings: ($4,157,835)
Emp.: 6
Fiscal Year-end: 07/31/15

Wireless Medical Equipment Mfr
N.A.I.C.S.: 339112
Kevin S. Cornell (Pres)

Subsidiaries:

Ambicom, Inc.   (1)
500 Alder Dr, Milpitas, CA 95035
Tel.: (408) 321-0822
Web Site: http://www.ambicom.com
Sales Range: $10-24.9 Million
Wireless Medical Equipment Mfr
N.A.I.C.S.: 339112
John Hwnd (Gen Mgr)

AMBIENT CONSULTING, LLC
5500 Wayzata Blvd Ste 1250, Minneapolis, MN 55416
Tel.: (763) 582-9000
Web Site:
   http://www.ambientconsulting.com
Year Founded: 1984
Sales Range: $10-24.9 Million
Emp.: 20
Management Consultants
N.A.I.C.S.: 541512
Andrew Gossmann (CEO)

AMBIENT TECHNOLOGIES, INC.
4610 Central Ave, Saint Petersburg, FL 33711
Tel.: (727) 328-0268   FL
Web Site:
   https://www.ambienttech.com
Year Founded: 1993
Sales Range: $1-9.9 Million
Emp.: 32
Scientific & Technical Consulting Services
N.A.I.C.S.: 541690
Carlos R. Lemos (CEO)
Albert Rodriguez (VP-Mktg)

Subsidiaries:

GeoView, Inc.   (1)
4610 Central Ave, Saint Petersburg, FL 33711
Tel.: (727) 209-2334
Web Site: http://www.geoviewinc.com
Sales Range: $1-9.9 Million
Emp.: 20
Geophysical Services
N.A.I.C.S.: 541360
Mike Wightman (Pres)
Christopher Taylor (VP)

AMBIENT WATER CORPORATION
7721 E Trent Ave, Spokane Valley, WA 99212
Tel.: (509) 474-9451   NV
Web Site:
   http://www.ambientwater.com
Year Founded: 2005
AWGI—(OTCBB)
Sales Range: Less than $1 Million
Emp.: 3
Potable Water Generating Appliances Deriving Water from Atmospheric Moisture
N.A.I.C.S.: 221310

AMBIENT WEATHER CO.
6845 W Frye Rd, Chandler, AZ 85226-3307
Tel.: (480) 346-3380
Web Site:
   https://www.ambientweather.com
Sales Range: $1-9.9 Million
Emp.: 8
Sells Weather-Monitoring Equipment
N.A.I.C.S.: 423610
Ed Edelman (CEO)

AMBIENTE H2O INC.
1500 W Hampden Ave Ste 5D, Denver, CO 80110
Tel.: (303) 433-0364

Ambiente H2O Inc.—(Continued)

Web Site:
https://www.ambienteh2o.com
Sales Range: $10-24.9 Million
Emp.: 8
Water Supply & Irrigation System
Services
N.A.I.C.S.: 221310
Steve Hansen (Pres)
Jane Harlow (Office Mgr)

AMBIR TECHNOLOGY, INC.
918 N Oaklawn Ave, Elmhurst, IL
60126-1015
Tel.: (630) 530-5400   IL
Web Site: http://www.ambir.com
Year Founded: 2001
Sales Range: $1-9.9 Million
Emp.: 14
Computer Peripherals
N.A.I.C.S.: 334118
Michael O'Leary (CEO)

AMBLER SAVINGS BANK
155 E Butler Ave, Ambler, PA 19002
Tel.: (215) 646-8400
Web Site:
https://www.amblersavingsbank.com
Year Founded: 1874
Sales Range: $10-24.9 Million
Emp.: 53
Savings Bank
N.A.I.C.S.: 522180
Thomas F. Keenan (CFO & Sr VP)
Joan M. Coleman (Sr VP-Lending)
Roger Zacharia (Pres & CEO)
Margaret Edgar (VP & Controller)
Patrick S. Rice (VP-Comml Lending)
Paula Marko (VP-Residential Lend-
ing)
Susan B. Look (Chief Risk Officer &
VP)
Geoffrey Ries (Chm)

AMBLING COMPANIES, INC.
348 Enterprise Dr, Valdosta, GA
31601
Tel.: (229) 244-2800
Web Site: https://www.ambling.com
Sales Range: $10-24.9 Million
Emp.: 350
Residential Construction Services
N.A.I.C.S.: 236118
Cynamon Willis (CFO)

AMBOY BANCORPORATION
3590 US Hwy 9 S, Old Bridge, NJ
08857
Tel.: (732) 591-8700
Web Site:
http://www.amboybank.com
Sales Range: $100-124.9 Million
Emp.: 28
Bank Holding Company
N.A.I.C.S.: 551111
Joseph DiSepio (Chm)
Eric Scharpf (Vice Chm)

AMBOY BANK
3590 US Hwy 9 S, Old Bridge, NJ
08857
Tel.: (732) 591-8700
Web Site:
https://www.amboybank.com
Year Founded: 1888
Sales Range: $75-99.9 Million
Emp.: 263
Full Service Commercial Bank
N.A.I.C.S.: 522110
Domenick Margiotta (Exec VP)
Mary Kay Riccardi (Exec VP)
Gregory Scharpf (Pres & CEO)

AMBROSIA SUBSTANCE
ABUSE TREATMENT CENTER
546 NW University Blvd Ste 103, Port
Saint Lucie, FL 34986
Tel.: (772) 323-2099
Web Site:
http://www.ambrosiatreatment.com
Year Founded: 2007
Sales Range: $10-24.9 Million
Emp.: 35
Substance Abuse Treatments & Re-
habilitation Programs
N.A.I.C.S.: 623220
Jerry Haffey (CEO)
Nicholas Alberto (COO)
Timothy Loceff (Chief Admin Officer)
Marc Chiurato (CFO)
Sal Raichbach (Dir-Clinical Svcs)
Lynne Davis-Tiedemann (Dir-
Programs)
Joseph Morrison (Dir-Ops & Mgr-
Projects)
Binny Montenegro (Dir-Ops/Medical
Liason)
Jerry Haffey Jr. (Dir-Mktg)

AMC TECHNOLOGY, L.L.C.
15521 Midlothian Tpke Ste 301, Mid-
lothian, VA 23113-7313
Tel.: (804) 419-8600
Web Site:
http://www.amctechnology.com
Year Founded: 1995
Sales Range: $10-24.9 Million
Emp.: 14
Call Center Information Software Mfr
N.A.I.C.S.: 541511
Anthony Uliano (Founder & CEO)
Rosemary Branch (COO)
Praveen Ravela (CTO)

AMCAN BEVERAGES, INC.
1201 Commerce Blvd, American Can-
yon, CA 94503-9611
Tel.: (707) 557-0500
Sales Range: $10-24.9 Million
Emp.: 125
Soft Drinks Mfr
N.A.I.C.S.: 312111
Frank Witbeck (Mgr-Info Sys)

AMCHI GENDYNAMY SCIENCE
CORPORATION
1809 Pritchard Way, Hacienda
Heights, CA 91745
Tel.: (626) 322-5205   DE
Year Founded: 2014
Emp.: 3
Biotechnology Research & Develop-
ment Services
N.A.I.C.S.: 541714
Wisdom Qiao (Pres, CEO, CFO &
Sec)

AMCO ENGINEERING CO
1 Innovation Dr, Des Plaines, IL
60016
Tel.: (847) 391-8100
Web Site:
http://www.amcoengineering.com
Year Founded: 1943
Sales Range: $10-24.9 Million
Emp.: 170
Mfr of Sheet Metalwork
N.A.I.C.S.: 332322

AMCO GROUP INC.
1020 NE 12th St, Fort Worth, TX
76102-1105
Tel.: (817) 336-5544
Web Site:
http://www.gesmechanical.com
Year Founded: 1982
Sales Range: $10-24.9 Million
Emp.: 25
Holding Company; Heating, Ventila-
tion, Air-Conditioning & Control Sys-
tems Contractor

N.A.I.C.S.: 551112
Judy C. Wooten (CEO)

Subsidiaries:

GES Mechanical Services, Inc.   (1)
1020 NE 12th St, Fort Worth, TX
76102-1105   (100%)
Tel.: (817) 589-7051
Web Site: http://www.gesmechanical.com
Emp.: 10
Heating, Ventilation, Air-Conditioning & Con-
trol Systems Contractor
N.A.I.C.S.: 238220
Judy C. Wooten (CEO)

AMCON BLOCK & PRECAST
INCORPORATED
2211 Hwy 10 S, Saint Cloud, MN
56304
Tel.: (320) 251-6030
Web Site:
http://www.amconblock.com
Sales Range: $10-24.9 Million
Emp.: 100
Blocks, Concrete Or Cinder: Standard
N.A.I.C.S.: 327331
David M. Pederson (Pres)
John C. Pederson (VP)
Jason Strusz (Controller)

AMD INDUSTRIES, INC.
4620 W 19th St, Cicero, IL 60804-
2502
Tel.: (708) 863-8900   IL
Web Site: https://www.amdpop.com
Year Founded: 1922
Rev.: $2,000,000
Emp.: 30
Mfr & Designer of Custom Point-of-
Purchase Displays
N.A.I.C.S.: 339950
David E. Allen (CEO)
Tessie Rivera (Controller)

AMDAHL MOTORS
950 7th St SE, Pipestone, MN 56164-
2067
Tel.: (507) 825-3321
Web Site:
http://www.amdahlmotors.com
Year Founded: 1938
Sales Range: $10-24.9 Million
Emp.: 31
New Car Whslr
N.A.I.C.S.: 441110
John Amdahl (Pres)

AMDEX CORPORATION
8403 Colesville Rd Ste 850, Silver
Spring, MD 20910
Tel.: (301) 588-4000
Web Site: http://www.amdexcorp.com
Year Founded: 1987
Sales Range: $25-49.9 Million
Emp.: 150
Business & Computer Consulting
Services
N.A.I.C.S.: 541611
Devinder K. Singh (Pres & CEO)

AME INCORPORATED
2467 Coltharp Rd, Fort Mill, SC
29715
Tel.: (803) 548-7766
Web Site:
https://www.ameonline.com
Sales Range: $25-49.9 Million
Emp.: 130
Industrial Buildings & Warehouses
N.A.I.C.S.: 236220
Nickie Hamrick (Dir-IT)

AME INTERNATIONAL
2347 Circuit Way, Brooksville, FL
34604
Tel.: (352) 799-1111
Web Site: https://www.ameintl.net

Year Founded: 2007
Sales Range: $1-9.9 Million
Emp.: 22
Mfr Tire-Changing Tools & Equipment
for Servicing Earth Movers & Con-
struction, Truck, Bus & Passenger
Vehicles
N.A.I.C.S.: 326211
Keith Jarman (Pres)
Tim Benoist (VP)
Brett Waggoner (VP-Domestic Sls)

AMEGA SALES INC.
111 Eastside Dr, Ashland, MO 65010
Tel.: (573) 657-2176
Web Site:
http://www.amegasales.com
Rev.: $35,318,557
Emp.: 85
Mobile Home Dealers
N.A.I.C.S.: 459930
Greg Deline (Owner)

AMELIA ISLAND COMPANY
6800 1st Coast Hwy, Amelia Island,
FL 32034
Tel.: (904) 261-6161
Web Site:
http://www.villasofameliaisland.com
Sales Range: $50-74.9 Million
Emp.: 1,000
Resort Villas
N.A.I.C.S.: 721110
Jack Healan (Pres)
Mike Wagner (Mgr-Sls)
Andrew Lott (Mgr-Sls)
Jamie Wilkinson (Reg Mgr-Sls)

AMENDOLAS FENCE CO.
1084 Sunrise Hwy, Amityville, NY
11701
Tel.: (631) 842-7800   NY
Web Site:
https://www.amendolas.com
Year Founded: 1964
Sales Range: $10-24.9 Million
Emp.: 140
Other Specialty Trade Contracting
Services
N.A.I.C.S.: 238990
Maryellen Ryan (VP)
Bob Amendola (Pres)
Jennifer Amandolas (Owner)

AMENITY HEALTH, INC.
8825 Rehco Rd Ste D, San Diego,
CA 92121
Web Site:
http://www.amenityhealth.com
Year Founded: 2011
Sales Range: $10-24.9 Million
Emp.: 16
Health Care Srvices
N.A.I.C.S.: 621610
Carl Melcher (Founder)

AMENTUM SERVICES, INC.
20501 Seneca Meadows Pkwy Ste
300, Germantown, MD 20876
Tel.: (301) 944-3100
Web Site: http://www.amentum.com
Year Founded: 2020
Technical And Engineering Services
Provider
N.A.I.C.S.: 541330
Charles Alexander Mathis (CFO &
Exec VP)
Charles Alexander Mathis (CFO &
Exec VP)
John Vollmer (Chm)
Jill Bruning (Exec VP & Gen Mgr)
Karl Spinnenweber (Exec Vp & Gen
Mgr)
Mark Whitney (Exec VP & Gen Mgr)
Jake Kennedy (CFO)

John Cooke (Exec VP-Risk & Strategy)
Stuart Young (Exec VP & Gen Counsel)
Bob Rudisin (Exec VP-HR)
Ron Hahn (Exec VP-Strategic Growth)
Carol Papillo (Sr VP-BD Ops)
John Heller (CEO)
Roela Santos (Sr VP-Comm & Mktg)
Sean Mullen (Exec VP-Bus Dev)
Dave Marlowe (VP)

Subsidiaries:

PAE Incorporated (1)
7799 Leesburg Pike Ste 300 N, Falls Church, VA 22043
Tel.: (703) 717-6000
Rev.: $2,714,628,000
Assets: $1,829,370,000
Liabilities: $1,672,718,000
Net Worth: $156,652,000
Earnings: $15,290,000
Emp.: 20,000
Fiscal Year-end: 12/31/2020
Holding Company
N.A.I.C.S.: 551112

Subsidiary (Domestic):

Courage Services, Inc. (2)
4121 Wilson Blvd Ste 301, Arlington, VA 22203
Tel.: (703) 276-7702
Web Site: http://www.courageservices.com
Research & Analysis Services
N.A.I.C.S.: 541990

Delta Bridge, Inc. (2)
1400A Duke St, Alexandria, VA 22314
Tel.: (703) 260-1545
Web Site: http://www.deltabridge.com
Satellite Communication Services
N.A.I.C.S.: 517410

Macfadden & Associates, Inc. (2)
1320 N Courthouse Rd Ste 700, Arlington, VA 22201
Tel.: (301) 588-5900
Web Site: http://www.macf.com
Management Consulting Services
N.A.I.C.S.: 541611
James R. Macfadden (Founder)

Metis Solutions LLC (2)
2001 Jefferson Davis Hwy Ste 401, Arlington, VA 22202
Emp.: 100
Business Management Consulting Services
N.A.I.C.S.: 541611

Subsidiary (Domestic):

Pluribus International Corporation (3)
5285 Shawnee Rd, Alexandria, VA 22312
Tel.: (571) 282-4830
Web Site: http://www.pluribusinternational.com
Industrial Building Construction
N.A.I.C.S.: 236210

Subsidiary (Non-US):

PAE (New Zealand) Limited (2)
PO Box 30 372, Lower Hutt, 5010, New Zealand
Tel.: (64) 45700560
Web Site: http://www.pae.co.nz
Facility Maintenance & Management Services
N.A.I.C.S.: 561210
Chris Pile (CEO)
Sheila McLeod (Gen Mgr-Govt & Comml)
Cormac Denton (Fin Dir)
Colin Devenish (Gen Mgr-Defence)
Bruce Thomas (Head-Bus Svcs)

Subsidiary (Domestic):

Pacific Architects & Engineers, Inc. (2)
7799 Leesburg Pike Ste 300 N, Falls Church, VA 22043-2408
Tel.: (703) 717-6175
Web Site: http://www.pae.com

Sales Range: Less than $1 Million
Facility Infrastructure, Aviation, Logistics, Training & National Security Support Services
N.A.I.C.S.: 541330
Clinton Bickett (Interim Pres/CFO & Mission Svcs-Global)
Charles Peiffer (Interim CEO & CFO)
Patricia Munchel (Chief HR Officer)
Whit Cobb (Gen Counsel)
James Benton (CIO & VP)
Adam Harrison (VP-Strategy & Corp Dev)

Subsidiary (Domestic):

FCi Federal, Inc. (3)
20135 Lakeview Ctr Plz Ste 300, Ashburn, VA 20147
Tel.: (703) 443-1888
Web Site: http://pae.com
Administrative Management & General Management Consulting Service
N.A.I.C.S.: 541611
Michael J. Petrucelli (Exec VP-Citizen, Immigration & Intl Travel & Gen Mgr)
Scott F. Miller (Pres)
Sharon D. Virts (Chm)
Claude Goddard (Chief Compliance Officer & Gen Counsel-Foreign Corrupt Practices)
Michael Mikuta (VP-Tech & Innovation)
Dawn Lewandowski (VP-Learning & Dev)
Susan M. Kirton (Chief Admin Officer)
William M. Thomas (VP-Pro Svcs)
Scott F. Miller (Pres & CEO)
Sharon D. Virts (Chm)

AMERASIA BANK
41-06 Main St, Flushing, NY 11355
Tel.: (718) 463-3600
Web Site: https://www.amerasiabankny.com
Year Founded: 1988
Sales Range: $10-24.9 Million
Emp.: 38
Banking Services
N.A.I.C.S.: 522110
Greta S. Chang (Comptroller)

AMERBELLE TEXTILES, LLC
104 E Main St, Vernon Rockville, CT 06066-0030
Tel.: (860) 979-0070
Sales Range: $75-99.9 Million
Emp.: 110
Dyeing, Finishing & Coating of Synthetic & Blend Fabrics
N.A.I.C.S.: 313310
Doug Rimsk (Pres)
Ted Brown (Mgr-IT)

AMERCABLE INCORPORATED
350 Bailey Rd, El Dorado, AR 71730
Tel.: (870) 862-4919
Web Site: http://www.amercable.com
Year Founded: 1899
Sales Range: $200-249.9 Million
Emp.: 400
Mfr of Steel, Aluminum & Vinyl Siding, Steel Wire & Electric Cable
N.A.I.C.S.: 423610
Rodney T. Cole (Pres)
Ben Corona (CFO & VP-Fin)

AMEREDEV II, LLC
2901 Via Fortuna Ste 600, Austin, TX 78746
Tel.: (737) 300-4700
Web Site: http://www.ameredev.com
Year Founded: 2015
Investment Services
N.A.I.C.S.: 523999
Parker Reese (Pres & CEO)
Floy Hammond (COO)
Ron Zboril (CFO)

AMEREDIA INCORPORATED
550 Montgomery St Ste 750, San Francisco, CA 94111
Tel.: (415) 788-5100
Web Site: http://www.ameredia.com
Year Founded: 2003

Sales Range: $1-9.9 Million
Emp.: 17
Integrated Marketing, Communications, Advertising & Media Services
N.A.I.C.S.: 541810
Pawan J. Mehra (Founder & Principal)

AMEREQUIP CORPORATION
1015 Calumet Ave, Kiel, WI 53042
Tel.: (920) 894-2000
Web Site: https://www.amerequip.com
Year Founded: 1920
Sales Range: $100-124.9 Million
Emp.: 195
Industrial & Farming Equipment: Compact Loaders, Post Hole Diggers, Back Hoes Mfr
N.A.I.C.S.: 333111
Mike Vander Zanden (Pres & CEO)
Fritz Heathman (Engr-Supplier Quality)
Charles Hoke (Chm)
Martin Schaefer (Coord-Safety)
Thomas Thiel (Plant Mgr)
Ted Torrison (Mgr-Customer Relationship)
Doug Thompson (VP-Ops)
Timothy A. Dorn (VP-Sls & Engrg)

AMEREX CORPORATION
7595 Gadsden Hwy, Trussville, AL 35173
Tel.: (205) 655-3271
Web Site: https://www.amerex-fire.com
Year Founded: 1971
Sales Range: $400-449.9 Million
Emp.: 500
Fire Extinguisher Equipment Mfr
N.A.I.C.S.: 332999
Harrison Bishop (Pres)
Larry Whitehead (CEO)
Andy Payant (Exec VP-Fin)
Mark Ross (VP)

AMEREX GROUP, INC.
512 7th Ave 9th Fl, New York, NY 10018
Tel.: (212) 609-3000   NY
Web Site: https://www.amerexgroup.com
Year Founded: 1940
Sales Range: $1-9.9 Million
Emp.: 48
Children's, Men's & Women's Outerwear
N.A.I.C.S.: 424350
Ira Ganger (Pres)
Stuart Cohen (Exec VP)
Perry Blonder (Mgr-EDI)
Brad Volenec (Dir-Creative)
Marsha Sokolovskaya (Sr VP)
Alexandra Grumet (Mgr-HR)

Subsidiaries:

Amerex Fashion Group (1)
512 7th Ave Fl 9, New York, NY 10018-0861
Tel.: (212) 609-3000
Mfg of Fashions
N.A.I.C.S.: 424350

Amerex Group (1)
512 7th Ave 9th Fl, New York, NY 10018
Tel.: (212) 609-3000
Web Site: http://www.amerexgroup.com
Clothing Stores
N.A.I.C.S.: 458110
Patty Crane (Mgr-Production)

Amerex Kid's Group (1)
Fl 9 512 Fashion Ave, New York, NY 10018-0861
Tel.: (212) 268-5656
Web Site: http://www.amerixgroup.com
Mfr Outerwear Clothing For Kids
N.A.I.C.S.: 315250

Amerex Ladies (1)
512 7th Ave Fl 9, New York, NY 10118
Tel.: (212) 609-3000
Ladies Clothing Mfr
N.A.I.C.S.: 458110
Ira Ganger (Pres)

Jones New York Outerwear (1)
512 7th Ave, New York, NY 10018-4603
Tel.: (212) 221-3151
Web Site: http://www.jonesnewyork.com
Mfg of Fashions
N.A.I.C.S.: 424350

AMERGINT TECHNOLOGIES, INC.
2315 Briargate Pkwy Ste 100, Colorado Springs, CO 80920
Tel.: (719) 522-2800
Web Site: http://www.amergint.com
Emp.: 100
Professional, Scientific & Technical Services
N.A.I.C.S.: 541990
Sean Conway (Exec VP)
Rob Andzik (Pres)
Larry Hill (CEO)

Subsidiaries:

Tethers Unlimited, Inc. (1)
11711 N Creek Pkwy S Ste D-113, Bothell, WA 98011-8804
Tel.: (425) 486-0100
Web Site: http://www.tethers.com
Aircraft Engine Parts Mfr
N.A.I.C.S.: 336412
Robert L. Forward (Co-Founder)
Robert P. Hoyt (Co-Founder & CEO)

AMERGRAPH CORPORATION
520 Lafayette Rd Rt 15, Sparta, NJ 07871
Tel.: (973) 383-8700
Web Site: https://www.amergraph.com
Year Founded: 1975
Emp.: 10
Graphic Arts Equipment Mfr & Distr
N.A.I.C.S.: 333310
Robert Lesko (Pres)

Subsidiaries:

HID Ultraviolet, LLC (1)
520 Lafayette Rd, Sparta, NJ 07871
Tel.: (973) 383-8535
Web Site: http://www.hid.com
Mfr of Portable UV Floor Curing Equipment
N.A.I.C.S.: 238330
Robert Lesko (Pres)

AMERHART LIMITED
2455 Century Rd, Green Bay, WI 54303
Tel.: (920) 494-4744
Web Site: http://www.amerhart.com
Year Founded: 1940
Sales Range: $125-149.9 Million
Emp.: 200
Lumber: Rough, Dressed & Finished
N.A.I.C.S.: 423310
Mark Kasper (CEO)
Cindy Johnson (Dir-Corp Trng)
Matthew Kuepers (Mgr-Credit)
Craig Goodman (Branch Mgr)
Jac Carr (Mgr-Warehouse)
Timothy Stoeffler (Branch Mgr)
Jeff Verboncouer (Mgr-Acct-Natl)
Paul DesJardins (Branch Mgr)
Erik Gustafson (Branch Mgr)
Dave Destiche (VP-Sls & Mktg)
Tom Miller (VP-Supply Chain)
Chad Warpinski (Pres)
Timothy Schneider (Mgr-Warehouse)
Rick Johnson (VP-IT)
Jackie Bartanen (CFO)

Subsidiaries:

Wind Mill Woodworking, Inc. (1)

Amerhart Limited—(Continued)

200 Balsam Rd, Sheboygan Falls, WI
53085   **(100%)**
Tel.: (920) 467-2402
Web Site: http://www.windmillslatwall.com
Sales Range: $1-9.9 Million
Emp.: 50
Stock & Custom Retail Display Panels &
Fixtures Mfr
N.A.I.C.S.: 333514
Jay Hogfeldt *(Owner & Pres)*
Mark Radtke *(Exec VP)*
Mandy Berres *(Project Mgr)*
Lance Dedering *(Plant Mgr)*
Dave Herold *(Mgr-Sls-East)*
Vickie McCabe *(Mgr-Admin)*
Karen Mueller *(Project Mgr)*
Adam Murray *(Project Mgr)*
Gregg Hilbelink *(Coord-Maintenance)*
Joan Kersten *(Mgr-Mktg)*
Mandy Scharenbroch *(Project Mgr)*
Randy Barthels *(Project Mgr)*
Steve Henschel *(Coord-Production)*

AMERI FINANCIAL GROUP, INC.

1946 Washington Ave S, Stillwater,
MN 55082
Tel.: (651) 351-1200   **MN**
Web Site: https://www.myfrbank.com
Year Founded: 2016
Bank Holding Company
N.A.I.C.S.: 551111
John Seidel *(Pres & CEO)*

Subsidiaries:

First Resource Bank   **(1)**
7449 Vlg Dr, Lino Lakes, MN 55014
Tel.: (651) 785-9320
Web Site: http://www.myfrbank.com
Sales Range: $1-9.9 Million
Commercial Banking
N.A.I.C.S.: 522110
Steve Cerven *(Sr VP)*
Pat Henderson *(VP-Loan Admin)*

AMERI LIFE & HEALTH SERVICES

2650 McCormick Dr, Clearwater, FL
33759
Tel.: (727) 726-0726
Web Site: http://www.amerilife.com
Year Founded: 1971
Sales Range: $1-4.9 Billion
Emp.: 350
Insurance Agents, Brokers & Service
N.A.I.C.S.: 524210
Tim North *(CEO)*
Gary Jenkins *(Pres)*
Mark Graham *(Dir-Bus Dev)*
Derek Richardson *(CMO)*
Karen Surplus *(Chief Acctg Officer)*
Paul Carter *(COO)*
Jerry Cwiok *(Head-New Initiatives &
Integration)*
Billy Hill *(Head-Product Dev)*

AMERI METRO, INC.

2575 Eastern Blvd Ste 102, York, PA
17402
Tel.: (717) 434-0668   **DE**
Web Site: https://ameri-metro.com
Year Founded: 2011
Rev.: ($6,144,812)
Assets: $4,848
Liabilities: $59,099,820
Net Worth: ($59,094,972)
Earnings: ($6,149,130)
Emp.: 8
Fiscal Year-end: 07/31/21
Holding Company; Transportation Infrastructure Development
N.A.I.C.S.: 551112
Shahjahan Charles Mathias *(Exec
VP)*
James Becker *(Pres)*
John W. Thompson *(Gen Counsel)*
Bryan Elicker *(COO)*

Shah Mathias *(Founder, CEO, Treas
& Sec)*
Philip M. Hicks *(CFO)*
Chris J. Quick *(Chief Risk Officer)*

AMERI-FORCE, INC.

9485 Regency Sq Blvd Ste 340,
Jacksonville, FL 32225-8194
Tel.: (904) 633-9918   **FL**
Web Site: http://www.ameriforce.com
Year Founded: 1991
Sales Range: $25-49.9 Million
Emp.: 200
Holding Company; Skilled & Unskilled
Labor Staffing Services
N.A.I.C.S.: 551112
Steve Sanchez *(CIO)*
Lisa Boyd *(Controller)*

Subsidiaries:

Ameri-Force Craft Services, Inc.   **(1)**
9485 Regency Sq Blvd Ste 340, Jacksonville, FL 32225   **(100%)**
Tel.: (904) 633-9918
Web Site: http://www.ameriforce.com
Sales Range: $100-124.9 Million
Skilled Labor Staffing Services
N.A.I.C.S.: 561311
Austin Fricks *(VP)*

Ameri-Force Industrial Services,
Inc.   **(1)**
9485 Regency Sq Blvd Ste 300, Jacksonville, FL 32225
Tel.: (904) 633-9918
Employee Placement Services
N.A.I.C.S.: 561311

Ameri-Force Labor Services, Inc.   **(1)**
9485 Regency Square Blvd Ste 300, Jacksonville, FL 32225   **(100%)**
Tel.: (904) 633-9918
Web Site: http://www.ameriforce.com
Sales Range: $25-49.9 Million
Emp.: 20
Semi-Skilled & Unskilled Labor Staffing
Services
N.A.I.C.S.: 561311
John Glover *(Pres)*

Ameri-Force Professional Services,
Inc.   **(1)**
714 High St, Portsmouth, VA 23704
Tel.: (757) 393-2581
Web Site: http://www.ameriforce.com
Employee Placement Services
N.A.I.C.S.: 561311
Brandy Davies *(Mgr-Pro Svcs)*

AMERI-KLEEN

328 E Lake Ave, Watsonville, CA
95076
Tel.: (831) 722-8888
Web Site: http://www.ameri-
kleen.com
Year Founded: 1968
Sales Range: $10-24.9 Million
Emp.: 566
Janitorial & Other Facility Related
Maintenance Services
N.A.I.C.S.: 561720
Brett Meyers *(Pres)*
Gayle Moore *(Mgr-HR)*

AMERIBANCSHARES, INC.

2732 Midwestern Pkwy, Wichita Falls,
TX 76308
Tel.: (940) 397-2300   **TX**
Web Site: http://www.amnat.com
Year Founded: 1994
Rev.: $49,388,000
Assets: $885,411,000
Liabilities: $797,401,000
Net Worth: $88,010,000
Earnings: $9,703,000
Emp.: 200
Fiscal Year-end: 12/31/19
Bank Holding Company
N.A.I.C.S.: 551111
Dwight Berry *(Pres & CEO)*

Subsidiaries:

American National Bank & Trust   **(1)**
2732 Midwestern Pkwy, Wichita Falls, TX
76308
Tel.: (940) 397-2300
Web Site: http://www.amnat.com
Sales Range: $10-24.9 Million
Emp.: 100
National Commercial Banks
N.A.I.C.S.: 522110
Michael W. Boyle *(Sr VP)*
Randy R. Martin *(Officer-Trust & Exec VP)*
Kelly J. Smith *(Officer-Trust & Sr VP)*
Paula A. Walmer *(VP-Trust Ops)*
Brad Davidson *(Sr VP)*
Caroline Groves *(Officer-Loan)*
Chris Rogers *(Asst VP)*
Donna Adair *(Sr VP)*
Kristin Morris *(VP)*
Micha Lambeth *(Officer-Loan)*
Morgan Mori *(Officer-Loan)*
Fred Ingham *(Sec)*

AMERICA ACHIEVES

21 W 46th St Ste 905, New York, NY
10036
Tel.: (202) 465-8700   **NY**
Web Site:
    http://www.americaachieves.org
Year Founded: 2012
Sales Range: $10-24.9 Million
Emp.: 26
Educational Support Services
N.A.I.C.S.: 611710
Jon Schnur *(Chm)*

AMERICA CHUNG NAM LLC

1163 Fairway Dr, City of Industry, CA
91789
Tel.: (909) 839-8383   **CA**
Web Site: https://www.acni.net
Year Founded: 1990
Rev.: $188,524,046
Emp.: 35
Industrial & Personal Service Paper
N.A.I.C.S.: 424130
Yan Cheung *(Founder)*
Chung Liu Ming *(Co-Founder)*
Eddie Yeung *(Sr VP-Logistics & Plng)*
Ken Liu *(Vice Chm)*
Kevin Zhao *(CFO)*
Sam Liu *(COO)*
Teresa Cheung *(CEO)*

Subsidiaries:

ACN Recycling Industries LLC   **(1)**
1163 Fairway Dr, City of Industry, CA 91789
Tel.: (909) 839-8383
Web Site: http://www.acni.net
Intermodal Transloading Services, Storage
& Quality Inspection
N.A.I.C.S.: 562920
Sam Luu *(COO)*

America Chung Nam Transportation
LLC   **(1)**
1163 Fairway Dr, City of Industry, CA 91789
Tel.: (909) 839-8383
Web Site: http://www.acni.net
Emp.: 100
Local Trucking without Storage
N.A.I.C.S.: 424130

AMERICA II ELECTRONICS, INC.

2600 118th St N, Saint Petersburg,
FL 33716
Tel.: (727) 573-0900
Web Site: http://www.americaii.com
Year Founded: 1989
Sales Range: $200-249.9 Million
Emp.: 600
Electronic Parts & Equipment Distr
N.A.I.C.S.: 423690
Michael Galinski *(Founder & CEO)*
Mike Pointer *(Gen Counsel & VP-HR)*
Brian Ellison *(Pres)*
Pat O'Brien *(VP-Strategic Sls)*
Anton Wurr *(Dir-Mktg)*

Rick Kauchak *(VP-Sls)*
Dimitra Tsekos *(VP-Sls Ops)*
Jed Pecchioli *(COO)*

AMERICA MIDWEST TRANSPORTATION, LLC.

148 Zieske Rd, Courtland, MN
56021-4327
Tel.: (507) 359-4450
Web Site: https://www.america-
midwest.com
Year Founded: 2003
Sales Range: $10-24.9 Million
Emp.: 30
Transportation Support Services
N.A.I.C.S.: 488999
Barry M. Bloedel *(CEO)*
Garland Bloedel *(Pres)*

AMERICA VOTES

1155 Connecticut Ave NW Ste 600,
Washington, DC 20036
Tel.: (202) 962-7240   **DC**
Web Site:
    http://www.americavotes.org
Year Founded: 2009
Sales Range: $10-24.9 Million
Emp.: 38
Civil & Social Organization
N.A.I.C.S.: 813410
Sara Schreiber *(Mng Dir)*

AMERICA WORKS OF NEW YORK INC.

228 E 45th St 16th Fl, New York, NY
10017
Tel.: (212) 599-5627
Web Site:
    https://www.americaworks.com
Year Founded: 1984
Sales Range: $1-9.9 Million
Emp.: 50
Employment Agencies
N.A.I.C.S.: 561311
Lee Bowes *(CEO)*
Peter Cove *(Founder)*
David Aguado *(Dir-Ops)*
Maureen Rowson *(Assoc Dir)*
Bill Clinton *(Pres)*
Dan Quayle *(VP)*

AMERICA'S BODY COMPANY

3 Acorn Dr, Cleveland, OH 44146
Tel.: (440) 439-4805
Automobiles & Other Motor Vehicles
N.A.I.C.S.: 423110

AMERICA'S CAPITAL PARTNERS, LLC

1 Alhambra Plz Ste 1450, Coral
Gables, FL 33134
Tel.: (305) 995-9998
Web Site:
    https://www.americascapital.com
Year Founded: 1998
Sales Range: Less than $1 Million
Emp.: 12
Real Estate Services Including Asset
Management, Leasing, Accounting &
Construction Management
N.A.I.C.S.: 531390
Sergio G. Socolsky *(CEO)*
Jude M. Williams *(Pres)*
Forrest Jones *(VP-Dev)*
Judi A. Sponsel *(VP)*
Stephen P. Sauriol *(Dir-Engrg)*
Mary M. Cook *(Gen Mgr)*
Emily White *(Gen Mgr)*
Raimundo Echeverria *(Mgr-Portfolio)*
Keith J. Richard *(VP-Acquisitions)*
Carlton L. Harden *(VP & Reg Mgr)*

AMERICA'S CATCH, INC.

46623 Co Rd 523, Itta Bena, MS
38941
Tel.: (662) 254-7200

Web Site: https://www.catfish.com
Sales Range: $50-74.9 Million
Emp.: 300
Sales of Fresh or Frozen Packaged
Fish
N.A.I.C.S.: 311710
Dick Carr *(CFO)*
Bobby Giachelli *(VP-Sls)*
Solon Scott III *(Pres)*

AMERICA'S CHARITIES
14150 Newbrook Dr Ste 110, Chan-
tilly, VA 20151
Tel.: (800) 458-9505   DC
Web Site: http://www.charities.org
Year Founded: 1988
Sales Range: $10-24.9 Million
Emp.: 42
Individual & Family Support Services
N.A.I.C.S.: 624190
Kimberly H. Young *(VP-Business De-
velopment)*
James E. Starr *(Pres & CEO)*
Robyn Neal *(VP-Client Engagement
Solutions)*
Patrick R. Gaston *(Sec)*

AMERICA'S CHRISTIAN CREDIT UNION
2100 E Route 66, Glendora, CA
91740
Tel.: (626) 208-5546   CA
Web Site:
    https://www.americaschristian.com
Year Founded: 1958
Sales Range: $10-24.9 Million
Emp.: 108
Credit Union
N.A.I.C.S.: 522130
Terri Snyder *(COO & Sr VP)*
Norm Sauve *(Chm)*
Mendell L. Thompson *(Pres, CEO &
Treas)*
Sylvia Nash *(Sec)*
Jerry Ferguson *(Vice Chm)*

AMERICA'S HOME PLACE INC.
2144 Hilton Dr, Gainesville, GA
30501
Tel.: (770) 536-9847
Web Site:
    http://www.americashomeplace.com
Sales Range: $75-99.9 Million
Emp.: 400
New Construction, Single-Family
Houses
N.A.I.C.S.: 236115
Claudette Bragg *(Dir-Fin)*
Sonya Brown *(Mgr-Fin)*
Leah Bagwell *(Office Mgr)*

AMERICA'S INCREDIBLE PIZZA COMPANY
909 Twin Oaks Office Park E, Spring-
field, MO 65807
Tel.: (417) 890-1408
Web Site:
    http://www.incrediblepizza.com
Year Founded: 2002
Sales Range: $1-9.9 Million
Emp.: 2,100
Full-Service Restaurants
N.A.I.C.S.: 722511
George R. Ward II *(CFO)*
Cheryl Barsness *(Sec)*
Rick Barsness *(Founder)*

AMERICA'S MORTGAGE PRO-FESSIONALS
2601 E Oakland Park Blvd Ste 500,
Fort Lauderdale, FL 33306
Tel.: (954) 332-6565
Web Site: http://www.amprefi.com
Year Founded: 2007
Sales Range: $1-9.9 Million

Emp.: 95
Mortgage Loan Brokers
N.A.I.C.S.: 522310
J. R. Boston *(Pres)*
Jamie Martinez *(Mgr-Licensing)*

AMERICA'S POWERSPORTS INC.
80 E McDermott Dr, Allen, TX 75002-
2802
Tel.: (972) 649-5490
Web Site:
    http://www.americaspowersport.com
Sales Range: $25-49.9 Million
Emp.: 250
Sports Clubs, Managers & Promoters
N.A.I.C.S.: 441227
Denise Armstrong *(Dir-Fin)*
Brenda Bova *(Dir-HR)*

AMERICA'S SUPER PAWN, INC.
5612 15th St E, Bradenton, FL 34203
Tel.: (941) 241-3362
Web Site:
    https://www.americasuperpawn.com
Sales Range: $25-49.9 Million
Emp.: 40
Pawnbrokers
N.A.I.C.S.: 522310
Greg Twarowski *(Owner)*
Stephanie Awad *(Asst Mgr)*

AMERICA, THE BEAUTIFUL DREAMER, INC.
9700 NE 126th Ave, Vancouver, WA
98682
Tel.: (360) 816-0167   WA
Web Site: https://www.atbd.com
Year Founded: 1970
Bedroom Furniture & Mattress Stores
Owner & Operator
N.A.I.C.S.: 449110

AMERICA-MIDEAST EDUCA-TIONAL & TRAINING SER-VICES, INC.
1730 M St NW Ste 1100, Washing-
ton, DC 20036-4505
Tel.: (202) 776-9600   NY
Web Site: http://www.amideast.org
Year Founded: 1951
Sales Range: $75-99.9 Million
Emp.: 338
Educational Support Services
N.A.I.C.S.: 611710
Vincent V. DeSomma *(VP-Business
Development)*
James T. Grabowski *(VP-Field Ops)*
Mary W. Gray *(Chm)*
Theodore H. Kattouf *(Pres & CEO)*
Nicholas A. Veliotes *(Vice Chm)*
Leslie S. Nucho *(VP-Programs)*

AMERICAN ACADEMY OF DERMATOLOGY
1445 New York Avenue, Washington,
DC 20005
Tel.: (847) 240-1280   MN
Web Site: http://www.aad.org
Year Founded: 1959
Sales Range: $25-49.9 Million
Emp.: 95
Leadership Development & Training
Services
N.A.I.C.S.: 611430
Brett M. Coldiron *(Pres)*

AMERICAN ACADEMY OF NEUROLOGY
201 Chicago Ave, Minneapolis, MN
55415
Tel.: (612) 928-6000   MN
Web Site: http://www.aan.com
Year Founded: 2007

Sales Range: $10-24.9 Million
Emp.: 158
Neurologist Association
N.A.I.C.S.: 621111
Jason Kopinski *(Deputy Exec Dir)*
Timothy Engel *(CFO & CTO)*
Aaron E. Miller *(Sec)*
Terrence L. Cascino *(Pres)*
Angela Babb *(Chief Comm Officer)*
Chris Becker *(Chief Bus Dev Officer)*
Ann Tilton *(VP)*
Mary Post *(CEO)*

AMERICAN ACADEMY OF OTOLARYNGOLOGY-HEAD AND NECK SURGERY
1650 Diagonal Rd, Alexandria, VA
22314-2857
Tel.: (703) 836-4444   DC
Web Site: http://www.entnet.org
Year Founded: 1981
Sales Range: $10-24.9 Million
Emp.: 85
General Medical Services
N.A.I.C.S.: 622110
David R. Nielsen *(CEO & Exec VP)*
Richard Waguespack *(Pres)*

AMERICAN ACADEMY OF PERIODONTOLOGY
737 N Michigan Ave Ste 800, Chi-
cago, IL 60611-6660
Tel.: (312) 787-5518   IL
Web Site: https://www.perio.org
Year Founded: 1914
Sales Range: $10-24.9 Million
Dental Care Services
N.A.I.C.S.: 621210
Steven R. Daniel *(Pres)*
Richard Kao *(VP)*

AMERICAN ACADEMY OF PHYSICAL MEDICINE & REHA-BILITATION
9700 W Bryn Mawr Ave Ste 200,
Rosemont, IL 60018
Tel.: (847) 737-6000   IL
Web Site: https://www.aapmr.org
Year Founded: 1951
Sales Range: $10-24.9 Million
Emp.: 57
Medical Professional Association
N.A.I.C.S.: 813920
Thomas E. Stautzenbach *(Exec Dir)*

AMERICAN ACADEMY OF SLEEP MEDICINE
2510 N Frontage Rd, Darien, IL
60561
Tel.: (630) 737-9700   MN
Web Site: http://www.aasmnet.org
Year Founded: 1975
Sales Range: $10-24.9 Million
Sleep Medicine Health Care Ser-
vices, Education & Research
N.A.I.C.S.: 621498
Kelly Carden *(Treas & Sec)*
Ilene Rosen *(Pres)*
Jerome A. Barrett *(Exec Dir)*

AMERICAN ACCESSORIES INTERNATIONAL LLC
550 W Main St Ste 825, Knoxville,
TN 37902
Tel.: (865) 525-9100
Web Site:
    https://www.americanaccessory.com
Year Founded: 1995
Cosmetic Bags
N.A.I.C.S.: 316990
Eric Zeanah *(Pres)*
Cassie McMahan *(Sec)*

AMERICAN ACCOUNTS & AD-VISERS

7460 80th St S, Cottage Grove, MN
55016-3007
Tel.: (651) 405-9760
Web Site: http://www.amaccts.com
Year Founded: 1986
Sales Range: $10-24.9 Million
Emp.: 25
Collection Agency Services
N.A.I.C.S.: 561440
Bryan McGroarty *(Pres)*
Phil Fahey *(VP)*
Dick Ryans *(Office Mgr)*

AMERICAN ACE INTERNA-TIONAL CO.
313 Newquist Ave Ste A, City of In-
dustry, CA 91745
Tel.: (626) 937-6116
Sales Range: $10-24.9 Million
Emp.: 25
Groceries, General Line
N.A.I.C.S.: 424410

AMERICAN ACTION NET-WORK
1747 Pennsylvania Ave NW, Wash-
ington, DC 20006
Tel.: (202) 559-6420   DE
Web Site:
    http://www.americanactionnet.org
Year Founded: 2009
Sales Range: $10-24.9 Million
Emp.: 11
Community Action Services
N.A.I.C.S.: 624190
Brian O. Walsh *(Pres)*

AMERICAN AGCO INC.
7900 97Th St S, Cottage Grove, MN
55016
Tel.: (651) 451-1349
Web Site:
    https://www.americanagco.com
Rev.: $72,000,000
Emp.: 108
Pet Foods
N.A.I.C.S.: 424490
D. J. Johnson *(Mgr)*
Melissa Schmidt *(Mgr-Feed Ingredi-
ent)*

AMERICAN AGCREDIT
400 Aviation Blvd Ste 100, Santa
Rosa, CA 95403
Tel.: (707) 545-7100
Web Site: http://www.agloan.com
Sales Range: $25-49.9 Million
Emp.: 6
Member-Owned Cooperative Offering
Financial Services to Agricultural &
Rural Customers in 30 States
N.A.I.C.S.: 522310
Charles Talbott *(Chm)*
George Fontes *(Vice Chm)*
Lynn Scherler *(Chief Lending Officer)*
Gary Harshberger *(Vice Chm)*
Greg Somerhalder *(COO)*
Rachel Angress *(Gen Counsel & Sr
VP)*
Mike Banks *(Chief Credit Officer & Sr
VP)*
Roger Bastow *(Chief Admin Officer &
Exec VP)*
Chase Hafner *(CTO & Sr VP)*
Sean O'Day *(Chief Banking Officer &
Exec VP)*
Paula Olufs *(Chief Innovation Officer
& Sr VP)*

Subsidiaries:

American AgCredit FLCA   (1)
3201 W Monte Vista Ave, Turlock, CA
95380
Tel.: (209) 667-5101

American AgCredit—(Continued)

Web Site: http://www.agloan.com
Emp.: 15
Farm Credit Services
N.A.I.C.S.: 523999
Stephen Moitovo (Gen Mgr)

American AgCredit PCA (1)
1440 W Williams Ave, Fallon, NV 89406
Tel.: (775) 423-3136
Farm Credit Services
N.A.I.C.S.: 523999

AMERICAN AGENCIES CO. INC.
1554 Ave Ponce De Leon, San Juan, PR 00902
Tel.: (787) 758-6300
Web Site:
http://www.americanagencies.com
Year Founded: 1956
Rev.: $26,603,138
Emp.: 30
Structural Shapes, Iron or Steel
N.A.I.C.S.: 423510
George Vendrell (VP)

Subsidiaries:

New Steel Inc. (1)
1554 Ave Ponce De Leon, San Juan, PR 00902
Tel.: (787) 758-6300
Web Site: http://www.carbe.net
Sales Range: $10-24.9 Million
Emp.: 18
Steel Structural Shapes & Pilings
N.A.I.C.S.: 331110
Omir Mendez (Chm)
George Vendrell (VP)

AMERICAN AGENCY INC.
5851 Cedar Lake Rd S, Minneapolis, MN 55416
Tel.: (952) 545-1230
Web Site:
http://www.americanagencymn.com
Sales Range: $25-49.9 Million
Emp.: 49
Insurance Agents
N.A.I.C.S.: 524210
Bob Clemants (Pres)
Paul Anderson (VP)

AMERICAN AIR SYSTEMS, INC.
181 Hobbs St PO Box 2241, Conway, NH 03818
Tel.: (603) 447-2136   **NH**
Web Site:
http://www.americanairsystems.net
Rev.: $29,435,564
Emp.: 15
Plumbing, Heating, Air-Conditioning
N.A.I.C.S.: 238220
Robert Franz (Pres)

AMERICAN AIRCRAFT PARTS MANUFACTURING CO.
17917 Masonic Blvd, Fraser, MI 48026-3160
Tel.: (586) 294-3300   **MI**
Year Founded: 1952
Sales Range: $75-99.9 Million
Emp.: 100
Mfr of Precision Aircraft Parts
N.A.I.C.S.: 336412
Richard Gordon (Pres & CEO)
Herb Richter (Controller)
Michael Thomas (Gen Mgr)

AMERICAN AIRPORTS CORPORATION
2425 Olympic Blvd Ste 650E, Santa Monica, CA 90404
Tel.: (310) 752-0555   **CA**
Web Site:
http://www.americanairports.com
Year Founded: 1997

Sales Range: $10-24.9 Million
Airport Services
N.A.I.C.S.: 488119
David G. Price (Chm & CEO)
Edward R. Sause (Pres)
Scott A. Wardle (Reg Dir-Ops)

AMERICAN ALARM & COMMUNICATIONS, INC.
297 Broadway, Arlington, MA 02474
Tel.: (781) 641-2000
Web Site:
https://www.americanalarm.com
Sales Range: $25-49.9 Million
Emp.: 100
Security Systems Integration & Monitoring Services
N.A.I.C.S.: 561621
Wells Sampson (Pres)
Louis Sampson (CFO & VP)
Dale Rawlinson (Mgr-Ops)
Joseph Doyle (Mgr-Corp HR)

AMERICAN ALLOY STEEL INC.
6230 N Houston Rosslyn Rd, Houston, TX 77091
Tel.: (713) 462-8081
Web Site: https://www.aasteel.com
Sales Range: $50-74.9 Million
Emp.: 95
Steel
N.A.I.C.S.: 423510
Arthur J. Moore (Pres)
Julio Cedeno (VP & Gen Mgr-Sls Div-Latin America)

AMERICAN ALUMINUM EXTRUSION COMPANY, LLC.
1 St Lawrence Ave, Beloit, WI 53511
Tel.: (608) 361-1800
Web Site:
http://www.americanaluminum.com
Year Founded: 2001
Sales Range: $10-24.9 Million
Emp.: 80
Aluminum Extruded Product Mfr
N.A.I.C.S.: 331315
Steve Mootz (Project Mgr)

AMERICAN APPAREL, INC.
107 Selma Bypass, Selma, AL 36701
Tel.: (334) 872-6337   **AL**
Web Site: http://www.amappinc.com
Sales Range: $25-49.9 Million
Emp.: 400
Military Uniforms Mfr
N.A.I.C.S.: 315250

AMERICAN APPAREL, INC.
747 Warehouse St, Los Angeles, CA 90021
Tel.: (213) 488-0226   **DE**
Web Site:
http://www.americanapparel.net
Year Founded: 2005
Sales Range: $600-649.9 Million
Apparel Mfr, Distr & Retailer
N.A.I.C.S.: 315990
Thoryn Stephens (Chief Digital Officer)
Cynthia Erland (Sr VP-Mktg)
Paul Charron (Chm)

Subsidiaries:

American Apparel (Carnaby)
Limited (1)
3 Carnaby Street, Soho, London, W1F 9PB, United Kingdom
Tel.: (44) 2077344477
Apparel Mfr & Distr
N.A.I.C.S.: 315990

American Apparel (UK) Limited (1)
3rd Floor National House 60-66 Wardour Street, London, W1F 0TA, United Kingdom
Tel.: (44) 2032062046

Web Site: http://www.americanapparel.net
Sales Range: $100-124.9 Million
Emp.: 40
Apparel Sales
N.A.I.C.S.: 458110
Sarah Haith (Mng Dir)

American Apparel Australia Pty
Ltd. (1)
262 Chapel St, Prahran, Melbourne, 3181, VIC, Australia
Tel.: (61) 395296852
Web Site: http://www.americanapparel.net
Apparel Mfr & Distr
N.A.I.C.S.: 315990
Esther Brown (Mgr)

American Apparel Canada Retail
Inc. (1)
5430 Ferrier, Montreal, H4P 1M2, QC, Canada
Tel.: (514) 939-0245
Web Site: http://www.americanapparel.net
Sales Range: $100-124.9 Million
Emp.: 100
Apparel Sales
N.A.I.C.S.: 458110
Caroline Ramirez (Mgr-Customer Svc)
Carlina Ramirez (Mgr-Customer Svc)

American Apparel Deutschland
GmbH (1)
Zollhof 10, 40 221, Dusseldorf, Germany
Tel.: (49) 2113854090
Web Site: http://americanapparel.net
Sales Range: $100-124.9 Million
Emp.: 20
Apparel Sales
N.A.I.C.S.: 458110
Sara Haith (Mng Dir)

American Apparel Dyeing & Finishing,
Inc. (1)
12641 Industry St, Garden Grove, CA 92841-3911
Tel.: (213) 488-0226
Web Site: http://www.americanapparel.net
Textile Dyeing & Finishing Mill Operator
N.A.I.C.S.: 313310
Monica Ramos (Dir-Plng)

American Apparel Japan Yuger
Kaisha (1)
Harajuku Yamada Building 4th Floor, 6-12-23 Jingumai, Shibuya-ku, Tokyo, 150-0001, Japan
Tel.: (81) 354673213
Sales Range: $150-199.9 Million
Apparels Mfr
N.A.I.C.S.: 315250

AMERICAN ARBITRATION ASSOCIATION
120 Broadway 21st Fl, New York, NY 10271
Tel.: (212) 716-5800   **NY**
Web Site: https://www.adr.org
Year Founded: 1926
Sales Range: $150-199.9 Million
Emp.: 750
Arbitration, Mediation & Conciliation Service
N.A.I.C.S.: 813910
Mark Appel (Sr VP)
Luis Martinez (VP)

AMERICAN ARCHITECTURAL DESIGN SPECIALTIES, INC.
1122 Old Chattahoochee Ave Nw Ste E, Atlanta, GA 30318
Tel.: (404) 367-0400   **GA**
Web Site: http://www.adsreps.com
Year Founded: 1983
Sales Range: $1-9.9 Million
Furniture & Other Interior & Exterior Products Whslr
N.A.I.C.S.: 423210
Ken Erdoes (Founder)

AMERICAN ARMED FORCES MUTUAL AID ASSOCIATION
102 Sheridan Ave, Fort Myer, VA 22211-1100

Tel.: (703) 707-4600   **VA**
Web Site: https://www.aafmaa.com
Year Founded: 1879
Sales Range: $100-124.9 Million
Emp.: 75
Armed Forces Mutual Aid Association
N.A.I.C.S.: 813920
Michael J. Meese (COO & Sec)
Merilynn Bergstresser (Controller)
Donald M. Babers (Chm)
Walter R. Lincoln (Pres & Treas)
Jack N. Merritt (Vice Chm)
Kevin A. Kincaid (VP-Ops)
Carrie L. Clark (Officer-Trust & Exec VP)

AMERICAN ART CLAY CO., INC.
6060 Guion Rd, Indianapolis, IN 46254-1222
Tel.: (317) 244-6871
Web Site: https://www.amaco.com
Year Founded: 1919
Rev.: $21,500,000
Emp.: 130
Ceramic Clay & Accessories
N.A.I.C.S.: 327992
Lester B. Sandoe Jr. (Pres & COO)

AMERICAN ASPHALT PAVING CO.
500 Chase Rd, Shavertown, PA 18708
Tel.: (570) 696-1181
Web Site:
https://www.amerasphalt.com
Year Founded: 1952
Sales Range: $10-24.9 Million
Emp.: 300
Highway & Street Paving Contractor
N.A.I.C.S.: 237310
Tommy Opeka (Superintendent)
Justin Schwartztrauber (Mgr-Sls)
Bernard C. Banks Jr. (Pres)

AMERICAN ASPHALT REPAIR & RESURFACING
24200 Clawiter Rd, Hayward, CA 94545-2216
Tel.: (510) 723-0280   **CA**
Web Site:
https://www.americanasphalt.com
Rev.: $10,700,000
Emp.: 35
Resurfacing Contractor
N.A.I.C.S.: 237310
Allan Henderson (Owner)
Kim Henschel (VP)
Steve Aguirre (COO)

AMERICAN ASSOCIATION FOR CANCER RESEARCH
615 Chestnut St 17th Fl, Philadelphia, PA 19106-4404
Tel.: (215) 440-9300   **NY**
Web Site: https://www.aacr.org
Year Founded: 1907
Sales Range: $50-74.9 Million
Emp.: 184
Disease Research Services
N.A.I.C.S.: 813212
Richard G. Buck (Sr Dir-Comm & PR)
Jon Retzlaff (Chief Policy Officer & VP-Science Policy & Govt Affairs)

AMERICAN ASSOCIATION FOR CLINICAL CHEMISTRY, INC.
1850 K St NW Ste 625, Washington, DC 20006-2213
Tel.: (202) 857-0717   **NY**
Web Site: http://www.aacc.org
Year Founded: 1948
Sales Range: $10-24.9 Million

Emp.: 74
Medical Professional Association
N.A.I.C.S.: 813920
David D. Koch *(Pres)*
Michael J. Bennett *(Treas)*

AMERICAN ASSOCIATION FOR LABORATORY ACCREDITATION
5202 Presidents Ct Ste 220, Frederick, MD 21703
Tel.: (301) 644-3248   MD
Web Site: http://www.a2la.org
Year Founded: 1978
Laboratory Accreditation Services
N.A.I.C.S.: 561990
Robert Miller *(Gen Mgr-Accreditation Svcs)*
Trace McInturff *(Sr Dir-Accreditation Svcs)*
Timothy Osborne *(Sr Dir-Trng Svcs)*
David Fischer *(Treas)*
Dean Williams *(Sec)*
Lonnie Spires *(Pres & CEO)*
Robin Stombler *(Vice Chm)*

AMERICAN ASSOCIATION FOR THE STUDY OF LIVER DISEASES
1001 N Fairfax St Ste 400, Alexandria, VA 22314
Tel.: (703) 299-9766   IL
Web Site: http://www.aasld.org
Year Founded: 1950
Sales Range: $1-9.9 Million
Health Care Srvices
N.A.I.C.S.: 622110
Gyongyi Szabo *(Pres)*
Gary L. Davis *(Sec)*
W. Ray Kim *(Treas)*
Bruce A. Luxon *(Co-Treas)*
Kimberly A. Brown *(Sec)*

AMERICAN ASSOCIATION OF AIRPORT EXECUTIVES
601 Madison St Ste 400, Alexandria, VA 22314
Tel.: (703) 824-0500   IL
Web Site: https://www.aaae.org
Year Founded: 1928
Sales Range: $10-24.9 Million
Emp.: 86
Airport Executive Association
N.A.I.C.S.: 813920
Joel Bacon *(Exec VP-Govt & Pub Affairs)*
Todd Hauptli *(Pres & CEO)*
Brad Van Dam *(Sr VP-Govt Affairs)*
Colleen Chamberlain *(VP-Transportation Security Policy)*
Melissa Sabatine *(Sr VP-Regulatory Affairs)*
Todd McNamee *(Treas & Sec)*
Stephanie Gupta *(Sr VP-Security & Facilitation-Federal Affairs Dept)*

AMERICAN ASSOCIATION OF NURSE ANESTHETISTS
222 S Prospect Ave, Park Ridge, IL 60068-4001
Tel.: (847) 692-7050   IL
Web Site: http://www.aana.com
Year Founded: 1948
Sales Range: $10-24.9 Million
Emp.: 171
Professional Support Services
N.A.I.C.S.: 813920

AMERICAN ASSOCIATION OF NURSE PRACTITIONERS
901 S Mopac Expy Bldg II Ste 450, Austin, TX 78746
Tel.: (512) 442-4262   TX
Web Site: http://www.aanp.org
Year Founded: 1985

Sales Range: $10-24.9 Million
Emp.: 53
Nursing Professional Association
N.A.I.C.S.: 813920
Joyce M. Knestrick *(Treas)*
April N. Kapu *(Pres)*
Jon Fanning *(CEO)*

AMERICAN ASSOCIATION OF ORAL AND MAXILLOFACIAL SURGEONS
9700 W Bryn Mawr Ave, Rosemont, IL 60018-5701
Tel.: (847) 678-6200   IL
Web Site: https://www.myoms.org
Year Founded: 1918
Sales Range: $10-24.9 Million
Emp.: 57
Oral & Maxillofacial Surgeon Association
N.A.I.C.S.: 813920
Scott Farrell *(CFO)*
Louis K. Rafetto *(VP)*
A. Thomas Indresano *(Pres)*
Douglas W. Fain *(VP)*
B. D. Tiner *(VP)*
Jolene Kremer *(Assoc Exec Dir-Comm & Publications)*

AMERICAN ASSOCIATION OF ORTHOPAEDIC SURGEONS
9400 W Higgins Rd, Rosemont, IL 60018
Tel.: (847) 823-7186   IL
Web Site: http://www.aaos.org
Year Founded: 1999
Sales Range: $10-24.9 Million
Medical Professional Association
N.A.I.C.S.: 813920
William Bruce *(CTO)*
Will Shaffer *(Dir-Medical)*
Ellen Moore *(Chief Education Officer)*
Richard J. Stewart *(CFO & COO)*
Richard N. Peterson *(Gen Counsel)*
David Teuscher *(Pres)*
Gerald R. Williams *(First VP)*
Frederick M. Azar Jr. *(Treas)*

AMERICAN ASSOCIATION OF STATE COLLEGES AND UNIVERSITIES
1307 New York Ave NW 5th Fl, Washington, DC 20005
Tel.: (202) 293-7070   DC
Web Site: http://www.aascu.org
Year Founded: 1961
Sales Range: $10-24.9 Million
Emp.: 106
Educational Support Services
N.A.I.C.S.: 611710

AMERICAN ASSOCIATION OF STATE HIGHWAY & TRANSPORTATION OFFICIALS
444 N Capitol St NW Ste 249, Washington, DC 20001
Tel.: (202) 624-5800   DC
Web Site: http://www.transportation.org
Year Founded: 1914
Sales Range: $50-74.9 Million
Emp.: 153
Transportation Official Association
N.A.I.C.S.: 813910
Clarisse Bernardes Coble *(Mgr-HR)*
Robert Cullen *(Mgr-Info Resource)*
Jenet Adem *(Dir-Finance-Administration)*
Jim Tymon *(COO & Dir-Policy & Mgmt)*
Monica Russell *(Dir-Meetings-Member Services)*
Jim McDonnell *(Dir-Program-Engrg)*
Erin K. Grady *(Dir-Publ Production)*
Joung Lee *(Dir-Policy)*

Matthew Hardy *(Dir-Program-Planning-Policy)*
Kelly Hardy *(Sr Mgr-Engrg Program-Safety)*

AMERICAN AUCTIONEERS LLC
10165 Cribari Dr, Yucaipa, CA 92399-6007
Tel.: (909) 790-0433
Web Site: http://www.americanauctioneer.com
Year Founded: 1983
Sales Range: $1-9.9 Million
Emp.: 10
Antique Dealer
N.A.I.C.S.: 459510
Dan Dotson *(Owner)*

AMERICAN AUTOMATED PAYROLL
901 Old Trolley Rd Ste A, Summerville, SC 29485
Tel.: (843) 851-2289
Web Site: http://www.aappayroll.com
Year Founded: 1996
Sales Range: $1-9.9 Million
Emp.: 27
Payroll Services
N.A.I.C.S.: 541214
Bill Streyffeler *(CEO)*

AMERICAN BAILEY CORPORATION
120 Long Ridge Rd, Stamford, CT 06902-1839
Tel.: (203) 348-8700   DE
Web Site: http://www.americanbailey.com
Year Founded: 1984
Sales Range: $25-49.9 Million
Emp.: 10
Investment Company
N.A.I.C.S.: 523910
Ralph E. Bailey *(Chm)*
Douglas G. Bailey *(Pres & CEO)*

AMERICAN BANCARD, LLC
1081 Holland Dr, Boca Raton, FL 33487
Tel.: (561) 961-1353
Web Site: http://www.americanbancard.com
Year Founded: 2001
Sales Range: $1-9.9 Million
Emp.: 50
Credit Card Processing Services
N.A.I.C.S.: 561499
Sam Zietz *(CEO)*
Steven Scop *(Dir-Mktg)*
Ron Schnell *(CTO)*

AMERICAN BANCOR, LTD.
46 1st W, Dickinson, ND 58601-5106
Tel.: (701) 483-6811
Year Founded: 1985
Multi-Bank Holding Company
N.A.I.C.S.: 551111
David Ehlis *(Pres & CEO)*

Subsidiaries:

Bravera Bank   (1)
220 1st Ave W, Dickinson, ND 58601-5689
Tel.: (701) 483-6811
Web Site: https://www.bravera.bank
Commericial Banking
N.A.I.C.S.: 522110
Dave Ehlis *(Pres & CEO)*

United Community Bank of North Dakota   (1)
105 Central Ave S, Leeds, ND 58346
Tel.: (701) 466-2000
Web Site: http://www.ucbnd.bank
Sales Range: $1-9.9 Million
Commericial Banking
N.A.I.C.S.: 522110

Bill Kuntz *(Pres & CEO)*
Kelly Fischer *(Pres-Leeds)*

AMERICAN BANCORP OF OKLAHOMA
15 E 15th St, Edmond, OK 73013
Tel.: (405) 341-8222
Web Site: http://www.kirkpatrickbank.com
Year Founded: 1970
Sales Range: $1-9.9 Million
Emp.: 2
State Commercial Banks
N.A.I.C.S.: 522110
George Drew *(Pres)*
Christian K. Keesee *(Chm)*

Subsidiaries:

Kirkpatrick Bank   (1)
15 E 15th St, Edmond, OK 73013
Tel.: (405) 341-8222
Web Site: http://www.kirkpatrickbank.com
Sales Range: $50-74.9 Million
Emp.: 55
National Commercial Banks
N.A.I.C.S.: 522110
George Drew *(Pres)*
Christian K. Keesee *(Chm)*
Christine Sanford *(VP)*
Grace Meyer *(Sec & Sr VP)*
John Steen *(Officer-Ops)*
James A. Shane *(CFO & Sr VP)*
Trenton Stafford *(Pres-Colorado Market)*
Doris Rigoni *(Pres-Denver)*
Christopher Lueth *(VP-Comml Lending)*

AMERICAN BANCORPORATION OF MINNESOTA, INC.
7638 Woida Rd, Baxter, MN 56425
Tel.: (218) 829-1484   MN
Web Site: http://www.anbmn.com
Year Founded: 2001
Sales Range: $10-24.9 Million
Emp.: 61
Bank Holding Company
N.A.I.C.S.: 551111
Thomas J. Johnson *(Pres & CEO)*

Subsidiaries:

American National Bank of Minnesota   (1)
7638 Woida Rd, Baxter, MN 56425
Tel.: (218) 829-1484
Web Site: http://www.anbmn.com
Sales Range: $10-24.9 Million
Emp.: 64
Commercial Bank Services
N.A.I.C.S.: 522110

AMERICAN BANK & TRUST COMPANY
6060 American Plz, Tulsa, OK 74135
Tel.: (918) 481-3000
Web Site: https://www.americanbanktulsa.com
Year Founded: 1971
Sales Range: $1-9.9 Million
Emp.: 42
Provider of Banking & Trust Services
N.A.I.C.S.: 522110
Lisa Carr *(Controller)*
Michael P. Oonk *(VP-Comml Loan Dept)*
Frank X. Henke III *(Chm)*

AMERICAN BANK HOLDING INC.
4301 E 53rd St, Davenport, IA 52807-3861
Tel.: (563) 344-9500
Web Site: http://www.ambankqc.com
Sales Range: $10-24.9 Million
Emp.: 150
Bank Holding Company
N.A.I.C.S.: 551111
James V. Russell *(Vice Chm)*
Richard Emery *(Officer-Trust & Sr VP-Quad Cities & Kane County)*

American Bank Holding Inc.—(Continued)

Matt Phares *(CFO)*
Jeffrey P. Rose *(Pres & CEO)*
Rakesh Alla *(Chm)*
Mark B. Werning *(COO & Sec)*
Dan P. Jaros *(Chief Lending Officer & Sr VP)*

Subsidiaries:

American Bank & Trust Company   (1)
4301 E 53rd St, Davenport, IA 52807
Tel.: (563) 344-9500
Web Site: http://www.ambankqc.com
Rev.: $18,020,000
Emp.: 50
National Commercial Banks
N.A.I.C.S.: 522110
James V. Russell *(Vice Chm)*
Jeffrey P. Rose *(Pres & CEO)*
John D. Timmer *(Vice Chm)*
Rakesh Alla *(Chm)*
Charles E. Sorensen *(Sr VP & Mgr-Consumer Loan)*
Dan P. Jaros *(Chief Lending Officer & Sr VP)*
Garrett E. Buhle *(Sr VP & Mgr-Comml Market)*
Matt Phares *(CFO)*
Rebecca Skafidas *(Officer-Credit & Sr VP)*
Richard Emery *(Officer-Trust & Sr VP)*

AMERICAN BANKNOTE CORPORATION
2200 Fletcher Ave, Fort Lee, NJ 07024
Tel.: (201) 592-3400   DE
Web Site:
http://www.americanbanknote.com
Year Founded: 1795
Sales Range: $150-199.9 Million
Emp.: 2,520
Engraving & Printing Securities, Food Coupons, Travellers Cheques, Postage Stamps, Stock & Bond Gift Certificates, State Vital Documents, Gift Certificates, Business Checks
N.A.I.C.S.: 551112
David M. Kober *(Gen Counsel & Exec VP)*
Richard Taylor *(Sr VP-Global Strategy)*
Rola Hamandi *(Sr VP-Sls-Intl & Bus Dev)*
Thomas Ziemkus *(CTO-Global & Sr VP)*
Gregoire Maes *(COO-Global)*
William Brown *(CEO)*
Tim Perry *(Country Mgr-ABCorp NZ Limited)*

Subsidiaries:

ABCorp USA   (1)
225 Rivermoor St, Boston, MA 02132
Tel.: (617) 325-9600
Web Site: http://www.abnote.com
Private Label Plastic Card Mfr
N.A.I.C.S.: 326199

ABnote Australasia Pty. Ltd.   (1)
1 Dunlopillo Drive, Dandenong South, 3175, VIC, Australia
Tel.: (61) 395569111
Web Site: http://www.abnote.com.au
Sales Range: $25-49.9 Million
Emp.: 500
Commercial Printing Services
N.A.I.C.S.: 323111

ABnote NZ Ltd   (1)
25 Halwyn Drive, Hornby, Christchurch, 8042, New Zealand
Tel.: (64) 3 349 9500
Sales Range: $25-49.9 Million
Emp.: 160
Plastic Laminated Card Mfr & Supplier
N.A.I.C.S.: 326199

ABnote North America   (1)
225 Rivermoor St, Boston, MA 02132-4905
Tel.: (617) 325-9600
Web Site: http://www.abnote.com

Sales Range: $25-49.9 Million
Emp.: 200
Specialty Printing & Integrated Card Solutions
N.A.I.C.S.: 326113
Jeffery White *(Mgr-Pre-Press)*
Joe Caffarella *(Sr VP-Govt Contracts)*
Rola Hamandi *(Sr VP-Intl Sls & Bus Dev)*
James Ellis *(Sr VP-Sls & Mktg)*
John Ekers *(Global CIO & Sr VP)*
Michael Connors *(VP-Ops)*
Gregoire Maes *(COO-Global)*
Richard Taylor *(Sr VP-Global Strategy)*
Thomas Ziemkus *(CTO-Global & Sr VP)*

ABnote North America   (1)
2520 Metropolitan Dr, Trevose, PA 19053
Tel.: (215) 396-8707
Web Site: http://www.abncompany.com
Sales Range: $10-24.9 Million
Emp.: 20
Engraving & Printing Securities, Food Coupons, Travellers Cheques, Postage Stamps, Stock & Bond Gift Certificates, State Vital Documents, Gift Certificates, Business Checks
N.A.I.C.S.: 323111
Michael Zanoni *(VP-Mktg & Bus Dev)*

AMERICAN BAPTIST HOMES OF THE MIDWEST
14850 Scenic Heights Rd Ste 125, Eden Prairie, MN 55344
Tel.: (952) 941-3175   MN
Web Site: https://www.abhomes.net
Year Founded: 1930
Sales Range: $50-74.9 Million
Emp.: 1,526
Elder Care Services
N.A.I.C.S.: 624120
Jeff Hongslo *(CFO & Treas)*
David Charron *(Dir-Crest Svcs)*
Roger Hennen *(Dir-IT)*
Diane Baumgartner *(Dir-Mktg)*
Tim O'Brien *(Sec & VP-Program)*

AMERICAN BARCODE AND RFID
3431 E Elwood St, Phoenix, AZ 85040
Tel.: (602) 651-1684   AZ
Web Site: https://www.abr.com
Year Founded: 1980
Supply Chain Management Services
N.A.I.C.S.: 423430
Michael E. Stryczek *(CEO)*
Dino D. Farfante *(Pres & COO)*
Brian Krueger *(Acct Mgr-Western Arizona, Nevada & Utah)*
Gary Randall *(VP-Bus Dev & VP-Bus Dev & Sls)*
Mark Steger *(Dir-Pro Svcs)*
Ted Morgan *(VP-Strategic Dev)*
Patrick Mahony *(Acct Mgr-East Coast Reg)*
Drew Henderson *(Acct Mgr-Texas, New Mexico, Oklahoma, Louisiana & Arkansas)*
Jason Miller *(Sls Mgr-Eastern Arizona)*
Bradley Bast *(Acct Mgr-Southern California)*
Chris Coffman *(Acct Mgr-Northern California & Reno)*
Brett Bordes *(Acct Mgr-Washington, Oregon & Idaho)*
Ted Morgan *(VP-Strategic Dev)*
Gary Randall *(VP-Bus Dev & Sls)*

AMERICAN BATH GROUP
435 Industrial Rd, Savannah, TN 38372
Tel.: (800) 443-7269   TN
Web Site:
http://www.americanbathgroup.com
Year Founded: 1993
Sales Range: $350-399.9 Million
Emp.: 3,400
Bath Product Mfr

N.A.I.C.S.: 332913
Jason Burdette *(Sr VP-Svc, Mktg & Sls Admin)*

Subsidiaries:

MAAX Bath Inc.   (1)
160 Saint Joseph Blvd, Lachine, H8S 2L3, QC, Canada
Tel.: (514) 844-4155
Web Site: http://www.maax.com
Kitchen Cabinets, Bathroom Fixtures, Spas & Accessories Mfr
N.A.I.C.S.: 337110

Branch (US):

MAAX Bath Inc. - Plymouth   (2)
1001 N Oak Dr, Plymouth, IN 46563-3428
Tel.: (574) 936-3838
Web Site: http://www.maax.com
Plastic Plumbing Fixtures Mfr
N.A.I.C.S.: 326191

Subsidiary (Domestic):

MAAX Canada Inc.   (2)
4225 Spallumcheen Road, Armstrong, V0E 1B6, BC, Canada
Tel.: (250) 546-8701
Web Site: http://www.maax.com
Bathroom Plumbing Fixture Mfr
N.A.I.C.S.: 332913

Branch (US):

MAAX Inc.-Minneapolis   (2)
7767 Elm Creek Blvd Ste 310, Maple Grove, MN 55369
Tel.: (763) 424-3335
Web Site: http://www.maax.com
Sauna & Acrylic Spa Mfr
N.A.I.C.S.: 326191

MAAX Inc.-Valdosta   (2)
1625 James P Rogers Rd, Valdosta, GA 31601
Tel.: (229) 247-2364
Web Site: http://www.maax.com
Bathroom Plumbing Fixture Mfr
N.A.I.C.S.: 332913

Subsidiary (US):

MAAX Spas Industries Corp.   (2)
25605 S Arizona Ave, Chandler, AZ 85248
Tel.: (480) 895-0598
Web Site: http://www.maaxspas.com
Sauna & Acrylic Spas Mfr
N.A.I.C.S.: 326191
John Johnson *(Pres & Gen Mgr)*

AMERICAN BATTERY CO. INC.
2080 Springdale Rd, Cherry Hill, NJ 08003
Tel.: (856) 797-2979
Sales Range: $10-24.9 Million
Emp.: 240
Automotive Batteries
N.A.I.C.S.: 423120
Louis Fishman *(Pres)*
Carla Fishman *(Treas)*

AMERICAN BEAUTY CORP
20750 Ventura Blvd Ste 240, Woodland Hills, CA 91364-6235
Tel.: (818) 981-4900   CA
Web Site: http://www.abdco.com
Year Founded: 1972
Sales Range: Less than $1 Million
Emp.: 2
New Construction of Single-Family Houses
N.A.I.C.S.: 237210
Jack Shine *(Principal)*
Daniel Shine *(Principal)*

AMERICAN BEVERAGE ASSOCIATION
1275 Pennsylvania Ave NW Ste 1100, Washington, DC 20004
Tel.: (202) 463-6732   DC
Web Site: http://www.ameribev.org
Year Founded: 1921
Sales Range: $50-74.9 Million

Emp.: 41
Beverage Association
N.A.I.C.S.: 813910
William Dermody *(VP-Policy)*
Kevin W. Keane *(Exec VP-Govt & Pub Affairs)*
Mark Hammond *(CFO & Exec VP)*
Amy E. Hancock *(Sec)*
Kirk Tyler *(Chm)*
Marie Franco *(VP-Fin & Admin)*
Tracey A. Halliday *(VP-Comm)*
Barbara Hiden *(VP-Federal Affairs)*
Maia M. Jack *(VP-Science & Regulatory Affairs)*
Sean Krispinsky *(Sr VP)*
Fredericka McGee *(VP-California Govt Affairs & Ops)*
Bill McManus *(VP-Govt Affairs & Outreach)*
Patrice Webb *(VP-Social Commitment)*
Katherine G. Lugar *(Pres & CEO)*
Ralph D. Crowley Jr. *(Treas)*

AMERICAN BIOTECH LABS
705 E 50 S, American Fork, UT 84003
Tel.: (801) 756-1000
Web Site:
http://www.americanbiotechlabs.com
Year Founded: 1998
Rev.: $6,000,000
Emp.: 30
Pharmaceutical Preparation Mfr
N.A.I.C.S.: 325412
Dawn Valdez *(Mgr)*
Keith Moeller *(CEO)*
Scott Moeller *(CFO)*

AMERICAN BIRD CONSERVANCY
4249 Loudoun Ave, The Plains, VA 20198-2237
Tel.: (540) 253-5780   DE
Web Site: http://www.abcbirds.org
Year Founded: 1986
Sales Range: $10-24.9 Million
Emp.: 70
Bird Conservancy Services
N.A.I.C.S.: 712190
Rita Fenwick *(VP-Dev)*
Merrie Morrison *(VP-Admin)*
Clare Nielsen *(VP-Comm)*
V. Richard Eales *(Vice Chm & Treas)*
Lawrence A. Selzer *(Chm)*
Michael J. Parr *(Pres)*
David Younkman *(VP-Western Reg)*
David Roos *(CFO & VP-Fin)*
Shawn Graff *(VP-Great Lakes)*
Daniel Lebbin *(VP-Intl Programs)*

AMERICAN BLOCK-CHAINBIOCHAR CORPORATION
14500 Roscoe Blvd Ste 203, Panorama City, CA 91402
Tel.: (805) 340-2484   DE
Year Founded: 2017
Investment Services
N.A.I.C.S.: 523999
Mahesh Talwar *(CEO)*
James McKillop *(Chief Bus Officer)*

AMERICAN BOARD OF MEDICAL SPECIALTIES
353 N Clark St Ste 1400, Chicago, IL 60654
Tel.: (312) 436-2600   IL
Web Site: http://www.abms.org
Year Founded: 1935
Sales Range: $10-24.9 Million
Emp.: 82
Medical Professional Association
N.A.I.C.S.: 813920

Laura Skarnulis *(COO)*
Jennifer Michael *(COO)*
Krista Allbee *(VP-Intl Programs)*
Mira Irons *(Sr VP-Academic Affairs)*
Jennifer J. Fronek *(VP-Fin)*
Robert H. Miller *(Treas & Sec)*
John C. Moorhead *(Chm)*
Carol Clothier *(VP-State Health Policy & Pub Affairs)*
Thomas Granatir *(Sr VP-Policy & External Rels)*
John D. Mandelbaum *(Chief Legal Officer)*
David B. Swanson *(VP-Academic Programs & Svcs)*
Rich Waters *(VP-Mktg & Comm)*
Richard E. Hawkins *(Pres & CEO)*

AMERICAN BORATE CORPORATION

5701 Cleveland St Ste 350, Virginia Beach, VA 23462
Tel.: (757) 490-2242
Web Site:
   https://www.americanborate.com
Year Founded: 1990
Sales Range: $10-24.9 Million
Emp.: 10
Borate Compounds (Natural) Mining
N.A.I.C.S.: 212390
James Sparks *(CEO)*
Bob Reid *(Mgr-Natl Sls)*
Bryant Baker *(Mgr-Technical)*
Pat Riddle *(Mgr-Logistics & Sourcing)*
Kristin Sparks *(COO)*
Paul Wilcox *(Reg.Mgr-Sls)*
Linda Bowers *(CFO)*

AMERICAN BOTANICALS, LLC

24750 Highway FF, Eolia, MO 63344
Tel.: (573) 485-2300   MO
Web Site:
   https://www.americanbotanicals.com
Rev.: $1,700,000
Emp.: 100
Buys, Sells & Exports Various Roots & Herbs for Pharmaceutical & Natural Herbal Product Manufacturing
N.A.I.C.S.: 325412
Belinda Ellsworth *(Office Mgr)*
Don Stock *(CEO)*

Subsidiaries:

Aloha Medicinals, Inc.   **(1)**
2300 Arrowhead Dr, Carson City, NV 89706
Tel.: (775) 886-6300
Web Site: http://www.alohamedicinals.com
Sales Range: $1-9.9 Million
Emp.: 122
Producer of Organic Medicinal Mushrooms
N.A.I.C.S.: 111411
John Holliday *(Pres)*

AMERICAN BULK COMMODITIES INC.

8063 Southern Blvd, Youngstown, OH 44512-6306
Tel.: (330) 758-0841
Year Founded: 1992
Sales Range: $25-49.9 Million
Emp.: 600
Provider of Trucking & Shipping Services
N.A.I.C.S.: 484110
Rob Reed *(CFO)*

Subsidiaries:

R & J Trucking Inc.   **(1)**
8063 Southern Blvd, Youngstown, OH 44512-6306   **(100%)**
Tel.: (330) 758-0841
Web Site: http://www.rjtrucking.com
Sales Range: $25-49.9 Million
Emp.: 400
Provider Of Trucking & Shipping Services
N.A.I.C.S.: 484110
Dennis Coe *(VP-Sls & Mgr-Terminal)*
Chris Asher *(Mgr-Terminal)*

Jeff Caltrider *(Mgr-Maintenance)*
Bill Gates *(Mgr-Maintenance)*
Zach Miller *(Mgr-Maintenance)*

AMERICAN BUREAU OF SHIPPING

ABS Plz 16855 Northchase Dr, Houston, TX 77060
Tel.: (281) 877-5700
Web Site: https://www.eagle.org
Year Founded: 1862
Sales Range: $450-499.9 Million
Emp.: 3,300
Ship & Marine Facility Classification Society
N.A.I.C.S.: 926120
Christopher J. Wiernicki *(Chm)*
Jeffrey J. Weiner *(CFO & Exec VP)*
Laura C. Fulton *(CFO & Sr VP)*
Howard Fireman *(CTO & Sr VP)*
Bret Montaruli *(VP)*
Derek Novak *(Pres-ABS Pacific Div)*
Eric Kleess *(Pres-ABS Greater China Div)*
Joseph A. Riva *(VP)*
Kenneth Richardson *(Exec VP-Global Offshore)*
Tony Nassif *(COO & Exec VP)*
Bob Clyne *(Gen Counsel, Sec & Sr VP)*
Adam Moilanen *(VP-Health, Safety, Quality & Environment)*

Subsidiaries:

ABS Europe Ltd.   **(1)**
ABS House 1 Frying Pan Alley, London, E1 7HR, United Kingdom
Tel.: (44) 2072473255
Web Site: http://www.eagle.org
Sales Range: $100-124.9 Million
Emp.: 150
Ship & Marine Facility Classification, Engineering & Survey Services
N.A.I.C.S.: 551114
Antonio C. Lino Costa *(VP-Global Mktg)*
Gillian Smyth *(Mgr-Mktg & Comm-Europe)*
James Hall *(Mgr-Reward)*

ABS Group of Companies, Inc.   **(1)**
ABS Plz 16855 Northchase Dr, Houston, TX 77060
Tel.: (281) 673-2800
Web Site: http://www.abs-group.com
Sales Range: $150-199.9 Million
Emp.: 100
Holding Company; Risk Management, Safety, Quality & Environmental Consulting & Certification Services
N.A.I.C.S.: 551112
Jeffrey J. Weiner *(CFO & Treas)*
Christopher J. Wiernicki *(Chm)*
Suresh S. Bheema *(VP-Technical Inspection & Verification)*

Division (Domestic):

ABS InfoLink Inc.   **(2)**
16855 Northchase Dr, Houston, TX 77060-6008
Tel.: (281) 877-5750
Information Technology Management Services & Software Publisher
N.A.I.C.S.: 541513

Subsidiary (Domestic):

ABS Nautical Systems LLC   **(3)**
ABS Plz 16855 Northchase Dr, Houston, TX 77060
Tel.: (281) 877-5700
Web Site: http://www.abs-ns.com
Sales Range: $25-49.9 Million
Emp.: 300
Fleet Management Software Developer & Publisher
N.A.I.C.S.: 513210
Joe Woods *(VP-Sls & Mktg)*

Branch (Non-US):

ABS Maritime Services - Hellas   **(4)**
6 Skouze Street Floor 4A, GR-185 10, Piraeus, Greece
Tel.: (30) 2104294046
Web Site: http://www.abs-ns.com

Sales Range: $50-74.9 Million
Emp.: 12
Fleet Management Software Developer & Publisher
N.A.I.C.S.: 513210

ABS Nautical Systems Asia Pacific   **(4)**
438 Alexandra Rd Fl 10 Unit 10 Alexandra Pt, Singapore, 119958, Singapore
Tel.: (65) 62768700
Web Site: http://www.abs-ns.com
Sales Range: $50-74.9 Million
Emp.: 3
Fleet Management Software Developer & Publisher
N.A.I.C.S.: 513210

ABS Nautical Systems Chile   **(4)**
Torre Marina Arauco, Av Libertad No 1348 Of 702, Vina del Mar, Chile
Tel.: (56) 322381440
Web Site: http://www.abs-ns.com
Sales Range: $50-74.9 Million
Emp.: 1
Fleet Management Software Developer & Publisher
N.A.I.C.S.: 513210

ABS Nautical Systems Malaysia   **(4)**
Lot F1-06 1 FL Compalex Dayabumi, 50050, Kuala Lumpur, Malaysia
Tel.: (60) 322722732
Web Site: http://www.abs-ns.com
Sales Range: $50-74.9 Million
Emp.: 2
Fleet Management Software Developer & Publisher
N.A.I.C.S.: 513210

Division (Domestic):

ABSG Consulting Inc.   **(2)**
140 Heimer Rd Ste 300, San Antonio, TX 78232
Tel.: (210) 495-5195
Sales Range: $150-199.9 Million
Risk Management & Consulting Services
N.A.I.C.S.: 541618

Division (Non-US):

ABS Consulting Ltd.   **(3)**
EQE House The Beacons Warrington Road, Birchwood, Warrington, WA3 6W3, Cheshire, United Kingdom
Tel.: (44) 1925287300
Sales Range: $25-49.9 Million
Emp.: 50
Risk Management & Consulting Services
N.A.I.C.S.: 541618
Simon Wong *(Gen Mgr)*
Brad Eccles *(Gen Mgr)*

Subsidiary (Non-US):

ABS Group Services de Mexico, S.A. de C.V.   **(3)**
Hamburgo 254-201, Col Juarez, Mexico, 6600, Mexico
Tel.: (52) 5555114240
Sales Range: $10-24.9 Million
Emp.: 30
Risk Management & Consulting Services
N.A.I.C.S.: 541618
Miguel Angel Cinta Meza *(Country Mgr)*

ABS Group Services do Brasil Ltda.   **(3)**
Av Venezuela 3 18th Andar, Centro, Rio de Janeiro, 20081 310, RJ, Brazil
Tel.: (55) 2132321700
Sales Range: $25-49.9 Million
Emp.: 100
Risk Management & Consulting Services
N.A.I.C.S.: 541618

Branch (Domestic):

ABSG Consulting - Irvine   **(3)**
300 Commerce Dr Ste 200, Irvine, CA 92602-1305
Tel.: (714) 734-4242
Web Site: http://www.abs-groupe.com
Sales Range: $25-49.9 Million
Emp.: 34
Risk Management & Consulting Services
N.A.I.C.S.: 541618
Tom Roche *(VP-US Nuclear-Energy Sector)*

ABSG Consulting - Knoxville   **(3)**
10301 Technology Dr, Knoxville, TN 37932-3392
Tel.: (865) 966-5232
Sales Range: $25-49.9 Million
Emp.: 70
Risk Management & Consulting Services
N.A.I.C.S.: 541618
David Whittle *(Dir-Process Safety Competency Center)*
David Walker *(Sr VP-Pub Sector)*

ABSG Consulting - Lakewood   **(3)**
3075 Windridge Cir, Littleton, CO 80126-8006
Tel.: (303) 674-2990
Web Site: http://www.absconsulting.com
Sales Range: $25-49.9 Million
Emp.: 1
Risk Management & Consulting Services
N.A.I.C.S.: 541618

Division (Non-US):

ABSG Consulting - Middle East   **(3)**
Sheikh Zayed Rd After The 3rd Interchange Aljoud Ctr 1st Fl Ofc 111, PO Box 282229, Dubai, 282229, United Arab Emirates
Tel.: (971) 43306116
Sales Range: $25-49.9 Million
Emp.: 30
Risk Management & Consulting Services
N.A.I.C.S.: 541618
Gary Graham *(Gen Mgr)*

Branch (Domestic):

ABSG Consulting - Rockville   **(3)**
1309 Piccard Dr Ste 350, Rockville, MD 20850
Tel.: (301) 907-9100
Sales Range: $25-49.9 Million
Emp.: 12
Risk Management & Consulting Services
N.A.I.C.S.: 541618
Mark Abrams *(Mgr-Tech)*

ABSG Consulting - Saint Louis   **(3)**
77 Westport Plz Ste 210, Saint Louis, MO 63146-3121
Tel.: (314) 994-7007
Sales Range: $25-49.9 Million
Emp.: 15
Risk Management & Consulting Services
N.A.I.C.S.: 541618
Nathan Gould *(Gen Mgr)*

ABSG Consulting - Salt Lake City   **(3)**
310 S Main St Ste 300, Salt Lake City, UT 84101-2105
Tel.: (801) 333-7676
Web Site: http://www.absconsulting.com
Sales Range: $25-49.9 Million
Emp.: 17
Risk Management & Consulting Services
N.A.I.C.S.: 541618

ABSG Consulting - San Antonio   **(3)**
14607 San Pedro Ste 215, San Antonio, TX 78232-2252
Tel.: (210) 495-5195
Sales Range: $25-49.9 Million
Emp.: 24
Risk Management & Consulting Services
N.A.I.C.S.: 541618

ABSG Consulting - Wilmington   **(3)**
5301 Limestone Rd Ste 225, Wilmington, DE 19808-1265
Tel.: (302) 239-7310
Risk Management & Consulting Services
N.A.I.C.S.: 541618

Division (Non-US):

ABSG Consulting Inc.   **(3)**
438 Alexandra Road 09-01, Alexandra Point, Singapore, 119958, Singapore
Tel.: (65) 62708663
Emp.: 100
Risk Management & Consulting Services
N.A.I.C.S.: 541618
Henrique Paula *(Pres)*
Suresh S. Bheema *(VP)*
Andre du Plessis *(Head-Risk Consulting)*
Mohamed Hatta *(Head-Marine Svcs)*
Amar Hanspal *(Head-Trng & Consulting)*

Branch (Non-US):

ABSG Consulting - Taiwan   **(4)**

American Bureau of Shipping—(Continued)

Room 606 168 Chung Cheng 4th Rd, Ka-
ohsiung, 801, Taiwan
Tel.: (886) 72713463
Sales Range: $50-74.9 Million
Emp.: 5
Risk Management & Consulting Services
N.A.I.C.S.: 541618
Yong Ling N. Fong (Country Mgr)

Subsidiary (Non-US):

ABSG Consulting de Venezuela,
C.A.   (3)
Centro Ciudad Comercial Tamanaco, Torre
A Fl 3 Oficina A-309, Chuao, Caracas,
1064, Venezuela
Tel.: (58) 2129597442
Sales Range: $10-24.9 Million
Emp.: 8
Risk Management & Consulting Services
N.A.I.C.S.: 541618
Victor Martinez (Country Mgr)

Subsidiary (Domestic):

EQECAT, Inc.   (3)
475 14th Ste 550, Oakland, CA
94612   (100%)
Tel.: (510) 817-3100
Web Site: http://www.eqecat.com
Sales Range: $25-49.9 Million
Emp.: 60
Risk Management Software & Consulting
Services
N.A.I.C.S.: 541618
David Smith (Sr VP-Model Dev)
Maiclaire Bolton (Mgr-Global Earthquake
Product)

ABS Pacific   (1)
438 Alexandra Rd No 10-00, Alexandra
Point, Singapore, 119958, Singapore
Tel.: (65) 62768700
Web Site: http://www.eagle.org
Sales Range: $125-149.9 Million
Emp.: 300
Ship & Marine Facility Classification, Engi-
neering & Survey Services
N.A.I.C.S.: 551114
Mark A. McGrath (Chief Learning Officer)
Edwin King (Dir-HR)
Caroline Zubbr (Mgr-Mktg & Comm)

AMERICAN BURN ASSOCIA-
TION

311 S Wacker Dr Ste 4150, Chicago,
IL 60606
Tel.: (312) 642-9260   IL
Web Site: https://www.ameriburn.org
Year Founded: 1948
Sales Range: $10-24.9 Million
Emp.: 14
Burn Injury Treatment Services
N.A.I.C.S.: 622110
David H. Ahrenholz (Pres)
Linwood R. Haith (Co-Pres)
William G. Cioffi Jr. (Sec)

AMERICAN BUSINESS SOLU-
TIONS, INC.

8850 Whitney Dr, Lewis Center, OH
43035
Tel.: (614) 917-2274   OH
Web Site: https://www.absi-usa.com
Year Founded: 1998
Sales Range: $1-9.9 Million
Emp.: 84
IT Services & Solutions
N.A.I.C.S.: 519290
Manisha Dixit (VP)
Rajeev Dubey (Founder)
Neil Hudson (Mgr-HR & Sls)
Nitin Sharma (Sr Mgr)

AMERICAN CABLE COMPANY
INC.

1200 E Erie Ave, Philadelphia, PA
19124
Tel.: (215) 456-0700
Web Site:
https://www.americancableco.com

Year Founded: 1976
Rev.: $20,000,000
Emp.: 200
Custom Mfr of Battery Cables, Elec-
trical Wiring Harnesses, Electrical
Panel & Control Assemblies & Re-
lated Components
N.A.I.C.S.: 336390
Pat Sabre (Sls Mgr)
Daryl Greene (Mgr-Quality)
Carlos M. Gonzales Jr. (Pres & CEO)

AMERICAN CANNABIS INNO-
VATIONS CONGLOMERATED

14065 Proton Rd, Farmers Branch,
TX 75244
Tel.: (214) 937-9097
Web Site:
https://www.aciconglomerated.com
Holding Company
N.A.I.C.S.: 551112
Steven Rash (CEO)

Subsidiaries:

Puration, Inc.   (1)
1584 County Rd 613, Farmersville, TX
75442
Tel.: (214) 937-9097
Web Site: http://www.purationinc.com
Water Purification Products Mfr & Distr
N.A.I.C.S.: 333310
Brian Shibley (Chm & CEO)

Subsidiary (Domestic):

Telluride Health Company   (2)
309 N Oak St, Telluride, CO 81435
Tel.: (800) 852-0426
Cannabis Health Products Developer
N.A.I.C.S.: 541714
Yasmine Acebo (Pres)

AMERICAN CAPITAL SENIOR
FLOATING, LTD.

245 Park Ave 42nd Fl, New York, NY
10167
Tel.: (212) 750-7300   MD
Web Site:
http://www.americancapital.com
Year Founded: 2013
Sales Range: $10-24.9 Million
Investment Management Service
N.A.I.C.S.: 523940
Mitchell S. Goldstein (VP)
Scott C. Lem (Chief Acctg Officer-Los
Angeles)
Miriam G. Krieger (Chief Compliance
Officer- Washington D.C.)
Joshua M. Bloomstein (Asst Sec &
VP)
Kevin Braddish (Pres & CEO)
Penni F. Roll (CFO)
Carl G. Drake (Partner-Pub IR &
Head-Pub IR & Comm-Atlanta)
Veronica Mendiola (VP-Pub IR &
Comm)
Shelly Cleary (VP & Portfolio Mgr)
Ian Fitzgerald (Gen Counsel, Sec &
VP)

AMERICAN CARPET ONE

302 Sand Island Access Rd, Hono-
lulu, HI 96819
Tel.: (808) 447-2751
Web Site:
http://www.americancarpetone.com
Rev.: $10,000,000
Emp.: 130
Floor Covering Stores
N.A.I.C.S.: 449121
David Arita (Pres)
Aaron Okamoto (Gen Mgr)

AMERICAN CASEIN COMPANY

109 Elbow Ln, Burlington, NJ 08016
Tel.: (609) 387-3130
Web Site:
http://www.americancasein.com

Sales Range: $10-24.9 Million
Emp.: 50
Dried Milk & Preparations
N.A.I.C.S.: 311514
Roger Hare (Controller)

AMERICAN CAST IRON PIPE
COMPANY

1501 31st Ave N, Birmingham, AL
35207-4101
Tel.: (205) 325-7701   AL
Web Site: http://www.american-
usa.com
Year Founded: 1905
Sales Range: $600-649.9 Million
Emp.: 2,600
Mfr of Ductile Iron Pipe; Cast Iron &
Ductile Iron Fittings, Valves & Hy-
drants; Rubber Gaskets; Centrifugally
Cast Carbon & Alloy Steel Tubes &
Static Castings; Steel Pipe
N.A.I.C.S.: 331511
Ian K. Willoughby (Mgr-Sls)
Jon Noland (Mgr-Sls-Electric Resis-
tance Welded Steel Pipe-Natl)
Barry Sadler (Mgr-AMERICAN Perfor-
mance System)
Paul Freund (Asst Mgr-Sls-
AMERICAN Steel Pipe)
Don Greer (Gen Mgr-Acctg)

Subsidiaries:

AMERICAN SpiralWeld Pipe Com-
pany, LLC   (1)
2061 American Italian Way, Columbia, SC
29209
Tel.: (803) 695-2200
Steel Pole Mfr
N.A.I.C.S.: 331210
Patrick Hook (VP-Ops)
Christopher Jarrett (Asst Mgr-Div Sls)
W. D. Benton (Mgr-Div Sls)

American Castings   (1)
5265 Hunt St, Pryor, OK 74361-0549
Tel.: (918) 476-8321
Web Site: http://www.americancastings.com
Sales Range: $25-49.9 Million
Emp.: 570
Gray & Ductile Iron Foundry
N.A.I.C.S.: 331511

American Ductile Iron Pipe Div.   (1)
1501 31st Ave N, Birmingham, AL 35207-
4101
Tel.: (205) 325-7733
Sales Range: $10-24.9 Million
Emp.: 100
Cast Iron Pipe Sales
N.A.I.C.S.: 331511
Christopher Jarrett (Asst Mgr-Div Sls)
W. D. Benton (Mgr-Div Sls)

American Flow Control   (1)
1501 31st Ave N, Birmingham, AL 35207
Tel.: (205) 325-7701
Web Site: http://www.american-usa.com
Sales Range: $300-349.9 Million
Manufacture of pipe & valve
N.A.I.C.S.: 331511
John Hagelskamp (Mgr-Sls)

American Steel Pipe Div.   (1)
1501 31St Ave N, Birmingham, AL
35207-4101   (100%)
Tel.: (205) 325-7742
Sales Range: $100-124.9 Million
Emp.: 2,100
Electric Resistance Weld Mill
N.A.I.C.S.: 331110
Mark Schach (Mgr-Outside Sls)

American Valve & Hydrant Co.   (1)
3350 Hollywood St, Beaumont, TX
77701-3820   (100%)
Tel.: (409) 832-7721
Web Site: http://www.avhmc.com
Sales Range: $25-49.9 Million
Emp.: 175
Valves & Hydrants
N.A.I.C.S.: 332911
Tim Sudela (Pres)

Intercast SA   (1)
Highway MG 050 Km 92, PO Box 535,

35680-108, Itauna, Minas Gerais, Brazil
Tel.: (55) 37 3249 7000
Web Site: http://www.intercast.com.br
Sales Range: $25-49.9 Million
Emp.: 400
Cast Iron Pipe Mfr
N.A.I.C.S.: 331511
Silvestre de Andrade Neto (Dir-Comm)
Denia Marcia Franco (Mgr-Sls)
Horacio Paiva da Rocha (Mgr-Special Acct)

Specification Rubber Products
Inc.   (1)
1568 1st St N, Alabaster, AL 35007
Tel.: (205) 663-2521
Web Site: http://www.specrubber.com
Sales Range: $10-24.9 Million
Emp.: 60
Gasket Material Mfr
N.A.I.C.S.: 339991
Lonnie Thompson (Mgr-Mktg & Sls)
Jonadtaen Davis (Mgr-Mfg)

Waterous Company   (1)
125 Hardman Ave S, South Saint Paul, MN
55075-1129   (100%)
Tel.: (651) 450-5000
Web Site: http://www.waterousco.com
Sales Range: $100-124.9 Million
Emp.: 240
Fire Hydrants, Fire Pumps & Valves Mfr
N.A.I.C.S.: 332911
Gregg Geske (Dir-Sls-North America)
Mike Sterbentz (Mgr-OEM Sls)
Steve Morelan (Mgr-Customer Svc)
Peter A. Ledgar (Mgr-Sls-Europe, Middle
East, Africa & England)
Dominick Monico (Exec Dir-Sls, Mktg & Bus
Dev-Global)
Jay Rought (Coord-Customer Trng)
Matt Wolf (Mgr-OEM Sls)
Keith Klassen (Mgr-Instruction Program)
Mark Tracy (Coord-Instruction)
Bill Smith (CEO)
Dan Reese (VP-Ops)

AMERICAN CASTING &
MANUFACTURING CORPORA-
TION

51 Commercial St, Plainview, NY
11803-2401
Tel.: (516) 349-7010   NY
Web Site:
http://www.americancasting.com
Year Founded: 1910
Sales Range: $75-99.9 Million
Emp.: 50
Mfr, Designer & Producer of Seals
N.A.I.C.S.: 339991
James Wenk (VP-Sls & Mktg)
Joseph Wenk (VP)
Norman Wenk III (Pres)

AMERICAN CENTURY COMPA-
NIES, INC.

4500 Main St, Kansas City, MO
64111-1816
Tel.: (816) 531-5575   MO
Web Site:
https://www.americancentury.com
Year Founded: 1958
Sales Range: $1-4.9 Billion
Emp.: 2,900
Investment Brokerage Advisory Ser-
vice; Mutual Funds
N.A.I.C.S.: 523940
John Small Jr. (Portfolio Mgr)

Subsidiaries:

American Century Brokerage,
Inc.   (1)
PO Box 419146, Kansas City, MO 64141-
6146
Tel.: (888) 345-2071
Investment Advisory Management Services
N.A.I.C.S.: 523940

American Century Investments   (1)
4500 Main St, Kansas City, MO 64111-1816
Tel.: (816) 340-4200
Web Site: http://www.americancentury.com

Sales Range: $250-299.9 Million
Emp.: 1,300
Investment Management Service
N.A.I.C.S.: 523999
Jonathan Thomas (Pres & CEO)
Patrick Bannigan (CFO & Exec VP)
Joseph G. Schultz (Chief Client Officer)
Vinod Chandrashekaran (Chief Investment Officer-Disciplined Equity)
Victor Zhang (Chief Investment Officer & Sr VP)
Peruvemba Satish (Sr VP, Dir-Global Analytics & Portfolio Mgr)
Abdelak Adjriou (VP & Mgr-Portfolio)
Jay Hummel (VP-Direct Sls & Svc)
Edward Rosenberg (Sr VP & Head-Exchange Traded Funds)
Tsuyoshi Ozaki (Portfolio Mgr-Disciplined Equity Grp)
Matt Lewis (VP & Head-Exchange Traded Funds Implementation & Capital Markets)
Tony Archer (Head-Asia-Pacific)
Michelle Kidd (VP-Institutional Advisory Grp)
Rick Luchinsky (Sr VP-Bus-DC)
Jamie Downing (Mng Dir & VP-EMEA)
John Pak (Gen Counsel)
Sarah Bratton Hughes (Sr VP & Head-ESG & Sustainable Investing)
Tanya S. Beder (Chm)

AMERICAN CHEMET CORPORATION
740 Waukegan Rd Ste 202, Deerfield, IL 60015-4374
Tel.: (847) 948-0800   MT
Web Site: https://www.chemet.com
Year Founded: 1946
Sales Range: $10-24.9 Million
Emp.: 104
Mfr & Marketer of Cuprous Oxide, Copper Powder, Cupric Oxide, Zinc Oxide, Dispersion Strengthened Copper & Copper-Based Agricultural Fungicides
N.A.I.C.S.: 325180
Joanne Alexander (Coord-Export Sls)
April Myers (Office Mgr)
Jeff King (Mgr-Sls)
W.W. Shropshire Jr. (Chm)

Subsidiaries:

American Chemet Export
Corporation   (1)
740 Waukegan Rd Ste 202, Deerfield, IL 60015-4374
Tel.: (847) 948-0800
Sales Range: Less than $1 Million
Metals Service Centers & Offices
N.A.I.C.S.: 325180
William H. Shropshire (Pres)

Royal Metal Powders Inc.   (1)
433 Continental Dr, Maryville, TN 37804
Tel.: (865) 982-8096
Web Site:
http://www.royalmetalpowders.com
Copper Powder Mfr
N.A.I.C.S.: 331410

AMERICAN CLASSIFIED SERVICES, INC.
1809 W Main Ste 304, Carbondale, IL 62901
Tel.: (406) 446-1542   IL
Web Site:
https://www.advertisingresults.com
Year Founded: 1997
Sales Range: $1-9.9 Million
Emp.: 3
Advetising Agency
N.A.I.C.S.: 541810
Leigh Ann Kristiansen (Pres & CEO)

AMERICAN CLEANERS & LAUNDRY CO.
13960 Manchester Rd, Ballwin, MO 63011
Tel.: (636) 227-8299
Rev.: $15,000,000
Emp.: 200

Drycleaning Plants, Except Rugs
N.A.I.C.S.: 812320
Joseph Mach Jr. (Pres)

AMERICAN COALITION FOR CLEAN COAL ELECTRICITY
1152 15th St NW Ste 400, Washington, DC 20005
Tel.: (202) 459-4800   VA
Web Site:
http://www.americaspower.org
Year Founded: 1992
Sales Range: $10-24.9 Million
Emp.: 11
Energy Conservation Services
N.A.I.C.S.: 813312
Michelle Bloodworth (Pres & CEO)

AMERICAN COATINGS
11917 Cutten Rd, Houston, TX 77066
Tel.: (281) 351-1776
Web Site:
http://www.americancoatings.com
Year Founded: 1985
Sales Range: $10-24.9 Million
Emp.: 50
Paint & Coating Mfr
N.A.I.C.S.: 325510
Jim Adams (Co-Owner)
Jim Morrison (Co-Owner)
John Burton (Controller)
Gary Moyer (Dir-R&D)
Juan De La Garza (Plant Mgr)
Kirby Meyer (Mgr-Pur)
Danny Miller (Mgr-Quality Control)
Bill Osters (Dir-Sls)

AMERICAN COFFEE COMPANY, INC.
640 Magazine St, New Orleans, LA 70130-3616
Tel.: (504) 581-7234   LA
Web Site:
http://www.frenchmarketcoffee.com
Year Founded: 1890
Sales Range: $75-99.9 Million
Emp.: 150
Roasted Coffee, Chicory & Tea Mfr
N.A.I.C.S.: 311920
Fraiser Bartlett (Pres)

AMERICAN COLD STORAGE
5220 McKinney Ave Ste 201, Dallas, TX 75205
Tel.: (214) 692-0220
Web Site:
http://www.americancold.com
Year Founded: 1981
Storage, Frozen Or Refrigerated Goods
N.A.I.C.S.: 493120
Sam C. Bradshaw (Pres & CEO)
Teresa M. Belden (VP-Fin)
Jerry Miles (Chief Engr)

AMERICAN COLLEGE OF CARDIOLOGY
2400 N St NW, Washington, DC 20037
Tel.: (202) 375-6000   DC
Web Site: https://www.acc.org
Year Founded: 2001
Sales Range: $10-24.9 Million
Emp.: 500
Cardiovascular Health Research & Educational Support Services
N.A.I.C.S.: 813212
Richard A. Chazal (Pres)
Michael C. Valentine (VP)
Cathleen C. Gates (COO)

AMERICAN COLLEGE OF GASTROENTEROLOGY
6400 Goldsboro Rd Ste 200, Bethesda, MD 20817
Tel.: (301) 263-9000   DE

Web Site: https://www.gi.org
Year Founded: 1932
Sales Range: $10-24.9 Million
Emp.: 23
Health Care Srvices
N.A.I.C.S.: 622110
Irving M. Pike (Treas)
Carol A. Burke (VP)
Sunanda V. Kane (Sec)
Daniel J. Pambianco (Pres)

AMERICAN COLLEGE OF RHEUMATOLOGY, INC.
2200 Lake Blvd NE, Atlanta, GA 30319
Tel.: (404) 633-3777   IL
Web Site:
https://www.rheumatology.org
Year Founded: 1985
Sales Range: $10-24.9 Million
Emp.: 91
Medical Association
N.A.I.C.S.: 813920
Joseph Flood (Pres)
David R. Karp (Pres-Foundation)
Paula Marchetta (Treas)
Mark Andrejeski (CEO)

AMERICAN COLLEGE OF SPORTS MEDICINE
401 W Michigan St, Indianapolis, IN 46202-3233
Tel.: (317) 637-9200   WI
Web Site: http://www.acsm.org
Year Founded: 1923
Sales Range: $10-24.9 Million
Emp.: 48
Sports Medicine Research Services
N.A.I.C.S.: 541715
Carl Foster (Treas)
Kristin Belleson (CEO)
William E. Kraus (Pres)

AMERICAN COLLEGIATE MARKETING
4440 Hagadorn Rd, Okemos, MI 48864
Tel.: (517) 336-1600
Web Site:
http://www.magazineline.com
Rev.: $13,781,794
Emp.: 60
Magazines, Mail Order
N.A.I.C.S.: 459210
Roberta Myers (Controller)
Jason Salsbury (VP-Mktg)
Lee Kile (Mgr-Call Center)
Irving A. Lesher III (Pres)

AMERICAN COMMERCE SOLUTIONS, INC.
1400 Chamber Dr, Bartow, FL 33830
Tel.: (863) 533-0326   DE
Web Site:
http://www.aacssymbol.com
Year Founded: 1991
Sales Range: $1-9.9 Million
Emp.: 33
Holding Company; Metalworking Machinery & Fiberglass Motorcycle Bodies Mfr
N.A.I.C.S.: 551112

AMERICAN COMMITTEE FOR THE WEIZMANN INSTITUTE OF SCIENCE, INC.
633 3rd Ave, New York, NY 10017
Tel.: (212) 895-7900   NY
Web Site: https://www.weizmann-usa.org
Year Founded: 1944
Rev.: $5,900,000
Emp.: 86
Fiscal Year-end: 12/31/06
Noncommercial Research Organizations, Nsk

N.A.I.C.S.: 813211
Molly Morse (Pres)
Dave Doneson (CEO)

AMERICAN COMMODITIES INC.
2945 Davison Rd, Flint, MI 48506
Tel.: (810) 767-3800
Web Site:
https://www.aciplastics.com
Sales Range: $10-24.9 Million
Emp.: 75
Recycler of Engineered Thermoplastics: Compounding Services
N.A.I.C.S.: 562920
Scott Melton (Pres)

AMERICAN COMMUNICATIONS GROUP, INC.
21311 Madrona Ave Ste 101, Torrance, CA 90503
Tel.: (310) 530-4100
Web Site: http://www.acgmedia.com
Year Founded: 1987
Sales Range: $500-549.9 Million
Advertising, Local Marketing, Market Research, Media Buying Services & Media Planning
N.A.I.C.S.: 541830
Christopher Cope (Pres & CEO)
Jamie Shaw (CFO & Exec VP)
Christi Ware (VP-Acct)

AMERICAN COMPLIANCE TECHNOLOGIES, INC.
1875 W Main St, Bartow, FL 33830
Tel.: (863) 533-2000
Web Site: https://www.a-c-t.com
Sales Range: $10-24.9 Million
Emp.: 100
Environmental Engineering & Consulting Services
N.A.I.C.S.: 541330
Robert Kincart (Pres)
Larry Legg (Dir-Environmental Construction)

AMERICAN COMPRESSED GASES INC.
189 Central Ave, Old Tappan, NJ 07675
Tel.: (201) 767-3200
Web Site:
https://www.dryicecorp.com
Sales Range: $25-49.9 Million
Emp.: 170
Distr of Compressed Gas
N.A.I.C.S.: 457210
Marita Viray (Controller)
Keith Ramsdell (VP)
Arthur F. Ramsdell Jr. (Pres)

Subsidiaries:

Dry Ice Corp.   (1)
189 Central Ave, Old Tappan, NJ 07675
Tel.: (201) 767-3200
Web Site: http://www.firstharrison.com
Sales Range: $10-24.9 Million
Emp.: 36
Distr of Compressed Gas
N.A.I.C.S.: 459999
Author Ransdell (Pres & CEO)
Marita Viray (Controller)

AMERICAN COMPUTER DEVELOPMENT, INC.
5350 Partners Ct, Frederick, MD 21703
Tel.: (301) 620-0900
Web Site: http://www.acdi.com
Printed Circuit Assembly Mfr
N.A.I.C.S.: 334418
William Hornbaker (Pres & CEO)

American Computer Development, Inc.—(Continued)

Subsidiaries:

Enhanced Manufacturing Solutions, LLC   (1)
925 Industrial Park Rd NE, Brookhaven, MS 39601-8951
Tel.: (601) 182-2017
Web Site: http://www.enhanced-mfg.com
Motor Vehicle Parts Mfr
N.A.I.C.S.: 336390
Lester Donald (Mgr)

AMERICAN CONSERVATORY THEATRE
30 Grant Ave FL 6, San Francisco, CA 94108
Tel.: (415) 834-3200
Web Site: http://www.act-sf.org
Year Founded: 1965
Sales Range: $10-24.9 Million
Emp.: 300
Theatrical Production
N.A.I.C.S.: 711110
Carey Perloff (Dir-Artistic)
Melissa Smith (Dir-Conservatory)
Elizabeth Brodersen (Dir-Education & Community Programs)
Jerry Lopez (Dir-Fin Aid)
Thomas Morgan (Dir-Information Technology)

AMERICAN CONSOLIDATED INDUSTRIES
30775 Solon Industrial Pkwy, Solon, OH 44139-4338
Tel.: (440) 461-0900
Web Site: http://www.anchor-online.com
Sales Range: $125-149.9 Million
Emp.: 45
Molded Rubber Products
N.A.I.C.S.: 326299
Doug Kaufman (Pres)

Subsidiaries:

Monarch Steel Alabama Inc.   (1)
1425 Red Hat Rd, Decatur, AL 35601
Tel.: (256) 301-5730
Web Site: http://www.monarchsteel.com
Steel Foundries, Nec
N.A.I.C.S.: 331513

Monarch Steel Company   (1)
4650 Johnston Pkwy, Cleveland, OH 44128
Tel.: (216) 587-8000
Web Site: http://www.monarchsteel.com
Rev.: $12,700,000
Metals Service Centers & Offices
N.A.I.C.S.: 423510

AMERICAN CONSOLIDATED MEDIA LP
7301 N State Hwy 161 Ste 270, Irving, TX 75039
Tel.: (214) 691-4066
Web Site:
     http://www.amconmedia.com
Year Founded: 1998
Holding Company; Newspaper Publishers
N.A.I.C.S.: 551112
Michelle Smith (VP-Sls)
Scott A. Wright (CEO)

Subsidiaries:

Alice Echo-News, Inc.   (1)
405 E Main St, Alice, TX 78332
Tel.: (361) 664-6588
Web Site: http://www.alicetx.com
Sales Range: $1-9.9 Million
Emp.: 18
Newspaper Publishers
N.A.I.C.S.: 513110
Bill Weaver (Publr)

Brownwood Newspapers, Inc.   (1)
700 Carnegie St, Brownwood, TX 76801
Tel.: (325) 646-2541
Web Site: http://www.brownwoodtx.com

Sales Range: $1-9.9 Million
Emp.: 54
Newspaper Publishers
N.A.I.C.S.: 513110

Chesapeake Publishing & Printing   (1)
29088 Airpark Dr, Easton, MD 21601-7000
Tel.: (410) 770-4124
Web Site: http://www.chespub.com
Sales Range: $25-49.9 Million
Emp.: 300
Newspaper Publishing
N.A.I.C.S.: 513110
David Alltop (Reg Mgr-IT)
Kevin Fike (Dir-Circulation)
Bethany Ziegler (Editor-Community)

Miami Newspapers, Inc.   (1)
14 1st Ave NW, Miami, OK 74354-6224
Tel.: (918) 542-5533
Web Site: http://www.miaminewsrecord.com
Sales Range: $10-24.9 Million
Emp.: 20
Newspaper Publishers
N.A.I.C.S.: 513110
Jim Ellis (Editor)

Superior Publishing, Inc.   (1)
1105 Tower Ave, Superior, WI 54880
Tel.: (715) 395-5725
Sales Range: $25-49.9 Million
Emp.: 585
Newspaper Publishing & Printing Services
N.A.I.C.S.: 513110

Subsidiary (Domestic):

Hibbing Daily Tribune   (2)
2142 1st Ave, Hibbing, MN 55746-1805
Tel.: (218) 262-1011
Web Site: http://www.hibbingmn.com
Rev.: $1,800,000
Emp.: 25
Newspaper Publishers
N.A.I.C.S.: 513110
Gary Giombetti (Editor-Sports)
Ida Meyer (Mgr-Circulation)

The Daily Press   (2)
122 W 3rd St, Ashland, WI 54806-1620
Tel.: (715) 682-2313
Web Site: http://www.ashlandwi.com
Sales Range: $25-49.9 Million
Emp.: 50
Newspapers
N.A.I.C.S.: 513110

The Gladwin County Record   (2)
700 E Cedar Ave, Gladwin, MI 48624-2218
Tel.: (989) 426-9411
Web Site: http://www.gladwinmi.com
Rev.: $320,000
Emp.: 7
Newspaper Publishers
N.A.I.C.S.: 513110
Dawn Laidlaw (Office Mgr)
Carissa Petherbridge (Mgr-Production)

The Athens Messenger   (1)
9300 Johnson Rd, Athens, OH 45701-9028
Tel.: (740) 592-6612
Web Site: http://www.athensmessenger.com
Newspaper Publishers
N.A.I.C.S.: 513110
Chana Powell (Bus Mgr)
Joe Higgins (Editor)
Kevin Wiseman (Editor-Sports)
Glenn Christensen (Mgr-Comml Printing)
Jeff Bunch (Dir-Advertising)

Waxahachie Newspapers, Inc.   (1)
200 W Marvin Ave, Waxahachie, TX 75165
Tel.: (972) 937-3310
Web Site: http://www.waxahachietx.com
Sales Range: $10-24.9 Million
Emp.: 55
Newspaper Publishers
N.A.I.C.S.: 513110
Marvin Clark (Mgr-Circulation)
Shelly Conlon (Mng Editor)
Beverly Harris (Mgr-Bus)

AMERICAN CONSOLIDATED NATURAL RESOURCES, INC.
46226 National Rd, Saint Clairsville, OH 43950
Tel.: (740) 338-3100   DE
Web Site: http://www.acnrinc.com

Holding Company
N.A.I.C.S.: 551112
Robert D. Moore (Pres & CEO)

Subsidiaries:

Murray Energy Corporation   (1)
153 Hwy 7 S, Powhatan Point, OH 43942
Tel.: (740) 795-5220
Web Site:
     http://www.murrayenergycorp.com
Sales Range: $450-499.9 Million
Emp.: 2,400
Holding Company; Coal Mining
N.A.I.C.S.: 551112
John R. Forrelli (Sr VP)
Michael T. W. Carey (VP-Govt Affairs)
Michael O. McKown (Sr VP)
Roy A. Heidelbach (Asst VP-Ops)
Ryan M. Murray (VP-Ops)
Todd Adkins (VP-Mktg & Sls-Louisville)
James R. Turner Jr. (Sr VP)

AMERICAN CONSTRUCTION SUPPLY & RENTAL INC.
601 N 36th St, Nampa, ID 83687
Tel.: (208) 467-4591
Web Site:
     http://www.americansupplyinc.com
Sales Range: $10-24.9 Million
Emp.: 45
Concrete Construction Supplies
N.A.I.C.S.: 444140
Joe Wheeler (Pres)
Diane Banner (Mgr-Accts Receivable)

AMERICAN CONSTRUCTORS LP
4330 Gines Ranch Loop Ste 230, Austin, TX 78735
Tel.: (512) 328-2026
Web Site: http://www.acitexas.com
Rev.: $20,500,000
Emp.: 100
Commercial & Office Building, New Construction
N.A.I.C.S.: 236220
William A. Heine (Chm)
Marty Burger (CEO)
Joe Charlton (COO)
Joe Moore (CFO)

AMERICAN CONSUMER CREDIT COUNSELING, INC.
130 Rumford Ave Ste 202, Auburndale, MA 02466-1317
Tel.: (617) 559-5700   MA
Web Site:
     https://www.consumercredit.com
Year Founded: 1992
Sales Range: $10-24.9 Million
Emp.: 174
Consumer Credit Counseling Services
N.A.I.C.S.: 541990
Kim Sheehan (Mgr-Fin)
Donna Conley (VP & Mgr-Disbursements)
Steven R. Trumble (Pres & CEO)
Sandra Castellano (Office Mgr)

AMERICAN CONSUMER FINANCIAL NETWORK
6th Fl Community Twr 111 W Saint John St, San Jose, CA 95113
Tel.: (888) 794-2236
Web Site:
     http://www.acfnfranchised.com
Year Founded: 1996
Sales Range: $1-9.9 Million
ATM Services
N.A.I.C.S.: 522320

AMERICAN CONSUMER NEWS, LLC
326 E 8th St Ste105, Sioux Falls, SD 57103
Web Site: http://www.marketbeat.com

Year Founded: 2008
Sales Range: $1-9.9 Million
Emp.: 10
Investment Services
N.A.I.C.S.: 523940
Matthew Paulson (Founder)

AMERICAN CONTINENTAL BANCORP
17700 Castleton St Ste 100, City of Industry, CA 91748
Tel.: (626) 363-8988   CA
Web Site:
     https://www.americancontinental.com
Emp.: 100
Bank Holding Company
N.A.I.C.S.: 551111

Subsidiaries:

American Continental Bank   (1)
17700 Castleton St, City of Industry, CA 91748
Tel.: (626) 363-8988
Web Site:
     http://www.americancontinentalbank.com
Sales Range: $1-9.9 Million
Emp.: 14
Commercial Bank
N.A.I.C.S.: 522110
Terry Lou (Pres & CEO)
Donald Dang (CFO & Sr VP)
Vera Wang (First VP & Branch Mgr)
Sandy Yang (COO & Exec VP)

AMERICAN CONTRACT BRIDGE LEAGUE, INC.
6575 Windchase Blvd, Horn Lake, MS 38637-1523
Tel.: (662) 253-3100   TN
Web Site: https://www.acbl.org
Year Founded: 1937
Sales Range: $10-24.9 Million
Emp.: 206
Contract Bridge Game Promotion Services
N.A.I.C.S.: 713210
Kelley McGuire (Sec)
Joseph Jones (CFO)
Mitchell Hodus (CIO)
Dan Storch (CMO)

AMERICAN CONTRACTING INC.
1722 S Main, Dickinson, ND 58601
Tel.: (701) 225-1579
Web Site:
     http://www.americancontracting.com
Sales Range: $10-24.9 Million
Emp.: 10
Provider of Excavation & Grading Services
N.A.I.C.S.: 238910

AMERICAN CONTROLS INC.
20764 Whitlock St, Farmington Hills, MI 48336
Tel.: (248) 476-7782
Web Site:
     http://www.americancontrolsinc.com
Year Founded: 1969
Rev.: $12,545,000
Emp.: 28
Industrial Machinery & Equipment
N.A.I.C.S.: 423830
Craig A. Maass (Pres)
Hans Czeranna (Mgr-Engrg)
Jonathan Pillsbury (Mgr-Shipping Receiving)
Steve McMaster (Mgr-Sls)

AMERICAN CORRECTIONAL SOLUTIONS, INC.
741 E Ball Rd Ste 101, Anaheim, CA 92805
Tel.: (714) 538-0200   CA
Web Site:
     https://www.correctionalsolutions.com

Year Founded: 1985
Sales Range: $10-24.9 Million
Emp.: 100
On-site Correctional Facility Inmate
Medical Care Services
N.A.I.C.S.: 812199
Barry Goldstein *(Pres)*
Scott Fredrickson *(Controller)*
Diane Zelna *(Bus Mgr)*

AMERICAN COUNCIL OF LEARNED SOCIETIES
633 3rd Ave 8th Fl, New York, NY 10017-6706
Tel.: (212) 697-1505   DC
Web Site: https://www.acls.org
Year Founded: 1924
Sales Range: $10-24.9 Million
Emp.: 27
Educational Support Services
N.A.I.C.S.: 611710
Andrzej W. Tymowski *(Dir-Intl Programs)*
Steven C. Wheatley *(VP)*
Sandra Bradley *(Dir-Member Rels)*
Simon Guzman *(Dir-Fin)*

AMERICAN COUNCIL ON THE TEACHING OF FOREIGN LANGUAGES
1001 N Fairfax St Ste 200, Alexandria, VA 22314
Tel.: (703) 894-2900   NY
Web Site: https://www.actfl.org
Year Founded: 1977
Sales Range: $10-24.9 Million
Emp.: 26
Foreign Language Teaching Services
N.A.I.C.S.: 611630
Paul Sandrock *(Dir-Education)*
Julia Richardson *(Dir-Convention & Mktg)*
Zerihun Haile-Selassie *(Dir-Fin)*
Howard Berman *(Dir-Membership & Admin)*
Marty Abbott *(Exec Dir)*

AMERICAN COUNCILS FOR INTERNATIONAL EDUCATION
1828 L St NW Ste 1200, Washington, DC 20036
Tel.: (202) 833-7522   MD
Web Site: https://www.americancouncils.org
Year Founded: 1974
Sales Range: $75-99.9 Million
Emp.: 257
Educational Support Services
N.A.I.C.S.: 611710
John Henderson *(CFO)*
Michael Curtis *(VP-Program & Bus Dev)*
David Patton *(Pres & CEO)*
Robert M. Rhea *(Chm)*
Edith Falk *(Vice Chm)*
Karen Witt *(Dir-HR)*
Lisa Choate *(Exec VP)*

AMERICAN CRANE & EQUIPMENT CORPORATION
531 Old Swede Rd, Douglassville, PA 19518-1205
Tel.: (610) 385-6061   PA
Web Site: http://www.americancrane.com
Year Founded: 1972
Sales Range: $100-124.9 Million
Emp.: 180
Overhead Electrical Cranes & Hoists Mfr
N.A.I.C.S.: 333923
Oddvar Norheim *(Founder & Chm)*
Dave Hope *(CFO, Gen Counsel & VP)*
Scott Harner *(Reg Mgr-Svc)*

Bonnie Marquette *(Mgr-HR)*
Jami Rubendall *(VP-Comml Nuclear)*
Frank Yurich *(VP-Quality & Performance Improvement)*
Mike Myers *(VP & Mgr-Natl Svc)*
Karen Norheim *(Pres & CEO)*

Subsidiaries:

American Crane & Equipment Corporation - Service, Parts & Standard
Crane Division   **(1)**
1440 Ben Franklin Hwy, Douglassville, PA 19518
Tel.: (484) 945-0420
Crane & Hoist Mfr
N.A.I.C.S.: 333923
David Scherr *(Mgr-Quality Control)*

AMERICAN CREDIT ALLIANCE INC.
PO Box 939, Morrisville, PA 19067
Tel.: (609) 393-5400
Web Site: http://www.501plan.com
Rev.: $25,000,000
Emp.: 30
Personal Financial Services
N.A.I.C.S.: 812990
Alan Franklin *(Pres)*

AMERICAN CRITICAL CARE SERVICES
221 Ruthers Rd Ste 103, Richmond, VA 23235
Tel.: (804) 320-1113
Web Site: http://www.accsnurses.com
Rev.: $10,100,000
Emp.: 900
Medical Help Service
N.A.I.C.S.: 561320
Carolyn W. McCrocklin *(Pres)*

AMERICAN CRITTER COLLEGE, INC.
271 Serenity Pl, Newport, VA 24128
Tel.: (540) 641-0159   DE
Web Site: http://americancrittercollege.com
Pet Training Schools
N.A.I.C.S.: 812910
Hunt Keith *(Pres, CEO, CFO & Treas)*
Mark N. Radford *(Sec & VP)*

AMERICAN CRYSTAL HOLDINGS, INC.
888 Washington St, Dedham, MA 02026
Tel.: (781) 251-8000
Year Founded: 1995
Sales Range: $10-24.9 Million
Emp.: 2,000
Employment Agencies
N.A.I.C.S.: 561311
Daniel A. Lasman *(CFO & VP)*

Subsidiaries:

TAC Worldwide Companies   **(1)**
888 Washington St, Dedham, MA 02027-9100
Tel.: (781) 251-8000
Temporary Help Supply Services
N.A.I.C.S.: 561320

AMERICAN CUSTOM YACHTS, INC.
6800 Jack James Dr, Stuart, FL 34997
Tel.: (772) 221-9100   FL
Web Site: http://www.americanyachts.com
Year Founded: 1992
Sales Range: $10-24.9 Million
Emp.: 86
Boat Building & Repairing
N.A.I.C.S.: 336612

Chris Shultz *(Dir-Mktg)*
Ed Kelley *(Controller)*
John Resnik *(Dir-Admin)*
Dominick La Combe Sr. *(Pres)*

AMERICAN CYBERSYSTEMS, INC.
2400 Meadowbrook Pkwy, Duluth, GA 30096-4635
Tel.: (770) 493-5588   GA
Web Site: https://www.acsicorp.com
Year Founded: 1998
Sales Range: $200-249.9 Million
Emp.: 2,500
Information Technology Consulting, Staffing & Payroll Services
N.A.I.C.S.: 541612
Rajiv Sardana *(Pres & CEO)*
Sanjeev Sardana *(COO)*
Ruby Pandit *(Sr Mgr-Client Svcs)*
Toral Kapur *(Asst Controller)*

Subsidiaries:

Analysts International
Corporation   **(1)**
7700 France Ave S Ste 200, Minneapolis, MN 55435
Tel.: (952) 838-3000
Web Site: http://www.analysts.com
Rev.: $105,790,000
Assets: $24,719,000
Liabilities: $5,571,000
Net Worth: $19,148,000
Earnings: $330,000
Emp.: 871
Fiscal Year-end: 12/29/2012
Information Technology & Business Consulting Services
N.A.I.C.S.: 541690
Paul Cmiel *(VP-Sls)*
Skip Fogus *(CIO)*
Jeff Hoekstra *(VP-Solutions)*

Division (Domestic):

Analysts International-Lawson
Practice   **(2)**
7700 France Ave S, Minneapolis, MN 55435-5242
Tel.: (952) 835-5900
Web Site: http://www.analysts.com
Sales Range: $50-74.9 Million
Emp.: 220
Computer Consultancy Services
N.A.I.C.S.: 541511

Analysts International-Managed Services Group   **(2)**
6660 Delmonico Dr Suite 432, Greenwood Village, CO 80919
Tel.: (303) 721-6200
Sales Range: $10-24.9 Million
Emp.: 25
IT Services
N.A.I.C.S.: 541511

COMFORCE Corporation   **(1)**
999 Stewart Ave Ste 100, Bethpage, NY 11714
Tel.: (516) 437-3300
Web Site: http://www.comforce.com
Sales Range: $150-199.9 Million
Temporary Staffing & Consulting Services
N.A.I.C.S.: 561320

Subsidiary (Domestic):

COMFORCE Information Technologies, Inc.   **(2)**
1000 Pittsford Victor Rd, Pittsford, NY 14534
Tel.: (585) 381-2300
Web Site: http://www.temporarydirecthirestaffing.com
Emp.: 5
Information Technology Temporary Staffing & Consulting Services
N.A.I.C.S.: 561320
Allison Gross *(Pres)*
Jo Eaton *(Branch Mgr)*

COMFORCE Technical Services, Inc.   **(2)**
13208 NE 20th St Ste 100, Bellevue, WA 98005-2027

Tel.: (425) 883-2233
Web Site: http://www.temporarydirecthirestaffing.com
Engineering & Technical Support Temporary Staffing & Consulting Services
N.A.I.C.S.: 561320

COMFORCE Telecom, Inc.   **(2)**
2960 S McCall Rd Ste 201, Englewood, FL 34224
Tel.: (941) 475-6600
Web Site: http://www.temporarydirecthirestaffing.com
Telecommunications Contingent Staffing & Consulting Services
N.A.I.C.S.: 561320

CrossUSA, Inc.   **(1)**
13754 Frontier Ct Ste 106, Burnsville, MN 55337
Tel.: (952) 432-3775
Web Site: http://www.cross-usa.com
Sales Range: $10-24.9 Million
Emp.: 75
Computer System Design Services
N.A.I.C.S.: 541512
Brian Soderholm *(Chief Sls Officer)*
P. Nick Goel *(Chief Acctg Officer)*
Terry Bretzman *(VP-Ops)*
Doug Michelz *(Dir-Ops)*

Volt Information Sciences, Inc.   **(1)**
2401 N Glassell St, Orange, CA 92865
Tel.: (714) 921-8800
Web Site: https://www.volt.com
Rev.: $885,393,000
Assets: $260,104,000
Liabilities: $229,011,000
Net Worth: $31,093,000
Earnings: $1,374,000
Emp.: 15,400
Fiscal Year-end: 10/31/2021
Electronic Publishing Systems, Staffing, Database Management & Telephone Directory Services
N.A.I.C.S.: 561320
Raj Sardana *(Chm & CEO)*
Sonia Sardana *(Chief Transformation Officer)*
Brian Soderholm *(Chief Revenue Officer)*
Brad Doss *(CFO & Grp VP)*
Jeff DeWitt *(Grp VP)*
Matthew Alderete *(Sr VP-Retail Sls)*
Allen Brown *(VP-Enterprise West)*
Marne Oberg *(VP-Human Resources)*

Subsidiary (Non-US):

Arctern Consulting Private
Limited   **(2)**
4th Floor 410/381/290 Siddappa Layout Madiwala Post, Bommanahalli, Bengaluru, 560 068, Karnataka, India
Tel.: (91) 8068103300
Web Site: http://www.arctern.com
Human Resource Consulting Services
N.A.I.C.S.: 541612

Subsidiary (Domestic):

Arctern, Inc.   **(2)**
10332 Main Str Ste 150, Fairfax, VA 22030
Tel.: (703) 738-6669
Web Site: http://www.arctern.com
Human Resource Consulting Services
N.A.I.C.S.: 541612
Bijal Mehta *(Founder, CEO & Mng Dir)*
Ruhi Sharma *(VP)*
Surya Katakam *(VP-Tech)*
Sudhakar Vishwanath *(Corp Counsel)*
Sherly Chacko *(Head-Admin & Procurement & Asst Dir-Admin & Procurement)*
Subhashini Ponnappa *(Head-HR)*

Century Reprographics   **(2)**
2040 Avenue of the Stars Ste 105, Los Angeles, CA 90067-4703
Tel.: (310) 553-8383
Office Furniture & Equipment Installation Services
N.A.I.C.S.: 238390

DataServ, Incorporated   **(2)**
1 Tarablvd Ste 102, Nashua, NH 03062
Tel.: (402) 339-8700
Web Site: http://www.dataservinc.com
Emp.: 125
Software Publishing Services
N.A.I.C.S.: 513210

American CyberSystems, Inc.—(Continued)

Fidelity National Credit Services Ltd. (2)
2421 N Glassell St, Orange, CA 92865
Tel.: (714) 921-0271 **(100%)**
Sales Range: $100-124.9 Million
Credit Collection Services
N.A.I.C.S.: 561440

Subsidiary (Non-US):

Maintech Europe Limited (2)
Dolphin House Windmill Road, Sunbury-on-Thames, TW16 7HT, United Kingdom
Tel.: (44) 1932755588
Software Development Services
N.A.I.C.S.: 541511

Subsidiary (Domestic):

Momentum, A Volt Information Sciences Company, Inc. (2)
1002 15 St SW, Auburn, WA 98001
Tel.: (253) 733-3060
Web Site: http://www.volt.com
Emp.: 25
Human Resource Consulting Services
N.A.I.C.S.: 541612

Sierra Technology Corporation (2)
4150 Manzanita Ave 100, Carmichael, CA 95608
Tel.: (916) 488-4960
Emp.: 3
Software Development Services
N.A.I.C.S.: 541511

Subsidiary (Non-US):

Tainol, S.A. (2)
Sancho Panza 3087, Montevideo, 11600, Uruguay
Tel.: (598) 24879347
Web Site:
http://www.imprasorasudramericani.uy
Commercial Printing & Book Binding Services
N.A.I.C.S.: 323113
Steven A. Shaw (Pres)

Subsidiary (Domestic):

The Community Phone Book, Inc. (2)
3221 Hill St, Duluth, GA 30096
Tel.: (770) 232-7887
Advertising Services
N.A.I.C.S.: 541810

Subsidiary (Non-US):

VMC Consulting Europe Limited (2)
110 Buckingham Avenue, Slough, SL1 4PF, Berkshire, United Kingdom
Tel.: (44) 1753849700
Web Site: http://www.vmc.com
Software Development Services
N.A.I.C.S.: 541511

Volt Asia Enterprises (Taiwan) Co, Ltd. (2)
2F No 499 Zhonghe Rd, Yonghe Dist, New Taipei City, 234, Taiwan
Tel.: (886) 222328226
Web Site: http://www.volttaiwan.com
Human Resource Consulting Services
N.A.I.C.S.: 541612

Volt Consulting Group Limited (2)
Volt House 3 Chapel Road, Redhill, RH1 1QD, Surrey, United Kingdom
Tel.: (44) 173 777 4100
Web Site:
https://www.voltconsultinggroup.com
Human Resource Consulting Services
N.A.I.C.S.: 541612

Subsidiary (Domestic):

Volt Consulting Group, Ltd. (2)
50 Charles Lindbergh Blvd Ste 206, Uniondale, NY 11553
Tel.: (516) 228-6700
Web Site:
http://www.voltconsultinggroup.com
Management Consulting Services
N.A.I.C.S.: 541618

Subsidiary (Non-US):

Volt Europe (Belgium) SPRL (2)
Jules Bordet 166 Jules Bordetlaan, 1140, Brussels, Belgium
Tel.: (32) 27271130
Web Site: https://www.voltinternational.be
Sales Range: $10-24.9 Million
Emp.: 18
Software Services for Telecommunications Companies
N.A.I.C.S.: 541511
Alessandra Dorato (Mgr-Acct Dev)
Valeria Bonaccorso (Mgr-Acct Dev)

Volt Europe (France) SARL (2)
WTC Batiment D 1300 Route Des Cretes, Valbonne, 06560, Sophia-Antipolis, France **(100%)**
Tel.: (33) 422840131
Web Site: http://www.volt.com
Sales Range: $1-9.9 Million
Staffing Services
N.A.I.C.S.: 561320

Volt Europe (Germany) GmbH (2)
Theodor-Heuss-Allee 112, 60486, Frankfurt, Hessen, Germany
Tel.: (49) 69247557350
Human Resource Consulting Services
N.A.I.C.S.: 541612

Volt Europe Holdings Limited (2)
Volt House 3 Chapel Road, Redhill, RH1 1QD, Surrey, United Kingdom
Tel.: (44) 1737774100
Web Site: http://www.volt.com
Holding Company
N.A.I.C.S.: 551112

Volt Europe Limited (2)
Volt House 3 Chapel Road, Redhill, RH1 1QD, Surrey, United Kingdom
Tel.: (44) 173 777 4100
Web Site: http://www.volt.eu.com
Sales Range: $25-49.9 Million
Emp.: 80
Staffing Services
N.A.I.C.S.: 541511
Francois Debertrand (CFO-Intl)
Andy Wyatt (Mgr)
Geoff King (Mgr-Delivery-IT)
Ben Batten (Mng Dir & Sr VP-Intl)
Garry Jones (Sr Mgr-Acct Dev)
Lee Howard (Sr Mgr-Engrg & Mfg)
Josh Miles (Sr Mgr-Life Sciences)

Branch (Domestic):

Volt Information Sciences-West (2)
2401 N Glassell St, Orange, CA 92865-2705
Tel.: (714) 921-8800
Sales Range: $75-99.9 Million
Emp.: 450
Technical Contact Personnel
N.A.I.C.S.: 541211
Bob Houghton (CIO)
Nancy Avedissian (Chief Legal Officer, Sec & Sr VP)

Subsidiary (Domestic):

Volt Management Corp. (2)
3733 National Dr Ste 100, Raleigh, NC 27612-4845
Tel.: (919) 782-7440
Web Site: http://www.volt.com
Emp.: 100
Human Resource Consulting Services
N.A.I.C.S.: 541612

Volt Road Boring Corp. (2)
5000 S Shore Dr, New Port Richey, FL 34652
Tel.: (727) 571-2268
Commercial Printing & Publishing Services
N.A.I.C.S.: 323113

Subsidiary (Non-US):

Volt Service Corporation Pte, Ltd. (2)
6 Temasek Boulevard 25-05 Suntec Tower 4, Singapore, 038986, Singapore
Tel.: (65) 6 701 1500
Web Site:
https://www.voltinternational.com.sg
Human Resource Consulting Services
N.A.I.C.S.: 541612

Subsidiary (Domestic):

Volt Technical Resources, LLC (2)
1065 Ave of the Americas, New York, NY 10018
Tel.: (212) 719-7800
Web Site: http://www.volt.com
Sales Range: $75-99.9 Million
Emp.: 300
Staffing Services
N.A.I.C.S.: 561320

Volt Telecommunications Group, Inc. (2)
218 Helicopter Cir, Corona, CA 92880-2531 **(100%)**
Tel.: (212) 704-2400
Web Site: http://www.volt-telecom.com
Sales Range: $75-99.9 Million
Turnkey Solutions
N.A.I.C.S.: 517810

Division (Domestic):

Volt Telecom Group (3)
1065 Ave nue of the Americas 20th Fl, New York, NY 10018
Tel.: (212) 704-2400
Web Site: http://www.volt.com
Turnkey Telecommunications Services
N.A.I.C.S.: 517810

Volt Telecommunicaitons Group (3)
2090 Palm Beach Lakes Blvd Ste 200, Royal Palm Beach, FL 33409-6507
Tel.: (561) 357-9779
Web Site: http://www.volt-telecom.com
Sales Range: $10-24.9 Million
Emp.: 2
Turnkey Telecommunications Solutions
N.A.I.C.S.: 541690
Brian Liegey (Mgr)

Volt Telecommunications Group (3)
218 Helicopter Cir, Corona, CA 92880
Tel.: (951) 493-8900
Web Site: http://www.volt-telecom.com
Sales Range: $75-99.9 Million
Provider of Engineering Services; Communications & Power Line Construction
N.A.I.C.S.: 541611

Subsidiary (Domestic):

Volt Temporary Services (2)
2401 N Glassell St, Orange, CA 92865-2705 **(100%)**
Tel.: (714) 921-1870
Sales Range: $150-199.9 Million
Emp.: 1,000
Personnel Placement
N.A.I.C.S.: 541690
Jerome Shaw (Sec & Exec VP)

Volt VIEWtech, Inc. (2)
4761 E Hunter Ave, Anaheim, CA 92807 **(100%)**
Tel.: (714) 695-3385
Sales Range: $25-49.9 Million
Emp.: 50
Water Power Construction
N.A.I.C.S.: 522310

Volt Workforce Solutions, Inc. (2)
900 Long Lake Rd Ste 310, New Brighton, MN 55112
Tel.: (651) 633-3889
Web Site: http://www.volt.com
Contingent Staffing
N.A.I.C.S.: 541612

AMERICAN DAWN INC.
401 W Artesia Blvd, Los Angeles, CA 90220
Tel.: (310) 223-2000
Web Site:
https://www.americandawn.com
Rev.: $86,000,000
Emp.: 100
Textiles, Woven, Nec
N.A.I.C.S.: 424310
Mahmud Rawjee (Chm)
Karim Patel (Mgr-Sls & Mktg)
Seve Locsin (Dir-Plng)
Terri Tankiss (Mgr-Pur & Traffic)
Helen Mengel (Mgr-Svc Solutions)
Ron Rajesh Kothari (Dir-Sls)
Kathleen Healy (Dir-Sourcing)

AMERICAN DECORATIVE FABRICS, LLC
295 Fifth Ave Ste 812, New York, NY 10016
Tel.: (212) 689-3579
Designer & Mfr of Fabrics & Textiles
N.A.I.C.S.: 314120
Erica Youngleson (Dir-Design)

AMERICAN DENTAL EDUCATION ASSOCIATION
655 K St NW Ste 1100, Washington, DC 20005
Tel.: (202) 289-7201
Web Site: http://www.adea.org
Year Founded: 1923
Sales Range: $10-24.9 Million
Emp.: 79
Dental Education Support Services
N.A.I.C.S.: 611310

AMERICAN DESIGN LTD.
70 S Potomac St, Aurora, CO 80012
Tel.: (303) 695-8478
Web Site:
https://www.americandesignltd.com
Sales Range: $10-24.9 Million
Emp.: 50
Art Dealers
N.A.I.C.S.: 459920
Paul Zueger (Pres)
Darren Zueger (Gen Mgr)

AMERICAN DINING CORPORATION
1000 Conshohocken Rd, Conshohocken, PA 19428
Tel.: (215) 244-6325
Rev.: $12,944,290
Emp.: 7
Fast-Food Restaurant, Chain
N.A.I.C.S.: 722513

AMERICAN DISTILLING & MANUFACTURING CO.
31 E High St, East Hampton, CT 06424
Tel.: (860) 267-4444
Web Site:
http://www.americandistilling.com
Toilet Preparation Mfr
N.A.I.C.S.: 325620
Doug Logan (Plant Mgr)

AMERICAN DOUGLAS METALS INC.
783 Thorpe Rd, Orlando, FL 32824
Tel.: (407) 855-6590
Web Site:
https://www.americanmetals.com
Year Founded: 1976
Sales Range: $25-49.9 Million
Emp.: 33
Steel Distr
N.A.I.C.S.: 423510
Steven Powers (Pres & COO)
Edward Raimonde (CEO)

AMERICAN DRAPERY BLIND & CARPET, INC.
700 S 3rd St, Renton, WA 98057
Tel.: (425) 255-3893
Web Site: http://www.american-drapery.com
Rev.: $18,000,000
Emp.: 110
Draperies, Plastic & Textile: From Purchased Materials
N.A.I.C.S.: 314120

AMERICAN DREAM HOME IMPROVEMENT, INC.
3040 Finley Rd ste 200, Downers Grove, IL 60515
Tel.: (630) 353-1900

Web Site:
    http://www.americandream.com
Year Founded: 2007
Sales Range: $25-49.9 Million
Emp.: 160
Building Remodeling Services
N.A.I.C.S.: 236118
Michael Gray *(Pres)*

AMERICAN DRILL BUSHING CO.
5740 Hunt Rd, Valdosta, GA 31606-2445
Web Site:
    https://www.americanbushing.com
Year Founded: 1943
Bushings, Tooling Components & Toggle Clamps Mfr
N.A.I.C.S.: 333515

AMERICAN EAGLE CO., INC.
2741 Paldan Dr, Auburn Hills, MI 48326
Tel.: (248) 340-7210
Web Site:
    https://www.teachersdiscovery.com
Rev.: $17,203,617
Emp.: 100
Distributes School Supplies Catalogs
N.A.I.C.S.: 423490
Bruce C. McWilliams *(Pres)*
Neil Silver *(CFO)*

AMERICAN EAGLE DISTRIB-UTING CO.
3800 Clydesdale Pkwy, Loveland, CO 80538
Tel.: (970) 663-1690   CO
Web Site:
    http://www.americaneagledistr.com
Year Founded: 1980
Sales Range: $10-24.9 Million
Emp.: 18
Beer & Other Fermented Malt Liquors
N.A.I.C.S.: 424810
Jerry Helgeson *(Pres)*
Sam Goffena *(VP-Fin)*
Nicole Hockley *(Mgr-HR)*

AMERICAN EAGLE EXPRESS INC.
PO Box 42977, Philadelphia, PA 19101
Tel.: (484) 768-1200
Web Site: http://www.aexgroup.net
Rev.: $14,571,851
Emp.: 50
Courier Or Messenger Service
N.A.I.C.S.: 561499
J. D. Gamble *(Pres & CEO)*
Gina Goldsmith *(Dir-Customer Rels)*

AMERICAN EAGLE LIFECARE CORPORATION
3819 Hawk Crest Rd, Ann Arbor, MI 48103
Tel.: (615) 252-2305   TN
Year Founded: 2002
Sales Range: $50-74.9 Million
Emp.: 1,172
Elder Care Services
N.A.I.C.S.: 624120
Elan Ruggill *(Sr VP)*

AMERICAN EAGLE MORT-GAGE CO., LLC
6145 Park Square Dr Ste 4, Lorain, OH 44053
Tel.: (440) 988-2900   OH
Web Site: http://www.aemc.cc
Year Founded: 2001
Sales Range: $10-24.9 Million
Emp.: 120
Mortgage Banking
N.A.I.C.S.: 522310

Diane Schrenkel *(Sec)*
Dave Berry *(CFO)*
Heath Lee *(Mgr-Ops)*
John Schrenkel *(Pres)*
Matt Yacobozzi *(VP-HR & Mktg)*

AMERICAN EAGLE STEEL CORP.
716 Gittings Ave Ste 214, Annapolis, MD 21401
Tel.: (904) 285-5999
Web Site:
    http://www.americaneaglesteel.com
Sales Range: $10-24.9 Million
Emp.: 10
Bars, Metal
N.A.I.C.S.: 423510
Joseph Camac *(Pres)*
Sandra Baldwin *(Controller)*

AMERICAN EAGLE SYSTEMS INC.
160 Libur Pl Ste 600, Bohemia, NY 11716
Tel.: (631) 207-4400
Web Site:
    http://www.americaneaglesys.com
Year Founded: 1976
Sales Range: $10-24.9 Million
Emp.: 30
Computers, Peripherals & Software
N.A.I.C.S.: 423430
William Herrschaft *(CEO)*

AMERICAN EAGLE WHEEL CORP.
5780 Soestern Ct, Chino, CA 91710
Tel.: (909) 590-8828
Web Site:
    http://www.americaneaglewheel.com
Sales Range: $100-124.9 Million
Emp.: 300
Wheels, Motor Vehicle
N.A.I.C.S.: 423120
Margo Furbolow *(CEO)*
Richard Wedge Jr. *(Mgr-Sls)*

AMERICAN EAR HEARING AND AUDIOLOGY, LLC
1950 Tamarack Rd, Newark, OH 43055
Tel.: (740) 784-4562
Web Site:
    https://www.americanear.com
Year Founded: 2005
Rev.: $3,100,000
Emp.: 22
Health Care Srvices
N.A.I.C.S.: 524114
Scott W. Sirles *(Pres)*

AMERICAN EDUCATIONAL RESEARCH ASSOCIATION
1430 K St NW Ste 1200, Washington, DC 20005
Tel.: (202) 238-3200   DC
Web Site: https://www.aera.net
Year Founded: 1968
Sales Range: $10-24.9 Million
Emp.: 36
Educational Support Services
N.A.I.C.S.: 611710
George Wimberly *(Dir-Pro Dev Social Justice)*
Shannon Luo *(Mgr-Acctg)*
Tony Pals *(Dir-Comm)*
Norman Tenorio *(Dir-Fin & Admin)*
Felice J. Levine *(Exec Dir)*
John Neikirk *(Dir-Publ)*
Joyce E. King *(Pres)*
Juliane Baron *(Dir-Govt Rels)*
Sylvie Nguyen-Fawley *(Mgr-Governance)*

AMERICAN EFFICIENT LLC

703 Foster St, Durham, NC 27701
Tel.: (919) 590-0327   DE
Web Site:
    http://www.americanefficient.com
Year Founded: 2011
Energy Efficiency & Environmental Consulting Services
N.A.I.C.S.: 541690
Bo Clayton *(CIO)*
Angela Fox *(Head-Market Ops)*
Sterling Bowen *(Head-Residential EE)*

Subsidiaries:

PlotWatt, Inc.   (1)
703 Foster St, Durham, NC 27701
Tel.: (844) 756-8928
Web Site: http://www.plotwatt.com
Data Processing, Hosting & Related Services
N.A.I.C.S.: 518210

AMERICAN ELECTRIC CO. LLC
799 Kahelu Ave, Mililani, HI 96789
Tel.: (808) 848-0751   HI
Web Site:
    http://www.americanelectric.com
Year Founded: 1969
Sales Range: $50-74.9 Million
Emp.: 60
Industrial Construction & Electrical Contractor Services
N.A.I.C.S.: 238210
Thomas Vincent *(CEO)*
Sandra Brewer *(CFO)*

AMERICAN ELECTRIC SUP-PLY INC.
1872 W Pomona Rd, Corona, CA 92880
Tel.: (951) 734-7910
Web Site: http://www.amelect.com
Rev.: $33,336,688
Emp.: 76
Electrical Fittings & Construction Materials
N.A.I.C.S.: 423610
Herlinda Guadiana *(Mgr-Accts Payable)*
Anne Montejano *(Mgr-Inventory)*
Shannon Winans *(Mgr-Mktg)*
Barry Bonds *(Branch Mgr-Outside Sls)*

AMERICAN ELECTRONIC COMPONENTS INC.
90 Fanny Rd, Boonton, NJ 07005-1065
Tel.: (973) 402-8282
Web Site: https://www.aeciusa.com
Year Founded: 1978
Sales Range: $10-24.9 Million
Emp.: 20
Supplier of Electronic Parts & Equipment
N.A.I.C.S.: 423690
Andy Franks *(VP)*
Ron Frank *(CEO)*
Melisa Hensinger *(Mgr-Sls)*

AMERICAN ELECTRONIC COMPONENTS, INC.
1101 Lafayette St, Elkhart, IN 46516
Tel.: (574) 295-6330   DE
Web Site:
    https://www.aecsensors.com
Sales Range: $75-99.9 Million
Emp.: 320
Custom Sensors, Industrial Relays & Switches & Other Electromechanical Products Mfr
N.A.I.C.S.: 334413
Keith L. Vanderbosch *(VP)*

AMERICAN ELECTRONIC RE-SOURCE
3505 Cadillac Ave Ste A, Costa Mesa, CA 92626
Tel.: (714) 338-4400   CA
Web Site: http://www.aeri.com
Year Founded: 1994
Sales Range: $10-24.9 Million
Emp.: 30
Electronic Parts
N.A.I.C.S.: 423690
Rebecca Chehade *(VP-Ops & VP-Ops-North America)*
Brandon Northrop *(Mgr-Sls-North America)*
Tony Romano *(CFO & VP)*
Trent Ober *(Mgr-Pur-North America)*
Robb Hammond *(Pres & CEO)*
Shon Engle *(Acct Exec)*
Edward Limjoco *(Mgr-ESD Compliance-North America)*
Brian Herrick *(Mgr-Quality Control-North America)*
Justin Han *(Mgr-Shipping-North America)*
David Millet *(Mgr-Sls-Europe)*
Alex Sapp *(VP-Bus Dev-North America)*
Alex Sapp *(VP-Bus Dev-North America)*
Rebecca Chehade *(VP-Ops-North America)*

AMERICAN ELEVATOR GROUP
352 7th Ave 4th Fl, 10001, New York, NY
Tel.: (915) 856-7757
Web Site:
    http://www.americanelevator.com
Emp.: 100
Elevator & Moving Stairway Mfr
N.A.I.C.S.: 333921
Dave Stepp *(Owner)*
Bryan Clairmont *(Pres)*

Subsidiaries:

Madden Elevator Company   (1)
9462 Brownsboro Rd Ste 132, Louisville, KY 40241
Tel.: (502) 290-8878
Web Site: http://www.maddenelevator.com
Building Equipment Contractors
N.A.I.C.S.: 238290
Sean Madden *(Pres)*

AMERICAN ENDOWMENT FOUNDATION
1521 Georgetown Rd Ste 104, Hudson, OH 44236
Tel.: (330) 655-7552   OH
Web Site: http://www.aefonline.org
Year Founded: 1993
Sales Range: $125-149.9 Million
Emp.: 11
Grantmaking Services
N.A.I.C.S.: 813211
John Farren *(Exec VP & Dir-Dev)*
Cheryl Gerbracht *(Dir-Grants)*
Lori Page *(Mgr-Fund Admin)*
Shannon Baker *(VP-Development)*
Eric Kinaitis *(Editor)*

AMERICAN ENERGY PRO-DUCTION, INC.
6073 Hwy 281 S, Mineral Wells, TX 76067
Tel.: (940) 445-0698   DE
Web Site:
    http://www.americanenergy.com
Year Founded: 2000
Sales Range: $1-9.9 Million
Emp.: 9
Oil & Gas Exploration, Production & Sales
N.A.I.C.S.: 211120

American Energy Production, Inc.—(Continued)

Charles Bitters *(Pres, CEO & CFO)*

AMERICAN ENGINEERING AS-SOCIATES - SOUTHEAST, P.A.
8008 Corporate Center Dr Ste 110, Charlotte, NC 28226
Tel.: (704) 375-2438   **NC**
Web Site: https://www.american-ea.com
Year Founded: 1974
Engineeering Services
N.A.I.C.S.: 541330
Scott D. Stone *(Pres-American Engrg)*

AMERICAN ENTERPRISE IN-STITUTE FOR PUBLIC POLICY RESEARCH
1150 17th St NW, Washington, DC 20036-4603
Tel.: (202) 862-5800   **DC**
Web Site: http://www.aei.org
Year Founded: 1943
Sales Range: $10-24.9 Million
Emp.: 150
Nonprofit, Nonpartisan, Publicly Supported Educational Research Organization
N.A.I.C.S.: 541720
David Gerson *(Exec VP)*
Jason Bertsch *(Sr VP-Dev & Comm)*
Michael Pratt *(Dir-Digital Strategy)*
Christy Sadler *(Dir-Editing & Publ)*
John Cusey *(Dir-Govt Rels)*
Janine Nichols *(Mgr-External Rels)*
Toby Stock *(VP-Dev & Academic Programs)*

AMERICAN ENTERPRISE MU-TUAL HOLDING COMPANY
601 6th Ave, Des Moines, IA 50334-0001
Tel.: (515) 245-2000
Web Site:
  http://www.americanrepublic.com
Mutual Holding Company
N.A.I.C.S.: 551112
Thomas A. Swank *(Pres & CEO)*

Subsidiaries:

American Enterprise Group, Inc. **(1)**
601 6th Ave, Des Moines, IA 50309
Tel.: (515) 245-2000
Web Site:
  http://www.americanenterprise.com
Sales Range: $350-399.9 Million
Emp.: 400
Holding Company; Health & Life Insurance Products & Services
N.A.I.C.S.: 551112
Michael E. Abbott *(Chm)*
Linda Abel *(Supvr-Hosting Svcs)*
Thomas Swank *(CEO)*
Dave Keith *(COO)*
Kenn Peterson *(VP-Sls-Preneed)*
Jennifer Kaset *(Acct Mgr-Natl)*

Subsidiary (Domestic):

American Republic Insurance
Company   **(2)**
601 6th Ave, Des Moines, IA 50334-0001
Tel.: (515) 245-2000
Web Site: http://www.americanrepublic.com
Sales Range: $350-399.9 Million
Comprehensive Health, Life & Long Term Care Insurance Products & Services
N.A.I.C.S.: 524114
Michael E. Abbott *(Pres & CEO)*

Medico Insurance Company   **(1)**
1515 S 75th St, Omaha, NE 68124
Tel.: (402) 391-6900
Web Site: http://www.gomedico.com
Sales Range: $150-199.9 Million
Emp.: 95
Specialty Health & Life Insurance Products & Services
N.A.I.C.S.: 524114

AMERICAN EQUIPMENT & TRAILER, INC.
610 N Grand St, Amarillo, TX 79107
Tel.: (806) 383-8831
Web Site:
  https://www.americantrailer.com
Year Founded: 1953
Sales Range: $10-24.9 Million
Emp.: 62
Trailers For Trucks, New & Used
N.A.I.C.S.: 423110
Mike Morehead *(Controller)*
Christopher Tardy *(Mgr-Trailer & Fin)*

AMERICAN EQUITY MORT-GAGE INC.
11933 Westline Industrial Dr, Saint Louis, MO 63146
Tel.: (314) 878-9999
Web Site:
  http://www.americanequity.com
Year Founded: 1992
Sales Range: $50-74.9 Million
Emp.: 500
Mortgage Bankers & Loan Correspondents
N.A.I.C.S.: 522310
Deanna Daughhetee *(Pres & CEO)*

AMERICAN EUROPEAN GROUP, INC.
605 Third Ave Fl 9, New York, NY 10158
Tel.: (212) 355-3310
Web Site:
  http://www.aeiginsurance.com
Year Founded: 1986
Sales Range: $50-74.9 Million
Emp.: 25
Holding Company; Insurance
N.A.I.C.S.: 524126
Nachum John Stein *(Chm)*
Peter J. Livaich *(Sr VP-AE Specialty)*

Subsidiaries:

Merchants Group, Inc.   **(1)**
250 Main St, Buffalo, NY 14202
Tel.: (716) 849-3333
Web Site: http://www.merchantsgroup.com
Sales Range: $25-49.9 Million
Property & Casualty Insurance Services
N.A.I.C.S.: 524126
Robert M. Zak *(Chm)*
Marge Kafka *(VP-Corp Svcs)*
Tina Schaedler *(Reg Mgr)*
Lisa Wishman *(Asst VP-Mktg)*
Cammy Belser *(Reg Mgr)*
Samuel Guarnieri *(Reg Mgr)*
Charles E. Makey III *(Pres)*

Subsidiary (Domestic):

Merchants Mutual Insurance
Company   **(2)**
250 Main St, Buffalo, NY 14202-0903
Tel.: (716) 849-3333
Web Site: http://www.merchantsgroup.com
Property & Casualty Insurance Services
N.A.I.C.S.: 524126
Gregory Robinson *(Reg Mgr)*

Rutgers Casualty Insurance Co   **(1)**
2250 Chapel Ave W Ste 200, Cherry Hill, NJ 08002
Tel.: (856) 779-0600
Sales Range: $10-24.9 Million
Automobile Insurance
N.A.I.C.S.: 524126

United International Insurance
Co.   **(1)**
444 Madison Ave Ste 501, New York, NY 10022
Tel.: (212) 355-3310
Fire, Marine & Casualty Insurance & Carriers
N.A.I.C.S.: 524126
Nachum J. Stein *(Pres)*

AMERICAN EXCELSIOR COM-PANY

850 Ave H E, Arlington, TX 76011-7720
Tel.: (817) 385-3500   **TX**
Web Site:
  https://www.americanexcelsior.com
Year Founded: 1888
Sales Range: $150-199.9 Million
Emp.: 500
Urethane Foam, Polyethylene, Polystyrene, Carpet Underlay, Packaging & Erosion Control Products Mfr & Distr
N.A.I.C.S.: 326150
Todd A. Eblen *(CFO & VP)*
Kenneth E. Starrett *(VP-Sls & Mktg)*
Terry A. Sadowski *(Pres & CEO)*
Kevin E. Stewart *(VP-Foam Ops)*
Marsha Shaw *(Dir-Customer Svc)*
Rocky A. Van Gilder *(VP-Wood Ops)*
William D. Albers *(Owner & Chm)*

Subsidiaries:

Earth Science Division   **(1)**
850 Ave H E, Arlington, TX
76011-7720   **(100%)**
Tel.: (817) 385-3500
Web Site: http://www.curlex.com
Sales Range: $10-24.9 Million
Emp.: 40
Erosion
N.A.I.C.S.: 326150
Earl Alexander *(Controller)*

AMERICAN EXCHANGE GROUP
1400 Broadway 18th Fl, New York, NY 10018
Tel.: (212) 287-9001
Web Site:
  https://www.axnygroup.com
Year Founded: 2007
Fashion Accessories, Watches, Jewelry & Footwear Mfr & Whslr
N.A.I.C.S.: 423940
Alen Mamrout *(CEO)*
Steve Velasquez *(Chief Strategy Officer)*

Subsidiaries:

Danecraft Inc.   **(1)**
1 Baker St, Providence, RI 02905-4417
Tel.: (401) 941-7700
Web Site: https://www.danecraft.com
Sterling Silver & Fashion Jewelry Mfr
N.A.I.C.S.: 339910
Jerry Sestric *(Natl Sls Mgr)*
Bob Soltys *(Pres)*
Carol Cooper *(VP-Strategic Plng)*
Tony Buonanno *(VP-Ops)*
Michele Masse *(VP-Product Dev)*
Gail Gesmundi *(CFO)*
Victor Primavera III *(CEO)*

HatchBeauty Agency LLC   **(1)**
10951 W Pico Blvd Ste 300, Los Angeles, CA 90064
Tel.: (855) 895-6980
Web Site: http://www.hatchbeauty.com
Sales Range: $50-74.9 Million
Cosmetic Products Mfr & Distr
N.A.I.C.S.: 456120
Tracy Holland *(CEO)*
Kristin Bibb *(Pres & Chief Comml Officer)*

AMERICAN EXHIBITIONS, INC.
6001 Broken Sound Pkwy NW Ste 404, Boca Raton, FL 33487-2754
Tel.: (561) 482-2088
Web Site:
  http://www.americanexhibitions.com
Emp.: 10
Touring Exhibitions
N.A.I.C.S.: 713990
Marcus W. Corwin *(Pres & Gen Counsel)*

Subsidiaries:

Mummies of The World Touring Company Inc.   **(1)**

6001 Broken Sound Pkwy NW Ste 404, Boca Raton, FL 33487-2754
Tel.: (561) 482-2088
Web Site:
  http://www.mummiesoftheworld.com
Touring Exhibitions
N.A.I.C.S.: 713990

AMERICAN EXTERIORS, LLC
1169 W Littleton Blvd, Littleton, CO 80120
Tel.: (303) 794-6369
Web Site: http://www.amext.com
Year Founded: 1993
Rev.: $26,400,000
Emp.: 208
Construction Services
N.A.I.C.S.: 238170
Ed Rand *(CFO & COO)*
Nadine McLemore *(Mgr-Fin)*
Thomas Roos *(Controller)*
Jeremy Hayes *(Mgr-Trng)*
Steve Henry *(Dir-Call Center)*
Al Courtney *(Mgr-Sls & Ops)*
Lance Keiser *(Pres)*
Elliott Crutchfield *(Chm)*

AMERICAN FABRICATION CORPORATION
2891 E Via Martens, Anaheim, CA 92806-1751
Tel.: (714) 632-1709
Year Founded: 1973
Sales Range: $10-24.9 Million
Emp.: 20
Plastics Product Mfr
N.A.I.C.S.: 326199
Greg Knox *(Pres)*

AMERICAN FABRICATORS
615 S Springbrook Rd, Newberg, OR 97132
Tel.: (503) 538-1260
Web Site:
  http://www.harristhermal.com
Rev.: $10,079,616
Emp.: 100
Process Vessels Mfr
N.A.I.C.S.: 238120
Arnold Fuchs *(Pres)*

AMERICAN FABRICATORS, INC.
570 Metroplex Dr, Nashville, TN 37211-3133
Tel.: (615) 834-8700   **TN**
Web Site:
  https://www.americanfabricators.com
Year Founded: 1984
Sheet Metal Fabrication
N.A.I.C.S.: 332322
Milton R. Grief *(Pres)*
Tony Massa *(COO)*
Paul Sutter *(Dir-Sls)*
Jonathan Gregory *(Mgr-Sls)*
G. Scott Graves *(CEO & Co-Owner)*

AMERICAN FACILITY SER-VICES
1325 Union Hill Industrial Ct Ste A, Alpharetta, GA 30004
Tel.: (770) 740-1613
Web Site:
  https://www.americanfacilities.com
Year Founded: 1991
Sales Range: $10-24.9 Million
Emp.: 460
Janitorial Services
N.A.I.C.S.: 561720
Kevin McCann *(CEO)*

AMERICAN FAMILY ASSOCIA-TION, INC.
PO Drawer 2440, Tupelo, MS 38803
Tel.: (662) 844-5036   **MS**
Web Site: http://www.afa.net

Year Founded: 1977
Sales Range: $25-49.9 Million
Emp.: 144
Christian Ministry Services
N.A.I.C.S.: 813110
Timothy B. Wildmon *(Pres)*

AMERICAN FAMILY CARE, INC.
3700 Cahaba Beach Rd, Birmingham, AL 35242
Tel.: (205) 421-2092
Web Site:
   http://www.afcurgentcare.com
Year Founded: 1982
Sales Range: $50-74.9 Million
Emp.: 700
Specialty Hospital Services
N.A.I.C.S.: 622310
D. Bruce Irwin *(Founder & CEO)*
Joseph Hawley *(CFO & Exec VP)*
Randy Johansen *(Pres)*
William L. Koleszar *(Chief Mktg Officer)*
Claudius Moore *(CIO)*

AMERICAN FAMILY MUTUAL INSURANCE COMPANY
6000 American Pkwy, Madison, WI 53783
Tel.: (608) 242-4100   WI
Web Site: http://www.amfam.com
Year Founded: 1927
Rev.: $12,166,506,000
Assets: $31,123,650,000
Liabilities: $21,360,521,000
Net Worth: $9,763,129,000
Earnings: $455,934,000
Fiscal Year-end: 12/31/19
Auto Home Health Life & Business Insurance Consumer Finance Services
N.A.I.C.S.: 524113
Jack C. Salzwedel *(Chm & CEO)*

Subsidiaries:

American Family Brokerage, Inc.   (1)
6000 American Pkwy, Madison, WI 53783-0001   (100%)
Tel.: (608) 249-2111
Web Site: http://www.amfam.com
Sales Range: $25-49.9 Million
Emp.: 25
Insurance Brokerage
N.A.I.C.S.: 524210
Darrel Snyder *(Sr Mgr-External Markets)*

American Family Financial Services, Inc.   (1)
6000 American Pkwy, Madison, WI 53783-0001   (100%)
Tel.: (608) 249-2111
Web Site:
   http://www.americanfamilyinsurance.com
Financial Services
N.A.I.C.S.: 523999

American Family Insurance Company   (1)
6000 American Pkwy, Madison, WI 53783-0001   (100%)
Tel.: (608) 249-2111
Web Site: http://www.amfam.com
Sales Range: $1-4.9 Billion
Property, Casualty & Health Insurance
N.A.I.C.S.: 524113
Jack Salzeedel *(Chm & CEO)*
Bill Westrate *(Pres)*
Mary A. Theilen *(Pres-Personal Lines)*
Telisa L. Yancy *(Grp Pres)*

American Family Life Insurance Co.   (1)
6000 American Pkwy, Madison, WI 53783-0001   (100%)
Tel.: (608) 249-2111
Web Site: http://www.amfam.com
Sales Range: $750-799.9 Million
Emp.: 3,000
Life Insurance
N.A.I.C.S.: 524113
Rich Steffen *(Pres)*

American Standard Insurance Company of Wisconsin   (1)
6000 American Pkwy, Madison, WI 53783-0001   (100%)
Tel.: (608) 249-2111
Web Site: http://www.amfam.com
Sales Range: $1-4.9 Billion
Special Property & Casualty Risk Insurance
N.A.I.C.S.: 524210

Ameriprise Auto & Home Insurance Agency Inc.   (1)
3500 Packerland Dr, De Pere, WI 54115-9070
Sales Range: $50-74.9 Million
Emp.: 1,000
Insurance Services
N.A.I.C.S.: 524298
Jessie Stauffacher *(Pres & CEO)*
Sharena Ali *(COO)*

Networked Insights, Inc.   (1)
350 N Orleans Ste 850, Chicago, IL 60654
Tel.: (312) 985-9700
Custom Computer Programming Services
N.A.I.C.S.: 541511

The Main Street America Group   (1)
4601 Touchton Rd E Ste 3400, Jacksonville, FL 32246
Tel.: (904) 380-7281
Web Site: http://www.msagroup.com
Insurance Holding Company
N.A.I.C.S.: 551112
Bruce Fox *(Gen Counsel, Sec & Sr VP)*
Jeff Kusch *(COO)*
Dave Medvidofsky *(Sr VP-HR)*
Janet Root *(VP-Internal Audit)*
Chris Listau *(Pres & CEO)*
Theresa Breunig-Silbernagel *(Sr VP-Enterprise Solutions)*
Joe Freitas *(CFO)*

Holding (Domestic):

Grain Dealers Mutual Insurance Company Inc.   (2)
6325 Digital Way Ste 101, Indianapolis, IN 46278
Tel.: (317) 388-4500
Web Site: http://www.graindealers.com
Insurance Services
N.A.I.C.S.: 524126

NGM Insurance Company   (2)
55 W St, Keene, NH 03431
Tel.: (603) 352-4000
Web Site: http://www.msagroup.com
Fire, Marine & Casualty Insurance
N.A.I.C.S.: 524126
Tom Frazier *(CIO)*

AMERICAN FARMLAND TRUST
1150 Connecticut Ave NW Ste 600, Washington, DC 20036
Tel.: (202) 331-7300   DC
Web Site: https://www.farmland.org
Year Founded: 1980
Rev.: $11,026,619
Assets: $26,812,245
Liabilities: $2,052,823
Net Worth: $24,759,422
Earnings: $883,427
Emp.: 62
Fiscal Year-end: 09/30/14
Farmland Protection Services
N.A.I.C.S.: 813910
Jimmy Daukas *(Sr Program Officer & VP-Programs)*
John Larson *(Sr VP & Exec Dir-Programs)*
Brian Brandt *(Dir-Agriculture Conservation Innovations)*
Cris Coffin *(Dir-National Agricultural Land Network)*
David Haight *(VP-Programs & Dir-New York State)*
Jennifer Dempsey *(Dir-Farmland Information Center)*
John Piotti *(Pres & CEO)*
Beth Sauerhaft *(VP-Programs)*
Ashley Bovino *(CFO & VP-Finance & Administration)*

Phoebe Silag *(VP-Communications)*
Lea Harvey *(VP-Development)*
Rick Monk *(Gen Counsel & VP)*
Tim Fink *(VP-Policy)*

AMERICAN FARMS LLC
1484 Keane Ave SW, Naples, FL 34117
Tel.: (239) 455-0300
Web Site: https://www.american-farms.com
Year Founded: 1991
Sales Range: $10-24.9 Million
Emp.: 170
Nursery Stock
N.A.I.C.S.: 424930
Cindy Swanson *(Acct Mgr)*
Christine Raber *(Mng Dir)*

AMERICAN FASTENERS INC.
9129 E US Hwy 36, Avon, IN 46123
Tel.: (317) 271-6100
Web Site: http://www.amfast.com
Rev.: $13,083,192
Emp.: 40
Nuts (Hardware)
N.A.I.C.S.: 423710
Jim Delp *(Pres)*

AMERICAN FEDERATION FOR AGING RESEARCH
55 W 39th St 16th Fl, New York, NY 10018
Tel.: (212) 703-9977   NY
Web Site: https://www.afar.org
Year Founded: 1981
Sales Range: $10-24.9 Million
Emp.: 13
Biomedical Research Services
N.A.I.C.S.: 541715
Riki Blum *(Fin Dir)*
Catherine Cullar *(Mgr-Admin)*

AMERICAN FELT & FILTER COMPANY
361 Walsh Ave, New Windsor, NY 12553-6727
Tel.: (845) 561-3560   NY
Web Site: http://www.affco.com
Year Founded: 1899
Sales Range: $75-99.9 Million
Emp.: 250
Mfr & Fabricator of Natural & Synthetic Felts
N.A.I.C.S.: 333998
Wilson H. Pryne *(Pres & CEO)*
Mark A. Pryne *(Sec)*
Scott H. Pryne *(VP)*
Phyllis Pryne *(Asst Controller)*

AMERICAN FENCE COMPANY, INC.
2502 N 27th Ave, Phoenix, AZ 85009
Tel.: (602) 272-2333   AZ
Web Site:
   https://www.americanfence.com
Year Founded: 1948
Special Trade Contractors; Construction Materials Whslr
N.A.I.C.S.: 238990
Daniel Van Denburgh *(Pres)*

Subsidiaries:

American Fence & Security Company   (1)
2502 N 27th Ave, Phoenix, AZ 85009
Tel.: (602) 272-2333
Web Site: https://www.americanfence.com
Sales Range: $200-249.9 Million
Emp.: 900
Special Trade Contractors; Whslr of Construction Materials
N.A.I.C.S.: 238990
David S. Vandenburgh *(Chm & CEO)*
Douglas Waslaski *(CFO)*
Lois J. Maurin *(Treas & Sec)*

American Fence Company of Arizona, Inc.   (1)
2502 N 27th Ave, Phoenix, AZ 85009
Tel.: (602) 272-2333
Construction Material Merchant Whslr
N.A.I.C.S.: 423390

Subsidiary (Domestic):

Allstate Rent A Fence, Inc.   (2)
210 S 55th Ave, Phoenix, AZ 85043
Tel.: (602) 233-1433
Web Site: http://www.allstaterentafence.com
Sales Range: $1-9.9 Million
Emp.: 40
Construction Materials Distr
N.A.I.C.S.: 423390
Duayne Dougherty *(Pres)*

AMERICAN FIBER & FINISHING INC.
225 N Depot St, Albemarle, NC 28001
Tel.: (704) 983-6102
Web Site: https://www.affinc.com
Year Founded: 1986
Sales Range: $10-24.9 Million
Emp.: 50
Producer of Broadwoven Cotton Fabric
N.A.I.C.S.: 313210
E. Carle Shotwell *(VP-Sales-Marketing)*

AMERICAN FIDELITY CORPORATION
2000 N Classen Blvd, Oklahoma City, OK 73107
Tel.: (405) 523-2000   OK
Web Site:
   http://www.afadvantage.com
Year Founded: 1960
Sales Range: $50-74.9 Million
Emp.: 1,350
Insurance & Financial Services
N.A.I.C.S.: 524114
Robert Brearton *(COO, Treas & Exec VP)*
David R. Carpenter *(Exec VP)*
Jeanette M. Rice *(Sr VP-HR)*
Al Litchenburg *(Exec VP)*
Brett Barrowman *(VP-Conference & Travel)*

Subsidiaries:

American Fidelity Assurance Company   (1)
9000 Cameron Pkwy, Oklahoma City, OK 73114   (100%)
Tel.: (405) 523-2000
Web Site: http://www.afadvantage.com
Emp.: 1,200
Insurance Services
N.A.I.C.S.: 524113

Subsidiary (Domestic):

American Fidelity Securities, Inc.   (2)
2000 N Classen Blvd, Oklahoma City, OK 73106-6023   (100%)
Tel.: (405) 523-2000
Web Site: http://www.afadvantage.com
Sales Range: $125-149.9 Million
Broker & Dealer Issuing Variable Annuity Policies
N.A.I.C.S.: 541613
David R. Carpenter *(Pres, CEO, CFO & Treas)*

First Financial Group of America   (2)
515 N Sam Houston Pkwy E, Houston, TX 77060-4034   (100%)
Tel.: (281) 847-8422
Web Site: http://www.ffga.com
Sales Range: $100-124.9 Million
Emp.: 150
Securities Broker & Dealer
N.A.I.C.S.: 524210
Larry Forrester *(CFO)*

American Fidelity International Holdings, Inc.   (1)

American Fidelity Corporation—(Continued)

2000 N Classen Blvd, Oklahoma City, OK 73106-6023 **(100%)**
Tel.: (405) 523-5065
Web Site: http://www.americanfidelity.com
Sales Range: $50-74.9 Million
Emp.: 80
Holding Company for All International Projects
N.A.I.C.S.: 524113

American Fidelity Property Company **(1)**
2000 N Classen Blvd, Oklahoma City, OK 73106-6023 **(100%)**
Tel.: (800) 654-8489
Web Site: http://www.afadvantage.com
Sales Range: $125-149.9 Million
Emp.: 1,300
Manage & Lease Various Real Estate Holdings
N.A.I.C.S.: 531210

Enrollcom, Inc. **(1)**
2000 N Classen Blvd, Oklahoma City, OK 73106-6023 **(100%)**
Web Site: http://www.enrollcom.com
Any Lawful Act or Activity
N.A.I.C.S.: 517810

InvesTrust, N.A. **(1)**
5100 N Classen Blvd, Oklahoma City, OK 73118-4433 **(100%)**
Tel.: (405) 843-7177
Web Site: http://www.investrust.com
Sales Range: $25-49.9 Million
Emp.: 26
Investment & Investment Custodial Services
N.A.I.C.S.: 523150
David Thompson (Chm & CEO)
Steve Replogle (Dir-Trust Svcs)

AMERICAN FILM INSTITUTE
2021 N Western Ave, Los Angeles, CA 90027-1657
Tel.: (323) 856-7600
Web Site: https://www.afi.com
Year Founded: 1967
Sales Range: $25-49.9 Million
Emp.: 120
Motion Picture Industry Support & Education Services
N.A.I.C.S.: 813990
Bruce Neiner (CFO & Treas)
Paul Jacques (Chief Info & Infrastructure Officer)
Nancy Harris (COO)
Bob Gazzale (Pres & CEO)
Juli Goodwin (Chief Comm Officer)

AMERICAN FINDINGS CORPORATION
10441 N Scottsdale Rd, Scottsdale, AZ 85253
Tel.: (480) 367-1717   **AZ**
Web Site:
  https://www.londongold.com
Year Founded: 1980
Sales Range: $10-24.9 Million
Emp.: 35
Jewelry, Precious Stones & Precious Metals
N.A.I.C.S.: 458310
Benyamin Avrahami (Pres)

AMERICAN FIRE PROTECTION, INC.
5525 Eastcliff Industrial Loop, Birmingham, AL 35210
Tel.: (205) 591-9111   **AL**
Web Site:
  https://www.americanfireinc.com
Year Founded: 2004
Sales Range: $1-9.9 Million
Emp.: 35
Plumbing, Heating & Air-Conditioning Contractors
N.A.I.C.S.: 238220
Kim Muir (Office Mgr)
Josh Crow (COO)

Josh Whaley (Pres & CEO)
Matt Mullinax (Exec VP)
Randy Treglown (Exec VP)

AMERICAN FIRE RESTORATION, LLC
71-02 80th St, Glendale, NY 11385-7715
Tel.: (718) 383-7006
Web Site:
  https://www.amfirerestoration.com
Year Founded: 2000
Sales Range: $1-9.9 Million
Emp.: 12
Insurance Services
N.A.I.C.S.: 524298
Adam Gass (Gen Mgr)
Chris Croner (Project Mgr)
Phyllis Iacontino (Project Mgr)

AMERICAN FIREGLASS
592 Crane St, Lake Elsinore, CA 92530
Tel.: (951) 245-5151
Web Site:
  http://www.americanfireglass.com
Year Founded: 2004
Sales Range: $1-9.9 Million
Emp.: 11
Mfr & Distr of Crushed Fireglass for Fireplaces & Firepits in both Home & Commercial Applications
N.A.I.C.S.: 333994
Matt Doll (Founder & CEO)

AMERICAN FIRST CREDIT UNION
700 N Harbor Blvd, La Habra, CA 90631
Tel.: (800) 290-1112   **CA**
Web Site: http://www.amerfirst.org
Year Founded: 1989
Sales Range: $25-49.9 Million
Emp.: 143
Credit Union
N.A.I.C.S.: 522130
Danny Doss (Chm)
Patti Malott (Treas & Sec)
Priscilla Lam (Asst Mgr-Mktg)
Jon Shigematsu (Pres & CEO)
Julie Glance (CFO)

AMERICAN FIRST NATIONAL BANK NA
9999 Bellaire Blvd, Houston, TX 77036
Tel.: (713) 596-2888
Web Site: https://www.afnb.com
Sales Range: $25-49.9 Million
Emp.: 200
National Commercial Banks
N.A.I.C.S.: 522110
Bruce Chang (Pres & CEO)
Sook Kim (VP-Mktg)

AMERICAN FLORIST SUPPLY INC.
1 Progress Way, Wilmington, MA 01887
Tel.: (978) 658-2400
Sales Range: $25-49.9 Million
Emp.: 250
Flowers & Florists Supplies
N.A.I.C.S.: 424930
John T. Dickinson (Owner)
Steve Moscaritolo (Mgr-Accts)
Jessica Scammell (Mgr-Payroll & HR)
Robert Cote (Gen Mgr-Bedford)

AMERICAN FOOD & VENDING CORP.
124 Metropolitan Park Dr, Liverpool, NY 13088
Tel.: (315) 457-9950

Web Site:
  http://www.americanvending.com
Rev.: $35,000,000
Emp.: 40
Merchandising Machine Operators
N.A.I.C.S.: 445132
Martin Wells (VP)
Allyson Ciampi (Mgr-Relief)
Clayton Hargrove (Reg VP)
Samuel Melamedas (Dir-Pur)
Kathlyne Sommers (Mgr-HR)

AMERICAN FOOD DISTRIBUTORS
49 Wireless Blvd, Hauppauge, NY 11788
Tel.: (631) 864-5400
Web Site: http://www.amfood.com
Sales Range: $100-124.9 Million
Emp.: 29
Groceries, General Line
N.A.I.C.S.: 424410
John Cannistra (VP)

Subsidiaries:

Drl Group Ltd. **(1)**
325 Wireless Blvd, Hauppauge, NY 11788
Tel.: (631) 864-5400
Web Site: http://www.amfood.com
Health Foods
N.A.I.C.S.: 424490

AMERICAN FOOD DISTRIBUTORS, LLC
8402 Lemon Rd, Port Richey, FL 34668
Tel.: (727) 848-1010
Web Site: https://www.afdllc.com
Year Founded: 1997
Sales Range: $75-99.9 Million
Emp.: 105
Food Distr
N.A.I.C.S.: 424490
Bill Loiacano (CEO)

AMERICAN FOODSERVICE CORP.
400 Drew Ct, King of Prussia, PA 19406
Tel.: (610) 277-5010   **DE**
Year Founded: 1972
Sales Range: $10-24.9 Million
Emp.: 300
Mfr of Hamburgers
N.A.I.C.S.: 311612
Ronald G. Allen (Chm & CEO)
Barry Renninger (Pres & COO)
Ed McGroarty (Controller)

AMERICAN FOREST PRODUCTS LLC
1620 Webster Ave, Bronx, NY 10457
Tel.: (718) 901-1700
Web Site:
  http://www.tulnoylumber.com
Sales Range: $10-24.9 Million
Emp.: 100
Lumber, Plywood & Millwork
N.A.I.C.S.: 423310
Steven Tulchin (Pres)

AMERICAN FOUNDRY GROUP, INC.
14602 S Grant St, Bixby, OK 74008
Tel.: (918) 366-4401   **OK**
Web Site:
  https://www.americanfoundry.com
Year Founded: 1966
Sales Range: $150-199.9 Million
Emp.: 485
Casting Foundries
N.A.I.C.S.: 331523

Subsidiaries:

American Foundry **(1)**
612 S 45th St, Muskogee, OK 74403

Tel.: (918) 366-4401
Web Site: http://www.americanfoundry.com
Sales Range: $10-24.9 Million
Emp.: 60
Non-Ferrous Foundry
N.A.I.C.S.: 331529
Jerry McGouldrick (Mgr-Sls)

AMERICAN FROZEN FOODS, INC.
155 Hill St, Milford, CT 06460
Tel.: (203) 882-6200   **CT**
Web Site:
  http://www.americanfoods.com
Year Founded: 1921
Sales Range: $75-99.9 Million
Emp.: 15
Supplier of Meat & Fish
N.A.I.C.S.: 445110
William Rappoport (Pres)
Palma DiCaprio (VP-Admin)

AMERICAN FUEL AND PETROCHEMICAL MANUFACTURERS
1667 K St NW Ste 700, Washington, DC 20006
Tel.: (202) 457-0480   **DE**
Web Site: http://www.afpm.org
Year Founded: 1961
Sales Range: $25-49.9 Million
Emp.: 48
Fuel & Petrochemical Manufacturer Association
N.A.I.C.S.: 813910
Gregory J. Goff (Chm)
Geoff Moody (Sr Dir-Govt Rels)
Diana Cronan (Dir-Comm)
Rebecca H. Adler (Sr Dir-Comm)
Sarah Magruder Lyle (VP-Strategic Initiatives)
Richard Meeks (Treas)
Brendan E. Williams (Exec VP)
Lawrence M. Ziemba (Vice Chm)
Chet M. Thompson (Pres)
Wade L. Easter (Sr Dir-Acctg)
Jared Hawes (Mgr-Outreach)
Richard S. Moskowitz (Gen Counsel)
Gordon Robertson (Dir-Technical Programs)
Lauren Sheehan (Sr Mgr-Govt Rels)
Daniel Strachan (Dir-Indus Rels & Programs)
Gerald R. Van De Velde (CFO)
Colleen Van Gieson (Mgr-Meetings)
Susan E. Yashinskie (Sr VP-Member Svcs & Programs)
Merla Zollinger (Sr Mgr-Convention Svcs)
David N. Friedman (VP-Regulatory Affairs)
Robert McArver (VP-Petrochemicals)
Don Thoren (VP-State & Local Outreach)

AMERICAN FURNITURE MANUFACTURING, INC.
604 Pontotoc County Industrial Park Rd, Ecru, MS 38841
Tel.: (662) 489-2633   **MS**
Web Site:
  http://www.americanfurn.net
Year Founded: 1998
Upholstered Furniture Mfr
N.A.I.C.S.: 337121
Randall C. Spak (CEO)

AMERICAN FURNITURE RENTAL
720 Hylton Rd, Pennsauken, NJ 08110
Tel.: (856) 406-1200
Web Site:
  https://www.rentfurniture.com
Sales Range: $10-24.9 Million
Emp.: 112

Furniture Rental
N.A.I.C.S.: 459510
Neil Scholnick *(CEO)*
Joseph Culver *(Dir-Tech)*
Grace Capato *(Mgr-Inventory Control)*
Deborah Howell *(Reg Mgr)*
Adam Scholnick *(Chief Admin Officer)*
Norman Imaoka *(VP-Mdse)*

AMERICAN FURNITURE WAREHOUSE
8820 American Way, Englewood, CO 80112
Tel.: (303) 799-9044
Web Site: http://www.afwonline.com
Year Founded: 1975
Sales Range: $250-299.9 Million
Emp.: 2,700
Furniture Stores
N.A.I.C.S.: 423220
Jake Jabs *(Pres & CEO)*
David Annable *(Asst Mgr-RTA)*
Jeff Bomstein *(Mgr)*
Susie Duff *(Mgr-Sls)*
Dave Duncomb *(Mgr-Adv)*
Darby Gaetano *(Mgr-Customer Svc)*
Desean Lydia *(Mgr-Digital Print)*
Rob Naish *(Mgr)*
Lee Nelson *(Mgr-Fin)*
Jon Neuenschwander *(Mgr-Inventory Ops)*
Kate Uhlar *(Mgr-Online)*
Bruce Garrett *(Mgr-Sls)*
Dion Chavez *(Mgr-Warehouse)*
James Secreto *(Mgr-Fleet Maintenance)*
Tierra Smith *(Mgr-Distr)*
Tom Salazar *(Mgr-Shop)*
Dan George *(Asst Mgr)*
Bob Schwartz *(Controller)*
Joe Straface *(Dir-Adv)*
Becky L. Moul *(Dir-HR & Mgr-Risk)*
Carrie Mitchell *(Mgr)*
Michael Munsell *(Mgr-Customer Svc)*
Mike Buscietta *(Mgr-Facility)*
Chris Gibson *(Mgr-IT)*
Scott Brianne *(Mgr-Staging)*
Nolan Morrison *(Reg Mgr-Facility)*
Jode Baerga *(Mgr-Customer Svc)*

AMERICAN FUTURE SYSTEMS INC.
370 Technology Dr, Malvern, PA 19355
Tel.: (610) 695-8600
Web Site: https://www.pbp.com
Year Founded: 1989
Sales Range: $25-49.9 Million
Emp.: 400
Newsletter Publishing
N.A.I.C.S.: 513199
Jim Brown *(VP)*

AMERICAN GARDENWORKS
205 W Mauzy St, Boswell, IN 47921
Tel.: (765) 869-4033
Sales Range: $10-24.9 Million
Emp.: 20
Bar, Rod & Wire Products
N.A.I.C.S.: 331110

AMERICAN GAS & CHEMICAL CO., LTD.
220 Pegasus Ave, Northvale, NJ 07647-1904
Tel.: (201) 767-7300   NJ
Web Site: https://www.amgas.com
Year Founded: 1953
Sales Range: $125-149.9 Million
Emp.: 30
Leak Testing & Gas Monitoring Products Mfr
N.A.I.C.S.: 325180
Gerald L. Anderson *(Pres & CEO)*
Melanie Kershaw *(VP-Mktg)*

Subsidiaries:

Delphian Corporation   (1)
220 Pegasus Ave, Northvale, NJ 07647
Tel.: (201) 767-7300
Web Site: http://www.delphian.com
Sales Range: $25-49.9 Million
Emp.: 20
Gas Detection Instrument Mfr
N.A.I.C.S.: 334519
Melanie Kershaw *(VP)*

AMERICAN GENE ENGINEER CORP.
521 5th Ave Ste 1718, New York, NY 10175
Tel.: (212) 292-4325   DE
Year Founded: 2010
Investment Services
N.A.I.C.S.: 523999
Ming Lin *(Pres & CEO)*
Han-Chen Lin *(Chm & CFO)*

AMERICAN GENERAL SUPPLIES, INC.
7840 Airpark Rd, Gaithersburg, MD 20879
Tel.: (301) 590-9200
Web Site: https://www.agsusa.com
Sales Range: $10-24.9 Million
Emp.: 30
Aircraft Equipment & Supplies, Nec
N.A.I.C.S.: 423860
Kassa Maru *(Pres & Chm)*

AMERICAN GIFT FUND
4550 Linden Hill Rd Ste 200, Wilmington, DE 19808
Tel.: (302) 892-6900   DE
Web Site: https://www.giftfund.org
Year Founded: 1998
Sales Range: $10-24.9 Million
Grantmaking Services
N.A.I.C.S.: 813211
David E. Davis *(Chm)*

AMERICAN GLOBAL HEALTH GROUP, LLC.
11808 Northup Way Ste W-105, Seattle, WA 98005-1922
Tel.: (206) 420-1194
Web Site: http://www.aghg.us
Year Founded: 1999
Sales Range: $10-24.9 Million
Emp.: 170
Beauty Care & Medical Product Mfr & Distr
N.A.I.C.S.: 325412
Douglas N. Jewett *(Chm)*
Justin Featherman *(CFO)*
Paul Nazarov *(Owner)*

AMERICAN GOLF CORPORATION
909 N Pacific Coast Hwy, El Segundo, CA 90245
Tel.: (310) 664-4000   CA
Web Site: https://www.americangolf.com
Year Founded: 1968
Golf Course Management Services
N.A.I.C.S.: 713910
Craig Kniffen *(Sr VP-Maintenance)*
Jim Hinckley *(Pres & CEO)*
Rick Rosen *(CFO)*
Lee Finkel *(Sr VP-Publics)*
Ken Hultz *(Sr VP-Private Clubs)*
Paul Ballam *(Sr VP-Bus Dev)*

AMERICAN GOVERNMENT SERVICES CORP.
3812 W Linebaugh Ave, Tampa, FL 33618
Tel.: (813) 933-3322   FL
Web Site: https://www.agsres.com
Year Founded: 2003
Sales Range: $1-9.9 Million

Emp.: 20
Title Insurance
N.A.I.C.S.: 524127
Tammy Mehl *(Sr VP)*
Wendi McAleese *(Pres)*

AMERICAN GRANBY, INC.
7652 Morgan Rd, Liverpool, NY 13090-3433
Tel.: (315) 451-1100   NY
Web Site:
https://www.americangranby.com
Year Founded: 1997
Sales Range: $75-99.9 Million
Emp.: 45
Wholesale Distributor of Water System Accessories & Plant Watering Equipment
N.A.I.C.S.: 423830
John Lowe *(Owner)*
Mary Lanzafame *(VP-Ops)*
Gary Palley *(VP-Mktg & Sls)*
Denise Gerould *(VP-Fin)*

Subsidiaries:

CB Supplies Ltd.   (1)
8125 North Fraser Way, Burnaby, V5J 5M8, BC, Canada
Tel.: (604) 431-5088
Web Site: http://www.cbsupplies.ca
Plumbing Equipment Distr
N.A.I.C.S.: 423720

Subsidiary (Domestic):

Seymour Industries Ltd.   (2)
8125 North Fraser Way, Burnaby, V5J 5M8, BC, Canada
Tel.: (888) 258-3370
Web Site: http://www.seymourind.com
Plumbing Equipment Whslr
N.A.I.C.S.: 423720

AMERICAN GRINDING AND MACHINE COMPANY
2000 N Mango Ave, Chicago, IL 60639-2899
Tel.: (773) 889-4343
Web Site:
https://www.americangrinding.com
Rev.: $13,186,046
Emp.: 75
Machine Shop, Jobbing & Repair
N.A.I.C.S.: 332710
Greg Leonard *(Pres)*

AMERICAN GROUP, LLC.
25 S Arizona Pl Ste 300, Chandler, AZ 85225
Tel.: (480) 406-6102
Web Site: https://www.shipag.com
Sales Range: $1-9.9 Million
Emp.: 10
Freight Transportation Services
N.A.I.C.S.: 484122
Daniel Krivickas *(Pres & CEO)*

AMERICAN HAKKO PRODUCTS, INC.
28920 Avenue Williams, Valencia, CA 91355
Tel.: (661) 294-0090
Web Site: https://www.hakkousa.com
Rev.: $5,300,000
Emp.: 30
Industrial Supplies Merchant Whslr
N.A.I.C.S.: 423840
Hitoshi Fujiwara *(Pres)*
Toru Furukubo *(Treas & Sec)*
Andy Mitchell *(Sr Mgr-Customer Rels Div)*

AMERICAN HANDLING SYSTEMS, INC.
191 N Rush Lake Rd, Laurens, IA 50554
Tel.: (712) 841-4548
Web Site: https://www.positech.com

Year Founded: 1951
Sales Range: $1-9.9 Million
Emp.: 50
Material Handling Equipment Mfr
N.A.I.C.S.: 333248
Brenda Slama *(Mgr-Sls)*

AMERICAN HARTFORD GOLD GROUP LLC
11900 W Olympic Blvd 7th Fl, Los Angeles, CA 90064
Web Site:
http://www.americanhartfordgold.com
Year Founded: 2015
Sales Range: $25-49.9 Million
Emp.: 40
Precious Metal Distr
N.A.I.C.S.: 423940
Sanford Mann *(CEO)*
Scott Gerlis *(Pres)*

AMERICAN HARVEST BAKING
823 E Gate Dr Unit Ste 3, Mount Laurel, NJ 08054
Tel.: (856) 642-9955
Web Site: http://www.ahbfoods.com
Sales Range: $10-24.9 Million
Emp.: 100
Bakery Products Mfr
N.A.I.C.S.: 311812
Jay Roseman *(Pres)*
Robert W. Bennett *(Dir-Ops)*
Barry Kratchman *(Principal)*

AMERICAN HEALTH INFORMATION MANAGEMENT ASSOCIATION
233 N Michigan Ave Ste 21, Chicago, IL 60601-5519
Tel.: (312) 233-1100   IL
Web Site: http://www.ahima.org
Year Founded: 1928
Rev.: $7,500,000
Emp.: 100
Fiscal Year-end: 12/31/07
Professional Organizations
N.A.I.C.S.: 813920
Kevin Klauer *(CEO)*
Jennifer Mueller *(Chm & Pres)*

AMERICAN HEALTH LAWYERS ASSOCIATION INC.
1620 Eye St NW 6th Fl, Washington, DC 20006-4010
Tel.: (202) 833-1100   DC
Web Site:
http://www.healthlawyers.org
Year Founded: 1973
Sales Range: $1-9.9 Million
Emp.: 47
Lawyer Association
N.A.I.C.S.: 813920
Carine Brice *(Mgr-Dispute Resolution Svc)*
David S. Cade *(CEO & Exec VP)*
Geoff A. Drucker *(Sr Mgr-Dispute Resolution Svc)*

AMERICAN HEALTHCARE INVESTORS LLC
18191 Von Karman Ave Ste 300, Irvine, CA 92612
Tel.: (949) 270-9200
Web Site:
http://www.americanhealthcare.com
Healthcare Industry Real Estate Investment & Portfolio Management
N.A.I.C.S.: 523940
Jeffrey T. Hanson *(Co-Founder & Principal)*
Danny Prosky *(Pres & CEO)*
Mathieu B. Streiff *(Co-Founder & Principal)*
Cora Lo *(Sr VP)*
Damon Elder *(Sr VP-Mktg & Comm)*

American Healthcare Investors LLC—(Continued)

Wendie Newman *(Exec VP-Asset Mgmt)*
Mark E. Foster *(Gen Counsel & Exec VP)*

Subsidiaries:

American Healthcare REIT, Inc. **(1)**
18191 Von Karman Ave 3rd Fl, Irvine, CA 92612
Tel.: (949) 270-9200
Web Site:
  https://www.americanhealthcarereit.com
Rev.: $1,643,175,000
Assets: $4,786,698,000
Liabilities: $3,137,335,000
Net Worth: $1,567,765,000
Earnings: ($73,383,000)
Emp.: 113
Fiscal Year-end: 12/31/2022
Healthcare Industry Real Estate Investment Trust
N.A.I.C.S.: 525990
Danny Prosky *(Pres & CEO)*
Brian S. Peay *(CFO)*
Gabe Willhite *(COO)*
Mark Foster *(Gen Counsel, Sec & Exec VP)*
Stefan Oh *(Chief Investment Officer)*
Kenny Lin *(Chief Acctg Officer, Deputy CFO & Exec VP)*
Wendie Newman *(Exec VP-Asset Mgmt)*
Ray Oborn *(Exec VP-Asset Mgmt)*
Charlynn Diapo *(Sr VP-Accounting & Finance)*

Subsidiary (Domestic):

Griffin-American Healthcare REIT III, Inc. **(2)**
18191 Von Karman Ave Ste 300, Irvine, CA 92612
Tel.: (949) 270-9200
Web Site: http://www.healthcarereit3.com
Rev.: $1,244,301,000
Assets: $3,234,937,000
Liabilities: $2,200,454,000
Net Worth: $1,034,483,000
Earnings: $2,163,000
Emp.: 50
Fiscal Year-end: 12/31/2020
Healthcare Industry Real Estate Investment Trust
N.A.I.C.S.: 525990
Jeffrey T. Hanson *(Chm & CEO)*
Danny Prosky *(Pres & COO)*
Brian S. Peay *(CFO)*
Mathieu B. Streiff *(Gen Counsel & Exec VP)*
Stefan K. L. Oh *(Sr VP-Acquisitions)*
Cora Lo *(Sec)*

Joint Venture (Domestic):

Trilogy Health Services LLC **(3)**
303 N Hurstbourne Pkwy Ste 200, Louisville, KY 40222 **(70%)**
Tel.: (502) 412-5847
Web Site: https://www.trilogyhs.com
Women Healthcare Services
N.A.I.C.S.: 532283
Randall J. Bufford *(Pres & CEO)*

AMERICAN HEALTHCARE PRODUCTS, INC.

1028 Westminster Ave, Alhambra, CA 91803
Tel.: (626) 588-2788
Web Site: http://www.uniseal.net
Year Founded: 1991
Sales Range: $10-24.9 Million
Emp.: 14
Medical Equipment & Supplies
N.A.I.C.S.: 423450
Modesto Cabral *(Gen Mgr)*

AMERICAN HEALTHCARE SYSTEMS CORP., INC.

505 N Brand Blvd Ste 1110, Glendale, CA 91203
Tel.: (818) 646-9933   NV
Web Site:
  https://www.amhealthsystems.com
Emp.: 100

Health Care Srvices
N.A.I.C.S.: 621999
Michael Sarian *(Chm & CEO)*

Subsidiaries:

ProMedica Health System, Inc. **(1)**
1801 Richards Rd, Toledo, OH 43607
Tel.: (419) 291-3000
Web Site: http://www.promedica.org
Sales Range: $500-549.9 Million
Emp.: 56,000
Health System
N.A.I.C.S.: 622110
Gary Cates *(Chief Philanthropy Officer)*
Dawn Buskey *(Pres-Acute Care)*
Lori A. Johnston *(Executives)*
Holly Bristol *(Chief Integration Officer)*
Arturo Polizzi *(Pres & CEO)*
Terry Metzger *(CFO)*

Subsidiary (Domestic):

Paramount Health Systems **(2)**
1901 Indian Wood Cir, Maumee, OH 43537-4055
Tel.: (419) 887-2500
Web Site:
  http://www.paramounthealthcare.com
Sales Range: $25-49.9 Million
Emp.: 360
Health Insurance Services
N.A.I.C.S.: 524114

ProMedica Endoscopy Center **(2)**
5700 Monroe St Ste 102, Sylvania, OH 43560
Tel.: (419) 843-7993
Web Site: http://www.promedica.org
Endoscopy Center
N.A.I.C.S.: 621112

ProMedica Senior Care **(2)**
333 N Summit St, Toledo, OH 43604-2617
Tel.: (419) 252-5500
Web Site: http://promedicaseniorcare.org
Short-Term Post-Acute Medical Care & Rehabilitation & Long-Term Skilled Nursing Care
N.A.I.C.S.: 623110
Steven M. Cavanaugh *(CEO)*

Subsidiary (Domestic):

Heartland Rehabilitation Services, LLC **(3)**
5630 Harroun Rd, Sylvania, OH 43560
Tel.: (419) 540-6000
Web Site: http://www.heartland-manorcare.com
Health Care Srvices
N.A.I.C.S.: 621610

MileStone Health Systems, LLC **(3)**
275 W Campbell Rd Ste 300, Richardson, TX 75080
Tel.: (972) 813-4001
Web Site: http://www.milestonehealth.com
Health Care Srvices
N.A.I.C.S.: 623110
Lana Buley *(VP-Ops)*
Gail Grace *(Reg Dir-Ops)*

AMERICAN HERITAGE BANK

2 S Main St, Sapulpa, OK 74066
Tel.: (918) 224-3210
Web Site: http://www.ahb-ok.com
Year Founded: 1905
Rev.: $7,500,000
Emp.: 42
Banking Services
N.A.I.C.S.: 522110
Jennifer Dilley *(VP-Mktg)*
Randall C. Vaughn *(CFO & Sr VP)*
William L. Berry *(Chm)*
Guy L. Berry *(Vice Chm)*

Subsidiaries:

Osage Bancshares, Inc. **(1)**
239 E Main St, Pawhuska, OK 74056
Tel.: (918) 287-2919
Sales Range: $1-9.9 Million
Emp.: 35
Bank Holding Company
N.A.I.C.S.: 551111
Mark S. White *(Pres & CEO)*
Sue Allen Smith *(CFO & VP)*

Martha M. Hayes *(Sr VP)*
Frances Altaffer *(Sec & VP)*
Richard J. Trolinger *(Exec VP & Chief Lending Officer)*

Subsidiary (Domestic):

Osage Federal Bank **(2)**
239 E Main St, Pawhuska, OK 74056
Tel.: (918) 287-2919
Web Site: http://www.osagefed.com
Commericial Banking
N.A.I.C.S.: 522110
Mark S. White *(Pres & CEO)*

AMERICAN HERITAGE NATIONAL BANK

24 2nd St S, Long Prairie, MN 56347-0509
Tel.: (320) 732-6131
Web Site: https://www.logbank.com
Sales Range: $10-24.9 Million
Emp.: 60
National Commercial Banks
N.A.I.C.S.: 522110
Rodger J. Johnston *(Chm)*
Denis G. Irsfeld *(Sec)*
Jay Johnston *(CEO & Pres)*

AMERICAN HERITAGE PUBLISHING COMPANY

500 N Washington St, Rockville, MD 20849-1488
Tel.: (301) 706-4179
Web Site:
  https://www.americanheritage.com
Year Founded: 1949
Magazine Publisher
N.A.I.C.S.: 513199
Melissa Hunsiker *(VP-Admin)*

AMERICAN HOFMANN CORPORATION

3700 Cohen Pl, Lynchburg, VA 24501
Tel.: (434) 522-0300   VA
Web Site: https://www.hofmann-global.com
Year Founded: 1932
Sales Range: $10-24.9 Million
Emp.: 89
Balancing Machines (Machine Tool Accessories) Mfr
N.A.I.C.S.: 333515
Stephen Cavanaugh *(Mgr-Product-Aerospace, Turbine, Universal)*

AMERICAN HOLDCO INC.

175 Alley St, Lynn, MA 01905
Tel.: (781) 593-1737
Web Site:
  http://www.eastcoastseafood.com
Rev.: $127,109,495
Emp.: 50
Holding Company
N.A.I.C.S.: 551112
Michael J. Tourkistas *(Pres & CEO)*
James C. Bouras *(CFO)*

Subsidiaries:

East Coast Seafood Inc. **(1)**
175 Alley St, Lynn, MA 01905
Tel.: (781) 593-1737
Web Site: http://www.eastcoastseafood.com
Sales Range: $10-24.9 Million
Emp.: 30
Seafoods
N.A.I.C.S.: 424460
Michael J. Tourkistas *(Founder)*
Chris Maze *(CEO)*
Kourtney Corcoran *(CFO)*

Seatrade International Company, Inc. **(1)**
105 Bartlett St, Portsmouth, NH 03801
Tel.: (603) 431-5184
Web Site: http://www.seatrade-international.com
Sales Range: $25-49.9 Million
Emp.: 40
Seafood Mfr

N.A.I.C.S.: 311710
Stephen C. Barndollar *(Founder & Pres)*

Worldwide Perishables Enterprise Inc. **(1)**
50 Eastern Ave, Chelsea, MA 02150
Tel.: (857) 776-7701
Web Site: http://www.shipwwp.com
Sales Range: $10-24.9 Million
Emp.: 25
Refrigerated Products Transport
N.A.I.C.S.: 484230
Michael Tourkitas *(Pres)*

AMERICAN HOME MORTGAGES

538 Broadhollow Rd Fl 4, Melville, NY 11747-3638
Tel.: (410) 872-2000
Rev.: $82,000,000
Emp.: 1
Mortgage Banker
N.A.I.C.S.: 522292

AMERICAN HOME PARTNERS, INC.

1154 Highland Ave, Cheshire, CT 06410
Tel.: (203) 699-3400
Year Founded: 1946
Sales Range: $1-9.9 Million
Emp.: 35
Home Mortgage Services
N.A.I.C.S.: 522310
Thomas P. Heneghan *(Executives)*

AMERICAN HOMES, INC.

1900 E I 30, Rockwall, TX 75087-6203
Tel.: (972) 771-9204
Web Site:
  http://deliveringthedream.com
Sales Range: $10-24.9 Million
Emp.: 40
Mobile Home Dealer Services
N.A.I.C.S.: 459930
Tav Blankenship *(Gen Mgr)*

AMERICAN HOMESTAR CORPORATION

2450 S Shore Blvd Ste 300, League City, TX 77573-2997
Tel.: (281) 334-9700   TX
Web Site:
  http://www.americanhomestar.com
Year Founded: 1971
Sales Range: $100-124.9 Million
Emp.: 600
Manufactured Homes Mfr & Distr
N.A.I.C.S.: 321991

AMERICAN HOTEL REGISTER COMPANY

100 S Milwaukee Ave, Vernon Hills, IL 60061
Tel.: (847) 743-1000
Web Site:
  http://www.americanhotel.com
Sales Range: $100-124.9 Million
Emp.: 900
Hotel Equipment & Supplies
N.A.I.C.S.: 423440
Tom Leahy *(Vice Chm)*
Larry Morse *(Pres & CEO)*
Jim Leahy *(Chm)*
Deidre Schwartz *(Dir-FF&E Design & Social Responsibility)*

AMERICAN HOUSE

5737 Darlington Rd, Pittsburgh, PA 15217
Tel.: (412) 422-5951
Year Founded: 1985
Rev.: $10,000,000
Emp.: 9
General Merchandise & Non-Durable Goods
N.A.I.C.S.: 424990

AMERICAN HOUSING CORPORATION
6580 72nd Ave, Pinellas Park, FL 33781
Tel.: (727) 546-6611
Web Site:
http://www.americanhousing.com
Year Founded: 1990
Sales Range: $10-24.9 Million
Emp.: 9
New Home Construction
N.A.I.C.S.: 236115
Mick McKenzie (Co-Owner)
Lee Kretzer (Co-Owner)
Stuart Cohen (Co-Owner)

AMERICAN HUTS INC.
2 Fl 350 Passaic Ave, Fairfield, NJ 07004-2007
Tel.: (973) 808-9525
Web Site: http://www.adfmgt.com
Sales Range: $50-74.9 Million
Emp.: 5,000
Franchise Owner of Fast-Food Restaurants
N.A.I.C.S.: 722513
Donald Harty (Pres)

AMERICAN IMMIGRATION LAWYERS ASSOCIATION
1331 G St NW Ste 300, Washington, DC 20005-3142
Tel.: (202) 507-7600   NY
Web Site: https://www.aila.org
Year Founded: 1946
Sales Range: $10-24.9 Million
Immigration Services
N.A.I.C.S.: 928120
Theresa A. Waters (Sr Dir-HR & Admin)
George Paul Tzamaras (Sr Dir-Comm & Outreach)
Jennifer English Lynch (Sr Dir-Membership)
Torey Carter-Conneen (Deputy Dir-Fin & Ops)
Benjamin Johnson (Exec Dir)
Robert P. Deasy (Deputy Dir-Programs)
Grace Woods (Sr Dir-Education)
Barry Collins (Mgr-Education Process)
Regchenal Johnson (Coord-Acctg)
Jorge Cardona (Mgr-Online Svcs)
Betsy Lawrence (Dir-Liaison)
Robert Bequeaith (Mgr-Creative Svcs)
Gillian Shurland (Sr Mgr-HR & Admin)
Reid F. Trautz (Dir-Practice & Professionalism)
Daniel M. Polen (Dir-Publ & Online Resources)
Rachel Pulda (Mgr-Online Editorial)
Sarah Redzic (Mgr-Publ)

AMERICAN INCORPORATORS LTD.
1013 Ctr Rd Ste 403A, Wilmington, DE 19805
Tel.: (302) 421-5752
Web Site: http://www.ailcorp.com
Sales Range: $1-9.9 Million
Emp.: 25
Company Incorporating Services
N.A.I.C.S.: 561499
Ann Shilton (CEO)
Laura Bryda (VP-Admin)
Jeff Tindall (Supvr-Accts-Intl)
Janet M. Caruccio (Supvr-Accts-Intl)
Murray H. Sawyer Jr. (Founder & Chm)

AMERICAN INDUSTRIAL ACQUISITION CORPORATION
250 Park Ave, New York, NY 10177
Tel.: (212) 572-4853   DE
Web Site: http://www.aiac.com
Year Founded: 1995
Investment Holding Company
N.A.I.C.S.: 551112
L. M. Levie (Chm)
Marc Renard-Payen (Mng Dir-Europe)
Bertrand Talabart (Deputy Mng Dir-Europe)
Lawrence W. Schwoeri (Mng Dir)
Jean Franco Montalvan (Exec VP)

Subsidiaries:

Avara Pharmaceutical Services, Inc.   (1)
101 Merritt 7, Norwalk, CT 06851
Tel.: (203) 655-1333
Web Site: http://www.avara.com
Contract Pharmaceutical Products Mfr & Developer
N.A.I.C.S.: 325412
William L. Pasek (Chief Comml Officer & Exec VP)
Andy Glanville (CFO & Exec VP)
Charlie Lickfold (CIO & Exec VP)
Paul Fioravanti (CEO)
Scott Aladeen (Exec VP-Ops & Special Projects)
Warren Horton (Exec VP-Quality Assurance & Regulatory Affairs-Global)

Subsidiary (Domestic):

Avara Aiken Pharmaceutical Services, Inc.   (2)
65 Windham Blvd, Aiken, SC 29805-9384
Tel.: (803) 649-3471
Web Site: http://www.avara.com
Pharmaceuticals Mfr
N.A.I.C.S.: 325412

Avara Pharmaceutical Technologies, Inc.   (2)
3300 Marshall Ave, Norman, OK 73072
Tel.: (405) 217-6400
Pharmaceuticals Product Mfr
N.A.I.C.S.: 325412
Pam Maguire (Sr Mgr-HR)
Eric Brown (Mgr-Mfg)
Daehwan Kim (Mgr-Site Svcs)
Victor Voronyuk (Mgr-Validation)
Ben Duphorne (Sr Mgr-Quality Assurance)

Champlain Cable Corp.   (1)
175 Hercules Dr, Colchester, VT 05446-5925
Tel.: (802) 654-4200
Web Site: http://www.champcable.com
Sales Range: $10-24.9 Million
Emp.: 100
High Temperature Insulated Wires & Cables Mfr
N.A.I.C.S.: 332618
Bill Riechert (Pres & CEO)

Eurofoil Luxembourg S.A.   (1)
Zone Industrielle de Riedgen, BP 91, Dudelange, 3401, Luxembourg
Tel.: (352) 51 8664 1
Web Site: http://www.eurofoil.com
Sales Range: $25-49.9 Million
Emp.: 300
Aluminum Foil & Packaging Product Mfr
N.A.I.C.S.: 331315
Falcie Antonio (Mng Dir)

InnovioPapers BV   (1)
Ambachtsweg 2, 6541 DB, Nijmegen, Netherlands
Tel.: (31) 243710911
Web Site: http://www.innoviopapers.com
Sales Range: $50-74.9 Million
Emp.: 200
Paper Mills
N.A.I.C.S.: 322120
Wayne Thomas (Dir-Mill)

iP3 Lyons   (1)
Rue Grange Morin, BP 178, 69656, Villefranche-sur-Saone, France
Tel.: (33) 474656080
Web Site: http://www.ip3plastics.com
Sales Range: $25-49.9 Million
Emp.: 100
Plastic Motor Vehicle Component Mfr

N.A.I.C.S.: 326199

AMERICAN INDUSTRIAL CORPORATION
1400 American Way, Greenwood, IN 46143
Tel.: (317) 859-9900
Web Site: http://www.teamaic.com
Year Founded: 1969
Sales Range: $25-49.9 Million
Emp.: 35
Sales, Engineering, Service, Repair & Manufacturing of Liquid & Powder Finishing Equipment, Systems & Components
N.A.I.C.S.: 423830
Dave Jacks (Pres)
Mark Schriver (Controller)
Melanie Gorrell (Mgr-Fin)

AMERICAN INDUSTRIAL HYGIENE ASSOCIATION
3141 Fairview Park Dr Ste 777, Falls Church, VA 22042
Tel.: (703) 849-8888   IL
Web Site: https://www.aiha.org
Year Founded: 1956
Sales Range: $10-24.9 Million
Emp.: 55
Occupational Safety & Health Administration Services
N.A.I.C.S.: 926150
Sue Marchese (Dir-Mktg & Comm)

AMERICAN INNOTEK, INC
2320 Meyers Ave, Escondido, CA 92029
Tel.: (760) 741-6600
Web Site:
http://www.americaninnotek.com
Year Founded: 1988
Sales Range: $10-24.9 Million
Emp.: 50
Sanitary Product Mfr & Distr
N.A.I.C.S.: 322291
Clarence A. Cassidy (Chm & CEO)

AMERICAN INSTANTS, INC.
117 Bartley Flanders Rd, Flanders, NJ 07836
Tel.: (973) 584-8811
Web Site:
http://www.americaninstants.com
Year Founded: 1961
Sales Range: $10-24.9 Million
Emp.: 60
Instant Beverage Mfr
N.A.I.C.S.: 424490
Chris Roche (CEO)
Jim Mioduszewski (Controller)

AMERICAN INSTITUTE FOR CHARTERED PROPERTY CASUALTY UNDERWRITERS
720 Providence Rd Ste 100, Malvern, PA 19355
Tel.: (610) 644-2100   PA
Web Site:
https://www.theinstitutes.org
Year Founded: 1942
Sales Range: $50-74.9 Million
Emp.: 186
Educational Support Services
N.A.I.C.S.: 611710
Anita Z. Bourke (Exec VP)
Kevin H. Brown (Sr VP & Exec Dir)
Jeffrey Scheidt (Sr VP)
Elizabeth A. Sprinkel (Sr VP)

AMERICAN INSTITUTE FOR FOREIGN STUDY, INC.
1 High Ridge Park, Stamford, CT 06905-1322
Tel.: (203) 399-5000   DE
Web Site: https://www.aifs.com
Year Founded: 1964

Sales Range: $125-149.9 Million
Emp.: 410
Organizes Cultural Exchange Programs Worldwide
N.A.I.C.S.: 611710
William L. Gertz (Chm, Pres & CEO)

Subsidiaries:

American Council for International Studies Inc.   (1)
343 Congress St Ste 3100, Boston, MA 02210
Tel.: (617) 236-2051
Web Site: http://www.acis.com
Rev.: $4,500,000
Emp.: 60
Operates High School Programs that Take High School Students Abroad to Study
N.A.I.C.S.: 611699
Peter Jones (Founder & Pres)

Division (Domestic):

American Council for International Studies, Inc. - Encore Tours Division   (2)
343 Congress St Ste 3100, Boston, MA 02210
Tel.: (877) 460-3801
Web Site: http://www.encoretours.com
Emp.: 150
Tour Operator
N.A.I.C.S.: 561520
Catherine Coggins (Mgr-HR)

American Institute For Foreign Study (Deutschland) GmbH   (1)
Cudateftr Str Asse 4, Bonn, 53111, Germany
Tel.: (49) 228 957 300
Web Site: http://www.aifs.de
Emp.: 70
Educational Support Services
N.A.I.C.S.: 611710
Thomas Kiechle (Office Mgr)

American Institute for Foreign Study   (1)
37 Queens Gate, London, SW7 5HR, United Kingdom
Tel.: (44) 2075817300
Web Site: http://www.aifs.co.uk
Sales Range: $25-49.9 Million
Emp.: 75
Educational Exchange Programs
N.A.I.C.S.: 611710

American Institute for Foreign Study College Division   (1)
1 High Ridge Pk, Stamford, CT 06905
Tel.: (203) 399-5000
Web Site: http://www.aifsabroad.com
Rev.: $34,000,000
Emp.: 200
Provides Overseas Educational Programs for U.S. Students
N.A.I.C.S.: 611710

Au Pair in America   (1)
1 High Ridge Park, Stamford, CT 06905   (100%)
Tel.: (203) 399-5000
Web Site: http://www.aupairinamerica.com
Rev.: $17,000,000
Emp.: 100
Childcare & Cultural Exchange Program; Enables Young Adults to Live with American Families & Care for Their Young Children
N.A.I.C.S.: 611710
Ruth Frizell Ferry (Sr VP)
Jean Quinn (Asst VP)

Camp America   (1)
1 High Ridge Park, Stamford, CT 06905
Tel.: (203) 399-5414
Web Site: http://www.campamerica.com
Sales Range: $25-49.9 Million
Emp.: 250
Exchange Program for Foreign Students Interested in Working as Camp Counselors in the U.S.
N.A.I.C.S.: 611710
Dennis Regan (Sr VP)
Victoria Pannett (Asst VP)
Andrew Newberry (Dir-Client Dev)

Cultural Insurance Services International, Inc.   (1)

American Institute for Foreign Study,
Inc.—(Continued)

1 High Ridge Park, Stamford, CT 06905
Tel.: (203) 399-5130
Web Site: http://www.culturalinsurance.com
General Insurance Services
N.A.I.C.S.: 524210

Global Experiences, Inc. **(1)**
14 Annapolis St, 21401, Annapolis, MD
Tel.: (410) 267-7306
Web Site: http://www.globalexperiences.com
Education Training & Support Services
N.A.I.C.S.: 611710
Peter Ballagh *(Dir-Dublin Program)*
Claire Betts *(Program Dir-London)*
Jessica Burns *(Dir-Ops)*
Jordan Caley *(Coord-Paris)*
Jaci Corvino *(Mgr-Acct)*
Emily Merson *(Co-Founder & CEO)*

AMERICAN INSTITUTE OF GASTRIC BANDING

630 N Coit Rd Ste 2200, Richardson,
TX 75080-3764
Tel.: (214) 389-7400
Web Site: http://www.aigb.com
Year Founded: 2003
Sales Range: $10-24.9 Million
Emp.: 225
Surgical Center Operator
N.A.I.C.S.: 541720
Peter Gottlieb *(CEO)*
Roy Russell *(CMO)*

AMERICAN INSTITUTE OF PHYSICS INC.

1 Physics Ellipse, College Park, MD
20740
Tel.: (301) 209-3100
Web Site: http://www.aip.org
Year Founded: 1931
Sales Range: $50-74.9 Million
Emp.: 100
Publisher of Physics Trade Journals
N.A.I.C.S.: 513120
Catherine Swartz *(CFO)*
Catherine O'Riordan *(COO)*
Michael H. Moloney *(CEO)*
David J. Helfand *(Chm)*
Kevin Watkins *(Chief Federation Officer)*

AMERICAN INSTITUTE OF STEEL CONSTRUCTION

1 E Wacker Dr Ste 700, Chicago, IL
60601-1802
Tel.: (312) 670-2400   IL
Web Site: http://www.aisc.org
Year Founded: 1921
Sales Range: $10-24.9 Million
Emp.: 79
Trade Assocation
N.A.I.C.S.: 813910
Charles J. Carter *(Pres)*
David B. Ratterman *(Exec Officer)*
David Zalesne *(Chm)*
Jack Klimp *(Vice Chm)*
Dan Kadrmas *(Treas)*
Larry Kruth *(VP-Market Dev)*

AMERICAN INSTITUTE OF TOXICOLOGY, INC.

2265 Executive Dr, Indianapolis, IN
46241
Tel.: (317) 243-3894
Web Site: http://www.aitlabs.com
Year Founded: 1990
Sales Range: $50-74.9 Million
Emp.: 480
Toxicology & Forensics Laboratories
N.A.I.C.S.: 621511
Michael A. Evans *(Founder)*
Andrea Terrell *(Chief Scientific Officer & VP)*
Eric A. Orme *(COO & VP)*
Todd Pedersen *(VP-Corp Dev)*

AMERICAN INSURANCE MANAGEMENT GROUP

3101 Towercreek Pkwy SE # 750,
Atlanta, GA 30339
Tel.: (770) 980-0591
Rev.: $10,000,000
Emp.: 36
Insurance Agents, Brokers & Service
N.A.I.C.S.: 524210

AMERICAN INTEGRATION CONTRACTORS, LLC

430 Eraste Landry Rd, Lafayette, LA
70506-2329
Web Site: http://www.getaic.com
Electrical Contractor
N.A.I.C.S.: 238210
Todd Mouton *(Co-Owner & VP)*
Craig Noel *(Co-Owner & CEO)*

Subsidiaries:

Accel Protection & Technologies,
LLC.   **(1)**
1510 Rees St, Breaux Bridge, LA 70517
Tel.: (337) 332-2730
Sales Range: $1-9.9 Million
Emp.: 23
Security System Services
N.A.I.C.S.: 561621
Griffin Huval *(COO & Dir-Mktg)*
Levi Landry *(Dir-Protective Svcs)*
Pat Papillion *(Project Mgr)*

AMERICAN INTEGRITY INSURANCE COMPANY OF FLORIDA, INC.

5426 Bay Center Dr 6th Fl Ste 650,
Tampa, FL 33609
Web Site: https://www.aiicfl.com
Year Founded: 2006
Property & Casualty Insurance Services
N.A.I.C.S.: 524126
Robert Ritchie *(Pres & CEO)*
Gloria Hendrickson *(Sr VP-Risk Mgmt)*
Angie Quinn *(Chief HR Officer & Sr VP)*
Jon Ritchie *(Sr VP-Ops)*
Patrick Madigan *(VP-Underwriting & Client Svcs)*
Victor Mandes *(VP-IT)*
Steve Kolk *(Asst VP-Pricing)*
Anne Kevlin *(Dir-Litigation)*
Toni Logan *(Dir-Mktg)*
Danny Pringle *(Asst VP-Product Dev)*
Cory Brown *(CFO)*
Justin Waters *(VP-Sls)*
Wei Xie *(VP-Pricing & Actuarial Svcs)*
Dick Dowd *(Exec VP)*

AMERICAN INTERNATIONAL COMMUNICATIONS, INC.

6760 Jimmy Carter Blvd Ste 185,
Norcross, GA 30071
Tel.: (770) 447-8666
Web Site:
    http://www.aicconverge.com
Year Founded: 1986
Sales Range: $25-49.9 Million
Emp.: 150
Telecommunications Solutions & Services
N.A.I.C.S.: 334419
William Abram *(Chm & CEO)*

Subsidiaries:

American International Communications Jacksonville   **(1)**
6684 Columbia Park Dr Ste 1, Jacksonville,
FL 32258
Tel.: (904) 363-0033
Web Site: http://www.aicconverge.com
Rev.: $1,300,000
Emp.: 20
Telecommunications Solutions & Services
N.A.I.C.S.: 334419

AMERICAN INTERNATIONAL CONTRACTORS INC.

4600 N Fairfax Dr Ste 1004, Arlington, VA 22203
Tel.: (703) 524-5454   MD
Web Site: http://www.aici-ho.com
Year Founded: 1974
Industrial Buildings & Warehouses
N.A.I.C.S.: 236220
Francois Antypas *(Sr VP)*
Daniel Grey *(Pres)*
William Sheedy *(Program Mgr)*
Agustin O Eustaquio *(VP-Fin)*
Emad Salah *(Ops Mgr)*

AMERICAN INTERNATIONAL HEALTH ALLIANCE

1225 Eye St NW Ste 205, Washington, DC 20005
Tel.: (202) 789-1136   DE
Web Site: http://www.aiha.com
Year Founded: 1992
Sales Range: $10-24.9 Million
Community Care Services
N.A.I.C.S.: 624190
Alan Weinstein *(Chm & Treas)*
Inna Jurkevich *(Dir-Program)*
David Greeley *(Pres & CEO)*

AMERICAN INTERNATIONAL INDUSTRIES COMPANY

2220 Gaspar Ave, Los Angeles, CA
90040-1516
Tel.: (323) 728-2999   CA
Web Site: https://www.aiibeauty.com
Year Founded: 1971
Sales Range: $75-99.9 Million
Emp.: 22
Health & Beauty Aids Mfr
N.A.I.C.S.: 424210
Zvi Ryzman *(Pres & CEO)*
Terri Cooper *(Exec VP)*

Subsidiaries:

All Clubman   **(1)**
2220 Gaspar Ave, Los Angeles, CA 90040
Tel.: (323) 728-2999
Sales Range: $50-74.9 Million
Mfr of Health & Beauty Aids
N.A.I.C.S.: 424210
Zvi Ryzman *(Pres & CEO)*

Andrea International   **(1)**
2220 Gaspar Ave, City of Commerce, CA
90040
Tel.: (323) 728-2999
Web Site: http://www.andrea.com
Sales Range: $50-74.9 Million
Eye Care Products Mfr
N.A.I.C.S.: 339115
Zvi Ryzman *(CEO)*
Charlie Loveless *(CFO)*

Ardell International, Inc.   **(1)**
2220 Gaspar Ave, City of Commerce, CA
90040   **(100%)**
Tel.: (323) 728-2999
Web Site: http://www.aii.com
Sales Range: $50-74.9 Million
Mfr of Health & Beauty Aids
N.A.I.C.S.: 424210
Zvi Ryzman *(Pres & CEO)*
Terry Cooper *(Exec VP)*

SuperNail   **(1)**
2220 Gaspar Ave, City of Commerce, CA
90040
Tel.: (323) 728-2999
Web Site: http://www.aiibeauty.co
Sales Range: $25-49.9 Million
Mfr of Professional Nail Care Products
N.A.I.C.S.: 424210
Zvi Ryzman *(Pres & CEO)*
Terri Cooper *(Exec VP)*
Mark Moesta *(VP-Sls)*

AMERICAN INTERNATIONAL RELOCATION SOLUTIONS LLC

6 Penn Ctr W, Pittsburgh, PA 15276
Tel.: (412) 788-0461

Web Site: https://www.aires.com
Year Founded: 1981
Rev.: $12,500,000
Emp.: 500
Relocation Services
N.A.I.C.S.: 481212
Joleen Lauffer *(VP-Ops)*
Michael Drew II *(Dir-Consulting Svc)*
Ed Hartman *(Dir-Fin)*
Tony Dougherty *(Mgr-Accts)*
Eric Reed *(Dir-Corp Bus-West Coast Reg)*
Bryan Putt *(CEO)*
Eric Tate *(VP-East)*
Jeffrey Wangler *(Pres)*

AMERICAN INTERNATIONAL SUPPLY INC.

575 Independent Rd, Oakland, CA
94621
Tel.: (510) 834-7222   CA
Web Site: https://www.aisi.com
Year Founded: 1983
Sales Range: $10-24.9 Million
Emp.: 50
Provider of Plumbing Fixtures, Equipment & Supplies
N.A.I.C.S.: 423720
Jed Myle *(Pres)*

AMERICAN IRON & STEEL COMPANY

2800 Pacific St, Minneapolis, MN
55411
Tel.: (612) 529-9221
Web Site: http://www.scrappy.com
Year Founded: 1885
Rev.: $32,000,000
Emp.: 50
Ferrous Metal Scrap & Waste
N.A.I.C.S.: 423930
Steve Ettinger *(Pres)*

AMERICAN IRON WORKS

5010 Inwood St, Hyattsville, MD
20781
Tel.: (301) 277-8444
Web Site:
    https://www.americanironworks.com
Year Founded: 1948
Sales Range: $25-49.9 Million
Emp.: 211
Ornamental & Architectural Metal Work Mfr
N.A.I.C.S.: 332323
Savvas Savopoulos *(Pres & CEO)*

AMERICAN IT SOLUTIONS, INC. (AIT)

420 Center St, Wallingford, CT 06492
Tel.: (203) 269-1900
Web Site:
    https://www.americanitsolutions.com
Year Founded: 2005
Sales Range: $1-9.9 Million
Emp.: 112
Nationwide Onsite Computer & Network Support for Small & Midsize Businesses
N.A.I.C.S.: 541511
Bryan Kane *(Mng Partner)*

AMERICAN JEBCO CORPORATION

11330 W Melrose Ave, Franklin Park,
IL 60131-1367
Tel.: (847) 455-3150
Web Site:
    http://www.americanjebco.com
Year Founded: 2001
Sales Range: $25-49.9 Million
Emp.: 100
Rivets & Cold-Headed Special Fasteners Mfr
N.A.I.C.S.: 332722

Matthew Connor *(Pres, Treas & Sec)*
John Drinan *(Controller)*
Jeff Kaup *(Mgr-Customer Svc)*
Pete O'Connor *(Mgr-Pur)*

AMERICAN JEWELRY & LOAN
20450 Greenfield Rd, Detroit, MI 48235
Tel.: (313) 345-4000
Web Site: http://www.americanjewelry.com
Year Founded: 1978
Sales Range: $1-9.9 Million
Emp.: 50
Pawn Shop Owner
N.A.I.C.S.: 459510
Leslie Gold *(Co-Owner & Pres)*
Seth Gold *(Gen Mgr)*
Ashley Broad *(Asst Mgr)*
Lili Gold *(Co-Owner)*

AMERICAN JEWISH COMMITTEE
165 E 56th St, New York, NY 10022
Tel.: (212) 751-4000   NY
Web Site: http://www.ajc.org
Year Founded: 1906
Sales Range: $50-74.9 Million
Emp.: 303
Human Right Services
N.A.I.C.S.: 813311
Victoria E. Schonfeld *(COO)*
David Harris *(CEO)*
Janet Besso Becker *(Mng Dir-HR & Strategic Implementation & Assoc Exec Dir)*
Julie Schair *(Mng Dir-Resource Dev & Assoc Exec Dir)*
Richard Hyne *(CFO)*
Marc Stern *(Gen Counsel)*
Andrew Baker *(Dir-Jewish Affairs-Intl)*
Richard Foltin *(Dir-Legislative Affairs-Natl)*
Julie Fishman Rayman *(Dir-Political Outreach)*
Kenneth Bandler *(Dir-Media Rels)*
Lawrence Grossman *(Dir-Publications)*
Richard Hirschhaut *(Dir-Los Angeles)*
Holly Huffnagle *(Dir-Combating Anti-Semitism)*

AMERICAN JEWISH CONGRESS INC.
115 E 57 St Ste 11, New York, NY 10022
Tel.: (212) 879-4500
Web Site: http://www.ajcongress.org
Year Founded: 1918
Rev.: $10,500,000
Emp.: 40
Magazine Publisher
N.A.I.C.S.: 513120
Jack Rosen *(Pres)*

AMERICAN JEWISH WORLD SERVICE, INC.
45 W 36th St, New York, NY 10018
Tel.: (212) 792-2900   NY
Web Site: http://www.ajws.org
Year Founded: 1985
Rev.: $40,227,642
Assets: $50,639,183
Liabilities: $5,309,791
Net Worth: $45,329,392
Earnings: ($4,065,715)
Fiscal Year-end: 04/30/19
Human Rights Organizations
N.A.I.C.S.: 813311
Robert Bank *(Pres & CEO)*
Jacqueline Hart *(VP-Strategic Learning, Res & Evaluation)*
Stuart Schear *(VP-Comm & Mktg)*
Kristine A. Stallone *(VP-Fin & Admin)*
Eric Sahn *(Vice Chm)*
Jim Koshland *(Treas)*

Marion J. Bergman *(Vice Chm)*
Russ Pratt *(Pres-Pratt Company)*
Bradley Abelow *(Chm)*
Sharon Leslie *(Vice Chm)*
Margo Bloom *(VP-Dev)*
Danielle Edwards *(VP-Fin & Admin)*
Amy Pasquale *(Exec VP)*
Shari Turitz *(VP-Programs)*

AMERICAN JOURNAL EXPERTS, LLC
3211 Shannon Rd Ste 500, Durham, NC 27707
Tel.: (919) 704-4253
Web Site: http://www.journalexperts.com
Year Founded: 2004
Sales Range: $10-24.9 Million
Emp.: 90
Manuscript Publisher
N.A.I.C.S.: 513199
Amy Rawls *(Dir-HR)*
Jenny Evans *(Mgr-Ops Support)*
Afton Thompson *(Dir-Dev Svcs)*
Allison McMullen *(Project Mgr)*
April Troester *(Dir-Customer Svcs)*
Brandon Jernigan *(Dir-Editing Svcs)*
Flavia Jaszczak *(Mgr-Acct Dev)*
Kurt Spurlock *(Mgr-Quality)*
Michelle Ebbs *(Partner-Res Comm)*
Sarah Smith-Brady *(Mgr-Team)*
Sarah Taylor *(VP-Ops)*

AMERICAN KITCHEN DELIGHTS
15320 Cooper Ave, Harvey, IL 60426-2922
Tel.: (708) 210-3200
Web Site: https://www.americankitchens.com
Sales Range: $10-24.9 Million
Emp.: 100
Convenience Foods Mfr
N.A.I.C.S.: 311991
Shahnawaz Hasan *(Pres)*

AMERICAN LABELMARK COMPANY INC.
5724 N Pulaski Rd, Chicago, IL 60646
Tel.: (773) 478-0900
Web Site: https://www.labelmaster.com
Year Founded: 1967
Dangerous Goods Shipping & Hazardous Materials Logistics
N.A.I.C.S.: 541614
Dwight E. Curtis *(Vice Chm)*
Alan J. Schoen *(Pres)*
Robert Finn *(VP-Mktg & Product Mgmt)*
Michael J. Kaufman *(VP-Production & Tech)*
Peggi Boyd *(Compliance Officer)*
Gary S. Mostow *(Chm)*
Heidi Lohmann *(VP-Sls)*
Mario Sagastume *(VP-Customer Success)*

AMERICAN LABORATORIES
35 Broadway, Hicksville, NY 11801
Tel.: (516) 822-8700
Web Site: http://www.americandental.com
Rev.: $13,800,000
Emp.: 7
Dentists' Professional Supplies
N.A.I.C.S.: 423450

AMERICAN LABORATORIES INC.
4410 S 102nd St, Omaha, NE 68127
Tel.: (402) 339-2494
Web Site: http://www.americanlaboratory.com
Year Founded: 1967

Sales Range: $10-24.9 Million
Emp.: 50
Processor & Supplier of Raw Materials
N.A.I.C.S.: 325412
Jeffrey E. Jackson *(CEO)*

AMERICAN LAND VENTURES, LLC
800 Brickell Ave Ph 1, Miami, FL 33131
Tel.: (305) 350-1901
Web Site: http://www.americanventures.com
Year Founded: 1982
Sales Range: $1-9.9 Million
Emp.: 10
Land Subdivision
N.A.I.C.S.: 237210
Granvil Tracy *(Pres)*
James Cuddy *(VP-Construction)*
Jason Robertson *(VP-Dev)*
Tammy Britton *(Exec Dir-Property Mgmt)*

AMERICAN LASER CENTERS
24555 Hallwood Ct, Farmington Hills, MI 48334
Tel.: (248) 426-8250
Web Site: http://www.americanlaser.com
Year Founded: 2002
Sales Range: $125-149.9 Million
Emp.: 1,711
Personal Care Services
N.A.I.C.S.: 812111
Steven Brown *(Chm)*
Bob Mack *(VP-Ops)*
Jacqueline Segal *(VP & Controller)*
Steven C. Straus *(CEO)*
Cheryl Vogel *(Dir-Treasury)*

AMERICAN LAUBSCHER CORPORATION
80 Finn Ct, Farmingdale, NY 11735-1107
Tel.: (631) 694-5900   NY
Web Site: http://www.alcprecision.com
Year Founded: 1950
Sales Range: $75-99.9 Million
Emp.: 50
Mfr of Precision Components; Screw Machine Products; Jewel Bearings; Wire Guides; Ground Shafts
N.A.I.C.S.: 423830
Lloyd Miller *(Pres)*
Richard Fox *(CFO)*

AMERICAN LAWN MOWER COMPANY
2100 N Granville Ave, Muncie, IN 47303-2153
Tel.: (765) 288-6624
Web Site: http://www.reelin.com
Rev.: $5,000,000
Emp.: 60
Mfr of Hand Lawn Mowers, Reel Power Mowers & Gang Mowers
N.A.I.C.S.: 333112
R.E. Kersey *(Pres & Gen Mgr)*

Subsidiaries:

Great States Corp.   (1)
830 Webster St, Shelbyville, IN 46176-1961   (100%)
Tel.: (317) 392-3615
Web Site: http://www.earthwisetools.com
Sales Range: $25-49.9 Million
Emp.: 20
Lawn Mower Replacement Parts Mfr
N.A.I.C.S.: 333112
R. E. Kersey *(CEO)*

AMERICAN LEARNING CORPORATION
1 Jericho Plz, Jericho, NY 11753

Tel.: (516) 938-8000   NY
Web Site: http://www.americanlearningco.com
Year Founded: 1982
Sales Range: $1-9.9 Million
Emp.: 79
Services to Children with Disabilities
N.A.I.C.S.: 624190
Gary Gelman *(Chm, Pres & CEO)*
Gary J. Knauer *(CFO, Treas & Sec)*

Subsidiaries:

Interactive Therapy Group Consultants, Inc.   (1)
1 Adler Dr, East Syracuse, NY 13057
Tel.: (315) 469-1189
Web Site: http://www.interactivetherapygroup.com
Speech Therapy Services
N.A.I.C.S.: 621340
Jared M. Bauer *(Pres)*
Delilah Morales *(Dir-Program-Hudson Valley)*
Celi Alvarez *(Mgr-Acctg)*
Gary J. Knauer *(CFO)*

Signature Learning Resources, Inc.   (1)
19 W 21st St Ste 701, New York, NY 10010
Tel.: (646) 230-8190
Web Site: http://www.signaturelearningresources.com
Speech Therapy Services
N.A.I.C.S.: 621340
Jared M. Bauer *(Pres)*
Vanessa R. Evans *(Dir-Reg Program)*
Olga Martes *(Dir-HR)*

AMERICAN LEGAL SEARCH, LLC
PO Box 43391, Birmingham, AL 35243
Tel.: (205) 397-9500
Web Site: http://www.americanlegalsearch.com
Year Founded: 2001
Emp.: 6
Legal Search & Consulting Services
N.A.I.C.S.: 541199
Joseph D. Freedman *(Chm)*
Rhonda Singer *(Sr Mng Dir-Ops-East Coast)*
Carter Hoyt *(Mng Dir-Ops-Atlanta)*

AMERICAN LEGEND COOPERATIVE
200 SW 34th St, Renton, WA 98057
Tel.: (425) 251-3200   WA
Web Site: http://www.americanlegend.com
Year Founded: 1986
Rev.: $80,000,000
Emp.: 40
Mink Producer & Mink Products Mfr
N.A.I.C.S.: 112930
Anne Daffern *(CFO)*

AMERICAN LICORICE CO. INC.
2796 NW Clearwater Dr, Bend, OR 97701-7008
Tel.: (541) 617-0800
Web Site: http://www.americanlicorice.com
Rev.: $100,000,000
Emp.: 500
Licorice Candy Mfr
N.A.I.C.S.: 311340
John Kretchmer *(CEO)*
Jeff Gorden *(Dir-Acctg & Fin)*
Madalyn Friedman *(Dir-Mktg, Sls & Fin)*

AMERICAN LIFT TRUCK SERVICES LLC

American Lift Truck Services LLC—(Continued)

298 Quality Dr Ste 1, Byhalia, MS
38611-6519
Tel.: (901) 366-1842   TN
Year Founded: 2005
Sales Range: $10-24.9 Million
Emp.: 20
Industrial Lift Truck Sales, Rental,
Parts & Repair Services
N.A.I.C.S.: 423830

AMERICAN LIST COUNSEL, INC.
4300 US Hwy 1 CN 5219, Princeton,
NJ 08543
Tel.: (609) 580-2800   NJ
Web Site: http://www.alc.com
Year Founded: 1978
Sales Range: $150-199.9 Million
Emp.: 182
Direct Mail Advertising Services
N.A.I.C.S.: 541860
Donn Rappaport *(Founder & Chm)*
Susan Rappaport *(Pres & COO)*
Steve Jones *(Mgr-Smart Data Solutions Acct)*
Fran Green *(Pres-SMART Data Solutions)*
Peter DeRosa *(CFO-Bus Svcs)*
Rachel Mercer *(Sr VP-Data Acq)*
David Dotson *(Mng Partner-Data Acq)*
Laurie Cole *(Exec VP-Data Acq)*
Susan Rudy *(Sr VP & Acct Dir)*
Patricia Stecher *(Exec VP-IT)*
Britt Vatne *(Pres-Data Mgmt)*
Bruce Kimmel *(VP-Data Mgmt)*
Michael Reckinger *(VP-Data Svcs)*
Bernadette Joachim *(VP-Insert Media)*
Bryan MacDonald *(Exec VP-Strategic Plng)*
Kathryn Moreci *(VP-Data Acquisition)*
Maryann Posten *(VP-Smart Bus Solutions)*
Holly Hammond Romer *(Mng Partner-Data Acquisition)*
Elizabeth Schreiber *(VP-Bus Svc)*
Greg Westrick *(Sr VP-Sls Remarketable)*

AMERICAN LITHIUM MINERALS, INC.
2850 W Horizon Rdg Pkwy Ste 200,
Henderson, NV 89052
Tel.: (416) 214-0049
Mineral Exploration Services
N.A.I.C.S.: 212290
Hugh Aird *(Pres & CEO)*

AMERICAN LITHO INC.
175 Mercedes Dr, Carol Stream, IL
60188-9409
Tel.: (630) 462-1700
Web Site: https://www.alitho.com
Year Founded: 1994
Sales Range: $50-74.9 Million
Emp.: 145
Commercial Web Printing Services
N.A.I.C.S.: 323111
Mike Fontana *(Pres & CEO)*
Frank Arostegui *(Exec VP-Sls & Customer Care)*

Subsidiaries:

Berlin Division   (1)
175 Mercedes Dr, Carol Stream, IL 60188-9409
Tel.: (630) 682-0600
Commercial Printing
N.A.I.C.S.: 323111

AMERICAN LOCKER GROUP INCORPORATED
700 Freeport Pkwy Ste 300, Coppell,
TX 75019
Tel.: (817) 329-1600   DE
Web Site:
   http://www.americanlocker.com
Year Founded: 1958
Sales Range: $10-24.9 Million
Emp.: 120
Coin Key & Electronically Controlled
Security Locker & Lock Plastic Centralized Mail & Parcel Distibution
Locker Mfr
N.A.I.C.S.: 337215

Subsidiaries:

American Locker Company, Inc.   (1)
2701 Regent Blvd Ste 200, Dallas-Fort
Worth Airport, TX 75261   **(100%)**
Tel.: (817) 329-1600
Web Site: http://www.americanlocker.com
Holding Company
N.A.I.C.S.: 337126
David Vonzqrnqehlen *(VP-Sls)*

American Locker Security Systems,
Inc.   (1)
815 S Main St, Grapevine, TX
76051-5535   **(100%)**
Tel.: (817) 329-1600
Web Site: http://www.americanlocker.com
Coin Operated Checking Lockers, Mini-
Check Valuables Lockers, Police Evidence
Lockers, Law Enforcement Pistol Lockers,
Computer Print-Out Lockers, Parcel Post &
Hotel Lockers
N.A.I.C.S.: 337215

Canadian Locker Company of
Canada, Ltd.   (1)
151 Nashdene Rd Unit 13, Scarborough,
M1V 2T3, ON, Canada   **(100%)**
Tel.: (416) 439-5992
Sales Range: $1-9.9 Million
Emp.: 8
Secure Mailbox Mfr & Distr
N.A.I.C.S.: 561621

Subsidiary (Domestic):

Canadian Locker Co., Ltd.   (2)
931 Progress Ave Unit 5, Scarborough,
M1G 3V5, ON, Canada   **(100%)**
Tel.: (416) 439-5992
Sales Range: $1-9.9 Million
Distribution of Coin & Key Controlled Lockers & Locks
N.A.I.C.S.: 423440

Security Manufacturing Corp   (1)
700 Freeport pakrway Ste 300, Coppell, TX
75019   **(100%)**
Tel.: (817) 329-1600
Web Site:
   http://www.securitymanufacturing.com
Sales Range: $10-24.9 Million
Emp.: 50
Mailbox Mfr
N.A.I.C.S.: 337215

Security Manufacturing
Corporation   (1)
2701 Regent Blvd, Grapevine, TX
75261   **(100%)**
Tel.: (817) 329-1600
Web Site:
   http://www.securitymanufacturing.com
Secure Mailbox Mfr & Distr
N.A.I.C.S.: 332439

AMERICAN LOUVER COMPANY
7700 Austin Ave, Skokie, IL 60077-
2603
Tel.: (847) 470-3300   IL
Web Site:
   http://www.americanlouver.com
Year Founded: 1946
Sales Range: $75-99.9 Million
Emp.: 130
Louvers & Lenses, Security Mirrors,
Shopping Baskets, Plastic Barricades
& Traffic Devices & Plastic Sign
Stands Mfr
N.A.I.C.S.: 335132

Walter Glass *(Founder)*
Lucy Polk *(CFO)*
Donner Kelner *(Dir-Mktg)*
Geoffrey Glass Jr. *(Pres)*

AMERICAN LUMBER COMPANY INCORPORATED
1 American Way, Walden, NY 12586
Tel.: (845) 778-1111
Web Site:
   https://www.americanlumberco.com
Sales Range: $10-24.9 Million
Emp.: 40
Lumber: Rough, Dressed & Finished
N.A.I.C.S.: 423310
John Harrington *(Controller)*

AMERICAN LUMBER COMPANY LP
4002 Legion Dr, Hamburg, NY 14075
Tel.: (814) 438-7888
Web Site: https://www.alumber.com
Year Founded: 1953
Sales Range: $10-24.9 Million
Emp.: 75
Supplier of Lumber & Plywood Products
N.A.I.C.S.: 423310

AMERICAN MADE, LLC
19 Leonberg Rd, Cranberry Township, PA 16066
Tel.: (724) 776-4800   PA
Web Site: http://www.american-madellc.com
Year Founded: 1983
Sales Range: $10-24.9 Million
Glass-Reinforced Thermoplastic
Composite Products Mfr
N.A.I.C.S.: 326199

Subsidiaries:

American Made Liner Systems   (1)
2600 Neville Rd, Pittsburgh, PA 15225
Tel.: (412) 771-3300
Web Site: http://www.linersystems.com
Reinforced Thermoplastic Dump Truck Bed
Liner Mfr
N.A.I.C.S.: 326199
Michael LaRocco *(Founder, Pres & CEO)*

AMERICAN MANAGEMENT SERVICES LLC
Pier 70 2801 Alaskan Way Ste 200,
Seattle, WA 98121
Tel.: (206) 215-9700
Web Site:
   http://www.pinnaclerealty.com
Year Founded: 2003
Sales Range: $50-74.9 Million
Emp.: 2,500
Real Estate Manangement Services
N.A.I.C.S.: 531390
John A. Goodman *(Chm)*

Subsidiaries:

Aspen Apartments   (1)
1800 Aspen Dr Apt 103, Hudson, WI 54016
Tel.: (715) 386-6228
Web Site: http://www.pinnacleams.com
Rev.: $120,000
Emp.: 3
Apartment Building Operator
N.A.I.C.S.: 531110
Ron Konickson *(Mgr-Property)*

Pinnacle AMS Development Company LLC   (1)
11235 SE 6th St Ste 200, Bellevue, WA
98004
Tel.: (206) 215-9700
Web Site: http://www.pinnacleliving.com
Real Estate Manangement Services
N.A.I.C.S.: 531390
Stan Harrelson *(Pres & CEO)*
Mary J. Bunt *(Dir-Natl Tech Trng)*

AMERICAN MARINE HOLDINGS, LLC

1653 Whichards Beach Rd, Washington, NC 27889
Tel.: (252) 975-2000   FL
Web Site:
   http://www.donzimarine.com
Sales Range: $50-74.9 Million
Emp.: 30
Holding Company & Fiberglass Pleasure Boat Services
N.A.I.C.S.: 551112
Josh Stickles *(VP-Mktg)*
Chuck Wagner *(VP-Customer Svc)*
Joseph G. Wortley *(Principal)*
Craig Tompkins *(Principal)*
Carol Price *(Mgr-Sls)*
Pam Campbell *(Mgr-Social Media & Web)*

Subsidiaries:

Baja Marine, Inc.   (1)
1653 Whichards Beach Rd, Washington,
NC 27889
Tel.: (252) 975-2000
Web Site: http://www.bajamarine.com
Sport Boats
N.A.I.C.S.: 336612
Craig Barrie *(VP-Sls & Gen Mgr)*
Blane Aarup *(Dir-Sls)*
Nick Miller *(VP)*
Presley Eley *(Mgr-Lamination)*
B. K. Millaway *(Dir-Customer Svc)*
Carol Price *(Mgr-Sls)*

Donzi Marine Corporation   (1)
7110 21st St E, Sarasota, FL 34243-3916
Tel.: (941) 727-0622
Web Site: http://www.donzimarine.com
Sales Range: $25-49.9 Million
Mfr of Luxury Speedboats & Sportsboats
N.A.I.C.S.: 336612

Fountain Powerboats, Inc.   (1)
1653 Whichards Beach Rd, Washington,
NC 27889
Tel.: (252) 975-2000
Web Site:
   http://www.fountainpowerboats.com
Sport Boat Mfr
N.A.I.C.S.: 336612
John Walker *(Pres & CEO)*
Craig Barrie *(Gen Mgr)*

Pro-Line Boats   (1)
1520 S Suncoat Blvd, Homosassa, FL
34448
Tel.: (352) 795-4111
Web Site: http://www.prolineboats.com
Boat Builders
N.A.I.C.S.: 336612
Dan Atwood *(Founder)*

AMERICAN MARITIME HOLDINGS, INC.
555 E Main St Ste 1212, Norfolk, VA
23510
Tel.: (757) 961-9311   VA
Web Site:
   http://www.americanmaritime.com
Year Founded: 2005
Holding Company; Ship Repair &
Maintenance Services
N.A.I.C.S.: 551112
Gary Brandt *(Chm & CEO)*
Michael S. Torrech *(Pres & COO)*

Subsidiaries:

Tecnico Corporation   (1)
831 Industrial Ave, Chesapeake, VA 23324-
2614
Tel.: (757) 545-4013
Web Site: http://www.tecnicocorp.com
Sales Range: $50-74.9 Million
Emp.: 600
Marine & Industrial Contractor
N.A.I.C.S.: 238990
Mark Oakley *(Sr VP & Dir-Divs)*
Lisa Stuchell Foley *(Controller)*
Danny Oertel *(VP-Ops)*
Al Lowe *(Mgr-Estimating)*
Armando Smith *(Mgr-Project-Contract)*
Tim Varvel *(Mgr)*

AMERICAN MARKETING &

MAILING SERVICES, INC.
9427 Corporate Lake Dr, Tampa, FL 33634
Tel.: (813) 886-5597
Web Site:
https://www.americanmarkets.com
Year Founded: 1994
Sales Range: $10-24.9 Million
Emp.: 70
Direct Marketing Services
N.A.I.C.S.: 541860
Rick Davis (Mgr-IT)
Sandi Sawyer (VP-Customer Rels)
Charles Fest Jr. (VP-Wholesale Sls)

AMERICAN MARKING SYSTEMS, INC.
1015 Paulison Ave, Clifton, NJ 07011-3610
Tel.: (973) 478-5600   NJ
Web Site: https://www.ams-stamps.com
Year Founded: 1898
Sales Range: $50-74.9 Million
Emp.: 80
Mfr of Marking Devices & ID Products such as Rubber, Self-Inking & Pre-Inked Stamps, Signs, Name Plates, Badges, Daters, Seals, Other Office Products & Industrial Marking Products
N.A.I.C.S.: 339940
John A. Collins (Pres)
Ronald Cochran (Mgr-Mktg & Sls)

Subsidiaries:

Baumgarten Stamp Co.   (1)
1305 St Pauls St, Baltimore, MD 21201-4301   (100%)
Tel.: (410) 727-3733
Web Site: http://www.ams-stamps.com
Sales Range: $10-24.9 Million
Emp.: 5
Custom Rubber Stamps Mfr
N.A.I.C.S.: 339940

Harrisburg Stamp Co.   (1)
3362 Paxton St, Harrisburg, PA 17111-1030
Tel.: (717) 236-9000
Web Site: http://www.ams-stamps.com
Sales Range: $25-49.9 Million
Emp.: 6
Mfr Rubber Stamps
N.A.I.C.S.: 339940

Paterson Stamp Works   (1)
1015 Paulison Ave, Clifton, NJ 07011-3610
Tel.: (973) 478-5600
Sales Range: $25-49.9 Million
Emp.: 20
Mfg Marking Devices
N.A.I.C.S.: 339940
Ron Cochran (Dir-Mktg)

Quaker City Stamp & Stencil   (1)
12285 McNulty Rd Bldg 103, Philadelphia, PA 19154-1210
Tel.: (215) 969-9800
Web Site: http://www.ams-stamps.com
Sales Range: $25-49.9 Million
Emp.: 5
Stamps & Signs Mfr
N.A.I.C.S.: 339940
Jack Shaughnessy (Mgr-Sls)
John Collins Jr. (Pres)

AMERICAN MEDIA INTERNATIONAL LTD.
2609 Tucker St Ext, Burlington, NC 27215-8857
Tel.: (336) 229-5554
Web Site: http://www.ami-media.com
Year Founded: 1981
Sales Range: $10-24.9 Million
Emp.: 80
Provider of Prerecorded Audio & Visual Duplication Services
N.A.I.C.S.: 334610
Richard Clark (Pres)

AMERICAN MEDICAL ADMIN-

ISTRATORS, INC.
10345 Watson Rd, Saint Louis, MO 63127
Tel.: (866) 668-2188   DE
Web Site:
https://www.amadministrators.com
Health Care Srvices
N.A.I.C.S.: 621999
Jonathan Loutzenhiser (CEO)

Subsidiaries:

Pediatrics & Adolescent Medicine, PC   (1)
2155 Post Oak Tritt Rd Ste 100, Marietta, GA 30062-1651
Tel.: (404) 255-6335
Web Site: http://www.pampapediatrics.com
Freestanding Ambulatory Surgical & Emergency Centers
N.A.I.C.S.: 621493
Jane Rogers (Office Mgr)
Andrew Beach (Head)

AMERICAN MEDICAL GROUP LLC
1698 Post Rd E, Westport, CT 06880
Tel.: (203) 292-8444
Web Site:
https://www.americanmeds.com
Healtcare Services
N.A.I.C.S.: 621999
Dom Gatto (Pres)

Subsidiaries:

Solos Endoscopy, Inc.   (1)
1698 Post Rd E Ste 3C, Westport, CT 06880
Tel.: (617) 360-9700
Web Site: http://www.solosendoscopy.com
Medical Device Mfr
N.A.I.C.S.: 339112
Amanda Segersten (VP)
Dom L. Gatto (Chm & CEO)

AMERICAN MERCHANDISE LIQUIDATORS, INC.
15810 A Hwy 59, Foley, AL 36535
Tel.: (251) 970-1100
Web Site: http://www.amlinc.com
Year Founded: 1992
Sales Range: $10-24.9 Million
Emp.: 22
General Merchandise Services
N.A.I.C.S.: 455219
Gerald Hughes (Pres)

AMERICAN METAL & PLASTICS INC.
450 32nd St SW, Grand Rapids, MI 49548-1021
Tel.: (616) 452-6061   MI
Web Site: https://www.ampi-gr.com
Year Founded: 1968
Sales Range: $100-124.9 Million
Emp.: 100
Provider of Automotive Stampings & Molded Plastics
N.A.I.C.S.: 326199
Dave Visch (Mgr-Engrg)
Tom Maxwell (Mgr-Production & Shipping)
John Pohl (Mgr-Pur)
Tom Cook (Pres & CEO)

AMERICAN METAL MOULDING CORP.
1801 N American St, Philadelphia, PA 19122
Tel.: (215) 634-3100
Web Site:
https://www.kbkitchenbath.com
Rev.: $12,000,000
Emp.: 30
Distributing Wood Flooring
N.A.I.C.S.: 423220
Herbert Lewenthal (Pres)
Alan Lewenthal (VP & Gen Mgr)

AMERICAN METAL TECHNOLOGIES, LLC
8213 Durand Ave, Sturtevant, WI 53177
Tel.: (262) 633-1756
Web Site:
https://www.amermetals.com
Year Founded: 2000
Rev.: $43,000,000
Emp.: 200
Machine Tools Mfr
N.A.I.C.S.: 333517
Ram Thukkaram (CEO)
David Becker (VP-Sls & Mktg)

AMERICAN METALS COMPANY, INC.
740 W Broadway Rd, Mesa, AZ 85210
Tel.: (480) 834-1923
Web Site:
https://www.amcrecycling.com
Year Founded: 1975
Sales Range: $10-24.9 Million
Emp.: 50
Scrap Metal Processing Services
N.A.I.C.S.: 423930
Irwin Sheinben (Pres)
Tony Di Santi (VP-Sls)

AMERICAN MILLS INCORPORATED
1120 Everee Inn Rd, Griffin, GA 30224
Tel.: (770) 228-3010
Web Site:
http://www.americanmillsinc.com
Rev.: $39,413,000
Emp.: 100
Tablecloths & Table Settings
N.A.I.C.S.: 314120
Joe Brown (Pres)

AMERICAN MINORITY BUSINESS FORMS, INC.
106 1st St SE PO Box 337, Glenwood, MN 56334-0337
Tel.: (800) 754-8831
Web Site:
http://www.americandiv.com
Year Founded: 1992
Sales Range: $10-24.9 Million
Business Forms & Office Supplies Distr
N.A.I.C.S.: 424120
Erica Van Beck (VP)

AMERICAN MORTGAGE SERVICES
8086 US Hwy 51 N, Millington, TN 38053
Tel.: (901) 873-1400
Web Site:
http://www.amortgageservices.com
Sales Range: $10-24.9 Million
Emp.: 16
Mortgages & Loans
N.A.I.C.S.: 522310
Monte Connell (Pres)

AMERICAN MOTEL MANAGEMENT
200 Northlake Pkwy S 277, Tucker, GA 30084-4023
Tel.: (770) 939-1801
Web Site:
https://www.americanmotels.com
Sales Range: $10-24.9 Million
Emp.: 100
Real Estate Services
N.A.I.C.S.: 531311
Deborah Harrell (VP)

Subsidiaries:

M&H Properties Ltd.   (1)

2200NLake Pkwy Ste 277, Tucker, GA 30084
Tel.: (770) 939-1801
Rev.: $15,213,876
Emp.: 6
Provider of Real Estate Services
N.A.I.C.S.: 531210
Melton Harrell (Pres)

AMERICAN MUNICIPAL POWER-OHIO, INC.
1111 Schrock Rd Ste 100, Columbus, OH 43229
Tel.: (614) 337-6222
Web Site: http://www.amp-ohio.org
Year Founded: 1971
Sales Range: $200-249.9 Million
Emp.: 85
Wholesale Provider of Electrical Power
N.A.I.C.S.: 221118
Marc S. Gerken (Pres & CEO)
Bob Trip (VP-Fin)
Ray Merill (Asst VP-Fin)
Jolene Thompson (Exec Dir)
Rachel Gerrick (Deputy Gen Counsel)
Bobby Little (Sr VP-Risk Control)
John Christopher Easton (VP-Bus Ops)
Scott Kiesewetter (Sr VP-Generation Ops)

AMERICAN NATIONAL CORPORATION
8990 W Dodge Rd, Omaha, NE 68114
Tel.: (402) 399-5000   NE
Web Site: http://www.anbank.com
Year Founded: 1979
Rev.: $34,878,414
Emp.: 400
Bank Holding Company
N.A.I.C.S.: 551111
Steven Ritzman (Pres)

Subsidiaries:

American National Bank Inc.   (1)
8990 W Dodge Rd, Omaha, NE 68114-3329
Tel.: (402) 399-5079
Web Site: http://www.anbank.com
Commercial Banking Services
N.A.I.C.S.: 522110
John F. Kotouc (Chm & CEO)
Bill Klein (CEO)
Curt W. Becker (CFO)
Jason L. Hansen (Sr VP)
Grant Empson (Treas & First VP)
Christopher Reiner (VP)
Craig Wilkins (Head-Corp Lending)
Anguel Lindarev (CIO)

Subsidiary (Domestic):

Residential Mortgage Services, Inc.   (2)
12829 W Dodge Rd Ste 203, Omaha, NE 68154
Tel.: (402) 514-3908
Web Site:
http://www.residentialmortgages.com
Sales Range: $1-9.9 Million
Residential Mortgage Services
N.A.I.C.S.: 522292

AMERICAN NATURAL ENERGY CORPORATION
6100 S Yale Ste 2010, Tulsa, OK 74136
Tel.: (918) 481-1440
Web Site: http://www.annrg.com
Sales Range: $1-9.9 Million
Emp.: 6
Oil & Gas Exploration Services
N.A.I.C.S.: 213112
Michael K. Paulk (Pres & CEO)
Steven P. Ensz (CFO & VP-Fin)
Richard O. Mulford (Mgr-Ops)
Robert G. Snead (Mgr-Exploitation)

American News Company, LLC—(Continued)

AMERICAN NEWS COMPANY, LLC
1955 Lk Park Dr Ste 400, Smyrna, GA 30080
Tel.: (800) 929-8274   DE
Web Site: http://anc365.com
Magazine & Newspaper Whslr
N.A.I.C.S.: 424920
David Parry (Pres & CEO)
Ted Kallgren (CFO & Exec VP-Fin)
Dan McLaughlin (COO & Exec VP-Logistics)
Ingris Jakabcsin (Exec VP-Publ.& Distr)
Michael Rogge (Sr VP-HR & Risk Mgmt)
David Forsman (Exec VP-Sls & Mktg)
Chris Vealey (Exec VP-Retail Solutions)
Dan Pittman (Gen Counsel)

AMERICAN NEWSPAPER REPRESENTATIVES, INC.
2075 W Big Beaver Rd Ste 310, Troy, MI 48084-3439
Tel.: (248) 643-9910   MI
Web Site: http://www.anrinc.net
Year Founded: 1943
Sales Range: Less than $1 Million
Emp.: 5
Media Buying Solutions
N.A.I.C.S.: 541830
Dean Bevacqua (Mgr-Natl Sls)
John Jepsen (Pres)

AMERICAN NICARAGUA FOUNDATION
1000 NW 57th Ct Ste 170, Miami, FL 33126
Tel.: (305) 374-3391   FL
Web Site: https://www.anfnicaragua.org
Year Founded: 1992
Sales Range: $100-124.9 Million
Emp.: 8
Community Care Services
N.A.I.C.S.: 624190
Damaris Oporta (Mgr-Acctg)

AMERICAN NOVELTY INC
7099 Huntley Rd Ste 105, Columbus, OH 43229
Tel.: (614) 848-6764
Sales Range: $10-24.9 Million
Emp.: 10
Snack Foods
N.A.I.C.S.: 424450
Diab Ellen (Pres)

AMERICAN OCCUPATIONAL THERAPY ASSOCIATION, INC.
4720 Montgomery Ln Ste 200, Bethesda, MD 20814-3449
Tel.: (301) 652-6611   DC
Web Site: http://www.aota.org
Year Founded: 1917
Sales Range: $10-24.9 Million
Emp.: 80
Occupational Therapist Association
N.A.I.C.S.: 813920
Frederick P. Somers (Exec Dir)
Tracy Hammond (Mgr-Sls)

AMERICAN OFFICE EQUIPMENT CO. INC.
309 N Calvert St, Baltimore, MD 21202
Tel.: (410) 539-7529   MD
Web Site: http://www.aofurn.com
Year Founded: 1935
Sales Range: $75-99.9 Million
Emp.: 169
Whslr of Office Furniture
N.A.I.C.S.: 423210

David Kuntz (Pres)
Patricia Norman (Dir-Sls)

AMERICAN ONION INC.
28790 Westport Rd, Hermiston, OR 97838-9576
Tel.: (541) 564-0866
Sales Range: $10-24.9 Million
Emp.: 50
Fruit & Vegetable Canning Services
N.A.I.C.S.: 311421
Craig Reeder (Mgr-Sys)
Jeff Mason (Mgr-Farm)
Douglas Hale (Pres-Eastern Ops)
Bob Hale (CEO)
Rick Hale (Pres-Overall Ops)

AMERICAN OPPORTUNITY FOR HOUSING, INC.
7334 Blanco Rd Ste 200, San Antonio, TX 78216
Tel.: (210) 341-8097   KS
Web Site: http://www.aoh-inc.com
Year Founded: 1992
Sales Range: $50-74.9 Million
Community Housing Services
N.A.I.C.S.: 624229
David Starr (Pres)
James H. Shipley (Sec)

AMERICAN OPTOMETRIC ASSOCIATION
243 N Lindbergh Blvd, Saint Louis, MO 63141-7881
Tel.: (314) 991-4100   MO
Web Site: https://www.aoa.org
Year Founded: 1936
Sales Range: $10-24.9 Million
Emp.: 131
Optometric Association
N.A.I.C.S.: 813920
David A. Cockrell (Pres)
Christopher J. Quinn (Treas & Sec)
Andrea P. Thau (VP)
Chase Cannon (Assoc Dir-Govt Rels)

AMERICAN OSMENT
2923 5th Ave S, Birmingham, AL 35233
Tel.: (205) 326-3456
Web Site: https://www.americanosment.com
Year Founded: 1974
Sales Range: $200-249.9 Million
Emp.: 125
Wholesale Distributor of Industrial Chemicals & Paper Products
N.A.I.C.S.: 424690
Steven K. Mote (Pres)
Tom Hamm (Mgr-Credit)
Robbie Medley (Gen Mgr)

AMERICAN OSTEOPATHIC ASSOCIATION
142 E Ontario St, Chicago, IL 60611-2864
Tel.: (312) 202-8000   IL
Web Site: http://www.osteopathic.org
Year Founded: 1897
Sales Range: $25-49.9 Million
Emp.: 158
Health Care Srvices
N.A.I.C.S.: 622110
Joshua Prober (Gen Counsel)
Frank W. Bedford (Controller)
Adrienne White-Faine (CEO)
Kenya D. McRae (VP-R&D)
Boyd R. Buser (Pres)
Sally Szumlas (COO)

AMERICAN PACESETTERS ENTERPRISE LLC.
2238 S McClintock Ste 1, Tempe, AZ 85282
Tel.: (480) 784-2270
Sales Range: $10-24.9 Million

Emp.: 150
Accounting & Auditing Services
N.A.I.C.S.: 541211
William Randall (Principal)

AMERICAN PACIFIC GROUP, LLC
201 Mission Str Ste 1330, San Francisco, CA 94105
Tel.: (415) 578-1600
Web Site: http://www.americanpacific.com
Investment Services
N.A.I.C.S.: 523999
Fraser Preston (Founder & Mng Partner)

Subsidiaries:

Fresche Solutions Inc.   (1)
995 Wellington Suite 200, Montreal, H3C 1V3, QC, Canada
Tel.: (514) 747-7007
Web Site: http://www.freschesolutions.com
Sales Range: $25-49.9 Million
Emp.: 400
Legacy Computer System Management Services
N.A.I.C.S.: 541512
Andrew Kulakowski (Founder)
Garry Ciambella (VP-Engrg)
Christopher Koppe (VP-Consulting & Portfolio Mgmt)
Jennifer Fisher (VP-Sls & Mktg)
Emmanuel Tzinevrakis (VP-Pre-Sls Solutions)
Maria G. Anzini (VP-HR)
Christine McDowell (VP-Corp Mktg)
Marcel Sarrasin (VP-Mktg)
Brendan Kay (CTO)
Patrick Thibault (CFO)
Mathieu Alarie (VP-Employee Experience)
Stephen Woodard (Pres & CEO)

Subsidiary (US):

Abacus Solutions LLC   (2)
1190 Kennestone Clr Ste 120, Marietta, GA 30066
Tel.: (770) 738-1101
Web Site: http://www.abacusllc.com
Sales Range: $25-49.9 Million
Emp.: 55
IT Infrastructure Products
N.A.I.C.S.: 541512
Ken Snuggs (Co-Founder & Pres)
Joseph Corbett (COO)
Steve White (CFO)
Patrick Schutz (Dir-Managed Svcs)
Rob Wentz (Dir-Mktg & Bus Dev)
Kimberly Christopher (Mgr-Logistics)
Tricia Dukes (Mgr-HR)
Tom Sellers (Dir-Infrastructure Computing Svcs)

Quadrant Software, Inc.   (2)
124 Grove St, Franklin, MA 02038
Tel.: (508) 594-2700
Web Site: http://www.quadrantsoftware.com
Software Publisher
N.A.I.C.S.: 513210
John Clark (VP-Engrg)

AMERICAN PACIFIC INVESTCORP, LP
295 Madison Ave 2nd Fl, New York, NY 10017
Tel.: (212) 545-1100   DE
Year Founded: 2010
Real Estate Investment Services
N.A.I.C.S.: 525990
Philip Pilevsky (Chm)
Michael Arons (CFO)
Michael Pilevsky (Co-Pres & Co-CEO)
Seth Pilevsky (Co-Pres & Co-CEO)

AMERICAN PACIFIC MORTGAGE
3000 Lava Ridge Ct Ste 200, Roseville, CA 95661
Tel.: (916) 960-1325

Web Site: https://www.apmortgage.com
Sales Range: $50-74.9 Million
Emp.: 2,000
Mortgage Lending Services
N.A.I.C.S.: 522310
Kurt Reisig (Founder & Chm)
Bill Lowman (CEO)
Matt Brinitzer (VP-Corp Svcs)
David Mack (Chief Origination Practices Officer)

Subsidiaries:

Petaluma Home Loans   (1)
628 E Washington St Ste B, Petaluma, CA 94952
Tel.: (707) 773-4200
Web Site: http://www.petalumahomeloans.com
Sales Range: $25-49.9 Million
Emp.: 10
Mortgage Bankers & Broker
N.A.I.C.S.: 522292
Ken Mccoy (Branch Mgr)

AMERICAN PACKAGING CORPORATION
777 Driving Pk Ave, Rochester, NY 14613-1591
Tel.: (585) 254-9500   PA
Web Site: http://www.ampkcorp.com
Year Founded: 1902
Sales Range: $150-199.9 Million
Emp.: 700
Mfr of Bags, Coated, Laminated Paper Films & Foils; Flexo & Roto Printing Up to Ten Colors
N.A.I.C.S.: 322220
Peter B. Schottland (Co-Chm & CEO)
Debby Pruismann (Coord-Sls & Mktg)
Sue Rotolo (Mgr-Bus Dev)
Jeffrey T. Huber (Dir-Pur)
Steve Schottland (Co-Chm)
Jeff Koch (Pres)

Subsidiaries:

American Packaging Corporation   (1)
103 W Broad St, Story City, IA 50248-1003
Tel.: (515) 733-1400
Web Site: http://www.ampkcorp.com
Sales Range: $25-49.9 Million
Emp.: 175
Flexible Packaging Mfr
N.A.I.C.S.: 322211
Chad Gray (Controller)

American Packaging Corporation - Extrusion Division   (1)
777 Driving Park Ave, Rochester, NY 14613
Tel.: (585) 254-9500
Extrusion Lamination Services
N.A.I.C.S.: 326130

American Packaging Corporation - Flexographic Division   (1)
103 W Broad St, Story City, IA 50248
Tel.: (515) 733-1400
Web Site: http://www.ampkcorp.com
Emp.: 330
Bag & Pouch Mfr
N.A.I.C.S.: 322220
Debby Pruismann (Coord-Corp Mktg)

American Packaging Corporation - Roto Grauvre Division   (1)
850 W James St, Columbus, WI 53925-1024   (100%)
Tel.: (920) 623-2291
Web Site: http://www.ampkcorp.com
Sales Range: $25-49.9 Million
Emp.: 200
Label & Wrapper Printing Services
N.A.I.C.S.: 322220
Jeff Koch (VP-Ops)

AMERICAN PAINTING AND RENOVATIONS, INC.
1325 Satellite Blvd Nw Ste 101, Suwanee, GA 30024-4697
Tel.: (770) 995-8787
Web Site: http://www.amerapaint.com

Year Founded: 1991
Rev.: $13,600,000
Emp.: 11
Construction Services
N.A.I.C.S.: 238320
Linda Brewer (Mgr)
Sidney H. Theus (CEO)
Christopher R. Theus (COO)

AMERICAN PAPER & TWINE COMPANY

7400 Cockrill Bend Blvd, Nashville, TN 37209
Tel.: (615) 350-9000
Rev.: $72,000,000
Emp.: 150
Industrial & Personal Service Paper
N.A.I.C.S.: 424130
Robert S. Doochin (Pres & CEO)
David Morris (CFO & Exec VP)
Elaine Brian (Supvr-Comm)
Gary Dotson (Dir-Office Products)
Mark Wright (Sr VP)

AMERICAN PAPER TOWEL CO. LLC

10 Industrial Rd, Carlstadt, NJ 07072
Tel.: (201) 939-4200
Web Site:
https://www.americanpaperco.com
Sales Range: $10-24.9 Million
Emp.: 45
Distr of Tissue & Towel Products
N.A.I.C.S.: 424130
Jonathan Shapiro (Pres)

AMERICAN PARA PROFESSIONAL SYSTEMS, INC.

1 Jericho Plz, Jericho, NY 11753
Tel.: (516) 822-6230   NY
Web Site:
http://www.appsnational.com
Year Founded: 1973
Sales Range: $1-9.9 Million
Paramedical Services
N.A.I.C.S.: 621999
Gary Gelman (CEO)

AMERICAN PARKING SYSTEM INC.

Calle Rarterial Behostos 18 Newsan 1 Bldg Fl 2, Hato Rey, PR 00917
Tel.: (787) 725-9184
Web Site:
http://www.americanparking.com
Sales Range: $25-49.9 Million
Emp.: 630
Owner & Operator of Parking Lots
N.A.I.C.S.: 812930
Miguel Cabral Vera (Pres)
Asbertly Rosa (CFO)

AMERICAN PARTNERS INC.

1005 Main St Ste 2205, Pawtucket, RI 02860
Tel.: (401) 312-4262
Web Site:
http://www.americanpartnersinc.com
Year Founded: 2007
Sales Range: $25-49.9 Million
Emp.: 23
IT Consulting Services
N.A.I.C.S.: 541690
David McIntyre (Mgr-Bus Dev)

AMERICAN PASTEURIZATION COMPANY

2675 N Mayfair Rd Ste 680, Wauwatosa, WI 53226
Tel.: (414) 453-7522
Web Site:
https://www.americanpasteuri
zationcompany.com
Year Founded: 2017
Food Storage & Packaging Services
N.A.I.C.S.: 561910

Enrique Hernandez (Mgr-Shipping & Receiving)

AMERICAN PATRIOT BRANDS, INC.

4570 Campus Dr Ste 1, Newport Beach, CA 92660
Tel.: (949) 478-2571   NV
Year Founded: 2009
Mobile Food Services
N.A.I.C.S.: 722330
Robert Lee (Chm, CEO & Principal Accounting Officer)

AMERICAN PAWN & JEWELRY, INC.

1785 E Interstate 30, Garland, TX 75043
Tel.: (972) 240-1300   TX
Year Founded: 1981
Rev.: $13,911,613
Emp.: 35
Pawn Shop
N.A.I.C.S.: 522299
Morgan Jones (Pres)
Charles Valdez (Mgr-Reg)

AMERICAN PAYDAY LOANS INC.

3609a S Noland Rd, Independence, MO 64055
Tel.: (816) 833-1644
Web Site: http://www.dfg.com
Rev.: $10,600,000
Emp.: 3
Short-Term Business Credit Institutions, Except Agricultural
N.A.I.C.S.: 522299

AMERICAN PENSION SERVICES, INC.

2451 McMullen Booth Rd Ste 200, Clearwater, FL 33759
Tel.: (813) 281-0707
Web Site:
http://www.americanpension.net
Year Founded: 2000
Sales Range: $1-9.9 Million
Emp.: 17
Insurance Related Activities
N.A.I.C.S.: 524298
Terrance P. Power (Pres)

AMERICAN PERFORMANCE INDUSTRIES

109 McNeil Rd, Sanford, NC 27330
Tel.: (919) 775-7321
Sales Range: $1-9.9 Million
Emp.: 100
Fabrication & Machining, Powdering, Coating & Assembly Mfr
N.A.I.C.S.: 333248

Subsidiaries:

The Phoenix Grill Company   (1)
109 McNeill Rd, Sanford, NC 27330-9451
Tel.: (919) 775-7321
Mfr of Gas Grills
N.A.I.C.S.: 423220

AMERICAN PETRO-HUNTER INC.

250 N Rock Rd Ste 365, Wichita, KS 67206
Tel.: (316) 201-1853   NV
Web Site:
http://www.americanpetrohunter.com
Year Founded: 1996
Sales Range: Less than $1 Million
Oil & Gas Exploration Services
N.A.I.C.S.: 213112

AMERICAN PETROLEUM EQUIPMENT & CONSTRUCTION COMPANY, INC.

63 Orange Ave, Walden, NY 12586
Tel.: (845) 778-5110
Web Site: https://www.apecco.biz
Year Founded: 2003
Sales Range: $10-24.9 Million
Emp.: 68
Construction Engineering Services
N.A.I.C.S.: 541330
Patrick Dunn (Mgr-Environmental Ops)

AMERICAN PETROLEUM TANKERS PARTNERS LP

600 W Germantown Pk Ste 400, Plymouth Meeting, PA 19462
Tel.: (610) 947-1677   DE
Year Founded: 2013
Petroleum Products Transportation
Tankers Owner, Operator & Acquirer
N.A.I.C.S.: 488390
Philip J. Doherty (CFO)

AMERICAN PHILOSOPHICAL SOCIETY

104 S 5th St, Philadelphia, PA 19106-3387
Tel.: (215) 440-3400   PA
Web Site: https://www.amphilsoc.org
Year Founded: 1743
Sales Range: $10-24.9 Million
Emp.: 75
Historical Resource Preservation Services
N.A.I.C.S.: 712110
Merrill Mason (Dir-Museum)
Brunilda Matraku (Controller)
Mary C. McDonald (Dir-Publ)
Nora Monroe (Dir-Membership & Prizes)

AMERICAN PHOENIX INC.

800 Wisconsin St Ste 11, Eau Claire, WI 54703
Tel.: (715) 831-0966
Web Site: http://www.apimix.net
Rev.: $27,900,000
Emp.: 245
Custom Compounding of Rubber Materials
N.A.I.C.S.: 326299
Clement A. Nelson (Pres)

AMERICAN PHOTONICS CO.

6621 19th St E, Sarasota, FL 34243
Tel.: (941) 752-5811
Web Site:
http://www.americanphotonics.com
Year Founded: 2000
Sales Range: $1-9.9 Million
Emp.: 30
Optical Instrument & Lens Mfr
N.A.I.C.S.: 333310
Ana Piumbini (CEO)

AMERICAN PHYSICAL SOCIETY

1 Physics Ellipse, College Park, MD 20740-3844
Tel.: (301) 209-3200
Web Site: https://www.aps.org
Year Founded: 1899
Sales Range: $25-49.9 Million
Emp.: 200
Publisher of Periodicals
N.A.I.C.S.: 513120
Matt Wascavage (Mgr-Sls-Ops)
Sara Conners (Dir-Comm)
Jeanette Russo (Mgr-Programs-OPA)
Jim Egan (Dir-IT & Member Svcs)
Hopkins Gould (CFO)
Matthew Salter (Publr)
Jonathan Bagger (CEO)
Rachel Burley (Chief Publications Officer)

AMERICAN PHYSICIAN PARTNERS, LLC

5121 Maryland Way Ste 300, Brentwood, TN 37027
Tel.: (855) 246-8607
Web Site: http://www.appartners.com
Year Founded: 2015
Hospital & Healthcare Services
N.A.I.C.S.: 621999
John Rutledge (Pres & CEO)
Andy McQueen (Chief Dev Officer & Sr VP)
Matt Stapleton (COO)

Subsidiaries:

Progressive Medical Associates, PLLC   (1)
1660 S Alma School Rd Ste 213, Mesa, AZ 85210
Tel.: (480) 456-9500
Office Of Physician
N.A.I.C.S.: 621111

AMERICAN PILEDRIVING EQUIPMENT, INC.

7032 S 196th St, Kent, WA 98032
Tel.: (253) 872-0141
Web Site: http://www.apevibro.com
Sales Range: $10-24.9 Million
Emp.: 100
Metals Service Centers & Offices
N.A.I.C.S.: 423510
Dan Collins (Controller)
Kelly Goranson (Mgr-Production)
Steve Cress (Mgr)

AMERICAN PIZZA PARTNERS LP

7700 E Polo Dr, Wichita, KS 67206
Tel.: (316) 634-1190
Sales Range: $50-74.9 Million
Emp.: 1,500
Pizza Restaurants Operator
N.A.I.C.S.: 722513

Subsidiaries:

American Seafood Partners LP   (1)
3020 N Cypress Rd Ste 100, Wichita, KS 67226
Tel.: (316) 634-1190
Rev.: $12,247,923
Emp.: 40
Seafood Restaurants
N.A.I.C.S.: 722511

AMERICAN PLANNING ASSOCIATION

205 N Michigan Ave Ste 1200, Chicago, IL 60601-5927
Tel.: (312) 431-9100   DC
Web Site: https://www.planning.org
Year Founded: 1978
Sales Range: $10-24.9 Million
Emp.: 119
Educational Support Services
N.A.I.C.S.: 611710
Ann Simms (CFO & COO)
Felicia Braunstein (Dir-Pro Practice)
Deene Alongi (Dir-Meetings & Conferences)
Mark Ferguson (CIO)
Jason Jordan (Dir-Policy & Govt Affairs)

AMERICAN PLANT FOOD CORP.

903 Mayo Shell Rd, Galena Park, TX 77547
Tel.: (713) 675-2231
Web Site: http://www.apfcorp.net
Year Founded: 1964
Sales Range: $100-124.9 Million
Emp.: 61
Fertilizer Mfr
N.A.I.C.S.: 325314

American Plant Food Corp.—(Continued)

Donald R. Ford (Pres)
John Twardowski (Mgr-Fleet)
Toby Hlavinka (VP-Sls)

AMERICAN PLASTIC MOLDING CORP.

965 S Elm St, Scottsburg, IN 47170-2173
Tel.: (812) 752-7000
Web Site: https://www.apmc.com
Year Founded: 1971
Sales Range: $10-24.9 Million
Emp.: 110
Plastics Product Mfr
N.A.I.C.S.: 326199
Alan Myers (Plant Mgr)
Jeff Hougland (Mgr-Engrg)
Anne Coates (Pres)

AMERICAN PLASTIC TOYS INC.

799 Ladd Rd, Walled Lake, MI 48390-3025
Tel.: (248) 624-4881
Web Site:
  https://www.americanplastictoy.com
Year Founded: 1961
Sales Range: $150-199.9 Million
Emp.: 600
Mfr of Toys
N.A.I.C.S.: 339930
David B. Littleton (Chm)
John Gessatt (Pres)
Susan Gessert (Mgr-HR)
Hailey Mann (Mgr-Quality & Engrg)
Jim Grau (Treas)
Steve Mellos (Dir-Sls)
Shea Mellendorf (Mgr-Traffic)
Glenn Miller (Engr-Design)

AMERICAN POOL MANAGEMENT CORP.

11515 Cronridge Dr Ste Q, Owings Mills, MD 21117
Tel.: (410) 363-6800
Web Site:
  http://www.americanpool.com
Year Founded: 1985
Sales Range: $10-24.9 Million
Emp.: 300
Services to Buildings & Dwellings
N.A.I.C.S.: 561790
Michelle Porter (Pres)

AMERICAN POOLPLAYERS ASSOCIATION INC.

1000 Lake Saint Louis Blvd Ste 325, Lake Saint Louis, MO 63367
Tel.: (636) 625-8611
Web Site:
  https://www.poolplayers.com
Year Founded: 1979
Sales Range: $10-24.9 Million
Emp.: 65
Amateur Pool League
N.A.I.C.S.: 711211

AMERICAN POP CORN COMPANY

1 Fun Pl, Sioux City, IA 51102
Tel.: (712) 239-1232
Web Site: https://www.jollytime.com
Year Founded: 1914
Sales Range: $100-124.9 Million
Emp.: 150
Popcorn Mfr
N.A.I.C.S.: 311999
Garrett K. Smith (Pres)
Tom Elsen (VP-Mktg)
Steve Juisenga (VP-Sls)
Carlton P. Smith (Chm)
Cloid H. Smith (Founder)
Wrede H. Smith (Co-Pres)

AMERICAN POWER SYSTEMS, LLC

26507 79th Ave S, Kent, WA 98032
Tel.: (253) 852-4839
Web Site:
  https://www.ampowersys.com
Sales Range: $10-24.9 Million
Emp.: 40
Batteries
N.A.I.C.S.: 423610
Gary Hughes (Pres)
Ben Gillihan (Dir-Ops)

AMERICAN PRESS LLC

1 American Pl, Gordonsville, VA 22942
Tel.: (540) 832-2253
Year Founded: 1978
Sales Range: $25-49.9 Million
Emp.: 300
Publisher of Lithographic, Commercial Printing
N.A.I.C.S.: 323111
Charly Petigrove (Pres)
Marshall Petigrove (Owner)
Eddie Owens (Vp-Mfg)
Paul Grieco (VP-Sls)

AMERICAN PRINTING COMPANY INC.

2909 Syene Rd, Madison, WI 53713
Tel.: (608) 271-6544
Web Site:
  https://www.americanprintingco.com
Rev.: $12,000,000
Emp.: 90
Offset Printing
N.A.I.C.S.: 323111
Ajay Lamb (Dir-Tech)
Therese Gulbransen (VP-Sls & Mktg)
Vance Kataltzynski (Pres)
Samantha Engelhart (VP-Sls & Mktg)

AMERICAN PRODUCT DISTRIBUTORS, INC.

8350 Arrowridge Blvd, Charlotte, NC 28273
Tel.: (704) 522-9411
Web Site:
  http://www.americanproduct.com
Year Founded: 1992
Sales Range: $10-24.9 Million
Emp.: 100
Office, Industrial, Janitorial & Business Imaging Supplies Distr & Sales
N.A.I.C.S.: 561720
C. Ray Kennedy (CEO & Founder)
Eva G. Dinion (Sr VP-Ops & Tech)
Cy Kennedy (Pres)

AMERICAN PRODUCTS, L.L.C.

597 Evergreen Rd, Strafford, MO 65757
Tel.: (417) 736-2135
Web Site: https://www.amprod.us
Sales Range: $10-24.9 Million
Emp.: 120
Sheet Metal Work Mfg
N.A.I.C.S.: 332322
Mike Springer (Exec Dir-Sls-Southeast Territory)
Mike Henderson (Exec Dir-Sls-Northwest Territory)
Steve Smith (CEO)
Matt Calton (Exec Dir-Sls & Engrg-Sls-Southwest Territory)
Gary Hasler (VP-Sls)

AMERICAN PROPERTY GROUP OF SARASOTA INC.

7750 S Tamiami Trl, Sarasota, FL 34231
Tel.: (941) 923-0535
Web Site:
  https://www.americanproperty.com
Sales Range: $10-24.9 Million

Emp.: 10
Real Estate Broker
N.A.I.C.S.: 531210
Barry Seidel (Pres)

AMERICAN PROPERTY MANAGEMENT CORPORATION

8910 University Center Ln Ste 640, San Diego, CA 92122-1016
Tel.: (858) 964-5500
Web Site:
  https://www.pacificpearlhotels.com
Rev.: $285,000,000
Emp.: 1,000
Owner & Operator of Hotels
N.A.I.C.S.: 531210
Michael Gallegos (CEO)

AMERICAN PROTEINS INC.

4705 Leland Dr, Cumming, GA 30041
Tel.: (770) 886-2250
Web Site:
  http://www.americanproteins.com
Year Founded: 1949
Sales Range: $10-24.9 Million
Emp.: 22
Provider of Ingredients for Prepared Feeds
N.A.I.C.S.: 311119
Hoyt Langford (Controller)
Ken Thompson (Controller-Cumming Div)
James Sanford (Controller-Hanceville Div)
Janet Adams (Coord-Corp Sls)
Mark Ham (Pres)
Jonathan Green (Gen Mgr-Cumming Div)
Jason Spann (Gen Mgr-Hanceville Div)
Scott Duchette (Mgr-Ampro)
Brandon Kyzar (Mgr-Cuthbert)
Stan Gudenkauf (VP-Sls & Mktg)
Richard Stewart (VP-Bus Dev)

Subsidiaries:

AMPRO Laboratories, Inc.   (1)
4480 Keith Bridge Rd, Cumming, GA 30131
Tel.: (770) 887-6011
Emp.: 14
Laboratory Testing Services
N.A.I.C.S.: 541380
Wanda Ledford (Gen Mgr)

Ampro Products Inc.   (1)
2305 Okelly Rd, Gainesville, GA 30507
Tel.: (770) 535-6646
Web Site: http://www.ampro.com
Sales Range: $10-24.9 Million
Emp.: 20
Prepared Feeds, Nec
N.A.I.C.S.: 311119
Toby Miller (Mgr)

AMERICAN PSYCHIATRIC ASSOCIATION

1000 Wilson Blvd Ste 1825, Arlington, VA 22209-3901
Tel.: (703) 907-7300
Web Site: http://www.psychiatry.org
Year Founded: 2000
Sales Range: $75-99.9 Million
Emp.: 235
Medical Professional Association
N.A.I.C.S.: 813920
Maria A. Oquendo (Pres)
Frank W. Brown (Treas)

AMERICAN PSYCHOLOGICAL ASSOCIATION

750 1st St NE, Washington, DC 20002-4242
Tel.: (202) 336-5500
Web Site: https://www.apa.org
Year Founded: 1925
Sales Range: $100-124.9 Million
Emp.: 722
Psychological Organization

N.A.I.C.S.: 622210
Tony Habash (Chief Information Officer)
Jaime L. Diaz Granados (Exec Dir-Education Directorate)
Jean A. Carter (Treas)

AMERICAN PUBLIC MEDIA GROUP

480 Cedar St, Saint Paul, MN 55101
Tel.: (651) 290-1500
Web Site:
  http://www.americanpublicmedia.org
Year Founded: 1967
Rev.: $134,704,000
Assets: $337,371,000
Liabilities: $74,836,000
Net Worth: $262,535,000
Fiscal Year-end: 06/30/18
Public Media Administration Organization
N.A.I.C.S.: 813990
Bradbury H. Anderson (Chm)
Jon R. McTaggart (Pres & CEO)
David W. Kansas (COO & Sr VP)
Mary Keith Brainerd (Vice Chm & Sec)
Emery Koenig (Treas)
Mette McLoughlin (Chief HR Officer & VP)
Sylvia Strobel (Gen Counsel & Sr VP)
Carmen Rodriguez Johnson (CMO & Sr VP-Audience Dev)
Liliana Kim (Mng Dir-Podcasts)
Phyllis Fletcher (Editor-Podcast)
Morris Goodwin Jr. (CFO & Sr VP)

Subsidiaries:

American Public Media   (1)
480 Cedar St, Saint Paul, MN 55101
Tel.: (651) 290-1373
Web Site:
  http://www.americanpublicmedia.org
Radio Broadcasting Services
N.A.I.C.S.: 516210
David Kansas (COO & Exec VP)
Jon McTaggart (Pres & CEO)
Randi Yoder (Chief Dev Officer & Sr VP)
Angie Andresen (Dir-Comm)
Nick Kereakos (CTO, Sr VP & Gen Mgr-Reg Svcs)

Classical South Florida Inc   (1)
330 SW 2nd St Ste 207, Fort Lauderdale, FL 33312
Tel.: (954) 522-8755
Web Site:
  http://classicalsouthflorida.publicradio.org
Radio Broadcasting Services
N.A.I.C.S.: 516210
Mary Lou Dasburg (Co-Founder)
Betty MacMillan (Co-Founder)

Greenspring Company   (1)
480 Cedar St, Saint Paul, MN 55101-2217
Tel.: (651) 290-1552
Web Site: http://www.mpr.org
Radio Broadcasting Stations
N.A.I.C.S.: 424990

Minnesota Public Radio Inc.   (1)
480 Cedar St, Saint Paul, MN 55101-2202
Tel.: (651) 290-1500
Web Site: http://www.mpr.org
Rev.: $100,762,000
Assets: $150,645,000
Liabilities: $56,281,000
Net Worth: $94,364,000
Earnings: ($895,000)
Emp.: 484
Fiscal Year-end: 06/30/2014
Radio Broadcasting Stations
N.A.I.C.S.: 516110
Jon R. McTaggart (CEO)
Chris Worthington (Mng Dir & Editor-in-Chief)
Lisa Radzak (Mng Dir-Community & Govt Rels)
Mary Brainerd (Chm)
Dave Murphy (Vice Chm)

Julie Amacher *(Program Dir-Classical MPR & Mgr-C24)*
Angie Andresen *(Dir-Comm)*
Mike Edgerly *(Exec Editor-News)*
Barb Gehlen *(Dir-Reg Underwriting)*
Chandra Kavati *(Mng Dir-Dev Strategy & Ops)*
Brian Newhouse *(Mng Dir-Classical Programming)*
David Safar *(Mng Dir)*
Kristen Wesloh *(Dir-Institutional Giving)*
Mike Reszler *(Chief Digital Officer & Sr VP)*
Nick Kereakos *(Sr VP & Gen Mgr)*
Duchesne Drew *(Pres):*

Unit (Domestic):

The Fitzgerald Theater Company Inc. (2)
10 E Exchange St, Saint Paul, MN 55101 **(100%)**
Tel.: (651) 290-1200
Web Site: http://www.fitzgeraldtheater.org
Sales Range: $25-49.9 Million
Emp.: 40
Nonresidential Building Operators
N.A.I.C.S.: 531120
Joanna Schnedler *(Gen Mgr)*

Southern California Public Radio (1)
474 S Raymond Ave, Pasadena, CA 91105
Tel.: (626) 585-7000
Web Site: http://www.scpr.org
Rev.: $2,549,800
Emp.: 100
Radio Stations
N.A.I.C.S.: 516110
Doug Johnson *(Dir-Brdcst & Tech)*
Alex Schaffert *(Dir-Digital Media)*
Melanie Sauer *(Dir-Fin & Bus Svcs)*
C. Douglas Kranwinkle *(Sec)*
Charles Woo *(Treas)*
Carol Komatsuka *(VP-Dev)*
Carla Wohl *(Sr VP-Dev)*
Drew Murphy *(Vice Chm)*
Herb Scannell *(Pres & CEO)*
Catherine Ward *(Vice Chm)*

AMERICAN PUBLIC TELEVISION
55 Summer St, Boston, MA 02110
Tel.: (617) 338-4455   MA
Web Site: http://www.aptonline.org
Year Founded: 1960
Sales Range: $10-24.9 Million
Emp.: 34
Television Broadcasting Services
N.A.I.C.S.: 516120
Terry Mena *(Controller)*
Eric Luskin *(VP-Premium Svc & Syndication)*
Judy Barlow *(VP-Bus Dev & Intl Sls)*
Jamie Haines *(VP-Comm)*
Gerry Field *(VP-Tech)*
Larry Unger *(Treas)*
Rosemary Marbach *(Office Mgr)*
Kevin McKenna *(Dir-Intl Sls)*
Tom Davison *(Dir-Bus Dev)*
Shawn Halford *(VP-Exchange Content & Digital Svcs)*
Paul Higgins *(VP-Fin & Admin)*
James E. Dunford *(Pres & CEO)*
Mare Mazur *(Chm)*
Olivia Wong *(VP-Mktg & Comm)*

AMERICAN PUBLIC WORKS ASSOCIATION
2345 Grand Blvd Ste 700, Kansas City, MO 64108-2625
Tel.: (816) 472-6100   IL
Web Site: http://www.apwa.net
Year Founded: 1937
Sales Range: $10-24.9 Million
Emp.: 62
Business Associations
N.A.I.C.S.: 813910
Brenda Shaver *(Mgr-Meetings)*
Andrea Eales *(Dir-Govt Affairs)*
Anne Jackson *(Dir-Sustainability)*

AMERICAN PULVERIZER COMPANY
1319 Macklind Ave, Saint Louis, MO 63110
Tel.: (314) 781-6100
Web Site: https://www.ampulverizer.com
Rev.: $20,000,000
Emp.: 60
Mining Machinery
N.A.I.C.S.: 333131
Chris Griesedieck *(Pres)*
Paul Griesedieck *(VP)*
Roger Hershey *(Mgr-Parts)*
Steve Rogan *(VP-Engrg)*
Skip Anthony *(VP-Sls)*

AMERICAN QUALITY FOODS
353 Banner Farm Rd, Mills River, NC 28759
Web Site: https://www.americanfoods.com
Year Founded: 1994
Emp.: 35
Pasta Mfr
N.A.I.C.S.: 311824
Rhonda Byas *(Sls Mgr-Diet & Gluten Free Dessert Mixes)*

AMERICAN READING COMPANY
201 S Gulph Rd, King of Prussia, PA 19046
Tel.: (610) 992-4150
Web Site: http://www.americanreading.com
Sales Range: $10-24.9 Million
Emp.: 100
Children's Books, Teaching Materials & Software Supplier
N.A.I.C.S.: 423490
Jane Hileman *(Founder & CEO)*
Kate Henry *(Acct Mgr-Kentucky, Southern Indiana & Southern Ohio)*
Al Struzinski *(Pres)*
Megan Maloney *(Chief Academic Officer)*
Nate Smith *(CTO)*
Tamiko Lowery Jones *(VP-Academic Partnerships)*
Tony Hicks *(Chief Strategic Officer)*

AMERICAN READY MIX INC.
1475 E Greg St, Sparks, NV 89431
Tel.: (775) 786-4773
Web Site: https://www.americanreadymix.com
Sales Range: $10-24.9 Million
Emp.: 100
Ready Mixed Concrete
N.A.I.C.S.: 327320
Ken Longballa *(Dir-Sls)*

AMERICAN REALTY ADVISORS
801 N Brand Blvd Ste 800, Glendale, CA 91203
Tel.: (818) 545-3762   CA
Web Site: http://www.americanreal.com
Year Founded: 1985
Rev.: $5,700,000,000
Institutional Real Estate Investment Management Services
N.A.I.C.S.: 523940
Scott W. Darling *(Pres & Exec Mng Dir-Portfolio Mgmt)*
Daniel Robinson *(Mng Dir-Fin & Investment Consulting)*
Stanley L. Iezman *(Chm & CEO)*
Jay Butterfield *(Mng Dir-Fund Ops-Glendale)*
Teri Noble *(Dir-Mktg & Client Svc-Glendale)*
Chris Macke *(Mng Dir-Res & Strategy)*
Kristin Adrian *(Chief Compliance Officer & Gen Counsel)*

Kirk Helgeson *(Chief Investment Officer)*
Richelle Hayes *(Dir-Mktg & Client Svc-Orlando)*
Robert Samuel *(Dir-Mktg & Client Svc-Santa Fe)*
Todd Fowler *(Dir-Mktg & Client Svc-Chicago)*
Paul Vacheron *(Mng Dir-Asset Mgmt)*
Michael Gelber *(Sr Dir-Asset Mgmt)*
David Hubbs *(Sr Portfolio Mgr)*
Martha Shelley *(Sr Portfolio Mgr)*
Doug Vikser *(Sr Mgr-Capital Markets)*
Shelley Santulli *(Exec VP-Portfolio Mgmt)*
Glen Weisberg *(Exec VP-Portfolio Mgmt & Multifamily Investments-Chicago)*

AMERICAN RECOVERY SERVICE INC.
555 Saint Charles Dr Ste 100, Thousand Oaks, CA 91360
Tel.: (805) 379-8500
Web Site: http://www.arsigroup.com
Rev.: $40,000,000
Emp.: 175
Debt Collection Services
N.A.I.C.S.: 561440
Thomas C. Baxter *(Pres)*
Lane McCarthy *(CMO)*
Sarah Vargas *(Dir-Ops)*
Keith Richardson *(Mgr-Network)*

AMERICAN RED CROSS
431 18th St NW 5th Fl, Washington, DC 20006
Tel.: (202) 737-8300
Web Site: https://www.redcross.org
Year Founded: 1881
Emp.: 35,000
Disaster Relief & Humanitarian Services
N.A.I.C.S.: 813311
Bonnie McElveen-Hunter *(Chm)*
Gail J. McGovern *(Pres & CEO)*
Suzy C. DeFrancis *(Chief Pub Affairs Officer)*
Peggy Dyer *(CMO)*
Vanessa Davis *(Dir-Ops-Central Indiana Chapter)*
Lori Pampilo Harris *(Exec Dir-Greater Orlando Chapter)*
Phyllis Harris *(Chief Compliance Officer & Gen Counsel)*

AMERICAN REFINING GROUP INC.
100 4 Falls Corp Ctr Ste 215, West Conshohocken, PA 19428
Tel.: (610) 940-4420   PA
Web Site: http://www.amref.com
Year Founded: 1975
Sales Range: $125-149.9 Million
Emp.: 250
Petroleum Refining Services
N.A.I.C.S.: 324110
William F. Murray *(VP-Supply Chain & Logistics)*
Rick Smith *(VP & Gen Counsel)*
Sarah Hayden *(Dir-HR)*
Robin Augustine *(Sr VP-Ops)*
Brian J. Zolkos *(CFO)*
David O. Krantz *(VP-Research & Dev)*
Robert C. Esch *(VP-External Affairs)*
Jeannine T. Schoenecker *(Pres & COO)*
Timothy Brown *(CEO)*
David Breitigam *(VP-Environmental, Health & Safety)*
Mike Speaker *(Dir-Ops-Bradford Refinery)*
Harry R. Halloran Jr. *(Chm)*

AMERICAN REGISTRY FOR

DIAGNOSTIC MEDICAL SONOGRAPHY, INC.
1401 Rockville Pike Ste 600, Rockville, MD 20852-1402
Tel.: (301) 738-8401   OH
Web Site: https://www.ardms.org
Year Founded: 1975
Sales Range: $10-24.9 Million
Emp.: 54
Medical Professional Certification Provider
N.A.I.C.S.: 561990
Thomas D. Shipp *(Chm)*
Erika Mann *(Vice Pres)*
Daniel Merton *(Treas & Sec)*

AMERICAN REGISTRY FOR INTERNET NUMBERS, LTD.
PO Box 232290, Centreville, VA 20120
Tel.: (703) 227-9840   VA
Web Site: https://www.arin.net
Year Founded: 1997
Sales Range: $10-24.9 Million
Emp.: 100
Internet Registry Management Services
N.A.I.C.S.: 513140
Richard Jimmerson *(CIO)*
Nate Davis *(COO)*
Erin Alligood *(Dir-HR & Admin)*
Cathy Handley *(Exec Dir-Govt Affairs & Pub Policy)*
Mark Kosters *(CTO)*
Debra Martin *(Sr Project Mgr)*
Garth Dubin *(Mgr-Technical)*
Hollis Kara *(Mgr-Comm)*
John Curran *(Pres & CEO)*
Jonathan Worley *(Mgr-Technical Svcs)*
Octavis Jones *(Engr-Support)*
Rob Atkinson *(Engr-Support)*
Sherrie Link *(Project Mgr)*

AMERICAN RELIANCE INC.
9040 Telstar Ave Ste 127, El Monte, CA 91731
Tel.: (626) 482-1862
Web Site: http://www.amrel.com
Sales Range: $10-24.9 Million
Emp.: 100
Mobile Computer Products Mfr
N.A.I.C.S.: 334118
Edward Chen *(CEO)*
Linda Talcott *(Dir-Mktg)*
Tom Lewis *(Dir-Federal Computer Sls)*
Richard Lane *(VP-Bus Dev)*
Kalvin Chen *(VP-Ops)*

AMERICAN RENAISSANCE CAPITAL, INC.
3699 Wilshire Blvd Ste 610, Los Angeles, CA 90010
Tel.: (310) 895-1839   CA
Web Site: http://www.amrecapital.com
Year Founded: 2012
Rev.: $682,003
Assets: $1,606,423
Liabilities: $1,740,888
Net Worth: ($134,465)
Earnings: $86,383
Emp.: 1
Fiscal Year-end: 12/31/16
Consulting & Advisory Services
N.A.I.C.S.: 541611
Frank Igwealor *(Pres, CEO, CFO, Principal Acctg Officer, Treas & Sec)*
Solomon K N Mbagwu *(Exec Chm)*
Janet Allen *(VP-Fin)*
Kareem Davis *(Mng Dir)*
Fola Bryan Ade *(Dir-Acctg)*
Martin Nwaege *(Controller-Fin)*

American Repertory Theater—(Continued)

AMERICAN REPERTORY THEATER
64 Brattle St, Cambridge, MA 02138
Tel.: (617) 547-8300   MA
Web Site:
https://www.americanrepertory.org
Year Founded: 1979
Sales Range: $10-24.9 Million
Emp.: 314
Live Theater Operator
N.A.I.C.S.: 711310
Anna Fitzloff (Mng Dir)
Skip Curtiss (Dir-Technical)

AMERICAN REPORTING COMPANY, LLC
6628 212th St SW, Lynnwood, WA 98036
Tel.: (425) 563-1900
Web Site: http://www.arcreports.com
Year Founded: 1986
Sales Range: $10-24.9 Million
Emp.: 27
Credit Reporting Services
N.A.I.C.S.: 561450
Francois L. Madath (Pres)

AMERICAN RESIDENTIAL MORTGAGE LP
235 Roselawn Ave E Ste 12, Maplewood, MN 55117
Tel.: (651) 488-1801
Web Site: http://www.armlp.com
Sales Range: $250-299.9 Million
Emp.: 100
Mortgage Bankers & Loan Correspondents
N.A.I.C.S.: 522310

AMERICAN RESTAURANT GROUP, INC.
4410 El Camino Real, Los Altos, CA 94022
Tel.: (650) 949-6400   DE
Web Site:
http://www.stuartandersons.com
Sales Range: $300-349.9 Million
Emp.: 7,000
Restaurant Owner & Operator
N.A.I.C.S.: 722511
George G. Golleher (Chm)

Subsidiaries:

Stuart Anderson's Black Angus & Cattle Company Restaurants   (1)
4410 El Camino Real Ste 201, Los Altos, CA 94022-1049
Tel.: (650) 949-6400
Web Site: http://www.stuartandersons.com
Rev.: $260,000,000
Emp.: 6,000
Steakhouse Restaurant
N.A.I.C.S.: 722511

AMERICAN RESTAURANT HOLDINGS, INC.
18818 Teller Ave Ste 115, Irvine, CA 92612
Tel.: (949) 825-5090   DE
Web Site:
http://www.americanrestaurant.com
Year Founded: 2013
Food Service Industry Investment Holding Company
N.A.I.C.S.: 551112
Tim M. Betts (Pres & CEO)
Noel DeWinter (Interim CFO)
Kurt Schaefer (VP-Ops)

Subsidiaries:

American Restaurants, LLC   (1)
18818 Teller Ave Ste 115, Irvine, CA 92612
Tel.: (949) 825-5090
Food Service Industry Investment Services
N.A.I.C.S.: 523999

Tim M. Betts (Pres & CEO)
Noel DeWinter (Interim CFO)
Kurt Schaeffer (VP-Ops)

Fresca's Mexican Grill, Inc.   (1)
20060 Santa Ana Ave, Costa Mesa, CA 92626
Tel.: (714) 557-6822
Web Site: http://www.frescas.com
Sales Range: $1-9.9 Million
Emp.: 65
Restaurant
N.A.I.C.S.: 722511
Thomas Ryder (Founder)

Jojo's Pizza Kitchen Inc.   (1)
2923 Chino Ave Ste H1, Chino Hills, CA 91709
Tel.: (951) 464-0015
Web Site: http://www.jojospizza.com
Full-Service Restaurants
N.A.I.C.S.: 722511
Joe Bonafede (Founder)

Muscle Maker Franchising LLC   (1)
15 Prospect Lane Suite 2 AB, Colonia, NJ 07067
Tel.: (732) 669-1200
Web Site: http://www.musclemakergrill.com
Sales Range: $1-9.9 Million
Emp.: 12
Limited Service Restaurants Franchisor
N.A.I.C.S.: 533110
Rodney Silva (Founder)
Arthur G. Gunther (Pres)
Robert E. Morgan (Pres & CEO)
Gordon Abbott (Dir-Ops)
Ben Ross (Dir-Franchise Dev)
T.J. Disney (Mgr-Franchise Support)
Joe Jaeger (Dir-Franchise Dev-West Coast)
Scott Carlock (CFO)
Derek Bogner (VP-Franchise Ops)
David LaPointe (Dir-Corp Ops)
Patrick Chiacchia (Dir-Non-Traditional Dev)
James Ginger (Dir-Construction)

AMERICAN RESURGENS MANAGEMENT CORPORATION
2929 Lenox Rd NE, Atlanta, GA 30324
Tel.: (404) 261-7855
Web Site: http://www.armcorp.com
Sales Range: $25-49.9 Million
Emp.: 12
Real Estate Asset Managers & Developers
N.A.I.C.S.: 237210
James L. McMahan (Chm)

AMERICAN RIVER VENTURES, LLC
21355 38th St, Sacramento, CA 95816
Tel.: (916) 780-2828
Web Site: http://www.arventures.com
Year Founded: 2001
Privater Equity Firm
N.A.I.C.S.: 523999
Harry Laswell (Co-Founder)
Cheryl Beninga (Mng Dir)

AMERICAN RIVER-PACKAGEONE INC.
4225 Pell Dr, Sacramento, CA 95838
Tel.: (916) 929-7969
Rev.: $14,000,000
Emp.: 500
Mfr of Corrugated Boxes
N.A.I.C.S.: 322211
Tom Kandris (Co-Founder & CEO)

AMERICAN ROAD LINE, INC.
1155 Stoops Ferry Rd, Moon Township, PA 15108
Tel.: (412) 264-6996
Web Site: http://www.arlnetwork.com
Sales Range: $50-74.9 Million
Emp.: 50
Trucking Except Local
N.A.I.C.S.: 484121

Ronald K. Faherty (Pres)
Tom Lioi (Dir-IT)
John Lioi (Dir-HR)

AMERICAN ROCK SALT COMPANY LLC
3846 Retsof Rd, Retsof, NY 14539
Tel.: (585) 243-9510   NY
Web Site:
http://www.americanrocksalt.com
Sales Range: $150-199.9 Million
Emp.: 266
Industrial Salts Mfr
N.A.I.C.S.: 212311
Gunther K. Buerman (Chm)
Gregory J. Norris (Plant Mgr)
Barb Heller (Mgr-Comml Sls)
Mark Assini (Chief Admin Officer)

AMERICAN ROLL FORMED PRODUCTS CORP.
892 Callendar Blvd, Painesville, OH 44077
Tel.: (440) 352-0753
Web Site: http://www.arfpcorp.com
Year Founded: 1960
Sales Range: $50-74.9 Million
Emp.: 125
Fabricated Pipe & Pipe Fitting Mfr
N.A.I.C.S.: 332996
Phil Misch (Pres)
Randy Myers (Dir-Sls & Engrg)
Joshua Perkins (Dir-Mktg)

AMERICAN ROLLER BEARING CO., INC.
400 2nd Ave NW, Hickory, NC 28601
Tel.: (828) 624-1460
Web Site: http://www.amroll.com
Year Founded: 1911
Sales Range: $25-49.9 Million
Emp.: 400
Ball & Roller Bearing Mfr
N.A.I.C.S.: 332991
Benjamin Succop (Pres)

AMERICAN ROLLER BEARING COMPANY
400 2nd Ave NW, Hickory, NC 28601
Tel.: (828) 624-1460
Web Site: http://www.amroll.com
Rev.: $39,000,000
Emp.: 400
Roller Bearings & Parts
N.A.I.C.S.: 332991
Lawrence N. Succop (Chm)

AMERICAN ROLLER COMPANY
1440 13th Ave, Union Grove, WI 53182
Tel.: (262) 878-8665
Web Site:
https://www.americanroller.com
Sales Range: $50-74.9 Million
Emp.: 25
Printing Trades Machinery
N.A.I.C.S.: 333248
Daniel J. Cahalane (Pres)
David L. Turbiville (CFO)

AMERICAN ROOFING & METAL CO. INC.
801 Wyoming St, San Antonio, TX 78203
Tel.: (210) 224-6463
Web Site:
https://www.amerroofing.com
Year Founded: 1904
Sales Range: $10-24.9 Million
Emp.: 150
Roofing Contractors
N.A.I.C.S.: 238160
Edward W. Spalten (Pres)

AMERICAN SALE, INC.
8401 W 185th St, Tinley Park, IL 60487
Tel.: (708) 623-1481
Web Site:
https://www.americansale.com
Rev.: $13,000,000
Emp.: 8
Variety Stores
N.A.I.C.S.: 455219
Robert A. Jones Jr. (Owner, Pres & CEO)

AMERICAN SANDS ENERGY CORP.
4760 S Highland Dr Ste 341, Salt Lake City, UT 84117
Tel.: (801) 699-3966
Year Founded: 2011
Oil & Gas Exploration Services
N.A.I.C.S.: 213112
William C. Gibbs (Chm & CEO)

AMERICAN SCHOOL OF CORRESPONDENCE
2200 E 170th St, Lansing, IL 60438-1002
Tel.: (708) 418-2800
Web Site:
https://www.americanschoolcorr.com
Year Founded: 1897
Sales Range: $75-99.9 Million
Emp.: 200
Education Services
N.A.I.C.S.: 611519
Roberta R. Allen (Exec VP & Dir-Curriculum)
Gary R. Masterton (Pres)
Valerie Riley (Asst Dir-Adv)

AMERICAN SEAFOODS, LP
Market Place Tower 2025 1st Ave Ste 900, Seattle, WA 98121
Tel.: (206) 448-0300
Web Site:
https://www.americanseafoods.com
Sales Range: $500-549.9 Million
Emp.: 1,200
Seafood Mfr & Distr
N.A.I.C.S.: 311710
Inge Andreassen (Pres)
Trent Hartill (VP-Fisheries & Sustainability)
Kevin McMenimen (CFO)
Rasmus Soerensen (Exec VP-Sls-Global)
Margery Schelling (Exec VP-Mktg, Strategy & Innovation)
Scott McNair (Exec VP-Product & Bus Dev)
Valentina Zackrone (Chief HR Officer)
Trond Ringstad (Mng Partner)

Subsidiaries:

American Seafoods Group LLC   (1)
Marketplace Tower 2025 1st Ave Ste 900, Seattle, WA 98121
Tel.: (206) 374-1515
Web Site:
http://www.americanseafoods.com
Sales Range: $10-24.9 Million
Emp.: 100
Fresh & Frozen Seafood Processing Services
N.A.I.C.S.: 311710
Bernt O. Bodal (Chm)
Brad Bodenman (Treas)
Matthew D. Latimer (Chief Legal Officer & Gen Counsel)
Kevin McMenimen (CFO)

Subsidiary (Domestic):

American Seafoods Company   (2)
Marketplace Tower 2025 1st Ave Ste 900, Seattle, WA 98121
Tel.: (206) 448-0300
Web Site:
http://www.americanseafoods.com

Emp.: 100
Manager of Fishing Vessels; Catcher & Processor of Seafood
N.A.I.C.S.: 541611
Inge Andreassen *(Pres)*
Kevin McMenimen *(CFO)*
Margery Schelling *(Exec VP-Mktg, Strategy & Innovation)*
Rasmus Soerensen *(Exec VP-Sls-Global)*
Scott McNair *(Exec VP-Product & Bus Dev)*
Valentina Zackrone *(Chief HR Officer)*

AMERICAN SEATING COMPANY

401 American Seating Ctr NW, Grand Rapids, MI 49504-4455
Tel.: (616) 732-6600   DE
Web Site:
   http://www.americanseating.com
Year Founded: 1886
Sales Range: $100-124.9 Million
Emp.: 300
Seating Product Mfr
N.A.I.C.S.: 337214
Dave McLaughlin *(VP & Gen Mgr-Sls)*
Edward J. Clark *(Chm)*
Anthony Tomasello *(Mgr-Sls-Northeast)*
Tom Bush *(Pres & CEO)*
Brian Chappell *(Natl Sls Mgr)*
Karen Dhanie *(VP-Bus Dev)*

Subsidiaries:

Otaco Seating Co., Ltd.   (1)
Harvie Settlement Rd, PO Box 2310, Orillia, L3V 6S2, ON, Canada   **(100%)**
Tel.: (705) 325-7052
Web Site: http://www.otacoseating.com
Sales Range: $10-24.9 Million
Emp.: 35
Mfr of Seats for Buses
N.A.I.C.S.: 336360

AMERICAN SECURITIES LLC

590 Madison Avenue, 38th Floor, New York, NY 10022
Tel.: (212) 476-8000   NY
Web Site: http://www.american-securities.com
Year Founded: 1994
Rev.: $42,000,000,000
Emp.: 109,900
Privater Equity Firm
N.A.I.C.S.: 523999
Michael G. Fisch *(CEO & Founder)*
David L. Horing *(Mng Dir)*
Lee Dranikoff *(Mng Dir)*
David Maue *(Mng Dir & Chief Admin Officer)*
Scott Wolff *(Mng Dir)*
Loren Easton *(Mng Dir)*
Michael Sand *(Mng Dir)*
Bill Fry *(Mng Dir)*
Helen A. Chiang *(Mng Dir)*
Benjamin B. Dickson *(Mng Dir)*
Mark Lovett *(Mng Dir)*
Will Manuel *(Mng Dir)*
Noah Scherz *(Principal)*
David Portnoy *(Principal)*
Jared Sperling *(VP)*
Kevin Penn *(Mng Dir)*
Aaron Maeng *(Mng Dir)*
Dan Thau *(VP)*
Kevin S. Penn *(Mng Dir)*
Anthony Grillo *(Founder)*

Subsidiaries:

ASP Westward, L.P.   (1)
523 N Sam Houston Pkwy E Ste 600, Houston, TX 77060
Tel.: (281) 668-1100
Web Site: http://www.aspwestward.com
Newspaper Publishing Services
N.A.I.C.S.: 513110
James W. Hopson *(Pres & CEO)*
Monica Liban *(VP-Sls & Mktg)*

Air Methods Corporation   (1)

5500 S Quebec St Ste 300, Greenwood Village, CO 80111
Tel.: (303) 792-7400
Web Site: http://www.airmethods.com
Holding Company; Medical Emergency & Scenic Helicopter Transportation & Support Services
N.A.I.C.S.: 551112
Sharon J. Keck *(Chief Acctg Officer)*
Michael D. Allen *(Pres-Air Medical Svcs)*
Chris Meinhardt *(Sr Dir-Maintenance)*
Crystal L. Gordon *(Gen Counsel, Sec & Exec VP)*
David M. Doerr *(Exec VP-Tourism Div)*
Kevin Campbell *(Sr VP-Fin)*
Doni Perry *(VP-IT)*
Tina Giangrasso *(VP-Clinical Svcs)*
Mike Slattery *(Pres-United Rotorcraft)*
Leo Morrissette *(Sr VP-Aviation Ops)*
Heather Dumas *(Sr VP-HR)*
David Stuhlmiller *(Chief Medical Officer)*
Cory Theriot *(VP-Safety & Risk Mgmt)*
Alan Einisman *(Chief Compliance Officer & VP)*
Carolyn Mayle *(VP-Govt Affairs)*
John Baumgarten *(VP-Strategic Alliances)*
Christina Ward *(Dir-Corp Comm)*
Aaron D. Todd III *(CEO)*

Subsidiary (Domestic):

Helicopter Consultants of Maui, LLC   (2)
1 Kahului Airport Rd Ste 105, Kahului, HI 96732
Tel.: (808) 871-6657
Web Site: http://www.bluehawaiian.com
Scenic Helicopter Tour Services
N.A.I.C.S.: 487990
Gregg Lundberg *(Pres & CEO)*
Meghan Lee *(Dir-Sls & Mktg)*

Sundance Helicopters, Inc.   (2)
5596 Haven St, Las Vegas, NV 89119
Tel.: (702) 736-0606
Web Site:
   http://www.sundancehelicopters.com
Scenic Helicopter Transportation Services
N.A.I.C.S.: 487990
Eric Filipcic *(Head-Sls)*
John Wells *(Dir-IT)*
Pavy Mueller *(Dir-Sls-Intl)*

United Rotorcraft Solutions, LLC   (2)
1942 N Trinity St, Decatur, TX 76234
Tel.: (940) 627-0626
Web Site: http://www.unitedrotorcraft.com
Helicopter & Fixed-Wing Completions Center; Aircraft Maintenance Services
N.A.I.C.S.: 488190
Everett Horst *(Dir-Decatur Ops)*
Michael Slattery *(Pres)*
William Salus *(Sr Dir-Ops)*
Jon Warneke *(Sr Dir-Program Mgmt)*
Frank Graham *(Sr Dir-Global Sls & Mktg)*
Robert Brodin *(Dir-Govt Programs)*
Christen Duncan *(Dir-Quality Sys)*
Trina Reish *(Dir-Customer Support)*
Kenneth Reincke *(Mgr-Contracts)*
Matt Hoadley *(Mgr-Sls Support)*
Art Torwirt *(Sr Mgr-Govt Bus Dev)*
CJ Daniel *(Mgr-Decatur-Part 145 Acct)*

Aramsco, Inc.   (1)
1480 Grandview Ave, Paulsboro, NJ 08066
Tel.: (856) 686-7700
Web Site: http://www.aramsco.com
Sales Range: $50-74.9 Million
Environmental Safety Supply Distr Owned by Summit Partners LP & by WSG Partners LLC
N.A.I.C.S.: 423840
Curt Massey *(Treas & VP)*
Rich Salerno *(CEO)*
Andrew Liebert *(VP)*

Joint Venture (Domestic):

Allen Equipment, Inc.   (2)
600 S 56th St Ste 3, Chandler, AZ 85226-4207
Tel.: (480) 961-5307
Equipment Electrical Repair & Supplies Merchant Whslr
N.A.I.C.S.: 423850

Subsidiary (Domestic):

Retailers Supply Co Inc.   (2)
4398 Security Pkwy, New Albany, IN 47150

Tel.: (812) 948-1163
Web Site: http://www.retailersupply.com
Industrial & Personal Service Paper Merchant Whslr
N.A.I.C.S.: 424130

Blount International, Inc.   (1)
4909 SE International Way, Portland, OR 97222-4679
Tel.: (503) 653-8881
Web Site: http://www.blount.com
Sales Range: $800-899.9 Million
Emp.: 1,200
Industrial & Outdoor Power Cutting Equipment Mfr
N.A.I.C.S.: 332994
David A. Willmott *(Pres & COO)*
Chad E. Paulson *(Gen Counsel, Sec & VP)*
Dave P. Gillrie *(Sr VP-Global Sls & Mktg-FLAG Div)*
David K. Parrish *(Sr VP-Global Supply Chain)*
Kevin M. Trepa *(CIO & Sr VP-Global Plng & Logistics)*
Valdir R. Viana *(VP-FLAG Mfg Ops)*
Todd H. Hall *(Pres-Farm, Ranch & Agriculture Div-Woods Equipment)*
Bob Hickson *(CFO)*
Paul Tonnesen *(CEO)*

Subsidiary (Domestic):

Blount, Inc.   (2)
4909 SE International Way, Portland, OR 97222-4679
Tel.: (503) 653-8881
Web Site: http://www.oregonproducts.com
Emp.: 3,000
Outdoor Power Equipment & Tools Mfr & Marketer
N.A.I.C.S.: 333112

Subsidiary (Non-US):

Blount Europe, S.A.   (3)
Rue Emile Francqui 5, 1435, Mont-Saint-Guibert, Belgium
Tel.: (32) 10301111
Web Site: http://www.oregonproducts.eu
Cutting Systems & Farm Equipment Mfr
N.A.I.C.S.: 333515

Blount GmbH   (3)
Lise-Meitner-Strasse 4, 70736, Fellbach, Germany
Tel.: (49) 71130033400
Web Site: http://www.oregonproducts.de
Industrial Garden & Forestry Cutting Product Mfr
N.A.I.C.S.: 333515
Ralf Geiger *(Mng Dir)*
Jochen Weber *(Mng Dir)*

Blount Industrial Ltda.   (3)
Rua Emilio Romani 1630 CIC, CEP 81460-020, Curitiba, Parana, Brazil
Tel.: (55) 4121695800
Web Site: http://www.oregonbrasil.com.br
Cutting Chains, Bars & Accessories Mfr
N.A.I.C.S.: 332216

Blount Japan, Inc.   (3)
Queens Tower C 12F 2-3-5 Minatomirai, Nishi-Ku, Yokohama, 220-6212, Japan
Tel.: (81) 456824433
Web Site: http://www.oregonchain.jp
Cutting Chain, Bars & Machine Tool Acessories Mfr
N.A.I.C.S.: 333515
Junko Ito *(Dir)*

Blount UK Ltd.   (3)
Unit 3 Formal Business Park Northway Lane, Tewkesbury, GL20 8GY, Gloucestershire, United Kingdom
Tel.: (44) 1684297600
Web Site: http://www.oregonproducts.co.uk
Industrial, Garden & Forestry Cutting Products Mfr
N.A.I.C.S.: 333515

Oregon Distribution Ltd   (3)
505 Edinburgh Road North, Guelph, N1H 6L4, ON, Canada
Tel.: (519) 822-6870
Web Site: http://www.oregonproducts.com
Industrial Machinery & Equipment Mfr & Distr
N.A.I.C.S.: 333998

Subsidiary (Domestic):

Blount Canada Ltd.   (4)
505 Edinburgh Road North, Guelph, N1H 6L4, ON, Canada
Tel.: (519) 822-6870
Web Site: http://www.oregonproducts.com
Cutting Chain Bar & Accessory Mfr
N.A.I.C.S.: 332216

Subsidiary (Non-US):

Svenska Blount AB   (3)
PO Box 1104, 432 15, Varberg, Sweden
Tel.: (46) 340645480
Web Site: http://www.oregonproducts.se
Industrial Machinery & Equipment Distr
N.A.I.C.S.: 423830

Subsidiary (Domestic):

SpeeCo, Inc.   (2)
2606 S Illinois Route 2, Oregon, IL 61061
Tel.: (800) 525-8322
Web Site: http://www.speeco.com
Farm Accessories & Equipment Mfr
N.A.I.C.S.: 333111

Woods Equipment Company   (2)
2606 S Illinois Rte 2, Oregon, IL 61061
Tel.: (815) 732-2141
Web Site: http://www.woodsequipment.com
Emp.: 550
Agricultural & Construction Machinery Mfr
N.A.I.C.S.: 333111
Angela Kay Larson *(VP-Mktg)*

Blue Bird Corporation   (1)
3920 Arkwright Rd Ste 200, Macon, GA 31210   **(57%)**
Web Site: https://www.blue-bird.com
Rev.: $683,995,000
Assets: $356,020,000
Liabilities: $388,676,000
Net Worth: ($32,656,000)
Earnings: ($289,000)
Emp.: 1,702
Fiscal Year-end: 10/02/2021
Holding Company; School Bus Mfr & Whslr
N.A.I.C.S.: 551112
Kevin S. Penn *(Chm)*
Felix Lin *(VP-HR & External Affairs)*
Ted Scartz *(Corp Counsel)*
Razvan Radulescu *(CFO)*
Jeff Sanfrey *(COO & Sr VP)*
Jolene O'Brien Paver *(Chief HR Officer & Sr VP)*
Philip Horlock *(Pres & CEO)*

Conair Corporation   (1)
150 Milford Rd, East Windsor, NJ 08520-6124
Web Site: http://www.conair.com
Electronic & Kitchen Appliance Mfr
N.A.I.C.S.: 335210
Ronald T. Diamond *(Pres & CEO)*
Stacey DeFelice *(Mgr-PR)*
Martin A. Cohen *(VP-Mktg)*

Subsidiary (Domestic):

Allegro Manufacturing, Inc.   (2)
9350 Rayo Ave, South Gate, CA 90280
Tel.: (323) 724-0101
Web Site: http://www.allegromfg.com
Sales Range: $10-24.9 Million
Emp.: 100
Travel Bag Mfr & Supplier
N.A.I.C.S.: 316990
John Dunkel *(VP-Ops)*

Subsidiary (Non-US):

Babyliss SA   (2)
99 Avenue Aristide Briand, PO Box 72, 92120, Montrouge, France   **(100%)**
Tel.: (33) 146564757
Web Site: http://www.babyliss.fr
Sales Range: $10-24.9 Million
Emp.: 60
Mfr of Personal Care Products
N.A.I.C.S.: 812199
Corinne Philippe *(Gen Mgr)*

Division (Domestic):

Conair Consumer Appliances Division   (2)
150 Milford Rd, East Windsor, NJ 08520   **(100%)**
Tel.: (203) 351-9000

American Securities LLC—(Continued)

Web Site: http://www.conair.com
Electric Housewares & Fans Mfr
N.A.I.C.S.: 335210

Subsidiary (Non-US):

Conair Consumer Products Inc. (2)
100 Conair Pkwy, Woodbridge, L4H 0L2,
ON, Canada
Tel.: (905) 265-4500
Web Site: http://www.conaircanada.ca
Personal Care, Dental & Beauty Aid Products, Consumer Electronic & Kitchen Appliances Mfr & Developer
N.A.I.C.S.: 335210

Division (Domestic):

Conair Corporation - Waring
Division (2)
314 Ella T Grasso Ave, Torrington, CT
06790
Tel.: (203) 975-4600
Web Site: http://www.waringproducts.com
Household Cooking Appliance Mfr
N.A.I.C.S.: 335220

Subsidiary (Non-US):

Conair Far East Limited (2)
Rm 3307-10 Millennium City 388 Kwun
Tong Road, Standard Chartered Tower,
Kowloon, China (Hong Kong)
Tel.: (852) 2751 4604
Personal Care Appliance Mfr
N.A.I.C.S.: 335220

Division (Domestic):

Conair Liquids Division (2)
1 Cummings Point Rd, Stamford, CT 06902
Tel.: (203) 351-9000
Web Site: http://www.conair.com
Hair Care Products Mfr
N.A.I.C.S.: 325620

Subsidiary (Domestic):

ConairPRO Inc. (2)
1 Cummings Point Rd, Stamford, CT
06902-7901
Tel.: (800) 726-4202
Web Site: http://www.conairpro.com
Electrical Personal Care Appliance Mfr
N.A.I.C.S.: 333310

Subsidiary (Non-US):

Continental Conair, Ltd. (2)
Room 604 New World Centre, 18-24 Salisbury, Kowloon, China (Hong Kong) (100%)
Mfr of Personal Care Products
N.A.I.C.S.: 812199

Division (Domestic):

Cuisinart Inc. (2)
1 Cummings Point Rd, Stamford, CT 06902
Tel.: (203) 351-9000
Web Site: http://www.cuisinart.com
Sales Range: $25-49.9 Million
Emp.: 300
Cooking Equipment Mfr & Retailer
N.A.I.C.S.: 449129
Mary Rodgers (Dir-Mktg Comm)
Ron Diamond (Pres)

Rusk, Inc. (2)
1 Cummings Point Rd, Stamford, CT 06902
Tel.: (203) 351-9000
Web Site: http://www.rusk1.com
Sales Range: $25-49.9 Million
Emp.: 300
Hair-Care Products for Beauty Salons
N.A.I.C.S.: 424210
Ron Diamond (Pres)

Subsidiary (Domestic):

SalonQuest, LLC (2)
7185 Chagrin Rd Ste A, Chagrin Falls, OH
44023
Tel.: (877) 238-1100
Web Site: http://www.aquage.com
Piece Goods, Notions & Other Dry Goods
Merchant Whslr
N.A.I.C.S.: 424310
Shawn Long (Reg Sls Mgr)

Division (Domestic):

Waring Products, Inc. (2)
1 Cummings Point Rd, Stamford, CT
06902-7901
Tel.: (203) 975-4600
Web Site: http://www.waringproducts.com
Sales Range: $25-49.9 Million
Emp.: 400
Commercial & Consumer Portable Electrical
Appliances Mfr
N.A.I.C.S.: 335220

FiberMark Inc. (1)
161 Wellington Rd, Brattleboro, VT 05301
Tel.: (802) 257-0365
Sales Range: $150-199.9 Million
Specialty Fiber-Based Materials Mfr
N.A.I.C.S.: 322130
Jonathan Robson (Mng Dir-United Kingdom)

Branch (Domestic):

FiberMark
45 N 4th St, Quakertown, PA 18951-1239
Tel.: (215) 536-4600
Sales Range: $75-99.9 Million
Specialty Fiber-Based Materials Mfr
N.A.I.C.S.: 322130

FiberMark North America, Inc. (2)
70 Front St, West Springfield, MA 01089
Tel.: (413) 533-0699
Decorative Covering Materials For Books
Specialty Packaging & Stationery Product
Mfr
N.A.I.C.S.: 322220
Mark Gaspari (Mgr-Support Svcs)

FleetPride, Inc. (1)
600 E Las Colinas Blvd Ste 400, Irving, TX
75039
Web Site: http://www.fleetpride.com
Heavy-Duty Truck & Trailer Parts Distr;
Truck Repair & Maintenance Service Facilities Operator
N.A.I.C.S.: 423120
Kenny Wagers (Chief Financial Officer)
Mike Harris (Pres-Parts)
Beth Corl (Sr VP-HR)
Ashley Adams (Gen Counsel & VP)
Michael A. Duffy (CEO)
Mike Duffy (CEO)

Subsidiary (Domestic):

Albert's Truck Service & Supply,
Inc. (2)
4900 S Frontage Rd, Weatherford, OK
73096
Tel.: (580) 772-6065
General Automotive Repair Services
N.A.I.C.S.: 811111

Best Deal Spring Inc. (2)
444 E 100 N, Payson, UT 84657
Web Site: http://www.bestdealspring.com
Tire Dealers
N.A.I.C.S.: 441340

Bolin Auto & Truck Parts Co.,
Inc. (2)
1211 S 10th St, Saint Joseph, MO 64503
Tel.: (816) 232-4477
Web Site: http://www.bolintruckparts.com
Rev.: $1,900,000
Emp.: 12
Auto & Truck Components Mfr
N.A.I.C.S.: 333924

Division (Domestic):

FleetPride - Northeast (2)
269 State St, North Haven, CT 06473-5049
Tel.: (203) 281-0111
Web Site: http://www.fleetpride.com
Sales Range: $25-49.9 Million
Emp.: 100
Heavy-Duty Truck Parts Distr; Truck Repair
& Maintenance Facilities Operator
N.A.I.C.S.: 423120
Mitch Gallignano (Gen Mgr)

FleetPride - Southeast (2)
2403 21st St N, Birmingham, AL 35234
Tel.: (205) 322-5621
Web Site: http://www.fleetpride.com
Sales Range: $25-49.9 Million
Emp.: 25

Distr of Heavy-Duty Truck Parts; Operator
of Truck Repair & Maintenance Facilities
N.A.I.C.S.: 423120
Harold Johnson (Reg VP-South)

FleetPride - Western/Central (2)
424 Port Ave, Corpus Christi, TX 78405
Tel.: (866) 221-2484
Web Site: http://www.fleetpride.com
Heavy-Duty Truck & Trailer Parts Distr;
Truck Repair & Maintenance Service Facilities Operator
N.A.I.C.S.: 423120

Subsidiary (Domestic):

Frame Service Inc. (2)
4210 Goshen Rd, Fort Wayne, IN 46818
Tel.: (260) 423-3336
Web Site: http://www.frameservice.com
Automotive Repair Services
N.A.I.C.S.: 811111

Keystone Spring Service, Inc. (2)
112 35th St, Pittsburgh, PA 15201
Tel.: (412) 621-4800
Web Site: http://www.keystonespring.com
Rev.: $7,000,000
Emp.: 35
Motor Vehicle Supplies & New Parts Merchant Whslr
N.A.I.C.S.: 423120
Edward A. Valant (VP & Sec)

Knowles On Site Repair, Inc. (2)
7481 N Palafox St, Pensacola, FL 32503-
7078
Tel.: (850) 994-4211
Mobile Repair Services
N.A.I.C.S.: 811198

L & N Truck Service of Ellenwood,
LLC (2)
5291 Hwy 42, Ellenwood, GA 30294
Tel.: (770) 961-2505
Web Site: http://www.lntruck.com
General Freight Trucking
N.A.I.C.S.: 484122
Ned Coleman (Pres)

MTR Fleet Services, LLC (2)
2520 Jake Dr, Cumming, GA 30028-4304
Tel.: (678) 947-9068
Web Site: http://www.mtrfleetservices.com
General Automotive Repair
N.A.I.C.S.: 811111

National Truck Repair (2)
185 Kyle Wilson Rd, Longview, TX 75602-
7375
Tel.: (903) 234-9051
Web Site:
   http://www.nationaltruckrepair.com
General Automotive Repair
N.A.I.C.S.: 811111
Justin Head (Mgr)

Powers Truck and Trailer Sales
LLC (2)
911 S Main St, Seminole, TX 79360-5505
Tel.: (432) 758-3734
Web Site:
   http://www.powerstrucktrailersales.com
General Automotive Repair Services
N.A.I.C.S.: 811111

Raney's Truck Center, Inc. (2)
1550 NW 38th Ave, Ocala, FL 34482-4019
Tel.: (352) 789-6701
Web Site: http://www.raneystruckparts.com
Motor Vehicle Supplies & New Parts Merchant Whslr
N.A.I.C.S.: 423120

Steubenville Truck Center, Inc. (2)
620 South St, Steubenville, OH 43952
Tel.: (740) 282-2711
Web Site:
   http://www.steubenvilletruckcenter.com
Sales Range: $1-9.9 Million
Emp.: 25
General Automotive Repair
N.A.I.C.S.: 811111
Larry A. Remp (Pres)
Mary Stead (Office Mgr)

Tam Truck & Trailer Services
LLC (2)
2071 Industrial Dr, Gainesville, GA 30504-
5855
Tel.: (770) 287-1900

Web Site: http://www.tamtruckandtrailer.com
General Automotive Repair
N.A.I.C.S.: 811111

Truck Parts & Equipment Inc. (2)
4501 Esthner St, Wichita, KS 67209
Tel.: (316) 942-4251
Truck Parts & Accessories
N.A.I.C.S.: 423120

Foundation Building Materials,
Inc. (1)
2520 Red Hill Ave, Santa Ana, CA 92705
Tel.: (714) 380-3127
Web Site: http://www.fbmsales.com
Holding Company; Building Materials Distr
N.A.I.C.S.: 551112
John Gorey (CFO)
Peter A. Welly (COO)
Alan Kirby Thompson (Chief Sls Officer)
Richard J. Tilley (Gen Counsel, Sec & VP)
Onur Demirkaya (CFO)

Subsidiary (Domestic):

American Wal-Board LLC (2)
3520 Sky Harbor Cove, Memphis, TN
38118
Tel.: (901) 362-1845
Web Site: http://www.americanwal-
board.com
Sales Range: $1-9.9 Million
Emp.: 30
Wall Insulation, Fireplace & Ceiling Products Distr
N.A.I.C.S.: 423310
Jeff Hudson (Controller)

Associated Drywall Suppliers,
Inc. (2)
6250 Fern Vly Pass, Louisville, KY 40228-
1001
Tel.: (502) 966-3323
Web Site: http://www.adrywall.net
Construction & Mining Machinery
N.A.I.C.S.: 423810
Charles Nutt (Pres)

Dominion Interior Supply
Corporation (2)
2109 Westmoreland St, Richmond, VA
23230
Tel.: (804) 355-5888
Web Site: http://dominioninterior.com
Acoustical Ceiling Supplier
N.A.I.C.S.: 423330

Foundation Building Materials,
LLC (2)
2741 Walnut Ave Ste 200, Tustin, CA
92780-6992
Tel.: (714) 380-3127
Web Site: http://www.fbmsales.com
Building Materials Distr
N.A.I.C.S.: 423990
Ruben D. Mendoza (Pres & CEO)
John Gorey (CFO)
Pete Welly (COO)
Kirby Thompson (Sr VP-Sls & Mktg)
Ray Sears (Sr VP-Mechanical Insulation)
Jim Carpenter (VP-Bus Dev)

Subsidiary (Domestic):

A & D Supply of Okc, Inc. (3)
801 S Agnew Ave, Oklahoma City, OK
73108
Tel.: (405) 236-0076
Web Site: http://www.adsupplyco.com
Sales Range: $1-9.9 Million
Emp.: 22
Lumber, Plywood, Millwork & Wood Panel
Merchant Whslr
N.A.I.C.S.: 423310
George Hughes (Pres)

Henrietta Building Supplies, Inc (3)
1 Riverton Way, West Henrietta, NY 14586
Tel.: (585) 334-4020
Web Site:
   https://www.hbsbuildingsupplies.com
Sales Range: $10-24.9 Million
Emp.: 85
Building Materials, Interior
N.A.I.C.S.: 423310
Erin Eratsley (Office Mgr)
Tim Stahl (Gen Mgr & Sr Project Mgr)
John Black (Mgr)
Thomas Morgan (Mgr-Pur & Inventory Control)

Erin Cratsley *(Mgr-Office & HR)*
John Wilcox *(Project Mgr)*
Tony Agnello *(Controller)*

MarJam Supply Company, Inc. (3)
885 Conklin St, Farmingdale, NY 11735
Tel.: (631) 249-4900
Web Site: http://www.marjam.com
Sales Range: $25-49.9 Million
Emp.: 700
Building Materials & Supplies
N.A.I.C.S.: 423310

Holding (Domestic):

Unified Door & Hardware Group, LLC (3)
1650 Suckle Highway, Pennsauken, NJ 08110
Tel.: (856) 488-8843
Web Site: https://udhgroup.com
Wholesale Building Materials
N.A.I.C.S.: 236210

Subsidiary (Domestic):

The A.G. Mauro Company (4)
310 Alpha Dr, Pittsburgh, PA 15238-2908
Tel.: (412) 782-6600
Web Site: http://www.agmauro.com
Hardware, Doors & Frames Mfr
N.A.I.C.S.: 423710

Subsidiary (Domestic):

Gypsum Wallboard Supply Inc. (2)
10745 A St S, Tacoma, WA 98444
Tel.: (253) 537-3310
Wood Panel Whslr
N.A.I.C.S.: 423310

Marriott Drywall Materials, Inc (2)
W229n2514 Duplainville Rd, Waukesha, WI 53186
Tel.: (262) 548-9599
Web Site: http://www.marriottdrywall.com
Brick, Stone & Related Construction Material Merchant Whslr
N.A.I.C.S.: 423320
Mark Tojek *(Controller)*
Harry Panagiotopoulos *(Gen Mgr)*

Virginia Builders' Supply, Inc. (2)
3008 Impala Pl, Richmond, VA 23228-4206
Tel.: (804) 264-2572
Web Site: http://www.vabuilderssupply.com
Drywall, Plaster, Steel Structures & Other Home Construction Materials Distr
N.A.I.C.S.: 444110
Anthony Bertozzi *(Founder & Pres)*

Wallboard, Inc. (2)
5346 Industrial Boulevard NE, Fridley, MN 55421
Tel.: (763) 571-0062
Web Site: http://wallboardinc.com
Drywall Distr
N.A.I.C.S.: 423310
Bill Goodman *(Owner)*

Frontier Spinning Mills, Inc. (1)
1823 Boone Trail Rd, Sanford, NC 27330
Tel.: (919) 776-9940
Web Site: http://www.frontierspinning.com
Sales Range: $100-124.9 Million
Cotton & Cotton Blend Spun Yarn Mfr
N.A.I.C.S.: 313110
Barbara F. Walton *(CFO & Exec VP)*
John M. Maness *(Exec VP-Mfg)*
John L. Bakane *(Chm)*
George R. Perkins *(Co-CEO)*
George W. Parker *(Pres-Mktg)*

General Chemical Performance Products LLC (1)
90 E Halsey Rd, Parsippany, NJ 07054 **(100%)**
Tel.: (973) 515-0900
Web Site: http://www.generalchemical.com
Sales Range: $25-49.9 Million
Performance Chemicals Mfr
N.A.I.C.S.: 325180
Vincent Opalewski *(VP)*
Douglas McFarland *(VP-Product Dev, Brand Dev & Res)*
Willam E. Redmond Jr. *(Pres & CEO)*

Global Tel Link Corporation (1)
2609 Cameron St, Mobile, AL 36607-3104
Tel.: (251) 479-4500
Web Site: http://www.gtl.net

Sales Range: $500-549.9 Million
Developer & Mfr of Telecommunications Systems with Surveillance Features for Use in Prisons
N.A.I.C.S.: 334210
Hal Howard *(Sr VP-Procurement)*
Teresa Ridgeway *(Sr VP-Admin)*
Brian Oliver *(CEO)*
Tom Sweeney *(VP-Sls-Southeast)*
Garth Johnson *(Sr VP-Ops)*
Lauren Studebaker *(Sr VP-Svcs)*
Chris Tarbert *(VP-Mktg)*
Andrew J. Ritter *(VP-Strategy & Corp Dev)*

Subsidiary (Domestic):

DSI-ITI, LLC (2)
5000 Sixth Ave Ste 1, Altoona, PA 16602 **(100%)**
Tel.: (888) 222-3081
Web Site: http://www.dsiiti.com
Sales Range: $50-74.9 Million
Emp.: 120
Offender Management Software Solutions for Corrections Industry
N.A.I.C.S.: 513210
Anthony Bambocci *(Pres)*
James Rokosky *(Sr VP-Ops)*
Jim Bradley *(Dir-Client Svcs)*
Ed Adams *(Exec Dir-Project Svcs)*

Unit (Domestic):

Global Tel Link Corporation - Validation Station (2)
5959 Corporate Dr, Houston, TX 77056
Tel.: (713) 777-1663
Web Site: http://www.gtl.net
Sales Range: $10-24.9 Million
Emp.: 4
Prison Telecommunications Support Services
N.A.I.C.S.: 517810

Hexion Holdings Corporation (1)
180 E Broad St, Columbus, OH 43215
Tel.: (614) 225-4000
Web Site: http://www.hexion.com
Rev.: $3,374,000,000
Assets: $4,146,000,000
Liabilities: $3,071,000,000
Net Worth: $1,075,000,000
Earnings: $2,805,000,000
Fiscal Year-end: 12/31/2019
Holding Company; Specialty Chemical Products Mfr
N.A.I.C.S.: 551112
George F. Knight III *(CFO & Exec VP)*
George F. Knight *(CFO & Exec VP)*
John P. Auletto *(Exec VP-HR)*
Paul Barletta *(Exec VP-Ops)*
Nathan Fisher *(Chief Procurement Officer & Exec VP)*
Douglas A. Johns *(Gen Counsel & Exec VP)*
Matthew A. Sokol *(Chief Admin Officer & Exec VP)*
Mark Bidstrup *(Treas & Sr VP)*
Stephanie Couhig *(Sr VP-Environmental Health & Safety)*
Dennis Ryan *(CIO & Sr VP)*

Subsidiary (Non-US):

Hexion B.V. (2)
Seattleweg 17, Rotterdam, Pernis, 3195, Netherlands
Tel.: (31) 331355349
Web Site: http://www.hexion.com
Binders & Adhesives Mfr
N.A.I.C.S.: 325211

Branch (Non-US):

Hexion B.V. - Rotterdam, Botlek (2)
Chemiestraat 30, Habour no 4203, 3197 KB, Botlek, Netherlands
Tel.: (31) 102630000
Web Site: http://www.hexion.com
Sales Range: $25-49.9 Million
Emp.: 9
Chemicals Mfr
N.A.I.C.S.: 325998

Subsidiary (Non-US):

Hexion Canada Inc. (2)
12621 156th St NW, Edmonton, T5V 1E1, AB, Canada
Tel.: (614) 986-2497

Web Site: http://www.hexion.com
Emp.: 70
Chemicals Mfr
N.A.I.C.S.: 325998

Hexion GmbH (2)
Gennaer Strasse 2-4, 58642, Iserlohn, Germany
Tel.: (49) 23749250
Web Site: http://www.hexion.com
Sales Range: $125-149.9 Million
Emp.: 400
Chemicals Mfr
N.A.I.C.S.: 325998

Subsidiary (Domestic):

Hexion Inc. (2)
180 E Broad St, Columbus, OH 43215
Tel.: (614) 225-4000
Web Site: http://www.hexion.com
Rev.: $2,510,000,000
Assets: $4,002,000,000
Liabilities: $3,179,000,000
Net Worth: $823,000,000
Earnings: ($230,000,000)
Emp.: 2,600
Fiscal Year-end: 12/31/2020
Industrial Chemicals Mfr
N.A.I.C.S.: 325199
Nathan E. Fisher *(Exec VP-Procurement)*
Douglas A. Johns *(Gen Counsel & Exec VP)*
Mark Bidstrup *(Treas & Sr VP)*
Colette Barricks *(Sr VP & Controller)*
John P. Auletto *(Exec VP-HR)*
Matthew A. Sokol *(Chief Admin Officer & Exec VP)*
Paul G. Barletta *(Exec VP-Ops)*

Subsidiary (Non-US):

Hexion Specialty Chemicals Iberica, S.A. (2)
Calle Ante Pardo 7, Pol Industrial Lantaron, 01213, Lantaron, Spain
Tel.: (34) 945 332 744
Plastics Product Mfr
N.A.I.C.S.: 326199

Hexion UK Ltd. (2)
Sully Moors Road, Sully, Penarth, CF64 5YU, South Glamorgan, United Kingdom
Tel.: (44) 1446725500
Web Site: http://www.hexion.com
Emp.: 50
Mfr of Industrial Chemicals
N.A.I.C.S.: 325998

Plant (Non-US):

Hexion UK Ltd. - Peterlee (2)
Mill Hill North West Industrial Estate Peterlee Co, Durham, SR8 2HR, United Kingdom
Tel.: (44) 1915863239
Web Site: http://www.hexion.com
Emp.: 34
Mfr of Industrial Chemicals
N.A.I.C.S.: 325998

Hexion UK Ltd. - Stirling (2)
Station Road, Cowie, Stirling, FK7 7BQ, United Kingdom
Tel.: (44) 1786814045
Web Site: http://www.hexion.com
Mfr of Industrial Chemicals
N.A.I.C.S.: 325998

Learning Care Group, Inc. (1)
21333 Haggerty Rd Ste 300, Novi, MI 48375
Tel.: (248) 697-9000
Web Site: http://www.learningcaregroup.com
Sales Range: $600-649.9 Million
Emp.: 17,000
Child Day Care Services
N.A.I.C.S.: 624410
Mark R. Bierley *(CEO)*
Susan Canizares *(Chief Academic Officer)*
Sean Sondreal *(CMO)*
Douglas R. Baker *(CFO)*
Judy Fimiani *(Chief HR Officer)*
Nicholas Strange *(COO)*
Daniel Follis Jr. *(Chief Compliance Officer, Gen Counsel & Exec VP)*

Subsidiary (Domestic):

Creative Kids, Inc. (2)
5025 Bond St, Las Vegas, NV 89118
Tel.: (702) 871-0078

Web Site: http://www.creativekidslearningcenter.com
Child Day Care & Tutorial Services
N.A.I.C.S.: 624410

U-GRO Learning Centres, Inc. (2)
1223 Research Blvd, Harrisburg, PA 17111
Tel.: (717) 561-2201
Web Site: http://www.u-gro.com
Rev.: $6,100,000
Emp.: 275
Child Day Care Services
N.A.I.C.S.: 624410
Karen Grissom *(Dir-Education & Curriculum)*

MW Industries, Inc. (1)
9501 Technology Blvd Ste 401, Rosemont, IL 60018
Tel.: (847) 349-5760
Web Site: http://www.mw-ind.com
Springs & Fasteners Mfr & Distr
N.A.I.C.S.: 332613

Subsidiary (Domestic):

Atlantic Spring (2)
137 US RT 202, Ringoes, NJ 08551
Tel.: (908) 788-5800
Web Site: http://www.mw-ind.com
Spring & Coils Mfr
N.A.I.C.S.: 332613

Automatic Spring Coiling (2)
4045 W Thorndale Ave, Chicago, IL 60646
Tel.: (773) 539-5600
Web Site: http://www.mw-ind.com
Precision Compression Springs Mfr
N.A.I.C.S.: 332613

Capital Spring (2)
2000 Jetway Blvd, Columbus, OH 43219
Tel.: (614) 418-0250
Web Site: http://www.mw-ind.com
Coils & Springs Mfr
N.A.I.C.S.: 332613

Century Spring Corp. (2)
5959 Triumph St, Commerce, CA 90040
Tel.: (213) 749-1466
Web Site: http://www.centuryspring.com
Spring Mfr
N.A.I.C.S.: 332613
Ayda Mashhadchi *(Mgr-Quality)*
Shara Hughes *(Mgr-Customer Svc)*

Duer Carolina Coil, Inc. (2)
2375 Hwy 101 S, Greer, SC 29651
Tel.: (864) 989-4141
Web Site: http://www.dccoil.com
Machine Product Mfr
N.A.I.C.S.: 333517
Tom Armstrong *(CEO)*
Steve Wunder *(Pres)*
Peter Netherton *(CFO)*
Rick Eitel *(VP-Mfg)*
Jeff Randall *(Mgr-Bus Dev)*
Marilyn Hendricks *(Mgr-Pur)*
Nathan Jolley *(Engr-Product)*

ESSC Holdings, Inc. (2)
29 DePaolo Dr, Southington, CT 06489
Tel.: (860) 621-7358
Web Site: http://www.mw-ind.com
Wire Forms, Metal Stampings & Spring Mfr
N.A.I.C.S.: 332613

Engineered Spring Products, Inc. (2)
7400 Pinemont Dr, Houston, TX 77040
Tel.: (713) 690-0391
Web Site: http://www.mw-ind.com
Spring Mfr
N.A.I.C.S.: 332613
Karen Douglas *(Fin Mgr)*

Helical Products Company (2)
901 W McCoy Ln, Santa Maria, CA 93455
Tel.: (805) 928-3851
Web Site: http://www.heli-cal.com
Machined Springs, Couplings & Joints Mfr
N.A.I.C.S.: 332613
Alyssa Newman *(Coord-Mktg)*

Hi-Performance Fastening Systems (2)
733 Maple Ln, Bensenville, IL 60106
Tel.: (630) 860-7766
Web Site: http://www.mw-ind.com
Industrial Fastener Mfr
N.A.I.C.S.: 332722

American Securities LLC—(Continued)

Maryland Precision Spring (2)
8900 Kelso Dr, Baltimore, MD 21221
Tel.: (410) 391-7400
Web Site: http://www.mw-ind.com
Springs & Coils Mfr
N.A.I.C.S.: 332613
Maureen Wisnewski (Office Mgr)

Matthew Warren Spring (2)
500 E Ottawa St, Logansport, IN 46947-7008
Tel.: (574) 722-8200
Web Site: http://www.mw-ind.com
Industrial Springs, Stampings & Rings Mfr
N.A.I.C.S.: 332613

Maudlin & Son Manufacturing Co., Inc. (2)
1929 Hwy 146, Kemah, TX 77565
Tel.: (281) 334-7566
Web Site: http://www.maudlinproducts.com
Coil Spring & Other Metal Products Mfr
N.A.I.C.S.: 332613
Autumn Tindall (Controller)
Kirk Tindall (VP & Gen Mgr)
Lee Cruz (Dir-Safety)
Reed Leistad (Mgr-SES Mktg)
Elizabeth Shellabarger (Sls Mgr-Shim Products)
Wade Countryman (Sls Mgr-North America)
Jesus Garcia (Mgr-Shipping)
Warren Trahan (Mgr-Shearing)
Dago Garza (Mgr-Engrg Quality)
Daniel Cruz (Plant Mgr)
Paul Ciolli (Mgr-Laser & Spring Products)
Rod Marquis (Sls Mgr-Custom Shims)
Joe Walton (Mgr-EDM Program)
Doug Folkens (Mgr-Tool Die & Stamping)
Blake Tindall (Mgr-Spring)
Paul Noble (Mgr-Web Design & Mktg)

Mohawk Spring (2)
9505 Winona Ave, Schiller Park, IL 60176
Tel.: (847) 671-6767
Web Site: http://www.mw-ind.com
Spring Mfr
N.A.I.C.S.: 332613

Pontotoc Spring (2)
260 Industrial Dr, Pontotoc, MS 38863
Tel.: (662) 489-7846
Web Site: http://www.mw-ind.com
Coil Spring Mfr
N.A.I.C.S.: 332613
Allen Roye (Gen Mgr)
Milfy Weeks (Engr)

Precision Manufacturing Group, LLC (2)
501 Little Falls Rd, Cedar Grove, NJ 07009
Tel.: (973) 785-4630
Web Site: http://www.servometer.com
Electrodeposited Miniature Metal Bellows, Bellows Assemblies, Contact Springs, Flexible Shaft Couplings Mfr
N.A.I.C.S.: 332999

Subsidiary (Domestic):

BellowsTech, LLC (3)
1289 N US Highway 1, Ormond Beach, FL 32174
Tel.: (386) 615-7530
Web Site: http://www.bellowstech.com
Metal Edge Welded Bellows & Assemblies Mfr
N.A.I.C.S.: 333995
Brad Merkel (VP & Gen Mgr)

Subsidiary (Domestic):

Springmasters (2)
1450 S Buncombe Rd, Greer, SC 29651
Tel.: (864) 877-5100
Web Site: http://www.mw-ind.com
Springs & Coils Mfr
N.A.I.C.S.: 332613

Tri-Star Industries, Inc. (2)
101 Massirio Dr, Berlin, CT 06037
Tel.: (860) 828-7570
Web Site: http://www.tristar-inserts.com
Threaded Inserts & Screw Machine Products Mfr
N.A.I.C.S.: 332722
Jim Haste (Mgr-Sls & Engrg)
Tom Marrone (Mgr-Quality)
Greg Fontaine (Ops Mgr)
Aaron Edelson (Engr-Sls)

USA Fastener Group Inc (2)
1300 Gazin St, Houston, TX 77020
Tel.: (713) 641-4600
Web Site: http://www.mw-ind.com
Industrial Supplies Merchant Whslr
N.A.I.C.S.: 423840
Michael Dierschke (Pres & Gen Mgr)
Allan Jacob (Mgr-Quality)

Milk Specialties Company (1)
7500 Flying Cloud Dr Ste 500, Eden Prairie, MN 55344
Tel.: (952) 942-7310
Web Site: http://www.milkspecialties.com
Emp.: 900
Specialty Protein Reinforced Dairy Products Mfr
N.A.I.C.S.: 311511
David Lenzmeier (CEO)
Tom Benson (Exec VP & VP-Strategic Resourcing)
Eddie Wells (Pres)
Mark Nelson (Pres-Animal Nutrition)
Brad Berentson (CFO)
Paul Lombard (Exec VP)
Brian Lundquist (Sr VP-Ops)
Stacey Pexa (VP-HR)
Michael Hiron (VP-Sls-Human Nutrition Ingredients)
Steve Erickson (VP-Fin)
David Horing (Mng Dir)
Helen Chiang (Principal)
Bahaa Naamani (VP)

Subsidiary (Domestic):

Kay's Processing, Inc. (2)
PO Box 669, Clara City, MN 65222
Tel.: (320) 847-3220
Web Site: http://www.kaysprocess.com
Sales Range: $1-9.9 Million
Emp.: 18
Breakfast Cereal Mfr
N.A.I.C.S.: 311230
Massoud Kazemzadeh (Chm & COO)

Mortgage Contracting Services LLC (1)
350 Highland Dr Ste 100, Lewisville, TX 75067
Tel.: (813) 387-1100
Web Site: http://www.mcs360.com
Property Inspection, Preservation & Real Estate Owned Property Maintenance Services
N.A.I.C.S.: 561499
Chad Mosley (Pres)
Len Suazo (CFO)
Craig Torrance (CEO)
John Bacon (CMO)
Marin Ursu (CIO)

Subsidiary (Domestic):

M&M Mortgage Services, Inc. (2)
12901 SW 132 Ave, Miami, FL 33186
Tel.: (305) 232-4300
Ambulatory Health Care Services
N.A.I.C.S.: 621999

NWN Corporation (1)
271 Waverley Oaks Rd, Waltham, MA 02452
Tel.: (781) 472-3400
Web Site: http://www.nwnit.com
Sales Range: $100-124.9 Million
Emp.: 550
Information Technology Management & Consulting Services
N.A.I.C.S.: 541519
Mont Phelps (Founder)
Skip Tappen (CEO)
Bill Nelson (Acct Exec-Oil, Gas & Healthcare)
Jessica Krause (Acct Exec)
Jillian Bartkus (Acct Exec)
Drew Phelps (Exec VP-Svc Delivery-Natl)
Richard E. Johnson (CFO)
Scott Pintsopoulos (Exec VP-Sls & Mktg)

Subsidiary (Domestic):

Carousel Industries of North America, Inc. (2)
659 S County Trl, Exeter, RI 02822
Tel.: (401) 667-5400
Web Site: http://www.carouselindustries.com
Sales Range: $100-124.9 Million
Emp.: 325
Technology Services

N.A.I.C.S.: 517810
Jeff Gardner (CEO)
Bill Thompson (Exec VP-Ops)
Dan Tassone (VP-Sls-East)
Jody Grandpre (VP-Sls-West)
Jason Albuquerque (Chief Info Security Officer)
Meredith Lawrence (VP-Mktg)
Jen Vahtola (VP-Ops)
Mark Moretti (VP-Data & Security)
Nancy Contillo (Chief People Officer)
Rhonda Wingate (VP-Visual Collaboration Sls)
Tim Hebert (Chief Managed Svcs Officer)
Robert Taylor (VP-Southwest)
Jason Cherry (CFO)
Jason Viera (CTO)
Paul Pinto (Exec VP-Svcs)
Pundari Pothini (Dir-Customer Experience Tech)
Andrew Rogers (Dir-Contact Center Tech)
Stephen Drew (VP-Contact Center)
Kelly Santos (Dir-Content & Comm)
Adam Anderson (VP-Cisco Sls)
Zane West (VP-Cybersecurity Sls & Strategy)
Lee Kayne (VP-Contact Center Solutions)
James R. Marsh III (Chief Revenue Officer)

Subsidiary (Domestic):

TriNET Systems, Inc. (3)
659 South County Trl, Exeter, RI 02822
Tel.: (888) 874-6383
Web Site: http://www.carouselindustries.com
Sales Range: $25-49.9 Million
Emp.: 200
Computer Network Design Services
N.A.I.C.S.: 541512

Subsidiary (Domestic):

NWN Corporation (2)
10661 Rockley Rd, Houston, TX 77099
Tel.: (281) 983-9955
Web Site: http://www.nwnit.com
Sales Range: $50-74.9 Million
Emp.: 35
Computer Networking Services & Solutions
N.A.I.C.S.: 541512
Stephanie Clark (Acct Exec)

Subsidiary (Domestic):

Leverage Information Systems, Inc. (3)
17280 Wdnville Redmond Rd, Woodinville, WA 98072
Tel.: (425) 481-6300
Web Site: http://www.leverageis.com
Sales Range: $1-9.9 Million
Emp.: 19
Computers, Peripherals, And Software, Nsk
N.A.I.C.S.: 423430
Doug Chesler (Pres)

Subsidiary (Domestic):

NWN Corporation (2)
Meadow Brook Corporate Park 100 Corporate Pkwy Ste 300, Birmingham, AL 35242
Tel.: (205) 329-7300
Web Site: http://www.nwnit.com
Sales Range: $10-24.9 Million
Emp.: 35
Custom Computer Programming Services
N.A.I.C.S.: 541511
Mont Phelps (CEO)
Terry Joslin (Exec VP)
Jane Linder (Mng Dir)
Skip Tappen (Pres & CEO)

Trace3, Inc. (1)
7565 Irvine Center Dr Ste 200, Irvine, CA 92618
Tel.: (949) 333-2300
Web Site: http://www.trace3.com
Sales Range: $100-124.9 Million
Emp.: 160
IT Services
N.A.I.C.S.: 541512
Hayes Drumwright (Founder & Chm)
David Titov (Dir-Pro Svcs)
Todd Gallina (VP-Mktg)
Tony Olzak (CTO)
Guthrie Paterson (Exec VP-Engrg)
Mark Campbell (Chief Innovation Officer)
Michael Fitzgerald (VP-Sls)
Tony Bushell (Exec VP-Engrg)
Bryan Kissinger (Chief Info Security Officer & VP)
Rich Fennessy (CEO)

Subsidiary (Domestic):

Groupware Technology, Inc. (2)
541 Division St, Campbell, CA 95008
Tel.: (408) 540-0090
Web Site: http://www.groupwaretechnology.com
Sales Range: $100-124.9 Million
Emp.: 87
Technology Solutions Including Rapid Design, Procurement, Testing & Integration
N.A.I.C.S.: 541512
Mike Thompson (CEO)
Anthony Miley (Pres & COO)
Josh Avila (VP-Ops)
John Barnes (Dir-Sls)
Renata Elias (Mgr-Inside Sls)
Jeremy Morris (Mgr-Sls)
Samara Halterman (VP-Mktg)
Vinay Prabhu (Sr Dir-Engrg)
Amrinderpal Oberai (Dir-Data & AI)

LaSalle Systems Leasing, Inc. (2)
9550 W Higgins, Rosemont, IL 60018
Tel.: (847) 823-9600
Web Site: http://www.elasalle.com
Sales Range: $100-124.9 Million
Emp.: 40
Equipment Leasing Services
N.A.I.C.S.: 532420

Set Solutions Inc. (2)
550 Westcott St Ste 470, Houston, TX 77007
Tel.: (713) 956-9677
Web Site: http://www.setsolutions.com
Rev.: $4,000,000
Emp.: 7
Computer & Computer Peripheral Equipment & Software Merchant Whslr
N.A.I.C.S.: 423430
R. Moore (Pres)
John Marler (CEO)
Josh Tatum (VP-Engrg)
Matt Miller (VP-Sls)

Vibrantz Technologies Inc (1)
, Houston, TX
Web Site: https://www.vibrantz.com
Emp.: 5,400
Mineral-Based Specialty Additives; Pigment & Colorants & Mfr
N.A.I.C.S.: 325130
Scott T. Becker (Pres-Color Solutions)
Matthias Bell (Pres-Performance Coatings)
Barry Misquitta (Pres- Advance Materials)
Andrew T. Henke (VP)
Michael Wilson (Pres & CEO)
Glenn Fish (CFO & Exec VP)
Mark Whitney (Gen Counsel, Sec & Sr VP)
Imelda Torres-Laborde (Chief HR Officer & Sr VP)
Suresh Rao (Sr VP-Information Technology)

Subsidiary (Domestic):

Chromaflo Technologies Corporation (2)
2600 Michigan Ave, Ashtabula, OH 44005
Tel.: (440) 997-5137
Web Site: http://www.chromaflo.com
Pigment & Chemical Dispersion Services
N.A.I.C.S.: 325130
Elizabeth Campbell (Bus Dir-Coatings-Americas)
Ben Arnold (Bus Dir-Thermosets-Americas)
Eric Thiele (VP)
Casey Webster (Mgr-HR-Americas)
John Dry (VP & Mng Dir-Asia Pacific)
Holger Spieckermann (VP & Mng Dir-Europe)
Brij Mohal (VP-Innovation & Tech)
Andrea G. Singer (VP-HR)
Steve Riccardi (Dir-Global & Bus Dev)
Frank Huynen (Dir-Procurement-Global)
Kristine Eisemon (Mgr-Global Industry-Thermosets)
Michael McCormick (Mgr-Global Industry-Industrial Coatings)
Larry Haines (VP-Mergers & Acq)
Maricarmen Eguiliz (Mgr-Mexico)
Fernando Rodriguez (Sls Mgr-Northern Mexico)
Dean Doza (Mng Dir-Americas & VP)
Jolyon Stickels (Dir-Mergers & Acq-EMEA)
Kamilah King (Mgr-Supply Chain)
Ivone Beato (Mgr-Comml)
Sergio Duenas (Country Mgr-Mexico)
Benjamin Woeste (Sls Mgr-Coatings & Thermosets-Southwest)

Subsidiary (Non-US):

Chromaflo Technologies China Manufacturing Ltd. (3)
No 655 ShenFu Road, XinZhuang Industrial Zone, Shanghai, 201108, China
Tel.: (86) 21 2416 9200
Web Site: http://www.chromaflo.com
Coating Mfr
N.A.I.C.S.: 325510

Chromaflo Technologies Europe B.V. (3)
Nusterweg 98, 6136 KV, Sittard, Netherlands
Tel.: (31) 464570100
Web Site: http://www.chromaflo.com
Colorants, Chemical & Additive Dispersions Mfr
N.A.I.C.S.: 325510

Chromaflo Technologies Finland Oy (3)
Vernissakatu 1, 01300, Vantaa, Finland
Tel.: (358) 20 7188 000
Web Site: http://www.chromaflo.com
Tinting Product Distr
N.A.I.C.S.: 424950

Subsidiary (Domestic):

Ferro Corporation (2)
6060 Parkland Blvd Ste 250, Mayfield Heights, OH 44124
Tel.: (216) 875-5600
Web Site: http://www.ferro.com
Rev.: $1,126,264,000
Assets: $1,290,024,000
Liabilities: $741,921,000
Net Worth: $548,103,000
Earnings: $148,831,000
Emp.: 3,585
Fiscal Year-end: 12/31/2021
Technology-Based Performance Materials & Chemicals Mfr
N.A.I.C.S.: 325510

Subsidiary (Non-US):

Cappelle Pigments NV (3)
Kortrijkstraat 153, 8930, Menen, Belgium
Tel.: (32) 56521200
Pigment Mfr
N.A.I.C.S.: 325510

Subsidiary (Non-US):

Ferro Performance Pigments France SAS (4)
92 Rue de la Lys, 59250, Halluin, France
Tel.: (33) 320239226
Color & Coating Mfr
N.A.I.C.S.: 325510

Subsidiary (Non-US):

Dip Tech Ltd. (3)
5 Atir Yeda St, Kfar Saba, Israel
Tel.: (972) 97908400
Digital Printer Whslr
N.A.I.C.S.: 423430

Subsidiary (Domestic):

Electro-Science Laboratories, LLC (3)
416 E Church Rd, King of Prussia, PA 19406-2625
Tel.: (610) 272-8000
Web Site: http://www.electroscience.com
Conductors, Dielectrics, Resistors & Other Electronic Components Mfr
N.A.I.C.S.: 325998

Subsidiary (Non-US):

Endeka Ceramics S.A. (3)
Botiguers Parq Emp Tactica 3 4-I, 46980, Paterna, Valencia, Spain
Tel.: (34) 961344500
Web Site: http://www.endekaceramics.com
Paint & Coating Distr
N.A.I.C.S.: 424950

Subsidiary (Non-US):

Endeka Ceramics SpA (4)
Via Statale 242, Fiorano-Modenese, 41042, Italy
Tel.: (39) 0536864511
Web Site: http://www.endekaceramics.com

Ceramic Materials Mfr
N.A.I.C.S.: 327120

Subsidiary (US):

Zircosil (USA) Inc. (4)
11400 New Berlin Rd, Jacksonville, FL 32226
Tel.: (904) 751-2828
Web Site: http://www.zircosil.com
Ceramic Materials Mfr
N.A.I.C.S.: 212323

Subsidiary (Non-US):

Endeka Ceramics S.r.l. (3)
Via Marzabotto 16, Fiorano-Modenese, 41042, Modena, Italy
Tel.: (39) 0536864511
Color & Coating Mfr
N.A.I.C.S.: 325510

Ferro (Great Britain) Ltd (3)
Nile Street, Stoke-on-Trent, ST6 2BQ, United Kingdom (100%)
Tel.: (44) 1782 820400
Web Site: http://www.ferro.com
Sales Range: $250-299.9 Million
Emp.: 21
Technology-Based Performance Materials & Chemicals Supplier
N.A.I.C.S.: 325510

Ferro (Suzhou) Performance Materials Co., Ltd. (3)
No 178 Suhong West Road, Suzhou Industrial Park, Suzhou, 215021, Jiangsu, China
Tel.: (86) 51262562258
Web Site: http://www.ferro.com
Sales Range: $50-74.9 Million
Emp.: 200
Paint & Coating Distr
N.A.I.C.S.: 424950

Ferro (Thailand) Co. Ltd. (3)
CW Tower Unit 1804 Tower B 90 Ratchadapisek Rd, Huai Khwang Sub-district Huai Khwang District, Bangkok, 10310, Thailand (100%)
Tel.: (66) 21683295
Web Site: http://www.ferro.com
Sales Range: $50-74.9 Million
Emp.: 150
Paint & Coating Distr
N.A.I.C.S.: 424950

Ferro Argentina, S.A. (3)
Gibraltar 1365 B1872CWC Sarandi, Buenos Aires, 2908, Argentina (100%)
Tel.: (54) 1142052662
Sales Range: $50-74.9 Million
Emp.: 150
Porcelain Enamel Frits; Glaze Frits; Colorants for Ceramics & Plastics; Engineering Services Mfr
N.A.I.C.S.: 325510
Carlos M. Rosso *(Mgr-Fin)*

Ferro B.V. (3)
Roer 266, 2908 MC, Capelle aan den IJssel, Netherlands (100%)
Tel.: (31) 104784911
Web Site: http://www.ferro.com
Sales Range: $50-74.9 Million
Emp.: 35
Holding Company
N.A.I.C.S.: 551112

Subsidiary (Non-US):

Ferro (Belgium) Sprl (4)
Granbonpre 11, 1348, Louvain-la-Neuve, Belgium
Tel.: (32) 10685300
Web Site: http://www.ferro.com
Sales Range: $25-49.9 Million
Emp.: 11
Chemical Products Mfr
N.A.I.C.S.: 325998

Subsidiary (Domestic):

Ferro (Holland) B.V. (4)
Waalhaven Zuidzijde 2c, 3088 HH, Rotterdam, Netherlands
Tel.: (31) 104784911
Web Site: http://www.ferro.com
Paint & Coating Distr
N.A.I.C.S.: 424950

Subsidiary (Non-US):

Ferro Egypt for Glaze (S.A.E.) (4)
First Industrial Zone Kom Oshim, Faiyum, 63511, Egypt
Tel.: (20) 842215151
Tile Coating Product Mfr
N.A.I.C.S.: 325998

Ferro France S.a.r.l. (4)
43 Rue Jeanne d'Arc, 52115, Saint Dizier, Cedex, France (100%)
Tel.: (33) 325073333
Web Site: http://www.ferro.com
Sales Range: $50-74.9 Million
Porcelain Enamel Frits; Glaze Frits; Colorants for Ceramics & Plastics Mfr
N.A.I.C.S.: 325510

Subsidiary (Domestic):

Ferro Couleurs France SA (5)
2 Avenue Du President John Kennedy, BP 540, Limoges, 87011, France
Tel.: (33) 555315050
Web Site: http://www.ferro.com
Sales Range: $50-74.9 Million
Emp.: 200
Paint & Coating Distr
N.A.I.C.S.: 424950

Subsidiary (Non-US):

Ferro India Private Limited (4)
601 Amar Neptune Baner, Pune, 411045, India
Tel.: (91) 2067703500
Web Site: http://www.ferro.com
Sales Range: $25-49.9 Million
Emp.: 4
Chemical Products Mfr
N.A.I.C.S.: 325998

Ferro Industrias Quimicas (Portugal) Lda (4)
Apartado 10 Av Carlos Leal, 2601-906, Lisbon, Portugal (100%)
Tel.: (351) 263280900
Web Site: http://www.ferro.com
Sales Range: $75-99.9 Million
Emp.: 250
Mfr of Porcelain Enamel Frits; Glaze Frits; Colorants for Ceramics & Plastics; Specialty Chemicals
N.A.I.C.S.: 325510

Ferro Specialty Materials, LLC (4)
Leninsky prospect 160A Office 613-06, 196247, Saint Petersburg, Russia
Tel.: (7) 8126128581
Sales & Technical Support for Performance Coatings & Colors
N.A.I.C.S.: 424690

Subsidiary (Non-US):

Ferro Colombia Pigmentos S.A.S. (3)
Calle 7 No 23 C 10, Antioquia, 51030, Colombia
Tel.: (57) 44444646
Chemical Paint Mfr
N.A.I.C.S.: 325510

Ferro Colores SA de CV (3)
Oriente 171 No 450 Colonia Santa Coleta, GUSTAVO A MADERO, 7470, Mexico, Mexico
Tel.: (52) 5557907200
Chemical Products Mfr
N.A.I.C.S.: 325998

Ferro Corporation (Australia) Pty. Ltd. (3)
21 South Link Dandenong South, Melbourne, 3175, VIC, Australia (100%)
Tel.: (61) 387820847
Web Site: http://www.ferro.com
Sales Range: $25-49.9 Million
Emp.: 6
Paint & Coating Distr
N.A.I.C.S.: 424950

Division (Domestic):

Ferro Corporation - Color Division (3)
4150 E 56th St, Cleveland, OH 44105 (100%)
Tel.: (216) 875-5600

Web Site: http://www.ferro.com
Sales Range: $25-49.9 Million
Emp.: 100
Oxides & Specialty Colorants for the Porcelain Enamel, Ceramics, Paint & Coatings Industries; Forehearth Colorants for Glass Mfr
N.A.I.C.S.: 325510

Plant (Domestic):

Ferro Corporation - Edison Specialty Plastics Plant (3)
54 Kellogg Ct, Edison, NJ 08817-2509
Tel.: (732) 287-1930
Web Site: http://www.ferro.com
Sales Range: $50-74.9 Million
Emp.: 60
Color Pigments Mfr
N.A.I.C.S.: 332812

Division (Domestic):

Ferro Corporation - Industrial Coatings Division (3)
1000 Lakeside Ave, Cleveland, OH 44114-7000 (100%)
Tel.: (216) 641-8580
Web Site: http://www.ferro.com
Sales Range: $25-49.9 Million
Emp.: 75
Epoxy, Polyester, Acrylic & Hybrid Powder Coating Mfr
N.A.I.C.S.: 325510

Ferro Corporation - Performance Colors & Glass Division (3)
251 W Wylie Ave, Washington, PA 15301
Tel.: (724) 207-2300
Web Site: http://www.ferro.com
Sales Range: $150-199.9 Million
Emp.: 390
Colors & Colorings for Glass, Porcelain Enamel Mfr
N.A.I.C.S.: 325130

Plant (Domestic):

Ferro Corporation - Performance Colors & Glass, Orrville Plant (4)
1560 N Main St, Orrville, OH 44667
Tel.: (330) 765-4400
Web Site: http://www.ferro.com
Emp.: 20
Color Pigments & Glass Mfr
N.A.I.C.S.: 325130

Division (Domestic):

Ferro Corporation - Specialty Color Division (3)
4150 E 56th St, Cleveland, OH 44105 (100%)
Tel.: (216) 875-5600
Web Site: http://www.ferro.com
Sales Range: $50-74.9 Million
Emp.: 40
Inorganic Paint Mfr
N.A.I.C.S.: 325110

Subsidiary (Domestic):

Ferro Electronic Materials Inc. (3)
1395 Aspen Way, Vista, CA 92081 (100%)
Tel.: (760) 305-1000
Web Site: http://www.ferro.com
Sales Range: $50-74.9 Million
Emp.: 160
Paint & Coating Distr
N.A.I.C.S.: 424950

Plant (Domestic):

Ferro Electronic Materials Inc. - Penn Yan (4)
1789 Transelco Dr, Penn Yan, NY 14527-9752
Tel.: (315) 536-3357
Web Site: http://www.ferro.com
Sales Range: $75-99.9 Million
Ceramic Polishing Compounds; Barium Titanate, Electronic Ceramics
N.A.I.C.S.: 325180

Subsidiary (Non-US):

Ferro Enamel do Brasil Ltda. (3)
885/897 Dona Maria Helena Dias De Castro Pereira Avenue, Santa Gertrudes, 13511-000, Sao Paulo, Brazil

American Securities LLC—(Continued)

Tel.: (55) 1935451613
Web Site: http://www.ferro.com
Paint & Coating Mfr
N.A.I.C.S.: 325510

Subsidiary (Domestic):

Ferro Enamel do Brasil Industria e
Comercio Ltda.   (4)
6500 Florindo Cibin Street, Sao Jeronimo,
Americana, 13470-437, Sao Paulo, Brazil
Tel.: (55) 1921089900
Web Site: http://www.ferro.com
Paint & Coating Distr
N.A.I.C.S.: 424950

Subsidiary (Non-US):

Ferro Far East Company SDN,
BHD   (3)
D-5-13 Southgate Commercial Centre No 2
Jalan Dua, Off Jalan Chan Sow Lin, 55200,
Kuala Lumpur, Malaysia
Tel.: (60) 392212128
Web Site: http://www.ferro.com
Sales Range: $25-49.9 Million
Emp.: 10
Chemical Products Mfr
N.A.I.C.S.: 325998

Ferro Far East Ltd.   (3)
Suite 01 66/F The Center 99 Queen's
Road, Central, China (Hong Kong) **(100%)**
Tel.: (852) 27246193
Web Site: http://www.ferro.com
Sales Range: $900-999.9 Million
Paint & Coating Distr
N.A.I.C.S.: 424950

Subsidiary (Non-US):

PT Ferro Materials Utama   (4)
Jl Raya Mojosari Japanan Lor Embong Ds
Jasem Kec Ngoro Kabupaten, Mojokerto,
Indonesia
Tel.: (62) 3216820554
Chemical Paint Mfr
N.A.I.C.S.: 325510
Agus Purnomo (Head-Production)

Subsidiary (Non-US):

Ferro Holding GmbH   (3)
Gutleutstrasse 215, 60327, Frankfurt am
Main, Germany
Tel.: (49) 69271160
Web Site: http://www.ferro.com
Sales Range: $250-299.9 Million
Emp.: 250
Paint & Coating Distr
N.A.I.C.S.: 424950

Subsidiary (Domestic):

Ferro GmbH   (4)
Gutleutstrasse 215, Frankfurt am Main,
60327, Germany
Tel.: (49) 69 271160
Coatings, Colors & Colorings for Glass,
Porcelain Enamel Mfr
N.A.I.C.S.: 325510

Subsidiary (Domestic):

Ernst Diegel GmbH   (5)
Ernst Diegel Str 1-3, 36304, Alsfeld, Ger-
many
Tel.: (49) 66317850
Web Site: http://www.diegel.de
Plastic Coating Mfr
N.A.I.C.S.: 326150

Branch (Domestic):

Ferro GmbH   (5)
Furtweg 23, 04680, Colditz, Germany
Tel.: (49) 343818370
Web Site: http://www.ferro.com
Paint & Coating Distr
N.A.I.C.S.: 424950

Subsidiary (Non-US):

Ferro Performance Pigments Belgium
NV   (5)
Kortrijkstraat 153, 8930, Menen, Belgium
Tel.: (32) 56521200
Chemical Paint Mfr
N.A.I.C.S.: 325510

Subsidiary (Non-US):

Ferro Japan K.K.   (3)
21 Kasuminosato Ami-machi Inashiki-gun,
Ibaraki, 300-0315, Japan
Tel.: (81) 29 889 2144
Web Site: http://www.ferro.com
Paint & Coating Distr
N.A.I.C.S.: 424950

Ferro Kaplama Malzemeleri Limited
Sirketi   (3)
75 Yil Mah Organize Sanayi Bolgesi
Teknoloji Bulvari No 17 Odunpazari, Odun-
pazari, Eskisehir, Turkiye
Tel.: (90) 2122824385
Ceramic Coating Product Mfr
N.A.I.C.S.: 332812
Eyup Koray Oztan (Mgr-Sls)

Ferro Mexicana, S.A. de C.V.   (3)
Carretera Celaya Salamanca Km 12 5 Ran-
cho El Pintor, Del Gustavo A Madero,
38260, Villagran, Mexico   **(100%)**
Tel.: (52) 4111551125
Web Site: http://www.ferromexicana.com.mx
Sales Range: $150-199.9 Million
Emp.: 73
Mfr of Porcelain Enamel Frits; Glaze Frits;
Colorants for Ceramics & Plastics; Chemi-
cals & Stabilizers; Specialty Refractories
N.A.I.C.S.: 325510

Ferro Performance Pigments Spain
S.L.   (3)
Pablo Iglesias 98-100, 08908, L'Hospitalet
de Llobregat, Barcelona, Spain
Tel.: (34) 933435750
Web Site: http://www.ferropigments.com
Paint & Coating Distr
N.A.I.C.S.: 424950

Subsidiary (Non-US):

Ferro Performance Pigments (Shang-
hai) Co., Ltd.   (4)
Room 709 Tower B Far East International
Plaza No 317 Xianxia Road, Changning
District, Shanghai, 200051, China
Tel.: (86) 2133352258
Coating Chemical Mfr
N.A.I.C.S.: 325510

Ferro Performance Pigments Roma-
nia SRL   (4)
Aleea Sinaia nr 120, Doicesti Jud Dambo-
vita, 137195, Targoviste, Romania
Tel.: (40) 245227100
Color & Coating Mfr
N.A.I.C.S.: 325510

Subsidiary (Domestic):

Ferro Pfanstiehl Laboratories,
Inc.   (3)
1219 Glen Rock Ave, Waukegan, IL
60085-6230   **(100%)**
Tel.: (847) 623-0370
Web Site: http://www.pfanstiehl.com
Sales Range: $50-74.9 Million
Emp.: 120
Industrial Organic Chemicals Mfr
N.A.I.C.S.: 325199
Cynthia Kerker (Pres)

Subsidiary (Non-US):

Ferro Spain SA   (3)
Carretera Valencia - Barcelona Km 61 5,
12550, Almazora, Spain
Tel.: (34) 964504450
Sales Range: $250-299.9 Million
Emp.: 800
Chemical Products Mfr
N.A.I.C.S.: 325998
Luca Pecorara (Gen Mgr)

Subsidiary (Domestic):

Ferro Enamel Espanola, S.A.   (4)
Carretera Valencia - Barcelona Km 61 5,
Almazora, 12550, Castellon de la Plana,
Spain   **(100%)**
Tel.: (34) 964504450
Web Site: http://www.ferro.com
Sales Range: $350-399.9 Million
Emp.: 800
Porcelain Enamel Frits, Glaze Frits, Colo-
rants for Ceramics & Plastics & Specialty
Refractories Mfr; Engineering Services

N.A.I.C.S.: 325510

Gardenia-Quimica SA   (4)
Av Real de Extremadura 25, 12200, Onda,
Castellon, Spain
Tel.: (34) 964604000
Web Site: http://www.gardeniaquimica.com
Chemicals Mfr
N.A.I.C.S.: 325998

Quimicer, S.A.   (4)
Carretera Onda-Ribesalbes Km 5, 12200,
Onda, Castellon, Spain
Tel.: (34) 964776666
Chemical Paint Mfr
N.A.I.C.S.: 325510

Subsidiary (Non-US):

Quimicer Polska Sp. z o.o.   (5)
ul Przemyslowa 5, Opoczno, Poland
Tel.: (48) 447556982
Chemical Paint Mfr
N.A.I.C.S.: 325510

Quimicer Portugal S.A.   (5)
Mamodeiro Apartado 33 Costa Do Valado,
3811-501, Aveiro, Portugal
Tel.: (351) 234940220
Chemical Paint Mfr
N.A.I.C.S.: 325510

Subsidiary (Non-US):

Ferro Taiwan Ltd   (3)
6 Fl-3 408 Ruiguang Road, Neihu District,
Taipei, 114, Taiwan
Tel.: (886) 227990886
Web Site: http://www.ferro.com
Emp.: 8
Chemical Products Mfr
N.A.I.C.S.: 325998

Subsidiary (Domestic):

Uwiz Technology Co., Ltd.   (4)
No 33 Dongyuan Rd Zhongli, Taoyuan,
32063, Taiwan
Tel.: (886) 34357367
Web Site: http://www.uwiz.com.tw
Semiconductor Devices Mfr
N.A.I.C.S.: 334413

Subsidiary (Non-US):

Ferro Turkey Kaplama Cam ve Renk
Cozumleri Sanayi ve Ticaret Limited
Sirketi   (3)
Osmangazi Mah Mimar Sinan Cad No 3
E-Blok, 43030, Kutahya, Turkiye
Tel.: (90) 2742300110
Color & Coating Mfr
N.A.I.C.S.: 325510

Jem Finco Limited   (3)
Suite 1 3rd Floor 11-12 St James S Square,
London, SW1Y 4LB, United Kingdom
Tel.: (44) 2081443935
Web Site: http://www.jem-finco-limited.co
Shipping Services
N.A.I.C.S.: 488510

Nubiola Bulgaria ODD   (3)
133 Bulgaria Blvd East Industrial Zone,
7009, Ruse, Bulgaria
Tel.: (359) 82841339
Inorganic Pigments Mfr
N.A.I.C.S.: 325130

Nubiola Colombia Pigmentos
S.A.S.   (3)
Carrera 46 52 82 Piso 9, Medellin, 050001,
Colombia
Tel.: (57) 5744444646
Paint & Coating Distr
N.A.I.C.S.: 424950
Ana Mercedes Garces Lengua (Mgr-IT)

Subsidiary (Domestic):

Nubiola India Private, Limited   (3)
6th fl B Suite Kences Towers 1 Ra-
makrishna Street T Nagar, Chennai, 600
017, India
Tel.: (91) 4426810978
Web Site: http://www.nubiola.net
Inorganic Pigments Mfr
N.A.I.C.S.: 325130

Nubiola Pigments (Shanghai) Co.,
Ltd.   (3)
Room 302 Building 3 Yihong Science &
Technology Park II, 142 Tian Lin Road,

Shanghai, 200233, China
Tel.: (86) 2151692808
Inorganic Pigments Mfr
N.A.I.C.S.: 325130
David Yang (Gen Mgr)

Nubiola Romania SRL   (3)
Str Mircea Cel Batran, Dambovita, Targov-
iste, 130023, Romania
Tel.: (40) 245217125
Inorganic Pigments Mfr
N.A.I.C.S.: 325130
Stanciu Dragos (Mgr-Maintenance)

Subsidiary (Domestic):

Nubiola USA, Inc.   (3)
6369 Peachtree St, Peachtree Corners, GA
30071
Tel.: (770) 277-8819
Inorganic Pigments Mfr
N.A.I.C.S.: 325130
Kaylene Carley (Mgr-Admin)

Subsidiary (Non-US):

Oximet S.r.l.   (3)
Viale Regina Pacis 200, 41049, Sassuolo,
MO, Italy
Tel.: (39) 0536800801
Web Site: http://www.oximet.com
Ceramic Tile Mfr
N.A.I.C.S.: 327110

PT Ferro Ceramic Colors
Indonesia   (3)
Dusun Beringin Kulon No 35 RT/RW
008/004 Bringinbendo-Taman, Sidoarjo,
61257, Indonesia
Tel.: (62) 317882828
Chemical Products Mfr
N.A.I.C.S.: 325998

PT Ferro Mas Dinamika   (3)
Jl Raya Cikarang Ds Pasir Sari, Tegal
Gede, Cibarusah-Bekosi, 17550,
Indonesia   **(55%)**
Tel.: (62) 218934751
Sales Range: $150-199.9 Million
Porcelin Enamel Frits, Glass Frits & Colo-
rant for Ceramics Mfr
N.A.I.C.S.: 325998

Pinturas Benicarlo, S.L.   (3)
Partida Covatellas Poligono 18 Apartado de
Correos 247, 12580, Benicarlo, Castellon,
Spain
Tel.: (34) 964461697
Web Site: http://www.pinturasbenicarlo.com
Paint Mfr & Distr
N.A.I.C.S.: 325510

Smalti Per Ceramica S.r.l.   (3)
Via Canaletto 138/140, 41042, Fiorano-
Modenese, Italy
Tel.: (39) 0536845509
Web Site: http://www.spccolor.com
Glaze Mfr
N.A.I.C.S.: 327120

Vetriceramici Polska spoka z ogranic-
zona odpowiedzialnoscia   (3)
Ul Piaskowa 147-151, 97-200, Tomaszow
Mazowiecki, Poland
Tel.: (48) 447260260
Web Site: http://www.vetriceramici.com
Emp.: 12
Semi-Finished Porcelain Product Production
& Research Services
N.A.I.C.S.: 327999

Vetriceramici S.p.A.   (3)
Maggio 35, Casola Valsenio, 48010,
Ravenna, Italy
Tel.: (39) 054676711
Web Site: http://www.vetriceramici.com
Semi-Finished Porcelain Product Production
& Research Services
N.A.I.C.S.: 327999

Vetriceramici Seramik Mamulleri
Hizmetleri Sanayi ve Ticaret Limited
Sirketi   (3)
Ayazmadere Caddesi No 6 Dikilitas, Istan-
bul, Turkiye
Tel.: (90) 2123470647
Chemicals Mfr
N.A.I.C.S.: 325998

Vetriceramici de Mexico, S. de R.L.
de C.V.   (3)

Av San Fernando 101 Fracc Valle de Santa Maria, 66670, Pesqueria, NL, Mexico
Tel.: (52) 8140008400
Paint & Coating Distr
N.A.I.C.S.: 424950
Luca Ghilardini Marazzi *(Dir Gen)*

Zibo Ferro Performance Materials Company, Limited (3)
No 263 Tielu Street, Kunlun Town Zichuan District, Zibo, 255129, Shandong, China
Tel.: (86) 5335769609
Chemical Products Mfr
N.A.I.C.S.: 325998

Subsidiary (Domestic):

Prince International Corporation (2)
15311 Vantage Pkwy W Ste 350, Houston, TX 77032
Tel.: (646) 747-4222
Web Site: http://www.princecorp.com
Sales Range: $10-24.9 Million
Specialty Minerals Distr
N.A.I.C.S.: 423520
J. F. Alewijnse *(Sr VP-Bus Dev)*

Subsidiary (Non-US):

Castle Colours Ltd. (3)
3 Morgan Way, Norwich, NR5 9JJ, United Kingdom
Tel.: (44) 1603 741278
Web Site: http://www.castlecolour.co.uk
Blister Packaging Services
N.A.I.C.S.: 561910

Subsidiary (Domestic):

Densimix-E&B Inc. (3)
13501 Industrial Rd, Houston, TX 77015
Tel.: (646) 747-2952
Web Site: http://www.densimix-eb.com
Emp.: 12
Iron Oxide Distr
N.A.I.C.S.: 423520
Bobby Woods *(Plant Mgr)*

Grinding & Sizing Company LLC (3)
307 Webber, Lufkin, TX 75904
Tel.: (936) 634-7718
Web Site: http://www.grindsize.com
Sales Range: $10-24.9 Million
Grinding, Bending, Packaging & Fabrication Services
N.A.I.C.S.: 561910
Robert Pike *(Dir-Tech)*
Harvey Oyler *(Pres)*

Pemco Corporation (3)
100 Pemco Dr, Leesburg, AL 35983
Tel.: (256) 526-8522
Web Site: http://www.pemco-intl.com
Sales Range: $10-24.9 Million
Vitreous Enamel Coatings Mfr & Marketer
N.A.I.C.S.: 325510
Jonathan Davies *(Pres)*
David Banfield *(VP-Ops)*
Janet Kessler *(Dir-Supply Chain)*

Subsidiary (Non-US):

PEMCO Emelier S.A. (4)
Bouchard 3040, Lanus Este, Buenos Aires, 1825, Argentina
Tel.: (54) 11 42892430
Enamel Coating Mfr
N.A.I.C.S.: 325510
Diego Calvo *(Gen Mgr)*

Pemco Brugge BVBA (4)
Pathoekeweg 116, 8000, Brugge, Belgium
Tel.: (32) 50 456 411
Emp.: 130
Enamel Coating Mfr
N.A.I.C.S.: 325510
Johan De Soete *(Mgr-Technical Svc & Dev)*

Prince Minerals Italy S.r.l. (4)
Via delle Industrie 9, 24040, Filago, BG, Italy
Tel.: (39) 035 9002011
Enamel Coating Mfr
N.A.I.C.S.: 325510

Subsidiary (Non-US):

Prince Minerals, GmbH (3)
Tauberstrasse 32, 97922, Lauda-Konigshofen, Baden-Wurttemberg, Germany

Tel.: (49) 9343 60000 0
Chemical Product Whslr
N.A.I.C.S.: 424690

Prince Minerals, Ltd. (3)
Duke Street, Fenton, Stoke-on-Trent, ST4 3NR, Staffordshire, United Kingdom
Tel.: (44) 1782 343 000
Web Site: http://www.princecorp.com
Emp.: 45
Mineral Mfr & Whslr
N.A.I.C.S.: 212323
Craig Cherry *(Mng Dir)*

Prince Minerals, S.A. (3)
Klein Veerle 103, 2960, Brecht, Belgium
Tel.: (32) 3 315 01 67
Emp.: 3
Chemical Product Whslr
N.A.I.C.S.: 424690

AMERICAN SECURITY, L.L.C.
1717 University Ave W, Saint Paul, MN 55104
Tel.: (651) 644-1155
Web Site:
   https://www.americansecurityllc.com
Year Founded: 1959
Sales Range: $75-99.9 Million
Emp.: 1,000
Protective Services, Guard
N.A.I.C.S.: 561612
Anson Watson *(Acct Mgr)*
Dick Kohl *(Exec VP)*
Joel Crandall *(Supvr-Security Site)*
Lyle Lange *(Supvr-Security)*
Tim Knutsen *(Dir-Safety Dev & Trng)*

AMERICAN SENIOR SERVICES, INC.
5051 66th St N, Saint Petersburg, FL 33709
Tel.: (888) 245-9001
Web Site:
   http://www.truefreedomcare.com
Sales Range: $1-9.9 Million
Emp.: 7
Women Healthcare Services
N.A.I.C.S.: 621610
Bobby Gross *(Co-Founder & Principal)*
Bob Doolan *(Co-Founder & Principal)*
Marc Sinton *(VP-Sls)*
Scott Gross *(Dir-Mktg & Trng)*
Jim Tran *(Chief Technical Officer)*

AMERICAN SENIORS FOUNDATION INC
205 Powell Pl, Brentwood, TN 37027
Tel.: (615) 369-0620   OH
Year Founded: 1990
Sales Range: $10-24.9 Million
Emp.: 2
Lifecare Retirement Community Operator
N.A.I.C.S.: 623311
R. Murray Hatcher Sr. *(Chm & Pres)*

AMERICAN SERVICE CENTER ASSOCIATES LLC
585 N Glebe Rd, Arlington, VA 22203
Tel.: (703) 525-2100
Web Site:
   https://www.justmercedes.com
Sales Range: $50-74.9 Million
Emp.: 550
Automobile Sales, Repair & Maintenance Services
N.A.I.C.S.: 441110
Ralph Mastantuono *(Gen Mgr)*

AMERICAN SHARE INSURANCE
5656 Frantz Rd, Dublin, OH 43017
Tel.: (614) 764-1900   OH
Web Site:
   http://www.americanshare.com
Year Founded: 1974

Sales Range: $10-24.9 Million
Emp.: 34
Deposit Insurance Service Provider
N.A.I.C.S.: 524128
Curt Robson *(Treas & VP-Fin)*
Kurt Kluth *(VP-IT)*
Kurt Loose *(VP-Examination & Insurance)*
Dennis R. Adams *(Pres & CEO)*
Kevin W. Willour *(Vice Chm)*

AMERICAN SHIPPING CO. INC.
250 Moonachie Rd 5th Fl, Moonachie, NJ 07074
Tel.: (201) 478-4600
Web Site:
   https://www.shipamerican.com
Year Founded: 1899
Sales Range: $10-24.9 Million
Emp.: 75
Freight Transportation Arrangement
N.A.I.C.S.: 488510
Ralph Natale *(CEO)*
Marc S. Greenberg *(Pres)*

Subsidiaries:

American Cartage & Distribution, LLC (1)
650 Belleville Tpke Ste 6, Kearny, NJ 07032
Tel.: (201) 941-4990
Web Site: http://www.shipamerican.com
Emp.: 3
Logistics Consulting Servies
N.A.I.C.S.: 541614
Ray Davies *(Gen Mgr)*

American International Cargo Service (1)
250 Moonachie Rd Fl 5, Moonachie, NJ 07074
Tel.: (201) 585-1800
Web Site: http://www.shipamerican.com
Sales Range: $10-24.9 Million
Emp.: 40
Cargo Loading & Unloading Services
N.A.I.C.S.: 488210
Marc S. Greenberg *(Pres & COO)*

American International Cargo Services (China) Limited (1)
Room 2012 20/Fl Shenhua Commercial Building 2018 Jiabin Road, Shenzhen, 518001, China
Tel.: (86) 755 8248 0829
Air & Sea Freight Transportation Services
N.A.I.C.S.: 481112
Ebbie Tang *(Mgr)*

AMERICAN SLIDE-CHART CO.
25W550 Geneva Rd, Carol Stream, IL 60188
Tel.: (630) 665-3333
Web Site:
   https://www.americanslidechart.com
Sales Range: $75-99.9 Million
Emp.: 100
Custom Dimensional Marketing Products Mfr
N.A.I.C.S.: 323111
David P. Johnson *(Co-Pres)*
Bob Irving *(Reg Mgr-Sls)*
Harold Wiese *(Plant Mgr)*
Don Hoff *(COO & VP)*
Craig E. Johnson *(Co-Pres)*

AMERICAN SMALL BUSINESS ALLIANCE, INC.
6021 University Blvd Ste 160, Ellicott City, MD 21043
Tel.: (443) 325-5020
Web Site: http://www.asballiance.com
Year Founded: 2001
Sales Range: $1-9.9 Million
Emp.: 15
Business Event Organizing Services
N.A.I.C.S.: 711310
Tariq Shane *(Founder & Pres)*

AMERICAN SMOOTH WAVE VENTURES, INC.
73726 Alessandro Dr Ste 103, Palm Desert, CA 92260
Tel.: (595) 851-9632   IA
Year Founded: 2008
Candy, Sweets, Food & Bakery Products
N.A.I.C.S.: 311340
Baofu Ding *(CEO)*
Wing Sang Lo *(CFO)*
Baojian Ding *(COO)*

AMERICAN SOCCER CORPORATION
1919 San Diego Ave, San Diego, CA 92110
Tel.: (619) 756-7528
Web Site:
   http://www.americansoccercorp.com
Soccer Holding Company
N.A.I.C.S.: 551112
Yan Skwara *(Founder)*

AMERICAN SOCIETY FOR BIOCHEMISTRY AND MOLECULAR BIOLOGY
11200 Rockville Pike Ste 302, Rockville, MD 20852-3110
Tel.: (240) 283-6600   NY
Web Site: http://www.asbmb.org
Year Founded: 1919
Sales Range: $10-24.9 Million
Emp.: 45
Biochemistry & Molecular Biologist Association
N.A.I.C.S.: 813920
Ned Maher *(Acct Mgr)*

AMERICAN SOCIETY FOR CLINICAL PATHOLOGY
33 W Monroe St Ste 1600, Chicago, IL 60603
Tel.: (312) 541-4999   IL
Web Site: https://www.ascp.org
Year Founded: 1922
Sales Range: $25-49.9 Million
Emp.: 169
Pathologist & Laboratory Professional Association
N.A.I.C.S.: 813920
William E. Schreiber *(Pres)*

AMERICAN SOCIETY FOR GASTROINTESTINAL ENDOSCOPY
3300 Woodcreek Dr, Downers Grove, IL 60515
Tel.: (630) 573-0600   IL
Web Site: https://www.asge.org
Year Founded: 1941
Sales Range: $10-24.9 Million
Emp.: 54
Health Care Srvices
N.A.I.C.S.: 622110
Barbara Connell *(COO)*
Jennifer Michalek *(Chief Comm Officer)*
Linda Tyler *(Sr Dir-Sls & Bus Dev)*
Karen L. Woods *(Pres)*

AMERICAN SOCIETY FOR MICROBIOLOGY
1752 N St NW, Washington, DC 20036-2904
Tel.: (202) 737-3600   DC
Web Site: https://www.asm.org
Year Founded: 1899
Sales Range: $50-74.9 Million
Emp.: 198
Medical Professional Association
N.A.I.C.S.: 813920
Alex Merchan *(CMO)*
Ron Bension *(Pres & CEO)*

American Society for Radiation Oncology—(Continued)

AMERICAN SOCIETY FOR RADIATION ONCOLOGY
8280 Willow Oaks Corporate Dr Ste 500, Fairfax, VA 22031
Tel.: (703) 502-1550   IL
Web Site: http://www.astro.org
Year Founded: 1958
Sales Range: $10-24.9 Million
Emp.: 88
Cancer Research & Treatment Services
N.A.I.C.S.: 813212
Laura Thevenot (CEO)
Jeff M. Michalski (Treas & Sec)
Chris Neumann (VP-Learning & Education)
Kirsta Suggs (Dir-Diversity, Equity & Inclusion)

AMERICAN SOCIETY FOR TESTING & MATERIALS
100 Barr Harbor Dr, West Conshohocken, PA 19428-2959
Tel.: (610) 832-9585   PA
Web Site: http://www.astm.org
Year Founded: 1898
Sales Range: $75-99.9 Million
Emp.: 222
Business Associations
N.A.I.C.S.: 813910
Brian Meincke (Asst VP-Bus Dev)
Katharine Morgan (Pres)
Philip Lively (VP-IT Dev & Application)
John Pace (VP-Publications & Mktg)
James S. Thomas (Asst VP-Publications, SIs & Mktg)
Dale F. Bohn (Vice Chm)
Terry Wohlers (Head-Additive Mfg Market Intelligence)
Noah Mostow (Mgr-Market Intelligence & Analytics)

Subsidiaries:

Wohlers Associates Inc.   (1)
1511 River Oak Dr, Fort Collins, CO 80525
Tel.: (970) 225-0086
Web Site:
  http://www.wohlersassociates.com
Technical & Strategic Consulting Services
N.A.I.C.S.: 541690

AMERICAN SOCIETY FOR THE PREVENTION OF CRUELTY TO ANIMALS
424 E 92nd St, New York, NY 10128-6804
Tel.: (212) 876-7700
Web Site: https://www.aspca.org
Emp.: 500
Promoter of Humane Treatment, Cruelty Prevention & Fear & Pain Allieviation of Animals
N.A.I.C.S.: 813312
Elizabeth J. Estroff (Sr VP-Comm)
Matt Bershadker (Sr VP-Anti Cruelty Grp)
Fredrik G. Gradin (Treas)
Sally Spooner (Sec)
Frederick Tanne (Vice Chm)
Tim F. Wray (Chm)
Sarah Levin Goodstine (Sr VP-Ops)
Todd Hendricks (Sr VP-Dev)
Beverly Jones (Chief Legal Officer & Sr VP)
Julie Morris (Sr VP-Community Outreach)
Johanna Richman (CFO & Sr VP)
Jed Rogers (Sr VP-Animal Health Svcs)
Bert Troughton (Sr VP-Strategy)
Stacy Wolf (Sr VP-Anti-Cruelty Grp)

AMERICAN SOCIETY FOR YAD VASHEM
500 5th Ave 42nd Fl, New York, NY 10110-4299
Tel.: (212) 220-4304   NY
Web Site:
  https://www.yadvashemusa.org
Year Founded: 1981
Sales Range: $10-24.9 Million
Emp.: 14
Museum Operator
N.A.I.C.S.: 712110
Marlene W. Yahalom (Dir-Education)
Leonard Wilf (Chm)
Rachelle Grossman (Coord-Event)
Ira Drukier (Sec-Natl)

AMERICAN SOCIETY OF ANESTHESIOLOGISTS
1061 American Ln, Schaumburg, IL 60173-4973
Tel.: (847) 825-5586   NY
Web Site: http://www.asahq.org
Year Founded: 1936
Sales Range: $25-49.9 Million
Emp.: 163
Medical Professional Association
N.A.I.C.S.: 813920
Paul Pomerantz (CEO)
Manuel Bonilla (Chief Advocacy Officer)
Thomas Conway (COO)
Christopher J. Wehking (Chief Program Officer)
DeLaine Schmitz (Chief Quality Officer)
Ed Dellert (Chief Learning Officer)
Jason Hansen (Dir-State Affairs)
Matthew Popovich (Dir-Quality & Regulatory Affairs)
Daniel Barron (Dir-IT)
Danielle L. Urbina (Dir-Meetings & Exhibits)
Elizabeth Lepkowski (Dir-Education)
Jeremy Lewin (Gen Counsel)
Sara Curtis (Dir-HR)
Michael W. Champeau (First VP)
Beverly K. Philip (Pres)

AMERICAN SOCIETY OF APPRAISERS
11107 Sunset Hills Rd Ste 310, Reston, VA 20190
Tel.: (703) 478-2228   VA
Web Site: http://www.appraisers.org
Year Founded: 1952
Real Estate Valuation Professional Organization
N.A.I.C.S.: 813920
David Villani (CFO)

Subsidiaries:

National Association of Independent Fee Appraisers, Inc.   (1)
330 N Wabash Ave Ste 2000, Chicago, IL 60611
Tel.: (312) 321-6830
Web Site: http://chicagonaifa.com
Real Estate Valuation Professional Organization
N.A.I.C.S.: 813920

AMERICAN SOCIETY OF CATARACT AND REFRACTIVE SURGERY
4000 Legato Rd Ste 700, Fairfax, VA 22033
Tel.: (703) 591-2220   CA
Web Site: http://www.ascrs.org
Year Founded: 1974
Sales Range: $10-24.9 Million
Emp.: 56
Health Care Srvices
N.A.I.C.S.: 622310

AMERICAN SOCIETY OF MECHANICAL ENGINEERS
2 Park Ave, New York, NY 10016-5990
Tel.: (973) 882-1170
Web Site: https://www.asme.org
Year Founded: 1880
Rev.: $117,699,245
Assets: $180,301,159
Liabilities: $71,918,827
Net Worth: $108,382,332
Fiscal Year-end: 06/30/18
Services to Mechanical Engineers
N.A.I.C.S.: 561990
William W. Predebon (VP-Engrg Education)
Chitra Sethi (Mng Editor)
Tom Costabile (Exec Dir)

AMERICAN SOCIETY OF NEPHROLOGY
1510 H St NW Ste 800, Washington, DC 20005
Tel.: (202) 640-4660   DC
Web Site: http://www.asn-online.org
Year Founded: 1966
Sales Range: $25-49.9 Million
Emp.: 32
Kidney Disease Treatment Services
N.A.I.C.S.: 621492
Tod Ibrahim (Exec Dir)
Gisela Deuter (Dir-Continuing Pro Dev)
Bob Henkel (Dir-Comm)
Shari Leventhal (Mng Editor)
Bonnie O'Brien (Mng Editor)

AMERICAN SOCIETY OF PENSION PROFESSIONALS & ACTUARIES, INC.
4245 Fairfax Dr Ste 750, Arlington, VA 22203
Tel.: (703) 516-9300   TX
Web Site: http://www.asppa.net
Year Founded: 1966
Sales Range: $10-24.9 Million
Emp.: 61
Professional Organizations
N.A.I.C.S.: 813920
Brian H. Graff (Exec Dir)
Richard A. Hochman (Pres)
James R. Nolan (VP)

AMERICAN SOCIETY OF RADIOLOGIC TECHNOLOGISTS
15000 Central Ave SE, Albuquerque, NM 87123-3909
Tel.: (505) 298-4500   IL
Web Site: https://www.asrt.org
Year Founded: 1932
Sales Range: $10-24.9 Million
Emp.: 125
Health Care Srvices
N.A.I.C.S.: 622110
Sal Martino (CEO)
Greg Morrison (COO)
Myke Kudlas (Chief Academic Officer)
Keith Greer (Mgr-Dev)
Sandra Hayden (Pres)
Melissa Jackowski (Treas & Sec)
Amanda Garlock (Pres)
Laura Niel (CFO)
Liana Watson (Chief Governance & External Affairs Officer)
Dana Aragon (Chief Governance Officer)
Lisa DeTemple (VP-HR)
Mark Ryerson (VP-Mktg & Bus Dev)
William J. Brennan Jr. (Chm)

AMERICAN SOCIETY OF SAFETY ENGINEERS
520 N Northwest Hwy, Park Ridge, IL 60068
Tel.: (847) 699-2929   IL
Web Site: http://www.asse.org
Year Founded: 1911

Sales Range: $10-24.9 Million
Emp.: 74
Professional Development Services
N.A.I.C.S.: 611430
Stephanie A. Helgerman (VP-Fin)
James D. Smith (Sr VP)
Michael Belcher (Pres)
Dennis Hudson (Exec Dir)

AMERICAN SOIL TECHNOLOGIES, INC.
9018 Balboa Blvd Ste 558, Northridge, CA 91304
Tel.: (818) 899-4686   NV
Web Site:
  http://www.americansoiltech.com
Year Founded: 1993
Rev.: $3,043
Assets: $9,653
Liabilities: $8,342,644
Net Worth: ($8,332,991)
Earnings: ($558,116)
Emp.: 3
Fiscal Year-end: 09/30/15
Soil Products & Fertilizers Mfr
N.A.I.C.S.: 115112
Diana Visco (Sec)
Neil C. Kitchen (VP)
Carl P. Ranno (Pres, CEO & CFO)

AMERICAN SOLAR ELECTRIC, INC.
1475 N Scottsdale Rd Ste 410, Scottsdale, AZ 85257
Tel.: (480) 994-1440
Web Site:
  http://www.americanpv.com
Year Founded: 2001
Sales Range: $1-9.9 Million
Emp.: 25
Solar-Electric Power Systems for Commercial, Residential & Industrial Buildings
N.A.I.C.S.: 221118
Sean M. Seitz (COO)
Craig Murphy (Project Mgr)

AMERICAN SOLUTIONS FOR BUSINESS
31 E Minnesota Ave, Glenwood, MN 56334-1625
Tel.: (320) 634-5471   MN
Web Site:
  https://www.americanbus.com
Year Founded: 1981
Sales Range: $25-49.9 Million
Emp.: 200
Office Supplies Distr
N.A.I.C.S.: 424120
Larry Zavadil (Founder & CEO)
Wayne Martin (VP-SIs Resource Grp)
Katie Hallstrom (VP-HR)
Michael Pfeiffer (VP-IT)
Maggie Leland (Dir-GPO Svcs)
Monique Gregoire (VP-Fin & Acctg)
Glenn Miller (VP-Bus Solutions)
Justin Zavadil (Pres)

Subsidiaries:

Peter E. Kleine Co.   (1)
30 Wright Ave, Lititz, PA 17543
Tel.: (717) 627-0370
Web Site: http://www.pkcomp.com
Business Promotional Products
N.A.I.C.S.: 541890
Peter E. Kleine (Founder)

AMERICAN SOUTHERN HOMES, LLC
1768 Business Ctr Dr Ste 350, Reston, VA 20190
Tel.: (888) 503-1603
Web Site:
  http://www.americansouthern.com
Year Founded: 2017
Building Construction Services

N.A.I.C.S.: 236115
Greg Benson (Pres & COO)

Subsidiaries:

Dorn Homes, Inc.   (1)
600 W Gurley St Ste 200, Prescott, AZ
86305
Tel.: (928) 442-1111
Web Site: http://www.dornhomes.com
Sales Range: $25-49.9 Million
Emp.: 29
Building Construction Services
N.A.I.C.S.: 236115
Jim Gunby (VP-Sls, Mktg & Acq)
David Grounds (CEO)

AMERICAN SOYBEAN ASSO-CIATION

12125 Woodcrest Executive Dr Ste
100, Saint Louis, MO 63141-5009
Tel.: (314) 576-1770   IA
Web Site:
     http://www.soygrowers.com
Year Founded: 1946
Sales Range: $25-49.9 Million
Emp.: 30
Soybean Industry Association
N.A.I.C.S.: 813910
Jordan Bright (Mgr-Comm)
Michael Jones (Mgr-Ops)
Richard Wilkins (Co-Chm)
Wade Cowan (Co-Chm)
Bill Gordon (VP)
Bret Davis (Sec)
Kevin Scott (Pres)
Brian Vaught (CFO)
Ryan Findlay (CEO)
John Gordley (Dir-Washington)
Wendy Brannen (Dir-Policy Comm-Washington)

AMERICAN SPECIALTIES INC.

441 Saw Mill River Rd, Yonkers, NY
10701-4913
Tel.: (914) 476-9000   NY
Web Site:
     https://www.americanspecialty.com
Year Founded: 1961
Sales Range: $350-399.9 Million
Emp.: 2,100
Washroom/Hospital Accessories,
Public Telephone Enclosures & Mall
Kiosks Mfr
N.A.I.C.S.: 332999
Peter M. Rolla (CEO)
Charles V. Labarbera (COO)
Gary Drossman (CFO)

AMERICAN SPECIALTY HEALTH, INC.

10241 Wateridge Cir, San Diego, CA
92121-2797
Tel.: (619) 578-2000
Web Site:
     http://www.ashcompanies.com
Year Founded: 1987
Sales Range: $125-149.9 Million
Emp.: 681
Direct Health & Medical Insurance
Carriers
N.A.I.C.S.: 524114
R. Douglas Metz (Exec VP & Chief
Health Svcs Officer)
Robert P. White (Pres & COO)
Jerome Bonhomme (CTO)
George T. DeVries III (Chm & CEO)

AMERICAN SPEECH-LANGUAGE-HEARING ASSO-CIATION

2200 Research Blvd, Rockville, MD
20850-3289
Tel.: (301) 296-5700   KS
Web Site: https://www.asha.org
Year Founded: 1947
Sales Range: $50-74.9 Million
Emp.: 311

Medical Professional Association
N.A.I.C.S.: 813920

AMERICAN SPICE COMPANY INC.

PO Box 420531, Miami, FL 33242
Tel.: (305) 634-3534
Web Site:
     http://www.americanspice.us
Sales Range: $10-24.9 Million
Emp.: 15
Mayonnaise, Dressing & Prepared
Sauce Mfg
N.A.I.C.S.: 311941
Robert Urra (Pres)

AMERICAN SPIRIT GRAPHICS CORPORATION

801 9th St SE, Minneapolis, MN
55414
Tel.: (612) 623-3333
Web Site: http://www.asgc.com
Sales Range: $10-24.9 Million
Emp.: 325
Commercial Printing, Lithographic
N.A.I.C.S.: 323111
A. Oscar Carlson (Chm)
Gale Bakeberg (Mgr-Production)
Brad Bloss (VP-Natl Accts)
Robert Dorsey (Mgr-Estimating)
Lauren Drevlow (Exec VP)
Mark McHugh (Mgr-Press Room)
Tom Syvertson (Mgr-Production)
Dane Weeks (Mgr-HR)
Tim Franzen (VP & Gen Mgr)
Darin Tysdal (VP-Fin)

AMERICAN SPRING WIRE CORP.

26300 Miles Rd, Bedford, OH 44146-1410
Tel.: (216) 292-4620
Web Site:
     http://www.americanspringwire.com
Year Founded: 1968
Sales Range: $25-49.9 Million
Emp.: 565
Mfr of Valve & Commercial Spring
Wire
N.A.I.C.S.: 331222
Timothy W. Selhorst (Pres & CEO)
Darlynn Connor (Mgr-Customer Svc)
Rick Baker (Engr-Mechanical)
Elizabeth Jaworski (Mgr-HR)
Ralph Friedel (Project Mgr)

AMERICAN STAIR CORPORA-TION

642 Forestwood Dr, Romeoville, IL
60446
Tel.: (815) 886-9600
Web Site:
     http://www.americanstair.com
Year Founded: 1956
Sales Range: $10-24.9 Million
Emp.: 120
Design & Fabrication of Steel Stairs
& Railings
N.A.I.C.S.: 332323
Gordon Fitzsimmons (Pres)
Bob Danaher (Mgr)
Sam Sy (Mgr)
Andrew Combs (Mgr-Sls-Natl)

AMERICAN STANDARD TEST-ING BUREAU

40 Water St, New York, NY 10004
Tel.: (212) 943-3160
Web Site: http://www.nortrax.com
Sales Range: $25-49.9 Million
Emp.: 475
Research Services
N.A.I.C.S.: 541380
Gary Uhl (Dir-Design)
Martin Montoya (Dir-Fin)

Karen Dowd (Dir-Fin-Integrated Sup-ply Chain)
Lisa Escudero (Dir-HR)
Larry Van House (Mgr-Pkg Engrg)
Margaret Monteleone (Product Dir-Luxury)
Chris Buhowski (Product Mgr)
Debbie Guarriello (Sr Dir-Fin)
David Goldblatt (VP-Mktg Retail
Channel)
Steve Tardosky (Acct Mgr-Natl)
Stanimir Stoynov (Dir-Fin-Faucets)
Tommy Lu (Sr Mgr-Sourcing)

AMERICAN STATE BANCSHARES, INC.

1321 Main St, Great Bend, KS 67530
Tel.: (620) 793-5900   KS
Year Founded: 1984
Sales Range: $10-24.9 Million
Emp.: 143
Bank Holding Company
N.A.I.C.S.: 551111
Donald R. LacKamp (Pres & CEO)
Alan H. Schmidt (Dir-Residential
Mortgage Lending)

Subsidiaries:

American State Bank & Trust
Company   (1)
1321 Main St, Great Bend, KS 67530
Tel.: (620) 793-5900
Web Site:
     http://www.americanstatebankna.com
Sales Range: $10-24.9 Million
Emp.: 54
Retail & Commercial Banking
N.A.I.C.S.: 522110
Donald R. LacKamp (CEO)
Bruce Frost (Sr VP)
Alana Neale (CFO)
Erica Haskins (VP/Dir-Treasury Mgmt)

First National Bank of Holcomb   (1)
401 N Henderson St, Holcomb, KS 67851
Tel.: (620) 277-0077
Web Site: http://www.fnbholcomb.com
Sales Range: $1-9.9 Million
Retail & Commercial Banking
N.A.I.C.S.: 522110

Peoples Exchange Bank   (1)
1404 28th St, Belleville, KS 66935
Tel.: (785) 527-2213
Web Site: http://www.pebank.net
Sales Range: $1-9.9 Million
Emp.: 21
Retail & Commercial Banking
N.A.I.C.S.: 522110
James Koch (Pres)
Randy Wise (Sr VP-Belleville Branch)
Edmund Rudolph (VP-Concordia Branch)
Tom Baxa (VP-Concordia Branch)

Rose Hill Bank   (1)
107 N Rose Hill Rd, Rose Hill, KS 67133
Tel.: (316) 776-2131
Web Site: http://www.rosehillbank.com
Sales Range: $1-9.9 Million
Emp.: 68
Retail & Commercial Banking
N.A.I.C.S.: 522110
Roger Kepley (Pres)
Matt Allred (VP-Comml Lending)
Lisa Kelley (VP)
Joe Goedert (Sr VP)
Stephanie Lock (Mgr-HR)
Kathy Gomez (Asst VP)
Alison Dowell (VP)

AMERICAN STATE BANK HOLDING COMPANY, INC.

223 Main St, Williston, ND 58802
Tel.: (701) 774-4100   ND
Web Site: https://www.asbt.com
Sales Range: $10-24.9 Million
Emp.: 96
Bank Holding Company
N.A.I.C.S.: 551111
David N. Hanson (Pres & CEO)
Patrick Sogard (Chm)

Subsidiaries:

American State Bank & Trust Com-pany of Williston   (1)
223 Main St, Williston, ND 58801
Tel.: (701) 774-4100
Web Site: http://www.asbt.com
Emp.: 80
Retail & Commercial Banking
N.A.I.C.S.: 522110
Dave N. Hanson (Pres & CEO)

AMERICAN STATE EQUIP-MENT CO. INC.

2055 S 108th St, Milwaukee, WI
53227-1103
Tel.: (414) 541-8700   WI
Web Site: https://www.amstate.com
Year Founded: 1957
Sales Range: $10-24.9 Million
Emp.: 100
Construction & Mining Machinery
N.A.I.C.S.: 423810
Stephen Kraut (Chm & CEO)
Jim Drought (Sr VP)
Curt Ripke (CFO)
Timothy Kraut (Pres & COO)

Subsidiaries:

Finkbiner Equipment Co. Inc.   (1)
15 W 400 N Frntage Rd, Hinsdale, IL
60527   (100%)
Tel.: (630) 654-3700
Web Site: http://www.amstete.com
Sales Range: $10-24.9 Million
Emp.: 20
Construction & Mining Machinery
N.A.I.C.S.: 423810

AMERICAN STATIONERY CO., INC.

100 N Park Ave, Peru, IN 46970-1701
Tel.: (765) 473-4438   IN
Web Site:
     https://www.americanstationery.com
Year Founded: 1919
Sales Range: $100-124.9 Million
Emp.: 175
Fine Stationery & Personalized Paper
Products Distr & Mfr
N.A.I.C.S.: 322230
Michael Bakehorn (Pres)
Jim Cooper (Mgr-Warehouse Safety)
Joyce McCarty (Controller)
Kathy Calderbank (CFO)
Mark Brown (Dir-Mktg)

Subsidiaries:

The Rytex Company   (1)
100 N Park Ave, Peru, IN 46970 (100%)
Web Site: http://www.rytex.com
Rev.: $10,000,000
Emp.: 150
Mfr & Distributor of Fine Stationery & Per-sonalized Paper Products
N.A.I.C.S.: 322230

AMERICAN STEEL & SUPPLY INC.

8900 IH 37, Corpus Christi, TX 78409
Tel.: (361) 241-3265
Web Site:
     https://www.americansteelsupply.com
Year Founded: 1983
Sales Range: $10-24.9 Million
Emp.: 21
Metal Product Distr
N.A.I.C.S.: 423510
Bradley Pickens (Owner)

AMERICAN STEEL INC.

2500 Agnes St, Corpus Christi, TX
78405-1618
Tel.: (361) 241-3265
Web Site:
     http://www.americansteelsupply.com
Year Founded: 1938

American Steel Inc.—(Continued)

Sales Range: $10-24.9 Million
Emp.: 104
Distr of Furniture & Steel Products
N.A.I.C.S.: 423220

AMERICAN STRATEGIC INSURANCE CORP.

1 ASI Way N, Saint Petersburg, FL 33702
Tel.: (727) 821-8765
Web Site: http://www.americanstrategic.com
Year Founded: 1997
Sales Range: $800-899.9 Million
Emp.: 240
Property Insurance
N.A.I.C.S.: 524126
John F. Auer (Pres & CEO)
Kevin R. Milkey (Exec VP)
Jacob Peters (Natl Acct Exec)
Michael Tharpe (Acct Exec)
Jessica Peskin (VP-Mktg-Builders Div)
Philip Brubaker (VP-Product Mgmt)
Angel Conlin (VP-Product Mgmt)
Tanya Fjare (VP-Bus Analysis & Project Mgmt)
Mary Frances Fournet (VP-Natl Accounts & Corp Svcs)
Jeff Hannon (VP-Mktg)
Trevor Hillier (VP-Fin)
Patrick T. McCrink (VP-Claims)

AMERICAN STRUCTUREPOINT INC.

7260 Shadeland Sta, Indianapolis, IN 46256
Tel.: (317) 547-5580
Web Site: http://www.structurepoint.com
Year Founded: 1966
Emp.: 375
Engineeering Services
N.A.I.C.S.: 541330
Willis Conner (Pres, Partner & COO)
Gregory H. Henneke (Partner & Exec VP)
Jack Lashenik (Partner & VP)
Kenton M. Moore (Partner & VP)
Chritopher F. Murphy (VP)
Valerie Klingman (Sr Project Mgr)
Rick Paul (Project Mgr)
Rad Hudson (Project Mgr)
Ricardo Zamarripa (VP)
Cash Canfield (Partner & VP)
Steven J. Davidson (Partner & VP)
Scott Scoville (CFO)
Steve Fleming (VP)
Mike McBride (VP)
Ben Braun (VP)
Walid Gemayel (Sr VP)
Will Conley (Principal)
Andy Clemens (Dir-Project Dev)
Preston Ray (Project Mgr-Investigative Grp)
Joe Rebber (Project Mgr-Healthcare Practice)
David Mohler II (Partner & VP)
Bob Kuederle Jr. (VP)

AMERICAN STUDENT ASSISTANCE

100 Cambridge St Ste 1600, Boston, MA 02114
Tel.: (617) 426-9434
Web Site: http://asa.org
Rev.: $36,725,000
Student Loan Marketing Association
N.A.I.C.S.: 522299
Susan H. J. Nathan (COO)
Donald Reaves (Chm)
Angie Castera (Chief HR Officer)
Jean Eddy (Pres & CEO)

AMERICAN SUBSTANCE ABUSE PROFESSIONALS, INC.

1421 Clarkview Rd Ste 130, Baltimore, MD 21209
Tel.: (410) 366-3899
Web Site: http://www.go2asap.com
Year Founded: 1999
Rev.: $3,600,000
Emp.: 33
Specialized Health Care Services
N.A.I.C.S.: 621498
Reed Morrison (Pres)

AMERICAN SUNREX CORPORATION

671 Brea Canyon Rd Ste 1, Walnut, CA 91789
Tel.: (909) 839-1985
Web Site: https://www.usasunrex.com
Rev.: $3,300,000
Emp.: 18
Computer & Computer Peripheral Equipment & Software Merchant Whslr
N.A.I.C.S.: 423430
Huo-Lu Tsai (Pres)

AMERICAN SUNROOF CORPORATION

9240 Dowdy Dr, San Diego, CA 92126
Tel.: (562) 634-0466
Web Site: https://www.americansunroof.com
Year Founded: 1965
Sales Range: $10-24.9 Million
Emp.: 20
Provider of Customized Automotive Repair & Installation Services
N.A.I.C.S.: 811198
Myron Hankins (Gen Mgr)

AMERICAN SUPERIOR FEEDS INC.

200 Mill St SE, Ardmore, OK 73401
Tel.: (580) 223-3010
Web Site: http://www.bluebonnetfeed.com
Year Founded: 1972
Sales Range: $25-49.9 Million
Emp.: 95
Livestock Feeds
N.A.I.C.S.: 311119
Dale Downs (Pres)

AMERICAN SUPPORT LLC

1480 Environ Way, Chapel Hill, NC 27517-4433
Tel.: (919) 237-4900
Web Site: http://www.americansupport.com
Year Founded: 2006
Sales Range: $1-9.9 Million
Emp.: 103
Outsourced Billing & Technical Support Services
N.A.I.C.S.: 541219
Matt Zemon (Founder, Pres & CEO)
Chad Rycenga (CIO)

AMERICAN SWISS PRODUCTS CO, INC.

1987 Jefferson Rd W, Pittsford, NY 14534
Tel.: (585) 292-1720
Web Site: https://www.americanswiss.com
Year Founded: 1954
Sales Range: $1-9.9 Million
Emp.: 9
Industrial Machinery & Equipment Merchant Whslr
N.A.I.C.S.: 423830

Rebecca J. Luce (Pres)
Stacy Cowley (Mgr-Sls & Compliance)
Zahl Cama (Mgr-Quality)

AMERICAN SYNERGY CORPORATION

28436 Satellite St, Hayward, CA 94545
Tel.: (510) 259-1700
Web Site: http://www.synergycompanies.org
Year Founded: 1981
Rev.: $10,000,000
Emp.: 50
Asbestos Removal & Encapsulation
N.A.I.C.S.: 238310
David C. Clark (Pres)
Steve Shallenberger (Pres)

AMERICAN SYSTEMS CORPORATION

14151 Park Meadow Dr, Chantilly, VA 20151-2272
Tel.: (703) 968-6300
Web Site: http://www.americansystems.com
Year Founded: 1975
Sales Range: $250-299.9 Million
Emp.: 1,500
Government & Private Sector Consulting, Professional, Technical, Systems Engineering & Managed Services
N.A.I.C.S.: 541618
Brian Neely (CTO & CIO)
William C. Hoover (Chm)
Chris Braccio (VP-HR)
Peter Whitfield (CFO)
Jeff Jancek (VP & Dir-Live, Virtual & Constructive Trng)
Michael Dolton (Dir-Comm)
John Steckel (VP-Corp Dev)
Sheri Murphy (VP-Quality Assurance & Continuous Improvement)

AMERICAN TANK & FABRICATING COMPANY

12314 Elmwood Ave, Cleveland, OH 44111-5906
Tel.: (216) 252-1500
Web Site: http://www.amtank.com
Year Founded: 1940
Sales Range: $75-99.9 Million
Emp.: 100
Mfr & Retailer of Steel Plates
N.A.I.C.S.: 332313
Terry Ripich (Chm & Pres)
Chris Disanto (Mgr)
Rick Sykora (Controller)

Subsidiaries:

AT&F Advanced Metals LLC (1)
95 N Swinehart Rd, Orrville, OH 44667
Tel.: (330) 684-1122
Sales Range: $1-9.9 Million
Fabricated Structural Metal Mfr
N.A.I.C.S.: 332312
John Deily (Gen Mgr)
Tom Pindroh (Project Engr)

AT&F India Fabrication Pvt. Ltd. (1)
902 9th Fl Sanjona Apts Opp IIPS Govandi Station Rd Deonar, Mumbai, 400098, India
Tel.: (91) 976 997 0135
Web Site: http://www.atfindia.com
Emp.: 18
Fabricated Structural Metal Mfr
N.A.I.C.S.: 332312
Shivkumar Menon (Project Mgr)

AT&F Marine (1)
3 Broad St Ste 400-4, Charleston, SC 29401
Tel.: (216) 246-5933
Web Site: http://www.atfco.com
Marine Engineering Services
N.A.I.C.S.: 541330
Michael Ripich (CEO)

AMERICAN TANK & VESSEL INC.

1005 Govt St, Mobile, AL 36604
Tel.: (251) 432-8265
Web Site: https://www.at-v.com
Year Founded: 1982
Sales Range: $25-49.9 Million
Emp.: 300
Provider of Steel Construction Services
N.A.I.C.S.: 238120
William J. Cutts (CEO)
Dean Carlisle (Project Mgr)
Rhonda Green (Office Mgr)
Joe Watts (Mgr-Traffic)
Jake Davidson (Project Mgr)

AMERICAN TECHNICAL PUBLISHERS, INC.

10100 Orland Pkwy Ste 200, Orland Park, IL 60467
Tel.: (708) 957-1100
Web Site: http://www.go2atp.com
Year Founded: 1898
Sales Range: $50-74.9 Million
Emp.: 50
Publisher of Vocational & Technical Textbooks
N.A.I.C.S.: 513130
Robert D. Deisinger (Chm, Pres, CEO & CFO)
David J. Holloway (Sr VP)
Jonathan F. Gosse (Editor-in-Chief)

AMERICAN TECHNOLOGIES, INC.

210 Baywood Ave, Orange, CA 92865
Tel.: (714) 939-4940
Web Site: http://www.amer-tech.com
Rev.: $20,909,869
Emp.: 225
Restoration & Remediation Services
N.A.I.C.S.: 562910
Steven E. Pace (CFO)
Aaron Murray (Reg Mgr)
Barry Metcalf (Reg Mgr)
Eric Gotham (Reg Mgr)
Gregg Zembik (Reg Mgr)
Jeff Huddleston (Sr VP)
Kyle Pickett (Exec VP)
Marc Oberacker (Reg Mgr)
Mark Schafer (Dir-Technical Svcs)
Roy Hawkins (Mgr-Tucson)
Rudi Suminski (Dir-Consulting Svcs)

AMERICAN TECHNOLOGY SERVICES INC

2751 Prosperity Ave 6th Fl, Fairfax, VA 22031
Tel.: (703) 876-0300
Web Site: https://www.networkats.com
Sales Range: $1-9.9 Million
Emp.: 65
IT Consulting Services
N.A.I.C.S.: 541990
Calvin E. Schafer (Treas & Sec)
Jeff Chandler (Pres)
Tim Baer (VP)
Alex Koludrovic (VP)
Barbara Kent (CFO & VP)
Danesh Hussain (Dir-Network Svcs)
Meg Riat (Mgr-HR)
Felicia Engdahl (Mgr-Support)
Sherrie Bakshi (Project Mgr)
Brisbane Benedicto (Project Mgr)
Christine Rand (Project Mgr)
Matthew Valleskey (VP-Mktg & Sls)

AMERICAN TEL-A-SYSTEMS INC.

4800 Curtin Dr, McFarland, WI 53558
Tel.: (608) 838-4194
Web Site: https://www.amtelco.com

Year Founded: 1978
Rev.: $10,800,000
Emp.: 120
Telephone & Telegraph Apparatus
N.A.I.C.S.: 334210
Tom Curtin (Pres)

AMERICAN TELECARE, INC.
15159 Technology Dr, Eden Prairie, MN 55344
Tel.: (952) 897-0000
Web Site:
http://www.americantelecare.com
Year Founded: 1993
Sales Range: $10-24.9 Million
Emp.: 4
Healthcare Software Development Services
N.A.I.C.S.: 541511
Edward Bergmark (CEO)
Dennis J. Duval (Pres & COO)
Allen U. Lenzmeier (Chm)

AMERICAN TELECOMMUNI-CATIONS INC.
250 47th St, Brooklyn, NY 11220
Tel.: (718) 439-5333
Web Site: http://www.atiglobal.com
Rev.: $28,900,000
Emp.: 120
Electronic Parts & Equipment Merchant Whslr
N.A.I.C.S.: 423690
Michael Ziegler (CFO)
Nathan Yanovitch (Pres)

AMERICAN TELETIMER CORP.
1167 Globe Ave, Mountainside, NJ 07092
Tel.: (908) 654-4200   NY
Web Site: http://www.teletimer.com
Year Founded: 1938
Sales Range: $1-9.9 Million
Emp.: 40
Relay & Industrial Control Mfr
N.A.I.C.S.: 335314
Joel Rosenzweig (Pres & CEO)
Ron Couturier (COO & Exec VP)
Eric Barthelemy (Sr VP)

AMERICAN TEXTILE MAINTE-NANCE COMPANY
1667 W Washington Blvd, Los Angeles, CA 90007
Tel.: (323) 731-3132
Web Site:
https://www.republicmasters.com
Sales Range: $10-24.9 Million
Emp.: 500
Linen Supply
N.A.I.C.S.: 812331
Gail Reynolds (Controller)

AMERICAN THERMOPLASTIC COMPANY
106 Gamma Dr, Pittsburgh, PA 15238-2920
Tel.: (412) 967-0900
Web Site: http://www.binders.com
Year Founded: 1954
Sales Range: $100-124.9 Million
Emp.: 7
Looseleaf Binders & Related Products Mfr
N.A.I.C.S.: 323111
Barry Franklin (Gen Mgr)

Subsidiaries:

Four Point Products   (1)
106 Gamma Dr, Pittsburgh, PA 15238
Tel.: (412) 967-0900
Web Site: http://www.binders.com
Sales Range: $10-24.9 Million
Mfr Looseleaf Binders & Related Prods.
N.A.I.C.S.: 323111
Barry Franklin (Gen Mgr)

AMERICAN TOOLING CEN-TER, INC.
4111 Mount Hope Rd, Grass Lake, MI 49240
Tel.: (517) 522-8411
Web Site:
http://www.americantooling.com
Sales Range: $100-124.9 Million
Emp.: 140
Mfr of Tools & Dies
N.A.I.C.S.: 333514
John J. Basso (Pres)
Gary Gizinski (CFO)

Subsidiaries:

Midland Design Service Inc.   (1)
31435 Stephenson Hwy, Madison Heights, MI 48071-1424   (100%)
Tel.: (248) 588-1100
Web Site:
http://www.midlanddesignservice.com
Sales Range: $10-24.9 Million
Emp.: 19
Engineering Services
N.A.I.C.S.: 541330

AMERICAN TORCH TIP CO. INC.
6212 29th St E, Bradenton, FL 34203
Tel.: (941) 753-7557
Web Site:
https://www.americantorchtip.com
Sales Range: $10-24.9 Million
Emp.: 200
Welding Apparatus
N.A.I.C.S.: 333992
Jack McCulloch (Dir-Sls-Western Reg & Bus Mgr)
Daniel Engel (CFO)
John D. Walters Jr. (Pres)

AMERICAN TRADING & PRO-DUCTION CORPORATION
10 E Baltimore St Ste 1600, Baltimore, MD 21202
Tel.: (410) 347-7150   MD
Web Site: http://www.atapco.com
Year Founded: 1931
Sales Range: $75-99.9 Million
Emp.: 25
Owner & Operator of Real Estate Properties
N.A.I.C.S.: 531210
Daniel B. Hirschhorn (Chm)
Shirley MacNeal (Mgr-HR)

AMERICAN TRADING INTER-NATIONAL
19 Microlab Rd Ste C, Livingston, NJ 07039
Tel.: (973) 740-9270
Web Site: https://www.amtinet.com
Year Founded: 1986
Sales Range: $10-24.9 Million
Emp.: 15
Importer & Exporter of Computer Related Products
N.A.I.C.S.: 424610
Barbera Dersovitz (VP)

AMERICAN TRIM LLC
1005 W Grand Ave, Lima, OH 45801-3429
Tel.: (419) 228-1145   OH
Web Site: https://www.amtrim.com
Year Founded: 1951
Sales Range: $350-399.9 Million
Emp.: 1,900
Automotive Stampings & Metal Products Mfr
N.A.I.C.S.: 332119
Jeffrey A. Hawk (CEO)
Robert Stead (VP-HR)

Subsidiaries:

American Trim - Cullman   (1)
1909 Beech Ave SE, Cullman, AL 35055

Tel.: (256) 734-4921
Sales Range: $25-49.9 Million
Emp.: 230
Mfr of Roll Forms & Decorative Products
Brian Ritter (Sr Engr-Tooling)

Angell-Demmel North America Corporation   (1)
1516 Stanley Ave, Dayton, OH 45404
Tel.: (937) 461-5800
Web Site: http://www.angell-demmel.com
Sales Range: $50-74.9 Million
Emp.: 20
Metal Automotive Part Mfr
N.A.I.C.S.: 336390
Diana Brelsford (Project Coord)
Rick Pfeifer (CEO)

Division (Domestic):

Angell-Demmel North America   (2)
810 W Main St, Lebanon, KY 40033
Tel.: (270) 692-2142
Sales Range: $50-74.9 Million
Aluminum Wheelcovers, Automotive Interior Trim Products, Aluminum Appliance Panels & General Nameplates & Escutcheons Mfr
N.A.I.C.S.: 336390
Marty Asberry (Mgr-Engrg)

AMERICAN TRUCK & BUS INC.
195 Defense Hwy, Annapolis, MD 21401
Tel.: (410) 224-9775
Web Site: http://www.american-bus.com
Emp.: 200
Wholesale Distribution of Buses & other Motor Vehicles
N.A.I.C.S.: 423110
Steven R. Leonard (Pres)
Karen Thiemeyer (Controller)

AMERICAN TRUCKING ASSO-CIATION
80 M St SE Ste 800, Washington, DC 20003
Tel.: (703) 838-1700
Web Site: https://www.trucking.org
Year Founded: 1933
Trucking Industry Services
N.A.I.C.S.: 484121

AMERICAN TRUST SENIOR CARE LLC
3301 Bonita Beach Rd Ste 208, Bonita Springs, FL 34134
Tel.: (239) 908-2921
Web Site:
http://www.discoverymgt.com
Year Founded: 1994
Sales Range: $50-74.9 Million
Emp.: 980
Luxury Senior Living Communities Developer & Manager
N.A.I.C.S.: 237210
Thomas J. Harrison (Co-Founder & CEO)
Diana Ferrante Thies (Sr VP-Mktg & Sls)
Thomas J. Costello (Sr VP-Fin, Acctg & IT)
Richard L. Rekar (VP-Acctg)
Randy P. Smith (Sr VP-Ops)
Tammy Kaminski (VP-Construction)

AMERICAN TUBE CORP.
603 Grenar Rd, Nazareth, PA 18064
Tel.: (610) 759-8700
Web Site: http://www.amtubeco.com
Rev.: $13,200,000
Emp.: 100
Tubes, Seamless Steel
N.A.I.C.S.: 331210

AMERICAN TURNED PROD-UCTS, INC.
7626 Klier Dr, Fairview, PA 16415

Tel.: (814) 474-4200
Web Site: https://www.atpteam.com
Year Founded: 1984
Sales Range: $25-49.9 Million
Emp.: 140
Hand & Edge Tool Mfr
N.A.I.C.S.: 332216
Jerry Eighmy (Founder)
B. Scott Eighmy (Co-Owner & CEO)
Harry Eighmy (Co-Owner & COO)
Jim Osmanski (VP-Fin)
Drew Hoffman (VP-Client Rels)
Jerry Sargent (Gen Mgr)
Karen Andrews (Mgr-HR)

AMERICAN TV & APPLIANCE OF MADISON, INC.
2404 W Beltline Hwy, Madison, WI 53713-2346
Tel.: (608) 271-1000   WI
Web Site: http://www.americantv.com
Year Founded: 1954
Sales Range: $500-549.9 Million
Emp.: 1,000
Retailer of Furniture & Electrical Appliances Including Stereos, Televisions & Computers
N.A.I.C.S.: 449210
Tina Walters (Mgr)

AMERICAN UNDERWATER PRODUCTS
2002 Davis St, San Leandro, CA 94577
Tel.: (510) 562-0500
Web Site:
http://www.oceanicworldwide.com
Rev.: $13,500,000
Emp.: 100
Skin Diving Equipment, Scuba Type
N.A.I.C.S.: 339920
Robert Hollis (CEO & Founder)

AMERICAN UNITED MUTUAL INSURANCE HOLDING COM-PANY
1 American Sq, Indianapolis, IN 46282
Tel.: (317) 285-1111   IN
Web Site:
http://www.oneamerica.com
Year Founded: 2000
Sales Range: $1-4.9 Billion
Emp.: 1,000
Holding Company
N.A.I.C.S.: 551112
Dayton H. Molendorp (Chm & CEO)

Subsidiaries:

OneAmerica Financial Partners, Inc.   (1)
1 America Sq, Indianapolis, IN 46282   (100%)
Tel.: (317) 285-1111
Web Site: http://www.oneamerica.com
Sales Range: $150-199.9 Million
Life Insurance, Retirement Planning, Employee Benefits & Reinsurance Products & Services
N.A.I.C.S.: 551112
Jeffrey D. Holley (Exec VP-Fin, Ops & Institutional Markets)
J. Scott Davison (Chm, Pres & CEO)
John Mason (Chief Investment Officer & Sr VP)
Karin Sarratt (Chief HR Officer & Sr VP)
Dennis Martin (Pres-Individual Life & Fin Svcs)
Sandy McCarthy (Pres-Retirement Svcs)
Andrew Michie (Sr VP & Controller)
David Brentlinger (Chief Actuary & Sr VP)
Gene P. Berry (CIO & Sr VP)
Kelly Huntington (Sr VP-Enterprise Strategy & Mktg)
Richard M. Ellery (Gen Counsel & Sr VP)
Mark Scalercio (Sr VP & Head-Distr-Individual Life & Fin Svcs Line)

American United Mutual Insurance Holding
Company—(Continued)

Subsidiary (Domestic):

AUL Reinsurance Management Services, LLC (2)
20 Security Dr, Avon, CT 06001
Tel.: (860) 677-7300
General Insurance Services
N.A.I.C.S.: 524298

**Pioneer Mutual Life Insurance
Company** (2)
101 N 10th St, Fargo, ND 58108
Tel.: (701) 297-5700
Web Site: http://www.pmlife.com
Rev.: $32,100,000
Emp.: 41
Life Insurance & Annuity
N.A.I.C.S.: 525110

AMERICAN VAN EQUIPMENT INC.
149 Lehigh Ave, Lakewood, NJ
08701
Tel.: (732) 905-5900   NJ
Web Site:
   https://www.americanvan.com
Year Founded: 1978
Commercial Truck & Van Accessories
N.A.I.C.S.: 441330
Charles B. Richter (Pres)
Joseph W. Fallon Sr. (VP-Sls)

AMERICAN VENDING SALES, INC.
750 Morse Ave, Elk Grove Village, IL
60007
Tel.: (847) 439-9400   IL
Web Site:
   http://www.americanvending.com
Sales Range: $10-24.9 Million
Emp.: 35
Vending Machines, Coin-Operated
N.A.I.C.S.: 423440
Jim McAllister (CFO)
Vince Gumma (Pres)
Cortney Black Kinzler (Dir-Mktg)
Jeff Yoder (VP & Gen Mgr)
Kurk Johnson (Head-Sls-Vending)

Subsidiaries:

Lieberman Companies, Inc. (1)
9549 Penn Ave S, Bloomington, MN 55431
Tel.: (952) 887-5299
Web Site:
   http://www.liebermancompanies.com
Sales Range: $10-24.9 Million
Amusement, Gaming & Vending Machines
& Equipment Distr
N.A.I.C.S.: 423850
Harold L. Lieberman (Pres & CEO)
Linda Winstead (Head-Sls)

AMERICAN VISION WINDOWS, INC.
2125 Madera Rd, Simi Valley, CA
93065
Tel.: (805) 468-4316
Web Site:
   https://www.americanwindows.com
Year Founded: 1999
Sales Range: $10-24.9 Million
Emp.: 215
Personal & Household Goods Repair
& Maintenance Services
N.A.I.C.S.: 811490
Bill Herren (CEO)
Chris Perez (VP-Sls)
Armen Hovakimyan (Project Mgr)
Awan Diles (Project Mgr)
Brad Hopper (VP-Sls)
Brian Ohl (Project Mgr)
Cybill Wolfstein (Project Mgr)
Gina Perin (Project Mgr)
Gonzo Raymond (Project Mgr)
Mike Wilson (Project Mgr)
Steve Huffman (Project Mgr)
Tim Hess (Project Mgr)

AMERICAN WASTE INDUSTRIES
11266 Peoria St, Sun Valley, CA
91352
Tel.: (818) 768-1492
Web Site:
   http://www.americanwaste.com
Rev.: $17,514,987
Emp.: 154
Garbage Collection & Transport, No
Disposal
N.A.I.C.S.: 562111
Mego Godjamanian (Pres)

AMERICAN WEB INC.
4040 Dahlia St, Denver, CO 80216
Tel.: (303) 321-2422
Web Site:
   http://www.americanwebinc.com
Sales Range: $10-24.9 Million
Emp.: 110
Offset Printing
N.A.I.C.S.: 323111
Gary E. Hansen (Chm)

AMERICAN WEST HOMES INC.
250 Pilot Rd Ste 140, Las Vegas, NV
89119
Tel.: (702) 736-6434
Web Site:
   http://www.americanhomes.com
Year Founded: 1984
Subdividers & Developers
N.A.I.C.S.: 237210
Lawrence D. Canarelli (Founder)

AMERICAN WEST WORLD-WIDE EXPRESS INC.
51 Zaca Ln Ste 120, San Luis
Obispo, CA 93401
Tel.: (562) 692-2660
Web Site: https://www.awest.com
Year Founded: 1993
Sales Range: $10-24.9 Million
Emp.: 100
Provider of Trucking Services
N.A.I.C.S.: 484121
Josh Brown (Founder & CEO)
Michelle Crow (VP)
Israel Gonzalez (Mgr-Warehouse)

AMERICAN WHOLESALERS INC.
3509 American Way, Evansville, IN
47711
Tel.: (812) 464-8781
Web Site:
   http://www.americanwindows.com
Sales Range: $10-24.9 Million
Emp.: 44
Construction Services & Products
N.A.I.C.S.: 423330
Stacey Paulstring (Controller)
Jack Starks (Gen Mgr)

AMERICAN WINDOW & GLASS INC.
2715 Lynch Rd, Evansville, IN 47711
Tel.: (812) 464-9400
Web Site:
   http://www.americanwindows.com
Sales Range: $10-24.9 Million
Emp.: 120
Awnings, Fiberglass & Plastics Combination
N.A.I.C.S.: 326199
Stacy Palstring (Controller)
Jeff Wigington (Gen Mgr)

AMERICAN WIRE & CABLE COMPANY
7951 Bronson Rd, Olmsted Falls, OH
44138
Tel.: (440) 235-3303

Web Site:
   https://www.americanwirecable.com
Rev.: $15,000,000
Emp.: 40
Nonferrous Wiredrawing & Insulating
N.A.I.C.S.: 332618
Richard M. McClain (Pres)

AMERICAN WOOD FIBERS, INC.
9841 Brokenland Pkwy, Columbia,
MD 21046-1169
Tel.: (410) 290-8700
Web Site: http://www.awf.com
Year Founded: 1988
Sales Range: $100-124.9 Million
Emp.: 300
Mfr of Wood Products
N.A.I.C.S.: 321999
Steve Radant (VP-Fin)
Stephen Faehner (CEO)

AMERICAN WOOD MOULDING, LLC
7458 New Rdg Rd, Hanover, MD
21076-3101
Tel.: (410) 850-5430
Web Site:
   http://www.americanmoulding.com
Year Founded: 1996
Sales Range: $200-249.9 Million
Emp.: 450
Lumber, Plywood & Millwork
N.A.I.C.S.: 423310
Matthew Hagen (Pres & CEO)
Clayton Waskiewicz (VP-Logistics)
Steve Anstett (VP-Mktg & Bus Dev)
Kevin Blum (VP-Supply Chain)
Fred Cooper (CFO)

AMERICAN WORDATA, INC.
13529 Prestige Pl Ste 112, Tampa,
FL 33635
Tel.: (800) 358-6664
Web Site: http://www.awdata.com
Year Founded: 1981
Sales Range: $1-9.9 Million
Emp.: 12
Computer & Software Stores
N.A.I.C.S.: 449210
Traci Weston (CEO)

AMERICAN WRECKING INC.
2549 Lee Ave Ste1, South El Monte,
CA 91733
Tel.: (626) 350-8303
Web Site:
   https://www.americanwrecking.com
Sales Range: $10-24.9 Million
Emp.: 70
Site Preparation Contractor
N.A.I.C.S.: 238910
Robert Hall (VP)
Jose L. Galaviz Sr. (Pres)

AMERICAN XANTHAN CORPORATION
1712 Pioneer Ave Ste 1749, Cheyenne, WY 82001
Tel.: (307) 778-4713   WY
Year Founded: 2013
Xanthan Gum Mfr & Distr
N.A.I.C.S.: 325194
Henry Luce (CEO)

AMERICAN YOUTH SOCCER ORGANIZATION
19750 S Vermont Ave Ste 200, Torrance, CA 90502
Tel.: (424) 221-7910   CA
Web Site: http://www.ayso.org
Year Founded: 1964
Sales Range: $50-74.9 Million
Emp.: 56
Soccer Association
N.A.I.C.S.: 711211

Matt Winegar (Pres)
Eileen Tabert (VP-Admin)
Michael Karon (Treas)

AMERICAN-MARSH PUMPS
185 Progress Rd, Collierville, TN
38017
Tel.: (901) 860-2300
Web Site: http://www.american-marsh.com
Year Founded: 1873
Sales Range: $10-24.9 Million
Emp.: 95
Pumps & Pumping Equipment, Nec
N.A.I.C.S.: 423830
Ron Cheek (CEO)
Michael Florio (VP-Mktg)
Pat Dickey (VP-Engrg)

AMERICANA COMPANIES INC.
415 N Burnett St, Shenandoah, IA
51601
Tel.: (800) 833-7555
Web Site:
   http://www.americanacompanies.com
Sales Range: $50-74.9 Million
Emp.: 130
Industrial Machinery & Equipment
Merchant Whslr
N.A.I.C.S.: 423830
Ted Swanson (VP)
Phillip Lamb (Mgr-Plant)

AMERICANA COMPANIES, INC.
415 N Burnett, Shenandoah, IA
51601
Tel.: (712) 246-3458
Web Site:
   http://www.americanacompanies.com
Year Founded: 1975
Sales Range: $10-24.9 Million
Emp.: 45
Shopping Carts, Parts & Accessories
& Hand Baskets Mfr
N.A.I.C.S.: 332999
Terry Swanson (Pres)
Ted Swanson (Sec)

Subsidiaries:

American Shopping Carts Inc (1)
PO Box 250, Shenandoah, IA 51601
Tel.: (712) 246-3458
Web Site:
   http://www.americanacompanies.com
Shopping Cart Repair
N.A.I.C.S.: 322299

AMERICANA COMPANY INC.
11130 Bloomfield Ave, Santa Fe
Springs, CA 90670-4603
Tel.: (310) 354-1377
Web Site:
   http://www.americanasportswear.com
Sales Range: $25-49.9 Million
Emp.: 22
Sportswear, Women's & Children's
N.A.I.C.S.: 424350

AMERICANA LLC
2140 E Pebble Rd 160, Las Vegas,
NV 89123
Tel.: (702) 796-7777
Web Site:
   http://www.americanagroup.com
Year Founded: 1979
Real Estate Agency
N.A.I.C.S.: 531210
Mark Stark (Owner)
Gordon Miles (COO)

AMERICANEAGLE.COM, INC.
2600 S River Rd, Des Plaines, IL
60018
Tel.: (847) 699-0300

Web Site:
https://www.americaneagle.com
Sales Range: $10-24.9 Million
Emp.: 196
Website Design Services
N.A.I.C.S.: 541511
Tony Svanascini *(CEO)*
Nick Goodrum *(Partner)*
Shawn Griffin *(Partner)*
Phil Kubel *(VP-Digital Media & Tech)*
Pierre D'Arbost *(Gen Mgr-UK & Europe)*

AMERICANS FOR JOB SECURITY
107 SW St PMB 551, Alexandria, VA 22314
Tel.: (703) 535-3110   DC
Web Site: http://www.savejobs.org
Year Founded: 1998
Sales Range: $50-74.9 Million
Emp.: 1
Workforce Development Services
N.A.I.C.S.: 561311
Stephen DeMaura *(Pres & Sec)*

AMERICANS FOR PROSPERITY
2111 Wilson Blvd Ste 350, Arlington, VA 22201
Tel.: (703) 224-3200   DC
Web Site:
http://www.americanprosperity.org
Year Founded: 2004
Sales Range: $25-49.9 Million
Civic & Social Organization
N.A.I.C.S.: 813410
Teresa Oelke *(Sr VP-State Ops)*
Brent Gardner *(Chief Govt Affairs Officer)*
Emily Seidel *(CEO)*
Tim Phillips *(Pres)*
Victor E. Bernson Jr. *(Gen Counsel & VP)*

AMERICARX.COM
19-35 Hazen St, East Elmhurst, NY 11370
Tel.: (718) 204-7211
Web Site:
https://www.myotcstore.com
Year Founded: 1999
Rev.: $13,700,000
Emp.: 50
Pharmacies & Drug Stores
N.A.I.C.S.: 456110
Pavankumar Darisi *(CEO)*

AMERICATOWNE HOLDINGS, INC.
4700 Homewood Ct Ste 100, Raleigh, NC 27609   NV
Year Founded: 1969
Rev.: $376,540
Assets: $4,750,806
Liabilities: $2,440,988
Net Worth: $2,309,818
Earnings: ($1,615,316)
Emp.: 24
Fiscal Year-end: 12/31/18
Holding Company
N.A.I.C.S.: 551112

AMERICH CORPORATION
13212 Saticoy St, North Hollywood, CA 91605
Tel.: (818) 982-1711
Web Site: https://www.americh.com
Rev.: $18,000,000
Emp.: 50
Whirlpool Baths, Hydrotherapy Equipment
N.A.I.C.S.: 339113
Edward Richmond *(Pres)*

AMERICHEM INC.

2000 Americhem Way, Cuyahoga Falls, OH 44221-3309
Tel.: (330) 929-4213
Web Site: http://www.americhem.com
Year Founded: 1941
Sales Range: $25-49.9 Million
Emp.: 900
Mfr of Custom Color Concentrates
N.A.I.C.S.: 325130
Matt Miklos *(VP-Global Tech & Innovation)*
Rob Gudbranson *(CFO)*
Vimal Sharma *(VP & Gen Mgr-Global Ops)*
Diane Shields *(VP-Global HR)*
Stanley Teoh *(VP)*

AMERICHIP, INC.
19032 S Vermont Ave, Los Angeles, CA 90248-1011
Tel.: (310) 323-3697   CA
Web Site: https://www.americhip.com
Year Founded: 2001
Sales Range: $10-24.9 Million
Emp.: 100
Audio, Visual & Dimensional Print Products & Technologies Designer & Mfr
N.A.I.C.S.: 323111
Tim Clegg *(Founder & CEO)*
John Clegg *(VP-Sls)*
Angie Davis *(Mgr-Production)*
Kevin Clegg *(Pres)*
Primoz Samardzija *(Exec VP)*

AMERICOLLECT, INC.
1851 S Alverno Rd, Manitowoc, WI 54220
Tel.: (920) 682-0311   WI
Web Site:
https://www.americollect.com
Sales Range: $1-9.9 Million
Emp.: 62
Adjustment/Collection Services & Legal Services
N.A.I.C.S.: 561440
Kenlyn T. Gretz *(Pres)*
Julie Bruckschen *(Mgr-HR)*

AMERICRAFT CARTON, INC.
7400 State Line Rd Ste 206, Prairie Village, KS 66208-3445
Tel.: (913) 387-3700   MO
Web Site: https://www.americraft.com
Year Founded: 1983
Sales Range: $25-49.9 Million
Emp.: 600
Folding Paperboard Boxes
N.A.I.C.S.: 322212
Richard Horton *(VP)*
C. Allen Booe *(CFO)*
Rick N. Johnson *(Pres)*

Subsidiaries:

Americraft Carton Group, Inc.   (1)
164 Meadowcroft St, Lowell, MA 01853-5326   (100%)
Tel.: (978) 459-9328
Web Site: http://www.americraft.com
Sales Range: $10-24.9 Million
Emp.: 70
Mfr of Folding Paperboard Boxes
N.A.I.C.S.: 322130
Ernest George *(Controller)*
Terri Aquaviva *(Dir-Bus Dev)*
Kristine Tamblingson *(Reg VP & Gen Mgr)*
Kim Houston *(Office Mgr)*

Americraft Carton Inc.   (1)
403 Fillmore Ave E, Saint Paul, MN 55107-1205
Tel.: (651) 227-6655
Web Site: http://www.americraft.com
Sales Range: $25-49.9 Million
Emp.: 150
Mfr Of Setup Paperboard Boxes
N.A.I.C.S.: 322219
Todd Butcher *(Gen Mgr)*

Americraft Carton Inc.   (1)

320 W Hanes Mill Rd, Winston Salem, NC 27105-9135   (100%)
Tel.: (336) 744-1222
Web Site: http://www.americraft.com
Sales Range: $10-24.9 Million
Emp.: 120
Folding Paperboard Boxes
N.A.I.C.S.: 322212
James T. Kleinfeld *(Gen Mgr)*
Ray Taylor *(VP-Sls)*

Americraft Carton Inc.   (1)
305 W S St, Sturgis, MI 49091-2149   (100%)
Tel.: (269) 651-2365
Web Site: http://www.americraft.com
Sales Range: $10-24.9 Million
Emp.: 110
Folding Paperboard Box Mfr
N.A.I.C.S.: 322212

Americraft Carton Inc.   (1)
835 S Bellevue Blvd, Memphis, TN 38104-4643
Tel.: (901) 725-5100
Web Site: http://www.americraft.com
Sales Range: $10-24.9 Million
Emp.: 100
Folding Paperboard Boxes
N.A.I.C.S.: 322212
Joe Creel *(Mgr-Die Cutting)*
Andy Clayton *(Mgr-Maintenance)*

Americraft Carton, Inc. - Lowell Plant   (1)
164 Meadowcroft St, Lowell, MA 08152
Tel.: (978) 459-9328
Folding Paperboard Carton Mfr
N.A.I.C.S.: 322212
Kristine Tamblingson *(Gen Mgr)*

Americraft Carton, Inc. - Memphis Plant   (1)
835 S Bellevue Blvd, Memphis, TN 38104
Tel.: (901) 725-5100
Folding Cartons Mfr
N.A.I.C.S.: 322212

Americraft Carton, Inc. - Norwalk Plant   (1)
209 Republic St, Norwalk, OH 44857
Tel.: (419) 668-1006
Folding Cartons Mfr
N.A.I.C.S.: 322212

Americraft Carton, Inc. - St. Paul Plant   (1)
403 Fillmore Ave, Saint Paul, MN 55107
Tel.: (651) 227-6655
Folding Cartons Mfr
N.A.I.C.S.: 322212

Americraft Carton, Inc. - Sturgis Plant   (1)
305 WSSt, Sturgis, MI 49091
Tel.: (269) 651-2365
Folding Paperboard Carton Mfr
N.A.I.C.S.: 322212
Eric Hansen *(Gen Mgr)*

Americraft Carton, Inc. - Winston-Salem Plant   (1)
320 W Hanes Mill Rd, Winston Salem, NC 27105
Tel.: (336) 744-1222
Folding Paperboard Box Mfr
N.A.I.C.S.: 322212

AMERIDIAL, INC.
4535 Strausser St NW, Canton, OH 44720
Tel.: (330) 497-4888
Web Site: http://www.ameridial.com
Year Founded: 1987
Sales Range: $25-49.9 Million
Emp.: 800
Telemarketing Services
N.A.I.C.S.: 561422
James A. McGeorge *(Founder & Chm)*
Terri Peterman *(Gen Mgr)*
Craig Vretas *(Dir-Bus Dev)*
Topaz Roberts *(Dir-Program Mgmt)*

AMERIDIAN SPECIALTY SERVICES INC.

11520 Rockfield Ct, Cincinnati, OH 45241
Tel.: (513) 769-0150
Web Site:
http://www.ameridiansvcs.com
Year Founded: 1999
Sales Range: $1-9.9 Million
Emp.: 30
Commercial & Residential Roofing & Construction Services
N.A.I.C.S.: 236220
Matt Owens *(Pres)*
Brian Crawley *(Mgr-Roofing Ops)*
Geoff Griffiths *(CFO)*

AMERIFIRST HOME MORTGAGE
616 W Ctr Ave, Portage, MI 49024
Tel.: (269) 324-4240
Web Site: http://www.amerifirst.com
Year Founded: 1987
Sales Range: $10-24.9 Million
Emp.: 267
Residential Mortgage Services
N.A.I.C.S.: 531210
Mark A. Jones *(Co-Founder)*
David N. Gahm *(Co-Founder)*
Dan Moyle *(Dir-Creative-Mktg)*
Joe Hufnagel *(Dir-HR)*
Sandra Cartwright *(Sr VP-HR)*
Doug Long *(Pres-Southeast)*
Jamie Brown *(Mgr-Southeast)*

AMERIGLOBE FIBC SOLUTIONS
153 S Long St, Lafayette, LA 70506
Tel.: (337) 234-3211
Web Site: https://www.ameriglobe-fibc.com
Year Founded: 1985
Sales Range: $50-74.9 Million
Emp.: 200
Mfr of Plastic Bags: Made From Purchased Materials
N.A.I.C.S.: 326111
Daniel R. Schnaars *(Pres)*
Randy Diraourd *(Controller)*

AMERIGO RESTAURANT CORPORATION
1922 W End Ave, Nashville, TN 37203
Tel.: (615) 321-6024
Web Site: http://www.amerigo.net
Sales Range: $10-24.9 Million
Emp.: 80
Restaurant
N.A.I.C.S.: 722511
Brandie Gartman *(Gen Mgr)*

AMERIGROW RECYCLING - DELRAY, LIMITED PARTNERSHIP
10320 W Atlantic Ave, Delray Beach, FL 33446
Tel.: (561) 499-8148
Web Site:
https://www.amerigrow.com
Year Founded: 1995
Rev.: $10,949,728
Emp.: 80
Mulch & Soil Products Whslr
N.A.I.C.S.: 424910
Janet Tomlinson *(Pres)*

AMERIHEALTH NEW JERSEY
259 Prospect Plains Rd Bldg M, Cranbury, NJ 08512-3706
Tel.: (609) 662-2400
Web Site:
https://www.amerihealthnj.com
Year Founded: 1994
Sales Range: $600-649.9 Million
Emp.: 162

AmeriHealth New Jersey—(Continued)

Innovative & Affordable Health Plans for Residents of the State of New Jersey
N.A.I.C.S.: 524114
Michael Munoz (Pres-Market)
Michael Zollenberg (VP-Provider Network Ops)
Ken Kobylowski (Sr VP-Provider Contracting & Network Ops)
Jill Roman (Mgr-PR)
Ryan J. Petrizzi (VP-Sls)

AMERIKAS, INC.
1412 Broadway Ste 2136, New York, NY 10018
Tel.: (212) 957-1200
Web Site: http://www.amerikas.com
Year Founded: 2013
Sales Range: $1-9.9 Million
Emp.: 6
Cosmetic Product Distr
N.A.I.C.S.: 456120
Jose Penalba (CEO)
Fabrizio Bird (Partner)
Ruby Lock (Partner)

AMERIKOHL MINING INC.
202 Sunset Dr, Butler, PA 16001-1368
Tel.: (724) 282-2339   PA
Web Site: http://www.amerikohl.com
Year Founded: 1978
Sales Range: $25-49.9 Million
Emp.: 150
Bituminous Coal & Lignite-Surface
N.A.I.C.S.: 212114
Jamie Stilley (VP-Amerikohl Aggregates-Stahlstown)
John Saugrich (VP-Operations-Geologist)
David Maxwell (VP-Ops-Stahlstown)
Jake Stilley (VP-Patriot Exploration-Stahlstown)
Todd Fiedor (VP-Fin & Controller)
Mike Jurcevich (Mgr-Aggregates)

AMERILUX INTERNATIONAL, LLC.
1212 Enterprise Dr, De Pere, WI 54115-3193
Tel.: (920) 336-9300
Web Site:
    https://www.ameriluxnational.com
Sales Range: $10-24.9 Million
Emp.: 50
Plastic Material & Basic Form & Shape Object Whslr
N.A.I.C.S.: 424610
Kurt Voss (CEO)
Betty Reed (Mgr-Customer Rels)
Patrick Gauthier (VP & Gen Mgr)
Joe Nick (VP-Ops)
Julia VerHaagh (CFO)

AMERINAC HOLDING CORP.
5936 SR 15, Chillicothe, OH 45601
Tel.: (614) 836-1050   DE
Web Site: https://www.amerinac.com
Year Founded: 2005
PAOS—(OTCBB)
Rev.: $44,388,579
Assets: $20,575,550
Liabilities: $12,131,043
Net Worth: $8,444,507
Earnings: $1,685,382
Emp.: 80
Fiscal Year-end: 12/31/19
Holding Company; Specialty Fastener Mfr & Distr
N.A.I.C.S.: 551112
John F. Wachter (Mng Partner)
William J. Golden (Mng Partner)
John F. Wachter (Chm & CEO)
William J. Golden (CFO, Gen Counsel & Sec)

Brian Corcoran (Controller-Operations & Dir)
Kristin Newberry (Dir-North American Ops)
Ben Crunkhorn (Dir-European Ops)
Michael Lynn (Dir-Primary Metals)

Subsidiaries:

Prime Metals & Alloys, Inc.   (1)
101 Innovation Dr, Homer City, PA 15748
Tel.: (724) 479-4155
Web Site: http://www.primemetals.net
Metal Product Mfr & Whlsr
N.A.I.C.S.: 332999
Brian K. Knupp (VP-Mfg, Safety & Environmental)
Michael Lynn (VP-Sls, Quality & Purchasing)

AMERINDIA TECHNOLOGIES, INC.
666 Plainsboro Rd Ste 545, Plainsboro, NJ 08536
Tel.: (609) 632-1285
Web Site: http://www.AmerIndia.net
Year Founded: 2004
Sales Range: $1-9.9 Million
Emp.: 27
Information Technology Services
N.A.I.C.S.: 423430
Arun Mehta (Co-Founder & CEO)
Rajesh Mittal (Co-Founder & VP-Tech)

AMERIPIPE SUPPLY, INC.
11430 Denton Dr, Dallas, TX 75229
Tel.: (972) 241-1666
Web Site: https://www.ameripipe.com
Year Founded: 1979
Sales Range: $25-49.9 Million
Emp.: 100
Supplier of Pipes, Valves, Fittings & Fabrication Services
N.A.I.C.S.: 423510
Randy Ensch (COO)
Brent Kirk (Mgr-Credit)
Ken Comrie (Dir-IT)
Becky Clark (Mgr-Pur)
Blair Franklin (Pres & CEO)
Chris James (Treas & VP)
Jack McKendrick (Dir-Mechanical, Indus & Oilfield Sls)
Jeff Obitz (Mgr-Fabrication)
Mike Sisti (Mgr-Warehouse)

Subsidiaries:

Premier Fab, Inc.   (1)
10224 Sibley Hole Rd, Mabelvale, AR 72103
Tel.: (501) 455-5991
Web Site: http://www.premierfab.biz
Sales Range: $1-9.9 Million
Emp.: 25
Fabricated Metal Products Mfr & Distr
N.A.I.C.S.: 332999
Danny Heathcock (Pres)
Tim Hatley (Branch Mgr)

AMERIPLAN CORPORATION
5700 Democracy Dr, Plano, TX 75024
Tel.: (469) 229-4503
Web Site:
    http://www.ameriplanusa.com
Year Founded: 1992
Sales Range: $10-24.9 Million
Emp.: 250
Direct Health & Medical Insurance Carrier Services
N.A.I.C.S.: 524114
Clifford Ritch (Reg Dir-Sls)
Randelle Arena Ash (Reg Dir-Sls)
Dennis Bloom (Owner)
Daniel Bloom (Owner)

AMERIPRO HEALTH LLC
9 Dunwoody Park S, Ste 126, Atlanta, GA 30338

Tel.: (855) 277-6367
Web Site:
    https://www.ameriprohealth.com
Year Founded: 2018
Emp.: 109
Emergency & Non-Emergency Transportation
N.A.I.C.S.: 621910
Suhas Uppalapati (CEO)

AMERIQUEST BUSINESS SERVICES
457 Haddonfield Rd Ste 220, Cherry Hill, NJ 08002
Tel.: (856) 773-0600
Web Site:
    http://www.ameriquestcorp.com
Year Founded: 1996
Sales Range: $600-649.9 Million
Emp.: 160
Transportation & Logistics Services
N.A.I.C.S.: 488510
James Guice (Exec VP)
William J. McCouch (Sr VP-Procurement Svcs)
David Nitzsche (Sr VP-Supply Mgmt)
Kate Freer (VP-Mktg)
Mike Rowbotham (VP-Strategy & Innovation)
Glenn R. Boyet (Dir-Strategic Comm)
Patrick Gaskins (Sr VP-Fin Svcs)
Robert Upton (VP-Fin Svcs-AmeriQuest Transportation Svcs)
Sean Bliss (VP-Sls-Indirect Spend Solutions)
Patrick Barrett (VP-Fin Svcs)
Patrick Moynahan (Dir-Mktg)
Douglas W. Clark (Chm, Pres & CEO)
Mark P. Joyce (CFO & Exec VP)

Subsidiaries:

National Truck Leasing System   (1)
2651 Warrenville Rd Ste 560, Downers Grove, IL 60515
Tel.: (630) 925-7693
Web Site: http://www.nationalease.com
Sales Range: $200-249.9 Million
Emp.: 30
Full Service Truck, Tractor & Trailer Leasing Services
N.A.I.C.S.: 532120
Dean Vicha (Pres)
Jane Clark (VP-Member Svcs)
Dave Renz (Chm)

AMERIQUEST CAPITAL CORPORATION
1100 W Town and Country Rd, Orange, CA 92868-4600
Tel.: (714) 564-0600
Year Founded: 1994
Sales Range: $1-4.9 Billion
Emp.: 4,000
Investment Capital
N.A.I.C.S.: 522310

Subsidiaries:

Town & Country Credit Corp.   (1)
2010 Main St Ste 800, Irvine, CA 92614
Tel.: (949) 474-9577
Sales Range: $50-74.9 Million
Emp.: 80
Credit Lending Services
N.A.I.C.S.: 522310

AMERISCAPE USA, INC.
9702 Harney Rd, Thonotosassa, FL 33592
Tel.: (813) 948-3938   FL
Web Site:
    http://www.ameriscapeusa.com
Year Founded: 2002
Sales Range: $1-9.9 Million
Emp.: 60
Landscape Architectural Services
N.A.I.C.S.: 541320
Joe Chiellini (Pres & CEO)

AMERISTAR JET CHARTER INC.
4400 Glenn Curtiss Dr Ste 202, Addison, TX 75001
Tel.: (972) 248-2478
Web Site:
    http://www.ameristarjet.com
Sales Range: $10-24.9 Million
Emp.: 163
Flying Charter Service
N.A.I.C.S.: 481219
Tom Wachendorfer (Founder & Pres)
Stacy Muth (VP-Ops)
Bryan Blue (Mgr-IT)

AMERISURE MUTUAL INSURANCE COMPANY
26777 Halsted Rd, Farmington Hills, MI 48331-3586
Tel.: (248) 615-9000   MI
Web Site: http://www.amerisure.com
Year Founded: 1912
Sales Range: $550-599.9 Million
Emp.: 630
Casualty & Property Insurance Services
N.A.I.C.S.: 524126
Kevin Clary (VP-Risk Mgmt)
Angela McBride (COO)
Gregory J. Crabb (Pres & CEO)
Matthew Ford (Sr VP-Field Underwriting & Partnerships)
Shawn O'Rourke (CTO)
Todd B. Ruthruff (Chief Relationship Officer)
Erin Buddie (Chief HR Officer)
Jayashree Ishwar (Chief Underwriting Officer)
Jessica Soufrine (VP-Field Mktg & Underwriting)
Chelcee McGowan (VP & Controller)
Chris Spaude (CFO & Treas)
Frank A. Hammers (Reg VP-North Region)
Shannon Anderson Alt (Gen Counsel, Sec & VP)
Rod Labbe (VP-Risk Mgmt-North & West)
George Pavarini (VP-Liability Technical Claims)
Steve Donnelly (Chief Svc Officer)
Kimberly Vaughn (VP-Claims)
Phillip E. Love Jr. (Chm)

Subsidiaries:

Amerisure Insurance Company Inc   (1)
26777 Halsted Rd, Farmington Hills, MI 48331-3560
Tel.: (248) 615-9000
Web Site: http://www.amerisure.com
Sales Range: $50-74.9 Million
Emp.: 260
Provider of Fire Marine & Casualty Insurance Services
N.A.I.C.S.: 524126
Matt Simon (CFO & Treas)
Daniel J. Graf (Chief Investment Officer)
Todd B. Ruthruff (Chief Relationship Officer)
Chris Spaude (VP-Fin)
Stephanie Haas (Gen Counsel, Sec & VP)
Greg Crabb (Pres & CEO)
Anastasia Gale (VP & Asst Gen Counsel)

AMERITAS MUTUAL HOLDING COMPANY
5900 O St, Lincoln, NE 68501
Tel.: (402) 467-1122   NE
Web Site: http://www.ameritas.com
Sales Range: $1-4.9 Billion
Emp.: 2,400
Mutual Holding Company; Insurance, Investment & Banking Products & Services

N.A.I.C.S.: 551112
JoAnn M. Martin *(Vice Chm)*
William W. Lester *(Pres & COO)*
Robert-John H. Sands *(Gen Counsel, Sec & Sr VP)*
Tim L. Stonehocker *(Exec VP-Individual, AIC & Retirement Plans)*
Susan K. Wilkinson *(CFO & Sr VP)*
Steven J. Valerius *(Pres-Individual Div)*
Jim Barone *(Sr VP-MGA Distr & Bus Dev-Grp Div)*
Karen M. Gustin *(Exec VP-Grp Div)*
Kelly J. Wieseler *(Sr VP-Actuarial & Underwriting-Grp Div)*
Cheryl L. Heilman *(Pres-Ameritas Investment Corp)*
Robert M. Jurgensmeier *(Chief Actuary & Sr VP-Individual Div)*
Lisa A. Mullen *(Sr VP-Individual Fin Ops)*
Bruce E. Mieth *(Sr VP-Grp Ops)*
Linda A. Whitmire *(Chief Actuary & Sr VP)*
Richard A. Wiedenbeck *(CIO & Sr VP-IT)*
Randee Manley *(Chief HR Officer & Sr VP)*
Brent Korte *(CMO & Sr VP)*
Drew Fleming *(Sr VP-Natl Accts & Key Partnering Relationships-Grp Div)*
April Rimpley *(Sr VP-HR)*

Subsidiaries:

Ameritas Investment Partners, Inc. (1)
390 N Cotner Blvd, Lincoln, NE 68505
Tel.: (877) 731-3336
Web Site:
http://www.summitinvestmentpartners.com
Investment Advisory Services
N.A.I.C.S.: 523940

Ameritas Life Insurance Corp. (1)
5900 O St, Lincoln, NE 68510 (100%)
Tel.: (402) 467-1122
Web Site: http://www.ameritas.com
Sales Range: $550-599.9 Million
Emp.: 2,000
Life Insurance, Retirement Plans & Annuities, Savings & Investment Products & Services
N.A.I.C.S.: 524113
JoAnn M. Martin *(Vice Chm)*
William W. Lester *(Pres & CEO)*
Kelly J. Wieseler *(Sr VP & Chief Actuary-Individual Div)*
Steven J. Valerius *(Pres-Individual Div)*

Subsidiary (Domestic):

Acacia Life Insurance Company (2)
7315 Wisconsin Ave 10th Fl, Bethesda, MD 20814-3202 (100%)
Tel.: (301) 280-1000
Web Site: http://www.unificompanies.com
Sales Range: $50-74.9 Million
Emp.: 65
Life Insurance & Annuities Products & Services
N.A.I.C.S.: 524113
Barbara Janet Krumsiek *(Chm)*

Subsidiary (Domestic):

Calvert Investments, Inc. (3)
4550 Montgomery Ave Ste 1125, Bethesda, MD 20814-3304 (100%)
Tel.: (301) 951-4800
Web Site: http://www.calvert.com
Holding Company; Mutual Fund, Pension & Other Investment Fund Products & Management Services
N.A.I.C.S.: 551112
Kathy Torrence *(VP-Corp Sustainability & Community Partnerships)*
Hope Brown *(Chief Compliance Officer & VP-Calvert Funds)*
Vicki Benjamin *(CFO, COO & Exec VP)*
Jason Rosenberg *(Chief Compliance Officer-Investment Advisor & Broker-Dealer)*
Stu Dalheim *(VP-Shareholder Advocacy)*
John H. Streur *(CEO)*

Subsidiary (Domestic):

Calvert Administrative Services Company (4)
4550 Montgomery Ave Ste 1000N, Bethesda, MD 20814-3304 (100%)
Tel.: (301) 951-4800
Web Site: http://www.calvert.com
Emp.: 180
Fund Administration Services
N.A.I.C.S.: 524292
Barbara Janet Krumsiek *(Chm, Pres & CEO)*

Calvert Asset Management Company, Inc. (4)
4550 Montgomery Ave Ste 1000N, Bethesda, MD 20814-3304
Tel.: (301) 951-4800
Web Site: http://www.calvert.com
Fixed-Income Investment & Equity Fund Management Services
N.A.I.C.S.: 523940
Barbara Janet Krumsiek *(Chm, Pres & CEO)*

Calvert Distributors, Inc. (4)
4550 Montgomery Ave Ste 1000N, Bethesda, MD 20814-3304
Tel.: (301) 951-4800
Web Site: http://www.calvert.com
Sales Range: $150-199.9 Million
Emp.: 100
Mutual Fund Underwriting & Distribution Services
N.A.I.C.S.: 525910
Alison Smith *(VP-Client Svcs)*
Stan Young *(VP-Client Svcs)*
David W. Leach *(VP-Bank Trust Dept & Corp Cash Mgmt)*

Calvert Shareholder Services, Inc. (4)
4550 Montgomery Ave Ste 1000N, Bethesda, MD 20814-3304
Tel.: (301) 951-4800
Web Site: http://www.calvert.com
Sales Range: $50-74.9 Million
Emp.: 100
Shareholder Support Services
N.A.I.C.S.: 561421
Barbara Janet Krumsiek *(Chm, Pres & CEO)*
Chris Dyson *(Office Mgr)*

Subsidiary (Domestic):

Ameritas Investment Corp. (2)
5900 O St, Lincoln, NE 68510
Tel.: (402) 325-4000
Web Site: http://www.ameritas.com
Sales Range: $1-4.9 Billion
Emp.: 1,500
Securities Brokerage, Dealing & Investment Advisory Services
N.A.I.C.S.: 523150
Salene Hitchcock-Gear *(CEO)*
Cheryl Heilman *(Pres)*
Ryan C. Beasley *(Sr VP-Individual Div)*
Jim Kais *(Sr VP-Retirement Plans)*

First Ameritas Life Insurance Corp. of New York (2)
400 Rella Blvd Ste 304, Suffern, NY 10901 (100%)
Tel.: (845) 357-3816
Web Site: http://www.first.ameritas.com
Life Insurance, Retirement Plan, Dental & Other Specialty Health Insurance Products & Services
N.A.I.C.S.: 524113

AMERITEC CORPORATION
760 Arrow Grand Cir, Covina, CA 91722
Tel.: (626) 915-5441
Web Site: http://www.ameritec.com
Year Founded: 1980
Sales Range: $100-124.9 Million
Emp.: 130
Telephone & Telegraph Apparatus
N.A.I.C.S.: 334210
Thomas Hollfelder *(Owner)*
Brett Isley *(VP-Sls)*

AMERITEL CORPORATION
15010 Broschart Rd, Rockville, MD 20850
Tel.: (301) 251-0222
Web Site:
https://www.ameritelcorporation.com
Year Founded: 1984
Rev.: $14,700,000
Emp.: 87
Miscellaneous Store Retailers
N.A.I.C.S.: 459999
Anita C. Stonebraker *(VP-Admin)*
David Kaufman *(CEO)*

AMERITEL INNS INCORPORATED
10200 W Emerald St, Boise, ID 83704
Tel.: (208) 375-2323
Web Site:
http://www.ameritelinns.com
Sales Range: $10-24.9 Million
Emp.: 17
Hotel & Motels
N.A.I.C.S.: 721110
Glen Black *(Pres)*
Costin Pirvu *(Controller)*

AMERITEMPS INC.
6100 Rockside Wood Blvd Ste 350, Independence, OH 44131
Tel.: (216) 447-9700
Web Site:
http://www.ameritemps.com
Year Founded: 1970
Sales Range: $10-24.9 Million
Emp.: 145
Temporary Help Service
N.A.I.C.S.: 561320
Jerry Nalipa *(Pres)*

AMERITRUST MORTGAGE CORPORATION
15009 Lancaster Hwy, Charlotte, NC 28277
Tel.: (704) 909-5555 NC
Web Site: http://www.ameritrust.com
Year Founded: 1970
Sales Range: $10-24.9 Million
Emp.: 125
Mortgage Services
N.A.I.C.S.: 522310
John J. Owens *(CEO)*

AMERLING COMPANY
170-178 Boston Post, West Haven, CT 06516
Tel.: (203) 934-7901
Sales Range: $10-24.9 Million
Emp.: 12
Automotive Supplies & Parts
N.A.I.C.S.: 423120
Robert L. Jacobs *(Pres)*

AMEROP PRODUCTS
1800 Broadway Ste 100, Boulder, CO 80302
Tel.: (303) 938-9836
Year Founded: 1975
Sales Range: $1-9.9 Million
Emp.: 1
Farm & Garden Machinery Mfr
N.A.I.C.S.: 423820
Leonard Wessell *(Pres)*

Subsidiaries:

Ingersoll Products Company (1)
11323 Steeplechase Pkwy, Orland Park, IL 60467-5898
Tel.: (773) 264-7800
Web Site: http://www.ingersoll-products.com
Mfr of Plow Discs & Blades for Farming Machinery
N.A.I.C.S.: 333111

AMERTAC HOLDINGS INC.
250 Boulder Dr, Breinigsville, PA 18031
Tel.: (610) 336-1330
Web Site: https://www.amertac.com
Year Founded: 1996
Sales Range: $10-24.9 Million
Emp.: 53
Holding Company for Electrical Equipment & Supplies
N.A.I.C.S.: 334419
Chris Kokkinakis *(Controller)*

Subsidiaries:

American Tack & Hardware Co. Inc. (1)
Saddle River Executive Ctr 1 Rte 17 S, Upper Saddle River, NJ 07458-2386
Tel.: (201) 934-3224
Web Site: http://www.amertac.com
Electrical Equipment & Supplies
N.A.I.C.S.: 334419

Westek Lighting (1)
Saddle River Executive One Route 17 South, Saddle River, NJ 07458
Tel.: (201) 934-3224
Sales Range: $10-24.9 Million
Emp.: 40
Residential Lighting Fixtures
N.A.I.C.S.: 334419

AMERY REGIONAL MEDICAL CENTER
265 Griffin St E, Amery, WI 54001
Tel.: (715) 268-8000
Web Site:
http://www.amerymedicalcenter.org
Year Founded: 1956
Health Care Srvices
N.A.I.C.S.: 622110
Debra Rudquist *(Pres & CEO)*
Patrick Sura *(Chief Medical Officer)*
Sandi Reed *(VP-Ambulatory Svcs)*
Joyce Schaefer *(VP-Patient Care Svcs)*
Joanne Jackson *(Exec Dir-HR, Community Rels & Foundation)*

AMES CONSTRUCTION, INC.
2000 Ames Dr, Burnsville, MN 55306
Tel.: (952) 435-7106
Web Site: http://www.amesco.com
Year Founded: 1960
Sales Range: $400-449.9 Million
Emp.: 1,200
Provider of Heavy Civil & Industrial Design-Build General Contracting Services
N.A.I.C.S.: 237310
John A. Ames *(Sr VP & Reg Mgr)*
Ronald L. Ames *(Sr VP & Mgr-Midwest)*
Todd M. Goderstad *(VP)*
Roger L. McBride *(Sr VP-Safety, Risk Mgmt & HR)*

AMES GOLDSMITH CORP.
50 Harrison Ave, South Glens Falls, NY 12803
Tel.: (518) 792-5808
Web Site:
http://www.amesgoldsmith.com
Year Founded: 1978
Sales Range: $750-799.9 Million
Emp.: 50
Primary Metal Products
N.A.I.C.S.: 331492
Frank Barber *(Pres & CEO)*
Steve Macy *(VP)*
Michael Herman *(VP-Global Market Dev)*

Subsidiaries:

Ames Goldsmith UK Ltd (1)
Acornfield Road Knowsley Industrial Estate, Kirkby, L33 7UF, Merseyside, United Kingdom
Tel.: (44) 151 548 5427
Web Site: http://www.amesgoldsmith.co.uk
Silver Nitrate & Oxide Distr
N.A.I.C.S.: 423520

Ames Goldsmith Corp.—(Continued)

Catalyst Refiners (1)
21 Rogers St, Glens Falls, NY 12801-3821
Tel.: (518) 792-7435
Sales Range: $10-24.9 Million
Emp.: 8
Industrial Inorganic Chemicals
N.A.I.C.S.: 325180
Ronald F. Davies (Chm)
Frank Barber (Pres)

AMES SCULLIN O'HAIRE
245 Peachtree Ctr Ave 23rd Fl, Atlanta, GA 30303
Tel.: (404) 659-2769   GA
Web Site: http://www.asoy.com
Year Founded: 1997
Emp.: 34
Advetising Agency
N.A.I.C.S.: 541810
John F. Ames (Mng Partner)
Tony O'Haire (Mng Partner)
Patrick Scullin (Mng Partner-Creative)
Mike Bourne (Dir-Creative)
Steve Harding (Partner-Engagement)
Katie Kiefer (Assoc Dir-Engagement)
Ryan Mikesell (Partner-Creative)
Jim Crone (Partner-Strategy)
Maureen Dabrowa (Acct Dir)
Michelle Chong (Assoc Dir-Engagement)
Sandra Love (Dir-Art)

Subsidiaries:

The Hauser Group (1)
245 Peachtree Center Ave Ne Ste 2300, Atlanta, GA 30303-1224
Tel.: (404) 222-0600
Web Site: http://www.hausergroup.com
Emp.: 20
Advetising Agency
N.A.I.C.S.: 541810

AMES TEXTILE CORPORATION
710 Chelmsford St, Lowell, MA 01851
Tel.: (978) 458-3321
Web Site:
http://www.amestextile.com
Year Founded: 1865
Sales Range: $25-49.9 Million
Emp.: 35
Mfr Of Knit Goods & Textiles
N.A.I.C.S.: 313240
Josh Miner (Sr VP)
Richard Gilman (Mgr-Cost & Credit)

AMES WALKER INTERNATIONAL INC.
300 Industrial Park Ave, Asheboro, NC 27205
Tel.: (336) 355-7577
Web Site:
https://www.ameswalker.com
Sales Range: $10-24.9 Million
Emp.: 25
Medical Supplies Merchant Whslr
N.A.I.C.S.: 423450
Ryan Zell (Owner)
Kaki Zell (Owner)

Subsidiaries:

Venosan North America, Inc. (1)
300 Industrial Park Ave, Asheboro, NC 27205
Tel.: (336) 629-7181
Web Site: http://www.venosanusa.com
Medical Supplies Distr
N.A.I.C.S.: 423450

AMES WATSON HOLDING LLC
6100 Merriweather Dr Ste 210, Columbia, MD 21044
Tel.: (202) 210-2234
Web Site:
http://www.ameswatson.com
Year Founded: 2018

Privater Equity Firm
N.A.I.C.S.: 523940
Lawrence Berger (Co-Founder & Partner)

Subsidiaries:

South Moon Sales, Inc. (1)
183 Harry S Truman Pkwy, Annapolis, MD 21401
Tel.: (410) 641-1644
Web Site: http://www.southmoonunder.com
Women's & Men's Apparel & Accessories Designer, Whslr & Online Retailer
N.A.I.C.S.: 424350
Michael Smith (CEO)
Patricia Smith (Chief Creative Officer)

AMF ELECTRICAL CONTRACTORS, INC.
1627 Sublette Ave, Saint Louis, MO 63110-1924
Tel.: (314) 647-4066
Web Site:
https://www.amfelectric.com
Sales Range: $10-24.9 Million
Emp.: 120
Electrical Wiring Services
N.A.I.C.S.: 238210
Scott Hearst (Project Mgr)
Ryan Bell (Project Mgr)
Nick Vitale (Project Mgr)
Chris Hunter (Project Mgr)

AMF SUPPORT SURFACES INC.
1691 N Delilah St, Corona, CA 92879
Tel.: (909) 549-6800
Web Site: http://www.amfsupport.com
Rev.: $10,900,000
Emp.: 130
Therapeutic Pads
N.A.I.C.S.: 337910

AMFAR
120 Wall St 13th Fl, New York, NY 10005-3908
Tel.: (212) 806-1600   NY
Web Site: https://www.amfar.org
Year Founded: 1983
Sales Range: $25-49.9 Million
Emp.: 91
AIDS Research Services
N.A.I.C.S.: 813212
Annmarie Shannahan (VP-Pub Info)
Kevin Robert Frost (CEO)
Anthony Ancona (VP & Dir-HR)
Bradley Jensen (CFO)
Rowena Johnston (VP & Dir-Res)
Bill Roedy (Vice Chm)
John C. Simons (Treas)
Greg Millett (VP)
Phill Wilson (Pres & CEO)

AMFED COMPANIES, LLC
576 Highland Colony Pkwy Ste 300, Ridgeland, MS 39157
Tel.: (601) 853-4949
Web Site: http://www.amfed.com
Rev.: $13,083,808
Emp.: 100
Insurance Information & Consulting Services
N.A.I.C.S.: 524298
Michael G. Richardson (VP)
Greg T. McLemore (CFO & VP-Acctg & Fin)
Sarah Watters (CFO & Dir-Insurance Acctg Ops)

AMG & ASSOCIATES, INC.
28296 Constellation Rd, Valencia, CA 91355
Tel.: (661) 251-7401
Web Site:
http://www.amgassociatesinc.com
Year Founded: 2005
Sales Range: $10-24.9 Million

Emp.: 16
Building Contractors
N.A.I.C.S.: 236220
Albert Giacomazzi (Pres & CEO)
Anthony Traverso (VP-Pur)
Gregory Barrow (Sec)
Scott Sampson (Dir-Bus Dev)

AMG NATIONAL TRUST BANK
1155 Canyon Blvd Ste 310, Boulder, CO 80302
Tel.: (303) 473-4860
Web Site:
https://www.amgnational.com
Year Founded: 1972
Sales Range: $10-24.9 Million
Emp.: 130
Trust, Fiduciary & Custody Activity Services
N.A.I.C.S.: 523991
Thomas B. Chesney (Pres-Comml Banking Div)
Earl L. Wright (Co-Founder & Chm)
Michael D. Bergmann (Co-Founder & Sr Exec VP)
Sheryl L. Bollinger (Pres & CEO)

AMG RESOURCES CORP.
2 Robinson Plz Ste 350, Pittsburgh, PA 15205-1045
Tel.: (412) 331-0770
Web Site:
http://www.amgresources.com
Sales Range: $1-9.9 Million
Emp.: 75
Tin-Free Steel
N.A.I.C.S.: 331110
Allan Goldstein (CEO)
Ron Zorn (COO-Pittsburgh)
Lee Dezzutti (VP-Bus Dev)
Brian Cohen (CFO)
Garey Rittenhouse (VP-Non-Ferrous Metals)
Kevin O'Bryan (Controller)
Norman LeVesque (Mgr-Bus Dev)
Ronnie Silber (Mgr-Mktg-Baltimore)
Scott Duffey (VP)

Subsidiaries:

AMG Alliance LLC (1)
1220 Brick Ave, Red Wing, MN 55066
Tel.: (651) 388-1790
Ferrous & Non Ferrous Scrap Metal Processing Services
N.A.I.C.S.: 331492

AMG Resources Corp. - Baltimore Facility (1)
2415 Grays Rd, Baltimore, MD 21222
Tel.: (410) 477-0300
Steel Mfrs
N.A.I.C.S.: 331110

AMG Resources Corp. - Gary Facility (1)
459 N Cline Ave, Gary, IN 46406
Tel.: (219) 949-8150
Web Site: http://www.amgresources.com
Emp.: 15
Steel Mfrs
N.A.I.C.S.: 331110

AMG Resources Corp. - Llanelli Facility (1)
Nevills Dock, Dyfed, Llanelli, SA15 2HD, United Kingdom
Tel.: (44) 1554 750791
Scrap Metal Mfr
N.A.I.C.S.: 333998

AMG Resources Corp. - Milwaukee Facility (1)
11000 W Brown Deer Pl, Milwaukee, WI 53224
Tel.: (414) 357-8770
Steel Mfrs
N.A.I.C.S.: 331110

AMG Resources Corp. - Newark Facility (1)
317 Frelinghuysen Ave, Newark, NJ 07114
Tel.: (973) 242-4177

Steel Mfrs
N.A.I.C.S.: 331110

AMG Resources Corp. - St. Joseph Facility (1)
2435 S 6th St, Saint Joseph, MO 64504
Tel.: (816) 364-1335
Steel Mfrs
N.A.I.C.S.: 331110

AMG Resources Corp. - St. Paul Facility (1)
1303 Red Rock Rd, Saint Paul, MN 55119
Tel.: (651) 739-6080
Web Site: http://www.amgresources.com
Steel Mfrs
N.A.I.C.S.: 331110

AMG Resources Pacific Corp (1)
15332 McKinley Ave, Lathrop, CA 95330
Tel.: (209) 858-2458
Web Site: http://www.amgresources.com
Rev.: $890,000
Emp.: 7
Ferrous Metal Scrap & Waste
N.A.I.C.S.: 423930
Jim Orendorff (Pres & Dir-Mktg)
Brian Cohen (CFO)
Ronald Zorn (COO)
Sean Kerrigan (Deputy Mng Dir & Dir-Comml)
Bob Chevalier (Pres & COO)
Don Forlani (Chief Comml Officer & Sr VP)
Allan Goldstein (CEO)
Eric Goldstein (Pres)
Kevin O'Bryan (Controller)

Allegheny Raw Materials, LLC (1)
206 Bilmar Dr, Pittsburgh, PA 15205
Tel.: (412) 424-4415
Web Site:
http://www.alleghenyrawmaterials.com
Scrap Recycling Services
N.A.I.C.S.: 423930
Damian Eonta (Pres)
John Greco (Sr VP)
Nick Katsafanas (VP-Ops)

Midwest Steel & Alloy, Inc. (1)
200 Division St, Youngstown, OH 44510
Tel.: (330) 792-0600
Ferrous & Non Ferrous Scrap Metal Processing Services
N.A.I.C.S.: 331492

AMGLO KEMLITE LABORATORIES INC.
215 Gateway Rd, Bensenville, IL 60106
Tel.: (630) 350-9470
Web Site: https://www.amglo.com
Sales Range: $10-24.9 Million
Emp.: 120
Tubes, Electric Light
N.A.I.C.S.: 335139
James H. Hyland (Chm)
Larry Kerchenfaut (Pres)

AMGRAPH PACKAGING INC.
90 Paper Mill Rd, Baltic, CT 06330
Tel.: (860) 822-2000
Web Site: https://www.amgraph.com
Rev.: $22,600,000
Emp.: 130
Flexible Packaging Mfr
N.A.I.C.S.: 322220
Ken Fontaine (Pres & CEO)
John M. Timken Jr. (Co-Founder)
Kathy Bouchey (Exec Dir-HR)
Michael Nickerson (Mgr-Extrusion)
Greg Minnette (Mgr-Customer Svcs & Pur)
Jeff Mee (Mgr-IS)
Sherry Kosma (Coord-Customer Svc)
Sean Evans (Dir-R&D)
Michael Drab (Mgr-Sls-Natl)
Robert Brooks (CFO)

AMHEARST GLEN, INC.
3481 Golden Creek Cir, Riverton, UT 84065
Tel.: (801) 742-1543   NV
Year Founded: 2009

Investment Services
N.A.I.C.S.: 523150
Lori Barland (Pres, Sec & Treas)

AMHERST SECURITIES GROUP LP
Ste 850 1300 Post Oak Blvd, Houston, TX 77056-3218
Tel.: (713) 888-9100
Web Site:
http://www.amherstsecurities.com
Rev.: $52,000,000
Emp.: 120
Security Brokers & Dealers
N.A.I.C.S.: 523150
Sean Dobson (Chm & CEO)
Darla Bartkowiak (Sr VP & Chief Compliance Officer)
Alan Gilbert (Vice Chm)
Steven Gorman (Sr VP-IT)
Steve Coale (Mng Dir)
Michael Sullivan (CFO & Sr VP)
Terence Browne (COO & Sr VP)
Doug Fashenpour (VP-IT)
Chris McDowell (Mng Dir-Fixed Income Trading & Sls)

AMI BEARINGS, INC.
570 N Wheeling Rd, Mount Prospect, IL 60056
Tel.: (847) 759-0620
Web Site:
https://www.amibearings.com
Sales Range: $10-24.9 Million
Emp.: 40
Industrial Supplies Merchant Whslr
N.A.I.C.S.: 423840
Wally Budzielek (VP-Sls)
Steve Zimmerman (Pres)
Paul Olund (Mgr-Acctg)

AMI INDUSTRIES, INC.
5093 N Red Oak Rd, Lewiston, MI 49756
Tel.: (989) 786-3755   MI
Web Site: http://www.ami-lewiston.com
Year Founded: 2000
Sales Range: $50-74.9 Million
Emp.: 225
Automotive Tube Fabrication Industry Manufacturing Equipment Mfr
N.A.I.C.S.: 333248
Jeffery Evans (Pres)

AMI MANCHESTER, LLC
17951 W Austin Rd, Manchester, MI 48158
Tel.: (734) 428-8301
Web Site:
http://www.amistamping.com
Year Founded: 1963
Automotive Stamping Mfr
N.A.I.C.S.: 336370
Vincent J. Henderson (Chm)
John Kampf (Sr VP-Ops)
Warren Hughes (Controller)
Michelle Chang (Mgr-HR)

AMICA MUTUAL INSURANCE CO.
100 Amica Way, Lincoln, RI 02865
Tel.: (401) 334-4241   RI
Web Site: http://www.amica.com
Year Founded: 1973
Rev.: $2,412,202,000
Assets: $5,360,644,000
Liabilities: $2,577,781,000
Net Worth: $2,782,863,000
Earnings: $158,119,000
Emp.: 3,800
Fiscal Year-end: 12/31/19
Personal Lines Property & Casualty Insurance
N.A.I.C.S.: 524126
Edmund Shallcross III (Pres & CEO)

Subsidiaries:
Amica Lloyd's of Texas   (1)
14090 SW Fwy Ste 500, Sugar Land, TX 77478-3677
Sales Range: $50-74.9 Million
Provider of Property & Casualty Insurance
N.A.I.C.S.: 524126

AMICALOLA ELECTRIC MEMBERSHIP CORPORATION
544 Hwy 515 S, Jasper, GA 30143-4884
Tel.: (706) 253-5200
Web Site:
https://www.amicalolaemc.com
Rev.: $11,069,572
Emp.: 110
Distribution, Electric Power
N.A.I.C.S.: 221122

AMICK CONSTRUCTION, INC.
PO Box 568492, Orlando, FL 32856-8492
Tel.: (407) 293-6562   FL
Web Site: http://www.amickinc.com
Emp.: 125
Highway & Heavy Construction Services
N.A.I.C.S.: 237310
Jeffrey B. Fuqua (Pres)
Conan Martin (VP)
Cheryl Gotsis (Controller)

AMICK PROCESSING INC.
2079 Batesburg Hwy, Batesburg, SC 29006
Tel.: (803) 532-1400   SC
Web Site:
https://www.amickfarms.com
Year Founded: 1948
Sales Range: $75-99.9 Million
Emp.: 1,650
Provider of Poultry Processing Services
N.A.I.C.S.: 112340

AMICUS SEARCH GROUP LLC
4245 N Central Expressway Ste 200, Dallas, TX 75205
Tel.: (512) 322-3217
Web Site:
http://www.amicussearch.com
Year Founded: 2005
Rev.: $3,500,000
Emp.: 9
Employment Placement Agencies
N.A.I.C.S.: 561311
Lee Allbritton (Principal)
Alysa Schildcrout (Principal)
Mike Danforth (Mng Dir-Amicus Consultants)

AMIDA CARE INC.
14 Penn Plz 2nd Fl, New York, NY 10122
Tel.: (646) 757-7000   NY
Web Site:
https://www.amidacareny.org
Year Founded: 2000
Sales Range: $250-299.9 Million
Emp.: 209
Health Care Srvices
N.A.I.C.S.: 621610
Felice Kussoy (CFO)
Jerome Ernst (Chief Medical Officer)
Charles King (Sec)
Doug Wirth (Pres & CEO)
Emma DeVito (Vice Chm)

AMIGO CHEVROLET
1900 S 2nd St, Gallup, NM 87301
Tel.: (505) 722-7701
Year Founded: 1989
Sales Range: $10-24.9 Million
Emp.: 80
Car Whslr

N.A.I.C.S.: 441110
Terry Proffitt (Owner)

AMIGO MOBILITY INTERNATIONAL, INC.
6693 Dixie Hwy, Bridgeport, MI 48722
Tel.: (989) 777-0910
Web Site: https://www.myamigo.com
Year Founded: 1968
Rev.: $13,400,000
Emp.: 80
Electromedical & Electrotherapeutic Apparatus Mfr
N.A.I.C.S.: 334510
Mike Galer (Controller & Dir-Fin)
Mike LaBrake (Dir-Ops)
Beth L. Thieme (Founder & Chm)
Tim Drumhiller (Pres)

AMIGO TRUCK & EQUIPMENT, LLC.
710 McCarty St, Houston, TX 77029
Tel.: (713) 675-7575
Web Site:
http://www.amigotruckusa.com
Sales Range: $10-24.9 Million
Emp.: 40
Motor Vehicle Supplies & New Parts Merchant Whslr
N.A.I.C.S.: 423120
Charlie McDaniel (Owner & Pres)

AMIGOS LIBRARY SERVICES
14400 Midway Rd Ste 200, Dallas, TX 75244-6179
Tel.: (972) 851-8000   TX
Web Site: http://www.amigos.org
Year Founded: 1974
Sales Range: $10-24.9 Million
Emp.: 34
Library Management Services
N.A.I.C.S.: 519210
Connie Burnett (Mgr-Accounting)
Tracy Byerly (Chief Programs Officer)
Keith Gaertner (CFO)

AMIKAM & PARAS DIAMOND CORPORATION
70 W 36th St Rm 500, New York, NY 10018-8050
Tel.: (212) 869-1366
Web Site: http://www.amikam-paras.com
Sales Range: $50-74.9 Million
Emp.: 30
Diamond Trading Services
N.A.I.C.S.: 423940
Samir Mehta (Pres)
Ravi Gopalan (Controller)

AMIKIDS, INC.
5915 Benjamin Center Dr, Tampa, FL 33634
Tel.: (813) 887-3300
Web Site: https://www.amikids.org
Year Founded: 1969
Sales Range: $50-74.9 Million
Emp.: 1,671
Youth Care Services
N.A.I.C.S.: 624110
Heyward Golden (Sr VP-Ops)
Shannon Jager (VP-Resource Dev)
Rontel Batie (Dir-Corp Sponsorships-Natl)
Jessica R. Aspiras (Dir-Mktg)
Cassandra Griggs-Frierson (Exec Dir)
Michael Thornton (Pres & CEO)
Brenda Birkett (Chm)

AMINCO INTERNATIONAL (USA) INC.
20571 Crescent Bay Dr, Lake Forest, CA 92630-8825
Tel.: (949) 457-3261

Web Site:
https://www.amincousa.com
Year Founded: 1978
Sales Range: $10-24.9 Million
Emp.: 60
Brass Goods & Logo Pins Mfr
N.A.I.C.S.: 423990
William Wu (Pres)

AMIT CHILDREN, INC.
817 Broadway 3rd Fl, New York, NY 10003
Tel.: (212) 477-4720   NY
Web Site: http://www.amitchildren.org
Year Founded: 1925
Sales Range: $1-9.9 Million
Emp.: 37
Child Care Services
N.A.I.C.S.: 624110
Sharon Merkin (Treas)
Suzanne Doft (Chm)
Connie Kadish (VP-Programming-Israel)
Audrey Trachtman (VP-Strategic Plng)
Andrew S. Goldsmith (Exec VP)

AMITAL SPINNING CORP.
197 Bosch Blvd, New Bern, NC 28562-6924
Tel.: (252) 672-7384   DE
Web Site: https://www.amital.net
Year Founded: 1986
Sales Range: $25-49.9 Million
Emp.: 157
Yarn Spinning Mills
N.A.I.C.S.: 313110
Milton E. Gold Jr. (Pres)

AMITE CITY FORD INC.
11239 Hwy 16 Fl 1, Amite, LA 70422
Tel.: (985) 748-9026
Rev.: $13,500,000
Emp.: 45
New Car Dealers
N.A.I.C.S.: 441110
Gene Anglebrandt (VP)
B. L. Kilbride (VP)
Samuel D. Johnson (Pres)

AMITY TECHNOLOGY LLC
2800 7th Ave N, Fargo, ND 58102
Tel.: (701) 232-4199
Web Site: https://www.amitytech.com
Year Founded: 1979
Sales Range: $10-24.9 Million
Emp.: 290
Mfr of Farm Machinery & Equipment
N.A.I.C.S.: 333111
Howard Dahl (Co-Founder, Owner & Pres)
Brian Dahl (Co-Founder)

AMK INSURANCE AGENCY, INC.
6855 Via Del Oro, San Jose, CA 95119
Tel.: (408) 224-9101
Year Founded: 1993
Sales Range: $10-24.9 Million
Emp.: 17
Insurance Agency & Brokerage Services
N.A.I.C.S.: 524210
Alan M. Kirchick (Pres)

AML RIGHTSOURCE LLC
200 Public Sq Ste 3100, Cleveland, OH 44114
Web Site:
http://www.amlrightsource.com
Year Founded: 2004
Sales Range: $50-74.9 Million
Emp.: 5,000
Financial Services
N.A.I.C.S.: 522110

AML RightSource LLC—(Continued)

Frank H. Ewing (CEO)
Paul W. Linehan (Pres)
John J. Byrne (Vice Chm)
Todd Ayers (CFO)
Joe McNamara (Mgr-Mktg)

AMLOID CORPORATION
9 Mt Pleasant Ste 202, Cedar Knolls,
NJ 07927
Tel.: (973) 328-0654   NJ
Web Site: http://www.amloid.com
Year Founded: 1916
Sales Range: $10-24.9 Million
Emp.: 4
Mfr of Plastic Toys
N.A.I.C.S.: 339930
Dan McMahon (Exec VP)
Eric Kiel (VP-sls)
Michael Albarelli Jr. (Chm & Pres)

AMMARS INC.
710 S College Ave, Bluefield, VA
24605
Tel.: (276) 322-4686
Web Site:
   http://www.magicmartstores.com
Sales Range: $75-99.9 Million
Emp.: 160
Provider of Discount Apparel
N.A.I.C.S.: 455110
Trey A. Ammar (Pres)
Kaleel A. Ammar Jr. (Chm)

AMMD, LLC
12117 FM 2244 Bldg 1 Ste 201, Bee
Cave, TX 78738
Tel.: (512) 721-0424   TX
Web Site:
   http://www.amymyersmd.com
Year Founded: 2015
Sales Range: $10-24.9 Million
Emp.: 18
Nutritional Food Distr
N.A.I.C.S.: 456191
Amy Myers (Founder & CEO)

AMMO BROTHERS
15979 S Piuma Ave, Cerritos, CA
90703
Tel.: (562) 865-3980
Web Site:
   https://www.ammobros.com
Year Founded: 2003
Sales Range: $10-24.9 Million
Emp.: 55
Gunsmithing Services & Sales of
Guns & Ammunition
N.A.I.C.S.: 332993
Dustin Mohacsi (VP)

**AMMON & RIZOS COMPANY
INC.**
901 Waterfall Way Ste 701, Richard-
son, TX 75080
Tel.: (972) 644-5591
Web Site:
   http://www.ammonrizos.com
Sales Range: $10-24.9 Million
Emp.: 20
Mfr & Distributor of Electronic Parts
N.A.I.C.S.: 423690
Rick Rizos (Partner)
Dave Rizos (Pres)

AMMUNITION LLC
1500 Sansome St, San Francisco,
CA 94111
Tel.: (415) 632-1170
Web Site:
   https://www.ammunitiongroup.com
Sales Range: $10-24.9 Million
Emp.: 50
Product Designing Services
N.A.I.C.S.: 541490

Robert Brunner (Partner)
Brett Wickens (Partner)
Matt Rolandson (Partner)
Victoria Slaker (VP-Product Design)
Jeremy Matthews (Principal-Graphic
Design)
Darcy DiNucci (VP-User Experience)
Nick Barrett (VP-Client Svcs)
Peter Rack (Mng Dir)
David Summers (VP-Design Strategy)
Christopher Kuh (VP-Indus Design
Studio)
Sara Munday (VP-Mktg)
Ty Whittington (VP-Visual Design)

**AMNET DATA SOLUTIONS
INC.**
41-26 27th St, Long Island City, NY
11101
Tel.: (212) 935-9200   NY
Web Site:
   http://www.amnetdatasolutions.com
Year Founded: 1995
Electronics Stores
N.A.I.C.S.: 449210
David Abrahiman (Pres)

AMNET NEW YORK, INC.
19 W 44th St Ste 407, New York, NY
10036
Tel.: (212) 247-1900   NY
Web Site:
   http://www.travelwithamnet.com
Year Founded: 1988
Travel Agency
N.A.I.C.S.: 561510
Yuichiro Tanaka (Branch Mgr)
Fujio Nakagawa (Pres & CEO)

**AMON CARTER MUSEUM OF
AMERICAN ART**
3501 Camp Bowie Blvd, Fort Worth,
TX 76107
Tel.: (817) 738-1933   TX
Web Site:
   https://www.cartermuseum.org
Year Founded: 1961
Sales Range: $10-24.9 Million
Emp.: 142
Art Museum
N.A.I.C.S.: 712110
Andrew J. Walker (Exec Dir)
Amanda Blake (Dir-Education & Li-
brary Svcs)

AMORE CONSTRUCTION CO.
8409 Laurel Fair Cir 103, Tampa, FL
33610
Tel.: (813) 246-4200
Year Founded: 1995
Sales Range: $10-24.9 Million
Emp.: 8
Residential Remodeler
N.A.I.C.S.: 236118
David B. Amore (Pres)

AMOS & CONNORS, INC.
5590 E Yale Ave Ste 101, Denver,
CO 80222
Tel.: (303) 691-2900
Web Site:
   http://www.amosandconnors.com
Rev.: $15,000,000
Emp.: 4
Builders' Hardware, Nec
N.A.I.C.S.: 311821
Steve Connors (Pres)

AMOS PRESS, INC.
911 Vandemark Rd, Sidney, OH
45365
Tel.: (937) 498-2111
Web Site: http://www.amospress.com
Sales Range: $50-74.9 Million
Emp.: 370
Periodical Publishers

N.A.I.C.S.: 513120
Bruce Daniel Boyd (Pres)
Margie Bruns (Dir-Sls Ops)
Annie Niemiec (Editor)
Steve Collins (VP-Ops)
April Winemiller (Mgr-Circulation
Mktg)
Harry Haberer (Dir-HR)
Mary Holthaus (Mgr-Fin Ops)
Becky Schloss I (Mgr-Customer Svc)

Subsidiaries:

Amos Craft Publishing   (1)
4660 N Austin Ave Apt 310, Chicago, IL
60630-3182
Tel.: (847) 635-5800
Sales Range: $10-24.9 Million
Emp.: 30
Craft Magazines Publisher
N.A.I.C.S.: 513120

AMOS-HILL ASSOCIATES, INC.
112 Shelby Ave, Edinburgh, IN
46124-1042
Tel.: (812) 526-2671   IN
Web Site: http://www.amoshill.com
Year Founded: 1982
Sales Range: $100-124.9 Million
Emp.: 145
Mfr of Decorative Hardwood Veneer
N.A.I.C.S.: 321211
Angie Banks (Dir-HR)
Ken M. Brown (Plant Mgr)
Bill Costoplos (Pres)
Michael Bell (Controller)

AMOSKEAG BEVERAGES INC.
510 Hall St, Bow, NH 03304-3105
Tel.: (603) 224-3348   NH
Web Site: https://www.amoskeagbe
   verages.com
Year Founded: 1947
Sales Range: $25-49.9 Million
Emp.: 200
Sales of Beer & Other Fermented
Malt Liquors
N.A.I.C.S.: 424810
Thomas Bullock (Pres)
Ed Murphy (VP)

AMOTEC, INC.
1220 W 6th St Ste 407, Cleveland,
OH 44113
Tel.: (440) 250-4600   OH
Web Site: http://www.amotecinc.com
Year Founded: 2000
Sales Range: $1-9.9 Million
Emp.: 54
Recruitment & Placement Services
N.A.I.C.S.: 541612
Carmen Izzo (CEO)
Mark Simonetti (Mgr-Recruiting)

AMP AGENCY
77 N Washington St, Boston, MA
02114
Tel.: (617) 723-8929
Web Site:
   http://www.ampagency.com
Year Founded: 1984
Sales Range: $125-149.9 Million
Emp.: 100
Advertising Services
N.A.I.C.S.: 541810
Gary Colen (CEO)
Josh Pike (Sr VP-Shopper Digital)
Steve McCall (Exec VP-Bus Dev &
Ops)
Michael Mish (Sr VP-Bus Dev)
Colin Booth (Dir-Creative)
Kevin Casey (Assoc Creative Dir)
Matt Jacobs (Mng Dir-New York &
VP)
Doug Grumet (Sr VP-Media)
Nicole Peterson (VP)
Rich Grogan (VP-Measurement &
Analytics)

AMP SECURITY
1261 S 820 E Ste 300, American
Fork, UT 84003
Tel.: (800) 817-3918
Web Site:
   http://www.ampsecurity.com
Year Founded: 2007
Sales Range: $25-49.9 Million
Emp.: 550
Sales & Installation of Security Sys-
tems
N.A.I.C.S.: 561621
Johnny Hebda (VP-Sls)
Kevin Longust (Co-Mgr)
Scott Brown (Co-Mgr)

AMPAC ENTERPRISES INC.
4621 192nd St E, Tacoma, WA
98446-2753
Tel.: (253) 875-6900
Year Founded: 1992
Sales Range: $10-24.9 Million
Emp.: 130
Mfr of Doors & Glass
N.A.I.C.S.: 327215
John Ham (Pres)

AMPAC SCIENTIFIC INC.
1799 Bayshore Hwy Ste 238, Burlin-
game, CA 94010-1312
Tel.: (650) 259-7678
Web Site: http://www.ampacnet.com
Rev.: $10,000,000
Emp.: 45
Computer Software Development &
Applications
N.A.I.C.S.: 541511
Yu Zhou (Pres)

AMPACET CORPORATION
660 White Plains Rd, Tarrytown, NY
10591-5130
Tel.: (914) 631-6600   NY
Web Site: https://www.ampacet.com
Year Founded: 1937
Sales Range: $150-199.9 Million
Emp.: 880
Color Concentrates & Plastics
N.A.I.C.S.: 326199
Andrew McClellan (CFO & Sr VP)

Subsidiaries:

Ampacet (Thailand) Company,
Ltd.   (1)
64/19 Moo 4 Highway 331, Pluakdaeng,
21140, Rayong, Thailand
Tel.: (66) 38927999
Sales Range: $25-49.9 Million
Emp.: 300
Plastics Product Mfr
N.A.I.C.S.: 326199
Ajay Bajwa (Gen Mgr)

Ampacet Europe, S.A.   (1)
Zoning Industriel Riedgen, 3451, Dude-
lange, Luxembourg
Tel.: (352) 2920991
Web Site: http://www.ampacet.com
Emp.: 117
Plastics Product Mfr
N.A.I.C.S.: 326199

Ampacet Shanghai (Trading) Co.,
Ltd.   (1)
Building 8 No 191 Hua Jin Road, Min Hang
District, Shanghai, 201108, China
Tel.: (86) 21 6489 7660
Color Master Batch Mfr
N.A.I.C.S.: 325199

Ampacet South America S.R.L.   (1)
Dardo Rocha 2454-2nd Floor, San Isidro,
1640, Buenos Aires, Argentina
Tel.: (54) 1141104200
Sales Range: $25-49.9 Million
Emp.: 200
Plastic Masterbatch Distr
N.A.I.C.S.: 424950

Ampacet Specialty Products Private
Ltd.   (1)

D-276 D-277 & D-283 Ranjangaon Industrial Area, Shirur, Pune, 412210, India
Tel.: (91) 2138 611999
Web Site: http://www.ampacet.com
Emp.: 80
Color Master Batch Mfr
N.A.I.C.S.: 325199
Ajay Bijwe (Gen Mgr)

AMPCO PRODUCTS INC.
11400 NW 36th Ave, Miami, FL 33167
Tel.: (305) 821-5700
Web Site: http://www.ampco.com
Sales Range: $10-24.9 Million
Emp.: 65
Carrier Trays, Wood
N.A.I.C.S.: 321920
Michael O'Neill (COO)

AMPCUS INC.
14900 Conference Ctr Dr, Chantilly, VA 20151
Tel.: (703) 637-7299
Web Site: http://www.ampcus.com
Sales Range: $10-24.9 Million
Emp.: 110
Information Technology Consulting & Staffing Services
N.A.I.C.S.: 541512
Anjali Ramakumaran (Founder & CEO)
Ramana Challa (COO)
Charles R. McMahon (Exec VP)
Samir Sankaran (Mgr-PMO Program)
Venkat Rao (Dir-Practice)
R. J. Koechlin (Dir-Alliances)
Donna W. Erhardt (Sr VP-Bus Dev)
Vinay Mahamankar (CEO-Asia Pacific)
Tom Doran (Dir-Strategic Sls)
Craig Thompson (Sr VP)
Ajit Walker (Sr VP-Comml Sls)
Karen Kok (VP)

Subsidiaries:

Itech Solutions, Inc. (1)
30 Stanford Dr, Farmington, CT 06032
Tel.: (860) 674-1636
Web Site: http://www.itechsolutions.com
Sales Range: $10-24.9 Million
Emp.: 99
IT Consulting & Staffing
N.A.I.C.S.: 541519
Kay B. Lukas (Pres)
Chris Lukas (Founder & COO)
Amber Girardin (Coord-Event)

AMPED WIRELESS LIMITED
13089 Peyton Dr Ste C307, Chino Hills, CA 91709
Tel.: (909) 217-3229
Web Site: http://www.ampedwireless.com
Year Founded: 2008
Sales Range: $10-24.9 Million
Emp.: 26
Wireless Device Mfr
N.A.I.C.S.: 334210
Jason Owen (CEO)

AMPERAGE, LLC
6711 Chancellor Dr, Cedar Falls, IA 50613
Tel.: (319) 268-9151   IA
Web Site: https://www.amperagemarkets.com
Year Founded: 1996
Sales Range: $1-9.9 Million
Emp.: 50
Advetising Agency
N.A.I.C.S.: 541810
Bryan Earnest (Pres & Partner)
Mark Mathis III (Partner & Chief Strategy Officer)

Subsidiaries:

AMPERAGE Marketing (1)

200 1st St SE Ste 105, Cedar Rapids, IA 52401
Tel.: (319) 298-0242
Web Site: http://www.amperagemarketing.com
Sales Range: $1-9.9 Million
Emp.: 17
Advetising Agency
N.A.I.C.S.: 541810
Erin Bishop (Coord-Mktg Res)
Monte Bowden (Dir-Creative)
Maureen Burum (Coord-Media)
Bryan Earnest (Pres & CEO)
Brian Foelske (Dir-Video Content)
Denise Hesser (Dir-Media)
Leana Place (Dir-First Impressions)
Emily Smedley (Coord-Billing)
Julie Weiand (Coord-Client Svcs)

AMPERE COMPUTING LLC
4655 Great America Pkwy Ste 601, Santa Clara, CA 95054
Tel.: (669) 770-3700
Web Site: http://www.amperecomputing.com
Year Founded: 2018
Semiconductor Product Mfr
N.A.I.C.S.: 334413
Chi Miller (CFO & COO)
Atiq Bajwa (CTO)
Rohit Vidwans (Exec VP-Engrg)
Jeff Wittich (Sr VP-Products)
Kit Ho Chee (Chief Revenue Officer)
Matt Taylor (Sr VP-Worldwide Sls & Bus Dev)
Ben Lenhart (Gen Counsel)
Melissa Moore (VP-People & Culture)
Mauri Whalen (VP-Software Engrg)
Betsey Signol (VP-Global Mktg)
Sean Mirkes (VP-Logic Dev)
Mitrajit Chatterjee (VP-Silicon Engrg)
Renee J. James (Founder, Chm & CEO)

AMPERSAND CONSTRUCTION, LLC
428 Lemon Ave, Sarasota, FL 34236
Tel.: (941) 914-6446
Web Site: http://www.ampersandconstruct.com
Year Founded: 1999
Sales Range: $1-9.9 Million
Residential Construction & Remodeling Services
N.A.I.C.S.: 236115
Allan Livesey (Pres)
John E. Hermansen (VP & Dir-Bus Dev)

AMPERSAND MANAGEMENT LLC
55 William St Ste 240, Wellesley, MA 02481
Tel.: (781) 239-0700   DE
Web Site: http://www.ampersandcapital.com
Year Founded: 1980
Privater Equity Firm
N.A.I.C.S.: 523999
David J. Parker (Gen Partner)
Dave Patteson (Partner)
Henry Dubina (Operating Partner)
Jay Ray (Operating Partner)
Dana L. Niles (Partner & COO)
David Q. Anderson (Partner)
Geoffrey P. Teillon (Partner)
Marina Pellon-Consunji (Partner)
Trevor L. Wahlbrink (Partner)
Franklin R. Witney (Operating Partner)

Subsidiaries:

American Laboratory Products Company, Ltd. (1)
26 Keewaydin Dr G, Salem, NH 03079
Tel.: (603) 893-8914
Web Site: http://www.alpco.com
Rev.: $5,196,000

Emp.: 12
Office Supplies & Stationery Stores
N.A.I.C.S.: 459410
Collin Shaw (Product Mgr)
Richard Conley (Owner)

Elite One Source Nutrisciences (1)
13840 Magnolia Ave, Chino, CA 91710
Tel.: (909) 902-5005
Nutritional Supplements Mfr
N.A.I.C.S.: 325411
Thomas W. Burnell (Pres & CEO)
Tom Burnell (Pres & CEO)

Subsidiary (Domestic):

Nutramed, Inc. (2)
13840 Magnolia Ave, Chino, CA 91710
Tel.: (909) 902-5005
Web Site: http://www.nutramedinc.com
Nutritional Supplements Mfr
N.A.I.C.S.: 325411
Tom Burnell (Pres & CEO)

Nutritional Laboratories International, Inc. (2)
1001 S 3rd St W, Missoula, MT 59801
Tel.: (406) 273-5493
Web Site: http://www.nutritionallaboratories.com
Emp.: 140
Nutritional Supplements Mfr
N.A.I.C.S.: 325411
Tito Flores (Mgr-Sls)
Titut Yokelson (VP-R&D)
Steve Dybdal (Dir-Ops)
Jerale Smith (Dir-Quality Assurance)
Doug Lefler (Dir-Sls & Mktg)

Genezen Laboratories Inc. (1)
9900 Westpoint Dr Ste 128, Indianapolis, IN 46256
Tel.: (317) 822-8330
Web Site: https://www.genezen.com
Gene & Cell Therapy Mfr
N.A.I.C.S.: 541715

Subsidiary (Non-US):

uniQure N.V. (2)
Paasheuvelweg 25a, 1105 BP, Amsterdam, Netherlands
Tel.: (31) 202406000
Web Site: https://www.uniqure.com
Rev.: $15,843,000
Assets: $831,689,000
Liabilities: $624,019,000
Net Worth: $207,670,000
Earnings: ($308,478,000)
Emp.: 480
Fiscal Year-end: 12/31/2023
Human Gene Therapy Research
N.A.I.C.S.: 541715
Christian Klemt (CFO)
David Cerveny (Chief Legal Officer, Gen Counsel & Sec)
Pierre Caloz (COO)
Amin Abujoub (Chief Quality Officer)
Erin Boyer (Chief People Officer)
Richard Porter (Chief Bus Officer & Chief Scientific Officer)
Jeanette Potts (Chief Legal Officer)
Matthew Kapusta (CEO)

HSRL Holdings LLC (1)
5930 Main St, Mount Jackson, VA 22842
Tel.: (513) 204-4400
Web Site: https://www.stagebio.com
GLP-compliant Research & Clinical Histology, Pathology & Specimen Archiving Services
N.A.I.C.S.: 541714
Lori A. Ball (CEO)
Tom Galati (Founder)
Carrie Harris (VP-Pathology Svcs)
Damon Lusk (CFO)
Ayse Bal (Mng Dir)

Subsidiary (Domestic):

Tox Path Specialists, LLC (2)
8747 Chestnut Grove Rd, Frederick, MD 21701
Tel.: (301) 378-0505
Web Site: http://www.toxpath.net
Professional, Scientific & Technical Services
N.A.I.C.S.: 541990
Mark Butt (Owner)

Microtest Laboratories, Inc. (1)

104 Gold St, Agawam, MA 01001
Tel.: (413) 786-1680
Web Site: http://www.microtestlabs.com
Sales Range: $1-9.9 Million
Surgical & Medical Instrument Mfr
N.A.I.C.S.: 339112
Steven G. Richter (Founder)
Pat Walsh (COO)

Nexelis (1)
645 Elliott Ave W Ste 300, Seattle, WA 98119
Tel.: (206) 298-0068
Web Site: http://www.nexelis.com
Medical & Bioanalytical Development Services
N.A.I.C.S.: 541714
Benoit Bouche (Pres & CEO)

Subsidiary (Domestic):

AIT Bioscience LLC (2)
7840 Innovation Blvd, Indianapolis, IN 46278
Tel.: (317) 715-8800
Web Site: http://www.aitbioscience.com
Sales Range: $1-9.9 Million
Emp.: 43
Biological Research & Development Services
N.A.I.C.S.: 541715
Michael A. Evans (Founder)
Ron Shoup (Chief Scientific Officer)
Terri Pascarelli (CEO)
Timothy Grever (Dir-Laboratory Ops)

Rand A Technology Corporation (1)
151 Courtney Park Dr W, Mississauga, L5W 1Y5, ON, Canada
Tel.: (905) 625-2000
Sales Range: $100-124.9 Million
Engineering & Information Technology
N.A.I.C.S.: 541512
Bill Zavadil (Pres)
Dominic Yu (VP)
Jamie Chevalier (VP)
Jess McCormick (VP)
John Kuta (CFO)
Chantale Marchand (VP)

Specac Limited (1)
Science And Innovation Centre Unit 12 Halo Business Park Cray Ave, Orpington, London, BR5 3FQ, Kent, United Kingdom
Tel.: (44) 1689873134
Web Site: https://specac.com
Electronic Measuring & Testing Equipment Design & Mfr
N.A.I.C.S.: 334519
Dave Patteson (Interim CEO)

Subsidiary (US):

Harrick Scientific Products, Inc. (2)
141 Tompkins Ave, Pleasantville, NY 10570
Tel.: (914) 747-7202
Web Site: http://www.harricksci.com
Rev.: $3,000,000
Emp.: 25
Optical Instrument & Lens Mfr
N.A.I.C.S.: 333310
N. N. (Founder & Pres)
Susan Berets (Mgr-MIS)
Linda Marshall (Mgr-Fin)

Specac Inc. (2)
50 Sharpe Dr, Cranston, RI 02920
Tel.: (401) 854-5281
Web Site: http://www.specac.com
Rev.: $1,000,000
Emp.: 3
Instruments & Related Products Manufacturing for Measuring, Displaying & Controlling Industrial Process Variables
N.A.I.C.S.: 334513
Forrest Imhoff (Bus Mgr)

Sterlingtech, Inc. (1)
250 Moonachie Rd., Ste 400, Moonachie, NJ 07074
Tel.: (201) 479-9746
Web Site: http://www.sterlingtechsoftware.com
Sales Range: $1-9.9 Million
Emp.: 18
Computer & Computer Peripheral Equipment & Software Merchant Whslr
N.A.I.C.S.: 423430
Bruce Swope (VP)
Dan Sterling (Founder & Pres)
John Campbell (Dir-Quality)
David Montecalvo (CEO)

Ampersand Management LLC—(Continued)

Subsidiary (Domestic):

RBC Development, LLC **(2)**
15200 Santa Fe Trail Dr Ste 100, Lenexa, KS 66219
Tel.: (913) 385-5700
Web Site: https://rbccorp.com
Rev.: $3,600,000
Emp.: 34
Custom Computer Programming Services
N.A.I.C.S.: 541511
Carl Mayer *(Pres & Founder)*
David Montecalvo *(CEO)*

Vivitide, LLC **(1)**
65 Zub Ln, Gardner, MA 01440
Tel.: (978) 630-0020
Web Site: https://vivitide.com
Rev.: $3,200,000
Emp.: 28
Pharmaceutical Preparation Mfr
N.A.I.C.S.: 325412

Subsidiary (Domestic):

Peptides International, Inc. **(2)**
11621 Electron Dr, Louisville, KY 40299
Tel.: (502) 266-8787
Web Site: http://www.pepnet.com
Biological Product, except Diagnostic, Mfr
N.A.I.C.S.: 325414
Rosendo Estrada *(VP-Ops)*

AMPEX CORPORATION

500 Broadway St, Redwood City, CA 94063-3199
Tel.: (650) 367-4111   DE
Web Site: http://www.ampex.com
Year Founded: 1944
Sales Range: $25-49.9 Million
Emp.: 112
Digital Data Recorders & Systems for Corporate, Government, Network, Entertainment & Telecommunications Applications
N.A.I.C.S.: 334112
Joel D. Talcott *(Sec & VP)*
Ramon C. H. Venema *(VP & Controller)*
D. Gordon Strickland *(Chm, Pres & CEO)*
Raymond F. Weldon *(Mng Dir)*
Christopher Lake *(CFO, Treas & VP)*
Donald L. Hawks III *(Mng Dir)*

Subsidiaries:

Ampex Corporation - Colorado Springs Service Facility **(1)**
4184 E Bijou St, Colorado Springs, CO 80909
Tel.: (719) 596-2000
Digital Storage Equipment Mfr
N.A.I.C.S.: 334419

Ampex Data International Corporation **(1)**
26460 Corporate Ave, Hayward, CA 94545
Tel.: (650) 367-3365
Web Site: http://www.ampex.com
Emp.: 52
Digital Storage Equipment Mfr
N.A.I.C.S.: 334419
Jim Orahood *(Gen Mgr)*

Ampex Data Systems Corporation **(1)**
500 Broadway, Redwood City, CA 94063-3199 **(100%)**
Tel.: (650) 367-2011
Web Site: http://www.ampexdata.com
Sales Range: $10-24.9 Million
Emp.: 70
Designs & Markets Digital Storage Systems
N.A.I.C.S.: 334112
Donald Downing *(Mgr-Bus Dev)*
Tracy Wood *(Mgr-Bus Dev)*

Ampex Great Britain Ltd. **(1)**
Ampex House Beechwood Chineham Business Park, Chineham, Basingstoke, RG24 8WA, United Kingdom **(100%)**
Tel.: (44) 256814410
Web Site: http://www.ampexdata.com

Sales Range: $25-49.9 Million
Emp.: 7
Provider of Recording Products
N.A.I.C.S.: 334610

Ampex Japan Ltd. **(1)**
Ikedaya Shinagawa Building 5th Floor
12-27 Konan 2-chome, Minato-ku, Tokyo, 108 0075, Japan **(100%)**
Tel.: (81) 364339081
Web Site: http://www.ampex.co.jp
Sales Range: $50-74.9 Million
Emp.: 5
Markets & Supports Products for Broadcast Industry
N.A.I.C.S.: 423990
Kazunori Yagyuda *(Pres)*

AMPHIL

PO Box 1480, Hockessin, DE 19707
Tel.: (302) 635-7354
Web Site: https://www.amphil.com
Year Founded: 2009
Management Consulting Services
N.A.I.C.S.: 541618

AMPHORA, INC.

10370 Richmond Ave Ste 300, Houston, TX 77042-4182
Tel.: (713) 339-5600   DE
Web Site: http://www.amphorainc.com
Year Founded: 1997
Commodity Trading & Risk Management Software Publisher
N.A.I.C.S.: 513210
Antonio Albiero *(COO)*
Davinder Virk *(Pres-India)*
Donald Levantin *(CEO)*
Ken Anderson *(CTO)*
Lynn Lattimer *(Head-Sls-Global)*
Maarten-Jan Waasdorp *(VP-Fin & HR)*
Rick Nelson *(Pres)*
John R. Beaty II *(Pres-Americas)*

AMPIRICAL SOLUTIONS LLC

4 Sanctuary Blvd Ste 100, Mandeville, LA 70471-2939
Tel.: (985) 809-5240
Web Site: http://www.ampirical.com
Year Founded: 2006
Sales Range: $25-49.9 Million
Emp.: 50
Designs Electrical Transmission & Distribution Systems
N.A.I.C.S.: 541330
Matthew Saacks *(Pres)*
Mike Sulzer *(Exec VP-Ops)*
Mark Stephens *(Exec VP-Engrg)*
Ed Tafelski *(Dir-Bus Dev)*
Jeff Spence *(Dir-Substation)*
Kurt Traub *(Dir-Transmission)*

AMPLEX INC.

13100 34th St N, Clearwater, FL 33762
Tel.: (727) 572-4546
Web Site: https://www.aboutamplex.com
Sales Range: $10-24.9 Million
Emp.: 80
Flowers & Florists Supplies
N.A.I.C.S.: 424930
George D. Kostilnik *(Pres)*
Tami McKnight *(VP)*

AMPLIFIER TECHNOLOGIES, INC.

1749 Chapin Rd, Montebello, CA 90640
Tel.: (323) 278-0001   CA
Web Site: https://www.ati-amp.com
Year Founded: 1971
Sales Range: $10-24.9 Million
Emp.: 48
Professional & Commercial Audio Power Amplifiers

N.A.I.C.S.: 334310
Morris Kessler *(Pres)*

AMPLIO DIGITAL, LLC

1300 Walnut St Ste 20, Boulder, CO 80302
Tel.: (415) 746-9850
Web Site: http://www.ampliodigital.com
Year Founded: 2014
Sales Range: $1-9.9 Million
Emp.: 20
Digital Marketing Services
N.A.I.C.S.: 541810
Marshall Hayes *(Founder)*

AMPM, INC.

7403 W Weckley St, Midland, MI 48642-7344
Tel.: (989) 837-8800   MI
Web Site: http://www.ampminc.com
Year Founded: 1969
Sales Range: $1-9.9 Million
Emp.: 13
Advertising Agency Services
N.A.I.C.S.: 541810
Mark Bush *(Partner)*
Ty Smith *(Assoc Dir-Creative)*
Angela Harrington *(Mgr-Ops)*

Subsidiaries:

AMPM, Inc. Detroit **(1)**
21442 Beauford Ln, Northville, MI 48167
Tel.: (248) 477-0400
Web Site: http://www.ampminc.com
Emp.: 2
Advetising Agency
N.A.I.C.S.: 541810
Dave Well *(Partner)*

AMPRITE ELECTRIC COMPANY INC.

929 5th Ave S, Nashville, TN 37203
Tel.: (615) 255-5593
Web Site: http://www.amprite.com
Sales Range: $10-24.9 Million
Emp.: 85
General Electrical Contractors; Industrial Electrical Work & Engineering
N.A.I.C.S.: 238210
Emory Lester *(VP-Construction)*
Chuck Roberts *(Pres)*

AMPRO INC.

250 W Lake St, Barrington, IL 60010
Tel.: (847) 381-3387
Rev.: $22,000,000
Emp.: 2
Financial Services
N.A.I.C.S.: 541611

AMPRO INDUSTRIES INC.

6240 Poplar Ave, Memphis, TN 38119
Tel.: (901) 527-5365
Web Site: http://www.amprogel.com
Rev.: $11,605,064
Emp.: 75
Hair Preparations, Including Shampoos
N.A.I.C.S.: 325620
Jack Sammons *(Pres)*
Henry G. Rudner *(CEO)*
Cheri L. Rudner *(Chm)*
Tricia Snead *(Brand Mgr)*

AMRO FABRICATING CORPORATION

1430 Amro Way, El Monte, CA 91733
Tel.: (626) 579-2200
Web Site: http://www.amrofab.com
Sales Range: $10-24.9 Million
Emp.: 150
Aircraft Parts & Equipment
N.A.I.C.S.: 336413

Steven M. Riley *(VP)*
John E. Hammond *(VP-Mktg & Sls)*
Steve Walleman *(VP)*

AMROD CORP.

305A Craneway St, Newark, NJ 07114
Tel.: (973) 344-3806   NJ
Web Site: https://www.amrod.com
Year Founded: 1983
Rev.: $13,700,000
Emp.: 80
Copper Rod Mfr
N.A.I.C.S.: 331420
Edward Gollob *(Chm)*
Timothy Anglim *(CFO & Controller)*
Mark Woehnker *(Pres)*

AMRON INTERNATIONAL INC.

1380 Aspen Way, Vista, CA 92081-8349
Tel.: (760) 208-6500
Web Site: https://www.amronintl.com
Rev.: $44,700,000
Emp.: 80
Sporting & Athletic Goods Mfr
N.A.I.C.S.: 339920
Robin Butts *(Mgr-Production Control)*
Scott Ritchie *(VP-Mfg)*
Debra L. Ritchie *(Pres)*
Mike Malone *(Mgr-Sls & Mktg)*

AMROSE OIL COMPANY

3525 Sage Rd Ste 1416, Houston, TX 77056
Tel.: (713) 280-5173   NV
Web Site: http://www.amroseoil.com
Year Founded: 2011
Sales Range: $25-49.9 Million
Emp.: 5
Oil & Gas Exploration
N.A.I.C.S.: 211120
James William Anderson *(Chm & CEO)*
Vic Devlaeminck *(CFO)*
Bob Ouriel *(Gen Counsel)*

AMS CORPORATION

9119 Cross Park Dr, Knoxville, TN 37923
Tel.: (865) 691-1756
Web Site: https://www.ams-corp.com
Sales Range: $10-24.9 Million
Emp.: 80
Measuring & Testing Equipment Sales & Maintenance Services
N.A.I.C.S.: 423830
H. M. Hashemian *(Pres & CEO)*
Dan D. Beverly *(CTO)*
Mehred Hashemian *(Mgr-Field Testing)*
Darrell W. Mitchell *(Mgr-Technical Svc)*
Greg W. Morton *(Mgr-Software Dev)*

AMS FULFILLMENT , INC.

29010 Commerce Center Dr, Valencia, CA 91355
Tel.: (661) 775-0611
Web Site: https://www.amsfulfillment.com
Year Founded: 2002
Sales Range: $25-49.9 Million
Emp.: 292
Electronic Order Processing Services
N.A.I.C.S.: 458110
Ken Wiseman *(CEO & Mng Partner)*
Jay Catlin *(Pres & Mng Partner)*
Rose Huttas *(Sr Acct Exec)*

AMS MECHANICAL SYSTEMS, INC.

140 E Tower Dr, Burr Ridge, IL 60527
Tel.: (630) 887-7700

Web Site:
http://www.amsmechanics.com
Rev.: $83,000,000
Emp.: 170
Provider of Warm Air Heating & Air Conditioning Contracting Services
N.A.I.C.S.: 238220
Mike Roberts *(CFO & VP)*
Bill Montgomery *(VP-Business Development)*
John Berzanskis Jr. *(Pres & CEO)*

AMS PICTURES
16986 N Dallas Pkwy, Dallas, TX 75248
Tel.: (972) 818-7400
Web Site:
https://www.amspictures.com
Year Founded: 1982
Emp.: 200
Broadcast Media & Video Production Services
N.A.I.C.S.: 512110
Andy Streitfeld *(Founder & CEO)*
Brad Osborne *(Dir)*
Stacy Thiele *(VP-Ops)*
Amanda Metz *(Sr Mgr-Production)*

AMS PRESS INC.
63 Flushing Ave Bldg 292, Brooklyn, NY 11205
Tel.: (212) 777-4700
Web Site:
http://www.amspressinc.com
Rev.: $11,700,000
Emp.: 10
Academic Publishing Services
N.A.I.C.S.: 424920
Gabriel Hornstein *(Pres)*

AMS STAFF LEASING
4455 LBJ Fwy Ste 1080, Dallas, TX 75244
Tel.: (972) 404-1615
Web Site:
http://www.amsstaffleasing.com
Year Founded: 1996
Sales Range: $150-199.9 Million
Emp.: 100
Employment Services
N.A.I.C.S.: 561311
Jack Young *(Mgr-IT Ops)*
Judy Milner *(Mgr-HR)*
Kristin Wynn *(Controller)*
Tameshia Crowe *(Supvr-Unemployment Dept)*

AMSCO SCHOOL PUBLICATIONS, INC.
315 Hudson St, New York, NY 10013
Tel.: (212) 886-6500   NY
Web Site: http://www.amscopub.com
Year Founded: 1935
Sales Range: $75-99.9 Million
Emp.: 120
Publisher of Books
N.A.I.C.S.: 513130
Henry Brun *(Pres)*

AMSCO STEEL COMPANY
3430 McCart Ave, Fort Worth, TX 76110
Tel.: (817) 926-3355
Web Site:
http://www.amscosteel.com
Rev.: $27,468,400
Emp.: 65
Structural Shapes, Iron Or Steel
N.A.I.C.S.: 423510
Stephen S. Sikes *(Pres)*
Howard Pena *(VP-Fin)*
Robert Pilson *(Mgr-Programming, IT & Pur)*
Ferrell Wright *(VP-Production)*

AMSCO WEAR PRODUCTS INC.
5 Hatfield Ln, Goshen, NY 10924
Tel.: (845) 294-1600
Web Site: http://www.amsco.us
Sales Range: $50-74.9 Million
Emp.: 9
Mfr of Steel Castings
N.A.I.C.S.: 423510
Sheerin Morris *(CFO)*
Art Borin Jr. *(Pres)*

AMSCOT HOLDINGS INC.
4808 E Broadway, Tampa, FL 33605
Tel.: (813) 248-4140
Web Site:
http://www.amscotfinancial.com
Year Founded: 1989
Sales Range: $150-199.9 Million
Emp.: 2,000
Tax Return Preparation & Other Financial Services
N.A.I.C.S.: 541213
Ian A. MacKechnie *(Chm & CEO)*

Subsidiaries:

Amscot Corporation   (1)
600 N Westshore Blvd Ste 1200, Tampa, FL 33609
Tel.: (813) 637-6100
Web Site: http://www.amscot.com
Sales Range: $150-199.9 Million
Emp.: 1,300
Tax Return Preparation & Other Financial Services
N.A.I.C.S.: 541213
Ian A. MacKechnie *(Pres & CEO)*

AMSDELL COMPANIES
1 International Pl 20445 Emerald Pkwy Dr SW Ste 220, Cleveland, OH 44135
Tel.: (216) 458-0670
Web Site:
http://www.amsdellcompanies.com
Rev.: $16,900,000
Emp.: 280
Real Estate Development Services
N.A.I.C.S.: 236220
Todd Amsdell *(Pres)*

AMSOIL INC.
925 Tower Ave, Superior, WI 54880
Tel.: (715) 392-7101
Web Site: https://www.amsoil.com
Year Founded: 1972
Sales Range: $100-124.9 Million
Emp.: 315
Lubricating Oils & Greases Mfr
N.A.I.C.S.: 324191
Dean Alexander *(Co-Pres & CFO)*
Alan Amatuzio *(Chm & CEO)*

Subsidiaries:

ALTRUM   (1)
Amsoil Bldg, Superior, WI 54880
Tel.: (715) 392-7101
Web Site: http://www.altrumonline.com
Sales Range: $10-24.9 Million
Emp.: 250
Nutritional Supplements, Natural Lawn & Garden Products & Water Filter Mfr
N.A.I.C.S.: 335220
A. L. Amatuzio *(Founder)*

Aerospace Lubricants, Inc.   (1)
1600 Georgesville Road, Columbus, OH 43228
Tel.: (614) 878-3600
Web Site:
http://www.aerospacelubricants.com
Rev.: $1,333,333
Emp.: 10
Petroleum Lubricating Oil & Grease Mfr
N.A.I.C.S.: 324191
Dave Meyer *(Pres)*

Benz Oil Inc.   (1)
2724 W Hampton Ave, Milwaukee, WI 53209
Tel.: (414) 442-2900

Web Site: https://www.benz.com
Sales Range: $10-24.9 Million
Emp.: 60
Oils & Greases, Blending & Compounding
N.A.I.C.S.: 324191
Dixon W. Benz *(Pres)*
Terry Brazell *(VP-Fin)*

Oil Analyzers, Inc.   (1)
1101 Susquehanna Ave, Superior, WI 54880
Web Site: http://www.oaitesting.com
Laboratory Testing Services
N.A.I.C.S.: 541380
Allen Bender *(Mgr)*

AMSTED INDUSTRIES INCORPORATED
111 S Wacker Dr Ste 4400, Chicago, IL 60606
Tel.: (312) 645-1700   DE
Web Site: https://www.amsted.com
Year Founded: 1902
Sales Range: $1-4.9 Billion
Emp.: 15,000
Steel Foundries (except Investment)
N.A.I.C.S.: 331513
Stephen R. Smith *(Chm, Pres & CEO)*
Steven E. Obendorf *(VP-Audit)*
Marilyn D. Franson *(VP)*
Christopher G. Athas *(Gen Counsel, Sec & VP)*
Luke Penskar *(Treas)*
Chris Meyers *(CFO & VP-Fin)*
Rajeev Batra *(Vice Chm)*
Jack A. Cumming *(Treas)*

Subsidiaries:

AMSTED Canada Inc.   (1)
2500 Day St, Winnipeg, R2C 3A4, MB, Canada   (100%)
Tel.: (204) 222-4252
Web Site: http://www.amstedrail.com
Sales Range: $25-49.9 Million
Emp.: 100
Mfr of Steel Railroad Wheels & Composition Brake Shoes
N.A.I.C.S.: 331513
Pierre MacKay *(Controller)*

Acieries De Ploermel   (1)
BP 103, 56804, Ploermel, Cedex, France   (100%)
Tel.: (33) 297732470
Web Site: http://www.krec.de
Sales Range: $10-24.9 Million
Emp.: 150
Mfr of European Railcar Cushioning Devices
N.A.I.C.S.: 336510

American Steel Foundries   (1)
1700 Walnut St, Granite City, IL 62040-3708
Tel.: (618) 452-2111
Web Site: http://www.asfglobal.com
Sales Range: $50-74.9 Million
Emp.: 900
Mfr of Cast Steel Freight Car Components, Steel Springs & Fifth Wheels
N.A.I.C.S.: 336510
Paul Limbach *(VP-Opers)*

Amsted Rail Company, Inc.   (1)
311 S Wacker Ste 5300, Chicago, IL 60606
Tel.: (312) 922-4501
Web Site: http://www.amstedrail.com
Sales Range: $25-49.9 Million
Emp.: 35
Steel Railroad Wheel Mfr
N.A.I.C.S.: 423860
John Wories Jr. *(Pres)*

Division (Domestic):

Amsted RPS   (2)
8400 W 110th St Ste 300, Overland Park, KS 66210   (100%)
Tel.: (913) 345-4807
Web Site: http://www.amstedrps.com
Sales Range: $25-49.9 Million
Rail Fastening Systems Mfr & Distr
N.A.I.C.S.: 339993

Wes Hodges *(Pres)*
Janine Judd *(Dir-HR)*
John Stout *(VP-Sls & Mktg)*
Kendra Wilson *(Mgr-Mktg & Comm)*

Amsted Rail Company, Inc. - ASF Keystone   (2)
3420 Simpson Ferry Rd, Camp Hill, PA 17011-6410   (100%)
Tel.: (717) 761-3690
Web Site: http://www.amstedrail.com
Sales Range: $25-49.9 Million
Railcar Shock Absorbant Products Mfr
N.A.I.C.S.: 336510
Steve A. Brough *(Gen Mgr)*
William P. O'Donnell *(VP-Sls & Mktg)*
John Wories *(Pres)*

Baltimore Aircoil Company   (1)
7600 Dorsey Run Rd, Jessup, MD 20794-9323
Tel.: (410) 799-6200
Web Site: http://www.baltimoreaircoil.com
Sales Range: $100-124.9 Million
Emp.: 1,200
Cooling Water Recovery System Cooling Tower Evaporative Condenser Closed Circuit Cooling Tower Thermal Storage Unit & Heat Exchanger Thermal Storage Mfr
N.A.I.C.S.: 333415
Brad Considine *(Dir-Sls-Americas)*
Don Fetzer *(Pres)*

Subsidiary (Non-US):

BAC Cooling Systems (Suzhou) Co., Ltd.   (2)
Rm 2204 Litong Plaza No 1350 North Sichuan Rd, Shanghai, 200080, China
Tel.: (86) 2160723600
Web Site: http://www.baltimoreaircoil.cn
Sales Range: $25-49.9 Million
Emp.: 460
Air Conditioning Equipment Mfr
N.A.I.C.S.: 333415
Zhang Anne *(Plant Mgr)*

BAC Dalian Co., Ltd.   (2)
No 65 Guangxian Road Hi-Tech Zone, Dalian, 116023, Liaoning, China
Tel.: (86) 411 8479 3275
Web Site: http://www.baltimoreaircoil.cn
Air Conditioning Equipment Mfr
N.A.I.C.S.: 333415

BAC Japan Co., Ltd.   (2)
2-27-4 Shinmachi, Setagaya-ku, Tokyo, 154-0014, Japan
Tel.: (81) 3 5450 6161
Web Site: http://www.bacj.co.jp
Air Conditioning Equipment Mfr
N.A.I.C.S.: 333415
Masanori Harada *(Pres)*

BAC Malaysia, Sdn. Bhd.   (2)
628 6th Floor Block A Damansara Intan No 1 Jalan SS20/27, Darul Ehsan, 47400, Petaling Jaya, Selangor, Malaysia
Tel.: (60) 3 7725 4917
Web Site: http://www.baltimoreaircoil.com
Sales Range: $10-24.9 Million
Emp.: 2
Air Conditioning Equipment Mfr
N.A.I.C.S.: 333415

BALTIMORE AIRCOIL Aust. Pty.Ltd.   (2)
Wisemans Ferry Road 120, Somersby, 2250, NSW, Australia
Tel.: (61) 2 4340 1200
Web Site:
http://www.baltimoreaircoil.com.au
Sales Range: $25-49.9 Million
Emp.: 100
Air Conditioning Equipment Mfr
N.A.I.C.S.: 333415

BALTIMORE AIRCOIL INTERNATIONAL NV   (2)
Industriepark-Zone A, Heist-op-den-Berg, 2220, Belgium
Tel.: (32) 15 257 700
Web Site: http://www.baltimoreaircoil.eu
Emp.: 320
Air Conditioning Equipment Mfr
N.A.I.C.S.: 333415
Don Setzer *(Gen Mgr)*
David Jacobs *(Gen Mgr)*

BALTIMORE AIRCOIL ITALIA s.r.l.   (2)

AMSTED Industries Incorporated—(Continued)

Via Nazionale Localita Giardini 15, Chiuro,
23030, Sondrio, Italy
Tel.: (39) 0342 485 111
Web Site: http://www.baltimoreaircoil.com
Sales Range: $25-49.9 Million
Emp.: 120
Air Conditioning Equipment Mfr
N.A.I.C.S.: 333415
Marco Verri (Mng Dir)

Baltimore Aircoil Company S.A. (Pty)
Ltd.   (2)
Portland Road, Philippi, Cape Town, 7785,
South Africa
Tel.: (27) 21 371 7121
Web Site: http://www.baltimoreaircoil.co.za
Air Conditioning Equipment Mfr
N.A.I.C.S.: 333415
Jose Fernandes (Gen Mgr)

Brenco, Inc.   (1)
2580 Frontage Rd, Petersburg, VA
23805   (100%)
Tel.: (804) 732-0202
Web Site: http://www.amstedrail.com
Sales Range: $75-99.9 Million
Emp.: 550
Railroad Bearings & Components Mfr
N.A.I.C.S.: 336510
Arun Dhir (VP-Intl Bus)

Burgess-Norton Manufacturing
Company   (1)
737 Peyton St, Geneva, IL 60134-2150
Tel.: (630) 232-4100
Web Site: http://www.burgessnorton.com
Sales Range: $50-74.9 Million
Emp.: 500
Piston Pins & Powder Metal Parts, Dulcite
& Gray Iron Castings & Assembled Parts
Mfr
N.A.I.C.S.: 541330
Tom Stockwell III (VP-Piston Pin Sls-Global)

Subsidiary (Non-US):

Salvadori Spinotti S.r.l.   (2)
Via Pinerolo 23/B, 10060, Torino, Italy
Tel.: (39) 011 985 4311
Sales Range: $25-49.9 Million
Emp.: 125
Piston Rings Mfr
N.A.I.C.S.: 336310

Xinyang Burgess-Norton Yinguang
Piston pin Co., Ltd.   (2)
No 669 Gongqu Road, Xinyang, 464000,
Henan, China
Tel.: (86) 376 659 5990
Piston Rings Mfr
N.A.I.C.S.: 336310

Consolidated Metco Inc.   (1)
5701 SE Columbia Way, Vancouver, WA
98661   (100%)
Tel.: (360) 828-2599
Web Site: http://www.conmet.com
Sales Range: $25-49.9 Million
Emp.: 50
Lightweight Aluminum Components Mfr
N.A.I.C.S.: 331524
Mike Hurley (VP-OEM Sls)
Beto Dantas (VP-Mktg, Strategy & Innova-
tion)
John Waters (Pres)

Subsidiary (Non-US):

ConMet de Mexico   (2)
Avenidas De Las Americas 100, Cienega
de Flores, Nuevo Leon, Mexico
Tel.: (52) 818 154 7703
Mold Aluminum Casting Mfr
N.A.I.C.S.: 331524

Means Industries, Inc.   (1)
1860 S Jefferson Ave, Saginaw, MI
48601-2824   (100%)
Tel.: (989) 754-3300
Web Site: http://www.meansindustries.com
Sales Range: $10-24.9 Million
Emp.: 100
Mfr Of Precision High Volume Stamped
Metal Components For The Auto Industry
N.A.I.C.S.: 336370
Jeremy Holt (Pres)

AMSTEK METAL

2408 W McDonough, Joliet, IL 60436
Tel.: (815) 725-2520
Web Site:
   https://www.amstekmetal.com
Year Founded: 1987
Sales Range: $10-24.9 Million
Emp.: 27
Distr of Steel
N.A.I.C.S.: 423510
Charles K. Stevens (CEO, Chm &
Pres)
Gene Burda (Mgr-Ops)
Thomas Hunt (Mgr-Sls)

AMSTER KIRTZ CO.

2830 Cleveland Ave NW, Canton, OH
44709
Tel.: (330) 493-1800
Web Site: http://www.amsterkirtz.com
Sales Range: $100-124.9 Million
Emp.: 84
Provider of Cigarettes
N.A.I.C.S.: 424940
Everat Manors (Mgr-Sls)
James Ulery (Pres)

**AMSTERDAM HOUSE CON-
TINUING CARE RETIREMENT
COMMUNITY, INC.**

1060 Amsterdam Ave, New York, NY
10025
Tel.: (212) 575-3322   NY
Year Founded: 2004
Sales Range: $10-24.9 Million
Emp.: 240
Continuing Care Retirement Commu-
nity Operator
N.A.I.C.S.: 623311
Mark Pancirer (CFO)
James Davis (CEO)

AMSTORE CORPORATION

3951 Trade Dr SE, Grand Rapids, MI
49508
Tel.: (616) 247-7100   MI
Web Site: https://www.amstore.com
Year Founded: 1914
Sales Range: $75-99.9 Million
Emp.: 150
Provider of Store Fixtures & Wood
Showcases
N.A.I.C.S.: 337212
Richard F. Kaufman (COO)
Greg Kaufman (Pres & CEO)
Tammy Guiles (CFO)

**AMT DATASOUTH CORPORA-
TION**

803 Camarillo Springs Rd Ste D, Ca-
marillo, CA 93012
Tel.: (805) 388-5799   CA
Web Site:
   https://www.amtdatasouth.com
Year Founded: 1982
Rev.: $30,000,000
Emp.: 15
Designer, Developer & Distributor of
Computer Printers
N.A.I.C.S.: 541715
Joseph Eichberger (Pres & CEO)
Kim Stovall (Mgr-Natl Sls)
James Nolan (VP-Ops)
Mike Denny (Reg Mgr-East Territory)

Subsidiaries:

AMT Datasouth Corporation   (1)
5033 Sironx, Charlotte, NC 28273 (100%)
Tel.: (704) 523-8500
Web Site: http://www.amtprinters.com
Sales Range: $10-24.9 Million
Mfr of Computer Printers
N.A.I.C.S.: 334118

AMTEC CORPORATION

500 Wynn Dr NW Ste 314, Huntsville,
AL 35816

Tel.: (256) 722-7200
Web Site: http://www.amtec-corp.com
Rev.: $19,000,000
Emp.: 250
Research Services
N.A.I.C.S.: 541910
Larry Johnson (Dir-Test Ops)
Judy Behrens (Engr-Quality)
Phil Thompson (Engr-Product & Proj-
ect)
James Sheehy (Dir-Survivability Pro-
grams)
Shirley Hinkle (Mgr-HR)

**AMTEL SECURITY SYSTEMS,
INC.**

1 Amtel Plz 1691 NW 107th Ave, Mi-
ami, FL 33172-2707
Tel.: (305) 591-8200   FL
Year Founded: 1982
Sales Range: $50-74.9 Million
Emp.: 25
Mfr of Pre-Entry Telephonic Security
Systems, Alarm Panels & Parking
Barrier Gates
N.A.I.C.S.: 335999
Suresh Gajwani (Pres)

AMTEX BANCSHARES INC.

6608 Interstate Route 10 W, Orange,
TX 77632
Tel.: (409) 882-0071
Sales Range: $10-24.9 Million
Emp.: 87
State Commercial Banking Services
N.A.I.C.S.: 522110
Ben Thacker (CFO)

Subsidiaries:

Bridge City State Bank   (1)
701 W Roundbunch, Bridge City, TX 77611
Tel.: (409) 735-3516
Web Site:
   http://www.bridgecitystatebank.com
Sales Range: $25-49.9 Million
Emp.: 33
State Commercial Banks
N.A.I.C.S.: 522110
Scott Hale (Pres)

Pavillion Bank   (1)
1200 W Cambell Rd, Richardson, TX 75080
Tel.: (972) 380-0700
Web Site: http://www.pavillionbank.com
Sales Range: $25-49.9 Million
Emp.: 18
State Commercial Banks
N.A.I.C.S.: 522110
Steve Storey (Pres)

Peoples State Bank   (1)
5850 Hwy 59 S, Shepherd, TX 77371
Tel.: (936) 628-3312
Web Site: http://www.psbtexas.com
Sales Range: $25-49.9 Million
Emp.: 30
State Commercial Banks
N.A.I.C.S.: 522110
Mark Hamilton (Pres & CEO)

AMTEX SYSTEMS INC.

50 Broad St Rm 801, New York, NY
10004
Tel.: (212) 269-6448   DE
Web Site:
   http://www.amtexsystems.com
Year Founded: 1995
Sales Range: $10-24.9 Million
Emp.: 180
Provider of Computer Related Con-
sulting Services
N.A.I.C.S.: 541512
Sainath Pokala (Pres)
Thomas Chandy (Mgr-Resource)
Mallika Kasbekar (Sr Acct Mgr)
Donna Lester (Acct Mgr)
Glenn Knowles (Mgr-Bus Dev)
Rishi Keshavalu (Acct Mgr)

Sara Kaur (VP-IT Consulting & Solu-
tions & Staffing)
Dinu Kotian (CFO)
Deepa Lokendernath (Mgr-Sls)

AMTRAC OF OHIO, INC.

11842 Lincolnway E, Wooster, OH
44667
Tel.: (330) 683-7206
Web Site: http://www.amtracohio.com
Year Founded: 1969
Sales Range: $10-24.9 Million
Emp.: 55
Other Heavy & Civil Engineering
Construction Services
N.A.I.C.S.: 237990
Rick Geib (Pres)

AMTREX, INC.

5000 Birch St Ste 8000, Newport
Beach, CA 92660
Tel.: (949) 833-0500
Web Site: http://www.amtrex.com
Rev.: $30,000,000
Emp.: 25
Freight Transportation Arrangement
N.A.I.C.S.: 488510
Eric Scott (Co-Founder & Chm)

**AMULET CAPITAL PARTNERS,
L.P.**

55 Railroad Ave Ste 302, Greenwich,
CT 06830
Tel.: (646) 561-6655
Web Site:
   http://www.amuletcapital.com
Privater Equity Firm
N.A.I.C.S.: 523999
Ramsey Frank (Co-Founder & Part-
ner)
Jay Rose (Co-Founder & Co-Partner)
Nick Amigone (Partner)
Gabriel Luft (Principal)

Subsidiaries:

Genetics & IVF Institute, Inc.   (1)
3015 Williams Dr, Fairfax, VA 22031
Tel.: (703) 698-7355
Web Site: https://www.givf.com
Sales Range: $25-49.9 Million
Emp.: 350
Comprehensive Fertility Services
N.A.I.C.S.: 621511
Don Marazzo (Dir-MicroSort Medical)
Lauren Haring (Mgr-Practice & Dir-Nursing)
Weipeng Zhao (Pres-Intl Div)
Sean Swindell (Co-CEO)
Nadeem Malik (Co-CEO)

Unlock Health, Inc.   (1)
209 10th Ave S Ste 530, Nashville, TN
37203
Tel.: (615) 266-0790
Web Site: https://www.unlockhealthnow.com
Business Consulting & Services
N.A.I.C.S.: 541618

Subsidiary (Domestic):

SPM Marketing & Communications,
LLC   (2)
15 W Harris Ave Ste 300, La Grange, IL
60525-2498
Tel.: (708) 246-7700
Web Site: http://www.spmmarketing.com
Advertising Agencies
N.A.I.C.S.: 541810
Larry Margolis (Mng Partner)
Donna L. Greene (VP & Acct Director)
Dan Miers (Chief Strategy Officer)
Patti Winegar (Mng Partner)
Amy Ralston (Dir-Integrated Media)
Laura Roberts (VP & Acct Dir)
Shannon Curran (Sr V& & Group Acct Dir)
Bill Tourlas (Sr VP-Innovation and Engage-
ment)
Jim Larmon (Exec Dir-Creative)
Julie Hubert (VP & Acct Director)
Cori Ahrens (VP & Acct Director)
Kara Rozek (Dir-Group Media)
Kaela Carey (Digital Strategist)
Maggie Checinski (Dir-Integrated Media)

Marty Horn (Dir-Consumer Insights & Res)
Lei Wang (Dir-Consumer Insights & Res)
Bob Konold (Dir-Creative)
Laura Eboli (Dir-Creative)
Frank Oles (Dir-Creative)
Devin Grimes (Dir-Creative)

Subsidiary (Domestic):

Centretek Solutions, LLC (3)
8318 Forrest St Ste 2, Ellicott City, MD 21043-4769
Tel.: (410) 465-4880
Web Site: http://www.centretek.com
Data Processing, Hosting & Related Services
N.A.I.C.S.: 518210
Jerry A. Hanline (Pres)

AMUNDSEN DAVIS LLC
150 N Michigan Ave Ste 3300, Chicago, IL 60601
Tel.: (312) 894-3200
Web Site:
   https://www.amundsendavislaw.com
Year Founded: 1997
Emp.: 134
Law firm
N.A.I.C.S.: 541110
Heather A. Bailey (Partner)
Molly A. Arranz (Partner)
Kristina Clarke (Sec-Legal)
Jayne Long (Sec-Legal)
Alicia McKenzie (Sec-Legal)
Elizabeth Lum (Atty)
Heather Bub (Partner)
Stephen Stitle (Mng Partner-Indiana)
Moses Suarez (Partner)
Elisabeth Townsend Bridge (Partner-Intellectual Property Grp-Milwaukee)
Joe Trevino (Partner)

Subsidiaries:

Crabbe Brown & James, LLP (1)
500 S Front St Ste 1200, Columbus, OH 43215
Tel.: (614) 228-5511
Web Site: http://www.cbjlawyers.com
Emp.: 29
Law firm
N.A.I.C.S.: 541110
John P. Kennedy (Partner)
Vincent J. Lodico (Partner)
Richard D. Wetzel (Partner)
David Edelstein (Mng Partner)
Larry H. James (Mng Partner)
John C. Albert (Partner)
Diane Artz (Paralegal)
Robert C. Buchbinder (Partner)
Christina L. Corl (Partner)
Matthew Planey (Partner)

Davis & Kuelthau, s.c. (1)
N42 W7346 W Pointe Ct, Cedarburg, WI 53012-2279
Tel.: (414) 276-0200
Web Site: http://www.dkattorneys.com
Emp.: 64
Law firm
N.A.I.C.S.: 541110
Cynthia G. Fletcher (Atty)
Scott E. Fiducci (Atty)
Joseph S. Heino (Atty)
Charles I. Henderson (Atty)
James E. Braza (Atty)
Pagette K. Fischer (Dir-Mktg & Bus Dev)
Brian F. Langenbach (Dir-IT)
Matthew R. McClean (Chm-Litigation)
Kathy L. Nusslock (COO)
Mark Andres (Atty)
Ryan Wiesner (Assoc Atty)
Joseph E. Tierney IV (Pres)

AMUNEAL MANUFACTURING CORPORATION
4737 Darrah St, Philadelphia, PA 19124
Tel.: (215) 535-3000
Web Site: https://www.amuneal.com
Year Founded: 1965
Sales Range: $1-9.9 Million
Emp.: 80
Magnetic Shield Mfr

N.A.I.C.S.: 332322
Rodney Griffin (VP-Quality Assurance)
Adam Kamens (CEO)
Symond Brain (VP-Fin & Admin)

AMURCON CORPORATION
32100 Telegraph Rd Ste 220, Bingham Farms, MI 48025-2454
Tel.: (248) 646-0202   MI
Web Site: http://www.amurcorp.com
Year Founded: 1971
Sales Range: $200-249.9 Million
Emp.: 350
Property Management Services
N.A.I.C.S.: 531210
Maureen Patterson (Dir-Human Svcs)

Subsidiaries:

Amurcon Corporation of Virginia (1)
1111 E Main St Ste 1100, Richmond, VA 23219-3547
Tel.: (804) 644-1020
Web Site: http://www.amurcon.com
Sales Range: $50-74.9 Million
Emp.: 13
Property Management
N.A.I.C.S.: 523940

AMUSEMENTS OF AMERICA INC.
24 Federal Rd, Monroe Township, NJ 08831
Tel.: (732) 446-7144
Web Site: https://www.amusementsof
   america.com
Year Founded: 1939
Sales Range: $10-24.9 Million
Emp.: 70
Operator of Mobile Carnivals
N.A.I.C.S.: 713990

AMUZA, INC.
10060 Carroll Canyon Rd Ste 100, San Diego, CA 92131
Tel.: (858) 225-6869
Web Site: http://www.amuzainc.com
Year Founded: 2012
Sales Range: $1-9.9 Million
Emp.: 9
Laboratory Equipment Distr
N.A.I.C.S.: 423490
Shinji Azuma (Pres)

AMWAT MOVING WAREHOUSING & STORAGE
319 Ross Rd, Tallahassee, FL 32305
Tel.: (850) 877-7131
Web Site:
   https://www.amwatmovers.com
Year Founded: 1997
Sales Range: $1-9.9 Million
Moving, Warehousing & Storage
N.A.I.C.S.: 484110
Gloria Pugh (Pres & CEO)
Dean Pugh (COO)

AMWELD BUILDING PRODUCTS INC.
PO Box 516, North Jackson, OH 44451
Tel.: (330) 527-4385
Web Site: http://www.amweld.com
Year Founded: 1946
Rev.: $23,100,000
Emp.: 175
Mfr of Metal Doors
N.A.I.C.S.: 332321
Michael Morgan (Pres)
Dan Smith (Mgr-Natl Field Sls)
John Goforth (National Sls Mgr)
Frank Berning (Acct Mgr)
John Kish (Dir-Corp Mktg)

AMWINS GROUP, INC.
4725 Piedmont Row Dr Ste 600, Charlotte, NC 28210-4283

Tel.: (704) 749-2700   DE
Web Site: http://www.amwins.com
Year Founded: 1998
Specialty Insurance Products Wholesale Distr & Services
N.A.I.C.S.: 524298
Scott M. Purviance (CEO)
Samuel H. Fleet (Pres-Grp Benefits Div)
Kristin L. Downey (Dir-HR)
Donna L. Hargrove (Gen Counsel)
James C. Drinkwater (Pres & Chm-Amwins Global Risks)
Tom Lott (Dir-Mktg, Practices & Client Relationships)
Benjamin Sloop (COO)
Todd Atwood (CIO)
William Nichols (Dir-Bus Dev)
Darin K. Stafford (CFO)
James Gresham (Pres-Access)
Alex Kaplan (Exec VP-Alternative Risk)
Mark R. Bernacki (Pres-Special Risk Underwriters & Exec VP)
Matthew Crane (Pres-Intl Div)
Tom Graham (Dir-Casualty-Amwins Global Risks)
Roddy Graham (Mng Dir-Amwins Global Risks)
Lisa Kuszmar (Sr VP)
Sam Baig (Co-Pres-Amwins Brokerage)
Jeff McNatt (Co-Pres-Amwins Brokerage)
Ryan Armijo (Pres-Underwriting)

Subsidiaries:

AmWINS Group, Inc. - Redondo Beach (1)
435 N Pacific Coast Hwy #200, Redondo Beach, CA 90277
Tel.: (310) 372-9115
Web Site: http://www.bgsurplus.com
Insurance Brokerage Services
N.A.I.C.S.: 524210
Andrea Riccardi (Asst VP)
Becky Martin (Asst Mgr-Acctg)
Corinne M. Jones (Dir-Ops)
Lori Rodriguez (Sr VP)
Michael Hansard (Mgr-Acctg Ops)
Nancy Petru (VP)
Robert Abramson (Exec VP)
Tiffany McPartland (Sr VP)
Alyssa Scruggs (Coord-Surplus Lines)
Doug Pohlner (Mgr-Claims)
Jeff Tuccinardi (VP)
Jenni Boyer (VP)
Kay Fourquet (VP)
Linda Long (VP)
Lindsay Leamy (VP)
Liz Kaintz (Mgr-Client Svcs)
Michael Nguyen (VP)
Monique Echols (Mgr-HR)
Pam Streeter (VP)
Shane Bouma (Sr VP)
Cindy Hand (VP)
John Trittipo (Asst VP)
Kelly Scherm (VP)
Wade Lupe (VP)

American Southwest Insurance Managers, Inc. (1)
2600 N Central Expy Ste 700, Richardson, TX 75080-1316
Tel.: (972) 238-4000
Web Site:
   http://www.americansouthwest.com
Sales Range: $10-24.9 Million
Insurance Agents, Brokers & Service
N.A.I.C.S.: 524210
Doug Hite (Mgr-IT)
Gigi Iskander (Controller)

Atlantic Risk Specialists, Inc. (1)
1 International Blvd Ste 350, Mahwah, NJ 07495
Tel.: (201) 661-2300
Web Site: http://www.arspecialists.com
Insurance Products Wholesale & Management Services
N.A.I.C.S.: 524210
Larry Maier (CEO)

Connected Risk Solutions, LLC (1)

30 S Wacker Dr St 1425, Chicago, IL 60606
Tel.: (847) 832-9100
Insurance Brokerage Services
N.A.I.C.S.: 524210

Subsidiary (Domestic):

Highland Risk Services LLC (2)
2 Northfield Plz 570 Rd Ste 330, Northfield, IL 60093
Tel.: (847) 832-9100
Web Site: http://www.highlandrisk.com
Leather Goods Mfr
N.A.I.C.S.: 315210
Brian G. Daly (Pres)

Gresham & Associates, Inc. (1)
1 Gresham Landing, Stockbridge, GA 30281
Tel.: (770) 389-1600
Web Site: http://www.gresham-inc.com
Sales Range: $150-199.9 Million
Emp.: 220
Insurance Brokers
N.A.I.C.S.: 524210
James V. Gresham (Founder & Chm)
Tony Gresham (Pres)
George L. Abernathy (Vice Chm)
Betty Porter (Sr VP-Property & Casualty Underwriter)
Bob Reardon (VP & Dir-Mktg)

Group Benefit Services Inc. (1)
6 N Park Dr Ste 310, Hunt Valley, MD 21030
Tel.: (410) 832-1300
Web Site: http://www.g-b-s.com
Insurance Agents
N.A.I.C.S.: 524210
Greg Troupe (VP-Sls & Dir-Voluntary Benefits)
Cameira Taylor (Mgr-HR)
Dave Abeshouse (VP-Info Tech)
Cynthia A. Whitehead (VP-Admin)
James M. Deren (CEO)
Michael CalhoonRe (Reg Dir-Mktg)
Larry Gibson (Mktg Dir-Northern Missouri & Eastern Kansas)
Lewis E. LeBrun II (VP-Claims, CarePlus & Bus Analysis)
David Cardwell Sr. (Exec VP-Bus Dev)

Impact Interactive, LLC (1)
5400 Laurel Springs Pkwy Ste 1003, Suwanee, GA 30024-6025
Tel.: (800) 768-6856
Web Site: http://www.impact.amwins.com
Emp.: 20
Benefits Enrollment & Administration Services
N.A.I.C.S.: 425120

M.T. Donahoe & Associates, LLC (1)
9841 Broken Land Pkwy Ste 116, Columbia, MD 21046
Web Site: http://www.mtda.com
Financial & Support Services
N.A.I.C.S.: 561990
Patrick Donahoe (VP-New Bus Dev)
Heather Edwards (Office Mgr)
Michael Donahoe Jr. (Pres)

National Truck Underwriting Managers, Inc. (1)
5001 American Blvd W # 801, Minneapolis, MN 55437
Tel.: (952) 893-1234
Web Site: http://www.ntuminc.com
Sales Range: $10-24.9 Million
Emp.: 49
Insurance Agencies & Brokerages
N.A.I.C.S.: 524210
James Joyce Jr. (Pres)

Partners Specialty Group LLC (1)
100 Tournament Dr Ste 214, Horsham, PA 19044
Tel.: (484) 322-0400
Web Site: http://www.psgins.com
Emp.: 160
Specialty Insurance Broker
N.A.I.C.S.: 524210
Daniel McDonnell (Founder & CEO)

THB Group Limited (1)
Murray House Murray Road, Orpington, BR5 3QY, Kent, United Kingdom
Tel.: (44) 1689883500
Web Site: http://www.thbgroup.com

AmWINS Group, Inc.—(Continued)

Sales Range: $1-9.9 Million
Holding Company; Insurance & Reinsurance Brokerage & Risk Management Services
N.A.I.C.S.: 551112
Rob S. Wilkinson (Comml Dir)
Stephen D. Crowe (Sec)
Sasa Brcerevic (COO)
Joaquim Caria (Mng Dir-Europe)
Rodrigo Botelho (Dir-Europe)
Kay Smith (Grp CFO)
Malcolm Beane (Chm)
Matthew Crane (CEO)

Subsidiary (Domestic):

Thompson Heath & Bond
Limited   (2)
Ground Floor 107 Leadenhall Street, London, EC3A 4AF, United Kingdom
Tel.: (44) 8707515077
Web Site: http://www.thbgroup.com
Insurance Brokers
N.A.I.C.S.: 524210
Robert S. Wilkinson (Dir-Fin)

Subsidiary (Non-US):

PWS East Asia Pte Limited   (3)
600 N Bridge Rd 14-09/10, Parkview Sq, Singapore, 188778, Singapore
Tel.: (65) 63361771
Reinsurance Brokerage Services
N.A.I.C.S.: 524130

Subsidiary (US):

THB International Inc   (3)
801 Brickell Ave Ste 943, Miami, FL 33131-2987
Tel.: (786) 375-5015
Securities Brokerage Services
N.A.I.C.S.: 523150

Subsidiary (Domestic):

THB UK Limited   (3)
107 Leadenhall Street, London, EC3A 4AF, United Kingdom
Tel.: (44) 8707 515077
Web Site: http://www.thbgroup.com
Emp.: 300
General Insurance Services
N.A.I.C.S.: 524210
Frank Murthy (Mng Dir)

Subsidiary (Domestic):

Cardinus Risk Management
Limited   (4)
4th Floor East Grinstead House Wood Street, East Grinstead, RH19 1UZ, West Sussex, United Kingdom
Tel.: (44) 20 7469 0200
Web Site: http://www.cardinus.com
Emp.: 35
Risk Management Software Solutions
N.A.I.C.S.: 513210
Andrew Hawkes (CEO)
James Truscott (Chm)
Jon Abbott (Mng Dir-Cardinus Ergonomics & Safety)
Marcus Noble (Dir-Customer Svcs)
Barbara Snape (Dir-IT)

THB Risk Solutions Limited   (4)
10 Flag Bus Exchange, Vicarage Farm Rd, Peterborough, PE1 5SL, United Kingdom
Tel.: (44) 1733426000
Emp.: 35
Insurance Products & Services Dsitr
N.A.I.C.S.: 524298
Claire Carpenter (Sec)
Darren Nightingale (CEO)
Declan Durkan (Mng Dir)

Division (Non-US):

Thompson Heath & Bond Limited -
European Division   (3)
Building Parktoren Van Heuven Goedhart-laan 7-13, Diemen, 1181 LE, Amsterdam, Netherlands
Tel.: (31) 20 695 9798
Reinsurance Brokerage Services
N.A.I.C.S.: 524130

The American Equity Underwriters,
Inc.   (1)

11 N Water St 32nd Fl, Mobile, AL 36602
Tel.: (251) 431-6112
Web Site: http://www.amequity.com
Insurance Services
N.A.I.C.S.: 524210
Michael L. Lapeyrouse (Pres & CEO)
Jimmy Burgin (Sr VP & Dir-Loss Control)
Julie Bland (Sr VP-Underwriting)
Donna Long (Sr VP-Claims)
Jack Martone (Sr VP-Advisory Svcs)
Andrea Mills (Sr VP & Dir-Bus Dev & Comm)
Mike Adams (Exec VP & Dir-Advantage)
Holly Chapman (CFO)
Tim Dunne (Sr VP & Dir-Info Sys)
Amanda Knapstein (Sr VP & Dir-Fin)
Sandra Parker (Sr VP & Dir-Acct Mgmt)
Royce Ray (Sr VP & Dir-Special Investigations)
Adele Hapworth (COO)
Tim Finnorn (Mng Dir)
Teresa Rowell (Mng Dir)
Winchester Thurber (Mng Dir)
Will Scheffler (Sr VP & Dir-Claims Svcs)

WEBTPA, Inc.   (1)
8500 Freeport Pkwy, Irving, TX 75063-1937
Tel.: (469) 417-1700
Web Site: http://www.webtpaes.com
Data Processing, Hosting & Related Services
N.A.I.C.S.: 518210
Michael McCabe (Pres & CEO)
Megan Rigby (Chief Growth Officer)
Scott Chapman (VP-Bus Dev)

Worldwide Facilities, LLC   (1)
725 S Figeroa St 19th Fl, Los Angeles, CA 90017
Tel.: (213) 236-4500
Web Site: http://www.wwfi.com
Wholesale Insurance Broker
N.A.I.C.S.: 524210
Davis D. Moore (CEO)
Ronald Austin (Pres)
Cameron Kelly (COO)
Eric Stuckman (Pres-Brokerage)
Nicole Rickett (VP-Transportation-Chicago & Atlanta)
Garett Kaneko (Exec VP-Natl Client Mgmt & Sls)
Juliet Carrillo (Asst VP)
John Curry (Sr VP-New York)
Frank Caplan (Asst VP-New York)
John Baran (Gen Counsel)
Gary Kitchen (Pres-MGA)
Hank Haldeman (Pres-Programs)

Subsidiary (Domestic):

Clearwater Underwriters, Inc.   (2)
50 S Belcher Rd Ste 101, Clearwater, FL 33765
Tel.: (727) 791-6030
Web Site:
    http://www.clearwaterunderwriter.com
Insurance Agencies & Brokerages
N.A.I.C.S.: 524210
Guy Waters (Sr VP)
Don Waters (Pres)

Division (Domestic):

McClelland & Hine   (2)
2200 Thousand Oaks Ste 100, San Antonio, TX 78232
Tel.: (210) 366-2500
Web Site: http://www.mhi-mga.com
Commercial Auto & Life Insurance Services
N.A.I.C.S.: 524210
Amicia Hine (Pres & CEO)
Lorrie Cheshier (Sr VP & Branch Mgr)
Micayla Brooks (Dir-Bus Dev)
Dave Jones (VP-Excess & Brokerage Casualty)
Lynn Bordelon (Sr VP-Dallas)
Shannon Dahlke Applegate (Sr VP-Houston & Atlanta)
Robert McCallum (CTO)
Ron Lloyd (CFO)
Gilbert C. Hine Jr. (Chm & Chief Strategic Officer)

Subsidiary (Domestic):

Royal Oak Underwriters, Inc.   (2)
8417 Patterson Ave, Richmond, VA 23229
Tel.: (804) 741-7999
Web Site:
    http://www.royaloakunderwriters.com

Insurance Management Services
N.A.I.C.S.: 524298
Bev Gravatt (Office Mgr)
Patti Nunnally (CEO)

Division (Domestic):

Trinity Underwriting Managers,
Inc.   (2)
2100 Pooler Pkwy, Pooler, GA 31322
Tel.: (912) 450-7500
Web Site: http://www.tumi-ins.com
Insurance Agencies & Brokerages
N.A.I.C.S.: 524210
Stephen Standing (Principal)

eReinsure.com, Inc.   (1)
420 E S Temple Ste 400, Salt Lake City, UT 84111
Tel.: (801) 521-0600
Web Site: http://www.ereinsure.com
Insurance & Reinsurance Services
N.A.I.C.S.: 524210
David Winslow (VP-Dev)
Dion Davidson (Mgr-Product)
Igor Best-Devereux (Pres)
Joel Barraza (VP-Ops)
Mark Nielson (VP-Quality Assurance)

Subsidiary (Non-US):

eReinsure (UK) Limited   (2)
Suite 820 Lloyds Building 1 Lime Street, London, EC3M 7HA, United Kingdom
Tel.: (44) 2073273555
Insurance & Reinsurance Services
N.A.I.C.S.: 524130
Drew Bolton (Product Mgr-European)

AMX INTERNATIONAL, INC.
346 Grand Loop, Rexburg, ID 83440
Tel.: (208) 523-3671
Web Site: http://www.amxinc.com
Rev.: $16,800,000
Emp.: 100
Software Publisher
N.A.I.C.S.: 513210
Jay Price (Founder, Pres & CEO)
Andy MacKay (Founder & CTO)
Scott Sears (VP-Software Svcs & Sls)
Darin Stoddard (VP-Strategic Alliances & Mktg)

AMY LYNN, INC.
5800 Maple Ave, Dallas, TX 75235
Tel.: (214) 350-2488
Rev.: $10,170,248
Emp.: 50
Gift Shop
N.A.I.C.S.: 424940
Gerald A. Shults (Pres)

AMY'S KITCHEN, INC.
2330 Northpoint Pkwy, Santa Rosa, CA 95407
Tel.: (707) 578-7270
Web Site: http://www.amys.com
Year Founded: 1987
Rev.: $200,000,000
Emp.: 900
Healthy Food Mfr
N.A.I.C.S.: 311999
Andy Berliner (Founder)
Tom Mello (Mgr-Organic Agriculture)
Rachel Berliner (Co-Owner)
Damien Threadgold (Dir-Sls-UK)
Xavier Unkovic (CEO)

AMYX, INC.
12355 Sunrise Valley Dr, Reston, VA 20191
Tel.: (703) 373-1984
Web Site: http://www.amyx.com
Year Founded: 1999
Sales Range: $10-24.9 Million
Emp.: 115
Information Technology & Engineering Services
N.A.I.C.S.: 541330
Scott Amey (Chm)
Faye Granger (VP-Bus Ops)

Michael Kleeblatt (VP-Bus Dev)
William Schaefer (Pres & CEO)
Christopher Ziniti (VP-Defense)
Roman Dzialo (VP-Strategic Programs)
Ryan Marsden (CFO)
Alex Forti (Dir-Bus Dev)

AMZ FINANCIAL INSURANCE SERVICES, LLC
1107 Investment Blvd Ste 150, El Dorado Hills, CA 95762
Tel.: (916) 939-3765
Web Site:
    http://www.amzfinancial.com
Insurance Provider
N.A.I.C.S.: 524298
Allie Miller (CEO)
Jason Konopik (CFO)
Joseph Zuccolotto (Pres & COO)
Dave Zuccolotto (VP-Mktg)

Subsidiaries:

Partners Advantage Insurance
Services   (1)
4204 Riverwalk Pkwy Ste 300, Riverside, CA 92505
Tel.: (951) 977-2600
Web Site:
    http://www.humana.partnersadvantage.com
Insurance Agencies & Brokerages
N.A.I.C.S.: 524210
Charlie Gipple (Sr VP-Sls & Mktg)
James Wong (Pres-Platinum Distr)
Scott Tietz (CEO)
Patrick Amaya (Gen Counsel)
Chris Griffith (CFO)
Jeff Janes (CMO)
Jake Marxen (Sr VP-Premier Distr)
Louis Slagle (Sr VP-Advantage Distr)
Joe Zuccolotto (COO)

AMZAK CAPITAL MANAGEMENT, LLC
980 N Federal Hwy Ste 315, Boca Raton, FL 33432
Tel.: (561) 953-4164
Web Site: http://www.amzak.com
Year Founded: 2008
Privater Equity Firm
N.A.I.C.S.: 523999
Michael David Kazma (Pres & CEO)
Gerald J. Kazma (Chm)
Beatriz Beltranena (Gen Counsel)
Mark Fields (Operating Partner)
Andres Bethencourt (VP-Direct Investments)
Luis Espinal (VP-Direct Investments)
Eduardo Arguello (VP-Direct Investments)
Chris Woodburn (VP-Direct Investments)
Joanne Rodriguez (Controller)
Marco Mendez (Mgr-Info)

Subsidiaries:

Stamptech, Inc.   (1)
445 W Queen St, Southington, CT 06489
Tel.: (860) 628-9090
Web Site: http://www.stamptechinc.com
Metal Stamping Equipment Distr
N.A.I.C.S.: 423510
Eric Kubeck (Mgr-Ops)
Tony Amato (Pres)
Pat Clavet (Office Mgr)

AMZUR TECHNOLOGIES, INC.
405 N Reo St Ste110, Tampa, FL 33609
Tel.: (813) 600-4060
Web Site: https://www.amzur.com
Year Founded: 2004
Sales Range: $1-9.9 Million
Emp.: 100
Software Development Services
N.A.I.C.S.: 513210
Bala Nemani (CEO)

Subsidiaries:

Amzur Technologies (I) Private
Limited (1)
9-29-22 2nd Floor Pioneer Sankar Shantini-
ketan, Balaji Nagar, Siripuram, Visakhapat-
nam, 530003, India
Tel.: (91) 891 6451882
Software Development Services
N.A.I.C.S.: 513210

AN GLOBAL I.T. S.A.P.I. DE C.V.
222 Urban Towers Ste 1650 E, Irving,
TX 75039
Tel.: (972) 501-1441
Web Site: http://www.anglobal.com
Software Development Services
N.A.I.C.S.: 513210
Manuel Senderos (Chm, Pres &
Founder)

Subsidiaries:

Motivus (1)
222 W Las Colinas Blvd Ste 1650 E, Irving,
TX 75039
Tel.: (971) 501-1440
Web Site: https://motivus.com
Emp.: 176
Software Publisher
N.A.I.C.S.: 513210
Manuel Senderos (Chm & CEO)

AN INTERNET GROUP
858 Alta Vista Dr, Pacifica, CA
94044-3486
Tel.: (650) 359-8800
Sales Range: $10-24.9 Million
Emp.: 40
Wired Telecommunication Services
N.A.I.C.S.: 517111
Myles Kleinfeld (Principal)

ANABIOS CORPORATION
3030 Bunker Hill St Ste 312, San Di-
ego, CA 92109-5754
Tel.: (858) 366-8608
Web Site: http://www.anabios.com
Research & Development in Biotech-
nology
N.A.I.C.S.: 541714
Andre Ghetti (CEO)
Blake Anson (VP-Bus Dev)

Subsidiaries:

Cell Systems LLC (1)
12815 NE 124th St Ste A, Kirkland, WA
98034-8313
Tel.: (425) 823-1010
Web Site: http://www.cell-systems.com
Biotechnology Research & Development
Services
N.A.I.C.S.: 541714
Jesse Damm (CEO)

ANABOLIC LABORATORIES INC.
17802 Gillette Ave, Irvine, CA 92614
Tel.: (949) 863-0340
Web Site:
http://www.anaboliclabs.com
Year Founded: 1925
Rev.: $60,000,000
Emp.: 190
Mfr of Pharmaceuticals & Dietary
Supplements
N.A.I.C.S.: 424210
Steven Brown (Pres)
Mark Nishi (CFO)

ANACONDA SPORTS, INC.
85 Katrine Ln, Lake Katrine, NY
12449
Tel.: (845) 336-4550
Web Site:
http://www.anacondasports.com
Sales Range: $125-149.9 Million
Emp.: 140
Sporting & Recreation Goods

N.A.I.C.S.: 423910
Miles Joseph (VP-Product Dev)
Ralph Weekly (Dir-Dev)

ANADARKO INDUSTRIES, LLC
17625 El Camino Real Ste 410,
Houston, TX 77058
Tel.: (281) 286-9200   TX
Web Site: http://www.anadarko-
industries.com
Year Founded: 2003
Sales Range: $25-49.9 Million
Emp.: 154
Engineering, IT & Logistics
N.A.I.C.S.: 541330
Mike Reeves (VP-Bus Dev)
Kenn Hall (Pres & CEO)

ANAHEIM AMATEUR HOCKEY ASSOCIATION
300 W Lincoln Ave, Anaheim, CA
92805
Tel.: (714) 545-7465
Web Site: http://www.jrducks.com
Rev.: $3,939,437
Emp.: 1
Fiscal Year-end: 06/30/14
Hockey League Organizer
N.A.I.C.S.: 711211
Cindy Frazier (VP)
Art Trottier (Pres)
Chris Carcerano (VP)
Carrie Collodel (CFO)
Craig Johnson (Dir-Coaches)

ANAHEIM DUCKS HOCKEY CLUB, LLC
Honda Ctr 2695 E Katella Ave, Ana-
heim, CA 92806
Tel.: (714) 940-2900   CA
Web Site: http://www.ducks.nhl.com
Year Founded: 1992
Sales Range: $10-24.9 Million
Emp.: 200
Professional Hockey Club
N.A.I.C.S.: 711211
Michael Schulman (CEO)
Bob Murray (Pres-Hockey Ops)
David McNab (Sr VP-Hockey Ops)
Doug Heller (CFO & VP-Fin)
Susan Samueli (Co-Owner)
Tim Ryan (COO & Exec VP)
Rick Paterson (Dir-Player Personnel)
Martin Madden (Dir-Scouting, Pro &
Amateur)
Doug Shearer (Mgr-Equipment)
Aaron Teats (CMO & VP)
Alex Gilchrist (Dir-Media & Comm)
Matt Savant (Dir-Mktg & Brand Mgmt)
Melody Martin (Controller)
Adam Brady (Dir-Publ & New Media)
Jim Panetta (Dir-Premium Sls & Svc)
Lisa Johnson (Dir-Ticket Sls & Svcs)
Jay Scott (VP-HR)
Ari Segal (Pres-Bus Ops)
Bill Pedigo (Chief Comm Officer)
Bob Ferguson (Gen Mgr)
Henry Samueli (Co-Owner)

ANAHEIM TRANSPORTATION NETWORK
1354 S Anaheim Blvd, Anaheim, CA
92805
Tel.: (714) 563-5287   CA
Web Site: https://www.rideart.org
Year Founded: 1995
Sales Range: $10-24.9 Million
Emp.: 36
Transportation Services
N.A.I.C.S.: 488999
Diana Kotler (Exec Dir)
Paul Sanford (Chm)

ANALYSIS & MEASUREMENT SERVICES CORPORATION

9119 Cross Park Dr, Knoxville, TN
37923
Tel.: (865) 691-1756
Web Site: https://www.ams-corp.com
Year Founded: 1977
Sales Range: $1-9.9 Million
Emp.: 55
Instrument Manufacturing for Measur-
ing & Testing Electricity & Electrical
Signals
N.A.I.C.S.: 334515
H. M. Hashemian (Pres & CEO)
Darrell W. Mitchell (Mgr-Technical
Svcs)
Mehrad Hashemian (Mgr-Field Test-
ing)
Greg W. Morton (Mgr-Software Dev)

ANALYSIS GROUP, INC.
111 Huntington Ave 13th Fl, Boston,
MA 02199
Tel.: (617) 425-8000
Web Site:
https://www.analysisgroup.com
Year Founded: 1981
Sales Range: $10-24.9 Million
Emp.: 300
Economic, Financial & Business
Strategy Consulting Services
N.A.I.C.S.: 541611
Martha S. Samuelson (Pres & CEO)
Nicholas I. Crew (Mng Principal)
Carla S. Mulhern (Mng Principal)
Richard M. Starfield (Mng Principal)
Eric Qiong Wu (Mng Principal)
Bruce F. Deal (Mng Principal)
Brian S. Gorin (Mng Principal)
John C. Jarosz (Mng Principal)
Marc Van Audenrode (Mng Principal)
Mihran Yenikomshian (Mng Principal)
Aaron Yeater (Mng Principal)
Min Yang (Mng Principal)
Hongbo Yang (Mng Principal)
Andrew Wong (Mng Principal)
Alan G. White (Mng Principal)
Kenneth Weinstein (Mng Principal)
Samuel Weglein (Mng Principal)
R. Jeffrey Malinak (Mng Principal)
Paul E. Greenberg (Mng Principal &
Dir-Health Care Practice)
Mark H. Egland (Mng Principal)
Jeffrey H. Kinrich (Mng Principal)

ANALYTIC SERVICES, INC.
5275 Leesburg Pike Ste N-5000,
Falls Church, VA 22041
Tel.: (703) 416-2000   CA
Web Site: http://www.anser.org
Year Founded: 1958
Research & Analysis Services
N.A.I.C.S.: 541715
Carmen J. Spencer (Pres & CEO)
Steve Hopkins (Pres & CEO)
Gary Struzik (CFO & VP)
Jessica Albosta (VP-Analysis & Secu-
rity)
Paul N. Stockton (Chm)

Subsidiaries:

Advanced Technology
International (1)
315 Sigma Dr, Summerville, SC 29486
Tel.: (843) 760-4500
Web Site: http://www.ati.org
Emp.: 200
Research & Analysis Services
N.A.I.C.S.: 541715
Chris Van Metre (Pres & CEO)
Robert Tuohy (COO)
Julia Martin (CFO)
Buddy McAlister (CIO)
Brian Piedfort (VP-Bus Dev & Comm)
Scott A. Savoie (Sr VP-Corp Contracts)
Ronald L. Kerber (Chm)
Ronald E. Cuneo (Vice Chm)
Kelly Cusanelli (VP-Compliance)
Brian Fitzpatrick (Chief Growth Officer)

ANALYTICAL SERVICES & MATERIALS, INC.
107 Research Dr, Hampton, VA
23666
Tel.: (757) 865-7093
Web Site: https://www.asm-usa.com
Year Founded: 1983
Rev.: $20,901,049
Emp.: 80
Research & Engineering Services
N.A.I.C.S.: 541330
Jalaiah Unnam (Pres)

ANALYTICS8, LLC
150 N Michigan Ave Ste 1580, Chi-
cago, IL 60601
Tel.: (312) 878-6600
Web Site: https://www.analytics8.com
Computer Software Development
Services
N.A.I.C.S.: 513210
David Fussichen (Pres)
Tracey Doyle (VP-Mktg)

ANALYTIX ON DEMAND, INC.
2 Park Plz Ste 200, Irvine, CA 92614
Tel.: (949) 552-4323   CA
Web Site:
http://www.analytixondemand.com
Business Information Services
N.A.I.C.S.: 519290
Vik Torpunuri (Founder & CEO)

Subsidiaries:

CentraMed, Inc. (1)
2714 Loker Ave W Ste 200, Carlsbad, CA
92010
Tel.: (760) 476-0077
Web Site: http://www.centramed.co
Sales Range: $1-9.9 Million
Emp.: 30
Healthcare Analytic Services
N.A.I.C.S.: 541618
Vik Torpunuri (CEO)

ANAM INC.
1600 E Hanley Blvd No 128, Tucson,
AZ 85737
Tel.: (520) 742-7007
Sales Range: $10-24.9 Million
Emp.: 8
Crude Petroleum Production
N.A.I.C.S.: 211120
Jennifer Sacksen (Pres)

Subsidiaries:

Bounty Holdings Inc (1)
1600 East Hanley Blvd # 128, Tucson, AZ
85737
Tel.: (520) 742-7007
Crude Petroleum Production
N.A.I.C.S.: 211120

ANAMET INC.
739 Roosevelt Rd, Glen Ellyn, IL
60137-5877
Tel.: (630) 469-1364   DE
Sales Range: $150-199.9 Million
Emp.: 800
Flexible Metal Hoses, Electrical Con-
duits & Automotive Parts
N.A.I.C.S.: 334519

Subsidiaries:

Anamet Canada, Inc. (1)
118 Lakeport Rd, PO Box 550, Colborne,
K0K 1S0, ON, Canada   (100%)
Tel.: (905) 355-2122
Web Site: http://www.anametcanada.com
Sales Range: $10-24.9 Million
Emp.: 54
Mfr of Flexible Conduits
N.A.I.C.S.: 335932

Anamet Europe B.V. (1)
Galwin 5, 1046 AW, Amsterdam,
Netherlands   (100%)
Tel.: (31) 205863586
Web Site: http://www.anameteurope.com

Anamet Inc.—(Continued)
Sales Range: $1-9.9 Million
Emp.: 40
Motor Vehicle Body Parts Mfr
N.A.I.C.S.: 336370
Cen Zanten (Mng Dir)

Flexider S.p.A.   (1)
Corso Romania 501 24, 10156, Turin, Italy
Tel.: (39) 0112627111
Web Site: http://www.flexider.com
Sales Range: $25-49.9 Million
Emp.: 250
Automotive & Aerospace Components Mfr
N.A.I.C.S.: 336110

ANANIA & ASSOCIATES INVESTMENT COMPANY LLC
2 Portland Fish Pier Ste 214, Portland, ME 04101-4698
Tel.: (207) 518-6791
Web Site: https://anania.biz
All Other Personal Services
N.A.I.C.S.: 812990
Peter Anania (Pres)
Peter V. Anania (Pres)

ANASTASI CONSTRUCTION COMPANY, L.L.C.
511 Torrance Blvd, Redondo Beach, CA 90277
Tel.: (310) 376-8077
Web Site: http://www.anastasi.com
Year Founded: 1962
Rev.: $13,000,000
Emp.: 100
Developer of Single Family Homes
N.A.I.C.S.: 237210
Wayne Anastasi (Pres)
John Dimperio (Controller)

ANASTASI DEVELOPMENT COMPANY, LLC.
511 Torrance Blvd 2nd Fl, Redondo Beach, CA 90277
Tel.: (310) 376-8077
Web Site: https://www.anastasi.com
Year Founded: 1962
Sales Range: $75-99.9 Million
Emp.: 135
Land Subdivision Services
N.A.I.C.S.: 237210
Scott Anastasi (Sr VP)

ANATOMY IT, LLC
10 New King St Ste 215, White Plains, NY 10604
Tel.: (914) 683-0005
Web Site: http://www.stratxit.com
Year Founded: 1997
Healthcare IT Integration & Support Services
N.A.I.C.S.: 541690
Tom A. Telesca (Partner)
Jennifer Driscoll (Mktg Dir)
Curt Thornton (Chief Comml Officer)
Jennifer Clarke (Sr VP-People)
Frank Forte (CEO)
David F. Smith III (CFO)

Subsidiaries:

Compufit, Inc.   (1)
1 W Red Oak Ln, White Plains, NY 10604
Tel.: (914) 741-6500
Sales Range: $1-9.9 Million
Emp.: 12
Computer & Software Stores
N.A.I.C.S.: 449210
Tara Lansen (Pres & CEO)

Iris Solutions, LLC   (1)
8700 Red Oak Blvd, Ste H, Charlotte, NC 28217
Tel.: (704) 523-3880
Web Site: http://www.irissol.com
Computer Related Services
N.A.I.C.S.: 541519
Bill Chamberlin (Owner)

ANATOMY SUPPLY PARTNERS
3450 Atlanta Industrial Pkwy, Atlanta, GA 30331
Tel.: (404) 696-6999
Web Site: http://www.anatomysupply.com
Year Founded: 2003
Rev.: $6,300,000
Emp.: 9
Medical & Hospital Equipment Whslr
N.A.I.C.S.: 423450
Lorne Tritt (Partner)
Linda Perez (Mgr-Corp Pur)
Jeffrey Bell (Controller)

ANCAP MANAGEMENT INC.
517 S Kingshighway, Cape Girardeau, MO 63703
Tel.: (573) 335-5581   MO
Web Site: http://www.coadfamilyofdealers.com
Sales Range: $25-49.9 Million
Emp.: 50
Holding Company; New & Used Car Dealership Owner & Operator
N.A.I.C.S.: 551112
Jim Smith (Pres)
Greg Kennard (Gen Mgr)

Subsidiaries:

Coad Chevrolet Inc.   (1)
517 S Kings Hwy St, Cape Girardeau, MO 63703
Tel.: (573) 335-5581
Web Site: http://www.coadchevrolet.com
New & Used Car Dealer
N.A.I.C.S.: 441110
Michael Coad (Pres)

Coad Chevrolet-Cadillac, Inc.   (1)
2525 E Vienna St, Anna, IL 62906
Tel.: (618) 833-2166
Web Site: http://www.coadchevy.com
Rev.: $6,700,000
Emp.: 27
New & Used Car Dealer
N.A.I.C.S.: 441110

ANCERO, LLC
1001 Briggs Rd Ste 220, Mount Laurel, NJ 08054
Tel.: (856) 210-5800
Web Site: http://www.ancero.com
Year Founded: 1979
Rev.: $5,800,000
Emp.: 46
Computers & Peripherals Equipment Whslr
N.A.I.C.S.: 423990
Robert Hogg (Mng Dir)
Paul Boyer (Mng Partner)
Scott Zadina (Dir-Sls)
Chad Muckenfuss (Dir-Channel Sls)

ANCHIN, BLOCK & ANCHIN LLP
1375 Broadway, New York, NY 10018
Tel.: (212) 840-3456
Web Site: https://www.anchin.com
Year Founded: 1923
Rev.: $18,200,000
Emp.: 360
Accounting, Financial & Business Services
N.A.I.C.S.: 541211
Matt J. Mullaney (Partner-Tax)
Steven Kahn (Partner)
Clarence G. Kehoe (Partner)
David J. Lamb (Partner)
Robert S. Gilman (Partner)
Marc G. Goldberg (Partner)
Scott A. Goldfond (CFO)
David Finkelstein (Dir-HR)
Michael E. Cirenza (Partner)
Kuldeepak Acharya (Partner)
Frederick Ackerman (Partner)
Fred Barotz (Dir-Tax)

Michael R. Belfer (Partner)
Peter L. Berlant (Partner)
Ehud Sadan (Partner)
Frank A. Schettino (Mng Partner-CPA)
Mark Schneider (Partner-Tax)
Jeffrey Perelman (Partner-Tax)
Mitchell Rosenthal (Partner)
Phillip M. Ross (Partner)
Carolyn Sekosan (Sr Mgr-Audit)
Daniel Shea (Sr Mgr)
Jane E. Bernardini (Partner-Tax)
Anish Shah (Dir-Audit)
Christopher J. Noble (Partner)
Antonia Greenwald (Dir-Tax)
Chris Kelly (Partner)
Jeffrey M. Palley (Partner-Tax)
Terry Pissi (Partner)
E. George Teixeira (Partner)
Edward F. Thorp (Partner)
Greg A. Wank (Partner)
Gregory Dalto (Sr Mgr-Audit)
Howard Krams (Partner)
Russell B. Shinsky (Partner)
Stephen Plattman (Partner)
Paul Gevertzman (Partner-Tax)
Deborah de Vries (Partner)
Jeffrey Bowden (Partner-Tax)
Laurence I. Feibel (Partner-Tax)
Tamir Dardashtian (Principal-Tax)
Yair Holtzman (Partner)
Gary S. Castle (Principal)
David J. Emmer (CIO)
Laurie Fasinski (Principal)
Mela Garber (Principal-Tax)
Olamide Ajibesin (Mng Dir)
E. Richard Baum (Partner-Tax)
Marc A. Federbush (Partner)
Jared Feldman (Partner)
James K. Ferrara (Partner-Tax)
David Horton (Partner)
John Ingrassia (Partner-Tax)
Michael Meehan (Partner)
Ling Ou (Partner)
Keith Peterka (Partner)
Baggeri Raymond (Partner)
Michael Greenfield (Partner-Consumer Products Grp)

Subsidiaries:

ABA Stephenson & Brook   (1)
86 Highland Ave, Salem, MA 01970
Tel.: (978) 740-6962
Web Site: http://www.stephensonandbrook.com
Sales Range: $10-24.9 Million
Emp.: 16
Risk Managemeng Srvices
N.A.I.C.S.: 541611
Bonnie Brook (Co-Founder & Pres)

Anchin Capital Advisors LLC   (1)
1375 Broadway, New York, NY 10018
Tel.: (212) 536-6859
Web Site: http://www.anchincapital.com
Emp.: 400
Investment Advisory Services
N.A.I.C.S.: 523940
Sol Lipshitz (Partner)

ANCHOR BANK
13951 Us Highway 1, Juno Beach, FL 33408
Tel.: (561) 383-3150
Web Site: http://www.anchorbank.com
Rev.: $7,845,000
Emp.: 44
Banking Services
N.A.I.C.S.: 522110
Bruce Mahon (Chm)
John Kapsis (CFO)
Nelson Hinojosa (CEO)

ANCHOR CAPITAL ADVISORS LLC
1 Post Office Sq Ste 3850, Boston, MA 02109

Tel.: (617) 338-3800
Web Site: http://www.anchorcapital.com
Year Founded: 1983
Emp.: 47
Investment Management Service
N.A.I.C.S.: 523940
David J. Watson (First VP)
J. Blake Taylor (VP-South)
Jeffrey L. Deaner (VP-West)
Daniel A. Doucette (VP-Northeast)
Jean A. Fidone-Schroer (VP-Central-West)
Jack R. Kulpa (VP-Mid-Atlantic)
Casey M. Gober (VP-Central-East)
Daniel P. Carr (VP)
Diane M. DeBono Schafer (Chief Compliance Officer)
Mark D. Bergen (Pres & COO)
Michael C. Pierre (Portfolio Mgr)
William J. Hickey (Portfolio Mgr)
Jennifer K. DeSisto (Portfolio Mgr)
Andrew P. St Martin (Portfolio Mgr)
John P. Boles (Dir-Institutional Mktg)
Robert P. Zielinski (Mktg Mgr)
George N. Whitmore (Dir-Private Clients)
Michael K. Serchen (Dir-Managed Accts)
William P. Rice Sr. (Founder & Chm)
Stephen Mead Jr. (First VP)
William P. Rice Jr. (CEO & Chief Investment Officer)

ANCHOR CNGO CORP.
301 N E St, Lake Worth, FL 33460
Tel.: (908) 892-4958   FL
Year Founded: 2012
Compressed Natural Gas Motor Vehicle Fueling Stations
N.A.I.C.S.: 457120
Gregory C. Liddy (Pres & CEO)
George B. Liddy (Sec)

ANCHOR COMMERCIAL REALTY CORP.
500 S Florida Ave Ste 700, Lakeland, FL 33801
Tel.: (863) 682-6173
Rev.: $10,977,400
Emp.: 50
Real Estate Services
N.A.I.C.S.: 531120
Benjamin Falk (CEO)

ANCHOR COMPUTER INC.
1900 New Hwy, Farmingdale, NY 11735
Tel.: (631) 293-6100
Web Site: http://www.anchorcomputer.com
Year Founded: 1974
Sales Range: $25-49.9 Million
Emp.: 150
Data Processing Services
N.A.I.C.S.: 518210
Mark Schenker (Pres)
Len Shenker (Founder & CEO)
Fred Milman (Head-Pro Consulting Svcs)

Subsidiaries:

Anchor Computer Inc.   (1)
600 Fairway Dr Ste 205, Deerfield Beach, FL 33441
Tel.: (954) 428-2270
Web Site: http://www.anchorcomputer.com
Sales Range: $1-9.9 Million
Emp.: 15
Data Processing Services
N.A.I.C.S.: 518210
Lenord Schenker (Owner)

Anchor Software LLC   (1)
400 Chisholm Pl Ste 300, Plano, TX 75075-6911
Tel.: (972) 881-2424

Web Site:
http://www.anchorcomputersoftware.com
Emp.: 18
Software Publisher
N.A.I.C.S.: 513210
Gary M. Siegel (Pres)

ANCHOR CONSTRUCTION CORPORATION

2254 25th Pl NE, Washington, DC 20018-1404
Tel.: (202) 269-6694
Web Site:
https://www.anchorconst.com
Sales Range: $25-49.9 Million
Emp.: 150
General Contractor, Highway & Street Construction
N.A.I.C.S.: 237310
Florentino Gregorio (Pres)
William Custead (Exec VP)
Trupti Kulkarni (Engr-Project Mgmt)

ANCHOR FABRICATION LTD.

1200 Lawson Rd, Fort Worth, TX 76131-2722
Tel.: (817) 232-4575
Web Site:
http://www.anchorfabrication.com
Fabricated Metal Product Manufacturing
N.A.I.C.S.: 332999

Subsidiaries:

Quality Industries, Inc.   **(1)**
130 Jones Blvd, La Vergne, TN 37086
Tel.: (615) 793-3000
Web Site: http://www.qualityindustries.com
Reusable Containers Designer & Mfr
N.A.I.C.S.: 326199
Stanley Bryan (Dir-Sls & Customer Svc)
Mike Bolden (Dir-IT)
Gary Carter (Pres)
Ricky Chaney (Gen Mgr-QI Texas)
Chad Grief (Dir-Bus Dev & Strategic Plng)
Robert Holman (Dir-Mfg & Engrng)
Cory Newsom (Controller)
Don Pettry (Dir-HR)
Mike Swift (Dir-Quality & Continuous Improvement)
JT Tapp (Mgr-Engrng)

ANCHOR GASOLINE CORPORATION

114 E 5th St, Tulsa, OK 74103-4605
Tel.: (918) 584-5291   OK
Year Founded: 1940
Sales Range: $75-99.9 Million
Emp.: 10
Extractor of Petroleum Products
N.A.I.C.S.: 445131
Wanda McCreedy (Sec)
Newman Cooke (Pres)

Subsidiaries:

Cove Petroleum   **(1)**
114 E 5th St, Tulsa, OK 74103-4605   **(100%)**
Tel.: (918) 584-5291
Sales Range: $25-49.9 Million
Emp.: 4
Oil & Gas Exploration
N.A.I.C.S.: 211120
Bill Williams (VP-Ops)

ANCHOR GENERAL INSURANCE AGENCY, INC.

10256 Meanley Dr, San Diego, CA 92131
Tel.: (858) 527-3600
Web Site:
http://www.anchorgeneral.com
Year Founded: 1995
Sales Range: $10-24.9 Million
Emp.: 203
Insurance Agency & Brokerage Services
N.A.I.C.S.: 524210
Annie Strandberg (Dir-HR)

ANCHOR INDUSTRIES, INC.

7701 Hwy 41 N, Evansville, IN 47725-1702
Tel.: (812) 867-2421   DE
Web Site: https://www.anchorinc.com
Year Founded: 1892
Sales Range: $150-199.9 Million
Emp.: 500
Mfr of Canvas Awnings, Fabric & Vinyl-Laminated Tents, Trailer & Patio Awnings & Tarpaulins, Safety Pool Covers, Custom Canvas & Synthetic Fabric Industrial Covers, Private Label Bags
N.A.I.C.S.: 314910
Pete Mogavero (Pres)
David Conner (CFO)
Roger Krebsbach (Dir-HR)
Bryan Peelman (Dir-Ops & Quality Assurance)
John Fuchs (Gen Mgr-Special Events)
Biff Gentsch (Mgr-Sls-Natl)
Joey Ruffin (VP-Engrg)
Mike Crews (Dir-Clear Span Bus & Product Dev)

Subsidiaries:

Anchor Industries, Inc. - LEISURE POOLS FACTORY   **(1)**
3567 I H 35 S, New Braunfels, TX 78132
Tel.: (830) 387-4020
Tent & Canopy Mfr
N.A.I.C.S.: 336214

Pool and Patio Works Inc.   **(1)**
178 State St, North Haven, CT 06473-2207
Tel.: (203) 239-6575
Web Site:
http://www.poolandpatioworksinc.com
Emp.: 25
Swimming Pool Maintenance Services
N.A.I.C.S.: 561790
Sandy Menillo (Owner)

ANCHOR INNOVATION, INC.

208 Golden Oak CT Ste 121, Virginia Beach, VA 23452
Tel.: (757) 962-9175
Web Site: http://www.anchori.com
Year Founded: 2002
Rev.: $3,400,000
Emp.: 7
Management Services
N.A.I.C.S.: 561110
Stephen Palmer (Founder & CEO)
Jamie Palmer (VP)
Christopher Powell (Pres)

ANCHOR MANUFACTURING GROUP, INC.

11830 Brookpark Rd, Cleveland, OH 44130-1138
Tel.: (216) 362-1850   OH
Web Site: http://www.anchor-mfg.com
Year Founded: 1970
Sales Range: $50-74.9 Million
Emp.: 300
Mfr of Tools, Dies, Jigs, Fixtures & Metal Stampings; Machining & Welding Services & Assembly
N.A.I.C.S.: 336370
Edward Pfaff (Founder & Chm)
Frederick A. Pfaff (Pres & CEO)
Robert E. Pfaff (Gen Counsel)
James Walker (CFO)

Subsidiaries:

Anchor Die Technologies   **(1)**
4541 Industrial Pkwy, Cleveland, OH 44135-4541
Tel.: (216) 671-6000
Web Site: http://www.anchordietech.com
Sales Range: $25-49.9 Million
Emp.: 9
Tool & Die Construction; Machining
N.A.I.C.S.: 336370

Anchor Metal Processing   **(1)**
11830 Brookpark Rd, Cleveland, OH 44130-1138
Tel.: (216) 362-1850
Web Site: http://www.anchor-mfg.com
Sales Range: $25-49.9 Million
Emp.: 35
MfrSheet Metal Fabrication Precision Machining Assembly Welding & Powder Coating
N.A.I.C.S.: 332710
Edward Pfaff (Chm)
Frederick A. Pfaff (Pres & CEO)
Judy Cuayle (Exec Sec)
James Walker (CFO)

ANCHOR PAINT MANUFACTURING CO. INC.

6707 E 14th St, Tulsa, OK 74112-6615
Tel.: (918) 836-4626   OK
Web Site:
https://www.anchorpaint.com
Year Founded: 1962
Sales Range: $25-49.9 Million
Emp.: 175
Mfr of Paints & Allied Products
N.A.I.C.S.: 325510

Subsidiaries:

Anchor Paint Co. of Denver Inc.   **(1)**
7205 Gilpin Way Ste 200, Denver, CO 80229
Tel.: (303) 744-2361
Web Site: http://www.archpaint.com
Sales Range: $10-24.9 Million
Emp.: 10
Paints, Varnishes & Supplies
N.A.I.C.S.: 424950

Anchor Paint Co. of Oklahoma City Inc.   **(1)**
6707 E 14th St, Tulsa, OK 74112-6615
Tel.: (918) 836-4626
Web Site: http://www.anchorpaint.com
Sales Range: $10-24.9 Million
Emp.: 3
Paint, Varnishes & Supplies
N.A.I.C.S.: 424950
Chip Meade (Co-Owner)
Justin Meade (Co-Owner)

ANCHOR PAPER COMPANY

480 Broadway St, Saint Paul, MN 55101
Tel.: (651) 298-1311
Web Site:
http://www.anchorpaper.com
Year Founded: 1923
Sales Range: $200-249.9 Million
Emp.: 150
Fine Paper
N.A.I.C.S.: 424110
Dan Anderson (Mgr-Sls)

ANCHOR PHARMACY & MEDICAL SUPPLIES

205 Washington Heights Medical Ctr, Westminster, MD 21157-5632
Tel.: (410) 848-8901
Web Site: https://www.anchorrx.com
Year Founded: 1984
Sales Range: $10-24.9 Million
Emp.: 48
Pharmaceutical Product Whslr
N.A.I.C.S.: 424210
Jeff Disney (Mgr)

ANCHOR POST PRODUCTS OF TEXAS, INC.

9765 Harry Hines Blvd, Dallas, TX 75220
Tel.: (214) 350-1900
Web Site:
https://www.anchortexas.com
Sales Range: $10-24.9 Million
Emp.: 40
Fence Construction
N.A.I.C.S.: 238990
Mike Irwin (VP)

ANCHOR QEA, LLC

720 Olive Way Ste 1900, Seattle, WA 98101
Tel.: (206) 287-9130
Web Site: http://www.anchorqea.com
Rev.: $30,000,000
Emp.: 380
Scientific & Technical Consulting Services
N.A.I.C.S.: 541690
Ed Berschinski (Partner)
Leilani McSpadden (Mgr-Acctg)
Derek Ormerod (Engr-Water Resources)

ANCHOR STONE COMPANY

4124 S Rockford Ave Ste 201, Tulsa, OK 74105-4248
Tel.: (918) 744-8820
Web Site: http://www.anchor-stone.com
Sales Range: $10-24.9 Million
Emp.: 15
Crushed & Broken Limestone Distr
N.A.I.C.S.: 212312
Tom Snyder (CEO)
Joseph L. Parker Jr. (Chm)

ANCHOR SUBARU

949 Eddie Dowling Hwy, North Smithfield, RI 02896
Tel.: (401) 769-1199
Web Site:
https://www.anchorsubaru.com
Year Founded: 1983
Sales Range: $10-24.9 Million
Emp.: 35
Car Whslr
N.A.I.C.S.: 441110
Robert B. Benoit (Owner)
Chris Benoit (VP)

ANCHOR TAMPA, INC.

3907 W Osborne Ave, Tampa, FL 33614
Tel.: (813) 879-8685
Web Site:
https://www.anchortampa.com
Year Founded: 1979
Sales Range: $10-24.9 Million
Emp.: 55
Electronic Services
N.A.I.C.S.: 236220
Jim Fowler (VP)
Paula Pino (Mgr-HR)

ANCHOR WORLDWIDE, LLC

333 Hudson St, New York, NY 10013
Tel.: (917) 472-7260
Web Site: http://www.anchorww.com
Year Founded: 2015
Sales Range: $10-24.9 Million
Emp.: 110
Media Advertising Services
N.A.I.C.S.: 541840
Sebastian Eldridge (Co-Founder & CEO)
Eric Ditzian (Co-Founder & Head-Strategy)
David Gross (Co-Founder & Head-Digital)
Saxon Eldridge (Co-Founder & Head-Production)
Javier Bonifaz (Co-Founder & Chief Creative Officer-Global)

ANCHORAGE CAPITAL GROUP, L.L.C.

610 Broadway 6th Fl, New York, NY 10012
Tel.: (212) 432-4600   NY
Web Site:
https://www.anchoragecap.com
Year Founded: 2003
Private Investment Firm
N.A.I.C.S.: 523999

Anchorage Capital Group, L.L.C.—(Continued)

Michael Charlton (Mng Dir)

Subsidiaries:

Ideal Standard International NV   (1)
Ikaroslaan 18, 1930, Zaventem, Belgium
Tel.: (32) 23256600
Web Site: http://www.idealstandard.be
Emp.: 60
Shower Enclosure & Bathroom Fixture Mfr
N.A.I.C.S.: 325620
Torsten Tuerling (CEO)

Subsidiary (Non-US):

Ideal Standard (UK) Ltd.   (2)
The Bathroom Works National Avenue,
Kingston upon Hull, HU5 4HS, United King-
dom
Tel.: (44) 1482346461
Web Site: http://www.ideal-standard.co.uk
Shower Enclosure & Bathroom Fixture Mfr
& Distr
N.A.I.C.S.: 327110
Keith Boad (Mng Dir)

Ideal Standard France   (2)
165 Avenue Du Bois De La Pie, 95920,
Roissy-en-France, France
Tel.: (33) 149382800
Web Site: http://www.idealstandard.com
Sales Range: $25-49.9 Million
Shower Enclosure & Bathroom Fixture Mfr
& Distr
N.A.I.C.S.: 327110

Ideal Standard GmbH   (2)
Euskirchener Strasse 80, PO Box 1809,
53121, Bonn, Germany
Tel.: (49) 2285210
Web Site: http://www.idealstandard.de
Sales Range: $25-49.9 Million
Shower Enclosure & Bathroom Fixture Mfr
& Distr
N.A.I.C.S.: 327110

Branch (Non-US):

Ideal Standard GmbH Zweignieder-
lassung Osterreich   (3)
Murbangasse 8, 1108, Vienna, Austria
Tel.: (43) 125662220
Web Site: http://www.idealstandard.de
Shower Enclosure & Bathroom Fixture Mfr
& Distr
N.A.I.C.S.: 327110

Subsidiary (Non-US):

Ideal Standard Italia S.r.l.   (2)
Via Domodossola 19, 20145, Milan, Italy
Web Site: http://www.idealstandard.it
Shower Enclosure & Bathroom Fixture Mfr
& Distr
N.A.I.C.S.: 327110

Ideal Standard S.A.I.   (2)
265 Messogion Avenue, 15451, Athens,
Greece
Tel.: (30) 2106790800
Web Site: http://www.idealstandard.gr
Sales Range: $25-49.9 Million
Emp.: 60
Shower Enclosure & Bathroom Fixture Mfr
& Distr
N.A.I.C.S.: 327110

Ideal Standard s.r.o.   (2)
Zemska 623, Teplice, 41501, Czech Repub-
lic
Tel.: (420) 417592111
Web Site: http://www.idealstandard.cz
Sales Range: $50-74.9 Million
Kitchen & Bathroom Products Mfr & Distr
N.A.I.C.S.: 332913
Jiri Tourek (Gen Mgr)

Quality Ceramic (Arklow) Limited   (2)
South Quay, Co Wicklow, Arklow, Ireland
Tel.: (353) 40231288
Sales Range: $25-49.9 Million
Emp.: 50
Vitreous China Plumbing Fixture & China &
Earthenware Bathroom Accessories Mfr
N.A.I.C.S.: 327110

Subsidiary (Domestic):

Quality Ceramics (Sales) Limited   (3)

South Quay, Co Wicklow, Arklow, Wicklow,
Ireland
Tel.: (353) 40 231288
Bathroom Fixtures Whslr
N.A.I.C.S.: 423720
John O'Loughlin (Mng Dir)

Subsidiary (Non-US):

Quay Bathrooms Limited   (2)
South Quay, Arklow, Wicklow, Ireland
Tel.: (353) 40 231288
Bathroom Fixture Mfr
N.A.I.C.S.: 327110

Shires (Ireland) Limited   (2)
Broomhill Road, Tallaght, Dublin, 24, Ireland
Tel.: (353) 1 4047600
Sales Range: $25-49.9 Million
Emp.: 45
Plumbing & Heating Equipment & Supplies
Hydronics Merchant Whslr
N.A.I.C.S.: 423720

Koosharem, LLC   (1)
3820 State St, Santa Barbara, CA 93105
Tel.: (805) 882-2200
Web Site: http://www.selectstaffing.com
Sales Range: $1-4.9 Billion
Emp.: 1,250
Holding Company; Temporary Personnel
Services
N.A.I.C.S.: 551112
Paul J. Sorensen (Pres)
Laurie C. Maxwell (VP-Ops)
Richard K. Hulme (Chief Admin Officer)
Melissa J. Porter (Chief Sls Officer)
Mark R. McComb (COO)
Gunnar Gooding (Sr VP)
Irwin Much (Pres-Franchise Div)
Fred R. Herbert (Pres-RemX Specialty
Staffing)
Thomas A. Bickes (CEO)
Shawn W. Poole (CFO & Exec VP)

Holding (Domestic):

Remedy Intelligent Staffing, Inc.   (2)
3820 State St, Santa Barbara, CA 93105
Tel.: (805) 882-2200
Web Site: http://www.remedystaff.com
Emp.: 100
Staffing & People Placement
N.A.I.C.S.: 561311
Melissa J. Porter (Chief Sls Officer)

Select Staffing   (2)
Park Central Bldg 410 Ware Blvd Ste 205,
Tampa, FL 33619
Tel.: (813) 830-7700
Web Site: http://www.selectremedy.com
Sales Range: $125-149.9 Million
Emp.: 100
Staffing Services
N.A.I.C.S.: 561320
Shawn Levisky (Gen Mgr & Dir-IT)
Lori Weathers (Dir-Sls & Mktg)

SelectRemedy   (2)
3820 State St, Santa Barbara, CA 93105-
3112
Tel.: (805) 882-2200
Web Site: http://www.selectremedy.com
Temporary Employment Services
N.A.I.C.S.: 561320
Laurie Maxwell (COO)
Melissa J. Porter (Chief Sls Officer)

ANCHORAGE SUZUKI ARCTIC CAT

3054 Comml Dr, Anchorage, AK
99501
Tel.: (907) 272-2412
Web Site:
http://www.anchoragearcticcat.com
Sales Range: $10-24.9 Million
Emp.: 8
Snowmobiles; Motorcycles;
4-Wheelers
N.A.I.C.S.: 423110
Dennis Dunham (Owner)

ANCHORFREE, INC.

450 National Ave, Mountain View, CA
94043-2238
Tel.: (408) 744-1002
Web Site: http://www.anchorfree.com

Year Founded: 2006
Sales Range: $25-49.9 Million
Emp.: 50
Software Developer
N.A.I.C.S.: 513210
David Gorodyansky (Co-Founder &
CEO)
Michael Geer (COO)
Peter Hoag (Co-Founder & Exec VP-
Fin & Admin)
Eugene Lapidous (VP-Engrg & Chief
Architect)
Eugene Malobrodsky (Co-Founder &
CTO)
Baglan Nurhan Rhymes (Chief Digital
Officer)

ANCILLA SYSTEMS INCORPO-RATED

1419 S Lk Park Ave, Hobart, IN
46342-5958
Tel.: (219) 947-8500
Web Site: http://www.ancilla.org
Year Founded: 1982
Sales Range: $10-24.9 Million
Emp.: 12
Operates Hospital & Health Care
Services
N.A.I.C.S.: 621491
Fred Arand (VP-Fin)
J. R. Daves (VP-Support Svcs)
Herlinda Castro (Mgr-Facilities)
Jane Bomberger (Dir-Donor Rels)

ANCIRA ENTERPRISES INC.

6111 Bandera Rd, San Antonio, TX
78238-1643
Tel.: (210) 681-4900
Web Site: http://www.ancira.com
Year Founded: 1983
Sales Range: $125-149.9 Million
Emp.: 300
New & Used Automobiles Retailer
N.A.I.C.S.: 441110
Ernesto Ancira (Owner)
Greg Spence (Exec VP)
Betty Ferguson (CFO)
Joey Blackmon (VP-Ops)

ANCO INSURANCE MANAG-ERS INC.

1111 Briarcrest Dr, Bryan, TX 77802
Tel.: (979) 776-2626
Web Site: http://www.anco.com
Sales Range: $10-24.9 Million
Emp.: 103
Insurance Services
N.A.I.C.S.: 524210
John L. Lynn (Sr VP-Acctg & Control-
ler)
S. W. Cauthorn (Chm)
Adrian G. McDonald Jr. (Sr VP)
Sid Alexander (Sr VP-Comml)
Roy Gunnels (Sr VP-Life & Health)
Todd Gunnels (Sr VP-Life & Health)
Tony Jernigan (Sr VP-Comml)
Nick Schrader (Sr VP-Comml)
Don Smith (Sr VP-Comml)
Juanice Smith (Sr VP-Comml)
Guy Cauthorn (VP-Comml)
Duane Arbuckle (Sr VP-Comml)

Subsidiary:

Anco Insurance Services   (1)
1111 Briarcrest Dr, Bryan, TX 77802
Tel.: (979) 776-2626
Web Site: http://www.anco.com
Rev.: $13,200,000
Emp.: 100
Insurance Services
N.A.I.C.S.: 524210
Kathy Gregory (Pres)

ANCON CONSTRUCTION COMPANY

2146 Elkhart Rd, Goshen, IN 46526

Tel.: (574) 533-9561
Web Site:
https://www.anconconstruction.com
Year Founded: 1975
Sales Range: $25-49.9 Million
Emp.: 75
Industrial Buildings, New Construction
N.A.I.C.S.: 236210
Andrew W. Frech (Founder)
Steve Brindle (Project Mgr)
Rick Dieringer (Project Mgr)
Rhett M. Fisher (CFO)
John D. Place (Pres)
Doug VonGunten (Project Mgr)
Gary Wetzel (VP-Bus Dev)
Ken Wright (Project Mgr)
Seth Hartman (Project Mgr-ABS)

ANCON MARINE, LLC

2250 E Dominguez St, Carson, CA
90810
Tel.: (310) 522-5110
Web Site:
http://www.anconmarine.com
Year Founded: 1968
Sales Range: $10-24.9 Million
Emp.: 150
General Freight Trucking, Local
N.A.I.C.S.: 484110
Bret Hardin (Pres & CEO)

Subsidiaries:

Ancon KOT Logistics   (1)
11355 Arrow Rte, Rancho Cucamonga, CA
91730
Tel.: (909) 987-3939
Web Site: http://www.ancon-kot.com
Logistics & Supply Chain
N.A.I.C.S.: 484110

ANCONA ENTERPRISES INC

1000 N Rogers Rd, Olathe, KS
66062-1086
Tel.: (913) 782-3636
Web Site:
http://www.frankanconahonda.com
Rev.: $19,400,000
Emp.: 75
New Car Dealers
N.A.I.C.S.: 441110
Frank Ancona (Owner & CEO)
Michael Ancona (Gen Mgr)
Jason Heard (Gen Mgr)

ANCONA GRAIN INC.

107 E Wall Sreet, Ancona, IL 61311
Tel.: (815) 672-7511
Sales Range: $10-24.9 Million
Emp.: 11
Grain Elevators
N.A.I.C.S.: 424510
Greg Lovins (Gen Mgr)

ANCOR HOLDINGS, L.P.

2720 E State Hwy 114, Southlake,
TX 76092-2846
Tel.: (817) 877-4458
Web Site:
https://www.ancorcapital.com
Sales Range: $25-49.9 Million
Emp.: 11
Privater Equity Firm
N.A.I.C.S.: 523999
Timothy J. McKibben (Partner)
J. Randall Keene (Partner)
Raymond H. Kingsbury (Partner)
Brook M. Smith (Partner)
Mitchell A. Green (CFO)
Victor L. Keller Jr. (Mng Partner)

Subsidiaries:

Alliance Family of Companies,
LLC   (1)
4545 Fuller Dr Ste 100, Irving, TX 75038
Tel.: (888) 982-8492
Web Site: http://www.afcompanies.com
Diagnostic Testing Services

N.A.I.C.S.: 334515
Justin Magnuson *(CEO)*
Conor Butts *(Pres)*
Andrea Bohannon *(CFO)*
Jeremy Slater *(Chief Medical Officer)*
Zach Williams *(VP-Sls)*
Pamela Wagner *(Gen Counsel)*
Kent Harris *(Dir-HR)*
Zachary Mandler *(VP-Ops)*

Subsidiary (Domestic):

Telemedx Corp. (2)
2550 S Sam Houston Pkwy W, Houston, TX 77047
Tel.: (713) 655-7600
Web Site: http://www.telemedx.com
Sales Range: $1-9.9 Million
Emp.: 24
Medical Laboratories
N.A.I.C.S.: 621511
Ray Mitchell *(Co-Founder)*

Identity Group Holdings Corp. (1)
51 Century Blvdd Ste 100, Nashville, TN 37214
Tel.: (931) 432-4000
Web Site: http://www.identitygroup.com
Sales Range: $25-49.9 Million.
Emp.: 250
Signs, Stamps & Stationery Mfr
N.A.I.C.S.: 339940
Lee Brantley *(Exec VP-HR)*
Paul Morgan *(Mgr-Mfg Engrg)*
Brad Wolf *(Pres & CEO)*
Brian Mogensen *(CFO & Exec VP)*
David Durfee *(Exec VP-Ops)*
Warren Soltis *(Exec VP-Info Svcs)*

LSC Environmental Products, LLC (1)
2183 Pennsylvania Ave, Apalachin, NY 13732
Tel.: (607) 625-3050
Web Site: http://www.landfill.com
Environmental Products & Equipments Mfr
N.A.I.C.S.: 423830
Joseph W. Donze *(CEO)*
Joel E. Lanz *(Pres)*
Karen P. Welch *(CFO)*

Subsidiary (Domestic):

Mat Nuwood, LLC. (2)
811 Price Pl, Lenoir, NC 28645
Tel.: (828) 758-4463
Sales Range: $1-9.9 Million
Emp.: 50
Paperboard Product Recycling Services
N.A.I.C.S.: 322130
Ronald G. Ruzynski *(Mgr)*
Patti J. Karpik *(Mgr)*

PMA Industries (1)
18008 N Black Canyon Hwy, Phoenix, AZ 85053
Tel.: (602) 278-7800
Web Site: https://pmaindustriesinc.com
Photo-Chemical Etching Mfr
N.A.I.C.S.: 333310
Jim Everson *(Pres & CEO)*

Subsidiary (Domestic):

United Western Enterprises, Inc. (2)
850 Flynn Rd, Camarillo, CA 93012
Tel.: (805) 389-1077.
Web Site: http://www.uweinc.com
Sales Range: $1-9.9 Million
Emp.: 29
Coating/Engraving Service
N.A.I.C.S.: 332812

ANCORA COFFEE & TEA
3701 Orin Rd, Madison, WI 53704
Tel.: (608) 255-2900
Web Site:
   http://www.ancoracoffee.com
Year Founded: 1994
Sales Range: $10-24.9 Million
Emp.: 20
Roasted Coffee & Tea Mfr
N.A.I.C.S.: 311920
Tori Johnson *(Owner)*

ANDALAY SOLAR, INC.

2071 Ringwood Ave Unit C, San Jose, CA 95131
Tel.: (408) 402-9400   DE
Web Site:
   http://www.andalaysolar.com
Year Founded: 2001
Sales Range: $1-9.9 Million
Emp.: 10
Solar Power Systems Designer & Installer
N.A.I.C.S.: 237130
Edward L. Bernstein *(Pres, CEO & Interim CFO)*
Mark L. Kalow *(Chm)*
Mark L. Kalow *(Chm)*

ANDALE FARMERS COOP-ERATIVE CO.
219 N Main St, Andale, KS 67001
Tel.: (316) 444-2141
Sales Range: $25-49.9 Million
Emp.: 20
Grains
N.A.I.C.S.: 424510
Steven Shaver *(Gen Mgr)*

ANDALE INC.
300 Ferguson Dr, Mountain View, CA 94043-5227
Tel.: (650) 230-3000
Web Site: http://www.andale.com
Year Founded: 1999
Sales Range: $10-24.9 Million
Emp.: 75
Selling Tools & Management Services for Online Auction Merchants
N.A.I.C.S.: 561499
Linda Hayes *(Pres & CEO)*
Timothy Vago *(Dir-Fin)*

ANDALUSIA DISTRIBUTING COMPANY INC.
117 Allen Ave, Andalusia, AL 36420
Tel.: (334) 222-3671
Web Site: https://www.adc1.com
Rev.: $107,000,000
Emp.: 60
Tobacco & Tobacco Product Merchant Whslr
N.A.I.C.S.: 424940
Michael L. Jones *(Pres)*
Richard E. Jones *(Treas & Sec)*

ANDAVO TRAVEL
8450 E Crescent Pkwy Ste 410, Greenwood Village, CO 80111
Tel.: (303) 694-3322   CO
Web Site: http://www.andavo.com
Year Founded: 1990
Sales Range: $250-299.9 Million
Emp.: 155
Travel Agency
N.A.I.C.S.: 561510
Brenda Rivers *(Pres & CEO)*
Max Garcia *(Dir-Corp Sls)*
Meredith Price *(Mgr-Leisure Ops)*
Kirsten Little *(Mgr-Leisure & Host Agency Div)*

ANDCO CONSULTING, LLC
4901 Vineland Rd Ste 600, Orlando, FL 32811
Tel.: (866) 240-7932
Web Site:
   http://www.andcoconsulting.com
Year Founded: 2000
Investment Advice & Consulting Services
N.A.I.C.S.: 523940
Bryan Bakardjiev *(Exec Dir)*
Mike Welker *(Pres & CEO)*
Troy Brown *(Exec Dir)*
Steve Gordon *(Exec Dir)*
Kim Spurlin *(Exec Dir)*
Jason Purdy *(Dir-IT)*

Matt Deconcini *(Chief Compliance Officer)*
Jerry Camel *(Dir-Software Dev)*
Kim Goodearl *(Head-RFP Team)*
Derek Tangeman *(Dir-Mktg)*
Rachel Brignoni *(Dir-HR)*

ANDELCARE, INC.
14400 Bel-Red Rd Ste 109, Bellevue, WA 98007
Tel.: (425) 283-0408
Web Site: https://www.andelcare.com
Year Founded: 2003
Sales Range: $1-9.9 Million
Emp.: 199
Senior Citizen Home Care Services
N.A.I.C.S.: 624120
Marla Beck *(Owner & Pres)*

ANDERSEN & ASSOCIATES INC.
30575 Anderson Ct, Wixom, MI 48393-2817
Tel.: (248) 960-6800   MI
Web Site:
   http://www.andersenassoc.com
Year Founded: 1960
Rev.: $35,399,127
Emp.: 135
Industrial Machinery & Equipment
N.A.I.C.S.: 423830
Thomas M. Campau *(Chm)*
James O'Dette *(Pres)*
Pat Feheley *(VP-Sls)*
Heather Fannon *(Mgr-Parts)*

ANDERSEN CORPORATION
100 4th Ave N, Bayport, MN 55003
Tel.: (651) 264-5150   MN
Web Site:
   https://www.andersenwindows.com
Year Founded: 1903
Sales Range: Less than $1 Million
Emp.: 12,000
Offices of Other Holding Companies
N.A.I.C.S.: 551112
Jay Lund *(Chm, Chm, CEO, CEO & Sr VP-Sls & Mktg)*
Steve Berg *(VP-R&D & Innovation)*
Karen Richard *(Chief HR Officer & Sr VP)*
Philip E. Donaldson *(CFO & Exec VP)*
Grant Davis *(Gen Mgr-Residential & Comml Pro Div & VP)*
Chris Galvin *(Pres & CEO)*
Andrea Nordaune *(Chief Legal Officer, Sec & Sr VP)*

Subsidiaries:

Andersen Windows, Inc. (1)
100 4th Ave N, Bayport, MN 55003-1058
Tel.: (651) 264-5150
Web Site: http://www.andersenwindows.com
Window Mfr
N.A.I.C.S.: 321911

Custom Pultrusions, Inc. (1)
1331 S Chillicothe Rd, Aurora, OH 44202-8066
Tel.: (330) 562-5201
Sales Range: $25-49.9 Million
Emp.: 100
Pultruded Plastic Products Mfr
N.A.I.C.S.: 326199

EMCO Enterprises, Inc. (1)
2121 E Walnut St, Des Moines, IA 50317-2264
Tel.: (515) 265-6101
Web Site: http://www.andersoncorp.com
Sales Range: $25-49.9 Million
Emp.: 900
Metal Doors, Sash & Trim Mfr
N.A.I.C.S.: 332321

Eagle Window & Door, Inc. (1)
2045 Kerper Blvd, Dubuque, IA 52001
Tel.: (563) 556-2270
Web Site: http://www.eaglewindow.com

Sales Range: $25-49.9 Million
Emp.: 500
Windows & Doors Mfr
N.A.I.C.S.: 321911

Frontier Tooling & Design, Inc. (1)
5120 Guyan River Rd, Huntington, WV 25702
Tel.: (304) 529-0115
Special Die & Tool, Die Set, Jig & Fixture Mfr
N.A.I.C.S.: 333514

Renewal by Andersen Corporation (1)
9900 Jamaica Ave S, Cottage Grove, MN 55016
Tel.: (651) 264-4056
Web Site:
   http://www.renewalbyandersen.com
Sales Range: $50-74.9 Million
Emp.: 550
Window Replacement Services
N.A.I.C.S.: 236118
Paul Delahunt *(Pres)*
Troy Barrow *(VP-Mktg)*
Grant Davis *(VP-Company Owned Retail Ops)*
Jeanne Junker *(VP-Affiliate Retail Ops)*

Tashco Industries, Inc. (1)
1503 W San Pedro St, Gilbert, AZ 85233
Tel.: (480) 892-2600
Web Site: http://www.heritagewindows.com
Metal Window & Door Mfr
N.A.I.C.S.: 332321

Weiland Sliding Doors & Windows, Inc. (1)
2601 Industry St, Oceanside, CA 92054
Tel.: (760) 722-8828
Web Site:
   http://www.weilandslidingdoors.com
Sales Range: $1-9.9 Million
Emp.: 45
Metal Sliding Doors & Windows Mfr & Whslr
N.A.I.C.S.: 332321
Steve Donner *(Gen Mgr)*

ANDERSEN DAIRY INC.
305 E Main St, Battle Ground, WA 98604
Tel.: (360) 687-7171
Web Site: https://andersendairy.com
Rev.: $17,900,000
Emp.: 100
Fluid Milk Mfr
N.A.I.C.S.: 311511
Jack Dunn *(Pres)*

ANDERSON & HOWARD ELECTRIC INC.
1791 Reynolds Ave, Irvine, CA 92614-5711
Tel.: (949) 250-4555
Web Site: http://aandh.com
Year Founded: 1963
Sales Range: $10-24.9 Million
Emp.: 250
Power & Communication Line Construction Services
N.A.I.C.S.: 237130
Greg Elliott *(Pres)*

ANDERSON & HOWARD ELECTRIC, INC.
1791 Reynolds Ave, Irvine, CA 92614
Tel.: (949) 250-4555
Web Site: http://www.aandh.com
Year Founded: 1964
Sales Range: $25-49.9 Million
Emp.: 300
Provider of Electrical Contracting Services
N.A.I.C.S.: 238210
Teresa Viloria *(Controller)*

ANDERSON & MIDDLETON COMPANY
111 Market St NE Ste 360, Olympia, WA 98501
Tel.: (360) 533-2410

Anderson & Middleton
Company—(Continued)

Web Site:
http://www.andersonmiddleton.com
Sales Range: $50-74.9 Million
Emp.: 150
Timber & Agricultural Services
N.A.I.C.S.: 113310
Kevin James (Sec & Controller)

ANDERSON & VREELAND, INC.
15348 US Hwy 127 EW, Bryan, OH 43506
Tel.: (973) 227-2270   NJ
Web Site:
http://www.andersonvreeland.com
Year Founded: 1961
Sales Range: $75-99.9 Million
Emp.: 135
Supplier of Flexographic Platemaking Equipment & Materials for the Graphic Arts
N.A.I.C.S.: 333248
Darin Lyon (Pres & CEO)
Lonnie Grieser (Mgr-Warehouse-East)
Bill Bower (Dir-Sls)
Sean Sawa (Dir-Photoengraving)
Lee Zerfass (Mgr-Digital Bus Dev)
Anthony Gilski (Mgr-Central)
Peter Spain (Mgr-Sls-East)
Don Archer (Reg Acct Mgr)
Jack Cook (Acct Mgr-Southern California, Arizona & New Mexico)
Dave Miller (Dir-Creative)
Melissa Hubbard (Coord-Customer Relationship Mgmt & Mktg)
Bryan Thrasher (Acct Mgr)
Cory Whitton (Acct Mgr-North Carolina, South Carolina & Tennessee)
Larry Dingman (Mgr-Sls-West)
Paige Green (Acct Mgr-Central)
Jessica Harrell (Dir-Technologies)
Andy Gillis (VP-Sls & Gen Mgr)
Paul Teachout (Mgr-Bus Dev-Narrow Web)
Tim Brannon (Acct Mgr)

Subsidiaries:

Anderson & Vreeland Inc.   (1)
5435 Rue Francois-Cusson, Lachine, H8T 3J4, QC, Canada
Web Site: http://www.andersonvreeland.ca
Flexographic Printing Services
N.A.I.C.S.: 323111
Andy Gillis (VP)
Darin Lyon (Pres)
Howard Vreeland Jr. (Chm & CEO)

The Provident Group   (1)
15 Pleasant St Ste 7, Concord, NH 03301
Tel.: (603) 230-9680
Web Site: http://www.providentgrp.com
Printing Equipment Mfr
N.A.I.C.S.: 333248
Andrew Gillis (Gen Mgr)

ANDERSON AUTO PARTS CO. INC.
508 S Main St, Anderson, SC 29624-2304
Tel.: (864) 224-6321   SC
Year Founded: 1976
Sales Range: $10-24.9 Million
Emp.: 55
Provider of Auto Supplies
N.A.I.C.S.: 423120
Hampton Anderson III (Pres)

ANDERSON AUTOMOTIVE GROUP
2500 Wildcat Dr, Lincoln, NE 68521
Tel.: (402) 458-9800
Web Site:
https://www.andersonautogroup.com
Year Founded: 1986

Sales Range: $25-49.9 Million
Emp.: 100
Automobiles, New & Used
N.A.I.C.S.: 441110
Scott Heaton (CFO)
Mike Anderson (Pres)

ANDERSON AUTOMOTIVE GROUP INC.
10125 York Rd, Cockeysville, MD 21030-3305
Tel.: (410) 467-8800   MD
Web Site:
http://www.andersonautomotive.com
Rev.: $69,814,058
Emp.: 256
Automobile Dealers
N.A.I.C.S.: 441110
Bruce Mortimer (Owner)
Karen Kuhn (Dir-HR & Office Mgr)

ANDERSON BROTHERS CONSTRUCTION CO. BRAINERD, INC.
11325 Hwy 210 E, Brainerd, MN 56401
Tel.: (218) 829-1768   MN
Web Site:
https://www.andersonbrothers.com
Year Founded: 1940
Sales Range: $125-149.9 Million
Emp.: 150
Provider of Road Construction Services
N.A.I.C.S.: 237310
James Anderson (Chm)
Ron Wickhan (VP-Aggregates)
Dana Hegarty (CFO)

ANDERSON CHRYSLER JEEP INC.
2 Capella S, Newport, RI 02840-1506
Tel.: (508) 222-4500
Sales Range: $10-24.9 Million
Emp.: 30
Sales of Automobiles
N.A.I.C.S.: 441110
Gerald Farinelli (VP & Gen Mgr)

ANDERSON COLUMBIA CO. INC.
871 Guerdon St, Lake City, FL 32055
Tel.: (386) 752-7585
Web Site:
http://www.andersoncolumbia.com
Year Founded: 1958
Sales Range: $75-99.9 Million
Emp.: 2,000
General Contracting Services
N.A.I.C.S.: 237310
Joey Anderson (Pres)
John Godbold (Controller)
Susan Chappell (Mgr-Credit)
Shawn Snyder (VP)
Walter Edwards (Mgr-Construction)

Subsidiaries:

Suwannee American Cement Co Inc   (1)
5117 N US Hwy 27, Branford, FL 32008
Tel.: (386) 935-5000
Web Site: http://www.suwanneecement.com
Rev.: $780,000
Emp.: 70
Portland Cement
N.A.I.C.S.: 327310
Tom Messer (Mgr-Plant-Branford)
Dana Moran (VP-Sls & Mktg)
Monica Manolas (Pres)

ANDERSON COMPANIES, INC.
4511 Helton Dr, Florence, AL 35630
Tel.: (256) 766-3824   DE
Sales Range: $1-4.9 Billion
Emp.: 9,800
Holding Company
N.A.I.C.S.: 551112

Charles Anderson (CEO)

Subsidiaries:

American Promotional Events, Inc.   (1)
4511 Helton Dr, Florence, AL 35630
Tel.: (256) 764-6131
Web Site: http://www.tntfireworks.com
Rev.: $18,400,000
Emp.: 120
Fireworks Distr
N.A.I.C.S.: 423990
Tommy Glasgow (Pres)

Subsidiary (Domestic):

American Promotional Events, Inc.   (2)
2120 Milwakee Way, Tacoma, WA 98424
Tel.: (253) 922-0800
Web Site: http://www.tntfireworks.com
Fireworks
N.A.I.C.S.: 423920

Anderson Merchandisers, L.P.   (1)
421 E 34th Ave, Amarillo, TX 79103-1702
Tel.: (806) 376-6251
Web Site:
http://www.andersonmerchandisers.com
Sales Range: $75-99.9 Million
Emp.: 100
Retailer of Durable Goods
N.A.I.C.S.: 423990
Bill Lardie (Pres)

Subsidiary (Domestic):

Liquid Digital Media   (2)
999 Main St, Redwood City, CA 94063-4748
Tel.: (650) 549-2000
Web Site: http://www.liquid.com
Sales Range: $25-49.9 Million
Emp.: 40
Software & Computer Related Services
N.A.I.C.S.: 512290

ANDERSON CONCRETE CORP.
400 Frank Rd, Columbus, OH 43207
Tel.: (614) 443-0123
Web Site:
https://www.andersonconcrete.com
Sales Range: $25-49.9 Million
Emp.: 130
Ready Mixed Concrete
N.A.I.C.S.: 327320
Douglas Anderson (Pres)
Michael Anderson (VP)
Gary Conley (CFO)

ANDERSON CONSTRUCTION COMPANY OF FORT GAINES
58 Crozier Ln, Fort Gaines, GA 39851
Tel.: (229) 768-2555
Web Site: https://www.accofg.com
Year Founded: 1964
Rev.: $16,320,225
Emp.: 150
Construction Services
N.A.I.C.S.: 236220
Jerry Anderson (CEO)
Trey Anderson (Pres)
David Anderson (VP)
Sheriee Bryan (Sec & Treas)

ANDERSON CUSTOM PROCESSING, INC.
105 1/2 N Minnesota St, New Ulm, MN 56073
Tel.: (507) 233-2800
Web Site:
http://www.andersonprocessing.com
Year Founded: 1972
Sales Range: $10-24.9 Million
Emp.: 70
Mfr & Distributor of Corn Starch
N.A.I.C.S.: 311221
Brian G. Anderson (Pres)

Subsidiaries:

Anderson Custom Processing, Inc. - Belleville Plant   (1)
220 Serv Us St, Belleville, WI 53508
Tel.: (608) 424-3321
Web Site:
http://www.andersonprocessing.com
Sales Range: $10-24.9 Million
Emp.: 22
Mfr & Distributor of Corn Starch
N.A.I.C.S.: 311221

ANDERSON DAIRY, INC.
801 Searles Ave, Las Vegas, NV 89101
Tel.: (702) 642-7507
Web Site:
https://www.andersondairy.com
Year Founded: 1907
Sales Range: $75-99.9 Million
Emp.: 200
Fluid Milk Mfr & Distr
N.A.I.C.S.: 311511
Harry Anderson (Founder)

ANDERSON ELECTRIC, INC.
3501 S 6th St Hwy W Ste 1, Springfield, IL 62703-4771
Tel.: (217) 529-5471   DE
Web Site: http://www.anderson-electric.com
Year Founded: 1918
Sales Range: $25-49.9 Million
Emp.: 175
Electrical Contractors Serving Commercial, Industrial, Institutional & Power Generating Customers
N.A.I.C.S.: 238210
Marsha S. Landers (Treas)
Teri Starkey (Sec)
Lucky L. Brown (VP-Safety)
David J. Bruce (VP-Bloomington Branch)
Annette Ogden (Mgr-IT)
Wes Anderson (Pres)
Bryan Allison (Sr VP)

ANDERSON EQUIPMENT CO., INC.
1000 Washington Pike, Bridgeville, PA 15017
Tel.: (412) 343-2300
Web Site:
https://www.andersonequip.com
Emp.: 100
Construction Equipment Distr
N.A.I.C.S.: 532412
Judi Anderson (Pres)

ANDERSON ERICKSON DAIRY COMPANY
2420 E University Ave, Des Moines, IA 50317-6559
Tel.: (515) 265-2521   IA
Web Site: https://www.aedairy.com
Year Founded: 1930
Sales Range: $25-49.9 Million
Emp.: 520
Milk & Dairy Products Mfr
N.A.I.C.S.: 311511
Miriam Erickson Brown (Pres & CEO)

Subsidiaries:

AE Farms, Inc.   (1)
2420 E University Ave, Des Moines, IA 50317-6559   (100%)
Tel.: (515) 243-1637
Web Site: http://www.aedairy.com
Sales Range: $10-24.9 Million
Emp.: 15
Provider of Ice Cream Sales & Delivery
N.A.I.C.S.: 311520

ANDERSON FORD MAZDA LLC
3900 Clemson Blvd, Anderson, SC 29621

Tel.: (864) 225-4151   DE
Web Site:
   https://www.andersonfordsc.com
Sales Range: $10-24.9 Million
Emp.: 70
New & Used Automobile Dealer
N.A.I.C.S.: 441110
Dan Parks (Owner)

ANDERSON FOREST PRODUCTS INC.
1267 Old Edmonton Rd, Tompkinsville, KY 42167
Tel.: (270) 487-6778
Web Site: https://www.afp-usa.com
Rev.: $10,220,707
Emp.: 110
Pallets, Wood
N.A.I.C.S.: 321920
Billy J. Anderson (Pres)
Ina Graves (Mgr-HR)

ANDERSON GAS & PROPANE INC.
6216 Hwy 45, Hindsville, AR 72738-9038
Tel.: (479) 789-5188
Sales Range: $10-24.9 Million
Emp.: 20
Petroleum Products Sales
N.A.I.C.S.: 424720
Don Anderson (Pres)

ANDERSON HARDWOOD FLOORS
384 Torrington Rd, Clinton, SC 29345-4635
Tel.: (864) 833-6250   SC
Web Site:
   http://www.andersonfloors.com
Year Founded: 1946
Sales Range: $150-199.9 Million
Emp.: 400
Hardwood, Veneer & Plywood Flooring Mfr
N.A.I.C.S.: 321211
Don Finkell (Pres)

ANDERSON HAY & GRAIN CO. INC.
910 Anderson Rd, Ellensburg, WA 98926
Tel.: (509) 925-9818
Web Site: https://www.anderson-hay.com
Rev.: $24,000,000
Emp.: 350
Hay
N.A.I.C.S.: 424910
Mark Anderson (CEO)
Heidi Nollan (Coord-HR)
Laura Daniels (Mgr-Transportation)

ANDERSON INDUSTRIES LLC
200 4th Ave SE, Mapleton, ND 58059
Tel.: (701) 281-1111
Web Site: http://www.anderson-industries.com
Emp.: 35
Metal Products Mfr
N.A.I.C.S.: 332322
Kory Anderson (Pres)

Subsidiaries:

Dakota Foundry, Inc.   (1)
20 Park Ln, Webster, SD 57274
Tel.: (605) 345-3349
Web Site: http://www.dakotafoundry.com
Sales Range: $1-9.9 Million
Emp.: 50
Malleable Iron Foundry
N.A.I.C.S.: 331511
Josh Bartos (VP-Ops)

ANDERSON INTERNATIONAL CORP.

6200 Harvard Ave, Cleveland, OH 44105-4861
Tel.: (216) 641-1112
Web Site: http://www.andersonintl.net
Year Founded: 1888
Sales Range: $75-99.9 Million
Emp.: 85
Food Processing Equipment Mfr
N.A.I.C.S.: 333241
Vincent J. Vavpot (Mgr-Worldwide Bus)
Len Trocono (Pres)
Kathleen Ohearn (Controller)
Rob Williams (VP-Engrg)

ANDERSON MACHINERY COMPANY
6535 Leopard St, Corpus Christi, TX 78409
Tel.: (361) 289-6043
Web Site:
   https://www.andersonmachines.com
Sales Range: $10-24.9 Million
Emp.: 30
Road Construction Equipment
N.A.I.C.S.: 423810
Jim Anderson (Pres)
Kirk Anderson (VP)
Beth Unland (Controller)

ANDERSON MARKETING GROUP
7420 Blanco Rd Ste 200, San Antonio, TX 78216
Tel.: (210) 223-6233   TX
Web Site: http://www.andadv.com
Year Founded: 1970
Sales Range: $10-24.9 Million
Emp.: 30
Advertising Services
N.A.I.C.S.: 541810
Charles J. Anderson (CEO)
Julius Germano (COO)
Ken Clegg (CFO)
Kim Gresham (Pres)
Dirk Ronk (Assoc Dir-Creative)
Jacqueline Yarrington (Sr Acct Exec)

ANDERSON MOTORS
170 Amaral St, East Providence, RI 02915
Tel.: (401) 434-5900
Web Site:
   https://www.andersonmotors.com
Year Founded: 1964
Sales Range: $10-24.9 Million
Emp.: 30
Car Whslr
N.A.I.C.S.: 441110
John E. Anderson (Pres)

ANDERSON OIL COMPANY INCORPORATED
1101 Hugh St, Barnwell, SC 29812
Tel.: (803) 259-7578
Rev.: $21,615,117
Emp.: 12
Petroleum Bulk Stations
N.A.I.C.S.: 457210
Terrill Tuten (Pres)

ANDERSON PARTNERS
444 Regency Parkway Dr Ste 311, Omaha, NE 68114
Tel.: (402) 341-4807
Web Site:
   https://www.andersonpartners.com
Year Founded: 1989
Sales Range: $25-49.9 Million
Emp.: 13
Advertising Agencies
N.A.I.C.S.: 541810
Krista Meisinger (CFO)
Deborah Murray (Pres)

ANDERSON PRESS INC

3101 Clairmont Rd Ste G, Atlanta, GA 30329
Tel.: (404) 214-4300
Web Site:
   http://www.andersonpress.com
Sales Range: $10-24.9 Million
Emp.: 75
Book Publishers
N.A.I.C.S.: 513130
Taylor Anderson (Dir-New Bus Dev)

ANDERSON REGIONAL HEALTH SYSTEM
2124 14th St, Meridian, MS 39301
Tel.: (601) 553-6000
Web Site:
   https://www.andersonregional.org
Year Founded: 1928
Health Care Srvices
N.A.I.C.S.: 622110
Joseph M. S. Anderson (Chm)
John G. Anderson (Pres & CEO)
W. Scot Bell (Chief Medical Officer)
Steven Brown (CFO)
Betty Cryer (Chief Nursing Officer)
Wanda Cooper (VP-Professional Rels)
Denton Farr (VP-Ops)

Subsidiaries:

Anderson Regional Medical Center   (1)
2124 14th St, Meridian, MS 39301
Tel.: (601) 553-6000
Health Care Srvices
N.A.I.C.S.: 622110
John G. Anderson (Pres & CEO)

Baptist Memorial Health Care Corporation   (1)
350 N Humphreys Blvd, Memphis, TN 38120
Tel.: (901) 227-4500
Web Site: https://www.baptistonline.org
Sales Range: $900-999.9 Million
Emp.: 12,000
Health Care Services Organization
N.A.I.C.S.: 813920
Paul DePriest (COO & Exec VP)
Jason Little (Pres & CEO)

Subsidiary (Domestic):

ECC West Tennessee MC, LLC   (2)
1995 Highway 51 S, Covington, TN 38019
Tel.: (901) 476-2621
Web Site: http://www.baptistonline.org
Emergency Care Services
N.A.I.C.S.: 621493

ANDERSON SERVICES
475 Moore Ln, Billings, MT 59101
Tel.: (713) 840-8087
Web Site:
   https://andersonserviceinc.com
Year Founded: 1988
Sales Range: $1-9.9 Million
Emp.: 15
Industrial Machinery & Equipment Merchant Whslr
N.A.I.C.S.: 423830

ANDERSON STEEL SUPPLY, INC.
3811 River Dr N, Great Falls, MT 59405
Tel.: (406) 761-4354
Web Site:
   http://www.andersonsteel.com
Sales Range: $25-49.9 Million
Emp.: 75
Fabricated Structural Metal Services
N.A.I.C.S.: 332312
Susan R. Humble (Pres)
Todd D. Humble (Owner & Treas)

ANDERSON TECHNOLOGIES INC.

14000 172nd Ave, Grand Haven, MI 49417
Tel.: (616) 844-2505
Web Site: http://www.andtec.com
Sales Range: $10-24.9 Million
Emp.: 100
Injection Molding Of Plastics
N.A.I.C.S.: 326199
Glenn C. Anderson (Pres)

ANDERSON TRUCKING SERVICE INC.
725 Opportunity Dr, Saint Cloud, MN 56301
Tel.: (320) 255-7400   MN
Web Site: https://www.atsinc.com
Year Founded: 1955
Sales Range: $250-299.9 Million
Emp.: 250
Provider of Trucking Services
N.A.I.C.S.: 484121
Rollie Anderson (CEO)
Brent Anderson (COO)
Scott Anderson (Treas & Exec VP)

Subsidiaries:

ATS Specialized, Inc.   (1)
725 Opportunity Dr, Saint Cloud, MN 56301-5886
Tel.: (320) 255-7400
General Freight Trucking Services
N.A.I.C.S.: 484121
Jim Fagan (Dir-Risk Policy & Customer Compliance)
Tom Roholt (Mgr-Fleet-Heavy Haul-Wind Grp)
Marty Brix (Acct Mgr)

Sunbelt Furniture Xpress, Inc.   (1)
3255 20th Ave SE, Hickory, NC 28602
Tel.: (828) 464-7240
Web Site: http://www.sbfx.us
General Freight Trucking Services
N.A.I.C.S.: 484121
Stan Froneberger (VP & Gen Mgr)
Carola Crisp (Dir-Mktg)
Brett Kiser (VP-Ops)
Brian Canipe (Mgr-Ops)
Ben Crawley (Dir-Freight Mgmt)
James R. Edwards (CFO & Sec)
Jake Wood (Pres)
Brian Cochran (Dir-Safety)
John Cranford (Mgr-Ops)
Alan Dillard (Mgr-Shop)
Ron Easter (Reg Mgr-Sls)
Ed Fleming (Mgr-Sls-Natl)
Nancy Hollar (Mgr-Credit)
Eric Hoover (Reg Mgr-Sls)
Deidra Locklear (Coord-Logistics)
Nichole Mellon (Mgr-Claims)
Gary York (Reg Mgr-Sls)

ANDERSON WEBER TOYOTA-LINCOLN-MERCURY
3450 Center Grove Dr, Dubuque, IA 52003
Tel.: (563) 556-3281
Web Site:
   http://www.andersonweber.com
Year Founded: 1957
Sales Range: $10-24.9 Million
Emp.: 50
Sales of New & Used Automobiles
N.A.I.C.S.: 441110
Jeffrey Weber (Gen Mgr)
Tim Weber (Dir-Svc)
Lynn Morrison (Mgr-Parts)
Mike Hefel (Mgr-Fin)
Chris Lapier (Mgr-Sls)
Michael Manning (Mgr-Mktg)
Ashley Jacks (Mgr-Parts)
Carla Orr (Mgr-Body Shop)
Dave Bigelow (Mgr-Body Shop)
Larry Covents (Mgr-Fin)
Mike Crane (Gen Mgr)

ANDERSON ZURMUEHLEN & CO., PC
828 Great Northern Blvd, Helena, MT 59601

Anderson ZurMuehlen & Co., PC—(Continued)

Tel.: (406) 442-1040
Web Site: https://www.azworld.com
Rev.: $13,000,000
Emp.: 81
Certified Public Accountants
N.A.I.C.S.: 541211
Robert Culpon (COO)
Brea Bauer (Mgr-Acctg & Auditing Svcs)
Chad Miller (Sr Mgr-Consulting & Advisory Svcs)
Jessica Van Voast (Sr Mgr-Acctg & Auditing Svcs)

ANDERSON-COOK INC.
17650 15 Mi Rd, Fraser, MI 48026-3450
Tel.: (586) 293-0800   MI
Web Site:
   https://www.andersoncook.com
Year Founded: 1970
Sales Range: $10-24.9 Million
Emp.: 80
Machine Tools, Metal Forming Type
N.A.I.C.S.: 333517
Craig Everlove (Pres)

Subsidiaries:

Anderson-Cook Inc. - Clinton Twp.
Plant   (1)
44785 Macomb Industrial Dr, Clinton Township, MI 48036
Tel.: (586) 954-0700
Machine Tools Mfr
N.A.I.C.S.: 333517

Anderson-Cook Inc. - Fraser
Plant   (1)
17650 15 Mile Rd, Fraser, MI 48026
Tel.: (586) 293-0800
Machine Tools Mfr
N.A.I.C.S.: 333517

Anderson-Cook Inc. - Shanghai
Plant   (1)
Unit 103 T22-33 351 Jin Zang Road, Qiao Export Processing Zone, Shanghai, 201206, China
Tel.: (86) 215 055 0886
Machine Tools Mfr
N.A.I.C.S.: 333517

Anderson-Cook Inc. - Stratford
Plant   (1)
251 Lorne Ave West, Stratford, N5A 6S4, ON, Canada
Tel.: (519) 273-5760
Web Site: http://www.andersoncorp.com
Emp.: 100
Machine Tools Mfr
N.A.I.C.S.: 333517

LM Gear Company, Inc.   (1)
50550 E Russell Schmidt Blvd, Chesterfield, MI 48051-2451
Tel.: (586) 949-6800
Web Site: http://www.lmgear.com
Motor Vehicle Parts & Accessories
N.A.I.C.S.: 336350

ANDERSON-GILYARD
12431 Pine St, Becker, MN 55308
Tel.: (763) 261-5161
Rev.: $10,400,000
Emp.: 40
Petroleum Bulk Stations
N.A.I.C.S.: 424710
Virgil E. Gilyard (CEO)

ANDERSON-MCQUEEN COMPANY
2201 Dr Martin Luther King St N, Saint Petersburg, FL 33704-3205
Tel.: (727) 258-2929
Web Site:
   https://www.andersonmcqueen.com
Year Founded: 1952
Sales Range: $1-9.9 Million
Emp.: 50

Funeral Home & Funeral Services
N.A.I.C.S.: 812210
John T. McQueen (Owner & Pres)
Nicole McQueen (VP)
Jim Hobbs (Controller)
Pyong Benney (Dir-Facilities)

ANDERSON-TULLY CO.
775 Rigelake Blvd Ste 105, Memphis, TN 38120-1704
Tel.: (901) 576-1400   TN
Web Site:
   http://www.andersontully.com
Year Founded: 1889
Sales Range: $100-124.9 Million
Emp.: 200
Mfr & Retailer of Kiln-Dried Hardwood, Industrial Floor Blocks & Laminated Truck Flooring
N.A.I.C.S.: 113110
Roy James (VP-Ops)

ANDES 7, INC.
424 Clay St Lower Level, San Francisco, CA 94111
Tel.: (415) 463-7827   DE
Year Founded: 2015
Rev.: $12,997
Assets: $582,287
Liabilities: $1,574,771
Net Worth: ($992,484)
Earnings: ($256,101)
Emp.: 11
Fiscal Year-end: 12/31/19
Investment Services
N.A.I.C.S.: 523999
Andrew Poh Kiang Khor (Chm, Pres & CEO)
Kok Keing Lee (CFO)
Jannie Gui Honey (Sec)
Mooi Eng Ng (Treas)
Choon Moh Khor (COO)

ANDEX INDUSTRIES INC.
1911 4th Ave N, Escanaba, MI 49829
Tel.: (906) 786-6070
Web Site: http://www.andex.net
Sales Range: $10-24.9 Million
Emp.: 140
Coated & Laminated Packaging Mfr
N.A.I.C.S.: 322220
John T. Anthony (Pres)
James Roberts (Supvr-Maintenance)

ANDGAR CORPORATION
PO Box 2708, Ferndale, WA 98248
Tel.: (360) 366-9900
Web Site: http://www.andgar.com
Year Founded: 1999
Sales Range: $10-24.9 Million
Emp.: 140
Plumbing, Heating & Air-Conditioning Contracting Services
N.A.I.C.S.: 238220
Dave Hofford (Mgr)
Bryan Van Loo (Mgr-Renewable Energy Construcion)

ANDINO CEMENTS USA, LLC
121 Alhambra Plz Ste 1202, Coral Gables, FL 33134
Tel.: (786) 306-8229
Web Site:
   http://www.andinocements.com
Sales Range: $300-349.9 Million
Emp.: 5,000
Cement, Aggregates & Construction Materials Supplier
N.A.I.C.S.: 423320
Hector Bello (Chm)
Agustin Restrepo (Dir-Bus Dev)

ANDIS ADVERTISING
1800 Renaissance Blvd, Sturtevant, WI 53177
Tel.: (262) 884-2600

Web Site: https://www.andis.com
Year Founded: 1922
Sales Range: $1-9.9 Million
Emp.: 5
In House Advertising Agency
N.A.I.C.S.: 541810
Matthew L. Andis (Pres)
Fred Koeller (VP-Mktg & Intl Sales)
Mary L. Kosch (VP-HR)
B. Elayne Severson (Mgr-DP)
Brian Schalk (Mgr-Pur)

ANDIS COMPANY
1800 Renaissance Blvd, Sturtevant, WI 53177-1743
Tel.: (262) 884-2600   WI
Web Site: https://www.andis.com
Year Founded: 1922
Sales Range: $150-199.9 Million
Emp.: 450
Clippers, Blow Driers & Hair Care Products Mfr
N.A.I.C.S.: 339999
Fred Koeller (VP-Intl Sls)
Gary Stanczyk (VP-Sls)
Marcia Andis (Sr VP-Market Dev)
Karen Formico (VP-Mktg)
Barbara Jewell (Dir-Acctg)
Julianne Hlavka (Mgr-Customer Svc)
Hector Contreras (Mgr-Sls-Central & South America)
Bruce Bock (Mgr-Mktg Comm)
Aileen Nunez (Mgr-Intl-Education & Style)
Jeffrey Wolf (Dir-Product Engrg)
Iris Huang (VP-Supply Chain)
Matt K. Andis (Pres)
Al Arends (Mgr-Mktg Product)
Serena Sretenovich (Coord-Mktg Comm)

ANDISCH, INC.
4703 Boardwalk Dr Bldg A, Fort Collins, CO 80525
Tel.: (970) 226-3990   CO
Web Site: http://www.rmfa.com
Year Founded: 1985
Sales Range: $10-24.9 Million
Emp.: 210
Real Estate Brokers & Agents
N.A.I.C.S.: 531210
Allen E. Vaughan (Owner)
Hazel Reed (Mgr-Fort Collins South)

ANDLINGER & COMPANY, INC.
520 White Plains Rd Ste 500, Tarrytown, NY 10591-5118
Tel.: (914) 332-4900   DE
Web Site: https://www.andlinger.com
Year Founded: 1976
Management Investment Broker
N.A.I.C.S.: 523999
Gerhard R. Andlinger (Founder & Chm)
Merrick G. Andlinger (Pres)
Charles E. Ball (Mng Dir-Florida)
Mark F. Callaghan (Mng Dir-New York)
Hermann Lutzenberger (Partner)
Ivar W. Mitchell (Mng Dir-Florida)
George Doomany (Mng Dir-New York)
Stephen A. Magida (Mng Dir-New York)
Rainer Ullmann (Partner)
Johan Volckaerts (Sr Partner)
Annie De Smedt (Office Mgr)
Judith Haas (Office Mgr)
Alain Engelschenschilt (Partner)
Ernst Reichmayr (Partner)
Hans Jorg Kaltenbrunner (Partner)
Olivier Bru (Partner-Brussels)
Sylvia Gilis (Sr Partner)

Subsidiaries:

Andlinger & Company CVBA   (1)

Avenue Louise 149, PO Box 24, 1050, Brussels, Belgium
Tel.: (32) 26478070
Web Site: http://www.andlinger.com
Sales Range: $10-24.9 Million
Emp.: 5
Management Consulting Services
N.A.I.C.S.: 541611
Johan Volckaerts (Mng Partner)
Alain Pronost (Partner)

Andlinger & Company GmbH   (1)
Sieveringer Strasse 36/9, 1190, Vienna, Austria
Tel.: (43) 1 328 7145
Web Site: http://www.andlinger.com
Investment Management Service
N.A.I.C.S.: 523940
Ernst Reichmayr (Partner)
Gerhard Unterganschnigg (Partner)
Hans Jorg Kaltenbrunner (Partner)
Judith Haas (Office Mgr)

Crown Van Gelder B.V.   (1)
Eendrachtsstraat 30, 1951 AZ, Velsen, Netherlands
Tel.: (31) 251262233
Web Site: http://www.cvg.nl
Sales Range: $150-199.9 Million
Emp.: 280
Specialty Paper Mfr
N.A.I.C.S.: 322220
Henk van der Zwaag (CFO)
Miklas Dronkers (CEO)
Hans Ekelmans (Dir-Sls & Mktg)
Ad Sies (Mgr-Bus Dev)
Jan Rops (Product Mgr-Digital)
Bernard Wesselink (Product Mgr-Digital)
Eric Koops (Product Mgr-Label & Packaging)

ETI Elektroelement, d.d.   (1)
Obrezija 5, 1411, Izlake, Slovenia (99.43%)
Tel.: (386) 35657570
Web Site: http://www.eti.si
Electrical Equipment & Supplies
N.A.I.C.S.: 333992
Tomaz Berginc (CEO)
Marjan Kramar (Chm-Supervisory Bd)
Peter Gasperlin (Dir-Sls Network)

Subsidiary (Non-US):

ETI B   (2)
Brace Jerkovic 120, 11000, Belgrade, Serbia
Tel.: (381) 113961668
Web Site: http://www.etib.rs
Electrical Equipment & Supplies
N.A.I.C.S.: 335999

ETI DE GmbH   (2)
Dorfwiesenweg 13, 63828, Kleinkahl, Bavaria, Germany
Tel.: (49) 6024639710
Web Site: http://www.eti-de.de
Electrical Equipment & Supplies
N.A.I.C.S.: 335999

ETI ELB s.r.o.   (2)
Potocna 42, District of Pezinok, 90084, Bahon, Bratislava Region, Slovakia
Tel.: (421) 33645 52 92
Web Site: http://www.eti.szm.sk
Switchgear & Switchboard Apparatus Mfr
N.A.I.C.S.: 335313

ETI Polam Sp.zo.o.   (2)
ul Jana Pawla II 18, 06 100, Warsaw, Poland
Tel.: (48) 236919300
Web Site: http://www.etipolam.com.pl
Electrical Apparatus & Equipment Whslr
N.A.I.C.S.: 423610

ETI Sarajevo d.o.o.   (2)
Hifzi Bjelevca 13, Sarajevo, 71 000, Bosnia & Herzegovina
Tel.: (387) 33775250
Web Site: http://www.eti.ba
Electrical Equipment & Supplies
N.A.I.C.S.: 335999

ETI Ukraine Ltd.   (2)
Ul Akademika Tupoleva 19a of 216, 04128, Kiev, Ukraine
Tel.: (380) 44 494 2180
Web Site: http://www.eti.org.ua
Electrical Equipment & Supplies
N.A.I.C.S.: 423610

ETIBALTUS UAB (2)
Tilzes 41a, 47187, Kaunas, Lithuania
Tel.: (370) 37261582
Web Site: http://www.etibaltus.lt
Electrical Equipment & Supplies
N.A.I.C.S.: 423610
Rumunas Gumis (Mng Dir)

SUSPA GmbH (1)
Muhlweg 33, 90518, Altdorf, Bavaria, Germany (80%)
Tel.: (49) 9187930
Web Site: http://www.suspa.com
Sales Range: $200-249.9 Million
Emp.: 1,400
Mfr of Gas Springs, Hydraulic Dampers, Piston Rods & Shock Absorbers
N.A.I.C.S.: 336390
Timo Stahl (Member-Mgmt Bd)
Michael M. Wengler (Member-Mgmt Bd)
Thomas Peuker (Member-Mgmt Bd)

Subsidiary (Non-US):

SUSPA Compart Asia Pte. Ltd. (2)
4 Changi S Ln, No 05-04 Nan Wah Bldg, 486127, Singapore, Singapore
Tel.: (65) 67878727
Web Site: http://www.suspa.com.sg
Sales Range: $10-24.9 Million
Emp.: 7
Mfr of Gas Cylinders, Hydraulic Dampers & Height Adjustment Systems
N.A.I.C.S.: 332999
Ben Tan (Gen Mgr)

SUSPA Nanjing Co. Ltd. (2)
Bai-Jia Hu Industry Park, 211100, Nanjing, China
Tel.: (86) 2552727058
Web Site: http://www.suspa.com
Sales Range: $25-49.9 Million
Emp.: 400
Motor Vehicle Parts Mfr
N.A.I.C.S.: 336390
Shen Jin (Gen Mgr)

SUSPA Pneumatics India Pvt. Ltd. (2)
Guduvancheri-Tiruporur Road Pandur Village No 16, Kayarambedu PO, Chennai, 603 202, Tamil Nadu, India
Tel.: (91) 4427438135
Sales Range: $25-49.9 Million
Emp.: 190
Commercial & Service Industry Machinery Mfr
N.A.I.C.S.: 333310

Subsidiary (Domestic):

SUSPA Tec AG (2)
Muhlweg 33, 90518, Altdorf, Germany
Tel.: (49) 9187930253
Emp.: 700
Chemical Product & Preparation Mfr
N.A.I.C.S.: 325998

Subsidiary (Non-US):

SUSPA UK Ltd. (2)
104 Dudley Road, Sedgley, Dudley, DY3 1TA, West Midlands, United Kingdom
Tel.: (44) 1902597216
Web Site: http://www.suspa.com
Emp.: 2
Gas Spring Hydraulic Damper Piston Rods & Shock Absorber Mfr
N.A.I.C.S.: 332999
Keith Parker (Mng Dir)

Subsidiary (Domestic):

SUSPA Vertriebsgesellschaft mbH (2)
Siemensstrasse 28, Kleve, 47533, Germany
Tel.: (49) 28217115890
Sales Range: $25-49.9 Million
Emp.: 50
Pesticide & Agricultural Chemical Mfr
N.A.I.C.S.: 325320
Lothar Gertlowski (Mgr-Mktg)

Subsidiary (US):

SUSPA, Inc. (2)
3970 Roger B Chaffee Dr SE, Grand Rapids, MI 49548-3497
Tel.: (616) 241-4200
Web Site: http://www.suspa.com

Sales Range: $25-49.9 Million
Emp.: 150
Lift Systems & Gas Cylinders
N.A.I.C.S.: 333995
Jason Robinson (Mgr-IT)

Seitz LLC (1)
212 Industrial Ln, Torrington, CT 06790-2325
Tel.: (860) 489-0476
Web Site: http://www.seitzllc.com
Sales Range: $25-49.9 Million
Emp.: 150
Engineering Services & Industrial Plastic Molds Mfr
N.A.I.C.S.: 333511
Mike Beaman (VP-Sls & Mktg)
Evan Berns (Pres & CEO)

ANDOVER COMMUNICATIONS, INC.
1 Bridge Plz N Ste 275, Fort Lee, NJ 07024-7586
Tel.: (201) 947-4133
Web Site:
 https://www.andovercommunications.com
Year Founded: 1989
Sales Range: $1-9.9 Million
Emp.: 3
Public Relations Agency
N.A.I.C.S.: 541820
Steven Clark (Pres)

ANDOVER NATIONAL CORPORATION
333 Ave of the Americas Ste 2000, Miami, FL 33131
Tel.: (786) 871-3333   DE
Web Site:
 http://www.andovernational.com
Year Founded: 2014
Rev.: $18,686,786
Assets: $35,120,921
Liabilities: $6,409,572
Net Worth: $28,711,349
Earnings: ($8,311,162)
Emp.: 206
Fiscal Year-end: 12/31/21
Data Processing Services
N.A.I.C.S.: 518210
Milun K. Patel (CFO & Head-Corp Dev)
Peter Anthony Cohen (Chm, CEO & Principal Acctg Officer)

ANDRE PROST, INC.
680 Middlesex Tpke, Old Saybrook, CT 06475
Tel.: (860) 388-0838
Web Site:
 https://www.andreprost.com
Year Founded: 1923
Sales Range: $10-24.9 Million
Emp.: 20
Dried & Dehydrated Food Mfr
N.A.I.C.S.: 311423
Frank Landrey (Pres)
Charles Landrey (VP)
Peter Cumings (VP)
Wendy Lewis (Treas)
Lori Montano (Sec)
Mike Souza (Mgr-Sls)

ANDRE-BOUDIN BAKERIES INC.
221 Main St Ste 1230, San Francisco, CA 94105
Tel.: (415) 913-1849
Web Site:
 http://www.boudinbakery.com
Rev.: $38,000,000
Emp.: 25
Breads, Rolls & Buns
N.A.I.C.S.: 311812
Sharon Duvall (CEO)

ANDREAS FURNITURE COMPANY INC.
114 Dover Rd NE, Sugarcreek, OH 44681
Tel.: (330) 852-2494   OH
Web Site:
 https://www.andreasfurniture.com
Year Founded: 1948
Sales Range: $10-24.9 Million
Emp.: 130
Provider of Home Furnishings & Accessories
N.A.I.C.S.: 449110
Terry Andreas (VP)

ANDREESSEN HOROWITZ
2865 Sand Hill Rd Ste 101, Menlo Park, CA 94025
Tel.: (650) 798-3900
Web Site: http://www.a16z.com
Year Founded: 2009
Venture Capital Investment Services
N.A.I.C.S.: 523999
Alastair Rampell (Gen Partner)
Lars Dalgaard (Gen Partner)
Ben Horowitz (Founder)
Alex Rampell (Gen Partner)
Robert H. Swan (Operating Partner)
Jorge Conde (Gen Partner)
Andrew Chen (Gen Partner)
Connie Chan (Gen Partner)
David Ulevitch (Gen Partner)
Jeffrey Jordan (Mng Partner)
Vineeta Agarwala (Gen Partner)
Marc L. Andreessen (Gen Partner)
Asiff S. Hirji (Partner)
William H. Shrank (Venture Partner-Bio & Health)
Vijay Pande (Gen Partner)

ANDRELL INC.
4525 Vliet St SW, Canton, OH 44710
Tel.: (330) 478-3248
Sales Range: $10-24.9 Million
Emp.: 40
Contracting & Construction Services
N.A.I.C.S.: 237310
Andrea Richardson (Pres)
Bill Richardson (Sr VP)
Mary Richardson (VP)

ANDRES CONSTRUCTION SERVICES INC.
3710 Rawlins St Ste 1510, Dallas, TX 75219-4273
Tel.: (512) 291-5430   TX
Web Site:
 http://www.andresconstruction.com
Year Founded: 1991
Sales Range: $10-24.9 Million
Emp.: 35
Provider of Contracting & Construction Services
N.A.I.C.S.: 541618
Wade Andres (Pres)
Gil H. Andres (Chm & CEO)
Dinah Hayes (CFO)

ANDRESS ENGINEERING ASSOCIATES INC.
131 Airpark Industrial Rd, Alabaster, AL 35007
Tel.: (205) 620-9777
Web Site:
 https://www.andressengineers.com
Rev.: $22,000,000
Emp.: 40
Industrial Machinery & Equipment Merchant Whslr
N.A.I.C.S.: 423830
Thomas R. Armstrong (Pres & Treas)
Carl R. Majors (Sec)

ANDRETTI PETROLEUM, LLC
1324 5th St, Eureka, CA 95501
Tel.: (707) 443-3069

Web Site: https://andretti1.com
Year Founded: 1997
Petroleum Products Marketer
N.A.I.C.S.: 424720
Michael Andretti (Owner)

Subsidiaries:

Colvin Oil Company Inc. (1)
2520 Foothill Blvd, Grants Pass, OR 97526-3603
Tel.: (541) 479-5343
Petroleum Bulk Stations & Terminals
N.A.I.C.S.: 424710

ANDRETTI WINERY
4162 Big Ranch Rd, Napa, CA 94558
Tel.: (707) 259-6777
Web Site:
 http://www.andrettiwinery.com
Year Founded: 1996
Sales Range: $1-9.9 Million
Emp.: 15
Winery
N.A.I.C.S.: 312130
Joseph E. Antonini (Co-Founder & Chm)
Mario Andretti (Co-Founder)

ANDREW CHRISTIAN, INC.
1631 Gardena Ave, Glendale, CA 91204
Tel.: (818) 508-9195
Web Site:
 https://www.andrewchristian.com
Year Founded: 1997
Sales Range: $10-24.9 Million
Emp.: 45
Men's Swimwear
N.A.I.C.S.: 315990
Andrew Christian (Pres)

ANDREW CONSTRUCTION CO II, INC.
209 E Mckinley St, Osceola, IA 50213
Tel.: (641) 342-4869
Web Site:
 https://www.andrewconstruction.com
Year Founded: 1934
Residential Remodeler
N.A.I.C.S.: 236118
Randall Andrew (Pres)

ANDREW LAUREN CO. INC.
8909 Kenamar Dr Ste 101, San Diego, CA 92121
Tel.: (858) 793-5319
Web Site:
 http://www.andrewlauren.com
Sales Range: $10-24.9 Million
Emp.: 100
Carpets
N.A.I.C.S.: 423220
David Dominguez (Pres)
Jim Delaurentis (CFO)

ANDREW R. MANCINI ASSOCIATES, INC.
129 Odell Ave, Endicott, NY 13760
Tel.: (607) 754-7070
Web Site: http://www.armoggi.com
Year Founded: 1967
Sales Range: $10-24.9 Million
Emp.: 75
Commercial & Office Building, New Construction
N.A.I.C.S.: 236220
Americo Dicamillo (Pres)
Ellie Tassey (Treas)

ANDREW SPORTS CLUB INC.
5 Empire Blvd, South Hackensack, NJ 07606
Tel.: (201) 662-8200   NJ
Year Founded: 1983
Rev.: $92,000,000
Emp.: 73

Andrew Sports Club Inc.—(Continued)

Fashion Garments for Young Girls, Young Boys & Men Whslr
N.A.I.C.S.: 424350
Andrew Kirpalani *(Pres & CEO)*
P.J. Lalwani *(COO, CIO, Sec & Controller)*
Anil Anand *(CFO)*
John Kirpalani *(VP-Mktg & Sls)*
Lorraine Emilius *(Mgr-Sls-Natl)*

Subsidiaries:

Coliseum (1)
5 Empire Blvd, South Hackensack, NJ 07606 **(100%)**
Tel.: (201) 662-8200
Sales Range: $10-24.9 Million
Emp.: 14
Importer & Distributor of Mens Apparel
N.A.I.C.S.: 424350

Plugg (1)
5 Empire Blvd, South Hackensack, NJ 07606 **(100%)**
Tel.: (201) 662-8200
Sales Range: $25-49.9 Million
Emp.: 60
Importer & Distributor of Jeans
N.A.I.C.S.: 424350

ANDREW TOYOTA
1620 W Silver Spring Dr, Milwaukee, WI 53209
Tel.: (414) 228-1450
Web Site:
https://www.andrewtoyota.com
New & Used Car Retailer
N.A.I.C.S.: 441110
K. C. Han *(Gen Mgr)*
Michael Oppermann *(Sls Mgr-Leasing)*
John Moore *(Sls Mgr-Used Car)*
Cristian Coroian *(Sls Mgr-New Car)*
Laurie Differt *(Mgr-Fin)*
Jared Johnson *(Mgr-Fin)*
Shelby Loth *(Sls Mgr-Internet)*
Allen Good *(Mgr-Svc)*
Duane Domagalski *(Dir-Svc Dept)*
Bob Bielejeski *(Asst Mgr-Parts)*
Mike Brockhaus *(Asst Mgr-Parts)*
Vince Miserendino *(Fin Mgr)*
Andrew C. Schlesinger *(Owner & Pres)*

ANDREW W. BYRD & CO., LLC
1 American Ctr Ste 500 3100 W End Ave, Nashville, TN 37203
Tel.: (615) 256-8061   TN
Web Site: http://www.tvvcapital.com
Year Founded: 1997
Emp.: 6
Private Equity Firm Services
N.A.I.C.S.: 523999
Andrew W. Byrd *(Founder & Pres)*
Ken Weaver *(Mng Dir)*
Jim Gaittens *(Mng Dir)*
Jeremy Wilkinson *(Mng Dir)*
Andrew W. Byrd Jr. *(Mng Dir)*

Subsidiaries:

Bigham Brothers, Inc. (1)
705 E Slaton Rd, Lubbock, TX 79404
Tel.: (806) 745-0384
Web Site: http://www.bighambrothers.com
Sales Range: $10-24.9 Million
Farm Machinery & Equipment Mfr
N.A.I.C.S.: 333111
Lucas Sutterer *(CFO)*

Sur-Form Corporation (1)
50320 E Russell Schmidt Blvd, Chesterfield, MI 48051
Tel.: (586) 221-1950
Web Site: http://www.sur-form.com
Sales Range: $1-9.9 Million
Emp.: 36
Reusable Materials Handling Equipment Mfr
N.A.I.C.S.: 333248

Aaron Redman *(Project Mgr)*
Patty Densmore *(Mgr-Production)*
Edward Stacey Jr. *(Pres)*

ANDREWS & CO, LLC
30 Sparta Ave, Sparta, NJ 07871
Tel.: (973) 383-3193   NJ
Web Site:
https://www.andrewscleaning.biz
Year Founded: 1979
Sales Range: $1-9.9 Million
Emp.: 75
Janitorial Services
N.A.I.C.S.: 561720
Nadja Meo *(CEO & CFO)*
Joe Paulo *(Partner & Head-Ops)*
Jamie Krulikowsky *(Head-HR)*

ANDREWS DISTRIBUTING COMPANY, LLC
2730 Irving Blvd, Dallas, TX 75207
Tel.: (361) 696-7400   TX
Web Site:
https://www.andrewsdistributing.com
Year Founded: 1976
Sales Range: $400-449.9 Million
Emp.: 1,100
Beer Distr
N.A.I.C.S.: 424810
Barry G. Andrews *(Founder & Chm)*
Sean Murphy *(VP & Gen Mgr-Fort Worth & Corpus Christi Sls)*
Michael McGuire *(Pres & CEO)*
Roy Foster *(CFO & Exec VP)*
David Holt *(Exec VP-Mktg)*
John Ross *(Exec VP-IT)*
Mike Barnes *(Exec VP & Gen Mgr-Revenue)*
Maryam Morse *(Exec VP-HR)*
Dan Betz *(Exec VP-Ops)*

Subsidiaries:

Andrews Distributing Company of North Texas, LLC (1)
2730 Irving Blvd, Dallas, TX 75207
Tel.: (214) 525-9400
Web Site:
http://www.andrewsdistributing.com
Sales Range: $25-49.9 Million
Beer Distr
N.A.I.C.S.: 424810
Barry G. Andrews *(Chm)*
Michael McGuire *(Pres & CEO)*
Mike Barnes *(Exec VP & Gen Mgr-Revenue)*
Dan Betz *(Exec VP-Ops)*
Roy Foster *(CFO & Exec VP)*
David Holt *(Exec VP-Mktg)*
Nick Lake *(VP-Comml Strategy)*
Sean Murphy *(VP & Gen Mgr-Sls-Fort Worth & Corpus Christi)*
John Ross *(Exec VP-IT)*
Katy Wittig *(VP-Strategic Execution & Comm)*
Maryam Morse *(Exec VP-HR)*

ANDREWS GROUP
1801 Walters Ct, Fairfield, CA 94533
Tel.: (707) 422-4844
Sales Range: $10-24.9 Million
Emp.: 80
Mechanical Contractor
N.A.I.C.S.: 238220
Frank J. Andrews Jr. *(Pres)*

Subsidiaries:

Amos & Andrews Inc. (1)
PO Box 250, Fairfield, CA 94533
Tel.: (707) 422-4844
Sales Range: $10-24.9 Million
Emp.: 5
Mechanical Contractor
N.A.I.C.S.: 238220
Gary Andrews *(Pres)*

Pacific Power Services Corp. (1)
1801 Walters Ct, Fairfield, CA 94533
Tel.: (707) 422-4844
Rev.: $250,000
Emp.: 4

Industrial Equipment & Generators Service & Installation
N.A.I.C.S.: 811210

ANDREWS LOGISTICS, INC.
2445 E Southlake Blvd, Southlake, TX 76092
Tel.: (817) 527-2770
Web Site:
https://www.andrewslogistics.com
Year Founded: 1997
Emp.: 15
Hazardous Materials & Liquids Transportation Services
N.A.I.C.S.: 484230
Brian Jarvis *(Pres & COO)*
J. Darron Eschle *(Chm & CEO)*
Randall Ingo *(Exec VP)*
Griff Odgers *(Sr VP-Safety & Risk Mgmt)*
Ayman Kawache *(VP-IT)*

Subsidiaries:

Andrews Transportation, Inc. (1)
5601 Denton Hwy, Fort Worth, TX 76148-3754 **(100%)**
Tel.: (817) 498-6000
Web Site: http://www.andrews-transport.com
Sales Range: $25-49.9 Million
Bulk Liquid Trucking Transport
N.A.I.C.S.: 484230
Gary Andrews *(Chm & CEO)*
Randall Ingo *(Pres & COO)*
Jim Hawarden *(CFO & VP)*

ANDREWS MCMEEL UNIVERSAL
1130 Walnut St, Kansas City, MO 64106
Tel.: (816) 581-7500   DE
Web Site:
http://www.amuniversal.com
Year Founded: 1970
Sales Range: $75-99.9 Million
Emp.: 180
Books, Calendars, Greeting Cards & Stationery Products Mfr & Distr
N.A.I.C.S.: 513130
Hugh T. Andrews *(Chm)*
Andy Sareyan *(Pres & CEO)*
Sue Roush *(VP & Mng Editor)*
Les Hinmon *(CFO & Sr VP)*
Kathy Hilliard *(VP-Mktg)*
Bridget McMeel *(Partner)*
Kevin Greenlee *(VP-Tech)*
Andy Sareyan *(Pres & CEO)*
Andrea Colvin *(VP-Content)*
Andy Sareyan *(Pres & CEO)*
Brent Bartram *(VP-Fin)*
Cliff Koehler *(VP-Production)*
Dan Boston *(VP-Sls)*
James Andrews *(VP-Licensing)*
Kathy Hilliard *(VP-Mktg)*
Kevin Greenlee *(VP-Tech)*
Michael Stewart *(VP-HR)*
Jennifer Sussman *(Chief Digital Officer)*
Susan Johnson *(CMO)*
Linda Jones *(Sr VP-Sls & Licensing)*
Brent Bartram *(VP-Fin)*
Lynne McAdoo *(VP-Sls-Books)*

ANDREWS OIL COMPANY
206 E 9th St, Mount Carmel, IL 62863
Tel.: (618) 263-3896
Sales Range: $25-49.9 Million
Emp.: 15
Petroleum Bulk Stations
N.A.I.C.S.: 424710
Rick Andrews *(Pres)*
Becky Andrews *(VP)*

ANDROMEDA SYSTEMS INC.
615 Lynnhaven Pkwy Ste 104, Virginia Beach, VA 23452
Tel.: (757) 340-9070

Web Site:
https://www.androsysinc.com
Year Founded: 2005
Sales Range: $1-9.9 Million
Emp.: 65
Professional & Technical Engineering Services
N.A.I.C.S.: 541330
John H. Kobelski *(CEO)*
John W. Henson *(Pres)*
Robert Ward *(CFO)*
Carl T. Sawyer *(CIO)*
Ron Wagner *(CTO & VP-Innovation)*

ANDROSCOGGIN HOME HEALTH SERVICES, INC.
15 Strawberry Ave, Lewiston, ME 04240
Tel.: (207) 777-7740   ME
Web Site: http://www.ahch.org
Year Founded: 1966
Sales Range: $25-49.9 Million
Hospice Care Services
N.A.I.C.S.: 621610
Kathleen Applin *(CFO)*
Ann Weaver *(Dir-HR)*
Kenneth Albert *(Pres & CEO)*
Miles C. Hunt *(Vice Chm)*
Alex Roy *(Vice Chm)*
Christopher D. Gagnon *(Treas)*

ANDROSCOGGIN SAVINGS BANK
30 Lisbon St, Lewiston, ME 04240
Tel.: (207) 784-9164   ME
Web Site:
http://www.androscogginbank.com
Year Founded: 1870
Sales Range: $25-49.9 Million
Emp.: 155
Community Bank
N.A.I.C.S.: 522180
Paul H. Andersen *(Pres & CEO)*
Lena Hann *(Officer-Bus & Govt Svcs & VP)*
Denise Tabet *(Mgr-Retail)*
Eric Hansen *(Officer-Comml Loan & VP)*
Melissa Knutson *(Officer-Comml Loan & VP)*
Dawn Youland *(Mgr-Central Maine Market)*

ANDROSCOGGIN VALLEY HOSPITAL
59 Page Hill Rd, Berlin, NH 03570
Tel.: (603) 752-2200   NH
Web Site: https://www.avhnh.org
Year Founded: 1971
Sales Range: $50-74.9 Million
Emp.: 418
Health Care Srvices
N.A.I.C.S.: 622110
Russell Keene *(CEO)*
Mark Kelley *(Chm)*
Alta Chase *(Sec)*
Donna Goodrich *(Co-Chm)*

ANDURIL INDUSTRIES, INC.
1400 Anduril, Costa Mesa 92626
Tel.: (949) 891-1607   DE
Web Site: https://www.anduril.com
Year Founded: 2017
Defense & Space Manufacturing
N.A.I.C.S.: 928110
Palmer Luckey *(Co-Founder)*
Brian Schimpf *(Co-Founder & CEO)*
Trae' Stephens *(Co-Founder & Exec Chm)*
Matt Grimm *(Co-Founder & COO)*

Subsidiaries:

Blue Force Technologies, Inc. (1)
627 Distribution Dr Ste D, Morrisville, NC 27560-7100
Tel.: (919) 443-1660

Aircraft Mfr
N.A.I.C.S.: 336411
Shawn Herrmann (Project Engr)

ANDWIN CORPORATION
6636 Variel Ave, Woodland Hills, CA 91303
Tel.: (818) 999-2828
Web Site: http://www.andwin.com
Sales Range: $10-24.9 Million
Emp.: 30
Kits For Labs
N.A.I.C.S.: 339113
Natalie L. Sarraf (CEO)
Abner Ledy (Pres)

ANDY BUSINESS CONGLOM-ERATE, USA
8565 S Eastern Ave Ste 136, Las Vegas, NV 89123
Tel.: (702) 576-1187   NV
Year Founded: 2011
Emp.: 1
Business Consultants
N.A.I.C.S.: 541611
Andy Z. Fan (Chm, Pres, CEO & Treas)

ANDY GUMP INC.
26954 Ruether Ave, Santa Clarita, CA 91351
Tel.: (661) 251-7721
Web Site: https://www.andygump.com
Sales Range: $10-24.9 Million
Emp.: 215
Provider of Portable Sanitation, Temporary Fencing, Power & Septic Services
N.A.I.C.S.: 562991
Barry Gump (Pres & CEO)
Patricia Gump (VP)
Sharon Manly (Controller)

ANDY M. CAMACHO INC.
845 N Alameda St, Los Angeles, CA 90012
Tel.: (213) 626-5554
Rev.: $13,800,000
Emp.: 15
Mexican Restaurant
N.A.I.C.S.: 722511
Andy M. Camacho (CEO)

ANDY MOHR BUICK GMC
9295 E 131st St, Fishers, IN 46038
Tel.: (317) 632-6300
Web Site: http://www.andymohrbg.com
Sales Range: $10-24.9 Million
Emp.: 63
Car Dealer
N.A.I.C.S.: 441120
Bob Siderys (Mgr-Used Car Sls)
Steve Faulkner (Gen Mgr)
Dave Parker (Mgr-Svc)
John Ramsey (Mgr-Parts)

ANDY MOHR FORD
2713 E Main St, Plainfield, IN 46168
Tel.: (317) 342-0833
Web Site: https://www.andymohrford.com
Year Founded: 1995
Sales Range: $10-24.9 Million
Emp.: 75
Car Whslr
N.A.I.C.S.: 441110
Calvin Young (Mgr-Parts)
Chris Huston (Gen Mgr)
Austin Williams (Mgr-Fin)
David Wilson (Mgr-Sls)
Dennis Pennington (Mgr-Used Car)
Dwayne Deppe (Mgr-Fin)
Jack McKinney (Mgr-Fin)
Jon Blakely (Mgr-Sls)

Keri Price (Mgr-Fin)
Nikki Smythe (Mgr-Fin)
Scott Gardner (Mgr-Fin)
Shannon Buck (Mgr-Used Car)

ANDY MOHR NISSAN, INC.
4302 Lafayette Rd, Indianapolis, IN 46254
Tel.: (317) 794-2165
Web Site: https://www.andymohr-nissan.com
Sales Range: $10-24.9 Million
Emp.: 50
New Car Dealers
N.A.I.C.S.: 441110
Brian Webb (Gen Mgr)
Mike Hopper (Gen Mgr)
Doug Currie (Mgr-Fin)
Karen Hardwick (Mgr-Parts)

ANDY MOHR TRUCK CENTER
1301 S Holt Rd, Indianapolis, IN 46241
Tel.: (317) 244-6811
Web Site: http://www.andymohrtrucks.com
Year Founded: 1964
Rev.: $40,200,000
Emp.: 50
Authorized Dealer for Ford, Volvo & UD Trucks
N.A.I.C.S.: 441110
Andy Jeanor (Mgr-Sls & Fin)

ANDY SHAW FORD
1231 E Main St, Sylva, NC 28779
Tel.: (828) 586-0900
Web Site: https://www.andyshawford.com
Sales Range: $10-24.9 Million
Emp.: 35
New Car Retailer
N.A.I.C.S.: 441110
David Rogers (Mgr-Svc)

ANDY'S ASSURANCE AGENCY
1441 W Flagler St, Miami, FL 33135
Tel.: (305) 642-8407
Web Site: https://www.andysassurance.net
Year Founded: 1969
Sales Range: $10-24.9 Million
Emp.: 20
Insurance Agency & Brokerage Services
N.A.I.C.S.: 524210
Loreta Rodriguez (Owner)

ANDY'S RESTAURANTS, INC.
514 Hwy 274, Camden, AR 71701
Tel.: (870) 574-0407   AR
Web Site: http://www.andys-restaurant.com
Year Founded: 1977
Sales Range: $1-9.9 Million
Emp.: 126
Fast Food Services
N.A.I.C.S.: 722513
Chad Hause (Pres & CEO)

ANEMOI LLC
PO Box 692, Morgantown, WV 26507
Tel.: (304) 381-3660
Web Site: http://www.anemoiservices.com
Year Founded: 2014
Sales Range: $1-9.9 Million
Emp.: 27
Wind Turbine Mfr
N.A.I.C.S.: 333611
Matthew Smith (Founder & Pres)

ANESTHESIA BUSINESS CONSULTANTS

255 W Michigan Ave, Jackson, MI 49201-1909
Tel.: (517) 787-6440
Web Site: https://www.anesthesiallc.com
Year Founded: 1987
Sales Range: $100-124.9 Million
Emp.: 250
Anesthesia Billing
N.A.I.C.S.: 541219
Tony Mira (Co-Founder, Co-Owner, Pres & CEO)
Sue Mira (Co-Founder & Co-Owner)
Trevor Myers (Pres)

ANEW MARKETING GROUP
811 W Jericho Tpke Ste 109E, Smithtown, NY 11787
Tel.: (631) 982-4000
Year Founded: 1973
Rev.: $20,000,000
Emp.: 31
N.A.I.C.S.: 541810
Charles B. Macleod (Pres & CEO)
Jan Krsanac (Dir-Mktg)

Subsidiaries:

ANEW Marketing Group   (1)
445 Park Ave 9th Fl, New York, NY 10022
Tel.: (212) 333-8683
N.A.I.C.S.: 541810
Jan Krsanac (Dir-Mktg)
Charles B. Macleod (Pres & CEO)

ANEXIO, INC.
1 Bank of America Plz 421 Fayetteville St, Raleigh, NC 27601
Tel.: (941) 556-3410
Web Site: http://www.anexio.com
Sales Range: $10-24.9 Million
Emp.: 13
Custom Computing Services
N.A.I.C.S.: 541511
James E. Griffin (Sr VP)
Tony Pompliano (Pres & CEO)
Scott Hauff (VP-Sls-Worldwide)
Kevin Burns (COO)
John Kraft (Sr VP-Corp Dev)
Alex Reppen (CTO)
Dane Vincent (CFO)

Subsidiaries:

Pragmatix, Inc.   (1)
565 Taxter Rd, Elmsford, NY 10523
Tel.: (914) 345-9444
Web Site: http://www.pragmatix.net
Sales Range: $1-9.9 Million
Emp.: 15
IT Support & Consulting Services
N.A.I.C.S.: 541512
William Abram (Founder & Pres)
Barbara Abram (CEO)

ANGARAI INTERNATIONAL, INC.
7331 Hanover Pkwy Ste C & D, Greenbelt, MD 20770
Tel.: (410) 472-5000
Web Site: http://www.angarai-intl.com
Year Founded: 2003
Sales Range: $1-9.9 Million
Emp.: 17
Consulting Services
N.A.I.C.S.: 541611
Venkat A.R. Subramanian (Founder, Pres & CEO)

ANGEL BROTHERS ENTERPRISES INC.
5210 W Rd, Baytown, TX 77521-9022
Tel.: (281) 471-6730
Web Site: http://www.angelbrothers.com
Year Founded: 1972
Sales Range: $50-74.9 Million
Emp.: 400

Provider of Excavation & Construction Services
N.A.I.C.S.: 238910
Greg Angel (Pres & Partner)
Kenneth Kitchen (Mgr-IT)

ANGEL PARK GOLF, LLC
100 S Rampart Blvd, Las Vegas, NV 89145
Tel.: (702) 254-4653
Web Site: https://www.angelpark.com
Year Founded: 1995
Sales Range: $10-24.9 Million
Emp.: 200
Golf Club Operator
N.A.I.C.S.: 713910
David Bogue (Gen Mgr)
Rich Feuerstein (Dir-Food & Beverage)
Jeremy Adkins (Dir-Maintenance)
Brenda Raffety (Mgr-HR)
Jed Francese (Mgr-Grp Sls)
Jessie Reid (Mgr-Special Events)
Bill Sheehan (Accountant)

ANGEL STAFFING, INC.
1202 E Sonterra Ste 501, San Antonio, TX 78258
Tel.: (210) 616-9526   TX
Web Site: https://www.angelstaffing.net
Year Founded: 2002
Sales Range: $10-24.9 Million
Emp.: 1,500
Employment Services
N.A.I.C.S.: 561311
Shannon Ralston (Founder, Pres & CEO)
Kathy Gallagher (COO)

ANGEL WAREHOUSE INC.
12882 Pierce St, Pacoima, CA 91331
Tel.: (818) 834-2774
Web Site: http://www.angelwarehouse.net
Sales Range: $10-24.9 Million
Emp.: 25
Automotive Supplies
N.A.I.C.S.: 423120
John Gilmour (Gen Mgr)

ANGELES EQUITY PARTNERS, LLC
11661 San Vicente Blvd Ste 808, Los Angeles, CA 90049
Tel.: (310) 844-9200   DE
Web Site: http://www.angelesequity.com
Year Founded: 2014
Privater Equity Firm
N.A.I.C.S.: 523999
Jordan W. Katz (Co-Founder & Mng Partner)
Timothy P. Meyer (Co-Founder & Mng Partner)
Annie Chau (COO & Chief Compliance Officer)
Sameer Patel (Mng Dir)
Sam Heischuber (Mng Dir)
Frank Spelman (Mng Dir)
Martin Mumford (Operating Partner)
Matthew Hively (Operating Partner)
Te'Rhon O'Neal (VP)
Jamie Brown (VP)

Subsidiaries:

AEP NVH OpCo, LLC   (1)
1001 State St, Chicago Heights, IL 60411-2907
Tel.: (708) 758-0211
Web Site: http://www.aainvh.com
Sales Range: $10-24.9 Million
Automotive Acoustic Products Mfr
N.A.I.C.S.: 336390

Angeles Equity Partners, LLC—(Continued)

Larry Hagood (CEO)
David Marshall (CFO)
Tony Daines (CMO)
Rich Baumstein (VP-Ops)

Data Clean Corp. (1)
1033 Graceland Ave, Des Plaines, IL 60016
Tel.: (858) 693-6004
Web Site: http://www.dataclean.com
Rev.: $1,240,000
Emp.: 10
Data Center Cleaning & Maintenance Services
N.A.I.C.S.: 518210
Bill Stephenson (Mgr)
Richard Hill (Pres)

Subsidiary (Domestic):

SML Enterprises Inc. (2)
7950 Gainsford Ct, Bristow, VA 20136
Tel.: (703) 361-1959
Rev.: $4,410,000
Emp.: 30
Environmental Cleaning Services
N.A.I.C.S.: 541620

Sealco LLC (2)
1751 International Pkwy Ste 115, Richardson, TX 75081
Tel.: (972) 234-5567
Web Site: http://www.sealco.net
Sales Range: $10-24.9 Million
Computer & Office Machine Repair & Maintenance Services
N.A.I.C.S.: 811210
Eddie Dulaney (VP)

ERP Power LLC (1)
893 Patriot Dr Ste E, Moorpark, CA 93021
Tel.: (805) 517-1300
Web Site: http://www.erp-power.com
Appliance & Electronics Mfg.
N.A.I.C.S.: 423620
Abdul Sher-Jan (Pres & COO)
Michael Archer (Founder & CEO)

Subsidiary (Domestic):

Lumenetix, Inc. (2)
4742 Scotts Vly Dr, Scotts Valley, CA 95066
Tel.: (877) 805-7284
Electronic Parts & Equipment Merchant Whslr
N.A.I.C.S.: 423690

Edwards Building Center, Inc. (1)
33636 Highway 6, Edwards, CO 81632
Tel.: (970) 926-3381
Web Site:
http://edwardsbuildingcenterinc.net
Hardware Stores; Batteries, Chainsaw & Trimmers
N.A.I.C.S.: 444140

Lapmaster Group Holdings LLC (1)
501 W Algonquin Rd, Mount Prospect, IL 60056-5705
Tel.: (224) 659-7101
Web Site: http://www.lapmaster.com
Emp.: 600
Industrial Machinery Mfr
N.A.I.C.S.: 333248
Chelsea A. Grayson (Chm)

Subsidiary (Non-US):

Lapmaster Wolters GmbH (2)
Buesumer Strasse 96, 24768, Rendsburg, Germany
Tel.: (49) 43314580
Web Site: http://www.lapmaster-wolters.de
Precision Machine Tools & Systems Mfr
N.A.I.C.S.: 333248
Sebastian Jessen (Dir-Sls Admin)

Subsidiary (Non-US):

Lapmaster India Private Limited (3)
Plot 55 1st Floor 2nd Street Samayapuram Main Road, Karambakkam Porur, Chennai, 600 116, Tamil Nadu, India
Tel.: (91) 4465356555
Web Site: http://www.lapmasterindia.com
Precision Machine Tool & System Mfr
N.A.I.C.S.: 333515

Subsidiary (US):

Lapmaster Wolters LLC (3)

14 High St, Plainville, MA 02762
Tel.: (508) 695-7151
Web Site: http://www.lapmaster-wolters.de
Emp.: 15
Precision Machine Tool & System Mfr
N.A.I.C.S.: 333248
Scott Schuster (Product Mgr-Fine Grinding Products)

Subsidiary (Non-US):

Lapmaster Wolters Limited (3)
Lee Mill Industrial Estate Unit 1 North Road, Ivybridge, Devon, PL21 9EN, United Kingdom
Tel.: (44) 1752893191
Web Site: http://www.lapmaster.co.uk
Precision Machine Tools & Systems Mfr & Distr
N.A.I.C.S.: 333248
Kevin M. Hook (Mgr-Quality)
Martin Nicholas (Mgr-Technical)

Peter Wolters Japan Co., Ltd. (3)
Daisho Bldg 6th Floor Room 601 12-28 Esaka-cho 1-chome, Suita, 564-0063, Osaka, Japan
Tel.: (81) 668217024
Web Site: http://www.peter-wolters.com
High Precision Machine Tools & Systems Mfr
N.A.I.C.S.: 333515
Keiko Hoshikawa (Mgr-Acctg)
Kosaku Matsuno (Sr Mgr-Bus Dev)

Meek's Lumber Company (1)
1311 E Woodhurst Dr, Springfield, MO 65804-4282
Tel.: (417) 521-2801
Web Site: http://www.meeklumber.com
Sales Range: $300-349.9 Million
Emp.: 700
Home Improvement Centers Operator
N.A.I.C.S.: 444110
Terry O. Meek (Pres)
Charlie Meek (Gen Mgr)
Kent May (CFO)

Subsidiary (Domestic):

Meek's, Inc. (2)
1651 Response Rd Ste 200, Sacramento, CA 95815
Tel.: (916) 576-3042
Web Site: http://www.meeks.com
Home Improvement Centers Operator
N.A.I.C.S.: 444110

Primus Aerospace, Inc. (1)
938 Quail Street, Lakewood, CO 80215
Tel.: (303) 235-8944
Web Site: https://primusaero.com
Emp.: 86
Aerospace Component & Mfg.
N.A.I.C.S.: 336415
Randall Brodsky (Pres)
Nick McGrath (CFO)
Kyle Brengel (COO)
Scott Miller (CEO)

Subsidiary (Domestic):

Raloid Corporation (2)
109 Wabash Ave, Reisterstown, MD 21136
Tel.: (410) 833-2272
Web Site: http://www.raloid.com
Rev.: $5,000,000
Emp.: 55
All Other Miscellaneous Fabricated Metal Product Mfr
N.A.I.C.S.: 332999
David Sandy (Exec VP)
Nicholas Kalathas (Pres)

RoBEX LLC (1)
8600 S Wilkinson Way, Perrysburg, OH 43551
Tel.: (734) 432-5055
Web Site: https://robex.us
Robotics Automation Services
N.A.I.C.S.: 541511

Subsidiary (Domestic):

Acieta LLC (2)
N25 W23790 Commerce Cir Ste F, Waukesha, WI 53188
Tel.: (844) 422-4382
Web Site: https://www.acieta.com
Industrial Robotics Automation Services
N.A.I.C.S.: 423830

Vistech Manufacturing Solutions, LLC (1)
1156 Scenic Dr Ste 120, Modesto, CA 95350
Tel.: (209) 544-9333
Web Site: http://www.vistechmfg.com
Sales Range: $1-9.9 Million
Emp.: 33
Packaging Machinery, Nsk
N.A.I.C.S.: 333993
John Jacinto (Principal)

Subsidiary (Domestic):

NVH Acquisition Holdings LLC (2)
500 E Statler Rd, Piqua, OH 45356
Tel.: (937) 778-0585
Web Site:
http://www.industryproductsco.com
Sales Range: $1-9.9 Million
Emp.: 310
Welding Repair
N.A.I.C.S.: 811490

Worthington Industries Engineered Cabs, Inc. (1)
315 Airport Dr, Watertown, SD 57201
Tel.: (605) 886-5681
Heavy Mobile Equipment Designer & Mfr.
N.A.I.C.S.: 336390

Subsidiary (Domestic):

Worthington Industries Engineered Cabs, LLC (2)
315 Airport Dr, Watertown, SD 57201
Tel.: (605) 886-5681
Custom Metal Fabrications Mfr
N.A.I.C.S.: 336390

Xanitos, Inc. (1)
17 Campus Blvd Ste 150, Newtown Square, PA 19073
Tel.: (484) 654-2300
Web Site: http://www.xanitos.com
Industrial Janitorial Services
N.A.I.C.S.: 561720
Dwight Sypolt (Sr VP-HR & Admin)
David Crothall (CEO)

ANGELES WELDING & MFG., INC.
9747 S Norwalk Blvd, Santa Fe Springs, CA 90670
Tel.: (562) 692-0876
Year Founded: 1935
Sales Range: $10-24.9 Million
Emp.: 110
Steel Service Center
N.A.I.C.S.: 423510

ANGELI-MENOMINEE INC.
1401 8th Ave, Menominee, MI 49858
Tel.: (906) 863-5575
Web Site:
http://www.angelisfresh.com
Sales Range: $25-49.9 Million
Emp.: 250
Owner & Operator of Grocery Stores
N.A.I.C.S.: 445110
Fred Angeli (Owner)

ANGELLE CONCRETE GROUP, LLC
2638 S Sherwood Forest Blvd Ste 200, Baton Rouge, LA 70816-3404
Tel.: (225) 304-5873
Web Site:
http://www.angelleconcrete.com
Year Founded: 1946
Sales Range: $10-24.9 Million
Emp.: 30
Readymix Concrete Mfr.
N.A.I.C.S.: 327320
Brian Trauernicht (CEO & CFO)
Allan Sanchez (Sls Mgr)

ANGELO'S FRESH MARKET, INC.
4400 W Elm St, McHenry, IL 60050-4036
Tel.: (815) 385-1430

Year Founded: 1999
Supermarket Operator
N.A.I.C.S.: 445110
Chris Christou (Mgr-HR)

Subsidiaries:

Angelo's Fresh Food Market, LLC (1)
9914 N Main St, Richmond, IL 60071
Tel.: (815) 678-6011
Web Site:
https://www.angelosfreshmarket.com
Supermarket Operator
N.A.I.C.S.: 445110

ANGELOU ECONOMIC ADVISORS INC.
8121 Bee Cave Rd Ste 200, Austin, TX 78746
Tel.: (512) 225-9320
Web Site:
http://www.angeloueconomics.com
Sales Range: $1-9.9 Million
Emp.: 9
Economic Development & Site Selection Consulting Services
N.A.I.C.S.: 541611
Angelos Angelou (Founder & Exec Officer)
Esther Angelou (Owner-Fin Mgmt)
Steve Vierck (Pres & CEO-New Mexico Partnership)
William Mellor (VP & Gen Mgr-Economic Impact & Res)

Subsidiaries:

Angelou Economic Advisors Inc. (1)
Dubai Media City Building 8 Ste 319, PO Box 500657, Dubai, United Arab Emirates
Tel.: (971) 4 3633472
Economic Development & Site Selection Consulting Services
N.A.I.C.S.: 541611

ANGELS BASEBALL, L.P.
2000 Gene Autry Way, Anaheim, CA 92806-6100
Tel.: (714) 940-2000
Web Site: http://www.mlb.com
Year Founded: 1961
Sales Range: $50-74.9 Million
Emp.: 1,400
Professional Baseball Club Services
N.A.I.C.S.: 711211
Dennis Kuhl (Chm)
Bill Beverage (CFO)
John Carpino (Pres)
Molly Taylor Jolly (Sr VP-Fin & Admin)
Neil Viserto (VP-Sls)

Subsidiaries:

Salt Lake Bees (1)
77 W 1300 S, Salt Lake City, UT 84115-5326
Tel.: (801) 325-2273
Web Site: http://www.slbees.com
Sales Range: $50-74.9 Million
Emp.: 500
Baseball Team
N.A.I.C.S.: 711211
Marc Amicone (VP & Gen Mgr)
Brad Tammen (Asst Gen Mgr)

ANGELUS BLOCK CO. INC.
11374 Tuxford St, Sun Valley, CA 91352
Tel.: (818) 767-8576
Web Site:
https://www.angelusblock.com
Rev.: $15,900,000
Emp.: 50
Manufactures Concrete & Cinder Block
N.A.I.C.S.: 444180
Tom Berry (Mgr-Credit)
Tom Reed (Mgr-Sls)
Walter Wright (Supvr-Maintenance)
Tom Murphy (Mgr-Paver Sls)

**ANGELUS FURNITURE OUT-
LET INC.**
7227 Edinger Ave, Huntington Beach,
CA 92647
Tel.: (714) 908-5754
Web Site: http://www.thomasville.com
Year Founded: 1904
Sales Range: $10-24.9 Million
Emp.: 15
Furniture Retailer
N.A.I.C.S.: 449110
Irwin Greenberg (Owner)

**ANGELVISION TECHNOLO-
GIES, INC.**
7320 SW Hunziker Ste 200, Portland,
OR 97223
Tel.: (503) 620-3377
Web Site:
 http://www.angelvisiontech.com
Year Founded: 2001
Sales Range: $10-24.9 Million
Emp.: 80
Digital Video Production
N.A.I.C.S.: 512110
Michael Jingozian (Founder, Pres &
CEO)
Mike Williams (Dir-Impact Books)

ANGLERS MARINE
3475 E La Palma Ave, Anaheim, CA
92806-2024
Tel.: (714) 666-2628
Web Site:
 https://www.anglersmarine.com
Sales Range: $10-24.9 Million
Emp.: 19
Boat Whslr
N.A.I.C.S.: 441222
Richard Grover (CEO)

**ANGLIN REICHMANN SNELL-
GROVE & ARMSTRONG, P.C.**
305 Quality Cir, Huntsville, AL 35806-
4542
Tel.: (256) 533-1040
Web Site: https://www.anglincpa.com
Year Founded: 1990
Emp.: 55
General Management Consulting
Services
N.A.I.C.S.: 541611
Jason L. Miller (Partner)
Kandy Gardner (Partner)
N. Scott Hand (Partner)
Luke C. Kinzer (Partner)
Jeremy D. Mosteller (Partner)
Jay Reichmann (Partner)
Tracy L. Sams (Partner)
Steve Schickel (Partner)
Brandon C. Smith (Partner)

**ANGOLA WIRE PRODUCTS
INC.**
803 Wohlert St, Angola, IN 46703
Tel.: (260) 665-9447
Web Site: http://www.angolawire.com
Sales Range: $10-24.9 Million
Emp.: 180
Miscellaneous Fabricated Wire Prod-
ucts
N.A.I.C.S.: 332618
Roy Abriani (Mgr-Retail POP Sls)

ANGSTROM USA, LLC.
26980 Trolley Indus Dr, Taylor, MI
48180
Tel.: (313) 295-0100 MI
Web Site: http://www.angstrom-
 usa.com
Year Founded: 2003
Sales Range: $10-24.9 Million
Emp.: 30
Narrow Fabric Mills
N.A.I.C.S.: 313220

Nagesh Palakurthi (Pres & CEO)
Scott Cowan (Acct Mgr)
Jayanth Karnam (Plant Mgr)
Ronald Housley (Mgr-Quality
Assurance-OEM)
Subsidiaries:
Wrena LLC   (1)
265 Lightner Rd, Tipp City, OH 45371
Tel.: (937) 667-4403
Sales Range: $10-24.9 Million
Emp.: 65
Automotive Stamping Services
N.A.I.C.S.: 336370
Pam Melish (Mgr-Pur)

**ANHEUSER-BUSCH BUSCH
EMPLOYEES BENEFIT TRUST**
PO Box 535007, Pittsburgh, PA
15253-5007
Tel.: (412) 236-7175 NY
Year Founded: 1985
Sales Range: $10-24.9 Million
Fire Insurance Services
N.A.I.C.S.: 524113
Brent Heintzelman (VP)

ANIMAID PET HOSPITAL
7080 Katella Ave, Stanton, CA 90680-
2805
Tel.: (714) 897-2429
Web Site:
 http://www.animaidpethospital.com
Veterinary Services
N.A.I.C.S.: 541940
Won Seung (Owner)

ANIMAL HAVEN INC.
251 Center St, New York, NY 10013
Tel.: (212) 274-8511
Year Founded: 1967
Sales Range: $1-9.9 Million
Emp.: 19
Animal Care Services
N.A.I.C.S.: 812910
Tiffany Lacey (Exec Dir)

ANIMAL HUMANE SOCIETY
845 Meadow Ln N, Golden Valley,
MN 55422
Tel.: (763) 522-4325 MN
Web Site: http://www.animalhumane
 society.org
Year Founded: 1878
Sales Range: $10-24.9 Million
Emp.: 381
Animal Care Services
N.A.I.C.S.: 812910
Kathy Mock (Chief Govt Affairs &
Outreach Officer)
Eileen Lay (CFO & COO)
Scott Schroepfer (Treas)
Maureen McDonough (Sec)
Janelle Dixon (Pres & CEO)
Lisa B. Bonds (Chief Advancement
Officer)

**ANIMAL RESCUE LEAGUE OF
BOSTON**
10 Chandler St, Boston, MA 02116
Tel.: (617) 426-9170 MA
Web Site: https://www.arlboston.org
Year Founded: 1899
Sales Range: $10-24.9 Million
Emp.: 109
Animal Rescue Services
N.A.I.C.S.: 813312
Julie Chirillo (Dir-HR)
Nadine Pellegrini (Dir-Advocacy)
Angela Altobelli (Dir-Mktg & Comm)
Constance de Brun (CFO & COO)

**ANIMALFEEDS INTERNA-
TIONAL CORPORATION**
77 Brandt Ave, Clark, NJ 07066-1540
Tel.: (732) 827-0660

Web Site:
 https://www.animalfeeds.com
Year Founded: 1955
Sales Range: $150-199.9 Million
Emp.: 50
Mfr, Packer & Distributor of Protein &
Oil
N.A.I.C.S.: 531190
Celia Meilan (Founder & VP)
Subsidiaries:
Atlantic Shippers Inc.   (1)
77 Brant Ave Ste 315, Clark, NJ 07066-
1540
Tel.: (252) 726-6833
Sales Range: $10-24.9 Million
Emp.: 4
Provider of Terminal Services
N.A.I.C.S.: 493110
Atlantic Shippers of Texas, Inc. (1)
6400 Procter Ext, Port Arthur, TX
77642-0905   (100%)
Tel.: (409) 962-2457
Web Site: http://www.animalfeeds.com
Sales Range: $10-24.9 Million
Emp.: 9
Provider of Terminal Services
N.A.I.C.S.: 488510
Robert Pastore (CEO)

ANIMALSCAN
934 Charter St, Redwood City, CA
94063
Tel.: (650) 480-2001
Web Site:
 http://www.as.blacklabs.space
Year Founded: 2008
Sales Range: $1-9.9 Million
Emp.: 12
Veterinary MRI Imaging Services
N.A.I.C.S.: 621512
James J. Stuppino (Pres & CEO)
Subsidiaries:
AnimalScan MRI   (1)
328 Maple Ave E, Vienna, VA 22180
Tel.: (703) 281-9440
Web Site: http://www.animalscan.org
Animal Diagnostic Solutions
N.A.I.C.S.: 621512
Jill K. Maney (Med Dir)
AnimalScan MRI   (1)
934 Charter St, Redwood City, CA 94063
Tel.: (650) 480-2001
Web Site: http://www.animalscan.com
Animal Diagnostic Solutions
N.A.I.C.S.: 621512
William Cain (COO)
AnimalScan MRI   (1)
1596 Hockett Rd Manakin-Sabot, Rich-
mond, VA 23102
Tel.: (877) 838-6747
Web Site: http://www.animalscan.org
Animal Diagnostic Solutions
N.A.I.C.S.: 621512
Heather Jones (Medical Dir)
AnimalScan MRI-NC School of Vet-
erinary Medicine   (1)
1060 William Moore Dr, Raleigh, NC 27607
Tel.: (919) 838-5209
Web Site: http://www.animalscan.org
Animal Diagnostic Solutions
N.A.I.C.S.: 621512
Richard Broadstone (Dir-Medical)
Mike Caglia (VP-Sls & Dev)
William Cain (COO)
Michael Defrancesco (CFO)
Dana Guffy (Dir-HR)
Lara Warren (Coord-Dev)

ANIMART INC.
1240 Green Valley Rd, Beaver Dam,
WI 53916
Tel.: (920) 885-2800
Web Site: http://www.animart.com
Sales Range: $10-24.9 Million
Emp.: 60
Pets & Pet Supplies
N.A.I.C.S.: 459910

Ruth Metz (Founder)
Dan Ellsworth (Pres & CEO)
James Metz (Founder)
Subsidiaries:
Midwest Supply & Distributing (1)
828 19th Ave NE, Saint Joseph, MN 56374
Tel.: (320) 363-4700
Web Site: http://www.mws-d.com
Farming Supplies & Animal Health Products
Whslr & Distr
N.A.I.C.S.: 115210
Rick Zabloski (Sls Mgr)
Tom Hanamann (Territory Mgr)
Jeff Spranger (Territory Mgr)
Tara Bauer (Territory Mgr)
Breck Kruger (Territory Mgr)
Patty Barnes (Territory Mgr)
Jackie Todd (Inside Sls Mgr)
Stockmen's Supply, Inc. (1)
802 W Main Ave, West Fargo, ND 58078
Tel.: (701) 282-3255
Web Site: http://www.stockmens.com
Sales Range: $1-9.9 Million
Emp.: 25
Farm Supplier & Wholesaler
N.A.I.C.S.: 424910
Robert Jameson (Pres)

ANIMATED DESIGNS LLC
31336 Via Colinas Ste 103, Westlake
Village, CA 91362-6784
Tel.: (818) 889-2348
Web Site: http://www.anides.com
Year Founded: 1992
Rev.: $5,000,000
Emp.: 19
Automotive, E-Commerce, Entertain-
ment, Fashion/Apparel, Financial, In-
teractive, Internet/Web Design, Media
Buying Services, Real Estate
N.A.I.C.S.: 541810
Mike Johnson (COO)

ANIMATION COLLECTIVE
148 W 37th St, New York, NY 10018
Tel.: (212) 947-1099
Year Founded: 2004
Rev.: $1,100,000
Emp.: 10
Fiscal Year-end: 12/31/06
N.A.I.C.S.: 541810
Larry Schwarz (Founder & CEO)

ANIMEIGO INC.
6810 Finian Dr, Wilmington, NC
28409
Tel.: (910) 251-1850
Web Site: http://www.animeigo.com
Year Founded: 1989
Sales Range: $1-9.9 Million
Emp.: 15
Video Production Services
N.A.I.C.S.: 512110

ANIMUS SOLUTIONS INC.
2202 N Westshore Blvd Ste 200,
Tampa, FL 33607
Tel.: (813) 321-7355
Web Site:
 http://www.animussolutions.com
Sales Range: $1-9.9 Million
Emp.: 15
Technology Consulting Services
N.A.I.C.S.: 541690
Phara E. McLachlan (CEO)
Jamie Zinober (Dir-PR)
Taylor Thanas (Coord-Internal Comm)

ANISA INTERNATIONAL, INC.
55 Peachtree Park Dr Ne, Atlanta,
GA 30309
Tel.: (404) 869-6475
Web Site: http://www.anisa.com
Year Founded: 1992
Rev.: $21,600,000
Emp.: 20

Anisa International, Inc.—(Continued)

Miscellaneous Nondurable Goods Merchant Whslr
N.A.I.C.S.: 424990
Zhanna Gershanok-Moody (Dir-HR)
Julie Scudder-Feldman (Sr VP-Bus Dev)
Jeremiah Johnson (Sr VP-Supply Chain & Mfg)
Catie Helms (Assoc Dir-Acct Mgmt)
Gary Heege (CFO)
Heather Sumner (Mgr-Bus Dev)
Mary Campbell (Dir-Creative)
Scott Piedmont (Mgr-Fin)

ANJANEYAP GLOBAL INC.
830 Hillview Ct Suite 140, Milpitas, CA 95035
Tel.: (408) 922-9690
Web Site:
    http://www.anjaneyapglobal.com
Year Founded: 2008
Sales Range: $10-24.9 Million
Emp.: 200
IT Consulting, Staffing & Project Management & Application Development
N.A.I.C.S.: 561311
Puja Kumar (Coord-HR)
Mani Thakur (Mgr-Bus Dev)

ANJANI ETECH SOLUTIONS, INC.
34475 Mound Rd Ste A, Sterling Heights, MI 48310
Tel.: (586) 979-4554
Web Site:
    https://www.aetsolutions.com
Year Founded: 2000
Rev.: $6,100,000
Emp.: 40
Software Consulting, Development & Training
N.A.I.C.S.: 334610
Gayatri Ponnam (Founder & CEO)

ANJOST CORP.
138 Bruckner Blvd, Bronx, NY 10454-4620
Tel.: (718) 993-5600
Sales Range: $10-24.9 Million
Emp.: 200
Baked Goods Mfr
N.A.I.C.S.: 311811
Joseph Zaro (Treas)
Stuart Zaro (Pres)

ANKA BEHAVIORAL HEALTH, INC.
1850 Gateway Blvd Ste 900, Concord, CA 94520
Tel.: (925) 825-4700   CA
Web Site: http://www.ankabhi.org
Year Founded: 1973
Sales Range: $25-49.9 Million
Behavioral Healthcare Services
N.A.I.C.S.: 623220
Naja W. Boyd (COO)
Nzinga Harrison (Chief Medical Officer)
Sharene Kacyra (Dir-Project Mgmt)
Kevin Andrews (VP-IT)
Chris Withrow (Co-CEO)
Janice Washburn (CFO)
Todd Dangott (Dir-Risk Mgmt)
Stephen Hahn-Smith (VP-Quality Mgmt)

ANKOR ENERGY, LLC.
1615 Poydras St Ste 1100, New Orleans, LA 70112
Tel.: (504) 596-3700
Web Site:
    http://www.ankorenergy.com
Year Founded: 2008
Sales Range: $300-349.9 Million

Emp.: 160
Oil & Gas Operating Services
N.A.I.C.S.: 213112
W. Denton Copeland (VP-Ops)

ANKURA CONSULTING GROUP, LLC
15950 Dallas Pkwy Ste 750, Dallas, TX 75248
Tel.: (214) 200-3680   DE
Web Site: http://www.ankura.com
Emp.: 500
Corporate Consulting Services
N.A.I.C.S.: 541611
Roger D. Carlile (Founder)
Roger Carlile (Founder)
Philip Daddona (Chm)
Kevin Lavin (CEO)
Kelly Kittrell (CFO)
Prashant Lamba (Mng Dir-Regulatory & Contractual Compliance Grp-Washington)
Richard M. Cameron (Sr Mng Dir)
David Sawyer (Sr Mng Dir)
Ted Theisen (Sr Mng Dir-Risk, Resilience & Geopolitical Grp)
Luke Tenery (Sr Mng Dir)
Steven Richards (Sr Mng Dir)
Robert Reyburn (Mng Dir)
Isaac Lee (Mng Dir)
Thomas Vasquez (Sr Mng Dir)
Josh Johnston (Sr Mng Dir-Litigation, Disputes, Investigations & Acctg Advisory)
Jonathan Morrison (Mng Dir-Chicago)
Evelyn Ni (Mng Dir-Turnaround & Restructuring Grp-Chicago)
Rasmus Kristoffer Gerdeman (Mng Dir)
Martin Wilczynski (Sr Mng Dir)
Jim Barratt (Mng Dir-Investigations & Acctg Advisory Practice-Washington)
Michael Schultz (Mng Dir-New York)
F. Lisa Murtha (Sr Mng Dir-Philadelphia)
Adrian Frankum (Sr Mng Dir-New York)
John Levitske (Sr Mng Dir-Chicago)
Daron M. Hartvigsen (Mng Dir-Washington)
Christopher Todd Doss (Mng Dir-Washington)
Angela L. Cinefro (Chief People Officer-Chicago)
Ben Seto (CFO-Washington)
Christopher Balsley (Chief Acctg Officer)
Orion C. Corcilius (Mng Dir)
Jeffrey J. Berardi (Chief Mktg & Comm Officer)
Mary Beth Edwards (Sr Mng Dir)
Richard Merino (Sr Mng Dir-Washington)
Scott A. Fowler (Sr Mng Dir-Houston)
William Brown (Mng Dir)
Robert Unell (Mng Dir)
Anthony C. Schnur (Sr Mng Dir-Houston)
Philip J. Gund (Sr Mng Dir)
Ryan Rubin (Sr Mng Dir)
Bob Olsen (Head-Cybersecurity & Privacy-Global)
Elliot Fuhr (Sr Mng Dir)
Joe D'Ascoli (Sr Mng Dir)
Dave Owen (Sr Mng Dir)
Tom Crawford (Chief Dev Officer)
Mark Furgeson (Sr Mng Dir)
Fernando Batlle (Chm-Latin America & Caribbean)
Kasey Rosado (Sr Mng Dir)

Subsidiaries:

284 Partners LLC   (1)
215 E Washington Ste 201, Ann Arbor, MI 48104-2041
Tel.: (734) 369-8723

Web Site: http://www.284partners.com
Scientific & Technical Consulting Services
N.A.I.C.S.: 541690
Michael J. Lasinski (CEO & Mng Dir)

ANLIN INDUSTRIES
1665 Tollhouse Rd, Clovis, CA 93611
Tel.: (559) 322-1531
Web Site: https://www.anlin.com
Year Founded: 1990
Sales Range: $10-24.9 Million
Emp.: 250
Flat Glass Mfr
N.A.I.C.S.: 327211
Eric Vidmar (VP)
Thomas Vidmar (Founder)
John J. Maloney (Exec VP)
Greg Vidmar (VP)
John Vidmar (Pres)

ANMED HEALTH
800 N Fant St, Anderson, SC 29621
Tel.: (864) 512-1000   SC
Web Site:
    http://www.anmedhealth.org
Year Founded: 1906
Sales Range: $450-499.9 Million
Emp.: 3,600
Health & Medical Services
N.A.I.C.S.: 622110
Garrick Chidester (Exec VP-Network Ops)
Christine Pearson (CFO)
Tina Jury (Chief Nursing Officer & Exec VP-Hospital Ops)
Bill Manson (CEO)

Subsidiaries:

AnMed Health Medical Center   (1)
800 N Fant St, Anderson, SC 29621-5708
Tel.: (864) 261-1000
Web Site: http://www.anmedhealth.org
Sales Range: $250-299.9 Million
Emp.: 3,500
Medical Center
N.A.I.C.S.: 622110
Anna McCormick (Coord-PreAnalytical)
Nedra Brown (Dir-Orthopedic Svc)
Ronny Gann (Dir-Engrg Svc)
Lagena Fant (Coord-Continuing Medical Education)
Lori Lucas (Coord-Reimbursement)

ANN & HOPE INC.
1 Ann & Hope Way, Cumberland, RI 02864-6918
Tel.: (401) 722-1000   RI
Web Site:
    http://www.curtainandbathoutlet.com
Year Founded: 1954
Sales Range: $25-49.9 Million
Emp.: 200
Home Furnishings Stores
N.A.I.C.S.: 455110
Irwin Chase (Pres)
Michael Chase (Controller)

ANN & ROBERT H. LURIE CHILDREN'S HOSPITAL OF CHICAGO
225 E Chicago Ave, Chicago, IL 60611
Tel.: (312) 227-4000   IL
Web Site:
    https://www.luriechildrens.org
Year Founded: 1894
Sales Range: $650-699.9 Million
Emp.: 4,671
Health Care Srvices
N.A.I.C.S.: 622110
Stanley B. Krok (CIO)
Patrick Magoon (Pres & CEO)
Michelle Stephenson (COO & Exec VP)
Monica Heenan (Chief Strategy Officer & Sr VP)

Elizabeth Hood (Sr Dir-Pediatric Surgery)
Elizabeth Alpern (Head-Emergency Medicine)

ANN ARBOR FIRE PROTECTION INC.
3735 Plz Dr, Ann Arbor, MI 48108
Tel.: (734) 761-7767
Sales Range: $1-9.9 Million
Emp.: 15
Fire Sprinkler System Installation
N.A.I.C.S.: 238220
Samuel M. Callan (Pres)
David Pietrzyk (Mgr-Pur)
Jeff Pegeon (VP)

ANN STORCK CENTER, INC.
1790 SW 43rd Way, Fort Lauderdale, FL 33317
Tel.: (954) 584-8000   FL
Web Site:
    https://www.annstorckcenter.org
Year Founded: 1980
Sales Range: $10-24.9 Million
Emp.: 448
Developmental Disability Assistance Services
N.A.I.C.S.: 623210

ANNA MARIA VACATIONS
3018 Ave C, Holmes Beach, FL 34217
Tel.: (941) 778-4178
Web Site:
    https://www.annamaria.com
Sales Range: $1-9.9 Million
Emp.: 20
Vacation Rental Property
N.A.I.C.S.: 531110
Joe Varner (Owner)

ANNABELLE CANDY COMPANY, INC.
27211 Industrial Blvd, Hayward, CA 94545-3347
Tel.: (510) 783-2900   CA
Web Site: http://www.annabellecandy.com
Year Founded: 1950
Sales Range: $75-99.9 Million
Emp.: 65
Candy Mfr
N.A.I.C.S.: 311352
Annabelle Block (Chm)
Susan Gampson Karl (Pres & CEO)
Jim McIntyre (Plant Mgr)

ANNAGEN, LLC
2330 Vartan Way Ste 185, Harrisburg, PA 17110
Tel.: (717) 447-5715
Web Site: http://www.netrepid.com
Year Founded: 2013
Sales Range: $1-9.9 Million
Emp.: 21
Information Technology Services
N.A.I.C.S.: 541512
Sam Coyl (Pres & CEO)

ANNAPOLIS MICRO SYSTEMS, INC.
190 Admiral Cochrane Dr Ste 130, Annapolis, MD 21401
Tel.: (410) 841-2514
Web Site:
    https://www.annapmicro.com
Rev.: $11,300,000
Emp.: 60
Computer Terminal Mfr
N.A.I.C.S.: 334118
Patrick Stover (VP-Sls)
Laura Breshearf (Acct Mgr)

ANNE KLEIN COMMUNICATIONS GROUP, LLC

1000 Atrium Way Ste 102, Mount Laurel, NJ 08054
Tel.: (856) 866-0411
Web Site:
http://www.annekleincg.com
Year Founded: 1982
Sales Range: $1-9.9 Million
Emp.: 8
Public Relations Agency
N.A.I.C.S.: 541820
Anne Sceia Klein *(Pres)*
Gerhart L. Klein *(Exec VP)*
Christopher Lukach *(Co-Owner & VP)*
Elizabeth Archer *(VP)*

ANNEX CAPITAL MANAGEMENT LLC
350 S County Rd Ste 102, Palm Beach, FL 33480-4432
Tel.: (516) 674-8969
Investment Services
N.A.I.C.S.: 523999

Subsidiaries:

Wholesome & Hearty Foods Company **(1)**
15615 Alton Pkwy Ste 450, Irvine, CA 92618-3308
Tel.: (949) 255-2000
Web Site: http://www.gardenburger.com
Sales Range: $50-74.9 Million
Emp.: 156
Meatless Food Products Mfr & Distr
N.A.I.C.S.: 311412

ANNEX MANUFACTURING, INC.
3050 SE Loop 820, Fort Worth, TX 76140-1014
Tel.: (817) 293-8762
Web Site: http://www.annexac.com
Year Founded: 1988
Sales Range: $10-24.9 Million
Emp.: 25
Fluid Power Valve & Hose Fitting Mfr
N.A.I.C.S.: 332912
Raul Castillo-Gonzalez *(Mgr-Quality)*
Kris Gilman *(Acct Mgr)*
Jill Vierra *(Mgr-Customer Svc)*
Scott Lemser *(Mgr-Warehouse)*
Jose Ibarra *(Controller)*
Mike Milliman *(Mgr-Engrg)*
Pat Mulholland *(VP-Aftermarket Sls & Svc)*
Rick Steen *(VP-OEM/OES Sls & Svc)*
Steven D. Gilman *(Pres)*
Stephen Mott *(Product Mgr-Heat Exchanger & Acct Exec)*
Tony Rhinehart *(Mgr-Pur)*
Maria Guzman *(Mgr-Customer Billing & Invoicing)*
Scott Gilman *(Project Mgr)*
Ashley Reitzer *(Coord-AP & AR)*
Jerry Arivett *(Supvr-Quality Dept)*

ANNIN & COMPANY
105 Eisenhower Pkwy Ste 203, Roseland, NJ 07068-1800
Tel.: (973) 228-9400 **NY**
Web Site: https://www.annin.com
Year Founded: 1847
Sales Range: $150-199.9 Million
Emp.: 500
Mfr of Flags, Banners, Pennants & Flagpoles
N.A.I.C.S.: 314999
Dale Coots *(Mgr-Mktg)*
Robert Goman *(Dir-HR)*
Nick Minniti *(Dir-Tech)*
Carter Beard *(Pres)*
Cameron Randolph Beard II *(Chm)*

ANNUAL REVIEWS
4139 El Camino Way, Palo Alto, CA 94306
Tel.: (650) 493-4400 **CA**

Web Site:
https://www.annualreviews.org
Year Founded: 1934
Sales Range: $1-9.9 Million
Emp.: 74
Philanthropic Services
N.A.I.C.S.: 813211
Jennifer Jongsma *(Dir-Production)*
Paul Calvi *(Dir-Tech)*
Lisa Wucher *(Dir-HR)*
Steve Castro *(CFO)*
Richard Gallagher *(Pres & Editor-in-Chief)*

ANOCOIL CORPORATION
60 E Main St, Rockville, CT 06066-3245
Tel.: (860) 871-1200 **DE**
Web Site: http://www.anocoil.com
Year Founded: 1960
Sales Range: $25-49.9 Million
Emp.: 115
Mfr of Anodized Aluminum & Lithographic Printing Plates
N.A.I.C.S.: 323120
Howard A. Fromson *(Chm & Pres)*
Timothy A. Fromson *(VP)*
Jay Faulkner *(Dir-Sls & Mktg)*

ANOKA HENNEPIN SCHOOL DISTRICT CREDIT UNION, INC.
3505 Northdale Blvd NW, Minneapolis, MN 55448
Tel.: (763) 422-0290 **MN**
Year Founded: 1963
Rev.: $6,300,000
Emp.: 12
Fiscal Year-end: 12/31/06
Federal Credit Unions
N.A.I.C.S.: 522130

ANOPLATE CORPORATION
459 Pulaski St, Syracuse, NY 13204
Tel.: (315) 471-6143
Web Site: https://www.anoplate.com
Sales Range: $10-24.9 Million
Emp.: 200
Metal Electroplating Services
N.A.I.C.S.: 332813
Chris Koch *(VP-Process & Product Quality Engrg)*
Peter Clark *(Engr-Quality)*
Brian Arnold *(Supvr-Trng)*

ANOTEROS, INC.
609 Deep Valley Dr Ste 200, Los Angeles, CA 90274
Tel.: (218) 940-2274 **NV**
Sales Range: Less than $1 Million
Emp.: 1
Children's Book Publisher; Educational & Entertainment Services
N.A.I.C.S.: 513130
Blain Burke *(Pres, CEO, CFO & Sec)*

ANOVA HEALTHCARE SERVICES, INC.
875 Greentree Rd 2 Pkwy Ctr Ste 120, Pittsburgh, PA 15220
Tel.: (888) 266-8211 **PA**
Web Site:
http://www.anovahomehealth.com
Women Healthcare Services
N.A.I.C.S.: 621610

ANOVA MICROSYSTEMS INC.
1830 Houret Ct, Milpitas, CA 95035
Tel.: (408) 941-1888
Web Site: http://www.anova.com
Rev.: $240,000
Emp.: 5
Personal Computers
N.A.I.C.S.: 541512
Raymond Chuang *(Pres)*
Matthew Toone *(CEO)*
Martin Carter *(Chm)*

Subsidiaries:

ISA Intelligent Sensing Anywhere SA **(1)**
Instituto Pedro Nunes Rua Pedro Nunes Edificio, 3030-199, Coimbra, Portugal
Tel.: (351) 239791090
Web Site: http://www.isasensing.com
Emp.: 44
Hardware Mfr & Distr
N.A.I.C.S.: 332510
Diamantino Costa *(Chm & CEO)*
Joao Vasco Ribeiro *(Vice Chm)*
Miguel Franco *(Head-MarCom & Partner Acq)*
Helder Ferreira *(Head-Svcs & Product Delivery)*
Luis Carvalho *(Head-Tech)*
Fernando Cortez *(Head-Sls)*
Pedro Oliveira *(Head-Mfg & Logistics)*
Jorge Pinto *(Product Mgr)*

ANREDER & CO.
286 Madison Ave Ste 907, New York, NY 10017
Tel.: (212) 532-3232
Web Site: http://www.anreder.com
Year Founded: 1990
Sales Range: $1-9.9 Million
Emp.: 12
Public Relations, Investor Relations, Crisis Communications
N.A.I.C.S.: 541820
Steven S. Anreder *(Owner)*

Subsidiaries:

Anreder & Company **(1)**
622 N Palm Dr, Los Angeles, CA 90210 **(100%)**
Tel.: (310) 278-8802
Web Site: http://www.anreder.com
Corporate Communications, Strategic Counseling & Public Relations
N.A.I.C.S.: 541820

ANRO INC.
931 S Matlack St, West Chester, PA 19382
Tel.: (610) 687-1200 **PA**
Web Site: https://www.anro.com
Year Founded: 1953
Sales Range: $25-49.9 Million
Emp.: 120
Provider of Full Service Commercial Printing
N.A.I.C.S.: 323111
David Spinelli *(CFO)*
James Spinelli *(Owner & Pres)*

ANSAFONE CONTACT CENTERS
145 E Columbine Ave, Santa Ana, CA 92707
Tel.: (714) 560-1000
Web Site: http://www.ansafone.com
Sales Range: $1-9.9 Million
Emp.: 318
Answering Service
N.A.I.C.S.: 561421
Randall Harmat *(Pres & CEO)*
Jennifer Oliveros *(VP)*
Carrie Gill *(Dir-Client Svcs)*
Jared Mendez *(Dir-IT & Integration)*
Robert Martinez *(Dir-Support Ops)*
Lynda Owens *(Dir-Ops-East Coast)*
Timothy M. Clarke *(Bus Mgr-East Coast)*
Meredith Gaitanis *(Controller)*
Tim Austrums *(VP-Sls & Mktg)*

ANSAY & ASSOCIATES INC.
101 E Grand Ave Ste 11, Port Washington, WI 53074
Tel.: (262) 284-7174
Web Site: https://www.ansay.com
Year Founded: 1946
Sales Range: $75-99.9 Million
Emp.: 200
Insurance Agents, Nec

N.A.I.C.S.: 524210
Michael G. Ansay *(Chm & CEO)*
Patt Miller *(Mng Dir)*

ANSAY & ASSOCIATES, LLC.
101 E Grand Ave Ste 11, Port Washington, WI 53074
Tel.: (262) 284-7174 **WI**
Web Site: https://www.ansay.com
Year Founded: 1981
Sales Range: $10-24.9 Million
Emp.: 220
Insurance Agencies & Brokerages
N.A.I.C.S.: 524210
A. John Ansay *(Principal)*
Stacey Robertson *(Acct Exec-Employee Benefits)*

Subsidiaries:

Wojta-Hansen Insurance Agency **(1)**
3618 Calumet Ave, Manitowoc, WI 54220
Tel.: (920) 682-8858
Web Site: http://www.ansay.com
Direct Life Insurance Carriers
N.A.I.C.S.: 524113

ANSCA HOMES
7593 Boynton Beach Blvd Ste 220, Boynton Beach, FL 33437
Tel.: (561) 364-3653
Web Site:
http://www.anscahomes.com
Sales Range: $10-24.9 Million
Emp.: 140
New Single Family Housing Construction Services
N.A.I.C.S.: 236115
Charles Scardina *(Pres)*

ANSEN CORPORATION
100 Chimney Point Dr, Ogdensburg, NY 13669
Tel.: (315) 393-3573
Web Site:
https://www.ansencorp.com
Year Founded: 1982
Microelectronic Systems & Components
N.A.I.C.S.: 334412
Rod Bush *(VP & Gen Mgr)*

ANSIRA PARTNERS, INC.
2300 Locust St, Saint Louis, MO 63103
Tel.: (314) 783-2300 **DE**
Web Site: http://www.ansira.com
Emp.: 800
Advetising Agency
N.A.I.C.S.: 541810
Andy Arnold *(Exec VP-Client Partnership)*
Tom Cole *(Pres)*
Gary Weller *(CFO & Exec VP)*
Trae Clevenger *(Chief Strategy Officer & Exec VP)*
Judge Graham *(CMO, Chief New Bus Officer & Exec VP)*
Con McGrath *(Chief Talent Officer & Exec VP)*
Jim Badum *(Exec VP-Client Partnership)*
John Holmes *(Exec VP-Creative)*
Tom Millweard *(Exec VP-Client Partnership)*
Kelly Jo Sands *(Exec VP-Mktg Tech)*
Gabe Winslow *(Exec VP-Media)*
Jim Warner *(Chm)*
Ed McLaughlin *(Chief Product & Tech Officer)*
Jay Dettling *(CEO)*

Subsidiaries:

BrightWave Marketing, LLC **(1)**
3340 Peachtree Rd NE Ste 400, Atlanta, GA 30326
Tel.: (404) 253-2544
Web Site: http://www.brightwave.com

Ansira Partners, Inc.—(Continued)

Email Marketing & Digital Messaging Services
N.A.I.C.S.: 541613
Simms Jenkins *(Founder & CEO)*
Brent Rosengren *(Chief Client Officer)*
Laura Giles *(Acct Dir)*
Matthew Stewart *(Sr Dir-Art)*
Laura Sullivan *(Dir-Creative)*
Amanda Tuttle *(Dir-Ops & Strategic Plng)*
Kristen Speagle *(Dir-Strategic Svcs)*
Thomas Barnhart *(VP-Bus Dev)*
Jessica Higgins *(Sr VP-Creative Svcs)*
Laura Sutton Middleton *(Sr Dir-Client Solutions)*
Raj Choudhury *(Pres)*
Felipe Buccianti *(Dir-Art)*

LBN Partners LLC (1)
1030 Doris Rd, Auburn Hills, MI 48326
Tel.: (248) 499-5251
Web Site: http://www.localbiznow.com
Advetising Agency
N.A.I.C.S.: 541810
Todd Webber *(Founder & CEO)*
Mandy Stonerock *(Dir-Client Svcs)*
Jon Bennett *(VP-Sls)*
Paul Manns *(VP-Client Programs)*
Mike Talovich *(VP-Enterprise Accts)*
Dane Vettraino *(Controller)*
Ross Kittredge *(Creative Dir)*

Branch (Domestic):

LBN Partners LLC - Los Angeles Office (2)
5657 Wilshire Blvd Ste 475, Los Angeles, CA 90036-3736
Tel.: (323) 932-1780
Web Site: http://www.localbiznow.com
Advetising Agency
N.A.I.C.S.: 541810
Dan Petersen *(CTO)*
Matt Blackmore *(VP-Digital Mktg)*

SproutLoud Media Networks, LLC (1)
15431 SW 14th St, Sunrise, FL 33326
Tel.: (954) 476-6211
Web Site: http://www.sproutloud.com
Sales Range: $10-24.9 Million
Emp.: 55
Online Brokerage Services
N.A.I.C.S.: 524210
Anjan Upadhya *(Chief Architect & Mng Partner)*
Gary Ritkes *(Pres & Mng Partner)*
Dave Kinsella *(COO & Mng Partner)*
David Spinola *(CFO)*

ANSLEY ATLANTA REAL ESTATE,LLC
3035 Peachtree Rd Ste 202, Atlanta, GA 30305
Tel.: (404) 480-4663
Web Site: http://ansleyatlanta.com
Year Founded: 2015
Sales Range: $10-24.9 Million
Emp.: 22
Real Estate Services
N.A.I.C.S.: 531390
Bonneau Ansley *(Co-Founder & CEO)*
Chris Burell *(Chief Motivation Officer)*
Hil Harper *(Co-Founder & VP)*
Julie Harris *(Chief People Officer)*
Lane McCormack *(Chief Strategy Officer)*

ANSLEY GOLF CLUB
196 Montgomery Ferry Dr NE, Atlanta, GA 30309
Tel.: (404) 875-1687   GA
Web Site:
http://www.ansleygolfclub.org
Year Founded: 1912
Sales Range: $10-24.9 Million
Emp.: 341
Golf Club
N.A.I.C.S.: 713910
Andy Feinour *(Pres)*
Jim Schwarzkopf *(Treas)*
Phil Beatty *(Chm-Grounds)*

Guy Thompson *(Chm)*
Tracy Roberts *(Chm-Tennis)*
Emily Burdette *(Mgr-Catering)*

ANSON INDUSTRIES, INC.
1959 Anson Dr, Melrose Park, IL 60160-1018
Tel.: (708) 681-1300   DE
Web Site:
http://www.ansonindustries.com
Year Founded: 1940
Sales Range: $250-299.9 Million
Emp.: 20
Plastering Drywall Acoustical Insulation Roofing & Sheet Metal Work; Special Trade Contractors
N.A.I.C.S.: 238300
John R. Andrzejewski *(Pres & CEO)*
Kathleen A. Tomaska *(CFO & Treas)*

Subsidiaries:

Anning Johnson Co. (1)
1959 Anson Dr, Melrose Park, IL 60160-1018   (100%)
Tel.: (708) 681-1300
Web Site: http://www.ajvoton.com
Sales Range: $10-24.9 Million
Plastering Drywall, Acoustical Insulation, Roofing, Sheet Metal & Special Trade Contractors
N.A.I.C.S.: 238310
John Stralka *(Mgr-Sls)*
Jim Kasella *(VP & District Mgr)*

Branch (Domestic):

Anning Johnson Company (2)
1901 MacArthur Blvd NW, Atlanta, GA 30318-2025
Tel.: (404) 355-1680
Web Site: http://www.anningjohnson.com
Dry Wall & Roof Teck
N.A.I.C.S.: 238310
Corey Bolden *(Mgr-Construction)*

Anning Johnson Company (2)
13250 Temple Ave, City of Industry, CA 91746
Tel.: (626) 369-7131
Web Site: http://www.anningjohnson.com
Emp.: 100
Construction Services
N.A.I.C.S.: 238990
Larry J. Domino *(Pres)*
Andy Widin *(Mgr-Metal Deck Sls)*

Anning Johnson San Francisco (2)
22955 Kidder St, Hayward, CA 94545-1670
Tel.: (510) 670-0100
Web Site: http://www.ansonindustries.com
Emp.: 50
Construction Services
N.A.I.C.S.: 238310
Angelica Munoz *(Office Mgr)*

Restec Contractors Inc. (1)
22959 Kidder St, Hayward, CA 94545-1670
Tel.: (510) 732-1996
Web Site: http://www.resteccontractors.com
Sales Range: $10-24.9 Million
Provides Abatement Services with Asbestos, Lead, Mold & Hazardous Materials
N.A.I.C.S.: 562910
Angelica Munoz *(Office Mgr)*

ANSON PARTNERS LLC
4005 Northwest Expy Ste 400, Oklahoma City, OK 73116
Tel.: (405) 848-0525
Rev.: $34,600,000
Emp.: 6
Investor
N.A.I.C.S.: 211120
Carl B. Anderson Jr. *(Mgr)*

ANSON-STONER INC.
111 E Fairbanks Ave, Winter Park, FL 32789-7004
Tel.: (407) 629-9484   FL
Web Site: https://www.anson-stoner.com
Year Founded: 1983
Sales Range: $25-49.9 Million

Emp.: 20
Advetising Agency
N.A.I.C.S.: 541810
Andrew Anson *(Pres)*
Tom Macaluso *(Sr VP & Creative Dir)*
Karen Madanick *(VP & Dir-Media)*
Megan Gooding *(Acct Supvr)*
Justin Bohn *(VP & Dir-Fin)*

ANSONIA COPPER & BRASS INC.
75 Liberty St, Ansonia, CT 06401
Tel.: (203) 732-6600
Web Site: http://www.ansoniacb.com
Sales Range: $50-74.9 Million
Emp.: 170
Copper Rolling & Drawing
N.A.I.C.S.: 331420
Raymond Mcgee *(Pres)*
Steve Turner *(CFO & Sec)*

ANSWER-1 COMMUNICA-TIONS
3820 N 3rd St, Phoenix, AZ 85012
Tel.: (602) 234-0111
Web Site: http://www.answer1.com
Year Founded: 1982
Sales Range: $1-9.9 Million
Emp.: 59
Telephone Answering Services
N.A.I.C.S.: 561421
Chris Hudock *(Mgr-Ops)*
Cameron Reichert *(Mgr-Customer Svc)*

ANSWERFIRST COMMUNICA-TIONS, INC.
1602 N 21st St, Tampa, FL 33605
Tel.: (813) 882-5307
Web Site:
https://www.answerfirst.com
Year Founded: 1985
Sales Range: $1-9.9 Million
Emp.: 35
Telephone Answering Services
N.A.I.C.S.: 561421
Matt Herron *(Pres & CEO)*
Penny Herron *(Dir-Contact Center Ops)*
Michael Stroud *(Coord-IT)*
Chris Culverhouse *(Coord-Client Loyalty)*

ANSWERNET EDUCATION SERVICES, INC.
21410 N 19th Ave Ste 210, Phoenix, AZ 85027
Tel.: (310) 905-8300   AZ
Web Site:
https://www.answereducation.com
Business Process Outsourcing Call Center Services
N.A.I.C.S.: 517810
Gary Pudles *(Pres & CEO)*

ANSWERNET, INC.
3930 Commerce Ave, Willow Grove, PA 19090
Tel.: (267) 942-6000
Web Site:
https://www.answernet.com
Year Founded: 1998
Sales Range: $75-99.9 Million
Emp.: 1,600
Telemessaging Call Center; Telephone Answering Service & Outsourced Contact Center Fulfillment Services
N.A.I.C.S.: 561421
Rebecca Lorden *(Assoc Dir-Mktg)*

Subsidiaries:

Cerida (1)
1 Griffin Brook Dr, Methuen, MA 01844
Tel.: (978) 659-6500
Web Site: http://www.cerida.com

Sales Range: $10-24.9 Million
Emp.: 44
Business to Business Telesale Professionals; Lead Pipeline & Sales Development
N.A.I.C.S.: 561422
Gary Pudles *(Owner, Pres & CEO)*

Signius Corp. (1)
2325 Maryland Rd Ste 210, Willow Grove, PA 19090
Web Site: http://www.signius.com
Sales Range: $100-124.9 Million
Emp.: 1,400
Telephone Answering Services
N.A.I.C.S.: 561421
William Robertshaw *(CEO)*

Subsidiary (Domestic):

Signius Communications (2)
8915 Knight Rd, Houston, TX 77054-4303
Tel.: (713) 799-9000
Web Site: http://www.signius.com
Sales Range: $25-49.9 Million
Emp.: 70
Provider of Business Services
N.A.I.C.S.: 561410
Tara Washington *(Gen Mgr)*

Signius Investment Corporation (2)
8915 Knight Rd, Houston, TX 77054
Tel.: (817) 261-4488
Web Site: http://www.signius.com
Sales Range: $25-49.9 Million
Emp.: 20
Call Center Operations
N.A.I.C.S.: 561421
William Robertshaw *(CEO-Signius Corp & Signius Investment)*

ANSWERPHONE
1230 Central Ave, Albany, NY 12205
Tel.: (518) 489-1552
Web Site:
https://www.abetteranswer.net
Year Founded: 1967
Sales Range: $1-9.9 Million
Emp.: 95
Outsourced Calling & Messaging Services in a Wide Range of Industries
N.A.I.C.S.: 561421
Ed Courcelle *(Mgr-Sls)*
Jason Schmidt *(Mgr)*

ANTAEAN SOLUTIONS, LLC
11700 Preston Rd Ste 660-213, Dallas, TX 75230
Tel.: (214) 987-3439
Web Site: http://www.antaeans.com
Year Founded: 1997
Sales Range: $10-24.9 Million
Emp.: 10
Financial Institution Consulting Services
N.A.I.C.S.: 541618
Jim Kemp *(Mng Partner)*
Randy Ripple *(Mng Partner)*

ANTARCTICA CAPITAL, LLC
712 5th Ave 24th Fl, New York, NY 10019
Tel.: (212) 983-1602   DE
Web Site:
http://www.antarcticacapital.com
Privater Equity Firm
N.A.I.C.S.: 523999
Chandra Patel *(Mng Partner)*

Subsidiaries:

Midwest Holding Inc. (1)
2900 S 70th St Ste 400, Lincoln, NE 68506
Tel.: (402) 817-5701
Web Site: https://www.midwestholding.com
Rev.: $30,049,000
Assets: $1,920,431,000
Liabilities: $1,886,054,000
Net Worth: $34,377,000
Earnings: $7,140,000
Emp.: 91
Fiscal Year-end: 12/31/2022
Holding Company; Life Insurance Products & Services
N.A.I.C.S.: 551112

Subsidiary (Domestic):

American Life & Security Corp. (2)
2900 S 70th St Ste 400, Lincoln, NE 68506
Tel.: (402) 489-8266
Web Site: https://www.american-life.com
Emp.: 21
Life Insurance Products & Services
N.A.I.C.S.: 524113
Todd Christopher Boeve (COO, Sec & VP)

Seneca Reinsurance Company,
LLC (2)
126 College St Ste 300, Burlington, VT
05401
Tel.: (802) 735-1682
Web Site: https://www.seneca-
reinsurance.com
Reinsurance Services
N.A.I.C.S.: 524130

ANTARES CAPITAL CORPO-
RATION
PO Box 330309, Miami, FL 33233-
0309
Tel.: (305) 894-2888
Web Site:
http://www.antarescapital.com
Year Founded: 1993
Sales Range: Less than $1 Million
Emp.: 2
Privater Equity Firm
N.A.I.C.S.: 523999
Randall E. Poliner (Founder)
Monica Kelsey (CFO)
Benjamin Concessi (Head-Strategy &
Corp Dev)
Timothy Lyne (CEO)

ANTARES GROUP, INC.
1429 Iris Dr SE, Conyers, GA 30013
Tel.: (770) 785-7855
Web Site:
https://www.antarescpas.com
Accounting Services
N.A.I.C.S.: 541219
Emmitt W. White (CEO & Partner)
Jennifer Singleton (Dir-HR)
Aimee Gartner (Mgr-Comm & Mktg)
Mat Payne (Dir-Tech)
Les Atkins (Mgr-Dev)
Sonya Powers (Mgr-Back Office)
Deanna Olton (Dir-Tax)
Carolyn Allen (Mgr-Tax)
Carrie Smith (Mgr-Acctg)
Tracy Young (Mgr-Acctg)

Subsidiaries:

Gray, Gray & Gray, LLP (1)
150 Royall St Ste 102, Canton, MA 02021
Tel.: (781) 407-0300
Web Site: http://www.gggcpas.com
Offices of Certified Public Accountants
N.A.I.C.S.: 541211
C. Joseph Ciccarello (Partner)
Bradford Carlson (Partner)
James Donellon (Partner)
Marty Kirshner (Chm-Energy Indus Practice
Grp & Dir-Client Svcs Dept)
Mary Bibeau (Mgr-Tax)
Kimberly Benevides Lima (Mgr-Client Acctg
Svcs)
Susan Copeland (Mgr-Tax)
Aki Goto (Mgr-Assurance)
Richard Frizzell (Mgr-Audit)
Diane Gibson (Mgr)
Hank Wolfson (Partner)

ANTARES GROUP, INC.
5795 Canal Rd, Cleveland, OH
44125
Tel.: (216) 328-0012   OH
Web Site:
http://www.antaresgroupinc.com
Year Founded: 1974
Sales Range: $1-9.9 Million
Emp.: 700
Building Maintenance Services
N.A.I.C.S.: 444180

Patrick Cassese (Pres & CEO)
Tammy Daniel (COO)
Mark Kashgegian (Partner)

ANTARES, INC.
52 Mason St, Greenwich, CT 06831
Tel.: (203) 650-6000
Web Site:
http://www.antaresrealestate.com
Year Founded: 1998
Sales Range: $25-49.9 Million
Emp.: 200
Real Estate & Private Equity Invest-
ment Services
N.A.I.C.S.: 525990
Joseph P. Beninati (Co-Founder &
Partner)
James P. Cabrera (Co-Founder &
Partner)

ANTARRA COMMUNICATIONS
11601 Court Ln, Anaheim, CA 92804
Tel.: (714) 891-3660
Web Site: http://www.antarra.com
Year Founded: 2001
Sales Range: $10-24.9 Million
Emp.: 8
N.A.I.C.S.: 541810
Barbara Stracner (Acct Exec)
Rita Lee (Acct Mgr)

Subsidiaries:

Antarra Communications (1)
322 Bittlewood Ave, Berlin, NJ 08009
Tel.: (856) 626-0190
Web Site: http://www.antarra.com
N.A.I.C.S.: 541810
Doris Emich (VP-Mktg)

ANTEC INCORPORATED
47900 Fremont Blvd, Fremont, CA
94538
Tel.: (510) 770-1200   CA
Web Site: http://www.antec.com
Year Founded: 1986
Sales Range: $10-24.9 Million
Emp.: 50
Mfr of High-Performance Computer
Components & Accessories for Gam-
ing, PC Upgrade & Do-It-Yourself
Markets
N.A.I.C.S.: 334118
John Caezza (Pres)
Andrew Lee (Founder & Pres)
Shawn Carroll (Acct Mgr-Sls & Mgr-
Sls-Natl)
Michael Lowdermilk (Mgr-Bus Dev)
Kelvin Liu (Dir-Mktg & Bus Dev)
Shawn Carroll (Mgr-Sls-Natl)

ANTEKS HOME FURNISHINGS
INC.
1135 Dragon St, Dallas, TX 75207-
4207
Tel.: (214) 744-1318
Web Site:
http://www.antekshome.com
Sales Range: $10-24.9 Million
Emp.: 10
Antiques
N.A.I.C.S.: 459510
Rick Morris (Controller)
Jason Lenox (Pres & CEO)

ANTELOPE MEMORIAL HOS-
PITAL
PO Box 229, Neligh, NE 68756-0229
Tel.: (402) 887-4151   NE
Web Site: http://www.amhne.org
Year Founded: 1974
Sales Range: $10-24.9 Million
Emp.: 166
Health Care Srvices
N.A.I.C.S.: 622110
John Mlnarik (Pres)

ANTELOPE VALLEY EAST
KERN WATER AGENCY
6500 W Avenue N, Palmdale, CA
93551
Tel.: (661) 943-3201
Web Site: http://www.avek.org
Sales Range: $10-24.9 Million
Emp.: 27
Water Supply
N.A.I.C.S.: 221310
George M. Lane (VP)

ANTELOPE VALLEY FORD
1155 Auto Mall Dr, Lancaster, CA
93534-5867
Tel.: (661) 949-3586
Web Site: http://www.avford.com
Rev.: $45,500,933
Emp.: 100
Motor Vehicle Sales
N.A.I.C.S.: 441110
Michael Johnson (Pres)

ANTELOPE VALLEY NEWSPA-
PER INC.
37404 Sierra Hwy, Palmdale, CA
93550
Tel.: (661) 273-2700
Web Site: http://www.avpress.com
Sales Range: $10-24.9 Million
Emp.: 130
Newspapers, Publishing & Printing
N.A.I.C.S.: 513110

ANTELOPE VALLEY SCHOOL
TRANSPORTATION AGENCY
670 W Ave L8, Lancaster, CA 93534
Tel.: (661) 945-3621
Web Site: https://www.avsta.com
Year Founded: 1980
Sales Range: $10-24.9 Million
Emp.: 190
School & Employee Bus Transporta-
tion Services
N.A.I.C.S.: 485410
Sandi Vaughn (Mgr-Ops)
Terry Robertson (Mgr-Fleet)

ANTENNA RESEARCH ASSO-
CIATES, INCORPORATED
8880 Gorman Rd, Laurel, MD 20723
Tel.: (301) 937-8888   TX
Web Site: https://ara-inc.com
Year Founded: 1963
Antennas & RF Systems; Designer,
Developer & Mfr
N.A.I.C.S.: 541420
Logen Thiran (Pres & CEO)
David Thombs (Deputy CTO & VP-
Tech Strategy)

Subsidiaries:

SI2 Technologies, Inc. (1)
267 Boston Rd, North Billerica, MA 01862
Tel.: (978) 495-5300
Web Site: http://www.si2technologies.com
Rev.: $1,800,000
Emp.: 100
Marketing Research & Public Opinion Poll-
ing
N.A.I.C.S.: 541910
Joseph M. Kunze (Founder, CTO & Gen
Mgr)
Donald G. Flodin (COO & Exec VP)
Noel M. Burgoa (VP-Bus Admin)
Jonathan E. Lathrop (VP-Bus Dev)

ANTENNAS DIRECT
16388 Westwoods Business Park,
Ellisville, MO 63021
Tel.: (636) 587-3776
Web Site:
https://www.antennasdirect.com
Year Founded: 2003
Sales Range: $1-9.9 Million
Emp.: 11
Antenna Manufacturing

N.A.I.C.S.: 449210
Richard Schneider (Pres)

ANTHONY & SYLVAN POOLS
CORPORATION
Mt Vernon Sq 6690 Beta Dr Ste 300,
Mayfield Village, OH 44143-2359
Tel.: (440) 720-3301   OH
Web Site:
http://www.anthonysylvan.com
Year Founded: 1946
Sales Range: $75-99.9 Million
Emp.: 450
Designer & Retailer of Concrete
Swimming Pools & Spas
N.A.I.C.S.: 238990
Neil Coyne (Gen Mgr)
Dan Barrett (Gen Mgr-Austin & San
Antonio)
Jim Anderson (Mgr-Sls-Las Vegas)
Mike Exum (Mgr-Construction-
Charlotte)
Jason McBride (Asst Gen Mgr-New
York)
Jordan Schaeffer (Dir-Ops-Retail &
Svcs)
Corey Coughenour (Dir-Renovation &
Modernization Construction)
Bonnie Chong (CFO & Gen Counsel)

Subsidiaries:

Anthony & Sylvan Pools
Corporation (1)
Rte 611 N PO Box 1449, Doylestown, PA
18901
Tel.: (215) 348-9011
Web Site: http://www.anthonysylvan.com
Rev.: $191,725,000
Emp.: 100
Provider of Swimming Pool Construction
N.A.I.C.S.: 238990
Bill Lee (Gen Mgr-New Pools-Northeast)
Tony Monaco (Dir-Sls-Aftermarket)
William Meyerowitz (Dir-Tech & Processing)
Kevin Donaldson (Pres-New Pools)
Tom Waldin (Chm)
Jordan Schaeffer (VP/Gen Mgr-Renovations
& Aftermarket)
Brad Hill (CFO)
Bonnie Chong (CEO)

ANTHONY CHEVROLET CA-
DILLAC
1229 Country Club Rd, Fairmont, WV
26554
Tel.: (304) 366-3500
Web Site:
https://www.anthonychevrolet.com
Year Founded: 1955
Sales Range: $10-24.9 Million
Emp.: 34
New Car Retailer
N.A.I.C.S.: 441110
Jo Pitrolo (Pres)

ANTHONY FARMERS COOP
ELEVATOR CO.
519 W Main St, Anthony, KS 67003
Tel.: (620) 842-5181
Web Site:
http://www.anthonycoop.com
Sales Range: $25-49.9 Million
Emp.: 32
Grains Elevator Cooperative
N.A.I.C.S.: 424510
Dan Cashier (Gen Mgr)
Larry Whisman (VP)

ANTHONY PARASSON INC.
959 East Waterloo Rd, Akron, OH
44306
Tel.: (330) 724-9303
Rev.: $14,100,000
Emp.: 150
Italian Restaurant
N.A.I.C.S.: 722511
Nancy Parasson (Pres)

Anthony Pontiac GMC Buick, Inc.—(Continued)

ANTHONY PONTIAC GMC BUICK, INC.
7225 Grand Ave, Gurnee, IL 60031-5270
Tel.: (847) 856-3000
Year Founded: 1991
Sales Range: $25-49.9 Million
Emp.: 102
New Car Retailer
N.A.I.C.S.: 441110
Trent Tobias (VP)
Anthony Augelli (Pres)

ANTHONY TIMBERLANDS, INC.
111 S Plum St, Bearden, AR 71720-8800
Tel.: (870) 687-3611   AR
Web Site:
http://www.anthonytimberlands.com
Year Founded: 1969
Sales Range: $75-99.9 Million
Emp.: 600
Lumber Mill Seervices
N.A.I.C.S.: 113110
John Ed Anthony (Chm)
James Rick Green (CFO, Exec VP & Dir-Mktg)

Subsidiaries:

Anthony Hardwood Composites Inc   (1)
606 E Center St, Sheridan, AR 72150-0490
Tel.: (870) 942-4000
Web Site:
http://www.anthonycomposites.com
Sales Range: $1-9.9 Million
Hardwood Mfr
N.A.I.C.S.: 321211
Jon Fiutak (Gen Mgr)
Addison Anthony (Mgr-Contracts)

ANTHONY UNDERWOOD AUTOMOTIVE, INC.
4006 Bessemer Super Hwy, Bessemer, AL 35020
Tel.: (205) 424-4033
Web Site:
http://www.anthonyunderwood.com
Year Founded: 1994
Sales Range: $10-24.9 Million
Emp.: 38
Used Car Dealers
N.A.I.C.S.: 441120
Anthony Underwood (Owner)

ANTHONY VINEYARDS
5512 Valpredo Ave, Bakersfield, CA 93307
Tel.: (661) 858-6211
Web Site:
https://www.anthonyvineyards.com
Sales Range: $10-24.9 Million
Emp.: 150
Grape Vineyard Operating Services
N.A.I.C.S.: 111332
Bob Bianco (Owner)

ANTHONY'S COAL FIRED PIZZA
200 W Cypress Creek Rd Ste 220, Fort Lauderdale, FL 33309
Tel.: (954) 618-2000
Web Site: http://www.acsp.com
Year Founded: 2002
Sales Range: $50-74.9 Million
Italian Restaurant Owner & Franchisor
N.A.I.C.S.: 722511
Allison Cucinotta (Asst Mgr)
Jeremy Anderson (Gen Mgr)
Kevin L. May (VP & Controller)
Pat Marzano (Owner)
Sharon Mason-Lachat (Mgr-Acctg)
Darrin Vernale (Gen Mgr)

Jerry Fazio (Reg Mgr-Trng)
Rob Barker (Gen Mgr)
Shanda Peetros (Gen Mgr)

ANTHONY'S FISH GROTTO
5575 Lake Park Way Ste 211, La Mesa, CA 91942
Tel.: (619) 713-1950
Web Site:
http://www.gofishanthonys.com
Sales Range: $10-24.9 Million
Emp.: 500
Restaurant Operators
N.A.I.C.S.: 722511
Rick Ghio (Owner & Pres)
Janet Cepeda (Dir-Sls & Events)
Greer Williams (Mgr-Venue)

ANTHONY'S INC.
5000 Georgia Ave, West Palm Beach, FL 33405
Tel.: (561) 588-7336
Web Site:
https://www.anthonysfla.com
Sales Range: $10-24.9 Million
Emp.: 20
Women's Apparel
N.A.I.C.S.: 458110
Gary Morgan (VP)
Marvin P. Anthony Jr. (Pres)

ANTHONY, INC.
12391 Montero Ave, Sylmar, CA 91342
Tel.: (818) 365-9451   CA
Web Site:
https://www.anthonyintl.com
Year Founded: 1986
Sales Range: $25-49.9 Million
Emp.: 650
Display Case Doors, Shelving & Lighting Systems for the Refrigeration Industry
N.A.I.C.S.: 327215
Jeff Clark (Pres & CEO)
Tim Berberet (Mgr-Natl Accts)
Michael Murth (Mgr-Sls)
Daniel Zeddy (CFO)
Larry Rauzon (Dir-Intl Ops)
Will Pack (Mgr)

ANTHONY-THOMAS CANDY COMPANY
1777 Arlingate Ln, Columbus, OH 43228
Tel.: (614) 274-8405
Web Site: http://www.anthony-thomas.com
Year Founded: 1952
Sales Range: $10-24.9 Million
Emp.: 191
Candy Mfr
N.A.I.C.S.: 311352
Joe Zanetos (Pres)
Greg Zanetos (Exec VP-Admin & Fin)
Tim Zanetos (Exec VP-Production)

ANTI-HYDRO INTERNATIONAL, INC.
45 River Rd, Flemington, NJ 08822-6026
Tel.: (908) 284-9000   NJ
Web Site: https://www.anti-hydro.com
Year Founded: 1904
Sales Range: $50-74.9 Million
Emp.: 50
Building Construction Chemicals & Industrial Flooring Products Mfr
N.A.I.C.S.: 325211
Pankaj Desai (CEO)
Piyush Patel (Pres)

ANTILLEAN MARINE SHIPPING CORP.
3038 NW North River Dr, Miami, FL 33142

Tel.: (305) 633-6361   FL
Web Site: https://www.antillean.com
Year Founded: 1963
Sales Range: $10-24.9 Million
Emp.: 150
Provider of Freight Transportation
N.A.I.C.S.: 483111
Sara C. Babun (Pres & CEO)

ANTILLES CLEANING SERVICE INC.
Avenida Conquistador 103, Catano, PR 00962
Tel.: (787) 788-8080
Web Site: http://www.pr.com
Sales Range: $10-24.9 Million
Emp.: 1,280
Building Cleaning Services
N.A.I.C.S.: 561720
Jorge Lopez (Pres)

ANTIOCH CHRYSLER JEEP DODGE
1810 Auto Center Dr, Antioch, CA 94509-1353
Tel.: (925) 204-3721
Web Site:
https://www.antiochchrysler.com
Sales Range: $10-24.9 Million
Emp.: 130
Used Car Retailer
N.A.I.C.S.: 441120
John Ansaldo (Mgr-Svc)

ANTIOCH TIRE INC.
440 E Route 173, Antioch, IL 60002
Tel.: (847) 395-8196
Web Site: https://www.tredroc.com
Sales Range: $10-24.9 Million
Emp.: 150
Automotive Tires
N.A.I.C.S.: 441340
Mike Quit (Pres)

ANTIQUELAND USA INC.
5333 Forest Ln, Dallas, TX 75244
Tel.: (972) 661-0001
Web Site:
http://www.forestwoodantiques.com
Year Founded: 1994
Sales Range: $50-74.9 Million
Emp.: 325
Sub-Lessor of Real Estate; Retailer of Used Merchandise
N.A.I.C.S.: 531190
John Orton (Pres & CFO)
Courtland Logue Jr. (Chm)

ANTON CASTRO LAW, LLC
106 S Tampania, Tampa, FL 33609
Tel.: (813) 907-9807
Web Site:
http://www.tampaattorneys.org
Sales Range: $1-9.9 Million
Emp.: 11
Law firm
N.A.I.C.S.: 541110
Christina Anton Garcia (Partner)
John S. Castro (Partner)

ANTON/BAUER INCORPORATED
14 Progress Dr, Shelton, CT 06484
Tel.: (203) 929-1100
Web Site:
https://www.antonbauer.com
Sales Range: $10-24.9 Million
Emp.: 100
Cameras & Related Equipment
N.A.I.C.S.: 333310
Kristina Freund (Coord-Hr)

ANTONETTI CAPITAL MANAGEMENT, LLC
2590 Golden Gate Pkwy Ste 104, Naples, FL 34105

Tel.: (239) 403-0218
Web Site:
http://www.antonetticapital.com
Rev.: $100,000,000
Emp.: 4
Investment Advisory Services
N.A.I.C.S.: 523940
Pat Antonetti (Pres & Mng Partner)

ANTONIO SOFO & SON IMPORTING CO. INC.
253 Waggoner Blvd, Toledo, OH 43612-1988
Tel.: (419) 476-4211   OH
Web Site: https://www.sofofoods.com
Year Founded: 1954
Sales Range: $100-124.9 Million
Emp.: 350
Sale of Groceries & Related Products
N.A.I.C.S.: 424490
Michael Sofo (Owner)
Cos Figliomeni (COO)
Jeff Peer (Dir-Sls-Midwest Reg)
Kate Baker (Dir-HR)
Gary Tolles (VP-Ops)

Subsidiaries:

Sofo Food Co., Inc.   (1)
253 Waggoner Blvd, Toledo, OH 43612-1988
Tel.: (419) 476-4211
Sales Range: $25-49.9 Million
Emp.: 300
Grocery Store Services
N.A.I.C.S.: 445110
Michael Sofo (CEO)
Josesph Sofo (Pres)

ANTONIO'S MANUFACTURING INC.
800 2nd St, Cresson, PA 16630
Tel.: (814) 886-8171
Web Site:
https://www.antoniosmfg.com
Year Founded: 1971
Sales Range: $25-49.9 Million
Emp.: 13
Hair Products Mfr
N.A.I.C.S.: 326199
Anthony R. Romani II (Pres & CEO)

Subsidiaries:

Ajax Comb Company   (1)
800 2nd St, Cresson, PA 16630-1142
Tel.: (814) 886-8171
Web Site: http://www.antoniosmfg.com
Comb Mfr
N.A.I.C.S.: 326199
Anthony R. Romani II (Pres & CEO)

ANTRONIX INC.
440 Forsgate Dr, Cranbury, NJ 08512-3518
Tel.: (609) 395-1390
Web Site: http://www.antronix.net
Year Founded: 1980
Sales Range: $75-99.9 Million
Emp.: 2,000
Telecommunication & Cable Television Products Mfr
N.A.I.C.S.: 334220
Emily Bennett (Controller & Office Mgr)
Christine Mendelowitz (Mgr-HR)
Tony DiPace (Gen Mgr)
Juan Bravo (Chief Strategy Officer)
James Taxdahl (VP-Sls)
Neil Tang (Pres & CEO)

ANTS SOFTWARE INC.
4514 Chamblee Dunwoody Rd #188, Dunwoody, GA 30338
Tel.: (404) 216-2783   DE
Web Site: http://www.ants.com
Sales Range: $1-9.9 Million
Emp.: 68
Database Management & Consolidation Software

N.A.I.C.S.: 513210
Rick Cerwonka *(Pres-Svcs Div)*
Rik Sanchez *(Chm, Pres, CEO & Sec)*
Elise Vetula *(CFO)*

Subsidiaries:

Inventa Technologies Inc.   (1)
2040 Briggs Rd Ste B4, Mount Laurel, NJ 08054
Tel.: (856) 914-5200
Web Site: http://www.inventa.com
Office Computer Automation Systems Integration
N.A.I.C.S.: 541512
Derek Nash *(VP-Ops)*

ANTUIT, INC.
1010 Lk St Ste 300, Oak Park, IL 60301
Tel.: (214) 618-0939
Web Site: http://www.antuit.com
Forecasting & Supply Chain Analytics Services
N.A.I.C.S.: 541511
Craig Silverman *(CEO)*

Subsidiaries:

Forecast Horizon Inc.   (1)
6116 Telegraph Ave Ste 306, Oakland, CA 94609-1370
Tel.: (510) 213-9867
Web Site: http://www.forecasthorizon.com
Electronics Stores
N.A.I.C.S.: 449210
Kaushik Katari *(CEO)*

ANTWERP DIAMOND DISTRIBUTORS INC.
581 5th Ave Ste 560, New York, NY 10017-1921
Tel.: (212) 319-3300   NY
Web Site:
   http://www.antwerpdistributors.net
Year Founded: 1950
Sales Range: $50-74.9 Million
Emp.: 11
Producer & Retailer of Loose & Mounted Diamonds
N.A.I.C.S.: 339910
Phyllis Lisker *(Pres)*

ANTWERPEN MOTOR CARS LTD.
6440 Baltimore National Pike, Baltimore, MD 21228-3903
Tel.: (410) 788-6600
Web Site:
   http://www.antwerpenmotorcars.net
Year Founded: 1973
Sales Range: $25-49.9 Million
Emp.: 100
Motor Vehicle Sales
N.A.I.C.S.: 441110
Jacob M. Antwerpen *(Pres)*
Eric McMickings *(Dir-Customer Rels)*

ANU RESOURCES, INC.
5060 Parkcenter Ave Ste D, Dublin, OH 43017
Tel.: (614) 652-2700
Web Site:
   http://www.anuresources.com
Year Founded: 2002
Sales Range: Less than $1 Million
Emp.: 12
Employment Agencies
N.A.I.C.S.: 561311
Cynthia Hengeli Anu *(Founder, Pres & CEO)*

ANULEX TECHNOLOGIES, INC.
5600 Rowland Rd Ste 280, Minnetonka, MN 55343
Tel.: (952) 224-4000
Web Site: http://www.anulex.com

Year Founded: 2001
Sales Range: $1-9.9 Million
Emp.: 52
Mfr of Medical Devices for Spinal Disc Preservation & Anular Repair
N.A.I.C.S.: 339112
Tim Miller *(VP-Regulatory & Clinical Affairs)*
David Stassen *(Chm)*

ANUTRA CORP
248 Hatteras Ave, Clermont, FL 34711
Tel.: (321) 221-0233   DE
Year Founded: 2016
Investment Services
N.A.I.C.S.: 523999
Angelo S. Morini *(CEO & CFO)*

ANVIL ATTACHMENTS, LLC
261 Hwy 19, Slaughter, LA 70777-0216
Tel.: (225) 654-8223
Web Site:
   https://www.anvilattachments.com
Year Founded: 1968
Sales Range: $500-549.9 Million
Emp.: 80
Mfr of Bulk Material Clamshell Buckets, Grabs & Grapples
N.A.I.C.S.: 333120
John Craft *(Pres)*
Jeffery Wallace *(Mgr-Engrg)*
Johnny Gauthier *(Mgr-Ops)*

ANX E-BUSINESS CORP.
2000 Town Ctr Ste 2050, Southfield, MI 48075
Tel.: (248) 263-3400
Web Site: http://www.anx.com
Year Founded: 1998
Sales Range: $1-9.9 Million
Emp.: 80
Telephone Communications
N.A.I.C.S.: 517810
Mike Mahoney *(CFO)*
Rich Stanbaugh *(Pres & CEO)*
Cindy Swiantek *(VP-HR & Admin)*
Glenn Moore *(Sr VP-Corp Mktg)*
James Koessler *(Gen Counsel & VP)*
Jim Schmidt *(Controller)*
Ketan Patel *(VP-Svc & Support)*
Kevin Pierce *(Sr VP-Healthcare)*
Mark A. Wayne *(Exec VP-Sls)*
Stephen Koons *(Sr VP-Automotive)*

ANY BREAKERS, INC.
875 Malcom Rd, Burlingame, CA 94010
Tel.: (650) 697-3777
Web Site:
   http://www.anybreakers.com
Year Founded: 2001
Sales Range: $1-9.9 Million
Emp.: 5
Electrical Apparatus & Equipment Whslr
N.A.I.C.S.: 423610
Michael Feltsman *(Pres)*

ANY MOUNTAIN LTD.
71 Tamal Vista Blvd, Corte Madera, CA 94925
Tel.: (415) 927-2400
Web Site:
   http://www.anymountain.net
Rev.: $26,496,157
Emp.: 30
Skiing Equipment
N.A.I.C.S.: 459110
Bruno Gotzmer *(Area Mgr)*
Adam Turner *(Mgr-Mktg)*

ANYTHINGWEATHER COMMUNICATIONS, INC.

41701 Corporate Way Ste 6, Palm Desert, CA 92260
Tel.: (800) 845-0383
Web Site:
   http://www.anythingweather.com
Year Founded: 1999
Sales Range: $1-9.9 Million
Emp.: 20
Weather Data Services, Severe Weather Alerting Services, Weather Station Hardware & Monitoring Systems
N.A.I.C.S.: 517810
Gregg Potter *(Pres & CEO)*
Joshua Jans *(VP-Ops)*

ANZU PARTNERS, LLC
1399 New York Ave NW Ste 601, Washington, DC 20005
Tel.: (202) 742-5870
Web Site:
   http://www.anzupartners.com
Year Founded: 2014
Investment Firm
N.A.I.C.S.: 523999
Whitney Haring-Smith *(Founder & Mng Partner)*
David Michael *(Mng Partner)*
David Seldin *(Mng Partner)*
Greg Pope *(Principal)*
Debrah Herman *(CFO)*
Jaione Maiz *(Principal)*
William H. Strong *(Partner)*
Jimmy Kan *(Partner)*
Cathryn Paine *(Partner)*

Subsidiaries:

Pounce Technologies Inc.   (1)
LM 120 2303 4th Street SW, Calgary, T2S2S7, AB, Canada
Tel.: (403) 781-6671
Web Site: http://www.slyce.it
Rev.: $17,600
Assets: $52,697
Liabilities: $527,548
Net Worth: ($474,851)
Earnings: ($332,009)
Fiscal Year-end: 10/31/2019
Application Software Development Services
N.A.I.C.S.: 541511
Cameron Chell *(Founder)*

AO NORTH AMERICA
1700 Russell Rd, Paoli, PA 19301
Tel.: (610) 993-5100   PA
Web Site: http://www.aona.org
Year Founded: 2013
Sales Range: $10-24.9 Million
American Civic Association
N.A.I.C.S.: 813920
Michael Baumgaertner *(Chm)*

AOC KEY SOLUTIONS, INC.
14420 Albemarle Point Pl Ste 200, Chantilly, VA 20151-3283
Tel.: (703) 953-3838
Web Site:
   http://www.aockeysolutions.com
Year Founded: 1983
Market Assessment Consulting Services
N.A.I.C.S.: 541613
Greg McCarthy *(CEO)*
Kevin Berrigan *(CFO)*
Jean Watterson *(Sr VP-Ops)*

AOC SOLUTIONS, INC.
14151 Newbrook Dr Ste 200, Chantilly, VA 20151
Tel.: (703) 234-6300
Web Site:
   http://www.aocsolutions.com
Year Founded: 1996
Sales Range: $10-24.9 Million
Emp.: 250
Administrative & General Management Consulting Services
N.A.I.C.S.: 541611

Frank Sullivan *(VP-Program Dev)*
Larry J. Eisenhart *(VP-Fin Mgmt)*
Norwood J. Jackson Jr. *(VP)*

AOI MEDICAL, INC.
3251 Progress Dr Ste B2, Orlando, FL 32826
Tel.: (407) 770-1800
Web Site: http://www.aoimedical.net
Sales Range: $25-49.9 Million
Developer of Orthopaedic Medical Devices
N.A.I.C.S.: 339112
John D. Feltman *(Chm & CEO)*

AOS ADS
531 N 4th St, Tipp City, OH 45371
Tel.: (937) 667-2431
Year Founded: 1980
Sales Range: $1-9.9 Million
Advertising Agencies
N.A.I.C.S.: 541810
Heather Scaggs *(Dir)*

AOSS MEDICAL SUPPLY, INC.
4971 Central Ave, Monroe, LA 71203
Tel.: (318) 325-8290
Web Site:
   https://www.aossmedicalsupply.com
Year Founded: 1979
Sales Range: $10-24.9 Million
Emp.: 44
Medical Equipment & Supplies
N.A.I.C.S.: 423450
Eric Liew *(Co-Owner)*
Linda Pruett Liew *(Co-Owner)*

AOTCO METAL FINISHING LLC
11 Suburban Park Dr, Billerica, MA 01821
Tel.: (978) 667-8298
Web Site: http://www.aotco.com
Rev.: $4,160,000
Emp.: 40
Electroplating, Plating, Polishing, Anodizing & Coloring
N.A.I.C.S.: 332813
Jerry Paglia *(Mgr-Sls-Natl)*
Lynne M. Nason *(Mgr-Quality Assurance)*
Matt Smith *(Pres)*

Subsidiaries:

Plating for Electronics, LLC   (1)
94 Calvary St, Waltham, MA 02453
Tel.: (781) 893-2368
Web Site: http://www.p4e.com
Rev.: $3,300,000
Emp.: 44
Electroplating, Plating, Polishing, Anodizing & Coloring
N.A.I.C.S.: 332813
Michael Delaney *(Mgr)*
Peter Gigliotti *(VP)*
Stephen Davino *(Pres)*
Jim Hayes *(Mgr-Laboratory)*
Joseph LaSpada *(Sr VP-Ops)*
Karen Carter *(Mgr-Quality)*
Corie Davino *(Office Mgr-Customer Rels)*
Phillip Davino *(COO & Exec VP)*

AOXING PHARMACEUTICAL COMPANY, INC.
1098 Foster City Blvd Ste 106-810, Foster City, CA 94404
Tel.: (646) 367-1747
Web Site:
   http://www.aoxingpharma.com
Sales Range: $25-49.9 Million
Pharmaceutical Researcher, Developer, Mfr & Distr
N.A.I.C.S.: 325412
Zhenjiang Yue *(CEO)*
Guirong Zhou *(Pres-R&D)*
Jiang Peng *(Dir-Sls & Mktg)*

AP Atlantic Distribution, Inc.—(Continued)

AP ATLANTIC DISTRIBUTION, INC.
7190 NW 12th St, Miami, FL 33126-1304
Tel.: (305) 594-4022   FL
Web Site: http://www.apatlantic.com
Year Founded: 1995
Sales Range: $10-24.9 Million
Emp.: 7
Snacks & Confectionery Distr
N.A.I.C.S.: 424450
Orlando Alpizar (Pres)

AP CAPITAL INVESTMENT, LP
149 South Barrington Ave 815, Los Angeles, CA 90049
Tel.: (310) 593-4985
Web Site: http://apcinvest.com
Year Founded: 2007
Privater Equity Firm
N.A.I.C.S.: 523999
Bulend Corbacioglu (Founder & Mng Partner)

AP CONSTRUCTION INC.
915 S Black Horse Pike, Blackwood, NJ 08012-2815
Tel.: (856) 227-2030   NJ
Web Site: https://www.apconstruction.com
Year Founded: 1966
Sales Range: $10-24.9 Million
Emp.: 70
Water, Sewer & Utility Lines
N.A.I.C.S.: 237110
Michael Petrongolo (Mgr-Mktg)
Lee Norelli (Project Mgr)
Bill Twaddell (Project Mgr)
Robert Gillies (Project Mgr)

AP EMISSIONS TECHNOLOGIES, LLC
300 Dixie Trl, Goldsboro, NC 27530
Tel.: (919) 580-2000   DE
Web Site: http://apemissions.com
Year Founded: 1927
Automotive Exhaust & Emissions Products Mfr
N.A.I.C.S.: 336390
Gary Nix (Dir-Mktg & Product Mgmt)
Hope Abbott (Mgr-HR)
Danny Hammon (Mgr-Maintenance)
Jayme Farina (VP-Sls & Traditional Markets)
Dan Billie (Exec VP-Sls & Mktg)
Hugh Charvat (CEO)

AP PROFESSIONALS OF WNY LLC
5110 Main St, Williamsville, NY 14221
Tel.: (716) 635-0290
Web Site: https://www.approfessionals.com
Year Founded: 1993
Sales Range: $10-24.9 Million
Emp.: 100
IT Recruiting & Staffing Company
N.A.I.C.S.: 561311
Joe Kreuz (Founder & Partner)

APAC RUBBER, INC.
6851 McDivitt Dr Ste C, Bakersfield, CA 93313
Tel.: (661) 833-4421
Web Site: https://www.apacrubber.com
Year Founded: 2000
Sales Range: $1-9.9 Million
Emp.: 2
Produces Temperature Resistant Rubber Products
N.A.I.C.S.: 326291
Thai Tieu (Owner)

APACHE CONSTRUCTION COMPANY, INC.
1933 Coors Blvd SW, Albuquerque, NM 87121
Tel.: (505) 877-1155   NM
Web Site: https://www.valleyfenceco.com
Year Founded: 1981
Sales Range: $10-24.9 Million
Emp.: 70
Specialty Trade Contractors
N.A.I.C.S.: 238990
Paul Chavez (Pres)

Subsidiaries:

Valley Fence Company   (1)
1932 Coors Blvd SW, Albuquerque, NM 87121
Tel.: (505) 877-1155
Web Site: http://www.valleyfencecompany.com
Specialty Trade Contractors
N.A.I.C.S.: 238990
Paul Chavez (Pres & CEO)
Mariano Chavez (Founder & CFO)

APACHE MILLS INC.
18 Passaic Ave, Fairfield, NJ 07004-3845
Tel.: (973) 227-9080
Web Site: http://www.apachemills.com
Year Founded: 1971
Sales Range: $10-24.9 Million
Emp.: 3
Mfr of Miscellaneous Fabricated Wire Products
N.A.I.C.S.: 332618
Michael Wildstein (Pres)

APACHE MOTORCYCLES INC.
3618 W Camelback Rd, Phoenix, AZ 85019
Tel.: (602) 973-5111
Web Site: http://www.buyapache.com
Rev.: $28,537,536
Emp.: 45
Motorcycle Dealers
N.A.I.C.S.: 441227
Derek Vusovich (Mgr-Sls & Fin)
Josh Mueller (Mgr-Sls)
Kyle Asel (Gen Mgr-Parts)

APACHE NITROGEN PRODUCTS, INC.
1436 S Apache Powder Rd, Saint David, AZ 85630-6103
Tel.: (520) 720-2217   AZ
Web Site: https://www.apachenitrogen.com
Year Founded: 1920
Nitrate Products Mfr & Supplier
N.A.I.C.S.: 325311
Andy Hunter (VP & CFO)

APACHE STAINLESS EQUIPMENT CORP.
200 Industrial Dr, Beaver Dam, WI 53916-0538
Tel.: (920) 356-9900   WI
Web Site: https://www.apachestainless.com
Year Founded: 1975
Tanks & Metal Plates
N.A.I.C.S.: 332420
Ed Paradowski (Pres)
Kevin Paul (VP-Ops)

APARTMENT EXPRESS CORPORATE HOUSING INC.
5130 Dale Mabry Hwy S, Tampa, FL 33602
Tel.: (813) 864-0383
Web Site: http://www.wefindapartments.com
Sales Range: $1-9.9 Million
Emp.: 24

Short-term Luxury Housing
N.A.I.C.S.: 721110
David Lowrey (Pres)

APARTMENT LIFE
610 S Industrial Blvd Ste 170, Euless, TX 76040
Tel.: (817) 685-2963   TX
Web Site: https://www.apartmentlife.org
Year Founded: 2000
Sales Range: $10-24.9 Million
Emp.: 84
Community Care Services
N.A.I.C.S.: 624190
Kelly Jones (COO)

APARTMENT LIST
500 3rd St Ste 555, San Francisco, CA 94107
Tel.: (415) 817-1068
Web Site: http://www.apartmentlist.com
Year Founded: 2008
Sales Range: $10-24.9 Million
Emp.: 32
Apartment Rental Search Services
N.A.I.C.S.: 531110
John Kobs (Founder & CEO)

APAWAMIS CLUB
2 Club Rd, Rye, NY 10580
Tel.: (914) 967-2100   NY
Web Site: https://www.apawamis.org
Year Founded: 1891
Sales Range: $10-24.9 Million
Emp.: 220
Recreation Club Operator
N.A.I.C.S.: 713910
Paul Warren (Controller)
J. Hunter Baldwin (Pres)
William T. Henderson (Sec)
Alexander W. Vietor (Treas)
Richard F. Burke Jr. (VP)

APC POSTAL LOGISTICS, LLC
140 E Union Ave, East Rutherford, NJ 07073
Tel.: (201) 372-9700   MD
Web Site: https://www.apc-pli.com
Year Founded: 2002
Sales Range: $250-299.9 Million
Emp.: 88
International Mailing Solutions
N.A.I.C.S.: 481112
Michael Galianos (COO)
Amalyn Cruzado (Mgr-AP & AR)
John Barry (VP-Bus Mgmt)
Joe Calautti (Mgr-Ops)
Chris Serrano (Mgr-Export)
Carlos Alvarez (Mgr-IT)
Mike Panella (Pres)

APC WIRELESS
11910 Parklawn Dr, Rockville, MD 20852
Tel.: (301) 255-0410
Web Site: http://www.apcwireless.com
Sales Range: $25-49.9 Million
Emp.: 30
Tailored Electronic Solutions for Mobile Devices
N.A.I.C.S.: 517810
Paul Greene (CEO)
Jennifer Shappell (Dir-Sls)
John Chilufya (Mgr-Warehouse)

APCI, INC.
295 Athens Hwy, Loganville, GA 30052
Tel.: (770) 554-5050
Sales Range: $10-24.9 Million
Emp.: 150
Masonry Contracting Services
N.A.I.C.S.: 238140

Jesse Hutchinson (CEO)
Joy Hutchinson (CFO & Sec)

APCO EMPLOYEES CREDIT UNION
750 17th St N, Birmingham, AL 35203
Tel.: (205) 226-6800   AL
Web Site: https://www.apcocu.org
Year Founded: 1953
Sales Range: $50-74.9 Million
Emp.: 123
Credit Union
N.A.I.C.S.: 522130
Derrick Ragland (COO & Mgr-Facilities)
Blane Mink (CFO & VP)
Christopher Gerety (Mgr-Compliance & HR)

APCO GRAPHICS INC.
388 Grant St SE, Atlanta, GA 30312-2227
Tel.: (404) 688-9000
Web Site: https://www.apcosigns.com
Year Founded: 1966
Rev.: $13,000,000
Emp.: 300
Mfr of Architectural Signs
N.A.I.C.S.: 339950
Ronald Cobb (CEO)
Ratheal Watford (Mgr-Exterior Production)

APCO WORLDWIDE
700 1st St NW Ste 800, Washington, DC 20005
Tel.: (202) 778-1000
Web Site: http://www.apcoworldwide.com
Year Founded: 1984
Sales Range: $75-99.9 Million
Emp.: 575
Advertising Specialties
N.A.I.C.S.: 541810
Margery Kraus (Founder & Chm)
Evan Kraus (Pres-Global & Mng Dir-Ops)
Brad Staples (CEO)
Denise Teeling (CFO)
Nelson Fernandez (Chm-North America)
Karen Buerkle (Mng Dir-APCO insight)
Alicia Peterson Clark (Deputy Mng Dir)
Mamoon Sbeih (Pres)
Martina Tydecks (Exec Dir-Intl)
Andreas Constantinides (Chm-Tech Practice-Europe)
Theo Moore (Deputy Mng Dir)
Jen Young (Sr Dir-Global Health Care Practice)
Frank Lowenstein (Exec Dir-Solutions Practice-Global)
Brittney Manchester (Sr Assoc Dir-Healthcare Practice)
Dan Meyers (Head-Advocacy/Sr Dir-PA Practice)
James Yi (Mng Dir-South East Asia)
Kelly Williamson (Pres-North America)
Yash Kansal (Deputy Mng Dir)
Rahul Sharma (Mng Dir)
J. Todd Inman (Sr Dir)
Marta Ronquillo Newhart (CMO, Chief Comm Officer, Chief Brand Officer & Dir-Enterprise Leader)

Subsidiaries:

APCO Worldwide   (1)
4th Floor 2 Shabolovka Street, Moscow, 119049, Russia
Tel.: (7) 495 937 5525
Web Site: http://www.apcoworldwide.com

Sales Range: $10-24.9 Million
Emp.: 11
Public Relations
N.A.I.C.S.: 541820
Anna Gridneva *(Assoc Dir)*

APCO Worldwide (1)
47 Rue Montoyer 5th Floor, 1000, Brussels, Belgium
Tel.: (32) 2 645 98 11
Web Site: http://www.apcoworldwide.com
Sales Range: $25-49.9 Million
Emp.: 45
Communications, Public Relations
N.A.I.C.S.: 541820
Richard Bullard *(Dir-Pub Affairs)*
Claire Boussagol *(Mng Dir)*

APCO Worldwide (1)
90 Long Acre, London, WC2E 9RA, United Kingdom
Tel.: (44) 207 526 3600
Web Site: http://www.apcoworldwide.com
Sales Range: $25-49.9 Million
Emp.: 650
Public Relations
N.A.I.C.S.: 541820
James Tyrrell *(Chm-Health Practice)*

APCO Worldwide (1)
1201 K St Ste 1200, Sacramento, CA 95814-3953
Tel.: (916) 554-3400
Web Site: http://www.apcoworldwide.com
Sales Range: $10-24.9 Million
Emp.: 12
Public Relations
N.A.I.C.S.: 541820
Jose R. Hermocillo *(Mng Dir & Sr VP-Sacramento)*
Emily Johnson *(Dir-Digital Strategy)*
Jillian Hacker *(Assoc Dir)*

APCO Worldwide (1)
19/F Cambridge House Taikoo Place, 979 Kings Road, Central, China (Hong Kong)
Tel.: (852) 2866 2313
Web Site: http://www.apcoworldwide.com
Sales Range: $25-49.9 Million
Emp.: 25
Public Relations
N.A.I.C.S.: 541820

APCO Worldwide (1)
Suite 903 Tower C Office Park No 5 Jinghua South Street, Chaoyang District, Beijing, 100020, China
Tel.: (86).10 6505 5128
Web Site: http://www.apcoworldwide.com
Sales Range: $25-49.9 Million
Emp.: 50
Public Relations
N.A.I.C.S.: 541820

APCO Worldwide (1)
520 Pike St Ste 1001, Seattle, WA 98101-1385
Tel.: (206) 224-4340
Web Site: http://www.apcoworldwide.com
Sales Range: $10-24.9 Million
Emp.: 15
Public Relations
N.A.I.C.S.: 541820
Jon Ramsey *(Dir-Global Tech Practice)*
Tim Smith *(Mng Dir)*

APCO Worldwide (1)
255 Albert Street Suite 703, Ottawa, K1P 6A9, ON, Canada
Tel.: (613) 786-7600
Web Site: http://www.apcoworldwide.com
Sales Range: $10-24.9 Million
Emp.: 11
Public Relations
N.A.I.C.S.: 541820

APCO Worldwide (1)
Suites 2102-2103 CITIC Square, 1168 Nanjing Road West, Shanghai, 200041, China
Tel.: (86) 21 5298 4668
Web Site: http://www.apcoworldwide.com
Sales Range: $10-24.9 Million
Emp.: 16
Public Relations
N.A.I.C.S.: 541820
Kenneth Jarrett *(Vice Chm-Greater China)*
Linda Du *(Mng Dir)*
James Robinson *(Mng Dir)*
Jeff Astle *(Mng Dir)*

APCO Worldwide (1)

Unit 12 4/F Saigon Centre 65 Le Loi, District 1, Ho Chi Minh City, Vietnam
Tel.: (84) 8 821 7895
Web Site: http://www.apcoworldwide.com
Sales Range: $10-24.9 Million
Emp.: 4
Public Relations
N.A.I.C.S.: 541820

APCO Worldwide (1)
JFK Haus Rahel-Hirsch-Strasse 10, 10557, Berlin, Germany
Tel.: (49) 30 59 000 2010
Web Site: http://www.apcoworldwide.com
Sales Range: $10-24.9 Million
Emp.: 25
Public Relations Services
N.A.I.C.S.: 541820
Isabel Kassabian *(Deputy Mng Dir)*
Robert Ardelt *(Mng Dir)*

APCO Worldwide (1)
Via Condotti 61/A, 00187, Rome, 00187, Italy
Tel.: (39) 06 697 6661
Web Site: http://www.apcoworldwide.com
Sales Range: Less than $1 Million
Emp.: 7
Public Relations
N.A.I.C.S.: 541820
Paolo Compostella *(Mng Dir)*
Rossella Carrara *(Deputy Mng Dir)*

APCO Worldwide (1)
10th Floor World Trade Center Jl Jend Sudirman Kav 29-31, Jakarta, 12920, Indonesia
Tel.: (62) 21 5296 4611
Web Site: http://www.apcoworldwide.com
Sales Range: $25-49.9 Million
Emp.: 19
Public Relations
N.A.I.C.S.: 541820

APCO Worldwide (1)
Sroesischi Str 20, 0117, Berlin, Germany
Tel.: (49) 228 60 48 518
Web Site: http://www.apcoworldwide.com
Sales Range: $10-24.9 Million
Emp.: 35
Public Relations
N.A.I.C.S.: 541820
Robert Albert *(Mng Dir-Germany)*

APCO Worldwide (1)
360 Park Ave S 11th Fl, New York, NY 10010
Tel.: (212) 300-1800
Web Site: http://www.apcoworldwide.com
Sales Range: $10-24.9 Million
Emp.: 30
Lobbying Services
N.A.I.C.S.: 541820
Marc Johnson *(Mng Dir)*

APCO Worldwide (1)
Office No 433 Level 4 Dynasty Business Park A Wing, Andheri Kurla Road Andheri E, Mumbai, 400059, India
Tel.: (91) 22 4030 9380
Web Site: http://www.apcoworldwide.com
Sales Range: $10-24.9 Million
Emp.: 3
N.A.I.C.S.: 541810

APCO Worldwide (1)
9 Central Block 1st Floor ALPS Building 56 Janpath, Connaught Place, New Delhi, 110001, India
Tel.: (91) 11 4605 7700
Web Site: http://www.apcoworldwide.com
Sales Range: $10-24.9 Million
Emp.: 16
Advertising & Public Relation Agency Services
N.A.I.C.S.: 541810
Sukanti Ghosh *(Sr Dir-Houston)*
Rahul Sharma *(Mng Dir)*
Yash Kansal *(Deputy Mng Dir & Sr Dir)*

APCO Worldwide (1)
153/3 Goldenland Building 3rd Floor Room D3, Soi Mahardlekluang 1, Rajadamri Road, Bangkok, 10330, Thailand
Tel.: (66) 2652 2492
Web Site: http://www.apcoworldwide.com
Sales Range: $10-24.9 Million
Emp.: 6
N.A.I.C.S.: 541810

APCO Worldwide (1)

DIFC Ctr The Gate E Gate Fl 15 Office 13, Dubai, United Arab Emirates
Tel.: (971) 4 365 0410
Web Site: http://www.apcoworldwide.com
N.A.I.C.S.: 541820
Camilla d'Abo *(Mng Dir)*

APCO Worldwide - Paris (1)
12 bis Rue Kepler, Paris, 75016, France
Tel.: (33) 1 44 94 8666
Web Site: http://www.apcoworldwide.com
Public Relations Agency
N.A.I.C.S.: 541820
Veronique Ferjou *(Deputy Mng Dir)*

Gagen MacDonald, LLC (1)
343 West Erie St Ste 600, Chicago, IL 60610
Tel.: (312) 640-9100
Web Site: http://www.gagenmacdonald.com
Rev.: $9,459,676
Emp.: 40
Administrative Management & General Management Consulting Service
N.A.I.C.S.: 541611
Maril MacDonald *(CEO)*
Brad Messinger *(CMO)*
Sherry Scott *(Pres)*

StrawberryFrog (1)
60 Madison Ave Ph, New York, NY 10010
Tel.: (212) 366-0500
Web Site: http://www.strawberryfrog.com
Sales Range: $10-24.9 Million
Emp.: 60
Advetising Agency
N.A.I.C.S.: 541810
Scott Goodson *(Co-Founder, CEO & Mng Dir)*
Karin Drakenberg *(Co-Founder)*
Raj Kamble *(Mng Partner-India)*
Craig Love *(Exec Dir-Creative)*

Branch (Non-US):

PeraltaStrawberryFrog (2)
Avenida Mofarrej 1200, 2 Piso Andar Vila Leopoldina, Sao Paulo, 05311-000, Brazil
Tel.: (55) 11 3834 8344
N.A.I.C.S.: 541810

APELLA CAPITAL LLC
151 National Dr, Glastonbury, CT 06033
Tel.: (860) 785-2260   KY
Web Site: https://apellawealth.com
Emp.: 100
Investment Advisor
N.A.I.C.S.: 523940

Subsidiaries:

Structured Asset Management Inc. (1)
37 N Vly Rd, Paoli, PA 19301
Tel.: (610) 648-0766
Web Site: http://www.samasset.com
Investment Advice
N.A.I.C.S.: 523940
William Suplee *(Pres)*

APELON INC.
100 Danbury Rd Ste 202, Ridgefield, CT 06877
Tel.: (203) 431-2530
Web Site: http://www.apelon.com
Sales Range: $10-24.9 Million
Emp.: 45
Medical Computer Software
N.A.I.C.S.: 423450
Stephen Coady *(CEO)*
Jack Bowie *(Sr VP-Product Svcs)*
Tony Weida *(Sr VP-Consulting Svcs)*

APERION MANAGEMENT
1185 Ave of the Americas 20th Flr, New York, NY 10036
Tel.: (212) 300-0279
Web Site: http://aperionmgt.com
Privater Equity Firm
N.A.I.C.S.: 523999
Kyun Park *(Mng Dir)*

Subsidiaries:

JP Piccinini Real Estate Services LLC (1)
6136 Frisco Square Blvd Ste 200, Frisco, TX 75034
Tel.: (972) 836-9295
Web Site: http://www.jpar.net
Sales Range: $1-9.9 Million
Emp.: 580
Real Estate Brokerage Services
N.A.I.C.S.: 531210
J. P. Piccinini *(Founder)*
Howard Ashkinos *(Dir-Franchise Sls-Natl)*
Debbie Viverito *(Dir-Recruiting)*
Shannon Ashkinos *(Dir-Career Dev)*
Jonathan Garza *(Controller & Dir-Bus to Bus)*

APERION MANAGEMENT GROUP LLC
20310 Empire Ave Ste A-103, Bend, OR 97703
Tel.: (541) 389-3172   OR
Web Site:
http://www.aperionmgmt.com
Privater Equity Firm
N.A.I.C.S.: 523999
Katie Anderson *(Founder)*

APET INC.
195 Prairie Lk Rd, East Dundee, IL 60118
Tel.: (630) 595-6808
Web Site: http://www.apetinc.com
Rev.: $16,000,000
Emp.: 121
Pets & Pet Supplies; Distribution
N.A.I.C.S.: 424990
Mark Shilkus *(Pres)*
Tom Scianna *(Acct Mgr-Sls)*
Jovan Goral *(Mgr-Logistic)*

APEX 2, INC.
1300 N Vosburg Dr, Azusa, CA 91702
Tel.: (612) 961-5656   DE
Year Founded: 2011
Assets: $19,689
Liabilities: $211,428
Net Worth: ($191,739)
Earnings: ($70,307)
Fiscal Year-end: 12/31/18
Investment Services
N.A.I.C.S.: 523999
Xiang Dong Wang *(Chm, Pres, CEO, CFO & Treas)*
Lowell Thomas Holden *(Sec)*

APEX ACCOUNTING AND TAX, INC.
7800 S Elati St Ste 320, Littleton, CO 80120
Tel.: (303) 797-1070
Web Site:
https://www.apexaccountingtax.com
Public Accounting firm
N.A.I.C.S.: 541219

Subsidiaries:

Phases Accounting & Tax Services (1)
1445 N. Union Blvd., Colorado Springs, CO 80909
Tel.: (719) 548-1646
Web Site: http://www.phasesaccounting.com
Other Accounting Services
N.A.I.C.S.: 541219
Debby Miller *(Owner)*

APEX BULK COMMODITIES INC.
12531 Violet Rd, Adelanto, CA 92301-2705
Tel.: (760) 246-6077   CA
Web Site: https://www.apexbulk.com
Year Founded: 1991
Sales Range: $25-49.9 Million

Apex Bulk Commodities Inc.—(Continued)

Emp.: 320
Local Trucking
N.A.I.C.S.: 484220
Glenn Warner (CEO)
Denny Wyatt (VP-Sls & Customer Support)

APEX COMPANIES, LLC
15850 Crabbs Branch Way Ste 200, Rockville, MD 20855-2616
Tel.: (301) 417-0200
Web Site: http://www.apexcos.com
Year Founded: 1988
Environmental & Engineering Services
N.A.I.C.S.: 541620
Pam Semler (Exec Dir-HR)
Brian Burke (CFO)
Darwin Nelson (COO)
Amandeep Kang (VP-West Reg)
Brian Pine (VP-Northeast Reg)
Diane Anderson (VP-Southeast Reg)
Ryan Trahan (VP-Infrastructure)
Edward Coleman (VP-Comml Stormwater)
Jim Cochrane (CIO)
Stephen Choi (Controller)
Erin Kane (Exec Dir-Mktg)
Matt Hardesty (VP-Fin)
David Fabianski (Pres & CEO)

Subsidiaries:

GIF Enterprises, Inc.   (1)
6622 Gordon Rd Ste K, Wilmington, NC 28411
Tel.: (910) 313-6830
Stormwater Management Services
N.A.I.C.S.: 562998

Johnson Engineering, Inc.   (1)
2122 Johnson St, Fort Myers, FL 33901
Tel.: (239) 334-0046
Web Site:
   http://www.johnsonengineering.com
Sales Range: $10-24.9 Million
Emp.: 100
Engineering, Surveying, Environmental, Water Resources & Landscape Architecture Services
N.A.I.C.S.: 541330
Kevin Winter (Chm)
Lonnie V. Howard (Pres)
Andrew Tilton (VP)
Michael Dickey (VP-Engrg)

The Source Group Inc.   (1)
3478 Buskirk Ave Ste 100, Pleasant Hill, CA 94523   (100%)
Tel.: (925) 944-2856
Web Site: http://www.thesourcegroup.net
Emp.: 100
Environmental Consulting & Engineering Services
N.A.I.C.S.: 541330
Kirsten L. Duey (Sr Engr-Chemical)

APEX CONTRACTING & RESTORATION, INC.
4421 Glacier Ave, San Diego, CA 92120
Tel.: (619) 255-3022   CA
Web Site: http://www.apex411.com
Year Founded: 2004
Sales Range: $10-24.9 Million
Emp.: 55
General Contractors
N.A.I.C.S.: 236115
Patrick Bodine (Pres)
Jimmy Pettit (Dir-Ops)

APEX COVANTAGE
198 Van Buren St Ste 100, Herndon, VA 20170-5338
Tel.: (703) 709-3000
Web Site:
   https://www.apexcovantage.com
Sales Range: $150-199.9 Million
Emp.: 2,500

Outsourcing Services, Digital Content Services (Digital Libraries & Databases Building) & Print Production for Publishing Companies
N.A.I.C.S.: 541690
James O. Edwards (Chm)
Shashikant Gupta (Co-Founder & CEO)
Margaret Boryczka (Co-Founder & Exec VP)

APEX DENTAL PARTNERS, LP
15660 Dallas Pkwy Ste 925, Dallas, TX 75248
Tel.: (214) 702-0720   DE
Web Site: http://www.apexdp.com
Year Founded: 2014
Sales Range: $10-24.9 Million
Emp.: 150
Dental Care Services
N.A.I.C.S.: 621399
David Lohmann (Co-Founder & CEO)
Matt Hale (Co-Founder, Pres & COO)

APEX ENGINEERING INC.
1234 Wellington Pl, Wichita, KS 67203
Tel.: (316) 262-1494
Web Site: http://www.aeiinc.com
Sales Range: $10-24.9 Million
Emp.: 150
Aircraft Parts & Equipment
N.A.I.C.S.: 336413
Jeff Landreth (Pres & CEO)

Subsidiaries:

Apex Composites Inc.   (1)
414 Chamber Loop, Ada, OK 74820
Tel.: (580) 436-6444
Web Site: http://www.apexcomposites.com
Rev.: $4,300,000
Emp.: 45
Aircraft Parts & Equipment
N.A.I.C.S.: 336413

APEX FACILITY RESOURCES, INC.
4435 Colorado Ave S, Seattle, WA 98134
Tel.: (206) 686-3357
Web Site: http://www.apexfacility.com
Year Founded: 1997
Sales Range: $10-24.9 Million
Emp.: 40
New & Used Office Furniture Distr & Office Facilities Coordinator
N.A.I.C.S.: 423210
Marlaine R. McCauley (Founder)
Rochelle Martin (Acct Mgr)
Nicole Schmidt (Project Coord)

APEX FINTECH SOLUTIONS LLC
888 7th Ave 32nd Fl, New York, NY 10106
Tel.: (212) 658-1173
Web Site:
   http://www.apexfintechsolutions.com
Digital Wealth Management; Cryptocurrency Trading & Custody Services
N.A.I.C.S.: 522320
Bill Capuzzi (CEO)
Jon Patullo (Chief Product Officer-Advisory)
Olivia Eisinger (Gen Mgr-Advisory Solutions)

Subsidiaries:

Apex Clearing Corporation   (1)
1 Dallas Ctr 350 N Saint Paul St Ste 1300, Dallas, TX 75201
Tel.: (888) 268-6220
Web Site: http://www.apexclearing.com
Financial Clearing & Execution Services
N.A.I.C.S.: 522320
Hannah Shaw Grove (CMO)
Bill Capuzzi (CEO)
Lucille Mayer (COO)

Chris Fesle (CTO)
William Brennan (CFO)
Reluca Marin (Chief People Officer)

Silver Management Group, Inc.   (1)
114 Rabbit Hill Rd, Princeton Junction, NJ 08550
Tel.: (609) 275-9221
Web Site:
   http://www.silvermanagement.com
Management Consulting Services
N.A.I.C.S.: 541611
Blake Henry (CEO)
Neal Ruskin (Mng Partner-Product)
Robert Benkovitz (Mng Partner-Tech)

APEX GLOBAL BRANDS INC.
5990 Sepulveda Blvd, Sherman Oaks, CA 91411
Tel.: (818) 908-9868   DE
Web Site:
   http://www.apexglobalbrands.com
Year Founded: 1973
Rev.: $21,041,000
Assets: $82,922,000
Liabilities: $77,575,000
Net Worth: $5,347,000
Earnings: ($11,500,000)
Emp.: 37
Fiscal Year-end: 02/01/20
Licenser of Branded Apparel, Shoes & Accessories to Retailers & Wholesalers
N.A.I.C.S.: 533110
Howard Siegel (Pres, COO & Sec)
Henry Stupp (CEO)
Steven L. Brink (CFO)

Subsidiaries:

Hi-Tec Sports International Holdings B.V.   (1)
Paasheuvelweg 22a, Zuidoost, 1105 BJ, Amsterdam, Netherlands
Tel.: (31) 207118400
Web Site: http://sp.hi-tec.com
Footwear Distr
N.A.I.C.S.: 424340
Frank Van Wezel (Founder)

APEX HOME LOANS, INC.
3204 Tower Oaks Blvd Ste 400, Rockville, MD 20852
Tel.: (301) 610-9600
Web Site:
   http://www.apexhomeloans.com
Year Founded: 1998
Sales Range: $10-24.9 Million
Emp.: 61
Mortgage Banking Services
N.A.I.C.S.: 522292
Craig Strent (CEO)
Eric D. Gates (Pres)
Michael C. Parsons (Chm)
Stewart A. Zemil (COO)
Glen Lazovick (VP-Residential Lending)
Francki DiFrancesco (VP-Residential Lending)
Brian Du Plessis (Mgr-Herndon)
Jennifer Du Plessis (VP & Reg Dir-Sls)
Kevin Michno (Sr VP-Expansion & Bus Dev)
Judy Blank (Chief Compliance Officer)
Steve Dorfman (Chief Experience Officer)

APEX HOMES INC.
7172 US Hwy 522 N, Middleburg, PA 17842
Tel.: (570) 837-2333
Web Site:
   http://www.apexhomesinc.com
Sales Range: $25-49.9 Million
Emp.: 230
Prefabricated Wood Modular Homes
N.A.I.C.S.: 321992

Brian Troutman (Mgr-Svcs)
Kyle Nornhold (Dir-Engrg)

APEX INCORPORATED
100 Main St, Pawtucket, RI 02860-4107
Tel.: (401) 723-6108   RI
Web Site: http://www.apexstores.com
Year Founded: 1942
Sales Range: $25-49.9 Million
Emp.: 500
Provider of Retail Services
N.A.I.C.S.: 455110

APEX INFINITE SOLUTIONS LLC
8801 N Meridian St Ste 209, Indianapolis, IN 46260
Tel.: (317) 974-0382   IN
Web Site: http://www.aisllp.com
Year Founded: 2012
Sales Range: $1-9.9 Million
Emp.: 7
Information Technology Consulting Services
N.A.I.C.S.: 541690
Lamont Hatcher (CEO)

APEX INFORMATION TECHNOLOGIES
100 S Owasso Blvd W, Saint Paul, MN 55117
Tel.: (866) 676-2739
Web Site:
   http://www.apexinformationtech.com
Year Founded: 1995
Sales Range: $25-49.9 Million
Emp.: 78
Back-End Segment of Revenue Cycle Management in the Healthcare Industry
N.A.I.C.S.: 513210
Brian Kueppers (CEO)
Patrick Maurer (Pres)
Warren Becker (CFO)
Greg Barmore (Exec VP-Sls & Bus Dev)
Carrie Romandine (VP-Solutions & Svcs)
Ryan Dotson (VP-Product Dev)

APEX INSTRUMENTS, INC.
204 Technology Park Ln, Fuquay Varina, NC 27526
Tel.: (919) 557-7300
Web Site: https://www.apexinst.com
Year Founded: 1988
Sales Range: $1-9.9 Million
Emp.: 31
Measuring Machinery & Equipment Mfr
N.A.I.C.S.: 334513
William H. Howe (Pres)
Chris Green (Dir-Bus Dev)
Sung Jun Lee (Dir-Analytical Div)
Angela Vargas (Mgr-Pur)
Jim Cothran (Project Mgr)
Ben Rogers (Mgr-Warehouse)
Tony Miller (Mgr-Production)
Michael Zulpo (Dir-Sls & Mktg)

APEX MACHINE CO.
3000 NE 12th Ter, Fort Lauderdale, FL 33334
Tel.: (954) 566-1572
Web Site:
   https://www.apexmachine.com
Sales Range: $10-24.9 Million
Emp.: 65
Printing Machinery
N.A.I.C.S.: 333248
A. Robert Coningsby (Chm & CEO)
Chris Bardelang (Controller)
Chris Dunn (Dir-Sls-Europe & Africa)
Russell Coningsby (Mgr-Natl Sls)
Todd D. Coningsby (Pres)

Gregg Coningsby *(Mgr-Engrg)*
Ernesto Paez *(Mgr-MIS)*
Anita Rice *(Mgr-Traffic)*
Raghav Podar *(Mng Dir)*

Subsidiaries:

Desco Equipment Corp. **(1)**
1903 Case Pkwy, Twinsburg, OH 44087-2343
Tel.: (330) 405-1581
Web Site: http://www.descoequipment.com
Sales Range: $1-9.9 Million
Emp.: 38
Printing Machinery & Equipment Mfr
N.A.I.C.S.: 333248
Leo E. Henry *(Pres)*

APEX MEDICAL COMMUNICA-TIONS, INC.
611 US Highway 46 W, Hasbrouck Heights, NJ 07604
Tel.: (201) 288-4800
Web Site: http://www.apexcom.com
Year Founded: 1994
Sales Range: $1-9.9 Million
Emp.: 84
Administrative Management & General Management Consulting Service
N.A.I.C.S.: 541611

APEX MILLS CORPORATION
168 Doughty Blvd, Inwood, NY 11096
Tel.: (516) 239-4400
Web Site: https://www.apexmills.com
Sales Range: $75-99.9 Million
Emp.: 22
Mfr of Manmade Broadwoven Fabrics & Knitted Netting Solid Fabrics
N.A.I.C.S.: 313210
David Kurz *(VP & Controller)*
Jonathan Kurz *(Pres)*

APEX OFFICE PRODUCTS, INC.
5209 N Howard Ave, Tampa, FL 33603
Tel.: (813) 871-2010   FL
Web Site: https://www.apexop.com
Year Founded: 1981
Sales Range: $10-24.9 Million
Emp.: 60
Stationery, Office Supplies & Furniture Merchant Whslr
N.A.I.C.S.: 424120
Alex Llorente *(Pres & CEO)*
Michele Adams *(Acct Mgr)*
Nick Muley *(Exec VP)*

APEX OIL COMPANY, INC.
8235 Forsyth Blvd Ste 400, Saint Louis, MO 63105-3923
Tel.: (314) 889-9600   MO
Web Site: https://www.apexoil.com
Year Founded: 1932
Sales Range: $1-4.9 Billion
Emp.: 700
Offices of Other Holding Companies
N.A.I.C.S.: 551112

Subsidiaries:

Apex Towing Company **(1)**
8235 Forsyth Blvd Ste 400, Saint Louis, MO 63105
Tel.: (314) 889-9600
Towboat Hiring Services
N.A.I.C.S.: 532120

Petroleum Fuel & Terminal Company **(1)**
8235 Forsyth Blvd Ste 400, Saint Louis, MO 63105-3786   **(100%)**
Tel.: (314) 889-9600
Web Site: http://www.apexoil.com
Sales Range: $10-24.9 Million
Emp.: 70
Petroleum Terminal Operator & Distr
N.A.I.C.S.: 424710

Trinidad Resort & Club, LLC **(1)**

5780 Shanty Creek Rd, Bellaire, MI 49615
Tel.: (231) 533-8621
Web Site: http://www.shantycreek.com
Hotel Operating Services
N.A.I.C.S.: 721110

APEX OUTSOURCING, INC.
2525 Main St Ste 360, Irvine, CA 92614
Tel.: (949) 486-4800
Web Site: http://www.apexbroker.com
Sales Range: $25-49.9 Million
Emp.: 21
Insurance Agency & Brokerage Services
N.A.I.C.S.: 524210
Darren Sugiyama *(Pres)*

APEX PRECISION TECHNOL-OGY INC.
8824 Union Mills Dr, Camby, IN 46113-9705
Tel.: (317) 821-1000   IN
Web Site:
  http://www.apexprecision.com
Year Founded: 1951
Sales Range: Less than $1 Million
Emp.: 45
Mfr of Aircraft Engine Components & Transmission Parts
N.A.I.C.S.: 333914
Bob Venton *(VP-Mktg & Sls)*
Bryson Ocker *(Pres)*

APEX RESOURCES, INC.
13191 Crossroads Pkwy N Ste 200, City of Industry, CA 91746
Tel.: (626) 910-5101   NV
Web Site: http://www.apexr.com
Year Founded: 1996
Assets: $56,711
Liabilities: $758,994
Net Worth: ($702,283)
Earnings: ($630,489)
Emp.: 3
Fiscal Year-end: 06/30/19
Industrial Grade Water Soluble Polymers
N.A.I.C.S.: 325180
Jeff Bodnar *(Pres & CEO)*
Linda Bao *(CFO, Treas & Sec)*
Xiaoya Deng *(Chm)*

APEX RESTAURANT MAN-AGEMENT, INC.
4117 N Josey Ln, Carrollton, TX 75007
Tel.: (972) 394-8519   CA
Web Site: http://www.apex-brands.com
Year Founded: 2005
Fast Food Restaurant Owner & Operator
N.A.I.C.S.: 722513
Tabbassum Mumtaz *(Pres & CEO)*
Ajay Dhillon *(CFO)*
Ray Walia *(COO)*

Subsidiaries:

Morgan's Foods, Inc. **(1)**
4829 Galaxy Pkwy Ste S, Cleveland, OH 44128
Tel.: (216) 359-9000
Web Site: http://www.morgansfoods.com
Sales Range: $75-99.9 Million
Emp.: 1,500
Fast Food Restaurant Franchise Owner & Operator
N.A.I.C.S.: 722513
James J. Liguori *(Pres & COO)*
Kenneth L. Hignett *(CFO, Sec & Exec VP)*
Ramesh J. Gursahaney *(VP-Ops Support Svcs)*

APEX SERVICE PARTNERS LLC
201 E Kennedy Blvd. Ste 1600, Tampa, TX 33602

Tel.: (813) 658-6100
Web Site:
  https://apexservicepartners.com
Emp.: 100
HVAC, Plumbing & Electrical Service
N.A.I.C.S.: 238220
Andrew Brown *(CEO)*

Subsidiaries:

Frontier Service Partners **(1)**
625 Bakers Bridge Ave Ste 105, Franklin, TN 37067
Tel.: (615) 406-8440
Web Site:
  http://www.frontierservicepartners.com
Residential Service Company
N.A.I.C.S.: 811310
Dean Fulton *(CEO)*

Subsidiary (Domestic):

Haley Mechanical, LLC **(2)**
8415 Dexter-Chelsea Rd, Dexter, MI 48130
Tel.: (734) 424-9170
Web Site: http://www.haleymechanical.com
Plumbing, Heating & Air-Conditioning Contractors
N.A.I.C.S.: 238220
Henry Haley *(Gen Mgr)*

APEX SUPPLY COMPANY
180 Oak Lawn Ave, Dallas, TX 75207
Tel.: (214) 741-5463
Web Site:
  http://www.apexsupplyco.com
Sales Range: $25-49.9 Million
Emp.: 80
Plumbing Fittings & Supplies
N.A.I.C.S.: 423720
Stephen Lerer *(Pres)*
Bob Janney *(Controller)*
Ross Cates *(Gen Counsel)*

APEX TECHNOLOGY GROUP, INC.
2703 Merrywood Dr, Edison, NJ 08817
Tel.: (732) 819-7550
Web Site: https://www.apextgi.com
Year Founded: 2001
Rev.: $14,600,000
Emp.: 142
Computer System Design Services
N.A.I.C.S.: 541512
Chhavi Dharaya *(VP)*
Sarvesh Dharayan *(Pres)*

APEXCCTV
22 Prestige Cir Ste 100, Allen, TX 75002
Tel.: (972) 312-1713
Web Site: http://www.apexcctv.com
Year Founded: 2006
Sales Range: $1-9.9 Million
Emp.: 27
Security & Surveillance Distribution & Support Services
N.A.I.C.S.: 561621
Donald Bennett *(Pres & CEO)*

APEXICAL, INC.
1905 New Cut Rd, Spartanburg, SC 29303
Tel.: (864) 578-0030
Web Site: https://www.apexical.com
Year Founded: 1900
Sales Range: $10-24.9 Million
Emp.: 25
Mfr & Sales of Specialty Chemicals
N.A.I.C.S.: 325998
Steven A. Baer *(Pres)*
Dana Shinta *(Office Mgr)*
Larry Morda *(Plant Mgr)*
Ted Dickson *(VP-Bus Dev)*

APEXTERIORS INC.
376 Pr Hill Rd, South Beloit, IL 61080
Tel.: (815) 624-2161

Web Site:
  http://www.apexexterior.com
Year Founded: 2006
Sales Range: $1-9.9 Million
Emp.: 7
Roof, Siding & Gutter Restoration
N.A.I.C.S.: 238160
Jim Stringham *(Owner)*

APG ELECTRIC INC.
4825 140th Ave N, Clearwater, FL 33762-3822
Tel.: (727) 530-0077
Web Site: https://www.apg.company
Year Founded: 1983
Sales Range: $25-49.9 Million
Emp.: 250
Electrical Engineering Services
N.A.I.C.S.: 238210
Chris M. Johnson *(Exec VP)*
Justin Foster *(CIO)*
Stephen A. Tallyn *(VP-Bus Dev)*
Tim White *(Mgr-Svc Grp)*
Michael D. Henley *(Pres)*
Trina M. Rodriguez *(CFO)*
Jerry Lightner *(COO)*
Mike Dobbs *(VP-Engrg)*
Lester Weil *(Mgr-Tech Grp)*
Pete Hyneman *(Mgr-Electric Svc)*
B. J. Klingensmith *(Mgr-Life Safety Grp)*
Kevin Dewitt *(Mgr-Automation Grp)*

APG INTERNATIONAL INC.
70 Sewell St Ste C, Glassboro, NJ 08028
Tel.: (856) 863-6620
Web Site: http://www.apgintl.com
Sales Range: $25-49.9 Million
Emp.: 35
Glass & Glazing Work
N.A.I.C.S.: 238150
Thomas Salver *(Pres)*
Mary Mattia *(Controller)*
Thomas Salzer *(Mgr)*
Chris Karafonda *(Project Mgr)*

Subsidiaries:

APG Europe Ltd. **(1)**
Unit 9 Chancery Gate, West Drayton, UB7 8EB, Middlesex, United Kingdom
Tel.: (44) 189 5445 222
Glazing Contracting Services
N.A.I.C.S.: 238150
Mark Pendle *(Mng Dir)*

APG Far East Ltd. **(1)**
129/176 M 8 Bangkok Blvd Ratchapruek-Rama 5 Rd T Bangkrang A Muang, Non-thaburi, 11000, Thailand
Tel.: (66) 2 422 5821
Glazing Contracting Services
N.A.I.C.S.: 238150
Chalermchai Suttayamullee *(Mng Dir)*

APG Middle East FZC **(1)**
SAIF-Zone, PO Box 9745, Sharjah, United Arab Emirates
Tel.: (971) 6 557 8010
Glazing Contracting Services
N.A.I.C.S.: 238150
Dirk Schulte *(Mng Dir)*

APG-Europe GmbH **(1)**
Brueckenstrasse 24, 97199, Ochsenfurt, Germany
Tel.: (49) 933180252
Web Site: http://www.apgeurope.de
Glass & Glazing
N.A.I.C.S.: 238150

APG POLYTECH, LLC
27610 Huntington Rd, Apple Grove, WV 25502
Tel.: (304) 576-2041
Polymer Product Distr
N.A.I.C.S.: 424610

APH INC.

APH Inc.—(Continued)

5750 W 95th St Ste 300, Overland
Park, KS 66207-2969
Tel.: (913) 890-8250   DE
Web Site: http://www.codero.com
Year Founded: 1992
On-Demand Cloud Data Hosting &
Related Services
N.A.I.C.S.: 518210
Leo Staurulakis *(Chm)*

API CONTROL SYSTEMS SO-LUTIONS INC
218 Hector Connoly Rd, Carencro,
LA 70520
Tel.: (337) 896-9090
Web Site: http://www.apicss.com
Sales Range: $10-24.9 Million
Emp.: 60
Electrical Equipment & Supplies, Nec
N.A.I.C.S.: 334419
John Danos *(Owner & Pres)*
Felix Dominique *(Gen Mgr-Automation & Field Svs)*
Lucas Comeaux *(Gen Mgr-Sys Mfg)*
Issac Dantin *(Mgr-Safety)*
Alan Broxson *(Mgr-Div-I&E)*

API INDUSTRIES INC.
2 Glenshaw St, Orangeburg, NY
10962-1207
Tel.: (845) 365-2200   NJ
Web Site: http://www.alufplastics.com
Year Founded: 1977
Sales Range: $75-99.9 Million
Emp.: 300
Mfr & Distributor of Plastic Bags
N.A.I.C.S.: 326111
Gabriel Kahana *(VP)*

API INTERNATIONAL INC.
12505 SW Herman Rd, Tualatin, OR
97062-6950
Tel.: (503) 692-3800
Web Site: https://www.apiint.com
Sales Range: $10-24.9 Million
Emp.: 30
Whslr of Motor Vehicle Parts & Sup-plies
N.A.I.C.S.: 423120
M. Hasan Behbahany *(Pres)*
Cyrus Behbahany *(VP)*
Ross Tamini *(VP)*

API, INC.
27413 Tourney Rd Ste 200, Valencia,
CA 91355-5606
Tel.: (661) 702-0988
Web Site: http://www.apitire.com
Sales Range: $10-24.9 Million
Emp.: 25
Tires & Tubes
N.A.I.C.S.: 423120
Jeri Harp *(Controller)*

APIARY MEDICAL, INC.
12711 Big Bend Way, Valley Center,
CA 92082-6451
Web Site:
   http://www.apiarymedical.com
Medical, Dental & Hospital Equipment
& Supplies Merchant Whslr
N.A.I.C.S.: 423450
Christopher Hadsall *(CEO)*
Pamela Wiedenkeller *(Pres)*

Subsidiaries:

Manus Medical, LLC   (1)
3420 Pump Rd Ste 348, Richmond, VA
23233-1111
Web Site: http://www.manusmed.com
Surgical & Medical Instrument Mfr
N.A.I.C.S.: 339112
Bob Minnick *(Pres)*

APISCENT LABS, LLC

4170 S Nevada St, Saint Francis, WI
53235
Tel.: (414) 744-3993
Web Site: http://www.apiscent.com
Sales Range: $10-24.9 Million
Emp.: 50
Ingredients Mfr for Flavors, Fra-grances & Pharmaceuticals
N.A.I.C.S.: 325998
Tom Schaefer *(CFO)*
Patrick McComis *(Pres & Co-Owner)*
Lisa Mills *(Mgr-Customer Svc)*
Matt Cwiklinski *(Sr Mgr-Bus Dev)*
Joe Froehlich *(Co-Owner)*

APLJ CAPITAL MANAGEMENT LLC
1188 Royal Glen Dr Apt 321, Glen
Ellyn, IL 60137
Tel.: (630) 706-8222
Web Site:
   https://www.apljcapitalmanage.com
Investment Services
N.A.I.C.S.: 523999
Andri Teneqexhi *(Founder & Princi-pal)*

Subsidiaries:

Gregg Communications Systems,
Inc.   (1)
555 Waters Edge Ste 200, Lombard, IL
60148-7044
Tel.: (630) 706-8222
Web Site: http://www.greggcomm.com
Sales Range: $1-9.9 Million
Emp.: 15
Communications Solutions Services
N.A.I.C.S.: 541618
Andri Teneqexhi *(CEO)*
Dave LeTourneau *(CIO)*
Karen Drinkard *(COO)*
Janet Mackin *(Office Mgr)*
Wayne Helder *(Dir-Tech)*

APM, INC.
Ste 112 3610 American River Dr,
Sacramento, CA 95864-5999
Tel.: (707) 745-8060   CA
Year Founded: 1977
Sales Range: $10-24.9 Million
Emp.: 100
Mfr & Distributor of Wine & Food
Packaging Supplies
N.A.I.C.S.: 321999

APO HOLDINGS INC.
6607 Chittenden Rd, Hudson, OH
44236
Tel.: (216) 447-9190
Web Site:
   http://www.airpowerofohio.com
Year Founded: 1967
Sales Range: $10-24.9 Million
Emp.: 55
Whslr & Repairer of Air Compressors
& Pumps
N.A.I.C.S.: 423830
Ted Mailey *(Pres)*

APODACA WALL SYSTEMS, INC.
5740 W Buckeye Rd, Phoenix, AZ
85043
Tel.: (602) 269-7744
Web Site:
   https://www.apodacainc.com
Year Founded: 2002
Sales Range: $10-24.9 Million
Emp.: 50
Building Construction Services
N.A.I.C.S.: 236220
Arnold Apodaca *(Pres & CEO)*
Ernest Miera *(Office Mgr)*

APOGEE JETS
1111 Brickell Ave Ste 1100, Miami, FL
33131

Tel.: (305) 913-7120
Web Site: http://www.apogeejets.com
Year Founded: 2006
Sales Range: $1-9.9 Million
Emp.: 1
Aircraft Charter Services
N.A.I.C.S.: 481211
Kevin Parrott *(Pres & CEO)*

APOGEE RESULTS
11044 Research Blvd Ste A 500, Aus-tin, TX 78759
Tel.: (512) 381-7000   TX
Web Site:
   http://www.apogeeresults.com
Sales Range: $1-9.9 Million
Emp.: 20
Search Engine Optimization, Online
Media Planning & Buying
N.A.I.C.S.: 541810
William R. Leake *(Founder & CEO)*

APOLLO ACQUISITION COR-PORATION
800 E Colorado Blvd Ste 888, Pasa-dena, CA 91101
Tel.: (626) 683-9120   Ky
Year Founded: 2006
Investment Services
N.A.I.C.S.: 523999
Shuning Luo *(Sec)*
Wing Tak Jack Law *(Chm, Pres & CEO)*
Jun Yan *(CFO)*

APOLLO CASUALTY INSUR-ANCE CO.
1001 E Touhy Ave Ste 200, Des
Plaines, IL 60018-5800
Tel.: (847) 635-5600
Year Founded: 1995
Sales Range: $25-49.9 Million
Emp.: 54
Direct Property & Casualty Insurance
Services
N.A.I.C.S.: 524126
Bruce Arneson *(Pres)*
Deborah Tau *(VP-Claims)*
Karen Lockwood *(Dir-Mktg)*

APOLLO CHEMICAL CORP.
1105 Sutherland St, Graham, NC
27253-1757
Tel.: (336) 226-1161   NC
Web Site:
   http://www.apollochemical.com
Year Founded: 1968
Sales Range: $10-24.9 Million
Emp.: 74
Provider of Industrial Chemicals
N.A.I.C.S.: 325180
Ed Rish *(Pres & COO)*
Richard Barnhardt *(Dir-Technical)*
Richard Smith *(Mgr-Facility)*

APOLLO COLORS INC.
1401 Mound Rd, Rockdale, IL 60436-2859
Tel.: (815) 741-2588   IL
Web Site:
   https://www.apollocolors.com
Year Founded: 1969
Sales Range: $50-74.9 Million
Emp.: 100
Mfr of Organic Color Pigments
N.A.I.C.S.: 325130
Larry Bykerk *(VP-Sls)*
David Klebine *(Pres)*
Matt McClure *(VP & Dir-Tech)*
Bruce Wright *(VP-Mfg)*
Richard P. Milord *(Treas)*
Jim Daniels *(Mgr-Tech Sls)*

APOLLO DEBT SOLUTIONS BDC
9 W 57th St, New York, NY 10019

Tel.: (212) 515-3450   DE
Year Founded: 2020
Rev.: $252,301,000
Assets: $4,506,220,000
Liabilities: $2,351,287,000
Net Worth: $2,154,933,000
Earnings: $147,863,000
Fiscal Year-end: 12/31/22
Investment Management Service
N.A.I.C.S.: 523999
Eric Rosenberg *(CFO)*
Earl Hunt *(Chm & CEO)*
Adam Eling *(COO)*
Kristin Hester *(Chief Legal Officer)*
Meredith Coffey *(Trustee)*

APOLLO DISPLAY TECH-NOLOGIES CORP.
87 Raynor Ave, Ronkonkoma, NY
11779
Tel.: (631) 580-4360
Web Site: http://www.datadisplay-group.com
Year Founded: 1987
Emp.: 50
Electronic Parts & Equipment
N.A.I.C.S.: 423690
Joanne Sottile *(CFO & VP)*
Bernhard Staller *(Pres & CEO)*
Scott Makboulian *(VP-Sls & Tech)*

APOLLO ENTERPRISE SOLU-TIONS, LTD.
111 W Ocean Blvd Ste 1625, Long
Beach, CA 90802
Tel.: (949) 633-3381   BM
Web Site: http://www.aestrue.com
Year Founded: 2012
Sales Range: Less than $1 Million
Holding Company; Interactive Bank-ing Software Developer & Publisher
N.A.I.C.S.: 551112
Joseph Konowiecki *(Chm & CEO)*

Subsidiaries:

Apollo Enterprise Solutions, Inc.   (1)
111 W Ocean Blvd Ste 1625, Long Beach,
CA 90802
Tel.: (949) 633-3381
Web Site: http://www.aestrue.com
Sales Range: $1-9.9 Million
Emp.: 28
Computer & Computer Peripheral Equip-ment & Software Merchant Whslr
N.A.I.C.S.: 423430
Joseph Konowiecki *(Chm & CEO)*

APOLLO HAIR SYSTEMS INC
2255 NW Vivion Rd, Kansas City,
MO 64150
Tel.: (816) 741-5700
Web Site: http://www.apollonow.com
Sales Range: $10-24.9 Million
Emp.: 50
Hair Replacement
N.A.I.C.S.: 424990
Timothy Stansberry *(Exec VP)*

APOLLO INDUSTRIES INC.
1850 S Cobb Indus Blvd, Smyrna,
GA 30082
Tel.: (770) 433-0210
Web Site: http://www.apolloind.com
Year Founded: 1998
Sales Range: $25-49.9 Million
Emp.: 150
Mfr of Industrial Gases & Specialty
Chemicals
N.A.I.C.S.: 325612
Tracy Wadford *(Mgr-Info Svs)*
Ann-Marie Hahn *(Mgr-Pur)*
Michael Espinosa *(Mgr-Production
Scheduling & Plng)*
Ian Johnston *(Sr VP-Ops)*
Lydia Rivera *(Mgr-Laboratory)*

APOLLO INTERACTIVE, INC.

139 Illinois St, El Segundo, CA
90245-4312
Tel.: (310) 836-9777   CA
Web Site:
    http://www.apollointeractive.com
Year Founded: 1995
Emp.: 40
Advetising Agency
N.A.I.C.S.: 541810
Justin Woo (CEO)
David Bohline (COO)
Richard Balue (CTO)
Matthew J. Beshear (VP & Grp Acct Dir)
Coleman Engellennar (Dir-Adv)
Erik Brannon (Grp Dir-Acct)

Subsidiaries:

Apollo Interactive, Inc. - Dallas   (1)
Republic Ctr 325 N Saint Paul St Ste 1575,
Dallas, TX 75201
Tel.: (214) 580-2021
Web Site: http://apollointeractive.com
Emp.: 12
Advetising Agency
N.A.I.C.S.: 541810

APOLLO INTERNATIONAL FORWARDERS, INC.
2455 E Sunrise Blvd Ste 801, Fort
Lauderdale, FL 33304
Tel.: (954) 565-9801
Web Site: http://www.apollo-intl.com
Sales Range: $10-24.9 Million
Emp.: 6
Provider of Foreign Freight Forward-
ing Services
N.A.I.C.S.: 488510
Armando Gomez (Pres & Mng Dir)

APOLLO JETS LLC
220 W 42nd St, New York, NY 10036
Tel.: (212) 889-5387
Web Site: http://www.apollojets.com
Year Founded: 2008
Sales Range: $10-24.9 Million
Emp.: 30
Luxury Private Jet Charter Services
N.A.I.C.S.: 481211
Al Palagonia (Mng Dir)
Dean Giasi (Dir-Sls)
Aileen Diaz (Controller)
Steve Tabb (VP-Sls)

APOLLO MED INNOVATIONS LLC
6120 Powers Ferry Rd NW, Atlanta,
GA 30339
Tel.: (844) 698-4782   DE
Web Site:
    http://apollomedinnovations.com
Aesthetic Products Distr
N.A.I.C.S.: 456120
Randy Wright (CEO)

Subsidiaries:

Cosmedical Spa   (1)
401 Hwy 74 N, Peachtree City, GA 30269-
1169
Tel.: (770) 632-5500
Web Site: http://www.cosmedicalspaptc.com
Medical Spa & Beauty Salon
N.A.I.C.S.: 812112
Andrea Mobley (Mgr)
Julie Robbins (Dir-Ops)
Andrew Nobles (Mgr-Sls Ops)

APOLLO OIL LLC
1175 Early Dr, Winchester, KY
40391-3012
Tel.: (859) 744-5444   KY
Web Site: http://www.apollooil.com
Year Founded: 1970
Sales Range: $25-49.9 Million
Emp.: 140
Petroleum Products
N.A.I.C.S.: 424720
Phil Holley (Pres)

APOLLO PARTNERS LLC
500 5th Ave Ste 3520, New York, NY
10110
Tel.: (212) 840-9145
Sales Range: $50-74.9 Million
Emp.: 30
Investment Services
N.A.I.C.S.: 523999

APOLLO REALTY INCOME SO-LUTIONS, INC.
9 W 57th St 42nd Fl, New York, NY
10019
Tel.: (212) 515-3200   MD
Web Site: https://www.apollo.com
Year Founded: 2021
Rev.: $6,912,000
Assets: $609,671,000
Liabilities: $66,795,000
Net Worth: $542,876,000
Earnings: $12,759,000
Fiscal Year-end: 12/31/23
Investment Management Service
N.A.I.C.S.: 523999

APOLLO SHEET METAL INC.
1207 W Columbia Dr, Kennewick,
WA 99336
Tel.: (509) 586-1104
Web Site:
    http://www.apollomech.com
Year Founded: 1981
Sales Range: $25-49.9 Million
Emp.: 300
Mechanical Contractor
N.A.I.C.S.: 238220
Bruce W. Ratchford (Pres & CEO)
Dan Briscoe (VP-Bus Dev)
Bob Hightower (Pres)

APOLLO SUNGUARD SYS-TEMS, INC.
4487 A Ashton Rd, Sarasota, FL
34233
Tel.: (941) 925-3000
Web Site:
    https://www.apollosunguard.com
Year Founded: 2001
Sales Range: $1-9.9 Million
Emp.: 15
Shade Mfr
N.A.I.C.S.: 337920
Kevin Connelly (Pres)
Ernesto de Oliveira (Dir-Engrg & Product Design)

APOLLO WOOD RECOVERY INC.
14253 Whittram Ave, Fontana, CA
92335
Tel.: (909) 356-2735
Web Site:
    http://www.apollowood.com
Sales Range: $10-24.9 Million
Emp.: 12
Wood Recycling Services
N.A.I.C.S.: 562920
Pat Heaney (CEO & CFO)

APOLLO, INC.
1133 W Columbia Dr, Kennewick, WA
99338
Tel.: (509) 586-1104
Web Site: https://www.apollo-gc.com
Year Founded: 1982
Sales Range: $25-49.9 Million
Emp.: 250
Nonresidential Construction Services
N.A.I.C.S.: 236220
Dan Bruscoe (VP)
Alex van Hoek (Partner)

APOLLOMD, INC.
5665 New Northside Dr Ste 200, Atlanta, GA 30328
Tel.: (770) 874-5400

Web Site: https://www.apollomd.com
Sales Range: $250-299.9 Million
Emp.: 998
Multispecialty Physician Services
N.A.I.C.S.: 622110
Christopher Krubert (CEO)
Michael Dolister (Pres)
Bobby Ryan (Chief Growth Officer)
Amy Katnik (COO)
Wendy Parker (VP-Hospital Transi-tions)
Jackie Newman (Sr VP-Ops)
John Friedel (Sr VP-Radiology)
Lindsay Carmichael (VP-Ops & Anes-thesia Svcs)
Ginni Viscardi (VP-Radiology)

APP INCLINE CORPORATION
1510 Longbranch Ave, Grover Beach,
CA 93433
Tel.: (805) 704-9310   NV
Web Site: http://www.appincline.com
Year Founded: 2015
Sales Range: Less than $1 Million
Mobile Application Publishing Ser-
vices
N.A.I.C.S.: 513210
Adam Elmquist (Chm, Pres, CEO,
CFO, Treas & Sec)

APPALACHIAN CAST PROD-UCTS, INC.
26372 Hillman Hwy, Abingdon, VA
24210
Tel.: (276) 619-5080
Web Site:
    https://www.appalachiancast.com
Year Founded: 1999
Sales Range: $10-24.9 Million
Emp.: 138
Aluminum Die-Casting Services
N.A.I.C.S.: 331524
Greg Willis (Mgr-Sls)
Richard Cocilova (VP-Ops)
Steve Canonico (Mgr-Engrg)

APPALACHIAN EMERGENCY PHYSICIANS
1019 W Oakland Ave Ste 207, John-
son City, TN 37604
Tel.: (804) 967-9604   VA
Year Founded: 2010
Sales Range: $25-49.9 Million
Physician Association
N.A.I.C.S.: 813920
C. Steven Kilgore (Pres)
Candace Jennings (Sec)

APPALACHIAN LOG STRUC-TURES
234 Fair Oaks Way, Ripley, WV
25271
Tel.: (304) 372-6410
Web Site: https://www.applog.com
Rev.: $10,000,000
Emp.: 25
Prefabricated Log Home Mfr
N.A.I.C.S.: 321992
Douglas Parsons (Pres)
Anthony Nichols (Mgr-Info Sys)
Dorie Workman (VP-Adv & Mktg)
Mark Feder (VP-Sls)

APPALACHIAN REGIONAL HEALTHCARE, INC.
80 Hospital Dr, Barbourville, KY
40906
Tel.: (606) 546-4175   KY
Web Site: https://www.arh.org
Year Founded: 1956
Emp.: 5,000
Medical Health Network
N.A.I.C.S.: 622110

Joe Grossman (Pres & CEO)
Thomas Hyatt (Chm)
Greg Pauley (Vice Chm)
Duanne Thompson (Treas & Sec)

APPALACHIAN TIRE PROD-UCTS INC.
2907 4th Ave, Charleston, WV 25387
Tel.: (304) 744-9473
Web Site: http://www.apptire.com
Year Founded: 1947
Sales Range: $25-49.9 Million
Emp.: 250
Provider of Tires & Tubes
N.A.I.C.S.: 423130
Walter B. Dial Jr. (Chm)

Subsidiaries:

Glenn Roberts Tire & Recapping Co.
Inc.   (1)
2907 4th Ave, Charleston, WV 25312-1721
Tel.: (304) 744-9474
Sales Range: $10-24.9 Million
Emp.: 2
Provider of Tires & Tubes
N.A.I.C.S.: 423130

Mountain Mining & Supply Company
Inc.   (1)
2907 Fourth Ave, Charleston, WV 25312-
1721
Tel.: (304) 744-9474
Sales Range: $10-24.9 Million
Emp.: 4
Provider of Tires & Tubes
N.A.I.C.S.: 423130
Greg Stover (Mgr-Sls & Mktg)

APPALACHIAN UNDERWRIT-ERS, INC.
800 Oak Ridge Tpke Ste A 1000,
Oak Ridge, TN 37830
Tel.: (865) 457-0981
Web Site: http://www.appund.com
Sales Range: $25-49.9 Million
Emp.: 30
Insurance Services
N.A.I.C.S.: 524210
Robert J. Arowood (Principal)
Eric Dail (VP-West)
Rhonda Henze (Dir-Comml Specialty)
William Chambers (Dir-Digital Part-
nerships)

Subsidiaries:

Appalachian Underwriters, Inc. - Oak
Ridge   (1)
800 Oakridge Tpke Ste A1000, Oak Ridge,
TN 37830
Tel.: (888) 376-9633
Web Site: http://www.appund.com
Insurance Services
N.A.I.C.S.: 524210

APPAREL RESOURCES INC.
110 W 40th 18th Fl, New York, NY
10018
Tel.: (212) 764-2484
Web Site: http://www.yansifugel.com
Sales Range: $10-24.9 Million
Emp.: 26
Mfr of Womens Clothing
N.A.I.C.S.: 315250
Yansi Molamusa Fugel (Pres)
Claudia Kyteser (Mgr-Sls)

APPARELWAY, INC.
2007 Lee Ave S, El Monte, CA
91733-2505
Tel.: (626) 448-6888
Sales Range: $50-74.9 Million
Emp.: 15
Apparels Mfr
N.A.I.C.S.: 315250
Don X. Ho (Pres)

APPAREO SYSTEMS, LLC

Appareo Systems, LLC—(Continued)

1810 NDSU Research Cir N, Fargo, ND 58102
Tel.: (701) 356-2200
Web Site: https://www.appareo.com
Year Founded: 2003
Sales Range: $1-9.9 Million
Emp.: 190
Designs & Manufactures Electronic, Mechanical & Software Products for Aerospace, Defense & Transportation Applications
N.A.I.C.S.: 513210
Barry D. Batcheller (Pres & CEO)
Bob Allen (Mgr-Hardware Engrg)
Robert Weinmann (Dir-Engrg)
Bruce Wheeler (Dir-Mfg)
Elliot Kirschmann (Engr-Electronics Design)
Casey Delanghe (Mgr-Sls)
Travis Wiertzema (Engr-Software)

APPDIRECT INC.
650 California St 25th Fl, San Francisco, CA 94108
Tel.: (415) 852-3919
Web Site: https://www.appdirect.com
Year Founded: 2009
Emp.: 150
Cloud Marketplace Software & Solutions
N.A.I.C.S.: 513210
Nicolas Desmarais (Chm & Co-CEO)
Daniel Saks (Pres & & Co-CEO)
Andy Sen (CTO)
Mark Liu (Gen Counsel)

Subsidiaries:

Enterprise jBilling Software Ltd.   (1)
343 Preston St Ste 330, Ottawa, K1S 1N4, ON, Canada
Tel.: (866) 920-4348
Web Site: http://www.jbilling.com
Billing Software Developer
N.A.I.C.S.: 513210
Emiliano Conde (Pres)

Wmode Inc.   (1)
3553 31 Street NW, Calgary, T2L 2K7, AB, Canada
Tel.: (403) 260-8690
Web Site: http://www.wmode.com
Sales Range: $10-24.9 Million
Emp.: 70
Digital Media Distribution Solutions
N.A.I.C.S.: 513210
Emanuel Bertolin (CEO)

Subsidiary (Domestic):

NeoSystems Inc.   (2)
603 7th Ave SW Ste 550, Calgary, T2P 2T5, AB, Canada
Tel.: (403) 225-9020
Software Development Services
N.A.I.C.S.: 541511
Richard Link (Mgr-Client Relationship)

World Telecom Group   (1)
22619 Pacific Coast Hwy Ste A310, Malibu, CA 90265
Tel.: (310) 456-2200
Web Site:
   http://www.worldtelecomgroup.com
Sales Range: $1-9.9 Million
Emp.: 15
Telecom Brokerage Services
N.A.I.C.S.: 517121
Vince Bradley (Pres & CEO)
Jeremy Hopkins (CFO & CIO)
Susan Penevolpe (VP-Sls)
Julie Dzubay (VP-Sls)
William Lombardo (Sr Mgr-Channel-East)

APPERSON PRINT RESOURCES, INC.
13910 Cerritos Corporate Dr, Cerritos, CA 90703-2457
Tel.: (562) 356-3333   CA
Web Site:
http://www.appersonprint.com

Year Founded: 1955
Sales Range: $10-24.9 Million
Emp.: 150
Business Form Mfr
N.A.I.C.S.: 323111
Kelly Doherty (Pres & CEO)
Carey Thompson (VP-Fin)
Robert P. Apperson (Owner & Chm)

Subsidiaries:

Apperson Print Resources, Inc. - Apperson Education Products
Division   (1)
851 SW 34th St Bldg B, Renton, WA 98057
Tel.: (425) 251-1850
Web Site: http://www.apperson.com
Sales Range: $10-24.9 Million
Emp.: 35
Commercial Printing Services
N.A.I.C.S.: 323111
Bill Apperson (CEO)

APPLE AMERICAN GROUP LLC
6200 Oak Tree Blvd Ste 250, Independence, OH 44131   DE
Tel.: (216) 525-2775
Web Site:
   http://www.appleamerican.com
Year Founded: 1998
Sales Range: $800-899.9 Million
Emp.: 20,000
Holding Company; Franchise Bar-Restaurants Owner & Operator
N.A.I.C.S.: 551112
Lorin Cortina (CFO & Exec VP)
Brad Pettinger (COO)
Dan Krebsbach (VP-Ops & Pres-Washington & New England Markets)
Gary Koch (Pres-New Jersey/Delaware Market)
Keith Morrow (Pres-Indiana Market)
Mike Hebert (Pres-Southern California & Southern Nevada Markets)
Ron Bellamy (Chief Improvement Officer)
Ron Igarashi (VP-Fin)
Kasey Mania (VP-Procurement)
Betsy Mercado (VP-HR)

APPLE BANK FOR SAVINGS
1395 Northern Blvd, Manhasset, NY 11030
Tel.: (914) 902-2775
Web Site: http://www.applebank.com
Year Founded: 1863
Rev.: $340,728,000
Assets: $14,307,238,000
Liabilities: $13,111,395,000
Net Worth: $1,195,843,000
Earnings: $100,901,000
Emp.: 785
Fiscal Year-end: 12/31/18
Full Service Banking Provider
N.A.I.C.S.: 522180
Robin Thomson (Exec VP)
Steven C. Bush (Chm, Pres & CEO)
Lee Swedowsky (First VP)
Howard Hsu (Sr VP)
Susan Kay (VP)
Jay Rosen (VP)
Soo Ho Choi (Asst VP)

APPLE BUS COMPANY
PO Box 155, Cleveland, MO 64734
Tel.: (816) 618-3310
Web Site:
   http://www.applebuscompany.com
Year Founded: 2001
Sales Range: $25-49.9 Million
Emp.: 850
Full Service Transportation
N.A.I.C.S.: 485410
Michael Oyster (Owner)
Reid Oyster (VP)
Mindy Johnson (CFO)

APPLE CHEVROLET INCORPORATED
1200 Loucks Rd, York, PA 17404
Tel.: (717) 848-1300
Web Site:
   http://www.applechevrolet.com
Rev.: $71,300,000
Emp.: 150
Automobiles, New & Used
N.A.I.C.S.: 441110
Steve Ball (Gen Mgr)

APPLE CORE ENTERPRISES INC.
PO Box 969, Minot, ND 58702
Tel.: (701) 838-2822
Sales Range: $10-24.9 Million
Emp.: 2,000
Restaurant Operators
N.A.I.C.S.: 722511
Myron D. Thompson (Pres)
Bret Ruff (VP-People)

APPLE CREEK BANC CORP.
3 W Main, St, Apple Creek, OH 44606
Tel.: (330) 698-2631   OH
Web Site:
   https://www.applecreekbank.com
Year Founded: 1904
Sales Range: $25-49.9 Million
Emp.: 50
Bank Holding Company
N.A.I.C.S.: 551111
Leo J. Miller (Pres & CEO)
Jeff Smith (Chief Lending Officer)
Mike Force (Officer-Comml Loan)
Theresa Taylor (Officer-Comml Loan)
Connie Hartzler (Officer-Retail Banking)

Subsidiaries:

The Apple Creek Banking
Company   (1)
3 W Main Apple Creek, Apple Creek, OH 44606
Tel.: (330) 698-2631
Web Site: http://www.applecreekbank.com
Commercial Banking Services
N.A.I.C.S.: 522110

APPLE FARM SERVICE INC.
10120 W Versailles Rd, Covington, OH 45318
Tel.: (937) 526-4851
Web Site:
   https://www.applefarmservice.com
Sales Range: $10-24.9 Million
Emp.: 50
Provider of Agricultural Machinery
N.A.I.C.S.: 423820
William Apple (Pres & CEO)
Doug Shoenleben (Mgr-Parts)
Jeff Tomlinbuckeyes I (Mgr-West College Corner)

APPLE FORD
3250 Cape Horn Rd, Red Lion, PA 17356
Tel.: (717) 244-7677
Web Site: http://www.apple-ford.com
Sales Range: $10-24.9 Million
Emp.: 90
New Car Retailer
N.A.I.C.S.: 441110
Craig Lilliedahl (Coord-Internet)
Damien Fortson (Mgr-New Car)
Brandon Butler (Mgr-Parts)
Rob Dell (Gen Mgr)
Mike Elliott (Mgr-Production-Collision Center)
Steve Martin (Mgr-Collision Center)
Travis Motley (Mgr-Sls)
Jake Nelson (Mgr-Bus)
Scott Rudisill (Mgr-Svc)
Herb Uffleman (Mgr-Fleet)
Andy Nyeste (Dir-Internet)

Mike Colen (Mgr-Bus)
Ted Grothe (Mgr-Fleet)
Tom Godfrey (Mgr-Used Car)

APPLE FORD INC.
8800 Stanford Blvd, Columbia, MD 21045
Tel.: (410) 290-1100
Web Site: https://www.appleford.net
Rev.: $61,000,000
Emp.: 200
Automobiles, New & Used
N.A.I.C.S.: 441110
George L. Doetsch (Co-Owner & Co-Pres)
Chip Doetsch (Co-Owner & Co-Pres)

APPLE GROWTH PARTNERS
1540 W Market St, Akron, OH 44313-7114
Tel.: (330) 867-7350
Web Site:
   http://www.applegrowth.com
Year Founded: 1943
Offices of Certified Public Accountants
N.A.I.C.S.: 541211
Erin McCafferty (Dir-Ops)
Jeff Stinson (Dir-Strategic Core Svcs)
Chuck Mullen (Chm)
Dirk Ahlbeck (Principal-Tax)
Erica Ishida (Pres)

APPLE HEALTH CARE INC.
21 Waterville Rd, Avon, CT 06001-2039
Tel.: (860) 678-9755   CT
Web Site: http://www.apple-rehab.com
Year Founded: 1983
Sales Range: $10-24.9 Million
Emp.: 46
Provider of Nursing Care Services
N.A.I.C.S.: 623110
Brian J. Foley (Pres)

APPLE LEISURE GROUP
7 Campus Blvd, Newtown Square, PA 19073
Tel.: (610) 359-6500
Web Site:
   http://www.appleleisuregroup.com
Year Founded: 1969
Holding Company; Travel Agencies
N.A.I.C.S.: 551112
Alejandro Zozaya Gorostiza (Chm)
Javier Coll (Chief Strategy Officer & Exec VP)
Cory Shade (Chief Legal Officer)
Inaki Cebollero (Chief People Officer)

Subsidiaries:

Apple Vacations, LLC   (1)
7 Campus Blvd, Newtown Square, PA 19073
Tel.: (610) 359-6500
Web Site: http://www.applevacations.com
Wholesale Vacation Services
N.A.I.C.S.: 561510
Timothy Mullen (Pres)
Peter Bowler (Pres-Distr Grp)
Scott Quigley (VP-Global Call Center)
Bob Thye (Sr VP-Revenue Mgmt)
Cory Klatt (CIO)

CheapCaribbean.com, Inc.   (1)
2003 S Easton Rd Ste 100, Doylestown, PA 18901
Tel.: (215) 348-8775
Web Site: http://www.cheapcaribbean.com
Sales Range: $500-549.9 Million
Online Travel Services
N.A.I.C.S.: 561599
Steve Dumaine (Pres)

Funjet Vacations Inc.   (1)
8907 N Port Washington Rd, Milwaukee, WI 53217
Tel.: (414) 351-3553
Web Site: http://www.funjet.com

Travel & Tourism Services
N.A.I.C.S.: 561599

Subsidiary (Domestic):

Trans National Group Services,
LLC　　　　　　　　　　　　　(2)
2 Charlesgate W, Boston, MA 02215
Tel.: (617) 262-9200
Travel Agency
N.A.I.C.S.: 561520

Subsidiary (Domestic):

TN Marketing, LLC　　　　　　(3)
1903 Wayzata Boulevard East, Wayzata,
MN 55391
Tel.: (763) 577-1200
Web Site: http://www.tnmarketing.com
Sales Range: $1-9.9 Million
Emp.: 47
Mail-Order Houses
N.A.I.C.S.: 455219
Steve Belkin (Principal)
Cal Franklin (Pres & CEO)

Subsidiary (Domestic):

Sympoz, LLC　　　　　　　　　(4)
2150 W 29th Ave, Denver, CO 80211
Tel.: (415) 867-8617
Web Site: http://www.sympoz.com
Online Educational & Information Services
N.A.I.C.S.: 519290

Travel Impressions, Ltd.　　　(1)
465 Smith St Ste A, Farmingdale, NY
11735-1106　　　　　　　　(100%)
Tel.: (631) 845-8000
Web Site: http://www.travimp.com
Sales Range: $75-99.9 Million
Emp.: 500
Travel Services & Tour Operators
N.A.I.C.S.: 561520
Marcelle DiPasca (Mgr-Airline & Car Rental
Rels)
Erin McCarthy (VP-Mktg)
Greg Bernd (VP-Sls)
Scott Wiseman (Pres)

APPLE METRO INC.
550 Mamaroneck Ave Ste 204, Harri-
son, NY 10528
Tel.: (914) 777-2331
Web Site:
　https://www.applerestaurants.com
Sales Range: $50-74.9 Million
Emp.: 5,500
Restaurant Operators
N.A.I.C.S.: 722511
Roy Raeburn (Pres)
Frank Venice (CFO & Exec VP)
Zane Tankel (Chm & CEO)
K. Feldman (VP-Mktg)

APPLE ONE SERVICE ARI-
ZONA INC.
327 W Broadway, Glendale, CA
91204
Tel.: (818) 240-8688
Web Site: http://www.appleone.com
Sales Range: $10-24.9 Million
Emp.: 20
Employment Agencies
N.A.I.C.S.: 561311
Bernard Howroyd (Pres)

APPLE ROCK
7602 Business Park Dr, Greensboro,
NC 27409
Tel.: (336) 232-4800　　　　　NC
Web Site: https://www.applerock.com
Year Founded: 1988
Sales Range: $10-24.9 Million
Emp.: 60
Advetising Agency
N.A.I.C.S.: 541810
Eric Burg (CEO)
Randy Neese (Dir-Fin)
Allison O'Neal (Sr Dir-Global Sls)

APPLE RUBBER PRODUCTS
INC.
310 Erie St, Lancaster, NY 14086-
9504
Tel.: (716) 684-6560
Web Site:
　https://www.applerubber.com
Sales Range: $10-24.9 Million
Emp.: 130
Hard Rubber & Molded Rubber Prod-
ucts
N.A.I.C.S.: 326299
Steven L. Apple (Pres)

APPLE SAUCE, INC.
741 Centre View Blvd, Crestview
Hills, KY 41017
Tel.: (859) 331-3900
Web Site:
　http://www.applesauceinc.com
Sales Range: $75-99.9 Million
Restaurant Franchise Owner & Op-
erator
N.A.I.C.S.: 722511
W. Curtis Smith (Pres)
Jerry Kreger (CFO & VP)
Rod Ward (Mgr-Pur)
Russ Hoffecker (Controller)
George Werden (Gen Counsel)
Ron Long (VP)

APPLE SEEDS
10 W 25th St, New York, NY 10010
Tel.: (212) 792-7590
Web Site:
　https://www.appleseedsplay.com
Year Founded: 2007
Sales Range: $1-9.9 Million
Emp.: 70
Operates Indoor Playgrounds
N.A.I.C.S.: 713990
Allison Schlanger (Co-Founder)
Alison Qualter Berna (Co-Founder)
Robert Berna (Co-Founder)
Craig Schlanger (Co-Founder)

APPLE SUITES REALTY
GROUP, INC.
814 E Main St, Richmond, VA 23219
Tel.: (804) 344-8121　　　　　VA
Web Site:
　http://www.applereitcompanies.com
Sales Range: $1-4.9 Billion
Emp.: 49
Hotel Real Estate Investment Trust
Management & Properties Broker
N.A.I.C.S.: 531390
Bryan F. Peery (CFO & Exec VP)
Glade M. Knight (Chm)
Justin G. Knight (Pres-REITs)
Kristian M. Gathright (COO & Exec
VP)
David McKenney (Pres-Capital
Markets-REITs)
David Buckley (Exec VP & Chief Le-
gal Counsel)

Subsidiaries:

Apple Hospitality REIT, Inc.　　(1)
814 E Main St, Richmond, VA 23219
Tel.: (804) 344-8121
Web Site:
　https://www.applehospitalityreit.com
Rev.: $1,343,800,000
Assets: $4,937,298,000
Liabilities: $1,613,317,000
Net Worth: $3,323,981,000
Earnings: $177,489,000
Emp.: 63
Fiscal Year-end: 12/31/2023
Real Estate Investment Trust
N.A.I.C.S.: 525990
Glade M. Knight (Founder)
Justin G. Knight (CEO)
Nelson G. Knight (Pres-Real Estate & In-
vestments)
Jeanette A. Clarke (Chief Capital Invest-
ments Officer & Sr VP)
Kelly Clarke (VP-IR)
Matthew Rash (Chief Legal Officer, Sec &
Sr VP)

Rachel S. Labrecque (Chief Acctg Officer)
Karen C. Gallagher (COO)
Elizabeth S. Perkins (CFO)

APPLE TREE HONDA
195 Underwood Rd, Fletcher, NC
28732
Tel.: (828) 684-4400
Web Site:
　https://www.appletreeautos.com
Year Founded: 1970
Sales Range: $1-4.9 Billion
Emp.: 119
Car Whslr
N.A.I.C.S.: 441110
Jason Locke (Gen Mgr-Sls)

APPLEBY & STERLING, INC.
2290 Agate Ct Ste D, Simi Valley, CA
93065-1935
Tel.: (805) 583-9828
Web Site:
　http://www.applebyandsterling.com
Year Founded: 1983
Insurance Agencies & Brokerages
N.A.I.C.S.: 524210
Mike Maurer (Pres)

APPLEGATE MEDIA GROUP
405 Lexington Ave 26th Fl, New York,
NY 10174
Tel.: (203) 261-5248
Web Site:
　http://www.applegatemedia.com
Year Founded: 1991
Sales Range: $10-24.9 Million
Emp.: 17
N.A.I.C.S.: 541830
Susan Y. Applegate (Chief Executive
Officer-Chief Strategist)
Melisa Cehajic (VP & Dir-Media)
Jeannie Cahill (Sr VP & Grp Dir-
Media)

APPLEGATE, INC
485 E South St, Jackson, MI 49203
Tel.: (517) 783-2646
Year Founded: 1959
Sales Range: $25-49.9 Million
Emp.: 250
Heating & Air Conditioning Services
N.A.I.C.S.: 238220
Gary Applegate (Pres)
Eric Holmes (Project Mgr)
Samuel Vansickle (Project Mgr)

APPLEJAM INC.
8905 Lake Ave Fl 1, Cleveland, OH
44102-6319
Tel.: (770) 923-6001
Sales Range: $25-49.9 Million
Emp.: 1,500
Restaurant Operators
N.A.I.C.S.: 722513
Frank S. DeAngelo (Pres)

Subsidiaries:

Applejam of GA Inc.　　　　　(1)
8905 Lake Ave Fl 1, Cleveland, OH 44102-
6319
Tel.: (770) 923-6001
Sales Range: $10-24.9 Million
Emp.: 12
Restaurant Operators
N.A.I.C.S.: 722513

Applejam of TX Inc.　　　　　(1)
8905 Lake Ave Fl 1, Cleveland, OH 44102-
6319
Tel.: (770) 923-6001
Sales Range: $75-99.9 Million
Emp.: 1,100
Restaurant Operators
N.A.I.C.S.: 722511

APPLEPIE CAPITAL, INC.
235 Pine St Fl 13, San Francisco, CA
94104

Tel.: (800) 720-0241　　　　　DE
Web Site:
　http://www.applepiecapital.com
Year Founded: 2014
Online Financial Lender
N.A.I.C.S.: 523999
Denis Thomas (Founder & CEO)
Geoff Thompson (Gen Counsel)
Ron Feldman (Chief Dev Officer)
Natasha Lala (COO)
Randy Jones (Head-Originations)
John Neff (CMO)

APPLETON LEARNING COR-
PORATION
200 Clinton Ave Ste 1000, Huntsville,
AL 35801
Tel.: (256) 325-2616
Web Site:
　http://www.appletonlearning.com
Year Founded: 2004
Sales Range: $1-9.9 Million
Emp.: 20
Academic Coaching, Test Preparation
& Academic Assessments for All Stu-
dents
N.A.I.C.S.: 923110
Glenn Clayton (Founder, Pres &
CEO)
Philip Kovacs (Dir-Education)
Lindsay Phillips (Mgr-School Pro-
gram)
Sonia Robinson (VP)

APPLETREE ANSWERING
SERVICES, INC.
1521 Concord Pike Ste 202, Wilming-
ton, DE 19803
Tel.: (302) 656-0630
Web Site:
　http://www.appletreeanswers.com
Sales Range: $1-9.9 Million
Emp.: 100
Telephone Answering Services
N.A.I.C.S.: 561421
John H. Ratliff (Founder, Pres &
CEO)
Jane Tshudy (Mgr-Customer Svc)

APPLETREE MARKETS
7676 Hillmont St Ste 204, Houston,
TX 77040-6469
Tel.: (713) 895-5223　　　　　DE
Year Founded: 1986
Sales Range: $125-149.9 Million
Emp.: 250
Operator of Grocery Stores
N.A.I.C.S.: 445110
R.T. Kubicek (Pres & CEO)
Denise Bennett (Controller)

APPLIANCE FACTORY OUT-
LET & MATTRESSES, INC.
6005 E Evans Ave, Denver, CO
80222
Tel.: (303) 759-5555
Web Site:
　http://www.appliancefactory.com
Year Founded: 1986
Sales Range: $25-49.9 Million
Emp.: 45
Household Appliance Stores
N.A.I.C.S.: 449210
Cleat Crocker (Dir-Mktg)
Charles Ewing (Pres & Co-CEO)

APPLIANCE PARTS DEPOT
INC.
4754 Almond Ave, Dallas, TX 75247
Tel.: (214) 631-4298
Web Site: http://www.apdepot.com
Year Founded: 1957
Rev.: $12,000,000
Emp.: 140
Appliance Parts Distr

Appliance Parts Depot Inc.—(Continued)
N.A.I.C.S.: 423620
Bill W. Parker *(Founder & Pres)*

APPLIANCE WAREHOUSE OF EXETER

6 Smiths Ln Rte 1 Traffic Cir, Seabrook, NH 03874
Tel.: (603) 474-8333
Web Site:
  https://www.appliancewarehouse.net
Rev.: $10,000,000
Emp.: 10
Electric Household Appliances, Major
N.A.I.C.S.: 449210
Je Tres *(Pres)*

APPLICATION CONSULTING GROUP

1639 State Rte 10 Ste 107, Parsippany, NJ 07054
Tel.: (973) 898-0012
Web Site: https://www.acgi.com
Sales Range: $25-49.9 Million
Emp.: 25
Custom Computer Programming Services
N.A.I.C.S.: 541690
Peter Edwards *(Pres)*
Margaret Langley *(Mgr-Fin & Admin)*
Rob Haraj *(Dir-Sls & Mktg)*

APPLICATION CONSULTING TRAINING SOLUTIONS INC.

100 N Laura St Ste 700, Jacksonville, FL 32202
Tel.: (904) 317-2140
Web Site: http://www.actsolution.net
Year Founded: 2002
Sales Range: $1-9.9 Million
Emp.: 15
Technical Support Services
N.A.I.C.S.: 541990
James Farhat *(CEO)*
Naro Sreeram *(Dir-IT Svcs)*

APPLICATION DEVELOPMENT CONSULTANTS, LLC

6011 Benjamin Rd Ste 107, Tampa, FL 33634
Tel.: (813) 849-1818
Web Site: https://upshop.com
Year Founded: 1994
Sales Range: $1-9.9 Million
Emp.: 25
Custom Computer Programming Services
N.A.I.C.S.: 541511
Shamus Hines *(CEO)*

Subsidiaries:

Itasca Retail Information Systems, Inc.   (1)
140 S 68th St Ste 1103, West Des Moines, IA 50266
Tel.: (515) 223-0045
Web Site: http://www.itasca-retail.com
Sales Range: $1-9.9 Million
Software Development Services
N.A.I.C.S.: 541511
Jeff Kennedy *(Co-Founder & Pres)*
Mike Miller *(Co-Founder & CTO)*

APPLICATION DEVELOPMENT RESOURCES, INC.

3015 Windward Plz Ste 120, Alpharetta, GA 30005
Tel.: (770) 772-0347
Web Site:
  https://www.appdevinc.com
Year Founded: 2001
Sales Range: $10-24.9 Million
Emp.: 75
Custom Computer Programming Services
N.A.I.C.S.: 541511

Daksha Choksey *(Pres)*
Adil Choksey *(CEO)*

APPLICATIONS SOFTWARE TECHNOLOGY LLC

4343 Commerce Ct Ste 701, Lisle, IL 60532
Tel.: (630) 778-1180
Web Site:
  http://www.astcorporation.com
Year Founded: 1995
Sales Range: $25-49.9 Million
Emp.: 175
Application Software Development Services
N.A.I.C.S.: 541511
Pankaj Mundra *(VP)*
Patrick Callahan *(VP-BI-EPM)*
Prasad Nettem *(VP-ERP)*
Justin Winter *(CEO)*

Subsidiaries:

Computer Technology Resources, Inc.   (1)
16 Technology Dr Ste 210, Irvine, CA 92618-2329
Tel.: (714) 665-6507
Web Site: http://www.ctrworld.com
Data Processing, Hosting & Related Services
N.A.I.C.S.: 518210

APPLICATOR SALES & SERVICE

400 Warren Ave, Portland, ME 04103
Tel.: (207) 797-7950
Web Site:
  http://www.applicatorssales.com
Year Founded: 1997
Sales Range: $25-49.9 Million
Emp.: 15
Whslr of Siding Materials
N.A.I.C.S.: 423330
Scott D. Koocher *(Pres)*
Gary Koocher *(Controller)*

APPLIED AVIONICS, INC.

3201 Sandy Ln, Fort Worth, TX 76112
Tel.: (817) 451-1141
Web Site:
  http://www.vivisunavionics.com
Year Founded: 1968
Sales Range: $1-9.9 Million
Emp.: 59
Aircraft Switches & Indicators Mfr
N.A.I.C.S.: 336413
Loren Jensen *(Pres & CEO)*
Matt Hawkins *(VP & CFO)*

Subsidiaries:

SELECTaero   (1)
PO Box 186, Evesham, WR11 1WW, United Kingdom
Tel.: (44) 1386 442836
Web Site: http://www.selectaero.com
Lighted Switches, Rugged LCD Modules, Back Lights & Illuminated Switch Panels
Aerospace Mfr
N.A.I.C.S.: 336413

APPLIED CARD HOLDINGS INC.

50 Applied Card Bank Blvd, Glen Mills, PA 19342
Tel.: (484) 840-1700
Web Site:
  http://www.cardcenter.bank.com
Sales Range: $50-74.9 Million
Emp.: 300
Financial Transactions Processing, Reserve & Clearinghouse Activities
N.A.I.C.S.: 522320
Walter Sockoloskie *(VP-Fin)*
Rocco A. Abessinio *(Chm & Pres)*

APPLIED CARD SYSTEMS INC.

5401 Broken Sound Blvd NW, Boca Raton, FL 33487
Tel.: (561) 995-8820
Web Site:
  https://www.appliedcard.com
Year Founded: 1987
Sales Range: $50-74.9 Million
Emp.: 250
Credit Card Processing
N.A.I.C.S.: 522320
Rocco Abessinio *(CEO)*
Isaac Silverman *(Mgr-Dialer Ops)*

APPLIED CONTROL ENGINEERING, INC.

700 Creek View Rd, Newark, DE 19711
Tel.: (302) 738-8800
Web Site: https://www.ace-net.com
Year Founded: 1991
Rev.: $15,600,000
Emp.: 105
Computer Programming Services
N.A.I.C.S.: 541511
Gary A. Hida *(VP)*
Dean B. DeGrazia *(Mgr-Ops)*

APPLIED DYNAMICS INTERNATIONAL

3800 Stone School Rd, Ann Arbor, MI 48108-2414
Tel.: (734) 973-1300
Web Site: https://www.adi.com
Year Founded: 1957
Sales Range: $10-24.9 Million
Emp.: 53
Electronic Computers
N.A.I.C.S.: 334111
Dave Hickman *(Treas & VP-Fin)*
Scott Klamerus *(Dir-Software Engrg)*
Clare Savaglio *(Mgr-Applications Engrg)*
Bryan Ellinger *(Product Mgr)*

Subsidiaries:

Applied Dynamics International, Ltd.   (1)
1450 Montagu Ct, Kettering Venture Pk, Kettering, NN15 6XR, United Kingdom   (100%)
Tel.: (44) 536410077
Web Site: http://www.adi.com
Sales Range: $10-24.9 Million
Emp.: 7
Electronic Computers
N.A.I.C.S.: 334111

APPLIED ENERGY SOLUTIONS

1 Technology Pl, Caledonia, NY 14423-1246
Tel.: (800) 836-2132
Web Site:
  http://www.appliedenergysol.com
Year Founded: 1949
Electronic Components & Battery Chargers Mfr
N.A.I.C.S.: 335999
Vern P. Fleming *(Pres & CEO)*
Ken Selbig *(VP-Technical, Svc & Quality)*
Brandy Selover *(Coord-Svc & Warranty)*
Randy Dickes *(Coord-Installation)*

APPLIED FIBER MANUFACTURING, LLC

25 Garrett Dr, Havana, FL 32333
Tel.: (850) 539-7720
Web Site: https://www.appliedfiber.com
Year Founded: 2003
Sales Range: $1-9.9 Million
Emp.: 25

Rope, Cordage & Twine Mills
N.A.I.C.S.: 314994
Richard Campbell *(Owner)*

APPLIED FLUID POWER INC.

7900 Whitepine Rd, Richmond, VA 23237
Tel.: (804) 275-1436
Web Site: http://www.afpind.com
Sales Range: $10-24.9 Million
Emp.: 60
Hydraulic Systems Equipment & Supplies
N.A.I.C.S.: 423830
Richard W. Kish *(Pres)*
Frank Kish *(Co-Founder)*
Dick Kish *(Co-Founder)*

APPLIED FOOD TECHNOLOGIES, INC.

12085 Research Dr, Alachua, FL 32615
Tel.: (386) 418-3661
Web Site:
  http://www.appliedfoodtech.com
Food Product Research & Development Services
N.A.I.C.S.: 541715
LeeAnn Applewhite *(CEO)*

APPLIED GLOBAL TECHNOLOGIES

1006 Pathfinder Way, Rockledge, FL 32955
Tel.: (321) 638-2007
Web Site:
  http://www.appliedglobal.com
Year Founded: 1993
Sales Range: $25-49.9 Million
Emp.: 98
Outsourcing & Managed Services Within Voice, Video & Data Collaboration Networks
N.A.I.C.S.: 541512
Michael J. Valletutti *(Co-Founder)*
Todd Jacobson *(VP-Product Dev)*
Mark Cray *(Co-Owner & CEO)*
Justin Mason *(Dir-Engrg)*
Darryl Bailey *(Dir-Client Care)*
Jarrett Lowman *(Dir-Enterprise Sls)*
Melissa Hudson *(Dir-PR & Mktg)*
Trippe Wilkes *(Dir-QA Engrg)*

APPLIED HANDLING INC.

15200 Century Dr, Dearborn, MI 48120
Tel.: (313) 336-8020
Web Site:
  https://www.appliedhandling.com
Rev.: $30,000,000
Emp.: 45
Materials Handling Machinery
N.A.I.C.S.: 423830
Bruce R. Bacon *(Pres)*
Kevin Roy *(Mgr-Global Accts)*
Mike Wozniak *(Mgr-New Equipment Sls)*

APPLIED IMAGE GROUP INC.

1653 E Main St, Rochester, NY 14609
Tel.: (585) 482-0300
Web Site:
  http://www.appliedimage.com
Sales Range: $10-24.9 Million
Emp.: 35
Optical Elements & Assemblies Mfr
N.A.I.C.S.: 333310
Glenn Jackling *(Pres)*

APPLIED INFORMATION SCIENCES, INC.

11400 Commerce Park Dr Ste 600, Reston, VA 20191
Tel.: (703) 860-7800

Web Site: http://www.appliedis.com
Rev.: $19,389,905
Emp.: 40
Computer Integrated Systems Design
N.A.I.C.S.: 541512
Larry Katzman *(Pres & CEO)*
Kimberly Pack *(Pres-Federal Unit)*

Subsidiaries:

XGILITY, LLC.   **(1)**
44258 Mercure Cir Ste 102B, Dulles, VA
20166
Web Site: http://www.xgility.com
Label Printing Services
N.A.I.C.S.: 561910
Kurt Greening *(Dir-Productivity Solutions)*
Chris Hornbecker *(Pres & CEO)*
Christi Luther *(Dir-Client Solutions)*

APPLIED INTUITION, INC.
145 E Dana St, Mountain View, CA
94041
Tel.: (630) 935-8986
Web Site:
https://www.appliedintuition.com
Emp.: 100
Software Publisher
N.A.I.C.S.: 513210
Qasar Younis *(CEO)*

Subsidiaries:

Embark Technology, Inc.   **(1)**
321 Alabama St, San Francisco, CA 94110
Tel.: (415) 671-9628
Web Site: https://www.embarktrucks.com
Rev.: $2,221,000
Assets: $214,730,000
Liabilities: $29,756,000
Net Worth: $184,974,000
Earnings: ($103,163,000)
Emp.: 2
Fiscal Year-end: 12/31/2022
Investment Services
N.A.I.C.S.: 523999
Qasar Younis *(Treas)*
Morgan Dioli *(Principal Fin Officer & Principal Acctg Officer)*
Peter Ludwig *(Pres & Sec)*

Subsidiary (Non-US):

The Lion Electric Co.   **(2)**
921 Chemin De La Riviere-du-Nord, Saint-
Jerome, J7Y 5G2, QC, Canada
Tel.: (450) 432-5466
Web Site: https://www.thelionelectric.com
Rev.: $139,914,470
Assets: $710,410,912
Liabilities: $273,294,139
Net Worth: $437,116,773
Earnings: $17,775,766
Emp.: 1,400
Fiscal Year-end: 12/31/2022
Electronic Battery Mfr
N.A.I.C.S.: 335910
Marc Bedard *(Founder & CEO)*
Mark-Andre Page *(VP-Comml Ops)*
Nicolas Brunet *(Pres, CFO & Exec VP)*
Yannick Poulin *(COO)*
Nathalie Giroux *(Chief People Officer)*
Benoit Morin *(VP-Sls-Canada)*
Richard Coulombe *(CFO)*
Dominique Perron *(Sec & Chief Legal Counsel)*
Philippe LeBlanc *(VP-Advanced Engrg)*
Vince Spadafora *(Treas & Sr VP-Finance)*
Christina Ameigh *(VP-Truck Sls)*
Nate A. Baguio *(Sr VP-Comm Dev)*
Patrick Gervais *(VP-Trucks & Public Affairs)*
Patrick Richter *(VP-Svcs & Product Support)*
Maxime Gauvin *(VP-Corporate Development)*
David Sicotte *(Sr VP-Product Development)*
Pierre Larochelle *(Chm)*

Mechanical Simulation Corp.   **(1)**
755 Phoenix Dr, Ann Arbor, MI 48108-2222
Tel.: (734) 668-2930
Web Site: http://www.carsim.com
Software Publisher
N.A.I.C.S.: 513210
Michael Sayers *(Co-Founder)*

APPLIED MECHANICAL SYSTEMS, INC.

5598 Wolf Creek Pike, Dayton, OH
45426
Tel.: (937) 854-3073
Web Site:
http://www.appliedmechanics.com
Year Founded: 1974
Sales Range: $25-49.9 Million
Emp.: 260
Plumbing Contractor
N.A.I.C.S.: 238220
Edward W. Kelker *(VP-Ops)*
Raymond Sebaali *(VP-Engrg & Estimating)*
Richard Geyer *(CFO & Treas)*
Brian Daugherty *(Mgr-HR)*
Carol Kniesly *(VP-Svc)*

APPLIED MEDICAL CORPORATION
22872 Avenida Empresa, Rancho
Santa Margarita, CA 92688
Tel.: (949) 713-8000   DE
Web Site:
https://www.appliedmedical.com
Year Founded: 1987
Sales Range: $250-299.9 Million
Emp.: 2,250
Medical Device Mfr
N.A.I.C.S.: 339112
Gary Johnson *(Pres-Surgical-Grp)*

APPLIED NANOTECH, INC.
8200 Cameron Rd Ste B160, Austin,
TX 78754
Tel.: (512) 339-5020   DE
Web Site:
http://www.appliednanotech.net
Year Founded: 1989
Emp.: 100
Nanomaterial Development Services
N.A.I.C.S.: 541713

APPLIED NATURAL GAS FUELS, INC.
31111 Agoura Rd Ste 208, Westlake
Village, CA 91361
Tel.: (818) 450-3650   NV
Web Site: http://www.altlng.com
Year Founded: 1995
Sales Range: $10-24.9 Million
Emp.: 24
Liquefied Natural Gas Mfr, Distr &
Sales
N.A.I.C.S.: 325120
Frank Martelli *(VP-Ops)*
Greg Roche *(VP-Sls & Mktg)*

APPLIED POWER PRODUCTS INC.
1240 Trapp Rd, Eagan, MN 55121
Tel.: (651) 452-2250
Web Site:
http://www.appliedpowerprod.com
Sales Range: $25-49.9 Million
Emp.: 100
Provider of Industrial Supply Services
N.A.I.C.S.: 423840
Alan Luthi *(VP-Fin)*

APPLIED RESEARCH ASSOCIATES, INC.
4300 San Mateo Blvd NE Ste A-220,
Albuquerque, NM 87110-1295
Tel.: (505) 881-8074   NM
Web Site: https://www.ara.com
Year Founded: 1979
Engineering Research & Development
N.A.I.C.S.: 541715
Robert Sues *(Pres & CEO)*
Will Goodman *(Sr VP)*
James P. Allen *(Chm)*
James Myers *(VP-Program Innovation & Growth)*
James Kainz *(Sr VP)*

Subsidiaries:

Applied Research Associates Emerald Coast Division   **(1)**
956 W John Sims Pkwy, Niceville, FL
32578-1823
Tel.: (850) 678-5222
Web Site: http://www.ara.com
Sales Range: $25-49.9 Million
Emp.: 65
Engineering, Research & Development
N.A.I.C.S.: 541860

Applied Research Associates Mid-Atlantic Division   **(1)**
4000 Pemberton Sq Blvd, Vicksburg, MS
39180-5160   **(100%)**
Tel.: (601) 629-6165
Web Site: http://www.ara.com
Sales Range: $10-24.9 Million
Emp.: 40
Engineering Research & Consulting Services
N.A.I.C.S.: 541715
Curt Beckmeyer *(Sr VP)*

Applied Research Associates Midwest Division   **(1)**
100 Trade Center Dr Ste 200, Champaign,
IL 61820-3915
Tel.: (217) 356-4500
Web Site: http://www.ara.com
Sales Range: $10-24.9 Million
Emp.: 50
Pavement Engineering Specialists
N.A.I.C.S.: 541330
Curt Beckmeyer *(VP & Sector Mgr)*

Applied Research Associates North
Florida Division   **(1)**
430 W 5th St Ste 700, Panama City, FL
32401-6357
Tel.: (850) 914-3188
Web Site: http://www.ara.com
Sales Range: $10-24.9 Million
Emp.: 50
Engineering, Research & Development
N.A.I.C.S.: 541611

Applied Research Associates Rocky
Mountain Division   **(1)**
7921 Shaffer Pkwy, Littleton, CO 80127-
3734
Tel.: (303) 795-8106
Web Site: http://www.ara.com
Provide Explosive & Computational Fluid
Dynamics Services
N.A.I.C.S.: 541715

Applied Research Associates Shock
Physics Division   **(1)**
3751 F Wyoming Blvd SE, Kirtland AFB,
NM 87117-5388
Tel.: (505) 846-0487
Web Site: http://www.ara.com
Sales Range: $10-24.9 Million
Emp.: 60
Provides Cost Effective Test Support to a
Wide Variety of Government Agencies &
Commercial Clients
N.A.I.C.S.: 541330

Applied Research Associates Southeast Division   **(1)**
8537 6 Forks Rd Ste 600, Raleigh, NC
27615-6545
Tel.: (919) 582-3300
Web Site: http://www.ara.com
Sales Range: $25-49.9 Million
Emp.: 103
Research & Development
N.A.I.C.S.: 541330

Applied Research Associates Southwest Division   **(1)**
4300 San Mateo Blvd NE Ste A220, Albu-
querque, NM 87110-1295   **(100%)**
Tel.: (505) 883-3636
Web Site: http://www.ara.com
Sales Range: $25-49.9 Million
Emp.: 120
Engineering & Research
N.A.I.C.S.: 541715

Berriehill Research Corporation   **(1)**
7735 Paragon Rd, Dayton, OH 45459
Tel.: (937) 435-1016
Web Site: http://www.berriehill.com
Hardware & Software Services

N.A.I.C.S.: 541330
Jeff Berrie *(VP & Mgr-Div)*
David Hughes *(Mgr-Asst Div)*

Neya Systems, LLC   **(1)**
555 Keystone Dr, Warrendale, PA 15086
Tel.: (724) 799-8078
Web Site: http://www.neyasystems.com
Robotics Company
N.A.I.C.S.: 541715

APPLIED SCIENTIFIC INSTRUMENTATION, INC.
29391 W Enid Rd, Eugene, OR
97402
Tel.: (541) 461-8181
Web Site: http://www.asiimaging.com
Year Founded: 1990
Sales Range: $10-24.9 Million
Emp.: 25
Electronic Components Mfr
N.A.I.C.S.: 334419
Vik Kopuri *(Engr-Electrical)*
Gary Rondeau *(Dir-Tech)*
Cliff Turpin *(Mgr-Pur)*
Kimberly Zemek *(Sec)*
John Zemek *(Pres)*

APPLIED SOFTWARE TECHNOLOGY, INC.
5901 Peachtree Dunwoody Rd Ste
C230, Atlanta, GA 30328
Tel.: (404) 633-8660
Web Site: http://www.asti.com
Year Founded: 1982
Software Consulting, Implementation,
Customization & Training Services
N.A.I.C.S.: 541519
Richard Burroughs *(Pres)*
Clay Smith *(COO)*

APPLIED TECHNOLOGIES ASSOCIATES
3025 Buena Vista Dr, Paso Robles,
CA 93446
Tel.: (805) 239-9100
Web Site: http://www.ata-sd.com
Sales Range: $10-24.9 Million
Emp.: 225
Surveying Instruments & Accessories
N.A.I.C.S.: 334519
Gene Chang *(Engr-Embedded Sys)*
Holly Driver *(Coord-HR)*
Joseph Edone *(Mgr-Production Logging Svcs)*
Pat Gibson *(Engr-Electronic)*
Tim Whitacre *(Engr-Res)*

Subsidiaries:

Scientific Drilling   **(1)**
1100 Rankin Rd, Houston, TX 77073
Tel.: (281) 443-3300
Web Site: http://www.scientificdrilling.com
Developer of Technology for Survey, Pro-
duction Logging & Directional Drilling
N.A.I.C.S.: 213111
Gerald Heisig *(Sr VP-Res & Tech Dev)*
Phil Longorio *(Pres & CEO)*
Dana Armstrong *(CFO & Sr VP)*
Chip Abrant *(Sr VP-Global Ops & Sls)*
Doug McGregor *(Sr VP-Drilling & Measurements)*
Dan Carter *(Gen Counsel & Sr VP)*

Scientific Production Services   **(1)**
Hwy 723, Lafayette, LA 70507
Tel.: (337) 232-7302
Web Site: http://www.scientificdrilling.com
Developer of Memory Production Logging
Systems
N.A.I.C.S.: 237120

APPLIED TECHNOLOGY SERVICES, INC.
11615 Crossroads Cir, Middle River,
MD 21220
Tel.: (410) 344-1256
Web Site:
http://www.appliedtechnology.com

Applied Technology Services, Inc.—(Continued)
Year Founded: 2001
Sales Range: $25-49.9 Million
Information Technology Services
N.A.I.C.S.: 541512
Danielle Burnett (Pres)
Bob Marchese (VP-Bus Dev)
Tina Marchese (VP-Fin)
Paula Carter (Mgr-Sls Ops)
Jonathan Harris (Acct Mgr)

APPLIED VALUE LLC
300 Brickstone Sq Ste 201, Andover, MA 01810
Tel.: (978) 631-4142 MA
Web Site: https://appliedvaluegroup.com
Year Founded: 1997
Investment, Management & Consulting Services
N.A.I.C.S.: 523999
Bruce Grant (Chm)
Maximillian Sultan (Partner)

APPLIED VISIONS, INC.
6 Bayview Ave, Northport, NY 11768
Tel.: (631) 759-3900 NY
Web Site: http://www.avi.com
Year Founded: 1986
Computer Software
N.A.I.C.S.: 541512
Frank Zinghini (Pres & CEO)
Anita D'Amico (Dir-Secure Decisions Div)
Lynn Antunovich (Mgr-Talent)
Alex Thomas (Engr-Project)
David D'Amico (Engr-Project)
Michael Rosenstein (Engr-Project)
Kelly Bennett (Controller)
Jesse Smith (Sr Engr-Software)
Ken Prole (Engr-Software)

Subsidiaries:

Software Design Solutions Inc. (1)
4091 Saltzburg Rd Ste S, Murrysville, PA 15668
Tel.: (412) 793-3973
Web Site: http://www.softwaredesignsolutions.com
Electronics Stores
N.A.I.C.S.: 449210
Edward Kuzemchak (CTO & Dir-Embedded & IoT Engrg)
Frank Zinghini (Pres & CEO)

APPLING HEALTHCARE SYSTEM
163 E Tollison St, Baxley, GA 31513
Tel.: (912) 367-9841
Web Site: http://www.applinghospital.org
Sales Range: $10-24.9 Million
Emp.: 350
Healtcare Services
N.A.I.C.S.: 621999
Ray Ledbetter (Interim CEO)
Brian Wesbury (Dir-Safety, Security & Nuclear Medicine-RSO)
Melissa Hood (Dir-Revenue Cycle)
Joy Kicklighter (Dir-HIM)

APPOGEE, LLC
418 Evans St Ste 201, Greenville, NC 27858
Web Site: http://www.appogee.com
Year Founded: 2008
Sales Range: $10-24.9 Million
Emp.: 13
Information Technology Development Services
N.A.I.C.S.: 541511
Kristie King (Co-Founder)
Tim Hassett (Co-Founder)
Jake Jacob (Head-Bus Ops)
Kirstie Ivie (Fin Dir)
Ginger Dennis (Dir-Client Svcs)

APPRENTICE & JOURNEYMEN TRAINING TRUST FUND OF THE SOUTHERN CALIFORNIA PLUMBING & PIPING INDUSTRY
7850 Haskell Ave, Van Nuys, CA 91406
Tel.: (310) 604-0892 CA
Web Site: https://www.ajtraining.org
Year Founded: 1956
Sales Range: $10-24.9 Million
Emp.: 168
Educational Support Services
N.A.I.C.S.: 611710

APPRIO INC.
425 3rd St SW Ste 600, Washington, DC 20024
Tel.: (202) 863-9281
Web Site: https://www.apprioinc.com
Year Founded: 1998
Sales Range: $1-9.9 Million
Emp.: 47
Information Technology Services
N.A.I.C.S.: 541512
Darryl F. Britt (Founder & Pres)
H. Allen Dobbs (Chief Medical Info Officer)
Jennifer Gilliam-Hooker (Mgr-Ops Bus)
Kevin Mesiah (Exec VP-Defense & Dev-Intl)
Michael Pena (Exec VP-Homeland Security Ops)
Marvin Huber (Controller)
Eric Huweart (VP-Military & Veteran Healthcare)
Gloria-Ann Norwood (VP-Ops)
Chloe Madden (Chief Human Capital Officer)
Nicholas Tomlin (VP-Info Security)
Donny Zamora (Pres-Comml Health Care Div)
Mark Patzschke (VP-Corp Growth-Federal Health Practice)
Erika Capobianco (CFO)
Trenton Janda (Chief Medical Innovation Officer)

APPRISE MEDIA, LLC
595 Madison Ave 16th Fl, New York, NY 10022
Tel.: (212) 751-3182
Year Founded: 2004
Privater Equity Firm
N.A.I.C.S.: 523999
Michael P. Behringer (Principal & Mng Dir)

APPRISS HOLDINGS, INC.
9901 Linn Station Rd Ste 500, Louisville, KY 40223
Tel.: (502) 561-8463
Web Site: https://apprisscorp.com
Data Analysis Solutions
N.A.I.C.S.: 518210
Krishnan Sastry (Pres & Dir)

Subsidiaries:

Appriss, Inc. (1)
10401 Linn Station Rd Ste 200, Louisville, KY 40223-3842
Tel.: (502) 561-8463
Web Site: http://www.appriss.com
Sales Range: $10-24.9 Million
Emp.: 200
Provider of Voice Activated Applications to Business & Government Agencies
N.A.I.C.S.: 541199
Mike Davis (CEO)
Brian Oldham (CIO)
Robert A. Cohen (Pres-Healthcare)
Krishnan Sastry (Chief Strategy Officer)
Kathy Sue Bennett (Mgr-Mktg)

Subsidiary (Domestic):

Appriss Retail (2)

6430 Oak Canyon Ste 250, Irvine, CA 92618
Tel.: (866) 277-7477
Web Site: https://apprissretail.com
Artificial Intelligence-Based Solution
N.A.I.C.S.: 513210
Kara Holthaus (VP-Customer Success)
Pedro Ramos (Chief Revenue Officer)
Michael Osborne (CEO)
Emily Rhodes (VP-Mktg)
Heather Magaro (CFO)
Melissa Trelfa (Chief People Officer)

Securitec Screening Solutions, Inc. (2)
3800Electric Rd Ste 300, Roanoke, VA 24018-2301
Tel.: (540) 725-1571
Web Site:
http://www.securitecscreening.com
Employment Placement Agencies
N.A.I.C.S.: 561311
Jessica James (Owner)

The Retail Equation Inc. (2)
6430 Oak Cyn, Irvine, CA 92618
Tel.: (949) 262-5100
Web Site: http://www.theretailequation.com
Rev.: $1,600,000
Emp.: 14
Data Processing, Hosting & Related Services
N.A.I.C.S.: 518210
Jim Ibert (VP-Reg Sls)
David Justus (Co-Founder & Chm)

APPRO DEVELOPMENT, INC.
21476 Grenada Ave, Lakeville, MN 55044
Tel.: (952) 469-2171
Web Site: https://www.approdevelopment.com
Sales Range: $10-24.9 Million
Emp.: 10
Commercial & Institutional Building Construction Services
N.A.I.C.S.: 236220
Jack Matasosky (Co-Owner & CEO)
Jim Connelly (Co-Owner & Project Mgr)
Kathy Morse (Co-Owner & CFO)
Andrea Kaderlik (Coord-Mktg)
Cam Luong (Project Mgr)
Gordy Schiltz (Project Mgr)

APPROACH RESOURCES INC.
One Ridgmar Ctr 6500 W Fwy Ste 800, Fort Worth, TX 76116
Tel.: (817) 989-9000 DE
Web Site: http://www.approachresources.com
Year Founded: 2002
Rev.: $114,035,000
Assets: $1,084,647,000
Liabilities: $495,402,000
Net Worth: $589,245,000
Earnings: ($19,911,000)
Emp.: 99
Fiscal Year-end: 12/31/18
Natural Gas & Oil Properties Exploration, Development, Exploitation, Production & Acquisition
N.A.I.C.S.: 211120
Troy A. Hoefer (Exec VP-Ops)
Suzanne L. Ogle (VP-IR & Corp Comm)
Joshua E. Dazey (Sec & Exec VP-Legal)
Sergei Krylov (Pres & CEO)
James C. Crain (Chm)

Subsidiaries:

Approach Oil & Gas Inc. (1)
1 Ridgmar Ctr 6500 W Freeway Ste 800, Fort Worth, TX 76116
Tel.: (817) 989-9000
Web Site:
http://www.approachresources.com
Emp.: 40
Oil & Gas Field Services
N.A.I.C.S.: 213112

Approach Operating, LLC (1)
638 State Hwy 163 N, Ozona, TX 76943
Tel.: (325) 392-8900
Emp.: 50
Business Management Consulting Services
N.A.I.C.S.: 541618
Cole Wadsworth (Branch Mgr)

APPSFLYER INC.
100 1st St 25th Fl, San Francisco, CA 94105
Tel.: (415) 636-9430 DE
Web Site: http://www.appsflyer.com
Year Founded: 2011
Sales Range: $75-99.9 Million
Emp.: 493
Software Development Services
N.A.I.C.S.: 541511
Oren Kaniel (Co-Founder & CEO)
Reshef Mann (Co-Founder & CTO)
Brian Quinn (Pres & Gen Mgr-North America)
Chad L. Greenleaf (Sr VP-Client Success)

APPTECH INC.
2011 Palomar Airport Rd Ste 102, Carlsbad, CA 92011
Tel.: (760) 707-5955
Web Site:
http://www.apptechcorp.com
Rev.: $3,000,000
Emp.: 17
Computer System Design Services
N.A.I.C.S.: 541512
Luke D'Angelo (CEO)
Steven Cox (Pres)

Subsidiaries:

Transcendent One, Inc. (1)
2011 Palomar Airport Rd Ste 102, Carlsbad, CA 92011
Tel.: (760) 707-5959
Web Site: http://www.transcendentone.com
Sales Range: $1-9.9 Million
Emp.: 10
Electronic Transactions Processing Services
N.A.I.C.S.: 518210
Steve Cox (Exec VP)

APPWORX LLC
3701 FAU Blvd Ste 210, Boca Raton, FL 33431
Tel.: (561) 237-5500
Web Site:
http://www.myappworx.com
Sales Range: $1-9.9 Million
Medical-Based Mobile Applications
N.A.I.C.S.: 513210
Ariel Soffer (Co-Founder & Chm)
Christopher Cabell (Co-Founder & CTO)
Jim Clark (CEO)

APR CONSULTING INC.
22632 Golden Springs Dr No 380, Diamond Bar, CA 91765
Tel.: (909) 396-5375
Web Site:
http://www.aprconsulting.com
Sales Range: $10-24.9 Million
Emp.: 135
Computer Related Consulting Services
N.A.I.C.S.: 561311
Erlinda R. Stone (Pres)
Darrell Stone (Pres)
Ajay Kumar (Mgr-IT)

APR SUPPLY CO.
749 Guilford St, Lebanon, PA 17046
Tel.: (717) 274-5999
Web Site: http://www.aprsupply.com
Plumbing, Heating & Cooling Supplies Mfr
N.A.I.C.S.: 423720
Scott Weaver (Pres & CEO)

APRICOT OFFICE SUPPLIES & FURNITURE, INC.

1000 S Federal Hwy Ste 200, Fort Lauderdale, FL 33316-1237
Tel.: (305) 463-8872
Web Site: http://www.apricotos.com
Sales Range: $10-24.9 Million
Emp.: 18
Office Supplies & Furniture Retailer
N.A.I.C.S.: 459410
Basil Bernard (Pres)
Greg Silvera (VP & Mgr-Sls)
Marlene Bernard (Treas & VP)
Yvette Benjamin (Office Mgr)
Adley Clarke (Acct Exec)
Larry Johnson (Acct Exec)
Sherie Strangwayes (Acct Exec)
Paul Wright (Acct Exec)

APRIL CORNELL HOLDINGS

131 Battery St, Burlington, VT 05401
Tel.: (802) 879-1271   NY
Web Site: http://www.aprilcornell.com
Year Founded: 1981
Sales Range: $75-99.9 Million
Emp.: 300
Holding Company; Home Furnishings & Apparel Mfr
N.A.I.C.S.: 551112
Donna Larrabee (VP-Brand Dev & Design)

APRIO, LLP

5 Concourse Pkwy Ste 1000, Atlanta, GA 30328
Tel.: (404) 892-9651
Web Site: http://www.aprio.com
Year Founded: 1952
Emp.: 400
Accounting, Tax & Consulting Services
N.A.I.C.S.: 541211
Yelena Epova (Mng Partner)
Jeff Grosoff (Partner-Quality Control)
Kurt Huntzinger (Partner & Chief Risk Officer)
Mitchell S. Kopelman (Partner & Head-Bus Tax, Tech & Biosciences)
Robert Casey (Partner)
Frank H. Gudger (Partner & Head-Assurance Svcs)
Richard Kopelman (CEO & Mng Partner)
Richard A. Rubin (Partner-Pro Svcs Grp)
Edward D. Deck (Partner)
Darrin Friedrich (Partner)
Lisa C. Haynor (Partner)
Angela Dotson (Partner-Pro Svcs Grp)
Alison Fossyl (Partner)
Matt Wise (Partner)
Cardell McKinstry (Partner-Transaction Advisory Svcs)
Kristin Maeckel (Partner)
Charles Webb (Partner)
Kevin Williams (VP-Fin)
Alan Vaughn (Partner, Exec VP & Head-Real Estate & Construction)
Carli McDonald (Partner-R&D Tax Credit Svcs)
Carrie Zhou (Dir-Transaction Advisory Svcs)
Christopher Davis (Partner-Private Client Svcs)
Chris Esworthy (Dir-Information Assurance Svcs)
Derek Pitts (Partner-Transaction Advisory Svcs)
Scott Rittenberg (Partner)
Tony Mills (Exec VP)
Lee Fields (Partner & Head-Advisory Svcs)
Keith Greenwald (Partner & Head-Private Client Svcs)
Larry Sheftel (VP-HR)

Sam Tuck (Partner & Head-Tax Svcs)
Danielle Berg (CMO & Chief Corp Comm Officer)
Dna Mallory (VP-Tech)
Jim Canfield (Mng Dir-CEO Tools)
Leanne Gould (Dir-Litigation Support & Forensic Acctg Svcs)
Kelli Winter (Partner-Assurance-Real Estate & Construction Grp)
Robert Melnick (Mng Dir-Outsourced Acctg Svcs)
Rob Shirley (Partner-Birmingham)
Julie Chesebro (Dir-Tax)
Jagruti Solanki (Partner-Assurance-Tech & Blockchain)
Thomas Scott (Partner-Tech & Blockchain-Tax Practice)
Thomas Prevatt (Partner-Pro Svcs-Tax Grp)
Michael Lange (Partner-Mfg & Distr-Assurance Practice)
Jessica Hussain (Partner-Retail, Franchise & Hospitality Grp)
Cheryl Leydon (Dir-Tax-Global Mobility Svcs)
Shay Eubanks (Dir-Tax-Tax practice)
Ben Magoon (Partner)
Claire Jones (Partner)
Irvin Rabinowitz (Partner)
Jeffrey C. Glickman (Partner-State & Local Tax)
Karen Bates (Partner)
Kerry Defler (Partner)
Leslie Balmforth (Partner-Learning & Dev)
Ori Epstein (Partner)
Rebecca McCune (Partner)
Rick Bernstein (Partner)
Robert Greenberger (Partner)
Ryan Ahn (Partner)
Sammy Freeman (Partner)
Sandi Buttram (Partner)
Scott Barnett (Partner)
Scott Hutchinson (Partner)
Sheldon Zimmerman (Partner)
Thomas Carr (Partner)
Timothy Sumrall (Partner)
Brett Williams (Partner-Info Assurance Svcs)
Adam Venokur (Mng Partner-Northeast)
Charity Monk (Partner-Audit)
Bill Dupee (Partner)
David Zafft (Partner)
Jed Rogers (Partner)
Rob Stroud (Partner)
Alison Sellers (Partner)
David Siegel (Partner)
Brent McDaniel (Chief Digital Officer)
Joe Spain Jr. (Partner)

Subsidiaries:

Aprio Benefit Advisors, LLC   **(1)**
5 Concourse Pkwy Ste 1000, Atlanta, GA 30328
Tel.: (404) 892-9651
Web Site: http://www.aprio.com
Retirement Benefits Planning, Advisory & Administration Services
N.A.I.C.S.: 524292
Keith Greenwald (Partner & Head-Private Client Svcs)
Tim Baker (Dir-Ops-Retirement Plan)
Mary Jenkins (Dir-Svcs-Retirement Plan)

Aprio Wealth Management, LLC **(1)**
5 Concourse Pkwy Ste 1000, Atlanta, GA 30328
Tel.: (404) 892-9651
Web Site: http://www.aprio.com
Financial Advisory & Retirement Plan Consulting Services
N.A.I.C.S.: 523940
Keith Greenwald (Partner & Head-Private Client Svcs)
Carrie Zhou (Dir-Valuation Svcs)
Tim Baker (Dir-Retirement Plan Ops)
Jon Dangar (Dir-Mergers & Acq)
Richard Schriefer (Partner-New York City)

Gomerdinger & Associates, LLC **(1)**
9000 E Nichols Ave, Centennial, CO 80112
Tel.: (720) 488-1926
Web Site: http://www.gomerdingercpas.com
Offices of Certified Public Accountants
N.A.I.C.S.: 541211
Cindy Gomerdinger (Owner)

Kirsch Kohn & Bridge LLP   **(1)**
15910 Ventura Blvd Ste 1100, Encino, CA 91436
Tel.: (818) 907-6500
Web Site: http://www.kkbcpa.com
Rev.: $4,000,000
Emp.: 30
Other Accounting Services
N.A.I.C.S.: 541219
Wesley Hartman (Mgr-IT)

LBA Haynes Strand, PLLC   **(1)**
212 W Matthews St Ste 102, Matthews, NC 28105
Tel.: (704) 841-1120
Web Site: http://www.lbahs.com
Financial Services
N.A.I.C.S.: 541611
Casey O'Keefe (Mgr-Audit)

Pontiff & Associates, P.C.   **(1)**
1979 W Littleton Blvd, Littleton, CO 80120-2022
Tel.: (303) 813-1561
Web Site: http://www.pontiffcpa.com
Other Accounting Services
N.A.I.C.S.: 541219
Matt Pontiff (Owner)

Ridout Barrett & Co PC   **(1)**
901 NE Loop 410, San Antonio, TX 78209-1307
Tel.: (210) 829-1793
Web Site: http://www.ridoutbarrett.com
Offices of Certified Public Accountants
N.A.I.C.S.: 541211
Anthony Ridout (Partner)
Sarita Akin (Dir-Tax)

Tobin & Collins Cpa, Pa.   **(1)**
75 Essex St Ste 200, Hackensack, NJ 07601
Tel.: (201) 487-7744
Web Site: http://www.tccpa.net
Sales Range: $1-9.9 Million
Emp.: 19
Tax Preparation Accounting Auditing & Bookkeeping Services
N.A.I.C.S.: 541219
Kevin J. Collins (Partner)
Richard C. Tobin (Partner)
James P. King (Partner)

APRIORI CAPITAL PARTNERS L.P.

4470 W Sunset Blvd Ste 92879, Los Angeles, CA 90027
Tel.: (212) 325-2000
Web Site:
   http://www.aprioricapital.com
Year Founded: 1985
Private Equity Investment Firm
N.A.I.C.S.: 523999
Colin Taylor (Mng Partner)
Maximilian Hofert (Partner & Mng Dir)
Robert Espinoza (CFO)
Susan C. Schnabel (Mng Partner)

Subsidiaries:

Merrill Corporation   **(1)**
1 Merrill Cir, Saint Paul, MN 55108   **(58%)**
Tel.: (651) 646-4501
Web Site: http://www.merrillcorp.com
Sales Range: $750-799.9 Million
Emp.: 5,000
Business Communication & Information Management Outsourcing Services
N.A.I.C.S.: 561410
Roy Gross (COO-Mktg & Comm Solutions)
Brenda J. Vale (Chief Admin Officer)
Katherine L. Miller (Chief Acctg Officer & Controller)
James V. Continenza (Chm)
Rusty Wiley (Pres & CEO)
Todd R. Albright (Global Chief Revenue Officer)
Tom Donnelly (CFO)

Thomas Fredell (Chief Product Officer)
Axel Kirstetter (VP-Product Mktg)
Deven Lindemann (Exec VP-Client Svcs)
Gretchen Dahlberg (Gen Counsel)
Dixon Gould (CIO)
Deborah LaMere (VP-HR)

Branch (Domestic):

Merrill Corporation - Chicago Office   **(2)**
311 S Wacker Dr Ste 1800, Chicago, IL 60606-6620
Tel.: (312) 786-6300
Web Site: http://www.merrillcorp.com
Provider of Financial, Legal, Commercial & Corporate Printing Services
N.A.I.C.S.: 323111
John W. Castro (Chm & CEO)

Merrill Corporation - Denver Office   **(2)**
1225 17th St Ste 2800, Denver, CO 80202-5599
Tel.: (303) 572-3889
Web Site: http://www.merrillcorp.com
Sales Range: $75-99.9 Million
Emp.: 50
Provide Financial, Legal, Commercial & Corporate Printing Services
N.A.I.C.S.: 323111

Merrill Corporation - Houston Office   **(2)**
Bayou Pl 315 Capitol St Ste 210, Houston, TX 77002
Tel.: (713) 650-9640
Web Site: http://www.merrillcorp.com
Sales Range: $75-99.9 Million
Emp.: 20
Financial, Legal, Commercial, Corporate & DRG Printing
N.A.I.C.S.: 323111

Merrill Corporation - Irvine Office   **(2)**
2603 Main St Ste 100, Irvine, CA 92614-4242
Tel.: (949) 252-9449
Web Site: http://www.merrillcorp.com
Financial, Legal, Commercial, Corporate & DRG Printing
N.A.I.C.S.: 323111

Merrill Corporation - La Mirada Office   **(2)**
16200 Trojan Way, La Mirada, CA 90638-5600
Tel.: (213) 765-7000
Web Site: http://www.merrillcorp.com
Financial, Legal, Commercial & Corporate Printing
N.A.I.C.S.: 323111

Merrill Corporation - Los Angeles (South Grand) Office   **(2)**
350 S Grand Ave Ste 3000, Los Angeles, CA 90071-3424
Tel.: (213) 253-5900
Web Site: http://www.merrillcorp.com
Financial, Legal, Commercial, Corporate & DRG Printing
N.A.I.C.S.: 323111

Merrill Corporation - Monroe Office   **(2)**
14640 172nd Dr SE, Monroe, WA 98272-1076
Tel.: (360) 794-3157
Web Site: http://www.merrillcorp.com
Sales Range: $75-99.9 Million
Emp.: 50
Financial Legal Commercial Corporate & DRG Printing
N.A.I.C.S.: 323111

Merrill Corporation - St. Cloud Office   **(2)**
4110 Clearwater Rd, Saint Cloud, MN 56301-9634
Tel.: (320) 656-5000
Web Site: http://www.merrillcorp.com
Financial, Legal, Commercial, Corporate & DRG Printing
N.A.I.C.S.: 323111
Katherine Miller (Chief Acctg Officer, Sr VP & Controller)
Rod Johnson (COO-Legal & Fin Svcs)

aPriori Capital Partners L.P.—(Continued)

Merrill Corporation - Washington, DC
Office   (2)
1325 G St NW Ste 200, Washington, DC
20005-3104
Tel.: (202) 331-2424
Web Site: http://www.merrillcorp.com
Sales Range: $100-124.9 Million
Emp.: 60
Financial Legal Commercial Corporate &
DRG Printing
N.A.I.C.S.: 323111

Subsidiary (Non-US):

Merrill Corporation Canada   (2)
1 Adelaide St E Ste 3000, Toronto, M5C
2V9, ON, Canada
Tel.: (416) 214-2448
Web Site: http://www.merrillcorp.com
Sales Range: $50-74.9 Million
Emp.: 35
Printing Services
N.A.I.C.S.: 323111

Branch (Domestic):

Merrill Corporation Canada   (3)
1111 West Hastings Street Suite 333, Van-
couver, V6E 2J3, BC, Canada
Tel.: (604) 682-8594
Web Site: http://www.merrillcorp.com
Sales Range: $10-24.9 Million
Emp.: 3
Financial Printing Services
N.A.I.C.S.: 323111

Subsidiary (Non-US):

Merrill Corporation Limited   (2)
101 Finsbury Pavement, London, EC2A
1ER, United Kingdom   (100%)
Tel.: (44) 2074226100
Web Site: http://www.merrillcorp.com
Sales Range: $75-99.9 Million
Emp.: 100
Financial, Legal, Commercial, Corporate &
DRG Printing
N.A.I.C.S.: 323111
Todd Albright (Chief Revenue Officer)
Deven Lindemann (Exec VP-Client Svcs)
Doug Cullen (CMO)
Gretchen Dahlberg (Gen Counsel)
Thomas Fredell (Chief Product Officer)
Thomas Donnelly (CFO)
Dixon Gould (CIO)
Mark Williams (Chief Revenue Officer-
Americas)
Katherine Miller (Chief Acctg Officer)

Merrill France S.A.R.L.   (2)
11 rue de Tehéran, Paris, 75008, France
Tel.: (33) 1 40 06 13 00
Web Site: http://www.merrillcorp.com
Business Communication & Information
Management Outsourcing Services
N.A.I.C.S.: 561410

Merrill Germany GmbH   (2)
An der Welle 8, 60322, Frankfurt am Main,
Germany   (100%)
Tel.: (49) 69 244 321 450
Web Site: http://www.merrillcorp.com
Emp.: 12
Business Communication & Information
Management Outsourcing Services
N.A.I.C.S.: 561410
Sarah Andres (Gen Mgr)

Subsidiary (Domestic):

Merrill/Daniels, Inc.   (2)
40 Commercial St, Everett, MA
02149-5507   (100%)
Tel.: (617) 389-7900
Web Site: http://www.danielsprinting.com
Sales Range: $300-349.9 Million
Emp.: 270
Commercial & Financial Printing
N.A.I.C.S.: 323111

**APRIORI TECHNOLOGIES,
INC.**
300 Baker Ave, Concord, MA 01742
Tel.: (978) 371-2006   DE
Web Site: http://www.aPriori.com
Year Founded: 2003
Sales Range: $1-9.9 Million

Emp.: 35
Custom Computer Programming Ser-
vices
N.A.I.C.S.: 541511
Stephanie A. Feraday (Pres & CEO)
Rick Burke (VP-Mktg)
Stephanos Bacon (VP-Engrg)
John Busa (VP-Cost Modeling)
Julie Driscoll (VP-Strategic Mktg &
Product Mgmt)
Michael Philpott (Founder)
Michael Knox (VP-Pro Svcs)
Scott Carlyle (VP-Sls)
Jeannine Flynn (CFO)
Whitney Repetto (VP-People)
Ranae Mogensen (Dir-Mktg Comm &
PR)

**APS BUILDING SERVICES,
INC.**
11050 W Little York Rd Bldg P, Hous-
ton, TX 77041
Tel.: (713) 979-0720
Web Site: http://www.apshou.com
Year Founded: 2014
Sales Range: $10-24.9 Million
Emp.: 81
Building Construction Services
N.A.I.C.S.: 236115
Russell Griffin (Pres)
Ron Brittain (Exec VP-Ops)

APS TECHNOLOGY, INC.
7 Laser Ln, Wallingford, CT 06492
Tel.: (860) 613-4450
Web Site: https://www.aps-tech.com
Sales Range: $25-49.9 Million
Emp.: 100
Drilling Technology Engineering &
Design Services
N.A.I.C.S.: 541330
William E. Turner (Founder & CEO)
Denis Biglin (Exec VP)
Christopher Abbamonte (CFO)
Lawrence Weiner (Sr VP-Bus & Legal
Affairs)
Craig Brown (VP-Bus Dev)
Paul J. G. Seaton (Chief Acctg Offi-
cer & VP-Fin)
Maria Pangakis (Dir-HR)
Berzis Irani (Dir-Sls-Asia Pacific)
William J. Gowrie (VP-Quality & Reli-
ability)
Dirk Bosman (VP-Eastern Reg)
Ron Dirksen (VP-Western Reg)
Robert T. Kramer Jr. (Controller)

**APSCO APPLIANCE & TV
CENTERS, INC.**
2905 E Bay Dr, Largo, FL 33771
Tel.: (727) 535-5585   FL
Web Site: https://www.apsco.com
Year Founded: 1972
Sales Range: $10-24.9 Million
Emp.: 3
Electric Household Appliances Re-
tailer
N.A.I.C.S.: 449210
Alfred C. Greco (Co-Owner & Pres)

APT, INC.
1801 Se Commerce Ave, Battle
Ground, WA 98604-8963
Tel.: (510) 770-9100
Web Site:
    http://www.aptsystems.com
Rev.: $12,000,000
Emp.: 30
Provider of Wafers & Semiconductor
Devices
N.A.I.C.S.: 541613
Dale Morsette (Gen Mgr-APT)

Subsidiaries:

TFI Telemark   (1)

1801 SE Commerce Ave, Battle Ground,
WA 98604-8963
Tel.: (510) 887-2225
Web Site: http://www.telemark.com
Rev.: $1,400,000
Emp.: 20
Electron Beam Generator Tubes
N.A.I.C.S.: 334419

APTARIS LLC
2502 Rocky Point Dr Ste 1070,
Tampa, FL 33607
Tel.: (888) 804-5008   DE
Web Site: http://goaptaris.com
Management & Enterprise Software
Publisher
N.A.I.C.S.: 513210
Tom O'Reilly (Pres & CEO)
Ken Scrase (VP)
Christine Vaughn (Pres-Creative Svcs
Div)
Bill Morrell (CTO)
Marsha Shapiro (Sr VP-Product
Mgmt & Customer Success)

APTECH GROUP, INC.
11411 Williamson Rd, Blue Ash, OH
45241
Tel.: (513) 761-8111
Web Site:
    http://www.aptechgroup.com
Sales Range: $1-9.9 Million
Emp.: 11
Solid Water Treatment Chemicals Mfr
N.A.I.C.S.: 424690
Jim Heimert (CEO)
Al Heimert (Pres-Solid Concentrates)
Todd Lee (VP-Ops)
Matt Horine (VP-Engrg)
Kathleen Collier (Dir-Creative & Mktg)

APTIMA, INC.
12 Gill St Ste 1400, Woburn, MA
01801
Tel.: (781) 935-3966
Web Site: https://www.aptima.com
Year Founded: 1995
Sales Range: $10-24.9 Million
Emp.: 113
Human Centered Research & Devel-
opment Services
N.A.I.C.S.: 541715
Daniel Serfaty (Chm & CEO)
Margaret Clancy (Founder)
Thomas J. McKenna (CFO & COO)
Frederick J. Diedrich (Pres)
Christopher Brouady (VP-Contracts)
Shawn Weil (Exec VP-Bus Strategy)
Michael J. Garrity (Exec VP-Govt
Programs)
Adam Fouse (Dir-Performance Aug-
mentation Sys-R&D Grp)
Krista Ratwani (Dir-Learning & Trng
Sys-R&D)
Charlotte Shabarekh (Dir-Intelligent
Analytic Technologies)
Kara Orvis (VP-R&D Grp)
Kevin Sullivan (VP)
Kent Halverson (Dir-Performance As-
sessment Tech-R&D Grp)
Sterling Wiggins (VP-Transformation)

APTO SOLUTIONS, INC.
1910 MacArthur Blvd NW, Atlanta,
GA 30318
Tel.: (404) 605-0992
Web Site:
    https://www.aptosolutions.com
Year Founded: 2001
Sales Range: $10-24.9 Million
Emp.: 104
Asset Recovery Services
N.A.I.C.S.: 541611
Jeffrey Jones (Co-Founder & CEO)
James Kilkelly (Co-Founder & Pres)
Elona Bray (Mgr-HR)

**APTUS COURT REPORTING,
LLC**
600 W Broadway Ste 300, San Di-
ego, CA 92101-3352
Web Site: http://www.aptuscr.com
Court Reporting & Stenotype Ser-
vices
N.A.I.C.S.: 561492
Mick Gallagher (CEO)
Sandy Waite (COO)
Ronald Harrison (Mng Dir-Northern
California)
Derek Berg (Pres)
Michael McGowan (Mng Dir-New
York City)
Cathy Chu (Dir-Sls)

Subsidiaries:

Barristers' Reporting Service,
Inc.   (1)
160 S Old Springs Rd, Anaheim, CA 92808
Tel.: (714) 444-4100
Court Reporting & Stenotype Services
N.A.I.C.S.: 561492
Beth Drain (Owner)

AQABA TECHNOLOGIES
36150 Dequindre Ste 610, Sterling
Heights, MI 48310
Tel.: (248) 275-1222
Web Site: http://www.aqabatech.com
Year Founded: 2003
Sales Range: $1-9.9 Million
Online Advertising & Marketing Ser-
vices
N.A.I.C.S.: 541890
Adam Sgamotta (Project Mgr)

AQIWO
1225 S Clark St Ste 1301, Arlington,
VA 22202
Tel.: (703) 416-8590
Web Site: http://www.aqiwo.com
Year Founded: 2002
Sales Range: $10-24.9 Million
Emp.: 30
Computer System Design Services
N.A.I.C.S.: 541512
Stephen Mills (Founder, Pres & CEO)
Eric L. Blackmon (COO & VP)

**AQR CAPITAL MANAGEMENT,
LLC**
2 Greenwich Plz, Greenwich, CT
06830-6353
Tel.: (203) 742-3600   DE
Web Site: http://www.aqrcapital.com
Year Founded: 1998
Sales Range: $100-124.9 Million
Emp.: 200
Investment Management Service
N.A.I.C.S.: 523940
David G. Kabiller (Co-Founder &
Principal)
Jacques A. Friedman (Principal)
Brian K. Hurst (Principal)
Brian S. Posner (Chm)

AQUA AIR PRODUCTS INC.
3638 W Cypress St, Tampa, FL
33607
Tel.: (813) 885-4988
Web Site: http://www.aquaairfl.com
Sales Range: $10-24.9 Million
Emp.: 15
Warm Air Heating & Air Conditioning
N.A.I.C.S.: 238220
Martin A. Vicari (Pres)
Song Sayprasith (Acct Mgr)

AQUA MIZER INC.
6578 Palmer Park Cir, Sarasota, FL
34238
Tel.: (941) 487-7329
Web Site:
    http://www.aquamizerinc.com

Sales Range: $1-9.9 Million
Plumbing Fixtures
N.A.I.C.S.: 326191
David Seaman (Pres)

AQUA POOL & SPA, INC.
2111 Moffat Blvd, Manteca, CA 95336
Tel.: (209) 249-6800
Rev.: $12,900,000
Emp.: 210
Specialty Trade Contractors
N.A.I.C.S.: 238990
Corie Bisio (Acct Mgr)
Richard Townsend (Pres)
Alan Wong (CFO)

AQUA SUN PROPERTIES
3 Sunshine Blvd, Ormond Beach, FL 32174
Tel.: (386) 677-0573
Web Site: http://www.aquasun.com
Sales Range: $10-24.9 Million
Emp.: 92
Condominium Developers
N.A.I.C.S.: 236117
William Carlson (Pres)

AQUA YIELD OPERATIONS, LLC
12754 S 125 E, Draper, UT 84020
Tel.: (801) 449-9220
Web Site: http://www.aquayield.com
Year Founded: 2014
Sales Range: $1-9.9 Million
Emp.: 27
Agricultural Research Services
N.A.I.C.S.: 115112
Warren T. Bell (Co-Founder & Chm)
Clark T. Bell (Co-Founder & CEO)
Mike Bullock (Co-Founder, Pres & COO)
Landon Bunderson (Chief Science Officer)
Jim Krebsbach (VP-Sls)

AQUA-GON INC.
1728 N Aurora Rd, Naperville, IL 60563
Tel.: (630) 355-5363
Web Site: http://www.aquagon.com
Sales Range: $10-24.9 Million
Emp.: 19
Whslr of Sporting & Recreational Supplies
N.A.I.C.S.: 423910
Phil Horvath (Pres)
Jeff Heise (Branch Mgr)
Richard Sletten (Dir-Fin)

AQUABEST SEAFOOD, LLC.
14335 SW 120th St Ste 213, Miami, FL 33186-7296
Tel.: (305) 386-1772
Web Site:
  http://www.aquabestseafood.com
Year Founded: 2009
Sales Range: $10-24.9 Million
Emp.: 2
Fish & Other Seafood Whslr
N.A.I.C.S.: 424460
Robert Tate (Mgr-Sls)
Cesar G. Cantos (Acct Exec)
Lucille M Comprosky (Mgr-Ops)
Federica Hulett (CEO)

AQUARIUS IRRIGATION SUPPLY INC.
1120 Goffle Rd, Hawthorne, NJ 07506
Tel.: (973) 423-0222
Web Site:
  https://www.aquariussupply.com
Year Founded: 1969
Sales Range: $10-24.9 Million
Emp.: 45
Irrigation Equipment

N.A.I.C.S.: 423820
Mark Harabedian (CFO)
Robert Beausoleil (Pres)

AQUARIUS LTD. INC.
3200 S Kingshighway Blvd, Saint Louis, MO 63139-1114
Tel.: (314) 664-4498   MO
Web Site:
  https://www.aquariusltd.com
Year Founded: 1969
Sales Range: $10-24.9 Million
Emp.: 115
Provider of Apparel & Accessories
N.A.I.C.S.: 424350
Alexander Schonwald (Pres)
Carl Ranger (CFO)
Cathy Bone (Mgr-Hr)

AQUATEC INC.
1235 Shappert Dr, Machesney Park, IL 61115
Tel.: (815) 654-1500
Web Site: http://www.aquatecinc.com
Sales Range: $10-24.9 Million
Emp.: 20
Pollution Control Equipment
N.A.I.C.S.: 423830
Richard J. Ryan (Pres)
Jeffrey Strey (Mgr-Ops)

AQUATECH INTERNATIONAL CORP.
1 4 Coins Dr, Canonsburg, PA 15317
Tel.: (724) 746-5300
Web Site: https://www.aquatech.com
Sales Range: $10-24.9 Million
Emp.: 125
Water Treatment Equipment, Industrial
N.A.I.C.S.: 333310
Venkee N. Sharma (Pres & CEO)
Patrick Randall (Dir-Sls)
Devesh Mittal (VP-Indus Solutions)

AQUATHERM INTERNATIONAL
500 S 500 W Bldg 1, Lindon, UT 84042
Tel.: (801) 805-6657
Web Site: http://www.aquatherm-pipesystems.com
Year Founded: 2007
Sales Range: $10-24.9 Million
Emp.: 30
Plastic & Metal Pipes For Plumbing
N.A.I.C.S.: 326122
Adam Clark (Pres & COO)
Jordan Hardy (CFO)
David Chen (CEO)

AQUATIC DEVELOPMENT GROUP, INC.
13 Green Mountain Dr, Cohoes, NY 12047-4865
Tel.: (518) 783-0038   NY
Web Site:
  https://www.aquaticgroup.com
Year Founded: 1994
Rev.: $30,000,000
Emp.: 100
Specialty Trade Contractors
N.A.I.C.S.: 238990
Ken Ellis (CEO)
David Savage (Mgr-Architecture & Engrg)
Steve Biernacki (Mgr-Bus Dev)
Robin Cuddey (Controller)
Thomas A. Lampron (Project Mgr-Construction)
Jim Dunn (Pres)
Bruce Quay (COO)

Subsidiaries:

Aquatic Amusement Associates
Ltd.   (1)

13 Green Mtn Dr, Cohoes, NY
12047-4865   (100%)
Tel.: (518) 783-0038
Web Site: http://www.aquaticgroup.com
Specialty Trade Contractors
N.A.I.C.S.: 238990
Ken Ellis (Pres)

Aquatic Builders Ltd.   (1)
13 Green Mtn Dr, Cohoes, NY 12047-4865
Tel.: (518) 783-0038
Web Site: http://www.aquaticgroup.com
Sales Range: $25-49.9 Million
Emp.: 80
Specialty Trade Contractors
N.A.I.C.S.: 238990
Ken Ellis (Owner)

Aquatic Construction Ltd.   (1)
13 Green Mountain Dr, Cohoes, NY 12047-4865
Tel.: (518) 783-0038
Web Site: http://www.aquaticgroup.com
Sales Range: $25-49.9 Million
Emp.: 80
Specialty Trade Contractors
N.A.I.C.S.: 238990
Ken Ellis (Pres)

AQUATIC VEGETATION CONTROL INC.
1860 W 10th St, Riviera Beach, FL 33404
Tel.: (561) 845-5525
Web Site:
  https://www.avcaquatic.com
Rev.: $20,000,000
Emp.: 100
Soil Preparation, Planting & Cultivating
N.A.I.C.S.: 115112
Christy Barton (Mgr-HR)
Todd Olson (CMO)
Sharon Gillenwalters (CFO)
Angel Lopez (VP-Ops)
James L. Burney Jr. (Pres)

AQUENT INC.
501 Boylston St 3rd Fl, Boston, MA 02116
Tel.: (617) 535-5000   MA
Web Site: http://www.aquent.com
Year Founded: 1986
Sales Range: $300-349.9 Million
Emp.: 387
Marketing & Creative Staffing Services
N.A.I.C.S.: 561311
John H. Chuang (Co-Founder, Chm & CEO)
Steven M. Kapner (Co-Founder & Mng Dir)
Larry Bolick (CIO)
Nunzio Domilici (CFO)
Mia Wenjen (Co-Founder)
Steve Dempsey (COO)
Kelly Boykin (Sr VP-Fin Svcs & Professional Svcs Industries)

Subsidiaries:

Aquent GmbH & Co. KG   (1)
Prunnstrasse 5, 80331, Munich,
Germany   (100%)
Tel.: (49) 892370960
Web Site: http://www.aquent.de
Sales Range: $10-24.9 Million
Emp.: 9
Information Technology Consulting
N.A.I.C.S.: 541512

RitaSue Siegel Resources   (1)
162 5th Ave 11th Fl, New York, NY 10010
Tel.: (212) 682-2100
Web Site: http://www.ritasue.com
Sales Range: $10-24.9 Million
Emp.: 70
Marketing & Creative Staffing Services
N.A.I.C.S.: 561311

AQUILINE CAPITAL PARTNERS LLC

535 Madison Ave, New York, NY 10022
Tel.: (212) 624-9500   DE
Web Site: http://www.aquiline.com
Privater Equity Firm
N.A.I.C.S.: 523999
Jeffrey W. Greenberg (Chm & CEO)
Geoffrey Kalish (Partner & COO)
Richard Rosenbaum (Founder)
Vincenzo La Ruffa (Pres)

Subsidiaries:

Altegris Investments, Inc.   (1)
1200 Prospect St Ste 400, La Jolla, CA 92037
Tel.: (858) 459-7040
Web Site: http://www.altegris.com
Rev.: $2,430,000,000
Alternative Investment Management Services
N.A.I.C.S.: 523940
Jon C. Sundt (Founder & Chm)
Jack Leon Rivkin (Chief Investment Officer)
Ken McGuire (Co-Pres)
David Mathews (Gen Counsel & Sr VP)
Laura Pyle (Sr VP & Chief of Staff)
Robert J. Murphy (Deputy Chief Investment Officer)

Subsidiary (Domestic):

Altegris Advisors, LLC   (2)
1200 Prospect St Ste 400, La Jolla, CA 92037
Tel.: (858) 459-7040
Web Site: http://www.altegris.com
Investment Advisory Services
N.A.I.C.S.: 523940
Allen Cheng (Chief Investment Officer, Sr VP & Portfolio Mgr)
Jack Leon Rivkin (Vice Chm & CEO)
Kenneth Ives McGuire (Pres & COO)
Robert Naka (COO)

Altegris Portfolio Management,
Inc.   (2)
1200 Prospect St Ste 400, La Jolla, CA 92037
Tel.: (858) 459-7040
Web Site: http://www.altegris.com
Portfolio Management Services
N.A.I.C.S.: 523940
Jon C. Sundt (Pres & CEO)
Allen Cheng (Sr VP & Co-Portfolio Mgr-Mutual Funds)

Ascensus, LLC   (1)
200 Dryden Rd, Dresher, PA 19025
Tel.: (800) 346-3860
Web Site: https://www.ascensus.com
Financial Retirement Services
N.A.I.C.S.: 524292
Raghav Nandagopal (Chief Corp Dev Officer)
James M. Lucania (CFO)
Joe Dansky (Chief Compliance Officer, Chief Legal Officer & Chief Risk Officer)
Amy Walker (Chief HR Officer)
David L. Musto (Pres & CEO)
Carl Negin (CMO)
Kevin Cox (Pres-Retirement & Head-Retirement Bus)
Peg Creonte (Head-Gov Savings)
Jim Gearin (COO)
Kurt Laning (Pres-Institutional Solutions)
James Lucania (CFO)
Clay Kennedy (VP-Insurance & Nonqualified Retirement Plan Sls)

Subsidiary (Domestic):

Beneco Systems, Inc.   (2)
8655 East Via de Ventura Ste G-200, Scottsdale, AZ 85258
Tel.: (800) 965-2702
Web Site: http://www.beneco.com
Human Resources & Executive Search Consulting Services
N.A.I.C.S.: 541612

Benefits of Missouri Inc.   (2)
14323 S Outer 40 Ste 600N, Chesterfield, MO 63017-5747
Tel.: (314) 576-5880
Portfolio Management
N.A.I.C.S.: 523940

Intac Actuarial Services, Inc.   (2)

Aquiline Capital Partners LLC—(Continued)

50 Tice Blvd Ste 151, Woodcliff Lake, NJ 07677
Tel.:(201) 447-2525
Web Site: http://www.intacinc.com
Human Resources & Executive Search
Consulting Services
N.A.I.C.S.: 541612
Harry Rosenberg (VP)

National Retirement Services, Inc. (2)
5832 Bolsa Ave 100, Huntington Beach, CA 92649
Tel.: (714) 622-3188
Pension Funds & Retirement Services
N.A.I.C.S.: 525110

Polycomp Administrative Services, Inc. (2)
3000 Lava Ridge Ct Ste 130, Roseville, CA 95661
Tel.: (916) 773-3480
Web Site: http://www.polycomp.net
Insurance Services
N.A.I.C.S.: 524298
NaKendra Stewart (Dir-Qualified Plans)
Christopher Mastrianni (Dir-Benefit Trust Svcs)

Provident Trust Group, LLC (2)
8880 W Sunset Rd Ste 250, Las Vegas, NV 89148
Tel.: (702) 434-0023
Web Site: http://www.trustprovident.com
Trust, Custody, Administration & Escrow Services
N.A.I.C.S.: 523991
Michael Vavruska (Mgr-Sr Bus Dev)

Qualified Plans, LLC (2)
2702 Whatley Ave Ste A-1, Savannah, GA 31404
Tel.: (912) 356-1120
Web Site: http://www.qplans.com
Third Party Retirement Plan Services
N.A.I.C.S.: 623311
Joanna M. Fenske (Partner)

TCFCW, LLC (2)
113 Seaboard Ln Ste B150, Franklin, TN 37067
Tel.: (615) 467-7090
HR Consulting Services
N.A.I.C.S.: 541612

The Newport Group, Inc. (2)
1350 Treat Blvd Ste 300, Walnut Creek, CA 94597
Tel.: (925) 328-4540
Web Site: http://www.newportgroup.com
Emp.: 1,200
Asset Management, Retirement Plans & Insurance Services
N.A.I.C.S.: 524113
Amy K. Parker (Mng Dir-Fiduciary Consulting Svcs)
Greg Tschider (CEO)
Laura Ramanis (COO)
Sean N. Havlin (CFO)
Jacqueline Ward (Chief HR Officer)
Kurt J. Laning (Exec VP)
Micah DiSalvo (Sr VP-Institutional Sls)
Whitney Ames (Gen Counsel)
Geraldine O'Brien (VP-Comm)
Andre Mintz (Chief Info Security Officer)

Subsidiary (Domestic):

Plan Administrators, Inc. (3)
1300 Enterprise Dr, De Pere, WI 54115
Tel.: (920) 337-9906
Web Site: http://www.pai.com
Sales Range: $1-9.9 Million
Emp.: 100
Management Consulting Services
N.A.I.C.S.: 541611
Michael Kiley (VP-Sls & Mktg)
Kelly Skenandore-Holtz (Coord-Trng & Dev)
Drew Meyers (Dir-Customer Care Center)
Tracy Ruh (CEO)

Subsidiary (Domestic):

United Retirement Plan Consultants, Inc. (2)
545 Metro Pl S Ste 240, Dublin, OH 43017
Tel.: (614) 923-8822
Web Site: http://www.unitedretirement.com

Sales Range: $25-49.9 Million
Retirement, Pension Administration & Investment Management Services
N.A.I.C.S.: 524292

Subsidiary (Domestic):

MGA Consultants, Inc. (3)
6031 University Blvd Ste 300, Ellicott City, MD 21043
Tel.: (301) 614-0957
Web Site: http://www.mgaconsultants.net
Financial Services
N.A.I.C.S.: 525990
Lee Bachu (CEO)

Axiom Re, Inc. (1)
1000 SE Monterey Commons Blvd Ste 301, Stuart, FL 34996
Tel.: (772) 781-5280
Web Site: http://www.evergreenre.com
Managed Care Reinsurance Broker
N.A.I.C.S.: 524210
Ronald K. Taylor (Pres & CEO)
Charles Crispin (Sr VP)
Rhonda Parry (VP)

Subsidiary (Domestic):

Axia Strategies, Inc. (2)
8688 Eagle Creek Cir, Savage, MN 55378
Tel.: (952) 945-3535
Web Site: http://www.axiastrategies.com
Administrative Management & General Management Consulting Service
N.A.I.C.S.: 541611
Tom Schori (Principal)
Mike Harrington (Principal)
Bob Ziomek (Principal)

Independent Pharmaceutical Consultants, Inc. (2)
1061 Peruque Crossing Ct, O'Fallon, MO 63366
Tel.: (636) 614-1344
Web Site: http://www.ipc-inc.com
Emp.: 13
Prescription Benefit Consulting Services
N.A.I.C.S.: 541690
Christine Johnston (Mng Dir)
Ronald K. Taylor (Sr Mng Dir)

CoAdvantage Corporation (1)
3350 Buschwood Park Dr Ste 200, Tampa, FL 33618
Tel.: (813) 935-2000
Web Site: http://www.coadvantage.com
Emp.: 50,000
Medical Human Resources Services
N.A.I.C.S.: 541612
Wade Latham (Sr VP-Risk Mgmt & Corp Strategy)
Mark Zimmerman (CIO)
Clinton Burgess (Pres & CEO)
Peter Grabowski (CFO)
Scott Gordon (Sr VP-Sls)
John McAllister (Sr VP-Benefit Products)
Kat Bush (Sr VP-Payroll & Benefits Ops)
Kimberley A. Robbins (Chief Legal Officer)
John Hale (CTO)
Lori Martin (Sr VP-Fin)

Subsidiary (Domestic):

Momentum Resources, Inc. (2)
139 Drayton St, Savannah, GA 31401-3745
Tel.: (912) 238-5200
Web Site: https://www.momentumhr.net
Professional Employer Organizations
N.A.I.C.S.: 561330
David Kindred (CEO)

Remedy Employer Services, LLC (2)
300 Riverside Dr E Ste 3100, Bradenton, FL 34208
Tel.: (941) 722-3344
Web Site: http://www.remedyes.com
Professional Employer Organizations
N.A.I.C.S.: 561330

SourcePointe, LLC (2)
2000B Southbridge Pkwy Ste 200, Birmingham, AL 35209
Tel.: (251) 340-8333
Web Site: http://sourcepointe.com
Sales Range: $1-9.9 Million
Emp.: 200
Human Resources & Executive Search Consulting Services
N.A.I.C.S.: 541612

National Medical Billing Services LLC (1)
7 Arnage Rd, Saint Louis, MO 63005
Tel.: (877) 236-5245
Web Site: http://www.nationalascbilling.com
Healthcare Revenue Cycle Management Services
N.A.I.C.S.: 541512
Nader Samii (CEO)

Subsidiary (Domestic):

Medi Corp, Inc. (2)
25 Commerce Dr 2, Cranford, NJ 07016
Tel.: (908) 653-9399
Web Site: http://www.medi-corp.com
Sales Range: $1-9.9 Million
Emp.: 35
Accounting Services
N.A.I.C.S.: 541219
David Kadish (Pres & CEO)
Adis Whartnaby (Exec VP)
Greg Maccia (CTO)

mdStrategies, Inc. (2)
23 Forest Green Trl, Kingwood, TX 77339
Tel.: (281) 358-0300
Web Site: http://www.mdstrategies.com
Sales Range: $1-9.9 Million
Emp.: 14
Management Consulting Services
N.A.I.C.S.: 541618
Scott Megason (Pres)

Ontellus (1)
1010 Lamar St 18th Fl, Houston, TX 77002
Tel.: (713) 224-6865
Web Site: http://www.ontellus.com
Record Retrieval & Analysis Services
N.A.I.C.S.: 519290
Newton Ross (Pres)
Melanie Pita (Chief Legal Officer)
Lori Neal (Sr VP-HR)
Darren Klauser (CEO)
Aaron Deister (CFO)
Cynthia Ledlow (COO)
Brian James (CIO)
Todd Smith (Exec VP-Customer Care)
Mason Ross (Sr VP-California Ops)
Tim Kennedy (VP-Sls)
Michelle Ritchey (VP-Strategic Accts)
Dan Sandman (Pres-AMFS)
Joe Brito (VP-HR)
M. Neil Kallmeyer (Chm)

Subsidiary (Domestic):

Aboingo Services (2)
225 W Winton Ave Ste 203, Hayward, CA 94544-1219
Tel.: (877) 475-6161
Law firm
N.A.I.C.S.: 541199

Plante & Moran, PLLC (2)
27400 NW Hwy, Southfield, MI 48034
Tel.: (248) 352-2500
Web Site: http://www.plantemoran.com
Emp.: 3,100
Accounting, Auditing & Consulting Services
N.A.I.C.S.: 541211
Gordon Krater (Partner)
Ron Eckstein (Partner)
Frank Audia (Mng Partner, Partner & Chief Risk Officer)
Jim Proppe (Dir-Socio)
Sue Novak (Partner)
Keith Martinez (Partner-Columbus)
Dave Plomin (Partner-Chicago)
Sherrie Krowczyk-Mendoza (Partner-Chicago)
Greg Alonso (Principal)
Dave Andrea (Principal)
Jeff Antaya (Partner & CMO)
Dennis Bagley (Partner)
Theresa Banka (Partner)
Mark Barrott (Principal)
John R. Bebes (Partner)
Anthony Belloli (Partner-Wealth Mgmt)
Beth Bialy (Partner)

Second Image National, Inc. (2)
170 E Arrow Hwy, San Dimas, CA 91773
Tel.: http://www.secondimage.com
Document Preparation Services
N.A.I.C.S.: 561410
Rebecca Williams (Acct Exec-Natl)

Output Services Group, Inc. (1)
775 Washington Ave, Carlstadt, NJ 07072

Tel.: (201) 871-1100
Web Site: https://osgconnect.com
Electronic Billing & Payment Services
N.A.I.C.S.: 522320
Eric Blassberg (CIO)
Kevin Keleghan (CEO)
Phil Hoggarth (Pres-UK)
Eric W. Ek (Interim Pres & CFO)
Steve Karp (Chief Product Officer)
Ken Powell (Chief Comml Officer)
Patrick O'Hara (Chief Performance Officer)

Subsidiary (Domestic):

Applied Information Group Inc. (2)
100 Market St, Kenilworth, NJ 07033
Tel.: (908) 241-7007
Web Site: http://www.appliedinfogroup.com
Sales Range: $1-9.9 Million
Emp.: 30
Software Publisher
N.A.I.C.S.: 513210
Mitch Rubin (Pres)

Subsidiary (Non-US):

Communisis plc (2)
10 Little Portland Street, London, W1W 7JG, United Kingdom
Tel.: (44) 207 382 8950
Web Site: http://www.communisis.com
Rev.: $507,086,989
Assets: $441,614,195
Liabilities: $253,903,035
Net Worth: $187,711,160
Earnings: $15,881,841
Emp.: 2,073
Fiscal Year-end: 12/31/2017
Printing Management Services; Specialist Printing & Direct Mail Services
N.A.I.C.S.: 323111
Andy Blundell (CEO)
Sarah Caddy (Sec)

Subsidiary (Domestic):

Communisis Europe Limited (3)
Communisis House Manston Lane, Leeds, LS15 8AH, West Yorkshire, United Kingdom
Tel.: (44) 113 277 0202
Web Site: http://www.communisis.com
Emp.: 30
Fiscal Year-end: 12/31/2017
Management Services
N.A.I.C.S.: 551114

Communisis UK Limited (3)
Communisis House Manston Lane, Leeds, LS15 8AH, West Yorkshire, United Kingdom (100%)
Tel.: (44) 1132770202
Web Site: http://www.Communisis.co.uk
Sales Range: $25-49.9 Million
Emp.: 80
Commercial Printing
N.A.I.C.S.: 323111
Andy Blundell (Exec Dir)

Subsidiary (Domestic):

Diamond Marketing Solutions Group, Inc. (2)
900 Kimberly Dr, Carol Stream, IL 60188
Tel.: (630) 597-9100
Web Site: http://www.dmsolutions.com
Advertising & Marketing Services
N.A.I.C.S.: 541810
Mark Helland (Exec VP & CIO)
Jim Renella (Sr VP-Special Projects)
Mark Selland (Pres-West Coast Ops)
Greg Waite (Pres)
Michael Nevolo (Exec VP-Corp Sls & Mktg)
Cyndi Greenglass (Sr VP-Strategic Solutions)
Dawn Mellas (Sr VP-Chicago Ops)
Sherrie Miller (VP-Print Production Svcs)
Louis J. Sedivy IV (Exec VP & CFO)

DoublePositive Marketing Group, Inc. (2)
kySong 1 Ste 140 1475 North Scottsdale Rd, Scottsdale, AZ 85257
Tel.: (410) 332-0464
Web Site: http://www.doublepositive.com
Online Marketing Services
N.A.I.C.S.: 541613
Joey Liner (Pres)
John Nuclo (Mng Dir)

Miria Systems, Inc. (2)

2570 Blvd of the Generals Ste 222, Norristown, PA 19043
Tel.: (484) 446-3300
Software Publisher
N.A.I.C.S.: 513210
George Thomas (VP-Sls)

Subsidiary (Domestic):

Paybox Corp (3)
150 S Pine Island Rd Ste 300, Plantation, FL 33324
Tel.: (954) 510-3750
Web Site: http://www.gopaybox.com
Electronic Invoice Management & Workflow
Compliance Reconciliation for Accounts
Payable & Accounts Receivable
N.A.I.C.S.: 541512
Matthew E. Oakes (Pres)
Robert Gilbert (Dir-Sls)
Harold Yamcek (VP-Fin)
Joe Vosilla (Sr Dir-Dev & Delivery)
Jorge Ferrer (Sr Dir-IT)

Subsidiary (Domestic):

NCP Solutions, LLC (2)
5200 E Lake Blvd, Birmingham, AL 35217
Tel.: (205) 849-5200
Web Site: http://www.ncpsolutions.com
Sales Range: $50-74.9 Million
Receipt, Invoice & Memorandum Books Mfr
N.A.I.C.S.: 323111
Tim Cooper (Sr VP-IT)
Mark Harris (Sr VP & Gen Mgr)

National Business Systems, Inc. (2)
2919 W Service Rd, Eagan, MN 55121
Tel.: (651) 688-0202
Web Site: http://www.nbsusa.com
Data Entry Services
N.A.I.C.S.: 518210

TeleReach, Inc. (2)
90 Whiting St, Plainville, CT 06062
Tel.: (860) 793-3480
Web Site: http://www.telereachinc.com
Telephone Answering Services
N.A.I.C.S.: 561421
Gary Reach (Founder & Pres)
Mike Prince (Dir-Call Center)
Linnette Algarin (Dir-Call Center)
Cam Craig (Coord-Major Accts)

The Garfield Group, Inc. (2)
325 Chestnut St Ste 405, Philadelphia, PA 19106
Tel.: (215) 867-8600
Web Site: http://www.garfieldgroup.com
Emp.: 4
Advertising & Public Relations Agency
N.A.I.C.S.: 541810
Larry Garfield (Founder & Pres)
Les Brokaw (VP-Ops)
Byron Lomas (VP-Creative)
Matt Pfluger (VP-Strategy)
Alexis Sawyer (Assoc Dir-Creative)
Ken Wilsbach (Dir-Tech)
David Saba (Dir-Public Rels)
Brian Beltz (Mgr-Digital Campaign)
Doug Eckard (Dir-New Bus)

WhatCounts, Inc. (2)
3445 Peachtree Rd NE Ste 600, Atlanta, GA 30326
Tel.: (404) 995-8600
Web Site: http://www.whatcounts.com
Web-Based E-Mail Marketing
N.A.I.C.S.: 541613
Daniel Caplin (Pres)

Windsor Circle Inc. (2)
212 West Main St Ste 400, Durham, NC 27701
Tel.: (877) 848-4113
Customer Retention Automation Software
N.A.I.C.S.: 513210
Erik Nieman (Dir-Acct Mgmt)

Relation Insurance, Inc. (1)
Walnut Creek Office 1277 Treat Blvd Ste 400, Walnut Creek, CA 94597
Tel.: (925) 937-5858
Web Site: http://www.relationinsurance.com
Insurance Brokerage: Risk-Management & Benefits-Consulting Services
N.A.I.C.S.: 524298
Joseph L. Tatum (CEO)
Edward Nathan Page (Pres & COO)
Keri Lopez (Pres-Employee Benefits)

Kendra Butler (Executives)
Jonathan W. Cooper (Pres-East Reg)
Kate Rager (Gen Counsel)
Neil Majors (Pres-Education Practice)
Timothy Hall (Exec VP & Head-M&A)
Vincent Bell (VP)
Russell Brown (Chief Revenue Officer)

Subsidiary (Domestic):

Clark Farley Insurance Agency, Inc. (2)
9300 Two Notch Rd Ste N, Columbia, SC 29223
Tel.: (803) 788-4211
Web Site: http://www.clarkfarleyinsurance.com
Sales Range: $1-9.9 Million
Emp.: 10
Insurance Agencies & Brokerages
N.A.I.C.S.: 524210
Clark Farley (Principal)

Dahlmeier Insurance Agency, Inc. (2)
2080 Myers St, Chico, CA 95966-5368
Tel.: (530) 533-3424
Web Site: http://www.dahlmeier.com
Sales Range: $1-9.9 Million
Emp.: 15
Insurance Brokerage Services
N.A.I.C.S.: 524210
Don Schukraft (CEO)
Mike Barry (Controller)

Dunn Insurance, Inc. (2)
198 S Main St, Middletown, CT 06457-3727
Tel.: (860) 347-4924
Rev.: $1,300,000
Emp.: 9
Insurance Agencies & Brokerages
N.A.I.C.S.: 524210
Ron Dunn (Pres)

J Deutsch Associates Inc. (2)
111 John St, New York, NY 10038
Tel.: (212) 693-3717
Insurance Agencies & Brokerages
N.A.I.C.S.: 524210

Relation Insurance Services Inc. (2)
1277 Treat Blvd Ste 400, Walnut Creek, CA 94597
Web Site: http://www.ascensionins.com
Sales Range: $150-199.9 Million
Emp.: 400
Insurance Products & Employee Benefits
Management Services
N.A.I.C.S.: 524210
Tuan Nguyen (VP-Ascension Benefits & Insurance Solutions)
Edward Nathan Page (COO)
Jonathan W. Cooper (Mng Dir-Eastern)
Keri Lopez (Pres-Employee Benefits)
Daniel Granieri (Officer-Tech)
Kendra Butler (Dir-Corp HR)
Neil Majors (Pres-Education Practice)
Clark Palmer (COO-Eastern)
Lee Paige (VP-Bus Integration)
Natalie Zensius (VP-Mktg & Comm)
Scott Machado (VP-IT)
Tim Hall (CEO)
Katy Ringeman (Pres-Relation Select)
Russell Brown (Pres)
Charissa Hartmann (CFO)

Division (Domestic):

Ascension Benefits & Insurance Solutions (3)
1277 Treat Blvd Ste 650, Walnut Creek, CA 94597
Web Site: http://www.ascensionbenefitsins.com
Benefits & Insurance Solutions
N.A.I.C.S.: 524298

Unit (Domestic):

Ascension Collegiate Solutions (4)
12121 Wilshire Blvd Ste 1001, Los Angeles, CA 90401
Tel.: (310) 394-0440
Web Site: http://www.ascensioncollegiate.com
Emp.: 20
Insurance Agencies & Brokerages
N.A.I.C.S.: 524210
Neil Majors (COO)

Subsidiary (Domestic):

Belvedere Pacific LLC (3)
145 Corte Madera Town Ctr Ste 435, Corte Madera, CA 94925
Tel.: (415) 891-3304
Web Site: http://www.belvederepacificgroup.com
Employee Benefit Consulting Services
N.A.I.C.S.: 541612
Michael P. Stallone (Principal)

Consultative Insurance Group Inc. (3)
25800 N Depot St Ste 200, Olmsted Falls, OH 44138
Tel.: (612) 590-6454
Web Site: http://www.consultativeinsurance.com
Insurance Agencies & Brokerages
N.A.I.C.S.: 524210
Susan Jones (Mgr)
Ron Smith (VP)
Kindra Smith (Ops Mgr)

Hooper, Spuhler & Sturgeon Insurance Services, Inc. (3)
133 N L St, Tulare, CA 93274
Tel.: (559) 686-3442
Web Site: http://www.hssins.com
Insurance Related Activities
N.A.I.C.S.: 524298
Mike Muller (Partner)
Kristi Koetsier (Acct Exec)

Transure Services, Inc. (3)
7261 Burlington Rd, Whitsett, NC 27377
Tel.: (336) 584-9494
Web Site: http://www.transure.com
Sales Range: $1-9.9 Million
Emp.: 12
Trucking & Transportation Industry Insurance Products & Services
N.A.I.C.S.: 524210
Stan H. Sharpe (Principal)
Bob Gunn (Pres)
Deb Aldridge (Mgr-Mktg Acct)
Sherrie Allen (Mgr-Mktg Acct)
Rick Joyce (Controller)
Paul Fazekas (Acct Exec)
Chris Huneycutt (Mgr-Mktg)

Truck Insurance Mart Inc. (3)
10027 Woodend Rd, Kansas City, KS 66111-1763
Tel.: (913) 344-0349
Web Site: http://www.truckinsurancemart.com
Insurance Agencies & Brokerages
N.A.I.C.S.: 524210
Lucy Harrity (CEO)

Walter L. Clark & Associates, Inc. (3)
7673 N Ingram Ave, Fresno, CA 93711
Tel.: (559) 222-0300
Insurance Brokerage Services
N.A.I.C.S.: 524210

Subsidiary (Domestic):

S.T. Good Insurance, Inc. (2)
875 AAA Blvd Ste A, Newark, DE 19713
Tel.: (302) 328-1888
Web Site: http://www.thegoodagency.com
Insurance Agencies & Brokerages
N.A.I.C.S.: 524210
Daniel Good (VP)
Barbara Donahue (Acct Mgr-Comml)

Santo Insurance & Financial Services, Inc. (2)
224 Main St Ste 2A, Salem, NH 03079
Tel.: (603) 890-6439
Web Site: http://www.santoinsurance.com
Insurance Related Activities
N.A.I.C.S.: 524298
Jamie Santo (Pres)

Sleeper Sewell Insurance Services, Inc. (2)
12400 Coit Rd Ste 1100, Dallas, TX 75251
Tel.: (972) 419-7500
Web Site: http://www.sleepersewell.com
Insurance Related Activities
N.A.I.C.S.: 524298
Michael Darnell (Exec VP)

Summers Thompson Lowry, Inc. (2)

100 Europa Dr Ste 571, Chapel Hill, NC 27517
Tel.: (939) 969-5332
Web Site: http://www.stlinsure.com
Insurance Agencies & Brokerages
N.A.I.C.S.: 524210
Larry A. Summers (Pres)

Taylor & Associates Benefits (2)
1501 F St, Modesto, CA 95354-2522
Tel.: (209) 338-1012
Web Site: http://www.taylorandassociatesbenefit.com
Insurance Agencies & Brokerages
N.A.I.C.S.: 524210
Chris Taylor (Owner)

Shepard Insurance (1)
5801 N 10th St, McAllen, TX 78504-2609
Tel.: (956) 686-3888
Web Site: http://www.shepins.com
Insurance Agencies & Brokerages
N.A.I.C.S.: 524210
Ken Shepard (Owner)

Worley Claims Services, LLC (1)
303 Timber Creek, Hammond, LA 70403
Tel.: (985) 542-2369
Web Site: http://www.worleyco.com
Insurance Claims Adjusting Services
N.A.I.C.S.: 524291

Subsidiary (Domestic):

Apex Claims Services of New England (2)
94 N Elm St, Westfield, MA 01085-1643
Tel.: (413) 562-7502
Web Site: http://www.apexclaims.com
Claims Adjusting
N.A.I.C.S.: 524291
Tom Abel (Partner)
Marion Guzik (Partner)
Doug DeSaulnier (Partner)
Tammy Breton (Office Mgr)

Audit Services, Inc. (2)
2123 Eastview Pkwy, Conyers, GA 30013
Tel.: (770) 388-0222
Web Site: http://www.asiclaims.com
Insurance Related Activities
N.A.I.C.S.: 524298

National Catastrophe Adjusters LLC (2)
9725 Windermere Blvd, Fishers, IN 46037
Tel.: (317) 915-8888
Web Site: http://www.ncagroup.com
Insurance Adjusting & Catastrophe Claims Management
N.A.I.C.S.: 524291
Jim Pearl (Pres)

Reid, Jones, McRorie & Williams, Inc. (2)
2200 Executive St, Charlotte, NC 28208-3652
Tel.: (704) 537-0012
Web Site: http://www.rjmw.com
Insurance Claims Adjusting Services
N.A.I.C.S.: 524291
Robert McRorie (Owner, Pres & CEO)

AQUION PARTNERS L.P.
101 S Gary Ave, Roselle, IL 60172
Tel.: (847) 437-9400   IL
Web Site: https://www.aquion.com
Year Founded: 1989
Sales Range: $50-74.9 Million
Emp.: 130
Water Treatment
N.A.I.C.S.: 333310
Steve Swiderski (VP-Mfg)
Mike Madsen (CFO & Exec VP)

Subsidiaries:

RainSoft Water Treatment Systems (1)
2080 E Lunt Ave, Elk Grove Village, IL 60007-5606
Tel.: (847) 437-9400
Web Site: http://www.rainsoft.com
Sales Range: $10-24.9 Million
Emp.: 100
Water Softening & Purification Equipment Mfr
N.A.I.C.S.: 333310

Aquion Partners L.P.—(Continued)

Ed Meil *(VP-Fin)*
Rich Verson *(Dir-Mktg)*

AR GLOBAL INVESTMENTS, LLC

405 Park Ave, New York, NY 10022
Tel.: (212) 415-6500   DE
Web Site: http://www.ar-global.com
Emp.: 150
Holding Company; Real Estate Investment & Fund Management Services
N.A.I.C.S.: 551112
Edward Michael Weil Jr. *(CEO)*

Subsidiaries:

AR Capital, LLC   (1)
405 Park Ave 15th Fl, New York, NY 10022
Tel.: (212) 415-6500
Web Site:
http://www.americanrealtycap.com
Real Estate Investment Trust Management Services
N.A.I.C.S.: 523940
Edward Michael Weil Jr. *(CEO)*
Patrick A. O'Malley *(Mng Dir-Acq)*
Jason Slear *(Mng Dir-Acq & Dispositions)*
Peter M. Budko *(Chief Investment Officer)*
Jesse Galloway *(Exec VP & Gen Counsel)*
Nick Radesca *(CFO)*
Louisa Quarto *(Exec VP)*
Katie Kurtz *(Dir-Fin)*

Affiliate (Domestic):

American Realty Capital - Retail Centers of America II, Inc.   (2)
405 Park Ave, New York, NY 10022
Tel.: (212) 415-6500
Web Site: http://www.ar-global.com
Real Estate Investment Trust
N.A.I.C.S.: 525990
Patrick J. Goulding *(CFO, Treas & Sec)*

American Realty Capital Daily Net Asset Value Trust, Inc.   (2)
405 Park Ave 14th Fl, New York, NY 10022
Tel.: (212) 415-6500
Rev.: $2,840,000
Assets: $36,398,000
Liabilities: $19,762,000
Net Worth: $16,636,000
Earnings: ($435,000)
Fiscal Year-end: 12/31/2014
Real Estate Investment Trust
N.A.I.C.S.: 525990
Edward Michael Weil Jr. *(Chm, Pres & CEO)*

American Realty Capital Global Trust II, Inc.   (2)
405 Park Ave 14th Floor, New York, NY 10022
Tel.: (212) 415-6500
Web Site: http://www.arcglobaltrust2.com
Rev.: $21,648,000
Assets: $677,120,000
Liabilities: $476,989,000
Net Worth: $200,131,000
Earnings: ($44,515,000)
Fiscal Year-end: 12/31/2015
Real Estate Investment Trust
N.A.I.C.S.: 525990
Scott J. Bowman *(Pres & CEO)*
Timothy Salvemini *(CFO, Treas & Sec)*

American Realty Capital New York City REIT II, Inc.   (2)
405 Park Ave 14th Fl, New York, NY 10022
Tel.: (212) 415-6500
Real Estate Investment Trust
N.A.I.C.S.: 525990
Patrick A. O'Malley *(Chief Investment Officer)*
Michael A. Happel *(Pres, CEO & Sec)*
Gregory W. Sullivan *(CFO, COO & Treas)*

American Strategic Investment Co.   (2)
650 5th Ave 30th Fl, New York, NY 10019
Tel.: (212) 415-6500
Web Site:
https://www.americaninvestment.com
Rev.: $64,005,000
Assets: $790,455,000

Liabilities: $468,879,000
Net Worth: $321,576,000
Earnings: ($45,896,000)
Emp.: 8
Fiscal Year-end: 12/31/2022
Real Estate Investment Trust
N.A.I.C.S.: 525990
Michael Anderson *(CEO)*
Michael LeSanto *(CFO)*
Michael Weil *(Chm)*
Christopher Chao *(Sr VP-Asset Mgmt)*
Ori Kravel *(Sr VP-Corp Dev)*
Boris Korotkin *(Sr VP-Capital Markets)*
Jason Slear *(Exec VP-Real Estate Acquisitions & Dispositions)*

Global Net Lease, Inc.   (2)
650 5th Ave 30th Fl, New York, NY 10019
Tel.: (332) 265-2020
Web Site: https://www.globalnetlease.com
Rev.: $515,070,000
Assets: $8,098,977,000
Liabilities: $5,459,828,000
Net Worth: $2,639,149,000
Earnings: ($211,910,000)
Emp.: 77
Fiscal Year-end: 12/31/2023
Real Estate Investment Trust
N.A.I.C.S.: 525990
Edward Michael Weil Jr. *(Pres & CEO)*
Christopher J. Masterson *(CFO)*
Jason Slear *(Exec VP-Acquisitions)*
Alex Wagstaff *(VP-Asset Mgmt)*
Jacqui Shimmin *(Mng Dir)*
Michael Weil *(CEO)*
Jesse Galloway *(Gen Counsel & Exec VP)*
Ori Kravel *(Sr VP-Corporate Development)*
Stephanie Drews *(VP-Reg Asset Mgmt)*
Donald Foster *(VP-Reg Asset Mgmt)*
Peter Aburrow *(Mgr-Asset)*
Preston Pillsbury *(Mgr-Asset)*
Starr Duvall *(Dir-Construction)*
Jay Kanik *(Dir-Property Mgmt)*

Subsidiary (Domestic):

The Necessity Retail REIT, Inc.   (3)
650 5th Ave 30th Fl, New York, NY 10019
Tel.: (212) 415-6500
Web Site:
https://www.necessityretailreit.com
Rev.: $446,438,000
Assets: $4,586,054,000
Liabilities: $2,998,581,000
Net Worth: $1,587,473,000
Earnings: ($105,854,000)
Fiscal Year-end: 12/31/2022
Real Estate Investment Trust
N.A.I.C.S.: 525990
Jason Doyle *(CFO, Treas & Sec)*

Affiliate (Domestic):

Hospitality Investors Trust, Inc.   (2)
Park Ave Tower 65 E 55th St Ste 801, New York, NY 10022
Tel.: (571) 529-6390
Web Site: http://www.hitreit.com
Rev.: $236,766,000
Assets: $1,776,146,000
Liabilities: $1,827,226,000
Net Worth: ($51,080,000)
Earnings: ($223,989,000)
Emp.: 24
Fiscal Year-end: 12/31/2020
Hospitality Real Estate Investment Trust
N.A.I.C.S.: 525990
Bruce G. Wiles *(Chm)*
Paul C. Hughes *(Gen Counsel & Sec)*
Mark Fowler *(Sr VP-Asset Mgmt)*
Bruce A. Riggins *(Pres, CFO & Treas)*

Retail Credit Property Trust, Inc.   (2)
405 Park Ave 14th Fl, New York, NY 10022
Tel.: (212) 415-6500
Real Estate Investment Trust
N.A.I.C.S.: 525990
Nicholas A. Radesca *(CFO, Treas & Sec)*

AR MEDIA

601 W 26th St Ste 810, New York, NY 10001
Tel.: (212) 739-5500
Web Site: http://www.arnewyork.com
Year Founded: 1997
Sales Range: $10-24.9 Million
Emp.: 45
Advetising Agency

N.A.I.C.S.: 541810
Gavin Manley *(Dir-New Bus & Mktg)*
Raul Martinez *(Principal & Chief Creative Officer)*
Dianne Desroches *(CEO & Principal)*
David Israel *(Exec Dir-Brand Strategy)*

AR SANDRI INC.

400 Chapman St, Greenfield, MA 01301
Tel.: (413) 315-5370
Web Site: https://www.sandri.com
Sales Range: $75-99.9 Million
Emp.: 120
Gasoline
N.A.I.C.S.: 424720
Mike Behn *(COO)*
Christina Wysk *(Mgr-Credit Residential Accts)*

AR WILFLEY & SONS INC.

7350 E Progress Pl Ste 200, Englewood, CO 80111
Tel.: (303) 779-1777
Web Site: http://www.wilfley.com
Sales Range: $10-24.9 Million
Emp.: 130
Industrial Pumps & Parts
N.A.I.C.S.: 333914
Michael Wilfley *(Pres)*
Douglas Segovia *(Reg Mgr-Sls)*
Troy Zellers *(VP-Engrg)*

AR-BE DOORS INC.

7211 S Lockwood Ave, Bedford Park, IL 60638
Tel.: (708) 458-2345
Web Site: http://www.ar-be.com
Sales Range: $10-24.9 Million
Emp.: 60
Garage Door & Entry Door; Installation or Erection
N.A.I.C.S.: 238130
Joe Bladi *(Pres)*

AR-EX LTD.

1282 Old Skokie Valley Rd, Highland Park, IL 60035-3016
Tel.: (847) 579-1408   IL
Web Site: http://www.ar-ex.com
Year Founded: 1938
Sales Range: $1-9.9 Million
Emp.: 40
Hypo-Allergenic Cosmetics & Personal Care Products Whslr
N.A.I.C.S.: 424210
Perry Blatt *(Pres)*
John Floodas *(Controller)*

ARA PARTNERS GROUP

5300 Memorial Dr Ste 500, Houston, TX 77007
Tel.: (713) 337-9150
Web Site:
http://www.arapartners.com
Privater Equity Firm
N.A.I.C.S.: 523940
Charles Cherington *(Mng Partner)*
Troy W. Thacker *(Mng Partner)*
Tuan Tran *(Partner)*
Katy Terrell *(VP)*
David Touhey *(Mng Dir-Portfolio Svcs Grp)*
Charles Cherington *(Mng Partner)*

Subsidiaries:

Anesco Limited   (1)
The Green Easter Park Benyon Road, Reading, RG7 2PQ, Berkshire, United Kingdom
Tel.: (44) 845 894 4444
Web Site: http://www.anesco.co.uk
Sales Range: $25-49.9 Million
Emp.: 100
Energy Efficiency Consultancy Services
N.A.I.C.S.: 541350

Adrian Pike *(CEO)*
Tim Payne *(COO)*
Steve Shine *(Chm)*
Delvin Lane *(Dir-Comml)*
Luke Mann *(Dir-Energy Svcs)*

Fluitron, Inc.   (1)
30 Industrial Dr, Ivyland, PA 18974
Tel.: (215) 355-9970
Web Site: http://www.fluitron.com
Pump & Pumping Equipment Mfr
N.A.I.C.S.: 333914
James G. Leaming-Engineer *(Mgr-Quality Control)*
Robert Chiccarine *(VP)*
Anthony Chiccarine *(Pres)*

Genera Energy, LLC   (1)
2450 E J Chapman Dr Ste 216, Knoxville, TN 37996-0001
Tel.: (423) 884-4110
Web Site: http://www.generaenergy.com
Research & Development in the Physical, Engineering & Life Sciences
N.A.I.C.S.: 541715
Sam Jackson *(VP-Bus Dev)*

Vacuumschmelze GmbH & Co., KG   (1)
Gruener Weg 37, 63450, Hanau, Germany
Tel.: (49) 6181380
Web Site:
https://www.vacuumschmelze.com
Emp.: 4,300
Magnetic Materials, Parts, Inductive Components, Assemblies & Systems Mfr
N.A.I.C.S.: 331110
Erik Eschen *(CEO)*
James Voss *(Member-Mgmt Bd)*
Edward Yocum *(Member-Mgmt Bd)*
Ralf Koch *(VP)*

Subsidiary (Non-US):

VAC Magnetic Japan K.K.   (2)
4-9-14 Takadanobaba, Shinjuku-Ku, Tokyo, 169-0075, Japan
Tel.: (81) 353378522
Web Site: https://www.vac-magnetic-japan.com
Magnetic & Related Product Mfr
N.A.I.C.S.: 332999

VAC Magnetic Korea Ltd.   (2)
A-504 Pyeongchon Acrotower 230 Simin-Daero, Dongan-Gu, Anyang, 014-067, Gyeonggi-Do, Korea (South)
Tel.: (82) 313831728
Magnetic & Related Product Mfr
N.A.I.C.S.: 332999

Subsidiary (US):

VAC Magnetics LLC   (2)
2935 Dolphin Dr, Elizabethtown, KY 42701
Tel.: (270) 769-1333
Web Site: http://www.vacuumschmelze.com
Magnetic Materials, Parts, Inductive Components, Assemblies & Systems Mfr & Distr
N.A.I.C.S.: 335999

Subsidiary (Non-US):

VAC Netherlands B.V.   (2)
Steenovenweg 5, 5708 HN, Helmond, Netherlands
Tel.: (31) 492472432
Magnetic & Related Product Mfr
N.A.I.C.S.: 332999

ARABELLA ADVISORS, LLC

1201 Connecticut Ave NW Ste 300, Washington, DC 20036
Tel.: (202) 595-1020
Web Site:
http://www.arabellaadvisors.com
Year Founded: 2005
Emp.: 500
Advisory Services
N.A.I.C.S.: 541618
Tara Abrahams *(Mng Dir)*
Rick Cruz *(Chief Revenue Officer)*

Sharyn Church *(Mng Dir)*
Sampriti Ganguli *(CEO)*
Chris Hobbs *(COO)*

Subsidiaries:

Redstone Strategy Group, LLC **(1)**
3223 Arapahoe Ave Ste 210, Boulder, CO 80303-1092
Tel.: (303) 606-7100
Web Site: http://www.redstonestrategy.com
Emp.: 100
General Management Consulting Services
N.A.I.C.S.: 541611
Ivan Barkhorn *(Mng Dir)*

ARABELLA EXPLORATION, INC.
509 Pecan St Ste 200, Fort Worth, TX 76102
Tel.: (432) 897-4755   Ky
Web Site: http://www.arabellaexploration.com
Year Founded: 2010
Rev.: $1,515,456
Assets: $8,836,209
Liabilities: $29,251,685
Net Worth: ($20,415,476)
Earnings: ($31,656,273)
Emp.: 5
Fiscal Year-end: 12/31/15
Oil & Gas Exploration Services
N.A.I.C.S.: 211120
Jason Hoisager *(Pres, CEO & Interim CFO)*

ARABLE CAPITAL PARTNERS LLC
10655 NE 4th St Ste 705, Bellevue, WA 98004
Tel.: (866) 927-2253
Web Site: http://www.arablecp.com
Private Equity Firm
N.A.I.C.S.: 523999
Greg Richards *(Founder & Mng Dir)*

Subsidiaries:

Pacific Trellis Fruit LLC **(1)**
5108 E Clinton Way Ste 108, Fresno, CA 93727
Tel.: (559) 255-5400
Web Site: http://www.pacifictrellisfruit.com
Fruit Farming
N.A.I.C.S.: 111998
David Sullivan *(CEO)*

Subsidiary (Domestic):

Dulcinea Farms, LLC **(2)**
111 Corporate Dr, Ladera Ranch, CA 92694
Tel.: (949) 429-1200
Web Site: http://www.dulcinea.com
Sales Range: $75-99.9 Million
Emp.: 35
Fruit Farming
N.A.I.C.S.: 111339
Steve Dabich *(Dir-Sls)*

Progressive Produce LLC **(2)**
5790 Peachtree St, Los Angeles, CA 90040   **(65%)**
Tel.: (323) 890-8100
Web Site: http://www.progressiveproduce.com
Fresh Produce Company
N.A.I.C.S.: 424480

Subsidiary (Domestic):

Keystone Fruit Marketing Inc. **(3)**
11 N Carlisle St Ste 102, Greencastle, PA 17225-1493
Tel.: (717) 597-2112
Web Site: http://www.keystonefruit.com
Fresh Fruit & Vegetable Merchant Whslr
N.A.I.C.S.: 424480
Marty Kamer *(Owner)*

Division (Domestic):

Progressive Farms **(3)**
12100 Edison Hwy, Edison, CA 93220
Tel.: (661) 366-4557
Web Site: http://www.progressiveproduce.com

Emp.: 50
Potatoes, Yams & Onions Farming
N.A.I.C.S.: 111211

Royal Ridge Fruit & Cold Storage, LLC **(1)**
13215 Road F SW, Royal City, WA 99357
Tel.: (509) 346-1520
Web Site: http://www.royalridgefruits.com
Sales Range: $1-9.9 Million
Emp.: 45
Postharvest Crop Services
N.A.I.C.S.: 115114
Kevin Dorsing *(CEO)*

ARACOMA DRUG CO. INC.
604 Stratton St, Logan, WV 25601-4029
Tel.: (304) 752-3812   WV
Year Founded: 1961
Sales Range: $10-24.9 Million
Emp.: 28
Provider of Pharmaceutical Services
N.A.I.C.S.: 456110
George A. Kostas *(Pres)*

ARADIANT CORP.
Ste 150 2468 Historic Decatur Rd, San Diego, CA 92106-6113
Tel.: (858) 654-9090
Rev.: $26,411,000
Emp.: 225
Telephone Communication, Except Radio
N.A.I.C.S.: 517121
Linda Hobbs *(Pres & CEO)*
Mark Wooster *(CFO)*

ARAG INSURANCE COMPANY INC.
500 Grand Ave Ste 100, Des Moines, IA 50309
Tel.: (515) 246-1200
Web Site: http://www.araglegal.com
Sales Range: $25-49.9 Million
Emp.: 140
Insurance Agents
N.A.I.C.S.: 524210
Steve L. Champion *(Mng Dir-South)*
Rick Cavanaugh *(Mng Dir-Northeast)*
Mike Sweeney *(Mng Dir-West)*

Subsidiaries:

Arag Services LLC **(1)**
400 Locust St Ste 480, Des Moines, IA 50309
Tel.: (515) 246-1200
Web Site: http://www.araggroup.com
Rev.: $5,300,000
Emp.: 120
Financial Services
N.A.I.C.S.: 524210

ARAGON LLC.
142 W 57th St 9th Fl, New York, NY 10019
Tel.: (212) 937-9600
Year Founded: 2000
Sales Range: $50-74.9 Million
Emp.: 60
Housing Construction Services
N.A.I.C.S.: 236117
Danielle Fanduiz *(CFO)*
Alex Getelman *(Pres)*

ARAKELIAN ENTERPRISES, INC.
14048 E Valley Blvd, City of Industry, CA 91746
Tel.: (626) 336-3636
Web Site: http://www.athensservices.com
Year Founded: 1957
Waste Collection & Recycling Company
N.A.I.C.S.: 562111
Eric Hollman *(Supvr-Ops)*

Subsidiaries:

Recology Inc. **(1)**

50 California St 24th Fl, San Francisco, CA 94111
Tel.: (415) 875-1000
Web Site: http://www.recology.com
Waste Management; Garbage Collection, Disposal & Recycling
N.A.I.C.S.: 562111
Mark R. Lomele *(*)*
Michael J. Sangiacomo *(Pres & CEO)*
Mark J. Arsenault *(COO & Exec VP)*
Catherine Langridge *(CFO & Sr VP)*
Julie Bertani-Kiser *(Chief HR Officer & Sr VP)*
Dennis Wu *(Chm)*

Subsidiary (Domestic):

Nature's Needs LLC **(2)**
9570 NW 307th Ave, North Plains, OR 97133
Tel.: (503) 647-9489
Waste Treatment & Disposal Services
N.A.I.C.S.: 562219

Recology Ashland **(2)**
170 Oak St, Ashland, OR 97520
Tel.: (541) 482-1471
Web Site: http://www.recology.com
Waste Treatment & Disposal Services
N.A.I.C.S.: 562219

Recology CleanScapes, Inc. **(2)**
7303 8th Ave S, Seattle, WA 98108
Tel.: (206) 859-6700
Waste Management; Garbage Collection, Disposal & Recycling
N.A.I.C.S.: 562111

Subsidiary (Domestic):

Sunset Garbage Collection, Inc. **(3)**
9035 SE Henderson St, Portland, OR 97266
Tel.: (503) 774-4122
Web Site: http://www.sunsetgarbage.com
Rev.: $1,736,000
Emp.: 8
Hazardous Waste Treatment & Disposal
N.A.I.C.S.: 562211

Subsidiary (Domestic):

Recology Del Norte, Inc. **(2)**
2675 Lake Earl Dr, Crescent City, CA 95531
Tel.: (707) 464-4181
Web Site: http://www.recology.com
Waste Treatment & Disposal Services
N.A.I.C.S.: 562219

Recology Environmental Solutions Inc. **(2)**
235 N 1st St, Dixon, CA 95620
Tel.: (800) 208-2370
Web Site: http://www.recology.com
Waste Treatment & Disposal Services
N.A.I.C.S.: 562219
Paul Yamamoto *(Gen Mgr)*

Recology Hay Road **(2)**
6246 Hay Rd, Vacaville, CA 95687
Tel.: (707) 678-4718
Solid Waste Landfill
N.A.I.C.S.: 562212

Recology Mountain View **(2)**
935 Terra Bella Ave, Mountain View, CA 94043
Tel.: (650) 967-3034
Web Site: http://www.recology.com
Waste Treatment & Disposal Services
N.A.I.C.S.: 562219

Recology Ostrom Road **(2)**
5900 Ostrom Rd, Wheatland, CA 95692
Tel.: (800) 208-2371
Web Site: http://www.recology.com
Waste Treatment & Disposal Services
N.A.I.C.S.: 562219

Recology Portland Inc. **(2)**
9345 N Harborgate St, Portland, OR 97203
Tel.: (503) 283-2015
Web Site: http://www.recology.com
Waste Treatment & Disposal Services
N.A.I.C.S.: 562219

Recology San Francisco **(2)**
501 Tunnel Ave, San Francisco, CA 94134
Tel.: (415) 330-1400
Web Site: http://www.recology.com

Waste Treatment & Disposal Services
N.A.I.C.S.: 562219

Recology Vacaville Solano **(2)**
1 Town Sq Ste 200, Vacaville, CA 95688
Tel.: (707) 448-2945
Web Site: http://www.recology.com
Waste Treatment & Disposal Services
N.A.I.C.S.: 562219

Recology Yuba-Sutter **(2)**
3001 N Levee Rd, Marysville, CA 95901
Tel.: (530) 743-6933
Web Site: http://www.recology.com
Waste Treatment & Disposal Services
N.A.I.C.S.: 562219

ARAM INCORPORATED
7920 Belt Line Rd Ste 960, Dallas, TX 75254
Tel.: (972) 690-9793   TX
Web Site: http://www.holdenbrand.com
Year Founded: 1975
Sales Range: $10-24.9 Million
Emp.: 20
Mfr of Looseleaf Binders
N.A.I.C.S.: 424120
Marnie Holden *(Owner)*
Carrie Shanks *(Mgr-Mktg)*

ARAPAHOE HOUSE
8801 Lipan St, Thornton, CO 80260
Tel.: (205) 619-2891   CO
Web Site: https://www.arapahoehouse.org
Year Founded: 1975
Sales Range: $10-24.9 Million
Emp.: 458
Individual & Family Support Services
N.A.I.C.S.: 624190
Aleah Horstman *(COO)*
Sheryl Blythe *(Dir-HR)*
Mike Butler *(Pres & CEO)*
Kelly Mahncke *(CFO)*
Sara Kemp *(Chief Clinical Officer)*

ARAPAHOE MOTORS, INC.
1003 Plum Vly Ln, Highlands Ranch, CO 80129
Tel.: (303) 798-1500   CO
Web Site: http://www.ralphschomp.com
Year Founded: 1941
New & Used Car Dealer
N.A.I.C.S.: 441110
Lisa J. Schomp *(Pres & CEO)*

ARARAT HOME OF LOS ANGELES, INC.
15105 Mission Hills Rd, Mission Hills, CA 91345
Tel.: (818) 365-3000   CA
Web Site: https://www.ararathome.org
Year Founded: 1949
Sales Range: $10-24.9 Million
Emp.: 312
Elder Care Services
N.A.I.C.S.: 623312
Derik Ghookasian *(COO)*
Debbie Avedian *(Asst Sec)*
Ronald Nazeley *(Asst Treas)*
Arthur Zabounian *(Asst Sec)*
Gary Kaloostian *(Asst Treas)*
Michael Surmeian *(Chm)*
Vahe Vartanian *(Treas)*

ARAS CORP
100 Brickstone Square Ste 100, Andover, MA 01810-1492
Tel.: (978) 806-9400   DE
Web Site: http://www.aras.com
Year Founded: 2000
Software Publisher
N.A.I.C.S.: 513210
Peter Schroer *(Founder & CEO)*
John Yee *(CFO)*

Aras Corp—(Continued)

Subsidiaries:

Comet Solutions, Inc. (1)
9380 Montgomery Rd Ste 206, Cincinnati,
OH 45242
Tel.: (248) 766-2329
Web Site: http://cometsolutions.com
Sales Range: $1-9.9 Million
Emp.: 27
Custom Computer Programming Services
N.A.I.C.S.: 541511
Geoffrey S. Flagg (CFO)
Steve Brown (VP-Global Sls)
Malcolm Panthaki (Founder & CTO)
Tim Keer (VP-Technical Svcs & Customer
Success)

ARAWAK PAVING CO. INC.
7503 Weymouth Rd, Hammonton, NJ
08037
Tel.: (609) 561-4100
Web Site: https://www.arawakpci.com
Rev.: $18,338,387
Emp.: 25
Highway & Street Paving Contractor
N.A.I.C.S.: 237310

ARB MIDSTREAM, LLC
1600 Broadway Ste 2400, Denver,
CO 80202
Tel.: (720) 600-7500   DE
Web Site:
https://www.arbmidstream.com
Year Founded: 2014
Crude Oil Multimodal Transportation
Services
N.A.I.C.S.: 488510
Adam Bedard (CEO)
Rogan McGillis (CFO)

Subsidiaries:

InCorr Energy Group LLC (1)
13275 E Fremont Pl Ste 200, Centennial,
CO 80112-3986
Tel.: (303) 249-5569
Web Site: www.incorrenergy.com
Crude Oil Marketing & Trading Services
N.A.I.C.S.: 424720
Joe Purdy (Co-Founder & Pres)
Mark Edward Wysooki (Co-Founder & VP-
Ops)

ARBEE ASSOCIATES INC.
1531 S Washington Ave, Piscataway,
NJ 08854-5076
Tel.: (732) 424-3900   NJ
Web Site: https://www.arbee.net
Year Founded: 1973
Sales Range: $25-49.9 Million
Emp.: 230
Provider of Furniture
N.A.I.C.S.: 423210
Howard Berkowitz (Chm)
Nancy Berkowitz (Pres, CEO & Prin-
cipal)
Vincent Marron (CFO)
Ellen Berkowitz (Principal & VP-Corp
Dev)
Chris Hanes (COO)

ARBELLA INSURANCE
GROUP
1100 Crown Colony Dr, Quincy, MA
02269
Tel.: (617) 328-2800   MA
Web Site: http://www.arbella.com
Year Founded: 1917
Sales Range: $750-799.9 Million
Fire, Marine & Casualty Insurance
N.A.I.C.S.: 541611
John F. Donohue (Chm, Pres & CEO)
Janet R. Corcoran (COO & Exec VP)
Steve Jacobs (VP-Sls & Mktg)
Gayle O'Connell (CMO & Exec VP)
James S. Hyatt (Chief Underwriting
Officer & Exec VP)

Lynellen M. Ramirez (Chief Actuary &
VP-Res Analytics)
Paul J. Brady (Sr VP & Head-Tech &
Ops)
Allen Chaves (Dir-Data Governance
& Res Analytics)
Hugh Thai (Asst VP-Actuarial & Res
Analytics)
Karen Jansky (Dir-Application Dev-IT)
Matthew Postulka (CIO & VP)
Ellen Mann (Asst VP-HR)
Karin Martin (Asst VP-Contact Cen-
ters)
Andrew O'Donoghue (Asst VP-Sls &
Mktg)
Mark Wheeler (Dir-Personal Lines
Underwriting)
Julia Kim (Asst VP-Application Dev &
Architecture)
Candice Lohmeier (Dir-Claim)
Megan Glynn (Dir-Digital Strategy-
Corp Comm)

Subsidiaries:

Arbella Incorporated (1)
1100 Crown Colony Dr, Quincy, MA
02269-9103   (100%)
Tel.: (617) 328-2800
Web Site: http://www.arbella.com
Rev.: $131,133,000
Emp.: 1,000
Fire, Marine & Casualty Insurance
N.A.I.C.S.: 524126
John F. Donohue (Pres)

Arbella Indemnity Insurance Co. (1)
1100 Crown Colony Dr, Quincy, MA 02269-
0934
Tel.: (617) 328-2800
Web Site: http://www.arbella.com
Sales Range: $200-249.9 Million
Emp.: 800
N.A.I.C.S.: 524128
John Donohue (Chm & CEO)

Arbella Insurance Group (1)
1450 Southford Rd Ste 11, Southbury, CT
06488
Tel.: (203) 267-2701
Web Site: http://www.arbella.com
Sales Range: $25-49.9 Million
Emp.: 20
Provider of Insurance Services
N.A.I.C.S.: 524210
Tony Cervone (Gen Mgr-Sls)

Arbella Mutual Insurance Co. (1)
1100 Crown Colony Dr, Quincy, MA 02269
Tel.: (617) 328-2800
Web Site: http://www.arbella.com
Sales Range: $100-124.9 Million
Emp.: 700
N.A.I.C.S.: 524128
John Donohue (Pres & CEO)

Arbella Protection Insurance Com-
pany Inc. (1)
1100 Crown Colony Dr, Quincy, MA
02269   (100%)
Tel.: (617) 328-2800
Web Site: http://www.arbella.com
Sales Range: $250-299.9 Million
Insurance Agents, Brokers & Service
N.A.I.C.S.: 524210

Arbella Service Company Inc. (1)
1100 Crown Colony Dr, Quincy, MA 02269-
0934
Tel.: (617) 328-2800
Web Site: http://www.arbella.com
Sales Range: $100-124.9 Million
Emp.: 700
Management Consulting Services
N.A.I.C.S.: 524126
John Donahue (CEO)

ARBEN GROUP
175 Marble Ave, Pleasantville, NY
10570
Tel.: (914) 741-5459
Web Site:
http://www.arbengroup.com
Sales Range: $10-24.9 Million
Emp.: 40

Specialized Public Building Contrac-
tors
N.A.I.C.S.: 236220
Mark A. Ronnow (VP & Sr Project
Mgr)

ARBEN GROUP LLC.
175 Marble Ave, Pleasantville, NY
10570
Tel.: (914) 741-5459
Web Site:
https://www.arbengroup.com
Year Founded: 1986
Sales Range: $10-24.9 Million
Emp.: 40
Commercial & Institutional Building
Construction Services
N.A.I.C.S.: 236220
Ross Pepe (Pres)
David Weiss (Project Mgr)

ARBICO EAST LLC
1135 Volunteer Pkwy Ste 16, Bristol,
TN 37620
Tel.: (423) 968-2729
Web Site: http://www.arbys.com
Sales Range: $10-24.9 Million
Emp.: 300
Franchise Owner of Fast-Food Res-
taurants
N.A.I.C.S.: 722513
Donald H. Shawl (Pres)
Rudy Johnson (Controller)
Ben Frizzell Jr. (Chm)

ARBILL INDUSTRIES INC.
10450 Drummond Rd, Philadelphia,
PA 19154
Tel.: (215) 501-0305   PA
Web Site: http://www.arbill.com
Year Founded: 1945
Sales Range: $10-24.9 Million
Emp.: 7
Provider of Industrial Supplies
N.A.I.C.S.: 423840
Julie Copeland (CEO)

ARBITECH
64 Fairbanks, Irvine, CA 92618
Tel.: (949) 376-6650
Web Site: https://www.arbitech.com
Year Founded: 2000
Sales Range: $10-24.9 Million
Emp.: 70
Computer Products Distributor
N.A.I.C.S.: 423430
Torin Pavia (Chm & CEO)
Frank G. Llaca (Gen Counsel & VP-
Bus Rels)
Peter Freix (Pres)

ARBITRATION FORUMS, INC.
3820 Northdale Blvd Ste 115, Tampa,
FL 33624
Tel.: (813) 931-4004
Web Site: https://www.arbfile.org
Year Founded: 1943
Sales Range: $25-49.9 Million
Emp.: 250
Arbitration Services
N.A.I.C.S.: 561499
Jay Arcila (CFO)

ARBOL INC.
445 Park Ave Ste 931, New York, NY
10022
Tel.: (839) 712-3224   DE
Web Site: https://www.arbol.io
Year Founded: 2018
Software Development Services
N.A.I.C.S.: 513210
Siddhartha Jha (Founder & CEO)

Subsidiaries:

Lilypad Insurance Company (1)

6751 Professional Pkwy W Ste 105, Sara-
sota, FL 34240
Tel.: (844) 544-5459
Web Site: https://lilypad-
insurance.webflow.io
Insurance Services
N.A.I.C.S.: 524298
Ricardo Espino (CEO)
Traci Stillwagon (COO)

ARBOR BANCORP, INC.
125 S 5th Ave, Ann Arbor, MI 48104
Tel.: (734) 662-1600
Web Site:
http://www.bankofannarbor.com
Bank Holding Company
N.A.I.C.S.: 551111
Tim Marshall (Pres & CEO)
Charlie Crone (Chief Revenue Officer
& Exec VP)
Patti Jackson (COO & Exec VP)
Cindy Livesay (Chief Credit Officer &
Exec VP)
Mark Slade (CFO & Exec VP)

Subsidiaries:

Bank of Ann Arbor (1)
125 S 5th Ave, Ann Arbor, MI 48104
Tel.: (734) 662-1600
Web Site: http://www.bankofannarbor.com
Commericial Banking
N.A.I.C.S.: 522110
Tim Marshall (Pres & CEO)
Rich Spencer (Chief Info & Innovation Offi-
cer & Sr VP)

ARBOR CONSULTING RE-
SOURCES INC.
7777 Bonhomme, Saint Louis, MO
63105
Tel.: (314) 725-7510
Sales Range: $10-24.9 Million
Emp.: 50
Computer System Design Services
N.A.I.C.S.: 541512
Arjomand Kalayeh (Principal)

ARBOR CONTRACT CARPET
INC.
2213 E Pioneer Dr, Irving, TX 75061
Tel.: (972) 445-2235   TX
Web Site:
https://www.arborcarpet.com
Year Founded: 1981
Sales Range: $25-49.9 Million
Emp.: 200
Provider of Floor Covering Products
& Services
N.A.I.C.S.: 238330
Matt Gilbreth (Pres)

ARBOR INVESTMENT GROUP
39400 Woodward Ave, Bloomfield
Hills, MI 48304
Tel.: (248) 593-8840
Rev.: $6,030,000
Emp.: 15
Investment Banking & Securities
Dealing
N.A.I.C.S.: 523150
Eugene Applebaum (Owner)

Subsidiaries:

Hudson Baking Company LLC (1)
1300 Beaudry Blvd, Hudson, WI 54016
Tel.: (715) 386-1034
Sales Range: $1-9.9 Million
Grocery & Related Products Merchant
Whslr
N.A.I.C.S.: 424490
Kristen Rieser (Pres)

ARBOR MATERIAL HANDLING
INC.
2465 Maryland Rd, Willow Grove, PA
19090
Tel.: (215) 657-2700   PA
Web Site: https://www.arbor-inc.com

Year Founded: 1951
Sales Range: $10-24.9 Million
Emp.: 70
Provider of Material Handling Machinery & Equipment
N.A.I.C.S.: 423830
David C. Bennett (Pres)
Ron Bancroft (Controller)
Craig Walker (Mgr-HR)

ARBOR PRIVATE INVESTMENT COMPANY, LLC
676 N Michigan Ave, Chicago, IL 60611-2883
Tel.: (312) 981-3770   DE
Web Site: http://www.arborpic.com
Year Founded: 1999
Privater Equity Firm
N.A.I.C.S.: 523999
Gregory J. Purcell (CEO)
Dennis M. Malchow (Sr Partner-Operating)
Siegfried E. Buck (Operating Partner)
Steven D. Zoll (Operating Partner)
Ryan R. McKenzie (Chief Admin Officer)
J. David Foster (CFO)
Roberta R. McQuade (Sr VP-Organizational Strategy & Talent)
Jerry B. Cronin (VP-IT & Acctg)
Sylvia L. Lauener (Controller)
Alan A. Weed (Partner)
Brody D. Lynn (Partner)
Jason L. Booth (Gen Counsel)
Timothy G. Fallon (Chm & Interim CEO)
Christopher G. A. Tuffin (Partner)
John M. Camp (Mng Dir-Bus Dev)
Richard P. Distasio (Operating Partner)
Bing L. Graffunder (Operating Partner)
Alison B. Miller (Chief Mktg Officer)
Peter G. Bradley (Operating Partner)
Carl Allegretti (Pres)

Subsidiaries:

Dunn Paper, Inc.   (1)
218 Riverview St, Port Huron, MI 48060
Tel.: (810) 984-5521
Web Site: http://www.dunnpaper.com
Specialty Coated & Uncoated Paper Mfr
N.A.I.C.S.: 322120
Brent Earnshaw (Founder & CEO)
Rick Voss (VP-Sls & Mktg)
Wade Kemnitz (Pres)

Midland Container Corporation   (1)
3545 Nicholson Rd, Franksville, WI 53126
Tel.: (262) 886-8851
Web Site: http://www.midlandcontainer.com
Rev.: $15,000,000
Emp.: 100
Corrugated Packaging & Display Mfr
N.A.I.C.S.: 322211
Siegfried E. Buck (CEO)
Terry Skalmoski (Pres)

New Carbon Co, LLC   (1)
4101 William Richardson Dr, South Bend, IN 46628
Tel.: (888) 596-4040
Web Site: http://www.goldenmalted.com
Waffle Mix & Cooking Equipment Mfr
N.A.I.C.S.: 311824

Rice Garden Inc.   (1)
2121 W Mission Rd Ste 301, Alhambra, CA 91803
Tel.: (626) 281-2392
Web Site: http://www.ricegarden.com
Sales Range: $10-24.9 Million
Emp.: 9
Fast Food Restaurant Operator
N.A.I.C.S.: 722513
Gill Sommers (Branch Mgr)

ARBOUR NATIONAL
801 N. W St, Raleigh, NC 27603
Tel.: (919) 653-7499
Web Site: https://arbournational.com

Year Founded: 2021
Insurance Holding Company
N.A.I.C.S.: 524126

ARBUTUS PARK RETIREMENT COMMUNITY
207 Ottawa St, Johnstown, PA 15904
Tel.: (814) 266-8621   PA
Web Site:
http://www.arbutusparkmanor.com
Year Founded: 1969
Sales Range: $10-24.9 Million
Emp.: 260
Lifecare Retirement Community Operator
N.A.I.C.S.: 623311
Brooke Patterson (Dir-Nursing)
Lisa Arcuril (Dir-Admissions)

ARC ABATEMENT, INC.
225 S 12th St, Waco, TX 76701
Tel.: (254) 755-6700
Web Site:
https://www.arcabatement.com
Rev.: $17,500,000
Emp.: 375
Remediation Services
N.A.I.C.S.: 562910
Ron Daniel (Founder, Pres & CEO)
Don Daniel (Gen Mgr-Austin Div)
Steve Chappell (Gen Mgr-Dallas Div)
Mike Daniel (Gen Mgr-Remediation-Waco Div)

ARC ASPICIO LLC
3318 Lorcom Ln, Arlington, VA 22207
Tel.: (703) 465-2060
Web Site: http://www.arcaspicio.com
Year Founded: 2004
Sales Range: $1-9.9 Million
Emp.: 24
Management & IT Consulting
N.A.I.C.S.: 541618
Lynn Ann Casey (CEO)
Robert O'Keefe (CTO)
Lisa Barsa (Mgr-Ops)

ARC CONTRACTING, INC.
2300 Holly Rd, Neenah, WI 54956
Web Site:
http://www.arccontracting.com
Year Founded: 2006
Sales Range: $10-24.9 Million
Emp.: 42
Roofing Contracting Construction Services
N.A.I.C.S.: 238160
Jesse Chase (Pres)

ARC ENTERTAINMENT LLC.
3212 Nebraska Ave, Santa Monica, CA 90404
Tel.: (310) 857-5200
Web Site: http://www.arc-ent.com
Sales Range: $10-24.9 Million
Emp.: 15
Photographic Equipment & Supplies Whslr
N.A.I.C.S.: 423410
Trevor Drinkwater (CEO)
Bobby Gerber (Exec VP & Gen Mgr-Entertainment)
Scott Moesta (VP-Digital & VOD)

ARC EXCESS & SURPLUS LLC
113 S Service Rd, Jericho, NY 11753
Tel.: (516) 747-4100
Web Site:
https://www.arcbrokers.com
Sales Range: $10-24.9 Million
Emp.: 82
Insurance Services
N.A.I.C.S.: 524210

Christopher J. Cavallaro (CEO & Mng Dir)
John Semeraro (Dir-Sls)
Joan Brunjes (CFO)

Subsidiaries:

ARC Excess & Surplus of MidSouth, LLC   (1)
110 Painters Mill Rd Ste101, Owings Mills, MD 21117
Tel.: (410) 427-9564
Web Site: http://www.arcbrokers.com
Emp.: 5
Insurance & Brokerage Services
N.A.I.C.S.: 524210
Larry Jones (CEO)

ARC Excess & Surplus of New England, LLC   (1)
1224 Mill St Bldg A, East Berlin, CT 06023
Tel.: (860) 517-3102
Insurance & Brokerage Services
N.A.I.C.S.: 524210

ARC MidAtlantic   (1)
129 B Johnson Rd Ste 5, Turnersville, NJ 08012
Tel.: (856) 401-8070
Web Site: http://www.arcbrokers.com
Rev.: $750,000
Emp.: 10
Insurance Agents, Brokers & Service
N.A.I.C.S.: 524210

ARC South, LLC   (1)
2205 Riverstone Blvd Ste 204, Canton, GA 30114
Tel.: (404) 474-4301
Insurance & Brokerage Services
N.A.I.C.S.: 524210

ARC Specialty Brokerage, LLC   (1)
1122 Franklin Ave, Garden City, NY 11530-9240
Tel.: (516) 408-5717
Property & Casualty Insurance Services
N.A.I.C.S.: 524126

ARC OF GREATER NEW ORLEANS
925 S Labarre Rd, Metairie, LA 70001
Tel.: (504) 837-5140   LA
Web Site: https://www.arcgno.org
Year Founded: 1953
Sales Range: $10-24.9 Million
Emp.: 373
Disability Assistance Services
N.A.I.C.S.: 624120
Cliff Doescher (Exec Dir)
Michelle Chaisson (Dir-Admin Supports)
Malbert Helton (Dir-Maintenance)
Milton Batiste (Dir-Transportation)
Debbie Armstrong (Sec)
Marc Chevis (Pres)
Jennifer O'Neal (Sec)
Glenda Dickinson (Dir-Project Help)
Katy Wahl (Dir-Family Svc Coordination)
Lori Malbroue (Dir-Supported Living)
Nicole Blair (Dir-Arc Enterprises)
Tom Barnes (Dir-Employment Svcs)

ARC OF THE UNITED STATES
1825 K St NW Ste 1200, Washington, DC 20006
Tel.: (202) 534-3700   MD
Web Site: https://www.thearc.org
Year Founded: 2000
Sales Range: $1-9.9 Million
Emp.: 53
Developmental Disability Assistance Services
N.A.I.C.S.: 624120
Laura Schroeder (Mgr-Dev)
Peter V. Berns (CEO)
Shaw Fodor (Mgr-HR)

ARC OUTDOORS

5425 S 99th East Ave, Tulsa, OK 74146
Tel.: (877) 974-4353
Web Site:
http://www.arcoutdoors.com
Year Founded: 1998
Sales Range: $1-9.9 Million
Emp.: 14
Sportswear & Accessories Mfr
N.A.I.C.S.: 315250

ARC-COM FABRICS INCORPORATED
33 Ramland Rd S, Orangeburg, NY 10962
Tel.: (845) 365-1100
Web Site: https://www.arc-com.com
Year Founded: 1972
Sales Range: $10-24.9 Million
Emp.: 75
Textile Converters
N.A.I.C.S.: 314999
Jeffrey Layne (Pres)
Brian Connor (Mgr-IT)
Peter Layne (Owner)
Ann Lyons (Mgr-Customer Svc)
Larry Lamicella (Mgr-Facilities)
Sherman Pollack (VP-Production)

ARC3 ARCHITECTURE, INC.
6699 13th Ave N Ste 4A, Saint Petersburg, FL 33710
Tel.: (727) 381-5220
Web Site: https://www.arc-3.com
Sales Range: $1-9.9 Million
Emp.: 10
Architectural Services
N.A.I.C.S.: 541310
Steve Vinci (Pres)

ARCADE CHINA ACQUISITION CORP.
62 LaSalle Rd Ste 304, West Hartford, CT 06107
Tel.: (860) 236-6320   DE
Year Founded: 2011
Sales Range: $25-49.9 Million
Emp.: 3
Investment Services
N.A.I.C.S.: 523999
Jonathan R. Furer (Chm)
John M. Chapman (CFO & Chief Acctg Officer)

ARCADIA CHEVROLET BUICK PONTIAC INC.
210 S Brevard Ave, Arcadia, FL 34266
Tel.: (863) 494-3838
Web Site:
http://www.arcadiachevrolet.com
Rev.: $22,300,000
Emp.: 65
New Car Dealers
N.A.I.C.S.: 441110
Douglas D. Plattner (Owner)

ARCADIA PUBLISHING, INC.
420 Wando Park Blvd, Mount Pleasant, SC 29464
Tel.: (843) 853-2070   SC
Web Site:
https://www.arcadiapublishing.com
Year Founded: 1993
Sales Range: $1-9.9 Million
Emp.: 90
Book Publishers
N.A.I.C.S.: 513130
Richard Joseph (Pres & CEO)

Subsidiaries:

The History Press, Inc.   (1)
645 Meeting St Ste 200, Charleston, SC 29403
Tel.: (843) 577-5971
Web Site: http://www.historypress.net

Arcadia Publishing, Inc.—(Continued)

Emp.: 30
Books Publishing Services
N.A.I.C.S.: 513130
Adam Ferrell (Dir-Publ)
Brittain Phillips (COO)
Kelly Bowen (Dir-Mktg)
Kate Everingham (Dir-Sls)
Richard Joseph (CEO)
Katie Kellett (Dir-Imprints)
Paul Raffle (COO)
Steve Sawyer (Dir-Production)

ARCADIAN HEALTHCARE INC.
45 Rt 46E Ste 606, Pine Brook, NJ
07058
Rev.: $14,100,000
Emp.: 40
Medical Equipment Rental
N.A.I.C.S.: 532283

Subsidiaries:

Medicare Supply Centers Inc   (1)
45 Rt 46E Ste 606, Pine Brook, NJ 07058
Web Site:
  http://www.millenniumhomecare.com
Rev.: $6,261,836
Emp.: 5
Medical Apparatus & Supplies
N.A.I.C.S.: 456199

ARCAMAX PUBLISHING, INC.
729 Thimble Shoals Blvd Ste 1-B,
Newport News, VA 23606
Tel.: (757) 596-9730
Web Site: https://www.arcamax.com
Year Founded: 2004
Rev.: $4,900,000
Emp.: 20
Miscellaneous Publishing
N.A.I.C.S.: 513199
Charles Strauss (Mgr)
Scott Wolf (CEO)

ARCENEAUX FORD INC.
1407 Center St, New Iberia, LA
70560
Tel.: (337) 364-9721
Web Site:
  http://www.arceneauxford.com
Rev.: $13,300,000
Emp.: 35
Automobiles, New & Used
N.A.I.C.S.: 441110
Thomas McMath (Pres)

ARCET EQUIPMENT COM-
PANY
1700 Chamberlayne Ave, Richmond,
VA 23222
Tel.: (804) 644-4521
Web Site: http://www.arcet.com
Rev.: $22,000,000
Emp.: 35
Welding Machinery & Equipment
N.A.I.C.S.: 423830
Parker Dillard (Pres)
Doug Carpenter (Mgr)
Glenda Groome (Controller)
Buz Edwards (Dir-Pur)

ARCH EQUITY PARTNERS,
LLC
2381 Centerline Industrial Dr Ste 200,
Saint Louis, MO 63146
Tel.: (314) 409-0264
Web Site:
  http://www.archequitypartners.com
Year Founded: 2008
Sales Range: $100-124.9 Million
Privater Equity Firm
N.A.I.C.S.: 523999
William J. Lindenmayer (Mng Partner)
John Mandelker (Mng Partner)

Subsidiaries:

Chandler Industries, Inc.   (1)
1654 N Ninth St, Montevideo, MN 56265

Tel.: (320) 269-8893
Sales Range: $50-74.9 Million
Emp.: 100
Contract Mfr of Precision Machined Compo-
nents, Fabrications, Complex Assemblies &
Weldments
N.A.I.C.S.: 332999
Don Alter (Pres)

Division (Domestic):

Chandler Industries - Lake Country
Division   (2)
513 6th St NE, Long Prairie, MN 56347
Tel.: (320) 732-3454
Web Site:
  http://www.chandlerindustries.com
Sales Range: $1-9.9 Million
Emp.: 35
Machine Shops
N.A.I.C.S.: 332710

Chandler Industries - Stremel
Division   (2)
260 Plymouth Ave N, Minneapolis, MN
55411
Tel.: (612) 339-8261
Web Site:
  http://www.chandlerindustries.com
Sales Range: $25-49.9 Million
Emp.: 85
Miscellaneous Fabricated Metal Product Mfr
N.A.I.C.S.: 332999
Chris May (Gen Mgr)

Chandler Industries -Arrow
Division   (2)
10488 W Centennial Rd, Littleton, CO
80127
Tel.: (303) 904-2626
Web Site:
  http://www.chandlerindustries.com
Sales Range: $25-49.9 Million
Emp.: 80
Tubular Component Mfr
N.A.I.C.S.: 332999
Jed Klayman (Mgr-Shipping & Receiving)

ARCH PROMO GROUP LLC
1 Gemini Industrial Dr., Roxana, IL
62084
Web Site:
  https://archpromogroup.com
Glasses, Beer Mugs & cups Mfg.
N.A.I.C.S.: 327212
Steve Ehlert (Gen Mgr)

Subsidiaries:

Howw Manufacturing Company
Inc.   (1)
28 W 020 Commercial Ave, Barrington, IL
60010
Tel.: (847) 382-4380
Web Site: http://www.howw.com
Rev.: $2,800,000
Emp.: 25
All Other Basic Inorganic Chemical Mfr
N.A.I.C.S.: 325180
Clemmons Kalamaras (Pres)
Mike Kalamaras (Pres)

ARCH VENTURE PARTNERS
1700 Owens St Ste 535, San Fran-
cisco, CA 94158-0002
Tel.: (773) 380-6600
Web Site:
  http://www.archventure.com
Intermediation
N.A.I.C.S.: 523910
Keith L. Crandell (Co-Founder & Mng
Dir)
E. Kevin Hrusovsky (Venture Partner)
Jami Rubin (Venture Partner)
George A. Scangos (Venture Partner)
Kristina M. Burow (Mng Dir)
Kaye I. Foster-Cheek (Venture Part-
ner)
Robert Nelsen (Co-Founder & Mng
Dir)
Keith R. Leonard Jr. (Venture Part-
ner)
Jake B. Bauer (Venture Partner)
Jonathan E. Lim (Venture Partner)

Subsidiaries:

Hibercell, Inc.   (1)
619 W 54th St 8th Fl, New York, NY 10019
Tel.: (212) 601-2800
Web Site: http://www.hibercell.com
Research & Development in Biotechnology
N.A.I.C.S.: 541714
Julio Aguirre-Ghiso (Co-Founder)
Debra Artura (Office Mgr)
Mark J. Mulvihill (Chief Scientific Officer)
Alan Rigby (Co-Founder & CEO)

ARCHBROOK CAPITAL MAN-
AGEMENT LLC
100 Front St Ste 570, Conshohocken,
PA 19428-2889
Tel.: (610) 684-4900
Web Site: https://www.archbrook.com
Year Founded: 2002
Privater Equity Firm
N.A.I.C.S.: 523999
David F. Apple (Founder & Partner)
John F. McGlinn II (Partner)

Subsidiaries:

Tray-Pak Corp.   (1)
Tuckerton Rd & Reading Crest Ave, Read-
ing, PA 19605
Tel.: (484) 637-9081
Web Site: http://www.traypak.com
Sales Range: $50-74.9 Million
Emp.: 275
Thermoformed Plastic Packaging
N.A.I.C.S.: 326199
Scott Myers (CEO)

ARCHELON LLC
200 S Wacker Dr Ste 2400, Chicago,
IL 60606
Tel.: (312) 461-0300
Web Site:
  http://www.archelongroup.com
Sales Range: $25-49.9 Million
Emp.: 40
Security Brokers & Dealers
N.A.I.C.S.: 523150
Charles Tall (Pres)
Robert Stranz (Supvr-Ops-United
States)
John Koltes III (Owner)

ARCHER & GREINER P.C.
1 Centennial Square 33 E Euclid Ave,
Haddonfield, NJ 08033
Tel.: (856) 795-2121
Web Site: http://www.archerlaw.com
Year Founded: 1928
Sales Range: $75-99.9 Million
Emp.: 347
Law firm
N.A.I.C.S.: 922130
John M. Cantalupo (Partner)
James H. Carll (Partner)
Alex Paul Genato (Partner)
Christopher R. Gibson (Pres &
Partner-Haddonfield)
Lisa Stewart Albright (Partner)
Michael F. Floyd (Partner)
Robert S. Davis (Vice Chm-Real Es-
tate Dept & Partner)
Andrew J. Cevasco (Partner)
David W. Carickhoff (Partner)
John C. Connell (Partner)
Kerri E. Chewning (Partner)
Kimberly Anne Capadona (Partner)
Matthew Conley (Partner)
Richard J. Contant (Partner)
Ronald D. Coleman (Partner)
Trevor J. Cooney (Partner)
Vincent P. Sarubbi (Partner)

ARCHER COMMUNICATIONS,
INC.
252 Alexander St, Rochester, NY
14607-2515
Tel.: (585) 461-1570   NY
Web Site: http://www.archercom.com

Year Founded: 1997
Sales Range: $10-24.9 Million
Emp.: 10
Advertising Agencies
N.A.I.C.S.: 541810
Jeff Lennox (CEO)

ARCHER EXTERIORS
341 Harding Hwy, Pittsgrove, NJ
08318
Tel.: (856) 363-7000
Web Site:
  https://www.archerexteriors.com
Rev.: $15,532,229
Emp.: 40
Siding Contractors
N.A.I.C.S.: 238170
Lhann David (Mgr-Contract)
Jim Losasso (Mgr-Contract)

ARCHER MALMO
65 Union Ave Ste 500, Memphis, TN
38103-5137
Tel.: (901) 523-2000   TN
Web Site:
  https://www.archermalmo.com
Year Founded: 1952
Sales Range: $100-124.9 Million
Emp.: 160
Advertising Agencies
N.A.I.C.S.: 541810
Gary Backaus (Chief Creative &
Strategy Officer)
Russ Williams (CEO)
Mary Lynn Gratzer (Sr VP & Dir-
Client Svcs)
Arlene Goldner (Sr VP & Dir-Media
Svcs)
Mike Butler (Sr VP & Grp Acct Dir)
Ken Rohman (Chief Digital Officer)
Naomi Bata (Chief PR Officer & Sr
VP)
Beverly Mattingly (Sr VP & Grp Acct
Dir)
Fred Nichols (VP & Acct Dir)
Colin Gilligan (VP-Media & Plng-
Austin)
Matt Rand (VP & Exec Dir-Creative-
Austin)
Tom Barzizza (Pres-Retail Mktg Grp)
Simon Hjorth (Sr VP & Dir-Client
Svcs-Austin)
Patricia Emory-Walker (Sr VP & Dir-
Acct Grp)
Robby Grant (VP-Dev & Tech)
Rob Hoerter (VP & Dir-Acct)
Gokben Yamandag (Sr VP-Digital
Strategy & Analysis)
Gorkem Yamandag (VP-Digital Proj-
ect Mgmt & Production)
Brad Carmony (VP-PR)
Brad Carmony (VP-PR)

ARCHER RV
10711 SW Fwy, Houston, TX 77074
Tel.: (713) 995-8585
Web Site: https://www.archerrvs.com
New & Used Car Dealers
N.A.I.C.S.: 441110

ARCHER SCREW PRODUCTS
INC.
11341 Melrose Ave, Franklin Park, IL
60131
Tel.: (847) 451-1150
Web Site:
  https://www.archerscrew.com
Year Founded: 1975
Sales Range: $10-24.9 Million
Emp.: 63
Screws
N.A.I.C.S.: 423710
Timothy Coffee (Pres)
Tom Zoccoli (VP-Ops)
William Clark (Mgr-Inventory Control)

ARCHERHALL, LLC
2081 Arena Blvd Ste 200, Sacramento, CA 95834
Tel.: (855) 839-9084
Web Site: http://www.archerhall.com
Year Founded: 1997
Digital Document Solution Services
N.A.I.C.S.: 561410
Dave Wilkinson (Co-Owner & Pres)
Lucas Mageno (Founder & Co-Owner)
Dave Baer (Gen Mgr)
Ron Bodenmann (Dir-Computer Forensics & Trng)
Ignacio Solorio (Acct Exec)
Thon Kong (Mgr-Production)
Nicolas C. Anderson (Executives)

Subsidiaries:

eDiscovery Inc.   (1)
15600 NE 8th St Ste B1, Bellevue, WA
98008-3958
Tel.: (425) 373-3349
Web Site: http://www.ediscoveryinc.com
Engineeering Services
N.A.I.C.S.: 541330
Allison Goodman (Pres)

ARCHGATE TMS SOLUTIONS LLC
17W662 Butterfield Rd Ste 305, Oakbrook Terrace, IL 60181
Tel.: (847) 696-9000
Web Site:
    http://www.archgatetms.com
Year Founded: 2013
Sales Range: $10-24.9 Million
Emp.: 50
Logistic & Transportation Services
N.A.I.C.S.: 488510
Linda Lewin-Haralampopoulo (Mgr-Bus Dev)

ARCHIE COMIC PUBLICATIONS INC.
629 Fifth Ave, Pelham, NY 10803
Tel.: (914) 381-5155
Web Site:
    http://www.archiecomics.com
Year Founded: 2003
Sales Range: $1-9.9 Million
Television, Film, Home Video, Music & Comics Producer & Distr
N.A.I.C.S.: 512110
Victor Gorelick (Co-Pres & Editor-in-Chief)
Roberto Aguirre-Sacasa (Chief Creative Officer)
Jon Goldwater (CEO & Publr)

ARCHIMEDES GLOBAL, INC.
3001 N Rocky Point Dr E, Tampa, FL 33607
Tel.: (800) 670-2390
Web Site:
    http://www.archimedesglobal.com
Year Founded: 2005
Sales Range: $10-24.9 Million
Emp.: 35
Government Energy & Information Technology Services
N.A.I.C.S.: 921190
Dan Shiels (Dir-HR Ops)

ARCHITEC HOUSEWARES
350 SE 1st St, Delray Beach, FL 33483
Tel.: (561) 272-0018
Web Site:
    http://www.architecproducts.com
Year Founded: 1980
Rev.: $18,100,000
Emp.: 16
Home Furnishing Merchant Whslr
N.A.I.C.S.: 423220
Jenna Miller (VP)
Jenna Sellers (Pres)

ARCHITECTS ORANGE LLP
144 N Orange St, Orange, CA 92866
Tel.: (714) 639-9860
Web Site:
    http://www.architectsorange.com
Year Founded: 1974
Sales Range: $1-9.9 Million
Emp.: 75
Architectural Services
N.A.I.C.S.: 541310
Darrel Hebenstreit (Partner)
Ed Cadavona (Partner)
Jim Dietze (Partner)
Hugh Rose (Partner)
Bruce Greenfield (Principal)
Jack Selman (Partner)
Jeffrey Rabbitt (Principal)
Kebin Yu (Principal)
Ken Smith (Partner)
Michael Heinrich (Principal)
Robert Budetti (Partner)
Samuel Saludo (Principal)
Douglas White (Principal)

Subsidiaries:

WHL Architects & Planners, Inc.   (1)
1289 Reamwood Ave Ste B, Sunnyvale, CA
94089-2261
Tel.: (408) 730-9500
Web Site: http://www.whlarchitects.com
Architectural Services
N.A.I.C.S.: 541310

ARCHITECTURAL DOORS & WINDOWS
865 Spring St, Westbrook, ME 04092-3828
Tel.: (207) 879-7800   ME
Web Site: https://www.a-d-w.biz
Year Founded: 1947
Sales Range: $10-24.9 Million
Emp.: 40
Provider of Curtainwall Store Front Windows Replacement & New Construction
N.A.I.C.S.: 236220
Jonathan Cohen (Pres & CEO)
Rory Huntley (Project Mgr)

ARCHITECTURAL DOORS INC.
11700 Monarch St, Garden Grove, CA 92841
Tel.: (714) 898-3667
Web Site: http://www.adi-usa.com
Year Founded: 1978
Sales Range: $10-24.9 Million
Emp.: 100
Provider of Building Products
N.A.I.C.S.: 423310
Robert Crane (Pres & CEO)

ARCHITECTURAL FLOORING RESOURCE, INC.
135 W 27th St 6th Fl, New York, NY 10001
Tel.: (212) 290-0200
Web Site: https://www.afrny.com
Year Founded: 1993
Rev.: $16,800,000
Emp.: 20
Flooring Contractors
N.A.I.C.S.: 238330
Catherine Leidersdorff (Founder, CEO & Pres)
Lydia Corchado (Project Mgr)

ARCHITECTURAL GLASS & ALUMINUM CO. INC.
1151 Marina Village Pkwy Ste 101, Alameda, CA 94501
Tel.: (510) 444-6100
Web Site: http://www.aga-ca.com
Year Founded: 1970
Sales Range: $10-24.9 Million
Emp.: 50

Provider of Architectural Construction Services
N.A.I.C.S.: 238150
Joseph Brescia (CEO)
Mark Tofflemire (VP-Engrg)

ARCHITECTURAL PANEL PRODUCTS, INC.
1175 NW 17th Ave, Delray Beach, FL 33445
Tel.: (561) 265-0707
Web Site: http://www.appi.us
Year Founded: 1994
Sales Range: $10-24.9 Million
Emp.: 38
Wood Panel & Component Product Whslr
N.A.I.C.S.: 423830
Donald Boyd (Acct Mgr)

ARCHITECTURAL SURFACES GROUP, LLC
401 Ctr Rdg Dr, Austin, TX 78753
Tel.: (512) 263-7625   DE
Web Site:
    http://www.arcsurfacesgroup.com
Year Founded: 2017
Holding Company; Granite Countertops Distr
N.A.I.C.S.: 551112
Sunil Palakodati (CEO)

Subsidiaries:

Architectural Granite & Marble, LLC   (1)
19012 State Hwy 71 W, Spicewood, TX
78669-6935
Tel.: (512) 263-7625
Web Site: http://www.agmgranite.com
Sales Range: $1-9.9 Million
Emp.: 23
Granite Countertops Distr
N.A.I.C.S.: 423320
Jesse Bogan (Mgr-Sls)
Sunil Palakodati (Grp CEO)

Cosmic Stone & Tile Distributors, Inc.   (1)
502 Jersey Ave, New Brunswick, NJ 08901
Tel.: (732) 937-5400
Web Site: http://www.cosmicstone.com
Sales Range: $1-9.9 Million
Emp.: 15
Construction Materials Whslr
N.A.I.C.S.: 423320
Venkat Malladi (Founder)

Modul Marble & Granite   (1)
4850 E La Palma Ave, Anaheim, CA 92807
Tel.: (714) 465-5220
Web Site: http://www.modulmarble.com
Rev.: $2,880,000
Emp.: 6
Brick, Stone & Related Construction Material Merchant Whslr
N.A.I.C.S.: 423320
Vinny Akpulat (VP-Mktg)

Pental Granite & Marble, LLC   (1)
713 S Fidalgo St, Seattle, WA 98108
Tel.: (206) 768-3200
Web Site: http://www.pentalonline.com
Granite Countertops Distr
N.A.I.C.S.: 423320

ARCHITECTURAL SYSTEMS INC.
4470 Spring Valley Rd, Dallas, TX 75244
Tel.: (972) 960-8726
Web Site:
    http://www.architecturalsystems.org
Sales Range: $10-24.9 Million
Emp.: 3
Construction Product Mfr
N.A.I.C.S.: 423310
Michael F. Gibbons (Owner & Pres)
Cheryl Gardner (VP & Mgr-Sls)
Travis Sursa (VP-Sls & Mktg)

ARCHITECTURAL WOODS INC.
801 E 25th St, Tacoma, WA 98421-2393
Tel.: (253) 383-5484
Web Site: https://www.awi-wa.com
Rev.: $10,800,000
Emp.: 50
Construction Product Mfr
N.A.I.C.S.: 423310
Tim Thomson (Mgr)

ARCHITECTURE DESIGN COLLABORATIVE, INC.
23231 S Pointe Dr, Laguna Hills, CA 92653
Tel.: (949) 267-1660
Web Site:
    http://www.adcollaborative.com
Year Founded: 2014
Sales Range: $1-9.9 Million
Architectural Services
N.A.I.C.S.: 541310
Craig Chinn (Pres & Principal)
Kent Miyake (Sr Project Mgr)
Marie Delwiche (Project Mgr-Design)
Sorlanda Moron Velez (Project Mgr)

ARCHITECTUREPLUS INTERNATIONAL, INC.
2709 N Rocky Point Dr Ste 201, Tampa, FL 33607
Tel.: (813) 281-9299   FL
Web Site: https://www.apiplus.com
Year Founded: 1990
Sales Range: $1-9.9 Million
Emp.: 21
Architectural Services
N.A.I.C.S.: 541310
Juan Romero (Pres & CEO)
Thomas Henken (VP & Dir-Design)

ARCHITEX INTERNATIONAL
3333 Commercial Ave, Northbrook, IL 60062
Tel.: (847) 205-1333
Web Site: https://www.architex-ljh.com
Sales Range: $50-74.9 Million
Emp.: 50
Textile Mfr
N.A.I.C.S.: 424310
Robert Korn (Dir-Sls)
Keith Gordon (Pres)
Lauren Williams (Dir-Mktg Svcs)

ARCHLYNK, LLC
3 E 3rd Ave Ste 200, San Mateo, CA 94401
Tel.: (650) 249-3200   DE
Web Site: https://archlynk.com
Year Founded: 2022
Information Technology Consulting Services
N.A.I.C.S.: 541511
Jigish Shah (Pres)
Joerg Rohde (Chief Strategy Officer)
Sekhar Puli (CEO-Global)

Subsidiaries:

Krypt Inc.   (1)
1250 Oakmead Pkwy Ste 210, Sunnyvale, CA 94085
Tel.: (408) 338-0029
Web Site: http://www.kryptinc.com
Custom Computer Programming Services
N.A.I.C.S.: 541511
Niki Vyas (Dir-HR)

Novigo Inc.   (1)
3 E 3rd Ave Ste 200, San Mateo, CA 94401
Tel.: (650) 249-3200
Web Site: https://novigo.com
Information Technology Consulting Services
N.A.I.C.S.: 541690

ArchLynk, LLC—(Continued)

ARCHON INFORMATION SYS-TEMS, L.L.C.
PO Box 52138, New Orleans, LA 70152
Tel.: (504) 267-0065
Web Site:
http://www.archoninfosys.com
Year Founded: 2008
Sales Range: $1-9.9 Million
Emp.: 58
Delinquent Tax Collection, Online Property Tax Auctions & Tax Collection Software
N.A.I.C.S.: 513210
Bryan P. Barrios (CEO)
William Sossamon (CTO)
Brian Danos (CIO)

ARCHRIVAL, INC.
720 O St, Lincoln, NE 68508
Tel.: (402) 435-2525
Web Site: http://www.archrival.com
Year Founded: 1997
Sales Range: $10-24.9 Million
Emp.: 20
Advertising Services
N.A.I.C.S.: 541810
Bart Johnston (Head-Digital)
Dan Gibson (Dir-Creative)
Jesseca Marchand (Dir-Ops)

ARCIS EQUITY PARTNERS LLC
5221 N O'Connor Blvd Ste 700, Irving, TX 75039
Tel.: (972) 532-4391
Web Site:
https://www.arcisequity.com
Privater Equity Firm
N.A.I.C.S.: 523940
Blake S. Walker (CEO & Mng Dir)

Subsidiaries:

Evergreen Alliance Golf Ltd (1)
13727 Noel Rd Ste 1000, Dallas, TX 75240
Tel.: (214) 722-6000
Web Site: https://www.arcisgolf.com
Golf Club
N.A.I.C.S.: 713940
Dirk Burghartz (Pres)
Blake S. Walker (Founder & CEO)
Julian Potter (CFO)
Chris J. Crocker (CMO)
Scott Siddons (Gen Counsel)

Subsidiary (Domestic):

The Dominion Golf Group (2)
4207 River Pl Blvd, Austin, TX 78730
Tel.: (512) 346-1114
Private Country Clubs
N.A.I.C.S.: 713990

ARCLIGHT CAPITAL HOLD-INGS, LLC
200 Clarendon St 55th Fl, Boston, MA 02116
Tel.: (617) 531-6300   DE
Web Site: https://www.arclight.com
Year Founded: 2001
Emp.: 50
Holding Company; Energy Investment Services
N.A.I.C.S.: 551112
Daniel R. Revers (Founder & Mng Partner)
Carter A. Ward (Partner)
Theodore D. Burke (Partner & Gen Counsel)
Kevin M. Crosby (Partner)
John F. Erhard (Partner)
Mark A. Tarini (Partner & Head-Portfolio Mgmt)
Timothy M. Evans (Principal)
Adam N. Kuhnley (Principal)
Evan M. Schwartz (Principal)
Lucius H. Taylor (Principal)

Subsidiaries:

ArcLight Capital Partners, LLC (1)
200 Clarendon St 55th Fl, Boston, MA 02117
Tel.: (212) 901-1500
Web Site: http://www.arclightcapital.com
Rev.: $10,000,000,000
Energy Investment Private Equity Firm
N.A.I.C.S.: 523999
Daniel R. Revers (Co-Founder & Mng Partner)
John F. Erhard (Partner)
Robb E. Turner (Co-Founder & Sr Partner)
Mark A. Tarini (Partner, Head & Portfolio Mgr)
Christine Miller (Assoc Gen Counsel)
Heidi D. Milne (Dir-PR)
Robert M. Trevisani (CFO)
Kevin M. Crosby (Partner)
Philip A. Messina (Principal-Dev)
Thomas J. Teich (Dir-Portfolio Mgmt)
Robert S. McGaughey (Head-Commodity Markets)
Patricia R. Winton (Principal-Strategy & Human Capital)
Timothy M. Evans (Principal)
John F. Mahoney (Controller)
Carter A. Ward (Partner)
Theodore D. Burke (Gen Counsel & Partner)
Rebecca S. Cooke (Office Mgr)
Karen E. Finn (Dir-HR)
Ross A. Murphy (Dir-IR)
Ashley S. Nahmias (Coord-IR)
Matthew E. Nelson (Head-IR)
Elisabeth A. Wallace (Coord-Legal)
Melissa A. Waystack (Controller)
Michelle M. Wright (Asst Controller)
John J. McNaught III (Dir-IT)

Holding (Domestic):

Gulf Oil, LP (2)
80 William St Ste 400, Wellesley Hills, MA 02481
Tel.: (339) 933-7200
Web Site: http://www.gulfoil.com
Petroleum Products Whslr & Terminal Operator
N.A.I.C.S.: 424710
Ron Sabia (Chief Strategy Officer)
Mike Campbell (CFO)
Todd O'Malley (Chief Comml Officer)
Chris Paul (Gen Counsel)
Michael DuBois (CIO)
Eric Johnson (Pres & CEO)
Belinda Foxworth (Gen Counsel & Sr VP)
Sue Hayden (CMO & Exec VP)
Winston Eaton (Exec VP-Corp Dev & Strategy)

Midcoast Energy Partners, L.P. (2)
1100 Louisiana St Ste 3300, Houston, TX 77002
Tel.: (713) 821-2000
Web Site: http://www.midcoastenergy.com
Natural Gas Exploration, Production, Distribution & Pipeline Transportation
N.A.I.C.S.: 211130

Terra-Gen Power, LLC (2)
565 5th Ave 27th FL, New York, NY 10017
Tel.: (646) 829-3900
Web Site: http://www.terra-genpower.com
Holding Company; Geothermal, Wind & Solar Power Generation
N.A.I.C.S.: 551112
Jim Pagano (CEO)

Subsidiary (Domestic):

Coso Operating Company, LLC (3)
PO Box 1690, Inyokern, CA 93527-1690
Tel.: (760) 764-1300
Web Site: http://www.terra-genpower.com
Sales Range: $10-24.9 Million
Geothermal, Wind & Solar Energy Generation
N.A.I.C.S.: 221118
Chris Ellis (Gen Mgr)

Terra-Gen Operating Company, LLC (3)
565 5th Ave 27th Fl, New York, NY 10017
Tel.: (646) 829-3900
Geothermal, Wind & Solar Power Generation
N.A.I.C.S.: 221118

Branch (Domestic):

Terra-Gen Operating Co., LLC (4)
9590 Prototype Ct Ste200, Reno, NV 89521
Tel.: (775) 851-1125
Renewable Energy Power Plants Operation & Maintenance Services
N.A.I.C.S.: 221118

Holding (Domestic):

TransMontaigne GP L.L.C. (2)
1670 Broadway Ste 3100, Denver, CO 80202
Tel.: (303) 626-8200
Holding Company
N.A.I.C.S.: 551112
Frederick W. Boutin (CEO)
Robert T. Fuller (CFO, Chief Acctg Officer, Treas & Exec VP)

Griffith Energy, LLC (1)
3375 W Navajo Dr, Golden Valley, AZ 86413
Tel.: (928) 718-0102
Electric Power Generation
N.A.I.C.S.: 221118

Third Coast Midstream, LLC (1)
2103 City W Blvd Bldg 4 Ste 800, Houston, TX 77042
Tel.: (346) 241-3400
Web Site:
http://www.americanmidstream.com
Rev.: $805,354,000
Assets: $1,687,696,000
Liabilities: $1,562,618,000
Net Worth: $125,078,000
Earnings: ($7,764,000)
Emp.: 490
Fiscal Year-end: 12/31/2018
Natural Gas Energy Services
N.A.I.C.S.: 211130
Matthew W. Rowland (Pres & CEO)
Rene L. Casadaban (COO & Sr VP)
Edward E. Greene (VP-Gathering, Processing & Terminals)
Ryan K. Rupe (Chief Comml Officer & Sr VP)
Karen S. Acree (Chief Acctg Officer & Sr VP)

Subsidiary (Domestic):

American Midstream (Mississippi), LLC (2)
1614 15th St Ste 300, Denver, CO 80202
Tel.: (720) 457-6060
Natural Gas Transmission Services
N.A.I.C.S.: 486210

Blackwater Georgia, LLC (2)
211 Newcastle St, Brunswick, GA 31520
Tel.: (912) 265-5860
Liquid Storage Services
N.A.I.C.S.: 424710

Blackwater Midstream Corp. (2)
660 LaBauve Dr, Westwego, LA 70094
Tel.: (504) 340-3000
Web Site:
http://www.blackwatermidstream.com
Sales Range: $75-99.9 Million
Emp.: 24
Liquid Storage Services
N.A.I.C.S.: 424710

Blackwater New Orleans, LLC (2)
660 La Bauve Dr, Westwego, LA 70094
Tel.: (504) 340-3000
Emp.: 8
Natural Gas Transmission Services
N.A.I.C.S.: 486210

High Point Gas Transmission, LLC (2)
919 Milam St Ste 2450, Houston, TX 77002
Tel.: (713) 815-3900
Natural Gas Transmission Services
N.A.I.C.S.: 486210
Charlie Bilberry (Dir-Producer Svcs)
Ryan Rupe (VP-Comml Ops)
Avery Plank (Dir-Bus Dev)
Lauren Kaestner (Dir-Comml Ops)
Buddy Gray (Mgr-Comml)

Main Pass Oil Gathering Company (2)
550 Westlake Park Blvd, Houston, TX 77079-2661

Tel.: (281) 366-7651
Oil & Gas Transportation Services
N.A.I.C.S.: 484220

Thorntons Inc (1)
10101 Linn Sta Rd Ste 200, Louisville, KY 40223-3819
Tel.: (502) 425-8022
Web Site: http://www.thorntonsinc.com
Sales Range: $1-4.9 Billion
Emp.: 950
Operator of Gasoline Service Stations & Convenience Stores
N.A.I.C.S.: 445131
James H. Thornton (Founder)

TransMontaigne Partners LLC (1)
1670 Broadway Ste 3100, Denver, CO 80202   (100%)
Tel.: (303) 626-8200
Web Site:
https://www.transmontaignepartners.com
Rev.: $666,395,000
Assets: $1,376,023,000
Liabilities: $1,389,885,000
Net Worth: ($13,862,000)
Earnings: $41,949,000
Emp.: 532
Fiscal Year-end: 12/31/2022
Oil & Gas Services
N.A.I.C.S.: 486110
Randal T. Maffett (CEO)
Lisa M. Kearney (Chief Acctg Officer)
Matt White (Gen Counsel)

ARCLIGHT CINEMA COMPANY
6360 W Sunset Blvd, Los Angeles, CA 90028
Tel.: (323) 464-4226
Web Site:
http://www.arclightcinemas.com
Sales Range: $10-24.9 Million
Emp.: 300
Movie Theatre Operator
N.A.I.C.S.: 512131
Christopher S. Forman (Pres)

ARCLINE INVESTMENT MAN-AGEMENT LP
4 Embarcadero Ctr Ste 2660, San Francisco, CA 94111
Tel.: (415) 801-4570   DE
Web Site: http://arcline.com
Year Founded: 2018
Privater Equity Firm
N.A.I.C.S.: 523999
Rajeev Amara (CEO)
Shyam Ravindran (Pres)
Gib Efird (CFO & Head-IR)
Robert Nelson (Chief Compliance Officer & Gen Counsel)

Subsidiaries:

Air Comm Corporation (1)
1575 W 124th Ave Ste 210, Westminster, CO 80234
Tel.: (303) 440-4075
Web Site: http://www.aircommcorp.com
Emp.: 120
Flight Control Systems Mfr
N.A.I.C.S.: 334513
Keith Steiner (CEO)
Rick Steiner (Exec VP)
Mark Shankland (Mgr-Supply Chain-CO)
Chad Rhoades (Dir-Ops)
Chuck Barrineau (Mgr-Supply Chain-TX)
John Fiala (Mgr-Corp Quality)
Dave Harrison (Chm)

Division (Domestic):

Air Comm Corporation - Addison (2)
4554 Claire Chennault, Addison, TX 75001
Tel.: (972) 407-1234
Web Site: http://www.keithproducts.com
Aircraft Air Conditioning, Heating & Ventilation Systems Mfr
N.A.I.C.S.: 336413
Chuck Barrineau (Mgr-Supply Chain)
Jeff Baird (Dir-Ops)
David Benedetti (Dir-Fin)
John Fiala (Mgr-Corp Quality)
Mark Krause (Dir-Bus Dev)
Danny Ogle (Mgr-Production)
Chad Rhoades (Mgr-Ops)

Norm Steiner *(Founder)*
Richard Voorhees *(Mgr-Sls & Customer Svc)*
Louise Wilson *(Dir-HR)*
Keith Steiner *(CEO)*
Rick Steiner *(Exec VP)*

American Holt Corp. (1)
203 Carnegie Row, Norwood, MA 02062
Tel.: (781) 440-9993
Web Site: http://www.americanholt.com
Rev.: $2,500,000
Emp.: 10
Industrial Supplies Merchant Whslr
N.A.I.C.S.: 423840
Jon Levy *(CEO)*

BEI Precision Systems & Space Company, Inc. (1)
1100 Murphy Dr, Maumelle, AR 72113
Tel.: (501) 851-4000
Web Site: http://www.beiprecision.com
Rotary Optical Encoders, Accelerometers & Servo Systems Design & Mfr
N.A.I.C.S.: 335312
Jeff Sponsler *(Program Mgr)*

Subsidiary (Domestic):

Wenzel Associates, Inc. (2)
2215 Kramer Ln, Austin, TX 78758
Tel.: (512) 835-2038
Web Site: http://www.wenzel.com
Electrical Instrument Testing Mfr
N.A.I.C.S.: 334515
James White *(Engr-Quality)*
Joseph Ybarbo *(Comptroller)*
Kevin Golliher *(CFO)*
Paul Cole *(Engr-Sls)*

Subsidiary (Non-US):

Wenzel International Inc. (3)
500 Beech Street, Whitby, L1N 7T8, ON, Canada
Tel.: (905) 668-3324
Web Site: http://www.crovencrystals.com
Sales Range: $75-99.9 Million
Emp.: 150
Quartz Crystal Mfr
N.A.I.C.S.: 334220
Luke Mueller *(Pres)*

Cooper Machinery Services (1)
16250 Port NW Dr, Houston, TX 77041
Tel.: (713) 354-1900
Web Site: http://www.bhge.com
Engines & Compression Equipment Mfr
N.A.I.C.S.: 333912
John Sargent *(CEO)*

Subsidiary (Domestic):

Sinor Engine Company, Inc. (2)
1100 Georgia, Deer Park, TX 77536
Tel.: (281) 930-0060
Web Site: http://www.sinorengine.com
Oil & Gas Operations
N.A.I.C.S.: 213111
Dale L. Sinor *(Pres, Treas & Sec)*

Corry Micronics, Inc. (1)
761 Commonwealth Dr #201, Warrendale, PA 15086
Tel.: (814) 664-7728
Web Site: http://www.cormic.com
Rev.: $4,000,000
Emp.: 29
Electronic Capacitor Mfr
N.A.I.C.S.: 334416
Don Pavlek *(Pres & CEO)*

Dwyer Instruments, LLC (1)
102 Indiana Hwy 212, Michigan City, IN 46360-1956
Tel.: (219) 879-8000
Web Site: http://www.dwyer-inst.com
Sales Range: $150-199.9 Million
Emp.: 700
Industrial Instruments & Controls Mfr
N.A.I.C.S.: 334513
Mark Fisher *(VP-Sls, Engrg, and Mktg)*
Brian Palmer *(Mgr-Product Support & Enhancement)*
Peggy Stover *(Plant Mgr)*

Subsidiary (Domestic):

Automation Components, Inc. (2)
2305 Pleasant View Rd, Middleton, WI 53562
Tel.: (608) 831-2585
Sales Range: $1-9.9 Million
Emp.: 95
Automatic Environmental Control Mfr for Residential, Commercial & Appliance Use
N.A.I.C.S.: 334512
Brian Statz *(Dir-Sls)*
Bill Kubsh *(Mgr-Engrg)*
Connor Meloy *(VP)*
Lois Ripp *(Office Mgr)*
Randi Biech *(Mgr-Pur)*

Subsidiary (Non-US):

Dwyer Instruments Ltd (2)
Unit 16 The Wye Estate London Road, High Wycombe, HP11 1LH, Bucks, United Kingdom
Tel.: (44) 1494 461707
Web Site: http://www.dwyer-inst.co.uk
Sales Range: $10-24.9 Million
Emp.: 8
Industrial Instrument Mfr
N.A.I.C.S.: 334513
Bradley Chapman *(Mng Dir)*

Dwyer Instruments Pty Ltd (2)
Unit 1 11 Waverley Drive, PO Box 359, Unanderra, 2526, NSW, Australia
Tel.: (61) 2 4272 2055
Web Site: http://www.dwyer-inst.com.au
Sales Range: $10-24.9 Million
Emp.: 6
Industrial Instrument Mfr
N.A.I.C.S.: 334513
Andrea Jonker *(Gen Mgr)*

Division (Domestic):

Love Controls Corporation (2)
102 Indiana Hwy 212, Michigan City, IN 46360-1956 **(100%)**
Tel.: (219) 879-8000
Web Site: http://www.love-controls.com
Sales Range: $25-49.9 Million
Emp.: 200
Temperature Sensors & Controls Mfr
N.A.I.C.S.: 334512
Stephen S. Clark *(Chm)*
Rom Bellisario *(Pres)*

Mercoid Div. (2)
102 Indiana Hwy 212, Michigan City, IN 46360 **(100%)**
Tel.: (219) 879-8000
Web Site: http://www.dwyer-inst.com
Sales Range: $10-24.9 Million
Emp.: 200
Mercoid Pressure Temperature & Level Controls
N.A.I.C.S.: 334513
Mark Fisher *(Pres)*

Subsidiary (Domestic):

Miljoco Corp. (2)
14335 E 9 Mile Rd, Warren, MI 48089
Tel.: (586) 777-4280
Web Site: http://www.miljoco.com
Sales Range: $1-9.9 Million
Emp.: 35
Process Control Instruments
N.A.I.C.S.: 334513
Ben Spencer *(Dir & Mgr)*

Subsidiary (Domestic):

Weiss Instruments, Inc. (3)
905 Waverly Ave, Holtsville, NY 11742
Tel.: (631) 207-1200
Web Site: http://www.weissinstruments.com
Sales Range: $1-9.9 Million
Emp.: 100
Instruments & Related Products Mfr for Measuring, Displaying & Controlling Industrial Process Variables
N.A.I.C.S.: 334513
John Weiss *(Pres)*
Frank A. Ancona *(Mgr-Field Sls)*
Karen Drago *(Asst Mgr-Sls Distr)*
Richard Schwab *(Dir-Creative Adv)*
Ken Goodwin *(Mgr-Quality Assurance)*
Kenneth Weiss *(Plant Mgr)*
Sandy Renner *(Asst Mgr-OEM Sls)*
Steve Weiss *(Sec)*
William Weiss *(Treas)*

Division (Domestic):

Proximity Controls Corp. (2)
1431 Hwy 210 E, Fergus Falls, MN 56537
Tel.: (218) 739-3364
Web Site: http://www.proximitycontrols.com
Sales Range: $10-24.9 Million
Emp.: 10
Liquid & Dry Bulk Level Controls & Valve Position Indicating Switches & Transmitters Mfr
N.A.I.C.S.: 335314
Curt Biegler *(Plant Mgr)*

Subsidiary (Domestic):

Universal Flow Monitors, Inc. (2)
1755 E 9 Mile Rd, Hazel Park, MI 48030
Tel.: (248) 542-9635
Web Site: http://www.flowmeters.com
Sales Range: $1-9.9 Million
Emp.: 45
Instruments & Related Products Mfr for Measuring, Displaying & Controlling Industrial Process Variables
N.A.I.C.S.: 334513
Lars Rosaen *(Pres)*

Division (Domestic):

W.E. Anderson Div. (2)
250 High Grove Rd, Grandview, MO 64030-5614
Tel.: (816) 966-2000
Sales Range: $10-24.9 Million
Emp.: 60
Temperature Sensors & Controls Mfr
N.A.I.C.S.: 334513
Sue McHenry *(Office Mgr)*

Evans Capacitor Company (1)
72 Boyd Ave, East Providence, RI 02914
Tel.: (401) 435-3555
Web Site: http://www.evanscap.com
Rev.: $6,600,000
Emp.: 18
Metal Stamping
N.A.I.C.S.: 332119
Charles Dewey *(CEO)*

Fairbanks Morse, LLC (1)
701 White Ave, Beloit, WI 53511-5447
Tel.: (512) 215-4452
Web Site: http://www.fairbanksmorse.com
Sales Range: $100-124.9 Million
Emp.: 350
Diesel Engine Generator Systems; Diesel Engines for Industry, Drives; Marine Diesel Propulsion Systems; Engine Accessories-Magnetos, Starters & Clutches
N.A.I.C.S.: 333618
George Whittier *(CEO)*
Deepak Navnith *(Pres)*
Pat Bussie *(VP-Sls-Marine Segment)*
Tricia Blackwell *(Mgr-Acctg)*
James McFadyen *(VP & Gen Mgr-Aftermarket)*
Michael E. Clark *(COO)*

Subsidiary (Domestic):

Ammcon Corp. (2)
21450 Nw West Union Rd, Hillsboro, OR 97124
Tel.: (503) 645-5206
Web Site: http://www.ammcon.com
Rev.: $6,534,000
Emp.: 46
All Other Miscellaneous Fabricated Metal Product Mfr
N.A.I.C.S.: 332999
Randy Grow *(VP)*
Darrell Grow *(Owner)*

Breco International Inc. (2)
6830 Lapaseo St, Houston, TX 77087
Tel.: (713) 641-6073
Web Site: http://www.brecointernational.net
Heavy & Civil Engineering Construction
N.A.I.C.S.: 237990
Gaynell Rodgers *(VP)*

Hunt Valve Company, Inc. (2)
1913 E State St, Salem, OH 44460
Tel.: (330) 337-9535
Specialty Valves, Cylinders & Systems Mfr
N.A.I.C.S.: 332912

Subsidiary (Domestic):

Hunt Valve - Actuator Division (3)
225 Glade View Dr Ne, Roanoke, VA 24012
Tel.: (540) 857-9871
Web Site: http://www.huntvalveactuators.com
All Other Miscellaneous Electrical Equipment & Component Mfr
N.A.I.C.S.: 335999
Brad Sterner *(Pres & CEO)*
Charles Ferrer *(VP & Gen Mgr)*
Michael Johnston *(VP-Ops & Supply Chain)*

Pima Valve, Inc. (3)
6525 W Allison Rd #5010, Chandler, AZ 85226
Tel.: (480) 646-8456
Metal Valve & Pipe Fitting Mfr
N.A.I.C.S.: 332919

Division (Non-US):

Tecnometal (3)
Edif Losoles PD 19 Av Lazaro Cardens 2400, Garza Garcia, 66200, N.L., Mexico **(100%)**
Tel.: (52) 818 363 2449
Web Site: http://www.huntvalve.com
Sales Range: $10-24.9 Million
Emp.: 3
Specialty Metal Valve Engineering Mfr
N.A.I.C.S.: 332911
Cesar Ruelas *(Gen Mgr)*

Subsidiary (Domestic):

Ward Leonard CT LLC (2)
401 Watertown Rd, Thomaston, CT 06787
Tel.: (860) 283-5801
Web Site: http://www.wardleonard.com
Electrical & Electronic Control Products
N.A.I.C.S.: 335314
Jon Carter *(CEO)*
Alder H. Crocker *(Dir-Mktg)*
Michael Clute *(Pres)*

Subsidiary (Domestic):

Houma Armature Works & Supply, Inc. (3)
2534 Cummins Road, Houma, LA 70363
Tel.: (985) 876-0198
Web Site: http://www.houmaarmature.com
Sales Range: $1-9.9 Million
Emp.: 45
Electric Motor & Generator Systems Maintenance, Repair & Overhaul
N.A.I.C.S.: 238210
Jeremy Luke *(Mgr-Sls)*
Roy Corbitt *(Mgr-Ops)*
Mark Welch *(Gen Mgr)*
Dustin Graham *(Mgr-Svc)*
Taeger Gisclair *(Asst Mgr-Ops)*
Jeremiah Pellegrin *(Project Mgr)*

Glebar Company, Inc. (1)
565 E Crescent Ave, Ramsey, NJ 07446
Tel.: (201) 337-1500
Web Site: http://www.glebar.com
Machine Tools, Metal Cutting Type
N.A.I.C.S.: 333517
Robert Gleason *(VP-Engrg)*
Adam Cook *(Pres)*
Mark Bannayan *(VP-Sls & Mktg)*
Jason Habib *(Engr-Sls-Midwest)*

Subsidiary (Domestic):

Everite Machine Products Co. (2)
1555 Rte 73 S, Pennsauken, NJ 08110
Tel.: (856) 330-6700
Web Site: http://www.everite.com
Machine Tool, Metal Cutting Types, Mfr
N.A.I.C.S.: 333517

Hartzell Engine Technologies LLC (1)
2900 Selma Hwy, Montgomery, AL 36108
Tel.: (334) 386-5400
Web Site: http://www.hartzell.aero
Emp.: 100
Aircraft Components Mfr
N.A.I.C.S.: 336412
Keith Bagley *(Pres)*

Subsidiary (Domestic):

Kelly Aerospace Inc. (2)
1400 E South Blvd, Montgomery, AL 36116
Tel.: (334) 286-8551
Web Site: http://www.kellyaerospace.com
Sales Range: $25-49.9 Million
Emp.: 12
Aviation Parts & Accessories Mfr

Arcline Investment Management LP—(Continued)

N.A.I.C.S.: 336413
Kent Kelly (Chm)
Jeffrey D. Kelly (Pres)
Walter Dodge (Dir-Ops)

Integrated Polymer Solutions, Inc. (1)
3701 Conant St, Long Beach, CA 90808
Tel.: (562) 354-2920
Web Site:
　http://www.integratedpolymersolution.com
Investment Holding Company
N.A.I.C.S.: 551112
Eric Sanders (Chm & Owner)
Karrie Hatfield (Mgr-Personnel)
Stuart Lowndes (VP-Demand Creation)
Rich McManus (Pres & CEO)

Subsidiary (Domestic):

Mast Technologies, Inc. (2)
6370 Nancy Rdg Dr Ste 103, San Diego, CA 92121-3212
Tel.: (858) 452-1700
Web Site: http://www.masttechnologies.com
All Other Manufacturing
N.A.I.C.S.: 339999
Andrew Sundsmo (Pres & CEO)

Seal Science, Inc. (2)
17131 Daimler, Irvine, CA 92614
Tel.: (949) 253-3130
Web Site: http://www.sealscience.com
Gasket, Packing & Sealing Device Mfr
N.A.I.C.S.: 339991
Gregory Bloom (Pres)

Swift Textile Metalizing LLC (2)
23 Britton Dr, Bloomfield, CT 06002
Tel.: (860) 243-1122
Web Site: http://www.swift-textile.com
Fabrics Mfr
N.A.I.C.S.: 313320
Patricia Clarke (Mgr-Customer Svc)
Steve Sigmon (Pres)

International Mezzo Technologies, Inc. (2)
7167 Florida Blvd, Baton Rouge, LA 70806
Tel.: (225) 706-0191
Plate Work Mfr
N.A.I.C.S.: 332313
Kevin Kelly (Pres)
Mark Turner (Dir-Fin)

International Water-Guard Industries Inc. (1)
Building 7 15050 54A Avenue, Surrey, V3S 5X7, BC, Canada
Tel.: (604) 255-5555
Web Site: http://www.water.aero
Aircraft Water Treatment & Solutions
N.A.I.C.S.: 325998
Steven Bis (Pres)

Jersey Elevator Co. Inc. (1)
657 Line Rd, Aberdeen, NJ 07747
Tel.: (732) 290-2991
Web Site: http://www.jerseyelevator.com
Sales Range: $1-9.9 Million
Emp.: 30
Building Equipment Installation Services
N.A.I.C.S.: 238290
John Sweeney (Pres)

Kaman Corporation (1)
1332 Blue Hills Ave, Bloomfield, CT 06002
Tel.: (860) 243-7100
Web Site: http://www.kaman.com
Rev.: $687,961,000
Assets: $1,491,332,000
Liabilities: $807,353,000
Net Worth: $683,979,000
Earnings: ($46,226,000)
Emp.: 3,063
Fiscal Year-end: 12/31/2022
Aerospace Component & Industrial Supplies Mfr & Distr
N.A.I.C.S.: 423840
Roy Dilig (VP-IT)
Matthew Petterson (Chief Acctg Officer, VP & Controller)
Carroll K. Lane (Interim CFO & Sr VP)
Kristen M. Samson (CMO & VP)
Richard S. Smith Jr. (Gen Counsel)
John Michelon Jr. (VP)

Ian K. Walsh (Chm, Pres & CEO)
Megan Morgan (Chief HR Officer & VP)
Richard S. Smith Jr. (Gen Counsel, Sec & Sr VP)

Subsidiary (Domestic):

EXTEX Engineered Products, Inc. (2)
340 E Germann Rd Ste 113, Gilbert, AZ 85297
Tel.: (480) 632-1039
Web Site: https://www.extexengineered.com
Aerospace Overhaul & Repair Services
N.A.I.C.S.: 423860

Subsidiary (Non-US):

Gebr. Reinfurt GmbH & Co. KG (2)
Niederhoferstrasse 105, Rimpar, 97222, Wurzburg, Germany
Tel.: (49) 93658190
Web Site: https://www.grw.de
Emp.: 600
Ball & Roller Bearing Mfr
N.A.I.C.S.: 332991

Subsidiary (Domestic):

Kaman Aerospace Group, Inc. (2)
1332 Blue Hills Ave, Bloomfield, CT 06002-5302
Tel.: (860) 243-7100
Web Site: http://www.kaman.com
Holding Company; Aircraft Components Mfr & Distr
N.A.I.C.S.: 551112

Subsidiary (Domestic):

Bal Seal Engineering, Inc. (3)
19650 Pauling, Foothill Ranch, CA 92610-2610
Tel.: (949) 460-2100
Web Site: https://www.balseal.com
Metal Mining Support Services
N.A.I.C.S.: 213114

Subsidiary (Non-US):

Bal Seal Asia, Ltd. (4)
Suite 901 Chinachem Century Tower 178 Gloucester Road, Wanchai, China (Hong Kong)
Tel.: (852) 28681860
Motor Vehicle Electrical Mfr
N.A.I.C.S.: 336320
Shawn Noh (Mng Dir)

Bal Seal Engineering Europe BV (4)
VIDA Building 1st Floor Kabelweg 57, 1014 BA, Amsterdam, Netherlands
Tel.: (31) 206386523
Motor Vehicle Electrical Mfr
N.A.I.C.S.: 336320

Subsidiary (Domestic):

Kaman Aerospace Corporation (3)
50 Old Windsor Rd, Bloomfield, CT 06002-0002 (100%)
Tel.: (860) 242-4461
Web Site: https://www.kaman.com
Sales Range: $200-249.9 Million
Emp.: 500
Mfr & Design of Helicopters & Aircraft Parts
N.A.I.C.S.: 336413

Subsidiary (Domestic):

K-MAX Corporation (4)
1332 Blue Hills Ave, Bloomfield, CT 06002-5302
Tel.: (860) 243-7100
Aerospace Product Whslr
N.A.I.C.S.: 423860
Neil Keating (CEO)

Subsidiary (Non-US):

Kaman Composites - UK Holdings Limited (3)
Holding Company; Aerospace Composite Products Mfr & Distr

Subsidiary (Non-US):

Kaman Fabricated Products Limited (4)
Emp.: 2
Aerostructure Assembly Mfr

Subsidiary (Domestic):

Kaman Composites - Vermont, Inc. (3)
25 Performance Dr, Bennington, VT 05201-1947
Tel.: (802) 442-9964
Web Site: http://www.kaman.com
Fibre Reinforced Advanced Composite Components Mfr for Aerospace, Medical, X-Ray & Other Industrial Applications
N.A.I.C.S.: 326199

Kaman Composites - Wichita, Inc. (3)
1650 S McComas St, Wichita, KS 67213
Tel.: (316) 942-1241
Web Site: https://www.kaman.com
Aerospace Component Mfr
N.A.I.C.S.: 336413

Kaman Engineering Services, Inc. (3)
11323 Commando Rd W Ste 200, Everett, WA 98204-1302
Tel.: (425) 367-4477
Web Site: https://www.kaman.com
Sales Range: $25-49.9 Million
Emp.: 100
Aerospace Engineering Services
N.A.I.C.S.: 541330

Kaman Precision Products, Inc. (3)
6655 E Colonial Dr, Orlando, FL 32807-5200
Tel.: (407) 282-1000
Web Site: https://www.kamansensors.com
Aerospace Fuzing & Precision Products Designer, Mfr & Distr
N.A.I.C.S.: 336419

Unit (Domestic):

Kaman Precision Products, Inc. - Middletown (4)
217 Smith St, Middletown, CT 06457-8750
Tel.: (860) 632-1000
Web Site: https://www.kamansensors.com
Emp.: 180
Aerospace Fuzing & Precision Products Designer & Distr
N.A.I.C.S.: 336419
William E. Seitz (Pres & CEO)

Subsidiary (Non-US):

Kaman Specialty Bearings & Engineered Products, GmbH (3)
Medbacher Weg 1, Hochstadt an der Aisch, Germany
Tel.: (49) 919350105100
Industrial Product Distr
N.A.I.C.S.: 423840

Subsidiary (Domestic):

Kamatics Corporation (3)
1330 Blue Hills Ave, Bloomfield, CT 06002-0003 (100%)
Tel.: (860) 243-9704
Web Site: https://www.kamatics.com
Sales Range: $125-149.9 Million
Emp.: 450
Mfr of Bearings
N.A.I.C.S.: 333613

Subsidiary (Non-US):

RWG Germany GmbH (3)
Medbacher Weg 1, 91315, Burgebrach, Germany
Tel.: (49) 919350105100
Web Site: https://www.rwg-germany.de
Engineering Equipment Mfr
N.A.I.C.S.: 336310
Robert Paterson (Mng Dir)
Stefan Daub-Klose (Mng Dir)

Subsidiary (Domestic):

Ovation Instruments (2)
37 Greenwoods Road, New Hartford, CT 06057
Tel.: (860) 379-7575
Web Site: http://www.ovationguitars.com
Musical Instrument Mfr
N.A.I.C.S.: 339992
Frank Untermyer (Mgr)

Subsidiary (Non-US):

Reinfurt-CR, k.s. (2)
Prumyslova 1366, 383 01, Prachatice, Czech Republic
Tel.: (420) 380601039
Ball & Roller Bearing Mfr
N.A.I.C.S.: 332991

Kings III of America, LLC (1)
751 Canyon Dr Ste 100, Coppell, TX 75019
Tel.: (682) 503-1455
Web Site: http://www.kingsiii.com
Communication Equipment Repair & Maintenance Services
N.A.I.C.S.: 811210
David Bryant (VP-Sls)
Dennis Mason (CEO)

OMEGA Engineering, Inc. (1)
1 Omega Dr, Stamford, CT 06907-2390
Tel.: (203) 359-1660
Web Site: http://www.omega.com
Sales Range: $150-199.9 Million
Emp.: 800
Process Control Instrumentation & Publisher of Technical & Scientific Literature Mfr
N.A.I.C.S.: 334513
Joe Vorih (Pres)

Affiliate (Non-US):

JAKAR Electronics, spol. s r.o. (2)
Frystatska 184/46, 733 01, Karvina, Czech Republic (100%)
Tel.: (420) 59 631 1899
Web Site: https://www.jakar.cz
Sales Range: $1-9.9 Million
Emp.: 10
Instruments for Measuring & Testing of Electricity & Electrical Signals Distr
N.A.I.C.S.: 423690

Newport Electronics B.V. (2)
Postbus 8034, 1180 LA, Amstelveen, Netherlands (100%)
Tel.: (31) 203472121
Web Site: http://www.newport.nl
Provider of Digital Electronic Measurement Instruments
N.A.I.C.S.: 334515

Affiliate (Domestic):

Newport Electronics, Inc. (2)
2229 S Yale St, Santa Ana, CA 92704-4401
Tel.: (714) 540-4914
Web Site: http://www.newportus.com
Sales Range: $25-49.9 Million
Emp.: 65
Mfr of High-Technology Digital Measurement Instrumentation
N.A.I.C.S.: 334513

Affiliate (Non-US):

Omega Engineering GmbH (2)
Daimlerstrasse 26, 75392, Deckenpfronn, Germany (100%)
Tel.: (49) 705693980
Web Site: http://www.omega.de
Emp.: 15
Digital Electronic Measurement Instruments Mfr & Distr
N.A.I.C.S.: 334515

Subsidiary (Non-US):

Omega Engineering Ltd. (2)
1 Omega Drive Northbank, Irlam, Manchester, M44 5BD, United Kingdom (100%)
Tel.: (44) 161 777 6611
Web Site: https://www.omega.co.uk
Sales Range: $25-49.9 Million
Emp.: 40
Provider of Digital Electronic Measurement Instruments
N.A.I.C.S.: 334515

Omega Environmental, Inc. (2)
82 Boul Arthur Sauve, Saint-Eustache, J7R 2H7, QC, Canada (100%)
Tel.: (514) 856-6928
Web Site: http://www.omega.ca
Sales Range: $25-49.9 Million
Emp.: 13
Process Control Instrumentation Sales & Repair
N.A.I.C.S.: 811310

Subsidiary (Domestic):

Omegadyne, Inc. (2)
149 Stelzer Ct, Sunbury, OH 43074-8528
Tel.: (740) 965-9340
Web Site: http://www.omegadyne.com
Sales Range: $25-49.9 Million
Emp.: 100
Mfr of Pressure Measuring Equipment, including Controllers, Indicators, Gauges, Sensors & Transmitters for the Aerospace Industry
N.A.I.C.S.: 334519
Gesling Ken (Mgr-IT & Engr-Automation)

Ohmega Technologies, Inc. (1)
4031 Elenda St, Culver City, CA 90232
Tel.: (310) 559-4400
Web Site: http://www.ohmega.com
Sales Range: $1-9.9 Million
Emp.: 20
Electronic Components Mfr
N.A.I.C.S.: 334419
Andrew Fructuoso (Controller)
Bruce P. Mahler (VP)
Daniel D. Brandler (Dir-Techical)
Marian Yacoub (Mgr-Admin)

Planar Monolithics Industries, Inc. (1)
7311 Grove Rd Ste F, Frederick, MD 21704-5178
Tel.: (301) 662-5019
Web Site: http://www.pmi-rf.com
Monolithic Based Product Mfr
N.A.I.C.S.: 334419
Ashok Gorwara (Pres & CEO)
Sebastian Palacio (Gen Mgr)

Pride Engineering, LLC (1)
10301 Xylon Ave N Ste 100, Minneapolis, MN 55445
Tel.: (763) 427-6250
Web Site: http://www.pridecan.com
Soft Drinks Mfr
N.A.I.C.S.: 312111
Dave Gadow (Dir-Ops)
Greg Pickert (Pres & CEO)

Signia Aerospace (1)
1575 W 124th Ave., Westminster, CO 80234
Tel.: (727) 403-4507
Web Site: https://signiaaerospace.com
Aviation & Aerospace Component Mfg
N.A.I.C.S.: 334511
Ralph A. DeMarco (Chief Comml Officer)

Subsidiary (Domestic):

Lifesaving Systems Corp. (2)
220 Elsberry Rd, Apollo Beach, FL 33572
Tel.: (813) 645-2748
Web Site: http://www.lifesavingsystems.com
Sales Range: $1-9.9 Million
Emp.: 20
Surgical Appliances And Supplies, Nsk
N.A.I.C.S.: 339113
Barbara Maness (Sec & VP)

Syneo, LLC (1)
3875 Fiscal Ct Ste 300, West Palm Beach, FL 33404
Tel.: (561) 848-6684
Web Site: http://www.syneoco.com
Cutting Tools & Hole-Making Machines & Systems Developer
N.A.I.C.S.: 333515
Tyler Wackman (CEO)
Crew Feighery (VP-Bus Dev)
Vincent Levannier (Mgr-Global Pressfit)
Tim Hammill (Ops Mgr-Machine)
Brian Sandberg (Mgr-Ops)
Lauren Hadley (Controller)

Union Technology Corp. (1)
718 Monterey Pass Rd, Monterey Park, CA 91754
Tel.: (323) 266-6603
Web Site: http://www.uniontechcorp.com
Sales Range: $1-9.9 Million
Emp.: 50
Electronic Parts & Equipment Merchant Whslr
N.A.I.C.S.: 423690
Robert Boughrum (VP-Sls & Mktg)
David Chu (Pres & CEO)
Gary Koniow (Mgr-Quality Assurance)
Benja Choonhauri (Mgr-Customer Svc)
Raj Amin (Dir-Technical)
Peter He (Gen Mgr)

ARCO CONSTRUCTION COMPANY INC.
900 N Rock Hill Rd, Saint Louis, MO 63119-1315
Tel.: (314) 963-0715   MO
Web Site: https://arcoconstruction.com
Year Founded: 1992
Sales Range: $25-49.9 Million
Emp.: 1,250
Engineeering Services
N.A.I.C.S.: 541330
Stephen F. Holste (VP-Finance)
Jeff Cook (Co-Founder)

ARCO ELECTRIC, INC.
597 W 9320 S, Sandy, UT 84070
Tel.: (801) 566-1695
Web Site: https://www.arcoelectric.com
Year Founded: 1972
Rev.: $21,800,000
Emp.: 170
Electrical Contractor
N.A.I.C.S.: 238210
Dee Clark (Pres)

ARCO INCORPORATED
17 Westgate Blvd, Savannah, GA 31405
Tel.: (912) 233-6914
Web Site: http://www.arcosav.com
Sales Range: $10-24.9 Million
Emp.: 30
General Contractor, Highway & Street Construction
N.A.I.C.S.: 237310
Joseph G. Arsenault (Founder)
Keith Trotheer (Pres)

ARCO INDUSTRIAL SALES INC.
5380 S Riley Ln, Salt Lake City, UT 84107
Tel.: (801) 261-4455   UT
Web Site: http://www.arcopackaging.com
Sales Range: $10-24.9 Million
Emp.: 40
Distribution of Packaging & Janitorial Materials
N.A.I.C.S.: 424130
John A. Mitchell (Pres)

ARCO/MURRAY NATIONAL CONSTRUCTION COMPANY, INC.
3110 Woodcreek Dr, Downers Grove, IL 60515
Tel.: (331) 251-2726
Web Site: https://www.arcomurray.com
Year Founded: 1992
Sales Range: $75-99.9 Million
Emp.: 70
Construction Engineering Services
N.A.I.C.S.: 237310
Brad Dannegger (Pres)
Joe Pomerenke (Principal & Dir-Bus Dev)
Elliot Mata (Principal & Dir-Ops Process Div)
Leonidas Stellakis (Principal & Dir-Ops BTS Natl Accts)
Chris Niedhammer (Principal & Dir-Ops-Interiors Div)

ARCOM PUBLISHING INC.
9 E Market St, Leesburg, VA 20176
Tel.: (703) 777-1111
Web Site: http://www.timescommunity.com
Sales Range: $10-24.9 Million
Emp.: 100
Newspapers; Publishing & Printing
N.A.I.C.S.: 513110

Peter Arundel (Pres & Publr)

ARCON CONSTRUCTION & MANAGEMENT SERVICES, INC.
8 Railroad Ave, Albany, NY 12205
Tel.: (518) 459-1128   NY
Web Site: https://www.arconconstruction.net
Year Founded: 1996
Sales Range: $1-9.9 Million
Emp.: 24
Construction, Management, Electrical & Project Services
N.A.I.C.S.: 236220
Paul Winne (Pres)

Subsidiaries:

ARCON Electric, LLC (1)
8 Railroad Ave, Albany, NY 12205   (100%)
Tel.: (518) 459-1128
Web Site: http://www.arconelectric.com
Electrical Contractor
N.A.I.C.S.: 238210
Meryl Winnie (Pres)
Bob Moroukian (VP)

ARCOS COMMUNICATIONS
341 W 38th St 12th Fl, New York, NY 10018
Tel.: (212) 807-1337
Web Site: http://www.arcos-ny.com
Year Founded: 1996
Sales Range: Less than $1 Million
Emp.: 5
Event Marketing, Full Service, Public Relations, Publicity/Promotions
N.A.I.C.S.: 541810
Roy Cosme (Pres)
T. Marc Newell (Exec VP)
Lisa Garza (Sr Acct Exec)

ARCOS INDUSTRIES LLC
1 Arcos Dr, Mount Carmel, PA 17851-2504
Tel.: (570) 339-5200   PA
Web Site: http://www.arcos.us
Sales Range: $10-24.9 Million
Emp.: 65
Mfr of Welding Wire
N.A.I.C.S.: 335999
Harry Wehr (Gen Mgr)
Bob Hopkins (Mgr-Automotive Indus)
Bob Bush (Mgr-Customer Service)
John Abbitt (Mgr-Sales-Maryland, Virginia, West Virginia Reg)
Paul Sherman (Mgr-Sls-Midwest & East Reg)
Larry Miller (Mgr-Sls-Midwest & West Reg)
Todd Haegele (Mgr-Sls-Illinois, Iowa, Wisconsin, Minnesota & Dakotas)
William Goodwyn (Mgr-Sls-Southeast & Southwest Reg)
Rick Tidwell (Mgr-Sales-Tennessee, Kentucky, Carolinas)
David Braden (Product Mgr-Hardfacing)
Richard Poe (Product Mgr-Stainless-High Alloys)

ARCS INVESTMENTS, LLC
2244 Trade Center Way, Naples, FL 34109
Tel.: (239) 254-1664   FL
Web Site: https://www.gulfstreamhomes.com
Year Founded: 1998
Sales Range: $10-24.9 Million
Emp.: 5
Residential Homes Designer & Builder
N.A.I.C.S.: 236115
Michael J. Peel (Co-Founder)
Jeneane Paula Bennett (Mng Dir-Bus Ops)
Dale Hogue (Mgr-Construction)
Dominic Buzzy (Mgr-Field)

ARCSOFT, INC.
46601 Fremont Blvd, Fremont, CA 94538
Tel.: (510) 440-9901
Web Site: https://www.arcsoft.com
Sales Range: $10-24.9 Million
Emp.: 395
Multimedia Software Developer for OEM Customers
N.A.I.C.S.: 541511
Michael Deng (CEO)

ARCSOURCE GROUP, INC.
9250 Bendix Rd N Ste 125, Columbia, MD 21045
Tel.: (410) 750-2973
Web Site: http://arcsourcegroup.com
Year Founded: 2000
Sales Range: $1-9.9 Million
Emp.: 10
Information Technology Services
N.A.I.C.S.: 541512
Megan Pulliam (Pres & CEO)

ARCTIC CIRCLE ENTERPRISES INC.
3812 Spenard Rd, Anchorage, AK 99517
Tel.: (907) 272-4366
Web Site: http://www.aceak.com
Rev.: $24,000,000
Emp.: 40
Embroidered Products Mfr
N.A.I.C.S.: 313310
Kim van der Linden (Mng Dir-Strategic Brand)

ARCTIC EXPRESS INC.
4277 Lyman Dr, Hilliard, OH 43026-1227
Tel.: (614) 876-4008   DE
Web Site: http://www.arcticexpress.com
Year Founded: 1981
Sales Range: $25-49.9 Million
Emp.: 150
Provider of Trucking Services
N.A.I.C.S.: 484121
Richard Durst (Chm & CEO)
Michael Ott (Mgr-Recruiting)
Stephanie Tovine (Mgr-Billing)
Ernie Thornton (VP-Sls & Mktg)
John Durst (Mgr-Fleet & OTR Breakdown)

ARCTIC FALLS SPRING WATER, INC.
58 Sand Park Rd, Cedar Grove, NJ 07009
Tel.: (973) 857-3000
Web Site: https://www.arcticfalls.com
Year Founded: 1985
Sales Range: $1-9.9 Million
Emp.: 24
Water & Coffee Services for Home & Office
N.A.I.C.S.: 424490
Frank Lipari (Co-Owner & Pres)
Michelle Lipari (Office Mgr)

ARCTIC OFFICE MACHINE INC.
100 W Fireweed, Anchorage, AK 99503
Tel.: (907) 276-2322
Web Site: https://www.arcticoffice.com
Sales Range: $10-24.9 Million
Emp.: 100
Office Supplies Sales
N.A.I.C.S.: 424120

ARCTIC SLOPE REGIONAL CORPORATION
1230 Agvik St, Utqiagvik, AK 99723
Tel.: (907) 852-8633   AK

Arctic Slope Regional Corporation—(Continued)

Web Site: https://www.asrc.com
Year Founded: 1972
Emp.: 14,174
Offices of Other Holding Companies
N.A.I.C.S.: 551112
Patsy Pausan Aamodt *(Treas)*
Crawford Ahkivgak Patkotak *(Chm)*
Mary Ellen Qariuluk Ahmaogak *(Sec)*
Glen Edwin Solomon *(VP-Kaktovik)*
Charlie Kozak *(CFO & Exec VP)*
Butch Lincoln *(COO & Exec VP)*
Matt Waldron *(Gen Counsel & Exec VP)*
Avaiyak Burnell *(VP)*
Thomas K. Napageak Jr. *(VP-Nuiqsut)*
Rex Allen Kakianaaq Rock Sr. *(Pres & CEO)*
Paul Bodfish Sr. *(Vice Chm)*

Subsidiaries:

ASRC Construction Holding Company, LLC **(1)**
3900 C St Ste 301, Anchorage, AK 99503
Tel.: (907) 339-5900
Web Site: http://www.asrcconstruction.com
Construction Services
N.A.I.C.S.: 237990
Brady Strahl *(Pres & CEO)*

Subsidiary (Domestic):

ASRC Civil Construction, LLC **(2)**
1211 E 80th Ave, Anchorage, AK 99518
Tel.: (907) 339-5600
Web Site:
http://www.asrccivilconstruction.com
Construction Services
N.A.I.C.S.: 237990

ASRC SKW Eskimos, Inc. **(2)**
3900 C St Ste 308, Anchorage, AK 99503-5938
Tel.: (907) 339-6700
Web Site: http://www.skweskimos.com
General Construction Contractor Services
N.A.I.C.S.: 236220

ASRC Energy Services **(1)**
3900 C St Ste 701, Anchorage, AK 99503
Tel.: (907) 339-6200
Web Site: http://www.asrcenergy.com
Sales Range: $350-399.9 Million
Emp.: 5,000
Oil Field Services
N.A.I.C.S.: 237120
Doug Smith *(Pres & CEO)*

Subsidiary (Domestic):

ASRC Energy Services Power & Communications, LLC **(2)**
3900 C St Ste 602, Anchorage, AK 99503
Tel.: (907) 339-6411
Web Site: http://www.asrcenergy.com
Sales Range: $1-9.9 Million
Emp.: 35
Oil Field Services
N.A.I.C.S.: 237120

Petrochem Insulation, Inc. **(2)**
110 Corporate Pl, Vallejo, CA 94590-6968
Tel.: (707) 644-7455
Web Site: http://www.petrocheminc.com
Sales Range: $100-124.9 Million
Emp.: 230
Industrial Contracting Services
N.A.I.C.S.: 238990
Brian Benson *(VP-Mktg & Bus Dev)*
Bill Wright *(Pres & CEO)*
Candy Hourmouzus *(Branch Mgr-Safety)*

ASRC Federal Holding Company **(1)**
7000 Muirkirk Meadows Dr Ste 100, Beltsville, MD 20705
Tel.: (301) 837-5500
Web Site: http://www.asrcfederal.com
Technical Consulting Services
N.A.I.C.S.: 541690
Greg Resutek *(CFO)*
Charlie Bengston *(Pres-Operating-Engrg, Aerospace & Mission Sys)*
Lexi Alexander *(Sr VP-Bus Dev & Corp Strategy)*

Cynthia Achorn *(Sr VP-Corp Initiatives & Comm)*
Cliff Greenblatt *(Chief Compliance Officer & Gen Counsel)*
Leif Henecke *(CIO)*
Elizabeth Malone *(VP-Contracts & Procurement)*
Cass Panciocco *(Sr VP-Corp Dev)*
Richard Terry *(VP)*
Mike Molino *(Exec VP-Corp Dev)*
Jason Nichols *(Sr VP-Corp Bus Dev)*
Mike Teegardin *(Sr VP-Mktg & Comm)*
Scott Altman *(Sr VP-Engrg, Aerospace & Mission Sys-Civil Ops)*
Steve Ennis *(Pres-Infrastructure Support & Professional Svcs-Operating Grp)*
Wayne Lucernoni *(Pres-Information Sys & Tech-Operating Grp)*
Jennifer Felix *(Pres & CEO)*
George Morrow *(VP-Space Strategy)*
Carlo Uchello *(Pres-Civilian & Health Bus)*
Shaveta Joshi *(Chief HR Officer)*
Robert Huebner *(VP-Bus Dev)*

Subsidiary (Domestic):

ASRC Management Services, Inc. **(2)**
3900 C St Ste 801, Anchorage, AK 99503-5963
Tel.: (907) 339-6000
Web Site: http://www.asrcms.com
Management Consulting Services
N.A.I.C.S.: 541618

Analytical Services, Inc. **(2)**
350 Voyager Way, Huntsville, AL 35806-3200
Tel.: (256) 562-2100
Web Site: http://www.asi-hsv.com
Engineering, Scientific, Research & Computer Consulting Services
N.A.I.C.S.: 541715

Mission Solutions, LLC **(2)**
121 Whittendale Dr, Moorestown, NJ 08057
Tel.: (856) 291-2346
Web Site: http://www.missionse.com
Engineering Services
N.A.I.C.S.: 541330

ASRC Industrial Services LLC **(1)**
1 Concord Ctr 2300 Clayton Rd Ste 1050, Concord, CA 94520 **(100%)**
Tel.: (480) 646-3157
Web Site: http://www.asrcindustrial.com
Industrial, Remediation & Response Services
N.A.I.C.S.: 562910
Brent Renfrew *(Pres & CEO)*
Andrew McClain *(VP-Bus Dev)*
Steve Ennis *(COO & Exec VP)*
Tony Spagnola *(CFO & Sr VP)*
Chad Horner *(Gen Counsel & Sr VP)*

Subsidiary (Domestic):

Brad Cole Construction Company, Incorporated **(2)**
2250 Lovvorn Rd, Carrollton, GA 30117-0117
Tel.: (770) 834-4681
Web Site:
http://www.bradcoleconstruction.com
Heavy Civil Construction & Sitework Firm
N.A.I.C.S.: 236210
Bobbi Spears *(Mgr-HR Mgmt)*
Terri Watson *(Controller)*
Stephen Christensen *(Pres & Gen Mgr)*
Jason Hoffman *(Mgr-Ops)*
Timothy Johnson *(Dir-Safety)*
David Walker *(Dir-Equipment & Assets)*
Tory Passalacqua *(Mgr-Program)*
Kyle Miller *(Mgr-Program)*

F.D. Thomas Inc. **(2)**
217 Bateman Dr, Central Point, OR 97502
Tel.: (541) 664-3010
Web Site: http://www.fdthomas.com
Industrial Painting
N.A.I.C.S.: 238320
F. Dan Thomas *(Pres)*
Stuart Hunter *(VP-Waterproofing, Sealents & Roofing Div)*

Subsidiary (Domestic):

Redwood Painting Co, Inc. **(3)**
620 W 10th St, Pittsburg, CA 94565
Tel.: (925) 432-4500

Web Site: http://www.redwoodptg.com
Sales Range: $1-9.9 Million
Emp.: 110
Painting & Wall Covering Contractors
N.A.I.C.S.: 238320
Charles D. Monte *(Pres)*

Subsidiary (Domestic):

K2 Industrial Services, Inc. **(2)**
3838 N Sam Houston Pkwy E Ste 285, Houston, TX 77032
Tel.: (800) 347-4813
Web Site: http://www.k2industrial.com
Industrial Cleaning, Tank Cleaning, Coatings, Insulation Products Mfr & Scaffolding Services
N.A.I.C.S.: 562991
Ted Mansfield *(CEO)*
Tony Bochniak *(Pres)*
Rick Napier *(VP)*

Mavo Systems, Inc. **(2)**
4330 Centerville Rd, White Bear Lake, MN 55127
Tel.: (763) 788-7713
Web Site: http://www.mavo.com
Construction Services; Environmental / Specialty Contractor
N.A.I.C.S.: 236220
Christopher Schmitt *(Dir-Safety)*

Northwest Demolition & Dismantling, Inc. **(2)**
8200 SW Hunziker St, Tigard, OR 97223
Tel.: (503) 638-6900
Web Site: http://www.nwdemolition.com
Demolition & Dismantling, Environmental, Consulting & Asset Management services
N.A.I.C.S.: 238910
Richard Wayper *(Pres)*
Dave Williams *(VP-Ops)*
Chad Hoffart *(VP-Admin)*
Dan Leibelt *(Mgr-Senior Program & Mgr-Bus Dev-National)*
Bob Anderson *(Dir-Bus Dev)*
David McClure *(Controller)*
Patty Radcliff *(Mgr-Office)*
Andy Vogt *(Mgr-Corp Safety)*

ASRC Service Center, Inc. **(1)**
3900 C St, Anchorage, AK 99503
Tel.: (907) 339-6800
Web Site: http://www.asrc.com
Sales Range: $1-9.9 Million
Emp.: 16
IT Consulting Services
N.A.I.C.S.: 541618
Rex Rock *(Pres)*

Alaska Growth Capital Bidco, Inc. **(1)**
3301 C St Ste 100, Anchorage, AK 99503
Tel.: (907) 339-6760
Web Site: http://www.alaskagrowth.com
Sales Range: $1-9.9 Million
Emp.: 16
Renting Services
N.A.I.C.S.: 522310
Logan Beirch *(Pres)*

Arctic Pipe Inspection, Inc. **(1)**
9500 Sheldon Rd, Houston, TX 77049
Tel.: (281) 456-8300
Web Site: http://www.arctic-companies.com
Sales Range: $1-9.9 Million
Emp.: 64
Oil & Gas Pipe Inspection Services
N.A.I.C.S.: 213112
Ken Lopez *(Ops Mgr)*
Jim Hildebrandt *(Pres & Gen Mgr)*

Subsidiary (Domestic):

Arctic Pipe Engineering, Inc. **(2)**
Pouch 3400-37, Prudhoe Bay, AK 99734-0037
Tel.: (907) 659-2873
Web Site: http://www.arctic-companies.com
Sales Range: $1-9.9 Million
Oil & Gas Pipe Inspection & Engineering Services
N.A.I.C.S.: 213112

Eskimos, Inc. **(1)**
3417 Stevenson St, Barrow, AK 99723
Tel.: (907) 852-8000
Sales Range: $1-9.9 Million
Emp.: 16
Motor Vehicle Supplies & New Parts Whslr

N.A.I.C.S.: 441330

Petro Star Inc. **(1)**
3900 C St Ste 802, Anchorage, AK 99503-5966
Tel.: (907) 339-6600
Web Site: http://www.petrostar.com
Sales Range: $25-49.9 Million
Emp.: 200
Petroleum Refining, Distribution & Marketing Services
N.A.I.C.S.: 324110
Shirley Merkley *(Gen Mgr)*
Lisa Lewis *(Dir-Govt Compliance & Safety)*
Mark W. John *(VP-Bus Dev)*
Nicole Stewart *(Mgr-Bus Dev & Comm)*
Don Castle *(VP-Sls & Ops)*
Doug Richmond *(Dir-Sourdough Fuel Sls & Ops)*
Donna Bellows *(Mgr-Credit)*
Antwuan Cooks *(Coord-Sourdough Fuel Adv)*

Division (Domestic):

Sourdough Fuel, Inc. **(2)**
1555 Van Horn Rd, Fairbanks, AK 99701
Tel.: (907) 456-7798
Web Site: http://www.sourdoughfuel.com
Sales Range: $50-74.9 Million
Emp.: 150
Fuel Distr
N.A.I.C.S.: 457210
David Atlee *(Dir-Retail Sls & Ops)*
Doug Richmond *(Dir-Sls & Ops)*
Antwuan Cooks *(Mgr-Mktg & Adv)*

Piquniq Management Corp. **(1)**
6613 Brayton Dr, Anchorage, AK 99507
Tel.: (907) 522-5234
Web Site: http://www.alaska.net
Telecommunication Servicesb
N.A.I.C.S.: 517810

Top of the World Hotel **(1)**
3060 Eben Hopson St, Barrow, AK 99723 **(100%)**
Tel.: (907) 852-3900
Web Site: http://www.tundratoursinc.com
Sales Range: $10-24.9 Million
Emp.: 40
Hotel
N.A.I.C.S.: 485113

Tundra Tours, Inc. **(1)**
PO Box 189, Barrow, AK 99723 **(100%)**
Tel.: (907) 852-3900
Web Site: http://www.tundratoursinc.com
Sales Range: $10-24.9 Million
Emp.: 20
Tour Operator
N.A.I.C.S.: 485113
Monica Rowe *(Mgr)*

ARCTIC SNOW & ICE CONTROL INC.
22763 S Center Rd, Frankfort, IL 60423-1668
Tel.: (815) 469-8001
Web Site:
https://www.arcticsnowandice.com
Year Founded: 1978
Sales Range: $10-24.9 Million
Emp.: 20
Food Transportation Services
N.A.I.C.S.: 488490
Randy Strait *(Pres & CEO)*
Rick Bell *(Gen Mgr)*
Tim Rieken *(CFO & COO)*
Jeremy Hicks *(Acct Exec-Ops)*
Linda Zoller *(Office Mgr)*
John Starek *(Dir-Ops)*
Patrick Ryan *(Dir-Sls)*

ARCTIC STRUCTURES LLC
9312 Vanguard Dr Ste 200, Anchorage, AK 99507
Tel.: (907) 522-2425
Rev.: $15,509,297
Emp.: 25
Developers of Construction Modular Units
N.A.I.C.S.: 423220

ARCW INSURANCE, INC.

9067 Belcher Rd, Pinellas Park, FL 33782-4423
Tel.: (727) 544-8841
Web Site: https://arcwinsurance.com
Insurance Agencies & Brokerages
N.A.I.C.S.: 524210
Chuck Wasson *(Owner)*
Adam Sechrest *(COO)*
Deborah Wyzinski *(Mgr-Personal Lines)*
Gary Irby *(Acct Mgr-Comml Lines)*

ARD CONTRACTING, INC.
120 Office Park Dr Ste 200, Birmingham, AL 35223-3407
Tel.: (205) 870-0035
Web Site:
   https://www.ardcontracting.com
Sales Range: $25-49.9 Million
Emp.: 300
Concrete Finishing Services
N.A.I.C.S.: 238140
Garry Ard *(Pres)*
Jimmie Ard *(Pres)*
Tammy Davidson *(Office Mgr)*

ARD DISTRIBUTORS INC.
1600 NW 159th St, Miami, FL 33169-5637
Tel.: (305) 624-0106   FL
Web Site: http://www.ardonline.com
Year Founded: 1978
Sales Range: $25-49.9 Million
Emp.: 500
Appliance Distr
N.A.I.C.S.: 423620
Barry Hall *(Mgr-Ops-Florida)*

ARD INC.
2200 E Hwy 67, Cleburne, TX 76031
Tel.: (817) 517-2200
Web Site: http://www.funtimerv.com
Rev.: $43,000,000
Emp.: 100
Retailer of Recreational Vehicles
N.A.I.C.S.: 812112
Sam Kidd *(Pres)*
Doug Kacsir *(CFO)*

ARDEN COMPANIES
30400 Telegraph Rd Ste 200, Bingham Farms, MI 48025
Tel.: (248) 415-8500
Web Site:
http://www.ardencompanies.com
Year Founded: 1964
Sales Range: $100-124.9 Million
Emp.: 90
Household Furnishings
N.A.I.C.S.: 314120
Carol Embach *(Acct Coord)*
Ruth Hoon *(Asst Controller)*
Cecil Kearse *(Pres)*
Benjamin Rapp *(VP-Supply Chain)*
Jan Regal *(Dir-Styling)*
Sarah Wisner *(Mgr-Customer Compliance)*
Zvonko Kolar *(CTO & VP)*
Ralph Gardella *(Mgr-Studio Design)*

ARDEN ENGINEERING CONSTRUCTORS LLC
505 Narragansett Park Dr, Pawtucket, RI 02861
Tel.: (401) 727-3500   RI
Web Site: https://www.ardeneng.com
Year Founded: 1986
Sales Range: $10-24.9 Million
Emp.: 300
Mechanical Contracting Service
N.A.I.C.S.: 238220
Timothy Elliott *(Dir-Design & Engrg)*
Norman Brothers *(Gen Mgr)*
Jeff Potter *(VP-Svc)*
Kenneth Demers *(Sr VP)*
Gordon Fletcher *(CFO)*

Subsidiaries:
M.J. Daly LLC   (1)
110 Mattatuck Heights Rd, Waterbury, CT 06705
Tel.: (203) 753-5131
Web Site: http://www.ardeneng.com
Fire Protection Power Piping Fabricator; Heating, Ventilating, Plumbing & Sheet Metal Contractors
N.A.I.C.S.: 238220
Edward Carvalho *(Pres)*
Salie Cameron *(Svc Coord)*

ARDENT MANAGEMENT CONSULTING, INC
1840 Michael Faraday Dr Ste 130, Reston, VA 20190
Tel.: (703) 964-8010
Web Site: http://www.ArdentMC.com
Sales Range: $1-9.9 Million
Emp.: 25
Business Consulting Services
N.A.I.C.S.: 541618
Brandon LaBonte *(Co-Founder & CEO)*
Matt Kelley *(Co-Founder & VP-Homeland Security Div)*
Michael Matechak *(VP-Federal Civilian Div)*

ARDENTE SUPPLY CO. INC.
404 Valley St, Providence, RI 02908
Tel.: (401) 861-1324   RI
Web Site: https://www.ardente.com
Year Founded: 1946
Sales Range: $10-24.9 Million
Emp.: 45
Supplier of Industrial Heating & Plumbing
N.A.I.C.S.: 423720
Mark Ardente *(Co-Owner & Pres)*
Paul Ardente *(Co-Owner & Sec)*

ARDEO EDUCATION SOLUTIONS, LLC
PO Box 1476, Bloomington, IN 47402   DC
Web Site:
http://www.ardeoeducation.org
Year Founded: 2008
Sales Range: $1-9.9 Million
Emp.: 40
Educational Support Services
N.A.I.C.S.: 611710
Peter Samuelson *(Pres)*
Justin Mead *(COO)*
Matt Osborne *(Sr VP-Client Svc)*
Jonathan Shores *(Sr VP-Client Svc)*
Roger Kieffer *(VP-Client Service)*

ARDMORE NISSAN
265 E Lancaster Ave, Wynnewood, PA 19096
Tel.: (610) 649-4400
Web Site:
http://www.ardmorenissan.com
Year Founded: 2002
Sales Range: $25-49.9 Million
Emp.: 40
Car Dealer
N.A.I.C.S.: 441110
Brian Hansell *(Mgr-Internet)*
Don Spence *(Mgr-Svc)*

ARDSLEY PARTNERS
262 Harbor Dr Fl 4, Stamford, CT 06902
Tel.: (203) 355-0700
Web Site: https://www.ardsley.com
Sales Range: $10-24.9 Million
Emp.: 20
Investment Advice
N.A.I.C.S.: 523940
Steven Napoli *(CFO)*

AREA AGENCY ON AGING

FOR SOUTHWEST FLORIDA INC.
15201 N Cleveland Ave Ste 1100, North Fort Myers, FL 33903
Tel.: (239) 652-6900   FL
Web Site: http://www.aaaswfl.org
Year Founded: 1978
Sales Range: $10-24.9 Million
Emp.: 39
Elderly Health Care Services
N.A.I.C.S.: 624120
Marianne Lorini *(Exec Dir)*

AREA AGENCY ON AGING OF CENTRAL FLORIDA
988 Woodcock Rd Ste 200, Orlando, FL 32803
Tel.: (407) 514-1800   FL
Web Site:
http://www.senioralliance.org
Year Founded: 1992
Sales Range: $10-24.9 Million
Emp.: 38
Elder Care Services
N.A.I.C.S.: 624120
Rob Gilts *(Chief Compliance Officer)*

AREA AGENCY ON AGING OF PALM BEACH/TREASURE COAST, INC.
4400 N Congress Ave, West Palm Beach, FL 33407
Tel.: (561) 684-5885   FL
Web Site:
http://www.youragingcenter.org
Year Founded: 1988
Sales Range: $10-24.9 Million
Emp.: 67
Elder Care Services
N.A.I.C.S.: 624120
Bonnie Conrad *(Dir-Elder Rights Project)*
Nancy Yarnall *(Dir-Plng & Consumer Care)*
Ligia Hardy *(Dir-Org Integrity)*
Trish Ernst *(Dir-Comm)*
Jaime Estremera-Fitzgerald *(CEO)*

AREA AGENCY ON AGING OF WESTERN ARKANSAS, INC.
524 Garrison, Fort Smith, AR 72902
Tel.: (479) 783-4500   AR
Web Site: https://www.agingwest.org
Year Founded: 1979
Sales Range: $10-24.9 Million
Emp.: 918
Elder Care Services
N.A.I.C.S.: 623312
Jennifer Hallum *(Pres & CEO)*

AREA AGENCY ON AGING REGION 9, INC.
60788 Southgate Rd, Byesville, OH 43723
Tel.: (740) 439-4478   OH
Web Site: http://www.aaa9.org
Year Founded: 1976
Sales Range: $25-49.9 Million
Emp.: 84
Aging Care Services
N.A.I.C.S.: 623312
Joyce Klingler *(Sec)*
Gwen Morgenstern *(VP)*

AREA AGENCY ON AGING, PSA2
40 W 2nd St Ste 400, Dayton, OH 45402
Tel.: (937) 341-4357   OH
Web Site: http://www.info4seniors.org
Year Founded: 1993
Sales Range: $75-99.9 Million
Emp.: 159
Elder Care Services
N.A.I.C.S.: 623312

Douglas McGarry *(Sec & Exec Dir)*
Daniel Auman *(Mgr-Information Sys)*
Jeanne Mbagwu *(Mgr-Community Svcs)*
Nicole Khaner *(Dir-Consumer Svcs)*

AREA COOPERATIVE EDUCATIONAL SERVICES
350 State St, North Haven, CT 06473
Tel.: (203) 498-6800
Web Site: http://www.aces.org
Year Founded: 1969
Sales Range: $75-99.9 Million
Emp.: 1,606
Educational Support Services
N.A.I.C.S.: 611710
Thomas M. Danehy *(Exec Dir)*
Sue Cohen *(Vice Chm)*
Edward Drapp *(Dir-Fiscal Svcs)*
Jeff Glagowski *(Mgr-Website)*
Sharon Locke *(Asst Dir-Pro Dev & School Improvement)*

AREA ENERGY & ELECTRIC, INC.
670-L Lakeview Plaza Blvd, Worthington, OH 45085
Tel.: (614) 888-8905
Web Site:
http://www.areaelectric.com
Sales Range: $1-9.9 Million
Emp.: 35
Electrical Contractor
N.A.I.C.S.: 238210
Todd Wiegandt *(Pres)*
Twila Stevens *(Dir-Mgmt Info Sys)*
Brian Moloney *(Gen Mgr)*
Joe Lachey *(VP)*
Ken Schlater *(Founder & CEO)*
Mike Marshall *(Mgr-HVAC & Residential-Div)*

Subsidiaries:
Brennan Electric, LLC   (1)
6859 Cemetary Dr, Miamitown, OH 45041
Tel.: (513) 353-2229
Web Site: http://www.brennanelectricllc.com
Electrical Contractor
N.A.I.C.S.: 238210

AREA ENERGY AND ELECTRIC INC.
2001 Commerce Dr, Sidney, OH 45365
Tel.: (937) 498-4784
Web Site:
https://www.areaelectric.com
Rev.: $23,000,000
Emp.: 300
Electrical Work
N.A.I.C.S.: 238210
Todd Weigandt *(CEO)*
Joe Lachey *(Branch Mgr)*
Twila Stevens *(Mgr-IT)*

AREA ERECTORS INC.
2323 Harrison Ave, Rockford, IL 61104-7339
Tel.: (815) 398-6700   IL
Web Site:
https://www.areaerectors.com
Year Founded: 1964
Sales Range: $50-74.9 Million
Emp.: 250
Provider of Structural Steel Services
N.A.I.C.S.: 238120
Jeff Hardison *(Dir-Corp Safety)*

AREA FIVE AGENCY ON AGING & COMMUNITY SERVICES, INC.
1801 Smith St, Logansport, IN 46947
Tel.: (574) 722-4451   IN
Web Site: https://www.areafive.com
Year Founded: 1974

Area Five Agency on Aging & Community Services, Inc.—(Continued)
Sales Range: $1-9.9 Million
Emp.: 204
Elder Care Services
N.A.I.C.S.: 624120
Michael Meagher *(Exec Dir)*
P. Daniel Casserly *(COO)*

AREA WHOLESALE TIRE COMPANY, LLC
5620 Airline Hwy, Baton Rouge, LA 70805
Web Site: https://www.areawholesale.com
Tire & Tube Merchant Whslr
N.A.I.C.S.: 423130
David Balfantz *(VP-Sls & Mktg)*
William B. Potter *(Pres & CEO)*

AREAWIDE COUNCIL ON AGING OF BROWARD COUNTY, INC.
5300 Hiatus Rd, Sunrise, FL 33351
Tel.: (954) 745-9567   FL
Web Site: https://www.adrcbroward.org
Year Founded: 1974
Sales Range: $10-24.9 Million
Emp.: 59
Disability Assistance Services
N.A.I.C.S.: 624120
Edith Lederberg *(Exec Dir)*

AREHNA ENGINEERING, INC.
5012 W Lemon St, Tampa, FL 33609
Tel.: (813) 944-3464
Web Site: https://www.arehna.com
Year Founded: 2009
Sales Range: $1-9.9 Million
Emp.: 35
Engineeering Services
N.A.I.C.S.: 541330
Jessica A. McRory *(Pres)*
Sonia R. Florence *(VP & Principal-Geotechnical Engr)*
John Melendez *(Dir-Bus Dev)*
Joseph E. Prendergast *(Sr Principal Geotechnical Engr)*
Peter R. Lehmann *(Sr Structural Engr)*
Amanda S. Pereira *(VP & Sr Geotechnical Engr)*

AREIAS SYSTEMS, INC.
5900 Butler Ln Ste 280, Scotts Valley, CA 95066
Tel.: (831) 440-9800
Web Site: https://www.areiasys.com
Year Founded: 2000
Sales Range: $1-9.9 Million
Emp.: 45
Electronics Design, Engineering, Prototyping & Mfr
N.A.I.C.S.: 541330
Clemm Noernberg *(Owner & CEO)*
Michael Nunns *(Mgr-NPI)*

ARENA COMMUNICATIONS
1780 W Sequoia Vista Cir, Salt Lake City, UT 84104
Tel.: (801) 595-8339   UT
Web Site: http://www.winningmail.com
Sales Range: $10-24.9 Million
Emp.: 10
Communications, Direct Response Marketing, Direct-to-Consumer, Government/Political/Public Affairs, Publicity/Promotions
N.A.I.C.S.: 541860
Peter Valcarce *(Pres)*

ARENA INVESTORS, LP
405 Lexington Ave 59th Fl, New York, NY 10174
Tel.: (212) 612-3205   DE
Web Site: http://www.arenaco.com
Year Founded: 2015
Investment Services
N.A.I.C.S.: 523999
Scott Gold *(Mng Dir)*
Ryan Houser *(Mng Dir & CTO)*
Lawrence Cutler *(COO)*

Subsidiaries:

GHS Interactive Security, LLC   (1)
21031 Warner Ctr Ln Ste D, Woodland Hills, CA 91367
Tel.: (833) 451-1015
Web Site: http://www.viosecurity.com
Home Security Products & Services
N.A.I.C.S.: 561621
John Bergher *(Mgr)*
Michael J. McLeod *(CEO)*

Strategic Resource Alternatives   (1)
112 West Park Dr Ste 200, Mount Laurel, NJ 08054
Tel.: (844) 567-7886
Accounting Auditing & Bookkeeping Services
N.A.I.C.S.: 541219
David White *(CEO)*

Subsidiary (Domestic):

J J Marshall & Associates, Inc.   (2)
6060 Collection Dr, Shelby, MI 48316
Tel.: (586) 992-3200
Web Site: http://www.jjmarshallinc.com
Sales Range: $1-9.9 Million
Emp.: 28
Collection Agencies
N.A.I.C.S.: 561440
John Angelo *(Pres)*

ARENA STAGE
1101 6th St SW, Washington, DC 20024
Tel.: (202) 554-9066   DC
Web Site: http://www.arenastage.org
Sales Range: $10-24.9 Million
Emp.: 150
Performing Arts Center
N.A.I.C.S.: 711310
Molly Smith *(Dir-Artistic)*

ARENDS BROS. INC.
Hwy 54 N, Melvin, IL 60952
Tel.: (217) 388-7717   IL
Web Site: http://www.arendsbros.com
Year Founded: 1932
Sales Range: $10-24.9 Million
Emp.: 100
Provider of Repair Services
N.A.I.C.S.: 423820
Kent Arends *(Pres)*
Mark Arends *(Treas & Sec)*
Phil Noellsch *(Mgr-Acctg)*

ARENDS, INC.
515 N River St Ste 101, Batavia, IL 60510
Tel.: (630) 482-9800
Web Site: http://www.arends-inc.com
Year Founded: 1958
Sales Range: $1-9.9 Million
Emp.: 11
Advertising Agencies
N.A.I.C.S.: 541810
John C. Arends *(CEO)*
Jim McMillen *(VP & Brand Mgr)*

ARENDS-AWE INC.
1285 Old Rte 36, Winchester, IL 62694
Tel.: (217) 742-3138
Web Site: http://www.arends-awe.com
Rev.: $17,000,000
Emp.: 22
Farm Equipment & Supplies
N.A.I.C.S.: 459999

Doug Awe *(Owner)*

ARENSON OFFICE FURNISHINGS INC.
1115 Brdwy 6th Fl, New York, NY 10010-2803
Tel.: (212) 633-2400
Web Site: http://www.aof.com
Year Founded: 1983
Sales Range: $50-74.9 Million
Emp.: 200
Office Furnishings
N.A.I.C.S.: 449110
Barry Gallo *(Acct Mgr)*
Arnold Manche *(CFO)*
Mary Stipisich *(Mgr-Sls State Contract)*
Dawn Garcia *(Project Mgr)*
John Green *(VP)*
Cathy Sandoval *(Project Mgr)*
Fred Frenzel *(Sr Acct Mgr)*
Ian Petrossian *(VP)*
Sue Marowitz *(VP-Ops)*
Betty Fredericks *(Acct Mgr)*

ARENTFOX SCHIFF LLP
1717 K St NW, Washington, DC 20036
Tel.: (202) 857-6000
Web Site: https://www.afslaw.com
Year Founded: 1942
Sales Range: $200-249.9 Million
Emp.: 325
Law firm
N.A.I.C.S.: 541110
David Hamill *(Partner)*
Mindy Hurwitz *(Partner)*
Kevin Pinkney *(Partner)*
Eleanor D. Zappone *(Partner)*
Janine Carlan *(Atty)*
Barbara S. Wahl *(Partner)*
Jackson D. Toof *(Partner)*
Brian Waldman *(Partner)*
Cristina A. Carvalho *(Mng Partner)*
Deborah S. Froling *(Partner)*
John Purcell *(Partner)*
Rachel Hold-Weiss *(Partner-New York)*
Peter J. Most *(Partner-Los Angeles)*
Glenn C. Colton *(Partner-Govt Enforcement & White Collar Grp-New York)*
Michelle J. Shapiro *(Partner-Govt Enforcement & White Collar Grp-New York)*
Jeffrey Tate *(Partner)*
Deborah Shelton *(Partner)*

Subsidiaries:

Schiff Hardin LLP   (1)
233 S Wacker Dr Ste 7100, Chicago, IL 60606-6473
Tel.: (312) 258-5500
Web Site: http://www.schiffhardin.com
Law firm
N.A.I.C.S.: 541110
Kenneth M. Roberts *(Partner)*
Marci A. Eisenstein *(Mng Partner)*
Peter L. Rossiter *(Partner)*
Bruce P. Weisenthal *(Partner)*
Lisa A. Brown *(Partner-Pro Dev)*
Valerie E. Ross *(Partner)*
Jill Berry *(Partner)*
John K. Hsu *(Partner)*
Christine R. W. Quigley *(Partner)*
Domenick Pugliese *(Partner)*
Marisa Murillo *(Partner)*
Kevin M. Nelson *(Partner-Intellectual Property Grp)*
Imron T. Aly *(Co-Chm-Pharmaceuticals & Biologics Patent Litigation & Partner)*
Sailesh K. Patel *(Co-Chm-Pharmaceuticals & Biologics Patent Litigation)*
Jill Himelfarb *(CMO)*
Derek G. Barella *(Partner-Labor & Employment Practice Grp-Chicago)*

ARES GROUP, INC.
8625 Engleside Ofc Park, Alexandria, VA 22309
Tel.: (703) 704-5351
Year Founded: 2001
Sales Range: $25-49.9 Million
Emp.: 900
Security Services
N.A.I.C.S.: 928110
William B. Moore *(Founder & Pres)*
Stanley Jones *(Sr VP)*

ARES SPORTSWEAR, LTD.
3704 Lacon Rd, Hilliard, OH 43026
Tel.: (614) 767-1950   OH
Web Site: http://www.areswear.com
Year Founded: 1991
Sales Range: $1-9.9 Million
Emp.: 65
Custom Embroidered, Screen-Printed & Decorated Athletic Uniforms & Apparel for Corporate Clients, Sports Teams & Athletic Associations
N.A.I.C.S.: 323113
Mike Leibrand *(Co-Owner)*
Michael Campbell *(Co-Owner)*
Chris Haubert *(Supvr-Warehouse Inventory)*
Jeff Bollinger *(Mgr-Sls)*
Katie Appel *(Coord-Mktg)*

ARETE ACQUISITIONS, LLC
3334 W Main St Ste 235, Norman, OK 73072
Web Site: http://www.areteacq.com
Year Founded: 2010
Sales Range: $1-9.9 Million
Emp.: 50
Financial Support Services
N.A.I.C.S.: 522220
Justin Burgess *(Founder & CEO)*
Tyler DaffineeCF *(CFO)*
Adam St Romain *(COO)*
Caitlyn Olivier VanCourt *(CMO)*

ARETE ASSOCIATES
9301 Carbin Ave Ste 2000, Northridge, CA 91324
Tel.: (818) 885-2200
Rev.: $12,200,000
Emp.: 95
Commercial Physical Research
N.A.I.C.S.: 541715
Christopher Choi *(CFO)*
David Kier *(Pres & CEO)*
Jill Cochran *(Mgr-Tech)*
Scott Dobson *(Mgr-Data Science & Analytic Engrg Grp)*

ARETT SALES CORPORATION
1152 Marlkress Rd, Cherry Hill, NJ 08003-2314
Tel.: (856) 751-1224   NJ
Web Site: http://www.arett.com
Year Founded: 1951
Sales Range: $25-49.9 Million
Emp.: 230
Farm, Lawn & Garden Supplies Distr
N.A.I.C.S.: 424910
Lindsey Chesbrough *(Pres)*

Subsidiaries:

Greensmith   (1)
1152 Marlkress Rd, Cherry Hill, NJ 08003-2314
Tel.: (856) 751-1224
Sales Range: $25-49.9 Million
Emp.: 100
Garden & Lawn Services
N.A.I.C.S.: 424910
Sal Intrieri *(Gen Mgr)*

AREVALO'S TORTILLIARIA INC.
1537 Mines Ave, Montebello, CA 90640
Tel.: (323) 888-1711
Web Site: https://www.arevalos.com

Sales Range: $10-24.9 Million
Emp.: 112
Tortilla Mfr
N.A.I.C.S.: 311830
Jose Arevalo (Owner)
Alex Arevalo (VP-Ops)
Leland Voelpz (Dir-Sls & Mktg)

AREWAY LLC
8525 Clinton Rd, Cleveland, OH
44144
Tel.: (216) 651-9020   OH
Web Site: http://arewayacq.com
Sales Range: $25-49.9 Million
Emp.: 30
Metal Polishing Products Mfr
N.A.I.C.S.: 332813
John S. Hadgis (Pres, CEO, Treas &
Sec)
Sidor Hadgis (Chm)

AREY COMPANY
1906 E Dixon Blvd, Shelby, NC
28152
Tel.: (704) 482-1445
Sales Range: $10-24.9 Million
Emp.: 120
Convenience Store Operator
N.A.I.C.S.: 445131
Roxanne Stiles (Controller)
Robert J. Arey Jr. (Pres)

ARFA ENTERPRISES INC.
4350 Haddonfield Rd Ste 200, Penn-
sauken, NJ 08109
Tel.: (856) 486-0550
Web Site: http://www.arfaoil.com
Year Founded: 1995
Sales Range: $10-24.9 Million
Emp.: 10
Gasoline Sales
N.A.I.C.S.: 457120
Sam Logovinsky (Pres)
Oleg Aliferov (COO)
Alex Prakhin (Pres)
Allen Gorin (Controller)

ARG FINANCIAL STAFFING
6223 Highland Place Way Ste 201,
Knoxville, TN 37919
Tel.: (865) 566-0700
Web Site: http://www.argjobs.com
Sales Range: $10-24.9 Million
Emp.: 12
Financial Staffing Services
N.A.I.C.S.: 561320
John Sharpe (Pres)
Wilma Hobby (Sr Mgr-Bus Dev)
Sarah Fortenberry (Dir-ARG Fin
Staffing & Staffsource Div)
Cecilee DeNardo (Mgr-Bus Dev)
Carol Fox (Dir-Permanent Placement)

ARG, INC.
8665 Sudley Rd Ste 313, Manassas,
VA 20110
Tel.: (703) 770-2400
Web Site: http://www.myarg.com
Information Technology Solutions
Services
N.A.I.C.S.: 518210
Greg Praske (CEO)
Mike Shonholz (Chief Revenue Offi-
cer)
Steve Kopp (Sr VP)

Subsidiaries:

Freedom Solutions Group Inc.   **(1)**
1600 Roseneath Rd Ste 202, Richmond, VA
23230-4449
Tel.: (804) 521-2977
Web Site: http://www.freedomsg.com
Data Processing, Hosting & Related Ser-
vices
N.A.I.C.S.: 518210
Walt McGraw (CEO)

ARGAND PARTNERS, LP
28 W 44th St Ste 501, New York, NY
10036
Tel.: (212) 588-6470   DE
Web Site:
https://www.argandequity.com
Year Founded: 2015
Privater Equity Firm
N.A.I.C.S.: 523999
Howard D. Morgan (Partner & Sr
Mng Dir)
Ryan Beres (VP)
Tariq Osman (Partner & Mng Dir)
Joseph Del Toro (Partner, CFO & Dir-
Portfolio Ops)
Joyce Schnoedl (Principal)
Patrick Gilrane (Chm-Sr Exec Advi-
sors)
Charlie Burns (VP)
Dino Sawaya (VP)
Nicole Narby (Office Mgr)
Catherine Mandell (Chief Compliance
Officer & Gen Counsel)
Kay Blackwell (Dir-IR & Corp Comm)
Heather L. Faust (Partner & Mng Dir)

Subsidiaries:

Brintons Carpets Limited   **(1)**
Stourport Road, Kidderminster, DY11 7PZ,
Worcs, United Kingdom
Tel.: (44) 1562820000
Web Site: http://www.brintons.net
Carpet & Rug Mfr
N.A.I.C.S.: 314110
Ian Barton (Bus Mgr)
James Brighton (Sls Mgr)

Subsidiary (Non-US):

Barrington Carpets Inc.   **(2)**
Unit 1110 11th Floor W Twr, Philippine
Stock Exchange Ortigas Center, Pasig,
Metro Manila, Philippines   **(100%)**
Carpet Mfr
N.A.I.C.S.: 314110
Aira Villanueva (Acct Exec)

Brintons Carpets Asia Pvt Ltd.   **(2)**
401 Wing A Lohia Jain IT Park Survey No
150 Paud Road, Kothrud, Pune, 411 038,
India   **(100%)**
Tel.: (91) 20 6646 5700
Web Site: http://www.brintons.net
Woolen Carpets Mfr
N.A.I.C.S.: 314110
Prakash Basannavar (Mng Dir)

Brintons France S.a.r.l.   **(2)**
95 Rue du Faubourg, Saint Honore, 75008,
Paris, France
Tel.: (33) 158183360
Carpet & Rugs Mfr
N.A.I.C.S.: 314110

Brintons Industria de Alcatifas
Lda.   **(2)**
Rebordinho, 3670-056, Coimbra, Portugal
Tel.: (351) 232750060
Web Site: http://www.brintons.pt
Carpet & Rug Mills
N.A.I.C.S.: 314110

Brintons Pty Ltd   **(2)**
Level 1 672 Lorimer Street, Port Melbourne,
3207, VIC, Australia
Tel.: (61) 96763333
Web Site: http://www.brintons.net
Carpet & Rug Mfr
N.A.I.C.S.: 314110

Subsidiary (US):

Brintons U.S. Axminster, Inc.   **(2)**
1000 Cobb Pl Blvd Bldg 200 Ste 200, Ken-
nesaw, GA 30144
Tel.: (678) 594-9300
Web Site: http://www.brintons.net
Carpet Mfr
N.A.I.C.S.: 314110
Johnny Massey (VP-Ops)

OASE GmbH   **(1)**
Tecklenburger Str 161, 48477, Horstel, Ger-
many
Tel.: (49) 541 93 39 99 800

Web Site: http://www.oase-livingwater.com
Water Gardening Products Designer, Devel-
oper & Mfr & Distr
N.A.I.C.S.: 423820
Thorsten Muck (CEO)

Subsidiary (US):

Atlantic Water Gardens   **(2)**
4494 Orchard St, Mantua, OH 44255-9049
Tel.: (330) 274-8317
Web Site:
http://www.atlanticwatergardens.com
Lawn & Garden Tractor; Home Lawn & Gar-
den Equipment Mfr
N.A.I.C.S.: 333112
Brandon Dwyer (VP-Product Dev)
James Lavery (Mgr-Natl Sls)
Debra Sue Tobak (Dir-Fin & HR)
Tim Fisher (Mgr-Ops)
Bill Lynne (Chm & CEO)

Subsidiary (Non-US):

OASE (UK) LTD.   **(2)**
The Old Cart Shed Apsley Barns, Andover,
SP11 6NA, Hampshire, United Kingdom
Tel.: (44) 1256 896886
Web Site: http://www.oase-livingwater.com
Gardening Equipment Distr
N.A.I.C.S.: 423820

OASE Asia Pacific PTE Ltd.   **(2)**
7030 Ang Mo Kio Ave 5 08-69 Northstar
Ang Mo Kio, Singapore, 569880, Singapore
Tel.: (65) 6337 2838
Web Site: http://www.oase-livingwater.com
Gardening Equipment Distr
N.A.I.C.S.: 423820

OASE China   **(2)**
No 80 North Dongting Road Taicang,
Shanghai, Jiangsu, China
Tel.: (86) 512 5371 9709
Web Site: http://www.oase-livingwater.com
Gardening Equipment Distr
N.A.I.C.S.: 423820

OASE Middle East FZE   **(2)**
Dubai Airport Free Trade Zone East Wing
Building 1E Unit 301, PO Box 54966,
Dubai, United Arab Emirates
Tel.: (971) 4 2994847
Web Site: http://www.oase-livingwater.com
Gardening Equipment Distr
N.A.I.C.S.: 423820

Subsidiary (US):

OASE North America, Inc.   **(2)**
721 N Poplar St, Orange, CA 92868
Tel.: (800) 365-3880
Web Site: http://www.oase-livingwater.com
Gardening Equipment Distr
N.A.I.C.S.: 423820

Subsidiary (Non-US):

OASE Turkiye   **(2)**
Uphill Towers Court A Ada Barbaros Mah
Dereboyu Cad, Ihlamur Hasat Sk B Blok D
55 Atasehir, Istanbul, Turkiye
Tel.: (90) 216 688 14 60
Web Site: http://www.oase-livingwater.com
Gardening Equipment Distr
N.A.I.C.S.: 423820

Sigma Electric Manufacturing
Corporation   **(1)**
120 Sigma Dr, Garner, NC 27529
Tel.: (919) 773-0011
Web Site: http://www.sigmaelectric.com
Electrical Equipment & Nonconductive Wir-
ing Devices Mfr
N.A.I.C.S.: 423610
Viren Joshi (Pres & CEO)

Subsidiary (Domestic):

Avalon Precision Casting Company,
LLC   **(2)**
15583 Brookpark Rd, Cleveland, OH 44142
Tel.: (216) 362-4100
Web Site: http://www.avalon-castings.com
Precision Investment Casting
N.A.I.C.S.: 331512
Kevin Glazier (VP-Engrg)
Donald Scott Ferguson (Dir-Global Sourc-
ing)
Tony Ansorge (Dir-Ops)

Gary Berghammer (Dir-Ops-Markesan Wis-
consin Facility)
John Pallenik (Sls Mgr)
Amy Gingerich (Mgr-HR & EHS)
David Palivec (Pres & CEO)
David J. Benisek Jr. (CFO)

Division (Domestic):

Avalon Precision Metalsmiths   **(3)**
2206 Sherman Rd, Jackson, WI 53037
Tel.: (262) 677-2280
Web Site: http://www.avalon-castings.com
Precision Metal Part Mfr
N.A.I.C.S.: 331512
John Pallenik (Sls Mgr)

ARGEN CORPORATION
5855 Oberlin Dr, San Diego, CA
92121
Tel.: (858) 455-7900
Web Site: http://www.argen.com
Rev.: $54,700,000
Emp.: 120
Precious Metals
N.A.I.C.S.: 331410
Jackie Woolf (Co-Owner & Pres)
Anton Woolf (CEO)
Paul Cascone (Sr VP-R&D)
Michael B. Clark (Sr VP-Domestic
Sls)
Neil Wainstein (CFO)
Connie Wedel (VP-HR)

ARGENT ASSOCIATES INC.
140 Fieldcrest Ave, Edison, NJ 08837
Tel.: (732) 512-9009
Web Site:
http://www.argentassociates.com
Year Founded: 1998
Sales Range: $100-124.9 Million
Emp.: 50
Telecom & IT Engineering, Design &
Installation Services
N.A.I.C.S.: 517810
Beatriz M. Manetta (Pres & CEO)
William C. Donadio (VP-Supply
Chain)
Joyce Hart (VP-Ops)
Lauren Peterson (Mgr-Sls)

**ARGENT CAPITAL MANAGE-
MENT, LLC**
100 S Brentwood Blvd Ste 110, Saint
Louis, MO 63105
Tel.: (314) 725-6000
Web Site:
https://www.argentcapital.com
Year Founded: 1998
Rev.: $5,300,000
Emp.: 26
Financial Services
N.A.I.C.S.: 523940
Scott A. Harrison (Portfolio Mgr)
Stephanie Dirscherl (Dir-Mktg)
Denise Pearman (Dir-Institutional Sls-
Denver)
Peter A. Roy (Portfolio Mgr-Small
Cap Strategy)
Carolyn Bowles (CFO)

**ARGENT FINANCIAL GROUP,
INC.**
500 E Reynolds Dr, Ruston, LA
71270
Tel.: (318) 251-5800   LA
Web Site:
http://www.argentfinancial.com
Year Founded: 1990
Rev.: $5,500,000,000
Emp.: 270
Holding Company; Investment Advi-
sory & Portfolio Management Ser-
vices
N.A.I.C.S.: 551112
Kyle McDonald (Founder & CEO)
Laurie Parks (CFO)
Ryan Griep (CIO)

Argent Financial Group, Inc.—(Continued)

Aarin Alford (*Dir-HR & Pro Dev*)
John McCollum (*Sr VP-Investments*)
Byron R. Moore (*Mng Dir-Plng Grp*)
Cathy A. McKinzie (*Sr VP & Dir-Ops*)
Clay Hardy (*Sr VP*)
David Luke (*Pres*)
Mark C. Hartnett (*Mng Dir*)
Mike Jones (*Mng Dir-Investment Grp*)
Richard Funchess (*Sr VP*)
Samuel Boldrick (*Sr VP & Dir-Fixed Income*)
Kimberly Breithaupt (*Chief Risk Officer*)
Brooks M. Campany (*VP & Dir-Mktg & PR*)
Jason McDavid (*VP*)
Vince Chamblee (*Sr VP*)
Stephen B. Payne Jr. (*Vice Chm-Corp Dev*)
Charles R. Dudley II (*VP*)

Subsidiaries:

Argent Advisors, Inc.   (1)
1609 Stubbs Ave, Monroe, LA 71201
Tel.: (318) 324-8000
Web Site: http://www.argentmoney.com
Financial Investment Advice
N.A.I.C.S.: 523940
Dean Mailhes (*Pres*)
Vaughn Antley (*Sr VP*)
Trey Curtis (*VP*)
Mike Jones (*Mng Dir-Investment Grp-Ruston*)
Byron R. Moore (*Mng Dir-Plng Grp-Ruston*)

Argent Fiduciary Consulting Services, LLC   (1)
500 E Reynolds Dr, Ruston, LA 71270
Tel.: (318) 251-5800
Web Site: http://www.argentmoney.com
Fiduciary Consulting Services
N.A.I.C.S.: 541611
Robert W. Barrett (*Mng Dir*)

Argent Property Services, LLC   (1)
500 E Reynolds Dr, Ruston, LA 71270
Tel.: (318) 251-5800
Web Site: http://www.argentmoney.com
Management of Property Interests
N.A.I.C.S.: 531390
Matt Barham (*VP*)

Argent Trust Company of Tennessee   (1)
3102 Wend Ave Ste 775, Nashville, TN 37203
Tel.: (615) 385-2345
Web Site: http://www.argentmoney.com
Emp.: 10
Trust Services
N.A.I.C.S.: 525920
Howard Safer (*CEO*)
David Franks (*Pres-Market-Memphis*)

Argent Trust Company, N.A.   (1)
500 E Reynolds Dr, Ruston, LA 71270
Tel.: (318) 251-5800
Web Site: http://www.argentmoney.com
Emp.: 55
Trust Services
N.A.I.C.S.: 525920
Ann Marie Mills (*Sr VP-Employee Benefits*)
Mark Shorthouse (*VP*)
Timothy G. Barrett (*Sr VP-Louisville*)
Ed Brundick (*Pres-Market-Memphis*)
Jordan Earle (*Mng Dir-Greenville*)
Steve Fisher (*Officer-Trust-Greenville*)
Frank Hosse (*Chief Investment Officer-Nashville*)
Nicole Jacobsen-Nally (*Pres-Market-Louisville*)
David H. Williams (*Gen Counsel, Exec VP & Mgr-Atlanta*)
David Redding (*Pres-Austin*)
Mark Milton (*Sr VP-Institutional Svcs*)
Mollie Seymour (*Sr VP-Birmingham*)
Amy Rhodes (*VP*)
Deanna Rankin (*Chief Compliance Officer*)
Ken Alderman (*Pres*)
Steve Jackson (*Sr VP-Funeral & Cemetery Div*)
James Breaux (*Sr VP*)
Michael S. Nutter (*Sr VP-Dallas*)

Linda S. Baker (*Pres-Dallas*)
Jon K. Daubert (*Sr VP-San Antonio*)
Reid Harrell (*Chief Fiduciary Officer*)
Steve Gutermuth (*Sr VP-Louisville*)
John O. Allen Jr. (*Pres-Market-Greenville*)
Sidney Roebuck Jr. (*Sr VP*)

Highland Capital Management, LLC   (1)
6075 Poplar Ave, Memphis, TN 38119-5797
Tel.: (901) 761-9500
Web Site: http://www.highlandcap.com
Sales Range: $1-4.9 Billion
Emp.: 15
Investment Advisory & Management Services
N.A.I.C.S.: 523940
Steven Wishnia (*CEO*)
David Thompson (*Portfolio Mgr*)
Jed Miller (*Dir-Fixed Income*)
Bart McMurry (*Dir-Equity Investments*)
Steve Stack (*COO*)

The Trust Company   (1)
755 E Mulberry Ave Ste 400, San Antonio, TX 78212
Tel.: (210) 352-2410
Web Site: http://www.thetrustcompany.com
Sales Range: $1-9.9 Million
Emp.: 22
Trust Services
N.A.I.C.S.: 525920
Michael R. Sierra (*VP*)
Jay Thompson (*Sr VP & Mgr-Relationship-Southwest*)
Samuel N. Boldrick III (*Mng Dir & Chief Investment Officer*)
James M. Pettus III (*Sr VP*)

ARGENT INTERNATIONAL

41016 Concept Dr, Plymouth, MI 48170
Tel.: (734) 582-9800
Web Site: https://www.argent-international.com
Sales Range: $25-49.9 Million
Emp.: 150
Automotive Accessories Mfr
N.A.I.C.S.: 322220
Fred Ashline (*Mgr-Acct*)
Gregg Merians (*Mgr-Acct-Automotive Sls*)
Shawn Fitzpatrick (*Supvr-AR*)
Tina Farris (*Mgr-Acct*)
Chris Gariepy (*Mgr-Acct*)
Mary Kay Renaud (*Mgr-Acct*)
Tomas Flores (*Mgr-Sls*)

ARGENT VENTURES, LLC

551 5th Ave 34th Fl, New York, NY 10176
Tel.: (212) 692-5400
Web Site:
  https://www.argentventures.com
Year Founded: 1997
Sales Range: $10-24.9 Million
Emp.: 10
Real Estate Services
N.A.I.C.S.: 531390
Andrew Penson (*Pres*)

Subsidiaries:

Hilton Miami Downtown   (1)
1601 Biscayne Blvd, Miami, FL 33132
Tel.: (305) 374-0000
Web Site:
  http://www.hiltonmiamidowntown.com
Sales Range: $10-24.9 Million
Hotel Services
N.A.I.C.S.: 721110
Farooq Rehmatwala (*Gen Mgr*)
Susana Vento (*Dir-Sls & Mktg*)

ARGENTINE BETTERMENT CORPORATION

PO Box 6613, Kansas City, KS 66106
Tel.: (913) 730-0241   **KS**
Year Founded: 2009
Sales Range: $1-9.9 Million
Emp.: 3

Neighborhood People Support Services
N.A.I.C.S.: 624190
Leticia DeCaigny (*Treas*)
Monica DeLeon (*Sec & VP*)

ARGENTS EXPRESS GROUP LTD

206 Watersedge, Hilton Head Island, SC 29928
Tel.: (843) 785-8700
Web Site: http://www.argents.com
Rev.: $10,512,508
Emp.: 35
Freight Forwarding
N.A.I.C.S.: 488510
William Chiappetta (*Founder, Owner & Pres*)
Cynthia Chiappetta (*VP, Controller & Dir-HR*)

ARGI FINANCIAL GROUP

2110 High Wickham Pl, Louisville, KY 40245
Tel.: (502) 753-0609
Web Site:
  http://www.argifinancialgroup.com
Year Founded: 1995
Sales Range: $1-9.9 Million
Emp.: 49
Financial Planning Services
N.A.I.C.S.: 523940
Ron Butt (*Partner*)
Joe Reeves (*Mng Partner*)
Neil Quinlan (*Partner*)
Joe Tichenor (*Partner*)
Jason Brangers (*CFO & Head-Tax & Bus Svc Div*)
Jan Peebles (*Chief Compliance Officer*)
Denise Bright (*COO*)
Steve Wahl (*Partner*)
Dan Cupkovic (*Dir-Investments-Louisville*)
Doug Whyte (*Chief Dev Officer*)
Erin Haynes Reed (*Dir-Mktg & Bus Dev*)
Cindy Lofton (*Mgr-Client Svc*)

ARGIX DIRECT INC.

100 Middlesex Ctr Blvd, Jamesburg, NJ 08831
Tel.: (732) 656-2550
Web Site: http://www.argixdirect.com
Sales Range: $75-99.9 Million
Emp.: 500
Provider of Trucking Services
N.A.I.C.S.: 484121
Richard Mitschke (*Mgr*)

ARGO DATA RESOURCE CORPORATION

1500 N Greenville, Richardson, TX 75081
Tel.: (972) 866-3300
Web Site: https://www.argodata.com
Rev.: $28,939,555
Computer Software Development
N.A.I.C.S.: 541511
Max Martin (*Chm & CEO*)
Brent Tompkins (*Project Mgr*)

ARGO INFRASTRUCTURE PARTNERS LLC

1155 Avenue of The Americas 15th Fl, New York, NY 10036
Tel.: (212) 521-5159
Web Site: http://www.argoip.com
Infrastructure Investment Services
N.A.I.C.S.: 523999
Jason Zibarras (*Founding Partner*)

Subsidiaries:

Corning Natural Gas Holding Corporation   (1)
330 W William St, Corning, NY 14830,

Tel.: (607) 936-3755
Web Site: https://www.corninggas.com
Rev.: $35,235,545
Assets: $144,054,747
Liabilities: $103,601,635
Net Worth: $40,453,112
Earnings: $1,280,640
Emp.: 73
Fiscal Year-end: 09/30/2021
Holding Company
N.A.I.C.S.: 551112
Michael I. German (*Pres & CEO*)
Julie Lewis (*Sec & VP-Energy Supply*)
Jeffery Spear (*COO*)
Charlene Faulk (*VP-Information Technology & Customer Service*)
Kevin Fink (*VP-Operations & Engineering*)

Subsidiary (Domestic):

Corning Natural Gas Corporation   (2)
330 W William St, Corning, NY 14830
Tel.: (607) 936-3755
Web Site: http://www.corninggas.com
Emp.: 58
Natural Gas Distr
N.A.I.C.S.: 221210
Firouzeh Sarhangi (*CFO & Treas*)
Matthew J. Cook (*VP-Ops*)
Russell S. Miller (*VP-Energy Supply & Bus Dev*)

Pike County Light & Power Company   (2)
105 Schneider Ln, Milford, PA 18337   (100%)
Web Site: http://www.pclpeg.com
Electric & Gas Utility
N.A.I.C.S.: 221122

Cross Sound Cable Company, LLC   (1)
200 Donald Lynch Boulevard Suite 300, Marlborough, MA 01581
Tel.: (508) 229-0208
Web Site: http://www.crosssoundcable.com
Rev.: $1,600,000
Emp.: 11
Electrical Transmission Services
N.A.I.C.S.: 487110

ARGO PRODUCTS CO.

3500 Goodfellow Blvd, Saint Louis, MO 63120
Tel.: (314) 385-1803
Web Site:
  https://www.argoproducts.com
Rev.: $10,000,000
Emp.: 145
Metal Products Mfr
N.A.I.C.S.: 332618
George Goldstein (*CEO*)
Kenneth Goldstein (*Owner*)
Fred Faust (*VP-Sls*)
Lee Barman (*Controller*)

ARGO TURBOSERVE CORPORATION

681 5th Ave, New York, NY 10022
Tel.: (201) 804-6200   **DE**
Web Site: http://www.argoturbo.com
Year Founded: 1996
Sales Range: $25-49.9 Million
Emp.: 140
Provider of Industrial Machinery & Equipment Services
N.A.I.C.S.: 541611
Dan Tenzer (*Pres-ATC Govt & Turbine*)
Rob Bruinsma (*Pres-Aerospace*)
John Calicchio (*Chm & CEO*)
Jason Kirshner (*Pres*)
Lynda McGonigle (*CFO*)
Steve Rai (*CIO*)

Subsidiaries:

Argo International Corporation   (1)
160 Chubb Ave, Lyndhurst, NJ 07071   (100%)
Tel.: (212) 431-1700
Web Site: http://www.argointl.com
Sales Range: $25-49.9 Million
Emp.: 56

Distr of Mechanical & Electrical Components, Renewal Parts & General Supplies for Marine & Industrial Use
N.A.I.C.S.: 423830
John Calicchio (Chm)

ARGONAUT CONSTRUCTORS, INC.
1236 Central Ave, Santa Rosa, CA 95402
Tel.: (707) 542-4862
Web Site:
    http://www.argonautconstructor.com
Year Founded: 1957
Sales Range: $75-99.9 Million
Emp.: 200
Water & Sewer Line Structures Construction Services
N.A.I.C.S.: 237110
Michael D. Smith (Pres)
Michael A. Smith (VP)

ARGONAUT PRIVATE EQUITY, LLC
7030 S Yale Ave Ste 810, Tulsa, OK 74136
Tel.: (918) 392-9650   OK
Web Site:
    https://www.argonautpe.com
Year Founded: 2002
Privater Equity Firm
N.A.I.C.S.: 523999
Steven R. Mitchell (CEO)
Phil VanTrease (CFO & Gen Counsel)
Patrick Sullivan (Chief Compliance Officer)
Joey Wignarajah (VP)
John Young (VP)
Kelby Hagar (Pres)
Chong Wang (VP)

Subsidiaries:

JAC Holdings, LLC   (1)
3937 Campus Dr, Pontiac, MI 48341
Tel.: (248) 874-1800
Web Site: http://www.jacproducts.com
Holding Company; Plastic Injection Molding Products Mfr
N.A.I.C.S.: 551112
Mike Wood (Pres & CEO)
Peter Steffes (CFO)

Subsidiary (Domestic):

JAC Products, Inc.   (2)
3937 Campus Dr, Pontiac, MI 48341
Tel.: (248) 874-1800
Web Site: http://www.jacproducts.com
Plastic Injection Molding Products Mfr
N.A.I.C.S.: 326199
Mike Wood (Pres & CEO)
Stuart McRobbie (COO)
Mike Gallico (VP-HR & Admin)
Gordon Michie (VP-Advanced Product Dev)
Alex Hall (Dir-Product Engrg)
Dennis Kirby (CFO)
Ricardo Neves (Mng Dir-Europe)
Tony Yuan (Mng Dir-China)

Plant (Domestic):

JAC Products, Inc. - JAC Molding Plant   (3)
225 S Industrial Dr, Saline, MI 48176
Tel.: (734) 944-8844
Plastic Injection Molding Products Mfr
N.A.I.C.S.: 326199

Miratech Corp.   (1)
420 S 145th E Ave, Tulsa, OK 74108
Tel.: (918) 622-7077
Web Site: http://www.miratechcorp.com
Catalysts, Silencers, Control & Monitoring Systems for Emission Solutions for Industrial Engines Mfr
N.A.I.C.S.: 334519
John Sartain (Sr VP-Engrg & Product Dev)
David Zenthoefer (CEO)
Nick Detor (Sls Mgr-Power Generation)
Doug Janes (CFO)
Shawn Bailes (CFO-OEM Catalyst Mfg)
Steve Decicco (COO-OEM Catalyst Mfg)

Elizabeth Wells Burden (Gen Counsel & Dir-Employee Engagement)
Eddie Hollomon (VP-Ops)

ARGONNE CAPITAL GROUP, LLC
3060 Peachtree Rd NW Ste 425, Atlanta, GA 30305-2256
Tel.: (404) 364-2984   GA
Web Site:
    https://www.argonnecapital.com
Year Founded: 2002
Sales Range: $25-49.9 Million
Emp.: 7
Private Investment Firm
N.A.I.C.S.: 523999
Michael Klump (Founder, Pres & CEO)
Karl F. Jaeger (Sr Mng Dir)
Layton Grisette (Mng Dir)
Bill Weimar (Mng Dir)
R. Patrick Anderson (VP)

Subsidiaries:

The Lube Stop, Inc.   (1)
201 Front St Ste 200, Berea, OH 44017
Tel.: (440) 891-2378
Web Site: http://www.lubestop.com
Automotive Oil Change Services
N.A.I.C.S.: 811191

ARGOSY CAPITAL GROUP, LLC
950 W Valley Rd Ste 2900, Wayne, PA 19087-1845
Tel.: (610) 971-9685   PA
Web Site:
    https://www.argosycapital.com
Year Founded: 1990
Rev.: $2,300,000,000
Investment Management Service
N.A.I.C.S.: 523999
John P. Kirwin III (Founder, Chm & Partner)
Sarah M. Busch (Principal-IR & VP-IR)
Melanie Cafe Lyren (Chief Compliance Officer & VP-Compliance & Tech)
Sarah G. Roth (CEO)
Keith S. Marlowe (Gen Counsel-Legal & Compliance)
Keven Shanahan (Partner)

Subsidiaries:

Anderson Cargo Services, LLC   (1)
1045 Gemini Rd, Saint Paul, MN 55121
Tel.: (651) 556-3400
Web Site: http://www.andersoncargo.com
Sales Range: $1-9.9 Million
Emp.: 13
Freight Transportation Arrangement
N.A.I.C.S.: 488510
Robert Masters (CEO)

Argosy Healthcare Partners   (1)
900 W Vly Rd Ste 1000, Wayne, PA 19087
Tel.: (610) 971-9685
Web Site: https://argosycapital.com
Investment Services
N.A.I.C.S.: 523999

Subsidiary (Domestic):

Art Robbins Instruments, LLC   (2)
1293 Mt View Alviso Rd Ste D, Sunnyvale, CA 94089-2241
Tel.: (408) 734-8400
Web Site: http://www.artrobbins.com
Professional Equipment & Supplies Merchant Whslr
N.A.I.C.S.: 423490
David Wright (Gen Mgr)

Argosy Real Estate Management, LLC   (1)
950 W Vly Rd Ste 2900, Wayne, PA 19087-1845
Tel.: (610) 971-0558
Web Site: http://www.argosyrealestate.com
Rev.: $175,000,000
Emp.: 12

Real Estate Investment & Asset Management Services
N.A.I.C.S.: 531390
Richard C. Schwenk Jr. (CFO & COO)
John P. Kirwin III (CEO & Partner)
David J. Butler (Mng Partner)
Andrew J. Stewart (Mng Partner)
Sarah M. Busch (VP-IR)
Melanie C. Lyren (VP-Compliance & Investor Reporting)
Elizabeth S. Tucker (Controller)
Joshua S. Cohen (Portfolio Mgr)
Nancy H. Mourse (VP-HR)
David J. Butler (Co-CEO & Mng Partner)
Andrew J. Stewart (Co-CEO & Mng Partner)
Sara N. Doelger (Principal)

Asia America Corporation   (1)
1301 Westinghouse Blvd Ste I, Charlotte, NC 28273
Tel.: (704) 843-9292
Web Site: http://www.asiaamericacorp.com
Emp.: 20
Industrial Manufacturing Components Distr & Support Services
N.A.I.C.S.: 423840
John Hornberger (Sr Acct Mgr-Strategic)
Dave Rowles (Pres)
Keenan Acradoville (CFO & Controller)
Sri Burugapalli (CEO)

Enefco International, Inc.   (1)
1130 Minot Ave, Auburn, ME 04210
Tel.: (207) 784-6933
Web Site: http://www.enefco.com
Sales Range: $10-24.9 Million
Emp.: 90
Holding Company; Footwear Heel Components, Industrial Cutting Dies & Cleaning Cards Mfr
N.A.I.C.S.: 551112
Peter Klein (Pres & CEO)

Subsidiary (Domestic):

Enefco USA, Inc.   (2)
1130 Minot Ave, Auburn, ME 04211-1120
Tel.: (207) 784-6933
Web Site: http://www.enefco.com
Footwear Heel Components, Industrial Cutting Dies & Cleaning Cards Mfr
N.A.I.C.S.: 339999
Peter Klein (Pres & CEO)
John Condon (Dir-Ops)

Division (Domestic):

Enefco USA, Inc. - GlobalDie Division   (3)
1130 Minot Ave, Auburn, ME 04211-1120
Tel.: (207) 514-7252
Web Site: http://www.globaldie.com
Emp.: 65
Specialty Cutting Die Mfr
N.A.I.C.S.: 333514
John Condon (Dir-Ops)

Subsidiary (Domestic):

KICTeam, Inc.   (3)
1130 Minot Ave, Auburn, ME 04211-1120
Tel.: (207) 514-7030
Web Site: http://www.kicteam.com
Emp.: 60
Cleaning Card Mfr
N.A.I.C.S.: 339999
Glen Bailey (VP-Product Dev)
Joline Bell (VP-Bus Dev)
Duncan Fielding (Head-Europe)
Ian McCormick (Pres & CEO)

Geneva Scientific, Inc.   (1)
11 N Batavia Ave, Batavia, IL 60510-1961
Web Site: http://www.barcoproducts.com
Plastics Product Mfr
N.A.I.C.S.: 326199
Judy Leonard (Dir-Mktg)

Groome Industrial Service Group   (1)
22 Audrey Pl, Fairfield, NJ 07004
Tel.: (201) 445-6100
Web Site: http://www.groomeindustrial.com
Highway, Street & Bridge Construction
N.A.I.C.S.: 237310
Jeff Bause (Pres & CEO)

Subsidiary (Domestic):

Blasting Solutions Inc.   (2)

1377 S 2500 W, Syracuse, UT 84075-6941
Tel.: (801) 776-0068
Web Site:
    http://www.blastingsolutionsinc.com
Site Preparation Contractor
N.A.I.C.S.: 238910
Steve Woodhall (Mgr)

Hudson Robotics, Inc.   (1)
3300 Sirius Ave Ste 103, Las Vegas, NV 89102-7821
Tel.: (973) 376-7400
Electrical Contractor
N.A.I.C.S.: 238210
Jeffrey Hibler (Pres)

Panhandle Oilfield Service Companies, Inc.   (1)
221 S Country Estates Rd, Liberal, KS 67905
Tel.: (405) 608-5330
Web Site: http://www.posci.net
Sales Range: $10-24.9 Million
Oil & Gas Operation Support Services
N.A.I.C.S.: 213112
Tim Long (Founder, COO & VP-Artificial Lift)
Bill Massa (Chm & CEO)

Richwood Industries, Inc.   (1)
2700 Buchanan SW, Grand Rapids, MI 49548
Tel.: (616) 243-2700
Web Site: http://www.richwoodind.com
Sales Range: $1-9.9 Million
Emp.: 24
Wood Products Mfr
N.A.I.C.S.: 321999
Kelley Barr (Coord-Sls & Mktg)
Dan Springer (Pres)

SinterFire, Inc.   (1)
200 Industrial Park Rd, Kersey, PA 15846
Tel.: (814) 885-6672
Web Site: http://www.sinterfire.com
Sales Range: $1-9.9 Million
Emp.: 11
Lead-Free Frangible Ammunition Components Mfr
N.A.I.C.S.: 332992
Amy Brennan (Controller)
Mike Goetz (Officer-Water Supply)
Mike Sloff (Co-COO)
Brandon Graves (Co-COO)
Todd Alexander (CFO & Plant Mgr)

Sussex Wire, Inc.   (1)
4 Danforth Dr, Easton, PA 18045
Tel.: (610) 250-7750
Web Site: http://www.sussexwire.com
Custom Cold-Formed Metal Components Mfr
N.A.I.C.S.: 332999
Timothy Kardish (Pres & CEO)
Madan Mathevan (VP & Gen Mgr)
Megan Pierzga (Mgr-Quality Control)

Subsidiary (Domestic):

Marox Corp.   (2)
373 Whitney Ave, Holyoke, MA 01040
Tel.: (413) 536-1300
Web Site: https://www.marox.com
Orthopedic Implants & Instruments Mfr
N.A.I.C.S.: 339112

Wittenbach Business Systems, Inc.   (1)
100 Sparks Vly Rd Ste B, Sparks Glencoe, MD 21152-9234
Web Site: http://www.wittenbach.com
Commercial, Industrial Machinery & Equipment Repair & Maintenance
N.A.I.C.S.: 811310
Nathan Derr (Sr VP-Sls)
Bernard Goode (VP-Warehouse & Fleet Ops)
Sanford Levitt (VP-IT)

Subsidiary (Domestic):

The Gilbertson Group, Inc.   (2)
795 Fox Chase, Coatesville, PA 19320
Tel.: (610) 466-9600
Web Site: http://www.gilbertsongroup.com
Rev.: $2,100,000
Emp.: 50
Security Systems Services, except Locksmiths
N.A.I.C.S.: 561621

Argosy Capital Group, LLC—(Continued)

Ronald Gilbertson (CEO)

Wize Solutions Inc. (1)
2500 S Decker Lk Blvd #30, West Valley,
UT 84119
Tel.: (801) 966-0210
Web Site: www.wizesolutions.com
Industrial Building Construction
N.A.I.C.S.: 236210
Tyson Bigelow (Mgr-Sls-Natl)

ARGOSY CONSOLE, INC.
402 Indus Park Dr, Eldon, MO 65026
Tel.: (573) 557-3150 MO
Web Site: https://argosyconsole.com
Year Founded: 1994
Technical Furniture, Ergonomics, Design & Control Room Transformation
N.A.I.C.S.: 337214
Tim Thompson (Pres & CEO)

ARGOSY INTERNATIONAL INC.
225 W 34th St Ste 800, New York,
NY 10122
Tel.: (212) 268-0003
Web Site:
https://www.argosyinternational.com
Rev.: $15,000,000
Emp.: 30
Sporting & Recreational Goods &
Supplies Merchant Whslr
N.A.I.C.S.: 423910
Paul Marks (Chm & CEO)
Ryan Flugel (VP-Sls & Mktg-Seattle)

ARGUINDEGUI OIL COMPANY
4506 State Hwy 359, Laredo, TX
78043
Tel.: (956) 722-5251
Web Site:
http://www.aocpetroleum.com
Sales Range: $50-74.9 Million
Emp.: 133
Petroleum Bulk Stations
N.A.I.C.S.: 424710
Alfonso Arguindegui (Pres)
Jonathan Owens (CFO)

ARGUS
280 Summer St, Boston, MA 02210
Tel.: (617) 261-7676
Web Site: http://www.thinkargus.com
Year Founded: 1997
Sales Range: $10-24.9 Million
Emp.: 13
Advertising Agencies, Advertising
Specialties, African-American Market,
Bilingual Marketing, Full Service, Hispanic Marketing
N.A.I.C.S.: 541810
Lucas H. Guerra (Principal & Dir-Creative)
Zamawa Arenas (Principal)
Cheryl Hammond (Dir-Client Svcs)

ARGUS DENTAL PLAN, INC.
410 W State St, Tampa, FL 33609
Tel.: (813) 864-0625
Web Site:
http://www.argusdental.com
Year Founded: 2007
Sales Range: $1-9.9 Million
Dental Insurance
N.A.I.C.S.: 524114
Jeff Parslow (CFO)
Zee M. Yee (VP-Network Dev)
Michael Hagan (Mgr-Ops)
Cathy Sharp (Dir-Provider Rels &
Network Dev)
Crystal Roznak (Chief Legal Officer)
Lewis Sollner (Dir-Sls-Florida)
Marissa Fernandez (Mgr-Compliance)
Nicholas M. Kavouklis (Pres & CEO)
Richard Bosley (CIO)
Roger W. Skinner (VP)

ARGUS ENERGY LLC.
3026 Big Sandy River Rd, Kenova,
WV 25530
Tel.: (304) 453-6140
Rev.: $11,700,000
Emp.: 172
Coal & Other Mineral & Ore Merchant
Whslr
N.A.I.C.S.: 423520
Terry Hensley (Controller)

ARGUS LIMITED
2099 Gaither Rd Ste 100, Rockville,
MD 20850
Tel.: (301) 948-0448
Web Site:
http://www.arguslimited.com
Sales Range: $25-49.9 Million
Construction Machinery Mfr & Pipe-
lines Repair Services
N.A.I.C.S.: 333120
Olga Korsakovr (Project Mgr)
Ruth Ploff (Dir-HR)

ARGUS TECHNICAL SER-
VICES INC.
2835 N Mayfair Rd, Milwaukee, WI
53222
Tel.: (414) 774-5996
Web Site: https://www.argus-
tech.com
Year Founded: 1974
Rev.: $12,377,000
Emp.: 30
Technical Contracting Services
N.A.I.C.S.: 561320
Brian Smith (Acct Mgr)
David Ernst (Acct Mgr)

ARGY, WILTSE & ROBINSON,
P.C.
8405 Greensboro Dr Ste 700,
McLean, VA 22102
Tel.: (703) 893-0600
Year Founded: 1991
Sales Range: $25-49.9 Million
Emp.: 200
Audit, Tax & Business Advisory Ser-
vices; Human Resources Consulting
& Support; Outsourced Accounting
Solutions & Information Technology
Consulting & Support
N.A.I.C.S.: 541219
Paul Argy (Pres & CEO)
Mary Karen Wills (Partner-Bus Con-
sulting)
Darren Mills (Principal-Intl Corp Svcs)
Bill Keating (Partner)

ARGYLE EXECUTIVE FORUM,
LLC
122 W 26th St 2nd Fl, New York, NY
10001
Tel.: (646) 839-0012 DE
Web Site:
http://www.argyleforum.com
Executive Content, Events, Lead
Generation & Professional Network-
ing Services
N.A.I.C.S.: 513199
Danny Phillips (CEO)
Scott Kenerly (Pres)
Fred Ibarra (VP-Mktg)
Joe Rosenbaum (VP-HR)
Tim Skennion (VP-Sls)
Dan Cannici (Dir-Meeting Mgmt &
Ops)
Lauren Everhart (Dir-Acct Mgmt)
Gerry Marletta (Dir-Tech Ops)
Lauren Meyer (Dir-Content)
Luke Bilton (VP-Audience & Content)

ARI PRODUCTS INC.
102 Gaither Dr Ste 3, Mount Laurel,
NJ 08054
Tel.: (856) 234-0757

Web Site:
https://www.ariproducts.com
Sales Range: $10-24.9 Million
Emp.: 20
Sales & Installation of Floor Products
N.A.I.C.S.: 238330
Ross Gilfillan (Pres)
Terrence Barone (VP-New York Sls)
Janice Villa (Controller)

ARIAS INTEL CORP.
442 W Kennedy Blvd Ste 200,
Tampa, FL 33606
Tel.: (877) 749-5909 NV
Year Founded: 2013
Assets: $801,232
Liabilities: $4,149,750
Net Worth: ($3,348,518)
Earnings: ($10,219,920)
Fiscal Year-end: 03/31/18
Digital Media Platform Developer
N.A.I.C.S.: 541511
Kevin Gillespie (Pres & CEO)

ARIAT INTERNATIONAL, INC.
3242 Whipple Rd, Union City, CA
94587
Tel.: (510) 477-7000 CA
Web Site: https://www.ariat.com
Year Founded: 1989
Sales Range: $300-349.9 Million
Footwear & Apparel Mfr
N.A.I.C.S.: 316210
Audrey Gonzales (Mgr-Call Center)
Jack Teague (VP-Mfg)
Randy Gaines (Mgr-Design)
Soyala Breen (Product Mgr)
Thadd Curry (Mgr-Credit & Collec-
tions)
Katie Rosson (VP-HR)
Todd Levy (VP-Fin)
Janel Organo (Asst Mgr-Mktg)
Gina Del Vecchio (VP-Supply Chain)
Cynthia Relander (Dir-Acctg)

ARIEL CAPITAL MANAGE-
MENT LLC
200 E Randolph St Ste 2900, Chi-
cago, IL 60601
Tel.: (312) 726-0140
Web Site:
https://www.arielinvestments.com
Sales Range: $10-24.9 Million
Emp.: 70
Investment Advisory Services
N.A.I.C.S.: 523940
Christopher G. Kennedy (Chm)
James W. Compton (CEO)
Sabrina Carollo (Sr VP & Dir-Res
Ops)

ARIEL CLINICAL SERVICES
2938 North Ave Ste G, Grand Junc-
tion, CO 81504
Tel.: (970) 245-1616 CO
Web Site: https://www.arielcpa.org
Year Founded: 1993
Sales Range: $1-9.9 Million
Emp.: 182
Community Health Care Services
N.A.I.C.S.: 621498
Brandi Black (Mgr-Community Sup-
port Svcs)
Rebecca Ely (Mgr-Therapeutic Foster
Care-Grand Junction)
Sarah Marshall (Dir-Fin)

ARIEL CORPORATION
35 Blackjack Rd, Mount Vernon, OH
43050-9480
Tel.: (740) 397-0311 OH
Web Site: https://www.arielcorp.com
Year Founded: 1966
Sales Range: $100-124.9 Million
Emp.: 1,200
Mfr of Reciprocating Compressors

N.A.I.C.S.: 333912
Karen Buchwald Wright (Pres &
CEO)

ARIENS COMPANY INC.
655 W Ryan St, Brillion, WI 54110-
1072
Tel.: (920) 756-2141 WI
Web Site: http://www.ariens.com
Year Founded: 1933
Mowers, Tillers, Tractors & Snow
Blowers Mfr
N.A.I.C.S.: 333112
Larry Weyers (Grp Pres)

Subsidiaries:

Parker Company, Inc (1)
655 W Ryan St, Brillion, WI 54110
Tel.: (920) 756-4688
Web Site: http://www.parkersweeper.com
Sales Range: $25-49.9 Million
Emp.: 400
Grounds Maintenance Equipment Mfr
N.A.I.C.S.: 333310

ARIES ELECTRONICS INC.
2609 Bartram Rd, Bristol, PA 19007-
6810
Tel.: (215) 781-9956
Web Site: https://www.arieselec.com
Year Founded: 1972
Sales Range: $10-24.9 Million
Emp.: 50
Electronic Products Mfr
N.A.I.C.S.: 334419
William Sinclair (Pres & CEO)
Frank Folmsbee (Mgr-Sls)
Michael Salerno (Mgr-Engrg)
Jonathan Robb (Product Mgr)

ARIES GLOBAL LOGISTICS,
INC.
365 Franklin Ave, Franklin Square,
NY 11010
Tel.: (516) 328-2500
Web Site: https://www.ariesgl.com
Rev.: $21,000,000
Emp.: 150
Freight Forwarding & Customs Bro-
kerage Services
N.A.I.C.S.: 488510
Frank D'Ambra (Pres)
Joe Greco (VP)
Laura Amico (Controller)

ARIES INDUSTRIES INC.
550 Elizabeth St, Waukesha, WI
53186
Tel.: (262) 896-7205
Web Site:
https://www.ariesindustries.com
Rev.: $23,000,000
Emp.: 110
Closed Circuit Television Equipment
Mfr
N.A.I.C.S.: 334220
Nick Kroll (Pres & CEO)
Steven Cantwell (VP-Sls)

Subsidiaries:

Aries Canada Ltd. (1)
1081 Meyerside Drive Units 1 & 2, Missis-
sauga, L5T 1M4, ON, Canada
Tel.: (905) 795-7913
Closed Circuit Television Equipment Distr
N.A.I.C.S.: 423690

CCV Engineering & Mfg., Inc. (1)
5748 E Shields Ave, Fresno, CA 93727
Tel.: (559) 291-0383
Web Site: http://www.ariesindustries.com
Rev.: $3,000,000
Emp.: 30
Supplier of Water Well (borehole) CCTV
Camera Inspection Systems
N.A.I.C.S.: 449210
Timothy Papenthien (Gen Mgr)

ARIES MARINE CORPORATION

309 La Rue France Ste 100, Lafayette, LA 70508
Tel.: (337) 232-8147
Web Site:
http://www.ariesmarine.com
Rev.: $23,000,000
Emp.: 6
Rental & Leasing Services of Boats & Ships
N.A.I.C.S.: 532411
Dwight S. Ramsay *(Chm & CFO)*
Jeannine Holden *(Controller)*
Court B. Ramsay *(Pres & CEO)*

ARIES PREPARED BEEF CO.

17 W Magnolia Blvd, Burbank, CA 91502
Tel.: (818) 845-4807
Web Site: http://www.ariesbeef.com
Rev.: $24,047,428
Emp.: 250
Meats & Meat Products
N.A.I.C.S.: 311612
Fred Scholder *(Owner & Pres)*
Sandra Nelson *(Controller)*
Rob R. Unal *(Dir-Quality Control)*
Ken McLaughlin *(Exec VP)*

ARIMON TECHNOLOGIES INC.

251 E 5th St, Montello, WI 53949
Tel.: (608) 297-9244
Web Site:
http://www.arimontechnologies.com
Year Founded: 1944
Sales Range: $50-74.9 Million
Emp.: 85
Electronic Components Mfr
N.A.I.C.S.: 334419
Douglas Bessette *(Pres)*

ARING EQUIPMENT COMPANY INC.

13001 W Silver Spring Dr, Butler, WI 53007-1012
Tel.: (262) 781-3770
Web Site:
https://www.aringequipment.com
Year Founded: 1939
Sales Range: $10-24.9 Million
Emp.: 75
Distr of Construction Equipment
N.A.I.C.S.: 423810
Jeff Lemanczyk *(CEO)*
Jim King *(Mgr-Equipment)*
Rick Frost Frost *(Mgr-Equipment Inventory)*

ARIS HORTICULTURE, INC.

115 3rd St SE, Barberton, OH 44203-0230
Tel.: (330) 745-2143   OH
Web Site: http://www.arishort.com
Year Founded: 1920
Sales Range: $25-49.9 Million
Emp.: 650
Ornamental Nursery Products
N.A.I.C.S.: 111421
William G. Rasbach *(Vice Chm)*
Scott Schaefer *(Pres & CEO)*

Subsidiaries:

Aris Horticultural Services   (1)
7401 Moyer Rd, Harrisburg, PA 17112
Tel.: (800) 321-9573
Web Site: http://www.arishortservices.com
Plant & Flower Retailer
N.A.I.C.S.: 424930

Green Leaf Plants   (1)
2369 Old Philadelphia Pike, Lancaster, PA 17602
Tel.: (717) 299-0300
Web Site: http://www.glplants.com
Plant & Flower Whslr
N.A.I.C.S.: 424930

Rich Hollenbach *(Mgr-Facility Maintenance, Production Plng & Inventory Control)*
Mickey Young *(Dir-Sls)*
Nancy Parr *(Mgr-Bus & Customer Svc)*
Cindy Myers *(Mgr-Ops & HR)*
Blair Hoey *(Mng Dir)*

Keepsake Plants LTD   (1)
PO Box 370, Leamington, N8H 3W3, ON, Canada
Tel.: (519) 791-6709
Web Site: http://www.keepsakeplants.com
Emp.: 50
Horticultural Services
N.A.I.C.S.: 561730
Tracy Wiper *(Dir-Sls)*
Tara Wigle *(Mgr-Customer Svc)*

ARIS SOLUTIONS INC.

72 S Main St, White River Junction, VT 05001
Tel.: (802) 280-1911   VT
Web Site:
http://www.arissolutions.org
Year Founded: 1996
Sales Range: $50-74.9 Million
Emp.: 50
Finance Research & Educational Support Services
N.A.I.C.S.: 541611
Jason Richardson *(CFO)*
Cheryl Thrall *(Exec Dir)*
Mary Ann Lauder *(Sec)*
Ron Poe *(VP)*
William Ashe *(Exec Dir)*
Robert Gay III *(Controller)*

ARISTA AIR CONDITIONING CORPORATION

3826 10th St, Long Island City, NY 11101
Tel.: (718) 937-1400
Web Site: https://www.aristair.com
Rev.: $10,800,000
Emp.: 90
Heating & Air Conditioning Contractors
N.A.I.C.S.: 238220
Scott L. Berger *(Pres)*
Craig Berger *(VP-Installations)*
Haroon Muggo *(Mgr-Acctg)*
Michael Piecyk *(Acct Mgr)*
Yvette Gitelman *(VP-Fin & Admin)*
Vinny Eckerson *(VP-Ops)*

ARISTA FINANCIAL CORP.

51 JFK Pkwy 1st Fl W, Short Hills, NJ 07078
Tel.: (973) 218-2428   NV
Web Site: http://www.aristacapital.net
Year Founded: 2009
Rev.: $13,948
Assets: $96,470
Liabilities: $986,992
Net Worth: ($890,522)
Earnings: ($1,164,692)
Emp.: 3
Fiscal Year-end: 12/31/18
Holding Company; Commercial Lending Finance Services
N.A.I.C.S.: 551112
Paul Patrizio *(Chm & CEO-Arista Capital Ltd)*
David Carver *(Dir-Bus Dev-Arista Capital Ltd)*

Subsidiaries:

Arista Capital Ltd.   (1)
51 JFK Pkwy 1st Fl W, Short Hills, NJ 07078
Tel.: (973) 218-2428
Web Site: http://www.aristacapital.net
Commercial Lending Finance Services
N.A.I.C.S.: 522299
Paul Patrizio *(Chm & CEO)*
Kenneth Mathews *(Vice Chm & Treas)*
David Carver *(Dir-Bus Dev)*
Walter A. Wojcik Jr. *(CFO)*

ARISTA INVESTORS CORP.

15 Maiden Ln Ste 905, New York, NY 10038
Tel.: (212) 964-2150   DE
Web Site: https://www.aristacorp-tpa.com
Year Founded: 1978
Sales Range: $1-9.9 Million
Emp.: 7
Insurance Services
N.A.I.C.S.: 524292
Dan Saltzman *(VP-HR)*

ARISTOCRAT VOLKSWAGEN INC.

4175 Orlando Dr, Sanford, FL 32773
Tel.: (407) 365-3300
Web Site: https://www.sanfordvw.com
Year Founded: 1989
Sales Range: $25-49.9 Million
Emp.: 55
Car Whslr
N.A.I.C.S.: 441110
Nestor Mena *(Gen Mgr)*

ARISTOTLE CAPITAL MANAGEMENT, LLC

20 Pacifica Ste 1050, Irvine, CA 92618-7463
Tel.: (949) 681-2100
Web Site:
http://www.aristotlecap.com
Investment Advice
N.A.I.C.S.: 523940
Janet Francis *(Office Mgr)*
Richard S. Hollander *(Chm)*
Richard Schweitzer *(CFO & COO)*

Subsidiaries:

Aristotle Pacific Capital, LLC   (1)
700 Newport Center Dr, Newport Beach, CA 92660
Tel.: (949) 219-1656
Web Site: http://www.pam.pacificlife.com
Asset Management Services
N.A.I.C.S.: 523940
Dominic Nolan *(CEO)*

ARIXA MANAGEMENT, LLC

10960 Wilshire Blvd Ste 1050, Los Angeles, CA 90024
Tel.: (310) 905-3050
Web Site:
http://www.arixacapital.com
Year Founded: 2006
Sales Range: $1-9.9 Million
Emp.: 25
Real Estate Investment Services
N.A.I.C.S.: 531390
Jan Brzeski *(Mng Dir & Chief Investment Officer)*
Gregory Hebner *(Mng Dir)*
Doug Cochrane *(VP-Loan Production)*
Jerry Feinstein *(Sr VP)*
Dan Frankel *(Dir-IR & Bus Dev)*

ARIZON COMPANIES

11880 Dorsett Rd, Saint Louis, MO 63043
Tel.: (314) 739-0037
Web Site:
http://www.arizoncompanies.com
Year Founded: 1921
Sales Range: $50-74.9 Million
Emp.: 490
Mfr & Creator Air-Supported Structures of Fabric, Frames & Tension that House Sports Complexes, Manufacturing, Warehousing, Architecture & Other Commercial Enterprises
N.A.I.C.S.: 236220
Ron Scharf *(Chm)*
Tim Scharf *(COO & VP)*
Matt Polizzi *(Dir-Mktg)*
Jane Pfister *(Mgr-HR)*
Dawn Covili *(Office Mgr)*

Max Havens *(Coord-Sls & Mktg)*
Catherine McComish *(Coord-Corp Office)*
Veronica Milligan *(Coord-Acctg)*
Megan Edwards *(Coord-Sls & Mktg)*
Mitchell Donahoe *(Engr-Inside Sls)*
Tom Buhr *(Engr-Application Piping)*
Kevin Gentsch *(Engr-Application)*
Andrew Rains *(Engr-Market Dev Sls)*
Theresa Barnicle *(Coord-Fin Office)*
Jason Lintker *(Mgr-Technical Bus Dev)*

ARIZONA BEHAVIORAL HEALTH CORPORATION

1406 N 2nd St, Phoenix, AZ 85004
Tel.: (602) 712-9200   AZ
Web Site: http://www.azabc.org
Year Founded: 1997
Sales Range: $10-24.9 Million
Emp.: 11
Behavioral Healthcare Services
N.A.I.C.S.: 623210
Jenny McLellan *(Mgr-Ops)*
Art Medis *(Fin Mgr)*
Kirby Gibbar *(Mgr-IT)*
Ted Williams *(Pres & CEO)*

ARIZONA BIKE WEEK CHARITIES

104 S Robson, Mesa, AZ 85210-1334
Tel.: (480) 644-9314   AZ
Web Site:
http://www.arizonabiker.com
Year Founded: 2003
Sales Range: $1-9.9 Million
Emp.: 3
Veteran Association
N.A.I.C.S.: 813410
Bradley Bennet *(Pres)*
Lisa Cyr *(VP)*
Todd Snedeker *(Treas)*

ARIZONA BLINDS

8550 N 91st Ave Ste 96, Peoria, AZ 85345
Tel.: (520) 784-8266
Web Site: http://www.azblinds.com
Sales Range: $1-9.9 Million
Emp.: 9
Shutters & Drapery Installation Services
N.A.I.C.S.: 238390
Michael O'Daniel *(Pres)*

ARIZONA CARDINALS FOOTBALL CLUB, INC.

8701 S Hardy Dr, Tempe, AZ 85284
Tel.: (602) 379-0101   AZ
Web Site:
http://www.azcardinals.com
Year Founded: 1920
Sales Range: $75-99.9 Million
Emp.: 200
Professional Football Franchise
N.A.I.C.S.: 711211
Michael J. Bidwill *(Pres)*
Mark Feller *(VP-Technology)*
Steve Bomar *(Sr VP-Ticketing)*
Lisa Manning *(VP-Mktg)*
Mark Dalton *(VP-Media Rels)*
Steve Ryan *(VP-Bus Dev)*
John Misch *(Sr Mgr-Corp Hospitality Sls)*
Chris Melvin *(Mgr-Media Rels)*
Darren Urban *(Sr Mgr-Website)*
Steve Keim *(Gen Mgr)*
Cari Belanger-Maas *(Dir-Premium Svcs-Guest Rels)*
Orlando Avila *(Mgr-Mktg & Brdcst Svcs)*
Rolando Cantu *(Mgr-Intl Bus Ventures)*
Greg Lee *(CFO)*
Quentin Harris *(Dir-Pro Scouting)*

Arizona Cardinals Football Club, Inc.—(Continued)

Jeff Wallo (Asst Dir-Video)
Christine Harms (Controller)
Mike Chavez (Mgr-Creative Svcs)
Mike Iaquinta (Dir-Bus Dev)
Todd Santino (Mgr-Business Development)
Tim DeLaney (VP-Brdcst & Digital Content)
Ron Campbell (Sr Dir-Ticket Sls)

ARIZONA CENTRAL CREDIT UNION
2020 N Central Ave Rm 1200, Phoenix, AZ 85004
Tel.: (602) 264-6421　　AZ
Web Site: http://www.azcentralcu.org
Year Founded: 1939
Sales Range: $25-49.9 Million
Emp.: 227
Credit Union
N.A.I.C.S.: 522130

ARIZONA COMMERCIAL TRUCK SALES, LLC.
2560 E Main St, Mesa, AZ 85213
Tel.: (480) 833-2200
Web Site:
　https://www.azcommercialtrucks.net
Sales Range: $10-24.9 Million
Emp.: 20
Commercial Truck Supplier
N.A.I.C.S.: 423440
John Verdone (Owner)
Monty Winn (Dir-Fin)
Paul Brockmeyer (Dir-Ops)

ARIZONA DIAMONDBACKS
401 E Jefferson St, Phoenix, AZ 85004
Tel.: (602) 462-6000
Web Site:
　http://arizona.diamondbacks.com
Year Founded: 1995
Sales Range: $75-99.9 Million
Emp.: 200
Professional Baseball Club
N.A.I.C.S.: 711211
Derrick Hall (Pres)
Thomas Harris (CFO & Exec VP)
Roger Riley (Sr Dir-Team Travel & Mgr-Home Clubhouse)
Craig Bradley (VP-Fin)
Earl G. Kendrick (Mng Gen Partner)
Mike Chipman (Gen Partner)
Jeff Royer (Gen Partner)
Cullen Maxey (Exec VP-Bus Ops)
Robert Zweig (CIO & VP)
Chris James (Dir-Acctg)
Jeff Jacobs (Dir-Fin Mgmt)
Bob Gebhard (VP)
Scott Geyer (VP-Brdcst)
Luis Calderon (Sr Mgr-Ticket Ops)
Kenny Farrell (VP-Mktg & Analytics)
Casey Wilcox (Dir-Player & Media Rels)
Jeff Rodin (Dir-Baseball Outreach & Dev)
Sean Maguire (Dir-Security)
Russ Amaral (VP-Facilities & Event Svcs)
Bryan White (Dir-Event Svcs)
Jim White (Dir-Facilities Engrg)
Marshall Cheever (Sr Mgr-Facilities Engrg)
Gregory Green (Sr Mgr)
John Fisher (Sr VP-Ticket Sls & Mktg)
Tim Martin (Mgr-Hospitality & Bus Dev)
Diney Ransford (Mgr-Premium Svcs)
Graham Rossini (VP-Special Projects & Fan Experience)
Marian Rhodes (Chief HR & Diversity Officer & Sr VP)

Caleb Jay (Sr Dir-Legal Affairs & Assoc Gen Counsel)
Karina Bohn (Sr Dir-Mktg)
Debbie Castaldo (VP-Corp & Community Impact)
Billy Ryan (Asst Gen Mgr)
Josh Rawitch (Sr VP-Comm)
Judd Norris (VP-Corp Partnerships)
Tony La Russa (Chief Baseball Officer)
De Jon Watson (Sr VP-Baseball Ops)
Chip Hale (Mgr)
Bryan Minniti (Asst Gen Mgr)
Ed Lewis (Dir-Baseball Analytics & Res)
Brad Arnsberg (Coord-Rehab Pitching)
Deric Ladnier (Dir-Scouting)
Jeff Cederbaum (Mgr-Video Production)
Jeffrey Barnes (Supvr-Acctg)
John Prewitt (Supvr-Social Media)
Kyle Payne (Coord-Social Media)
Leah Brandenburg (Accountant)
Mike Bell (Dir-Player Dev)
Sam Eaton (Dir-Baseball Ops)
Shawn Marette (Sr Mgr-Player Dev)
Mike Hazen (Exec VP & Gen Mgr)
Pat Courtney (Chief Comm Officer)
Tony Petitti (COO)
Bob Bowman (Pres-Bus & Media)
Matthew Gould (VP-Corp Comm)

ARIZONA ELECTRIC POWER COOPERATIVE INC.
1000 S Hwy 80, Benson, AZ 85602-7007
Tel.: (520) 586-3631　　AZ
Web Site: https://www.azgt.coop
Year Founded: 1961
Sales Range: $25-49.9 Million
Emp.: 261
Producer of Electrical Services
N.A.I.C.S.: 221118
Geoff Oldfather (Mgr-Comm & PR)
Charles Reece (Plant Mgr-Engrg)
Daniel Beck (Engr-Mechanical)
Walter Bray (Mgr-Power Scheduling & Trading)

ARIZONA FUEL DISTRIBUTORS LLC
2727 W Baseline Rd Ste 13, Tempe, AZ 85283
Tel.: (602) 437-4515
Web Site:
　http://www.azfueldistributors.com
Sales Range: $50-74.9 Million
Emp.: 10
Petroleum Products
N.A.I.C.S.: 424720
Larry Davis (Mgr-Ops)
Ken Kennigs (Controller)

ARIZONA GRAINS INC.
601 E Main Ave, Casa Grande, AZ 85122
Tel.: (520) 836-8228　　AZ
Web Site:
　https://www.arizonagrain.com
Year Founded: 1972
Sales Range: $75-99.9 Million
Emp.: 85
Grain & Feed Mfr
N.A.I.C.S.: 424510
Eric Wilkey (Pres)
Subsidiaries:

Arizona Grain Valley Seed　　(1)
601 E Main Ave, Casa Grande, AZ 85222　　(100%)
Tel.: (520) 836-8228
Web Site: http://www.arizonagrain.com
Sales Range: $25-49.9 Million
Emp.: 38
Agricultural Seed Processing Services

N.A.I.C.S.: 424510
Eric Wilkey (Pres)

ARIZONA HOUSING, INC.
230 S 12th Ave, Phoenix, AZ 85007
Tel.: (602) 228-7832　　AZ
Web Site:
　http://www.azhousinginc.org
Year Founded: 1995
Sales Range: $1-9.9 Million
Housing Assistance Services
N.A.I.C.S.: 624229
Mark Holleran (CEO)

ARIZONA HUMANE SOCIETY
1521 W Dobbins Rd, Phoenix, AZ 85041
Tel.: (602) 997-7585　　AZ
Web Site: https://www.azhumane.org
Year Founded: 1957
Sales Range: $10-24.9 Million
Emp.: 271
Animal Protection Services
N.A.I.C.S.: 813312
Steven R. Hansen (Pres & CEO)
Michelle L. Giesen (CFO & VP-Fin)
Elizabeth Claxton (VP-Bus Ops)
Robyn Jaynes (VP-Medical Svcs)
Kelsea Patton (VP-External Affairs)
Jill Santa (VP-HR)

ARIZONA INSTRUMENT LLC
3375 N Delaware St, Chandler, AZ 85225
Tel.: (602) 470-1414　　DE
Web Site: http://www.azic.com
Year Founded: 1981
Sales Range: $10-24.9 Million
Emp.: 60
Quality Control Instruments & Environmental Monitoring Instruments Mfr, Designer & Marketer
N.A.I.C.S.: 334513
George G. Hays (Pres & CEO)
Linda Shepherd (Controller)
Rick Ervin (Dir-Sls)

ARIZONA LABOR FORCE INC.
6363 S Kyrene Rd, Tempe, AZ 85283-1736
Tel.: (480) 820-1234
Web Site:
　http://www.laborsystems.com
Sales Range: $25-49.9 Million
Emp.: 400
Temporary Help Service
N.A.I.C.S.: 561320
Denise Hobart (Controller)
Gail Martin (Mgr-Ops)
Amy Falk (VP-Ops)

ARIZONA LEATHER COMPANY INC.
4235 Schaefer Ave, Chino, CA 91710
Tel.: (909) 393-6776
Web Site:
　https://www.arizonaleather.com
Sales Range: $10-24.9 Million
Emp.: 10
Mfr of Customized Furniture & Cabinets
N.A.I.C.S.: 337212
Rob Cannon (Mgr-Sls)
John McCluney (Mgr-Store)

ARIZONA MACHINERY CO.
11111 W McDowell Rd, Avondale, AZ 85323
Tel.: (623) 936-7131
Web Site:
　http://www.arizonamachinery.com
Sales Range: $25-49.9 Million
Emp.: 102
Farm Equipment & Supplies
N.A.I.C.S.: 423820

Ferenc E. Rosztoczy (CEO)
Tom Rosztoczy (Pres)

ARIZONA PARTSMASTER INC.
7125 W Sherman St, Phoenix, AZ 85043
Tel.: (602) 233-3580
Web Site:
　http://www.azpartsmaster.com
Year Founded: 1985
Sales Range: $10-24.9 Million
Emp.: 36
Whslr of Plumbing Fittings & Supplies
N.A.I.C.S.: 423720
David D. Schlecht (Pres)
Brad Schlecht (VP)

ARIZONA PEPPER PRODUCTS CO., INC.
PO Box 40605, Mesa, AZ 85274
Tel.: (480) 844-0302
Web Site:
　http://www.azgunslinger.com
Year Founded: 1985
Sales Range: $10-24.9 Million
Emp.: 15
Dried & Dehydrated Food Mfr
N.A.I.C.S.: 311423
Anne Gentuso (Exec VP)
Bill Marko (Pres)

ARIZONA PIPE LINE COMPANY INC.
17372 Lilac St, Hesperia, CA 92345-5162
Tel.: (760) 244-8212
Web Site:
　https://www.arizonapipeline.com
Year Founded: 1979
Sales Range: $25-49.9 Million
Emp.: 500
Water, Sewer & Utility Line Construction Services
N.A.I.C.S.: 237110
Nina Moyers (Pres & CEO)
Arne Grant (Mgr-Phoenix)
Phyllis Moyers (Sec)
Kevin Senart (Mgr-Hesperia)
John W. Gulzow (COO)
Tom Seals (Mgr-Equipment)
Steven Lords (CFO & VP)
Cathy Whitener (Exec VP)
Brion C. Morris (Mgr-IT)
Glen Gray (Mgr-Reno Div)
Jim Harris (Mgr-Risk)
Charlie Manherz (Mgr-Tucson)
Alan Hart (Project Mgr-Steel Pipeline Div)

ARIZONA STATE CREDIT UNION
2355 W Pinnacle Peak Rd, Phoenix, AZ 85027
Tel.: (602) 467-4088　　AZ
Web Site: http://www.azstcu.org
Year Founded: 1951
Sales Range: $75-99.9 Million
Emp.: 557
Credit Union
N.A.I.C.S.: 522130
Jon Borge (Treas)
Sam Wheeler (Chm)
Martha Rozen (Sec)
Shane Siren (Vice Chm)
Dave Dos (Gen Mgr)

ARIZONA STATE TRAILERS SALES, INC.
2038 N Country Club Dr, Mesa, AZ 85201
Tel.: (480) 834-9581
Web Site: https://www.littledealer.com
Year Founded: 1966
Sales Range: $10-24.9 Million
Emp.: 40

Sales of Recreational Vehicles
N.A.I.C.S.: 441210
Larry Samtsom *(Mgr-Sls)*

ARIZONA STATE UNIVERSITY
300 E University Dr Ste 245, Tempe, AZ 85281
Tel.: (480) 965-0335
Web Site: http://www.ui.asu.edu
University
N.A.I.C.S.: 611310
Jose Aguinaga Cardenas *(Gen Counsel & Sr VP)*
Michael M. Crow *(Pres)*
Morgan R. Olsen *(CFO, Treas & Exec VP)*
Daniel Dillon *(CMO & Sr VP)*
Kevin J. Salcido *(Chief HR Officer & VP-HR)*
Lisa Grace *(Exec Dir-University Audits)*
Joshua LaBaer *(Exec Dir-Biodesign Institute)*
Sethuraman Panchanathan *(Chief Res & Innovation Officer & Exec VP-Knowledge Enterprise Dev)*
Lee E. Ohanian *(Dir-Center for the Study of Economic Liberty)*
Paul Carrese *(Dir-Civic, Economic Thought & Leadership)*
Lev Gonick *(CIO)*
Ann Toca *(Chief Mktg Officer & Sr VP)*
Mark Searle *(Exec VP)*
James Rund *(Sr VP-Education Outreach & Student Svcs)*
Christine K. Wilkinson *(Sr VP-ASU Alumni Association)*
Jim O'Brien *(Sr VP-University Affairs)*
Richard Stanley *(Sr VP)*
Laura Roskind *(Co-Chm)*
Bob Zollars *(Co-Chm)*

Subsidiaries:

Thunderbird School of Global
Management　　　　　　　　(1)
400 E Van Buren St Ste 900, Phoenix, AZ 85004
Tel.: (602) 496-7000
Web Site: http://www.thunderbird.asu.edu
Emp.: 200
Graduate & Undergraduate College
N.A.I.C.S.: 611310
Bronwyn Beabeau *(COO)*
Patrick McDermott *(Chief Engagement Officer)*

ARIZONA STONE & ARCHITECTURAL, LLC.
4502 E Virginia St, Mesa, AZ 85215
Tel.: (480) 641-1042
Web Site:
　　https://www.arizonastone.com
Year Founded: 2002
Sales Range: $10-24.9 Million
Emp.: 10
Brick, Stone & Related Construction Material Whslr
N.A.I.C.S.: 423320
Duree O'Daniel *(Mgr-Ops)*
Terri Sotelo *(Mgr-Acctg)*

ARIZONA TILE SUPPLY, INC.
8829 S Priest Dr, Tempe, AZ 85284-1905
Tel.: (480) 893-9393　　　　AZ
Web Site:
　　https://www.arizonatile.com
Year Founded: 1978
Sales Range: $50-74.9 Million
Emp.: 500
Ceramic Tile Importer & Distr
N.A.I.C.S.: 444180
John G. Huarte *(Owner & CEO)*
Don Kesteloot *(VP-Fin)*
Roy Kunihiro *(Gen Mgr-Stone Div)*

Subsidiaries:

Arizona Tile-Anaheim　　　　　(1)
1620 S Lewis St, Anaheim, CA 92805
Tel.: (714) 978-6403
Web Site: http://www.arizonatile.com
Sales Range: $25-49.9 Million
Emp.: 200
Ceramic Wall & Floor Tile Mfr
N.A.I.C.S.: 423320
Mark Huarte *(Pres)*

ARIZONA WHOLESALE SUPPLY COMPANY
2020 E University Dr, Phoenix, AZ 85034-6731
Tel.: (602) 258-7901　　　　AZ
Web Site:
　　http://www.arizonawholesale.com
Year Founded: 1944
Sales Range: $125-149.9 Million
Emp.: 82
Electronic Products, Consumer Appliances & Flooring Distr
N.A.I.C.S.: 423620
Larry Eglinton *(VP)*
Michele Garrett *(Pres)*

Subsidiaries:

QDI　　　　　　　　　　　　(1)
2424 S 21st St, Phoenix, AZ
85034　　　　　　　　　　(100%)
Tel.: (602) 445-2600
Web Site: http://www.qdiwireless.com
Sales Range: $25-49.9 Million
Emp.: 55
Wireless Dealer Programs
N.A.I.C.S.: 517112
Donna Juarez *(Mgr-Mktg)*
Garry Hill *(Mgr-Pur)*
Bill Abbott *(Owner)*

ARIZONA'S CHILDREN ASSOCIATION
711 E Missouri Ste 200, Phoenix, AZ 85014
Tel.: (520) 622-7611　　　　AZ
Web Site:
　　http://www.arizonaschildren.org
Year Founded: 1915
Sales Range: $25-49.9 Million
Emp.: 1,023
Community Mental Health Services
N.A.I.C.S.: 623220
Ellen Howlett *(Treas)*
Harold Magalnick *(Chm)*

ARK ROYAL INSURANCE COMPANY
1 ASI Way N, Saint Petersburg, FL 33702
Tel.: (727) 456-1673　　　　FL
Web Site: http://www.arkroyalins.com
Year Founded: 2007
Property & Casualty Insurance Services
N.A.I.C.S.: 524126

ARK TECHNOLOGIES INC.
3655 Ohio Ave, Saint Charles, IL 60174
Tel.: (630) 377-8855
Web Site: https://www.arktechno.com
Year Founded: 1980
Sales Range: $10-24.9 Million
Emp.: 100
Precision Instrument Springs Mfr
N.A.I.C.S.: 332613
Al Kabeshita *(Chm)*
Eric Takeda *(Mgr-Pur)*

ARKADIUM, INC.
920 Broadway 2nd Fl, New York, NY 10010
Tel.: (212) 337-3701
Web Site: http://www.arkadium.com
Year Founded: 2001
Sales Range: $1-9.9 Million

Emp.: 106
Wired Telecommunications Carriers
N.A.I.C.S.: 517111
Kenny Rosenblatt *(Co-Founder, Pres & CEO)*
Jessica Rovello *(Co-Founder & Exec Chm)*
Jordan Fox *(CFO)*
David Hague *(Gen Mgr)*

ARKANSAS & MISSOURI RAILROAD CO.
306 E Emma Ave, Springdale, AR 72764
Tel.: (479) 751-8600
Web Site:
　　http://www.arkansasmissouri-rr.com
Rev.: $12,500,000
Emp.: 70
Railroads Line-Haul Operating
N.A.I.C.S.: 482111
G. Brent McCready *(Pres)*
Maria Andreadis *(Office Mgr & Asst Controller)*
Casey Shepherd *(Chief Mechanical Officer)*
Rick Hall *(CFO)*
Caren Kraska *(Chm)*

ARKANSAS CHILDREN'S HOSPITAL
1 Childrens Way, Little Rock, AR 72202-3591
Tel.: (501) 364-1100　　　　AR
Web Site: http://www.archildrens.org
Year Founded: 1912
Sales Range: $500-549.9 Million
Emp.: 4,617
Healthcare Services
N.A.I.C.S.: 622110
Marcella L. Doderer *(Pres & CEO)*
Kris Maddalena *(Chief Nursing Officer & Sr VP)*

ARKANSAS ELDER OUTREACH OF LITTLE ROCK, INC.
10632 Hillary Ct, Baton Rouge, LA 70810
Tel.: (225) 769-7960　　　　IA
Web Site:
　　http://www.elderoutreach.org
Year Founded: 2003
Sales Range: $50-74.9 Million
Emp.: 1,880
Elder Care Services
N.A.I.C.S.: 624120
Billy Amons *(Mgr-Ops)*
Dorrie Rambo *(CFO)*
Todd Desormeaux *(Dir-IT)*

ARKANSAS ELECTRIC COOPERATIVES, INC.
1 Cooperative Way, Little Rock, AR 72209-5433
Tel.: (501) 570-2200　　　　AR
Web Site: http://www.aeci.com
Year Founded: 1942
Sales Range: $50-74.9 Million
Emp.: 398
Mfr & Wholesale Distributor of Electrical Equipment; Electrical Construction Management & Maintenance
N.A.I.C.S.: 423610
Michael W. Henderson *(CFO & Exec VP)*
Robert H. McClanahan *(CTO & VP)*
Bill Conine *(Interim Pres & CEO)*

Subsidiaries:

Electric Research & Manufacturing
Cooperative, Inc. (ERMCO)　　(1)
2225 Industrial Rd, Dyersburg, TN
38024-2344　　　　　　　　(100%)
Tel.: (731) 285-9121

Web Site: http://www.ermco-eci.com
Rev.: $76,025,000
Emp.: 395
Mfr of Transformers
N.A.I.C.S.: 335311
Craig Tennant *(Mgr-Sls)*

ARKANSAS ELECTRICAL OUTLET INC.
1735 E Broadway, Forrest City, AR 72335
Tel.: (870) 633-4997
Web Site: http://www.aeoinc.net
Sales Range: $10-24.9 Million
Emp.: 6
Electrical Apparatus & Equipment
N.A.I.C.S.: 423610
Billy Paulman *(Owner)*

ARKANSAS FARM BUREAU FEDERATION
10720 Kanis Rd, Little Rock, AR 72211-3825
Tel.: (501) 224-4400　　　　AR
Web Site: https://www.arfb.com
Year Founded: 1935
Sales Range: $150-199.9 Million
Emp.: 325
Farm Bureau Membership Organization
N.A.I.C.S.: 813910
Randy Veach *(Pres)*
Mike Solomon *(VP-Fin & Ops)*
Zac Bradley *(Dir-Pub Affairs & Govt Rels)*
Bryan Pistole *(Coord-Graphic Design & Editorial)*
Rich Hillman *(VP)*
Stanley Hill *(VP-Pub Affairs & Govt Rels)*
Leigh Pruss *(Dir-Fin)*
John Bailey *(Dir-Environmental & Regulatory Affairs)*
Warren Carter *(Exec VP)*
Evan Teague *(VP-Commodity & Regulatory Affairs)*
Rob Anderson *(VP-PR)*
Steve Eddington *(VP-PR)*
Chuck Tucker *(Exec VP)*
Karen Wood *(Sec)*
Jessica Clowser Burkham *(Dir-Policy Dev & Legislative Res)*
John McMinn *(Dir-Commodity Activities & Economics)*

Subsidiaries:

Arkansas Casualty Investment　(1)
10720 Kanis Rd, Little Rock, AR
72211-0000　　　　　　　　(100%)
Tel.: (501) 224-4400
Web Site: http://www.afbic.com
Sales Range: $75-99.9 Million
Holding Company: Insurance Services
N.A.I.C.S.: 551112

Arkansas Farm Bureau
Investment　　　　　　　　(1)
10720 Kanis Rd, Little Rock, AR
72211-3825　　　　　　　　(100%)
Tel.: (501) 224-4400
Web Site:
　　http://www.arkansasfarmbureau.com
Sales Range: $25-49.9 Million
Insurance Company
N.A.I.C.S.: 813910
Rodney Baker *(VP)*
Randy Veach *(Pres)*

Farm Bureau Building, Inc.　　(1)
10720 Kanis Rd, Little Rock, AR
72211-3825　　　　　　　　(100%)
Tel.: (501) 224-4400
Web Site: http://www.arfb.com
Sales Range: $25-49.9 Million
Emp.: 300
Overseer of Properties
N.A.I.C.S.: 531190

Farm Bureau Casualty Insurance
Co.　　　　　　　　　　　(1)

Arkansas Farm Bureau Federation—(Continued)

10720 Kanis Rd, Little Rock, AR
72211-3825   **(100%)**
Tel.: (501) 224-4400
Web Site: http://www.arfd.com
Farm Bureau Insurance Company
N.A.I.C.S.: 524126

Farm Bureau Mutual Insurance Co. of
Arkansas   **(1)**
10720 Kanis Rd, Little Rock, AR
72211-3825   **(100%)**
Tel.: (501) 224-4400
Web Site: http://www.afbic.com
Sales Range: $100-124.9 Million
Farm Bureau Insurance Company
N.A.I.C.S.: 524126
David Moore *(VP & Gen Mgr)*

ARKANSAS FEDERAL CREDIT UNION
2424 Marshall Rd, Jacksonville, AR
72076
Tel.: (501) 982-1000
Web Site: https://www.afcu.org
Financial Cooperative & Investment
Services
N.A.I.C.S.: 523999
Alan Harrison *(VP-Bus Svcs)*

ARKANSAS FOUNDATION FOR MEDICAL CARE, INC.
1020 W 4th St Ste 300, Little Rock,
AR 72201
Tel.: (501) 212-8600   AR
Web Site: http://www.afmc.org
Year Founded: 1972
Sales Range: $10-24.9 Million
Emp.: 219
Health Care Srvices
N.A.I.C.S.: 622110
Ray Hanley *(Pres & CEO)*
Peggy Starling *(Chief Outreach Svcs Officer)*
Catherine Bain *(Chief Admin Officer)*
Marilyn Little *(COO)*
Susie Moore *(Chief Compliance Officer)*
Nathan Ray *(CTO)*

ARKANSAS GLASS CONTAINER CORP.
516 W Johnson Ave, Jonesboro, AR
72401
Tel.: (870) 932-4564   AR
Web Site: http://www.agcc.com
Year Founded: 1956
Glass Container Mfr
N.A.I.C.S.: 327213
Brian Richey *(Dir-Mfr)*
LuAnn Sutton *(Dir-HR)*
Vicki Rampley *(COO)*
Chris Tyree *(Dir-Purchasing)*

ARKANSAS HOSPICE, INC.
14 Parkstone Cir, North Little Rock,
AR 72116
Tel.: (501) 748-3333   AR
Web Site:
https://www.arkansashospice.org
Year Founded: 1992
Sales Range: $25-49.9 Million
Emp.: 484
Hospice Care Services
N.A.I.C.S.: 623110
Judith S. Wooten *(Pres & CEO)*
Brian Bell *(Chief Medical Officer & VP)*

ARKANSAS METHODIST MEDICAL CENTER
900 W Kingshighway, Paragould, AR
72450
Tel.: (870) 239-7000   AR
Web Site: https://www.myammc.org
Year Founded: 1949
Sales Range: $50-74.9 Million

Emp.: 811
Healtcare Services
N.A.I.C.S.: 622110
Brad Bloemer *(CFO & VP-Fin)*
Barry Davis *(Pres & CEO)*
Lana Williams *(Chief Nursing Officer)*
Kevin Thielemier *(Dir-HR)*
Jon Collier *(Sec)*
Teresa Ervin *(Sec-Nursing)*
Bill Fisher *(Treas)*
Janette Iglehart *(Dir-Physician Svcs)*
Robin Patten *(Dir-Social Svcs)*
David Dudley *(Chm)*

ARKANSAS MILL SUPPLY COMPANY
701 Commerce Rd, Pine Bluff, AR
71601
Tel.: (870) 534-6540
Web Site:
http://www.arkansasmill.com
Sales Range: $10-24.9 Million
Emp.: 70
Industrial Supplies
N.A.I.C.S.: 423840
Jill Drake *(Controller)*
Cliff Cheatwood *(Chm)*
David Brown *(Pres)*

ARKANSAS PACKAGING PRODUCTS, INC.
7701 Industry Dr, North Little Rock,
AR 72117
Tel.: (501) 945-1400
Web Site:
http://www.arkansaspackaging.com
Year Founded: 1973
Sales Range: $25-49.9 Million
Emp.: 30
Adhesives, Tape & Plasters
N.A.I.C.S.: 423840
Mark Schaefer *(Pres)*

ARKANSAS REGIONAL ORGAN RECOVERY AGENCY
1701 Aldersgate Rd Ste 4, Little
Rock, AR 72205
Tel.: (501) 907-9150   AR
Web Site: http://www.arora.org
Year Founded: 1987
Sales Range: $10-24.9 Million
Emp.: 74
Organ Transplantation Services
N.A.I.C.S.: 621991

ARKANSAS RICE DEPOT, INC.
4301 W 65th St, Little Rock, AR
72209
Tel.: (501) 565-8855   AR
Web Site: http://www.ricedepot.org
Year Founded: 1982
Sales Range: $10-24.9 Million
Emp.: 60
Fiscal Year-end: 12/31/15
Community Food Services
N.A.I.C.S.: 624210
Brandi Johnston *(Dir-Dev)*
Phyllis Parrish *(Dir-Programs)*
Frank Harrison *(Mgr-Warehouse & Facilities)*
Rhonda Sanders *(Pres & CEO)*

ARKANSAS TRAILER MANUFACTURING CO., INC.
3200 S Elm St, Little Rock, AR 72204
Tel.: (501) 666-5417
Web Site:
http://www.arkansastrailer.com
Sales Range: $10-24.9 Million
Emp.: 68
Truck Parts & Accessories
N.A.I.C.S.: 423120
Guy Campbell *(CEO)*
Greg Campbell *(Pres)*

ARKANSAS VALLEY ELEC-

TRIC COOPERATIVE CORPORATION
1811 W Commercial St, Ozark, AR
72949-2905
Tel.: (479) 667-2176   AR
Web Site: http://www.avecc.com
Year Founded: 1937
Sales Range: $25-49.9 Million
Emp.: 150
Electronic Services
N.A.I.C.S.: 221118
Larhonda Melton *(CEO & Sec)*

ARKANSAS VALLEY STATE BANK
322 S Main St, Broken Arrow, OK
74012
Tel.: (918) 251-9611
Web Site: http://www.bankavb.com
Year Founded: 1905
State Commercial Banks
N.A.I.C.S.: 522110

ARKAY PACKAGING CORPORATION
100 Marcus Blvd Ste 2, Hauppauge,
NY 11788-3749
Tel.: (631) 273-2000   NY
Web Site: http://www.arkay.com
Year Founded: 1922
Sales Range: $100-124.9 Million
Emp.: 220
Mfr of Folding Cartons & Custom
Packaging
N.A.I.C.S.: 322212
Laura Carey *(Dir-Sls)*
Patricia Hunold *(Coord-Sls)*
Steve Tily *(Dir-Sls)*
Gregg Goldman *(Dir-Sls)*

ARKEL CONSTRUCTORS, INC.
1048 Florida St, Baton Rouge, LA
70802
Tel.: (225) 344-1023
Web Site:
https://www.arkelconstructors.com
Year Founded: 1981
Sales Range: $10-24.9 Million
Emp.: 40
Nonresidential Construction Services
N.A.I.C.S.: 236220
Johnny Fife *(Pres)*
Derek Fife *(VP)*
John Bourgeois *(Gen Superintendent)*
Greg Friedland *(Sr Project Mgr)*

ARKEL INTERNATIONAL INC.
1055 Convention St, Baton Rouge,
LA 70802
Tel.: (225) 343-0525
Web Site: http://www.arkel.com
Year Founded: 1956
Sales Range: $10-24.9 Million
Emp.: 30
Industrial Buildings & Warehouses
N.A.I.C.S.: 236220
Homer Knost *(Chm)*
Maureen Kelley *(VP)*

ARKION LIFE SCIENCES L.L.C.
551 Mews Dr Ste J, New Castle, DE
19720
Tel.: (302) 504-7400   DE
Web Site: https://www.arkionls.com
Year Founded: 1992
Sales Range: $100-124.9 Million
Emp.: 300
Environmentally Friendly, Natural &
Nature-Identical Bioactive Compounds Mfr
N.A.I.C.S.: 325998
Rick L. Stejskal *(CFO)*
Ernest W. Porta *(Pres & CEO)*
Harvey L. Weaver *(VP-Market Dev)*
Chris Widrig *(Pres-Airepel)*

Subsidiaries:
Bio-Technical Resources   **(1)**
1035 S 7th St, Manitowoc, WI 54220
Tel.: (920) 684-5518
Web Site: http://www.biotechresources.com
Emp.: 12
Biotechnology Research & Development
Services
N.A.I.C.S.: 541714
Reinhardt A. Rosson *(Pres)*

ARKNETMEDIA INC.
401 Franklin Ave Ste 102A, Garden
City, NY 11530
Web Site:
http://www.arknetmedia.com
Year Founded: 2006
Sales Range: $1-9.9 Million
Emp.: 20
Interactive Agency & Owner Of Portfolio Of Online Companies
N.A.I.C.S.: 541890
Ryan Alovis *(Founder & CEO)*
Justin Tamburro *(VP-Ops)*
Rob Reynolds *(VP-Dev)*

ARLAN'S MARKET INC.
909 Curtis Ave, Schertz, TX 78154
Tel.: (281) 326-4363
Web Site:
https://www.arlansmarket.com
Sales Range: $10-24.9 Million
Emp.: 450
Supermarket
N.A.I.C.S.: 445110
Ames Hal Arlan *(Pres)*
Mike Grant *(VP)*

ARLAND TOOL & MANUFACTURING INC.
421 Main St, Sturbridge, MA 01566
Tel.: (508) 347-3368
Web Site: http://www.arland.com
Year Founded: 1948
Rev.: $11,900,000
Emp.: 130
Machine Bases, Metal
N.A.I.C.S.: 332999
Tye Baker *(Coord-Sls)*
Keith Gagnon *(Gen Mgr)*
Dan Benoit *(Mgr-Mgmt Info Sys)*

ARLEE HOME FASHIONS INC.
261 5th Ave Fl 6, New York, NY
10016-7601
Tel.: (212) 689-0020   DE
Year Founded: 1976
Sales Range: $25-49.9 Million
Emp.: 500
Household Furnishings
N.A.I.C.S.: 314120
Jack Kleiner *(Controller)*
Allen Manzell *(CFO)*
Lisa Battaglia *(Dir-Product Dev)*
Oscar Lugo *(Dir-Textile Design)*

ARLEY WHOLESALE INC.
700 N South Rd, Scranton, PA 18504
Tel.: (570) 344-9874
Web Site:
https://www.arleywholesale.com
Rev.: $18,500,000
Emp.: 66
Tile & Clay Products
N.A.I.C.S.: 423320
Saul M. Levy *(Co-Owner & Pres)*
Arlene Gevanthor *(Co-Owner)*
Brenda Walker *(Asst Comptroller)*
David Lowe *(VP-Sls)*

ARLINGTON CAPITAL PARTNERS LLC
5425 Wisconsin Ave Ste 200, Chevy
Chase, MD 20815
Tel.: (202) 337-7500

Web Site:
   http://www.arlingtoncap.com
Year Founded: 1999
Private Equity Investment Firm
N.A.I.C.S.: 523999
Peter M. Manos *(Mng Partner)*
Matthew L. Altman *(Mng Partner)*
Deneshea L. Phelps *(CFO & Chief Compliance Officer)*
Michael H. Lustbader *(Mng Partner)*
David C. Wodlinger *(Mng Partner)*
Bilal Noor *(VP)*
C. Malcolm Little *(Partner)*
Erica S. Son *(VP)*
Henry H. Albers *(VP)*
Gordon Auduong *(VP)*
Benjamin J. Raymundo *(VP)*

Subsidiaries:

Advanced Health Media, LLC (1)
420 Mountain Ave, New Providence, NJ 07974
Tel.: (908) 393-8700
Web Site: http://www.ahmdirect.com
Sales Range: $400-449.9 Million
Medical Communications & Marketing Services
N.A.I.C.S.: 519290
Kevin McMurtry *(Founder & Chm)*
Peter Collins *(Sr VP-Strategic Acct Mgmt-Global)*
Christine Croft *(CEO)*
Susan Hill *(Sr VP-Products & Solutions-Global)*
Karen Villarreal *(Sr VP-Product Delivery)*
Frank Spender *(CFO & Sr VP)*

AeroCision, LLC (1)
12A Inspiration Ln, Chester, CT 06412-1366
Tel.: (860) 526-9700
Web Site: http://www.aerocision.com
Aircraft Part & Auxiliary Equipment Mfr
N.A.I.C.S.: 336413

Avalign Technologies, Inc. (1)
2275 Half Day Rd Ste 126, Bannockburn, IL 60015
Tel.: (847) 457-5300
Web Site: http://www.avalign.com
Implants, Cutting & Precision Machined Surgical Instruments Mfr
N.A.I.C.S.: 339112
Forrest R. Whittaker *(CEO)*
Barbara Sullivan *(CFO)*
McNeil Brown *(VP-Sls & Mktg)*
Scott Gareiss *(VP-R&D & Bus Dev)*
Tony O'Neill *(Sr VP-Ops)*
Paul Rice *(VP-Quality Assurance & Regulatory Affairs)*
Gary Fromm *(VP-Cases & Trays Ops)*
Rick Link *(VP-Instruments & Implants Ops)*
Dave Cummings *(VP-Cutting Instruments Ops)*
Manfred Klingel *(Pres-German Specialty Instruments)*
Eric Graham *(VP-Sls & Mktg-German Specialty Instruments)*

Subsidiary (Domestic):

Avalign Cases & Trays (2)
2121 Southtech Dr Ste 600, Greenwood, IN 46143
Tel.: (317) 859-2300
Web Site: http://www.avaligntech.com
Metal & Theraformed Medical Cases & Trays Mfr
N.A.I.C.S.: 339112

Instrumed International, Inc. (2)
626 Cooper Ct, Schaumburg, IL 60173
Tel.: (847) 908-0292
Web Site: http://www.instrumedinc.biz
German Specialty Medical Instruments Mfr & Distr
N.A.I.C.S.: 339112

Millennium Surgical Corp (2)
822 Montgomery Ave Ste 205, Narberth, PA 19072
Tel.: (610) 771-0850
Web Site:
   http://www.surgicalinstruments.com
Surgical Instrument Distr
N.A.I.C.S.: 423450
Robert Edelstein *(Pres)*
Bill Kearns *(Dir-Sls)*

Thortex (2)
15045 NE Mason St, Portland, OR 97230-4357
Tel.: (503) 654-5726
Web Site: http://www.thortexinc.com
Metal Heat Treating
N.A.I.C.S.: 332811
David Walker *(Pres)*

Avenu Insights & Analytics LLC (1)
5860 Trinity Pkwy Ste 120, Centreville, VA 20120
Tel.: (800) 927-5125
Web Site: https://www.avenuinsights.com
Analytics & Administrative Solutions Provider
N.A.I.C.S.: 561110
Paul Colangelo *(CEO)*

Subsidiary (Domestic):

Grids Information Technologies, Inc. (2)
108 Exchange Pl Ste 210, Lafayette, LA 70503
Tel.: (337) 232-4470
Web Site: http://www.gridsinc.com
Electronics Stores
N.A.I.C.S.: 449210

Interware Development Company, Inc. (2)
22 Gregory St, Mont Vernon, NH 03057-1303
Web Site: http://www.interwaredev.com
Custom Computer Programming Services
N.A.I.C.S.: 541511
Nichole Sperry *(Product Mgr)*

BlueHalo, LLC (1)
410 Jan Davis Dr, Huntsville, AL 35806
Tel.: (256) 922-0802
Web Site: http://www.aegistg.com
Sales Range: $25-49.9 Million
Emp.: 325
Computer Modeling & Engineering Services
N.A.I.C.S.: 541330
Steve Hill *(Founder & Pres)*
Lance Cooper *(Exec VP-Corp Strategy)*
Del Beilstein *(VP-Bus Dev)*
Patrick M. Cannon *(VP-Ops-Western)*
Rodney Kreps *(CFO)*
Jonathan P. Moneymaker *(CEO)*
Patrick Markus *(Gen Mgr-Cyber & Intelligence)*
Vikram Manikonda *(CTO)*
Trip Ferguson *(COO)*
Mary Clum *(Exec VP & Gen Mgr-Product Innovation & Mfg)*
Mark McNeely *(Chief Admin Officer)*

Subsidiary (Non-US):

AEgis Simulation Technologies UK, Ltd. (2)
BCM Aegis, London, WC1N 3XX, United Kingdom
Tel.: (44) 7930174542
Web Site: http://www.aegistg.com
Sales Range: $10-24.9 Million
Emp.: 3
Computer Modeling & Engineering Services
N.A.I.C.S.: 541330
Mark Dumble *(Dir-Ops)*

Subsidiary (Domestic):

Asymmetrik, Ltd. (2)
300 Sentinel Dr Ste 210, Annapolis Junction, MD 20701-1058
Tel.: (301) 490-9569
Web Site: http://www.asymmetrik.com
Custom Computer Programming Services
N.A.I.C.S.: 541511
Mike Frentz *(Co-Founder & CEO)*
Amit Singh *(Co-Founder & CTO)*

Excivity, Inc. (2)
14020 Thunderbolt Pl Ste 100, Chantilly, VA 20151-3293
Tel.: (571) 267-4222
Web Site: http://www.excivity.com
Computer System Design Services
N.A.I.C.S.: 541512
Michael Parker *(Engr-Software)*

Verus Technology Group, Inc. (2)
20130 Lakeview Ctr Plz Ste 400, Ashburn, VA 20176-7837
Tel.: (703) 496-4264

Web Site:
   http://www.verustechnologygroup.com
Computer System Design Services
N.A.I.C.S.: 541512
John Abbey *(Founder & CEO)*

Cadence Aerospace, LLC (1)
3150 E Miraloma Ave, Anaheim, CA 92806
Tel.: (949) 877-3630
Web Site:
   http://www.cadenceaerospace.com
Aerospace Components & Assemblies Mfr
N.A.I.C.S.: 336413
Joyce Pae *(CFO)*
Maria M. Danburg *(Chief HR Officer)*
Nick Guerra *(CTO)*
Kevin W. Martin *(CIO)*
Jeff Capponi *(Sr VP-Sls & Mktg)*
Robert Saia *(Sr VP-Bus Dev)*
Olivier Jarrault *(CEO)*

Subsidiary (Domestic):

Arden Engineering, Inc. (2)
3130 E Miraloma Ave, Anaheim, CA 92806
Tel.: (714) 998-6410
Machined Aerospace Components & Assemblies Mfr
N.A.I.C.S.: 332999

Astro Spar, Inc. (2)
3130 E Miraloma Ave, Anaheim, CA 92806
Tel.: (714) 998-6410
Aircraft Parts & Auxiliary Equipment Mfr
N.A.I.C.S.: 336413

B&E Group, LLC (2)
10 Hudson Dr, Southwick, MA 01077
Tel.: (413) 569-5585
Web Site:
   http://www.beaerospacegroup.com
Precision Machined Components Mfr
N.A.I.C.S.: 811210
Vin Misciagna *(CEO)*
Bob Quaglia *(Pres & COO)*

Subsidiary (Domestic):

Safe Fuel Systems, Inc. (3)
860 W 84 St, Hialeah, FL 33004
Tel.: (954) 929-7233
Web Site: http://www.safefuelsystems.com
Other Airport Operations
N.A.I.C.S.: 488119
Rafael Fuentes *(Sr VP-Ops)*

Subsidiary (Domestic):

Giddens Industries (2)
2600 94th St SW Ste 150, Everett, WA 98204
Tel.: (425) 353-0405
Web Site: http://www.giddens.com
Precision Machining, Sheet Metal & Metal Forming Products
N.A.I.C.S.: 332322

Perfekta Inc. (2)
480 E 21st St N, Wichita, KS 67214
Tel.: (316) 263-2056
Web Site: http://www.perfekta-inc.com
Fabricated Metal Products Mfr
N.A.I.C.S.: 332999

Precision Machine Works, Inc. (2)
2024 Puyallup Ave, Tacoma, WA 98421
Tel.: (253) 272-5119
Web Site:
   http://www.cadenceaerospace.com
Machine Supplier Specializing in Complex Machine Parts & Assemblies
N.A.I.C.S.: 336413

Quality Forming, LLC (2)
22906 Frampton Ave, Torrance, CA 90501
Tel.: (310) 539-2855
Sheet Metal Products Used for Production of Aerospace Equipment Mfr
N.A.I.C.S.: 332322

Tell Tool, Inc. (2)
35 Turnpike Industrial Rd, Westfield, MA 01085
Tel.: (413) 568-1671
Aircraft Engine & Hydraulic Components Mfr
N.A.I.C.S.: 336412

CollabraSpace, Inc. (1)
306 Sentinel Dr Ste 350, Annapolis Junction, MD 20701

Tel.: (410) 224-4343
Web Site: https://www.collabraspace.com
Sales Range: $1-9.9 Million
Emp.: 70
Web-Based Collaboration Software Developer
N.A.I.C.S.: 513210
Ray Schwemmer *(Co-Founder, Pres & CEO)*
Chris Murphy *(Co-Founder & VP-Engrg)*
Rick Havrilla *(Founder & CTO)*
Shawn Davis *(COO)*

Daily Racing Form, Inc. (1)
708 3rd Ave Fl 12, New York, NY 10017-4129
Tel.: (212) 366-7600
Web Site: http://www.drf.com
Sports Magazine Publisher
N.A.I.C.S.: 513120
Brent Diamond *(CEO)*
Ben Cambra *(Sr VP-Bus Dev & Sponsorships)*
James Zenni *(Chm)*
Itay Fisher *(CTO)*
Jim Kostas *(Pres)*

Eqlipse Technologies (1)
2350 Corporate Park Dr Ste #110, Herndon, VA 20171
Tel.: (262) 827-4647
Web Site: https://www.eqlipsetechnologies.com
IT Consulting & Services
N.A.I.C.S.: 541690
Dennis Kelly *(CEO)*

Exostar LLC (1)
2325 Dulles Corner Blvd Ste 600, Herndon, VA 20171
Tel.: (703) 561-0500
Web Site: http://www.exostar.com
Cloud-Based IT Solutions
N.A.I.C.S.: 541512
Richard Addi *(Pres & CEO)*
Paul G. Kaminski *(Chm)*
Vijay Takanti *(VP-Security & Collaboration Solutions)*
Doug Russell *(VP-Bus Solutions)*
Patrick Kannan *(CFO)*
Dipto Chakravarty *(CTO)*
Venencia Magnusen *(VP-HR)*
Mike Castle *(VP-Sls & Mktg)*

Subsidiary (Non-US):

Pirean Ltd. (2)
Faretec Cams Hall Estate, Fareham, PO16 8UY, Hampshire, United Kingdom
Tel.: (44) 8452260542
Web Site: http://www.pirean.com
Sales Range: $10-24.9 Million
Emp.: 66
IT Services
N.A.I.C.S.: 541512

Forged Solutions Group, Ltd (1)
Dale Rd N Darly Dale, Matlock, DE4 2JB, Derbyshire, United Kingdom
Tel.: (44) 1142193000
Web Site:
   https://www.forgedsolutionsgroup.com
Sales Range: $50-74.9 Million
Emp.: 350
Automotive & Aircraft Forged Metal Product Mfr
N.A.I.C.S.: 331318

Subsidiary (US):

Continental Forge Company (2)
412 E El Segundo Blvd, Compton, CA 90222-2399
Tel.: (310) 603-1014
Web Site: https://www.cforge.com
Sales Range: $50-74.9 Million
Emp.: 130
Provider of Aluminum Forgings
N.A.I.C.S.: 332112
Margaret A. Haueisen *(CFO)*
Stan Curtis *(Treas, Sec & Controller)*

Steel Industries Inc. (2)
12600 Beech Daly Rd, Redford, MI 48239-2455
Tel.: (313) 534-2165
Web Site: https://www.steel-industries.com
Iron & Steel Forging
N.A.I.C.S.: 332111
Guy Williams *(Dir-IT)*

Arlington Capital Partners LLC—(Continued)

Integrated Data Services, Inc. (1)
4151 Rosecrans Blvd Ste 2, El Segundo, CA 90245
Tel.: (310) 416-9898
Web Site: http://www.get-integrated.com
Sales Range: $1-9.9 Million
Emp.: 100
Custom Computer Programming Services
N.A.I.C.S.: 541511
Ellie Castro-Bordano (Mgr)
Rick Tiffin (Reg Dir)
James Truhe (CEO)

Intelesys Corporation (1)
6797 Dorsey Rd Ste 5, Elkridge, MD 21075
Tel.: (410) 540-9755
Web Site: http://www.intelesyscorp.com
Sales Range: $1-9.9 Million
Emp.: 50
Computer System Design Services
N.A.I.C.S.: 541512

Intellectual Technology, Inc. (1)
1901 Camino Vida Roble Ste 204, Carlsbad, CA 92008
Tel.: (800) 488-2774
Web Site: http://www1.iti4dmv.com
Hardware & Software System Integration Solutions
N.A.I.C.S.: 513210
Craig Litchin (CEO)
Drew Nicholson (COO)
John Low (CFO)
Von Swalley (VP-Sls)
Byron Thomas (Dir-Bus Dev)

Keel Holdings, LLC (1)
9801 US-78 Building 1, Ladson, SC 29456
Tel.: (843) 737-9900
Web Site: https://keelusa.com
Steel Fabrication Services
N.A.I.C.S.: 238120
Brian Carter (CEO)

Subsidiary (Domestic):

Metal Trades, LLC (2)
4194 Hwy 165, Hollywood, SC 29449
Tel.: (843) 889-6441
Web Site: http://www.metaltrades.com
Sales Range: $100-124.9 Million
Emp.: 200
Provider of Building & Repair of Combat Vessels, Crew Boats, Dredges & Troop Transport Vessels
N.A.I.C.S.: 332322
Krist Rowe (Mgr-HR)

Pegasus Steel, LLC (2)
1 Alliance Dr, Goose Creek, SC 29445
Tel.: (843) 737-9900
Web Site: http://www.pegasussteel.com
Sales Range: $1-9.9 Million
Emp.: 68
Steel Fabrication Services
N.A.I.C.S.: 331110
Anthony Deering (Founder & CEO)
Portia Sisk (VP-HR)
John Mei (VP-Fin)

MCR, LLC (1)
2010 Corporate Rdg Ste 350, McLean, VA 22102-7853
Tel.: (703) 506-4600
Web Site: http://www.mcri.com
Sales Range: $10-24.9 Million
Emp.: 60
Integrated Program Management Services; Consulting Services
N.A.I.C.S.: 541512
Chris Neubauer (Sr VP-Corp Ops)
Michael P. Galvin (Chm)
Jason Dechoretz (Chief Strategy Officer & Sr VP)
John Cochran (Sr VP-Bus Dev)
Karen Bertha (Chief Ethics & Compliance Officer)
Ken Newcomer (Sr VP-Bus Dev)
Bill Parker (Pres & CEO)

Micron Technologies, Inc. (1)
333 Phoenixville Pike, Malvern, PA 19355
Tel.: (610) 251-7400
Web Site: http://www.microntech.com
Sales Range: $25-49.9 Million
Emp.: 55
Particle Size Reduction & Analytical Contract Services

N.A.I.C.S.: 541990
Kathleen Donelly (Gen Mgr)

Numet Machining Techniques, LLC (1)
235 Edison Rd, Orange, CT 06477
Tel.: (203) 375-4995
Web Site: http://www.numet.net
Jet Turbine Engine Parts & Assemblies Mfr
N.A.I.C.S.: 336412
Mark Roscio (VP-Sls)
Joseph Sartori (COO)
Tim Ulles (Pres & CEO)

Octo Consulting Group, Inc. (1)
10780 Parkridge Blvd 4th Fl, Reston, VA 20191
Tel.: (571) 423-0200
Web Site: http://www.octoconsulting.com
Sales Range: $10-24.9 Million
Emp.: 25
Management & Technical Consulting
N.A.I.C.S.: 541611
Mehul Sanghani (Founder & CEO)
Jay Shah (COO)
Greg Nowak (Dir-Contracts)
Mike Raymond (Chief Strategy Officer)
Sujey Edward (CTO)
Tom Lee (Sr VP-Natl Security Bus)
Ethan Meurlin (VP-Mktg & Corp Partnerships)
Simon Godwin (VP-Federal Civilian Programs)
Craig Summers (VP-Commerce Accts)
Harold Poston (VP-Defense Accts)
Jim Vant (Exec VP-Defense & Intelligence)
Sam Stollar (Sr VP-Intelligence Programs)
Cynthia Walker (VP-Data Center of Excellence)

Subsidiary (Domestic):

Connexta, LLC (2)
1860 N 95th Ln Ste 325, Phoenix, AZ 85037
Tel.: (602) 714-1459
Custom Computer Programming Services
N.A.I.C.S.: 541511

Sevatec, Inc. (2)
2815 Oddley Hwy, Fairfax, VA 22031
Tel.: (571) 766-1300
Web Site: http://www.sevatec.com
Sales Range: $25-49.9 Million
Emp.: 120
Business Consulting Services
N.A.I.C.S.: 541618
Joan Moret (VP-HR)
Sonny Kakar (Founder & CEO)
Balan R. Ayyar (Pres)
Richard J. Roth (CFO)
Aslam Nawabzada (CTO)
Angela Butler (VP-Bus Dev-Federal Civilian Practice)
Chris Cole (Sr VP-DHS & Natl Intelligence)
Angela Leno (VP-Internal Ops)
Steven Smith (Sr VP-Federal Civilian Programs)
Tim May (Chief Growth Oficer & Exec VP)
Steve Schefer (VP-Bus Dev)
Troy Holmes (VP)

PlattForm Advertising, Inc. (1)
15500 W 113 Ste 200, Lenexa, KS 66219
Tel.: (913) 254-6000
Web Site: http://www.plattformad.com
Sales Range: $25-49.9 Million
Advetising Agency
N.A.I.C.S.: 541810
Michael D. Platt (Founder & Chm)
Dave Admire (Pres & Chief Integrity Officer)
Steve Booth (Chief Culture Officer)
Brad Gibbs (Chief Growth Officer)
John VanFleet (Chief Interactive Officer)
Tracy Kreikemeier (CMO)
Mike McHugh (Grp Pres-Integrated Mktg)
Jai B. Shankar (CTO)
Justin Gill (Chief Media Officer & Chief Analytics Officer)
Aaron Edwards (VP-Bus Dev)
Stephen C. Fireng (CEO)

Quantum Spatial, Inc. (1)
10033 MLK St N Ste 200, Saint Petersburg, FL 33716
Tel.: (920) 457-3631
Web Site: http://www.quantumspatial.com
Emp.: 600
Photogrammetry & Geospatial Data Solutions

N.A.I.C.S.: 541360
Peter Manos (Chm)
Peter LaMontagne (Pres & CEO)
Mark Abatto (CFO)
Anand Iyer (Sr VP-Products & Mktg)
Mark Meade (Sr VP-Shared Svcs)
Russ Faux (Sr VP-Growth Initiatives)

Radius Aerospace, Inc. (1)
153 Extrusion Pl, Hot Springs, AR 71901
Tel.: (501) 321-9325
Aerospace Forming & Fabricating Business
N.A.I.C.S.: 423860
Tony Johnson (CEO)
Chris Blair (Head-Bus Dev)
Beverly Joe (VP-HR)

Subsidiary (Non-US):

Radius Aerospace UK Ltd. (2)
Whitchurch Road, Shrewsbury, SY1 4DP, Shropshire, United Kingdom
Tel.: (0) 1743454300
Web Site: http://www.doncasters.com
Aerospace Gas Turbine Components Mfr
N.A.I.C.S.: 336412

Subsidiary (Domestic):

Radius Aerospace, Inc. - Shelbyville (2)
850 Elston Dr, Shelbyville, IN 46176-1823
Tel.: (317) 398-6684
Web Site: http://radiusaerospace.com
Sheet Metal Parts Mfr
N.A.I.C.S.: 332812

Triumph Fabrications-Fort Worth, Inc. (2)
7445 E Lancaster Ave, Fort Worth, TX 76112
Tel.: (817) 451-0620
Web Site: http://radiusaerospace.com
Metal & Composite Aircraft Component Mfr
N.A.I.C.S.: 332710

Triumph Fabrications-San Diego, Inc. (2)
203 N Johnson Ave, El Cajon, CA 92020-3111
Tel.: (619) 440-2504
Web Site: http://radiusaerospace.com
Sheet Metal Assemblies Mfr
N.A.I.C.S.: 336412

Riverpoint Medical, LLC (1)
825 NE 25th Ave, Portland, OR 97232
Tel.: (503) 517-8001
Web Site: http://www.rpmed.com
Medical, Dental & Hospital Equipment & Supplies Merchant Whslr
N.A.I.C.S.: 423450

Systems Planning and Analysis, Inc. (1)
2001 N Beauregard St, Alexandria, VA 22311
Tel.: (703) 931-3500
Web Site: https://spa.com
Security Business Solutions Services
N.A.I.C.S.: 561499
Michelle Howell (Chief HR Officer)
David C. Wodlinger (Chm)
Rich Sawchak (CEO)
Andrew Pahutski (VP-Economic Security Programs)

Tex-Tech Industries, Inc. (1)
1 City Ctr 11th Fl, Portland, ME 04101
Tel.: (207) 756-8606
Web Site: http://www.textechindustries.com
Specialty Materials Mfr & Distr
N.A.I.C.S.: 339999
Ciaran F. Lynch (Pres & CEO)
Ben Havey (Sls Mgr-Aerospace)
Chris Fritch (Mgr-Sls & Seat Fire Blocking)
Chris Spencer (Dir-Safety & Composites)
Edward Bower (Dir-Quality & Tech)
Eoin Lynch (Exec Dir-Sls & Mktg)
Lee Hubley (Dir-Weaving)
Moe Maheux (Dir-Ops)
Stephen Rogers (Mng Dir-Thailand)
John Stankiewicz (CFO & COO)
Seamus Mulrooney (Dir-Sls-Europe)
Sean Goggin (Controller)
Steve Judge (Exec VP)
Vincent Gallacher (Dir-Global Tech)
Simone Ryle (Mgr-Customer Svc)
Tim Cashell (Dir-Protective Markets)
Jack Woolston (Mgr-Filtration Technical Sls)

Scott Janco (Engr-Ballistic Product Dev)
Simon Walker (Mgr-Technical)
Jake Hirschi (Gen Mgr-CarbonX)
Jeremy Parkinson (Fin Dir)
David Parente (Engr-New Product Dev)
James J. Stahl (Engr-R&D)

Tyto Athene, LLC (1)
510 Spring St Ste 200, Herndon, VA 20170
Tel.: (703) 885-7900
Web Site: http://gotyto.com
Information Technology & Services
N.A.I.C.S.: 541512
John West (VP-Bus Dev & Strategy)
Dan Smith (CTO)
Carl Tegen (Sr VP)
Bill Lantzy (Sr VP)
Hector Pelayo (VP-Air & Space Forces)
Jeff Wolfe (VP-Integration Mgmt Office)
Peter O'Donoghue (CTO)
Dennis Kelly (CEO)

Subsidiary (Domestic):

AT&T Government Solutions, Inc. (2)
1900 Gallows Rd, Vienna, VA 22182
Tel.: (703) 506-5000
Web Site: http://www.att.com
Integrated & Network-Enabled Information Technology Services
N.A.I.C.S.: 541690

Subsidiary (Domestic):

AT&T Alascom (3)
505 E Bluff Dr, Anchorage, AK 99501　　　　　　(100%)
Tel.: (907) 264-7000
Sales Range: $150-199.9 Million
Emp.: 300
Telecommunications, Cable Television & Internet Services
N.A.I.C.S.: 517410

AT&T Technical Services Company (3)
1900 Gallows Rd, Vienna, VA 22182　　　　　　(100%)
Tel.: (703) 506-5000
Web Site: http://www.att.com
Sales Range: $10-24.9 Million
On-Site Telecommunications Consulting Services
N.A.I.C.S.: 541690

Subsidiary (Domestic):

Microtel LLC (2)
7703 Belle Point Dr, Greenbelt, MD 20770-3300
Tel.: (452) 020-7703
Web Site: http://www.microtel-llc.com
Research & Development in the Physical, Engineering & Life Sciences
N.A.I.C.S.: 541715
Kevin Phillips (Engr-Software)
Jerry Hengemihle (CEO)

Virgo Publishing, LLC (1)
3300 N Central Ave Ste 300, Phoenix, AZ 85012
Tel.: (480) 990-1101
Web Site: http://www.vpico.com
Trade Magazine Publisher
N.A.I.C.S.: 513120
John Siefert (CEO)
Sabrina Wolf (Dir-HR)
Jon Benninger (VP-Health & Nutrition Network)
Jose Copado (CIO)
Danica Cullins (VP-Sls, Health & Nutrition Networks)
Danielle Dunlap (VP-Mktg Svcs)
John Lybarger (CTO)
Kelly Ridley (CFO & Exec VP)

ARLINGTON COAL & LUMBER CO. INC.
41 Pk Ave, Arlington, MA 02476-4114
Tel.: (781) 643-8100　　　　　　MA
Web Site: http://www.arlcoal.com
Year Founded: 1962
Sales Range: $25-49.9 Million
Emp.: 27
Lumber & Other Building Materials
N.A.I.C.S.: 423310
Robert W. McNamara (Pres & Treas)

Subsidiaries:

Chelmsford Lumber Company   (1)
201 Boston Rd, Chelmsford, MA 01824
Tel.: (978) 244-0222
Lumber Distr
N.A.I.C.S.: 423310

Sudbury Lumber Company Inc.   (1)
28 Union Ave, Sudbury, MA 01776-2247
Tel.: (978) 443-1680
Web Site: http://www.sudburylumber.com
Sales Range: $10-24.9 Million
Emp.: 21
Distribution of Lumber , Plywood & Millwork
N.A.I.C.S.: 423310

Wilmington Builders Supply Company Inc.   (1)
334 Main St, Wilmington, MA 01887-2725
Tel.: (978) 658-4621
Web Site: http://www.wilmbuild.com
Sales Range: $10-24.9 Million
Emp.: 25
Selling Lumber & Other Building Materials
N.A.I.C.S.: 423310

ARLINGTON COMPUTER PRODUCTS

851 Commerce Ct, Buffalo Grove, IL 60089
Tel.: (847) 541-6333
Web Site: http://www.arlingtoncp.com
Sales Range: $75-99.9 Million
Emp.: 40
Computers, Peripherals & Software
N.A.I.C.S.: 423430
Arlington A. Guenther (CEO)
Mark Buchek (VP-Ops)
John Callaghan (Gen Mgr)
Scott Dunsire (Pres)

ARLINGTON CONTACT LENS SERVICE, INC.

4265 Diplomacy Dr, Columbus, OH 43228
Tel.: (614) 921-9892
Web Site: http://www.aclens.com
Year Founded: 1995
Sales Range: $25-49.9 Million
Emp.: 53
Contact Lens Sales
N.A.I.C.S.: 456130
Peter Clarkson (Founder, Pres & CEO)
Philip Dietrich (CTO)

ARLINGTON INDUSTRIES INC.

1 Stauffer Industrial Park, Scranton, PA 18517
Tel.: (570) 562-0270
Web Site: https://www.aifittings.com
Sales Range: $50-74.9 Million
Emp.: 320
Electronic Products Mfr
N.A.I.C.S.: 335932
Don Ambrose (Dir-Sls & Mktg)
Joe Sullivan (VP-Ops)
Steven Finnerty (Mgr-Engrg)
Stephen Hayes (Mgr-South)
Jim Cortese (Natl Sls Mgr)
Ray Barnes (Treas & VP)
Elizabeth Stark (Chm)

ARLINGTON METALS CORPORATION

11355 Franklin Ave, Franklin Park, IL 60131
Tel.: (847) 451-9100
Web Site: https://www.arlingtonmetals.com
Year Founded: 1971
Sales Range: $100-124.9 Million
Emp.: 150
Steel
N.A.I.C.S.: 423510
Bonnie Wener (Controller)

ARLINGTON RACK & PACKAGING CO.

6120 N Detroit Ave, Toledo, OH 43612
Tel.: (419) 476-7700
Web Site: http://www.racksandpackaging.com
Sales Range: $10-24.9 Million
Emp.: 9
Manufacture Motor Vehicle Parts & Accessories
N.A.I.C.S.: 336390

ARLINGTON RESOURCES, INC.

4902 Tollview Dr, Rolling Meadows, IL 60008
Tel.: (224) 232-5900
Web Site: http://www.arlingtonresources.com
Year Founded: 1997
Rev.: $6,000,000
Emp.: 25
Employment Placement Agencies
N.A.I.C.S.: 561311
Patricia Casey (Pres)
Denise Young (Dir-Sls & Recruiting)

ARLINGTON SALVAGE & WRECKER CO.

3261 Phillips Hwy, Jacksonville, FL 32207
Tel.: (904) 744-4933
Web Site: http://www.arlingtonwrecker.com
Sales Range: $10-24.9 Million
Emp.: 30
Trucking Service
N.A.I.C.S.: 484121
Corey Phelps (Mgr)

ARLINGTON TOMORROW FOUNDATION

PO Box 90231 MS 29-0100, Arlington, TX 76004-3231
Tel.: (817) 459-6419   TX
Web Site: http://www.arlingtonfoundation.org
Year Founded: 2007
Sales Range: $10-24.9 Million
Community Development Program Services
N.A.I.C.S.: 923120
Charlie Parker (Sec)
Carolyn Mentesana (Exec Dir)
Robert Shephard (Vice Pres)
Jimmy Bennett (Treas)
W. Jeff Williams (Pres)

ARLUN FLOOR COVERINGS INC.

6250 Corporate Dr, Colorado Springs, CO 80919
Tel.: (719) 599-4175
Web Site: https://www.arlun.com
Sales Range: $25-49.9 Million
Emp.: 80
Sales of Floor Coverings
N.A.I.C.S.: 423220
Steve Hoppe (Pres & CEO)

ARM NATIONAL FOOD INC.

1546 Lamberton Rd, Trenton, NJ 08611
Tel.: (609) 394-0431
Rev.: $13,767,877
Emp.: 18
Groceries, General Line
N.A.I.C.S.: 424410
Armando Rienzi (Pres)

ARMA GLOBAL CORP.

2701 N Rocky Point Dr Ste 1150, Tampa, FL 33607
Tel.: (866) 554-9333

Web Site: http://www.arma-global.com
Sales Range: $150-199.9 Million
Emp.: 800
Professional, Defense, Peacekeeping & Systems Integration Services
N.A.I.C.S.: 541611
Todd Schweitzer (CEO)
James Fugit (Pres)
Brian Overstreet (COO)

ARMADA ENTERPRISES, LP

40 Wall St 28th Fl, New York, NY 10005
Tel.: (646) 483-9671   DE
Year Founded: 2014
Liabilities: $1,052,890
Net Worth: $1,052,890
Earnings: ($2,367,025)
Fiscal Year-end: 12/31/17
Investment Services
N.A.I.C.S.: 523999

ARMADA GROUP, LTD.

645 Alpha Dr., Pittsburgh, PA 15238
Tel.: (412) 406-5700   PA
Web Site: https://www.armada.net
Year Founded: 1909
Emp.: 1,000
Offices of Other Holding Companies
N.A.I.C.S.: 551112
John Burke (Chm)

Subsidiaries:

Armada Supply Chain Solutions, LLC   (1)
641 Alpha Dr, Pittsburgh, PA 15238
Tel.: (412) 406-5700
Web Site: http://www.armada.net
Logistics & Warehousing Services
N.A.I.C.S.: 493110
Joseph Dominijanni (CEO)
Joseph Dominijanni (CEO)

Subsidiary (Domestic):

ATEC Systems, Ltd.   (2)
650 Northlake Blvd, Altamonte Springs, FL 32701
Tel.: (407) 740-5565
Web Site: https://www.atecsystems.com
Sales Range: $1-9.9 Million
Emp.: 35
Freight Transportation Arrangement
N.A.I.C.S.: 488510
Donald Krueger (Principal)
Dylan Denicola (Dir-Info Sys)
Martha Paez (Mgr-Customer Svc & Logistics)

Sunset Transportation, LLC   (1)
10877 Watson Rd, Saint Louis, MO 63127
Tel.: (314) 849-0685
Web Site: https://www.sunsettrans.com
Sales Range: $25-49.9 Million
Emp.: 47
Freight Transportation Arrangement
N.A.I.C.S.: 488510
Tracy Meetre (Chief Comml Officer)
Lindsey Williams (Pres & CEO)
Mark Cammarata (CFO)
James Williams (Founder, Chm & CEO)
Mick McGrory (COO)
Lindsey Graves (VP-Ops)
Mick McGrory (VP)
Jill Gross (VP-Strategic Accts)
Craig Marton (Pres & COO)
Mark Cammarata (CFO)
Tracy Meetre (Chief Comml Officer)

ARMADA MATERIALS, LLC

442 W. Kennedy Blvd., Ste 300, Tampa, FL 33606
Tel.: (813) 588-3250
Web Site: https://armadamaterials.com
Year Founded: 2022
Emp.: 100
Construction Industry
N.A.I.C.S.: 236210
Rob Duke (Founder & CEO)

Subsidiaries:

Wright Paving Contractors Inc   (1)
372 Shelbyville Hwy, Fayetteville, TN 37334
Tel.: (931) 433-7938
Rev.: $7,000,000
Emp.: 8
Highway, Street & Bridge Construction
N.A.I.C.S.: 237310
Tommy Wright (Pres)
Grad Wright (Ops Mgr)

ARMADA NANO TECHNOLOGIES GROUP INC.

48-51 Oceania St, Bayside, NY 11364
Tel.: (917) 582-0011   NV
Web Site: http://www.armada-battery.com
Year Founded: 2017
Nano Silicon Battery Distr
N.A.I.C.S.: 423610
David Champ (Pres, CEO & CFO)
Catherine Wang (Sec)

ARMADA WATER ASSETS, INC.

2425 Fountain View Dr Ste 300, Houston, TX 77057
Tel.: (832) 804-8312   NV
Web Site: http://www.armadawater.com
Year Founded: 2012
Sales Range: $10-24.9 Million
Emp.: 147
Water Supply, Treatment & Disposal
N.A.I.C.S.: 221310
Mitch Burroughs (VP-Corp Dev)
Richard Schaeffer (Chm)
Maarten Propper (Pres & CEO)
Oliver Laurence (VP-Innovation & Engrg)
Lee Washington (Regional Mgr-West Texas)
Zach Donaldson (Regional Mgr-Colorado/Utah)

ARMADALE CAPITAL INC.

99 Madison Ave Ste 608, New York, NY 10016
Tel.: (646) 430-5748
Web Site: http://www.armadalecapital.com
Year Founded: 2008
Sales Range: $1-9.9 Million
Emp.: 2
Financial Services to Healthcare Industries
N.A.I.C.S.: 525990
Stephen R. Pack (Pres)

ARMADILLO CONSTRUCTION COMPANY, LTD.

119 Tranquilo Dr, Laredo, TX 78045
Tel.: (956) 724-1811
Rev.: $43,942,479
Emp.: 40
Single-Family Home Remodeling, Additions & Repairs
N.A.I.C.S.: 811411
Robert Gutierrez (CEO)
Jeffrey J. Czar (COO)
Brian Nanney (Dir-Construction)

ARMADILLO ENTERPRISES, INC.

4924 W Waters Ave, Tampa, FL 33634
Tel.: (813) 600-3920
Web Site: https://www.armadilloent.com
Year Founded: 1994
Sales Range: $1-9.9 Million
Emp.: 50
Musical Instruments Mfr & Distr
N.A.I.C.S.: 339992
Jeff McDonald (Mgr-Warehouse)

Armaly Sponge Company, Inc.—(Continued)

ARMALY SPONGE COMPANY, INC.
1900 Easy St, Walled Lake, MI 48390
Tel.: (248) 669-2100   MI
Web Site:
https://www.armalybrands.com
Year Founded: 1973
Plastics Product Mfr
N.A.I.C.S.: 326199
Ann Armaly (Treas)

Subsidiaries:

Acme Sponge Company   (1)
855 E Pine St, Tarpon Springs, FL 34689
Tel.: (727) 937-3222
Web Site: http://www.acmesponge.com
Chamois Leather
N.A.I.C.S.: 316110
Jim Cantonis (Pres)
Stephen Heller (Exec VP)

ARMANINO LLP
12657 Alcosta Blvd Ste 500, San Ramon, CA 94583
Tel.: (925) 790-2600
Web Site:
https://www.armaninollp.com
Year Founded: 1969
Sales Range: $100-124.9 Million
Emp.: 260
Accounting & Business Consulting Services
N.A.I.C.S.: 541211
Brad Cless (Partner-In-Charge-Tax)
Thomas E. Gard (Partner)
Tom Mescall (Partner-Consulting)
Lori Colvin (CMO & Partner)
David Davis (Partner)
Daniel Bowen (Partner)
Theresa Brown (Partner)
Dave Burlington (Partner)
John Dunican (Partner)
Ricardo Martinez (Partner)
Josh Nevarez (Partner)
Monika Pelz (Partner)
Matthew Perreault (Partner)
Jeremy Sucharski (Partner)
Kevin Wise (Partner)
Larry Hancock (Partner & VP-AMF Medical Grp)
Chris Carlberg (Gen Counsel/Partner-San Ramon))

ARMANINO LLP
12657 Alcosta Blvd Ste 500, San Ramon, CA 94583-4406
Tel.: (604) 428-8834
Web Site:
http://www.amfmediagroup.com
Year Founded: 2007
Advertising & Public Relations Agency
N.A.I.C.S.: 541810
Oshi Jauco (Grp Acct Dir)
Michael Clinebell (Sr Dir-Content Svcs)
Jeffery Davis (Sls Dir-Natl)
Larry Hancock (VP)
Joe Lopez (Creative Dir)
Peggy Spear (Dir-Editorial)
Bill Hattox (Partner)
Matt Armanino (CEO & Mng Partner)
Carolyn Bremer (Partner-Consulting-Dallas)
Darice Chan (Partner-Tax-San Francisco)
Matt Gard (Partner-Audit)
Jonathan March (Partner-Tax-Dallas)
Chris Mays (Partner-Bus Mgmt-Los Angeles)
Ryan Prindiville (Partner-Consulting)
Scott Schwartz (Partner-Consulting-San Francisco)

Carol Ann Nash (Chief People Officer)
Maggie Cox (Pres)
Dave Cox (VP)

Subsidiaries:

Barnett Cox & Associates   (1)
711 Tank Farm Rd Ste 210, San Luis Obispo, CA 93401
Tel.: (805) 545-8887
Emp.: 20
Advertising Agencies
N.A.I.C.S.: 541810
Maggie Cox (Founder)

ARMATRON INTERNATIONAL, INC.
15 Highland Ave, Malden, MA 02148
Tel.: (781) 321-2300
Web Site: https://www.flowtron.com
Year Founded: 1920
Sales Range: $150-199.9 Million
Emp.: 75
Electronic Pesticide & Lawn & Garden Power Equipment Mfr
N.A.I.C.S.: 333992
Charles J. Housman (Chm, Pres & Treas)
Jerry Cassealno (VP-Sls & Mktg)

Subsidiaries:

Flowtron Outdoor Products   (1)
15 Highland Ave, Malden, MA 02148   (100%)
Tel.: (781) 321-2300
Web Site: http://www.flowtron.com
Sales Range: $50-74.9 Million
Emp.: 55
Electronic Pesticide & Lawn & Garden Power Equipment Mfr
N.A.I.C.S.: 561710
Jerry Casselano (VP-Sls & Mktg)
Charles Housman (Pres)

ARMCO METALS HOLDINGS, INC.
1730 S Amphlett Blvd 230, San Mateo, CA 94402
Tel.: (650) 212-7620   NV
Web Site:
http://www.armcometals.com
Year Founded: 2001
Sales Range: $100-124.9 Million
Metal Ores & Non-Ferrous Metals Distr
N.A.I.C.S.: 423510
Kexuan Yao (Chm & CEO)
Fengtao Wen (CFO)

Subsidiaries:

Armco Metals (Shanghai) Holdings, Ltd.   (1)
Room 808 Aetna Tower No 107 Zunyi Road, Shanghai, 200051, China
Tel.: (86) 2162375286
Web Site: http://www.armcometals.com
Investment Management Service
N.A.I.C.S.: 523940

Henan Armco & Metawise Trading Co., Ltd.   (1)
Room 1706 A Jincheng International Plaza No 66 Jingsan Road, Zhengzhou, 450008, China
Tel.: (86) 37165861171
Web Site: http://www.armcometals.com
Metal Ore Mining Services
N.A.I.C.S.: 212290

ARMED FORCES COMMUNICATIONS, INC.
151 W 26th St 12th Fl, New York, NY 10001
Tel.: (646) 571-2600
Web Site:
http://www.refuelagency.com
Advertising Services
N.A.I.C.S.: 541810
Derek White (Pres & CEO)

Subsidiaries:

Armed Forces Communications, Inc. - Cranbury   (1)
10 Abeel Rd, Cranbury, NJ 08512
Tel.: (609) 655-8878
Emp.: 203
Advertising Agencies
N.A.I.C.S.: 541613
Chris Cassino (COO)

ARMED FORCES INSURANCE EXCHANGE
550 Eisenhower Rd, Leavenworth, KS 66048
Tel.: (913) 727-5500
Web Site: http://www.afi.org
Year Founded: 1982
Sales Range: $25-49.9 Million
Emp.: 220
Management Services
N.A.I.C.S.: 561110
Arlen Briggs (Pres & CEO)
Stanley E. Clarke III (Chm)

ARMEDIA LLC
2000 Riveredge Pkwy Ste 775, Atlanta, GA 30328
Tel.: (678) 945-4417
Web Site: http://www.armedia.com
Year Founded: 2002
Sales Range: $10-24.9 Million
Emp.: 15
Custom Computer Programming Services
N.A.I.C.S.: 541511
Jim Nasr (CEO)
John Shinnick (CTO)
James Bailey (Pres & CFO)
Vicentee Ferguson (VP-Federal Svcs)

ARMELLINI INDUSTRIES, INC.
3446 SW Armellini Ave, Palm City, FL 34990-8129
Tel.: (772) 287-0575   FL
Web Site: https://www.armellini.com
Year Founded: 1984
Sales Range: $75-99.9 Million
Emp.: 1,000
Flower Trucking Services
N.A.I.C.S.: 484121
Jules Armellini (Chm)
Richard Armellini (Pres-California Div)
David Armellini (Pres)

Subsidiaries:

Armellini Air Express, Inc.   (1)
2811 NW 74th Ave, Miami, FL 33122
Tel.: (305) 468-8745
Web Site: http://www.armellini.com
Air Freight Transportation Services
N.A.I.C.S.: 481212
Carlos Velarde (Gen Mgr)

Armellini Express Lines Inc.   (1)
3446 SW Armellini Ave, Palm City, FL 34990-8129
Tel.: (772) 287-0575
Web Site: http://www.armellini.com
Sales Range: $25-49.9 Million
Emp.: 650
Non-Local Trucking
N.A.I.C.S.: 484121
James Kraft (Controller)
Coraly Ramos (Coord-Sls & Mktg)
Eric McManis (Dir-IT)
Mark Sterling (Dir-Terminal Ops)
Maria Morgan (Mgr-Admin)
Michael Thomas (Mgr-Help Desk & Comm)
Conrado Lopez (Mgr-JAF Dispatch & Maintenace)
Judy Dusharm (VP)
David Armellini (Pres)

JA Flowers Services Inc.   (1)
2003 NW 70th Ave, Miami, FL 33122-1811
Tel.: (305) 592-5198
Sales Range: $10-24.9 Million
Emp.: 35
Freight Transportation Arrangement
N.A.I.C.S.: 488510

North Star Transportation Inc.   (1)
2811 NW 74th Ave, Miami, FL 33122-1423   (100%)
Tel.: (305) 592-7008
Web Site: http://www.armellini.com
Sales Range: $10-24.9 Million
Emp.: 12
Non-Local Trucking
N.A.I.C.S.: 484121
Enrique Lima (Gen Mgr)

ARMEN CADILLAC
1441 Ridge Pike, Plymouth Meeting, PA 19462-2725
Tel.: (484) 751-9178
Web Site:
https://www.armencadillac.com
Sales Range: $10-24.9 Million
Emp.: 50
Car Whslr
N.A.I.C.S.: 441110
Cynthia Artz (Chm)

ARMET ALARM & ELECTRONICS INC.
424 W Colorado St Ste 200A, Glendale, CA 91204-4817
Tel.: (818) 242-0022
Web Site:
http://www.armetalarm.com
Year Founded: 1983
Electrical Apparatus & Equipment, Wiring Supplies & Related Equipment Merchant Whslr
N.A.I.C.S.: 423610
Souren Achemian (Mgr)

Subsidiaries:

San Fernando Valley Alarm, Inc.   (1)
8111 San Fernando Rd, Sun Valley, CA 91352
Tel.: (818) 787-0999
Web Site: http://www.valleyalarm.com
Sales Range: $1-9.9 Million
Emp.: 20
Electronic Security Services
N.A.I.C.S.: 561621
Bob Michel (Pres)

ARMINTOOL MANUFACTURING & ARMIN MOLD CORPORATION
1500 N LaFox St, South Elgin, IL 60177
Tel.: (847) 742-1864
Web Site: https://www.armin-ind.com
Sales Range: $10-24.9 Million
Emp.: 80
Injection Molding
N.A.I.C.S.: 333514
Paul Stoll (Pres)

ARMISTEAD MECHANICAL INC.
168 Hopper Ave, Waldwick, NJ 07463
Tel.: (201) 447-6740
Web Site:
https://www.armisteadmechanics.com
Year Founded: 1956
Sales Range: $10-24.9 Million
Emp.: 50
Provider of Mechanical Contracting Services
N.A.I.C.S.: 238220
Robert T. Armistead (Pres & CEO)
Chris Vavrinec (Project Mgr)
Steve Wanderling (Project Mgr)

ARMON INC.
2265 Carlson Dr, Northbrook, IL 60062
Tel.: (847) 498-4800
Sales Range: $125-149.9 Million
Emp.: 125
Holding Company; Warm Air Heating & Air Conditioning Contractor
N.A.I.C.S.: 551112

Joseph Larson *(CFO)*
Brian Moran *(CEO)*

Subsidiaries:

F.E. Moran **(1)**
2265 Carlson Dr, Northbrook, IL 60062
Tel.: (847) 498-4800
Web Site: http://www.femoran.com
Service & Maintenance for Mechanical Systems, Plumbing, Fire Protection Systems & Security Systems
N.A.I.C.S.: 238220
Brian Moran *(CEO)*
Joseph Larson *(CFO)*

ARMOR DESIGNS, INC.

2500 N 24th St, Phoenix, AZ 85008
Tel.: (602) 275-4633   DE
Web Site:
    http://www.armordesigns.com
Rev.: $97,494
Assets: $2,974,051
Liabilities: $13,858,582
Net Worth: ($10,884,531)
Earnings: ($4,826,065)
Fiscal Year-end: 12/31/13
Armor Materials Mfr
N.A.I.C.S.: 339999
David L. Oliveira *(CEO)*
Ruth G. Covey *(Head-Operating & Mfg Sys & Sr Dir-Ops)*
Subramaniam Rajan *(Dir-R&D)*

ARMORCAST PRODUCTS COMPANY

13230 Saticoy St, North Hollywood, CA 91605
Tel.: (818) 982-3600
Web Site:
    http://www.armorcastprod.com
Year Founded: 1966
Sales Range: $50-74.9 Million
Emp.: 530
Plastic & Fiberglass Product Mfr & Distr
N.A.I.C.S.: 423390
Michele Boghossian *(CEO)*
H. Paul Boghossian Sr. *(Founder)*
H. Paul Boghossian Jr. *(Pres)*

Subsidiaries:

Armorcast Rotational Molding **(1)**
500 South DuPont Ave, Ontario, CA 91761
Tel.: (909) 390-1365
Web Site: http://www.armorcastprod.com
Sales Range: $10-24.9 Million
Emp.: 75
Unsupported Plastics Profile Shape Mfr
N.A.I.C.S.: 326121
Paul Boghossian *(Pres)*

ARMSTRONG AIR & HEATING INC.

671 Business Park Blvd, Winter Garden, FL 34787
Tel.: (407) 877-8090   FL
Web Site:
    https://www.armstrongairinc.com
Year Founded: 1995
Sales Range: $25-49.9 Million
Emp.: 160
Plumbing, Heating & Air-Conditioning Contractors
N.A.I.C.S.: 238220
Paul Richards *(Pres)*
Kevin Abraham *(Mgr-Multi Family Div)*
Lisa Porter *(Office Mgr)*
Norma Ocampo *(CFO)*
Alen Oster *(Acct Mgr)*
Ana Alvarez *(Mgr-Svc & Warranty)*
Carrie Dinger *(Mgr-Acct & Bus Dev)*
Danny Sanz *(Mgr-Multi Family Construction)*
Jose Perez *(Mgr-Warehouse Ops)*

Tommy Young *(Mgr-Residential New Construction)*
Whitney Porter *(Sr Acct Mgr)*
Tom Hyatt *(Mgr-Sls & Mktg-Residential)*

ARMSTRONG BUICK VOLKSWAGEN

20000 McLoughlin Blvd, Gladstone, OR 97027
Tel.: (503) 656-2924
Web Site:
    https://www.armstrongvw.com
Year Founded: 1986
Rev.: $21,300,000
Emp.: 40
Automobiles, New & Used
N.A.I.C.S.: 441110
Don Woodruff *(Owner)*

ARMSTRONG COUNTY MEMORIAL HOSPITAL

1 Nolte Dr, Kittanning, PA 16201
Tel.: (724) 543-8500   PA
Web Site: https://www.acmh.org
Year Founded: 1874
Sales Range: $75-99.9 Million
Emp.: 1,120
Health Care Srvices
N.A.I.C.S.: 622110
Pat Burns *(CFO & VP)*
Mona Rupert *(VP-Clinical Svcs)*
Anne Remaley *(VP-HR)*
Harold Altman *(Chief Medical Officer)*
Chase McClister *(Chm)*
John Lewis *(Pres & CEO)*
Volker Zaun *(Treas & Sec)*
Mark Snyder *(Vice Chm)*
Jodi Beers *(Exec Dir)*
Wendell S. Davis *(Vice Chm)*
Nichole Geraci *(VP-Patient Svcs & Ops)*

ARMSTRONG FORENSIC ENGINEERS, INC.

17844 N US Hwy 41, Lutz, FL 33549
Tel.: (813) 948-8010
Web Site:
    https://www.armstrongforensic.com
Year Founded: 2003
Sales Range: $10-24.9 Million
Emp.: 20
Forensic Consulting Services
N.A.I.C.S.: 541690
Jeffrey D. Armstrong *(Founder & Chm)*
Daniel J. Melcher *(Dir-Engrg)*

ARMSTRONG GARDEN CENTERS, INC.

2200 E Rte 66 Ste 200, Glendora, CA 91740
Tel.: (626) 914-1091   CA
Web Site:
    https://www.armstronggarden.com
Year Founded: 1889
Sales Range: $50-74.9 Million
Emp.: 600
Nursery & Garden Center
N.A.I.C.S.: 444240
Mike D. Kunce *(Pres/CEO-Atlanta)*
David Weisman *(CFO & VP)*
Monte Enright *(Pres & COO)*
Gary Jones *(VP-Mktg)*

Subsidiaries:

Pike Nurseries Acquisition, LLC **(1)**
3555 Koger Blvd Ste360, Duluth, GA 30096
Tel.: (770) 921-1022
Web Site: http://www.pikenursery.com
Sales Range: $50-74.9 Million
Emp.: 30
Nursery & Garden Center Operator
N.A.I.C.S.: 444240
Michael Kunce *(CEO)*

ARMSTRONG HOLDINGS, INC.

1 Armstrong Pl, Butler, PA 16001
Tel.: (724) 283-0925   DE
Web Site:
    http://www.armstrongonewire.com
Year Founded: 1986
Sales Range: $350-399.9 Million
Emp.: 2,000
Holding Company; Telecommunications, Security Systems, Restaurant Franchising & Real Estate Investment Services
N.A.I.C.S.: 551112
David R. Jamieson *(Gen Counsel)*

Subsidiaries:

AccuSpec Electronics, LLC **(1)**
8140 Hawthorne Dr, Erie, PA 16509
Tel.: (814) 464-2000
Web Site:
    http://www.accuspecelectronic.com
Electronic Components Mfr
N.A.I.C.S.: 334419
Mike Jenkins *(CFO)*
Bob Borgia *(Mgr-Sls)*
Tom Rettger *(Mgr-Pur & Matls)*
Michael Sementelli *(VP-Sls & Mktg)*
Patty Schenker *(Mgr-HR)*
Joe Rogers *(VP-Ops)*

Armstrong Development Properties, Inc. **(1)**
1370 Washington Pike Ste 305, Bridgeville, PA 15017
Tel.: (412) 381-1122
Web Site: http://www.armstrongdev.com
Commercial Real Estate Development & Property Management Services
N.A.I.C.S.: 531390
Michaelann Murphy *(Mgr-Real Estate)*

Armstrong Telephone Company **(1)**
1 Armstrong Pl, Butler, PA 16001
Tel.: (724) 283-0925
Web Site: http://www.telephone.agoc.com
Sales Range: $25-49.9 Million
Emp.: 220
Wired Voice, Data & Internet Telecommunications Services
N.A.I.C.S.: 517111

Armstrong Utilities, Inc. **(1)**
1 Armstrong Pl, Butler, PA 16001
Tel.: (724) 283-0925
Web Site: http://www.cable.agoc.com
Sales Range: $10-24.9 Million
Emp.: 100
Cable Television, Internet & Voice Telecommunications Services
N.A.I.C.S.: 517810
Jeffrey A. Ross *(Pres)*

Guardian Protection Services, Inc. **(1)**
174 Thorn Hill Rd, Warrendale, PA 15086 **(100%)**
Tel.: (412) 788-2580
Web Site:
    http://www.guardianprotection.com
Sales Range: $100-124.9 Million
Emp.: 650
Residential & Commercial Security System Sales, Installation & Monitoring Services
N.A.I.C.S.: 561621
Russell C. Cersosimo *(CEO)*
Brian Helt *(VP-Authorized Dealer Program)*
Richard Bishop *(VP-Corp Sls)*
Bryan Cipoletti *(Pres)*
James Ward *(Gen Mgr-Nashville)*
John Olon *(CFO)*
Darren Crawford *(VP & Gen Mgr-Bus Sls)*

Subsidiary (Domestic):

Vintage Security LLC **(2)**
8220 Stayton Dr, Jessup, MD 20794
Tel.: (410) 888-9030
Web Site: http://www.vintagesecurity.com
Rev.: $3,290,000
Emp.: 5
Security Monitoring Services
N.A.I.C.S.: 561621
Jeff Smith *(Mgr-Comml Div)*

ARMSTRONG INTERNATIONAL, INC.

816 Maple St, Three Rivers, MI 49093-2345
Tel.: (269) 273-1415   MI
Web Site: http://www.armstrong-intl.com
Year Founded: 1907
Sales Range: $150-199.9 Million
Emp.: 600
Steam Traps; Steam Humidifiers; Purgers for Refrigeration; Pipe Line Strainers; Air Vents; Fishing & Marine Equipment Mfr
N.A.I.C.S.: 332911

Subsidiaries:

Armstrong Fluid Handling **(1)**
221 Armstrong Blvd, Three Rivers, MI 49093-2374 **(100%)**
Tel.: (269) 278-6500
Web Site: http://www.armintl.com
Sales Range: $10-24.9 Million
Emp.: 8
Mfr of Condensate Traps
N.A.I.C.S.: 333996

Armstrong Global Holdings, Inc. **(1)**
32451 Golden Lantern Ste 202, Laguna Niguel, CA 92677-5344
Tel.: (949) 313-7737
Investment Management Service
N.A.I.C.S.: 523940

Armstrong Heat Transfer Group **(1)**
648 Moeller St, Granby, J2G 8N1, QC, Canada
Tel.: (450) 378-2655
Web Site:
    http://www.armstronginternational.com
Sales Range: $10-24.9 Million
Emp.: 50
Metal Heat Treatment Services
N.A.I.C.S.: 332811
Claude Levesque *(Pres)*

Armstrong International Italiana S.r.l **(1)**
Via Orbetello 81, 10148, Turin, Italy
Tel.: (39) 011200035
Web Site:
    http://www.armstronginternational.com
Sales Range: $10-24.9 Million
Emp.: 15
Energy Consulting Services
N.A.I.C.S.: 541690
Ottorino Menardi *(Mng Dir)*

Armstrong International Mexico S de RL de CV **(1)**
Calle Industria 1228 A, Col El Mirador Zona Oblatos, Guadalajara, 44380, Jalisco, Mexico
Tel.: (52) 3338831790
Industrial Machinery Mfr
N.A.I.C.S.: 333998

Armstrong International Private Limited **(1)**
P46 Mahindra World City Eighth Avenue, Anjur Village Nathm Sub, Chengalpattu, 603002, India
Tel.: (91) 4437474444
Web Site:
    http://www.armstronginternational.in
Sales Range: $10-24.9 Million
Emp.: 120
Automatic Environmental Control Mfr
N.A.I.C.S.: 334512
Mahijeet Mishra *(Mng Dir)*

Armstrong International SA **(1)**
Manchester Business Park 3000 Aviator Way, Manchester, M22 5TG, United Kingdom
Tel.: (44) 1612662279
Sales Range: $10-24.9 Million
Emp.: 70
Energy Consulting Services
N.A.I.C.S.: 541690

Armstrong International, S.A. **(1)**
2nd Ave Parc Industrial Des Hauts Sarts, B 4040, Herstal, Liege, Belgium **(100%)**
Tel.: (32) 42409090
Web Site:
    http://www.armstronginternational.eu
Sales Range: $25-49.9 Million
Emp.: 60
Mfr of Steam Traps

Armstrong International, Inc.—(Continued)

N.A.I.C.S.: 332911

Armstrong Service France S.A. (1)
Port 4008-Route du Hoc, Gonfreville-
l'Orcher, 76700, France
Tel.: (33) 235536835
Automatic Environmental Control Mfr
N.A.I.C.S.: 334512

Armstrong Service, Inc. (1)
816 Maple St, Three Rivers, MI 49093
Tel.: (269) 273-1415
Web Site: http://www.armstrongservice.com
Water Heater Control System Mfr
N.A.I.C.S.: 334512
Liam Hickey (Mgr-Dev & Svc)

Armstrong-Yoshitake, Inc. (1)
816 Maple St, Three Rivers, MI 49093
Tel.: (269) 273-1415
Web Site: http://www.yoshitake.jp
Industrial Water Heaters & Valves Mfr
N.A.I.C.S.: 332410
Patrick B. Armstrong (Pres & Dir)

Computrol, Inc. (1)
499 E Corporate Dr, Meridian, ID
83642-3503   (96%)
Tel.: (208) 887-1000
Web Site: http://www.computrol.com
Sales Range: $10-24.9 Million
Emp.: 250
Electronics Contract Mfr
N.A.I.C.S.: 334412
Steve Dillon (Mgr-Production)
Jon Hanson (VP-Sls & Mktg)
Farid Anani (VP-Ops)

Everlasting Valve Co. (1)
108 Somogyi Ct, South Plainfield, NJ
07080-4816   (100%)
Tel.: (908) 769-0700
Sales Range: $10-24.9 Million
Emp.: 28
Mfr of Service Specialty Valves
N.A.I.C.S.: 332919

Sturgis Foundry Corp. (1)
1000 W W St, Sturgis, MI 49091   (100%)
Tel.: (269) 651-8544
Web Site: http://www.sturgisfoundry.com
Sales Range: $10-24.9 Million
Emp.: 98
Gray Iron Foundry
N.A.I.C.S.: 331511

ARMSTRONG MOLD CORP.
6910 Manlius Center Rd, East Syra-
cuse, NY 13057-9597
Tel.: (315) 437-1517
Web Site:
    http://www.armstrongmold.com
Year Founded: 1968
Emp.: 200
Mfr of Industrial Machinery
N.A.I.C.S.: 333998
John A. Armstrong (Founder)

ARMSTRONG MOVING & STORAGE INC.
2401 Double Creek Dr, Round Rock,
TX 78664
Tel.: (512) 244-1112
Web Site:
    http://www.armstrongmoving.com
Sales Range: $75-99.9 Million
Emp.: 47
Household Goods Moving & Storage
Services
N.A.I.C.S.: 484210
Charles Wolchansky (Dir-Mktg)

ARMSTRONG STEEL
2 Inverness Dr E #200, Englewood,
CO 80112
Web Site:
    http://www.armstrongsteel.com
Year Founded: 2006
Sales Range: $1-9.9 Million
Emp.: 50
Metal Structure Construction
N.A.I.C.S.: 236220
Ethan Chumley (Founder & CEO)

ARMSTRONG TEASDALE LLP
7700 Forsyth Blvd Ste 1800, Saint
Louis, MO 63105
Tel.: (314) 621-5070
Web Site:
    http://www.armstrongteasdale.com
Year Founded: 1901
Sales Range: $100-124.9 Million
Emp.: 201
Legal Advisory Services
N.A.I.C.S.: 541110
Karen A. Baudendistel (Partner & Atty)
Derick E. Allen (Partner & Atty)
Christopher D. Baucom (Partner)
Lori L. Bockman (Partner)
David W. Braswell (Mng Partner)
Patrick E. Brennan (Partner)
Richard L. Bridge (Partner)
Maureen O. Bryan (Partner)
Erin M. Florek (Partner)
Christopher LaRose (Partner)
Richard L. Brophy (Partner)
Paul M. Croker (Partner & Atty)
Mary D. Rychnovsky (Partner)
Eric M. Trelz (Partner-Litigation Prac-
tice Grp)
Michael A. Chivell (Chm)
Cristian M. Stevens (Partner-
Litigation Practice)
Donald M. Flack (Partner-Litigation)
Ray Foumie (Partner)
Marc W. Vander Tuig (Partner)
Kenneth H. Amorello (Assoc Atty-
New York)
Abraham Ally Dayon (Assoc Atty-New
York)
Jack Dayon (Assoc Atty-New York)
Denise DeNicola (Assoc Atty-New
York)
Thomas Juneau (Assoc Atty-New
York)
Daniel Lavian (Assoc Atty-New York)
Marijana Predovan (Assoc Atty-New
York)
Jose Saladin (Assoc Atty-New York)
Jeffrey Wurstx (Partner-New York)
Richard W. Engel Jr. (Mng Partner)
Martha Hereford (Partner)
William M. Ojile Jr. (Partner)
Joseph Hipskind Jr. (Partner-Fin &
Real Estate Svcs)

Subsidiaries:

Novack and Macey LLP (1)
100 N Riverside Plz, Chicago, IL 60606-
1501
Tel.: (312) 419-6900
Web Site: http://www.novackmacey.com
Emp.: 30
Law firm
N.A.I.C.S.: 541110
Andrew D. Campbell (Partner)
Kristen Werries Collier (Partner)
P. Andrew Fleming (Partner & Atty)
Steven J. Ciszewski (Partner)
Richard G. Douglass (Partner)

ARMSTRONG TECHNOLOGY INC.
1121 Elko Dr, Sunnyvale, CA 94089
Tel.: (408) 734-4434
Web Site: https://www.armstrong-
tech.com
Sales Range: $10-24.9 Million
Emp.: 100
Mechanical & Electromechanical
Counters & Devices
N.A.I.C.S.: 332710
Mark Richardson (Sys Engr-
Manufacturing)

ARMTECH, INC.
7101 82nd St, Lubbock, TX 79424-
4703
Tel.: (806) 473-0333
Web Site: http://www.armt.com

Year Founded: 1996
Sales Range: $10-24.9 Million
Emp.: 269
Direct Property & Casualty Insurance
Services
N.A.I.C.S.: 524126
Mike Jones (CFO & Sr VP)
Tom Gowdy (Exec VP)
Sam Scheef (Pres)
Jay Rushing (VP)
Jake Rinehart (VP-Ops)
Buckles Bryant (Mgr-Natl Claims)
Melissa Williams (Dir-Underwriting)
Franchesca Peralez (Mgr-
Underwriting-Natl)
Zane Vaughn (Gen Counsel)
Michael Smith (Pres & CEO)
Sam Bruce (Sr Mgr-Litigation)

ARMY EMERGENCY RELIEF
200 Stovall St, Alexandria, VA 22332
Tel.: (703) 428-0000   DC
Web Site: http://www.aerhq.org
Year Founded: 1942
Sales Range: Less than $1 Million
Financial Services
N.A.I.C.S.: 523999
Thomas P. Carney (VP-Admin)
Dennis J. Reimer (Pres)
Eldon Mullis (COO & Deputy Dir)
Joel J. Levesque (CFO)

ARNAV INDUSTRIES, INC.
441 W End Ave Fl 1A, New York, NY
10024
Tel.: (212) 532-6268   DE
Year Founded: 1959
Sales Range: $25-49.9 Million
Emp.: 20
Mfr of Women's Jackets & Vests, Ex-
cept Fur & Leather; Women's,
Misses' & Juniors' Suits
N.A.I.C.S.: 315250
Leonard Wassner (Pres)
Joseph Wassner (VP-Fin)
Judah Wassner (Controller)

ARNELL-WEST INC.
3441 S 2200 W, Salt Lake City, UT
84119
Tel.: (801) 975-9966
Web Site: https://www.arnell-
west.com
Sales Range: $25-49.9 Million
Emp.: 43
Provider of Commercial & Office
Building Construction Services
N.A.I.C.S.: 236220
Arnold West (Owner)

ARNIE BAUER, INC.
5525 Miller Cir Dr, Matteson, IL
60443
Tel.: (708) 720-1900
Sales Range: $50-74.9 Million
Emp.: 78
Car Whslr
N.A.I.C.S.: 441110
Les Brewer (Principal)
Mike Dykstra (Dir-Svc)
Cynthia Pykstra (Sec)
Deborah Wheeler (Office Mgr)

ARNIES RESTAURANT
300 Admiral Way Ste 211, Edmonds,
WA 98020
Tel.: (425) 771-5688
Web Site:
    https://www.arniesrestaurant.com
Rev.: $12,000,000
Emp.: 275
Restaurant Services
N.A.I.C.S.: 722511
Scott Howes (Dir-Food & Beverage)
Rob Davis (Gen Mgr-Mukilteo)
Fran Lumm (Gen Mgr)

ARNIS INC.
2200 Elmwood Ave, Lafayette, IN
47904
Tel.: (765) 838-2985
Web Site:
    http://www.meetyouatarnis.com
Sales Range: $10-24.9 Million
Emp.: 450
Restaurant Operators
N.A.I.C.S.: 722511
Kurt Cohen (VP)
Bradley Cohen (VP)
Chuck Petry (Mgr)

ARNOLD & O'SHERIDAN, INC.
1111 Deming Way Ste 200, Madison,
WI 53717
Tel.: (608) 821-8500
Web Site:
    http://www.arnoldandosheridan.com
Rev.: $12,000,000
Emp.: 50
Engineeering Services
N.A.I.C.S.: 541330
Ben Miller (CFO)
Brian Hanson (Pres)
Steven Roloff (COO)

ARNOLD & PORTER KAYE SCHOLER LLP
601 Massachusetts Ave NW, Wash-
ington, DC 20001-3743
Tel.: (202) 942-5000   DE
Web Site:
    https://www.arnoldporter.com
Year Founded: 2017
Emp.: 1,000
Law firm
N.A.I.C.S.: 541110
Richard M. Alexander (Partner)
Peter J. Levitas (Partner)
Thomas H. Milch (Partner)
Daniel A. Kracov (Partner)
Kenneth L. Schwartz (Partner)
John P. Barker (Partner)
Elissa J. Preheim (Partner)
Eric A. Rubel (Partner)
Frank Liss (Partner)
Jonathan S. Martel (Partner)
Keri Arnold (Partner)
Marty Duvall (Chief Mktg Officer)
Michael B. Mierzewski (Partner)
Roberta L. Horton (Partner)
Christopher L. Allen (Partner)
Janet Robin (Chief HR Officer)
David R. Marsh (Partner)
John E. Nilsson (Partner)
Michael T. Shor (Partner)
Peggy Otum (Partner)
Raul R. Herrera (Partner)
Craig A. Holman (Partner)
Paul E. Pompeo (Partner)
Alexander Shaknes (Partner-New
York)
Daphne O'Connor (Partner)
Daniel M. Hawke (Partner)
Edward McTiernan (Partner)
Kevin O'Neill (Partner)
Michael Bywell (Partner-London)
R. Reeves Anderson (Partner)
Stephen Martin (Partner)
Adela Williams (Partner)
Carey W. Smith (Partner)
Gregory Harrington (Partner)
Jeffrey L. Handwerker (Partner)
Lincoln Tsang (Partner)
Matthew T. Heartney (Partner)
Susan E. Hendrickson (Partner)
Teresa L. Johnson (Partner)
Anthony Samson (Atty)
Sean Curran (Partner)
Michael Folkes (CIO)
Sean Howell (CFO)
Catherine Zawierka (Chief Talent Offi-
cer)
Michael D. Daneker (Partner)

Anne P. Davis (*Partner*)
Evan Rothstein (*Partner-Denver*)
Timothy Macdonald (*Head-Denver*)
Arthur E. Brown (*Partner*)
Thad Thano Dameris (*Partner*)
Luc Gyselen (*Partner*)
Ingrid Kalisch (*Partner*)
Sean Morris (*Partner*)
D. Tyler Nurnberg (*Partner*)
Douglas A. Winthrop (*Partner*)
Jun Hee Kim (*Partner*)
Charles Yi (*Partner-Fin Svcs & Legislative & Pub Policy Practices*)
John Elwood (*Partner*)
Michael McGill (*Partner-Govt Contracts Practice*)

ARNOLD AUTOMOTIVE AND OIL CO.
5909 Burleson Rd, Austin, TX 78744
Tel.: (512) 476-2401
Web Site: https://www.arnoldoil.com
Rev.: $21,200,000
Emp.: 65
Petroleum Products
N.A.I.C.S.: 424720
James Arnold (*Pres & CEO*)
Kurt Filbert (*Dir-Sls & Mktg*)

ARNOLD BERNHARD & CO.
551 Fifth Ave 3rd Fl, New York, NY 10176
Tel.: (212) 907-1500   NY
Web Site: http://www.valueline.com
Year Founded: 1931
Sales Range: $50-74.9 Million
Emp.: 180
Holding Company; Miscellaneous Investments
N.A.I.C.S.: 513120
Stephen R. Anastasio (*Treas*)

Subsidiaries:

Value Line, Inc.   (1)
551 5th Ave 3rd fl, New York, NY 10176-0001   (87.9%)
Tel.: (212) 907-1500
Web Site: https://www.valueline.com
Rev.: $37,487,000
Assets: $136,035,000
Liabilities: $45,242,000
Net Worth: $90,793,000
Earnings: $19,016,000
Emp.: 122
Fiscal Year-end: 04/30/2024
Investment Periodical Publications & Information Services
N.A.I.C.S.: 513120
Stephen R. Anastasio (*Treas & VP*)
Mary Bernstein (*Dir-Acctg*)

Subsidiary (Domestic):

Compupower Corporation   (2)
125 E Union Ave, East Rutherford, NJ 07073
Tel.: (201) 842-8000
Periodical Publishing Subscription Fulfillment Services
N.A.I.C.S.: 561499

The Vanderbilt Advertising Agency, Inc.   (2)
551 Th Ave 3 Fl, New York, NY 10016
Tel.: (212) 907-1500
Web Site: http://www.valueline.com
Emp.: 190
Advertising Services
N.A.I.C.S.: 541810
Howard A. Brecher (*Pres*)

Value Line Distribution Center, Inc.   (2)
125 East Union Ave, East Rutherford, NJ 07073   (100%)
Tel.: (201) 842-8000
Web Site: http://www.valueline.com
Sales Range: $25-49.9 Million
Fulfillment Service for Publishers
N.A.I.C.S.: 518210
Stephen R. Anastasio (*Treas & VP*)

Value Line Publishing LLC   (2)

485 Lexington Ave 9th Fl, New York, NY 10017-5891
Tel.: (212) 907-1500
Web Site: http://www.valueline.com
Periodical Publishing Services
N.A.I.C.S.: 513120
Jisela Panchana (*Mgr-Recruiting & HR Admin*)

ARNOLD LUMBER COMPANY
251 Fairgrounds Rd, West Kingston, RI 02892
Tel.: (401) 783-2266   RI
Web Site: https://www.arnoldlumber.com
Year Founded: 1911
Sales Range: $25-49.9 Million
Emp.: 165
Provider of Home Planning & Contractor Services
N.A.I.C.S.: 423310
Paul Nadau (*Controller*)
Christine Sykes (*Mgr-Payroll*)
Ray Dreczko (*Mgr-Ops*)
Arthur P. Arnold Jr. (*Chm & CEO*)

ARNOLD MACHINERY COMPANY
2975 W 2100 S, Salt Lake City, UT 84119-1207
Tel.: (801) 972-4000   UT
Web Site: https://www.arnoldmachinery.com
Year Founded: 1929
Sales Range: $200-249.9 Million
Emp.: 497
Industrial Equipment, Construction & Material Handling Equipment & Implements, Concrete Aggregate Equipment & Large Buckets, Shovels & Loaders Distr
N.A.I.C.S.: 423810
Thomas O'Byrne (*COO & Pres-Mining Equipment*)
Brent Kunz (*Branch Mgr*)
Michael Hale (*Branch Mgr*)
Terry Walls (*Branch Mgr*)
Jon Pugmire (*CFO*)
Mike Miles (*Pres-Construction Equipment*)
Mike Brown (*Pres-Material Handling Equipment*)
Kirk Reese (*Pres-Material Handling Equipment*)
Darrell Buttars (*Pres-Gen Implement Distributors*)

Subsidiaries:

Arnold Machinery Co - Construction & Mining Division   (1)
2975 W 2100 S, Salt Lake City, UT 84119
Tel.: (801) 972-4000
Web Site: http://www.arnoldmachinery.com
Sales Range: $50-74.9 Million
Sales of Construction Machinery & Equipment Distr
N.A.I.C.S.: 423810
Kayden Bell (*Pres & CEO*)
Jon Pugmire (*CFO*)

Arnold Machinery Company - Material Handling Division   (1)
2921 W 2100 S, Salt Lake City, UT 84119-1207   (100%)
Tel.: (801) 974-4000
Web Site: http://www.arnoldmachinery.com
Sales Range: $25-49.9 Million
Emp.: 50
Construction Machinery & Equipment
N.A.I.C.S.: 423830
Mike Brown (*Co-Pres*)

General Implement Distributors   (1)
2955 W 2100 S, Salt Lake City, UT 84119-1207
Tel.: (801) 972-4321
Web Site: http://www.generalimp.com
Sales Range: $25-49.9 Million
Emp.: 45
Construction Machinery & Equipment
N.A.I.C.S.: 423820

Buz Nelson (*Pres*)
Darrell Buttars (*Pres*)
Matt Sieverts (*Branch Mgr*)
Mark Tibbitts (*VP-Sls*)

Subsidiary (Domestic):

R.M. Wade & Co.   (2)
10025 SW Allen Blvd, Beaverton, OR 97005-4124
Tel.: (503) 641-1865
Web Site: http://www.rmwade.com
Sales Range: $25-49.9 Million
Farm & Outdoor Power Equipment Distr
N.A.I.C.S.: 423820

ARNOLD MOTOR SUPPLY, LLP
601 1st Ave SW, Spencer, IA 51301-5302
Tel.: (712) 262-1141
Web Site: https://www.arnoldmotorsupply.com
Year Founded: 1927
Motor Vehicle Supplies & Parts Whslr
N.A.I.C.S.: 423120
Grant Schenk (*Mgr-Store*)

ARNOLD OIL CO. INC.
5422 Ayers St, Corpus Christi, TX 78415
Tel.: (361) 884-6621
Web Site: https://www.arnoldoilco.com
Rev.: $12,078,354
Emp.: 40
Lubricating Oils & Greases
N.A.I.C.S.: 424720
Randall Arnold (*Pres*)

ARNOLD PALMER'S BAY HILL CLUB & LODGE
9000 Bay Hill Blvd, Orlando, FL 32819
Tel.: (407) 876-8030
Web Site: http://www.bayhill.com
Year Founded: 1961
Sales Range: $10-24.9 Million
Emp.: 200
Golf Course & Lodge
N.A.I.C.S.: 713910
Terry McMullen (*Dir-Ops*)
Brian Dorn (*Dir-Golf*)
Carole Lasky (*Dir-Membership*)
Roy Schindele (*Dir-Sls & Mktg*)
Leigh Anne Huckaby (*Mgr-Mktg*)
Don Emery (*Pres & Gen Mgr*)

ARNOLD SHAPIRO PRODUCTIONS, INC.
11311 Camarillo St, Toluca Lake, CA 91602
Tel.: (818) 487-5125   CA
Web Site: http://www.arnoldshapiroprods.com
Year Founded: 1981
Sales Range: $10-24.9 Million
Emp.: 40
Television & Motion Pictures Production & Distribution
N.A.I.C.S.: 512110
Arnold Shapiro (*Pres*)
John Gengl (*Supvr-Post Production*)

ARNOLD STEEL COMPANY, INC.
79 Randolph Rd, Howell, NJ 07731
Tel.: (732) 363-1079   NJ
Web Site: https://www.arnoldsteel.com
Year Founded: 1961
Sales Range: $75-99.9 Million
Emp.: 100
Provider of Fabrication & Erection of Steel
N.A.I.C.S.: 238120
Leon Pflaster (*Pres*)
Tina Pflaster (*CFO*)

Vincent DiGioia (*Project Mgr*)
David Lidberg (*Mgr-Fabrications Ops*)
Frank Weaver (*Project Mgr*)

ARNOLD'S OF WILLMAR INCORPORATED
4773 Hwy 71 S, Willmar, MN 56201
Tel.: (320) 235-4898
Web Site: https://arnoldsinc.com
Sales Range: $10-24.9 Million
Emp.: 30
Agricultural Machinery & Equipment
N.A.I.C.S.: 423820
John Arnold (*Pres*)

ARNOLD-BAKER CHEVROLET
619 S Washington, Magnolia, AR 71753-3929
Tel.: (870) 234-1200
Web Site: https://www.abchevy.com
Rev.: $13,000,000
Emp.: 45
Sales New & Used Automobiles
N.A.I.C.S.: 441110
James W. Arnold (*Pres*)

ARNOLD-WILBERT CORP.
1401 W Grantham St, Goldsboro, NC 27530
Tel.: (919) 735-5008
Web Site: https://www.arnoldwilbert.com
Year Founded: 1932
Sales Range: $10-24.9 Million
Emp.: 75
Concrete Products Mfr
N.A.I.C.S.: 327390
Stephen L. Velker (*VP & Gen Mgr*)
Ronald K. Turner (*Sec*)
Les King (*Asst Mgr-Ops*)
Mike King (*Mgr-Ops*)

ARNTZEN CORPORATION
1025 School St, Rockford, IL 61101
Tel.: (815) 964-9413
Web Site: http://www.arntzenrolling.com
Sales Range: $10-24.9 Million
Emp.: 56
Pipe, Standpipe & Culverts
N.A.I.C.S.: 332313
Richard Arntzen (*Pres*)
John Arntzen (*VP*)
Robert Arc (*CFO*)

ARO LIQUIDATION, INC.
125 Chubb Ave, Lyndhurst, NJ 07071
Tel.: (646) 485-5410   DE
Web Site: http://www.aeropostale.com
Year Founded: 1987
Sales Range: $1-4.9 Billion
Holding Company; Clothing Designer, Marketer & Retailer
N.A.I.C.S.: 551112
Steve Lubomski (*VP-Mktg*)

ARO-SYSTEMS INC.
1811 Sherman Dr Ste 10, Saint Charles, MO 63303
Tel.: (636) 947-6404
Rev.: $29,100,098
Emp.: 2
Convenience Store
N.A.I.C.S.: 445110
Charles J. Geno Jr. (*Pres*)

AROG PHARMACEUTICALS, INC.
5420 LBJ Freeway Ste 410, Dallas, TX 75240
Tel.: (214) 593-0500   DE
Web Site: http://www.arogpharma.com
Year Founded: 2010
Emp.: 20

Arog Pharmaceuticals, Inc.—(Continued)

Biopharmaceutical Product Research
& Development Services
N.A.I.C.S.: 541714
Vinay K. Jain (Founder & Chm)
M. Scott Salka (CEO)
Dean Ferrigno (CFO)
Edward McDonald (Gen Counsel &
Sec)

AROGAS INC.
1811 Sherman Dr Ste 1, Saint
Charles, MO 63303-3976
Tel.: (636) 947-0255   MO
Year Founded: 1970
Sales Range: $10-24.9 Million
Emp.: 10
Gasoline Service Stations
N.A.I.C.S.: 424720
Patrick T. Manning (Pres & CEO)
Kevin Manning (VP)
Richard Orcutt (Project Mgr)

AROK INC.
2819 W Grovers Ave, Phoenix, AZ
85053
Tel.: (602) 997-1492
Web Site: http://www.arokteam.com
Sales Range: $10-24.9 Million
Emp.: 120
Nonresidential Construction
N.A.I.C.S.: 236220
Brent Cooper (Pres)
Ana Cannon (Controller)
Nathan Firnstahl (Mgr-Safety)

AROMATIC FUSION
3185 Tucker Rd, Bensalem, PA
19020
Tel.: (215) 244-1830
Web Site:
 https://www.aromaticfusion.com
Year Founded: 2003
Sales Range: $1-9.9 Million
Emp.: 5
Engineers, Develops & Manufactures
Fragrance Delivery Systems for
Home & Commercial Users
N.A.I.C.S.: 561499
Eric Albee (Pres)
Sandra Kelley (Co-Founder)

AROMATIQUE INC.
3421 Highway 25B N, Heber Springs,
AR 72543
Tel.: (501) 362-7511   AR
Web Site:
 https://www.aromatique.com
Year Founded: 1982
Fragrances, Oils, Room Sprays,
Candles, Bath Products & Decorative
Containers & Accessories Mfr
N.A.I.C.S.: 339999
Carlton Collier (Exec VP)

ARONA CORPORATION
1001 Grand Ave W, Des Moines, IA
50312
Tel.: (515) 225-9029
Year Founded: 1996
Sales Range: $50-74.9 Million
Emp.: 400
Consumer Goods Lease to Own Re-
tailer
N.A.I.C.S.: 532289
Thomas R. Bernau (Pres)

ARONSON ASSOCIATES INC.
3798 Paxton St, Harrisburg, PA 17111
Tel.: (717) 564-1657   PA
Web Site:
 https://www.serviceoilco.com
Year Founded: 1922
Sales Range: $10-24.9 Million
Emp.: 28
Seller & Installer of Air Conditioners

N.A.I.C.S.: 457120
Raphael Aronson (CEO & Treas)
Rick Barbush (VP-Sls)
Steve Nicholson (Mgr-Sls)
Dorothea Aronson (VP & Sec)

ARONSON LLC
805 King Farm Blvd Ste 300, Rock-
ville, MD 20850
Tel.: (301) 231-6200   MD
Web Site: http://www.aronsonllc.com
Year Founded: 1962
Emp.: 225
Audit, Tax & Consulting Services
N.A.I.C.S.: 541618
Brenda L. Jayne (Partner)
Barbara Morgan (Partner)
Greg Plotts (Partner)
Larry Davis (Mng Partner)
Kevin M. Gerrity Jr. (Chief People
Officer & Dir-Recruiting)

Subsidiaries:

Washington Management Group,
Inc.   (1)
1990 M St NW No 400, Washington, DC
20036-3420
Tel.: (202) 833-1120
Sales Range: $25-49.9 Million
Business Management Consultant
N.A.I.C.S.: 541618

**ARONSON-CAMPBELL INDUS-
TRIAL SUPPLY INC.**
1700 136th Pl NE, Bellevue, WA
98005
Tel.: (425) 372-2000   WI
Web Site: https://www.aronson-
campbell.com
Year Founded: 1900
Sales Range: $10-24.9 Million
Emp.: 44
Distr of Industrial Supplies
N.A.I.C.S.: 423840
Bruce Buchberger (Owner)
John Buchberger (Pres)

ARORA ENGINEERS, INC.
61 Wilmington W Chester Pike,
Chadds Ford, PA 19317
Tel.: (610) 459-7900   PA
Web Site:
 https://www.aroraengineers.com
Year Founded: 1986
Emp.: 100
Engineering Services
N.A.I.C.S.: 541304
Kalpesh S. Trivedi (VP-PM/CM)
Manohar L. Arora (Founder)
Manik K. Arora (Pres & CEO)
Earl M. Carter (Mgr-BIM & CAD)
James Falvey (VP-New England)
Chase J. Miller (VP-Fire & Life Safety
Practice Lead)
Adam Oliver (CMO)
Anthony J. Vitullo (CFO)
Karen Hierman (VP-Admin & Comm)
Vincent De Meis (VP-Middle States)
Jocelyn Dugdale Bernhardt (Dir-Mid-
Atlantic)
Steve Bisch (VP-Enterprise Solutions)
Marco Viola (VP-Global Bus Dev &
Enterprise Solutions)

Subsidiaries:

Electronic Data, LLC   (1)
400 Carillon Pkwy Ste 100, Saint Peters-
burg, FL 33716
Tel.: (727) 299-9304
Web Site: http://edatai.com
Computer Consultants
N.A.I.C.S.: 541512
Jay Chauncey (Dir-EAM Solutions)
Jenna Riffer (Dir-EAM Svcs & Customer
Care)
Joe Mahaz (Founder)
Brian Benedict (Dir-Dev)
Raelyn Davis (Office Mgr)

**AROUND THE CLOCK A/C
SERVICE, LLC**
11840 NW 41st St, Coral Springs, FL
33065
Tel.: (954) 742-5544
Web Site: http://www.atcair.com
Year Founded: 1988
Sales Range: $10-24.9 Million
Emp.: 140
Appliance Repair Services
N.A.I.C.S.: 811412
Eric Pereira (Pres)
Steven Cartier (Owner)
Scott Davis (Mgr-Ops)
Joe Guerrieri (Mgr)

ARQUEST INC.
101 Interchange Plz, Cranbury, NJ
08512
Tel.: (609) 395-9500
Sales Range: $200-249.9 Million
Emp.: 20
Mfr & Distributor of Disposable Dia-
pers & Training Pants
N.A.I.C.S.: 322291
Matthew Rinaldi (Pres & CEO)

ARR INVESTMENTS, LLC
3400 N Main Ave, Scranton, PA
18508
Tel.: (570) 701-8682
Web Site:
 https://www.toyotaofscranton.com
Emp.: 100
Car Dealer
N.A.I.C.S.: 441110
Patrick Rogers (CFO)

Subsidiaries:

James W. Halterman, Inc.   (1)
400 Analomink Rd, East Stroudsburg, PA
18301
Tel.: (570) 421-6930
Web Site: http://www.haltermantoyota.com
Automotive Repair & Maintenance
N.A.I.C.S.: 811198
Andrew Stratz (Mgr-Sls)

**ARRAY INFORMATION TECH-
NOLOGY, INC.**
7474 Greenway Center Dr Ste 600,
Greenbelt, MD 20770-3504
Tel.: (301) 345-8188
Web Site:
 http://www.arrayinfotech.com
Year Founded: 1997
Sales Range: $10-24.9 Million
IT Services
N.A.I.C.S.: 541512
Sumeet Shrivastava (Pres)
Bob Deegan (CFO & Sr VP)
Hafidh A. A. Ghalib (VP-Science &
Tech)
Jon C. Dittmer (Sr VP & Gen Mgr)
Chuck Gillies (Dir-Quality Assurance)

ARRAY NETWORKS, INC.
1371 McCarthy Blvd, Milpitas, CA
95035
Tel.: (408) 240-8700
Web Site:
 https://www.arraynetworks.com
Computer & Computer Peripheral
Equipment & Software Merchant
Whslr
N.A.I.C.S.: 423430
Rich Siegel (VP-Sls & Bus Dev)
Vinod Pisharody (CTO)
Michael Zhao (Pres & CEO)
Joseph Lien (Chm)
Joe Hwang (CEO)
Sameena Ahmed (Pres & Gen Mgr)
Sean Fang (CFO)
Roland Hsu (CTO)
Blank Nguyen (Chief Customer Suc-
cess Officer)

Hao Sam (Chief Mfg Officer)
Shibu Paul (VP-Sls International)
Paul Andersen (VP-Sls North
America)

**ARRAY PRODUCTS COM-
PANY, LLC**
15900 Morales Rd, Houston, TX
77032-2126
Tel.: (918) 682-7952
Web Site:
 http://www.arrayproducts.com
Rev.: $12,300,000
Emp.: 10
Valve, Actuator & Flow Control Prod-
ucts Mfr
N.A.I.C.S.: 332912
Michael Johnson (Pres)
Kent Watts (Exec VP)
Jack Davies (VP-Sls)
Johnny Gates (Mgr-Engrg)
Geo George (Mgr-Quality & Logistics)
Andrea Riggins (Gen Mgr-Acctg)
Georgia Pequet (Mgr-HR)
Richard Mitchell (Mgr-IT)

Subsidiaries:

E&S Manufacturing, Inc.   (1)
506 W Harrison Rd, Longview, TX 75604
Tel.: (903) 759-2326
Web Site: http://www.esvalve.com
Sales Range: $10-24.9 Million
Mfr Fluid Power Valves & Hose Fittings
N.A.I.C.S.: 332912

ARRAYA SOLUTIONS, INC.
523 Plymouth Rd Ste 212, Plymouth
Meeting, PA 19462
Web Site:
 http://www.arrayasolutions.com
Year Founded: 1999
Sales Range: $25-49.9 Million
Emp.: 51
IT Consulting Services
N.A.I.C.S.: 541690
Daniel J. Lifshutz (Co-Founder &
CEO)
David Bakker (Co-Founder & CTO)

ARRC TECHNOLOGY
1600 Mill Rock Way, Bakersfield, CA
93311
Tel.: (661) 281-4000
Web Site: https://www.arrc.com
Year Founded: 1992
Rev.: $6,400,000
Emp.: 65
Consumer Electronics Repair & Main-
tenance
N.A.I.C.S.: 811210
David A. Rogers (Pres)
Monique Rogers (CFO & Treas)
Roy Cullipher (Owner)

**ARRESTAGE INTERNA-
TIONAL, INC.**
20343 N Hayden Rd Ste 101, Scotts-
dale, AZ 85255
Tel.: (480) 710-2229   NV
Web Site:
 http://www.arrestagenational.com
Year Founded: 2011
Rev.: $500
Assets: $1,786
Liabilities: $280,667
Net Worth: ($278,881)
Earnings: ($84,790)
Emp.: 4
Fiscal Year-end: 12/31/19
Cosmetic Product Mfr & Distr
N.A.I.C.S.: 325620
Kimberly Shapiro (Chm)
Greg Washington (Dir-Mktg)
John W. Muldoon III (CEO)

ARREVA LLC

3511 W Commercial Blvd Ste 404, Fort Lauderdale, FL 33309
Tel.: (800) 750-6418   DE
Web Site: http://www.arreva.com
Computer Software Developer
N.A.I.C.S.: 513210
David Blyer *(Pres, CEO & Co-Founder)*
Susan Packard Orr *(Co-Founder & Chm)*
Subsidiaries:

MaestroSoft, Inc.   (1)
1200 112th Ave NE Ste C250, Bellevue, WA 98004-3741
Web Site: http://www.maestrosoft.com
Computer Related Services
N.A.I.C.S.: 541519
Kenneth R. Kleve *(Co-Pres & COO)*
Jay Fiske *(Co-Pres)*

ARRINGTON LUMBER & PALLET COMPANY, INC.
PO Box 1900, Jacksonville, TX 75766
Tel.: (903) 586-4070
Web Site:
    https://www.arringtonlumber.com
Year Founded: 1963
Sales Range: $10-24.9 Million
Emp.: 170
Wood Container & Pallet Mfr
N.A.I.C.S.: 321920
Eddie Arrington *(CEO)*
Kyle Arrington *(COO)*
Brian Gorham *(Controller)*
Ec Blount *(Acct Mgr)*

ARROW COMPANIES, LLC
1501 E Wisconsin St Ste 2, Delavan, WI 53115
Tel.: (262) 724-8822
Web Site:
    http://www.arrowcompaniesllc.com
Investment Services
N.A.I.C.S.: 523999
Peter Wright *(CFO)*
Jerry Voors *(Pres)*
Hether Miles-Fiess *(VP-Cabinet Div)*

ARROW CONCRETE COMPANY
202 51st St, Vienna, WV 26105
Tel.: (304) 485-2191
Sales Range: $10-24.9 Million
Emp.: 30
Ready Mixed Concrete
N.A.I.C.S.: 327320

ARROW ELECTRIC CO. INC.
317 Wabasso Ave, Louisville, KY 40209
Tel.: (502) 367-0141
Web Site:
    http://www.arrowelectric.com
Sales Range: $10-24.9 Million
Emp.: 200
General Electrical Contractor
N.A.I.C.S.: 238210
Bob Allgeier *(CEO)*
Alan Kopp *(Mgr-HR & Safety)*

ARROW EXTERMINATORS INC.
8613 Roswell Rd Bldg Ste 4, Atlanta, GA 30350
Tel.: (770) 552-4943   GA
Web Site:
    http://www.arrowexterminators.com
Year Founded: 1964
Sales Range: $100-124.9 Million
Emp.: 1,000
Disinfecting & Pest Control Services
N.A.I.C.S.: 561710
Emily Thomas Kendrick *(CEO)*
Tim Pollard *(Pres & COO)*

Shay Jones Runion *(Chief HR Officer & Sr VP-Professional Development)*
Joey Holland *(CFO)*
Subsidiaries:

5 Star Termite & Pest Control, Inc.   (1)
1002 S Pantano Rd, Tucson, AZ 85710
Tel.: (520) 886-0045
Web Site:
    https://www.arrowexterminators.com
Exterminating & Pest Control Services
N.A.I.C.S.: 561710

Bugmaster Termite & Pest Control   (1)
795 Russell Palmer Rd, Kingwood, TX 77339   **(100%)**
Tel.: (281) 812-3532
Web Site:
    http://www.arrowexterminators.com
Exterminating & Pest Control Services
N.A.I.C.S.: 561710
Samuel White *(Project Mgr)*
Emely Thomas *(Pres)*

Cannon Pest Control   (1)
404 Opelika Rd Ste A, Auburn, AL 36830-3906
Tel.: (334) 482-3049
Web Site:
    http://www.cannonpestandtermite.com
Exterminating & Pest Control Services
N.A.I.C.S.: 561710
Darryl Cannon *(Owner)*

DC Scientific Pest Control, Inc.   (1)
1814 Greensboro Ave, Tuscaloosa, AL 35401
Tel.: (205) 758-9029
Web Site: http://www.dcspestcontrol.com
Sales Range: $1-9.9 Million
Emp.: 30
Disinfecting & Pest Control Services
N.A.I.C.S.: 561710
Barbara Moore *(VP)*

Frye Exterminating Co   (1)
3033 Stonybrook Dr Ste 5, Raleigh, NC 27604
Tel.: (919) 713-4346
Web Site: http://www.fryeexterminating.com
Rev.: $1,760,000
Emp.: 16
Exterminating & Pest Control Services
N.A.I.C.S.: 561710
Les Preece *(Pres)*

Hughes Exterminators, Inc.   (1)
2506 Manatee Ave W, Bradenton, FL 34205
Tel.: (941) 748-2260
Web Site: http://www.hughes-exterminators.com
Exterminating & Pest Control Services
N.A.I.C.S.: 561710
Danny Nix *(Mgr-Svc Center)*

Nader's Pest Raiders, Inc.   (1)
96014 Chester Rd, Yulee, FL 32097
Tel.: (904) 225-9425
Web Site: http://www.naderspestraiders.com
Sales Range: $1-9.9 Million
Exterminating & Pest Control Services
N.A.I.C.S.: 561710
Terri Mills *(Office Mgr)*

ARROW FORD INC.
4001 S 1st St, Abilene, TX 79605-1529
Tel.: (325) 692-9500   TX
Web Site: https://www.arrowford.net
Year Founded: 1964
Sales Range: $75-99.9 Million
Emp.: 150
New & Used Car Dealers
N.A.I.C.S.: 441110
Seaton Higginbothom *(Gen Mgr)*

ARROW GEAR COMPANY
2301 Curtiss St, Downers Grove, IL 60515-4055
Tel.: (630) 969-7640   IL
Web Site: https://www.arrowgear.com
Year Founded: 1947

Loose Gears & Gear Boxes For Aerospace Mfr
N.A.I.C.S.: 336412
Kerry Klein *(VP-Sls & Mktg)*
Bob Bonomo *(Supvr-Shop)*

ARROW GLASS & MIRROR, INC.
9201 Brown Ln Ste 280, Austin, TX 78754
Tel.: (512) 336-0400
Web Site:
    https://www.glassgang.com
Year Founded: 1994
Sales Range: $1-9.9 Million
Emp.: 45
Glass & Glazing Contractors
N.A.I.C.S.: 238150
Dan Robb *(Pres)*
Barry Easley *(Mgr-Ops)*

ARROW INTERNATIONAL, INC.
9900 Clinton Rd, Cleveland, OH 44144-1034
Tel.: (216) 961-3500   OH
Web Site:
    https://www.arrowinternational.com
Sales Range: $800-899.9 Million
Emp.: 1,000
Mfr of Charitable & Social Gaming Solutions
N.A.I.C.S.: 323111
John Simonelli *(Co-Controller)*
Richard Kebert *(Co-Controller)*
John E. Gallagher Jr. *(Pres)*
Subsidiaries:

Arrow Games Corporation   (1)
9515 Montrose Road Unit 2, Port Robinson, L0S 1K0, ON, Canada   **(100%)**
Tel.: (905) 354-7300
Web Site: http://www.arrowgames.com
Sales Range: $50-74.9 Million
Emp.: 150
Bingo & Pull-Tab Gaming Products, Equipment & Accessories Mfr
N.A.I.C.S.: 323111

Subsidiary (Domestic):

Bazaar & Novelty Ltd.   (2)
612 Squier Street, Thunder Bay, P7B 6A8, ON, Canada
Tel.: (807) 345-3784
Web Site: http://www.bazaarandnovelty.ca
Emp.: 100
Bingo & Pull-Tab Gaming Products & Accessories Mfr
N.A.I.C.S.: 323111
Roy Lister *(Pres)*

Bingo King Company   (1)
2807 Lincoln Way, Lynnwood, WA 98087
Tel.: (425) 745-3700
Web Site: http://www.bingoking.com
Bingo & Pull-Tab Gaming Products, Equipment & Accessories Mfr
N.A.I.C.S.: 323111
Clem Chantiam *(Pres)*

Cowells Arrow Bingo   (1)
9900 Clinton Rd, Cleveland, OH 44144-1034
Tel.: (216) 961-3500
Web Site: http://www.arrowgames.com
Commercial Printing
N.A.I.C.S.: 423320

Specialty Manufacturing, Inc.   (1)
6605 Hardeson Rd Ste A, Everett, WA 98203
Tel.: (425) 407-1475
Web Site:
    http://www.specialtymanufacturing.com
Sales Range: $10-24.9 Million
Emp.: 75
Commercial Printing
N.A.I.C.S.: 323111

ARROW LUMBER & HARDWARE LLC

28280 Hwy 410 E, Buckley, WA 98321
Tel.: (360) 829-9049
Web Site:
    http://www.arrowlumber.com
Sales Range: $10-24.9 Million
Emp.: 55
Sales of Lumber & Other Building Materials
N.A.I.C.S.: 423310
Barney Wagner *(Pres & Co-Owner)*
Shawn Roehr *(Mgr-Store & Co-Owner)*
Ted Cebula *(Mgr-Store)*

ARROW PARTNERSHIP, LLC
8055 E Tufts Ave Suite 710, Denver, CO 80237
Tel.: (303) 321-8500
Web Site:
    http://www.arrowpartnership.com
Year Founded: 1999
Sales Range: $1-9.9 Million
Emp.: 25
Management & IT Consulting Services
N.A.I.C.S.: 541618
Chan Pollock *(Mng Partner)*
Mike Jones *(Partner)*
Stephen Barnett *(CEO)*
Wendy Campbell *(Partner)*

ARROW PNEUMATICS INC.
2111 W 21st St, Broadview, IL 60155-4627
Tel.: (708) 343-9595   IL
Web Site:
    http://www.arrowpneumatics.com
Year Founded: 1914
Sales Range: $50-74.9 Million
Emp.: 100
Compressed Industrial Air Dryers Mfr
N.A.I.C.S.: 333415
Benny Kawa *(Pres)*
Adelaida Teruel *(Controller)*
Larry Adams *(Mgr-Sls-Natl)*
Subsidiaries:

Arrow Fluid Power   (1)
2111 W 21st St, Broadview, IL 60155-4627
Tel.: (708) 343-9595
Web Site: http://www.arrowpneumatics.com
Fluid Power Accessories Mfr
N.A.I.C.S.: 333415
Benny Kawa *(Pres)*

Arrow Sintered Products   (1)
2111 W 21st St, Broadview, IL 60155   **(100%)**
Tel.: (708) 343-9595
Sales Range: $10-24.9 Million
Emp.: 50
Custom Sintered Bronze Parts Mfr
N.A.I.C.S.: 333998

ARROW RESOURCES DEVELOPMENT, INC.
Carnegie Hall Tower 152 W 57th St 27 Fl, New York, NY 10019
Tel.: (212) 262-2300   DE
Year Founded: 1968
Land & Natural Resource Development Services
N.A.I.C.S.: 925120
Peter John Frugone *(Chm, Pres, CEO, CFO, Principal Acctg Officer)*

ARROW ROAD CONSTRUCTION COMPANY
3401 S Busse Rd, Mount Prospect, IL 60056
Tel.: (847) 437-0700
Web Site: https://www.arrowroad.com
Sales Range: $10-24.9 Million
Emp.: 30
Highway & Street Paving Contractor
N.A.I.C.S.: 237310

Arrow Road Construction
Company—(Continued)

Wayne E. Healy (Chm)
John F. Healy (Pres & CEO)
Mike Salmon (CFO)

ARROW SAFETY DEVICE COMPANY
123 Dixon St, Selbyville, DE 19975
Tel.: (302) 856-2516
Web Site:
http://www.arrowsafetydevice.com
Year Founded: 1930
Sales Range: $50-74.9 Million
Emp.: 50
Vehicle Lighting Systems & Accessories Mfr
N.A.I.C.S.: 336320
Dave Speier (Chm & CEO)

ARROW SECURITY, INC.
300 W Main St, Smithtown, NY 11787
Tel.: (631) 675-2430   NY
Web Site:
https://www.arrowsecurity.net
Year Founded: 1985
Sales Range: $1-9.9 Million
Emp.: 375
Security Guards & Patrol Services & Security Management Services
N.A.I.C.S.: 561612
Alexander J. Caro (CEO)

ARROW STRATEGIES, LLC
27777 Franklin Rd Ste 1200, Southfield, MI 48034
Tel.: (248) 502-2500   MI
Web Site:
https://www.arrowstrategies.com
Year Founded: 2002
Sales Range: $10-24.9 Million
Emp.: 250
Full Service Staffing Solutions
N.A.I.C.S.: 561330
Jeffrey Styers (Founder & CEO)
Kim Dzierzawski (VP-Fin)
John Ninkovich (Pres)

ARROW TANK & ENGINEERING CO.
8950 Evergreen Blvd, Coon Rapids, MN 55433-6042
Tel.: (763) 786-9510   MN
Web Site: https://www.arrowtank.com
Year Founded: 1958
Sales Range: $75-99.9 Million
Emp.: 200
Distr of Pressure Vessels
N.A.I.C.S.: 332420
John Stark (Pres & CFO)
Ron Lingscheit (Chief Engr)
Dave Haskins (Owner & Mgr-Tech Div)
Tim Schweppe (Gen Mgr-Propane Div)
Kelly Schlickenmayer (Mgr-Mfg)
Randy Robinson (Mgr-Quality Control)
Tom Stratton (Officer-Compliance)

Subsidiaries:

Arrow Tech High Purity Division   (1)
8950 Evergreen Blvd, Coon Rapids, MN 55433
Tel.: (763) 786-9510
Web Site: http://www.arrowtank.com
Provider of Engineering Services
N.A.I.C.S.: 332420
Dan Haskins (Div Mgr)

ARROW TECHNOLOGIES, LLC
2110 Maples Pl, Highlands Ranch, CO 80129
Tel.: (303) 694-4390

Web Site:
http://www.arrowtechnologiesllc.com
Year Founded: 2002
Sales Range: $1-9.9 Million
Emp.: 12
Telecommunications Network Infrastructure, Design & Installation
N.A.I.C.S.: 517810
Messiah G. Willis (Owner)

ARROW TRUCK SALES INCORPORATED
3200 Manchester Trfwy, Kansas City, MO 64129
Tel.: (816) 923-5000
Web Site:
https://www.arrowtruck.com
Rev.: $170,000,000
Emp.: 95
Trucks, Tractors & Trailers Sales
N.A.I.C.S.: 441227
Dildeep Johal (Branch Mgr)

ARROWAC FISHERIES INC.
Fishermans Commerce Bldg 4039 21st Ave W Ste 200, Seattle, WA 98199-1252
Tel.: (206) 282-5655   WA
Web Site: http://www.arrowac-merco.com
Year Founded: 1978
Sales Range: $10-24.9 Million
Emp.: 3
Fresh & Frozen Packaged Fish Mfr & Distr
N.A.I.C.S.: 311710
Frank M. Mercker (Pres)

ARROWHEAD ADVERTISING
16155 N 83rd Ave Ste 205, Peoria, AZ 85382
Tel.: (623) 979-3000
Web Site:
http://www.arrowheadadv.com
Year Founded: 2003
Rev.: $3,800,000
Emp.: 89
Advertising & Marketing
N.A.I.C.S.: 541810
Kyle Eng (Pres & CEO)

ARROWHEAD CONVEYOR CORPORATION, INC.
3255 Medalist Dr, Oshkosh, WI 54902-7123
Tel.: (920) 235-5562
Web Site:
http://www.arrowheadconveyor.com
Year Founded: 1998
Sales Range: $75-99.9 Million
Emp.: 310
Tabletop, Belt & Case-Handling Conveyors; Custom Steel & Stainless Steel Mfr
N.A.I.C.S.: 333922
Ben Trustem (Mgr-Applications Engrg)
Eric Gagnon (Engr-Electrical Project)
Jeff Bakran (Engr-Electrical Applications)
Tim Krueger (Mgr-Mfg)
Wesley Behling (Engr-Mechanical)

Subsidiaries:

Busse/SJI   (1)
124 N Columbus St, Randolph, WI 53956-1204
Tel.: (920) 326-3131
Web Site:
http://www.arrowheadsystems.com
Sales Range: $10-24.9 Million
Emp.: 100
Mfr of Bulk Palletizers & Bulk Depalletizers for Container Handling; Manufacturer of Case & Pallet Washers, Warmers & Coolers & Twist Rinsers
N.A.I.C.S.: 333922

Tom Young (Owner)
Scott Brenner (Engr-Electrical)

ARROWHEAD CREDIT UNION
PO Box 735, San Bernardino, CA 92402
Tel.: (909) 383-7300   CA
Web Site:
https://www.arrowheadcu.org
Year Founded: 1949
Sales Range: $50-74.9 Million
Emp.: 352
Credit Union
N.A.I.C.S.: 522130
Michele Megill (Sr VP-Operations)

ARROWHEAD EQUIPMENT INC.
106 Luzerne Rd, Queensbury, NY 12212
Tel.: (518) 793-2265
Year Founded: 1987
Heavy-Duty Truck Equipment Distr
N.A.I.C.S.: 423110
Corey A. Soprano (Mgr-Comml Sls)

ARROWHEAD PLASTIC ENGINEERING, INC.
2909 S Hoyt Ave, Muncie, IN 47302
Tel.: (765) 286-0533
Web Site:
https://www.arrowheadinc.com
Year Founded: 1972
Rev.: $13,000,000
Emp.: 56
Plastics Processing
N.A.I.C.S.: 326199
Thomas W. Kishel (Pres)
Carol Gregory (Mgr-Pur)
Monte Foist (Engr-Sys)
Jeff Miller (Mgr-Tank Sls)

ARROWHEAD PROMOTION & FULFILLMENT COMPANY, INC.
1105 SE 8th St, Grand Rapids, MN 55744-4082
Tel.: (218) 327-1165
Web Site:
https://arrowheadpromotion.com
Year Founded: 1983
Sales Range: $10-24.9 Million
Emp.: 280
Advertising Services
N.A.I.C.S.: 541860
Danica Salisbury (Controller)
Tim McDonald (VP-Ops)
Katie Prokop (CEO)

ARROWHEAD WEST, INC.
1100 E Wyatt Earp Blvd, Dodge City, KS 67801
Tel.: (620) 227-8803   KS
Web Site:
https://www.arrowheadwest.org
Year Founded: 1976
Sales Range: $10-24.9 Million
Emp.: 403
Disabled People Assistance Services
N.A.I.C.S.: 624120

ARROWPAC INCORPORATED
85 Twin Rivers Dr, East Windsor, NJ 08520
Tel.: (201) 330-7800
Web Site: https://www.arrowpac.com
Year Founded: 1980
Sales Range: $10-24.9 Million
Emp.: 11
Freight Forwarding Services
N.A.I.C.S.: 488510
Walter Kenney (Pres)
Tom Parshall (VP-Ops-United States)

ARROWPOINT ASSET MANAGEMENT LLC
100 Fillmore St Ste 325, Denver, CO 80206
Tel.: (303) 398-2929
Web Site: http://www.ap-am.com
Sales Range: $10-24.9 Million
Investment Firm
N.A.I.C.S.: 523940
Christopher Dunne (Mng Dir-IR)
David Corkins (Founder & Mng Partner)
Minyoung Sohn (Portfolio Mgr-Meridian Equity Income Fund)
Rick Grove (COO & Chief Compliance Officer)
Karen Reidy (Principal)

ARROWPOINT CAPITAL CORP.
3600 Arco Corporate Dr Ste 100, Charlotte, NC 28273
Tel.: (704) 522-2000   DE
Web Site:
http://www.arrowpointcap.com
Year Founded: 1985
Sales Range: $1-4.9 Billion
Emp.: 5,700
Personal & Commercial Insurance Products & Services
N.A.I.C.S.: 524126
Sean Beatty (CFO)
John Tighe (Pres & CEO)
Dennis Cahill (COO)
Julie Fortune (Chief Claims Officer)
Andre Lefebvre (Officer-Fin Risk)
Jim Meehan (Gen Counsel)
Dave Davenport (Controller)
Dave Shumway (Chief Investment Officer)
Dan Keddie (Head-Corp Actuarial)

Subsidiaries:

Arrowood Indemnity Company   (1)
3600 Arco Corporate Dr, Charlotte, NC 28201
Tel.: (704) 522-2000
Property & Casualty Insurance Services
N.A.I.C.S.: 524126

Royal Indemnity Co.   (1)
Whitehall Corporate Ctr 3 3600 Arco Corporate Dr, Charlotte, NC 28273
Tel.: (704) 522-2000
Sales Range: $1-4.9 Billion
Emp.: 200
Specialty Insurance Services
N.A.I.C.S.: 524126

ARROWPOINT CORPORATION
5999 Stevenson Ave Ste 403, Alexandria, VA 22304
Tel.: (703) 778-3900
Web Site: http://www.arrowpoint.net
Sales Range: $25-49.9 Million
Emp.: 150
Information Technology Services
N.A.I.C.S.: 541512
Chris W. Small (Chm & CEO)
Greg Krinock (MGR-PETROLEUM DISPATCH)
Kevin Martin (CTO & VP)

ARROWWOOD CABINETRY, INC.
3331 N Panam Expy, San Antonio, TX 78219-2313
Tel.: (210) 344-4151
Web Site:
http://www.arrowwoodcab.com
Year Founded: 1995
Rev.: $16,000,000
Emp.: 50
Custom Cabinet Construction
N.A.I.C.S.: 337110

ARROYO & COMPANY
425 California St Ste 2000, San Francisco, CA 94104
Tel.: (415) 445-7800

Web Site: http://www.a-c.com
Year Founded: 1988
Sales Range: $10-24.9 Million
Emp.: 57
Real Estate Advisory & Brokerage Services
N.A.I.C.S.: 531210
Pedro S. Arroyo *(Co-Founder & CEO)*
David Kram *(VP)*
Ursula Dalzell *(Dir-Ops)*

ARROYO PROCESS EQUIPMENT INC.

13750 Automobile Blvd, Clearwater, FL 33762
Tel.: (727) 573-5294
Web Site:
   http://www.arroyoprocess.com
Year Founded: 1968
Sales Range: $10-24.9 Million
Emp.: 30
Pumps, Pumping Equipment, Strainers, Gear Boxes, Mixers, Motors & Drives Distr
N.A.I.C.S.: 423830
Diane Schleicher *(Pres)*
Dick Puhak *(Mgr-Svcs)*

ARS ADVERTISING, LLC.

626 W Jackson Blvd Ste 100, Chicago, IL 60661
Tel.: (866) 787-9275
Web Site: http://www.aislerocket.com
Sales Range: $10-24.9 Million
Emp.: 40
Advetising Agency
N.A.I.C.S.: 541810
Ronda Scalise *(Pres)*
Ross Shelleman *(CEO)*
Greg Slama *(Exec VP-Media)*
Subsidiaries:

ARS Advertising   (1)
511 Renaissance Dr Ste 150, Saint Joseph, MI 49085
Tel.: (269) 982-6600
Advetising Agency
N.A.I.C.S.: 541810

ARS Advertising   (1)
2800 W. Higgins Rd Ste 1200, Hoffman Estates, IL 60169
Tel.: (847) 882-9703
Web Site: http://thinkars.com
Emp.: 30
Advetising Agency
N.A.I.C.S.: 541810

Target Data, Inc.   (1)
626 W Jackson Blvd Ste 100, Chicago, IL 60661
Tel.: (312) 508-4305
Web Site: https://www.aislerocket.com
Advertising Services
N.A.I.C.S.: 541810
Scott Bailey *(Exec VP-Strategy & Analytics)*
Craig Leidlein *(VP-Fin & Admin)*
Don Aicklen *(Chief Revenue Officer)*
Jen Strojin *(VP-Client Svcs)*
Laura Ziemer *(Dir-Strategy)*
Dave Cameron *(VP-Analytics)*
Edward Yeh *(VP-Tech)*
Joseph Lavan *(VP-Digital Strategy)*
David E. Cook Jr. *(Sr VP-Sls)*

Subsidiary (Domestic):

Social Fulcrum LLC   (2)
109 Kingston St Fl 4, Boston, MA 02111
Tel.: (617) 820-5270
Online Advertising Services
N.A.I.C.S.: 541840

ARS WEALTH ADVISORS, LLC

111 2nd Ave NE Ste 1600, Saint Petersburg, FL 33701
Tel.: (727) 322-7681
Web Site: http://www.arswealth.com
Year Founded: 1997
Rev.: $249,000,000
Emp.: 8

Investment Banking & Advisory Services
N.A.I.C.S.: 523150
Anthony A. Anderson *(CEO & Mng Partner)*

ARSALON TECHNOLOGIES, LLC

10605 W 84th Terr, Lenexa, KS 66214
Tel.: (913) 339-6260
Web Site: http://www.arsalon.net
Year Founded: 2001
Sales Range: $1-9.9 Million
Emp.: 25
Hosting Services
N.A.I.C.S.: 518210
Bryan Porter *(Co-Owner)*
Gary Hall *(Co-Owner)*
Brad Hajek *(Dir-Engrg)*
Annie Brock *(Dir-Sls)*

ARSENAL CAPITAL MANAGEMENT LP

100 Park Ave 31st Fl, New York, NY 10017
Tel.: (212) 771-1717   DE
Web Site:
   http://www.arsenalcapital.com
Year Founded: 2000
Privater Equity Firm
N.A.I.C.S.: 523999
David Spaight *(Operating Partner)*
Terrence M. Mullen *(Co-Founder & Mng Partner)*
Jeffrey B. Kovach *(Mng Partner)*
Joelle Marquis *(Sr Partner-Human Capital)*
John Y. Televantos *(Sr Partner)*
Timothy J. Zappala *(Sr Partner)*
Stephen M. McLean *(Sr Partner)*
Brian Orkin *(Partner-Investment)*
Eugene Gorbach *(Partner-Investment)*
Joseph Rooney *(Partner-Investment)*
Frank D. Scrudato *(CFO & Chief Compliance Officer)*
Patricia Grad *(Partner & Head-IR)*
Michelle Nasir *(Chief Talent Officer)*
Marc Tremblay *(Operating Partner)*

Subsidiaries:

Accumen, Inc.   (1)
3333 N Hayden Rd, Suite 1, Scottsdale, AZ 85251
Tel.: (800) 860-5454
Web Site: http://www.accumen.com
Healtcare Services
N.A.I.C.S.: 621999
George H. Ellis *(CFO)*
BG Porter *(CEO)*
Joanna Peyton *(COO & Chief HR Officer)*
John McGahey *(Chief Revenue Officer)*
George H. Ellis *(CFO)*

Allied Blending & Ingredients, Inc.   (1)
121 Royal Rd, Keokuk, IA 52632
Tel.: (319) 526-6440
Web Site: http://www.alliedblending.com
Fiber & Starch Based Products Mfr
N.A.I.C.S.: 311999
Tara Perry *(Dir-Sls & Mktg Admin)*
Chandrani Atapattu *(Dir-Ingredient Innovations)*
Veronica Banuelos *(Mgr)*

Subsidiary (Domestic):

Ingredients Unlimited, Inc.   (2)
5690 Lindbergh Ln, Bell, CA 90201
Tel.: (319) 526-6448
Web Site: http://www.alliedblending.com
Ingredient Blending
N.A.I.C.S.: 311999

Mississippi Blending Company, Inc.   (2)
121 Royal Rd, Keokuk, IA 52632
Tel.: (319) 526-6440
Web Site: http://www.alliedblending.com

Fiber & Starch Based Products Mfr
N.A.I.C.S.: 311999

CPS Performance Materials Corp.   (1)
100 W Main St, Bound Brook, NJ 08805
Tel.: (732) 469-7760
Web Site:
   http://cpsperformancematerials.com
Specialty Chemicals Mfr
N.A.I.C.S.: 325998
Jeremy Steinfink *(CEO)*
Robert Nobile *(CFO)*

Subsidiary (Domestic):

Cyalume Technologies Holdings, Inc.   (2)
910 SE 17th St Ste 300, Fort Lauderdale, FL 33316
Tel.: (888) 858-7881
Web Site: http://www.cyalume.com
Holding Company; Chemical & Electronic Light Systems Mfr
N.A.I.C.S.: 551112
Earl Cranor *(VP-Tech)*
Donald Schmidt *(Sr VP-Products, Program Mgmt & Sls)*
Robert Nobile *(CFO)*
Jeremy Steinfink *(CEO)*

GEO Specialty Chemicals, Inc.   (2)
300 Brookside Ave Bldg 23 Ste 100, Ambler, PA 19002-3420
Tel.: (215) 773-9280
Web Site: http://www.geosc.com
Dispersant Specialty Chemicals Mfr
N.A.I.C.S.: 325998
Caren Shedd *(Dir-Payroll & Corp HR Policy)*

Plant (Domestic):

GEO Specialty Chemicals - Bastrop   (3)
1502 N Washington St, Bastrop, LA 71220-2419
Tel.: (318) 281-5131
Web Site: http://www.geosc.com
Water Treatment Chemical Products Mfr
N.A.I.C.S.: 325998

GEO Specialty Chemicals - Cedartown   (3)
701 Wissahickon Ave, Cedartown, GA 30125-2562
Tel.: (770) 748-1200
Web Site: http://www.geosc.com
Sales Range: $25-49.9 Million
Emp.: 75
Construction & Industrial Chemical Products Mfr
N.A.I.C.S.: 325998
Mike Hunter *(Plant Mgr)*

Carolina Color Corporation   (1)
100 E 17th St, Salisbury, NC 28144
Tel.: (704) 637-7000
Web Site: http://www.carocolor.com
Plastics Industry Customized Color Concentrates Developer & Mfr
N.A.I.C.S.: 325211
Matt Barr *(Chm & CEO)*
Jeff Smink *(Pres)*

Subsidiary (Domestic):

Carolina Color Corporation of Ohio   (2)
100 Colomet Dr, Delaware, OH 43015
Tel.: (740) 363-6622
Web Site: http://www.carolinacolor.com
Plastics Industry Customized Color Concentrates Developer & Mfr
N.A.I.C.S.: 325211
Bryan Ball *(Mgr-Quality Control)*
Bryan Artrip *(Plant Mgr)*
Kim Caldwell *(Mgr-Customer Svc)*
Rick Martz *(Mgr-Lab)*

Chroma Color Corporation   (2)
3900 W Dayton St, McHenry, IL 60050-8378
Tel.: (815) 385-8100
Web Site: http://www.chromacolors.com
Sales Range: $1-9.9 Million
Color & Additive Compounding for Thermoplastics
N.A.I.C.S.: 325510

Howard DeMonte *(Pres)*
Matt Barr *(Vice Chm)*
Gerald Baillargeon *(CFO)*
Shruti Singhal *(Pres & CEO)*

Subsidiary (Domestic):

Epolin, LLC   (3)
358-364 Adams St, Newark, NJ 07105
Tel.: (973) 465-9495
Web Site: http://www.epolin.com
Infrared & Laser Absorbing Dyes Developer, Mfr & Marketer
N.A.I.C.S.: 325130
Michael Crosby *(Pres)*

Spectra Color, Inc.   (3)
9116 Stellar Ct, Corona, CA 92883
Tel.: (951) 277-0200
Rev.: $7,353,100
Emp.: 42
Elevator & Moving Stairway Mfr
N.A.I.C.S.: 333921
Robert Shedd *(Pres)*
Mike Bills *(Engr-Maintenance)*

CellCarta Precision Medicine Inc.   (1)
201 ave President Kennedy Ste 3900, Montreal, H2X 3Y7, QC, Canada
Tel.: (514) 360-3600
Web Site: http://www.caprion.com
Pharmaceutical Research & Development Services
N.A.I.C.S.: 541715
Martin LeBlanc *(Pres & CEO)*
Daniel Chelsky *(Chief Scientific Officer)*
Eustache Paramithiotis *(VP- Discovery)*
Normand Rivard *(Sr VP & CFO)*
Carol Barry *(Sr VP & Chief Bus Officer)*
Patrick Tremblay *(Sr VP-Corp Dev)*
Lorella Di Donato *(Sr VP-Scientific Ops)*
Laura McIntosh *(VP-Translational Res)*
Benoit Houle *(VP-Bus Dev)*

Subsidiary (US):

Primity Bio, Inc.   (2)
48383 Fremont Blvd Ste 118, Fremont, CA 94538
Tel.: (510) 210-0605
Web Site: http://www.primitybio.com
Biotechnology Research & Development
N.A.I.C.S.: 541714

Reveal Biosciences, Inc.   (2)
6760 Top Gun St Ste 110, San Diego, CA 92121
Tel.: (858) 274-3663
Web Site: http://www.revealbio.com
Research & Development in Biotechnology
N.A.I.C.S.: 541714
Claire Weston *(Founder & CEO)*

Cello Health plc   (1)
Queens House 8-9 Queen Street, London, EC4N 1SP, United Kingdom
Tel.: (44) 2078128460
Web Site: http://www.cellohealthplc.com
Rev.: $218,735,532
Assets: $183,275,114
Liabilities: $75,196,651
Net Worth: $108,078,463
Earnings: ($1,236,839)
Emp.: 907
Fiscal Year-end: 12/31/2019
Advertising Services
N.A.I.C.S.: 541810
Mark Scott *(CEO)*
Mark Bentley *(Dir-Fin Grp)*
Stephen Highley *(COO)*
Andy Brown *(Sec)*
Jacqueline Briggs *(Chief HR Officer)*

Subsidiary (Domestic):

2CV Limited   (2)
12 Flitcroft Street Covent Garden, London, WC2H 8DL, United Kingdom
Tel.: (44) 20 7 655 9900
Web Site: http://www.2cv.com
Emp.: 100
Consumer Research Agency Services
N.A.I.C.S.: 541910
Mark Bagnall *(Mng Dir)*

Subsidiary (US):

2CV Inc   (3)
460 Bush St FL 1 180 mount gomergung str 1550, San Francisco, CA 94104
Tel.: (415) 956-1004

ARSENAL CAPITAL MANAGEMENT LP

U.S. PRIVATE

Arsenal Capital Management LP—(Continued)

Web Site: http://www.2cv.com
Emp.: 20
Consumer Research Agency Services
N.A.I.C.S.: 541910
Maria Joan Payuran (Controller-Quality)

Subsidiary (US):

Advantage Healthcare, Inc. (2)
475 Wall St, Princeton, NJ 08540
Tel.: (609) 683-1911
Web Site: http://www.advantageh.com
Management Consulting Services
N.A.I.C.S.: 541618
Debbie Glick (Mng Partner)
Leslie Goldberg (Mng Partner)

Subsidiary (Domestic):

Brightsource Limited (2)
St James House St James Square, Chel-
tenham, GL50 3PR, United Kingdom
Tel.: (44) 1242 534200
Web Site: http://www.brightsource.co.uk
Emp.: 80
General Marketing Services
N.A.I.C.S.: 541613
Barney Hosey (Mng Dir)
Eddie Sheppard (Dir-Ops)
Emily Gore (Mng Partner)
Karen Mason (Dir-Project Delivery)
Minh Huynh (Dir-Fin)
Peter Frings (Mng Dir)
Rupert Tucker (Head-Creative Dev)
Tim Jones (Head-Studio Svcs)

Division (Domestic):

Cello Health (2)
11-13 Charterhouse Buildings, London,
EC1M 7AP, United Kingdom
Tel.: (44) 20 7812 8460
Web Site: http://www.cellohealth.com
Emp.: 130
Healthcare Industry Advertising Services
N.A.I.C.S.: 541810
Jon Bircher (Chief Comml Officer)
Isaac Batley (COO-Europe)
Steve Smith (Chief Comml Dev Officer-
Europe)
Rick Lang (Sr VP-Digital)
Craig Lipski (Sr Dir-Application Dev)
John Howley (Mng Dir-Comm-MedErgy)
Duncan Munro (Head-Specialist Quantita-
tive Res Practice IQ-Insight)
Mark Scott (CEO)

Subsidiary (US):

Defined Health, Inc. (3)
25-B Hanover Rd Ste 320, Florham Park,
NJ 07932
Tel.: (973) 292-5001
Web Site: http://www.definedhealth.com
Management Consulting Services
N.A.I.C.S.: 541618
Edward C. Saltzman (Executives)
Edward C. Saltzman (Executives)
Jeffrey M. Bockman (Exec VP & Head-
Oncology Practice)
Ginger S. Johnson (CEO)
Ginny E. Llobell (Sr VP-Bus Dev & Mktg)
Ed Saltzman (Exec Chm)
Janet Czachura (Principal)
David J. Lomb (Assoc Principal)
Danielle M. Marra (Assoc Principal)
Michael C Rice (Principal)
Joel S. Sandler (Assoc Principal)

MedErgy HealthGroup Inc. (3)
790 Township Line Rd Ste 200, Yardley, PA
19067-4261
Tel.: (215) 504-5082
Web Site: http://www.medergygroup.com
Advertising Services
N.A.I.C.S.: 519290
Julia Ralston (Pres & CEO)
Rhea Ogawa (VP & Grp Acct Supvr)

Subsidiary (Domestic):

Scifluent Communications Inc (4)
790 Township Line Rd Ste 210, Yardley, PA
19067
Tel.: (267) 364-6070
Web Site: http://www.scifluent.com
Medical Writing Services
N.A.I.C.S.: 541990

Jacqueline Briggs (Dir-HR & Admin)
Kathleen A. McConnell (Mng Dir)

Subsidiary (US):

Promedica Inc. (3)
577 Airport Blvd Ste 130, Burlingame, CA
94010-2021
Tel.: (650) 344-6242
Web Site: http://www.promedicainc.com
Marketing Research Consulting Services
N.A.I.C.S.: 541613
Joan Day (Co-Founder & Pres)
Susan Rowen (Co-Founder & Exec VP)
Richard Burke (VP)
Robert Singer (VP)

Division (Domestic):

Cello Signal (2)
86 Commercial Quay Commercial Street,
Edinburgh, EH6 6LX, United Kingdom
Tel.: (44) 1312420005
Web Site: http://www.cellosignal.com
Advertising Services
N.A.I.C.S.: 541810

Subsidiary (Domestic):

Blonde Digital Ltd. (3)
86/3 Commercial Quay Commercial Street,
Edinburgh, EH6 6LX, United Kingdom
Tel.: (44) 131 526 303
Web Site: http://www.blonde.net
Emp.: 60
Advertising Services
N.A.I.C.S.: 541810
Pete Burns (Mng Dir)

Subsidiary (Domestic):

Line Digital Limited (4)
77 Brunswick St, Edinburgh, EH7 5HS,
Scotland, United Kingdom
Tel.: (44) 131 524 3260
Web Site: http://www.line.uk.com
Sales Range: $1-9.9 Million
Emp.: 20
Digital Advertising Services
N.A.I.C.S.: 541810
Ross Laurie (Co-Founder & Mng Dir)
Ben Ausden (Dir-Technical & Co-Founder)

Subsidiary (Domestic):

**Leapfrog Research & Planning
Limited** (3)
Priory House Cloisters Business Centre
Battersea Park Rd, London, SW8 4BG,
United Kingdom
Tel.: (44) 1753 271 400
Web Site: http://www.leapfrogresearch.co.uk
Emp.: 50
Advertising Services
N.A.I.C.S.: 541830
Julie Hindmarch (Mgr-Qualitative)
Chrissie Wells (Head-Quantitative)
Kate Anderson (Gen Mgr)

The Leith Agency (3)
86/2 Commercial Quay, Leith, Edinburgh,
EH6 6LX, United Kingdom
Tel.: (44) 131 561 8600
Web Site: http://www.leith.co.uk
Emp.: 60
Advertising Agencies
N.A.I.C.S.: 541810
Richard Marsham (Mng Partner)
Ed Brooke (Head-Leith)
Troy Farnworth (Dir-Creative)
Phil Evans (Dir-Creative)
Brian Coane (Partner)
Fiona Burton (Partner-Client)

Subsidiary (US):

**Innovative Science Solutions,
LLP** (2)
67 E Park Pl, Morristown, NJ 07960
Tel.: (973) 889-1600
Web Site: http://www.innovativescience.net
Sales Range: $1-9.9 Million
Teleproduction & Other Postproduction Ser-
vices
N.A.I.C.S.: 512191
Steven M. Weisman (Owner)
David H. Schwartz (Chief Scientific Officer)

Subsidiary (Domestic):

Mash Health Limited (2)

Harlequin House 7 High Street, Teddington,
TW11 8EE, United Kingdom
Tel.: (44) 20 8977 6364
Web Site: http://www.mashhealth.com
Healthcare Management Consulting Ser-
vices
N.A.I.C.S.: 621491
Jane Ayton (Pres, CEO & Mng Dir)

Opticomm Media Limited (2)
31 Old Nichol Street, London, E2 7HR,
United Kingdom
Tel.: (44) 2078746573
Web Site: http://www.opticomm.co.uk
Emp.: 15
Media Buying Agency
N.A.I.C.S.: 541830

RS Consulting Limited (2)
11-13 Charterhouse Buildings, London,
EC1M 7AP, United Kingdom
Tel.: (44) 20 7627 7700
Web Site:
    http://www.breakingblueresearch.com
General Marketing Services
N.A.I.C.S.: 541613
Andrew Wood (Dir-Res)
Amie Luther (Mgr-Res)
Christoph Koerbitz (Assoc Dir)
Kate Anderson (Mng Dir)
Martin Wootton (Dir-Res)

Tangible Group Limited (2)
The Brass Foundry 7 Midford Place, Lon-
don, W1T 5BG, United Kingdom
Tel.: (44) 20 7881 3200
Emp.: 30
Consumer Research Agency Services
N.A.I.C.S.: 541910
Liz Hanks (Head-Data & Insight)
John Rowley (Chm)
Jonathan Spooner (Exec Dir-Creative)
Karen Trickett (CEO)
Michael White (Mgr-Mktg Sys)
Minh Huynh (Dir-Fin)
Sue Byde (Sr Dir-Acct)
Nathan Shilton (Head-Data Mgmt)
Paul Becque (Chief Strategy Officer)

The Value Engineers Limited (2)
12 Flitcroft Street, London, WC2H 8DL,
Buckinghamshire, United Kingdom
Tel.: (44) 2039543032
Web Site:
    http://www.thevalueengineers.com
General Marketing Services
N.A.I.C.S.: 541613
Paul Walton (Founder)

Danlin Industries Corp. (1)
601 E Fresco St, Thomas, OK 73669
Tel.: (580) 661-3248
Web Site: http://www.danlin.us
Sales Range: $1-9.9 Million
Oil/Gas Field Machinery Mfr
N.A.I.C.S.: 333132
Jimmy Johnson (Acct Mgr)

H A Eckhart & Associates, Inc. (1)
16185 National Pkwy, Lansing, MI 48906
Tel.: (517) 321-7700
Web Site: http://www.eckhartusa.com
Emp.: 400
Industrial Machinery Mfr
N.A.I.C.S.: 333248
Bob Breard (VP)
Daniel Burseth (VP)
Michael Stob (Treas)
Andy Storm (Pres & CEO)

Subsidiary (Domestic):

Auto Craft Tool & Die Co. (2)
1800 Fruit St, Algonac, MI 48001
Tel.: (810) 794-4929
Web Site: http://www.auto-craft.com
Sales Range: $10-24.9 Million
Emp.: 45
Manufacture Special Dies, Tools, Jigs &
Fixtures
N.A.I.C.S.: 333514

Eagle Engineering, Inc. (2)
2701 South First St, Eldridge, IA 52748
Tel.: (563) 285-7515
Web Site: http://www.eckhartusa.com
Civil, Geotechnical & Environmental Engi-
neering, Land Surveying & Materials Testing
N.A.I.C.S.: 237990
Bryan Purdy (Pres)

Gasper Engineering, Inc (2)
3450 4th St, North Vernon, IN 47265
Tel.: (812) 346-2323
Other Commercial & Service Industry Ma-
chinery Mfr
N.A.I.C.S.: 333310

International Fiber Corp. (1)
50 Bridge St, North Tonawanda, NY 14120-
6842
Tel.: (716) 693-4040
Web Site: http://www.ifcfiber.com
Sales Range: $50-74.9 Million
Fiber Processor for Food, Cheese, Pharma-
ceutical, Pet Food & Industrial Applications
N.A.I.C.S.: 325220
Jit Ang (Exec VP-New Bus Dev)
Peter Vogt (Exec VP-Mfg)

Subsidiary (Domestic):

Fibred-Maryland, Inc. (2)
543 National Hwy, La Vale, MD 21502-7043
Tel.: (301) 724-6050
Web Site: http://www.fibred.com
Sales Range: $1-9.9 Million
Emp.: 45
Soy Fiber Products Mfr
N.A.I.C.S.: 339999
Rhonda Niland (Mgr-Quality Assurance)
Karen Ort (VP-Sls)

Lockwood Industries Inc. (1)
28525 W Industrial Dr, Valencia, CA 91355
Tel.: (661) 702-6999
Web Site: http://www.fralock.com
Insulators & Insulation Materials, Electrical
N.A.I.C.S.: 335932
Marc Haugen (CEO)
Marc Haugen (CEO)

Subsidiary (Domestic):

Career Technologies USA (2)
9134 Independence Ave, Chatsworth, CA
91311
Tel.: (818) 701-5391
Web Site: http://www.careertech-usa.com
Circuit Design & Fabrication Services
N.A.I.C.S.: 541490

Lenthor Engineering, LLC (2)
311 Turquoise St, Milpitas, CA 95035
Tel.: (408) 945-8787
Web Site: http://www.lenthor.com
Bare Printed Circuit Board Mfr
N.A.I.C.S.: 334412
Mark Lencioni (Pres)

Oasis Materials Corporation (2)
12131 Community Rd Ste D, Poway, CA
92064-8893
Tel.: (858) 486-8846
Web Site: http://www.oasismaterials.com
Performance Ceramic Heaters Mfr
N.A.I.C.S.: 333414
Frank Polese (Pres)
Steve Nootens (VP)

Lumanity, Inc. (1)
7315 Wisconsin Ave 950 W Tower,
Bethesda, MD 20814
Tel.: (702) 776-0985
Web Site: https://lumanity.com
Information Research Services
N.A.I.C.S.: 519290
Edward C. Saltzman (Head-Biotech Strat-
egy)
Edward C. Saltzman (Head-Biotech Strat-
egy)
Jon Williams (CEO)

Subsidiary (Domestic):

Clarion Healthcare, LLC (2)
1 Financial Ctr Ste 1610, Boston, MA 02111
Tel.: (617) 757-7850
Web Site: http://www.clarionhealthcare.com
Life Sciences Strategy & Organizational
Consulting Services
N.A.I.C.S.: 541715
Daniel J. Hawkins (Co-Founder & Mng Dir)
Jessica Blaustein (Dir-Mktg)

Marlen Textiles Inc. (1)
500 Orchard St, New Haven, MO 63068-
1108
Tel.: (573) 237-4444
Web Site: http://www.marlentextiles.com
Sales Range: $1-9.9 Million
Emp.: 24

Coated, Laminated & Solution Dyed Polyester Fabrics Mfr
N.A.I.C.S.: 313320
Rodney Washburn (Pres)

Meridian Adhesives Group LLC (1)
2 Memorial City Plz 820 Gessner Rd Ste 1145, Houston, TX 77024
Tel.: (800) 868-4583
Web Site: http://www.meridianadhesives.com
Adhesives & Sealants Mfr
N.A.I.C.S.: 339991
Daniel Pelton (CEO)
John Knudsen (CFO)

Subsidiary (Domestic):

Adhesives Technology Corp. (2)
450 E Copans Rd, Pompano Beach, FL 33064
Tel.: (800) 892-1880
Web Site: http://www.atcepoxy.com
Adhesive Mfr
N.A.I.C.S.: 325520
Joseph Hanley (Dir-Engrg)

American Sealants, Inc. (2)
3806 Option Pass, Fort Wayne, IN 46818
Tel.: (260) 489-0728
Web Site: http://www.americansealantsinc.com
Rev.: $4,666,666
Emp.: 20
Adhesive Mfr
N.A.I.C.S.: 325520
Brian Harruff (Mgr-Sls)
Andrew Zaremba (Pres)

Evans Adhesive Corporation (2)
925 Old Henderson Rd, Columbus, OH 43220-3722
Tel.: (614) 451-2665
Web Site: http://www.evansadhesive.com
Sales Range: $75-99.9 Million
Emp.: 65
Industrial & Commercial Adhesives & Related Products Mfr
N.A.I.C.S.: 325520
Will Little (Controller)
Rusty Thompson (Pres)
Jean Hollo (VP-Sls)
Jeff Swoboda (Dir-R&D & Laboratory Svcs)

FRI Resins Holding Co. (2)
21 Starline Way, Cranston, RI 02921
Tel.: (401) 946-5564
Web Site: http://www.epoxies.com
Other Chemical & Allied Products Merchant Whslr
N.A.I.C.S.: 424690

WF Taylor Co., Inc. (2)
11545 Pacific Ave, Fontana, CA 92337
Tel.: (951) 360-6677
Web Site: http://www.wftaylor.com
Sales Range: $10-24.9 Million
Emp.: 60
Adhesives & Sealants
N.A.I.C.S.: 325520
Barry Wright (Exec VP)
Michael J. Raidy (VP-Sls-Western)
Robert Ddamulira (VP-R&D & Ops)
Kenneth R. Sandefur (Treas & VP)
Paul K. Murfin (Pres)
John E. Raidy Sr. (CEO)

Peach State Lab, LLC (1)
180 Burlington Rd, Rome, GA 30162-1087
Tel.: (706) 291-8743
Web Site: http://www.peachstatelabs.com
Emp.: 25
Polymer Chemicals Mfr
N.A.I.C.S.: 424690
Dennis Nance (VP)

Polycorp Ltd. (1)
One University Avenue Suite 402, Toronto, M5J 2P1, ON, Canada
Tel.: (416) 364-2241
Web Site: http://www.poly-corp.com
Rev.: $13,800,000
Emp.: 100
Polymer Product Mfr
N.A.I.C.S.: 326299
Andrew Haber (VP & Gen Mgr)
Pramod Kumar (Dir-Mining Products)

Polytek Development Corp. (1)
55 Hilton St, Easton, PA 18042
Tel.: (610) 559-8620
Web Site: http://www.polytek.com

Specialty Polymers & Synthetic Rubber Mfr
N.A.I.C.S.: 325212
Joseph Lawrence (Mgr)

Subsidiary (Domestic):

Alumilite, Inc (2)
1458 S 35th St, Galesburg, MI 49053
Tel.: (269) 488-4000
Web Site: http://www.alumilite.com
All Other Plastics Product Mfr
N.A.I.C.S.: 326199

BCC Products Inc. (2)
2140 Earlywood Dr, Franklin, IN 46131-8870
Tel.: (317) 736-4090
Web Site: http://www.bccproducts.com
Plastics Material & Resin Mfr
N.A.I.C.S.: 325211

California Medical Innovations (2)
872 Towne Ctr Dr, Pomona, CA 91767
Tel.: (909) 621-5871
Web Site: http://www.cal-med-innovations.com
Natural Rubber Latex, Plastisols (PVCs) & Thermoplastic Elastomers Mfr
N.A.I.C.S.: 326299

Endurance Technologies, Inc. (2)
275 Bridgepoint Dr, South Saint Paul, MN 55075
Tel.: (651) 451-8000
Web Site: http://www.epoxi.com
Sales Range: $1-9.9 Million
Emp.: 13
Plastics Material & Resin Mfr
N.A.I.C.S.: 325211
Peter Hoeffel (CEO)

Environmental Technology, Inc. (2)
PO Box 365, Fields Landing, CA 95537
Tel.: (707) 443-9323
Web Site: http://www.eti-usa.com
Plastics Material & Resin Mfr
N.A.I.C.S.: 325211
David Fonsen (Pres)

Revolution Sustainable Solutions, LLC (1)
8801 Frazier Pike, Little Rock, AR 72206
Tel.: (800) 277-9172
Web Site: http://www.revolutioncompany.com
Plastics Material & Resin Mfr
N.A.I.C.S.: 325211
Sean Whiteley (CEO)

Subsidiary (Domestic):

Jadcore LLC (2)
300 N Fruitridge Ave, Terre Haute, IN 47803
Tel.: (812) 234-2724
Web Site: http://www.jadcore.com
Emp.: 250
Plastics Material & Resin Mfr
N.A.I.C.S.: 325211
Jim Hensle (Dir-Info Sys)
Rob Doti (Pres)
Dean Doti (VP-Sls)

Norflex, Inc. (2)
720 Norflex Dr, Hudson, WI 54016
Tel.: (715) 386-0887
Web Site: http://www.norflex.com
Rev.: $2,500,000
Emp.: 25
Fiscal Year-end: 12/31/2006
Mfg Unsupported Plastic Film/Sheet
N.A.I.C.S.: 326113

The Copernicus Group, Inc. (1)
5000 CentreGreen Way Ste 200, Cary, NC 27513
Tel.: (919) 465-4310
Web Site: http://www.cgirb.com
Clinical Trial Review Organization
N.A.I.C.S.: 813920
Donald A. Deieso (Chm)
Andrew Messick (CFO)
Dawn Pope (COO)
Jennifer Sodrel (CTO)
Angie Gustafson (Assoc Dir-Study Mgmt Ops)
Megan Aiken (Dir-Ops)
Dave Borasky (VP-Quality)

Velsicol Chemical Corporation (1)

10400 W Higgins Rd Ste 700, Rosemont, IL 60018-3713
Tel.: (847) 813-7888
Web Site: http://www.velsicol.com
Sales Range: $25-49.9 Million
Emp.: 9
Specialty Chemicals Mfr
N.A.I.C.S.: 325180

Western Institutional Review Board, Inc. (1)
1019 39th Ave SE Ste 120, Puyallup, WA 98374
Tel.: (360) 252-2500
Web Site: http://www.wirb.com
Medical Review Organization
N.A.I.C.S.: 813920
Laurie L. Jackson (CFO & COO)
David G. Forster (Chief Compliance Officer)
R. Bert Wilkins (Dir-Regulatory Affairs)

ARSENAL GROUP, LLC
21 Greene Ave, Amityville, NY 11701
Tel.: (631) 608-8900
Web Site: http://www.arsenalgrp.com
Equity Investment Firm
N.A.I.C.S.: 523999
Gary Kania (Mng Dir)
Lionel Singh (CFO)

ARSENAL SECURITY GROUP, INC.
1750 Tysons Blvd 4th Fl, McLean, VA 22102
Tel.: (703) 986-1700
Year Founded: 2005
Rev.: $3,800,000
Emp.: 30
Management Consulting Services
N.A.I.C.S.: 541611
Russell Teague (Pres & Sr Partner)

ARSENAL STRENGTH LLC
11234 Gilbert Dr, Knoxville, TN 37932
Tel.: (865) 333-5444   TN
Web Site: http://www.myarsenalstrength.com
Year Founded: 2014
Sales Range: $1-9.9 Million
Emp.: 4
Gym Equipment Distr
N.A.I.C.S.: 423910
Jamie Kelling Hall (Founder)

ARSO RADIO CORPORATION
Luis Munoz Marin Ave 24, Caguas, PR 00725
Tel.: (787) 744-3131
Web Site: http://www.salsoul.com
Rev.: $10,708,004
Emp.: 35
Radio Broadcasting Stations
N.A.I.C.S.: 516110
Jesus M. Soto (CEO)

ART & FRAME DIRECT INC.
11423 Satellite Blvd, Orlando, FL 32837
Tel.: (407) 857-6000
Web Site: https://www.afdhome.com
Rev.: $26,221,768
Emp.: 80
Frames For Artists' Canvases
N.A.I.C.S.: 339940
George A. Eouse (Pres & CEO)

ART & LOGIC, INC.
2 N Lake Ave Ste 1050, Pasadena, CA 91101
Tel.: (818) 500-1933
Web Site: http://www.artandlogic.com
Year Founded: 1991
Sales Range: $50-74.9 Million
Emp.: 50
Software Developer
N.A.I.C.S.: 541512
Paul Hershenson (Founder)
Bob Bajoras (Pres)

ART GAMBLIN MOTORS
1047 Roosevelt Ave, Enumclaw, WA 98022
Tel.: (360) 825-3567
Web Site: http://www.gamblinmotors.com
Year Founded: 1969
Sales Range: $25-49.9 Million
Emp.: 65
Sales of Automobiles
N.A.I.C.S.: 441110
Alan Gamblin (Owner & Pres)
Mark Maxey (Controller)
Rick Josie (Mgr-Sls)
Ken Brons (Mgr-Parts)

ART GUILD INC.
300 Wolf Dr, West Deptford, NJ 08086
Tel.: (856) 853-7500
Web Site: https://www.artguildinc.com
Rev.: $10,000,000
Emp.: 100
Creation & Management of 3-D Marketing & Educational Programs
N.A.I.C.S.: 339950
John Seyler (Acct Mgr)
Om Machhar (Exec VP)
Dave Chan (Dir-Creative)
Bonnie J. Sanders (Mgr-Pur)
Diane Riffitts (Mgr-IT)
John Breshock (Mgr-Logistics)
Randy Murschell (Mgr-Logistics)
Doug Zegel (Pres)
Joe Simpson (Project Mgr)
Mark Weaver (Project Mgr)
Brian Fijalkowski (Project Mgr-Retail Displays & Fixtures)
Danielle Forte (Sr Acct Mgr)
Kenneth Kunz (Supvr-Graphics Storage)
Meghan Costello (Sr Acct Mgr)
Jeff Jamison (VP-Bus Dev)

ART HAUSER INSURANCE, INC.
8260 Northcreek Dr Ste 200, Cincinnati, OH 45236
Tel.: (513) 745-9200   OH
Web Site: http://www.hauser1.com
Year Founded: 1981
Insurance, Employee Benefits & Investment Products & Services
N.A.I.C.S.: 524210
Jeffrey Dixon (Mgr-Claims-Corp Risk)
Joseph M. Worrall (Pres-Corp Risk)
James Stines (CEO-Employee Benefits)
Mitch Stookey (VP-Individual Risk)
Cameron Martin (Exec VP)

Subsidiaries:

Hauser Capital Markets LLC (1)
5905 E Galbraith Rd Ste 9000, Cincinnati, OH 45236   **(100%)**
Tel.: (513) 745-9200
Web Site: http://www.thehausergroup.com
Emp.: 70
Corporate Investment Services
N.A.I.C.S.: 523999
Paul Swanson (Pres & CEO)
Janna Laudato (Mng Dir)
Daniel Heidenreich (Principal)
Jeff Dixon (Mgr-Claims)

ART HILL INC.
901 W Lincoln Hwy, Merrillville, IN 46410
Tel.: (219) 738-5300
Web Site: https://www.arthillautogroup.com
Sales Range: $50-74.9 Million
Emp.: 75
Automobiles, New & Used
N.A.I.C.S.: 441110

Art Hill Inc.—(Continued)
Arthur Fairchild (Co-Pres)
William Fairchild (Co-Pres)

ART IRON, INC.
860 Curtis St, Toledo, OH 43609-2304
Tel.: (419) 241-1261   **OH**
Web Site: http://www.artiron.com
Year Founded: 1905
Metals, Steel & Aluminum Distr & Mfr
N.A.I.C.S.: 423510
Robert Schlatter (Pres)
Ron Grothaus (Project Coord)

ART LEWIN & CO.
112 W Ninth St Showroom 626, Los Angeles, CA 90015
Tel.: (213) 785-2400
Web Site:
     http://www.losangelesbespoke.com
Year Founded: 1997
Sales Range: $1-9.9 Million
Emp.: 60
Custom & Ready-Made Executive Clothiers
N.A.I.C.S.: 315250
Art Lewin (Pres)

ART LINE INC.
5200 Proviso Dr, Melrose Park, IL 60162
Tel.: (708) 449-8100
Rev.: $30,000,000
Emp.: 140
Lawn Ornaments
N.A.I.C.S.: 339999
Marcie Hooker (Office Mgr)

ART MORAN PONTIAC-GMC TRUCK-MITSUBISHI INC.
29300 Telegraph Rd, Southfield, MI 48034
Tel.: (248) 353-9000   **MI**
Web Site: http://www.artmoran.com
Year Founded: 1972
Sales Range: $125-149.9 Million
Emp.: 137
Sales of Automobiles & Trucks
N.A.I.C.S.: 441110
Arthur Moran (Owner)
Carol Charron (Treas, Sec & Controller)

ART OF BUSINESS, INC.
345 Morgantown Rd, Reading, PA 19611
Tel.: (610) 376-4871   **PA**
Web Site:
     http://www.artofbusiness.com
Year Founded: 1953
Sales Range: $10-24.9 Million
Beauty Parlor Equipment & Supplies Distr
N.A.I.C.S.: 423850
Howard Hafetz (Treas)
Joshua Hafetz (Pres)
Chriz Raszkiewicz (VP)
Elaine Hafetz (Sec)

ART RESOURCE, INC.
65 Bleecker St 12th Fl, New York, NY 10012
Tel.: (212) 505-8700   **NY**
Web Site: https://www.artres.com
Year Founded: 1967
Sales Range: $10-24.9 Million
Emp.: 35
Fine Art Stock Photo Archives
N.A.I.C.S.: 519290
Theodore Feder (Pres)

ART STONE THEATRICAL CORP.
1795 Express Dr N, Smithtown, NY 11787
Tel.: (631) 582-9500
Web Site:
     http://www.artstonecostumes.com
Rev.: $16,800,000
Emp.: 300
Mail-Order Houses
N.A.I.C.S.: 424340
Arthur Stone (Pres)

ART SUPPLY ENTERPRISES INC.
1375 Ocean Ave, Emeryville, CA 94608-1128
Tel.: (510) 428-9011
Web Site:
     http://www.macphersonart.com
Rev.: $45,601,398
Emp.: 200
Artists' Materials
N.A.I.C.S.: 424990

ARTCO GROUP INTERNATIONAL, INC.
711 Westchester Ave Ste 2, White Plains, NY 10604-3539
Tel.: (914) 286-5200
Web Site: http://artcosteel.com
Year Founded: 1948
Sales Range: $10-24.9 Million
Emp.: 40
Metal Service Center & Other Metal Whslr
N.A.I.C.S.: 423510
Jeffrey A. Himmel (CEO)

ARTCRAFT PROMOTIONAL CONCEPTS
1270 Glen Ave, Moorestown, NJ 08057
Tel.: (856) 727-5200
Web Site:
     https://www.artcraftpromos.com
Year Founded: 1946
Marketing & Advertising
N.A.I.C.S.: 541613
Judith Zimmermann (Pres & CEO)
Herold Zimmermann (VP)
Todd Zimmermann (Partner & Sr Acct Mgr)
Philip A. Edelstein (CFO)

Subsidiaries:

Corporate Marketing, Inc.   **(1)**
185 Industrial Pkwy Ste D, Somerville, NJ 08876
Tel.: (908) 429-7650
Web Site: http://www.corpmktg.com
Promotional Products, Awards, Incentives, Business Gifts & Imprinted Wearables Distr
N.A.I.C.S.: 424990

ARTE DE MEXICO INCORPORATED
1000 Chestnut St, Burbank, CA 91506
Tel.: (818) 753-4559
Web Site:
     https://www.artedemexico.com
Year Founded: 1972
Sales Range: $10-24.9 Million
Emp.: 200
Wood & Upholstered Household Furniture
N.A.I.C.S.: 337121
Gerald Stoffers (Pres)

ARTECH INFORMATION SYSTEMS LLC
360 Mt Kemble Ave Ste 2000, Morristown, NJ 07960
Tel.: (973) 998-2500
Web Site: http://www.artechinfo.com
Year Founded: 1992
Sales Range: $350-399.9 Million
Emp.: 5,500

Information Technology Consulting
N.A.I.C.S.: 541511
Ranjini Poddar (Pres)
Antonio Carrion (Dir-Mktg & Comm)
Kapil Kumar (Asst Mgr-Recruitment-United States)

Subsidiaries:

Artech China Limited   **(1)**
210-211 Building 9 Dalian Software Park No 18 Software Road, Dalian, 116023, China   **(100%)**
Tel.: (86) 41166863668
Web Site: http://www.artechinfo.com.cn
Information Technology Consulting
N.A.I.C.S.: 519290

Artech China Limited   **(1)**
11F Tai Bang Building High-Tech Park, Nanshan District, Shenzhen, 518005, China   **(100%)**
Tel.: (86) 755 2641 1934
Web Site: http://www.artechinfo.com.cn
Information Technology Consulting Services
N.A.I.C.S.: 519290

Artech China-Shanghai   **(1)**
Room No 1103 Bldg 5 No 299 West Jiang Chang Road, 200 436, Shanghai, Zhabei Distrct, China   **(100%)**
Tel.: (86) 21 6107 9166
Web Site: http://www.artechinfo.com.cn
Information Technology Consulting
N.A.I.C.S.: 519290

Artech Infosystems Private Limited   **(1)**
Infospace B2 Tower 2 Ground Fl Sector 62, Noida, 201 307, India   **(100%)**
Tel.: (91) 120 666 6333
Web Site: http://www.artechinfo.in
Information Consulting Services
N.A.I.C.S.: 519290
Shivnath Ghosh (Sr VP)

Artech Infosystems Private Limited   **(1)**
Cyber Park 1st Fl Block B Plot No 76 & 77 Electronic City Phase 1, Doddathogur Hosur Road, 560100, Bengaluru, India   **(100%)**
Tel.: (91) 80 490 83500
Web Site: http://www.artechinfo.in
Information Technology Services
N.A.I.C.S.: 519290
Varun Mehra (VP-Bus Practice)

ARTEFACT
619 Western Ave Ste 500, Seattle, WA 98104
Tel.: (206) 384-4952
Web Site:
     http://www.artefactgroup.com
Sales Range: $10-24.9 Million
Emp.: 40
Product Design Services
N.A.I.C.S.: 541490
Gavin Kelly (Co-Founder & Principal)
Rob Girling (Co-Founder & Principal)
Tom Dabson (Dir-Engrg)

ARTEL, INC.
13665 Dulles Technology Dr, Herndon, VA 20171
Tel.: (703) 620-1700
Web Site: http://www.artelinc.com
Year Founded: 1986
Sales Range: $100-124.9 Million
Emp.: 200
Provider of Telephone Communication Services
N.A.I.C.S.: 517121
Abbas Yazdani (Founder)
Paul Domorski (Pres & CEO)
Greg Fornino (CIO & Dir-Engrg)
X. T. Vuong (VP & Project Mgr-FSCA)

ARTEMIS CAPITAL PARTNERS MANAGEMENT CO., LLC
160 Federal St 23rd Fl, Boston, MA 02110
Tel.: (857) 327-5606   **DE**

Web Site: http://www.artemislp.com
Year Founded: 2010
Holding Company; Private Equity Firm
N.A.I.C.S.: 551112
Peter A. Hunter (Founder, Chm & Mng Dir)
James Ward (Mng Dir)

Subsidiaries:

Adcole Corporation   **(1)**
669 Forest St, Marlborough, MA 01752-3067
Tel.: (508) 485-9100
Web Site: http://www.adcole.com
Search & Navigation Equipment, Automotive Measuring & Guages
N.A.I.C.S.: 334511
Stephen Corrado (Sr Engr)
Jeff Walker (Pres & CEO)
Paul Richards (VP-Engrg)
Cathy King (VP-Fin)
Gordon Scott (Dir-Ops)

Subsidiary (Domestic):

Adcole Corporation   **(2)**
1481 SW 5th Ct, Pompano Beach, FL 33069-3524   **(100%)**
Tel.: (954) 785-8665
Sales Range: $10-24.9 Million
Emp.: 5
Ball & Roller Bearings
N.A.I.C.S.: 332991

Division (Domestic):

Adcole Corporation - Aerospace Division   **(2)**
669 Forest St, Marlborough, MA 01752
Tel.: (508) 485-9100
Web Site: http://www.adcole.com
Sensor Mfr
N.A.I.C.S.: 334413
Michael Foley (Pres)

Subsidiary (Non-US):

Adcole Far East Ltd.   **(2)**
EBUCHI building 1F 3-24-13 Minamioi, Shinagawa, Tokyo, 140 0013, Japan
Tel.: (81) 3 5471 7710
Web Site: http://www.adcole-far-east.co.jp
Measuring Instruments Mfr
N.A.I.C.S.: 334513

Adcole GmbH   **(2)**
Am Stadion 6, 45659, Recklinghausen, Germany
Tel.: (49) 2361 9196 0
Web Site: http://www.adcole.eu
Measuring Instruments Mfr
N.A.I.C.S.: 334513

Maury Microwave Inc.   **(1)**
2900 Inland Empire Blvd, Ontario, CA 91764
Tel.: (909) 987-4715
Web Site: http://www.maurymw.com
Electronic Components Mfr
N.A.I.C.S.: 334419
Michael Howo (CEO)
Rusty Myers (Dir-Engrg)
Greg Maury (Pres & CEO)
Jim Adamson (Dir-Customer Solutions)
Steve Dudkiewicz (VP-Mktg & Bus Dev)
Gary Simpson (CTO)
Sathya Padmanabhan (Dir-Product Dev)
Ted Lewis (VP-Sls)

Subsidiary (Domestic):

Wireless Telecom Group, Inc.   **(2)**
9 Entin Rd Ste 101, Parsippany, NJ 07054
Tel.: (973) 386-9696
Web Site:
     https://www.wirelesstelecomgroup.com
Rev.: $22,367,000
Assets: $44,973,000
Liabilities: $3,935,000
Net Worth: $41,038,000
Earnings: $14,589,000
Emp.: 68
Fiscal Year-end: 12/31/2022
Solid State Noise Sources, Noise Based Test Equipment & Wireless Telecommunication Test Equipment Mfr
N.A.I.C.S.: 334514
Michael Kandell (CFO)

Subsidiary (Domestic):

Boonton Electronics Corp. (3)
25 Eastmans Rd, Parsippany, NJ 07054
Tel.: (973) 386-9696
Web Site: https://www.boonton.com
Electricity & Signal Testing Instrument Mfr
N.A.I.C.S.: 334515
Alan L. Bazaar *(Chm)*

Holzworth Instrumentation, Inc. (3)
2540 Frontier Ave Ste 200, Boulder, CO
80301-2400
Tel.: (303) 325-3473
Web Site: https://www.holzworth.com
Emp.: 8
Electronic Test & Measurement Instrument
Mfr
N.A.I.C.S.: 334515

Microlab LLC (3)
300 Interpace Pkwy, Parsippany, NJ 07054
Tel.: (862) 328-1101
Web Site: https://microlabtech.com
Sales Range: $1-9.9 Million
Emp.: 50
Microwave Component & Instrument Services
N.A.I.C.S.: 561499

McDanel Advanced Material Technologies LLC (1)
510 9th Ave, Beaver Falls, PA 15010
Tel.: (724) 843-8300
Web Site: https://mcdanelceramics.com
Ceramic Components Mfg.
N.A.I.C.S.: 327110

Subsidiary (Domestic):

Rayotek Scientific, Inc. (2)
11494 Sorrento Valley Rd, San Diego, CA
92121
Tel.: (858) 558-3671
Web Site: http://www.rayotek.com
Sales Range: $1-9.9 Million
Emp.: 51
Semiconductor & Related Device Mfr
N.A.I.C.S.: 334413
William Raggio *(Pres)*
Jessica Alegre *(Project Mgr-Engrg)*
Randy Weber *(Project Mgr-IT)*
Ernesto Garcia *(Engr-Staff Mechanical)*

Omega Optical, LLC (1)
Delta Campus 21 Omega Dr, Brattleboro,
VT 05301
Tel.: (802) 254-2690
Web Site: http://www.omegafilters.com
Sales Range: $10-24.9 Million
Emp.: 125
Optical Filters
N.A.I.C.S.: 423490
Robert Johnson *(Dir-Tech)*
Kieran Gallagher *(Co-COO & Dir-Sls & Bus Dev)*
Robert Stillings *(Co-COO & Dir-Production)*
Gary Carver *(Dir-R&D)*
Jennifer LoCascio *(Dir-HR)*
Scott Mitchell *(Mgr-Sls & Bus Dev)*
Kim Cook *(Sr Acct Mgr-OEM Sls)*
Laura Cutter *(Acct Mgr-OEM Sls)*
Kirk Winchester *(Project Mgr-Astronomy & Product Dev)*
Tina Hoppock *(Acct Mgr-OEM Sls)*
Deb Tillinghast *(Mgr-End User Sls)*
Jim Waters *(Mgr-End User Sls Acct)*
Iain Tweedy *(Acct Mgr-Sls)*
Peter Hunter *(Chm)*
Michael J. Cumbo *(Pres & CEO)*

Unit (Domestic):

Spectral Systems LLC (2)
35 Corporate Park Dr, Hopewell Junction,
NY 12533
Tel.: (845) 896-2200
Web Site: http://www.spectral-systems.com
Rev.: $10,000,000
Emp.: 51
Optical Fiber Components Mfr
N.A.I.C.S.: 333310
Carlos Guajardo *(Mgr-Sls)*
Bruce Capuano *(Mgr)*
Tim Olsen *(Gen Mgr)*

Superior Technical Ceramics Corp. (1)
600 Industrial Park Rd, Saint Albans, VT
05478

Tel.: (802) 527-7726
Web Site: https://www.ceramics.net
Sales Range: $1-9.9 Million
Noncurrent-Carrying Wiring Device Mfr
N.A.I.C.S.: 335932

Tekscan, Inc. (1)
307 W First St, Boston, MA 02127-1309
Tel.: (617) 464-4500
Web Site: http://www.tekscan.com
Tactile Pressure & Force Measurement Systems & Sensors Mfr
N.A.I.C.S.: 334513
Adam Corthell *(Engr-R&D)*
Dennis Parrish *(VP-Ops)*
Ken Soltz *(Mgr-Sls-Europe)*
Mike Harty *(Mgr-Applications Engrg)*
Jeff Ames *(Pres & CEO)*
Peter A. Hunter *(Chm)*
Kerry Sullivan *(Dir-Mktg Comm)*

ARTEMIS ELECTRONICS LLC.

13400 W Hwy 42 Ste 180, Prospect,
KY 40059
Tel.: (502) 292-0890
Web Site:
https://www.artemiselectronics.com
Year Founded: 2005
Sales Range: $1-9.9 Million
Emp.: 20
Electronic Material Repair Services &
Mfr
N.A.I.C.S.: 811210
Dean Dickinson *(Founder & CEO)*
Mellody Green *(Mgr-Pur)*
David Thomas *(Supvr-Production)*

ARTHREX, INC.

1370 Creekside Blvd, Naples, FL
34108-1945
Web Site: https://www.arthrex.com
Year Founded: 1984
Sales Range: Less than $1 Million
Emp.: 4,500
Surgical & Medical Instrument Manufacturing
N.A.I.C.S.: 339112
Lisa Gardiner *(Mgr-Comm)*
Diane Mills *(Sr Mgr-Software Quality Assurance)*

Subsidiaries:

Arthrex BvbA (1)
Technologiepark Satenrozen Satenrozen
1A, 2550, Kontich, Belgium
Tel.: (32) 33340100
Web Site: http://www.arthrex.be
Emp.: 6
Orthopedic Product Distr
N.A.I.C.S.: 423450
Luc Peeters *(Mgr)*

Arthrex California Inc. (1)
20509 Earlgate St, Walnut, CA 91789
Tel.: (909) 869-6671
Sales Range: $10-24.9 Million
Emp.: 30
Surgical & Medical Instrument Mfr
N.A.I.C.S.: 339112

Arthrex Danmark A/S (1)
Islands Brygge 43, 2300, Copenhagen,
Denmark
Tel.: (45) 32 31 50 30
Web Site: http://www.arthrex.dk
Emp.: 7
Orthopedic Products
N.A.I.C.S.: 339112
Graham Ross *(Dir-Intl Reg)*

Arthrex Espana & Portugal (1)
Parque Empresarial La Finca, P Club Deportivo 1 Ediofio 17 Pozuelo de Alarcon,
28223, Madrid, Spain
Tel.: (34) 911115835
Orthopedic Products
N.A.I.C.S.: 339112

Arthrex GesmbH (1)
Triesterstrasse 10/1, 2351, Wiener Neudorf,
Austria
Tel.: (43) 2236 893 350 0
Orthopedic Products
N.A.I.C.S.: 339112

Arthrex Korea (1)
#201 Hashin CYLUX West B/D, 716
Sooseo Dong, Kangnam Ku, Seoul, 135-
744, Korea (South)
Tel.: (82) 2 445 30 26
Orthopedic Products
N.A.I.C.S.: 339112

Arthrex Ltd. (1)
Unit 5 3 Smithy Wood Drive, Smithy Wood
Business Park, Sheffield, S35 1QN, United
Kingdom
Tel.: (44) 114 23 291 80
Orthopedic Products
N.A.I.C.S.: 339112
Terry Byca *(Gen Mgr)*

**Arthrex Medizinische Instrumente
GmbH** (1)
Erwin-Hielscher-Strasse 9, 81249, Munich,
Germany
Tel.: (49) 8131 5957 0
Web Site: http://www.arthrex.de
Emp.: 311
Orthopedic Products
N.A.I.C.S.: 339112
Hans Dorzapf *(Mgr-Bus Dev)*
Ralf Mullers *(Sr Mgr-Strategy & Implementation)*

Arthrex Mexico, S.A. de C.V. (1)
Insurgentes Sur 600 Mezanine, Col Del
Valle, Mexico, 6100, Mexico
Tel.: (52) 55 36 01 2800
Web Site: http://www.arthrex.com
Orthopedic Products
N.A.I.C.S.: 339112
Fernando Rovriguez *(Gen Mgr)*

Arthrex Nederland B.V. (1)
't Kempke 1, 5845 GB, Sint Anthonis, Netherlands
Tel.: (31) 485 38 29 43
Web Site: http://www.arthrex.nl
Emp.: 35
Orthopedic Products
N.A.I.C.S.: 339112
Georg Osterhoff *(Gen Mgr)*

Arthrex S.A.S. (1)
5 Avenue Pierre et Marie Curie, 59260, Lezennes, France
Tel.: (33) 3 20 05 72 72
Web Site: http://www.arthrex.fr
Orthopedic Products
N.A.I.C.S.: 339112

Arthrex Sverige AB (1)
Textilgatan 43, 120 30, Stockholm, Sweden
Tel.: (46) 855681000
Web Site: http://www.arthrex.com
Emp.: 14
Orthopaedic Product Mfr
N.A.I.C.S.: 339112
Vassilis Rabbat *(Mgr)*
Johan Karlsson *(Mgr)*

Arthrex Swiss AG (1)
Huhnerhubelsrasse 60, Belp, 3123, Bern,
Switzerland
Tel.: (41) 31 810 66 00
Web Site: http://www.arthrex.ch
Emp.: 3
Orthopedic Products
N.A.I.C.S.: 339112
Daniel Burkhalter *(Gen Mgr)*

Arthrex do Brazil (1)
Rua Doutor Renato Paes de Barros 750
conjunto 36, Itaim Bibi, Sao Paulo,
4530001, Brazil
Tel.: (55) 11 3078 7042
Web Site: http://www.arthrex.com
Emp.: 6
Orthopedic Products
N.A.I.C.S.: 339112

ARTHRITIS FOUNDATION, INC.

1355 Peachtree Ste 600, Atlanta, GA
30309
Tel.: (404) 872-7100
Web Site: http://www.arthritis.org
Year Founded: 1948
Sales Range: $1-9.9 Million
Emp.: 185
Disease Awareness Fundraising Services
N.A.I.C.S.: 813212

Ann M. Palmer *(Pres & CEO)*
Guy S. Eakin *(Sr VP-Scientific Strategy)*
Melissa Honabach *(Sr VP-Mktg, Comm & ECommerce)*
Jill Lopez *(Chm)*
Cindy McDaniel *(Sr VP-Consumer Health & Impact)*
David McLoughlin *(COO)*
Ann McNamara *(Sr VP-Revenue Strategy)*
Ingrid Montecino *(Reg VP)*
Laura Rosseisen *(Reg VP)*
Rick Willis *(Sr VP-Field Mgmt)*

ARTHROSCOPY ASSOCIATION OF NORTH AMERICA

9400 W Higgins Rd Ste 200, Rosemont, IL 60018
Tel.: (847) 292-2262   IL
Web Site: https://www.aana.org
Year Founded: 1981
Sales Range: $10-24.9 Million
Emp.: 17
Medical Professional Association
N.A.I.C.S.: 813920

ARTHUR BROWN & BRO., INC.

2 W 45th St, New York, NY 10036-
4502
Tel.: (212) 575-5555
Web Site: http://www.artbrown.com
Year Founded: 1924
Rev.: $1,700,000
Emp.: 10
Writing Instruments & Artists & Drafting Supplies Distr
N.A.I.C.S.: 424120
B. Warren Brown *(Pres)*
David Brown *(VP-Corp Sls)*
Debbie Silver *(Controller)*

Subsidiaries:

The International Pen Shop (1)
2 W 45th St, New York, NY 10036
Tel.: (212) 575-5555
Pen & Desk Accessories Retailer
N.A.I.C.S.: 459410

ARTHUR COMPANIES INC.

429 Main St, Arthur, ND 58006
Tel.: (701) 967-8312
Web Site:
http://www.arthurcompanies.com
Sales Range: $50-74.9 Million
Emp.: 75
Grain Elevators
N.A.I.C.S.: 424510
Frederick Burgum *(Pres)*
Joel Moore *(Gen Mgr)*
Scott Kroger *(Office Mgr)*
Travis Larson *(Mgr-Agronomy)*

ARTHUR G. LOMBARD & SONS INC.

330 Willow St, New Haven, CT
06511-2432
Tel.: (203) 776-4853
Rev.: $15,000,000
Emp.: 6
Wine & Distilled Alcoholic Beverage
Merchant Whslr
N.A.I.C.S.: 424820
Sonia Rainey *(VP)*
Frank Vollero *(Pres)*

ARTHUR J. HURLEY COMPANY, INC.

2500 Washington St, Boston, MA
02119
Tel.: (617) 442-9200
Web Site:
https://www.hurleywire.com
Year Founded: 1929
Sales Range: $10-24.9 Million

Arthur J. Hurley Company, Inc.—(Continued)

Emp.: 45
Electrical Apparatus & Equipment
Whslr
N.A.I.C.S.: 423610
Jim Clark (CFO & Exec VP)
Kevin Sodden (Acct Mgr-Utility, Municipal & Engrg-New England)
Camilo Pereira (Bus Mgr)
Arthur J. Hurley III (Pres & CEO)

ARTHUR J. ROGERS & CO
1559 Elmhurst Rd, Elk Grove Village, IL 60007-6414
Tel.: (847) 297-2200
Web Site:
　http://www.arthurjrogers.com
Sales Range: $10-24.9 Million
Emp.: 45
Real Estate Brokers & Agents
N.A.I.C.S.: 531210
William G. Schmitz (Pres & CEO)
Carole Caveney (VP)
Patrick Napue (CFO)
George Crawford (Mgr-Property)
Mark Baumhart (VP)
Connie Kennelly (Partner & Exec VP)
Jeanne Rogers (Partner & Exec VP)
Kathi Rogers (Partner & Exec VP)

ARTHUR LAUER, INC.
47 Steve's Ln, Gardiner, NY 12525
Tel.: (845) 255-7871
Web Site: http://www.arthurlauer.com
Year Founded: 1983
Rev.: $11,000,000
Emp.: 30
Mfr of Teak Outdoor Furniture
N.A.I.C.S.: 337122
Sue Hamel (VP-Mktg)
Thomas J. Reynolds (VP)

ARTHUR MURRAY INTERNATIONAL, INC.
1077 Ponce De Leon Blvd, Coral Gables, FL 33134-3319
Tel.: (305) 445-9645
Web Site:
　https://www.arthurmurray.com
Year Founded: 1912
Sales Range: $75-99.9 Million
Emp.: 15
American, Latin, Social & Ballroom Dance Instruction
N.A.I.C.S.: 533110
Wayne A. Smith (Exec VP-Franchising)

Subsidiaries:

Arthur Murray Enterprises, Inc.　　(1)
1077 Ponce De Leon Blvd, Coral Gables, FL 33134-3319
Tel.: (305) 445-9646
Sales Range: $10-24.9 Million
Franchisor; Dance Studios
N.A.I.C.S.: 533110
Minerva Mesa (Gen Mgr)

ARTHUR RUTENBERG HOMES INC.
13922 58th St N, Clearwater, FL 33760
Tel.: (727) 536-5900
Web Site: http://www.arhomes.com
Year Founded: 1953
Sales Range: $100-124.9 Million
Emp.: 50
Real Estate Development Services
N.A.I.C.S.: 236115
Arthur Rutenberg (Chm)
Jamie Caffelle (Mgr-Community Sls)

ARTHUR SCHUMAN INC. (ASI)
40 New Dutch Lane, Fairfield, NJ 07004
Tel.: (973) 227-0030

Web Site:
　http://www.arthurschuman.com
Year Founded: 1944
Sales Range: $500-549.9 Million
Emp.: 150
Importer, Mfr & Domestic Producer of Italian & Italian-Style Cheese
N.A.I.C.S.: 311513
Rich Phillips (Exec VP-Sls, Mktg & Food Ingredients)
Joan Allen (Mgr-Exports)
Neal Schuman (Chm)
Melissa Shore (Dir-Mktg)
Larry Schaefer (CFO)
Steve K. Snyder (CEO)

ARTHUR SHUSTER INC.
1995 Oakcrest Ave, Saint Paul, MN 55113
Tel.: (651) 631-9200
Sales Range: $25-49.9 Million
Emp.: 45
Interior Designer
N.A.I.C.S.: 541410
Stanford Shuster (Chm)
Charles Shuster (Pres & CEO)
Joan Nicol-Hoium (VP-Design)
Jerel Williams (Supvr-Installation)
Sara Henry (Project Coord)
Judy Koniges (Project Mgr)

ARTHUR STATE BANK
100 E Main St, Union, SC 29379
Tel.: (864) 427-1213
Web Site:
　https://www.arthurstatebank.com
Sales Range: $10-24.9 Million
Emp.: 150
State Commercial Banks
N.A.I.C.S.: 522110
J. Carlisle Oxner (Chm)
Daniel O. Cook (CFO, COO & Exec VP)
Cynthia C. Pike (VP & Branch Mgr)
Jennifer C. Murphy (Asst VP & Mgr-Fin)
Susan C. Hicks (Asst VP & Asst Branch Mgr)
John H. Fallaw (VP)
W. Lee Miller (VP)
Steve S. Southwell (Sr VP)
Kelly G. Banks (VP)
Rhonda J. Hughey (Officer-Loan & Sr VP)
Keith Hughes (VP & Mgr)
Harry A. Oxner (Pres & CEO)
J. Carlisle Oxner III (Pres & CEO)

ARTHUR'S ENTERPRISES, INC.
310 Davis Rd, Culloden, WV 25703-1108
Tel.: (304) 523-7491　　　　　WV
Web Site:
　http://www.stateelectric.com
Year Founded: 1986
Sales Range: $75-99.9 Million
Emp.: 850
Holding Company
N.A.I.C.S.: 551112

Subsidiaries:

Service Wire Co.　　　　　　　　　(1)
310 Davis Rd, Culloden, WV 25510
Tel.: (304) 743-8650
Web Site: http://www.servicewire.com
Sales Range: $25-49.9 Million
Emp.: 150
Mfr of Electrical Wire & Cable
N.A.I.C.S.: 335929
Louis Weisberg (Pres & CEO)
Bruse Kesler (Reg Mgr-Sls)
Mel Meineke (Dir-Strategic Accts-Americas & Sls-Canada)
Kyle Kroening (VP-Mfg & Distr)
Tammi Comley (Acct Mgr-California & Northeast Nevada)
Corey Jarvis (Asst Mgr-Sls)

Lorenzo Valverde (Mgr-Phoenix Mfg Facility)
Rachel Ramsey (Coord-Mktg-Corp Mktg Dept)
Jeff Lovett (Sls Mgr-Phoenix Sls Office)
Rodney Smith (Sls Mgr-Culloden Sls Office)
Jason Cao (Sls Mgr-Phoenix Sls Office)
Joe DeBellis (Dir-Sls-Houston & Natl Sls Mgr-Utility & Transit)
Collin McCray (Asst Mgr-Credit)
Charles F. Oldaker Jr. (CFO & Exec VP)

State Electric Supply Company　　(1)
2010 2nd Ave, Huntington, WV 25703
Tel.: (681) 203-2090
Web Site: http://www.stateelectric.com
Sales Range: $50-74.9 Million
Emp.: 700
Electrical & Electronic Supplies Distr
N.A.I.C.S.: 423610
Clarence Martin (CEO & CFO)

Subsidiary (Domestic):

Ligon Electric Supply Company Inc.
of NC　　　　　　　　　　　　　　(2)
1221 National Dr, Winston Salem, NC 27103
Tel.: (336) 723-9656
Web Site: http://www.stateelectric.com
Sales Range: $25-49.9 Million
Emp.: 100
Electrical Apparatus & Equipment Distr
N.A.I.C.S.: 423610
John Spoor (Pres)

SESCO DataComm　　　　　　　(2)
405 12th St, Dunbar, WV 25064
Tel.: (304) 768-3600
Web Site: http://www.stateelectric.com
Emp.: 8
Communication Equipment Distr
N.A.I.C.S.: 423690
Dan Vandegrift (Branch Mgr)

State Electric Supply Co.　　　　(2)
801 S George St, Goldsboro, NC 27530
Tel.: (919) 735-1701
Web Site: http://www.stateelectric.com
Electrical Equipment Distr
N.A.I.C.S.: 423610
Chris Faucette (Branch Mgr)

State Electric Supply Co.　　　　(2)
2045 8th St, Portsmouth, OH 45662
Tel.: (740) 354-3141
Web Site: http://www.stateelectric.com
Electrical Equipment Distr
N.A.I.C.S.: 423610
John Spoor (Pres & COO)
Clarence Martin (CEO & CFO)

Division (Domestic):

State Electric Supply Company　　(2)
986 Route 50, Clarksburg, WV
26302-0986　　　　　　　　　(100%)
Tel.: (304) 624-7467
Web Site: http://www.stateelectric.com
Sales Range: $25-49.9 Million
Emp.: 42
Electrical Equipment Distr
N.A.I.C.S.: 423610
Mike Rieser (Branch Mgr)
Terry Booth (Mgr-Showroom)
Bill Blevins (Branch Mgr)
Robert Lowe (Branch Mgr)
Mike Smiley (Branch Mgr)
Mitch Treadway (Branch Mgr)

ARTHUR'S GARDEN DELI INC.
1400 1st Ave, Rock Falls, IL 61071
Tel.: (815) 625-0011
Rev.: $16,700,000
Emp.: 5
Delicatessen Stores
N.A.I.C.S.: 445110
Scott A. Wolber (Pres & CEO)
Lisa Winstead (Mgr)

ARTIC CIRCLE, INC.
411 W 7200 S Ste 200, Midvale, UT 84047-1058
Tel.: (801) 561-3620　　　　　UT
Web Site: http://www.acburger.com
Year Founded: 1992
Sales Range: $10-24.9 Million

Emp.: 1,200
Restaurant Operators
N.A.I.C.S.: 722513
Gary Roberts (Pres & CEO)
Kasey Christensen (COO)
Frank L. Christianson (CFO)
Bonnie Anisworth (Treas & Controller)

Subsidiaries:

Arctic Circle Restaurants, Inc.　　(1)
411 W 7200 S Ste 200, Midvale, UT 84047-1058
Tel.: (801) 561-3620
Web Site: http://www.arcticcirclerest.com
Sales Range: $10-24.9 Million
Emp.: 25
Restaurant Operators
N.A.I.C.S.: 722513
Frank L. Christianson (CFO)
Carol Brown (VP-Mktg)
William Gee (Exec VP)
Gary Roberts (Pres & CEO)
George Morgan (Exec VP)
Mike Larsen (VP-Ops)
Bonnie Anisworth (Treas & Controller)
Kasey Christensen (COO)
Steve Heal (Dir-Franchise Ops)

ARTICULATE COMMUNICATIONS INC.
40 Fulton St 15th Fl, New York, NY 10038
Tel.: (212) 255-0080
Web Site:
　http://www.articulatecomms.com
Year Founded: 2002
Sales Range: $10-24.9 Million
Emp.: 16
Public Relations Agency
N.A.I.C.S.: 541820
Adrienne Robbins (Office Mgr)
Audra Tiner (Pres & CEO)

Subsidiaries:

Articulate Communications Inc.　　(1)
548 Tremont St # 3, Boston, MA 02116-6314
Tel.: (781) 990-3455
Public Relations Agency
N.A.I.C.S.: 541820

ARTICUS LTD. MARKETING COMMUNICATIONS
1528 Walnut St Ste 701, Philadelphia, PA 19102
Tel.: (215) 564-1213
Web Site: http://www.articus.com
Year Founded: 1986
Rev.: $10,500,000
Emp.: 10
Fiscal Year-end: 12/31/01
N.A.I.C.S.: 541810
Eric Van Der Vlugt (Principal)
Gillian Van Der Vlugt (Dir-Ops)
Debra Pusak (Acct Exec)
Jeff Biglan (Sr Dir-Art)
Sarah G. Salmon (Sr Acct Exec)

ARTIFAX
117 Delmonico Pl, Valley Stream, NY 11581
Tel.: (516) 593-4844
Year Founded: 1981
Sales Range: Less than $1 Million
Emp.: 1
Arts, Brand Development & Integration, Graphic Design, Newspaper, Publicity/Promotions
N.A.I.C.S.: 541810
Joe Vissichelli (Dir-Creative)

ARTIFEX TECHNOLOGY CONSULTING, INC.
614 George Washington Hwy, Norwell, RI 02865
Tel.: (401) 723-6644
Web Site: http://www.artifextech.com

Year Founded: 2002
Rev.: $2,300,000
Emp.: 19
Management Consulting Services
N.A.I.C.S.: 541618
Jenna L. Schmidt *(Founder & Pres)*
Myra Durfee *(Office Mgr)*
Tyler James *(Asst Mgr-Dev)*
Vandara Peou *(Engr-Software)*
Paul Duffy *(Mgr-Dev)*
Matthew Charron *(Project Mgr-Tech)*

ARTILLERY MARKETING COMMUNICATIONS LLC
1709 Colley Ave Ste 308, Norfolk, VA 23517
Tel.: (757) 627-4800
Year Founded: 2001
Sales Range: Less than $1 Million
Emp.: 12
Full Service
N.A.I.C.S.: 541810
Douglas Burdett *(Founder & Pres)*

ARTIS-NAPLES
5833 Pelican Bay Blvd, Naples, FL 34108-2740
Tel.: (239) 597-1900   FL
Web Site: http://www.artisnaples.org
Year Founded: 1983
Sales Range: $25-49.9 Million
Emp.: 381
Visual Art Program Administration Services
N.A.I.C.S.: 926110
Ned C. Lautenbach *(Chm)*

ARTISAN DESIGN GROUP
888 W Ash St, San Diego, CA 92101-2407
Tel.: (619) 269-1211
Web Site:
http://www.interiorsbyadg.net
Sales Range: $1-9.9 Million
Interior Design Services
N.A.I.C.S.: 541410
Jaimi Julian Thompson *(Founder & Pres)*

ARTISAN INFRASTRUCTURE INC.
12400 Hwy 71 W Ste 350-407, Austin, TX 78738
Tel.: (512) 600-4300
Web Site:
http://www.artisaninfrastructure.com
Year Founded: 2001
Emp.: 95
Software Solutions
N.A.I.C.S.: 513210
Brian Hierholzer *(CEO)*
Larry Hart *(Sr VP-Strategic Alliances)*
Stuart Clark *(Chief Info Security Officer)*
Mark Almeida-Cardy *(CTO)*

Subsidiaries:

Neverfail Group Ltd.   (1)
Merlin House Brunel Rd, Theale, RG7 4AB, Berks, United Kingdom
Tel.: (44) 8707771500
Web Site: http://www.neverfailgroup.com
Sales Range: $10-24.9 Million
Emp.: 150
Business Continuity Solutions
N.A.I.C.S.: 513210
Paul Dossey *(VP-Global Support)*
Ashwin Kotian *(Chief Product Officer)*
Michele Cadd *(CFO)*
Eric Vaughn *(Chief Revenue Officer)*
Paolo Di Leo *(Dir-Sls-EMEA)*
Jason White *(Chief Strategy Officer)*

ARTISANAL BRANDS, INC.
483 Tenth Ave, New York, NY 10018
Tel.: (212) 871-3150   NY

Web Site:
http://www.artisanalcheese.com
Sales Range: $1-9.9 Million
Cheese Mfr, Online Retailer & Mail Order
N.A.I.C.S.: 311513
Daniel W. Dowe *(Pres & CEO)*

ARTISANS INC.
W 4146 2nd St, Glen Flora, WI 54526
Tel.: (715) 322-5285
Web Site:
https://www.artisansinc.com
Year Founded: 1974
Sales Range: $10-24.9 Million
Emp.: 75
Mfr of Screen Printing & Embroidery
N.A.I.C.S.: 314999
Gordie Dukerschein *(CEO)*

ARTISANS' BANK
2961 Centerville Rd, Wilmington, DE 19808
Tel.: (302) 884-6985
Web Site:
https://www.artisansbank.com
Year Founded: 1861
Sales Range: $50-74.9 Million
Emp.: 132
Banking Services
N.A.I.C.S.: 522180
Lynn Petrone *(VP-HR)*
Robert P. Cox *(VP-Comml Lending Div-New Castle County Reg)*
Thomas D. Keehan *(Officer-Loan)*
Kirby C. Fitzgerald *(VP-Comml Banking & Mgr-Comml Relationship-Sussex County)*

ARTISON INVESTMENTS, LTD.
16526 106th Ct, Orland Park, IL 60647
Tel.: (408) 385-9449   NV
Year Founded: 2010
Sales Range: $10-24.9 Million
Emp.: 60
Bamboo Composite Laminates & Synthetic Resin Mfr
N.A.I.C.S.: 325211
Debopam Mukherjee *(Pres, CEO, CFO, Chief Acctg Officer, Treas & Sec)*

ARTISSIMO HOLDINGS, INC.
841 Apollo St Ste 400, El Segundo, CA 90245
Tel.: (310) 802-7900   DE
Web Site:
http://www.artissimoholdings.com
Year Founded: 1998
Sales Range: $50-74.9 Million
Emp.: 100
Holding Company; Licensed Wall Art Reproductions Mfr & Distr
N.A.I.C.S.: 551112
Matthew Mann *(Dir-Bus & Legal Affairs)*
Kari Nikolish *(VP-Sls-Walmart)*
Chuck McGonigle *(CEO)*

Subsidiaries:

Artissimo Designs Inc.   (1)
415 Annagem Blvd, Mississauga, L5T 3A7, ON, Canada
Tel.: (514) 363-7171
Web Site: http://www.artissimoholdings.com
Licensed Wall Art Reproductions Mfr & Distr
N.A.I.C.S.: 323113
Mitchell Rubin *(CFO & Sr VP)*

Artissimo U.S., LLC   (1)
841 Apollo St Suite 400, El Segundo, CA 90245
Tel.: (310) 802-7900
Web Site: http://www.artissimoholdings.com
Licensed Wall Art Reproductions Mfr & Distr
N.A.I.C.S.: 323113

Ken Floyd *(CEO)*

ARTISTIC COUNTERS, INC.
18630 Goll St, Garden Ridge, TX 78266
Tel.: (210) 651-3281
Web Site: http://www.artisticcounters.com
Year Founded: 1991
Sales Range: $10-24.9 Million
Emp.: 120
Cut Stone & Stone Product Mfr
N.A.I.C.S.: 327991
Scott Tonick *(Pres)*
Susan Tonick *(VP)*
Steve Hearn *(Mgr-Home Center)*

ARTISTIC FRAME CO., INC.
14 Whale Sq, Brooklyn, NY 11232
Tel.: (212) 289-2100
Web Site:
http://www.artisticframe.com
Rev.: $71,200,000
Emp.: 110
Wood Frames for Upholstered Furniture Mfr
N.A.I.C.S.: 337215
David Bibi *(Office Mgr)*

ARTISTIC FRAMING INC.
860 Chaddick Dr, Wheeling, IL 60090
Tel.: (847) 808-0200
Web Site:
https://www.artisticframing.com
Rev.: $25,000,000
Emp.: 200
Picture Frames, Metal
N.A.I.C.S.: 332999
Thomas Wolk *(Pres)*

ARTISTIC PAVERS MANUFAC-TURING, INC.
120 NE 179th St, Miami, FL 33162
Tel.: (305) 653-7283   FL
Web Site:
http://www.artisticpavers.com
Year Founded: 2000
Emp.: 100
Asphalt Paving Mixture & Block Mfr
N.A.I.C.S.: 324121
Daniel Essig *(Founder & Pres)*
Matthew Wayman *(CEO)*

ARTISTIC TILE INC.
520 Secacus Rd, Secaucus, NJ 07094-2502
Tel.: (201) 864-7000
Web Site: https://www.artistictile.com
Sales Range: $25-49.9 Million
Emp.: 100
Bathroom Fixtures, Equipment & Supplies
N.A.I.C.S.: 444180
Nancy Epstein *(Founder & CEO)*
Lauren Cherkas *(Pres)*
Richard Johnson *(VP-PR)*
Jill Cohen *(Dir-Design)*
Mary Beth Brintz *(Mgr-Client Svcs)*
Stephanie Rakotz *(Mgr-Ops)*
Joshua Levinson *(Pres)*
Gerard Esmail *(VP-Ops)*
Lucinda Deichmeister *(Mgr-Show Room)*
Michael Epstein *(VP-Mktg)*
Alba Hannagan *(Project Mgr)*
Carol Schreck-Butsko *(VP-Sls-Wholesale Div)*

ARTISTREE LANDSCAPE MAINTENANCE & DESIGN
160 Pond Cypress Rd Ste B, Venice, FL 34292
Tel.: (941) 488-8897
Web Site: https://www.artistree.com
Year Founded: 1990
Sales Range: $10-24.9 Million

Emp.: 240
Lawn & Garden Services
N.A.I.C.S.: 561730
Joseph Gonzalez *(CEO)*
Sara Roberts *(Dir-Mktg & PR)*
Scott Acton *(Dir-Lawn & Ornamental-Landscape Maintenance Div)*
Paul Hurlock *(Mgr-Fleet-Landscape Maintenance Div)*
Pam Lasota *(Dir-Acctg & Admin)*
Maria Muhlhahn *(Mgr-Pur-Landscape Design Div)*
Frank Fistner *(Pres)*
Debra Morrow *(VP-Mktg)*
Chris Barber *(Mgr-Production-Design Div)*
Tim White *(Mgr-Lawn & Ornamental-Landscape Maintenance Div)*
Jeremy Lepper *(Mgr-North-Maintenance Div)*
Ginger Watson *(Acct Exec)*
Alan Williams *(Acct Exec)*
Bill Walters *(VP-Ops-Maintenance)*
Conan Michel *(Mgr-Ops)*
Anita Nichols *(Office Mgr)*
Jennifer Lassen *(Project Coord)*
Luis Garcia *(Supvr-Production)*
Joe Mantkowski *(Gen Mgr-Landscape)*

ARTISTS' FRAME SERVICE, INC.
1867 N Clybourn Ave, Chicago, IL 60614
Tel.: (773) 248-7713
Web Site:
http://www.artistframeservice.com
Rev.: $11,000,000
Emp.: 100
Picture Framing, Custom
N.A.I.C.S.: 811490
Jay Goltz *(Pres)*
Jim Pierce *(CFO)*

ARTIVA BIOTHERAPEUTICS, INC.
5505 Morehouse Dr Ste 100, San Diego, CA 92121
Tel.: (858) 267-4467   DE
Web Site: https://www.artivabio.com
Year Founded: 2019
Assets: $29,234,000
Liabilities: $50,801,000
Net Worth: ($21,567,000)
Earnings: ($17,991,000)
Emp.: 25
Fiscal Year-end: 12/31/20
Biotechnology Research & Development Services
N.A.I.C.S.: 541714
Fred Aslan *(Pres & CEO)*
Thomas J. Farrell *(Founder & Chief Strategy Officer)*
Michael E. Faerm *(CFO)*
Peter Flynn *(COO)*
Esther Van den Boom *(Chief Acctg Officer)*
Jennifer Bush *(Chief Legal & People Officer, Sec & Exec VP)*
Eugene Helsel *(VP-Regulatory Affairs & Quality)*
John Lim *(VP-Clinical Ops)*
Heather Raymon *(VP-Early Dev & Program Mgmt)*
Brian Daniels *(Chm)*
Thorsten Graef *(Chief Medical Officer)*

ARTMAR INC.
900 E Expy 83, San Juan, TX 78589
Tel.: (956) 781-7900
Rev.: $10,100,000
Emp.: 20
Trucks, Tractors & Trailers: New & Used
N.A.I.C.S.: 441110

Artmar Inc.—(Continued)

ARTSONIA, LLC
1350 Tri-State Pkwy Ste 106,
Gurnee, IL 60031
Tel.: (224) 538-5060
Web Site: https://www.artsonia.com
Year Founded: 2000
Sales Range: $1-9.9 Million
Student Art Gallery Website
N.A.I.C.S.: 513140
Jim Meyers (Co-Founder & CEO)
Eric Meidel (Co-Founder & Pres)
Tiffany Rahn (Dir-Education)

ARTSPACE PROJECTS INC
250 3rd Ave N Ste 500, Minneapolis,
MN 55401
Tel.: (612) 333-9012
Web Site: https://www.artspace.org
Year Founded: 1998
Sales Range: $1-9.9 Million
Emp.: 23
Lessors of Nonresidential Buildings
(except Miniwarehouses)
N.A.I.C.S.: 531120
Mark Conrad (CFO)

ARTSQUEST
25 W 3rd St, Bethlehem, PA 18015
Tel.: (610) 332-1300   PA
Web Site: https://www.artsquest.org
Year Founded: 1983
Sales Range: $10-24.9 Million
Emp.: 426
Arts Promotion Services
N.A.I.C.S.: 711310
Kassie Hilgert (Pres & CEO)
Walter Keiper (Sr VP-Bus Admin)
Ron Unger (VP-Admin)
Curt Mosel (Sr VP-Mktg & Corp Partnerships)
Nicole Dotta (Dir-New Bus Partnerships)

ARTUR EXPRESS, INC.
10352 Lk Bluff Dr, Saint Louis, MO
63102
Tel.: (314) 714-3400
Web Site:
    http://www.arturexpress.com
Year Founded: 1998
Sales Range: $50-74.9 Million
Emp.: 42
Transportation & Logistics Services
N.A.I.C.S.: 488999
Artur Wagrodzki (Co-Pres)
Tomasz Tokarczyk (Co-Pres)
Mark Lesher (Dir-Sls)

ARTUS CORPORATION
201 S Dean St, Englewood, NJ
07631-4107
Tel.: (201) 568-1000
Web Site: http://www.artuscorp.com
Year Founded: 1941
Sales Range: $1-9.9 Million
Emp.: 100
Plastic, Aluminum & Metal Shims Mfr
N.A.I.C.S.: 326199
Sam Levi (Plant Mgr)

**ARTUSO PASTRY FOODS,
CORP.**
49 S Macquesten Pkwy, Mount Vernon, NY 10550
Tel.: (914) 663-8806   NY
Web Site:
    https://www.artusopastry.com
Year Founded: 1940
Sales Range: $1-9.9 Million
Emp.: 40
Pasta Mfr
N.A.I.C.S.: 311813
Dianne Campanaro (Mgr-Fin)
Anthony Artuso Sr. (Owner)

ARTWALK TILE, INC.
28 Atlantic Ave, Rochester, NY 14607
Tel.: (585) 563-6701
Web Site: http://www.artwalktile.com
Year Founded: 2000
Sales Range: $1-9.9 Million
Emp.: 7
Tile & Flooring Product Distr
N.A.I.C.S.: 423320
Joseph Ventura (Owner)

ARUNDEL COMMUNITY DEVELOPMENT SERVICES, INC.
2666 Riva Rd Ste 210, Annapolis,
MD 21401
Tel.: (410) 222-7600   MD
Web Site: https://www.acdsinc.org
Year Founded: 1993
Sales Range: $10-24.9 Million
Emp.: 29
Community Care Services
N.A.I.C.S.: 624190
Chauncey A. Hall (Dir-Program)
James C. Sylvester (Dir-Fin & Admin)
William F. Gibbons (Project Dir)
Kathleen M. Koch (Exec Dir)

ARUNDEL FORD
38-40 Portland Rd, Kennebunk, ME
04043
Tel.: (207) 985-7171
Web Site: http://www.arundelfd.com
Sales Range: $10-24.9 Million
Emp.: 34
Car Whslr
N.A.I.C.S.: 441110
Elliot R. Levine (Pres)

ARUP LABORATORIES
500 Chipeta Way, Salt Lake City, UT
84108-1221
Tel.: (200) 510-1905
Web Site: http://www.aruplab.com
Research & Development in the
Physical, Engineering & Life Sciences
N.A.I.C.S.: 541715
Edgar Braendle (Pres & CEO)
Peter Jensen (Chm)
Julio Delgado (Chief Medical Officer
& Dir-Laboratories)

ARVADA EXCAVATING CO.
6205 W 52nd Ave, Arvada, CO 80002
Tel.: (303) 422-1822
Web Site:
    https://www.arvadaexcavating.com
Year Founded: 1968
Sales Range: $25-49.9 Million
Emp.: 10
Excavation Services
N.A.I.C.S.: 238910
Ed Radatz (Controller)

ARVADA RENT-ALLS
10675 Ralston Rd, Arvada, CO
80004
Tel.: (303) 309-4240
Web Site:
    https://www.arvadarentalls.com
Year Founded: 1963
Rev.: $3,660,000
Emp.: 20
Consumer Electronics & Appliances
Rental
N.A.I.C.S.: 532210
Luke Heesacker (Co-Owner, Pres &
CEO)

ARVCO CONTAINER CORPORATION
845 Gibson St, Kalamazoo, MI
49001-2573
Tel.: (269) 381-0900   MI
Web Site: https://www.arvco.com
Year Founded: 1971
Sales Range: $100-124.9 Million

Emp.: 230
Corrugated & Solid Fiber Boxes Mfr
N.A.I.C.S.: 322211
Kevin Kellogg (Mgr-Product Dev)
Brian Oviatt (Coord-Sls)
Timothy Pickett (Dir-Tech)
Doug Kool (Mgr-Sls)
Jim Thomas (VP-Sls)
Jonathon Henry (Supvr-Production)

ARVEST BANK GROUP, INC.
201 W Walnut St, Rogers, AR 72756
Tel.: (479) 621-1775
Web Site: http://www.arvest.com
Year Founded: 1976
Sales Range: $1-4.9 Billion
Emp.: 6,393
Bank Holding Company
N.A.I.C.S.: 551111
K. Kevin Sabin (Pres & CEO)
Keith Kersten (Exec VP)
Janice Fox (Sr VP & Mgr-HR)
William Fisher (Sr VP-Comml
Banking-Morrilton)
Kirk Israel (Sr VP-Arvest Wealth
Mgmt)
David Norris (VP)
Cara James (Chief Risk Officer)
Ninish Ukkan (CTO)
Bryan Hicks (Head-Product-
Application Programming Interfaces &
Third-Party Integration)
Laura Merling (Chief Transformation
& Ops Officer)

Subsidiaries:

Arvest Bank   (1)
75 NE Ave, Fayetteville, AR 72701-6171
Tel.: (479) 575-1000
Web Site: http://www.arvest.com
Sales Range: $1-4.9 Billion
Commericial Banking
N.A.I.C.S.: 522110
Jason Kincy (Mktg Dir)
K. Kevin Sabin (Pres & CEO)
Jayme Vaughan (Mktg Mgr-Siloam Springs)
Jim Bates (Mgr-Credit Admin-Arvest Equipment Fin)
Eric Bunnell (Pres-Arvest Equipment Fin)
Doug Heck (Exec Dir-Consumer Lending-Overland Park)
Mike Willard (Pres/CEO-North Central Arkansas)
Jaren Beavers (Mktg Mgr-North Central Arkansas)

Subsidiary (Domestic):

Arvest Asset Management   (2)
201 W Walnut St, Rogers, AR 72756
Tel.: (479) 621-4877
Web Site: http://www.arvest.com
Sales Range: $50-74.9 Million
Emp.: 53
Asset Management Services
N.A.I.C.S.: 523940
Larry Cowger (VP)
Sonya Reed (VP)
Roger Bryles (VP)
Paul Krus (Sr VP & Mgr-Oklahoma City,
Shawnee & Southwest Oklahoma)

Arvest Bank Operations, Inc.   (2)
103 S Bloomington, Lowell, AR 72745
Tel.: (479) 750-5400
Web Site: http://www.arvest.com
Rev.: $6,100,000
Emp.: 120
Retail Bank Office Administrative Services
N.A.I.C.S.: 561110

Arvest Mortgage Company   (2)
PO Box 399, Lowell, AR 72745
Tel.: (479) 750-6932
Rev.: $3,300,000
Emp.: 90
Mortgage Bankers & Correspondents
N.A.I.C.S.: 522292
Keri Cook (Mgr-Call Center)
Susan Kuehn (Mgr-Call Center)
Jessica Trantham (Mgr-Call Center)
Steven Plaisance (Pres & CEO)

Superior Finance Company   (2)

305-1 Rayfine Blvd, Roland, OK 74954
Tel.: (918) 427-0486
Web Site:
    http://www.superiorfinancecompany.com
Financial Management Services
N.A.I.C.S.: 523999

ARVIG ENTERPRISES, INC.
160 2nd Ave SW, Perham, MN
56573-1409
Tel.: (218) 346-4227   MN
Web Site: http://www.arvig.com
Year Founded: 1950
Sales Range: $25-49.9 Million
Emp.: 300
Holding Company; Telecommunications Services
N.A.I.C.S.: 551112
David Arvig (COO & VP)
Brad Kirckof (Reg Mgr)
Andy Klinnert (Dir-Net Ops)
Ray Sonnenberg (Supvr-
Construction)
Steve Malikowski (Supvr-
Construction)
Tim Heggestuen (Controller)
Shannon Wegner (Coord-Security)
David Pratt (Dir-Video)
Lisa Greene (Sr Mgr-Mktg)

Subsidiaries:

All State Communications, Inc.   (1)
5114 Marson Dr, Sauk Rapids, MN 56379
Tel.: (320) 203-1511
Web Site: http://www.allstatecom.com
Sales Range: $1-9.9 Million
Emp.: 40
Data, Voice & Building Management Systems Contractor
N.A.I.C.S.: 238210
Jared Gapinski (Pres)
Becky Monson (Office Mgr)
Bob Burt (Mgr-Acct)
Dan Hoops (Dir-Engrg)
Clint Namenuik (Project Mgr)
Frank Petykowski (Dir-Fire & Security)
Scott Woodward (Mgr-Bus Dev)
David Schornack (Pres)

Arvig Communications Systems   (1)
150 2nd Ave SW, Perham, MN
56573   (100%)
Tel.: (218) 346-5500
Web Site: http://www.arvig.com
Sales Range: $10-24.9 Million
Emp.: 16
Telephone Communication Services
N.A.I.C.S.: 517121
Shaun Carlson (Mgr-Network Engrg)

Joint Venture (Non-US):

Hector Communications
Corporation   (2)
Tel.: (507) 354-2500
Holding Company; Local Telecommunication Services
N.A.I.C.S.: 551112

Subsidiary (Non-US):

Eagle Valley Telephone
Company   (3)
Tel.: (218) 756-2312
Web Site: http://www.eaglevalleytel.net
Sales Range: $10-24.9 Million
Emp.: 1
Telecommunications & Internet Services
N.A.I.C.S.: 517121

Pine Island Telephone Company   (3)
Tel.: (507) 356-8302
Web Site: http://www.pitel.net
Sales Range: $10-24.9 Million
Emp.: 12
Telephone Services
N.A.I.C.S.: 517111

Sleepy Eye Telephone Company   (3)
Tel.: (507) 794-3361
Sales Range: $10-24.9 Million
Emp.: 20
Telephone Services
N.A.I.C.S.: 517121

East Otter Tail Telephone Company Inc. (1)
150 2nd Ave SW, Perham, MN 56573-1409
Tel.: (218) 346-5500
Web Site: http://www.arvig.com
Sales Range: $10-24.9 Million
Emp.: 100
Telephone Communications
N.A.I.C.S.: 517121
David Arvig (COO & VP)
Josey Winkels (Mng Dir)

Image Office Services (1)
300 33rd Avenue S Suite 101, Waite Park, MN 56387
Tel.: (320) 255-5455
Web Site:
http://www.imageofficeservices.com
Emp.: 150
Call-Answering Center
N.A.I.C.S.: 561421
Jamie DesJardins (Pres)

Security Plus Alarms, LLC (1)
609 Bemidji Ave N, Bemidji, MN 56601
Tel.: (218) 751-7847
Web Site: http://www.securityplusmn.com
Alarm & Security System Mfr
N.A.I.C.S.: 334290

Tekstar Cablevision Inc. (1)
150 2nd Ave SW, Perham, MN 56573-1409
Tel.: (218) 346-5500
Web Site: http://www.arvig.com
Cable & Other Pay Television Services
N.A.I.C.S.: 516210

ARVIN-EDISON WATER STORAGE DISTRICT
20401 E Bear Mountain Blvd, Arvin, CA 93203
Tel.: (661) 854-5573
Web Site: https://www.aewsd.org
Sales Range: $10-24.9 Million
Emp.: 52
Agricultural Water
N.A.I.C.S.: 221310
David A. Nixon (Asst Mgr)
Edwin A. Camp (VP & Dir-Div 6)
Jeffrey G. Giumarra (VP)

ARVIXE, LLC
23801 Calabasas Rd Suite 2005, Calabasas, CA 91302-1547
Tel.: (707) 304-5520
Web Site: http://www.arvixe.com
Year Founded: 2003
Sales Range: $1-9.9 Million
Emp.: 60
Hosts Personal, Small Business & Enterprise Websites
N.A.I.C.S.: 517810
Arvand Sabetian (Founder & CEO)

ARVO COMMUNICATIONS, INC.
1544 Hunters Mill Pl, Oviedo, FL 32765-8452
Tel.: (407) 671-0185   FL
Year Founded: 1976
Sales Range: $25-49.9 Million
Emp.: 8
Advetising Agency
N.A.I.C.S.: 541810
Thomas R. Arvo (Chm & CEO)
Carol Arvo (Pres)

ARYA SCIENCES ACQUISITION CORP.
Tel.: (212) 284-2300   Ky
Year Founded: 2018
Rev.: $3,353,229
Assets: $148,776,423
Liabilities: $143,776,420
Net Worth: $5,000,003
Earnings: $2,578,622
Emp.: 2
Fiscal Year-end: 12/31/19
Investment Services
N.A.I.C.S.: 523999

Adam Stone (CEO)
Joseph Edelman (Chm)
Adam Stone (CEO)
Michael Altman (CFO)

ARYAKA NETWORKS INC.
3945 Freedom Cir Ste 1100, Santa Clara, CA 95054
Tel.: (408) 273-8420
Web Site: https://www.aryaka.com
Year Founded: 2009
Sales Range: $10-24.9 Million
Emp.: 150
Wide Area Network Optimization & Application Acceleration Services
N.A.I.C.S.: 541512
Ashwath Nagaraj (Founder & CTO)
Vikas Garg (Sr VP-Engrg & Ops)
Ram Gupta (Chm)
Randolph Barr (Chief Security Officer)
Nick Fan (VP/Gen Mgr-Americas)
Mike Hoffman (Chief Revenue Officer & Sr VP-Sls-Global)
Matthew Carter Jr. (Pres)
Deepak Kumar (Sr VP-Customer Success)
Christiana Khostovan (Gen Counsel & Corp Sec)
Mario Vecchio (Sr VP-Asia Pacific)
Karen Freitag (Chief Revenue Officer)
Brad Kinnish (CFO)
Ed Pearce (Dir-Channel-North America)
Craig Patterson (VP-Sls-Americas)

Subsidiaries:

Aryaka Networks India Pvt. Ltd. (1)
35/B 1st Main 3rd Phase, JP Nagar, Bengaluru, 560078, India
Tel.: (91) 80 42563300
Web Site: http://www.aryaka.com
Wide Area Network Optimization & Application Acceleration Services
N.A.I.C.S.: 541512
Frederick Griffe (Mng Dir)

AS CAPITAL, INC.
Ste 430 1110 Brickell Ave, Miami, FL 33131
Tel.: (305) 853-8178   ID
Web Site: https://as-capital.com
Year Founded: 2015
BRMT—(OTCIQ)
Rev.: $1,195,460
Assets: $178,352
Liabilities: $130,750
Net Worth: $47,602
Earnings: $83,584
Emp.: 5
Fiscal Year-end: 10/31/19
Real Estate Investment Company
N.A.I.C.S.: 531390
John Karatzaferis (Pres, CEO, CFO, Treas & Sec)

ASA APPLE INC.
377 Roosevelt Ave, Carteret, NJ 07008
Tel.: (732) 969-2900
Web Site: http://www.asaapple.com
Sales Range: $25-49.9 Million
Emp.: 30
General Warehousing & Storage
N.A.I.C.S.: 493110
Williams Ferriera (Asst Mgr & Supvr)
Willie Ortiz (Mgr-Transportation)
John Cholowinski (VP-Ops)

ASA INTERNATIONAL LTD.
25 Manchester St Ste 100, Merrimack, NH 03054
Tel.: (508) 626-2727   DE
Web Site: http://www.asaint.com
Year Founded: 1969
Sales Range: $10-24.9 Million

Emp.: 110
Business Software & Systems
N.A.I.C.S.: 541512
Christopher Crane (Vice Chm)

ASA MARKETING
5339 SW 22nd Pl, Topeka, KS 66614
Tel.: (785) 273-5411
Sales Range: Less than $1 Million
Emp.: 15
Advetising Agency
N.A.I.C.S.: 541810
JD Dienes (Dir-New Media)

ASAEL FARR & SONS COMPANY
2575 S 300 W, Salt Lake City, UT 84115
Tel.: (801) 484-8724   UT
Web Site:
http://www.farrsicecream.com
Year Founded: 1920
Rev.: $19,510,201
Emp.: 80
Ice Cream Mfr, Distr & Retailer
N.A.I.C.S.: 311520
Michael Farr (Pres)

ASANTE TECHNOLOGIES, INC.
2223 Oakland Rd, San Jose, CA 95131-1402
Tel.: (408) 435-8388   DE
Web Site: http://www.asante.com
Year Founded: 1988
Sales Range: $50-74.9 Million
Emp.: 45
High-Performance Networking Solutions for the Digital Graphics Communications & Education Markets
N.A.I.C.S.: 334118
Anthony Contos (Controller)
Mike Tobin (Mgr-Sls-EMEA)

ASAP SOLUTIONS GROUP, LLC
3885 Holcomb Bridge Rd, Norcross, GA 30092
Tel.: (770) 246-1718
Web Site: https://www.myasap.com
Year Founded: 1989
Sales Range: $50-74.9 Million
Emp.: 798
Information Technology Services
N.A.I.C.S.: 449210
Kathy Dowling (Exec VP-Managed Svcs)
Norma Lizotte (Coord-TPA)

ASAP TOWING & STORAGE COMPANY
10053 103rd St, Jacksonville, FL 32210
Tel.: (904) 771-7111   FL
Web Site:
https://www.asaptowing.net
Year Founded: 1995
Sales Range: $1-9.9 Million
Emp.: 35
Automotive & Heavy Equipment Towing Services
N.A.I.C.S.: 488410
Vanice Serrano (Co-Owner & VP)
Vincent Serrano (Co-Owner & Pres)

ASB CAPITAL MANAGEMENT, LLC
7501 Wisconsin Ave Ste 1300W, Bethesda, MD 20814
Tel.: (240) 482-2900   MD
Web Site:
https://www.asbrealestate.com
Rev.: $29,000,000,000
Real Estate, Institutional Equity & Fixed Income Investment Management Services
N.A.I.C.S.: 523940

Bernard Francis Saul II (Chm)
Robert Bellinger (Pres & CEO)

ASBURY COMMUNITIES, INC.
20030 Century Blvd Ste 300, Germantown, MD 20874
Tel.: (301) 250-2100   MD
Web Site: http://www.asbury.org
Year Founded: 1994
Sales Range: $10-24.9 Million
Emp.: 80
Continuing Care Retirement Services
N.A.I.C.S.: 623311
Andrew Jeanneret (CFO)
Doug Leidig (Pres & CEO)

ASC COMMUNICATIONS, LLC
17 N State St Ste 1800, Chicago, IL 60602
Web Site:
http://www.beckershospital.com
Year Founded: 1996
Sales Range: $25-49.9 Million
Emp.: 56
Media Advertising Services
N.A.I.C.S.: 541840
Scott Becker (Founder)
Jessica Cole (Pres & CEO)
Jim Milligan (CFO)
Katie Atwood (COO)
Ally Warner (VP-Sls)

ASC GLOBAL INC.
4710 Mainsail Dr, Bradenton, FL 34208
Tel.: (631) 397-1111   NV
Web Site: https://ascglobal.us
Year Founded: 2020
Holding Company; Corporate & Real Estate Investment
N.A.I.C.S.: 551112
David Chen (Pres & CEO)

Subsidiaries:

American Software Capital Inc. (1)
4710 Mainsail Dr, Bradenton, FL 34208
Tel.: (631) 397-1111
Corporate Investment
N.A.I.C.S.: 523999
David Chen (Pres & CEO)
Xiangru Lin (COO)

Holding (Domestic):

Token Communities Ltd. (2)
850 Tidewater Shore Loop Ste 402, Bradenton, FL 34208   (83.26%)
Tel.: (631) 397-1111
Emp.: 4
Holding Company; Holistic & Naturopathic Supplement Developer, Mfr & Marketer
N.A.I.C.S.: 551112
David Chen (Chm, Pres, CEO & Interim CFO)
Alex Lightman (CEO)

Subsidiary (Domestic):

Elements of Health and Wellness, Inc. (3)
850 Tidewater Shore Loop Ste 402, Bradenton, FL 34208   (90%)
Tel.: (631) 397-1111
Web Site:
https://www.elementsofhealth.com
Holistic & Naturopathic Supplement Developer, Mfr & Marketer
N.A.I.C.S.: 325411

ASC MACHINE TOOLS INC.
900 N Fancher Rd, Spokane, WA 99212
Tel.: (509) 534-6600
Web Site: https://www.ascmt.com
Year Founded: 1982
Sales Range: $10-24.9 Million
Emp.: 120
Paper Industries Machinery
N.A.I.C.S.: 333243
James Dunn (VP)

ASCC, Inc.—(Continued)

ASCC, INC.
130 Wisconsin Ave, Cranberry Township, PA 16066
Tel.: (724) 772-2722
Web Site: http://www.ascc-inc.com
Sales Range: $10-24.9 Million
Emp.: 50
Sales & Service of Communication Equipment
N.A.I.C.S.: 423690
John Ball (VP-Sls & Mktg)
Lynn Marx (VP-Gen Svcs)
Mark Bodo (Acct Mgr)
Shannen Tkatch (Engr-Sls)

ASCEND INTEGRATED MEDIA, LLC
7171 W 95th St Ste 300, Overland Park, KS 66212
Tel.: (913) 469-1110
Web Site:
   http://www.ascendintegrated.com
Year Founded: 2002
Sales Range: $1-9.9 Million
Emp.: 60
Business-to-Business Media
N.A.I.C.S.: 513120
Kate Hegarty (VP-Procurement)
Tricia Walsh (VP-Media Dev)
Rhonda Wickham (VP-Content)

Subsidiaries:

Practice Builders (1)
945 E Main St Ste 4, Spartanburg, SC 29302
Tel.: (714) 751-7960
Web Site: http://www.practicebuilders.com
Healthcare Marketing Services
N.A.I.C.S.: 541613
David Aguilar (Mgr-Implementation)
Sharon Mason Parker (CEO)

ASCEND MANAGEMENT INNOVATIONS LLC
840 Crescent Centre Dr Ste 400, Franklin, TN 37067-4667
Web Site: http://www.ascendami.com
Ambulance Service
N.A.I.C.S.: 621910
Teri Lepley (CEO)

ASCEND ONE CORPORATION
9755 Patuxent Woods Dr Ste 100, Columbia, MD 21046
Tel.: (410) 910-1735
Web Site: http://www.ascendone.com
Sales Range: $10-24.9 Million
Emp.: 200
Holding Company
N.A.I.C.S.: 541199
Bernaldo Dancel (Pres & CEO)
Robert Miller (COO)
Sherry Myers (Sr Dir)
Jiunn Tan (CIO)
John Mill (CFO)

Subsidiaries:

Amerix Corporation (1)
9755 Patuxent Woods Dr, Columbia, MD 21046-5805 (100%)
Tel.: (410) 910-1834
Web Site: http://www.careone.com
Consumer Debt Management Programs
N.A.I.C.S.: 541199
Bernie Dancel (Chm & CEO)

ASCEND PLASTIC SURGERY PARTNERS
2 Ravinia Dr NE Ste 970, Atlanta, GA 30346
Tel.: (833) 902-4574
Web Site:
   https://www.ascendpsp.com
Plastic Surgery & Aesthetics
N.A.I.C.S.: 621111
William Hedden (Founding Partner)

Subsidiaries:

Ponte Vedra Plastic Surgery (1)
209 Ponte Vedra Park Dr, Ponte Vedra Beach, FL 32082-6600
Tel.: (904) 273-6200
Web Site: http://www.pvps.com
Freestanding Ambulatory Surgical & Emergency Centers
N.A.I.C.S.: 621493
Mary Daniel (Mgr)

ASCEND TECHNOLOGIES, LLC
3915 Harrison Rd Ste 100, Loganville, GA 30052-5896
Tel.: (770) 788-8089
Web Site:
   http://www.ascendtechnologies.com
Research & Development in Biotechnology
N.A.I.C.S.: 541714
David Roberts (Owner)

Subsidiaries:

Infogressive, Inc. (1)
6200 S 58th St Ste A, Lincoln, NE 68516
Tel.: (402) 261-0123
Web Site: http://www.infogressive.com
Sales Range: $1-9.9 Million
Emp.: 12
Information Security Management Services
N.A.I.C.S.: 541512
Justin Kallhoff (CEO)

ASCEND VENTURE GROUP, LLC
129 W 29th St 5th Fl, New York, NY 10001
Tel.: (212) 324-2222
Web Site:
   http://www.ascendventures.com
Year Founded: 2000
Rev.: $150,000,000
Emp.: 10
Venture Capital Investment & Portfolio Management Firm
N.A.I.C.S.: 523999
Darryl Wash (Mng Partner)
Susan Levy (Partner)
Kylie A. D. Sachs (Partner)

ASCENDANT COMPLIANCE MANAGEMENT
194 Main St, Salisbury, CT 06068
Tel.: (860) 435-2255
Web Site:
   http://www.ascendantcomply.com
Sales Range: $1-9.9 Million
Emp.: 30
Business Management Consulting Services
N.A.I.C.S.: 541611
Jon Higgins (Pres & Partner)
Jacqueline Hallihan (Partner)
John J. Gentile (Partner)
Keith Marks (Partner)
Sally Cole (Dir-Conferences & Education & Mgr)
Roger Crain (Partner)
Melissa Maleri (Dir-Mktg)
Mike Mirantz (Partner & Mgr-Client Svcs)

ASCENDO RESOURCES, LLC
2 Alhambra Plz PH 2-A, Coral Gables, FL 33134
Tel.: (305) 423-1221
Web Site:
   http://www.ascendoresources.com
Sales Range: $1-9.9 Million
Emp.: 40
Staffing Services
N.A.I.C.S.: 561311
Gustavo Pena (Mng Partner)
Ronei Foumia (Partner)
Peter Soto (Mng Dir-Lauderdale)
Joan Sturge (Mgr-Bus Dev)

Eli Halabu (Mng Dir-Miami)
Eugene Holzer (Mng Partner-Miami)
Jodi Jaiman (Mng Dir-Central Florida)
John Moorhouse (Mng Dir-New York)
Mark Poolos (Mng Dir-Chicago)
Rick Ferretti (Partner)
Orlando Perez (Mng Dir)
Kelly Lintz (Mng Dir-Tampa)

ASCENDTECH, INC.
4772 E 355th St, Willoughby, OH 44094
Tel.: (216) 458-1101
Web Site: https://www.ascendtech.us
Year Founded: 2002
Rev.: $9,400,000
Emp.: 30
Computer & Computer Peripheral Equipment & Software Merchant Whslr
N.A.I.C.S.: 423430
Igor Lapinskiy (Pres)
Valeri Sakhanevitch (Gen Mgr)

ASCENSION HEALTH ALLIANCE
101 S Hanley Rd Ste 450, Saint Louis, MO 63105
Tel.: (314) 733-8000
Web Site: http://www.ascension.org
Year Founded: 2011
Health Care Services Organization
N.A.I.C.S.: 813920
Eduardo F. Conrado (Pres)
Joseph R. Impicciche (CEO)
Christine Kocot McCoy (Gen Counsel & Exec VP)
Craig Cordola (COO & Exec VP)

Subsidiaries:

AH Holdings, LLC (1)
5451 Lakeview Pkwy S Dr, Indianapolis, IN 46268
Tel.: (317) 275-5544
Holding Company
N.A.I.C.S.: 551112

Subsidiary (Domestic):

MedXcel, LLC (2)
5451 Lakeview Pkwy S Dr, Indianapolis, IN 46268
Tel.: (317) 275-5544
Web Site: http://www.medxcelglobal.com
Health Technology Services
N.A.I.C.S.: 561110
Greg Ranger (Pres)
Barbara Burcope (Chief Responsibility Officer & Sr VP-HR)
Jeff Dodson (VP-Info Svcs)
Jim Fanelli (CFO)
Tim McGeath (Gen Counsel & Sr VP)
Jennefer Pursifull (VP-Mktg)
Douglas Folsom (CIO)
Robert Duffy (VP-Value Chain)
Ron Brown (VP-Real Estate)
Carla Shade (VP)
Michael Argir (CEO)

Subsidiary (Domestic):

Axess Ultrasound, LLC (3)
8148 Woodland Dr, Indianapolis, IN 46278
Tel.: (317) 275-5554
Ultrasound Services, Repair & Training
N.A.I.C.S.: 334510

TriMedx International, LLC (3)
5451 Lakeview Pkwy S Dr, Indianapolis, IN 46268
Tel.: (317) 275-5544
Web Site: http://www.trimedx.com
Clinical Engineering Services & Medical Equipment Management
N.A.I.C.S.: 811210
Henry Hummel (CEO)
Chris Dunkerley (CFO)
Tim McGeath (Chief Compliance Officer & Gen Counsel)
Gene Schrecengost (Chief HR Officer)
Doug Folsom (CIO)
LeAnne Hester (CMO)
Jay Khan (Exec VP-Ops)

Ramy Boghdadi (Exec VP-Strategic Client Value & Relationships)
Shane Landrum (Sr VP-Comml Ops)

Subsidiary (Domestic):

TriMedx, LLC (4)
5451 Lakeview Pkwy S Dr, Indianapolis, IN 46268
Web Site: http://www.trimedx.com
Healthcare Technology Equipment Services
N.A.I.C.S.: 541990
Henry Hummel (CEO)

Subsidiary (Domestic):

Aramark Healthcare Technologies, LLC (5)
10510 Twin Lake Pkwy, Raleigh, NC 28269
Tel.: (704) 948-1110
Life & Health Insurance Services
N.A.I.C.S.: 524210
Timothy Moss (Mgr-Laboratory Product)

Centurion Service Group, LLC (5)
3325 Mount Prospect Rd, Franklin Park, IL 60131
Tel.: (708) 761-6655
Web Site: http://www.centurionservice.com
Electronic Auctions
N.A.I.C.S.: 455219
Julie Ball (VP-Sls)
Erik Tivin (CEO)

Subsidiary (Non-US):

TriMedx India Pvt. Ltd. (5)
No. 258/A Bomassandra Industrial Area, Anekal Taluk, 560099, Bengaluru, Karnataka, India
Tel.: (91) 80 7122 2222
Healthcare Technology Management Services
N.A.I.C.S.: 541618
Mike Zess (Reg Dir)

Subsidiary (Domestic):

eProtex, LLC (3)
5451 Lakeview Pkwy S Dr, Indianapolis, IN 46268
Tel.: (317) 275-5544
Web Site: http://www.eprotex.com
Medical Device Security
N.A.I.C.S.: 541990
Derek Brost (Chief Security Officer)
David Elisea (Dir-Ops)

Alexian Brothers Health System, Inc. (1)
3040 Salt Creek Ln, Arlington Heights, IL 60005
Tel.: (847) 385-7100
Web Site:
   http://www.alexianbrothershealth.org
Sales Range: $500-549.9 Million
Emp.: 5,000
Owns & Operates Specialty Hospitals, Ambulatory Care Clinics, Senior Living Facilities & Rehabilitation Centers
N.A.I.C.S.: 622310
Mark A. Frey (Pres & CEO)
Patricia Cassidy (Chief Strategy Officer & Sr VP)
Paul Belter (CFO & Sr VP)

Borgess Health Alliance, Inc. (1)
110 N Elm Ave, Jackson, MI 49202
Tel.: (269) 226-7000
Holding Company; Hospitals & Medical Centers Operator
N.A.I.C.S.: 551112

Subsidiary (Domestic):

Ascension Borgess Lee Hospital (2)
420 W High St, Dowagiac, MI 49047-1943
Tel.: (269) 782-8681
Web Site: http://healthcare.ascension.org
Emp.: 275
General Medical & Surgical Hospitals
N.A.I.C.S.: 622110

Borgess Medical Center (2)
1521 Gull Rd, Kalamazoo, MI 49048
Tel.: (269) 226-7000
Web Site: http://www.borgess.com
Sales Range: $700-749.9 Million
Emp.: 4,000
Hospital Operations
N.A.I.C.S.: 622110

Tim A. Fischell *(Dir-Cardiovascular Res)*
Beth Brutsche *(Sec)*
Joni Knapper *(Vice Chm)*
Susan Pozo *(Treas)*

Textile Systems, Inc. (2)
817 Walbridge St, Kalamazoo, MI 49007-3573
Tel.: (269) 552-2050
Web Site: http://www.tsi.borgess.com
Sales Range: $10-24.9 Million
Emp.: 125
Linen Supply & Laundry Services
N.A.I.C.S.: 812331

Carondelet Health Corporation (1)
1000 Carondelet Dr, Kansas City, MO 64114-4673
Tel.: (816) 942-4400
Web Site: http://www.carondelethealth.org
Sales Range: $10-24.9 Million
Emp.: 154
Health Care Services Association
N.A.I.C.S.: 813910
Michael Dorsey *(Interim CEO)*

Subsidiary (Domestic):

Carondelet Management Company, Inc. (2)
1000 Carondelet Dr, Kansas City, MO 64114-4673
Tel.: (816) 942-4400
Healthcare Facilities Management & Administration Services
N.A.I.C.S.: 561110
Robert J. Erickson *(CEO)*

Unit (Domestic):

Carondelet Manor (2)
621 Carondelet Dr, Kansas City, MO 64114-4670
Tel.: (816) 943-4777
Web Site: http://www.carondeletmanor.com
Provider of Nursing Services
N.A.I.C.S.: 623110
Christie Deininger *(Dir-HR)*

Subsidiary (Domestic):

Carondelet Pharmacy at Saint Joseph Health Center Inc. (2)
1000 Carondelet Dr Ste 120, Kansas City, MO 64114-4673
Tel.: (816) 943-4879
Web Site: http://www.stjosephkc.com
Drug Stores & Proprietary Stores
N.A.I.C.S.: 456110
Loren Holtz *(Mgr)*

Unit (Domestic):

St. Mary's Manor (2)
111 Mock Ave, Blue Springs, MO 64014
Tel.: (816) 228-5655
Web Site: http://www.stmary.com
Provider of Nursing Services
N.A.I.C.S.: 623110
Bridget Jurgensmeyer *(Dir-Nursing)*

Villa Saint Joseph (2)
11901 Rosewood Dr, Overland Park, KS 66209-3533
Tel.: (913) 345-1745
Web Site: http://www.carondelethealth.org
Nursing Services
N.A.I.C.S.: 623110
Rebecca Slavens *(Dir-Admissions)*

Carondelet Health Network (1)
2202 N Forbes Blvd, Tucson, AZ 85745
Tel.: (520) 872-7790
Web Site: http://www.carondelet.org
Sales Range: $700-749.9 Million
Emp.: 4,000
Non-Profit Healthcare Services & Hospital Network Operator
N.A.I.C.S.: 622110
Leticia Ramirez *(CMO & Chief Plng Officer)*
Kim Commins *(Chief Legal Officer)*
James K. Beckmann *(Pres & CEO)*
Martha Gerganoff *(Chief Nursing Officer & Sr VP)*
Tawnya Tretschok *(VP & Exec Dir-Physician Practices)*

Subsidiary (Domestic):

Holy Cross Hospital (2)

1171 W Target Range Rd, Nogales, AZ 85621-2497
Tel.: (520) 285-3000
Web Site: http://www.carondelet.org
Sales Range: $75-99.9 Million
Emp.: 230
Hospital Operator
N.A.I.C.S.: 622110
Wanona Fritz *(Pres & CEO)*
Loretta Ortiz y Pino *(Chief Medical Officer)*

St. Joseph's Hospital (2)
350 N Wilmot Rd, Tucson, AZ 85711
Tel.: (520) 873-3000
Web Site: http://www.carondelet.org
Sales Range: $250-299.9 Million
Emp.: 1,670
Hospital Operator
N.A.I.C.S.: 622110
Scott Schmidly *(CEO-Atlanta)*
Mark Benz *(CEO)*

St. Mary's Hospital (2)
1601 W Saint Marys Rd, Tucson, AZ 85745
Tel.: (520) 872-3000
Web Site: http://www.carondelet.org
Sales Range: $250-299.9 Million
Emp.: 1,710
Hospital Operator
N.A.I.C.S.: 622110
Amy Beiter *(Pres & CEO)*
Lea Marquez Peterson *(Chm)*
Michael Duperret *(Vice Chm)*

Tucson Heart Hospital (2)
4888 N Stone Ave, Tucson, AZ 85704 **(78.8%)**
Tel.: (520) 696-2300
Sales Range: $100-124.9 Million
Emp.: 350
Cardiovascular Healthcare Services & Hospital Operator
N.A.I.C.S.: 622310

Columbia St. Mary's Inc. (1)
2301 N Lake Dr, Milwaukee, WI 53211
Tel.: (414) 291-1704
Web Site: http://www.columbia-stmarys.org
Sales Range: $10-24.9 Million
Medical Health Network
N.A.I.C.S.: 622110
Jo Ann Hankwitz *(VP-HR-Interim)*
Kevin Kluesner *(VP-Clinical Svcs-Hospital Div)*
Richard Shimp *(Chief Medical Officer)*
Gerri Staffileno *(Chief Nursing Officer & VP-Hospital Ops)*

Lourdes Health Network (1)
520 N 4th Ave, Pasco, WA 99301-5257
Tel.: (509) 547-7704
Web Site:
    http://www.lourdeshealthnetwork.org
Sales Range: $75-99.9 Million
Emp.: 750
Non-Profit Hospitals & Clinics Healthcare Network Operator & Support Services
N.A.I.C.S.: 622110
Frank Becker *(CFO & VP-Fin)*
Anita Kongslie-Lourdes *(Dir-Risk Mgmt)*
Melanie Johnston *(Dir-Mktg)*
Mark Gregson *(Interim CEO)*

Subsidiary (Domestic):

Lourdes Counseling Center (2)
1175 Carondelet Dr, Richland, WA 99354-3300
Tel.: (509) 943-9104
Web Site: http://www.lourdeshealth.net
Sales Range: $50-74.9 Million
Emp.: 145
Psychiatric & Behavioral Health Services
N.A.I.C.S.: 622210
Kaila Mitchell *(Mgr-Out Patient Mental Health Case-MSW)*
Lorena Herrera *(Mgr-Social Svcs)*

Lourdes Medical Center (2)
520 N 4th Ave, Pasco, WA 99301 **(100%)**
Tel.: (509) 547-7704
Web Site: http://www.lourdeshealth.net
Sales Range: $100-124.9 Million
Hospital; General & Ambulatory Health Services
N.A.I.C.S.: 622110
Denise Clapp *(Exec Dir-Patient Care)*

Presence Health (1)
7435 W Talcott Ave, Chicago, IL 60631

Tel.: (737) 774-8000
Web Site: http://www.amitahealth.org
Hospital Operator
N.A.I.C.S.: 622110

Sacred Heart Health System (1)
5151 N 9th Ave, Pensacola, FL 32504
Tel.: (850) 416-7000
Web Site: http://www.sacred-heart.org
Hospital Owner & Operator
N.A.I.C.S.: 622110
Robert A. Emmanuel *(Chm)*
Quint Studer *(Vice Chm)*
Terri Smith *(COO)*
Henry Stovall *(Pres & CEO)*

Saint Thomas Health Services (1)
102 Woodmont Blvd Ste 800, Nashville, TN 37205
Tel.: (615) 284-7847
Web Site: http://www.sths.com
Sales Range: $10-24.9 Million
Emp.: 50
Health Care System
N.A.I.C.S.: 531120
Greg Pope *(Chief Ministry Officer)*
Karen Springer *(Pres & CEO)*
Gregory James *(Chief Clinical Officer)*
Michelle Robertson *(COO)*
Dawn Rudolph *(Chief Experience Officer)*

Subsidiary (Domestic):

Saint Thomas Highlands Hospital, LLC (2)
401 Sewell Dr, Sparta, TN 38583
Tel.: (931) 738-9211
Web Site:
    http://www.highlandsmedicalcenter.net
Hospital Operator
N.A.I.C.S.: 622110
Cynthia Strong *(Dir-Bus Dev)*
Teresa Roberts *(Chief Nursing Officer)*
Andy Wachtel *(CEO)*
Richard Tumlin *(Chief Admin Officer)*

Saint Thomas Midtown Hospital (2)
2000 Church St, Nashville, TN 37236
Tel.: (615) 284-5555
Web Site: http://www.sthealth.com
Healthcare Services
N.A.I.C.S.: 622110
Jeremy Gray *(COO)*
Marco Fernandez *(Chief Nursing Officer)*
Geoffrey Smallwood *(Chief Medical Officer)*

Subsidiary (Domestic):

Baptist Hospital Foundation Inc. (3)
2000 Church St, Nashville, TN 37236-0001
Tel.: (615) 284-8211
Web Site: http://www.baptisthospital.com
Sales Range: $250-299.9 Million
Emp.: 3,000
Health Care Srvices
N.A.I.C.S.: 813410

Subsidiary (Domestic):

Saint Thomas Stones River Hospital, LLC (2)
324 Doolittle Rd, Woodbury, TN 37190
Tel.: (615) 563-4001
Web Site:
    http://www.stonesriverhospital.com
Emp.: 90
Hospital Operator
N.A.I.C.S.: 622110
Brian Gill *(Chief Admin Officer)*

St. John Providence Health System (1)
28000 Dequindre Rd, Warren, MI 48092-2468
Tel.: (586) 753-0500
Web Site: http://www.stjohnprovidence.org
Sales Range: $650-699.9 Million
Emp.: 14,028
Medical Hospital Network
N.A.I.C.S.: 622110
Patrick McGuire *(CFO & Exec VP)*

Subsidiary (Domestic):

St. John Conner Creek Village (2)
4777 E Outer Dr, Detroit, MI 48234
Tel.: (313) 369-9100
Web Site: http://www.stjohn.org
Sales Range: $75-99.9 Million
Emp.: 1,000
Emergency Health Services

N.A.I.C.S.: 622110

St. John Hospital & Medical Center (2)
22101 Morose Rd, Detroit, MI 48236
Tel.: (313) 343-4000
Web Site: http://www.ascension.org
Hospital Services
N.A.I.C.S.: 622110
Tomasine Marx *(VP-Fin Svcs)*
David Brooks *(CEO)*

St. John Macomb Hospital (2)
11800 E 12 Mile Rd, Warren, MI 48093
Tel.: (586) 573-5000
Web Site: http://www.ascenion.org
Sales Range: $125-149.9 Million
Emp.: 1,000
Hospital Services
N.A.I.C.S.: 622110
Randolph H. Kummler *(CFO)*
Joseph Tasse *(Pres)*

St. John Oakland Hospital (2)
27351 Dequindre Rd, Madison Heights, MI 48071-3487
Tel.: (586) 573-5000
Web Site: http://www.stjohnprovidence.org
Sales Range: $75-99.9 Million
Emp.: 700
Hospital Services
N.A.I.C.S.: 622110

St. John River District Hospital (2)
4100 River Rd, East China, MI 48054
Tel.: (810) 329-7111
Web Site: http://www.stjohn.org
Sales Range: $50-74.9 Million
Emp.: 386
Hospital Services
N.A.I.C.S.: 622110
Frank Poma *(Pres)*
Phil Wild *(Controller)*

St. Joseph Regional Medical Center (1)
415 6th St, Lewiston, ID 83501
Tel.: (208) 743-2511
Web Site: http://www.sjrmc.org
Sales Range: $75-99.9 Million
Emp.: 1,000
Medical Facility
N.A.I.C.S.: 622110
John Grauke *(Dir-Sleep Center)*
D. Blain Claypool *(Pres, CEO & Sec)*
Colin Doyle *(Chm)*

St. Mary's Hospital (1)
427 Guy Park Ave, Amsterdam, NY 12010-1054
Tel.: (518) 842-1900
Web Site: http://www.smha.org
Sales Range: $50-74.9 Million
Emp.: 1,000
Health Care Srvices
N.A.I.C.S.: 621111
Victor Giulianelli *(Pres & CEO)*
Michele Walsh *(VP-Nursing)*
Joan Ehlinger *(VP-Fin)*
Duane Miller *(VP-Behavioral Health Svcs)*
Andrew Heck *(Vice Chm)*
Emily Etzkorn *(Chm)*
Mary Anne Heenan *(Sec)*
Thomas Cichy *(Treas)*

St. Vincent's HealthCare (1)
1 Schircliff Way, Jacksonville, FL 32204
Tel.: (904) 308-7300
Web Site: http://www.jaxhealth.com
Emp.: 5,000
Hospital Owner & Operator
N.A.I.C.S.: 622110
Ann Carey *(CIO & VP)*
Bill Mayher *(Officer-Corp Responsibility & VP-Reg Dev)*
David Meyer *(Chief Strategy Mktg Officer-Ministry Market-Jacksonville)*
Hugh Middlerooks *(Chief Legal Officer)*
Kyle Sanders *(Pres-Population Health & Care Continuum)*
Michael Zwetschkenbaum *(VP-Fin & Revenue cycle)*
Tom VanOsdol *(CEO)*
David G. Kulik *(Vice Chm)*
Huson Gilberstadt *(Chief Clinical Officer)*
Maureen Martin *(VP-Fin)*
Estrellita Redmon *(VP-Clinical Integration)*
Sidney S. Simmons *(Chm)*
Ricardo Morales Jr. *(Treas & Sec)*

Ascension Health Alliance—(Continued)

Subsidiary (Domestic):

St. Catherine Laboure Manor, Inc. (2)
1750 Stockton St, Jacksonville, FL 32204
Tel.: (904) 308-4706
Sales Range: $25-49.9 Million
Emp.: 230
Nursing Care Facilities
N.A.I.C.S.: 623110
Maureen Gartland (VP)

St. Vincent's HealthCare Foundation (2)
1 Shircliff Way, Jacksonville, FL 32203
Tel.: (904) 308-7306
Web Site: http://stvincentsfoundation.org
Emp.: 12
Hospital Foundation
N.A.I.C.S.: 813219
Jane Lanier (Pres)
Moody Chisholm (Pres)
Bridget S. Markley (Coord-Donor & Campaign Svcs)
Jim Towler (Dir-Donor Svcs)
Tracie Loftis (VP-Mission Integration)
Willie Roberts (Coord-Program-FCN)
Rita Driskill (Mgr-Lab)

St. Vincent's Medical Center Riverside (2)
1 Shircliff Way, Jacksonville, FL 32204
Tel.: (904) 308-7300
Web Site: http://www.jaxhealth.com
Emp.: 5,000
Hospital Operations
N.A.I.C.S.: 622110
Tom Van Osdol (Plant Mgr)

St. Vincent's Medical Center Southside (2)
4201 Belfort Rd, Jacksonville, FL 32216
Tel.: (904) 296-3700
Web Site: http://www.jaxhealth.com
Sales Range: $125-149.9 Million
Emp.: 1,400
Hospital Operations
N.A.I.C.S.: 622110
Kyle Sanders (Pres & COO)
Lorraine Keith (COO & Chief Nursing Officer)

ASCENSION ST JOHN FOUNDATION
1923 S Utica Ave, Tulsa, OK 74104
Tel.: (918) 744-2186
Web Site: https://www.givestjohn.org
Health Care Srvices
N.A.I.C.S.: 621610

ASCENT BANCORP
1721 11th Ave, Helena, MT 59601-4665
Tel.: (406) 442-8870   MT
Web Site: http://www.fsb-hln.com
Year Founded: 2015
Bank Holding Company
N.A.I.C.S.: 551111
Loren J. Brown (Pres & CEO)
Tom McGree (COO)
Amy Caruso Quarles (CFO)

Subsidiaries:

First Security Bank of Helena (1)
1721 11th Ave, Helena, MT 59601-4665
Tel.: (406) 442-8870
Web Site: http://www.fsb-hln.com
Sales Range: $1-9.9 Million
Emp.: 9
Commericial Banking
N.A.I.C.S.: 522110
Loren J. Brown (Pres & CEO)
Tom McGree (COO)
Tyler Armstrong (Chief Credit Officer)

ASCENT CAPITAL GROUP, INC.
5251 DTC Pkwy Ste 1000, Greenwood Village, CO 80111
Tel.: (303) 628-5600   DE
Web Site: http://ir.ascentcapitalgroupinc.com

Year Founded: 2008
Sales Range: $500-549.9 Million
Emp.: 1,190
Holding Company
N.A.I.C.S.: 551112

Subsidiaries:

Ascent Media Group, LLC (1)
520 Broadway 5th Fl, Santa Monica, CA 90401-2420   (100%)
Tel.: (310) 434-7000
Web Site: http://www.ascentmedia.com
Sales Range: $10-24.9 Million
Emp.: 50
Post-Production Sound & Video Services
N.A.I.C.S.: 512191

Unit (Domestic):

Cinetech (2)
27200 Tourney Rd Ste 100, Valencia, CA 91355
Tel.: (661) 222-9073
Web Site: http://www.cinetech.com
Film Restoration & Preservation Services
N.A.I.C.S.: 512191
Suzy Galvez (VP-Film Restoration & Laboratory Svcs)

RIOT (2)
3399 Peachtree Rd NE, Atlanta, GA 30326
Tel.: (404) 237-9977
Web Site: http://www.riotatlanta.com
Motion Picture Sound Effects & Music Production Services
N.A.I.C.S.: 512191
Buddy Hall (Mng Dir)

Monitronics International, Inc. (1)
1990 Wittington Pl, Farmers Branch, TX 75234
Tel.: (972) 243-7443
Web Site: https://www.brinkshome.com
Rev.: $503,597,000
Assets: $1,346,663,000
Liabilities: $1,186,070,000
Net Worth: $160,593,000
Earnings: ($181,756,000)
Emp.: 1,280
Fiscal Year-end: 12/31/2020
Security Alarm Monitoring Systems
N.A.I.C.S.: 561621
Sara Harshbarger (Chief Transformation Officer)
Bob Reedy (Sr VP-Ops)
Dinesh Kalwani (Sr VP-Sls Ops)
Sava Tsvetkov (Sr VP-Finance & Strategy)
Philip Kolterman (Sr VP-Digital Transformation & Information Technology)
Veronica Moturi (Sr VP-Customer Experience)
Mike Hackett (Sr VP-Enterprise Bus Dev)

Subsidiary (Domestic):

Security Networks LLC (2)
3223 Commerce Pl Ste 101, West Palm Beach, FL 33407
Tel.: (561) 655-9956
Web Site: http://www.securitynetworks.net
Sales Range: $75-99.9 Million
Security System Monitoring Services
N.A.I.C.S.: 561621
Gary Franklyn (VP)

ASCENT INNOVATIONS LLC
Woodfield Corporate Ctr 475 N Martingale Rd Ste 820, Schaumburg, IL 60173-2435
Tel.: (847) 572-8000
Web Site: http://www.ascent365.com
Year Founded: 2009
Sales Range: $1-9.9 Million
Software Development Services
N.A.I.C.S.: 541511
Sohena Hafiz (Partner)

ASCENTIUM CORPORATION
3601 Rigby Rd Ste 420, Miamisburg, OH 45342
Tel.: (206) 403-1773
Web Site: http://www.smithcommerce.com
Sales Range: $10-24.9 Million
Emp.: 370

Integrated Technology & Marketing Consulting Services
N.A.I.C.S.: 541690
James Beebe (Pres & Partner)
Steven Salta (Partner & VP-Consulting Svcs)
Ross Porter (Partner & VP-Delivery Svcs)
Romi Mahajan (CMO)
Colleen Lillie (CFO)
Tony Steel (CEO)

Subsidiaries:

Adept Marketing Outsourced LLC (1)
855 Grandview Ave Ste 140, Columbus, OH 43215
Tel.: (614) 285-3044
Web Site: http://www.marketingadept.com
Sales Range: $1-9.9 Million
Emp.: 20
General Marketing Services
N.A.I.C.S.: 541613
Danielle Walton (Founder & CEO)
Gail Sech (VP-Bus Dev)
Justin Hines (Dir-Website Design & Dev)
Paul Woodhouse (Dir-SEO)
Nancy Cloutier (Chief Growth Officer)

Ascentium-MWR
518 W Riverside Ave, Spokane, WA 99201-0504
Tel.: (509) 455-4300
Web Site: http://www.ascentium.com
Rev.: $33,000,000
Emp.: 42
Advertising Agencies
N.A.I.C.S.: 541810
Curt Doolittle (CEO)
Colleen Lillie (CFO)
James Kim (Chief Strategy Officer)

Branch (Domestic):

Miller.whiterunkle (2)
1230 Peachtree St Ste 1800, Atlanta, GA 30309
Tel.: (404) 942-2830
Web Site: http://www.millerwr.com
N.A.I.C.S.: 541810
Joanne Hunt (Gen Mgr)

ASCH/GROSSBARDT, INC.
580 5th Ave Ste 918, New York, NY 10036
Tel.: (212) 302-3942   NY
Web Site: http://www.aschgrossbardt.com
Year Founded: 1987
Sales Range: $10-24.9 Million
Emp.: 7
Fine Inlaid Gold Jewelry Mfr
N.A.I.C.S.: 423940
Eric Grossbardt (Owner)

ASCHINGER ELECTRIC CO.
877 Horan Dr, Fenton, MO 63026
Tel.: (636) 343-1211
Web Site: https://www.aschinger.com
Year Founded: 1912
Sales Range: $25-49.9 Million
Emp.: 210
Electronic Services
N.A.I.C.S.: 238210
Emily Aschinger Martin (Pres)
Jack Aschinger (Sr VP)
Keith Aschinger (VP-Admin & Sec)
Scott Aschinger (VP-Ops)

ASCO SINTERING CO.
2750 Garfield Ave, Commerce, CA 90040
Tel.: (323) 725-3550
Web Site: https://www.ascosintering.com
Sales Range: $10-24.9 Million
Emp.: 110
Hardware
N.A.I.C.S.: 332510

Robert LeBrun (CFO)
Ian Harris (Plant Mgr)
Bob LeBrun (Mgr-HR)

ASCORP, INC.
217 College Ave Ste 5, Orofino, ID 83544
Tel.: (208) 476-3617
Web Site: https://www.debcousa.com
Sales Range: $10-24.9 Million
Emp.: 100
Heavy Construction & Project Management Services
N.A.I.C.S.: 237110
Lonnie E. Simpson (Pres)
Shannon Simpson (Sec)
Linda Applington (Mgr-Safety)
Diana Upton (Mgr-Payroll)
Chuck Martinez (Project Mgr)

ASCOT ENTERPRISES, INC.
503 S Main St, Nappanee, IN 46550-2531
Tel.: (574) 773-7751   IN
Web Site: http://www.ascotent.com
Year Founded: 1976
Sales Range: $25-49.9 Million
Emp.: 550
Curtains, Draperies, Bedspreads & Blinds
N.A.I.C.S.: 314120
Ken Manning (Pres)

ASE TECHNOLOGY INC.
7113 Peach Ct Ste 200, Brentwood, TN 37027
Tel.: (615) 595-8990   TN
Web Site: http://www.asetechnology.com
Year Founded: 2002
Sales Range: $1-9.9 Million
Emp.: 30
Printing & Photocopying Equipment Sales, Leasing & Servicing
N.A.I.C.S.: 561499
Judson H. Clift (Pres & CEO)
Allison Smock (Mgr-Accts Receivable)
Wesley Wright (Dir-Fin)

ASEL ART SUPPLY INC.
2701 Cedar Springs Rd, Dallas, TX 75201
Tel.: (214) 871-2425
Web Site: http://www.aselart.com
Sales Range: $10-24.9 Million
Emp.: 85
Artists' Supplies & Materials
N.A.I.C.S.: 459999

ASERA INC.
600 Clipper Dr Ste 100, Belmont, CA 94002
Tel.: (650) 769-1234
Web Site: http://www.asera.com
Rev.: $26,600,000
Emp.: 250
Computer Software Development
N.A.I.C.S.: 541511

ASFG, INC.
13911 Ridgedale Dr Ste 477, Eden Prairie, MN 55305
Tel.: (952) 348-0480
Mortgage Brokerage Services
N.A.I.C.S.: 522310
Timothy R. Duoos (Chm)

ASGARD PARTNERS & CO., LLC
12 E 49th St 11th Fl, New York, NY 10017
Tel.: (646) 867-7230   NY
Web Site: http://asgardpartners.com
Privater Equity Firm
N.A.I.C.S.: 523999

Karan Rai *(Founder & Mng Partner)*

Subsidiaries:

Angstrom Technology Ltd. (1)
3509 3 Mile Rd Nw Ste 3, Rockford, MI
49534
Web Site: http://angstromtechnology.com
Industrial Launderers
N.A.I.C.S.: 812332
Matt Isard *(Pres)*
Matt Purvis *(VP-Ops)*

Revision Military Ltd. (1)
7 Corporate Dr, Essex Junction, VT 05452
Tel.: (802) 879-7002
Web Site: http://www.revisionmilitary.com
Protective Soldier Equipment Mfr & Distr
N.A.I.C.S.: 423990
Amy Coyne *(CEO)*

ASGCO MANUFACTURING, INC.
301-323 Gordon St, Allentown, PA
18102
Tel.: (610) 821-0216
Web Site: http://www.asgco.com
Year Founded: 1972
Sales Range: $10-24.9 Million
Emp.: 100
Belt Conveyor Systems; General Industrial Use
N.A.I.C.S.: 333922
A. Todd Gibbs *(Co-Founder)*
Beth Hertzler *(Dir-Safety)*

Subsidiaries:

Esbelt, S.A. (1)
Provenca 385, Barcelona, 8025, (100%)
Spain
Tel.: (34) 932073311
Web Site: http://www.esbelt.com
Sales Range: $10-24.9 Million
Emp.: 30
Mfr & Supplier of Conveyor Belts, Power
Transmission Belts, Cleats & Sidewalls,
Round & V-belts for Lightweight Conveying
N.A.I.C.S.: 333922

ASH BROKERAGE CORP.
7609 W Jefferson Blvd, Fort Wayne,
IN 46804
Tel.: (260) 478-2604
Web Site:
    http://www.ashbrokerage.com
Year Founded: 1971
Insurance Agency & Brokerage Services
N.A.I.C.S.: 524210
Tim Ash *(Pres & CEO)*

Subsidiaries:

Target Insurance Services Inc. (1)
11020 Oakmont, Overland Park, KS 66210
Tel.: (913) 384-6300
Web Site: http://www.targetins.com
Sales Range: $50-74.9 Million
Emp.: 35
Insurance Agents
N.A.I.C.S.: 524210
Matthew McAvoy *(Pres)*
Nita Mead *(Dir-Ops)*
Kevin Coughlin *(Dir-Large Case Underwriting)*

ASH CREEK ENTERPRISES, INC.
1110 Broadbridge Ave, Stratford, CT
06615
Tel.: (203) 572-0200
Web Site: http://www.ashcreek.com
Year Founded: 1999
Sales Range: $1-9.9 Million
Emp.: 10
Data Processing, Hosting & Related
Services
N.A.I.C.S.: 518210
Mark Calzone *(Pres)*

ASH SHIPPING, INC.

961 Industry Dr, Savannah, GA
31415
Tel.: (912) 232-2639
Web Site:
    http://www.savannahcandy.com
Sales Range: $25-49.9 Million
Emp.: 200
Dry, Condensed & Evaporated Dairy
Product Mfr
N.A.I.C.S.: 311514
Stanley E. Strickland *(Pres)*
Tonya Strickland *(VP)*

ASHAWAY LINE & TWINE MFG. CO.
24 Laurel St, Ashaway, RI 02804-
1515
Tel.: (401) 377-2221
Web Site:
    https://www.ashawayusa.com
Year Founded: 1824
Sales Range: $75-99.9 Million
Emp.: 74
Mfr of Fishing Lines, Racket Strings,
Industrial Cordage & Surgical Sutures
N.A.I.C.S.: 314994
Pamela A. Crandall *(Chm)*
Wendy H. Crandall *(VP-Mfg)*
Katherine Crandall *(Pres & Treas)*

ASHBRIDGE OIL CO. INC.
335 Nees Ave, Johnstown, PA 15904
Tel.: (814) 266-5829
Sales Range: $25-49.9 Million
Emp.: 7
Gasoline Station Supply & Services
N.A.I.C.S.: 424720
Frank A. Ashbridge Jr. *(Pres)*

ASHBY LUMBER CO.
824 Ashby Ave, Berkeley, CA 94710
Tel.: (510) 843-4832
Web Site:
    http://www.ashbylumber.com
Sales Range: $25-49.9 Million
Emp.: 100
Retailer of Lumber & Building Materials
N.A.I.C.S.: 444140
Jeffrey Hogan *(Co-Owner)*
Nadya Cook *(Mgr-HR)*
Rick Kelly *(Gen Mgr-Store)*
Emily Morgan *(Co-Owner & CEO)*

ASHCO EXTERIORS INC.
1819 Bemidji Ave N Suite 24, Bemidji, MN 56601
Tel.: (218) 751-1040
Web Site:
    http://www.ashcoexteriors.com
Year Founded: 2001
Sales Range: $10-24.9 Million
Emp.: 20
Real Estate Restoration Specialists
N.A.I.C.S.: 236116
Greg Anderson *(CEO)*

ASHEBORO ELASTICS CORPORATION
150 N Park St, Asheboro, NC 27203
Tel.: (336) 629-2626
Web Site:
    http://www.asheboroelastics.com
Year Founded: 1986
Sales Range: $10-24.9 Million
Emp.: 60
Mfr of Elastic Narrow Fabrics, Woven
Or Braided
N.A.I.C.S.: 313220
Keith Crisco *(Founder & Partner)*
Jeff Crisco *(VP-Sls)*
Charles Adams *(Pres)*
Larry Himes *(CEO)*

ASHEBORO PAPER & PACKAGING, INC.

4441 N Fayetteville St, Asheboro, NC
27203-3288
Tel.: (336) 683-0200
Web Site:
    http://www.asheboropaper.com
Year Founded: 1997
Sales Range: $10-24.9 Million
Emp.: 65
Non-Durable Goods Whslr
N.A.I.C.S.: 424990
Joanne O'Grady *(Owner)*

ASHER AGENCY, INC.
535 W Wayne St, Fort Wayne, IN
46802-2123
Tel.: (260) 424-3373   IN
Web Site:
    https://www.asheragency.com
Year Founded: 1974
Sales Range: $25-49.9 Million
Emp.: 60
Advertising Services
N.A.I.C.S.: 541810
Thomas K. Borne *(CEO)*
Larry Wardlaw *(VP-Acct Svc)*
Jill Brown *(Sr VP & Dir-Media)*
Sasha Skow-Lindsey *(Supvr-Acct)*
Kara Kelley *(Pres)*
Kelly Gayer *(VP & Dir-Creative)*
Dan Schroeter *(VP & Dir-Creative)*
Margaret Davidson *(VP-Strategic
Dev)*
Steve Morrison *(VP & Gen Mgr)*
Megan Bennett *(CFO)*

Subsidiaries:

Asher Agency, Inc. - Lexington (1)
4101 Tates Creek Ctr Dr Ste 150, Lexington, KY 40517-3096
Tel.: (859) 273-5530
Web Site: http://www.asheragency.com
Advertising Services
N.A.I.C.S.: 541810
Jill Brown *(Sr VP & Dir-Media)*
Kelley Gayer *(VP & Dir-Creative)*
Margaret Davidson *(VP-Strategic Dev)*
Kara Kelley *(Sr VP)*
Steve Morrison *(VP & Gen Mgr)*
Karen Richter *(CFO & VP)*

ASHER MEDIA, INC.
15303 Dallas Pkwy Ste 1300, Addison, TX 75001
Tel.: (972) 732-6464   TX
Web Site:
    http://www.ashermedia.com
Year Founded: 1999
Sales Range: $1-9.9 Million
Emp.: 22
Advertising Agencies
N.A.I.C.S.: 541810
Kalyn Asher *(Pres)*
Lora Funderberk *(Dir-Media Plng)*
Jackie Barrera *(Dir-Media Buying)*

ASHER'S CHOCOLATES, INC.
80 Wambold Rd, Souderton, PA
18964
Tel.: (215) 721-3000
Web Site: http://www.ashers.com
Year Founded: 1892
Sales Range: $1-9.9 Million
Emp.: 120
Candy & Snack Mfr
N.A.I.C.S.: 311352
John Asher *(Co-Chm)*
Robert Asher *(Co-Chm)*
Charles Clark *(CFO)*
Steve Marcanello *(VP-Ops)*
Jeff Asher *(VP-Sls/Mktg & Product
Dev)*
Steve Mercogliana *(Mgr-Pur)*

ASHEVILLE CHEVROLET INC.
205 Smokey Park Hwy, Asheville, NC
28806-1140
Tel.: (828) 665-4444

Web Site:
    https://www.ashevillechevrolet.com
Year Founded: 1998
Sales Range: $25-49.9 Million
Emp.: 50
Dealers of New & Used Automobiles
N.A.I.C.S.: 441110
Diane Hemphill *(CFO)*

ASHFIELD CAPITAL PARTNERS, LLC
801 Montgomery St Ste 200, San
Francisco, CA 94133
Tel.: (415) 391-4747   DE
Web Site: https://www.ashfield.com
Year Founded: 1973
Sales Range: $25-49.9 Million
Emp.: 29
Asset Management & Investment Advisory Services
N.A.I.C.S.: 523940
J. Stephen Lauck *(Pres, CEO & Co-CIO)*
Lesley Jones *(Chief Compliance Officer)*
Peter A. Johnson *(Co-CEO & Mgr-Portfolio)*
Marc W. Lieberman *(Dir-Res & Portfolio Mgr)*
Lyman D. Howard *(Portfolio Mgr)*

ASHH, INC.
13231 Northend Ave, Oak Park, MI
48237
Web Site:
    http://www.oozewholesale.com
Year Founded: 2015
Sales Range: $25-49.9 Million
Emp.: 30
Smoking Product & Accessory Retailer
N.A.I.C.S.: 459991
Gjergj Sinishtaj *(CEO & Partner)*

ASHLAND OFFICE SUPPLY, INC.
2100 29th St, Ashland, KY 41101
Tel.: (606) 329-1400
Web Site:
    https://www.ashlandoffice.com
Rev.: $10,000,000
Emp.: 50
Retailer of Office Equipment
N.A.I.C.S.: 423420
Thomas L. Burnette *(Pres)*

ASHLAND TECHNOLOGIES, INC.
218 Dell Rd, Hegins, PA 17938
Tel.: (570) 682-0933
Web Site: https://www.ash-tec.com
Sales Range: $1-9.9 Million
Emp.: 38
Contract Mfr of Machined & Fabricated Parts
N.A.I.C.S.: 333515
Connie Wydra *(Office Mgr & Mgr-Acctg)*
Jim Miller *(Supvr-Second Shift)*
Roger Strohecker *(Mgr-HR)*
William Wydra Jr. *(Pres)*

ASHLEY CAPITAL LLC
60 E 42nd St Ste 4530, New York,
NY 10165
Tel.: (212) 755-1900
Web Site:
    http://www.ashleycapital.com
Year Founded: 1984
Sales Range: $10-24.9 Million
Emp.: 45
Real Estate Agents & Managers
N.A.I.C.S.: 531210
Paul D. Rubacha *(Co-Founder &
Principal)*
Rick Morton *(Co-Founder & Principal)*

Ashley Capital LLC—(Continued)

Lori Roth *(Sr Mng Dir-Finance-New York)*
Susan Harvey *(Sr VP-Leasing & Acq)*
Bob Auskalnis *(CFO & VP-Midwest Reg-Chicago)*
Richard Borthwick *(VP-Leasing)*
Peter Pfeiffer *(VP-Property Mgmt-Midwest Reg)*
Ken Bowen *(VP-Construction)*
Kevin Hegg *(VP-Leasing)*
Gary Rosecrans *(VP-Leasing-Acquisitions)*
Tim Schneider *(VP-Leasing & Acq)*

ASHLEY F. WARD, INC.
7490 Easy St, Mason, OH 45040-9423
Tel.: (513) 398-1414   OH
Web Site:
    https://www.ashleyward.com
Year Founded: 1908
Sales Range: $10-24.9 Million
Emp.: 250
Mfr of Lighters & Screw Machine Products
N.A.I.C.S.: 332721
William Ward *(Chm)*
Terry Bien *(Pres)*
Pam Stephenson *(Dir-Accounting-Finance)*
Larry Sutter *(Mgr-Quality Control)*

ASHLEY FURNITURE INDUSTRIES, INC.
1 Ashley Way, Arcadia, WI 54612-1218
Tel.: (608) 323-3377   WI
Web Site:
    https://www.ashleyfurniture.com
Year Founded: 1945
Sales Range: $1-4.9 Billion
Emp.: 3,500
Nonupholstered Wood Household Furniture Manufacturing
N.A.I.C.S.: 337122
Todd R. Wanek *(Pres & CEO)*

Subsidiaries:

Ashley Distribution Services, Ltd. (1)
1 Ashley Way, Arcadia, WI 54612-1218
Tel.: (608) 323-3377
Web Site: http://www.ashleyfurniture.com
Sales Range: $100-124.9 Million
Emp.: 350
Furniture Whslr, Warehousing & Transportation Services
N.A.I.C.S.: 423210
Todd R. Wanek *(Pres & CEO)*
Ron Wanek *(Founder & Chm)*
Nathan Sanders *(Sr VP)*

Ashley HomeStores, Ltd.   (1)
2998 Broadway Center Blvd, Brandon, FL 33510
Tel.: (813) 620-3444
Web Site:
    http://www.ashleyfurniturehomestore.com
Sales Range: $1-4.9 Billion
Emp.: 5,000
Retail Furniture Store Licensing & Development
N.A.I.C.S.: 533110
Chuck Spang *(Bus Dev & Property Mgmt)*
Bill Dixon *(Gen Mgr-Jacksonville)*
Chris Caprio *(Pres & Partner)*
Howard Fineman *(CEO)*

ASHLEY IMPORTS, LLC
1555 W 16th St, Merced, CA 95340
Tel.: (209) 384-2000   CA
Web Site: http://mercedkia.com
Year Founded: 1961
Sales Range: $10-24.9 Million
Emp.: 47
Automobiles, New & Used
N.A.I.C.S.: 441330
Sargiz Isaac *(Owner)*

ASHMORE BROS., INC.
1880 S Hwy 14, Greer, SC 29650
Tel.: (864) 879-7311
Web Site:
    http://www.ashmorebros.com
Year Founded: 1930
Sales Range: $10-24.9 Million
Emp.: 200
Provider of Construction Preparation Services
N.A.I.C.S.: 237310
David C. Hughey *(Controller)*
Ken Atwood *(Coord-Safety Compliance)*
Scott Short *(Mgr-Acctg)*

ASHOKA
1700 N Moore St Ste 2000 20th Fl, Arlington, VA 22209
Tel.: (703) 527-8300   VA
Web Site: https://www.ashoka.org
Year Founded: 1980
Sales Range: $25-49.9 Million
Emp.: 400
Social Entrepreneur Support Services
N.A.I.C.S.: 561499
Maria Valeria Budinich *(Mgr)*
Allen Hammond *(Mgr)*

ASHTON ATLANTA RESIDENTIAL LLC
3820 Mansell Rd Ste 300, Alpharetta, GA 30022
Tel.: (770) 642-6123
Web Site:
    http://www.ashtonwoodshomes.com
Sales Range: $10-24.9 Million
Emp.: 85
Single-Family Housing Construction
N.A.I.C.S.: 236115
Dawn Stokley *(Office Mgr)*
Detrick Childers *(Office Mgr)*

ASHTON BANCSHARES, INC.
317 3rd St, Ashton, IA 51232
Tel.: (712) 724-6326
Web Site:
    http://www.ashtonstatebank.com
Sales Range: $1-9.9 Million
Bank Holding Company
N.A.I.C.S.: 551111
Brian D. Mino *(Pres & CEO)*

Subsidiaries:

Ashton State Bank   (1)
317 3rd St, Ashton, IA 51232
Tel.: (712) 724-6326
Web Site: http://www.ashtonstatebank.com
Commericial Banking
N.A.I.C.S.: 522110
Brian D. Mino *(Pres & CEO)*
Karen A. Simington *(VP)*

Subsidiary (Domestic):

Ashton State Bank Agency, Inc. (2)
317 3rd St, Ashton, IA 51232
Tel.: (712) 724-6326
Web Site: http://www.ashtonstatebank.com
Insurance Agents
N.A.I.C.S.: 524210
Karen A. Simington *(VP)*

ASHTON COMPANY, INC.
2727 S Country Club Rd, Tucson, AZ 85713
Tel.: (520) 624-5500
Web Site:
    https://www.ashtoncoinc.com
Year Founded: 1946
Sales Range: $200-249.9 Million
Emp.: 325
Heavy & Civil Engineering Construction Services
N.A.I.C.S.: 237990

William R. Vail *(Pres & CEO)*
Douglas J. Humphreys *(VP)*
Brian Andrews *(VP)*
Marc J. Dotseth *(VP)*

ASHTON GARDENS HOUSTON
21919 Inverness Forest Blvd, Houston, TX 77073
Tel.: (281) 362-0011
Web Site:
    http://www.ashtongardens.com
Year Founded: 2004
Sales Range: $1-9.9 Million
Emp.: 90
High-End Wedding Venues
N.A.I.C.S.: 711310
Stephanie Selaiden *(Dir-Sls & Mktg)*
Rex O. Grey *(Owner & CEO)*
Cesar Garcia *(Mgr-Ops)*

ASHTON WOODS HOMES
1405 Old Alabama Rd Ste 200, Roswell, GA 30076
Tel.: (770) 998-9663   TX
Web Site:
    http://www.ashtonwoods.com
Year Founded: 1994
Sales Range: $10-24.9 Million
Emp.: 60
Residential Construction
N.A.I.C.S.: 236115
Ken Balogh *(Pres & CEO)*
Deborah M. Danzig *(Chief Legal Officer)*
Thad DiGiuro *(Sr VP-Land Acq-Strategy)*
Jay Kallos *(VP-Architecture)*
Karin Shaban *(VP-HR)*
Ryan Lewis *(COO)*
Zack Sawyer *(VP & Controller)*
Onex Evans *(Mgr)*
Cory Jacobs Boydston *(CFO)*

ASHWORTH BROS., INC.
Ste 3 222 Milliken Blvd, Fall River, MA 02721-1623
Tel.: (508) 674-4693   MA
Web Site: http://www.ashworth.com
Year Founded: 1894
Sales Range: $150-199.9 Million
Emp.: 450
Mfr of Metal & Plastic Conveyor Belting & Conveyor Systems
N.A.I.C.S.: 333922
Vincent Moretti *(Pres)*
Tom Flynn *(Mgr-Acctg)*

Subsidiaries:

Ashworth Belts B.V.   (1)
Kabelweg 57, 1014 BA, Amsterdam, Netherlands
Tel.: (31) 20 581 3220
Web Site: http://ashworth-belts-bv.business.site
Emp.: 8
Conveyor Belts Mfr
N.A.I.C.S.: 332618
Joe Lackner *(Head-Sls)*

Ashworth Europe, LTD   (1)
Unit E5 The Wallows Industrial Estate Fens Pool Avenue, Brierley Hill, DY5 1QA, West Midlands, United Kingdom
Tel.: (44) 1 384 355000
Emp.: 4
Conveyor Belts Mfr
N.A.I.C.S.: 332618
David Stackhouse *(Area Mgr-Sls)*

Ashworth Factory Service
Corporation   (1)
1405 Cannon Cir Ste 15, Faribault, MN 55021
Tel.: (866) 204-1414
Web Site: http://www.ashworth.com
Emp.: 8
Conveyor Belts Mfr
N.A.I.C.S.: 333922
Bryan Hobbs *(Gen Mgr)*

Ashworth Japan K.K.   (1)
M Plus Building Room No 601 6-2-13 Ueno, Taito-ku, Tokyo, 110-0005, Japan
Tel.: (81) 3 6806 0745
Conveyor Belts Mfr
N.A.I.C.S.: 332618

ASI AVIATION, INC.
8521 Leesburg Pike Ste 175, Vienna, VA 22182
Tel.: (703) 657-9909   NV
Year Founded: 2015
Emp.: 2
Aircraft Components Mfr
N.A.I.C.S.: 336413
B. B. Sahay *(Chm & CEO)*
James P. Flynn *(Pres)*
James L. Silvester *(CFO)*
Carl Jacobsen *(VP-Admin)*
Danette Penenburgh *(Sec)*

ASI BUILDING PRODUCTS
4720 Adamo Dr, Tampa, FL 33605
Tel.: (813) 247-4667
Web Site: http://www.asibp.com
Rev.: $34,000,000
Sales Range: $10-24.9 Million
Emp.: 66
Building Products
N.A.I.C.S.: 423330
Alvin Neff *(Mgr-Production)*
Ervin Rodriguez *(VP-HR)*
Jesse Severn *(Branch Mgr)*
Jamica Smith *(Dir-Mktg)*
Mitch Mells *(Mgr-Patio Div)*
Nevin Ashe *(Product Mgr)*
Ronald Neidert *(Reg Mgr-Sls)*
Victoria Stuben *(Asst Mgr-Credit)*
Cookie Brinkman *(VP-Mktg)*
Karim Kharroubi *(VP-Fin)*

ASI BUSINESS SOLUTIONS INC.
2200 Renaissance Blvd, King of Prussia, PA 19406
Tel.: (610) 265-9400
Web Site: https://www.asi-solutions.com
Year Founded: 1990
Rev.: $10,500,000
Emp.: 50
Computer Software Development
N.A.I.C.S.: 541511
Jim Alonso *(Pres & CEO)*
Alyssa Carey *(Acct Exec)*

ASI CORPORATION
48289 Fremont Blvd, Fremont, CA 94538
Tel.: (510) 226-8000   CA
Web Site: http://www.asipartner.com
Year Founded: 1987
Sales Range: $900-999.9 Million
Emp.: 541
Computer Hardware & Software Distr
N.A.I.C.S.: 423430
Christine Liang *(Founder)*

ASI SYSTEM INTEGRATION, INC.
48 W 37th St, New York, NY 10018
Tel.: (212) 736-0111
Web Site: http://www.asisystem.com
Year Founded: 2005
Sales Range: $150-199.9 Million
Emp.: 625
Information Technology Services
N.A.I.C.S.: 449210
Sonny Chabra *(Chm & CEO)*
Chris Mammano *(Pres)*
Narinder Chabra *(COO)*
Mark Romanowski *(Exec VP)*
Ravi Thakur *(CFO)*
Sonny Bindra *(VP)*
Kathleen Riley *(Dir-Bus Dev & Mktg)*

Harry Taluja *(Dir-Consulting & Integration)*
Joe Roman *(Dir-Support Svcs)*
Angel L. Pineiro Jr. *(Sr VP-Svcs)*

ASIA ACCESS TELECOM, INC.
197 Turnpike Plz Ste 305, East Brunswick, NJ 08816
Tel.: (732) 828-9002   DE
Web Site: https://www.asiaat.com
Sales Range: $250-299.9 Million
Emp.: 50
Telephone Communication, Except Radio
N.A.I.C.S.: 517121
Norman Rosenberg *(Mgr)*

ASIA CHEMICAL CORPORATION INC.
11950 Airline Dr Ste 300, Houston, TX 77037
Tel.: (281) 445-1793
Web Site: https://www.asiachem-tx.com
Rev.: $36,000,000
Emp.: 50
Plastics Resins
N.A.I.C.S.: 424610
George C. Yang *(Chm & CEO)*
Yung Chang *(Pres)*

ASIAN AMERICAN DRUG ABUSE PROGRAM
2900 S Crenshaw Blvd, Los Angeles, CA 90016
Tel.: (323) 293-6284
Web Site: http://www.aadapinc.org
Year Founded: 1972
Sales Range: $1-9.9 Million
Emp.: 177
Substance Abuse Rehabilitation Services
N.A.I.C.S.: 623220
Michael Watanabe *(Pres & CEO)*
Karl K. Nobuyuki *(Vice Chm)*
Danny Torii *(Chm)*

ASIAN COUNSELING & REFERRAL SERVICE
3639 Martin Luther King Jr Way S, Seattle, WA 98144
Tel.: (206) 695-7600   WA
Web Site: https://www.acrs.org
Year Founded: 1973
Sales Range: $10-24.9 Million
Emp.: 272
Behavioral Healthcare Services
N.A.I.C.S.: 623220
Juliana Wong *(First VP)*
Jeffrey Liang *(Second VP)*
Anita Rodgers *(Treas)*

ASIAN HEALTH SERVICES
818 Webster St, Oakland, CA 94607
Tel.: (510) 986-6800   CA
Web Site:
   https://www.asianhealthservices.org
Year Founded: 1974
Sales Range: $25-49.9 Million
Emp.: 361
Health Care Srvices
N.A.I.C.S.: 622110
Carl Chan *(Chm)*
Gavin Funabiki *(Sec)*
Tervina Moy *(Vice Chm)*
Vance Yoshida *(Treas)*
Dong Suh *(COO)*
George Lee *(Chief Medical Officer)*
Huong Le *(Chief Dental Officer)*
Rose Tam *(CFO)*

ASIAN PACIFIC HEALTH CARE VENTURE, INC.
4216 Fountain Ave, Los Angeles, CA 90029

Tel.: (323) 644-3880   CA
Web Site: https://www.aphcv.org
Year Founded: 1987
Sales Range: $10-24.9 Million
Emp.: 181
Healtcare Services
N.A.I.C.S.: 622110
Kazue Shibata *(CEO)*
John Hoh *(Dir-Medical)*
Michael Epstein *(VP)*

ASIAN WORLD OF MARTIAL ARTS, INC.
9400 Ashton Rd, Philadelphia, PA 19114
Tel.: (215) 969-3500
Web Site: http://www.awma.com
Sales Range: $10-24.9 Million
Emp.: 50
Sporting & Recreation Goods
N.A.I.C.S.: 423910
Georgette Ciukurescu *(Pres)*

ASIANA CUISINE ENTERPRISES, INC.
22771 S Western Ave, Torrance, CA 90501
Tel.: (310) 327-2223
Web Site: https://www.acesushi.com
Sales Range: $25-49.9 Million
Emp.: 560
Convenience Foods Mfr
N.A.I.C.S.: 311991
Brian Tan *(Sr VP-Sls & Ops)*
Harlan Chin *(Pres)*
Gary Chin *(CFO)*

ASIANWEEK
564 Market St Ste 320, San Francisco, CA 94104
Tel.: (415) 397-0220
Web Site: http://www.asianweek.com
Sales Range: Less than $1 Million
Emp.: 9
Online Newspaper
N.A.I.C.S.: 513110
Ted Fang *(Editor & Publr)*
James Fang *(Pres)*

Subsidiaries:

Asian Week Foundation   (1)
564 Market St Ste 320, San Francisco, CA 94104
Tel.: (415) 397-0220
Web Site: http://www.asianweek.com
Online Newspaper Focusing on Asian Pacific American Community
N.A.I.C.S.: 513110

ASIGNET USA, INC.
90 Et Halsey Rd, Parsippany, NJ 07054
Tel.: (973) 387-1050
Web Site: https://asignet.com
Year Founded: 2006
It Consulting
N.A.I.C.S.: 513210
Claudio Lopez Silva *(Founder & CEO)*

Subsidiaries:

Xigo, LLC   (1)
5870 Trinity Pkwy, Centreville, VA 20120
Tel.: (703) 334-0070
Web Site: http://www.xigo.com
Sales Range: $25-49.9 Million
Emp.: 100
Telecommunications Expense Management Software Solutions
N.A.I.C.S.: 513210
David Spofford *(CEO)*
Robert Smith *(CTO)*
Scott Little *(COO & Chief Security Officer)*
Dave Snow *(CMO)*
Robin Boniface *(COO & Chief Security Officer)*

ASK FOODS INC.

77 N Hetrick Ave, Palmyra, PA 17078
Tel.: (717) 838-6356
Web Site: https://www.askfoods.com
Rev.: $21,607,889
Emp.: 140
Salads, Fresh or Refrigerated
N.A.I.C.S.: 311991
Wendie DiMatteo *(CEO)*
Jere Maurer *(Controller)*
Matthew Corbett *(Coord-Trng)*
George Loverich *(Mgr-Sanitation)*

ASK STAFFING, INC.
3805 Crestwood Pkwy NW Ste 260, Duluth, GA 30096-3339
Tel.: (770) 813-8947
Web Site: http://www.askstaffing.com
Sales Range: $10-24.9 Million
Emp.: 31
Professional Staffing Services
N.A.I.C.S.: 561311
Amanda Poland *(Acct Mgr)*

ASL INTERPRETER REFERRAL SERVICE, INC.
21 Clyde Rd Ste 103, Somerset, NJ 08873
Tel.: (732) 873-6401
Web Site: https://www.aslirs.com
Year Founded: 1997
Rev.: $2,000,000
Emp.: 8
School & Educational Services
N.A.I.C.S.: 611699
Kathy Kady-Hopkins *(Pres)*
Christine Sherwood *(VP)*

ASLAN CONSTRUCTION INC.
120 Bunyan Ave Ste 200, Berthoud, CO 80513
Tel.: (970) 344-1040
Web Site:
   https://www.aslanconstruction.com
Year Founded: 2001
Sales Range: $10-24.9 Million
Emp.: 50
Construction Engineering Services
N.A.I.C.S.: 237310
Michael Pelphrey *(Pres)*

ASOCIACION PUERTORRIQUENOS EN MARCHA FOR EVERYONE
4301 Rising Sun Ave, Philadelphia, PA 19140
Tel.: (267) 296-7200   PA
Web Site: http://www.apmphila.org
Year Founded: 1971
Sales Range: $10-24.9 Million
Emp.: 139
Family Support Services
N.A.I.C.S.: 624190
Donald E. Price *(VP-Health Svcs)*
Rose Gray *(Sr VP-Community-Economic Dev)*
Rasak Azeez *(CFO & Sr VP-Admin & Fin)*
Elizabeth Colon *(VP-Org Integration)*
Nilda Iris Ruiz *(Pres & CEO)*

ASP FIBERMARK HOLDINGS LLC.
70 Front St, West Springfield, MA 01089
Tel.: (413) 736-4554
Sales Range: $200-249.9 Million
Emp.: 591
Investment Management Service
N.A.I.C.S.: 523999
Matthew Lebaron *(Pres)*
Eric Schondorf *(VP)*
Matthew Levine *(VP & Treas)*

ASPECT CONSULTING, INC.
20140 Valley Forge Cir, King of Prussia, PA 19406

Tel.: (610) 783-0600
Web Site: https://www.aspect-consulting.com
Year Founded: 1994
Sales Range: $1-9.9 Million
Emp.: 21
Data Warehousing & Data Management & Application Development Services
N.A.I.C.S.: 541511
John Abrams *(Pres & Co-Founder)*
Joseph McMonagle *(Dir-Recruiting & Staffing)*
Joe-Ellen Zaspel *(Co-Founder)*

ASPECT HOLDINGS, LLC
1775 Sherman St Ste 2400, Denver, CO 80203
Tel.: (303) 573-7011   CO
Web Site:
   http://www.aspectenergy.com
Year Founded: 1993
Rev.: $150,000,000
Emp.: 35
Oil & Gas Exploration
N.A.I.C.S.: 213112
Alex Cranberg *(Chm)*
Lora Mays *(Chief Admin Officer & Gen Counsel)*
Codey James *(VP-Engrg & Ops)*

ASPECT RATIO INC.
5161 Lankershim Blvd, Hollywood, CA 91601
Tel.: (323) 467-2121
Web Site: http://www.aspectratio.com
Rev.: $11,200,000
Emp.: 100
Motion Picture Film Processing & Editing Services
N.A.I.C.S.: 512191
Dennis Hamilton *(CFO)*
Jeff Niford *(Mgr-IT)*

ASPECT SOFTWARE GROUP HOLDINGS LTD.
300 Apollo Drive, Chelmsford, MA 01824
Tel.: (978) 250-7900   Ky
Web Site: http://www.aspect.com
Year Founded: 1973
Software Publisher & Whslr
N.A.I.C.S.: 513210
Christopher Koziol *(Pres & CEO)*
James Freeze *(CMO & Sr VP)*
Michael Regan *(Sr VP-R&D)*
Gwen Braygreen *(Sr VP-Aspect Customer Care)*
Jim Haskin *(CIO & Sr VP)*
Joe Gagnon *(Sr VP & Gen Mgr-Cloud Solutions)*
Manish Bajaj *(Mgr-India & Middle East)*
Jagannath Narendran *(Sr VP-Asia & Middle East)*
Shailendra Tanwar *(Head-Mktg-India & Middle East)*
Tom Davies *(Sr VP-Cloud Ops)*
Bob Segert *(Chm)*

ASPEN DISTRIBUTION SERVICES, INC.
1711 S 4650 W, Salt Lake City, UT 84104
Tel.: (801) 973-2622
Web Site: http://aspenlogistics.com
Sales Range: $25-49.9 Million
Emp.: 150
General Warehousing
N.A.I.C.S.: 424460
Garry Barfuss *(Gen Mgr)*

ASPEN EXTERIORS, INC.
14245 Saint Francis Blvd Ste 101, Ramsey, MN 55303
Tel.: (763) 434-3687

Aspen Exteriors, Inc.—(Continued)

Web Site:
https://www.aspenexteriors.com
Sales Range: $1-9.9 Million
Emp.: 7
Home Remodeling & Storm Damage
Services
N.A.I.C.S.: 236220
Joseph W. Jelinek *(Owner)*
Matthew LaBine *(Pres)*

ASPEN GROVE LANDSCAPE COMPANIES, LLC

708 Blair Mill Rd, Willow Grove, PA
19090
Tel.: (855) 588-5452   PA
Web Site:
http://www.aspengrovelg.com
Year Founded: 2018
Holding Company; Commercial Land-
scaping Firm
N.A.I.C.S.: 551112

Subsidiaries:

Long Brothers Landscaping, LLC   (1)
6460 Mount Heman Rd, Raleigh, NC 27617
Tel.: (919) 782-2809
Web Site:
http://www.longbrotherslandscaping.com
Specialty Trade Contractors
N.A.I.C.S.: 238990

The Landscape Partners, Ltd.   (1)
7231 Baker Blvd, Fort Worth, TX 76118
Tel.: (817) 284-7900
Web Site: http://thelandscapepartners.com
Landscape Services
N.A.I.C.S.: 541320

ASPEN HEALTHCARE SERVICES

314 W Main St Ste 100, Lewisville,
TX 75057
Tel.: (972) 316-2035
Web Site:
https://www.aspenhealthcare.com
Year Founded: 2006
Sales Range: $1-9.9 Million
Emp.: 90
Quality Home Health Care Services
N.A.I.C.S.: 621610
Ron Davis *(VP-Bus Dev)*
Cynthia Blair *(Dir-HR)*
Sandy Long *(Mgr-Fin)*

ASPEN MORTGAGE CORP.

2460 Lemoine Ave, Fort Lee, NJ
07024-6231
Tel.: (201) 944-5040   NJ
Year Founded: 1993
Sales Range: $25-49.9 Million
Emp.: 1
Mortgage Bankers & Correspondents
N.A.I.C.S.: 522310
Daniel Back *(Pres)*

ASPEN OF DC

1200 18th St NW Ste 1001, Washing-
ton, DC 20036
Tel.: (202) 380-9930
Web Site: http://www.aspenofdc.com
Year Founded: 2003
Sales Range: $10-24.9 Million
Emp.: 10
Staffing Solutions
N.A.I.C.S.: 561311
Brandy Butler *(Pres & CEO)*
Gwen Henderson *(Dir-Ops)*
Adriana Spikes-Freeman *(Dir-Mktg & Comm)*

ASPEN SQUARE MANAGE-MENT, INC.

380 Union St, West Springfield, MA
01089
Tel.: (413) 781-0712

Web Site:
http://www.aspensquare.com
Sales Range: $10-24.9 Million
Emp.: 100
Apartment Building Operator
N.A.I.C.S.: 531311
Harold Grinspoon *(Pres & CEO)*
Ann Berezin *(Dir-Affordable Housing)*
Dave Grzybowski *(Mgr-Natl Asset)*
David Chabot *(Gen Counsel)*
Wendy Crate *(Dir-Property Mgmt)*
Bobbie Longo *(Mgr-Property)*
Chris Wood *(Dir-Procurement)*
James Gennari *(Mgr-Real Estate As-set)*
Roger Cherewatti *(Partner)*
Liz Craig *(Mgr-Contract)*

ASPEN TRANSPORTATION, LLC

2608 Fair Park Blvd, Jonesboro, AR
72401
Tel.: (870) 910-5712   AR
Web Site:
http://www.aspentransportation.com
Year Founded: 2002
Sales Range: $10-24.9 Million
Emp.: 19
Supply Chain Management Services
N.A.I.C.S.: 541614
Stephanie Mize *(Mgr)*

ASPEN WASTE SYSTEMS INC.

2951 Weeks Ave SE, Minneapolis,
MN 55414
Tel.: (651) 644-3488
Web Site:
http://www.aspenwaste.com
Rev.: $12,100,672
Emp.: 75
Rubbish Collection & Disposal
N.A.I.C.S.: 562111
Robert E. Kircher *(Founder, Owner, Pres & CEO)*
Thor Nelson *(COO)*

Subsidiaries:

Aspen Waste System of Missouri   (1)
13710 Green Ash Ct, Saint Louis, MO
63045
Tel.: (314) 890-9100
Web Site: http://www.aspenwaste.com
Rev.: $2,400,000
Emp.: 40
Refuse System
N.A.I.C.S.: 562219
Robert Kircher *(Owner & CEO)*

ASPENPOINTE

675 Southpointe Ct Ste 210, Colo-
rado Springs, CO 80906
Tel.: (719) 572-6100   CO
Web Site: http://www.aspenpointe.org
Year Founded: 2003
Sales Range: $25-49.9 Million
Emp.: 648
Individual & Family Support Services
N.A.I.C.S.: 624190
Kevin Light *(CFO)*
Mick Pattinson *(Pres & CEO)*
Kevin Porter *(VP-Sls & Mktg)*

ASPENWARE, INC.

6000 Greenwood Plz Blvd Ste 110,
Englewood, CO 80111
Tel.: (303) 798-5458
Web Site: http://www.aspenware.com
Sales Range: $1-9.9 Million
Emp.: 17
Software Services
N.A.I.C.S.: 513210
Josh Swihart *(CEO)*
Zaneta Kelsey *(Dir-Mktg)*

ASPHALT CONTRACTORS INC.

6730 Taylor Cir, Montgomery, AL
36117
Tel.: (334) 279-5228
Sales Range: $10-24.9 Million
Emp.: 115
Highway & Street Paving Contractor
N.A.I.C.S.: 237310

ASPHALT SPECIALTIES CO. INC.

10100 Dallas St, Henderson, CO
80640
Tel.: (303) 289-8555
Web Site:
https://www.asphaltspecialties.com
Sales Range: $50-74.9 Million
Emp.: 300
Highway & Street Paving Contractor
N.A.I.C.S.: 238110
Daniel Hunt *(Owner)*
Greg Simmons *(Project Mgr)*

ASPINWALL COOPERATIVE CO.

201 Main St, Aspinwall, IA 51432
Tel.: (712) 653-3441   IA
Web Site:
http://www.aspinwallcoop.com
Year Founded: 1942
Sales Range: $10-24.9 Million
Emp.: 30
Retail of Grain Field Beans, Fuel
Seed & Petroleum
N.A.I.C.S.: 424510
Jeff Nelson *(Gen Mgr)*

ASPIRANET

400 Oyster Point Blvd Ste 501, South
San Francisco, CA 94080
Tel.: (650) 866-4080   CA
Web Site: https://www.aspiranet.org
Year Founded: 1975
Sales Range: $25-49.9 Million
Emp.: 1,389
Individual & Family Support Services
N.A.I.C.S.: 624190
Holly Thauwald *(Dir-HR)*
John Reiber *(CFO)*

ASPIRE CHICAGO

1815 S Wolf Rd, Hillside, IL 60162
Tel.: (708) 547-3560
Web Site:
https://www.aspirechicago.com
Individual & Family Services
N.A.I.C.S.: 624190
Taryn Wagner *(Mgr-Case)*

ASPIRE CONSULTING GROUP LLC

8220 Crestwood Heights Dr, McLean,
VA 22102
Tel.: (571) 888-0009
Web Site:
http://www.aspire.consulting
Year Founded: 2015
Emp.: 50
Information Technology Solutions
N.A.I.C.S.: 541614
Mark S. Johnson *(Pres)*
David Thielen *(CEO-Aspire Consult-ing & Exec VP-Textmunication Hold-ings)*

ASPIRE HEALTH PARTNERS, INC.

5151 Adanson St Ste 200, Orlando,
FL 32804
Tel.: (407) 245-0045   FL
Web Site: http://www.cfdfl.com
Year Founded: 1972
Sales Range: $25-49.9 Million
Emp.: 708
Behavioral Healthcare Services
N.A.I.C.S.: 623220

Joe Goldstein *(Treas)*
Paul F. Bryan *(Chm)*
Karen Florio *(Sec)*

Subsidiaries:

Aspire Health Partners - Fernpark
Facility   (1)
237 Fernwood Blvd, Fern Park, FL 32730
Tel.: (407) 831-2411
Web Site:
http://www.aspirehealthpartners.org
Rev.: $13,570,916
Assets: $11,495,259
Liabilities: $2,399,343
Net Worth: $9,095,916
Earnings: $400,832
Emp.: 205
Fiscal Year-end: 06/30/2012
Behavioral Healthcare Services
N.A.I.C.S.: 623220
Debbie R. Driskell *(Exec VP)*
Scott Charles Griffiths *(Sr VP)*
Valerie Westhead-Tonner *(Dir-Medical)*

Aspire Health Partners - Princeton
Plaza   (1)
1800 Mercy Dr, Orlando, FL 32808
Tel.: (407) 875-3700
Web Site: http://www.lakesidecares.org
Sales Range: $25-49.9 Million
Emp.: 1,000
Behavioral Healthcare Services
N.A.I.C.S.: 623220
Vicki Garner *(Exec VP-Ops)*
Carla Caponi *(Exec VP & CFO)*
John G. Kassab *(Pres & CEO)*
Peg Seykora *(VP-Outpatient Svcs)*
Tom Greenman *(VP-Acute Care Svcs)*
Paula Bateman *(VP-HR)*

ASPIRE OF ILLINOIS

1815 S Wolf Rd, Hillside, IL 60162
Tel.: (708) 547-3550   IL
Web Site:
https://www.aspirechicago.com
Year Founded: 1960
Sales Range: $10-24.9 Million
Emp.: 638
Disability Assistance Services
N.A.I.C.S.: 624310
Jim Kales *(Pres & CEO)*

ASPIRE OF WESTERN NEW YORK, INC.

2356 N Forest Rd, Getzville, NY
14068
Tel.: (716) 324-2744   NY
Web Site: http://www.aspirewny.org
Year Founded: 1947
Sales Range: $50-74.9 Million
Emp.: 1,902
Developmental Disability Assistance
Services
N.A.I.C.S.: 623210

ASPIRE REAL ESTATE INVES-TORS, INC.

1920 Main St Ste 150, Irvine, CA
92614
Tel.: (949) 269-4700   MD
Year Founded: 2020
Real Estate Investment Services
N.A.I.C.S.: 531210
Daryl J. Carter *(Pres & CEO)*

ASPIREHR

5151 Belt Line Rd Ste 1125, Dallas,
TX 75254
Tel.: (214) 880-0099
Web Site: https://www.aspirehr.com
Year Founded: 1998
Rev.: $15,700,000
Emp.: 50
Management Consulting Services
N.A.I.C.S.: 541618
Mike Braun *(Acct Mgr)*
Brian Collett *(Partner-Dev Svcs)*
Randy Griffith *(Pres)*

ASPIRIANT HOLDINGS, LLC

11100 Santa Monica Blvd Ste 600, Los Angeles, CA 90025
Tel.: (310) 806-4000 DE
Web Site: https://www.aspiriant.com
Wealth Management Services
N.A.I.C.S.: 523999
Rob Francais *(CEO)*
Marc Castellani *(Principal & Mng Dir-Investment Strategy & Res)*
Adam Stanley *(Principal)*
Doug Hendrickson *(CFO)*
Nathan S. Kublank *(Principal & Dir-Investment Advisory)*
Tom Tracy *(Chief Client Officer & Principal)*
John Allen *(Chief Investment Officer & Principal)*
Cammie Doder *(Principal & Dir-Mktg)*
Ken Anderson *(Principal & Dir-Wealth Mgmt)*
Michael S. Angell *(Principal & Dir-Wealth Mgmt)*
Lisa Barnea *(Principal & Dir-Fin)*
Ryan P. Benson *(Principal & Mgr-Wealth Mgmt)*
Karen Blodgett *(Principal & Dir-Wealth Mgmt)*
Sandi Bragar *(Principal & Mng Dir-Planning Strategy & Res)*
Lisa Colletti *(Principal & Mng Dir-Planning Strategy & Res)*
John Collins *(Principal & Dir-Investment Advisory)*
Sandra Conners *(Principal & Dir-Wealth Mgmt)*
Helen A. Dietz *(Principal & Dir-Wealth Mgmt)*
Gregory P. Fasig *(Principal & Dir-Investment Advisory)*
Mike Fitzhugh *(Principal & Dir-Wealth Mgmt)*
Carl Forster *(Principal & Dir-Investment Advisory)*
Lorraine Fox *(Principal & Dir-Wealth Mgmt)*
Brett Gookin *(Principal & Dir-Wealth Mgmt)*
David Grecsek *(Principal & Mng Dir-Investment Strategy-Res)*
Andy Hamilton *(Principal & Dir-Wealth Mgmt)*
Lani Kapur *(Principal & Mgr-Wealth Mgmt)*
Phil J. Kastenholz *(Principal & Dir-Investment Strategy & Res)*
Young Kim *(Principal & Mng Dir-Investment Ops)*
Ginny King *(Principal & Dir-Wealth Mgmt)*

ASPIRITY HOLDINGS, LLC
701 Xenia Ave Ste 475, Minneapolis, MN 55416
Tel.: (763) 432-1500 MN
Web Site:
http://www.aspirityholdings.com
Sales Range: $10-24.9 Million
Emp.: 11
Holding Company; Electric Power Distr
N.A.I.C.S.: 551112
Timothy S. Krieger *(Chm & Interim CEO)*
Scott C. Lutz *(Pres & CEO)*

ASPLUNDH FAMILY PUBLIC FOUNDATION INC.
708 Blair Mill Rd, Willow Grove, PA 19090
Tel.: (215) 784-4200 PA
Year Founded: 2009
Sales Range: $1-9.9 Million
Healthcare Support Services
N.A.I.C.S.: 813910
Edward K. Asplundh *(Pres)*
Christopher B. Asplundh *(VP)*

Kurt H. Asplundh *(Sec)*
Joseph P. Dwyer *(Treas)*

ASPLUNDH TREE EXPERT CO.
708 Blair Mill Rd, Willow Grove, PA 19090-1701
Tel.: (215) 784-4112 PA
Web Site: https://www.asplundh.com
Year Founded: 1928
Sales Range: $1-4.9 Billion
Emp.: 34,819
Landscaping Services
N.A.I.C.S.: 561730
Matt Asplundh *(CEO)*

Subsidiaries:

American Electrical Testing Co., Inc. **(1)**
480 Neponset St, Canton, MA 02021-0267
Tel.: (781) 821-0121
Web Site: http://www.99aetc.com
Emp.: 55
Electrical Testing Services
N.A.I.C.S.: 541380
Charles K. Blizard *(Pres & CEO)*
Scott Blizard *(VP-Field Ops)*

ArborMetrics Solutions, Inc. **(1)**
224 Thompson St 104, Hendersonville, NC 28792
Tel.: (866) 685-1880
Web Site:
http://www.arbormetricssolutions.com
Sales Range: $10-24.9 Million
Emp.: 137
Vegetation Management Services
N.A.I.C.S.: 561730
Robert Richard *(Gen Mgr)*

Arborchem Products **(1)**
943 Nixon Dr, Mechanicsburg, PA 17055
Tel.: (717) 766-6661
Web Site: http://www.arborchem.com
Vegetation Management Services
N.A.I.C.S.: 561730

Asplundh Brush Control Co. **(1)**
94 Park St, Whitney Point, NY 13862
Tel.: (607) 692-4711
Line Clearance & Vegetation Management Services
N.A.I.C.S.: 238910

Asplundh Canada ULC **(1)**
128 Drull Av W Vita, Winnipeg, MB, Canada
Tel.: (613) 223-4154
Vegetation Management Services
N.A.I.C.S.: 561730

Asplundh Tree Expert (Australia) PTY Ltd **(1)**
PO Box 165, Doonside, Sydney, 3199, NSW, Australia **(100%)**
Tel.: (61) 397831000
Web Site: http://www.asplundh.com.au
Sales Range: $10-24.9 Million
Emp.: 130
Provider of Landscape Management Services
N.A.I.C.S.: 561730

Asplundh Tree Expert (NZ) Ltd. **(1)**
27-29 Kitchener Rd Pukekohe, Auckland, 2012, New Zealand
Tel.: (64) 95708041
Web Site: http://www.asplundh.co.nz
Sales Range: $10-24.9 Million
Emp.: 75
Landscape Management Services
N.A.I.C.S.: 561730

Asplundh Tree Service ULC **(1)**
82 Ray, Fall River, B2T 1J5, NS, Canada
Tel.: (902) 818-3142
Landscaping Services
N.A.I.C.S.: 561730

Blume Tree Services, Inc. **(1)**
5165 Old Summer Rd, Memphis, TN 38122
Tel.: (901) 682-0279
Web Site: http://www.blumetree.org
Vegetation Management Services
N.A.I.C.S.: 561730

UtiliCon Solutions, Ltd. **(1)**
708 Blair Mill Rd, Willow Grove, PA 19090

Tel.: (877) 884-5426
Web Site: http://www.utiliconltd.com
Utility Construction Services
N.A.I.C.S.: 237130

Subsidiary (Domestic):

American Lighting and Signalization, Inc. **(2)**
12712 E Us Hwy 92, Dover, FL 33527-4100
Tel.: (813) 719-2211
Lighting & Signalization Construction Services
N.A.I.C.S.: 237130

Asplundh Environmental Services, Inc. **(2)**
11639 Davis Creek Rd E, Jacksonville, FL 32256
Tel.: (904) 260-2600
Web Site:
http://www.asplundhenvironmental.com
Emergency Recovery Services
N.A.I.C.S.: 624230

BNK Advisory Group, Inc. **(2)**
1605 Valley Ctr Pkwy, Bethlehem, PA 18017
Tel.: (610) 867-2717
Rev.: $3,000,000
Emp.: 10
Securities Brokerage
N.A.I.C.S.: 523150
John P. Brew Jr. *(Chm, Pres & CEO)*

Highlines Construction Company, Inc. **(2)**
701 Bridge City Ave, Westwego, LA 70096-0408
Tel.: (504) 436-3961
Web Site: http://www.highlines.com
Electrical Transmission Line Construction Services
N.A.I.C.S.: 811310
Rick Chanove *(Mgr-Admin)*

Musgrove Construction, Inc. **(2)**
8708 US Hwy 90, Live Oak, FL 32060
Tel.: (386) 362-7048
Sales Range: $25-49.9 Million
Emp.: 170
Construction Engineering Services
N.A.I.C.S.: 541330
Tim Smith *(Gen Mgr)*

Utility Lines Construction Services, Inc. **(2)**
617 1st St N, Birmingham, AL 35203
Tel.: (205) 226-5400
Sales Range: $25-49.9 Million
Emp.: 130
Construction Engineering Services
N.A.I.C.S.: 237990
Jim Marsh *(VP)*

VSI Meter Services, Inc. **(1)**
500 W Dutton Mill Rd, Aston, PA 19014
Web Site: http://www.vsimeterservices.com
Sales Range: $25-49.9 Million
Emp.: 250
Installer of Meters for Utilities & Municipalities
N.A.I.C.S.: 423430

ASR INTERNATIONAL CORPORATION
580 Old Willets Path, Hauppauge, NY 11788
Tel.: (631) 231-1086
Web Site: https://www.asrintl.com
Year Founded: 1986
Sales Range: $10-24.9 Million
Emp.: 450
Administrative Management & General Management Consulting Services
N.A.I.C.S.: 541611
Sandeep Manne *(Project Mgr)*

ASSABET VALLEY BANCORP
42 Main St, Hudson, MA 01749
Tel.: (978) 567-3515
Web Site: http://www.avidiabank.com
Year Founded: 1997
Sales Range: $1-9.9 Million
Emp.: 100

Mutual Holding Company
N.A.I.C.S.: 551111
Oliver F. Nunes *(Pres)*
Paul Blazar *(Chm)*

Subsidiaries:

Avidia Bank **(1)**
42 Main St, Hudson, MA 01749
Tel.: (978) 562-6944
Web Site: http://www.avidiabank.com
Savings Institutions, Except Federal
N.A.I.C.S.: 522180
Mark R. O'Connell *(Pres & CEO)*
Margaret B. M. Sullivan *(CFO & Exec VP)*
Rita Janeiro *(Sr VP-Community Banking)*
Andrea Blood *(VP-Comml Loan Admin)*
Avnish Puri *(Officer-Relationship & VP-Comml)*
David Morticelli *(VP)*
Stephanie Luz *(Officer-Bus Banking & Asst VP)*
Paul Blazar *(Chm)*
Robert W. Conery *(Co-COO & Exec VP)*
Gerald L. Curley *(Co-COO & Exec VP)*
Thomas Allain *(Officer-Comml Relationship & Sr VP)*
Jocelyn Arsenault *(Sr VP-Internal Audit)*
Emily Braga *(Sr VP-Deposit Ops)*
Neil Buckley *(Sr VP-Security & Compliance)*
Charles Budd *(Officer-Comml Relationship & Sr VP)*
Thomas Doane *(Sr VP-HR)*
Nicolas Karmelek *(Chief Risk Officer & Sr VP)*
Philip Maio *(Chief Info Security Officer & Sr VP)*
Stephen McAndrew *(Officer-Comml Relationship & Sr VP)*
Andrew Miller *(Officer-Comml Relationship & Sr VP)*
Sharon Quinn *(Sr VP-Cash Mgmt)*
Dick Schrader *(Officer-Comml Lending & Sr VP)*
Joseph Sova *(Officer-Comml Relationship & Sr VP)*
Lee Thompson *(Chief Credit Officer & Sr VP)*
James Wilkins *(Officer-Comml Relationship & Sr VP)*
Ronald Fraser *(Officer-Comml Relationship & VP)*
Ron Notaro *(Officer-Comml Relationship & VP)*
Maureen Marshall *(Officer-Comml Relationship & VP)*
Edward Perachi *(Officer-Mortgage Loan & VP)*
Daniel Provencher *(Officer-Comml Relationship & VP)*
Charles L. Park Jr. *(VP & Mgr-Workout)*
Bartholomew H. Murphy Jr. *(Chief Lending Officer & Exec VP)*
Donald Frost III *(Sr VP-Residential Lending)*
Daniel J. Serafin Sr. *(CIO & Sr VP)*

ASSEMBLY & MANUFACTURING SYSTEMS, INC.
3204 Darby St Unit 218, Simi Valley, CA 93063-5390
Tel.: (805) 583-8961
Sales Range: $10-24.9 Million
Emp.: 45
Custom Machine Builder & Systems Integrator
N.A.I.C.S.: 333998

ASSEMBLY FASTENERS INC.
255 Semoran Commerce Pl, Apopka, FL 32703-4632
Tel.: (407) 703-1582
Web Site: https://www.afi.cc
Sales Range: $10-24.9 Million
Emp.: 70
Hardware Distr
N.A.I.C.S.: 423710
Hubert L. Watson *(Pres)*
Judy Watson *(VP)*

ASSET ALLIANCE CORPORATION
800 3rd Ave, New York, NY 10022
Tel.: (212) 207-8786

Asset Alliance Corporation—(Continued)

Web Site:
http://www.assetalliance.com
Sales Range: $10-24.9 Million
Emp.: 20
Investment Banking & Management
N.A.I.C.S.: 523150
Bruce H. Lipnick (Co-Founder, Chm & CEO)
Arnold L. Mintz (Co-Founder, Pres & COO)
Nathan C. Gorin (CFO & Sr VP)
Michael Wu (Exec VP)
Steve Stanton (Head-Sls-Total Traffic Mgmt Div-Wolverhampton)
David Potter (Dir-Comml Dev)

Subsidiaries:

Asset Alliance Advisors Inc　　(1)
800 3rd Ave, New York, NY 10022
Tel.: (212) 207-8786
Web Site: http://www.assetalliance.com
Rev.: $190,000
Security Brokers & Dealers
N.A.I.C.S.: 523150
Bruce H. Lipnick (Chm)

Asset Alliance Holding Group　　(1)
800 3rd Ave Fl 22, New York, NY 10022
Tel.: (212) 207-8786
Web Site: http://www.assetalliance.com
Security Brokers & Dealers
N.A.I.C.S.: 523150
Bruce H. Lipnick (Co-Founder, Chm & CEO)

ASSET INTERTECH, INC.
2201 N Central Expy Ste 105, Richardson, TX 75080
Tel.: (972) 437-2800
Web Site: http://www.asset-intertech.com
Year Founded: 1995
Computer Debugging, Validation & Testing Solutions
N.A.I.C.S.: 513210
Alan Sguigna (VP-Sls)
Gerry Morgan (VP-Product Dev)
Glenn Woppman (Chm, Pres & CEO)
Larry Traylor (VP-Software Debug & Trace)
Brent Troxel (CFO & VP)

ASSET MANAGEMENT COMPANY, LLC
2100 Geng Rd Ste 200, Palo Alto, CA 94303
Tel.: (650) 621-8808　　　CA
Web Site: http://www.assetman.com
Year Founded: 1967
Venture Capital Firm
N.A.I.C.S.: 523999
Mike Knych (CFO)
Skip Fleshman (Partner)
Louis G. Lange (Gen Partner)
Rich Simoni (Partner)

ASSET MARKETING SYSTEMS INSURANCE SERVICES, LLC
15050 Avenue Of Science Ste 100, San Diego, CA 92128-3418
Web Site:
http://www.assetmarketing.net
Year Founded: 1996
Rev.: $1,600,000,000
Emp.: 175
Annuities & Life Insurance Services
N.A.I.C.S.: 524128
Dee Costa (Sr VP-Bus Consultant)
Louise Erdman (Exec VP-Consulting Div)
Jennifer Metcalfe-Schendel (Pres & CEO)
Merrit Strunk (CMO)
Ricky Metcalfe (Owner & Dir-Producer Rels)

ASSET PLUS COMPANIES LP

950 Corbindale Rd Ste 300, Houston, TX 77024
Tel.: (713) 782-5800
Web Site:
http://www.assetpluscorp.com
Year Founded: 1986
Sales Range: $10-24.9 Million
Emp.: 1,803
Real Estate Manangement Services
N.A.I.C.S.: 531390
Michael S. McGrath (Chm & Pres)
Ryan McGrath (CEO)
Barrett Kirk (Sr VP-Dev)
Mark Lindley (Sr VP-Construction)
Randall Husmann (CFO)
Ruth Ford (Controller)
Nancy Kovar (Controller-Houston)
Stephen Mitchell (Exec VP-Bus Dev)
David Hargrove (COO)
Monica Morrison (Chief Acctg Officer)

Subsidiaries:

Alpha Barnes Real Estate Services, LLC　　(1)
12720 Hillcrest Rd Ste 400, Dallas, TX 75230-2087
Tel.: (972) 643-3200
Web Site: http://www.alpha-barnes.com
Real Estate Services
N.A.I.C.S.: 531210
Jeff A. Barnes (Pres)
Michael Clark (Partner)

ASSET PROTECTION & SECURITY SERVICES, L. P.
5502 Burnham Dr Ste A, Corpus Christi, TX 78413
Tel.: (361) 906-1552
Web Site: http://www.asset-security-pro.com
Year Founded: 1990
Sales Range: $10-24.9 Million
Emp.: 425
Security Guard Services
N.A.I.C.S.: 561612
Ron Gates (VP-Bus Dev)
Scott Mandel (Pres & CEO)
Thelma Garza (CFO)
Brian Mandel (VP-Innovation & Strategy)
Alfred Legler (VP-Ops)
Timothy Perry (VP-Govt Rels)
Ronald Berglund (Mgr-HR)
Kevin Mandel (Mgr-Transportation)

ASSET REALTY GROUP
121 Lake St S Ste 201, Kirkland, WA 98033
Tel.: (425) 250-3301
Web Site:
http://www.assetrealtygroup.com
Year Founded: 2005
Sales Range: $1-9.9 Million
Emp.: 21
Real Estate Brokerage Software Solutions
N.A.I.C.S.: 513210
Chad Storey (Founder & Principal)

Subsidiaries:

Asset Realty　　(1)
3906 S 74th St, Tacoma, WA 98409　　(100%)
Tel.: (425) 250-3301
Web Site: http://www.assetrealtygroup.com
Real Estate Services
N.A.I.C.S.: 531210

Asset Realty　　(1)
3710 168th St NE Ste C101, Arlington, WA 98223　　(100%)
Tel.: (425) 409-9800
Web Site: http://www.assetrealtygroup.com
Real Estate Brokerage Services
N.A.I.C.S.: 531210
Chad Storey (Owner)
Michelle Wilson (Owner)

ASSET STAFFING INCORPO-RATED
30 Broad St Ste 1202, New York, NY 10004
Tel.: (212) 430-1060
Web Site:
https://www.assetstaffing.com
Year Founded: 1986
Sales Range: $10-24.9 Million
Emp.: 100
Temporary Personnel for Financial & Legal Firms
N.A.I.C.S.: 561311
Ed Giannattasio (CEO)

Subsidiaries:

Northpointe Personnel　　(1)
80 River St Ste D, Hoboken, NJ 07030　　(100%)
Tel.: (201) 418-9500
Web Site: http://www.assetstaffing.com
Sales Range: $10-24.9 Million
Emp.: 6
Temporary Administrative & Back-Office Personnel
N.A.I.C.S.: 561311
Nancy Regan (Pres)

ASSET STRATEGY RETIRE-MENT CONSULTANTS, LLC
5 Commonwealth Rd Ste 3A, Natick, MA 01760
Tel.: (781) 235-4426　　　MA
Web Site:
http://www.assetstrategyrc.com
Sales Range: $10-24.9 Million
Emp.: 5
Financial Services
N.A.I.C.S.: 561499
Kent A. Fitzpatrick (Pres)

ASSETCO FREIGHT BRO-KERS INC.
8005 NW 80 St, Miami, FL 33166
Web Site: http://www.gofreighthub.io
Year Founded: 2006
Sales Range: $10-24.9 Million
Emp.: 154
Logistic & Transportation Services
N.A.I.C.S.: 541614
Luis Lopez (Pres & CEO)

ASSETT, INC.
11220 Assett Loop Ste 101, Manassas, VA 20109
Tel.: (703) 365-8950
Web Site: http://www.assett.net
Year Founded: 2001
Rev.: $7,000,000
Emp.: 45
Engineering & Design Services
N.A.I.C.S.: 541512
Robert L. McCaig (Sr VP & Founder)
George T. Dasher (Pres)

ASSIGNED COUNSEL INCOR-PORATED
950 W Valley Rd Ste 2600, Wayne, PA 19087
Tel.: (610) 964-8300
Web Site:
http://www.assignedcounsel.com
Year Founded: 1992
Rev.: $6,700,000
Emp.: 12
Temporary Help Service
N.A.I.C.S.: 561320
Joel Adams (Co-Founder)
Cheri Holdan (Mgr-Admin)
Robert Murphy Jr. (Co-Founder)

ASSOCIATED
133 N Swift Rd, Addison, IL 60101
Tel.: (630) 588-8800
Web Site: https://www.associated-solutions.com
Year Founded: 1960

Sales Range: $150-199.9 Million
Emp.: 365
Business Consultants
N.A.I.C.S.: 541611

ASSOCIATED ADVERTISING AGENCY, INC.
330 N Mead Ste 200, Wichita, KS 67202
Tel.: (316) 683-4691
Year Founded: 1946
Rev.: $20,000,000
Emp.: 38
Asian Market, Business-To-Business, Financial, Health Care, Strategic Planning/Research
N.A.I.C.S.: 541810
Susan K. Leasure (Exec VP)
Patrick Dreiling (VP & Dir-Production)
Dave Stewart (Exec Dir-Creative)
Brian Schoenthaler (VP & Acct Team Leader)
Shawn Steward (Dir-PR)
Sean Amore (Mgr-Pub Rel)
Bill Fialka (CEO)
Scott Nosenko (Assoc Dir-Creative)
Eric Finkelstein (Exec Dir-Creative)

ASSOCIATED AIRCRAFT COMPANY LLC
3250 Stone Myers Pkwy, Grapevine, TX 76051
Tel.: (214) 331-4381
Web Site: https://www.associated-aircraft.com
Year Founded: 1953
Sales Range: $10-24.9 Million
Emp.: 30
Distr of Electronic Aircraft Parts
N.A.I.C.S.: 336413
Darrin Ross (Sr Acct Exec)
Jason Frazier (CEO)

ASSOCIATED AIRCRAFT MANUFACTURING & SALES, INC.
2735 NW 63 Ct, Fort Lauderdale, FL 33309-1711
Tel.: (954) 772-6606
Web Site: https://www.aamsi.com
Year Founded: 1953
Sales Range: $25-49.9 Million
Emp.: 85
Aircraft Parts Mfr & Sales
N.A.I.C.S.: 336413
David Clark (VP-Defense & Aerospace)
Dennis Zalupski (Pres & CEO)

ASSOCIATED ALUMINUM PRODUCTS CO., LLC
Ellsmere Ave 2550, Norfolk, VA 23513-2423
Tel.: (804) 271-2500
Web Site: http://www.aapco.com
Rev.: $14,600,000
Emp.: 85
Siding
N.A.I.C.S.: 444110
Jim Renault (Mgr-Sls)

ASSOCIATED AUTO PARTS
300 E Elizabeth Ave, Linden, NJ 07036
Tel.: (908) 862-0600　　　NJ
Web Site:
http://www.associatedauto.com
Year Founded: 1940
Sales Range: $1-9.9 Million
Emp.: 50
Sales of Automotive Supplies & Parts
N.A.I.C.S.: 423120
Ronald Brody (Pres)

ASSOCIATED BRIGHAM CON-TRACTORS

75 N 900 W, Brigham City, UT 84302
Tel.: (435) 723-8529
Web Site: https://www.abc-concrete.com
Rev.: $28,992,538
Emp.: 125
Industrial Buildings & Warehouses
N.A.I.C.S.: 236220
Bruce McFarland *(Dir-Safety)*
Corey Schultz *(Project Mgr)*
Dennis R. Racine *(Treas, Sec & Controller)*
Ted E. Valentine *(VP)*
Heidi Hansen *(Mgr)*
C. J. Nix *(Mgr)*
Kevin McBride *(Project Mgr)*

ASSOCIATED COMMUNITY BANCORP, INC.
115 E Putnam Ave, Greenwich, CT 06830
Tel.: (203) 618-8900   DE
Web Site:
http://www.ccbankonline.com
Bank Holding Company
N.A.I.C.S.: 551111
William Robert Berkley *(Chm)*

Subsidiaries:

Connecticut Community Bank, N.A.   (1)
1495 Post Rd E, Westport, CT 06880
Tel.: (203) 319-6260
Web Site: http://www.ccbankonline.com
Savings Bank
N.A.I.C.S.: 522180

ASSOCIATED CONSTRUCTION PUBLICATIONS LLC
1028 Shelby St, Indianapolis, IN 46203
Tel.: (317) 423-7080   MN
Web Site: http://www.acppubs.com
Sales Range: $1-9.9 Million
Emp.: 33
Construction Magazine Publisher
N.A.I.C.S.: 513120
Gregory A. Sitek *(VP-Editorial)*
John White *(Pres & Publr)*

ASSOCIATED CONSULTING INTERNATIONAL, INC.
955 N Pennsylvania Ave, Winter Park, FL 32789
Tel.: (407) 740-8405
Web Site: https://www.acistudios.com
Sales Range: $1-9.9 Million
Emp.: 20
Architectural Services
N.A.I.C.S.: 541310
John Cunningham *(Co-Founder)*
Joanne Adams *(Co-Founder)*
Larry Adams Jr. *(Co-Founder)*

ASSOCIATED COST ENGINEERS INC.
801 N Pine Hills Rd, Orlando, FL 32808-7209
Tel.: (407) 648-4915
Web Site: http://www.acecm.biz
Rev.: $400,000
Emp.: 3
Office Administrative Services
N.A.I.C.S.: 561110
Jaja Wade *(Pres)*

ASSOCIATED COUNSEL FOR THE ACCUSED
110 Prefontaine Pl S Ste 200, Seattle, WA 98104
Tel.: (206) 624-8105   WA
Web Site:
http://www.acawashington.org
Year Founded: 1973
Sales Range: $10-24.9 Million
Emp.: 152

Public Defender Services
N.A.I.C.S.: 922130
Don Madsen *(Mng Dir)*
Charlene Curtiss *(Pres)*
Greg Girard *(Sec)*
Tom Schwanz *(VP)*

ASSOCIATED CRAFTS, INC.
1700 W Washington St 105, Gilbert, AZ 85295
Tel.: (888) 503-1184
Web Site: http://www.church-stained-glass-windows.com
Year Founded: 1997
Stained Glass Window Production, Repair & Restoration Services
N.A.I.C.S.: 238150
Mary Phillips *(VP-Special Projects)*
Robert Bohannon *(VP-Ops)*
Tim Hudson *(VP-Consultation)*
John D. Phillips Jr. *(Pres & CEO)*

Subsidiaries:

Willet Hauser Architectural Glass, Inc.   (1)
1685 Wilkie Dr, Winona, MN 55987-6203
Tel.: (507) 457-3500
Web Site: http://www.stained-glass-window.us
Sales Range: $1-9.9 Million
Emp.: 60
Stained Glass Window Production & Repair Services
N.A.I.C.S.: 238150

ASSOCIATED CREDIT UNION OF TEXAS
1095 League City Pkwy, League City, TX 77573
Tel.: (409) 945-4474   TX
Web Site: http://www.acutx.org
Year Founded: 2012
Rev.: $29,507,095
Assets: $398,567,137
Liabilities: $359,467,020
Net Worth: $39,100,117
Fiscal Year-end: 12/31/18
Credit Union Operator
N.A.I.C.S.: 522130
Charis Pollard *(Chief HR Officer)*
Jay Coppock *(COO)*
Jack Click *(Pres & CEO)*
Clay Franks *(CFO)*
David DeAnda *(Chief Legal Officer)*
John Blair *(Vice Chm)*
Mark Kline *(Chm)*
Mark Rodriguez *(Treas)*

ASSOCIATED CREDITORS EXCHANGE, INC.
3443 N Central Ave, Phoenix, AZ 85012
Tel.: (602) 954-6554
Web Site: http://www.ace-collects.com
Sales Range: $10-24.9 Million
Emp.: 280
Debt Collection Services
N.A.I.C.S.: 561440
Joseph A. Berardi *(Pres)*
Matthew Berardi *(VP)*
Cindy Olson *(Controller)*

ASSOCIATED ELECTRIC COOPERATIVE INC.
2814 S Golden Ave, Springfield, MO 65807-3213
Tel.: (417) 881-1204   MO
Web Site: https://www.aeci.org
Year Founded: 1961
Sales Range: $500-549.9 Million
Emp.: 672
Electric Power Distr
N.A.I.C.S.: 221122
O. B. Clark *(Pres)*
R. Layne Morrill *(Sec)*
Meretith Roberts *(Controller)*

Shawn Calhoun *(Dir-HR)*
Brent W. Bossi *(CIO)*
Joseph E. Wilkinson *(Dir-Member Svcs & Corp Comm)*
Kenneth S. Wilmot *(Dir-Power Production)*
T. E. Fisher *(Treas)*
John B. Killgore *(VP)*
Emery O. Geisendorfer Jr. *(Pres)*

ASSOCIATED ENVIRONMENTAL SYSTEMS
8 Post Office Sq, Acton, MA 01720
Tel.: (978) 772-0022   MA
Web Site:
https://www.associatedsystems.com
Year Founded: 1959
Sales Range: $50-74.9 Million
Emp.: 50
Mfr of Environmental Simulation Equipment
N.A.I.C.S.: 334516
Ryan Kenny *(Engr-Mechanical Design)*
David Rockwood *(Mgr)*
Evan Nelson *(Supvr-Production)*
Steven Farnsworth *(Dir-Mfg)*

ASSOCIATED EQUIPMENT COMPANY OF DELAWARE
1230 E I 65 Service Rd N, Mobile, AL 36617-1505
Tel.: (251) 476-1082   DE
Web Site:
https://www.associatedinc.com
Year Founded: 1955
Sales Range: $10-24.9 Million
Emp.: 60
Distr of Heating & Air Conditioning Equipment
N.A.I.C.S.: 423730
Luther Clemons *(Pres)*
Norman Walker *(Comptroller)*

ASSOCIATED EQUIPMENT SALES CO.
14535 W 96 Ter, Lenexa, KS 66215
Tel.: (913) 894-4455
Web Site: https://www.aeskc.com
Year Founded: 2004
Sales Range: $10-24.9 Million
Emp.: 15
Industrial Machinery & Equipment Whslr
N.A.I.C.S.: 423830
Keith Williams *(Owner)*
Eric Smith *(Project Mgr)*

ASSOCIATED FABRICS CORPORATION
15-01 Pollitt Dr Unit 7, Fair Lawn, NJ 07410
Tel.: (800) 232-4077   NY
Web Site: http://www.afc-fabrics.com
Year Founded: 1928
Sales Range: $10-24.9 Million
Emp.: 10
Theatrical Fabrics
N.A.I.C.S.: 313310
Bruce Nocera *(Dir-Sls)*
Sam Samson *(Dir-Ops)*

ASSOCIATED FINANCIAL CORP.
12100 Wilshire Blvd Ste 1400, Los Angeles, CA 90025
Tel.: (310) 207-0704
Rev.: $11,200,000
Real Estate Managers
N.A.I.C.S.: 523999
Dean Ross *(Pres)*

ASSOCIATED FIRE PROTECTION
2316 S 24th St, Omaha, NE 68108

Tel.: (402) 733-2800
Web Site:
http://www.associatedfireprotection.com
Year Founded: 1993
Sales Range: $1-9.9 Million
Emp.: 44
Design, Equipment, Installation, Maintenance & Start-Up Services for Fire Protection
N.A.I.C.S.: 922160
Jim Blaszak *(Owner & Pres)*

ASSOCIATED FOOD STORES, INC.
1850 W 2100 S, Salt Lake City, UT 84119
Tel.: (801) 973-4400   UT
Web Site: https://www.afstores.com
Year Founded: 1940
Sales Range: $450-499.9 Million
Emp.: 1,500
Distr of Groceries
N.A.I.C.S.: 424410
Steve Miner *(VP-Store Dev)*
Wayne Dalton *(Mgr-Creative Svcs)*
Robert Opray *(CFO)*
Bret Gallacher *(VP-Mktg)*

Subsidiaries:

AFS Insurance Services, Inc.   (1)
1850 W 2100 S, Salt Lake City, UT 84119-1304   (100%)
Tel.: (801) 978-8336
Web Site: http://www.afsstores.com
Sales Range: $25-49.9 Million
Emp.: 11
Insurance Services
N.A.I.C.S.: 524126
Don Noyes *(Mgr)*

ASSOCIATED FOOD STORES, INC.
99 Seaview Blvd, Port Washington, NY 11050
Tel.: (516) 256-3100   NY
Web Site:
http://www.associatedmarkets.com
Sales Range: $125-149.9 Million
Emp.: 21
Groceries
N.A.I.C.S.: 551112
Ira Gober *(Chm & CEO)*
Sheryl Harding *(Controller)*
Robert A. Sigel *(Pres)*
Zulema Wiscovitch *(Chief Admin Officer & Exec VP)*

ASSOCIATED FUIG LLC
102 S 2nd St, Oakland, MD 21550
Tel.: (301) 334-3343
Web Site: http://www.fuig.net
Sales Range: $1-9.9 Million
Emp.: 15
Insurance Services
N.A.I.C.S.: 524298
Denny Mears *(Pres & CEO)*
Erick Johnson *(VP-Durant)*

ASSOCIATED GLASS, INC.
1233 Cordova St, Billings, MT 59101
Tel.: (406) 259-1352   MT
Web Site:
https://www.associatedglass.com
Year Founded: 1975
Sales Range: $50-74.9 Million
Emp.: 35
Glass Products Mfr, Distr & Installation Services
N.A.I.C.S.: 423390
Stewart Russell *(Owner)*

ASSOCIATED GROCERS OF NEW ENGLAND, INC.

Associated Grocers of New England, Inc.—(Continued)

11 Cooperative Way, Pembroke, NH 03275
Tel.: (603) 223-6710   **NH**
Web Site: http://www.agne.com
Year Founded: 1946
Sales Range: $200-249.9 Million
Emp.: 500
Wholesale & Distribution of Groceries
N.A.I.C.S.: 424410
Michael J. Daley (Chm)
Sam F. Adams (Vice Chm)

Subsidiaries:

AG Supermarkets Inc.   (1)
11 Cooperative Way, Pembroke, NH 03275   (100%)
Tel.: (603) 223-6710
Web Site: http://www.agne.com
Sales Range: $25-49.9 Million
Emp.: 100
Food Products Distr
N.A.I.C.S.: 424450

Associated Lease Corp.   (1)
725 Gold St, Manchester, NH 03108-5200   (100%)
Tel.: (603) 669-3250
Sales Range: $50-74.9 Million
Emp.: 400
Grocery Distr
N.A.I.C.S.: 423740

Certified Wholesalers Inc.   (1)
725 Gold St, Manchester, NH 03108   (100%)
Tel.: (603) 669-3250
Sales Range: $25-49.9 Million
Emp.: 160
Groceries Whslr
N.A.I.C.S.: 424410

French & Bean   (1)
725 Gold St, Manchester, NH 03108   (100%)
Tel.: (603) 669-3250
Sales Range: $50-74.9 Million
Emp.: 350
Grocery Products Mfr & Distr
N.A.I.C.S.: 424410

ASSOCIATED GROCERS OF THE SOUTH, INC.
3600 Vanderbilt Rd, Birmingham, AL 35217-4256
Tel.: (205) 841-6781   **AL**
Web Site: https://www.agsouth.com
Year Founded: 1927
Sales Range: $200-249.9 Million
Emp.: 500
Wholesale Grocery Services
N.A.I.C.S.: 424410
Jackie Plott (VP-Fin)
Leland Slay (VP-HR)
Larry Wilson (VP-Transportation & Warehousing)
Ron Burke (VP-IT)

ASSOCIATED GROCERS, INC.
8600 Anselmo Ln, Baton Rouge, LA 70810
Tel.: (225) 444-1000   **LA**
Web Site: https://www.agbr.com
Year Founded: 1950
Groceries Distr
N.A.I.C.S.: 424410
John P. Schittone (VP-HR)
Randy Fletcher (Sr VP-WholesalOps)
Emile R. Breaux (Pres & CEO)

ASSOCIATED HANGAR INC.
8321 Lemmon Ave, Dallas, TX 75209
Tel.: (214) 350-4111
Rev.: $20,700,000
Emp.: 250
Hangar Operation
N.A.I.C.S.: 488119

ASSOCIATED HEALTH SERVICES INC

615 Douglas St Ste 700, Durham, NC 27705
Tel.: (919) 613-8997   **NC**
Year Founded: 1984
Sales Range: $10-24.9 Million
Healthcare Services
N.A.I.C.S.: 622110
Kenneth C. Morris (Treas)
Leighton Roper (Sec)
Kerry Watson (Pres)
Jane C. Mangum (VP)

ASSOCIATED INDUSTRIES
11347 Vanowen St, North Hollywood, CA 91605
Tel.: (818) 760-1000
Web Site: https://www.associated-ind.com
Rev.: $11,000,000
Emp.: 30
Communications Equipment
N.A.I.C.S.: 423690
Devin Semler (Pres)
Ravi Achar (VP)

ASSOCIATED INDUSTRIES OF MASSACHUSETTS MUTUAL INSURANCE COMPANY
54 3rd Ave, Burlington, MA 01803
Tel.: (781) 221-1600
Web Site: http://www.aimmutual.com
Sales Range: $50-74.9 Million
Emp.: 150
Workers Compensation Insurance
N.A.I.C.S.: 524126
John A. Myers (Chm)
Michael Standing (CEO)
Glen Pitruzzello (Dir-Claim)

ASSOCIATED LIGHTING REPRESENTATIVES, INC.
7777 Pardee Ln, Oakland, CA 94621
Tel.: (510) 638-3800
Web Site: http://www.alrinc.com
Year Founded: 1961
Emp.: 100
Agency Representatives to Lighting Fixtures, Commercial & Industrial Mfrs
N.A.I.C.S.: 335132
Dave Ruth (Principal & Controller)
Russ Thomas (Mgr-Bay Area)
Darrell Packard Jr. (Mgr-Inside Sls & Principal)

ASSOCIATED MICROBREWERIES LTD.
5985 Santa Fe St, San Diego, CA 92109
Tel.: (858) 273-2739
Web Site: http://www.karlstrauss.com
Rev.: $34,000,000
Emp.: 700
Beer (Alcoholic Beverage)
N.A.I.C.S.: 312120
Chris Cramer (Founder & CEO)
Matt Rattner (Co-Founder & Pres)
Colleen Harvey (Controller)

ASSOCIATED MILK PRODUCERS, INC.
315 N Broadway, New Ulm, MN 56073
Tel.: (507) 354-8295   **KS**
Web Site: http://www.ampi.com
Year Founded: 1969
Sales Range: $10-24.9 Million
Emp.: 1,200
Regional Dairy Products Cooperative Mfr
N.A.I.C.S.: 311514
Sheryl Doering Meshke (Co-Pres & Co-CEO)
Donn DeVelder (Co-Pres & Co-CEO)

Brad Nevin (Treas)
Steve Schlangen (Chm)
Doug Temme (Vice Chm)
Bruce Maas (Sec)

Subsidiaries:

Cass-Clay Creamery   (1)
200 20th St N, Fargo, ND 58102
Tel.: (701) 293-6455
Web Site: http://www.cassclay.com
Dairy Products Mfr
N.A.I.C.S.: 311511
Scott Boll (Dir-Sls)
Teresa Benson (Coord-Mktg)

ASSOCIATED OF LOS ANGELES
2585 E Olympic Blvd, Los Angeles, CA 90023-2605
Tel.: (323) 268-8411   **CA**
Web Site:
http://www.associatedla.com
Year Founded: 1928
Sales Range: $75-99.9 Million
Emp.: 65
Distr of Electrical Equipment & Supplies
N.A.I.C.S.: 423610
Don Fagan (Mgr-Inside Sls)
David Gomez (Engr-Application Sls)
Duane Scott (Mgr-Procurement)
Janeece Layman (Engr-Application Sls)
Lou Pontarelli (Mgr-Sls & Mktg)
Manuel Ochoa (Engr-Application Sls)
Maria Uzarski (Engr-Application Sls)

Subsidiaries:

Associated Wholesale Electric Co.   (1)
2585E Olympic Blvd, Los Angeles, CA 90023   (100%)
Tel.: (323) 268-8411
Web Site:
http://www.associatedwholesale.com
Rev.: $6,000,000
Emp.: 26
Electrical Distributors
N.A.I.C.S.: 423610

ASSOCIATED OUTDOOR CLUBS, INC.
8300 N Nebraska Ave, Tampa, FL 33604
Tel.: (813) 932-4313   **FL**
Web Site: http://www.tampadogs.com
Year Founded: 1933
Sales Range: $50-74.9 Million
Emp.: 180
Dog Racing
N.A.I.C.S.: 711219
Mike Hater (Pres & Gen Mgr)
Theresa Hughes (Mgr-Maintanance)
Harry J. Hater (Chm & Treas)
Millie Licata (Office Mgr)

ASSOCIATED PACKAGING INC.
435 Calvert Dr, Gallatin, TN 37066-5402
Tel.: (615) 452-2131   **TN**
Web Site:
https://www.associatedpacking.com
Year Founded: 1980
Sales Range: $10-24.9 Million
Emp.: 100
Packaging Products Mfr
N.A.I.C.S.: 424990
Joseph R. Smith (Founder & Co-CEO)
Kevin Miller (Pres)
Michael Boyette (CFO)

ASSOCIATED PAPER INC.
1202 Royal Dr, Conyers, GA 30094
Tel.: (770) 929-1987

Web Site:
https://www.associatedpaper.com
Year Founded: 1967
Sales Range: $10-24.9 Million
Emp.: 43
Pressure Sensitive Tape Mfr
N.A.I.C.S.: 423850
Ronnie Kent (Pres)
Stephanie Alexander (Acct Mgr-Inside)
Jack Clark (Acct Mgr-Metro Atlanta)
Mark Davis (Acct Mgr-Metro Atlanta)

ASSOCIATED PARTNERS, LP
660 Madison Ave Ste 1435, New York, NY 10065
Tel.: (212) 301-2800
Web Site:
http://www.associatedpartnerslp.com
Investment Services
N.A.I.C.S.: 523999
William Berkman (Mng Dir)
David J. Berkman (Mng Partner)

ASSOCIATED PETROLEUM CARRIERS
1746 Union St, Spartanburg, SC 29302-4133
Tel.: (864) 573-9301   **SC**
Web Site:
https://www.apccorporate.com
Year Founded: 1950
Sales Range: $50-74.9 Million
Emp.: 10
Petroleum Transport Services
N.A.I.C.S.: 484230
Sanders O'Neil (Pres)
Mike Stepp (Office Mgr)

ASSOCIATED PETROLEUM PRODUCTS INC.
2320 Milwaukee Way, Tacoma, WA 98421-2710
Tel.: (253) 627-6179
Web Site:
http://www.associatedpetroleum.com
Year Founded: 1972
Sales Range: $25-49.9 Million
Emp.: 160
Petroleum Products Distr
N.A.I.C.S.: 424720
Kelli McCann (Mgr-Pricing)
Shannon Feichter (Mgr-Mktg)

ASSOCIATED PHARMACIES INC.
211 Lonnie E Crawford Blvd, Scottsboro, AL 35769-7408
Tel.: (256) 574-6819
Web Site: http://www.apirx.com
Sales Range: $10-24.9 Million
Emp.: 55
Pharmaceutical Services
N.A.I.C.S.: 424210
Clint King (VP & Gen Mgr)
Paul Carlin (Treas, Sec & Controller)
Brandy Presley (Dir-HR)
Mark Metzger (Dir-Mdsg)
Jon Copeland (CEO)

ASSOCIATED PIPE LINE CONTRACTORS, INC.
3535 Briarpark Dr Ste 135, Houston, TX 77042-5233
Tel.: (713) 789-4311
Web Site:
http://www.associatedpipelines.inc
Year Founded: 1993
Sales Range: $75-99.9 Million
Emp.: 500
Pipeline Contractor
N.A.I.C.S.: 237120
Paul G. Somerville (Chm & CEO)
Gene Bell (VP)

ASSOCIATED POWER, INC.
1741 E Colon St, Wilmington, CA 90744-2210
Tel.: (310) 835-3161   CA
Web Site: http://www.assocpower.com
Year Founded: 1957
Sales Range: $75-99.9 Million
Emp.: 40
Retailer of Diesel Engines, Generator Sets, Welders & Portable Light Towers; Provider of Maintenance for Diesel Engines
N.A.I.C.S.: 423830
Marvin L. Johnson (Pres)

ASSOCIATED PRODUCE DEALERS & BROKERS OF L.A - INSURANCE TRUST
1601 E Olympic Blvd Ste 312, Los Angeles, CA 90021-1942
Tel.: (213) 623-6293   CA
Year Founded: 1961
Sales Range: $10-24.9 Million
Business Support Services
N.A.I.C.S.: 561439
Ronald Bateman (Sec & Exec Dir)
Mark Tanimura (Pres)
Tracy Hellman (Treas)

ASSOCIATED PRODUCTION SERVICE
325 Andrews Rd, Trevose, PA 19053
Tel.: (215) 364-0211
Web Site: http://www.erols.com
Sales Range: $10-24.9 Million
Emp.: 100
Packaging & Labeling Services
N.A.I.C.S.: 561910
Jay Belting (Pres)
Samantha Adams (Dir-Production Svcs)

ASSOCIATED RACK CORPORATION
1245 16th St, Vero Beach, FL 32960
Tel.: (772) 567-2262
Web Site: http://www.associatedrack.com
Sales Range: $10-24.9 Million
Emp.: 100
Rack Metal Fixtures Finishers
N.A.I.C.S.: 337126
W. L. Faulman (Pres)
Richard Rexford (Engr-Sls)

ASSOCIATED READY MIX CONCRETE
2730 E Washington Blvd, Los Angeles, CA 90023
Tel.: (323) 260-5350
Web Site: http://www.aareadymix.com
Rev.: $36,900,000
Emp.: 65
Selling & Manufacturing Ready Mix Concrete
N.A.I.C.S.: 327320
Kurt Callier (Pres)
Bonnie Baker (Controller)

ASSOCIATED RECOVERY SYSTEMS
201 W Grand Ave, Escondido, CA 92025
Tel.: (760) 735-2700
Web Site: http://www.arsnational.com
Sales Range: $50-74.9 Million
Emp.: 300
Collection Agency
N.A.I.C.S.: 561440

ASSOCIATED RECREATION COUNCIL
100 Dexter Ave N, Seattle, WA 98109

Tel.: (206) 615-1276   WA
Web Site: http://www.arcseattle.org
Year Founded: 1975
Sales Range: $10-24.9 Million
Emp.: 1,027
Recreational Services
N.A.I.C.S.: 624110

ASSOCIATED SALES & BAG COMPANY INCORPORATED
400 W Boden St, Milwaukee, WI 53207
Tel.: (414) 769-1000
Web Site: https://www.associatedbag.com
Sales Range: $25-49.9 Million
Emp.: 169
Industrial & Personal Service Paper
N.A.I.C.S.: 424130
Herbert Rubenstein (Owner)
Thad Moris (Mgr-Fin)

ASSOCIATED SERVICE SPECIALIST
870 High St Ste 2, Chestertown, MD 21620
Tel.: (410) 778-9114
Sales Range: $10-24.9 Million
Emp.: 12
Investment Holding Companies, Except Banks
N.A.I.C.S.: 551112
D. Cherry Jones (Pres)

ASSOCIATED SPECIALTY CONTRACTING, INC.
98 Lacrue Ave, Glen Mills, PA 19342
Tel.: (610) 364-9622
Web Site: https://www.associated.com
Sales Range: $10-24.9 Million
Emp.: 20
Environmental Remediation, Demolition & Carpentry Contracting Services
N.A.I.C.S.: 238990
James P. Vail (Owner & Pres)

ASSOCIATED STEEL WORKERS, LTD.
91-156 Kalaeloa Blvd, Kapolei, HI 96707
Tel.: (808) 682-5588   HI
Web Site: http://www.aswcranes.com
Year Founded: 1948
Sales Range: $10-24.9 Million
Emp.: 125
Structural Steel Erection Contractors
N.A.I.C.S.: 238120
Ronald Fujikawa (Pres & Treas)
Fe Yoshida (Controller)
Rob Oliver (Supvr-Crane & Rigging)

ASSOCIATED SUPPLY COMPANY INC
6330 Sandhill Rd Ste 5-7, Las Vegas, NV 89119
Tel.: (702) 739-8129
Web Site: http://www.associatedsupply.com
Rev.: $17,900,000
Emp.: 70
Computer Software & Accessories
N.A.I.C.S.: 449210
Perry Binen (Pres)
Lisa Roe (CFO)

ASSOCIATED SUPPLY COMPANY INC.
2102 Slaton Rd, Lubbock, TX 79404
Tel.: (806) 745-2000
Web Site: https://www.ascoeq.com
Year Founded: 1960
Sales Range: $75-99.9 Million
Emp.: 250
Materials Handling Machinery Sales & Rentals

N.A.I.C.S.: 423830
John W. Wright (Chm)
W. B. Wright (CEO)
Nathan Swindel (Controller)
Steve Wright (Pres)
Courtney Vanderham (VP)
Chase Key (VP)

Subsidiaries:

ASCO Equipment San Antonio   (1)
4146 Interstate 10 E, San Antonio, TX 78219
Tel.: (210) 333-8000
Web Site: http://www.ascoeq.com
Sales Range: $10-24.9 Million
Emp.: 50
Building Equipment Rental Services
N.A.I.C.S.: 532412

OCT Equipment LLC   (1)
7100 SW 3rd St, Oklahoma City, OK 73128
Tel.: (405) 789-6812
Web Site: http://www.octequipment.com
Construction & Mining Machinery & Equipment Merchant Whslr
N.A.I.C.S.: 423810
Clay Schuster (Mgr-Parts)

ASSOCIATED TELEPHONE DESIGN INC.
45W 36th St Fl 5, New York, NY 10018-4328
Tel.: (212) 532-6800   NY
Web Site: http://www.bmwautohaus.com
Year Founded: 1981
Sales Range: $10-24.9 Million
Emp.: 30
Electronic Parts & Equipment
N.A.I.C.S.: 423690
George Schoenberg (Pres & CEO)

ASSOCIATED TERMINALS LLC
9100 Safety Dr, Convent, LA 70723
Tel.: (225) 399-3010
Web Site: https://www.associatedterminal.com
Year Founded: 1990
Emp.: 450
Marine Cargo Handling Services
N.A.I.C.S.: 488320
Todd Fuller (Pres)
Kevin Tarleton (Co-CFO)
Ann Thibodeaux (Co-CFO)
Barry Hoth (VP)
Brian Harden (Gen Mgr)
Daniel Talley (Mgr-Ops)
Dawn Lopez (VP-Mktg & PR)
Frankie Walker (VP-Bulk Ops)
Greg Miller (Mgr-Ops)
Terry May (Sr VP)
Gary Poirrier (Vice Chm)
Matthew Magnuson (CTO)
Glenn Schexnayder (Sr VP-Sls)
David Wilkins (Sr VP)
Zeljko Franks (Sr VP)

ASSOCIATED THIRD PARTY ADMINISTRATORS
1640 S Loop Rd, Alameda, CA 94502
Tel.: (510) 337-3050
Web Site: http://www.atpa.com
Rev.: $121,500,000
Emp.: 400
Employee Benefit Administration Services
N.A.I.C.S.: 541612
Kirsten Brooks (Sr VP)
Peter Herrling (Exec VP)

ASSOCIATED TIME & PARKING CONTROLS, INC.
9104 Diplomacy Row, Dallas, TX 75247
Tel.: (214) 637-2763
Web Site: https://www.associatedtime.com

Year Founded: 1996
Commercial Equipment Merchant Whslr
N.A.I.C.S.: 423440
Christopher J. Archer (Pres)
Andrew White (VP-Bus Dev)
Edward J. Lammer (VP-Ops)
Robert J. Collier (Sr VP-Tech)
Adriane B. Kearney (VP-Fin)

Subsidiaries:

C.T.E. Systems, Inc.   (1)
565-A W Lambert Rd, Brea, CA 92821
Tel.: (714) 257-6440
Web Site: http://www.ctesystems.com
Electrical Apparatus & Equipment Mfr
N.A.I.C.S.: 423610
Kathleen Albers (Pres)

ASSOCIATED TRANSFER & STORAGE INC.
301 E Wilbur Ave, Champaign, IL 61822
Tel.: (217) 359-6250
Web Site: https://www.gowithats.com
Rev.: $14,000,000
Emp.: 50
Local Trucking with Storage
N.A.I.C.S.: 484110
Art Warren (Pres)

ASSOCIATED WELDING SUPPLY INC.
3002 S Main St, Pearland, TX 77581
Tel.: (281) 485-2755   TX
Web Site: http://www.associated-welding.com
Year Founded: 1963
Sales Range: $10-24.9 Million
Emp.: 15
Welding Machinery & Equipment
N.A.I.C.S.: 423830
Paul DeLisi (Controller)
Jesse Vasquez (VP)

ASSOCIATED WHOLESALE GROCERS, INC.
5000 Kansas Ave, Kansas City, KS 66106-1135
Tel.: (913) 288-1000   MO
Web Site: http://www.awginc.com
Year Founded: 1926
Sales Range: $5-14.9 Billion
Emp.: 2,000
Co-Operative Grocery Distr
N.A.I.C.S.: 424410
Joe Busch (VP-Sls)
Steve Arnold (Sr VP-Oklahoma City)
Dan Funk (Chief Supply Chain & Mdsg Officer)
David Smith (Pres & CEO)
Linda Lawson (Sr VP-Fort Worth)
Tye Anthony (VP-Great Lakes)
Jeff Pedersen (Chief Sls & Support Officer & Exec VP)
Danny Lane (Sr VP-Grocery)
Steve James (Assoc Gen Counsel)
Stephanie Becker (Chief Legal Officer, Gen Counsel, Sec & Sr VP)
Scott Welman (Chief Dev Officer)
David Gates (Sr VP-Kansas City)

Subsidiaries:

Homeland Stores, Inc.   (1)
390 NE 36th St, Oklahoma City, OK 73105
Tel.: (405) 290-3000
Web Site: http://www.homelandstores.com
Sales Range: $500-549.9 Million
Emp.: 50
Grocery Stores, Chain
N.A.I.C.S.: 445110
Sonny Sanchez (Mgr-Category)
Jerry Heidenreich (VP-Ops)

Associated Wholesale Grocers, Inc.—(Continued)

ASSOCIATES IN MEDICAL PHYSICS, LLC
7501 Greenway Center Dr, Suite 1001, Greenbelt, MD 20770
Tel.: (301) 220-3580
Web Site: http://www.ampglobal.net
Year Founded: 2000
Healtcare Services
N.A.I.C.S.: 622110
Brian Pellegrini (CEO)

Subsidiaries:

Keystone Physics Limited   (1)
153 Scarborough Ln, Millersville, PA 17551-0000
Web Site: http://www.keystonephysics.com
Scientific & Technical Consulting Services
N.A.I.C.S.: 541690
Jay M. Yoder (Principal)

ASSOCIATES INSURANCE AGENCY, INC.
11470 N 53rd St, Temple Terrace, FL 33617
Tel.: (813) 988-1234
Web Site:
  https://www.associatesins.com
Year Founded: 1991
Insurance Brokers
N.A.I.C.S.: 524210
Mike Rogers (Pres)

ASSOCIATION FOR AD-VANCED LIFE UNDERWRITING
11921 Freedom Dr Ste 1100, Reston, VA 20190
Tel.: (703) 641-9400   DC
Web Site: http://www.aalu.org
Year Founded: 1998
Sales Range: $10-24.9 Million
Emp.: 30
Fire Insurance Services
N.A.I.C.S.: 524113
Marc Cadin (COO)
Gonzalo Abrigo (Dir-Ops)
Richard A. DeVita (Treas & VP)
Tracy Mawyer (CFO & VP-HR)
Chris Morton (Sr VP-Govt Affairs)
David Hollingsworth (Dir-Pub Policy)
Emily Ward (Asst VP-Federal Advocacy Svcs)
Josh Caron (Dir-Political Fin)
Kevin Tangney (Dir-Corp Partnerships)
Laura Henry (Asst VP-Meetings & Events)
Marilyn Maticic (VP-Member Experience)
Will Swaim (Asst VP-Client Experience)
Eric Lundberg (VP-Political Affairs)

ASSOCIATION FOR COMPUT-ING MACHINERY
2 Penn Plz Ste 701, New York, NY 10121-0701
Tel.: (212) 626-0500   DE
Web Site: https://www.acm.org
Year Founded: 1947
Sales Range: $50-74.9 Million
Emp.: 92
Professional Organizations
N.A.I.C.S.: 813920
Vicki L. Hanson (CEO)
Bernard Rous (Dir-Publ)
Cherri M. Pancake (Pres)
Elizabeth Churchill (VP)
Yannis Ioannidis (Treas & Sec)
Andrew Sears (Founder/Editor-In-Chief-ACM Transactions on Accessible Computing)

ASSOCIATION FOR MOLECU-LAR PATHOLOGY
9650 Rockville Pike Ste E133, Bethesda, MD 20814
Tel.: (301) 634-7939   MD
Web Site: http://www.amp.org
Year Founded: 1999
Sales Range: $1-9.9 Million
Medical Professional Association
N.A.I.C.S.: 813920
Mary Steele Williams (Exec Dir)

ASSOCIATION FOR TALENT DEVELOPMENT
PO Box 1443, Alexandria, VA 22313-1443
Tel.: (703) 683-8100   WI
Web Site: http://www.td.org
Year Founded: 1957
Sales Range: $25-49.9 Million
Emp.: 142
Professional Organizations
N.A.I.C.S.: 813920
Tony Bingham (Pres & CEO)
Charles Fred (Chm)

ASSOCIATION FOR THE DE-VELOPMENTALLY DISABLED
769 Brooks Edge Blvd, Worthington, OH 43081
Tel.: (614) 486-4361   OH
Web Site: http://www.addohio.org
Year Founded: 1971
Sales Range: $10-24.9 Million
Emp.: 619
Disability Assistance Services
N.A.I.C.S.: 623102
Greg Snyder (CFO)
Sid Geller (Sec)
Valorie Schwarzmann (Treas)
Patrick A. Devine (Vice Chm)
Daniel K. Glessner (VP)
Dennis Allen (CEO & Sec)
Michael J. Weinhardt (Pres, Treas & Sr VP-Investments)
Nicholas Lopick (Sr Mgr-Assurance Svcs)
Catherine Schwartz (Chief Dev Officer)
Sandy Cinch (VP-Quality Improvement & Compliance)

ASSOCIATION MEMBER BEN-EFITS ADVISORS, LLC
6034 W Courtyard Dr. Ste 300, Austin, TX 78730
Tel.: (800) 258-7041
Web Site: https://www.amba.info
Insurance Services
N.A.I.C.S.: 524210

Subsidiaries:

Oozle Media, Inc.   (1)
11339 S 700 E Ste 300, Sandy, UT 84070
Tel.: (801) 562-8557
Web Site: http://www.oozlemedia.com
Information Services
N.A.I.C.S.: 519290
Travis Ashby (Co-Founder)

ASSOCIATION OF AMERICAN RAILROADS
425 3rd St SW, Washington, DC 20024
Tel.: (202) 639-2100   US
Web Site: https://www.aar.org
Year Founded: 1934
Railroad Regulation & Administration Association
N.A.I.C.S.: 926120
Kathryn D. Kirmayer (Gen Counsel & Sr VP-Law)
Michael Rush (Sr VP-Safety & Ops)
Kristin Smith (Sr VP-Comm)
Paul Hedrick (CFO & Sr VP-Fin & Admin)
Ian Jefferies (Pres & CEO)

Subsidiaries:

Railinc Corp.   (1)
7001 Weston Pkwy Ste 200, Cary, NC 27513-2125   (100%)
Tel.: (877) 724-5462
Web Site: https://public.railinc.com
Custom Computer Programming Services
N.A.I.C.S.: 541511
E. Allen West (Pres & CEO)
Todd M. Rynaski (Chm)

ASSOCIATION OF CHRISTIAN SCHOOLS INTERNATIONAL
731 Chapel Hills Dr, Colorado Springs, CO 80920
Tel.: (719) 528-6906   CA
Web Site: http://www.acsiglobal.org
Year Founded: 1965
Sales Range: $10-24.9 Million
Emp.: 165
Christian Ministry Services
N.A.I.C.S.: 813110
Joel Farlow (Vice Chm)
Robert Gutzwiller (Sec)
Larry Taylor (Pres)
Michael D. Epp (Sr VP-Global)
Stephen G. Reel (VP)
Bret Wichert (VP-Fin)
Kevin Wilson (VP-IT & Customer Improvement)
Julee Mecham (VP-Programs & Res)
Chris Marchand (VP-Purposeful Design Publications)
Juan Cabrera (CIO)
David Balik (VP-USA)
Edward Bunn (Program Dir-Leadership)
Jeff Mattner (Sr Dir-Central)
Cecil Swetland (Sr Dir-Western)
Caitlyn Berman (Coord-Pub & Media Rels)
Larry Lincoln (Chief Comm & Engagement Officer)
Sarah Loncar (Dir-Digital Initiatives)
Althea Penn (Dir-Early Education)

ASSOCIATION OF GOVERN-ING BOARDS OF UNIVERSI-TIES AND COLLEGES
1133 20th St NW Ste 300, Washington, DC 20036
Tel.: (202) 296-8400   DC
Web Site: https://www.agb.org
Year Founded: 1974
Sales Range: $10-24.9 Million
Emp.: 42
Educational Support Services
N.A.I.C.S.: 611710
Maria Nazareth (VP-Fin)
Susan Whealler Johnston (COO & Exec VP)
Helen Woelk (Dir-HR & Office Mgmt)
Mary A. Papazian (Exec VP)
Charles R. Pruitt (Vice Chm)
Charles A. Shorter (Vice Chm)
David Miles (Chm)
Joyce M. Roche (Vice Chm)
Kristen Hodge-Clark (Dir-Res)
Melissa Decosmo (Mgr-Publications)
Audrey Young (Dir-Conferences & Events)
Andy Lounder (Dir-Special Projects)
Angel L. Mendez (Sec)
Merrill Schwartz (Sr VP-Consulting)
Timothy J. McDonough (VP-Govt & Pub Affairs)
Michelle Sparacino (VP-Member Svcs)
Mark Kelly (VP-Mktg & Comm)
Henry Stoever (Pres & CEO)

ASSOCIATION OF NATIONAL ADVERTISERS, INC.
708 3rd Ave 33rd Fl, New York, NY 10017

Tel.: (212) 697-5950   NY
Web Site: http://www.ana.net
Year Founded: 1910
Trade Assocation
N.A.I.C.S.: 813910
Daniel L. Jaffe (Exec VP-Govt Rels)
Christine Manna (Pres & COO)
Bill Duggan (Exec VP)
Keith Scarborough (Sr VP)
Douglas J. Wood (Gen Counsel)
Robert Rothe (Exec VP)
Kristen McDonough (Sr VP)
Tracy Owens (Sr VP)
Mark Liebert (VP)
John Wolfe (Dir-Comm)
Marc Pritchard (Chm)
Ken Beaulieu (Sr VP)
Christina Curry (VP)
Duke Fanelli (Exec VP)
Marni Gordon (Sr VP)
Lisa Guhanick (VP)
Andrea Kislan (Sr VP)
Lan Phan (Sr VP)
Nick Primola (Exec VP)
Kristina Sweet (Sr VP)
Arthur Tharpe (Sr Dir-AFE)
Vivian Frouxides (VP)
Bill Tucker (Exec VP)
Christopher Oswald (Sr VP)
Edward Kabak (Sr VP)
Mike Kaufman (Sr VP)
Neil O'Keefe (Sr VP)
Senny Boone (Sr VP)
Paul G. Alexander (Treas)
Deborah Wahl (Vice Chm)
Deborah L. Wahl (Vice Chm)
Gilbert R. Davila (Co-Founder)

Subsidiaries:

Business Marketing Association, Inc.   (1)
708 3rd Ave, New York, NY 10017
Tel.: (212) 697-5950
Web Site: http://www.marketing.org
Sales Range: Less than $1 Million
Business-to-Business Marketing & Communications Organization
N.A.I.C.S.: 813910
Maralah Rose-Asch (Sec)
Stephen Liguori (Chm)
Arthur Tharpe (Sr Dir)
Lana Mavreshko (Dir-Fin)
Michael Palmer (Exec Dir)
Ned Clausen (Exec Dir)
Mark Mastroianni (VP)
Tom Hadlock (Treas & VP)

ASSOCIATION OF PERIOP-ERATIVE REGISTERED NURSES
2170 S Parker Rd Ste 300, Denver, CO 80231
Tel.: (303) 755-6304   CO
Web Site: http://www.aorn.org
Year Founded: 1971
Sales Range: $10-24.9 Million
Emp.: 140
Nursing Care Services
N.A.I.C.S.: 623110
Linda Groah (Exec Dir & CEO)

ASSOCIATION OF PRIVATE SECTOR COLLEGES AND UNI-VERSITIES
1101 Connecticut Ave NW Ste 900, Washington, DC 20036
Tel.: (202) 336-6700   DC
Web Site: http://www.career.org
Year Founded: 1991
Sales Range: $10-24.9 Million
Emp.: 60
Educational Support Services
N.A.I.C.S.: 611710

ASSOCIATION OF PUBLIC HEALTH LABORATORIES

8515 Georgia Ave Ste 700, Silver
Spring, MD 20910
Tel.: (240) 485-2745   DC
Web Site: https://www.aphl.org
Year Founded: 1991
Sales Range: $25-49.9 Million
Emp.: 112
Health Care Srvices
N.A.I.C.S.: 621511
Christine Bean (Pres)
Judith C. Lovchik (Treas & Sec)

ASSOCIATION OF SCHOOLS AND PROGRAMS OF PUBLIC HEALTH

1900 M St NW Ste 710, Washington,
DC 20036
Tel.: (202) 296-1099   PA
Web Site: http://www.aspph.org
Year Founded: 1959
Sales Range: $10-24.9 Million
Emp.: 49
Educational Support Services
N.A.I.C.S.: 611710
Laura Magana Valladares (Pres & CEO)

ASSOCIATION OF SOCIAL WORK BOARDS

400 Southridge Pkwy Ste B, Cul-
peper, VA 22701
Tel.: (540) 829-6880   VA
Web Site: http://www.aswb.org
Year Founded: 1979
Sales Range: $10-24.9 Million
Emp.: 43
Civic & Social Organization
N.A.I.C.S.: 813410
Jayne Wood (Dir-Comm & Mktg)
Stacey Hardy-Chandler (CEO)
Roxroy A. Reid (Co-Pres)

ASSOCIATION OF TEXAS PROFESSIONAL EDUCATORS

305 E Huntland Dr Ste 300, Austin,
TX 78752-3792
Tel.: (512) 467-0071   TX
Web Site: https://www.atpe.org
Year Founded: 1980
Sales Range: $10-24.9 Million
Emp.: 76
Educational Support Services
N.A.I.C.S.: 611710

ASSOCIATION OF THE UNITED STATES ARMY

2425 Wilson Blvd, Arlington, VA
22201
Tel.: (703) 841-4300   VA
Web Site: https://www.ausa.org
Year Founded: 1950
Sales Range: $25-49.9 Million
Emp.: 105
Professional Organizations
N.A.I.C.S.: 813920
Jerry Sinn (VP-Fin & Admin)
Kenneth O. Preston (VP-
Noncommissioned Officer & Soldier
Programs)
Ann Belyea (Sec)
David H. Ohle (Vice Chm-Retiree &
Veteran Affairs)
Jack L. Tilley (Vice Chm-
Noncommissioned Officer & Soldier
Programs)
Guy C. Swan III (VP-Education)

ASSOCIATION OF WOMEN'S HEALTH, OBSTETRIC & NEO-NATAL NURSES

2000 L St NW Ste 740, Washington,
DC 20036
Tel.: (202) 261-2400   DC
Web Site: http://www.awhonn.org
Year Founded: 1969

Sales Range: $10-24.9 Million
Emp.: 54
Women Healthcare Services
N.A.I.C.S.: 622110

ASSOCIATIONS, INC.

5401 N Central Expy, Dallas, TX
75205   TX
Web Site:
    https://www.associaonline.com
Year Founded: 1979
Property & Association Management
Services
N.A.I.C.S.: 531311
Matthew Kraft (Sr VP-Sls & Mktg)
Andrew S. Fortin (Sr VP-External Af-
fairs)
Jose Bosco Maldonado (CFO & Exec
VP)
Max Freedman (Reg VP-Northeast)
Patrick Brensinger (Pres & COO)
Michael Packard (Sr VP-Acq)
Ron Duprey (Sr VP-Associa Direct
Connect)
Craig Koss (Sr VP-Central Reg Ops)
Tom Buechel (Sr VP-Fin Plng & Re-
porting)
Andrew Brock (CIO & Exec VP)
Helen Eden Carona (Chief Corp Offi-
cer & Exec VP)
Chelle O'Keefe (Chief HR Officer &
Exec VP)
John Ingenito (Sr VP-Internal & Acq)
Brian Kruppa (Gen Counsel & Sr VP)
Matt Steele (Sr VP-Integrated Svcs)
Shannon Streenz (Sr VP-Client Svc
Ops-Richardson)
Nick Mazzarella (Reg VP)
Angela Frieling (Sr VP-Mktg)
Craig Lubaczewski (Sr VP-East Reg
Ops)
George Zalitis (Sr VP-West Reg Ops)
Sean West (Sr VP-Sls)
Nancy Hastings (Sr VP-Ops)
John J. Carona Sr. (Chm & CEO)

Subsidiaries:

Community Development, Inc.   (1)
7100 Madison Ave W, Golden Valley, MN
55427
Tel.: (763) 225-6400
Web Site:
    http://www.developcommunity.com
Community Management Services
N.A.I.C.S.: 925120
Charles Schneider (CEO)

McKay Management Corporation   (1)
5 Riverchase Rdg, Birmingham, AL 35244
Tel.: (205) 733-6700
Web Site:
    http://www.mckaymanagement.com
Sales Range: $1-9.9 Million
Emp.: 17
Property Management, Subdivider & Devel-
oper Services
N.A.I.C.S.: 237210
Jada Hilyer (Pres)
Hope Mills (Dir-Fin Mgmt)
Andrew Brock (CIO & Exec VP)
Tom Buechel (Sr VP-Fin Plng & Reporting)
Helen Eden Carona (Chief Corp Officer &
Exec VP)
John J. Carona (Chm & CEO)
Andrew S. Fortin (Sr VP-External Affairs)
Craig Koss (Sr VP-Field Ops)
Matt Kraft (Sr VP-Sls & Mktg)
Jose Bosco Maldonado (Sr VP-Fin & Acctg)
Michael Packard (Sr VP-Ops & Acq)
Matt Steele (Sr VP-Field Ops)

ASSUMPTION COOPERATIVE GRAIN COMPANY

104 W N St, Assumption, IL 62510
Tel.: (217) 226-3213
Web Site: http://www.acoop.com
Sales Range: $25-49.9 Million
Emp.: 25
Grain Elevators
N.A.I.C.S.: 424510

Matt Yepsen (Comptroller)
Kim Peterson (Mgr-Ops)
Mike Pinkston (Pres)

ASSURANCE FORENSIC AC-COUNTING CPAS, LLC

5755 N Point Pkwy Ste 92, Atlanta,
GA 30328
Tel.: (678) 578-2525
Web Site:
    http://www.assurancefa.com
Year Founded: 2004
Sales Range: $1-9.9 Million
Emp.: 51
Public Accounting Services Specializ-
ing in Forensic Accounting & Fraud
Examination
N.A.I.C.S.: 541219
Dennis Neas (Owner)
Chad Thompson (Partner)
Neelima Sunder (Mgr)
William Beecken (Dir-Fraud Svcs)

ASSURANCE TECHNOLOGY CORPORATION

84 S St, Carlisle, MA 01741-1515
Tel.: (978) 369-8848   MA
Web Site: http://www.assurtech.com
Year Founded: 1969
Sales Range: $25-49.9 Million
Emp.: 280
Engineeering Services
N.A.I.C.S.: 541330
Warren Tolman (Sr VP)

ASSURANCEAMERICA COR-PORATION

5500 Interstate N Pkwy Ste 600, At-
lanta, GA 30328
Tel.: (770) 952-0200
Web Site:
    http://www.assuranceamerica.com
Year Founded: 1998
Sales Range: $75-99.9 Million
Emp.: 147
Insurance Services
N.A.I.C.S.: 524298
Guy W. Millner (Chm)
David H. Anthony (CIO & Sr VP)

ASSURE AMERICA CORP.

3546 Pennsylvania Ave, Weirton, WV
26062
Tel.: (304) 723-4600
Web Site:
    https://www.assureamerica.com
Year Founded: 1920
Rev.: $100,000,000
Emp.: 6
Insurance Services
N.A.I.C.S.: 524298
Matthew A. Mangone (Pres)
Angela Frazier (Exec VP-Personal
Lines)

ASSURE HOLDINGS, LLC

6510 Millrock Dr Ste 400, Salt Lake
City, UT 84121
Web Site: http://www.assure.co
Year Founded: 2014
Sales Range: $10-24.9 Million
Emp.: 53
Financial Services
N.A.I.C.S.: 523999
Jeremy Neilson (Co-CEO)
Katie Neilson (Co-CEO)
John Wallace (COO)

ASSURED AGGREGATES COMPANY

520A Crazy Horse Canyon Rd, Sali-
nas, CA 93907
Tel.: (831) 443-8644
Web Site:
    https://www.donchapin.com
Rev.: $12,186,583

Emp.: 60
Trucking Service
N.A.I.C.S.: 484110
Don Chapin Jr. (Pres)

Subsidiaries:

Hollister Landscape Supply   (1)
520A Crazy Horse Canyon Rd, Salinas, CA
93907
Tel.: (831) 443-8644
Rev.: $1,000,000
Emp.: 10
Ready Mixed Concrete
N.A.I.C.S.: 327320
Barbara A. Chapin (Pres)
Janet Sondberly (Branch Mgr)

ASSURED INFORMATION SE-CURITY, INC.

153 Brooks Rd, Rome, NY 13441
Tel.: (315) 336-3306
Web Site: https://www.ainfosec.com
Year Founded: 2001
Sales Range: $1-9.9 Million
Emp.: 100
Computer Network Security Services
N.A.I.C.S.: 541519
Charles Green (CEO)
Steven Flint (COO)
James Reilly (Engr-Res)
Timothy Hanna (Engr-Software)

ASSURED TRANSPORTATION SERVICES

4425 Enterprise Dr, Bartonville, IL
61607
Tel.: (309) 697-8200
Web Site:
    http://www.thrifttrucking.com
Sales Range: $10-24.9 Million
Emp.: 60
Trucking Service
N.A.I.C.S.: 484110

Subsidiaries:

Thrift Trucking Incorporated   (1)
4425 Enterprise Dr, Bartonville, IL 61607
Tel.: (309) 697-8200
Web Site: http://www.thrifttrucking.com
Rev.: $1,900,000
Emp.: 45
Local Trucking without Storage
N.A.I.C.S.: 484110
Edward Roeder (Pres)
Jenny Juskiv (Controller)

ASSURITY SECURITY GROUP INC.

PO Box 82533, Lincoln, NE 68501-
2625
Tel.: (402) 476-6500
Web Site: http://www.assurity.com
Sales Range: $50-74.9 Million
Emp.: 375
Holding Company
N.A.I.C.S.: 551112
Marvin P. Ehly (CFO)

Subsidiaries:

Assurity Life Insurance Company   (1)
2000 Q St, Lincoln, NE 68503
Tel.: (402) 476-6500
Web Site: http://www.assurity.com
Life, Annuity & Disability Insurance Services
N.A.I.C.S.: 524210
Marvin P. Ehly (CFO, Treas & VP)
Todd W. Reimers (Chief Mktg & Sls Officer
& Sr VP)
David D. Lockwood (Chief Investment Offi-
cer & VP)
Eric L. Otterstein (CIO & VP)
John Sharp (Gen Counsel, Sec & VP)
Susan Becker (VP-HR)
Susie Keisler-Munro (Chm, Pres & CEO)

ASSYRIAN NATIONAL COUN-CIL OF ILLINOIS

2450 W Peterson, Chicago, IL 60659
Tel.: (773) 262-5589   IL

Assyrian National Council of
Illinois—(Continued)

Web Site: http://www.ancil.org
Year Founded: 1986
Sales Range: $10-24.9 Million
Emp.: 974
Grantmaking Services
N.A.I.C.S.: 561499

**ASSYRIAN UNIVERSAL ALLI-
ANCE FOUNDATION, INC.**
4343 W Touhy Ave, Lincolnwood, IL
60712
Tel.: (773) 274-9262   IL
Web Site: https://www.auaf.us
Year Founded: 1978
Sales Range: $25-49.9 Million
Emp.: 2,040
Refugee & Elderly People Welfare
Services
N.A.I.C.S.: 624120
Kenneth Jacobs (Treas)
Homer Ashurian (CEO)
Robert Sargis (Asst Treas)
Ronald Sargis (Pres)

ASTA FUNDING, INC.
210 Sylvan Ave, Englewood Cliffs, NJ
07632
Tel.: (201) 567-5648   DE
Web Site:
     http://www.astafunding.com
Year Founded: 1994
Rev.: $21,113,000
Assets: $90,685,000
Liabilities: $1,516,000
Net Worth: $89,169,000
Earnings: $7,175,000
Emp.: 56
Fiscal Year-end: 09/30/19
Purchaser, Liquidator & Manager of
Distressed Consumer Receivables
N.A.I.C.S.: 522220
Gary Stern (Chm, Pres & CEO)
Seth Berman (Chief Compliance Offi-
cer & Gen Counsel)
Ricky Stern (Pres-GAR Disability Ad-
vocates LLC & Sr VP)
Lorri Smith (VP-Bus Dev)
David Cavill (Dir-Bus Intelligence)
Steven Leidenfrost (CFO)
Alexandra Vivero (Mgr-Bus Dev-Intl)

Subsidiaries:

CBC Settlement Funding, LLC   (1)
1 W 1st Ave Ste 310, Conshohocken, PA
19428
Tel.: (610) 825-4098
Web Site:
     http://www.cbcsettlementfunding.com
General Insurance Services
N.A.I.C.S.: 524210
Kenneth Barnett (Pres)

Palisades Collection, LLC   (1)
210 Sylvan Ave, Englewood Cliffs, NJ
07632
Tel.: (800) 414-8319
Asset Management Services
N.A.I.C.S.: 531390

Pegasus Funding, LLC   (1)
14 Wall St Ste 6a, New York, NY
10005   (80%)
Tel.: (212) 227-1008
Asset Management Services
N.A.I.C.S.: 531390

ASTARA, INC.
10700 Jersey Blvd Ste 450, Rancho
Cucamonga, CA 91730
Tel.: (909) 948-7412   CA
Web Site: http://www.astara.org
Year Founded: 1951
Sales Range: $50-74.9 Million
Emp.: 9
Religious & Educational Book Pub-
lisher
N.A.I.C.S.: 513130

Dean Zakich (Gen Mgr)
Sally Fleck (Mgr-Member Records)
Samantha Pennala (Mgr-Mktg)

**ASTATINE INVESTMENT
PARTNERS LLC**
33 Benedict Pl 2nd Fl, Greenwich,
CT 06830
Tel.: (203) 930-3800
Web Site: https://astatineip.com
Emp.: 100
Investment Services
N.A.I.C.S.: 523999

Subsidiaries:

Astatine Capital Partners LLC   (1)
100 West Putnam Ave, Greenwich, CT
06830
Tel.: (203) 930-3800
Web Site: http://www.alinda.com
Privater Equity Firm
N.A.I.C.S.: 523999
Christopher W. Beale (Chm & Mng Partner)
Joe Kelleher (Partner & Gen Counsel)

Subsidiary (Domestic):

Alinda Investments LLC   (2)
150 E 58th St, New York, NY 10155
Tel.: (212) 838-6400
Web Site: http://www.alinda.com
Sales Range: $50-74.9 Million
Investment
N.A.I.C.S.: 523999

Holding (Non-US):

Energy Assets Group Limited   (2)
6 Almondvale Business Park Almondvale
Way, Livingston, EH54 6GA, United King-
dom
Tel.: (44) 1506405405
Web Site: http://www.energyassets.co.uk
Sales Range: $50-74.9 Million
Emp.: 500
Gas Metering Services
N.A.I.C.S.: 213112
John McMorrow (CFO)
David Sing (Mng Dir-Assets)
Stewart Love (Dir-Comml Grp)
Colin Lynch (CEO)
Craig Topley (Mng Dir-Construction Grp)
Steven Miller (Controller-Fin)
James Walker (Head-IT)

Subsidiary (Domestic):

Bglobal Metering Limited   (3)
Arkwright House 2 Arkwright Court, Com-
mercial Road, Darwen, BB3 0FG, Lancs,
United Kingdom
Tel.: (44) 1254819600
Web Site: http://www.energyassets.co.uk
Metering Services
N.A.I.C.S.: 561990
Steve Whitehead (Head-Bus Strategy)
Martin Thomasson (Dir-Data Svcs)
Pauline Bryon (Mgr-Customer Support)
Susan Handford (Mgr-Direct Sls, Customer
Svcs & Data Quality)

McKeil Marine Limited   (1)
208 Hillyard St, Hamilton, ON, Canada
Tel.: (905) 528-4780
Web Site: http://www.mckeil.com
Rev.: $22,259,925
Emp.: 200
Marine Transportation Services
N.A.I.C.S.: 488390
Robert Dionisi (VP-Comml)
Scott Bravener (CEO)

ASTEK WALLCOVERING, INC.
15924 Arminta St, Van Nuys, CA
91406
Tel.: (818) 901-9876   CA
Web Site:
     http://www.astekwallcovering.com
Year Founded: 1980
Sales Range: $1-9.9 Million
Emp.: 20
Specialty Wall Coverings
N.A.I.C.S.: 424950
Aaron Kirsch (Pres)
Sarah LaVoie (Dir-Creative)

ASTENJOHNSON, INC.
4399 Corporate Rd, Charleston, SC
29405
Tel.: (843) 747-7800
Web Site:
     https://www.astenjohnson.com
Year Founded: 1931
Sales Range: $200-249.9 Million
Emp.: 80
Specialty & Filtration Fabrics, Fila-
ments & Paper Machine Clothing Mfr;
Paper Industry Machinery Mfr
N.A.I.C.S.: 314999
Kevin Frank (Pres & CEO)
Steve Gray (CFO)

Subsidiaries:

AstenJohnson, Inc. - Kanata R&D
Facility   (1)
1243 Teron Road, Kanata, K2K 1X2, ON,
Canada
Tel.: (613) 592-5851
Web Site: http://www.astenjohnson.com
Sales Range: $25-49.9 Million
Emp.: 65
Dryer Fabrics Research & Development
N.A.I.C.S.: 314999

ASTERI HOLDINGS
333 Market St, Shreveport, LA 71101
Tel.: (318) 216-5709
Web Site:
     http://www.asteriholdings.com
Online Gaming & Advertising
N.A.I.C.S.: 541890
Steve Gray (CEO)
Bill Macdonald (Chief Creative Offi-
cer)
Marcus Morton (Pres)

Subsidiaries:

Prima Games   (1)
3000 Lava Ridge Ct Ste 100, Roseville, CA
95661
Tel.: (916) 787-7000
Web Site: http://www.primagames.com
Book Publishers
N.A.I.C.S.: 513130
Debra Kempker (Pres)

ASTIR IT SOLUTIONS, INC.
50 Cragwood Rd Ste 219, South
Plainfield, NJ 07080
Tel.: (908) 279-8670
Web Site: https://www.astirit.com
Year Founded: 2001
Sales Range: $1-9.9 Million
Emp.: 200
Corporate Information Technology
Consulting Services
N.A.I.C.S.: 541690
Kishore Ganji (Pres & CEO)
Sarad Bhattaram (Engr-Software)
Ravi Shankar (Mgr-Resource)

Subsidiaries:

Sysnet Technology Solutions,
Inc.   (1)
4320 Stevens Creek Blvd Ste 229, San
Jose, CA 95129
Tel.: (408) 248-5000
Web Site: http://www.sysnetts.com
Sales Range: $1-9.9 Million
Emp.: 50
Software Development & Computer Con-
sulting
N.A.I.C.S.: 541512

**ASTLEFORD INTERNATIONAL
TRUCKS, INC.**
3000 Broadway St NE, Minneapolis,
MN 55413
Tel.: (612) 378-1660
Web Site: https://www.astleford.com
Year Founded: 1945
Sales Range: $25-49.9 Million
Emp.: 150
Truck Dealership Owner & Operator

N.A.I.C.S.: 423110
Scott Dawson (Owner & Pres)
Tom Mike (Mgr-Ops)
Scott Loyd (Controller)

Subsidiaries:

G&H Truck Leasing Inc.   (1)
3000 Broadway St NE, Minneapolis, MN
55413
Tel.: (612) 378-1660
Web Site: http://www.astleford.com
Rev.: $2,400,000
Emp.: 50
Truck Leasing, Without Drivers
N.A.I.C.S.: 532120
Scott Dawson (Pres)
Jim Woodison (Mgr-New Truck Sls)

ASTON HOTELS & RESORTS
2155 Kalakaua Ave Ste 500, Hono-
lulu, HI 96815-2355
Tel.: (808) 931-1400
Web Site:
     http://www.astonhotels.com
Year Founded: 1967
Sales Range: $50-74.9 Million
Emp.: 1,821
Hotel Services
N.A.I.C.S.: 721110
Wes Murasaki (Sr Dir-Sls)
James Farquhar (Mgr-Rooms Div)
Kaniela Neves (Gen Mgr)
Matt Bailey (Pres)

ASTONISH
300 Metro Center Blvd, Warwick, RI
02886
Tel.: (401) 921-6220
Web Site: http://www.astonish.com
Year Founded: 2006
Sales Range: $10-24.9 Million
Emp.: 100
Digital Web Development & Market-
ing Services for Insurance Agencies
N.A.I.C.S.: 541613
Adam Degraide (Co-Founder)
John Boudreau (Co-Founder & CEO)
Tim Sawyer (Co-Founder & Pres)
Rishi Bhatia (CTO)
Teri Shipp (Exec VP-Sls)
Jackie Dube (VP-HR)

**ASTOR & BLACK CUSTOM
CLOTHIERS, LTD.**
81 S 5th St, Columbus, OH 43215
Tel.: (614) 857-9000   OH
Web Site:
     http://www.astorandblack.com
Year Founded: 2005
Sales Range: $10-24.9 Million
Emp.: 120
Clothing & Accessories Sales
N.A.I.C.S.: 458110
Richard Norris (CFO)

**ASTOR & SANDERS CORPO-
RATION**
9900 Belward Campus Dr Ste 275,
Rockville, MD 20850
Tel.: (301) 838-3420
Web Site: https://www.astor-
     sanders.com
Year Founded: 2000
Sales Range: $1-9.9 Million
Emp.: 88
IT, Telecommunications, Management
& Financial Consulting & Administra-
tive Support Services
N.A.I.C.S.: 519290
Andrew Iserson (Program Mgr)
Omar Karim (Sr Analyst-Systems III)
Thomas N. Flagg (Mgr-Projects)

ASTOR CHOCOLATE CORP.
651 New Hampshire Ave, Lakewood,
NJ 08701
Tel.: (732) 901-1000

Web Site:
   https://www.astorchocolate.com
Sales Range: $10-24.9 Million
Emp.: 65
Chocolate Candy, Solid
N.A.I.C.S.: 311351
Ron Lutz (Mgr-Print Shop)

ASTORG FORD LINCOLN-MERCURY OF PARKERS-BURG, INC.
2028 7th St, Parkersburg, WV 26101
Tel.: (304) 422-6403   **WV**
Web Site: http://www.astorgauto.com
Year Founded: 1967
Sales Range: $25-49.9 Million
Emp.: 100
Automobiles, New & Used
N.A.I.C.S.: 441110
Paul Astorg (Pres)

ASTORG MOTOR CO.
2028 7th St, Parkersburg, WV 26101
Tel.: (304) 485-8585
Web Site:
   https://www.astorgauto.com
Sales Range: $10-24.9 Million
Emp.: 100
Car Whslr
N.A.I.C.S.: 441110
Carolyn Cooke (Office Mgr)

ASTOUND COMMERCE CORP.
1111 Bayhill Dr Ste 425, San Bruno, CA 94066
Web Site:
   http://www.astoundcommerce.com
Year Founded: 2000
Information Technology Services & Software Publishing
N.A.I.C.S.: 541519
Roman Martynenko (Co-Founder & Exec VP-Global Sls)
Igor Gorin (Co-Founder & CEO)
Ilya Vinogradsky (Co-Founder, CTO & Exec Vp-Commerce Delivery)
Terry Hunter (Mng Dir-UK)
James Joyce (Dir-Mktg & Brand)
Omar Jabbour (Gen Counsel & Chief Compliance Officer)
Igor Peshkov (VP-Global Alliances)
Sean Sanders (VP-Bus Dev)
Vlad Veksler (VP-Engrg)
David Murack (VP-Tech Svcs)
Michael Kahn (CEO-Global)

Subsidiaries:

Fluid, Inc.   (1)
1611 Telegraph Ave Ste 400, Oakland, CA 94612
Tel.: (415) 898-5652
Web Site: http://www.configureid.com
Digital Commerce Solutions
N.A.I.C.S.: 541511
Andrew Guldman (Principal)
Sara Arias (Mgr-Product)

Site 9, Inc.   (1)
610 SW Alder St Ste 515, Portland, OR 97205-3606
Tel.: (503) 248-4440
Web Site: http://www.protoshare.com
Software Publisher
N.A.I.C.S.: 513210
Robert Wiggins (Sec)
Andrew S. Mottaz (Founder, Pres & CEO)

the e-tailing group, Inc.   (1)
1743 W Wellington Ave, Chicago, IL 60657
Tel.: (773) 975-7280
Web Site: http://www.e-tailing.com
Emp.: 5
Marketing Consulting Services
N.A.I.C.S.: 541613
Lauren Freedman (Pres)

ASTRA CAPITAL MANAGEMENT LLC
900 16th St NW Ste 450, Washington, DC 20006
Tel.: (202) 930-7000
Web Site:
   http://www.astracapitalmgmt.com
Privater Equity Firm
N.A.I.C.S.: 523999
William E. Kennard (Co-Founder & Partner)
Mark Johnson (Co-Founder & Mng Partner)
Matthew Murphy (Co-Founder)
Todd M. Crick (Co-Founder)
Kevin L. Beebe (Partner)
Brian R. Kirschbaum (Partner)
Raj Kumar (Gen Counsel & Partner)
James G. Martin (Partner & CFO)
Daniel A. Ben-Ami (VP)
Nia G. White (Partner & Head-IR & External Affairs)

Subsidiaries:

DartPoints LLC   (1)
2001 Bryan St Ste 1325, Dallas, TX 75201
Tel.: (888) 257-7462
Web Site: http://www.dartpoints.com
Data Center & Managed Care Services
N.A.I.C.S.: 518210
Scott Willis (CEO)
Angelika Torres (CFO)

Subsidiary (Domestic):

Venyu Solutions Inc.   (2)
7127 Florida Blvd 1, Baton Rouge, LA 70806
Tel.: (225) 214-3800
Sales Range: $10-24.9 Million
Emp.: 75
Data Processing, Hosting & Related Services
N.A.I.C.S.: 518210
Chris Davis (CFO)
Tommy Curb (Exec VP-Bus Dev & Legal Affairs)
Gerry Boudreau (VP-Datacenter Design Construction, WAN Strategy & Peering)
Brian Vandegrif (Exec VP-Sls & Innovation)
Mark Baker (Dir-Infrastructure)
Jerrod LeMaire (Exec VP-Ops & Infrastructure)
Janet Britton (Gen Counsel & Exec VP-HR)
Toby Dubois (Exec VP-Consumer Sls & Mktg)
Tressy Leindecker (Exec VP-Sls)
Peter Louviere (CFO)
Harris Miller (Exec VP-Tech & Innovation)
Kevin Phillips (Exec VP-IT & Project Mgmt)
John D. Scanlan (CEO)
Arthur Scanlan (Chm)

LOGIX Communications, L.P.   (1)
2950 N Loop W 8th Fl, Houston, TX 77092
Tel.: (281) 688-6231
Web Site: http://www.logixcom.com
Telecommunication Servicesb
N.A.I.C.S.: 517121
Shane Schilling (CTO)
Mary Malsch (Chief Customer Officer)
Stephen Erickson (Chief Admin Officer)
Amit Rai (Interim CFO)
Scott Brueggeman (Chief Sls & Mktg Officer)
Adam Sheiner (VP-Sls)
Craig Collins (CEO)

Subsidiary (Domestic):

Alpheus Communications LP   (2)
211 E 7th St Ste 620, Austin, TX 78701
Tel.: (877) 257-4387
Telecommunication Servicesb
N.A.I.C.S.: 517810
Ed Stacey (CFO)

Subsidiary (Domestic):

Net Star Telecommunications, Inc.   (3)
505 Julie Rivers Dr Ste 170, Sugar Land, TX 77478
Tel.: (281) 240-7300
Web Site: http://www.netstartel.com
Technology Consulting Services
N.A.I.C.S.: 517810

ASTRA FOODS, INC.
6430 Market St, Upper Darby, PA 19082
Tel.: (610) 352-4400
Web Site:
   https://www.astrafoods.com
Year Founded: 1978
Sales Range: $10-24.9 Million
Emp.: 300
Beef & Chicken Steak Mfr
N.A.I.C.S.: 311611
Demosthenes Vasiliou (Co-Founder & Pres)
Spiros Poulimenos (Co-Founder & VP)

ASTRA INC.
1660 NW 65th Ave Ste 1, Plantation, FL 33313
Tel.: (954) 583-5677
Web Site:
   http://www.astraservices.com
Sales Range: $10-24.9 Million
Emp.: 9
Transportation Agents & Brokers
N.A.I.C.S.: 488510
Tom Przybojewski (Pres)

ASTRA SPACE, INC.
1900 Skyhawk St, Alameda, CA 94501   **DE**
Web Site: https://astra.com
Year Founded: 2020
ASTR—(NASDAQ)
Rev.: $9,370,000
Assets: $174,699,000
Liabilities: $92,389,000
Net Worth: $82,310,000
Earnings: ($411,438,000)
Emp.: 359
Fiscal Year-end: 12/31/22
Other Guided Missile & Space Vehicle Parts & Auxiliary Equipment Manufacturing
N.A.I.C.S.: 336419
Axel Martinez (CFO)
Chris Kemp (Founder, Chm & CEO)

ASTRAL BRANDS, INC.
6120 Power Ferry Rd NW Ste 300, Atlanta, GA 30339
Tel.: (678) 303-3088
Web Site:
   http://www.astralbrands.com
Makeup & Skincare Products Mfr
N.A.I.C.S.: 456120
Adeline Riggle (Partner)
Elise Von Der Porten (Sr Dir-Sls-Canada)
Robert K. Cohen (Exec Chm & CEO)

Subsidiaries:

Butter LONDON LLC   (1)
3535 Factoria Blvd SE Ste 440, Bellevue, WA 98006-1209
Tel.: (206) 525-0847
Web Site: http://www.butterlondon.com
Beauty Product Mfr
N.A.I.C.S.: 456120
Sasha Muir (Founder)

ASTRAL EXTRACTS, LTD.
160 Eileen Way, Syosset, NY 11791
Tel.: (516) 496-2505
Web Site:
   http://www.astralextracts.com
Sales Range: $10-24.9 Million
Emp.: 14
Supplier of Raw Materials & Specialty Ingredients for the Flavor, Fragrance & Beverage Industries
N.A.I.C.S.: 424490
Cynthia Astrack (Chm & Pres)
Joan Pace (Gen Mgr)

ASTRE CORPORATION

3801 Mount Vernon Ave, Alexandria, VA 22313-5766
Tel.: (703) 548-1343   **DE**
Web Site: http://www.astrecg.com
Year Founded: 1976
Sales Range: $100-124.9 Million
Emp.: 244
Research & Development; Product Design & Process Development
N.A.I.C.S.: 541715
Roy A. Ackerman (CEO)

ASTREYA PARTNERS, INC.
1515 Wyatt Dr, Santa Clara, CA 95054
Tel.: (408) 790-5900
Web Site: http://www.astreya.com
Year Founded: 2001
Rev.: $18,400,000
Emp.: 136
Temporary Help Service
N.A.I.C.S.: 561320
Jeffrey Freeland (Founder & Chm)
Jay Preston (Sr VP-Svc Delivery-Global)
Monica Hushen (CFO & COO)
Sunitha Krishnaswamy (VP/Controller-Silicon Valley)
Andrea Bendzick (Pres & CEO)
Sonali Chatterji (Chief Sls Officer)

ASTRIA HEALTH
900 W Chestnut Ave, Yakima, WA 98902
Tel.: (509) 837-1330
Web Site: http://www.astria.health
Non Profit Healthcare System
N.A.I.C.S.: 621999
John Gallagher (Pres & CEO)
Cary Rowan (CFO)
John Andersen (Sr Dir- Info Svcs)
Daniel Burtnett (Interim Sr Dir-Revenue Cycle)
Joe Ketterer (Sr Dir-Physician Practices)
Dawn R. O'Polka (CMO & Comm Exec)
Les Abercrombie III (Chief HR Officer)

Subsidiaries:

Astria Sunnyside Hospital   (1)
1016 Tacoma Ave, Sunnyside, WA 98944
Tel.: (509) 837-1500
Web Site: http://www.astria.health
Healtcare Services
N.A.I.C.S.: 622110
Brian Gibbons (CEO)
Eric Strokes (COO)
Michael Long (CFO)
Cynthia Lewis (Chief Nursing Officer)

Subsidiary (Domestic):

Astria Regional Medical Center   (2)
110 S 9th Ave, Yakima, WA 98902
Tel.: (509) 575-5000
Web Site: http://www.yakimaregional.com
Hospital Services
N.A.I.C.S.: 622110
Darrin Cook (COO)
Mark Hartman (Acting CFO)
Sara Williamson (Chief Nursing Officer)

Astria Toppenish Hospital   (2)
502 W 4th Ave, Toppenish, WA 98948
Tel.: (509) 865-3105
Web Site: http://www.astria.health
General Medical And Surgical Hospitals, N
N.A.I.C.S.: 622110
Eric Jensen (CEO)
Kyla Wright (CFO)
Terra Palomarez (Chief Nursing Officer)
Rhonda Wellner (Dir-Quality & Risk Mgmt & Compliance Officer)

ASTRIX TECHNOLOGY GROUP, INC.
125 Half Mile Rd Ste 200, Red Bank, NJ 07701

Astrix Technology Group, Inc.—(Continued)

Tel.: (732) 661-0400
Web Site:
http://www.astrixsoftware.com
Year Founded: 1983
Sales Range: $10-24.9 Million
Emp.: 100
Custom-Made Software
N.A.I.C.S.: 513210
Jim Cotter *(Project Mgr-Tech)*
Chelsey Rodier *(Acct Mgr)*
Jeffrey Policastro *(VP-Bus Dev)*
Dale Curtis *(Pres)*

ASTRO APPAREL, INC.
300 Brook St, Scranton, PA 18505
Tel.: (570) 346-1700
Web Site:
https://www.astroapparel.com
Year Founded: 1946
Clothing Mfr
N.A.I.C.S.: 315210
James Alperin *(Owner & CEO)*
Ronald Daniels *(CFO)*
Phylis Regan *(Mgr-Info Sys)*
James Pusateri *(VP-Ops)*
Gene Baronski *(Mgr-ISO)*
Pat Laskowski *(Dir-HR)*
Ellie McCauley *(Asst CFO)*
Bobbie Kromko *(Controller)*

ASTRO COMMUNICATIONS SERVICES, INC.
68 Fogg Rd, Epping, NH 03042
Tel.: (603) 734-4300
Web Site: http://www.astrocom.com
Year Founded: 1973
Sales Range: Less than $1 Million
Emp.: 2
Astrology Services; Publisher of
Books, Charts, Reports & Software
N.A.I.C.S.: 812990
Tom Canfield *(Office Mgr)*

ASTRO INC.
1955 Fairmont Ave, Fairmont, WV
26554
Tel.: (304) 366-4460
Sales Range: $10-24.9 Million
Emp.: 20
Sales of New & Used Automobiles
N.A.I.C.S.: 441110
Joseph Asterino *(Pres)*

ASTRO LINCOLN, MERCURY, INC.
6350 Pensacola Blvd, Pensacola, FL
32505
Tel.: (850) 478-8531
Web Site: http://www.astroauto.com
Year Founded: 1968
Sales Range: $10-24.9 Million
Emp.: 60
New Car Dealers
N.A.I.C.S.: 441110
M. W. Culbertson *(Pres)*
B. S. Culbertson *(VP)*
J. Morris *(Treas & Sec)*

ASTRO MANUFACTURING & DESIGN, INC.
34459 Curtis Blvd, Eastlake, OH
44095-4011
Tel.: (440) 946-8171   OH
Web Site: https://www.astromfg.com
Year Founded: 1977
Sales Range: $25-49.9 Million
Emp.: 250
Medical, Aerospace & Automotive
Component Mfr
N.A.I.C.S.: 333998
Mike Watts Jr. *(Pres)*

Subsidiaries:

AMD Fabricators, Inc.   **(1)**

4580 Beidler Road, Willoughby, OH 44094
Tel.: (440) 946-8855
Web Site: https://astromfg.com
Rev.: $1,300,000
Emp.: 20
Fiscal Year-end: 12/31/2006
Sheet Metal Work Mfg
N.A.I.C.S.: 332322
Gus DeAngelo *(CFO)*

ASTRO PAK CORPORATION
270 E Baker St Ste 100, Costa Mesa,
CA 92626
Tel.: (866) 492-7876
Web Site: http://www.astropak.com
Year Founded: 1959
Sales Range: $10-24.9 Million
Building Cleaning & Maintenance
Services
N.A.I.C.S.: 561720
Ken Verheyen *(CEO)*
Ken Carroll *(Pres)*
Tim Sowell *(Sr VP)*
Robert Pozil *(Sr VP-Sls & Mktg)*
Brent Ekstrand *(VP-Science & Tech)*
Tom Tate *(VP-Field Svcs-Western Ops)*
Gordon Hanscom *(Gen Mgr-Downey Cleanroom)*
Todd Dean *(COO)*
Jeff Wassenaar *(VP-Field Svcs & Sls)*
Keith Marlin *(VP-Field Svcs-Eastern Ops)*
Jennifer Kaushek *(VP-People & Culture)*
Jeremy Galtier *(VP-Environment, Health, Safety & Regulatory)*
Michael Johnson *(Dir-Technical Svcs)*
Jonathan Hopkins *(VP-Ops-Cleanroom Svcs)*

Subsidiaries:

Chemko Technical Services, Inc.   **(1)**
5325 US Hwy 1, Mims, FL 32754
Tel.: (321) 269-4573
Web Site: http://www.astropak.com
Sales Range: $1-9.9 Million
Emp.: 15
Instruments & Related Products Mfr for
Measuring, Displaying & Controlling Indus-
trial Process Variables
N.A.I.C.S.: 334513
Kenneth Verheyen *(CEO)*

ASTRO-TEC MANUFACTUR- ING, INC.
550 Elm Ridge Ave, Canal Fulton,
OH 44614-0608
Tel.: (330) 854-2209
Web Site: https://www.astro-tec.com
Year Founded: 1963
Sales Range: $10-24.9 Million
Emp.: 20
Mfr of Planetarium Domes
N.A.I.C.S.: 327215
Clayton Hopper *(Pres)*
Stephanie Hopper *(VP)*
Sophia Haines *(Office Mgr)*
Derl Wells *(Engr-Design)*

ASTROCHEF, INC.
1111 S Mateo St, Los Angeles, CA
90021
Tel.: (213) 627-9860
Web Site:
http://www.pegasusfoodsinc.com
Year Founded: 1998
Sales Range: $10-24.9 Million
Emp.: 55
Frozen Food Mfr
N.A.I.C.S.: 311412
Jim Zaferis *(Owner)*
Rudolph Cheng *(Controller)*
Colin Sarantis *(Mgr)*
Evangelos Ambatielos *(Pres)*
Laurie Morgan *(Office Mgr)*

ASTRONAUTICS CORPORA-

TION OF AMERICA
4115 N Teutonia Ave, Milwaukee, WI
53209
Tel.: (414) 449-4000   WI
Web Site:
http://www.astronautics.com
Year Founded: 1959
Sales Range: $125-149.9 Million
Emp.: 2,600
Aircraft Instruments, Flight Control
Systems, Guidance & Navigation
Systems, Robotics, Thermal Magnetic
Refrigeration, Avionic Displays & Dis-
play Processors & Systems Integra-
tors Mfr
N.A.I.C.S.: 334511
Ronald E. Zelazo *(Chm & CEO)*
Stephen Givant *(CFO)*
Chad Cundiff *(Pres)*

Subsidiaries:

Astronautics C.A. Ltd.   **(1)**
16 Martin Gehl, PO Box 3351, Petah Tiqwa,
49130, Israel   **(100%)**
Tel.: (972) 39251555
Web Site: http://www.astronautics.co.il
Sales Range: $10-24.9 Million
Emp.: 85
Mfr of Aircraft Instruments & Controls, Avi-
onics Displays & Display Processors, Guid-
ance & Navigation Systems
N.A.I.C.S.: 334511
Zvi Krepel *(Gen Mgr)*

Astronautics Corporation of America -
Plant 4   **(1)**
1426 W National Ave, Milwaukee, WI
53204-2116
Tel.: (414) 671-5500
Avionic System Mfr
N.A.I.C.S.: 334511

Astronautics U.K.   **(1)**
28 Tekels Avenue, Camberley, GU15 2LB,
Surrey, United Kingdom   **(100%)**
Tel.: (44) 276677365
Web Site: http://www.astronautics.com
Mfr of Aircraft Instruments & Controls, Avi-
onics, Guidance & Navigation Systems
N.A.I.C.S.: 334511

Kearfott Corporation   **(1)**
1150 McBride Ave, Little Falls, NJ 07424-
2500
Tel.: (973) 785-6000
Web Site: http://www.kearfott.com
Sales Range: $100-124.9 Million
Emp.: 262
Guidance & Navigational Systems Mfr
N.A.I.C.S.: 334511
Ronald Zelazo *(Chm & CEO)*

Kearfott Guidance & Navigation
Corporation   **(1)**
1150 McBride Ave, Little Falls, NJ 07424-
2500
Tel.: (973) 785-6000
Web Site: http://www.kearfott.com
Sales Range: $75-99.9 Million
Emp.: 1,400
Inertial Navigation Systems for Land, Sea,
Air & Space Designer, Developer, Mfr &
Servicer
N.A.I.C.S.: 334511
Stephen Givant *(VP-Fin & HR)*
Walter Peters *(VP)*

Division (Domestic):

Kearfott Guidance & Navigation Cor-
poration - Kearfott Motion System
Division   **(2)**
2858 US Highway 70 W, Black Mountain,
NC 28711-9111
Tel.: (828) 350-5300
Web Site: http://www.kearfott.com
Sales Range: $50-74.9 Million
Emp.: 325
Motion Sensor Device Mfr
N.A.I.C.S.: 334511
Greg Scott *(Pres)*

ASTRUP DRUGS, INC.
905 N Main St, Austin, MN 55912-
3357

Tel.: (507) 433-4586   MN
Web Site:
https://www.astrupdrug.com
Year Founded: 1952
Sales Range: $125-149.9 Million
Emp.: 300
Retailer of Drugs, Sundries & Gen-
eral Merchandise
N.A.I.C.S.: 456110
Chris Astrup *(CEO)*
Dan Astrup *(Treas, Sec & VP)*

ASTUTE, INC.
2400 Corporate Exchange Dr Ste
150, Columbus, OH 43231
Tel.: (614) 508-6100   OH
Web Site:
http://www.astutesolutions.com
Year Founded: 1996
Sales Range: $10-24.9 Million
Emp.: 100
Customer Service Software
N.A.I.C.S.: 513210
Alex George *(Pres & CTO)*
Shellie Vornhagen *(Chief Customer Experience Officer)*
Dave Butler *(VP-Sls-North America)*
Mark Zablan *(CEO)*
Zarnaz Arlia *(CMO)*
Peter Bennfors *(CFO)*

ASTYRA CORPORATION
411 E Franklin St Ste 105, Richmond,
VA 23219
Tel.: (804) 433-1100
Web Site: https://www.astyra.com
Year Founded: 1997
Rev.: $9,800,000
Emp.: 235
Employment Placement Agencies
N.A.I.C.S.: 561311
Ken Ampy *(CEO)*
Sam Young *(Pres)*
Melissa Silver *(Dir-Ops)*
Mark Thompson *(CFO)*
Melanie Parrish *(Dir-Client Accts)*

ASU GROUP
2120 University Park Dr, Okemos, MI
48805-0077
Tel.: (517) 349-2212
Web Site: https://www.asugroup.com
Year Founded: 1952
Rev.: $31,954,846
Emp.: 70
Insurance Agents, Brokers & Service
N.A.I.C.S.: 524210
Cheryl Hendrixson *(Dir-Case Mgmt Svcs)*
Debra Claeys *(Pres & CEO)*
Chad Johnson *(Dir-Risk Mgmt Svcs-Michigan Clients)*

ASURION LLC
648 Grassmere Pk, Nashville, TN
37211
Tel.: (615) 837-3000
Web Site: http://www.asurion.com
Year Founded: 1994
Sales Range: $25-49.9 Million
Technology Warranty & Mobile Sup-
port Services
N.A.I.C.S.: 561499
Bret Comolli *(Chm)*
Kevin Taweel *(CEO)*
Rodney Schlosser *(Sr VP-Bus Dev & Strategic Partnerships)*
Jim Flautt *(Sr VP-Global Supply Chain Mgmt)*
Charles A. Laue *(CEO)*
Cindy Christy *(Pres)*
Anthony P. Nader III *(Vice Chm)*
Tony Detter *(CEO)*
Rob DiRocco *(Sr VP & Gen Mgr-Retail Solutions)*

John Leonard *(Sr VP-Global Product Mgmt)*
Tony Nader *(Vice Chm)*
Sue Nokes *(Sr VP-Growth Initiatives-Global & Operational Plng)*
Gus Puryear *(Gen Counsel & Sr VP-HR)*
Tim Stadthaus *(Sr VP-Mktg & Customer Experience)*
Chuck Stewart *(CEO-Europe)*
Barry Vandevier *(COO)*
Ken Wirth *(Sr VP & Gen Mgr-Americas Mobility)*
Mark Gunning *(CFO)*
John Storey *(Sr VP-Corp Dev & Strategy)*
Tiffany Whaley *(Mgr-Talent Aq Mktg)*
Casey Santos *(CIO)*

Subsidiaries:

uBreakiFix **(1)**
11779 E Colonial Dr, Orlando, FL 32817
Tel.: (407) 243-9994
Web Site: http://www.ubreakifix.com
Sales Range: $10-24.9 Million
Emp.: 180
Repair Services for Electronic Devices
N.A.I.C.S.: 811210
Justin Wetherill *(Founder & CEO)*
Rolando Bencomo *(Owner)*
Scott Jones *(VP-Strategy)*

ASW HOLDING CORPORATION

750 W Lake Cook Grove Ste 480, Buffalo Grove, IL 60089
Tel.: (847) 202-7000
Web Site: http://www.gmt-inc.com
Year Founded: 1987
Sales Range: $10-24.9 Million
Emp.: 15
Abrasive Products
N.A.I.C.S.: 332999
Norman Soep *(Pres)*
Rob Krebs *(CFO)*

Subsidiaries:

Global Material Technologies, Inc. **(1)**
750 W Lakecook Rd, Buffalo Grove, IL 60089-8320 **(100%)**
Tel.: (847) 202-7000
Web Site: http://www.globalmaterials.com
Abrasive Products
N.A.I.C.S.: 332999

ASW LOGISTICS INC.

3375 Gilchrist Rd, Mogadore, OH 44260
Tel.: (330) 733-6291
Web Site:
http://www.aswservices.com
Rev.: $13,500,000
Emp.: 150
General Warehousing & Storage
N.A.I.C.S.: 493110
Philip H. Maynard *(Vice Chm)*

AT CONFERENCE, INC.

33 Flying Point Rd, Southampton, NY 11968
Tel.: (631) 204-1891   NY
Year Founded: 2005
Sales Range: $10-24.9 Million
Emp.: 36
Audio & Web Conference Services
N.A.I.C.S.: 517810

AT INDUSTRIES, INC.

4915 Stilwell St, Kansas City, MO 64120
Tel.: (816) 242-0400
Sales Range: $25-49.9 Million
Emp.: 100
Holding Company; Specialty Contractors
N.A.I.C.S.: 551112

Salvatore T. Curiale *(Pres)*
Grace A. Curiale *(Owner & VP)*
David Masrud *(Project Mgr)*
Greg Nitcher *(VP-Project Mgmt)*
Rick Kooser *(Project Mgr)*
Tom Curiale *(VP)*
Kristin Seybold *(Controller)*

Subsidiaries:

AT Abatement Services, Inc. **(1)**
4915 Stilwell St, Kansas City, MO 64120
Tel.: (816) 242-0400
Web Site:
http://www.abatementservices.com
Rev.: $5,883,362
Emp.: 20
Asbestos Removal & Encapsulation
N.A.I.C.S.: 562910
Salvatore T. Curiale *(Pres)*
David Masrud *(Project Mgr)*
Greg Nitcher *(VP-Project Mgmt)*

AT Industrial Sheet Metal, Inc. **(1)**
4915 Stilwell St, Kansas City, MO 64120
Tel.: (816) 231-6696
Web Site: http://www.atindustriesinc.com
Rev.: $5,326,857
Emp.: 40
Sheet Metalwork
N.A.I.C.S.: 238390
Rick Kooser *(Project Mgr)*
Salvatore T. Curiale *(Pres)*

All Temp, Inc. **(1)**
4915 Stilwell St, Kansas City, MO 64120
Tel.: (816) 483-0028
Rev.: $8,371,345
Emp.: 75
Acoustical & Insulation Work
N.A.I.C.S.: 238310

AT INFORMATION PRODUCTS

575 Corporate Dr, Mahwah, NJ 07430-2330
Tel.: (201) 529-0202   NJ
Web Site: https://www.atip-usa.com
Sales Range: $1-9.9 Million
Emp.: 6
Bar Code & Other Printing Services
N.A.I.C.S.: 333248
Joseph Traut *(Pres)*
Roger Angrick *(Gen Mgr)*

AT LAST NATURALS, INC.

401 Columbus Ave, Valhalla, NY 10595
Tel.: (914) 747-3599   NY
Web Site:
https://www.atlastnaturals.com
Year Founded: 1967
Sales Range: $75-99.9 Million
Emp.: 50
Cosmetics & Pharmaceuticals Mfr
N.A.I.C.S.: 325620
Fred Rosen *(Gen Counsel & Exec VP)*

AT SURGICAL COMPANY, INC.

115 Clemente St, Holyoke, MA 01040-5644
Tel.: (413) 532-4551
Web Site: http://www.atsurgical.com
Year Founded: 1969
Rev.: $3,000,000
Emp.: 15
Elastic Surgical Supports Mfr
N.A.I.C.S.: 339113
Mark Shoham *(CEO)*

AT THE TABLE PUBLIC RELATIONS

301 W Platt St Ste 414, Tampa, FL 33606
Tel.: (813) 251-4242
Web Site:
https://www.atthetablepr.com
Sales Range: $1-9.9 Million
Emp.: 10
Public Relations Agency
N.A.I.C.S.: 541820

Cheryl Miller *(CEO & Principal)*
Candace Rotolo *(Acct Mgr)*

AT-NET SERVICES, INC.

9625-D S Pine Blvd, Charlotte, NC 28273
Tel.: (704) 831-2500   SC
Web Site: http://www.at-net.net
Year Founded: 1999
Sales Range: $10-24.9 Million
Emp.: 80
Data, Voice, Video & Security Products/Services; Network Systems Integration
N.A.I.C.S.: 518210
Jeff King *(Founder & Pres)*
David Berman *(COO)*
Joel Sosebee *(Dir-Sls)*
Dan Dunkin *(CTO)*

Subsidiaries:

At-Net Services-Greenville, Inc. **(1)**
111 Smith Hines Rd Ste A & B, Greenville, SC 29607
Tel.: (864) 679-0006
Web Site: http://www.expertit.net
Sales Range: $10-24.9 Million
Emp.: 35
Network Software, Hardware Design & Installation Services
N.A.I.C.S.: 541511
David Berman *(CFO)*

ATA - A.T APPARELS, INC.

8020 Arcadian Ct, Mount Dora, FL 32757
Tel.: (352) 735-1588
Sales Range: $25-49.9 Million
Emp.: 1,200
Textile Products Mfr
N.A.I.C.S.: 314999
Rajesh S. Tari *(Pres)*

ATAIROS GROUP, INC.

620 5th Ave 6th Fl Rockefeller Plz, New York, NY 10020
Tel.: (646) 690-5252
Web Site: http://www.atairos.com
Year Founded: 2016
Privater Equity Firm
N.A.I.C.S.: 523999
Michael J. Angelakis *(Chm & CEO)*
Rachael A. Wagner *(Partner & Mng Dir)*
David L. Caplan *(Partner & Gen Counsel)*
Alexander D. Evans *(Partner)*
Jackson Phillips *(Mng Dir)*
Clare McGrory *(CFO & Chief Compliance Officer)*
Kellen Brown *(Controller)*
Melissa Bethell *(Mng Partner)*
Rachael A. Wagner *(Mng Dir)*
Robert Slinkard *(Mng Dir-Strategic Initiatives)*
Michael J. Angelakis *(Chm & CEO)*

Subsidiaries:

Learfield Communications, LLC **(1)**
505 Hobbs Rd, Jefferson City, MO 65109-6829
Tel.: (573) 893-7200
Web Site: http://www.learfield.com
News & Sports Multimedia Syndicate
N.A.I.C.S.: 516210
Greg Brown *(Pres & CEO)*
Jeff Martin *(VP-HR)*
Phil Atkinson *(VP-IT)*
Tom Boman *(VP-Brdcst Ops)*
Aaron Worsham *(Sr VP-Affiliate Rels & Broadcast Ops)*
Jennifer Heim *(VP & Corp Controller)*
Bob Agramonte *(Chief Business Development)*
Bob Bernard *(Pres-Learfield Licensing Partners)*
Lori Bland *(VP-Partnership Mgmt)*
Jeff Bolitho *(VP-Multimedia-Rights)*
Keith Bradshaw *(VP-Multi-Media Rights)*

Eric Buchanan *(VP-Training & Dev)*
Spencer Christiansen *(Sr VP-Multi-Media Rights)*
Tom Wistrcill *(VP-Multi-Media Rights)*
Andrew Wheeler *(Exec VP-Multimedia Rights)*

Division (Domestic):

Learfield Communications, LLC **(2)**
2400 Dallas Pkwy Ste 500, Plano, TX 75093
Tel.: (469) 241-9191
Web Site: http://www.learfield.com
Sports Multimedia Syndicate
N.A.I.C.S.: 533110
Steven H. Gowan *(Sr VP-Sls Ops)*
Greg Brown *(Pres & CEO)*
Roy Seinfeld *(Exec VP-Natl Sls)*
Matt Hupfeld *(CFO-ANC)*
Bob Agramonte *(Chief Bus Dev Officer)*
Spencer Christiansen *(Sr VP-Multi-Media Rights)*
John Raleigh *(Chief Legal Officer)*
Bob Bernard *(Pres & CEO-Learfield Licensing Partners)*
Gil Beverly *(VP-Sponsorship Mktg & Natl Sls)*
Lori Bland *(VP-Partnership Mgmt)*
Jeff Bolitho *(VP-Multi-Media Rights)*

Subsidiary (Domestic):

ANC Sports Enterprises, LLC **(3)**
2 Manhattanville Rd Ste 402, Purchase, NY 10577
Tel.: (914) 696-2100
Web Site: http://www.ancsports.com
Multimedia Sports Marketing & Information Systems Developer
N.A.I.C.S.: 541613
Mark J. Stross *(CTO-Tech Dev)*
Siobhan Mason *(Sr VP-Admin)*
Chris Mascatello *(Exec VP-Tech Solutions)*
Joe Morgan *(VP-Fin & Acctg)*
Jerry Cifarelli *(Co-Founder, Pres & CEO)*
Aj Faxel *(Sr VP-Ops)*
Malik Khan *(Sr VP-Integration & Product Dev)*
Steve Kerepesi *(Exec VP & Chief Revenue Officer)*
Michael Hopkins *(Sr VP-External Comm)*
Colleeen Brace *(Sr VP-Sls & Venue Svcs)*
Joseph Occhipinti *(VP-Ops)*
Jude Bucci *(VP-Projects)*
Dave Watroba *(VP-Sls)*
Josh Keeler *(Creative Dir)*

Cyclone Sports Properties, LLC **(3)**
yclone Sports Properties 10609 Justin Dr, Urbandale, IA 50322
Tel.: (515) 222-9393
Web Site: http://www.cyclones.com
Sports Multimedia Broadcasting Rights Lessor
N.A.I.C.S.: 711310
Tim Atterberg *(Assoc Gen Mgr)*
Brett Cooper *(Mgr-Bus Dev)*
Brendan Falvey *(Mgr-Bus Dev)*
Chris Andrews *(Gen Mgr)*
Ryan Baade *(Mgr-Bus Dev)*
Samantha McPherson *(Mgr-Partnership Svcs)*
Tyler Smaha *(Coord-Sls Ops)*
Chelsea Cline *(Coord-Sls Ops)*

GoVision, LP **(3)**
8291 Gateway Dr Ste 100, Argyle, TX 76226
Tel.: (940) 464-2320
Web Site: http://www.jumbo.tv
Mobile Video Screen Solutions
N.A.I.C.S.: 334310
Christopher Curtis *(Pres & CEO)*
Adam Vahl *(Mgr-Field Svcs)*
Brett Amman *(Mgr-Golf Sls & Ops)*
Jeff Williams *(VP-Ops)*
Kim Hinnrichs *(Dir-Copr Admin)*
Kristy Johnston *(VP-Fin)*
Robert Rhodes *(Mgr-Natl Acct)*
Steve Daniels *(Mgr-Fleet)*
Scott McKinnon *(Exec VP-Sls & Mktg)*
Kevin Faciane *(Exec VP)*
Mark Johnson *(VP-Bus Dev)*
Todd Wickstrum *(VP-Design & Engrg)*
Josh Echo-hawk *(VP-Creative Svcs)*
Brad Merriman *(Mgr-Bus Dev)*

Learfield Licensing Partners, LLC **(3)**

Atairos Group, Inc.—(Continued)

442 Century Ln Ste 100, Holland, MI 49423
Tel.: (616) 395-0808
Web Site: http://www.learfieldlicensing.com
Sports Licensing & Trademark Management Services
N.A.I.C.S.: 533110
Bob Bernard (Pres & CEO)
Bill Haut (Gen Counsel)
Eric Johnson (COO)
Tony Johnson (Exec VP)

Mogo Marketing & Media, Inc.   (3)
21 Tamal Vista Blvd Ste 207, Corte Madera, CA 94925
Tel.: (844) 214-6693
Web Site: http://www.mogointeractive.com
Digital Marketing Services
N.A.I.C.S.: 541613
Doug Mowbray (CEO)
Sheri Mowbray (Founder & CFO)
Danielle Johnson (COO)
Anna Nogueiro (Sr Dir-Culture)
Jill Vived (Dir-Ops)
Jonathon Hunt (Dir-Product)
Amanda Deely (Dir-Partnerships)
Susan Paine (Dir-Fin)

SME, Inc.   (3)
530 7th Ave Fl M-1, New York, NY 10018
Tel.: (212) 924-5700
Web Site: http://www.smebranding.com
Graphic Design Services
N.A.I.C.S.: 541430
Ed O'hara (Pres & Chief Creative Officer)
Greg Economou (Chm)
Sabara Heath (VP-Ops)
Jason Vogel (Assoc Dir-Creative)
Morgan Salvan (Assoc Dir)
Ronald Goldberg (Mgr-Bus Dev)
Brandon Cabassa (Dir-Sr Art)
Alex Kurr (Art-Art)
Mark Davis (Dir-Junior Art)

Division (Domestic):

Learfield News   (2)
505 Hobbs Rd, Jefferson City, MO 65109
Tel.: (573) 893-7200
Web Site: http://www.learfield.com
News Syndicates
N.A.I.C.S.: 516210

Spectra Venue Management   (1)
3601 S Broad St, Philadelphia, PA 19148
Tel.: (215) 389-9477
Web Site:
    http://www.spectraexperiences.com
Commercial Facilities Maintenance Services
N.A.I.C.S.: 561210

ATALANTA SOSNOFF CAPITAL, LLC
505 5th Ave, New York, NY 10017
Tel.: (212) 867-5000   DE
Web Site:
    https://www.atalantasosnoff.com
Sales Range: $10-24.9 Million
Emp.: 50
Discretionary Investment Management, Brokerage & Other Related Services
N.A.I.C.S.: 523940
Martin T. Sosnoff (Founder)
Craig Steinberg (Pres & Dir-Res)
Kevin Kelly (CFO, COO & Chief Compliance Officer)
Richard Maresca (Sr Mng Dir)
Ted Bellis (Mng Dir-Natl Sls & Mktg)
Donn M. Goodman (Sr VP)
Morton A. Millhauser (Sr VP)
Robert Ruland (Sr VP & Portfolio Mgr)
John McMullan (Sr VP & Portfolio Mgr)
Douglas Reid (Sr VP & Portfolio Mgr)
Bill DiPietro (Sr VP & Dir-Client Svcs)
Steve Gesing (Sr VP)
Robert Ohanesian (Portfolio Mgr-Fixed Income)
Edward Killea (Sr VP)
Tonianne Russo (Asst VP)
Jerry Thunelius (Mng Dir & Sr Portfolio Mgr-Fixed Income)

Joseph V. Sileo Jr. (Mng Dir & Sr Portfolio Mgr-Fixed Income)

ATALY, INC.
5828 Johns Rd, Tampa, FL 33634
Tel.: (813) 882-0815   FL
Web Site: https://www.ataly.com
Year Founded: 1981
Sales Range: $1-9.9 Million
Emp.: 20
Embroidery, Screen Printing & Graphic Design
N.A.I.C.S.: 314999

ATAMIAN VOLKSWAGEN & HONDA, INC.
150 Main St, Tewksbury, MA 01876
Tel.: (978) 851-4356
Web Site:
    https://www.hondaatamian.com
Year Founded: 1969
Sales Range: $10-24.9 Million
Emp.: 75
Car Whslr
N.A.I.C.S.: 441110
Terry Atamian (Pres)

ATAR CAPITAL, LLC
1999 Ave of the Stars Ste 2810, Los Angeles, CA 90067
Tel.: (310) 870-0808   DE
Web Site: http://www.atarcapital.com
Year Founded: 2016
Privater Equity Firm
N.A.I.C.S.: 523999
Cyrus Nikou (Founder & Mng Partner)
Robert Lezec (Sr Mng Dir)
Stanley Huang (Mng Dir)
Vijay K Mony (Mng Dir)
T. J. McCaffrey (Dir)

Subsidiaries:

New WinCup Holdings, Inc.   (1)
55 Ivan Allen Jr Blvd NW Ste 900, Atlanta, GA 30308
Tel.: (770) 872-7614
Web Site: https://wincup.com
Holding Company; Polystyrene Foam Product Mfr
N.A.I.C.S.: 551112
Michael Winters (Pres & Chief Revenue Officer)
Brad Laporte (CEO)
Matthew Marrazza (CIO)

Pathways Health and Community Support LLC   (1)
10304 Spotsylvania Ave Ste 300, Fredericksburg, VA 22408
Tel.: (540) 710-6085
Web Site: http://www.pathways.com
Healthcare Services
N.A.I.C.S.: 624190
Joyce Montes (VP-Compliance and Regulatory Affairs)

Subsidiary (Domestic):

AmericanWork, Inc.   (2)
507 Ocean Blvd Suites 203 204 & 205, Savannah, GA 31522
Tel.: (912) 638-0350
Web Site: http://www.pathways.com
Outpatient Mental Health Services
N.A.I.C.S.: 621420
Partic Waters (COO)

Camelot Care Centers, Inc   (2)
333 W Pierce Rd Ste 175, Itasca, IL 60143-3120
Tel.: (630) 773-1985
Web Site:
    http://www.camelotcarecenters.com
Behavioral Health Services
N.A.I.C.S.: 621330
Nick Szara (Dir-Reg)
Amber Rakoczy (Dir-Compliance & QA)
Lauren White (Dir-Reg-Matteson Office)
Kathy Henke (Dir-Reg-Peoria & Springfield Office)
Penny Hurlbut (Dir-Reg-Rockford Office)

Ronica Patel (Exec Dir-State)
Shannon Pociecha (Dir-Clinical)
Jamin Wright (Mgr-Clinical)
Angela Zumbek (Dir-Clinical)
Dorothy Rhodes (Dir-Clinical)

Children's Behavioral Health, Inc.   (2)
College Park Plaza Ste 203, Johnstown, PA 15904
Tel.: (814) 262-0768
Web Site: http://www.childrensbh.com
Behavioral Health Services
N.A.I.C.S.: 621330

Choices Group, Inc.   (2)
800 S Valley View Blvd, Las Vegas, NV 89107
Tel.: (702) 252-8342
Behavioral Health Services
N.A.I.C.S.: 621330

College Community Services   (2)
4281 Katella Ave Ste 20, Los Alamitos, CA 90720
Tel.: (562) 467-5440
Web Site: http://www.pathways.com
Mental Health Services
N.A.I.C.S.: 621420
Breeann Hoerning (VP-Ops)
Gail Laporte (Dir-State)
Katherine Lee (Dir-State Clinical)
Marni Orsbern (Dir-QI & Privacy Officer)
Michelle Molnar (Dir-Billing)
Sonya Zhang (Dir-Fin)

Dockside Services, Inc.   (2)
9008 Cline Ave, Highland, IN 46322
Tel.: (219) 838-8001
Healtcare Services
N.A.I.C.S.: 524114

Family Preservation Services, Inc.   (2)
615 Jefferson Davis Hwy Ste 101, Fredericksburg, VA 22408
Tel.: (540) 710-5810
Web Site: http://fpscorp.com
Behavioral Health Services
N.A.I.C.S.: 621330
Michael Fidgeon (Pres)
Jon Morris (Dir-State)
Challen Mabry (Chief Clinical Officer)
Carla Warner (Chief Compliance Officer)
Sam Funkhouser (Dir-Mgmt-Risk)
Megan Hall (Dir-Clinical Svcs)
Tami King (Asst Dir-State)
Kyle McMahon (Asst Dir-State)
Rod McMurray (Asst Dir-State)
Mark Lester (Asst Dir-State)

Subsidiary (Domestic):

Family Preservation Services of North Carolina, Inc.   (3)
2300 Sardis Rd Ste M, Charlotte, NC 28227
Tel.: (704) 344-0491
Web Site: http://www.pathways.com
Behavioral Health Services
N.A.I.C.S.: 621330
Rick Smith (Reg VP-Pathways-Eastern Div)
Cindy Davis-Bryant (Dir-State)
Matthew Joseph (Dir-Medical)
Kevin Anders (Dir & Privacy Officer)
Carson Ojamaa (Dir-Clinical)
Krista Zappia (Dir-Ops)
Joe Yurchak (Dir-Dev)
Jada Ware (Reg Dir-Charlotte)
Derek Littlefield (Coord-Clinical-Reg)
Laurie Mills (Reg Dir)
Sara Spotila (Reg Dir)
Samantha Morrison (Dir-Clinical-Reg)

Family Preservation Services of Washington, D.C., Inc.   (3)
3341 Benning Rd NE, Washington, DC 20019
Tel.: (202) 543-0387
Web Site: http://www.pathways.com
Behavioral Health Services
N.A.I.C.S.: 621330
Roeathea Butler (Exec Dir)

Subsidiary (Domestic):

Human Resource Training, Inc.   (2)
5501 North 19th Ave, Phoenix, AZ 85015
Tel.: (602) 433-1344
Web Site: http://www.hrtaz.com
Rev.: $7,000,000

Emp.: 70
Other Management Consulting Services
N.A.I.C.S.: 541618
Dawn Wallschlaeger (Dir)
Sally Jones (CEO)

Maple Star Nevada, Inc.   (2)
050 E Flamingo Road S-107, Las Vegas, NV 89119
Tel.: (702) 733-8098
Web Site: http://www.pathways.com
Mental Health Services
N.A.I.C.S.: 621420
Thomas Criste (Dir-State)
Darlene Dufault (Dir-State)

Pathways Community Services LLC   (2)
208 S Centre St, Pottsville, PA 17901
Tel.: (570) 622-6417
Web Site: http://www.pathways.com
Mental Health Care Services
N.A.I.C.S.: 524114
Breeann Hoerning (VP-Ops)
Gail Laporte (Dir-State)
Katherine Lee (Dir-State Clinical)
Marni Orsbern (Dir-QI & Officer-Privacy)
Michelle Molnar (Dir-Billing)
Sonya Zhang (Dir-Fin)

Pathways Community Services LLC   (2)
208 S Ctr St, Pottsville, PA 17901
Tel.: (570) 628-5215
Web Site: http://pathwaysofpa.com
Behavioral Health Services
N.A.I.C.S.: 621330

Pathways of Arizona, Inc.   (2)
2830 W Glendale Ave Suite 16, Phoenix, AZ 85051
Tel.: (602) 455-4626
Web Site: http://www.pathwaysofaz.com
Behavioral Health Services
N.A.I.C.S.: 621330
Cindy Greer (CEO)

Pathways of Delaware, Inc.   (2)
101 Rogers Rd Ste 102 or 201B, Wilmington, DE 19801
Tel.: (302) 573-5073
Web Site: http://www.pathways.com
Mental Health Care Services
N.A.I.C.S.: 524114
Malik Muhammad (VP-Mid-Atlantic Reg)
Christina Watlington (Dir-State Clinical)
Gail Evans (Principal-Parkway Academy-Central)
William Fuller (Principal)

Pathways of Maine, Inc.   (2)
14 Maine St Ste 202 Box 50, Brunswick, ME 04011
Tel.: (207) 373-0620
Web Site: http://www.pathways.com
Behavioral Health Services
N.A.I.C.S.: 621330

Pathways of Massachusetts, LLC   (2)
511 E Columbus Ave, Springfield, MA 01105-2506
Tel.: (508) 753-2900
Healtcare Services
N.A.I.C.S.: 621491
Anthony Boswell (Mgr)

Pathways of Washington, Inc.   (2)
1050 N Argonne Rd. Suite 100, Spokane Valley, WA 99212
Tel.: (509) 209-8990
Web Site: http://www.pathways.com
Child Placing Agency
N.A.I.C.S.: 624410
Amika Taniguchi (Dir-State)

Unit (Domestic):

Pioneer Health Resources   (2)
545 N Benjamin Ste 185, Boise, ID 83704
Tel.: (208) 322-1026
Web Site:
    http://www.pioneerhealthresources.com
Ambulatory Health Care Services
N.A.I.C.S.: 621999

Subsidiary (Domestic):

Raystown Developmental Services, Inc.   (2)

710 Mt Vernon Ave, Huntingdon, PA 16652
Tel.: (814) 643-0366
Web Site: http://www.rdsinc.org
Residential Management Services
N.A.I.C.S.: 623990

The ReDCo Group, Inc. (2)
210 S Ctr St, Pottsville, PA 17901
Tel.: (570) 628-5215
Web Site: http://www.redcogrp.com
Behavioral Health Services
N.A.I.C.S.: 524114
Virginia Schenk *(COO & Asst Dir-State)*
Sharon Angelo *(VP-Workforce Investment Networks)*
Jill Bainbridge *(Exec Dir-Behavioral Health Svcs)*
Timothy Sohosky *(VP-Developmental Support Svcs)*
Elizabeth Simpson *(Exec Dir)*
Melissa Woznicki-Marshall *(VP-Behavioral Health Rehabilitative Svcs)*

Transitional Family Services, Inc. (2)
3643 Walton Way Extension Ste 4, Atlanta, GA 30909
Tel.: (706) 364-1404
Web Site: http://www.tfsga.org
Family Preservation Services
N.A.I.C.S.: 624190
Nicole Aldred *(Dir-State)*
Faye Anders *(Mgr-Reg)*
Dawn Peebles *(Dir-Clinical)*
Bernadette Vipond *(Office Mgr)*
Patrick Waters *(COO)*

Recycling & Waste Solutions, LLC (1)
3 Dickinson Dr 4 Bldg, Chadds Ford, PA 19317
Tel.: (610) 358-3400
Web Site: http://recyclingwaste.com
Waste Management Services
N.A.I.C.S.: 562998
Jeff Roney *(VP-Ops)*

ATASCOSA NATIONAL BANK
1525 W Oaklawn Rd, Pleasanton, TX 78064
Tel.: (830) 569-2507 TX
Web Site:
 https://www.atascosabank.com
Year Founded: 1982
Sales Range: $25-49.9 Million
Emp.: 13
Commericial Banking
N.A.I.C.S.: 522110
Buddy Bingham *(Pres)*

ATC GROUP, INC.
101 Parker Dr, Andover, OH 44003
Tel.: (440) 293-4064 OH
Web Site: https://www.atc-lighting-plastics.com
Year Founded: 1984
Sales Range: $10-24.9 Million
Emp.: 250
Vehicular Lighting Equipment
N.A.I.C.S.: 336320
Seymour S. Stein *(Pres)*

Subsidiaries:

ATC Lighting & Plastics Inc. (1)
101 Parker Dr, Andover, OH 44003
Tel.: (440) 293-4064
Web Site: http://www.atc-lighting-plastics.com
Sales Range: $10-24.9 Million
Emp.: 35
Vehicular Lighting Equipment Mfr
N.A.I.C.S.: 336320
Seymour S. Stein *(Pres)*

ATC Nymold Corporation (1)
101 Parker Dr, Andover, OH 44003
Tel.: (440) 293-4064
Web Site:
 http://www.atc-lighting-plastics.com
Rev.: $6,900,000
Emp.: 50
Plastics Products
N.A.I.C.S.: 326199

Advanced Medical Systems Inc. (1)

101 Parker Dr, Andover, OH 44003 **(100%)**
Tel.: (440) 293-4064
Sales Range: $10-24.9 Million
Emp.: 2
X-Ray Apparatus & Tubes
N.A.I.C.S.: 334517

Advanced Technology Corp. (1)
101 Parker Dr, Andover, OH 44003-9456 **(100%)**
Tel.: (440) 293-4064
Web Site:
 http://www.atc-lighting-plastics.com
Rev.: $11,300,000
Emp.: 50
Vehicular Lighting Equipment
N.A.I.C.S.: 336320
Sherry Epstein *(Treas)*

KD Lamp Co (1)
101 Parker Dr, Andover, OH 44003
Tel.: (440) 293-4064
Emp.: 50
Lighting Equipment Mfr
N.A.I.C.S.: 335139

ATC HEALTHCARE, INC.
1983 Marcus Ave Ste E122, Lake Success, NY 11042-1016
Tel.: (516) 750-1600 DE
Web Site:
 https://www.atchealthcare.com
Year Founded: 1982
Sales Range: $75-99.9 Million
Emp.: 27
Temporary Personnel Services
N.A.I.C.S.: 561311
Stephen Savitsky *(Chm & Pres)*
David Savitsky *(CEO)*

Subsidiaries:

ATC Healthcare Services, Inc. (1)
1983 Marcus Ave, New Hyde Park, NY 11042-1029
Tel.: (516) 750-1600
Web Site: http://www.atchealthcare.com
Healthcare Personnel Services
N.A.I.C.S.: 561311
Stephen Savitsky *(Co-Founder, Chm & Pres)*
Dorika M. Beckett *(CEO)*

ATC MANAGEMENT INC.
N19 W234 N 2000 RidgeView Pkwy court, Waukesha, WI 53188-1000
Tel.: (262) 506-6700 WI
Web Site: https://www.atcllc.com
Emp.: 400
Electric Transmission & Gas Line Inspection Services Administration Organization
N.A.I.C.S.: 926130
John Procario *(Chm, Pres & CEO)*
Catherine E. Heigel *(Gen Counsel)*
Mike Rowe *(Chm, Pres & CEO)*

Subsidiaries:

American Transmission Company LLC (1)
PO Box 47, Waukesha, WI 53187-0047
Tel.: (262) 506-6700
Web Site: https://www.atcllc.com
Sales Range: $550-599.9 Million
Electric Transmission & Gas Line Inspection Services
N.A.I.C.S.: 541990
William Marsan *(Gen Counsel, Sec & Exec VP)*
Teresa Mogensen *(CEO)*
Jared Winters *(Sr VP- &)*
Eric Lundberg *(Treas)*
Debbie Masbruch *(VP-Supply Chain &)*
Ellen Nowak *(VP- &)*
Jake Stricker *(VP-Audit, Risk Management, and Compliance)*

ATC VENTURE GROUP INC.
5929 Baker Rd Ste 400, Minnetonka, MN 55345-5940
Tel.: (952) 215-3100 NV
Web Site: http://www.atcvg.com

Year Founded: 1981
Sales Range: $1-9.9 Million
Emp.: 92
Recreational & Power Sports Products Mfr & Sales
N.A.I.C.S.: 336991
Robert Davis *(Chm, CEO, CFO, COO, Treas & Sec)*

ATCO INCORPORATED
3815 N Osprey Ave, Sarasota, FL 34234
Tel.: (941) 355-7619
Sales Range: $10-24.9 Million
Emp.: 11
Petroleum Bulk Stations
N.A.I.C.S.: 424710
Alan Elwell *(Pres)*
Mark Hesser *(VP)*

ATCO INTERNATIONAL CORPORATION
1401 Barclay Cir SE, Marietta, GA 30060
Tel.: (770) 424-7550 GA
Web Site: http://www.atco-intl.com
Year Founded: 1961
Sales Range: $25-49.9 Million
Emp.: 135
Mfr of Water Treating Compounds & Specialty Chemicals
N.A.I.C.S.: 325998
Jerry Tillem *(CEO)*
Diane Milton *(VP)*
Teesha Evans *(Acct Exec)*

ATCOM, INC.
4920 S Alston Ave, Durham, NC 27713-4423
Tel.: (919) 314-1003 NC
Web Site: https://www.atcombts.com
Year Founded: 1979
Sales Range: $75-99.9 Million
Emp.: 49
Telecommunication Sales, Design & Service
N.A.I.C.S.: 238210
David Finch *(CEO)*
Sheldon Yarborough *(VP-Fin)*

ATCOMM PUBLISHING CORP.
3423 Piedmont Rd NE Ste 400, Atlanta, GA 30305
Tel.: (404) 249-1750
Web Site: http://www.atlanta.net
Sales Range: $1-9.9 Million
Emp.: 5
In House Advertising Agency
N.A.I.C.S.: 541810
Julie Minear *(Publr)*

ATD-AMERICAN CO. INC.
135 Greenwood Ave, Wyncote, PA 19095-1325
Tel.: (215) 576-1000 PA
Web Site: http://www.atd.com
Year Founded: 1931
Sales Range: $25-49.9 Million
Emp.: 142
Furniture, Textile, Office Products, Safety & Security & Police Items
N.A.I.C.S.: 313210
Janet Wischnia *(Pres)*
Ken Spector *(Mgr-Textile)*
Laurie Sawyer *(Dir-Art)*
Arnold Zaslow *(Exec VP)*

ATEC, INC.
12600 Executive Dr, Stafford, TX 77477
Tel.: (281) 276-2700
Web Site: https://www.atec.com
Year Founded: 1953
Emp.: 200

Design, Manufacturing, Construction & Maintenance of Test Stands for Aerospace & Energy Industry
N.A.I.C.S.: 332311
Howard Lederer *(Chm & CEO)*
Chris Elkins *(CFO & Dir-Fin & Controls)*

Subsidiaries:

Celtech Corp. (1)
1300 Terminal Dr, Carlsbad, NM 88220
Tel.: (575) 887-2044
Web Site: http://www.celtech.com
Sales Range: $1-9.9 Million
Emp.: 50
Jet Engine Testing Structures Mfr
N.A.I.C.S.: 332311
Tina Licon *(Coord-Admin)*

Hager Machine & Tool Inc. (1)
1303 Hugh Rd, Houston, TX 77067
Tel.: (281) 872-6393
Web Site: http://www.hagermachine.com
Sales Range: $1-9.9 Million
Emp.: 10
Precisioned Machined Products Mfr
N.A.I.C.S.: 332710
Greg Anspach *(Gen Mgr & Mgr-Sls)*

Vital Link, Inc. (1)
914 Bartlett Rd, Sealy, TX 77474
Tel.: (979) 885-4181
Web Site: http://www.vitallinkinc.com
Sales Range: $1-9.9 Million
Emp.: 100
Prefabricated Metal Building & Component Mfr
N.A.I.C.S.: 332311
Basil Greenwood *(Mgr-Ops)*
A. C. Kujawa *(VP-Contracts)*
Johnny Gunnels *(VP-Mfg & Field Ops)*
Guy Sessions *(Mgr-Sls)*
Russell Hankins *(Mgr-QA)*

ATEECO, INC.
600 E Center St, Shenandoah, PA 17976-0606
Tel.: (570) 462-2745
Web Site: http://www.pierogies.com
Sales Range: $100-124.9 Million
Emp.: 241
Frozen Food Mfr
N.A.I.C.S.: 311412
Frank Kass *(Mgr-Sanitation)*

ATEK COMPANIES, INC.
10025 Valley View Rd Ste 190, Eden Prairie, MN 55344
Tel.: (763) 553-7700 MN
Web Site: https://atekcompanies.com
Year Founded: 2008
Sales Range: $25-49.9 Million
Emp.: 10
Holding Company
N.A.I.C.S.: 551112
Kay Phillips *(Owner)*
Mark Osmanski *(Pres & CEO)*
Bill Bieber *(Founder)*
Jim Voiss *(Sec & Treas)*
Julie Mork *(VP-HR)*
Kevin Pollman *(CFO)*

Subsidiaries:

ATEK Access Technologies, LLC (1)
210 NE 10th Ave, Brainerd, MN 56401
Tel.: (218) 829-1481
Web Site: http://www.atekcompanies.com
Contract Manufacturing & Assembly Services
N.A.I.C.S.: 332710
Kay Phillips *(Owner)*
Julie Mork *(VP-HR)*
Mark Osmanski *(Pres & CEO)*
Kevin Pollman *(CFO)*
Jim Voiss *(Treas & Sec)*

ATEK Metal Technologies, LLC (1)
2205 Rusty Kennedy Rd, New Hampton, IA 50659
Tel.: (641) 394-1700
Web Site:
 http://www.atekmetaltechnologies.com

ATEK Companies, Inc.—(Continued)

Sales Range: $25-49.9 Million
Aluminum Casting Mfr
N.A.I.C.S.: 331523
Bruce Diiro (Dir-Quality)
John Cowan (VP-Engrg & Bus Dev)
Teresa Weber (Dir-HR)
Mark Osmanski (CEO)
Joe Brown (Pres)

ATEL CAPITAL GROUP

600 Montgomery St 9th Fl, San Francisco, CA 94111
Tel.: (415) 989-8800
Web Site: https://www.atel.com
Rev.: $20,083,667
Emp.: 60
Machinery & Equipment Finance Leasing
N.A.I.C.S.: 532490
Dean Cash (Pres & CEO)
Paritosh K. Choksi (CFO, COO & Exec VP)
Vasco Morais (Gen Counsel, Sec & Exec VP)
Russ Wilder (Chief Credit Officer & Exec VP)
Mari Lynch (Sr VP-HR)
Jim Ryan (VP)
Samuel Schussler (Chief Acctg Officer & Sr VP)
Leesa Nichols (Exec VP & Mgr-Sls-Natl)
Angelo Pirri (Dir-Institutional Sls)
Timothy Holmes (Dir-Institutional Sls-Fund Raising Efforts)

Subsidiaries:

ATEL Financial Services (1)
600 Montgomery St 9th Fl, San Francisco, CA 94111
Tel.: (415) 989-8800
Web Site: http://www.atel.com
Machinery & Equipment Lease Financing Services
N.A.I.C.S.: 522220
Bill Bullock (Sr VP-Direct Origination & Capital Markets)

Affiliate (Domestic):

ATEL 14, LLC (2)
The Transamerica Pyramid 600 Montgomery St 9th Fl, San Francisco, CA 94111
Tel.: (415) 989-8800
Web Site: http://www.atel.com
Rev.: $2,502,000
Assets: $10,342,000
Liabilities: $2,367,000
Net Worth: $7,975,000
Earnings: ($1,433,000)
Fiscal Year-end: 12/31/2021
Investment Fund Services; Equipment Leasing & Financing Services
N.A.I.C.S.: 523999
Dean Cash (Chm, Pres & CEO)

ATEL 15, LLC (2)
The Transamerica Pyramid 600 Montgomery St 9th Fl, San Francisco, CA 94111
Tel.: (415) 989-8800
Rev.: $4,111,000
Assets: $16,690,000
Liabilities: $3,442,000
Net Worth: $13,248,000
Earnings: ($872,000)
Fiscal Year-end: 12/31/2020
Investment Services
N.A.I.C.S.: 523999
Dean Cash (Chm, Pres & CEO)

Subsidiary (Domestic):

ATEL Equipment Corporation (2)
600 Montgomery St 9th Fl, San Francisco, CA 94111
Tel.: (415) 989-8800
Web Site: http://www.atel.com
Equipment Asset Management Services
N.A.I.C.S.: 523940
Thomas P. Monroe Jr. (Sr VP)

ATEL Investor Services (2)
3535 S Tamarac Dr, Denver, CO 80237
Tel.: (303) 221-6520

Web Site: http://www.atel.com
Rev.: $360,000
Emp.: 6
Investment Advisory Services
N.A.I.C.S.: 523940
Vasco Morais (Gen Counsel, Sec & Exec VP)

ATEL Securities Corporation (2)
600 Montgomery St 9th Fl, San Francisco, CA 94111
Tel.: (415) 989-8800
Web Site: http://www.atel.com
Rev.: $4,456,880
Securities Brokerage & Investment Banking Services
N.A.I.C.S.: 523150
Joseph Laganza (Sr VP-Natl Accts)
Craig Fisk (VP-RIA)
Audrey Kamin (VP-Southwest)
Mathew Travis (VP-Northwest)
Audrey Stein (Dir-Natl Accts)

ATEL Growth Capital Fund 8, LLC (1)
The Transamerica Pyramid 600 Montogomery St 9th Fl, San Francisco, CA 94111
Tel.: (415) 989-8800
Web Site: http://www.atel.com
Rev.: $541,000
Assets: $1,501,000
Liabilities: $119,000
Net Worth: $1,382,000
Earnings: $106,000
Fiscal Year-end: 12/31/2019
Investment Services
N.A.I.C.S.: 523999
Dean L. Cash (Chm, Pres & CEO)

ATEL Leasing Corporation (1)
600 Montana St 94, San Francisco, CA 94111
Tel.: (415) 989-8800
Web Site: http://www.atel.com
Vehicle & Equipment Leasing Services
N.A.I.C.S.: 532411
Bill Bullock (Sr VP & Mgr-Natl Sls)
Ken Fosina (Exec VP)
Taylor Sandoval (VP-Lease Originations)
Steven Spivey (Sr VP-Capital Markets-Maryland)

ATEL Ventures, Inc. (1)
600 Montgomery St 9th Fl, San Francisco, CA 94111
Tel.: (800) 543-2835
Web Site: http://www.atel.com
Equity Investment Firm
N.A.I.C.S.: 523999
Steven Rea (Pres)

ATERIAN INVESTMENT MANAGEMENT, L.P.

550 5th Ave 8th Fl, New York, NY 10036
Tel.: (646) 432-4405   DE
Web Site: https://www.aterianpartners.com
Year Founded: 2009
Investment Management Service
N.A.I.C.S.: 523999
Brandon Bethea (Co-Founder & Partner)
Michael Fieldstone (Co-Founder & Partner)
Christopher H. Thomas (Co-Founder & Partner)
Joshua Ciampa (Mng Dir)
Daniel Phan (Mng Dir)
Christian Remmel (Dir-Bus Dev)
Daniel Krasnow (Principal)
Jillian Boidy (CFO & Chief Compliance Officer)
Heidy Estrada (Office Mgr)
Martins Trautmanis (VP)

Subsidiaries:

Allentown, Inc. (1)
165 Route 526, Allentown, NJ 08501
Tel.: (609) 259-7951
Web Site: http://www.allentowninc.com
Sales Range: $1-9.9 Million
Emp.: 100
Sheet Metal Work Mfg

N.A.I.C.S.: 332322

Subsidiary (Domestic):

ClorDiSys Solutions Inc. (2)
50 Tannery Rd Ste #1, Branchburg, NJ 08876
Tel.: (908) 236-4100
Web Site: http://www.clordisys.com
Sales Range: $1-9.9 Million
Emp.: 25
Miscellaneous General Purpose Machinery Mfr
N.A.I.C.S.: 333998
Paul Lorcheim (Co-Founder & Dir)
Jennifer Czarneski (Pres)

Backyard Leisure Holdings, Inc. (1)
3001 N Rouse Ave, Pittsburg, KS 66762
Web Site: http://www.swingsetsonline.com
Doll, Toy & Game Mfr
N.A.I.C.S.: 339930
Ron Scripsick (CEO)

Bright International, LLC (1)
1301 W Industrial Dr, Coolidge, AZ 85228
Tel.: (520) 723-8001
Web Site: http://www.brightcorp.us
Rev.: $3,600,000
Emp.: 60
Engineering Services Mfg Toilet Preparations Whol Service Establishment Equipment
N.A.I.C.S.: 541330
Cal Bibars (Treas & VP)

Subsidiary (Domestic):

Bocchi Laboratories, Inc. (2)
26455 Ruether Ave, Santa Clarita, CA 91350-2621
Tel.: (661) 252-3807
Web Site: http://www.bocchilabs.com
Beauty Care & OTC Private Label Products Contract Mfr
N.A.I.C.S.: 325620
Joe Perider (CEO)
Shelly Cazan (Mgr-HR)
Jason McLarty (Mgr-Compounding)
Albert Lising (Dir-Ops)

Contract Pharmaceuticals Limited (1)
7600 Danbro Crescent, Mississauga, L5N 6L6, ON, Canada
Tel.: (905) 821-7600
Web Site: https://www.cplltd.com
Pharmaceuticals Product Mfr
N.A.I.C.S.: 325412
Jan Sahai (CEO)
Caitlin Wege (Exec Chm)
John Wilkening (VP)
Shannon Meijer (VP)
Colin Watson (VP)
Cameron Carvalho (VP)

Eaglestone, LLC (1)
370 Lexington Ave Ste 606, New York, NY 10017
Web Site: http://www.eaglestoneny.com
Holding Company
N.A.I.C.S.: 551112
Andru Coren (CEO)

Holding (Domestic):

Commonwealth Electrical Technologies, Inc. (2)
125 Blackstone River Rd, Worcester, MA 01607-1491
Tel.: (508) 421-6600
Web Site: http://www.comelectrical.com
Electrical Contractor
N.A.I.C.S.: 238210
John P. Duquette Sr. (Pres)

Hain Pure Protein Corporation (1)
304 S Water St, New Oxford, PA 17350
Poultry Processing
N.A.I.C.S.: 311615
Jay Lieberman (CFO & COO)
Jeff Brown (CEO)

Kane Infrastructure Services Holdings, LLC (1)
7047 E Greenway Pkwy Ste 455, Scottsdale, AZ 85254
Tel.: (602) 805-1750
Web Site: https://kane.com

Structured Cabling & Utility Construction Services
N.A.I.C.S.: 517810
John Wozniak (CEO)

Subsidiary (Domestic):

Net100 Ltd. (2)
3675 Concorde Pkwy Ste 800, Chantilly, VA 20151
Tel.: (703) 818-8606
Web Site: http://www.net100ltd.com
Rev.: $15,500,000
Emp.: 190
Communication Service
N.A.I.C.S.: 238210
Rodney W. Cannon (Pres)
William J. Paris (VP)
Ron Langowski (Acct Mgr)
Michael Whalen (Mgr-Ops-Baltimore)

Outlook Group Corp. (1)
1180 American Dr, Neenah, WI 54956-1306
Tel.: (920) 722-2333
Web Site: https://www.outlookgroup.com
Sales Range: $75-99.9 Million
Emp.: 300
Holding Company; Printing, Packaging & Direct Marketing Services; Owned by Milestone Partners & by John Hancock Life Insurance Company
N.A.I.C.S.: 561910
Sherry Olig (Mgr-Mktg)
Brian Conrad (Mgr-Market-Labels)

Pioneer Metal Finishing LLC (1)
486 Globe Ave, Green Bay, WI 54304
Tel.: (920) 499-6996
Web Site: http://www.pioneermetal.com
Sales Range: $25-49.9 Million
Emp.: 650
Plating & Polishing Services
N.A.I.C.S.: 332813
Scott Turner (VP-Tech)
Steve King (CFO)
Bob Pyle (CEO)
Christopher Knuth (Plant Mgr)
Dale Seidl (Engr-Sls)
Josh Engels (Plant Mgr)

Subsidiary (Domestic):

Electrochem Solutions, LLC (2)
32500 Central Ave, Union City, CA 94587
Tel.: (510) 476-1840
Web Site: http://www.electro-chem.com
Electroplating, Plating, Polishing, Anodizing & Coloring
N.A.I.C.S.: 332813
David Rossiter (Pres & CEO)
Janet Nielsen (Mgr-Sls)
Frank Ruano (Mgr-Ops)

Indianhead Plating, Inc. (2)
1610 Palmer St, Chippewa Falls, WI 54729
Tel.: (715) 723-8558
Web Site: http://www.indianheadplating.com
Rev.: $3,300,000
Emp.: 92
Fiscal Year-end: 12/31/2009
Electroplating, Plating, Polishing, Anodizing & Coloring
N.A.I.C.S.: 332813
John Altmann (Pres)

Metal Prep Technology, Inc. (2)
5650 W Jefferson Ave, Detroit, MI 48209
Tel.: (313) 843-2890
Plating & Polishing Services
N.A.I.C.S.: 332813

Pilkington Metal Finishing LLC (2)
1225 Legacy View St, Salt Lake City, UT 84104
Tel.: (801) 972-2146
Web Site: http://www.pilkingtonanodizing.com
Electroplating, Plating, Polishing, Anodizing & Coloring
N.A.I.C.S.: 332813
Van Pilkington (Pres)
Michael McNally (Coord-Delivery)

Plant (Domestic):

Pioneer Metal Finishing LLC - Anodizing & Plating Facility (2)
19005 SW 125th Ct, Tualatin, OR 97062
Tel.: (503) 692-4202
Web Site: http://www.pioneermetal.com
Plating & Polishing Services

N.A.I.C.S.: 332813
Rob Abfall (VP-Ops-Finishing)

Division (Domestic):

Pioneer Metal Finishing LLC - Gaffney Division   (2)
254 Henderson St, Gaffney, SC 29341
Tel.: (864) 488-1210
Plating & Polishing Services
N.A.I.C.S.: 332813

Pioneer Metal Finishing LLC - Minneapolis Division   (2)
4800 Quebec Ave N, Minneapolis, MN 55428
Tel.: (612) 588-0855
Web Site: http://www.pioneermetal.com
Emp.: 90
Plating & Polishing Services
N.A.I.C.S.: 332813
Chris Knuth (Plant Mgr)

Pioneer Metal Finishing LLC - Monroe Division   (2)
525 Ternes Dr, Monroe, MI 48162
Tel.: (888) 217-7634
Plating & Polishing Services
N.A.I.C.S.: 332813

Pioneer Metal Finishing LLC - Oshkosh Division   (2)
480 Pilgrim Way Ste 1400, Green Bay, WI 54304
Tel.: (920) 235-2124
Plating & Polishing Services
N.A.I.C.S.: 332813

Pioneer Metal Finishing LLC - South Bend Division   (2)
2424 N Foundation Dr, South Bend, IN 46628
Tel.: (574) 287-7239
Plating & Polishing Services
N.A.I.C.S.: 332813

Subsidiary (Domestic):

Superior Metal Finishing, Inc.   (2)
18240 SW 100th Ct, Tualatin, OR 97062
Tel.: (503) 692-4252
Web Site:
    http://www.superiormetalfinishing.com
Sales Range: $10-24.9 Million
Emp.: 20
Component Finishing Services
N.A.I.C.S.: 332813

The Step2 Company LLC   (1)
10010 Aurora-Hudson Rd, Streetsboro, OH 44241
Tel.: (330) 656-0440
Web Site: http://www.step2company.com
Children Toy Products Mfr
N.A.I.C.S.: 326199

Subsidiary (Domestic):

Infantino, LLC   (2)
4920 Carroll Canyon Rd Ste 200, San Diego, CA 92121
Tel.: (858) 457-9797
Web Site: http://www.infantino.com
Juvenile Accessories Whslr
N.A.I.C.S.: 423990
Wendy Mclean (Chief Bus Dev Officer & VP-Sls)
Colette Cosky (VP-Mktg & Creative)

U.S. Zinc Corporation   (1)
6020 Esperson St, Houston, TX 77011-2330
Tel.: (713) 926-1705
Web Site: http://www.uszinc.com
Zinc Metal Products Mfr
N.A.I.C.S.: 331420
Tracy Baugh (Pres & CEO)
Francisco Moriera (VP-Fin)

Vander-Bend Manufacturing, LLC   (1)
2701 Orchard Pkwy, San Jose, CA 95134
Tel.: (408) 245-5150
Web Site: http://www.vander-bend.com
Precision Machining, Sheet Metal Fabrication & Electro-Mechanical Assembly Services
N.A.I.C.S.: 811210
Greg Biggs (CEO)
Aaron Bennett (Pres-TMK)

HT Myburg (Dir-Engrg)
Ted Perry (Dir-Mfg)
Sigal Pashinski (Dir-quality)
Tom Spies (Dir-Assembly)
Holly Bugaj (Dir-HR)
Nate Spang (CFO)
Jonathan Iddings (COO)
Brett Catterall (Dir-Supply Chain)
Noah Rodriguez (Dir-IT)

Subsidiary (Domestic):

J.L. Haley Enterprises, Inc.   (2)
3510 Luyung Dr, Rancho Cordova, CA 95742
Tel.: (916) 631-6375
Web Site: http://www.jlhaleyinc.com
Miscellaneous Fabricated Metal Product Mfr
N.A.I.C.S.: 332999
Steven Butts (Gen Mgr)
Steven Butts (Gen Mgr)

Omni Components Corp.   (2)
46 River Rd, Hudson, NH 03051
Tel.: (603) 882-4467
Web Site: http://www.omnicomponents.com
Sales Range: $1-9.9 Million
Emp.: 52
Precision Turned Product Mfr
N.A.I.C.S.: 332721
William R. Holka (Chm & Pres)
Larry Cuneo (VP-Sls & Customer Svc)
Shelby Overbeck (COO & VP)
Frank Stone Jr. (CEO & Exec VP)

TMK Manufacturing, Inc.   (2)
386 Laurelwood Rd, Santa Clara, CA 95054
Tel.: (408) 844-8289
Web Site: http://www.tmk-inc.com
Special Die & Tool, Die Set, Jig & Fixture Mfr
N.A.I.C.S.: 333514
Aaron Bennett (Pres)
Israel Sanchez (VP-Ops)

Xpress Global Systems, LLC   (1)
6137 Shallowford Rd, Chattanooga, TN 37421
Tel.: (844) 947-7447
Web Site: http://www.xgsi.com
Specialized Freight Trucking Services
N.A.I.C.S.: 484230
Dale Davis (COO)
Dan Martin (CEO)
Roger Silva (CFO)

ATF, INC.
3550 W Pratt Ave, Lincolnwood, IL 60712-3745
Tel.: (847) 677-1300   DE
Web Site: https://www.atf-inc.com
Year Founded: 1946
Sales Range: $50-74.9 Million
Emp.: 240
Screws, Bolts, Rivets, Metal Components & Assembly Mfr
N.A.I.C.S.: 332722
Donald E. Surber (CEO)
Lauren Wilson (Dir-HR)

Subsidiaries:

ATF Aerospace LLC   (1)
2609 N Ogden Ste 101, Mesa, AZ 85215
Tel.: (480) 218-0918
Web Site: http://www.atfaerospace.com
Aircraft Parts Distr
N.A.I.C.S.: 423860
Jim Costello (Mgr-Program)

ATG TITLE
11320 Random Hills Rd Ste 120, Fairfax, VA 22030
Tel.: (703) 934-2100
Web Site: https://www.atgtitle.com
Year Founded: 2008
Sales Range: $1-9.9 Million
Emp.: 60
Real Estate Title & Closing Services
N.A.I.C.S.: 531210
Mo Choumil (Pres & Founder)

ATH POWER CONSULTING CORPORATION
100 Burtt Rd, Andover, MA 01810

Tel.: (978) 474-6464
Web Site: http://www.athpower.com
Year Founded: 1997
Sales Range: $1-9.9 Million
Emp.: 26
Market Research, Mystery Shopping, Employee Training & Strategic Planning Consulting Services
N.A.I.C.S.: 541611
Francis J. Aloi (Pres & CEO)

ATHENA HEALTH CARE SYSTEMS
135 South Rd, Farmington, CT 06032
Tel.: (860) 751-3900
Web Site:
    https://www.athenahealthcare.com
Year Founded: 1984
Sales Range: $10-24.9 Million
Emp.: 50
Nursing Home & Personal Care Facility Manager
N.A.I.C.S.: 561110
Lawrence G. Santilli (Pres & CEO)

Subsidiaries:

Laurel Ridge Health Care Center   (1)
642 Danbury Rd, Ridgefield, CT 06877
Tel.: (203) 438-8226
Web Site: http://www.athenahealthcare.com
Nursing Home Operator
N.A.I.C.S.: 621498
Thora Perkins (Dir-Recreation)

ATHENA MANUFACTURING, LP.
15900 Bratton Ln, Austin, TX 78728
Tel.: (512) 928-2693
Web Site:
    https://www.athenamfg.com
Year Founded: 2000
Sales Range: $10-24.9 Million
Emp.: 100
Machine Shop Operator
N.A.I.C.S.: 332710
Bill Johnson (Pres)
John Newman (CFO)
Gary Payne (Mgr-Sls-Aerospace Products)
Javier Ortiz (Supvr-Mfg Specialist & Fab Shop Engrg)

ATHENIAN VENTURE PARTNERS LP
340 West State St Unit 29, Athens, OH 45701
Tel.: (614) 360-1155
Web Site: http://www.athenianvp.com
Year Founded: 1997
Rev.: $105,000,000
Emp.: 14
Venture Capital
N.A.I.C.S.: 523999
Karl O. Elderkin (Founder & Mng Partner)
Francois Helou (Sr Partner)
Mary A. Strother (Mng Dir-IR)

ATHENIUM ANALYTICS LLC
616 H Street NW 400, Washington, DC 20001   DE
Web Site: http://www.athenium.com
Year Founded: 2005
Weather Analytics Software Publisher
N.A.I.C.S.: 513210
Beverly Parker (Pres & COO)
Bill Pardue (Co-Founder, Chm & CEO)
Jordan Foley (Chief Strategy Officer)
Ellen Cousins (Chief Science & Tech Officer)
Audra Ryan (CFO)
Susan Grady (Exec VP-Client Solutions)
Jake Gerber (Sr VP-Pro Svcs)
Kyle Davis (VP-Corp Dev)

Cyrena-Marie Arnold (VP-Customer Success)
Ganesh Kannan (Sr Dir-Engrg)
Lindsay Gray (VP-Earth Sciences)
Ashley Deveny (VP-Product & Content Dev)

Subsidiaries:

Athenium, LLC   (1)
75 3rd Ave 2nd Fl, Waltham, MA 02451
Tel.: (781) 250-1720
Web Site: http://www.athenium.com
Insurance Claims & Underwriting Assessment Software Publisher
N.A.I.C.S.: 513210

ATHENS ADMINISTRATORS
2552 Stanwell Dr, Concord, CA 94520-4851
Tel.: (866) 482-3535
Web Site:
    http://www.athensadmin.com
Year Founded: 1976
Insurance Agencies & Brokerages
N.A.I.C.S.: 524210
James C. Jenkins (Pres)
Douglas Gibb (Exec VP-Workers Compensation)
Guy Mastrangelo (Exec VP-Programs)
Janet McClain (Exec VP-HR)
Michael Landa (Exec VP-Acct Mgmt & Bus Dev)
Raffy Daghlian (Exec VP-Programs)

ATHENS FOODS, INC.
13600 Snow Rd, Cleveland, OH 44142-2596
Tel.: (216) 430-3456
Web Site:
    https://www.athensfoods.com
Year Founded: 1958
Sales Range: $25-49.9 Million
Emp.: 170
Fillo Dough Product Mfr & Distr
N.A.I.C.S.: 311813
Robert Tansing (Mgr-Fin)
Candy Janes (Dir-R&D)
Bill Buckingham (VP-Sls & Mktg)
Jeff Swint (VP-Ops)
Pat Shrimpton (Mgr-HR)

ATHENS PAPER COMPANY, INC.
1898 Elm Tree Dr, Nashville, TN 37210-3727
Tel.: (615) 889-7900   TN
Web Site:
    https://www.athenspaper.com
Year Founded: 1952
Sales Range: $300-349.9 Million
Emp.: 300
Tape Distr
N.A.I.C.S.: 424110
Harold Sparks (CFO)
Mark Griffin (Pres)
W. Donald Jenkins Jr. (Chm & CEO)

Subsidiaries:

Athens Paper Co.   (1)
605 Best Friend Ct Ste 600, Norcross, GA 30071
Tel.: (404) 696-8900
Web Site: http://www.athenspaper.com
Sales Range: $25-49.9 Million
Emp.: 60
Fine Paper Sales
N.A.I.C.S.: 424110
Bill Blair (Gen Mgr)

Athens Paper Co.   (1)
7925 National Tpke, Louisville, KY 40214-4901   (100%)
Tel.: (502) 361-3800
Web Site: http://www.athenspaper.com
Emp.: 12
Wholesale Paper Distributor
N.A.I.C.S.: 424110
Barry Lugar (Division Mgr)

Athens Paper Company, Inc.—(Continued)

Athens Paper Co. - Distribution **(1)**
2005 Amnicola Hwy, Chattanooga, TN
37406-2304   **(100%)**
Tel.: (423) 493-5900
Web Site: http://www.athenspaper.com
Sales Range: $25-49.9 Million
Emp.: 30
Wholesale Paper Distributor
N.A.I.C.S.: 424110

ATHENS SEED COMPANY
63 Depot St, Watkinsville, GA 30677
Tel.: (706) 769-0828
Sales Range: $10-24.9 Million
Emp.: 25
Farm Supplies
N.A.I.C.S.: 424910
James R. Willis *(Pres)*

ATHENS UTILITY BOARD
100 New Englewood Rd, Athens, TN
37303
Tel.: (423) 745-4501
Web Site: https://www.aub.org
Rev.: $17,700,000
Emp.: 100
Natural Gas Distribution
N.A.I.C.S.: 221210
Eric Newberry *(Gen Mgr)*

ATHERONOVA INC.
2301 Dupont Dr Ste 525, Irvine, CA
92612
Tel.: (949) 476-1100   DE
Web Site: http://www.atheronova.com
Year Founded: 1997
Sales Range: Less than $1 Million
Emp.: 3
Pharmaceuticals Mfr
N.A.I.C.S.: 325412
Thomas W. Gardner *(Chm, Pres &
CEO)*
Mark Selawski *(CFO & Sec)*
Balbir S. Brar *(Dir-Cosmeceutical
Dev)*
Randolph M. Johnson *(COO)*
Lisa A. Bauman *(Exec Dir-Clinical
Ops)*
Mark K. Wedel *(Chief Medical Officer
& Sr VP-Clinical Affairs)*
Mark K. Wedel *(Chief Medical Officer
& Sr VP-Clinical Affairs)*

ATHERTON BAPTIST HOMES
214 S Atlantic Blvd, Alhambra, CA
91801
Tel.: (626) 289-4178   CA
Web Site: https://www.abh.org
Year Founded: 1914
Sales Range: $10-24.9 Million
Emp.: 297
Continuing Care Retirement Community Operator
N.A.I.C.S.: 623311
Catherine C. Griffin *(Dir-Nursing)*
Willis R. Hull III *(Dir-Sls)*

ATHLEISURE INC.
2081 Las Parmas Dr, Carlsbad, CA
92011
Tel.: (760) 476-9201
Web Site: http://www.sundiego.com
Sales Range: $10-24.9 Million
Emp.: 155
Sports Apparel
N.A.I.C.S.: 458110
Michael Leighty *(Asst Mgr)*

**ATHLETES' PERFORMANCE,
INC.**
2629 E Rose Garden Ln, Phoenix,
AZ 85050
Tel.: (480) 449-9000   DE
Web Site: http://www.teamexos.com
Year Founded: 1999
Emp.: 4,500

Training, Nutrition & Physical Therapy
Services
N.A.I.C.S.: 713940
Mark Verstegen *(Founder & Pres)*
Jon Zerden *(CTO)*
Dan Burns *(CEO)*
Rick Smith *(CFO)*
Todd Smith *(CMO)*
Jeff Sassone *(Pres-Sports & Tactical)*
Jeff Terrill *(Pres-Employer & Community)*
Bill Bourque *(Pres-Acct Mgmt & Field
Ops)*
Brandon Parise *(Chief People Officer)*
John Golden *(Pres-Product)*
Kurt Atherton *(Pres-Commuity Svcs)*
Andy Bhatt *(Sr VP-Creative)*
Matt Cadile *(VP-Dev)*
David Canter *(VP-Client Performance
Solutions)*
Amanda Carlson-Phillips *(VP-
Nutrition & Res)*
Chris Dubek *(VP-Amateur Sports)*
Chris Cherry *(Sr Dir-Acct Mgmt)*
John Stemmerman *(VP-Performance)*

Subsidiaries:

D1 Sports Holdings, LLC **(1)**
7115 S Springs Dr, Franklin, TN 37067
Tel.: (615) 778-1893
Web Site: http://www.d1sportstraining.com
Sports Training Facilities Owner & Franchisor
N.A.I.C.S.: 713940
Will Bartholomew *(Founder & CEO)*
Matt Kite *(Dir-Education)*
Mike Abramson *(Pres)*

Medifit Corporate Services Inc. **(1)**
25 Hanover Rd, Florham Park, NJ 07932
Tel.: (973) 593-9000
Web Site: http://www.medifit.com
Fitness Management & Wellness Program
Services
N.A.I.C.S.: 541611
Vincent Deprossino *(Founder & Exec Dir)*
Dan Burns *(CEO)*
Jeff Terrill *(Pres)*
Bill Bourque *(Pres-Client Svcs)*
Kurt Atherton *(Pres-Community Svcs)*
Carl Walker *(Chief Legal Officer & Sr VP-
HR)*
Pete Coletto *(CFO)*
Kristine Holbrook *(Sr VP-Employer, Health
& Wellness)*
Garrett D. Felix *(Officer-Privacy & Info Security)*

ATHLETICA INC.
Ste 600 15300 25th Ave N, Minneapolis, MN 55447-2080
Tel.: (952) 925-2325
Web Site: http://www.athleticainc.com
Year Founded: 1993
Sales Range: $10-24.9 Million
Emp.: 100
Sporting & Recreation Goods
N.A.I.C.S.: 339920

ATHLETICO LTD.
625 Enterprise Dr, Oak Brook, IL
60523
Tel.: (630) 575-6200
Web Site: http://www.athletico.com
Year Founded: 1991
Physical Therapy & Rehabilitation
Center
N.A.I.C.S.: 621340
Mark Kaufman *(Pres)*
Melissa McMahon *(Sr VP-HR)*
Carrie Bienkowski *(CMO & Chief
Digital Experience Officer)*
Larry Benz *(CEO)*
Khymberly Booth *(Chief HR Officer)*

Subsidiaries:

**C. Weaver Physical Therapy,
Inc.** **(1)**
1720 Abbey Rd, East Lansing, MI 48823
Tel.: (517) 333-6692

Web Site: http://www.athletico.com
Process, Physical Distribution & Logistics
Consulting Services
N.A.I.C.S.: 541614
Carl Weaver *(Pres)*

**Maximum Impact Physical Therapy
Services, LLC** **(1)**
6970 N Oracle Rd Ste 130, Tucson, AZ
85704-4237
Tel.: (520) 219-5825
Web Site:
http://www.maximumimpactpt.com
Occupational & Speech Therapists & Audiologists
N.A.I.C.S.: 621340
Darren Bayliss *(Pres)*

Pivot Health Solutions **(1)**
501 Fairmount Ave Ste 302, Towson, MD
21286
Tel.: (844) 748-6878
Web Site: http://www.pivoths.com
Emp.: 3,000
Health Care Srvices
N.A.I.C.S.: 812199
Todd L. Herring *(Dir-Market)*

Subsidiary (Domestic):

Onsite Innovations, Inc. **(2)**
125 Gaither Dr Ste K, Mount Laurel, NJ
08054
Tel.: (610) 365-1492
Professional, Scientific & Technical Services
N.A.I.C.S.: 541990
Lawrence J. Goren *(CEO)*

The Work Center, Inc. **(1)**
11971 Westline Industrial Dr, Saint Louis,
MO 63146
Tel.: (314) 434-2886
Web Site: http://www.theworkcenterinc.com
Physical Distribution & Logistics Consulting
Services
N.A.I.C.S.: 541614
Michael Fallwell *(Co-Founder)*
Dennis Lloyd *(Co-Founder)*

**ATHLETICS INVESTMENT
GROUP, LLC**
7000 Coliseum Way, Oakland, CA
94621-1917
Tel.: (510) 638-4900   CA
Web Site: https://www.mlb.com
Sales Range: $25-49.9 Million
Emp.: 150
Athletic Club Services
N.A.I.C.S.: 551112
Billy Beane *(Exec VP-Baseball Ops)*
David Kaval *(Pres)*
Chris Giles *(COO)*

Subsidiaries:

**Oakland Athletics Limited
Partnership** **(1)**
7000 Coliseum Way, Oakland, CA 94621
Tel.: (510) 638-4900
Web Site:
http://www.oakland.athletics.mlb.com
Sales Range: $75-99.9 Million
Professional Baseball Club
N.A.I.C.S.: 711211
Michael Crowley *(Co-Pres)*
David Rinetti *(VP-Stadium Ops)*
Keith Lieppman *(Dir-Player Dev)*
Eric Kubota *(Dir-Scouting)*
Pamela Pitts *(Dir-Baseball Admin)*
Steve Fanelli *(VP-Ticket Ops & Svcs)*
David Forst *(Gen Mgr)*
Billy Owens *(Dir-Player Personnel)*
Steve Vucinich *(Mgr-Equipment)*
Mike Ono *(Mgr-Creative Svcs)*
Heather Rajeski *(Sr Mgr-Ballpark Events)*
Detra Paige *(Dir-Alumni & Family Rels)*
David Don *(Sr Dir-Engrg & Multimedia
Svcs)*
John Fisher *(Mng Partner)*
Chris Giles *(COO)*
David Kaval *(Co-Pres)*
Billy Beane *(Exec VP-Baseball Ops)*

**ATHLETX SPORTS GROUP,
LLC**

11221 Plantside Dr, Louisville, KY
40299
Web Site: http://www.athletx.com
Year Founded: 2012
Sales Range: $1-9.9 Million
Emp.: 41
Sports Event Management Services
N.A.I.C.S.: 711320
Jim Haddaway *(Co-Founder & CEO)*
Aaron Flaker *(Co-Founder & Chief
Bus Dev Officer)*
John Ruby *(Co-Founder & Chief Digital Officer)*
Matt Roberts *(Partner, CMO & Chief
Media Officer)*
Rich Janor *(Partner & Pres-Game
Day USA)*

ATHLON HOLDINGS, INC.
2451 Atrium Way, Nashville, TN
37214
Tel.: (615) 327-0747   TN
Web Site:
http://www.athlonmediagroup.com
Year Founded: 2012
Holding Company; Magazine Publisher
N.A.I.C.S.: 551112
Charles Allen *(Pres & CEO)*
Mary Lee Vanderkooi *(CFO & Treas)*
Tracey Altman *(Exec VP-New Ventures & Bus Dev)*
Amy Chernoff *(Chief Revenue
Officer-Brand Sls)*
Lisa Delaney *(Chief Content Officer &
Sr VP)*
Marie Tassini *(Sr VP-Direct Response
Media)*
Monique Kakar *(Chief Mktg Officer-
Digital & Sr VP)*
Corrine Barcia *(VP-Integrated Mktg-
New York)*
Michael McCracken *(Chief Digital Officer & Sr VP)*
Tom Meisel *(Sr VP-Mfg & Distr)*
Kevin Craig *(Sr VP & Dir-Newspaper
Rels Grp)*

Subsidiaries:

**Athlon Sports Communications,
Inc.** **(1)**
2451 Atrium Way, Nashville, TN 37214
Tel.: (615) 327-0747
Web Site: http://www.athlonsports.com
Sports & Entertainment Magazine Publisher
N.A.I.C.S.: 513120
Mitch Light *(Editor)*

ATHOL SAVINGS BANK INC.
444 Main St, Athol, MA 01331
Tel.: (978) 249-3200
Web Site: http://www.atholsb.com
Sales Range: $250-299.9 Million
Emp.: 100
Banking Services
N.A.I.C.S.: 522110
Peter J. Russell *(Sr VP-Comml Lending)*
Kathleen G. Matewsky *(Asst VP-
Residential Lending)*
Mark W. Millett *(Asst VP-Learning &
Dev)*
Sarah A. Galvin *(VP)*
Dan Zona *(Pres & CEO)*

ATI JET, INC.
7007 Boeing Dr, El Paso, TX 79925
Tel.: (915) 772-1449
Web Site: https://www.atijet.com
Year Founded: 2002
Rev.: $9,100,000
Emp.: 36
Logistics & Transportation
N.A.I.C.S.: 485999
Lyle Byrum *(Pres)*
Connie Parsons *(Comptroller)*

ATI WAREHOUSE INC.
2045-51 W Sylvania Ave, Toledo, OH 43613
Tel.: (419) 472-2128
Web Site:
http://www.shradertireandoil.com
Sales Range: $100-124.9 Million
Emp.: 100
Tires & Tubes
N.A.I.C.S.: 423130
Mark P. Meyer (Controller)

ATI WINDOWS
1455 Columbia Ave, Riverside, CA 92507
Tel.: (909) 946-3697
Web Site:
https://www.vinylwindows.co
Sales Range: $10-24.9 Million
Emp.: 150
Mfr of Metal Storm Doors & Windows
N.A.I.C.S.: 332321
Dan Swartz (Pres)
Daniel Schwartz (Controller)
Marcos Sotomayor (Plant Mgr)

ATIA GROUP LTD.
1061 1/2 N Spaulding Ave, West Hollywood, CA 90046
Tel.: (323) 822-1750
Web Site: http://www.atiagroup.com
Year Founded: 2000
Real Estate Management & Development Services
N.A.I.C.S.: 531390
Shalom Atia (VP)
Yossi Atia (CEO)

ATICO INTERNATIONAL USA, INC.
501 S Andrews Ave, Fort Lauderdale, FL 33301
Tel.: (954) 779-2500
Web Site:
http://www.aticointernational.com
Sales Range: $125-149.9 Million
Emp.: 160
Non-Durable Goods Distr
N.A.I.C.S.: 424990
Steve Felkowitz (CEO)
John Clarke (VP-Sls)
Dan Forbes (Gen Counsel)

ATKINS INC.
15510 Stony Creek Way, Noblesville, IN 46060
Tel.: (317) 773-3330
Sales Range: $10-24.9 Million
Emp.: 125
Cakes, Bakery: Except Frozen
N.A.I.C.S.: 311812
J. Atkins (Pres & CEO)

ATKINSON CANDY COMPANY
1608 W Frank Ave, Lufkin, TX 75904
Tel.: (936) 639-2333
Web Site:
https://www.atkinsoncandy.com
Year Founded: 1932
Sales Range: $10-24.9 Million
Emp.: 170
Candy Mfr
N.A.I.C.S.: 311340
Amy Atkinson Voltz (Exec VP)
Doyle Huntsman (Exec VP-Sls & Mktg)
Basil E. Atkinson III (Pres)
Basil E. Atkinson Jr. (CEO)

ATKINSON GRAIN & FERTILIZER INC.
400 N Spring St, Atkinson, IL 61235
Tel.: (309) 936-7177
Web Site:
https://www.atkinsongrain.com
Year Founded: 1968

Sales Range: $10-24.9 Million
Emp.: 20
Whslr of Agricultural Chemicals, Grain, Feed, Fertilizer & Seed
N.A.I.C.S.: 424910
Dan Callison (Gen Mgr)

ATKINSON TRUCK SALES INC.
11541 US Hwy 29, Chatham, VA 24531
Tel.: (434) 432-9770
Web Site:
http://www.atkinsontrucksales.com
Sales Range: $50-74.9 Million
Emp.: 45
Trucks, Commercial
N.A.I.C.S.: 423110
Jackie Ray Atkinson (Pres)

ATKINSON'S MARKET INC.
451 4th St E, Ketchum, ID 83340
Tel.: (208) 726-5668   ID
Web Site: http://www.atkinsons.com
Year Founded: 1956
Sales Range: $25-49.9 Million
Emp.: 150
Grocery Stores
N.A.I.C.S.: 445110
Charles Atkinson (Pres)

ATKINSON-BAKER, INC
500 N Brand Blvd 3rd Fl, Glendale, CA 91203
Tel.: (818) 551-7300
Web Site: https://www.depo.com
Sales Range: $25-49.9 Million
Emp.: 170
Court Reporting Service
N.A.I.C.S.: 561492
Sheila Atkinson-Baker (Pres)
Diana Pozo (Mgr-Acct)
Jamison Fornelli (Dir-Client Svc)
Myriam Wunder (Dir-Client Svcs)
Rebecca Stone (Dir-Client Svcs)
Raeanne Pineda (Mgr-Interpreter)
Cristina Garcia (Sr VP-Production)
Richard Wadsworth (Supvr-Quality Control)
Charles Savage (VP-IT)

ATKINSON-CRAWFORD SALES CO.
11999 Plano Rd, Dallas, TX 75243
Tel.: (972) 234-0947
Web Site: https://www.acsales.net
Sales Range: $10-24.9 Million
Emp.: 37
Bond Brokers
N.A.I.C.S.: 424410
Bruce Gibbons (Pres)

ATL PARTNERS, LLC
320 Park Ave Ste 1400, New York, NY 10022
Tel.: (646) 926-5841   DE
Web Site: http://www.atlpartners.com
Investment Services
N.A.I.C.S.: 523999
Paul Teske (Co-Founder & Partner)
Frank V. Nash (Co-Founder & Mng Partner)
Sanjay Arora (Partner)
Kirby Fine (Principal)
Michael Kramer (Principal)
Gabi Peic (Head-Mktg & IR)

Subsidiaries:

Geost LLC   (1)
3855 W River Rd, Tucson, AZ 85741-3794
Tel.: (520) 789-7100
Web Site: http://www.geost.com
Engineeering Services
N.A.I.C.S.: 541330
Anthony Gleckler (Pres)

LightRidge Solutions   (1)

3855 W River Rd, Tucson, AZ 85741
Tel.: (520) 789-7101
Web Site:
https://www.lightridgesolutions.com
Aerospace & Defense
N.A.I.C.S.: 334511
Bill Gattle (CEO)
Skip Williams (CTO)
Jim Congdon (Chief Software Officer)

Subsidiary (Domestic):

Trident Systems Incorporated   (2)
10201 Fairfax Blvd, Fairfax, VA 22030
Tel.: (703) 273-1012
Web Site: http://www.tridsys.com
Sales Range: $50-74.9 Million
Emp.: 80
Provider of Computer Systems Engineering
N.A.I.C.S.: 541512
Nicholas Karangelen (Founder & Chm)
John Broglio (Pres)
Ponnie Egwarger (CFO)
James O'Looney (Dir-Integrated C4I Sys)
Jim Nieves (Mgr-Contracts)
Pavel Santos (Dir-IT)
Nguyen Ha (Engr-Sys)

Rock-It Cargo USA LLC   (1)
1800 Byberry Rd Ste 810, Huntingdon Valley, PA 19006
Tel.: (215) 947-5400
Web Site: http://www.rockitcargo.com
Sales Range: $25-49.9 Million
Emp.: 100
Freight Forwarding & Logistics Services
N.A.I.C.S.: 488510
Daniel Rosenthal (Pres & CEO)

Subsidiary (Domestic):

Airworks LLC   (2)
6725 Suitland Rd, Suitland, MD 20746
Tel.: (301) 967-4060
Web Site: http://www.airworksllc.com
Passenger Air Transportation Services
N.A.I.C.S.: 481211

Dell Will Customs Brokers (U.S.A.) Inc.   (2)
26480 Northline Commerce, Taylor, MI 48180
Tel.: (734) 946-3040
Sales Range: $1-9.9 Million
Emp.: 15
Freight Transportation Arrangement Services
N.A.I.C.S.: 488510
Joe Clairmont (Pres)
David McMillan (VP)
Marty Bloch (Founder & VP-Motorsports Customs Brokerage)

Dietl International Services, Inc.   (2)
207 W 25th St 3 Fl, New York, NY 10001
Tel.: (212) 400-9555
Web Site: http://www.dietl.com
Sales Range: $1-9.9 Million
Emp.: 60
Freight Transportation & Logistics Services for Fine Arts Industry
N.A.I.C.S.: 488510
Fritz Dietl (Pres)
Dave Preston (Gen Mgr)
Derrick Hilbertz (Mgr-Ops)
Diane Hill (Mgr-Acctg)
Suzy Kim (Sr Project Mgr)
Justin Goldner (Mgr-Art Fair Svcs)

Rock-It Air Charter, Inc.   (2)
140 Blackburn Ter, Pacifica, CA 94044
Tel.: (310) 702-6770
Web Site: http://www.rockitair.com
Passenger Air Transportation Services
N.A.I.C.S.: 481211

Branch (Domestic):

Rock-It Cargo USA LLC - Los Angeles-RIC   (2)
5343 W Imperial Hwy Ste 900, Los Angeles, CA 90045
Tel.: (310) 410-0935
Web Site: http://www.rockitcargo.com
Freight Forwarding & Logistics Services; Executive Office
N.A.I.C.S.: 488510
David Charles Bernstein (Chm & CEO)
Andy Dietz (Exec VP)
Gus Garcia (Mgr-Import Ops)

Anderson Maae (Mgr-Logistics & Warehouse)
Christy MacNicoll (Mgr-HR)
Lou M. Kerpan Jr. (Dir-US Event Ops & Licensed Custom)

Subsidiary (Domestic):

SOS Global Express Inc.   (2)
2803 Trent Rd, New Bern, NC 28562
Tel.: (252) 635-1400
Web Site: http://www.sosglobal.com
Freight Transportation Arrangement Services
N.A.I.C.S.: 488510
Fernando Soler (Pres)

Valence Surface Technologies LLC   (1)
1790 Hughes Landing Blvd Ste 300, The Woodlands, TX 77380
Tel.: (888) 540-0878
Web Site: http://valencesurfacetech.com
Aerospace & Defense Metal Finishing Services
N.A.I.C.S.: 334511
James Mitchell (CFO)
Jorge Della Costa (CTO)
Tim Mickael (Exec VP-Corp Dev)
Steve Cooper (VP-Information Sys)
Simone Murphy-Fickenworth (VP-Quality Assurance & Compliance)
Chris Celtruda (CEO)
David Camilleri (Chm)
Julie Sims (Dir-Mktg & Comm)

Subsidiary (Domestic):

B & M Painting Co., Inc.   (2)
347 Van Buren St NE, Camden, AR 71701-4017
Tel.: (870) 836-3388
Web Site: http://www.bandmpainting.com
Sales Range: $1-9.9 Million
Emp.: 50
Automotive Body, Paint & Interior Repair & Maintenance Services
N.A.I.C.S.: 811121
Brian McCasland (VP)
Shelley Johnson (Pres)
Tracy Payne (VP & Gen Mgr)
Mike Tidwell (Office Mgr)

Triumph Processing, Inc.   (2)
2605 Industry Way, Lynwood, CA 90262-4088
Tel.: (323) 563-1338
Metal Mining Services
N.A.I.C.S.: 213114
Peter J. LaBarbera (Pres)

Triumph Structures-Los Angeles, Inc.   (2)
9301 Mason Ave, Chatsworth, CA 91311-5202
Tel.: (818) 341-1314
Web Site: http://www.triumphgroup.com
Job Machine Shop For Aircraft Parts
N.A.I.C.S.: 332710

ATL TECHNOLOGY, INC.
1335 W 1650 N, Springville, UT 84663
Tel.: (801) 489-9100
Web Site:
https://www.atltechnology.com
Sales Range: $1-9.9 Million
Emp.: 20
Engineeering Services
N.A.I.C.S.: 541330
Brad Brown (CEO)
David Smith (VP-Sls & Mktg-Global)
John Scadden (CFO)
Dave Gens (Pres & COO)

Subsidiaries:

Catheter Research, Inc.   (1)
5610 W 82nd St, Indianapolis, IN 46278
Tel.: (317) 872-0074
Web Site: http://www.catheterresearch.com
Emp.: 116
Medical Device Mfr
N.A.I.C.S.: 339112
Mike Andrus (VP-Sls & Mktg)
Gary T. Cerasale (Mgr-Extrusion & Ops)

ATL Technology, Inc.—(Continued)

Brian Bading (Engr-Mfg)
Christine Cook (COO)
Andy Beard (Engr-Mfg)

Medconx, Inc.　　　　　　　　(1)
2901 Tasman Dr Ste 211, Santa Clara, CA 95054
Tel.: (408) 330-0003
Web Site: http://www.medconx.com
Sales Range: $1-9.9 Million
Medical Cables & Connectors Mfr
N.A.I.C.S.: 339112
Hal Kent (Pres & CEO)
William Diehl (CFO)

ATLAN PLASTICS INC.
13911 Distribution Way, Dallas, TX 75234
Tel.: (972) 484-1661
Web Site:
　　http://www.plasticstoday.com
Sales Range: $10-24.9 Million
Emp.: 3
Plastics Product Mfr
N.A.I.C.S.: 424610
Frank Stieler (CEO)

Subsidiaries:

Adco Inc.　　　　　　　　　　(1)
7600 Sovergin Row, Dallas, TX 75247
Tel.: (972) 484-6177
Web Site: http://www.gluestick.com
Rev.: $4,800,000
Emp.: 2
Hot Melt Glue Mfr & Sales
N.A.I.C.S.: 325520

ATLANTA ASSOCIATION FOR CONVALESCENT AGED PERSONS INC.
1821 Anderson Ave NW, Atlanta, GA 30314-1897
Tel.: (404) 794-2477　　　　GA
Year Founded: 1947
Sales Range: $10-24.9 Million
Emp.: 259
Nursing Care Services
N.A.I.C.S.: 623110
Nova Jane McCombs (Vice Chm)
Marla V. Jones (Sec)
Samuel Bacote (Chm)
Charles Robinson Jr. (Pres & CEO)
Peter Hayley Jr. (Treas)

ATLANTA ATTACHMENT COMPANY, INC.
362 Industrial Park Dr, Lawrenceville, GA 30046-4648
Tel.: (770) 963-7369　　　　GA
Web Site: https://www.atlatt.com
Year Founded: 1969
Sales Range: $10-24.9 Million
Emp.: 130
Mfr of Sewing Products
N.A.I.C.S.: 333248
Randy Clark (VP-Sls-Mid-West Div)
Farrell Wilkins (COO)
Hank Little (Pres)
William Richey (VP)
John Price (VP-Folder Div)
George Price (VP-Electrical Engrg)
Eugenio Fonts (Dir-Sls-Intl)
Darrel Miller (Reg Mgr-Sls)
Jurgen Van Osch (VP-Customer Svc)
Sandra Morrison (VP)

ATLANTA BEVERAGE CO.
5000 Fulton Industrial Blvd, Atlanta, GA 30336
Tel.: (404) 699-6700　　　　GA
Web Site:
　　https://www.atlantabev.com
Year Founded: 1930
Sales Range: $100-124.9 Million
Emp.: 315
Wholesale Beer Distributor
N.A.I.C.S.: 424810

Greg Elliott (VP)
C. Mark Pirrung (Owner)
Kelly Akins (Mgr-HR)

ATLANTA BONDED WAREHOUSE CORPORATION
3000 Cobb Intl Blvd, Kennesaw, GA 30152
Tel.: (770) 425-3000
Web Site:
　　https://www.atlantabonded.com
Rev.: $18,000,000
Emp.: 301
Frozen Food Storage Services
N.A.I.C.S.: 493120
Fred Keith (Chm & CEO)
Andy Womack (Gen Mgr-Dedicated Ops)
Clay Foxworth (Mgr-Customer Logistics)
Bryan McBrayer (Mgr-Inventory Control)
John Harris (Mgr-IT)
Joe Keith (Pres)
Jeff Holton (Project Mgr-IT & IS)
Hal Justice (VP-Sls & Ops)
Troy Snelson (Gen Mgr)

ATLANTA BOTANICAL GARDEN, INC.
1345 Piedmont Ave NE, Atlanta, GA 30309
Tel.: (404) 876-5859　　　　GA
Web Site:
　　http://www.atlantabotanicals.org
Year Founded: 1976
Sales Range: $10-24.9 Million
Emp.: 200
Botanical Garden
N.A.I.C.S.: 712130
Arthur Fix (COO)
Sabina Carr (VP-Mktg)
Mildred Fockele (VP-Horticulture)
Tracy McClendon (VP-Programs)
Mary Pat Matheson (Pres & CEO)
Emily Coffey (VP-Science & Conservation)
Mason W. Stephenson (Chm)
R. Samuel Fraundorf (Treas)
Marshall Norwood (CFO)
Carol B. Tome (Vice Chm)
John H. Crawford IV (Sec)

ATLANTA CAFE HOLDINGS CORP.
2525 Old Farm Rd Apt 2029, Houston, TX 77063
Tel.: (713) 781-6600
Rev.: $142,000,000
Emp.: 6
Land Subdividers & Developers, Commercial
N.A.I.C.S.: 237210

ATLANTA COMMERCIAL TIRE INC.
5067 Kennedy Rd, Forest Park, GA 30297
Tel.: (404) 351-8016
Web Site: https://www.actire.com
Sales Range: $10-24.9 Million
Emp.: 30
Tires Distr
N.A.I.C.S.: 423130
Dennis Stough (Pres)

ATLANTA DATACOM INC.
2915 Courtyards Dr Ste A, Norcross, GA 30071
Tel.: (770) 263-9756
Web Site:
　　http://www.adcomsolutions.com
Year Founded: 1985
Sales Range: $10-24.9 Million
Emp.: 64

Reseller of Data Communications Products & Services: Integrator of Networks
N.A.I.C.S.: 561421
R. J. Chapel (Pres)

ATLANTA FALCONS FOOTBALL CLUB, LLC
4400 Falcon Pkwy, Flowery Branch, GA 30542-3176
Tel.: (770) 965-3115
Web Site:
　　https://www.atlantafalcons.com
Sales Range: $50-74.9 Million
Emp.: 115
Professional Football Franchise
N.A.I.C.S.: 711211
Richard McKay (Pres & CEO-Atlanta Falcons)
Arthur M. Blank (Owner & Chm)
Timothy Zulawski (Chief Comml Officer & Sr VP)
Thomas Dimitroff (Gen Mgr)

ATLANTA FORKLIFTS, INC.
3111 E Ponce De Leon Ave, Scottdale, GA 30079
Tel.: (404) 373-1606　　　　GA
Web Site:
　　http://www.atlantaforklifts.com
Sales Range: $10-24.9 Million
Emp.: 200
Lift Trucks & Parts
N.A.I.C.S.: 423830
Robert Lee Smith Jr. (Pres)

Subsidiaries:

McGee Storage & Handling, Inc.　(1)
3480 Oakcliff Rd B1, Atlanta, GA 30340
Tel.: (770) 458-4346
Web Site: http://www.mcgeeatlanta.com
Rev.: $2,388,000
Emp.: 6
Other Commercial Equipment Merchant Whslr
N.A.I.C.S.: 423440
Kirk Anderson (Pres)

ATLANTA HARDWOOD CORPORATION
5596 Riverview Rd SE, Mableton, GA 30126-2914
Tel.: (404) 792-2290　　　　GA
Web Site:
　　https://www.hardwoodweb.com
Year Founded: 1952
Sales Range: $25-49.9 Million
Emp.: 200
Producer of Lumber, Plywood & Millwork
N.A.I.C.S.: 423310
Paul Harris (CFO)
Hal Mitchell (VP-Domestic Sls)
Dan Caldwell (Pres)
James W. Howard Jr. (CEO)

Subsidiaries:

Atlanta Hardwood Corporation - AHC Crystal Spring Division　　　(1)
45 S Valley Rd, Crystal Spring, PA 15536
Tel.: (814) 735-2050
Hardwood Mfr
N.A.I.C.S.: 321211

Atlanta Hardwood Corporation - AHC North Georgia Division　　　(1)
269 Appalachian Trl, Cleveland, GA 30528
Tel.: (706) 219-2099
Hardwood Mfr
N.A.I.C.S.: 321211

Hardwoods Incorporated　　　(1)
5400 Riverview Rd, Mableton, GA 30126
Tel.: (404) 792-0910
Web Site: http://www.hardwoodweb.com
Emp.: 30
Lumber Whslr
N.A.I.C.S.: 423310

Jim Howard (CEO)
Paul Harris (CFO)
John Biedermann (VP-Pur & Warehouse Ops)
Dam Caldwell (Pres)

ATLANTA HAWKS, L.P.
101 Marietta St NW Ste 1900, Atlanta, GA 30303
Tel.: (404) 878-3800　　　　GA
Web Site: http://www.nba.com
Year Founded: 1949
Professional Basketball Team & Sports Arena Operator
N.A.I.C.S.: 711211
Trey Feazell (Exec VP-Arena Programming)
Steven R. Koonin (CEO)
Jon Steinberg (Dir-Basketball Comm)
Dominique Wilkins (VP-Basketball)
T. Scott Wilkinson (Chief Legal Officer & Exec VP)
Andrew Saltzman (Chief Revenue Officer & Exec VP)
Tony Ressler (Owner & Chm)
Thad Sheely (COO)
Melissa McGhie Proctor (CMO & Exec VP)
Garin Narain (Sr VP-PR)
Nzinga Shaw (Chief Diversity & Inclusion Officer & Sr VP-Community)
Kyle Brunson (Sr VP-Ticket Sls & Svc)
Jeff Peterson (Asst Gen Mgr)
Malik Rose (Asst Gen Mgr)
Marcus Wasdin (CIO)
Travis Schlenk (Pres-Basketball Ops & Gen Mgr)
Chelsea Lane (VP-Athletic Performance & Sports Medicine)
Dan Martinez (VP-Team Ops)
Derek Pierce (VP-Player Personnel)
Mike McNeive (Dir-Player Personnel)
Daniel Starkman (Sr Mrg-Basketball-Ops)
Nick Ressler (Mgr-Basketball Ops)
Paul Jesperson (Asst Coord-Video)
Grant H. Hill (Co-Owner & Vice Chm)
Joel Browning (CFO & Exec VP)
Steve Koonin (CEO)
Dotun Akinwale Jr. (Dir-Scouting)

Subsidiaries:

Arena Operations, LLC　　　　(1)
1 Philips Dr, Atlanta, GA 30303　(100%)
Tel.: (404) 878-3000
Web Site: http://www.philipsarena.com
Sports & Entertainment Arena Operator
N.A.I.C.S.: 711310
Steven R. Koonin (CEO)
Garin Narain (Sr VP-PR)
Scott Wilkinson (Chief Legal Officer & Exec VP)
Brett Stefansson (Exec VP & Gen Mgr)
Camye Mackey (Chief People Officer & Sr VP)

ATLANTA HISTORY CENTER
130 W Paces Ferry Rd NW, Atlanta, GA 30305
Tel.: (404) 814-4000　　　　GA
Web Site:
　　https://www.atlantahistorycenter.com
Year Founded: 1927
Sales Range: $10-24.9 Million
Emp.: 160
Museum Operator
N.A.I.C.S.: 712110
Sheffield Hale (Pres & CEO)
Michael Rose (Exec VP)
Paul Crater (VP-Res Svcs)
Hillary Hardwick (VP-Mktg Comm)
Cheri Snyder (VP-Dev)

ATLANTA LEGAL AID SOCIETY, INC.
54 Ellis St NE, Atlanta, GA 30303

Tel.: (404) 524-5811 **GA**
Web Site:
    https://www.atlantalegalaid.org
Year Founded: 1924
Sales Range: $10-24.9 Million
Emp.: 140
Law firm
N.A.I.C.S.: 541199
Steven Gottlieb (Exec Dir)
Donald M. Coleman (Atty)
Stephen Krumm (Atty)
Jamie Aliperti (Atty)
Charles Bliss (Atty)

ATLANTA LIFE FINANCIAL GROUP
Herndon Plz 100 Auburn Ave NE, Atlanta, GA 30303
Tel.: (404) 659-2100
Year Founded: 1905
Sales Range: $50-74.9 Million
Emp.: 60
Financial Services
N.A.I.C.S.: 525990
Geoffrey Nnadi (Pres & CEO)
Donald E. Smart (Sec & VP & Gen Counsel)
Roosevelt Giles (Chm)
Leslie E. McCoy (CMO & VP-Mktg)
Randell A. Cain (Principal & Portfolio Mgr)
Drake Craig (COO, Portfolio Mgr & Principal)
Lydia Hancock (VP-HR)
William J. Stanley III (Vice Chm)

Subsidiaries:

Atlanta Life Insurance Company **(1)**
100 Auburn Ave NE, Atlanta, GA 30303-2527
Tel.: (404) 659-2100
Web Site: http://www.atlantalife.com
Sales Range: $50-74.9 Million
Life Insurance
N.A.I.C.S.: 524113
Leonard Bevard (Treas)

ATLANTA OFFICE TECHNOLOGIES, INC.
5600 Oakbrook Pkwy Ste 260, Norcross, GA 30093
Tel.: (770) 415-1720
Web Site: http://www.youraot.com
Year Founded: 2014
Sales Range: $1-9.9 Million
Emp.: 27
Commercial Office Equipment Distr
N.A.I.C.S.: 423420
Kevin Schmidt (Partner & Ops Mgr)

ATLANTA ORIENTAL FOOD WHOLESALE CO.
5600 Buford Hwy, Atlanta, GA 30340
Tel.: (770) 455-0770
Web Site: http://www.aofwc.com
Rev.: $31,080,190
Emp.: 300
Fish & Seafoods
N.A.I.C.S.: 424460

ATLANTA PEDIATRIC THERAPY, INC.
4961 Buford Hwy Ste 201, Chamblee, GA 30341
Tel.: (404) 575-4000
Web Site: http://www.aptherapy.com
Year Founded: 2002
Emp.: 100
Pediatric Healthcare Services
N.A.I.C.S.: 621340
George Rosero (Pres & CEO)

ATLANTA PLUMBERS & STEAMFITTERS
3855 Presidential Pkwy Ste 123, Atlanta, GA 30340

Tel.: (770) 455-3802 **GA**
Year Founded: 1973
Sales Range: $10-24.9 Million
Health Insurance Benefit Services
N.A.I.C.S.: 524114
Jon Sterling (Chm)

ATLANTA POSTAL CREDIT UNION
3900 Crown Rd, Atlanta, GA 30304
Tel.: (404) 768-4126 **GA**
Web Site: https://www.apcu.com
Year Founded: 1925
Sales Range: $50-74.9 Million
Emp.: 231
Credit Union
N.A.I.C.S.: 522130
Gary Kyle (CFO)
Charles Head (COO & Exec VP)
Janet Spruell (Sr VP-Ops)
Dianne Yost (Sr VP-Mktg)
Richard McCall (CIO)

ATLANTA REFRIGERATION SERVICE COMPANY, INC.
1231 Collier Rd NW Ste O, Norcross, GA 30318
Tel.: (404) 352-9222
Web Site:
    http://www.atlantarefrigeration.com
Year Founded: 1976
Sales Range: $1-9.9 Million
Emp.: 40
Heat, Air Conditioning, Refrigeration & Cooking Equipment Repair
N.A.I.C.S.: 238220
John Edgar Spivey (Office Mgr)

ATLANTA SYMPHONY ORCHESTRA
1280 Peachtree St, Atlanta, GA 30309-3552
Tel.: (404) 733-4900
Web Site:
    http://www.atlantasymphony.org
Sales Range: $75-99.9 Million
Emp.: 500
Symphony Orchestra
N.A.I.C.S.: 813990
Russell Williamson (Sr Mgr-Orchestra)
Susan Ambo (CFO)
Melanie Kite (Dir-Subscriptions & Patron Svcs)
Jennifer Barlament (Exec Dir)
Evans Mirageas (VP-Artistic Plng & Ops)
Clay Schell (VP-Programming)
Tammy Hawk (Dir-Comm)
Jessica Langlois (Dir-Dev)
Adam Fenton (Dir-Multimedia Tech)
Pam Kruseck (Sr Mgr-Sls & Bus Dev)

ATLANTIC 10 CONFERENCE
11827 Canon Blvd Ste 200, Newport News, VA 23606
Tel.: (757) 706-3054 **PA**
Web Site: http://www.atlantic10.com
Year Founded: 1976
Sales Range: $10-24.9 Million
Emp.: 18
Sport Promotion Services
N.A.I.C.S.: 711310

ATLANTIC AMERICAN FIRE EQUIPMENT COMPANY INC.
121 Titus Ave, Warrington, PA 18976
Tel.: (215) 491-9800
Web Site:
    http://www.atlantacamerican.com
Year Founded: 1985
Sales Range: $10-24.9 Million
Emp.: 50
Sprinkler Systems for Contractors Distr
N.A.I.C.S.: 423850

Paul Decamara (Founder & Pres)
Sam Kutterstein (Controller)

ATLANTIC AMERICAN PARTNERS, LLC
101 E Kennedy Blvd Ste 3300, Tampa, FL 33602
Tel.: (813) 318-9444
Web Site:
    https://www.atlanticamerican.com
Rev.: $57,000,000
Private Equity
N.A.I.C.S.: 523999
O. Garwood Lippincott (Mng Principal)
J. Patrick Michaels (Co-Founder)
Robert Moreyra (Co-Founder)
Brad Gordon (Co-Founder)
Bradley Snyder (Co-Founder & Principal)
JoAnn Covington (Mgr-Mktg-Chinese)
Ming Jung (CFO)
Monica Donosso (Controller-Fin)

ATLANTIC AUTOMALL
193 Sunrise Hwy 205, West Islip, NY 11795
Tel.: (631) 587-0700
Web Site:
    http://www.atlanticautomall.com
Rev.: $33,500,000
Emp.: 80
Automobiles, New & Used
N.A.I.C.S.: 441110

ATLANTIC AUTOMOTIVE CORP.
10 Olympic Pl, Towson, MD 21204
Tel.: (410) 602-6177 **MD**
Web Site:
    http://www.mileonecorporate.com
Year Founded: 1996
Sales Range: $125-149.9 Million
Emp.: 1,700
New & Used Car Dealer
N.A.I.C.S.: 441110
Steven B. Fader (Pres & CEO)
Louis S. Richards (CFO & VP)
Lonnie L. Swiger (Chief Admin Officer & VP)
Scott W. Fader (COO)
Peter M. Rubin (Gen Counsel & VP)
Mark Westerman (CMO)
Jamie Albertine (VP-Strategic Initiatives & Bus Dev)

Subsidiaries:

Allstate Leasing, Inc. **(1)**
1 Olympic Pl Ste 1010, Towson, MD 21204-4405 **(100%)**
Tel.: (410) 246-4394
Web Site: http://www.allstateleasing.com
Sales Range: $10-24.9 Million
Emp.: 65
Passenger Car & Vehicle Equipment Leasing Services
N.A.I.C.S.: 532112
Charlene Kurland (Officer-Bus Relationship)
Rick Sauter (VP-Ops)
Jay Jethwa (CFO)

BMW of Silver Spring **(1)**
3211 Automobile Blvd, Silver Spring, MD 20904
Tel.: (301) 890-3000
Web Site: http://www.bmwofsilverspring.com
Sales Range: $25-49.9 Million
Emp.: 120
Car Dealership
N.A.I.C.S.: 441110
Michael Bolgar (Mgr-Sls-New Vehicle)
Ron Ptak (Dir-Svc)
Donnie Mitchell (Dir-Parts)
Joseph Herche (Asst Mgr-Parts)
Joanna McCarthy (Mgr-Sls-New Vehicle)
Andrew Lippincott (Bus Mgr-Fin & Leasing)

Herb Gordon Mercedes-Benz **(1)**
3301 Briggs Chaney Rd, Silver Spring, MD 20904

Tel.: (301) 890-3030
Web Site:
    http://www.mercedesbenzsilverspring.net
Sales Range: $50-74.9 Million
Emp.: 200
Automobile Dealership
N.A.I.C.S.: 441110
Judy Rhodes (Mgr-HR)
Charles Mcfee (Controller)

Heritage Auto Mall of Bel Air Inc. **(1)**
716 Baltimore Pike, Bel Air, MD 21014-4222
Tel.: (410) 838-8787
Web Site: http://www.heritagejeepbelair.com
Sales Range: $25-49.9 Million
Emp.: 50
New & Used Cars Dealers
N.A.I.C.S.: 441110
Gary Kramer (Mgr)

Heritage Chevrolet, Inc. **(1)**
11234 Reisterstown Rd, Owings Mills, MD 21117-1908
Tel.: (410) 753-2480
Web Site: http://www.mileone.com
Sales Range: $10-24.9 Million
Emp.: 50
New & Used Cars Dealers
N.A.I.C.S.: 441110
Robert Lee (Gen Mgr)

Heritage Chrysler Dodge Jeep Ram **(1)**
11212 Reisterstown Rd, Owings Mills, MD 21117-1908
Tel.: (410) 356-6900
Web Site:
    http://www.saturnofowingsmills.com
Rev.: $38,000,000
Emp.: 45
New & Used Car Dealers
N.A.I.C.S.: 441110
Constantine Spivak (Office Mgr)

Heritage Imports Inc. **(1)**
9808 Reisterstown Rd, Owings Mills, MD 21117-4121
Tel.: (410) 363-8300
Web Site: http://www.mileone.com
Sales Range: $25-49.9 Million
Emp.: 75
New & Used Cars Dealers
N.A.I.C.S.: 441110
Phil Stillman (Gen Mgr)
Leonard Simon (Gen Mgr-Ops)

Motorworld Automotive Group **(1)**
150 Motorworld Dr, Wilkes Barre, PA 18702
Tel.: (570) 846-4498
Web Site: http://www.motorworldgroup.com
Rev.: $230,000,000
Emp.: 400
Automobile Sales & Service
N.A.I.C.S.: 532112
Rick Osick (Sr VP & Dir-Sls)

ATLANTIC BAY MORTGAGE GROUP LLC
600 Lynnhaven Pkwy, Virginia Beach, VA 23452
Tel.: (757) 502-9758
Web Site:
    https://www.atlanticbay.com
Emp.: 150
Mortgage Broker Services
N.A.I.C.S.: 522310
Brian Holland (Founder & CEO)
Brian Mason (Reg Pres)
Stan Holland (COO)
David Gowen (Mgr-Atlanta)
Stephen Templeton (VP-Strategic Growth-Florida)
Butch Holland II (VP)

ATLANTIC BOTTLING COMPANY
4 E 2nd St, Atlantic, IA 50022
Tel.: (712) 243-1440
Web Site:
    https://www.atlanticbottling.com
Sales Range: $10-24.9 Million
Emp.: 160
Soft Drink Bottling Services
N.A.I.C.S.: 312111

Atlantic Bottling Company—(Continued)

James R. Tyler *(Chm)*
Kirk J. Tyler *(Pres)*
Nathan Brown *(VP-Ops)*
John Otterbeck *(VP-Sls)*
Mike Pappas *(VP-Fin & Controller)*

ATLANTIC BUSINESS TECH-NOLOGIES, INC.

4509 Creedmoor Rd Ste 3, Raleigh, NC 27612-3813
Tel.: (919) 518-0670
Web Site: https://www.atlanticbt.com
Year Founded: 1998
Rev.: $2,200,000
Emp.: 68
Computer System Design Services
N.A.I.C.S.: 541512
Eileen Allen *(Dir-Creative)*
Matt Lemke *(Dir-IT)*
Jon Jordan *(Pres)*

ATLANTIC CAPITAL GROUP, INC.

1 Olympic Pl Ste 1220, Towson, MD 21204
Tel.: (410) 602-6020   NJ
Web Site:
    https://www.atcapgroup.com
Year Founded: 1989
Sales Range: $10-24.9 Million
Emp.: 10
Real Estate & Private Equity Investments
N.A.I.C.S.: 531390
Steven B. Fader *(Co-Founder & Chm)*
James M. Bannantine *(Mng Partner)*
Peter M. Rubin *(Co-Founder & Partner)*

Subsidiaries:

Stark Capital Management LLC   (1)
4550 Post Oak Pl Dr Suite 301, Houston, TX 77027   **(100%)**
Tel.: (713) 622-1595
Web Site: http://www.starkcapital.com
Emp.: 100
Investment Portfolio Management Services
N.A.I.C.S.: 523940
George Stark *(Pres & CEO)*
Fernando Perez *(Mng Dir)*
Jerry Axelrod *(Mng Dir)*
Christopher J. Dennis *(VP-Ops)*

ATLANTIC CASTING & ENGI-NEERING CORPORATION

810 Bloomfield Ave, Clifton, NJ 07012-0416
Tel.: (973) 779-2450
Web Site: https://www.atlantic-ce.com
Year Founded: 1938
Sales Range: $10-24.9 Million
Emp.: 140
Aluminum Foundry Services
N.A.I.C.S.: 331524
James E. Binns *(CEO)*
Brian McGrady *(Pres)*
Dan Lenino *(VP-Quality & Ops)*
Greg Rohrbacker *(VP-Sls & Engrg)*
Rob Zebick *(Dir-Ops)*

ATLANTIC CENTRAL ENTER-PRISES, INC.

336 Lpga Blvd, Daytona Beach, FL 32117
Tel.: (386) 255-9040   FL
Year Founded: 1996
Sales Range: $1-9.9 Million
Emp.: 23
Fabricated Structural Metal Mfr
N.A.I.C.S.: 332312
Steve Traulsen *(Pres)*

ATLANTIC CITY MUNICIPAL

UTILITIES AUTHORITY

401 N Virginia Ave, Atlantic City, NJ 08401
Tel.: (609) 345-3315
Web Site: https://www.acmua.org
Year Founded: 1978
Sales Range: $10-24.9 Million
Emp.: 100
Water Utility Services
N.A.I.C.S.: 221310

ATLANTIC COAST CONFER-ENCE

4512 Weybridge Ln, Greensboro, NC 27407
Tel.: (336) 854-8787   NC
Web Site: http://www.theacc.com
Year Founded: 1953
Sales Range: $200-249.9 Million
Emp.: 58
Athletic Event Organizer
N.A.I.C.S.: 711310
Robert Taggart *(VP)*
Sam Pardue *(Treas & Sec)*
Carolyn M. Callahan *(Pres)*
Bryan Kersey *(Coord-Men's Basket-ball Officiating)*

ATLANTIC COAST FOODS, INC.

112 Queens Creek Rd Ste 1, Swansboro, NC 28584-8530
Tel.: (910) 326-2300
Web Site:
    http://www.atlanticcoastfoods.com
Year Founded: 1984
Sales Range: $10-24.9 Million
Emp.: 10
Restaurant Operating Services
N.A.I.C.S.: 722513
Rodney E. Martin *(Pres)*

ATLANTIC COAST MEDIA GROUP

100 Town Sq Pl, Jersey City, NJ 07310
Tel.: (201) 942-2366
Web Site:
    http://www.atlanticcoastmedia.com
Year Founded: 2005
Sales Range: $100-124.9 Million
Emp.: 285
Mfr of Luxury Skin Care Products
N.A.I.C.S.: 325620
Andrew Surwilo *(Co-Founder & CEO)*
Thomas Shipley *(Co-Founder)*
Darek Hrynkiewicz *(VP-Ops)*

ATLANTIC COASTAL ACQUISI-TION CORP.

6 St Johns Ln 5th Fl, New York, NY 10013
Tel.: (248) 890-7200   DE
Year Founded: 2020
ACAH—(NASDAQ)
Rev.: $23,617,162
Assets: $350,656,275
Liabilities: $367,946,131
Net Worth: ($17,289,856)
Earnings: $17,994,321
Emp.: 5
Fiscal Year-end: 12/31/22
Investment Holding Company
N.A.I.C.S.: 551112
Burt Jordan *(Pres)*
Anthony D. Eisenberg *(Chief Strategy Officer)*
Ned Sizer *(COO)*

ATLANTIC COASTAL ELEC-TRONICS

1875 Lake Markham Preserve Trl, Sanford, FL 32771-8101
Tel.: (407) 328-1040

Web Site:
    http://www.atlanticelectronics.com
Sales Range: $10-24.9 Million
Emp.: 178
Surgical & Medical Instruments
N.A.I.C.S.: 339112
Debbie Fogleman *(Pres)*

ATLANTIC COMMUNITY BANKERS BANK

1400 Market St, Camp Hill, PA 17011-4831
Tel.: (717) 737-9335
Web Site: https://www.acbb.com
Year Founded: 1983
Sales Range: $10-24.9 Million
Banking Services
N.A.I.C.S.: 522110
Jon S. Evans *(Pres & CEO)*
Laura L. Gibboney *(COO, Sec & Exec VP)*
Amy Braun *(CFO & VP)*
Regina Malloy *(Chief Risk Officer, Officer-Info Sys & Compliance & VP)*
Lyle Myers *(Officer-Comml Loan & Asst VP)*
Gerald Lake *(Officer-Comml Loan & Asst VP)*
Janine Salisbury *(VP & Mgr-Deposit Ops)*
William Sayre *(Chief Credit Officer & Exec VP)*
R. Michael Briggs *(Vice Chm)*
Peter A. Michelotti *(Chm)*
Tracy Coles *(Officer-Loan Ops)*
Brian Good *(Officer-Correspondent Banking & VP)*
Brandi Lambert *(Officer-Loan Admin, Asst VP & Mgr-Loan Documentation)*
Karen A. Maydick *(Officer-Comml Loan & VP)*
Mary Anne Willow *(Officer-Deposit Ops)*
Virginia Wright *(Officer-Customer Rels)*
Donald Loser *(Controller)*
Sabina Barresi *(Asst VP & Mgr-Relationship-England)*
Nancy Lake *(Dir-Compliance Anchor)*

ATLANTIC CONCRETE PROD-UCTS, INC.

8900 Old Bristol Pike, Tullytown, PA 19007-0098
Tel.: (215) 945-5600   PA
Web Site:
    https://www.atlanticconcrete.com
Year Founded: 1969
Sales Range: $25-49.9 Million
Emp.: 40
Sales of Pre-cast Concrete Products
N.A.I.C.S.: 327390
Jerry Donahue *(Mgr-Sls)*
Steve Schlussel *(Mgr-Accounts Receivable)*

Subsidiaries:

Atlantic Concrete Products, Inc. - Cockeysville Plant   (1)
10823 Beaver Dam Rd, Cockeysville, MD 21030
Tel.: (410) 785-1777
Precast Concrete Products Mfr
N.A.I.C.S.: 327390
Bob Weller *(Mgr-Sls)*
Jim Bolich *(Gen Mgr)*

Puerto Rico Precast Concrete, Inc.   (1)
PO Box 51059, Toa Baja, PR 00950-1059
Tel.: (787) 786-8108
Precast Concrete Products Mfr
N.A.I.C.S.: 327390

ATLANTIC CONTAINER SER-VICE INC.

124 Prosperity Dr, Garden City, GA 31408
Tel.: (912) 964-0933
Web Site: http://www.acslanport.com
Sales Range: $10-24.9 Million
Emp.: 102
Maintenance & Repair of Steamship Intermodal Equipment
N.A.I.C.S.: 488490
Steven G. Miller *(Pres)*

ATLANTIC CORPORATE INTE-RIORS, INC.

6940 Columbia Gateway Dr Ste 350, Columbia, MD 21046
Tel.: (301) 931-3600
Web Site: https://www.aciinc.com
Rev.: $25,000,000
Emp.: 28
Furniture Merchant Whslr
N.A.I.C.S.: 423210
David Todd *(CFO)*

ATLANTIC CORPORATION

806 N 23rd St, Wilmington, NC 28405
Tel.: (910) 343-0624   NC
Web Site: http://www.atlanticpkg.com
Year Founded: 1946
Sales Range: $150-199.9 Million
Emp.: 900
Paper, Packaging Materials & Paper Related Products Distr & Whslr
N.A.I.C.S.: 322299
Norm Dunlap *(VP-Pkg Products)*

Subsidiaries:

Atlantic Corporation - Charleston Facility   (1)
101 Spaniel Ln, Summerville, SC 29483
Tel.: (843) 552-7616
Web Site: http://www.atlanticpkg.com
Emp.: 45
Packaging & Labeling Services
N.A.I.C.S.: 561910
Bruce Cantley *(Mgr-Pur)*

Atlantic Corporation - Charlotte Facility   (1)
12201 Steele Creek Rd, Charlotte, NC 28273
Tel.: (704) 588-1400
Web Site: http://www.atlanticpkg.com
Sales Range: $25-49.9 Million
Emp.: 100
Packaging & Labeling Services
N.A.I.C.S.: 561910
Eric Farmer *(Gen Mgr)*

Atlantic Corporation - Greensboro Facility   (1)
4229 Beechwood Dr, Greensboro, NC 27410
Tel.: (336) 668-0081
Sales Range: $25-49.9 Million
Emp.: 67
Packaging & Labeling Services
N.A.I.C.S.: 561910
Norman Dunlap *(Gen Mgr)*

Coastal Corrugated, Inc.   (1)
5101 Coosaw Creek Blvd, Charleston, SC 29420
Tel.: (843) 552-2697
Web Site: http://www.coastalcorr.com
Rev.: $8,000,000
Emp.: 48
Corrugated & Solid Fiber Box Mfr
N.A.I.C.S.: 322211
James Bozard *(Co-Founder & Chm)*
Cathy Bozard *(Co-Founder)*
David Bozard *(Co-CEO)*
Jenn Bozard *(Co-CEO)*
Sam Gilner *(CFO)*

ATLANTIC COUNTY UTILITIES AUTHORITY

6700 Delilah Rd, Egg Harbor Township, NJ 08234
Tel.: (609) 272-6950
Web Site: https://www.acua.com
Sales Range: $25-49.9 Million

Emp.: 240
Sewerage Systems
N.A.I.C.S.: 221320
Richard S. Dovey (Pres)

ATLANTIC DATA SERVICES, INC.
30 Braintree Hill Office Park Ste 201, Braintree, MA 02184
Tel.: (617) 770-3333   MA
Web Site: http://www.adsfs.com
Year Founded: 1980
Sales Range: $10-24.9 Million
Emp.: 50
Information Technology Consulting & Systems for the Financial Industry
N.A.I.C.S.: 541511
Robert W. Howe (Co-Founder & Chm)
William H. Gallagher (Co-Founder & CEO)
Bond Isaacson (CEO)

ATLANTIC DETROIT DIESEL-ALLISON, LLC
180 Route 17 S, Lodi, NJ 07644-3809
Tel.: (201) 489-5800   NJ
Web Site: http://www.atlanticdda.com
Year Founded: 1975
Sales Range: $200-249.9 Million
Emp.: 400
Industrial Machinery & Equipment
N.A.I.C.S.: 423830

Subsidiaries:

Atlantic Detroit Diesel-Allison   (1)
169 Old New Brunswick Rd, Piscataway, NJ 08854-3708
Tel.: (732) 752-7100
Web Site: http://www.atlanticdda.com
Sales Range: $10-24.9 Million
Emp.: 12
Industrial Machinery & Equipment
N.A.I.C.S.: 493110
Elaine Loss (Office Mgr)
Brian Belew (Branch Mgr)
Scott Brandstetter (Mgr)
Ivan Francis (Mgr)
Bob Light (Mgr-Vehicle Sys Svc)
Bob Smith (Mgr-Power Sys)
John Stefano (Mgr)

Atlantic Detroit Diesel-Allison - Power Systems   (1)
33 Gregg St, Lodi, NJ 07644-2704
Tel.: (201) 291-0300
Web Site: http://www.atlanticdda.com
Sales Range: $25-49.9 Million
Emp.: 30
Industrial Machinery & Equipment
N.A.I.C.S.: 424720
John Stefano (Mgr-Ops)
Arty Labarbera (Dir-Sls & Ops)
Nick Enea (Mgr-Makes Parts Sls)
Karen Gallagher (Mgr-Ops & Sls)
Bob Mangs (VP-Parts Ops)
Elaine Loss (Office Mgr)

ATLANTIC FIELD PLUME DE VEAU INC.
275 Morgan Ave, Brooklyn, NY 11211
Tel.: (718) 599-6400
Rev.: $81,600,000
Emp.: 140
Meat, Frozen: Packaged
N.A.I.C.S.: 424420
Phillip Peerless (Pres)

ATLANTIC FISH & DISTRIBUTING CO.
430 6th St SE, Canton, OH 44702
Tel.: (330) 454-1307
Web Site:
    https://www.atlanticfoods.biz
Year Founded: 1960
Sales Range: $10-24.9 Million
Emp.: 41
General Line Grocery Whslr
N.A.I.C.S.: 424410

Stan Manolakis (Pres & CEO)

ATLANTIC GASKET CORP.
3908 Frankford Ave, Philadelphia, PA 19124
Tel.: (215) 533-6400
Web Site:
    https://www.atlanticgasket.com
Year Founded: 1947
Sales Range: $10-24.9 Million
Emp.: 27
Mufflers & Related Product Mfr
N.A.I.C.S.: 333514
Steve Gordon (VP-Sls)

Subsidiaries:

Centek Industries Inc   (1)
116 Plantation Oak Dr, Thomasville, GA 31792
Tel.: (229) 228-7653
Web Site: http://www.centekindustries.com
Mufflers (Exhaust), Motor Vehicle
N.A.I.C.S.: 336390
Robin Bullard (Mgr-Fin)

ATLANTIC GREAT DANE INC.
1 Hemco Rd, South Portland, ME 04106
Tel.: (207) 799-4700
Web Site:
    http://www.atlanticgreatdane.com
Sales Range: $10-24.9 Million
Emp.: 34
Trucks, Tractors & Trailers: New & Used
N.A.I.C.S.: 441110
Scott Lamb (Pres)
Todd Vachon (Controller)

ATLANTIC GROUP
1156 6th Ave 9th Fl, New York, NY 10036
Tel.: (212) 977-6688
Web Site:
    http://www.furnituresystems.com
Year Founded: 1996
Sales Range: $50-74.9 Million
Emp.: 51
Office Furniture Whslr
N.A.I.C.S.: 423210
Michael Garla (Pres)

ATLANTIC HEALTH SYSTEM INC.
475 South St, Morristown, NJ 07962
Tel.: (973) 660-3143
Web Site:
    http://www.atlantichealth.org
Sales Range: $1-4.9 Billion
Emp.: 8,510
General Hospital
N.A.I.C.S.: 622110
Madeline Ferraro (VP-Govt & Pub Affairs)
Kevin Lenahan (CFO, Chief Admin Officer & Sr VP)
Dexter D. Earle (Chm)
Nikki Sumpter (Chief HR Officer & Sr VP)
Jan Schwarz-Miller (Chief Medical & Academic Officer & Sr VP)
Deborah Cancilla (CIO & VP)
Sheilah O'Halloran (Gen Counsel & VP-Legal Affairs)
Alan Lieber (VP)
David M. Schreck (VP)
Joseph DiPaolo (VP)
Stephanie Bloom-Schwartz (VP)
Thomas Kloos (VP)
Trish O'Keefe (VP)
Katharine Driebe (VP-Fin)
Armond Kinsey (Chief Diversity Officer)
Amy Perry (CEO-Hospital & Sr VP-Integrated Care Delivery)

Sylvia Romm (Chief Innovation Officer)
Brian A. Gragnolati (Pres & CEO)
Abhishek Singh (Dir-Medical -Heart Success Program)

Subsidiaries:

Hackettstown Medical Center   (1)
651 Willow Grove St, Hackettstown, NJ 07840
Tel.: (908) 852-5100
Web Site: http://www.atlantichealth.org
Sales Range: $75-99.9 Million
Emp.: 995
General Hospital Services
N.A.I.C.S.: 622110

Thompson Medical & Chiropractic LLC   (1)
424 S Main St, Forked River, NJ 08731
Tel.: (609) 971-3500
Web Site: http://www.thsm.info
Sales Range: $25-49.9 Million
Emp.: 155
Health Care Srvices
N.A.I.C.S.: 621610
Robert Thompson (CEO & Founder)

ATLANTIC HOSIERY, INC.
13449 Nw 42nd Ave, Opa Locka, FL 33054-4513
Tel.: (305) 685-7617   FL
Web Site: http://atlantichosieryllc.com
Year Founded: 1967
Sales Range: $10-24.9 Million
Emp.: 80
Whslr of Women's Hosiery
N.A.I.C.S.: 424350
Ruben Kloda (VP)
Neil Gottlieb (VP)
Daniel Whitebrook (Pres)
Howard Willen (Controller)

ATLANTIC HOUSING FOUNDATION, INC.
5910 N Central Expy Ste 1310, Dallas, TX 75206
Tel.: (469) 206-8900   SC
Web Site:
    http://www.atlantichousing.org
Year Founded: 1999
Sales Range: $50-74.9 Million
Emp.: 239
Elderly & Disabled People Housing Assistance Services
N.A.I.C.S.: 624120
Liz Snyder (Controller)
Kent Foster (Mgr-Asset)
Leonard Freeman (Mgr-Community Svcs)
Dan French (Founder, Chm & Exec VP)
Michael Nguyen (Pres & CEO)

ATLANTIC HOUSING PARTNERS, LLLP
700 W Morse Blvd Ste 220, Winter Park, FL 32789
Tel.: (407) 741-8500   FL
Web Site:
    http://www.atlantichousing.com
Multi-Family Housing Operative Builder
N.A.I.C.S.: 236117
Scott Culp (Exec VP)
Kerry French (Controller)
Lori Holycross (Supvr-Accts Payable)

ATLANTIC INVESTMENT COMPANY
2 Buckhead Plz 3050 Peachtree Rd NW Ste 200, Atlanta, GA 30305
Tel.: (404) 523-6057
Web Site:
    http://www.atlanticinvestment.com
Sales Range: $10-24.9 Million
Emp.: 9

Commercial & Industrial Building Operation
N.A.I.C.S.: 531120
R. W. Courts II (Chm)

ATLANTIC LIFT TRUCK INC.
2945 Whittington Ave, Baltimore, MD 21230
Tel.: (410) 644-7777
Web Site: http://www.atlanticlift.com
Sales Range: $10-24.9 Million
Emp.: 54
Lift Trucks & Parts
N.A.I.C.S.: 423830
Glenn R. Baer (Pres & CEO)
Brittany Yannuzzi (Coord-Rental New & Used Sls)

ATLANTIC LIMOUSINE INC.
130 N Florida Ave, Atlantic City, NJ 08401
Tel.: (609) 348-2683
Web Site: http://www.atlanticlimo.com
Rev.: $10,711,101
Emp.: 5
Limousine Rental Services
N.A.I.C.S.: 532111
Daniel P. Geiger (Pres)

ATLANTIC MEDIA SERVICES
PO Box 566, Voorhees, NJ 08043-0566
Tel.: (856) 489-6961   NJ
Year Founded: 1999
Sales Range: Less than $1 Million
Emp.: 3
Media Buying Solutions
N.A.I.C.S.: 541810
Kent Warder (Owner)

ATLANTIC MERCHANT CAPITAL INVESTORS, LLC
501 E Kennedy Blvd Ste 810, Tampa, FL 33602
Tel.: (813) 443-0745
Web Site: https://www.amci360.com
Year Founded: 2009
Sales Range: $1-9.9 Million
Emp.: 6
Privater Equity Firm
N.A.I.C.S.: 523999
Allan S. Martin (CEO)

ATLANTIC MUTUAL COMPANIES
100 Wall St, New York, NY 10005
Tel.: (212) 943-1800   NY
Year Founded: 1842
Sales Range: $1-4.9 Billion
Emp.: 1,800
Property & Casualty Insurance Services
N.A.I.C.S.: 524126

Subsidiaries:

Atlantic Mutual Insurance Company   (1)
Fl 28 100 Wall St, New York, NY 10005-3743
Tel.: (212) 943-1800
Web Site: http://www.atlanticmutual.com
Sales Range: $150-199.9 Million
Emp.: 100
Corporate Office
N.A.I.C.S.: 524126

ATLANTIC PARTNERS CORP.
6001 Broken Sound Pkwy Ste 506, Boca Raton, FL 33487
Tel.: (561) 912-9363
Web Site:
    https://www.atlanticpartnerscorp.com
Sales Range: $10-24.9 Million
IT Staffing Solutions
N.A.I.C.S.: 561311
Monroe Gang (CEO)

Atlantic Paste & Glue Co. Inc.—(Continued)

ATLANTIC PASTE & GLUE CO. INC.
170 53rd St, Brooklyn, NY 11232
Tel.: (718) 492-3648
Web Site:
http://www.catchmaster.com
Rev.: $12,000,000
Emp.: 40
Adhesives
N.A.I.C.S.: 325520
Ilona Frisch (Pres)

ATLANTIC PLUMBING SUPPLY CORP.
702 Joline Ave, Long Branch, NJ 07740
Tel.: (732) 229-0334
Web Site:
http://www.atlanticplumbing.net
Year Founded: 1929
Sales Range: $10-24.9 Million
Emp.: 17
Whslr of Plumbing Fittings & Supplies
N.A.I.C.S.: 423720
Barry Ratner (Pres)
Bob Sabat (Branch Mgr)
Patrick Mason Jr. (Mgr-Waterworks)

ATLANTIC PRO-NUTRIENTS, INC.
6900 Kingspointe Pkwy, Orlando, FL 32819
Tel.: (407) 445-0203   FL
Web Site: https://www.xymogen.com
Year Founded: 2002
Sales Range: $10-24.9 Million
Emp.: 100
Vitamin Supplement Developers & Marketers
N.A.I.C.S.: 325412
Brian Blackburn (CEO)
Duck Williams (VP-Pharmaceutix Medical Foods)

ATLANTIC RELOCATION SYS-TEMS
1314 Chattahoochee Ave NW, Atlanta, GA 30318-2829
Tel.: (404) 351-5311   GA
Web Site:
http://www.atlanticrelocation.com
Year Founded: 1966
Sales Range: $75-99.9 Million
Emp.: 40
Intrastate & Interstate Moving & Storage Services
N.A.I.C.S.: 484210
Rich Reed (CFO)

ATLANTIC SELF STORAGE
Ste 300 7880 Gate Pkwy, Jacksonville, FL 32256-7285
Tel.: (904) 545-6726
Web Site:
http://www.atlanticselfstorage.com
Sales Range: $10-24.9 Million
Emp.: 80
Storage Facilities Operator
N.A.I.C.S.: 531130
Mike Ash (Pres)
Michael Torres (Mgr)
Stephanie Fletchall (Mgr-Relief)

ATLANTIC SERVICES
1445 N Rock Rd Ste 200, Wichita, KS 67206
Tel.: (316) 634-2133
Sales Range: $50-74.9 Million
Emp.: 750
Pizzeria Franchise
N.A.I.C.S.: 722513
Ronda Schultz (Office Mgr)

ATLANTIC STREET CAPITAL

MANAGEMENT LLC
145 Mason St 2nd Fl, Greenwich, CT 06830
Tel.: (203) 428-3158
Web Site:
http://www.atlanticstreetcapital.com
Privater Equity Firm
N.A.I.C.S.: 523999
Peter Shabecoff (Mng Partner)
Andrew Wilkins (Mng Partner)
Phil Druce (Partner)
Whit Williams (Mng Partner)
Johnny Conklin (Partner)
Jay Steinle (Partner)
Larry Hicks (CEO-Medical Imaging Platform)

Subsidiaries:

Advancing Eyecare Holdings, Inc.   (1)
11825 Central Pkwy, Jacksonville, FL 32224
Tel.: (855) 777-2020
Web Site:
http://www.advancingeyecare.com
Holding Company
N.A.I.C.S.: 551112

Subsidiary (Domestic):

Generations in Aviation, Inc.   (2)
11825 Central Pkwy, Jacksonville, FL 32224
Tel.: (904) 642-9330
Optical Instrument & Lens Mfr
N.A.I.C.S.: 333310

Lombart Brothers, Inc.   (2)
5358 Robin Hood Rd, Norfolk, VA 23513-2430
Tel.: (757) 853-8888
Web Site: http://www.lombartinstrument.com
Ophthalmic Goods Merchant Whslr
N.A.I.C.S.: 423460
Mike Leidy (Ops Mgr)
Lou Ann Joyner (Mgr-Pur)
Rose Vallera (Mgr-Inventory)
Bill Barnes (Mgr-Used Equipment)
Ron Lee (Mgr-Svc)
Jim Campbell (Mgr-Parts Dept)
Debby Elder (Mgr-Receiving)
Jerry Talliere (Mgr-Warehouse)
Tai Nguyen (Mgr-Rep Air Dept)
Richard Lombart (Pres)

All Star Auto Lights, Inc.   (1)
300 W Grant St, Orlando, FL 32806
Tel.: (407) 271-8949
Web Site: http://www.allstarautolights.com
Replacement Alternative Lighting Products (for Auto Body) Distr
N.A.I.C.S.: 423120
Noel Ranka (Chief Revenue Officer)
Greg Butler (COO)
Matt Immerfall (CEO)
Tom Murray (CFO)
Beth Zefo (VP-HR)
AJ Tyler (Sls Dir)
Kelly Parker (Mgr-HR)
Carolyne Candell (Sls Mgr-Inbound)

Subsidiary (Domestic):

Autolights, LLC   (2)
1000 Hilton Rd, Ferndale, MI 48220-2523
Tel.: (313) 766-4090
Web Site: http://www.autolightsparts.com
Automotive Parts & Accessories Stores
N.A.I.C.S.: 441330
Shannon Croombs (Mgr)

Brown's Medical Imaging, LLC   (1)
14315 C Cir, Omaha, NE 68144-3349
Web Site:
http://www.brownsmedicalimaging.com
Irradiation Apparatus Mfr
N.A.I.C.S.: 334517
Brett Brown (Engr-Svcs)
Chad Brown (Pres)

Double B Foods, Inc.   (1)
800 W Arbrook Blvd Ste 210, Arlington, TX 76015-4393
Tel.: (469) 567-6000
Web Site: http://www.doubleb.com
Sales Range: $50-74.9 Million
Food Mfr
N.A.I.C.S.: 311999

Matt Goldthwaite (Dir-Sls & Mktg)
Gay Cooper (Supvr-HR)
Gordon Parnell (Coord-Cost Acctg & Inventory Control)

GAT Airline Ground Support, Inc.   (1)
246 City Cir Ste 2200, Peachtree City, GA 30269
Tel.: (404) 209-8690
Web Site: http://www.gatags.com
Airline Ground Support; Airports, Flying Fields & Services
N.A.I.C.S.: 488119
Scott Stewart (CFO)

Lab Logistics LLC   (1)
1156 Whitegate Court O, Fallon, MO 63366
Tel.: (855) 522-5644
Web Site: https://www.lablogistics.com
Emp.: 156
Medical Laboratories & Healthcare Services
N.A.I.C.S.: 621511
Brian McArdle (Pres & CEO)
Walter Humphrey (Sr VP)

Subsidiary (Domestic):

The Allied Group Inc.   (2)
25 Amflex Dr, Cranston, RI 02921-2028
Tel.: (401) 946-6100
Web Site: http://www.thealliedgrp.com
Commercial Printing Services
N.A.I.C.S.: 323111
Richard S. Riley (VP-Sls)

Prescott's, Inc.   (1)
18940 Emigrant Trl E, Monument, CO 80132-9041
Web Site:
http://www.surgicalmicroscopes.com
Surgical & Medical Instrument Mfr
N.A.I.C.S.: 339112
Mark Redner (CEO)
Dylan DiJulio (CEO)

Subsidiary (Domestic):

Preventive Maintenance Medical Inc.   (2)
301 Harcourt Rd, Mount Vernon, OH 43050
Tel.: (740) 397-9777
Web Site: http://www.preventivemedical.com
Janitorial Services
N.A.I.C.S.: 561720
John Hubbard (Gen Mgr)

Prestige Medical Imaging LLC   (1)
289 North Plank Road Suite 4, Newburgh, NY 12550
Tel.: (845) 561-6947
Web Site:
http://www.prestigemedicalimaging.com
Radiographic Services
N.A.I.C.S.: 339112
David Eveland (Pres)
Bill Haussmann (CEO)

Subsidiary (Domestic):

X-Ray Visions, Inc.   (2)
5410 Port Royal Rd, Springfield, VA 22151
Tel.: (703) 321-8400
Web Site: https://xrvhealthcare.com
Rev.: $3,000,000
Emp.: 16
Medical, Dental & Hospital Equipment & Supplies Merchant Whslr
N.A.I.C.S.: 423450
Mike Butler (Mgr-Svc)
Aaron Kawa (COO)

U.S. Hospitality Publishers, Inc.   (1)
2926 Kraft Dr, Nashville, TN 37204-3623
Web Site: http://www.uniguest.com
Sales Range: $10-24.9 Million
Hospitality Industry Software Developer
N.A.I.C.S.: 513210
Gillian Tierney (Chief People Officer)
Jeff Hiscox (CEO)
Matt Goche (COO)
Lee Horgan (Chief Revenue Officer)
Joan Stone (CFO)
Steve Rickless (CEO-Tripleplay Div)

Subsidiary (Domestic):

Showcase Technology, Inc.   (2)
19815 Hamilton Ave, Torrance, CA 90502
Tel.: (310) 769-1700
Web Site: http://www.showcasetech.com

Sales Range: $1-9.9 Million
Emp.: 10
Software Developer
N.A.I.C.S.: 513210
Paul Rajewski (Pres & CEO)

Subsidiary (Non-US):

Touchtown Inc.   (2)
Tel.: (412) 826-0460
Web Site: https://www.touchtown.com
Content Management Software Publisher
N.A.I.C.S.: 513210

Subsidiary (Domestic):

Vertical Systems, Inc.   (2)
1392 Borregas Ave, Sunnyvale, CA 94089
Tel.: (408) 752-8100
Web Site: http://www.ver-sys.com
Sales Range: $1-9.9 Million
Emp.: 60
Hospitality Industry Management Software Developer & Publisher
N.A.I.C.S.: 513210
Nabeel Saeed (Product Mgr-Mktg)

ATLANTIC TESTING LABORA-TORIES, LTD.
Potsdam Canton Rd, Canton, NY 13617
Tel.: (315) 386-4578   NY
Web Site:
http://www.atlantictesting.com
Year Founded: 1967
Sales Range: $1-9.9 Million
Emp.: 125
Engineeering Services
N.A.I.C.S.: 541330
Christian J. Roderick (VP-Technical Svcs)
James J. Kuhn (Pres)
Marijean B. Remington (CEO)
Scott M. McCasland (VP-Quality)
Royce A. Knowlton (Mgr-Ops)
Daniel R. Owens (Mgr-Ops-Syracuse)
Arthur T. Cross (Mgr-Ops-Plattsburgh)
Timothy J. Gavin (Mgr-Ops-Subsurface Investigations)
Thomas R. Bundle (Mgr-Corp Risk)
Andrew A. Jarmak (Mgr-Ops)
Justin M. Seymour (Mgr-Ops)
Michael N. DelSanto (Mgr-Ops)

Subsidiaries:

Sjb Services, Inc.   (1)
5167 S Park Ave, Hamburg, NY 14075
Tel.: (716) 649-8110
Web Site: http://www.sjbegs.com
Sales Range: $1-9.9 Million
Emp.: 120
Provides Geotechnical And Environmental Drilling And Testing Of Construction Materials
N.A.I.C.S.: 237110
Richard Zynda (Project Mgr)

ATLANTIC THEATER COM-PANY
336 W 20th St, New York, NY 10011
Tel.: (212) 691-5919   VT
Web Site:
https://www.atlantictheater.org
Year Founded: 1985
Sales Range: $1-9.9 Million
Theater Operator
N.A.I.C.S.: 711110
Olaf Olafsson (Chm)
Carol Auerbach (Vice Chm)
Jeffory Lawson (Mng Dir)
Heather Baird (Dir-Education-Recruitment)
Alison Beatty (Dir-School Artistic)
Pamela Adams (Gen Mgr)
Neil Pepe (Dir-Artistic)

ATLANTIC TOOL & DIE COM-PANY INC.

19963 Progress Dr, Strongsville, OH 44149-3211
Tel.: (440) 238-6931   OH
Web Site:
   https://www.atlantictool.com
Year Founded: 1937
Sales Range: $25-49.9 Million
Emp.: 476
Metal Stampings & Assemblies Mfr
N.A.I.C.S.: 332119
Frank Mehwald (Pres)
Michael S. Mehwald (Exec VP)

Subsidiaries:

Atlantic-Durant Technology Inc.   (1)
5801 Progress Dr, Harlingen, TX 78550
Tel.: (440) 238-6931
Web Site: http://www.atlantictool.com
Rev.: $6,052,018
Emp.: 1
Mfr of Metal Stampings
N.A.I.C.S.: 332119
Frank Mehwald (Pres & CEO)
Jennifer Dumm (Partner-HR)

ATLANTIC TOYOTA
200 Sunrise Hwy, Amityville, NY 11701
Tel.: (631) 789-2700
Web Site:
   http://www.atlantictoyotascion.com
Sales Range: $10-24.9 Million
Emp.: 65
Car Whslr
N.A.I.C.S.: 441110
Pablo Feliz (Mgr-Fin)

ATLANTIC TRACK & TURN-OUT CO.
270 Broad St, Bloomfield, NJ 07003
Tel.: (973) 748-5885
Web Site:
   http://www.atlantictrack.com
Sales Range: $75-99.9 Million
Emp.: 90
Railroad Equipment & Supplies
N.A.I.C.S.: 423860
Peter H. Hughes (Pres)
Charles Killeen (VP)
John McDonald (Mgr-Sls-NE)

ATLANTIC UTILITY TRAILER SALES, INC.
137 Crown Point Rd, Thorofare, NJ 08086
Tel.: (856) 384-7800
Web Site:
   http://www.atlanticutility.com
Rev.: $3,581,500
Emp.: 15
Business to Business Electronic Markets
N.A.I.C.S.: 425120
Spencer Kiernan (CFO & COO)

Subsidiaries:

Utility Trailer Sales of New Jersey, Inc.   (1)
589 Nassau St, North Brunswick, NJ 08902
Tel.: (732) 745-1222
Web Site: http://www.utilityofnj.com
Sales Range: $1-9.9 Million
Emp.: 20
Automobiles And Other Motor Vehicles, Nsk
N.A.I.C.S.: 423110
Elaine Dwyer (Sec)

ATLANTIC VENEER CORPORATION
2457 Lennoxville Rd, Beaufort, NC 28516
Tel.: (252) 728-3169
Web Site:
   http://www.atlanticveneercorp.com
Sales Range: $10-24.9 Million
Emp.: 121
Plywood, Hardwood Or Hardwood Faced

N.A.I.C.S.: 321211
Michael Kraszcski (Pres)
Carmen Garcia (Mgr-HR)

ATLANTIC.NET, INC.
440 W Kennedy Blvd Ste 3, Orlando, FL 32810
Tel.: (352) 375-2912   DE
Web Site: https://www.atlantic.net
Rev.: $16,000,000
Emp.: 65
Internet Service Provider
N.A.I.C.S.: 423430
Marty Puranik (Pres & CEO)
Jacques Ward (Gen Counsel)
Richard Schwartz (VP)
George Kleven (Sec)

ATLANTIX PARTNERS LLC
800 Corporate Dr Ste 408, Fort Lauderdale, FL 33334
Tel.: (954) 734-2360
Web Site:
   https://www.atlantixpartners.com
Sales Range: $1-9.9 Million
Emp.: 16
Business Consulting Services
N.A.I.C.S.: 541611
Michael Moffitt (Mng Partner)
Jennifer Kreis (Dir-Mktg & Comm)
Walter Mores (Partner)
Alex Davis (Mng Dir)

ATLAPAC TRADING COMPANY, INC.
2240 S Garfield Ave, Commerce, CA 90040-1808
Tel.: (323) 722-2472   CA
Web Site:
   http://www.atlapactrading.com
Year Founded: 1981
Sales Range: $75-99.9 Million
Emp.: 18
Wholesale Distributor of Canned Foods
N.A.I.C.S.: 424490
Timothy F. Torrington (Chm & Pres)
William Nelson (Gen Counsel)
Debra Jenkins (Sec)

ATLAS ADVERTISING, LLC
1128 Grant St, Denver, CO 80203
Tel.: (303) 292-3300
Web Site: http://www.atlas-advertising.com
Sales Range: $1-9.9 Million
Advetising Agency
N.A.I.C.S.: 541810
Ben Wright (Founder)
Guillermo Mazier (CEO)
Hugh Daly (Mgr-Ops)
Nikki Molina (Acct Dir)
Bradley Hein (Assoc Dir-Creative)
Lucy Bowman (Dir-Creative Svcs)
Craig Shannon (Mgr-Dev)
Polo Willman (Mgr-Digital Relationship)
Tori Repetti (Mgr-Fin & Admin)
Tyler Hearn (Sr Acct Mgr)
Shayna Miller (Sr Acct Mgr)
Sandy Hazzard (Sr Project Mgr)
Lauren Weston (Sr Project Mgr)

ATLAS ALARM CORPORATION
1239 Washington St, Weymouth, MA 02189
Tel.: (781) 337-8866
Web Site: http://www.atlasalarm.com
Year Founded: 1945
Sales Range: $10-24.9 Million
Emp.: 100
Electrical Contracting Services
N.A.I.C.S.: 238210
Michael J. Rich (Pres)

ATLAS AMERICAN CORPORATION
1111 W 22nd St, Hialeah, FL 33010
Tel.: (305) 885-8941   DE
Web Site: http://www.asltg.com
Year Founded: 1967
Sales Range: $10-24.9 Million
Lighting Equipment & Associated Electrical Supplies Distr
N.A.I.C.S.: 423610
Alan Gordich (Pres)
Dimas Ortega (Controller)

ATLAS ASIA PACIFIC INCORPORATED
100 N El Camino Real, San Mateo, CA 94401-2705
Tel.: (650) 347-3691
Sales Range: $10-24.9 Million
Emp.: 9
Lubricating Oils & Greases
N.A.I.C.S.: 424720
Frank Ryan (VP-Sls & Mktg)

ATLAS ASPHALT INC.
1333 Airport Rd, Jonesboro, AR 72402
Tel.: (870) 932-1246
Web Site:
   https://www.atlasasphaltinc.com
Rev.: $13,300,000
Emp.: 80
Asphalt Product Mfr
N.A.I.C.S.: 324121
Tony Carter (Superintendent-Paving)
Brian Fulkerson (VP-Jonesboro Div)
David Shetron (Asst VP)
Joe Harlan (Mgr-Laboratory)

ATLAS BOX & CRATING CO. INC.
223 Worcester Providence Tpke, Sutton, MA 01590-2905
Tel.: (508) 865-1155
Web Site: http://www.atlasbox.net
Sales Range: $10-24.9 Million
Emp.: 200
Cargo Containers, Wood
N.A.I.C.S.: 321920
Arthur Mahassel (Pres)
Joe Lambert (Engr-Sls)

ATLAS BRONZE
445 Bunting Ave, Trenton, NJ 08611
Tel.: (609) 599-1402
Web Site:
   https://www.atlasbronze.com
Year Founded: 1995
Sales Range: $1-9.9 Million
Emp.: 25
Iron Products Distr
N.A.I.C.S.: 423510
Thomas Smith (Founder)
Eric Grabowski (Mgr-Sls)
Jason Borrero (Mgr-Warehouse)

ATLAS BUTLER HEATING & COOLING
4849 Evanswood Dr, Columbus, OH 43229
Tel.: (614) 681-2167
Web Site:
   https://www.atlasbutler.com
Sales Range: $10-24.9 Million
Emp.: 80
Warm Air Heating & Air Conditioning Contractor
N.A.I.C.S.: 238220
Mark Swepston (Pres)
Greg Benua (Dir-HR)
Jeff Starkey (Mgr-Svcs & Installation)

ATLAS CAPITAL GROUP, LLC
450 Park Ave, New York, NY 10022
Tel.: (212) 554-2250   DE
Web Site: http://www.atlas-cap.com

Year Founded: 2006
Real Estate Investment, Development, Construction & Asset Management Services
N.A.I.C.S.: 531390
Jeffrey A. Goldberger (Co-Founder & Principal)
Andrew B. Cohen (Co-Founder & Principal)
Christopher W. Flynn (CFO)
Stephen Nuckel (Dir-Dev & Construction)
Jacob S. Wood (Dir-Acq & Analysis)
Gene A. Daversa (Mgr-Construction)
Jay Fehskens (Mgr-US Comml Asset)
Carl Weng (Officer-Acctg)
Heather Restino (Chief Acctg Officer)
Carlo Zola (Founder)
Louis B. Blum Jr. (Dir-Construction & Building Ops)

ATLAS COMPANIES, LLC
30 NE Industrial Rd, Branford, CT 06405
Tel.: (203) 483-9013
Web Site:
   https://www.atlasoutdoor.com
Rev.: $15,265,228
Emp.: 70
Fence Construction
N.A.I.C.S.: 238990
Ray Falkoff (Controller)
Ken Dippold (Mgr)

ATLAS CONSTRUCTION SUPPLY INC.
4640 Brinnell St, San Diego, CA 92111
Tel.: (858) 277-2100
Web Site: https://www.atlasform.com
Rev.: $21,095,110
Emp.: 100
Concrete Building Products
N.A.I.C.S.: 423320
Brian Quinn (Pres)
Tom Bargas (VP)
Gerald Schatzberg (Controller)
Tim Jordan (Product Mgr)

ATLAS CONTAINER CORPORATION
8140 Telegraph Rd, Severn, MD 21144
Tel.: (410) 551-6300
Web Site:
   https://www.atlascontainer.com
Year Founded: 1968
Sales Range: $50-74.9 Million
Emp.: 350
Corrugated Packaging & Display Product Mfr
N.A.I.C.S.: 322211
Paul Centenari (Owner & Pres)
Bill McKee (CFO)
Lavell Maddox (Mgr-Production)

Subsidiaries:

Atlas Container LLC   (1)
119 Empire Ave, Meriden, CT 06450
Tel.: (203) 235-2551
Web Site: http://www.atlascontainer.com
Sales Range: $10-24.9 Million
Emp.: 105
Corrugated Packaging & Display Product Mfr
N.A.I.C.S.: 322211

ATLAS DEVELOPMENT CORPORATION
26679 W Agoura Rd Ste 200, Calabasas, CA 91302
Tel.: (818) 340-7080
Web Site: http://www.atlasdev.com
Year Founded: 1989
Sales Range: $10-24.9 Million
Emp.: 110
Software Developer

Atlas Development Corporation—(Continued)
N.A.I.C.S.: 513210
Anahita Villafane (CFO)
Russell von Blanck (CIO)
Michael Epplen (Pres)
Lisa Conley (Sr VP-Growth)
Preston Law (Chief Dev Officer)

Subsidiaries:

Atlas Consulting　　　　　　　　　(1)
26679 W Agoura Rd Ste 200, Calabasas,
CA 91302
Tel.: (818) 340-7080
Web Site:
　http://www.atlasconsultingdivision.com
Sales Range: $25-49.9 Million
Emp.: 80
Custom Software Development & Support
Services
N.A.I.C.S.: 513210
Robert D. Atlas (Pres & CEO)

Atlas Medical　　　　　　　　　　(1)
26679 W Agoura Rd Ste 200, Calabasas,
CA 91302
Tel.: (818) 340-7080
Web Site: http://www.atlasmedical.com
Sales Range: $25-49.9 Million
Emp.: 90
Software Solutions for the Medical Outreach
Market
N.A.I.C.S.: 513210
Robert D. Atlas (Founder)
Lisa Conley (Sr VP-Growth)
Michelle Del Guercio (VP-Mktg)
Mike Epplen (Pres)
Preston Law (Chief Dev Officer)
Anahita Villafane (CFO)
Russell Von Blanck (CIO)

Atlas Public Health　　　　　　　(1)
26679 W Agoura Rd Ste 200, Calabasas,
CA 91302
Tel.: (818) 340-7080
Web Site: http://www.atlaspublichealth.com
Sales Range: $25-49.9 Million
Emp.: 100
Software Development for Private Health-
care & Public Agencies
N.A.I.C.S.: 513210

ATLAS EXCAVATING INC.
4740 Swisher Rd Bldg A, West Lafay-
ette, IN 47906
Tel.: (765) 429-4800
Web Site:
　https://www.atlasexcavating.com
Rev.: $25,000,000
Emp.: 180
Highway, Street & Bridge Construc-
tion
N.A.I.C.S.: 237310
Keisha Dillon (Controller)
Steve Rich (Project Mgr)
Ryan Golden (Mgr-Shop)
Andrew Dodson (Project Mgr)

ATLAS FIBRE COMPANY
3721 W Chase Ave, Skokie, IL 60076
Tel.: (847) 674-1234
Web Site: http://www.atlasfibre.com
Metal Products Manufacturing
N.A.I.C.S.: 332999
Richard Welch (Pres)

Subsidiaries:

Assured Quality Technology, Ltd.　(1)
1521 Mark St, Elk Grove Village, IL 60007-
6716
Tel.: (847) 766-7727
Web Site: http://www.aqtillinois.com
Rev.: $1,000,000
Emp.: 9
Electronic & Precision Equipment Repair &
Maintenance
N.A.I.C.S.: 811210

**ATLAS FOOD SYSTEMS &
SERVICES, INC.**
205 Woods Lk Rd, Greenville, SC
29607-2739
Tel.: (864) 232-1885

Web Site: http://www.atlasfoods.com
Year Founded: 1957
Sales Range: $200-249.9 Million
Emp.: 350
Provider of Merchandising Machine
Operators
N.A.I.C.S.: 445132
Alex Kiriakides (Chm)
Terry Elgin (VP-HR)

**ATLAS FUTURES FUND, LIM-
ITED PARTNERSHIP**
505 Brookfield Dr, Dover, DE 19901
Year Founded: 1998
Sales Range: Less than $1 Million
Bond Investment Services
N.A.I.C.S.: 523150
Michael Pacult (Pres)

**ATLAS GROWTH PARTNERS,
L.P.**
2400 Market St Ste 230, Philadel-
phia, PA 19103
Tel.: (412) 489-0006　　　　　DE
Year Founded: 2013
Rev.: $2,853,000
Assets: $6,914,000
Liabilities: $3,187,000
Net Worth: $3,727,000
Earnings: ($7,637,000)
Fiscal Year-end: 12/31/20
Natural Gas Pipeline Transportation
Services
N.A.I.C.S.: 486210
Daniel P. Flannery (Chm)

**ATLAS HEALTH CARE LINEN
SERVICES CO.**
414 W Taylor St, Syracuse, NY
13202
Tel.: (315) 475-9945
Web Site:
　http://www.atlashealthlinen.com
Rev.: $14,002,137
Emp.: 200
Linen Supply
N.A.I.C.S.: 812331
Scott Wakeman (VP)
John Ralph (Bus Unit Mgr)
Chuck Allen (Plant Mgr)
Thomas Baron (Plant Mgr)

ATLAS HOLDINGS, LLC
100 Northfield St, Greenwich, CT
06830
Tel.: (203) 622-9138　　　　　CT
Web Site:
　http://www.atlasholdingsllc.com
Year Founded: 2002
Investment Holding Company
N.A.I.C.S.: 551112
Andrew M. Bursky (Mng Partner)
Philip E. Schuch (Partner)
Daniel E. Cromie (Partner)
Edward J. Fletcher (Partner)
Jacob D. Hudson (Partner)
Margaret D. DeFonce (Mgr-Admin)
Troy E. Schirk (CIO)
Cheri Reeve (CFO)
Nicholas A. Liso (Controller-Fund)
Jerome E. Lay (Principal)
Michael W. Sher (Partner)
Jason M. Squire (Principal)
Neil Mahajan (Partner)
Timothy J. Fazio (Co-Founder & Co-
Mng Partner)

Subsidiaries:

Banker Steel Co., LLC　　　　　(1)
1619 Wythe Rd, Lynchburg, VA 24501
Tel.: (434) 847-4575
Web Site: http://www.bankersteel.com
Fabricated Structural Metal Mfr
N.A.I.C.S.: 332312
Chet McPhatter (COO)
Linda Whitmore (Dir-HR)
Rob Glass (Sr VP-Sls & Estimating)

Finch Paper LLC　　　　　　　　(1)
1 Glen St, Glens Falls, NY 12801
Tel.: (518) 793-2541
Web Site: http://www.finchpaper.com
Specialty Paper Mfr & Converting Services
N.A.I.C.S.: 322120
Debabrata Mukherjee (Pres & CEO)
Greg Maio (VP-Sls & Mktg)
Michael McLarty (VP-Forestry & Wood Pro-
curement)
Tracey Riley (VP-HR)
Eric Wood (VP-Mfr & Supply Chain)
Alex Rotolo (VP & CFO)

Subsidiary (Domestic):

French Paper Co.　　　　　　　　(2)
100 French St, Niles, MI 49120-2854
Tel.: (269) 683-1100
Web Site: http://www.frenchpaper.com
Paper Mill Operator
N.A.I.C.S.: 322120
Lee Batin (Dir-West Reg Sls)

Flagstone Foods Inc.　　　　　　(1)
380 St. Peter St Ste 1000, Saint Paul, MN
55102
Tel.: (651) 348-4100
Web Site: http://www.flagstonefoods.com
Healthy Snacks Mfr & Distr
N.A.I.C.S.: 311919
Kim Ewanika Kim has a account (Mktg Dir)
Robert Scalia (CEO)

Foster Farms LLC　　　　　　　(1)
PO Box 306, Livingston, CA 95334
Web Site: https://www.fosterfarms.com
Emp.: 10,000
Poultry Hatcheries
N.A.I.C.S.: 112340
Terry Martin (Chm)

Division (Domestic):

Crystal Cream & Butter
Company　　　　　　　　　　　(2)
529 Kansas Ave, Modesto, CA 95321
Tel.: (209) 576-3400
Web Site: http://www.crystalcreamery.com
Sales Range: $150-199.9 Million
Emp.: 630
Dairy Products Mfr
N.A.I.C.S.: 311511
Frank Otis (Pres & CEO)
Mark Shaw (CFO)
Dennis Dalton (VP-Ops)
Luis Miranda (VP-HR)

International Wire Group, Inc.　　(1)
12 Masonic Ave, Camden, NY 13316
Tel.: (315) 245-3800
Web Site:
　http://www.internationalwiregroup.com
Sales Range: $650-699.9 Million
Emp.: 1,600
Bare & Tin-Plated Wire Products & High
Performance Alloy Conductor Developer &
Mfr
N.A.I.C.S.: 331420
Gregory J. Smith (Pres & CEO)

Division (Domestic):

International Wire Co.　　　　　　(2)
12 Masonic Ave, Camden, NY 13316-1202
Tel.: (315) 245-2000
Web Site: http://www.iwgcorp.net
Sales Range: $150-199.9 Million
Emp.: 450
Mfr of Insulated Wire & Cable
N.A.I.C.S.: 423510
Dince Donaldson (Mgr-Sls)

International Wire Group - Insulated
Division　　　　　　　　　　　(2)
1115 W North St, Bremen, IN 46506-2053
Tel.: (260) 897-2535
Sales Range: $50-74.9 Million
Emp.: 100
Mfr of Polyvinyl Chloride & Insulated Cop-
per Wire
N.A.I.C.S.: 332618

International Wire Group-High Perfor-
mance Conductors　　　　　　(2)
1570 Campton Rd, Inman, SC 29349
Tel.: (864) 472-9022
Web Site: http://www.iwghpc.com
Sales Range: $250-299.9 Million
Emp.: 390
High-Performance Conductor Mfr

N.A.I.C.S.: 335929
International Wire Group-Wyre
Wynd　　　　　　　　　　　　(2)
12 Masonic Ave, Camden, NY 13316-1202
Tel.: (860) 376-2516
Web Site:
　http://www.internationalwiregroup.com
Sales Range: $25-49.9 Million
Emp.: 210
Copper Wire & Conductor Developer & Mfr
N.A.I.C.S.: 331420

Subsidiary (Domestic):

Owl Wire & Cable, LLC　　　　　(2)
3127 Seneca Tpke, Canastota, NY 13032
Tel.: (315) 697-2011
Web Site: http://www.owlwire.com
Sales Range: $75-99.9 Million
Wire Copper & Alloy
N.A.I.C.S.: 331420

LSC Communications Inc.　　　　(1)
4101 Winfield Rd, Warrenville, IL 60555
Tel.: (844) 572-5720
Web Site: https://www.lsccom.com
Commercial Printing Services
N.A.I.C.S.: 323111

Subsidiary (Non-US):

Lakeside Book Company　　　　(2)
Tel.: (844) 572-5720
Web Site:
　https://www.lakesidebookcompany.com
Printing Services
N.A.I.C.S.: 323117

Subsidiary (US):

Phoenix Color Corp.　　　　　　(3)
18249 Phoenix Dr, Hagerstown, MD 21742
Tel.: (301) 733-0018
Web Site: https://www.phoenixcolor.com
Full-service & Full-color Printing Services
N.A.I.C.S.: 323111

Subsidiary (Domestic):

Color Optics Inc.　　　　　　　　(4)
40 Green Pond Rd, Rockaway, NJ 07866
Tel.: (973) 664-3100
Web Site: http://www.coloroptics.com
Prepress Services
N.A.I.C.S.: 323120
Mitchell Librot (VP-Sls)

LSC Communications LLC　　　　(1)
4101 Winfield Rd, Warrenville, IL 60555
Tel.: (773) 272-9200
Web Site: https://www.lsccom.com
Rev.: $3,326,000,000
Assets: $1,649,000,000
Liabilities: $1,721,000,000
Net Worth: ($72,000,000)
Earnings: ($295,000,000)
Emp.: 20,000
Fiscal Year-end: 12/31/2019
Holding Company; Commercial Printing
Services
N.A.I.C.S.: 551112
Stephanie K. Mains (CEO)

Subsidiary (Domestic):

Clark Holdings, Inc.　　　　　　(2)
443 S Cayuga Rd, Buffalo, NY 14221
Tel.: (716) 636-1966
Web Site: http://www.clarkgroupinc.com
Holding Company
N.A.I.C.S.: 551112

Subsidiary (Domestic):

The Clark Group, Inc.　　　　　　(3)
258 Prospect Plains Rd, Cranbury, NJ
08512
Tel.: (717) 505-7170
Web Site: http://www.clarkgroupinc.com
Logistics & Freight Transportation Services
N.A.I.C.S.: 484121

Subsidiary (Domestic):

Clark Distribution Systems, Inc.　(4)
3705 Quakerbridge Rd Ste 116, Hamilton,
NJ 08619
Tel.: (717) 505-7170
Web Site: http://www.clarkgroupinc.com
Local Periodical Distribution Services
N.A.I.C.S.: 484220

Branch (Domestic):

Clark Distribution Systems,
Inc.-Mechanicsburg (5)
400 Capital Ln, Middletown, PA 17057
Tel.: (717) 505-7170
Web Site: http://www.clarkgroupinc.com
Freight Distribution Services
N.A.I.C.S.: 484220
Marc Waldman (Dir-Transportation)

Subsidiary (Domestic):

Creel Printing, LLC (2)
6330 W Sunset Rd, Las Vegas, NV 89118
Tel.: (702) 735-8161
Web Site: http://www.creelprint.com
Commercial Printing
N.A.I.C.S.: 323111

Fairrington Transportation Corp. (2)
553 S Joliet Rd, Bolingbrook, IL 60440-3631
Tel.: (630) 783-9200
Web Site: http://www.fairrington.com
Local Transportation Services
N.A.I.C.S.: 484110
Victor Warren (Founder & CEO)
Monte Fosher (Dir-Client Sys Integration)
Jim Slattery (VP-Ops)
Michele DeGuido (Mgr-Sls Support & Data Svcs)
Jim Reifenberg (VP-Natl Accts)
Paula Stoskopf (Dir-Mktg & Industry Rels)
Phillip C. Warren (Exec VP-Sls)
Rich Nathan (Mgr-Client Svcs)
Rick Warren (Acct Mgr)
Brian Wojciechowski (Mgr-Data Analysis)

LibreDigital, Inc. (2)
1835-B Kramer Ln Ste 150, Austin, TX 78758
Tel.: (512) 334-5100
Web Site: http://www.libredigital.com
Digital Content Publishing Services
N.A.I.C.S.: 513199

Subsidiary (Non-US):

Marquis Book Printing Inc. (2)
350 rue des Entrepreneurs, Montmagny, G5V 4T1, QC, Canada
Tel.: (855) 566-1937
Web Site: https://www.marquisbook.com
Printing Services
N.A.I.C.S.: 323113

Subsidiary (Domestic):

National Publishing Company (2)
11311 Roosevelt Blvd, Philadelphia, PA 19154 (100%)
Tel.: (215) 676-1863
Web Site: http://www.lsccom.com
Printing & Binding Bibles, Medical Reference Texts & Other Books
N.A.I.C.S.: 513130

Subsidiary (Domestic):

Dover Publications, Inc. (3)
31 E 2nd St, Mineola, NY 11501 (100%)
Tel.: (516) 294-7000
Web Site: http://www.doverpublications.com
Book Publishers
N.A.I.C.S.: 513130

Research & Education Association,
Inc. (3)
61 Ethel Rd W, Piscataway, NJ 08854
Tel.: (732) 819-8880
Web Site: http://www.rea.com
Educational Materials Publisher
N.A.I.C.S.: 513130

Plant (Non-US):

Planta San Juan del Rio Unidad de
Negocios Impresion Comercial (2)
Av Central Num 235 Col Zona Industrial
Valle De Oro, San Juan del Rio, 76802, Mexico
Tel.: (52) 4272719200
Web Site: http://www.lsccom.com
Commercial Lithographic Printing Services
N.A.I.C.S.: 323111

Subsidiary (Domestic):

Publishers Press, LLC (2)

13487 S Preston Hwy, Lebanon Junction, KY 40150 (100%)
Web Site: http://www.pubpress.com
Commercial Printing Services
N.A.I.C.S.: 323117
Michael J. Simon (Pres)

TriLiteral LLC (2)
100 Maple Rdg Dr, Cumberland, RI 02864
Tel.: (401) 658-4226
Web Site: http://www.triliteral.org
Commercial Printing Mfr
N.A.I.C.S.: 323111
Bob Ohandley (Dir-Ops)
Jennifer Amaral (Mgr-HR)
Cathy Morrone (Mgr-Customer Svc)
Jeff Pepin (Mgr-Distr)
Tom Hall (Mgr-Credit & Collections)

Millar Western Forest Products
Ltd. (1)
16640 - 111 Avenue, Edmonton, T5M 2S5, AB, Canada
Tel.: (780) 486-8200
Web Site: http://www.millarwestern.com
Lumber & Pulp Mills Operator
N.A.I.C.S.: 321113
H. MacKenzie Millar (Chm)
David Anderson (Pres & CEO)
Brian McConkey (VP-HR & Corp Affairs)
Jacob Hudson (Partner)

Division (Domestic):

West Fraser Timber Co., Ltd. - Ques-
nel River Pulp Division (2)
1000 Finning Road, Quesnel, V2J 6A1, BC, Canada
Tel.: (250) 992-8919
Sales Range: $50-74.9 Million
Emp.: 135
Pulp & Paper Product Mfr
N.A.I.C.S.: 322299
Dave Needham (Gen Mgr)

West Fraser Timber Co., Ltd. - Slave
Lake Pulp Division (2)
PO Box 1790, Slave Lake, T0G 2A0, AB, Canada
Tel.: (780) 849-7777
Web Site: https://www.westfraser.com
Sales Range: $25-49.9 Million
Timber & Plywood Product Mfr
N.A.I.C.S.: 321211

Permasteelisa S.p.A. (1)
Via E Mattei 21/23, 31029, Vittorio Veneto, TV, Italy
Tel.: (39) 0438505000
Web Site: http://www.permasteelisa.com
Sales Range: $1-4.9 Billion
Emp.: 5,531
Architectural Services
N.A.I.C.S.: 332321
Davide Croff (Chm)
Klaus Lother (Pres)

Subsidiary (Non-US):

Josef Gartner GmbH (2)
Gartnerstrasse 20, Gundelfingen, 89423, Germany
Tel.: (49) 9073840
Web Site: http://www.josef-gartner.de
Curtain Wall Mfr
N.A.I.C.S.: 332323
Klaus Lother (Gen Mgr)
Jurgen Wax (Gen Mgr)
Fritz Gartner (Chm-Supervisory Bd)

Subsidiary (Domestic):

Gartner Steel and Glass GmbH (3)
Beethovenstr 5c, Wurzburg, 97080, Germany
Tel.: (49) 931 797 39 0
Web Site: http://www.gartnersteel.com
Sales Range: $25-49.9 Million
Emp.: 70
Architectural Components Mfr
N.A.I.C.S.: 337212
Frank Kusters (Dir-Sls)
Nikolaus Rennon (Dir-Engrg & Design)
Stefan Zimmermann (Dir-Ops)

Subsidiary (Non-US):

Josef Gartner & Co. UK Ltd (3)
26 Mastmaker Road, London, E14 9UB, United Kingdom

Tel.: (44) 20 7531 4600
Architectural Components Mfr
N.A.I.C.S.: 337212

Josef Gartner Switzerland AG (3)
Schorenweg 10, 4144, Arlesheim, Switzerland
Tel.: (41) 61 417 1111
Web Site: http://www.josef-gartner.ch
Emp.: 20
Curtain Wall Mfr
N.A.I.C.S.: 332323

Subsidiary (Non-US):

OOO Josef Gartner (2)
Business Centre Arma 5/18 Nizhniy Susalniy Pereulok, 105064, Moscow, Russia
Tel.: (7) 4951327380
Web Site: http://josef-gartner.permasteelisagroup.com
Sales Range: $25-49.9 Million
Emp.: 8
Curtain Wall Mfr
N.A.I.C.S.: 332323
Andreas Bachmann (Exec Dir)

Permasteelisa (Victoria) PTY
Ltd. (2)
21 Translink Dr Keilor Pk, Melbourne, 3042, VIC, Australia
Tel.: (61) 393578122
Architectural Components Mfr
N.A.I.C.S.: 337212

Subsidiary (US):

Permasteelisa Cladding Tech (2)
2060 Centre Pointe Blvd 10, Mendota Heights, MN 55120
Tel.: (651) 686-8035
Commercial & Institutional Building Construction
N.A.I.C.S.: 236220

Permasteelisa Cladding
Technologies (2)
1240 Ala Moana Blvd Ofc, Honolulu, HI 96814
Tel.: (808) 589-1510
Web Site: http://www.permasteelisausa.com
Sales Range: $25-49.9 Million
Emp.: 14
Commercial & Institutional Building Construction
N.A.I.C.S.: 236220

Subsidiary (Non-US):

Permasteelisa Espana S.A.U (2)
Calle Mar Adriatico 4 Poligono Industrial, 28830, San Fernando de Henares, Madrid, Spain
Tel.: (34) 91 7000494
Architectural Components Mfr
N.A.I.C.S.: 337212

Permasteelisa France S.a.s. (2)
Immeuble Le Monge 22 Place des Vosges, La Defense, 92979, Paris, France
Tel.: (33) 1 46 88 94 40
Web Site: http://www.permasteelisa.fr
Emp.: 36
Architectural Components Mfr
N.A.I.C.S.: 337212
Stephane Bedell (Gen Mgr)

Division (Domestic):

Permasteelisa Impianti S.r.l.- FCC
Planterm Division (2)
Viale E Mattei 21/23, 31029, Vittorio Veneto, Treviso, Italy
Tel.: (39) 0438505274
Web Site: http://www.fccplanterm.com
Sales Range: $25-49.9 Million
Emp.: 20
Architectural Components Mfr
N.A.I.C.S.: 337212
Feedrica Sem (Mng Dir)

Subsidiary (Domestic):

Permasteelisa Interiors S.r.l. (2)
Viale E Mattei 21/23, 31029, Vittorio Veneto, Treviso, Italy
Tel.: (39) 0438505000
Architectural Components Mfr
N.A.I.C.S.: 337212

Subsidiary (Non-US):

Permasteelisa Ireland Ltd. (2)
3 Westland Square Pearse Street, Dublin, Ireland
Tel.: (353) 861713503
Web Site: http://www.permasteelisa.it
Architectural Components Mfr
N.A.I.C.S.: 337212

Subsidiary (US):

Permasteelisa North America
Corp. (2)
123 Day Hill Rd, Windsor, CT 06095
Tel.: (860) 298-2000
Web Site: http://www.permasteelisagroup.com
Sales Range: $50-74.9 Million
Emp.: 200
Engineering, Project Management, Manufacturing & Installation of Architectural Envelopes & Interior Systems
N.A.I.C.S.: 541330

Branch (Domestic):

Permasteelisa North America Corp. -
Miami (3)
7955 NW 12 St Ste 222, Doral, FL 33126
Tel.: (305) 592-1212
Web Site: http://www.permasteelisagroup.com
Emp.: 50
Engineering & Architectural Services to Building Exteriors
N.A.I.C.S.: 541330
Roberto Bicciarelli (Mgr-Bus Dev)

Division (Non-US):

Permasteelisa Pacific Holdings
Ltd. (2)
2 International Business Park 1111 Tower 1 Strategy, Singapore, 609930, Singapore
Tel.: (65) 68614733
Sales Range: $50-74.9 Million
Emp.: 100
Holding Company; Manufacturer, Designer & Installer of Architectural Curtain Wall Claddings for the Building Industry
N.A.I.C.S.: 551112

Subsidiary (Domestic):

Global Tech Design Pte Ltd. (3)
2 International Business Park 11-07 Tower 1 Strategy, Singapore, 609930, Singapore
Tel.: (65) 63161680
Emp.: 10
Architectural Components Mfr
N.A.I.C.S.: 337212
Famy Sanna (Mng Dir)

Subsidiary (Non-US):

Global Wall Malaysia Sdn. Bhd. (3)
3B-21-3 Block 3B level 21 plaza Sentral Jalan Stesen Sentral 5, Kuala Lumpur, 50470, Malaysia (70%)
Tel.: (60) 379579222
Web Site: http://www.permasteelisa.com
Sales Range: $1-9.9 Million
Emp.: 20
Provider of Architectural Services
N.A.I.C.S.: 541310

Josef Gartner & Co. UK Ltd. (3)
24 Mastmaker Rd, London, E14 9UB, United Kingdom
Tel.: (44) 2075314630
Web Site: http://www.josef-gartner.co.uk
Curtain Wall Mfr
N.A.I.C.S.: 332323

Josef Gartner Curtain Wall (Shang-
hai) Co. Ltd. (3)
11/F City Point No 1600 ZhongHua Road, Huangpu, Shanghai, 200021, China
Tel.: (86) 2163299988
Web Site: http://www.permasteelisa.com
Sales Range: $25-49.9 Million
Emp.: 20
Curtain Wall Mfr
N.A.I.C.S.: 332323

Josef Gartner Curtain Wall (Suzhou)
Co. Ltd (3)
9 Qiangxing Road Liu Jia Gang Fu Qiao Town, Taicang, Jiangsu, China

Atlas Holdings, LLC—(Continued)
Tel.: (86) 51253378800
Architectural Components Mfr
N.A.I.C.S.: 337212

Permasteelisa (India) Private Limited (3)
No 110/3 Lalbhag Cross Road Krishnappa Layout, Bengaluru, 2170, 560027, India
Tel.: (91) 80 42441000
Architectural Components Mfr
N.A.I.C.S.: 337212
Andreas Sbroggio (Gen Mgr)

Permasteelisa (Thailand) Ltd. (3)
700/379 Moo 6 Amata Nakom Industrial Estate, Tumbon Don Hua Lor, Chon Buri, 20000, Thailand
Tel.: (66) 663846825877
Architectural & Construction Services
N.A.I.C.S.: 541310

Permasteelisa Hong Kong Ltd. (3)
Unit 2701-07B Island Place Tower 510 King's Road, North Point, China (Hong Kong) (100%)
Tel.: (852) 22016800
Web Site:
http://www.permasteelisagroup.com
Architectural Curtain Wall Claddings Mfr
N.A.I.C.S.: 332323

Permasteelisa Pty Ltd (3)
13-15 Governor Macquarie Drive, Chipping Norton, 2170, NSW, Australia (100%)
Tel.: (61) 297551788
Web Site: http://www.permasteelisa.com.au
Emp.: 45
Mfr, Designer & Installer of Architectural Curtain Wall Claddings for the Building Industry
N.A.I.C.S.: 332323
Andrew Vatiliotis (Mng Dir)

Permasteelisa-Gartner Taiwan Ltd. (3)
10 Fl No 171 Sung Teh Rd, Taipei, 110, Taiwan
Tel.: (886) 227283331
Web Site: http://www.permasteelisa.com
Sales Range: $10-24.9 Million
Emp.: 50
Architectural Services
N.A.I.C.S.: 541310

Subsidiary (Non-US):

Permasteelisa Taiwan Ltd. (2)
9F No 410 Chung Hsiao East Road Section 5, Taipei, 11061, Taiwan
Tel.: (886) 2 8780 0822
Architectural Components Mfr
N.A.I.C.S.: 337212

Permasteelisa UK Ltd. (2)
One Old Jewry 2nd floor, London, EC2R 8DN, United Kingdom
Tel.: (44) 2076180400
Web Site: http://www.permasteelisa.it
Sales Range: $25-49.9 Million
Emp.: 30
Architectural Components Mfr
N.A.I.C.S.: 337212

RI.ISA D.o.o. (2)
Petra Kobeka 13, 51000, Rijeka, Croatia
Tel.: (385) 51323006
Web Site: http://www.ri-isa.com
Emp.: 30
Architectural Engineering Services
N.A.I.C.S.: 541330

Scheldebouw B.V. (2)
Herculesweg 17, 4338 PL, Middelburg, Netherlands
Tel.: (31) 118697900
Web Site:
http://www.scheldebouw.group.com
Emp.: 500
Architectural Components Mfr
N.A.I.C.S.: 337212

RedBuilt LLC (1)
200 E Mallard Dr, Boise, ID 83706
Tel.: (208) 364-1316
Web Site: http://www.redbuilt.com
Sales Range: $100-124.9 Million
Emp.: 30
Engineered Structural Wood Products Designer, Mfr & Distr

N.A.I.C.S.: 321215
Kurt Liebich (Chm & CEO)
Don Schwabe (Pres)
Bruce Murphy (CFO & Sr VP)
Ted Osterberger (VP-Ops)
Randy Ruim (VP-Mktg & Bus Dev)
Darren Lehto (Mgr-Sls-North Pacific)
Dave Thompson (Mgr-Sls-Eastern)
Jason Weber (VP-Sls)
Mike Hayley (Mgr-Sls-South Coast)
Steve Aikman (Mgr-Indus Sls)

Saxco International, LLC (1)
1855 Gateway Blvd Ste 400, Concord, CA 94520
Tel.: (877) 641-4003
Web Site: http://www.saxco.com
Emp.: 250
Glass Container Mfr & Distr
N.A.I.C.S.: 327213
David Schwandt (VP-Wine Category)
Rich Bouwer (Gen Mgr-West Coast Grp)
H. Benjamin Samuels (Chm)
Rick Schwartz (Gen Mgr-Product Lines-East Coast & Canada)
Kevin Brownrigg (Mgr-Reg Sls)
Rob Belke (VP-Sls)
Guy Marsala (Pres & CEO)
John Kellogg (Chief Sls & Mktg Officer)
William N. Knopka Jr. (Mgr-Sls-Wine Category)

Subsidiary (Domestic):

Demptos Glass Company (2)
Spring River Bus Pk 2301 River Rd Ste 101, Louisville, KY 40206-1010
Tel.: (502) 326-8456
Web Site: http://www.demptos.com
Sales Range: $10-24.9 Million
Emp.: 36
Glass Wine & Spirits Bottles Mfr
N.A.I.C.S.: 327213
Rob Belke (VP & Gen Mgr)

Square Peg Packaging & Printing, LLC (2)
5260 Anna Ave, San Diego, CA 92110
Tel.: (858) 486-6000
Web Site: http://www.teamsquarepeg.com
Packaging & Labeling Services
N.A.I.C.S.: 561910
John Kellogg (Founder)

Shorewood Packaging LLC (1)
400 Atlantic St 14th Fl, Stamford, CT 06921
Tel.: (203) 541-8100
Web Site: http://www.asg-worldwide.com
Sales Range: $75-99.9 Million
Emp.: 235
Retail Packaging
N.A.I.C.S.: 322219
Mark Caines (CEO)

Unit (Domestic):

Amaray (2)
45 Downing Pkwy, Pittsfield, MA 01201-3879
Tel.: (413) 499-3550
Web Site: http://www.asg-amaray.com
Sales Range: $75-99.9 Million
Emp.: 220
Injection Molded Plastics Packaging Mfr
N.A.I.C.S.: 326112
Barbara Ferguson (Mgr-Customer Svc)
Ted Brown (VP & Gen Mgr-North America)

Plant (Domestic):

Shorewood Packaging LLC - Hendersonville Plant (2)
200 Tabor Rd, East Flat Rock, NC 28726
Tel.: (828) 692-6254
Web Site: http://www.agishorewood.com
Sales Range: $50-74.9 Million
Emp.: 160
Commercial Printing
N.A.I.C.S.: 323111

Shorewood Packaging LLC - Los Angeles Plant (2)
5890 W Jefferson Blvd Studio A, Los Angeles, CA 90016
Tel.: (310) 280-1700
Web Site: http://www.agishorewood.com
Sales Range: $25-49.9 Million
Emp.: 43
Folding Paperboard Boxes Designer & Mfr
N.A.I.C.S.: 322212

Shorewood Packaging LLC - Louisville Plant (2)
4501 Allmond Ave, Louisville, KY 40209-1401
Tel.: (502) 368-7777
Web Site: http://www.agishorewood.com
Sales Range: $50-74.9 Million
Emp.: 107
Color Lithography
N.A.I.C.S.: 322219
Jim Parenti (Gen Mgr)

Shorewood Packaging LLC - Melrose Park (2)
1950 N Ruby St, Melrose Park, IL 60160-1110
Tel.: (708) 344-9100
Web Site: http://www.agishorewood.com
Sales Range: $75-99.9 Million
Emp.: 100
Commercial Printing; Paperboard Cartons Mfr
N.A.I.C.S.: 323111

Soundview Paper Co. LLC (1)
1 Market St, Elmwood Park, NJ 07407
Tel.: (201) 796-4000
Web Site: http://www.soundviewpaper.com
Sales Range: $150-199.9 Million
Emp.: 1,000
Consumer & Institutional Tissue Products Mfr
N.A.I.C.S.: 322291
Karl L. Meyers (CEO)
Carrie Williamson (Sec & Sr VP)
Karl Meyers (CEO)
Rob Baron (Pres)
Jim Andrews (CFO & VP)
M. J. Dickson (VP-HR)
John Glaze (Exec VP-Sls & Mktg)
William Schlenger (VP-Pur)

Division (Domestic):

von Drehle Corporation (2)
612 3rd Ave NE, Hickory, NC 28601-5164
Tel.: (828) 322-1805
Web Site: http://www.vondrehle.com
Sales Range: $10-24.9 Million
Emp.: 250
Sanitary Paper Product Mfr
N.A.I.C.S.: 322291
Randy Bergman (COO)

Tecumseh Products Company LLC (1)
5683 Hines Dr, Ann Arbor, MI 48108
Tel.: (734) 585-9500
Web Site: http://www.tecumseh.com
Sales Range: $700-749.9 Million
Compressors, Small Engines, Power-Train Products & Pump Mfr
N.A.I.C.S.: 333912
Jay Pittas (Chm)
Ricardo Maciel (CEO)
Phyllis Knight (CFO)
Chris Wiseman (Pres)
Stan Gilhool (Gen Counsel)
Regis Marques (VP)
Greg Dwyer (VP)
Hiroshi Saito (VP-Mktg)
Ricardo Ferreira (Mng Dir)
Hin Choy Chong (Mng Dir)
Sandeep Chaudhry (Mng Dir)

Subsidiary (Non-US):

Tecumseh Euro-Malaysia SDN. BHD (2)
No 18 Jalan Sultan Mohamed 4 Selat Klang Utara, 42200, Port Klang, Selangor Darul Ehsan, Malaysia
Tel.: (60) 331763886
Web Site: http://www.tecumseh.com
Hermetic Compressors Mfr
N.A.I.C.S.: 333415
HinChoy Chong (Mng Dir)

Tecumseh Europe SA (2)
2 Avenue Blaise Pascal, 38090, Vaulx-Milieu, France
Tel.: (33) 474822400
Web Site: http://www.tecumseh.com
Hermetic Compressors Mfr
N.A.I.C.S.: 333415

Division (Domestic):

Tecumseh Products Company-Paris Division (2)

2700 W Wood St, Paris, TN 38242
Tel.: (731) 642-6394
Web Site: http://www.tecumotor.com
Emp.: 80
Generator Design Services; Hermetic Motors Mfr
N.A.I.C.S.: 335312
Jeff Fowlkes (Supvr-Product Engrg)
Joseph Holland (Mgr-Product Engrg)

Subsidiary (Non-US):

Tecumseh Products India Pvt. Ltd. (2)
667P 784P Shed B and C, Kistapur Village Medchal Nagar Panchayat Medchal - Malkajgiri, Hyderabad, 501401, Andhra Pradesh, India
Tel.: (91) 4023078103
Web Site: http://www.tecumseh.com
Air & Gas Compressor Mfr
N.A.I.C.S.: 333912

Tecumseh do Brasil, Ltda. (2)
Rua Ray Wesley Herrick 700 Jardim Jockey Club, 700 Jardim Jockey Club, Sao Carlos, 13565-900, SP, Brazil
Tel.: (55) 1633637000
Web Site: http://www.tecumseh.com.br
Refrigeration & Air Conditioning Compressors Mfr
N.A.I.C.S.: 333415

Veritas Steel LLC (1)
1901 Butterfield Rd Ste 810, Downers Grove, IL 60515
Tel.: (630) 423-8708
Web Site: http://www.veritassteel.com
Structural Steel Bridge Components Fabricator
N.A.I.C.S.: 332312
Alan Sobel (CFO)
Rick Daniels (VP-Engrg)
Henrik Jensen (CEO)
Richard Phillips (VP-Bus Dev)

Plant (Domestic):

Veritas Steel LLC - Eau Claire Plant (2)
2800 Melby St, Eau Claire, WI 54703-0562
Tel.: (715) 835-2800
Web Site: http://www.veritassteel.com
Sales Range: $50-74.9 Million
Emp.: 120
Structural Steel Bridge Components Fabricator
N.A.I.C.S.: 332312
Aaron Bialzik (Gen Mgr)

ATLAS HOTELS, INC.
500 Hotel Cir N, San Diego, CA 92108-3005
Tel.: (619) 291-7131   DE
Web Site:
https://www.towncountry.com
Year Founded: 1953
Sales Range: $1-4.9 Billion
Emp.: 5
Holding Company; Hotel, Restaurant & Resort Owner & Operator
N.A.I.C.S.: 551112
C. Terry Brown (Pres & CEO)
Rachel Ashcraft (Dir-Corp Admin)

Subsidiaries:

Town & Country Hotel, LLC (1)
500 Hotel Cir N, San Diego, CA 92108-3005
Tel.: (619) 291-7131
Web Site: http://www.towncountry.com
Sales Range: $50-74.9 Million
Hotel & Resort Services
N.A.I.C.S.: 721110
Michael Sloffer (Mng Dir)

ATLAS INDUSTRIAL CONTRACTORS, LLC
5275 Sinclair Rd, Columbus, OH 43229
Tel.: (614) 841-4500   DE
Web Site: https://www.atlascos.com
Sales Range: $100-124.9 Million
Emp.: 400
Electrical Work

N.A.I.C.S.: 238210
Randy Goddard (Sr VP)
George Ghanem (Pres & CEO)

ATLAS INDUSTRIES INC.
1750 E State St, Fremont, OH 43420
Tel.: (419) 355-1000
Web Site: http://www.atlas-industries.com
Sales Range: $25-49.9 Million
Emp.: 231
Crankshafts & Camshafts, Machining
N.A.I.C.S.: 333998
R. James Elfring (Dir-Mktg & Sls)
Kay Miller (Mgr-HR)

ATLAS LIFT TRUCK RENTALS & SALES, INC.
1815 Landmeier Rd, Elk Grove Village, IL 60007
Tel.: (847) 678-3450
Web Site: https://www.atlaslift.com
Year Founded: 1951
Sales Range: $125-149.9 Million
Emp.: 265
Distr of Material Handling Equipment & Fork Lifts
N.A.I.C.S.: 423830
Larry Hirsch (CFO)

Subsidiaries:

Atlas Bobcat, Inc.   (1)
1160 Mccabe avenue Eokgrove Village, Schiller Park, IL 60176
Tel.: (847) 678-3633
Web Site: http://www.atlasbobcat.com
Rev.: $17,600,000
Emp.: 70
General Construction Machinery & Equipment
N.A.I.C.S.: 423810
Bob Loula (VP-Sls)
John Johnson (Exec VP)
Tony Hilgart (Mgr-Rental)
Andy Hubbard (Mgr-Parts)
Jason Kalandyk (Mgr-Parts)
John Pobuta (Mgr-Svc)
Matt Sobacki (Mgr-Parts)
Brian Soderstrom (Mgr-Svc)

Atlas International Lift Trucks   (1)
1850 Touhy Ave Oak 60007, Schiller Park, IL 60176
Tel.: (847) 233-7200
Web Site: http://www.atlaslifttruck.com
Sales Range: $10-24.9 Million
Emp.: 25
Used Forklift Truck Sales
N.A.I.C.S.: 423830
Gary Klein (VP & Gen Mgr)
Ivelisse Romero (Coord-Freight)

Atlas Toyota Material Handling
Inc   (1)
1815 Landmeier Rd, Elk Grove Village, IL 60007
Tel.: (847) 678-3450
Web Site: http://www.atlastoyota.com
Forklift Truck Distr
N.A.I.C.S.: 423830
Asya Erhart (Dir-HR)

ATLAS MACHINE AND SUPPLY INC.
7000 Global Dr, Louisville, KY 40258
Tel.: (502) 584-7262
Web Site: https://www.atlasmachine.com
Sales Range: $10-24.9 Million
Emp.: 118
Industrial Machinery & Equipment
N.A.I.C.S.: 332710
Jeremy Rydberg (VP-Bus Dev)
Brian Pait (Mgr-HR)

ATLAS MACHINING & WELDING, INC.
777 Smith Lane, Northampton, PA 18067
Tel.: (610) 262-1374
Web Site: https://www.atlasmw.com

Year Founded: 1981
Sales Range: $10-24.9 Million
Emp.: 60
Machining, Welding, Laser Cutting, Mechanical Repair & Assembly
N.A.I.C.S.: 332710
Harold Keeney (Founder & CEO)
Lisa Keeney (Pres)

ATLAS MERCHANT CAPITAL LLC
375 Park Ave, New York, NY 10152
Tel.: (212) 883-4330
Web Site: http://www.atlasmerchantcapital.com
Year Founded: 2013
Privater Equity Firm
N.A.I.C.S.: 523999
Thomas C. King (Operating Partner)
Robert E. Diamond Jr. (Founder, CEO & Partner)
Ty E. Wallach (Mng Dir & CIO)
Bob Diamond (Co-Founder & CEO)
David Schamis (Co-Founder & CIO)
Timothy J. Kacani (Mng Dir & COO)
Ned Dybvig (Mng Dir)

Subsidiaries:

Atlas Merchant Capital UK LLP   (1)
5 Welbeck Street, London, W1G 9YQ, United Kingdom
Tel.: (44) 20 3551 7850
Web Site: http://www.atlasmerchantcapital.com
Privater Equity Firm
N.A.I.C.S.: 523999
Matthew Hansen (Mng Dir & Head-UK & Europe Bus)
Abigail May (Mng Dir)

Panmure Gordon & Co. Limited   (1)
One New Change, London, EC4M 9AF, United Kingdom
Tel.: (44) 207 886 2500
Web Site: https://www.panmure.com
Sales Range: $10-24.9 Million
Holding Company; Corporate Finance, Securities Brokerage, Institutional Trading, Equity Research & Market Maker Services
N.A.I.C.S.: 551112
Barrie Cornes (Head-Res)
Erik Anderson (Head-Corp Broking)

Subsidiary (Domestic):

Panmure Gordon (Broking) Limited   (2)
Moorgate Hall 155 Moorgate, London, EC2M 6XB, United Kingdom
Tel.: (44) 2074593600
Web Site: http://www.panmuregordon.com
Sales Range: $50-74.9 Million
Emp.: 90
Stock Brokerage Services
N.A.I.C.S.: 523150

Panmure Gordon (UK) Limited   (2)
Moorgate Hall 155 Moorgate, London, EC2M 6XB, United Kingdom
Tel.: (44) 2074593600
Stock Brokerage Services
N.A.I.C.S.: 523150

ATLAS METAL & IRON CORPORATION
1100 Umatilla St, Denver, CO 80204
Tel.: (303) 825-7166
Web Site: http://www.atlasmetal.com
Sales Range: $25-49.9 Million
Emp.: 105
Ferrous Metal Scrap & Waste
N.A.I.C.S.: 423930
Donald Rosen (Chm)

ATLAS METAL PRODUCTS COMPANY
5101 Commerce Crossing Dr, Louisville, KY 40229
Tel.: (502) 779-2100
Web Site: https://www.atlas-co.com
Year Founded: 1972

Sales Range: $25-49.9 Million
Emp.: 36
Architectural Products Mfr
N.A.I.C.S.: 423390
Andrew Keith (Pres)
Jonathan Keith (Controller)

ATLAS MINERALS & CHEMICALS, INC.
1227 Valley Rd, Mertztown, PA 19539-8827
Tel.: (610) 682-7171
Web Site: http://www.atlasmin.com
Year Founded: 1892
Sales Range: $10-24.9 Million
Emp.: 48
Corrosion-Resistant Cements, Linings, Coatings, Rigid Plastics & Pipe Jointing Compounds, Adhesive Putties
N.A.I.C.S.: 325520
Francis X. Hanson (Pres)
Scott Gallagher (Mgr-Mktg)
Brenda Isamoyer (Coord-Logistics)

ATLAS MORTGAGE & INSURANCE CO., INC.
7120 Beneva Rd, Sarasota, FL 34238-2850
Tel.: (941) 366-8424
Web Site: https://www.atlasinsurance.com
Year Founded: 1953
Emp.: 41
Insurance Agency & Mortgage Services
N.A.I.C.S.: 524210
Tommy W. Kochis (VP-Sls)
Robert W. Brown (Pres)
Darren Howard (VP)
Michelle Barrow (Mgr-Comml Lines)
Annie LaRiviere (Project Mgr)
Cynthia Fitzgibbons (Mktg Mgr)
Dawn Genther (Jr Acct Mgr)
Julie Saunier (Jr Acct Mgr)
Laura Dansky (Acct Mgr)
Lisa Speights (Acct Mgr-Comml)
Nancy Perin (Acct Mgr-Comml)
Pam Shepard (Acct Exec)
Sheri Deer (Acct Mgr-Comml)
Beth Manley (Acct Mgr-Personal Lines)
Terri Thompson (Acct Mgr-Personal Lines)
Karen Gray (Dir-Ops)

ATLAS OPERATIONS, INC.
325 SW 15th Ave, Pompano Beach, FL 33069
Tel.: (954) 788-1200   FL
Web Site: http://www.atlas-operations.com
Year Founded: 1996
Sales Range: $100-124.9 Million
Emp.: 100
Dietary Supplement Whslr
N.A.I.C.S.: 424210
Gustavo Barni (Pres)
Melanie Barni (Sec)

ATLAS PACIFIC ENGINEERING COMPANY, INC.
1 Atlas Ave, Pueblo, CO 81002-0500
Tel.: (719) 948-3040   DE
Web Site: http://www.atlaspacific.com
Year Founded: 1945
Sales Range: $25-49.9 Million
Emp.: 300
Food Product Machinery Mfr
N.A.I.C.S.: 333241
Don Freeman (VP-Sls)
Mary Bailey (Mgr-Pur)
David Bullock (Sr Project Engr & Supvr-IT)

Subsidiaries:

Magnuson Corporation   (1)
1 Magnuson Ave, Pueblo, CO 81001-4889
Tel.: (719) 948-9500
Web Site: http://www.magnusoncorp.com
Sales Range: $25-49.9 Million
Emp.: 200
Food Product Machinery Mfr & Distr
N.A.I.C.S.: 333241
Craig Furlo (CEO)

ATLAS PEN & PENCIL CORP.
408 Madison St Ste 126, Shelbyville, TN 37160
Tel.: (954) 920-4444   FL
Web Site: http://www.atlaspen.com
Year Founded: 1948
Sales Range: $25-49.9 Million
Emp.: 200
Pens & Pencils Custom Engraving & Imprinting for Advertising & Promotion
N.A.I.C.S.: 332812
Dave Thomas (Pres)

ATLAS PROFESSIONAL SERVICES, INC.
9560 W Linebaugh Ave, Tampa, FL 33626
Tel.: (813) 999-4499
Web Site: http://www.atlasps.com
Year Founded: 2006
Sales Range: $1-9.9 Million
Emp.: 20
IT Consulting Services
N.A.I.C.S.: 541690
Gregory A. Zolkos (CEO)
Adrian Swaim (CFO)

ATLAS REAL ESTATE PARTNERS
226 5th Ave 2nd Fl, New York, NY 10001
Tel.: (646) 863-9765
Web Site: https://www.atlasrep.com
Year Founded: 2009
Sales Range: $1-9.9 Million
Real Estate Investment & Management Services
N.A.I.C.S.: 523999
Arvind Chary (Co-Founder & Mng Partner)
Alex Foster (Co-Founder & Mng Partner)
Aubrey Duffy (Dir-Bus Dev)
Dave Wallace (Chief Investment Officer)
Joe Stampone (VP-Investments)

ATLAS REFINERY, INC.
142 Lockwood St, Newark, NJ 07105-4719
Tel.: (973) 589-2002   DE
Web Site: http://www.atlasrefinery.com
Year Founded: 1887
Sales Range: $75-99.9 Million
Emp.: 36
Specialty Chemicals, Lubricants, Emulsifiers, Wetting Agents & Surfactants Mfr
N.A.I.C.S.: 325613
Steven B. Schroeder (Owner)
Joseph Gargano (Dir-Fin)
Bill Baumann (Mgr-Ops)
Steven Shroeder Jr. (Pres)

ATLAS RFID SOLUTIONS, INC.
1500 1st Ave N Ste 10, Birmingham, AL 35203
Tel.: (205) 383-4428
Web Site: http://www.atlasrfid.com
Year Founded: 2006
Sales Range: $1-9.9 Million
Emp.: 50
Software Development for Industrial Construction

Atlas RFID Solutions, Inc.—(Continued)
N.A.I.C.S.: 513210
Jon Chesser (VP-Sls)
Robert Ball (COO)
Andrew Ryan (VP-Product Mgmt)
Lance Hendrix (Sr VP-Bus Dev)
Jessica Vance (Dir-Mktg)
Robert L. Fuqua Jr. (Founder & CEO)

ATLAS ROOFING CORP.
2000 RiverEdge Pkwy Ste 800, Atlanta, GA 30328
Tel.: (601) 484-8900   MS
Web Site:
  http://www.atlasroofing.com
Year Founded: 1982
Sales Range: $400-449.9 Million
Emp.: 1,800
Roofing Materials Mfr
N.A.I.C.S.: 326150
Kenneth Farrish (Pres)
Kirk Villar (VP-Sls & Mktg)
Jennifer Sansone (Mgr-Sls-Midwest)
Michael McCaig (VP-Ops-Shingle & Underlayment Div)
Gus Harkins (Dir-Natl Accts-Shingles & Underlayments)
Stan Bastek (VP-Sls & Mktg)
Cathy Capellan (Sls Mgr-Shingles & Underlayments-Atlantic)
Darren Skaggs (Sls Dir-Shingles & Underlayments-North)

Subsidiaries:

ACH Foam Technologies, LLC   (1)
8700 Turnpike Dr Ste 400, Westminster, CO 80031
Tel.: (855) 594-4427
Web Site: http://www.achfoam.com
Sales Range: $100-124.9 Million
Emp.: 550
Mfr of Expanded Polystyrene Insulation & Roofing Products
N.A.I.C.S.: 326140
Mary Burk (Dir-Sls & Mktg)

Subsidiary (Domestic):

ACH Foam Technologies, LLC   (2)
4001 Kaw Dr, Kansas City, KS 66102
Tel.: (913) 321-4114
Web Site: http://www.achfoam.com
Rev.: $20,085,316
Emp.: 150
Mfr of Expanded Polystyrene Insulation & Roofing Products
N.A.I.C.S.: 326140
Chuck Hogue (Plant Mgr)

ACH Foam Technologies, LLC   (2)
809 E 15th St, Washington, IA 52353
Tel.: (319) 653-7429
Web Site: http://www.achfoam.com
Rev.: $2,800,000
Emp.: 30
Mfr of Expanded Polystyrene Insulation & Roofing Products
N.A.I.C.S.: 326140

ACH Foam Technologies, LLC - Fond DuLac   (2)
90 Trowbridge Dr, Fond Du Lac, WI 54937
Tel.: (920) 924-4050
Web Site: http://www.achfoam.com
Expanded Polystyrene Insulation & Roofing Products Mfr
N.A.I.C.S.: 326140

Plant (Domestic):

ACH Foam Technologies, LLC - Georgia Plant   (2)
2731 White Sulphur Rd, Gainesville, GA 30501
Tel.: (770) 536-7900
Foam Products Mfr
N.A.I.C.S.: 326140

ACH Foam Technologies, LLC - Nevada Plant   (2)
775 Waltham Way Ste 105, Sparks, NV 89434
Tel.: (775) 355-7655
Foam Products Mfr

N.A.I.C.S.: 326140
Mark Willis (Plant Mgr)

ACH Foam Technologies, LLC - Utah Plant   (2)
111 W Fireclay Ave, Murray, UT 84107
Tel.: (801) 265-3465
Foam Products Mfr
N.A.I.C.S.: 326140

Atlas EPS   (1)
8240 Byron Ctr Ave SW, Byron Center, MI 49315   (100%)
Tel.: (616) 878-1568
Web Site: http://www.atlaseps.com
Sales Range: $25-49.9 Million
Emp.: 175
Mfr of Expanded Polystyrene
N.A.I.C.S.: 326150
Miki Horton (Mgr-Customer Ops-HR Div)
Ken Dietz Jr. (Supvr-Production)

Atlas Roofing Corp.   (1)
2300 Hwy 142 E, Ardmore, OK 73401
Tel.: (580) 226-3283
Web Site: http://www.atlasroofing.com
Sales Range: $25-49.9 Million
Emp.: 100
Roofing Shingles Mfr
N.A.I.C.S.: 324122

Atlas Roofing Corp.   (1)
1100 Georgia Pacific Dr, Daingerfield, TX 75638-0700   (100%)
Tel.: (903) 645-3988
Web Site: http://www.atlasroofing.com
Sales Range: $25-49.9 Million
Emp.: 180
Production & Sales of Roofing Materials
N.A.I.C.S.: 324122
Greg Frost (Plant Mgr)

Atlas Roofing Corp.   (1)
100 Pine View Dr, Hampton, GA 30228-3141   (100%)
Tel.: (770) 946-4571
Web Site: http://www.atlasroofing.com
Sales Range: $25-49.9 Million
Emp.: 150
Production & Sales of Roofing Materials
N.A.I.C.S.: 324122

ATLAS STAFFING INC.
189 7th Pl E, Saint Paul, MN 55101-2344
Tel.: (651) 222-5894
Web Site: http://www.atlasstaffing.com
Rev.: $10,000,000
Emp.: 15
Provider of Staffing Services
N.A.I.C.S.: 561330
Kelly Severson (Mgr)
Sandy Olafson (Mgr)
Vicky Ponce (Mgr)
Kim Gelao (Mgr-Acct)
Wendy Van Bergen (Mgr-Acct)

ATLAS STEEL PRODUCTS CO. INC.
7990 Bavaria Rd, Twinsburg, OH 44087-2252
Tel.: (330) 425-1600
Web Site: https://www.atlassteel.com
Year Founded: 1983
Sales Range: $10-24.9 Million
Emp.: 90
Aluminum Steel & Aluminized Tubing
N.A.I.C.S.: 423510
John Adams (Pres)
Vicki Widmor (VP-Sls)

ATLAS TOOL INC.
29880 Groesbeck Hwy, Roseville, MI 48066-1925
Tel.: (586) 778-3570   MI
Web Site: http://www.atlastool.com
Year Founded: 1962
Sales Range: $150-199.9 Million
Emp.: 340
Mfr of Special Dies & Tools
N.A.I.C.S.: 333514

Elizabeth Schmidt (CEO)
Mark R. Schmidt (Pres)
Eric Hanpeter (CFO)

ATLAS TRANSFER & STORAGE CO.
13026 Stowe Dr Ste A, Poway, CA 92064
Tel.: (858) 513-3800
Web Site: https://www.atlasallied.com
Rev.: $11,953,101
Emp.: 88
Trucking Service
N.A.I.C.S.: 484121
Linda J. Oakley (VP)
Tom Oakley (Pres)

ATLAS TRAVEL INTERNATIONAL
1 Maple St Ste 3, Milford, MA 01757
Tel.: (508) 478-8626
Web Site: http://www.atlastravel.com
Year Founded: 1986
Sales Range: $1-9.9 Million
Emp.: 105
Travel Agencies
N.A.I.C.S.: 561510
Elaine Osgood (CEO)
Mimi Cleary (VP-Supplier Rels & Strategic Sourcing)
Dan Reagan (CTO)
Karen McCrink (Dir-Leisure Travel Svcs)
Lea Cahill (Pres)
Christy Conrow (VP-Bus Dev & Program Mgmt)
John Hannon (CFO)

ATLAS TUBULAR LP
1710 South Hwy 77, Robstown, TX 78380
Tel.: (361) 387-7505
Web Site:
  http://www.atlastubular.com
Year Founded: 1977
Sales Range: $10-24.9 Million
Emp.: 60
Pipe & Tubing, Steel
N.A.I.C.S.: 423510
John Hubbard (Pres & CEO)
Tracy Barrett (COO & Sec)

ATLAS WATER SYSTEMS, INC.
301 2nd Ave, Waltham, MA 02451
Tel.: (781) 373-4700
Web Site: http://www.atlaswater.com
Direct Selling Establishments
N.A.I.C.S.: 423110
Cindyann D. Mealey (Sec & Treas)

ATLAS WIRE CORPORATION
1601 Glenlake Ave, Itasca, IL 60143
Tel.: (847) 678-1210   IL
Web Site:
  https://www.atlaswirecorp.com
Year Founded: 1970
Sales Range: $50-74.9 Million
Emp.: 30
Mfr of Wire
N.A.I.C.S.: 332618
Bruce Leska (Pres & CEO)
Hector Ayala (Mgr-Shipping & Receiving)

ATLAS WORLD GROUP, INC.
1212 Saint George Rd, Evansville, IN 47711-2364
Tel.: (812) 424-2222   DE
Web Site:
  http://www.atlasworldgroup.com
Year Founded: 1994
Emp.: 100
Holding Company
N.A.I.C.S.: 551112
Jack Griffin (Chm & CEO)
Donald Breivogel Jr. (CFO & Sr VP)

Subsidiaries:

American VanPac Carriers, Inc.   (1)
9750 3rd Ave NE Ste 200, Seattle, WA 98115-0628
Tel.: (800) 877-0444
Web Site: http://www.vanpac.com
Freight Transportation Services
N.A.I.C.S.: 488510

Atlas Logistics Inc.   (1)
1212 St George Rd, Evansville, IN 47711
Tel.: (800) 446-2079
Web Site: http://www.awglogistics.com
Logistics Management Consulting Services
N.A.I.C.S.: 541614
Garrett Hall (Coord-LTL)
Phil Wahl (Pres & COO)

Subsidiary (Domestic):

TopHat Logistical Solutions, LLC   (2)
547 Ctr St, Lake Geneva, WI 53147
Tel.: (262) 581-4300
Web Site: http://www.tophatls.com
Logistic Services
N.A.I.C.S.: 492110
Ryan Clark (Reg Mgr)
Steve Trensch (Partner)

Atlas Van Lines (Canada) Ltd.   (1)
485 North Service Road East, Oakville, L6H 1A5, ON, Canada   (95%)
Tel.: (905) 844-0701
Web Site: http://www.atlasvanlines.ca
Sales Range: $10-24.9 Million
Emp.: 110
Household Goods Moving Services
N.A.I.C.S.: 484210
Fred A. Haladay (Pres & COO)
Shirley C. Sveda (CFO & Sr VP)

Atlas Van Lines, Inc.   (1)
1212 Saint George Rd, Evansville, IN 47711-2364   (100%)
Tel.: (812) 424-2222
Web Site: http://www.atlasvanlines.com
Domestic & International Transportation of Household Goods & Sensitive Shipments
N.A.I.C.S.: 484210
Howard E. Parker (Sr VP-Fin & Admin)
Dennie D. Lynn (Sr VP-Transportation Svcs)
Marian Weilert Sauvey (Gen Counsel, Sec & VP)
Jeff Schimmel (VP-Transportation Svcs)
Steve Hermann (VP-Agency Dev)
Dave Coughlin (VP-Ops)
Glen Dunkerson (Chm & CEO)
Donald Hill (Pres)
Shirley Sveda (Co-CFO & Sr VP)
Kelly Foreman (VP-HR)
Donald Breivogel Jr. (Co-CFO & Sr VP)

Division (Domestic):

Atlas Terminal Co. Inc.   (2)
1212 St George Rd, Evansville, IN 47711   (100%)
Tel.: (812) 424-2222
Web Site: http://www.atlasvanlines.com
Rev.: $8,990,000
Emp.: 24
Sales of Trailers, Tractors & Trucks
N.A.I.C.S.: 423110
Rick Olson (CFO & Sr VP)
Jack Griffin (Pres)

Subsidiary (Domestic):

Atlas Van Lines Intl.   (2)
9750 3rd Ave NE Ste 200, Seattle, WA 98115-2022   (100%)
Tel.: (206) 526-1137
Web Site: http://www.atlasintl.com
Sales Range: $10-24.9 Million
Emp.: 75
International Freight Forwarder
N.A.I.C.S.: 488510

Atlas World-Class Travel   (2)
1212 St George Rd, Evansville, IN 47711-2364   (100%)
Tel.: (812) 421-7168
Web Site: http://www.atlasworldgroup.com
Sales Range: $10-24.9 Million
Emp.: 4
Travel Agency
N.A.I.C.S.: 561510

Avail Resource Management, Inc.   (1)

5715 N Fares Ave, Evansville, IN 47711
Tel.: (800) 259-1277
Web Site: http://www.availmm.com
Food Transportation Services
N.A.I.C.S.: 484121

Champion International Moving,
Ltd. (1)
1 Champion Way, Canonsburg, PA 15317
Tel.: (724) 873-8000
Web Site: http://www.champmove.com
All Other Support Services
N.A.I.C.S.: 561990

Cornerstone Relocation Group,
LLC. (1)
106 Allen Rd, Basking Ridge, NJ 07920
Tel.: (908) 580-9600
Web Site: http://www.crgglobal.com
Sales Range: $10-24.9 Million
Emp.: 50
Relocation Services
N.A.I.C.S.: 484210
Janelle Piatkowski (Founder, Pres & CEO)
Mark Rabe (Sr VP-Global Bus Dev & Mktg)
Debra Frost (Sr VP-Global Svcs)

Titan Global Distribution, Inc. (1)
11973 Westline Industrial Dr Ste 200, Saint
Louis, MO 63143
Tel.: (314) 817-0051
Web Site: http://www.atlaslogistics.com
Emp.: 30
Logistics Management Consulting Services
N.A.I.C.S.: 541614
Stan Eisen (VP-Ops)

ATLAST FULFILLMENT
22100 E 26th Ave, Aurora, CO 80019
Tel.: (303) 662-1041
Web Site:
http://www.atlastfulfillment.com
Year Founded: 2003
Sales Range: $10-24.9 Million
Emp.: 200
E-commerce & Catalog Warehouse,
Order Fulfillment & Customer Service
Outsource Staffing
N.A.I.C.S.: 561311
Ted Tanner (Pres & CEO)

ATM CORPORATION OF AMERICA
345 Rouser Rd, Coraopolis, PA
15108
Tel.: (412) 299-6200
Year Founded: 1993
Sales Range: $10-24.9 Million
Emp.: 485
Real Estate Services
N.A.I.C.S.: 531320
Chris Ruehrshneck (Principal)

ATM RECYCLING, INC.
2620 Kirby Cir NE, Palm Bay, FL
32905-3404
Tel.: (321) 237-2762
Web Site:
http://www.atmrecyclingco.com
Sales Range: $1-9.9 Million
Emp.: 30
Metals Recycling
N.A.I.C.S.: 423930
Greg Velasquez (Mgr)

ATMI DYNACORE LLC
960 Ridgeway Ave, Aurora, IL 60506
Tel.: (630) 896-4679
Web Site:
https://www.atmiprecast.com
Sales Range: $10-24.9 Million
Emp.: 75
Concrete Products, Precast
N.A.I.C.S.: 327390
John B. Armbruster (Product Mgr)

ATMI PRECAST INC.
960 Ridgeway Ave, Aurora, IL 60506
Tel.: (630) 896-4679
Web Site:
https://www.atmiprecast.com
Rev.: $20,000,000
Emp.: 12
Concrete Products, Precast
N.A.I.C.S.: 327390
Rhonda McCormick (VP-Admin)
Mike Walsh (VP)
Al Baysek (VP-Engrg)
Chris Barone (Mgr-Ops-Waubonsee
Dev)
Dave Nowak (Project Mgr)
Edward Schulze (Project Mgr)
Joe Pozzi (Sr Project Mgr)
Ken Graef (Sr Project Mgr)
Mike Pelz (Mgr-Ops-Mfg)
Paul Carr (COO)
Sudhir Singamsethi (Mgr-Engrg)

ATMOSERA, INC.
9705 SW Sunshine Ct, Beaverton,
OR 97005
Tel.: (503) 646-8400
Web Site: http://www.easystreet.com
Year Founded: 1995
Sales Range: $10-24.9 Million
Emp.: 35
Data Processing, Hosting & Related
Services
N.A.I.C.S.: 518210
Jon Crowhurst (Co-Founder & Dir-
Tech Svc)
Kami Olszewski (Project Mgr)
Breanne Antonius (Sr Acct Mgr)
Charles Schwenger (VP-Sls)
Benjamin Gallo (VP-Sls & Gen Mgr)
Jon Thomsen (CEO)
Miran Baric (VP-Sls)

Subsidiaries:

Infinity Internet, Inc. (1)
1101 SE Tech Center Dr, Vancouver, WA
98683
Tel.: (360) 735-3700
Web Site: http://www.iinet.com
Sales Range: $1-9.9 Million
Information Retrieval Services
N.A.I.C.S.: 517810

Wintellect LLC (1)
10207 Technology Dr Ste 302, Knoxville,
TN 37932
Web Site: http://www.wintellect.com
Sales Range: $1-9.9 Million
Emp.: 30
Computer Consulting & Training
N.A.I.C.S.: 541519
Jeffrey Richter (Co-Founder)
John Robbins (Co-Founder)
Jeff Prosise (Co-Founder)

ATNA RESOURCES LTD.
14142 Denver W Pkwy Ste 250,
Golden, CO 80401
Tel.: (303) 278-8464   BC
Web Site: http://www.atna.com
Sales Range: Less than $1 Million
Emp.: 116
Gold Exploration & Mining Services
N.A.I.C.S.: 212220
William R. Stanley (VP-Exploration)
Daniel Saint Don (COO & VP)

Subsidiaries:

CR Briggs Corporation (1)
PO Box 668, Trona, CA 93592
Tel.: (760) 372-4233
Sales Range: $75-99.9 Million
Gold Mining Services
N.A.I.C.S.: 212220
Larry Turner (Gen Mgr)
Joe Balas (Mgr-Process)

CR Kendall Corporation (1)
PO Box 799, Hilger, MT 59451-0799
Tel.: (406) 538-2501
Web Site: http://www.atna.com
Sales Range: $50-74.9 Million
Emp.: 3
Gold & Silver Mining
N.A.I.C.S.: 212220

Jim Volberding (Mgr-Ops)

ATOMATIC MECHANICAL SERVICES, INC.
3733 N Ventura Dr, Arlington Heights,
IL 60004
Tel.: (847) 818-4300
Web Site: https://www.atomatic.com
Rev.: $14,900,000
Emp.: 130
Mechanical Contractor
N.A.I.C.S.: 238220
Richard D. Hoffman (Co-Owner &
CEO)
Steven Wiet (CFO)
Frank Bisceglie (Project Mgr)
Glen Ruiz (VP-Svc)
Rich Janota (Engr-Svc Sls)
Matt Turk (Co-Owner)
Don Kaslofski (VP-Svc Sls)

ATOMIC CREDIT UNION, INC.
711 Beaver Creek Rd, Piketon, OH
45661
Tel.: (740) 289-5060   OH
Web Site: http://www.2mycu.com
Year Founded: 1955
Sales Range: $10-24.9 Million
Emp.: 160
Credit Union
N.A.I.C.S.: 522130
Thomas Griffiths (Pres & CEO)
Jerod Wiley (CFO)
Aaron Michael (COO)
Curtis Green (CIO & Sr VP)

ATOMIC DATA, LLC.
250 Marquette Ave S Ste 225, Minneapolis, MN 55401
Tel.: (612) 466-2000
Web Site:
https://www.atomicdata.com
Year Founded: 2001
Sales Range: $10-24.9 Million
Emp.: 75
Information Technology Services
N.A.I.C.S.: 541512
Mark Abbott (Chief Legal Officer)

ATOMIC DIRECT, LLC
1219 SE Lafayette St, Portland, OR
97202
Tel.: (503) 296-6131
Web Site:
http://www.atomicdirect.com
Year Founded: 1998
Sales Range: $10-24.9 Million
Emp.: 8
Advetising Agency
N.A.I.C.S.: 541810
Doug Garnett (Founder & CEO)
John Gurney (Exec Producer)
Skye Weadick (Acct Dir)
Shelby Brill (Mgr-Mktg & Campaign)

ATOMIC OBJECT LLC
941 Wealthy St SE, Grand Rapids,
MI 01034
Tel.: (616) 776-6020
Web Site:
http://www.atomicobject.com
Year Founded: 2001
Sales Range: $1-9.9 Million
Emp.: 40
Software Development Services
N.A.I.C.S.: 541511
Carl Erickson (Co-Founder & Pres)
Michael Marsiglia (VP)
Mary O'Neill (Bus Mgr)

ATOMIC PLAYPEN
701 Xenia Ave S Ste 200, Minneapolis, MN 55416
Tel.: (763) 231-3400   MN
Year Founded: 1999
Rev.: $2,300,000

Emp.: 30
Fiscal Year-end: 12/31/06
Advertising, Digital/Interactive
N.A.I.C.S.: 541810
Michael Kretsinger (Founder & Partner)

ATOMIC TATTOOS, LLC
9041 Ulmerton Rd, Largo, FL 33771
Tel.: (727) 518-7819
Web Site:
http://www.atomictattoos.com
Year Founded: 2001
Sales Range: $1-9.9 Million
Emp.: 100
Tattoo Shop Owner
N.A.I.C.S.: 459999
Stephen Cannon (CEO)

ATP TOUR, INC.
201 ATP Tour Blvd, Ponte Vedra
Beach, FL 32082-3211
Tel.: (904) 285-8000   DE
Web Site:
http://www.atpworldtour.com
Year Founded: 1972
Sales Range: $25-49.9 Million
Emp.: 80
Men's & Women's Professional Tennis
N.A.I.C.S.: 813920
Philip Galloway (COO)
Graeme Agars (VP-Media Rels)
Mark Young (CEO)

Subsidiaries:

ATP Europe BVBA (1)
Monte-Carlo Sun 74 Boulevard d'Italie,
98000, Monaco, Monaco
Tel.: (377) 97 97 04 04
Web Site: http://www.atptour.com
Tennis Event Organizer
N.A.I.C.S.: 711219

ATP International Group (1)
Ste 208 46A Macleay Street Potts Point,
Sydney, 2011, NSW, Australia
Tel.: (61) 2 9336 7000
Web Site: http://www.atpworldtour.com
Emp.: 4
Tennis Event Organizer
N.A.I.C.S.: 711219
Karina Duckitt (Office Mgr)

ATP London (1)
Palliser House Palliser Road, London, W14.
9EB, United Kingdom (100%)
Tel.: (44) 2073817890
Web Site: http://www.atptour.com
Rev.: $29,095,527
Emp.: 7
Management Consulting Services for Tennis
Professionals
N.A.I.C.S.: 541611
Chris Kermode (Chm & Pres-Monaco)
Ross Hutchins (Chief Player Officer)

ATR INTERNATIONAL, INC.
1230 Oakmead Pkwy, Sunnyvale, CA
94085
Tel.: (408) 328-8000
Web Site:
http://www.atrinternational.com
Sales Range: $25-49.9 Million
Emp.: 800
Employment Placement Agencies
N.A.I.C.S.: 561311
Jerry Brenholz (Pres & CEO)
Theresa Siegfried (VP-Fin)
Wendy Sun (VP-Recruiting)
Jeff Monaghan (Dir-Mktg)
Maria Novoa (Founder)
Joel Benevides (VP-Bus Dev)
Maggie Morelle (CIO)

ATR LIGHTING ENTERPRISES, INC.
10 Industrial Rd, Richland, MO 65556
Tel.: (573) 765-5219
Web Site: https://www.atrlighting.com

Atr Lighting Enterprises, Inc.—(Continued)

Year Founded: 1984
Sales Range: $1-9.9 Million
Emp.: 47
Electronic Part & Equipment Whslr
N.A.I.C.S.: 423610
Tom Reagan (Pres)

ATRAX MARKETING

7065 Belding Rd NE, Rockford, MI 49341
Tel.: (616) 915-2121
Web Site:
  http://www.atraxmarketing.com
Year Founded: 2004
Sales Range: Less than $1 Million
Emp.: 1
Advetising Agency
N.A.I.C.S.: 541810
Richard Hill (Pres)

ATREL VIDEOSYSTEMS

5B Lyberty Way, Westford, MA 01886
Tel.: (978) 263-5775
Web Site: http://www.artel.com
Year Founded: 2001
Sales Range: $10-24.9 Million
Emp.: 35
Electronic Hardware Supplier
N.A.I.C.S.: 423690
Richard Dellacanonica (Founder, Pres & CEO)
Richard Lee Harrington (VP-Ops)
Kevin Ancelin (VP-Sls & Bus Dev-Jacksonville)

Subsidiaries:

Artel (1)
5B Lyberty Way, Westford, MA 01886
Tel.: (978) 263-5775
Web Site: http://www.artel.com
Rev.: $18,000,000
Provider of Fiber Optic Video Transmission Equipment
N.A.I.C.S.: 334220

ATREND USA

2701 Lively Blvd, Elk Grove Village, IL 60007
Web Site: http://www.atrendusa.com
Year Founded: 1996
Sales Range: $1-9.9 Million
Emp.: 35
Manufactures & Designs High-end Car Audio Accessories & Sub-Woofer Enclosures
N.A.I.C.S.: 334310
Kevin Hundal (CEO)

ATREX INC.

175 Industrial Loop S, Orange Park, FL 32073
Tel.: (904) 264-9086
Web Site: http://www.atrexinc.com
Rev.: $20,000,000
Emp.: 100
Telephone & Communication Line Construction
N.A.I.C.S.: 237130
David Brafford (Pres)
Bill Musser (VP)

ATRIA CONSULTING, LLC

112 W 34th St 18th Fl, New York, NY 10102
Tel.: (646) 722-8700
Web Site:
  http://www.atriaconsulting.com
Year Founded: 2006
Sales Range: $1-9.9 Million
Human Resource Consulting Services
N.A.I.C.S.: 541612
Michelle Arakaki (Mgr-Staffing)

ATRIA SENIOR LIVING, INC.

300 E Market St Ste 100, Louisville, KY 40202
Tel.: (502) 779-4700
Web Site:
  http://www.atriaseniorliving.com
Sales Range: $450-499.9 Million
Emp.: 9,000
Continuing Care Retirement Communities Operator
N.A.I.C.S.: 623311
John Moore (CEO)
Walter Hall (Dir-HR)
Eli Stull (Dir-Culinary Svcs)
Todd Kiziminski (Dir-Recruitment)
Eric Leef (Chief HR Officer)
Regan Atkinson (Sr VP-Product Dev)
Kelli Corney (VP-Strategic Mktg & Creative)
Michael Brown Jr. (Exec Dir)

Subsidiaries:

Atria Guilderland (1)
300 Melrose Ct, Guilderland, NY 12084
Tel.: (518) 218-0233
Sales Range: $1-9.9 Million
Emp.: 40
Continuing Care Retirement Community Operator
N.A.I.C.S.: 623311

Atria Huntington (1)
165 Beverly Rd, Huntington Station, NY 11746
Tel.: (631) 714-6332
Web Site: http://www.atriaseniorliving.com
Sales Range: $1-9.9 Million
Emp.: 65
Continuing Care Retirement Community Operator
N.A.I.C.S.: 623311
Jerry Ruark (Dir)
Khristine Rogers (VP)

Atria Palm Desert (1)
44300 San Pasqual Ave Ofc, Palm Desert, CA 92260
Tel.: (760) 773-3772
Web Site: http://www.atriaseniorliving.com
Sales Range: $1-9.9 Million
Emp.: 41
Continuing Care Retirement Community Operator
N.A.I.C.S.: 623311
Vicki Mariger (Exec Dir)

ATRIUM CENTERS, LLC

2 Easton Oval Ste 210, Columbus, OH 43219-6013
Tel.: (614) 416-0600
Web Site:
  http://www.atriumlivingcenters.com
Sales Range: $50-74.9 Million
Emp.: 4,000
Assisted Living & Rehabilitation Services
N.A.I.C.S.: 621610
Dennis Lockhart (Controller)
Pam Reese (Chief Clinical Officer)
Gertie Dickey (VP-Clinical Compliance)
Graham Phillips (Chief Dev Officer)
Blake Church (CFO)

ATRIUM DEVELOPMENT INC.

115 Atrium Way Ste 204, Columbia, SC 29223
Tel.: (803) 736-7716
Web Site:
  https://www.atriumdevelopment.com
Sales Range: $10-24.9 Million
Emp.: 4
Land Subdivider & Developer Services
N.A.I.C.S.: 237210
David H. Jacobs (Pres)

ATRIUM STAFFING SERVICES LTD.

71 5th Ave Ste 1415 3rd Fl, New York, NY 10003

Tel.: (212) 292-0550
Web Site: http://www.atriumstaff.com
Sales Range: $10-24.9 Million
Emp.: 40
Temporary Help & Staffing Service
N.A.I.C.S.: 561311
Rebecca Cenni (Founder)
John Liscinsky (CFO)
Juliana No (Mgr-Bus Dev)

ATRIUS HEALTH, INC.

275 Grove St Ste 3-300, Newton, MA 02466
Tel.: (617) 559-8000   MA
Web Site: http://www.atriushealth.org
Year Founded: 2004
Sales Range: $25-49.9 Million
Health Care Srvices
N.A.I.C.S.: 622110
Leland Stacy (CFO)
Daniel Moriarty (CIO)
Kimberly Nelson (Chief Legal Officer)
Joe Kimura (Chief Medical Officer)
Marci Sindell (Chief Strategy Officer & Sr VP-External Affairs)
Gerard Velasco (VP-Performance Excellence)
Rachel Rosenblum (COO)
Jane F. Fogg (Dir-Specialty-Internal Medicine & Population Health)
Richard Lopez (Sr VP-Population Health)
Jennifer Derkazarian (Sr Dir-Nursing)

ATRONIX INC.

6401 S Country Club Rd Ste 101, Tucson, AZ 85706
Tel.: (978) 313-2500
Web Site: http://www.atronix.com
Rev.: $25,000,000
Emp.: 80
Computer Peripheral Equipment; Manufacturing & Assembly
N.A.I.C.S.: 334118
Peter Schofield (Pres)
Sandra Apostolos (Mgr-Acctg & HR)

ATS ACOUSTICS

15 W Main St, Piper City, IL 60959
Tel.: (815) 686-2705
Web Site:
  http://www.atsacoustics.com
Year Founded: 2005
Sales Range: $1-9.9 Million
Emp.: 20
Mfr & E-Commerce Sales of Acoustical Panels & Other Acoustical Products
N.A.I.C.S.: 334310
Mark Aardsma (Owner)

ATS AUTOMATION INC.

450 Shaptuck Ave, Renton, WA 98055
Tel.: (425) 251-9680
Web Site: http://www.atsinc.org
Year Founded: 1986
Rev.: $10,000,000
Emp.: 75
Automatic Environmental Control Manufacturing for Residential, Commercial & Appliance Use
N.A.I.C.S.: 334512
Jerry Weatherhogg (Mgr-IT)
Ken Duncan (Project Mgr)
Lucy Gedney (VP-Sls & Mktg)
Josh Cales (Pres)
Brian Allen (CEO)

Subsidiaries:

WayPoint Systems, Inc. (1)
10 Mansell Court E Ste 200, Roswell, GA 30076
Tel.: (770) 649-6100
Web Site: http://www.waypointsys.com
Electrical Contractor
N.A.I.C.S.: 238210

Roger T. Bennett (Pres)
Andrew Segal (VP-Sls)
Ray Gregory (Engr-Low Voltage Sys & Sls)
Phil Lambert (Project Mgr)
Daniel West (Project Mgr)

ATS ELECTRIC, INC.

840 N 52nd Ave, Phoenix, AZ 85043
Tel.: (602) 943-6120
Web Site:
  http://www.atselectricinc.com
Year Founded: 2001
Rev.: $16,500,000
Emp.: 50
Electrical Contractor
N.A.I.C.S.: 238210
Vincent Streech (Chm)
Beth Sutton (Office Mgr)
David Duran (Mgr-HR)
David Shaub (VP-Ops)
Robert Sutton (Pres)
Tim Tucker (Controller)

ATS GROUP, LLC

613 N Euchee Vly Rd, Cushing, OK 74023
Tel.: (918) 225-1010   DE
Web Site:
  http://www.alliancetankservice.com
Year Founded: 2008
Metal Tank Engineering, Fabrication, Inspection & Repair Services
N.A.I.C.S.: 332420
John Allcorn (Pres & CEO)

ATS PRODUCTS INC.

2785 Goodrick Ave, Richmond, CA 94801
Tel.: (510) 234-3173
Web Site: https://www.atsduct.com
Year Founded: 1978
Sales Range: $10-24.9 Million
Emp.: 15
Plastics Hardware & Building Products: Corrosion Resistant, Fire Retardant Duct Systems
N.A.I.C.S.: 326199
Jeff Shea (Pres & CEO)
Doug Williams (VP-Sls & Engrg)
Kathleen Passalacqua (Head-Acctg)
Lou Flores (Mgr-Sls)

ATS TRAINING, LLC.

65 Bonneau Rd, Claremont, NH 03743
Tel.: (603) 727-7304
Sales Range: $25-49.9 Million
Emp.: 800
Electrical Wiring Services
N.A.I.C.S.: 238210
Alan Donohue (Dir-Ops)

ATSCO FOOTWEAR GROUP

755 Dedham St, Canton, MA 02021-1402
Tel.: (508) 583-7600
Web Site: http://www.khombu.com
Rev.: $50,000,000
Emp.: 25
Footwear
N.A.I.C.S.: 424340
Alan Colman (CEO)

ATSIGN, INC.

1900 Camden Ave Ste 101, San Jose, CA 95124
Tel.: (650) 339-9451
Software Development Services
N.A.I.C.S.: 541511

ATTACHE

10 E Weber Rd # A, Columbus, OH 43202-1448
Tel.: (614) 268-9484
Web Site:
  http://www.abandonconvention.com
Sales Range: $1-9.9 Million

Emp.: 10
Communication & Staffing Services
N.A.I.C.S.: 561499
Cheryl Rodeheffer (Pres)

ATTACK MARKETING, LLC
367 Nineth St Ste B, San Francisco, CA 94103
Tel.: (415) 433-1499
Web Site:
    http://www.attackmarketing.net
Year Founded: 2003
Sales Range: $1-9.9 Million
Emp.: 15
Advertising, Graphic Design, Guerilla Marketing, In-Store Advertising, Mobile Marketing, Out-of-Home Media, Outdoor
N.A.I.C.S.: 541890
Andrew Loos (Owner & Mng Partner)
Pete D'Andrea (VP-Partnerships-New York)
Christian Jurinka (Co-Founder & CEO)

ATTAIN, LLC
1600 Tysons Blvd Ste 1400, McLean, VA 22102
Tel.: (703) 857-2200
Web Site: http://www.attain.com
Research & Development in the Physical, Engineering & Life Sciences
N.A.I.C.S.: 541715
Greg J. Baroni (Chm & CEO)
Simon Szykman (Partner & CTO-Federal Svcs)
Manish Agerwal (Pres & COO)
Ravichandra Mudumby (Partner)
John Mandell (Mng Dir-Natl Security Practice)
Joseph Kehoe (Mng Dir)

Subsidiaries:

ACF Solutions, LLC.   (1)
11800 Sunrise Vly Dr Ste 424, Reston, VA 20191-5302
Tel.: (703) 834-6996
Web Site: http://www.acfsolutions.com
Rev.: $1,500,000
Emp.: 15
Computer System Design Services
N.A.I.C.S.: 541512
Doug Sharpe (CTO)
Kristin Sharpe (Pres)
Aimee Cubbage (VP-Ops)

ATTARCO INC.
2400 Florida Ave, Richmond, CA 94804
Tel.: (510) 525-3333
Web Site: http://www.attarco.com
Sales Range: $10-24.9 Million
Emp.: 50
Import Engines & Transmissions
N.A.I.C.S.: 459999
T. Attar (Pres)

ATTEA & ATTEA, P.C.
11 Main St, Hamburg, NY 14075
Tel.: (716) 648-7000
Web Site: https://www.attealaw.com
Year Founded: 1972
Law firm
N.A.I.C.S.: 541110
Richard J. Attea (Sr Partner)
Brian F. Attea (Mng Partner)
Ryan F. McCann (Partner)

ATTEBURY GRAIN, LLC
2025 S Hughes St Ste 100, Amarillo, TX 79110
Tel.: (806) 335-1639
Web Site: https://www.attebury.com
Year Founded: 1954
Rev.: $100,190,772
Emp.: 300
Grain Warehousing & Distribution
N.A.I.C.S.: 424510

Susan Attebury (Pres)

ATTENSITY GROUP, INC.
1600 Seaport Blvd Ste 200, Redwood City, CA 94063
Tel.: (650) 433-1700   DE
Web Site: http://www.attensity.com
Year Founded: 2006
Sales Range: $50-74.9 Million
Emp.: 100
Holding Company; Business Intelligence & Information Management Software & Services
N.A.I.C.S.: 551112
Howard Lau (Chm & CEO)
Frank Brown (CFO)
James Purchase (VP-Bus Dev)
Cary Fulbright (Chief Strategy Officer)
Mark Schmelzenbach (CTO)
David Pikal (Gen Counsel)
Mike White (VP-Ops & IT Security)

Subsidiaries:

Attensity Corporation   (1)
1600 Seaport Blvd Ste 200, Redwood City, CA 94063
Tel.: (650) 433-1700
Web Site: http://www.attensity.com
Business Intelligence & Information Management Software & Services
N.A.I.C.S.: 513210
Howard Lau (Chm & CEO)
Frank Brown (COO)
Mark Schmelzenbach (CTO)
Cary Fulbright (Chief Strategy Officer)
Mark White (VP-Ops & IT Security)

ATTERBERY TRUCK SALES, INC.
524 Pamco Rd, Lake Charles, LA 70615
Tel.: (337) 433-0675
Sales Range: $10-24.9 Million
Emp.: 39
Car Whslr
N.A.I.C.S.: 441110
Ted S. Atterbery (Chm)

ATTIC LIGHT ENTERTAIN-MENT, INC.
23 Corpoate Plz Ste 248, Newport Beach, CA 92661
Tel.: (310) 906-0607   NV
Web Site:
    http://www.atticlightentertains.com
Year Founded: 2007
All-Digital Motion Picture Production Services
N.A.I.C.S.: 512110
Paul Winze (Dir-Creative)
Ashley Sandberg (VP-Dev)
Rob Nederhorst (CTO)
Stephen M. Griffith Jr. (Pres & CEO)

ATTIS INDUSTRIES INC.
12540 Broadwell Rd Ste 1203, Milton, GA 30004
Tel.: (678) 580-5661   NY
Web Site: http://attisind.com
Year Founded: 1993
Holding Company; Sustainable Materials; Diagnostic & Healthcare Solutions; Renewable Biofuel Production
N.A.I.C.S.: 551112
Jeffrey S. Cosman (Chm & CEO)
Joe D'Arelli (Dir-Compliance)
Greg Hamilton (CFO)

ATTITUDE DRINKS INCORPORATED
11231 US Hwy 1 Ste 200, North Palm Beach, FL 33408
Tel.: (561) 227-2727   DE
Web Site:
    http://www.attitudedrinks.com
Year Founded: 1988
Rev.: $738,465

Assets: $1,581,898
Liabilities: $18,524,276
Net Worth: ($16,942,378)
Earnings: ($5,030,873)
Emp.: 48
Fiscal Year-end: 03/31/15
Holding Company; Milk-based Sports Recovery & Nutritional Supplement Beverage Mfr & Marketer
N.A.I.C.S.: 551112
John L. Shea (Exec VP-Sls)
Craig A. Peters (Exec VP-Ops & Production)

Subsidiaries:

Attitude Drink Company, Inc.   (1)
712 US Hwy 1 Ste 200, North Palm Beach, FL 33408
Tel.: (561) 227-2727
Web Site: http://www.attitudedrinks.com
Milk-based Sports Recovery & Nutritional Supplement Beverages Mfr & Marketer
N.A.I.C.S.: 311511
Roy G. Warren (Chm, Pres & CEO)
Tommy E. Kee (CFO)
John L. Shea (Exec VP-Sls)
Craig A. Peters (Exec VP-Ops & Production)
Niki Fuller (VP & Brand Mgr)
Debbie Lieblong (VP-Corp Svcs)

Harrison, Vickers & Waterman, Inc.   (1)
5781 Schaefer Ave, Chino, CA 91710
Tel.: (310) 755-4033
Web Site:
    https://www.modernprosolutions.com
Commercial Loan Leader Services
N.A.I.C.S.: 522291
Robert Tetsch (CEO)

ATTITUDES IN DRESSING INC.
107 Trumbull St Bldg B8, Elizabeth, NJ 07206
Tel.: (908) 354-7218
Web Site:
    http://www.bodywrappers.com
Year Founded: 1980
Rev.: $18,795,888
Emp.: 50
Athletic Clothing: Women's, Misses' & Juniors' Mfr
N.A.I.C.S.: 315250
Marie West (Pres)
Michael Rubin (CEO & Partner)

ATTO TECHNOLOGY, INC.
155 Crosspoint Pkwy, Getzville, NY 14068
Tel.: (716) 691-7166
Web Site: http://www.attotech.com
Year Founded: 1988
Emp.: 137
Storage Connectivity & Infrastructure Solution Services
N.A.I.C.S.: 493110
Timothy J. Klein (Co-Founder, Pres & CEO)
David A. Snell (Co-Founder, CTO & VP-Engrg)
James F. Masiello (VP-Fin & HR)
Timothy J. Boser (VP-Ops)

ATTORNEYS' TITLE GUARANTY FUND, INC.
7600 E Eastman Ave Ste 130, Denver, CO 80231
Tel.: (303) 292-3055   CO
Web Site: https://www.atgf.net
Year Founded: 1950
Sales Range: $25-49.9 Million
Emp.: 20
Title Insurance Underwriter
N.A.I.C.S.: 524127
Eric Morgan (Pres)
Christine Sparks (COO)
Tania M. S. Stori (VP-Claims & Litigation)

Arden K. Miner (VP-Underwriting, Support & Dev)
Chris Burhans (CIO & Sr VP)
Deborah Frank Feinen (VP-Downstate)

ATTORNEYS' TITLE INSURANCE FUND
6545 Corporate Centre Blvd, Orlando, FL 32822-3217
Tel.: (407) 240-3863   FL
Web Site: https://www.thefund.com
Year Founded: 1947
Rev.: $111,839,907
Emp.: 900
Title Insurance & Title Information
N.A.I.C.S.: 524127
Jimmy R. Jones (Pres)
B. Gwen Geier (COO & Exec VP)
Sharon K. Priest (Sr VP-Production Ops)
Deanna Bolger (CFO & Sr VP)
G. Robert Arnold (VP-Legal Svcs)
Ted Conner (VP & Assoc Gen Counsel)
Melissa Scaletta (VP-Underwriting & Mgr-Education)
Jeff Rogero (CIO & Sr VP)
Melissa Jay Murphy (Gen Counsel & Sr VP)

Subsidiaries:

Attorneys' Title Fund Services, LLC   (1)
6545 Corporate Centre Blvd, Orlando, FL 32822
Tel.: (407) 240-3863
Real Estate Management Services
N.A.I.C.S.: 531390
Joann Cherrington (Mgr-HR)

ATTRONICA COMPUTERS INC.
15867 Gaither Dr, Gaithersburg, MD 20877-1403
Tel.: (301) 417-0070   MD
Web Site: http://www.attronica.com
Year Founded: 1983
Sales Range: $50-74.9 Million
Emp.: 85
Computers, Peripherals & Software
N.A.I.C.S.: 541512
Ali Tajdar (VP-Engrg Svcs)
Esmail Sadeghi (VP-Mgmt Info Svcs)
Vivek Karkhanis (Pres & COO)

ATTUNE FOODS, INC.
790 Tennessee St, San Francisco, CA 94107
Tel.: (415) 401-0080
Web Site:
    http://www.worldpantry.com
Year Founded: 2003
Emp.: 50
Cereals & Snacks Mfr
N.A.I.C.S.: 311230
David Miller (Pres)
Peter Harris (CEO)
Rob Goluba (Dir-Mktg)

Subsidiaries:

Peace Cereal   (1)
2545 Prairie Rd, Eugene, OR 97402
Tel.: (541) 461-2160
Web Site: http://www.peacecereal.com
Breakfast Cereal Mfr
N.A.I.C.S.: 311230

ATTUNIX CORPORATION
10500 NE 8th St Suite 625, Bellevue, WA 98004
Tel.: (206) 774-3163
Web Site: http://www.attunix.com
Year Founded: 2006
Sales Range: $1-9.9 Million
Emp.: 26
Business Consulting & Technology Services Including Mobile, Cloud

Attunix Corporation—(Continued)

Computing, Portals & Collaboration, Application Development & Enterprise Systems Integration
N.A.I.C.S.: 541618
Matt O'Donnell (Pres)
Marcy Knott (Mgr-Bus Dev)

ATW COMPANIES INC.
55 Service Ave, Warwick, RI 02886
Tel.: (401) 739-0740
Web Site: http://www.atwcompanies.com
Rev.: $35,000,000
Emp.: 50
Investment Holding Company
N.A.I.C.S.: 551112
Mike Howard (Pres-Judson Smith)
Rob Hall (Pres-Parmatech)

Subsidiaries:

Parmatech Corporation   (1)
2221 Pine View Way, Petaluma, CA 94954-5688
Tel.: (707) 778-2266
Web Site: http://www.parmatech.com
Sales Range: $10-24.9 Million
Emp.: 85
Mfr of Complex Injection-Molded Parts from Powder Metals
N.A.I.C.S.: 331221
Thomas Chagnon (Engr-Sls)
Bob DeQuattro (Mgr-Quality)
Anthony Girard (Plant Mgr)
Anita Shah (Mgr-Ops)
Suzanne Stites (Mgr-Quality)
Melissa Tentnowski (Mgr-HR-California)

ATWATER REAL ESTATE
42 7th St Ste 102A, Astoria, OR 97103-4226
Tel.: (503) 325-7653
Web Site: http://www.atwaterastoria.com
Sales Range: $10-24.9 Million
Emp.: 4
Real Estate Agent & Brokerage Services
N.A.I.C.S.: 531210
Randy Bowe (Owner)

ATWELL MEDIA SERVICES, INC.
15101 Seguridad Sloughhouse, Rancho Murieta, CA 95683
Tel.: (916) 354-8585
Web Site: http://www.atwellmediaservices.com
Year Founded: 2002
Sales Range: $25-49.9 Million
Emp.: 3
Media Buying Services
N.A.I.C.S.: 541830
Brian Atwell (Owner)

ATWELL, LLC
2 Towne Sq Ste 700, Southfield, MI 48076
Tel.: (248) 447-2000   MI
Web Site: https://www.atwell-group.com
Engineering, Construction Management & Technical Consulting Services
N.A.I.C.S.: 541330
David L. Richter (Chief Growth Officer & Exec VP)
Brian Wenzel (CEO)
Kurt Beleck (VP-Program Mgmt)
Timothy Augustine (Partner & VP)
Donna Jakubowicz (Dir-Mktg)
Alan N. Harris (Gen Counsel & VP)
Thomas Lucey (Dir-Land Dev-Cleveland)
Jim Curry (Project Mgr-Land Solutions-Lakewood)
Matthew Bissett (Pres)

Sam Lichenstein (Project Mgr-Land Solutions, Power & Energy-San Antonio)
John Gleason (Project Mgr-Land Svcs, Power & Energy)
Mark Prawl (Sr Project Engr-Power & Energy-Denver)
Tara Corbett (Project Mgr-Environmental-Colorado)
Richard Weed (Sr Project Mgr-Land Dev Grp-Denver)
Michael Ritch (Sr Project Mgr-Real Estate & Land Dev)
Adrian Reyes (Sr Project Mgr-Oil & Gas)
Christopher R. Rutledge (VP-Environmental Svcs)
Dan McNulty (COO)
Justin Faughn (Dir-Oil and Gas)
Ryan Hayse (Project Mgr-Oil & Gas Team)
John R. Stone (Pres-Strategic Construction Solutions, Inc)
Debriah Wilson (VP)
Elizabeth Babcock (Sr Project Mgr-Power & Energy, Land & ROW Solutions Grp-Lakewood)
Tracey Dubuque (VP)
Bourke Thomas (Dir-Environmental Svcs)
Jeff Williams (Project Mgr-Environmental Grp)

Subsidiaries:

Atwell AZ, LLC   (1)
4700 E Southern Ave, Mesa, AZ 85206
Tel.: (480) 218-8831
Web Site: http://www.atwell-group.com
Sales Range: $25-49.9 Million
Emp.: 50
Engineering, Construction Management & Technical Consulting Services
N.A.I.C.S.: 541330

Bay Engineering, Inc.   (1)
2661 Riva Rd Bldg 800, Annapolis, MD 97401-2749
Tel.: (717) 889-2066
Web Site: https://www.bayengineering.com
Engineeering Services
N.A.I.C.S.: 541330
Tim Martin (Pres)

Biscayne Engineering Company, Inc.   (1)
529 W Flagler St, Miami, FL 33130
Tel.: (305) 324-7671
Web Site: https://www.biscayneengineering.com
Emp.: 100
Engineering Services
N.A.I.C.S.: 334516

Hydro Consultants Inc.   (1)
10275 Siegen Ln, Baton Rouge, LA 70810
Tel.: (225) 766-4422
Rev.: $2,370,000
Emp.: 30
Geophysical Surveying & Mapping Services
N.A.I.C.S.: 541360
Ernie Gammon (Pres)

Mead Gilman & Associates   (1)
17625 130th Ave NE Ste 104, Woodinville, WA 98072-8706
Tel.: (425) 486-1252
Web Site: http://www.meadgilman.com
Surveying & Mapping Services
N.A.I.C.S.: 541370
Timothy Griffin (Partner)
Shane Barnes (Principal)

Peak Civil Consultants Inc.   (1)
200 W Hampden Ave Ste 200, Englewood, CO 80110
Tel.: (720) 855-3859
Web Site: http://www.peakcivil.com
Emp.: 10
Engineeering Services
N.A.I.C.S.: 541330
Jeff French (Pres)
L. Kelley Stevenson (Mgr-Survey)
Bob Kelsey (VP)
Allison Rice (Engr-Project)

Peak Power Engineering, Inc.   (1)
143 Union Blvd Ste 800, Lakewood, CO 80228
Tel.: (303) 462-1100
Web Site: http://www.peakpwr.com
Power System Engineering & Consulting Services
N.A.I.C.S.: 541330

W Dexter Bender & Associates, LLC   (1)
2052 Virginia Ave, Fort Myers, FL 33901
Tel.: (239) 334-3680
Web Site: http://www.dexbender.com
Sales Range: $1-9.9 Million
Emp.: 20
Scientific & Technical Consulting Services
N.A.I.C.S.: 541690
Tyler C. King (Pres)

Waldrop Engineering, P.A.   (1)
28100 Bonita Grande Dr Ste 305, Bonita Springs, FL 34135
Tel.: (239) 405-7777
Web Site: http://www.waldropengineering.com
Sales Range: $1-9.9 Million
Emp.: 20
Civil Engineering, Landscape Architecture & Planning
N.A.I.C.S.: 237990
Ronald Waldrop (Founder & CEO)
Ryan Binkowski (Dir-Plng & Landscape Architecture)
Eric Dunning (Project Mgr)
Victor Barbosa (Dir-Engrg)

ATWOOD CHEVROLET INC.
2339 N Frontage Rd, Vicksburg, MS 39180
Tel.: (601) 501-7055
Web Site: https://www.atwoodchevrolet.com
Rev.: $16,700,000
Emp.: 60
New & Used Car Dealer
N.A.I.C.S.: 441110
Debbie Berry (Bus Mgr-Sls)

ATWOOD DISTRIBUTING, INC.
500 S Garland, Enid, OK 73703
Tel.: (580) 233-3702   OK
Web Site: https://www.atwoods.com
Year Founded: 1960
Sales Range: $500-549.9 Million
Emp.: 1,000
General Merchandise, Hardware & Automotive Supplies
N.A.I.C.S.: 444230
Gary A. Atwood (CEO)
Brian Atwood (Pres)
Shirley Groom (Mgr-Acctg)
Jeff Gwin (VP)

ATWOOD ENTERPRISES INC.
4863 American Rd, Rockford, IL 61109
Tel.: (815) 873-9710
Rev.: $25,400,000
Emp.: 6
Commercial & Industrial Building Operation
N.A.I.C.S.: 531120
Seth G. Atwood (Pres)

Subsidiaries:

United Realty Corporation   (1)
4863 American Rd, Rockford, IL 61109
Tel.: (815) 873-9710
Commercial & Industrial Building Operation
N.A.I.C.S.: 531120

ATWOOD FENCE COMPANY INC.
2048 Attala Rd 2202, Kosciusko, MS 39090
Tel.: (662) 289-6338
Web Site: http://www.atwoodfenceco.com
Year Founded: 1971
Rev.: $16,300,000

Emp.: 40
Highway & Street Construction Trade Contractor
N.A.I.C.S.: 237310
Kay Atwood (Pres)

ATWORKGROUP LLC
6700 Baum Dr Ste 25, Knoxville, TN 37919
Tel.: (865) 444-3530   TN
Web Site: http://www.atwork.com
Temporary Staffing
N.A.I.C.S.: 533110
Joseph Moore (CFO)
Mike Baumgardner (Sr VP-Ops)
Kim Baumgardner (Sr VP-Administration & Controller)
Jason Leverant (Pres & COO)
Cliff Harber (VP-Franchise Sls)
Benjamin Hubbard (VP)
John D. Hall Jr. (CEO)

Subsidiaries:

Desert Personnel Services   (1)
73350 El Paseo Ste 205, Palm Desert, CA 92260-4240
Tel.: (760) 346-3945
Web Site: http://www.desertpersonnel.com
Employment Placement Agencies
N.A.I.C.S.: 561311
Sarah Seils (Owner)

Momentum Specialized Staffing   (1)
3118 W Thomas Rd Ste 711, Phoenix, AZ 85017-5308
Tel.: (602) 477-8193
Web Site: http://www.peckerman.com
Employment Agencies
N.A.I.C.S.: 561311
Michael D. Hayes (Owner)
Raina Fuentes (Office Mgr)
Todd Johnson (Co-Owner)
Bill Begina (Office Mgr)

ATZENHOFFER CHEVROLET COMPANY
3211 N Navarro St, Victoria, TX 77901
Tel.: (361) 582-9041
Web Site: https://www.atzenhoffer.com
Year Founded: 1926
Sales Range: $100-124.9 Million
Emp.: 163
Car Whslr
N.A.I.C.S.: 441110
Tommy Taylor (Gen Mgr)

AUA PRIVATE EQUITY PARTNERS LLC
1 N Clematis St Ste 500, West Palm Beach, FL 33401
Tel.: (561) 851-9500
Web Site: https://auaequity.com
Emp.: 100
Privater Equity Firm
N.A.I.C.S.: 523999

AUBERGEDUSOLEIL
180 Rutherford Hill Rd, Rutherford, CA 94573
Tel.: (707) 963-1211
Web Site: http://www.aubergedusoleil.com
Sales Range: $10-24.9 Million
Emp.: 270
French Restaurant
N.A.I.C.S.: 721110
Jessica Watts (Mgr-Event)
Veronica King (Mgr-Food & Beverage)
Deanna Montoro (Dir-Ops)
Demetri Smith (Mgr-Food & Beverage)
Kris Margerum (Dir-Wine)
Bradley Reynolds (Mgr)

AUBERLE

1101 Hartman St, McKeesport, PA
15132
Tel.: (412) 673-5800   PA
Web Site: https://www.auberle.org
Year Founded: 1952
Emp.: 100
Child & Family Care Services
N.A.I.C.S.: 624190
Stephanie Walsh (COO)
John P. Lydon (CEO)

Subsidiaries:

Ward Home, Inc.   (1)
2275 Swallow Hill Rd Bldg 800, Pittsburgh,
PA 15220
Tel.: (412) 722-1404
Youth Care Services
N.A.I.C.S.: 624110

AUBREY ORGANICS INC.
5046 W Linebaugh Ave, Tampa, FL
33624
Tel.: (813) 877-4186
Web Site: http://www.aubrey-
organics.com
Year Founded: 1967
Sales Range: $10-24.9 Million
Emp.: 50
Toilet Preparations & Cosmetics Mfr
N.A.I.C.S.: 325620
Aubrey W. Hampton (Founder &
CEO)
Patricia Basin (Mgr-Ops & Mktg
Svcs)
Karen Ress (Exec Dir-Natl Sls)

**AUBREY SILVEY ENTER-
PRISES INC.**
371 Hamp Jones Rd, Carrollton, GA
30117-9492
Tel.: (770) 834-0738   GA
Web Site: https://www.silvey.com
Year Founded: 1971
Rev.: $26,127,531
Emp.: 300
Heavy Construction, Power Equip-
ment Services & Mfr
N.A.I.C.S.: 237990
Tommy Muse (Pres)
Mike Vines (CFO & VP)
Anne Daniel (Bus Mgr)
Stephen Hodge (Mgr-Indus Rels-Corp
Loss Control)
Charles Bolton (Mgr-Power Equip-
ment Svcs)
Baiju Gajjar (Project Mgr-EPC Grp)
Joseph Murrah (Mgr-Sls)
Jose Soria (Superintendent)
Trent Gable (Superintendent)

Subsidiaries:

Associated Substation Engineering
Inc.   (1)
919 Alabama Ave S, Bremen, GA 30110-
2006
Tel.: (770) 537-0033
Web Site: http://www.aseng.com
Sales Range: $10-24.9 Million
Emp.: 20
Engineeering Services
N.A.I.C.S.: 541330
Van Pelt (CFO)

Sefcor Inc.   (1)
1150 Uniform Rd, Griffin, GA
30224   (100%)
Tel.: (770) 227-8297
Web Site: http://www.sefcor.com
Rev.: $4,854,291
Emp.: 50
Mfr Power Work Connectors
N.A.I.C.S.: 335931
Mark Miller (Gen Mgr)
William Gatlin (Supvr-Inventory)

Silvey Information Systems Inc.   (1)
136 Windemere Dr, Bremen, GA 30110-
2318
Tel.: (770) 834-9892
Web Site: http://www.silveyis.com

Sales Range: $10-24.9 Million
Emp.: 4
Computer Integrated Systems Design
N.A.I.C.S.: 541512

AUBUCHON HOMES, INC.
4707 SE 9th Pl, Cape Coral, FL
33904
Tel.: (239) 549-6358   FL
Web Site:
    https://www.aubuchonhomes.com
Year Founded: 1992
Sales Range: $1-9.9 Million
Emp.: 14
New Single-Family Housing Con-
struction
N.A.I.C.S.: 236115
Gary Aubuchon (Pres)
Jim Aubuchon (VP)
Cindy Cross (CFO)
Justin Einstein (Dir-Ops)
Kyle Lantz (Controller)
Diane VanArsdale (Dir-Mktg & Sls)
Jeff Miloff (Dir-Sls)
Linda Whitmore (Mgr-Design Ctr)
Matt Henry (Controller)
Karen LaRoc (Coord-Selections)
Joe Sealey (Dir-New Home Sls)
Wes Allen (Mgr-Info Sys)
Steve Santora (Mgr-Warranty)

**AUBURN COMMUNITY HOSPI-
TAL**
17 Lansing St, Auburn, NY 13021
Tel.: (315) 255-7011   NY
Web Site:
    http://www.auburnhospital.org
Year Founded: 1878
Sales Range: $75-99.9 Million
Emp.: 1,035
Community Health Care Services
N.A.I.C.S.: 621498
Christopher Ryan (CIO)
R. J. Cruz (Controller)
Ann E. Mahon (VP-Quality)
Scott Andrew Berlucchi (Pres & CEO)
William Dorr (Sec)
Anthony D. Franceschelli (Vice Chm)
Joseph P. Bartolotta (Chm)
Jason Lesch (CFO)
Michael G. Wilson (Chief Medical
Officer)

AUBURN CORPORATION
10490 164th Pl, Orland Park, IL
60467
Tel.: (708) 349-7676
Web Site:
    https://www.auburncorp.com
Sales Range: $10-24.9 Million
Emp.: 10
Windows
N.A.I.C.S.: 423310
Albert Gierut (Pres)
Dave Arcand (Project Mgr-Comml
Sls)
Doug Schuetz (Project Mgr)

**AUBURN MANUFACTURING
INC.**
34 Walker Rd, Mechanic Falls, ME
04256
Tel.: (207) 345-8271
Web Site: http://www.auburnmfg.com
Sales Range: $10-24.9 Million
Emp.: 46
Fire Resistance Finishing: Manmade
& Silk Broadwoven
N.A.I.C.S.: 313310
Kathie M. Leonard (Pres & CEO)
Matt Lampron (Mgr-Bus Dev)
Steven P. Boulet (Mgr-HR)
Garrett VanAtta (VP-Mfg)

AUBURN MOTOR SALES

699 Center St Rte 4 N, Auburn, ME
04210
Tel.: (207) 784-2321
Web Site:
    http://www.roweauburn.com
Sales Range: $50-74.9 Million
Emp.: 120
New & Used Automobiles Dealers
N.A.I.C.S.: 441110
Michelle Pettengill (Treas & Control-
ler)
Thomas Mooney (Mgr-Lease & Fleet)

AUBURN SUPPLY CO. INC.
3850 W 167th St, Markham, IL 60428
Tel.: (708) 596-9800
Web Site:
    https://www.auburnsupply.com
Sales Range: $10-24.9 Million
Emp.: 74
Plumbing Supplies
N.A.I.C.S.: 423720
William Smith (VP)
James Smith (VP)
Jim Kolebes (Controller)

**AUCTION BROADCASTING
CO. LLC**
1919 S Post Rd, Indianapolis, IN
46239
Tel.: (317) 862-7325
Web Site:
    http://www.auctionbroadcasting.com
Sales Range: $50-74.9 Million
Emp.: 1,000
Automobile Auction
N.A.I.C.S.: 423110

**AUCTION SYSTEMS AUCTION-
EERS & APPRAISERS, INC.**
951 W Watkins St, Phoenix, AZ
85007
Tel.: (602) 252-4842   AZ
Web Site:
    http://www.auctionandappraise.com
Year Founded: 1995
Sales Range: $75-99.9 Million
Emp.: 71
Auctions
N.A.I.C.S.: 541618
Deborah A. Weidenhamer (Founder &
CEO)

AUCTION WORLD USA, LLC
7722 US Open Loop, Lakewood
Ranch, FL 34202
Tel.: (941) 907-2004
Web Site:
    https://www.auctionworldusa.com
Commercial Real Estate Broker &
Auctioneer
N.A.I.C.S.: 531210
Mark Henderson (Owner)

AUDACIOUS INQUIRY, LLC
5523 Research Park Dr Ste 370, Bal-
timore, MD 21228
Tel.: (301) 560-6999
Web Site: https://www.ainq.com
Year Founded: 2004
Sales Range: $1-9.9 Million
Emp.: 30
Business Management Consulting
Services
N.A.I.C.S.: 561499
Christopher Brandt (Mng Partner)
Scott Afzal (Partner)
Robert Horst (Principal)
Greg Farnum (Principal)
Kelly Carulli (Mgr)
Marc Falcone (Mgr)
Karan Mansukhani (Mgr-Sls)
Tim Mooney (Sr Mgr)
King Yip (Sr Mgr)
Jeremy Wong (Sr Mgr)

Christopher Watson (Engr-Software)
Sandeep Savarala (Engr-Software)
Jacob Lambert (Engr-Software)
Anusha Kanuri (Engr-Software)
Danny Krifcher (CFO)

AUDAX CREDIT BDC INC.
101 Huntington Ave, Boston, MA
02199
Tel.: (617) 859-1500   DE
Web Site:
    https://www.audaxcreditbdc.com
Year Founded: 2015
Rev.: $29,658,516
Assets: $443,650,195
Liabilities: $15,172,517
Net Worth: $428,477,678
Earnings: $23,817,808
Fiscal Year-end: 12/31/22
Management Investment Services
N.A.I.C.S.: 523999
Michael P. McGonigle (Chm, Pres &
CEO)
Richard T. Joseph (CFO & Treas)

**AUDAX GROUP, LIMITED
PARTNERSHIP**
101 Huntington Ave 25th Ave, Bos-
ton, MA 02199
Tel.: (617) 859-1500   DE
Web Site:
    http://www.audaxgroup.com
Year Founded: 1999
Emp.: 300
Investment Holding Company
N.A.I.C.S.: 551112
Edgar W. Soule (Mng Dir-IR)
Keith Palumbo (Mng Dir)
Donald G. Bramley (Mng Dir)
Young J. Lee (Mng Dir)
Erik-Jan Dubovik (CIO & Mng Dir)
Daniel H. Weintraub (Chief Admin &
Legal Officer & Mng Dir)
Alexander A. Casale (Mng Dir-IR)
Jason G. Currier (CFO)
Joshua Aronson (Mng Dir & Deputy
Gen Counsel)
Ryan Bruehlmann (Mng Dir)
Mark Cordes (Mng Dir-Capital Mar-
kets)
Matthew Dewey (Principal)
Brian Doherty (Mng Dir-Capital Mar-
kets)
Daniel Doran (VP)
Michael Fondo (Mng Dir-Tax & Coun-
sel)
Asheesh Gupta (Mng Dir-Portfolio
Support)

Subsidiaries:

Audax Management Company,
LLC   (1)
101 Huntington Ave Fl 25, Boston, MA
02199
Tel.: (617) 859-1500
Web Site:
    http://www.audaxprivateequity.com
Sales Range: $50-74.9 Million
Privater Equity Firm
N.A.I.C.S.: 523999
Pamela F. Martin (Mng Dir)
Young J. Lee (Mng Dir)
Donald G. Bramley (Mng Dir)
Adam A. Abramson (Mng Dir)
Timothy S. Mack (Mng Dir)
Mark Cordes (Mng Dir-Capital Markets)
David J. Wong (Mng Dir)
Asheesh Gupta (Mng Dir-Portfolio Support)
David A. Goldenheim (Mng Dir)
David C. Winterle (Sr VP-Portfolio Support)
Gregory S. Smith (Principal)
Jay W. Petricone (Principal)
Matthew G. Gosselin (Principal)
Mauricio Sanchez (Sr VP)
Steven H. Maxwell (Sr VP-Human Capital-
Portfolio)
William G. Gonzalez (Mng Dir-Bus Dev)
Alicia Alexander (VP)
William Allen (Mng Dir)

Audax Group, Limited Partnership—(Continued)

Peter Arcoma (Sr VP-Financial Diligence)
Tripp Ateyeh (VP)
Peter Awad (VP)
Lauren Baldwin (VP)
Sean Bartlett (VP)
Iveshu Bhatia (Mng Dir)
Michelle Bitman (VP-Bus Dev)
Katherine Brackett (VP-Financial Diligence)
Richard Broughton (Sr VP)
Robert Connors (Sr VP-IR)
Kevin Cox (Pres)
Matthew Cross (Mng Dir-IR)
James Deng (VP-Portfolio Support)
Tuck Welch (VP-Bus Dev)
Joseph P. Rogers Jr. (Mng Dir)

Holding (Domestic):

48forty Solutions, LLC   (2)
13100 NW Freeway 450, Houston, TX
77040
Tel.: (713) 332-6145
Web Site: http://www.48forty.com
International Logistics Services
N.A.I.C.S.: 321920
Mike Hachtman (CEO)
Jennifer Thomas (CFO)
Jon Cline (VP-Ops)
LeRoi Cochran (VP-Supply Chain)
Kyle Eberlin (VP-Natl Sls & East Area Ops)
Scott Sowa (VP-West Ops)

Subsidiary (Domestic):

**Allegheny Recycled Products,
Inc.**   (3)
4201 Grand Ave, Pittsburgh, PA 15225
Tel.: (412) 331-6704
Web Site: http://www.arpallet.com
Rev.: $5,000,000
Emp.: 40
Wood Container & Pallet Mfr
N.A.I.C.S.: 321920
William E. Biedenbach (Chm)
John Cory (CEO)

Bo's Pallets, Inc.   (3)
2427 Hwy 140, Adairsville, GA 30103
Tel.: (770) 773-3054
Web Site: http://www.bospallets.com
Sales Range: $1-9.9 Million
Emp.: 48
Wood Container & Pallet Mfr
N.A.I.C.S.: 321920
Greg Bowen (Pres)

Unit (Domestic):

IFCO Systems US, LLC   (3)
3030 Rocky Point Dr Ste 300, Tampa, FL
33607
Tel.: (813) 463-4100
Web Site: http://www.ifco.com
Reusable Plastic Containers Mfr
N.A.I.C.S.: 811210
Wolfgang Orgeldinger (CEO)
Julian zu Putlitz (CFO)

Subsidiary (Domestic):

Industrial Pallet, LLC   (3)
27 Chaplin Rd, Eastford, CT 06242
Tel.: (860) 974-0093
Web Site: http://www.industrialpallet.com
Sales Range: $1-9.9 Million
Emp.: 46
Wood Container & Pallet Mfr
N.A.I.C.S.: 321920
Randy Therrien (Founder, VP & Gen Mgr)
Ken Fournier (Asst Gen Mgr)
Joe O'Brien (Principal)

Nazareth Pallet Co., Inc.   (3)
800 Held Dr, Northampton, PA 18067
Tel.: (610) 262-9232
Web Site: http://www.nazpallet.com
Rev.: $6,666,666
Emp.: 45
Wood Container & Pallet Mfr
N.A.I.C.S.: 321920
George Frack (Pres)

Taylor Pallets & Recycling , Inc   (3)
3571 Abbeville Hwy, Anderson, SC 29624
Tel.: (864) 296-5001
Web Site: http://www.taylorpallets.com
Rev.: $1,100,000
Emp.: 15
Wood Container & Pallet Mfr

N.A.I.C.S.: 321920
Greg Taylor (Pres)
Drew Simpson (Plant Mgr)

Joint Venture (Domestic):

**APC Automotive Technologies,
LLC**   (2)
300 Dixie Trail, Goldsboro, NC 27530
Tel.: (919) 580-2000
Web Site: http://www.apcautotech.com
Underbody Vehicle Products Supplier
N.A.I.C.S.: 336340
James McCoy (COO)

Holding (Domestic):

Affordable Interior Systems, Inc.   (2)
4 Bonazzoli Ave, Hudson, MA 01749
Tel.: (978) 562-7500
Web Site: http://www.ais-inc.com
Sales Range: $100-124.9 Million
Wood Office Furniture
N.A.I.C.S.: 337214
Arthur Maxwell (Founder & Chm)
Bryan Poist (CFO)
Steve Savage (COO)
Greg Scher (VP-Ops)
Meaghan Avellaneda (VP-Strategic Accts)
Todd Hartman (VP-Midwest)
Brian Sheehan (VP)
Jason Lauro (Sls Dir-North California)
Nick Haritos (Exec VP-Sls & Distr)

AllOver Media, Inc.   (2)
16355 36th Ave Ste 700, Minneapolis, MN
55446
Tel.: (763) 762-2000
Web Site: http://www.allovermedia.com
Out-of-Home Display Advertising Services
N.A.I.C.S.: 541850
Dustin Benz (VP-Ops)
Jake Johnson (Dir-Natl Sls)
Rochelle Castiglione (Dir-Franchise Ops)
Jordan Schumack (Sr Dir-Ops)
Steve Hutchinson (Dir-Print & Svcs)
Cody Cagnina (VP-Natl Accounts)
Hester Downing (Dir-Creative)
Jeff Griffing (CEO)
Billy Corvalan (VP-Brand Partnerships-Los
Angeles)

Andrews International   (2)
27959 Smyth Dr, Valencia, CA 91355
Tel.: (661) 775-8400
Web Site:
http://www.andrewsinternational.com
Sales Range: $1-4.9 Billion
Emp.: 15,000
Security & Risk Mitigation Services
N.A.I.C.S.: 928110
Randy Andrews (CEO)
Bill Farrar (Sr VP-Media, Entertainment &
Special Armed Svcs)
Kevin Coughenour (CIO)
William Besse (VP)
Thomas Cseh (Deputy Dir-Mexico)
Blanca Fernandez Ramirez (Deputy Dir-
Mexico)
Robert Knapp (Sr VP-Consulting & Investi-
gations)
Jim Milford (Sr VP-Consulting & Investiga-
tions)
D. C. Page (Sr VP-Intl Ops & Consulting)
John F. Timoney (Sr VP-Consulting)
Andrew Lamprey (VP-Consulting)
Anthony Velazquez (VP-Ops-Consulting &
Investigations)
Brian Gimlett (Sr VP-Consulting)
John Keeney (Sr Dir-Consulting)
Nick Alleva (Sr Project Mgr)

Branch (Domestic):

Andrews International   (3)
475 Park Ave S 12th Fl, New York, NY
10016
Tel.: (718) 518-8055
Web Site:
http://www.andrewsinternational.com
Sales Range: $25-49.9 Million
Emp.: 20
Contract Security Services
N.A.I.C.S.: 561621
Brian Gimlett (Sr VP-Consulting, Investiga-
tions & Intl)

Subsidiary (Domestic):

**Andrews International Government
Services, Inc.**   (3)

5870 Trinity Pkwy Ste 300, Centreville, VA
20120
Tel.: (703) 592-1542
Web Site:
http://www.aigovernmentservices.com
Sales Range: $350-399.9 Million
Security & Risk Management Services
N.A.I.C.S.: 561611
Francis Coats (Chief Facility Security Offi-
cer)
Tom Carter (Dir-Ops)
John Cutler (Dir-Trng)
Obie R. Moore III (Pres)

Subsidiary (Non-US):

**Vance International de Mexico, S.A.
de C.V.**   (3)
Ejercito Nacional No 926 Piso 2 Desp 203,
Col Morales Secc Alameda, Mexico, 11510,
Mexico
Tel.: (52) 5515000440
Web Site:
http://www.andrewsinternational.com
Sales Range: $10-24.9 Million
Emp.: 60
Security & Risk Management Services
N.A.I.C.S.: 561612
Blanca Fernandez (Gen Mgr)

Holding (Domestic):

Aspen Surgical Products, Inc.   (2)
6945 Southbelt Dr SE, Caledonia, MI 49316
Tel.: (888) 364-7004
Web Site: http://www.aspensurgical.com
Disposable Medical Products Mfr
N.A.I.C.S.: 339112
Jeffrey Stephen (VP-Ops)
Jason Krieser (CEO)
Greg Muller (CFO)
Carl Hall (Chief Comml Officer)

Subsidiary (Domestic):

**Aspen Surgical Puerto Rico
Corp.**   (3)
Km 20 3 Rr 183, Las Piedras, PR 00771
Tel.: (787) 733-5813
Web Site: http://www.aspensurgical.com
Emp.: 200
Medical Device Equipment Mfr
N.A.I.C.S.: 339112

Precept Medical Products Inc.   (3)
370 Airport Rd, Arden, NC 28704
Tel.: (800) 438-5827
Web Site: http://www.preceptmed.com
Disposable Garments & Accessories
N.A.I.C.S.: 315250
Melissa Shealy (Mgr-Acctg & MIS)

Protek Medical Products, Inc.   (3)
4125 Westcor Ct, Coralville, IA 52241
Tel.: (319) 358-8080
Web Site: http://www.protekmedical.com
Engineeering Services
N.A.I.C.S.: 541330
Rick Pruter (CEO)

Symmetry Surgical Inc.   (2)
3034 Owen Dr, Antioch, TN 37013
Tel.: (615) 964-5532
Web Site: http://www.symmetrysurgical.com
Sales Range: $75-99.9 Million
Emp.: 196
Holding Company; Surgical Instruments Mfr
& Whslr
N.A.I.C.S.: 551112
Scott D. Kunkel (CFO & Sr VP)
Ronda L. Harris (Chief Acctg Officer & VP)
Jose E. Fernandez (CTO & Sr VP)
David C. Milne (Chief Admin Officer, Chief
Compliance Officer, Gen Counsel & Sec)
David C. Milne (Chief Admin Officer, Chief
Compliance Officer, Gen Counsel & Sec)

Subsidiary (Domestic):

**Specialty Surgical Instrumentation,
Inc.**   (4)
3034 Owen Dr, Antioch, TN 37013
Tel.: (800) 251-3000
Web Site: http://www.symmetrysurgical.com
Surgical Instruments & Supplies Mfr &
Whslr
N.A.I.C.S.: 339112
Thomas J. Sullivan (Pres & CEO)
Ronda L. Harris (Chief Acctg Officer)
Jose E. Fernandez (CTO)

David C. Milne (Chief Admin Officer, Chief
Compliance Officer, Gen Counsel & Sec)
Scott Kunkel (CFO & Sr VP)

Holding (Domestic):

Assistive Technology Group, Inc.   (2)
1111 Cromwell Pl Ste 601, Rocky Hill, CT
06067-3449
Tel.: (860) 257-3443
Web Site: http://www.atgrehab.com
Sales Range: $300-349.9 Million
Emp.: 2,000
Rehabilitation Equipment Distr & Support
Services
N.A.I.C.S.: 423450
Tamas Feitel (CFO)
Mike Swinford (CEO)

Beacon Mobility Corp.   (2)
70 Post Office Park Suite 7003, Wilbraham,
MA 01095
Tel.: (630) 432-9745
Web Site: https://gobeacon.com
School & Employee Bus Transportaion
N.A.I.C.S.: 485410

Subsidiary (Domestic):

**Midwest Paratransit Services
Inc.**   (3)
11785 Justen Cir, Maple Grove, MN 55369
Tel.: (763) 315-1074
Web Site:
http://www.midwestparatransitservices.com
Other Urban Transit Systems
N.A.I.C.S.: 485119
Bill Psterson (Mgr)

Holding (Domestic):

Broadcast Electronics, Inc.   (2)
4100 N 24th St, Quincy, IL 62305-3606
Tel.: (217) 224-9600
Web Site: http://www.bdcast.com
Rev.: $40,000,000
Emp.: 100
AM, FM & Internet Radio Broadcasting
Transmitter & Software Mfr
N.A.I.C.S.: 334220
Kim Winking (Mgr-Mktg Svcs)
Brent Whelan (VP-Technical Svcs & Prod-
uct Support)
Hector Brown (Mgr-Studio Technical Svcs)

Chase Industries, Inc.   (2)
10021 Commerce Park Dr, Cincinnati, OH
45246-1333
Tel.: (513) 860-5565
Web Site: http://www.chasedoors.com
Sales Range: $10-24.9 Million
Emp.: 300
Industrial Doors Mfr & Distr
N.A.I.C.S.: 332321
Jeffrey Stark (Chm)
Robert G. Isaman (Pres & CEO)

Subsidiary (Domestic):

**Door Engineering and Manufacturing
LLC**   (3)
400 W Cherry St, Kasota, MN 56050-0005
Tel.: (507) 931-6910
Web Site: http://www.doorengineering.com
Emp.: 50
Building & Warehouse Doors Design & Mfr.
N.A.I.C.S.: 332321
Steve Saggau (Pres)
Chris Adams (Product Mgr)
Jennifer George (Coord-Sls & Mktg)
Dwight Lowe (Sls Mgr-South Central)

Thermoseal Industries, LLC   (3)
600 Jersey Ave, Gloucester City, NJ 08030
Tel.: (856) 456-3109
Web Site: http://www.thermoseal.com
Sales Range: $10-24.9 Million
Emp.: 250
Doors & Insulating Glass Units Mfr & Sales
N.A.I.C.S.: 327215

Holding (Domestic):

**Checkers Industrial Products
LLC**   (2)
620 Compton St, Broomfield, CO 80020-
1635
Tel.: (720) 890-1187
Web Site: http://www.checkersindustrial.com

Sales Range: $25-49.9 Million
Safety Equipment Mfr
N.A.I.C.S.: 339999
Raymond Torres *(Pres)*

Subsidiary (Domestic):

Awecomm Technologies, LLC   (3)
165 Kirts Blvd Ste 400, Troy, MI 48084
Tel.: (248) 404-9910
Web Site: http://www.awecomm.com
Sales Range: $1-9.9 Million
Emp.: 50
Internet Service Provider
N.A.I.C.S.: 517810
Janet Nawrocki *(VP-Administration)*
Brent Yax *(CEO)*
David W. Townsend *(Pres & COO)*

**Notrax - Mats for Professional
Use**   (3)
5655 W 73rd St, Chicago, IL 60638
Tel.: (708) 458-4600
Web Site: http://www.notrax.com
Fabricated Rubber Products
N.A.I.C.S.: 326299
Mark McElhinny *(Pres & CEO)*

Subsidiary (Non-US):

**Superior Manufacturing Group Eu-
rope BV**   (4)
Achterzeedijk 57 - 1, 2992 SB, Baren-
drecht, Netherlands
Tel.: (31) 180 615 744
Web Site: http://www.notrax.eu
Emp.: 30
Industrial Floor Mat Mfr
N.A.I.C.S.: 326299
Rene Vieveen *(Exec VP)*
Arjan Fase *(Mgr-Ops)*
Michel Overvoorde *(Mgr-Sls)*

Subsidiary (Domestic):

**SVE Portable Roadway Systems,
Inc.**   (3)
6128 Brookshire Blvd Ste F, Charlotte, NC
28216-2423
Tel.: (704) 398-0007
Web Site: http://www.mudtraks.com
Plastics Product Mfr
N.A.I.C.S.: 326199
Dan Hammers *(Dir-Tech)*

Holding (Domestic):

**Chesapeake Urology Associates
PA**   (2)
6535 N Charles St Ste 500, Towson, MD
21204
Tel.: (410) 825-5454
Web Site:
    http://www.chesapeakeurology.com
Urologic Care Services
N.A.I.C.S.: 621493
Sanford Siegel *(CEO)*
Patricia Schnably *(VP-Mktg & Comm)*

Subsidiary (Domestic):

**Arizona Urology Specialists,
P.L.L.C.**   (3)
5750 W Thunderbird Rd Ste B200, Glen-
dale, AZ 85308
Tel.: (602) 222-1900
Web Site:
    http://www.arizonaurologyspecialists.com
Health Practitioners
N.A.I.C.S.: 621399
Christopher Stewart *(Chief Medical Officer)*

Holding (Domestic):

Colony Hardware Corp.   (2)
269 S Lambert Rd, Orange, CT 06477
Tel.: (203) 469-0000
Web Site: http://www.colonyhardware.com
General Purpose Machinery Manufacturing
N.A.I.C.S.: 333998
Christopher Lenzen *(Asst Controller)*
Michael Weiner *(Pres & CEO)*
Tim Rash *(CEO)*

Subsidiary (Domestic):

B&L Bolt, Inc.   (3)
4311 Commercial Ave, Portage, MI 49002
Tel.: (269) 327-9308
Web Site: http://www.blbolt.com

Hardware Merchant Whslr
N.A.I.C.S.: 423710
Dave Vander Ploeg *(CEO)*

Holding (Domestic):

Covercraft Industries Inc.   (2)
100 Enterprise, Pauls Valley, OK 73075-
9100
Tel.: (405) 238-9651
Web Site: http://www.covercraft.com
Sales Range: $25-49.9 Million
Emp.: 450
Mfr of Canvas & Related Products
N.A.I.C.S.: 314910
Howard Grider *(CFO)*
Mark Korros *(Pres)*
Bill McLaughlin *(Mgr-Sls-Southeastern)*
Erik Guldager *(Head-Sls)*

Subsidiary (Domestic):

DISA Global Solutions, Inc.   (2)
12600 Northborough Dr Ste 300, Houston,
TX 77067
Tel.: (281) 673-2400
Web Site: http://www.disa.com
Employee Drug Screening Services
N.A.I.C.S.: 621999
Colin Woods *(VP-Sls & External Ops)*
Jeff Boyle *(Pres & CEO)*
Brendon Brown *(VP-Internal Ops)*
Lisa Ellingsen *(VP-HR)*
Mark Mayo *(CFO)*

Subsidiary (Domestic):

Global Radar Acquisition LLC   (3)
9530 Marketplace Rd Ste 301, Fort Myers,
FL 33912
Tel.: (239) 274-0048
Web Site: http://www.ghrr.com
Background Screening & Other Human Re-
source Services
N.A.I.C.S.: 541612
Brandon Phillips *(Founder & Chief Revenue
Officer)*
Charlie Talbott *(VP-Integrations & Infrastruc-
ture)*
Kevin Smith *(Exec Chm & CEO)*

Subsidiary (Domestic):

**Employment Screening Services
(ESS)**   (4)
2500 Southlake Pk, Birmingham, AL 35244
Tel.: (205) 879-0143
Web Site: http://www.ess2.com
Sales Range: $1-9.9 Million
Emp.: 50
Employment Screening & Investigative Ser-
vices
N.A.I.C.S.: 561611
Russ Blitz *(VP-Sls)*
Tris Chapman *(Dir-Corp Solutions)*
Sheila Benson *(CEO)*
Jason Kimbrell *(COO)*
Tate Maddox *(Dir-Mktg)*
Dawn Carre *(VP-Criminal Svcs)*
Michele Adamson *(VP-HR)*
Mary Beth Brown *(Dir-Client Care)*
Brandt G. LaPish *(VP-Mktg)*

easyBackgrounds, Inc.   (4)
10 Main St, Newfields, NH 03856
Tel.: (603) 778-1820
Web Site: http://www.easybackgrounds.com
Investigation Services
N.A.I.C.S.: 561611
Brian McElwee *(Pres)*

Subsidiary (Non-US):

RS Occupational Health Ltd   (3)
Muirfield House Whitemyres Avenue, Aber-
deen, AB16 6HQ, United Kingdom
Tel.: (44) 1224 460044
Web Site: http://www.rsoh.co.uk
Health Care Srvices
N.A.I.C.S.: 621999
Patricia Douglas *(Mgr-Bus Dev)*
Andrew MacDonald *(Mng Dir)*
Graham Furnace *(Dir-Medical)*

Holding (Domestic):

EIS, Inc.   (2)
2018 Powers Ferry Rd Ste 500, Atlanta, GA
30339   (100%)
Tel.: (678) 255-3600

Web Site: http://www.eis-inc.com
Sales Range: $700-749.9 Million
Emp.: 1,200
Process Materials, Production Supplies &
Industrial Motor Repair Products Distr
N.A.I.C.S.: 423610
Larry L. Griffin *(Pres & CEO)*
Alexander Gonzalez *(Sr VP-Fabrication &
Coating)*
Peter Sheehan *(Sr VP)*
Ron Harris *(Sr VP)*
Marc Benesh *(CFO)*
Andrew Hartley *(CIO)*

Subsidiary (Domestic):

Cobra Wire & Cable Inc.   (3)
2930 Turnpike Dr, Hatboro, PA 19040
Tel.: (215) 674-8773
Web Site: http://www.cobrawire.com
Sales Range: $25-49.9 Million
Emp.: 35
Electronic Wire & Cable Mfr
N.A.I.C.S.: 423610
Brian Holtzman *(CFO)*
Tom Stone *(Mgr-Natl Sls)*
Peter Sheehan *(CEO)*

Division (Domestic):

EIS Fabrico   (3)
4175 Royal Dr Ste 800, Kennesaw, GA
30144   (100%)
Tel.: (678) 202-2700
Web Site: http://www.fabrico.com
Sales Range: $125-149.9 Million
Emp.: 90
Custom Converted Flexible Materials & En-
gineered Fabrication Services
N.A.I.C.S.: 326130

Branch (Domestic):

Fabrico Central   (4)
10436 N Port Washington Rd, Mequon, WI
53092   (100%)
Tel.: (262) 404-6000
Web Site: http://www.fabrico.com
Sales Range: $50-74.9 Million
Emp.: 30
Industrial Materials Engineered Conversion
N.A.I.C.S.: 333248
Ron Peszko *(Mng Dir)*

Branch (Domestic):

EIS, Inc.   (3)
2018 Powers Ferry Rd Ste 500, Atlanta, GA
30339   (100%)
Tel.: (678) 255-3600
Web Site: http://www.eis-inc.com
Sales Range: $150-199.9 Million
Emp.: 60
Industrial & Electrical Equipment Distr
N.A.I.C.S.: 423610

EIS, Inc.   (3)
1620 Fullerton Ct Ste 100, Glendale
Heights, IL 60139
Tel.: (630) 446-1210
Web Site: http://www.eis-inc.com
Sales Range: $25-49.9 Million
Emp.: 20
Industrial & Electrical Equipment Distr
N.A.I.C.S.: 423610
Douglas D. Dirks *(Pres & CEO)*

EIS, Inc. - Tempe   (3)
1524 W 14th St Ste 106, Tempe, AZ 85281
Tel.: (602) 325-3900
Web Site: http://www.eis-inc.com
Industrial & Electrical Equipment Distr
N.A.I.C.S.: 423610
Bob Thomas *(Pres)*
Mike Anecito *(Coord-eBus)*

Subsidiary (Domestic):

Electro-Wire Inc.   (3)
933 E Remington Rd, Schaumburg, IL
60173-4515
Tel.: (847) 944-1500
Web Site: http://www.electrowire.com
Sales Range: $10-24.9 Million
Emp.: 100
Wire & Cable Distr
N.A.I.C.S.: 423610
Jim Torok *(Mgr-Wireless Market-Natl)*
Kurt King *(Gen Mgr)*

Empire Wire & Supply, LLC   (3)

2119 Austin Ave, Rochester Hills, MI 48309
Tel.: (248) 853-6363
Web Site: http://www.empirewc.com
Other Communication & Energy Wire Mfr
N.A.I.C.S.: 335929
Milan Odovic *(Sls Mgr-Tech)*
Bill Brouwer *(Acct Mgr)*

Division (Domestic):

Tekra, LLC   (3)
16700 W Lincoln Ave, New Berlin, WI
53151-2728
Tel.: (262) 784-5533
Web Site: http://www.tekra.com
Sales Range: $75-99.9 Million
Emp.: 130
Wholesale Distr & Converter of Plastic
Films, Adhesive Tapes, Laminating Adhe-
sives, Hardcoated Plastics & Printable Top-
coated Films
N.A.I.C.S.: 326113
Kevin Suino *(Mgr-Market Dev)*

Division (Domestic):

Tekra - East Coast Division   (4)
3400 E Woodpark Blvd, Charlotte, NC
28206   (100%)
Tel.: (704) 588-9992
Sales Range: $25-49.9 Million
Wholesale Distributor, Converter of Plastic
Films, Adhesive Tapes, Laminating Adhe-
sives, Hardcoated Plastics & Printable Top-
coated Films
N.A.I.C.S.: 424990
Patrick Oram *(Dir-Sls)*

Division (Domestic):

Trient, LLC   (3)
480 Thompson Rd, Woodville, WI 54028
Tel.: (715) 698-3519
Web Site: http://www.trienttech.com
Commercial Printing
N.A.I.C.S.: 323111

Subsidiary (Domestic):

Eis Inc.   (2)
2018 Powers Ferry Rd SE Ste 500, Atlanta,
GA 30339
Tel.: (678) 255-3600
Web Site: https://www.eis-inc.com
Construction Engineering Services
N.A.I.C.S.: 541330
Glenn Pennycook *(CEO)*
James Shelby Marlow *(CFO)*
Louis Bacigalupo *(COO)*
Lisa Botz *(Chief HR Officer)*
Tom Ritter *(CIO)*
Chris Vierling *(VP-Corp Dev)*
Anshu Mehrotra *(Chief Comml Officer)*

Subsidiary (Domestic):

Gerome Technologies, Inc.   (3)
85 Broadway, Menands, NY 12204
Tel.: (518) 235-0235
Web Site: https://www.gerometech.com
Sales Range: $1-9.9 Million
Emp.: 15
Electronic Components Mfr
N.A.I.C.S.: 334419

Holding (Domestic):

**Fastener Distribution Holdings
LLC**   (2)
400 Continental Blvd Ste 280, El Segundo,
CA 90245
Tel.: (213) 620-9950
Web Site: http://www.fdhaero.com
Commercial Hardware & Replacement
Parts Mfr
N.A.I.C.S.: 336412
Scott Tucker *(CEO)*
Robert Earley *(CFO)*
Ryan Kinslow *(COO)*

Subsidiary (Domestic):

BJG Electronics, Inc.   (3)
141 Remington Blvd, Ronkonkoma, NY
11779
Tel.: (631) 737-1234
Web Site: http://www.bjgelectronics.com
Radio & Television Broadcasting & Wireless
Communications Equipment Mfr
N.A.I.C.S.: 334220

Audax Group, Limited Partnership—(Continued)

Subsidiary (Domestic):

Intro Corp. (4)
5121 Industry Dr, Melbourne, FL 32940
Tel.: (321) 757-6330
Web Site: http://www.introcorp.com
Electrical Connectors & Accessories Mfr
N.A.I.C.S.: 334417
Doug Chagnon (Pres & Gen Mgr)

Subsidiary (Domestic):

BTC Electronic Components, Inc. (3)
2709 Connector Dr, Wake Forest, NC 27587
Tel.: (800) 526-2828
Web Site: http://www.btcelectronics.com
Emp.: 70
Other Electronic Parts & Equipment Merchant Whslr
N.A.I.C.S.: 423690
Paul Moseley (Pres & CEO)
Gary Davis (Controller)
Devin Swann (Product Mgr)

Blue Sky Industries, Inc. (3)
595 Monterey Pass Rd, Monterey Park, CA 91754
Tel.: (213) 620-9950
Web Site: http://www.blueskyindustries.com
Sales Range: $1-9.9 Million
Emp.: 20
Transportation Equipment & Supplies (except Motor Vehicle) Merchant Whslr
N.A.I.C.S.: 423860

Electro Enterprises, Inc. (3)
3601 N I 35, Oklahoma City, OK 73111
Tel.: (405) 427-6591
Web Site: http://www.electroenterprises.com
Sales Range: $1-9.9 Million
Emp.: 35
Transportation Equipment And Supplies, Ns
N.A.I.C.S.: 423860
Marty Enright (Pres)
Chris Feltman (Dir-Production)

Stealth Aerospace, Inc. (3)
21520 Blythe St Unit D, Canoga Park, CA 91304
Tel.: (818) 716-5696
Web Site: http://www.stealthaerospace.com
Rev.: $2,050,000
Emp.: 10
Aircraft Parts & Auxiliary Equipment Mfr
N.A.I.C.S.: 336413
Alon Glickstein (Pres)

Holding (Domestic):

Flow Control Holdings, LLC (2)
900 N Michigan Ave Ste 1800, Chicago, IL 60611
Web Site:
http://www.flowcontrolholdings.com
Highly Engineered Sanitary & High Purity Flow Components
N.A.I.C.S.: 325612
Scott Kerns (CEO)

Subsidiary (Domestic):

DSO Fluid Handling Co., Inc. (3)
300 McGaw Dr, Raritan Center, Edison, NJ 08837
Tel.: (732) 225-9100
Web Site: https://www.dso-fluid.com
Industrial Replacement Parts Mfr & Distr
N.A.I.C.S.: 332919
Ed Kotarski (Gen Mgr)
Sandra Simeon (Mgr-Accounting)
Geoff LaPorte (Mgr-Sls-Natl)
Lisa Billian (Mgr-Pur)
Joel Cabrera (Mgr-Quality Assurance)
Michael Glaser (Pres)

Holding (Domestic):

Flexfit Hose LLC (3)
7950 E Baltimore St, Baltimore, MD 21224-2010
Tel.: (410) 327-0758
Web Site: http://www.flexfithose.com
Rubber & Plastics Hose & Belting Mfr
N.A.I.C.S.: 326220
Arjun Radhakrishnan (Mgr-Mktg)

Subsidiary (Domestic):

Flowtrend Inc. (3)
11512 Spc Ctr Blvd, Houston, TX 77059-3603
Tel.: (281) 487-3496
Industrial Machinery & Equipment Merchant Whslr
N.A.I.C.S.: 423830
Steve Stovall (Treas)
Jan Hansen (Pres)

Strahman Valves, Inc. (3)
2801 Baglyos Cir Lehigh Vly Indus Park VI, Bethlehem, PA 18020
Tel.: (484) 893-5080
Web Site: http://www.strahman.com
Sales Range: $50-74.9 Million
Emp.: 120
Wash Down Equipment & Industrial Valve Products Mfr
N.A.I.C.S.: 332919
Kevin Carroll (VP)
August Percoco (Pres & CEO)
William Doll (VP)
Jan-Willem Savelkoel (VP-Sls)
Eric Hays (Dir-IT)

Holding (Domestic):

GCX Corporation (2)
3875 Cypress Dr, Petaluma, CA 94954-5635
Tel.: (707) 773-1100
Web Site: http://www.gcx.com
Surgical & Medical Instrument Mfr
N.A.I.C.S.: 339112
Brad Cohen (Mgr-EMEA Bus Unit)

Innovative Chemical Products Group, LLC (2)
150 Dascomb Rd, Andover, MA 01810
Tel.: (978) 623-9980
Web Site: http://www.icpgroup.com
Holding Company; Coatings & Adhesives Mfr
N.A.I.C.S.: 551112
Doug Mattscheck (Pres & CEO)
Chad Crittendon (COO)
Pete Horan (CIO)

Subsidiary (Domestic):

California Products Corporation (3)
150 Dascomb Rd, Andover, MA 01810
Tel.: (978) 623-9980
Web Site: http://info.californiapaints.com
Paints, Tennis Court & Track Coating & Wood Stains
N.A.I.C.S.: 325510
Steven McMenamin (Pres)

Division (Domestic):

California Products Corp. - Paint Division (4)
150 Dascomb Rd, Andover, MA 01810
Tel.: (978) 965-2122
Web Site: http://www.californiapaints.com
Paints, Varnishes, Lacquers & Enamels Mfr
N.A.I.C.S.: 325510
Mike Gramke (Exec VP & Gen Mgr)

California Products Corp. - Recreational Products Division (4)
150 Dascomb Rd, Andover, MA 01810
Tel.: (978) 623-9980
Web Site: http://www.plexipave.com
Paints, Varnishes, Lacquers & Enamels Mfr
N.A.I.C.S.: 325510

Subsidiary (Domestic):

Fiberlock Technologies, Inc. (4)
150 Dascomb Rd, Andover, MA 01810
Tel.: (978) 623-9987
Web Site: http://www.fiberlock.com
Lead & Asbestos Encapsulants Mfr
N.A.I.C.S.: 334516
Kim Ware (Reg Sls Mgr-Southwest)
Chris August (Reg Sls Mgr-South Central Reg)
John Alvarez (Reg Sls Mgr-Southeast)
Jim Anders (Reg Sls Mgr-Northwest & Western Canada)
Sean O'Toole (Reg Mgr-Midwest)

Subsidiary (Domestic):

ICP Adhesives & Sealants, Inc. (3)
2775 Barber Rd, Barberton, OH 44203
Tel.: (330) 753-4585
Web Site: http://www.icpgroup.com
Polyurethane Foam Sealant & Adhesive Products Mfr
N.A.I.C.S.: 325520
Kristen Lewis (Natl Sls Mgr)
Kerry Armes (VP-Ops)
Rick Dodson (CFO & VP)
Doug Caffoe (VP-Bus & Market Dev)

ICP Building Solutions Group (3)
150 Dascomb Rd, Andover, MA 01810
Tel.: (978) 623-9980
Adhesives & Sealants Distr
N.A.I.C.S.: 423840

Subsidiary (Domestic):

Gardner-Gibson, Inc. (4)
4161 E 7th Ave, Tampa, FL 33605-4601
Tel.: (813) 248-2101
Web Site: http://www.gardner-gibson.com
Sales Range: $100-124.9 Million
Emp.: 225
Coatings & Other Construction Materials for Roofing, Waterproofing & Pavement Sealing Mfr & Marketer
N.A.I.C.S.: 324122
Sean Hyer (CEO)
Bern Gregory (Dir-Sls)

Subsidiary (Domestic):

Gardner APOC (5)
1001 Ashby Ave, Berkeley, CA 94710-2807 (100%)
Tel.: (510) 548-4887
Web Site: http://www.gardnerasphalt.com
Sales Range: $10-24.9 Million
Emp.: 10
Roofing Cements, Coatings & Adhesives Mfr
N.A.I.C.S.: 333243

Subsidiary (Domestic):

ICP Construction, Inc. (3)
150 Dascomb Rd, Andover, MA 01810
Tel.: (978) 623-9980
Construction Services
N.A.I.C.S.: 236220

Subsidiary (Domestic):

Arizona Polymer Flooring (4)
4565 W Watkins St, Phoenix, AZ 85043
Tel.: (623) 435-2277
Web Site: http://www.apfepoxy.com
Paint & Coating Mfr
N.A.I.C.S.: 325510
Adrienne Malek (VP-Cementitious Coatings)
Chris Fenoli (Dir-Technical)
Shannon Warner (Gen Mgr-Ops)
Mark Pyne (Plant Mgr-Specialty Flooring)
Jamie Budek (Mgr-EHS Compliance-Specialty Flooring)

Subsidiary (Domestic):

Super-Krete Products (5)
4565 W Watkins St, Phoenix, AZ 85043
Tel.: (623) 435-2277
Web Site: http://www.super-krete.com
Concrete Overlay Products Mfr
N.A.I.C.S.: 327390
Shannon Warner (Mgr-Gen Ops)
Mark Pyne (Plant Mgr-Specialty Flooring)
Adrienne Malek (VP-Cementitious Coatings)
Jamie Budek (Mgr-EHS Compliance-Specialty Flooring)
Chris Fenoli (Dir-Technical)

Subsidiary (Domestic):

Master Coating Technologies, Inc. (4)
2777 Eagandale Blvd, Eagan, MN 55121-1212
Tel.: (651) 332-5350
Web Site: http://www.mastercoating.com
Paint & Coating Mfr
N.A.I.C.S.: 325510
Nancy Goethel (Mgr-Client Svcs)

Subsidiary (Domestic):

IdeaPaint, Inc. (3)
40 Broad Ste., Boston, MA 02109
Tel.: (800) 393-5250
Web Site: http://www.ideapaint.com

Emp.: 108
Paint & Coating Mfr
N.A.I.C.S.: 325510

Holding (Domestic):

Katena Products, Inc. (2)
6 Campus Dr Ste 310, Denville, NJ 07834
Tel.: (973) 989-1600
Web Site: http://www.katena.com
Emp.: 35
Medical, Dental & Hospital Equipment & Supplies Merchant Whslr
N.A.I.C.S.: 423450
Bryan Weinmann (VP-Ops-QA & RA)
Steve Blazejewski (CEO)

Subsidiary (Domestic):

Asico LLC (2)
26 Plz Dr, Westmont, IL 60559-1130
Tel.: (630) 986-8032
Web Site: http://www.asico.com
Surgical & Medical Instrument Mfr
N.A.I.C.S.: 339112
Ravi Nallakrishnan (Pres)

Eagle Vision, Inc. (3)
8500 Wolf Lake Dr Ste 110, Memphis, TN 38133 (100%)
Tel.: (901) 380-7000
Web Site: http://www.eaglevis.com
Rev.: $5,000,000
Emp.: 53
Surgical Appliance & Supplies Mfr
N.A.I.C.S.: 339113
Jerre M. Freeman (Mng Dir)

Rhein Medical, Inc. (3)
3360 Scherer Dr N, Saint Petersburg, FL 33716
Tel.: (727) 209-2244
Web Site: http://www.rheinmedical.com
Surgical & Medical Instrument Mfr
N.A.I.C.S.: 339112
John A. Bee (CEO)

Holding (Domestic):

Krayden, Inc. (2)
1491 W 124th Ave, Denver, CO 80234
Tel.: (720) 515-4583
Web Site: http://www.krayden.com
Industrial Supplies Merchant Whslr
N.A.I.C.S.: 423840
Gary Bowman (Mgr-Sls)
Wayne Wagner (CEO)

Laird Connectivity, Inc. (2)
50 S Main St Ste 1100, Akron, OH 44308
Tel.: (262) 375-4400
Web Site: https://www.lairdconnect.com
Wireless Connectivity Solutions
N.A.I.C.S.: 517111

Subsidiary (Domestic):

Boundary Devices, LLC. (3)
7 Orchard Rd Ste 102, Lake Forest, CA 92630
Tel.: (602) 758-5159
Sales Range: $1-9.9 Million
Emp.: 12
Computer & Computer Peripheral Equipment & Software Merchant Whslr
N.A.I.C.S.: 423430

Holding (Domestic):

Liquid Environmental Solutions of Texas, LLC (2)
7651 Esters Blvd Ste 200, Irving, TX 75063-4034
Web Site: http://www.liquidenviro.com
Waste Management Services
N.A.I.C.S.: 562998
Alan Viterbi (Exec Chm)
Jerry Sheridan (CEO)
Gene Cookson (Pres & COO)
William Bergstrom (CFO & Sr VP)
Peter Crane (VP-Customer Solutions)
Brian Bidelspach (VP-Expansion Ops)
Mike Urban (VP-IT)
Tom Hillstroam (VP-Treatment & Recovery)
Fln Neve (VP-Svcs & Solutions)
Robin Fiddes (VP-HR)
Catherine McCord (VP-Environmental Health & Safety)

Subsidiary (Domestic):

Atlas Pumping Service (3)

12740 Vigilante Rd, Lakeside, CA 92040
Tel.: (619) 443-7867
Web Site:
   http://www.atlaspumpingservice.com
Commercial & Institutional Building Construction
N.A.I.C.S.: 236220
Kelly Stonesifer (Office Mgr)

Holding (Domestic):

Luminator Holding LP (2)
900 Klein Rd, Plano, TX 75074-8522
Tel.: (972) 424-6511
Web Site:
   http://www.luminatortechnologygroup.com
Sales Range: $50-74.9 Million
Emp.: 300
Transportation Lighting & Communication
Products Mfr & Distr
N.A.I.C.S.: 335132
Dave Cauchi (Mgr-Sls-Canadian)
Rick Kimbrough (Mgr-Field Svc)
John Obert (Mgr-Sls-OEM-Natl)
Magnus Friberg (CEO)
David Coppe (Chm)

Holding (Non-US):

Mobitec AB (3)
Olltorps Industrial Area 4, PO Box 97, 524
21, Herrljunga, Sweden
Tel.: (46) 51322900
Web Site: http://www.mobitec.eu
Sales Range: $25-49.9 Million
Emp.: 50
Public Transportation Information Systems
N.A.I.C.S.: 423860
Jenz Torstensson (Mng Dir)
Fredrick Varnbremk (Area Mgr-Sls)

Subsidiary (Non-US):

Mobitec Brasil Ltda (4)
Rua Rosangela Rosa Terres 1401, Bairro
Sao Caetano, Caxias do Sul, 95095-500,
Rio Grande do Sul, Brazil
Tel.: (55) 5432098500
Web Site: http://www.mobitec.com.br
Sales Range: $10-24.9 Million
Public Transportation Information Systems
Mfr
N.A.I.C.S.: 336999
Guilherme Demore (Mng Dir)

Mobitec GmbH (4)
Stockfeldstrasse 1, 76437, Rastatt, Germany
Tel.: (49) 7243761750
Web Site: http://www.mobitec.eu
Sales Range: $10-24.9 Million
Emp.: 10
Public Transportation Information Systems
Mfr
N.A.I.C.S.: 336999

Division (Domestic):

TwinVision (3)
900 Klein Rd, Plano, TX 75074
Tel.: (972) 424-6511
Web Site: http://www.luminatorusa.com
Sales Range: $10-24.9 Million
Designs, Manufactures, Sells & Services
Electronic Destination Sign Systems Used
on Transit & Transportation Vehicles
N.A.I.C.S.: 336320
Daniel Kelleher (VP-Sls & Mktg)

Holding (Domestic):

**Monarch Landscape Holdings
LLC** (2)
550 S Hope St. Ste 1675, Los Angeles, CA
90071
Tel.: (213) 797-5934
Web Site:
   https://www.monarchlandscape.com
Emp.: 147
Facilities Services
N.A.I.C.S.: 561730
Brian Helgoe (Founder & CEO)

Subsidiary (Domestic):

Environmental Design, Inc. (3)
12511 E 112th Ave, Brighton, CO 80640
Tel.: (303) 287-9113
Web Site:
   https://www.environmentaldesigns.com

Emp.: 100
Lawn & Garden Services
N.A.I.C.S.: 561730
Shawn Ryan (Pres)
Pat McDonough (Principal)

Holding (Domestic):

**PHOENIX Rehabilitation & Health
Services, Inc.** (2)
2000 Westinghouse Drive I Suite 200,
Cranberry Township, PA 16066
Tel.: (724) 343-4060
Web Site: http://www.phoenixrehab.com
Emp.: 1,000
Physical Therapy & Rehabilitation Services
N.A.I.C.S.: 621340
Anthony Giannetta (VP-Compliance)
David Angelo (Chief Growth Officer)
Robert Kohn (Exec VP-Ops)
Christine Osman (Exec VP-Ops)
Chris Ciatto (CEO)
Robert Gallo (Chief Legal Officer)
Drew Hurt (CFO)

Subsidiary (Domestic):

Aldridge Physical Therapy, LLC (3)
2408 E University Dr Ste 106, Auburn, AL
36830-9404
Tel.: (334) 275-4636
Offices of Physical, Occupational & Speech
Therapists & Audiologists
N.A.I.C.S.: 621340

**Black Mountain Physical Therapy
LLC** (3)
997 Old US Hwy 70 W, Black Mountain, NC
28711-2665
Tel.: (828) 669-6896
Offices of Physical, Occupational & Speech
Therapists & Audiologists
N.A.I.C.S.: 621340

Physical Therapy Etc. (3)
142 Franklin Farm Ln, Chambersburg, PA
17202
Tel.: (717) 263-5147
Web Site:
   http://www.physicaltherapyetc.com
Offices of All Other Miscellaneous Health
Practitioners
N.A.I.C.S.: 621399
John Hostetler (Pres)

**The Advanced Center for Physical
Therapy** (3)
2114 Angus Rd Ste 107, Charlottesville, VA
22901-2769
Tel.: (434) 295-4473
Web Site: http://www.advancedcpt.com
Emp.: 6
Physical Therapy Services
N.A.I.C.S.: 621340
Dave Watson (CEO)

**The Physical Therapy Connection,
Inc.** (3)
4001 Miller Rd, Wilmington, DE 19802
Tel.: (302) 764-2008
Web Site:
   http://www.physicaltherapyconnection.com
Physical Therapy Office
N.A.I.C.S.: 621340
Kim M. Dare (Dir)
Marie Snyder (Office Mgr)

Holding (Domestic):

Renovo Home Partners (2)
101 Huntington Ave 25th Fl, Boston, MA
02199
Web Site:
   https://www.renovohomepartners.com
Home Improvement Solutions & Services
N.A.I.C.S.: 236118
John Dupuy (CEO)

Subsidiary (Domestic):

Reborn Cabinets, Inc. (3)
2981 E La Palma Ave, Anaheim, CA 92806
Tel.: (714) 630-2220
Web Site: http://www.reborncabinets.com
Sales Range: $1-9.9 Million
Emp.: 120
Wood Kitchen Cabinets
N.A.I.C.S.: 337110
Anthony Nardo (CFO)
Vinny Nardo (Chm)

Subsidiary (Domestic):

Rensa Filtration, Inc. (2)
100 Illinois St Ste 200, Saint Charles, IL
60174
Tel.: (630) 797-2165
Web Site: http://www.rensafiltration.com
Air Filtration Products Mfr
N.A.I.C.S.: 333413
Brandon Ost (Founder & CEO)

Subsidiary (Domestic):

Air Filter Supply, Inc. (3)
10087 Mills Sta Rd Ste C, Sacramento, CA
95827-2200
Tel.: (916) 364-5200
Web Site: http://www.airfiltersupply.com
Warm Air Heating & Air-Conditioning Equipment Supplies Merchant Whslr
N.A.I.C.S.: 423730
Brandon Smith (Branch Mgr)

Custom Filter, LLC (3)
2300 Raddant Rd Ste 100, Aurora, IL
60502
Tel.: (630) 906-2100
Web Site: http://www.customfilter.net
Sales Range: $10-24.9 Million
Air Purification Equipment Mfr
N.A.I.C.S.: 333413
John Copley (Pres)
Dan Plumb (Founder)
Bill Domenz (Mgr-Maintenance & Engr-Automation)
Bill Feilinger (Engr-Mfg)
Dave Fuller (Plant Mgr)
Martha Gass (Engr-Design)
Matt Lenell (Engr-Design)
Bill Moreland (Engr-Mfg)
Patrick O'Brien (CFO)
Oscar Pena (Engr-Mfg)
Bruce Plumb (VP)
Laura Yoho (Engr-Mfg)

Smith Filter Corporation (3)
5000 41st Street Ct, Moline, IL 61265
Tel.: (309) 764-8324
Web Site: http://www.smithfilter.com
Rev.: $6,200,000
Emp.: 44
Site Preparation Contractor
N.A.I.C.S.: 238910
Christine Zimmerman (Office Mgr)

Holding (Domestic):

Revolution Dancewear LLC (2)
6100 W Howard St, Niles, IL 60714
Web Site: http://www.revolutiondance.com
Dancewear Mfr
N.A.I.C.S.: 458110

**Senior Care Centers of America,
Inc.** (2)
6 Neshaminy Interplex Ste 401, Trevose,
PA 19053
Tel.: (215) 642-6600
Web Site: http://www.seniorcarectrs.com
Individual And Family Healthcare Services
N.A.I.C.S.: 624120
Howard Snyder (Dir-Bus Dev)

Subsidiary (Domestic):

Active Day Inc. (3)
6 Neshaminy Interplex Ste 401, Trevose,
PA 19053
Web Site: http://www.seniorcarectrs.com
Elderly & Disabled Adult Health Care & Social Services
N.A.I.C.S.: 624120

Subsidiary (Domestic):

Active Day of Randallstown (4)
6 Neshaminy Interplex Ste 401, Trevose,
PA 19053
Tel.: (410) 922-8600
Web Site: http://www.activeday.com
Elderly & Disabled Adult Health Care & Social Services
N.A.I.C.S.: 624120
Andrea Quarles (Dir)

Holding (Domestic):

**Source Refrigeration & HVAC,
Inc.** (2)
145 S State College Blvd Ste 200, Brea,
CA 92821

Tel.: (714) 701-8912
Web Site:
   http://www.sourcerefrigeration.com
Emp.: 1,000
Refrigeration Service & Repair
N.A.I.C.S.: 811412
Brad Howard (Founder)
Adam Coffey (Pres & CEO)
Ed Dunlap (CFO)
Amy Freeman (COO)
Burton Hong (Gen Counsel, Sec & Exec VP)
Mike Ochoa (Exec VP-Sls & Mktg)
Beth Goldstein (Exec VP-HR)
John Manzanares (Exec VP-IT)

Statlab Medical Products, LLC (2)
2090 Commerce Dr, McKinney, TX 75069
Tel.: (972) 436-1010
Web Site: http://www.statlab.com
Medical, Dental & Hospital Equipment &
Supplies Merchant Whslr
N.A.I.C.S.: 423450
John D. Bickel (VP-Product Dev)
Pete Ciaravino (VP-Channel Sls)
Mark Rees (VP-Advanced Diagnostics)
Gary Wiederhold (VP-R&D)
Sheri K. Gay (VP-Corp Accts)
Allan Couch (Dir-Quality & Regulatory Affairs)
Joe Bernardo (Exec Chm)
Todd Baldanzi (CFO)
John Martinson (COO)
Sung-Dae Hong (CEO)

Subsidiary (Domestic):

BBC Biochemical Corp (3)
409 Eleanor Ln, Mount Vernon, WA 98273-4518
Tel.: (360) 542-8400
Web Site: http://www.bbcus.com
Chemicals Mfr
N.A.I.C.S.: 325998
Adrian Biesecker (Pres)

Holding (Domestic):

Techniks Industries (2)
9930 E 56th St, Indianapolis, IN 46236
Tel.: (317) 803-8000
Web Site: http://www.techniksusa.com
Emp.: 60
Holding Company; Industrial Supplies Distr
N.A.I.C.S.: 551112
Vern Campell (VP-Acquisition)

Subsidiary (Domestic):

NAP GLADU (3)
1180 Wernsing Rd, Jasper, IN 47546
Tel.: (812) 482-2000
Web Site: http://www.napgladu.com
Carbide & Diamond Cutting Tools Designer,
Mfr & Whslr
N.A.I.C.S.: 333515
Trent Moss (VP-Sls)

Subsidiary (Non-US):

NAP GLADU - Marieville (4)
2115 Saint-Cesaire Street, Marieville, J3M
1E5, QC, Canada
Tel.: (450) 460-4481
Web Site: http://www.napgladu.com
Carbide & Diamond Cutting Tools Designer,
Mfr, Whslr & Services
N.A.I.C.S.: 333515

NAP GLADU - Toronto (4)
222 Evans Ave, Toronto, M8Z 1J8, ON,
Canada
Tel.: (416) 251-2236
Web Site: http://www.napgladu.com
Saw Blades & Other Industrial Supplies
Whslr
N.A.I.C.S.: 423840

Subsidiary (Domestic):

Riverside Tool Corp. (3)
3504 Henke St, Elkhart, IN 46514
Tel.: (574) 522-6798
Web Site: http://www.riversidetool.com
Emp.: 40
Sawmill & Woodworking Machinery Mfr
N.A.I.C.S.: 333243
Ronald Migedt (Gen Mgr)
Dustin Kessler (Mgr-Customer Svc)
Lori Yoder-Meyer (Mgr-Office & HR)

Audax Group, Limited Partnership—(Continued)

Brandon Denning *(Engr)*
Dave Michael *(Engr)*
John Baad *(Engr)*
Grant Sassaman *(Engr)*

Holding (Domestic):

Thalheimer Brothers, Inc. (2)
700 E Godfrey Ave, Philadelphia, PA 19124
Tel.: (215) 537-5200
Web Site:
   http://www.thalheimerbrothers.com
Recyclable Material Merchant Whslr
N.A.I.C.S.: 423930

Subsidiary (Domestic):

Ansam Metals LLC (3)
1026 E Patapsco Ave, Baltimore, MD
21225-2229
Tel.: (410) 355-8220
Web Site: http://www.ansammetals.com
Sales Range: $25-49.9 Million
Emp.: 55
Non-ferrous Metals Mfr
N.A.I.C.S.: 331410
Benjamin Zager *(Pres & CEO)*
Barry Stein *(VP-Pur)*
Dennis Epps *(Mgr-Plant Ops)*
Steve L. Steinbach *(Sr VP-Plant Ops)*
Jodi Glaser *(Mgr-Acctg)*
Evelyn M. Steinbach *(Mgr-Transportation)*
Anatoly Mendelson *(Mgr-MIS & QEHS)*

Division (Domestic):

Mega Metals, Inc. (3)
1323 N 22nd Ave, Phoenix, AZ 85009
Tel.: (602) 258-6677
Web Site: http://www.megametalsinc.com
Recyclable Material Merchant Whslr
N.A.I.C.S.: 423930
Robert Megdal *(Founder)*

Holding (Domestic):

The Chartis Group, LLC (2)
220 W Kinzie St 3rd Fl, Chicago, IL 60654
Tel.: (877) 667-4700
Web Site: http://www.chartis.com
Healthcare Industry Consulting Services
N.A.I.C.S.: 541611
Ken Graboys *(Co-Founder & CEO)*
Ethan Arnold *(Founder & Mng Dir)*
Shannon Brownell *(Chief Talent Officer)*
Adam Baker *(Principal)*
Brett Pederson *(Dir)*
Glenda Owen *(Principal)*
James Karpook *(Principal)*
Jodi L. Capistrant *(Principal)*
John Narcross *(Principal)*
Mark Krivopal *(Dir)*
Melissa H. Anderson *(Dir)*
Mike D'Olio *(Dir)*
Nathan Hall *(Principal)*
Parrish Aharam *(Dir)*
Ryan Langdale *(Dir)*
Sue Anderson *(Principal)*
Sue Atkinson *(Principal)*
Tonya Edwards *(Principal)*
Robert Christopher Regan *(Mng Dir)*

Subsidiary (Domestic):

Chartis Clinical Quality Solutions (3)
220 W Kinzie St 3 Floor, Chicago, IL 60654
Tel.: (305) 592-2000
Web Site: http://www.greeley.com
Healthcare Consulting
N.A.I.C.S.: 541611
Ted Pfeiffer *(VP-Product Innovation)*
Tim Barger *(Sr VP-Innovation)*

iVantage Health Analytics, Inc. (3)
509 Forest Ave Ste 250, Portland, ME
04101
Tel.: (207) 518-6700
Web Site: http://www.ivantagehealth.com
Healthcare Data & Analytics Software Services
N.A.I.C.S.: 423430
Araby Thornewill *(Exec VP)*
John Whittlesey *(VP-Client Svcs)*
Linda Albery *(Sr VP-Advisory Solutions)*
Courtney Morris *(Pres)*
Clayton Donahue *(Sr VP-Engrg)*
Lisa Weldon *(Sr VP-Sls)*

Subsidiary (Domestic):

Professional Data Services, Inc. (4)
1632 E 23rd Ave, Hutchinson, KS 67502-4705
Tel.: (800) 283-7543
Web Site: http://www.pdsmed.com
Medical Software Products Publisher
N.A.I.C.S.: 513210
Greg Newcomer *(Pres)*
Marc McCrary *(Dir)*
Les Jacobs *(Dir)*
Robert Pierce *(Dir)*

Subsidiary (Non-US):

Thermogenics Inc. (2)
6 Scanlon Court, Aurora, L4G 7B2, ON,
Canada
Tel.: (905) 727-8656
Web Site:
   http://www.thermogenicsboilers.com
Coiled Tube Steam Mfr
N.A.I.C.S.: 327332
Ross Garland *(CEO)*

Subsidiary (US):

Yown's Boiler & Furnace Service, Inc. (3)
3501 W 20th St, Jacksonville, FL 32254
Tel.: (904) 786-1645
Web Site: http://www.yowns.com
Commercial & Industrial Machinery &
Equipment (except Automotive & Electronic)
Repair & Maintenance
N.A.I.C.S.: 811310
Gary A. Yown *(Pres)*

Holding (Non-US):

Total PowerGen Solutions (2)
6450 Kestrel Road, Mississauga, L5T 1Z7,
ON, Canada
Tel.: (888) 870-9152
Web Site: https://www.tpgs.ca
Electrical Equipment Supplier
N.A.I.C.S.: 423610

Subsidiary (Domestic):

Total Power Ltd. (3)
6450 Kestrel Road, Mississauga, L5T 1Z7,
ON, Canada
Tel.: (905) 670-1535
Web Site: https://www.totalpower.ca
Rev.: $11,255,253
Emp.: 90
Electrical Equipment Supplier
N.A.I.C.S.: 423610
Graham Clark *(Pres)*

Holding (Domestic):

United Recovery Systems, LP (2)
5800 N Course Dr, Houston, TX 77072
Tel.: (713) 977-1234
Web Site:
   http://www.unitedrecoverysystems.com
Debt Collection Services
N.A.I.C.S.: 561440
Kevin Keleghan *(Pres & CEO)*
Drew Anderson *(Exec VP & Coord-Ops)*

Subsidiary (Domestic):

Enterprise Recovery Systems, Inc. (3)
840 S, Woodridge, IL 60517
Tel.: (630) 574-3113
Web Site: http://www.ersinc.com
Sales Range: $10-24.9 Million
Collection Agency, Except Real Estate
N.A.I.C.S.: 561440
Scott Nicholson *(Pres)*
Steve Recchia *(Dir-Sls & Client Svcs)*
Corey Soderquist *(CIO)*

Plaza Recovery, Inc. (3)
370 7th Ave Ste 1200, New York, NY 10001
Tel.: (212) 695-8750
Web Site: http://www.plazaassociates.com
Sales Range: $10-24.9 Million
Collection Agencies
N.A.I.C.S.: 561440
Ira Dauber *(CFO)*

Audax Mezzanine (1)
20 St Park Ave 19th Fl, New York, NY
10017
Tel.: (212) 703-2700

Web Site: http://www.audaxmezzanine.com
Sales Range: $25-49.9 Million
Emp.: 20
Equity Investment Firm
N.A.I.C.S.: 523999
Kevin P. Magid *(Mng Dir)*
Marc B. Wolpow *(Co-CEO)*
Geoffrey S. Rehnert *(Co-CEO)*
U. Peter C. Gummeson *(Mng Dir)*
Rahman Vahabzadeh *(Mng Dir)*
Steven V. Ruby *(Mng Dir)*
Ryan N. Benedict *(Mng Dir)*
Adam J. Weiss *(Mng Dir)*
Blake Loweth *(Principal)*
Shehzad Ajmal *(Principal)*
Remington Chin *(Principal)*
Bryant Shain *(VP)*
Peter K. Stern *(Principal)*
Robin Dholarla *(VP)*

Genuine Cable Group LLC (1)
8770 W Bryn Mawr Ave Ste 1200, Chicago,
IL 60631
Tel.: (847) 944-1500
Web Site: https://www.genuinecable.com
Wire, Cable, Connectivity & Automation
Distr
N.A.I.C.S.: 332618
Steve Maucieri *(CEO)*

Subsidiary (Domestic):

Paige Electric Company, LLP (2)
1160 Springfield Rd PO Box 368, Union, NJ
07083-0368
Tel.: (908) 687-7810
Web Site: http://www.paigeelectric.com
Sales Range: $150-199.9 Million
Emp.: 50
Specialty Electrical Wire, Cable & Accessories Distr
N.A.I.C.S.: 423610
Louis W. Grotta *(Pres)*
William Watkins *(CFO)*
Jodi Conaty *(VP-Sls)*

PlayMonster LLC (1)
1400 E Inman Pkwy, Beloit, WI 53511
Tel.: (608) 362-6896
Web Site: http://www.playmonster.com
Board Games & Toys Whslr
N.A.I.C.S.: 423920
Darby Zahradnik *(Dir-Natl Accounts)*
Amy Graczyk *(Chief People Officer)*
Steve Adolph *(CEO)*
Sharon Fosbery *(Chief Brands & Strategy Officer)*
Bryan Margner *(CFO)*

Subsidiary (Domestic):

The Automoblox Company (2)
18 N Salem St, Dover, NJ 07801 (100%)
Tel.: (973) 442-9444
Web Site: http://www.automoblox.com
Emp.: 10
Wooden Car Toys Mfr & Sales
N.A.I.C.S.: 332994
Patrick Calello *(Pres)*

TPC Holdings, LLC (1)
9600 Valley View Rd, Macedonia, OH
44056
Tel.: (800) 211-4520
Web Site: https://trexonglobal.com
Electrical & Electronic Cord, Cable & Accessories Distr
N.A.I.C.S.: 423610
Mark C. J. Twaalfhoven *(Pres & CEO)*

Subsidiary (Domestic):

C E Precision Assemblies, Inc. (2)
6501 W Frye Rd, Chandler, AZ 85226
Tel.: (480) 940-0740
Web Site: http://www.cepaino.com
Sales Range: $1-9.9 Million
Emp.: 40
Fabricated Wire Product Mfr
N.A.I.C.S.: 332618
Susan Ross *(CEO)*
Mark Schwartz *(Mgr-Quality Assurance)*

TPC Wire & Cable Corp. (2)
9600 Valley View Rd, Macedonia, OH
44056
Tel.: (800) 211-4520
Web Site: http://www.tpcwire.com
Electrical & Electronic Cord, Cable & Accessories Distr

N.A.I.C.S.: 423610

AUDETTE CADILLAC, INC.
7100 Orchard Lake Rd, West Bloomfield, MI 48322
Tel.: (248) 851-7200
Year Founded: 1975
Sales Range: $10-24.9 Million
Emp.: 80
New Car Dealers
N.A.I.C.S.: 441110
Frank B. Audette Sr. *(Pres)*

AUDI OF BERNARDSVILLE
65 Morristown Rd, Bernardsville, NJ
07924
Tel.: (908) 766-0900
Web Site:
   http://www.audibernardsville.com
Sales Range: $10-24.9 Million
Emp.: 30
Automobiles, New & Used
N.A.I.C.S.: 441110
Dave Cozza *(Mgr-Used Car)*
Paul Reynolds *(Pres, CEO & Principal)*
Sandy Hogan *(Gen Mgr)*

AUDI PEMBROKE PINES
15000 Sheridan St, Pembroke Pines,
FL 33331
Tel.: (954) 620-2150
Web Site:
   https://www.audipembrokepines.com
Rev.: $16,100,000
Emp.: 80
New Car Dealers
N.A.I.C.S.: 441110
Joseph Sparacino *(Gen Mgr)*
Mark Davis *(Mgr-Fin)*
Jordano Jimenez *(Mgr-PDI & Inventory Maintenance)*

AUDIA INTERNATIONAL, INC.
450 Racetrack Rd, Washington, PA
15301
Tel.: (724) 228-1260   PA
Web Site:
   http://washingtonpennplastic.com
Emp.: 1,000
Holding Company; Resins & Plastic
Products Mfr & Distr
N.A.I.C.S.: 551112
Robert Andy *(Pres & CEO)*
Randy Lueth *(CFO)*

Subsidiaries:

Southern Polymer, Inc. (1)
6190 Powers Ferry Rd NW Ste 290, Atlanta, GA 30339
Tel.: (770) 916-0607
Web Site: http://www.southernpolymer.com
Emp.: 13
Polyethylene & Polyproplene Resins Mfr &
Distr
N.A.I.C.S.: 325211
Seth Stewart *(Acct Mgr)*
Bobby Halcomb *(Bus Mgr)*

Uniform Color Company (1)
942 Brooks Ave, Holland, MI 49423
Tel.: (616) 394-3800
Web Site: http://www.uniformcolor.com
Custom Color Concentrates Mfr
N.A.I.C.S.: 325991
Kim Miller *(Dir-HR)*
Brian Coleman *(Dir-Tech)*

Washington Penn Plastic Co., Inc. (1)
450 Racetrack Rd, Washington, PA 15301
Tel.: (724) 228-1260
Web Site:
   http://www.washingtonpennplastic.com
Sales Range: $25-49.9 Million
Emp.: 350
Custom Compounded Polypropylene &
Polyethylene Products Mfr
N.A.I.C.S.: 325991
Robert Andy *(CEO)*

Plant (Domestic):

Washington Penn Plastic Co., Inc. - Frankfort Division **(2)**
290 Chenault Rd, Frankfort, KY 40601
Tel.: (502) 695-7771
Web Site: http://www.washpenn.com
Custom Compounded Polypropylene & Polyethylene Products Mfr
N.A.I.C.S.: 325991
Jay Greenwell *(Mgr-Quality)*

AUDIENCE PRODUCTIONS, INC.
2311 N 45th St Ste 310, Seattle, WA 98103 **WA**
Year Founded: 2009
Film Production & Distribution Services
N.A.I.C.S.: 512110
Jay T. Schwartz *(Chm & Pres)*
George Brumder *(Treas)*
Julie Chase *(Sec)*

AUDIENCESCIENCE INC.
1120 112th Ave NE Ste 400, Bellevue, WA 98004
Tel.: (425) 201-3900 **DE**
Web Site:
http://www.audiencescience.com
Year Founded: 2000
Sales Range: $10-24.9 Million
Emp.: 100
Information Retrieval Services
N.A.I.C.S.: 541890
Basem Nayfeh *(CTO)*
Denise Colella *(Chief Revenue Officer)*
Tamara Santiago-Downes *(Dir-Mktg-Intl)*
Rob Gratchner *(VP-Privacy)*
Emily Riley *(VP-Mktg)*
Michael Greene *(Dir-Res & Mktg Strategy)*
Robert Chamberlain *(CFO)*
Natalie Mazer *(VP)*
Jeff Hochberg *(VP-Bus Dev)*
Danny Kim *(Dir-Innovation)*
Shelley Eleby *(VP-Mktg)*
Tim Barnes *(Chief Product Officer)*
Andrew Robinson *(Sr VP-Engrg)*
Ranbir Chawla *(Dir-Technical Ops)*
Alan Koslow *(Gen Counsel)*
Pawan Sadarangani *(Mng Dir-Ops-India)*
David deSimone *(COO)*
Patrick Reilly *(VP-Sls)*
Jana Whitcomb *(Chief Revenue Officer)*

Subsidiaries:

Consorte Media, Inc. **(1)**
332 Pine St 8th Fl, San Francisco, CA 94104
Tel.: (415) 677-4431
Web Site: http://www.consortemedia.com
Sales Range: $10-24.9 Million
Emp.: 10
Advetising Agency
N.A.I.C.S.: 541810

AUDIO FIDELITY COMMUNICATIONS CORP.
12820 W Creek Pkwy Ste M, Richmond, VA 23238
Tel.: (804) 273-9100
Web Site: http://www.whitlock.com
Sales Range: $25-49.9 Million
Emp.: 400
Distribute Electronic Video Equipment
N.A.I.C.S.: 423690
John D. Whitlock *(Chm)*
Doug Hall *(CEO)*
Mark Baker *(CFO)*
John Bailey *(VP-Sys Integration-Durham)*
Roger Patrick *(COO)*

AUDIO VIDEO SYSTEMS, INC. (AVS)
14566 Lee Rd Barthelson Plz, Chantilly, VA 20151
Tel.: (703) 263-1002
Web Site: http://www.avsinc.net
Year Founded: 1992
Sales Range: $50-74.9 Million
Emp.: 25
Audiovisual Systems, Engineering & Integration
N.A.I.C.S.: 334310
Peter Barthelson *(Founder)*

AUDIO VISUAL MANAGEMENT SOLUTIONS, INC.
814 6th Ave S, Seattle, WA 98134
Web Site: https://www.avms.com
Year Founded: 1999
Events Services
N.A.I.C.S.: 561920
Ric Maust *(Sls Mgr-Regional)*

AUDIO-DIGEST FOUNDATION
450 N Brand Blvd Ste 900, Glendale, CA 91203
Tel.: (818) 240-7500
Web Site:
http://www.audiodigest.com
Sales Range: $10-24.9 Million
Emp.: 75
Instructional Audio Tape Producer & Distr
N.A.I.C.S.: 334610
Fran Miller *(Dir-HR)*
Joe Strigle *(Engr-Audio Mastering)*
Ryan Mangano *(Engr-Audio)*
Todd Leafgreen *(Engr-Sound)*
Loree Allen *(Mgr-Print Production)*

AUDIOSEARS CORPORATION
2 S St, Stamford, NY 12167-1211
Tel.: (607) 652-7305
Web Site:
https://www.audiosears.com
Year Founded: 1956
Sales Range: Less than $1 Million
Emp.: 80
Mfr of Telephone & Telegraph Apparatus; Handsets, Headsets, Microphones & Receivers
N.A.I.C.S.: 334210
David Hartwell *(Pres)*
Nancy Rice *(Asst Mgr-Sls)*
Maureen O'Connor *(Project Mgr)*
Vincent Pricolo *(Mgr-Sls)*
Nichlaos Knoll *(Mgr-Pur)*

AUDITORY LEARNING FOUNDATION
1777 NE Loop 410 Ste 100, San Antonio, TX 78217
Tel.: (210) 824-0227 **TX**
Year Founded: 2002
Sales Range: $1-9.9 Million
Educational Support Services
N.A.I.C.S.: 611710
Fred H. Bull *(Sec)*
Jan Meadows *(Pres)*
Glenn G. Mortimer III *(VP)*
Paul McSween III *(Treas)*

AUDLEY TRAVEL US, INC.
77 N Washington St 6th Fl, Boston, MA 02114
Web Site:
http://www.audleytravel.com
Year Founded: 2013
Sales Range: $75-99.9 Million
Emp.: 216
Travel Agency Services
N.A.I.C.S.: 561510
Jacqui Lewis *(Pres)*

AUDUBON ENGINEERING

10205 Westheimer Ste 100, Houston, TX 77042
Tel.: (281) 669-0590
Web Site: http://www.audubon-engineering.com
Year Founded: 1997
Sales Range: $150-199.9 Million
Emp.: 750
Engineering Design, Management & Services
N.A.I.C.S.: 541330
Denis Taylor *(Co-Founder & Mng Partner)*
Dave Beck *(Mng Partner)*
Lee Beckett *(CEO & Mng Partner)*
Ryan Hanemann *(Co-Founder & Pres)*
Stafford Menard *(VP-Deepwater Dev)*
Ivonne Hallard *(Sr Dir-Mktg & Comm)*
David Robison *(CFO)*
Diego Ayala *(Mng Dir-Columbia)*
Florence Burk *(Dir-Inspection)*
Ginger Maness *(Dir-HR)*
Jeffrey Gernon *(Chief Comml Officer)*
Scott Dauzat *(VP-Bus Dev)*
Shawn Senf *(VP-Refining & Petrochemical)*
Terry Mienie *(VP-Offshore)*
Dan Wellons *(Gen Counsel)*
Kaushik Patrawala *(Exec VP-Downstream Ops)*
Kent McAllister *(VP-Projects)*

AUDUBON MACHINERY CORP.
814 Wurlitzer Dr, North Tonawanda, NY 14120
Tel.: (716) 564-5165 **NY**
Web Site: https://www.ogsi.com
Year Founded: 1995
Sales Range: $1-9.9 Million
Emp.: 50
Oxygen Generating Machinery
N.A.I.C.S.: 333998
Christopher Collins *(Chm)*
Joe McMahon *(CEO)*

AUDUBON NATURE INSTITUTE
6500 Magazine St, New Orleans, LA 70118
Tel.: (504) 861-2537
Web Site:
http://www.auduboninstitute.org
Sales Range: $10-24.9 Million
Emp.: 700
Zoological Gardens & Nature Preserve
N.A.I.C.S.: 712130
L. Ronald Forman *(Pres & CEO)*
Steve Dorand *(VP)*
Richard Buchsbaum *(VP-Food, Beverage & Special Events)*
Debra McGuire *(VP-Gift Shops)*
Boysie Bollinger *(Second VP)*
Chimene Granta *(VP-Mktg)*

AUER STEEL & HEATING SUPPLY CO. INC.
2935 W Silver Spring Dr, Milwaukee, WI 53209-4224
Tel.: (414) 463-1234 **WI**
Web Site: https://www.auersteel.com
Year Founded: 1940
Sales Range: $75-99.9 Million
Emp.: 182
Warm Air Heating & Air Conditioning Products Distr
N.A.I.C.S.: 423730
Don M. Curtes *(Founder)*
Tina Seibold *(Mgr-Mktg)*

Subsidiaries:

Auer Steel & Heating Supply Company, Twin Cities, Inc. **(1)**
865 Xenium Ln N, Plymouth, MN 55441 **(100%)**

Tel.: (763) 971-2910
Web Site: http://www.auersteel.com
Sales Range: $10-24.9 Million
Emp.: 60
Warm Air Heating & Air Conditioning Products Distr
N.A.I.C.S.: 423730
Aaron Tofte *(VP & Gen Mgr)*

AUFFENBERG IMPORTS INC.
1708 Newcar Dr, O'Fallon, IL 62269
Tel.: (618) 624-2277
Web Site: http://www.auffenberg.com
Rev.: $15,158,969
Emp.: 35
New & Used Car Dealers
N.A.I.C.S.: 441110
Jamie Auffenberg *(Pres)*
Greg Muren *(Mgr-Mktg)*

AUGEO AFFINITY MARKETING, INC.
2561 Territorial Rd, Saint Paul, MN 55114-1500
Tel.: (651) 917-9143 **DE**
Web Site:
https://www.augeomarketing.com
Year Founded: 2007
Sales Range: $10-24.9 Million
Emp.: 130
Marketing Consulting Services
N.A.I.C.S.: 541613
Daniel Kristal *(Gen Counsel & VP-Corp Svcs)*
David Kristal *(Founder, Co-Chm & CEO)*
Juan Sabater *(Co-Chm & Principal)*
Kenneth Greer *(CMO)*
Rita DiPalma *(Chief Dev Officer)*
Amy Murphy *(Pres-Loyalty & New Product Dev)*
Erik Sorensen *(Pres-Incentives & Recognition)*
Boris Kopilenko *(VP-IT)*
Tim Miller *(Pres-Membership & Benefit Programs)*
Jennifer Vanselow *(VP-Fin)*
Steven Van Fleet *(Pres-Card-Linked Offers)*
Mike Knoop *(Pres-Fin Institution Loyalty)*
Bob Dow *(Pres-Benefits Program)*
David Carlson *(Pres-Wholesale Membership)*
Karianne Avila *(VP-Ops)*
Nathaniel Engelsen *(VP-Software Engrg)*
Tom White *(Dir-Tech)*
Bill Morency *(Dir-Tech)*
Juliann Gilbert *(VP-Corp Mktg)*
Brian Conroy *(Dir-Client Svcs)*
Brian Anderson *(Dir-Ops-FI Loyalty)*
Randall Wakeford *(VP-Client Platform Dev)*
Chris Herbst *(VP-Sls-Natl & Bus Insights)*
John Sirvydas *(VP-Strategic Platform Dev)*
Dan Councill *(VP-Tech)*
Juan A. Sabater *(Co-Chm & Principal)*

Subsidiaries:

Brand Networks, LLC **(1)**
180 Canal St Ste 600, Boston, MA 02114
Tel.: (617) 275-7050
Social Software Solutions & Digital Marketing Services
N.A.I.C.S.: 541519
Jamie Tedford *(Co-Founder & Chm)*
Paul Falzone *(Pres)*

Deluxe Financial Services, Inc. **(1)**
3660 Victoria St N, Shoreview, MN 55126-2906
Tel.: (651) 490-8000
Web Site: http://www.deluxerewards.com
Customer Rewards & Loyalty Program Services

Augeo Affinity Marketing, Inc.—(Continued)

N.A.I.C.S.: 541612

Subsidiary (Domestic):

Wausau Financial Systems, Inc.   (2)
400 Westwood Dr Ste 100, Wausau, WI
54401
Tel.: (715) 359-0427
Computer System Design Services
N.A.I.C.S.: 541512

HSP EPI Acquisitions, LLC   (1)
1401 Crooks Rd Ste 150, Troy, MI 48084
Tel.: (248) 404-1000
Web Site: http://www.entertainment.com
Discount, Promotion & Coupon Book Publisher
N.A.I.C.S.: 513130

Motivaction LLC   (1)
16355 36th Ave N Ste 100, Minneapolis,
MN 55446-4600
Tel.: (763) 412-3000
Web Site: http://www.motivaction.com
Sales Range: $10-24.9 Million
Emp.: 100
Fiscal Year-end: 06/30/2015
Provider of Management Consulting Services
N.A.I.C.S.: 541612
William Bryson (CEO)
Mike Simon (CFO)
Kari Vrba (Sr VP-Bus Dev)
Joe Keller (Pres & COO)
Stephanie Teig (Chief Creative Officer)
Debbie Disch (Dir-Bus Dev)
Joy Hansen (Dir-Bus Dev)
Gretchen Harrington (Dir-Bus Dev)
Matt Robb (Dir-Bus Dev)
Joanie Miskowiec Phillips (Dir-Pur & Indus Rels)
Joyce Engberg (Mgr-Award Svcs)
Katie Huiras (Sr Mgr-Creative Project)
Julie Higgins (Supvr-Acct)
Greg Mazzuco (VP-Accts-Natl)

edo Interactive, Inc.   (1)
3841 Green Hills Village Dr Ste 425, Nashville, TN 37215
Tel.: (615) 297-6080
Web Site: http://www.edointeractive.com
Sales Range: $10-24.9 Million
Software Publisher
N.A.I.C.S.: 513210
Ed Braswell (Founder & CEO)
Tim Garnto (Sr VP-Tech)
Adie Magnuson (Dir-Product Mgmt)
Kevin Sagon (VP-Engrg)
Cary McNamara (CFO)

AUGERE CONSTRUCTION

115 Executive Pkwy No 200, Hudson,
OH 44236
Tel.: (330) 342-4287
Web Site:
    https://www.augereconstruction.com
Year Founded: 1989
Rev.: $10,600,000
Emp.: 7
Commercial & Institutional Building
Construction
N.A.I.C.S.: 236220
Diane Dombroski (Office Mgr)
Leah Roth (Mgr-Acctg)
James L. Stewart II (VP)
George W. Roth (Pres)

AUGES SALES & SERVICE

800 E River Rd, Belen, NM 87002
Tel.: (505) 355-2362
Web Site: https://www.augeboys.com
Year Founded: 1946
Sales Range: $25-49.9 Million
Emp.: 11
Car Whslr
N.A.I.C.S.: 441110
Robert Auge (Pres)

AUGMENTITY SYSTEMS

4951 Indiana Ave Ste 100, Lisle, IL
60532
Tel.: (312) 265-2640
Web Site: http://www.augmentity.com

Year Founded: 2001
Sales Range: $25-49.9 Million
Emp.: 30
Staffing Services
N.A.I.C.S.: 561320
Robert Nelson (CEO)

AUGSBURG FORTRESS

Ste 600 100 S 5th St PO Box 1209,
Minneapolis, MN 55402-1242
Tel.: (612) 330-3300   MN
Web Site:
    http://www.augsburgfortress.org
Year Founded: 1891
Sales Range: $25-49.9 Million
Emp.: 304
Mfr of Ecclesiastic Garments; Altar
Supplies; Religious Music; Publisher
of Religious Books & Periodicals
N.A.I.C.S.: 513130
Sandy Middendorf (VP-HR & Organizational Dev)
Beth A. Lewis (Pres & CEO)
John Rahja (CFO)

Subsidiaries:

Augsburg Fortress Canada   (1)
500 Trillium Drive, PO Box 9940, Kitchener,
N2G 4Y4, ON, Canada
Tel.: (519) 748-2200
Web Site: http://www.afcanada.com
Sales Range: $10-24.9 Million
Emp.: 15
Books Publishing Services
N.A.I.C.S.: 513130

Sparkhouse   (1)
510 S Marquette Ave Ste 800, Minneapolis,
MN 55402
Tel.: (877) 702-5551
Web Site: http://www.wearesparkhouse.org
Emp.: 100
Books Publishing Services
N.A.I.C.S.: 513130
Beth Lewis (CEO)

AUGUST CAPITAL

2480 Sand Hill Rd Ste 101, Menlo
Park, CA 94025
Tel.: (650) 234-9900
Web Site: http://www.augustcap.com
Rev.: $1,300,000,000
Emp.: 16
Privater Equity Firm
N.A.I.C.S.: 523999
John R. Johnston (Co-Founder)
David F. Marquardt (Co-Founder)
Abby Hipps (Gen Counsel)
Eric Carlborg (Gen Partner)
Howard Hartenbaum (Gen Partner)
Tripp Jones (Gen Partner)
Vivek Mehra (Gen Partner)
David M. Hornik (Executives)

AUGUST HOME PUBLISHING COMPANY

2200 Grand Ave, Des Moines, IA
50312
Tel.: (515) 282-7000
Web Site:
    http://www.augusthome.com
Sales Range: $10-24.9 Million
Emp.: 153
Magazines: Publishing Only, Not
Printed On Site
N.A.I.C.S.: 513120
Craig Stille (Controller)
Peter J. Larson (Dir-Photo)
Terry Strohman (Dir-Editorial Media)
Harlan Vanwyk (Mgr-Production)
Steven Nordmeyer (Dir-Editorial
Media)

AUGUST PACKAGING INC.

4156 Hoffmeister Ave, Saint Louis,
MO 63125
Tel.: (314) 772-5505

Web Site:
    http://www.augustpackaging.com
Sales Range: $10-24.9 Million
Emp.: 14
Mfr of Boxes, Paperboard & Disposable Plastic Packaging
N.A.I.C.S.: 424130
Della Whalen (Mgr-HR)

AUGUST WINTER & SONS INC.

2323 N Roemer Rd, Appleton, WI
54911
Tel.: (920) 739-8881
Web Site:
    https://www.augustwinter.com
Rev.: $18,522,351
Emp.: 200
Plumbing Contractor
N.A.I.C.S.: 238220
Mark Eimmerman (VP & Mgr-Production)

AUGUST, LANG & HUSAK, INC.

4630 Montgomery Ave Ste 400,
Bethesda, MD 20814-3443
Tel.: (301) 657-2772   MD
Web Site: http://www.alhadv.com
Year Founded: 1992
Rev.: $14,335,550
Emp.: 18
Advetising Agency
N.A.I.C.S.: 541810
Michael August (Dir-Client Svcs)
Bill Lang (Dir-Mktg)
Chuck Husak (Dir-Creative)
Bonnie Weaver (Pres)
Kandi Hopkins (Mgr-Acctg)
Owen Smith (Mgr-Strategic Dev)
Melissa Meyers (Dir-Creative)
Bryant Prince (Dir-Art)

AUGUSTA COATING & MANU-FACTURING, LLC

1048 Superior Way, Thomson, GA
30824
Tel.: (706) 597-0314
Web Site:
    https://www.augustacoating.com
Sales Range: $10-24.9 Million
Emp.: 30
Corrosion Resistant Finishing Systems
N.A.I.C.S.: 325510
Wayne Wallace (Pres)

AUGUSTA COOPERATIVE FARM BUREAU, INC.

1205 B Richmond Rd, Staunton, VA
24401
Tel.: (540) 885-1265
Web Site:
    https://www.augustacoop.com
Sales Range: $10-24.9 Million
Emp.: 81
Feed & Farm Supply
N.A.I.C.S.: 459999
Kevin McLaren (Gen Mgr)
Rick Miller (Comptroller)
Eric Holter (Mgr-Pur)
Mitchell Sutton (Branch Mgr)

AUGUSTA DODGE INC.

2220 Martin Rd, Augusta, GA 30906-
2892
Tel.: (706) 736-8414
Sales Range: $25-49.9 Million
Emp.: 24
Automobiles, New & Used
N.A.I.C.S.: 441110
Greg Helfrich (Owner)
Buddy Farrer (Dir-Fin)
James Toole (Mgr-Fin)
Darren Hackett (Mgr-Internet)

AUGUSTA IRON & STEEL WORKS

3781 Martinez Blvd, Augusta, GA
30907
Tel.: (706) 860-7719
Web Site:
    http://www.augustaironsteelwork.com
Rev.: $12,000,000
Emp.: 50
Bridge Sections, Prefabricated, Highway
N.A.I.C.S.: 332710
Ruth D. Bovard (Chm)
Grier Bovard (Pres)

AUGUSTA READY MIX INC.

100 APAC Indus Way, Augusta, GA
30907
Tel.: (706) 733-9781
Web Site:
    http://www.augustareadymixinc.com
Year Founded: 1985
Sales Range: $10-24.9 Million
Emp.: 50
Provider of Concrete Mixtures
N.A.I.C.S.: 423320
Michael Prouty (Mgr-Dispatch)
Bill Burch (Mgr-Sls)

AUGUSTA REGIONAL CLINIC

342 Mule Academy Rd, Fishersville,
VA 22939
Tel.: (540) 332-5619   VA
Web Site:
    http://www.augustafreeclinic.org
Year Founded: 2006
Sales Range: $10-24.9 Million
Emp.: 21
Dental Care Services
N.A.I.C.S.: 621210
Richard Mansfield (Dir-Dental)

AUGUSTA SYMPHONY INC.

1301 Greene St Ste 200, Augusta,
GA 30901
Tel.: (706) 826-4705
Web Site: http://www.soaugusta.org
Sales Range: $1-9.9 Million
Emp.: 90
Symphony Orchestra
N.A.I.C.S.: 711130
Arthur Ross (Principal)
Shizuo Kuwahara (Dir-Music)
Mieko Di Sano (Exec Dir)
Don Edmunds (Dir-Artistic Ops)
Ann Morrison (Dir-Dev)
Ansley Easterlin (Dir-Miller Dev)
Anne Catherine Murray (Exec Dir)
Camilia Heninger (Mgr-Mktg & Coord-Dev)
Pawel Kozak (Mgr-Personnel)
Todd Sullivan (Mgr-Stage)

AUI CONTRACTORS, LLC.

4775 N Freeway, Fort Worth, TX
76106
Tel.: (817) 926-4377
Web Site: http://www.auigc.com
Year Founded: 1983
Sales Range: $75-99.9 Million
Emp.: 315
Nonresidential Construction Services
N.A.I.C.S.: 236220
B. Douglas Alumbaugh (Owner &
Pres)
Glenn A. Strother (Owner & Exec VP)

AUI, INC.

7420 Reading Ave SE, Albuquerque,
NM 87105
Tel.: (505) 242-4848
Web Site: https://www.auiinc.net
Year Founded: 1981
Emp.: 156
Building Contracting Services
N.A.I.C.S.: 238190

Adam Triolo *(CEO)*

AULSON CO. INC.
49 Danton Dr, Methuen, MA 01844
Tel.: (978) 975-4500
Web Site: https://www.aulson.com
Sales Range: $25-49.9 Million
Emp.: 100
Decontamination Services
N.A.I.C.S.: 238990
Alan Aulson *(Chm)*

AUNALYTICS, INC.
460 Stull St Ste 100, South Bend, IN 46601
Tel.: (855) 799-3282
Web Site: http://www.aunalytics.com
Data Management Services
N.A.I.C.S.: 513210
Tracy D. Graham *(CEO)*
Kelly Jones *(Pres & COO)*

Subsidiaries:

Netgain Information Systems Co. LLC   **(1)**
220 Reynolds Ave, Bellefontaine, OH 43311
Tel.: (937) 593-7177
Web Site: http://www.netgainis.com
Sales Range: $10-24.9 Million
Emp.: 21
Network Design
N.A.I.C.S.: 541512
Michael Minnich *(OEO)*
Art Rogers *(Controller)*
Luke Skidmore *(CTO)*
Kelly Jones *(Pres)*
Rick Gerdeman *(CEO)*

AUNT SARAH'S LLC
9010 Brook Rd, Glen Allen, VA 23060
Tel.: (804) 264-9189
Web Site:
   http://auntsarahsbrookroad.com
Sales Range: $10-24.9 Million
Emp.: 100
Family Restaurant Chain
N.A.I.C.S.: 722511
Glenn Dankos *(Pres)*

AURA FINANCIAL CORPORATION
303 2nd St N Tower Ste 550, San Francisco, CA 94107
Web Site: http://www.myaura.com
Year Founded: 2012
Sales Range: $25-49.9 Million
Emp.: 161
Financial Investment Services
N.A.I.C.S.: 523940
James Gutierrez *(Co-Founder & CEO)*
Kevin Kang *(Co-Founder & VP-Risk Modeling)*
Randy Wong *(Co-Founder & CTO)*
Lynnette Carrasco *(VP-People)*
Bennett Fogel *(Chief Revenue Officer)*

AURELIO RESOURCE CORPORATION
275 Third St Ste 5, Elko, NV 89803-0454
Tel.: (775) 777-3999
Sales Range: Less than $1 Million
Gold Exploration
N.A.I.C.S.: 212220
Fred W. Warnaars *(Chm)*
Earl H. Detra *(VP-Exploration)*
Michael Galloro *(CFO)*

AUREON BIOSCIENCES, INC
28 Wells Ave 4th Fl, Yonkers, NY 10701
Tel.: (914) 377-4000   DE
Medical Testing & Research
N.A.I.C.S.: 621511
Robert Shovlin *(CEO)*

AURIC RESOURCES INTERNATIONAL, INC.
1020 W Wickenburg Way 9, Wickenburg, AZ 85390-3290
Tel.: (853) 903-3290   AZ
Web Site:
   http://www.auricresources.com
Year Founded: 1989
Gold, Gemstone & Mineral Exploration & Mining Services
N.A.I.C.S.: 212220
William C. Berridge *(Pres & Dir)*
Randolph A. Stewart *(Sec & VP)*
Jeffrey W. Berridge *(VP)*
Alan Wright *(VP)*

AURIEMMA CONSULTING GROUP, INC.
120 Broadway Ste 3401, New York, NY 10271
Tel.: (516) 333-4800   NY
Web Site:
   http://www.auriemmaconsulting.com
Year Founded: 1984
Sales Range: $1-9.9 Million
Emp.: 15
Management Consulting Services
N.A.I.C.S.: 541611
Michael Auriemma *(Pres)*
Mindy Harris *(Mng Dir & Gen Counsel)*
Marc Sacher *(Exec VP)*
John Costa *(Mng Dir)*
Marianne Berry *(Mng Dir)*
Mark Jackson *(Mng Dir, Mgr-UK & Head-Partnerships Practice-Intl)*
Tom LaMagna *(Mng Dir)*

Subsidiaries:

Edgar, Dunn & Company (EDC)   **(1)**
505 Montgomery St Ste 610, San Francisco, CA 94111
Tel.: (415) 977-1870
Web Site: http://www.edgardunn.com
Sales Range: $1-9.9 Million
Emp.: 45
Global Financial Services & Payments Consultancy
N.A.I.C.S.: 541611
Peter Sidenius *(Mng Dir-London)*
Volker Schloenvoigt *(Principal-London)*

AURIGO SOFTWARE TECHNOLOGIES INC.
12515 Research Blvd Bldg 7 Ste 300, Austin, TX 78759
Tel.: (512) 212-4999
Web Site: http://www.aurigo.com
Year Founded: 2003
Sales Range: $1-9.9 Million
Emp.: 500
Software Development Services
N.A.I.C.S.: 541511
Balaji Sreenivasan *(CEO)*
Kevin Koenig *(CTO)*
Ashish Agrawal *(VP-Product Strategy & Mktg)*
Josh Moriarty *(VP-Professional Svcs)*
Manish Sharma *(VP-Cloud Ops & Customer Success)*

AURORA BLACKTOP INC.
1065 Sard Ave, Montgomery, IL 60538
Tel.: (630) 892-7711
Web Site:
   http://www.aurorablacktop.com
Sales Range: $10-24.9 Million
Emp.: 60
Blacktop (Asphalt) Work
N.A.I.C.S.: 238990
Jerome Leifheit *(Pres & CEO)*

AURORA CAPITAL GROUP, LLC
11611 San Vicente Blvd Ste 800, Los Angeles, CA 90049
Tel.: (310) 551-0101   DE
Web Site: http://www.auroracap.com
Year Founded: 1991
Privater Equity Firm
N.A.I.C.S.: 523999
John T. Mapes *(Partner)*
Mark D. Rosenbaum *(Partner)*
Joshua R. Klinefelter *(Partner)*
Matthew B. Laycock *(Partner)*
Robert K. West *(CFO)*
M. Randy Moser *(Partner)*
Robert W. Fraser *(Partner)*
Andrew Wilson *(Partner)*
Philip Gross *(Principal)*
Robert Fraser *(Partner)*
Josh Klinefelter *(Partner)*

Subsidiaries:

Aurora Resurgence Management Partners LLC   **(1)**
10877 Wilshire Blvd 21st Fl, Los Angeles, CA 90024
Tel.: (310) 551-0101
Web Site: http://www.aurorares.com
Emp.: 12
Privater Equity Firm
N.A.I.C.S.: 523999
Gerald L. Parsky *(Chm)*
Gerald L. Parsky *(Chm)*
Steven Smith *(Mng Partner)*
Zach Mager *(Principal)*
Ayush Singhania *(Principal)*
Robert West *(CFO)*

Holding (Domestic):

Electric Coating Technologies, LLC   **(2)**
4407 Railroad Ave, East Chicago, IN 46312
Tel.: (219) 378-1930
Web Site: http://www.ectllc.com
Emp.: 35
Electro Galvanized Steel Producer
N.A.I.C.S.: 332812
Steve Tatalovich *(Pres)*
Kenneth Paxson *(Mgr-Quality Assurance)*
Timothy Levin *(Plant Mgr)*

Cold Chain Technologies, Inc.   **(1)**
135 Constitution Blvd, Franklin, MA 02038
Tel.: (508) 429-1395
Web Site: http://www.coldchaintech.com
Solid Fiber Box Mfr
N.A.I.C.S.: 322211
T. J. Rizzo *(Chief Comml Officer & Sr VP-Intl Ops)*
Geoff Kaiser *(Dir-Engrg & Technical Svcs)*
Dan McMahon *(VP-Ops)*
Deb Bousquet *(Dir-HR)*
Ranjeet Banerjee *(CEO)*

Curtis Bay Energy, Inc.   **(1)**
1501 S Clinton St Ste 130, Baltimore, MD 21224
Tel.: (410) 354-3228
Web Site: http://www.curtisbaymws.com
Medical Waste Processing Services
N.A.I.C.S.: 562998
Charlie Leonard *(Pres & COO)*
Mark Schifani *(CEO)*

Lexington Precision Corporation   **(1)**
800 3rd Ave, New York, NY 10022-5911
Tel.: (212) 319-4657
Web Site: http://www.lexingtonprecision.com
Sales Range: $50-74.9 Million
Mfr, Designer & Marketer of Metal & Rubber Component Parts
N.A.I.C.S.: 326299

National Technical Systems, Inc.   **(1)**
24007 Ventura Blvd Ste 200, Calabasas, CA 91302
Tel.: (818) 591-0776
Web Site: http://www.nts.com
Rev.: $184,547,000
Assets: $164,629,000
Liabilities: $96,177,000
Net Worth: $68,452,000
Earnings: $5,420,000
Emp.: 1,197
Fiscal Year-end: 01/31/2013
Holding Company; Product Design Consulting, Engineering, Supply Chain Management, Testing & Certification Services

N.A.I.C.S.: 551112
Douglas Briskie *(Chief Strategy Officer & Sr VP)*
Kevin Beard *(Pres-Svc Div)*
Dave Robertson *(Chief HR Officer & Sr VP)*
Michael Graham *(Gen Mgr-Testing Facility-Longmont)*
Hector Paez *(COO)*
Jeffrey Keene *(CIO)*
Rich Adams *(Pres & CEO)*
Sid Nayar *(CFO)*
Sarah Willis *(VP-Mktg)*

Unit (Domestic):

NTS Silicon Valley   **(2)**
41039 Boyce Rd, Fremont, CA 94538
Tel.: (510) 578-3500
Web Site: http://www.nts.com
Product Safety & Testing Services
N.A.I.C.S.: 541380
Sheareen Jacobs *(Gen Mgr)*

Subsidiary (Domestic):

NTS TECHNICAL SYSTEMS   **(2)**
5320 W 104th St, Los Angeles, CA 90045
Tel.: (310) 348-0900
Web Site: http://www.nts.com
Emp.: 30
Engineering & Testing Services
N.A.I.C.S.: 541330
Robert Bornino *(Mgr)*

National Technical Systems, Inc - Wichita   **(2)**
7447 W 33rd St N, Wichita, KS 67205
Tel.: (316) 832-1600
Web Site: http://www.nts.com
Emp.: 7
Firearms Function & Reliability Testing Services
N.A.I.C.S.: 541380
Matthew Lutz *(Gen Mgr)*

Unit (Domestic):

National Technical Systems, Inc. - Acton   **(2)**
533 Main St, Acton, MA 01720-3940
Tel.: (978) 263-2933
Web Site: http://www.nts.com
Sales Range: $10-24.9 Million
Emp.: 20
Testing Lab
N.A.I.C.S.: 541330
Steve Eisenberg *(Gen Mgr)*

National Technical Systems, Inc. - Detroit   **(2)**
12601 Southfield Rd Bldg J, Detroit, MI 48223-3463
Tel.: (313) 835-0044
Web Site: http://www.nts.com
Sales Range: $10-24.9 Million
Emp.: 30
Engineering Services for Military, Aerospace & Automobile Equipment
N.A.I.C.S.: 541715
Mark Maskio *(Gen Mgr)*

National Technical Systems, Inc. - Fullerton   **(2)**
1536 E Valencia Dr, Fullerton, CA 92831-4734
Tel.: (714) 879-6110
Web Site: http://www.nts.com
Sales Range: $10-24.9 Million
Testing Lab
N.A.I.C.S.: 541715

National Technical Systems, Inc. - Los Angeles   **(2)**
5320 W 104th St, Los Angeles, CA 90045-6010
Tel.: (310) 348-0900
Web Site: http://www.nts.com
Sales Range: $10-24.9 Million
Emp.: 20
Testing Lab
N.A.I.C.S.: 541715
Robert Bornino *(Gen Mgr)*

National Technical Systems, Inc. - Santa Clarita   **(2)**
20970 Centre Pointe Pkwy, Santa Clarita, CA 91350
Tel.: (661) 259-8184
Web Site: http://www.nts.com

Aurora Capital Group, LLC—(Continued)

Sales Range: $50-74.9 Million
Testing Lab
N.A.I.C.S.: 424990
John Czajkowski (VP)

New Axia Holdings Inc. (1)
3350 Breckinridge Blvd Ste 100, Duluth, GA
30096-4959
Tel.: (713) 425-2150
Holding Company
N.A.I.C.S.: 551112

Subsidiary (Domestic):

AXIA Incorporated (2)
3350 Breckinridge Blvd Ste 100, Duluth, GA
30096-4959
Tel.: (713) 425-2150
Sales Range: $400-449.9 Million
Hardware & Metal Stampings Mfr; Tools &
Equipment Mfr & Sales
N.A.I.C.S.: 333120

Subsidiary (Non-US):

**Ames Taping Tools Co. of Canada
Limited** (3)
2445 Caoe Ave, Burnaby, V3K 6A9, BC,
Canada
Tel.: (604) 468-7281
Web Site: http://www.amestools.com
Sales Range: $10-24.9 Million
Emp.: 1
Mfr of Hand & Edge Tools
N.A.I.C.S.: 332216

Division (Domestic):

Nestaway (3)
9501 Granger Rd, Cleveland, OH 44125-
5348
Tel.: (216) 587-1500
Web Site: http://www.nestawaywire.com
Sales Range: $10-24.9 Million
Mft & Sales Of Materials Handling Systems
& Coated Wire Products For Automatic
Dishwashers
N.A.I.C.S.: 331222

Northern Steel Group, Inc. (1)
195 Joe Orr Rd Ste 200, Chicago Heights,
IL 60411
Tel.: (708) 709-0800
Sales Range: $150-199.9 Million
Emp.: 400
Holding Company; Processing & Distribu-
tion of Steel Products
N.A.I.C.S.: 551112

PSC Group LLC. (1)
4949 Fairmont Pkwy Ste 203, Pasadena,
TX 77504
Tel.: (281) 991-3500
Web Site: http://www.petroleumservice.com
Product Handling Services & Logistics Solu-
tions
N.A.I.C.S.: 541614
Joel Dickerson (Pres & CEO)
Brian Camp (VP-Ops)

Subsidiary (Domestic):

Delta Petroleum Company Inc. (2)
10352 River Rd, Saint Rose, LA 70087
Tel.: (504) 467-1399
Web Site: http://www.deltacompanies.net
Sales Range: $75-99.9 Million
Emp.: 60
Oils & Greases, Blending & Compounding
N.A.I.C.S.: 324191

Subsidiary (Domestic):

Olympic Oil, Ltd. (3)
5000 W 41st St, Cicero, IL 60804
Tel.: (708) 876-7900
Web Site: http://www.deltacogroup.com
Lubricating Oils & Greases
N.A.I.C.S.: 324191

Subsidiary (Domestic):

Prokar, Inc. (2)
300 E Mcneese St, Lake Charles, LA 70605
Tel.: (337) 475-9955
Web Site: http://www.prokar.com
Rev.: $1,900,000
Emp.: 28
Railcar Repair Services

N.A.I.C.S.: 488210
Lee Schreve (Pres)
Tom White (Bus Mgr)

Randall-Reilly, LLC (1)
3200 Rice Mine Rd NE, Tuscaloosa, AL
35406-1510
Tel.: (855) 288-3783
Web Site: http://www.randallreilly.com
Media & Information Services
N.A.I.C.S.: 541890
Shane Elmore (COO)
Linda Longton (Sr VP-Editorial & Res)
Brent Reilly (Pres & CEO)
Robert Lake (Sr VP-Acq & Bus Dev)
Stacey McCants (VP-Events)
Scott Miller (Sr VP-Sls)
Julie Arsenault (Sr VP-Strategy & Mktg)
Nick Reid (Sr VP-Digital Svcs)
Shane Kilgore (VP-IT)
Prescott Shibles (Exec VP & Gen Mgr)
Kim Fieldbinder (CFO)
Jeff Crissey (Dir-OEM & Aftermarket)
Jason Cannon (Editor-Comml Carrier Jour-
nal)

Subsidiary (Domestic):

Central Analysis Bureau, Inc. (2)
150 Airport Rd Ste 1100, Lakewood, NJ
08701
Tel.: (212) 244-6575
Web Site: http://www.cabadvantage.com
Insurance Agents, Brokers, And Service, N
N.A.I.C.S.: 524298
Andrew Schindel (Pres)
Jean Gardner (CEO)
Shuie Yankelewitz (COO)
Chad Krueger (Sr VP)

Division (Domestic):

EquipmentWatch (2)
6190 Powers Ferry Rd Ste 320, Atlanta, GA
30339
Tel.: (800) 669-3282
Web Site: https://equipmentwatch.com
Database Information Products
N.A.I.C.S.: 519290

Northbrook Publishing (2)
21420 W Greenfield Ave, New Berlin, WI
53146
Tel.: (262) 650-9260
Web Site: http://northbrookpub.com
Customized Publishing Services
N.A.I.C.S.: 513120
Pete Sobic (Pres)
Kip Kusick (Assoc Publr)

Sharps Compliance Corp. (1)
9220 Kirby Dr Ste 500, Houston, TX 77054
Tel.: (713) 432-0300
Web Site: http://www.sharpsinc.com
Rev.: $76,424,000
Assets: $75,431,000
Liabilities: $28,847,000
Net Worth: $46,584,000
Earnings: $12,868,000
Emp.: 190
Fiscal Year-end: 06/30/2021
Medical Waste Management Services
N.A.I.C.S.: 562998
Gregory C. Davis (VP-Ops)
Dennis P. Halligan (VP-Mktg)
Eric T. Bauer (CFO & Exec VP)

Subsidiary (Domestic):

Citiwaste, LLC (2)
893 Shepherd Ave, Brooklyn, NY 11208
Tel.: (718) 372-3887
Waste Management Services
N.A.I.C.S.: 562998

**Sharps Environmental Services,
Inc.** (2)
1544 NE Loop, Carthage, TX 75633-1725
Tel.: (903) 693-2525
Web Site: https://www.sharpsinc.com
Emp.: 10
Waste Management Services
N.A.I.C.S.: 562211

VLS Recovery Services, LLC (1)
19500 Highway 249 Suite 440, Hockley, TX
77447-9109
Tel.: (713) 936-0960
Web Site: http://www.vlsrs.com
Waste Management Services

N.A.I.C.S.: 562998
Mike Dilick (CEO)
Bill Foran (Dir-Sls)
Tori Foerste (Acct Mgr)
Tony Clark (VP-Bus Dev)
John Magee (CEO)

Subsidiary (Domestic):

Lancaster Oil Company (2)
1076 Old Manheim Pike, Lancaster, PA
17601
Tel.: (717) 393-2627
Web Site: http://www.ercofusa.com
Rev.: $9,260,000
Emp.: 50
Hazardous Waste Treatment & Disposal
Services
N.A.I.C.S.: 562211
Richard Middleton (Pres)
Ken Lefever (CEO)

**Pacific Trans Environmental Services,
Inc.** (2)
1452 N Johnson Ave, El Cajon, CA 92020
Tel.: (619) 441-1818
Web Site: http://www.ptesinc.com
General Freight Trucking, Local
N.A.I.C.S.: 484110
Dave Kern (CFO)
Alberto Montero (Pres)
Horacio Fimbres (Mgr-Field Svcs & Trans-
portation)
Horacio Perez (Mgr-Ops & Environmental
Compliance-Mexico)
Karla Bibiano (Mgr-Customer Svc & Inside
Sls)
Karen Curiel (Mgr-Environmental
Regulations-US)
Michael Jeffries (VP & Gen Mgr)
Patrick Schuster (Mgr-Tech Svcs)
Ruben Verduzco (Mgr-Acctg)
Teri Bronold (Mgr-Admin)

**Westcoast Gate & Entry Systems,
Inc.** (1)
339 S Isis Ave, Inglewood, CA 90301
Tel.: (310) 445-5067
Web Site: http://www.westcoastgate.com
Rev.: $1,548,000
Emp.: 6
Custom Gate Installation & Repair Services
N.A.I.C.S.: 321911
Gary Ovsiowitz (Founder & Pres)

Subsidiary (Domestic):

Automated Gate Services, Inc. (2)
526 Princeland Ct, Corona, CA 92879
Tel.: (951) 689-9330
Web Site:
    http://www.automatedgateservices.com
Sales Range: $1-9.9 Million
Emp.: 20
Automatic Gated Entry Systems Installation
& Repair Services
N.A.I.C.S.: 238210
Carrie Johnson (CFO)
Sarah Hole (Project Mgr)
Steve Johnson (CEO)

AURORA CIVIL ENGINEERING INC.

610 E Morgan St, Brandon, FL 33510
Tel.: (813) 643-9907
Web Site:
    https://www.auroracivil.com
Year Founded: 2001
Sales Range: $1-9.9 Million
Emp.: 9
Engineering Services
N.A.I.C.S.: 541330
Christopher E. Weddle (Pres)
Michael Knight (Project Mgr)

AURORA COMMUNITY SER- VICES

406 Technology Dr E, Menomonie,
WI 54751
Tel.: (715) 235-1839
Web Site:
    https://www.auroraservices.com
Year Founded: 1986
Sales Range: $10-24.9 Million
Emp.: 790

Operation of Residential Buildings for
the Disabled
N.A.I.C.S.: 621610
Avis Wolski Baker (Chief Admin Offi-
cer)
Holly Hakes (Exec Dir)
Linda Aton (Dir-Admin Svcs)
Andy Wolf (Dir-Aurora Community
Counseling)
Candace Kapperman-Wolf (Dir-
Aurora Community Health)
Deena Black (Dir-Aurora Residential
Alternatives)
Terri Bollinger (Dir-Aurora Vocational
Svcs)
Cindy Smith (Dir-Fin)
Dustin Doornink (Dir-IT)
Dave Barnard (CEO)
Jim Newman (COO)

AURORA COOPERATIVE

2225 Q St, Aurora, NE 68818
Tel.: (402) 694-2106
Web Site:
    https://www.auroracoop.com
Sales Range: $200-249.9 Million
Emp.: 245
Grains; Agricultural Supplier
N.A.I.C.S.: 424510
Jeff Bart (Head-Employee Svcs)

AURORA DIAGNOSTICS HOLDINGS, LLC

11025 RCA Center Dr Ste 300, Palm
Beach Gardens, FL 33410
Tel.: (561) 626-5512
Web Site: http://www.auroradx.com
Year Founded: 2006
Sales Range: $250-299.9 Million
Emp.: 1,136
Holding Company; Medical Diagnos-
tic & Pathology Services
N.A.I.C.S.: 551112
Daniel D. Crowley (CEO)
Michael J. Null (Pres-Aurora Re-
search Institute)
Bruce C. Walton (Pres & COO)
Michael Grattendick (CFO)
Robert Pettit (VP-Revenue Cycle
Mgmt)
William Sutton (Chief Compliance
Officer, Chief Privacy Officer & Gen
Counsel)
Rei Lopez (VP-Hospital Ops)
F. Michael Walsh (Chief Medical Offi-
cer)
Christopher Rieder (CIO)

Subsidiaries:

**Cleveland Skin Pathology Laboratory
Inc.** (1)
3737 Park E Ste 202, Cleveland, OH
44122-4347
Tel.: (216) 464-7770
Web Site:
    http://www.clevelandskinpathology.com
Medical Laboratories Specializing in Pathol-
ogy
N.A.I.C.S.: 621511
Jerome R. Pomeranz (Founder)

CytoPath, P.C. (1)
1004 1st St N Ste 200, Alabaster, AL
35007-8796
Tel.: (205) 664-9797
Web Site: http://www.cytopathpc.com
Sales Range: $1-9.9 Million
Surgical Pathology & Cytopathology Ser-
vices
N.A.I.C.S.: 621511
Teresa Venz-Williamson (Pres)

AURORA PACKING CO., INC.

125 Grant St, North Aurora, IL 60542
Tel.: (630) 897-0551   IL
Web Site:
    https://www.aurorabeef.com
Year Founded: 1980

Sales Range: $100-124.9 Million
Emp.: 275
Meat Packing Services
N.A.I.C.S.: 311611
Marvin R. Fagel (Pres)

AURORA POWER RE-SOURCES INC.
10333 Richmond Ave Ste 710, Houston, TX 77042
Tel.: (281) 495-9957
Web Site:
   http://www.aurorapower.com
Sales Range: $1-9.9 Million
Emp.: 20
Natural Gas Marketing
N.A.I.C.S.: 221210
G. Scott Pfoff (Pres & COO)
David Boelens (VP-Ops-Alaska)

Subsidiaries:

Aurora Gas LLC   (1)
10333 Richmond Ave Ste 710, Houston, TX 77042
Tel.: (281) 495-9957
Web Site: http://www.aurorapower.com
Gas & Other Services
N.A.I.C.S.: 213112

Aurora Well Service, LLC   (1)
1029 W 3rd Ave, Anchorage, AK 99501-1981
Tel.: (907) 277-1003
Drilling Services
N.A.I.C.S.: 213111

AURORA TECHNOLOGIES INC.
19 Industrial Dr, Pacific, MO 63069
Tel.: (636) 257-6655
Web Site: https://www.ati-1.com
Year Founded: 1988
Sales Range: $10-24.9 Million
Emp.: 150
Custom Plastics Fabricator
N.A.I.C.S.: 326199
Thomas C. White (Pres)
Darren Winter (Mgr-IT)
Alicia Powell (Mgr-Accounts Payable)
Dina Lucas (Controller)
Kip Downhour (Gen Mgr)
Steve Archer (Mgr-Shipping)
Tracy Archer (Plant Mgr)
Jim Menees (Project Mgr)

AUS-TEX PRINTING & MAIL-ING
2431 Forbes Dr, Austin, TX 78754
Tel.: (512) 476-7581
Web Site: http://www.austex.com
Sales Range: $250-299.9 Million
Emp.: 50
Commercial Printing, Lithographic
N.A.I.C.S.: 323111
John Eastty (Pres)
Lynn Coleman (Mgr)
Mitzi Stiles (Mgr-HR)
Becky Ryan Harper (Acct Mgr)
Teri Lint (Acct Mgr)

AUSCO PRODUCTS, INC.
2245 Pipestone Rd, Benton Harbor, MI 49022-2425
Tel.: (269) 926-0700
Web Site:
   https://www.auscoproducts.com
Year Founded: 1908
Sales Range: $10-24.9 Million
Emp.: 110
Braking Equipment Mfr for Off-Highway Vehicles
N.A.I.C.S.: 336340
Dan Montey (Mgr-Ops)

AUSSIE PET MOBILE, INC.
95 Argonaut Ste 115, Aliso Viejo, CA 92656

Tel.: (949) 234-0680   AU
Web Site:
   https://www.aussiepetmobile.com
Year Founded: 1996
Sales Range: $1-9.9 Million
Emp.: 22
Mobile Pet Grooming Services Franchisor
N.A.I.C.S.: 812910

AUSSIEFIT
11589 Seminole Blvd, Seminole, FL 33778
Tel.: (727) 897-5405
Web Site: http://www.aussiefit.com
Sales Range: $10-24.9 Million
Emp.: 100
Fitness Center
N.A.I.C.S.: 713940
Geoff Dyer (Founder & CEO)

AUSTELL NATURAL GAS SYSTEM
2838 Joe Jerkins Blvd, Austell, GA 30106-3249
Tel.: (770) 948-1841   GA
Web Site: https://www.austellgas.com
Year Founded: 1954
Sales Range: $25-49.9 Million
Emp.: 120
Natural Gas Distribution
N.A.I.C.S.: 221210
Wanda Todd (Supvr-Pur)

AUSTEN RIGGS CENTER
25 Main St, Stockbridge, MA 01262
Tel.: (413) 298-5511   MA
Web Site:
   https://www.austenriggs.org
Year Founded: 1919
Sales Range: $10-24.9 Million
Emp.: 159
Psychiatric Treatment Services
N.A.I.C.S.: 622210

AUSTERLITZ ACQUISITION CORP I
1701 Village Center Cir, Las Vegas, NV 89134
Tel.: (702) 323-7330   Ky
Investment Management Service
N.A.I.C.S.: 523999

AUSTIN & WILLIAMS
125 Kennedy Dr Ste 100, Hauppauge, NY 11788-4017
Tel.: (631) 231-6600
Web Site: http://www.austin-williams.com
Year Founded: 1996
Sales Range: $10-24.9 Million
Emp.: 35
Advertising Agencies
N.A.I.C.S.: 541810
Ken Greenberg (Founder)
Rick Chiorando (Chief Creative Officer & Principal)
Eva LaMere (Principal)
Henry Luhmann (Dir-Production Svcs)
Sheira Rosenberg (Acct Dir)
Bryan Hynes (Dir-Creative)
Larry Baronciani (Sr Dir-Art)
Andria Osler (Acct Exec-Acct Mgmt Team)
Andrew Catalano (Chief Digital Officer)
Barbara Esposito (VP & Strategist-Comm)

AUSTIN BANK CORP., INC.
200 E Commerce, Jacksonville, TX 75766
Tel.: (903) 586-1526   TX
Web Site:
   https://www.austinbank.com

Year Founded: 1984
Sales Range: $50-74.9 Million
Emp.: 330
Banking Services
N.A.I.C.S.: 522110
Patty Steelman (Sr VP & Dir-Mktg)
Jeff Austin Jr. (Chm)
Jeff Austin III (Vice Chm)
Russ Gideon (COO)
Jason Petersen (Chief Lending Officer)
Mike Gunnels (Chief Credit Officer)
Lowell Little (Pres-Southeast & Exec VP)

Subsidiaries:

Austin Bank, Texas N.A.   (1)
200 E Commerce St, Jacksonville, TX 75766-4904   (100%)
Tel.: (903) 586-1526
Web Site: http://www.austinbank.com
Sales Range: $25-49.9 Million
Emp.: 309
National Commercial Banks
N.A.I.C.S.: 522110
John P. Williams (Pres & CEO)
Dawn DeVillers (Exec Admin Officer)

AUSTIN CAPITAL BANK
8100 Shoal Creek Blvd, Austin, TX 78757
Tel.: (512) 693-3600
Web Site:
   http://www.austincapitalbank.com
Year Founded: 2006
Sales Range: $1-9.9 Million
Emp.: 200
Banking Services
N.A.I.C.S.: 522110
Erik Beguin (Founder & CEO)

AUSTIN CHEMICAL COMPANY INC.
1565 Barclay Blvd, Buffalo Grove, IL 60089-4518
Tel.: (847) 520-9600
Web Site:
   http://www.austinchemical.com
Year Founded: 1976
Sales Range: $10-24.9 Million
Emp.: 35
Chemicals & Allied Products
N.A.I.C.S.: 424690
Samuel M. Ponticelli (Chm & CEO)
Deborah Green (Controller)

AUSTIN COMPANY
3336 Hwy 51 N, Fort Mill, SC 29715-8348
Tel.: (704) 332-1224
Web Site:
   http://www.theaustincompany.com
Year Founded: 1970
Sales Range: $10-24.9 Million
Emp.: 125
Drywall Installation Services
N.A.I.C.S.: 238310
Daniel Austin (Pres)
Sam Treadaway (Gen Mgr)

AUSTIN DISTRIBUTING & MANUFACTURING CORP.
4018 W 50th Ave, Amarillo, TX 79109
Tel.: (806) 355-8981
Web Site:
   http://www.austindistributing.com
Sales Range: $25-49.9 Million
Emp.: 50
Mfr & Distr of Industrial Supplies
N.A.I.C.S.: 423840
Jim Crimer (Pres)

AUSTIN ENERGY
721 Barton Springs Rd, Austin, TX 78704-1167
Tel.: (512) 322-6514

Web Site:
   http://www.austinenergy.com
Sales Range: $1-4.9 Billion
Emp.: 1,700
Electric Utility
N.A.I.C.S.: 221122
Kerry Overton (Deputy Gen Mgr)
Larry Weis (Gen Mgr)
Robert Cullick (Dir-Corp Comm)

AUSTIN ENGINEERING CO., INC.
3317 RR 620 N, Austin, TX 78734
Tel.: (512) 327-1464
Web Site: https://www.aecoi.net
Sales Range: $25-49.9 Million
Emp.: 250
Construction Engineering Services
N.A.I.C.S.: 237310
Buddy Keller (Owner)

AUSTIN GEOMODELING, INC.
River Pl Business Park 6500 River Pl Blvd Bldg I Ste 400, Austin, TX 78730
Tel.: (512) 257-8820
Web Site: http://www.austingeo.com
Year Founded: 1996
Sales Range: $1-9.9 Million
Emp.: 31
Computer Application Development
N.A.I.C.S.: 541519
Robin Dommisse (CEO)
Tron Isaksen (Pres)
Mauricio Arboleda (COO)

AUSTIN HARDWARE & SUPPLY INC.
950 NW Technology Dr, Lees Summit, MO 64086
Tel.: (816) 246-2800
Web Site:
   https://www.austinhardware.com
Rev.: $48,500,000
Emp.: 32
Hardware
N.A.I.C.S.: 423710
Donald A. Austin (Chm)
Mark Dudenhoeffer (Pres)
Gary Bobo (Product Mgr)
Joe Verdini (VP-Sls)
Teresa Meredith (Controller)

AUSTIN INDUSTRIES, INC.
3535 Travis St Ste 300, Dallas, TX 75204
Tel.: (214) 443-5500   DE
Web Site: https://www.austin-ind.com
Year Founded: 1918
Emp.: 7,000
Commercial & Institutional Building Construction
N.A.I.C.S.: 236220
Bernard Hewett (Exec Vp-Ops)
D. Steven Henry (Chief Legal Officer & Sr VP)
Joe McLaughlin (CFO)
David Walls (Co-Pres & CEO)
Michael Cox (Co-Pres)

Subsidiaries:

Austin Bridge & Road, Inc.   (1)
6330 Commerce Dr Ste 150, Irving, TX 75063-4412   (100%)
Tel.: (214) 596-7300
Web Site: http://www.austin-ind.com
Sales Range: $10-24.9 Million
Emp.: 100
Heavy Highway & Transportation Infrastructure Services
N.A.I.C.S.: 237310
Richard Mills (Pres)
Mike Manning (Exec VP-Ops)

Austin Commercial, Inc.   (1)
3535 Travis St, Dallas, TX 75204-1448   (100%)
Tel.: (214) 443-5100

Austin Industries, Inc.—(Continued)

Web Site: http://www.austin-ind.com
Sales Range: $10-24.9 Million
Emp.: 110
General Contractor & Commercial Construction
N.A.I.C.S.: 236220
David B. Walls (Pres)
Steve Rivers (VP-Southeast)
G. D. Soteropulos (VP-Ops-California)
Dianne Lee (Mgr-Bus Dev)
Davud Yeagy (Dir-Preconstruction)
Brian Andrews (Dir-Preconstruction)
David Graham (VP-Ops)
Pete Cesari (Sr Mgr-Ops-Southeast)
Bobby Terriaco (Sr Project Mgr-Southeast)
Michael Spencer (Sr Project Mgr-Orlando)
Kevin Glenn (Principal-Florida West Coast)
Jonathan Sheppeard (Sr Mgr-Preconstruction)

Austin Industrial, Inc. (1)
2801 E 13th St La Porte, Houston, TX 77571 (100%)
Tel.: (713) 641-3400
Web Site: http://www.austin-ind.com
Sales Range: $25-49.9 Million
Emp.: 75
Petro Chemical Contractor
N.A.I.C.S.: 238220
Don Fanning (Mgr-Mktg)
Barry Babyak (Pres)
Mike Morris (Dir-Health, Safety & Environmental)
Diana Aburub (Office Mgr-Noltex Site)

AUSTIN LAWRENCE GROUP

1266 E Main St Ste 700, Stamford, CT 06902
Tel.: (203) 391-3006 CT
Web Site:
http://www.austinlawrence.com
Year Founded: 1981
Sales Range: $10-24.9 Million
Emp.: 10
Advetising Agency
N.A.I.C.S.: 541810
Ken Lempit (Pres & Chief Mktg Officer)

AUSTIN MANUFACTURING SERVICES LP

4616 W Howard Ln, Austin, TX 78728
Tel.: (512) 491-7411
Web Site: http://www.austinmfg.com
Rev.: $17,000,000
Emp.: 40
Integrated Circuits, Semiconductor Networks
N.A.I.C.S.: 334413
Brad Scoggins (Pres & CEO)
Joseph Morgan (CFO)
Robert Wallace (Controller)
Iain Hurn (Exec VP & Gen Mgr)
Neil Ashley (VP-Corp & Bus Dev)

AUSTIN MUTUAL INSURANCE GROUP

15490 101st Ave N, Maple Grove, MN 55369
Web Site:
http://www.austinmutual.com
Sales Range: $50-74.9 Million
Emp.: 105
Fire, Marine & Casualty Insurance
N.A.I.C.S.: 524126
Jeffrey B. Kusch (Pres)
Wayne S. Cwik (Asst VP)
Thomas M. Van Berkel (Chm)

AUSTIN PRODUCTIONS INC.

835 Marconi Ave, Ronkonkoma, NY 11779
Tel.: (631) 981-7300 NY
Year Founded: 1953
Sales Range: $200-249.9 Million
Emp.: 550
Accessories for Home & Garden
N.A.I.C.S.: 449129

Pamela S. Pierce (Pres)
Andrew Cymrot (Exec VP)

AUSTIN PUMP & SUPPLY COMPANY INC

3803 Todd Ln, Austin, TX 78744
Tel.: (512) 442-2348
Web Site:
https://www.austinpump.com
Rev.: $18,048,691
Emp.: 40
Water Pumps (Industrial)
N.A.I.C.S.: 423830
Charles T. Sterzing II (Pres)

AUSTIN TRAFFIC SIGNAL CONSTRUCTION CO., LP

4615 Priem Ln, Pflugerville, TX 78660
Tel.: (512) 255-9951
Web Site: http://www.atscc.com
Year Founded: 1980
Sales Range: $10-24.9 Million
Emp.: 140
Traffic Signal & Roadway Electrical Construction Contracting Services
N.A.I.C.S.: 238210
Fred S. Shin (Pres)
Ed Schroeder (VP)
Steve Rutledge (VP)

AUSTIN VENTURES, LP

300 W 6th St Ste 2300, Austin, TX 78701-3902
Tel.: (512) 485-1900 TX
Web Site:
http://www.austinventures.com
Year Founded: 1984
Sales Range: $25-49.9 Million
Emp.: 16
Equity Investment Firm
N.A.I.C.S.: 523999
John Dirvin (COO & Partner)
Kevin Kunz (CFO)
Dave Benton (VP-Tech)
Ken DeAngelis (Gen Partner)
Christopher A. Pacitti (Gen Partner)
John Thornton (Gen Partner)
Vernon Bryant (Partner)

Subsidiaries:

AVP Management Services, Inc. (1)
300 W 6th St Ste 2300, Austin, TX 78701
Tel.: (512) 485-1900
Web Site: http://www.austinventures.com
Sales Range: $1-9.9 Million
Emp.: 55
Investment Management & Advisory Services
N.A.I.C.S.: 523940
Kim Hughes (Dir-Comm)
Dave Alter (Principal)
Joe Aragona (Gen Partner)
Vernon Bryant (Partner)
Ken Deangelis (Gen Partner)
Scott Donaldson (Partner)
Chris Pacitti (Gen Partner)
John Thornton (Gen Partner)

AUSTIN WHITE LIME COMPANY

4900 Howard Ln, Austin, TX 78728
Tel.: (512) 255-3646
Web Site:
http://www.austinwhitelime.com
Rev.: $16,700,000
Emp.: 150
Building Lime
N.A.I.C.S.: 327410
Lila Weirich (Mgr-Sls)

AUSTIN-MCGREGOR INTERNATIONAL

3500 Oaklawn Ste 550, Dallas, TX 75219
Tel.: (972) 488-0500

Web Site:
http://www.austinmcgregor.com
Sales Range: $10-24.9 Million
Emp.: 20
Employment Agencies
N.A.I.C.S.: 561311
Charles McCreary (Founder)
Stephen Sterett (Mng Partner)
Paul Bailey (Mng Partner)
Logan Moodley (Mng Partner)
Angie Benninghoff (Partner)

AUSTINREALESTATE.COM

3103 Bee Caves Rd Ste 102, Austin, TX 78746
Tel.: (512) 344-6000
Web Site:
https://www.austinrealestate.com
Year Founded: 2007
Sales Range: $1-9.9 Million
Emp.: 36
Real Estate Brokerage Services
N.A.I.C.S.: 531210
Jim Olenbush (Co-Founder)
Crystal Olenbush (Co-Founder)

AUTCO DISTRIBUTING INC.

10900 Midwest Industrial Blvd, Saint Louis, MO 63132
Tel.: (314) 426-6524
Web Site: https://www.autco.com
Year Founded: 1970
Sales Range: $10-24.9 Million
Emp.: 20
Video Cassette Recorders & Accessories
N.A.I.C.S.: 423620
Michael F. Hennessey (Pres)
Timothy Meyer (Dir-Inside Sls)
Shaun Murphy (Acct Mgr)

AUTEX INC.

94 Key Rd, Keene, NH 03431
Tel.: (603) 276-3520
Web Site: http://www.autexinc.com
Rev.: $14,300,000
Emp.: 25
General Automotive Repair Shops
N.A.I.C.S.: 811111
Thomas Bogar (Owner & Pres)

AUTHENTIC AUTOGRAPHS UNLIMITED, INC.

500 N Rainbow Blvd Ste 300, Las Vegas, NV 89107
Tel.: (702) 257-7111 NV
Web Site:
https://www.aaunlimited.com
Year Founded: 1996
Autographed Memorabilia Authenticating Services
N.A.I.C.S.: 541990
Marc S. Goldman (Pres)

AUTHENTIC CUSTOM HOMES, LLC

2422 NW 178th St, Edmond, OK 73012
Tel.: (405) 595-1000
Web Site:
http://www.buildauthentic.com
Year Founded: 2006
Sales Range: $10-24.9 Million
Emp.: 16
Real Estate Investment Management Services
N.A.I.C.S.: 531390
Kenyon Woods (Co-Founder & Co-Owner)
Brandi Woods (Co-Founder & Co-Owner)
Brent Beard (Pres)
David Cumming (VP-Construction)
Debbie Beard (Dir-Pur)

AUTHENTICOM, INC.

400 Main St Ste 300, La Crosse, WI 54601
Tel.: (608) 796-1167 WI
Web Site:
https://www.authenticom.com
Year Founded: 2002
Sales Range: $10-24.9 Million
Emp.: 100
Automotive Industry Data Management Services
N.A.I.C.S.: 541513
Stephen Cottrell (Founder & CEO)
Brian Clements (Dir-Software Dev)
Drew Williams (Creative Dir)
Jason Tryfon (Pres-Intl Ops & Global Growth-Canada)

AUTISM SERVICES, INC.

4444 Bryant Stratton Way, Williamsville, NY 14221
Tel.: (716) 631-5777 NY
Web Site: http://www.autism-services-inc.org
Year Founded: 1982
Sales Range: $10-24.9 Million
Emp.: 471
Family Support Services
N.A.I.C.S.: 624190
Veronica Federiconi (Exec Dir)
Thomas Mazur (Pres)

AUTISM SOCIETY OF NORTH CAROLINA, INC.

505 Oberlin Rd Ste 230, Raleigh, NC 27605
Tel.: (919) 743-0204 NC
Web Site: http://www.autismsociety-nc.org
Year Founded: 1970
Sales Range: $10-24.9 Million
Emp.: 1,257
Autism Support Services
N.A.I.C.S.: 813212
Kerri Erb (Chief Program Officer)
Jennifer Mahan (Dir-Advocacy & Pub Policy)
David Laxton (Dir-Comm)
Kristy White (Chief Dev Officer)
Paul Wendler (CFO)
Elizabeth Phillippi (Chm)
John Delaloye (Treas)
John Townson (Sec)
Ruth Hurst (Vice Chm)
Tracey Sheriff (CEO)
Maureen Morrell (Dir-Chapter)
Kate Hall (Dir-Ops)
Aleck Myers (Dir-Clinical)
Kari Johnston (Dir-Svcs)
Betty Camp (Co-Founder)
Joann Jeffries (Co-Founder)
Mary Lou Warren (Co-Founder)

AUTO ACCESSORIES GARAGE INC.

28 W Nebraska St, Frankfort, IL 60423-1483
Tel.: (708) 444-2580
Web Site:
https://www.autoaccessories.com
Year Founded: 2005
Sales Range: $1-9.9 Million
Emp.: 11
Online Retailer of Automotive Parts
N.A.I.C.S.: 441330
Steve Therriault (Pres)

AUTO BODY TOOLMART

2545 Millennium Dr, Elgin, IL 60124
Tel.: (847) 462-9243
Web Site: http://www.abtm.com
Year Founded: 1981
Sales Range: $10-24.9 Million
Emp.: 25
Motor Vehicle Supplies & New Parts
N.A.I.C.S.: 423120

Matthew Dorfman (Pres)
David Gauze (Mgr-Adv)
Suzanne Weiner (Mgr-HR & Pur)

AUTO BUTLER INC.
4701 Humboldt Ave N, Minneapolis, MN 55430
Tel.: (612) 529-3345
Web Site: http://www.autobutler.net
Sales Range: $10-24.9 Million
Emp.: 20
Car Washing Machinery
N.A.I.C.S.: 333310
Keith Schleeter (Pres)

AUTO CUSTOM CARPETS INC.
1429 Noble St, Anniston, AL 36201
Tel.: (256) 236-1118
Web Site: http://www.accmats.com
Rev.: $25,300,000
Emp.: 30
Automobile Floor Coverings Mfr
N.A.I.C.S.: 314110
Ken Howell (Pres)
Randall Bates (Mgr-Sls)
Tim Sparks (Plant Mgr)

AUTO DATA, INC.
6111 Blue Cir Dr, Minneapolis, MN 55343
Tel.: (952) 938-4710   MN
Web Site: http://www.autodata.com
Year Founded: 1993
Packaged Productivity Software Programs Mfr
N.A.I.C.S.: 513210
Jim Vereide (Dir-Bus)

AUTO EQUIPMENT INC.
2846 Salisbury Hwy, Statesville, NC 28687
Tel.: (704) 872-4116
Web Site: https://www.autoequipmentinc.com
Year Founded: 1928
Rev.: $15,000,000
Emp.: 25
Trucks, Tractors & Trailers: New & Used
N.A.I.C.S.: 441110
Dick Reavis (Pres)
Richard A. Reavis Sr. (CEO)

AUTO EUROPE, LLC
39 Commercial St, Portland, ME 04101
Tel.: (207) 842-2000
Web Site: http://www.autoeurope.com
Year Founded: 1954
Sales Range: $1-4.9 Billion
Emp.: 400
Automobile Rental Services
N.A.I.C.S.: 561599
Imad Khalidi (CEO)
Joshua Nagine (Mgr-Reservations)
Brian Lutz (Dir-e-Commerce-SEO & SEM)
Dan Petlon (CIO)

AUTO EXECUTIVES
7493 N Oracle Rd Ste 105, Tucson, AZ 85704
Tel.: (520) 297-3787
Web Site: http://www.autoexecutives.com
Sales Range: $10-24.9 Million
Emp.: 2
New & Used Car Dealers
N.A.I.C.S.: 441110
John M. Almond (Founder & Co-Owner & Pres)
Brenda Almond (Co-Owner & VP)

AUTO EXPEDITING INC.

12300 Farmington Rd, Livonia, MI 48150
Tel.: (734) 522-2224
Web Site: https://www.ryantransportation.com
Sales Range: $10-24.9 Million
Emp.: 65
Trucking Except Local
N.A.I.C.S.: 484121
Gary England (Gen Mgr)

Subsidiaries:

Ryan Transportation Group, Inc.   (1)
12300 Farmington Rd, Livonia, MI 48150
Tel.: (734) 522-7382
Web Site: http://www.ryantransportation.com
Sales Range: Less than $1 Million
Emp.: 5
Management Services
N.A.I.C.S.: 541611

Ryan Transportation Inc.   (1)
12300 Farmington Rd, Livonia, MI 48150
Tel.: (734) 522-7382
Web Site: http://www.ryantransportation.com
Sales Range: $1-9.9 Million
Local Trucking without Storage
N.A.I.C.S.: 484110

AUTO GLASS SERVICE LLC.
131 John Rice Blvd Ste B, Murfreesboro, TN 37129-4165
Tel.: (615) 867-3500
Web Site: https://www.glassusa.com
Rev.: $11,200,000
Emp.: 200
Automotive Glass Replacement Shops
N.A.I.C.S.: 811122
Rich West (Partner)

AUTO MALL 46, INC.
440 Rte 46 E, Totowa, NJ 07512
Tel.: (973) 256-1200   NJ
Web Site: https://www.route46autos.com
New & Used Car Dealerships Owner & Operator
N.A.I.C.S.: 441110
Frank Esposito (Pres & Owner)

Subsidiaries:

Route 33 Nissan   (1)
951 US Hwy 33, Hamilton Square, NJ 08690
Tel.: (609) 586-1900
Web Site: http://www.route33nissan.com
New & Used Car Dealers
N.A.I.C.S.: 441110

AUTO MANAGEMENT INC.
9896 Bissonnet St, Houston, TX 77036
Tel.: (713) 596-8000
Sales Range: $50-74.9 Million
Emp.: 900
Automobiles, New & Used
N.A.I.C.S.: 445298

AUTO PARTS COMPANY
203 N Tennessee St, Cartersville, GA 30120-1450
Tel.: (770) 382-1881
Web Site: http://www.autopartinc.com
Year Founded: 1945
Sales Range: $10-24.9 Million
Emp.: 65
Motor Vehicle Parts Whslr
N.A.I.C.S.: 423120
Lawrence S. Pritchard (CEO, CFO & Sec)

AUTO PARTS WAREHOUSE INC.
1073 E Artesia Blvd, Carson, CA 90746
Tel.: (310) 884-5000
Web Site: http://www.apwks.com
Year Founded: 1972
Rev.: $20,000,000

Emp.: 170
Automotive Supplies & Parts
N.A.I.C.S.: 423120

Subsidiaries:

APW International (USA), Inc.   (1)
1073 E Artesia Blvd, Carson, CA 90746
Tel.: (310) 884-5000
Web Site: http://www.apwks.com
Auto Parts Mfr
N.A.I.C.S.: 423140
T. Young Suhr (Pres)

AUTO RECYCLERS LLC
1400 Sycamore Ave, Buena Vista, VA 24416
Tel.: (540) 261-9991
Web Site: https://www.autorecyclersllc.com
Year Founded: 2004
Sales Range: $1-9.9 Million
Emp.: 25
Automobile Parts Recycling
N.A.I.C.S.: 811198
Paul Palma (CEO)

AUTO REFINISH DISTRIBUTORS HOLDING CORP.
1120 N Iroquois Ave, Tulsa, OK 74106
Tel.: (918) 587-6727
Web Site: http://ardwd.com
Sales Range: $10-24.9 Million
Emp.: 45
Whslr of Paints, Varnishes & Related Supplies
N.A.I.C.S.: 424950
Stephen C. Clark (Pres)
Elena White (Controller)

Subsidiaries:

Auto Refinish Distributors   (1)
10820 Composite Dr, Dallas, TX 75220
Tel.: (972) 484-9545
Web Site: http://www.ardwd.com
Sales Range: $10-24.9 Million
Emp.: 15
Paints Varnishes & Supplies
N.A.I.C.S.: 424950
Travis Powell (Branch Mgr)

AUTO SOUND COMPANY INCORPORATED
109 Washington St, Plainville, MA 02762
Tel.: (508) 643-9925
Web Site: https://www.autosound.com
Year Founded: 1971
Sales Range: Less than $1 Million
Emp.: 20
Radios, Motor Vehicle
N.A.I.C.S.: 423620
Ronald B. Needleman (Pres)

AUTO SUPPLY COMPANY INC.
3740 N Patterson Ave, Winston Salem, NC 27105
Tel.: (336) 661-6113
Web Site: http://www.ascodc.com
Year Founded: 1945
Sales Range: $25-49.9 Million
Emp.: 50
Automotive Supplies & Parts
N.A.I.C.S.: 423120
R. Daniel Luper (VP-Bus Dev)
Charles A. Key Jr. (Owner)

AUTO TEMP, INC.
950 Kent Rd, Batavia, OH 45103
Tel.: (513) 732-6969
Web Site: https://www.autotempinc.com
Year Founded: 1992
Sales Range: $10-24.9 Million
Emp.: 85
Glass Products Mfr

N.A.I.C.S.: 327215
Bernard Fassler (Pres)
Kim Kinder (Mgr-HR & Environmental)

AUTO WAREHOUSING COMPANY
2810-B Marshall Ave, Tacoma, WA 98421-3135
Tel.: (253) 922-0540
Web Site: https://www.autowc.com
Year Founded: 1962
Rev.: $60,000,000
Emp.: 1,000
Automobile Warehousing & Storage Services
N.A.I.C.S.: 811198
Dennis Matteo (CFO)
Ian McRae (Dir-Fin & Controller)
Robert Mullen (VP-IT)
Mike Collison (Dir-IT Ops)
Micheal Leinstock (VP-Safety, Claims & Risk Mgmt)
Mark Berg (Dir-Sls-West Coast)
Marty Colbeck (Dir-Sls-East Coast)
Brett Witzig (Reg VP-Ops)
Brian Taylor (Reg VP-Ops)
Jim Strong (Reg VP-Ops)
Ben Seher (Co-Pres)
Chris Seher (Co-Pres)
Julie MacDonald (VP-HR)
Steve Seher (Pres & CEO)
Bob Wisler (Mgr-District)
Don Dickson (Mgr-District)
Eric Bonwell (Mgr-District)
Gary Stancato (Dir-Quality Assurance)

AUTO'S ETC. LTD.
3301 E Central Texas Expy, Killeen, TX 76543
Tel.: (254) 699-2629
Year Founded: 1996
Sales Range: $25-49.9 Million
Emp.: 135
Car Whslr
N.A.I.C.S.: 441110
Larry Mulcahy (Principal)

AUTO-OWNERS INSURANCE GROUP
6101 Anacapri Blvd, Lansing, MI 48917
Tel.: (517) 323-1200   MI
Web Site: http://www.auto-owners.com
Year Founded: 1916
Sales Range: $5-14.9 Billion
Emp.: 3,270
Holding Company; Insurance Products & Services
N.A.I.C.S.: 551112
Jeffrey F. Harrold (Chm & CEO)

Subsidiaries:

Auto-Owners Insurance Company   (1)
6101 Anacapri Blvd, Lansing, MI 48917
Tel.: (517) 323-1200
Web Site: http://www.auto-owners.com
Property & Casualty Insurance Products & Services
N.A.I.C.S.: 524126
Jeffrey S. Tagsold (Chm & CEO)
Daniel J. Thelen (Pres)
Carolyn B. Muller (Exec VP)

Auto-Owners Life Insurance Co.   (1)
6101 Anacapri Blvd, Lansing, MI 48917-3968   (100%)
Tel.: (517) 323-1200
Web Site: http://www.auto-owners.com
Rev.: $79,968,000
Emp.: 2,000
Life Insurance, Health Insurance & Annuities
N.A.I.C.S.: 524126

Home-Owners Insurance Co.   (1)

Auto-Owners Insurance Group—(Continued)

6101 Anacapri Blvd, Lansing, MI 48917-3968
Tel.: (517) 323-1200
Web Site: http://www.auto-owners.com
Rev.: $89,978,000
Emp.: 3,200
Home Insurance Services
N.A.I.C.S.: 524126
Jeff Harrold (CEO)

Owners Insurance Company (1)
6101 Anacapri Blvd, Lansing, MI 48917-3968
Tel.: (517) 323-1200
Web Site: http://www.orders-ownersinsurancecompany.com
Emp.: 2,000
Home & Auto Insurance Services
N.A.I.C.S.: 524126
Jeff Harrold (CEO)

Property-Owners Insurance Co. (1)
3950 W Delphi Pke, Marion, IN 46952-9266
Tel.: (765) 384-5461
Web Site: http://www.auto-owners.com
Sales Range: $50-74.9 Million
Emp.: 82
Insurance Services
N.A.I.C.S.: 524210
Jeff Herrald (Pres)

Southern-Owners Insurance Company (1)
2710 W Memorial Blvd, Lakeland, FL 33815
Tel.: (863) 687-4505
Web Site: http://www.aoins.com
Sales Range: $50-74.9 Million
Emp.: 163
Property & Casualty Insurance Products & Services
N.A.I.C.S.: 524126
Greg Shell (Pres-Reg)

AUTO-TROL TECHNOLOGY CORPORATION
6011 W Courtyard Dr Ste 250, Austin, TX 78730-5119
Tel.: (303) 452-4919 CO
Web Site: http://www.auto-trol.com
Year Founded: 1962
Rev.: $7,000,000
Emp.: 22
Product Data Management, Electronic Data Management, Physical Network Management & Technical Illustration Software Services, Mfr, Developer & Marketer
N.A.I.C.S.: 541512
Bryan Oldham (Product Mgr-KONFIG CM)
Raghu Kalavacherla (Mgr-Graphics R & D)
Sheila Finan (Controller)

Subsidiaries:

Auto-trol Technology Australia (1)
PO Box 301, Milsons Point, 1565, NSW, Australia (100%)
Tel.: (61) 299232977
Web Site: http://www.auto-trol.com
Computers & Software
N.A.I.C.S.: 541512

Auto-trol Technology Canada Ltd. (1)
200 7326 10th St NE, Calgary, T2E 8W1, AB, Canada (100%)
Tel.: (403) 250-1232
Web Site: http://www.autotrol.com
Sales Range: $10-24.9 Million
Emp.: 5
Computers & Software
N.A.I.C.S.: 541512

Auto-trol Technology GmbH (1)
Heltorfer Strasse 6, 40472, Dusseldorf, Germany
Tel.: (49) 211907950
Sales Range: $10-24.9 Million
Software Sales
N.A.I.C.S.: 541512

Centra 2000, Inc. (1)

16441 Spc Ctr Blvd Bldg C #100, Houston, TX 77058-3165 (100%)
Tel.: (281) 486-7070
Sales Range: $10-24.9 Million
Research & Development of Software
N.A.I.C.S.: 541511

AUTO-WARES, LLC
440 Kirtland SW, Grand Rapids, MI 49507-2331
Tel.: (616) 245-1353 MI
Web Site: https://www.autowares.com
Year Founded: 1976
Sales Range: $50-74.9 Million
Emp.: 750
Motor Vehicle Supplies & New Parts Distr
N.A.I.C.S.: 423120
Nick Hinkle (Coord-Info)
Rob Kiel (Mgr-Acctg)
Jim Malott (Mgr-Accts Receivable)
Chris Stevens (Mgr-Loss Prevention & Risk Mgmt)
Gordon Gillman (VP-Product & Pricing)
Steve Gould (VP-IT)
Todd Leimenstoll (Co-Pres)

Subsidiaries:

A-1 Truck Parts (1)
3868 N Euclid Ave, Bay City, MI 48706
Web Site: http://www.a1truckparts.com
Emp.: 10
Truck Parts Distr
N.A.I.C.S.: 423120
Dan Bond (Mng Dir)

Auto Paint (1)
440 Kirtland St SW, Grand Rapids, MI 49507-2331
Tel.: (616) 243-2125
Web Site: http://www.autowares.com
Motor Vehicle Supplies & New Parts
N.A.I.C.S.: 423120
Scott Stauffer (Gen Mgr)

Auto Performance, Inc. (1)
440 Kirtland St SW, Grand Rapids, MI 49507-2331
Tel.: (616) 243-2125
Web Site: http://www.autowares.com
Rev.: $720,000
Emp.: 100
Motor Vehicle Supplies & New Parts
N.A.I.C.S.: 423120
Bill Haynes (Gen Mgr)

Auto-Wares OE (1)
6638 Weiss Rd, Saginaw, MI 48603
Tel.: (989) 793-6241
Web Site: http://www.autowaresoe.com
Motor Vehicle Parts Distr
N.A.I.C.S.: 423120

Auto-Wares Tools, Inc. (1)
2153 Richfield Rd, Flint, MI 48506
Tel.: (810) 736-0301
Web Site: http://www.autowares.com
Sales Range: $10-24.9 Million
Emp.: 30
Motor Vehicle Supply & New Parts Distr
N.A.I.C.S.: 423120
Linda Schuemaker (Dir-HR)
Barry Hill (Pres-Auto Wares)

Battery Specialists, Inc. (1)
440 Kirtland St SW, Grand Rapids, MI 49507-2331
Tel.: (616) 243-7788
Web Site: http://www.autowares.com
Rev.: $320,000
Emp.: 4
Motor Vehicle Supplies & New Parts
N.A.I.C.S.: 423120
Todd Leimenstoll (Pres)

Foreign Parts Specialists (1)
440 Kirtland SW St, Grand Rapids, MI 49507
Tel.: (616) 243-2125
Automotive Part Whslr
N.A.I.C.S.: 423120

AUTOBAHN MOTORCAR GROUP

3000 White Settlement Rd, Fort Worth, TX 76107
Tel.: (817) 336-0885
Web Site: http://www.shopautobahn.com
Rev.: $125,000,000
Emp.: 250
New & Used Cars Sales
N.A.I.C.S.: 441110
Chad Chase (VP)

AUTOCLAIMS DIRECT, INC.
3196 Willow Creek Rd Ste A103 & 230, Prescott, AZ 86301
Tel.: (480) 282-8412
Web Site: http://www.autoclaimsdirect.com
Year Founded: 2004
Rev.: $3,200,000
Emp.: 8
Business Services Fire & Casualty Insurance Carrier
N.A.I.C.S.: 524126
Tara Esquivel (Co-Founder & VP-Corp Acct)
Ernest Bray (Co-Founder & CEO)
Brian Bray (VP-Ops)
Michael O'Leary (Sr Dir-Bus Dev)
Brandon Bryant (Dir-Bus Dev)

AUTOCOM ASSOCIATES
74 W Long Lk Rd Ste 103, Bloomfield Hills, MI 48304-2770
Tel.: (248) 647-8621
Web Site: http://www.usautocom.com
Year Founded: 1995
Sales Range: $10-24.9 Million
Emp.: 17
Automotive, High Technology
N.A.I.C.S.: 541820
Lawrence A. Weis (Pres & CEO)
Jack R. Harned (Sr Partner)
Kenneth A. Levy (Sr Partner & Pres-Intl Ops)
Holly Clark (Acct Exec)
Lynn Koretz (Mgr-Bus)
Jim Meloche (Partner & Sr VP-Mktg)

AUTOCRAT, LLC
10 Blackstone Vly Pl, Lincoln, RI 02865
Tel.: (401) 333-3300
Web Site: http://www.autocrat.com
Year Founded: 1895
Emp.: 107
Food Products Mfr
N.A.I.C.S.: 311999
Patrick Holmes (CEO)
Ann Malinowski (CFO)
Steve Olyha (COO)
Scott Tittle (Dir-Ops)
Kim Cipriano (Mktg Dir)
Patricia McGovern (Dir-HR)

AUTODEMO LLC
1129 Payne St, Louisville, KY 40204
Tel.: (502) 581-1300
Web Site: https://www.autodemo.com
Year Founded: 1998
Sales Range: $1-9.9 Million
Emp.: 12
Software Publisher
N.A.I.C.S.: 513210
J.C. Stites (Owner & CEO)
Tim Williams (Project Mgr)
Dedra Carricato (Bus Mgr)

AUTODRIVE1
181 S Main St, West Bridgewater, MA 02379
Tel.: (508) 584-8200
Web Site: http://www.autodrive1.com
Year Founded: 2000
Sales Range: $10-24.9 Million
Emp.: 15

Auto Financing for Individuals with Credit Problems
N.A.I.C.S.: 921130
Joseph DiBiasio (Owner & Pres)

AUTOGATOR, INC.
1961 PFE Rd, Roseville, CA 95747
Tel.: (916) 783-5216
Web Site: https://www.autogator.com
Year Founded: 1981
Sales Range: $1-9.9 Million
Emp.: 18
Automotive Salvage Operations & Sales
N.A.I.C.S.: 811198
Ron Dumas (Pres)

AUTOHAUS ARIZONA, INC.
2850 S Roosevelt St Ste 102, Tempe, AZ 85282
Tel.: (602) 243-4287 AZ
Web Site: http://www.autohausaz.com
Year Founded: 1996
Sales Range: $10-24.9 Million
Emp.: 23
Internet Based Auto Parts Warehouse
N.A.I.C.S.: 423120
Dmitri Aleksandrov (Dir-IT)

AUTOHAUS BMW
3015 S Hanley, Saint Louis, MO 63143
Tel.: (314) 727-8870 MO
Web Site: https://www.bmwautohaus.com
Year Founded: 1961
Sales Range: $25-49.9 Million
Emp.: 100
New & Used Car Dealers
N.A.I.C.S.: 441110
Anita Fink (Owner)
Joe Emerson (Mgr-Sls)

AUTOHAUS LANCASTER, INC.
1373 Manheim Pike, Lancaster, PA 17601
Tel.: (717) 299-2801
Web Site: https://www.autohaus.com
Year Founded: 1964
Sales Range: $25-49.9 Million
Emp.: 62
New Car Retailer
N.A.I.C.S.: 441110
Tom Wanner (Owner & Pres)

AUTOHAUS ON EDENS INC.
1600 Frontage Rd, Northbrook, IL 60062-4129
Tel.: (847) 272-7900
Web Site: https://www.autohausonedens.com
Sales Range: $10-24.9 Million
Emp.: 80
Automobiles; New & Used
N.A.I.C.S.: 441110
Kris Pitt (Office Mgr)
Peter Laskowski (Mgr-Body Shop)

AUTOMARKET/LOTUS OF ORANGE COUNTY
2115 Harbor Blvd, Costa Mesa, CA 92627
Tel.: (949) 722-6555
Rev.: $30,000,000
Emp.: 6
Automotive Supplies & Parts
N.A.I.C.S.: 441120

AUTOMAT PICTURES, INC.
3255 Wilshire Blvd, Los Angeles, CA 90010
Tel.: (213) 351-0444 CA
Web Site: http://www.automatpictures.com
Year Founded: 2001

Sales Range: $1-9.9 Million
Emp.: 10
Film Producer & Distr
N.A.I.C.S.: 512110
Jeffrey Schwarz *(Pres & CEO)*

AUTOMATED BUILDING COMPONENTS, INC.
2359 Grant Rd, North Baltimore, OH 45872
Tel.: (419) 257-2152
Web Site: https://www.abctruss.com
Sales Range: $10-24.9 Million
Emp.: 30
Roof Trusses & Floor Trusses: Wooden
N.A.I.C.S.: 321215
Marshall McCarty *(Pres)*

AUTOMATED COLLECTION SERVICES, INC. (ACSI)
25802 Opryland Dr, Nashville, TN 37214
Tel.: (615) 690-1801
Web Site: http://www.automatedcollection.com
Year Founded: 1988
Sales Range: $10-24.9 Million
Emp.: 152
Total Recovery Management Services & Accounts Receivable to Government, Healthcare & Education Sectors
N.A.I.C.S.: 561440
Robert Duffy *(CEO)*

AUTOMATED FINANCIAL SYSTEMS INC.
123 Summit Dr, Exton, PA 19341-2842
Tel.: (610) 524-9300   PA
Web Site: http://www.afsvision.com
Year Founded: 1970
Prepackaged Financial Software
N.A.I.C.S.: 513210
John Shain *(Chm)*
Jim Greenwood *(Chm & CEO)*
Rick Bare *(CFO & Exec VP)*
Jeff Baldyga *(Gen Counsel & Exec VP)*
Melissa Hofer *(Chief Product Officer & Exec VP)*
Dean Snyder *(Exec VP & Head-Bus Solutions)*
Rene Baron Coady *(Dir-Mktg)*

AUTOMATED HEALTHCARE SOLUTIONS, LLC
2901 SW 149th Ave, Miramar, FL 33027
Web Site: http://www.ahcs.com
Year Founded: 1997
Sales Range: $1-9.9 Million
Medical Software Publisher
N.A.I.C.S.: 513210
Dave Bowen *(Pres)*

AUTOMATED INDUSTRIAL MACHINERY, INC.
502 S Vista Ave, Addison, IL 60101-4423
Tel.: (630) 458-0008
Web Site: https://www.aimmachines.com
Year Founded: 1992
Sales Range: $10-24.9 Million
Emp.: 40
Automated Industrial Machinery Mfr & Whslr
N.A.I.C.S.: 333998
Constantine Grapsas *(Founder & CEO)*

AUTOMATED OUTLET, INC.
708 Valley Ridge Cir, Lewisville, TX 75057-3307
Tel.: (214) 245-4594
Web Site: http://www.automatedoutlet.com
Year Founded: 2002
Sales Range: $1-9.9 Million
Emp.: 13
Automated Household Product Distr
N.A.I.C.S.: 423220
Martin Custer *(Pres)*

AUTOMATED PETROLEUM & ENERGY COMPANY, INC.
1201 Oakfield Dr Ste 109, Brandon, FL 33511
Tel.: (813) 681-4279   FL
Web Site: https://www.automatedpetro.com
Year Founded: 1981
Sales Range: $1-4.9 Billion
Emp.: 30
Gasoline Stations
N.A.I.C.S.: 457120
Katheryn McKnight *(Office Mgr)*
Bill McKnight *(Pres)*

AUTOMATED POWER EXCHANGE INC.
224 Airport Pkwy Ste 600, San Jose, CA 95110
Tel.: (408) 517-2100
Web Site: http://www.apx.com
Year Founded: 1996
Sales Range: $10-24.9 Million
Emp.: 60
Electricity Contractor Services
N.A.I.C.S.: 523160
Jason Brome *(CTO-Environmental & Power Markets)*

AUTOMATED RESOURCE MANAGEMENT ASSOCIATES, INC.
962 Wayne Ave Ste 320, Silver Spring, MD 20910-3389
Tel.: (301) 587-7077
Web Site: http://www.armainc.com
Sales Range: $1-9.9 Million
Emp.: 75
Computer Related Services
N.A.I.C.S.: 541519
Thomasine Bannister *(Pres & CEO)*

AUTOMATED SYSTEMS INC.
2400 Communication Dr, Auburn Hills, MI 48326
Tel.: (248) 373-5600
Web Site: http://www.automatedsysteminc.org
Sales Range: $10-24.9 Million
Emp.: 20
Elevators & Moving Stairways
N.A.I.C.S.: 333921
Bruce Claycomb *(Pres)*

AUTOMATED TECHNOLOGY MACHINES INCORPORATED
400 Poydras St Ste 1650, New Orleans, LA 70130
Tel.: (504) 836-2331
Rev.: $12,298,443
Emp.: 46
Banking Services
N.A.I.C.S.: 561499

AUTOMATEDQA CORP.
100 Cummings Ctr Ste 420B, Beverly, MA 01915
Tel.: (978) 236-7900
Web Site: http://www.automatedqa.com
Year Founded: 1999
Rev.: $10,500,000
Emp.: 30

Custom Computer Programming Services
N.A.I.C.S.: 541511
Bryan Semple *(CMO)*
Dmitry Fonarev *(Sr VP-Product Dev)*
Doug McNary *(CEO)*
Kevin Gillis *(VP-Products for Dev & Testing)*
Lance Levy *(Gen Counsel & Sr VP)*
Ole Lensmar *(CTO)*
Shawn Garrett *(CFO)*

AUTOMATIC APARTMENT LAUNDRIES, INC.
30295 Schoolcraft Rd, Livonia, MI 48150
Tel.: (734) 427-8990   MI
Web Site: http://www.aalaundries.com
Year Founded: 1946
Sales Range: $25-49.9 Million
Emp.: 45
Provider of Laundry Facilities
N.A.I.C.S.: 812310
Richard D. Colton *(Pres)*

AUTOMATIC EQUIPMENT CORPORATION
4699 Interstate Dr, Cincinnati, OH 45246
Tel.: (513) 771-3833   OH
Web Site: https://www.aecmagnetics.com
Year Founded: 1961
Sales Range: $25-49.9 Million
Emp.: 19
Electro Magnets Lifting Equipment
Permanent Magnetic Sweepers Magnetic Assemblies Mfr
N.A.I.C.S.: 332999
William Klaus *(Pres)*
Michael Sprague *(Exec VP & Mgr-Traffic)*

AUTOMATIC EQUIPMENT MANUFACTURING CO.
1 Mill Rd, Pender, NE 68047
Tel.: (402) 385-3051   NE
Web Site: http://www.aemfg.com
Year Founded: 1925
Sales Range: $25-49.9 Million
Emp.: 125
Earthmovers, Guidance Systems, Rollermills & Mixers; Towing Products Mfr
N.A.I.C.S.: 336990
Ellen Kietzmann *(Pres & CEO)*
Jeff Carlson *(VP-Ops)*
Laura Henry *(Mgr-Inside Sls)*
Jim Klynman *(Mgr-Dealer Sls)*
Sean Carrigan *(Mgr-Dealer Dev-Western Canada)*

AUTOMATIC MACHINE PRODUCTS COMPANY
400 Constitution Dr, Taunton, MA 02780
Tel.: (508) 822-4226   MA
Web Site: https://www.ampcomp.com
Year Founded: 1923
Sales Range: $75-99.9 Million
Emp.: 166
Mfr of Steel & Brass Valves
N.A.I.C.S.: 332919
John S. Holden III *(Pres)*

AUTOMATIC SPRING PRODUCTS CORP.
803 Taylor Ave, Grand Haven, MI 49417
Tel.: (616) 842-7800
Web Site: https://www.automaticspring.com
Sales Range: $25-49.9 Million
Emp.: 400

Steel Springs, Except Wire
N.A.I.C.S.: 332613
Steven P. Moreland *(Pres & CEO)*
Patrick DeShaw *(COO)*
Tim Benningfield *(Mgr-Ops)*

AUTOMATION & MODULAR COMPONENTS, INC.
10301 Enterprise Dr, Davisburg, MI 48350-1312
Tel.: (248) 922-4740
Web Site: https://www.amcautomation.com
Year Founded: 1991
Rev.: $11,500,000
Emp.: 75
Conveyors & Conveying Equipment
N.A.I.C.S.: 333922
Dave O'Nions *(VP)*

AUTOMATION ENGINEERING CO., INC.
1220 Washington Ave, Cedarburg, WI 53012
Tel.: (262) 377-7500
Year Founded: 1961
Sales Range: $10-24.9 Million
Emp.: 30
Distr of Electrical Apparatus & Equipment
N.A.I.C.S.: 423610
Mike Byers *(Pres)*

AUTOMATION ENGINEERING CORPORATION
110 Smith Rd, Greenville, SC 29615
Tel.: (864) 679-8024
Web Site: http://www.teamaec.com
Year Founded: 1981
Sales Range: $10-24.9 Million
Emp.: 64
Designs, Builds & Integrates Custom Manufacturing Equipment
N.A.I.C.S.: 333998
Gary Foster *(Pres)*
Manfred Gollent *(Pres)*

AUTOMATION GROUP INC.
10497 Town & Country Way Ste 600, Houston, TX 77024
Tel.: (713) 860-5200
Web Site: http://www.tagsite.com
Rev.: $13,500,000
Emp.: 80
Custom Computer Programming Services
N.A.I.C.S.: 541511
Kem Lam *(Controller)*

AUTOMATION PERSONNEL SERVICES, INC.
401 Southgate Dr, Pelham, AL 35124
Tel.: (205) 733-3700
Web Site: http://www.atstemps.com
Sales Range: $25-49.9 Million
Emp.: 20
Temporary Help Service
N.A.I.C.S.: 561320
Steve Nordness *(Owner)*
Allison Bevelheimer *(Branch Mgr)*
Julie Williams *(Branch Mgr)*
Leslie Nordness *(Owner)*
Heidi Doss *(Coord-Staffing)*

AUTOMATION SPECIALISTS, INC.
12555 Superior Ct, Holland, MI 49424-8287
Tel.: (616) 738-8288
Web Site: http://www.automationspecialists.com
Year Founded: 1994
Sales Range: $1-9.9 Million
Emp.: 15
Metalworking Machines Mfr
N.A.I.C.S.: 333519

Automation Specialists, Inc.—(Continued)

Mitch Weener (*Founder, Owner & Pres*)

AUTOMATION TECHNOLO-GIES, INC.
8219 Leesburg Pike Ste 401, Vienna, VA 22182-2655
Tel.: (703) 883-1410
Web Site: http://www.ati4it.com
Year Founded: 1994
Sales Range: $1-9.9 Million
Emp.: 35
IT Consulting Services
N.A.I.C.S.: 541690
Gary Webb (*Dir-Fed Ops*)

AUTOMATION TOOL COM-PANY
101 Mill Dr, Cookeville, TN 38501
Tel.: (931) 528-5417
Web Site:
http://www.automationtool.com
Year Founded: 1977
Sales Range: $25-49.9 Million
Emp.: 125
Assembly Machines, Non-Metalworking
N.A.I.C.S.: 333998
Adam Bernhardt (*Controller*)
Bill Curran (*CEO*)

AUTOMATION-X CORPORA-TION
159 Lincoln St, Lander, WY 82520
Tel.: (307) 332-0422
Web Site: http://www.automation-x.com
Sales Range: $50-74.9 Million
Emp.: 75
Miscellaneous Store Retailers
N.A.I.C.S.: 459999
Alex Schultejann (*Exec VP-Mktg & Sls*)
Tami Scott (*Mgr-Fin & Acctg*)
Daniel Schultejann (*Chm & CEO*)
Michael Harris (*Mgr-IT*)

AUTOMATTIC INC.
60 29th St #343, San Francisco, CA 94110
Tel.: (877) 273-3049   DE
Web Site: http://automattic.com
Year Founded: 2005
Web Developer
N.A.I.C.S.: 513210
Matt Mullenweg (*CEO*)

Subsidiaries:

WPVIP Inc.   **(1)**
60 29th St Ste 343, San Francisco, CA 94110
Tel.: (877) 273-3049
Web Site: http://www.wpvip.com
Custom Computer Programming Services
N.A.I.C.S.: 541511
Nick Gernert (*CEO*)

Subsidiary (Domestic):

Parsely, Inc.   **(2)**
989 6th Ave 3rd Fl, New York, NY 10018
Tel.: (212) 920-6846
Web Site: http://www.parsely.com
Custom Computer Programming Services
N.A.I.C.S.: 541511
Andrew Montalenti (*Co-Founder*)
Sachin Kamdar (*Co-Founder & CEO*)

AUTOMAX CHRYSLER DODGE JEEP RAM
2815 Stratford Rd, Delaware, OH 43015
Tel.: (740) 369-9611
Web Site:
http://www.automaxchrysler.com
Sales Range: $50-74.9 Million

Emp.: 64
Car Dealership Owner & Operator
N.A.I.C.S.: 441110
Brian Bauer (*Mgr-New Car*)
Ashley Schwyn (*Coord-PR & Retention*)
Austin Walden (*Mgr-Fin*)
Chad Hart (*Mgr-Used Car*)
Dawn Brown (*Mgr-Parts*)
Dennis Thompson (*Dir-Fin*)
Denny Friermood (*Gen Mgr*)
Derek Price (*Mgr-Svc*)
Leigh Ann Ragan (*Dir-Internal Audit & Compliance*)

AUTOMOBILE INSURANCE PLANS SERVICE OFFICE
302 Central Ave, Johnston, RI 02919
Tel.: (401) 946-2310
Web Site: http://www.aipso.com
Sales Range: $10-24.9 Million
Emp.: 400
Insurance Services
N.A.I.C.S.: 524210
Lawrence M. Iacoi (*Gen Counsel, Sec & VP*)
Thomas J. Neagle (*VP-Ops*)
Charles P. Kwolek Jr. (*Pres*)

AUTOMOBILES OF STATES-VILLE, INC.
1015 Folger Dr, Statesville, NC 28625
Tel.: (704) 873-0699
Sales Range: $10-24.9 Million
Emp.: 50
New Car Dealers
N.A.I.C.S.: 441110
Ralph E. Everhart (*Pres*)
Larry W. Nichols (*Sec*)

AUTOMOTIVE AFTER MAR-KET INC.
10425 S La Cienega Blvd, Los Angeles, CA 90045
Tel.: (310) 793-7079
Web Site:
https://www.completesplus.com
Sales Range: $10-24.9 Million
Emp.: 85
Automotive Supplies & Parts
N.A.I.C.S.: 423120
Jack R. Hubka (*Pres*)
Manuela Degirmen (*Controller*)
Jim Hubka (*Mgr-Mktg & Sls*)
Eric Katnic (*Mgr-Pur*)

AUTOMOTIVE CLIMATE CON-TROL, INC.
22150 Challenger Dr, Elkhart, IN 46514
Tel.: (574) 264-2190
Web Site:
http://www.accclimatecontrol.com
Year Founded: 1948
Sales Range: $10-24.9 Million
Emp.: 30
Heating & Air Conditioning Services
N.A.I.C.S.: 333415
Dave Sanders (*Pres & CEO*)

AUTOMOTIVE CONCEPTS OF NORTH AMERICA
513 Horsham Rd, Horsham, PA 19044
Tel.: (215) 443-5420
Year Founded: 1982
Rev.: $10,900,000
Emp.: 37
Automotive Customizing Services, Nonfactory Basis
N.A.I.C.S.: 811198

AUTOMOTIVE DISTRIBUTORS CO., INC.

2981 Morse Rd, Columbus, OH 43231-6035
Tel.: (614) 476-1315
Web Site: https://www.adw1.com
Year Founded: 1985
Rev.: $54,883,144
Emp.: 250
Automotive Supplies & Parts
N.A.I.C.S.: 423120
Robert Yeoman (*Pres & CEO*)
Ron Elkins (*Mgr-Ops*)
Tim Gallagher (*Mgr-Accessory Sls*)

AUTOMOTIVE FASTENERS INC.
2111 S Elm Eugene St, Greensboro, NC 27406
Tel.: (336) 274-3731
Web Site:
http://www.automotivefasteners.com
Sales Range: $10-24.9 Million
Emp.: 110
Automotive Fasteners
N.A.I.C.S.: 423840
Charles Causey (*Mgr-Maintenance & Special Projects*)

AUTOMOTIVE HARD PARTS INC.
199 Union St, Rockland, MA 02370
Tel.: (781) 878-7555
Rev.: $10,000,000
Emp.: 29
Automotive Supplies
N.A.I.C.S.: 423120
Thomas Borr (*Pres*)

AUTOMOTIVE IMPORTING MANUFACTURING, INC.
3920 Security Park Dr, Rancho Cordova, CA 95742
Tel.: (916) 985-8505
Web Site: http://www.aim-soft.com
Rev.: $25,000,000
Emp.: 12
Automotive Supplies & Parts
N.A.I.C.S.: 423120
Frank G. Seabourne (*Pres*)
Darrrell Mathews (*Controller*)

AUTOMOTIVE INTERNET ME-DIA, INC.
322 W Burlington, La Grange, IL 60525
Tel.:
Web Site: http://www.aimyes.com
Year Founded: 2009
Sales Range: $1-9.9 Million
Emp.: 15
Media Advertising Services
N.A.I.C.S.: 541840
Tony French (*Co-Founder & Pres*)
Mike McDonnell (*Co-Founder & CEO*)
David McGarry (*Co-Founder & Exec VP-Digital Strategy & Ops*)

AUTOMOTIVE MANAGEMENT GROUP, INC.
730 N. Main St, Honea Path, SC 29654
Tel.: (864) 369-7376   SC
Web Site: http://www.carolinaford.net
Sales Range: $10-24.9 Million
Emp.: 10
New & Used Car Dealer
N.A.I.C.S.: 441110
Berry Woods (*Pres*)
Carol Fenn (*Controller*)

AUTOMOTIVE MANAGEMENT SERVICES, INC.
505 S Flagler Dr Ste 700, West Palm Beach, FL 33401
Tel.: (561) 578-8520
Emp.: 10,000
Holding Company; Car Dealerships
N.A.I.C.S.: 551112

Joe Sassin (*Dir-Fixed Ops*)
Terry Taylor (*Owner & Pres*)
Angelina Raffo (*Mgr-Corp Rels*)
Steve Suggs (*Dir-Sls & Tech Ops*)
Todd Patton (*Dir-IT*)
Denise Owens (*Dir-HR*)
Stephen Terry (*Sec*)
Nancy Cera (*Asst Sec*)

AUTOMOTIVE MANUFACTUR-ING & SUPPLY CO.
90 Plant Ave Ste 1, Hauppauge, NY 11788
Tel.: (631) 435-1400
Web Site: http://www.amscovf.com
Year Founded: 1921
Sales Range: $10-24.9 Million
Emp.: 28
Automotive Supplies & Parts
N.A.I.C.S.: 423120
Melvin Minoff (*Pres*)

AUTOMOTIVE PARTS EX-PRESS INC.
Ste 7 11290 St Johns Indus Pkwy N, Jacksonville, FL 32246-6632
Tel.: (904) 641-8181
Sales Range: $10-24.9 Million
Emp.: 60
Whslr of Motor Vehicle Parts & Supplies
N.A.I.C.S.: 423120
Richard Bennett (*Pres*)

AUTOMOTIVE PARTS HEAD-QUARTERS, INC.
2959 Clearwater Rd, Saint Cloud, MN 56301
Tel.: (320) 252-5411   MN
Web Site:
http://www.autopartshq.com
Year Founded: 1965
Automobile Parts Distr
N.A.I.C.S.: 423120
Corey Bartlett (*Pres & CEO*)
Kevin Mack (*VP-Mdsg*)
Jesse Westrup (*COO*)

Subsidiaries:

OK Automotive   **(1)**
1726 W Michigan St, Duluth, MN 55806-2131
Tel.: (218) 722-6233
Web Site: http://www.okautomotive.com
Sales Range: $10-24.9 Million
Emp.: 35
Automotive Replacement Parts
N.A.I.C.S.: 423120

AUTOMOTIVE PETROLEUM AND ALLIED INDUSTRIES EM-PLOYEES WELFARE FUND
9040 Lackland Rd, Saint Louis, MO 63114
Tel.: (314) 426-5909   MO
Year Founded: 1951
Sales Range: $10-24.9 Million
Emp.: 3
Health & Welfare Benefit Services
N.A.I.C.S.: 525120
Rod Joggerst (*Treas*)
Thomas A. Dinkins III (*Chm*)

AUTOMOTIVE PRODUCT CON-SULTANTS, INC.
770 Spirit of St Louis Blvd, Chesterfield, MO 63005
Web Site:
http://www.apcwarranties.com
Rev.: $17,340,000
Automobile & Consumer Finance Companies
N.A.I.C.S.: 522220

AUTOMOTIVE RACING PROD-UCTS

1863 Eastman Ave, Ventura, CA
93003
Tel.: (805) 339-2200
Web Site: https://www.arp-bolts.com
Rev.: $19,146,619
Emp.: 30
Hardware
N.A.I.C.S.: 332510
Mike Holzapfel *(Pres)*
Kelly Schau *(CFO)*
Gary Holzapfel *(Founder & CEO)*
Robert Florine *(VP)*

AUTOMOTIVE SERVICE INC.
910 Mountain Home Rd, Reading, PA
19608
Tel.: (610) 678-3421
Web Site: http://www.reladyne.com
Rev.: $16,591,907
Emp.: 17
Fuel Oil Dealers
N.A.I.C.S.: 457210
John K. Palmer *(Pres)*

AUTOMOTIVE SERVICE NET-WORK, INC.
1011 N Wymore Rd Ste 100, Winter
Park, FL 32789
Tel.: (407) 539-6500   FL
Year Founded: 1976
Sales Range: $1-9.9 Million
Emp.: 80
Automobile Dealership; Accounting
Services & Automotive Repair
N.A.I.C.S.: 441110
Juliette Holler *(Principal)*
Roger Holler Jr. *(Pres)*

AUTOMOTIVE SUPPLY ASSO-CIATES, INC.
129 Manchester St, Concord, NH
03301-5118
Tel.: (603) 225-4000   NH
Year Founded: 1989
Sales Range: $200-249.9 Million
Emp.: 375
Wholesale Distr of Automotive & In-
dustrial Parts & Supplies
N.A.I.C.S.: 423120
David Segal *(Pres)*

Subsidiaries:

Sanel Auto Parts Co.   (1)
219 S Main St, Concord, NH 03301-3405
Tel.: (603) 225-4100
Sales Range: $25-49.9 Million
Emp.: 60
Wholesale Distributor of Automotive Parts &
Supplies & Industrial Supplies
N.A.I.C.S.: 441330
Tom Houghes *(Mgr-Store)*

AUTOMOTIVE TESTING AND DEVELOPMENT SERVICES, INC.
400 Etiwanda Ave, Ontario, CA
91761
Tel.: (909) 390-1100
Web Site:
https://www.automotivetesting.com
Rev.: $12,900,000
Emp.: 185
Emissions Testing Without Repairs,
Automotive
N.A.I.C.S.: 811198
Linwood Farmer *(VP)*

AUTOPLEX AUTOMOTIVE LP
4600 Canyon Dr, Amarillo, TX 79109
Tel.: (806) 359-2886
Web Site: http://www.autoplex-tx.com
Rev.: $60,200,000
Emp.: 75
Holding Company; New & Used Car
Dealers
N.A.I.C.S.: 551112

Johnson Poe *(Gen Mgr)*
Joe Harless *(Gen Mgr)*

Subsidiaries:

Autoplex BMW   (1)
4700 Canyon Dr, Amarillo, TX 79109
Tel.: (806) 359-2886
Web Site: http://www.autoplex-tx.com
Rev.: $870,000
Emp.: 50
Body Shop, Automotive
N.A.I.C.S.: 811121
Edward W. Bradley *(Owner)*

Frontier Dodge   (1)
5801 Spur 327, Lubbock, TX 79424
Tel.: (806) 798-4500
Web Site: http://www.frontierdodge.com
New & Used Car Dealers
N.A.I.C.S.: 441110
Bobby Ray *(Gen Mgr)*
Ralph Meadows *(Mgr-Comml)*
Richard Fish *(Mgr-Sls)*
Caroline George *(Mgr-Internet)*
Paul Herrera *(Mgr-Fin)*
Larry Klafka *(Mgr-Svc)*
Jared Knight *(Dir-Internet Sls)*
Ruben Madrigal *(Mgr-Sls)*
Daniel Tovar *(Mgr-Sls)*
Brad Townley *(Mgr-Fin)*
Jimmy Ware *(Mgr-Parts)*
Terry Wilcox *(Mgr-Sls)*

AUTORAMA INC.
5389 Poplar Ave, Memphis, TN
38119
Tel.: (901) 345-6211
Web Site:
https://www.mbofmemphis.com
Sales Range: $10-24.9 Million
Emp.: 65
Car Dealership
N.A.I.C.S.: 441110
Gunter Stephan *(Pres)*
Wayne Scroggins *(Gen Mgr-Sls)*
Danny Reed *(Controller)*

AUTORE OIL & PROPANE COMPANY
670 W Michigan Hwy 134, Cedarville,
MI 49719-9543
Tel.: (906) 484-2233
Web Site: http://www.autoreoil.com
Year Founded: 1955
Sales Range: $10-24.9 Million
Emp.: 60
Fuel Services
N.A.I.C.S.: 424720
Steve Autore *(Pres)*

Subsidiaries:

Newberry BP Express Market   (1)
PO Box 52, Newberry, MI 49868   (100%)
Tel.: (906) 293-3564
Sales Range: $10-24.9 Million
Emp.: 7
Provider of Gasoline Services
N.A.I.C.S.: 457110
Steve Autore *(Pres)*

AUTOREVO, LTD
7920 Belt Line Rd Ste 450, Dallas,
TX 75254
Tel.: (972) 715-8600
Web Site: http://www.autorevo.com
Year Founded: 2001
Sales Range: $1-9.9 Million
Emp.: 25
Auto Dealers
N.A.I.C.S.: 441227
Randy Roberts *(Co-Founder)*

AUTOS ETC INC.
3301 E Central Texas Expy, Killeen,
TX 76543
Tel.: (254) 699-2629
Web Site: http://www.automax.com
Sales Range: $25-49.9 Million
Emp.: 135
New & Used Car Dealers

N.A.I.C.S.: 441120
Bradley Whitis *(Pres)*

AUTOS VEGA INC.
227 Marginal JF Kennedy, San Juan,
PR 00920
Tel.: (787) 782-4030
Web Site: http://www.autosvega.com
Rev.: $49,100,000
Emp.: 165
New & Used Automobiles
N.A.I.C.S.: 441110
Ramon Vega Jr. *(Pres)*

AUTOSALES, INC.
1200 Southeast Ave, Tallmadge, OH
44278
Tel.: (330) 630-0270   OH
Web Site:
http://www.summitracing.com
Year Founded: 1969
Sales Range: $1-9.9 Million
Emp.: 17
Automotive Parts & Accessories
Stores & Mail Order
N.A.I.C.S.: 441330
Paul Sergi *(CEO)*
Scott Peterson *(Pres & COO)*

AUTOSHOP SOLUTIONS INC.
942 Windy Rd, Apex, NC 27502
Tel.: (888) 847-7036
Web Site:
http://www.autoshopsolutions.com
Year Founded: 1998
Sales Range: $1-9.9 Million
Emp.: 24
Website Design & Internet Marketing
Services to Auto Repair Shops, Tire
Dealers & Collision & Transmission
Shops
N.A.I.C.S.: 811114
Bryan Minihan *(CTO)*
Danny Sanchez *(Founder)*
Margaret Palango *(CEO)*
Tony Mercury *(VP-Revenue)*

AUTOSOURCE MOTORS LLC
2023 S 625 W, Woods Cross, UT
84087   UT
Web Site:
http://www.myautosource.com
Year Founded: 2003
Sales Range: $150-199.9 Million
Emp.: 285
Automotive Retailer
N.A.I.C.S.: 441110
Brett Parham *(CEO)*
Rich Jackson *(Pres & COO)*
Jeremy Baker *(CFO)*
Sariah Heaton *(VP-Mktg)*
Nik Barnard *(Dir-HR)*

AUTOSPLICE INC.
10121 Barnes Cyn Rd, San Diego,
CA 92121
Tel.: (858) 535-0077
Web Site: http://www.autosplice.com
Sales Range: $50-74.9 Million
Emp.: 175
Electric Connectors
N.A.I.C.S.: 335931
Santosh Rao *(CEO)*
Miguel Aguilar *(Engr-Mfg)*
Samuel Rosas *(Mgr-Engrg)*
Jeff Cartwright *(CFO)*
Kevin Barry *(COO)*
Takeshi Yoshikawa *(Dir-Ops-Japan &
Korea)*
Anthony Marcione *(Mgr-Bus Dev)*
Gerardo Vera *(Mgr-Bus Dev)*
Joseph Chia *(Mng Dir-Autosplice Asia
Pacific)*

AUTOTEC LLC

2200 Woodcrest Pl Ste 200, Birming-
ham, AL 35209
Tel.: (205) 414-2700   AL
Web Site: https://www.autotec.com
Year Founded: 1997
Sales Range: $1-9.9 Million
Emp.: 60
Software for the Automotive Remar-
keting Industry
N.A.I.C.S.: 513210
Tom Adams *(Chm)*
Adam Sparks *(Engr-Help Desk)*
Chuck Redden *(Pres)*
Ben Puckett *(Pres-Auction Insurance
Agency)*
Charlie Adams *(VP-Bus Dev)*
Brent Gillis *(VP-Auction Insurance
Agency)*
Brandon Walton *(COO & Sr VP-
Auction Insurance Agency)*
Bryan Benson *(VP-Auction Insurance
Agency)*
Tony Zeidler *(Sr VP)*
Esther Peek *(VP-Customer Svcs,
Red Mountain Tech & AutoCheck
Auctions)*
John McElrath *(VP-Sls & Mktg-Red
Mountain Technologies & AutoCheck
Auctions)*
Lee Mahoney *(CTO)*
Richard Adams *(VP)*
Steve DeMedicis *(Pres-Red Mountain
Tech & AutoCheck Auctions)*
William Cain *(CFO)*

AUTOTECH ENGINEERING
10580 Mulberry Ave, Fontana, CA
92337
Tel.: (909) 428-9072
Web Site: http://www.autotech.com
Sales Range: $10-24.9 Million
Emp.: 50
Automotive Supplies & Parts
N.A.I.C.S.: 336350
Tig Wongthaweesap *(Controller)*

AUTOVATIVE TECHNOLO-GIES, INC.
1010 Industrial Rd #70, Boulder City,
NV 89005
Tel.: (760) 732-5868   NV
Year Founded: 2012
Automotive Specialty Parts Distr
N.A.I.C.S.: 423120
David Funderburk *(Pres, CEO, CFO,
Principal Acctg Officer, Treas & Sec)*

AUTOWORLD KIA
2520 Hempstead Tpke, East
Meadow, NY 11554
Tel.: (516) 938-4542
Web Site: http://www.kiagiant.com
Sales Range: $10-24.9 Million
Emp.: 33
Car Whslr
N.A.I.C.S.: 441110
Joseph G. Catalanotto *(Pres)*

AUTRONIC PLASTICS INC.
1150 Motor Pkwy Central Islip NY
11722, Westbury, NY 11590
Tel.: (516) 333-7577
Web Site: http://www.apisolution.com
Sales Range: $10-24.9 Million
Emp.: 100
Injection Molding Of Plastics
N.A.I.C.S.: 326199
Michael Lax *(Chm & CEO)*
Tim Keuning *(Pres)*
Agjah I. Libohova *(Dir-R&D)*
Suresh Desai *(Mgr-Quality Control)*
Karen Ledoux *(Asst Controller)*
Bill Stubbs *(Dir-Sls)*
Fred Van Koot *(Engr-Mfg)*
Jim Jacoby *(Plant Mgr)*
Roy Jacob *(Engr-Electrical)*

Autronic Plastics Inc.—(Continued)

Phil Tjimos *(Mgr-Ops)*
Jerzy Prochnicki *(Mgr-Tool Room)*
HaoPing Qi *(Engr-Design)*

AUTRY GREER & SONS, INC.
2850 W Main St, Prichard, AL 36612-2043
Tel.: (251) 457-8655   DE
Web Site: http://www.greers.com
Year Founded: 1916
Sales Range: $200-249.9 Million
Emp.: 600
Grocery Store Chain; General Line of Groceries
N.A.I.C.S.: 445110
Robert A. Greer *(Sec & VP)*
Barton Greer Jr. *(Chm)*
Jack V. Greer Sr. *(Pres)*
O. M. Otts III *(CEO)*
Jack Greer Jr. *(Treas & VP)*

AUTUMN SENIOR LIVING, LLC
8307 Championship Ct, Lakewood Ranch, FL 34202
Tel.: (727) 342-0253
Web Site:
http://www.autumnassistliving.com
Sales Range: $10-24.9 Million
Emp.: 3
Senior Living Facilities Owner & Operator
N.A.I.C.S.: 623312
Jim Soper *(CEO)*
Robert Ross *(Chief Dev Officer)*
Kerry Bingaman *(Chief Admin Officer)*
John A. DePizzo Jr. *(Chm)*

AUVIL FRUIT COMPANY, INC.
21902 US 97, Orondo, WA 98843
Tel.: (509) 784-1033
Web Site: https://www.auvilfruit.com
Year Founded: 1928
Sales Range: $25-49.9 Million
Emp.: 100
Fresh Fruit Production; Apple Orchards
N.A.I.C.S.: 111331
Stan Sheumann *(CFO & Mgr-Mktg)*
Laurie Hough *(Mgr-Sls Data)*
Mike Claphan *(Pres & Gen Mgr)*

AUX SABLE LIQUID PRODUCTS LP
6155 E US Route 6, Morris, IL 60450
Tel.: (815) 941-5800
Web Site: https://www.auxsable.com
Rev.: $365,000,000
Emp.: 100.
Natural Gas Liquids Production
N.A.I.C.S.: 211130
Katherine Dodds *(Gen Counsel & VP)*
Glenn Luce *(Dir-Mktg & Bus Dev)*

AUXILLIUM ENERGY, INC.
1065 Dobbs Ferry RdÂ., White Plains, NY 10607
Tel.: (647) 456-4002
Year Founded: 2009
Oil & Gas Exploration Services
N.A.I.C.S.: 213112
Warmond Fang *(Pres & CEO)*

AUXO INVESTMENT PARTNERS, LLC
146 Monroe Ctr NW Ste 1125, Grand Rapids, MI 49503
Tel.: (616) 980-9810   DE
Web Site:
http://www.auxopartners.com
Year Founded: 2016
Privater Equity Firm
N.A.I.C.S.: 523999
Jeff Helminski *(Mng Partner)*
Jack Kolodny *(Mng Partner)*

Fred Tedori *(Mng Partner)*
Kimberly Beute *(CFO)*
Brian Dora *(Principal)*

Subsidiaries:

Andrie, Inc.   **(1)**
561 E Western Ave, Muskegon, MI 49442
Tel.: (231) 728-2226
Web Site: http://www.andrie.com
Great Lakes Frght Trans Heavy Construction
N.A.I.C.S.: 483113
Stanley Andrie Jr. *(CEO)*

Atlas Die, LLC   **(1)**
2000 Middlebury St, Elkhart, IN 46516
Tel.: (574) 295-0050
Web Site: http://www.atlasdie.com
Steel Rule Dies & Industrial Molds Mfr
N.A.I.C.S.: 333514
Jim White *(VP-Sls)*

Plant (Domestic):

Atlas Die, LLC - Atlanta Plant   **(2)**
5205 Snapfinger Woods Dr, Decatur, GA 30035
Tel.: (770) 981-6585
Web Site: http://www.atlasdie.com
Automotive Parts & Accessories Mfr
N.A.I.C.S.: 333514
Jim White *(VP-Sls)*
Philip Sexton *(Plant Mgr)*

Division (Domestic):

Atlas Die, LLC - Chem-Milling Division   **(2)**
1627 W Lusher Ave, Elkhart, IN 46517-1421
Tel.: (574) 295-0277
Web Site: http://www.atlasdie.com
Steel Rule Dies, Tools & Jigs Mfr
N.A.I.C.S.: 333511
Kevin Deckard *(Gen Mgr)*

Plant (Domestic):

Atlas Die, LLC - Chicago Plant   **(2)**
2000 Bloomingdale Rd Ste 235, Glendale Heights, IL 60139-2182
Tel.: (630) 351-5140
Web Site: http://www.atlasdie.com
Steel Rule Die Mfr
N.A.I.C.S.: 332216
Ed Singleton *(Dir-Mfg)*

Atlas Die, LLC - Greensboro Plant   **(2)**
510 Corliss St Ste B, Greensboro, NC 27406-5273
Tel.: (336) 627-5212
Web Site: http://www.sedie.com
Special Die & Tool, Die Set, Jig & Fixture Mfr
N.A.I.C.S.: 333514
Rob Causey *(Mgr)*
Robert Ficquette *(Plant Mgr)*

Avon Machining LLC   **(1)**
11968 Investment Dr, Shelby, MI 48315-1794
Tel.: (586) 884-2200
Web Site: http://www.avonmachining.com
Heavy Equipment Precision Parts Mfr
N.A.I.C.S.: 332721
Chad Fietsam *(CEO)*

Bernal, LLC   **(1)**
2960 Technology Dr, Rochester Hills, MI 48309
Tel.: (248) 299-3600
Web Site: http://www.bernalrotarydies.com
Sales Range: $1-9.9 Million
Emp.: 60
Paper Idustry Machinery Mfr
N.A.I.C.S.: 333243

M/G Transport Services, Inc.   **(1)**
3838 N Causeway Blvd Ste 3, Metairie, LA 70002
Tel.: (504) 836-7080
Web Site: http://www.mg-transport.com
Sales Range: $1-9.9 Million
Emp.: 3
River-Based Transportation Services
N.A.I.C.S.: 483211

Midway Die, LLC   **(1)**
811 Progress Ct, Williamston, MI 48895
Tel.: (517) 655-5631
Web Site: http://www.midwayrotary.com
Emp.: 50
Rotary Die Mfr
N.A.I.C.S.: 333514
Mike Fitchett *(Mgr-Bus Dev)*

Precision Products Group, Inc.   **(1)**
10201 N Illinois St Ste 390, Indianapolis, IN 46290
Tel.: (800) 887-1475
Web Site: http://www.ppgintl.com
Sales Range: $150-199.9 Million
Emp.: 400
Springs & Tubes Mfr
N.A.I.C.S.: 332613
Dave Hooe *(CEO)*
Heather Weglein *(Mgr-Inside Sls)*

Subsidiary (Non-US):

Huizhou Fusheng Insulation Materials Ltd, Inc.   **(2)**
3rd District Tahsin Group, Chenjiang Town, Huizhou, 516229, Guangdong, China
Tel.: (86) 752 3230169
Web Site: http://www.ppgfs.com
Sales Range: $10-24.9 Million
Emp.: 100
Precision Tube Mfr
N.A.I.C.S.: 332996

Division (Domestic):

Paramount Tube   **(2)**
1430 Progress Rd, Fort Wayne, IN 46808   **(100%)**
Tel.: (260) 484-4111
Web Site: http://www.paramounttube.com
Sales Range: $10-24.9 Million
Emp.: 45
Spiral Wound Paper Tubes for Electrical, Automotive & Packaging Application Mfr
N.A.I.C.S.: 322219

Precision Products   **(2)**
1210 Barranca Dr, El Paso, TX 79935-4601
Tel.: (915) 593-8125
Sales Range: $10-24.9 Million
Emp.: 13
Mfr of Springs
N.A.I.C.S.: 332613

Stone Industrial   **(2)**
9207 51st Ave, College Park, MD 20740
Tel.: (301) 474-3100
Web Site: http://www.stoneindustrial.com
Sales Range: $25-49.9 Million
Emp.: 150
Mfr of Spiral Wound Tubes
N.A.I.C.S.: 322219

Prestige Stamping, Inc.   **(1)**
23513 Groesbeck Hwy, Warren, MI 48089-4253
Tel.: (586) 773-2700
Web Site: http://www.prestigestamping.com
Metal Washers, Fasteners, Metal Stampings & Assemblies & Mfr
N.A.I.C.S.: 332722
Chris Rink *(COO)*
Rosemary Wilson *(Mgr-Accts Payable)*
Tammy Beardsley *(Mgr-Accts Receivable)*
Rick Wyckhuys *(Mgr-Plant)*
Frank Schubert *(Mgr-Quality)*

AV BUILDER CORP.
6373 Nancy Ridge Dr, San Diego, CA 92121
Tel.: (858) 622-9200
Web Site: https://www.avbuilder.com
Sales Range: $50-74.9 Million
Emp.: 12
Hotel/Motel & Multi-Family Home Renovation Services
N.A.I.C.S.: 236220
A. V. Madureira *(Founder & Pres)*
Lindsey King *(Dir-Mktg)*
Keith Pheifer *(Mgr-Ops)*

AV CAPITAL HOLDINGS MANAGEMENT, LLC
300 W 6th St Ste 2300, Austin, TX 78701-3902

Tel.: (512) 485-1945   DE
Year Founded: 2015
Privater Equity Firm
N.A.I.C.S.: 523999
Vernon Bryant *(Mng Partner)*
Dave Alter *(Partner)*

AV THERAPEUTICS, INC.
20 E 68th St Ste 204, New York, NY 10065
Tel.: (917) 497-5523   DE
Web Site:
http://www.avtherapeutics.com
Year Founded: 2011
Pharmaceuticals Mfr
N.A.I.C.S.: 325412
Abraham Mittelman *(Chm, Pres & CEO)*
Raj Kumar Tiwari *(Chief Scientific Officer)*
Jan Geliebter *(Sec)*

AV THOMAS PRODUCE
3900 Sultana Dr, Atwater, CA 95301-9605
Tel.: (209) 394-7514
Web Site:
https://www.avthomasproduce.com
Year Founded: 1920
Sales Range: $25-49.9 Million
Emp.: 8
Potato Farming Services
N.A.I.C.S.: 111211
Rick Vieira *(VP-Farming Div)*
Carlos Vieira *(VP-Packing & Sls Div)*
Manuel Eduardo Vieira *(Owner & Pres)*
Frank Lucas *(Coord-Food Safety & Security)*
Brian Henrique Escobar *(Dir-Organic Ops)*
Manuel E. Silva Jr. *(Mgr-Sls)*

AVA ADVERTISING
259 S St, Waukesha, WI 53186
Tel.: (262) 523-9200   WI,
Year Founded: 1979
Sales Range: $25-49.9 Million
Emp.: 6
Advertising Agencies
N.A.I.C.S.: 541810
Millie Crawford *(Office Mgr)*

AVA GALLERY & ART CENTER
11 Bank St, Lebanon, NH 03766
Tel.: (603) 448-3117   NH
Web Site: http://www.avagallery.org
Year Founded: 1973
Rev.: $1,133,146
Assets: $4,796,325
Liabilities: $440,134
Net Worth: $4,356,191
Earnings: $344,362
Emp.: 5
Fiscal Year-end: 08/31/14
Visual Art Promotion Services
N.A.I.C.S.: 711310
Bente Torjusen *(Exec Dir)*
Maggie Burnett *(Office Mgr)*
Althea Goundrey *(Mgr-Studio)*
Adam Blue *(Dir-Education)*

AVA-RUHA CORP.
1890 Newport Blvd, Costa Mesa, CA 92627
Tel.: (949) 631-4741
Web Site:
http://www.mothersmarket.com
Sales Range: $50-74.9 Million
Emp.: 350
Grocery Stores, Independent
N.A.I.C.S.: 445110
Bruce Mac Gurn *(Chm)*
Sally Ann Kawamoto *(Dir-HR)*

AVAAP INC.
510 Thornall St Ste 250, Edison, NJ 08837
Tel.: (732) 710-3425
Web Site: http://www.avaap.com
Sales Range: $1-9.9 Million
Emp.: 50
Software Services
N.A.I.C.S.: 541511
Dhiraj Shah *(Pres)*
Ria Aggarwal *(Controller-Fin)*

Subsidiaries:

Falcon Consulting Group, LLC   **(1)**
5 Great Valley Pkwy Ste 120, Malvern, PA 19335   **(100%)**
Tel.: (610) 363-0815
Web Site: http://www.falconnest.com
Rev.: $2,300,000
Emp.: 30
Consulting & Implementation for Health Care
N.A.I.C.S.: 518210
Cheryl J. Priest *(VP-Res Quality & Compliance Svcs)*

Navigator Management Partners LLC   **(1)**
450 S Front St, Columbus, OH 43215
Tel.: (614) 796-0090
Web Site: http://www.navmp.com
Sales Range: $10-24.9 Million
Emp.: 65
Management & Information Technology Consulting Services
N.A.I.C.S.: 541611
David K. Schoettmer *(Founder & CEO)*
Kameron de Vente *(COO & Sr VP)*
Jeffrey Brown *(VP-Consulting Svcs)*
Heather Bodak *(VP-Fin)*
Kelly Reo *(VP-Mktg & Enterprise Information)*
Derek Sharp *(Sr VP)*
Richard Walega *(Sr VP)*
Mike Waller *(VP-Consulting Svcs)*
Casey Cramer *(Mgr-Mktg)*
Glenn Small *(VP)*
John DeLeo *(Dir-Consulting Svcs)*
Tom Okonak *(Dir-Consulting Svcs)*
Marcelo Casella *(VP-Consulting Svcs)*
Michael Stevenson *(Sr VP-Consulting Svcs)*

AVADIAN CREDIT UNION
1 Riverchase Pkwy S, Hoover, AL 35244
Tel.: (205) 985-2828
Web Site: https://www.avadiancu.com
Year Founded: 1934
Sales Range: $25-49.9 Million
Emp.: 214
Credit Union
N.A.I.C.S.: 522130
Linda Cencula *(Pres & CEO)*

AVAIL-TVN
1881 Campus Commons Dr Ste 101, Reston, VA 20191
Tel.: (571) 485-2760
Web Site: http://www.avail-tvn.com
Sales Range: $200-249.9 Million
Emp.: 215
Video Production Services
N.A.I.C.S.: 512191
Phil Herget *(Chm)*

AVALEX TECHNOLOGIES CORPORATION
2665 Gulf Breeze Pkwy, Gulf Breeze, FL 32563
Tel.: (850) 470-8464   **GA**
Web Site: https://www.avalex.com
Year Founded: 1993
Sales Range: $10-24.9 Million
Emp.: 65
Flat Panel Navigation Displays, Digital Mapping & Sensor Pointing Systems for Airborne & Military Surveillance
N.A.I.C.S.: 334511

Tad Ihns *(CEO)*
Terri Wojtys *(Mgr-Sls)*

AVALON CONSULTING, LLC
6841 Virginia Pkwy Ste 103 425, McKinney, TX 75071
Tel.: (469) 424-3449
Web Site: http://www.avalonconsult.com
Year Founded: 2003
Rev.: $6,900,000
Emp.: 55
Management Consulting Services
N.A.I.C.S.: 541618
Mike Green *(Mng Dir-Dallas/National Consulting Practice)*
Casey Green *(Principal & Exec VP-Corp Strategy)*
Tom Reidy *(Founder, Pres & Principal)*

AVALON DOCUMENTS SERVICES
901 N State St, Syracuse, NY 13208
Tel.: (315) 471-3333   **NY**
Web Site: https://www.teamavalon.com
Sales Range: $1-9.9 Million
Emp.: 66
Business Services
N.A.I.C.S.: 513199
Shawn Thrall *(Pres)*
J. P. Midgley *(CEO)*
Lukas Kleppe *(Dir-Client Svcs)*
Lewis Airth *(Mng Partner-Utica)*
Patrick Beckett *(Mng Partner-Buffalo)*
Marty Bohn *(Mng Partner-Cleveland)*
Michael Byrne *(Mng Partner-Rochester)*
Andrew Guffey *(Mng Partner-Tampa)*
Robert DeStefanis *(Mng Partner-Cleveland)*
Chris Haag *(Chief Sls Officer)*
Kyle Cavalieri *(CIO)*

Subsidiaries:

Digits LLC   **(1)**
490 Ctr Rd Ste 200, Buffalo, NY 14224-2170
Web Site: http://www.digitsllc.com
Scientific & Technical Consulting Services
N.A.I.C.S.: 541690
Michael G. McCartney *(Pres & CEO)*

AVALON EXHIBITS, INC.
65 Lukens Dr Riveredge Park, New Castle, DE 19720
Tel.: (302) 654-1633   **DE**
Sales Range: $1-9.9 Million
Emp.: 90
Designing & Manufacturing Displays
N.A.I.C.S.: 541850

AVALON GLASS & MIRROR COMPANY
642 E Alondra Blvd, Carson, CA 90746
Tel.: (323) 321-8806
Web Site: https://www.avalonmirrorglass.com
Sales Range: $10-24.9 Million
Emp.: 160
Mirrored Glass
N.A.I.C.S.: 327215
Randy Steinberg *(CEO)*

AVALON GLOBAL GROUP, INC.
2350 34th St N 2nd Fl, Saint Petersburg, FL 33713
Tel.: (727) 328-8666
Year Founded: 2001
Sales Range: $50-74.9 Million
Emp.: 450
Car Rental & Sales
N.A.I.C.S.: 532111

Feng Lin *(CEO)*

AVALON HEALTH SERVICES, LLC
3405 W Dr Martin Luther King Jr Blvd Ste 200, Tampa, FL 33607
Tel.: (813) 751-3800
Web Site: http://www.avalonhcs.com
Year Founded: 2013
Sales Range: $1-9.9 Million
Emp.: 200
Health Care Srvices
N.A.I.C.S.: 621610
Pamela Stahl *(Pres)*
Bill Kerr *(CEO)*
John Adams *(CFO)*
Jason Bush *(Chief Data Officer)*
Barry Davis *(Chief Growth Officer)*
Shantha Diaz *(COO)*
Michele Norton *(Sr VP-Product Mktg)*

AVALON PARK GROUP MANAGEMENT, INC.
3680 Avalon Park E Blvd Ste 300, Orlando, FL 32828
Tel.: (407) 658-6565
Web Site: http://www.avalonparkgroup.com
Year Founded: 1995
Rev.: $300,000,000
Emp.: 45
Property Management & Development Services
N.A.I.C.S.: 237210
Beat Kahli *(Pres & CEO)*
Eric Marks *(Pres-Avex Homes)*
Ross Halle *(Sr VP)*
Stephanie Hodson *(Sr VP-Mktg & Community Rels)*
Marybel Defillo *(CFO & Exec VP)*
Richard Kunz *(Pres-Avalon Park Texas LP)*
Marta Pierliusi *(Sr VP & Controller)*
Mari Robles *(Sr VP & Dir-HR)*
J. J. Soffarelli *(Asst VP-Orlando)*
Thomas Lang *(Pres-Pasco Mine)*

Subsidiaries:

Avalon Park   **(1)**
3680 Avalon Park E Blvd Ste 300, Orlando, FL 32828
Tel.: (407) 658-6565
Web Site: http://www.avalonpark.com
Sales Range: $10-24.9 Million
Emp.: 10
Residential Properties
N.A.I.C.S.: 236116
Beat Kahli *(Pres)*

AVALON PETROLEUM COMPANY
200 E Court St Ste 720, Kankakee, IL 60901
Tel.: (708) 720-3060
Web Site: http://www.avalonpetroleum.com
Sales Range: $50-74.9 Million
Emp.: 58
Gasoline Distr
N.A.I.C.S.: 424720
John J. Eckenstein *(Pres)*
Bill Katzenberger *(VP-Sls)*
Rich Unger *(VP-Fin)*
Matt Kalivoda *(Mgr-Ops)*

AVALON RISK MANAGEMENT, INC.
150 NW Point Blvd 2nd Fl, Elk Grove Village, IL 60007
Tel.: (847) 700-8100
Web Site: https://www.avalonrisk.com
Sales Range: $50-74.9 Million
Emp.: 130
Risk Managemeng Srvices
N.A.I.C.S.: 524210
Denise Lee Chipman *(VP-Ops)*
James Zuhlke *(Chm)*

Dave Huck *(Controller & Treas)*
Nathan Baylor *(VP)*
Michael Brown *(Exec VP & VP-East Coast)*
Andrea Lanouette *(VP-Los Angeles)*
Christine Wade *(Asst VP-Natl Accts)*
Deirdre Hudson *(VP-San Francisco)*
Kathy Schricker *(VP-Boston)*
Leslie Carril *(VP-Miami)*
Lisa Vranich *(Mgr-South)*
Terrie Sapronetti *(Asst VP-Underwriting)*
Wanda Sample *(VP-New York)*
Gary C. Bhojwani *(Founder)*

AVALOTIS CORPORATION
400 Jones St, Verona, PA 15147
Tel.: (412) 828-9666
Web Site: https://www.avalotis.com
Year Founded: 1967
Sales Range: $25-49.9 Million
Emp.: 400
Exterior Commercial Painting Contracting Services
N.A.I.C.S.: 238320
Chris Aivaliotis *(VP)*
Gerard Masters *(Mgr-Corp Safety & Quality Control)*
Zack Jeney *(Mgr-Project Safety)*

AVALT, LLC
79 Newbury St, Boston, MA 02116
Tel.: (617) 874-5880   **DE**
Web Site: http://www.avalt.com
Investment Services
N.A.I.C.S.: 523999
Marko Kivisto *(Partner)*

Subsidiaries:

Ned Stevens Gutter Cleaning & General Contracting, Inc.   **(1)**
11 Daniel Rd E, Fairfield, NJ 07004
Tel.: (973) 830-1515
Web Site: http://www.nedstevens.com
Sales Range: $1-9.9 Million
Emp.: 23
Roofing, Siding & Gutter Cleaning Services
N.A.I.C.S.: 238390
Ned Stevens *(Pres)*
Jahaira Cortes-Guilbe *(Mgr-Sls)*
Rob Rapuano *(CEO)*

AVANCE INVESTMENT MANAGEMENT, LLC
650 5th Ave 23rd Fl Ste 2320, New York, NY 10019
Tel.: (646) 568-7397   **DE**
Web Site: https://avanceinv.com
Year Founded: 2020
Privater Equity Firm
N.A.I.C.S.: 523999
John Civanto *(Sr Partner)*

Subsidiaries:

RIA Advisory LLC   **(1)**
2000 Ponce De Leon Blvd Ste 600, Coral Gables, FL 33134
Tel.: (305) 421-6303
Web Site: https://riaadvisory.com
Revenue Management Services
N.A.I.C.S.: 541618
Saket Pabby *(CEO)*

Subsidiary (Domestic):

TMG Consulting LLC   **(2)**
9210 Honeycomb Dr, Austin, TX 78737
Tel.: (512) 288-2655
Sales Range: $1-9.9 Million
Emp.: 10
Management Consulting Services
N.A.I.C.S.: 541611
Gregory Galluzzi *(Pres)*
Jason C. Kinslow *(VP-AMI & Smart Grid Svcs)*
Mario Bauer *(CEO)*

AVANCEON LTD.
300 Eagleview Blvd Ste 100, Exton, PA 19341

Avanceon Ltd.—(Continued)
Tel.: (610) 458-8700
Web Site: https://www.avanceon.com
Year Founded: 1984
Engineering Services
N.A.I.C.S.: 541330
Brian Fenn (COO & VP-Ops)
Matt Ruth (Pres & CEO)
Tracey Johnson (VP-Operations)
Susan Schlegel (VP-Sales)
Bryan Little (Ops Mgr)
Nicholas Imfeld (Ops Mgr)
Bruce Slusser (Dir-Digital Transformation Practice)
Michael Fazzini (Ops Mgr)

AVANGARD CAPITAL GROUP, INC.
2708 Commerce Way Ste 300, Philadelphia, PA 19154
Tel.: (215) 464-7300   NV
Web Site:
http://www.avangardcapital.com
Sales Range: Less than $1 Million
Emp.: 1
Automobile Financing
N.A.I.C.S.: 522220
Simon Friedman (Chm, Interim CEO & Sec)

AVANKIA LLC
750 Old Hickory Blvd Ste 150, Brentwood, TN 94566
Tel.: (615) 429-5462
Web Site: https://www.avankia.com
Year Founded: 2002
Sales Range: $1-9.9 Million
Emp.: 33
Computer Networking Software Mfr & Technology Consulting Services
N.A.I.C.S.: 541690
Reena Gupta (CEO)
Rajeev Gupta (CTO)
Muralidhar Koteshwar (Mng Dir-Global Ops)

AVANT COMMUNICATIONS, INC.
2 N. Riverside Plaza Suite 2450, Chicago, IL 60606
Tel.: (312) 281-9052
Web Site:
http://www.avantcommunication.net
Emp.: 219
Wired Telecommunications Carriers
N.A.I.C.S.: 517111
Ted Schuman (Chief Experience Officer)
Chris Werpy (Chief Innovation Officer)
Melissa Campbell (Project Mgr)
Ron Hayman (Chief Cloud Officer)
Alex Danyluk (Chief Strategy Officer)
Ian Kieninger (CEO)
Shane McNamara (Exec VP-Channel Sls-East)
Jen Gallego (Exec VP-Channel Sls)
Rick Reed (Sr Dir-Channel Sls-South Central)

Subsidiaries:

PlanetOne Communications Inc.   (1)
9845 E Bell Rd Ste 130, Scottsdale, AZ 85260
Tel.: (877) 487-8353
Web Site: http://www.planetone.net
Sales Range: $10-24.9 Million
Emp.: 15
Telecommunications Resellers
N.A.I.C.S.: 517121

AVANT CREDIT CORP.
640 N La Salle Dr Ste 535, Chicago, IL 60654
Tel.: (800) 712-5407
Web Site: http://www.avantcredit.com

Emp.: 500
Loan Brokerage Services
N.A.I.C.S.: 522310
Al Goldstein (CEO)
John Sun (Chief Credit Officer)
Paul Zhang (CTO)
Adam Hughes (COO)
Anna Fridman (Gen Counsel & Chief Compliance Officer)
David Pickel (Controller)
Ryan McLennan (Gen Counsel)

AVANT MARKETING GROUP
1922 Prospector Ave, Park City, UT 84060
Tel.: (435) 608-0294
Web Site: http://www.avantlink.com
Sales Range: $1-9.9 Million
Advertising & Marketing Affiliate Network Services
N.A.I.C.S.: 541890
Scott Kalbach (Co-Founder & CEO)
Paul Kalbach (Co-Founder & VP-Sls)

AVANT PUBLICATIONS LLC
116 Morlake Dr Ste 203, Mooresville, NC 28117
Tel.: (704) 897-6048
Web Site: http://www.avantpubs.com
Newspaper Publishers
N.A.I.C.S.: 513110
Scott Champion (Co-CEO)
Andrew Mok (Co-CEO)
Corey Champion (CFO)
Nick DeLorenzo (Chief Digital Officer)

AVANT SERVICES CORPORATION
60 E 42nd St Lowr Level, New York, NY 10165
Tel.: (212) 687-5145
Web Site:
http://www.nymessenger.com
Year Founded: 1925
Rev.: $12,900,000
Emp.: 400
Courier Or Messenger Service
N.A.I.C.S.: 561499
Charles C. Chiusano (CEO)
James Chiusano (VP-Sls & Mktg)

AVANT TECHNOLOGIES OF PR, INC.
Rd 156 Caguas W Industrial Park Bldg 39, Caguas, PR 00725
Tel.: (787) 746-9191
Sales Range: $1-9.9 Million
Emp.: 45
Computer Mfr; Networked Digital Video Surveillance Systems Mfr & Designer
N.A.I.C.S.: 334111
Luis Diaz (Mgr-Mktg)

AVANT-GARDE ADVISORS LLC
9155 E Nichols Ave Ste 175, Centennial, CO 80112
Tel.: (303) 900-1370
Web Site:
http://www.avantgardewm.com
Year Founded: 2009
Asset & Cash Management & Financial Planning Services
N.A.I.C.S.: 523999
Jennifer Gregory (Ops Mgr)
Austin Coose (Portfolio Mgr)
Jennifer Patton (Treas)
Eric Patton (Chief Compliance Officer)

AVANTE CAPITAL PARTNERS
11150 Santa Monica Blvd Suite 1470, Los Angeles, CA 90025
Tel.: (310) 667-9242
Web Site: https://avantecap.com

Year Founded: 2009
Privater Equity Firm
N.A.I.C.S.: 523999

AVANTE MEZZANINE PARTNERS, INC.
11150 Santa Monica Blvd Ste 1470, Los Angeles, CA 90025
Tel.: (310) 667-9242   DE
Web Site:
http://www.avantemezzanine.com
Equity Investment Firm
N.A.I.C.S.: 523999
Jeri J. Harman (CEO & Mng Partner)
Stephen Adamson (Mng Partner)
Natasha V. Fox (Mng Partner)
Cliff Lyon (CFO & Partner-Admin)
Ivelisse Rodriguez Simon (Partner)
Paul Hayama (Partner)
Dan Moss (Principal)
Aaron DiCenzo (VP)

AVANTECH, INC.
95-A Sunbelt Blvd, Columbia, SC 29203
Tel.: (803) 407-7171   SC
Web Site:
http://www.avantechinc.com
Year Founded: 1999
Sales Range: $10-24.9 Million
Emp.: 56
Industrial Water Treatment Equipment Sales & Maintenance Services
N.A.I.C.S.: 423830
Steven Gagnon (VP-Sls)
Dave Langan (VP-Quality & Compliance)
Marvin Memmert (Dir-Procurement)
Tracy Barker (CTO)
Larry Beets (VP-Ops)
Gary A. Benda (Sr VP-Bus Dev)
Mike Goodrich (CFO)

AVANTI CIGAR CORPORATION
200 Keystone Industrial Park, Dunmore, PA 18512
Tel.: (570) 344-8566
Web Site: http://www.avanticigar.com
Year Founded: 1913
Sales Range: $25-49.9 Million
Emp.: 33
Mfr of Cigars
N.A.I.C.S.: 312230
Luciano Simeone (COO)

AVANTI HEALTH SYSTEMS
300 Villa Dr, Hurley, WI 54534-1523
Tel.: (715) 561-3200   WI
Web Site: https://www.avantihs.com
Year Founded: 1985
Sales Range: $50-74.9 Million
Emp.: 50
Nursing & Assisted Living Facilities Operator
N.A.I.C.S.: 813212
Lisa Jusula (Mgr-Payroll)

AVANTI LINENS, INC.
234 Moonachie, Moonachie, NJ 07074
Tel.: (201) 641-7766   NJ
Web Site:
https://www.avantilinens.com
Year Founded: 1969
Sales Range: $10-24.9 Million
Emp.: 200
Table Linens & Kitchen Textiles Mfr
N.A.I.C.S.: 313310

AVASANT LLC
1960 E Grand Ave Ste 1050, El Segundo, CA 90245
Tel.: (310) 643-3030
Web Site: http://www.avasant.com

Process, Physical Distribution & Logistics Consulting Services
N.A.I.C.S.: 541614
Kevin S. Parikh (CEO & Sr Partner)
Jemie Sae Koo (VP-Mktg)

Subsidiaries:

Strativa, Inc.   (1)
2082 Business Center Dr Ste 240, Irvine, CA 92612
Tel.: (949) 442-0099
Web Site: http://www.strativa.com
Administrative Management & General Management Consulting Service
N.A.I.C.S.: 541611

AVATAR INTEGRATED SYSTEMS, INC.
2111 Tasman Dr, Santa Clara, CA 95054
Tel.: (669) 230-0100
Web Site: http://www.avatar-da.com
Year Founded: 2017
Software Company
N.A.I.C.S.: 513210
Jingyuan Han (Chm)

Subsidiaries:

ATopTech, Inc.   (1)
2111 Tasman Dr, Santa Clara, CA 95054
Tel.: (408) 550-4085
Computer & Electronic Equipment Distr
N.A.I.C.S.: 423690

AVATAR STUDIOS
2675 Scott Ave Ste G, Saint Louis, MO 63103
Tel.: (314) 533-2242
Web Site: https://www.avatar-studios.com
Year Founded: 1973
Sales Range: $50-74.9 Million
Emp.: 35
Video Production
N.A.I.C.S.: 512110
Bill Faris (Pres)

AVATEL TECHNOLOGIES, INC.
220 S Hilltop Rd, Brandon, FL 33511
Tel.: (813) 314-2111   FL
Web Site: https://www.avatel.us
Year Founded: 2000
Sales Range: $1-9.9 Million
Emp.: 60
Electrical Contractor
N.A.I.C.S.: 238210
Jamie Wood (Exec VP)

AVATRIA INC.
10 S LaSalle St Ste 320, Chicago, IL 60603
Tel.: (312) 600-7758
Web Site: http://www.avatria.com
Year Founded: 2014
Sales Range: $1-9.9 Million
Emp.: 13
Digital Marketing Services
N.A.I.C.S.: 541810
John McDonough (Project Mgr)

AVC CORP.
17707 S Santa Fe Ave, Rancho Dominguez, CA 90221
Tel.: (310) 533-5811
Web Site: https://www.avccorp.com
Sales Range: $50-74.9 Million
Emp.: 82
Tapes & Cassettes, Duplicate DVD's
N.A.I.C.S.: 423990
Moshe Begim (Pres)
Sharon Van Roo (VP-Mdsg)
Guy Marom (Exec VP)

AVCENTER INC.
1483 Flightline, Pocatello, ID 83204
Tel.: (208) 234-2141

Web Site: https://www.avcenter.com
Rev.: $13,300,000
Emp.: 70
Aircraft Fueling Services
N.A.I.C.S.: 424720
Shane Palagi (Dir-Maintenance)
Melvin Wagoner (Owner & Dir-Ops)

AVEANNA HEALTHCARE, LLC
400 Interstate N Pkwy Ste 1600, Atlanta, GA 30339
Tel.: (770) 441-1580
Web Site: https://www.aveanna.com
Year Founded: 2017
N.A.I.C.S.:
Rod Windley (CEO)
Dave Afshar (CFO)
Jeff S. Shaner (COO)
Beth Rubio (Chief Clinical Officer)
Patrick Cunningham (Chief Compliance Officer)
Ed Reisz (Chief Admin Officer)
Shannon Drake (Gen Counsel)

AVEDIS FOUNDATION
3903 N Harrison, Shawnee, OK 74804
Tel.: (405) 273-4055   OK
Web Site:
     http://www.avedisfoundation.org
Year Founded: 1989
Sales Range: $50-74.9 Million
Emp.: 761
People Welfare Services
N.A.I.C.S.: 624190

AVEDIS ZILDJIAN COMPANY INC.
22 Longwater Dr, Norwell, MA 02061-1612
Tel.: (781) 871-2200   MA
Web Site: https://www.zildjian.com
Sales Range: $75-99.9 Million
Emp.: 170
Cymbals & Drumsticks Mfr
N.A.I.C.S.: 339992
Craigie Zildjian (CEO)
Debbie Zildjian (VP-HR)
Paul R. Struble (VP-Ops)
Victor Filonovich (Mgr-Category-Cymbals)
Neil Larrivee (VP-Education & Drumstick Product Dev)
John Stephans (Pres)

AVELLA OF DEER VALLEY, INC.
24416 N 19th Ave, Phoenix, AZ 85085
Tel.: (623) 742-1700   AZ
Web Site: http://www.avella.com
Year Founded: 1996
Sales Range: $300-349.9 Million
Emp.: 450
Specialty Pharmaceutical Preparations Services
N.A.I.C.S.: 325412
John D. Musil (Founder)
Nathan Downhour (Exec VP-Strategic Programs)
Rebecca M. Shanahan (CEO)
Wes Edwards (CFO)
Eric S. Sredzinski (Exec VP-Clinical Affairs & Quality Assurance & Program Dir-ADAP)
Joshua A. Rademacher (Exec VP-Bus Dev & Enterprise Solutions)
Ron Geguzys (Exec VP-Ops & IT)
Nancy McCutcheon (Sr VP-Strategic Sls)
Todd Speranzo (VP-Mktg)
A. Hamilton Baiden IV (Exec VP-Sls)

Subsidiaries:

Avella of Scottsdale, Inc.   (1)

9111 N 91st St Ste C-102, Scottsdale, AZ 85258
Tel.: (480) 451-3771
Web Site: http://www.avella.com
Sales Range: $1-9.9 Million
Specialty Pharmaceutical Preparations Services
N.A.I.C.S.: 325412
Sarjit Patel (Mgr-Pharmacy)

Oncology Plus, Inc.   (1)
1070 E Brandon Blvd, Brandon, FL 33511
Tel.: (813) 689-2069
Web Site: http://www.oncologyplus.com
Sales Range: $1-9.9 Million
Emp.: 15
Pharmacies & Drug Distr
N.A.I.C.S.: 456110
Zach Scholl (Pres)

AVEM PARTNERS, LLC
10350 Santa Monica Blvd Ste 295, Los Angeles, CA 90025
Tel.: (310) 228-6904
Web Site: http://avempartners.com
Investment Services
N.A.I.C.S.: 523940
Mike Fourtiq (Partner)
Ken Walter (Partner)
Brian Leibl (Partner)

Subsidiaries:

Future Tech Metals, Inc.   (1)
2926 Rubidoux Blvd, Riverside, CA 92509
Tel.: (951) 781-4801
Web Site: http://www.futuretechmetals.com
Machine Shops
N.A.I.C.S.: 332710

AVENTIS SYSTEMS
200 Galleria Pkwy SE Ste 250, Atlanta, GA 30339
Tel.: (866) 714-9138
Web Site:
     https://www.aventissystems.com
Year Founded: 2008
Sales Range: $10-24.9 Million
Emp.: 40
Sales of Dell & HP Servers & Storage Equipment & Cisco Networking Equipment, Workstations, Desktops, Laptops & Hardware Components
N.A.I.C.S.: 334112
Hesam Lamei (Founder & Pres)
Tiffany Bloomer (Dir-Mktg & Bus Dev)

AVENTURE AVIATION
108 International Dr, Peachtree City, GA 30269
Tel.: (770) 632-7930
Web Site:
     https://www.aventureaviation.com
Year Founded: 2001
Sales Range: $1-9.9 Million
Emp.: 17
Aviation Parts Supplier & Service
N.A.I.C.S.: 441227
Zaheer Faruqi (Pres)
Amyr Qureshi (VP)
Vic Daniel (Dir-Military Sls)

AVENUE CAPITAL GROUP, LLC
399 Park Ave 6th Fl, New York, NY 10022-4693
Tel.: (212) 878-3500   DE
Web Site:
     http://www.avenuecapital.com
Year Founded: 1995
Rev.: $12,200,000,000
Emp.: 204
Distressed Debt Market Investment Firm
N.A.I.C.S.: 523999
Marc Lasry (Co-Founder, Chm & CEO)
Thomas More Larkin (CFO)
Randolph Scott Takian (Sr Mng Dir & Head-Pub Fund Strategy)

Sonia E. Gardner (Co-Founder, Pres & Mng Partner)
Nish Wijerathna Kolonne (CTO)
Todd Greenbarg (Sr Mng Dir-Legal)
Julie Baumann (Sr Mng Dir-IR)
Richard Furst (Chief Investment Officer & Head-Strategy-Europe)
Cherie Alcoff (Sr Mng Dir-Bus Dev)
John Larkin (Sr Mng Dir & Head-Impact Investments)
Anil Gorthy (Sr Portfolio Mgr-Asia Strategy)
Richard Cocozza (Chief Risk Officer)

Subsidiaries:

Avenue Capital Management II, L.P.   (1)
399 Park Ave 6th Fl, New York, NY 10022
Tel.: (212) 878-3500
Web Site: http://www.avenuecapital.com
Distressed Debt Market Investment Management Services
N.A.I.C.S.: 523940
Marc Lasry (Chm & CEO)
Jeffrey J. Gary (Sr Portfolio Mgr-Enhanced Credit Strategy)
Randal T. Klein (Portfolio Mgr-Trade Claims & Restructurings-US Strategy)

Affiliate (Domestic):

Avenue Capital Mortgage REIT Inc.   (2)
399 Park Ave, New York, NY 10022
Tel.: (212) 878-3500
Web Site: http://www.avenuecapital.com
Real Estate Investment Trust
N.A.I.C.S.: 525990
Marc Lasry (Chm & CEO)
Thomas More Larkin (CFO)
Randolph Scott Takian (Pres)
Jeffrey B. Lown II (Chief Investment Officer & Portfolio Mgr)

AVENUE100 MEDIA SOLUTIONS INC.
10 Presidential Way, Woburn, MA 01801
Tel.: (781) 683-3300
Web Site: http://www.avenue100.com
Year Founded: 2009
Education Training Services
N.A.I.C.S.: 611710
Rob Carbonaro (CEO)
Mary Long (Gen Counsel)
Lisa Mastrangelo (COO & CFO)
Chris Marshall (Dir-Engrg)
Cliff Libby (Exec VP-Sls & Mktg)

AVERA HEALTH
3900 W Avera Dr, Sioux Falls, SD 57108
Tel.: (605) 322-4700   SD
Web Site: https://www.avera.org
Year Founded: 1982
Sales Range: $25-49.9 Million
Emp.: 100
Health Care Srvices
N.A.I.C.S.: 524114
James Veline (CIO & Sr VP)
Rob Bates (Sr VP-Managed Care Svcs)
Rich Korman (Gen Counsel & Sr VP)
Steve Statz (Sr VP-Bus Dev)
Tom Clark (Reg Pres)
David Flicek (Chief Admin Officer-Avera Medical Grp)
Richard Molseed (Exec VP-Strategy & Governance)
Bob Sutton (CEO)
Joan Reichelt Sr. (Exec VP-Culture)

Subsidiaries:

Avera Tyler Hospital   (1)
240 Willow St, Tyler, MN 56178
Tel.: (507) 247-5521
Web Site: http://www.avera.org
Primary Care Clinics & Physician Offices
N.A.I.C.S.: 623110

AVERITT EXPRESS INC.
1415 Neal St, Cookeville, TN 38502-3166
Tel.: (931) 526-3306   TN
Web Site:
     http://www.averittexpress.com
Year Founded: 1986
Sales Range: $800-899.9 Million
Emp.: 6,500
Logistic Services
N.A.I.C.S.: 484121
Gary D. Sasser (Chm & CEO)
Wayne Spain (Pres & COO)
Phil Pierce (Exec VP-Sls & Mktg)
Johnny Fields (CFO & Exec VP)

AVERTEST, LLC
2916 W Marshall St Ste A, Richmond, VA 23230
Web Site: http://averhealth.com
Year Founded: 1995
Sales Range: $10-24.9 Million
Emp.: 500
Mental Health Care Services
N.A.I.C.S.: 621330
Jason Herzog (Co-Chm & Co-CEO)
Jeff Herr (Co-Chm & Co-CEO)
Dominique Delagnes (COO)
David Flood (CFO)
Justin Manni (Dir-Bus Dev)

AVESI PARTNERS, LLC
4 Star Point Ste 202, Stamford, CT 06902
Tel.: (475) 333-3470
Web Site: https://avesipartners.com
Holding Company
N.A.I.C.S.: 551112
George Parry (Mng Dir)

Subsidiaries:

Danforth Advisors, LLC   (1)
91 Middle Rd, Southborough, MA 01772
Tel.: (617) 686-7679
Web Site: http://www.danforthadvisors.com
General Management Consulting Services
N.A.I.C.S.: 541611
Gregg Beloff (Co-Founder & Mng Dir)
Bill Romeo (Mng Dir-Healthcare Tech Practice)
G. Hamilton Mehlman (COO)
Paul Falvey (Dir-Healthcare Svcs Practice)
Timothy M. Cunningham (CFO)
Chris Connors (Pres)
Barbara Carlin (Mng Dir-Mid-Atlantic)
John Hallinan (Chief Dev Officer)
Stephen J. DiPalma (Mng Dir)
Daniel E. Geffken (Co-Founder)

Subsidiary (Domestic):

Argot Partners, LLC   (2)
200 Park Ave S Ste 1515, New York, NY 10003
Tel.: (212) 600-2126
Web Site: http://www.argotpartners.com
Media Streaming Services
N.A.I.C.S.: 518210
David M. F. Pitts (Partner)
Andrea F. Rabney (Pres & CEO)
Laura Perry (Mng Dir)
Lourdes Catala (VP)
Susan Kim (Mng Dir)
Angeli Kolhatkar (Mng Dir)
David Rosen (Sr VP)
Eliza Schleifstein (Mng Dir)
Glenn Garmont (VP)
Kimberly Minarovich (Mng Dir)
Maeva Conneighton (VP)
Sam Martin (Mng Dir)
Michelle Pappanastos (Sr Mng Dir)

AVESTA COMPUTER SERVICES LTD.
23 Emmet Ct, Piscataway, NJ 08854-5579
Tel.: (201) 369-9400
Web Site: http://www.avestacs.com
Year Founded: 1994
Sales Range: $10-24.9 Million

Avesta Computer Services Ltd.—(Continued)

Emp.: 5
Global IT Solutions
N.A.I.C.S.: 541512
Cyrus H. Davierwalla *(Founder & CEO)*
Rushad E. Cassad *(Pres)*

AVESTA HOMES LLC

Tampa Bay Hillsborough Ave N 56th St, Tampa, FL 33680
Tel.: (800) 467-3330
Web Site:
  http://avestacommunities.com
Year Founded: 2010
Sales Range: $1-9.9 Million
Apartment Owner & Operator
N.A.I.C.S.: 531311
Peter Reynolds *(Mng Dir)*
Nathaniel Fischer *(Mng Dir)*
Scott Bigham *(Mng Dir)*
Joseph Facchini *(Mng Dir)*

AVESTA HOUSING DEVELOP-MENT CORP.

307 Cumberland Ave, Portland, ME 04101
Tel.: (207) 553-7777
Web Site:
  https://www.avestahousing.org
Year Founded: 1971
Sales Range: $25-49.9 Million
Emp.: 65
Housing Construction Services
N.A.I.C.S.: 236117
Eric Boucher *(CFO)*
Dana Totman *(Pres)*
Kim Farrar *(VP-Residential Svcs)*
Matthew Peters *(VP-Real Estate Svcs)*
Michael L. Rayder *(Assoc Dir-Dev)*

AVFUEL CORPORATION

47 W Ellsworth, Ann Arbor, MI 48108-2206
Tel.: (734) 663-6466
Web Site: https://www.avfuel.com
Year Founded: 1984
Sales Range: $10-24.9 Million
Emp.: 95
Aviation Fuel Product & Services
N.A.I.C.S.: 424720
Craig R. Sincock *(Pres & CEO)*

Subsidiaries:

Avplan Trip Support   (1)
47 W Ellsworth Rd, Ann Arbor, MI 48108
Tel.: (734) 272-4120
Web Site: http://www.avplantripsupport.com
Flight Planning & Ground Handling Services
N.A.I.C.S.: 488119
Phil Tyler *(Mgr-Ops)*
Russ Standefer *(VP-Trip Support & Sr Acct Exec)*
Craig R. Sincock *(Pres & CEO)*

Avsurance Corporation   (1)
47 W Ellsworth, Ann Arbor, MI 48108-2206
Tel.: (734) 663-6466
Web Site: http://www.avfuel.com
Aviation Insurance Product & Services
N.A.I.C.S.: 524210
Edmund Underwood *(Pres)*

AVG ADVANCED TECHNOLO-GIES LP

363 Saint Paul Blvd, Carol Stream, IL 60188
Tel.: (630) 668-3900
Web Site:
  http://www.autotechcontrols.net
Rev.: $78,100,000
Emp.: 100
Printed Circuit Boards
N.A.I.C.S.: 334412

Subsidiaries:

AVG-LTI LP   (1)

363 St Paul Blvd, Carol Stream, IL 60188
Tel.: (630) 668-8886
Web Site: http://www.avg.net
Sales Range: $1-9.9 Million
Emp.: 30
Electronic Circuits
N.A.I.C.S.: 334419

Autotech Tech Limited
Partnership   (1)
363 St Paul Blvd, Carol Stream, IL 60188
Tel.: (630) 668-3900
Web Site: http://www.avg.net
Sales Range: $25-49.9 Million
Switches & Electronic Applications Mfr
N.A.I.C.S.: 334419

AVI FOODSYSTEMS INC.

2590 Elm Rd NE, Warren, OH 44483
Tel.: (330) 372-6000   OH
Web Site:
  https://www.avifoodsystems.com
Year Founded: 1960
Sales Range: $150-199.9 Million
Emp.: 2,000
Food Service
N.A.I.C.S.: 445132
John Payiavlas *(Founder)*
Jane Ferguson *(Dir-Resident)*
Jen Chesser *(Mgr-Ops)*
Mary Pasternak *(Dir-Admin)*
Sandy Gray *(Dir-HR)*
Tammy Esquivel *(Mgr-Retail)*
Terry Nichols *(Mgr-Ops)*
Keith McDonald *(Mgr-Benefits)*
Douglas Stoll *(VP-Procurement)*
Neal Rupert *(Dir-Creative)*

AVI PARTNERS, LLC

555 E Lancaster Ave Ste 520, Radnor, PA 19087
Tel.: (610) 816-6660
Web Site: http://www.avipartners.com
Private Investment Firm
N.A.I.C.S.: 523999
Darren Wallis *(Mng Partner)*
Jay Dunn *(Mng Partner)*

AVI SYSTEMS, INC.

9675 W 76th St Ste 200, Eden Prairie, MN 55344
Tel.: (952) 949-3700   ND
Web Site: http://www.avisys.com
Year Founded: 1979
Rev.: $96,603,000
Emp.: 134
Audio Visual & Communications Support Services
N.A.I.C.S.: 561499
Michael Fornander *(VP-Northwest Area)*
Jeff Stoebner *(Pres & CEO)*
Brad Sousa *(CTO)*
Joe Stoebner *(Founder & Chm)*
Christopher Mounts *(CFO)*
Joel Lehman *(COO)*
Bill Smith *(Reg Mgr-Fin)*

Subsidiaries:

AVI Systems Company   (1)
1930 E Century Ave, Bismarck, ND 58503
Tel.: (701) 258-6360
Web Site: http://www.avisys.com
Sales Range: $10-24.9 Million
Emp.: 20
Equipment Rental & Leasing Services
N.A.I.C.S.: 532210
Jeff Stoebner *(Pres & CEO)*

Neurilink LLC   (1)
623 S Americana Blvd, Boise, ID 83702-6732
Tel.: (208) 426-8238
Web Site: http://www.neurilink.com
Audio & Video Equipment Mfr
N.A.I.C.S.: 334310
Michael Fornander *(Founder)*

AVIAN ENGINEERING, LLC

22111 3 Notch Rd, Lexington Park, MD 20653
Tel.: (301) 866-2070
Web Site: http://www.avianllc.com
Year Founded: 2005
Sales Range: $1-9.9 Million
Emp.: 90
Technical Consultation & Acquisition Services to the Department of Defense & the Commercial Market
N.A.I.C.S.: 541690
Jeff Sherman *(Co-Founder & Pres)*
Kevin Switick *(Acting CEO & VP-Pro Svcs)*
Jeffrey M. Danielson *(Dir-Test & Evaluation)*
John Slaughter *(VP-Bus Dev)*

AVIAN ENTERPRISES, LLC

221 Ocean Grande Blvd Ste 801, Jupiter, FL 33477
Web Site:
  https://www.aviancontrolinc.com
Bird Repellant Mfr
N.A.I.C.S.: 325998
Jon Stone *(Pres)*
Steven Stone *(Exec VP)*
Kenneth Stone *(VP)*
Dan Kramer *(Dir-Technical)*
Jacqueline Elchemmas *(Office Mgr)*
Lisette Thomas *(Mgr-Accts Receivable)*

AVIATECH CORPORATION

104 Lindbergh Dr, Roanoke, TX 76762
Tel.: (817) 430-4784
Web Site:
  https://www.aviatechcorp.com
Year Founded: 1970
Sales Range: $10-24.9 Million
Emp.: 6
Transportation Equipment & Supplies Whslr
N.A.I.C.S.: 423860
Patrick Carr *(Mgr)*

AVIATION CHARTER INC.

9960 Flying Cloud Dr, Eden Prairie, MN 55347
Tel.: (952) 943-1519
Web Site: http://www.aviation-charter.com
Year Founded: 1982
Sales Range: $10-24.9 Million
Emp.: 80
Charter Services
N.A.I.C.S.: 481219
Shirley Wikner *(Pres)*
Kirk Otteson *(Dir-Ops)*

AVIATION FACILITIES COM-PANY, INC.

45025 Aviation Dr Ste 100, Dulles, VA 20166
Tel.: (703) 902-2900
Web Site: http://www.afcoinc.com
Year Founded: 1990
Sales Range: $10-24.9 Million
Emp.: 20
Air Cargo Property Management & Development Services
N.A.I.C.S.: 531210
Daniel S. Ungerleider *(CFO & Exec VP)*
Charles V. Stipancic *(Pres & CEO)*
Suzanne L. Smith *(VP-Acctg & Admin)*
Kimberly Maddox *(VP-HR)*
Steve R. Forrer *(Chief Investment Officer & Exec VP)*
Alan Kral *(COO & Exec VP)*
John A. Northcott Jr. *(VP-Facilities)*

Subsidiaries:

AFCO Global Ports LLC   (1)

7600 Colshire Dr Ste 240, McLean, VA 22102
Tel.: (703) 902-2900
Web Site: http://www.afcoinc.com
Rev.: $840,000
Emp.: 5
Land Subdividers & Developers, Commercial
N.A.I.C.S.: 237210

AVIATION INVENTORY RE-SOURCES, INC.

12240 E FM Rd 917, Alvarado, TX 76009
Tel.: (817) 672-0060
Web Site: http://www.avinvres.com
Year Founded: 1999
Deep Sea Freight Transportation
N.A.I.C.S.: 483111
Paul Wahlstrom *(Owner)*

AVIATION LABORATORIES, INC.

5401 Mitchelldale St Ste B6, Houston, TX 77092
Tel.: (713) 864-6677
Web Site: https://www.avlab.com
Year Founded: 1985
Sales Range: $10-24.9 Million
Emp.: 45
Transportation Equipment & Supplies Whslr
N.A.I.C.S.: 423860
Wayne Odegard *(Gen Mgr & VP)*
Scott Hitterman *(Acct Mgr)*

AVIATION MINING SOLU-TIONS, INC.

170 S William Dillard Dr Ste -100, Gilbert, AZ 85233
Tel.: (480) 878-4230   DE
Year Founded: 2018
Emp.: 10
Aircraft Parts Distr
N.A.I.C.S.: 423860
John Hudnall *(CEO)*
Adam Fraser *(Pres & COO)*
Martha Jefferson *(Treas & Sec)*

AVIATION SPARES & SER-VICES INTERNATIONAL CO.

8920 152nd Ave NE, Redmond, WA 98052
Tel.: (425) 869-7799
Web Site: https://www.assic.com
Sales Range: $10-24.9 Million
Emp.: 11
Aircraft Equipment & Supplies Distr
N.A.I.C.S.: 423860
Zine A. Badissy *(Chm & CEO)*

AVICOM MARKETING COMMU-NICATIONS

2120 Pewaukee Rd Ste 200, Waukesha, WI 53188
Tel.: (262) 547-8000
Year Founded: 2001
Sales Range: $10-24.9 Million
Emp.: 15
Advertising Agencies
N.A.I.C.S.: 541810
Tim Kubina *(Pres)*
Tom Scheel *(Dir-Promos)*

Subsidiaries:

Avicom Marketing
Communications   (1)
150 River Rd Unit I-1, Montville, NJ 07045
Tel.: (973) 257-3500
Sales Range: $10-24.9 Million
Emp.: 2
Advertising Agencies
N.A.I.C.S.: 541810

AVID CENTER

9797 Aero Dr Ste 100, San Diego, CA 92123

Tel.: (858) 380-4800   CA
Web Site: https://www.avid.org
Year Founded: 1992
Sales Range: $25-49.9 Million
Emp.: 782
Educational Support Services
N.A.I.C.S.: 611710
Michelle Mullen (Exec VP-Curriculum & Learning)
Sandy Husk (CEO)
Steve Silberman (Exec VP)
Edward Lee Vargas (Exec VP)
Mary Catherine Swanson (Founder)
Stephen Weber (Chm)
Matt Gianneschi (Vice Chm)
Thuan Nguyen (Exec VP)
Kenn Young (Chief Div Support Officer)

AVID TECHNICAL RESOURCES, INC.

185 Devonshire St Ste 100, Boston, MA 02110
Tel.: (617) 951-1880
Web Site: https://www.avidtr.com
Year Founded: 2003
Sales Range: $10-24.9 Million
Emp.: 24
Staffing & IT Services
N.A.I.C.S.: 541612
Brian Tomasello (Founder & Partner)
John-Paul Treacy (Co-Founder)
Chip Kakas (VP-Sls)

AVIDIAN TECHNOLOGIES, INC.

3633 136th Pl SE Ste 107, Bellevue, WA 98006
Tel.: (206) 686-3001
Web Site: http://www.avidian.com
Year Founded: 2002
Sales Range: $1-9.9 Million
Emp.: 25
CRM Software
N.A.I.C.S.: 513210
James Wong (Founder & Chm)
Roger Johnson (Acct Mgr)
Keith Clements (CEO)
Rose Glitschka (Mgr-Support Svcs)
Mark Johnson (Acct Exec)
David Archer (Chief Sls Officer)
Dennis Sanchez (Acct Exec)
Donnita Weese (Acct Exec)
Kaye Weese (Acct Exec)
Melissa Bay (CFO)
Amanda Gardner (Project Mgr)
Chantelle Wilkins (Project Mgr)
Shelly McNaught (Project Mgr)
Matt Cannard (VP-Mktg)
Eric Bolstad (VP-Software Dev)

AVIDIAN WEALTH SOLUTIONS, LLC

CityCentre One 800 Town & Country Blvd Ste 220, Houston, TX
Tel.: (281) 572-5770   TX
Web Site: https://avidianwealth.com
Year Founded: 2002
Financial Services
N.A.I.C.S.: 523999
Luke Patterson (CEO & Chief Investment Officer)

Subsidiaries:

Stone Asset Management, Inc. (1)
703 W 19th St, Austin, TX 78701
Tel.: (512) 469-9152
Web Site: http://www.stoneasset.com
Investment Advice
N.A.I.C.S.: 523940
Morgan Stone (Founder & Pres)

AVILA CONSTRUCTION COMPANY INC

912 Bordentown Rd, Columbus, NJ 08022

Tel.: (609) 298-7540
Rev.: $12,632,953
Emp.: 15
Nonresidential Construction
N.A.I.C.S.: 236220
Louis Rivera (VP)

AVILA'S GARDEN ART

14608 Merrill Ave, Fontana, CA 92335
Tel.: (909) 350-4546
Web Site:
   http://www.avilasgardenart.com
Year Founded: 1980
Sales Range: $10-24.9 Million
Emp.: 121
Garden Precast Concrete Mfr
N.A.I.C.S.: 327390
Lawrence Avila (Pres)

AVINEON, INC.

4825 Mark Ctr Dr Ste 700, Alexandria, VA 22311
Tel.: (703) 671-1900
Web Site: http://www.avineon.com
Sales Range: $300-349.9 Million
Emp.: 1,200
Holding Company; Information Technology, Geospatial & Engineering Services
N.A.I.C.S.: 551112
Karlu Rambhala (Pres & CEO)
Heesun Robertson (COO)
Eric Martin (VP-Federal Sys)
Joel Campbell (VP-Comml Sys)

Subsidiaries:

Avineon India Private Limited (1)
Block A 1st floorCyber Gateway, Madhapur, Hyderabad, 500 081, India
Tel.: (91) 4066632452
Web Site: http://www.avineonindia.com
Sales Range: $250-299.9 Million
Emp.: 1,000
Information Technology, Geospatial & Engineering Services
N.A.I.C.S.: 541519
Raghu Ganeshan (Pres)

North Point Geographic
Solutions (1)
31 W Superior St Ste 100D, Duluth, MN 55802
Tel.: (218) 720-6747
Web Site: http://www.northpointgis.com
Environmental Consulting Services
N.A.I.C.S.: 541620
Jesse Adams (Principal)

AVINS INDUSTRIAL PRODUCTS CORPORATION

2 N Rd, Warren, NJ 07059
Tel.: (732) 469-8800
Web Site: http://www.avins.com
Sales Range: $10-24.9 Million
Emp.: 13
Nonferrous Metal Sheets, Bars & Rods
N.A.I.C.S.: 423510
Mark Boyce (Mgr-Sls)

AVIO GLOBAL, INC.

8525 120th Ave NE Ste 300, Kirkland, WA 98033
Tel.: (425) 739-6800   DE
Web Site:
   http://www.aviosupport.com
Sales Range: $10-24.9 Million
Holding Company; Aircraft Spare Parts Mfr & Whslr
N.A.I.C.S.: 551112
Gordon Kirkland (CEO)
Anne Pernaa (Mgr-Accts)

Subsidiaries:

Aviosupport, Inc. (1)
8525 120th Ave NE 3rd Fl, Kirkland, WA 98033
Tel.: (425) 739-6800

Web Site: http://www.aviosupport.com
Sales Range: $10-24.9 Million
Aircraft Parts Mfr & Distr
N.A.I.C.S.: 336413
Gordon Kirkland (CEO)
Ken Kirkland (Pres)

Gemini Management Ltd. (1)
8525 120th Ave NE, Kirkland, WA 98033
Tel.: (425) 739-6800
Emp.: 25
Aircraft Parts & Equipment Engineering Services
N.A.I.C.S.: 541330
Gordon Kirkland (CEO)

Spectralux Corporation (1)
12335 134th Ct NE, Redmond, WA 98052
Tel.: (425) 285-3000
Web Site: http://www.spectralux.com
Aerospace Electronics Equipment Developer & Mfr
N.A.I.C.S.: 336413
Scott McCammant (Pres)
Brian Brooks (Dir-Ops)
Tom Henderson (Dir-Sls & Mktg)
Frank Hummel (Dir-Engrg)
Fred Anderson (CFO)

AVION SOLUTIONS, INC.

4905 Research Dr NW, Huntsville, AL 35805
Tel.: (256) 721-7006
Web Site: https://avionsolutions.com
Emp.: 100
Aerospace Engineering, Software Development & Programming Services
N.A.I.C.S.: 334511
Evan Wagner (Pres & CEO)

Subsidiaries:

Synectic Research & Analysis, Inc. (1)
6700 Odyssey Dr NW, Huntsville, AL 35806
Tel.: (256) 705-8820
Web Site: http://sra-hsv.com
Sales Range: $1-9.9 Million
Emp.: 25
Steel Investment Foundries
N.A.I.C.S.: 331512
Jonathan Hall (Controller)
Leonard Williams (Engr-Optical)

AVIONTE

1270 Eagan Industrial Rd Ste 150, Eagan, MN 55121
Tel.: (651) 556-2121
Web Site: http://www.avionte.com
Year Founded: 2006
Sales Range: $1-9.9 Million
Emp.: 140
Staffing Software Development Services
N.A.I.C.S.: 541511
John Long (Founder & Co-Chm)
Jason Ortner (VP-Sls-West)
Mike Scoville (VP-Sls-Midwest & Northeast)
Brenda Long (Dir-Mktg)
Jami Timmons (VP-Product Mgmt)
Kevin Frick (Co-Chm)
Andy Zark (Chief Revenue Officer)
Rishabh Mehrotra (CEO)
Christopher Ryan (Chief Strategy & Mktg Officer)
Chris Johnson (VP-Professional Svcs)

AVIS FORD INC.

29200 Telegraph Rd, Southfield, MI 48034-7602
Tel.: (248) 355-7500   MI
Web Site: https://www.avisford.com
Year Founded: 1946
Sales Range: $100-124.9 Million
Emp.: 150
Sales of Automobiles
N.A.I.C.S.: 441110
James Witmer (Gen Mgr)
Mark A. Douglas (Pres)
Natalie Farrell (Office Mgr)

AVIS INDUSTRIAL CORPORATION

1909 S Main St, Upland, IN 46989
Tel.: (765) 998-8100   IN
Web Site:
   https://www.avisindustrial.com
Year Founded: 1959
Sales Range: $75-99.9 Million
Emp.: 1,200
Mfr of Industrial & Automotive Locks, Industrial Steel Tubing, Machine Tools, Miscellaneous Automotive Parts & Forgings
N.A.I.C.S.: 332510
Leland E. Boren (CEO)
Gregory L. King (Pres & CEO)

Subsidiaries:

AI International, Inc. (1)
8055A National Tpke, Louisville, KY 40214
Tel.: (502) 873-4575
Web Site: http://www.avisindustrial.com
Emp.: 50
Construction Engineering Services
N.A.I.C.S.: 541330
Troy Grant (Project Mgr)
John Senninger (Acct Mgr)

American Baler Company (1)
800 E Center St, Bellevue, OH 44811-0029   (100%)
Tel.: (419) 483-5790
Web Site: http://www.americanbaler.com
Sales Range: $10-24.9 Million
Emp.: 60
Baling Equipment Mfr
N.A.I.C.S.: 333998
Carmen Loparo (Mgr-Customer Svcs)

Crankshaft Machine Company (1)
314 N Jackson St, Jackson, MI 49201
Tel.: (517) 787-3791
Web Site: http://www.crankshaft.net
Sales Range: $10-24.9 Million
Emp.: 30
Designer & Builder of Special Purpose Machine Tools; Designer & Installer of Flexible Turn-Key Systems
N.A.I.C.S.: 333517
Kevin Glaspie (Mgr-Svc)

Division (Domestic):

U.S. Broach & Machine
Company (2)
314 N Jackson St, Jackson, MI 49201
Tel.: (517) 841-4062
Web Site: http://www.crankshaft.net
Mfr of Vertical Broaching Machines
N.A.I.C.S.: 333517
Greg little (Pres)

Cumsa Corp. (1)
4656 Towerwood Dr, Brownsville, TX 78521
Tel.: (956) 838-2480
Web Site: http://www.lockcraftproducts.com
Electrical & Automotive Security Product Mfr
N.A.I.C.S.: 335999
Francisco Hinojosa (Mgr-Sls)

Edgerton Forge, Inc. (1)
257 E Morrison St, Edgerton, OH 43517-9302
Tel.: (419) 298-2333
Web Site: http://www.edgertonforge.com
Sales Range: $10-24.9 Million
Emp.: 60
Forged Products Mfr
N.A.I.C.S.: 332111
Pam Fitzcharles (Controller)

James Steel & Tube Company (1)
29774 Stephenson Hwy, Madison Heights, MI 48071   (100%)
Tel.: (248) 547-4200
Web Site: http://www.jamessteel.com
Sales Range: $25-49.9 Million
Emp.: 33
Mfr of Cold Formed Welded Structural Tubing
N.A.I.C.S.: 331210
Jim Petkus (Pres)

Pacific Forge, Inc. (1)
10641 Etiwanda Ave, Fontana, CA 92337-6909
Tel.: (909) 390-0701

Avis Industrial Corporation—(Continued)

Web Site: http://www.pacificforge.com
Sales Range: $10-24.9 Million
Emp.: 50
Mfr of High Quality Forgings for the Aircraft, Chemical, Nuclear, Ordnance, Orthopedic Implant & Petroleum Industries
N.A.I.C.S.: 332111
Jacqualine Dyer *(Controller)*
Cesar Gervas *(Engr-Maintenance)*

Peninsular Cylinder Co., **(1)**
27650 Groesbeck Hwy, Roseville, MI 48066
Tel.: (586) 775-7211
Web Site:
  http://www.peninsularcylinders.com
Air & Hydraulic Cylinder Mfr
N.A.I.C.S.: 333995
Richard Haver *(Plant Mgr-Second Shift)*

Sellick Equipment Limited **(1)**
358 Erie Street North, PO Box 1000, Harrow, N0R 1G0, ON, Canada
Tel.: (519) 738-2255
Web Site: http://www.sellickequipment.com
Emp.: 70
Forklift Mfr
N.A.I.C.S.: 333924
Howard Sellick *(Pres)*

The Pierce Co., Inc. **(1)**
35 N 8th St, Upland, IN 46989
Tel.: (765) 998-2712
Sales Range: $25-49.9 Million
Emp.: 50
Mfr of Engineered Assemblies for the Auto Industry; Formed Wire Products, Engine Speed Controls, Water Pumps, Aftermarket Fuel Pumps & Castings
N.A.I.C.S.: 336390

AVISCO INC.
1005 Clarence Larson Dr, Oak Ridge, TN 37830
Tel.: (865) 689-6383
Web Site: http://www.avisco.com
Sales Range: $10-24.9 Million
Emp.: 60
Toxic Or Hazardous Waste Cleanup
N.A.I.C.S.: 562910
Avis A. Phillips *(Owner & Pres)*
Patricia Ferguson *(Sec)*
Jerry L. Hampton *(VP & Project Mgr)*
Mitch Carpenter *(VP & Mgr-Site Ops)*
Jerry Hanson *(VP)*

AVISENA, INC.
6100 Blue Lagoon Dr Ste 450, Miami, FL 33126
Tel.: (786) 621-4400 FL
Web Site: http://www.avisena.com
Year Founded: 2001
Sales Range: $10-24.9 Million
Emp.: 70
Revenue Cycle Management Solutions for Medical Professionals
N.A.I.C.S.: 524292
Keith Ashley *(VP-Product Dev)*

AVISTA CAPITAL PARTNERS, L.P.
65 E 55th St, New York, NY 10022
Tel.: (212) 593-6900 DE
Web Site: http://www.avistacap.com
Year Founded: 2005
Privater Equity Firm
N.A.I.C.S.: 523999
Thompson Dean *(Co-CEO & Mng Partner)*
David F. Burgstahler *(Co-CEO & Mng Partner)*
Joshua A. Tamaroff *(Principal)*
Amanda Heravi *(Head-IR)*
Robert Girardi *(Partner)*
John Cafasso *(CFO)*
Sriram Venkataraman *(Partner)*
Alex Yu *(Principal)*
Jeremy Konyves *(Controller-Fund)*
Anthony Russo *(Controller)*
Roshni Charles *(Mgr-Tax)*
Hector Cortes *(Controller-Mgmt Company)*

Subsidiaries:

Avista Capital Holdings, L.P. **(1)**
65 E 55th St 18th Fl, New York, NY 10022
Tel.: (212) 593-6900
Web Site: http://www.avistacap.com
Investment Holding Company
N.A.I.C.S.: 551112
Thompson Dean *(Co-CEO & Mng Partner)*
Joshua A. Tamaroff *(VP)*
John Cafasso *(CFO)*
Hector Cortes *(Controller-Mgmt)*
Jeremy Konyves *(Controller-Fund)*
Anthony Russo *(Controller)*

Joint Venture (Non-US):

Acino Holding AG **(2)**
Dornacherstrasse 114, 4147, Aesch, Switzerland
Tel.: (41) 613386000
Web Site: http://www.acino-pharma.com
Sales Range: $10-24.9 Million
Emp.: 836
Holding Company; Pharmaceuticals Mfr
N.A.I.C.S.: 551112
Jean-Daniel Bonny *(Head-R&D)*
Kalle Kand *(Chief Comml Officer)*
Konstantin V. Bakaykin *(Head-Bus Dev)*
Sven Hakan Bjorklund *(Chm)*
Toni Weitzberg *(Vice Chm)*
Geir Myklebust *(Head-Projects, Process Improvement & IT)*
Barthold Piening *(COO)*
Christina Roelli Schwethelm *(Chief HR Officer)*
Christina Peusch *(Chief Legal Officer)*
Ulrike Seminati *(Head-Comm)*

Subsidiary (Domestic):

Acino Pharma AG **(3)**
Birsweg 2, 4253, Liesberg, Switzerland
Tel.: (41) 617758000
Web Site: http://www.acino-pharma.com
Emp.: 350
Pharmaceuticals Product Mfr
N.A.I.C.S.: 325412
Kalle Kand *(Mng Dir)*

Acino Supply AG **(3)**
Pfeffingerring 205, 4147, Aesch, Switzerland
Tel.: (41) 61 756 40 00
Pharmaceutical Products Distr
N.A.I.C.S.: 424210

Holding (Domestic):

Anthony International, Inc. **(2)**
12391 Montero Ave, Sylmar, CA 91342
Tel.: (818) 365-9451
Web Site: http://www.anthonyintl.com
Sales Range: $125-149.9 Million
Mfr of Commercial Glass Refrigerator & Freezer Doors, Frames, Lighting Systems & Related Accessories
N.A.I.C.S.: 327215
Greg Little *(Pres)*

Joint Venture (Domestic):

ConvaTec Ltd. **(2)**
Centerpointe II 1160 Route 22 E Ste 201, Bridgewater, NJ 08807
Tel.: (908) 231-2179
Web Site: http://www.convatec.com
Sales Range: $1-4.9 Billion
Medicinal Product Mfr
N.A.I.C.S.: 339112
Supratim Bose *(Pres-APAC & Exec VP)*
Kjersti Grimsrud *(Pres-EMEA)*
George Poole *(Pres-Americas)*
Frank Gehres *(Pres-Continence & Critical Care)*
John Lindskog *(Pres-B2B & Infusion Devices)*
David Shepherd *(Pres-Advanced Wound Care)*
Sean McGrath *(Exec VP-HR)*
Adam Deutsch *(Gen Counsel & Exec VP)*
Robert Steele *(Exec VP-Quality, Regulatory & Clinical Affairs)*
Donal Balfe *(Exec VP-Ops-Global)*
Steve Holliday *(Deputy Chm)*
Frank Schulkes *(CFO)*

Subsidiary (Domestic):

180 Medical, Inc. **(3)**

8516 NW Expy, Oklahoma City, OK 73162
Tel.: (405) 702-7700
Web Site: https://www.180medical.com
Medical, Dental & Hospital Equipment & Supplies Merchant Whslr
N.A.I.C.S.: 423450
Todd Brown *(Founder & CEO)*

Holding (Domestic):

GCM Holding Corporation **(2)**
1350 Atlantic St, Union City, CA 94587
Tel.: (510) 475-0404
Web Site: http://www.gogcm.com
High Precision Components & Assemblies Mfr
N.A.I.C.S.: 332311
Seamus Meagher *(Pres)*

Subsidiary (Domestic):

GCM Medical & OEM, Inc. **(3)**
1350 Atlantic St, Union City, CA 94587
Tel.: (510) 475-0404
Web Site: http://www.gcmfg.com
Sales Range: $1-9.9 Million
Engineering, Manufacturing & Assembly Services
N.A.I.C.S.: 339999
Seamus Meagher *(Pres & Principal)*

Holding (Domestic):

InvestorPlace Media, LLC **(2)**
9201 Corporate Blvd, Rockville, MD 20850
Tel.: (301) 250-2201
Web Site: http://www.investorplace.com
Publisher of Investment Advisory Information Targeted to Individual Investors
N.A.I.C.S.: 513199

Kramer Laboratories, Inc. **(2)**
440 US Hwy 22 Ste 210, Bridgewater, NJ 08807
Web Site: http://www.kramerlabs.com
Drugs & Druggists' Sundries Merchant Whslr
N.A.I.C.S.: 424210

Lantheus Holdings, Inc. **(2)**
201 Burlington Rd S Bldg, Bedford, MA 01730
Tel.: (978) 671-8001
Web Site: https://www.lantheus.com
Rev.: $1,296,429,000
Assets: $1,651,149,000
Liabilities: $835,257,000
Net Worth: $815,892,000
Earnings: $326,661,000
Emp.: 834
Fiscal Year-end: 12/31/2023
Holding Company; Diagnostic Medical Imaging Agents & Products
N.A.I.C.S.: 551112
Brian A. Markison *(CEO)*
Robert J. Marshall Jr. *(CFO & Treas)*
Carol Walker *(Sr VP-Quality)*
Jeffrey S. Humphrey *(Chief Medical Officer)*
Linda Lennox *(VP-Corp Comm)*
Mark Kinarney *(VP-IR)*
Melissa Downs *(Sr Dir-Corp Comm)*
Daniel M. Niedzwiecki *(Chief Admin Officer, Gen Counsel & Sec)*
Dorothy Barr *(Sr VP-Mfg & Tech Ops)*
Jean-Claude Provost *(Chief Science Officer)*
Paul Blanchfield *(Pres)*
Amanda Morgan *(Chief Comml Officer & Sr VP)*
Jamie Spaeth *(Chief People Officer)*
Cheryl Ball *(Sr VP-Strategy & Enterprise Plng)*
Lee Anne Howe *(CIO)*
Joann Nestor *(Sr VP-Legal Affairs)*
Kimberly Brown *(Chief Acctg Officer)*
Andrea Sabens *(VP-Bus Optimization)*

Subsidiary (Non-US):

EXINI Diagnostics AB **(3)**
Ideon Science Park Scheelevagen 27, 223 70, Lund, Sweden
Tel.: (46) 462865420
Web Site: http://www.exini.com
Medical Image Analysis Software Services
N.A.I.C.S.: 513210
Jens Richter *(Dir-Machine Learning)*

Subsidiary (Domestic):

Lantheus Medical Imaging, Inc. **(3)**

331 Treble Cove Rd, North Billerica, MA 01862
Tel.: (978) 671-8001
Web Site: http://www.lantheus.com
Sales Range: $250-299.9 Million
Emp.: 519
Medical Imaging Products
N.A.I.C.S.: 339112
John K. Bakewell *(CFO)*
Robert J. Marshall Jr. *(CFO & Treas)*
William Dawes *(VP-Mfg & Ops)*
Michael P. Duffy *(Gen Counsel, Sr VP-Bus Dev & Strategy)*
Simon Robinson *(VP-Res & Pharmaceutical Dev)*
Cyrille Villeneuve *(VP-Intl)*
Cesare Orlandi *(Chief Medical Officer)*
Carol Walker *(VP-Quality)*
Joyce G. Leger *(Dir-HR)*
Etienne Montagut *(Sr VP-Corp Dev)*
John Bolla *(Sr VP-Technical Ops)*
Sarah Le Roy *(Sr VP-HR)*
Mark Kinarney *(Dir-IR)*

Progenics Pharmaceuticals, Inc. **(3)**
One World Trade Ctr 47th Fl Ste J, New York, NY 10007
Tel.: (646) 975-2500
Sales Range: $25-49.9 Million
Pharmaceuticals Mfr
N.A.I.C.S.: 325412
Jinti Peters *(Mgr-Clinical Data)*

Holding (Domestic):

National Spine & Pain Centers, LLC **(2)**
11921 Rockville Pike Ste 505, Rockville, MD 20852
Tel.: (301) 945-5111
Web Site: http://www.treatingpain.com
Spine & Specialty Health Care Services
N.A.I.C.S.: 621111
Marc Loev *(Co-Founder)*
Douglas W. Wisor *(Interim CEO & Pres)*
Les A. Zuckerman *(Co-Founder)*
Assaf T. Gordon *(Dir-Clinical Outcomes & Informatics)*
Peter S. Staats *(Chief Medical Officer)*
Amy J. Dilcher *(Gen Counsel & VP)*
Carol Drescher *(Dir-Clinical Quality & Education)*
Jody Walker *(Dir-Clinical Pharmacology)*

Subsidiary (Domestic):

Probo Medical, LLC **(2)**
9715 Kincaid Dr Ste 100, Fishers, IN 46037
Tel.: (317) 759-9210
Web Site: https://www.probomedical.com
Ultrasound Transducers & Stock Systems
N.A.I.C.S.: 423450
Michael Asmer *(CEO)*
Jay Burkhardt *(COO)*

Subsidiary (Domestic):

Medical Equipment Technologies, Inc. **(3)**
2172 NW Reserve Pk Trce, Port Saint Lucie, FL 34986
Tel.: (772) 460-0122
Web Site: http://www.remetronix.com
Medical, Dental & Hospital Equipment & Supplies Merchant Whslr
N.A.I.C.S.: 423450
Russell Knowles *(Pres & CEO)*
Nick Giallanzo *(VP & COO)*

National Ultrasound, Inc. **(3)**
2730 N Berkeley Lake Rd Ste B-400, Duluth, GA 30096
Tel.: (770) 551-8797
Web Site:
  http://www.nationalultrasound.com
Measuring & Controlling Devices Mfr
N.A.I.C.S.: 334510
Chris Williams *(CIO, CMO & Exec VP)*
Joe Lorren Wiliams *(Pres)*
Ivis Kamack *(Mgr-Sls-Latin America)*

SonoDepot, Inc. **(3)**
8 E 12th St, Saint Cloud, FL 34769
Tel.: (407) 892-5577
Web Site: http://www.sonodepot.com
Sales Range: $1-9.9 Million
Emp.: 18
Diagnostic Imaging Services
N.A.I.C.S.: 621512

Floyd McAuliffe *(Pres)*
Jack McAuliffe *(CEO)*

Tenvision, LLC (3)
1121 Gregory Dr, Gallatin, TN 37066-4910
Tel.: (615) 452-9770
Web Site: http://www.tenvisionllc.com
Medical, Dental & Hospital Equipment &
Supplies Merchant Whslr
N.A.I.C.S.: 423450
Kevin Gregory *(Pres)*

Trisonics, Inc. (3)
3535 Walnut St., Harrisburg, PA 17109
Tel.: (717) 759-9210
Ultrasound Medical Equipment Provider
N.A.I.C.S.: 621511

Holding (Domestic):

eMolecules, Inc. (2)
3430 Carmel Mountain Rd Ste 250, 92121,
San Diego, CA
Tel.: (858) 764-1941
Web Site: https://www.emolecules.com
Emp.: 100
Chemistry Search & Fulfillment Platform
N.A.I.C.S.: 541511
Niko Gubernator *(Pres & CEO)*

Subsidiary (Domestic):

Frontier Scientific, Inc. (3)
195 S 700 W, Logan, UT 84321-5023
Tel.: (435) 753-1901
Web Site: http://www.frontiersci.com
Contract Research Services
N.A.I.C.S.: 541715
Bert Israelsen *(COO)*
W. Tim Miller *(Pres & CEO)*
Charles Testa *(VP-R&D)*
Jerry Bommer *(VP-Porphyrin Res)*
Neil Jones *(Controller & Dir-HR)*
Mark Nelson *(Dir-Science & Bus Dev)*

Subsidiary (Domestic):

Echelon Biosciences Inc (4)
675 Arapeen Dr Ste 302, Salt Lake City, UT
84108
Tel.: (801) 588-0455
Web Site: http://www.echelon-inc.com
Sales Range: $10-24.9 Million
Emp.: 20
Commercial Physical & Biological Research
N.A.I.C.S.: 541714
Tim Miller *(Pres & CEO)*

Frontier Scientific Services, Inc. (4)
601 Interchange Blvd, Newark, DE 19711
Tel.: (302) 266-6891
Web Site: http://www.frontierssi.com
Sales Range: $10-24.9 Million
Emp.: 32
Chemicals Mfr
N.A.I.C.S.: 325998
W. Tim Miller *(Pres & CEO)*
Bert Israelsen *(COO)*
Kabana Perkins *(Sr VP & Gen Mgr)*
Neil Jones *(Controller & Dir-HR)*
Mark Nelson *(VP-Bus & Science Dev)*
Rick Hammar *(Sls Mgr-Global)*

Solmetex, LLC (1)
4 Mount Royal Ave Ste 4-250, Marlborough,
MA 01752
Tel.: (508) 393-1795
Web Site: https://solmetex.com
Emp.: 100
Medical Equipment Mfr
N.A.I.C.S.: 339112
Gene Dorff *(CEO)*
Nick Mozzicato *(Founder)*
Lauren Nagel *(COO)*

Subsidiary (Domestic):

Impladent, Ltd. (2)
19845 Foothill Ave, Jamaica, NY 11423
Tel.: (718) 465-1810
Web Site: http://www.impladentltd.com
Sales Range: $1-9.9 Million
Emp.: 20
Dental Equipment & Supplies Mfr
N.A.I.C.S.: 339114
Gisele Sasson *(Sec)*
Maurice Valen *(CEO & Founder)*

Sterisil, Inc. (2)
835 S Highway 105 Unit B, Palmer Lake,
CO 80133-9069

Tel.: (719) 481-0937
Web Site: http://www.sterisil.com
Rev.: $1,000,000
Emp.: 7
Commercial & Service Industry Machinery
Mfr
N.A.I.C.S.: 333310
Brad Downs *(CEO)*
Leah Light *(Office Mgr)*
Reid Cowan *(Coord-Sls-East Reg)*

Spear Education, LLC (1)
7201 E Princess Blvd, Scottsdale, AZ
85255
Tel.: (866) 781-0072
Web Site: http://www.speareducation.com
Education Services
N.A.I.C.S.: 923110
Imtiaz Manji *(Chm)*
Kaleim Manji *(CEO)*

**United BioSource Corporation
LLC** (1)
920 Harvest Dr, Blue Bell, PA
19422 (100%)
Tel.: (215) 591-2880
Web Site: http://www.ubc.com
Pharmaceutical Support Services With Au-
tomated Clinical Trial Management Systems
Using Voice Response (IVR) & Web-Based
Technologies
N.A.I.C.S.: 541519
Annette Stemhagen *(Sr VP-Chief Scientific
Officer)*
Patrick Lindsay *(Pres & CEO)*
Brett Huselton *(Sr VP & Head-Global Bus
Dev)*
Nicole Hebbert *(Sr VP & Head-Patient
Scvs)*
Sallyanne Williams *(Sr VP & Head-Global
Late Stage Svcs)*
Rich Hamel *(Sr VP & CFO)*
A.K. Gupta *(Sr VP & CIO)*
Lakshana Pujar *(Sr VP & Chief HR Officer)*
Jeff Ramage *(Sr VP & Gen Counsel)*

Subsidiary (Non-US):

**United BioSource (Germany)
GmbH** (2)
Wallbrunnstrasse 24, Lorrach, 79539, Ger-
many
Tel.: (49) 7621 98 67 00 0
Web Site: http://www.ubc.com
Emp.: 13
Automated Clinical Trial Management Sys-
tems Using Voice Response (IVR) & Web-
Based Technologies
N.A.I.C.S.: 541519

United BioSource (Suisse) SA (2)
16 Chemin des Coquelicots, 1214, Vernier,
Switzerland
Tel.: (41) 22 596 4444
Web Site: http://www.ubc.com
Emp.: 120
Pharmaceutical Support Services With Au-
tomated Clinical Trial Management Systems
Using Voice Response (IVR) & Web-Based
Technologies
N.A.I.C.S.: 541519
Veronique Basch *(Exec Dir-
Pharmacovigilance-Global)*

**United BioSource Holding (UK)
Limited** (2)
26-28 Hammersmith Grove, London, W6
7HA, United Kingdom
Tel.: (44) 20 8834 0100
Web Site: http://www.ubc.com
Emp.: 50
Pharmaceutical & Medicine Mfr
N.A.I.C.S.: 325412
Jess Sohal *(Exec Dir)*

**WellSpring Pharmaceutical
Corporation** (1)
5911 N Honore Ave Ste 211, Sarasota, FL
34243
Tel.: (844) 241-5454
Web Site: http://www.wellspringpharm.com
Pharmaceuticals Mfr
N.A.I.C.S.: 325412
Robert A. Vukovich *(Founder)*
Chris Brown *(CEO)*

**AVISTO CAPITAL PARTNERS,
LLC**

800 Isom Rd Ste 101, San Antonio,
TX 78216
Tel.: (210) 340-5900
Web Site: https://www.avistocap.com
Year Founded: 2005
Holding Company
N.A.I.C.S.: 551112

Subsidiaries:

PetroLedger LLC (1)
800 Isom Rd Ste 101, San Antonio, TX
78216
Tel.: (210) 340-5900
Web Site: https://www.petro-ledger.com
Oil & Gas Accounting & Transaction Ser-
vices
N.A.I.C.S.: 541219

Subsidiary (Domestic):

Associated Resources, Inc. (2)
5925 N Robinson Ave, Oklahoma City, OK
73118
Tel.: (918) 584-2111
Web Site: https://www.associated-
resources.com
Support Activities for Oil & Gas Operations
N.A.I.C.S.: 213112
Bill Harwell *(VP)*
Jeffrey Myers *(Pres)*

AVITA HEALTH SYSTEM
269 Portland Way S, Galion, OH
44833
Tel.: (419) 468-4841 OH
Web Site: https://www.avitahealth.org
Year Founded: 2011
Sales Range: $25-49.9 Million
Emp.: 210
Health Care Srvices
N.A.I.C.S.: 622110

AVITAS INC.
14520 Avion Pkwy Ste 300, Chantilly,
VA 20151-1114
Tel.: (703) 476-2300
Web Site: https://www.avitas.com
Year Founded: 1985
Sales Range: $10-24.9 Million
Emp.: 20
Aviation Consulting Services
N.A.I.C.S.: 541618
John W. Vitale *(Pres & CEO)*
Adam M. Pilarski *(Sr VP)*
Douglas B. Kelly *(Sr VP-Asset Valua-
tion)*
Stephen R. Jarvis *(Mng Dir)*
Chris Moore *(Dir-IT)*
William Whelan *(Sr Dir-Technical
Svcs)*
Tim Scott *(VP-Technical Svcs)*
Michael J. Miller *(VP-Valuation &
Consulting)*

AVITIDE, INC.
16 Cavendish Court, Lebanon, NH
03766
Tel.: (603) 965-2100
Web Site: http://www.avitide.com
Research & Development in Biotech-
nology
N.A.I.C.S.: 541714
Kevin Isett *(Pres & CEO)*
Scott Kennedy *(CFO)*
Karol Lacki *(VP-Tech Dev)*

AVIV CENTERS FOR LIVING
240 Lynnfield St, Peabody, MA 01960
Tel.: (978) 471-5100 MA
Web Site: http://www.avivliving.org
Year Founded: 1944
Sales Range: $10-24.9 Million
Emp.: 399
Elder Care Services
N.A.I.C.S.: 624120
Megin Hemmerling *(Exec Dir-
Assisted Living)*
Terry Halliday *(VP-Sls & Mktg)*
Jeffrey Gopen *(Exec Dir-Skilled Nurs-
ing)*

AVJET CORPORATION
4301 W Empire Ave, Burbank, CA
91505-1109
Tel.: (818) 841-6190 CA
Web Site: http://www.avjet.com
Year Founded: 1979
Sales Range: $200-249.9 Million
Nonscheduled Air Transportation
N.A.I.C.S.: 481219
Marc J. Foulkrod *(Chm & CEO)*
Andrew C. Bradley *(Pres-Global Sls)*
Leslie Cheshier *(VP-Charter Sls)*
Bruce Vogt *(Asst Dir-Maintenance)*
Richard W. Hildenbrand *(Co-Pres)*
William Tice *(Mgr-Boeing Completion)*
Megan Sayer *(Coord-Charter)*
Mark H. Lefever *(Co-Pres & COO)*
Karen M. Velligan *(CFO & VP)*
Gregory L. Wilcox *(Dir-Ops)*
Jeff W. Fritz *(VP-Maintenance Ops)*

Subsidiaries:

Avjet Asia Co., Ltd. (1)
3A-8-1 Office Zone Gimpo Airport Outlet
712-1 Bangwha2-dong, Gangseo-gu, Seoul,
157-854, Korea (South)
Tel.: (82) 2 6343 3092
Aircraft Ground Handling Services
N.A.I.C.S.: 488119
Chan Young Kim *(Pres)*

AVM ASSOCIATES LLC
777 Yamato Rd Ste 300, Boca Raton,
FL 33431
Tel.: (561) 544-4400
Web Site: http://www.avmlp.com
Sales Range: $25-49.9 Million
Emp.: 100
Security Brokers & Dealers
N.A.I.C.S.: 523150
Clifford G. Viner *(Co-Founder, Co-
CIO, Principal & Head-Rates Trading)*
Bob Hart *(Chief Risk Officer)*
Lester N. Coyle *(Co-CIO, Principal &
Portfolio Mgr-Credit)*
Deep Kumar *(Principal & Head-
Options)*
William P. McCauley *(CEO & Princi-
pal)*
Robert Printz *(Principal & Co-Head-
IR)*
Francis Feeney *(Principal & Co-
Head-IR)*
Garth Friesen *(Principal & Head-
Product Dev)*
Scott Wyler *(Gen Counsel & Princi-
pal)*
Thomas Olofsson *(Principal)*
Brandon Pellegrino *(Head-Structured
Credit)*
Jason Prest *(Head-US Rates & Mu-
nis)*
Yelena Anuar *(CFO)*
Mark Perry *(COO)*
Jose Morales *(CTO)*
Jeffrey S. Kidwell *(Dir-AVM Solutions)*
Warren B. Mosler *(Co-Founder)*

AVN CORPORATION
740 Union Carbide Dr, South
Charleston, WV 25303
Tel.: (304) 720-8612
Web Site: https://avncorp.com
Emp.: 100
Research & Development Services
N.A.I.C.S.: 541720
Steven Hedrick *(CEO)*

Subsidiaries:

**Mid-Atlantic Technology, Research &
Innovation Center, Inc.** (1)
3200 Kanawha Tpke Bldg 701, South
Charleston, WV 25303-2544
Web Site: http://www.matricresearch.com
Engineering Services
N.A.I.C.S.: 541330

Avon Plastics, Inc.—(Continued)

AVON PLASTICS, INC.
210 Ampe Dr, Paynesville, MN 56362
Tel.: (320) 243-7318
Web Site:
   https://www.avonplastics.com
Year Founded: 1966
Plastics Processing
N.A.I.C.S.: 326199
Mark Reum (CEO)

AVONDALE CONSULTING
640 N Lasalle Ste 670, Chicago, IL
60654
Tel.: (312) 676-9644
Web Site:
   http://www.avondaleconsulting.com
Sales Range: $1-9.9 Million
Emp.: 10
Financial Investment Advisory Services
N.A.I.C.S.: 523940
Karl Stark (Co-CEO & Mng Dir)
Bill Stewart (Co-CEO & Mng Dir)
Greg Stoklosa (Mng Dir)
Rob Crisp (Co-Founder & Mng Dir)

AVONDALE PARTNERS, LLC
3102 W End Ave Ste 1100, Nashville,
TN 37203-1302
Tel.: (615) 467-3500
Web Site:
   http://www.avondalepartnersllc.com
Year Founded: 2001
Emp.: 84
Investment Banking, Asset Management, Securities Brokerage & Trading Services
N.A.I.C.S.: 523150
Waymon Tipton (Mng Dir & Head-Wealth Mgmt)
Jonathan G. Morphett (Head-Investment Banking)
Joel Oertling (CFO)
David Morris (VP-Private Client Grp-Wealth Mgmt Div)
Richard Sale (Mng Dir-Municipal Bond Trading Dept)
Pat Shepherd (CEO)
Adam Shifrin (Head-Equity Capital Markets)
Philip Krebs (Pres & Sr Mng Partner)
Stephen Scott (Mng Dir-Investment Banking)

Subsidiaries:

Avondale Advisors, LLC   (1)
2 American Ctr 3102 W End Ave Ste 1100,
Nashville, TN 37203
Tel.: (615) 467-3500
Web Site:
   http://www.avondalepartnersllc.com
Emp.: 15
Investment Advisory & Asset Management Services
N.A.I.C.S.: 523940
Waymon Tipton (Mng Dir & Head-Wealth Mgmt)
David Gooch (Mng Dir)
Jim Bass (VP)
Angie Bates (Ops Mgr)
Steven Glasgow (Sr VP)
John Glennon (Mng Dir)
Ben May (Mng Dir)
David Morris (VP)
David Steine Jr. (Mng Dir)

AVONDALE STRATEGIC PARTNERS
640 N LaSalle Dr, Chicago, IL 60654
Tel.: (312) 676-9644
Web Site:
   http://www.avondalepartners.com
Sales Range: $1-9.9 Million
Emp.: 20
Financial Advisory Services
N.A.I.C.S.: 523940

Karl Stark (Co-CEO & Mng Dir)
Rob Crisp (Co-Founder & Mng Dir)
Bill Stewart (Co-CEO & Mng Dir)
Greg Stoklosa (Mng Dir)

AVOW HOSPICE, INC.
1095 B Whippoorwill Ln, Naples, FL
34105
Tel.: (239) 261-4404
Web Site:
   http://www.avowhospice.org
Year Founded: 1983
Sales Range: $10-24.9 Million
Emp.: 230
Hospice Services
N.A.I.C.S.: 621610
Karen Rollins (Pres & CEO)
Paul Mitchell (Chief Medical Officer)
Merrill Boone (CFO)
John Sannuto (VP-Hospice Ops)
Charles Hoffman (Chm)
Lavigne Ann Kirkpatrick (Mgr-External Affairs)

AVR REALTY COMPANY, LLC
1 Executive Blvd, Yonkers, NY 10701
Tel.: (914) 965-3990
Web Site: https://www.avrrealty.com
Sales Range: $10-24.9 Million
Emp.: 120
Commercial Real Estate Services
N.A.I.C.S.: 531120
Allan V. Rose (Pres)
Jeff Gansberg (VP)

Subsidiaries:

Northeast Hotel Associates   (1)
1 Executive Blvd, Yonkers, NY 10701
Tel.: (914) 965-3990
Web Site: http://www.avrrealty.com
Rev.: $5,000,000
Emp.: 50
Hotel
N.A.I.C.S.: 721110
Allan V. Rose (Pres)

AVRA SURGICAL ROBOTICS, INC.
c/o Stamell & Schager LLP 1 Liberty
Plz 35th Fl, New York, NY 10006
Tel.: (212) 566-4047
Web Site:
   http://www.avrasurgicalrobotics.com
Emp.: 4
Surgical Product Mfr
N.A.I.C.S.: 339112
Jared B. Stamell (Treas, Sec & VP)
A. Christian Schauer (CFO)

AVT SIMULATION INC.
2603 Challenger Tech Ct Ste 180,
Orlando, FL 32826
Tel.: (407) 381-7502
Web Site: http://www.avtsim.com
Year Founded: 1998
Sales Range: $10-24.9 Million
Emp.: 60
Simulation & Engineering Training Services
N.A.I.C.S.: 541330
Robert Abascal (Pres & CEO)
Nicholas Futch (Engr-Sys)
Kevin Vizzarri (VP & Dir-Bus Dev, Mktg & Proposals)
Stewart Grayson (CTO)
Jim Baka (Dir-Contracts)
Alicia Combs (Mgr-Corp Certification)
Margie Faulk (Mgr-HR)
Christina Wilson (Mgr-Ops)
Kevin Gregoire (VP-Strategic Fin)
Kyle E. Crooks (Pres)

AVTEC HOMES
1663 Georgia St NE Ste 600, Palm
Bay, FL 32907
Tel.: (321) 674-9395

Web Site:
   http://www.avtechomes.com
Year Founded: 2005
Sales Range: $10-24.9 Million
Emp.: 16
Residential Construction
N.A.I.C.S.: 236115
Larry Sietsma (Owner)

AVTEC INC.
100 Innovation Pl, Lexington, SC
29072
Tel.: (803) 358-3600
Web Site: https://www.avtecinc.com
Sales Range: $25-49.9 Million
Emp.: 69
Dispatching Consoles; Communications Equipment
N.A.I.C.S.: 334290
Michael Branning (CEO)
Wayne Hutchinson (Engr-Software)
Bob Kramer (Mgr-Sls Ops)
Dawn Fisher (Mgr-Customer Support)
Tim Shaffer (Dir-Admin)
Richard Kneece (Engr-Design)
Brian Wiger (Engr-QA-Automation)
Lisa Welborn (Engr-Quality Assurance)
Jeff Janvrin (Mgr-Software Dev)
Arjen Maarleveld (Pres)
Troy Branning (Founder)
Alphonso Hamilton (VP-Mfg Ops)
Heyward Leaphart (VP-Engr)

AW GOLDEN INC.
801 Lancaster Ave, Reading, PA
19607
Tel.: (610) 777-6521
Web Site: http://www.awgolden.com
Sales Range: $25-49.9 Million
Emp.: 100
Automobiles, New & Used
N.A.I.C.S.: 441110
Kate Goodman (Controller)
Pete Estes (Gen Mgr)
Albert W. Golden III (Pres)

AW INDUSTRIES, INC.
8415 Ardwick Ardmore Rd, Landover,
MD 20785
Tel.: (301) 322-1000
Web Site:
   http://www.awrestaurants.com
Rev.: $43,974,813
Emp.: 200
Mattresses & Foundations
N.A.I.C.S.: 337910
Stuart Bannett (Pres)

AW PROPERTY CO.
2801 PGA Blvd Ste 220, Palm Beach
Gardens, FL 33410
Tel.: (561) 687-5800
Web Site: http://www.awproperty.com
Year Founded: 2002
Emp.: 15
Real Estate Investment & Property Management
N.A.I.C.S.: 523999
Brian K. Waxman (Founder, Mng Dir & Partner)
Mujeeb Ahkter (Dir-Fin & Acctg)
Christopher Deveso (Assoc Dir-Leasing & Acq)

AWAD BROTHERS INC.
2400 Romig Rd Unit 67, Akron, OH
44322
Tel.: (330) 753-8999
Rev.: $30,000,000
Emp.: 10
Family Clothing Stores
N.A.I.C.S.: 448310

AWARD METALS INC.

1450 Virginia Ave, Baldwin Park, CA
91706
Tel.: (626) 814-4410
Web Site:
   http://www.awardmetals.com
Year Founded: 1962
Sales Range: $25-49.9 Million
Emp.: 250
Mfr of Sheet Metal Products
N.A.I.C.S.: 332322
Neville Kadimi (Controller)

AWARENESS TECHNOLOGY INC.
1935 SW Martin Hwy, Palm City, FL
34990-3228
Tel.: (772) 283-6540
Web Site: http://www.awaretech.com
Surgical & Medical Instrument Mfr
N.A.I.C.S.: 339112
Mary Freeman (Pres)

AWARENESS, INC.
25 Corporate Dr Ste 390, Boston, MA
01803
Tel.: (781) 270-2400
Web Site: http://awarenesshub.com
Social Media Marketing Software
N.A.I.C.S.: 513210
Brian Zanghi (CEO)
David Carter (Founder & CTO)
Melissa Leffler (VP-Engrg)
Stephen Tremblay (VP-Fin)

Subsidiaries:

Awareness Canada   (1)
5050 South Service Road Suite 100, Burlington, L7L 5Y7, ON, Canada
Tel.: (905) 635-3134
Social Media Marketing Software
N.A.I.C.S.: 513210

AWAREPOINT CORP.
600 W Broadway Ste 250, San Diego, CA 92101
Tel.: (858) 345-5000
Web Site: http://www.awarepoint.com
Year Founded: 2007
Sales Range: $10-24.9 Million
Emp.: 20
Real-Time Location Systems & Services
N.A.I.C.S.: 513210
Tim Roche (Pres & CEO)
Thomas Warlan (Sr VP-Software Engrg)
Bernard Lee (Dir-Product Mktg)
Karl Riesen (Dir-Bus Dev)
Gary Jorgensen (Sr VP-Hardware Engrg)
Karolina Wolf (VP-Pro Svcs & Support)

AWC FRAC VALVES INC.
11376 FM 2854, Conroe, TX 77304
Tel.: (936) 760-3431
Web Site:
   http://www.awcfracvalves.com
Emp.: 100
Valve Mfr & Distr
N.A.I.C.S.: 332911

Subsidiaries:

Regate Technology, Inc.   (1)
11816 County Road 302, Plantersville, TX
77363
Tel.: (936) 894-9555
Web Site: http://www.regate-technology.com
Sales Range: $1-9.9 Million
Emp.: 10
Construction And Mining Machinery
N.A.I.C.S.: 423810
Brett Bratcher (Pres)
Eric Dvorscak (Dir-Ops)

AWC INC.
6655 Exchequer Dr, Baton Rouge,
LA 70809-5148

Tel.: (225) 752-1100   LA
Web Site: http://www.awc-inc.com
Year Founded: 1965
Industrial Machinery & Equipment
N.A.I.C.S.: 423830
Jeremy Menter *(Sys Engr-Software)*

AWEBER COMMUNICATIONS, INC.

4275 County Line Rd Ste 20, Chalfont, PA 18914
Tel.: (215) 825-2196
Web Site: https://www.aweber.com
Year Founded: 1998
Sales Range: $10-24.9 Million
Emp.: 75
Email Marketing Software
N.A.I.C.S.: 513210
Tom Kulzer *(Founder & CEO)*
Sean Cohen *(COO)*
Brian Jones *(CTO)*
Brandyn Bissinger *(Dir-PR & Mktg Comm)*

AWESTRUCK MARKETING GROUP

180 Varick St Ste 1214, New York, NY 10014
Tel.: (212) 381-9500
Web Site:
   http://www.getawestruck.com
Year Founded: 1999
Sales Range: $1-9.9 Million
Emp.: 22
Online Marketing Services
N.A.I.C.S.: 541810

AWISCO NY CORPORATION

55-15 43rd St, Maspeth, NY 11378
Tel.: (718) 786-7788   NY
Web Site: https://www.awisco.com
Sales Range: $10-24.9 Million
Emp.: 60
Whslr of Welding Machinery & Equipment
N.A.I.C.S.: 423830
Lloyd Robinson *(Pres)*
Dennis Dicocchi *(VP-Sls)*

AWP INDUSTRIES INC.

616 Industrial Pk, Frankfort, KY 40601
Tel.: (502) 695-0070
Web Site: http://www.awpind.com
Rev.: $29,000,000
Emp.: 120
Baskets, Steel Wire
N.A.I.C.S.: 331222
Kara Oberlander *(Gen Mgr-Ops)*

AWP LLC

8130 NW 74th Ave, Medley, FL 33166-7402
Tel.: (305) 887-2646
Web Site: http://www.awpllc.com
Sales Range: $10-24.9 Million
Emp.: 180
Metal Doors & Windows
N.A.I.C.S.: 332321
Virginie Hoebanx *(Dir-Mktg & Customer Svc)*

AXAR CAPITAL MANAGEMENT L.P.

1330 Ave of the Americas 30th Fl, New York, NY 10019
Tel.: (212) 356-6130   DE
Web Site: http://www.axarcapital.com
Investment Advisory & Asset Management Services
N.A.I.C.S.: 523940
Andrew Axelrod *(Chm & CEO)*
Lionel Benichou *(Controller & Dir-Fin)*
Ricardo Mosquera *(COO)*
Timothy Parrott *(Pres)*
Mike Bernstein *(Head-IR)*

Subsidiaries:

Axar Acquisition Corp.   **(1)**
1330 Ave of the Americas 6th Fl, New York, NY 10019   **(85.8%)**
Tel.: (212) 356-6130
Rev.: $314,738
Assets: $25,372,874
Liabilities: $20,372,869
Net Worth: $5,000,005
Earnings: ($1,468,493)
Emp.: 3
Fiscal Year-end: 12/31/2016
Investment Holding Company
N.A.I.C.S.: 551112
Andrew Axelrod *(Chm & CEO)*
Lionel Benichou *(CFO, Treas & Sec)*

StoneMor Inc.   **(1)**
955 Keller Rd Ste 1500, Altamonte Springs, FL 32714   **(100%)**
Tel.: (407) 379-5700
Web Site:
   https://www.everstorypartners.com
Rev.: $322,842,000
Assets: $1,741,144,000
Liabilities: $1,886,886,000
Net Worth: ($145,742,000)
Earnings: ($55,279,000)
Emp.: 1,831
Fiscal Year-end: 12/31/2021
Funeral Homes & Funeral Services
N.A.I.C.S.: 812210
Andrew Axelrod *(Chm)*
Charlotte Igou *(VP-Acctg & Controller)*
Lorena Trujillo *(Gen Counsel & VP)*
Danielle Mehallo *(VP & Asst Gen Counsel)*
Lilly Donohue *(Pres & CEO)*
Scott Stefani *(Interim CFO)*
William Corbett *(Chief Investment Officer)*
Karen Sheean *(Chief People Officer)*
Laurianne Nolan *(VP-Tax)*
Derek D'Alessandro *(VP-IT)*
Michele Stone *(VP-Ops)*
Matt Sobon *(Reg VP-Ops & Ops-East)*
Alexandra Sandbach *(Sr VP-Accounting, Acquisitions, and Integrations)*
Kendra Stevens *(Sr VP-Sales & Marketing)*
Brooke Austin *(Reg VP-Operations)*
Lawrence W. Michael *(Reg VP-Operations)*
Gill Giddens *(Reg VP-Sales)*
Lilly H. Donohue *(Pres & CEO)*

Subsidiary (Domestic):

StoneMor Partners L.P.   **(2)**
3600 Horizon Blvd, Trevose, PA 19056
Tel.: (215) 826-2800
Web Site: http://www.stonemor.com
Rev.: $316,126,000
Assets: $1,669,101,000
Liabilities: $1,675,679,000
Net Worth: ($6,578,000)
Earnings: ($72,699,000)
Emp.: 2,630
Fiscal Year-end: 12/31/2018
Cemetery Subdividers
N.A.I.C.S.: 812220
Austin So *(Chief Legal Officer, Gen Counsel & Sec)*
James S. Ford *(COO & Sr VP)*
Garry Herdler *(CFO & Sr VP)*

Subsidiary (Domestic):

Alleghany Memorial Park LLC   **(3)**
7008 Winterberry Ave, Covington, VA 24426
Tel.: (540) 736-8347
Web Site: http://www.stonemor.com
Emp.: 5
Cemeteries & Crematories Operator
N.A.I.C.S.: 812220

Altavista Memorial Park LLC   **(3)**
642 Wards Rd, Altavista, VA 24517
Tel.: (434) 509-0325
Funeral Homes & Funeral Services
N.A.I.C.S.: 812210

Augusta Memorial Park Perpetual Care Company   **(3)**
1775 Goose Creek Rd, Waynesboro, VA 22980
Tel.: (540) 316-6061
Emp.: 5
Cemeteries & Crematories Operator
N.A.I.C.S.: 812220
Mark Colvin *(Mgr)*

Beth Israel Cemetery Association of Woodbridge   **(3)**

US Hwy 1 N, Woodbridge, NJ 07095
Tel.: (732) 634-2100
Cemeteries & Crematories Operator
N.A.I.C.S.: 812220

Birchlawn Burial Park LLC   **(3)**
177 Birchlawn Cir, Pearisburg, VA 24134
Tel.: (540) 736-8332
Cemeteries & Crematories Operator
N.A.I.C.S.: 812220

Bronswood Cemetery, Inc.   **(3)**
3805 Madison St, Oak Brook, IL 60523
Tel.: (630) 487-5003
Real Estate Asset Management Services
N.A.I.C.S.: 531390

Cedar Hill Funeral Home, Inc.   **(3)**
4111 Pennsylvania Ave, Suitland, MD 20746
Tel.: (301) 817-0120
Web Site:
   http://www.cedarhillfuneralhome.com
Emp.: 6
Funeral Homes & Funeral Services
N.A.I.C.S.: 812210

Chapel Hill Associates, Inc.   **(3)**
2894 Patterson Rd SE, Grand Rapids, MI 49512-1928
Tel.: (616) 965-1713
Web Site: http://www.chapelhill.com
Cemeteries & Crematories Operator
N.A.I.C.S.: 812220

Chapel Hill Funeral Home, Inc.   **(3)**
10776 McKinley Hwy, Osceola, IN 46561
Tel.: (574) 674-5991
Web Site:
   http://www.chapelhillmemorial.com
Sales Range: $10-24.9 Million
Emp.: 20
Funeral Homes & Funeral Services
N.A.I.C.S.: 812210
Richard G. Koschnick *(Gen Mgr)*
Julie Monroe *(Mgr-Cemetery Family Svcs)*
Rodney Urick *(Dir-Funeral)*

Clinch Valley Memorial Cemetery, Inc.   **(3)**
3201 W Front St, Richlands, VA 24641
Tel.: (276) 964-4410
Web Site: http://www.burialplanning.com
Emp.: 5
Funeral Homes & Funeral Services
N.A.I.C.S.: 812210

Columbia Memorial Park LLC   **(3)**
12005 Clarksville Pike, Clarksville, MD 21029
Tel.: (410) 205-2671
Web Site: http://www.stonemor.com
Cemeteries & Crematories Operator
N.A.I.C.S.: 812220

Cornerstone Family Services Inc.   **(3)**
311 Veterans Hwy Ste B, Levittown, PA 19056   **(100%)**
Tel.: (215) 826-2800
Web Site: http://www.stonemor.com
Rev.: $75,000,000
Emp.: 80
Funeral Service & Crematories
N.A.I.C.S.: 812210
Lawrence Miller *(Chm)*
Lawrence Miller *(Chm)*

Covington Memorial Gardens, Inc.   **(3)**
8408 Covington Rd, Fort Wayne, IN 46804
Tel.: (260) 432-2508
Web Site:
   http://www.covingtonmemorial.com
Emp.: 12
Cemeteries & Crematories Operator
N.A.I.C.S.: 812220

Eloise B. Kyper Funeral Home, Inc.   **(3)**
2702 Mount Royal Blvd, Glenshaw, PA 15116
Tel.: (412) 486-9086
Web Site: http://www.kyperfuneralhome.com
Funeral Homes & Funeral Services
N.A.I.C.S.: 812210

Forest Lawn Gardens, Inc.   **(3)**
3739 Washington Ave, McMurray, PA 15317
Tel.: (724) 821-9225
Cemeteries & Crematories Operator
N.A.I.C.S.: 812220

Forest Lawn Memorial Chapel, Inc.   **(3)**
1977 S State Rd 135, Greenwood, IN 46143
Tel.: (317) 491-1910
Funeral Homes & Funeral Services
N.A.I.C.S.: 812210

Forest Lawn Memory Gardens, Inc.   **(3)**
1977 S State Rd 135, Greenwood, IN 46143
Tel.: (317) 535-9003
Web Site: http://www.forestlawncemetery-fh.com
Emp.: 25
Funeral Homes & Funeral Services
N.A.I.C.S.: 812210

Henlopen Memorial Park LLC   **(3)**
28787 Lockerman Rd, Milton, DE 19968
Tel.: (302) 703-3003
Funeral Homes & Funeral Services
N.A.I.C.S.: 812210

Henry Memorial Park LLC   **(3)**
8443 Virginia Ave, Bassett, VA 24055
Tel.: (276) 365-3093
Cemeteries & Crematories Operator
N.A.I.C.S.: 812220

Highland Memorial Park, Inc.   **(3)**
264 S 12th St, Beloit, OH 44609
Tel.: (330) 525-7711
Cemeteries & Crematories Operator
N.A.I.C.S.: 812220

Juniata Memorial Park LLC   **(3)**
9010 Hwy 522 S, Lewistown, PA 17044-8908
Tel.: (717) 388-6261
Cemeteries & Crematories Operator
N.A.I.C.S.: 812220

Kingwood Memorial Park Association   **(3)**
8230 Columbus Pike, Lewis Center, OH 43035
Tel.: (740) 548-5509
Business Management Services
N.A.I.C.S.: 561110

Kirk & Nice, Inc.   **(3)**
80 Stenton Ave, Plymouth Meeting, PA 19462
Tel.: (610) 832-2064
Web Site: http://www.kirkandniceinc.com
Emp.: 52
Funeral Homes & Funeral Services
N.A.I.C.S.: 812210
Edwin D. MacFarland *(Dir-Funeral & Supvr)*
Charles A. Roman *(Dir-Funeral & Area Mgr)*
Nicholas R. Andreas *(Dir-Funeral)*
Travis Brown *(Dir-Funeral)*

Subsidiary (Domestic):

Kirk & Nice Suburban Chapel, Inc.   **(4)**
333 County Line Rd, Feasterville Trevose, PA 19053
Tel.: (215) 354-0085
Web Site:
   http://www.kirkandnicesuburban.com
Funeral Homes & Funeral Services
N.A.I.C.S.: 812210

Subsidiary (Domestic):

Montlawn Memorial Park, Inc.   **(3)**
2911 S Wilmington St, Raleigh, NC 27603   **(100%)**
Tel.: (919) 772-1073
Web Site: http://www.montlawn.com
Emp.: 25
Funeral Homes & Cremation Services
N.A.I.C.S.: 812210
Scott Wheeler *(Mgr-Funeral)*
Jason Abrams *(Dir-Funeral)*

Northlawn Memorial Gardens   **(3)**
4724 State Rd, Peninsula, OH 44264-9500
Tel.: (330) 929-2884
Web Site:
   http://www.northlawnmemorialgardens.com
Emp.: 5
Cemeteries & Crematories Operator
N.A.I.C.S.: 812220

Oak Hill Cemetery LLC   **(3)**

Axar Capital Management L.P.—(Continued)

1902 Plank Rd, Fredericksburg, VA 22401
Tel.: (540) 693-2961
Cemeteries & Crematories Operator
N.A.I.C.S.: 812220

Rockbridge Memorial Gardens
LLC   (3)
116 Peaceful Ln, Lexington, VA 24450-5721
Tel.: (540) 339-3700
Web Site: http://www.stonemor.com
Emp.: 4
Cemeteries & Crematories Operator
N.A.I.C.S.: 812220

Rolling Green Memorial Park
LLC   (3)
1008 W Chester Pike, West Chester, PA
19382
Tel.: (610) 590-5021
Cemeteries & Crematories Operator
N.A.I.C.S.: 812220
Jill Kiley (Office Mgr)
Daisy Grey (Office Mgr)

Rose Lawn Cemeteries Subsidiary,
Incorporated   (3)
4410 Lee Hwy, Marion, VA 24354
Tel.: (276) 325-5488
Cemeteries & Crematories Operator
N.A.I.C.S.: 812220

Roselawn Development LLC   (3)
103 Clearview Dr, Martinsville, VA 24112
Tel.: (276) 632-5141
Cemeteries & Crematories Operator
N.A.I.C.S.: 812220

Russell Memorial Cemetery LLC   (3)
154 Huckleberry Rd, Lebanon, VA 24266
Tel.: (276) 365-3099
Cemeteries & Crematories Operator
N.A.I.C.S.: 812220

Shenandoah Memorial Park LLC   (3)
1270 Front Royal Pike, Winchester, VA
22602
Tel.: (540) 931-0448
Web Site:
    http://www.shenandoahmemorialpark.com
Emp.: 5
Cemeteries & Crematories Operator
N.A.I.C.S.: 812220

Sierra View Memorial Park   (3)
4900 Olive Ave, Olivehurst, CA 95961-4767
Tel.: (530) 742-6957
Web Site: http://www.sierraviewfh.com
Cemeteries & Crematories Operator
N.A.I.C.S.: 812220

Springhill Memory Gardens LLC   (3)
27260 Ocean Gtwy, Hebron, MD 21830-
1040
Tel.: (410) 202-3030
Cemeteries & Crematories Operator
N.A.I.C.S.: 812220

Stephen R. Haky Funeral Home,
Inc.   (3)
603 N Gallatin Ave Ext, Uniontown, PA
15401
Tel.: (724) 437-2756
Web Site: http://www.hakyfuneralhome.com
Funeral Homes & Funeral Services
N.A.I.C.S.: 812210
Stephanie Haky Georgiana (Dir-Funeral,
Mgr & Supvr)

StoneMor Cemetery Products
LLC   (3)
311 Veterans Hwy Ste B, Levittown, PA
19056
Tel.: (215) 857-5000
Web Site:
    http://www.stonemorcemeteryprod.com
Cemeteries & Crematories Operator
N.A.I.C.S.: 812220

StoneMor Pennsylvania Subsidiary
LLC   (3)
311 Veterans Hwy Ste B, Levittown, PA
19056
Tel.: (215) 826-2800
Cemeteries & Crematories Operator
N.A.I.C.S.: 812220

StoneMor Puerto Rico LLC   (3)
Carr 119 Km 36 5, San Sebastian, PR
00685

Tel.: (787) 896-3535
Web Site: http://www.stonemor.com
Emp.: 11
Funeral Homes & Funeral Services
N.A.I.C.S.: 812210

Sunset Memorial Park Inc.   (3)
3600 Horizon Blvd, Trevose, PA 19056
Tel.: (215) 826-2800
Web Site: http://www.stonemor.com
Rev.: $500,000
Emp.: 10
Cemetery & Developers
N.A.I.C.S.: 812220

The Valhalla Cemetery Company
LLC   (3)
839 Wilkes Rd, Birmingham, AL 35228
Tel.: (205) 986-0364
Cemeteries & Crematories Operator
N.A.I.C.S.: 812220

XS Financial, Inc.   (1)
1901 Avenue of the Stars Ste 120, Los An-
geles, CA 90067
Tel.: (310) 683-2336
Web Site: https://www.xsfinancial.com
Rev.: $11,675,203
Assets: $84,091,723
Liabilities: $80,631,138
Net Worth: $3,460,585
Earnings: ($6,507,019)
Fiscal Year-end: 12/31/2023
Financial Investment Services
N.A.I.C.S.: 523999
David Kivitz (CEO)
Antony Radbod (COO)
Joel Fazzini (CFO)
Alex Karol (VP-Tech)
Jim Bates (Dir-Credit)

AXCESS INTERNATIONAL, INC.
16650 Westgrove Dr Ste 600, Addi-
son, TX 75001
Tel.: (972) 407-6080   DE
Web Site: http://www.axcessinc.com
Year Founded: 1982
Sales Range: $1-9.9 Million
Emp.: 12
Electronic Components Mfr
N.A.I.C.S.: 334419
Allan Griebenow (Pres & CEO)
Richard Cecil Eversfield Morgan
(Chm)

AXCHEM SOLUTIONS INC.
6 Oak Branch Dr Ste C, Greensboro,
NC 27407-2396
Tel.: (336) 632-0500
Web Site: http://www.axchem-
    group.com
Year Founded: 1980
Sales Range: $10-24.9 Million
Emp.: 12
Polyacrylamides & Other Process
Additives
N.A.I.C.S.: 424690
Peter Nichols (Pres)

AXEDA SYSTEMS INC.
Unit 3 25 Forbes Blvd, Foxboro, MA
02035-2873
Tel.: (508) 337-9200   DE
Web Site: http://www.axeda.com
Sales Range: $10-24.9 Million
Emp.: 116
Device Relationship Management
Software Developer
N.A.I.C.S.: 541512
Dale Calder (Founder)
Brian Anderson (VP-Mktg)
Rachael T. McCarthy (CFO)
Gave Camera (Controller)

AXEL AMERICAS LLC
1440 Erie St, Kansas City, MO 64116
Tel.: (816) 471-4590
Web Site:
    http://www.axelamericas.com
Sales Range: $10-24.9 Million
Emp.: 48

Lubricating Oils & Greases
N.A.I.C.S.: 324191
Clark Hoover (Treas & Controller)
Tim Skoch (Mgr-Pur & Customer Svc)
Tom Schroder (Pres)

AXEL PLASTICS RESEARCH LABORATORIES, INC.
PO Box 770855, Woodside, NY
11377
Tel.: (718) 672-8300   NY
Web Site:
    http://www.axelplastics.com
Sales Range: $10-24.9 Million
Emp.: 30
Mold Release Agents, Process Aid
Additives, Cleaners & Sealants De-
signer, Mfr & Marketer for the Plastic
& Rubber Industries
N.A.I.C.S.: 324191
Frank Axel (CEO)
Thomas Preisel (Dir-Sls & Mktg)

AXELERATE
14450 NE 29th Pl Ste 116, Bellevue,
WA 98007
Tel.: (425) 869-2255
Web Site: http://www.axelerate.com
Year Founded: 2003
Sales Range: $1-9.9 Million
Emp.: 33
Excutive Consulting Services
N.A.I.C.S.: 561312
Amy Bray (VP-Client Svcs)
Nancy Heen (Founder & CEO)

AXELGAARD MANUFACTUR-ING CO., LTD.
520 Industial Way, Fallbrook, CA
92028
Tel.: (760) 723-7554
Web Site: http://www.axelgaard.com
Year Founded: 1985
Sales Range: $10-24.9 Million
Emp.: 125
Electromedical Equipment
N.A.I.C.S.: 334510
Jens Axelgaard (Founder)
Ralynn Geiger (Controller)

AXELON SERVICES CORPO-RATION
44 Wall St Fl 18, New York, NY
10005-2408
Tel.: (212) 306-0100
Web Site: https://www.axelon.com
Year Founded: 1970
Sales Range: $25-49.9 Million
Emp.: 120
Computer Related Consulting Ser-
vices
N.A.I.C.S.: 541512
Tania Obeid (Pres & CEO)
Cynthia Lah (Mng Dir)
Keith Harper (Mng Dir)
Justin McCloskey (Mng Dir)

AXENICS, INC.
4 Townsend W Ste 5, Nashua, NH
03063
Tel.: (603) 595-9939   MA
Web Site: http://www.axenics.com
Year Founded: 1997
Sales Range: $1-9.9 Million
Emp.: 35
Mfg Valves/Pipe Fittings
N.A.I.C.S.: 332919
Haywood Schmidt (Pres & CEO)
James Gannon (Mgr-Production)

AXESS CORPORATION
91 Lukens Dr Ste E, New Castle, DE
19720-2799
Tel.: (302) 778-5285   DE
Year Founded: 1990
Rev.: $29,200,000

Emp.: 7
Holding Company
N.A.I.C.S.: 334516
Alexander F. Giacco (Chm)

Subsidiaries:

Empower Materials, Inc.   (1)
100 Interchange Blvd, Newark, DE 19711-
3549
Tel.: (302) 225-0100
Web Site:
    http://www.empowermaterials.com
Sales Range: $25-49.9 Million
Analytical Instruments
N.A.I.C.S.: 334516
Sugianto Hanggodo (Dir-Engrg)
Peter Ferraro (Dir-Bus Dev)

AXESSTEL, INC.
6815 Flanders Dr Ste 210, San Di-
ego, CA 92121
Tel.: (858) 625-2100   NV
Web Site: http://www.axesstel.com
Year Founded: 2000
Sales Range: $50-74.9 Million
Emp.: 35
Fixed Wireless Voice & Data Prod-
ucts Designer, Developer & Marketer
N.A.I.C.S.: 334290
Patrick Gray (CEO & CFO)

Subsidiaries:

Axesstel Korea, Inc.   (1)
KINS Tower 15F 25-1 Jeongja-dong
Bundang-gu Seongnam-si Gyeonggi, Seoul,
Korea (South)
Tel.: (82) 317848000
Sales Range: $10-24.9 Million
Wireless & Voice Data Research & Devel-
opment Services
N.A.I.C.S.: 334220
Marvin Tseu (CEO)

AXETURE CORP
76508 Sweet Pea Way, Palm Desert,
CA 92211
Tel.: (360) 224-5416   NV
Year Founded: 2015
Emp.: 1
Mobile Application Software Develop-
ment Services
N.A.I.C.S.: 541511
William Webber (Pres, CEO, CFO &
Treas)

AXIA CONSULTING, LLC
PO Box 21156, Columbus, OH 43221
Tel.: (614) 573-7650
Web Site:
    http://www.axiaconsulting.net
Year Founded: 2005
Sales Range: $1-9.9 Million
Emp.: 20
Technology & Business Consulting
Services
N.A.I.C.S.: 541618
Ed Mueller (CEO)
Paul Grove (Pres)
Tony Kopyar (VP)
Jon Riley (VP)
Nick Lemoine (Acct Mgr)
Brittany Marcellino (Mgr-HR)

AXIA PUBLIC RELATIONS
222 E Forsyth St, Jacksonville, FL
32202
Tel.: (904) 416-1500
Web Site: http://www.axia.net
Year Founded: 2002
Sales Range: $1-9.9 Million
Emp.: 20
Public Relations Agencies
N.A.I.C.S.: 541820
Jason Mudd (Pres & CEO)
Tabitha J. Mudd (Dir-Fin)

AXIOLOGIC SOLUTIONS, LLC
8280 Willow Oaks Corporate Dr Ste

450, Fairfax, VA 22031
Tel.: (703) 922-5500
Web Site:
http://www.axiologicsolutions.com
Computer Facilities Management
Services
N.A.I.C.S.: 541513
Tom Stauber *(Founder & Mng Partner)*
Andy Baratta *(Pres)*
Louis Chabot *(CTO)*
Chris Bibbee *(Chief Program Officer)*
Susan Moreira *(Chief Growth Officer)*

Subsidiaries:

Knowledge Link Inc. **(1)**
6861 Elm St, McLean, VA 22101
Tel.: (703) 827-8500
Web Site: http://www.knowledge-link.biz
Rev.: $4,193,000
Emp.: 30
Data Processing, Hosting & Related Services
N.A.I.C.S.: 518210
Donna Alligood *(CEO)*
Randall Stefano *(Pres)*
Rebecca Fortney *(Dir-Acctg)*

AXIOM
1702 Washington Ave, Houston, TX
77007
Tel.: (713) 523-5711
Web Site: http://www.axiomdg.com
Year Founded: 1998
Sales Range: $10-24.9 Million
Emp.: 13
Advertising Agencies
N.A.I.C.S.: 541810
Tom Hair *(Pres)*
David Lerch *(Dir-Creative)*
John Duplechin *(Mgr-Multimedia)*
Laura Paddock *(Acct Mgr)*
Mike Wu *(Sr Dir-Art & Designer)*

AXIOM AUTOMOTIVE TECH-NOLOGIES, INC
75 Spring St 8th Fl, New York, NY
10012
Tel.: (917) 237-2900
Web Site: http://www.axiom.com
Year Founded: 2000
Sales Range: $50-74.9 Million
Emp.: 500
Law firm
N.A.I.C.S.: 541110
Mark Harris *(Founder & CEO)*
Abbey Orlofsky *(Coord-Mktg)*
Adam Rosenfield *(Mgr-Fin Svcs)*
Ward Hendon *(Gen Mgr)*

Subsidiaries:

Axiom Legal London **(1)**
Floor 5 159-173 Saint John Street, London,
EC1V 4QJ, United Kingdom
Tel.: (44) 2073245300
Web Site: http://www.axiomlaw.co.uk
Sales Range: $10-24.9 Million
Emp.: 40
Law firm
N.A.I.C.S.: 541110
Mark Harris *(CEO)*

Axiom Legal, Inc.-San Francisco **(1)**
1000 Sansome St Ste 350, San Francisco,
CA 94111
Tel.: (415) 343-1070
Web Site: http://www.axiomlegal.com
Sales Range: $10-24.9 Million
Emp.: 25
Law firm
N.A.I.C.S.: 541110
Henry Jones *(Gen Mgr)*

AXIOM BANK, N.A.
258 Southhall Ln Ste 400, Maitland,
FL 32751
Tel.: (407) 732-5600
Web Site:
http://www.axiombanking.com
Year Founded: 1962

Federally Chartered Savings Bank
N.A.I.C.S.: 522180
Ron Strand-Sorrell *(COO)*
Debra Gaskin *(Sr VP-HR & Mktg)*
Lou Garcia *(Sr VP)*
Daniel Davis *(Pres & CEO)*
Perry Barbee *(Chief Credit Officer & Sr VP)*
Autumn Kircher *(Sr VP-Consumer Lending)*
Tom Coletta *(VP-Comml Lending)*
Jessica Ludvigsen *(Sr VP-Retail Banking)*
Trisha Delatte *(VP-Treasury & Mgr-Sls)*
Jerry Allen *(Sr VP-Comml Banking)*
Leah Douglas *(VP-SBA & Comml Lending)*
Jonathan Hawryschuk *(VP/Gen Mgr-West Florida)*
Scott Amatuccio *(VP & Mgr-Small Bus Admin)*
Amy Hammer *(VP/Mgr-Comml Relationship-Tampa)*
Aissam Haddouch *(VP & Mgr-Comml Relationship)*
Jason McKee *(VP & Mgr-Comml Relationship)*
Nina Howell *(VP-Comml & Mgr-Indus Relationship)*
Timothy Foreman *(CFO)*
Bryan Kazimierowski *(VP & Mgr-Customer Rels-Comml)*
Johan Cardenas *(VP & Mgr-Comml Relationship)*
Urjit Patel *(Exec VP-Consumer Banking)*
Glenda E. Hood *(Chm)*
Van Firios *(VP & Mgr-Comml Rels)*
Scott Leitner *(VP & Mgr-Comml Relationship)*
Pete Longo *(VP-Digital Banking & Mktg)*
Joshua Ocampo *(Mgr-Digital Banking Relationship)*
Lisa Johanning *(VP & Program Mgr-Consumer Loan)*
Joe Dear *(Sr VP)*
Ted Sheppe *(Exec VP-Comml Banking)*
Amy Carlson *(VP)*
Mercedis Couillard *(VP & Mgr-Payment Solutions Relationship)*
Susan Maurer *(Sr VP)*
Richard Jensen *(Sr VP & Mgr-Comml Relationship-Tampa)*
Dan Karas *(Exec VP-Allied Affiliated Funding)*
Mark J. Simshauser *(Sr VP-Allied Affiliated Funding)*
Jordan Wilson *(VP & Mgr-Relationship-Comml & Industrial Loan)*
Larry Swinney *(Sr VP-Bus Dev-Comml Fin)*
Michael Haddad *(Pres-Comml Fin)*

Subsidiaries:

Allied Affiliated Funding, LP **(1)**
5151 Beltline Rd Ste 500, Dallas, TX 75254
Tel.: (972) 776-5300
Web Site: http://www.axiombanking.com
Commercial Finance Services
N.A.I.C.S.: 522291
Gen Merritt-Parikh *(VP-Portfolio & Risk Mgmt)*
Karen Tramel *(Dir-Mktg & Adv)*
Katy Kashiwa *(Controller)*
David Lau *(CTO)*
Clay Tramel *(CEO)*
Joel Flig *(Mng Dir-Northeast)*

AXIOM CONSULTING PART-NERS, LLC
161 N Clark St Ste 4700, Chicago, IL
60601
Tel.: (312) 523-2123   DE

Web Site: http://www.axiomcp.com
Corporate Strategy, Organization &
Talent Consulting Services
N.A.I.C.S.: 541611
Steve Strelsin *(Partner)*
Garrett Sheridan *(Pres & Partner)*
Allan Ackerman *(Partner)*
Aaron Sorensen *(Partner)*
Dane Tyson *(Principal)*
Daniel Osafo *(Principal)*
Dave Kuhlman *(Partner)*
Donncha Carroll *(Principal)*
Don Ruse *(Partner)*
Isabelle Van Cauwenberge *(Principal)*
Juan Pablo Gonzalez *(Partner)*

AXIOM CORPORATION
Ste 100 2 Piedmont Ctr NE, Atlanta,
GA 30305-1502
Tel.: (404) 995-8880
Web Site: http://www.axiom-corp.com
Rev.: $10,377,597
Emp.: 20
Systems Engineering, Computer Related
N.A.I.C.S.: 541512
Tia Buckham-White *(Mgr-Bus Dev)*

AXIOM OIL AND GAS CORP.
1846 E Innovation Park Dr, Oro Valley, AZ 85755
Tel.: (303) 872-7814   NV
Web Site:
http://www.axiomgoldandsilver.com
Emp.: 2
Oil & Gas Exploration Services
N.A.I.C.S.: 211120
Robert Knight *(Chm)*
Ryan Kerr *(VP-Ops)*
Michael H. Altman *(Pres & CEO)*
Jill Mix *(CFO)*

AXIOM SALES FORCE DEVEL-OPMENT LLC
740 E Campbell Rd Ste 120, Richardson, TX 75081
Tel.: (972) 469-2450
Web Site: http://www.axiomsfd.com
Year Founded: 1990
Sales Range: $1-9.9 Million
Emp.: 25
Sales Training & Coaching
N.A.I.C.S.: 541618
Bob Sanders *(Pres & CEO)*
Ed McAdoo *(CTO)*
Steve Potts *(CMO & Chief Sls Officer)*
Rick Smith *(VP-Client Success)*

AXIOM WORLDWIDE INC.
5104 S Westshore Blvd, Tampa, FL
33634
Tel.: (813) 935-5500   FL
Web Site:
http://www.axiomworldwide.com
Year Founded: 2011
Sales Range: $10-24.9 Million
Medical, Dental & Hospital Equipment
& Supplies Merchant Whslr
N.A.I.C.S.: 423450
James J. Gibson *(Pres & CEO)*

AXIOM, INC.
295 Lafayette St 700, New York, NY
10012
Tel.: (917) 237-2900
Web Site: http://www.axiomlaw.com
Year Founded: 1998
Sales Range: $50-74.9 Million
Emp.: 305
Legal Consulting Services
N.A.I.C.S.: 541199
Alec Guettel *(Co-Founder)*
Mark Harris *(Co-Founder & Chm)*
Mathew Keshav Lewis *(Co-Head-Global Banking Practice)*

Barry Quinn *(Co-Head-Global Banking Practice)*
Doug Hebenthal *(CTO)*
Cathy Johnson *(CIO)*
Lisa Young *(Gen Counsel)*
Sloane Googin *(CFO)*
David K. McVeigh *(CEO)*

AXIOS INC.
801 Broadway NW Ste 200, Grand
Rapids, MI 49504
Tel.: (616) 949-2525
Web Site:
http://www.axiosincorporated.com
Year Founded: 1988
Sales Range: $100-124.9 Million
Emp.: 45
Employment Placement Agencies
N.A.I.C.S.: 561311
Dan Barcagski *(CEO)*
Ann Hayes *(VP-Ops)*
Kellie Haines *(Pres)*

AXIS BUSINESS SOLUTIONS, INC.
57 Green St, Portsmouth, NH 03801
Tel.: (603) 294-4256
Web Site:
http://www.axisbusiness.com
Sales Range: $100-124.9 Million
Emp.: 20
Computer Peripheral Equipment &
Software Merchant Whslr
N.A.I.C.S.: 423430
Peter Estes *(Owner & Founder)*

AXIS COMMUNICATIONS
1250 H St NW Ste 1101, Washington,
DC 20005
Tel.: (202) 347-0060
Web Site: http://www.axiscomm.com
Year Founded: 1991
Sales Range: $10-24.9 Million
Emp.: 19
N.A.I.C.S.: 541810
Dave Ihmels *(Dir-Acct Mgmt)*
Juan Pablo Tavil *(Reg Mgr-Sls-South America)*

AXIS GLOBAL SYSTEMS LLC
4635 54th Rd, Maspeth, NY 11378
Tel.: (718) 458-3666
Web Site: http://www.axisg.com
Sales Range: $10-24.9 Million
Emp.: 50
Domestic Freight Forwarding
N.A.I.C.S.: 488510
Scott Hodges *(VP)*
Tom Lopresti *(Mng Dir)*

AXIS GROUP, LLC
Connell Corp Ctr 400 Connell Dr Ste
6100, Berkeley Heights, NJ 07922
Tel.: (908) 988-0200   NJ
Web Site: http://www.axisgroup.com
Year Founded: 1996
Sales Range: $10-24.9 Million
Emp.: 35
Information Technology Consulting &
Services
N.A.I.C.S.: 541512
Albert J. Hughes *(Pres & CTO)*
Ranjan Sinha *(VP-Sls & Delivery)*
Mike Mahaney *(Dir-Project & Portfolio Mgmt)*
Scott Reedy *(Mgr-Practice-Bus Intelligence & Info Mgmt)*

AXIS MEDIA
30495 Canwood St, Agoura Hills, CA
91301
Tel.: (818) 264-1555
Web Site: http://www.axis-media.us
Year Founded: 2002
Sales Range: $1-9.9 Million
Emp.: 1

Axis Media—(Continued)

Advertising Specialties
N.A.I.C.S.: 541830
Tony Naish (Founder & Pres)

AXIS TEKNOLOGIES

8800 Roswell Rd, Atlanta, GA 30350
Tel.: (678) 441-0260
Web Site:
http://www.axisteknologies.com
Sales Range: $10-24.9 Million
Emp.: 118
Long Distance Communications Services
N.A.I.C.S.: 517112
Mark Keefe (Engr-Circuit Design)
Shawna Roberts (Bus Mgr)

AXISS ADVERTISING

2950 SW 27th Ave Ste 110, Miami,
FL 33133
Tel.: (305) 447-9300   FL
Year Founded: 1994
Sales Range: Less than $1 Million
Emp.: 7
Bilingual Marketing, Collateral, Corporate Identity, Graphic Design, Hispanic Marketing, Internet/Web Design, Logo & Package Design, Point of Purchase, Point of Sale
N.A.I.C.S.: 541810
Lexi Segre (Principal-Brand-Blaze)
Lilian Soeda (Co-Founder, Principal & Creative Dir)
Patricia Valdivia (Art Dir)

AXIUM INFRASTRUCTURE INC.

527 Madison Ave 21st Fl, New York,
NY 10022
Tel.: (646) 449-9058
Web Site: http://www.axiuminfra.com
Privater Equity Firm
N.A.I.C.S.: 523940
Pierre Anctil (Pres & CEO)

AXIUM PHARMACEUTICALS, INC.

265 Eastchester Dr Ste 133, High
Point, NC 27262   NC
Web Site: http://www.axium-pharma.com
Year Founded: 2017
Biopharmaceutical Research & Development Services
N.A.I.C.S.: 325412
Anthony Harrelson (CEO)
Kevin Beaumont (Sec)

AXIUM XTS CORPORATION

10200 SW Greenburg Rd Ste 600,
Portland, OR 97223
Tel.: (503) 688-5700
Web Site: http://www.axium.com
Sales Range: $1-9.9 Million
Emp.: 67
Software Solutions Provider
N.A.I.C.S.: 513210
Alan Mills (CEO)
Cathy Mills (Pres)
Ilene Ingram (VP-Ops)
D'Ann Laun (Dir-Sls & Svcs)
Jon Male (Dir-R&D)
Tony Williams (Mgr-Support)
Julie Ginn (Mgr-Mktg)

AXL MUSICAL INSTRUMENTS CO., LTD., CORP.

31067 San Clemente St, Hayward,
CA 94544
Tel.: (415) 508-1398
Web Site: http://www.axlusa.com
Sales Range: $10-24.9 Million
Emp.: 300
Musical Instrument Mfr

N.A.I.C.S.: 339992
Alan Liu (CEO)
Brad Townsend (Sr VP-Intl Sls & Mktg)

AXM PHARMA, INC.

3651 Lindell Rd Ste D344, Las Vegas, NV 89103
Tel.: (702) 932-7980
Pharmaceuticals Product Mfr
N.A.I.C.S.: 325412
Linda Forster (CEO)

AXTELL-TAYLOR GM, LLC.

1955 N Main St, Logan, UT 84341-1706
Tel.: (435) 752-6801
Web Site:
http://www.axtelltaylorgm.com
Sales Range: $10-24.9 Million
Emp.: 35
Car Whslr
N.A.I.C.S.: 441110
Michael Taylor (Mgr)

AXXESS TECHNOLOGY SOLUTIONS, INC

16000 Dallas Pkwy Ste 700N, Dallas,
TX 75248
Tel.: (214) 575-7711
Web Site: https://www.axxess.com
Year Founded: 2007
Emp.: 643
Home Health Care Management Software
N.A.I.C.S.: 513210
John Olajide (Founder & CEO)

Subsidiaries:

Complia Health, LLC   (1)
900 National Pkwy Ste 100, Schaumburg,
IL 60173
Tel.: (866) 802-7704
Web Site: https://www.compliahealth.com
Sales Range: $10-24.9 Million
Emp.: 150
Healthcare Software Development Services
N.A.I.C.S.: 541511
Scott Brashears (Sr VP-Sales Engrg)

AXYON CONSULTING, LLC

16300 Addison Rd Ste 300, Addison,
TX 75001
Tel.: (972) 473-4800
Web Site:
http://www.axyonconsulting.com
Sales Range: $1-9.9 Million
Emp.: 26
Business Consulting Services
N.A.I.C.S.: 541618
Daryl O. Blackwell (Pres, CEO & Sr Mng Partner)
Kristi Fruge (Co-Founder, Sr Partner & VP-Bus Solutions)

AXYS

330 Garden Oaks Blvd, Houston, TX
77018
Tel.: (713) 863-8588
Web Site: http://www.axyscorp.com
Year Founded: 2003
Sales Range: Less than $1 Million
Emp.: 3
Chemical & Allied Products Merchant
Whslr
N.A.I.C.S.: 424690
Jennifer Lamb (VP)
Kristina Wise (Office Mgr)
Brian Lamb (Pres)

AXYS INDUSTRIAL SOLUTIONS, INC.

330 Garden Oaks Blvd, Houston, TX
77018
Tel.: (713) 863-8588
Web Site: http://www.axyscorp.com
Sales Range: $1-9.9 Million

Emp.: 4
Specialty Chemical Mfr & Distr
N.A.I.C.S.: 325998
Brian Lamb (Pres)
Jennifer Lamb (VP)
Chris May (Partner)
Kristina Maduzia (Office Mgr)
Guillaume Gautier (Dir-Field Svcs-Nantes)

AYARS & AYARS INCORPORATED

2436 N 48th St, Lincoln, NE 68504
Tel.: (402) 435-8600
Web Site: http://www.ayarsayars.com
Year Founded: 1985
Sales Range: $25-49.9 Million
Emp.: 160
Nonresidential Construction
N.A.I.C.S.: 236220
Michael Ayars (Pres)
Gary Tucker (VP)

AYCO FARMS INC.

1501 NW 12th Ave Ste G, Pompano
Beach, FL 33069
Tel.: (954) 725-4700
Web Site:
https://www.aycofarms.com
Sales Range: $50-74.9 Million
Emp.: 15
Fresh Fruits & Vegetable Mfr & Distr
N.A.I.C.S.: 311421
Avi Nir (CEO)
Lou Kertesz (Mgr-Sls)
Luz Andrea Rodriguez (Mgr-Credit)
Daniel Ramirez Van Hoorde (Gen Mgr-Irapuato)

AYER SALES INC.

2 Industrial Pkwy, Woburn, MA 01801
Tel.: (781) 933-1141
Web Site: http://www.ayer.com
Year Founded: 1961
Rev.: $21,134,925
Emp.: 20
Plastics Materials & Basic Shapes
N.A.I.C.S.: 424610
David A. Ayer (Pres & CEO)

AYERS BASEMENT SYSTEMS, LLC.

2505 S Waverly Hwy, Lansing, MI
48911
Tel.: (517) 645-2013
Web Site:
https://www.ayersbasements.com
Sales Range: $25-49.9 Million
Emp.: 40
Specialty Trade Contractors
N.A.I.C.S.: 238910
Ed Krieger (Principal)

AYERS CHEVROLET & OLDSMOBILE, INC.

1 Route 46, Dover, NJ 07801
Tel.: (973) 366-1243
Web Site:
http://www.ayerschevrolet.com
Year Founded: 1928
Sales Range: $25-49.9 Million
Emp.: 58
Car Whslr
N.A.I.C.S.: 441110
David M. Ayers (Pres)

AYERS OIL CO. INC.

610 N 4th St, Canton, MO 63435
Tel.: (573) 288-4466
Sales Range: $25-49.9 Million
Emp.: 215
Petroleum Bulk Stations
N.A.I.C.S.: 424710
Robert Ayers (Chm, Pres & CEO)
Kenny Ott (Mgr-Parts)

AYRES ASSOCIATES INC.

3433 Oakwood Hills Pkwy, Eau
Claire, WI 54701-7698
Tel.: (715) 834-3161
Web Site:
https://www.ayresassociates.com
Year Founded: 1959
Sales Range: $25-49.9 Million
Emp.: 275
Engineeering Services
N.A.I.C.S.: 541330
Jan Zander (Exec VP)
Thomas Pulse (Pres)
Brian Schroeder (Supvr-Structural Inspection)
Disa Wahlstrand (VP)
Todd Rudolph (Engr-Water Resources)
Susan Leith (Mgr-Mktg)
Andrew Dana (Project Mgr)
Bruce Ommen (Exec VP)
Dale Mathison (Project Mgr)
Daniel Sydow (Engr-Structural)
Paul Clopper (Dir-Applied Tech)
Scott Wilson (VP)

AYRES KAHLER + SACCO

6800 Normal Blvd, Lincoln, NE
68506-2814
Tel.: (402) 450-7530
Web Site: http://
Year Founded: 1946
Rev.: $28,000,000
Emp.: 40
Advetising Agency
N.A.I.C.S.: 541810
Mick Sibbel (Pres)
Denise Donovan (Mgr-Production)
Bill Barma (Dir-Creative)

AYRES-DELTA IMPLEMENT, INC.

3180 Hwy 82 E, Greenville, MS
38703
Tel.: (662) 332-2683   MS
Web Site: http://www.delta-grp.com
Year Founded: 1987
Sales Range: $25-49.9 Million
Emp.: 100
Holding Company; Agricultural Machinery Sales & Leasing Services
N.A.I.C.S.: 551112
J. Terry Gibbs (Pres)
W. Stanley Ayres (Pres-Ayres)
Joseph J. Nash (Treas & Sec)
Richard Cousino (VP)

Subsidiaries:

Ayres-Delta Implement of Belzoni,
Inc.   (1)
118 N Hwy 49 W, Belzoni, MS
39038   (100%)
Tel.: (662) 247-1221
Web Site:
http://www.ayresdeltaimplement.com
Sales Range: $1-9.9 Million
Emp.: 11
Agricultural Machinery Sales & Leasing
Services
N.A.I.C.S.: 423820

Delta Implement Company   (1)
3180 Hwy 82 E, Greenville, MS
38703   (100%)
Tel.: (662) 332-2683
Web Site: http://www.deltaimplementco.com
Sales Range: $10-24.9 Million
Emp.: 50
Agricultural Machinery Sales & Leasing
Services
N.A.I.C.S.: 423820

Subsidiary (Domestic):

Delta Implement Co. of Rolling
Fork   (2)
101 Hwy 61 S, Rolling Fork, MS
39159   (100%)
Tel.: (662) 873-2661
Web Site: http://www.deltaimplementco.com

Sales Range: $1-9.9 Million
Emp.: 15
Agricultural Machinery Sales & Leasing Services
N.A.I.C.S.: 423820
Bubba Cooper *(Gen Mgr)*
James Kent *(Mgr-Svc)*
John Kerr *(Mgr-Parts)*

Planters Equipment Co.   (1)
Hwy 61 N, Cleveland, MS 38732   **(100%)**
Tel.: (662) 843-2741
Web Site: http://www.planterequipco.com
Rev.: $9,242,000
Emp.: 28
Agricultural Machinery Sales & Leasing Services
N.A.I.C.S.: 423820
Kenny Jones *(Gen Mgr-Sls)*
Ray Hodges *(Mgr-Parts)*

The Ayres Company   (1)
4507 Hwy 82 W, Leland, MS 38756
Tel.: (662) 686-2361
Web Site:
    http://www.ayresdeltaimplement.com
Sales Range: $10-24.9 Million
Emp.: 30
Agricultural Machinery Sales & Leasing Services
N.A.I.C.S.: 423820

AYU TECHNOLOGY SOLUTIONS LLC
2100 W Loop S Ste 900, Houston, TX 77027
Tel.: (888) 696-4513
Web Site:
    http://www.websitealive.com
Sales Range: $10-24.9 Million
Emp.: 10
Software Publisher
N.A.I.C.S.: 513210
Lois Brooks *(Dir-Ops)*
Lee Bratina *(Dir-Tech)*
Paul Glancy *(Mgr-Sls)*
Jarrell Liner *(Dir-Client Happiness)*
Dustin Yu *(Pres & CTO)*
Glenn Gutierrez *(COO)*

AYUDA MANAGEMENT CORPORATION
11800 Ridge Pkwy Ste 550, Broomfield, CO 80021
Tel.: (303) 999-2020
Web Site:
    http://www.ayudamanagement.com
Year Founded: 2002
Sales Range: $10-24.9 Million
Emp.: 45
Construction, Environmental Engineering, Construction Management & Remediation
N.A.I.C.S.: 236220
Maria A. Vogt *(Co-Owner, Pres & CEO)*
Sonya C. Yungeberg *(Co-Owner & Exec VP-Engrg)*

AYZENBERG GROUP, INC.
49 E Walnut St, Pasadena, CA 91103
Tel.: (626) 584-4070   CA
Web Site: http://www.ayzenberg.com
Year Founded: 1993
Sales Range: $50-74.9 Million
Emp.: 115
Advetising Agency
N.A.I.C.S.: 541810
Eric Ayzenberg *(Chief Creative Officer)*
Vincent Juarez *(Principal & Dir-Media)*
Chris Younger *(Pres)*
Steve Fowler *(Head-Mktg-Amazon Games)*
Gary Goodman *(Principal & Dir-Creative)*
Noah Eichen *(Assoc Dir-Creative)*
Bill Buckley *(VP-Brand Integration)*
Tanner Teale *(Assoc Dir-Creative)*

Matt Bretz *(VP & Dir-Creative)*
Joakim Baage *(Exec Dir)*
Terry City *(Head-Ops & Buzzfeed-West Coast)*
Andy Swanson *(VP-eSports)*
Edgar Davtyan *(CFO & Principal)*
Kai Mildenberger *(CTO)*
Victor M. Parker II *(Dir-Comm)*

AZAD INTERNATIONAL INC.
2 Daniel Rd E, Fairfield, NJ 07004
Tel.: (973) 808-1922
Rev.: $17,000,000
Emp.: 12
General Merchandise, Non-Durable
N.A.I.C.S.: 424990
Victor Khubani *(Pres)*

AZALEA CAPITAL, LLC
One Liberty Sq 55 Beattle Pl Ste 1500, Greenville, SC 29601
Tel.: (864) 235-0201
Web Site:
    http://www.azaleacapital.com
Year Founded: 1996
Sales Range: $1-9.9 Million
Emp.: 5
Privater Equity Firm
N.A.I.C.S.: 523999
Patrick A. Duncan *(Mng Partner)*
Ben C. Wallace *(Partner)*
Vicki L. Sorbin *(Mgr-IR)*
Barbara J. Anderson *(Chief Compliance Officer & Controller)*
Marshall H. Cole III *(CFO)*
Benny M. LaRusa Jr. *(Partner)*

AZALEA COLOR COMPANY
1300 Lower Rodi Rd, Turtle Creek, PA 15145
Tel.: (412) 829-2300
Web Site:
    http://www.azaleacolor.com
Sales Range: $10-24.9 Million
Emp.: 5
Chemicals & Paints Whslr
N.A.I.C.S.: 424950
Tim Smith *(Reg Mgr-Sls)*

AZALEA HEALTH INNOVATIONS, INC.
5871 Glenridge Dr NE Ste 480, Atlanta, GA 30328
Tel.: (877) 777-7686
Web Site:
    http://www.azaleahealth.com
Year Founded: 2008
Cloud-Based Healthcare Software & Client Services
N.A.I.C.S.: 513210
Baha Zeidan *(Co-Founder & CEO)*
Douglas Swords *(Co-Founder & VP-RCM)*
Brad Townsend *(CFO)*

Subsidiaries:

AO Capital Partners, LLC   (1)
808 Travis St Ste 415, Houston, TX 77002
Tel.: (713) 255-5580
Web Site:
    http://www.prognosisinnovation.com
Rural & Community Hospitals
N.A.I.C.S.: 622110

AZAR INCORPORATED
3400 E Coliseum Blvd Ste 100, Fort Wayne, IN 46805-9656
Tel.: (260) 424-1972
Sales Range: $50-74.9 Million
Emp.: 350
Owner & Operator of Hotels & Restaurants
N.A.I.C.S.: 721110
George Azar *(CEO)*
Yogesh Parikh *(Pres)*

AZARA HEALTHCARE LLC

70 Blanchard Rd Ste 100, Burlington, MA 01803
Tel.: (781) 365-2208
Web Site:
    http://www.azarahealthcare.com
Electronics Stores
N.A.I.C.S.: 449210
Jeff Brandes *(Pres)*
Kevin Weinstein *(Chief Growth Officer)*

AZAVEA INCORPORATED
990 Spring Garden St 5th Fl, Philadelphia, PA 19123
Tel.: (215) 925-2600
Web Site: https://www.azavea.com
Year Founded: 2000
Rev.: $2,200,000
Emp.: 65
Telecommunication Servicesb
N.A.I.C.S.: 517810
Rachel Cheetham-Richard *(VP-Product Mktg & HR)*
Chip Hitchens *(VP-Professional Services)*
Ester Needham *(Project Mgr)*

AZAZIE, INC.
148 E Brokaw Rd, San Jose, CA 95112
Tel.: (650) 422-2460
Web Site: http://www.azazie.com
Year Founded: 2014
Sales Range: $25-49.9 Million
Emp.: 55
Bridal Clothing & Accessory Retailer
N.A.I.C.S.: 458110
Anna Billings *(Mgr-Customer Experience)*

AZF AUTOMOTIVE GROUP INC.
1900 NW 79th Ave, Miami, FL 33126
Tel.: (305) 477-2425   FL
Year Founded: 1996
Sales Range: $10-24.9 Million
Emp.: 4
Automobile & Motor Vehicle Merchant Whslr
N.A.I.C.S.: 423110
Ivan Motta *(Pres)*

AZIEL CORP.
401 Ryland St Ste 200-A, Reno, NV 89502
Tel.: (830) 202-2010
Web Site:
    http://www.azielcorporation.com
Year Founded: 2007
Oil & Gas Consulting Services
N.A.I.C.S.: 541618

AZIMUTH FULL SCREEN PUBLICATIONS INC.
816 NW 11th St Ste 710, Miami, FL 33136
Tel.: (301) 792-0561   DE
Year Founded: 2005
Sales Range: $1-9.9 Million
Emp.: 10
Advertising Agencies
N.A.I.C.S.: 541810
April Scott *(Owner)*

AZLE ANTIQUE MALL
1951 NW Pkwy, Azle, TX 76020
Tel.: (817) 221-3257
Web Site:
    http://www.burlesonantiquemall.com
Sales Range: $10-24.9 Million
Emp.: 5
Antique Mall
N.A.I.C.S.: 531120

AZLEWAY, INC.

15892 County Rd 26, Tyler, TX 75707-9136
Tel.: (903) 566-8444   TX
Web Site: http://www.azleway.org
Year Founded: 1979
Sales Range: $10-24.9 Million
Child Care Services
N.A.I.C.S.: 624110
Sharon Roubinek *(Vice Chm)*
Brandi Haws *(VP-Child, Family, Managed Care & Ops)*
Jason DeaBueno *(VP-Health Svcs)*
Mark Vogtner *(VP-IT)*
Mary Ellen Benson *(VP-Healthcare Innovation)*
Susan Seiler *(COO)*
Todd Endres *(VP-HR)*
Gordon Roberts Jr. *(Chm)*

AZOFF MUSIC MANAGEMENT
1100 Glendon Ave Ste 2000, Los Angeles, CA 90024
Tel.: (310) 209-3100
Talent Management Services
N.A.I.C.S.: 711410
Irving L. Azoff *(Chm & CEO)*

Subsidiaries:

Azoff MSG Entertainment LLC   (1)
1100 Glendon Ave Ste 2000, Los Angeles, CA 90024   **(50%)**
Tel.: (310) 209-3100
Entertainment Services
N.A.I.C.S.: 711310
Irving L. Azoff *(Chm & CEO)*
Shelli Azoff *(CMO)*

AZON USA INC.
2204 Ravine Rd, Kalamazoo, MI 49004
Tel.: (269) 385-5942
Web Site: https://www.azonintl.com
Year Founded: 1977
Rev.: $21,872,076
Emp.: 50
Custom Compound Purchased Resins
N.A.I.C.S.: 325991
Tami Lee *(Dir-HR)*
Michael Vennix *(Mgr-Mktg)*
Patrick Muessig *(VP-Global Tech Ops)*
Jerry Schwabauer *(VP-Sls & Mktg)*

AZTALAN ENGINEERING, INC.
100 S Industrial Dr, Lake Mills, WI 53551
Tel.: (920) 648-3411   WI
Web Site: https://www.aztalan.com
Year Founded: 1978
Sales Range: $1-9.9 Million
Emp.: 52
Mfr of Precision Parts & Assemblies Used in Medical Equipment & Industrial Diagnostics Equipment
N.A.I.C.S.: 332710
Jim Brey *(Founder & Pres)*
Gerald Harris *(Engr-Maintenance)*
Kirk Kussman *(Dir-Sls & Mktg)*

AZTEC COMMUNICATIONS LTD.
5829 W Sam Houston Pkwy N Ste 108, Houston, TX 77041
Tel.: (713) 462-6707
Web Site: http://www.azteccom.com
Year Founded: 1987
Sales Range: $10-24.9 Million
Emp.: 50
Telephone & Telephone Equipment Installation Services
N.A.I.C.S.: 238210
David Yanez *(Mgr)*

AZTEC COMPONENTS, INC.
1201 Activity Dr, Vista, CA 92081
Tel.: (760) 305-0050

Aztec Components, Inc.—(Continued)

Web Site: https://www.aztecinc.com
Rev.: $12,700,000
Emp.: 42
Electronic Parts & Equipment Merchant Whslr
N.A.I.C.S.: 423690
Andria Stampfel (CEO)
Mindy Welch (Pres)
Alan Hamm (CFO)

AZTEC ENTERPRISES, INC.
12510 E Iliff Ave Ste 230, Aurora, CO 80014
Tel.: (949) 609-0560
Web Site:
https://www.triteksolutions.com
Year Founded: 1960
Sales Range: $10-24.9 Million
Emp.: 10
Manufacturers' Representative for Electronic Parts
N.A.I.C.S.: 423690
Donald Miller (Pres)
Brad Dannettell (Gen Mgr)

AZTEC FACILITY SERVICES INCORPORATED
11000 S Wilcrest Dr Ste 125, Houston, TX 77099-4309
Tel.: (281) 668-9000
Web Site:
http://www.aztecfacility.com
Year Founded: 1981
Rev.: $17,000,000
Emp.: 1,000
Building Maintenance & Janitorial Services
N.A.I.C.S.: 561720
Sherra Aguirre (Founder)
Kathleen Anglin (Sr VP-HR)
Rick Silverman (Exec VP-Fin)

AZTEC MATERIAL SERVICE CORP.
3624 W 26th St FL 2, Chicago, IL 60623
Tel.: (773) 521-0909
Sales Range: $10-24.9 Million
Emp.: 3
Ready Mixed Concrete
N.A.I.C.S.: 327320
Joel Arce (Pres)
Ralph Schilling (Mgr-Ops)

AZTEC NETWORKS, INC.
1 Park Plz Ste 600, Irvine, CA 92614
Tel.: (714) 373-1560
Web Site: http://www.aztecs.net
Wireless Telecommunication Services
N.A.I.C.S.: 517112
Kelly Foster (COO)
Robert J. Lopez (Founder, Pres & CEO)

AZTEC SHOPS LTD. INC.
San Diego State University, San Diego, CA 92182-1701
Tel.: (619) 594-6954   CA
Web Site:
https://www.aztecshops.com
Year Founded: 1932
Sales Range: $25-49.9 Million
Emp.: 800
Book Store & Food Management Services for Colleges
N.A.I.C.S.: 722514
Paul Melchior (Dir-Dining Svcs)
R. D. Williams (Dir-Business Development-Contract Housing)
Todd Summer (Dir-Campus Stores & Media Studies)
Jahan Jamshidi (Dir-Information Technology)

AZTEC WELL SERVICING CO. INC.
900 S Main Ave, Aztec, NM 87410
Tel.: (505) 334-6191
Web Site: http://www.aztecwell.com
Rev.: $46,518,758
Emp.: 450
Drilling Oil & Gas Wells
N.A.I.C.S.: 213111
Jerry W. Sandel (Pres)
Stewart Peterson (VP)
Carrie E. Cass (Comptroller)

AZTECA FOODS, INCORPORATED
5005 S Nagle Ave, Chicago, IL 60638
Tel.: (708) 563-6600   IL
Web Site:
http://www.aztecafoods.com
Year Founded: 1970
Sales Range: $100-124.9 Million
Emp.: 100
Tortillas, Salad Shells & Tortilla Chips Mfr
N.A.I.C.S.: 311830
Arthur R. Velasquez (Chm)
Joseph Klomes (VP-Fin)
Renee Togher (Pres)
Leticia Carcia (Dir-HR)
Julio Martinez (VP-Ops)

AZTECA RESTAURANT ENTERPRISES
15735 Ambaum Blvd SW, Burien, WA 98166
Tel.: (206) 243-7021
Web Site:
https://www.aztecamex.com
Sales Range: $25-49.9 Million
Emp.: 1,500
Mexican Restaurant
N.A.I.C.S.: 722511
Felipa Sanchez (Mgr-Mountlake Terrace)

AZTECH CONTROLS CORPORATION
324 S Bracken Ln, Chandler, AZ 85224
Tel.: (480) 782-6000
Web Site:
https://www.aztechcontrols.com
Year Founded: 1985
Sales Range: $10-24.9 Million
Emp.: 25
High Purity Fluid Handling Components: Instruments & Accessories
N.A.I.C.S.: 423830
Pat Frazier (CEO)
Jason Medhurst (Mgr-Sls)

AZTECH ELECTRIC INC.
5204 E Broadway, Spokane Valley, WA 99212-0904
Tel.: (509) 536-6200   WA
Web Site: http://www.aztech-electric.com
Year Founded: 1968
Sales Range: $10-24.9 Million
Emp.: 40
Electrical Work
N.A.I.C.S.: 238210
Andrew R. Dahlman (Pres)

AZTEX INTERNATIONAL
3010 Henson Rd, Knoxville, TN 37921
Tel.: (865) 588-5357   TN
Web Site:
http://www.candlemaking.com
Year Founded: 1986
Sales Range: $75-99.9 Million
Emp.: 4
Retailer of Candle Wax, Candle Making Accessories
N.A.I.C.S.: 457120

Gary Forrester (Pres)

AZTX CATTLE CO., LTD.
311 E Park Ave, Hereford, TX 79045
Tel.: (806) 364-8871
Web Site: http://www.aztx.com
Year Founded: 1983
Sales Range: $100-124.9 Million
Emp.: 162
Cattle Feedlots
N.A.I.C.S.: 112112
Bob Josserand (Chm)
John Josserand (Pres)

AZUL PARTNERS, INC.
625 N Michigan Ave Ste 1220, Chicago, IL 60611
Tel.: (773) 525-7406
Web Site:
http://www.azulpartners.com
Year Founded: 2004
Emp.: 15
Marketing Consulting Services
N.A.I.C.S.: 541613
Jason Busch (Co-Founder & Mng Dir-SolutionMap & Strategic Advisory)
Scott Slone (Mng Dir & CTO)
Lisa Reisman (Co-Founder, CEO & Mng Partner)
Pierre Mitchell (Chief Res Officer-UK)

Subsidiaries:

Spend Matters   (1)
625 N Michigan Ave Ste 1220, Chicago, IL 60611
Tel.: (773) 525-7406
Web Site: http://www.spendmatters.com
Research & Advisory Services
N.A.I.C.S.: 541910
Jason Busch (Founder & Mng Dir)
Scott Slone (CTO)

AZUL SYSTEMS, INC.
385 Moffett Park Dr Ste 115, Sunnyvale, CA 94089
Tel.: (650) 230-6500   DE
Web Site:
http://www.azulsystems.com
Year Founded: 2002
Sales Range: $10-24.9 Million
Emp.: 100
Data Processing Services; Data Networking
N.A.I.C.S.: 518210
Scott Sellers (Co-Founder, Pres & CEO)
Gil Tene (Co-Founder & CTO)
Anya Barski (VP-Engrg)
Howard Green (VP-Mktg)
Eric Graber (Exec VP-Field Ops-Global)
Andrew Savitz (CMO)
Peter J. Maloney (CFO & COO)

Subsidiaries:

Azul Systems United Kingdom
Limited   (1)
Albany House 14 Shute End, Wokingham, RG40 1BJ, Berkshire, United Kingdom
Tel.: (44) 8452508152
Web Site: http://www.azulsystems.com
Sales Range: $10-24.9 Million
Emp.: 5
Data Processing Services
N.A.I.C.S.: 518210

AZURE CAPITAL PARTNERS, LP
650 California St Fl 11, San Francisco, CA 94108
Tel.: (415) 276-5500
Web Site: http://www.azurecap.com
Year Founded: 2000
Sales Range: $10-24.9 Million
Emp.: 15
Venture Capital Firm
N.A.I.C.S.: 523999

Paul Weinstein (Gen Partner)
Paul A. Ferris (Gen Partner)
Mike Kwatinetz (Gen Partner)
Steve Gillan (CFO)
Andrea Drager (VP)

AZURE HOLDING GROUP CORP.
2091 Business Center Drive, Suite 212, Irvine, CA 92612
Tel.: (949) 272-3923   NV
Web Site:
http://www.azureholdinggroup.com
Year Founded: 2012
Metal Space Investment Services
N.A.I.C.S.: 523999

Subsidiaries:

Graffiti Entertainment, Inc.   (1)
30 N Gould St Ste 5291, Sheridan, WY 82801
Tel.: (307) 763-5334
Web Site:
http://www.graffitientertainment.com
Audio & Video Equipment Mfr
N.A.I.C.S.: 334310

AZURE STANDARD
79709 Dufur Valley Rd, Durfur, OR 97021
Tel.: (971) 200-8350
Web Site:
https://www.azurestandard.com
Year Founded: 1971
Sales Range: $10-24.9 Million
Emp.: 102
Food Products Mfr
N.A.I.C.S.: 311999
Shirley Kellogg (Mgr-HR)
David Stelzer (CEO)

AZZAM JORDAN
305 Washington Ave Ste 305, Baltimore, MD 21204
Tel.: (410) 825-1800
Year Founded: 1991
Sales Range: $10-24.9 Million
Emp.: 14
Advertising Agencies
N.A.I.C.S.: 541810
Linda Brooks (Controller)

AZZUR GROUP, LLC
330 S Warminster Rd Ste 341, Hatboro, PA 19040
Tel.: (215) 322-8322
Web Site: http://www.azzurgroup.com
Year Founded: 2007
Sales Range: $1-9.9 Million
Emp.: 60
Compliance Services to the Life Sciences Industry
N.A.I.C.S.: 541511
Mark O'Donnell (Pres)
Michael Khavinson (CEO)
Erik Zotter (VP)
Kevin Martin (Sr VP)
Anthony Lopez (Mng Dir)
Robert Reddick (Dir-Engrg Svcs-New England)
Cinta Burgos (VP-Consulting Svcs)
Kimberley Buytaert-Hoefen (Dir-Preclinical Consulting)
Scott Mitchell (Chief Admin Officer)
Ryan Ott (Chief Admin Officer)
Allison Kerska (Pres-Azzur Consulting)
Chris Mansur (Exec VP-Corp Dev)
Ravi Samavedam (Chief Innovation Officer)

B & B GERIG, INC.
38252 River Dr, Lebanon, OR 97355
Tel.: (541) 258-5668
Sales Range: $10-24.9 Million
Emp.: 7
Home Builder Services

N.A.I.C.S.: 236115
Bonnie L. Gerig *(Pres & Sec)*

B & G EQUIPMENT, INC.
10430 Rd 383, Philadelphia, MS
39350
Tel.: (601) 656-7011
Web Site:
https://www.bandgequip.com
Rev.: $10,800,000
Emp.: 60
Whole Construction & Mining Machine Repair Services
N.A.I.C.S.: 423810
Jeff Lee *(Mgr-Parts)*
Debbie Webb *(Pres)*
W. J. Bates *(CEO)*
Charles Martin *(Mgr-Svc)*
Justin Webb *(VP & Mgr-Sls)*
Kenny Sims *(Mgr-Svc)*
Rodney Kelley *(Branch Mgr)*
Ron Miles *(Mgr-Svc)*
Stephen Hudson *(Mgr-Svc)*
Randal Williamson *(Branch Mgr)*

B & G WHOLESALE DISTRIBUTING, INC.
6 Berry Rd, Houston, TX 77022
Tel.: (713) 691-1247
Web Site: https://www.bngdist.com
Year Founded: 1970
Rev.: $100,000,000
Emp.: 50
Tobacco & Tobacco Products
N.A.I.C.S.: 424130
Abe Baba *(CFO)*

B & I CONTRACTORS, INC.
2701 Prince St, Fort Myers, FL 33916
Tel.: (239) 332-4646
Web Site:
http://www.bandicontractors.com
Year Founded: 1960
Sales Range: $10-24.9 Million
Emp.: 520
Mechanical, Electrical & Plumbing
N.A.I.C.S.: 238210
Gary H. Griffin *(Pres)*
Jason N. Grabowski *(VP)*
Brian Kelly *(CFO, Treas & Sec)*

B & W MECHANICAL CONTRACTORS, INC.
1940 Riverside Pkwy, Lawrenceville, GA 30091
Tel.: (770) 449-6000
Sales Range: $10-24.9 Million
Emp.: 140
Plumbing, Heating & Air Conditioning Contractor Services
N.A.I.C.S.: 238220
James A. Hamilton *(CFO & Sec)*
Douglas D. Martin *(CEO)*

B B H SOLUTIONS, INC.
121 E 24th St, New York, NY 10010
Tel.: (212) 475-7100   NY
Web Site: http://www.bbhinc.com
Year Founded: 1989
Sales Range: $10-24.9 Million
Emp.: 85
Computer Integrated Systems Design
N.A.I.C.S.: 541512
John McCann *(Controller)*

B CAPITAL TECHNOLOGY OPPORTUNITIES CORP.
10 Hudson Yards, New York, NY 10001
Tel.: (310) 698-1270   Ky
Year Founded: 2021
Investment Services
N.A.I.C.S.: 523999

Howard Morgan *(Chm)*
Raj Ganguly *(CEO)*
Kabir Narang *(Pres)*
Angela Huang *(VP)*

B FERNANDEZ & HNOS INC.
Carr 5 Ste 305 Urb Industrial Luchetti, Bayamon, PR 00961
Tel.: (787) 288-7272
Web Site:
https://www.bfernandez.com
Rev.: $84,100,000
Emp.: 400
Beer & Other Fermented Malt Liquors; Distributors
N.A.I.C.S.: 424610
Jose Teixidor *(Chm)*
Jose Maltonado *(COO)*

B PLUS L TECHNOLOGIES INC.
3570 Charter Park, San Jose, CA 95136
Tel.: (408) 269-7884
Web Site: https://www.bplusl.com
Year Founded: 1991
Electronic Converters, Transformers & Electronic Ballasts Mfr
N.A.I.C.S.: 335311
David Wong *(Pres)*

B RESOURCE, INC.
2407 Timberloch Place Ste G, The Woodlands, TX 77380
Tel.: (281) 440-7300
Web Site: http://www.bresource.com
Year Founded: 2001
Sales Range: $1-9.9 Million
Emp.: 20
IT Systems Support, Network Design & Technical Services
N.A.I.C.S.: 519290
Hal Brumfield *(CEO)*

B SCENE ADVERTISING AGENCY
3419 Via Lido Ste 649, Newport Beach, CA 92663
Tel.: (949) 777-6772
Year Founded: 1985
Rev.: $10,000,000
Emp.: 33
N.A.I.C.S.: 541810
Caren Lancona *(CEO & Strategist)*

B&B AIR CONDITIONING & HEATING SERVICE COMPANY
12324 Wilkins Ave, Rockville, MD 20852
Tel.: (301) 881-2700
Web Site:
https://www.bbairconditioning.com
Year Founded: 1957
Sales Range: $10-24.9 Million
Emp.: 100
Air Conditioning Repair Services
N.A.I.C.S.: 811412
Louis C. Copeland *(Chm)*
Robin Rhodes *(Exec VP)*

B&B APPLIANCE COMPANY INC.
24470 Lakeland Blvd, Euclid, OH 44132
Tel.: (216) 261-5600   OH
Web Site:
http://www.bbappliance.com
Year Founded: 1924
Sales Range: $10-24.9 Million
Emp.: 45
Major Electric Household Appliances
N.A.I.C.S.: 449210
Jeffrey S. Blumenthal *(Pres)*
Mark Blumenthal *(VP)*

B&B ARMR CORPORATION

5900 S Lake Forest Dr Ste 230, McKinney, TX 75070
Tel.: (972) 385-7899
Web Site: http://www.bb-armr.com
Year Founded: 1925
Traffic Control Products, Crash Barriers, Warning Gates, Perimeter Security Gates & Railroad Crossing Safety Barriers Mfr
N.A.I.C.S.: 561621
Paul Matthews *(CEO)*

B&B BEST-BUY FOODS INC.
16 E Greenbrook Rd, Caldwell, NJ 07006-4320
Tel.: (201) 991-3919
Sales Range: $10-24.9 Million
Emp.: 33
Groceries, General Line
N.A.I.C.S.: 424410
Angelo Baldassare *(Pres)*

B&B BUILDERS, INC.
152 E Main St Ste 107, Rigby, ID 83442
Tel.: (208) 745-0870
Web Site: http://www.bbbuilders.com
Year Founded: 1993
Rev.: $7,700,000
Emp.: 17
Construction Services
N.A.I.C.S.: 238170
Brent Johnson *(Pres)*
Heather Hansen *(Office Mgr)*

B&B CONCRETE COMPANY INC.
130 N Industrial Rd, Tupelo, MS 38801
Tel.: (662) 842-6312
Web Site:
https://www.bbconcrete.com
Rev.: $17,500,000
Emp.: 68
Ready Mixed Concrete
N.A.I.C.S.: 327320
David E. Brevard *(Pres)*

B&B CONTRACTORS & DEVELOPERS
2781 Salt Springs Rd, Youngstown, OH 44509
Tel.: (330) 270-5020
Web Site: http://www.bbcdonline.com
Rev.: $23,212,081
Emp.: 40
Commercial & Office Building Contractors
N.A.I.C.S.: 236220
Philip M. Beshara *(Pres)*
Sam J. Decaria *(Treas)*

Subsidiaries:

B&B Construction Co. of Ohio   (1)
2781 Salt Springs Rd, Youngstown, OH 44509
Tel.: (330) 270-5020
Web Site: http://www.bbconline.com
Sales Range: $10-24.9 Million
Commercial & Office Building, New Construction
N.A.I.C.S.: 236220
Frank Beshara *(Pres)*

B&B CORPORATE HOLDINGS, INC.
927 US Hwy 301 S, Tampa, FL 33619
Tel.: (813) 621-6411   FL
Web Site: http://www.bnbch.com
Year Founded: 1995
Sales Range: $50-74.9 Million
Emp.: 750
Holding Company; Grocery Store Operator; Real Estate
N.A.I.C.S.: 551112
Jay Andrew Bever Jr. *(Pres)*

Subsidiaries:

B&B Cash Grocery Stores, Inc.   (1)
927 S US Hwy 301, Tampa, FL 33619-4338   (100%)
Tel.: (813) 621-6411
Grocery Stores
N.A.I.C.S.: 445110

Handy Food Stores Inc.   (1)
927 S US Hwy 301, Tampa, FL 33619-4338   (100%)
Tel.: (813) 621-6411
Sales Range: $1-9.9 Million
Emp.: 176
Grocery Stores
N.A.I.C.S.: 445131

B&B DEPARTMENT STORES SOUTH
254 Drum Point Rd, Ocean City, NJ 08226
Tel.: (732) 920-3300
Web Site: http://www.bnbstores.com
Sales Range: $10-24.9 Million
Emp.: 40
Ready-To-Wear Apparel, Women's
N.A.I.C.S.: 458110
Helen Bertole *(Owner)*

B&B ELECTRONICS MANUFACTURING COMPANY
707 Dayton Rd, Ottawa, IL 61350
Tel.: (815) 433-5100   DE
Web Site: http://www.bb-elec.com
Year Founded: 1981
Emp.: 100
Connectivity Technologies Developer & Mfr
N.A.I.C.S.: 334417
Dennis Martin *(Engr-Mfg Test Dev)*
Jerry O'Gorman *(Pres)*

Subsidiaries:

Quatech, LLC   (1)
5675 Hudson Industrial Pkwy, Hudson, OH 44236   (100%)
Tel.: (330) 655-9000
Web Site: http://www.quatech.com
Networking & Connectivity Solutions Developer
N.A.I.C.S.: 334417
Stewart Guy *(VP-Ops)*

B&B GLASS, INC.
1145 N Oro Vista Litchfield Park, Phoenix, AZ 85043
Tel.: (623) 580-8898
Year Founded: 1973
Sales Range: $10-24.9 Million
Emp.: 20
Glass & Glazing Work
N.A.I.C.S.: 238150
John Collier *(Sec)*
David Guerin *(Pres & CEO)*

B&B JOBBER SERVICES, INC.
303 Roosevelt Ave, Spring Valley, NY 10977
Tel.: (845) 352-4600
Web Site: http://www.autoprollc.com
Sales Range: $25-49.9 Million
Emp.: 50
Sales of Automotive Supplies & Parts
N.A.I.C.S.: 441330
Robert Mayer *(Mgr)*

B&B OFFICE SYSTEMS, INC.
3213 SW 42nd St, Gainesville, FL 32608
Tel.: (352) 335-3542   FL
Web Site: http://www.bbos.com
Year Founded: 1985
Sales Range: $1-9.9 Million
Emp.: 17
Office Equipment Retailer, Installer & Maintainer
N.A.I.C.S.: 423420

B&B Office Systems, Inc.—(Continued)

Harold Deck (Pres)
Rick Bolwan (Mgr-Svc)
Josh Rubinchik (Mgr-Mktg)

B&B SAAB
1011 E El Camino Real, Sunnyvale, CA 94087-3748
Tel.: (408) 247-3444
Web Site: http://www.bbsaab.com
Rev.: $19,800,000
Emp.: 36
New & Used Car Dealers
N.A.I.C.S.: 441110
Vincent Vandell (Dir-Svcs-Parts)

B&B SURPLUS, INC.
7020 Rosedale Hwy, Bakersfield, CA 93308-5842
Tel.: (661) 589-0381
Web Site: http://www.bbmetals.com
Year Founded: 1963
Sales Range: $10-24.9 Million
Emp.: 80
Pipe & Tubing, Steel
N.A.I.C.S.: 423510
Donice Boylan (VP)
Allen Arrington (Mgr-Ops)

B&D INDUSTRIAL, INC.
607 Lower Poplar St, Macon, GA 31201
Tel.: (478) 746-7623
Web Site:
   http://www.bdindustrial.com
Sales Range: $75-99.9 Million
Emp.: 350
Holding Company
N.A.I.C.S.: 551112
Andy Nations (CEO)
Lauren Lanter (CFO & Exec VP)
Benjamin Nations (Co-COO & Exec VP)
Brian Davis (Co-COO & Exec VP)

Subsidiaries:

B&D Technologies   (1)
588 12th St, Macon, GA 31201-3521
Tel.: (478) 742-8444
Web Site: http://www.bdindustrial.com
Sales Range: $75-99.9 Million
Emp.: 250
Industrial Supplies
N.A.I.C.S.: 423840
Andrew H. Nations (Pres & CEO)
Linda Miller (VP-HR & IT)
Harold Sharp (VP)
Don Upchurch (Gen Mgr-Ops & Scale Sys)
Brian Davis (VP)

Subsidiary (Domestic):

Simco Technologies Inc.   (2)
3905 Steve Reynolds Blvd Ste 100, Norcross, GA 30093-3097
Tel.: (770) 729-9100
Web Site: http://www.simcotech.com
Emp.: 20
Industrial Machinery & Equipment Distr
N.A.I.C.S.: 423830
Andy Nations (Owner)

Scale Systems Inc.   (1)
3905 Steve Reynolds Blvd Ste 100, Norcross, GA 30093-3097   **(100%)**
Tel.: (770) 921-1988
Web Site: http://www.scalesys.com
Sales Range: $10-24.9 Million
Emp.: 35
Industrial Equipment
N.A.I.C.S.: 423440
Don Upchurch (Gen Mgr)
Mark Burbine (VP-Sls)

B&D SALES & MARKETING, INC.
77 Brant Ave Ste 202, Clark, NJ 07066-1540
Tel.: (732) 340-1010   NJ

Web Site:
   http://www.bdsalesmarketing.com
Year Founded: 1986
Sales Range: $10-24.9 Million
Emp.: 15
General Line Groceries
N.A.I.C.S.: 424410
Andrew Michael Desalvo (Pres & CEO)
Wally Bycsek (VP)

B&F FINANCE CORP.
3000 S Stemmons, Lake Dallas, TX 75065
Tel.: (940) 497-5080
Year Founded: 1973
Sales Range: $25-49.9 Million
Emp.: 102
Personal Credit Institutions
N.A.I.C.S.: 522291
Robert C. Ramirez (Pres)

B&G FOOD ENTERPRISES INC.
1430 Sandra St, Morgan City, LA 70380
Tel.: (985) 384-3333
Web Site: https://www.bgfood.com
Year Founded: 1982
Rev.: $24,302,952
Emp.: 1,400
Fast Food Franchise Operator
N.A.I.C.S.: 722511
Brenda C. Hamer (Co-Founder & Sec)
Gregory J. Hamer (Co-Founder & CEO)
Jay Leblanc (VP-HR)
Ellen Pennison (CFO & VP)
John B. Hover Sr. (Exec VP-Ops)

Subsidiaries:

B&G Diversified Concepts LLC   (1)
1430 Sandra St, Morgan City, LA 70380
Tel.: (985) 384-3333
Web Site: http://www.bgfood.com
Fast-Food Restaurant, Chain
N.A.I.C.S.: 722513
Greg Hamer (Pres)

B&G Food Enterprises Texas LLC   (1)
1430 Sandra St, Morgan City, LA 70380
Tel.: (985) 384-3333
Web Site: http://bgfood.com
Rev.: $8,163,556
Fast-Food Restaurant, Chain
N.A.I.C.S.: 722513
Gregory J. Hamer Sr. (Founder & CEO)

B&G INDUSTRIES, LTD.
171 S Newman St, Hackensack, NJ 07601-3125
Tel.: (631) 669-6000
Web Site:
   http://www.bgelectrical.com
Rev.: $27,625,000
Electrical Contractor
N.A.I.C.S.: 238210
James T. Giorgio (Pres)
George Maley (Mgr-Acctg)

Subsidiaries:

B&G Electrical Contractors of NY   (1)
7100 New Horizon Blvd, Amityville, NY 11701   **(100%)**
Tel.: (631) 669-6000
Web Site: http://www.bgny.com
General Electrical Contractor
N.A.I.C.S.: 238210
Jim Turner (Controller)

B&G MANUFACTURING CO. INC.
3067 Unionville Pike, Hatfield, PA 19440-1822
Tel.: (215) 822-1925   PA
Web Site: https://www.bgmfg.com
Year Founded: 1989

Sales Range: $10-24.9 Million
Emp.: 300
Mfr of Bolts, Nuts, Rivets & Washers
N.A.I.C.S.: 332722
Bill Edmonds (Pres)
Rich Edmonds (VP)

B&G PLASTICS, INC.
37 Empire St, Newark, NJ 07114
Tel.: (973) 824-9220
Web Site: http://www.bgintr.com
Sales Range: $10-24.9 Million
Emp.: 120
Clothes Hangers, Plastics
N.A.I.C.S.: 326199
Chet Kolton (Pres)

B&G WHOLESALE DISTRIBUTING INC.
6th Berry Rd, Houston, TX 77022
Tel.: (713) 691-1247
Web Site: https://www.bngdist.com
Rev.: $130,500,000
Emp.: 50
Tobacco & Tobacco Product Merchant Whslr
N.A.I.C.S.: 424940
Jad Baba (VP)
Issa Baba (Pres)
Abe Baba (Gen Mgr)
Abraham Ganim (Treas)
Eisa Ganim (Sec)

B&H EDUCATION, INC.
501 S Beverly Dr Ste 240, Beverly Hills, CA 90212
Tel.: (310) 552-3838
Web Site:
   http://www.bheducation.com
Year Founded: 2003
Sales Range: $10-24.9 Million
Emp.: 200
Owner & Operator of Beauty Schools
N.A.I.C.S.: 611511
Nagui Elyas (Pres)
Rashed Elyas (CEO)
Michael Flecker (CFO)

Subsidiaries:

Marinello Schools of Beauty   (1)
12449 Putnam St, Whittier, CA 90602
Tel.: (562) 945-2211
Web Site: http://www.marinello.com
Sales Range: $10-24.9 Million
Emp.: 100
Beauty Schools
N.A.I.C.S.: 611511
Nagui Elyas (Pres & COO)
Devanshi Gandhi (Mgr-Bus Intelligence)
Marcus Vanderhoef (Mgr-Accts Payables)

B&H FOTO & ELECTRONIC CORP.
440 W 9th Ave, New York, NY 10001-1620
Tel.: (212) 239-7500   NY
Web Site:
   http://www.bhphotovideo.com
Year Founded: 1973
Sales Range: $75-99.9 Million
Emp.: 1,900
Photographic & Video Equipment Distr
N.A.I.C.S.: 449210
Sam Goldstein (Pres)

B&H MAINTENANCE & CONSTRUCTION INC.
S Hwy 207, Eunice, NM 88231
Tel.: (505) 394-2588   NM
Web Site: http://www.bhpipeline.com
Year Founded: 1969
Sales Range: $25-49.9 Million
Emp.: 600
Supplier of Water, Sewer & Utility Lines
N.A.I.C.S.: 237120

Dale Bettis (Pres & CEO)
Billy Thrash (VP)
Charlie Bettis (VP)
Scott Lee (Controller)
Gary Bettis (VP)

B&H MANUFACTURING COMPANY
3461 Roeding Rd, Ceres, CA 95307
Tel.: (209) 537-5785
Web Site:
   https://www.bhlabeling.com
Year Founded: 1969
Sales Range: $10-24.9 Million
Emp.: 45
Labelling Machinery Mfr
N.A.I.C.S.: 333993
Bob Adamson (VP-Sales)

B&I AUTO SUPPLIES INC.
135 Commerce Dr, Fort Washington, PA 19034
Tel.: (215) 643-9393
Web Site: http://bandiautosupply.com
Sales Range: $10-24.9 Million
Emp.: 200
Automotive Supplies
N.A.I.C.S.: 423120
Joseph Pluck (Pres & CEO)
Kevin Pluck (VP)
Lisa Bono (Office Mgr)
Mike Vixler (Gen Mgr)

B&J BUILDER'S SUPPLY & SERVICE
2325 Hutson Rd, Green Bay, WI 54303
Tel.: (920) 499-9778
Rev.: $10,000,000
Emp.: 39
Lumber, Plywood & Millwork
N.A.I.C.S.: 423310
Lawrence Burklund (Pres)
Rick Burklund (VP)

B&J PHOTO, INC.
525 N Main St, Findlay, OH 45840
Tel.: (419) 424-0903
Sales Range: $10-24.9 Million
Emp.: 8
Photographic Equipment & Supplies
N.A.I.C.S.: 423410

B&K COMPONENTS LTD.
2100 Old Union Rd, Buffalo, NY 14227
Tel.: (716) 656-0026
Web Site: http://www.bkcomp.com
Year Founded: 1981
Sales Range: $10-24.9 Million
Emp.: 34
Audio Electronic Systems Mfr
N.A.I.C.S.: 334310
John L. Beyer III (Pres)

B&K CONSTRUCTION CO. INC.
1905 Hwy 59, Mandeville, LA 70448
Tel.: (985) 626-1866
Web Site: https://www.bkconst.com
Sales Range: $10-24.9 Million
Emp.: 100
Underground Utilities Contractor
N.A.I.C.S.: 237110
Howard B. Kenyon (Owner & Pres)

B&K ELECTRIC WHOLESALE
1225 S Johnson Dr, City of Industry, CA 91745-2409
Tel.: (626) 965-5040
Web Site: https://www.bk-electric.com
Year Founded: 1958
Sales Range: $10-24.9 Million
Emp.: 90
Sales of Electrical Apparatus

N.A.I.C.S.: 423610
Kathleen Ellison (CEO)
Todd Brown (Pres)

B&K ENTERPRISES INC.
7109 Alexandria Pike, Alexandria, KY
41001
Tel.: (859) 635-1400
Web Site:
http://www.alexandriamarket.com
Rev.: $12,500,000
Emp.: 100
Independent Supermarket
N.A.I.C.S.: 445110
Dave Kramer (Owner)
Peggy Kramer (VP)

**B&L WHOLESALE SUPPLY
INC.**
70 Hartford St, Rochester, NY 14605-
2520
Tel.: (585) 546-6616   NY
Web Site:
http://www.blwholesale.com
Year Founded: 1950
Roofing, Siding & Insulation Whslrs
N.A.I.C.S.: 423330
Donald R. Tomeny (Pres)
Art Finocchario (VP)

B&M INDUSTRIAL, INC.
7170 Copperqueen Dr., El Paso, TX
79915-1225
Tel.: (915) 772-9007
Web Site: https://bmindustrial.com
Year Founded: 1946
Electric Power Transmission, Control
& Distr
N.A.I.C.S.: 221122

Subsidiaries:

C-D Electric, Inc.   (1)
617 High Starr Dr, Corpus Christi, TX
78408
Tel.: (361) 888-4133
Web Site: http://www.c-delectric.com
Sales Range: $1-9.9 Million
Emp.: 17
Electrical Apparatus And Equipment, Nsk
N.A.I.C.S.: 423610
William J. Pittaway (Principal)

B&M METALS LP
603 Major Acrombie Cir, Murrayville,
GA 30564
Tel.: (706) 864-6068
Web Site:
http://www.qualitymetalroofing.com
Year Founded: 1972
Sales Range: $25-49.9 Million
Emp.: 16
Metal Roofing Supplier
N.A.I.C.S.: 423330
Chris Bryan (Pres)
Angie Cain (Treas)

**B&M ROOFING OF COLO-
RADO. INC.**
3768 Eureka Way, Frederick, CO
80516
Tel.: (303) 443-5843
Web Site: https://www.bmroofing.com
Sales Range: $10-24.9 Million
Emp.: 65
Roofing Contractors
N.A.I.C.S.: 238160
Rick Rosendahl (CFO)

B&P MANUFACTURING
8051 E Boon Rd, Cadillac, MI 49601-
9013
Tel.: (231) 775-2229   MI
Web Site: https://www.bpmfg.com
Year Founded: 1984
Sales Range: $50-74.9 Million
Emp.: 50
Mfr of Material Handling Equipment

N.A.I.C.S.: 331318
Pat Mys (Mgr-Sls & Mktg)
Gale Merchant (CFO)

B&R MOLL, INC.
124 Railroad Dr Northhampton Park,
Ivyland, PA 18974
Tel.: (267) 288-0282
Web Site: http://www.moll.com
Sales Range: $10-24.9 Million
Emp.: 72
Industrial Machinery & Equipment
N.A.I.C.S.: 423830

B&R STORES INC.
4554 W St, Lincoln, NE 68503-2831
Tel.: (402) 464-6297   NE
Web Site: https://www.brstores.com
Year Founded: 1964
Emp.: 2,000
Grocery Store Services
N.A.I.C.S.: 445110
Pat Raybould (Pres)

B&R SUPERMARKET INC.
11 N Royal Poinciana Blvd, Miami
Springs, FL 33166
Tel.: (305) 884-4870
Sales Range: $25-49.9 Million
Emp.: 100
Grocery Stores
N.A.I.C.S.: 445110
Allen Milam (Pres)
Angie Herrera (Mgr-DP)

**B&S ELECTRIC SUPPLY CO.
INC.**
4505 Mills Pl SW, Atlanta, GA 30336
Tel.: (404) 696-8284
Web Site: http://www.b-s-electric.com
Sales Range: $25-49.9 Million
Emp.: 20
Electrical Supplies
N.A.I.C.S.: 423610
Clarence W. Robie (Pres)
Charlie Waits (Mgr-Sls)

**B&S FRAGRANCES & COS-
METICS INC.**
39-50 63rd St Woodside, New York,
NY 11377
Tel.: (212) 447-7206
Rev.: $19,832,760
Emp.: 9
Perfumes
N.A.I.C.S.: 424210
Saleem Khan (Pres)

B&S LOGGING INC.
4411 NW Elliott Ln, Prineville, OR
97754-8262
Tel.: (541) 447-3175
Rev.: $14,000,000
Emp.: 40
Logging
N.A.I.C.S.: 113310
Michael Brown (Pres)

B&T EXPRESS INC.
400 Miley Rd, North Lima, OH 44452
Tel.: (330) 549-0000
Web Site: https://www.btxpinc.com
Sales Range: $25-49.9 Million
Emp.: 75
Heavy Hauling Services
N.A.I.C.S.: 484121
Breen O'Malley (Pres)
William Rypcinski (VP-Ops)

B&T METALS CO.
425 W Town St, Columbus, OH
43215
Tel.: (614) 228-5411
Sales Range: $1-9.9 Million
Emp.: 2

Trim & Rims for Walls & Floors; In-
dustrial, Commercial & Architectural
Aluminum Extrusions, Fabrication &
Anodizing
N.A.I.C.S.: 332813
David Tolbert (Pres)
James Whitaker (CFO)

B&W PRESS, INC.
401 E Main St, Georgetown, MA
01833
Tel.: (978) 352-6100
Web Site: http://www.bwpress.com
Year Founded: 1966
Sales Range: $75-99.9 Million
Emp.: 50
Mfr of Direct Mail Bind-in Order Form
Envelopes for Catalogs, Magazines &
Direct Response Specialty Format
Mailers
N.A.I.C.S.: 322230
Paul Beegan (Owner)

B-B-F OIL COMPANY INC.
5506 Jefferson Pkwy, Pine Bluff, AR
71602
Tel.: (870) 247-5699
Web Site: http://www.bbfoil.com
Year Founded: 1968
Sales Range: $10-24.9 Million
Emp.: 63
Wholesale Distr of Petroleum Prod-
ucts
N.A.I.C.S.: 424720
Steven D. Ferren (Pres)

B-H TRANSFER CO
750 Sparta Rd, Sandersville, GA
31082
Tel.: (478) 552-5119
Web Site: https://www.b-
htransfer.com
Rev.: $24,000,000
Emp.: 140
Local Trucking without Storage
N.A.I.C.S.: 484110
Frank Young (Pres)
Jay Hinton (Dir-Maintenance)
Tommy Cauthen (Dir-Safety & Com-
pliance)
Rob Rowe (VP-Intermodal Ops)

B-LINE APPAREL, INC.
4671 E 11th Ave, Hialeah, FL 33013
Tel.: (305) 953-8300   FL
Web Site:
http://www.blineapparel.com
Year Founded: 1997
Sales Range: $1-9.9 Million
Emp.: 20
Advertising Specialties, Corporate
Identity, Fashion/Apparel, Point of
Sale, Print, Publicity/Promotions,
Sweepstakes, Travel & Tourism
N.A.I.C.S.: 541870
Jose Beguiristain (Pres & CEO)

B-SCADA, INC.
Tel.: (352) 564-9610   DE
Web Site: http://www.b-scada.com
Year Founded: 2003
SCDA—(OTCBB)
Online Graphics & Visualization Soft-
ware Products Developer
N.A.I.C.S.: 513210
Brian S. Thornton (VP)
Allen Ronald DeSerranno (CEO)

**B-SHARP MUSICAL PRODUC-
TIONS**
200 Frank Rd, Hicksville, NY 11801
Tel.: (516) 626-8300
Web Site: https://www.hanklane.com
Rev.: $10,000,000
Emp.: 30
Orchestras & Bands

N.A.I.C.S.: 711130
Hank Lane (Pres)

B. CATALANI, INC.
1500 S Zarzamora Unit 326, San An-
tonio, TX 78207-7210
Tel.: (210) 227-2266
Web Site: https://bcatalani.com
Year Founded: 1888
Sales Range: $10-24.9 Million
Emp.: 50
Fresh Fruit & Vegetable Whslr
N.A.I.C.S.: 424480
Dan Catalani (CEO)

B. DAZZLE, INC.
500 Meyer Ln, Redondo Beach, CA
90278
Tel.: (310) 374-3000
Web Site: https://www.b-dazzle.com
Year Founded: 1993
Sales Range: $1-9.9 Million
Emp.: 10
Puzzles, Games & Gifts Mfr
N.A.I.C.S.: 339930
Marshall P. Gavin (Exec VP)
Jorge Uribe (Mgr-Customer Svc)

B. GREEN & CO.
1300 S Monroe St, Baltimore, MD
21230-1712
Tel.: (410) 783-7777   MD
Web Site: http://www.bgreenco.com
Year Founded: 1915
Sales Range: $75-99.9 Million
Emp.: 200
Grocery Services
N.A.I.C.S.: 424410
Benjamin L. Green (Exec VP)
Ken Middleton (MIS Dir)
Cynthia Hoover (Mgr-AP)

**B. H. CRAIG CONSTRUCTION
COMPANY**
835 Wall St, Florence, AL 35630
Tel.: (256) 766-3350
Web Site:
https://www.bhcraigconst.com
Sales Range: $10-24.9 Million
Emp.: 75
Nonresidential Construction Services
N.A.I.C.S.: 236220
David Marbury (Pres)

B. LITTLE & COMPANY INC.
200 Park S Ste 117, New York, NY
10003
Tel.: (212) 328-3441
Web Site: http://www.blittle.com
Rev.: $14,700,000
Emp.: 11
Games, Toys & Children's Vehicles
N.A.I.C.S.: 339930
Kathy Vosters (Pres)
Bret Itskowitch (Exec VP & Dir-Client
Svcs & Bus Dev)

**B. MOSS CLOTHING COM-
PANY LTD.**
550 Meadowlands Pkwy, Secaucus,
NJ 07094
Tel.: (201) 866-6677
Rev.: $58,587,000
Emp.: 90
Women's Ready-To-Wear Apparel
N.A.I.C.S.: 458110
Richard Moss (Pres)

B. SCHOENBERG & CO. INC.
345 Kear St, Yorktown Heights, NY
10598
Tel.: (914) 962-1200
Web Site:
https://www.bschoenberg.info
Sales Range: $10-24.9 Million
Emp.: 25

B. Schoenberg & Co. Inc.—(Continued)
Buys & Sell Plastics Materials
N.A.I.C.S.: 424610
Brad Schoenberg (Pres)

B. SMITH ENTERPRISES LTD.
320 W 46th St, New York, NY 10108
Tel.: (212) 465-2284
Web Site: http://www.bsmith.com
Year Founded: 1986
Sales Range: $50-74.9 Million
Emp.: 35
Lifestyle Improvement, Advice, Skills, Guidance & Consumer Products Reaching Women & Men Through Television, Publishing, Restaurants, Merchandising & the Internet
N.A.I.C.S.: 722511
Dan Gasby (Founder)
Barbara L. Smith (Owner & Pres)

B.A. SWEETIE CANDY COMPANY
6770 Brookpark Rd, Cleveland, OH 44129
Tel.: (216) 739-2244   OH
Web Site:
    http://www.sweetiescandy.com
Year Founded: 1993
Sales Range: $1-9.9 Million
Emp.: 14
Whol Confectionery Ret Candy/Confectionery
N.A.I.C.S.: 424450
Tom Scheiman (Co-Owner & Pres)
Judi Scheiman (Co-Owner)

Subsidiaries:

The Humphrey Company   (1)
6770 Brookpark Rd, Cleveland, OH 44129
Tel.: (216) 739-2244
Web Site:
    http://www.humphreycompany.com
All Other Miscellaneous Crop Farming
N.A.I.C.S.: 111998

B.A.G. CORP.
1155 Kas Dr Ste 170, Richardson, TX 75081
Tel.: (214) 340-7060
Web Site: http://www.bagcorp.com
Year Founded: 1969
Sales Range: $25-49.9 Million
Emp.: 30
Bag Mfr
N.A.I.C.S.: 424130
Jodi Simons (Pres)
Bill Montgomery (Dir-IT)
Bobby Brown (Engr-Design)
Charlotte Chandler (Mgr-New Products & New Bus)
Cindy Finley (VP)
Nancy Cline (Dir-Quality Control)
Ron Futrell (CFO)
Dyrle Whipple (VP)
Deb Gilliam (Mgr-HR)

B.B. HOBBS, INC.
1340 Harry Byrd Hwy, Darlington, SC 29540
Tel.: (843) 395-2120
Web Site: http://www.bbhobbs.com
Year Founded: 1988
Sales Range: $10-24.9 Million
Emp.: 45
Farm & Garden Machinery Whslr
N.A.I.C.S.: 423820
Bryan B. Hobbs (Founder, Pres & CEO)

B.B.X. INC.
7310 Chestnut Rdg Rd, Lockport, NY 14094
Tel.: (716) 434-8200   NY
Web Site: https://www.bbxtrans.com
Year Founded: 1969

General & Specialized Freight Trucking Services
N.A.I.C.S.: 484121
Robert E. Lewis (Pres & CEO)

B.C. BUNDT, INC.
5221 Ehrlich Rd, Tampa, FL 33624
Tel.: (813) 963-2784
Web Site: http://www.bcbundt.com
Year Founded: 1986
Sales Range: $10-24.9 Million
Emp.: 8
Cakes, Bakery: Except Frozen
N.A.I.C.S.: 311812
James Hokes (COO)

B.C. CLARK INC.
101 Park Ave, Oklahoma City, OK 73102
Tel.: (405) 232-8806
Web Site: http://www.bcclark.com
Rev.: $16,679,197
Emp.: 26
Jewelry, Precious Stones & Precious Metals
N.A.I.C.S.: 458310
Jim C. Clark (Chm)
Colemann Clark (Pres)
Robert Mayberry (Mgr-Store Ops)

B.C. MOORE & SON INC
101 S Green St, Wadesboro, NC 28170-2782
Tel.: (704) 694-2171   GA
Year Founded: 1952
Sales Range: $10-24.9 Million
Emp.: 35
Department Stores
N.A.I.C.S.: 455110

B.C.S. FINANCIAL CORP.
2 Mid America Plz Ste 200, Oakbrook Terrace, IL 60181-4712
Tel.: (630) 472-7700
Web Site: http://www.bcsf.com
Year Founded: 1985
Sales Range: $250-299.9 Million
Emp.: 102
Insurance Services
N.A.I.C.S.: 524126
Edward J. Baran (Chm, Pres & CEO)
Peter L. Costello (Pres & CEO)
Susan C. Lindquist (Chief Talent Officer)
Terry M. Hackett (Gen Counsel & Sec)
James A. Drew (Sr VP-Strategic Ventures)
Wendell Ferguson (VP-IT)

Subsidiaries:

B.C.S. Insurance Company Inc.   (1)
676 N Saint Clair St, Chicago, IL 60611-2927
Tel.: (312) 951-7700
Sales Range: $50-74.9 Million
Emp.: 100
Accident & Health Insurance
N.A.I.C.S.: 524126

B.F. MYERS FURNITURE COMPANY, INC.
117 French St, Goodlettsville, TN 37072
Tel.: (615) 859-1301
Web Site:
    https://www.bfmyersfurniture.com
Sales Range: $10-24.9 Million
Emp.: 43
Furniture Whslr
N.A.I.C.S.: 449110
Bob Erwin (Owner)

B.F. RICH CO. INC.
322 Ruthar Dr, Newark, DE 19711
Tel.: (302) 894-0498
Web Site: http://www.bfrich.com

Year Founded: 1957
Sales Range: $10-24.9 Million
Emp.: 250
Windows, Plastics
N.A.I.C.S.: 326199
Terry T. Rex (Dir-Mktg)
Richard Rebmann (CFO)
George Simmons (Pres)
Chris Lorber (Mgr-Sls)

B.H. AIRCRAFT CO., INC.
2230 Smithtown Ave, Ronkonkoma, NY 11779
Tel.: (631) 981-4200   NY
Web Site: https://www.bhaircraft.com
Year Founded: 1933
Sales Range: $75-99.9 Million
Emp.: 150
Aircraft Engine Parts Mfr
N.A.I.C.S.: 336412
Vincent E. Kearns (Chm)
Robert J. Aversano (VP-Mfg)
Laura Bishop (Mgr-Pur)

B.H. BUNN COMPANY
2730 Drane Field Rd, Lakeland, FL 33811-1325
Tel.: (863) 647-1555
Web Site: https://www.bunntyco.com
Year Founded: 1907
Sales Range: $50-74.9 Million
Emp.: 15
Package Tying Machines, Strapping Equipment, Polypropylene Strapping, Strapping Hand Tools, Tying Twines & Poly Tape Mfr
N.A.I.C.S.: 333993
John R. Bunn (Pres)

B.H.T. ELECTRONICS PURCHASING INC.
29 W 46th St, New York, NY 10036-4119
Tel.: (212) 944-8417   NY
Year Founded: 1989
Sales Range: $10-24.9 Million
Emp.: 10
Electronic Parts & Equipment Retailer
N.A.I.C.S.: 423690
Hersel Torkian (Pres)

Subsidiaries:

Torkian-Zargari Trading Corp.   (1)
729 7th Ave, New York, NY 10019-6831
Tel.: (212) 302-5388
Sales Range: $10-24.9 Million
Radio, Television & Electronics Retailer
N.A.I.C.S.: 449210

B.J. ALAN COMPANY
555 Martin Luther King Jr Blvd, Youngstown, OH 44502-1102
Tel.: (330) 746-4129   OH
Web Site: http://www.fireworks.com
Year Founded: 1977
Sales Range: $200-249.9 Million
Emp.: 500
Consumer Fireworks Retailer
N.A.I.C.S.: 423920
William Weimer (Gen Counsel & VP)
Jerry Bostocky (VP-Sls)

B.J. BALDWIN ELECTRIC INC.
7060 Division Hwy, Narvon, PA 17555
Tel.: (717) 354-4651
Web Site: https://www.bjbaldwin.com
Year Founded: 1974
Sales Range: $10-24.9 Million
Emp.: 250
General Electrical Contractor
N.A.I.C.S.: 238210
Barry Baldwin (Owner)
Mic McKillips (Controller)
April Wilkinson (Treas)

B.J. CECIL TRUCKING INC.
5555 S Hospital Dr, Globe, AZ 85501
Tel.: (928) 425-5781   AZ
Web Site:
    https://www.bjceciltrucking.com
Year Founded: 1949
Sales Range: $10-24.9 Million
Emp.: 120
Trucking Service
N.A.I.C.S.: 484110
Don Amos (Mgr-Sls)
Chris Cecil (Owner)

B.J. MCGLONE CO. INC.
40 Brunswick Ave, Edison, NJ 08817
Tel.: (732) 287-8600
Web Site: http://www.bjmcglone.com
Year Founded: 1983
Sales Range: $25-49.9 Million
Emp.: 165
Contractors: Installers of Drywall
N.A.I.C.S.: 238310
Brian Mcglone (Pres)
Kevin Price (VP-Fin)
Gerry McCarthy (Dir-Sls)
Marc Coccoli (Project Mgr-LEED GA)

Subsidiaries:

B J McGlone Co   (1)
40 Brunswick Ave, Edison, NJ 08817
Tel.: (732) 287-8600
Web Site: http://www.bjmcglone.com
Rev.: $1,100,000
Emp.: 18
Drywall
N.A.I.C.S.: 238310
Brian McGlone (Pres)
Kevin Price (VP-Fin)

B.J. VINES INC.
498 Seventh Ave 21st Fl, New York, NY 10018-6798
Tel.: (212) 244-0843   NY
Web Site:
    http://www.betseyjohnson.com
Year Founded: 1978
Sales Range: $25-49.9 Million
Emp.: 200
Women's Clothing Store
N.A.I.C.S.: 458110
Betsey Johnson (Pres)

B.K. MILLER CO., INC.
9024 Old Branch Ave, Clinton, MD 20735-2594
Tel.: (301) 868-2500   DE
Web Site: https://www.bkmillers.com
Year Founded: 1991
Sales Range: $10-24.9 Million
Emp.: 47
Groceries & Related Products Retailer
N.A.I.C.S.: 424490
Blaise Miller (Pres & CEO)

B.L. HARBERT INTERNATIONAL, LLC
820 Shades Creek Pkwy Ste 3000, Birmingham, AL 35209
Tel.: (205) 802-2800   DE
Web Site: https://www.blharbert.com
Year Founded: 1990
Nonresidential Construction
N.A.I.C.S.: 236220
Alan Hall (Sr VP, CFO & Sec)
Johnny Garlington (Pres-US Grp)
Jim Stewart (COO-Bus Ops)
Charles A. Bohn (Pres-Intl Grp)
Matthew DeValk (Sr VP-Intl Grp)
Mike Veal (Sr VP-Intl Grp)
Ben Nevins (Sr VP & Mgr-Comml & Healthcare Div)
Matt Thompson (VP & Dir-US Estimating & Preconstruction)
Jim McGregor (VP-US Ops)
Billy L. Harbert Jr. (Chm & CEO)

B.L. SPILLE CONSTRUCTION, INC.

3140 Crescent Ave, Erlanger, KY 41018
Tel.: (859) 727-2800
Web Site: http://www.dpselectric.com
Year Founded: 1963
Sales Range: $10-24.9 Million
Emp.: 76
Commercial & Institutional Building Construction Services
N.A.I.C.S.: 236220
George A. Huser (Pres)

B.M. LAWRENCE & CO.

4300 Horton St Ste 15, Emeryville, CA 94608
Tel.: (415) 981-3650
Sales Range: $1-9.9 Million
Emp.: 10
Groceries & Related Products, Nec
N.A.I.C.S.: 424490
Hugh Ditzler (Pres & Treas)

B.O.P. PRODUCTS, LLC.

9118 Sweetbrush Dr, Houston, TX 77064
Tel.: (281) 955-6321
Web Site: https://www.bop-products.com
Year Founded: 2005
Sales Range: $10-24.9 Million
Emp.: 15
Oilfield Supporting Services
N.A.I.C.S.: 213112
Cliff Broughton (Co-Owner & Pres)
Leroy Hullum (Co-Owner & VP)

B.P. SHORT & SON PAVING CO.

1006 E Bank St, Petersburg, VA 23803
Tel.: (804) 732-8412
Sales Range: $10-24.9 Million
Emp.: 50
Highway & Street Paving Contractor
N.A.I.C.S.: 237310
Glenn Ricards (Controller)
Mike Cuilic (VP)
Burton P. Short III (Pres)

B.R. AMON & SONS INC.

W 2950 Hwy 11, Elkhorn, WI 53121
Tel.: (262) 723-2547
Web Site: http://www.bramon.com
Sales Range: $25-49.9 Million
Emp.: 150
General Contractor, Highway & Street Construction
N.A.I.C.S.: 237310
Thomas Amon (Pres)

B.R. FUNSTEN & CO., INC.

105 Industrial Park Dr, Manteca, CA 95337
Tel.: (209) 825-5375
Web Site: https://www.brfunsten.com
Year Founded: 1957
Sales Range: $50-74.9 Million
Emp.: 240
Flooring Product Whlsr
N.A.I.C.S.: 423220
James J. Funsten (Pres)

B.T. MANCINI CO., INC.

876 S Milpitas Blvd, Milpitas, CA 95036
Tel.: (408) 942-7900   CA
Web Site: https://www.btmancini.com
Year Founded: 1964
Sales Range: $125-149.9 Million
Emp.: 300
Provider of Contracting Services
N.A.I.C.S.: 238330
David Fan (Mgr-Sls)

B.W. WILSON PAPER COMPANY INCORPORATED

2501 Brittons Hill Rd, Richmond, VA 23230-2503
Tel.: (804) 358-6715   VA
Web Site: https://www.bwwilson.com
Year Founded: 1904
Sales Range: $10-24.9 Million
Emp.: 52
Printing & Writing Paper & Computer Supplies Distr
N.A.I.C.S.: 424110
Phil Knab (Dir-Sls)
Denise Hart (Sec)
Lawrence H. Rauppius Jr. (Pres)

B/R/S GROUP INC.

820 5th Ave Ste B, San Rafael, CA 94901
Tel.: (415) 526-2040
Web Site: http://www.brsgroup.com
Sales Range: $1-9.9 Million
Emp.: 4
Market Analysis, Business & Economic Research
N.A.I.C.S.: 541910
Lorne McMillan (Mng Partner)

B12 CAPITAL PARTNERS LLC

4900 Main St Ste 950, Kansas City, MO 64112
Tel.: (816) 994-8632
Web Site:
    http://www.b12capitalpartners.com
Holding Company
N.A.I.C.S.: 551112
Gregory L. Gaeddert (Co-Founder & Mng Partner)
Mike Wedel (Principal)

Subsidiaries:

S&H Products, LLC   (1)
5891 Nolan St Unit 1, Arvada, CO 80003
Tel.: (303) 421-2001
Web Site: http://www.shproductsllc.com
Aluminum Foundries
N.A.I.C.S.: 331524
Seth Larson (COO)
Josh Larson (CFO)

B2 INTERACTIVE

4223 S 143rd Cir, Omaha, NE 68137
Tel.: (402) 932-9990
Web Site:
    http://www.b2interactive.com
Year Founded: 2012
Emp.: 25
Digital Content Services
N.A.I.C.S.: 541519
Bill Hipsher (Co-Owner)
Brandon Taylor (Co-Owner)
Chris Gorman (Dir-Bus Dev)
Aaron Mackel (Dir-Content)
Angie Flaherty (Mgr-Bus & HR)

Subsidiaries:

U.S. Storage Search, Inc.   (1)
10840 Old Mill Rd, Omaha, NE 68154
Tel.: (866) 381-7930
Web Site: http://www.usstoragesearch.com
Online Self Storage Directory
N.A.I.C.S.: 513140
Michael G. Kucera (Pres, Sec & Treas)

B2A, LLC.

4550 S Windermere St, Englewood, CO 80110
Tel.: (303) 761-6975
Web Site:
    http://www.bettermanagers.com
Year Founded: 1989
Sales Range: $10-24.9 Million
Emp.: 105
Management Consulting Services
N.A.I.C.S.: 541611
Shiloh Kelly (VP-Mktg)

B2B CFO PARTNERS, LLC

3850 E Baseline Rd Ste 105, Mesa, AZ 85206
Tel.: (480) 397-0590
Web Site: https://www.b2bcfo.com
Year Founded: 1987
Sales Range: $10-24.9 Million
Emp.: 7
Financial & Other Senior Level Executive Services to Growing Companies
N.A.I.C.S.: 561311
Jerry L. Mills (Founder & CEO)
Tom Azzarelli (CFO-Chandler & Partner)
Wayne Lorgus (Partner)

B2B COMPUTER PRODUCTS, LLC

313 S Rohlwing Rd, Addison, IL 60101
Tel.: (630) 396-6300
Web Site: https://www.itsavvy.com
Year Founded: 2004
Rev.: $70,000,000
Emp.: 260
Computer & Computer Peripheral Equipment & Software Merchant Whslr
N.A.I.C.S.: 423430
Chris Kurpeikis (Exec VP-Bus Dev)
Wendy Belpedio (Mgr-Sls & Support)

B2B INDUSTRIES LLC.

313 S Rohlwing Rd, Addison, IL 60101
Tel.: (630) 396-6300
Web Site: https://www.itsavvy.com
Year Founded: 2004
Sales Range: $100-124.9 Million
Emp.: 111
Information Technology Support Services
N.A.I.C.S.: 541512
Mike Theriault (Pres & CEO)
Chris Kurpeikis (Exec VP-Bus Dev)
Scott W. Rose (VP-IT)

B2B STAFFING SERVICES, INC.

10073 Vly View St 280, Cypress, CA 90630
Tel.: (714) 243-4104
Web Site:
    http://www.b2bstaffingservices.com
Year Founded: 2006
Sales Range: $1-9.9 Million
Emp.: 450
Consulting, Temporary Placements, Permanent Full Time & Temp-to-Hire Services
N.A.I.C.S.: 561311
Brian Wigdor (Pres)

B3 SOLUTIONS, LLC

1225 W Beaver St Ste 108, Jacksonville, FL 32204
Tel.: (904) 695-4241
Web Site:
    http://www.b3solutions.com
Year Founded: 2003
Sales Range: $10-24.9 Million
Emp.: 97
Management Consulting Services
N.A.I.C.S.: 541611
Brenda Bearden (Pres)
William Almas (CEO)
Tracy Kerns (Assoc VP-HR)
Edward Marshall (VP-Homel & Security Sector)
James H. Washington (COO)
Mark Schuler (Pres & CFO-Alexandria)
Sharon Thorpe (Mgr-Contracts)
John W. Nyce (VP-Defense Sector)
Stacey Nelson (VP-Transportation Sector)

B4UTRADE.COM, CORP.

30 Montgomery St Ste 600, Jersey City, NJ 07302
Tel.: (201) 427-9060   CA
Web Site: http://www.b4utrade.com
Year Founded: 1999
Sales Range: $10-24.9 Million
Emp.: 15
Online Stock & Financial Information Services
N.A.I.C.S.: 541910
Angie Oaks (Co-Founder, COO & Exec VP)
Keith Savitz (Founder & Chm)
Dennis Cassidy (CEO)

BA-TAMPTE PICKLE PRODUCTS INCORPORATED

77 Brooklyn Terminal Market, Brooklyn, NY 11236
Tel.: (718) 251-2100
Web Site:
    https://www.batamptepickle.com
Sales Range: $10-24.9 Million
Emp.: 60
Pickles, Vinegar
N.A.I.C.S.: 311421
Barry Silberstein (Pres)

BABBITT FORD LINCOLN-MERCURY LLC

11 N Verde, Flagstaff, AZ 86001
Tel.: (928) 774-5063
Web Site: http://www.babbitt-ford.com
Year Founded: 1912
Sales Range: $10-24.9 Million
Emp.: 70
Automobiles, New & Used
N.A.I.C.S.: 441110
Alan Chan (Principal)

BABCO CONSTRUCTION INC.

1723 Howard St, Evanston, IL 60202-3735
Tel.: (847) 869-2100   WV
Year Founded: 1965
Sales Range: $50-74.9 Million
Emp.: 40
Nonresidential Construction Services
N.A.I.C.S.: 236220
Dan R. Sharps (Pres & CEO)
Jay S. Sharps (CFO, Treas & Sec)

BABCOCK & JENKINS, INC.

711 SW Alder Ste 200, Portland, OR 97205
Tel.: (503) 382-8500
Web Site: http://www.bnj.com
Year Founded: 1992
Sales Range: $1-9.9 Million
Emp.: 40
Advetising Agency
N.A.I.C.S.: 541810
Denise Barnes (Pres)
Lauren Goldstein (VP-Strategic Plng)

BABCOCK CENTER, INC.

2725 Banny Jones Ave, West Columbia, SC 29170
Tel.: (803) 799-1970   SC
Web Site:
    https://www.babcockcenter.org
Year Founded: 1970
Sales Range: $25-49.9 Million
Emp.: 1,485
Disability Assistance Services
N.A.I.C.S.: 624120
B. J. Simons (Dir-Clinical Svcs)
Dave Kammerer (Dir-Trng & Consumer Events)
Betsy Woodward (Dir-HR)
Gilda Williams (Dir-Residential-West)
Jennifer Brooks (Dir-Community Supports)
Judy E. Johnson (Pres & CEO)

Babcock Center, Inc.—(Continued)

Melissa Hallbick *(Sr Dir-Admin)*
Donna Hall *(Deputy Exec Dir)*
Andrew Saleeby *(Treas)*
Johnathan Stackhouse *(Vice Chm)*
Gary Dobson *(Vice Chm)*

BABCOCK LUMBER COMPANY
2220 Palmer St, Pittsburgh, PA 15218-2603
Tel.: (412) 351-3515 PA
Web Site:
http://www.babcocklumber.com
Year Founded: 1887
Sales Range: $150-199.9 Million
Emp.: 350
Whslr of Lumber & Building Supplies;
Processor of Domestic & Foreign
Hardwoods
N.A.I.C.S.: 321918
Maxine Perry *(Sec)*
Michael Johnston *(Pres)*
Stan Hoffman *(Dir-DP)*

Subsidiaries:

Babcock Lumber Company - FineWood Division (1)
135 Roaring Run Rd, Champion, PA 15622
Tel.: (724) 593-6127
Lumber Mfr
N.A.I.C.S.: 321113

BABCOCK POWER, INC.
26 Forest St Ste 300, Marlborough, MA 01752
Tel.: (508) 852-7100
Web Site:
https://www.babcockpower.com
Sales Range: $150-199.9 Million
Emp.: 450
Mfr of Industrial Blowers
N.A.I.C.S.: 333243
Anthony Brandano *(CFO, Treas & Exec VP)*
Douglas J. Harding *(Exec VP-Strategic Ops)*
Edward Dean *(Chief Construction Officer)*
John Heffernan *(Chief HR Officer & Exec VP)*
Michael Leclair *(Pres & CEO)*
Xavier Dorai *(COO)*
William Ferguson Jr. *(Gen Counsel, Sec & Exec VP-Admin)*
Stephen Scally *(Mgr-Engrg Support)*
Tim Persson *(Mgr-Facilities)*

Subsidiaries:

Babcock Power Environmental Inc. (1)
5 Neponset St, Worcester, MA 01615-0040
Tel.: (508) 852-7100
Web Site: http://www.babcockpower.com
Environmental Engineering Services
N.A.I.C.S.: 541330

Babcock Power Renewables LLC (1)
222 Rosewood Dr 3rd Fl, Dancers, MA 01923
Tel.: (978) 646-3300
Web Site: https://www.babcockpower.com
Energy & Environmental Services & Systems
N.A.I.C.S.: 221118

Subsidiary (Domestic):

Paradigm Enterprises, Inc. (2)
400 Center Ave W, Dilworth, MN 56529
Tel.: (218) 236-8795
Web Site:
http://www.paradigmenterprises.net
Sales Range: $1-9.9 Million
Emp.: 10
Landscaping Services
N.A.I.C.S.: 561730
Glen Morken *(Pres)*

Babcock Power Services Inc. (1)
5 Neponset St, Worcester, MA 01615-0040
Tel.: (508) 852-7100
Industrial Engineering Services
N.A.I.C.S.: 541330

Babcock Power UK Ltd. (1)
Bewley House Park Road, Esher, KT10 8NP, Surrey, United Kingdom
Tel.: (44) 1372 466 668
Sales Range: $10-24.9 Million
Emp.: 3
Steam Generator Mfr
N.A.I.C.S.: 335312

Boiler Tube Company of America (1)
506 Charlotte Hwy, Lyman, SC 29365
Tel.: (864) 439-4489
Web Site: http://www.boilertubes.com
Sales Range: $25-49.9 Million
Emp.: 150
Waste Heat Recovery Plants, Fired Boilers, Shell & Tube Heat Exchangers, Economisers, Feedwater Heaters, Condensers, Moisture Separator Reheaters & Boiler Spares
N.A.I.C.S.: 332313

Riley Power, Inc. (1)
5 Neponset St, Worcester, MA 01606-2714
Tel.: (814) 454-8164
Web Site: http://www.babcockpower.com
Sales Range: $25-49.9 Million
Emp.: 180
Provider of Service Maintenance for Steam Generators
N.A.I.C.S.: 333414

TEI Struthers Wells (1)
36 Clark St, Warren, PA 16365
Tel.: (814) 726-1000
Web Site: http://www.strutherswells.com
Sales Range: $10-24.9 Million
Emp.: 15
Engineering & Sales Office
N.A.I.C.S.: 333415

TEi Construction Services Inc. (1)
170 Tucapau Rd, Duncan, SC 29334
Tel.: (864) 485-0600
Web Site: http://www.babcockpower.com
Emp.: 34
Construction Engineering Services
N.A.I.C.S.: 541330
Eddie Hunt *(Mgr-Site Safety)*

Thermal Engineering International (USA), Inc. (1)
10375 Slusher Dr, Santa Fe Springs, CA 90670
Tel.: (323) 726-0641
Web Site: http://www.babcockpower.com
Sales Range: $25-49.9 Million
Emp.: 80
Holding Company
N.A.I.C.S.: 551112

Division (Domestic):

Thermal Engineering International (USA) Inc. - MSR Division (2)
10375 Slusher Dr, Santa Fe Springs, CA 90670
Tel.: (323) 838-1150
Power Boiler & Heat Exchanger Mfr
N.A.I.C.S.: 332410
Thomas Richardson *(Pres)*

Thermal Engineering International (USA) Inc. - Struthers Wells Division (2)
8825 N Sam Houston Pkwy, Houston, TX 77064
Tel.: (281) 664-8020
Thermal Engineering Services
N.A.I.C.S.: 541330

Subsidiary (Non-US):

Thermal Engineering International Limited (2)
Calder Vale Road, PO Box 80, Wakefield, WF1 5YS, West Yorkshire, United Kingdom
Tel.: (44) 1924780000
Web Site: http://www.tei.co.uk
Flexible Hose & Braiding; Bellows Expansion Joints; Drawn Seamless & Welded Tubing in Carbon, Alloy & Stainless Steel; Manipulated Tube; Steel Processing Equipment & Tools; Heat Treatment Services
N.A.I.C.S.: 313210

Vogt Power International Inc. (1)
13551 Triton Park Blvd Ste 2000, Louisville, KY 40223
Tel.: (502) 899-4500
Heat Exchanger Mfr
N.A.I.C.S.: 332410
Pat Sims *(Acct Mgr)*
Nicholas Barnes *(Mgr-Aftermarket Proposal)*
Tom Palermo *(Mgr-Subcontract)*
John Caudill *(Project Mgr)*
Dennie Hunt *(VP-Bus Dev)*

Welding Technologies, Inc. (1)
2330 Centennial Dr, Gainesville, GA 30504
Tel.: (770) 297-6441
Web Site: http://www.babcockpower.com
Emp.: 25
Welding Contract Services
N.A.I.C.S.: 238190
John Koslosky *(Mgr)*

BABCOX PUBLICATIONS INC.
3550 Embassy Pkwy, Akron, OH 44333-8318
Tel.: (330) 670-1234
Web Site: https://www.babcox.com
Rev.: $20,000,000
Emp.: 67
Publisher of Automotive Magazines
N.A.I.C.S.: 513120
William E. Babcox *(Pres)*
Greg Cira *(CFO & VP)*
Brendan Baker *(Editor)*
Doug Basford *(Reg Mgr-Sls)*
Tim Fritz *(Mng Editor)*
Jim Merle *(Publr-Tech Grp Properties)*
Karen Kaim *(Reg Mgr-Sls)*
John Zick *(Reg Mgr-Sls)*
John Hirnikl *(Designer-Graphic)*
Chuck Balazs *(Dir-IT)*
Jason Stahl *(Editor)*
Beth Scheetz *(Controller)*
Brandi Gangel *(Dir-Audience Data & Mktg)*
Mary DellaValle *(Editor)*
Michael Madej *(Dir-Digital Media)*

BABER INVESTMENT GROUP, INC.
80 E Sir Francis Drake Blvd Ste 3F, Larkspur, CA 94939
Tel.: (415) 591-9900
Web Site: http://www.msb-realestate.com
Year Founded: 1981
Sales Range: $10-24.9 Million
Emp.: 24
Real Estate Investment, Advisory & Asset Management Services
N.A.I.C.S.: 531390
Kenneth A. Baber *(Pres & CEO)*
Stewart F. Clark *(CFO & Exec VP)*
Steve D. Tovani *(Exec VP-Client Capital)*

BABERS INC.
3436 Main St, Moss Point, MS 39563
Tel.: (228) 312-0350
Web Site: https://www.babers.com
Sales Range: $10-24.9 Million
Emp.: 35
Home Appliance, Furniture & Entertainment Rental Services
N.A.I.C.S.: 561320
Shane Baber *(Owner)*

BABSCO SUPPLY, INC.
2410 S Main St, Elkhart, IN 46517
Tel.: (574) 293-0631
Web Site: https://www.babsco.com
Year Founded: 1998
Sales Range: $10-24.9 Million
Emp.: 17
Electrical Equipment Whslr
N.A.I.C.S.: 423610
Leo Stults *(VP)*
Jan Farron *(Pres)*
Joe Hammond *(Mgr)*

BABY TOGS, INC.
100 W 33rd St Ste 1400, New York, NY 10001
Tel.: (212) 868-2100 NY
Web Site: http://www.babytogs.com
Year Founded: 1942
Sales Range: $75-99.9 Million
Emp.: 100
Infant & Toddler Apparel Mfr
N.A.I.C.S.: 315250
Steve Hoffman *(Mgr-Sls & Mktg)*
Val Samaniego *(Mgr-Import)*

BABYEARTH
106 E Old Settlers Blvd Ste D 100, Round Rock, TX 78664
Tel.: (512) 275-6935
Web Site: http://www.babyearth.com
Year Founded: 2003
Sales Range: $1-9.9 Million
Emp.: 18
Environmentally Friendly Baby Products
N.A.I.C.S.: 339930
Heather Bendle *(Owner)*
Steve Steinberg *(VP)*

BABYHAVEN.COM INC.
10039 Painter Ave, Santa Fe Springs, CA 90670
Tel.: (877) 233-3432
Web Site: http://www.babyhaven.com
Year Founded: 2009
Sales Range: $10-24.9 Million
Emp.: 94
Online Retailer of Baby & Parenting Products
N.A.I.C.S.: 458110
Brett Schuber *(Mgr-Warehouse)*
Jason Becker *(CEO)*
Andrew Hunter *(Mgr-Product Submission)*

BACCO CONSTRUCTION CO.
PO Box 458, Iron Mountain, MI 49801
Tel.: (906) 774-2616 MI
Web Site:
http://www.baccoconstruction.com
Year Founded: 1930
Sales Range: $100-124.9 Million
Emp.: 200
Highway Construction Services
N.A.I.C.S.: 237310
Joseph J. Rigoni *(Chm)*
John Fortier *(Pres)*
Douglas R. Rigoni *(Treas)*
John A. Fortier Jr. *(VP)*

BACH TO ROCK MUSIC SCHOOL, INC.
4819 Saint Elmo Ave, Bethesda, MD 20814
Tel.: (301) 913-5757
Web Site: https://www.b2rmusic.com
Year Founded: 2007
Sales Range: $1-9.9 Million
Emp.: 111
Musical Education for Students of All Ages
N.A.I.C.S.: 459140
Nayan Bhula *(Reg Dir)*
Matt Cummings *(Dir-Music)*
Joey Baham *(Dir-Music)*

BACHMAN AUTO GROUP
9650 Bluegrass Pkwy, Louisville, KY 40299
Tel.: (502) 499-6161 KY
Web Site:
http://www.bachmanautogroup.com
Year Founded: 1985
Sales Range: $125-149.9 Million
Emp.: 300
Automobiles Retailer
N.A.I.C.S.: 441110

Tom Finley (Mgr-Parts)

BACHMAN'S, INC.
6010 Lyndale Ave S, Minneapolis, MN 55419-2225
Tel.: (612) 861-7676　　　　MN
Web Site:
　https://www.bachmans.com
Year Founded: 1885
Sales Range: $75-99.9 Million
Emp.: 1,000
Provider of Floral, Nursery, Garden & Gift Merchandise
N.A.I.C.S.: 459310
Dale L. Bachman (Chm)
Paul Bachman (VP-Admin)
Mary Fuller (CFO)

BACHMAN-BERNARD AUTO MALLS
300 Bachman Dr, Greeneville, TN 37745
Tel.: (423) 639-4141
Web Site: http://www.bbautomall.com
Sales Range: $10-24.9 Million
Emp.: 60
Car Dealership
N.A.I.C.S.: 441110
Myron N. Bernard (Owner)
Russ Kaufferd (Gen Mgr-Sls)
Philip M. Bachman Jr. (Owner)

BACHRODT MOTORS INC.
5695 E State St, Rockford, IL 61108
Tel.: (815) 226-9151
Web Site: http://www.bachrodt.com
Rev.: $45,000,000
Emp.: 85
New Car Dealers
N.A.I.C.S.: 441110
Patrick Bachrodt (Pres)

BACKBONE MEDIA, INC.
69 Milk St Ste 306, Westborough, MA 01581
Tel.: (508) 366-2100
Web Site:
　https://www.backbonemedia.com
Year Founded: 1996
Sales Range: $1-9.9 Million
Emp.: 16
Website Development, Marketing & Advertising
N.A.I.C.S.: 541890
Stephen Turcotte (Founder & Pres)
Paul Salvaggio (VP-Ops)
Brian Holcombe (Assoc Dir-PR)
Elizabeth Carey (Acct Mgr)
Charlie Lozner (Dir-Integrate Svcs)

BACKDRAFT BREWING COMPANY
35122 W Michigan Ave, Wayne, MI 48184-1614
Tel.: (734) 722-7639
Sales Range: $10-24.9 Million
Emp.: 100
Brewery Mfr
N.A.I.C.S.: 312120
George Riley (Co-Partner)
Michael Reddy (Co-Partner)

BACKE DIGITAL BRAND MARKETING
35 Cricket Ter Ctr, Ardmore, PA 19003-2203
Tel.: (610) 896-9260　　　　DE
Year Founded: 1997
Rev.: $40,000,000
Emp.: 30
Advetising Agency
N.A.I.C.S.: 541810
John E. Backe (CEO)
Michele Bennett (Sr VP-Interactive)
Larry Williams (Sr VP & Assoc Dir-Creative)

Roberta D'Emilio (Sr VP & Acct Supvr)
Robert Anthony (CFO & COO)
Lisa Gower (Media Dir)
Boyd Maits (Sr VP)
Malcolm Brown (Sr VP & Dir-Client Svcs)
Bob Hennessy (Dir-Mktg)

BACKGROUNDCHECKS.COM
12770 Coit Rd Ste 1150, Dallas, TX 75251
Tel.: (866) 766-4066
Web Site:
　http://www.backgroundchecks.com
Year Founded: 1999
Sales Range: $10-24.9 Million
Emp.: 60
Background Screening Services
N.A.I.C.S.: 541618
Michael Klazema (VP-Online Mktg & Product Mgmt)
Allison Sestak (VP-Sls)
Craig Kessler (Founder & Pres)
Bryan Mileger (CEO)

BACKJOY ORTHOTICS, LLC
25852 McBean Pkwy Ste 508, Valencia, CA 91351
Tel.: (310) 928-7751
Web Site: http://www.backjoy.com
Year Founded: 2005
Sales Range: $1-9.9 Million
Emp.: 3
Mfr & Designer of Back Orthotic Product
N.A.I.C.S.: 339113
Bing Howenstein (Owner & Pres)

BACKROADS INC.
801 Cedar St, Berkeley, CA 94710
Tel.: (510) 527-1555
Web Site:
　https://www.backroads.com
Rev.: $7,000,000
Emp.: 800
Tour Operator
N.A.I.C.S.: 561520
Alison Iles (Mgr-Canada)
Tom Hale (Founder & Pres)
Carlos Martinez Abad (Coord-Dev-Italy & Spain)
Jeff Cantarutti (Mgr-Italy)
Linda Cassell (Mgr-Southwest)
Christian Chumbley (Mgr-Africa)
Michelle Muench (Mgr-Latin)
Mark Selcon (Mgr-Europe)
Alexandre Visage (Coord-Dev-France)

BACKSTOP SOLUTIONS GROUP, LLC
233 S Wacker Ste 3960, Chicago, IL 60606
Tel.: (312) 277-7700
Web Site:
　http://www.backstopsolutions.com
Year Founded: 2003
Emp.: 52
Computer Software Development Services
N.A.I.C.S.: 541511
Clint Coghill (CEO)
Jim Schuler (CFO)
Michael Neuman (Chief Info Security Officer)
Chad Erwin (Sr VP-Asset Owners)
Greg Fujii (COO)
Kim Greuling (CTO)

Subsidiaries:

Barclay Hedge, Ltd.　　　　　(1)
2094 185th St Ste 1B, Fairfield, IA 52556-8758
Tel.: (641) 472-3456

Web Site: http://www.barclayhedge.com
Rev.: $1,000,000
Emp.: 16
Administrative Management & General Management Consulting Service
N.A.I.C.S.: 541611
Sol Waksman (Pres)
Richard Rubin (Exec VP-Sls)

Cogency Software, Inc.　　　　(1)
500 Airport Blvd Ste 152, Burlingame, CA 94010
Tel.: (650) 685-2500
Web Site: http://www.cogencysoft.com
Automated Management Solutions Developer
N.A.I.C.S.: 541511

ProTrak International, Inc.　　　(1)
237 W 35th St Ste 507, New York, NY 10001
Tel.: (212) 265-9833
Web Site: http://www.protrak.com
Computer Integrated Systems Design, Nsk
N.A.I.C.S.: 541512
Simon Koziel (Founder & Pres)
Gregory A. Kotlar (Dir-Product Dev)
Hania Jacobson (Dir-Consulting)
Edward G. Postrk (Dir-Client Svcs)

BACKUP MY INFO!, INC.
90 Broad St 6th Floor, New York, NY 10004
Tel.: (212) 599-7800　　　　FL
Web Site: http://www.bumi.com
Year Founded: 2003
Sales Range: $1-9.9 Million
Emp.: 10
Off-Site Data Protection & Continuity Services for Professional Services Firms
N.A.I.C.S.: 518210
Amaya Swanson (Mgr-Customer Svc)
Chris Conaboy (VP-Sls)
Raj Wakhale (Mgr-Sls)
Jennifer Walzer (CEO & Founder)

BACKUS TURNER INTERNATIONAL
3108 N Federal Hwy, Lighthouse Point, FL 33064
Tel.: (305) 573-9996　　　　FL
Web Site:
　http://www.backusturner.com
Year Founded: 1978
Rev.: $15,000,000
Emp.: 10
Advetising Agency
N.A.I.C.S.: 541810
Roberta Backus (CEO)
Rene Turner (VP & Media Dir)
Lawrence Turner (Owner)
Rachel Chin (Sr Art Dir)

BACKYARD PRODUCTIONS INC.
444 Washington Blvd, Marina Del Rey, CA 90292
Tel.: (310) 314-1122
Web Site: http://www.backyard.com
Rev.: $25,000,000
Emp.: 22
Commercials, Television: Tape Or Film
N.A.I.C.S.: 512110
Blair Stribley (Pres)

BACON COUNTY HEALTH SERVICES, LNC.
302 S Wayne St, Alma, GA 31510
Tel.: (912) 632-8961　　　　GA
Web Site:
　https://www.baconhospital.com
Year Founded: 1986
Sales Range: $25-49.9 Million
Emp.: 506
Health Care Srvices
N.A.I.C.S.: 622110
Cindy Turner (CEO)
Kyle Kimmel (CFO)

Lauris Mullis (Controller)
Deanna Williams (Dir-Nursing)
Patsy Smart (Dir-Nursing-Long Term Care)
Deanna Hoff (Dir-Nursing-Acute Care)

BACON GALLERIES INC.
17701 Murdock Cir, Port Charlotte, FL 33948
Tel.: (941) 625-4493
Web Site:
　https://www.baconsfurniture.com
Year Founded: 1972
Sales Range: $10-24.9 Million
Emp.: 45
Furniture Retailer
N.A.I.C.S.: 449110
William L. Bacon (Pres)

BACPLAS INC.
Montones Ward Carr 9939 Calle A Lote 9, Las Piedras, PR 00771
Tel.: (787) 275-7527　　　　PR
Web Site: http://www.bacplas.com
Year Founded: 1986
Sales Range: $25-49.9 Million
Emp.: 100
Injection Molding Of Plastics
N.A.I.C.S.: 326199
Joaquin Gonzalez (Mgr-Ops & Plan)
Manuel Coriano (Dir-Fin)

BACTOLAC PHARMACEUTICAL, INC.
7 Oser Ave Unit 14, Hauppauge, NY 11788
Tel.: (631) 951-4908　　　　TX
Web Site: http://www.bactolac.com
Sales Range: $10-24.9 Million
Emp.: 100
Pharmaceuticals Mfr
N.A.I.C.S.: 424210
Jeffrey G. McGonegal (Asst Sec)
Pailla M. Reddy (Pres & CEO)
Renee Reynolds (CFO & VP)
Vanessa Jackson (Mgr-Quality Assurance)
Pylla Chandrasheker Reddy (Mgr-Production)

BAD BOY WORLDWIDE ENTERTAINMENT GROUP
1710 Broadway, New York, NY 10019
Tel.: (212) 381-1540　　　　NY
Web Site:
　http://www.badboyonline.com
Year Founded: 1994
Sales Range: $300-349.9 Million
Emp.: 600
Music & Entertainment Producer; Advertising & Marketing Services; Restaurant Owner; Men's Clothing Designer
N.A.I.C.S.: 711130
Sean Combs (CEO)
Jon Cropper (CMO)

Subsidiaries:

Bad Boy Records　　　　　　(1)
1710 Broadway, New York, NY 10019
Tel.: (212) 381-1540
Web Site: http://www.badboyonline.com
Sales Range: $1-9.9 Million
Music Record Producer; Owned 50% by Bad Boy Worldwide Entertainment Group & 50% by Warner Music Group, Inc.
N.A.I.C.S.: 711130

BADCOCK HOME FURNITURE & MORE OF SOUTH FLORIDA
1409 10th St, Lake Park, FL 33403
Tel.: (561) 848-6200
Web Site: http://www.badcockinc.com
Sales Range: $25-49.9 Million
Emp.: 31

Badcock Home Furniture & More of South Florida—(Continued)

Furniture Retailer
N.A.I.C.S.: 449110
Robert Lee *(Mgr-Warehouse)*

BADEN GAGE & SCHROEDER, LLC
6920 Pointe Inverness Way Ste 300, Fort Wayne, IN 46804
Tel.: (260) 422-2551
Web Site: https://www.badencpa.com
Sales Range: $10-24.9 Million
Emp.: 70
Accounting Services & Auditing Services
N.A.I.C.S.: 541219
Maryann Ternet *(Sec)*
Mike Smith *(Sr Mgr-Bus Valuation Svcs)*

BADER RUTTER & ASSOCIATES, INC.
1433 N Water St Ste 100, Milwaukee, WI 53202
Tel.: (262) 784-7200   **WI**
Web Site: http://www.baderrutter.com
Year Founded: 1974
Sales Range: $25-49.9 Million
Emp.: 250
Advertising & Public Relations
N.A.I.C.S.: 541810
Greg Nickerson *(Chm)*
Jeff Young *(Pres & CEO)*
David Quigley *(Dir-Bus Dev)*
Ned Brown *(Chief Creative Officer)*
Eric Kirkhofer *(CFO)*
Linda Hogan *(Chief Talent Officer)*
JoDee George *(Chief Client Officer)*

Subsidiaries:

Bader Rutter & Associates, Inc.   **(1)**
808 P St Ste 210, Lincoln, NE 68508-2246
Tel.: (402) 434-5307
Sales Range: $10-24.9 Million
Emp.: 7
N.A.I.C.S.: 541810

BADGER & PARTNERS, INC.
261 5th Ave 26th Fl, New York, NY 10016
Tel.: (212) 533-3222   **NY**
Year Founded: 1994
Rev.: $58,000,000
Emp.: 38
Advetising Agency
N.A.I.C.S.: 541810
Madonna Badger *(Owner)*
Clark Fisher *(Dir-Creative)*
Jim Winters *(Pres)*
Linda Kim *(Dir-Creative)*
Caroline Frangos *(Mng Dir-Client Svcs)*

BADGER AIR BRUSH COMPANY
9128 W Belmont Ave, Franklin Park, IL 60131-2806
Tel.: (847) 678-3104   **IL**
Web Site: https://www.badgerairbrush.com
Year Founded: 1963
Sales Range: $50-74.9 Million
Emp.: 70
Airbrushes & Related Accessories Mfr
N.A.I.C.S.: 339940
Kenneth Schlotfeldt *(Pres)*
Candace Carnes *(Treas)*

BADGER CORRUGATING COMPANY
1801 W Ave S, La Crosse, WI 54601
Tel.: (608) 788-0100
Web Site: https://www.badgerlax.com
Rev.: $70,500,000
Emp.: 230

Lumber Plywood Millwork & Wood Panel Merchant Whslr
N.A.I.C.S.: 423310
Michael J. Sexauer *(Pres)*
Bruce Nordeen *(Treas & Sec)*

BADGER INCORPORATED
850 S Main St, Smithfield, UT 84335
Tel.: (435) 563-6251
Web Site: http://www.leesmarketplace.com
Rev.: $24,700,000
Emp.: 130
Independent Supermarket
N.A.I.C.S.: 445110
Shari Padger *(Pres)*

BADGER LIQUOR CO. INC.
850 Morris St, Fond Du Lac, WI 54935-5612
Tel.: (920) 923-8160
Web Site: https://www.badgerliquor.com
Year Founded: 1970
Sales Range: $25-49.9 Million
Emp.: 165
Wine & Distilled Beverages
N.A.I.C.S.: 424820
Gary Sadoff *(Pres)*
Tom Breecher *(Acct Mgr)*
Jeff Twohig *(Mgr-Fleet)*
Dan Werner *(Mgr-Sls)*
Tony Engedal *(VP)*
Joseph Rudolph *(VP)*
Krystal Schuh *(Mgr-HR)*

BADGER MAGNETICS, INC.
7939 W Tower Ave, Milwaukee, WI 53223
Tel.: (414) 362-4441
Web Site: http://www.badgermagnetics.com
Sales Range: $25-49.9 Million
Emp.: 75
Electromagnetic Products Mfr
N.A.I.C.S.: 334416
Pam Lefeber *(Mgr-Corp Sls)*

Subsidiaries:

Mag-Con Engineering   **(1)**
501 Apollo Dr, Lino Lakes, MN 55014   **(100%)**
Tel.: (651) 784-8888
Web Site: http://www.badgermagnetics.com
Sales Range: $10-24.9 Million
Emp.: 30
Custom Transformers Designer & Mfr
N.A.I.C.S.: 335311

BADGER MINING CORPORATION
409 S Church St, Berlin, WI 54923
Tel.: (920) 361-2388   **WI**
Web Site: https://www.badgerminingcorp.com
Year Founded: 1979
Sales Range: $25-49.9 Million
Emp.: 200
Industrial Sand Mining & Distr
N.A.I.C.S.: 212322
Tim Wuest *(Pres)*
Robert L. Brooks *(Treas & Sec)*
Sara Joyce *(VP-Quality & Tech Support)*
Stephen B. Ryan *(VP-Mktg, Sls, TDL & Customer Svc)*
Pam Leahy *(Coord-Production)*

BADGER MURPHY FOODSERVICES
652 N Western Ave, Chicago, IL 60612
Tel.: (773) 278-9100
Web Site: http://www.badgermurphy.com
Rev.: $45,000,000
Emp.: 20

Sales of Food Products
N.A.I.C.S.: 424430
Tona McGowan *(Mgr-Credit)*

BADGER MUTUAL INSURANCE COMPANY
1635 W National Ave, Milwaukee, WI 53204
Tel.: (414) 383-4143
Web Site: http://www.badgermutual.com
Year Founded: 1887
Emp.: 110
Insurance Management Services
N.A.I.C.S.: 524298
Laura Michna *(Asst VP-Administration)*
Dan Nigro *(Pres)*
Dan Wolfgram *(COO)*

BADGER PAPER MILLS, INC.
200 W Front St, Peshtigo, WI 54157
Tel.: (715) 582-4551
Converted Paper Product Mfr
N.A.I.C.S.: 322299
Jim Koronkiewicz *(Gen Mgr)*

BADGER PLUG COMPANY
N1045 Technical Dr, Greenville, WI 54942
Tel.: (920) 757-7300
Web Site: https://www.badgerplug.com
Rev.: $10,000,000
Emp.: 50
Molding Primary Plastics
N.A.I.C.S.: 326199
Dan Voissem *(Pres)*
Ted Voissem *(VP)*
Robert Nigh *(Controller)*

BADGER SHEET METAL WORKS OF GREEN BAY, INC.
1410 Partnership Dr, Green Bay, WI 54304
Tel.: (920) 435-8881
Web Site: https://www.bsmw.com
Year Founded: 1923
Sales Range: $10-24.9 Million
Emp.: 140
Sheet Metal Work Mfg
N.A.I.C.S.: 332322
Greg DeCaster *(CEO)*
Sam Thomas *(VP-Ops)*
Jeff Lindsley *(Mgr-Quality)*

BADGER STATE ETHANOL LLC
820 W 17th St, Monroe, WI 53566
Tel.: (608) 329-3900
Web Site: https://www.badgerstateethanol.com
Year Founded: 2000
Methanol Mfr
N.A.I.C.S.: 325193
Erik Huschitt *(CEO & Gen Mgr)*
Gary L. Kramer *(Pres & Sec)*
Jim Leitzinger *(CFO & Treas)*
Kevin Malchine *(Chm)*
Matt Hylen *(VP)*

BADGER STATE WESTERN INC.
710 S 4th St, Abbotsford, WI 54405
Tel.: (715) 223-2667
Web Site: http://www.bswinc.com
Sales Range: $10-24.9 Million
Emp.: 20
Trucking Service
N.A.I.C.S.: 484121
Richard C. Seefluth *(Pres)*
Kathy Lindgren *(Dir-Safety)*

BADGER TRUCK AND AUTOMOTIVE GROUP, INC.

2326 W St Paul Ave, Milwaukee, WI 53233-2522
Tel.: (414) 344-9500   **WI**
Web Site: http://www.badgertruck.com
Year Founded: 1965
Sales Range: $75-99.9 Million
Emp.: 110
Sale of Commercial Trucks; Motor Vehicle Supplies & New Parts
N.A.I.C.S.: 423110

Subsidiaries:

Badger Chevrolet Buick, Inc.   **(1)**
321 E Tyranena Park Rd, Lake Mills, WI 53551
Tel.: (920) 648-2388
Web Site: https://www.badgerchevroletbuick.com
Sales Range: $1-9.9 Million
Emp.: 15
New Car Dealers
N.A.I.C.S.: 441110

Siva Truck Leasing Inc.   **(1)**
2301 W Saint Paul Ave, Milwaukee, WI 53233-2540
Tel.: (414) 933-8355
Web Site: http://www.sivatruck.com
Sales Range: $10-24.9 Million
Emp.: 25
Sale of Commercial Trucks; Motor Vehicle Supplies & New Parts
N.A.I.C.S.: 532120

BADGER WELDING SUPPLIES INC.
101 S Dickinson St, Madison, WI 53703
Tel.: (608) 257-5606
Web Site: https://www.badgerwelding.com
Rev.: $12,400,000
Emp.: 34
Industrial Supplies Merchant Whslr
N.A.I.C.S.: 423840
Rick Maier *(Mgr-Sls)*
Jeff Richart *(Dir-Pur)*
Linda Strieff *(Office Mgr)*
Scott Griskavich *(VP)*

BADGER WIRE INC.
W 226 N 758 Eastmound Dr, Waukesha, WI 53186
Tel.: (262) 446-5500   **WI**
Web Site: https://www.badgerwire.com
Year Founded: 1989
Sales Range: $10-24.9 Million
Emp.: 10
Extruding Services
N.A.I.C.S.: 331420
Bill Harwood *(CEO)*

BADIA SPICES, INC.
1400 NW 93rd Ave, Miami, FL 33172
Tel.: (305) 629-8000
Web Site: https://www.badiaspices.com
Rev.: $15,500,000
Emp.: 102
Grocery & Related Products Merchant Whslr
N.A.I.C.S.: 424490
Kiara Curbelo-Infante *(Mgr-Pur)*
Alina M. Lastra *(Mgr-Audits & Regulatory Affairs)*
Jackie Luna *(Supvr-AP)*
Robert Vega *(Mgr-Sls)*

BAE SYSTEMS APPLIED INTELLIGENCE US CORP
440 Wheelers Farms Rd Ste 202, Milford, CT 06461
Tel.: (203) 541-3400   **DE**
Web Site: http://www.silversky.com
Year Founded: 1997
Computer Related Services
N.A.I.C.S.: 541519

Richard Dobrow (Chm & CEO)
Randal Skipper (Exec VP-Global Sls)
John Viega (Exec VP-Products, Strategy & Svcs)
Tim Harvey (CEO)

Subsidiaries:

Advanced Computer Solutions Group LLC (1)
Gateway Business Park 521 Fellowship Rd Ste 140, Mount Laurel, NJ 08054
Tel.: (856) 783-2980
Web Site: http://www.advancedcsg.net
Sales Range: $1-9.9 Million
Emp.: 50
IT Management Services
N.A.I.C.S.: 541511
Justin M. Jackson (CTO)

BAER'S FURNITURE CO. INC.
1589 NW 12th Ave, Pompano Beach, FL 33069-1730
Tel.: (954) 946-8001   FL
Web Site:
http://www.baersfurniture.com
Year Founded: 1968
Sales Range: $50-74.9 Million
Emp.: 240
Furniture Retailer
N.A.I.C.S.: 449110
Robert M. Baer (Pres)
Ronald Baer (VP)
Ira Baer (CFO)

BAERT MARINE INC.
7 River St, Middleton, MA 01949
Tel.: (978) 774-7712
Web Site:
https://www.baertmarine.com
Year Founded: 1972
Sales Range: $10-24.9 Million
Emp.: 20
Motor Boat Dealers
N.A.I.C.S.: 441222
Warren B. Kelly (Co-Founder & Pres-Mktg)
Bill Baert (Owner, Co-Pres & Treas)
Clyde Driscoll (Mgr-Svcs)

BAETA CORP.
1 Bridge Plz Ste 275, Fort Lee, NJ 07024
Tel.: (201) 471-0988   NJ
Web Site: http://www.baetacorp.com
Year Founded: 2007
Sales Range: Less than $1 Million
Pain Monitoring Products Designer & Developer
N.A.I.C.S.: 339112
Leonid Pushkantser (CEO)

BAETE FORSETH INC.
3521 S Norton Ave PO Box 1224, Sioux Falls, SD 57105
Tel.: (605) 336-0545
Web Site:
http://www.baeteforseth.com
Rev.: $10,720,885
Emp.: 70
Warm Air Heating & Air Conditioning Contractor
N.A.I.C.S.: 238220
Robert A. Dewit (Pres)
Vince Koltze (Mgr-Svc)
Dave Braley (Mgr-Shop)
Robert Ewit (CEO)

BAG BAZAAR LTD.
1 E 33rd St Fl 6, New York, NY 10016-5011
Tel.: (212) 931-5000   NY
Year Founded: 1961
Sales Range: $25-49.9 Million
Emp.: 200
Mfr of Handbags & Accessories
N.A.I.C.S.: 424350

Subsidiaries:

Accessory Exchange L.L.C. (1)
1 E 33rd St, New York, NY 10016-5011
Tel.: (212) 689-3508
Web Site: http://www.urrents.com
Rev.: $1,927,225
Emp.: 10
Mfr of Handbags
N.A.I.C.S.: 424350
Ken Singh (CFO)

BAG N BAGGAGE
8416 Preston Rd, Dallas, TX 75225-1551
Tel.: (214) 692-7275
Web Site:
http://www.bagnbaggage.com
Year Founded: 1987
Sales Range: $50-74.9 Million
Emp.: 500
Luggage & Leather Goods Stores
N.A.I.C.S.: 458320
Patrick Sullivan (Pres)
Rob Kuppens (CFO)

BAGBY ELEVATOR COMPANY, INC.
3608 Messer Airport Hwy, Birmingham, AL 35222
Tel.: (205) 591-4245   AL
Web Site:
https://www.bagbyelevator.com
Year Founded: 1920
Elevators & Equipment
N.A.I.C.S.: 333921
Arthur Bagby III (Pres)

BAGGETT TRANSPORTATION COMPANY
2 32nd St S, Birmingham, AL 35233
Tel.: (205) 322-6501
Web Site:
http://www.baggetttransport.com
Sales Range: $10-24.9 Million
Emp.: 30
Heavy Hauling
N.A.I.C.S.: 484121
Claiborne Crommelin (VP-Safety)
Scott Wheeler (VP-Ops)
David Crommelin (VP)
Joseph M. Donald III (Pres)

BAHAKEL COMMUNICATIONS, LTD.
1 Television Pl, Charlotte, NC 28205-7038
Tel.: (704) 372-4434   NC
Web Site: http://www.bahakel.com
Year Founded: 1949
Sales Range: $150-199.9 Million
Emp.: 391
Television & Radio Stations & Cable Systems
N.A.I.C.S.: 516120
Beverly Bahakel-Poston (Exec VP)
Gaston Bates (Gen Mgr-Sls)
John Hutchinson (Sr VP-Television)

Subsidiaries:

WDEF AM/FM (1)
2615 Broad St, Chattanooga, TN 37408-3100   (100%)
Tel.: (423) 321-6200
Web Site: http://www.sunny923.com
Sales Range: $10-24.9 Million
Emp.: 50
Radio Broadcasting Stations
N.A.I.C.S.: 516110
Chris Adams (Dir-Production)
Beverly Posten (Pres)
Bernie Barker (Gen Mgr)

BAHAMAS CONCIERGE, INC.
8076 Buttonwood Cir, Tamarac, FL 33321
Tel.: (954) 295-9754   NV

Web Site:
http://www.bahamasconcierge.com
Year Founded: 2011
Sales Range: Less than $1 Million
Emp.: 1
Concierge Services
N.A.I.C.S.: 812990
Nina Goldstein (Chm, CEO & CFO)

BAHNSON HOLDINGS, INC.
3901 Westpoint Blvd, Winston Salem, NC 27103
Tel.: (336) 760-3111
Web Site: http://www.bahnson.com
Sales Range: $25-49.9 Million
Emp.: 40
Holding Company
N.A.I.C.S.: 551112
Jim Hutcherson (Mgr-HR)

Subsidiaries:

Bahnson, Inc. (1)
3901 Westpoint Blvd, Winston Salem, NC 27103
Tel.: (336) 760-3111
Web Site: http://www.luwaamericas.com
Sales Range: $75-99.9 Million
Emp.: 1,000
Air Treatment Products, Systems & Services
N.A.I.C.S.: 333413

BAHR BROS MFG, INC.
2545 Lincoln Blvd, Marion, IN 46952
Tel.: (765) 664-6235   IN
Web Site: https://www.bahrbros.com
Year Founded: 1966
Sales Range: $10-24.9 Million
Emp.: 50
Steel Foundry
N.A.I.C.S.: 331513
Tim Street (Pres)
Jeffrey P. Jackson (Owner)
Matt Durbin (Mgr-Quality Control)
Scott Bratcher (VP & Mgr-Sls)
Steve Carl (Dir-Safety)

Subsidiaries:

Specialty Castings, Inc. (1)
211 Mill St, Springport, MI 49284-0129
Tel.: (517) 857-3660
Web Site: http://www.specialtycastings.com
Sales Range: $10-24.9 Million
Emp.: 35
Foundry Grey Iron & Ductile Iron Mfr
N.A.I.C.S.: 331511
John Drinkwater (Office Mgr)

BAI INC.
4600 Duke St Ste 303, Alexandria, VA 22304
Tel.: (703) 461-4713
Web Site: http://www.bai-inc.net
Year Founded: 1999
Rev.: $19,400,000
Emp.: 172
Government Services
N.A.I.C.S.: 334413
John T. Hardenbergh (CEO)
Adam Carrera (VP & Dir-Contracts)
David Cochran (VP-Bus Dev)
Lisa Shepherd (VP & Dir-HR)
Duval M. Williams Jr. (Pres)

BAI, INC.
21 Airport Blvd Ste B, South San Francisco, CA 94080
Tel.: (650) 872-1700   CA
Web Site: https://www.bai-inc.com
Year Founded: 1969
Sales Range: $10-24.9 Million
Emp.: 20
Wholesale Distribution of Aircraft Parts
N.A.I.C.S.: 423860

Tom Dolan (Pres)
George Jue (Controller)
Renat Deushev (Sr Acct Mgr)
Yuri Gelman (Dir-European Sls Ops)

BAILEY FEED MILL INC.
6421 Deans St, Bailey, NC 27807
Tel.: (252) 235-3961   NC
Web Site:
http://www.baileyfeedmill.com
Year Founded: 1932
Sales Range: $10-24.9 Million
Emp.: 35
Feed & Farm Supply Services
N.A.I.C.S.: 459999
Albert T. Daniel (Pres)

BAILEY GIBSON BUICK, PONTIAC & GMC, INC.
306 Happy Valley Rd, Glasgow, KY 42141
Tel.: (270) 651-8851
Web Site:
https://www.baileygibson.com
Year Founded: 1981
Sales Range: $10-24.9 Million
Emp.: 37
Car Whslr
N.A.I.C.S.: 441110
Danny R. Gibson (Pres)

BAILEY KENNEDY LLP
8984 Spanish Ridge Ave, Las Vegas, NV 89148-1302
Tel.: (702) 562-8820
Web Site:
https://www.baileykennedy.com
Year Founded: 2001
Sales Range: $1-9.9 Million
Emp.: 20
Law firm
N.A.I.C.S.: 541110
Dennis L. Kennedy (Partner)
Sarah E. Harmon (Atty)
Joshua M. Dickey (Atty)
Joseph A. Liebman (Atty)
John R. Bailey (Founder & Mng Partner)

BAILEY LAUERMAN
1299 Farnam St Ste 1400, Omaha, NE 68102
Tel.: (402) 475-2800   TN
Web Site:
http://www.baileylauerman.com
Year Founded: 1970
Sales Range: $50-74.9 Million
Emp.: 93
Advertising Agencies
N.A.I.C.S.: 541810
Carter Weitz (Chm & Chief Creative Officer)
Erica Lee (Dir-Media Strategy)
Greg Andersen (CEO)
Gwen Ivey (Grp Acct Dir)

Subsidiaries:

Bailey Lauerman (1)
1299 Farnam St Ste 930, Omaha, NE 68102-1157
Tel.: (402) 514-9400
Web Site: http://www.baileylauerman.com
Sales Range: $10-24.9 Million
Emp.: 25
Advertising Agency Services
N.A.I.C.S.: 541810
Carter Weitz (Chm & Co-CEO)

BAILEY NURSERIES INC.
1325 Bailey Rd, Saint Paul, MN 55119-6313
Tel.: (651) 459-9744   MN
Web Site:
https://www.baileynurseries.com
Year Founded: 1905
Sales Range: $800-899.9 Million
Emp.: 600

Bailey Nurseries Inc.—(Continued)

Ornamental Nursery Product Distr
N.A.I.C.S.: 424930
Terri McEnaney (Pres)
David Roberts (Head-Breeder & Gen Mgr)

Subsidiaries:

Bailey Nurseries Inc. - Sauvie Is
Division　　　　　　　　　　　　(1)
18616 Reeder Rd, Portland, OR 97231
Tel.: (503) 621-9710
Landscaping Services
N.A.I.C.S.: 561730

Bailey Nurseries Inc. - Sunnyside
Division　　　　　　　　　　　　(1)
1700 Holmason Rd, Sunnyside, WA 98944
Tel.: (509) 837-3002
Landscaping Services
N.A.I.C.S.: 561730

Bailey Nurseries-Sherman
Division
1300 Grove St, Charles City, IA
50616-2606　　　　　　　　(100%)
Tel.: (641) 228-1124
Web Site: http://www.baileynursery.com
Sales Range: $10-24.9 Million
Emp.: 50
Ornamental Nursery Products
N.A.I.C.S.: 111421

BAILEY PROPERTIES LLC
1400 W Markham St Ste 202, Little
Rock, AR 72201
Tel.: (501) 374-5050　　　　　　AR
Web Site: http://www.baileyapts.com
Year Founded: 1956
Sales Range: $10-24.9 Million
Emp.: 100
Real Estate Investment Properties
Services
N.A.I.C.S.: 531120
John Bailey (CEO & Mgr)
Patti Bailey (Partner)

BAILEY SOUTHWELL & CO.
5511 Virginia Way Ste 200, Brent-
wood, TN 37027
Tel.: (615) 800-6200
Web Site:
　https://www.baileysouthwell.com
Year Founded: 2005
Healthcare & Tech-enabled Services
N.A.I.C.S.: 541511
Jack Bailey (Co-Founder & Mng Dir)
Jeff Bailey (Co-Founder & Mng Dir)

BAILEY TIRE & AUTO SERVICE
811 S Federal Blvd, Riverton, WY
82501
Tel.: (307) 857-6750
Sales Range: $10-24.9 Million
Emp.: 75
Gasoline Stations
N.A.I.C.S.: 457120
Mike Bailey (Pres)

BAILEY'S MOVING AND STORAGE
400 N 700 W, Salt Lake City, UT
84054
Tel.: (801) 300-4086
Web Site:
　http://www.baileysallied.com
Year Founded: 1952
Household Goods Moving & Storage
N.A.I.C.S.: 484210
Cindee Holmes (Mgr-HR)
Steve Seljaas (Controller)
Kevin Beckstead (CEO)
Nancy Blegen (Gen Mgr)

BAILEY-HARRIS CONSTRUCTION, INC.

1552 Bailey Harris Dr, Auburn, AL
36830
Tel.: (334) 821-0807
Web Site: http://www.bailey-
　harris.com
Rev.: $17,700,000
Emp.: 100
Commercial & Institutional Building
Construction
N.A.I.C.S.: 236220
Allen C. Harris (Pres & CEO)
Steve Phillabaum (Project Mgr)

BAILEYS FURNITURE OUTLET INC.
350 W International Airport Rd Ste
100, Anchorage, AK 99518-1101
Tel.: (907) 563-4083
Web Site:
　http://www.baileysfurniture.com
Sales Range: $10-24.9 Million
Emp.: 100
Furniture Retailer
N.A.I.C.S.: 449110
Ronald C. Bailey (Pres)
Ruth Bailey (VP)

BAILEYS INC.
1210 Commerce Ave Ste 8, Wood-
land, CA 95776
Tel.: (707) 666-6133
Web Site: http://www.bbaileys.com
Year Founded: 1975
Sales Range: $10-24.9 Million
Emp.: 30
Tools & Hardware, Mail Order
N.A.I.C.S.: 444140
Janet Pepper (Controller)
Mick Bailey (Pres)

BAILLIE LUMBER CO., INC.
4002 Legion Dr, Hamburg, NY 14075
Tel.: (716) 649-2850　　　　　　NY
Web Site: https://www.baillie.com
Year Founded: 1923
Sales Range: $25-49.9 Million
Emp.: 500
Lumber Plywood & Millwork
N.A.I.C.S.: 423310

Subsidiaries:

American Hardwood Industries,
LLC　　　　　　　　　　　　　(1)
567 N Charlotte Ave, Waynesboro, VA
22980
Tel.: (540) 946-9150
Web Site: http://www.ahwood.com
Sales Range: $50-74.9 Million
Hardwood Lumber Sawmills & Products Mfr
N.A.I.C.S.: 321113
John O'Dea (CEO)
Dan Cumbo (Gen Mgr-Augusta Flooring)

Subsidiary (Domestic):

Blue Triangle Hardwoods, LLC　(2)
156 Industrial Blvd, Everett, PA 15537
Tel.: (814) 652-9111
Web Site: http://www.ahwood.com
Sales Range: $50-74.9 Million
Emp.: 399
Sawmills & Hardwood Sales
N.A.I.C.S.: 423310
John O'Dea (CEO)

Cross Creek Sales LLC　　　　　(2)
2608 Commons Blvd, Augusta, GA 30909-
2080
Tel.: (706) 738-4027
Web Site: http://www.ahwood.com
Sales Range: $10-24.9 Million
Emp.: 5
Lumber Whslr
N.A.I.C.S.: 423310
Terry Smith (Gen Mgr)

Graham Lumber Company, LLC　(2)
Hwy 412 W, Linden, TN 37096
Tel.: (931) 589-2143
Web Site: http://www.ahwood.com

Sales Range: $25-49.9 Million
Emp.: 85
Hardwood Lumber Sawmill & Products Mfr
N.A.I.C.S.: 321113

Baillie Lumber Co. Inc. - Boonville
Facility　　　　　　　　　　　　(1)
189 W St, Boonville, NY 13309
Tel.: (315) 942-5284
Emp.: 60
Lumber Mfr
N.A.I.C.S.: 321113
Michael Vaughan (Gen Mgr)

Baillie Lumber Co. Inc. - Galion
Facility　　　　　　　　　　　　(1)
3953 County Rd 51, Galion, OH 44833
Tel.: (419) 462-2000
Lumber Mfr
N.A.I.C.S.: 321113

Baillie Lumber Co. Inc. - Leitchfield
Facility　　　　　　　　　　　　(1)
279 Shaw Sta Rd, Leitchfield, KY 42754
Tel.: (270) 259-3104
Lumber Mfr
N.A.I.C.S.: 321113

Baillie Lumber Co. Inc. - Smyrna
Facility　　　　　　　　　　　　(1)
School St, Smyrna, NY 13464
Tel.: (607) 627-6547
Lumber Mfr
N.A.I.C.S.: 321113
Bob Steiner (Gen Mgr)

Baillie Lumber Co. Inc. - Titusville
Facility　　　　　　　　　　　　(1)
45529 State Hwy 27, Titusville, PA 16354
Tel.: (814) 827-1877
Emp.: 74
Lumber Mfr
N.A.I.C.S.: 321113
Dwayne Swift (Gen Mgr)

Baillie Lumber Sales Co. Inc.　　(1)
4002 Legion Dr, Hamburg, NY 14075-4508
Tel.: (716) 649-2850
Web Site: http://www.baillie.com
Sales Range: $10-24.9 Million
Emp.: 3
Lumber Mfr & Distr
N.A.I.C.S.: 321113

Clendenin Lumber Company　　　(1)
1225 Smith St Ext Donalds 29638, Green-
wood, SC 29638
Tel.: (864) 456-3494
Sales Range: $10-24.9 Million
Emp.: 120
Sawmills & Planing Mills
N.A.I.C.S.: 321912

Heritage Forest Products Inc.　　(1)
1990 Industrial Dr, Deland, FL
32724-2037　　　　　　　　(100%)
Tel.: (386) 738-2811
Web Site:
　http://www.heritageforestproducts.com
Sales Range: $10-24.9 Million
Emp.: 36
Lumber, Plywood & Millwork
N.A.I.C.S.: 423310
Peggy Hearrin (Controller)
Fred Blackmon (VP & Gen Mgr)
Greg Metts (Asst Gen Mgr)
Sam J. Sowers (Branch Mgr)

Branch (Domestic):

Heritage Forest Products　　　　(2)
101 Coleman Blvd Unit H, Savannah, GA
31408
Tel.: (912) 748-0869
Web Site:
　http://www.heritageforestproducts.com
Sales Range: $25-49.9 Million
Emp.: 10
Lumber, Plywood, Millwork & Wood Panel
Merchant Whslr
N.A.I.C.S.: 423310

Horizon Forest Products LP　　　(1)
4115 Commodity Pkwy, Raleigh, NC 27610
Tel.: (919) 424-8265
Web Site: http://www.horizonforest.com
Rev.: $6,000,000
Emp.: 40
Lumber, Plywood & Millwork
N.A.I.C.S.: 423310

David E. Williams (VP)
Robby Robertson (Mgr-Ops-Dallas)
Jerry Bell (Mgr-Ops-Sterling)
Christopher Williams (Branch Mgr)
Rex Holt (Mgr-Norfolk)
Patrick H. Hamill (Mgr-Dallas)

Mullican BA Lumber & Manufacturing
Co. Inc.　　　　　　　　　　　(1)
655 Woodlyn Rd, Johnson City, TN 37601
Tel.: (423) 283-4695
Web Site: http://www.mullicanflooring.com
Sales Range: $25-49.9 Million
Emp.: 125
Hardwood Floors Mfr
N.A.I.C.S.: 444110
Steve Smith (Gen Mgr)

World Wood Co., Inc.　　　　　(1)
12045 Hwy 70 E, Cove City, NC 28523
Tel.: (252) 523-0021
Rev.: $16,000,000
Emp.: 15
Lumber, Plywood & Millwork
N.A.I.C.S.: 423310

BAILLIO'S INC.
5301 Menaul Blvd NE, Albuquerque,
NM 87110-3113
Tel.: (505) 883-7511
Web Site: http://www.baillios.com
Year Founded: 1966
Sales Range: $25-49.9 Million
Emp.: 200
Retail Sales; Appliances & Electron-
ics
N.A.I.C.S.: 449210
Jack A. Baillio (Pres)

BAIM ENTERPRISES INC.
57 Haddonfield Rd Ste 100, Cherry
Hill, NJ 08002
Tel.: (856) 667-6656
Sales Range: $10-24.9 Million
Emp.: 5
Fast-Food Restaurant, Chain
N.A.I.C.S.: 722513
Edward Baim (Pres)
Philip Beebe (Mgr-Resturant)

BAIN & COMPANY, INC.
131 Dartmouth St, Boston, MA 02116
Tel.: (617) 572-2000　　　　　MA
Web Site: https://www.bain.com
Year Founded: 1973
Sales Range: $1-4.9 Billion
Emp.: 18,000
Administrative Management & Gen-
eral Management Consulting Ser-
vices
N.A.I.C.S.: 541611
Phyllis R. Yale (Partner-Advisory)
Manny Maceda (Mng Dir-Worldwide)
Tiaan Moolman (Mng Partner & Part-
ner)
Michael Robbins (Partner-
Washington)
Maureen Burns (Partner-Boston)
Terry Bradshaw (Partner)
Roger Zhu (Partner)
Richard Lichtenstein (Partner-New
York & VP)
Rebecca Burack (Partner-Boston)
Peter Shively (Partner)
Pedro Correa (Partner-Dallas)
Onyinye Ibeneche Avbovbo (Partner)
Neil Cherry (Partner-San Francisco)
Natasha Sommerfeld (Partner)
Orit Gadiesh (Chm)
Ravi K. Vijayaraghavan (Sr Partner &
Partner-Singapore)
Tim van Biesen (Partner-New York)
Matthew Crupi (Partner-Dallas)
Maria Teresa Tejada (Partner-San
Francisco)
Casey Carey (Partner-Chicago)
Michael Collins (Partner-London)
Linda M. Connly (Partner)
Tessa Bysong (Partner-Chicago)

Laura van Dijk *(Partner)*
Ivan Hindshaw *(Chief Talent Officer)*
Kim Burroughs *(Partner-Denver)*
Karl Zimmermann *(Partner)*
David Ellison *(Partner)*
Eugene Belashchenko *(Partner)*
Jim Harris *(Partner-Washington)*
Jim Drews *(Partner)*
Jennifer Rybak Kiernan *(Partner)*
Jen Smith *(Partner)*
Jeff Woods *(Partner)*
Jamie Cleghorn *(Partner-Chicago)*
James LaMontagne *(Partner)*
Erika Serow *(Partner & CMO)*
Elizabeth Pearsons *(Partner)*
Doug Truchan *(Partner)*
David Lipman *(Partner)*
Christophe De Vusser *(Mng Partner-Worldwide)*
Chuck Miller *(Partner)*
Bala Parameshwaran *(Partner)*
Andrea D'Arcy *(Partner)*
Stephen Caine *(Partner-Chicago)*
Steve Berez *(Partner-Advisory)*
Sandeep Heda *(Partner-Atlanta)*
Ron Kermisch *(Partner & Head-Global Talent Acquisition)*
Justin Murphy *(Partner-San Francisco)*
Julie Coffman *(Partner-Chicago)*
David Cooper *(Partner-New York)*
David Burns *(Partner-Chicago)*
Corrie Carrigan *(Partner-Denver)*
Andrew Noble *(Partner & Head-Americas Agile Innovation Practice)*
Aaron Cheris *(Partner-San Francisco)*
Tracy Thurkow *(Partner-Atlanta)*
Doug Fallon *(Partner)*
Glenn Engler *(Partner)*
Frederick F. Reichheld *(Founder-Loyalty Practice)*
David Cho *(Partner-Dallas)*

Subsidiaries:

Bain & Company (Hong Kong) **(1)**
30/F One International Finance Centre, 1 Harbour View Street, Central, China (Hong Kong) **(100%)**
Tel.: (852) 29788800
Web Site: http://bain.cn
Sales Range: $25-49.9 Million
Emp.: 34
Investment Banking
N.A.I.C.S.: 523150
Dale Cottrell *(Partner)*

Bain & Company Argentina S.R.L. **(1)**
Av Leandro N Alem 815 6th Floor, C1001AAD, Buenos Aires, Argentina
Tel.: (54) 11 4510 2600
Investment Management Service
N.A.I.C.S.: 523940
Federico Eisner *(Partner)*
Diego Garcia *(Partner)*
Nicolas Masjuan *(Partner)*
Pablo Sansuste *(Partner)*

Bain & Company Belgium, Inc. **(1)**
Avenue Louise 326, 1050, Brussels, Belgium
Tel.: (32) 2 626 2626
Web Site: http://www.bain.be
Emp.: 120
Business Management Consulting Services
N.A.I.C.S.: 541611
Anny Corstjens *(Mgr-Recruiting)*

Bain & Company Brazil, Inc. **(1)**
Av Republica do Chile 500 - 28 Andar, Rio de Janeiro, 20031-170, Brazil
Tel.: (55) 21 3528 2300
Web Site: http://www.bain.com.br
Emp.: 60
Investment Management Service
N.A.I.C.S.: 523940
Rodrigo Mas *(Partner)*
Jose de Sa *(Partner)*
Antonio Farinha *(Partner)*
Luiza Mattos *(Partner)*

Bain & Company Finland, Inc. **(1)**

Aleksanterinkatu 30-34, 00100, Helsinki, Finland
Tel.: (358) 9 6850 550
Web Site: http://www.bain.com
Emp.: 25
Business Management Consulting Services
N.A.I.C.S.: 541611
Timo Kairi *(Partner)*
Jani Kelloniemi *(Partner)*
Ilkka Leppavuori *(Partner)*
Timo Pohjakallio *(Partner)*

Bain & Company Germany, Inc. **(1)**
Karlsplatz 1, 80335, Munich, Germany
Tel.: (49) 89 5123 0
Web Site: http://www.bain.de
Business Management Consulting Services
N.A.I.C.S.: 541611
Rolf-Magnus Weddigen *(Partner)*
Pierre Deraed *(Dir-Mktg & Comm)*
Markus Bergmann *(Partner)*
Silvia Bergmann *(Partner)*
Imeyen Ebong *(Partner)*
Christina Ellringmann *(Partner)*
Marco Gerrits *(Partner)*
Christian Graf *(Partner)*
Hans Joachim Heider *(Partner)*
Marcus Hoffmann *(Partner)*
Serge Hoffmann *(Partner)*
Martin Holzapfel *(Partner)*
Ralf Kalmbach *(Partner)*
Arndt Kaminski *(Partner)*
Christian Kinder *(Partner)*
Franz-Robert Klingan *(Partner)*
Daniel Milleg *(Partner)*
Florian Mueller *(Partner)*
Richard Pelz *(Partner)*
Felix Reichardt *(Partner)*
Malte Reineke *(Partner)*
Michael Richthammer *(Partner)*
Michael Schertler *(Partner)*
Wilhelm Schmundt *(Partner)*
Franz-Josef Seidensticker *(Partner)*
Michael Staebe *(Partner)*
Mareike Steingrover *(Partner)*

Bain & Company Iberica, Inc. **(1)**
Paseo de la Castellana 35 6th Floor, 28046, Madrid, Spain
Tel.: (34) 91 790 3000
Web Site: http://www.bain.es
Business Management Consulting Services
N.A.I.C.S.: 541611
Jose Casas *(Partner)*
Pablo Cornicelli *(Partner)*
Jose Luis Del Prim *(Partner)*
Eduardo Gimenez *(Partner)*
Nicolas Lopez *(Partner)*
Antonio Martinez Leal *(Partner)*
Ignacio Otero *(Partner)*
Alvaro Pires *(Partner)*
Andre Pires de Carvalho *(Partner)*
Borja Tramazaygues *(Partner)*

Bain & Company India Pvt. Ltd. **(1)**
The Capital 13th Floor B Wing 1301 Plot No C 70 G Block, Bandra Kurla Complex, Mumbai, 400 051, India
Tel.: (91) 22 66289 600
Web Site: http://www.bain.in
Emp.: 90
Business Management Consulting Services
N.A.I.C.S.: 541611
Karan Singh *(Chm)*
Sri Rajan *(Partner-San Francisco)*
Ashish Singh *(Partner-Boston)*
Sriwatsan Krishnan *(Partner)*
Yaquta Mandviwala *(Partner)*
Sandeep Nayak *(Partner)*
Sambit Patra *(Partner)*
Nikhil Prasad Ojha *(Partner)*
Sudarshan Sampathkumar *(Partner)*
Arpan Sheth *(Partner)*
Saurabh Trehan *(Partner)*

Bain & Company Italy, Inc. **(1)**
Via Crocefisso 10, 20122, Milan, Italy
Tel.: (39) 02 58288 1
Web Site: http://www.bain.com
Business Management Consulting Services
N.A.I.C.S.: 541611

Bain & Company Japan, Inc. **(1)**
Midtown Tower Floor 8 9-7-1 Akasaka, Minato-ku, Tokyo, 107-6208, Japan
Tel.: (81) 3 4563 1100
Web Site: http://www.bain.co.jp
Sales Range: $50-74.9 Million
Emp.: 90
Investment Banking

N.A.I.C.S.: 523150
Toshihiko Hiura *(Partner)*
Jean-Philippe Biragnet *(Partner)*
Jim Verbeeten *(Partner)*
Kenji Govaers *(Partner)*
Junji Horinouchi *(Partner)*
Shigeki Ichii *(Partner)*
Junya Ishikawa *(Partner)*
Yusuke Morishima *(Partner)*
Fumihiko Nishiwaki *(Partner)*
Shingo Inoue *(Partner)*
Kazuki Okoshi *(Partner)*
Shintaro Okuno *(Partner)*
Hidenori Wakabayashi *(Partner)*
Hiroaki Adachi *(Principal)*
Sho Ikeno *(Principal)*
Masahiro Kubo *(Principal)*
Takashi Ohara *(Principal)*
Azusa Owa *(Principal)*
Yuta Suzuki *(Principal)*
Hiroaki Takagi *(Principal)*
Yukiko Tsukamoto *(Principal)*

Bain & Company Mexico, Inc. **(1)**
Paseo de Tamarindos 400A - 24 Bosques de las Lomas, DF 05120, Mexico, Mexico
Tel.: (52) 55 5267 1700
Web Site: http://www.bain.com.mx
Administrative Management Consulting Services
N.A.I.C.S.: 541611
Rodrigo Rubio *(Partner)*
Antonio Martinez Leal *(Partner-Madrid)*
Julio Rodriguez *(Partner)*
Eduardo Hutt Dorado *(Partner)*
Diego Santamaria *(Partner-Bogota)*
Francisco Barnes *(Partner)*
Jordi Ciuro *(Partner)*
Pino Del Sesto *(Partner)*
Juan Jimenez *(Partner)*
Luis Lapiedra Carmona *(Partner)*
Rodrigo Mayo *(Partner)*
Clara Albuquerque *(Principal)*
Carlos De Lascurain *(Principal)*
Marcelo Rodriguez *(Principal)*
Alejandro Yanez *(Principal)*
Claudia Lesseur *(Mgr)*
Gabriela Lozada Bosque *(Mgr)*

Bain & Company Middle East, Inc. **(1)**
Media 1 Tower Level 36, PO Box 502810, Dubai, United Arab Emirates
Tel.: (971) 4 365 7 365
Web Site: http://www.bain.com
Emp.: 100
Business Management Consulting Services
N.A.I.C.S.: 541611
Paul Rogers *(Partner)*
Houssem Jemili *(Partner)*

Bain & Company Netherlands, LLC **(1)**
Rembrandt Tower 32nd Floor Amstelplein 1, 1096 HA, Amsterdam, Netherlands
Tel.: (31) 20 7107 900
Emp.: 100
Business Management Consulting Services
N.A.I.C.S.: 541611
Klaasje Huijbregts *(Mgr-Recruiting)*
Bianca Bax *(Partner)*
Stephen Bertrand *(Partner)*
Mario Conde *(Partner)*
Jenny Davis-Peccoud *(Partner)*
Jeroen Hegge *(Partner)*
Michael Jongeneel *(Partner)*
Marc Lino *(Partner)*
Laurens-Jan Olsthoorn *(Partner)*
Robert Oushoorn *(Partner)*
Veronique Pauwels *(Partner)*
Lennert Spek *(Partner)*
Steven Tallman *(Partner)*
Anna Thal Larsen *(Partner)*
Fleur van Beem *(Partner)*
Allard Vegter *(Partner)*
Otto Verhage *(Partner)*
Kyle Weza *(Partner)*
Ewout Morks *(Principal)*

Bain & Company Russia, LLC **(1)**
Lotte Plaza Business Center 15th floor 8 Novinsky Boulevard, Moscow, 121099, Russia
Tel.: (7) 495 721 86 86
Web Site: http://www.bain.com.ru
Emp.: 100
Business Management Consulting Services
N.A.I.C.S.: 541611
Yury Spektorov *(Partner)*
Eugene Belashchenko *(Partner)*

Yegor Grygorenko *(Partner)*
Yuriy Kurganov *(Partner)*
Olya Linde *(Partner)*
Dmitry Naberezhnev *(Partner)*
Pierre-Laurent Wetli *(Partner)*

Bain & Company SE Asia, Inc. **(1)**
38 Beach Road Level 15 South Beach Tower, Singapore, 189767, Singapore
Tel.: (65) 62220123
Web Site: http://www.bain.com
Sales Range: $50-74.9 Million
Emp.: 150
General Management Consulting Services
N.A.I.C.S.: 541611
Karan Singh *(Head-Sustainability & Responsibility Practice)*
Wade Cruse *(Partner)*
Tony May *(Partner)*
Thomas Olsen *(Partner)*
Chew Seow-Chien *(Partner)*
Satish Shankar *(Mng Partner-Asia Pacific)*
Paolo Misurale *(Partner)*
Mike Booker *(Partner)*
Michael Egan *(Principal)*
Kevin Meehan *(Partner)*
Harshveer Singh *(Partner)*
Gwendolyn Lim *(Partner)*
Florian Hoppe *(Partner)*
Lin Edmund *(Partner)*
Dale Hardcastle *(Partner)*
Aadarsh Baijal *(Partner)*
Alessandro Cannarsi *(Partner)*
Francois Faelli *(Mng Partner-Environment, Sustainability & Governance-Global)*

Bain & Company South Africa, Inc. **(1)**
10 The High Street Melrose Arch, 2076, Johannesburg, South Africa
Tel.: (27) 11 012 9100
Web Site: http://www.bain.com
Emp.: 120
Business Management Consulting Services
N.A.I.C.S.: 541611

Bain & Company Switzerland, Inc. **(1)**
Sihlporte 3, 8001, Zurich, Switzerland
Tel.: (41) 44 668 80 00
Web Site: http://www.bain-company.ch
Emp.: 200
Business Management Consulting Services
N.A.I.C.S.: 541611
Thomas Lustgarten *(Chm & Partner)*
Enver Adakan *(Partner)*
Miltiadis Athanassiou *(Partner)*
Adrien Bron *(Partner)*
Hannes Brandli *(Partner)*
Jens Engelhardt *(Partner)*
Gilbert Grima *(Partner)*
Norbert Hueltenschmidt *(Partner)*
Mario Hauptli *(Partner)*
Massimo Lusardi *(Partner)*
Dieter Meyer *(Partner)*
David Michels *(Partner)*
Josef Ming *(Partner)*
Henrik Naujoks *(Partner)*
Pascal Roth *(Partner)*
Oliver Straehle *(Partner)*
Daniel Suter *(Partner)*
Moritz Vielhauer *(Partner)*
Eva-Maria Hempe *(Mgr)*
Melanie Oschlies *(Mgr)*
Bhavya Nand Kishore *(Dir-Practice-Global)*

Bain & Company Thailand, Inc. **(1)**
388 Exchange Tower Level 36 Unit 3602 Sukhumvit Road Khwaeng Klongtoey, Khet Klongtoey, Bangkok, 10110, Thailand
Tel.: (66) 2 0176 888
Business Management Consulting Services
N.A.I.C.S.: 541611
Sharad Apte *(Partner)*
Sen Ganesh *(Partner)*
Derek Keswakaroon *(Partner)*

Bain & Company, Inc. - New York **(1)**
1114 Ave of the Americas 43rd Fl, New York, NY 10036-6564
Tel.: (646) 562-8000
Web Site: http://www.bain.com
Business Consulting Services
N.A.I.C.S.: 541611
Preston Henske *(Partner)*
James Wright *(VP)*
Dan Pinkney *(Mgr-PR-Global)*
Andrew Mintz *(Partner)*

Bain & Company, Inc.—(Continued)

Atul Aggarwal *(Partner)*
Jason Barro *(Partner)*
Mike Baxter *(Partner)*
Mikaela Boyd *(Partner)*
Mark Brinda *(Partner)*
Gary Clare *(Partner)*
David Cooper *(Partner)*
Monisha De La Rocha *(Partner)*
Marissa Dent *(Partner)*
Paul DiPaola *(Partner)*
Joe Fielding *(Partner)*
David Fleisch *(Partner)*
Richard Fleming *(Partner)*
Sharon Fry *(Partner)*
Allison Gans *(Partner)*
Mattias Geise *(Partner)*
Melanie Harris *(Partner)*
Daniel Hong *(Partner)*
Nirad Jain *(Partner)*
Todd Johnson *(Partner)*
Kalyan Jonnalagadda *(Partner)*
Jeff Katzin *(Partner)*

Bain & Company, Inc. - San Francisco **(1)**
415 Mission St Ste 4800, San Francisco, CA 94105
Tel.: (415) 627-1000
Web Site: http://www.bain.com
Business Consulting Services
N.A.I.C.S.: 541611
Neil Cherry *(Partner)*
Bill Halloran *(Partner)*
Michael Mankins *(Partner)*
Steven Tallman *(Partner-Amsterdam)*
Savi Baveja *(Partner)*
Ann Bosche *(Partner)*
Chris Brahm *(Partner)*
Christian Buecker *(Partner)*
Greg Caimi *(Partner)*
Aaron CherisPartner *(Partner)*
Andrea D'Arcy *(Partner)*
Mark Daoust *(Partner)*
David Deming *(Partner)*
Asit Goel *(Partner)*
Adam Haller *(Partner)*
Peter Hanbury *(Partner)*
Joe Herger *(Partner)*
Tom Holland *(Partner)*
David Hoverman *(Partner)*
Pete Hultman *(Partner)*
Sam Israelit *(Partner)*
Chris Johnson *(Partner)*
Brian Krim *(Partner)*
Jordan Lee *(Partner)*
Justin Murphy *(Partner)*
Dunigan O'Keeffe *(Partner)*
Christopher Perry *(Partner)*
Raj Pherwani *(Partner)*

Bain & Company, Inc. - United Kingdom **(1)**
40 Strand, London, WC2N 5RW, United Kingdom **(100%)**
Tel.: (44) 2079696000
Web Site: http://www.bain.com
Sales Range: $100-124.9 Million
Emp.: 320
Investment Banking
N.A.I.C.S.: 523150
James Hadley *(Partner)*
Paul Meehan *(Partner)*
Waqar Alam *(Partner)*
James Allen *(Partner)*
Bharat Bansal *(Partner)*
Alex Bhak *(Partner)*
Florian Braun *(Partner)*
Andrew Carleton *(Partner)*
Robert Carse *(Partner)*
Luca Caruso *(Partner)*
Lili Chahbazi *(Partner)*
Nitin Chaturvedi *(Partner)*
Tim Cochrane *(Partner)*
Nigel Cornish *(Partner)*
Gemma Cotton *(Partner)*
Trevor Cotton *(Partner)*
Alexander DeMol *(Partner)*
Sanjay Dhiri *(Partner)*
Emilio Domingo *(Partner)*
Graham Elton *(Partner)*
Frank Ford *(Partner)*
Sinead Fox *(Partner)*
Jonathan Frick *(Partner)*
Michael Garstka *(Partner)*
Juan Carlos Gay *(Partner)*
Clare Gordon *(Partner)*
Jonny Holliday *(Partner)*

Bain International Inc. - Australia, Main Office **(1)**
Level 45 Governor Phillip Tower 1 Farrer Place, Sydney, 2000, NSW, Australia
Tel.: (61) 290248600
Web Site: http://www.bain.com.au
Emp.: 100
Business Consulting Services
N.A.I.C.S.: 541611
Edwina King *(Mgr-Media & PR)*
James Anderson *(Partner)*
Phil Barton *(Partner)*
Katrina Cuthell *(Partner)*
Lucy d'Arville *(Partner)*
Marco D'Avino *(Partner)*
David Ellis *(Partner)*
Pascal Gautheron *(Partner)*
Agathe Gross *(Partner)*
Richard Hatherall *(Partner)*
Simon Henderson *(Partner)*
Damian Stephenson *(Partner)*
Peter Stumbles *(Partner)*
Gary Turner *(Partner)*
Chio Verastegui *(Partner)*
James Viles *(Partner)*
Drew Woodhouse *(Partner)*
David Zehner *(Partner)*
Jose de Franca *(Principal)*
Nadja Kendlbacher *(Principal)*
Laird Rawsthorne *(Sr Mgr-Advanced Analytics Grp)*

Bain et Compagnie SNC **(1)**
25 Avenue Kleber, 75116, Paris, France
Tel.: (33) 1 44 55 75 75
Web Site: http://www.bain.fr
Emp.: 300
Business Management Consulting Services
N.A.I.C.S.: 541611
Laurent-Pierre Baculard *(Partner)*
Sabine Atieh *(Partner)*
Bernard Birchler *(Partner)*
Paolo Bordogna *(Partner)*
Emmanuel Coque *(Principal)*
Pierre De Raismes *(Partner)*
Ada Di Marzo *(Partner)*
Pierre-Antoine Dresco *(Partner)*
Doris Galan *(Partner)*
Camille Goossens *(Partner)*
John Hazan *(Partner)*
Marc-Andre Kamel *(Partner)*
Arnaud Leroi *(Partner)*
Francois Montaville *(Partner)*
Loic Plantevin *(Partner)*
Jean-Charles Redon *(Partner)*
Marie Saladin *(Partner)*
Daphne Vattier *(Partner)*
Matthieu Vigneron *(Partner)*

Pyxis Solutions, LLC **(1)**
55 Broad St Fl 28, New York, NY 10004-2501
Tel.: (212) 363-2828
Web Site: http://www.pyxissolutions.com
Software Development Services
N.A.I.C.S.: 541511
Ian Weber *(Co-Founder)*
Max Lee *(Co-Founder)*

BAIN CAPITAL, LP
200 Clarendon St, Boston, MA 02116
Tel.: (617) 516-2000 DE
Web Site:
https://www.baincapital.com
Year Founded: 1984
Emp.: 1,750
Privater Equity Firm
N.A.I.C.S.: 523999
Wayne S. Deveydt *(Operating Partner & Mng Dir)*
Ernesto Anguilla *(Partner & Head-Communications & Public Affairs)*
Paula Connolly *(Partner, Co-CTO & Head-Information Technology)*
Andrew A. F. Hack *(Partner)*
David W. Humphrey *(Partner, Mng Dir-Tech, Media, and Telecom-Vertical & Co-Head-North America Private Equity Bus)*
Max de Groen *(Partner & Mng Dir-Tech Vertical)*

Subsidiaries:

ADK Holdings Inc. **(1)**

23-1 Toranomon 1 chome, Minato-ku, Tokyo, 105-6312, Japan
Tel.: (81) 368303811
Web Site: http://www.adk.jp
Rev.: $3,082,344,540
Assets: $1,986,252,400
Liabilities: $996,665,900
Net Worth: $989,586,500
Earnings: $20,766,240
Emp.: 3,430
Fiscal Year-end: 12/31/2016
Holding Company; Advertising Services
N.A.I.C.S.: 551112
Shinichi Ueno *(Pres & CEO)*
Yoshiki Uemura *(Exec Dir)*
Hideaki Kido *(Chm)*
Noriyuki Nakai *(Exec Dir)*
Yoshitaka Ishiwata *(CFO)*

Subsidiary (US):

ADK America, Inc. **(2)**
405 Lexington Ave Spaces Chrysler Bldg Ste 865, 10174, New York, NY
Tel.: (646) 284-9801
Web Site: http://www.adkamerica.com
Advetising Agency
N.A.I.C.S.: 541810

Branch (Domestic):

ADK America, Inc. - New York Office **(3)**
515 W 20th St 6th fl, New York, NY 10011
Tel.: (646) 284-9811
Web Site: http://www.adkamerica.com
Advertising Services
N.A.I.C.S.: 541810

Subsidiary (Domestic):

ADK Emotions Inc. **(2)**
1-23-1 Toranomon Minato-ku, Tokyo, Japan
Tel.: (81) 3 6891 2311
Web Site: https://www.adkem.jp
Content Solutions & Rights Management
N.A.I.C.S.: 512120
Takahiro Noda *(Pres)*

ADK International Inc. **(2)**
Koishikawa Sakura Building 7F 1-28-1 Koishikawa Bunkyo-ku, Tokyo, 112-0002, Japan
Tel.: (81) 3 3546 9100
Web Site: http://www.adk-intl.jp
Emp.: 29
Communication & Marketing Services
N.A.I.C.S.: 541810
Wataru Sato *(Pres & CEO)*
Tomoya Takeda *(Exec Dir)*
Haruyuki Shimizu *(Exec Dir)*
Haruyuki Shimizu *(Auditor)*

Subsidiary (Non-US):

Asatsu (Thailand) Co., LTD. **(2)**
17th Floor Shinawatra Tower III 1010 Vibhavadi Rangsit Road Chatuchak, Bangkok, 10900, Thailand
Tel.: (66) 29492800
Advetising Agency
N.A.I.C.S.: 541810
Nutthawoot Lamsaard *(Dir-Comm Mgr)*

Asatsu Century (Shanghai) Advertising Co.,Ltd. **(2)**
Room 1007 887 Huaihai Road(M), Shanghai, 200020, China
Tel.: (86) 21 6474 8908
Web Site: http://www.adk-cn.com
Advertising Services
N.A.I.C.S.: 541810

Asatsu-DK Malaysia Sdn. Bhd. **(2)**
Level 9.01 Menara Amfirst No.1 Jalan 19/3, Petaling Jaya, 46300, Selangor, Malaysia
Tel.: (60) 3 7954 0388
Web Site: https://adk.com.my
Marketing & Advertising
N.A.I.C.S.: 541810
Hideki Ota *(Mng Dir)*
Pey Sun *(Media Dir)*

Asatsu-DK Singapore PTE. LTD. **(2)**
Tel.: (65) 6333 5115
Web Site: https://adk-connect.com
Advertising Services
N.A.I.C.S.: 541810

Asatsu-DK Vietnam Inc. **(2)**

Unit 16.07 & 16.08 Floor 16 Deutsches Haus Building 33 Le Duan Street Ben Nghe Ward District 1, Ho Chi Minh City, Vietnam
Tel.: (84) 8 38218852
Web Site: http://asatsu-dkvn.com
Online Advertising Services
N.A.I.C.S.: 541890

DIK-Ocean Advertising Co., Ltd. **(2)**
Tel.: (886) 2 8712 8555
Web Site: http://www.adk.com.tw
Marketing & Advertising
N.A.I.C.S.: 541810

DK Advertising (HK) Ltd. **(2)**
Suite 39 & 50 48/F Office Tower Langham Place, Kowloon, China (Hong Kong)
Tel.: (852) 852 2895 811
Online Advertising Services
N.A.I.C.S.: 541890

Shanghai Asatsu Advertising Co., Ltd. **(2)**
Room 1005 887 Huaihai Road(M), Shanghai, 200020, China
Tel.: (86) 21 6467 4118
Web Site: http://www.adk-cn.com
Advertising Services
N.A.I.C.S.: 541810

United Asatsu International Ltd. **(2)**
13F No 287 Nanking East Road Sec 3, Taipei, 105, Taiwan
Tel.: (886) 2 8712 8555
Web Site: http://www.adk.com.tw
Marketing & Advertising
N.A.I.C.S.: 541810

ASIMCO Technologies Limited **(1)**
7F Tower B Renji Plaza 101 Jingmi Road, Chaoyang District, Beijing, 100102, China
Tel.: (86) 10 5935 5000
Web Site: http://www.asimco.com
Sales Range: $500-549.9 Million
Automotive Components Mfr & Distr
N.A.I.C.S.: 336390
Bin Wang *(Pres & CEO)*
Michael Cronin *(VP-Corp Dev)*

Subsidiary (US):

ASIMCO International Inc. **(2)**
1000 Town Ctr Ste 1050, Southfield, MI 48075
Tel.: (248) 213-5200
Web Site: http://www.asimco.com
Emp.: 8
Motor Vehicle Parts Whslr
N.A.I.C.S.: 423120

Affiliate (Domestic):

ASIMCO Meilian Braking System (Langfang) Co., Ltd. **(2)**
No 1 Guangming W Rd, Langfang, 065000, Hebei, China
Tel.: (86) 3162684026
Web Site: http://www.asimco.com
Sales Range: $50-74.9 Million
Motor Vehicle Brakes Mfr
N.A.I.C.S.: 336340
Daniel Liu *(Gen Mgr)*

ASIMCO Tianwei Fuel Injection Equipment Stock Co., Ltd. **(2)**
Parkview Center 4 F 5 Fangyuan Xi Road, Chaoyang District, Beijing, 100016, China
Tel.: (86) 1063811155
Web Site: http://www.asimco.com
Sales Range: $250-299.9 Million
Fuel Injection Motor Vehicle Parts Mfr
N.A.I.C.S.: 336390
Wu Yingxue *(VP-Mfg Support)*

Subsidiary (Domestic):

Hubei Super-Elec Auto Electric Motor Ltd., Liability Co. **(2)**
No 276 Beijing East Road, Shashi, Jingzhou, 434001, Hubei, China
Tel.: (86) 71 6821 2419
Automotive Engine Parts Mfr
N.A.I.C.S.: 333618

Absolute Return Capital, LLC **(1)**
John Hancock Twr 200 Clarendon St, Boston, MA 02116-7615
Tel.: (617) 516-2000
Web Site: http://www.arc.baincapital.com

Fixed Income, Equity, Commodity & Currency Market Asset Management Services
N.A.I.C.S.: 523940
Jeffrey Woolbert (Mng Dir)
Jonathan J. Goodman (Mng Dir)

Ahlstrom-Munksjo Oyj (1)
Alvar Aallon katu 3 C, PO BOX 329, 00101, Helsinki, Finland (55%)
Tel.: (358) 108880
Web Site: http://www.ahlstrom-munksjo.com
Rev.: $3,295,736,392
Assets: $3,836,284,816
Liabilities: $2,381,311,712
Net Worth: $1,454,973,104
Earnings: $116,068,680
Emp.: 7,814
Fiscal Year-end: 12/31/2020
Fiber-based Materials Mfr; Specialty Paper Mfr
N.A.I.C.S.: 322120
Dan Adrianzon (Exec VP-Industrial Solutions)
Daniele Borlatto (Exec VP-Filtration & Performance Solutions)
Hans Sohlstrom (Pres & CEO)
Andreas Elving (Gen Counsel & Exec VP-Legal)
Tarja Takko (Exec VP-People, Safety & Comm)
Tomas Wulkan (Exec VP-Decor Solutions)
Mikko Lankinen (Exec VP-Corp Strategy & Dev)
Robin Guillaud (Exec VP-Sustainability, Innovation & Comml Excellence)
Johan Lindh (VP-Grp IR)
Ivano Sessa (Chm)
Robyn Buss (Exec VP-Food Pkg & Technical Solutions)
Markus Westerkamp (Exec VP-Advanced Solutions)
Jorn P. Jensen (CFO)

Subsidiary (Non-US):

Ahlstrom Asia Holdings Pte Ltd (2)
14 Ann Siang Road 02-01, Singapore, 69694, Singapore
Tel.: (65) 6861 2700
Web Site: http://www.ahlstrom-munksjo.com
Investment Management Service
N.A.I.C.S.: 523999

Subsidiary (Non-US):

Ahlstrom-Munksjo Fibercomposites (Binzhou) Limited (3)
Ahlstrom Binzhou No 209 Huanghe 5 Road, Binzhou, 256600, Shangdong, China
Tel.: (86) 543 340 9777
Web Site: http://www.ahlstrom-munksjo.com
Paper Products Mfr
N.A.I.C.S.: 322299

Ahlstrom-Munksjo Korea Co., Ltd. (3)
7 Keum Li Yuga Myoun Talsung County, Daegu, 711-882, Korea (South)
Tel.: (82) 536600491
Web Site: http://www.ahlstrom-munksjo.com
Automotive Filter Papers Mfr & Sales
N.A.I.C.S.: 322211

Subsidiary (Domestic):

Ahlstrom Seoul Co. Ltd (4)
Room 601 Kanglim Building 448-7 Seongnae-dong, Gangdong-gu, Seoul, 134884, Korea (South)
Tel.: (82) 2 3452 7314
Web Site: http://www.ahlstrom-munksjo.com
Pulp Paper Products Mfr & Distr
N.A.I.C.S.: 322120

Subsidiary (Non-US):

Ahlstrom-Munksjo Paper (Taicang) Co., Ltd. (3)
No 90 Fada Rd, Taicang Economic Development Area, Taicang, 215413, Jiangsu, China
Tel.: (86) 51253986618
Web Site: http://www.ahlstrom-munksjo.com
Insulation & Specialty Paper Mfr
N.A.I.C.S.: 322120

Ahlstrom-Munksjo Paper Trading (Shanghai) Co., Ltd. (3)
Unit BC 11F/L East Tower No 666 East Beijing Road, Huangpu District, Shanghai,

200001, China
Tel.: (86) 2123307330
Insulation & Specialty Paper Mfr
N.A.I.C.S.: 322120

PT Ahlstrom Indonesia (3)
Haryono Square-3rd Floor Room 303 MT Haryono Kav 10, 13330, Jakarta Timur, Indonesia
Tel.: (62) 2129067150
Insulation & Specialty Paper Mfr
N.A.I.C.S.: 322120

Subsidiary (Non-US):

Ahlstrom Munksjo Fiber Composites India Private Ltd (2)
Mundra Sez Textile & Apparel Park Plot No 7 Survey No 141, Mudra Kutch, Gujarat, 370 421, India
Tel.: (91) 2838 619100
Web Site: http://www.ahlstrom-munksjo.com
Fiber Composite Materials Mfr
N.A.I.C.S.: 322219

Ahlstrom Munksjo Fiber Composites India Private Ltd. (2)
Mundra Sez Textile and Apparel Park MI-TAP Plot No 7 Survey No 141, Mundra, Kutch, 370 421, India
Tel.: (91) 2838619100
Insulation & Specialty Paper Mfr
N.A.I.C.S.: 322120

Ahlstrom Research and Services SA (2)
Immeuble Perigares B 201 Rue Carnot, 94127, Fontenay-sous-Bois, France
Tel.: (33) 4 74 57 29 29
Paper Products Mfr
N.A.I.C.S.: 322299

Subsidiary (Domestic):

Ahlstrom Sales Helsinki Oy (2)
Alvar Aallon katu 3 C, PO Box 329, DI-00101, Helsinki, Finland
Tel.: (358) 10 8880
Specialty Papers & Packaging Materials Distr
N.A.I.C.S.: 424130

Subsidiary (Non-US):

Ahlstrom-Munksjo AB (2)
Barnarpsgatan 39 41, 553 33, Jonkoping, Sweden
Tel.: (46) 36303300
Insulation & Specialty Paper Mfr
N.A.I.C.S.: 322120

Ahlstrom-Munksjo Apprieu S.A.S (2)
Centre De recherche Apprieu 40 Rue Du Grand Champ, Apprieu, 38140, Isere, France
Tel.: (33) 476937271
Insulation & Specialty Paper Mfr
N.A.I.C.S.: 322120

Ahlstrom-Munksjo Arches S.A.S. (2)
48 Route de Remiremont, Arches, 88380, Les Marches, France
Tel.: (33) 329326000
Insulation & Specialty Paper Mfr
N.A.I.C.S.: 327910

Ahlstrom-Munksjo Aspa Bruk AB (2)
Fabriksvagen, Aspabruk, 696 80, Orebro, Sweden
Tel.: (46) 58381500
Insulation & Specialty Paper Mfr
N.A.I.C.S.: 322120

Ahlstrom-Munksjo Brasil Ltda. (2)
Rua Armando Steck 770 Bairro Capivari, CEP 13290-000, Louveira, Brazil
Tel.: (55) 19 3878 9238
Mfr & Sales of Specialty Fiber-Based Materials
N.A.I.C.S.: 322120

Subsidiary (Domestic):

Ahlstrom Brasil Ltda. (3)
Rua Armando Steck 770-Bairro Capivari, 13290-000, Louveira, Brazil
Tel.: (55) 1938789238
Insulation & Specialty Paper Mfr
N.A.I.C.S.: 322120

Ahlstrom-Munksjo Brasil Industria e Comercio de Papeis Especiais Ltda. (3)
Rod Euryale De Jesus Zerbine S/N P. 66 Km 84, Predio Industrial Paper Jardim Sao Gabriel, Jacarei, 12340-010, Sao Paulo, Brazil
Tel.: (55) 1221279300
Insulation & Specialty Paper Mfr
N.A.I.C.S.: 327910

Plant (Domestic):

Ahlstrom-Munksjo Oyj - Caieiras Plant (3)
Rod Pres Tancredo A Neves Km 34, PO Box 21, Caieiras, 07705-000, Sao Paulo, Brazil
Tel.: (55) 1144417800
Insulation & Specialty Paper Mfr
N.A.I.C.S.: 322120

Ahlstrom-Munksjo Oyj - Jacarei Plant (3)
Rod Euryale De Jesus Zerbine SN SP 66 Km 84 Jardim Sao Gabriel, Jacarei, 12340-010, Sao Paulo, Brazil
Tel.: (55) 1221279300
Insulation & Specialty Paper Mfr
N.A.I.C.S.: 322120

Ahlstrom-Munksjo Oyj - Louveira Plant (3)
Rua Armando Steck 770 Bairro Capivari, Louveira, 13290-000, Sao Paulo, Brazil
Tel.: (55) 1938789200
Insulation & Specialty Paper Mfr
N.A.I.C.S.: 322120

Subsidiary (Non-US):

Ahlstrom-Munksjo Brignoud SAS (2)
Rue Alfred Fredet, 38196, Brignoud, France
Tel.: (33) 4 7645 3515
Web Site: http://www.ahlstrom-munksjo.com
Paper Products Mfr
N.A.I.C.S.: 322299

Ahlstrom-Munksjo Chirnside Ltd. (2)
Chirnside, Duns, TD11 3JW, Berwickshire, United Kingdom
Tel.: (44) 1890818303
Web Site: http://www.ahlstrom-munksjo.com
Filters, Medical Fabrics, Life Science & Diagnostics, Wallcoverings, Tapes & Food & Beverage Packaging Mfr
N.A.I.C.S.: 322211

Plant (Domestic):

Ahlstrom-Munksjo Chirnside Limited - Manchester Plant (3)
Mount Sion Works Sion Street, Manchester, M26 3SB, United Kingdom
Tel.: (44) 1617255320
Insulation & Specialty Paper Mfr
N.A.I.C.S.: 322120

Subsidiary (Non-US):

Ahlstrom-Munksjo Falun AB (2)
Soldatvagen 14, 791 10, Falun, Sweden
Tel.: (46) 23705880
Web Site: http://www.ahlstrom-munksjo.com
Insulation & Specialty Paper Mfr
N.A.I.C.S.: 322120

Ahlstrom-Munksjo Germany Holding GmbH (2)
Nordlicher Stadtgraben 4, 73430, Aalen, Germany
Tel.: (49) 7361506111
Holding Company; Insulation & Specialty Paper Mfr
N.A.I.C.S.: 551112

Subsidiary (Domestic):

Ahlstrom-Munksjo Germany GmbH (3)
Niederschlag 1, 09471, Barenstein, Germany
Tel.: (49) 3 7347 830
Web Site: http://www.ahlstrom-munksjo.com
Holding Company; Paper Products Mfr & Distr
N.A.I.C.S.: 551112

Ahlstrom-Munksjo Paper GmbH (3)

Waldhauser Strasse 41, 73432, Aalen, Germany
Tel.: (49) 73615060
Insulation & Specialty Paper Mfr
N.A.I.C.S.: 322120

Subsidiary (Domestic):

Ahlstrom-Munksjo Glassfibre Oy (2)
Ahlstromintie 19, PO Box 140, 48601, Kotka, Finland
Tel.: (358) 1088811
Web Site: http://www.ahlstrom-munksjo.com
Fiber Glass Products Mfr
N.A.I.C.S.: 327215

Subsidiary (Non-US):

Ahlstrom-Munksjo Tver LLC (3)
Promyshlennaya Str 11, Redkino, 171261, Tver, Russia
Tel.: (7) 4956441350
Web Site: http://www.ahlstrom-munksjo.com
Glass Products Mfr
N.A.I.C.S.: 327215

Subsidiary (Non-US):

Ahlstrom-Munksjo Italia S.p.A. (2)
Localita Campoginepro 2 Frazione Gaville, 60041, Sassoferrato, Ancona, Italy
Tel.: (39) 073 29127
Web Site: http://www.ahlstrom-munksjo.com
Paper Products Mfr
N.A.I.C.S.: 322299

Ahlstrom-Munksjo Italia S.p.A. (2)
Via Stura 98, 10075, Mathi, Torino, Italy
Tel.: (39) 0119260111
Paper Impregnation Processes & Making Masking Tape
N.A.I.C.S.: 322211

Ahlstrom-Munksjo Japan Inc. (2)
Estage Osaki Bldg 3-5-2 Osaki, Shinagawa-ku, Tokyo, 141-0032, Japan
Tel.: (81) 3 5776 3600
Paper Product Distr
N.A.I.C.S.: 424130

Ahlstrom-Munksjo La Gere S.A.S. (2)
Usine de La Gere Chemin Cartallier, 38780, Pont-l'Eveque, France
Tel.: (33) 4 7416 1010
Web Site: http://www.ahlstrom-munksjo.com
Packaging Paper Products Mfr
N.A.I.C.S.: 322220

Ahlstrom-Munksjo Malmedy SA (2)
Avenue de Pont de Warche 1, 4960, Malmedy, Belgium
Tel.: (32) 8079 5411
Web Site: http://www.ahlstrom-munksjo.com
Paper Products Mfr
N.A.I.C.S.: 322299

Ahlstrom-Munksjo Monterrey, S. de R.L. de C.V. (2)
Lazaro Cardenas 2400 Col Residencial San Agustin, San Pedro Garza Garcia Nuevo Leon, 27000, Mexico, Mexico
Tel.: (52) 81 8104 0442
Web Site: http://www.ahlstrom-munksjo.com
Paper & Cardboard Products Distr
N.A.I.C.S.: 424130

Subsidiary (US):

Ahlstrom-Munksjo Nonwovens LLC (2)
2 Elm St, Windsor Locks, CT 06096-2335
Tel.: (860) 654-8300
Web Site: http://www.ahlstrom-munksjo.com
Specialty Paper Products Mfr
N.A.I.C.S.: 322299

Subsidiary (Domestic):

Ahlstrom-Munksjo Filtration LLC (3)
215 Nebo Rd, Madisonville, KY 42431
Tel.: (270) 821-0140
Web Site: http://www.ahlstrom-munksjo.com
Automotive Filters Mfr
N.A.I.C.S.: 336110

Plant (Domestic):

Ahlstrom-Munksjo Filtration LLC - Mount Holly Springs Plant (4)

Bain Capital, LP—(Continued)

122 W Butler St, Mount Holly Springs, PA
17065
Tel.: (717) 486-3438
Web Site: http://www.ahlstrom-munksjo.com
Filtration Papers Mfr
N.A.I.C.S.: 322120

**Ahlstrom-Munksjo Filtration LLC -
Taylorville Plant** (4)
1200 E Elm St, Taylorville, IL 62568
Tel.: (217) 824-9611
Web Site: http://www.ahlstrom-munksjo.com
Filtration Solutions
N.A.I.C.S.: 322120

Subsidiary (Domestic):

**Ahlstrom-Munksjo NA Specialty Solu-
tions LLC** (3)
600 Thilmany Rd, Kaukauna, WI 54130
Tel.: (920) 766-8440
Web Site: http://www.ahlstrom-munksjo.com
Paper & Packaging Products Mfr
N.A.I.C.S.: 322120

Plant (Domestic):

**Ahlstrom-Munksjo NA Specialty Solu-
tions LLC - Nicolet Plant** (4)
115 N 5th St, De Pere, WI 54115
Tel.: (920) 336-4211
Web Site: http://www.ahlstrom-munksjo.com
Insulation & Specialty Paper Mfr
N.A.I.C.S.: 322120

**Ahlstrom-Munksjo NA Specialty Solu-
tions LLC - Rhinelander Mill** (4)
515 W Davenport St, Rhinelander, WI
54501-3328
Tel.: (715) 369-4100
Web Site: http://www.ahlstrom-munksjo.com
Paper Products Mfr
N.A.I.C.S.: 322299

Subsidiary (Domestic):

Ahlstrom-Munksjo Paper Inc. (3)
100 Erdman Way Ste S100, Leominster,
MA 01453
Tel.: (978) 342-1080
Web Site: http://www.ahlstrom-munksjo.com
Decor Base Paper Mfr
N.A.I.C.S.: 322220

Subsidiary (Non-US):

Ahlstrom-Munksjo Paper S.A. (2)
Eldua Apartado 15, Berastegui, 20492, To-
losa, Spain
Tel.: (34) 943683032
Insulation & Specialty Paper Mfr
N.A.I.C.S.: 322120

**Ahlstrom-Munksjo Rottersac
S.A.S.** (2)
Usine Rottersac, Lalinde, 24150, Dordogne,
France
Tel.: (33) 553615400
Insulation & Specialty Paper Mfr
N.A.I.C.S.: 322120

Ahlstrom-Munksjo Rus LLC (2)
Ul Prechistenka 40/2 Building 1 6th Floor,
119034, Moscow, Russia
Tel.: (7) 4957853962
Insulation & Specialty Paper Mfr
N.A.I.C.S.: 322120

**Ahlstrom-Munksjo Specialties
S.A.S.** (2)
15 Rue des Papetiers, 27500, Pont Aude-
mer, Cedex, France
Tel.: (33) 2 3241 6100
Web Site: http://www.ahlstrom-munksjo.com
Paper Products Mfr
N.A.I.C.S.: 322299

Plant (Domestic):

**Ahlstrom-Munksjo Specialties S.A.S. -
Saint Severin Plant** (3)
Usine Du Marchais, Saint-Severin, 16390,
Saint-Yrieix-sur-Charente, France
Tel.: (33) 545985221
Web Site: http://www.ahlstrom-munksjo.com
Insulation & Specialty Paper Mfr
N.A.I.C.S.: 322120

Subsidiary (Non-US):

Ahlstrom-Munksjo Stalldalen AB (2)
Ställbergsvagen 30, Stalldalen, 71481,
Sweden
Tel.: (46) 58029100
Web Site: http://www.ahlstrom-munksjo.com
Filters, Medical Fabrics, Life Science & Di-
agnostics, Wallcoverings, Tapes & Food &
Beverage Packaging Mfr
N.A.I.C.S.: 322211

Subsidiary (Domestic):

Ahlstrom-Munksjo Tampere Oy (2)
Aunankaari 4, 33840, Tampere, Finland
Tel.: (358) 10 888 14
Web Site: http://www.ahlstrom-munksjo.com
Paper Products Mfr
N.A.I.C.S.: 322299

Apex Tool Group, LLC (1)
910 Ridgebrook Rd Ste 200, Sparks, MD
21152
Tel.: (410) 773-7800
Web Site: http://www.apextoolgroup.com
Sales Range: $1-4.9 Billion
Emp.: 8,000
Holding Company; Tool Mfr
N.A.I.C.S.: 551112
John P. Constantine (Pres-North American
Hand Tools & Sr VP)
James J. Roberts (CEO)
David Ling (Pres & Sr VP-Asia Pacific)
Jeff Campbell (VP-Sls & Channell Mktg-
North American Hand Tools)
Bob Kibbe (Pres-Power Tools-Global & Sr
VP)
Ross Porter (CFO & Sr VP)
Brad Opel (Sr VP-Corp Sls)
Ray Johnson (Sr VP-Ops & Supply Chain-
Global)
Jamie Raskin (Sr VP-Corp Dev & Brand
Mgmt)
Dave Sturgess (Gen Counsel, Sec & Sr VP)

Subsidiary (Domestic):

Apex Tool Group, LLC (2)
3000 W Kingsley Rd, Garland, TX 75041-
2313
Tel.: (972) 278-5678
Sales Range: $25-49.9 Million
Emp.: 270
Hand Tool Mfr
N.A.I.C.S.: 332216

Group (Domestic):

Cooper Tools, LLC (2)
1000 Lufkin Rd, Apex, NC 27539
Tel.: (919) 362-1670
Web Site: http://www.apextoolgroup.com
Sales Range: $125-149.9 Million
Hand Tool & Power Hand Tool Mfr
N.A.I.C.S.: 332216
William R. Bliss (Mgr-Mktg)

Subsidiary (Non-US):

**Apex Tool Group Germany
GmbH** (3)
Industriestrasse 1, D-73463, Westhausen,
Germany
Tel.: (49) 7363810
Web Site: http://www.apex-tools.eu
Sales Range: $75-99.9 Million
Emp.: 250
Hand Tools Mfr & Whslr
N.A.I.C.S.: 332216

Subsidiary (Domestic):

**Apex Tool Group GmbH & Co.
OHG** (4)
Industriestr 1, Westhausen, 73463, Ger-
many
Tel.: (49) 7363 81 0
Web Site: http://www.apexpowertools.com
Sales Range: $100-124.9 Million
Emp.: 250
Power Tool Mfr
N.A.I.C.S.: 333991
Andreas Kowol (Mng Dir)
Martin Kurzinger (Mng Dir)

Subsidiary (Non-US):

Apex Tool Group Pty. Ltd. (3)
519 Nurigong Street, PO Box 366, Albury,

2640, NSW, Australia
Tel.: (61) 260580300
Web Site: http://www.apextoolgroup.com.au
Sales Range: $50-74.9 Million
Emp.: 120
Hand Tool Mfr
N.A.I.C.S.: 332216
Peter Reynoldson (Mng Dir-Australia)

Division (Domestic):

**Apex Tool Group, LLC - Power Tool
Division** (3)
670 Industrial Dr, Lexington, SC 29072
Tel.: (803) 951-7510
Web Site: http://www.apexpowertools.com
Sales Range: $100-124.9 Million
Emp.: 1,500
Electric & Pneumatic Industrial Power Tools
Mfr
N.A.I.C.S.: 333991

Plant (Domestic):

**Apex Tool Group, LLC - Dayton
Power Tools Plant** (4)
762 W Stewart St, Dayton, OH 45417-1971
Tel.: (937) 222-7871
Web Site: http://www.apextoolgroup.com
Sales Range: $100-124.9 Million
Emp.: 250
Electric & Pneumatic Tools Mfr
N.A.I.C.S.: 333991

Subsidiary (Non-US):

Apex Tool S.r.l. (3)
Viale Europa 80, 20090, Cusago, MI, Italy
Tel.: (39) 02 9033101
Power & Hand Tools Whslr
N.A.I.C.S.: 423830

Cooper Tools SAS (3)
25 Av Maurice Chevalier, 77330, Ozoir-la-
Ferriere, Cedex, France
Tel.: (33) 160185540
Sales Range: $10-24.9 Million
Emp.: 14
Hand Tools Whslr
N.A.I.C.S.: 423830

Plant (Domestic):

**Cooper Tools, LLC - Sumter
Plant** (3)
1150 Clipper Rd Industrial Park, Sumter,
SC 29151
Tel.: (803) 481-1333
Web Site: http://www.cooperhandtools.com
Sales Range: $50-74.9 Million
Emp.: 53
Hand Tool Mfr
N.A.I.C.S.: 332216

Cooper Tools, LLC - York Plant (3)
3990 E Market St, York, PA 17402-2769
Tel.: (717) 755-2933
Sales Range: $100-124.9 Million
Emp.: 230
Welded & Weldless Chain Mfr
N.A.I.C.S.: 332999
Ray Grudi (Gen Mgr)

Subsidiary (Non-US):

**Nicholson Mexicana, S.A. de
C.V.** (3)
San Nicholas 18, Centro Industrial Tlal-
nepantla, Tlalnepantla, 54030, Mexico
Tel.: (52) 55 5310 1620
Sales Range: $25-49.9 Million
Emp.: 30
Hand Tool Mfr
N.A.I.C.S.: 332216
Manuel Aleman (Dir-Ops)
Hector Zago (Dir-Apex Bus Sys-Continuous
Improvement)

**Personeelsvereniging Lufkin Cooper
Tools** (3)
Phileas Foggstraat 16, 7821 AK, Emmen,
Netherlands
Tel.: (31) 591 667 500
Sales Range: $25-49.9 Million
Emp.: 25
Hand Tools Whslr
N.A.I.C.S.: 423440

Subsidiary (Domestic):

**Delta Consolidated Industries,
Inc.** (2)

4800 Krueger Dr, Jonesboro, AR 72401-
6716
Tel.: (870) 935-3711
Web Site: http://www.deltastorage.com
Sales Range: $125-149.9 Million
Emp.: 200
Truck & On-Site Tool Storage Products Mfr
N.A.I.C.S.: 332999
Roy Fannin (Dir-Ops)

Subsidiary (Non-US):

Weller Tools GmbH (2)
Carl-Benz-Strasse 2, 74354, Besigheim,
Germany
Tel.: (49) 7143 580 0
Web Site: http://www.weller-tools.com
Sales Range: $100-124.9 Million
Emp.: 80
Power Tools & Soldering Systems Mfr
N.A.I.C.S.: 333991
Bernd Fruehwald (Mng Dir)

Atento S.A. (1)
1 rue Hildegard Von Bingen, L-1282, Lux-
embourg, Luxembourg
Tel.: (352) 2678601
Web Site: http://www.atento.com
Rev.: $1,389,968,000
Assets: $885,972,000
Liabilities: $1,234,839,000
Net Worth: ($348,867,000)
Earnings: ($295,577,000)
Emp.: 127,158
Fiscal Year-end: 12/31/2022
Holding Company
N.A.I.C.S.: 551112
Jose Maria Perez Melber (Dir-Spain)
Carlos Lopez-Abadia (CEO)
Virginia Beltramini Trapero (Chief Legal Of-
ficer)
Dimitrius De Oliveira (Dir-Brazil)
Catherine Jooste (Dir-Comml)
Jose Antonio de Sousa Azevedo (CFO)
Kiomara Hidalgo (Chief HR Officer-Global)

Subsidiary (Non-US):

**Atento Inversiones y Teleservicios,
S.A.U.** (2)
Calle Quintanavides 17 Parque Empresarial
Via Norte Edificio 3, Las Tablas, 28050, Ma-
drid, Spain
Tel.: (34) 917407400
Web Site: http://www.atento.com
Sales Range: $1-4.9 Billion
Emp.: 15,200
Customer Support Call Center Services
N.A.I.C.S.: 561421
Alejandro Reynal Ample (CEO)
Diego Lopez (Dir-Sls & Bus Dev)
Inaki Cebollero (Dir-HR)
Reyes Cerezo (Sec & Dir-Legal & Regula-
tory Compliance)

Subsidiary (Domestic):

**Atento Teleservicios Espana,
S.A.U.** (3)
Santiago de Compostela 94, Madrid,
28035, Spain
Tel.: (34) 91 740 68 00
Web Site: http://www.atento.com
Emp.: 10,400
Customer Support Call Center Services
N.A.I.C.S.: 561421
Mariano Castanos Zemborain (Reg Dir-
EMEA)

BRP Inc. (1)
726 St-Joseph Street, Valcourt, J0E 2L0,
QC, Canada
Tel.: (450) 532-2211
Web Site: https://www.brp.com
Rev.: $7,848,928,152
Assets: $5,057,127,288
Liabilities: $4,634,617,860
Net Worth: $422,509,428
Earnings: $676,985,112
Emp.: 23,000
Fiscal Year-end: 01/31/2023
Personal Watercraft, Boats & All-Terrain Ve-
hicles Mfr
N.A.I.C.S.: 336999
Stephane Bilodeau (CIO)
Jose Boisjoli (Chm, Pres & CEO)
Sebastien Martel (CFO)
Patrick Dussault (Exec. VP-Global Mfg Ops)

Subsidiary (US):

Alumacraft Boat Company (2)

315 W Saint Julien St, Saint Peter, MN
56082
Tel.: (507) 931-1050
Web Site: http://www.alumacraft.com
Mfr of Aluminum Fishing Boats & Canoes
N.A.I.C.S.: 336612
Paul McDade *(Plant Mgr)*

Subsidiary (Domestic):

Alumacraft Boat Company **(3)**
1329 N 10th St, Arkadelphia, AR 71923-
2509
Tel.: (870) 246-5555
Web Site: http://www.alumacraft.com
Sales Range: $10-24.9 Million
Emp.: 80
Mfr of Small Boats & Canoes
N.A.I.C.S.: 336612

Subsidiary (Non-US):

BRP - Finland Oy **(2)**
Isoaavantie 7, PO Box 8040, 96101, Ro-
vaniemi, Finland
Tel.: (358) 408007700
Web Site: http://www.brp.com
Sales Range: $25-49.9 Million
Emp.: 280
Snowmobile Manufacturing
N.A.I.C.S.: 336999
Mika Muofku *(CFO)*

Subsidiary (US):

BRP Inc. **(2)**
1111 Ja Bombardier Blvd, Palm Bay, FL
32908
Tel.: (321) 722-4000
Web Site: http://www.brp.com
Sales Range: $25-49.9 Million
Emp.: 45
Mfr of Outboard Engines
N.A.I.C.S.: 423110

**BRP US Inc. - Outboard Engine
Division** **(2)**
10101 Science Dr, Sturtevant, WI 53177
Tel.: (262) 884-5000
Web Site: http://www.brp.com
Outboard Engines Mfr
N.A.I.C.S.: 336999

Subsidiary (Non-US):

BRP-Rotax GmbH & Co. KG **(2)**
Rotaxstrasse 1, PO Box 5, 4623, Gun-
skirchen, Austria
Tel.: (43) 72466010
Web Site: http://www.rotax.com
Sales Range: $300-349.9 Million
Motorized Recreational Vehicle Engines Mfr
N.A.I.C.S.: 336214
Peter Olsinger *(VP-Fin)*

Subsidiary (US):

**Bombardier Motor Corporation of
America** **(2)**
3225 Prairie Ave, Beloit, WI 53511
Tel.: (608) 364-3333
Web Site: http://www.brp.com
Sales Range: $10-24.9 Million
Emp.: 55
Distr of Ship Parts & Accessories for the
Marine Industry
N.A.I.C.S.: 336999

**Bombardier Motor Corporation of
America** **(2)**
10101 Science Dr, Sturtevant, WI 53177-
1757
Tel.: (262) 884-5000
Web Site: http://corp.brp.com
Sales Range: $25-49.9 Million
Emp.: 250
Mfr of Outboard Engines
N.A.I.C.S.: 336612

**Bombardier Motor Corporation of
America** **(2)**
1211 Greenwood Rd, Spruce Pine, NC
28777-8808
Tel.: (828) 765-4213
Sales Range: $25-49.9 Million
Emp.: 81
Mfr of Outboard Engines
N.A.I.C.S.: 331529

**Bombardier Motor Corporation of
America** **(2)**
12120 Ester Llama Dr Ste 114, El Paso, TX
79936
Tel.: (915) 595-8000
Web Site: http://www.brp.com
Sales Range: $25-49.9 Million
Emp.: 5
Mfr of Outboard Engines
N.A.I.C.S.: 441210
Silvan Blanchette *(VP)*

**Bombardier Recreational Products
Inc.** **(2)**
451 East Illinois Ave, Benton, IL 62812-
1996
Tel.: (618) 439-9444
Web Site: http://www.brp.com
Sales Range: $50-74.9 Million
Mfr of Outboard Engines
N.A.I.C.S.: 336612

Subsidiary (Domestic):

**Bombardier Recreational Products,
Inc.** **(2)**
565 De La Montaigne, Valcourt, G0E 2L0,
QC, Canada **(50%)**
Tel.: (819) 566-3000
Web Site: http://www.brp.com
Sales Range: $1-4.9 Billion
Emp.: 6,200
Designs, Develops, Builds, Distributes &
Markets Snowmobiles, Personal Watercraft
& Boats & All-Terrain Vehicles
N.A.I.C.S.: 336999
Jose Boisjoli *(Pres & CEO)*

Unit (Domestic):

**Bombardier Recreational Products -
Johnson & Evinrude** **(3)**
1789 Stenson Boulevard Unit 9, Peterbor-
ough, K9J7B6, ON, Canada **(80%)**
Tel.: (819) 566-3366
Web Site: http://www.brp.com
Sales Range: $10-24.9 Million
Emp.: 4
Sale of Outboard & Inboard-Outboard Mo-
tors; Parts & Accessories for Marine Indus-
try
N.A.I.C.S.: 333618

**Bain Capital Advisors (China)
Ltd.** **(1)**
46/F Two IFC 8 Century Boulevard, Shang-
hai, 200120, China
Tel.: (86) 2161632000
Capital Advisory Services
N.A.I.C.S.: 523940

**Bain Capital Advisors (India) Private
Limited** **(1)**
2nd Floor Free Press House, Nariman
Point, Mumbai, 400 021, India
Tel.: (91) 2267528000
Capital Advisory Services
N.A.I.C.S.: 523940

Bain Capital Asia, LLC **(1)**
51/F Cheung Kong Center 2 Queen's Road
Central, Hong Kong, China (Hong Kong)
Tel.: (852) 36566800
Investment Advisory Services
N.A.I.C.S.: 523940

**Bain Capital Beteiligungsberatung
GmbH** **(1)**
Maximilianstrasse 11, 80539, Munich, Ger-
many
Tel.: (49) 89244410700
Web Site: http://www.baincapital.com
Investment Management Service
N.A.I.C.S.: 523940

Bain Capital Double Impact, LP **(1)**
200 Clarendon St, Boston, MA 02116
Tel.: (617) 516-2000
Web Site:
http://www.baincapitaldoubleimpact.com
Investment Services
N.A.I.C.S.: 523999
Greg A. Shell *(Mng Dir)*
Matt Sears *(VP)*
Martha Obasi *(VP)*
Steve Rizoli *(VP)*
Amy Wang *(Sr VP)*
Alena Harrison *(Sr VP)*

Holding (Domestic):

Broadstep Behavioral Health **(2)**
8521 6 Forks Rd Ste 300, Raleigh, NC
27615
Tel.: (919) 589-1380
Web Site: http://www.broadstep.com
Residential & Community Based Services
N.A.I.C.S.: 623990
Lynn Mason *(Pres & CEO)*

Subsidiary (Domestic):

Pinelands Group Homes, Inc. **(3)**
201 E Luke Ave, Summerville, SC 29483
Tel.: (843) 851-0079
Web Site:
http://www.pinelandsgrouphome.com
Sales Range: $1-9.9 Million
Emp.: 30
Therapy & Medical Services
N.A.I.C.S.: 623220
Kristi Hudson *(Coord-Admissions)*

Holding (Domestic):

LivHOME, Inc. **(2)**
5670 Wilshire Blvd Ste 500, Los Angeles,
CA 90036
Tel.: (323) 933-5880
Web Site: http://www.livhome.com
Ambulatory Health Care Services
N.A.I.C.S.: 621999
Danny Gampe *(CFO)*
David Posner *(Exec Dir)*
Michael Nicholson *(CEO)*
Cody D. Legler *(Chief Clinical Officer)*

Subsidiary (Domestic):

**Advanced Care Management,
Inc.** **(3)**
1600 Prince St Ste 103, Alexandria, VA
22314-2836
Tel.: (703) 706-9595
Web Site:
http://www.advancedmanagement.com
Care Management Services for Elderly
N.A.I.C.S.: 621610
Joan Richardson *(Pres & CEO)*

Holding (Domestic):

MeTEOR Education LLC **(2)**
690 NE 23rd Ave Ste A, Gainesville, FL
32609
Tel.: (800) 699-7516
Web Site: https://www.meteoreducation.com
Sales Range: $1-9.9 Million
Emp.: 19
Education Administration Programs
N.A.I.C.S.: 923110
Carl B. Hedlund *(Chm)*
William Latham III *(CEO)*

Subsidiary (Domestic):

Blankenship Associates, Inc. **(3)**
980 Trinity Rd, Raleigh, NC 27607
Tel.: (919) 787-1346
Web Site:
http://www.blankenshipassociates.com
Rev: $6,000,000
Emp.: 10
Furniture Merchant Whslr
N.A.I.C.S.: 423210
Traci Smith *(CEO)*
Joe Daniels *(Sr Project Mgr)*
Teresa Snell *(Office Mgr & Mgr-Sls)*
Alan Winkler *(Dir-Ops)*

Holding (Domestic):

Rural Sourcing, Inc. **(2)**
817 W Peachtree St Ste 550, Atlanta, GA
30308
Tel.: (877) 887-4774
Web Site: http://www.ruralsourcing.com
Enterprise & Cloud Application Management
& IT Support
N.A.I.C.S.: 518210
Robin Stenzel *(Chief People Officer)*
Monty Hamilton *(CEO)*
Ingrid Miller Curtis *(Pres)*
Tre Sasser *(CFO)*
Alex Bruce *(Chief Revenue Officer)*
Scott Monnig *(Chief Client Officer)*
Derek Perry *(Sr VP-Engrg & Innovation)*
Jason Ward *(Sr VP-Consulting)*
John Lenzen *(CMO)*

Bain Capital Ltd. **(1)**
Devonshire House 5th Floor, London, W1J
8AJ, United Kingdom
Tel.: (44) 2075145252
Web Site: http://www.baincapital.co.uk
Sales Range: $50-74.9 Million
Emp.: 70
Privater Equity Firm
N.A.I.C.S.: 523999
Michel G. Plantevin *(Mng Dir)*
Blair E. Hendrix *(Mng Dir)*
Luca Bassi *(Principal)*
Stuart Gent *(Mng Dir)*
Ryan Cotton *(Mng Dir)*
Ajay Agarwal *(Mng Dir)*
Blair Hendrix *(Mng Dir)*
Brian J. Hirschfeld *(Mng Dir)*
Carolyn Hastings *(Mng Dir)*
Dan Cummings *(Mng Dir & Head-Real Es-
tate)*
Darren Abrahamson *(Mng Dir)*
Dewey Awad *(Mng Dir)*
Eric Anderson *(Exec VP)*
Jonathan Belitsos *(Principal)*
Joshua Ross *(Mng Dir)*
Kevin Gallagher *(Sr VP)*
Kyle Betty *(Mng Dir-IR)*
Matt Freeman *(Mng Dir)*
Michael McArdle *(Mng Dir-IR)*
Olof Bergqvist *(Mng Dir)*
Peter Saldarriaga *(Principal)*
Scott Friend *(Mng Dir)*
Steven Barnes *(Mng Dir)*
Tim Barns *(Mng Dir & Chief Credit Officer)*
Victoria Khanna *(Mng Dir-IR)*
Michael J. Bevacqua *(Mng Dir)*

Bain Capital Luxembourg S.a.r.l. **(1)**
4 rue Lou Hemmer, 1748, Luxembourg,
Luxembourg
Tel.: (352) 2678601
Web Site: http://www.baincapital.com
Emp.: 10
Investment Management Service
N.A.I.C.S.: 523940

Bain Capital NY, LLC **(1)**
5090 Madison Ave, New York, NY 10022
Tel.: (212) 326-9420
Web Site: http://www.baincapital.com
Privater Equity Firm
N.A.I.C.S.: 523999
Stephen M. Zide *(Mng Dir)*

Bain Capital Private Equity, LP **(1)**
200 Clarendon St, Boston, MA 02116
Tel.: (617) 516-2000
Web Site:
http://www.baincapitalprivateequity.com
Capital Advisory Services
N.A.I.C.S.: 523940
Susan Levine *(Mng Dir)*
Kenneth J. Hanau *(Mng Dir)*
David Humphrey *(Mng Dir)*
Max de Groen *(Mng Dir)*
Robert Farkas *(Operating Partner)*
Jonathon Penn *(Principal-Industrial & En-
ergy Vertical)*
Jonathan Zhu *(Mng Dir & Head-Asia Private
Equity)*

Holding (Non-US):

Chindata Group Holdings Limited **(2)**
No 47 Laiguangying East Road, Chaoyang
District, Beijing, 100012, China
Tel.: (86) 4008797679
Web Site: http://www.chindatagroup.com
Rev: $697,360,135
Assets: $3,539,186,392
Liabilities: $1,867,733,623
Net Worth: $1,671,452,768
Earnings: $99,836,232
Emp.: 1,450
Fiscal Year-end: 12/31/2022
Holding Company
N.A.I.C.S.: 551112

Estia Health Limited **(2)**
Level 9 227 Elizabeth Street, Sydney, 2000,
NSW, Australia
Tel.: (61) 292657900
Web Site: https://www.estiahealth.com.au
Rev: $514,164,825
Assets: $1,375,290,363
Liabilities: $960,216,891
Net Worth: $415,073,472
Earnings: ($40,119,241)
Emp.: 7,500

Bain Capital, LP—(Continued)

Fiscal Year-end: 06/30/2022
Elderly Health Care Services
N.A.I.C.S.: 623312
Sean Bilton *(CEO, Deputy CEO, Mng Dir & COO)*
Fiona Caldwell *(CIO)*
Damian Hiser *(COO & Chief Customer Officer)*
Leanne Laidler *(Chief Quality & Risk Officer)*
Suzy Watson *(Chief Privacy Officer & Gen Counsel)*
Leanne Ralph *(Sec)*
Ciara Rocks *(Chief Comml Officer & Chief Customer Officer)*
Anthony Rice *(CFO)*
Michael Lockwood *(Chief Dev Officer & Chief Property Officer)*
Cath Gillard *(Chief People Officer)*
Sam Winter *(Chief Bus Dev Officer)*
Gary H. Weiss *(Chm)*

Guidehouse LLP (2)
Tel.: (571) 633-1711
Web Site: http://guidehouse.com
Holding Company; Management, Technology & Risk Consulting Services
N.A.I.C.S.: 551112
Joy Jarrett *(CMO)*
Ed Meehan *(Chief Growth Officer)*
John Saad *(Head-Consolidated Defense & Natl Security Bus)*
Charles E. Beard Jr. *(COO)*
Scott McIntyre *(CEO)*
Debbie Ricci *(CFO)*
Ted Eich *(Gen Counsel)*
Jamila Taylor *(Chief HR Officer)*
Shamir Patel *(Chief Compliance Officer, Chief Ethics Officer & Deputy Gen Counsel)*
Chas Shaffer *(CIO)*
Paul Phaneuf *(Partner)*
Jessica Stallmeyer *(Partner)*
Gaurav Menon *(Partner)*
Dan Hushon *(CTO)*
Chris O'Brien *(Partner)*
Amy Howland *(Chief Information Security Officer)*
Alicia Harkness *(Partner)*
Ali Bokhari *(Partner)*

Subsidiary (Domestic):

Guidehouse Inc. (3)
150 N Riverside Plz Ste 1200, Chicago, IL 60606
Tel.: (312) 583-5700
Web Site: http://www.guidehouse.com
Sales Range: $700-749.9 Million
Litigation, Financial, Healthcare, Energy & Operational Consulting Services
N.A.I.C.S.: 541611
Gillian Forsyth *(Chief Acctg Officer)*

Subsidiary (Non-US):

Beijing Navigant Consulting Co., Ltd. (4)
Level 2 West Tower World Financial Centre, No 1 East 3rd Ring Middle Road Chaoyang District, Beijing, 100020, China
Tel.: (86) 10579932645
Management Consulting Services
N.A.I.C.S.: 541618

Subsidiary (Domestic):

Cymetrix Corporation (4)
2875 Michelle Dr Ste 250, Irvine, CA 92606
Tel.: (714) 361-6800
Web Site: http://www.cymetrix.com
Emp.: 600
Revenue Cycle Solutions for Hospitals & Healthcare Networks
N.A.I.C.S.: 541618

Dymedex Consulting, LLC (4)
4570 Churchill St Ste 200, Saint Paul, MN 55126 (100%)
Tel.: (651) 217-5990
Web Site: http://www.dymedex.com
Emp.: 100
Market Development Consulting Services
N.A.I.C.S.: 541990

Subsidiary (Non-US):

Ecofys Germany GmbH (4)

Am Wassermann 36, 50829, Cologne, Germany
Tel.: (49) 22127070100
Professional Consulting Services
Scott S. Harper *(Mng Dir)*
Julie M. Howard *(Mng Dir)*
Monica M. Weed *(Mng Dir)*

Ecofys Investments B.V. (4)
Kanaalweg 15-G, 3526 KL, Utrecht, Netherlands
Tel.: (31) 306623300
Professional Consulting Services
N.A.I.C.S.: 541611

Ecofys UK Limited (4)
Ecofys - A Navigant Company Woolgate Exchange 25 Basinghall Street, London, EC2V 5HA, United Kingdom
Tel.: (44) 2074230970
Professional Consulting Services
N.A.I.C.S.: 541611

Ecofys WTTS B.V. (4)
PO Box 8408, 3503 RK, Utrecht, Netherlands
Tel.: (31) 306623827
Web Site: http://www.ecofyswtts.com
Renewable Energy Device Testing Services
N.A.I.C.S.: 811310

Subsidiary (Domestic):

Leerink Partners LLC (4)
1 Federal St 37th Fl, Boston, MA 02110
Tel.: (617) 918-4000
Web Site: http://www.leerink.com
Emp.: 85
Financial Advisory Services for Healthcare Industries
N.A.I.C.S.: 523940
Jeffrey A. Leerink *(Founder, Chm & CEO)*
John L. Sullivan *(Sr Mng Dir-Equity Res)*
Joseph Gentile *(Chief Admin Officer)*
Tim Gerhold *(Gen Counsel)*

McKinnis Consulting Services, LLC. (4)
430 W Erie St Ste 300, Chicago, IL 60654
Tel.: (312) 216-2977
Web Site:
  http://www.mckinnisconsulting.com
Emp.: 738
Health Care Srvices
N.A.I.C.S.: 621610
Tim Kinney *(Mng Dir)*
James McHugh *(Mng Dir)*
Jake Morris *(Mng Dir)*
Patrik Vagenius *(Mng Dir)*
Caroline Jacobini *(Sr Mgr)*

Subsidiary (Non-US):

Navigant BPM (India) Private Limited (4)
Pamba Building 2nd Floor Technopark, Trivandrum, 695 581, India
Tel.: (91) 4713925900
Professional Consulting Services
N.A.I.C.S.: 541611
Paul Praveen *(COO)*
Shankar Lingam Sunnathi *(CIO)*
Mahendra Rawat *(Head-India)*
Vinod Mohan *(Dir-India)*
Unnikrishnan R. S. *(Dir-India)*

Subsidiary (Domestic):

Navigant Capital Advisors, LLC (4)
1180 Peachtree St Ste 1900, Atlanta, GA 30309
Tel.: (404) 575-4123
Web Site: http://www.navigant.com
Financial Advisory Services
N.A.I.C.S.: 523940

Subsidiary (Non-US):

Navigant Consulting (APAC) Pte. Ltd. (4)
460 Alexandra Road No 22-05 PSA Building, Singapore, 119963, Singapore
Tel.: (65) 62769050
Professional Consulting Services
N.A.I.C.S.: 541611
Jon Prudhoe *(Mng Dir-Construction)*
Gagan Puri *(Mng Dir-Financial Svcs)*
Kevin J. Attrill *(Dir-Construction)*
Premjit Dass *(Dir-Financial Svcs)*
Karen Fletcher *(Dir-Disputes & Economics)*

Navigant Consulting (Europe) Limited (4)
5th Floor Woolgate Exchange 25 Basinghall Street, London, EC2V 5HA, United Kingdom
Tel.: (44) 2074691111
Web Site: http://www.navigant.com
Financial Dispute Resolution & Investigation Services
N.A.I.C.S.: 561450
Andrew Caldwell *(Mng Dir-Disputes & Economics Practice)*

Subsidiary (Domestic):

Navigant Consulting (PI) LLC (4)
2 Houston Ctr 909 Fannin Ste 1900, Houston, TX 77010
Tel.: (713) 646-5000
Web Site: http://www.navigant.com
Emp.: 20
Financial Dispute Resolution & Investigation Services
N.A.I.C.S.: 561450

Subsidiary (Non-US):

Navigant Consulting Asia Limited (4)
108 Gloucester Road Suites 2901-4 29/F Everbright Centre, Wanchai, China (Hong Kong)
Tel.: (852) 22332500
Professional Consulting Services
N.A.I.C.S.: 541611
Kate Chan *(Mng Dir-Data & Analytics)*
Tanya Gross *(Mng Dir-Data & Analytics)*
Neill Poole *(Mng Dir-Disputes & Economics)*
Fred Chan *(Dir-Data & Analytics)*
Tim Cradock *(Assoc Dir-Construction)*

Navigant Consulting Ltd. (4)
Bay Adelaide Ctr, 333 Bay St Ste 1250, Toronto, M5H 2R2, ON, Canada
Tel.: (416) 777-2440
General Management Consulting Services
N.A.I.C.S.: 541611

Subsidiary (Domestic):

Navigant Economics, LLC (4)
30 S Wacker Dr Ste 3100, Chicago, IL 60606
Tel.: (312) 251-5900
Web Site:
  http://www.navianteconomics.com
Holding Company; Corporate, Legal & Government Economic & Financial Analysis Services
N.A.I.C.S.: 551112

Subsidiary (Domestic):

Empiris LLC (5)
2100 Main St NW Ste 604, Washington, DC 20037
Tel.: (202) 974-7960
Web Site: http://www.empiris.com
Corporate, Legal & Government Economic & Financial Analysis Services
N.A.I.C.S.: 541611
Jim Langenstld *(Dir-Navigant Economics)*

Branch (Domestic):

Navigant Economics, LLC - New York (5)
685 Third Av 14th Fl, New York, NY 10017
Tel.: (646) 227-4200
Web Site: http://www.navigant.com
Emp.: 5,900
Corporate, Legal & Government Economic & Financial Analysis Services
N.A.I.C.S.: 541611
Vikram Kapoor *(Mng Dir)*

Subsidiary (Non-US):

Navigant Europe Limited (4)
5th Floor Woolgate Exchange 25 Basinghall Street, London, EC2V 5HA, United Kingdom
Tel.: (44) 2038800800
Management Consulting Services
N.A.I.C.S.: 541611
Martin Parkinson *(Assoc Dir)*

Navigant Germany GmbH (4)
Albrechtstr 10 C, 10117, Berlin, Germany
Tel.: (49) 30297735790
Professional Consulting Services

N.A.I.C.S.: 541611

Holding (Domestic):

Harrington Industrial Plastics LLC (2)
14480 Yorba Ave, Chino, CA 91710
Tel.: (909) 597-8641
Web Site: http://www.hipco.com
Emp.: 550
Industrial Plastic Pipe Systems, Fittings, Valves, Fiberglass Fans & Air Washers Mfr
N.A.I.C.S.: 332996
Dave Abercrombie *(CEO)*
Bob Graham *(CEO)*

Subsidiary (Domestic):

Aetna Plastics Corp. (3)
1702 Saint Clair Ave NE, Cleveland, OH 44114
Tel.: (216) 781-4421
Web Site: http://www.aetnaplastics.com
Plastics Materials & Basic Forms & Shapes Merchant Whslr
N.A.I.C.S.: 424610
Gary Davis *(Pres)*
Alicia Cornelius *(Gen Mgr)*

Crist Group Inc. (3)
1324 E Beamer St, 95776, Woodland, CA
Tel.: (530) 661-0700
Web Site: http://www.cristgroup.com
Miscellaneous Durable Goods Merchant Whslr
N.A.I.C.S.: 423990
Paul Crist *(Pres)*

PumpMan Holdings LLC (3)
PO Box 837, 07663, Saddle Brook, NJ
Tel.: (201) 928-7355
Web Site: https://pumpman.com
Pump Systems, Pump Service & Repair
N.A.I.C.S.: 333996
Don Devine *(CEO)*

Subsidiary (Domestic):

PumpMan, LLC (4)
New Pehle Ave, Saddle Brook, NJ 07663
Tel.: (201) 928-7355
Web Site: http://www.pumpman.com
Pump System Repairs & Maintenance Services
N.A.I.C.S.: 333914
Donald Devine *(CEO)*

Subsidiary (Domestic):

ABC Electric Corp. (5)
2425 46th St, Astoria, NY 11103
Tel.: (718) 956-0000
Web Site: https://abcec.com
Industrial Equipment Whsr
N.A.I.C.S.: 423830

Alyan Pump Co. (5)
930 Henderson Blvd, Folcroft, PA 19032
Tel.: (610) 583-6900
Web Site: http://www.alyanpump.com
Sales Range: $1-9.9 Million
Holding Company; Pump & Pumping Equipment Mfr
N.A.I.C.S.: 333914

Federal Pump Corp. (5)
9802-9708 Ditmas Ave, Brooklyn, NY 11203
Tel.: (718) 451-2000
Web Site: http://www.federalpumps.com
Mfg Pumps/Pumping Equipment
N.A.I.C.S.: 333914
Chis Murtagh *(Pres & CEO)*

Flo Systems, Inc. (5)
905 Cherry Ln, Troy, IL 62294
Tel.: (618) 667-7890
Web Site: http://www.flosystems.com
Rev.: $5,000,000
Emp.: 12
Plumbing & Heating Equipment & Supplies, Hydronics, Merchant Whslr
N.A.I.C.S.: 423720
Bob Woods *(Mgr-Svc)*

Ransom Pump & Supply Inc. (5)
533 B St, Ramona, CA 92065-2029
Tel.: (760) 789-5955
Web Site: http://www.ransompump.com
Water & Sewer Line & Related Structures Construction
N.A.I.C.S.: 237110

Sommer Adams *(Gen Mgr)*

Southwest Waterworks Contractors, Inc. **(5)**
2205 W Grant St, Phoenix, AZ 85009-5835
Tel.: (602) 442-1110
Pump & Pumping Equipment Mfr
N.A.I.C.S.: 333914

Holding (Non-US):

Impact HD Inc. **(2)**
6F Tokken International Building 2-12-19
Shibuya, Shibuya-ku, Tokyo, 150-0002,
Japan **(81.06%)**
Tel.: (81) 354648321
Web Site: https://www.impact-h.co.jp
Rev.: $129,063,440
Assets: $86,171,360
Liabilities: $46,764,080
Net Worth: $39,407,280
Earnings: $11,693,440
Fiscal Year-end: 12/31/2021
Sales Support Services
N.A.I.C.S.: 561499
Kiyoto Sagae *(Pres & CEO)*

Subsidiary (Domestic):

Cabic Co., Ltd. **(3)**
617 Rokkaku-dori Manjuya -cho Karasuma-
dori, Nakagyo-ku Hexagon Hase Building
8th floor, Kyoto, 604-8161, Japan
Tel.: (81) 75 257 6868
Web Site: https://cabic.jp
Marketing Management Services
N.A.I.C.S.: 541613

Mediaflag Okinawa Inc. **(3)**
Multimedia Bld 1F 224-3 Toyohara, Nago,
905-2172, Okinawa, Japan
Tel.: (81) 980500144
Web Site: http://okinawa.mediaflag.co.jp
Marketing Support Services
N.A.I.C.S.: 561499
Rumi Sugiyama *(Office Mgr)*

Holding (Non-US):

Industria de Turbo Propulsores S.A. **(2)**
Parque Tecnologico Edificio 300, 48170,
Zamudio, Bizkaia, Spain
Tel.: (34) 944662100
Web Site: http://www.itp.es
Aeronautical Engines & Gas Turbines Engi-
neering, Research & Development, Casting
& Mfr
N.A.I.C.S.: 336413

Subsidiary (US):

Aeromaritime America Inc. **(3)**
4927 E Falcon Dr, Mesa, AZ 85215
Tel.: (480) 830-7780
Web Site: http://www.itpaero.com
Engine Overhaul & Repair Shop
N.A.I.C.S.: 811198

Plant (Domestic):

Industria de Turbo Propulsores S.A. - Ajalvir Plant **(3)**
Ctra Torrejon-Ajalvir M-108 Km 4, Ajalvir,
28864, Madrid, Spain
Tel.: (34) 912054500
Emp.: 1,990
Aircraft Equipment Distr
N.A.I.C.S.: 423830

Industria de Turbo Propulsores S.A. - Seville Plant **(3)**
Base Aerea de Moron de la Frontera Ctra
de Alcala de Guadaira, Moron de la Fron-
tera, 41530, Seville, Spain
Tel.: (34) 667649187
Aircraft Equipment Distr
N.A.I.C.S.: 423830

Subsidiary (Domestic):

PCB-Precicast Bilbao S.A. **(3)**
El Barracon 1, 48910, Barakaldo, Biscay,
Spain
Tel.: (34) 944184300
Web Site: https://www.itpaero.com
Super-alloys Microfusion
N.A.I.C.S.: 331511

Holding (Non-US):

OUTSOURCING Inc. **(2)**

19F Marunouchi Trust Tower Main 1-8-3
Marunouchi, Chiyoda-ku, Tokyo, 100-0005,
Japan **(85.72%)**
Tel.: (81) 332864888
Web Site: https://www.outsourcing.co.jp
Rev.: $4,557,495,870
Assets: $2,655,421,209
Liabilities: $2,132,388,503
Net Worth: $523,032,706
Earnings: $67,439,709
Emp.: 129,487
Fiscal Year-end: 12/31/2022
Outsourcing Services
N.A.I.C.S.: 561499
Haruhiko Doi *(Chm & CEO)*
Kenji Kamiyama *(Chm & CEO)*
Takayuki Yamazaki *(Pres & COO)*

Subsidiary (Non-US):

ALP Consulting Limited **(3)**
No 11/2 KHR House Palace Road Vasanth-
nagar, Bengaluru, 560 052, India
Tel.: (91) 7619569047
Web Site: https://alp.consulting
Consulting Services
N.A.I.C.S.: 541618
Jayachandran B. Pillai *(Co-Founder & Chm)*
Kishore V. N. *(Co-Founder & Mng Dir)*
Roopa Priyadarshini *(Co-Founder)*

Subsidiary (Domestic):

Datacore Technologies Private Limited **(4)**
No 11/2 KHR House Palace Road Vasanth-
nagar, Bengaluru, 560 052, India
Tel.: (91) 9663546688
Web Site: https://dcoretech.in
Emp.: 1,100
Consulting Services
N.A.I.C.S.: 541618

Subsidiary (Non-US):

Advantis Credit Limited **(3)**
Minton Hollins Building Shelton Old Road,
Stoke-on-Trent, ST4 7RY, Staffordshire,
United Kingdom
Tel.: (44) 1782401100
Web Site: https://www.advantiscredit.co.uk
Financial Processing Services
N.A.I.C.S.: 522320

Albacore Consulting Group Pty Ltd. **(3)**
Level 43 Australia Square 264-278 George
Street, Sydney, 2000, NSW, Australia
Tel.: (61) 292702691
Web Site:
   https://www.albacoreconsulting.com.au
Recruitment Services
N.A.I.C.S.: 561311

Allen Lane Limited **(3)**
33 King Street St James's, London, SW1Y
6RJ, United Kingdom
Tel.: (44) 2030319613
Web Site: https://www.allenlane.co.uk
Business Consulting Services
N.A.I.C.S.: 541618

Aro Recruitment (Singapore) Pte. Ltd. **(3)**
20 Bendemeer Road 03-12 BS Bendemeer
Centre, Singapore, 339914, Singapore
Tel.: (65) 63379733
Engineeering Services
N.A.I.C.S.: 541330

Bluefin Resources Pty. Limited **(3)**
Level 43 Australia Square 264-278 George
St, Sydney, 2000, NSW, Australia
Tel.: (61) 292702600
Web Site:
   https://www.bluefinresources.com.au
Consulting Services
N.A.I.C.S.: 541618
Simon Mills *(Asst Dir-Tech)*
Alex Slocombe *(Mgr-Div & Data Analytics)*
Paula Price *(Sr Mgr-Div, Banking, Wealth & Insurance)*

CPL Jobs Tunisie SARL **(3)**
Boulevard de la Terre Sana Business Cen-
ter Centre Urbain Nord, Bureau A7, Tunis,
Tunisia
Tel.: (216) 29337024
Web Site: https://cpljobs.com
Recruitment Services

N.A.I.C.S.: 561311

CPL Resources Limited **(3)**
One Haddington Buildings Haddington
Road, Dublin, D04 X4C9, Ireland
Tel.: (353) 16146000
Web Site: https://www.cpl.com
Recruitment Consulting Services
N.A.I.C.S.: 561311

Capacitygrid UK Ltd. **(3)**
5th Floor Knollys House 17 Addiscombe
Road, Croydon, CR0 6SR, United Kingdom
Tel.: (44) 2073783799
Web Site: http://www.capacitygrid.com
Emp.: 1,400
Business Development Services
N.A.I.C.S.: 541613

Subsidiary (Domestic):

Career Agent Co., Ltd. **(3)**
Tsukuba Building 2F 201 1-173 Tsukuba,
Kumagaya, 360-0037, Saitama, Japan
Tel.: (81) 485249811
Web Site: https://www.career-a.co.jp
Recruitment Services
N.A.I.C.S.: 561311

Subsidiary (Non-US):

Clicks Recruit (Australia) Pty. Ltd. **(3)**
Tel.: (61) 399634888
Web Site: http://clicks.com.au
Emp.: 80
Business Consulting Services
N.A.I.C.S.: 541618

Cpl Resources plc **(3)**
8-34 Percy Place, Dublin, 4, Ireland
Tel.: (353) 16146000
Web Site: http://www.cpl.ie
Rev.: $632,561,880
Assets: $214,111,633
Liabilities: $90,514,924
Net Worth: $123,596,708
Earnings: $23,884,374
Emp.: 11,250
Fiscal Year-end: 06/30/2019
Recruitment Services
N.A.I.C.S.: 561311
Anne Heraty *(CEO)*
Garret Roche *(Mng Dir-Recruitment & Tal-ent Solutions-Global)*
Niall McDevitt *(Dir-Healthcare)*
Lisa Holt *(Mng Dir-Professional Svcs Re-cruitment)*
Judith Moffett *(Dir-Technical Div)*
Suzanne Dolan *(Dir-Managed Svcs)*
Elaine Higgins *(Dir-Healthcare)*
Mary Carroll *(Dir-Learning & Dev)*
Siobhan O'Shea *(Dir-Client Svcs)*
Stephen Mullin *(Grp Dir-Sls & Bus Dev)*
Tina Dunne *(Mng Dir-Thornshaw Scientific)*
Lorna Conn *(CFO)*
Silvana Cuesta Carpio *(Mgr-Client Svcs)*
Libby Kelly *(Dir-Tech & Mgr-Tech)*
Ben McShane *(Dir-Fin Svcs)*
Barry Winkless *(Dir-Strategy & Innovation)*
Lauren Redmond *(Dir-Office Support, Mktg & Digital Permanent Svcs)*
Sharon Vize *(Dir-HR)*
James Louttit *(CIO)*

Subsidiary (Domestic):

CPL Solutions Limited **(4)**
83 Merrion Square, 2, Dublin, Ireland
Tel.: (353) 16146002
Web Site: http://www.cpl.ie
Emp.: 300
Employment Placement Agencies
N.A.I.C.S.: 561311
Edel Murphy *(Office Mgr)*

Careers Register Limited **(4)**
8-34 Percy Place, Dublin, Ireland
Tel.: (353) 1 5005900
Web Site: http://www.careers-register.com
Emp.: 25
Recruitment Consulting Services
N.A.I.C.S.: 541612
Lisa Holt *(Mng Dir)*
Paul McClatchie *(Dir)*

Computer Placement Limited **(4)**
Ross House Merchants Road, Galway,
Ireland **(100%)**
Tel.: (353) 91509740

Web Site: http://www.cpl.com
Sales Range: $25-49.9 Million
Emp.: 10
Business Support Services
N.A.I.C.S.: 561499
Ronan O. Sullivan *(Mgr)*

Subsidiary (Non-US):

Cpl (Northern Ireland) Limited **(4)**
20 Adelaide Street, Belfast, BT2 8GD,
United Kingdom
Tel.: (44) 2890725600
Web Site: http://www.cpl-ni.com
Sales Range: $25-49.9 Million
Emp.: 12
Staff Recruitment Consulting Services
N.A.I.C.S.: 541612
Paul Bacon *(Mng Dir)*

Cpl Jobs Kft **(4)**
Teve u 1 a-c, 1139, Budapest, Hungary
Tel.: (36) 15015460
Web Site: http://www.cpljobs.hu
Sales Range: $25-49.9 Million
Emp.: 40
Staff Recruitment Consulting Services
N.A.I.C.S.: 541612
Beatrrix Forkas *(Gen Mgr)*

Cpl Jobs S.r.o. **(4)**
Burzovni palac Rybna 14, Prague, 110 05,
Czech Republic
Tel.: (420) 221773611
Web Site: http://www.cpljobs.cz
Sales Range: $25-49.9 Million
Emp.: 20
Staff Recruitment Consulting Services
N.A.I.C.S.: 541612
Brigid Corby *(Mng Dir)*

Cpl Jobs S.r.o. **(4)**
Vysoka 14, Bratislava, 81106, Slovakia
Tel.: (421) 232191200
Web Site: http://www.cpljobs.sk
Emp.: 10
Staff Recruitment Consultancy Services
N.A.I.C.S.: 541612
Lenka Babelova *(Gen Mgr)*

Cpl Jobs Sp z.o.o **(4)**
Al Jerozolimskie 81, Warsaw, 2001, Poland
Tel.: (48) 224886500
Web Site: http://www.cpljobs.pl
Staff Recruitment Consultancy Services
N.A.I.C.S.: 541612
Renata Kozlowska *(Office Mgr)*

Cpl Resources plc. **(4)**
Gran via de les corts Catalanes 583 5
planta, 08011, Barcelona, Spain
Tel.: (34) 932752267
Web Site: http://www.cplspain.es
Recruitment Consulting Services
N.A.I.C.S.: 541612

Subsidiary (Domestic):

Cpl Training Limited **(4)**
83 Merrion Square, Dublin, Ireland
Tel.: (353) 16146000
Web Site: http://www.cpl.ie
Emp.: 100
Human Resource Consulting Services
N.A.I.C.S.: 541612
Gareth Roche *(Gen Mgr)*
Daniel Davies *(Grp CEO)*
Louise Sui *(Mng Dir)*

Flexsource Limited **(4)**
3 Main Street Blanchardstown, Dublin, Ire-
land
Tel.: (353) 16146000
Web Site: http://www.flexsource.ie
Recruitment Consulting Services
N.A.I.C.S.: 541612
Gareth Roche *(Gen Mgr)*

Kate Cowhig International Recruit-ment Limited **(4)**
49 Saint Stephen's Green, Dublin, Ireland
Tel.: (353) 16715557
Web Site: http://www.kcr.ie
Sales Range: $25-49.9 Million
Emp.: 15
Employment Placement Agencies
N.A.I.C.S.: 561311
Kate Cowhig *(CEO)*

Medical Recruitment Specialists **(4)**
84 Merrion Square, Dublin, 2, Ireland

Bain Capital, LP—(Continued)
Tel.: (353) 016146063
Web Site: http://www.mrs.ie
Medical Staffing Services
N.A.I.C.S.: 561311

Northside Recruitment Services Limited (4)
5 Saint Fintans N St, Dublin, Swoor, Ireland
Tel.: (353) 18346344
Employment Placement Agencies
N.A.I.C.S.: 561311

Subsidiary (Non-US):

NurseFindersUK Limited (4)
146A High Street, Tonbridge, TN9 1BB, Kent, United Kingdom
Tel.: (44) 1732355585
Web Site: http://www.nursefindersuk.com
Sales Range: $25-49.9 Million
Emp.: 3
Nursing Recruiters
N.A.I.C.S.: 561311

Subsidiary (Domestic):

Richmond Recruitment Limited (4)
83 Merrion Square, Dublin, Ireland
Tel.: (353) 16146000
Recruitment Consulting Services
N.A.I.C.S.: 541612

Servisource Healthcare Limited (4)
East Mid-Leinster Office International House Tara Street, Dublin, Ireland
Tel.: (353) 14730474
Health Care Srvices
N.A.I.C.S.: 621999

Servisource Recruitment Limited (4)
8-34 Percy Place, Dublin, 4, Ireland
Tel.: (353) 1 473 0474
Web Site: http://www.servisource.ie
Sales Range: $350-399.9 Million
Recruitment Consulting Services
N.A.I.C.S.: 541612
Declan Murphy (CEO)
Majella Hynes (Mgr-Healthcare)
Steven McDonnell (Mgr-Contracts)

Techskills Resources Limited (4)
25 Merrion Sq N, Dublin, 2, Ireland
Tel.: (353) 16390390
Web Site: http://www.techskills.ie
Sales Range: $25-49.9 Million
Emp.: 15
Engineeering Services
N.A.I.C.S.: 541330
Des Maguire (Mng Dir)

Subsidiary (Domestic):

DAISEI ENGINEERING Co., Ltd. (3)
1-2-10 Shinkawa Building 8th Floor Chuo-ku, Tokyo, 104 0033, Japan
Tel.: (81) 335533741
Web Site: http://www.daisei-eng.co.jp
Construction Engineering Services
N.A.I.C.S.: 541330

Dcom Co. Ltd. (3)
GYB Akihabara 12F 2-25 Kandasuda-cho, Chiyoda-ku, Tokyo, 101-0041, Japan
Tel.: (81) 332541700
Web Site: https://dcom-net.jp
Information Technology Consulting Services
N.A.I.C.S.: 541512

EcoCityService Corporation (3)
South Core 205 8-33 Chigasakichuo, Tsuzuki-ku, Yokohama, 224-0032, Kanagawa, Japan
Tel.: (81) 459415725
Web Site: https://www.ecocityservice.com
Water Supply Services
N.A.I.C.S.: 221310

Subsidiary (Non-US):

Eguridad Privada Active Security Company A.S.C. Cia. Ltda. (3)
Ciudadela La Garzota Manzana 92 Solar 7, Guayaquil, Ecuador
Tel.: (593) 46018258
Outsourcing Business Services
N.A.I.C.S.: 561439

FARO RECRUITMENT (HONG KONG) CO., LIMITED (3)

Suite 3202 32nd floor Landmark East AIA Kowloon Tower, 100 How Ming Street Kwun Tong, Kowloon, China (Hong Kong)
Tel.: (852) 25062676
Web Site: http://www.farorecruitment.com.hk
Emp.: 50
Temporary Staffing Services
N.A.I.C.S.: 561320
Connie Leung (Mng Dir)

FARO RECRUITMENT (SINGAPORE) PTE. LTD. (3)
230 Orchard Road 09-232 Faber House, Singapore, 238854, Singapore
Tel.: (65) 63379733
Emp.: 15
Temporary Staffing Services
N.A.I.C.S.: 561320
Samantha Tan (Gen Mgr)

Subsidiary (Domestic):

FOS Co., Ltd. (3)
Meiekiminami 1-chome 24th No 30 Nagoya Mitsui Building Main Building, 7th Floor Yubinbango Nakamura-ku, Nagoya, 450-0003, Aichi Prefecture, Japan
Tel.: (81) 525616005
Web Site: http://www.f-outsourcing.co.jp
Business Consulting Services
N.A.I.C.S.: 541618

Subsidiary (Non-US):

Faith Root Recruitment Vietnam Joint Stock Company (3)
Unit 701A 7th Floor Handi Resco Tower 521 Kim Ma street, Ba Dinh District, Hanoi, Vietnam
Tel.: (84) 2439743091
Web Site: http://www.farorecruitment.com.vn
Business Consulting Services
N.A.I.C.S.: 541618

Faro Recruitment (China) Co., Ltd. (3)
Unit 1201 CITIC Building Tower A 19 Jianguomenwai Street, Chaoyang District, Beijing, 100004, China
Tel.: (86) 1065270988
Web Site: http://www.farorecruitment.com
Business Consulting Services
N.A.I.C.S.: 541618

Subsidiary (Domestic):

GLocal Co., Ltd. (3)
3-1-4 Shin-Yokohama 402 Plastoria Building, Kohoku-ku, Yokohama, Kanagawa Prefecture, Japan
Tel.: (81) 457186271
Web Site: http://www.e-glocal.com
Business Process Outsourcing Services
N.A.I.C.S.: 541611

Subsidiary (Non-US):

Helpnet Ingenieria Y Servicios De Recursos Humanos S.A. (3)
Eliodoro Yanez 2416, Providencia, Santiago, Chile
Tel.: (56) 228620000
Web Site: http://www.helpnet.cl
Human Resource Consulting Services
N.A.I.C.S.: 541612

JBW Group Limited (3)
9th Floor Peninsular House Monument Street, London, EC3R 8LJ, United Kingdom
Tel.: (44) 3301070023
Web Site: http://www.jbwgroup.co.uk
Consulting Services
N.A.I.C.S.: 541618
Nick Tubbs (CEO)
Xiang Lu (CFO)
Lee Brown (COO)
John Mason (Officer-Client Svcs)
John Sweet-Escott (CTO)

Jigsaw Search Pty. Ltd. (3)
Tel.: (61) 399986261
Web Site: http://www.jigsawtm.com
Building Consulting Services
N.A.I.C.S.: 541310

Subsidiary (Domestic):

KEN Technology Co., Ltd. (3)
3-28-15 Shibuya Shibuya S Noguchi Bldg 9F, Shibuya-ku, Tokyo, 150-0002, Japan

Tel.: (81) 364271535
Web Site: http://www.kentechnology.co.jp
Business Process Outsourcing Services
N.A.I.C.S.: 541611

Kyodo Engineering Corporation (3)
17F Marunouchi Trust Tower Main Building 1-8-3 Marunouchi, Chiyoda-ku, Tokyo, 100-0005, Japan
Tel.: (81) 332867878
Web Site: https://www.kyodo-engine.com
Emp.: 3,697
Business Consulting Services
N.A.I.C.S.: 541618

Subsidiary (Non-US):

Liberata UK Ltd. (3)
5th Floor Knollys House 17 Addiscombe Road, Croydon, CR0 6SR, United Kingdom
Tel.: (44) 2073783700
Web Site: http://www.liberata.com
Business Process Outsourcing Services
N.A.I.C.S.: 561499
Charlie Bruin (CEO)
Robert Price (CFO)
Neil Simpson (Dir-Governance, Commi & Risk Mgmt)
Christopher Kelly (CIO)
Jonathan Watts (Dir-HR)

Subsidiary (Domestic):

Mobile Communications Co., Ltd. (3)
14th floor Akasaka Stargate Plaza 2-3-5 Akasaka, Minato-ku, Tokyo, 107-0052, Japan
Tel.: (81) 355492852
Web Site: https://www.mcoms.co.jp
Emp.: 1,300
Business Consulting Services
N.A.I.C.S.: 541618

Multi Tec Co., Ltd. (3)
9th Floor Kobe Sannomiya Hankyu Building 4-2-1 Kano-cho, Chuo-ku, Kobe, 650-0001, Hyogo, Japan
Tel.: (81) 782004590
Web Site: https://www.multi-tec.co.jp
Emp.: 230
Construction Assistance & Maintenance Services
N.A.I.C.S.: 811310

Natural Co., Ltd. (3)
1-5-12 Nihonbashi Horidomecho, Chuo-ku, Tokyo, 103-0012, Japan
Tel.: (81) 336620331
Web Site: http://www.nun.co.jp
Business Process Outsourcing Services
N.A.I.C.S.: 541611

Subsidiary (Non-US):

Ntrinsic Consulting Europe Limited (3)
Boulevard Brand Whitlock 114, 1200, Brussels, Belgium
Tel.: (32) 25040100
Consulting Services
N.A.I.C.S.: 541618
Kieran Kelly (Dir-Sls)

Ntrinsic Consulting Resources Limited (3)
Vine House 143 London Road, Kingston upon Thames, KT2 6NH, United Kingdom
Tel.: (44) 2085590666
Web Site: http://www.ntrinsic.net
Consulting Services
N.A.I.C.S.: 541618
Neil Chapman (CFO)

Subsidiary (Domestic):

ORJ Inc. (3)
2F Umeda Kita Place 1-14-8 Shibata, Kita-ku, Osaka, 530-0012, Japan
Tel.: (81) 662927540
Web Site: https://www.orj.co.jp
Business Consulting Services
N.A.I.C.S.: 541618

Subsidiary (Non-US):

OS (Thailand) Co., Ltd. (3)
179 Bangkok City Tower 5 Fl South Sathorn Rd, Thungmahamek Sathon, Bangkok, 10120, Thailand
Tel.: (66) 267950767
Web Site: https://www.os-thai.com

Business Process Outsourcing Services
N.A.I.C.S.: 561110

Subsidiary (Domestic):

OS Capital Partners Inc. (3)
19F Marunouchi Trust Tower Main Building 1-8-3 Marunouchi, Chiyoda-ku, Tokyo, 100-0005, Japan
Tel.: (81) 332865252
Web Site: https://www.oscp.co.jp
Business Process Outsourcing Services
N.A.I.C.S.: 541611

OS Facilities Co., Ltd. (3)
4-1-23 Shinjuku, Shinjuku-ku, Tokyo, 160-0022, Japan
Tel.: (81) 363842480
Web Site: https://www.os-facilities.co.jp
Emp.: 458
Human Resouce Services
N.A.I.C.S.: 541612

Subsidiary (Non-US):

OS HRS Sdn Bhd (3)
Suite 5-1 Level 5 Wisma UOA Damansara II No 6, Changkat Semantan Damansara Heights, 50490, Kuala Lumpur, Malaysia
Tel.: (60) 327778300
Business Process Outsourcing Services
N.A.I.C.S.: 541611

Subsidiary (Non-US):

OS HRS India Private Limited (4)
283/58/7 Devarabeesanahalli Village Varthur Hobli Bangalore East, Aurbis Business Park, Bengaluru, 560103, Karnataka, India
Tel.: (91) 8045616754
Business Process Outsourcing Services
N.A.I.C.S.: 541611

OS HRS Japan Inc. (4)
2F Marunouchi Trust Tower Main 1-8-3 Marunouchi, Chiyoda-ku, Tokyo, 100-0005, Japan
Tel.: (81) 332863999
Business Process Outsourcing Services
N.A.I.C.S.: 541611

Subsidiary (Domestic):

OS Logitec Co., Ltd. (3)
1131-6 Kamimikusa, Kato, 673-1472, Hyogo Prefecture, Japan
Tel.: (81) 7064009528
Web Site: https://www.os-logi.co.jp
Business Process Outsourcing Services
N.A.I.C.S.: 541611

OS Nano Technology Co., Ltd. (3)
Asahi Shimbun Dai-ichi Life Building 10F 4-7 Hanabatake-cho, Chuo-ku, Kumamoto, 860-0806, Kumamoto, Japan
Tel.: (81) 963425021
Web Site: https://www.os-nanotechnology.co.jp
Semiconductor Equipment Mfr
N.A.I.C.S.: 333242

OS Platinum Co., Ltd. (3)
1F Marunouchi Trust Tower Main Building 5F, Chiyoda-ku, Tokyo, 100-0005, Japan
Tel.: (81) 332867890
Web Site: http://www.os-platinum.co.jp
Business Process Outsourcing Services
N.A.I.C.S.: 541611

Subsidiary (Non-US):

OS Recruitment (Thailand) Co., Ltd. (3)
179 Bangkok City Tower 5 Fl South Sathorn Rd Thungmahamek, Sathorn, 10120, Thailand
Tel.: (66) 267950767
Web Site: http://www.outsourcing-thai.com
Consulting Services
N.A.I.C.S.: 541618

Subsidiary (Domestic):

OS Support Co., Ltd. (3)
Marunouchi Trust Tower Main Building 5F 8-3 Marunouchi, Chiyoda-ku, Tokyo, 100-0005, Japan
Tel.: (81) 332868686
Web Site: http://www.ossupport.co.jp
Business Process Outsourcing Services
N.A.I.C.S.: 541611

Subsidiary (Non-US):

OS Vietnam Co., Ltd. (3)
Room 12R 12 Floor Center Building No 1
Nguyen Huy Tuong Str, Thanh Xuan Trung
Ward Thanh Xuan Dist, Hanoi, Vietnam
Tel.: (84) 2462620122
Web Site: https://www.outsourcing-vn.com
Consulting Services
N.A.I.C.S.: 541618
Eiji Ryu *(Pres)*

Subsidiary (Domestic):

OSDC Co., Ltd. (3)
Marunouchi Trust Tower Main 19F 1-8-3
Marunouchi, Chiyoda-ku, Tokyo, 100-0005,
Japan
Tel.: (81) 332864141
Web Site: https://www.osdc.co.jp
Engineering Services
N.A.I.C.S.: 541330

OTS Inc. (3)
1-8-3 Marunouchi, Chiyoda-ku, Tokyo, 100-
0005, Japan
Tel.: (81) 332862001
Web Site: https://www.ots.co.jp
Human Resource Outsourcing Services
N.A.I.C.S.: 541612

Subsidiary (Non-US):

OTTO Work Force B.V. (3)
Keizersveld 51, 5803 AP, Venray, Nether-
lands
Tel.: (31) 478529999
Web Site: https://www.ottoworkforce.nl
Business Consulting Services
N.A.I.C.S.: 541618

OTTO Work Force Czech s.r.o. (3)
Palachovo namesti 1, 779 00, Olomouc,
Czech Republic
Tel.: (420) 603488040
Engineering Services
N.A.I.C.S.: 541330

OTTO Work Force Rom S.R.L. (3)
Bd Hristo Botev nr 5, Bucharest, Romania
Tel.: (40) 744668141
Engineering Services
N.A.I.C.S.: 541330

Subsidiary (Domestic):

Oomura Industrial Co., Ltd. (3)
Marunouchi Trust Tower Main 5F 1-8-3
Marunouchi, Chiyoda-ku, Tokyo, 100-0005,
Japan
Tel.: (81) 332862888
Web Site: https://www.outsourcing.co.jp
Business Consulting Services
N.A.I.C.S.: 541618

Subsidiary (Non-US):

Orizon Holding GmbH (3)
Berliner Allee 28 C, 86153, Augsburg, Ger-
many
Tel.: (49) 821509910
Web Site: https://www.orizon.de
Recruitment Services
N.A.I.C.S.: 561311

Os Power Vietnam Co., Ltd. (3)
Room 12P 12 Floor Center Building No 1
Nguyen Huy Tuong Str, Thanh Xuan Trung
Ward Thanh Xuan Dist, Hanoi, Vietnam
Tel.: (84) 2462620122
Web Site: https://www.outsourcing-vn.com
Recruitment Services
N.A.I.C.S.: 561311

Subsidiary (Domestic):

**Out-Sourcing System Consulting
Inc.** (3)
Marunouchi Trust Tower 5FL 1-8-3
Marunouchi, Chiyoda-ku, Tokyo, 100 0005,
Japan
Tel.: (81) 332867888
Web Site: http://www.ostechnology.co.jp
Temporary Placement Services
N.A.I.C.S.: 561320
Motegi Masaki *(Pres & CEO)*

Subsidiary (Non-US):

Outsourcing (Cambodia) Inc. (3)
No 394-396 Home City 1stFloor Monivong

Blvd, Khan Chamkamorn, Phnom Penh,
Cambodia
Web Site: https://www.oscambodia.com.kh
Consulting Services
N.A.I.C.S.: 541618

Subsidiary (Domestic):

**Outsourcing Business Service
Inc.** (3)
1-8-3 Marunouchi Marunouchi Trust Tower
Main Building 4F, Chiyoda-ku, Tokyo, 100-
0005, Japan
Tel.: (81) 332866661
Web Site: http://www.osbs.co.jp
Business Consulting Services
N.A.I.C.S.: 541618

**Outsourcing Communications Co.,
Ltd.** (3)
Marunouchi Trust Tower Main Building 1-8-3
Marunouchi, Chiyoda-ku, Tokyo, 100-0005,
Japan
Tel.: (81) 120179063
Web Site: https://www.oscom.co.jp
Business Process Outsourcing Services
N.A.I.C.S.: 541611

Subsidiary (Non-US):

Outsourcing Oceania Pty Ltd. (3)
Level 35 360 Collins St, Melbourne, 3000,
VIC, Australia
Tel.: (61) 399634850
Web Site:
    https://www.outsourcinginc.com.au
Recruitment Services
N.A.I.C.S.: 561311

Subsidiary (Domestic):

Outsourcing Technology Inc. (3)
16/17F Marunouchi Trust Tower Main Build-
ing 1-8-3 Marunouchi, Chiyoda-ku, Tokyo,
100-0005, Japan
Tel.: (81) 332864777
Web Site: https://www.ostechnology.co.jp
Business Consulting Services
N.A.I.C.S.: 541618

PCT Co., Ltd. (3)
Marunouchi Trust Tower Main Building 2F
1-8-3 Marunouchi, Chiyoda-ku, Tokyo, Ja-
pan
Tel.: (81) 332866555
Web Site: https://www.pctc.co.jp
Education Services
N.A.I.C.S.: 611710

PEO Co., Ltd. (3)
Nagoya Mitsui Building Honkan 7F 1-24-30
Meieki Minami, NakamuraKu, Nagoya, 450-
0003, Aichi Prefecture, Japan
Tel.: (81) 525623335
Web Site: https://www.peo.co.jp
Business Consulting Services
N.A.I.C.S.: 541618

**PEO Construction Machinery Opera-
tors Training Center Co., Ltd.** (3)
1-8-3 Marunouchi Tokyo Marunouchi Trust
Tower Main Building 2F, Chiyoda-ku, Tokyo,
100-0005, Japan
Tel.: (81) 332866555
Web Site: https://www.pctc.co.jp
Construction Services
N.A.I.C.S.: 236220

Subsidiary (Non-US):

PT. OS Selnajaya Indonesia (3)
Web Site: http://www.os-selnajaya.com
Business Consulting Services
N.A.I.C.S.: 541618

**Phoenix Commercial Collections
Limited** (3)
Paragon Business Park Chorley New Road,
Horwich, Bolton, BL6 6HG, Lancashire,
United Kingdom
Tel.: (44) 3333230333
Web Site:
    http://www.phoenixcommercial.co.uk
Collection Agency Services
N.A.I.C.S.: 561440
Paul Caddy *(Mng Dir)*
Andy Cummins *(Dir-Bus Dev & Client)*
Carole Kenney *(Dir-Customer Svcs & Per-
formance Delivery)*

**Project Management Partners Pty.
Ltd.** (3)
L5/45 Clarence Street, Sydney, 2000,
NSW, Australia
Tel.: (61) 1300701314
Web Site: https://www.pm-partners.com.au
Management Consulting Services
N.A.I.C.S.: 541618
Ken Sheargold *(CEO)*
Derek Quayle *(Dir-Programs & Quality As-
surance)*
Chris Hills *(CFO)*
Ray Wall *(Dir-Client Engagement)*
Tracey Copland *(Head-Dev)*

Subsidiary (Domestic):

RPM Co., Ltd. (3)
JRE Nishi-Shinjuku Terrace 5th floor 3-2-4
Nishi-Shinjuku, Shinjuku-ku, Tokyo, 160-
0023, Japan
Tel.: (81) 353255800
Web Site: https://www.rpmedical.co.jp
Emp.: 1,014
Pharmaceuticals Product Mfr
N.A.I.C.S.: 339112

Subsidiary (Non-US):

Red Appointments Pty Ltd. (3)
151 Henley Beach Road, Mile End, 5031,
SA, Australia
Tel.: (61) 870717350
Web Site: https://redappointments.com.au
Recruitment Services
N.A.I.C.S.: 561311

**Renovo Employment Group
Limited** (3)
Kings House 12 King Street, York, YO1
9WP, United Kingdom
Tel.: (44) 1904615163
Web Site: https://renovo.uk.com
Outplacement Services
N.A.I.C.S.: 561320

Rundle & Co., Limited (3)
53 Northampton Road, Market Harborough,
Leicestershire, United Kingdom
Web Site: http://www.rundles.org.uk
Financial Services
N.A.I.C.S.: 522320
Amy Collins *(Dir-Client Svcs)*
Tom Gover *(CEO)*
Andy Grice *(Dir-Sls & Mktg)*
Andrew Shornyk *(Dir-IT)*

Subsidiary (Domestic):

Sangatech Co., Ltd. (3)
200-2 Takei, Yonezawa, 992-0116, Yama-
gata, Japan
Tel.: (81) 238269235
Web Site: https://www.sangatech.co.jp
Industrial Machinery Mfr
N.A.I.C.S.: 333248

Sankyo Logi Associate. Co., Ltd. (3)
5-8-9 Sendagaya, Shibuya-ku, Tokyo, 151-
0051, Japan
Tel.: (81) 367346410
Web Site: https://www.ssgroup-jp.com
Logistics Management Services
N.A.I.C.S.: 541614

Subsidiary (Non-US):

Sanshin (Malaysia) Sdn. Bhd. (3)
Lot 55 Bakar Arang Industrial Estate,
08000, Sungai Petani, Kedah Darul Aman,
Malaysia
Tel.: (60) 4 421 6677
Web Site: http://www.saejpn.co.jp
Sales Range: $50-74.9 Million
Motor Vehicle Audio Equipment Mfr & Distr
N.A.I.C.S.: 334310

Subsidiary (Domestic):

Sanshin Electric Co., Ltd. (3)
1-13-1 Haramachida, Machida, 194-0013,
Tokyo, Japan
Tel.: (81) 427105544
Web Site: http://www.saejpn.co.jp
Sales Range: $50-74.9 Million
Motor Vehicle Audio Equipment Mfr & Distr
N.A.I.C.S.: 334310
Katsuhiro Hasegawa *(Pres)*

Subsidiary (Non-US):

**Santillana De Seguridad Vigilancia
Privada Ltda.** (3)

La Esperanza Av 95 A - 80 Tower II Room
303, Bogota, Colombia
Tel.: (57) 14321490
Web Site: https://santillanadeseguridad.com
Security Consulting Services
N.A.I.C.S.: 541690

**Seguridad Privada Active Security
Company A.S.C. Cia. Ltda.** (3)
Ciudadela La Garzota Manzana 92 Solar 7,
Guayaquil, Ecuador
Tel.: (593) 46018258
Business Consulting Services
N.A.I.C.S.: 541618

Subsidiary (Domestic):

Smart Robotics Co.Ltd. (3)
S-Gate Akihabara 8F 2-4-6 Higashi-Kanda,
Chiyoda-ku, Tokyo, 101-0031, Japan
Tel.: (81) 358353103
Engineering Services
N.A.I.C.S.: 541330

Subsidiary (Non-US):

Staff Solutions Australia Pty Ltd (3)
Suite 902 Level 9 50 Margaret Street, Syd-
ney, 2000, NSW, Australia
Tel.: (61) 292412455
Web Site: http://www.ssaust.com.au
General Management Consulting Services
N.A.I.C.S.: 541611

The Beddison Group Pty. Ltd. (3)
Level 35 360 Collins Street, Melbourne,
3000, VIC, Australia
Tel.: (61) 399634850
Web Site: http://www.beddison.com.au
Workforce Solution Services
N.A.I.C.S.: 541612

Subsidiary (Domestic):

Hoban Recruitment Pty. Ltd. (4)
Suite 5 Level 14 530 Collins Street, Mel-
bourne, 3000, VIC, Australia
Tel.: (61) 392034900
Web Site: https://www.hoban.com.au
Emp.: 100
Business Consulting Services
N.A.I.C.S.: 541618

Subsidiary (Non-US):

Index Consultants Pty. Ltd. (4)
Tel.: (61) 399634860
Web Site: http://www.index.com.au
Emp.: 4,000
Business Consulting Services
N.A.I.C.S.: 541618

Subsidiary (Domestic):

ThinkethBank Co., Ltd. (3)
Kubo Building 4F 2-9-2 Yoyogi, Shibuya-ku,
Tokyo, 151-0053, Japan
Tel.: (81) 368662031
Web Site: https://www.thinkethbank.co.jp
Management Development Training Ser-
vices
N.A.I.C.S.: 611430

Tryangle Co., Ltd. (3)
3-2-4 Nishi-Shinjuku Shinwa Building 5th
Floor, Shinjuku-ku, Tokyo, 160-0023, Japan
Tel.: (81) 353255600
Web Site: http://www.tryangle-cr.co.jp
Chemistry & Biochemistry Medical Product
Research Services
N.A.I.C.S.: 541714

Subsidiary (Non-US):

Whole Security S.A.C. (3)
Av Elmer Faucett Cdra/30 Modulo-E
Oficina-502, 5 to-Piso - Centro Aereo Com-
ercial, Callao, Peru
Tel.: (51) 16522370
Business Consulting Services
N.A.I.C.S.: 541618

orizon Gmbh (3)
Berliner Allee 28 c, 86153, Augsburg, Ger-
many
Tel.: (49) 82 150 9910
Web Site: https://www.orizon.de
Temporary Staffing Agency
N.A.I.C.S.: 561311
Jens Tettenborn *(Mng Dir)*

Bain Capital, LP—(Continued)

Holding (Non-US):

Snow Peak Inc. (2)
456 Nakanohara Sanjo-Shi, Niigata, 955- (59.55%)
0147, Japan
Tel.: (81) 256455858
Web Site: https://www.snowpeak.co.jp
Rev.: $220,642,410
Assets: $220,355,610
Liabilities: $110,962,920
Net Worth: $109,392,690
Earnings: $13,952,820
Emp.: 623
Fiscal Year-end: 12/31/2022
Outdoor Lifestyle Products Mfr
N.A.I.C.S.: 339920
Tohru Yamai (Pres & CEO)
Noriaki Sakamoto (Exec VP)

Subsidiary (Non-US):

Snow Peak Korea, Inc. (3)
602 GongHang-DaeRo, YangChen-Gu, 158-
807, Seoul, Korea (South)
Tel.: (82) 262031258
Web Site: http://www.snowpeak.co.kr
Apparel Distr
N.A.I.C.S.: 458110

Bain Capital Tech Opportunities,
LP (1)
200 Clarendon St, Boston, MA 02116
Tel.: (617) 516-2000
Web Site:
http://www.baincapitalopportunities.com
Technology-focused Private Equity Firm
N.A.I.C.S.: 523999
Dewey Awad (Partner)

Bain Capital Ventures, LLC (1)
John Hancock Tower 200 Clarendon St,
Boston, MA 02116
Tel.: (617) 516-2000
Web Site:
http://www.baincapitalventures.com
Rev.: $1,000,000,000
Equity Investment Firm
N.A.I.C.S.: 523999
Jeffrey R. Crisan (Mng Dir)
Michael A. Krupka (Mng Dir)
Ajay Agarwal (Mng Dir)
Paul Zurlo (COO)
Matt Harris (Partner)
Indy Guha (Partner-Palo Alto)
Jeff Williams (Operating Partner)
Andy Cleverdon (VP-Fin)
Kristen Deftos (VP-HR)
Brian Goldsmith (Principal-Boston)
David Friend (Principal-Boston)
Liz Bride (Dir-IR & Mktg-Boston)
Peter Apostolides (Dir-Fin-Boston)
Salil Deshpande (Mng Dir-Bay Area)
Yumin Choi (Mng Dir)
Annis Steiner (VP-Mktg)
Adam Levin (Partner)
Sarah Smith (Partner)
Keri Gohman (Operating Partner)

Joint Venture (Domestic):

Swift Prepaid Solutions, Inc. (2)
2150 E Lk Cook Rd Ste 150, Buffalo Grove,
IL 60089
Tel.: (847) 325-4330
Web Site: http://www.swiftprepaid.com
Custom Prepaid Credit Cards Issuing &
Support Services
N.A.I.C.S.: 522210
Brian Levin (VP-Fin & IT)
David Josephs (CEO)
Juli C. Spottiswood (Chm)

Bellsystem24, Inc. (1)
Harumi Island Triton Square Office Tower Y
8-11 Harumi 1-chome, Chuo-ku, Tokyo,
151-0051, Japan
Tel.: (81) 120024607
Web Site: http://www.bell24.co.jp
Telephone, Fax & Internet Marketing Ser-
vices
N.A.I.C.S.: 541613
Shiro Yahara (Pres & CEO)
Kenji Komatsu (COO)
Junjiro Iwashita (Exec VP)
Takehiko Go (Exec VP)
Manabu Sotomura (Sr VP)
Ichiro Tsuge (Pres & CEO)
Kimito Matsunaga (Sr VP)
Akihiko Kanazawa (Sr VP)

Subsidiary (Domestic):

Bell Medical Solutions Inc. (2)
2-16-8 Minami-Ikebukuro, Toshima-ku, To-
kyo, 171-0022, Japan
Tel.: (81) 3 5951 0024
Web Site: http://www.bell-medical.co.jp
Sales Range: $50-74.9 Million
Health Care Srvices
N.A.I.C.S.: 621999

Big Tex Trailer Manufacturing,
Inc. (1)
950 Interstate 30, Mount Pleasant, TX
75455
Tel.: (903) 575-0300
Web Site: http://www.bigtextrailers.com
Truck Trailer Mfr, Dealer & Parts Retailer
N.A.I.C.S.: 336212
Randy D. Homer (Pres & COO)
Richard W. Baker (Founder)

Subsidiary (Domestic):

American Trailer Works, Inc. (2)
1121 S Carroll Ave Ste 230, Southlake, TX
76092
Tel.: (706) 356-5379
Web Site:
http://www.americantrailerworks.com
Truck Trailer Mfr
N.A.I.C.S.: 333924
Rob McDevitt (VP-HR)

Subsidiary (Domestic):

Carry-On Trailer, Inc. (3)
101 Joe Harvey St, Lavonia, GA 30553
Tel.: (706) 356-5379
Web Site: http://www.carry-ontrailer.com
Trailer & Trailer Equipment Mfr
N.A.I.C.S.: 336214

PJ Trailers, Inc. (3)
1807 FM 2352, Sumner, TX 75486
Tel.: (903) 785-6879
Web Site: http://www.pjtrailers.com
Truck Trailer Mfr
N.A.I.C.S.: 333924

Subsidiary (Domestic):

Big Tex Trailer World, Inc. (2)
950 I 30 E, Mount Pleasant, TX 75455-
9596
Tel.: (903) 575-0300
Web Site: http://www.bigtextrailerworld.com
Truck Trailer Dealerships Operator
N.A.I.C.S.: 441227
Randy D. Homer (Pres & COO)

Branch (Domestic):

Big Tex Trailer World, Inc. -
Houston (3)
8404 N Fwy, Houston, TX 77037
Tel.: (281) 447-1414
Web Site: http://bigtextrailerworld.com
Emp.: 500
Trailer Dealer
N.A.I.C.S.: 441227
Tom McCoy (Gen Mgr)

Big Tex Trailer World, Inc. -
Tucson (3)
3150 W El Camino del Cerro, Tucson, AZ
85745
Tel.: (520) 834-8855
Web Site: http://bigtextrailerworld.com
Trailer Dealer
N.A.I.C.S.: 441227

Subsidiary (Domestic):

Circle J Trailers Limited (2)
312 W Simplot Blvd, Caldwell, ID 83605
Tel.: (208) 459-0842
Web Site: http://www.circlejtrailers.com
Horse Trailer Mfr
N.A.I.C.S.: 336214

Contract Manufacturer, L.L.C. (2)
103 Titan Rd, Kingston, OK 73439
Tel.: (580) 564-7537
Web Site: http://cmtruckbeds.com
Truck Trailer Mfr
N.A.I.C.S.: 336212

TexTrail, Inc. (2)
2424 W Ferguson, Mount Pleasant, TX
75455

Tel.: (903) 575-0300
Web Site: http://www.textrail.com
Truck Trailer Parts Distr & Retailer
N.A.I.C.S.: 423120

Division (Domestic):

TexTrail, Inc. - Fitzgerald (3)
223 Rip Wiley Rd, Fitzgerald, GA 31750
Tel.: (229) 409-0813
Web Site: http://www.textrail.com
Trailer Parts Whslr
N.A.I.C.S.: 423120

TexTrail, Inc. - Florida (3)
5181 N US 441, Ocala, FL 34475
Tel.: (800) 259-8712
Web Site: http://textrail.com
Trailer Parts Whslr
N.A.I.C.S.: 423120

TexTrail, Inc. - Georgia (3)
502 Midway Rd, Cordele, GA 31015
Tel.: (877) 224-1520
Web Site: http://www.textrail.com
Trailer Parts Whslr
N.A.I.C.S.: 423120

TexTrail, Inc. - Houston (3)
8404 N Fwy, Houston, TX 77037
Tel.: (281) 405-0825
Web Site: http://textrail.com
Truck Trailer Mfr
N.A.I.C.S.: 336212

TexTrail, Inc. - Idaho (3)
1802 Industrial Way, Caldwell, ID 83605
Tel.: (208) 459-0902
Web Site: http://www.textrail.com
Truck Trailer Mfr
N.A.I.C.S.: 336212

TexTrail, Inc. - Odessa (3)
13300 W I 20 E, Odessa, TX 79765
Tel.: (800) 333-1745
Web Site: http://www.texrail.com
Truck Trailer Mfr
N.A.I.C.S.: 336212

Subsidiary (Domestic):

Trailers Direct (2)
950 I-30 E, Mount Pleasant, TX 75455
Tel.: (903) 577-7418
Web Site: http://www.trailersdirect.com
Truck Trailer Whslr
N.A.I.C.S.: 423110

Blue Nile, Inc. (1)
411 1st Ave S Ste 700, Seattle, WA 98104
Tel.: (206) 336-6700
Web Site: http://www.bluenile.com
Rev.: $480,057,000
Assets: $157,414,000
Liabilities: $138,958,000
Net Worth: $18,456,000
Earnings: $10,534,000
Emp.: 335
Fiscal Year-end: 01/03/2016
Diamonds & Fine Jewelry Retailer
N.A.I.C.S.: 423940
Jonathan Sainsbury (Chief Strategy Officer
& Pres-Intl)
Carter A. Cast (Founder)
Ruth Sommers (COO)
David Fleischman (Chief Product Officer)
Katie Zimmerman (Chief Mdsg Officer)
Alexandra Wheeler (Chief Mktg Officer)
Sean Kell (CEO)

Bob's Discount Furniture Inc. (1)
428 Tolland Tpke, Manchester, CT 06042
Tel.: (860) 645-3208
Web Site: http://www.mybobs.com
Sales Range: $650-699.9 Million
Furniture Store Operator
N.A.I.C.S.: 449110
Robert Kaufman (Founder)
Ted J. English (Chm)
John Weldon (COO)
Carol Glaser (Exec VP-Mdsg)

Bright Horizons Family Solutions,
Inc. (1)
2 Wells Ave, Newton, MA 02459
Tel.: (617) 673-8000
Web Site: https://www.brighthorizons.com
Rev.: $2,418,257,000
Assets: $3,896,144,000
Liabilities: $2,683,468,000
Net Worth: $1,212,676,000

Earnings: $74,223,000
Emp.: 31,400
Fiscal Year-end: 12/31/2023
Employer-Sponsored Child Care, Early Edu-
cation & Worklife Consulting Services
N.A.I.C.S.: 624410
Stephen H. Kramer (Pres & CEO)
Elizabeth J. Boland (CFO)
Eric Lindgren (CIO)
Mandy Berman (COO)
Ros Marshall (Mng Dir & Mng Dir-
International)
Jason R. Janoff (Chief Acctg Officer)
Mary Lou Burke Afonso (COO-Ops-North
America Center)
John G. Casagrande (Gen Counsel & Sec)
Diane Bartoli (Sr VP-Education Advisory)
Melkeya McDuffie (Chief HR Officer)
Ryan Scott (CIO)
Sandy Wells (Chief Dev Officer)

Branch (Domestic):

Bright Horizons Family Solutions Cali-
fornia Regional Office (2)
880 Apollo St Ste 315, El Segundo, CA
90245
Tel.: (310) 640-2400
Web Site: http://www.brighthorizons.com
Employer-Sponsored Child Care, Early Education & Worklife Consulting Services
N.A.I.C.S.: 624410

Bright Horizons Family Solutions Chi-
cago Regional Office (2)
1011 Warrenville Rd Ste 160, Lisle, IL
60532
Tel.: (630) 724-8300
Web Site: http://www.brighthorizons.com
Employer-Sponsored Child Care, Early Education & Worklife Consulting Services
N.A.I.C.S.: 624410

Bright Horizons Family Solutions
Florida Regional Office (2)
2151 W Hillsboro Blvd Ste 210, Deerfield
Beach, FL 33442
Tel.: (954) 421-5077
Web Site: http://www.brighthorizons.com
Sales Range: $25-49.9 Million
Emp.: 2
Employer-Sponsored Child Care, Early Edu-
cation & Worklife Consulting Services
N.A.I.C.S.: 624410

Branch (Non-US):

Bright Horizons Family Solutions
Ireland (2)
Blanchardstown Corporate Park 2, Ste 4
Plz 212, Blanchardstown, Dublin, 15, Ire-
land
Tel.: (353) 18025140
Sales Range: $25-49.9 Million
Emp.: 200
Employer-Sponsored Child Care, Early Edu-
cation & Worklife Consulting Services
N.A.I.C.S.: 624410
David H. Lissy (CEO)

Subsidiary (Domestic):

Bright Horizons Family Solutions
LLC (2)
200 Talcott Ave S, Watertown, MA 02472
Tel.: (617) 673-8000
Web Site: http://www.brighthorizons.com
Child Care & Preschools Educational Advi-
sory Services
N.A.I.C.S.: 624410
David H. Lissy (CEO)
Linda A. Mason (Chm)
Elizabeth J. Boland (CFO)
Stephen I. Dreier (Sec & Exec VP)
Danroy T. Henry (Chief HR Officer)
Sandy Wells (Chief Dev Officer)

Subsidiary (Non-US):

BHFS One Limited (3)
2 Crown Court, Rushden, NN10 6BS,
Northamptonshire, United Kingdom
Tel.: (44) 1933415900
Educational Support Services
N.A.I.C.S.: 611710

Subsidiary (Domestic):

Bright Horizons LLC (3)
2419 Orofino Ct, Charlotte, NC 28269-2308

Tel.: (408) 623-5924
Child Care & Preschools Educational Advisory Services
N.A.I.C.S.: 624410

Subsidiary (Domestic):

Bright Horizons Children's Centers LLC (4)
400 Talcott Ave, Watertown, MA 02472
Tel.: (617) 924-4935
Web Site: http://www.brighthorizons.com
Emp.: 36
Child Care & Preschools Educational Advisory Services
N.A.I.C.S.: 624410

Work Options Group, Inc. (4)
1100 S McCaslin Blvd Ste 200, Superior, CO 80027
Tel.: (303) 604-6545
Professional Services & Educational Advisory Services
N.A.I.C.S.: 611430

Branch (Domestic):

Bright Horizons Family Solutions Maryland Regional Office (2)
16220 Frederick Rd Ste 410, Gaithersburg, MD 20877
Tel.: (301) 869-9110
Web Site: http://www.brighthorizons.com
Employer-Sponsored Child Care, Early Education & Worklife Consulting Services
N.A.I.C.S.: 624410

Bright Horizons Family Solutions Nashville Regional Office (2)
105 Westwood Pl Ste 125, Brentwood, TN 37027
Tel.: (615) 256-9915
Web Site: http://www.brighthorizons.com
Employer-Sponsored Child Care, Early Education & Worklife Consulting Services
N.A.I.C.S.: 624410

Bright Horizons Family Solutions Texas Regional Office (2)
8900 Freeport Pkwy, Irving, TX 75063
Tel.: (214) 596-5280
Web Site: http://www.brighthorizons.com
Sales Range: $25-49.9 Million
Emp.: 15
Employer-Sponsored Child Care, Early Education & Worklife Consulting Services
N.A.I.C.S.: 624410

Branch (Non-US):

Bright Horizons Family Solutions United Kingdom (2)
2 Crown Court, Rushden, NN10 6BS, Northamptonshire, United Kingdom
Tel.: (44) 1933415900
Web Site: http://www.brighthorizons.com
Sales Range: $1-4.9 Billion
Emp.: 16,000
Employer-Sponsored Child Care, Early Education & Worklife Consulting Services
N.A.I.C.S.: 624410

Subsidiary (Domestic):

Beehive Day Nurseries Limited (3)
Roughmoor Bishops Hull, Somerset, Taunton, TA1 5AA, Warwickshire, United Kingdom
Tel.: (44) 1823339110
Web Site: http://www.beehivedaynursery.co.uk
Child Care & Preschools Educational Advisory Services
N.A.I.C.S.: 624410

Bright Horizons Family Solutions Limited (3)
2 Crown Court, Rushden, NN10 6BS, Northamptonshire, United Kingdom
Tel.: (44) 8002471101
Web Site: http://www.brighthorizons.co.uk
Child Care & Preschools Educational Advisory Services
N.A.I.C.S.: 624410
Paul Quartly *(Mgr-Bus Dev)*
Naseem Smith *(Mgr-Bus Dev)*
Sanjay Chada *(Mgr-Bus Dev)*
Sara Macdonald *(Mgr-Back-Up Care Advantage Programme)*
Denise Priest *(Dir-Mktg & Strategic Partnerships)*

Branch (Domestic):

Bright Horizons Family Solutions Scotland Regional Office (3)
26 Whitehouse Road, Edinburgh, EH4 6PH, United Kingdom
Tel.: (44) 1313360900
Web Site: http://www.brighthorizons.co.uk
Sales Range: $25-49.9 Million
Emp.: 40
Employer-Sponsored Child Care, Early Education & Worklife Consulting Services
N.A.I.C.S.: 624410

Subsidiary (Domestic):

Bright Horizons Livingston Ltd. (3)
Bankton Square Murieston, Livingston, EH54 9EY, United Kingdom
Tel.: (44) 1506462200
Web Site: http://www.brighthorizons.co.uk
Sales Range: $10-24.9 Million
Emp.: 30
Employer-Sponsored Child Care, Early Education & Worklife Consulting Services
N.A.I.C.S.: 624410
Karen Bell *(Mgr)*

Daisies Day Nurseries Limited (3)
63 Main St Lowdham, Nottingham, NG14 7BD, United Kingdom
Tel.: (44) 1159665282
Web Site: http://www.daisiesdaynursery.co.uk
Emp.: 16
Child Care & Preschools Educational Advisory Services
N.A.I.C.S.: 624410

Dolphin Nurseries (Tooting) Ltd. (3)
75 Macmillan Way, London, SW17 6AT, United Kingdom
Tel.: (44) 2087672901
Sales Range: $10-24.9 Million
Emp.: 50
Child Care & Preschools Educational Advisory Services
N.A.I.C.S.: 624410
Emma Young *(Gen Mgr)*

Inglewood Day Nursery and College Ltd. (3)
Sonning Lane, Sonning, Reading, RG4 6ST, Berkshire, United Kingdom
Tel.: (44) 1189448338
Web Site: http://www.inglewooddaynursery.co.uk
Emp.: 50
Child Care & Preschools Educational Advisory Services
N.A.I.C.S.: 624410
Louise Chapman *(Deputy Mgr)*
Vicky McWilliams *(Deputy Mgr)*
Lauren Grant *(Deputy Mgr)*
Helen King *(Mgr-Kitchen)*
Emma Rapley *(Mgr-Unit-Willow & Acorn)*
Sarah Creech *(Mgr-Trng)*
Rachel Elford *(Mgr-Nursery)*

Springfield Lodge Day Nursery (Dartford) Ltd. (3)
Powder Mill Lane, Dartford, DA1 1NT, United Kingdom
Tel.: (44) 1322228154
Web Site: http://www.springfieldnursery-dartford.com
Child Care & Preschools Educational Advisory Services
N.A.I.C.S.: 624410
Melanie Pearce *(Mgr-Nursery)*
Stacey Dowsett *(Deputy Mgr)*
Emma La Roche *(Jr Deputy Mgr)*

Springfield Lodge Day Nursery (Swanscombe) Ltd. (3)
Craylands Lane, Swanscombe, DA10 0LP, Kent, United Kingdom
Tel.: (44) 1322389181
Web Site: http://www.springfieldnursery-swanscombe.com
Sales Range: $10-24.9 Million
Emp.: 40
Child Care & Preschools Educational Advisory Services
N.A.I.C.S.: 624410
Emma Lewing *(Mgr-Nursery)*
Sam Mummery *(Deputy Mgr)*
Josephine Johnston *(Mgr-Room-Pooh Bears)*

Samantha Lavington *(Mgr-Room-Tiggers)*
Natalie Barnes *(Mgr-Room-Piglets)*
Emma Knight *(Mgr-Room-Ladybirds)*
Sandie Kearns *(Mgr-Room-After School Club)*

Teddies Childcare Provision Limited (3)
North Lodge Queens Road, Maidstone, ME16 0JN, Kent, United Kingdom
Tel.: (44) 1622691700
Child Care & Preschools Educational Advisory Services
N.A.I.C.S.: 624410

Subsidiary (Domestic):

Children's Choice Learning Centers, Inc. (2)
3610 Shire Boulevard Ste 208, Richardson, TX 75074
Tel.: (972) 881-1900
Web Site: http://www.childrenschoice.com
Sales Range: $1-9.9 Million
Child Day Care Services
N.A.I.C.S.: 624410
Jack Wallace *(Exec VP-Bus Dev & Ops)*
Laura Holder *(VP-Ops)*

Subsidiary (Non-US):

Kindergarden Nederland B.V. (2)
Herengracht 250, Amsterdam, 1016 BV, Netherlands
Tel.: (31) 204235422
Web Site: http://www.kindergarden.nl
Emp.: 1,000
Child Care & Preschools Educational Advisory Services
N.A.I.C.S.: 624410
Nicole Krabbenborg *(Mng Dir)*

Subsidiary (Domestic):

Lipton Corporate Childcare, Inc. (2)
4 Gannett Dr, West Harrison, NY 10604
Tel.: (914) 696-1522
Child Care & Preschools Educational Advisory Services
N.A.I.C.S.: 624410

Sittercity Inc. (2)
20 W Kinzie St Ste 1500, Chicago, IL 60654
Tel.: (312) 428-4671
Web Site: http://www.sittercity.com
Sales Range: $10-24.9 Million
Online Babysitter & Nanny Directory & Background Information Publisher
N.A.I.C.S.: 513140
Naomi Sachs *(COO)*
Marty Hickey *(Sr VP-Mktg)*
Jeremy Gottschalk *(Gen Counsel)*
Sandra Dainora *(Sr VP-Product)*
Mark Row *(VP-Product)*
Zenobia Moochhala *(CEO)*

Broder Bros., Co. (1)
6 Neshaminy Interplex, Trevose, PA 19053
Tel.: (215) 291-6140
Web Site: http://www.alphabroder.com
Sales Range: $900-999.9 Million
Imprintable Sportswear Whslr & Distr
N.A.I.C.S.: 424350

Division (Domestic):

Alpha Shirt (2)
6 Neshaminy Interplex, Trevose, PA 19053
Tel.: (215) 291-0300
Web Site: http://www.alphashirt.com
Sales Range: $200-249.9 Million
Blank Apparel Whslr & Distr
N.A.I.C.S.: 424350

Brookside Capital, LLC (1)
200 Clarendon St, Boston, MA 02116
Tel.: (617) 516-2900
Web Site: http://www.brooksidefund.com
Sales Range: $50-74.9 Million
Emp.: 100
Equity Investment Firm
N.A.I.C.S.: 523999

Affiliate (Domestic):

Brookside Capital Partners Fund, L.P. (2)
John Hancock Tower 200 Clarendon St, Boston, MA 02116
Tel.: (617) 516-2900

Investment Management Service
N.A.I.C.S.: 523940

Burlington Stores, Inc. (1)
2006 Route 130 N, Burlington, NJ 08016
Tel.: (609) 387-7800
Web Site: https://www.burlington.com
Rev.: $9,727,467,000
Assets: $1,444,323,000
Liabilities: $447,391,000
Net Worth: $996,932,000
Earnings: $339,649,000
Emp.: 71,049
Fiscal Year-end: 02/03/2024
Department Store Retailer
N.A.I.C.S.: 551112
Michael O'Sullivan *(CEO)*
Travis R. Marquette *(Pres & COO)*
Michael O'Sullivan *(CEO)*
Kristin Wolfe *(CFO & Exec VP)*
Matt Pasch *(Chief HR Officer & Exec VP)*
Jennifer Vecchio *(Chief Mdsg Officer & Pres-Grp)*

Subsidiary (Domestic):

Burlington Coat Factory Investments Holdings, Inc. (2)
1830 Rte 130 N, Burlington, NJ 08016
Tel.: (609) 387-7800
Web Site: http://www.burlingtoncoatfactory.com
Rev.: $4,461,987,000
Assets: $2,613,936,000
Liabilities: $2,655,631,000
Net Worth: ($41,695,000)
Earnings: $43,750,000
Emp.: 30,095
Fiscal Year-end: 02/01/2014
Apparel, Shoes & Accessories for Men, Women & Children; Home Furnishings, Linens & Juvenile Furniture
N.A.I.C.S.: 455110
Paul C. Tang *(Gen Counsel & Exec VP)*
Bill Wagner *(Reg VP)*
Joyce Manning Magrini *(Exec VP-HR)*
Joyce Manning Magrini *(Exec VP-HR)*

Canada Goose Holdings Inc. (1)
(67.4%)
Tel.: (416) 780-9850
Rev.: $985,299,549
Assets: $1,094,481,791
Liabilities: $781,635,517
Net Worth: $312,846,273
Earnings: $42,919,406
Emp.: 4,462
Fiscal Year-end: 03/31/2024
Holding Company; Family Outerwear Designer, Mfr, Whslr & Retailer
N.A.I.C.S.: 551112
Dani Reiss *(CEO & Chm)*

Subsidiary (Domestic):

Baffin Inc. (2)
346 Arvin Ave, Stoney Creek, L8E 2M4, ON, Canada
Tel.: (905) 664-3930
Web Site: http://www.baffin.com
Work Boot & Arctic Footwear Mfr
N.A.I.C.S.: 316210

Canada Goose Inc. (2)
250 Bowie Avenue, Toronto, M6E 4Y2, ON, Canada
Tel.: (416) 780-9850
Web Site: http://www.canadagoose.com
Sales Range: $200-249.9 Million
Family Outerwear Designer, Mfr, Whslr & Retailer
N.A.I.C.S.: 315250
Tracy Reiman *(Pres)*
Carrie Baker *(Sr VP & Chief of Staff)*

China Fire & Security Group, Inc. (1)
B-2508 TYG Center C2 Dongsanhuanbeilu, Chaoyang District, Beijing, 100027, China
Tel.: (86) 10 8441 7566
Web Site: http://www.chinafiresecurity.com
Sales Range: $75-99.9 Million
Fire Safety Equipment
N.A.I.C.S.: 561621

Subsidiary (Domestic):

Sureland Industrial Fire Safety Limited (2)
22 Litian Road Nanbanbidian Industry Dis-

Bain Capital, LP—(Continued)

trict, Beijing Capital Airport, Beijing, 101304, China
Tel.: (86) 1081463816
Web Site: http://www.sureland.com
Sales Range: $25-49.9 Million
Emp.: 200
Fire Protection Products Design, Developer & Mfr
N.A.I.C.S.: 922160
Brian Lin *(CEO)*

Consolis SAS (1)
Tour Europe 33 place des Corolles, La Defense, F-92049, Puteaux, France
Tel.: (33) 146532400
Web Site: http://www.bonnasabla.com
Regional Managing Office; Prefabricated Concrete Products Mfr
N.A.I.C.S.: 551114

Subsidiary (Non-US):

Bonna Tunisia (2)
58 avenue Habib Bourguiba, TN-2033, Megrine, Tunisia
Tel.: (216) 71 434 455
Concrete Pipe & Other Concrete Products Mfr
N.A.I.C.S.: 327332

Branch (Non-US):

Consolis Oy AB (2)
Hiidenmaentie 20, Nummela, FI-03101, Finland
Tel.: (358) 20577577
Web Site: http://www.consolis.com
Regional Managing Office; Prefabricated Concrete Products Mfr
N.A.I.C.S.: 551114

Subsidiary (Non-US):

ASA Epitoipari Kft. (3)
Lajos utca 160-162, 1036, Budapest, Hungary
Tel.: (36) 12405455
Web Site: http://www.asa.hu
Prefabricated Reinforced Concrete Structural Components Designer, Mfr & Installer
N.A.I.C.S.: 327390

Affiliate (Non-US):

3betony Ltd. (4)
109 B Khmelnitsky str, 77300, Kalush, Ukraine (33.33%)
Tel.: (380) 347265002
Web Site: http://www.3betony.com
Prefabricated Reinforced Concrete Structural Components Designer, Mfr & Installer
N.A.I.C.S.: 327390
O.M. Domashchenko *(Gen Dir)*

Subsidiary (Non-US):

ASA Cons Romania s.r.l. (4)
str 22 Decembrie 1989 Nr 27, Turda, Cluj, Romania
Tel.: (40) 264312765
Web Site: http://www.asacons.ro
Prefabricated Reinforced Concrete Structural Components Designer, Mfr & Installer
N.A.I.C.S.: 327390
Bogdan Bulgaria *(CEO)*
Nicolae G. Pasca *(Dir-Factory)*
Andrei Ianos *(Dir-Sls)*
Daniela Dobra *(Dir-Procurement & Contrcat Mgmt)*
Ioan Oltean *(Dir-Occupational Health & Safety)*
Bogdan Daraban *(CFO)*
Simina Stoica *(Dir-HR)*

Subsidiary (Non-US):

Betonika UAB (3)
Placioji g 27 Senuju Traku km, LT-21146, Vilnius, Lithuania
Tel.: (370) 620 29463
Web Site: http://www.betonika.lt
Precast Concrete Products Mfr
N.A.I.C.S.: 327390

Consolis Polska Sp. z o.o. (3)
ul Wolczanska 128/134, PL-90 527, Lodz, Poland
Tel.: (48) 422035100
Web Site: http://www.consolis.pl

Prefabricated Concrete Building Products Mfr
N.A.I.C.S.: 327390

Subsidiary (Domestic):

Parastek Oy AB (3)
Hiidenmaentie 20, Nummela, FI-03101, Finland
Tel.: (358) 205775180
Prefabricated Concrete Building Products Mfr
N.A.I.C.S.: 327390

Parma Oy (3)
Hiidenmaenti 20, FI-03101, Nummela, Finland
Tel.: (358) 205775500
Web Site: http://www.parma.fi
Concrete Products Mfr & Construction Services
N.A.I.C.S.: 327390
Hovi Jani *(Mgr-Product)*
Markku Jarvelainen *(Mng Dir)*
Hakonen Joonas *(Mgr-Project)*
Launonen Juhani *(Mgr-Product)*
Loikkanen Aki *(Mgr-Product)*
Parviainen Jouko *(Mgr-Product)*
Valtanen Marko *(Head-Project Office)*
Airaksinen Antti *(Dir-Purchasing)*

Subsidiary (Non-US):

Spaencom A/S (4)
Akacievej 1, 2640, Hedehusene, Denmark
Tel.: (45) 8888 8200
Web Site: http://www.spaencom.dk
Concrete Structure Mfr & Installation Services
N.A.I.C.S.: 327390
Morten Chrone *(Dir-Sls)*
Magnus Strom *(Mgr-Admin)*
Nils Trier *(CFO)*
Kim Norrevang *(Dir-Product)*
Henrik Blaabjerg *(Dir-Prod)*
Per Bachmann *(Head-Comm)*
Sonja Jorgensen *(Dir-HR)*
Arnel Nuspahic *(Sr Mgr-Project)*

Spenncon AS (4)
Sentrum, PO Box 508, 3504, Honefoss, Norway
Tel.: (47) 6757 3900
Web Site: http://www.spenncon.no
Prefabricated Concrete Building Products Mfr
N.A.I.C.S.: 327390

Strangbetong AB (4)
Gjorwellsgatan 30, 112 60, Stockholm, Sweden
Tel.: (46) 86158200
Web Site: http://www.strangbetong.se
Custom Concrete Building Products Mfr & Construction Services
N.A.I.C.S.: 327390

Subsidiary (Non-US):

SIA Consolis Latvia (3)
22 Getlinu Street, LV-2130, Riga, Latvia
Tel.: (371) 7048300
Web Site: http://www.consolis.lv
Emp.: 175
Prefabricated Concrete Building Products Mfr
N.A.I.C.S.: 327390
Juris Germanis *(Mng Dir)*
Kristine Caune *(Dir-Fin)*
Oskars Zomerovskis *(Mgr-Product)*
Guntis Smits *(Sr Mgr-Project)*
Oskars Kopeika *(Mgr-Product)*

Wytwornia Podkladow Strunobetonowych S.A. (3)
Miroslaw 51, 64-850, Ujscie, Poland
Tel.: (48) 672840340
Web Site: http://www.wps-sa.com.pl
Concrete Railway Products Mfr
N.A.I.C.S.: 327390

Subsidiary (Non-US):

DW Beton GmbH (2)
Stockholmer Strasse 1, D-29640, Schnever-dingen, Germany
Tel.: (49) 5193850
Web Site: http://www.dw-beton.de
Holding Company; Prefabricated & Structural Precast Concrete Building Products Mfr

N.A.I.C.S.: 551112

Division (Domestic):

DW Schwellen GmbH (3)
Heerdterbuschstrasse 8, D-41460, Neuss, Germany
Tel.: (49) 21311860
Web Site: http://www.dw-schwellen.de
Precast Infrastructure Concrete Products Mfr
N.A.I.C.S.: 327390
Ingo Voss *(Exec Dir)*

DW Systembau GmbH (3)
Stockholmer Strasse 1, 29640, Schneverdingen, Germany
Tel.: (49) 5193850
Web Site: http://www.dw-systembau.de
Prestressed Concrete Building Products Mfr
N.A.I.C.S.: 327390
Eduard van der Meer *(Mng Dir)*
Herre Elsenga *(Mng Dir)*
Erwin Dedel *(Mng Dir)*

Subsidiary (Non-US):

H.A.N.S. Prefa a.s. (2)
Jedlickova 1190/1, Lysa nad Labem, 289 22, Czech Republic
Tel.: (420) 325510011
Web Site: http://www.hansprefa.cz
Precast Concrete Structures Mfr
N.A.I.C.S.: 327390
Michal Miksovsky *(Mng Dir)*
Martin Janik *(Dir-Plant)*
Martin Zalis *(Dir-Prod)*

Joint Venture (Non-US):

P.T. Bonna Indonesia (2)
JL Pertigaan Mercedes No 2 Tlajung Udik Gunung Putri, Bogor, 16962, West Java, Indonesia
Tel.: (62) 21 8670852
Web Site: http://www.bonna-indonesia.com
Concrete Pipe & Pre-Stressed Concrete Products Mfr; Owned by P.T. Duta Saraha Perkasa & by LBO France
N.A.I.C.S.: 327332

Subsidiary (Non-US):

Spanbeton B.V. (2)
Hoogewaard 207/209, NL-2396 AS, Koud-ekerk aan den Rijn, Netherlands
Tel.: (31) 713420200
Web Site: http://www.spanbeton.nl
Prestressed Concrete Products Mfr
N.A.I.C.S.: 327390

VBI Verenigde Bouwprodukten Industrie B.V. (2)
Looveer 1, NL-6851 AJ, Huissen, Netherlands
Tel.: (31) 263797979
Web Site: http://www.vbi.nl
Hollow Concrete Flooring Products Mfr
N.A.I.C.S.: 327390
Edward van de Meer *(Mng Dir)*

Contec Holdings, LLC (1)
1023 State St, Schenectady, NY 12307-1511
Tel.: (518) 382-8000
Web Site: http://www.gocontec.com
Sales Range: $25-49.9 Million
Emp.: 70
Cable Set-Top Box Repair & Maintenance Services
N.A.I.C.S.: 811210
Richard Kielb *(Sr VP-Sls)*
Hari Pillai *(Pres, CEO & Sec)*
Jochen Vogt *(CFO)*
Jyoti Kapoor *(COO)*
Brad Barcz *(Chm)*
Terry Le *(Exec VP-Supplier Mgmt)*

Subsidiary (Domestic):

Replico Corporation (2)
7700 Arroyo Cir, Gilroy, CA 95020
Tel.: (408) 842-8600
Web Site: http://www.replicocorp.com
Sales Range: $10-24.9 Million
Emp.: 35
Commercial Printing Services
N.A.I.C.S.: 323111
Julia Makie *(VP-Sls)*
Lisa Flohr *(VP-Fin & Admin)*
Michael A. Whitehead *(Pres)*
Nicki Kuzn *(Mgr-HR)*

D&M Holdings U.S. Inc. (1)
100 Corporate Dr, Mahwah, NJ 07430-1271
Tel.: (201) 762-6500
Web Site: http://www.dmglobal.com
Holding Company; Music Equipment Mfr & Distr
N.A.I.C.S.: 551112

Subsidiary (Domestic):

Boston Acoustics, Inc. (2)
300 Jubilee Dr, Peabody, MA 01960-4030
Tel.: (201) 762-2100
Web Site: https://www.bostonacoustics.com
Sales Range: $50-74.9 Million
Emp.: 192
High Quality Loudspeaker Systems Mfr for Home, Automotive, Business & Professional Use
N.A.I.C.S.: 334310

D&M Professional (2)
1100 Maplewood Dr, Itasca, IL 60143
Tel.: (630) 741-0330
Web Site: http://www.d-mpro.com
Sales Range: $25-49.9 Million
Emp.: 12
Professional Recording Equipment
N.A.I.C.S.: 423620

Subsidiary (Non-US):

Denon Corporation (2)
3-16-11 Yushima, Bunkyo Ku, Tokyo, 113-0034, Japan
Tel.: (81) 338375321
Web Site: http://www.denon.co.jp
Mfr of Household Audio & Video Equipment
N.A.I.C.S.: 334310

Subsidiary (US):

Denon Electronics USA LLC (3)
100 Corporate Dr, Mahwah, NJ 07430-2041
Tel.: (973) 396-0810
Web Site: http://www.usa.denon.com
Sales Range: $25-49.9 Million
Mfr of Audio & Video Equipment & Software Products
N.A.I.C.S.: 423990

Subsidiary (Non-US):

Marantz Japan Inc. (2)
Nisshin 2-1 D&M Building 4F Kawasaki-shi Kanagawa-ku, Kawasaki, 210-8569, Kanagawa, Japan
Tel.: (81) 570 200 288
Web Site: http://www.marantz.jp
Sales Range: $50-74.9 Million
Radio Equipment Mfr & Sales
N.A.I.C.S.: 334220

Subsidiary (US):

Marantz America Inc. (3)
1100 Maplewood Dr, Itasca, IL 60143
Tel.: (201) 762-6500
Web Site: http://www.marantz.com
Sales Range: $25-49.9 Million
Emp.: 15
Home Entertainment Equipment Retailer
N.A.I.C.S.: 423620

Subsidiary (Non-US):

Marantz Europe B.V. (3)
PO Box 8744, 5605 LS, Eindhoven, Netherlands
Tel.: (31) 402507850
Web Site: http://www.marantz.com
Sales Range: $10-24.9 Million
Emp.: 50
Audio & Video Equipment Mfr & Distr
N.A.I.C.S.: 334310

Marantz France SAS (3)
2 Rue Du Port Oaux Vins, 92150, Suresnes, France
Tel.: (33) 147281440
Sales Range: $10-24.9 Million
Emp.: 10
Audio & Video Equipment Mfr & Distr
N.A.I.C.S.: 334310

Marantz GmbH (3)
Hakenbusch 3, 49078, Osnabruck, Germany
Tel.: (49) 541404660
Web Site: http://www.marantz.de

Sales Range: $10-24.9 Million
Emp.: 11
Audio & Video Equipment Mfr & Distr
N.A.I.C.S.: 334310

Marantz Italy Srl (3)
Via Manfredi 98, 29122, Piacenza, Italy
Tel.: (39) 0523716899
Web Site: http://www.marantz.com
Sales Range: $10-24.9 Million
Emp.: 3
Audio & Video Equipment Mfr & Distr
N.A.I.C.S.: 334310

Marantz UK Ltd. (3)
Kingsbridge House Padbury Oaks, 575 583
Bath Rd Longford, West Drayton, UB7 0EH,
Middlesex, United Kingdom
Tel.: (44) 753680868
Web Site: http://www.marantz.com
Sales Range: $10-24.9 Million
Emp.: 15
Audio & Video Equipment Mfr & Distr
N.A.I.C.S.: 334310

**DSM Sinochem Pharmaceuticals
Netherlands B.V.** (1)
Alexander Fleminglaan 1, 2613 AX, Delft,
Netherlands
Tel.: (31) 152799111
Sales Range: $200-249.9 Million
Emp.: 1,000
Pharmaceutical Ingredient Mfr
N.A.I.C.S.: 325412
Stefan Doboczky (CEO)
Anurag Roy (Dir-New Bus-Asia Pacific,
Middle East & Africa)

Daymon Worldwide Inc. (1)
700 Fairfield Ave, Stamford, CT
06902-7526   (60%)
Tel.: (203) 352-7500
Web Site: http://www.daymon.com
Emp.: 40,000
Grocery Brand Development, Logistics Con-
sulting & Consumer Marketing Services
N.A.I.C.S.: 541613
Vipon Kumar (Chief Sourcing & Trading Of-
ficer)
James D. White (Chm)
Jim Holbrook (CEO)
Michael Bellman (Pres-SAS Retail Svcs)
Vasco Brinca (Pres-Intl)
Bharat Rupani (Pres-Retail Svcs & Intl-Asia)
Michael Taylor (Pres-North America Private
Brand)
Jim Clancy (Treas & Sr VP-Fin)
Rekha Ramesh (Sr VP-IT & Digital-Global)
Amy Sanderson (Sr VP-Growth & Strategy)
Jerrold Williams (Sr VP-HR)
Tim Garvey (VP-Process, Plng & Analysis)
Linda Stark (VP-Creative Svcs)

Subsidiary (Domestic):

Daymon Worldwide Trading Inc. (2)
333 Ludlow St 4th Fl, Stamford, CT 06902-
6982
Tel.: (203) 352-7500
Emp.: 200
International Trade Brokerage & Logistics
Services
N.A.I.C.S.: 425120

**Galileo Global Branding Group
Inc.** (2)
333 Ludlow St 5th Fl, Stamford, CT 06902
Tel.: (203) 352-7500
Web Site: http://www.galileobranding.com
Packaging Design & Print Management
Agency
N.A.I.C.S.: 541430
Linda Stark (Grp VP-Creative Svcs)

**Interactions Consumer Experience
Marketing Inc.** (2)
9555 Chesapeake Dr Ste 100, San Diego,
CA 92123
Tel.: (858) 581-8700
Web Site:
    http://www.interactionsmarketing.com
Consumer Marketing Research & Retail
Consulting Services
N.A.I.C.S.: 541910
Bharat Rupani (Pres)

**Omni Global Sourcing Solutions
Inc.** (2)
4050 S 26th St Ste 200, Philadelphia, PA
19112

Tel.: (215) 309-7129
Web Site: http://www.omnigss.com
Product Sourcing & Logistics Services
N.A.I.C.S.: 425120
Vipon Kumar (Chief Trading & Sourcing Of-
ficer)
Harry J. Warnaar (Sr Dir & Gen Mgr-Ops)
Thierno Barry (Sr Dir & Gen Mgr-Exports)
Asmita Pahwa (Sr Dir-Sourcing & Product
Dev-Global)
John Reilly (Dir-Quality Assurance)

SAS Retail Services, LLC (2)
1575 N Main St, Orange, CA 92867
Tel.: (714) 279-2660
Web Site: http://www.sasretail.com
Emp.: 20,000
Retail Merchandising Analytics, Logistics &
Consulting Services
N.A.I.C.S.: 541613
Michael Bellman (Pres)

Envestnet, Inc. (1)
1000 Chesterbrook Blvd Ste 250, Berwyn,
PA 19312
Tel.: (312) 827-2800
Web Site: https://www.envestnet.com
Rev.: $1,245,620,000
Assets: $1,877,252,000
Liabilities: $1,302,746,000
Net Worth: $574,506,000
Earnings: ($245,774,000)
Emp.: 3,100
Fiscal Year-end: 12/31/2023
Holding Company; Portfolio, Practice Man-
agement & Financial Reporting Services
N.A.I.C.S.: 551112
William C. Crager (Co-Founder)
Brandon Thomas (Co-Founder)
James L. Fox (Chm & Interim CEO)
James Lumberg (Co-Founder)
Shelly O'Brien (Chief Legal Officer, Gen
Counsel & Sec)
Dawn Newsome (Chief Bus Ops Officer)
Matthew J. Majoros (Sr VP-Fin Reporting)

Subsidiary (Domestic):

CastleRock Innovations, LLC (2)
216 S Jefferson St Ste 601, Chicago, IL
60661
Tel.: (312) 239-6090
Software Programming Services
N.A.I.C.S.: 541511

**Envestnet Portfolio Solutions,
Inc.** (2)
75 State St 6th Fl, Boston, MA 02110
Tel.: (866) 924-8912
Web Site: http://www.envestnet.com
Investment Management Service
N.A.I.C.S.: 523940

**Envestnet Retirement Solutions,
LLC** (2)
35 E Wacker Dr 22nd Fl, Chicago, IL 60601
Tel.: (312) 827-7957
Web Site: https://www.envestnetrs.com
Software Development Services
N.A.I.C.S.: 541511
Robert Bernstein (Founder)

Fiduciary Exchange, LLC (2)
450 N Brand Blvd Ste 600, Glendale, CA
91203
Tel.: (213) 260-0026
Web Site: http://www.fiduciaryexchange.com
Business Support Services
N.A.I.C.S.: 523940

Folio Dynamics Inc. (2)
1 Harmon Plz 6th Fl, Secaucus, NJ 07094
Tel.: (412) 225-4936
Advisory & Financial Services
N.A.I.C.S.: 523940

Oltis Software, LLC (2)
5151 E Broadway Blvd Ste 620, Tucson, AZ
85711
Tel.: (800) 557-1780
Web Site: http://www.financelogix.com
Emp.: 30
Investment Management Service
N.A.I.C.S.: 523940

**Portfolio Management Consultants,
Inc.** (2)
1801 California St 23 Fl, Denver, CO 80202
Tel.: (866) 924-8913
Web Site: http://www.investpmc.com

Emp.: 150
Investment Advisory Services
N.A.I.C.S.: 523940

Redi2 Technologies, Inc. (2)
205 Portland St Ste 202, Boston, MA 02114
Tel.: (510) 834-7334
Web Site: https://www.redi2.com
Sales Range: $1-9.9 Million
Emp.: 19
Prepackaged Software Services
N.A.I.C.S.: 513210
Fermin Garcia (Pres & COO)

Tamarac, Inc. (2)
701 5th Ave 14th Fl, Seattle, WA 98104
Tel.: (206) 428-4657
Web Site: https://www.tamaracinc.com
Software Development Services
N.A.I.C.S.: 541511

Wheelhouse Analytics (2)
117-123 W Gay St 3rd FL Ste 334, West
Chester, PA 19380
Tel.: (215) 240-7063
Web Site:
    http://www.wheelhouseanalytics.com
Computer Software Services
N.A.I.C.S.: 513210

Yodlee Canada, Inc. (2)
3600 Bridge Pkwy Ste 200, Redwood City,
CA 94065
Tel.: (650) 980-3600
Web Site: http://www.yodlee.com
Software Publishing Services
N.A.I.C.S.: 513210

Subsidiary (Non-US):

Yodlee Group Australia PTY Ltd. (2)
Level 4/11 York Street, Sydney, 2000,
NSW, Australia
Tel.: (61) 731213188
Software Publishing Services
N.A.I.C.S.: 513210

Yodlee Infotech Private Limited (2)
1st Floor Mercury 2B Block Prestige Tech-
nology Park, Sarjapura-Marathahalli Ring
Road, Bengaluru, 560 103, Karnataka, India
Tel.: (91) 8039805600
Web Site: http://www.yodlee.com
Software Publishing Services
N.A.I.C.S.: 513210

Subsidiary (Domestic):

Yodlee, Inc. (2)
999 Baker Way Ste 100, San Mateo, CA
94404   (100%)
Tel.: (650) 980-3600
Web Site: https://www.yodlee.com
Data Aggregation & Data Analytics Platform
& Services
N.A.I.C.S.: 513210
Bill Parsons (Pres-Data & AI/Analytics &
Intl)

Epic Health Services, Inc. (1)
5220 Spring Valley Rd Ste 400, Dallas, TX
75247
Tel.: (214) 466-1340
Web Site:
    http://www.epichealthservices.com
Healthcare Staffing Services
N.A.I.C.S.: 561311
Alex Jamieson (Dir-Client Rels)

Subsidiary (Domestic):

Option 1 Nutrition Holdings, LLC (2)
PO Box 11279, Chandler, AZ 85225
Web Site:
    http://www.epicmedicalsolutions.com
Business Support Services
N.A.I.C.S.: 561499
Dani Foster (Dir-Managed Care)

**Pediatric Services of America,
Inc.** (2)
6 Concourse Pkwy Ste 1100, Atlanta, GA
30028
Tel.: (770) 441-1580
Web Site: http://www.psahealthcare.com
Pediatric Health Care Services, Equipment,
Pharmaceutical Services, Infusion Therapy,
Pediatric Rehabilitation & Case Manage-
ment
N.A.I.C.S.: 621610

Jeffrey S. Shaner (COO)
Elizabeth A. Rubio (Chief Nursing Officer &
VP-Clinical Ops)
Shaner Jeff (COO)

Subsidiary (Domestic):

Assure Home Healthcare (3)
8700 Crownhill Blvd Ste 105, San Antonio,
TX 78209
Tel.: (210) 714-2805
Health Services & Private Duty Nursing
N.A.I.C.S.: 621610
Matt Strange (CEO)

Care Unlimited, Inc. (3)
3288 Babcock Blvd, Pittsburgh, PA 15237
Tel.: (412) 367-3620
Home Health Care Services to Medically
Complex Patients
N.A.I.C.S.: 621610

Gerard Lighting Pty Ltd (1)
Level 2 191 Fullarton Road, Dulwich, 5065,
SA, Australia
Tel.: (61) 1300799300
Web Site: http://www.gerardlighting.com.au
Lighting Product Mfr
N.A.I.C.S.: 335131
Les Patterson (CEO)

Subsidiary (Domestic):

Austube Pty Limited (2)
23 Foundry Road, Seven Hills, 2147, NSW,
Australia
Tel.: (61) 296749122
Web Site: http://www.austube.com.au
Emp.: 60
Tubular Lighting Systems Mfr
N.A.I.C.S.: 335132
Santina Dominguez (Controller-Fin)
Martin Kya (Gen Mgr)

Crompton Lighting Pty Limited (2)
96-112 Gow St, Padstow, 2211, NSW, Aus-
tralia
Tel.: (61) 2 9794 9393
Web Site: http://www.crompton.com.au
Sales Range: $50-74.9 Million
Emp.: 40
Lamps & Light Fittings Distr
N.A.I.C.S.: 423690
Margaret Gao (Mgr-Pur)

Subsidiary (Non-US):

Gerard Lighting (NZ) Limited (2)
59 Montgomerie Road, Airport Oaks, Auck-
land, 2022, New Zealand
Tel.: (64) 9 255 0006
Web Site: http://www.gerardlighting.co.nz
Sales Range: $25-49.9 Million
Emp.: 15
Lighting Product Mfr
N.A.I.C.S.: 335131

Subsidiary (Domestic):

Inlite Pty Limited (2)
44-46 Chippen St, Chippendale, 2008,
NSW, Australia
Tel.: (61) 283841000
Web Site: http://www.inlite.com.au
Sales Range: $25-49.9 Million
Emp.: 15
Lighting System Installation & Distr
N.A.I.C.S.: 238210
Jarrod Huxtable (Mgr-Natl Sls)

Lighting Corporation Pty Ltd (2)
12/37 O'Riordan Street, PO Box 7424, Alex-
andria, 2015, NSW, Australia
Tel.: (61) 283060900
Sales Range: $150-199.9 Million
Lighting Fixture Marketer & Distr
N.A.I.C.S.: 335131

Moonlighting Pty Limited (2)
351 King Street, Melbourne, 3000, VIC,
Australia
Tel.: (61) 392352400
Web Site: http://www.moonlighting.com.au
Sales Range: $25-49.9 Million
Emp.: 10
Lighting Fixtures Mfr & Distr
N.A.I.C.S.: 335131

Pierlite Australia Pty Limited (2)
96-112 Gow Street, Padstow, 2211, NSW,
Australia

Bain Capital, LP—(Continued)

Tel.: (61) 1300799300
Web Site: http://www.pierlite.com.au
Sales Range: $100-124.9 Million
Emp.: 500
Lighting Systems Mfr & Distr
N.A.I.C.S.: 335131
Simon Morrison (Mgr-Specification)
Geoff Daniow (Mgr-Bus Dev)
Andrew Nagy (Mgr-Application Engrg)

Guitar Center Holdings, Inc.   **(1)**
5795 Lindero Canyon Rd, Westlake Village, CA 91362
Tel.: (818) 735-8800
Web Site: http://www.guitarcenter.com
Sales Range: $1-4.9 Billion
Emp.: 7,738
Holding Company
N.A.I.C.S.: 551112

Subsidiary (Domestic):

Guitar Center, Inc.   **(2)**
5795 Lindero Canyon Rd, Westlake Village, CA 91362
Tel.: (801) 501-8847
Web Site: https://www.guitarcenter.com
Sales Range: $1-4.9 Billion
Emp.: 10,000
Musical Instrument & Supplies Retailers
N.A.I.C.S.: 459140
Michael Amkreutz (Exec VP-Mdsg, Sls & eCommerce)
Wayne Colwell (Exec VP-Stores)
Todd Lyche (CIO & Sr VP)
Michael Pendleton (Gen Counsel & Sr VP)
Jeannine D'Addario (Chief Customer Officer & Sr VP)
Anne Buchanan (Chief HR Officer & Sr VP)
Gabe Dalporto (CEO)

Subsidiary (Domestic):

Anaheim Band Instruments, Inc.   **(3)**
504 S State College Blvd, Anaheim, CA 92806
Tel.: (714) 999-5015
Web Site: http://www.abimusic.com
Sales Range: $1-9.9 Million
Emp.: 17
Musical Instrument Stores
N.A.I.C.S.: 459140

Music & Arts Center Inc.   **(3)**
5295 Westview Dr Ste 300, Frederick, MD 21703
Tel.: (301) 620-4040
Web Site: http://www.musicarts.com
Musical Instrument Store & Learning Center Distr
N.A.I.C.S.: 459140
Ashley Hartman (Mgr-Recruitment)

Musician's Friend, Inc.   **(3)**
931 Chevy Way, Medford, OR 97504
Tel.: (541) 772-5173
Web Site: http://www.musiciansfriend.com
Music Equipment & Products Catalogue & Online Sales
N.A.I.C.S.: 459140
Craig Johnson (Pres & COO)

Imperial Dade, LLC   **(1)**
255 Route 1 & 9, Jersey City, NJ 07306
Tel.: (201) 437-7440
Web Site: http://imperialdade.com
Food Service Disposables & Janitorial Supplies Distr
N.A.I.C.S.: 424130
Robert Tillis (Chm)
Jason Tillis (CEO)
Paul Cervino (Chief Admin Officer)
Jeffrey Burdick (VP)
Chris Freeman (VP-Sls)
Devashish Saxena (Chief Digital Officer)
Nick Morris (Owner)
Charlie D'Elia Jr. (Chief Comml Officer)

Subsidiary (Domestic):

Allston Supply Co., Inc.   **(2)**
2220 Main St, Springfield, MA 01104
Tel.: (413) 739-4797
Web Site: http://www.allstonsupply.com
Janitorial Product Whslr
N.A.I.C.S.: 423850
Robert Cohen (Exec VP)
Kent Domfried (Mgr-Sls)

Tania Curran (Mgr-Customer Svc)
Al White (Coord-Sve)
Roger Cohen (Pres & Treas)

Apache Group of Minnesota, Inc.   **(2)**
1787 Gateway Blvd, Saint Paul, MN 55112
Tel.: (651) 633-5555
Sales Range: $1-9.9 Million
Emp.: 24
Industrial & Personal Service Paper Merchant Whslr
N.A.I.C.S.: 424130
Jane Adrian (Sec)
Allison Adrian (CEO)
Joe Adrian (Founder)

Classic Solutions, Inc.   **(2)**
4140 Fisher Rd Ste A, Columbus, OH 43228
Tel.: (614) 351-3300
Web Site: http://www.classicsolutionsinc.com
Sales Range: $1-9.9 Million
Emp.: 28
Chemical & Allied Products Merchant Whslr
N.A.I.C.S.: 424690
James Creps (Pres)

Columbus Paper Company, Inc.   **(2)**
807 Joy Rd, Columbus, GA 31906
Tel.: (706) 689-1361
Web Site: http://www.copacoinc.com
Sales Range: $10-24.9 Million
Emp.: 35
Provider of Paper Products
N.A.I.C.S.: 424130
Michael A. Greenblatt (Pres & CEO)

Cosgrove Enterprises Inc.   **(2)**
14300 NW 77 Ct, Miami Lakes, FL 33016
Tel.: (305) 623-6700
Web Site: http://www.e-cosgrove.com
Sales Range: $10-24.9 Million
Emp.: 20
Janitors' Supplies
N.A.I.C.S.: 423850
Greg Rogers (Pres & CEO)
George Trotter (Sr Acct Mgr)
Maria Castellino (Sr Acct Mgr)
Raysa Alvarez (Acct Mgr)

Branch (Domestic):

Dade Paper & Bag, LLC   **(2)**
9601 NW 112th Ave, Miami, FL 33178
Tel.: (305) 592-1020
Web Site: http://www.imperialdade.com
Industrial & Personal Service Paper
N.A.I.C.S.: 424130

Subsidiary (Domestic):

Accommodation Mollen, Inc.   **(3)**
2150 Kubach Rd, Philadelphia, PA 19116-4203   **(100%)**
Tel.: (215) 739-2115
Web Site: http://www.accommodation-mollen.com
Rev.: $1,100,000
Emp.: 42
Distributes Cleaning & Safety Supplies & Equipment
N.A.I.C.S.: 423850
Dave Potack (Pres)
Richard Lawit (Partner)

Borax Paper Products   **(3)**
1390 Spofford Ave, Bronx, NY 10474-0474   **(100%)**
Tel.: (718) 665-8500
Web Site: http://www.boraxpaper.com
Emp.: 110
Distr of Food Packaging, Paper Products, Foodservice Disposables & Janitorial & Sanitary Supplies
N.A.I.C.S.: 322219
Marc Borak (CEO)
Howard Hirsch (VP)

Central Paper Products Co., Inc.   **(3)**
350 Gay St John C Mongan Indus Park, Manchester, NH 03103
Tel.: (603) 624-4064
Web Site: http://www.centralpaper.com
Industrial & Foodservice Supplies Mfr
N.A.I.C.S.: 424130
Bob Dalzell (Mgr-Logistics & Distr)
Cale Ellsworth (Mgr-Customer Svc)
Gordon Watson (Controller)
Matt Kfoury (Pres & CEO)

Mike Delahanty (Mgr-Credit)
Paul Hebert (Asst Mgr-Warehouse)
Christine Kfoury (VP-Fin)
Frederick Kfoury III (VP-Mktg)

DP Distribution LLC   **(3)**
9601 NW 112th Ave, Miami, FL 33178
Tel.: (305) 777-6108
Web Site:
   http://www.dadepaperdistribution.com
Grocery Product Whslr
Ruth Carr (Dir-Pur)

Plant (Domestic):

Dade Paper & Bag, LLC - Atlanta Facility   **(3)**
600 Hartman Industrial Ct SW Ste 200, Austell, GA 30168
Tel.: (678) 322-4444
Paper Product Distr
N.A.I.C.S.: 424130
Chuck Howard (Branch Mgr)

Dade Paper & Bag, LLC - Greensboro Facility   **(3)**
6530 A Judge Adams Rd, Whitsett, NC 27377
Tel.: (336) 603-5100
Web Site: http://www.dadepaper.com
Paper Product Distr
N.A.I.C.S.: 424130
Peter Nigro (Branch Mgr)

Dade Paper & Bag, LLC - Gulf States Facility   **(3)**
30427A County Rd 49, Loxley, AL 36551
Tel.: (251) 964-1500
Paper Product Distr
N.A.I.C.S.: 424130
Bob Worch (Branch Mgr)

Dade Paper & Bag, LLC - Jacksonville Facility   **(3)**
4102 Bulls Bay Hwy Unit 7, Jacksonville, FL 32219
Tel.: (904) 783-9490
Web Site: http://www.dadepaper.com
Emp.: 60
Paper Product Distr
N.A.I.C.S.: 424130
Jed Turner (Branch Mgr)

Dade Paper & Bag, LLC - Mid-Atlantic Facility   **(3)**
7605 Dorsey Run Rd Ste C, Jessup, MD 20794
Tel.: (301) 499-1700
Paper Product Distr
N.A.I.C.S.: 424130
David Holtz (Branch Mgr)

Dade Paper & Bag, LLC - Orlando Facility   **(3)**
2675 Directors Row, Orlando, FL 32809
Tel.: (407) 859-1020
Web Site: http://www.dadepaper.com
Paper Product Distr
N.A.I.C.S.: 424130
Scott Meltz (Branch Mgr)

Dade Paper & Bag, LLC - Puerto Rico Facility   **(3)**
PO Box 51535, Toa Baja, PR 00950-1535
Tel.: (787) 275-1414
Paper Product Distr
N.A.I.C.S.: 424130
Rafael O'Ferrall (Branch Mgr)

Dade Paper & Bag, LLC - Tri-State Facility   **(3)**
120 Tices Ln, East Brunswick, NJ 08816
Tel.: (888) 946-2671
Paper Product Distr
N.A.I.C.S.: 424130
Rick Tabit (Branch Mgr)

Division (Domestic):

Dade Paper Cruise Line   **(3)**
9601 NW 112th Ave, Miami, FL 33178
Tel.: (305) 805-2652
Web Site:
   http://www.dadepapercruisedivision.com
Paper Product Distr
N.A.I.C.S.: 424130
Andy Baltzell (Dir-Cruise Ops-Global)

Subsidiary (Domestic):

Franz Janitorial Service & Supply, Inc.   **(3)**

27 N Church St, Hazleton, PA 18201
Tel.: (570) 454-5256
Rev.: $1,500,000
Emp.: 15
Service Establishment Equipment & Supplies Merchant Whslr
N.A.I.C.S.: 423850
Anthony Franzosa Jr. (Pres)

Goldman Paper Company, Inc.   **(3)**
111 Constitution Blvd, Franklin, MA 02038
Tel.: (781) 963-9100
Web Site: http://www.goldmanpaper.com
Sales Range: $1-9.9 Million
Emp.: 30
Disposable Paper, Plastic & Janitorial Supplies Distr
N.A.I.C.S.: 424130
Bor Ajian (Mgr)

Kranz, Inc.   **(3)**
2200 De Koven Ave, Racine, WI 53403-2442
Tel.: (262) 638-2200
Web Site: http://www.kranzinc.com
Environmental Services
N.A.I.C.S.: 541620

Mid-Continent Paper & Distributing Company, Inc.   **(3)**
11809 Borman Dr, Saint Louis, MO 63146
Tel.: (314) 989-0894
Web Site:
   http://www.midcontinentpaper.com
Industrial & Personal Service Paper Merchant Whslr
N.A.I.C.S.: 424130
eff Schmiemeier (VP-Sls)

Peninsular Paper Company, Inc.   **(3)**
5101 E Hanna Ave, Tampa, FL 33610
Tel.: (813) 621-3091
Paper Products & Janitorial Supplies Distr
N.A.I.C.S.: 424130

Division (Domestic):

Philip Rosenau Co., Inc.   **(3)**
750 Jacksonville Rd, Warminster, PA 18974
Tel.: (215) 956-1980
Web Site: http://www.philiprosenau.com
Sales Range: $25-49.9 Million
Emp.: 55
Janitorial Supplies & Sanitary Maintenance Products Distr
N.A.I.C.S.: 423850
John Rosenau (Pres)

Subsidiary (Domestic):

Strauss Paper Co., Inc.   **(3)**
10 Slater St, Port Chester, NY 10573-4925
Tel.: (800) 927-2737
Web Site: http://www.strausspaper.com
Industrial & Personal Service Paper Mfr
N.A.I.C.S.: 424130
Stewart Strauss (Pres & Treas)

Subsidiary (Non-US):

EUGENE ALLARD PRODUITS D'EMBALLAGE & D'ENTRETIEN INC   **(2)**
2244 Chapais Street, Jonquière, G7X 7W8, QC, Canada
Tel.: (418) 547-6654
Web Site: http://www.eugeneallard.com
Packaging & Maintenance Products Distr
N.A.I.C.S.: 424130
Jean-Denis Allard (CEO)

Subsidiary (Domestic):

East Continental Supplies LLC   **(2)**
7955 W 20th Ave, Hialeah, FL 33014-3229
Tel.: (305) 887-0186
Web Site: http://www.ecsupplies.com
Investment Advice
N.A.I.C.S.: 523940
Dorothy Carvonel (Owner)

Focus Packaging & Supply Co.   **(2)**
2879 N Argyle Ave, Fresno, CA 93727-1305
Tel.: (559) 485-1261
Web Site:
   http://www.focuspackagingandsupply.com
Service Establishment Equipment & Supplies Merchant Whslr
N.A.I.C.S.: 423850

Garrett Paper, Inc.   **(2)**

3140 Park Ave, Saint Louis, MO 63104
Tel.: (314) 241-3060
Web Site: http://www.garrettpaper.com
Commercial Equipment Whslr
N.A.I.C.S.: 423440
Lisa Garrett (Pres)
Joseph Garrett Sr. (CEO)

Great Southwest Paper Co., Inc. (2)
5707 Harvey Wilson, Houston, TX 77220-5618
Tel.: (713) 223-5050
Web Site:
http://www.greatsouthwestpaper.com
Industrial Paper Whslr
N.A.I.C.S.: 424130
Andy Vannatta (CEO)

Insight Distributing, Inc. (2)
207 N Crestline St, Spokane, WA 99202
Tel.: (509) 534-5901
Sales Range: $1-9.9 Million
Emp.: 26
Commercial Equipment Merchant Whslr
N.A.I.C.S.: 423440
Kenneth Pearlstein (Pres & CEO)

Division (Domestic):

JAD Corporation (2)
2048 119th St, College Point, NY 11356
Tel.: (718) 762-8900
Sales Range: $1-9.9 Million
Emp.: 50
Mfg Bags-Plastic/Coated Paper Whol Service Establishment Equipment Whol Chemicals/Products
N.A.I.C.S.: 326111
Henry Schaeffer (CFO)

Subsidiary (Domestic):

Lovan Industries, Inc. (2)
8747 Governors Row, Dallas, TX 75247
Tel.: (214) 634-7345
Web Site: http://www.lovan.net
Sales Range: $1-9.9 Million
Emp.: 13
Industrial And Personal Service Paper, Ns
N.A.I.C.S.: 424130
Donna Norcott (Mgr-Ops)
Mike Gilliam (Pres & CEO)

Mailender, Inc. (2)
9500 Glades Dr, Hamilton, OH 45011
Tel.: (513) 942-5453
Web Site: http://www.mailender.com
Gasoline Engine & Engine Parts Mfr
N.A.I.C.S.: 336310
Chris Ward (VP)

Moresco Distributing Co. (2)
1120 Holm Rd, Petaluma, CA 94954-1105
Tel.: (707) 773-2500
Web Site: http://www.moresco.biz
Industrial & Personal Service Paper Merchant Whslr
N.A.I.C.S.: 424130
Ron Moresco (Owner)

Nichols Paper & Supply Co. Inc. (2)
1391 Judson Rd, Spring Lake, MI 49456
Tel.: (231) 799-2120
Web Site: http://www.enichols.com
Sales Range: $10-24.9 Million
Emp.: 200
Industrial & Personal Service Paper
N.A.I.C.S.: 424130
Mike Olthoff (CEO)
Robert Cloutier (Mgr-IT)
Tom Zeller (Mgr-IT)

Ohio & Michigan Paper Co. (2)
PO Box 621, Toledo, OH 43697-0621
Tel.: (419) 666-3768
Web Site: http://www.ompco.com
Office Supplies & Stationery Stores
N.A.I.C.S.: 459410
Kevin Leininger (Chm & Pres)

Russell Hall Co. (2)
19 N George St, Meriden, CT 06451-3234
Tel.: (203) 235-6391
Web Site: http://www.russellhall.com
Industrial Machinery & Equipment Merchant Whslr
N.A.I.C.S.: 423830
Bill Rosa (Principal)

Supreme Paper Supplies LLC (2)

8965 Pensacola Blvd, Pensacola, FL 32534
Tel.: (850) 478-9207
Web Site:
http://www.supremepapersupply.com
Rev.: $5,882,000
Emp.: 17
Cosmetics, Beauty Supplies & Perfume Stores
N.A.I.C.S.: 456120
Charles Kelly (Owner)

Tepe Sanitary Supply, Inc. (2)
52878 Frederic Dr, Elkhart, IN 46514
Tel.: (574) 293-7591
Web Site: http://www.tepesanitary.com
Sales Range: $1-9.9 Million
Emp.: 20
Service Establishment Equipment & Supplies Whslr
N.A.I.C.S.: 423850
Dave Goebel (Mgr-Sls)
Steve Tepe (Pres)
Dawn Evans (Office Mgr)
Mike Bujtas (Mgr-Svc Dept)

Triple F Holdings, LLC (2)
1845 Auiki St, Honolulu, HI 96819-3100
Tel.: (808) 842-9133
Web Site: http://www.fffhawaii.com
Food Service Contractors
N.A.I.C.S.: 722310
Kevin Wong (Mgr-Strategic Mktg)

Subsidiary (Non-US):

Veritiv Canada, Inc. (2)
125 Madill Blvd, Mississauga, L5W 0H1, ON, Canada
Tel.: Web Site: http://www.veritivcanada.ca
Packaging & Facility Maintenance Services
N.A.I.C.S.: 561910

Subsidiary (Domestic):

Wagner Supply Co, Inc. (2)
1349 W 42nd St, Odessa, TX 79764
Tel.: (432) 363-0433
Web Site: http://www.wagnersupply.com
Whol Service Establishment Equipment Ret Misc Merchandise Whol Sporting/Recreational Goods
N.A.I.C.S.: 423850
Brenda Wagner (Pres)

Western Paper Distributors, Inc. (2)
11551 E 45th Ave Ste A, Denver, CO 80239
Tel.: (303) 371-8710
Web Site: http://www.westernpaper.com
Sales Range: $25-49.9 Million
Emp.: 110
Janitorial Supplier & Hotel Supplier
N.A.I.C.S.: 424130
Jeff Hartman (Acct Mgr)
Suzanne Malom (Mgr-Fulfillment)
Katie Demarest (Mgr-Sls Support & Customer Care)

Subsidiary (Domestic):

Brown & White, Inc. (3)
501 E 30th St, Tucson, AZ 85713
Tel.: (520) 624-9860
Web Site: http://www.brownandwhiteinc.com
Sales Range: $1-9.9 Million
Emp.: 25
Disposable Foodservice Paper Mfr
N.A.I.C.S.: 322291
Pete Man (Founder)
Peter A. Granillo (Pres & CEO)

Italmatch Chemicals S.p.A. (1)
Via Magazzini del Cotone 17 Modulo 4, Tom Piane San Benigno, 16128, Genoa, Italy
Tel.: (39) 010 642081
Web Site: http://www.italmatch.com
Specialty Chemicals Mfr
N.A.I.C.S.: 325998
Sergio Iorio (CEO)

Subsidiary (US):

Italmatch USA Corporation (2)
5544 Oakdale Rd SE, Smyrna, GA 30082
Tel.: (404) 696-6711
Specialty Chemical Manufacturer
N.A.I.C.S.: 325998

Subsidiary (Domestic):

Compass Chemical International LLC (3)

5544 Oakdale Rd SE, Smyrna, GA 30082
Tel.: (404) 696-6711
Web Site: http://www.compasschemical.com
Rev.: $5,000,000
Emp.: 24
Other Chemical & Allied Products Merchant Mfr & Distr
N.A.I.C.S.: 333248
Daniel K. McCaul (Mgr-Mktg-Americas)
Ted Perez (Mgr-Sls-Midwest & Northeast)
Neil Williams (Mgr-Sls-Southwest)

The Elco Corp. (3)
1000 Belt Line Ave, Cleveland, OH 44109 (100%)
Tel.: (216) 749-2605
Web Site:
http://www.lubeperformanceadditives.com
Mfr & Marketer of Petroleum Additives for Hydraulic Fluids, Industrial Gear Oils, Greases & Metal Working Fluids
N.A.I.C.S.: 326122

Subsidiary (US):

Water Science Technologies, LLC (2)
5521 Parkwood Cir, Bessemer, AL 35022-5656
Tel.: (205) 426-4141
Chemical & Allied Products Merchant Whslr
N.A.I.C.S.: 424690
Lou LaFever (Mgr-Plant)

Jnana Therapeutics Inc (1)
1 Design Ctr Place Suite 19-400, Boston, MA 02210
Tel.: (857) 349-9200
Web Site: https://www.jnanatx.com
Biotechnology Company
N.A.I.C.S.: 541714

Keystone Agency Partners, LLC (1)
2600 Commerce Dr, Harrisburg, PA 17110
Tel.: (570) 473-4362
Web Site:
https://keystoneagencypartners.com
All Other Insurance Related Activities
N.A.I.C.S.: 524298

Subsidiary (Domestic):

Kai Yurconic Insurance Agency, LLC (2)
5910 Hamilton Blvd, Allentown, PA 18106
Tel.: (610) 770-6600
Web Site: http://www.yurconic.com
Sales Range: $1-9.9 Million
Emp.: 65
Auto, Home, Business, Life & Health Insurance Services
N.A.I.C.S.: 524210
John T. Yurconic (Pres)
Helena E. Yurconic (VP)
Richard V. Leonzi (CFO)
Ronald J. Hanna (Mgr-IT)
Jeff Boardman (Mgr-Bus Lines)
Kim Brown (Mgr-Vehicle Registration & Driver's License)
Christy Buchman (Mgr-Personal Lines)
Colleen Driscoll (COO)
Brenda Laughead (Mgr-Vehicle Registration & Driver's License)

Subsidiary (Domestic):

WR Sims Agency Incorporated (3)
1036 Washington Blvd, Williamsport, PA 17701
Tel.: (570) 326-4188
Web Site: http://www.wrsimsagency.com
Insurance Related Activities
N.A.I.C.S.: 524298
Cross Sam (Mgr-Comml Lines)

Subsidiary (Domestic):

LIFE QUOTES, INC. (2)
8205 S Cass Ave Ste 102, Darien, IL 60561
Tel.: (630) 515-0170
Web Site: http://www.lifequotes.com
Sales Range: $10-24.9 Million
Emp.: 106
Insurance Agency & Brokerage; Online Consumer Insurance Information Services
N.A.I.C.S.: 524210
Robert S. Bland (Founder & CEO)

Kirindo Holdings Co., Ltd. (1)
4F Central Shin Osaka Bldg 4-5-36 Miya-

hara, Yodogawa-ku, Osaka, 532-0003, Japan (69.75%)
Tel.: (81) 663940100
Web Site: https://www.kirindo-hd.co.jp
Rev.: $1,174,112,580
Assets: $458,082,660
Liabilities: $322,989,000
Net Worth: $135,093,660
Earnings: $13,327,260
Emp.: 1,620
Fiscal Year-end: 02/28/2019
Holding Company
N.A.I.C.S.: 551112
Toyohiko Teranishi (Pres & CEO)
Hayato Kondo (Auditor)
Kento Ogawa (Auditor)
Hiroyuki Teranishi (Mng Dir)
Ryuto Kobayashi (Mng Exec Officer)

MSX International, Inc. (1)
1 Detroit Center 500 Woodward Ave 19th Fl, Detroit, MI 48226
Tel.: (248) 829-6300
Web Site: http://www.msxi.com
Business Consulting Services
N.A.I.C.S.: 541618
Frederick Minturn (Chm & CEO)
Margaret Turner (Chief HR Officer & VP-HR-Global)
Brendan Walsh (CIO)
Pieter Van Rosmalen (Chief Product Officer & VP-Global)
Nils-Johan Andersson (CFO)

Subsidiary (Domestic):

Geometric Results, Inc. (2)
26555 Evergreen Rd Ste 710, Southfield, MI 48076
Tel.: (817) 999-7093
Web Site:
http://www.geometricresultsinc.com
Workforce Management Services
N.A.I.C.S.: 561311
David Cooper (Chief Comml Officer)
Art Knapp (CEO)
Jill Parrino (COO)
Salema Rice (Chief Data Officer)
Todd Hauser (CFO)
Mary Tucker (Chief HR Officer)
Jeffrey Hildreth (Sls Dir-Eastern US)
Patrick Aubry (Sls Dir-Central US)

Subsidiary (Non-US):

Geometric Results Holdings Limited (3)
Booths Park 1 Chelford Road, Knutsford, WA16 8GS, Cheshire, United Kingdom
Tel.: (44) 1565 682020
Web Site: http://www.geometricresults.co.uk
Workforce Management Services
N.A.I.C.S.: 561320
Andrew Preston (CEO)
Joe James (CTO)
Tim Flanagan (Dir-Strategy & Comml)

MYOB Limited (1)
12 Wesley Ct, Blackburn, 3151, VIC, Australia
Tel.: (61) 39222 9754
Web Site: http://www.myob.com
Sales Range: $150-199.9 Million
Emp.: 200
Business Management Software
N.A.I.C.S.: 513210
Tim Reed (CEO)
John Moore (Chief Strategy Officer)
Andrew Birch (Gen Mgr-Industry Solutions)
Kevin Rawlings (Gen Mgr-Practice Solutions)
Adam Ferguson (Gen Mgr-Engrg & Experience)
Alla Keogh (Head-People & Performance)
Steve Victor (Mgr-Sls-Enterprise Resource Plng Products-New Zealand)
Carolyn Luey (Gen Mgr-Enterprise Solutions)

Subsidiary (Non-US):

Asian Business Software Solutions Sdn. Bhd. (2)
A1-12 Kuchai Business Park No 2 Jalan 1/127 off Jalan, Kuchai Lama, 58200, Kuala Lumpur, Malaysia
Tel.: (60) 379890599
Web Site: http://www.myob.com.my
Business Software Solutions

Bain Capital, LP—(Continued)
N.A.I.C.S.: 513210

Dosh Software Ltd (2)
Westgate House, W Gate Ealing, London,
W51YY, United Kingdom
Tel.: (44) 1403273590
Business Management Software
N.A.I.C.S.: 513210

MYOB Asia Sdn Bhd (2)
Lot L5-I-1 Enterprise 4 Technology Park,
Bukit Jalil, 57000, Kuala Lumpur, Malaysia
Tel.: (60) 389910166
Web Site: http://www.myob.com.my
Sales Range: $25-49.9 Million
Emp.: 50
Business Management Software
N.A.I.C.S.: 513210

Subsidiary (Domestic):

MYOB Australia Pty Ltd (2)
L 14 383 Kent St, Sydney, NSW, Australia
Tel.: (61) 290899000
Web Site: http://myob.com
Business Management Software
N.A.I.C.S.: 513210

Subsidiary (Non-US):

MYOB Hong Kong Limited (2)
Room 1601 16th Fl Queen's Place, 74
Queen's Road Central, Central, China
(Hong Kong)
Tel.: (852) 34029888
Web Site: http://www.myob.com.hk
Sales Range: $10-24.9 Million
Emp.: 25
Exporter & Mfr of Electronic Appliances
N.A.I.C.S.: 335220
Tiffany Chan (Mgr-Mktg)

MYOB Singapore Pte Limited (2)
33 Ubi Avenue 3 08-67 Vertex, Singapore,
408868, Singapore
Tel.: (65) 64795779
Web Site: http://www.myob.com.sg
Sales Range: $25-49.9 Million
Emp.: 50
Business Management Software
N.A.I.C.S.: 513210
Lum Choong Eu (Country Mgr)

Macromill, Inc. (1)
Shinagawa East One Tower 11F 2-16-1 Ko-
nan, Minato-ku, Tokyo, 108-0075, Japan
Tel.: (81) 367160700
Web Site: http://www.macromill.com
Sales Range: $150-199.9 Million
Emp.: 684
Internet Research Services
N.A.I.C.S.: 541810
Tetsuya Sugimoto (Pres)
Toru Sasaki (CEO-Global)
Tetsuya Shinoda (Exec Officer)
Hironao Ashizawa (Exec Officer)
Hajime Takasaki (Exec Officer)
Kuniko Ogawa (CTO)
Masahiro Shimizu (CFO-Global)

Subsidiary (Domestic):

Brand Data Bank Inc. (2)
Shinagawa E One Tower 2-16-1 Konan 11F,
Minato-ku, Tokyo, 108-0075, Japan
Tel.: (81) 367160715
Web Site: http://www.branddatabank.com
Sales Range: $25-49.9 Million
Emp.: 9
Online Marketing Research Services
N.A.I.C.S.: 541910
Ken Miura (Gen Mgr)

**Mercury Payment Services
S.p.A.** (1)
Via Giulio Richard 7, 20143, Milan, Italy
Tel.: (39) 02 891371
Web Site: http://www.mercurypayments.it
Payment Processing Services
N.A.I.C.S.: 522320

**Mercury Processing Services Interna-
tional LLC** (1)
Radnicka cesta 50, 10000, Zagreb, Croatia
Tel.: (385) 1 645 60 41
Web Site: http://www.mercury-
processing.com
Credit Card Payment Processing Services
N.A.I.C.S.: 522320

Zdenek Houser (Chm-Mgmt Bd & Gen Dir)
Stuart James Ashley Gent (Chm-
Supervisory Bd)
Bernardo Mingrone (Vice Chm-Supervisory
Bd)
Alberto Barroero (Member-Mgmt Bd & Dir)
Irina Brucic (Member-Mgmt Bd & Dir)
Giovanni Cetrangolo (Member-Mgmt Bd &
Dir)
Tatjana Novak (Member-Mgmt Bd & Dir)

Subsidiary (Non-US):

**Mercury Processing Services Interna-
tional Payment Card Processing &
Development Ltd.** (2)
Slovenceva Ulica 24, 1000, Ljubljana, Slo-
venia
Tel.: (386) 1 568 03 00
Web Site: http://www.mercury-
processing.com
Credit Card Payment Processing Services
N.A.I.C.S.: 522320

Moorepay Limited (1)
Lowry Mill, Swinton, M27 6DB, Manchester,
United Kingdom
Tel.: (44) 8451844615
Web Site: http://www.moorepay.co.uk
Human Resources & Payroll Outsourcing
Services
N.A.I.C.S.: 923130

Nets A/S (1)
Klausdalsbrovej 601, DK-2750, Ballerup,
Denmark
Tel.: (45) 44684468
Web Site: http://www.nets.eu
Rev.: $1,264,993,856
Assets: $4,521,658,722
Liabilities: $2,816,559,886
Net Worth: $1,705,098,836
Earnings: $36,059,492
Emp.: 2,460
Fiscal Year-end: 12/31/2019
Holding Company; Payment Solutions, In-
formation Services & Digital Security Solu-
tions
N.A.I.C.S.: 551112
Soren Winge (Head-Media)
Bo Nilsson (CEO)
Pia Jorgensen (CIO)
Klaus Pedersen (CFO)
Robert Hoffmann (CEO-Merchant Svcs)
Gianluca Ventura (Chief HR Officer)
Christian Lintner (Sr Mgr-Treasury)

Subsidiary (Domestic):

Nets Denmark A/S (2)
Lautrupbjerg 10, DK-2750, Ballerup, Den-
mark
Tel.: (45) 4468 4468
Web Site: http://www.nets.eu
Payment, Card & Information Services
N.A.I.C.S.: 522320
Nevena Duric (Officer-Press)
Mads Allingstrup (Officer-Press)

Subsidiary (Non-US):

Nets Norway AS (2)
Haavard Martinsensvei 54, 0978, Oslo,
Norway
Tel.: (47) 22898989
Web Site: http://www.nets.eu
Payment Solutions
N.A.I.C.S.: 522320
Stein-Arne Tjore (Mgr-Press)

Nets Sweden AB (2)
Lumaparksvagen 11, 120 31, Stockholm,
Sweden
Tel.: (46) 8609 9400
Web Site: http://www.nets.eu
Electronic Payment Systems
N.A.I.C.S.: 522320
Soren Winge (Mgr-Press)

Nichiigakkan Co., Ltd. (1)
2-9 Kanda-Surugadai, Chiyoda-ku, Tokyo,
101-8688, Japan (82.27%)
Tel.: (81) 332912121
Web Site: http://www.nichiigakkan.co.jp
Rev.: $2,519,850,960
Assets: $1,689,322,320
Liabilities: $1,354,937,040
Net Worth: $334,385,280
Earnings: $7,583,520
Emp.: 20,393

Fiscal Year-end: 03/31/2018
Medical & Nursing Services
N.A.I.C.S.: 621610
Nobusuke Mori (Pres & Co-CEO)
Tsuyoshi Terada (Co-CEO & VP)
Shuji Otomaru (Auditor)

Subsidiary (Domestic):

Nichii Carenet Co., Ltd. (2)
2-5-12 Kanda Surugadai NMF Surugadai
Building 7F, Chiyoda, Tokyo, 101-0062,
Japan
Tel.: (81) 352811165
Web Site: http://www.nichii-carenet.com
Equipment Rental Services
N.A.I.C.S.: 532310

Nichii Carepalace Campany (2)
2-5-12 Kanda Surugadai NMF Surugadai
Building 6th Floor, Chiyoda, Tokyo, 101-
0062, Japan
Tel.: (81) 332918965
Web Site: http://www.nichii-carepalace.co.jp
Housing Rental Services
N.A.I.C.S.: 532310

Nichii Green Farm Company (2)
2-2-10 Sarugakucho, Kanda Chiyoda, To-
kyo, 101-0064, Japan
Tel.: (81) 475225266
Web Site: http://www.al-site.net
Fertilizer Mfr & Whslr
N.A.I.C.S.: 325312

Subsidiary (Non-US):

SELC Australia Pty. Ltd. (2)
495 Kent Street, Sydney, 2000, NSW, Aus-
tralia
Tel.: (61) 292675688
Education Management Services
N.A.I.C.S.: 611710

**SELC Career College Canada
Ltd.** (2)
2F 321 Water Street, Vancouver, V6B 1B8,
BC, Canada
Tel.: (604) 488-0780
Web Site: http://www.selccareercollege.com
Education Management Services
N.A.I.C.S.: 611710

**SELC English Language Centre
Canada Ltd.** (2)
2F 321 Water Street, Vancouver, V6B 1B8,
BC, Canada
Tel.: (604) 639-9075
Web Site: http://www.selceducation.com
Education Management Services
N.A.I.C.S.: 611710
Anna Raposo (Dir-Studies)
Joseph Ramos (Mktg Mgr)

OverIT S.p.A. (1)
Via Bassi 81, Fiume Veneto, 33080, Porde-
none, Italy
Tel.: (39) 0434562911
Web Site: http://www.overit.it
Software & IT Services
N.A.I.C.S.: 541511
Marco Zanuttini (Mng Dir)
Luca Turco (Mgr-IT Svcs)
Andrea Zamarian (Dir)
Paolo Bergamo (Chm & CEO)

PowerSchool Holdings, Inc. (1)
150 Parkshore Dr, Folsom, CA 95630
Web Site: https://www.powerschool.com
Rev.: $630,863,000
Assets: $3,583,395,000
Liabilities: $1,849,451,000
Net Worth: $1,733,944,000
Earnings: ($20,787,000)
Emp.: 3,232
Fiscal Year-end: 12/31/2022
Holding Company
N.A.I.C.S.: 551112
Hardeep Gulati (CEO)
Eric Shander (Pres & CFO)
Fred Studer (CMO)
Devendra Singh (CTO)
Paul Brook (Chief Customer Officer)
Tony Kender (Chief Revenue Officer)
Shivani Stumpf (Chief Product Officer &
Chief Innovation Officer)
Michael Bisignano (Chief Legal Officer)
Michele Haddad (Chief People Officer)
Darron Flagg (Chief Compliance Officer &
Chief Privacy Officer)

Rich Gay (Chief Information Security Officer
& VP-Development)
Grayson Williams (CIO)
Apoorav Nischal (Mng Dir-PowerSchool In-
dia)

Precinmac, LP (1)
79 Prospect Ave, South Paris, ME 04281
Tel.: (207) 743-6344
Web Site: https://www.precinmac.com
High Tolerance Precision Machined Compo-
nents & Assemblies Mfr
N.A.I.C.S.: 332721
Eric C. Wisnefsky (CEO)

Subsidiary (Domestic):

Petersen Inc. (2)
1527 N 2000 W, Ogden, UT 84404
Tel.: (801) 732-2000
Web Site: http://www.PetersenInc.com
Sales Range: $50-74.9 Million
Emp.: 445
Machinery Equipment Distr
N.A.I.C.S.: 423810
Jon Ballantyne (CEO)
Mark Jenkins (CEO)
Rob Despain (VP-Bus Dev)
Stephen Grange (VP-Ops)
Kirk Douglass (Dir-Quality)
Tom Burkland (Mgr-Engrg)
Dave Dixon (Mgr-HR)
Frank Shaw (Dir-Program Office)

RatePAY GmbH (1)
Franklinstrabe 28-29, 101587, Berlin, Ger-
many
Tel.: (49) 3033988560
Web Site: http://www.ratepay.com
Electronic Payment Services
N.A.I.C.S.: 522320
Miriam Wohlfarth (Founder & Mng Dir)
Jesper Wahrendorf (CEO)
Urs Bader (COO & Mng Dir)
Luise Linden (CTO)

Rocket Software, Inc. (1)
77 4th Ave, Waltham, MA 02451-1468
Tel.: (781) 577-4321
Web Site: http://www.rocketsoftware.com
Sales Range: $75-99.9 Million
Emp.: 1,000
Software Developer
N.A.I.C.S.: 513210
Andy Youniss (Founder & Chm)
David Reibel (Gen Counsel & Sr VP)
Kevin Thimble (CFO & Sr VP)
Jay Leader (CIO & Sr VP)
Bryan Smith (Co-CTO & VP-R&D)
P. Gary Gregory (Sr VP-Strategic Customer
Advocate)
Tom Brigiotta (Chief Revenue Officer & Sr
VP)
Anjali Arora (Chief Product Officer & Sr VP)
Joe Devlin (Co-CTO)
Christopher Wey (Pres- IBM i solutions)
Milan Shetti (Pres & CEO)

Subsidiary (Domestic):

OpenConnect Systems, Inc. (2)
2711 LBJ Fwy Ste 700, Dallas, TX 75234-
7323
Tel.: (800) 551-5881
Web Site: http://www.openconnect.com
e-Business Services & Solutions
N.A.I.C.S.: 334118
Charles Brockenbush (Exec VP, COO &
CFO)
Stuart Burris (CTO)
Mark Dailey (CEO)
Michael Cupps (Sr VP-Sls & Mktg)

Unit (Domestic):

Rocket OSS (2)
5915 Hollis St Bldg A Ste 201, Emeryville,
CA 94608
Tel.: (510) 749-8500
Web Site: http://www.rs.com
Sales Range: $25-49.9 Million
Emp.: 9
Communications Software Services
N.A.I.C.S.: 541512

STADA Arzneimittel AG (1)
Stadastrasse 2-18, 61118, Bad Vilbel, Ger-
many
Tel.: (49) 61016030

Web Site: http://www.stada.de
Rev.: $2,665,973,183
Assets: $4,072,036,518
Liabilities: $2,724,669,054
Net Worth: $1,347,367,463
Earnings: $355,183,396
Emp.: 10,416
Fiscal Year-end: 12/31/2018
Pharmaceuticals Mfr
N.A.I.C.S.: 325412
Jens Steegers *(Deputy Chm-Supervisory Bd)*
Kay Reubelt *(Dir-IR)*
Claudio Albrecht *(Chm-Exec Bd)*
Mark Keatley *(CFO & Member-Exec Bd)*
Barthold Piening *(CTO & Member-Exec Bd)*
Gunter Von Au *(Chm-Supervisory Bd)*
Leslie Iltgen *(VP-IR)*
Svenja Schildknecht *(Sr Mgr-IR)*

Subsidiary (Domestic):

ALIUD PHARMA GmbH (2)
Gottlieb-Daimler-Str 19, 89150, Laichingen, Germany
Tel.: (49) 73 33 96 51 0
Web Site: http://www.aliud.de
Emp.: 70
Pharmaceutical & Health Care Products Mfr
N.A.I.C.S.: 325412
Incrid Blumenthal *(Mgr)*

ALIUD PHARMA Verwaltungs-GmbH (2)
Gottlieb-Daimler-Str 19, Laichingen, 89150, Germany
Tel.: (49) 7333 965 10
Web Site: http://www.aliud.de
Sales Range: $25-49.9 Million
Emp.: 40
Pharmaceutical & Health Care Products Mfr
N.A.I.C.S.: 325412
Ingrid Blumbnthao *(Mng Dir)*

Subsidiary (Non-US):

Britannia Pharmaceuticals Ltd. (2)
200 Longwater Ave Queen Park, Reading, RG2 6GP, Berks, United Kingdom
Tel.: (44) 1635 568400
Web Site: http://www.britannia-pharm.co.uk
Pharmaceutical & Health Care Products Mfr
N.A.I.C.S.: 325412
Robert Wood *(Mng Dir)*

Centrafarm B.V. (2)
Nieuwe Donk 3, 4879 AC, Etten-Leur, Netherlands
Tel.: (31) 76 508 10 00
Web Site: http://www.centrafarm.nl
Sales Range: $50-74.9 Million
Emp.: 60
Pharmaceutical Products Distr
N.A.I.C.S.: 424210
Hans Stols *(Gen Mgr)*
Lian van Ginkel-Hereijgers *(Mgr-HR)*
Henry Tan *(Mgr-Sls)*
Albert Lankhuijzen *(Mgr-Logistics)*
Hans de Nijs *(Mgr-Quality Control & Quality Assurance)*
Ron de Koning *(Mgr-Fin & IT)*
Jack Janssens *(Mgr-Regulatory Affairs)*
Wendy Buijs *(Mgr-Mktg)*

Subsidiary (Domestic):

Centrafarm Nederland B.V. (3)
Nieuwe Donk 3, Etten-Leur, 4879 AC, Netherlands
Tel.: (31) 765081000
Web Site: http://www.centrafarm.nl
Emp.: 60
Pharmaceutical Products Mfr & Distr
N.A.I.C.S.: 325412

Subsidiary (Domestic):

Neocare B.V. (4)
Nieuwe Donk 3, Postbus 289, 4879 AC, Etten-Leur, Netherlands
Tel.: (31) 765081700
Web Site: http://www.neocare.nl
Sales Range: $25-49.9 Million
Emp.: 3
Pharmaceutical & Health Care Products Mfr
N.A.I.C.S.: 325412

Subsidiary (Domestic):

Centrafarm Pharmaceuticals B.V. (3)

Postbus 289, 4870 AG, Etten-Leur, Netherlands
Tel.: (31) 765081000
Pharmaceutical & Health Care Products Mfr
N.A.I.C.S.: 325412

HTP Huisapotheek B.V. (3)
Nieuwe Donk 3, Etten-Leur, 4879 AC, North Brabant, Netherlands
Tel.: (31) 765081000
Web Site: http://www.centrafarm.nl
Emp.: 50
Pharmaceutical & Health Care Products Mfr
N.A.I.C.S.: 325412

Healthypharm B.V. (3)
Nieuwe Donk 3, Postbus 289, 4879 AC, Etten-Leur, Netherlands
Tel.: (31) 765012045
Pharmaceutical & Health Care Products Mfr
N.A.I.C.S.: 325412

Subsidiary (Non-US):

Clonmel Healthcare Limited (2)
Waterford Road, E91 D768, Clonmel, Ireland
Tel.: (353) 52617 7777
Web Site: http://www.clonmel-health.ie
Pharmaceutical & Health Care Products Mfr
N.A.I.C.S.: 325412
Kieran Mulhall *(Dir-Ops)*
Martin E. Gallagher *(Dir-Mktg & Bus Dev)*
James Hanlon *(CEO)*
Gerard Roberts *(Dir-Quality & Regulatory Affairs)*

Croma Medic, Inc. (2)
Suite 301 Alegria Bldg 2229 Chino Roces Avenue, Makati, 1231, Philippines
Tel.: (63) 2 817 8541
Web Site: https://www.stada-apac.com
Pharmaceutical Products Mfr & Distr
N.A.I.C.S.: 325412

Crosspharma Ltd. (2)
22-26 Duncrue Road, Belfast, BT3 9BP, United Kingdom
Tel.: (44) 2890 776 877
Pharmaceutical & Health Care Products Mfr
N.A.I.C.S.: 325412

EG Labo SAS - Laboratoires Eurogenerics SAS (2)
Central Park 9-15 rue Maurice Mallet, 92130, Issy-les-Moulineaux, France
Tel.: (33) 146948686
Web Site: https://www.eglabo.fr
Pharmaceutical Product Mfr
N.A.I.C.S.: 325412

EG S.A. (2)
Heizel Esplanade B 22, Brussels, 1020, Belgium
Tel.: (32) 2 479 78 78
Web Site: https://www.eg.be
Emp.: 170
Pharmaceutical Product Mfr
N.A.I.C.S.: 325412

EG S.p.A. (2)
Via Pavia 6, Milan, 20136, Italy
Tel.: (39) 028310371
Web Site: http://www.eglab.it
Pharmaceutical & Health Care Products Mfr
N.A.I.C.S.: 325412

Forum Bioscience Holdings Ltd. (2)
Betchworth House 57-65 Station Rd, Redhill, RH1 1DL, Surrey, United Kingdom
Tel.: (44) 1737 857700
Web Site: http://www.forum.co.uk
Sales Range: $100-124.9 Million
Emp.: 125
Holding Company; Pharmaceutical Sales
N.A.I.C.S.: 551112

Genus Pharmaceuticals Ltd. (2)
Linthwaite Manchester Road, Huddersfield, HD7 5QH, United Kingdom
Tel.: (44) 1484 842217
Pharmaceutical & Health Care Products Mfr
N.A.I.C.S.: 325412

Hemofarm Koncern A.D. (2)
Beogradski Put BB, Vrsac, 26300, Serbia
Tel.: (381) 13803100
Web Site: http://www.hemofarm.com
Sales Range: $1-4.9 Billion
Emp.: 2,500
Pharmaceuticals Mfr

N.A.I.C.S.: 325412

Subsidiary (Domestic):

Hemofarm A.D. (3)
Beogradski put bb, 26300, Vrsac, Serbia
Tel.: (381) 13 803 100
Web Site: http://www.hemofarm.com
Emp.: 3,600
Pharmaceutical & Health Care Products Mfr
N.A.I.C.S.: 325412
Ronald Seeliger *(Gen Mgr)*
Nikola Turkan *(CFO & Sr Dir-Fin)*
Irina Skityaeva *(Sr Dir-HR)*
Veljko Pesic *(Sr Dir-Mktg & Sls)*
Ivan Tadic *(Sr Dir-Corp Dev)*
Jelena Rankov *(Sr Dir-Global Quality Control)*
Milan Smoljanovic *(Sr Dir-Corp Security)*
Sanda Savic *(Sr Dir-Corp Affairs & Comm)*
Sanja Manasijevski *(Sr Dir-Legal Affairs & Comml Projects)*
Sanja Ristic *(Sr Dir-Internal Audit)*
Tamara Tomic *(Sr Quality Dir-SEE Cluster)*

Subsidiary (Non-US):

Hemofarm Banja Luka d.o.o. (3)
Novakovici b b, Banja Luka, 78000, Bosnia & Herzegovina
Tel.: (387) 51 331 650
Web Site: https://www.hemofarm.ba
Emp.: 200
Pharmaceutical & Health Care Products Mfr
N.A.I.C.S.: 325412
Sasa Urosevic *(Dir)*
Tatjana Kvrgic *(Dir-Production)*
Bojana Gojic *(Quality Dir)*
Teodora Pasic *(Dir-Hemofarm Sarajevo)*

Hemomont d.o.o. (3)
8 Marta 55a, 20000, Podgorica, Montenegro
Tel.: (382) 81 662 322
Web Site: https://www.hemofarm.com
Pharmaceuticals Mfr
N.A.I.C.S.: 325412

Hemopharm GmbH (3)
Theodor-Heuss-Strasse 52, 61118, Bad Vilbel, Germany
Tel.: (49) 6101985740
Web Site: http://www.hemopharm.de
Pharmaceutical Mfr & Distr
N.A.I.C.S.: 325412
Christos Gallis *(Mng Dir)*
Holger Buschmann *(Mng Dir)*

OOO Hemofarm (3)
Kiyevskoye shosse 62, 249030, Obninsk, Russia
Tel.: (7) 4843990500
Web Site: https://www.stada.ru
Pharmaceutical & Health Care Products Mfr
N.A.I.C.S.: 325412

STADA Hemofarm S.R.L. (3)
Calea Torontalului km 6, 300633, Timisoara, Romania
Tel.: (40) 256203922
Web Site: http://www.hemofarm.com
Pharmaceutical Mfr & Distr
N.A.I.C.S.: 325412

Subsidiary (Non-US):

IZGRADNJA d.o.o. (2)
Kralja Zvonimira 45, 51260, Crikvenica, Croatia
Tel.: (385) 51241424
Web Site: http://www.izgradnja-ck.hr
Sales Range: $25-49.9 Million
Emp.: 59
Construction Engineering Services
N.A.I.C.S.: 541330
Goran Rubcic *(Dir-Tech)*

Laboratorio STADA, S.L (2)
Calle Frederic Mompou 5 Sant Just Desvern, Barcelona, 08960, Spain
Tel.: (34) 934738889
Web Site: http://www.stada.es
Pharmaceutical Mfr & Distr
N.A.I.C.S.: 325412

Subsidiary (Domestic):

ProtoPharma Gesellschaft fur Engineering und Consulting mbH (2)
Hessenring 107, 61348, Bad Homburg, Germany

Tel.: (49) 6172 27909 10
Web Site: http://www.protopharma.de
Sales Range: $25-49.9 Million
Emp.: 30
Pharmaceutical Industry Plant Design, Engineering & Consulting Services
N.A.I.C.S.: 541330

Subsidiary (Non-US):

STADA Arzneimittel Gesellschaft m.b.H. (2)
Muthgasse 36, 1190, Vienna, Austria
Tel.: (43) 1 367 85 85
Web Site: http://www.stada.at
Pharmaceutical & Health Care Products Mfr
N.A.I.C.S.: 325412
Martin Spatz *(Mng Dir)*

Subsidiary (Domestic):

STADA Consumer Health & STADAPHARM GmbH (2)
Stadastrasse 2 18, 61118, Bad Vilbel, Germany
Tel.: (49) 61016030
Web Site: http://www.stada.de
Pharmaceutical & Health Care Products Mfr
N.A.I.C.S.: 325412

STADA GmbH (2)
Stadastr 2-18, 61118, Bad Vilbel, Germany
Tel.: (49) 61016030
Pharmaceutical & Health Care Products Mfr
N.A.I.C.S.: 325412

Subsidiary (Non-US):

STADA PHARMA Bulgaria EOOD (2)
29 Atanas Dukov Street Floor 5 Rainbow Center, Sofia, 1407, Bulgaria
Tel.: (359) 29624626
Web Site: https://www.stada.com
Pharmaceutical & Health Care Products Mfr
N.A.I.C.S.: 325412

STADA PHARMA CZ, s.r.o. (2)
Siemensova 2717/4, 155 00, Prague, Czech Republic
Tel.: (420) 257 888 111
Web Site: http://www.stada-pharma.cz
Pharmaceuticals Product Mfr
N.A.I.C.S.: 325412

STADA Pharmaceuticals (Asia) Ltd. (2)
Room 13-18, 37/F Tower 1 Millennium City 1 388 Kwun Tong Road, Kwun Tong, Kowloon, China (Hong Kong)
Tel.: (852) 3156 7800
Web Site: https://www.stada-apac.com
Pharmaceutical & Health Care Products Mfr
N.A.I.C.S.: 325412
Zhou Fan *(Gen Mgr-Greater China)*
Simon Yung *(Dir-Portfolio & Comml Strategy-Emerging Markets)*

Subsidiary (Non-US):

STADA Pharmaceuticals (Beijing) Ltd. (3)
No 15 Yunteng Rd Industrial Development Zone, Beijing, 101500, China **(83.35%)**
Tel.: (86) 10 6907 6655
Web Site: https://www.stada.com
Pharmaceutical & Health Care Products Mfr
N.A.I.C.S.: 325412

Subsidiary (Domestic):

STADA R&D GmbH (2)
Stadastrasse 2 18, 61118, Bad Vilbel, Germany
Tel.: (49) 61016030
Pharmaceutical & Health Care Products Research & Development
N.A.I.C.S.: 325412

Subsidiary (Non-US):

STADA Service Holding B.V. (2)
Van de Reijtstraat 31-E, Breda, 4814, NE, Netherlands
Tel.: (31) 765081000
Web Site: http://www.centrafarm.nl
Pharmaceutical & Health Care Products Mfr
N.A.I.C.S.: 325412

Bain Capital, LP—(Continued)

Subsidiary (Domestic):

STADApharm GmbH (2)
Stadastrasse 2-18, 61118, Bad Vilbel, Germany
Tel.: (49) 61016030
Web Site: http://www.stada.de
Pharmaceutical & Health Care Products Mfr
N.A.I.C.S.: 325412

Subsidiary (Non-US):

Stada Nordic ApS (2)
Marielundvej 46 A, 2730, Herlev, Denmark
Tel.: (45) 44859999
Web Site: https://stada.dk
Pharmaceuticals Product Mfr
N.A.I.C.S.: 325412

Thornton & Ross Limited (2)
Linthwaite, Huddersfield, HD7 5QH, United Kingdom
Tel.: (44) 1484842217
Web Site: http://www.thorntonandross.co.uk
Pharmaceuticals Mfr
N.A.I.C.S.: 325412

Subsidiary (Domestic):

cell pharm Gesellschaft fur pharmazeutische und diagnostische Praparate mbH (2)
Theodor-Heuss-Str 52, 61118, Bad Vilbel, Germany
Tel.: (49) 610130420
Web Site: http://www.cellpharm.com
Sales Range: $25-49.9 Million
Emp.: 20
Pharmaceutical & Health Care Products Mfr
N.A.I.C.S.: 325412
Anne Demberg *(Pres)*

Sankaty Advisors, LLC (1)
200 Coarendon St, Boston, MA 02116
Tel.: (617) 516-2700
Web Site: http://www.sankaty.com
Rev.: $27,800,000,000
Emp.: 109
Fixed Income & Credit Instrument Portfolio Management & Investment Services
N.A.I.C.S.: 523940
Michael J. Bevacqua *(Mng Dir)*
Andrew Carlino *(Exec VP)*
Robert Cunjak *(Exec VP)*
Michael Ewald *(Mng Dir)*
Kimberly Harris *(Exec VP)*
Jeffrey Hawkins *(COO & Mng Dir)*
Viva Hyatt *(Exec VP)*
Susan Lynch *(Exec VP)*
David McCarthy *(Mng Dir)*
Jeffrey Robinson *(Exec VP)*

Holding (Domestic):

Encompass Group Affiliates, Inc. (2)
775 Tipton Industrial Dr, Lawrenceville, GA 30046
Tel.: (678) 405-5380
Web Site: http://www.encompassparts.com
Sales Range: $75-99.9 Million
Emp.: 250
Consumer Electronics & Computers repair & Distr
N.A.I.C.S.: 811210

Subsidiary (Domestic):

Cyber-Test, Inc. (3)
448 Commerce Way Ste 100, Longwood, FL 32750
Tel.: (407) 260-5600
Web Site: http://www.cybertest.com
Sales Range: $50-74.9 Million
Electronics Repair & Refurbishment Services
N.A.I.C.S.: 811210

Encompass Parts Distribution, Inc. (3)
775 Tipton Industrial Dr, Lawrenceville, GA 30046
Tel.: (410) 676-7300
Web Site: http://www.encompassparts.com
Electronics & Electronics Parts Warehousing & Supply Chain Management Services
N.A.I.C.S.: 493110

Subsidiary (Domestic):

Tritronics, Inc. (4)

1306 Continental Dr, Abingdon, MD 21009
Tel.: (410) 676-7300
Web Site: http://www.tritronicsinc.com
Sales Range: $10-24.9 Million
Emp.: 75
Electronic Parts
N.A.I.C.S.: 423690

Vance Baldwin, Inc. (4)
7060 State Rd 84 Ste 12, Fort Lauderdale, FL 33317
Tel.: (954) 723-9191
Web Site: http://www.encompassparts.com
Sales Range: $50-74.9 Million
Emp.: 100
Repair & Distribution of Consumer Electronics & Computers
N.A.I.C.S.: 423690

Subsidiary (Non-US):

Sankaty Advisors (Australia), Pty. Ltd (2)
101 Collins Street Level 20, Melbourne, 3000, VIC, Australia
Tel.: (61) 3 8102 8600
Web Site: http://www.sankatyadvisors.com
Emp.: 10
Capital Advisory Services
N.A.I.C.S.: 523940
Andrew Kateiva *(VP)*
Mitchell J. Stack *(Mng Dir)*

Subsidiary (Domestic):

Sankaty Advisors (NY), LLC (2)
590 Madison Ave 42nd Fl, New York, NY 10022
Tel.: (212) 326-9420
Investment Advisory Services
N.A.I.C.S.: 523940

Sankaty Advisors Illinois, LLC (2)
1603 Orrington Ave Ste 815, Evanston, IL 60201
Tel.: (847) 563-5330
Investment Advisory Services
N.A.I.C.S.: 523940

Subsidiary (Non-US):

Sankaty Advisors Ltd. (2)
Devonshire House 1st Floor Mayfair Place, London, W1J 8AJ, United Kingdom
Tel.: (44) 2075145757
Web Site: http://www.sankaty.com
Sales Range: $200-249.9 Million
Emp.: 200
Fixed Income & Credit Instrument Portfolio Management & Investment Services
N.A.I.C.S.: 523940
Jonathon DeSimone *(Mng Dir-Boston)*
David Ross *(VP)*

Sankaty European Investments, S.a.r.l (2)
4 rue Lou Hemmer, 1748, Luxembourg, Luxembourg
Tel.: (352) 26 78 66
Investment Advisory Services
N.A.I.C.S.: 523940

Securitas Direct AB (1)
Kalendegatan 26, Malmo, 203 20, Sweden
Tel.: (46) 40254500
Web Site: http://www.securitas-direct.com
Sales Range: $800-899.9 Million
Security Solution & Monitoring Services
N.A.I.C.S.: 561621
Henrik Heslyk *(Mgr-Human Capital)*
Fredrik Ostman *(CFO)*
Dick Seger *(Executives)*

Subsidiary (Non-US):

Verisure (2)
Drammensveien 175, 0277, Oslo, Norway
Tel.: (47) 23 68 90 99
Web Site: http://www.verisure.no
Sales Range: $50-74.9 Million
Home Security Services
N.A.I.C.S.: 561621
Thomas Berg *(Mgr-Ops)*
Cecilie Knudsen *(Mgr-HR)*

Showa Aircraft Industry Co., Ltd. (1)
600 Tanaka-cho, Akishima-shi, Tokyo, 196-8522, Japan
Tel.: (81) 42 541 2111
Web Site: http://www.showa-aircraft.co.jp
Rev.: $230,160,240

Assets: $571,975,920
Liabilities: $259,532,760
Net Worth: $312,443,160
Earnings: $11,288,760
Emp.: 400
Fiscal Year-end: 03/31/2019
Production & Sales of Aircraft Equipment & Components; Leasing of Real Estate
N.A.I.C.S.: 336413
Chiaki Tanuma *(Pres)*

Skylark Holdings Co., Ltd. (1)
1-25-8 Nishikubo, Musashino-shi, Tokyo, 180-8580, Japan
Tel.: (81) 422375310
Web Site: https://www.skylark.co.jp
Rev.: $2,515,751,790
Assets: $3,020,999,370
Liabilities: $1,870,363,270
Net Worth: $1,150,636,100
Earnings: $33,897,290
Emp.: 5,779
Fiscal Year-end: 12/31/2023
Family Restaurant Chain Operator
N.A.I.C.S.: 722511
Makoto Suzuki *(Auditor)*
Ikuo Umeki *(Mng Dir, Mng Dir, Exec Officer & Exec Officer)*
Hisashi Nakashima *(Mng Dir, Mng Dir, Mng Dir, Mng Dir, Exec Officer, Exec Officer, Exec Officer & Exec Officer)*
Makoto Tani *(Chm, Pres & CEO)*
Ichiro Takei *(Mng Dir, Mng Dir, Mng Dir, Exec Officer, Exec Officer, Exec Officer & Mng Dir-Admin Div)*
Minoru Kanaya *(Pres, COO, Mng Exec Officer & Mng Dir-Corp Support Div)*
Kouzou Nishida *(Exec Officer & Mng Dir-Human Capital Mgmt Div)*
Nobuyuki Katayama *(Exec Officer & Mng Dir-Supply Chain Pur Div)*

Subsidiary (Domestic):

BLDY Co., Ltd. (2)
1-25-8 Nishikubo Chi, Musashino, Tokyo, 180-8580, Japan
Tel.: (81) 4 2237 5265
Sales Range: $25-49.9 Million
Emp.: 100
Business Services
N.A.I.C.S.: 561499

Flo Japon Co., Ltd. (2)
1-25-8 Nishikubo, Musashino, Tokyo, 1800023, Japan
Tel.: (81) 422375267
Web Site: http://www.skylark.co.jp
French Brasseries Chain
N.A.I.C.S.: 722511

Hibari Development Co., Ltd. (2)
1-6-14 Nishikubo Musashino, Tokyo, 180-0013, Japan
Tel.: (81) 422375259
Rev.: $2,320,000
Emp.: 6
Damage Claim Insurance Agency
N.A.I.C.S.: 524298

Higashi-Matsuyama Skylark (2)
88-37-38 Shingo, Higashimatsuyama, 355 00111, Saitama-ken, Japan
Tel.: (81) 493238921
N.A.I.C.S.: 722511

Japan Cargo Co., Ltd. (2)
30 12 Ochayama Cho, Higashi, Matsuyama, 355 0032, Japan
Tel.: (81) 493246001
Web Site: http://www.skylark.co.jp
Sales Range: $10-24.9 Million
Emp.: 20
Logistic Operations
N.A.I.C.S.: 541614

Jonas & Co., Ltd. (2)
1 6 14 Nishikubo Musashino Shi, Tokyo, 180 8588, Japan
Tel.: (81) 422376111
Web Site: http://www.jonathan.co.jp
Sales Range: $10-24.9 Million
Emp.: 100
Coffee Shop Chain
N.A.I.C.S.: 722511

Jonathan's Co., Ltd. (2)
1-6--14 Nishikubo, Musashino, Tokyo, Japan
Tel.: (81) 422376111

Fast Food Restaurants
N.A.I.C.S.: 722513

Nilax Co., Ltd. (2)
1-6-14 Tokyo Nishikubo, Musashino Shi, Tokyo, 180 0013, Japan
Tel.: (81) 422376108
Web Site: http://www.nilax.jp
Sales Range: $250-299.9 Million
Emp.: 422
Restaurant Operators
N.A.I.C.S.: 722511
Sakita Haruyoshi *(Pres & CEO)*
Masao Tsutsumi *(Dir)*
Takuya Aizawa *(Dir)*
Makoto Suzuki *(Auditor)*

Nishinomiya Merchandising Center (2)
3-5-7 Naruohama, 663-8142, Nishinomiya, Hyogo, Japan
Tel.: (81) 798432081
Restaurant Merchandising Mfr & Distribution
N.A.I.C.S.: 455219
Makoto Tani *(Pres)*

Skylark Care Service Co., Ltd. (2)
Eclat Mitaka 9-24-25, Tokyo, Japan
Tel.: (81) 422375279
Web Site: http://www.skcare.co.jp
Sales Range: $10-24.9 Million
Emp.: 50
Nursing Care Services
N.A.I.C.S.: 623110

Skylark D&M Co., Ltd. (2)
1-6-14 Nishikubo Musashino-shi, Tokyo, 180-0013, Japan
Tel.: (81) 422 37 5801
Web Site: http://www.skylark-sdm.co.jp
Sales Range: $25-49.9 Million
Emp.: 265
Cleaning, Sales & Planning of Goods Sold in Restaurants
N.A.I.C.S.: 561210
Yanagisawa Michiyuki *(Pres & Dir)*

Subsidiary (Non-US):

Taiwan Skylark Co., Ltd. (2)
5th Floor No 410 Songhe Street, Nangang District, Taipei, 115, ROC, Taiwan
Tel.: (886) 226534008
Web Site: http://www.sky-lark.com.tw
Sales Range: $25-49.9 Million
Emp.: 150
Restaurant Operators
N.A.I.C.S.: 722513

Thai Skylark Co., Ltd. (2)
462 Srinakarin Road, Nongbon Pravet, Bangkok, 10250, Thailand
Tel.: (66) 27434773
Restaurant Operators
N.A.I.C.S.: 722513

Surgery Partners, Inc. (1)
340 7 Spgs Way Ste 600, Brentwood, TN 37027 **(54.9%)**
Tel.: (615) 234-5900
Web Site: https://www.surgerypartners.com
Rev.: $2,539,300,000
Assets: $6,682,100,000
Liabilities: $3,741,200,000
Net Worth: $2,940,900,000
Earnings: ($54,600,000)
Emp.: 9,100
Fiscal Year-end: 12/31/2022
Surgery Centers Support Services
N.A.I.C.S.: 622110
Wayne S. Deveydt *(Exec Chm)*
Jennifer B. Baldock *(Chief Admin & Dev Officer & Exec VP)*
Tony Taparo *(Chief Growth Officer)*
Roxanne Womack *(Chief Compliance Officer & Sr VP)*
Wayne S. DeVeydt *(Exec Chm)*
David T. Doherty *(CFO & Exec VP)*
Marissa Brittenham *(Chief Strategy Officer)*
Harrison Bane *(Pres)*
Danielle Burkhalter *(Chief HR Officer)*
Varun Gadhok *(CIO & Sr VP)*
Brent Jacobs *(Sr VP-Acquisitions & Development)*
Dawn Castro *(Chief Revenue Cycle Officer & Sr VP)*
Jackie Wright *(Chief Procurement Officer & Sr VP)*
Kelly T. Whelan *(Gen Counsel-American Grp & Sr VP)*

Neil Zieselman *(Sr VP & Controller-Finance)*
Shannon Yarrow *(Sr VP-Managed Care)*
Spencer Clark *(Gen Counsel & Sr VP)*
Tamala Norris-McJunkins *(Chief Clinical Officer & Sr VP-Enterprise)*
Alex Reynolds *(Sr VP-Emerging Markets)*
Fran Socash *(Sr VP-Operations)*
Jason Eric Evans *(CEO)*

Subsidiary (Domestic):

ARC of Georgia, LLC (2)
2420 Fletcher Ave, Santa Barbara, CA 93105
Tel.: (805) 898-1111
Web Site:
http://www.premiersurgerycenter.net
General Hospital Services
N.A.I.C.S.: 622110

Allcare Clinical Associates, PLLC (2)
2626 Glenwood Ave Ste 550, Raleigh, NC 27608
Tel.: (828) 274-3477
General Hospital Services
N.A.I.C.S.: 622110

Anesthesiology Professional Services, Inc. (2)
4919 Memorial HWY Ste 200, Tampa, FL 33634
Tel.: (813) 569-6500
Web Site: http://www.anesthesiaps.com
General Hospital Services
N.A.I.C.S.: 622110

Armenia Ambulatory Surgery Center, LLC (2)
4703 N Armenia Ave, Tampa, FL 33603
Tel.: (813) 514-0230
Web Site: https://armeniaasc.com
General Hospital Services
N.A.I.C.S.: 622110

Blue Ridge Surgical Center, LLC (2)
4240 Blue Ridge Blvd Ste 950, Kansas City, MO 64133
Tel.: (816) 358-9990
Web Site:
http://www.blueridgesurgicalcenter.com
Surgical & Emergency Center Operator
N.A.I.C.S.: 621493

Boulder Spine Center, LLC (2)
300 Exempla Cir Ste 130, Lafayette, CO 80026
Tel.: (303) 539-2533
Web Site: http://www.spinemisi.com
Spine Surgery Center
N.A.I.C.S.: 622110

Bristol Spine Center, LLC (2)
2365 E Fir Ave, Fresno, CA 93720
Tel.: (559) 797-9100
Web Site: http://www.rscfresno.com
Surgical Service Provider
N.A.I.C.S.: 622110
Jonathan Grossman *(Medical Dir)*
Britney Mehling *(Clinical Dir)*
Misty Castro *(Bus Office Mgr)*

CMSC, LLC (2)
3010 15th Ave S, Great Falls, MT 59405
Tel.: (406) 216-8000
Web Site: https://www.gfclinic.com
General Hospital Services
N.A.I.C.S.: 622110

Cape Coral Ambulatory Surgery Center, LLC (2)
2721 Del Prado Blvd, Cape Coral, FL 33904
Tel.: (239) 242-8010
Web Site:
http://www.capecoralsurgerycenter.com
Surgical Service Provider
N.A.I.C.S.: 622110

Community Care Channing Way, LLC (2)
2725 Channing Way, Idaho Falls, ID 83404
Tel.: (208) 525-8448
Web Site:
http://www.idahocommunitycare.com
Health Care Srvices
N.A.I.C.S.: 622110

Community Care West Side, LLC (2)
765 S Utah Ave, Idaho Falls, ID 83402

Tel.: (208) 525-2600
Web Site:
https://www.idahocommunitycare.com
Health Care Srvices
N.A.I.C.S.: 622110

Consultants in Pain Medicine, LLC (2)
3221 Glynn Ave, Brunswick, GA 31520
Tel.: (912) 466-9111
General Hospital Services
N.A.I.C.S.: 622110

Great Falls Clinic Surgery Center, LLC (2)
1509 29th St S, Great Falls, MT 59405
Tel.: (406) 454-2171
Web Site: http://www.gfclinic.com
Surgical Service Provider
N.A.I.C.S.: 622110

Honolulu Spine Center, LLC (2)
500 Ala Moana Blvd Bldg 1 Ste 301, Honolulu, HI 96813
Tel.: (808) 237-2970
Web Site: http://www.honoluluspine.com
Spine Surgery Center
N.A.I.C.S.: 622110

Lake Mary Surgery Center, L.L.C. (2)
460 St Charles Ct, Lake Mary, FL 32746
Tel.: (407) 585-0263
Web Site:
http://www.lakemarysurgerycenter.com
Surgical Service Provider
N.A.I.C.S.: 622110

Largo Endoscopy Center, L.P. (2)
7300 Bryan Dairy Rd Ste 495, Largo, FL 33777
Tel.: (727) 451-6780
Web Site:
http://www.tampabayregionalsurgery.com
Surgical Service Provider
N.A.I.C.S.: 622110

Largo Surgery, LLC (2)
1401 W Bay Dr, Largo, FL 33770
Tel.: (727) 585-9500
Web Site:
http://www.westbaysurgerycenter.com
Surgical Service Provider
N.A.I.C.S.: 622110

Laser and Outpatient Surgery Center, LLC (2)
6925 NW 11th Pl, Gainesville, FL 32605
Tel.: (352) 331-1590
Web Site:
http://www.laserandoutpatientsurgery.com
General Hospital Services
N.A.I.C.S.: 622110

Logan Laboratories, LLC (2)
5050 W Lemon St, Tampa, FL 33609
Tel.: (813) 316-4824
Medical Testing Laboratory Services
N.A.I.C.S.: 541380

Lubbock Heart Hospital, LLC (2)
4810 N Loop 289, Lubbock, TX 79416
Tel.: (806) 687-7777
Web Site: http://www.lubbockheart.com
General Hospital Services
N.A.I.C.S.: 622110
Terri Wheeler *(Coord-Medical Staff)*

MV Oncology, LLC (2)
Corp Trust Ctr 1209 Orange St, Wilmington, DE 19801
Tel.: (302) 658-7581
General Hospital Services
N.A.I.C.S.: 622110

Medical Billing Solutions, LLC (2)
625 Andover Park W Ste 101, Tukwila, WA 98188
Tel.: (206) 431-0138
Web Site: http://www.mbsmedicalbilling.com
Health Care Service Provider
N.A.I.C.S.: 621610

Midwest Uncuts, Inc. (2)
505 5th Ave Ste 729, Des Moine, IA 50309
Tel.: (515) 961-6593
Medical Testing Laboratory Services
N.A.I.C.S.: 541380

Millenia Surgery Center, L.L.C. (2)

4901 S Vineland Rd Ste 150, Orlando, FL 32811
Tel.: (407) 370-3272
Web Site:
http://www.milleniasurgerycenter.com
General Hospital Services
N.A.I.C.S.: 622110
Liz Algarin *(Coord-Office)*

Mountain View Hospital, LLC (2)
2325 Coronado St, Idaho Falls, ID 83404
Tel.: (208) 557-2700
Web Site:
http://www.mountainviewhospital.org
General Hospital Services
N.A.I.C.S.: 622110
Russell Taylor *(Controller)*

National Surgical Hospitals, Inc. (2)
250 S Wacker Dr Ste 500, Chicago, IL 60606
Tel.: (312) 627-8400
Web Site: http://www.surgerypartners.com
Surgical Facilities Management Services
N.A.I.C.S.: 561110

Subsidiary (Domestic):

Arizona Spine and Joint Hospital LLC (3)
4620 E Baseline Rd, Mesa, AZ 85206
Tel.: (480) 832-4770
Web Site: http://www.azspineandjoint.com
Surgical Hospital Operator
N.A.I.C.S.: 622110

Brentwood Surgery Center, LLC (3)
2400 Balfour Rd Ste 320, Brentwood, CA 94513
Tel.: (925) 626-9000
Web Site: http://www.brentwoodsurgery.com
Ambulatory Surgical Center Operator
N.A.I.C.S.: 621493

El Paso Specialty Hospital, Ltd. (3)
1755 Curie Dr Ste A, El Paso, TX 79902
Tel.: (915) 544-3636
Surgical Hospital Operator
N.A.I.C.S.: 622110
Sandra Morales *(Mgr-HR)*

North Carolina Specialty Hospital, LLC (3)
3916 Ben Franklin Blvd, Durham, NC 27704
Tel.: (919) 956-9300
Web Site: http://www.ncspecialty.com
Surgical Hospital Operator
N.A.I.C.S.: 622110
Randi Shults *(CEO)*
Bill Wilson *(CFO)*
John W. Medlin *(Chief Nursing Officer)*

North Idaho Day Surgery, LLC (3)
1593 E Polston Ave, Post Falls, ID 83854
Tel.: (208) 262-2300
Web Site:
http://www.northwestspecialtyhospital.com
Specialty Hospital Operator
N.A.I.C.S.: 622110
Rick Rasmussen *(CEO)*
Denise Fowler *(Chief Nursing Officer)*
Brian Brigham *(CFO)*
Chris Gregg *(Mgr-HR)*
Shelby Cathey *(Dir-Bus Office)*
Craig McIntosh *(Dir-IT)*
Mike Varga *(Dir-Pharmacy)*

Orthopedic & Spine Surgical Hospital of South Texas LP (3)
18600 N Hardy Oak Blvd, San Antonio, TX 78258
Tel.: (210) 404-0800
Web Site:
http://www.southtexassurgical.com
Surgical Hospital Operator
N.A.I.C.S.: 622110
Jesse Oviedo *(Mgr-Pharmacy)*
Denise Krajewski *(Chief Nursing Officer)*
Angie Kauffman *(CEO)*

Sequoia Surgical Center, L.P. (3)
2405 Shadelands Dr Ste # 200, Walnut Creek, CA 94598
Tel.: (925) 935-6700
Web Site: http://www.sequoiasurgery.org
Ambulatory Surgical Center Operator
N.A.I.C.S.: 621493
Gina Varela *(Dir-Bus Ops)*

Skyway Surgery Center, LLC (3)

121 Raley Blvd, Chico, CA 95928
Tel.: (530) 230-2000
Web Site:
https://www.skywaysurgerycenter.com
Ambulatory Surgical Center Operator
N.A.I.C.S.: 621493

Southeast Michigan Surgical Hospital, LLC (3)
21230 Dequindre Rd, Warren, MI 48091
Tel.: (586) 427-1000
Surgical Hospital Operator
N.A.I.C.S.: 622110

Subsidiary (Domestic):

NeoSpine Puyallup Spine Center, LLC (2)
1519 3rd St SE Ste 102, Puyallup, WA 98372
Tel.: (253) 841-8939
Web Site: http://www.mybackmylife.com
Spine Surgery Center
N.A.I.C.S.: 622110

New Tampa Surgery Center, LLC (2)
2407 Cypress Ridge Blvd, Wesley Chapel, FL 33544
Tel.: (813) 991-7575
Web Site: http://www.newtampasurgery.com
Surgical Service Provider
N.A.I.C.S.: 622110
Jackie Reynolds *(Coord-Front Office)*

North Dakota Surgery Center, LLC (2)
2600 47th Ave S, Grand Forks, ND 58201
Tel.: (701) 738-4240
Web Site:
https://northdakotasurgerycenter.com
Surgical Service Provider
N.A.I.C.S.: 622110

Northwest Ambulatory Surgery Services, LLC (2)
2075 Barkley Blvd Ste 101, Bellingham, WA 98226
Tel.: (360) 671-6933
Web Site: http://www.bellinghamasc.com
Surgical Service Provider
N.A.I.C.S.: 622110

NovaMed Eye Surgery Center of Maryville, LLC (2)
12 Professional Park Dr, Maryville, IL 62062
Tel.: (618) 288-7483
Web Site:
http://www.eyesofillinoissurgerycenter.com
Health Care Service Provider
N.A.I.C.S.: 621610

NovaMed Eye Surgery Center of New Albany, L.L.C. (2)
520 W 1st St, New Albany, IN 47150
Tel.: (812) 949-3442
Web Site: https://www.eyesurgeryna.com
Surgical Service Provider
N.A.I.C.S.: 622110

NovaMed Eye Surgery Center of North County, LLC (2)
12101 Woodcrest Executive Drive Suite 101, St Louise, MO 63141
Tel.: (314) 838-0321
Web Site:
https://woodcrestsurgerycenter.com
Health Care Service Provider
N.A.I.C.S.: 621610

NovaMed Eye Surgery Center of Overland Park, LLC (2)
5520 College Blvd Ste 200, Overland Park, KS 66211
Tel.: (913) 491-3040
Web Site:
http://www.overlandparkeyesurgery.com
Eye Care Service
N.A.I.C.S.: 622110

NovaMed Management Services, LLC (2)
3200 Downwood Cir NW Ste 240, Atlanta, GA 30327
Tel.: (404) 351-1990
Web Site:
https://www.atlantaeyesurgerycenter.com
Surgical Service Provider
N.A.I.C.S.: 622110

NovaMed Surgery Center of Baton Rouge, LLC (2)

Bain Capital, LP—(Continued)

8748 Bluebonnet Blvd, Baton Rouge, LA
70810
Tel.: (225) 329-2900
Web Site:
 http://www.surgerycenterbatonrouge.com
Surgical Service Provider
N.A.I.C.S.: 622110

**NovaMed Surgery Center of Chatta-
nooga, LLC** (2)
1949 Gunbarrel Rd Ste 200, Chattanooga,
TN 37421
Tel.: (423) 855-6861
Medical Center Operator
N.A.I.C.S.: 621491

**NovaMed Surgery Center of Chicago-
Northshore, LLC** (2)
3034 W Peterson Ave, Chicago, IL 60659
Tel.: (773) 973-7432
Web Site:
 http://www.novamedchicagonorth.com
Surgical Service Provider
N.A.I.C.S.: 622110

**NovaMed Surgery Center of Cleve-
land, LLC** (2)
137 25th St, Cleveland, TN 37311
Tel.: (423) 472-2881
Web Site:
 https://www.surgerycenterofcleveland.com
Surgical & Emergency Center Operator
N.A.I.C.S.: 621493

**NovaMed Surgery Center of Colorado
Springs, LLC** (2)
320 E Fontanero Ste 101, Colorado
Springs, CO 80907
Tel.: (719) 227-9711
Surgical & Emergency Center Operator
N.A.I.C.S.: 621493

**NovaMed Surgery Center of Denver,
LLC** (2)
3535 S Lafayette St Ste 200, Englewood,
CO 80113
Tel.: (303) 777-7303
Web Site:
 https://www.cherryhillssurgerycenter.com
Surgical & Emergency Center Operator
N.A.I.C.S.: 621493

**NovaMed Surgery Center of Jones-
boro, LLC** (2)
601 E Matthews Ave, Jonesboro, AR 72401
Tel.: (870) 935-6396
Web Site: https://www.arkansaslasik.com
Eye Care Service
N.A.I.C.S.: 622110

**NovaMed Surgery Center of Madison,
Limited Partnership** (2)
1200 John Q Hammons Dr Ste 102, Madi-
son, WI 53717
Tel.: (608) 827-5504
Web Site: https://novamedmadison.com
Surgical & Emergency Center Operator
N.A.I.C.S.: 621493

**NovaMed Surgery Center of Nashua,
LLC** (2)
5 Coliseum Ave, Nashua, NH 03063
Tel.: (603) 689-9240
Web Site:
 http://www.novamedsurgeryofnashua.com
Surgical & Emergency Center Operator
N.A.I.C.S.: 621493

**NovaMed Surgery Center of Oak
Lawn, LLC** (2)
6311 W 95th St, Oak Lawn, IL 60453
Tel.: (708) 499-3355
Web Site:
 http://www.reconstructivesurgery.com
Surgical & Emergency Center Operator
N.A.I.C.S.: 621493

**NovaMed Surgery Center of Orlando,
LLC** (2)
801 N Orange Ave Ste 630, Orlando, FL
32081
Tel.: (407) 650-0051
Web Site:
 http://www.downtownsurgerycenter.com
Surgical & Emergency Center Operator
N.A.I.C.S.: 621493

**NovaMed Surgery Center of River
Forest, LLC** (2)

7427 Lake St, River Forest, IL 60305
Tel.: (708) 488-1300
Web Site:
 http://www.novamedriverforesteyes.com
Surgical & Emergency Center Operator
N.A.I.C.S.: 621493
Cathleen Hopp (Coord-Surgery)

**NovaMed Surgery Center of San An-
tonio, L.P.** (2)
12838 Vista del Norte, San Antonio, TX
78216
Tel.: (210) 692-0218
Web Site:
 http://www.americansurgerycenter-
 novamed.com
Medical Center Operator
N.A.I.C.S.: 621491

**NovaMed Surgery Center of San-
dusky, LLC** (2)
2616 Hayes Ave, Sandusky, OH 44870
Tel.: (419) 626-2800
Web Site:
 http://www.surgerycenterofsandusky.com
Surgical & Emergency Center Operator
N.A.I.C.S.: 621493

**NovaMed Surgery Center of St. Pe-
ters, LLC** (2)
5200 Executive Ctr Parkway Ste 100, Saint
Peters, MO 63376
Tel.: (636) 928-1670
Web Site:
 http://www.novamedsurgerystpeters.com
Surgical & Emergency Center Operator
N.A.I.C.S.: 621493
Chris Schulz (VP-Ops)

**NovaMed Surgery Center of Tyler,
L.P.** (2)
802 Turtle Creek, Tyler, TX 75701
Tel.: (903) 595-4333
Web Site:
 https://novamedsurgerycenteroftyler.com
Eye Care Center Operator
N.A.I.C.S.: 622110

**NovaMed Surgery Center of War-
rensburg, LLC** (2)
506 Burkarth Rd Ste B, Warrensburg, MO
64093
Tel.: (660) 747-1888
Web Site:
 http://www.novamedsurgerycenter.com
Surgical & Emergency Center Operator
N.A.I.C.S.: 621493

**NovaMed Surgery Center of Whittier,
LLC** (2)
15141 E Whittier Blvd Ste 130, Whittier, CA
90603
Tel.: (562) 945-2832
General Hospital Services
N.A.I.C.S.: 622110

NovaMed, LLC (2)
4 Westchester Pl, Elmsford, NY 10523
Tel.: (914) 789-2100
Medical Supply Store Operator
N.A.I.C.S.: 456199

**Orange City Surgery Center,
LLC** (2)
975 Town Center Dr, Orange City, FL
32763
Tel.: (386) 456-5247
Web Site: http://www.orangecitysurgery.com
Surgical & Emergency Center Operator
N.A.I.C.S.: 621493

PSHS Alpha Partners, Ltd. (2)
7408 Lake Worth Rd Ste 900, Lake Worth,
FL 33467
Tel.: (561) 433-5700
Web Site: https://www.lakeworthsurgery.com
Surgical & Emergency Center Operator
N.A.I.C.S.: 621493

PSHS Beta Partners, Ltd. (2)
401 SW 42nd Ave Ste 201, Miami, FL
33134
Tel.: (305) 447-0882
Web Site:
 http://www.thegablessurgerycenter.com
Surgical & Emergency Center Operator
N.A.I.C.S.: 621493

Patient Education Concepts, Inc (2)

14614 Falling Creek Ste 210, Houston, TX
77068
Tel.: (281) 583-5577
Web Site:
 http://www.patienteducationconcepts.com
Laser Surgical Center Operator
N.A.I.C.S.: 621493
Robert Watson (Pres)

Physicians Surgical Care, Inc (2)
1245 Orange Ave, Winter Park, FL 32789
Tel.: (407) 647-5100
Web Site:
 http://www.physicianssurgicalcare.com
Surgical & Emergency Center Operator
N.A.I.C.S.: 621493

**Sarasota Ambulatory Surgery Center,
Ltd.** (2)
2821 Proctor Rd, Sarasota, FL 34231
Tel.: (941) 870-1872
Web Site:
 http://www.sarasotasurgicalcenter.com
Surgical & Emergency Center Operator
N.A.I.C.S.: 621493

**Sentry Anesthesia Management,
LLC** (2)
80 Newnan Sta Dr Ste A, Newnan, GA
30265
Tel.: (770) 251-2060
Web Site: http://www.sentryanesthesia.com
Ambulatory Surgical & Emergency Center
Operator
N.A.I.C.S.: 621493

**Southern Crescent Anesthesiology,
PC** (2)
2 Sun Ct Ste 400, Peachtree Corners, GA
30092
Tel.: (706) 882-1411
General Hospital Services
N.A.I.C.S.: 622110

**Southern Crescent Nurse Anesthesia,
LLC** (2)
2 Sun Ct Ste 400, Peachtree Corners, GA
75038
Tel.: (770) 655-3331
General Hospital Services
N.A.I.C.S.: 622110

**Space Coast Surgery Center
LLC** (2)
595 N Courtenay Pkwy Ste 103, Merritt Is-
land, FL 32953
Tel.: (321) 890-1800
Web Site:
 http://www.spacecoastsurgerycenter.com
Surgical & Emergency Center Operator
N.A.I.C.S.: 621493

Specialty Surgical Center, LLC (2)
380 Lafayette Rd Ste 110, Sparta, NJ
07871
Tel.: (973) 940-3166
Web Site:
 http://www.specialtysurgerycenter.org
Surgical & Emergency Center Operator
N.A.I.C.S.: 621493

**St. Louis Women's Surgery Center,
LLC** (2)
884 Woods Mill Rd Ste 100, Ballwin, MO
63011
Tel.: (636) 779-0079
Web Site: https://stlmultispecialty.com
Surgical & Emergency Center Operator
N.A.I.C.S.: 621493

**Suncoast Specialty Surgery Center,
LLLP** (2)
4519 US Hwy 19, New Port Richey, FL
34652
Tel.: (727) 835-7260
Web Site:
 http://www.suncoastspecialtysurgery.com
General Hospital Services
N.A.I.C.S.: 622110

Surgery Center Partners, LLC (2)
14825 N Outer 40 Rd Ste 100, Chesterfield,
MO 63017
Tel.: (636) 898-4695
Web Site:
 http://www.timberlakesurgerycenter.com
Surgical & Emergency Center Operator
N.A.I.C.S.: 621493

Surgery Center of Fremont, LLC (2)

2727 N Clarkson St, Fremont, NE 68025
Tel.: (402) 727-8500
Web Site:
 http://www.surgerycenteroffremont.com
Surgical & Emergency Center Operator
N.A.I.C.S.: 621493

**Surgery Center of Kalamazoo,
LLC** (2)
3200 W Centre Ave Ste 101, Portage, MI
49024
Tel.: (269) 323-9905
Web Site: http://www.scok.org
General Hospital Services
N.A.I.C.S.: 622110

Surgery Center of Lebanon, LP (2)
1840 Quentin Rd, Lebanon, PA 17042
Tel.: (717) 272-0007
Web Site:
 http://www.physicianssurgicalcenter.com
Medical Clinic Operator
N.A.I.C.S.: 621493

Subsidiary (Non-US):

Surgery Partners Holdings LLC (2)
Tel.: (813) 569-6500
Web Site: http://www.surgerypartners.com
Sales Range: $25-49.9 Million
Emp.: 50
Surgery Center Operator
N.A.I.C.S.: 622110

Subsidiary (Domestic):

**Ambulatory Surgery Center of Cool
Springs, LLC** (3)
2009 Mallory Ln Ste 100, Franklin, TN
37067
Tel.: (615) 468-2772
Web Site:
 http://www.coolspringssurgerycenter.com
Outpatient Surgical Services
N.A.I.C.S.: 621999

Animas Surgical Hospital, LLC (3)
575 Rivergate Ln, Durango, CO 81301
Tel.: (970) 247-3537
Web Site:
 http://www.animassurgicalhospital.com
Outpatient Surgery Center
N.A.I.C.S.: 621493

Bayside Endoscopy Center, LLC (3)
33 Staniford St, Providence, RI 02905
Tel.: (401) 274-1810
Outpatient Surgery Services
N.A.I.C.S.: 621999

Birmingham Surgery Center, LLC (3)
2621 19th St S, Birmingham, AL 35209
Tel.: (205) 271-8200
Web Site:
 http://www.birminghamsurgerycenter.com
Outpatient Surgical Services
N.A.I.C.S.: 621999

CMMP Surgical Center, L.L.C. (3)
1705 Christy Dr Ste 100, Jefferson City,
MO 65101
Tel.: (573) 635-7022
Web Site: http://cmmpsurgerycenter.com
Outpatient Surgery Services
N.A.I.C.S.: 621999

Cypress Surgery Center, LLC (3)
9300 E 29th St N Ste 100, Wichita, KS
67226
Tel.: (316) 634-0404
Web Site:
 http://www.cypresssurgerywichita.com
Outpatient Surgery Center
N.A.I.C.S.: 621493

**Delaware Outpatient Center for Sur-
gery, LLC** (3)
774 Christiana Rd Ste 2 Bldg B, Newark,
DE 19713
Tel.: (302) 738-0300
Web Site: http://www.dedocs.com
Freestanding Ambulatory Surgical & Emer-
gency Centers
N.A.I.C.S.: 621493

**Jacksonville Beach Surgery Center,
LLC** (3)
3316 S 3rd St Ste 200, Jacksonville Beach,
FL 32250
Tel.: (904) 247-8181
Web Site: http://www.jaxbeachsurg.com

Outpatient Surgery Services
N.A.I.C.S.: 621999

New Albany Outpatient Surgery, LLC (3)
2201 Green Valley Rd, New Albany, IN 47150
Tel.: (812) 949-1223
Outpatient Surgery Services
N.A.I.C.S.: 621999

Orthopaedic Surgery Center of Asheville, L.P. (3)
29 Nettlewood Dr, Asheville, NC 28803
Tel.: (828) 225-0861
Web Site: http://www.oscasheville.com
Outpatient Surgical Services
N.A.I.C.S.: 621999

Physicians Medical Center, LLC (3)
218 Corporate Dr, Houma, LA 70360
Tel.: (985) 853-1390
Web Site: http://physicianshouma.com
Outpatient Surgery Services
N.A.I.C.S.: 621999

Specialty Surgical Center of Arcadia, LLC (3)
51 N 5th Ave Ste 101, Arcadia, CA 91006
Tel.: (626) 471-9901
Web Site: http://www.sscarcadia.com
Outpatient Surgery Services
N.A.I.C.S.: 621999

Specialty Surgical Center of Beverly Hills, L.P. (3)
8670 Wilshire Blvd Ste 300, Beverly Hills, CA 90211
Tel.: (310) 275-1646
Web Site: http://sscbeverlyhills.com
Outpatient Surgery Services
N.A.I.C.S.: 621999

Specialty Surgical Center of Encino, LLC (3)
16501 Ventura Blvd Ste 103, Encino, CA 91436
Tel.: (818) 501-1080
Web Site: http://www.sscencino.com
Outpatient Surgery Services
N.A.I.C.S.: 621999

Specialty Surgical Center of Irvine, LLC (3)
15825 Laguna Canyon Rd Ste 200, Irvine, CA 92618
Tel.: (949) 341-3499
Web Site: http://sscirvine.com
Outpatient Surgery Services
N.A.I.C.S.: 621999

Texarkana Surgery Center GP, LLC (3)
5404 Summerhill Rd, Texarkana, TX 75503
Tel.: (903) 793-4872
Web Site:
http://www.texarkanasurgerycenter.com
Outpatient Surgery Services
N.A.I.C.S.: 621999

The Surgery Center of Ocala, LLC (3)
3241 SW 34th St, Ocala, FL 34474
Tel.: (352) 237-5906
Web Site: http://surgerycenterofocala.com
Outpatient Surgery Services
N.A.I.C.S.: 621999

The Surgery Center, LLC (3)
2548 Weems Rd, Columbus, GA 31909-6248
Tel.: (706) 323-8803
Web Site:
https://www.thesurgerycenterga.com
Outpatient Surgical Services
N.A.I.C.S.: 621999

Valley Ambulatory Surgery Center, L.P. (3)
2210 Dean St, Saint Charles, IL 60175
Tel.: (630) 584-9800
Web Site: http://www.valleyambulatory.com
Outpatient Surgery Services
N.A.I.C.S.: 621999

Valley Surgical Center, Ltd. (3)
2323 Sunset Blvd, Steubenville, OH 43952
Tel.: (740) 264-0145
Web Site:
http://www.valleysurgerycenter.com

Outpatient Surgery Services
N.A.I.C.S.: 621999

Subsidiary (Domestic):

Surgery Partners of Park Place, LLC (2)
2450 Maitland Center Pkwy Ste 100, Maitland, FL 32751
Tel.: (407) 875-0296
Web Site:
http://www.parkplacesurgerycenter.com
Outpatient Care Center Operator
N.A.I.C.S.: 621498

Surgical Hospital of Austin, L.P. (2)
3003 Bee Cave Rd, Austin, TX 78746-5542
Tel.: (512) 314-3800
Web Site:
http://www.arisemedicalcenter.com
General Hospital Services
N.A.I.C.S.: 622110

Tampa Pain Relief Center, Inc. (2)
403 South Kings Avenue Suite 201, Brandon, FL 33511
Tel.: (813) 872-4492
Web Site: https://yourpainreliefcenters.com
Pain Relief Center Operator
N.A.I.C.S.: 621498

The Cataract Specialty Surgical Center, LLC (2)
28747 Woodward Ave, Berkley, MI 48072
Tel.: (248) 584-4602
Web Site: https://cataractsurgicalcenter.com
Surgical & Emergency Center Operator
N.A.I.C.S.: 621493

The Center for Special Surgery, LLC (2)
556 Eagle Rock Ave, Roseland, NJ 07068
Tel.: (973) 226-3500
Web Site:
http://www.centersforspecialsurgery.com
Surgical & Emergency Center Operator
N.A.I.C.S.: 621493
David A Greuner (Chief Medical Officer)

The Center for Specialized Surgery, LP (2)
2851 Baglyos Cir Ste 100, Bethlehem, PA 18020
Tel.: (484) 821-0550
Web Site:
http://www.specializedsurgerycenter.com
Surgical & Emergency Center Operator
N.A.I.C.S.: 621493

The Surgery Center, L.L.C. (2)
3111 W Rawson Ave Ste 100, Franklin, WI 53132
Tel.: (414) 761-2600
Web Site: http://www.thesurgerycenter-llc.com
Surgical & Emergency Center Operator
N.A.I.C.S.: 621493

Village Surgicenter, Limited Partnership (2)
5473 Village Common Dr Ste 100, Erie, PA 16506-4961
Tel.: (814) 836-0770
Web Site: http://www.vscerie.com
Outpatient Care Center Operator
N.A.I.C.S.: 621498
John Desser (Dir-Clinical & Mgr-Clinical Nurse)
Heidi Andrews-Keys (Dir-Admin, Office Mgr & Bus Mgr)

Westchase Surgery Center, Ltd. (2)
10901 Sheldon Rd, Tampa, FL 33626
Tel.: (813) 343-3101
Web Site:
http://www.westchasesurgerycenter.com
Ambulatory Surgical & Emergency Center Operator
N.A.I.C.S.: 621493

Wilmington Surgery Center, L.P. (2)
1801 S 17th St, Wilmington, NC 28401
Tel.: (910) 763-4555
Web Site: http://www.surgcare.com
Outpatient Surgical Services
N.A.I.C.S.: 621999

TI Automotive Limited (1)
4650 Kingsgate, Oxford, OX4 2SU, United Kingdom

Tel.: (44) 1865 871820
Web Site: http://www.tiautomotive.com
Emp.: 24,000
Fuel Storage & Delivery Systems Mfr
N.A.I.C.S.: 336340
Tim Knutson (CFO)
Domenico Milicia (Chief Comm Officer & Chief HR Officer)
Matthew Paroly (Chief Legal Officer & Sec)
Hans Dieltjens (Exec VP-Fuel Tank & Delivery Svcs)
Al Deane (CTO)
Andy Ridgway (VP-Thermal Products)
Stefan Rau (Exec VP-Fluid Carrying Sys)

Subsidiary (US):

TI Automotive, LLC (2)
2020 Taylor Rd, Auburn Hills, MI 48326
Tel.: (248) 296-8000
Web Site: http://www.tiautomotive.com
Corporate Office; Automotive Fluid Carrying & Fuel Tank Systems Mfr
N.A.I.C.S.: 551114
Hans Dieltjens (Grp Exec VP-Fuel Tank & Delivery Systems)
Josie Archer (Chief Sls Officer & Sls Dir-Fluid Carrying Sys-Global)
Jay Phillion (Chief Pur & Quality Officer & VP-Fluid Carrying Div)
Al Deane (CTO-Global)

Subsidiary (Non-US):

TI Automotive Euro Holdings Limited (3)
4650 Kingsgate, Oxford, OX4 2SU, United Kingdom
Tel.: (44) 1865871820
Web Site: http://www.tiautomotive.com
Holding Company
N.A.I.C.S.: 551112
Tim Edwards (Controller)

Subsidiary (Non-US):

TI Poland Sp z o.o. (4)
Bestwinska 143 A, Bielsko-Biala, 43-346, Poland
Tel.: (48) 334992101
Fluid Carrying Systems Mfr
N.A.I.C.S.: 441330
Steve Taylor (Exec VP-Fluid Carrying Systems)

TOMS Shoes, LLC (1)
5404 Jandy Pl, Los Angeles, CA 90066 (50%)
Tel.: (310) 566-3170
Web Site: http://www.toms.com
Footwear Designer, Distr & Retailer
N.A.I.C.S.: 458210
Blake Mycoskie (Founder)
Pete Ferrer (VP-Sls & Mktg)
Mark Satkiewicz (Gen Mgr-Americas)
Magnus Wedhammar (CEO)
Dorothy Sadd (CFO-Global & COO-Global)

The Kantar Group Limited (1)
6 More London Pl, Tooley St, London, SE1 2QY, United Kingdom (60%)
Tel.: (44) 207 656 5700
Web Site: http://www.kantar.com
Sales Range: $25-49.9 Million
Marketing Research
N.A.I.C.S.: 541910
Adam Crozier (Chm)
Chris Jansen (CEO)

Unit (Domestic):

Kantar Retail (2)
6 More London Place Tooley Street, London, SE1 2QY, United Kingdom
Tel.: (44) 1932 83 3600
Web Site: http://www.kantarretail.com
Global Insight & Consulting Services
N.A.I.C.S.: 541618

Kantar Worldpanel (2)
Westgate Hanger Lane, London, W5 1UA, United Kingdom
Tel.: (44) 20 8967 0007
Web Site: http://www.kantarworldpanel.com
Marketing Research Service
N.A.I.C.S.: 541910

Subsidiary (Domestic):

TNS Group Holdings plc (2)

---

6 More London Place, London, SE1 2QY, United Kingdom
Tel.: (44) 2076565000
Web Site: http://www.tnsglobal.com
Sales Range: $1-4.9 Billion
Emp.: 800
Holding Company; Advertising & Marketing Agencies
N.A.I.C.S.: 551112

Subsidiary (Non-US):

Factum Invenio (3)
Tesnov 5, 110 00, Prague, Czech Republic (100%)
Tel.: (420) 224805651
Web Site: http://www.factum.cz
Sales Range: $50-74.9 Million
Emp.: 45
Market Information Services
N.A.I.C.S.: 541910

Kantar Deutschland GmbH (3)
Landsberger Str 284, 80687, Munich, Germany
Tel.: (49) 8956000
Web Site: http://www.kantardeutschland.de
Market Information Services
N.A.I.C.S.: 541910
Robert A. Wieland (Mng Dir)

Division (Domestic):

TNS Emnid (4)
Stieghorster Str 86-90, 33605, Bielefeld, Germany
Tel.: (49) 52192570
Web Site: http://www.tnsemnid.com
Sales Range: $150-199.9 Million
Emp.: 1,000
Market Information Services
N.A.I.C.S.: 541910

Subsidiary (Non-US):

NIPO BV (3)
Amsteldijk 166, 1079 LH, Amsterdam, Netherlands (100%)
Tel.: (31) 20 5225 989
Web Site: http://www.nipo.com
Market Information Services
N.A.I.C.S.: 541910
Ard Bisschop (Dir-Sls & Support & Mgr-Reg Sls-Europe)
Doris Fung (Mgr-Reg Sls)
Filip de Bruin (Dir-Product)

TNS Canadian Facts (3)
2 Glory St E Ste 900, Toronto, M4W 3H8, ON, Canada (100%)
Tel.: (416) 924-5751
Web Site: http://www.nfocfgroup.com
Sales Range: $25-49.9 Million
Emp.: 200
Market Information Services
N.A.I.C.S.: 541910
Morgan Mulvihill (CFO)
Maria Jenkins (Office Mgr)

TNS Gallup AS (3)
PO Box 9016, Gronland, 133, Oslo, Norway (100%)
Tel.: (47) 23291600
Web Site: http://www.tnsgallup.no
Sales Range: $25-49.9 Million
Emp.: 115
Market Information Services
N.A.I.C.S.: 541910

TNS Gallup SA (3)
Masnedoegade 22.24, 2100, Copenhagen, 2100, Denmark (100%)
Tel.: (45) 39272727
Web Site: http://www.gallup.dk
Sales Range: $25-49.9 Million
Emp.: 120
Market Information Services
N.A.I.C.S.: 541910

TNS India Pvt. Ltd. (3)
7th Floor Block 4-B DLF Corporate Park, DLF City Phase III MG Road, Gurgaon, 122002, India
Tel.: (91) 124 4488 877
Web Site: http://www.tnsglobal.com
Market Information & Advertising Services
N.A.I.C.S.: 541910

TNS Malaysia Sdn. Bhd. (3)
Level 33 Menara Multi-Purpose Capital Square, No 8 Jalan Munshi Abdullah, Kuala

Bain Capital, LP—(Continued)

Lumpur, 50100, Malaysia
Tel.: (60) 3 2787 8888
Web Site: http://www.tnsglobal.com
Market Information & Advertising Services
N.A.I.C.S.: 541910

TNS New Zealand (3)
Level 3 435 Khyber Pass Rd Newmarket
Millenium Centre, 602 Great South Road,
Auckland, 1023, New Zealand
Tel.: (64) 9 525 0934
Web Site: http://www.tns-global.com
Emp.: 30
Research Services
N.A.I.C.S.: 541910
Jason Shoebridge (Mng Dir)

TNS Philippines (3)
12 Fpsbank Center 777 Paseo De Roxas
Street, Salcedo Village, Makati, Philippines
Tel.: (63) 2 818 1150
Web Site: http://www.tnsglobal.com
Research Services
N.A.I.C.S.: 541910

TNS Singapore (3)
512A Thomson Road, 02 01 SLF Podium,
Singapore, 298137, Singapore
Tel.: (65) 6355 7910
Web Site: http://www.tns-global.com
Research Services
N.A.I.C.S.: 541910

Subsidiary (Domestic):

TNS UK Limited (3)
6 More London Place, London, SE1 2QY,
United Kingdom
Tel.: (44) 207 656 5000
Web Site: http://www.tnsglobal.com
Emp.: 400
Market Information & Advertising Services
N.A.I.C.S.: 541910

Subsidiary (Domestic):

Research International Limited (4)
6 More London Place, London, SE1 2QY,
United Kingdom
Tel.: (44) 20 7656 5500
Web Site: http://www.tnsglobal.com
Sales Range: $75-99.9 Million
Marketing & Advertising
N.A.I.C.S.: 541810

TNS Prognostics Ltd (4)
Green Pk 200 Brook Dr, Reading, RG2
6UB, Berkshire, United Kingdom (100%)
Tel.: (44) 189497099
Web Site: http://www.prognostics.com
Sales Range: $25-49.9 Million
Emp.: 4
Market Information Services
N.A.I.C.S.: 541910

**Taylor Nelson Sofres Group Holdings
Ltd** (4)
Tns House Westgate, London, W5 1UA,
United Kingdom
Tel.: (44) 20 8967 0007
Sales Range: $300-349.9 Million
Investment Management Service
N.A.I.C.S.: 523999
Alex Wright (Dir-Tech & Fin)

Subsidiary (US):

TNS US, LLC (3)
11 Madison Ave 12th Fl, New York, NY
10010
Tel.: (212) 991-6000
Web Site: http://www.tnsglobal.com
Market Information & Advertising Services
N.A.I.C.S.: 541910

Unit (Domestic):

TNS Intersearch (4)
700 Tresher Rd, Horsham, PA
19044-2012 (100%)
Tel.: (215) 442-9000
Sales Range: $75-99.9 Million
Emp.: 325
Custom Research Company
N.A.I.C.S.: 541910

**TNS Landis Strategy &
Innovation** (4)

4800 Riverside Dr Ste 200, Palm Beach
Gardens, FL 33410
Tel.: (561) 630-9500
Web Site: http://www.landis-si.com
Sales Range: $1-9.9 Million
Emp.: 40
Research-Based Consulting Services
N.A.I.C.S.: 541613

TNS Media Intelligence/CMR (4)
100 Park Ave Fl 4, New York, NY
10017 (100%)
Tel.: (212) 991-6000
Sales Range: $150-199.9 Million
Emp.: 663
Advertising Occurence & Expenditure Data
for Advertising Agencies, Advertisers,
Broadcasters & Publishers
N.A.I.C.S.: 541840

TNS Prognostics (4)
Stanford Research Park 900 Hansen Way,
Palo Alto, CA 94304 (100%)
Tel.: (650) 812-3900
Web Site: http://www.prognostics.com
Market Information Services
N.A.I.C.S.: 541910

Branch (Domestic):

TNS US, LLC - Toledo Office (4)
2700 Oregon Rd, Northwood, OH 43619
Tel.: (419) 666-8800
Web Site: http://www.tnsglobal.com
Sales Range: $100-124.9 Million
Emp.: 400
Market Information & Advertising Services
N.A.I.C.S.: 541910

Subsidiary (Non-US):

Taylor Nelson Sofres (3)
3 avenue Pierre Masse, 75014, Paris, Ce-
dex, France (100%)
Tel.: (33) 01 40 92 66 66
Web Site: http://www.tns-sofres.com
Market Information Services
N.A.I.C.S.: 541910
Ketty del Falco (Pres & CEO)
Arielle Belicha-Hardy (Chief Comml Officer)
Valerie Marc (Dir-Fin)
Laurence Geffray-Merger (Dir-HR)
Virginie Wong (COO)
Pierre Gomy (Mng Dir)
Marie-Agathe Nicoli (Deputy Chief Comml
Officer)
Sylvie Gassmann (Mng Dir-Quali Expertise)

Subsidiary (Domestic):

Louis Harris France SA (4)
46 Rue de l'Echiquier, 75010, Paris,
France (100%)
Tel.: (33) 55 33 20 00
Web Site: http://www.louis-harris.fr
Sales Range: $25-49.9 Million
Emp.: 114
Market Information Services
N.A.I.C.S.: 541910

Unit (Domestic):

TNS Secodip (4)
2 Rue Francis Pedron, Paris, 78241, Cham-
bourcy, France (100%)
Tel.: (33) 0130748080
Web Site: http://www.secodip.fr
Market Information Services
N.A.I.C.S.: 541910

Subsidiary (Non-US):

**Taylor Nelson Sofres Australia Pty.
Ltd.** (3)
Level 1 181 Miller Street, North Sydney,
2060, NSW, Australia
Tel.: (61) 2 9563 4200
Web Site: http://www.tnsaustralia.com
Market Information & Advertising Services
N.A.I.C.S.: 541910
Jon Foged (CEO-Insights Div)
Jonathan Sinton (Chief Comml Officer-
Insights Div)
Mark Henning (Exec Dir-Media & Digital)
Carolyn Reid (Exec Dir-Qualitative)
Gareth O'Neill (Exec Dir-Brand Guidance)
Ryan France (Exec Dir-Brand Strategy)
Simon Crisp (Exec Dir-Comml Fin)
John Cucka (Exec Dir-Analytics)
John Evans (Head-Ops-Insights Div)

Ilana Sanborn (Sr Dir-Marketplace)
Kim Ruyten (Sr Dir-Strategic Engagement)
Steven Howlett (Exec Dir-Insights Div-
Melbourne)

Taylor Nelson Sofres S.A. (3)
Cami De Can Calders 4, Sant Cugat Del
Valles, E 08173, Barcelona, Spain (100%)
Tel.: (34) 935819410
Web Site: http://www.tnf-global.com
Sales Range: $150-199.9 Million
Emp.: 550
Market Information Services
N.A.I.C.S.: 541910

Subsidiary (Domestic):

The Futures Company (2)
6 More London Place Tooley Street, Lon-
don, SE1 2QY, United Kingdom
Tel.: (44) 20 7955 1800
Web Site:
http://www.thefuturescompany.com
Sales Range: $10-24.9 Million
Emp.: 50
Investment Advice
N.A.I.C.S.: 541910

Subsidiary (US):

The Kantar Group (2)
401 Merritt 7, Norwalk, CT 06851
Tel.: (203) 330-5200
Web Site: http://www.kantargroup.com
Sales Range: $25-49.9 Million
Emp.: 150
Marketing Research
N.A.I.C.S.: 541613
Wayne Levings (Pres-Insights Div-APAC)
John Evans (Head-Ops-Australia)
Will Bordelon (CEO-Insights-Americas)

Subsidiary (Domestic):

Global Market Insite, Inc. (3)
1100 112th Ave NE Ste 200, Bellevue, WA
98004
Tel.: (206) 315-9300
Web Site: http://www.gmi-mr.com
Sales Range: $50-74.9 Million
Software Applications & Development Ser-
vices
N.A.I.C.S.: 541511

Kantar Media (3)
11 Madison Ave 12th Fl, New York, NY
10010
Tel.: (212) 991-6000
Web Site: http://www.kantarmediana.com
Solutions for Media Owners, Media Agen-
cies & Brand Owners
N.A.I.C.S.: 541910
Andy Brown (Chm & CEO-Global)
Richard Poustie (Mng Dir)
Richard Asquith (Chief Product Officer)
Manish Bhatia (CEO-North America)
Mark Inskip (CEO-UK & Ireland)
Pascale Anderson-Mair (Chief HR Officer-
Interim)
Phil Eames (COO-Interim)
Olivier Lefranc (Dir-Fin-Global)
Francois Nicolon (Chief Mktg Officer-
Interim)
Richard Wallace (CIO)

Subsidiary (Non-US):

Kantar IBOPE Media (4)
Alameda Santos 2 101, Cerqueira Cesar,
Sao Paulo, 01419 002, Brazil (84%)
Tel.: (55) 1130661500
Web Site: http://www.ibope.com.br
Emp.: 2,800
Research & Information Services
N.A.I.C.S.: 541910

Subsidiary (Domestic):

SRDS, Inc. (4)
1700 Higgins Rd, Des Plaines, IL 60018-
5621
Tel.: (847) 375-5000
Web Site: http://www.srds.com
Sales Range: $25-49.9 Million
Emp.: 150
Media Rates & Marketing Data Information
Services
N.A.I.C.S.: 513140
Emmanuel Debuyck (CEO)
Yigael Chetrit (CTO-Global)
Heather Petaccio (Pres)

Subsidiary (Domestic):

Millward Brown Inc. (3)
3333 Warrenville Rd, Lisle, IL 60532
Tel.: (630) 505-0066
Sales Range: $75-99.9 Million
Advetising Agency
N.A.I.C.S.: 541910

Branch (Non-US):

Colmar Brunton (4)
Level One 6-10 The Strand Takapuna,
Auckland, 0622, New Zealand
Tel.: (64) 9 919 9200
Web Site: http://www.colmarbrunton.co.nz
Sales Range: $10-24.9 Million
Emp.: 100
N.A.I.C.S.: 541810
Brian Turner (Exec Dir & Head-Client Svcs)
Jocelyn Rout (Exec Dir-Wellington)
Duncan Smith (Dir-Mktg Science)
Kathryn Robinson (Dir-Behavioural Insights-
Wellington)
Will Koning (Chief Data Officer)
Rachel Pita (Grp Acct Dir)
Yvette Basson (Grp Acct Dir)
Beth Rundle (Acct Dir)
Yasmin Handrich (Acct Dir)
Jessica Del Rosario (Acct Dir)
Annikki Delacey (Grp Acct Dir)
Kerri Tait (Chief Client Officer)
Adam Durant (Grp Acct Dir)
Sarah Bolger (Head-Colmar Brunton)
Sue Whitley (Dir-Creative & Multimedia)

Branch (Domestic):

Dynamic Logic (4)
60 Quaker Ln 4th Fl Ste 62, Warwick, RI
02886
Tel.: (401) 921-3681
N.A.I.C.S.: 541810

Dynamic Logic (4)
11 Madison 12 Fl, New York, NY 10010
Tel.: (212) 844-3700
Web Site: http://www.dynamiclogic.com
Sales Range: $25-49.9 Million
Emp.: 122
Consulting, Strategic Planning/Research
N.A.I.C.S.: 541810

Dynamic Logic (4)
303 2nd St N Tower 3rd Fl, San Francisco,
CA 94107
Tel.: (415) 268-1650
Web Site: http://www.dynamiclogic.com
Sales Range: $10-24.9 Million
Emp.: 22
N.A.I.C.S.: 541810

Dynamic Logic (4)
350 West Mart Center Dr Ste 1200, Chi-
cago, IL 60654
Tel.: (312) 577-4070
Web Site: http://www.dynamiclogic.com
Sales Range: $10-24.9 Million
Emp.: 18
N.A.I.C.S.: 541810

Branch (Non-US):

Japan Kantar Research (4)
Harmony Tower 11F 1-32-2 Honcho
Nakano-ku, Tokyo, 164-8721, Japan
Tel.: (81) 3 5365 6811
N.A.I.C.S.: 541810

Branch (Domestic):

Millward Brown (4)
11 Maidson Ave 12th Fl, New York, NY
10010
Tel.: (212) 548-7200
Brand Development, Consumer Marketing,
Planning & Consultation
N.A.I.C.S.: 541910

Millward Brown (4)
26555 Evergreen Rd Ste 600, Southfield,
MI 48076-4224
Tel.: (248) 351-2888
Sales Range: $10-24.9 Million
Emp.: 45
N.A.I.C.S.: 541810

Millward Brown (4)
2425 Olympic Blvd Ste 240-E, Santa
Monica, CA 90404
Tel.: (310) 309-3400

Sales Range: $10-24.9 Million
Emp.: 25
N.A.I.C.S.: 541810

Millward Brown (4)
3630 Peachtree Rd NE Ste 1200, Atlanta,
GA 30326
Tel.: (770) 343-6020
Sales Range: $10-24.9 Million
Emp.: 35
N.A.I.C.S.: 541810

Branch (Non-US):

Millward Brown Australia (4)
Level 11, 181 Miller St North, Sydney,
2060, Australia
Tel.: (61) 2 9927 1111
N.A.I.C.S.: 541810

Millward Brown Brazil (4)
Al Santos 2101 - 7 Andar, Sao Paulo,
01419-002, Brazil
Tel.: (55) 11 3069 3601
N.A.I.C.S.: 541810
Valkiria Garre (CEO)

Millward Brown Canada (4)
4950 Yonge Street Suite 600, Toronto, M2N
6K1, ON, Canada
Tel.: (416) 221-9200
Sales Range: $10-24.9 Million
Emp.: 55
Brand Development, Consulting, Consumer
Marketing, Planning & Consultation, Strate-
gic Planning/Research
N.A.I.C.S.: 541910

Millward Brown China (4)
Fl 17 Golden Bridge Plz, No 585 Xizang Rd
Middle, Shanghai, 200003, China
Tel.: (86) 21 6359 8622
Sales Range: $10-24.9 Million
Emp.: 100
N.A.I.C.S.: 541810
Adrian Gonzalez (CEO-Africa, Middle East
& Asia Pacific)

Millward Brown Columbia (4)
Carrera 13 No 94 A-26 5th Fl, Bogota, Co-
lombia
Tel.: (57) 1 747 7000
Sales Range: $50-74.9 Million
Emp.: 300
N.A.I.C.S.: 541810

Millward Brown Czech Republic (4)
Klimentska 10, 110 00, Prague, Czech Re-
public
Tel.: (420) 2 2530 0211
N.A.I.C.S.: 541810

Millward Brown Delfo (4)
Via Guglielmo Silva 36, 20149, Milan, Italy
Tel.: (39) 02 4399 5861
Sales Range: $10-24.9 Million
Emp.: 14
N.A.I.C.S.: 541810

Millward Brown Denmark (4)
Raadhuspladsen 45-47 5th Fl, 1550, Co-
penhagen, 1550, Denmark
Tel.: (45) 33 77 10 40
Web Site: http://www.millwardbrown.dk
Sales Range: $10-24.9 Million
Emp.: 30
N.A.I.C.S.: 541810

Millward Brown France (4)
16/18 quai de Loire, 75019, Paris, France
Tel.: (33) 1 5556 4000
Sales Range: $10-24.9 Million
Emp.: 100
N.A.I.C.S.: 541810

Millward Brown Germany GmbH (4)
Kleyerstrasse 88-90, Frankfurt am Main,
60326, Germany
Tel.: (49) 69 739 440
Sales Range: $10-24.9 Million
Emp.: 50
Marketing & Advertising
N.A.I.C.S.: 541810

Millward Brown Hungary (4)
Aradi u 8-10, Budapest, 1062, Hungary
Tel.: (36) 1 354 5200
Sales Range: $10-24.9 Million
Emp.: 60
N.A.I.C.S.: 541810

Millward Brown IMS (4)

Millbank House Arkle Road, Sandyford, 18,
Dublin, Ireland
Tel.: (353) 1 676 1196
Sales Range: $10-24.9 Million
Emp.: 55
N.A.I.C.S.: 541810
Will Galgey (CEO)

**Millward Brown Market Reseach
Services**
Mahalakshmi Chamber 3rd Fl Mahatma
Gandhi Rd, Bengaluru, 560001, India
Tel.: (91) 80 42927000
Sales Range: $10-24.9 Million
Emp.: 45
South Asian Market
N.A.I.C.S.: 541910
Pranay Singhvi (Dir-Fin-Mumbai)

Millward Brown Media Research (4)
Hae-Yang Bldg 1625-1, Seocho-Dong
Seocho-Gu, Seoul, 137-070, Korea (South)
Tel.: (82) 2 583 6655
N.A.I.C.S.: 541810

Millward Brown Mexico (4)
Avenida Tamaulipas 150-1202 Colonia Con-
desa, Mexico, 06140, DF, Mexico
Tel.: (52) 55 3098 1000
N.A.I.C.S.: 541810

Millward Brown Philippines (4)
8/F Equitable Bank Tower 8751 Paseo De
Roxas, Salcedo Village, Makati, 1226, Phil-
ippines
Tel.: (63) 2 864 8960
Sales Range: $10-24.9 Million
Emp.: 45
N.A.I.C.S.: 541810

Millward Brown Portugal (4)
Avenida Eng Duarte Pacheco Torre 1 - 90
Piso, 1070-101, Lisbon, Portugal
Tel.: (351) 213 581 130
N.A.I.C.S.: 541810

Millward Brown SMG/KRC (4)
Ul Branickiego 17, 02-972, Warsaw, Poland
Tel.: (48) 22 545 2000
Web Site: http://www.smgkrc.pl
Sales Range: $10-24.9 Million
Emp.: 300
N.A.I.C.S.: 541810
Marek Biskup (Dir-Client)

Millward Brown Singapore (4)
300 Beach Rd, #35-03 The Concourse, Sin-
gapore, 199555, Singapore
Tel.: (65) 6323 2273
Sales Range: $10-24.9 Million
Emp.: 80
N.A.I.C.S.: 541810

Millward Brown South Africa (4)
Black River Park North Fir Street, PO Box
12923, Mowbray, Cape Town, 7705, South
Africa
Tel.: (27) 21 442 3680
Sales Range: $25-49.9 Million
Emp.: 18
N.A.I.C.S.: 541810
Deepender Rana (CEO-Greater China)

Millward Brown Spain (4)
Alcala 474, Madrid, 28027, Spain
Tel.: (34) 91 325 4100
Sales Range: $10-24.9 Million
Emp.: 20
N.A.I.C.S.: 541810

Millward Brown Sweden (4)
Nybrokajen 7 6th Fl, Box 16356, 10326,
Stockholm, Sweden
Tel.: (46) 8 402 8970
N.A.I.C.S.: 541810

Millward Brown Taiwan (4)
7F-1 No 37 Sec 3, Minsheng E Rd, Taipei,
Taiwan
Tel.: (886) 2 7710 1200
N.A.I.C.S.: 541810

Millward Brown Thailand (4)
Level 14 Kamol Sukosol Bldg 317 Silom
Road, Bangrak, Bangkok, 10500, Thailand
Tel.: (66) 2 686 6400
N.A.I.C.S.: 541810

Millward Brown Turkey (4)
Buyukdere Caddesi Palazoglu Mevkii Cem
Is Merkezi No 23, Kat 1 34363 Sisli, Istan-
bul, Turkiye

Tel.: (90) 212 219 5350
Sales Range: $10-24.9 Million
Emp.: 80
N.A.I.C.S.: 541810

Millward Brown Ulster (4)
Aisling House, 50 Stranmillis Embankment,
Belfast, BT9 5FL, Northern Ireland, United
Kingdom
Tel.: (44) 28 9023 1060
Sales Range: $25-49.9 Million
Emp.: 160
N.A.I.C.S.: 541810

Branch (Domestic):

Millward Brown, Inc. (4)
501 Kings Hwy E, Fairfield, CT 06825-4859
Tel.: (203) 335-5222
Sales Range: $25-49.9 Million
Emp.: 200
N.A.I.C.S.: 541810

Branch (Non-US):

Millward Brown/Centrum (4)
Paulvan Vlissingen Scraac 10B, 1018 DH,
Amsterdam, Netherlands
Tel.: (31) 205566666
Sales Range: $10-24.9 Million
Emp.: 40
N.A.I.C.S.: 541810

Tri-Stage, Inc. (1)
21F Shiodome Building 2-20 Kaigan
1-chome, Minato-ku, Tokyo, 105-0022, Ja-
pan
Tel.: (81) 354024111
Web Site: https://www.tri-stage.jp
Rev.: $462,534,800
Assets: $141,951,600
Liabilities: $78,431,010
Net Worth: $63,520,590
Earnings: $1,668,940
Emp.: 354
Fiscal Year-end: 02/29/2020
Advertising Services
N.A.I.C.S.: 541890
Akio Maruta (Founder & Founder)
Yasuhisa Kurata (Pres)
Umimoto Keita (Exec VP)
Yusuke Shirai (Exec Officer)
Daisuke Teramae (Exec Officer)

Subsidiary (Domestic):

Adflex Communications Inc. (2)
KDX Hamamatsucho Center Building 3F
1-22-5, Minato-ku, Tokyo, 105-0013, Japan
Tel.: (81) 368236903
Web Site: http://www.ad-flex.com
Advertising Services
N.A.I.C.S.: 541613
Haruhiko Kuwahata (Pres)
Sadatomo Yanase (Auditor)

Mail Customer Center Co., Ltd. (2)
Shiodome Building 21st Floor 1-2-20 Kai-
gan, Minato-ku, Tokyo, 105-0022, Japan
Tel.: (81) 354023411
Web Site: http://www.mail-cc.com
Direct Mail Advertisement Services
N.A.I.C.S.: 541860

Subsidiary (Non-US):

PT. Merdis International (2)
DBS Bank Tower It 12 Suite 1202 Jl Prof
DR Satrio Kav 3-5, Ciputra World 1, Jakarta
Selatan, 12940, Indonesia
Tel.: (62) 2129888120
Web Site: http://www.merdis.co.id
Household Appliances Mfr
N.A.I.C.S.: 335220

Trinseo S.A. (1)
440 E Swedesford Rd Ste 301, Wayne, PA
19087 (89.5%)
Tel.: (610) 240-3200
Web Site: https://www.trinseo.com
Rev.: $4,965,500,000
Assets: $3,760,200,000
Liabilities: $3,339,900,000
Net Worth: $420,300,000
Earnings: ($430,900,000)
Emp.: 3,400
Fiscal Year-end: 12/31/2022
Emulsion Polymers & Plastics Mfr
N.A.I.C.S.: 325211

Frank A. Bozich (Pres & CEO)
David Stasse (CFO & Exec VP)
Roger E. Greene (VP)

Subsidiary (Non-US):

Styron (Hong Kong) Limited (2)
Room 3401- 3 34/F Central Plaza 18 Har-
bour Road, Wanchai, China (Hong Kong)
Tel.: (852) 3120 6300
Plastic, Latex & Rubber Mfr
N.A.I.C.S.: 325212

**Styron Deutschland Anlagengesell-
schaft mbH** (2)
Werk Rheinmunster Industriestr 1, 77836,
Rheinmunster, Germany
Tel.: (49) 7227 91 0
Web Site: http://www.styrondow.com
Emp.: 650
Plastic, Latex & Rubber Mfr
N.A.I.C.S.: 325211
Heiko Dahms (Gen Mgr)

Styron Deutschland GmbH (2)
Boehlen Olefinstrasse 1, 4564, Bohlen,
Saxony, Germany
Tel.: (49) 3461 49 6950
Plastic, Latex & Rubber Mfr
N.A.I.C.S.: 325211
Ralf Irmert (Mng Dir)

Styron France SAS (2)
10th floor - Tour Ariane 5 Place de la Pyra-
mide, La Defense 9, 92088, Paris, France
Tel.: (33) 1 55 68 10 10
Plastic, Latex & Rubber Mfr
N.A.I.C.S.: 325212

Styron Holdings Asia Pte Ltd. (2)
3 Killiney Road 07-08/09 Winsland House
1, Singapore, 239519, Singapore
Tel.: (65) 6895 1500
Plastic, Latex & Rubber Mfr
N.A.I.C.S.: 325212

Styron Italia s.r.l. (2)
Viale Certosa 2, 20155, Milan, Italy
Tel.: (39) 0291 326213
Plastic, Latex & Rubber Mfr
N.A.I.C.S.: 325212

Styron Korea Ltd. (2)
30/F Trade Tower 159-1 Samsung-dong,
Gangnam-gu, Seoul, 135 729, Korea
(South)
Tel.: (82) 2 6007 2180
Plastic, Latex & Rubber Mfr
N.A.I.C.S.: 325212

Subsidiary (Domestic):

Styron LLC (2)
1000 Chesterbrook Blvd, Berwyn, PA 19312
Tel.: (888) 789-7661
Web Site: http://www.styron.com
Sales Range: $5-14.9 Billion
Emp.: 2,100
Plastics, Latex & Rubber Mfr
N.A.I.C.S.: 326199

Subsidiary (Non-US):

Styron Spain, S.L. (2)
Ribera del Loria 46 Regus Offices, 28042,
Madrid, Spain
Tel.: (34) 915501720
Plastic, Latex & Rubber Mfr
N.A.I.C.S.: 325212

Styron Sverige AB (2)
Ramshallsvagen 2, Box 243, 601 04,
Norrkoping, Sweden
Tel.: (46) 11 245100
Plastic, Latex & Rubber Mfr
N.A.I.C.S.: 325211

**Styron do Brasil Comercio de Produ-
tos Quimicos Ltda.** (2)
Av Santos Dumont 4 444 Bairro Concei-
caozinha, Guaruja, 11460-007, SP, Brazil
Tel.: (55) 13 3358 8220
Plastic, Latex & Rubber Mfr
N.A.I.C.S.: 325211

Joint Venture (Non-US):

**Sumika Styron Polycarbonate
Limited** (2)
Nakajima Building 8-8 Nihonbashi-

Bain Capital, LP—(Continued)

Kabutocho, Chuo-ku, Tokyo, 103-0026,
Japan　　　　　　　　　　　　　　**(50%)**
Tel.: (81) 356444750
Web Site: http://www.sspc.com
Sales Range: $25-49.9 Million
Emp.: 120
Polycarbonate Resins Mfr & Sales; Owned
50 % by Trinseo S.A. & 50% by Sumitomo
Chemical Company, Ltd.
N.A.I.C.S.: 325998
Shin-Ichi Nakano (VP)
Hiroaki Sugimoto (Pres)

Subsidiary (Non-US):

Taiwan Styron Limited　　　　　　**(2)**
No 17 Renjen Road Hsinchu Industrial
Park, Hukou, Hsin-chu, 00303, Taiwan
Tel.: (886) 3 5432200
Web Site: http://www.trinseo.com
Sales Range: $25-49.9 Million
Emp.: 60
Plastic, Latex & Rubber Mfr
N.A.I.C.S.: 325212

Trinseo Europe GmbH　　　　　　**(2)**
Zugerstrasse 231, 8810, Horgen, Switzer-
land
Tel.: (41) 44 718 3600
Web Site: http://www.trinseo.com
Plastic, Latex & Rubber Mfr
N.A.I.C.S.: 325211

Trinseo Japan Y.K.　　　　　　　**(2)**
Shinagawa Grand Central Tower 8F 16-4
Konan 2-Chome, Minato-ku, Tokyo, 108-
0075, Japan
Tel.: (81) 364330228
Web Site: http://www.trinseo.com
Plastic, Latex & Rubber Mfr
N.A.I.C.S.: 325212

Trinseo Netherlands B.V.　　　　**(2)**
Herbert H Dowweg 5 4542 NM HOEK, PO
Box 48, 4530 AA, Terneuzen, Netherlands
Tel.: (31) 115 671616
Web Site: http://www.trinseo.com
Plastic, Latex & Rubber Mfr
N.A.I.C.S.: 325211

US LBM Holdings, Inc.　　　　　**(1)**
1000 Corporate Grove Dr, Buffalo Grove, IL
60089
Tel.: (847) 353-7800
Web Site: http://www.uslbm.com
Emp.: 7,300
Building Construction Material Distr
N.A.I.C.S.: 423390
L. T. Gibson (Pres & CEO)
Patrick McGuiness (CFO & Exec VP)
Jeff Umosella (Pres-Universal Supply Co &
COO)
Michelle Pollock (Gen Counsel, Sec & Sr.
VP)
Randy Aardema (Exec VP-Supply Chain)
Wendy Whiteash (Sr VP-Culture)
Jim Hooper (VP-Mergers & Acquisitions)
Senthil Arumugam (VP-Distr)
Enrico Batelli (VP-Corp Controller)
Greg Bossert (VP-Info Svcs)
Dale Carlson (VP-Ops)
Karen Charielle (VP-HR)
Brian Hein (VP-Fin Ops)
Young Nam (VP-Pricing & Procurement)
Scott Richter (VP-Midwest)

Subsidiary (Domestic):

Emerald Coast Truss, LLC　　　**(2)**
5817 Commerce Rd, Milton, FL 32583
Tel.: (850) 623-1967
Sales Range: $1-9.9 Million
Emp.: 26
Truss Mfr
N.A.I.C.S.: 321215
Darlene McKillip (Mgr)

U.S. LBM Holdings, LLC　　　　**(2)**
1000 Corporate Grove Dr, Buffalo Grove, IL
60089
Tel.: (847) 353-7800
Web Site: http://www.uslbm.com
Holding Company; Lumber & Building Prod-
ucts Mfr
N.A.I.C.S.: 551112
L. T. Gibson (Pres & CEO)
Jeff Umosella (Chief Dev Officer & Pres-
Universal Supply)

Karen Charielle (VP-HR)
Brian Hein (VP-Financial Ops)
Dale Carlson (VP-Midwest Ops)
Greg Bossert (VP-Info Svcs)
Wendy Whiteash (Exec VP-Culture)
Patrick McGuiness (CFO & Exec VP)
Michelle Pollock (Gen Counsel, Sec & Exec
VP)

Subsidiary (Domestic):

ALCO Doors, Inc.　　　　　　　**(3)**
520 S Caton Ave, Baltimore, MD 21229
Tel.: (410) 566-7800
Web Site:
　http://www.americanlumberonline.com
Sales Range: $1-9.9 Million
Wood Door Mfr & Whslr
N.A.I.C.S.: 321911
Howard Farbman (Pres)

**American Construction Source,
LLC**　　　　　　　　　　　　　　**(3)**
1311 E Woodhurst Dr, Springfield, MO
65804
Tel.: (417) 521-2801
Web Site: http://www.acs-lbm.com
Lumber & Building Materials Distr
N.A.I.C.S.: 423390

Subsidiary (Domestic):

**Breckenridge Building Center,
Inc.**　　　　　　　　　　　　　　**(4)**
13445 Hwy 9, Breckenridge, CO 80424
Tel.: (970) 453-2372
Web Site:
　http://breckenridgebuildingcenter.com
Lumber, Plywood & Millwork
N.A.I.C.S.: 423310
Dennis Rogstad (Gen Mgr)
Kari Marco (Acct Mgr)

Contractors Truss Systems, Inc.　**(4)**
2877 Cotter Rd, Cotter, AR 72626
Tel.: (870) 435-5655
Prefabricated Metal Buildings, Nsk
N.A.I.C.S.: 332311
Teresa Newman (Founder & Sec)
Brandt King (Mgr-Ops)

Freeborn Lumber Company　　　**(4)**
971 Plz St W, Albert Lea, MN 56007
Tel.: (507) 377-4284
Clay Building Material & Refractories Mfr
N.A.I.C.S.: 327120

Homewood Holdings, LLC　　　　**(4)**
1966 Homewood Dr, Altadena, CA 91001
Tel.: (916) 652-4655
Web Site: http://homewoodholdingsllc.com
Holding Company
N.A.I.C.S.: 551112
Jim Stockman (CEO)
Scott Blackburn (Pres-Washington Market)

Subsidiary (Domestic):

Eagle Creek Siding, LLC　　　　**(5)**
2975 Ferguson St SW, Tumwater, WA
98512
Tel.: (360) 570-0396
Roofing, Siding & Insulation Material Mer-
chant Whslr
N.A.I.C.S.: 423330
Ron McFarland (Mgr-Sls)
Jeff Fleury (Ops Mgr-Field)
Travis Houston (Mgr-Production Team)

Evergreen Lumber Inc.　　　　　**(5)**
1325 Lloyd Pkwy, Port Orchard, WA 98367-
9186
Tel.: (360) 876-3351
Web Site: http://www.evergreenlumber.com
Emp.: 45
Building Materials Whslr
N.A.I.C.S.: 423310
Keith Elledge (VP)

The Door Mill, Inc.　　　　　　**(5)**
1601 N Delaware St, Chandler, AZ 85225
Tel.: (480) 926-7112
Wood Window & Door Mfr
N.A.I.C.S.: 321911

Subsidiary (Domestic):

Tanco Lumber, L.L.C.　　　　　**(4)**
240 US Hwy 160, Forsyth, MO 65653
Tel.: (417) 546-3008
Web Site: http://www.tancolumber.net

Sales Range: $1-9.9 Million
Emp.: 8
Lumber & Building Material Whslr
N.A.I.C.S.: 444110
John Stauffer (Principal)

Subsidiary (Domestic):

BEP/Lyman, LLC　　　　　　　　**(3)**
520 3rd St Ste 200, Excelsior, MN 55331
Tel.: (952) 470-3600
Web Site: http://www.lymanlumber.com
Sales Range: $125-149.9 Million
Building Materials & Supply Distr
N.A.I.C.S.: 423310
Charlie Bradburn (Pres)

Subsidiary (Domestic):

**Automated Building Components,
Inc.**　　　　　　　　　　　　　　**(4)**
18800 W 78th St, Chanhassen, MN 55317
Tel.: (952) 937-9060
Web Site: http://www.abcmillowork.com
Sales Range: $25-49.9 Million
Emp.: 200
Supplier of Millwork to Professional Builders
N.A.I.C.S.: 423310
Charlie Bradburn (Branch Mgr)
Ron Fischer (Supvr-Warehouse)

Division (Domestic):

ABC Cabinetry　　　　　　　　　**(5)**
18800 W 78th St, Chanhassen, MN 55317
Tel.: (952) 937-9060
Web Site: http://www.abckitchens.com
Sales Range: $50-74.9 Million
Cabinet & Kitchen Mfr
N.A.I.C.S.: 337110
Lisa Oldakowski (Supvr-Inside Sls)
Anna Struss (Mgr-Cabinetry Sls)

Subsidiary (Domestic):

Carpentry Contractors Corp.　　　**(4)**
100 Zephyr Ave S, Montrose, MN 55363
Tel.: (763) 658-4000
Web Site:
　http://www.carpentrycontractors.com
Sales Range: $1-9.9 Million
Emp.: 30
Carpentry Contractor Services
N.A.I.C.S.: 561320
Scott Gertjejansen (Founder)

H&H Lumber Co., Inc.　　　　　**(4)**
1914 N 13th St, Superior, WI 54880
Tel.: (715) 392-2238
Web Site: http://www.hhlumber.com
Sales Range: $50-74.9 Million
Building Materials Distr
N.A.I.C.S.: 423310
Tim Heytens (Gen Mgr)
Chris Ellian (Branch Mgr)

Subsidiary (Domestic):

Bailey Lumber & Supply Co.　　　**(3)**
813 E Pass Rd, Gulfport, MS 39507
Tel.: (228) 896-6071
Web Site: http://www.baileylumber.com
Lumber & Other Building Materials
N.A.I.C.S.: 423310
Steve Braun (VP-Mktg)
Richard Kostal (COO)
Sherwood R. Bailey Jr. (Pres)

Barrons Enterprises, Inc.　　　　**(3)**
23 W Diamond Ave, Gaithersburg, MD
20877
Tel.: (301) 948-6600
Web Site: http://www.barronslumber.com
Sales Range: $10-24.9 Million
Emp.: 45
Building Materials Whslr
N.A.I.C.S.: 444180
Jim Davis (Co-Owner & Pres)
Terry Michnya (Co-Owner & Exec VP)
Annette Stuckey (Co-Owner, Treas & Con-
troller)
Mike Soulen (Co-Owner & VP)
Ann Clodfelter (Co-Owner & Mgr-Credit)
Steve James (Co-Owner & Gen Mgr)

**Bellevue Builders Supply - US LBM,
LLC**　　　　　　　　　　　　　　**(3)**
500 Duanesburg Rd, Schenectady, NY
12306-1015
Tel.: (518) 355-7190

Web Site: http://www.bellevuebuilders.com
Sales Range: $75-99.9 Million
Home Center Operator
N.A.I.C.S.: 444110
Gary Bloomer (Mgr)
Jim Bousa (Mgr)
Lisa Lamay (Mgr)
Patrick Wilsey (Mgr)

Deering Lumber Inc.　　　　　　**(3)**
3 Brown St, Kennebunk, ME 04043-7236
Tel.: (207) 985-4948
Web Site: http://www.deeringlumber.com
Hardware Stores
N.A.I.C.S.: 444140

Desert Lumber, Inc.　　　　　　**(3)**
4950 N Berg St, North Las Vegas, NV
89081
Tel.: (702) 642-7800
Web Site:
　http://www.desertcompaniesiv.com
Sales Range: $10-24.9 Million
Emp.: 230
Lumber Distr
N.A.I.C.S.: 423310
Terry Ono (Pres)
Danny Riley (Gen Mgr)
Nash Baltzer (Mgr)
Tyson Clayton (Mgr)
Jay Lewis (Mgr)

East Haven Builders Supply, Inc.　**(3)**
193 Silver Sands Rd, East Haven, CT
06512
Tel.: (203) 469-2394
Web Site: http://www.ehbuilders.com
Sales Range: $50-74.9 Million
Windows, Doors, Roofing, Siding, Decking
& Building Materials
N.A.I.C.S.: 321911
Neil Frederick (Mgr)

**GBS Building Supply - US LBM,
LLC**　　　　　　　　　　　　　　**(3)**
11 Geneva Ct, Greenville, SC 29607
Tel.: (864) 288-3627
Web Site: http://www.gbsbuilding.com
Sales Range: $25-49.9 Million
Lumber & Other Building Products, Solu-
tions & Services
N.A.I.C.S.: 423310
Robert J. Barreto (CEO)
Nick Campbell (VP-Sls)
Lawanna Dendy (VP-Administration)
Cindy Williams (VP-Pur)
Kim Martin (Mgr-Credit)
Bronson Whiteside (Dir-Ops)
Cammie Mackie (Dir-Mktg)
James Royals (Mgr-IT)
Derrin Morelly (Mgr-Inventory Control)

Gilcrest/Jewett Lumber Company　**(3)**
1100 Alices Rd, Waukee, IA 50263
Tel.: (515) 987-3600
Web Site: http://www.gilcrestjewett.com
Sales Range: $50-74.9 Million
Emp.: 215
Lumber & Other Building Materials
N.A.I.C.S.: 423310
Brad Schulte (Mgr-Door & Window Div)
Philip Jason Worth (Founder & Pres)

Higginbotham Bros. & Co., LLC　**(3)**
202 West Central Ave, Comanche, TX
76442
Tel.: (254) 965-3424
Web Site: http://www.higginbothams.com
Rev.: $2,322,000
Emp.: 9
Home Center Operator
N.A.I.C.S.: 444110
Daniel White (Mgr)

Branch (Domestic):

**Higginbotham Bros. & Co., LLC -
Gatesville**　　　　　　　　　　　**(4)**
2533 S State Highway 36, Gatesville, TX
76528
Tel.: (254) 865-8820
Rev.: $2,580,000
Emp.: 10
Home Center Operator
N.A.I.C.S.: 444110
Nate Byrd (Mgr)

Subsidiary (Domestic):

**Hines Building Supply - US LBM,
LLC**　　　　　　　　　　　　　　**(3)**

1050 Corporate Grove Dr, Buffalo Grove, IL 60089-4550
Tel.: (847) 353-7700
Web Site: http://www.hinessupply.com
Sales Range: $75-99.9 Million
Emp.: 115
Mfr & Distr of Custom Home Building Materials & Products
N.A.I.C.S.: 423310
Doug Jones (Pres)
Joe Stubler (Gen Mgr)

Holderness Building Materials, Inc. (3)
450 E Irvington Rd, Tucson, AZ 85714-2823
Tel.: (520) 889-1300
Web Site: https://holdernesssupplies.com
Sales Range: $10-24.9 Million
Emp.: 140
Lumber & Building Materials Mfr & Retailer
N.A.I.C.S.: 423310
Richard Alejos (Pres)
Patrick Carrico (CFO, Treas & Sec)

Homestead Building Systems Inc. (3)
10109 Piper Ln, Bristow, VA 20136
Tel.: (703) 331-5600
Web Site:
http://www.homesteadbuildingsystem.com
Rev.: $7,224,000
Emp.: 28
Home Center Operator
N.A.I.C.S.: 444110
Neal Scherer (VP-Sls)
Mike Hanlin (VP-Carpentry)

John H. Myers & Son Inc. (3)
2200 Monroe St, York, PA 17404
Tel.: (717) 792-2500
Web Site: http://www.jhmson.com
Sales Range: $50-74.9 Million
Building & Remodeling Products
N.A.I.C.S.: 423310
Robert Wood (Co-Pres)

Jones Lumber Company (3)
4500 Oak Cir, Boca Raton, FL 33431
Tel.: (561) 391-3995
Web Site: http://www.joneslumber.us
Sales Range: $1-9.9 Million
Lumber & Building Material Whslr
N.A.I.C.S.: 423310
Mark R. Jones (Pres)
Lander Talbott (Mgr)

Keene Lumber Co. (3)
346 W Laketon Ave, Muskegon, MI 49441-2630
Tel.: (231) 726-2706
Web Site: http://www.keenelumber.com
Sales Range: $1-9.9 Million
Emp.: 19
Lumber & Building Material Whslr
N.A.I.C.S.: 444110
Jerry Keene (Pres)

Kentucky Indiana Lumber - US LBM, LLC (3)
4010 Collins Ln, Louisville, KY 40245
Tel.: (502) 637-1401
Web Site: http://www.ki-lumber.com
Lumber, Millwork & Building Materials Distr
N.A.I.C.S.: 423310
Paul Miele (VP & Gen Mgr-Sls)
Scott Diebold (Mgr-Custom Mill)
John Thomas (Mgr-Roofing Div)

Maner Builders Supply Co. (3)
3717 Washington Rd, Augusta, GA 30907
Tel.: (706) 863-6191
Web Site: http://www.maner.com
Sales Range: $25-49.9 Million
Emp.: 110
Building Materials Distr
N.A.I.C.S.: 423310
Frank Chandler (Pres)

Manning Building Supplies, Inc. (3)
10900 Philips Hwy, Jacksonville, FL 32256-1551
Tel.: (904) 268-7000
Web Site: http://www.mbs-corp.com
Sales Range: $75-99.9 Million
Emp.: 420
Millwork, Lumber & Building Supplies
N.A.I.C.S.: 423310
James H. Cissel (Partner)
Rob Cashen (Mgr-Door Shop)

Massey Builders' Supply Corp. (3)
2303 Dabney Rd, Richmond, VA 23230-2947
Tel.: (804) 355-7891
Web Site: http://www.masseybuilders.com
Lumber & Building Products Distr
N.A.I.C.S.: 444180
Mike Christian (Pres)

Musselman Lumber Inc. (3)
200 Brimmer Ave, New Holland, PA 17557 (100%)
Tel.: (717) 354-4321
Web Site:
http://www.musselmanlumber.com
Sales Range: $10-24.9 Million
Lumber, Engineered Wood Products, Trusses, Windows, Doors, Siding, Roofing, Pre-Built Stairs, Pre-Hung Doors, Trim Packages & a Full Line of Hardware
N.A.I.C.S.: 444110
Galen Eby (Pres)

Raymond Building Supply LLC (3)
7751 Bayshore Rd, North Fort Myers, FL 33917-3506
Tel.: (239) 731-8300
Web Site: http://www.rbsc.net
Lumber & Other Building Materials Distr
N.A.I.C.S.: 423310
Greg Kelly (Mgr-Aluminum Window Div)
James Martin (VP-Ops)
John Cain (Supvr-Andersen Windows Sls Support)
Scott Botyos (Gen Mgr, Ops Mgr & Sls Mgr)
Danny Dunham (Coord-Special Project)

Ridout Lumber Cos., Inc. (3)
125 Henry Farrar Dr, Searcy, AR 72143
Tel.: (501) 268-3929
Web Site: http://www.ridoutlumber.com
Sales Range: $1-9.9 Million
Emp.: 17
Building Products & Materials Whslr
N.A.I.C.S.: 444180
Kristen Smith (VP)
Ross Ridout (Pres)

Subsidiary (Domestic):

Arkansas Wholesale Lumber, LLC (4)
125 Henry Farrar Dr, Searcy, AR 72143
Tel.: (501) 268-3929
Web Site: http://www.ridoutlumber.com
Sales Range: $25-49.9 Million
Emp.: 300
Provider of Lumber & Building Products
N.A.I.C.S.: 423310
Ross Ridout (VP)

Ridout Lumber Co. of Brinkley, Inc. (4)
3300 E Race Ave, Searcy, AR 72143
Tel.: (501) 268-0386
Web Site: http://www.ridoutlumber.com
Sales Range: $1-9.9 Million
Emp.: 12
Building Materials Whslr
N.A.I.C.S.: 423310
Homer Ridout (Founder)

Ridout Lumber Co. of Russellville, Inc. (4)
1717 E Main st, Russellville, AR 72801
Tel.: (479) 968-8900
Web Site: http://www.ridoutlumber.com
Sales Range: $1-9.9 Million
Emp.: 41
Building Materials Whslr
N.A.I.C.S.: 423310

Ridout Lumber Company of Batesville, LLC (4)
4489 Harrison St, Batesville, AR 72501
Tel.: (870) 793-4138
Web Site: http://www.ridoutlumber.com
Sales Range: $1-9.9 Million
Emp.: 23
Building Materials Whslr
N.A.I.C.S.: 423310

Ridout Lumber Company of Joplin, Inc. (4)
2500 W Seventh, Joplin, MO 64801
Tel.: (417) 624-5100
Web Site: http://www.ridoutlumber.com
Sales Range: $1-9.9 Million
Emp.: 28
Building Materials Whslr

N.A.I.C.S.: 423310

Subsidiary (Domestic):

Samuel Feldman Lumber Co., Inc. (3)
1281 Metropolitan Ave, Brooklyn, NY 11237-1909
Tel.: (718) 786-7777
Web Site: http://www.feldmanlumber.com
Lumber & Building Materials Distr
N.A.I.C.S.: 423310
Kenny Feldman (VP)

Shelly Enterprises, Inc. (3)
3110 Old State Rd, Telford, PA 18969 (100%)
Tel.: (215) 723-5108
Web Site: http://www.shellyssupply.com
Sales Range: $100-124.9 Million
Emp.: 500
Lumber, Hardware & Building Materials Retailer
N.A.I.C.S.: 444110
Keith Freed (Pres)
Katie Gulotta (Mgr-HR)

Standard Companies Inc. (3)
1535 Kalamazoo Ave SE, Grand Rapids, MI 49507-2129
Tel.: (616) 243-3655
Web Site:
http://www.standardcompanies.com
Holding Company; Building Materials & Household Appliances Whslr & Distr
N.A.I.C.S.: 551112
Timothy Rottschafer (Pres)
Ron Webb (Treas & Sec)

Subsidiary (Domestic):

Standard Supply & Lumber Co. (4)
1535 Kalamazoo Ave SE, Grand Rapids, MI 49507-2129
Tel.: (616) 243-3655
Web Site: http://www.standardlumber.com
Building Materials Mfr & Whslr
N.A.I.C.S.: 423310
Timothy Rottschafer (Pres)
Ron Webb (Treas & Sec)

Subsidiary (Domestic):

Truss Fab, LLC (3)
7831 N 67th Ave, Glendale, AZ 85301
Tel.: (623) 215-2738
Web Site: http://www.truss-fab.com
Sales Range: $1-9.9 Million
Emp.: 40
Truss Mfr
N.A.I.C.S.: 321215

Universal Supply Company Inc. (3)
582 S Egg Harbor Rd, Hammonton, NJ 08037-2017
Tel.: (609) 561-6300
Web Site: http://www.universalsupply.com
Sales Range: $75-99.9 Million
Emp.: 230
Roofing & Siding Materials Mfr
N.A.I.C.S.: 423330
Jeff Umosella (Pres)

Villaume Industries, Inc. (3)
2926 Lone Oak Cir, Saint Paul, MN 55121-1425
Tel.: (651) 454-3610
Web Site: http://www.villaume.com
Sales Range: $75-99.9 Million
Emp.: 150
Provider of Industrial Wood Products
N.A.I.C.S.: 321215
J. Nicholas Linsmayer (Pres)
Isaac Ganz (VP)
David Slettum (CFO)

VXI Global Solutions, Inc. (1)
220 West 1st St Ste 300, Los Angeles, CA 90012
Tel.: (213) 637-1300
Web Site: http://www.vxi.com
Sales Range: $75-99.9 Million
Business Process Outsourcing Services
N.A.I.C.S.: 561499
Nick Covelli (Sr VP-Sls & Mktg)
Eva Wang (Founder & Co-CEO)
David Zhou (Co-CEO)
Stephen Choi (CFO)
Jared Morrison (COO)

Dave Palmer (Sr VP-North America)
Joseph Wong (Sr VP-Bus Dev)
Mark Danielson (Sr VP-Ops-Americas)

Subsidiary (Non-US):

Symbio Finland Oy (2)
Finlaysoninkatu 5, Tampere, 32100, Finland
Tel.: (358) 108358300
Information Technology Application Software Engineering, Research & Development
N.A.I.C.S.: 541511

Branch (Domestic):

Symbio Finland Oy - Oulu (3)
Elektroniikkatie 8, 90590, Oulu, Finland
Tel.: (358) 10 8358 300
Web Site: http://www.symbio.fi
Emp.: 200
Information Technology Application Software Engineering, Research & Development
N.A.I.C.S.: 541511
Tero Lahteenmaki (Pres)

Varsity Brands Holding Co., Inc. (1)
4501 W 62nd St, Indianapolis, IN 46268
Tel.: (317) 297-3740
Web Site: http://www.varsitybrands.com
Emp.: 4,400
Holding Company; School & Institutional Products & Services
N.A.I.C.S.: 551112
Jeff Webb (Chm)
Adam Blumenfeld (CEO)
Joe Raines (Chief Supply Chain Officer & Exec VP)

Subsidiary (Domestic):

Herff Jones, Inc. (2)
4719 W 62nd St, Indianapolis, IN 46268-2587
Tel.: (317) 297-3740
Web Site: http://www.herffjones.com
Sales Range: $700-749.9 Million
Emp.: 2,000
School Graduation Products, Recognition & Motivational Awards, Photography & Multi-Media Instructional Programs; World Globes Mfr
N.A.I.C.S.: 339910
Joe Slaughter (Reg Mgr)
Clayton Chang (Mgr-Product Dev)
Tim Rauschenbach (VP-Customer Svc)
Maggie Waples (Sr VP & Gen Mgr-Yearbook)
Kyle Brown (Dir-Customer Svc)
Steve Down (Pres)
Salena Scardina (VP-Customer Experience)
Ronald Stoupa (Pres & CEO)

Subsidiary (Domestic):

BSN Sports, LLC (3)
1901 Diplomat Dr, Farmers Branch, TX 75234
Tel.: (972) 484-9484
Web Site: http://www.bsnsports.com
Sales Range: $200-249.9 Million
Sporting Goods & Sport Uniforms Mfr & Distr
N.A.I.C.S.: 339920
Terry Babilla (Pres)

Subsidiary (Domestic):

Athletics Unlimited, Inc. (4)
4648 Whitney Ave, Sacramento, CA 95821
Tel.: (916) 483-2352
Web Site: http://www.au1988.com
Sales Range: $1-9.9 Million
Emp.: 13
Whol Sporting/Recreational Goods Ret
Sporting Goods/Bicycles
N.A.I.C.S.: 423910
John England (Mgr)
Jordan Rasmussen (COE & Partner)

Teamline, Ltd. (4)
3117 Skyway Cir N, Irving, TX 75038
Tel.: (972) 471-0200
Web Site: http://catalog.eteamline.com
Sports Uniform & Apparel Distr
N.A.I.C.S.: 424350
Sue Ann Clark (Gen Mgr)

Division (Domestic):

Herff Jones, Inc. - Cap & Gown Division (3)

Bain Capital, LP—(Continued)

1000 N Market St, Champaign, IL 61820-3009
Tel.: (217) 351-9500
Web Site: http://www.herffjones.com
Sales Range: $25-49.9 Million.
Emp.: 215
Caps & Gowns, Choir & Judicial Robes Mfr
N.A.I.C.S.: 315250
Zach Baird (Plant Mgr)
Phil Reid (Plant Mgr)

Plant (Domestic):

Herff Jones, Inc. - Collegiate Cap & Gown, Arcola　　(4)
901 Bob King Dr, Arcola, IL 61910-1905
Tel.: (217) 268-4543
Web Site: http://www.herffjones.com
Sales Range: $25-49.9 Million
Caps & Gowns Mfr
N.A.I.C.S.: 315250
Howard Sutton (Mgr-HR)

Division (Domestic):

Herff Jones, Inc. - Jewelry　　(3)
4506 W 62nd St, Indianapolis, IN 46268-2593
Tel.: (317) 297-3740
Web Site: http://www.herffjones.com
Sales Range: $300-349.9 Million
Class Rings, Medals, Awards Mfr
N.A.I.C.S.: 339910
Jennifer Whitt (Assoc Dir-Strategic Plng & Process)
Pete Slamkowski (VP-Strategic Projects)

Herff Jones, Inc. - Yearbooks　　(3)
2525 Midpoint Dr, Edwardsville, KS 66111
Tel.: (913) 422-2400
Web Site:
　http://www.yearbookdiscoveries.com
Emp.: 300
Yearbook Production Services
N.A.I.C.S.: 513199
Greg Parkman (Plant Mgr)
Natalie Jones (Mgr-Customer Svc)

Subsidiary (Non-US):

Herff Jones Canada　　(4)
41 scufield blvd, Winnipeg, R3Y IG4, MB, Canada
Tel.: (204) 956-9920
Web Site: http://www.herffjones.com
Yearbooks Mfr
N.A.I.C.S.: 513199
Jocelyn Unrau (Specialist-Yearbook & Diploma)

Unit (Domestic):

Herff Jones, Inc. - Yearbook Marketing　　(4)
9525 Monroe Rd Ste 150, Charlotte, NC 28270
Tel.: (704) 847-9801
Web Site: http://www.herffjones.com
Emp.: 30
Yearbook Sales & Distribution Services
N.A.I.C.S.: 424920
Bruce Hartley (Gen Mgr)
Chris Glasgow (Mgr-Printing)

Plant (Domestic):

Herff Jones, Inc. - Yearbooks　　(4)
2800 Selma Hwy, Montgomery, AL 36108
Tel.: (334) 288-5260
Web Site: http://yearbookdiscoveries.com
Emp.: 70
Yearbook Production
N.A.I.C.S.: 323111
Julie Gunnell (Plant Mgr)
Donna Watson (Mgr-Customer Svc)
Adrienne Howard (Superintendent-Plant)

Herff Jones, Inc. - Yearbooks　　(4)
940 W 1400 N, Logan, UT 84323-3288
Tel.: (435) 753-7830
Web Site:
　http://www.yearbookdiscoveries.com
Yearbook Production
N.A.I.C.S.: 323111
Scott Marshall (Plant Mgr)

Division (Domestic):

Masters of Design, Inc.　　(3)

150 Herff Jones Way, Warwick, RI 02888-1332
Tel.: (401) 330-4272
Web Site: http://www.mastersofdesign.com
Sales Range: $25-49.9 Million
Award & Championship Rings, Emblematic Jewelry & Professional Awards Mfr
N.A.I.C.S.: 339910

Unit (Domestic):

Herff Jones Fine Papers　　(4)
4719 W 62nd St, Indianapolis, IN 46268-2593
Tel.: (317) 297-3740
Web Site: http://www.herffjones.com
Diplomas, Graduation Announcements & Other Related Printed Products Mfr
N.A.I.C.S.: 323111
Brian Webb (Plant Mgr)

Unit (Domestic):

Herff Jones Fine Papers - Iola　　(5)
2502 N State St, Iola, KS 66749
Tel.: (620) 365-5181
Web Site: http://www.herffjones.com
Emp.: 73
Diplomas, Graduation Announcements & Other Related Printed Products Mfr
N.A.I.C.S.: 323111

Subsidiary (Domestic):

Varsity Brands, Inc.　　(2)
6745 Lenox Ctr Ct Ste 300, Memphis, TN 38115
Tel.: (901) 387-4300
Web Site: http://www.varsitybrands.com
Sales Range: $150-199.9 Million
Emp.: 200
Cheerleading, Dance Apparel & Accessories Designer & Marketer; Cheerleading & Dance Camps Organizer
N.A.I.C.S.: 315250
Marlene Cota (VP-Corp Alliances & Bus Dev)
Sheila Noone (VP-PR)
Nicole Lauchaire (VP-Corp Mktg & Comm)
Lisa Autry (Supvr-Customer Care-Spirit Fashion)
Scott Borgmier (Mgr-Web Tech)
Jackie Martin (Mgr-Content)
Wayne Vacek (Chief Strategy Officer & VP)
Jaime Jaramillo (CTO)

Subsidiary (Domestic):

Varsity Spirit LLC　　(3)
6745 Lenox Center Ct Suite 300, Memphis, TN 38115
Tel.: (901) 387-4300
Web Site: http://www.varsity.com
Mfr & Whslr of Cheerleading & Dance Team Uniforms
N.A.I.C.S.: 611620
Nicole Lauchaire (Sr VP-Corp Comm)
Marlene Cota (VP-Corp Alliances & Bus Dev)
Bill Seely (Pres)
John Hutchinson (CFO-Brands & Exec VP)
Brett Gora (CFO)
Rick Brown (CIO)
Matt Deimund (Chief Transformation Officer)

Subsidiary (Domestic):

SA Feather Co., Inc.　　(4)
5852 Enterprise Pkwy, Fort Myers, FL 33905
Tel.: (239) 693-6363
Web Site:
　http://www.safeathercompany.com
Sales Range: $1-9.9 Million
Emp.: 27
Feather Goods Mfr & Sales
N.A.I.C.S.: 339999
Darren Samuel (CEO)

Stanbury Uniforms, Inc.　　(4)
108 Stanbury Industrial Dr, Brookfield, MO 64628
Tel.: (660) 258-2246
Web Site: http://www.stanbury.com
Band Uniforms & Marching Arts Mfr
N.A.I.C.S.: 315250
Carter Sappington (Dir-Mfg)
Steve Roberts (CEO)

Wittur Holding GmbH　　(1)

Rohrbachstrasse 26-30, 85259, Wiedenzhausen, Germany
Tel.: (49) 8134 18 0
Web Site: http://www.wittur.com
Emp.: 4,500
Holding Company; Elevators & Lift Components Mfr
N.A.I.C.S.: 551112
Sergio Biglino (Exec VP-Strategy)
Antoine Doutriaux (CEO)
Geoffroy Durandet (Mng Dir-Europe)
Aline Estevant-Rigaut (Chief HR Officer)
Christoph Kaml (CFO)
Ahmet Kanbolat (Mng Dir-Eurasia)
Hans Koenigshofer (COO)
Shaohua Li (Mng Dir-Asia)
Giorgio Scarabello (Mng Dir)
Suraj Thodimarath (Mng Dir-Asia Pacific)

Subsidiary (Domestic):

LM Liftmaterial GmbH　　(2)
Gewerbestrasse 1, Landsham, 85652, Pliening, Germany
Tel.: (49) 899099790
Web Site: http://www.wittur.com
Elevator Component Mfr
N.A.I.C.S.: 333921
Hartmut Liebig (Mng Dir)

Subsidiary (Non-US):

Sematic S.p.A.　　(2)
Via Zappa, Comm Francesco 5, 24046, Osio Sotto, Italy
Tel.: (39) 0354815100
Web Site: http://www.wittur.com
Elevator Products Mfr & Whslr
N.A.I.C.S.: 333921
Alfredo Pinotti (Dir-Global Pur)

Subsidiary (Domestic):

Computec Srl　　(3)
Via C A Dalla Chiesa, Lonato, 25017, Brescia, Italy
Tel.: (39) 030 9919700
Web Site: http://www.computeconline.it
IT Consulting Services
N.A.I.C.S.: 541690
Diego De Munari (Dir-IT & Engr-Sys)

Subsidiary (Non-US):

Sematic Elevadores Mexico S. de R.L. de C.V.　　(3)
Avenida Revolucion Mexicana n 1001 Col Barrera, Monclova, 25770, Coahuila, Mexico
Tel.: (52) 866 648 3365
Web Site: http://www.wittur.com
Elevator Component Mfr & Distr
N.A.I.C.S.: 333921

Sematic Elevator Products (Changshu) Co., Ltd.　　(3)
No 20 Jinmen Road Southeast Economic Zone, Changshu, 215533, Jiangsu, China
Tel.: (86) 512 5209 6363
Web Site: http://www.wittur.com
Elevator Component Mfr & Distr
N.A.I.C.S.: 333921

Sematic Hungaria Kft　　(3)
Debreceni ut 273, 4400, Nyiregyhaza, Hungary
Tel.: (36) 42 548 410
Web Site: http://www.wittur.com
Elevator Component Mfr & Distr
N.A.I.C.S.: 333921

Plant (Domestic):

Sematic S.p.A. - Suisio Plant　　(3)
Via dei Piazzoli 1/5, Suisio, 24040, Bergamo, Italy
Tel.: (39) 035 49 36 111
Web Site: http://www.wittur.com
Elevator Component Mfr
N.A.I.C.S.: 333921

Subsidiary (US):

Sematic USA, Inc.　　(3)
7852 Bavaria Rd, Twinsburg, OH 44087
Tel.: (216) 524-0100
Web Site: http://www.wittur.com
Emp.: 14
Elevator Mfr
N.A.I.C.S.: 333921
Roy Schaffer (Gen Mgr)

World Wide Packaging, LLC　　(1)
15 Vreeland Rd Ste 4, Florham Park, NJ 07932
Tel.: (973) 992-4994
Web Site: http://www.wwpinc.com
Cosmetic Packaging Mfr & Contract Manufacturing Services
N.A.I.C.S.: 326199
Barry Freda (CEO)
Kimyon Holmes (VP-Sls-West Coast)
Michael J. Dick (Mgr-Ops)
Rick Weisbrod (Exec VP-Global Ops)

WorldPay Ltd.　　(1)
The Science Park Milton Road Units 270-289, Cambridge, CB4 0WE, United Kingdom
Tel.: (44) 1223 258493
Web Site: http://www.worldpay.com
Online Payment Processing Services
N.A.I.C.S.: 522320
James Frost (CMO)
Ron M. Kalifa (Deputy Chm)
Mark Edwards (Grp Gen Counsel)
Michael Rake (Chm)
Asif Ramji (Chief Product Officer)

Subsidiary (US):

WorldPay US, Inc.　　(2)
600 Morgan Falls Rd Ste 260, Atlanta, GA 30350
Tel.: (770) 396-1616
Web Site: http://www.worldpay.us
Online Payment Processing Services
N.A.I.C.S.: 522320
Andy Doyle (Chief HR Officer)
Dave Hobday (Mng Dir-Worldpay UK)
Ron Kalifa (Vice Chm & Exec Dir)
Mark Kimber (CIO)
Rick Medlock (CFO)

Subsidiary (Domestic):

Century Payments, Inc.　　(3)
2601 Network Blvd Ste 200, Frisco, TX 75034
Tel.: (469) 252-0074
Web Site: http://www.centurypayments.com
Sales Range: $10-24.9 Million
Electronic Payment Processing Services
N.A.I.C.S.: 522320
Robert Wechsler (Co-Founder & CEO)
Patricia Keller (CFO & Chief Revenue Officer)
Thomas W. Bannon (COO)
Eric Frazier (Co-Founder & Chief Vision Officer)
Kristen Scott (Chief People Officer)
Irina Haydon (Chief Sls Officer)
Hila Shpigelman (CMO)
Lauren Harris (Sr VP-Sls-Inside, Trng & Customer Svc)

Zellis UK Limited　　(1)
740 Waterside Drive, Aztec West, Almondsbury, Bristol, BS32 4UF, United Kingdom
Tel.: (44) 2086021300
Web Site: https://www.zellis.com
Sales Range: $25-49.9 Million
Emp.: 100
HR, Payroll, Pensions & Reward Software & Services
N.A.I.C.S.: 923130

athenahealth, Inc.　　(1)
311 Arsenal St, Watertown, MA 02472
Tel.: (617) 402-1000
Web Site: http://www.athenahealth.com
Sales Range: $1-4.9 Billion
Emp.: 5,156
Internet-Based Healthcare Records Management Services
N.A.I.C.S.: 561499
Robert E. Segert (Chm & CEO)
Marc A. Levine (Chief Acctg Officer, Treas & Exec VP)
Stacy Simpson (CMO)
Jessica Collins (Sec)
David Young (Asst Treas)
Paul Brient (Chief Product Officer)
Caleb Anderson (Chief Sls Officer)
Rob Julavits (Exec Dir-External Comm)
George Hamilton (Chief Corp Strategy & Dev Officer)

esure Group plc　　(1)
The Observatory Castlefield Road, Reigate, RH2 0SG, Surrey, United Kingdom
Tel.: (44) 1737 222 222

Web Site: http://www.esuregroup.com
Rev.: $1,101,481,680
Assets: $2,975,495,760
Liabilities: $2,629,233,360
Net Worth: $346,262,400
Earnings: $7,344,960
Emp.: 1,835
Fiscal Year-end: 12/31/2019
Holding Company; General Insurance Products & Services
N.A.I.C.S.: 551112
Peter Wood (Founder)
Darren Boland (Chief Risk Officer)
Jon Wilshire (Chief Underwriting Officer)
Andy Haste (Chm)
David McMillan (CEO)
Peter Bole (CFO)
Andy Burton (CTO)
Justin Cockerill (Chief Comml Officer)
Graham Hughes (Chief Claims Officer)
Roy Jubraj (Chief Strategy & Transformation Officer)
Caroline Smith (Chief People Officer)
Kirsty Whitehead (Gen Counsel & Sec)
Chris Watts (Head-Investments)

Subsidiary (Domestic):

esure Insurance Ltd. (2)
The Observatory Castlefield Road, Reigate, RG2 0SG, Surrey, United Kingdom
Tel.: (44) 1737 222222
Web Site: http://www.esure.com
Sales Range: $900-999.9 Million
Emp.: 1,500
General Insurance Products & Services
N.A.I.C.S.: 524126
Jon Wilshire (Chief Underwriting Officer)

BAINBRIDGE & KNIGHT LABORATORIES
801 2nd Ave, New York, NY 10017
Tel.: (212) 986-5100
Web Site:
    http://www.bainbridgeandknight.com
Year Founded: 2009
Sales Range: $25-49.9 Million
Emp.: 50
Health Product Mfr
N.A.I.C.S.: 325412
Mark Horowitz (VP-Sls)
Carl Ruderman (Chm)
Linda McNicholas (Exec Dir-Corp Affairs)

BAINBRIDGE BANCSHARES, INC.
819 E Shotwell St, Bainbridge, GA 39819
Tel.: (229) 246-3131
Web Site: http://www.fnbdc.com
Year Founded: 2003
Emp.: 17
Bank Holding Company
N.A.I.C.S.: 551111
Donna H. Kelley (CFO & Sr VP)
Brad E. Barber (Pres & CEO)
Stephen G. Whittaker (Officer-Credit & VP)
Penny Wilson (Officer-Compliance & BSA & VP)

Subsidiaries:

First National Bank of Decatur
County (1)
819 E Shotwell St, Bainbridge, GA 39819
Tel.: (229) 246-3131
Web Site: http://www.fnbdc.com
Sales Range: $25-49.9 Million
Emp.: 15
Retail & Commercial Banking
N.A.I.C.S.: 522110
Donna H. Kelley (CFO & Sr VP)
James Reece (Sr VP-Bus & Ag Loans)
Brad E. Barber (Pres & CEO)
Stephen G. Whittaker (Officer-Credit & VP)
Ashley Vannoy (Pres-Market-Destin & Sr VP)
Barry Pollock (Pres-Market)

BAINBRIDGE INTERNATIONAL INC.
255 Revere St, Canton, MA 02021-2960
Tel.: (781) 821-2600
Web Site:
    http://www.bainbridgeint.com
Year Founded: 1917
Sales Range: $10-24.9 Million
Emp.: 35
Textile Converters
N.A.I.C.S.: 314999
Mike Cuscia (CEO)
Alan Meyers (Dir-Procurement & New Bus Dev)
Steven Collier (Mgr)
Matt Rosenberg (Mgr-Sls-Natl)
Bob Mills (Asst Mgr-Mktg)
Michael Suscia (CEO)

Subsidiaries:

Bainbridge International Ltd. (1)
8 Flanders Industrial Park Flanders Road
Hedge End, Southampton, SO30 2FZ, United Kingdom
Tel.: (44) 1489 776000
Sailcloth Mfr
N.A.I.C.S.: 314999
Jan O'Connor (Mng Dir)

BAINES MANAGEMENT CO.
Ste 601 1100 Wicomico St, Baltimore, MD 21230-2090
Tel.: (410) 783-8180   MD
Web Site: http://www.oursssave.com
Year Founded: 1986
Sales Range: $125-149.9 Million
Emp.: 300
Grocery Stores, Chain
N.A.I.C.S.: 445110
Lizanne Flowers (Controller)

BAIRD & WARNER REAL ESTATE, INC.
120 S La Salle St, Chicago, IL 60603-3564
Tel.: (312) 368-1855   IL
Web Site:
    http://www.bairdwarner.com
Year Founded: 1855
Sales Range: $100-124.9 Million
Emp.: 1,500
Residential Real Estate Brokerage & Residential Mortgage Brokerage
N.A.I.C.S.: 531210
Stephen W. Baird (Pres & CEO)
Mary Bozarth (CFO)
Wendy Dahm (Sr VP-Organizational Dev)
Tripti Kasal (Sr VP-Residential Sls)
Laura Ellis (Pres-Residential Sls & Exec VP)
Jennifer Alter Warden (COO)
Esther Phillips (Sr VP-Key Mortgage Svcs)
Jan Koch (VP-Residential Sls & Ops)
Jim Kinney (VP-Sls-Luxury Home)
Peter Papakyriacou (Sr VP-Mktg & Comm)
Steve DiMarco (Pres-Key Mortgage Svcs)
Warren Habib (Pres-Title Bus)
Elizabeth McGrath (VP-Relocation Svcs)

Subsidiaries:

Baird & Warner (1)
207 E Westminster Rd, Lake Forest, IL 60045-1881
Tel.: (847) 295-1855
Web Site: http://www.bairdwarner.com
Sales Range: $10-24.9 Million
Emp.: 40
Selling Real Estates
N.A.I.C.S.: 531210
Annette Fryzel (Dir-Bus Dev)
Troy Pieper (Comm Mgr)

BAIRD FINANCIAL GROUP, INC.
777 E Wisconsin Ave, Milwaukee, WI 53202
Tel.: (414) 765-3500   WI
Web Site: http://www.rwbaird.com
Year Founded: 2012
Rev.: $2,060,000,000
Emp.: 4,641
Fiscal Year-end: 12/31/19
Financial Holding Company
N.A.I.C.S.: 551112
Mary Ellen Stanek (Chief Investment Officer)
C. H. Randolph Lyon (Vice Chm)
Paul L. Schultz (Gen Counsel & Sec)
Steven G. Booth (Pres & CEO)
Terrance P. Maxwell (CFO)
Michael J. Schroeder (Pres-Private Wealth Mgmt)
Patrick S. Lawton (Dir-Fixed Income Capital Markets)
James R. Allen (Vice Chm)
Timothy Byrne (CIO)
Leslie Dixon (Chief HR Officer)
Rodney L. Jones-Tyson (Chief HR Officer-Global)
John Taft (Vice Chm)
Jonathan Kirkland (Dir-Global Tech & Svcs Practice-Govt & Defense)
Gary Baird Jr. (Founder & Owner)

Subsidiaries:

Robert W. Baird & Co.,
Incorporated (1)
777 E Wisconsin Ave, Milwaukee, WI 53202
Tel.: (414) 765-3500
Web Site: http://www.rwbaird.com
Investment Bankers
N.A.I.C.S.: 523150
Mary Ellen Stanek (Mng Dir & Dir-Asset Mgmt)
C. H. Randolph Lyon (Vice Chm)
Leslie H. Dixon (Chief Human Capital Officer)
Russell P. Schwei (COO)
Terrance P. Maxwell (CFO)
Michael J. Schroeder (Pres-Private Wealth Mgmt)
James H. Herrick (Mng Dir & Head-Global Trading)
Mark A. Roble (Dir-Risk Mgmt)
Patrick Steven Lawton (Mng Dir-Fixed Income Capital Markets)
Steven G. Booth (Pres & CEO)
Jeffrey F. Rogatz (Mng Dir)
Paul Schultz (Gen Counsel & Sec)
Karen Stepanski (Sr VP)
Chase Sanders (Mng Dir)
Charles B. Groeschell (Mng Dir & Sr Portfolio Mgr)
Peter J. Hammond (Mng Dir-Client Svcs)
Adrianne C. Limojoco (VP-Client Svcs)
Randall P. North (Sr VP-Client Svcs)
Warren D. Pierson (Mng Dir & Sr Portfolio Mgr)
Michael H. Possley (Mng Dir-Client Svcs)
Kathleen R. Ruidl (VP-Client Svcs)
Daniel A. Tranchita (Mng Dir & Sr Portfolio Mgr)
Kenneth Hemauer (Mng Dir & Sr Portfolio Mgr)
Brenda Hutchinson (Sr VP & Portfolio Mgr)
Timothy Steffen (Dir-Advanced Plng-Private Wealth Mgmt Bus)
Scott Grenier (Mgr-Fin & Estate Plng)
Burton Street (Sr VP & Mgr-Wealth Mgmt-Indianapolis)
John Taft (Vice Chm)
Jason P. Turetzky (Sr VP-Tucson)
Tom A. DuPlain (Sr VP-Tucson)
Dan Sullivan (Sr VP)
Richard Fisher (Sr VP)
Rudy Fernandez (Dir-Private Wealth Mgmt Div)
Hal Tearse (Sr VP)
Mark C. Micklem (Mng Dir)
Jon M. Earl (Dir)

Division (Domestic):

Baird Capital Partners (2)
227 W Monroe St Ste 1900, Chicago, IL 60606
Tel.: (312) 609-4700
Web Site: http://www.bairdcapital.com

Privater Equity Firm
N.A.I.C.S.: 523999
Gordon G. Pan (Pres)
David A. Gregorka (Partner-Venture)
Yongshan Zhang (Principal)
Alex Kessel (VP)
Scott Hoffman (Partner-Operating)
Melissa Mounce Mithal (VP-Human Capital)
Andrew Ferguson (Partner)
Chris Harper (Partner)
Michael Holgate (Mgr-Investment)
Michael Liang (Partner)
Melissa Mounce (Principal)
Benedict P. Rocchio (Partner)
Tom Smith (VP-Portfolio Ops)
Andy Tse (Partner)
Nicole Walker (Partner)
Kathleen Schultze (Mgr-IR-Global)
Donald W. Layden Jr. (Partner-Venture)

Subsidiary (Non-US):

Baird Capital Partners Europe
Limited (3)
Finsbury Circus House 15 Finsbury Circus, London, EC2M 7EB, United Kingdom
Tel.: (44) 2074881212
Web Site: http://www.bairdcapital.com
Sales Range: $75-99.9 Million
Emp.: 80
Investment Management Service
N.A.I.C.S.: 523940

Holding (Domestic):

SGX Sensortech Ltd. (4)
Sirius House Watery Lane, Wooburn Green, HP100AP, Buckingham, United
Kingdom (100%)
Tel.: (44) 1628533060
Web Site: http://www.e2vsi.com
Sales Range: $25-49.9 Million
Emp.: 30
Search Detection Navigation Guidance Aeronautical & Nautical System & Instrument Mfr
N.A.I.C.S.: 334511
Andy King (Dir-Fin)

The SR Group (UK) Ltd. (4)
95 Queen Victoria Street, London, EC4V 4HN, United Kingdom
Tel.: (44) 20 7415 0050
Web Site: http://www.thesrgroup.com
Recruitment Services
N.A.I.C.S.: 561499
David Buckley (CEO)
Alex Calcutt (CFO & COO)
Denis Turner (Head-Global Partnerships)
Stephen Menko (Head-South West & Midlands)

Holding (Domestic):

Cleanwater1, Inc. (3)
550 Sycamore Dr, Milpitas, CA 95035
Tel.: (858) 218-3745
Web Site: https://cleanwater1.com
Water Quality & Wastewater Treatment Products & Solutions
N.A.I.C.S.: 221310

Harris Research, Inc. (3)
124 12th Ave S Ste 300, Nashville, TN 37203
Tel.: (615) 739-5993
Web Site: http://www.hrisupport.com
Carpet & Upholstery Cleaner Franchise Operator
N.A.I.C.S.: 561740

Subsidiary (Domestic):

Delta Disaster Services LLC (4)
5535 W 56th Ave Unit 104, Arvada, CO 80002
Tel.: (720) 809-7335
Web Site: http://www.deltarestoration.com
Property Restoration & General Contracting
N.A.I.C.S.: 236118
Michael Mastous (Pres)

Subsidiary (Domestic):

Velocity Dynamics, LLC (3)
6595 Odell Pl Ste I, Boulder, CO 80301-3316
Tel.: (303) 530-3368
Web Site: http://www.polymersolution.com
Waste Management Services

Baird Financial Group, Inc.—(Continued)

N.A.I.C.S.: 562998
Paul Plache (Pres)

Subsidiary (Domestic):

Baird Financial Corporation (2)
777 E Wisconsin Ave, Milwaukee, WI 53202
Tel.: (414) 765-3500
Web Site:
http://www.bairdassetmanagement.com
Investment & Asset Management Services
N.A.I.C.S.: 523940

Division (Domestic):

Baird Advisors (3)
777 E Wisconsin Ave, Milwaukee, WI 53202
Tel.: (414) 765-3500
Web Site: http://www.rwbaird.com
Sales Range: $450-499.9 Million
Financial Investment Advisory & Management Services
N.A.I.C.S.: 523940
Mary Ellen Stanek (Co-Chief Investment Officer)

Subsidiary (Domestic):

Baird Funds, Inc. (3)
777 E Wisconsin Ave, Milwaukee, WI 53202
Tel.: (414) 765-3500
Web Site:
http://www.bairdassetmanagement.com
Emp.: 1,200
Open-End Investment Funds Management
N.A.I.C.S.: 525910
Mary Ellen Stanek (Pres)

Subsidiary (Domestic):

Chautauqua Capital Management LLC (2)
921 Walnut St Ste 250, Boulder, CO 80302-5152 (100%)
Tel.: (303) 541-1545
Web Site:
http://www.chautauquacapital.com
Sales Range: $1-9.9 Million
Global Equity Investment Strategies
N.A.I.C.S.: 523991
Brian Beitner (Mng Partner)
Daniel J. Boston (Partner)
David Lubchenco (Partner)
Haicheng Li (Partner)
Jesse Flores (Partner)
Michael T. Mow (Partner)

M. Griffith Investment Services, Inc. (2)
555 French Rd Bldg 2, New Hartford, NY 13413 (100%)
Tel.: (315) 797-0130
Web Site: http://www.bairdoffices.com
Investment Firm
N.A.I.C.S.: 523940

BAIRD HOME CORPORATION

3495 N US Hwy 441, Fruitland Park, FL 34731
Tel.: (352) 787-2500   FL
Web Site:
http://www.bairdhomecorp.com
Year Founded: 1947
Sales Range: $10-24.9 Million
Emp.: 15
Sales of Automotive Housing
N.A.I.C.S.: 459930
Clifton E. Baird (Founder)

BAIRD, PATRICK & CO., INC.

305 Plz 10 Harborside Financial Ctr, Jersey City, NJ 07311
Tel.: (201) 680-7300   DE
Web Site:
http://www.bairdpatrick.com
Year Founded: 1950
Sales Range: $150-199.9 Million
Emp.: 5
Dealer & Underwriter of Corporate & Municipal Securities, Stocks, Bonds & Mutual Fund Shares
N.A.I.C.S.: 523150
Stuart K. Patrick (Pres & CEO)

BAIRESDEV LLC

1 Embarcadero Ste 500, San Francisco, CA 94111
Tel.: (408) 915-4135
Web Site: http://www.bairesdev.com
Year Founded: 2009
Sales Range: $10-24.9 Million
Emp.: 700
Software Development Services
N.A.I.C.S.: 541511
Nacho De Marco (Co-Founder & CEO)
Pablo Azorin (Co-Founder & CTO)
Fernando Galano (Chief Strategy Officer)
Facundo Molina (Chief Bus Officer)
Pablo Chamorro (Chief Revenue Officer)

BAISCH & SKINNER INC.

2721 Lasalle St, Saint Louis, MO 63104
Tel.: (314) 664-1212
Web Site:
https://www.baischandskinner.com
Sales Range: $10-24.9 Million
Emp.: 55
Flowers & Florists Supplies
N.A.I.C.S.: 424930
John A. Baisch (Pres)

BAJA CONSTRUCTION CO. INC.

223 Foster St, Martinez, CA 94553
Tel.: (925) 229-0732
Web Site:
https://www.bajacarports.com
Sales Range: $75-99.9 Million
Emp.: 200
Structural Steel Erection
N.A.I.C.S.: 238120
Laura Daum (Pres)
Robert Hayworth (Owner)
Morayma Emerling (Project Mgr)
Gerardo Fernandez (Superintendent)
Joven Cuenco (Project Mgr)
Michael Franco (Superintendent)
Robert Boilini (Mgr-Bus Dev-Self Storage Div)

BAJA RANCH MARKET

328 W Huntington Dr, Monrovia, CA 91016-3304
Tel.: (626) 357-5051
Web Site:
http://www.bajaranchmarkets.com
Year Founded: 1979
Sales Range: $50-74.9 Million
Emp.: 400
Grocery Stores
N.A.I.C.S.: 445110
Sonia Bolanos (Gen Mgr)

BAJER DESIGN & MARKETING INC.

1801 Airport Rd, Waukesha, WI 53188
Tel.: (262) 650-6730
Web Site:
http://www.bajerdesign.com
Rev.: $20,000,000
Emp.: 20
Broadwoven Fabric Mills, Cotton
N.A.I.C.S.: 313210
Pamela Frontczak (Mgr-Direct Import)

BAKALARS SAUSAGE COMPANY, INC.

2219 South Ave, La Crosse, WI 54601
Tel.: (608) 784-0384
Web Site:
http://www.bakalarssausage.com
Rev.: $14,000,000
Emp.: 35

Packaged Frozen Food Merchant Whslr
N.A.I.C.S.: 424420
Nancy Wakefield (Office Mgr)
Michael E. Bakalars (Pres)
Pete Clements (Mgr-Sls)

BAKE 'N JOY FOODS INC.

351 Willow St S, North Andover, MA 01845
Tel.: (978) 683-1414
Web Site: https://www.bakenjoy.com
Sales Range: $25-49.9 Million
Emp.: 120
Cake Mixes, Prepared: From Purchased Flour
N.A.I.C.S.: 311824
Robert Ogan (Pres)
Tara O'Donovan (Mgr-Mktg)

BAKE CRAFTERS FOOD COMPANY

10673 S Lee Hwy, McDonald, TN 37353
Tel.: (423) 396-3392
Web Site:
https://www.bakecrafters.com
Year Founded: 1990
Sales Range: $50-74.9 Million
Emp.: 50
Bakery Products Mfr
N.A.I.C.S.: 311812
Michael Byrd (Pres)
Darryl Cordwell (VP-Ops)

BAKER & ASSOCIATES ADVERTISING, INC.

3963 E El Dorado, Springfield, MO 65809
Tel.: (417) 881-4704   MO
Year Founded: 1957
Sales Range: Less than $1 Million
Emp.: 4
Automotive, Financial, Health Care
N.A.I.C.S.: 541810
David B. Baker (Pres)
Susan Schule (Dir-Media)

BAKER & HOSTETLER LLP

Key Tower 127 Public Sq Ste 2000, Cleveland, OH 44114-1214
Tel.: (216) 621-0200
Web Site: https://www.bakerlaw.com
Year Founded: 1916
Sales Range: $350-399.9 Million
Emp.: 940
Law firm
N.A.I.C.S.: 541110
R. Steven Kestner (Sr Partner)
Hewitt B. Shaw (Mng Partner)
Arthur H. Lundberg (Partner)
Phillip M. Callesen (Partner)
George A. Stamboulidis (Mng Partner)
Dondi Duffy (Partner)
Elaine A. Hutchins (Partner)
Jennifer A. Mills (Partner)
Michele Gray Merrill (Exec Dir-HR)
Paul M. Schmidt (Chm-Tax Grp-Natl & Partner)
Ruth Ann Maloney (Partner)
Todd A. Dawson (Partner)
Gregory V. Mersol (Partner)
Matthew W. Caligur (Mng Partner)
Richard H. Bamberger (Partner)
Danyll W. Foix (Partner)
Teresa C. Chow (Partner)
Stephanie A. Lodise (Partner)
John F. Murphy (Partner)
Mark Hatcher (Partner)
James H. Nye (Partner)
Marie L. Carlisle (Partner)
Edward J. Jacobs (Partner)
Nicholas J. Cremona (Partner)
Dennis W. Russo (Partner)
Gina M. Mavica (Partner)

Patrick T. Lewis (Partner)
Richard M. Knoth (Partner)
Thomas R. Lucchesi (Partner)
Jason F. Hoffman (Partner-Washington)
Robert J. Tucker (Partner)
Kevin M. Bovard (Partner)
Jeffrey W. Lesovitz (Partner)
Kenneth B. Reisenfeld (Partner-Washington)
Benjamin C. Hsing (Partner)
Catherine E. Woltering (Partner)
Jennifer E. Edwards (Partner)
Trevor M. Stanley (Partner-Litigation & Political Law)
Katherine L. McKnight (Partner-Comml Litigation & Election Law)
Andrew M. Grossman (Partner-Constitutional Law & Legal Policy)
Hussein Akhavannik (Partner)
Joann Gallagher Jones (Mng Partner-Atlanta)
Steven M. Dettelbach (Partner-Litigation Grp)
L. Poe Leggette (Partner)
Mark L. Jones (Partner)
Curt Roy Hineline (Partner)
Albert T. Adams (Partner)
Alissa K. Lugo (Partner)
Amy M. Shepherd (Partner)
Adam R. Skilken (Partner)
Amy E. Vanderwal (Partner)
Alec Wightman (Partner)
Brandon T. Crossland (Partner)
Bruce W. Sanford (Partner)
Ronald B. Gaither (Partner-Atlanta)
Kevin M. Johnson (Partner-Tax-Philadelphia)
Joseph Lucci (Mng Partner-Philadelphia)
Tayan Patel (Partner)
Peter Fischer (Partner)
W. Barron Avery (Partner)
Matthew Thurlow (Partner-Washington)
Louis Cannon (Partner-Washington)
Glenn Benson (Partner)
G. Thomas Ball (Partner)
Numan Siddiqi (Partner-Bus Grp-Costa Mesa)
John Gherlein (Chm-Bus Grp)
Joseph N. Sacca (Partner-Litigation Grp-New York)
Sarah Zhao (Partner-Washington)
David G. Holcombe (Partner-Legal Svcs)
David A. Grant (Chm-Employment Grp)
Mark H. Tidman (Chm-Intellectual Property)
W. Ray Whitman (Chm-Litigation)
Ronald G. Linville (Mng Partner)
Laurin D. Quiat (Mng Partner)
Lauren J. Resnick (Mng Partner-Client Relationship)
James V. Etscorn (Mng Partner)
Jeffrey H. Paravano (Mng Partner)
Ronald S. Okada (Partner-Professional Dev)
John D. Parker (Partner & Gen Counsel)
Robert E. Craig (CIO)
Rick L. Johnson (CFO)
David D. Southern (Chief Mktg Officer)
Barbara Linney (Partner-Washington)
Marc Schildkraut (Partner-Washington)

BAKER & MCKENZIE LLP

300 E Randolph St Ste 3900, Chicago, IL 60601
Tel.: (312) 861-8000
Web Site:
http://www.bakermckenzie.com

Year Founded: 1949
Sales Range: $1-4.9 Billion
Emp.: 500
Law firm
N.A.I.C.S.: 541110
Edward Zulkey (Gen Counsel)
David P. Hackett (Partner)
Ian Siddell (Partner)
Daniel A. Rosen (Partner)
Michael Santa Maria (Partner)
James Colihan (Partner)
Michael DeFranco (Global Chm-M&A Practice)
Sinead Kelly (Partner)
Phillip Taylor (Partner-Tax Practice-Washington)
Daniel Stern (Partner-Tax Practice-Washington)
Nicole Calabro (Partner)
Paula Levy (Partner)
Kai Kramer (Partner)
Alison Stafford Powell (Partner)
Stephen Long (Partner)
Erik T. H. Scheer (Partner)
Robert Moore (Mng Partner-Miami)
Eric M. Lasry (Partner)
Summer Austin (Partner-Washington)
Jose Antonio Moran (Partner)
William Devaney (Partner-New York)
Jaclyn Pampel (Partner & Dir-Pro Bono Practice-North America)
Benjamin Ho (Partner-San Francisco)
Mackenzie Martin (Partner-Dallas)
Mark Hamer (Partner-Global Antitrust & Competition Practice-Washington)
Gary A. Seib (Partner-Hong Kong)
Jim Holloway (Partner-Toronto)
Ansgar Schott (Partner-Banking & Banking-Zurich)
Boris Wenger (Partner-Antitrust-Zurich)
Alessandro Celli (Partner-Intellectual Property & Intellectual Property-Zurich)
Narendra Acharya (Partner)
Adam Aft (Partner)
Melissa K. Allchin (Partner)
Matthew G. Allison (Partner)
Colleen Baime (Partner)
Christopher M. Bartoli (Partner)
Theodore R. Bots (Partner)
Colin Bowes-Carlson (Partner)
Addison Braendel (Partner)
Christina Sajous Bullock (Partner)
Michelle Carr (Partner)
Peter Chan (Partner)
Shusmita Chowdhury (Partner)
Robert A. Clary (Partner)
Jennifer Cohen (Partner)
Daniel F. Cullen (Partner)
Alexandra Daniels (Partner)
David J. Davis (Partner)
Hugo Dubovoy (Partner)
Michael A. Duffy (Partner)
William F. Dugan (Partner)
Elizabeth Ebersole (Partner)
Jon H. Ebner (Partner)
Michael J. Fieweger (Partner)
Milton W. M. Cheng (Chm)

BAKER & SONS AIR CONDITIONING, INC.

164 Sarasota Center Blvd, Sarasota, FL 34240
Tel.: (941) 377-3602
Web Site:
    http://www.bakerandsonsac.com
Year Founded: 1987
Sales Range: $1-9.9 Million
Emp.: 20
Heating & Air-Conditioning Contractor
N.A.I.C.S.: 238220
Bill Baker (Pres)

BAKER BARRIOS ARCHITECTS, INC.

189 S Orange Ave Ste 1700, Orlando, FL 32801
Tel.: (407) 926-3000   FL
Web Site:
    https://www.bakerbarrios.com
Year Founded: 1993
Sales Range: $1-9.9 Million
Emp.: 72
Architectural Services
N.A.I.C.S.: 541310
Carlos Barrios (Principal)
Shanon Larimer (Principal)
Ray Acosta (Principal)
Tim Baker (Founder & Principal)
Monte Olinger (Principal)
Robert K. Ledford (Principal)
Doug Leonard (Principal)
Chad Byerly (Principal)
Wayne Dunkelberger (Principal)
Mike Houseman (Principal)
Tyler Kirby (Principal)
Michael Ho-Useman (Principal-Architecture)
Michael Frohnappel (Principal)
John Slavens (Principal)
Darick Brokaw (Dir-Design Tech)
Corine Hall (Mgr-Mktg)
Kathryn Pankow (Mgr-Bus Dev)
Dan Engebretson (Principal)
Richard Jones (Principal & Dir-Plng & Landscape Architecture)

BAKER BOTTS L.L.P.

One Shell Plz 910 Louisiana St, Houston, TX 77002-4995
Tel.: (713) 229-1234   TX
Web Site: http://www.bakerbotts.com
Year Founded: 1840
Sales Range: $550-599.9 Million
Emp.: 1,001
Legal Advisory Services
N.A.I.C.S.: 541110
James H. Barkley (Partner)
John V. Anaipakos (Partner)
Michael B. Bennett (Partner)
Mark White (Chief Admin Officer)
Lydia Companion (CFO)
Tracy Hallenberger (Chief Knowledge Officer)
Gillian Ward (CMO)
John Meuser (Dir-HR & Admin Ops)
John Strange (Dir-Pricing & Project Mgmt)
George C. Lamb (Gen Counsel)
Thomas M. DiBiagio (Partner)
Kyle Clark (Partner)
William Lavery (Partner)
Andrew M. Behrman (Partner)
Lynn Neils (Partner-Litigation)
Stephen Weissman (Partner)
Megan Berge (Partner)
Nick Peacock (COO)
Barton E. Showalter (Partner)
Luke K. Pedersen (Partner)
John H. Bae (Partner-New York)
Kelly Rose (Chm-Corp Practice Grp)
Matthew Levitt (Partner-Antitrust Practice-Brussels)
Richard Brown (Partner)
Nick Collins (Partner)
John W. Martin (Mng Partner)
James A. Baker III (Partner)

BAKER BOY

170 GTA Dr, Dickinson, ND 58601
Tel.: (701) 225-4444
Web Site: https://www.bakerboy.com
Sales Range: $25-49.9 Million
Emp.: 254
Bakery Products Mfr
N.A.I.C.S.: 311919
Guy Moos (Pres)
Bill Newton (Mgr-Natl Sls)
Fred Schauer (Mgr-Safety & Environmental)

Bob Larson (COO & VP)
Melissa Krehlik (Mgr-Acctg)
Cole Simnioniw (Mgr-IT)

BAKER CAPITAL PARTNERS, LLC

575 Madison Ave 8th Fl, New York, NY 10022
Tel.: (212) 848-2000
Web Site:
    http://www.bakercapital.com
Year Founded: 1995
Sales Range: $25-49.9 Million
Emp.: 20
Investment Services
N.A.I.C.S.: 523999
Henry G. Baker (Founder & Partner)
Joseph R. Saviano (CFO)
Robert Manning (Gen Partner)

Subsidiaries:

MusicNet   (1)
220 W 42nd St 16th Fl, New York, NY 10036
Tel.: (212) 704-0280
Customized Music Download & Subscription Services
N.A.I.C.S.: 541519
Robert Glaser (Chm)
Jeff Wallace (CTO)
Frank Johnson (CEO)
Neil Smith (Exec VP-Bus Dev)

Wine.com, Inc.   (1)
222 Sutter St Ste 450, San Francisco, CA 94108
Tel.: (415) 291-9500
Web Site: http://www.wine.com
Sales Range: $1-9.9 Million
Online Wine Retailer
N.A.I.C.S.: 445320
Michael J. Osborn (Founder & VP-Mdsg)
Rich Bergsund (CEO)
David Do (VP-Ops)
William Tomaszewski (Gen Counsel)
Peter Elarde (CMO)

Subsidiary (Domestic):

A.K.A. Gourmet   (2)
1414 Harbour Way S, Richmond, CA 94804-3625
Tel.: (510) 903-7700
Web Site: http://www.akagourmet.com
Online Food & Gift Catalog
N.A.I.C.S.: 445298

BAKER CHEESE, INC.

N5279 County Rd G, Saint Cloud, WI 53079
Tel.: (920) 477-7871
Web Site:
    https://www.bakercheese.com
Rev.: $28,800,000
Emp.: 125
Cheese Mfr
N.A.I.C.S.: 311513
Brian Baker (Mng Dir)
Richard Baker (Pres)

BAKER COMMODITIES, INC.

4020 Bandini Blvd, Vernon, CA 90058-4605
Tel.: (323) 268-2801   CA
Web Site:
    https://www.bakercommodities.com
Year Founded: 1937
Sales Range: $200-249.9 Million
Emp.: 900
Rendering Company; Animal Fats & Oils, Tallow, Feed Fat, Meat & Bone Meal Producer & Distr
N.A.I.C.S.: 311613
James M. Andreoli (Pres & CEO)
Dennis N. Luckey (Exec VP)
Charlie Hernandez (Acct Mgr-Natl)
Jason Whittaker (Mgr-Info Sys)
Jesse Hernandez Jess (Plant Mgr)

Mingo Resendiz (Mgr-Corp Procurement Ops)
Ed Candioty (Acct Mgr-Natl & Mgr-Trade Show)

Subsidiaries:

Baker Commodities Inc.-Los Angeles   (1)
4020 Bandini Blvd, Vernon, CA 90058-4605   (100%)
Tel.: (323) 268-2801
Web Site:
    http://www.bakercommodities.com
Sales Range: $25-49.9 Million
Grease Removal Services
N.A.I.C.S.: 311225

One More Time Inc.   (1)
4144 Bandini, Vernon, CA 90058-4605
Tel.: (323) 268-2801
Sales Range: $25-49.9 Million
Emp.: 45
Collects Used Cooking Fats
N.A.I.C.S.: 562920

BAKER COMMUNICATIONS ADVERTISING, MARKETING & PUBLIC RELATIONS

128 E Reynolds Rd Ste 201, Lexington, KY 40517-1254
Tel.: (859) 245-1100   KY
Web Site:
    http://www.bakercomm.com
Year Founded: 1980
Sales Range: $10-24.9 Million
Emp.: 8
Communications, Consumer Marketing
N.A.I.C.S.: 541810
Thomas W. Baker (Pres)
Cindy W. Baker (Treas & Sec)
Beatrice Holland (Office Mgr)

BAKER COMPANY INC.

161 Gate House Rd, Sanford, ME 04073
Tel.: (207) 324-8773
Web Site: http://www.bakerco.com
Sales Range: $10-24.9 Million
Emp.: 155
Laboratory Apparatus & Furniture
N.A.I.C.S.: 337127
Dennis Eagleson (CEO)
David Eagleson (Pres)

BAKER CONCRETE CONSTRUCTION, INC.

900 N Garver Rd, Monroe, OH 45050-1241
Tel.: (513) 539-4000   OH
Web Site:
    https://www.bakerconcrete.com
Year Founded: 1968
Sales Range: $300-349.9 Million
Emp.: 3,500
Concrete Construction Services
N.A.I.C.S.: 238110
Daniel L. Baker (Owner)
Dennis W. Phillips (VP-Ops)
Tom Bell (Exec VP)

Subsidiaries:

Baker-Highrise Tunnel Form Operations   (1)
12000 Ford Rd, Dallas, TX 75234
Tel.: (972) 514-0055
Web Site: http://www.bakerconcrete.com
Sales Range: $10-24.9 Million
Emp.: 2
General Contractor & Developer of Concrete Buildings
N.A.I.C.S.: 238110

Dugan & Meyers LLC   (1)
11110 Kenwood Rd, Cincinnati, OH 45242-1818
Tel.: (513) 891-4300
Web Site: http://www.dugan-meyers.com
General Construction & Construction Management Services

Baker Concrete Construction, Inc.—(Continued)

N.A.I.C.S.: 236210
Linc Ketterer *(Sr VP)*
Steve Klinker *(Gen Mgr)*
Marcy Weaver *(Dir-HR)*
Jacob Becker *(Dir-Safety)*
Marty Schirmer *(Sr VP-Estimation & Pre-construction)*

Subsidiary (Domestic):

Dugan & Meyers Construction Services, Ltd.   (2)
8740 Orion Pl Ste 220, Columbus, OH 43240
Tel.: (614) 846-2826
Web Site: http://www.dugan-meyers.com
Commercial Construction
N.A.I.C.S.: 236210
Justin Koenes *(VP-Cincinnati/Columbus Ops)*

Dugan & Meyers LLC   (2)
2712 River Green Cir, Louisville, KY 40206-1085
Tel.: (502) 894-4481
Web Site: http://www.dugan-meyers.com
Commercial Construction
N.A.I.C.S.: 236220
Andy Zalla *(VP-Louisville Ops)*

BAKER DISTRIBUTING CORP.
395 N Shrewsbury Rd, North Clarendon, VT 05759-0050
Tel.: (802) 773-3397
Web Site:
  https://www.bakerdistributing.com
Rev.: $50,000,000
Emp.: 80
Distributes Beer & Other Fermented Malt Liquors
N.A.I.C.S.: 424810
David Baker *(Pres)*
Mike Lucas *(Gen Mgr)*
Paul Wells *(Coord-Safety)*

BAKER DONELSON BEARMAN CALDWELL & BERKOWITZ PC
1st Tennessee Bldg 165 Madison Ave Ste 2000, Memphis, TN 38103
Tel.: (901) 526-2000
Web Site:
  https://www.bakerdonelson.com
Year Founded: 1888
Sales Range: $250-299.9 Million
Emp.: 600
Law firm
N.A.I.C.S.: 541110
William S. Painter *(Chief Innovation Officer)*
Jennifer P. Keller *(Pres & CEO)*
Hugh Francis *(Atty)*
Christy Crider *(Chm-Health Care Litigation Practice Grp)*
Buckner Wellford *(Chm-Advocacy)*

BAKER DRYWALL CO. INC.
415 Hwy 80 E, Mesquite, TX 75150-5826
Tel.: (972) 289-5534   **TX**
Web Site:
  http://www.bakertriangle.com
Year Founded: 1974
Sales Range: $25-49.9 Million
Emp.: 500
Plastering Drywall Acoustic Ceiling & Insulation
N.A.I.C.S.: 238310
James Purser *(CFO)*
Michael Sireno *(Pres-San Antonio)*
Matthew Clark *(VP)*

BAKER ELECTRIC SOLAR
1298 Pacific Oaks Pl, Escondido, CA 92029
Tel.: (760) 690-5192
Web Site:
  http://www.BakerElectricSolar.com

Year Founded: 2005
Sales Range: $1-9.9 Million
Emp.: 25
Green Technology, Solar Panel Installation & Renewable Energy Systems
N.A.I.C.S.: 221114
Jessica McMurtrie *(Project Mgr)*
Kim Molzahn *(Dir-HR)*
Keith Randhahn *(Dir-Engrg)*
Scott Thorn *(Mgr-Ops-Controls Grp)*
Mike Teresso *(Pres)*
Jim Gagnon *(VP-Construction Ops)*
Cherri Ewing *(Controller)*
Ian Lochore *(Dir-Residential Sls)*
Jay Miller *(Dir-Ops)*
Kathi McCalligan *(Dir-Mktg)*
Brian Miliate *(CFO)*
Scott Williams *(VP-Comml, Utility Solar Ops & Safety)*

BAKER ENERGY INC.
38 Old Hickory Cove Ste A, Jackson, TN 38305
Tel.: (731) 664-1600
Rev.: $16,027,487
Emp.: 19
Petroleum Bulk Stations
N.A.I.C.S.: 424710

BAKER GROUP
1600 SE Corporate Woods Dr, Ankeny, IA 50021-7501
Tel.: (515) 262-4000
Web Site:
  https://www.thebakergroup.com
Year Founded: 1963
Sales Range: $25-49.9 Million
Emp.: 200
Plumbing, Heating & Air-Conditioning Services
N.A.I.C.S.: 238220
Gary Bridgewater *(Pres)*
Kathy Ladd *(COO & VP)*
Randy Helm *(CFO)*
Daryld Karloff *(Exec VP-Building Svcs)*
Dale J. Drent *(Mgr-Svc)*
Jim Cooper *(VP-Design & Pre-Construction)*
Mike Kordick *(VP-Fire & Security Sys)*
Doug Kumm *(VP-Mechanical Bus Unit)*
Tim Rabenberg *(VP-Control Sys Bus Unit)*
Tom Wengert *(VP-Sheet Metal Bus Unit)*
B. J. Baker III *(Chm & CEO)*

BAKER IMPLEMENT CO. INC.
915 Homecrest St, Kennett, MO 63857-1590
Tel.: (573) 888-4646
Web Site:
  https://www.bakerimplement.com
Year Founded: 1938
Sales Range: $100-124.9 Million
Emp.: 150
Farm & Garden Machinery & Equipment Distr
N.A.I.C.S.: 423820
Paul Combs *(Pres)*

BAKER INSTALLATIONS INC.
4121 Washington Rd, McMurray, PA 15317
Tel.: (724) 260-2200
Web Site: http://www.baker-installations.com
Sales Range: $25-49.9 Million
Emp.: 600
Communications Specialization
N.A.I.C.S.: 238210
Frederick Baker *(CEO)*
Jim Mazur *(COO)*
James Shaffer *(Supvr-Ops)*
John Shedd *(VP)*

BAKER MANUFACTURING COMPANY, INC.
75 Wadley St, Pineville, LA 71360-6678
Tel.: (318) 445-8015   **LA**
Web Site:
  http://www.bakermanufacturing.com
Year Founded: 1955
Sales Range: $100-124.9 Million
Emp.: 250
Mfr of Office Furniture, Except Wood
N.A.I.C.S.: 337214
Charles Martin *(Pres)*

BAKER MCMILLEN CO.
3688 Wyoga Lake, Stow, OH 44224
Tel.: (330) 923-8300
Web Site: http://www.baker-mcmillen.com
Rev.: $10,000,000
Emp.: 85
Carved & Turned Wood
N.A.I.C.S.: 321999

BAKER METAL PRODUCTS INC.
11140 Zodiac Ln, Dallas, TX 75229
Tel.: (972) 241-3553
Rev.: $11,100,000
Emp.: 135
Curtain Walls For Buildings, Steel
N.A.I.C.S.: 332321
Robert F. Baker *(Pres)*
David Wortman *(VP-Ops)*
Elson Brown *(Mgr-Product Dev)*
Mike Phares *(Project Mgr)*
Todd Hitt *(Mgr-Engrg)*

BAKER PUBLISHING GROUP
6030 E Fulton Rd, Ada, MI 49301-9106
Tel.: (616) 676-9185
Web Site:
  https://www.bakerpublishing.com
Year Founded: 1939
Sales Range: $25-49.9 Million
Emp.: 200
Books Publishing Services
N.A.I.C.S.: 513130
Richard Baker *(Chm)*
Jack Boers *(Mgr-IT)*
Jim Kinney *(Assoc Publr)*
Janelle Mahlmann *(Asst Mgr-Mktg)*
Jessica McGill *(Asst Mgr)*
John Vandenakker *(Mgr)*
Marv Moll *(Mgr-Payroll & AP)*
Michelle Plichta *(Asst Mgr-Customer Svc)*
Nathan Henrion *(Mgr-Natl Sls-ABA Digital)*
Wendy Wetzel *(Editor-Trade Books)*

Subsidiaries:

Bethany House Publishers   (1)
11400 Hampshire Ave S, Minneapolis, MN 55438
Tel.: (952) 829-2500
Web Site: http://www.bethanyhouse.com
Rev.: $37,934,188
Emp.: 40
Book Publishing & Printing
N.A.I.C.S.: 513130
Jennifer Huber *(Office Mgr)*

BAKER ROCK CRUSHING CO.
21880 SW Farmington Rd, Beaverton, OR 97007
Tel.: (503) 642-2531
Web Site: http://www.baker-rock.com
Year Founded: 1954
Sales Range: $10-24.9 Million
Emp.: 80
Highway & Street Paving Contractor
N.A.I.C.S.: 237310
Todd Baker *(Pres)*

Subsidiaries:

Baker Rock Resources   (1)
2245 NE Cumulus St Ave, McMinnville, OR 97128
Tel.: (503) 472-2189
Rev.: $13,561,113
Emp.: 10
Concrete Mixtures
N.A.I.C.S.: 423320

BAKER ROOFING COMPANY
517 Mercury St, Raleigh, NC 27603
Tel.: (919) 828-2975
Web Site:
  http://www.bakerroofing.com
Year Founded: 1915
Sales Range: $125-149.9 Million
Emp.: 775
Roofing Contractors
N.A.I.C.S.: 238160
Woody Baldwin *(CEO)*
Robert Hudson Jr. *(VP-Environmental Health & Safety)*

BAKER SPECIALTY & SUPPLY CO
701 711 Erie Ave, Logansport, IN 46947
Tel.: (574) 722-2000
Web Site:
  http://www.bakerspecialty.com
Rev.: $12,452,535
Emp.: 32
Industrial Supplies
N.A.I.C.S.: 423840
James Meyer *(Pres)*
Jeff Baker *(Pres)*

BAKER STREET PARTNERS
2410 Baker St, San Francisco, CA 94123
Tel.: (415) 659-3900   **CA**
Web Site:
  http://www.bakerstreetpartners.com
Year Founded: 1982
Sales Range: $10-24.9 Million
Emp.: 35
N.A.I.C.S.: 541810
Jack Boland *(Pres)*
Don Donovan *(Founder & CEO)*
Peter Angelos *(Owner)*
Glenn Yajko *(Dir-Media)*
Jim Willenborg *(Mng Partner)*

BAKER TECHNOLOGY ASSOCIATES, INC.
1512 16th St Ste 2, Santa Monica, CA 90404
Tel.: (310) 458-1752
Web Site: http://www.bakertech.com
Rev.: $15,419,157
Emp.: 3
Printed Circuit Boards
N.A.I.C.S.: 334412

BAKER TILLY US, LLP
205 N Michigan Ave, Chicago, IL 60601-5927
Tel.: (608) 249-6622   **IL**
Web Site: http://www.bakertilly.com
Year Founded: 1931
Emp.: 2,500
Accounting & Corporate Consulting Services
N.A.I.C.S.: 541211
Brandon D. Andries *(COO)*
Mark Alan T. Smith *(Partner)*
Kevin R. Heppner *(Mng Partner-Midwest)*
Stephen D. Levin *(Partner)*
Jean Mathews *(CFO)*
Christine M. Anderson *(Mng Partner-Growth & Specialization)*
V. Allen Smith *(CIO)*
Tammy Barboni *(CMO)*
Jeffrey L. Ferro *(CEO)*

John P. Nealon *(Mng Partner-Northern Pennsylvania)*
Todd Stokes *(Mng Partner-DC Metro Area)*
Daniel I. Altschul *(Partner)*
Jere Shawver *(Mng Partner-Assurance & Risk)*
Patrick Killeen *(Mng Partner-Michigan)*
Shawn Anderson *(Partner-Assurance Practice)*
Laura Gitlin *(Sr Mng Dir-Philadelphia)*
Tracey Nguyen *(Mng Dir)*
Michael Duke *(Principal-Healthcare Consulting Practice-North Carolina)*
Michael Ross *(Partner)*
Pietro Stuardi *(Partner)*
Christine Fenske *(Mng Partner)*
Brooke Borden *(Sr Mng Dir)*
Todd Carpenter *(Mng Partner-Real Estate & Construction Practice)*
Jaime Lawson *(Partner-Tysons)*
Cassandra Walsh *(Partner)*
Mike Zurenski *(Mgr-Comml Practice)*
Leah Makepeace *(Sr Mgr-Pub Sector & Not-for-Profit Practice)*
Alan D. Whitman *(Chm)*
Waqqas Mahmood *(Dir-Advanced Tech Innovation)*
John Doherty *(Sr Mgr-Enterprise Solutions Consulting Practice)*
David Ross *(Principal)*
Matt Rodgers *(Partner)*
Elaine Browne *(Dir-Bus Info Sys Consulting Grp)*
James Munuhe *(Partner)*
Nick Goodman *(Partner)*
Michael Perrine *(Mng Dir-Growing Transactions Practice-Austin)*
Nikki E. Bielick *(Sr Mgr-Comml Team)*
Derek V. Diethorn *(Sr Mgr-Comml Team)*
Kevin M. Brady *(Mgr-Comml Team)*
Nate J. Coblentz *(Mgr-Pub Sector & Not-for-Profit Team)*
Jonathan T. Marks *(Partner-Specialized Forensic Valuation Svcs Consulting Practice)*
Russell Fleming *(Dir-Construction & Real Estate Practice-Minneapolis)*
Rose Van Abraham *(Partner)*
Jim Alajbegu *(Partner)*
Joe Aldous *(Partner)*
Joseph A. Aldcowski *(Partner)*
Dan Andersen *(Partner)*
Anthony H. Anderson *(Partner)*
Stephen Aponte *(Partner-Tax)*
Bill Apple *(Partner)*
James H. Aronoff *(Principal)*
Ethan D. Bach *(Mng Partner)*
Matt Baker *(Partner)*
Mark T. Bakko *(Partner)*
Scott A. Barnard *(Partner)*
Jason C. Barnes *(Partner)*
Randall K. Barrus *(Partner)*
Ronald B. Barthell *(Partner)*
John Basile *(Partner)*
Paul F. Batchelor *(Partner)*
Donald N. Bernards *(Partner)*
Todd C. Bernhardt *(Partner)*
Jeremy J. Bivens *(Partner)*
Ann E. Blakely *(Principal)*
Jeff T. Blattner *(Partner)*
Todd R. Boslau *(Partner)*
Joe Schlueter *(Dir-Tax & Acct Exec)*
Kevin Brandt *(Principal-Bus Info Sys Practice)*
Joseph McCaffrey *(Partner-Govt Contractor Advisory Svcs Practice)*
Adam Grinde *(Mng Partner-Illinois)*

Subsidiaries:

Management Partners, Inc. **(1)**
1730 Madison Rd, Cincinnati, OH 45206
Tel.: (513) 861-5400

Web Site:
http://www.managementpartners.com
Rev.: $1,900,000
Emp.: 25
Fiscal Year-end: 12/31/2006
Business Management Consulting Services
N.A.I.C.S.: 541611
Gerald E. Newfarmer *(Founder, Pres & CEO)*

Middleton Raines + Zapata LLP **(1)**
9235 Katy Fwy Ste 400, Houston, TX 77024
Tel.: (713) 955-1123
Web Site: http://www.middletonraines.com
Accounting, Auditing & Tax Preparation Services
N.A.I.C.S.: 541211
Michael S. Parmet *(Partner)*
Wesley Middleton *(Partner-Tax)*
Stan Raines *(Partner-Tax)*
Liz Ngo *(Mgr-Audit)*
Carlee Stafford *(Mgr-Audit)*
Paige Baacke *(Mgr-Audit)*
Ricky Castillo *(Sr Mgr-Tax)*
Joe Gallegos *(Mgr-Tax)*
Catherine Seitz *(Dir-Mktg)*
Will Chambers *(Mgr-Tax)*
Janice Schoonover *(Mgr-Tax)*

True Partners Consulting LLC **(1)**
225 W Wacker Dr Ste 1600, Chicago, IL 60606
Tel.: (312) 235-3300
Web Site: http://www.tpctax.com
Sales Range: $25-49.9 Million
Emp.: 200
Tax & Business Advisory Services
N.A.I.C.S.: 541213
Stanley W. Jozefiak *(Mng Dir & Gen Counsel)*
Michael Chen *(Mng Dir-San Jose)*
Donald Bast *(Mng Dir)*
Gregg P. Dluginsky *(Mng Dir)*
Michael O'Connor *(Mng Dir)*
Nancy Barrett *(Mng Dir)*
John V. Aksak *(Mng Dir-Northeast)*
John P. Bennecke *(Mng Dir)*
Cathleen A. Bucholtz *(Mng Dir-Natl)*
Timothy L. Costello *(Mng Dir & CFO)*
Victor M. Polanco *(Mng Dir)*
Ross J. Valenza *(Mng Dir-Tampa)*
John E. Boseman *(Mng Dir)*
Christina Edson *(Mng Dir)*
Sonali Fournier *(Mng Dir-Tampa)*
Robert M. Gordon *(Mng Dir)*
Minah C. Hall *(Mng Dir-Chicago)*
James T. Hedderman *(Mng Dir-Chicago)*
Bernadette McConie *(Mng Dir-Long Island)*
Ryan McKenzie *(Mng Dir)*
Matthew McNally *(Mng Dir)*
Jim Sadik *(Mng Dir)*
Justin Smith *(Mng Dir)*
Steven Swaigenbaum *(Mng Dir)*
Ron L. Tambasco *(Mng Dir-Tampa)*
Robert M. Tucci *(Mng Dir)*
Troy R. Wangen *(Mng Dir)*

BAKERS INC.
85-91 Main St, Brattleboro, VT 05301
Tel.: (802) 254-2328   VT
Year Founded: 1985
Sales Range: $10-24.9 Million
Emp.: 12
Newspapers
N.A.I.C.S.: 424920
Stephen E. Baker *(Chm)*
Dennis Baker *(Pres)*

BAKERS MANAGEMENT INC.
243 W State St, Newcomerstown, OH 43832
Tel.: (740) 622-7979
Rev.: $13,383,438
Emp.: 140
Independent Supermarket
N.A.I.C.S.: 445110
Gary Baker *(Pres)*
Theresa Baker *(VP)*

BAKERS OF PARIS INC.
99 Park Ln, Brisbane, CA 94005
Tel.: (415) 468-9100
Web Site:
http://www.bakersofparis.com

Sales Range: $10-24.9 Million
Emp.: 28
Bakery Products
N.A.I.C.S.: 424490
Lionel Robbe-Jedeau *(Pres)*

BAKERSFIELD ARC
2240 S Union Ave, Bakersfield, CA 93307-4158
Tel.: (661) 834-2272   CA
Web Site: http://www.barc-inc.org
Year Founded: 1951
Sales Range: $10-24.9 Million
Emp.: 577
Intellectual & Developmental Disability Assistance Services
N.A.I.C.S.: 623210
Tracie Gray *(VP & Dir-HR)*
Jim Baldwin *(Pres & CEO)*
William Froning *(CFO & Sr VP)*
Dave Kyle *(Chief Compliance Officer & Sr VP)*
Mike Grover *(Chief Programs Officer & Sr VP)*
Doug Miller *(Chm)*
Eric Almberg *(Treas)*
Ray Creekbaum *(VP & Dir-Ops)*
Sally Rainey *(Sec)*

BAKERSFIELD PIPE & SUPPLY
3301 Zachary Ave, Shafter, CA 93263
Tel.: (661) 589-9141
Web Site:
http://www.bakersfieldpipe.com
Sales Range: $10-24.9 Million
Emp.: 70
Pipe & Tubing, Steel
N.A.I.C.S.: 423510
Erin Schutee *(Mgr-Acctg)*
Phillip Kessler *(Branch Mgr)*
Alex Gutierrez *(Mgr-HR & Ops)*

BAKERY BARN, INC.
111 Terence Dr, Pittsburgh, PA 15236
Tel.: (412) 655-1113
Web Site: http://www.bakery-barn.com
Year Founded: 2001
Sales Range: $10-24.9 Million
Emp.: 33
Grocery & Related Products Merchant Whslr
N.A.I.C.S.: 424490
Sean Perich *(Pres)*
James N. Perich *(VP)*
Joseph Hagan *(Sr Mgr-Pur & Plng)*
Matt Cruny *(CFO)*
Joe Holden *(Dir-Ops)*
Ryan Hirt *(Dir-R&D)*
Jessica Bindyke *(Mgr-Pur)*
Lee Lipper *(Sr Mgr-Ops)*

BAKERY EXPRESS - MID ATLANTIC, INC.
4711 Hollins Ferry Rd, Halethorpe, MD 21227
Tel.: (410) 281-2000
Web Site:
http://www.bakeryexpressusa.com
Sales Range: $10-24.9 Million
Emp.: 200
Cake & Dessert Mfr
N.A.I.C.S.: 311812
Steve Borsh *(VP)*
Ross Kendricks *(Asst Mgr-Production)*

BAL HARBOUR SHOPS, LLLP
9700 Collins Ave, Bal Harbour, FL 33154
Tel.: (305) 866-0311   FL
Web Site:
https://www.balharbourshops.com
Year Founded: 1965

Sales Range: $1-9.9 Million
Emp.: 76
Commercial Real Estate Operator
N.A.I.C.S.: 531120
Stanley Whitman *(Founder & Owner)*
Randall Whitman *(Mng Partner)*
Matthew Whitman Lazenby *(Partner & Dir-Leasing)*
Richard Lodes *(Gen Mgr)*
Cheryl Stephenson *(Dir-Mktg)*

BALANCE POINT CAPITAL ADVISORS, LLC
285 Riverside Ave Ste 200, Westport, CT 06880
Tel.: (203) 652-8250
Web Site:
http://www.balancepointcapital.com
Year Founded: 2007
Investment Management
N.A.I.C.S.: 523999
Eric J. Dale *(Partner)*
Seth W. Alvord *(Mng Partner)*
Amanda Meltzer *(CFO)*
Eric J. Dale *(Partner)*

Subsidiaries:

CraneTech, Inc. **(1)**
4082 Metro Dr., Stockton, CA 95215
Tel.: (209) 824-4500
Web Site: https://www.cranetechusa.com
Overhead Traveling Cranes Hoists And Monorail Systems
N.A.I.C.S.: 333923
Eric Factor *(CEO)*

Subsidiary (Domestic):

Ameracrane & Hoist, LLC. **(2)**
308 S Main St, Owasso, OK 74055
Tel.: (918) 274-3880
Rev.: $1,309,000
Emp.: 7
Construction, Mining & Forestry Machinery & Equipment Rental & Leasing
N.A.I.C.S.: 532412
Jim Kielty *(Coord-Production)*

Twin City Crane & Hoist Inc. **(2)**
2125 Washington St, Anthony, NM 88021
Tel.: (575) 882-5555
Web Site: http://www.twincitycrane.com
Commercial, Industrial Machinery & Equipment Repair & Maintenance Services
N.A.I.C.S.: 811310

BALANCE STAFFING, INC.
800 E Cypress Creek Rd Ste 300, Fort Lauderdale, FL 33334
Tel.: (954) 772-4888   FL
Web Site:
http://www.balancestaffing.com
Year Founded: 1997
Sales Range: $1-9.9 Million
Emp.: 82
Temporary Staff Recruiter
N.A.I.C.S.: 561320
Robert Feinstein *(Co-Founder & CEO)*

BALANCE TECHNOLOGY INC.
7035 Jomar Dr, Whitmore Lake, MI 48189
Tel.: (734) 769-2100
Web Site:
http://www.balancetechnology.com
Year Founded: 1968
Rev.: $20,000,000
Emp.: 115
Mfr of Industrial Balancing & Correction Systems
N.A.I.C.S.: 334519
Thomas P. Plunkett *(Pres)*
Bruce Mitchell *(VP-Mktg & Sls)*
Thomas Straub *(Supvr-Mfg)*

BALANCED BODY, INC.
5909 88th St, Sacramento, CA 95828
Tel.: (916) 388-2838
Web Site: https://www.pilates.com

Balanced Body, Inc.—(Continued)

Sales Range: $10-24.9 Million
Emp.: 150
Pilates Equipment
N.A.I.C.S.: 339920
Ken Endelman *(Founder & CEO)*
Dan Wilson *(Mgr-Comm)*

BALANCEPOINT, INC.
9201 Ward Pkwy Ste 200, Kansas
City, MO 64114
Tel.: (816) 268-1400
Web Site:
    http://www.balancepointcorp.com
Year Founded: 2004
Sales Range: $1-9.9 Million
Emp.: 30
Consulting Firm
N.A.I.C.S.: 541618
Jacquie Morgan *(Founder)*
Scott Lippert *(Founder)*

**BALBOA CAPITAL CORPORA-
TION**
535 Anton Blvd, Costa Mesa, CA
92626
Tel.: (949) 756-0800
Web Site:
    http://www.balboacapital.com
Sales Range: $10-24.9 Million
Emp.: 150
Machinery & Equipment Finance
Leasing
N.A.I.C.S.: 522220
Phil Silva *(Pres)*
Robert Rasmussen *(COO)*
Patrick Ontal *(VP-Sls)*
Mark Johnston *(Mgr-Sls-Equipment
Vendor Svcs Grp)*
Tom Miller *(Dir-Sls & Dealer Dev-
Equipment Dealer Financing Div)*
Kelly Cameron *(Program Mgr-
Equipment Dealer Financing Div)*
James Grant *(VP-Portfolio Mgmt)*
Matthew Goldenberg *(Treas)*
Heather Parker *(CFO)*
Michael Veneziano *(Acct Mgr-
Franchise Fin Div)*

**BALBOA TRAVEL MANAGE-
MENT**
5414 Oberlin Dr Ste 300, San Diego,
CA 92121
Tel.: (858) 678-3300
Web Site: https://www.balboa.com
Rev.: $27,100,000
Emp.: 100
Travel Agencies
N.A.I.C.S.: 561510
Jose G. Da Rosa *(Chm)*
Mary Alice Gonsalves *(Vice Chm)*
Denise Jackson *(Pres & CEO)*
John Cruse *(Mgr)*
Inez Reynolds *(Sr VP-Fin & Data So-
lutions)*
Bill Russell *(VP-IT)*
Phyllis Nakano *(Dir-Vendor Rels)*
Sandee Crouse *(Dir-Data Solutions)*
Tina Gilmore *(Dir-Airline Rels)*
Stephen Thomas-Schulere *(Sr VP-
Strategic Solutions)*
Thomas Cates *(Exec VP-Strategic
Bus Dev)*

BALCOM & MOE INC.
2520 Commercial Ave, Pasco, WA
99301
Tel.: (509) 547-3383
Web Site:
    https://www.balcomandmoe.com
Rev.: $13,200,000
Emp.: 100
Vineyard & Winery
N.A.I.C.S.: 111332

Jared W. Balcom *(Pres)*
Julie Shephard *(Treas & Sec)*
Maurice Balcom Jr. *(VP)*

BALCONES RECYCLING, INC.
9301 Johnny Morris Rd, Austin, TX
78724
Tel.: (512) 472-3355   TX
Web Site:
    https://www.balconesresources.com
Year Founded: 1994
Sales Range: $10-24.9 Million
Emp.: 165
Recycling, Document Destruction &
Alternative Energy Sourcing Services
N.A.I.C.S.: 562920
Kerry R. Getter *(Founder, Chm &
CEO)*
Sara Koeninger *(Sr VP-Corp Svcs)*
Russell Getter *(Pres & COO)*
Adam Vehik *(CFO)*

Subsidiaries:

Balcones Recycling, Inc. - Dallas
Facility   (1)
13921 Senlac Dr Ste 200, Farmers Branch,
TX 75234
Tel.: (972) 481-1400
Web Site:
    http://www.balconesresources.com
Recycling Services
N.A.I.C.S.: 562920
Russell Luker *(Gen Mgr)*

Balcones Recycling, Inc. - Little Rock
Facility   (1)
4501 Thibault Rd, Little Rock, AR 72206
Tel.: (501) 490-0500
Web Site:
    http://www.balconesresources.com
Rev.: $6,160,000
Emp.: 35
Recycling, Document Destruction & Alterna-
tive Energy Sourcing Services
N.A.I.C.S.: 562920

**BALDOR SPECIALTY FOODS
INC.**
155 Food Center Dr, Bronx, NY
10474
Tel.: (718) 860-9100
Web Site:
    https://www.baldorfood.com
Food Distr
N.A.I.C.S.: 424480
T. J. Murphy *(CEO)*
Michael Muzyk *(Pres)*

Subsidiaries:

Merex Food Corp.   (1)
1120 Saw Mill River Rd, Yonkers, NY
10710-3229
Tel.: (914) 376-0202
Sales Range: $10-24.9 Million
Emp.: 130
Specialty Fruit & Vegetable Distr
N.A.I.C.S.: 424480

Pierless Fish Corp.   (1)
63 Flushing Ave Ut313, Brooklyn, NY 11205
Tel.: (718) 222-4441
Web Site: http://pierlessfish.com
Sales Range: $1-9.9 Million
Emp.: 15
Fish & Seafood Markets
N.A.I.C.S.: 445250
Robert DeMasco *(Founder)*

**BALDRICA ADVERTISING &
MARKETING**
5660 Corporate Way, West Palm
Beach, FL 33407-2002
Tel.: (561) 683-0404
Web Site: http://www.baldrica.net
Sales Range: $10-24.9 Million
Emp.: 20
Advertising Agencies
N.A.I.C.S.: 541810

Bob Baldrica *(Mng Partner)*
John Garcia *(Dir-Digital)*
Lynn Chasmar *(Dir-Sls)*
Michael Bredahl *(Dir-Sls)*

BALDT, INC.
801 W 6th St, Chester, PA 19013-
3709
Tel.: (610) 447-5200   PA
Web Site: http://www.baldt.com
Year Founded: 1901
Sales Range: $50-74.9 Million
Emp.: 20
Mooring, Anchoring & Rigging Sys-
tems for Offshore Construction &
Commerical Shipping
N.A.I.C.S.: 332510

BALDWIN & OBENAUF, INC.
50 Division St Ste 401, Somerville,
NJ 08876
Tel.: (908) 685-1510   NJ
Web Site: http://www.bnoinc.com
Year Founded: 1981
Graphic & Web Design Services
N.A.I.C.S.: 541810
Joanne Obenauf *(Founder & CEO)*

Subsidiaries:

Graphic Matter, Inc.   (1)
50 Div St Ste 401, Somerville, NJ 08876
Tel.: (908) 685-1510
Web Site: http://www.gm.bnoinc.com
Graphic Design Services
N.A.I.C.S.: 541430

**BALDWIN & SHELL CON-
STRUCTION CO. INC.**
1000 W Capitol Ave, Little Rock, AR
72201
Tel.: (501) 374-8677   AR
Web Site:
    https://www.baldwinshell.com
Year Founded: 1971
Sales Range: $25-49.9 Million
Emp.: 150
General Contractors
N.A.I.C.S.: 236220
Scott Copas *(Pres & CEO)*
Doug Henson *(Exec VP)*
Hank Johns *(Exec VP-
Preconstruction Svcs)*
Karl Bartley *(VP-Field Ops)*
Steve Hurley *(Pres-Construction Svcs
Div)*
Tony Curtis *(VP-Central Arkansas
Team)*
Chuck Hesselbein *(VP-Estimating &
Preconstruction)*
Jeff Marcussen *(VP-Mktg & Bus Dev)*
Ron Pitts *(Controller)*
Sam Smith *(Dir-HR)*
Nick Copas *(Pres-Industrial Svcs)*
Rick Terry *(Pres-Northeast Arkansas)*
Laura McCabe *(Dir-Creative & Mktg)*
Adam Cunningham *(Project Mgr-
Construction Svcs Div)*
Maggie Estes *(Project Coord-
Construction Svcs Div)*
Michael Hansberry *(Project Mgr-
Central)*
Aristo C. Brizzola *(Principal & VP)*
Jim Minor *(COO & VP)*
Amanda Mack *(Head-HR)*
Bobby Gosser Jr. *(Pres-Central Ar-
kansas)*

Subsidiaries:

Baldwin & Shell Construction Co. Inc.
- Northeast Arkansas Division   (1)
110 Gee St, Jonesboro, AR 72401
Tel.: (870) 910-5400
Industrial Building Construction Services
N.A.I.C.S.: 236210
Rick Terry *(Pres)*
Libii Fairhead *(Dir-Bus Dev)*

Baldwin & Shell Construction Co. Inc.
- Northwest Arkansas Division   (1)
593 Horsebarn Rd Ste 100, Rogers, AR
72758
Tel.: (479) 845-1111
Industrial Building Construction Services
N.A.I.C.S.: 236210
Patrick Tenney *(Pres & Treas)*
Jim Minor *(COO & VP)*

**BALDWIN COUNTY MENTAL
HEALTH-MENTAL RETARDA-
TION SERVICES, INC.**
372 S Greeno Rd, Fairhope, AL
36532-1916
Tel.: (251) 928-2871   AL
Web Site: http://www.bcmhcal.com
Year Founded: 1974
Sales Range: $1-9.9 Million
Emp.: 50
Outpatient Mental Health & Sub-
stance Abuse Centers
N.A.I.C.S.: 621420
Carol A. Mann *(Dir-PR)*

Subsidiaries:

Cheaha Regional Mental Health
Center   (1)
351 W 3rd St, Sylacauga, AL 35150
Tel.: (256) 245-1340
Web Site: http://www.crmhc.org
Rev.: $8,060,910
Assets: $6,346,454
Liabilities: $857,293
Net Worth: $5,489,161
Earnings: $71,586
Emp.: 189
Fiscal Year-end: 09/30/2014
Intellectual Disability Assistance Services
N.A.I.C.S.: 623210
Shakil Khan *(Dir-Medical)*
Cynthia L. Atkinson *(Exec Dir)*
Karen McKinney *(Dir-Clinical-Mental Health
Svcs)*
David Stevens *(Dir-Substance Use & Pre-
vention Svcs)*
Ann Cunningham *(Coord-Intellectual Dis-
abilities Div)*
Keith Honeycutt *(Mgr-Physical Facilities)*
Michele Ryan *(Mgr-Bus Office)*
Mikah Campbell *(Coord-Info Tech)*

BALDWIN CPAS, PLLC
713 W Main St, Richmond, KY
40475-1351
Tel.: (859) 626-9040   KY
Web Site:
    https://www.baldwincpas.com
Sales Range: $10-24.9 Million
Accounting & Consulting Services
N.A.I.C.S.: 541211
G. Alan Long *(Mng Partner)*
Myron D. Fisher *(Partner)*
Chris Hatcher *(Partner)*

BALDWIN EMC
19600 Hwy 59, Summerdale, AL
36580
Tel.: (251) 989-6247
Web Site:
    https://www.baldwinemc.com
Sales Range: $50-74.9 Million
Emp.: 230
Electric Power Distr
N.A.I.C.S.: 221122
Clyde Abrams *(VP-Admin Svcs)*
Tim Hobbs *(Mgr-Pur & Warehouse)*
Chad Thomas *(Coord-Power Sys
Control)*

**BALDWIN FAMILY HEALTH
CARE, INC.**
1615 Michigan Ave, Baldwin, MI
49304
Tel.: (231) 745-4624   MI
Web Site:
    http://www.familyhealthcare.org
Sales Range: $25-49.9 Million
Emp.: 346

Health Care Srvices
N.A.I.C.S.: 621111
Kathy Sather (Pres & CEO)
Jocelyn Pouliot (Chief Medical Officer)
Bonnie Mapes (COO, Officer-HIPAA Compliance & Dir-Ops)
Kevin Halub (Chief Dental Officer)
Anne Featherstone (Chief Organizational Dev Officer & VP-HR)

BALDWIN PAVING COMPANY INC.

1014 Kenmill Dr NW, Marietta, GA 30060-7911
Tel.: (770) 425-9191   GA
Web Site: https://www.baldwin-paving.com
Year Founded: 1979
Sales Range: $10-24.9 Million
Emp.: 250
Highway & Street Construction
N.A.I.C.S.: 237310
Ernest L. Baldwin (Pres)

Subsidiaries:

Baldwin Paving Company Inc. - Plant 1   (1)
398 Marble Mill Rd, Marietta, GA 30060
Tel.: (770) 425-2839
Emp.: 5
Asphalt Paving Mixture Mfr
N.A.I.C.S.: 324121
Don Garrett (Plant Mgr)

Baldwin Paving Company Inc. - Plant 2   (1)
5396 W Lees Mill Rd, College Park, GA 30349
Tel.: (770) 907-7592
Asphalt Paving Mixture Mfr
N.A.I.C.S.: 324121

Baldwin Paving Company Inc. - Plant 3   (1)
6505 Bankhead Hwy, Douglasville, GA 30134
Tel.: (770) 920-9168
Asphalt Paving Mixture Mfr
N.A.I.C.S.: 324121

Baldwin Paving Company Inc. - Plant 4   (1)
290 Parks Mill Rd, Auburn, GA 30011
Tel.: (770) 237-3284
Web Site: http://www.baldwin-paving.com
Asphalt Paving Mixture Mfr
N.A.I.C.S.: 324121

Baldwin Paving Company Inc. - Plant 5   (1)
1535 Ronald Reagan Blvd, Cumming, GA 30041
Tel.: (678) 947-6564
Web Site: http://www.baldwinpaving.com
Emp.: 4
Asphalt Paving Mixture Mfr
N.A.I.C.S.: 324121
Benji Redington (Mgr)

Baldwin Paving Company Inc. - Plant 6   (1)
251 Elzie Johnson Rd, Newnan, GA 30265
Tel.: (770) 251-0006
Web Site: http://www.baldwin-paving.com
Asphalt Paving Mixture Mfr
N.A.I.C.S.: 324121

BALDWIN POLE & PILING COMPANY

1101 N Hwy 31, Bay Minette, AL 36507
Tel.: (251) 937-2141
Web Site: http://www.baldwinpole.com
Sales Range: $10-24.9 Million
Emp.: 80
Poles & Pole Crossarms, Treated Wood & Concrete
N.A.I.C.S.: 321114
Thomas A. McMillian (Pres)
Michelle Cox (Controller)

BALDWIN REDI-MIX CO. INC.

611 Martin Luther King Blvd, Baldwin, LA 70514
Tel.: (337) 923-4955
Sales Range: $10-24.9 Million
Emp.: 85
Ready Mixed Concrete
N.A.I.C.S.: 327320
Clint M. Bishop (VP)
Stewart J. Bishop (Treas)
Donald J. Bishop Jr. (Pres)

BALDWIN RICHARDSON FOODS COMPANY

1 Tower Ln Ste 2390, Oakbrook Terrace, IL 60181
Tel.: (630) 607-1780   IL
Web Site: https://www.brfoods.com
Year Founded: 1916
Sales Range: $50-74.9 Million
Emp.: 210
Food & Beverage Ingredient Mfr
N.A.I.C.S.: 311999

Subsidiaries:

Baldwin Richardson Foods Company - Macedon Manufacturing Facility   (1)
3268 Blue Heron View, Macedon, NY 14502
Tel.: (888) 273-6637
Perishable Prepared Food Mfr
N.A.I.C.S.: 311991

Baldwin Richardson Foods Corporation   (1)
3268 Blue Heron Dr, Macedon, NY 14502   (100%)
Tel.: (315) 986-2727
Web Site: http://www.brfoods.com
Sales Range: $25-49.9 Million
Toppings & Flavors for Ice Cream, Drink Syrups, Juice Bases, Ice Cream Cones, Mustard Relish & Sauces
N.A.I.C.S.: 311930
Eric Johnson (CEO)
Erin Tolefree (COO)

BALDWIN SUPPLY COMPANY

601-11th Ave S, Minneapolis, MN 55415
Tel.: (612) 338-6911
Web Site: https://www.baldwinsupply.com
Sales Range: $200-249.9 Million
Emp.: 100
Power Transmission Equipment, Electric
N.A.I.C.S.: 423610
Jim O'Connor (Exec VP)
Rob LaRue (Pres & COO)

BALE CHEVROLET

13101 Chenal Pkwy, Little Rock, AR 72211
Tel.: (501) 221-9191
Web Site: https://www.balechevrolet.com
Sales Range: $75-99.9 Million
Emp.: 120
New & Used Car Dealers
N.A.I.C.S.: 441110
Becky Shrum (Controller)
John H. Bale Jr. (Pres)

BALE OF KENTUCKY, INC.

1288 E Main St, Horse Cave, KY 42749-1626
Tel.: (270) 786-2124   KY
Year Founded: 1984
Sales Range: $125-149.9 Million
Emp.: 210
Tobacco Auctioning & Warehousing; Petroleum Bulk Stations; Bituminous Coal & Lignite-Surface; Tires, Tubes, Supplies & Parts Distr & Whslr
N.A.I.C.S.: 424710

Thomas M. Bale (Pres)
David Denton (CFO)
Lester Bale (CEO)

Subsidiaries:

Farmers Investment Company, Inc.   (1)
1288 E Main St, Horse Cave, KY 42749-1626
Tel.: (270) 786-2124
Sales Range: $10-24.9 Million
Emp.: 3
Tobacco Auctioning & Warehousing, Motels, Commercial & Industrial Building Operation
N.A.I.C.S.: 424590

BALES CONTINENTAL COMMISSION COMPANY

39763 US Hwy 14, Huron, SD 57350
Tel.: (605) 352-8682
Web Site: http://www.balesccc.com
Year Founded: 1939
Rev.: $38,000,000
Emp.: 45
Livestock Whslr
N.A.I.C.S.: 424520
Kent Bales (Co-Owner)
Alan Bales (Co-Owner)

BALES MOTOR COMPANY

630 Broadway St, Jeffersonville, IN 47130-3526
Tel.: (812) 282-4356   IN
Web Site: http://www.balesmotors.com
Year Founded: 1952
Sales Range: $75-99.9 Million
Emp.: 85
New & Used Cars Dealers
N.A.I.C.S.: 441110
Leslie D. Albro (Co-Pres)
David Lewis (Co-Pres)

BALFOUR TIMBER COMPANY INC.

1101 W Clay St, Thomasville, GA 31792
Tel.: (229) 228-1991
Sales Range: $10-24.9 Million
Emp.: 18
Timber Products Distr
N.A.I.C.S.: 423990
Charles A. Balfour (Pres)

BALI LEATHERS INC.

503 N Perry St, Johnstown, NY 12095
Tel.: (518) 762-0041
Rev.: $10,000,000
Emp.: 599
Gloves, Sport & Athletic: Boxing, Handball & Other Related Items
N.A.I.C.S.: 339920
John Widdemer (Pres)

BALIHOO, INC.

404 S 8th St Ste 300, Boise, ID 83702
Tel.: (208) 629-7520
Web Site: http://www.balihoo.com
Year Founded: 2004
Sales Range: $1-9.9 Million
Emp.: 42
Marketing Automation Software & Technology Services
N.A.I.C.S.: 513210
Paul Price (CEO)
Anne-Marie Packwood (VP-Fin)
Christopher Cunningham (VP-Sls & Strategic Partnerships)

BALISE MOTOR SALES CO.

1339 Riverdale St, West Springfield, MA 01089-4916
Tel.: (413) 734-8795   MA
Web Site: http://www.baliseauto.com
Year Founded: 1929

Sales Range: $25-49.9 Million
Emp.: 800
Automobile Dealership
N.A.I.C.S.: 441110
Dale A. MacDonald (Dir-Media)
James E. Balise Jr. (Pres)

BALKEMA EXCAVATING INC.

1500 River St, Kalamazoo, MI 49048
Tel.: (269) 345-5289
Rev.: $20,000,000
Emp.: 80
Underground Utilities Contractor
N.A.I.C.S.: 237110
Daniel Balkema (Pres)

BALL CHAIN MFG CO, INC.

741 S Fulton Ave, Mount Vernon, NY 10550
Tel.: (914) 664-7500   NY
Web Site: http://www.ballchain.com
Year Founded: 1938
Sales Range: $1-9.9 Million
Emp.: 90
Mfg Ball Type Chain
N.A.I.C.S.: 332111
James Taubner (Treas)
Bill Taubner (Pres)

Subsidiaries:

Jonmandy Corp.   (1)
151 Ella Grasso Ave, Torrington, CT 06790
Tel.: (860) 482-2354
Web Site: http://www.jonmandy.com
Electroplating, Plating, Polishing, Anodizing & Coloring
N.A.I.C.S.: 332813
Donald Nardozzi (Pres)

BALL HOMES INC.

3609 Walden Dr, Lexington, KY 40517
Tel.: (859) 268-1191   KY
Web Site: http://www.ballhomes.com
Year Founded: 1959
Sales Range: $25-49.9 Million
Emp.: 175
Single-Family Housing Construction Mfr
N.A.I.C.S.: 236115
Michael Ball (VP)
Lisa Ball (VP)
Don Ray Ball Jr. (Pres)

BALL HORTICULTURAL COMPANY

622 Town Rd, West Chicago, IL 60185-2698
Tel.: (630) 231-3600   IL
Web Site: https://www.ballhort.com
Year Founded: 1905
Sales Range: $300-349.9 Million
Emp.: 500
Horticultural Products Distr
N.A.I.C.S.: 111422
Anna C. Ball (Pres & CEO)

Subsidiaries:

Ball Colegrave Ltd   (1)
Milton Road West Adderbury, Banbury, OX17 3EY, Oxfordshire, United Kingdom
Tel.: (44) 12 95 810632
Web Site: http://www.ballcolegrave.co.uk
Sales Range: $10-24.9 Million
Emp.: 60
Seed & Plant Distr
N.A.I.C.S.: 115112
Sandy Shepherd (Mng Dir)

Ball Colombia Ltda.   (1)
Ave 82 7-22 Santafe de Bogota, Bogota, Colombia
Tel.: (57) 12 182861
Web Site: http://www.ballsb.com
Sales Range: $10-24.9 Million
Emp.: 50
Horticulture & Floriculture Distr
N.A.I.C.S.: 111422

Ball FloraPlant   (1)

Ball Horticultural Company—(Continued)

622 Town Rd, West Chicago, IL 60185-2698
Tel.: (630) 231-3600
Sales Range: $50-74.9 Million
Emp.: 350
Floraculture Production Services
N.A.I.C.S.: 111422

Ball Horticultural (Kunming) Co., Ltd. (1)
Dongtun Village Xiaojie Town, Songming County, Kunming, 651708, Yunnan, China
Tel.: (86) 871 7981621
Web Site: http://www.ballhort.cn
Horticulture & Floriculture Distr
N.A.I.C.S.: 115112

Ball Horticultural Company - Australia (1)
735 Western Port Hwy Cnr Hall Rd, Skye, Melbourne, 3977, VIC, Australia
Tel.: (61) 3 9798 5355
Web Site: http://www.ballaustralia.com
Sales Range: $10-24.9 Million
Emp.: 50
Horticulture & Floriculture Services
N.A.I.C.S.: 111422
Patrick Tai (Fin Mgr)
Russell Maxwell (Mgr-Ops)
Gideon Cox (Product Mgr)
Kate Grant (Mgr-Mktg)
Paul Boland (Mng Dir)

Ball Publishing (1)
622 Town Rd, West Chicago, IL 60186
Tel.: (630) 231-3675
Web Site: http://www.ballpublishing.com
Sales Range: $10-24.9 Million
Emp.: 24
Trade Journal Services
N.A.I.C.S.: 513120
Kathy Wootton (Mgr-Production)
Chris Truesdale (Dir-Creative)
Kim Brown (Mgr-Acct)
Jennifer Zurko (Mng Editor-Grower Talks)

Ball Seed Co. (1)
622 Town Rd, West Chicago, IL 60185-2698 (100%)
Tel.: (630) 231-3500
Web Site: http://www.ballseed.com
Sales Range: $10-24.9 Million
Emp.: 70
Distribution of Horticultural Products to Greenhouse Growers
N.A.I.C.S.: 111422
Peter Kruger (Gen Mgr)

Ball Straathof (Pty) Ltd. (1)
1550 Printech Ave Laserpark Ext 1, Honeydew, Roodepoort, 2040, South Africa
Tel.: (27) 11 794 2316
Web Site: http://www.ballstraathof.co.za
Sales Range: $25-49.9 Million
Emp.: 150
Horticulture & Floriculture Services
N.A.I.C.S.: 111422
Marlaen Straathof (Mng Dir)

Ball do Brasil (1)
Rua Campo de Pouso 1180 Bairro Centro, Holambra, 13825000, Sao Paulo, Brazil
Tel.: (55) 193802 9700
Horticulture & Floriculture Distr
N.A.I.C.S.: 111422

Bordon Hill Nurseries Ltd. (1)
Bordon Hill, Stratford-upon-Avon, CV37 9RY, Warwickshire, United Kingdom
Tel.: (44) 1789 292792
Web Site: http://www.bordonhill.com
Emp.: 100
Horticulture & Floriculture Distr
N.A.I.C.S.: 111422
Paul Kimbrey (Mgr-Ops)
Andrea Kingston (Acct Mgr)
Michelle Dale (Officer-HR)

KinderGarden Plants Ltd (1)
Sunnyfield Nurseries Wragg Marsh, Spalding, PE12 6HH, Lincolnshire, United Kingdom
Tel.: (44) 14 06 370239
Web Site: http://www.kindergarden.co.uk
Sales Range: $10-24.9 Million
Emp.: 4
Horticulture & Floriculture Distr
N.A.I.C.S.: 111422

Ian Cole (Gen Mgr)

Linda Vista S.A. (1)
100 S 50 E 600 S De Iglesia De Dulce Nombre De Car, Cartago, 2050, Costa Rica
Tel.: (506) 25504800
Sales Range: $75-99.9 Million
Horticulture & Floriculture Distr
N.A.I.C.S.: 111422

PanAmerican Seed Co. (1)
622 Town Rd, West Chicago, IL 60185-2614
Tel.: (630) 231-1400
Web Site: http://www.panamseed.com
Sales Range: $25-49.9 Million
Emp.: 100
Hybrid Flower Seed Distr
N.A.I.C.S.: 111422

The Conard-Pyle Company (1)
25 Lewis Rd, West Grove, PA 19390-9701
Tel.: (610) 869-2426
Web Site:
  http://www.starrosesandplants.com
Roses & Nursery Stock Whslr
N.A.I.C.S.: 111422
Steven Hutton (Pres)
Bradd Yoder (Dir-Sls)
Kyle McKean (Dir-Mktg)
Jacques Ferare (VP)

BALL OFFICE PRODUCTS
2100 Westmoreland St, Richmond, VA 23230
Tel.: (804) 204-1774
Web Site: https://www.ballop.com
Year Founded: 2000
Stationery Product Whslr
N.A.I.C.S.: 424120
Melissa Ball (Owner)

BALL STATE UNIVERSITY
2000 W University Ave, Muncie, IN 47306
Tel.: (765) 289-1241
Web Site: http://cms.bsu.edu
University
N.A.I.C.S.: 611310
Kay Bales (VP-Strategic Comm)
Julie Hopwood (Assoc VP-Bus & Auxiliary Svcs)
Alan Hargrave (Assoc VP-Student Affairs & Dir-Housing & Residence Life)
Becky Isaacs (Asst Dir-Admin Svcs)
Elijah Dotson (Asst Dir-Housing Sys)
Eva Newnam (Asst Dir-Bus Svcs)
Jeff Lodde (Asst Dir-Facilities)
Jeff Shoup (Asst Dir-Housing & Residence Life)
Joel Bynum (Asst Dir-Coordination Living & Learning Comm)
Lisa Walker (Asst Dir-University Apartments)
Matt Kovach (Asst Dir-Housing & Residence Life)
Kathy Wolf (VP-Mktg & Comm)
Mary Gerard Barr (Chief Creative Officer & Exec Dir-Creative Svcs)
Mike G. Goldsby (Chief Entrepreneurship Officer)
Tom B. Heck (Chief Investment Officer)
Dawn E. Miller (Chm & Principal)
Geoff S. Mearns (Pres)
Beth Goetz (Dir-Athletics)
Jean Crosby (Pres-Foundation & VP-University Advancement)
Dan Marino (Dir-Esports Program)
Charlene Alexander (Chief Strategy Officer)

Subsidiaries:

Ball State Innovation Corporation (1)
1208 W White River Blvd, Muncie, IN 47303
Tel.: (765) 285-5054
Web Site: http://www.bsic.com
Rev.: $303,197
Assets: $119,111

Liabilities: $240,003
Net Worth: ($120,892)
Earnings: $32,910
Fiscal Year-end: 06/30/2013
College Innovation Grantmaking Services
N.A.I.C.S.: 813219
Wil Davis (Pres)
Linn Crull (CFO-Acting)
Bernard Hannon (Chm)
Nicholas Tokar (Sec)

BALL TIRE & GAS INC.
620 S Ripley Blvd, Alpena, MI 49707
Tel.: (989) 354-4186   MI
Web Site: https://www.balltire.net
Year Founded: 1921
Sales Range: $10-24.9 Million
Emp.: 50
Sales & Services for Automotive Tires
N.A.I.C.S.: 424710
Pam Lane (Office Mgr)
James Wesley Ball Jr. (Pres)

BALL VOLVO & G M C TRUCKS
Hwy 136 E, Kahoka, MO 63445
Tel.: (660) 727-3358
Web Site: http://www.balltrucks.com
Year Founded: 1975
Sales Range: $10-24.9 Million
Emp.: 25
New Car Whslr
N.A.I.C.S.: 441110
Kenneth Ball (Owner)

BALL, BOUNCE & SPORT, INC.
1 Hedstrom Dr, Ashland, OH 44805
Tel.: (419) 289-9310   OH
Web Site: http://www.hedstrom.com
Year Founded: 2004
Sales Range: $10-24.9 Million
Emp.: 200
Toy & Plastics Products Mfr
N.A.I.C.S.: 423920
James Braeunig (CEO)

BALLARD COMPANIES, INC.
3555 Electric Ave, Rockford, IL 61109-2186
Tel.: (815) 229-1800
Web Site: https://www.ballardco.com
Year Founded: 1954
Sales Range: $10-24.9 Million
Emp.: 150
Electrical Wiring Services
N.A.I.C.S.: 238210
Deb Okeson (Principal)
Dave Voettcher (Pres)
Steve Peppers (Mgr-Ops)

BALLARD EXPLORATION COMPANY INC
1021 Main St Ste 2310, Houston, TX 77002
Tel.: (713) 651-0181
Web Site:
  http://www.ballardnatgas.com
Rev.: $48,000,000
Emp.: 24
Oil & Gas Exploration
N.A.I.C.S.: 213112
A. L. Ballard (Pres)
Nancy Snow (Controller)

BALLARD PARTNERS, INC.
201 E Park Ave 5th Fl, Tallahassee, FL 32301
Tel.: (850) 577-0444
Web Site: http://www.ballardpartners.com
Year Founded: 1998
Sales Range: $1-9.9 Million
Emp.: 20
Governmental & Public Affairs Consulting
N.A.I.C.S.: 541618

Brian D. Ballard (Pres)
Greg Turbeville (Sr VP)
Carol Bracy (VP)
Brady Benford (Partner)
Ana Cruz (Mng Partner)
Todd Josko (Mng Partner)

BALLARD REALTY CO INC.
5950 Carmichael Pl, Montgomery, AL 36117
Tel.: (334) 279-8646
Web Site:
  http://www.ballardcompanies.com
Rev.: $35,000,000
Emp.: 90
Lessors of Residential Buildings & Dwellings
N.A.I.C.S.: 531110
Bowen Ballard (CEO)

BALLARD SPAHR LLP
1735 Market St 51st Fl, Philadelphia, PA 19103-7599
Tel.: (215) 665-8500
Web Site:
  https://www.ballardspahr.com
Year Founded: 1886
Law firm
N.A.I.C.S.: 541110
Lynn R. Axelroth (Partner)
Valarie J. Allen (Partner)
John A. Chionchio (Partner)
Douglas Y. Christian (Partner)
Craig Circosta (Partner)
Brendan K. Collins (Partner)
Kevin R. Cunningham (Partner)
Dominic J. De Simone (Partner)
David J. Margules (Partner)
Mark S. Stewart (Chm & Partner)
Laura L. Seidel (Partner)
Bart I. Mellits (Chm-Real Estate & Partner)
Scott Pearson (Partner)
Booker T. Evans (Partner)
John G. Kerkorian (Partner)
Steven W. Suflas (Partner)
Jessica M. Anthony (Partner)
David M. Stauss (Partner)
Richard W. Miller (Partner)
Stefanie H. Jackman (Partner)
Debbie A. Klis (Partner)
Anna A. Mahaney (Partner)
Steve B. Park (Partner)
Christopher Bell (Partner)
Edward J. McAndrew (Partner)
Peter D. Hardy (Partner)
Mae Prestera (CFO)
Kevin W. Hathcock (Partner)
John Sadler (Partner)
Glenn Figurski (Partner)
Lindsey Ermey (Partner)
William B. Igoe (Partner)
Steve T. Park (Partner)
William A. Slaughter (Partner & Gen Counsel)
Raymond G. Truitt (Mng Partner-Fin & Ops)
Suzette Allaire (Chief Innovation Officer)
Cathyann Bixby (Chief Atty Recruitment & Integration Officer)
John T. DiBattista (Chief HR Officer)
Amy F. Shepherd (CMO & Chief Bus Dev Officer)
Melissa Prince (Chief Client Value Officer)
Kim A. Wismer (CIO)
Mark C. Langdon (Exec Dir-Admin)
John H. Harbison (Dir-Res & Info Center)
Nicholas J. Weeks (Dir-Risk Mgmt)
Virginia G. Essandoh (Chief Diversity Officer)
Martin C. Bryce Jr. (Partner)
Robert R. Baron Jr. (Partner)
John L. Culhane Jr. (Partner)

BALLARD TRUCK CENTER OF WORCESTER

442 Southwest Cutoff, Worcester, MA 01604-2717
Tel.: (508) 753-1403
Web Site:
http://www.ballardmack.com
Year Founded: 1906
Sales Range: $10-24.9 Million
Emp.: 60
Car Whslr
N.A.I.C.S.: 441110
Janet Grahn *(Treas)*
John Picking *(Pres)*

BALLARENA CONSTRUCTION

3727 SW 8th St Suite 105, Coral Gables, FL 33134
Tel.: (305) 441-9118
Web Site:
http://www.ballarenagroup.com
Year Founded: 2005
Sales Range: $1-9.9 Million
Emp.: 10
Construction & Management Services
N.A.I.C.S.: 236220
Jorge Ballarena *(Pres & CEO)*
Federico Reiners *(Project Mgr)*

BALLAST POINT VENTURES LP

880 Carillon Pkwy, Saint Petersburg, FL 33716
Tel.: (727) 567-1500
Web Site:
http://www.ballastpointventures.com
Year Founded: 2001
Rev.: $300,000,000
Emp.: 8
Venture Capital
N.A.I.C.S.: 523999
Drew Graham *(Partner)*
Matt Rice *(Partner)*
Robert Faber *(Principal)*
Carol Bear *(Dir-Admin)*
Sean Barkman *(VP)*

BALLAST WISE

677 Arrow Grand Cir, Covina, CA 91722-2146
Tel.: (626) 859-7475
Web Site: http://www.ballastwise.com
Sales Range: $25-49.9 Million
Emp.: 5
Commercial Lighting Fixtures
N.A.I.C.S.: 335132

BALLENISLES COUNTRY CLUB

100 BallenIsles Cir, Palm Beach Gardens, FL 33418
Tel.: (561) 622-0220   FL
Web Site: https://www.ballenisles.org
Year Founded: 1998
Sales Range: $10-24.9 Million
Country Club Operator
N.A.I.C.S.: 713910
Herbert Wender *(VP)*

BALLESTER HERMANOS INC.

Carr 869 Parque Industrial Westgate Barrio Palmas, Catano, PR 00962
Tel.: (787) 788-4110   PR
Web Site:
http://www.ballesterhermanos.com
Year Founded: 1914
Grocery Distr
N.A.I.C.S.: 424410
Alfonso F. Ballester *(Chm & Exec VP)*
Alejandro M. Ballester *(Pres)*
Reuben Medina *(Pres-Sr Exec)*
Luis A. Ballester *(Dir)*
Romulo J. Corrada *(Comptroller & CFO)*
Jose A. Acosta *(VP-HR & Dev)*
Rafael Moreno *(CTO)*

BALLET THEATRE FOUNDATION, INC.

890 Broadway, New York, NY 10003
Tel.: (212) 477-3030
Web Site: http://www.abt.org
Sales Range: $25-49.9 Million
Emp.: 165
Ballet Production Services
N.A.I.C.S.: 711120
Kevin McKenzie *(Dir-Artistic)*
David G. Lansky *(Gen Mgr)*
Danielle Ventimiglia *(Mgr-Production Stage)*
Brad Fields *(Dir-Lighting)*
Roseanne Forni *(Office Mgr)*
Mary Jo Ziesel *(Dir-Education & Trng)*
Brian Heidtke *(Pres)*
Bobby Godwin *(Mgr-Warehouse)*
Elizabeth Aymong *(Dir-Summer Intensive)*
Godwin Farrugia *(Dir-Fin)*
Grey C. Johnson *(Dir-Membership)*
J. Tim Landi *(Chief Advancement Officer)*
Jennifer McGrath *(Mgr-Stage)*
Richard Koch *(Dir-Technical)*
Janet Rolle *(CEO)*
Andrew Barth *(Chm)*

BALLEY PACIFIC PETROLEUM

166 Frank W Cir, Stockton, CA 95206
Tel.: (209) 948-9412
Web Site: http://www.vpps.net
Rev.: $300,000,000
Emp.: 175
Gasoline
N.A.I.C.S.: 531210
Norman E. Crum *(Pres)*
Dan Elmer *(VP-Comml)*

BALLOONS ARE EVERYWHERE, INC.

16474 Greeno Rd, Fairhope, AL 36532
Tel.: (251) 210-2100   AL
Web Site: https://www.balloons.com
Year Founded: 1981
Sales Range: $1-9.9 Million
Emp.: 45
Balloon & Party Supplies Merchant Whlsr
N.A.I.C.S.: 459420
Harry Palmer *(Pres)*

Subsidiaries:

Balloons Are Everywhere, Inc.   **(1)**
5733 E Shields Ave, Fresno, CA 93727
Tel.: (559) 294-1500
Web Site: http://www.balloons.com
Sales Range: $1-9.9 Million
Emp.: 31
Balloon & Party Supplies Merchant Whlsr
N.A.I.C.S.: 459420

BALLOU CONSTRUCTION COMPANY INCORPORATED

1100 W Grand Ave, Salina, KS 67401
Tel.: (785) 825-5303
Rev.: $16,591,929
Emp.: 5
General Contractor, Highway & Street Construction
N.A.I.C.S.: 237310
Don Kaiden *(Pres)*

BALLY RIBBON MILLS

23 N 7th St, Bally, PA 19503
Tel.: (610) 845-2211
Web Site:
https://www.ballyribbon.com
Rev.: $24,000,000
Emp.: 300
Manmade Fiber Narrow Woven Fabrics
N.A.I.C.S.: 313220

Raymond G. Harries *(Pres)*
Leo Frank *(Supvr-Electronic Tech)*
Blake Barthol *(Coord-Mfg)*
Amir Islam *(Dir-R&D)*

BALLYWHOSOCIAL

2654 Cypress Ridge Blvd, Wesley Chapel, FL 33544
Tel.: (813) 347-4400
Web Site:
http://www.ballwhosocial.com
Sales Range: $1-9.9 Million
Emp.: 10
Social Marketing & Advertising Services
N.A.I.C.S.: 541613
Elissa Nauful *(Founder & CEO)*
Caroline Jorgensen *(Mgr-Community)*

BALMORAL FUNDS LLC

11150 Santa Monica Blvd Ste 825, Los Angeles, CA 90025-3988
Tel.: (310) 473-3065
Web Site:
http://www.balmoralfunds.com
Year Founded: 2005
Rev.: $200,000,000
Privater Equity Firm
N.A.I.C.S.: 523999
Jonathan A. Victor *(Sr Mng Dir)*
Skip Victor *(Mng Dir)*
Robin Nourmand *(Mng Dir)*
Travis Haynes *(Mng Dir)*
Luke Mau *(CFO)*
David Shainberg *(VP)*

Subsidiaries:

Concurrent Manufacturing Solutions LLC   **(1)**
10773 NW 58th St Ste 100, Doral, FL 33178
Tel.: (305) 507-7413
Web Site: http://www.concurrentmfg.com
Contract Electronics Mfr
N.A.I.C.S.: 334418
Benjamin A. Teno *(Pres & CEO)*

DWFritz Automation Inc.   **(1)**
9600 SW Boeckman Rd, Wilsonville, OR 97070
Tel.: (503) 598-9393
Web Site: http://www.dwfritz.com
Rev.: $4,700,000
Emp.: 40
Precision Metrology, Inspection & Assembly Solutions Services
N.A.I.C.S.: 541690
Mike Fritz *(CEO)*
John Pence *(VP-High-Volume Inspection)*
Dennis Fritz *(Founder)*
Mukesh Dulani *(Pres)*

Epsilyte Holdings LLC   **(1)**
1330 Lke Robbins Dr Ste 310, The Woodlands, TX 77380
Tel.: (815) 224-1525
Polystyrene Resin Producer
N.A.I.C.S.: 325211
Bradley Crocker *(Pres & CEO)*
Brad Crocker *(Pres)*

MOOYAH Franchising, LLC   **(1)**
6865 Windcrest Dr Ste 400, Plano, TX 75024
Tel.: (214) 310-0768
Web Site: http://www.mooyah.com
Casual Dining
N.A.I.C.S.: 722513
Natalie Anderson *(VP-Mktg)*
Pamela Parham *(Mktg Mgr)*

R.H. Sheppard Co., Inc.   **(1)**
101 Philadelphia St, Hanover, PA 17331-2038
Tel.: (717) 637-3751
Web Site: https://www.rhsheppard.com
Motor Vehicle Parts, Accessories & Castings
N.A.I.C.S.: 336350
Neil Poffenberger *(VP-Foundry Div)*

Resco Products, Inc.   **(1)**
1 Robinson Plz, Pittsburgh, PA 15205
Tel.: (412) 494-4491

Web Site: http://www.rescoproducts.com
Refractories, Brick & Ceramic Minerals Mfr & Sales
N.A.I.C.S.: 327120
Richard W. Copp *(VP-Sls & Mktg)*
Timothy J. Powell *(CFO & VP-Fin)*
Gregory Kessler *(Sr Dir-Indus Sls)*
Mike Pannell *(Dir-Global HPI Market)*
Tom Tanaka *(Dir-Export Sls-Canada)*
Graham McDonough *(CFO & VP)*

Division (Domestic):

Cedar Heights Clay   **(2)**
3542 State Route 93, Oak Hill, OH 45656-0295   **(100%)**
Tel.: (740) 682-7794
Web Site: http://www.rescoproducts.com
Sales Range: $25-49.9 Million
Emp.: 20
Clay Mfr
N.A.I.C.S.: 327120
Linda Simpson *(Plant Mgr)*

Piedmont Minerals Division   **(2)**
231 Piedmont Dr, Hillsborough, NC 27278-0566   **(100%)**
Tel.: (919) 732-3981
Sales Range: $25-49.9 Million
Emp.: 10
N.A.I.C.S.: 327120
Doug Albert *(Pres)*

Resco Products Engineering Division   **(2)**
14801 S Anson Ave, Santa Fe Springs, CA 90670-5334
Tel.: (562) 802-2463
Sales Range: $25-49.9 Million
Emp.: 15
Bricks Mfr
N.A.I.C.S.: 327120
Itnacio Trejo *(Mgr-Production)*

Resco Products Greensboro   **(2)**
3514 W Wendover Ave, Greensboro, NC 27407
Tel.: (336) 299-1441
Sales Range: $25-49.9 Million
Refractories Mfr
N.A.I.C.S.: 327992

Resco Products Inc   **(2)**
PO Box 30169, Canton, OH 44730-0169
Tel.: (330) 488-1226
Web Site: http://www.rescoproducts.com
Sales Range: $25-49.9 Million
N.A.I.C.S.: 327120
Eric Mohney *(Area Mgr-Quality Assurance)*
Brian Lawrence *(Mgr-Production)*
Don Worley *(Mgr-Site)*
Mike Crabtree *(Supvr-Maintenance)*
Gregory Kessler *(Sr Dir-Indus Sls)*
Mike Pannell *(Dir-Global HPI Market)*
Tom Tanaka *(Dir-Canada & Export Sls)*

Subsidiary (Non-US):

Resco Products UK   **(2)**
Newbold, Coleorton, LE67 8PJ, Leicestershire, United Kingdom   **(100%)**
Tel.: (44) 1530222694
Web Site: http://www.rescoproduct.com
Sales Range: $25-49.9 Million
Emp.: 15
N.A.I.C.S.: 327120
Tucks Bury *(Office Mgr)*

Trecora, LLC   **(1)**
1330 Lake Robbins Dr Ste 200, The Woodlands, TX 77380
Tel.: (281) 980-5522
Web Site: https://www.trecora.com
Rev.: $272,690,000
Assets: $293,540,000
Liabilities: $93,567,000
Net Worth: $199,973,000
Earnings: $4,963,000
Emp.: 247
Fiscal Year-end: 12/31/2021
Petrochemical Mfr & Metal Mining Services
N.A.I.C.S.: 325110
Bradley Crocker *(Pres & CEO)*
Peter M. Loggenberg *(Chief Sustainability Officer & Exec VP-Specialty Polymers & Corporate Strategy)*
Christopher A. Groves *(CFO, Principal Acctg Officer & Controller)*
Matt Myren *(Gen Counsel)*

Balmoral Funds LLC—(Continued)

Shea Williamson (*Dir-Procurement*)
Andy Ternes (*Bus Dir-Specialty Chemicals*)
Erin Ballard (*Controller*)

Subsidiary (Domestic):

Chemtrade Phosphorous Specialties LLC (2)
440 N 9th St, Lawrence, KS 66044-5424
Tel.: (785) 843-2290
Industrial Chemical Whslr
N.A.I.C.S.: 424690

Gulf State Pipe Line Company (2)
7752 Hwy 418, Silsbee, TX 77656
Tel.: (409) 385-1400
Crude Oil Pipeline Transportation Services
N.A.I.C.S.: 486110

South Hampton Resources, Inc. (2)
7752 FM 418, Silsbee, TX 77656
Tel.: (409) 385-8300
Web Site: http://www.southhamptonr.com
Sales Range: $50-74.9 Million
Emp.: 160
Petrochemical Mfr
N.A.I.C.S.: 325110

Trecora Chemical, Inc (2)
12500 Bay Area Blvd, Pasadena, TX 77507
Tel.: (281) 474-7500
Web Site: https://www.trecchem.com
Chemical Products Mfr
N.A.I.C.S.: 325180

BALON CORPORATION
3245 S Hattie Ave, Oklahoma City, OK 73129
Tel.: (405) 677-3321
Web Site: https://www.balon.com
Rev.: $18,500,000
Emp.: 185
Valves & Pipe Fittings
N.A.I.C.S.: 332919
Bob Holden (*Mgr-EHS*)
Jim Turner (*Area Mgr*)
David Filler (*Engr-Mechanical*)

BALQON CORPORATION
1420 240th St, Harbor City, CA 90710
Tel.: (310) 326-3056
Web Site: http://www.balqon.com
Sales Range: $1-9.9 Million
Emp.: 8
Heavy Duty Electric Vehicles Designer, Assembler & Marketer
N.A.I.C.S.: 336110
Balwinder Samra (*Vice Chm, CEO & Interim CFO*)
Henry Velasquez (*VP-Engrg*)
Winston Hing Ka Chung (*Chm*)

BALSAM BRANDS
50 Woodside Plz Ste 111, Redwood City, CA 94061
Tel.: (336) 419-0960
Web Site:
http://www.balsambrands.com
Year Founded: 2006
Sales Range: $10-24.9 Million
Emp.: 36
Operates Branded Management Online Businesses Selling Specialty Products
N.A.I.C.S.: 459999
Thomas Harman (*Founder & CEO*)
Caroline Tuan (*COO*)
Kristen Gaisor (*Chief Mktg Officer*)
Sharon Gross (*Exec VP-ECommerce & Online Mdsg*)
David Gross (*Exec VP-ECommerce & Online Mdsg*)
Mike Rockwood (*VP-Fin*)
Claire Magat (*VP-People Initiatives & Strategic Projects*)

Subsidiaries:

Balsam Hill (1)

50 Woodside Plaza Ste 111, Redwood City, CA 94061 **(100%)**
Tel.: (336) 419-0960
Web Site: http://www.balsamhill.com
Retails High-Quality Realistic Artificial Christmas Trees & Accessories
N.A.I.C.S.: 459999

BALTER SALES CO. INC.
209 Bowery, New York, NY 10002
Tel.: (212) 674-2960
Web Site:
http://www.baltersalesstore.com
Sales Range: $10-24.9 Million
Emp.: 30
Sales of Restaurant Supplies
N.A.I.C.S.: 423220
Arnold Balter (*Pres*)
Lori Balter (*CFO*)

BALTIA AIR LINES, INC.
JFK International Airport Terminal 4
Room 262 089, Jamaica, NY 11430
Tel.: (718) 917-8052 NY
Web Site: http://www.baltia.com
Year Founded: 1989
Scheduled Passenger Air Transportation
N.A.I.C.S.: 481111
Brian Glynn (*VP-PR & IR*)
Anthony D. Koulouris (*Chm, Pres & CEO*)
Frank A. Acquavella (*VP-Ops*)
George W. Kelsey (*Gen Counsel*)
John W. Lampl (*VP-Corp Comm*)
Sheryle Milligan (*COO*)
Michael Jordan (*CFO*)

BALTIC LINEN COMPANY, INC.
1999 Marcus Ave, Lake Success, NY 11040
Tel.: (516) 791-4500 NY
Web Site: http://www.balticlinen.com
Year Founded: 1936
Sales Range: $50-74.9 Million
Emp.: 73
Whslr of Institutional Textiles
N.A.I.C.S.: 423220
Frank Greenberg (*Co-Owner*)
Mark Lichter (*Co-Owner*)
Lori Vaccariello (*Controller*)

BALTIMORE COMMUNITY FOUNDATION, INC.
2 E Read St 9th Fl, Baltimore, MD 21202
Tel.: (410) 332-4171 MD
Web Site: http://www.bcf.org
Year Founded: 1972
Sales Range: $25-49.9 Million
Emp.: 43
Philanthropic Services
N.A.I.C.S.: 813211
Gigi Casey Wirtz (*Dir-Comm*)
Patti Chandler (*VP-Fin & Admin*)
Shanaysha Sauls (*CEO*)
Dara Schapiro Schnee (*VP-Philanthropy*)
Ann K. Beegle (*VP-Strategic Investments*)

BALTIMORE COUNTRY CLUB
4712 Club Rd, Baltimore, MD 21210
Tel.: (410) 889-4400
Web Site: https://www.bcc1898.com
Sales Range: $10-24.9 Million
Emp.: 90
Recreational Services
N.A.I.C.S.: 713910
Mark Welsch (*Dir-Pur*)
Kevin Albertini (*Mgr-Food & Beverage*)
Preston Hardy (*Mgr-Club House*)
Ryan C. Granruth (*Asst Gen Mgr*)

Kate Beck (*Dir-Events*)
Debra Korb (*Dir-Club Events*)
Noelle Jewell (*Dir-Membership & Comm*)

BALTIMORE COUNTY REVENUE AUTHORITIES
115 Towsontown Blvd, Towson, MD 21286-5350
Tel.: (410) 887-3127
Web Site:
https://www.baltimoregolfing.com
Sales Range: $10-24.9 Million
Emp.: 155
Parking & Golfing
N.A.I.C.S.: 812930
Ken Mills (*Gen Mgr*)
John Hein (*Dir-Sls*)

BALTIMORE FREIGHTLINER
2723 Annapolis Rd, Baltimore, MD 21230
Tel.: (410) 685-4474
Web Site:
https://www.baltimorefreightliner.com
Sales Range: $50-74.9 Million
Emp.: 90
Commercial Trucking Services
N.A.I.C.S.: 423110
Edward S. Roberts (*Pres*)
John Blottenberger (*Mgr-Svcs*)
John Coombe (*Gen Mgr-Sls*)
Edward S. Dentz (*VP*)
Jack Patterson (*Controller*)
Bruce Doyle (*Mgr-Parts*)

BALTIMORE LIFE INSURANCE COMPANY INC.
10075 Red Run Blvd, Owings Mills, MD 21117-4871
Tel.: (410) 581-6600 MD
Web Site: https://www.baltlife.com
Year Founded: 1882
Sales Range: $100-124.9 Million
Emp.: 434
Life Insurance
N.A.I.C.S.: 524113
David K. Ficca (*Pres & CEO*)
Damian A. Salvi (*Chief Distr Officer & Sr VP*)
Stephanie L. Baker (*VP-Insurance Svcs*)
Richard A. Spencer III (*CFO, Treas & Sr VP*)

Subsidiaries:

Baltimore Financial Brokerage, Inc. (1)
10075 Red Run Blvd, Owings Mills, MD 21117
Tel.: (410) 581-6600
Financial Management Services
N.A.I.C.S.: 523940

Baltimore Financial Services Corporation (1)
10075 Red Run Blvd, Owings Mills, MD 21117-4865 **(100%)**
Tel.: (410) 581-6600
Web Site: http://www.baltlife.com
Sales Range: $50-74.9 Million
Emp.: 140
Insurance Agents, Brokers & Service
N.A.I.C.S.: 524210
David K. Ficca (*Pres*)

Baltimore Life Company (1)
10075 Red Run Blvd, Owings Mills, MD 21117-4865
Tel.: (410) 581-6600
Web Site: http://www.baltimorelife.com
Sales Range: $50-74.9 Million
Emp.: 147
Life Insurance
N.A.I.C.S.: 524113

BALTIMORE MEDICAL SYSTEM INC.

3501 Sinclair Ln, Baltimore, MD 21213-2037
Tel.: (410) 732-8800 MD
Web Site: https://www.bmsi.org
Year Founded: 1984
Sales Range: $25-49.9 Million
Emp.: 400
Health & Allied Services
N.A.I.C.S.: 621999
Michele Lagana (*CFO*)
James Bobbitt (*Sec*)
Shirley Sutton (*Pres & CEO*)

BALTIMORE ORIOLES, L.P.
333 W Camden St, Baltimore, MD 21201
Tel.: (410) 685-9800 MD
Web Site:
http://www.baltimore.orioles.mlb.com
Year Founded: 1954
Sales Range: $75-99.9 Million
Emp.: 200
Professional Baseball Club
N.A.I.C.S.: 711211
Peter G. Angelos (*Chm & CEO*)
Robert A. Ames (*CFO & Exec VP*)
John P. Angelos (*Exec VP*)
Lou Kousouris (*Exec VP*)
John Stockstill (*Dir-Player Dev*)
Mike Snyder (*Dir-Pacific Rim Ops & Baseball Dev*)
Carole Bohon (*Dir-Fin*)
Diane Schmitt (*Mgr-Accts Payable*)
H. Russell Smouse (*Gen Counsel*)
James L. Kline (*Dir-Info Sys*)
Kim Yancheski (*Mgr-Accts Receivable*)
Linda Ashauer (*Mgr-Pur*)
Lisa Tolson (*Sr VP-HR*)
Michael D. Hoppes (*VP-Fin*)
Pamela Nowicki (*Mgr-Payroll*)
Sharon Daniels (*Mgr-Bus Applications*)
Mike Elias (*Exec VP & Gen Mgr*)
Sig Mejdal (*Asst Gen Mgr-Analytics*)
Koby Perez (*Sr Dir-Intl Scouting*)
T. J. Brightman (*Chief Revenue Officer & Sr VP*)
Jennifer Grondahl (*Sr VP-Community Dev & Comm*)
Greg Bader (*Sr VP-Admin & Experience*)

BALTIMORE RAVENS LIMITED PARTNERSHIP
1 Winning Dr, Owings Mills, MD 21117
Tel.: (410) 701-4000 MD
Web Site:
https://www.baltimoreravens.com
Year Founded: 1946
Sales Range: $50-74.9 Million
Emp.: 130
Professional Football Franchise
N.A.I.C.S.: 711211
Kevin Byrne (*Sr VP-Pub & Community Rels*)
Jeff Goering (*CFO & Sr VP*)
Patti Holtery (*Sr Mgr-Payroll*)
Richard W. Cass (*Pres*)
Vincent Newsome (*Dir-Pro Personnel*)
Jim Coller (*VP-Fin*)
Harry Swayne (*Dir-Player Dev*)
Mark Bienvenu (*Dir-Football Video Ops*)
Elizabeth Jackson (*VP-HR*)
Chad Steele (*VP-PR*)
Michelle Andres (*Sr VP-Digital Media & Broadcasting*)
Darren Sanders (*Sr Dir-Security*)
Ozzie Newsome (*Exec VP & Gen Mgr*)
Jay O'Brien (*Mgr-Brdcst*)
John Cline (*Sr Mgr-Event & Guest Svcs*)

Nick Fusee *(Dir-IT)*
Josh Hartman *(Sr Mgr-Suite Sls & Svcs)*
Adam Mazalewski *(Sr Mgr-Ticket Ops)*
Mike Burke *(Sr Mgr-Ticket Sls & Hospitality)*
Jobie Waldt *(Mgr-Stadium Ops)*
Eric DeCosta *(Asst Gen Mgr)*
Bill Jankowski *(VP-IT)*
Kevin Rochlitz *(Sr VP-Corp Sls & Bus Dev)*
Sarah Ellison *(Editor-Digital Media)*
Roy Sommerhof *(Sr VP-Stadium Ops)*
Baker Koppelman *(Sr VP-Ticket Sls & Ops)*
Reba Koppelman *(Dir-Fin)*
Chad Alexander *(Asst Dir-Pro Personnel)*
Bob Eller *(Sr VP-Ops)*
William Sheridan *(Mgr-Equipment)*
Heather Darney *(Dir-Community Rels)*
Patrick Gleason *(Asst Dir-PR)*
Emily Scerba *(Mgr-Community Rels)*
Joe Hortiz *(Dir-College Scouting)*
Kate Kasabula *(Dir-Client Svcs)*
Mattie Wood *(Coord-Client Svcs)*
Tom Valente *(Mgr-PR)*
Kristin Stortini *(Asst Gen Counsel)*

BALTIMORE SYMPHONY ORCHESTRA
1212 Cathedral St, Baltimore, MD 21201
Tel.: (410) 783-8000
Web Site: https://www.bsomusic.org
Emp.: 200
Symphony Orchestra
N.A.I.C.S.: 531120
Tiffany Bryan *(Mgr-Front-House)*
Joanne Rosenthal *(Dir-Principal Gifts & Govt Rels)*
Peter Murphy *(Mgr-Ticket Svcs)*
Alice Simons *(Dir-Institutional Giving)*
John T. Verdon *(CFO & VP)*
Julia Kirchhausen *(Dir-PR)*
Kate Caldwell *(Dir-Philanthropic Plng)*
Katelyn Simon *(Mgr-Mktg)*
Katie Applefeld *(Dir-External Affairs)*
Nicholas Cohen *(Gen Mgr)*
Nick Skinner *(Dir-Ops)*
Peter T. Kjome *(Pres & CEO)*
Barbara Bozzuto *(Chm)*
Hilary Miller *(Vice Chm)*
Marin Alsop *(Dir-Music)*

BALTIMORE WASHINGTON THURGOOD MARSHALL INTERNATIONAL AIRPORT
750 Friendship Rd, Baltimore, MD 21240-0766
Tel.: (410) 859-7111
Web Site: http://www.bwiairport.com
Sales Range: $25-49.9 Million
Emp.: 500
Airport Operations
N.A.I.C.S.: 488119
Jonathan O. Dean *(Mgr-Comm)*
Asia Hemphill *(Mgr-Performance Mgmt)*

BALTZ & COMPANY
49 W 23rd St Fl 9, New York, NY 10010
Tel.: (212) 982-8300   NY
Web Site: http://www.baltzco.com
Sales Range: $1-9.9 Million
Emp.: 15
Public Relations Services
N.A.I.C.S.: 541820
Phillip Baltz *(Owner)*

Subsidiaries:

Baltz & Company   (1)

8335 W Sunset Blvd Suite 301, West Hollywood, CA 90069   **(100%)**
Tel.: (323) 337-9039
Web Site: http://www.baltzco.com
Public Relations
N.A.I.C.S.: 541820

Baltz & Company - Denver   (1)
3455 Ringsby Ct Ste 101, Denver, CO 80216
Tel.: (303) 296-2711
Web Site: http://www.baltzco.com
Public Relations Agency
N.A.I.C.S.: 541820

BALZER PACIFIC EQUIPMENT CO.
10830 SW Clutter Rd, Sherwood, OR 97140
Tel.: (971) 224-5225   OR
Web Site: https://www.balzerpacific.com
Year Founded: 1928
Sales Range: $10-24.9 Million
Emp.: 12
Aggregate, Concrete & Asphalt Equipment Mfr & Distr
N.A.I.C.S.: 333120
Mike Allen Sr. *(Pres)*

BAM ENTERPRISES, INC.
2937 Alt Blvd, Grand Island, NY 14072
Tel.: (716) 773-7634
Web Site: https://www.bamenterprisesinc.com
Holding Company
N.A.I.C.S.: 551112
Denise Serio *(Mgr-Marketing-Media)*

Subsidiaries:

Motor Components, LLC   (1)
2243 Corning Rd, Elmira, NY 14903-1031
Tel.: (607) 737-8011
Web Site: http://www.facet-purolator.com
Fuel Pumps Mfr
N.A.I.C.S.: 336310

NRD, LLC   (1)
2937 Alt Blvd, Grand Island, NY 14072
Tel.: (716) 773-7634
Web Site: http://www.nrdstaticcontrol.com
Emp.: 50
Static Control Equipment Mfr
N.A.I.C.S.: 335999
Douglas Fiegel *(Pres)*
Timothy Maroni *(Supvr-Engrg & Quality)*
William White *(Dir-OEM Sls-East Coast)*
John Glynn II *(Dir-Sls & Mktg)*

PMI Industries, Inc.   (1)
350 Buell Rd, Rochester, NY 14624
Tel.: (585) 464-8050
Web Site: http://www.pmiindustries.com
Sales Range: $1-9.9 Million
Emp.: 40
Industrial Mold Mfr
N.A.I.C.S.: 333511
Michael Jelfo *(Pres)*
Bill Brunelle *(Mgr-Ops)*

BAMA COMPANIES INC.
2745 E 11th St, Tulsa, OK 74104
Tel.: (918) 732-2584   OK
Web Site: https://www.bama.com
Year Founded: 1998
Sales Range: $25-49.9 Million
Emp.: 200
Packaged Frozen Goods
N.A.I.C.S.: 311812
Paula A. Marshall-Chapman *(Pres, CEO & Chief Inclusion Officer)*
Kevin McKenna *(Exec VP)*
Rocky Moore *(CFO)*
Eivind Djupedal *(Sr VP-Bus Dev-Intl)*

Subsidiaries:

Bama Frozen Dough LLC   (1)
2435 N Lewis Ave, Tulsa, OK 74110   **(100%)**
Tel.: (918) 732-2600
Web Site: http://www.bama.com

Sales Range: $25-49.9 Million
Packaged Frozen Goods
N.A.I.C.S.: 424420
Paula A. Marshall-Chapman *(Pres, CEO & Chief Inclusion Officer)*
William L. Chew *(CFO)*
Eivind Djupedal *(Sr VP-Intl Bus Dev)*
Kevin McKenna *(Exec VP)*
Bernard Sheridan *(VP & Gen Mgr-Asia)*

BAMA CONCRETE PRODUCTS CO., INC.
1608 17th St, Tuscaloosa, AL 35401
Tel.: (205) 345-6622
Web Site: https://www.bamaconcrete.com
Year Founded: 1950
Sales Range: $10-24.9 Million
Emp.: 85
Ready-Mix Concrete Supplier
N.A.I.C.S.: 327320
Tim Pearson *(Mgr-Credit)*
Tyler Davis *(VP)*

Subsidiaries:

Bama Concrete Birmingham, Inc. (1)
2180 Hwy 87, Alabaster, AL 35007
Tel.: (205) 663-6800
Web Site: http://www.bamaconcrete.com
Ready Mixed Concrete
N.A.I.C.S.: 327320

BAMA SEA PRODUCTS INC.
756 28th St S, Saint Petersburg, FL 33712-1907
Tel.: (727) 327-3474   FL
Web Site: https://www.bamasea.com
Year Founded: 1979
Sales Range: $100-124.9 Million
Emp.: 100
Producers of Seafoods
N.A.I.C.S.: 424460
John M. Stephens *(Pres)*
Adam Zewen *(Dir-Sls & Pur)*
Fredrik Stengard *(Dir-Res & Quality Control)*

BAMBACIGNO STEEL COMPANY, INC.
4930 McHenry Ave, Modesto, CA 95356
Tel.: (209) 524-9681
Web Site: https://www.bambacigno.com
Year Founded: 1955
Rev.: $15,000,000
Emp.: 55
Mfr, Designer & Erector of Structural Steel
N.A.I.C.S.: 238120
Lori Bambacigno *(Pres)*
Mary Bambacigno *(Owner)*
Rich Custer *(Project Mgr)*

BAMBECK & VEST ASSOCIATES INC.
49 E 4th St Ste 1020, Cincinnati, OH 45202
Tel.: (513) 621-5654
Web Site: http://www.bambeckandvest.com
Sales Range: $10-24.9 Million
Emp.: 35
Commercial & Office Building Construction Services
N.A.I.C.S.: 236220
Dianne C. Bambeck *(Pres)*

BAMBERGER POLYMERS, INC.
2 Jericho Plz, Jericho, NY 11753-1658
Tel.: (516) 622-3600   NY
Web Site: https://www.bambergerpolymer.com
Year Founded: 1967
Sales Range: $250-299.9 Million

Emp.: 112
Plastic Resins Distr
N.A.I.C.S.: 424610
Chris Hessenius *(Reg Sls Mgr)*

Subsidiaries:

Bamberger Polymers (Canada), Inc.   (1)
2000 Argentia Rd Plz 1, Mississauga, L5N 1P7, ON, Canada   **(100%)**
Tel.: (905) 821-9400
Web Site: http://www.bambergerpolymers.com
Sales Range: $50-74.9 Million
Emp.: 15
Distr of Chemicals & Allied Products
N.A.I.C.S.: 424690
Jeff MacLeod *(Gen Mgr)*
Marlo Mallari *(Asst Controller)*

Bamberger Polymers International Corp.   (1)
2 Jericho Plz, Jericho, NY 11753-1658
Tel.: (516) 622-3600
Web Site: http://www.bambergerpolymers.com
Sales Range: $10-24.9 Million
Emp.: 6
Plastics Materials & Basic Shapes
N.A.I.C.S.: 424610

BAMBOO MARKETING
c/o Bamboo Books 2200 Wilson Blvd Ste 102, Arlington, VA 22201
Tel.: (212) 969-8932
Web Site: http://www.bamboomarketing.com
Sales Range: Less than $1 Million
Emp.: 8
Advertising, Advertising Specialties, Arts, Collateral, Communications, Consulting, Corporate Communications, Corporate Identity, Crisis Communications
N.A.I.C.S.: 541820
Audra Dax *(Pres)*

BAMBOO PIPELINE, INC.
321 N Aviador St Ste 201, Camarillo, CA 93010
Tel.: (805) 764-2600
Year Founded: 2001
Sales Range: $10-24.9 Million
Emp.: 80
Retail Nurseries & Landscaping Supplies
N.A.I.C.S.: 444240
Matthew Fay *(Pres)*
Mike Cornell *(Exec VP)*
Martin Senn *(Sr VP)*

BAMCO CONSTRUCTION, INC.
PO Box 250, Boynton Beach, FL 33425
Tel.: (561) 732-2938
Web Site: https://www.bamcoconstruction.com
Sales Range: $10-24.9 Million
Emp.: 300
Housing Construction Services
N.A.I.C.S.: 236117
William McColman *(Pres)*

BAMCO INC.
30 Baekeland Ave, Middlesex, NJ 08846
Web Site: https://www.gobamco.com
Year Founded: 1986
Sales Range: $10-24.9 Million
Emp.: 85
Commercial, Institutional Construction Service
N.A.I.C.S.: 236220
Michael Biviano *(CEO)*
Allan Pasternak *(Treas & Sec)*
Robert Friedman *(CFO)*
Bob Balaam *(VP-Sls)*
Rick Marcavecchio *(VP-Fabrication Div)*

BAMCO inc.—(Continued)

Ron Palazzo *(VP-Field Ops)*
Jon Black *(Dir-Engrg)*
Judson Filkins *(Dir-Safety)*

BAMYAN MEDIA
2885 Sanford Ave SW 1953, Grand-
ville, MI 49418
Tel.: (720) 272-8942 DC
Web Site: http://www.bamyan.org
Year Founded: 2010
Sales Range: $1-9.9 Million
Emp.: 1
Entertainment Program Production
Services
N.A.I.C.S.: 711510
Anna Elliot *(CEO)*

BAN-KOE SYSTEMS COMPA-
NIES
9100 W Bloomington Freeway, Min-
neapolis, MN 55431
Tel.: (952) 888-6688
Web Site: http://www.bankoe.com
Sales Range: $10-24.9 Million
Emp.: 180
Computerized Time Clocks
N.A.I.C.S.: 423420
William L. Bangtson *(CEO & Owner)*

BANA INC.
624 E McLeroy Blvd, Saginaw, TX
76179
Tel.: (817) 232-3750
Web Site: https://www.banabox.com
Year Founded: 1969
Sales Range: $10-24.9 Million
Emp.: 120
Mfr of Corrugated Boxes
N.A.I.C.S.: 322211
David Boenker *(Owner & Mng Part-
ner)*
Angela Dill *(Owner & Mng Partner)*
Yvette Vaughn *(Controller)*

BANAH INTERNATIONAL
GROUP, INC.
215 SE 10th Ave, Hialeah, FL 33010
Tel.: (305) 285-3401
Web Site:
   http://www.banahsugar.com
Sales Range: $100-124.9 Million
Emp.: 90
Sugar Cane
N.A.I.C.S.: 311314
Alexander Perez *(Founder, Owner &
Pres)*
Manuel Arisso *(Dir-Sls-America &
Caribbean)*

BANANA BAY WATERFRONT
MOTEL
23285 Bayshore Rd, Port Charlotte,
FL 33980
Tel.: (941) 743-4441
Web Site:
   http://www.bananabaymotel.com
Sales Range: $1-9.9 Million
Hotel Operations
N.A.I.C.S.: 721110
Anand Desai *(Co-Owner)*
Jyoi Desai *(Co-Owner)*

BANC STATEMENTS, INC.
(BSI)
4700 Birmingham St, Birmingham, AL
35217
Tel.: (205) 956-5004
Web Site: http://www.bsisite.com
Year Founded: 2006
Sales Range: $1-9.9 Million
Emp.: 20
Outsourced Statement Printing &
Mailing Services for Community
Banks Nationwide

N.A.I.C.S.: 323120
David S. Yates *(VP-Sls)*
Bob Fairweather *(Pres & CEO)*
Lee Long *(COO)*
Lakyn Gaddy *(VP-Client Svcs)*
Kathy Taylor *(VP-Mktg)*
Eric McPherson *(Dir-Production)*
Larry Johnson *(Acct Exec-Midwest
Reg)*

BANC3, INC.
300 Alexander Park, Princeton, NJ
08540
Tel.: (609) 759-1900
Web Site: https://www.banc3.com
Year Founded: 1996
Sales Range: $1-9.9 Million
Emp.: 60
Engineering & IT Consulting Services
N.A.I.C.S.: 541330
Babu Cherukuri *(Pres)*
Jim Ott *(Dir-Bus Dev)*
Pam Puttagunta *(Dir-IT)*
Robert Lee *(Dir-Survey)*

BANCADVICE, LLC
850 Corporate Pkwy Ste 110, Bir-
mingham, AL 35242
Tel.: (205) 739-2265
Web Site:
   http://www.bankeradvice.com
Year Founded: 2008
Banking Services & Credit Unions
N.A.I.C.S.: 522110
Micah McCaleb *(Sr VP-Ops)*

Subsidiaries:

Fimac Solutions LLC (1)
7000 E Belleview Ste 310, Greenwood Vil-
lage, CO 80111-3330
Tel.: (303) 332-1900
Web Site: http://www.fimacsolutions.com
Financial Analytics, Asset / Liability Man-
agement & Consulting Services
N.A.I.C.S.: 523999
Greg Doner *(CEO)*
Richard B. Pennington *(Vice Chm)*
John Anton *(Pres & Mgr-Product)*
Randall Corwin *(Sr VP-Sls & Mktg)*

BANCINDEPENDENT INC.
710 S Montgomery Ave, Sheffield, AL
35660
Tel.: (256) 386-5000
Web Site: https://www.bibank.com
Bank Holding Company
N.A.I.C.S.: 551111
Macke Mauldin *(Pres)*

Subsidiaries:

Bank Independent (1)
710 S Montgomery Ave, Sheffield, AL
35660
Tel.: (256) 386-5000
Web Site: http://www.bibank.com
Sales Range: $10-24.9 Million
Emp.: 300
Banking Services
N.A.I.C.S.: 522110
Melissa Craig *(Sr VP)*
Macke Mauldin *(Pres)*
Anita Crittenden *(Officer-Sls)*
Hillard Whitlock *(Sr VP)*

Subsidiary (Domestic):

Interstate Billing Service Inc. (2)
1025 Fifth Ave SE PO Box 2250, Decatur,
AL 35609-2250 (100%)
Tel.: (256) 355-1750
Sales Range: $25-49.9 Million
Emp.: 100
Accounts Receivable, Billing & Collection
N.A.I.C.S.: 541219

BANCINSURANCE CORPORA-
TION
250 E Broad St 7th Fl, Columbus,
OH 43215
Tel.: (614) 220-5200 OH

Web Site:
   http://www.ohioindemnity.com
Year Founded: 1970
Sales Range: $25-49.9 Million
Emp.: 33
Property Insurance Holding Company
N.A.I.C.S.: 551111
John S. Sokol *(Chm, Pres & CEO)*
Matthew C. Nolan *(CFO, Treas, Sec
& VP)*

Subsidiaries:

Ohio Indemnity Company (1)
250 E Broad St 7th Fl, Columbus, OH
43215-3416
Tel.: (614) 228-2800
Web Site: http://www.ohioindemnity.com
Rev.: $12,076,742
Emp.: 30
Underwriters of Casualty & other Special-
ized Insurance Policies for Banks & other
Lending Institutions; Automobile Physical
Damage Coverage & Surety
N.A.I.C.S.: 524126
John S. Sokol *(Chm, Pres & CEO)*
Matt Nolan *(CFO, Treas, Sec & VP)*
Thomas Ryan *(Asst VP-Claims)*
Steve Toth *(VP)*

Division (Domestic):

Ohio Indemnity Company - OIC
Lender Services Division (2)
250 E Broad St 7th Fl, Columbus, OH
43215
Tel.: (800) 628-8581
Web Site: http://www.oiclenderservices.com
Financial Management Services
N.A.I.C.S.: 523940
Dan Stephan *(Pres)*
John Rodwell *(VP-Bus Dev)*
Thomas Ryan *(Asst VP-Claims)*
Michael Block *(Mgr-Product)*
Amy Miele *(Mgr-Client Svcs)*
John Sokol *(Chm, Pres & CEO)*
Margo Noreen *(VP-Tech)*
Matt Nolan *(CFO & VP)*

Ultimate Services Agency, LLC (1)
250 E Broad St, Columbus, OH 43215-
3416
Tel.: (614) 220-5200
Web Site: http://www.usagencyllc.com
Property & Casualty Insurance Services
N.A.I.C.S.: 524126
John S. Sokol *(Pres & CEO)*

BANCO PICHINCHA MIAMI
AGENCY
396 Alhambra Cir Penthouse 2, Coral
Gables, FL 33134
Tel.: (305) 372-3601
Web Site:
   http://www.pichinchamiami.com
Commercial Banking Services
N.A.I.C.S.: 522110
Ricardo De La Fuente *(CIO)*

BANCROFT BAG INC.
425 Bancroft Blvd, West Monroe, LA
71292-5703
Tel.: (318) 387-2550 LA
Web Site:
   https://www.bancroftbag.com
Year Founded: 1924
Sales Range: $75-99.9 Million
Emp.: 500
Mfr of Uncoated Paper & Multiwall
Bags
N.A.I.C.S.: 322220
Dennis Pace *(Mgr-Accts-Natl)*
Chris Collins *(Reg Mgr-Sls)*
Tom Gorman *(Mgr-Territory Sls)*
Brad Danger *(Mgr-Sls-Roscoe-IL)*
Gustavo Gonzalez *(Mgr-Sls-
Monterrey-Mexico Reg)*
Jay Wisecarver *(Dir-Tech)*
Nick Turner *(Mgr-Sls-Atlanta-GA)*
Robert T. Pipes *(VP-Sls-West
Monroe-LA)*

BANCROFT CONSTRUCTION
COMPANY
1300 N Grant Ave Ste 101, Wilming-
ton, DE 19806
Tel.: (302) 655-3434
Web Site:
   https://www.bancroftconstruction.com
Rev.: $101,500,000
Emp.: 125
Residential Building Construction
N.A.I.C.S.: 236116
Jack Barr *(CFO)*
Rob Jatick *(Dir-Sls & Mktg)*
Greg Sawka *(Pres)*

BANCROFT CONTRACTING
CORP.
23 Phillips Rd, South Paris, ME
04281
Tel.: (207) 743-8946
Web Site:
   https://www.bancroftcontracting.com
Sales Range: $10-24.9 Million
Emp.: 130
Paper/Pulp Mill Construction
N.A.I.C.S.: 236220
Mark Bancroft *(Pres)*
David Lepage *(VP-Fin)*
Harold Skelton *(Mgr-HR)*

BANCVUE, LTD.
4516 Seton Center Pkwy Ste 300,
Austin, TX 78759-5272
Tel.: (512) 418-9590
Web Site: http://www.bancvue.com
Year Founded: 2004
Sales Range: $10-24.9 Million
Emp.: 300
Bank & Credit Union Business Solu-
tions
N.A.I.C.S.: 561499
Gabriel Krajicek *(CEO)*
Don Shafer *(Chm)*
Marty Sunde *(Pres)*
John Waupsh *(Chief Innovation Offi-
cer & Chief Creative Officer)*
Steve Heston *(Chief Revenue Officer)*
Keith Brannan *(CMO)*

Subsidiaries:

BancLeasing Inc. (1)
660 N Central Expy, Plano, TX
75023 (100%)
Tel.: (972) 562-7480
Web Site: http://www.bancleasing.com
Sales Range: $10-24.9 Million
Emp.: 30
Equipment Leasing Services
N.A.I.C.S.: 532490

BAND OF CODERS, LP
1643 Mt Vernon Rd, Atlanta, GA
30338
Tel.: (470) 545-0767 GA
Web Site:
   https://www.bandofcoders.com
Year Founded: 2001
Software Design & Development Ser-
vices
N.A.I.C.S.: 541512
Jason Rhoades *(Sr Mng Partner)*
Bobby John *(CEO)*

Subsidiaries:

Toolbox No. 9 Inc. (1)
659 Auburn Ave NE Ste 254, Atlanta, GA
30312-1976
Tel.: (404) 434-4660
Web Site: http://www.toolbox9.com
Computer System Design Services
N.A.I.C.S.: 541512
Jason Rhoades *(Pres)*

BAND PRO FILM & DIGITAL
INC.
3403 W Pacific Ave, Burbank, CA
91505

Tel.: (818) 841-9655
Web Site:
http://www.bandprodigital.com
Year Founded: 1984
Sales Range: $10-24.9 Million
Emp.: 30
Retailer & Wholesaler of Video
Equipment
N.A.I.C.S.: 449210
Amnon H. Band *(Pres & CEO)*
Sandra Graves *(Controller)*

BANDANA'S BAR B Q

16141 Swingley Ridge Rd Ste 205,
Chesterfield, MO 63017
Tel.: (636) 537-8200
Web Site:
https://www.bandanasbbq.com
Year Founded: 2005
Sales Range: $1-9.9 Million
Emp.: 50
Restaurant
N.A.I.C.S.: 722511
Adam Craddock *(Principal)*

BANDERA ELECTRIC COOP-ERATIVE, INC.

3172 Hwy 16 N, Bandera, TX 78003
Tel.: (830) 796-3741
Web Site:
https://www.banderaelectric.com
Rev.: $25,000,000
Emp.: 100
Electronic Services
N.A.I.C.S.: 221118
Tim Landes *(Coord-Job Trng Safety
& Loss Control)*
David Swint *(Mgr-Special Projects)*
Lynn Midgette *(CFO)*
Shawna Frerich *(Mgr-Acctg)*
Richard McDonald *(Mgr-IT)*
Kurt Solis *(Treas & Sec)*

BANDES CONSTRUCTION COMPANY INC.

1368 Spalding Rd Ste C, Dunedin,
FL 34698
Tel.: (727) 733-5558
Web Site:
http://www.bandesconst.com
Year Founded: 1987
Sales Range: $25-49.9 Million
Emp.: 30
Commercial & Institutional Building
Construction
N.A.I.C.S.: 236220
Robert Bandes *(Pres)*
Mary Bandes *(Sec)*
Jim Dalka *(Sr Project Mgr)*
Lorraine Olgesby *(Mgr-Acctg)*
Mike Hovey *(Project Mgr)*

BANDIT LITES, INC.

2233 Sycamore Dr, Knoxville, TN
37921-1748
Tel.: (865) 971-3071   TN
Web Site: http://www.banditlites.com
Year Founded: 1968
Sales Range: $10-24.9 Million
Emp.: 80
Theatrical Producers & Services
N.A.I.C.S.: 541990
Michael T. Strickland *(Chm)*
Michael Golden *(VP)*
Matt King *(Project Mgr)*
Jake Tickle *(Dir-Technical Svcs)*
Allison Burchett *(Dir-Philanthropy)*
Chris Barbee *(Dir-Sls & Installations-Natl)*
Giff Swart *(Gen Mgr)*
Leonard Cox *(Dir-Logistics & Safety)*
Sharon Gross *(Coord-Media Rels)*
Brad Hylton *(Mgr-Warehouse)*
Brent Barrett *(Officer-Bus Dev)*

Jeff Vogt *(Dir-Computer Resources)*
Jimmy Hatten *(Project Mgr)*
Mark Steinwachs *(Gen Mgr)*

Subsidiaries:

Bandit Lites   (1)
1600 J P Hennessy Dr, La Vergne, TN
37086-3523
Tel.: (615) 641-9000
Web Site: http://www.banditlites.com
Entertainment Lighting
N.A.I.C.S.: 541990
Jason Workman *(Dir-Lighting)*

BANDUJO DONKER & BROTHERS

22 W 21st St 8th Fl, New York, NY
10010
Tel.: (212) 332-4100
Web Site: http://www.bandujo.com
Year Founded: 1993
Sales Range: $25-49.9 Million
Emp.: 10
Advertising Services
N.A.I.C.S.: 541810
Jose R. Bandujo *(Founder & Pres)*
Diego Rincon *(Dir-Art)*

BANDY CARROLL HELLIGE ADVERTISING

307 W Muhammad Ali Blvd, Louis-ville, KY 40202
Tel.: (502) 589-7711   KY
Web Site: https://www.bch.com
Year Founded: 1990
Sales Range: $25-49.9 Million
Emp.: 53
Advertising Services
N.A.I.C.S.: 541810
Susan Bandy *(Partner)*
Mark Carroll *(Partner)*
Tim Hellige *(Partner)*
Gary Sloboda *(Partner & Exec Cre-ative Dir)*
Matt Kamer *(Partner)*
Allison Pitman *(Partner & Dir-Acct)*
Cher Nelson *(Acct Mgr-PR)*
Andrew Tutt *(Acct Coord)*
Lauren Weitlauf *(Coord-PR)*
Danielle McKenzie *(Acct Mgr)*
Abigail Varner *(Acct Mgr)*
Sarah Bhatia *(Acct Mgr)*
Jan Kellogg *(Acct Dir-Brand Mgmt
Team)*
Julie Rudder *(Acct Dir-Brand Mgmt
Team)*
Shelby Nichols *(Dir-Digital Media)*
Molly Lucas *(Coord-Social Media)*
Alex Schoettmer *(Acct Coord)*
Trenton Schroeder *(Coord-Media)*

Subsidiaries:

Bandy Carroll Hellige Advertising -
Indianapolis   (1)
101 W Ohio St Ste 800, Indianapolis, IN
46204
Tel.: (317) 684-7711
Web Site: http://www.bch.com
Emp.: 10
Advertising Services
N.A.I.C.S.: 541810
Patrick Pfingsten *(Asst Mgr-Brand Engage-ment)*

BANES GENERAL CONTRAC-TORS, INC.

6001 Doniphan, El Paso, TX 79932
Tel.: (915) 584-0404
Web Site: https://www.banes-gc.com
Year Founded: 1946
Sales Range: $25-49.9 Million
Emp.: 20
Nonresidential Construction Services
N.A.I.C.S.: 236220
Dale Denney *(Principal)*

BANESCO USA

150 Alhambra Cir Ste 100, Coral
Gables, FL 33134
Tel.: (786) 725-3000   FL
Web Site:
http://www.banescousa.com
Year Founded: 2005
Sales Range: $10-24.9 Million
Emp.: 108
Retail & Commercial Banking
N.A.I.C.S.: 522110
Mercedes Escotet *(CFO & Exec VP)*
Carlos Palomares *(Chm)*
Alina D. Garcia-Duany *(Chief Lending
Officer & Exec VP)*
Leticia Pino *(Officer-Admin & Exec
VP)*
Alba Prestamo *(Chief Compliance &
Risk Officer & Exec VP)*
Jorge Salas *(Pres & CEO)*
Maritza Abadia *(Exec VP & Mgr-
Puerto Rico)*
Luis Alfredo Grau Guinand *(Sr VP &
Head-Intl)*
Jose E. Lopez *(Sr VP & Head-SMB
Lending & Branches)*
Michel Vogel *(Chief Credit Officer &
Sr VP)*
Julio Valle *(CIO & Exec VP)*
Kenneth Schoeni *(Chief Risk Officer)*
Amelia C. Rodriguez *(Sr VP)*
Ana Lorenzo *(Sr VP-Trade Fin
Lender)*
Martha S. Tabio *(Sr VP-Construction
Loan Div)*
Juan Babani *(Sr VP-Comml Lending)*
Rogelio Obeso *(Sr VP)*

BANFI PRODUCT CORP.

1111 Cedar Swamp Rd, Glen Head,
NY 11545-2109
Tel.: (516) 626-9200
Web Site: http://www.banfi.com
Sales Range: $75-99.9 Million
Emp.: 75
Mfr of Wines
N.A.I.C.S.: 424820
Harry Mariani *(Pres)*
John F. Mariani *(Chm & CEO)*
Marc Goodrich *(CFO & VP)*

Subsidiaries:

Banfi Vintners   (1)
1111 Cedar Swamp Rd, Glen Head, NY
11545-2109
Tel.: (516) 626-9200
Web Site: http://www.banfivintners.com
Sales Range: $25-49.9 Million
Wine Importer
N.A.I.C.S.: 424820
Lars Leicht *(VP & Dir-Comm)*
Neill Trimble *(VP-Adv)*
Cristina N. Mariani-May *(Pres & CEO)*
Rich Andrews *(COO)*

Subsidiary (Non-US):

Castello Banfi Srl   (2)
Castello di Poggio alle Mura, Montalcino,
53024, Siena, Sant Angelo Scalo, Italy
Tel.: (39) 0577877700
Web Site:
http://www.castellobanfiilborgo.com
Sales Range: $25-49.9 Million
Winery
N.A.I.C.S.: 312130
John F. Mariani Jr. *(CEO)*

Unit (Domestic):

House of Banfi   (2)
1111 Cedar Swamp Rd, Glen Head, NY
11545-2109
Tel.: (516) 626-9200
Web Site: http://www.banfi.com
Sales Range: $10-24.9 Million
Emp.: 30
Mfr of Wines
N.A.I.C.S.: 424820

Villadco Inc.   (2)
1111 Cedar Swamp Rd, Glen Head, NY
11545-2109

Tel.: (516) 626-9200
Web Site: http://www.banfivintners.com
Sales Range: $10-24.9 Million
Emp.: 10
Advetising Agency
N.A.I.C.S.: 541810
Neill Trimble *(VP-Adv)*

BANFIELD CHARITABLE TRUST

8000 NE Tillamook St, Portland, OR
97213-6655
Tel.: (503) 922-5801   OR
Web Site:
http://www.banfieldcharitabletrust.org
Year Founded: 2002
Sales Range: $1-9.9 Million
Emp.: 6
Animal Shelter Services
N.A.I.C.S.: 812910
Kristen Lane Murphy *(Program Mgr)*
Russ Kukini *(Mgr-Resource Dev)*
Kathryn Shimabukuro *(Dir-Mktg)*
Paul Lipscomb *(Exec Dir)*
Jim Cleary *(Chm)*
Keith Levy *(Vice Chm)*
Dave Pedersen *(Treas)*
Jeannine Taaffe *(Sec)*

BANG PRINTING

3323 Oak St, Brainerd, MN 56401
Tel.: (218) 829-2877
Web Site:
http://www.bangprinting.com
Year Founded: 1899
Emp.: 500
Commercial Printing
N.A.I.C.S.: 323111
Todd Vanek *(Pres)*

Subsidiaries:

Bang Printing - Valencia   (1)
28210 N Ave Stanford, Valencia, CA 91355-
3983
Tel.: (661) 257-0584
Sales Range: $25-49.9 Million
Emp.: 150
Books Printing
N.A.I.C.S.: 323117
Karen Matson *(VP-Admin & Customer Svc)*
Donna Beltran *(Mgr-Acctg)*
Jerry Bernstein *(VP-Sls)*
Patricia Medina *(Mgr-Bindery)*
Roger Butzen *(Dir-Bus Dev)*
Alice Zumstein *(VP-Production)*

Bang Printing of Ohio, Inc.   (1)
3765 Sunnybrook Rd, Brimfield, OH 44240-
7443
Tel.: (330) 678-5868
Web Site: http://www.hessprintsolutions.com
Sales Range: $25-49.9 Million
Emp.: 390
Commercial Printing & Lithographic Ser-vices
N.A.I.C.S.: 323111
Mark Berkey *(VP-Strategy & Corp Dev)*

Sentinel Printing Co., Inc.   (1)
250 N Hwy 10, Saint Cloud, MN 56304
Tel.: (320) 251-6434
Web Site: http://www.sentinelprinting.com
Sales Range: $1-9.9 Million
Emp.: 60
Book Printing Services
N.A.I.C.S.: 323117
Charles R. Manthey *(Pres)*
Doug Walter *(VP & Sls Mgr)*
Deb Finley *(Ops Mgr)*
Marcia Goss *(Mgr-HR)*

BANGKOK MARKET INC.

2916 Tanager Ave, Commerce, CA
90040
Tel.: (323) 585-5385
Web Site:
http://www.bangkokmarketinc.com
Year Founded: 1972
Sales Range: $1-9.9 Million
Emp.: 20
Oriental Grocery Retailer
N.A.I.C.S.: 424410

Bangkok Market Inc.—(Continued)

Mary Tila (Pres)
Marasri Tilakamonkul (CEO)

BANGOR PUBLISHING COMPANY
1 Merchant Plz, Bangor, ME 04402
Tel.: (207) 990-8000
Web Site:
https://www.bangordailynews.com
Sales Range: $25-49.9 Million
Emp.: 200
Newspapers, Publishing & Printing
N.A.I.C.S.: 513110
Richard J. Warren (Publr)
Jennifer Holmes (VP)
Mike Dowd (Editor-Metro & Standards)
Tod Benoit (Pres & COO)

BANGOR SAVINGS BANK
3 State St, Bangor, ME 04402
Tel.: (207) 907-7011   ME
Web Site: http://www.bangor.com
Year Founded: 1852
Sales Range: $200-249.9 Million
Emp.: 907
Savings Bank
N.A.I.C.S.: 522180
Gena R. Canning (Vice Pres)
Robert A. Strong (Chm)
Robert S. Montgomery-Rice (Pres & CEO)
Andrew J. Grover (Chief Risk Officer & Sr VP)
Joyce Clark Sarnacki (Chief Customer Experience Officer & Exec VP)

BANK ADMINISTRATION INSTITUTE
115 S Lasalle St, Chicago, IL 60603
Tel.: (312) 553-4600   IL
Web Site: http://www.bai.org
Year Founded: 1924
Sales Range: $10-24.9 Million
Emp.: 120
Business Associations
N.A.I.C.S.: 813910
Deborah L. Bianucci (Pres & CEO)
Austin A. Adams (Exec VP)
Holly Hughes (CMO)
Terry Badger (Mng Editor-BAI Banking Strategies)

BANK IOWA CORPORATION
1225 Jordan Creek Pkwy Ste 200, West Des Moines, IA 50266
Tel.: (515) 225-2333   IA
Web Site: http://www.bankiowa.bank
Year Founded: 1989
Sales Range: $50-74.9 Million
Emp.: 265
Bank Holding Company
N.A.I.C.S.: 551111
Bob Gagne (Chief Lending Officer & Exec VP)
Jim Plagge (Pres & CEO)
Jon Sarvis (CFO)

Subsidiaries:

Bank Iowa   (1)
1225 Jordan Creek Pkwy Ste 200, West Des Moines, IA 50266
Tel.: (515) 225-2333
Web Site: http://www.bankiowa.bank
Sales Range: $50-74.9 Million
Commericial Banking
N.A.I.C.S.: 522110
Jim Plagge (Pres & CEO)
Jon Sarvis (CFO)
Rich Davitt (Chief Credit Officer)
Kate Wolfe (Chief Admin Officer & Chief HR Officer)
Bob Gagne (Chief Lending Officer)
Chad Leighty (Pres-Denison)

BANK MIDWEST

1525 18th St, Spirit Lake, IA 51360
Tel.: (712) 336-0505
Web Site:
https://www.bankmidwest.com
Year Founded: 1882
Sales Range: $10-24.9 Million
Banking Services
N.A.I.C.S.: 522110
Stephen J. Goodenow (Chm)
Lisa Bowman (Mgr-Comml Banking Market)
Mary Kay Bates (Pres & CEO)

BANK OF AGRICULTURE & COMMERCE
2021 W March Ln, Stockton, CA 95207-6400
Tel.: (209) 473-6800   CA
Web Site: http://www.bankbac.com
Year Founded: 1965
Sales Range: $100-124.9 Million
Emp.: 100
Full-Service Banking
N.A.I.C.S.: 522110
Ronald A. Berberian (Chm & Pres)
William R. Trezza (CEO)
Dana Bockstahler (COO & Exec VP)
Janet Jenkins (Chief Credit Officer & Exec VP)
Jackie Verkuyl (CFO & Exec VP)
Linda Denos (Branch Mgr & Asst VP)

BANK OF ALMA
211 S Main St, Alma, WI 54610-0247
Tel.: (608) 685-4461
Web Site:
https://www.bankofalma.net
Sales Range: $25-49.9 Million
Emp.: 27
Commericial Banking
N.A.I.C.S.: 522110
William Bosshard (Pres)

BANK OF CENTRAL FLORIDA
5015 S Florida Ave, Lakeland, FL 33813
Tel.: (863) 701-2685
Web Site:
https://www.bankofcentralflorida.com
Year Founded: 2007
Sales Range: $10-24.9 Million
Emp.: 51
Commericial Banking
N.A.I.C.S.: 522110
Paul J. Noris (Chm & CEO)
Randell S. Hollen (Sr VP-Comml)
Jennifer L. Adams (Officer-Private Banking & Sr VP)
Gwyndolyn C. Hughes (Officer-Private Banking & VP)
David M. Brown (Sr VP)
Robert P. Kenney (CFO & Exec VP)
Jim Dugger (Chief Credit Officer & Exec VP)
Robert R. Wedlock (COO, CTO & Exec VP)
Marilyn Watson (VP)
Joseph Furnari III (Chief Sls Officer & Exec VP)

BANK OF CLARENDON
106 S Brooks St, Manning, SC 29102
Tel.: (803) 433-4451
Web Site:
http://www.bankofclarendon.com
Year Founded: 1932
Sales Range: $1-9.9 Million
Emp.: 50
Banking Services
N.A.I.C.S.: 522110
William O. Buyck (Chm & CEO)
J. Barry Ham (Pres)
Rose Buyck Newton (VP)
Jay Gardner (VP)

Thomas D. Ham (Asst.VP & Mgr-IT)
James Ham (VP)
Kendall Stewart (CFO & Exec VP)

BANK OF COMMERCE & TRUST CO.
326 N Ave G, Crowley, LA 70526
Tel.: (337) 783-2201
Web Site:
https://www.bankofcommerce.com
Sales Range: $75-99.9 Million
Emp.: 94
Commercial Bank
N.A.I.C.S.: 522110
John W. Sarver (Pres)
J. W. Landry Jr. (Chm)

BANK OF COMMERCE INC.
310 Howard St, Greenwood, MS 38930
Tel.: (662) 453-4142
Web Site: http://www.bankcom.com
Rev.: $10,315,097
Emp.: 35
State Commercial Banks
N.A.I.C.S.: 522110
Steve Lary (Exec VP)
Bryan Thornhill (Pres)
Zack Luke (Controller)

BANK OF HEMET
3715 Sunnyside Dr, Riverside, CA 92506
Tel.: (951) 248-2000
Web Site:
https://www.bankofhemet.com
Sales Range: $10-24.9 Million
Emp.: 89
Commercial & Private Banks
N.A.I.C.S.: 522110
Kevin Farrenkopf (Pres & CEO)

BANK OF JACKSON HOLE INC.
990 West Broadway, Jackson, WY 83002
Tel.: (307) 733-8064
Web Site: http://www.bojh.com
Rev.: $15,777,000
Emp.: 50
State Commercial Banks
N.A.I.C.S.: 522110
Brian Jones (Sr VP & Mgr-Trust Dept)
James Mazzarisi (VP-Comml Banker)

BANK OF LUXEMBURG
630 Main St, Luxemburg, WI 54217
Tel.: (920) 845-2345
Web Site:
https://www.bankofluxemburg.com
Rev.: $12,000,000
Emp.: 37
Commericial Banking
N.A.I.C.S.: 522110
Denise Kinjerski (VP-HR)
John Slatkey (CEO)

BANK OF MOUNT HOPE
602 Main St, Mount Hope, WV 25880
Tel.: (304) 877-5551   WV
Web Site:
http://www.mthopebank.com
Year Founded: 1902
Sales Range: $25-49.9 Million
Emp.: 35
Commericial Banking
N.A.I.C.S.: 522110
Ben M. Susman (Pres & CEO)
Ronald E. Clay (Chm)
Bradley P. Wartella (Sr VP)

BANK OF NEW ALBANY
133 E Bankhead, New Albany, MS 38652
Tel.: (662) 534-8171
Web Site: http://www.bnabank.com

Year Founded: 1896
Sales Range: $10-24.9 Million
Emp.: 77
Banking Services
N.A.I.C.S.: 522110
Vance Witt (Chm)
Robert Spencer (Officer-Compliance & Sr VP)
Mike Staten (Pres)
Mike Alef (Sr VP-Insurance & Investments)
Hugh Tate (Sr VP-Loans)
Peggy Crumpton (Asst VP)
Kay Darling (Asst VP)
Mike Nobles (VP-Loans)
Anita Speck (Asst VP-Retail)
Brad Kennedy (VP & Officer-Trust)
Michelle Kirk (VP-HR)
Gregory D. Pirkle (Atty)
William Thomas Shannon (Atty)
William O. Rutledge III (Atty)

Subsidiaries:

BNA Insurance & Investments, Inc.   (1)
133 E Bankhead St, New Albany, MS 38652
Tel.: (662) 534-8171
Web Site: http://www.bnabank.com
Sales Range: Less than $1 Million
Emp.: 3
Banking Services
N.A.I.C.S.: 522110
Mike Alef (VP-Investment Svcs)

BANK OF NORTH DAKOTA
1200 Memorial Hwy, Bismarck, ND 58506-5509
Tel.: (701) 328-5600   ND
Web Site: https://bnd.nd.gov
Year Founded: 1919
Sales Range: $250-299.9 Million
Emp.: 165
Commercial Banking Services
N.A.I.C.S.: 522110
Eric Hardmeyer (Pres)
Bonnie Schneider (Mgr-Mgmt Info Sys)
Tim Porter (CFO & Sr VP)
Kelvin Hullet (Mgr-Economic Dev & Govt Program Market)

BANK OF PUTNAM COUNTY
140 S Jefferson Ave, Cookeville, TN 38501
Tel.: (931) 528-5441
Web Site: http://www.bpc-financial.com
Year Founded: 1901
Sales Range: $10-24.9 Million
Emp.: 90
Banking Services
N.A.I.C.S.: 522110
David Williamson (Mgr)

BANK OF SOUTHSIDE VIRGINIA
17208 Halligan Park Rd, Carson, VA 23830
Tel.: (434) 246-5211
Web Site: https://www.bsvnet.com
Year Founded: 1905
Sales Range: $25-49.9 Million
Emp.: 115
Banking Services
N.A.I.C.S.: 522110
J. Peter Clements (Pres)
James Buren (Exec VP)
Joy Burroughs (Controller)

BANK OF THE LAKES NA
12401 E 86th St N, Owasso, OK 74055
Tel.: (918) 274-3535
Web Site:
http://www.bankofthelakes.com
Year Founded: 1976

Sales Range: $200-249.9 Million
Emp.: 50
Commercial Banking Services
N.A.I.C.S.: 522110
Robert F. Biolchini (Chm)
Lelia McCoy (Exec VP)
Stan Pinkham (CFO, COO & Exec VP)
Mark Charles (Officer-Info Security & VP-IT)
Doug DeJarnette (Sr VP & Dir-Private Bank)
Jeannine Hanner (Sr VP-Fin)
Starlene Warburton (Sr VP-Loan Ops)
Keri McSorley (Sr VP-Ops & Compliance)
Mike Judd (Sr VP-Retail Banking)
Shannon Habermehl (Sr VP-Treasury Svcs)
Lori Stevens (VP-HR)

BANK OF THE ORIENT
233 Sansome St, San Francisco, CA 94104-2305
Tel.: (415) 338-0668   CA
Web Site: http://www.bankorient.com
Sales Range: $25-49.9 Million
Emp.: 100
Banking Services
N.A.I.C.S.: 522110
Grace Yuen (Mgr-District & Sr VP)

BANK OF TRAVELERS REST INC.
42 Plaza Dr, Travelers Rest, SC 29690
Tel.: (864) 834-9031
Web Site:
   https://www.bankoftravelersrest.com
Year Founded: 1946
Sales Range: $10-24.9 Million
Emp.: 90
Banking Services
N.A.I.C.S.: 522110
Tom Britt (Pres)

BANK OF WASHINGTON INC.
200 W Main St, Washington, MO 63090
Tel.: (636) 239-7831
Web Site:
   http://www.bankofwashington.com
Rev.: $28,821,000
Emp.: 140
State Commercial Banks
N.A.I.C.S.: 522110
Chris Eckelkamp (Asst VP-Comml Lending)
Jay Nowak (Exec VP)
L. B. Eckelkamp Jr. (Chm & CEO)
Louis B. Eckelkamp III (Pres)

BANK OF WEDOWEE
112 W Broad St, Wedowee, AL 36278
Tel.: (256) 357-2132   AL
Web Site:
   http://www.bankofwedowee.com
Year Founded: 1906
Sales Range: $25-49.9 Million
Emp.: 37
Commericial Banking
N.A.I.C.S.: 522110
Roger E. Campbell (Pres)
McCakur Kay (VP)

BANK OF WISCONSIN DELLS
716 Superior St, Wisconsin Dells, WI 53965
Tel.: (608) 253-1111
Web Site: http://www.dellsbank.com
Rev.: $24,300,000
Emp.: 65
Commericial Banking
N.A.I.C.S.: 522110

Kelly Bauer (Sr VP)
Christine Lee (VP & Dir-IT)
Linda L. Sobojinski (Officer-Consumer & Mortgage Loan & Asst VP)
Scott Rockwell (Officer-Comml Loan & Asst VP)
John Bernander (CEO)
Connie R. Suemnicht (Officer-Comml Loan & VP)
Kim I. Pearson (VP & Mgr-Retail Sls)
Sean D. Brennan (Officer-Comml Loan & Asst VP)
Tracey M. Pierce (CFO & Sr VP)
Brian J. Jensen (VP)
Matthew J. Schaefer (VP-Loan Compliance)
Tammy Smith (VP-Ops)
Molly A. Bauer (VP-HR)
Jennifer J. Gilbertson (Officer-Loan Ops)
Tracy Stowell (Officer-Bank Secrecy, Act & Deposit Compliance)

BANK OF YORK
13 W Liberty St, York, SC 29745
Tel.: (803) 684-2265   SC
Web Site:
   https://www.bankofyork.com
Year Founded: 1935
Sales Range: $25-49.9 Million
Emp.: 50
State Commercial Banks
N.A.I.C.S.: 522110
Michael Hill (CEO)
William M. Langford (CFO)

BANK POLICY INSTITUTE
600 13th St NW Ste 400, Washington, DC 20005
Tel.: (202) 289-4322
Web Site: http://bpi.com
Year Founded: 2018
Financial Services
N.A.I.C.S.: 522320
Greg Baer (Pres & CEO)
Kate Childress (Exec VP & Head-Pub Affairs)
William Demchak (Chm)
Chris Feeney (Exec VP)
Bill Nelson (Exec VP)
William S. Demchak (Chm)

Subsidiaries:

New York Clearing House Association LLC   (1)
450 W 33rd St, New York, NY 10001
Tel.: (212) 612-9200
Web Site: http://www.theclearinghouse.org
Bank & Check Clearing Services
N.A.I.C.S.: 522320
James Aramanda (Pres)

Subsidiary (Domestic):

Financial Services Roundtable   (2)
600 13th St NW Ste 400, Washington, DC 20005
Tel.: (202) 289-4322
Web Site: http://www.fsroundtable.org
Advocacy Organization; Lobbying & Financial Advisory Services
N.A.I.C.S.: 813319
Christopher Feeney (Acting CEO)

BANKCARD USA MERCHANT SERVICES, INC.
5701 Lindero Canyon Rd, Westlake Village, CA 91362
Tel.: (818) 597-7000
Web Site:
   http://www.bankcardusa.com
Year Founded: 1993
Sales Range: $1-9.9 Million
Emp.: 85
Office Equipment
N.A.I.C.S.: 423420
Shawn Skelton (CEO)
Scott Hardy (Pres)

Felix Danciu (CFO)
Jason Hardy (COO)
William Hui-Chung Chang (Chm)

BANKERS BANCORP OF OKLAHOMA, INC.
9020 N May Ave, Oklahoma City, OK 73120
Tel.: (405) 848-8877   OK
Web Site:
   http://www.thebankersbank.com
Year Founded: 1985
Sales Range: $10-24.9 Million
Bank Holding Company
N.A.I.C.S.: 551111
Donald R. Abernathy Jr. (Pres & CEO)

Subsidiaries:

The Bankers Bank   (1)
9020 N May Ave, Oklahoma City, OK 73120
Tel.: (405) 848-8877
Web Site: http://www.tbb.bank
Sales Range: $10-24.9 Million
Emp.: 69
Commericial Banking
N.A.I.C.S.: 522110
Donald R. Abernathy Jr. (Pres & CEO)

BANKERS BUSINESS MANAGEMENT SERVICES, INC.
8121 Georgia Ave Ste 950, Silver Spring, MD 20910
Tel.: (301) 565-0601
Web Site:
   https://www.bankersbms.com
Year Founded: 1982
Rev.: $9,000,000
Emp.: 134
Business Services
N.A.I.C.S.: 561499
Mussie Betre (Pres, CEO & Treas-Fin)
Tselate Talley (Sec & VP)
Rhonda Mosley (Mgr-HR)
Shimelis Akalu (Mng Partner)

BANKERS HEALTHCARE GROUP, LLC
10234 W State Rd 84, Davie, FL 33324
Tel.: (954) 384-9119   FL
Web Site:
   http://www.bankershealthcare.com
Year Founded: 1992
Emp.: 200
Healthcare Professional Financial & Insurance Services
N.A.I.C.S.: 522299
Robert T. Castro (Co-Founder)
Eric R. Castro (Co-Founder)
Edmund Durant (CFO)
Christopher J. Cali (Chief Legal Officer)
Albert Crawford (Chm & CEO)
Juan Carlos Ortigosa (Chief Revenue Officer)
Chris Panebianco (CMO)
April Brissette (Chief Credit Officer)
Tyler Crawford (Chief Bus Dev Officer & CEO-Patient Lending)
Keith Gruebele (Sr VP-Sls)
Jim Kennedy (Chief Compliance Officer)
Dan McSherry (Sr VP-Analytics)
Tom Davis (Sr VP-Placements)
Juliana Haggerty (Sr VP-Collections)
Danielle Walker (Sr VP-Data Mgmt & Strategic Relationships)
Zach Raus (Pres-Lending Div)
Mark Schmidt (Chief Regulatory Rels Officer)

Subsidiaries:

Bankers Healthcare Group, LLC - Financial Headquarters   (1)

201 Solar St, Syracuse, NY 13204
Tel.: (315) 422-4350
Web Site:
   http://www.bankershealthcaregroup.com
Emp.: 320
Healthcare Professional Financial & Insurance Services
N.A.I.C.S.: 522299
Louise Stuenzi (Mgr-Payroll & Benefits)
April Brissette (Chief Lending Officer)
Melissa Whelan (Sr VP-Sls-Global)
Chris Panebianco (CMO)
Rosa M. Bernardi Pinti (Chief Acctg Officer)
Kristian Vartabedian (Mgr-Collections)
Brett Pugh (VP-Placements)

BANKERS INTERNATIONAL FINANCIAL CORPORATION
1101 Roosevelt Blvd N, Saint Petersburg, FL 33716
Tel.: (727) 823-4000   FL
Web Site:
   https://www.bankersinsurance.com
Year Founded: 1983
Sales Range: $200-249.9 Million
Emp.: 955
Insurance Agents & Broker Services
N.A.I.C.S.: 524210
David K. Meehan (Pres)
John Strong (Pres & CEO)

Subsidiaries:

Bankers Financial Corporation   (1)
11101 Roosevelt Blvd N, Saint Petersburg, FL 33716
Tel.: (727) 823-4000
Web Site:
   http://www.bankersfinancialcorp.com
Sales Range: $300-349.9 Million
Emp.: 750
Banking & Insurance Services
N.A.I.C.S.: 522110
John A. Strong (Chm & CEO)

Subsidiary (Domestic):

Bankers Insurance Group, Inc.   (2)
11101 Roosevelt Blvd N, Saint Petersburg, FL 33716-2340
Tel.: (727) 823-4000
Web Site: http://www.bankersinsurance.com
Sales Range: $125-149.9 Million
Emp.: 300
Fire, Marine & Casualty Insurance Services
N.A.I.C.S.: 524210
Bill Martin (Pres)

Subsidiary (Domestic):

Bankers Insurance Company   (3)
11101 Roosevelt Blvd N, Saint Petersburg, FL 33716-3857
Tel.: (727) 823-4000
Web Site: http://bankersinsurance.com
Rev.: $59,049,208
Emp.: 250
Fire, Marine & Casualty Insurance
N.A.I.C.S.: 524126

Bankers Insurance Services Inc.   (3)
11101 Roosevelt Blvd N, Saint Petersburg, FL 33716-2340
Tel.: (727) 823-4000
Web Site: http://www.bankersinsurance.com
Rev.: $111,871,168
Emp.: 400
Fire, Marine & Casualty Insurance
N.A.I.C.S.: 524126
David K. Meehan (Pres)
Rob Menke (Pres)

Bankers Life Insurance Company   (3)
11101 Roosevelt Blvd N, Saint Petersburg, FL 33716
Tel.: (727) 823-4000
Web Site:
   http://www.bankerslifeinsurance.com
Rev.: $26,727,577
Emp.: 250
Life Insurance
N.A.I.C.S.: 524210
Stuart Platter (Pres)

Bankers Surety Services   (3)
PO Box 33015, Saint Petersburg, FL 33733-8015

Bankers International Financial
Corporation—(Continued)

Tel.: (855) 890-6993
Web Site: http://www.bankerssurety.com
Emp.: 60
Insurance Management Services
N.A.I.C.S.: 524298
Brian Kesneck *(Pres)*
Joann Bjurholm *(Asst VP)*
Lisa Basta *(VP)*
Rob Southey *(VP)*
Kimberly Cheng *(Asst VP)*

Bonded Builders Warranty Group (3)
PO Box 33025, Saint Petersburg, FL
33733-8025
Tel.: (800) 749-0381
Web Site: http://www.bondedbuilders.com
Warranty Insurance Management Services
N.A.I.C.S.: 524128
Sheila Morgan *(Dir-Accts-Natl)*

Subsidiary (Domestic):

**Bonded Builders Insurance
Services** (4)
PO Box 33012, Saint Petersburg, FL 33733
Web Site: http://www.bbisinsurance.com
Insurance Management Services
N.A.I.C.S.: 524298
Shawn Heuton *(Mgr-Agency)*

Subsidiary (Domestic):

**G.D. van Wagenen Financial Ser-
vices, Inc.** (3)
6483 City W Pkwy, Eden Prairie, MN 55344
Tel.: (800) 346-9713
Web Site: http://www.vanwagenen.com
Insurance Management Services
N.A.I.C.S.: 524298
Randall Rempp *(VP & Gen Mgr)*

Subsidiary (Domestic):

Bankers Warranty Group (2)
11101 Roosevelt Blvd N, Saint Petersburg,
FL 33716
Tel.: (727) 823-4000
Warranty Services
N.A.I.C.S.: 561499
Michael Kelly *(VP-Sls)*

BANKERS' BANCORPORA-
TION, INC.
7700 Mineral Point Rd, Madison, WI
53717-1694
Tel.: (608) 833-5550   WI
Web Site:
http://www.bankersbank.com
Year Founded: 1983
Sales Range: $25-49.9 Million
Emp.: 127
Bank Holding Company
N.A.I.C.S.: 551111
Bradlee F. Stamper *(Pres & CEO)*

Subsidiaries:

Bankers' Bank (1)
7700 Mineral Point Rd, Madison, WI 53717
Tel.: (608) 833-5550
Web Site: http://www.bankersbank.com
Sales Range: $25-49.9 Million
Commercial, Investment & Mortgage Bank-
ing
N.A.I.C.S.: 522110
Tom Underkofler *(CFO & Sr VP)*
Carol Wanserski *(Chief Acctg Officer, Chief
Treasury Officer & Sr VP)*
Kara Hetzel *(Asst VP-HR)*
Bradlee F. Stamper *(Pres & CEO)*

BANKNEWPORT
184 John Clarke Rd, Middletown, RI
02842
Tel.: (401) 846-3400
Web Site:
http://www.banknewport.com
Year Founded: 1819
Sales Range: $25-49.9 Million
Emp.: 269
Federal Savings Bank
N.A.I.C.S.: 522180

Sandra J. Pattie *(Pres & CEO)*
Kenneth Burnett *(Sr VP & Dir-Comml
Relationships)*
Colleen J. Medeiros *(CTO & Sr VP)*
John P. Sullivan *(Exec VP-Digital &
Tech Strategy)*
George D. Duarte *(Officer-Bus Dev &
VP)*
Cidalia M. Rodrigues *(VP & Mgr-Sls)*
William J. Marcello *(VP & Mgr-Sls)*
F. Michael DeVito *(VP & Mgr-Sls)*
Linda Buchanan *(VP & Mgr-Sls)*
Paul J. Kloiber *(VP & Mgr-Sls)*
Joseph Bell *(VP & Mgr-Sls)*
Donna M. Giblin *(VP & Mgr-Sls)*
Mary Beth Manuel *(VP & Mgr-Branch
Ops)*
Victor Correia *(VP & Mgr-Sls)*
Thomas Beauchene *(Officer-Comml
Loan & VP)*
Sean McIntyre *(Officer-Comml Loan
& VP)*
Paul Disanto *(VP)*
Nate Colwell *(VP & Mgr-Sls)*
Daniel M. Silverman *(VP)*
Gina Campbell Helm *(VP)*
Gina M. Lauro *(VP & Sls Mgr-
Mortgage)*
Mark T. Carnevale *(VP)*
Christopher J. Sheehan *(Sr-VP &
Mgr-Bus Banking Grp)*
Nina Luchka *(Officer-Bus Dev & VP)*
Keith Lavimodiere *(Officer-Comml
Loan & VP)*
Maria T. Botelho *(Officer-Comml Loan
& VP)*
Nathan Colwell *(VP/Mgr-Sls-
Barrington)*
Jessica A. Almeida *(Asst VP)*
Ryan Galitskie *(VP & Reg Mgr-Sls)*
Paul A. Marchetti *(Chief Credit Offi-
cer, Chief Risk Officer & Sr VP)*
Gary Leveillee *(Officer-Mortgage
Loan & Asst VP)*
Sharon Medeiros *(Sr VP & Controller)*
Aman Rai *(VP & Branch Mgr-Sls)*
Jon Richmond *(VP & Branch Mgr-Sls)*
Laura Guillen *(VP & Branch Mgr-Sls)*
Susan M. Viveiros *(VP)*
Betsy L. Salisbury *(Sr VP & Mgr-
Retail Lending Ops)*
Isabel Tigano *(VP)*
Justin L. Lombardo *(VP & Mgr-Sls-
Barrington)*
Margaret McGreavy *(VP & Mgr-Sls-
Stone Bridge)*
Ronald P. Greenwood *(VP & Sls Mgr-
Cranston)*
Ann Ullucci *(VP & Sls Mgr-Coventry)*
Mathew Insana *(VP-Comml Lending
Team)*
Paul Sousa *(VP-Comml Lending
Team)*
Linda A. Dias *(VP)*
Erin L. Mallo *(VP & Sls Mgr-South
Angell Street)*
Marc Scanapieco *(Officer-Bus &
Comml Lending & VP)*
Thomas J. May Jr. *(Officer-Comml
Loan & VP)*

BANKNOTE CAPITAL CORP.
1629 Colonial Pkwy, Inverness, IL
60067
Tel.: (847) 991-0100   IL
Web Site: https://www.bncap.com
Investment Advisory, Private Equity &
Asset Management Services
N.A.I.C.S.: 523999
Thomas G. Fitzgerald *(Pres & CEO)*
Laurel Stewart *(Office Mgr)*

BANKO DESIGN LLC
2171 Kingston Ct Ste A, Marietta, GA
30067

Tel.: (678) 202-4812   GA
Web Site:
http://www.bankodesign.com
Interior Design Services
N.A.I.C.S.: 541410
Melissa Banko *(Founder & Principal)*

Subsidiaries:

Warner Design Associates, Inc. (1)
1510 Fashion Is Blvd Ste 240, San Mateo,
CA 94404
Tel.: (650) 274-0947
Web Site:
http://www.warnerdesignassociates.com
Commercial Interior Design Services
N.A.I.C.S.: 541410
Mark Warner *(Co-Founder)*
Cynthia J. Warner *(Co-Founder)*

BANKPLUS CORPORATION
1068 Highland Colony Pkwy, Ridge-
land, MS 39157
Tel.: (601) 898-8300
Web Site: https://www.bankplus.net
Rev.: $246,422,000
Assets: $7,034,821,000
Liabilities: $6,433,705,000
Net Worth: $601,116,000
Earnings: $60,775,000
Emp.: 1,173
Fiscal Year-end: 12/31/22
Bank Holding Company
N.A.I.C.S.: 551111
B. Bryan Jones III *(Chm)*
Randall E. Howard *(Vice Chm)*
William A. Ray *(Vice Chm, Pres &
CEO)*
Alison Tyler *(Chief HR Officer & Exec
VP)*

Subsidiaries:

BankPlus (1)
202 E Jackson St, Belzoni, MS 39038
Tel.: (662) 247-1811
Web Site: https://www.bankplus.net
Rev.: $99,749,000
Emp.: 18
Commericial Banking
N.A.I.C.S.: 522110
B. Bryan Jones III *(Chm)*
Randall E. Howard *(Vice Chm)*
Eugene F. Webb Jr. *(Pres)*
William A. Ray *(Vice Chm & CEO)*
Gaye Broyles *(First VP & Mgr-Comml Sls)*
Bruce Ulrich *(Asst VP & Mgr-Mktg Comm)*
Chris Roberts *(Asst VP-Madison)*
Lindsay Akers Tomlinson *(First VP & Dir-
Analytics-Mktg)*
Robert Hawkins *(Asst VP)*
Lee Hardy *(Asst VP-Flora)*
Toni Houston *(Asst VP-Jackson)*

BANKS BROS. CORPORATION
24 Federal Plz, Bloomfield, NJ
07003-5636
Tel.: (973) 680-4488
Web Site:
http://www.banksbroscorp.com
Year Founded: 1945
Sales Range: $25-49.9 Million
Emp.: 400
Mfr of Gaskets, Packing & Sealing
Devices
N.A.I.C.S.: 339991

Subsidiaries:

Larstan Industries, Inc. (1)
24 Federal Plz, Bloomfield, NJ 07003-5636
Tel.: (973) 680-4488
Web Site: http://www.larstan.net
Sales Range: $10-24.9 Million
Emp.: 40
Mfr of Fabricated Rubber Products
N.A.I.C.S.: 339991
Andrew Banks *(Dir-Sls)*

BANKS ENGINEERING, INC.
10511 6 Mile Cypress Pkwy Ste 101,
Fort Myers, FL 33966
Tel.: (239) 939-5490   FL

Web Site: http://www.bankseng.com
Year Founded: 1992
Sales Range: $1-9.9 Million
Emp.: 75
Engineering & Surveying Services
N.A.I.C.S.: 541330
Randy Banks *(Founder)*
Samuel Marshall *(Dir-Engrg)*
Richard Ritz *(Dir-Surveying)*
Bonny Thompson *(Controller)*
Todd Rebol *(Mgr-Port Charlotte
Branch)*
Shane Cooper *(Dir-Engrg)*
David Underhill Jr. *(Mgr-Naples
Branch)*
Thomas Lehnert Jr. *(Pres & CEO)*

BANKS HARDWOODS, INC.
69937 M 103, White Pigeon, MI
49099-9449
Tel.: (269) 483-2323   IN
Web Site:
https://www.bankshardwoods.com
Year Founded: 1985
Sales Range: $10-24.9 Million
Emp.: 150
Hardwood Lumber Distr
N.A.I.C.S.: 321999
Steven G. Banks *(CEO)*
James F. Clark *(Pres & CFO)*
Darren Hubartt *(VP-Purchasing)*

Subsidiaries:

Banks Hardwoods, Inc. (1)
2208 Wagner St, Menomonie, WI 54751
Tel.: (715) 235-5301
Web Site: http://www.bankshardwoods.com
Hardwood Mfr & Whslr
N.A.I.C.S.: 321211

Banks Hardwoods, Inc. (1)
9 Scarlett Maple Ct, Little Rock, AR 72223
Tel.: (501) 379-8846
Hardwood Mfr & Whslr
N.A.I.C.S.: 321211

Banks Hardwoods, Inc. - Menomonie
Facility (1)
2208 Wagner St, Menomonie, WI 54751
Tel.: (715) 235-5301
Web Site: http://www.bankshardwoods.com
Emp.: 50
Wood Products Mfr
N.A.I.C.S.: 321999
Steve Banks *(CEO)*

Banks Hardwoods, Inc. - Newberry
Facility (1)
6946 County Rd 392, Newberry, MI 49868
Tel.: (269) 483-2323
Hardwood Mfr
N.A.I.C.S.: 321918

BANNEKER PARTNERS, LLC
600 Montgomery Str 24th Fl, San
Francisco, CA 94111
Tel.: (415) 992-9017
Web Site:
http://www.bannekerpartners.com
Year Founded: 2010
Privater Equity Firm
N.A.I.C.S.: 523999
Stephen Davis *(Mng Partner)*
Matt McDonald *(Partner)*
Harjot Sachdeva *(Operating Partner)*
Kyle Hufford *(VP)*
Terrance Bei *(VP)*
Kenneth R. Frank *(Executives)*
Darryl Lewis *(Operating Partner)*

Subsidiaries:

HS GovTech Solutions Inc. (1)
Suite 303 750 West Pender St, Vancouver,
V6C 2T7, BC, Canada
Web Site: http://www.healthspace.com
Rev.: $5,677,868
Assets: $6,770,148
Liabilities: $2,117,230
Net Worth: $4,652,918
Earnings: ($4,990,352)
Emp.: 91

Fiscal Year-end: 12/31/2021
Computer System Design Services
N.A.I.C.S.: 541512
Dean Christie (CFO)
Andrew Silas Garrison (CEO)

Subsidiary (US):

Joule Microsystems Inc.   (2)
701 5th Ave Ste 3470, Seattle, WA 98104
Tel.: (206) 953-5578
Healthcare Software Development Services
N.A.I.C.S.: 541511

Integrated Computer Systems,
Inc.   (1)
3499 FM 1461, McKinney, TX 75071-3030
Tel.: (214) 544-0022
Web Site: https://www.athenaics.com
Software Publisher
N.A.I.C.S.: 513210
Thomas Galbraith (VP)
Kyle Indermuehle (CEO)

Versaterm Inc.   (1)
400-1331 Clyde Avenue, Ottawa, K2C 3G4,
ON, Canada
Tel.: (613) 820-0311
Web Site: https://www.versaterm.com
Emp.: 310
Software Publr
N.A.I.C.S.: 513210
Warren Loomis (CEO)

Subsidiary (US):

Justicetrax, Inc.   (2)
1 W Mn St, Mesa, AZ 85201
Tel.: (480) 222-8900
Web Site: http://justicetrax.com
Sales Range: $1-9.9 Million
Emp.: 23
Custom Computer Programing
N.A.I.C.S.: 541511
Jeffery Braucher (VP)
Simon Key (CEO)

BANNER COUNTY BAN COR-
PORATION
205 State St, Harrisburg, NE 69345
Tel.: (308) 436-5024   NE
Web Site: http://www.bcbank.net
Year Founded: 1984
Sales Range: $1-9.9 Million
Bank Holding Company
N.A.I.C.S.: 551111
Roger L. Wynne (Pres & CEO)
Kim Fanning (Sr VP)
Scott Prickett (Exec VP)

Subsidiaries:

Banner Capital Bank   (1)
205 State St, Harrisburg, NE 69345
Tel.: (308) 436-5024
Web Site: http://www.bcbank.net
Sales Range: $1-9.9 Million
Emp.: 29
Commericial Banking
N.A.I.C.S.: 522110
Roger Wynne (Exec VP-Harrisburg)
Don Ehrke (VP & Mgr-Alma Branch)
Kim Fanning (Sr VP-Harrisburg)
Brad Holtze (VP-Beaver City)
Audra Klotthor (VP-Alma)
Scott Prickett (Pres-Beaver City & Exec VP)
Janie Wyatt (CFO-Harrisburg)
Denise Brown (Officer-Compliance-Beaver
City)
Leonard Scoleri (Pres-Guernsey Branch)
Mark Miracle (Sr VP-Cheyenne)
Rich Petersen (Pres & CEO-Cheyenne)

Oregon Trail Bank   (1)
Cnr of US Hwy 26 & 17 N Wyoming,
Guernsey, WY 82214
Tel.: (307) 836-2344
Web Site: http://www.oregontrailbank.com
Sales Range: $1-9.9 Million
Emp.: 14
Commericial Banking
N.A.I.C.S.: 522110
Leonard Scoleri (Pres & CEO)

BANNER ENGINEERING
CORP.

9714 10th Ave N, Minneapolis, MN
55441-5019
Tel.: (763) 544-3164   MN
Web Site:
https://www.bannerengineering.com
Year Founded: 1966
Sales Range: $150-199.9 Million
Emp.: 400
Industrial Controls Manufacturing
N.A.I.C.S.: 335314
Victor Caneff (Bus Mgr-Automotive)

BANNER FORD
1943 N Causeway Blvd, Mandeville,
LA 70471
Tel.: (985) 234-5678
Web Site:
https://www.bannerford.com
Year Founded: 2002
Sales Range: $10-24.9 Million
Emp.: 75
Car Whslr
N.A.I.C.S.: 441110
Rj Flick (Owner)

BANNER FURNACE & FUEL
INC.
122 N Helena St, Spokane, WA
99202
Tel.: (509) 535-1711
Web Site:
https://www.bannerfuel.com
Sales Range: $10-24.9 Million
Emp.: 60
Heating & Air Conditioning Contrac-
tors
N.A.I.C.S.: 238220
Gary McLaughlin (Pres)
Sue LaRue (Mgr-Fuel)

BANNER HEALTH SYSTEM
1441 N 12th St 3rd Fl, Phoenix, AZ
85006
Tel.: (602) 747-4000   AZ
Web Site:
http://www.bannerhealth.com
Year Founded: 1999
Healtcare Services
N.A.I.C.S.: 623110
Peter S. Fine (Pres & CEO)
Christopher H. Volk (Chm)
Chuck Lehn (Pres-Banner Health
Network)
David Moromisato (Chief Medical Of-
ficer)
Quentin P. Smith Jr. (Chm)
Naomi Cramer (Chief HR Officer)
John Hensing (Sr VP-Clinical Quality)
Becky Kuhn (COO)
Alexandra Morehouse (CMO)
Rob Rohatsch (CEO-Banner Urgent
Care)
Larry Goldberg (Pres-University Medi-
cine Div)
David M. Bixby (Chief Legal Officer &
Gen Counsel)
Marjorie Bessel (Chief Clinical Offi-
cer)
Dennis Laraway (CFO)
D. Scott Nordlund (Chief Strategy &
Growth Officer)
Deanna L. Wise (CIO & Sr VP)
Alexandra Morehouse (CMO)

Subsidiaries:

Banner Health West   (1)
1441 N 12th St, Phoenix, AZ
85006   (100%)
Tel.: (602) 521-5000
Sales Range: $10-24.9 Million
Emp.: 6
Multi Hospital System
N.A.I.C.S.: 622110
Christopher H. Volk (Chm)
Kathy Bollinger (Pres-Arizona West Reg)
Marjorie Bessel (Chief Clinical Officer)

David M. Bixby (Chief Legal Officer & Gen
Counsel)
Dennis Laraway (CFO)
D. Scott Nordlund (Chief Strategy & Growth
Officer)

Payson Hospital Corporation   (1)
807 S Ponderosa, Payson, AZ 85541
Tel.: (928) 474-3222
Web Site: http://www.bannerhealth.com
Hospital Operator
N.A.I.C.S.: 622110
Lance Porter (CEO)
Pete Finelli (CFO)
Hart Hintze (Chief Nursing Officer)

BANNER INDUSTRIES INC.
1 Industrial Dr, Danvers, MA 01923
Tel.: (978) 777-0080
Web Site:
https://www.bannerindustries.com
Year Founded: 1985
Sales Range: $10-24.9 Million
Emp.: 7
Sales of Valves & Fittings
N.A.I.C.S.: 423830
Gary Richard (Pres)

BANNER MATTRESS COM-
PANY
1501 E Cooley Dr Unit B, Colton, CA
92324
Tel.: (909) 835-4200
Web Site:
http://www.bannermattresses.com
Sales Range: $10-24.9 Million
Emp.: 52
Mattress Mfr
N.A.I.C.S.: 337910
Lisa Scorziell (Pres)

BANNER PERSONNEL SER-
VICE INC.
53 W Jackson Blvd Ste 1219, Chi-
cago, IL 60604
Tel.: (312) 922-5400
Web Site:
https://www.bannerpersonnel.com
Year Founded: 1970
Sales Range: $10-24.9 Million
Emp.: 30
Temporary Help Service
N.A.I.C.S.: 561311
Emel Singer (Chm)

BANNER SUPPLY CO.
103 E Indianola Ave, Youngstown,
OH 44507
Tel.: (330) 782-1171
Web Site:
http://www.bannersupply.com
Sales Range: $10-24.9 Million
Emp.: 30
Building Material Retailer
N.A.I.C.S.: 444110
Richard W. Abel (Pres)

BANNER SUPPLY CO.
7195 NW 30th St, Miami, FL 33122
Tel.: (305) 593-2946
Web Site:
https://www.bannersupply.com
Rev.: $20,000,000
Emp.: 42
Lumber, Plywood, Millwork & Wood
Panel Merchant Whslr
N.A.I.C.S.: 423310
Arthur Landers (VP)
Barney Landers (Pres)

BANNER TRUCK & TRAILER
SALES, INC.
10000 State Hwy 57, Evansville, IN
47725
Tel.: (812) 867-2481
Web Site:
http://www.bannertruck.com
Sales Range: $10-24.9 Million

Emp.: 32
Automobile & Other Motor Vehicle
Whslr
N.A.I.C.S.: 423110
Phil Morelli (Pres)

BANNER WHOLESALE GRO-
CERS, INC.
3000 S Ashland Ave Ste 300, Chi-
cago, IL 60608-5333
Tel.: (312) 421-2650   IL
Web Site:
http://www.bannerwholesale.com
Year Founded: 1926
Sales Range: $25-49.9 Million
Emp.: 70
Groceries
N.A.I.C.S.: 424410
Richard B. Saltzman (Pres)
Irwin Friedman (Treas & Sec)
Jerry Dowl (Controller)
Mario Gomez (Dir-Sls)

BANSK GROUP LLC
340 Madison Ave, Ste 12C, New
York, NY 10173
Tel.: (646) 827-8710
Web Site:
https://www.banskgroup.com
Emp.: 100
Private Equity
N.A.I.C.S.: 523999

Subsidiaries:

PetIQ, Inc.   (1)
230 E Riverside Dr, Eagle, ID 83616
Tel.: (208) 939-9900
Web Site: https://www.petiq.com
Rev.: $800,305,000
Assets: $818,896,000
Liabilities: $607,103,000
Net Worth: $211,793,000
Earnings: ($48,208,000)
Emp.: 1,888
Fiscal Year-end: 12/31/2022
Pharmaceutical Preparation Manufacturing
N.A.I.C.S.: 325412
Zvi Glasman (CFO)
McCord Christensen (Co-Founder, Chm &
CEO)

Subsidiary (Non-US):

Mark & Chappell (Ireland)
Limited   (2)
Unit 1B The Renmore Business Complex
Kilcoole Industrial Estate, Kilcoole, Wicklow,
Ireland
Tel.: (353) 12872880
Web Site: https://markandchappell.com
Pet Product Distr
N.A.I.C.S.: 459910

Mark & Chappell Limited   (2)
Suite 2 248 Toddington Road, Luton, LU4
9DZ, United Kingdom
Tel.: (44) 1582583888
Web Site:
https://www.markandchappell.com
Pet Product Distr
N.A.I.C.S.: 459910

Subsidiary (Domestic):

Sergeant's Pet Care Products,
Inc.   (2)
10077 S 134th St, Omaha, NE 68138
Tel.: (800) 224-7387
Web Site: http://www.sergeants.com
Pet Care Products Mfr
N.A.I.C.S.: 339999

TruRX, LLC   (2)
230 E Riverside Dr, Eagle, ID 83616
Web Site: https://www.vetiq.com
Pet Product Mfr & Distr
N.A.I.C.S.: 311111

BANTERRA CORP.
1404 US Rte 45, Eldorado, IL 62930
Tel.: (618) 273-9346   IL
Web Site:
http://www.banterrabank.com

Banterra Corp.—(Continued)

Year Founded: 1981
Sales Range: $50-74.9 Million
Emp.: 321
Bank Holding Company
N.A.I.C.S.: 551111
Everett D. Knight *(Chm & CEO)*
Barbara L. McKenzie *(CFO, Sec & Exec VP)*
James W. Morris *(Exec VP)*
Robert J. May *(Pres)*
Janetta Flener *(Dir-HR)*
Steven R. Burroughs *(Exec VP)*
Debra Becht *(Sr VP & Dir-Retail Ops)*

Subsidiaries:

Banterra Bank　　　　　　　　　　**(1)**
3201 Banterra Dr, Marion, IL 62959-2434
Tel.: (618) 993-2678
Web Site: http://www.banterra.com
Sales Range: $50-74.9 Million
Emp.: 12
Commericial Banking
N.A.I.C.S.: 522110
Amber Pentecost *(Branch Mgr)*
Everett D. Knight *(Chm & CEO)*
Robert J. May *(Pres)*
Barbara L. McKenzie *(CFO, Sec & Exec VP)*
James W. Morris *(Exec VP)*
Steven R. Burroughs *(Chief Credit Officer & Exec VP)*
Debra Becht *(Sr VP & Dir-Retail Ops)*
Regina M. Davis *(VP & Comptroller)*
Ben Craft *(Mgr-Banking Center-Central Div)*
Anna Baumgart *(Mgr-Banking Center-Carmi)*

BANTON CONSTRUCTION COMPANY

339 Washington Ave, North Haven, CT 06473
Tel.: (203) 234-2353
Web Site: https://www.bantonconstruction.com
Year Founded: 1979
Sales Range: $25-49.9 Million
Emp.: 70
Commercial & Institutional Building Construction Services
N.A.I.C.S.: 236220
Holly M. Laprade *(Mgr-Mktg & Bus Dev)*

BANTRY BAY VENTURES-ASIA, LLC

40 Woodland St, Hartford, CT 06105
Tel.: (860) 727-5734
Investment Services
N.A.I.C.S.: 523999
Eric Zachs *(Mng Partner)*
Eli Katz *(Mng Partner)*

BANYAN AIR SERVICE INC.

5360 NW 20th Ter, Fort Lauderdale, FL 33309
Tel.: (954) 491-3170　　　　　　　**FL**
Web Site: https://www.banyanair.com
Sales Range: $50-74.9 Million
Emp.: 150
Aircraft Servicing & Repairing
N.A.I.C.S.: 488190
Donald A. Campion *(Pres & Head-Coach)*
James M. Barcel *(CFO)*
Dave Valenta *(Dir-Maintenance)*
Lynn Juengel *(VP-Maintenance)*
Michael O'Keeffe *(Sr VP)*
Lenny Baldwin *(Mgr-Svcs)*
J. Philip Jordan *(Sr Dir-Sls)*

BANYAN BIOMARKERS INC.

13400 Progress Blvd, Alachua, FL 32615
Tel.: (386) 462-6699
Web Site: http://www.banyanbio.com
Sales Range: $1-9.9 Million

Emp.: 25
In-Vitro Diagnostic Products
N.A.I.C.S.: 325413
Ronald L. Hayes *(Founder & Chief Science Officer)*
Henry L. Nordhoff *(Chm & CEO)*
Tony Grover *(VP-Bus Dev)*
Michael Catania *(VP-Product Dev)*
Julie Pashkowsky *(VP-Fin)*
Steven P. Richieri *(COO)*

BANYAN INVESTMENT GROUP

10065 Emerald Coast Pkwy Ste C101-A, Miramar Beach, FL 32550
Tel.: (850) 424-6431
Web Site: http://www.banyan-ig.com
Year Founded: 1977
Sales Range: $10-24.9 Million
Emp.: 138
Investment Management Service
N.A.I.C.S.: 523999
Rakesh Chauhan *(Pres & CEO)*
Manoj Chauhan *(Chief Dev Officer)*
Vick Chauhan *(Chief Legal Officer)*
Andy Chopra *(CIO)*
Chris Cooper *(VP-Project Dev)*
Michelle Wilson *(VP-Bus Dev)*
Mike Wells *(Sr VP-Fin)*
Ken Floyd *(Dir-Ops)*
Leanne Lloyd *(Dir-HR)*
Saleem Cross *(Mgr-Dev)*

BANYAN MEZZANINE FUND, L.P.

1111 Brickell Ave Ste 1300, Miami, FL 33131　　　　　　　　　　**DE**
Web Site:
　http://www.banyanmezzanine.com
Year Founded: 2002
Rev.: $400,000,000
Privater Equity Firm
N.A.I.C.S.: 523940
James W. Davidson *(Mng Partner)*

BANYAN SOFTWARE, INC.

303 Perimeter Ctr N Ste 450, Atlanta, GA 30346
Tel.: (857) 302-2990
Web Site:
　http://www.banyansoftware.com
Year Founded: 2016
Computer Software Solutions
N.A.I.C.S.: 513210
David Berkal *(Founder & CEO)*
Max Risen *(Head-M&A)*

Subsidiaries:

Dominion Leasing Software LLC　**(1)**
1545 Standing Ridge Dr Ste B, Powhatan, VA 23139
Tel.: (804) 477-8480
Web Site: http://www.dominionls.com
Lease Accounting Software & Services
N.A.I.C.S.: 541219
Clinton Dunlow *(Pres)*

HWA International, Inc.　　　　**(1)**
8363 Wolf Lake Dr 101, Memphis, TN 38133
Tel.: (901) 388-6120
Web Site: http://www.hwainternational.com
Rev.: $4,873,000
Emp.: 24
Software Publisher
N.A.I.C.S.: 513210
Donna Manley *(VP)*
Harry Sullivan *(Pres)*

Innovatum, Inc.　　　　　　　　**(1)**
1400 Buford Hwy, Sugar Hill, GA 30518
Tel.: (770) 945-4595
Web Site: http://www.innovatum.com
Custom Computer Programming Services
N.A.I.C.S.: 541511
Dana Buker *(VP-Ops)*
Ron Kohlhorst *(VP-Product Dev)*
Ardi Batmanghelidj *(CEO)*

Medicat LLC　　　　　　　　　　**(1)**

303 Perimeter Ctr N Ste 450, Sandy Springs, GA 30342
Tel.: (404) 252-2295
Web Site: http://www.medicat.com
Patient Health Management System
N.A.I.C.S.: 513210
Dave Berkal *(Chm)*
Daryl Rolley *(CEO)*
Ruth Pattern *(Dir-Client Dev)*
Isabella Vickers *(Dir-Mktg)*
Jay Spivey *(Mgr-Sls)*

PromoSuite　　　　　　　　　　**(1)**
65 Broadway 602, New York, NY 10006
Tel.: (212) 509-1200
Web Site: http://www.promosuite.com
Rev.: $2,586,886
Emp.: 12
Software Reproducing
N.A.I.C.S.: 334610
Niall Addison *(Mgr-Customer Success & Renewal Contract)*
Brian DAurelio *(Dir-Mktg)*
Chris Ackerman *(VP)*
Tripp Eldredge *(Pres & COO)*
Craig Zimmerman *(Mgr)*
Rachel Field *(Chief Revenue Officer)*
Rocco Macri *(CEO)*
Chris Bungo *(Founder & CTO)*
Chris Bungo *(CTO)*

vCreative, Inc.　　　　　　　　**(1)**
303 Perimeter Ctr N Ste 450, Atlanta, GA 30346
Tel.: (800) 605-9889
Web Site: https://vcreativeinc.com
Software Publisher
N.A.I.C.S.: 513210

BANYAN TECHNOLOGIES GROUP, LLC

Tel.: (734) 468-3621
Web Site:
　https://www.banyantechgroup.com
Year Founded: 2008
Emp.: 100
Private Equity
N.A.I.C.S.: 523999
Tanvir Arfi *(Founder & CEO)*

Subsidiaries:

HELM43, LLC　　　　　　　　　**(1)**
47911 Halyard Dr Ste 200, Plymouth, MI 48710
Tel.: (313) 865-5000
Web Site: http://www.helminc.com
Sales Range: $25-49.9 Million
Emp.: 150
Provider of Auto Repair Publications
N.A.I.C.S.: 561910
Dennis Gusick *(Pres)*

Subsidiary (Domestic):

Target Marketing Group　　　　**(2)**
11404 Cronridge Dr, Owings Mills, MD 21117-2217
Tel.: (443) 394-6677
Web Site: http://www.targetlogos.com
Services Related to Advertising
N.A.I.C.S.: 541890
Tracie Zaepfel *(Product Mgr)*

BAPKO METAL FABRICATORS INC.

180 S Anita Dr, Orange, CA 92868
Tel.: (714) 639-9380
Web Site: https://www.bapko.com
Sales Range: $10-24.9 Million
Emp.: 109
Structural Steel Erection
N.A.I.C.S.: 238120
Fred Bagatourian *(Pres)*

BAPTIST HEALTH MEDICAL CENTER

1001 Schneider Dr, Malvern, AR 72104
Tel.: (501) 332-1000　　　　　**AR**
Web Site: https://www.baptist-health.com
Year Founded: 1985
Healtcare Services
N.A.I.C.S.: 622110

Dee Schall *(Chief Nursing Officer)*
Michele Diedrich *(Chief Nursing Officer/VP-Patient Care-Little Rock)*
Nicole B. Thomas *(Co-Chm, Pres-South & Sr VP-Specialty Svcs)*

Subsidiaries:

Jacksonville Orthopedic Institute　**(1)**
1325 San Marco Blvd Ste 701, Jacksonville, FL 32207
Tel.: (904) 346-3465
Web Site: http://www.joionline.net
Health Care Srvices
N.A.I.C.S.: 622110
Bruce Steinberg *(Chm)*

BAPTIST HEALTH SOUTH FLORIDA, INC.

6855 Red Rd Ste 500, Coral Gables, FL 33143
Tel.: (305) 596-6534
Web Site: http://baptisthealth.net
Year Founded: 1960
Emp.: 19,500
Hospital Owner & Operator
N.A.I.C.S.: 622110
Jack Ziffer *(Chief Clinical Officer & Exec VP)*
Matthew Arsenault *(CFO & Exec VP)*
Bo Boulenger *(Pres, CEO, COO & Exec VP)*
Joe Natoli *(Chief Admin Officer & Exec VP)*
Barry T. Katzen *(Chief Medical Innovation Officer)*
Glenn Waters *(COO & Exec VP)*
David Friedman *(Gen Counsel & Sr VP)*
Adriene McCoy *(Chief People Officer & Sr VP)*
Nancy Batista-Rodriguez *(CEO-Baptist Outpatient Svcs)*

Subsidiaries:

Baptist Health Enterprises　　　**(1)**
1501 Venera Ave Ste 240, Coral Gables, FL 33146
Tel.: (786) 662-7000
Web Site: http://www.baptisthealth.net
Sales Range: $10-24.9 Million
Emp.: 141
Hospital Services
N.A.I.C.S.: 622110

Baptist Health South Florida Foundation　　　　　　　　　**(1)**
6855 Red Rd, Coral Gables, FL 33143
Tel.: (786) 662-7000
Sales Range: $10-24.9 Million
Emp.: 22
Hospital Foundation Services
N.A.I.C.S.: 813219
Alexandra Villoch *(CEO)*

Baptist Hospital of Miami　　　**(1)**
8900 N Kendall Dr, Miami, FL 33176
Tel.: (786) 596-1960
Web Site: http://www.baptisthealth.net
Sales Range: $250-299.9 Million
Emp.: 4,151
Hospital Operations
N.A.I.C.S.: 622110
Patricia Rosello *(CEO)*

Baptist Outpatient Services　　**(1)**
1501 Venera Ave Ste 240, Coral Gables, FL 33146
Tel.: (305) 596-6534
Web Site: http://www.baptisthealth.net
Sales Range: $25-49.9 Million
Emp.: 709
Hospital Outpatient Services
N.A.I.C.S.: 621498
Brian Keeley *(Gen Mgr)*

Boca Raton Regional Hospital, Inc.　　　　　　　　　　　　**(1)**
800 Meadows Rd, Boca Raton, FL 33486-2304　　　　　　　**(100%)**
Tel.: (561) 395-7100
Web Site: http://www.brrh.com
Hospital
N.A.I.C.S.: 622110

Mindy Raymond *(VP-HR)*
Dawn P. Javersack *(CFO & VP)*
Alexander D. Eremia *(Gen Counsel, Sec & VP)*
Melissa Durbin *(Chief Nursing Officer & VP)*
Thomas Chakurda *(VP-Mktg & Comm)*
C. Daniel Sacco *(VP-Strategic Affairs & Payer Rels)*
Mindy Sloane Shikiar *(COO)*
David G. Forcione *(Dir-Medical-Advanced Therapeutic Endoscopy)*
Stephen Steinberg *(Dir-Medical-Center for Advanced Therapeutic Endoscopy)*
Lincoln S. Mendez *(CEO)*

Doctors Hospital (1)
5000 University Dr, Coral Gables, FL 33146
Tel.: (786) 308-3000
Web Site: http://www.baptisthealth.net
Sales Range: $25-49.9 Million
Emp.: 947
Hospital Operations
N.A.I.C.S.: 622110
Ronald Gaudio *(Dir-Pastoral Care Svcs)*
Javier Hernandez-Lichtl *(CEO)*
Sheldon Anderson *(Vice Chm)*

Fishermen's Community Hospital, Inc. (1)
3301 Overseas Hwy, Marathon, FL 33050
Tel.: (305) 743-5533
Web Site:
    http://www.fishermenshospital.com
Sales Range: $25-49.9 Million
Emp.: 180
Hospital Services
N.A.I.C.S.: 622110
David Faulkner *(Interim CEO)*

Homestead Hospital (1)
975 Baptist Way, Homestead, FL 33033
Tel.: (786) 578-0114
Web Site: http://www.baptisthealth.net
Sales Range: $75-99.9 Million
Emp.: 1,117
Hospital Operations
N.A.I.C.S.: 622110

Mariners Hospital (1)
91500 Overseas Hwy, Tavernier, FL 33070
Tel.: (305) 434-3000
Web Site: http://www.baptisthealth.net
Emp.: 300
Hospital Operations
N.A.I.C.S.: 622110
Jay A. Hershoff *(Chm)*

South Miami Hospital (1)
6200 SW 73 St, South Miami, FL 33143
Tel.: (786) 662-4000
Web Site: http://www.baptisthealth.net
Sales Range: $75-99.9 Million
Emp.: 2,194
Hospital Operations
N.A.I.C.S.: 622110

South Palm Ambulatory Surgery Center, LLC (1)
1905 Clint Moore Rd Ste 115, Boca Raton, FL 33496
Tel.: (561) 509-5084
Health Care Srvices
N.A.I.C.S.: 621111

West Kendall Baptist Hospital (1)
9555 SW 162 Ave, Miami, FL 33196
Tel.: (786) 467-2000
Web Site: http://www.baptisthealth.net
Sales Range: $25-49.9 Million
Emp.: 475
Hospital Operation Services
N.A.I.C.S.: 622110
Aida Shafer *(Chm)*
Lourdes Boue *(CEO)*

BAPTIST HOMES SOCIETY
489 Castle Shannon Blvd, Pittsburgh, PA 15234
Tel.: (412) 563-6550   **PA**
Web Site:
    https://www.baptisthomes.org
Year Founded: 1910
Sales Range: $25-49.9 Million
Emp.: 753
Elderly People Welfare Services
N.A.I.C.S.: 624120
Jan O'Wenzel *(Chm)*
Valerie S. Faeth *(Sec)*

Thomas Ague *(Vice Chm)*
Brent V. Foster *(CFO & Asst Treas)*
Larry Jackley *(Treas)*
Eric Conti *(Dir-HR)*
Robert Kocent *(Exec Dir)*
Jack Miller *(VP-Dev)*
Alvin W. Allison Jr. *(Pres & CEO)*

BAPTIST HOSPITALS OF SOUTHEAST TEXAS
3080 College St, Beaumont, TX 77701-4606
Tel.: (409) 212-5000   **TX**
Web Site: https://www.bhset.net
Year Founded: 1945
Sales Range: $200-249.9 Million
Emp.: 2,194
Health Care Srvices
N.A.I.C.S.: 622110
Gary Troutman *(CFO)*
Bryan Chandler *(VP-Bus Dev)*
Reggie Wasson *(Officer-Safety)*
Lisa Feliciano *(VP-Quality & Risk Mgmt)*

BAPTIST MEDICAL & DENTAL MISSION INTERNATIONAL, INC.
11 Plaza Dr, Hattiesburg, MS 39402
Tel.: (601) 544-3586   **MS**
Web Site: http://www.bmdmi.org
Year Founded: 1991
Sales Range: $10-24.9 Million
Emp.: 39
Community Health Care Services
N.A.I.C.S.: 621498
Nicole Ruhnke *(Dir-Comm)*
Christy Draughn *(Office Mgr & Accountant)*

BAPTIST MISSIONS INC.
PO Box 381466, Germantown, TN 38183-1466
Tel.: (901) 289-1835   **TN**
Year Founded: 1964
Sales Range: $10-24.9 Million
Christian Ministry Services
N.A.I.C.S.: 813110
Connie Brandenburg *(VP)*
Cheryl Followell *(Sec)*
Larry Gurley *(Pres)*

BAR ALE, INC.
1011 5th St, Williams, CA 95993
Tel.: (530) 473-3333
Web Site: https://www.baraleinc.com
Sales Range: $25-49.9 Million
Emp.: 30
Poultry Feeds
N.A.I.C.S.: 311119
Paul A. Lewis *(CEO)*
Grant Garland *(VP)*
Joe Lemenager *(Supvr-Production)*

BAR HARBOR FOODS
1112 Cutler Rd, Whiting, ME 04691
Tel.: (207) 259-3341
Web Site:
    http://www.barharborfoods.com
Year Founded: 2003
Sales Range: $1-9.9 Million
Emp.: 25
Specialty Canned Seafood Soups & Sauces, Cooking Stocks, Clam Juice, Seafood Meats & Sustainable Fish Products for Retail & Wholesale
N.A.I.C.S.: 311710

BAR HARBOR LOBSTER COMPANY, INC.
2000 Premier Row, Orlando, FL 32809
Tel.: (407) 851-4001   **FL**
Web Site:
    http://www.bostonlobsterfeast.com

Year Founded: 1987
Sales Range: $10-24.9 Million
Emp.: 40
Seafood Restaurants Owner & Operator
N.A.I.C.S.: 722511
Jeff Hazell *(Founder)*
Dennis McGrath *(Controller)*
Len Lesperance *(CFO & Exec VP)*
Alonzo Campillo *(VP-Sls & Ops)*

BAR NONE, INC.
1302 Santa Fe Dr, Tustin, CA 92780
Tel.: (714) 259-8450   **CA**
Web Site: http://www.barnone.com
Credit Data Services
N.A.I.C.S.: 522299
R. J. Castelan *(Gen Mgr)*

BAR PROCCESSING CORP.
PO Box 1090, Flat Rock, MI 49134-1090
Tel.: (734) 782-4454
Web Site:
    https://www.barprocessingcorp.com
Steel Bar Mfr
N.A.I.C.S.: 332111
Paul Lanzon *(CEO)*

Subsidiaries:

Bar Processing - Wickliffe (1)
1271 E 289th St, Wickliffe, OH 44092
Tel.: (440) 943-0094
Rev.: $19,000,000
Emp.: 60
Bars & Bar Shapes, Steel, Cold-Finished: Own Hot-Rolled
N.A.I.C.S.: 331110
Denny Perrino *(VP)*

BAR'S PRODUCTS, INC.
720 W Rose St, Holly, MI 48442
Tel.: (248) 634-8278   **MI**
Web Site: https://barsleaks.com
Year Founded: 1970
Sales Range: $1-9.9 Million
Emp.: 25
Adhesives & Sealants Mfr
N.A.I.C.S.: 325520
Lisa Lewis *(Controller)*
Mike Mermuys *(Exec VP)*
Jim Miner *(Mgr-Plant)*

Subsidiaries:

Hy-Per Lube Corp. (1)
900 1st Ave S Ste 200, Seattle, WA 98134-1208
Tel.: (206) 381-3535
Web Site: http://www.hyperlube.com
Petroleum & Petroleum Products Merchant Whslr
N.A.I.C.S.: 424720
Harold Hilton *(Founder)*

BAR-ALL, INC.
9584 Hwy 46, Bon Aqua, TN 37025
Tel.: (931) 996-4234
Web Site:
    http://www.trimhealthymama.com
Year Founded: 2014
Sales Range: $10-24.9 Million
Health Product Distr
N.A.I.C.S.: 456199
Charlie Barrett *(CFO)*

BARABOO MOTORS INC.
640 US Hwy 12, Baraboo, WI 53913
Tel.: (608) 356-3968
Web Site:
    http://www.baraboomotors.net
Rev.: $20,000,000
Emp.: 33
Automobiles, New & Used
N.A.I.C.S.: 441110
Paul Romlow *(Pres)*
Pete Steinhauer *(Gen Mgr)*

BARANCORP, LTD.

214 N 2100 Rd, Lecompton, KS 66050
Tel.: (785) 887-6010   **KS**
Web Site: http://www.barancorp.com
Year Founded: 1975
Sales Range: $250-299.9 Million
Emp.: 6
Holding Company
N.A.I.C.S.: 551112
Dennis A. Baranski *(Pres & CEO)*
Linda D. Baranski *(VP)*

Subsidiaries:

Baranski & Associates (1)
214 N 2100 Rd, Lecompton, KS 66050   **(100%)**
Tel.: (785) 887-6010
Web Site: http://www.barancorp.com
Sales Range: $10-24.9 Million
Advertising, Consulting, Legal Services, Public Relations
N.A.I.C.S.: 541810
Dennis A. Baranski *(Chm)*

Baranski Publishing Company (1)
214 N 2100 Rd, Lecompton, KS 66050-4138   **(100%)**
Tel.: (785) 887-6010
Web Site: http://www.barancorp.com
Sales Range: $10-24.9 Million
Emp.: 4
Trade Book Publishers
N.A.I.C.S.: 513110
Dennis Baranski *(Pres)*

D.A. Baranski & Co. (1)
214 N 2100 Rd, Lecompton, KS 66050-4138   **(100%)**
Tel.: (785) 887-6010
Web Site: http://www.dabaranski.com
Sales Range: $10-24.9 Million
Emp.: 4
Art Brokerage, Art & Antiquities Appraisal Services, Fine Art Consulting, Administrators for the Modern Day Masters Project
N.A.I.C.S.: 513110
Dennis Baranski *(Chm, Pres & CEO)*

Joseph A. Baranski Literary Agency (1)
214 N 2100 Rd, Lecompton, KS 66050   **(100%)**
Tel.: (785) 887-6010
Web Site: http://www.barancorp.com
Rev.: $125,000
Emp.: 4
Authors Representatives, Foreign & Domestic
N.A.I.C.S.: 561499
Dennis A. Baransky *(Pres)*

Northern Cross, Ltd. (1)
214 N 2100 Rd, Lecompton, KS 66050   **(100%)**
Tel.: (785) 887-6010
Web Site: http://www.barancorp.com
Sales Range: $10-24.9 Million
Emp.: 4
Mfr of Survival Equipment, Including Emergency & Survival Kits for Motorists, Pilots, Backpackers & Hunters
N.A.I.C.S.: 339113
Dennis Baranski *(Pres)*

BARATZ & ASSOCIATES, PA
Eves Dr Ste A106 Bldg 4A, Marlton, NJ 08053
Tel.: (856) 985-5688   **NJ**
Web Site: http://www.baratzcpa.com
Year Founded: 1977
Rev.: $3,500,000
Emp.: 35
Fiscal Year-end: 12/31/06
Accounting, Auditing, And Bookkeeping
N.A.I.C.S.: 541211
Brian Baratz *(Pres)*

Subsidiaries:

Metter & Co. (1)
831 Dekalb Pike, Center Square, PA 19422-1215
Tel.: (610) 278-9444
Web Site: http://www.mettercpa.com
Offices of Certified Public Accountants

Baratz & Associates, PA—(Continued)
N.A.I.C.S.: 541211
Stan A. Metter (Owner)

BARBADOS TOURISM AU-THORITY
820 2nd Ave 5th Fl, New York, NY 10017-4709
Tel.: (212) 986-6516
Web Site:
http://www.visitbarbados.org
Year Founded: 1967
Sales Range: $100-124.9 Million
Emp.: 100
Barbados Travel Promoter
N.A.I.C.S.: 561510
Campbell Rudder (VP-Mktg-USA)

BARBARAS DEVELOPMENT, INC.
304 S Leighton Ave, Anniston, AL 36207
Tel.: (256) 235-2220   CA
Web Site: https://www.directex.net
Year Founded: 1991
Miscellaneous Fabricated Wire Products
N.A.I.C.S.: 332618
Billy Prickett (CFO)

BARBARICUM
1714 N St NW, Washington, DC 20036
Tel.: (202) 393-0873
Web Site:
https://www.barbaricum.com
Year Founded: 2008
Sales Range: $1-9.9 Million
Emp.: 47
Consulting Services in Strategic Communication, Analysis, Intelligence & Energy
N.A.I.C.S.: 541618
Brandon Bloodworth (Founder & Partner)
Scott Feldmayer (Partner)

BARBAROSSA AND SONS INC.
11000 93rd Ave N PO Box 367, Osseo, MN 55369
Tel.: (763) 425-4146
Sales Range: $10-24.9 Million
Emp.: 100
Underground Utilities Contractor
N.A.I.C.S.: 237110
Robert R. Barbarossa (Pres)
Paul Flykt (VP)
James Thompson (Treas)

BARBEAU-HUTCHINGS AD-VERTISING, INC.
30 Controls Dr, Shelton, CT 06484
Tel.: (203) 926-0040   CT
Web Site:
http://www.bhaadvertising.com
Year Founded: 1981
Sales Range: Less than $1 Million
Emp.: 10
Advertising Agencies
N.A.I.C.S.: 541810
Gregg Hutchings (Owner)

BARBEE JACKSON INSUR-ANCE COMPANY
2213 S Ferdon Blvd, Crestview, FL 32536
Tel.: (850) 389-2001
Web Site:
http://www.barbeejackson.com
Year Founded: 2009
Sales Range: $1-9.9 Million
Emp.: 7
Insurance Brokerage Services
N.A.I.C.S.: 524210

Craig Barbee (Chm & CEO)
Krystal Jackson (Partner)
Caleb Jackson (Partner)

BARBELLA CONSTRUCTION SERVICES, LLC
24 Tannery Rd, Somerville, NJ 08876
Tel.: (908) 534-1664
Web Site:
http://www.barbellaconstruction.com
Year Founded: 2005
Industrial Plant Construction
N.A.I.C.S.: 237990
Frank D. Barbella (Pres)
Alex Monteferrante (Treas-Chief Estimator)
Brian Barbella (VP)

BARBER & ROSS COMPANY INC.
255 Ft Collier Rd, Winchester, VA 22603
Tel.: (540) 722-9199   DE
Year Founded: 1971
Rev.: $45,000,000
Emp.: 425
Millwork
N.A.I.C.S.: 321911

Subsidiaries:

Barber & Ross Millwork Company Inc.   (1)
125 S Augusta St Ste 2000, Staunton, VA 24401-4386   (100%)
Tel.: (804) 354-0900
Sales Range: $10-24.9 Million
Emp.: 77
Millwork
N.A.I.C.S.: 321918

BARBER & SONS INVEST-MENT CO. INC.
11400 State Rte 7, Lees Summit, MO 64086-9368
Tel.: (816) 525-1737
Year Founded: 1969
Sales Range: $10-24.9 Million
Emp.: 7
Mfr of Tobacco & Tobacco Products
N.A.I.C.S.: 424940
Anthony Barber (Pres)

BARBER AUTO SALES INC.
4325 Sonoma Blvd, Vallejo, CA 94589-2243
Tel.: (707) 648-8500
Web Site: http://www.thomason.com
Year Founded: 1954
Sales Range: $25-49.9 Million
Emp.: 202
New & Used Car Dealers
N.A.I.C.S.: 441110
Scott Thomason (Pres)

BARBER BROTHERS CON-TRACTING COMPANY
2636 Dougherty Dr, Baton Rouge, LA 70805
Tel.: (225) 355-5611   LA
Web Site: https://www.barber-brothers.com
Year Founded: 1928
Sales Range: $100-124.9 Million
Emp.: 200
Highway & Street Contracting & Construction Services
N.A.I.C.S.: 237310
A. Lee Barber (Co-Founder & VP)
Lionel P. Barber (Co-Founder & Pres)

Subsidiaries:

Barber Brothers Contracting Company - Asphalt Plant 1   (1)
9604 Highway 75, Geismar, LA 70734
Tel.: (225) 744-3560
Asphalt Mfr
N.A.I.C.S.: 324121

Barber Brothers Contracting Company - Asphalt Plant 6   (1)
4411 N River Rd, Port Allen, LA 70734
Tel.: (225) 346-0505
Asphalt Mfr
N.A.I.C.S.: 324121

BARBER BROTHERS MOTOR COMPANY
1341 N Main St, Spanish Fork, UT 84660
Tel.: (801) 798-7431
Web Site:
http://www.barberbrothers.com
Rev.: $28,400,000
Emp.: 30
Automobiles, New & Used
N.A.I.C.S.: 441110
Fred Barber (Pres)
Becky Parke (Office Mgr)
Robby Lee (Head-Janitor)

BARBER FORD INC.
962 Wyoming Ave, Exeter, PA 18643
Tel.: (570) 654-3351
Web Site:
https://www.barberautogroup.com
Sales Range: $10-24.9 Million
Emp.: 12
Car Dealership
N.A.I.C.S.: 441110
Matthew DePrimo (Pres)

BARBER MARTIN & ASSOCI-ATES
7400 Beaufont Springs Dr Ste 201, Richmond, VA 23225-5519
Tel.: (804) 320-3232   DE
Year Founded: 1989
Sales Range: $10-24.9 Million
Emp.: 27
Advertising Agencies
N.A.I.C.S.: 541810
Robyn Deyo Zacharias (Pres & CEO)
Michael Mullen (Dir-Creative)
Matt Norton (Sr Dir-Art)
Megan Driscoll (Sr Mgr-Consumer Mktg)

BARBERINO BROTHERS, INC.
505 N Colony St, Wallingford, CT 06492-3145
Tel.: (203) 265-1611
Web Site:
https://www.barberinonissan.com
Year Founded: 1946
Sales Range: $25-49.9 Million
Emp.: 53
Car Whslr
N.A.I.C.S.: 441110
John Mocadlo (Gen Mgr)

BARBIZON LIGHTING COM-PANY
456 W 55th St, New York, NY 10019
Tel.: (212) 586-1620
Web Site: http://www.barbizon.com
Rev.: $64,244,568
Emp.: 23
Electrical Apparatus & Equipment
N.A.I.C.S.: 423610
Scott Sowden (Mgr-Acctg & Ops)
Thomas Augusta (Mgr-Natl Sls)
Vincent Syrek (Dir-IT)
Tobin Neis (Dir-Mktg)
Nicolas Cohen (Gen Mgr)
Angela Coutoumas (Mgr-Acctg)
Jim Maxwell (Mgr-Natl Pur)
Martin Kelly (Mgr-Ops)
Arnold Kramer (Mgr-Ops)
Allison Mutton (Branch Mgr)
Greg Kazanjian (Mgr-Pur)
Dawn Pollak (Mgr-Pur)
Jared Grohs (Mgr-Sls)
Danny Quiles (Mgr-Sls)
Esthere Strom (Mgr-Sls)

Mike Moore (Mgr-Sls & New Bus Dev)
Drew Bongiorno (Mgr-Sys)
Mark Fink (Mgr-Sys)
Edwin Diaz (Mgr-Warehouse)
Don Geist (Mgr-Warehouse)
Glen Pastores (Mgr-Warehouse)
Norman Pitts (Mgr-Warehouse)
Kathy Fogg (Office Mgr)
Tom Madden (Pres & CEO)
Case Lynch (Mng Dir)

BARBOUR CORPORATION
1001 N Montello St, Brockton, MA 02305
Tel.: (508) 583-8200
Web Site:
https://www.barbourcorp.com
Year Founded: 1892
Sales Range: $10-24.9 Million
Emp.: 120
Commercial & Industrial Products Mfr & Sales
N.A.I.C.S.: 316990
Rich Hynes (Pres & CEO)

Subsidiaries:

Barbour Welting Co.   (1)
1001 N Montello St, Brockton, MA 02305
Tel.: (508) 583-8200
Web Site: http://www.barbourcorp.com
Leather & Plastic Shoe Welting Mfr
N.A.I.C.S.: 316990
Mike Sallom (Gen Mgr)

BARBOUR INTERNATIONAL INC.
101 Cypress Way, Brandon, MS 39042
Tel.: (601) 591-1350
Web Site: http://www.barbour-int.com
Sales Range: $10-24.9 Million
Emp.: 25
Cooking Equipment, Commercial
N.A.I.C.S.: 423440
Rodney Barbour (Pres)
Donna Barbour (CFO)

BARBOUR STOCKWELL IN-CORPORATED
55 6th Rd, Woburn, MA 01801-1746
Tel.: (781) 933-5200
Web Site:
http://www.barbourstockwell.com
Sales Range: $25-49.9 Million
Emp.: 17
High Speed Vertical & Horizontal Air & Steam Turbines Mfr
N.A.I.C.S.: 333611
Kenneth Maillar (Pres)
Tony Enos (VP)
Robert Gauthier (VP-Testing)

BARC DEVELOPMENTAL SER-VICES
4950 York Rd, Holicong, PA 18928-0470
Tel.: (215) 794-0800   PA
Web Site:
https://www.barcprograms.org
Year Founded: 1951
Sales Range: $10-24.9 Million
Emp.: 324
Developmental Disability Assistance Services
N.A.I.C.S.: 624120

BARC ELECTRIC COOPERA-TIVE
84 High St, Millboro, VA 24460-0264   VA
Web Site:
https://www.barcelectric.com
Year Founded: 1938
Sales Range: $10-24.9 Million
Emp.: 52
Electric Power Distribution Services

N.A.I.C.S.: 221122
Dave Clinton *(Mgr-Fin & Member Svcs)*
Michael Keyser *(CEO)*
Jamie Lowry *(Mgr-Construction Svcs)*
C. Michael Sandridge *(VP)*
Gary R. Johnson *(Asst Treas & Asst Sec)*
John M. Quantz *(Treas & Sec)*
Keith L. Swisher *(Pres)*
William B. McClung *(Atty)*

BARCELO ENTERPRISES, INC.

1210 Rainbow Hills Rd, Fallbrook, CA 92028
Tel.: (760) 728-3444
Rev.: $15,500,000
Emp.: 100
Palm Tree Nursery
N.A.I.C.S.: 111421
Rosa H. Barcelo *(VP)*
Antonio Barcelo Sr. *(Pres)*

BARCELONA SONO

63-65 N Main St, South Norwalk, CT 06854
Tel.: (203) 899-0088
Web Site:
http://www.barcelonawinebar.com
Year Founded: 1996
Sales Range: $10-24.9 Million
Emp.: 350
Owner & Operator of Tapas & Wine Bars
N.A.I.C.S.: 722511
Sasa Mahr-Batuz *(Co-Founder)*
Scott Lawton *(COO)*
Craig Odierno *(Controller)*
Gretchen Thomas *(Dir-Wine & Spirits)*
Kim Fox *(Coord-Events)*
Adam Halberg *(Dir-Culinary)*
Andy Pforzheimer *(Co-Founder)*
Janice Orefice Dehn *(Dir-Mktg)*
Matt Wilber *(CFO)*

BARCHART.COM, INC.

330 S Wells St 6th Fl, Chicago, IL 60606
Tel.: (312) 554-8122
Web Site: http://www.barchart.com
Sales Range: $1-9.9 Million
Emp.: 30
Stock Information Services
N.A.I.C.S.: 561499
Andrew Lowdon *(COO)*
Eero Aleksander Pikat *(Pres)*
Mark Haraburda *(CEO)*
Michael Browne *(Head-AgriCharts)*
Colleen Sheeren *(Head-Mktg)*

BARCLAY DAMON, LLP

125 E Jefferson St, Syracuse, NY 13202
Tel.: (315) 425-2700   NY
Web Site:
http://www.barclaydamon.com
Year Founded: 1855
Law firm
N.A.I.C.S.: 541110
Jeffrey B. Andrus *(Partner)*
Peter J. Bilinski *(Partner)*
James J. Canfield *(Partner)*
Robert A. Barrer *(Partner)*
Brenda D. Colella *(Partner)*
David G. Burch *(Partner)*
Heather L. Sunser *(Partner)*
Thomas Hoehner *(Partner)*
John P. Langan *(Mng Partner)*
Michael R. Moore *(Partner)*
Frank V. Bifera *(Partner)*
Beth Ann Bivona *(Partner)*
Rosemary Enright *(Partner)*
Corey Auerbach *(Partner)*
Peter Marlette *(Mng Dir-Buffalo)*

Marc N. Henschke *(Partner-Intellectual Property Litigation Practice-Boston)*
Kevin Szczepanski *(Partner-Insurance Coverage & Regulation & Comml Litigation)*
Maureen E. Fyke *(Dir-Mktg & Bus Dev)*
Sharon Brown *(Partner-Pub Fin & Tax Practice)*
Lee Alcott *(Partner)*
Lisa C. Arrington *(Partner)*
J. Joseph Bainton *(Partner)*
Michael J. Balestra *(Partner)*
Teresa A. Bennet *(Partner)*
Susan A. Benz *(Partner)*
M. Cornelia Cahill *(Partner)*
John C. Canoni *(Partner)*
Richard R. Capozza *(Partner)*
Danielle M. Cardamone *(Partner)*
Christopher A. Cardillo *(Partner)*
Timothy C. Cashmore *(Partner)*
Christopher J. Centore *(Partner)*
J. Eric Charlton *(Partner)*
Linda J. Clark *(Partner)*
Roger F. Cominsky *(Partner)*
John D. Cook *(Partner)*
David M. Cost *(Partner)*
Thomas B. Cronmiller *(Partner)*
Peter J. Crossett *(Partner)*
Brian M. Culnan *(Partner)*
Jeffery D. Palumbo *(Partner)*
Alan R. Peterman *(Partner)*
Anthony J. Piazza *(Partner)*
Gary H. Abelson *(Partner)*
William A. Barclay *(Partner)*
Arthur A. Marrapese III *(Partner-Rapidly Expanding Employee Benefits Practice)*

Subsidiaries:

Menter, Rudin & Trivelpiece, P.C.   **(1)**
308 Maltbie St Ste 200, Syracuse, NY 13204-1439
Tel.: (315) 474-7541
Law firm
N.A.I.C.S.: 541110
Antonio E. Caruso *(Atty)*
Mitchell J. Katz *(Atty)*
Kevin M. Newman *(Atty)*
Jeffrey A. Dove *(Atty)*
F. Paul Vellano Jr. *(COO & Exec VP)*

Shapiro, Lifschitz and Schram, P.C.   **(1)**
1742 N St NW, Washington, DC 20036-2907
Tel.: (202) 689-1900
Web Site: http://www.slslaw.com
Emp.: 10
Law firm
N.A.I.C.S.: 541110
Judah Lifschitz *(Atty)*
Ronald S. Shapiro *(Principal & Co-Pres)*
George D. Carry *(Atty)*
Reed Sexter *(Principal & Exec VP)*
Robert Foster *(Sr VP)*
Susan A. Hubert *(Dir-Admin)*
Ann M. Moody *(Paralegal)*
Steven H. Schram *(Co-Pres & Principal)*
Timothy T. Unruh *(Paralegal)*
Barry Fleishman *(Principal-Trial Grp)*
Gregory Seador *(VP)*

BARCLAY DEAN, INC.

11100 NE 8th St Ste 900, Bellevue, WA 98004
Tel.: (425) 451-8940
Web Site:
http://www.barclaydean.com
Rev.: $15,500,000
Emp.: 100
Office Furniture
N.A.I.C.S.: 449110
Scott Harrison *(Pres)*
Hal Breier *(VP-Bus Dev)*

BARCLAYS DRYROCK ISSUANCE TRUST

1100 N Market St, Wilmington, DE 19890
Tel.: (302) 651-1000   DE
Investment Services
N.A.I.C.S.: 523999
Sean Sievers *(CFO)*

BARCO STAMPING CO

1095 Carolina Dr, West Chicago, IL 60185
Tel.: (630) 293-5155
Rev.: $25,000,000
Emp.: 50
Metal Stamping
N.A.I.C.S.: 332119
Thomas J. Mullally *(Pres)*
Brad Weber *(Principal)*
Ron Tampa *(Owner)*

BARCO UNIFORMS, INC.

350 W Rosecrans Ave, Gardena, CA 90247-0835
Tel.: (310) 323-7315   CA
Web Site:
https://www.barcouniforms.com
Year Founded: 1929
Sales Range: $100-124.9 Million
Emp.: 160
Mfr & Sales of Professional Apparel
N.A.I.C.S.: 315250
Michael Donner *(Owner & Pres)*
David Murphy *(Sr VP-Mktg & Sls)*
Joanne Lee *(Sr Mgr-Product Dev)*

BARCOM COMMERCIAL INC.

5826 Bear LN, Corpus Christi, TX 78405
Tel.: (361) 851-1000
Web Site: http://www.barcom.cc
Year Founded: 1986
Sales Range: $1-9.9 Million
Emp.: 25
Renovation & Repair of Commercial & Office Buildings
N.A.I.C.S.: 236220
Elaine Hoffman *(Pres)*
David W. Hoffman *(VP)*
Albert Saenz *(Dir-Ops)*
Ron Taylor *(Project Mgr)*

BARD & COMPANY, INC.

603 Park Pinte Dr Ste 200, Golden, CO 80401
Tel.: (303) 991-3000
Rev.: $1,000,000
Emp.: 8
Portfolio Management
N.A.I.C.S.: 523940
Jerry Melfi *(Treas)*

Subsidiaries:

Bard Capital Group, LLC   **(1)**
222 Greystone Rd, Evergreen, CO 80439
Tel.: (303) 679-0151
Privater Equity Firm
N.A.I.C.S.: 523999
Richard H. Bard *(Chm)*

Holding (Domestic):

Blastrac NA, Inc.   **(2)**
13201 N Santa Fe Ave, Oklahoma City, OK 73114
Tel.: (800) 256-3440
Web Site: http://www.blastrac.com
Sales Range: $1-9.9 Million
Emp.: 11
Construction Machinery Mfr
N.A.I.C.S.: 333120
Lenore Lipoufski *(Principal)*
Brian MacKenzie *(CEO)*

BARD HOLDING, INC.

54 E Bridge St, Morrisville, PA 19067
Tel.: (215) 825-8593   DE
Web Site:
http://www.bardholding.com
Year Founded: 2009
Sales Range: $10-24.9 Million

Emp.: 13
Composite Algae Based Biodiesel
N.A.I.C.S.: 324110
Howard L. Bobb *(Pres)*
Surajit Khanna *(Chm & Sec)*
Sohini Khanna *(Treas & Sr VP)*
Avery Hong *(VP-IR)*
Stephen Laksro *(Gen Counsel & VP)*
Sharon Miller *(VP-Strategic Plng)*
Larry Didonato *(Gen Counsel-Tax & VP)*
Syam Nutulapati *(VP-IT)*
Michelle McCurdy *(VP-Safety & Security & Health Environment)*
Sar Olivier *(VP-Environ Policy & Plng)*
Jonna Sawyer *(Dir-HR)*

BARD MANUFACTURING COMPANY

1914 Randolph Dr, Bryan, OH 43506-2253
Tel.: (419) 636-1194   OH
Web Site: https://www.bardhvac.com
Year Founded: 1914
Rev.: $69,928,208
Emp.: 300
Gas-Oil Heating Equipment, Air to Air & Water to Air Heat Pumps & Air Conditioning Equipment Mfr
N.A.I.C.S.: 333415
John V. Briggs *(VP-Pur)*
Bill Steel *(Chm, Pres & CEO)*
Robert S. Hood *(COO & VP-Mfg)*

BARD, RAO + ATHANAS CONSULTING ENGINEERS, LLC

10 Guest St 4th Fl, Boston, MA 02135-2783
Tel.: (617) 254-0016
Web Site: https://www.brplusa.com
Year Founded: 1975
Sales Range: $10-24.9 Million
Emp.: 350
Engineeering Services
N.A.I.C.S.: 541330
Eugéne Bard *(Co-Founder)*
Theodore Athanas *(Co-Founder, Principal & Exec VP)*
Allan Ames *(Pres & Principal)*
Grant Anderson *(Principal)*
Michael Benjamin *(Principal)*
Dan Caron *(Principal)*
Jonathan Chan *(Principal)*
Cris Copley *(Principal)*
Marco DiRenzo *(Principal)*
Patrick Duffy *(Principal)*
Mike Fahey *(Mng Principal & Sr VP)*
Ron Howie *(Principal)*
Carlos Jimenez *(Principal)*
Andrew Kozak *(Principal)*
Steven Levin *(Principal)*
Jean-Pierre Marjollet *(Principal)*
Brian Monahan *(Principal)*
John O'Leary *(Principal)*
Tony Petone *(Principal)*
Raymond Prucha *(Principal)*
Kurt Scheeren *(Principal)*
Richard Taylor *(Principal)*
Ari Tinkoff *(Principal)*
Steven Viehl *(Principal)*
Joe Witt *(Principal)*

Subsidiaries:

Bard, Rao + Athanas Consulting Engineers, LLC - New York   **(1)**
105 Madison Ave 10th Fl, New York, NY 10016
Tel.: (212) 840-0060
Web Site: http://www.brplusa.com
Engineeering Services
N.A.I.C.S.: 541330
Michael W. Fahey *(Mng Principal & Sr VP)*

BARDAHL MANUFACTURING CORPORATION

Bardahl Manufacturing Corporation—(Continued)

1400 NW 52nd St, Seattle, WA
98107
Tel.: (206) 783-4851   WA
Web Site: https://www.bardahl.com
Year Founded: 1939
Sales Range: $75-99.9 Million
Emp.: 35
Mfr of Auto Additives & Lubricants
N.A.I.C.S.: 324191
Evelyn Bardahl McNeil (Chm)
Eric Nicolaysen (VP)
Hugh M. Niel (Pres)
Dennis Amos (Plant Mgr)

Subsidiaries:

Bardahl Manufacturing Corporation -
Bardahl Europe Division   **(1)**
Town Hall Exchange Castle Street, Farn-
ham, GU9 7ND, United Kingdom
Tel.: (44) 1252 720 625
Sales Range: $10-24.9 Million
Emp.: 2
Petroleum Lubricating Oil Mfr & Distr
N.A.I.C.S.: 324191

BARDEN COMPANIES, INC.

400 Renaissance Ctr Ste 2400, De-
troit, MI 48243
Tel.: (313) 496-2900   MI
Sales Range: $125-149.9 Million
Emp.: 985
Investment Holding Company
N.A.I.C.S.: 551112
Michelle R. Sherman (CFO & VP)
Keyvan Pickett (Mgr-Property)

Subsidiaries:

Barden Development, Inc.   **(1)**
163 Madison Ave Ste 2000, Detroit, MI
48226
Tel.: (313) 496-2900
Casino Hotel Operator & Developer
N.A.I.C.S.: 721120

BARDONS & OLIVER, INC.

5800 Harper Rd, Solon, OH 44139-
1833
Tel.: (440) 498-5800   OH
Web Site:
https://www.bardonsoliver.com
Year Founded: 1892
Sales Range: $75-99.9 Million
Emp.: 450
Mfr of Turret Lathes, Cutting Lathes &
Special Machinery
N.A.I.C.S.: 333517
Bill Beattie (Pres)
Ben Bailey (Mgr-Sls Engrg & Cus-
tomer Fulfillment)
Brett Baldi (VP-Ops)
Matt Michalske (Mgr-Production Plng)
Rick Moscarino (VP-Engrg)
Tracy Mack (Mgr-HR)

BARDWIL INDUSTRIES INC.

1071 Avenue of the Americas, New
York, NY 10018-3704
Tel.: (212) 944-1870   DE
Web Site:
http://www.bardwilhome.com
Year Founded: 1940
Sales Range: $10-24.9 Million
Emp.: 60
Mfr of Table Linen
N.A.I.C.S.: 314120
George Bardwil (CEO)
Ronald Tassello (CFO)
Alan Kennedy (Pres)

BARE BONES SOFTWARE, INC.

73 Princeton St Ste 206, North
Chelmsford, MA 01863
Tel.: (978) 251-0500   MA

Web Site:
https://www.barebones.com
Year Founded: 1994
Sales Range: $10-24.9 Million
Emp.: 12
Software Publisher
N.A.I.C.S.: 541511
Rich Siegel (Founder & CEO)

BARE FEET ENTERPRISES, INC.

7-C Gwynns Mill Ct, Owings Mills,
MD 21117
Tel.: (410) 902-6090   MD
Sales Range: $10-24.9 Million
Women's Shoes & Clothing Accesso-
ries Stores Owner & Operator
N.A.I.C.S.: 458210
Meir A. Duke (Owner & Pres)

BARE FRUIT LLC

340 S Lemon Ave Ste 5475, Walnut,
CA 91789
Tel.: (509) 554-5540
Web Site:
http://www.barefruitsnacks.com
Year Founded: 2003
Sales Range: $1-9.9 Million
Emp.: 5
Organic Fruit Snacks
N.A.I.C.S.: 311919
Bradford Oberwager (Owner)

BARE INTERNATIONAL, INC.

3702 Pender Dr Ste 305, Fairfax, VA
22030
Tel.: (703) 591-9870
Web Site:
https://www.bareinternational.com
Year Founded: 1987
Sales Range: $10-24.9 Million
Emp.: 200
Marketing Research & Public Opinion
Polling
N.A.I.C.S.: 541910
Dale Bare (CEO)
Michael Bare (Founder & Pres)
Guy Caron (Mng Dir & VP)
Alicia Myers (Dir-Ops)
Melanie McConnell (Dir-Client Svcs)

BARED AND SONS INC.

209 San Just St, San Juan, PR
00901
Tel.: (787) 725-1346
Sales Range: $10-24.9 Million
Emp.: 35
Jewelry, Precious Stones & Precious
Metals
N.A.I.C.S.: 458310
Felix Bared Sr. (Pres)
Felix Bared Jr. (CEO)

BAREFOOT BOOKS, INC.

2067 Massachusetts Ave, Cambridge,
MA 02140
Tel.: (617) 576-0660
Web Site:
http://www.barefootbooks.com
Year Founded: 1992
Sales Range: $1-9.9 Million
Emp.: 25
Book Publishers
N.A.I.C.S.: 513130
Nancy Traversy (Co-Founder, Owner
& CEO)
Tessa Strickland (Co-Founder &
Editor-in-Chief)
Karen Janson (Dir-Ops)

BAREFOOT LUXURY, INC.

3333 Piedmont Rd Ste 2050, Atlanta,
GA 30305
Tel.: (404) 736-9431   GA
Web Site:
http://www.barefootluxury.com

Year Founded: 2016
Holding Company; Resorts, Marinas
& Other Travel Experiences Operator
N.A.I.C.S.: 551112
Joseph Patrick Hannan (Chm &
CEO)
Marcie Anderson (Head-Guest Rels)
Sara Crow (Head-Mktg)
Mike Milero (Head-Corp Dev)
Michael Joseph Hannan III (Gen
Counsel & Sec)

Subsidiaries:

Barefoot Lodge & Hiker Hostel,
LLC   **(1)**
7693 Hwy 19 N, Dahlonega, GA 30533-
1968
Tel.: (770) 312-7342
Web Site: http://www.hikerhostel.com
Sales Range: $1-9.9 Million
Hostel Operator
N.A.I.C.S.: 721199
Joshua Saint (Pres)

BAREMAN DAIRY INC.

234 Charles St, Holland, MI 49424
Tel.: (616) 396-0306
Web Site:
http://www.baremandairy.com
Sales Range: $75-99.9 Million
Emp.: 300
Fluid Milk
N.A.I.C.S.: 311511
Stanley Bareman (Pres)
Scoot Boldt (Controller)
Clare Weber (Dir-Safety)

BARGAIN SUPPLY COMPANY

844 E Jefferson St, Louisville, KY
40206-1618
Tel.: (502) 562-5000
Web Site:
https://www.bargainsupply.com
Year Founded: 1929
Sales Range: $75-99.9 Million
Emp.: 45
Retailer of General Merchandise
N.A.I.C.S.: 423710
Brad Ogden (Pres)

BARGE WAGGONER SUMNER & CANNON INC.

211 Commerce St Ste 600, Nashville,
TN 37201-1815
Tel.: (615) 254-1500
Web Site:
http://www.bargewaggoner.com
Year Founded: 1955
Sales Range: $25-49.9 Million
Emp.: 340
Engineeering Services
N.A.I.C.S.: 541330
Robert B. Higgins (Pres & CEO)
Carrie Stokes (Dir-Environment &
Water Resources)
R. Randolph Ferguson (COO & Exec
VP)
Matt Stovall (Dir-Land Resources)
Michele Herlein (Chief HR Officer &
Exec VP)
Daniel Spann (Dir-Transportation)
Jeffrey Weis (Dir-Industrial & Building
Svcs)
Cendy Dodd (CFO & Exec VP)
Mark Washing (Dir-Traffic Engrg
Svcs)
Jonathan Haycraft (Dir-Road &
Bridge)
Jason Burton (Engr-Water & Waste-
water)
John Greaud (Project Mgr-Aviation)
Paula E. Harris (Chief Mktg Officer &
Exec VP)

BARGERBURGER INC.

1001 Konnarock Rd, Kingsport, TN
37664

Tel.: (423) 247-3501
Web Site: http://www.palsweb.com
Rev.: $27,900,000
Restaurant Services
N.A.I.C.S.: 722511

BARGREEN-ELLINGSON INC.

2925 70th Ave E, Fife, WA 98424
Tel.: (253) 475-9201   WA
Web Site: http://www.bargreen.com
Year Founded: 1960
Rev.: $45,000,000
Emp.: 500
Food Service Equipment Distr
N.A.I.C.S.: 423440

Subsidiaries:

Specialty Wood Manufacturing
Inc.   **(1)**
7717 Portland Ave E, Tacoma, WA 98404-
3327
Tel.: (253) 531-1335
Web Site: http://www.specialtywoodmfg.com
Sales Range: $10-24.9 Million
Emp.: 45
Wood Partitions & Fixtures Mfr
N.A.I.C.S.: 337212
Richard Ellingson (VP)

The Restaurant Source   **(1)**
5005 Washington St, Denver, CO 80216
Tel.: (303) 296-1684
Web Site: http://www.bargreen.com
Sales Range: $10-24.9 Million
Emp.: 40
Commercial Restaurant Equipment & Bar
Supplies Whslr
N.A.I.C.S.: 423440
Jason Wirth (Gen Mgr)
Adam Deutschmann (Mgr)

BARHORST INSURANCE GROUP

8220 Jones Rd Ste 100, Houston, TX
77065
Tel.: (713) 856-5533
Web Site: http://www.big-usa.com
Year Founded: 1993
Sales Range: $1-9.9 Million
Emp.: 81
Insurance Services
N.A.I.C.S.: 524298
Warren E. Barhorst (Pres)
Karen Kominczak (Mgr-Customer
Svc)

BARI COSMETICS LTD

463 Temple Hill Rd, New Windsor,
NY 12553
Tel.: (845) 561-6330
Rev.: $11,100,000
Emp.: 12
Cosmetic Preparations
N.A.I.C.S.: 325620
Donald Harkness (Pres)

BARI-JAY FASHIONS INC.

225 W 37th St Fl 7, New York, NY
10018
Tel.: (212) 921-1551
Web Site: http://www.barijay.com
Sales Range: $10-24.9 Million
Emp.: 10
Gowns; Formal
N.A.I.C.S.: 315250

BARIBEAU IMPLEMENT COMPANY

1671 20 1/2 St, Rice Lake, WI 54868
Tel.: (715) 234-2144
Web Site:
http://www.baribeauimplement.com
Sales Range: $10-24.9 Million
Emp.: 25
Agricultural Machinery & Equipment
N.A.I.C.S.: 423820

Chris Gilchrist (*Mgr-Svc-St. Croix Falls*)
Mike Swartz (*Mgr-Svc-Rice Lake*)
Ray Baribeau Jr. (*Pres*)

BARINGS CAPITAL INVESTMENT CORPORATION

300 S Tryon St Ste 2500, Charlotte, NC 28202
Tel.: (704) 805-7200   MD
Year Founded: 2020
Rev.: $149,500,000
Assets: $1,414,849,000
Liabilities: $762,853,000
Net Worth: $651,996,000
Earnings: $79,947,000
Fiscal Year-end: 12/31/23
Investment Services
N.A.I.C.S.: 523940
Elizabeth A. Murray (*CFO, COO, Principal Acctg Officer & Treas-Private Equity Opportunities & Commitments Fund*)
Christopher A. DeFrancis (*Interim Chief Compliance Officer*)
Ian Fowler (*Pres & CEO*)
Elizabeth A. Murray (*Controller*)

BARINGS PRIVATE CREDIT CORPORATION

300 S Tryon St Ste 2500, Charlotte, NC 28202
Tel.: (704) 805-7200   MD
Year Founded: 2021
Rev.: $221,301,000
Assets: $2,599,334,000
Liabilities: $1,292,339,000
Net Worth: $1,306,995,000
Earnings: $145,730,000
Fiscal Year-end: 12/31/23
Investment Management Service
N.A.I.C.S.: 523999
Elizabeth A. Murray (*CFO, COO & Principal Acctg Officer*)

BARINGTON CAPITAL GROUP, L.P.

888 7th Ave 17th Fl, New York, NY 10019
Tel.: (212) 974-5710
Web Site: http://www.barington.com
Year Founded: 2000
Sales Range: $10-24.9 Million
Emp.: 8
Investment Banking
N.A.I.C.S.: 523150
James Anthony Mitarotonda (*Co-Founder, Chm, Pres & CEO*)
Jared L. Landaw (*Partner, COO & Gen Counsel*)
Christopher J. Pappano (*Partner & Head-Risk Mgmt*)
Nicole Luongo (*CFO*)
Sebastian Cassetta (*Partner & Sr Mng Dir*)
George W. Hebard III (*Partner & Dir-Res*)

Subsidiaries:

BCG Holdings Inc   (1)
888 7th Ave 17th Fl, New York, NY 10019
Tel.: (212) 974-5700
Web Site: http://www.barington.com
Sales Range: $1-9.9 Million
Emp.: 15
Investment Bankers
N.A.I.C.S.: 523150
James Anthony Mitarotonda (*Pres*)

BARINGTON/HILCO ACQUISITION CORP.

10990 Wilshire Blvd Penthouse, Los Angeles, CA 90024
Tel.: (310) 734-1310   DE
Year Founded: 2014
Sales Range: Less than $1 Million

Investment Services
N.A.I.C.S.: 523999
Jeffrey B. Hecktman (*Chm & CEO*)

BARKER ADVERTISING SPECIALTY COMPANY

27 Realty Dr, Cheshire, CT 06410
Tel.: (203) 272-2222
Web Site: http://www.barkerspecialty.com
Year Founded: 1951
Sales Range: $10-24.9 Million
Emp.: 88
Distr of Promotional Products & Premium Merchandise
N.A.I.C.S.: 424990
Gerald Barker (*Pres*)
Adrienne Barker (*Principal*)
Steven Barker (*Principal*)

BARKER AIR & HYDRAULICS INC.

1308 Miller Rd, Greenville, SC 29607
Tel.: (864) 288-3537
Web Site: https://www.barkerair.com
Sales Range: $10-24.9 Million
Emp.: 48
Pumps & Pumping Equipment
N.A.I.C.S.: 423830
John R. Barker (*CEO*)
Janet Mcdonough (*Controller*)
Drew Barker (*VP*)
Kelley Barker (*Mgr-Mktg*)

BARKER MANUFACTURING CO

730 E Michigan Ave, Battle Creek, MI 49014
Tel.: (269) 965-2371
Web Site: http://www.barkermfg.com
Rev.: $11,000,000
Emp.: 15
Motor Vehicle Parts & Accessories
N.A.I.C.S.: 336390
Norma Barker (*Pres*)

BARKER/DZP

30 Broad St Ph, New York, NY 10004
Tel.: (212) 226-7336   NY
Web Site: https://www.barkernyc.com
Year Founded: 2003
Sales Range: $10-24.9 Million
Emp.: 18
Advertising Agencies
N.A.I.C.S.: 541810
John R. Barker (*Pres*)

Subsidiaries:

Digital Zen   (1)
455 Broadway 5th Fl, New York, NY 10013
Tel.: (212) 226-7931
Advertising Agencies
N.A.I.C.S.: 541810

BARKERGILMORE

1387 Fairport Rd Ste 845, Fairport, NY 14450
Tel.: (585) 598-6555
Web Site: https://www.barkergilmore.com
Year Founded: 2006
Sales Range: $1-9.9 Million
Emp.: 12
Executive Search Service
N.A.I.C.S.: 561312
John Gilmore (*Mng Partner*)
Robert Barker (*Mng Partner*)

BARKLEY

1740 Main St, Kansas City, MO 64108
Tel.: (816) 842-1500   MO
Web Site: http://www.barkleyus.com
Year Founded: 1964
Sales Range: $450-499.9 Million
Emp.: 300

Advertising Services
N.A.I.C.S.: 541810
Jeff King (*CEO*)
Mark Logan (*Sr VP-Innovative Lab*)
Tim Galles (*Chief Idea Officer*)
Katy Hornaday (*Exec Dir-Creative*)
Paul Corrigan (*Exec Dir-Design*)
Amy Allen (*Exec VP-HR*)
Sara Buck (*Exec VP-Acct Leadership*)
Chris Cardetti (*VP & Dir-Strategy Grp*)
Brad Hanna (*Exec VP*)
Jason Parks (*Mng Dir & Exec VP*)
Suzanne Williams (*CFO*)
Graham Graham (*Mng Dir & Sr VP*)
Wade Paschall (*VP*)
Randy Rogers (*Grp Creative Dir*)
Stephanie Parker (*Sr VP-Brand Leadership*)

Subsidiaries:

Barkley   (1)
304 N Broadway, Saint Louis, MO 63102
Tel.: (314) 727-9500
Advertising Services
N.A.I.C.S.: 541810

Barkley REI   (1)
2740 Smallman St Ste 100, Pittsburgh, PA 15222
Tel.: (412) 683-3700
Web Site: http://www.barkleyrei.com
Sales Range: $25-49.9 Million
Emp.: 35
Advertising Agencies
N.A.I.C.S.: 541810
Scott Riemenschneider (*Dir-Art*)
Lynda Burkel (*Bus Mgr*)
Mike Kozak (*Acct Supvr*)
Michael Richardson (*Project Mgr*)
Shannon Lynch (*Mgr-Content*)

Blacktop Creative   (1)
512 Delaware St Ste 100, Kansas City, MO 64105
Tel.: (816) 221-1585
Web Site: http://www.blacktopcreative.com
Advertising Agencies
N.A.I.C.S.: 541810
Shawn Polowniak (*Pres*)
Dave Swearingen (*Dir-Creative*)

Callahan Creek, Inc.   (1)
805 New Hampshire St, Lawrence, KS 66044-2739
Tel.: (785) 838-4774
Rev.: $58,000,000
Emp.: 65
Fiscal Year-end: 03/31/2016
N.A.I.C.S.: 541810
John Kuefler (*Chief Strategy Officer & Exec VP*)
Sarah Etzel (*VP-Fin-Ops*)
Cecilia Riegel (*Dir-Paid Media*)
Tug McTighe (*VP & Exec Dir-Creative*)
Chris Marshall (*Pres & CEO*)
Chris Ralston (*Sr Dir-Art*)
Sarah Miller (*Grp Acct Dir*)
Stefan Mumaw (*Dir-Creative*)
Jan-Eric Anderson (*Chief Strategy Officer & VP*)
Mark Tribble (*Dir-Acct Mgmt*)
Dee Reser (*Dir-HR*)
Shelly Deveney (*Grp Acct Dir*)
Zack Pike (*VP-Data Strategy & Mktg Analytics*)

Branch (Domestic):

Callahan Creek   (2)
19001 S Western Ave T200, Torrance, CA 90501
Tel.: (310) 809-6124
Emp.: 10
N.A.I.C.S.: 541810
Martine Padilla (*Dir-Print*)
Cynthia Maude (*CEO*)
Steve Ward (*VP-Bus Dev*)
Paul Behnen (*Chief Creative Officer*)

Crossroads   (1)
1740 Main St, Kansas City, MO 64108
Tel.: (816) 842-1500
Web Site: http://www.crossroads.us
Sales Range: $100-124.9 Million
Public Relations
N.A.I.C.S.: 541820

Mike Swenson (*Pres*)
Lindsey DeWitte (*Sr VP*)
Jennifer Cawley (*Sr VP*)

Grenadier   (1)
2905 Central Green Ct Ste B, Boulder, CO 80301
Tel.: (303) 386-3957
Web Site: http://www.grenadierco.com
Emp.: 14
Advertising Agencies
N.A.I.C.S.: 541810
Randall Rogers (*Partner*)
Wade Paschall (*Partner*)
Madelaine Bess (*Mgr-Acct*)
Ryan Smith (*Supvr-Acct*)

BARKLEY HOLDING COMPANY, INC.

1740 Main St, Kansas City, MO 64108
Tel.: (816) 842-1500
Web Site: http://www.barkleyus.com
Sales Range: $10-24.9 Million
Emp.: 350
Design & Advertising Services
N.A.I.C.S.: 541810
Jeff Fromm (*Pres-Futurecast*)
Mike Swenson (*Pres-Crossroads*)
Jeff King (*CEO*)
Dan Fromm (*Pres & COO*)
Tim Galles (*Chief Idea Officer*)
Paul Corrigan (*Exec Dir-Design*)
Tom Demetriou (*VP & Dir-Creative*)
Bryan Herrman (*Sr VP*)
Jason Parks (*Mng Dir & Exec VP*)
Suzanne Williams (*CFO*)

BARKLEY SEED INC.

20th & Pacific Ave, Yuma, AZ 85366
Tel.: (928) 782-2571
Web Site: http://www.barkleyseed.com
Year Founded: 1988
Rev.: $29,000,000
Emp.: 30
Grain Whslr
N.A.I.C.S.: 424510
Robert Barkley (*Pres & CEO*)

BARKMAN HONEY, LLC

120 Santa Fe St, Hillsboro, KS 67063
Tel.: (620) 947-3173
Web Site: https://www.barkmanhoney.com
Year Founded: 1960
Sales Range: $10-24.9 Million
Emp.: 100
Honey Mfr & Distr
N.A.I.C.S.: 311999
Brent Barkman (*Owner & Chm*)
Doug Wienbrenner (*CEO*)

BARKMAN OIL CO. INC.

3793 Woodbury Pike, Woodbury, PA 16695
Tel.: (814) 766-2921
Web Site: http://www.barkmanoil.com
Sales Range: $10-24.9 Million
Emp.: 25
Retailer of Transport Gasoline & Heating Oil
N.A.I.C.S.: 424720
Dirk Barkman (*Pres*)
Lance Barkman (*VP*)

BARKSDALE FEDERAL CREDIT UNION

2701 Village Ln, Bossier City, LA 71112
Tel.: (318) 549-8065
Web Site: https://www.bfcu.org
Year Founded: 1954
Emp.: 108
Banking Services
N.A.I.C.S.: 523150
Patrick Gullatt (*Pres & CEO*)

Barksdale Federal Credit Union—(Continued)

BARLETTA MATERIALS & CONSTRUCTION
PO Box 550, Tamaqua, PA 18252-0550
Tel.: (570) 455-1511   **PA**
Web Site: http://www.glasgowinc.com
Year Founded: 1960
Sales Range: $125-149.9 Million
Emp.: 200
Highway Construction; Asphalt; Sand; Stone
N.A.I.C.S.: 423310
Karim Beily *(Dir-HR)*

Subsidiaries:

Lehigh Asphalt, Paving & Construction   **(1)**
Rte 209 1314 E Broad St, Tamaqua, PA 18252
Tel.: (570) 668-4303
Sales Range: $25-49.9 Million
Emp.: 60
Highway & Street Construction
N.A.I.C.S.: 237310
Caren Bailey *(Office Mgr)*

BARLEY SNYDER LLC
126 E King St, Lancaster, PA 17602-2893
Tel.: (717) 299-5201
Web Site: https://www.barley.com
Emp.: 63
Law firm
N.A.I.C.S.: 541110
Scott L. Kelley *(Executives)*
Kimberly J. Decker *(Partner)*
Lauralee B. Baker *(Partner)*
Michael W. Davis *(Partner)*
Christopher J. Churchill *(Chm-Sr Living Indus Grp)*
Jennifer L. Craighead *(Partner)*
Jennifer Good *(Dir-HR)*
Jeffrey D. Lobach *(Mng Partner)*
Paul G. Mattaini *(Partner)*
Ronald H. Pollock *(Partner)*
Russell Reed *(Dir-Acctg & Fin)*
Erin Saylor *(Dir-Bus Dev)*
William J. Zee *(Chm-Education Law Practice Grp)*
Jennifer Craighead Carey *(Partner)*

Subsidiaries:

Stonesifer & Kelley, P.C.   **(1)**
14 Ctr Sq, Hanover, PA 17331-2588
Tel.: (717) 632-0163
Web Site:
http://www.stonesiferandkelley.com
Law firm
N.A.I.C.S.: 541110

BARLEYCORN'S
1073 Industrial Rd, Cold Spring, KY 41076-9097
Tel.: (859) 442-3400
Web Site:
https://www.barleycorns.com
Sales Range: $75-99.9 Million
Emp.: 210
Operator of Casual Restaurant
N.A.I.C.S.: 722511
Tony Tontrup *(Mgr)*
Joe Heil *(Co-Owner)*
Rick Heil *(Co-Owner)*

BARLO PLASTICS CO. INC.
158 Greeley St, Hudson, NH 03051
Tel.: (603) 882-2638
Web Site:
https://www.barlosigns.com
Year Founded: 1969
Sales Range: $10-24.9 Million
Emp.: 70
Pylon & Wall Signs, Neon & LED Signs, Channel Letters, Electronic Message Centers & Illuminated Awnings, CNC Routing, Vinyl Lettering, Flag Poles & Menu Boards
N.A.I.C.S.: 339950
Arthur Bartlett *(Pres)*
Pamela Bartlett *(Treas & Sec)*

BARLOVENTO, LLC
431 Technology Dr, Dothan, AL 36303
Tel.: (334) 983-9979
Web Site:
https://www.barloventollc.com
Year Founded: 1996
Sales Range: $1-9.9 Million
Emp.: 62
Utility & General Contracting Services
N.A.I.C.S.: 236220
Jane Solomon *(Pres)*

BARLOW CHEVROLET
6057 Route 130, Delran, NJ 08075-1872
Tel.: (856) 335-7685
Web Site:
http://www.barlowcompany.com
Year Founded: 1970
Sales Range: $50-74.9 Million
Emp.: 90
Car Whslr
N.A.I.C.S.: 441110
Edward Barlow *(Principal)*

BARMAKIAN JEWELERS
300 Daniel Webster Hwy, Nashua, NH 03060
Tel.: (603) 888-7800
Web Site:
https://www.barmakian.com
Year Founded: 1921
Sales Range: $25-49.9 Million
Emp.: 65
Jewelry Whslr
N.A.I.C.S.: 458310
Eduardo Valdes *(Gen Mgr)*

BARMER ENTERPRISES LLC
401 S Powerline Rd, Pompano Beach, FL 33442
Tel.: (954) 570-8122
N.A.I.C.S.:
Gary Mercado *(Pres)*

Subsidiaries:

Bike America, Inc.   **(1)**
3150 N Federal Hwy, Boca Raton, FL 33431
Tel.: (561) 391-0800
Web Site: http://www.bikeam.com
Emp.: 20
Sporting Goods Whslr
N.A.I.C.S.: 459110
Gary Mercado *(Owner)*

BARN FURNITURE MART, INC.
6206 Sepulveda Blvd, Van Nuys, CA 91411
Tel.: (818) 551-6445
Web Site:
http://www.barnfurniture.com
Year Founded: 1890
Sales Range: $10-24.9 Million
Emp.: 25
Furniture Retailer
N.A.I.C.S.: 449110
Leon Tuberman *(Owner)*

BARNA & COMPANY
400 Bear Creek Rd, Oneida, TN 37841
Tel.: (423) 569-2180
Web Site: http://www.jimbarna-loghomes.com
Year Founded: 1976
Sales Range: $25-49.9 Million
Emp.: 125
Log Cabins, Prefabricated, Wood
N.A.I.C.S.: 321992
Shelly Valentine *(Sls Dir)*

BARNABAS FOUNDATION
18601 N Creek Dr Ste B, Tinley Park, IL 60477-6238
Tel.: (708) 532-3444   **IL**
Web Site:
http://www.barnabasfoundation.com
Year Founded: 1976
Sales Range: $25-49.9 Million
Emp.: 26
Christian Ministry Services
N.A.I.C.S.: 813110
Kurt Knoll *(Dir-Investment Svcs)*
David Schutt *(Dir-Administration & Fin Dir)*

BARNABAS HEALTH MEDICAL GROUP
101 Old Short Hills Rd Ste 201, West Orange, NJ 07052
Tel.: (973) 322-6333   **NJ**
Web Site: https://www.rwjbh.org
Year Founded: 1982
Health Care Srvices
N.A.I.C.S.: 621610
Glenn Miller *(Chief Dev Officer)*
Laura Schilare *(CFO)*
Vicki Robinson *(VP-Dev & Strategic Initiatives)*
Anne DeMesa *(VP-Gift Plng)*
Gregory Ellmer *(VP-Gift Plng)*
Stacy Buono *(Asst VP-Annual Giving & Donor Rels)*
Michael Wargo *(Asst VP-Corp & Foundation Rels)*
Jenny Mundell *(Sr Dir-Dev & Strategic Initiatives)*
Jodi Rostek *(Sr Dir-Data Mgmt)*
Mor Rubin *(Sr Dir-Porspect Res)*
Jane Cope *(Dir-Prospect Res)*
Maryann Mazur *(Mgr-Data Entry)*

Subsidiaries:

Robert Wood Johnson University Hospital Rahway   **(1)**
865 Stone St, Rahway, NJ 07065
Tel.: (732) 381-4200
Web Site: http://www.rwjuhr.com
Acute Care Hospital
N.A.I.C.S.: 622110
Kirk C. Tice *(Pres & CEO)*
Peter P. Bihuniak *(VP-Fin & CFO)*
Ann Marie Shears *(VP-Patient Svcs & Chief Nursing Officer)*
Barbara Mullery *(VP-Admin)*
Kevin M. Kramer *(VP-Legal Affairs & Gen Counsel)*
Heather Hays *(VP-RWJUH Rahway Foundation & Dev)*
Catherine Goodheart *(VP-Clinical Effectiveness)*
Sara Polak *(Dir-Patient Access)*
Ahmed Kheir *(Dir-Laboratory)*
Dave DePierro *(Dir-Food and Environmental Svcs)*
MaryAnne DeVenezia *(Dir-Medical Records)*
Oscar Gonzalez *(Dir-Plant Svcs)*
Denine Izzi *(Dir-Info Svcs)*
Karen Kowalenko *(Dir-Medical Mgmt)*
Mary Jackson *(Dir-Patient Experience)*
Terrence McCarthy *(Dir-Clinical Svcs)*
Sheetah Patel *(Dir-Pharmacy)*
Sheila Buthe *(Dir-HR)*
Victor Sanotsky *(Dir-Perioperative Svcs)*
Robert White *(Dir-Imaging Material Mgmt)*
Barbara Zidd *(Dir-Rehabilitation Svcs)*
Carol Ash *(Chief Medical Officer)*
Anu Chaudhry *(Pres)*
Mathew Cholankeril *(Treas & Sec)*

BARNABAS HEALTH, INC.
99 Hwy 37 W, Toms River, NJ 08755
Tel.: (732) 557-8000   **NJ**
Web Site: http://www.sbhcs.com
Year Founded: 1982
Sales Range: $600-649.9 Million
Emp.: 23,000
Health Care Association
N.A.I.C.S.: 813910
Ronald Delmauro *(Pres)*
Denise Clark *(Mgr-Mktg)*
Barbara Mintz *(VP-Healthy Living & Community Engagement)*
John Bonamo *(Chief Medical Officer & Exec VP)*
Stephen P. O'Mahony *(Chief Medical Info Officer)*
Robert T. Adamson *(Chief Pharmacy Officer)*
Frank J. Vozos *(Exec VP)*
David Mebane *(Exec VP)*

Subsidiaries:

Children's Hospital of New Jersey   **(1)**
201 Lyons Ave & Osborne Ter, Newark, NJ 07112
Tel.: (973) 926-4000
Web Site: http://www.sbhcs.com
Sales Range: $10-24.9 Million
Emp.: 75
Childrens Hospital
N.A.I.C.S.: 622110
Darrell K. Terry Sr. *(Pres & CEO)*

Clara Maass Medical Center   **(1)**
1 Clara Maass Dr, Belleville, NJ 07109-3550
Tel.: (973) 450-2000
Web Site:
http://www.claramaassmedicalcenter.com
Sales Range: $75-99.9 Million
Emp.: 1,700
General Health Care
N.A.I.C.S.: 622110
Keera Ferreira *(Dir-Case Mgmt & Social Svcs)*
Tara Florida Cullen *(Dir-Emergency Medicine Dept)*
Diana Wong *(Dir-Infection Prevention & Control)*
Mona Philips *(Dir-Pharmacy)*
Shelly Schneider *(Dir-Quality Standards)*
Sandra Mazzeo *(Dir-Radiation Oncology Svcs)*
Libby O'Donnell Naimo *(Dir-Radiology)*
Hanna Stickel *(Mgr-Admin-Medical Staff Office)*
Madeline Gale de Leon *(Mgr-Case)*
Kathleen Szymona *(Mgr-Clinical Nutrition)*
Barbara Ciccone *(Mgr-RN)*
Mary Ellen Clyne *(Pres & CEO)*
Alyssa Florio-August *(Sec)*
Cindy Pallante *(Sec)*
Jim Rolek *(VP-HR)*
Randi Hershkowitz *(Program Dir-Behavioral Health Svcs)*
Frank Dos Santos *(Chief Medical Officer)*

Community Medical Center   **(1)**
99 Hwy 37 W, Toms River, NJ 08755-6423
Tel.: (732) 557-8000
Web Site: http://www.barnabashealth.org
Sales Range: $250-299.9 Million
Emp.: 3,000
Healthcare Services
N.A.I.C.S.: 622110
Michael Corrigan *(Dir-Ops)*
Patricia Lees *(Dir-Peri-Ops Svcs)*
Awani Kumar *(Pres)*

Kimball Medical Center   **(1)**
600 River Ave, Lakewood, NJ 08701-5237
Tel.: (732) 363-1900
Web Site: http://www.sbhcs.com
Sales Range: $75-99.9 Million
Emp.: 1,100
Medical Center
N.A.I.C.S.: 622110

Monmouth Medical Center   **(1)**
300 2nd Ave, Long Branch, NJ 07740-6303
Tel.: (732) 222-5200
Web Site: http://www.barnabashealth.com
Sales Range: $100-124.9 Million
Emp.: 2,300
N.A.I.C.S.: 561110
Frank J. Vozos *(CEO-Southern Campus)*
Bill Arnold *(Pres & CEO)*
Mark K. Hirko *(Chm-Surgery)*
Eric Carney *(COO)*
Joanna P. Zimmerman *(Reg CFO)*

Newark Beth Israel Medical Center   **(1)**

201 Lyons Ave at Osborne Ter, Newark, NJ 07112
Tel.: (973) 926-7000
Web Site:
http://www.saintbarnabashealthcare.com
Sales Range: $100-124.9 Million
Emp.: 2,000
Health Care Srvices
N.A.I.C.S.: 561110
Mary Fuhro (VP-Patient Care Svcs & Outcome Mgmt)
Darrell K. Terry Sr. (Pres & CEO)

Saint Barnabas Medical Center   (1)
94 Old Short Hills Rd, Livingston, NJ 07039
Tel.: (973) 322-5000
N.A.I.C.S.: 561110
Victoria Taylor (Mgr-Central Distr & Receiving)
Jennifer A. O'Neill (Chief Nursing Officer & VP-Patient Care Svcs)
Stephen Zieniewicz (Pres & CEO)

Union Hospital   (1)
1000 Galloping Hill Rd, Union, NJ 07083-7951   (100%)
Tel.: (908) 687-1900
Web Site: http://www.sbnc.com
Sales Range: $25-49.9 Million
Emp.: 500
Hospital
N.A.I.C.S.: 622110

BARNARD CONSTRUCTION CO. INC.
701 Gold Ave, Bozeman, MT 59715
Tel.: (406) 586-1995   MT
Web Site: https://www.barnard-inc.com
Year Founded: 1975
Sales Range: $200-249.9 Million
Emp.: 500
Dam Construction & Rehabilitation
N.A.I.C.S.: 237110
Timothy Barnard (Chm)
Paul A. Franzen (Pres)
Jeff L. Higgins (CEO)
Tina M. Shepard (Mgr-Equipment)
Scott Lundberg (Dir-IT & Svcs)
Kevin Schneider (Mgr-Dams, Hydropower & Water Resources Bus Dev)

BARNES & THORNBURG LP
11 S Meridian St, Indianapolis, IN 46204-3535
Tel.: (317) 236-1313
Web Site: https://www.btlaw.com
Year Founded: 1982
Sales Range: $250-299.9 Million
Emp.: 470
Law firm
N.A.I.C.S.: 541110
David P. Durm (Partner-Real Estate Dept-Indianapolis & Atlanta)
Peter R. Spanos (Partner-Labor & Employment Law Dept-Atlanta & Washington)
Stephen Weizenecker (Partner)
David Spooner (Partner)
Connie A. Lahn (Partner)
Philip Westerman (Partner)
Bryan Venesy (Partner)
Erik Rickard (Partner)
Holly Heer (Partner)
Robert T. Grand (Partner)
Brian L. Burdick (Partner)
Bradley J. Olson (Partner)
Jon Hyland (Partner)
Thomas Haskins (Partner)
Anthony Burba (Partner)
Tabitha K. Meier (Partner-Litigation Dept-Indianapolis)
Michelle Mikol (Partner)
Scott Rothenberger (Partner)
Stephen Opler (Partner)
Stephanie Denby (Partner-Corp Dept & Private Client Svcs Practice-Chicago)
Claire M. Reed (Partner)
Angela K. Wessler (Partner)

Bradford G. Addison (Partner)
Carrie Marie Raver (Partner-Litigation Dept-Fort Wayne & Chicago)
Daniel P. Albers (Partner)
Donald E. Williams (Partner)
Heather H. Willey (Partner)
Michael A. Battle (Partner)
Anthony Son (Partner-Intellectual Property-Minneapolis)
David Wood (Partner-Los Angeles)
Frederick Schwartz (Partner-Chicago)
Christopher Fowlkes (Partner-Litigation)
Matthew O'Hanlon (Partner)
Gregory Gistenson (Partner-Litigation)
Christopher Knapp (Partner)
Malcolm Cox (Partner-Litigation)
Katrina Thompson (Partner)
Gregory Stype (Partner)
Lori Shannon (Partner-Corp Dept)
Robert Wade (Partner-Healthcare Dept-South Bend)
Robert Lockwood (Partner-IP-Atlanta)
Billy Martin (Partner-Washington)
G. Peter Nichols (Partner-Intellectual Property-Chicago)
Mark Rust (Mng Partner-Chicago)
Julia Gard (Chm-Intellectual Property)
William McErlean (Chm-Litigation Dept)
Marlen Cortez Morris (Partner-Litigation Dept-Chicago)
Mark Bayer (Mng Partner-Dallas)
Luke Wohlford (Partner-Litigation Dept-Dallas)
James Van Horn (Partner-Washington)
Meena Sinfelt (Partner-Washington)
Christine Sohar-Henter (Partner-Washington)
Roscoe Howard (Mng Partner-Washington)
Lee Hutton III (Partner-Minneapolis)

BARNES HEALTHCARE SERVICES
200 S Patterson St, Valdosta, GA 31601
Tel.: (229) 245-6013   GA
Web Site: https://www.barneshc.com
Year Founded: 1909
Surgical Equipment & Supplies Distr
N.A.I.C.S.: 423450
Robert Steedley (Chief Clinical Officer)
Karen Butterton (COO)
Becky Pitts (Asst VP-Respiratory Svcs)
Trey Bankson (Asst VP-Pharmacy Svcs)
Charles W. Barnes III (Owner & Chm)
Charles W. Barnes IV (CEO)

BARNES NURSERY, INC.
3511 W Cleveland Rd, Huron, OH 44839
Tel.: (419) 433-5525
Web Site:
https://www.barnesnursery.com
Year Founded: 1950
Sales Range: $25-49.9 Million
Emp.: 200
Nursery, Garden Center & Farm Supply Retailer
N.A.I.C.S.: 444240
Robert H. Barnes (Co-Owner & Pres)
Jarret S. Barnes (Co-Owner & VP)
Julie L. Barnes (Sec & Office Mgr)

BARNES PAPER COMPANY INCORPORATED
5638 Miller Industrial Blvd, Birmingham, AL 35210
Tel.: (205) 324-6262

Web Site:
http://www.barnespaper.com
Sales Range: $10-24.9 Million
Emp.: 18
Industrial & Personal Service Paper
N.A.I.C.S.: 424130
Ray Barnes (Pres)

BARNES-BAKER MOTORS INC.
1901 N Washington St, Chillicothe, MO 64601
Tel.: (660) 646-3156
Web Site:
http://www.barnesbaker.com
Year Founded: 1932
Rev.: $16,780,591
Emp.: 30
New & Used Car Dealers
N.A.I.C.S.: 441110
John Barnes (Mgr-Fin)
Brent Wyant (Owner & Gen Mgr)

BARNES-KASSON HOSPITAL
2872 Turnpike St, Susquehanna, PA 18847
Tel.: (570) 853-3135   PA
Web Site: https://www.barnes-kasson.org
Year Founded: 1904
Sales Range: $10-24.9 Million
Emp.: 313
Health Care Srvices
N.A.I.C.S.: 622110
Clay Weaver (VP)
Robert Burns (Pres)
John Kane (Sec)
Geraldine Lamb (Treas)

BARNESVILLE HOSPITAL
639 W Main St, Barnesville, OH 43713
Tel.: (740) 425-3941   OH
Web Site:
http://www.barnesvillehospital.com
Year Founded: 1940
Sales Range: $10-24.9 Million
Emp.: 333
Health Care Srvices
N.A.I.C.S.: 622110
Willie Cooper-Lohr (CFO)
David Phillips (CEO)
Cindy Touvelle (Chief Nursing Officer)

BARNETT & MURPHY, INC
1323 Brookhaven Dr, Orlando, FL 32803
Tel.: (407) 650-0264
Web Site: http://www.bmdm.com
Year Founded: 2002
Sales Range: $100-124.9 Million
Emp.: 14
Advertising Services
N.A.I.C.S.: 541810
Chuck Barnett (Co-Owner & CEO)

BARNETT CHRYSLER JEEP KIA
3610 Hwy 61 N, Saint Paul, MN 55110
Tel.: (651) 429-3391
Web Site:
http://www.barnettchrysler.com
Rev.: $29,600,000
Emp.: 100
New & Used Car Sales
N.A.I.C.S.: 441110
Bruce Barnett (Pres)
Nancy Greenberg (Controller)
Doug Lewis (Mgr-Svc)
Jeff Link (Mgr-Used Cars)
Tim Rogness (Mgr-New Cars)
Lou Henigin (Mgr-Fin)

BARNETT HARLEY-DAVIDSON

8272 Gateway Blvd E, El Paso, TX 79907
Tel.: (915) 592-0666
Web Site:
https://www.barnettharley.com
Rev.: $13,300,000
Emp.: 125
Motorcycles
N.A.I.C.S.: 441227
David Callendine (Mgr-MotorClothes)

BARNETT IMPLEMENT CO
4220 Old Hwy 99 S, Mount Vernon, WA 98273
Tel.: (360) 424-7995
Web Site:
http://www.barnettimplement.com
Year Founded: 1924
Sales Range: $10-24.9 Million
Emp.: 35
Lawn & Garden Equipment
N.A.I.C.S.: 444230
Bill Remmenga (Mgr-Sls)
Ben Pratt (Mgr-Svcs)

BARNETT MILLWORKS, INC.
4915 Hamilton Blvd, Theodore, AL 36582-8529
Tel.: (251) 443-7710   AL
Web Site:
http://www.barnettmillworks.com
Year Founded: 1945
Sales Range: $100-124.9 Million
Emp.: 175
Millwork Manufacturing
N.A.I.C.S.: 321918
Paul S. Barnett (Pres)
Dan Barber (VP)

BARNEYS PUMPS INC.
2965 Barneys Pump Pl, Lakeland, FL 33812
Tel.: (863) 665-8500
Web Site:
https://www.barneyspumps.com
Rev.: $18,656,908
Emp.: 70
Pumps & Pumping Equipment
N.A.I.C.S.: 423830
Greg Riching (Pres)
Karen Smith (Mgr-Credit)
Abilio Hernandez (Mgr-Acct)
Robbie Pearce (Acct Mgr)
Ryan Grymko (Engr-Sls)
Tom Gerardi (Mgr-Bridgeport)
Gene Hamilton (Mgr-Bridgeport)

BARNHARDT MANUFACTURING COMPANY
1100 Hawthorne Ln, Charlotte, NC 28205-2918
Tel.: (704) 376-0380   NC
Web Site: https://www.barnhardt.net
Year Founded: 1900
Sales Range: $150-199.9 Million
Emp.: 340
Mfr of Polyurethane Foam & Absorbent Cotton Products
N.A.I.C.S.: 326150
Lewis B. Barnhardt (Pres & COO)
Shawn P. Fitzgerald (Dir-Quality & Technical Svcs-Natural Fibers Div)
Wade Hubbard Jr. (Dir-Product Mgmt-Natural Fibers Div)

Subsidiaries:

Carolina Absorbent Cotton Company   (1)
1100 Hawthorne Ln, Charlotte, NC 28205-2918   (100%)
Tel.: (704) 376-0380
Web Site: http://www.carolinacotton.net
Sales Range: $10-24.9 Million
Emp.: 25
Supplier of Coil for Pharmaceutical & Vitamin Packaging
N.A.I.C.S.: 326150

Barnhardt Manufacturing Company—(Continued)

Intrinsics (1)
1100 Hawthorne Ln, Charlotte, NC 28205-2918
Tel.: (704) 376-0380
Sales Range: $25-49.9 Million
Emp.: 240
Mfr of Single Use Products for Salons & Spas
N.A.I.C.S.: 449110

North Carolina Foam Industries, Inc. (1)
1515 Carter St, Mount Airy, NC 27030-1528 (100%)
Tel.: (336) 789-9161
Web Site: http://www.ncfi.com
Sales Range: $50-74.9 Million
Emp.: 180
Plastic Materials Mfr
N.A.I.C.S.: 313210
Judd Brown (Exec VP)
Chip Holton (Pres)

Division (Domestic):

Barnhardt Cushion-Hickory Plant (2)
2725 Tate Blvd SE, Hickory, NC 28602-1449 (100%)
Tel.: (828) 328-1893
Web Site: http://www.barnhardt.net
Sales Range: $25-49.9 Million
Emp.: 75
Mfr of Cushions
N.A.I.C.S.: 314999

North Carolina Foam Industries, Inc. - Dalton Foam Division
4959 S Dixie Hwy, Dalton, GA 30719-4507
Tel.: (706) 277-1003
Carpet Cushion Mfr
N.A.I.C.S.: 326150

Richmond Dental (1)
1100 Hawthorne Ln, Charlotte, NC 28205-2918
Tel.: (704) 376-0380
Web Site: http://www.richmonddental.net
Sales Range: $50-74.9 Million
Emp.: 16
Cotton Dental Plugs
N.A.I.C.S.: 326140
Sara Evans (VP-Sls & Mktg)

BARNHARDT, DAY & HINES
56 Cabarrus Ave, W, Charlotte, NC 28026
Tel.: (704) 786-7193
Web Site: http://www.bdandh.com
Year Founded: 1983
Sales Range: $10-24.9 Million
Emp.: 11
Advertising Agencies
N.A.I.C.S.: 541810
Thomas Day (Pres & CEO)
Bev Stroman (Dir-Fin Svcs)
Laurey McElroy (VP-Acct Svcs)
Mike Scardino (Chief Creative Officer)
Darrel Myers (Dir-Creative)
Alaine Bollinger (Sr VP-Acct Svcs)

BARNHART
1641 California St Ste 400, Denver, CO 80202-1233
Tel.: (303) 626-7200 CO
Web Site:
http://www.barnhartusa.com
Year Founded: 1995
Sales Range: $50-74.9 Million
Emp.: 20
Advertising Agencies
N.A.I.C.S.: 541810
Christine Cowan (Grp Acct Dir)
Hannah Morris (Acct Exec-PR & Social Media)

BARNHART CRANE & RIGGING CO.
2163 Airways Blvd, Memphis, TN 38114-5208
Tel.: (901) 775-3000 DE

Web Site:
https://www.barnhartcrane.com
Year Founded: 1969
Specialized Heavy Lifting, Rigging & Transportation Solutions
N.A.I.C.S.: 238990
Alan Barnhart (Pres & CEO)
Gene Kaercher (Sr VP)
Chris Teague (Dir-Mktg)

Subsidiaries:

Armstrong Crane & Rigging Inc, (1)
717 1st St SW, New Brighton, MN 55112
Tel.: (651) 636-8129
Web Site:
http://www.armstrongcrane-rigging.com
Rev.: $9,350,000
Emp.: 30
Construction, Mining & Forestry Machinery & Equipment Rental & Leasing
N.A.I.C.S.: 532412

White Crane Co, Inc. (1)
3414 Augusta Rd, West Columbia, SC 29170
Tel.: (803) 794-7194
Web Site:
http://www.whitecranecompanyinc.com
Sales Range: $1-9.9 Million
Emp.: 30
Construction, Mining & Forestry Machinery & Equipment Rental & Leasing
N.A.I.C.S.: 532412
John Morris (Gen Mgr)

BARNHART INDUSTRIES, INC.
3690 Hwy M, Imperial, MO 63052-2932
Tel.: (636) 942-3133
Web Site: https://www.orthoband.com
Year Founded: 1939
Sales Range: $50-74.9 Million
Emp.: 25
Mfr of Soft Goods
N.A.I.C.S.: 339993
Kenneth J. DeWoskin (Owner)
Anna Boehm (Pres)
Brenda Marler (Controller)

Subsidiaries:

Orthoband Co., Inc. (1)
3690 Hwy M, Imperial, MO 63052
Tel.: (636) 942-3133
Web Site: http://www.orthoband.com
Sales Range: $25-49.9 Million
Emp.: 20
Mfr of Prosthetic Devices; Cervical Traction Bands, Neck Pads, Orthodontic Headgear
N.A.I.C.S.: 332215

BARNHART-REESE CONSTRUCTION INC.
10805 Thornmint Rd Ste 200, San Diego, CA 92127
Tel.: (858) 592-6500
Year Founded: 2007
Sales Range: $10-24.9 Million
Emp.: 11
Nonresidential Construction Services
N.A.I.C.S.: 236220
Douglas E. Bernhart (Chm)

BARNHILL CONTRACTING COMPANY
800 15 Blvd, Rocky Mount, NC 27804
Tel.: (252) 823-1021 NC
Web Site:
http://www.barnhillcontracting.com
Year Founded: 1949
Sales Range: $450-499.9 Million
Emp.: 1,000
General Contracting for Industrial, Highway & Commercial Construction
N.A.I.C.S.: 237310
Scott G. Fisher (VP-Info Svcs)
Chris Stroud (VP)
Barry Harden (VP-Building Div Ops)
Chad Webb (VP-Western Div)

Will Wilfong (VP-Rocky Mount & Greenville)
Shannon Douglas (VP)
Mike Bedell (VP-Charlotte)
Gail Suson (VP-Building Div Preconstruction Svcs)
Thumper Swann (VP-Coastal Div)
Jimmie Hughes (VP-HR & Safety)
Skip Partington (VP-Southeast Div)
Sidney Hughes (VP-HR)
Chris Freeman (Dir-Preconstruction Svcs)
Mike Lutz (VP-Triangle Div)
John Smith (VP-Eastern Div)
Randy Fichera (VP-Streamline Div)

BARNIE'S COFFEE & TEA COMPANY
2420 Lakemont Ave #160, Orlando, FL 32814
Tel.: (407) 854-6626 FL
Web Site:
http://www.barniescoffeeandtea.com
Year Founded: 1980
Sales Range: $10-24.9 Million
Emp.: 50
Coffee & Tea Shops
N.A.I.C.S.: 445298
Jonathan Smiga (Pres & CEO)

BARNMASTER INC.
3489 S Hwy 99 W, Corning, CA 96021
Web Site:
http://www.mdbarnmaster.com
Year Founded: 1983
Sales Range: $10-24.9 Million
Emp.: 50
Farm & Utility Buildings
N.A.I.C.S.: 332311
Bruce Thomas (CEO)

BARNWELL HOUSE OF TIRES INC.
2020 Lakeland Ave, Ronkonkoma, NY 11779
Tel.: (631) 737-8473
Web Site:
http://www.barnwellhousetires.com
Year Founded: 1939
Sales Range: $10-24.9 Million
Emp.: 85
Retail & Wholesale; Automotive & Truck Tires; Road Service
N.A.I.C.S.: 441340
James W. Gorman (Pres)
William Gorman (VP)
Calvin Norton (VP)

BAROLIN & SPENCER, INC.
1015 Main St, Voorhees, NJ 08043-4602
Tel.: (856) 424-7600 NJ
Web Site: http://www.barolin-spencer.com
Year Founded: 1988
Sales Range: $10-24.9 Million
Emp.: 8
Advetising Agency
N.A.I.C.S.: 541810
Anthony M. Barolin (Mng Partner)
Joel Spencer (Mng Partner)
Sue Spencer (Media Buyer)
Mark Laganella (Dir-Interactive)
Paul Young (Dir-Art)

BARON + DOWDLE CONSTRUCTION, LLC.
652 Old Ezell Rd, Nashville, TN 37217-2948
Tel.: (615) 399-0777
Sales Range: $10-24.9 Million
Emp.: 22
Nonresidential Construction Services
N.A.I.C.S.: 236220
Steve Mollenhour (Principal)

BARON BROS, INC.
239 50 Jericho Tpke, Floral Park, NY 11001
Tel.: (516) 358-2211
Web Site:
http://www.bestautooutlet1.com
Rev.: $35,000,000
Emp.: 6
New Car Dealers
N.A.I.C.S.: 441110
David Baron (Pres)
Ronald Baron (Sec)

BARON CAPITAL GROUP, INC.
767 5th Ave 48th Fl, New York, NY 10153
Tel.: (212) 583-2000 NY
Web Site: http://www.baronfunds.com
Year Founded: 1970
Sales Range: $75-99.9 Million
Emp.: 80
Brokers Security
N.A.I.C.S.: 523150
Ronald Baron (Founder, CEO, CIO & Portfolio Mgr)
Alex Umansky (VP & Mgr-Portfolio)
Linda Martinson (Pres & COO)
David Judice (VP & Head-Intermediary Sls & National Accts)
Peggy Wong (CFO, Treas & VP)
Pat Patalino (Gen Counsel, Sec & VP)
Glenn Smith (Mgr-Natl Sls)
Amy Low Chasen (VP & Dir-Res)
Cliff Greenberg (Sr VP & Mgr-Portfolio)
Andrew Peck (Sr VP & Mgr-Portfolio)
Michael Lippert (VP & Mgr-Portfolio)
Jeffrey Kolitch (VP & Mgr-Portfolio)
Michael Kass (VP & Mgr-Portfolio)
James H. Stone (VP & Mgr-Portfolio)
Laird Bieger (VP & Mgr-Portfolio)
Randolph Gwirtzman (VP & Mgr-Portfolio)
Ashim Mehra (VP)
David Baron (VP)
David Goldsmith (VP)
David Kirshenbaum (VP)
Kyuhey August (VP-Consumer-Intl)
Matthew Weiss (VP)
Michael Baron (VP & Asst Portfolio Mgr)
Neal Kaufman (VP)
Neal Rosenberg (VP & Asst Portfolio Mgr)
Rebecca Ellin (VP)
Susan Robbins (VP)
Stephanie Gisriel (VP & Dir-Natl Accounts)
Frank Maiorano (VP & Head-RIA Sls)

BARON GROUP LLC
3451 Executive Way, Miramar, FL 33025-3916
Tel.: (954) 435-3330
Web Site: http://www.baronintl.com
Sales Range: $10-24.9 Million
Emp.: 15
Aircraft Equipment & Supplies
N.A.I.C.S.: 336413
Steve Balaam (Pres)

BARONA VALLEY RANCH RESORT & CASINO
1932 Wildcat Canyon Rd, Lakeside, CA 92040
Tel.: (619) 443-2300 CA
Web Site: https://www.barona.com
Year Founded: 1932
Sales Range: $200-249.9 Million
Emp.: 3,600
Hotel & Casino
N.A.I.C.S.: 721120

Mike Patterson (VP-Table Game Ops)
Troy Simpson (Exec VP & Asst Gen Mgr)
Dean Allen (Sr VP-Admin)
Chuck Hickey (VP-Slot Ops)
Mike Murphy (VP-Tech)
Don King (Exec Dir-Golf)
Rick Salinas (Gen Mgr)
Linda Jordan (Sr VP-Ops)
Ed Fasulo (VP-Food & Beverage)

BARR & BARR, INC.
460 W 34th St 10th Fl, New York, NY 10001
Tel.: (212) 563-2330   NY
Web Site:
   http://www.barrandbarr.com
Year Founded: 1927
Sales Range: $250-299.9 Million
Emp.: 180
Contracting & Construction Services
N.A.I.C.S.: 236220
Glenn W. Kiefer (Sr Exec VP)
Keith W. Stanisce (Pres & CEO)
Thomas J. Lepage (Exec VP & Dir-Ops-Mid Atlantic)
Stephen Killian (COO, Exec VP & Dir-Ops-New England)

BARR AIR PATROL, LLC
1442 Airport Blvd Ste 11, Mesquite, TX 75181
Tel.: (972) 222-0229
Web Site:
   http://www.barrairpatrol.com
Year Founded: 1999
Sales Range: $1-9.9 Million
Emp.: 57
Professional, Scientific & Technical Services
N.A.I.C.S.: 541990
Clayton Chennault (Pres)

Subsidiaries:

Airborne Imaging Inc.   (1)
5757 4th St SE, Calgary, T2H 1K8, AB, Canada
Tel.: (403) 215-2963
Web Site:
   http://www.airborneimaginginc.com
Aircraft Charter Services
N.A.I.C.S.: 481219
Martin Maric (Sls Mgr)
Susan Muleme Kasumba (Mgr-Bus Dev)
Tamra Beaubouef (Mgr-Business Development-US)
Jocelyn Parent (Dir)

BARR BROTHERS & CO., INC.
39 Broadway 24th Fl, New York, NY 10006-3003
Tel.: (212) 269-4500   DE
Web Site: http://www.barrbros.com
Year Founded: 1913
Sales Range: $1-9.9 Million
Emp.: 16
Provider of Municipal Bond Trading & Investment Advice
N.A.I.C.S.: 523150

BARR CREDIT SERVICES, INC.
5151 E Broadway Blvd Ste 800, Tucson, AZ 85711-3705
Tel.: (520) 745-8701   AZ
Web Site: http://www.barrcredit.com
Year Founded: 1998
Emp.: 100
Commercial Credit & Collection Services
N.A.I.C.S.: 561440
Randy Frazee (CEO)
John Wieland (CFO)
George Kern (COO)
Jim Bessenbacher Jr. (Pres)

BARR ENGINEERING COMPANY
4300 Market Pointe Dr Ste 200, Minneapolis, MN 55435-4818
Tel.: (952) 832-2600   MN
Web Site: https://www.barr.com
Year Founded: 1953
Sales Range: $10-24.9 Million
Emp.: 800
Provider of Engineering Services
N.A.I.C.S.: 541330
Allan Gebhard (VP)
Greg Hill (VP)
Terry Khronberg (Controller)
John Lee (Pres & CEO)

Subsidiaries:

Barr Engineering Company, Ann Arbor   (1)
3005 Boardwalk St Ste 100, Ann Arbor, MI 48108   (100%)
Tel.: (734) 327-1200
Web Site: http://www.barr.com
Sales Range: $10-24.9 Million
Emp.: 44
Engineeering Services
N.A.I.C.S.: 541330
John T. Lee (CEO)
Christene Jones (VP)
Chris Toulouse (Engr-Structural)
Luke Mackewich (Engr-Environmental)
Michael Ellis (Engr-Environmental)
Neal Sheldon (Engr-Mechanical)
Sam Baushke (Engr-Environmental)

Barr Engineering Company, Duluth   (1)
325 S Lk Ave Ste 700, Duluth, MN 55802-1867
Tel.: (218) 529-8200
Sales Range: $10-24.9 Million
Emp.: 100
Engineering Services
N.A.I.C.S.: 541330

Barr Engineering Company, Hibbing   (1)
3128 14th Ave E, Hibbing, MN 55746
Tel.: (218) 262-8600
Web Site: http://www.barr.com
Engineering Services
N.A.I.C.S.: 541330
Doug Connell (Pres)

Barr Engineering Company, Jefferson City   (1)
1001 Diamond Rdg Ste 1100, Jefferson City, MO 65109-6839   (100%)
Tel.: (573) 638-5000
Web Site: http://www.bar.com
Sales Range: $10-24.9 Million
Emp.: 20
Engineeering Services
N.A.I.C.S.: 541330
Allen Fandrey (VP)

BARR INTERNATIONAL INC.
2407 N Salisbury Blvd, Salisbury, MD 21801
Tel.: (410) 546-1122
Web Site: http://www.barrtruck.com
Year Founded: 1969
Sales Range: $10-24.9 Million
Emp.: 85
Sales & Service of Trucks
N.A.I.C.S.: 423110
Thomas Murphy (CFO)
Nana Hirsch (Mgr-Parts)
Wayne Hoke (Mgr-Sls)
Rich Barr (Gen Mgr)
Richard S. Barr Sr. (Chm)
Richard S. Barr Jr. (Pres)

BARR LUMBER CO. INC.
1623 W San Bernardino Rd, West Covina, CA 91790-1020
Tel.: (909) 884-4744   CA
Web Site:
   http://www.barrlumber.doitbest.com
Year Founded: 1986
Sales Range: $50-74.9 Million
Emp.: 215

Lumber & Other Building Materials
N.A.I.C.S.: 444110
John Shirley (Pres)

Subsidiaries:

Barr Do it Best Lumber   (1)
7054 Old Woman Springs Rd, Yucca Valley, CA 92284-2913
Tel.: (760) 365-1000
Web Site: http://www.builderssupplyca.com
Sales Range: $25-49.9 Million
Emp.: 15
Lumber & other Building Materials
N.A.I.C.S.: 423310

BARR-NUNN ENTERPRISES LTD.
1803 Burr Oak Blvd, Granger, IA 50109
Tel.: (515) 999-2525   IA
Web Site: https://www.barr-nunn.com
Year Founded: 1985
Sales Range: $25-49.9 Million
Emp.: 1,000
Trucking Service
N.A.I.C.S.: 484121
Robert M. Sturgeon (Chm)
Rene Beacom (Pres)
Shari Proehl (CFO)

Subsidiaries:

Barr-Nunn Enterprises Ltd. - Ohio Orientation Facility   (1)
2351 New World Dr, Columbus, OH 43207
Tel.: (515) 999-2525
General Freight Trucking Services
N.A.I.C.S.: 484121

Barr-Nunn Logistics, Inc.   (1)
1803 Burr Oak Blvd, Granger, IA 50109
Tel.: (515) 999-2525
Web Site: http://www.barr-nunn.com
Emp.: 100
Freight Trucking Logistics
N.A.I.C.S.: 488510
Robert M. Sturgeon (Chm)

BARRACK'S CATER INN BANQUET CENTER & CATERING
1224 W Pioneer Pkwy, Peoria, IL 61615
Tel.: (309) 692-3990
Web Site: https://www.caterinn.com
Year Founded: 1930
Rev.: $2,200,000
Emp.: 50
Catering Services
N.A.I.C.S.: 722320
James Barrack (Pres & CEO)

BARRATT ASSET MANAGEMENT, LLC
602 N Capitol Ste 210, Indianapolis, IN 46204
Tel.: (317) 550-0214   IN
Web Site:
   http://www.barrattassetmanage.com
Year Founded: 2010
Sales Range: $1-9.9 Million
Emp.: 70
Asset Management Services
N.A.I.C.S.: 531390
Ivan Barratt (Founder & CEO)
Adam Ehret (Pres & COO)
Jerry Hyatt (Dir-Maintenance & Construction)
Catherine Azar (Dir-Property Mgmt)
Tony Landa (Chief Investment Officer)
Jeff King (VP-IR-BAM Capital)
Katherine Herron (VP)

BARREL ACCESSORIES & SUPPLY COMPANY, INC.
2595 Palmer Ave, University Park, IL 60484
Tel.: (708) 534-0900   DE
Web Site: https://www.bascousa.com

Year Founded: 1946
Sales Range: $10-24.9 Million
Emp.: 60
Industrial Supplies
N.A.I.C.S.: 423840
Richard Rudy (CEO)

BARRETT CHEVROLET, INC.
10419 Old Ocean City Blvd, Berlin, MD 21811-1121
Tel.: (410) 641-0444
Web Site: http://www.mybarrett.com
Year Founded: 1951
Sales Range: $10-24.9 Million
Emp.: 44
New Car Retailer
N.A.I.C.S.: 441110

BARRETT DISTRIBUTION CENTERS, INC.
15 Freedom Way, Franklin, MA 02038
Tel.: (508) 553-8800   MA
Web Site:
   http://www.barrettdistribution.com
Year Founded: 1953
Sales Range: $10-24.9 Million
Emp.: 25
General Warehousing
N.A.I.C.S.: 493110
Arthur Barrett (Pres)
Tim Barrett (COO)
Bob Willert (Sr VP-Ops)
Tim Barrett (COO)
Arthur Barrett (Pres)
Scott Hothem (Sr VP-Customer Solutions)

BARRETT GRILLO GROUP, INC.
3930 Utah St Ste E, San Diego, CA 92104
Web Site:
   http://www.resident360.com
Year Founded: 2011
Sales Range: $1-9.9 Million
Emp.: 14
Real Estate Management Services
N.A.I.C.S.: 531390
Josh Grillo (Co-Founder & Pres)
Michael Barrett (Co-Founder)

BARRETT HOLDING COMPANY INC.
1250 NE Loop 410 Ste 500, San Antonio, TX 78209
Tel.: (210) 829-7831
Rev.: $21,000,000
Emp.: 14
Concrete Plants
N.A.I.C.S.: 333120
Chris Waples (Pres)

BARRETT INC.
106 Mill Plain Rd, Danbury, CT 06811
Tel.: (203) 744-2780
Web Site:
   https://www.barrettroofing.com
Sales Range: $10-24.9 Million
Emp.: 50
Roofing Services
N.A.I.C.S.: 238160
John A. Lucchesi (Pres)

BARRETT INDUSTRIAL SUPPLY COMPANY
324 Henderson Ave, Joliet, IL 60432-2566
Tel.: (815) 726-4341   IL
Web Site:
   https://www.barrettindustrial.com
Year Founded: 1850
Hardware & Industrial Supplies Retailer & Whslr
N.A.I.C.S.: 444140

Barrett Industrial Supply Company—(Continued)

Robert A. Pierson *(Pres & CEO)*
Ben Pierson *(VP-Ops)*

BARRETT INDUSTRIES, INC.
3 Becker Farm Rd Ste 307, Roseland, NJ 07068
Tel.: (973) 533-1001
Web Site:
https://barrettindustries.com
Year Founded: 1854
Pavement Preservation, Aggregate Supply & Infrastructure Construction
N.A.I.C.S.: 423390
Robert Doucet *(Pres)*

Subsidiaries:

Upstone Materials Inc.   (1)
111 Quarry Rd, Plattsburgh, NY 12901
Tel.: (518) 561-5321
Web Site: http://upstonematerials.com
Hot Mix Asphalt, Aggregates & Ready Mix Concrete
N.A.I.C.S.: 327331
Danielle Godin *(Mgr-HR)*

Subsidiary (Domestic):

Graymont Materials (NY) Inc.   (2)
111 Quarry Rd, Plattsburgh, NY 12901
Tel.: (518) 561-5200
Stone Mining
N.A.I.C.S.: 212319

BARRETT MOTOR CARS
15423 IH 10 W, San Antonio, TX 78249
Tel.: (210) 341-2800
Web Site:
http://www.barrettmotorcars.com
Sales Range: $25-49.9 Million
Emp.: 35
Automobiles, New & Used
N.A.I.C.S.: 811111
Charles T. Barrett *(Pres & CEO)*

BARRETT-JACKSON AUCTION COMPANY LLC
7400 E Monte Cristo Ave, Scottsdale, AZ 85260
Tel.: (480) 663-6255
Web Site: http://www.barrett-jackson.com
Year Founded: 1971
Sales Range: $10-24.9 Million
Emp.: 50
Automobile Auction
N.A.I.C.S.: 441227
Craig Jackson *(Chm & CEO)*
Steve Davis *(Pres)*

BARRIE HOUSE COFFEE CO. INC.
945 Nepperhan Ave, Yonkers, NY 10703
Tel.: (914) 423-8400
Web Site:
http://www.barriehouse.com
Rev.: $16,234,292
Emp.: 75
Coffee Roasting (Except By Wholesale Grocers)
N.A.I.C.S.: 311920
Paul Goldstein *(Pres)*

BARRIER ISLAND STATION INC.
1 Cypress Knee Trl, Kitty Hawk, NC 27949
Tel.: (252) 261-4610
Web Site: http://www.bistation.com
Sales Range: $10-24.9 Million
Emp.: 70
Operative Builders
N.A.I.C.S.: 236117
Brad Weissman *(Exec VP-Hotel Ops)*
Brian Carson *(CFO)*

Bruce L. Thompson *(CEO)*
Bryan D. Cuffee *(VP-Dev)*
Chuck Sass *(Exec VP-Food & Beverage Ops)*
Elizabeth Weller *(Exec VP-Admin)*
Lee Westnedge *(Gen Counsel)*
Michael Woodhead *(VP-Mktg)*
Paul Grosch *(VP-IT)*
Robert Howard *(Chief Investment Officer)*

BARRIER MOTOR FUELS INC.
PO Box 690, Tarrytown, NY 10591-3668
Tel.: (914) 631-2272
Web Site: http://www.barrier.com
Year Founded: 1972
Sales Range: $100-124.9 Million
Emp.: 3
Retailer of Petroleum Products
N.A.I.C.S.: 424720
Elaine Jeffers *(VP)*

Subsidiaries:

Croton Equities Inc.   (1)
2030 Albany Post Rd, Croton on Hudson, NY 10591-3668
Tel.: (914) 631-2272
Web Site: http://www.barrier.com
Sales Range: $10-24.9 Million
Emp.: 2
Gasoline Service Stations
N.A.I.C.S.: 457120

BARRIER TECHNOLOGY CORP.
510 4th St N, Watkins, MN 55389
Tel.: (320) 764-5797
Web Site: http://www.intlbarrier.com
Year Founded: 1993
Sales Range: $1-9.9 Million
Emp.: 18
Adhesive Mfr
N.A.I.C.S.: 325520
Jane Waletzko *(Mgr-Admin)*

BARRIERE CONSTRUCTION CO. LLC
1 Galaria Blvd Ste 1650, Metairie, LA 70001
Tel.: (504) 581-7283
Web Site: https://www.barriere.com
Sales Range: $50-74.9 Million
Emp.: 400
General Contractor, Highway & Street Construction
N.A.I.C.S.: 237310
George H. Wilson Jr. *(Chm, Pres & CEO)*

BARRIERMED INC.
155 Technology Park, Lake Mary, FL 32746
Tel.: (407) 323-1604
Sales Range: $25-49.9 Million
Emp.: 8
Medical Device Company
N.A.I.C.S.: 541715
Victor J. Ragucci *(CEO)*

Subsidiaries:

Barriermed Glove Co. Inc.   (1)
155 Technology Park, Lake Mary, FL 32746
Tel.: (407) 323-1604
Web Site: http://www.barriermed.com
Sales Range: $10-24.9 Million
Gloves; Plastics
N.A.I.C.S.: 326199

BARRINGTON CHEMICAL CORP
500 Mamaroneck Ave, Harrison, NY 10528
Tel.: (914) 381-3500
Web Site:
http://www.barringtonchem.com
Sales Range: $10-24.9 Million

Emp.: 16
Chemicals & Allied Products
N.A.I.C.S.: 424690
Stuart R. Gelbard *(Pres)*

BARRINGTON DEVELOPMENT CORP.
120 Greenwich St, New York, NY 10006
Tel.: (212) 366-4877
Sales Range: $25-49.9 Million
Emp.: 4
Residential Building Operator
N.A.I.C.S.: 531120
Lawrence Devine *(Pres)*
John Struckhofs *(Office Mgr)*

BARRINGTON GROUP LTD.
2300 N Hasko Ave, Dallas, TX 75204
Tel.: (214) 528-6990
Web Site:
http://www.barringtongifts.com
Year Founded: 1991
Sales Range: $10-24.9 Million
Emp.: 30
Executive Writing Instruments, Leather Goods & Accessories for Corporate Environments
N.A.I.C.S.: 339940
David C. Gowdy *(Partner)*

BARRIOS DISTRIBUTING
5265 Lovelock St, San Diego, CA 92110
Tel.: (619) 295-3119
Web Site:
https://www.barriosdistributing.com
Rev.: $600,000
Emp.: 5
Grocery & Related Products Merchant Whslr
N.A.I.C.S.: 424490
Robert H. Barrios *(Owner)*

BARRIOS TECHNOLOGY LTD.
16441 Space Ctr Blvd Ste B-100, Houston, TX 77058
Tel.: (281) 280-1900
Web Site: http://www.barrios.com
Year Founded: 1980
Rev.: $60,000,000
Emp.: 600
Aerospace Engineering & Technology Services
N.A.I.C.S.: 541330
Sandra G. Johnson *(Pres)*
Anita Renteria *(Mgr-Bus Dev)*
Mark Polansky *(Sr Mgr-Program Integration)*

BARRISTER EXECUTIVE SUITES
11500 Olympic Blvd Ste 400, Los Angeles, CA 90064
Tel.: (310) 258-8000
Web Site: https://www.barrister-suites.com
Rev.: $15,300,000
Emp.: 15
Commercial & Industrial Building Operation
N.A.I.C.S.: 531120
Vince H. Otte *(Chm & CEO)*
Dorothy Bright *(Pres & COO)*
Alain Whittman *(CFO)*
Margaret Gunning *(Exec VP & Gen Mgr)*

BARRISTER GLOBAL SERVICES NETWORK, INC.
42548 Happywoods Dr, Hammond, LA 70401
Tel.: (985) 365-0400
Web Site: https://www.barrister.com
Year Founded: 1982
Sales Range: $10-24.9 Million

Emp.: 97
Multi-Vendor IT Services
N.A.I.C.S.: 541519
Jared Bowers *(VP-Bus Dev)*
Debra Bowers *(CEO)*
Byron Cain *(CFO & Sr VP)*
Brittany East *(Mgr-Ops)*

BARRON BUILDERS & MANAGEMENT COMPANY INC.
435 Spring Hill Dr, Spring, TX 77386-6001
Tel.: (281) 363-8705
Web Site:
http://www.barronmgmt.com
Sales Range: $25-49.9 Million
Emp.: 200
Remodeling & New Home Construction Services; Manager of Apartments
N.A.I.C.S.: 236118
Marquae Webb *(Reg Dir)*

BARRON COLLIER COMPANY, LTD.
2600 Golden Gate Pkwy, Naples, FL 34105
Tel.: (239) 262-2600
Web Site:
https://www.barroncollier.com
Year Founded: 1949
Emp.: 100
Holding Company; Real Estate, Agriculture & Energy Development
N.A.I.C.S.: 551112
Blake Gable *(Pres)*
Barron Collier III *(Founder)*

Subsidiaries:

Barron Collier Corporation   (1)
2600 Golden Gate Pkwy, Naples, FL 34105
Tel.: (239) 262-2600
Web Site: http://www.barroncollier.com
Residential & Commercial Real Estate Acquisition, Development & Property Management Services
N.A.I.C.S.: 237210

Subsidiary (Domestic):

Grey Oaks Country Club Inc.   (2)
2400 Grey Oaks Dr N, Naples, FL 34105
Tel.: (239) 262-5550
Web Site: http://www.greyoakscc.com
Country Club
N.A.I.C.S.: 713910
Tim Butler *(Gen Mgr)*

BARRON HEATING & AIR CONDITIONING INC.
5100 Pacific Hwy, Ferndale, WA 98248
Tel.: (360) 676-1131
Web Site:
https://www.barronheating.com
Year Founded: 1973
Sales Range: $10-24.9 Million
Emp.: 80
Plumbing, Heating & Air-Conditioning Contracting Services
N.A.I.C.S.: 238220
John Barron *(Co-Pres)*
Seth Bowman *(Mgr-Svc)*
Vivian O. Barron *(Sec)*
Dan Barron *(Co-Pres)*

BARRON MOTOR INC.
1850 McCloud Pl NE, Cedar Rapids, IA 52402
Tel.: (319) 393-6220
Web Site:
http://www.barronmotorsupply.com
Rev.: $10,700,000
Emp.: 50
Automotive Supplies & Parts
N.A.I.C.S.: 423120
John Barron *(VP)*
Dave Welter *(Mgr-Sls)*
William J. Barron III *(Pres)*

BARRON'S EDUCATIONAL SE-RIES, INC.
250 Wireless Blvd, Hauppauge, NY 11788
Tel.: (631) 434-3311
Web Site:
http://www.barronseduc.com
Year Founded: 1941
Sales Range: $75-99.9 Million
Emp.: 125
Book Publishing
N.A.I.C.S.: 513130
Manuel H. Barron (Chm)
Ellen Sibley (Pres)
Mike Rozansky (Controller)

BARROW FINE FURNITURE INC.
1220 Dr Martin Luther King Jr Expy, Andalusia, AL 36420
Tel.: (334) 222-6650
Web Site:
https://www.barrowfinefurniture.com
Rev.: $16,118,916
Emp.: 12
Furniture Retailer
N.A.I.C.S.: 449110
Patricia Northrop (VP)
Wilbur Hall Jr. (Pres)

BARROW INDUSTRIES IN-CORPORATED
3 Edgewater Dr, Norwood, MA 02062
Tel.: (781) 440-2666
Web Site:
https://www.barrowindustries.com
Year Founded: 1945
Rev.: $49,700,000
Emp.: 300
Drapery Material, Woven
N.A.I.C.S.: 424310
Dan O'Shea (Mgr-Sls)
William Fish (Sr VP-Sls & Mktg)
D. Harper (CFO)

BARROWS COAL CO. INC.
55 Depot St, Brattleboro, VT 05301
Tel.: (802) 254-4574   VT
Web Site: http://www.barrowsoil.com
Year Founded: 1969
Sales Range: $10-24.9 Million
Emp.: 9
Fuel Oil
N.A.I.C.S.: 424720
Lee Merrill (Pres)

BARRY ELECTRIC COOPERA-TIVE
4015 Main St, Cassville, MO 65625-0307
Tel.: (417) 847-2131   MO
Web Site:
http://www.barryelectric.com
Year Founded: 1946
Sales Range: $10-24.9 Million
Emp.: 33
Electric Power Distr
N.A.I.C.S.: 221122

BARRY ISETT & ASSOCIATES INC.
85 South Rte 100, Allentown, PA 18106
Tel.: (610) 398-0904
Web Site: https://www.barryisett.com
Year Founded: 1977
Sales Range: $1-9.9 Million
Emp.: 117
Civil, Structural & Environmental Engineering Services
N.A.I.C.S.: 541330
Barry Isett (Chm)
Kevin T. Campbell (Pres & CEO)
James Bonczek (Mgr-Forty Fort)

Ellen Ferretti (Sr Mgr-Environmental & Pub Sector Projects)
John Lewis (Mgr-Isett)
Subsidiaries:

BIA-Hazleton   **(1)**
100 W Broad St Suite 200, Hazleton, PA 18201-1064   **(100%)**
Tel.: (570) 455-2999
Web Site: http://www.barryisett.com
Environmental, Civil & Structural Engineering Services
N.A.I.C.S.: 237990
Barry Isett (Chm & CEO)

BIA-Phillipsburg   **(1)**
7 Union Square 3rd Floor, Phillipsburg, NJ 08865   **(100%)**
Tel.: (908) 454-9500
Web Site: http://www.barryisett.com
Survey, Environmental & Civil Engineering Services
N.A.I.C.S.: 541330

BIA-Phoenixville   **(1)**
1003 Egypt Rd, Phoenixville, PA 19460   **(100%)**
Tel.: (610) 935-2175
Web Site: http://www.barryisett.com
Environmental, Civil, Structural & Survey Engineering Services
N.A.I.C.S.: 237990
Jim Bonczek (Mgr-PR)

Code Master Inspection Services   (1)
1209 Hausman Rd, Allentown, PA 18104-9300
Tel.: (484) 223-0763
Web Site: http://www.codemaster.info
Building Inspection Services
N.A.I.C.S.: 541350
Sean Boyle (Owner)

BARRY PONTIAC-BUICK INC.
166 Connell Hwy, Newport, RI 02840
Tel.: (401) 847-5600   RI
Web Site:
https://www.barrymotors.com
Year Founded: 1949
Sales Range: $25-49.9 Million
Emp.: 53
Sales of New & Used Automobiles
N.A.I.C.S.: 441110
Peter W. Barry (Pres)

BARRY SALES ENGINEERING INC.
116 N Kirkwood Rd, Saint Louis, MO 63122-4302
Tel.: (314) 821-2525
Web Site:
http://www.barrysalesinc.com
Year Founded: 1974
Sales Range: $10-24.9 Million
Emp.: 15
Electrical Apparatus & Equipment
N.A.I.C.S.: 423610
Chris E. Barry (Pres)

BARRY SALES INC.
1323 Columbia Dr Ste 302, Richardson, TX 75081
Tel.: (972) 234-0255
Web Site: http://www.barrysales.com
Year Founded: 1974
Sales Range: $25-49.9 Million
Emp.: 5
Amateur Radio Communications Equipment
N.A.I.C.S.: 423690
Jack W. Barry (Owner)

BARRY SWENSON BUILDER
777 N 1st St Fl 5, San Jose, CA 95112
Tel.: (408) 287-0246
Web Site:
http://www.barryswensonbuilder.com
Year Founded: 1961
Sales Range: $100-124.9 Million
Emp.: 120

Commercial & Office Building Construction Services
N.A.I.C.S.: 236220
Barry Swenson (Pres)
Scott Connelly (Project Mgr)
Ron Cote (Sr VP-Construction)
Steve W. Andrews (Sr VP-Construction)
William Ryan (VP)
David A. Gibbons (Sr VP-Construction & Dev)
Lee Ann Woodard (CFO)
Jesse L. Nickell III (Sr VP-Construction & Dev)

BARRY'S CHEVROLET-BUICK, INC.
11380 State Route 41, West Union, OH 45693-2505
Tel.: (937) 544-2331
Web Site:
https://www.barryschevrolet.com
Year Founded: 1980
Sales Range: $10-24.9 Million
Emp.: 42
Car Whslr
N.A.I.C.S.: 441110
Barry McFarland (Pres)
Brad McFarland (Principal)

BARRY, BETTE & LED DUKE, INC.
302 Washington Ave Ext, Albany, NY 12203-5176
Tel.: (518) 452-8200   NY
Web Site: https://www.bblinc.com
Year Founded: 1973
Sales Range: $450-499.9 Million
Emp.: 1,000
Construction Management & General Construction
N.A.I.C.S.: 236220
Stephen Obermayer (Controller)
Subsidiaries:

Carlton, Inc.   (1)
900 Lee St E Ste 1400, Charleston, WV 25301
Tel.: (304) 345-1300
Web Site: http://www.bblcarlton.com
Rev.: $20,000,000
Emp.: 17
Commercial, Industrial & Institutional General Contractor & Construction Manager
N.A.I.C.S.: 236220

BARRY-WEHMILLER COMPA-NIES, INC.
8020 Forsyth Blvd, Saint Louis, MO 63105-1707
Tel.: (314) 862-8000   MO
Web Site: http://www.barry-wehmiller.com
Year Founded: 1885
Packaging Automation Machinery, Corrugating & Sheeting Equipment & Paper Converting System Mfr
N.A.I.C.S.: 333993
Robert H. Chapman (Chm & CEO)
Rhonda Spencer (Chief People Officer)
Joseph Wilhelm (Pres-Consulting Grp)
William Kuhn (VP-Fin)
Todd Finders (Chief Information Officer)
Stefano Rocca (Dir-Corp Dev-Europe)
Sara Hannah (Dir-Barry-Wehmiller University Academic)
Brian Wellinghoff (Dir-Living Legacy of Leadership)
Laurie Ferrendelli (Dir-Organizational Dev)
W. Kyle Chapman (Pres)

Subsidiaries:

Accraply, Inc.   **(1)**
3580 Holly Ln N, Plymouth, MN 55447-1269
Tel.: (763) 557-1313
Web Site: http://www.accraply.com
Sales Range: $25-49.9 Million
Emp.: 95
Product Identification, Labeling & Decorating Systems Mfr
N.A.I.C.S.: 333993
Seamus Lafferty (Pres)
Bruce Ewald (Mgr-Supply)
Aaron Fox (Engr-Design)
Jeff Strobach (VP-Sls & Mktg)

Subsidiary (Non-US):

Accraply Canada, Inc.   **(2)**
3070 Mainway Unit 16 19, Burlington, L7M 3X1, ON, Canada   **(100%)**
Tel.: (905) 336-8880
Web Site: http://www.accraply.com
Sales Range: $25-49.9 Million
Emp.: 28
Packaging & Labeling Services
N.A.I.C.S.: 325620

Subsidiary (Domestic):

Accraply, Inc.   **(2)**
10860 6th St, Rancho Cucamonga, CA 91730
Tel.: (909) 605-8200
Web Site: http://www.accraply.com
Sales Range: $10-24.9 Million
Emp.: 11
Product Identification, Labeling & Decorating Systems Mfr
N.A.I.C.S.: 333998

Barry-Wehmiller Design Group, Inc.   **(1)**
8020 Forsyth Blvd, Saint Louis, MO 63105-1707   **(100%)**
Tel.: (314) 862-8000
Web Site: http://www.3wdesign.com
Sales Range: $10-24.9 Million
Emp.: 100
Packaging Services
N.A.I.C.S.: 541330
Ed Perek (Partner)
Roger Mound (Controller)

Branch (Domestic):

Barry-Wehmiller Design Group   **(2)**
2012 Renaissance Blvd 110, King of Prussia, PA 19406
Tel.: (610) 239-7770
Web Site: http://www.bwdesigngroup.com
Emp.: 20
Engineering Services
N.A.I.C.S.: 541330

FleetwoodGoldcoWyard   **(1)**
1305 Lakeview Dr, Romeoville, IL 60446-3950   **(100%)**
Tel.: (630) 759-6800
Web Site:
http://www.bwcontainersystem.com
Sales Range: $25-49.9 Million
Emp.: 150
Conveying, Palletizing & Material Handling Equipment Mfr
N.A.I.C.S.: 333922
Mike Walraven (Mgr-Field Svc)

Branch (Domestic):

FleetwoodGoldcoWyard   **(2)**
5605 Goldco Dr, Loveland, CO 80538
Tel.: (970) 663-4770
Web Site: http://www.fgwa.com
Rev.: $8,300,000
Emp.: 115
Palletizers & Depalletizers
N.A.I.C.S.: 333922
Randy Pierce (Dir-Global Supply Chain)

Group (Domestic):

FleetwoodGoldcoWyard AMBEC, Inc.   **(2)**
10615 Beaver Dam Rd, Hunt Valley, MD 21030   **(100%)**
Tel.: (410) 785-1934
Web Site: http://www.fgwa.com

Barry-Wehmiller Companies, Inc.—(Continued)

Sales Range: $100-124.9 Million
Emp.: 7
Mfr of Stainless Steel Conveyor Products
N.A.I.C.S.: 333922
Tonya Neumeister (Mgr-Admin)

Hayssen Packing Technologies, Inc. (1)
225 Spartangreen Blvd, Duncan, SC 29334-9425
Tel.: (864) 486-4000
Web Site: http://www.hayssen.com
Sales Range: $25-49.9 Million
Emp.: 230
Mfr of Flexible Packaging Machinery
N.A.I.C.S.: 333993
Mike May (Pres)

MarquipWardUnited, Inc. (1)
1300 N Airport Rd, Phillips, WI 54555
Tel.: (715) 339-2191
Web Site:
    http://www.marquipwardunited.com
Sales Range: $25-49.9 Million
Emp.: 500
Corrugating Sheeting & Finishing Machinery
for the Corrugated Paperboard & Folding
Carton Industry Mfr
N.A.I.C.S.: 333243

Subsidiary (Domestic):

MarquipWardUnited, Inc. (2)
10615 Beaver Dam Rd, Hunt Valley, MD 21030
Tel.: (410) 584-7700
Web Site:
    http://www.marquipwardunited.com
Sales Range: $25-49.9 Million
Emp.: 250
Corrugated Container Machinery Mfr
N.A.I.C.S.: 333243
Markus Esch (Pres)

Paper Converting Machine Company (1)
2300 S Ashland Ave, Green Bay, WI 54304-9005
Tel.: (920) 494-5601
Web Site: http://www.pcmc.com
Sales Range: $200-249.9 Million
Emp.: 800
Flexographic Printing Presses & Converting
Machinery for the Production of Disposable
Cloths Designer & Mfr
N.A.I.C.S.: 333243
Steve Kemp (Pres)
Mark Zastrow (VP-Sls & Mktg)
Bill Easley (Mgr-Sls-North America)
Rich Rogals (Dir-Sls)
Dave Kessenich (Dir-Folding Intl Sls)
Rodney Pennings (Dir-Printing, Coating & Laminating Sls)

Subsidiary (Non-US):

Paper Converting Machine Company Far East (2)
43 Honcho 4 chome, Naka-ku, Yokohama, 231 0005, Kanagawa, Japan
Tel.: (81) 456715461
Web Site: http://www.pcmc.com
Sales Range: $10-24.9 Million
Emp.: 4
Retailer of Flexographic Printing Presses &
Converting Machinery for the Production of
Disposable Cloths
N.A.I.C.S.: 333243

Paper Converting Machine Company Far East (2)
Room B601 Tower B Kelun Bldg, 12A
Guang Hua Rd, Choa Yang District, 100020, Beijing, China
Tel.: (86) 106581 8397
Web Site: http://www.pcmc.com
Mfr & Retailer of Flexographic Printing
Presses & Converting Machinery for the
Production of Disposable Cloths
N.A.I.C.S.: 333243

Paper Converting Machine Company, Ltd. (2)
Southway Dr, Southway, Plymouth, PL6 6EL, Devon, United Kingdom
Tel.: (44) 752735881
Web Site: http://www.pcmc.com

Sales Range: $25-49.9 Million
Emp.: 75
Mfr & Retailer of Flexographic Printing
Presses & Converting Machinery for the
Production of Disposable Cloths
N.A.I.C.S.: 333243

Paper Converting Machine Europe GmbH (2)
Otto Hahn St No 54-63, Dreieich, 63303, Germany
Tel.: (49) 6103380995
Web Site: http://www.pcmc.com
Sales Range: $10-24.9 Million
Emp.: 3
Mfr & Retailer of Flexographic Printing
Presses & Converting Machinery for the
Production of Disposable Cloths
N.A.I.C.S.: 333243
Martin McTigue (Mng Dir)

Pneumatic Scale Corporation (1)
10 Ascot Pkwy, Cuyahoga Falls, OH 44223-3325
Tel.: (330) 923-0491
Web Site: http://www.psangelus.com
Sales Range: $25-49.9 Million
Emp.: 250
Packaging, Bottling Machinery & Parts Mfr
N.A.I.C.S.: 333993
Paul Kearney (VP-Sls)
Jim Foley (VP-Sls)
William Morgan (Pres)
Michael Mihalik (VP-Engrg)

Branch (Domestic):

PneumaticScaleAngelus (2)
10860 6thSt, Rancho Cucamonga, CA 91730
Tel.: (909) 527-7600
Web Site: http://www.psangelus.com
Sales Range: $75-99.9 Million
Emp.: 250
Mfr of Can Closing Machines
N.A.I.C.S.: 333993

Branch (Non-US):

PneumaticScaleAngelus (2)
De'Salis Drive, Hampton Lovett Indus Estate, Droitwich, WR9 0QE, Worcester, United Kingdom (100%)
Tel.: (44) 1905 779602
Web Site: http://www.psangelus.com
Sales Range: $25-49.9 Million
Emp.: 18
Mfr of Packaging & Bottling Machinery
N.A.I.C.S.: 333993
Nick Bemand (Mng Dir)

Thiele Technologies, Inc. (1)
315 27th Ave NE, Minneapolis, MN 55418-2715
Tel.: (612) 782-1200
Web Site: http://www.bwflexiblesystems.com
Sales Range: $50-74.9 Million
Emp.: 250
Flexible Packaging Machinery Mfr
N.A.I.C.S.: 333993
Larry Smith (Pres & CEO)
Al Bates (Controller)
Dean Grell (VP & Gen Mgr-Dairy Bus)
Brett Dexheimer (Gen Mgr)
Kip Boie (VP-Mktg & Sls)
John Curie (Head-Feeder Product Line Bus)

Subsidiary (Domestic):

The Hudson-Sharp Machine Company (2)
975 Lombardi Ave, Green Bay, WI 54304
Tel.: (920) 494-4571
Web Site: http://www.hudsonsharp.com
Sales Range: $50-74.9 Million
Emp.: 80
Packaging Machinery Mfr
N.A.I.C.S.: 333993
Paul Trousil (Mgr-Quality Assurance)
Justin Kusserow (Controller)
Larry Smith (Pres)
Moroni Mills (Coord-Mktg Comm)

Plant (Domestic):

Thiele Technologies - Reedley (2)
1949 E Manning Ave, Reedley, CA 93654
Tel.: (559) 638-8484
Web Site:
    http://www.bwintegratedsystems.com

Sales Range: $50-74.9 Million
Emp.: 215
Packaging Machinery Mfr
N.A.I.C.S.: 333993
Craig Friesen (Product Mgr)
Matt Garcia (Product Mgr-Robotics)
Ed Suarez (VP & Gen Mgr)

Winkler+Dunnebier GmbH (1)
Sohler Weg 65, 56564, Neuwied, Germany
Tel.: (49) 263184152
Web Site: http://www.w-d.de
Emp.: 300
Business Support Services
N.A.I.C.S.: 561499
Frank Eichhorn (CEO, Mng Dir & Member-Mgmt Bd)

Zepf Technologies (1)
5320 140th Ave N, Clearwater, FL 33760-3743
Tel.: (727) 535-4100
Web Site: http://www.zepf.com
Sales Range: $10-24.9 Million
Emp.: 60
Container Filling & Handling Systems Mfr
N.A.I.C.S.: 423840
Frank J. Zepf (Pres)

BARSCO INC.
4309 N Beltwood Pkwy, Dallas, TX 75244-3214
Tel.: (972) 231-8206
Web Site: https://www.barsco.com
Sales Range: $10-24.9 Million
Emp.: 95
Refrigeration Equipment Whslr
N.A.I.C.S.: 423740
Todd Schulz (Mgr)

BARSON COMPOSITES CORP.
160 Sweet Hollow Rd, Old Bethpage, NY 11804
Tel.: (516) 752-7882
Web Site: https://www.hitemco.com
Year Founded: 1974
Sales Range: $10-24.9 Million
Emp.: 100
Painting, Coating & Hot Dipping
N.A.I.C.S.: 332812
Terrill E. Barnard (Chm)

BARSTEEL CORP
484 Central Ave, Highland Park, IL 60035
Tel.: (847) 432-4618
Web Site:
    http://www.barsteelcorp.com
Sales Range: $10-24.9 Million
Emp.: 3
Iron & Steel (Ferrous) Products
N.A.I.C.S.: 423510
Stuart Barnett (Pres)
Sharon Temple (Office Mgr)
Drew Barnett (Pres)

BARSTOW MOTORS INC.
154 Market St, Potsdam, NY 13676
Tel.: (315) 265-8800
Web Site:
    http://www.barstownmotors.com
Sales Range: $200-249.9 Million
Emp.: 30
Automobiles, New & Used
N.A.I.C.S.: 441110
John M. Barstow (Chm & Principal)
Peter Burnham (Mgr-Sls)

BART & ASSOCIATES INC.
8300 Greensboro Dr Ste 900, McLean, VA 22102-3640
Tel.: (703) 821-0030
Web Site: https://www.bna-inc.com
Sales Range: $10-24.9 Million
Emp.: 25
Computer Software Development & Applications
N.A.I.C.S.: 541511
Paul Mangus (Co-Founder & Exec VP)

Jonathan Evans (Pres)
Syd Boyne (Sr VP)
Sang Cao (Engr-Software Test)
Jesus Medrano (Pres)
Jeannette Bernardo (Chief Bus Dev Officer)

Subsidiaries:

iDoxSolutions, Inc. (1)
7910 Woodmont Ave Ste 230, Bethesda, MD 20814-7058
Tel.: (301) 656-2300
Web Site: http://www.idoxsolutions.com
Information Services
N.A.I.C.S.: 519290
Carl Muller (COO)

BART RICH ENTERPRISES INC.
6060 Court St Rd, Syracuse, NY 13206-1746
Tel.: (315) 463-7181
Web Site: https://www.bartrich.com
Sales Range: $25-49.9 Million
Emp.: 300
Fast-Food Restaurant, Chain
N.A.I.C.S.: 722513
Julie Clarke (Mgr-HR)

BARTECH SYSTEMS INTERNATIONAL INC.
6000 S Eastern Ave Ste 12 A-B-C-D, Las Vegas, NV 89119
Tel.: (702) 369-5550
Web Site: https://www.bartech.com
Year Founded: 1988
Sales Range: $10-24.9 Million
Emp.: 65
Minibar Technology Services
N.A.I.C.S.: 722410
Sophie Longevialle (Dir-Mktg)
Vicente Martin-Pascual (Pres)

BARTELS LUTHERAN RETIREMENT COMMUNITY
1922 5th Ave NW, Waverly, IA 50677
Tel.: (319) 352-4540   IA
Web Site:
    https://www.bartelscommunity.org
Year Founded: 1950
Sales Range: $10-24.9 Million
Emp.: 330
Elder Care Services
N.A.I.C.S.: 623312
Deb Schroeder (Pres & CEO)

BARTHEL CONTRACTING COMPANY
155 W Congress Ste 400, Detroit, MI 48226
Tel.: (313) 963-1744
Web Site:
    http://www.barthelcontracting.com
Sales Range: $10-24.9 Million
Emp.: 29
General Contractor, Highway & Street Construction
N.A.I.C.S.: 237310
Lee Barthel (Pres)
Earl Baxtresser (Mgr)

BARTHOLOMEW COUNTY RURAL ELECTRIC MEMBERSHIP CORPORATION
1697 W Deaver Rd, Columbus, IN 47201
Tel.: (812) 372-2546   IN
Web Site: https://www.bcremc.com
Year Founded: 1935
Sales Range: $25-49.9 Million
Emp.: 34
Electric Power Distr
N.A.I.C.S.: 221122
Marty Lasure (VP-Comm & Member Svcs)
Marvin Book (Mgr-Engrg)

Matt Hackman *(Mgr-Corp Svcs)*
Jim Turner *(CEO & Gen Mgr)*
Curt Burbrink *(Pres)*
Janet Anthony *(Sec)*
Dan Fleming *(Treas)*
Larry Hoeltke *(VP)*

BARTLETT & CO. LLC

600 Vine St Ste 2100, Cincinnati, OH
45202-3896
Tel.: (513) 621-4612
Web Site:
https://www.bartlett1898.com
Year Founded: 1898
Sales Range: $1-4.9 Billion
Emp.: 45
Investment Management & Financial
Planning Services
N.A.I.C.S.: 523940
James A. Miller *(Chm)*
Kelley J. Downing *(Pres, CEO & Principal)*
Thomas A. Steele *(CFO, Principal & VP)*
Terrence T. Kelly *(Principal)*
David P. Francis *(Principal)*
James B. Hagerty *(Principal)*
Kenneth L. Schlachter *(Principal)*
Troy R. Snider *(Principal)*
Matthew P. Whalen *(Dir-IT)*
Joseph J. Walburg *(Dir-Ops)*
Marcia Pennekamp *(Mgr-Acctg)*

BARTLETT & COMPANY

4900 Main St Ste 1200, Kansas City,
MO 64112-2509
Tel.: (816) 753-6300   MO
Web Site:
http://www.bartlettandco.com
Year Founded: 1907
Sales Range: $200-249.9 Million
Emp.: 700
Grain Merchandising & Storage
N.A.I.C.S.: 424510
James B. Hebenstreit *(Pres & CEO)*

Subsidiaries:

Bartlett Cattle Company, L.P.   **(1)**
4900 Main St Ste 1200, Kansas City, MO
64112
Tel.: (816) 753-6300
Cattle Feeding Services
N.A.I.C.S.: 112112

Bartlett Grain Company, L.P.   **(1)**
4900 Main St Ste 1200, Kansas City, MO
64112-2509
Tel.: (816) 753-6300
Web Site: http://www.bartlettgrain.com
Emp.: 100
Grain Merchandiser
N.A.I.C.S.: 455219
Arnie Wheeler *(Controller)*

Bartlett Milling Company, L.P.   **(1)**
701 S Center St, Statesville, NC 28677
Tel.: (704) 873-8956
Web Site: http://www.bartlettmillingfeed.com
Animal Feed Mfr
N.A.I.C.S.: 311119
Earl W. Law *(Mgr-Sls)*

BARTLETT BEARING COMPANY INC.

10901 Decatur Rd, Philadelphia, PA
19154-3210
Tel.: (215) 743-8963   PA
Web Site:
http://www.bartlettbearing.com
Year Founded: 1951
Sales Range: $10-24.9 Million
Emp.: 140
Independent Distr of Bearings & Repair Parts for Electro-Mechanical Facilities Nationwide
N.A.I.C.S.: 423840
Gayle Musser *(Pres)*
Bill Potts *(Mgr-Ops)*
Vic McDevitt *(Mgr-Sls-Electric Motor Repair Div)*

Subsidiaries:

Bartlett Bearing Company Inc.   **(1)**
1497 Delta Dr, Gastonia, NC 28052
Tel.: (704) 915-3020
Web Site: http://www.bartlettbearing.com
Sales Range: $10-24.9 Million
Emp.: 100
Independent Distributor of Bearings & Repair Parts for Electro-Mechanical Facilities
N.A.I.C.S.: 423840

BARTLETT BRAINARD EACOTT, INC.

70 Griffin Rd S, Bloomfield, CT
06002-1352
Tel.: (860) 242-5565   CT
Web Site: https://www.bbeinc.com
Year Founded: 1921
Sales Range: $50-74.9 Million
Emp.: 100
Commercial & Industrial Building
Construction
N.A.I.C.S.: 236220
Thomas E. Anderson *(Dir-Engrg)*
Jim Arnold *(Controller)*
James H. Eacott III *(Pres)*

BARTLETT COCKE, LP

8706 Lockway St, San Antonio, TX
78217-4837
Tel.: (210) 655-1031   TX
Web Site:
https://www.bartlettcocke.com
Year Founded: 1959
Sales Range: $200-249.9 Million
Emp.: 400
Provider of General Contracting Services
N.A.I.C.S.: 236220
Randall J. Pawelek *(Chm & CEO)*
Kevin Byrd *(VP-Ops-Central Texas Reg)*
James Anderson *(VP-Ops-South Texas)*
Nathan Olson *(VP-PreConstruction)*
James Deaven *(Controller)*
Roberto Rios *(CFO)*
Jerry Hoog *(Sr VP-Ops-South Texas)*
T. J. Rogers *(VP-Estimating)*
Marty Garza *(VP-Ops-East Texas)*

BARTLETT MANAGEMENT SERVICES

70 Clinton Plz, Clinton, IL 61727
Tel.: (217) 935-3939
Web Site: http://www.bartlettms.com
Year Founded: 1999
Sales Range: $10-24.9 Million
Emp.: 750
Fast-Food Restaurant, Chain
N.A.I.C.S.: 722513
Darrell J. Valenti *(Chm & Pres)*
Francis J. Jahn *(Gen Counsel & Asst Sec)*
Peter J. Grant *(Sr VP)*
Steven M. Nesbitt *(Treas, Sec & Exec VP)*
Troy G. Valenti *(VP-Real Estate & Acq)*

BARTON COUNTY ELECTRIC COOPERATIVE INC.

91 W 160 Hwy, Lamar, MO 64759
Tel.: (417) 682-5636
Web Site:
https://www.bartonelectric.com
Year Founded: 1934
Sales Range: $10-24.9 Million
Emp.: 40
Electric Power Distribution Services
N.A.I.C.S.: 221118
Russell McCorkle *(CEO & Gen Mgr)*

BARTON COUNTY IMPLEMENT CO

510 W 12th St, Lamar, MO 64759

Tel.: (417) 682-5556
Web Site: http://www.legacyfal.com
Sales Range: $10-24.9 Million
Emp.: 125
Farm Equipment Distr
N.A.I.C.S.: 444240
Jack A. Purinton *(Pres)*

BARTON ENTERPRISES INC.

1416 Upfield Dr, Carrollton, TX 75006
Tel.: (972) 242-2711
Web Site:
http://www.finelinepackaging.com
Sales Range: $10-24.9 Million
Emp.: 50
Holding Company: Quality Gift Wrap,
Custom Packaging
N.A.I.C.S.: 322299
Les Barton *(Pres)*

BARTON GILANELLI & ASSOCIATES, INC.

51 N Mascher St, Philadelphia, PA
19106-2205
Tel.: (215) 592-8601   PA
Web Site: http://www.bartgil.com
Year Founded: 1985
Sales Range: $1-9.9 Million
Emp.: 10
Advertising & Public Relations
Agency
N.A.I.C.S.: 541810
Frank Gilanelli *(Pres)*

BARTON MALOW ENTERPRISES, INC.

26500 American Dr, Southfield, MI
48034
Tel.: (248) 436-5000   MI
Web Site:
https://www.bartonmalow.com
Year Founded: 1924
Sales Range: $1-4.9 Billion
Emp.: 3,000
Commercial & Institutional Building
Construction
N.A.I.C.S.: 236220
Benjamin C. Maibach III *(Chief Community Officer)*
Alex Ivanikiw *(Exec VP)*
Chuck Binkowski *(COO & Exec VP)*
Ryan Maibach *(Pres)*

Subsidiaries:

Barton Malow Company   **(1)**
26500 American Dr, Southfield, MI
48034   **(100%)**
Tel.: (248) 436-5000
Web Site: http://www.bartonmalow.com
Sales Range: $25-49.9 Million
Emp.: 180
Construction Management & General Contracting
N.A.I.C.S.: 236220
Benjamin C. Maibach III *(Chm & CEO)*
David Price *(VP)*
Paul Moffat *(Dir-Preconstruction)*
Jeff Baxa *(VP-Preconstruction)*
Crystal Carter *(Mgr-Bus Dev-Atlanta)*
David Keesler *(Sr Project Mgr-Atlanta)*
Doug Maibach *(Vice Chm & Exec VP)*

Barton Malow Company   **(1)**
5900 Windward Pkwy Ste 130, Alpharetta,
GA 30005   **(100%)**
Tel.: (678) 448-1100
Web Site: http://www.bmco.com
Sales Range: $25-49.9 Million
Emp.: 12
Construction Management, General Contracting, Facilities Services, Rigging & Machinery Installation
N.A.I.C.S.: 236220
Benjamin C. Maibach III *(Chm & CEO)*
Rod Creach *(VP)*
Ryan Maibach *(Pres)*

Barton Malow Company   **(1)**
300 W Pratt St Ste 310, Baltimore, MD
21201-6503
Tel.: (443) 757-1000

Web Site: http://www.bartonmalow.com
Sales Range: $25-49.9 Million
Emp.: 27
Construction Management, General Contracting, Facilities Services, Rigging & Machinery Installation
N.A.I.C.S.: 236220
Benjamin C. Maibach III *(Chm & CEO)*
Bob Grottenthaler *(VP)*

Barton Malow Company   **(1)**
4000 Legato Rd Ste 750, Fairfax, VA 22033
Tel.: (703) 592-0880
Web Site: http://www.bartonmalow.com
Construction Management, General Contracting, Facilities Services, Rigging & Machinery Installation
N.A.I.C.S.: 541618

Barton Malow Design   **(1)**
26500 American Dr Ste 451, Southfield, MI
48034   **(100%)**
Tel.: (248) 436-5158
Web Site:
http://www.bartonmalowdesign.com
Sales Range: $25-49.9 Million
Emp.: 100
Architectural Design, Interior Design &
Space Planning
N.A.I.C.S.: 541310
Benjamin C. Maibach III *(Chm & CEO)*
Doug Maibach *(Vice Chm & Exec VP)*

Barton Malow Yard   **(1)**
21090 Fern St, Oak Park, MI 48237-3229
Tel.: (248) 548-5000
Web Site: http://www.bartonmalow.com
Sales Range: $25-49.9 Million
Emp.: 70
Heavy Machinery Rigging & Erection
N.A.I.C.S.: 238290

BARTON MINES COMPANY LLC

6 Warren St, Glens Falls, NY 12801-
3438
Tel.: (518) 798-5462   PA
Web Site: https://www.barton.com
Year Founded: 1878
Sales Range: $150-199.9 Million
Emp.: 300
Garnet Abrasives Mfr
N.A.I.C.S.: 212390
R. Randolph Rapple *(Pres)*
Richard Jenks *(CFO-The Barton Grp)*
C. H. Bracken *(Chm)*

Subsidiaries:

Virginia Abrasives Corporation   **(1)**
2851 Service Rd, Petersburg, VA 23805
Tel.: (804) 732-0058
Web Site: http://www.virginiaabrasives.com
Sales Range: $10-24.9 Million
Emp.: 50
Abrasive Products Mfr
N.A.I.C.S.: 327910
Spencer Parkins *(Pres)*

BARTON NELSON INC.

13700 Wyandotte St, Kansas City,
MO 64145-1532
Tel.: (816) 942-3100   KS
Web Site: http://www.bebco.com
Year Founded: 1962
Sales Range: $100-124.9 Million
Emp.: 200
Promotional Products Mfr
N.A.I.C.S.: 322230
Dwight Nelson *(Pres, CEO & COO)*
Chuck Nelson *(Pres-Sls Promo Div)*
Rich Laudie *(Controller)*
Jill Woltering *(Dir-HR)*
Phil Beltkamp *(VP-DP)*

BARTON SOLVENTS INC.

1920 NE Broadway Ave, Des Moines,
IA 50306
Tel.: (515) 265-7998   IL
Web Site: https://www.barsol.com
Year Founded: 1938
Sales Range: $50-74.9 Million
Emp.: 145

Barton Solvents Inc.—(Continued)
Distr of Chemicals & Allied Products
N.A.I.C.S.: 424690
Leon Casten *(Chm & CEO)*
Ed Walsh *(VP)*
David Casten *(Pres)*

BARTOS INDUSTRIES LLC
10350 Olympic Dr, Dallas, TX 75220
Tel.: (214) 350-6871
Web Site:
    https://www.bartosindustries.com
Rev.: $12,000,000
Emp.: 36
Warm Air Heating & Air Conditioning
N.A.I.C.S.: 423730
William Shaw *(Pres)*
Spencer Shaw *(VP)*
Bill Barnes *(Engr-Sls)*
Pam Robertson *(Mgr-Staff Ops)*

BARUCH SLS, INC.
3196 Kraft Ave SE Ste 200, Grand
Rapids, MI 49512
Tel.: (616) 285-0563   MI
Web Site: http://www.baruchsls.org
Year Founded: 1997
Sales Range: $10-24.9 Million
Emp.: 333
Elder Care Services
N.A.I.C.S.: 623312
Connie Clauson *(VP-Ops)*
Thomas J. Nobel *(Founder & Co-Pres)*
Chris Murphy *(Treas & Sec)*

BARZ, GOWIE, AMON & FULTZ LLC
411 Old BAltimore Pike Ste 201,
Chadds Ford, PA 19317
Tel.: (610) 388-7800   DE
Web Site:
    http://www.barszgowie.com
Year Founded: 2017
Accounting & Auditing Firm
N.A.I.C.S.: 541219
William B. Gowie *(Mng Partner)*

BAS BROADCASTING, INC.
1281 N River Rd, Fremont, OH
43420
Tel.: (419) 332-8218   OH
Web Site: https://www.basohio.com
Year Founded: 2002
Sales Range: $10-24.9 Million
Emp.: 50
Radio Broadcasting Stations
N.A.I.C.S.: 516110
Tom Klein *(Pres)*
Jon Kerns *(Dir-Program)*

Subsidiaries:

BAS Broadcasting - Mount
Vernon   (1)
17421 Coshocton Rd, Mount Vernon, OH
43050
Tel.: (740) 397-1000
Web Site: http://www.basohio.com
Sales Range: $10-24.9 Million
Emp.: 12
Radio Broadcasting Stations
N.A.I.C.S.: 516110
Tom Klein *(Pres)*

BAS Broadcasting - Sandusky (1)
1640 Cleveland Rd, Sandusky, OH 44870-4357
Tel.: (419) 625-1010
Web Site: http://www.basohio.com
Sales Range: $10-24.9 Million
Emp.: 20
Radio Broadcasting Stations
N.A.I.C.S.: 516110
Tom Klein *(CEO)*

BAS PART SALES LLC
575 Ed Beegles LN, Greeley, CO
80631

Tel.: (970) 313-4823
Web Site: https://baspartsales.com
Emp.: 100
Aircraft Equipment & Supplies Merchant Whslr
N.A.I.C.S.: 423860
Jared Boles *(Pres)*

Subsidiaries:

White Industries, Inc.   (1)
N Outer Rd, Bates City, MO 64011
Tel.: (816) 690-8800
Web Site: http://www.whiteindustries.com
Sales Range: $1-9.9 Million
Emp.: 30
Whol Aircraft Parts
N.A.I.C.S.: 423860

BASA RESOURCES INC.
14875 Landmark Blvd 4th Fl, Dallas,
TX 75254
Tel.: (214) 559-4200
Web Site:
    https://www.basaresources.com
Sales Range: $10-24.9 Million
Emp.: 25
Crude Petroleum Production
N.A.I.C.S.: 211120
Michael N. Foster *(Co-Founder & Pres)*
Lary D. Knowlton *(Co-Founder & Exec VP)*
Steve Limke *(VP-Drilling)*

BASCO MANUFACTURING COMPANY
7201 Snider Rd, Mason, OH 45040
Tel.: (513) 573-1900
Web Site:
    https://www.bascoshowerdoor.com
Rev.: $30,220,000
Emp.: 163
Glass Door Mfr
N.A.I.C.S.: 327215

BASCOM HUNTER TECHNOLOGIES INC.
1 Bascom Way, Baton Rouge, LA
70809
Tel.: (225) 590-3553
Web Site:
    http://www.bascomhunter.com
Year Founded: 2011
Technological Networking & Communication Solutions
N.A.I.C.S.: 541330
Andrew McCandless *(Pres)*

Subsidiaries:

Seamech International, Inc.   (1)
24 Greenway Plaza #440, Houston, TX
77046
Tel.: (713) 660-0976
Web Site: http://www.seamech.com
Engineering Services
N.A.I.C.S.: 541330
Blaine Streeter *(Founder & Pres)*
Mike Gould *(Dir-Procurement & Mgr-Production)*
Mike Harness *(VP-Production Programs)*

Xcelaero Corp.   (1)
4540 Broad St Ste 120, San Luis Obispo,
CA 93401
Tel.: (877) 925-2376
Web Site: http://www.xcelaero.com
Analytical Laboratory Instrument Mfr
N.A.I.C.S.: 334516

BASCOM'S CHOP HOUSE
3665 Ulmerton Rd, Clearwater, FL
33762
Tel.: (727) 573-3363   FL
Web Site: https://www.bascoms.com
Year Founded: 2001
Sales Range: $1-9.9 Million
Emp.: 45
Restaurant
N.A.I.C.S.: 722511

Charles Macatee *(Mgr-Events)*

BASE CRAFT LLC
1200 Edwards Ave, Harahan, LA
70123
Tel.: (504) 305-2170
Web Site:
    http://www.basecraftllc.com
Year Founded: 2001
Truck, Utility Trailer & Recreational
Vehicle Rental & Leasing
N.A.I.C.S.: 532120
Jeffrey Gowing *(Co-Owner & Co-CEO)*
Welch Labeth *(Co-Owner & Co-CEO)*
Hunter Andrews *(COO)*
Stephanie Hilton *(CFO)*

Subsidiaries:

Hollywood Trucks, LLC   (1)
Raleigh Studios Celtic Media Centre 10000
Celtic Dr, Baton Rouge, LA 70809
Tel.: (225) 330-6126
Web Site: http://www.hollywoodtrucksllc.com
Sales Range: $1-9.9 Million
Emp.: 12
Transportation & Logistics to the Entertainment Industry
N.A.I.C.S.: 488510
Andre J. Champagne *(Founder & CEO)*
John DeVay *(Partner)*

BASE ENGINEERING INC.
1010 N Quebec St, Allentown, PA
18109
Tel.: (610) 437-0978
Web Site: https://www.baseeng.com
Year Founded: 1979
Sales Range: $1-9.9 Million
Emp.: 15
Technical & Consulting Engineering
Services
N.A.I.C.S.: 541330
Amit Mukherjee *(Pres & Principal Engr)*

BASE INTELLIGENCE, INC
2803 Western Trails Blvd, Austin, TX
78745
Tel.: (512) 548-4057   DE
Web Site: http://www.ba.se
Privater Equity Firm
N.A.I.C.S.: 523999
J. R. Kraft *(Founder & CEO)*
Cameron Lord *(CFO & Chief Investment Officer)*

Subsidiaries:

Move, Inc.   (1)
109 Brookville Ln, Lewistown, MT 59457
Tel.: (406) 366-2341
Web Site: http://www.movebumpers.com
Truck Bumper Mfr & Distr
N.A.I.C.S.: 336390
Lacey Steen *(Founder)*

BASE-LINE, INC.
30 Main St Ste 406, Danbury, CT
06810
Tel.: (203) 925-0240
Web Site: http://www.base-line.com
Press & Pre-Press Supplies Distr
N.A.I.C.S.: 423990
Howard E. Harper *(Pres & CEO)*

Subsidiaries:

GraphLine Inc.   (1)
1100 International Pkwy Ste 100, Sunrise,
FL 33323
Tel.: (954) 722-3000
Sales Range: $75-99.9 Million
Emp.: 100
Photo Electronic Imaging, Graphic Arts
Cameras & Computer Equipment Distr
N.A.I.C.S.: 423990

BASEBALL AMERICA, INC.
4319 S Alston Ave Ste 103, Durham,
NC 27713

Tel.: (919) 682-9635   NC
Web Site:
    https://www.baseballamerica.com
Year Founded: 1981
Baseball Trade Magazine Publisher
N.A.I.C.S.: 513120
J. J. Cooper *(Exec Editor)*
Matt Eddy *(Exec Editor)*

BASEBALLISM, INC.
2215 NW Quimby St, Portland, OR
97210
Tel.: (503) 206-6738
Web Site:
    http://www.baseballism.com
Year Founded: 2012
Sales Range: $10-24.9 Million
Emp.: 200
Family Clothing Retailer
N.A.I.C.S.: 458110
Travis Chock *(Founder & CEO)*

BASELINE SPORTS, INC.
5257 Cleveland St, Virginia Beach,
VA 23452
Tel.: (757) 626-1520
Sales Range: $1-9.9 Million
Emp.: 8
Furniture Mfr
N.A.I.C.S.: 337121
Red Barnes *(Owner)*

BASHAS' SUPERMARKETS
22402 S Basha Rd, Chandler, AZ
85248-4908
Tel.: (480) 895-5369   AZ
Web Site: http://www.bashas.com
Year Founded: 1932
Sales Range: $1-4.9 Billion
Emp.: 14,300
Retail Grocery Stores
N.A.I.C.S.: 445110
Robert Ortiz *(Sr VP-Ops)*
Karen Giroux *(Dir-Ops)*
Steve Mayer *(COO)*
Edward Basha *(Pres)*

BASHOR & LEGENDRE, LLP
4809 Ehrlich Rd Ste 203, Tampa, FL
33624
Tel.: (813) 961-3220
Web Site: https://www.blcpas.com
Sales Range: $1-9.9 Million
Emp.: 32
Certified Public Accountants
N.A.I.C.S.: 541211
Thomasena L. Bashor *(Partner)*
Percy J. Legendre III *(Mng Partner)*

BASIC ADHESIVES INC.
60 Webro Rd, Clifton, NJ 07012
Tel.: (201) 294-8423
Web Site:
    https://www.basicadhesives.com
Year Founded: 1960
Sales Range: $10-24.9 Million
Emp.: 40
Adhesives
N.A.I.C.S.: 325520
Yale E. Block *(Pres)*

BASIC AMERICAN FOODS, INC.
2999 Oak Rd Ste 800, Walnut Creek,
CA 94597
Tel.: (925) 472-4000   CA
Web Site: http://www.baf.com
Year Founded: 1933
Sales Range: $1-4.9 Billion
Emp.: 2,500
Dehydrated Potatoe Onion Garlic &
Refried Bean Mfr
N.A.I.C.S.: 311423
Bryan Reese *(Pres & CEO)*

Subsidiaries:

Basic American Foods, Inc. - Moses
Lake Processing Plant **(1)**
538 Potato Frontage Rd, Moses Lake, WA
98837
Tel.: (509) 765-8601
Vegetable Distr
N.A.I.C.S.: 424480

BASIC CARBIDE CORP
900 Main St, Lowber, PA 15660
Tel.: (724) 446-1630 PA
Web Site:
https://www.basiccarbide.com
Year Founded: 1981
Sales Range: $10-24.9 Million
Emp.: 100
Tungsten Carbide Preforms Mfr
N.A.I.C.S.: 327910
John Goodrum (Pres)
Jennifer Sampson (VP)
Jared P. Filapose (Gen Mgr-Sls)
Michael Ulyan (Mgr-Customer Svcs)

BASIC COMMERCE AND IN-DUSTRIES, INC.
304 Harper Dr Ste 203, Moorestown,
NJ 08057
Tel.: (856) 778-1660
Web Site: http://www.bcisse.com
Year Founded: 1981
Rev.: $30,800,000
Emp.: 216
Information Technology Services
N.A.I.C.S.: 541330
Frank Caruso (VP)

BASIC CONSTRUCTION COM-PANY
538 Oyster Point Rd, Newport News,
VA 23602-0000
Tel.: (757) 249-3789 VA
Web Site:
http://www.basicconstructionco.com
Year Founded: 1915
Sales Range: $125-149.9 Million
Emp.: 165
Construction of Asphalt Highways;
Utility Contractors
N.A.I.C.S.: 237310
C. Derek Patterson (Pres)
Lawrence Myers (VP-Fin)

Subsidiaries:

Basic Construction Company - New
Kent Facility **(1)**
7701 Parham Landing Rd, New Kent, VA
23181
Tel.: (804) 843-3905
Sales Range: $25-49.9 Million
Emp.: 100
Construction Services
N.A.I.C.S.: 237990
Derek Patterson (Gen Mgr)

Basic Construction Company - Oyster
Point Facility **(1)**
538 Oyster Point Rd, Newport News, VA
23602
Tel.: (757) 249-3801
Construction Services
N.A.I.C.S.: 237990

BASIC FUN, INC.
301 Yamato Rd Ste 2112, Boca Ra-
ton, FL 33431
Tel.: (561) 997-8901 DE
Web Site: http://www.basicfun.com
Children's Toy Mfr
N.A.I.C.S.: 339930
Jon Roman (VP-Mktg)

BASIC GRAIN PRODUCTS INC.
300 E Vine St, Coldwater, OH 45828
Tel.: (419) 678-2304
Year Founded: 1994
Sales Range: $10-24.9 Million

Emp.: 100
Cookie & Cracker Mfr
N.A.I.C.S.: 311821
Michael Chu (Sr VP-IT Svs)
Carol Knapke (Mgr-Sls)
Mark Aleong (Mgr-Ops)
Brent Aleong (CTO)
Jennifer Moe (Acct Coord)

BASIC MATERIALS
712 N Wall St, Calhoun, GA 30701
Tel.: (706) 629-2256
Web Site:
http://www.basicreadymix.com
Sales Range: $10-24.9 Million
Emp.: 25
Ready Mixed Concrete
N.A.I.C.S.: 327320
Tony Cantrell (Pres)
Tom Waguespack (VP)

BASIC RESOURCES INC.
928 12th St Ste 700, Modesto, CA
95354
Tel.: (209) 521-9771
Rev.: $55,000,000
Emp.: 50
Highway & Street Paving Contractor
N.A.I.C.S.: 237310
Wendy Stephens (Asst Mgr-Acctg)
Jack Van Kirk (Dir-Asphalt Tech)

BASIC SALES & MARKETING
1930 S Miles Stone Dr Ste A, Salt
Lake City, UT 84104
Tel.: (801) 363-4500
Web Site: http://www.basicsales.net
Rev.: $22,500,000
Emp.: 10
Bond Brokers
N.A.I.C.S.: 424410
Richard Balderston (Pres)

BASIN ELECTRIC POWER CO-OPERATIVE
1717 E Interstate Ave, Bismarck, ND
58503-0564
Tel.: (701) 223-0441 ND
Web Site:
https://www.basinelectric.com
Year Founded: 1961
Sales Range: $1-4.9 Billion
Emp.: 2,000
Electric Power Generation, Transmis-
sion & Distribution; Coal Gasification;
Bituminous Coal & Lignite Surface
N.A.I.C.S.: 221118
Shawn Deisz (VP & Controller)
Kermit Pearson (VP)
David Raatz (Sr VP-Asset Mgmt, Re-
source Plng & Rates)
Paul Sukut (CEO & Gen Mgr)
Mike Eggl (Sr VP-Comm & Admin)
Wayne Peltier (Pres)
Mike Risan (Sr VP-Transmission)
Mark Foss (Gen Counsel & Sr VP)
Chris Baumgartner (Sr VP-Member
Svcs & Admin)
Diane Paul (Sr VP-HR)
Steve Johnson (CFO & Sr VP)
Tom Christensen (Sr VP-
Transmission, Engrg & Construction)

Subsidiaries:

Basin Telecommunication, Inc. **(1)**
1717 E Interstate Ave, Bismarck, ND
58503-0542
Tel.: (701) 223-0441
Web Site: http://www.basin.com
Sales Range: $10-24.9 Million
Emp.: 15
Providers of Power Distribution Services
N.A.I.C.S.: 561421

Dakota Coal Company **(1)**
1717 E Interstate Ave, Bismarck, ND
58506-5540 **(100%)**
Tel.: (701) 223-0441

Web Site: http://www.basinelectric.com
Sales Range: $150-199.9 Million
Emp.: 400
N.A.I.C.S.: 221122
Ron Harper (COO & Gen Mgr)

Subsidiary (Domestic):

Montana Limestone Company **(2)**
PO Box 166, Frannie, WY 82423-0166
Tel.: (406) 764-2513
Web Site: http://www.basinelectric.com
Emp.: 16
Limestone Product Producer
N.A.I.C.S.: 212312

Dakota Gasification Company **(1)**
420 County Rd 26, Beulah, ND 58523-9400
Tel.: (701) 223-0441
Web Site: http://www.dakotagas.com
Sales Range: $150-199.9 Million
Emp.: 700
Electric Power Distr
N.A.I.C.S.: 221122
Dale Johnson (Mgr-Plant)
Dave Sauer (COO & Sr VP)
Paul Sukut (CEO & Gen Mgr-Basin Electric
Power Cooperative)
Allen Thiessen (Chm)

BASKETRY BY PHINA, LLC
425 Harrison Avenue, New Orleans,
LA 70124
Tel.: (504) 571-5169
Web Site: https://phinashop.com
Gift Shop
N.A.I.C.S.: 459420
Jenny McGuinness (Co-Founder &
Co-Owner)
Jessica Woodward (Co-Founder &
Co-Owner)

Subsidiaries:

Basketry Inc. **(1)**
12337 Hwy 90, Luling, LA 70070
Tel.: (985) 578-8769
Web Site: http://www.thebasketry.com
Gift, Novelty & Souvenir Stores
N.A.I.C.S.: 459420
Kristi Brocata (CEO & Founder)

BASKIN GROUP LIMITED
10203 Birchridge Dr Ste 500,
Humble, TX 77338-2227
Tel.: (936) 327-7140
Year Founded: 1972
Rev.: $24,160,742
Emp.: 13
Shoe Stores
N.A.I.C.S.: 458210
Don Baskin (Owner)

BASKIN TRUCK & TRACTOR, INC.
1844 Hwy 51 S, Covington, TN
38019-3622
Tel.: (901) 476-2626
Web Site:
http://www.baskintrandtr.com
Year Founded: 1957
Sales Range: $10-24.9 Million
Emp.: 50
New Car Whslr
N.A.I.C.S.: 441110
Donald Baskin Sr. (Principal)

BASLER ELECTRIC COMPANY
Rte 143, Highland, IL 62249
Tel.: (618) 654-2341 IL
Web Site: http://www.basler.com
Year Founded: 1942
Sales Range: $350-399.9 Million
Emp.: 1,090
Custom Transformers & Electric
Power Control Systems, Double
Sided Printed Circuit Boards Mfr
N.A.I.C.S.: 335311
William L. Basler (Chm, CEO &
Treas)
Gary D. Dolbeare (Pres & COO)

Gregory S. Basler (Exec VP)
Kenneth S. Parker (Sec & VP-Fin)
Matthew L. Basle (VP-Engrg)

Subsidiaries:

Basler Electric (Suzhou) Co., Ltd **(1)**
No 59 Heshun Rd, Loufeng District,
215122, Suzhou, China
Tel.: (86) 512 8227 2888
Web Site: http://www.Basler.com.cn
Emp.: 20
Excitation Control System Mfr
N.A.I.C.S.: 335999
Minthu Cao (Gen Mgr)

Basler Electric Company (Singapore)
Pte Ltd. **(1)**
111 North Bridge Road, 15-06 Peninsula
Plaza, Singapore, 179098, Singapore
Tel.: (65) 68446445
Web Site: http://www.basler.com
Emp.: 6
Electric Power Equipment Supplier
N.A.I.C.S.: 423610

Basler Electric Company - Basler
Electric Facility **(1)**
Interior Edificio 14, Piedras Negras, Coa-
huila, 26070, Mexico
Tel.: (52) 8787834644
Sales Range: $50-74.9 Million
Emp.: 400
Electric Equipment Mfr
N.A.I.C.S.: 334419

Basler Electric Company - Basler
Electric Facility **(1)**
204 Highland Dr, Taylor, TX 76574
Tel.: (512) 352-3154
Web Site: http://www.basler.com
Sales Range: $25-49.9 Million
Emp.: 45
Electric Equipment Mfr
N.A.I.C.S.: 334419
Anita Voyles (Gen Mgr)

Basler Electric France SAS **(1)**
27 Rue des Pins, Wasselonne, 67319,
France
Tel.: (33) 388871010
Web Site: http://www.basler.com
Sales Range: $10-24.9 Million
Emp.: 60
Electric Equipment Mfr
N.A.I.C.S.: 334419
Claude Ohlmann (Mgr-Fin)
Yves Chatelet (Mgr-HR)

Basler Plastics LLC **(1)**
201 Centerpoint Rd, San Marcos, TX 78666
Tel.: (512) 392-2800
Web Site: http://www.baslerplasticsllc.com
Sales Range: $25-49.9 Million
Emp.: 400
Plastics Product Mfr
N.A.I.C.S.: 326199
Kelly Beegle (Gen Mgr)

BASLER TURBO CONVER-SIONS, LLC.
255 W 35th Ave, Oshkosh, WI
54903-2305
Tel.: (920) 236-7820
Web Site:
https://www.baslerturbo.com
Sales Range: $50-74.9 Million
Emp.: 65
Aircraft Mfr
N.A.I.C.S.: 336411
Carrie Chappa (Controller)
Randy Myers (Dir-Production & En-
grg)
Brandon Saladin (Mgr-Matls & Cus-
tomer Support)

BASMAT INC.
1531W 240th St, Harbor City, CA
90710
Tel.: (310) 325-2063
Web Site: https://www.mcstarlite.com
Year Founded: 1955
Sales Range: $10-24.9 Million
Emp.: 95
Sheet Metalwork Mfr

Basmat Inc.—(Continued)
N.A.I.C.S.: 332322
John Basso (Pres)

BASS COMPUTERS INC.
10558 Bissonnet St, Houston, TX
77099
Tel.: (281) 776-6700   TX
Web Site:
https://www.basscomputers.com
Year Founded: 1991
Sales Range: $10-24.9 Million
Emp.: 80
Computers, Peripherals & Software
Provider
N.A.I.C.S.: 423430
Desiree Plumadore (Mgr-Acctg)
Aaron Reyna (Mgr-Sls)
Jason vonCordsen (Gen Mgr)
Melvin Alvie Hall Jr. (Pres & CEO)

BASS PROPERTIES, INC.
1291 Oleander Dr SW, Lilburn, GA
30047
Tel.: (770) 925-8879
Web Site:
http://www.basspropertiesinc.com
Sales Range: $10-24.9 Million
Emp.: 10
Home Builder Services
N.A.I.C.S.: 236115
Thomas W. Bass (CEO & CFO)
Thomas W. Bass Jr. (Sec)

BASSANI MANUFACTURING
2900 E La Jolla St, Anaheim, CA
92806-1305
Tel.: (714) 630-1821   CA
Web Site: http://www.bassani.com
Year Founded: 1969
Sales Range: $50-74.9 Million
Emp.: 45
Mfr of Motorcycle Exhaust Systems,
Tube Bending & Display Fixtures
N.A.I.C.S.: 332710
Darryl Bassani (Pres)
Frank Petersen (Supvr-Production)

BASSET CREEK CAPITAL,
INC.
1350 Douglas Dr Ste 117, Golden
Valley, MN 55422
Tel.: (612) 308-5741
Web Site:
https://www.bassettcreekcapital.com
Privater Equity Firm
N.A.I.C.S.: 523999
Rob Bauer (Mng Partner)

Subsidiaries:

J.R. Johnson, Inc.   (1)
9425 N Burrage Ave, Portland, OR 97217-
6966
Tel.: (503) 240-3388
Web Site: http://www.jrjohnsoninc.com
Sales Range: $1-9.9 Million
Building Repair & Restoration Services
N.A.I.C.S.: 238990
Clint Arp (Co-Pres & Partner)
Del Starr (Co-Pres & Partner)

BASSETT-HYLAND ENERGY
COMPANY
425 W Lockhart Ave, Coos Bay, OR
97420
Tel.: (541) 267-2107
Web Site:
http://www.bassetthyland.com
Sales Range: $10-24.9 Million
Emp.: 50
Petroleum Bulk Stations
N.A.I.C.S.: 424710
Scott Bassett (Pres)

BASSOTECH INC.

2981 W Commercial Blvd, Fort Lau-
derdale, FL 33309
Tel.: (954) 578-5005
Web Site: http://www.bassotech.com
Rev.: $13,865,627
Emp.: 17
Computer & Photocopying Supplies
N.A.I.C.S.: 424120
Al Debrito (Pres)

BAST HATFIELD INC.
1399 Crescent Vischer Ferry Rd Ste
2, Clifton Park, NY 12065
Tel.: (518) 373-2000
Web Site:
https://www.basthatfield.com
Sales Range: $150-199.9 Million
Emp.: 400
Civil Engineering Services
N.A.I.C.S.: 237310
Walt Rafferty (Product Mgr)

BASTA HOLDINGS, CORP.
1111 Kane Concourse Ste 518, Bay
Harbor Islands, FL 33154
Tel.: (305) 867-1228   NV
Year Founded: 2011
Sales Range: $1-9.9 Million
Emp.: 6
Copper Pipes & Fittings Distr
N.A.I.C.S.: 423510
Jacob Gitman (Pres)
Sophie Xue (VP-China & Asia Pa-
cific)
David Gitman (Project Mgr)
Michael S. Delin (CFO)
Dan Oran (CEO)

BASTIAN SOLUTIONS
10585 N Meridian St 3rd Fl, Carmel,
IN 46290
Tel.: (317) 575-9992
Web Site:
https://www.bastiansolutions.com
Year Founded: 1952
Sales Range: $125-149.9 Million
Emp.: 351
System Engineering, Design, Con-
sulting, Simulation, Project Manage-
ment & Automation Technologies
N.A.I.C.S.: 541715
Aaron Jones (Pres)
Eric Brunkow (Dir-Mktg)
Eric Cameron (VP-Software Sls)
Mark Colzani (Mgr-Corp Ops)
Derek Cribley (Dir-Advanced Tech)
Ron Daggett (VP-Controls Engrg)
Gregg Durham (Sec)
Lisa Rohe (Controller)
John Smith (CFO & Treas)
Greg Conner (VP-Sls)
Marvin Logan (VP-Consulting)
Ryan Petrancosta (Dir-Sys Engrg)
Stefanie Hardy (Mgr-Mktg)
Christopher Dyjak (Mgr-Cincinnati)
Jason Nowak (Dir-Bastian Robotics)
Demir Kantardzic (Pres-Software Div)
Bill Bastian II (Chm)

BAT INVESTMENTS, INC.
7910 Mowinkle Dr, Austin, TX 78736
Tel.: (512) 740-6665   TX
Year Founded: 2020
Financial Services
N.A.I.C.S.: 523999
Robert Priestley (Co-Founder & CEO)
Tanya Miller (Co-Founder & Pres)

BATANGA, INC.
2121 Ponce De Leon Blvd, Coral
Gables, FL 33134
Tel.: (305) 476-2974
Web Site:
http://www.batanganetwork.com
Year Founded: 1999
Sales Range: $25-49.9 Million

Emp.: 150
Digital Media Services
N.A.I.C.S.: 541890
Rafael Urbina (CEO)
Manny Borges (CFO)
Carlos Luchsinger (VP-Ops)
Natalia Borges (VP-Mktg)
Guillermo Abud (Head-Global Bus &
Programmatic)
Alexandre Jordao (Chief Revenue
Officer)
Rafael Garcia (VP-Content Dev)
Santiago Pehar (VP-Product)

BATCHELDER & COLLINS
INC.
2305 Granby St, Norfolk, VA 23517
Tel.: (757) 625-2506
Web Site: http://www.batchelder-
brick.com
Sales Range: $10-24.9 Million
Emp.: 50
Brick Sales
N.A.I.C.S.: 423320
Frank W. Wozniak (Pres)

BATEMAN BROTHERS LUM-
BER CO., INC.
89 Sand Rd, New Britain, PA 18901-
5122
Tel.: (215) 345-7331   DE
Web Site:
https://www.batemanlumber.com
Year Founded: 1946
Sales Range: $75-99.9 Million
Emp.: 30
Mfr & Retailer of Imported & Domes-
tic Lumber
N.A.I.C.S.: 423310

Subsidiaries:

E.D. Collier & Son   (1)
21 Reid St, Woodbury, NJ 08096-3219
Tel.: (856) 845-8100
Web Site: http://www.batemanlumber.com
Sales Range: $10-24.9 Million
Emp.: 15
Mfr & Distributor of Forest Products
N.A.I.C.S.: 423310

BATEMAN-HALL INC
1405 Foote Dr, Idaho Falls, ID 83402
Tel.: (208) 523-2681
Web Site: https://www.bateman-
hall.com
Sales Range: $50-74.9 Million
Emp.: 45
Commercial & Office Building New
Construction
N.A.I.C.S.: 236220
Ben Christensen (Project Mgr)
Doil Clements (Project Mgr)
Shay Moon (Pres)

BATES
ENGINEERS/CONTRACTORS
INC.
210 Airport Rd, Bainbridge, GA 39817
Tel.: (229) 246-4312   GA
Web Site: https://www.batesinc.com
Year Founded: 1962
Sales Range: $10-24.9 Million
Emp.: 120
Industrial Buildings & Warehouses
N.A.I.C.S.: 236210
Steven M. Lee (Pres)
Andrew Eckenrode (Mgr-CAD)
John Beers (VP)

BATES GROUP LLC
5005 Meadows Rd Ste 300, Lake
Oswego, OR 97035-5272
Tel.: (503) 670-7772
Web Site:
http://www.batesgroupllc.com
Year Founded: 1981

Investigation Services
N.A.I.C.S.: 561611
Jennifer Stout (Vice Chm)
Edward Longridge (Mng Dir-Financial
Crimes Practice-New York)
Benjamin R. Pappas (CEO)
Alex Russell (Mng Dir-Securities Liti-
gation & Regulatory Enforcement)
Julie R. Johnstone (Mng Dir-Retail
Litigation)
Andrew C. Daniel (Dir-Securities Liti-
gation Expert & Consultant)
Scott E. Lucas (Mng Dir-Regulatory &
Internal Investigations)
Josephine Vu (Dir-People & Culture)
Peter J. Klouda (Dir-Ops)
Ira D. Hammerman (Mng Dir)
Rob Lee (Chm)

Subsidiaries:

The Advisors Resource, Inc   (1)
6 Peony Springs Court, Spring, TX 77382-
2534
Tel.: (281) 298-7015
Web Site: http://www.batesgroup.com
Management Consulting Services
N.A.I.C.S.: 541618
Linda Shirkey (Founder & Pres)

BATES NISSAN INC.
5501 E Central Texas Expy, Killeen,
TX 76543
Tel.: (254) 987-6058
Web Site:
https://www.batesnissan.com
Year Founded: 1974
Sales Range: $10-24.9 Million
Emp.: 39
Car Whslr
N.A.I.C.S.: 441110
Bobby Bates (Owner)
John Johnston (Coord-Customer
Care)

BATES RV
4656 Mcintosh Rd, Dover, FL 33527-
4132
Tel.: (813) 659-0008
Web Site: http://www.batesrv.com
Sales Range: $10-24.9 Million
Emp.: 80
Recreational Vehicle Whslr
N.A.I.C.S.: 441210
Frank Bates (Owner)

BATES RV EXCHANGE
1018 US 41 Bypass, Venice, FL
34285-4335
Tel.: (941) 484-0001
Web Site: https://www.batesrv.com
Year Founded: 1986
Sales Range: $10-24.9 Million
Emp.: 80
Recreational Vehicle Whslr
N.A.I.C.S.: 441210
Frank Bates (Owner)

BATES SALES COMPANY INC.
5211 Northrup Ave, Saint Louis, MO
63110
Tel.: (314) 865-5211
Web Site:
http://www.batessalesco.com
Sales Range: $10-24.9 Million
Emp.: 30
Industrial Power Transmission
N.A.I.C.S.: 423610
Mike Adorjan (Pres)
Bob Cross (Controller)

BATES WHITE, LLC.
2001 K St NW N Bldg Ste 500,
Washington, DC 20006
Tel.: (202) 408-6110
Web Site:
https://www.bateswhite.com
Rev.: $7,300,000

Emp.: 120
Administrative Management & General Management Consulting Service
N.A.I.C.S.: 541611
Marc Scarcella (Mgr)
Charles Bates (Chm)
Meghan Benson (Mgr-HR)
Stacy Reyan (Chief People Officer)

BATES/LEE ADVERTISING
2950 Airway Ave Ste A9, Costa Mesa, CA 92626
Tel.: (714) 549-1757
Web Site: http://www.bates-lee.com
Year Founded: 1975
Rev.: $11,000,000
Emp.: 14
N.A.I.C.S.: 541810
Laura Lamude (Dir-Client Svcs)

BATESVILLE TOOL & DIE INC.
177 6 Pine Ranch Rd, Batesville, IN 47006
Tel.: (812) 934-5616
Web Site: http://www.btdinc.com
Sales Range: $75-99.9 Million
Emp.: 425
Metal Stamping
N.A.I.C.S.: 332119
Jody Fledderman (Chm & CEO)
Robert Holtel (Pres)

BATH COMMUNITY HOSPITAL
106 Park Ln, Hot Springs, VA 24445
Tel.: (540) 839-7000   VA
Web Site: http://www.bathhospital.org
Year Founded: 1925
Sales Range: $10-24.9 Million
Emp.: 167
Health Care Srvices
N.A.I.C.S.: 622110
Peter Faraone (Chm)
Kathy Landreth (CEO)
Deb Shipman (CFO)

BATH SAVER INC.
542 Industrial Dr, Lewisberry, PA 17339
Tel.: (717) 932-2500
Web Site: http://www.bathsaver.com
Rev.: $12,000,000
Emp.: 45
Single-Family Home Remodeling, Additions & Repairs
N.A.I.C.S.: 236118
Frank Ciccocioppo (VP-Sls)

BATH SAVINGS INSTITUTION
105 Front St, Bath, ME 04530
Tel.: (207) 442-7711
Web Site:
   http://www.bathsavings.com
Year Founded: 1852
Sales Range: $10-24.9 Million
Emp.: 300
Savings Institutions, Except Federal
N.A.I.C.S.: 522180
Glenn L. Hutchinson (Pres)
Barbara L. Gaul (VP-Mktg)
Michael W. Celeste (VP-Comml Lending)
Susan G. Carleton (Sr VP-HR)
Julia R. DeBery (Sr VP-Risk Mgmt & Internal Audit)
Joel E. Morley (VP-Facilities)
Sherry Y. Tremblay (Exec VP-Mortgage Lending)
Julie A. Wagoner (VP)
Maria E. Brown (VP-Ops)
Patricia A. Bernier (CIO & VP)
Mara K. Pennell (VP)
Marcia H. Hennessey (VP)
Michelle B. Farrin (VP)
Patty A. Erickson (VP)
Rebecca C. Launer (Sr VP)
Sharon M. Brobst (VP)

Theresa B. Hodge (VP)
Tyler Zamore (VP)
Virginia R. Hatch (VP)
Linda W. Anderson (VP)

BATJER SERVICE
2825 Pine St, Abilene, TX 79601-1535
Tel.: (325) 673-2556
Web Site: https://www.batjer.com
Year Founded: 1947
Sales Range: $10-24.9 Million
Emp.: 15
Plumbing Services
N.A.I.C.S.: 238220
Mark Sutphen (Gen Mgr)

BATON ROUGE AREA FOUNDATION
402 N 4th St, Baton Rouge, LA 70802
Tel.: (225) 387-6126   LA
Web Site: http://www.braf.org
Year Founded: 1964
Sales Range: $10-24.9 Million
Emp.: 29
Community Welfare Services
N.A.I.C.S.: 624190
Lauren Crapanzano Jumonville (Dir-Civic Leadership Initiatives)
John Spain (Exec VP)
Mukul Verma (Dir-Communications)
Annette D. Barton (Sec)
William E. Balhoff (Treas)
Edmund J. Giering IV (Gen Counsel)

BATON ROUGE JET CENTER LLC
4141 Chuck Yeager Ave, Baton Rouge, LA 70807
Tel.: (225) 355-9052
Web Site: http://www.btrjet.com
Oil Transportation Services
N.A.I.C.S.: 488190
Brett Furr (Pres)

Subsidiaries:

Executive Aviation Inc.   (1)
4490 Blanche Noyes Ave, Baton Rouge, LA 70807-4095
Tel.: (225) 355-5183
Airports, Flying Fields & Services
N.A.I.C.S.: 488119

Division (Domestic):

Millian Air Corp.   (2)
515 Eaton St, Saint Paul, MN 55107-2495
Tel.: (651) 227-2996
Airport
N.A.I.C.S.: 481219

BATON ROUGE TOBACCO CO. INC.
2326 Sorrel Ave, Baton Rouge, LA 70802
Tel.: (225) 343-7487
Sales Range: $25-49.9 Million
Emp.: 10
Tobacco & Tobacco Products
N.A.I.C.S.: 424940
Steven A. Shehane (Pres)

BATON ROUGE WATER WORKS COMPANY
8755 Goodwood Blvd, Baton Rouge, LA 70806-7916
Tel.: (225) 925-2011   LA
Web Site: https://www.brwater.com
Year Founded: 1888
Sales Range: $200-249.9 Million
Emp.: 195
Water Supply Distr
N.A.I.C.S.: 221310

E.H. Owen (CEO)
Hayes D. Owen (Chief Admin Officer & Sr VP)
J. Luther Jordan Jr. (Chm)

Subsidiaries:

Parish Water Company, Inc.   (1)
8755 Goodwood Blvd, Baton Rouge, LA 70806-7916
Tel.: (225) 928-1000
Sales Range: $25-49.9 Million
Emp.: 33
Water Utility
N.A.I.C.S.: 221310

Subsidiary (Domestic):

Ascension Water Co.   (2)
8755 Goodwood Blvd, Baton Rouge, LA 70806-7916
Tel.: (225) 928-1000
Sales Range: $50-74.9 Million
Emp.: 10
Water Supplier
N.A.I.C.S.: 221310

BATORY FOODS INC.
1700 E Higgins Rd Ste 300, Des Plaines, IL 60018
Tel.: (847) 299-1999
Web Site:
   http://www.batoryfoods.com
Sales Range: $10-24.9 Million
Emp.: 175
Sweetening Products
N.A.I.C.S.: 424490
Abel Friedman (Owner)
Alan Kessler (Controller)
Vince Pinneri (Pres)
Rita Ramirez (Chief People & Sustainability Officer)

BATTALIA WINSTON INTERNATIONAL
555 Madison Ave 19th Fl, New York, NY 10022
Tel.: (212) 308-8080
Web Site:
   http://www.battaliawinston.com
Year Founded: 1963
Sales Range: $10-24.9 Million
Emp.: 50
Management Consulting & Executive Search Services
N.A.I.C.S.: 541612
Dale Winston (Chm & CEO)
Rich Folts (Partner)
Terence Gallagher (Pres)
Ellen Romberg (Partner-Chicago)
Frederick Lamster (Partner-Retail Practice)
Doug Carrara (Partner-Life Science Practice)

BATTAT INC.
1560 Military Tpke, Plattsburgh, NY 12901-7458
Tel.: (518) 562-2200
Web Site: http://www.battatco.com
Rev.: $22,300,000
Emp.: 124
Toys
N.A.I.C.S.: 423920
Joe Battat (Owner & Pres)
Fonda Snyder (Exec VP-Entertainment)

BATTELLE MEMORIAL INSTITUTE
505 King Ave, Columbus, OH 43201-2696
Tel.: (614) 424-6424
Web Site: https://www.battelle.org
Year Founded: 1925
Sales Range: $5-14.9 Billion
Emp.: 20,000

Laboratory Management, Scientific Research & Technological Products Development & Commercialization Services
N.A.I.C.S.: 541715
Lewis F. Von Thaer (Pres & CEO)
Lou Von Thaer (Pres & CEO)
Aimee Kennedy (Sr VP-Human Resources-STEM Learning,Philanthropy)
Patrick Jarvis (Sr VP-Mktg & Comm)
Matt Vaughan (Pres-Applied Science & Technology & Sr VP-Contract Res)
Kirkland Donald (Chm)
Juan Alvarez (Exec VP-National Laboratory Mgmt & Operations)
Russell Austin (Gen Counsel, Sec & Sr VP)
Wes Hall (Sr VP-Philanthropy & Education)
Mike Haney (CIO)
Storm Woods (VP-Diversity, Equity, and Inclusion)

Subsidiaries:

Battelle India.   (1)
Unit No 302 3rd Floor Panchshil Technology Park, Hinjewadi, Pune, 411 057, India
Tel.: (91) 20 4021 1000
Web Site: http://www.battelle-india.com
Sales Range: $10-24.9 Million
Emp.: 25
Energy Research & Development Services
N.A.I.C.S.: 541715
Shalendra Porwal (CEO & Mng Dir)

Battelle UK Limited   (1)
Battelle House Fyfield Rd, Ongar, CM5 0GZ, United Kingdom
Tel.: (44) 1277 366100
Engineering Consulting Services
N.A.I.C.S.: 541330

Battelle Ventures, L.P.   (1)
100 Princeton South Corporate Ctr Ste 150, Ewing, NJ 08628
Tel.: (609) 921-1456
Web Site: http://www.battelleventures.com
Energy Research & Development Services
N.A.I.C.S.: 541715
Morton Collins (Gen Partner)

Pacific Northwest National Laboratory   (1)
902 Battelle Blvd, Richland, WA 99354
Tel.: (509) 375-2121
Web Site: http://www.pnl.gov
Sales Range: $600-649.9 Million
Emp.: 4,700
Energy & Environment Contract Research Services
N.A.I.C.S.: 541715
Paula Linnen (Exec Dir-External Affairs)
Vincent A. Branton (Gen Counsel)
Steven Ashby (Dir-Laboratory)
Malin M. Young (Deputy Dir-Science & Tech)
Brian Abrahamson (CIO & Assoc Dir-Laboratory-Comm & Tech)
Allison Campbell (Assoc Dir-Laboratory-Earth & Biological Sciences)
John P. LaFemina (Dir-Laboratory Plng & Performance Mgmt)
Larry Maples (Assoc Dir-Laboratory-Ops)
Tony Peurrung (Assoc Dir-Laboratory-Natl Security)
Michael Schlender (COO & Deputy Dir-Laboratory-Ops)
Louis Terminello (Assoc Dir-Laboratory, Physical & Computational Sciences)
Jud Virden (Assoc Dir-Laboratory-Energy & Environment)
Cheri Collins Wideman (Dir-HR)
Lee Cheatham (Dir-Tech Deployment & Outreach)
Tracie Cowen (CFO & Assoc Dir-Laboratory-Bus Svcs)

Scientific Advances, Inc.   (1)
601 W 5th Ave, Columbus, OH 43201-3174   (100%)
Tel.: (614) 424-7005
Sales Range: $25-49.9 Million
Emp.: 3
Venture Capital; Technical Products & Services

Battelle Memorial Institute—(Continued)
N.A.I.C.S.: 523160

BATTEN & SHAW, INC.
107 Music City Cir Ste 300, Nashville, TN 37214-1222
Tel.: (615) 292-2400
Sales Range: $10-24.9 Million
Emp.: 100
Civil Engineering Services
N.A.I.C.S.: 237310
Jimmy Batten (Pres)
Justin Saknini (Project Mgr)
Tony Gainous (Asst Project Mgr)
Andrew Lorenz (Asst Project Mgr)
Rachael Treadway (Coord-Mktg)
Aaron Talbot (VP-Ops)
Worth Scott (VP-Ops)
Colleen Mollica (Dir-HR)

BATTENFELD MANAGEMENT INC.
1174 Erie Ave, North Tonawanda, NY 14120-0728
Tel.: (716) 695-2100
Web Site: https://www.battenfeld-grease.com
Rev.: $28,340,802
Emp.: 70
Oils & Greases, Blending & Compounding
N.A.I.C.S.: 324191

Subsidiaries:

American Lubricants Inc (1)
619 Bailey Ave, Buffalo, NY 14206
Tel.: (716) 827-8300
Web Site:
http://www.americanlubricantsbflo.com
Rev.: $9,824,674
Emp.: 14
Lubricating Oils & Greases
N.A.I.C.S.: 424720

Battenfeld Grease & Oil Corp (1)
1174 Erie Ave, North Tonawanda, NY 14120
Tel.: (716) 695-2100
Web Site: http://www.battenfeld-grease.com
Rev.: $14,064,278
Emp.: 62
Oils & Greases, Blending & Compounding
N.A.I.C.S.: 324191
Daniel Ratka (Mgr-Shipping & Receiving)

Subsidiary (Non-US):

Battenfeld Grease (Canada) Ltd. (2)
68 Titan Road, Toronto, M8Z 2J8, ON, Canada
Tel.: (416) 239-1548
Emp.: 35
Lubricating Grease Distr
N.A.I.C.S.: 424720
Haresh Shah (Mgr-Quality Control)

Subsidiary (Domestic):

Battenfeld-American, Inc. (2)
1575 Clinton St, Buffalo, NY 14206-3064
Tel.: (716) 822-8410
Lubricating Grease & Oil Mfr
N.A.I.C.S.: 324191

BATTER UP, LLC
990 Biscayne Blvd Ste 502, Miami, FL 33132
Tel.: (786) 233-8660
Web Site:
http://www.thepipinggourmets.com
Year Founded: 2011
Sales Range: $1-9.9 Million
Emp.: 5
Bakery
N.A.I.C.S.: 311811
Carolyn Shulevitz (Co-Founder)
Leslie Kaplan (Co-Founder)

BATTERY RECYCLERS OF AMERICA, LLC
1920 Mckinney Ave 8th Fl, Dallas, TX 75201

Web Site:
http://www.batteryrecyclers.com
Year Founded: 2009
Sales Range: $10-24.9 Million
Emp.: 7
Battery Recycling Services
N.A.I.C.S.: 562920
Chad Sepulveda (Founder)

BATTERY SALES
12275 NE 13th Ave, Miami, FL 33161
Tel.: (305) 891-8355
Web Site:
https://www.batterysales.com
Year Founded: 1956
Sales Range: $10-24.9 Million
Emp.: 20
Electrical Apparatus & Equipment, Wiring Supplies & Related Equipment Whslr
N.A.I.C.S.: 423610
Stephen Stephens (Pres)

BATTERY SYSTEMS LLC
12322 Manhard St Garden Grove
948401, Long Beach, CA 90809-0906
Tel.: (310) 667-9320
Web Site:
http://www.batterysystems.net
Sales Range: $100-124.9 Million
Emp.: 210
Automotive Batteries
N.A.I.C.S.: 423120
Rick Campbell (VP)

BATTERY VENTURES, L.P.
1 Marina Park Dr Ste 1100, Boston, MA 02210
Tel.: (617) 948-3600
Web Site: http://www.battery.com
Year Founded: 1983
Privater Equity Firm
N.A.I.C.S.: 523999
Neeraj Agrawal (Gen Partner)
Karen Bommart (Partner & Head-IR)
Jesse Feldman (Gen Partner)
Marcus S. Ryu (Partner)
Shiran Shalev (Partner)
Morad Elhafed (Gen Partner)
Zak Ewen (Partner)
Russell L. Fleischer (Gen Partner)
Justin Rosner (Principal)
Rebecca Buckman (Partner-Mktg)
Michael Brown (Gen Partner)
Michael Brown (Gen Partner)

Subsidiaries:

1WorldSync, Inc. (1)
300 S Riverside Plz. Ste 1400, Chicago, IL 60606
Tel.: (866) 280-4013
Web Site: http://1worldsync.com
Software Publisher
N.A.I.C.S.: 513210

Subsidiary (Domestic):

PowerReviews, Inc. (2)
1 N Dearborn Ste 800, Chicago, IL 60602
Tel.: (312) 447-6100
Web Site: http://www.powerreviews.com
Social Commerce Network
N.A.I.C.S.: 516210
Matt Parsons (Chief Customer Officer)
Todd Caponi (CEO)
Theresa O'Neil (Sr VP-Mktg)
Marielle Lifshitz (Gen Counsel)
Kira Meinzer (VP-HR)
Kevin Rae (VP-Engrg)
Sheila Doolittle (VP-Customer Success)
Danny Harris (VP-Content Ops)
Duke Hoffman (VP-Implementation)
Dev Mukherjee (Pres & COO)
Kevin Clarke (VP-Fin)
Dave Hummel (VP-Tech)
Pete Lipovsek (VP-Strategic Enterprise Sls)
Anne Marie Olsen (VP-EMEA)
Erik Skurka (VP-Product Mgmt)
Sara Rossio (Sr VP-Product Mgmt)
Perry Marchant (CTO)

Mark Dillon (CEO)
Jillian Sheehan (CFO)
Robin L. Pederson (Exec Chm)

Subsidiary (Domestic):

BzzAgent, Inc. (3)
580 Harrison Ave Ste 101, Boston, MA 02118
Tel.: (617) 451-2280
Web Site: http://www.bzzagent.com
Social Marketing Services
N.A.I.C.S.: 541910
Paul Hunter (COO)
John Running (CTO)
Steve McLaughlin (CEO)

Alogent Corporation (1)
350 Technology Pkwy NW Ste 200, Peachtree Corners, GA 30092
Tel.: (678) 966-0844
Web Site: http://www.alogent.com
Electronic Document Management Services
N.A.I.C.S.: 541511
Robert Loughrey (CTO)
Kent Anderson (Sr VP-Bus Dev)
Dede Wakefield (CEO)
Nancy Nunn (CFO)
Jim Jones (Sr VP-Ops)
Jason Schwabline (Sr VP-Product Mgmt & Strategy)
Alissa Fry-Harris (Dir-Mktg)

Audio Precision, Inc. (1)
5750 SW Arctic Dr, Beaverton, OR 97005
Tel.: (503) 627-0832
Web Site: http://www.audioprecision.com
Rev.: $6,666,666
Emp.: 52
Instrument Manufacturing for Measuring & Testing Electricity & Electrical Signals
N.A.I.C.S.: 334515
Jayant Datta (CTO)

Battery Ventures, L.P. - Menlo
Park (1)
2884 Sand Hill Rd Ste 101, Menlo Park, CA 94025
Tel.: (650) 372-3939
Web Site: http://www.battery.com
Sales Range: $50-74.9 Million
Emp.: 15
Privater Equity Firm
N.A.I.C.S.: 523999
Chelsea R. Stoner (Gen Partner)
Chris Schiavo (CFO)
Dharmesh Thakker (Gen Partner)

Cimatron Ltd. (1)
11 Gush Etzion St, Giv'at Shemu'el, 54030, Israel
Tel.: (972) 732370237
Web Site: http://www.cimatron.com
Emp.: 90
Computer Software Designing Services
N.A.I.C.S.: 423430

Subsidiary (Non-US):

3D Systems Software GmbH (2)
Ottostrasse 2, 76275, Ettlingen, Germany
Tel.: (49) 724353880
Web Site: http://www.3dsystems-software.de
Computer Software Design Services
N.A.I.C.S.: 513210

Cimatron (Beijing) Technology Co. Ltd. (2)
Huibin Office B0415 No 8 Beichendong St, Chaoyang District, Beijing, 100101, China
Tel.: (86) 10 84978229
Web Site: http://www.cimatron.com
Computer Software Designing Services
N.A.I.C.S.: 423430

Subsidiary (US):

Cimatron Gibbs LLC (2)
323 Science Dr, Moorpark, CA 93021
Tel.: (805) 523-0004
Web Site: http://www.gibbscam.com
Computer Software Distr
N.A.I.C.S.: 423430

Subsidiary (Non-US):

Cimatron Technologies India Pvt. Ltd. (2)
107B Tejpal Ind Est Saki Naka, Mumbai, India

Tel.: (91) 9821125746
Web Site: http://www.cimatron.com
Computer Software Designing Services
N.A.I.C.S.: 423430

Subsidiary (US):

Cimatron Technologies, Inc. (2)
41700 Gardenbrook Rd Ste 100, Novi, MI 48375
Tel.: (248) 596-9700
Web Site: http://www.cimatron.com
Emp.: 21
Computer Software Distr
N.A.I.C.S.: 423430

Data Physics Corp. (1)
1741 Technology Dr Ste 260, San Jose, CA 95110
Tel.: (408) 437-0100
Web Site: http://www.dataphysics.com
Sales Range: $1-9.9 Million
Emp.: 40
Noise & Vibration Testing & Measurement Solutions
N.A.I.C.S.: 334513
Louis Pace (CEO)
Sabine Castagnet (COO)
David Stephens (Dir-DSP Engrg)
Thomas Reilly (Dir-Product Mgmt-SignalCalc & SignalStar)
Kevin W. McIntosh (VP-Global Shaker Bus Unit)

Subsidiary (Non-US):

Data Physics (Bharat/ India) Pvt. Ltd. (2)
411 15th Cross 2nd Block, Jayanagar, 560 011, Bangalore, India
Tel.: (91) 80 2656 5810
Vibration Test Equipment Distr
N.A.I.C.S.: 423830
Girish Doddamani (Reg Mgr)

Data Physics (Deutschland/ Germany) GmbH (2)
Business Center Gewerbepark C25, 93059, Regensburg, Germany
Tel.: (49) 9471 30 86 928
Web Site: http://www.data-physics.de
Vibration Test Equipment Distr
N.A.I.C.S.: 423830

Data Physics (France) S.A. (2)
142 avenue Joseph Kessel, 78960, Voisins-le-Bretonneux, France
Tel.: (33) 1 39 30 50 60
Vibration Test Equipment Distr
N.A.I.C.S.: 423830

Data Physics (UK) Ltd. (2)
South Road, Hailsham, BN27 3JJ, East Sussex, United Kingdom
Tel.: (44) 1323 846464
Vibration Test Equipment Distr
N.A.I.C.S.: 423830
Geoff Murphy (Mng Dir)

Subsidiary (Domestic):

Lansmont Corp. (2)
Ryan Ranch Research Pk 17 Mandeville Ct, Monterey, CA 93940
Tel.: (831) 655-6600
Web Site: http://www.lansmont.com
Sales Range: $1-9.9 Million
Emp.: 65
Noise & Vibration Testing Services
N.A.I.C.S.: 334519
Joe Driscoll (CEO)
Patti Monahan (CFO)
Dave Huntley (Pres)
Eric Joneson (VP-Mktg)
Eric Whitfield (VP-Quality & Ops)
Louis Pace (CEO)

Detcon, Inc. (1)
3200 Research Forest Dr, The Woodlands, TX 77381
Tel.: (281) 367-4100
Web Site: http://www.detcon.com
Sales Range: $1-9.9 Million
Emp.: 35
Commercial & Institutional Building Construction
N.A.I.C.S.: 236220
Robert Masi (Pres)
Tammy Bird-Scott (Mgr-Mktg & Comm)

James H. Heal & Company Limited (1)
Richmond Works, Halifax, HX3 6EP, United Kingdom
Tel.: (44) 1422366355
Web Site: http://www.james-heal.co.uk
Sales Range: $10-24.9 Million
Emp.: 110
Mfr of Testing Instruments for Textile & Garment Industry
N.A.I.C.S.: 339999
Lisa Earnshaw (Product Mgr)
Amanda McLaren (Mng Dir)

Jeeves Information Systems AB (1)
World Trade Center Kungsbron 1 Klarabergsviadukten 70, Stockholm, 10138, Sweden
Tel.: (46) 858709900
Web Site: http://www.jeevesearth.se
Emp.: 200
Business Systems Developer
N.A.I.C.S.: 519290
Marina Akerman (VP-Support & IT)
Gunilla Blixt (Dir-R&D)
Ann Fredriksson (Dir-HR)
Gronvik Magnus (Dir-Product Mgmt)
Andrea Wetterberg (Dir-Fin & Ops)
Christina Stange Skoster (Gen Mgr)

Subsidiary (Non-US):

Jeeves Deutschland GmbH (2)
An Der Leite 4, Rugendorf, Kulmbach, Bavaria, Germany
Tel.: (49) 9223 945 9018
Web Site: http://www.jeeves.se
Business Administration Software Development Services
N.A.I.C.S.: 541511

Jeeves France SAS (2)
67 Avenue Andre Morizet, 92100, Boulogne, Hauts-de-Seine, France
Tel.: (33) 146106520
Web Site: http://www.jeeves.fr
Business Administration Software Development Services
N.A.I.C.S.: 541511

Jeeves GmbH (2)
Eibenweg 26, 59423, Unna, Germany
Tel.: (49) 230396910
Web Site: http://www.jeeves.se
Sales Range: $25-49.9 Million
Emp.: 5
Non-Durable Goods Whslr
N.A.I.C.S.: 424990

Jeeves Information Systems Norway (2)
Thunes Vei 2, Oslo, 0274, Norway
Tel.: (47) 66818800
Web Site: http://www.jeeveserp.com
Emp.: 3
Software Development Consulting Services
N.A.I.C.S.: 541511
Jeff Tognoni (CEO)
Marina Akerman (VP-Support & IT)

Jeeves Information Systems UK Ltd (2)
PO Box 5116, Warwick, CV34 9JX, United Kingdom
Tel.: (44) 8443351115
Web Site: http://www.jeeves.se
Sales Range: $10-24.9 Million
Emp.: 2
Enterprise Resource Planning Systems Development Services
N.A.I.C.S.: 926110

LI-COR, Inc. (1)
4647 Superior St, Lincoln, NE 68504-5000
Tel.: (402) 467-0700
Web Site: http://www.licor.com
Surgical & Medical Instrument Mfr
N.A.I.C.S.: 339112
Jeff Harford (Sr Mgr-Product-Imaging Sys)
Bill Biggs (Co-Founder)
Elaine Biggs (Co-Founder)
Thomas Reslewic (CEO)

LightBox (1)
9 W 57th St, New York, NY 10001
Tel.: (212) 981-5600
Holding Company
N.A.I.C.S.: 523999
Eric Frank (CEO)
Anthony Bisseker (Mng Dir)

Subsidiary (Domestic):

Digital Map Products, Inc. (2)
5201 California Ave Ste 200, Irvine, CA 92617
Tel.: (949) 333-5111
Web Site: http://www.digmap.com
Sales Range: $10-24.9 Million
Custom Platform Data Services
N.A.I.C.S.: 518210
James Skurzynski (Founder, Pres & CEO)
Geoff Wade (CTO)
Nelson Greenwood (VP-Sls)
Annie Schwab (VP-Customer Success)
Steve Stautzenbach (VP-Product Mgmt)
Tara Bleakley (Dir-Data Analytics)
Steven Cheng (Dir-Data Dev)
Brendan McCann (Dir-IT)
Diane Rettew (Dir-HR & Talent Acq)
Thomas R. Patterson Jr. (COO & VP-Fin)

MadCap Software, Inc. (1)
11230 Sorrento Valley Rd, San Diego, CA 92121
Tel.: (858) 320-0387
Web Site: http://www.madcapsoftware.com
Rev.: $3,300,000
Emp.: 18
Fiscal Year-end: 12/31/2006
Software Development Services
N.A.I.C.S.: 513210
Anthony Olivier (CEO)

Subsidiary (Domestic):

Xyleme, Inc. (2)
1881 9th St Ste 300, Boulder, CO 80302-5148
Tel.: (303) 872-0233
Web Site: http://www.xyleme.com
Custom Computer Programming Services
N.A.I.C.S.: 541511
Gilles Arnaud (CFO)

Michell Instruments Limited (1)
48 Lancaster Way Business Park, Ely, CB6 3NW, Cambs, United Kingdom
Tel.: (44) 1353 658 000
Web Site: http://www.michell.com
Industrial Sensors & Instrumentation Designer, Mfr & Whslr
N.A.I.C.S.: 334513
Mike Bannister (CEO)
Adam Markin (Chm)

Subsidiary (US):

Michell Instruments, Inc. (2)
319 Newburyport Tpke Ste 207, Rowley, MA 01969
Tel.: (978) 484-0005
Web Site: http://www.michell.com
Industrial Sensors & Instrumentation Designer, Mfr & Whslr
N.A.I.C.S.: 334513
Nigel Futter (Product Mgr-Relative Humidity-Global)

Plixer International, Inc. (1)
68 Main St Ste 4, Kennebunk, ME 04073
Tel.: (207) 324-8805
Web Site: http://www.plixer.com
Custom Computer Programming Services
N.A.I.C.S.: 541511
Chris Moulas (VP-Global Sls)
Jeff Lindholm (Pres & CEO)
Paul Piccard (CTO & Sr VP-Engrg)
Thomas Pore (VP-Tech Svcs)
Bob Noel (VP-Mktg & Strategic Alliances)

Process Sensing Technologies Ltd. (1)
48 Lancaster Way Business Park, Ely, CB6 3NW, Cambs, United Kingdom
Web Site: http://www.processsensing.com
Electrical Products Mfr
N.A.I.C.S.: 335999

Subsidiary (US):

Analytical Industries Inc. (2)
2855 Metropolitan Pl, Pomona, CA 91767
Tel.: (909) 392-6900
Web Site: http://www.aii1.com
Process Control Instruments
N.A.I.C.S.: 334513
Patrick Prindible (VP)

Proemion Holding GmbH (1)
Donaustrase 14, Fulda, 36043, Germany

Tel.: (49) 66194900
Web Site: http://www.proemion.com
All Other Data Processing, Web Hosting & Computer Related Services
N.A.I.C.S.: 518210

ResourceWise (1)
15720 Brixham Hill Ave. Ste 550, Charlotte, NC 28277
Tel.: (704) 540-1440
Web Site: https://www.resourcewise.com
Environmental Services
N.A.I.C.S.: 541620
Matt Elhardt (VP-Sls)
Marko Summanen (VP-Bus Dev-Forest Vertical Europe)
Peter J. Stewart (CEO)
Peter Coutu (VP-Operational Excellence)

Subsidiary (Domestic):

Fisher International, Inc. (2)
15720 Brixham Hill Ave. Ste 550, Charlotte, NC 28277
Tel.: (203) 854-5390
Web Site: http://www.fisheri.com
Administrative Management & General Management Consulting Service
N.A.I.C.S.: 541611
Marko Summanen (VP-EMEA)
Marcello Collares (VP & Dir-Sls-Latin America)

Forest2Market, Inc. (2)
15720 John J Delaney Dr Ste 550, Charlotte, NC 28277
Tel.: (704) 540-1440
Web Site: http://www.forest2market.com
Wood Product Mfr & Distr
N.A.I.C.S.: 321999
Peter J. Stewart (Founder, Pres & CEO)
Suz-Anne Kinney (Dir-Mktg & Comm)

SaaSOptics, LLC (1)
6575 The Corners Pkwy NW Ste 400, Peachtree Corners, GA 30092
Tel.: (678) 510-8260
Web Site: http://www.saasoptics.com
Sales Range: $1-9.9 Million
Emp.: 58
Software Development Services
N.A.I.C.S.: 541511
Tim McCormick (CEO)
David Ryan (Chief Revenue Officer)
Chris Weber (COO)
Clayton Whitfield (Sr VP-Revenue Programs)
Matthew Woodard (Sr VP)

TrueContext Corporation (1)
2500 Solandt Rd 250, Kanata, K2K 3G5, ON, Canada
Tel.: (613) 599-8288
Web Site: https://truecontext.com
Rev.: $17,666,080
Assets: $13,564,924
Liabilities: $11,072,055
Net Worth: $2,492,869
Earnings: ($1,485,167)
Fiscal Year-end: 12/31/2020
Mobile Data Collection Applications
N.A.I.C.S.: 513210
David Croucher (CFO)
Glenn Chenier (Chief Product Officer)
Mansell Nelson (Sr VP-Bus Dev)
Lisa Scian (VP-People & Culture)
Cindy McGann (Gen Counsel)
Aly Mawani (VP)
Carl Turner (Gen Counsel)

Subsidiary (Domestic):

TrueContext Inc. (2)
800 - 535 Legget Drive, Ottawa, K2K 3B8, ON, Canada
Tel.: (613) 599-8288
Web Site: https://www.prontoforms.com
Sales Range: $10-24.9 Million
Emp.: 27
Business Solutions Provider
N.A.I.C.S.: 561400

VertiGIS Holdings Ltd. (1)
5 Fleet Place Farringdon, London, EC4M 7RD, United Kingdom
Tel.: (44) 2503813180
Geographic Information System & Software Developer
N.A.I.C.S.: 541512

Jason Kolt (CMO)
Andy Berry (CEO)

Subsidiary (US):

Mapcom Systems, LLC (2)
601 Southlake Blvd, Richmond, VA 23236-3921
Tel.: (804) 366-0727
Web Site: http://www.mapcom.com
Wholesale Trade Agents & Brokers
N.A.I.C.S.: 425120
John Granger (Pres)

BATTLE CREEK EQUIPMENT CO.
702 S Reed Rd, Fremont, IN 46737
Tel.: (269) 962-6181
Web Site:
   https://www.battlecreekequipco.com
Year Founded: 1931
Sales Range: $75-99.9 Million
Emp.: 45
Fitness Equipment, Portable Massage Tables, Automatic Moist Heat Pack, Air Purification Systems & Evaporative Humidifiers
N.A.I.C.S.: 423910
Mary Haywood Brown (VP-Sls & Mktg)
Austin McGregor (Supvr-Engrg)

BATTLE CREEK FARMERS COOP
83755 S Hwy 121, Battle Creek, NE 68715
Tel.: (402) 675-2375
Web Site: http://www.bccoop.com
Rev.: $43,355,945
Emp.: 100
Grains, Fertilizer, Fuel & Feed
N.A.I.C.S.: 424510
Ron Woslager (Mgr-Location)
Dennis Kuchar (Sec)
Paul Heybrock (Controller)

BATTLE INVESTMENT GROUP LLC
3715 Northside Pkwy NW Bldg 200 Ste 400, Atlanta, GA 30327 DE
Web Site:
   http://battleinvestmentgroup.com
Year Founded: 2015
Investment Services
N.A.I.C.S.: 523999
David Battle (Founder & Partner)

Subsidiaries:

Metal Finishing Technologies, Inc. (1)
60 Wooster Ct, Forestville, CT 06010
Tel.: (860) 582-9517
Web Site: http://www.mftech.com
Rev.: $8,103,000
Emp.: 75
Electroplating, Plating, Polishing, Anodizing & Coloring
N.A.I.C.S.: 332813
Michael Salamone (Pres)
Niko Giannopoulus (COO)

Subsidiary (Domestic):

Aqua Blasting Corp. (2)
2 Northwood Dr, Bloomfield, CT 06002
Tel.: (860) 242-8855
Web Site: http://www.aquablasting.com
Metal Heat Treating
N.A.I.C.S.: 332811
Victoria Stavola (Pres)

Oceus Networks Inc. (1)
1895 Preston White Dr 300, Reston, VA 20191-5449
Tel.: (703) 234-9200
Web Site: http://www.oceusnetworks.com
Government Communications Solutions
N.A.I.C.S.: 517810
Jim Patterson (VP-Special Programs)
Jeff Harman (Pres & CEO)
Kevin Stiles (CTO)
Kristen Carter (VP-HR)

Battle Investment Group LLC—(Continued)

Josh Montgomery (Treas & VP-Fin)
Brad Antle (Chm)
Paul McQuillan (Chief Growth & Strategy Officer)
Carm Caruso (CFO)

BATTLE LUMBER COMPANY INC.

11261 Hwy 1, Wadley, GA 30477
Tel.: (478) 252-5210　　　　**GA**
Web Site:
　https://www.battlelumberco.com
Year Founded: 1963
Sales Range: $10-24.9 Million
Emp.: 300
Wood Pallets & Skids
N.A.I.C.S.: 321920
Tommy Battle (VP-Ops)
Craig Miller (VP-Sls)
Rusty Logue (Gen Mgr-Dry Kiln Div & Lumber Sls)
David Brantley (Head-Forester)

BATTLEGROUND RESTAURANT GROUP INC.

1337 Winstead Pl, Greensboro, NC 27408-8024
Tel.: (336) 272-9355　　　　**NC**
Web Site: https://www.brginc.com
Year Founded: 1981
Restaurant Operators
N.A.I.C.S.: 722511
Tom Mincher (Pres)
Matt Stall (Controller)

BATTLES TRANSPORTATION INC.

3000 V St NE, Washington, DC 20018
Tel.: (202) 462-8658
Web Site: https://www.battles-transport.com
Rev.: $2,000,000
Emp.: 70
Urban Transit Systems
N.A.I.C.S.: 485119
McKinley Battle (Pres & CEO)
Danielle Battle (Mgr-Payroll)
Donna Thomas (Acct Mgr)
Thomas Dominique (CFO & COO)

BATTLEY HARLEY-DAVIDSON INC.

7830 Airpark Rd, Gaithersburg, MD 20879
Tel.: (301) 948-4581
Web Site: http://www.battley.com
Sales Range: $10-24.9 Million
Emp.: 35
Motorcycle Sales
N.A.I.C.S.: 441227
Devin Battley (Owner)
Kelly Gilbert (Bus Mgr)
Drew Alexander (Dir-Mktg)

BATTS INC.

108 S Main St, Advance, IN 46102
Tel.: (765) 676-5123
Web Site: https://www.battsinc.com
Roadway De-Icing Equipment Mfr & Whslr
N.A.I.C.S.: 332312

BATZER CONSTRUCTION, INC.

190 N Ross Ln, Medford, OR 97501
Tel.: (541) 773-7553
Web Site:
　http://www.batzerconstruction.com
Sales Range: $10-24.9 Million
Emp.: 80
Commercial & Institutional Building Construction Services
N.A.I.C.S.: 236220

Russ Batzer (Pres)
Pam Weeks (Supvr-AP)
Andy Batzer (VP)

BATZNER PEST MANAGEMENT, INC.

16948 W Victor Rd, New Berlin, WI 53151
Tel.: (262) 797-4160
Web Site: https://www.batzner.com
Sales Range: $1-9.9 Million
Emp.: 150
Pest Control & Exterminating Services
N.A.I.C.S.: 561710
Julie Wing (Mgr-HR)
Dennis Olijnyk (Mgr-Svc)

BAUER BUILT, INC.

1111 W Prospect St, Durand, WI 54736
Tel.: (715) 672-4295
Web Site: http://www.bauerbuilt.com
Year Founded: 1976
Sales Range: $50-74.9 Million
Emp.: 500
Auto & Home Supply Stores
N.A.I.C.S.: 441340
Jerry M. Bauer (Chm & CEO)

Subsidiaries:

Bauer Built Tire Center of Perry, IA　　　　　　　　　　　　　　(1)
First & Warford, Perry, IA 50220　　**(100%)**
Tel.: (515) 465-4675
Sales Range: $10-24.9 Million
Emp.: 4
Mfr of Tires & Tubes
N.A.I.C.S.: 423130

BAUER CORPORATION

2540 Progress Dr, Wooster, OH 44691
Tel.: (330) 262-3070
Web Site:
　https://www.bauerladder.com
Sales Range: $10-24.9 Million
Emp.: 30
Portable Ladder Mfr & Distr
N.A.I.C.S.: 332999
Marc Harrow McConnell (Pres)
Ward McConnell (Pres)

BAUER INDUSTRIES INC.

2021 Arden Way, Sacramento, CA 95825-2201
Tel.: (916) 648-9200
Year Founded: 1991
Sales Range: $10-24.9 Million
Emp.: 125
Sales of Automotive Accessories
N.A.I.C.S.: 441330
Greg Bauer (Pres & CEO)

BAUGHMAN GROUP LTD

4104 Eastmoor Rd, Louisville, KY 40218
Tel.: (502) 581-8770
Web Site:
　http://www.baughmangroup.com
Sales Range: $10-24.9 Million
Emp.: 10
Machine Shop, Jobbing & Repair
N.A.I.C.S.: 332710
David B. Baughman (Pres)

Subsidiaries:

Baughman Seals Inc　　　　　　　(1)
1226 Rowan St, Louisville, KY 40203
Tel.: (502) 581-8770
Web Site: http://www.baughmangroup.com
Rev.: $2,600,000
Emp.: 2
Industrial Supplies
N.A.I.C.S.: 423840
David B. Baughman (Pres)

BAUGHMAN TILE COMPANY, INC.

8516 Township Rd 137, Paulding, OH 45879
Tel.: (419) 399-3160
Web Site:
　https://www.baughmantile.com
Year Founded: 1883
Sales Range: $10-24.9 Million
Emp.: 100
Plastic Pipe & Pipe Fitting Mfr
N.A.I.C.S.: 326122
Gene A. Baughman (Pres)

BAUHAUS FURNITURE GROUP, LLC

1 Bauhaus Dr, Saltillo, MS 38866-6974
Tel.: (662) 869-2664　　　　**MS**
Web Site:
　http://www.bauhausfurniture.com
Year Founded: 1989
Emp.: 275
Furniture Mfr
N.A.I.C.S.: 337121
Blair Taylor (CFO)

BAUM BROTHERS IMPORTS INC.

350 5th Ave Ste 501, New York, NY 10118
Tel.: (212) 239-0080
Web Site: https://www.baum-essex.com
Rev.: $13,761,679
Emp.: 40
Umbrellas, Beach Products, Apparel & Ceramics Mfr & Whslr
N.A.I.C.S.: 423220
Charles Baum (Pres)

BAUM CAPITAL PARTNERS MANAGEMENT LLC

4801 Main St Ste 525, Kansas City, MO 64112
Tel.: (816) 283-5200
Web Site: http://baumpartners.com
Private Investment Firm
N.A.I.C.S.: 523999
Jonathan Baum (Mng Partner)

Subsidiaries:

Phoenix Peach, LLC　　　　　　　(1)
6521 W Post Rd Ste 1, Las Vegas, NV 89118
Tel.: (702) 623-0017
Web Site: http://www.goettl.com
Refrigeration & Heating Equipment Mfr
N.A.I.C.S.: 333415
Ken Goodrich (CEO)
Laura Rymut (VP-Customer Experience)

Subsidiary (Domestic):

Dutton Plumbing, Inc.　　　　　　(2)
997 Flower Glen, Simi Valley, CA 93065
Tel.: (844) 811-5449
Web Site: http://www.duttonplumbing.com
Plumbing, Heating & Air-Conditioning Contractors
N.A.I.C.S.: 238220

Las Vegas Air Conditioning, Inc.　　(2)
6220 Kimberly Ave Ste 13, Las Vegas, NV 89122
Tel.: (702) 437-1888
Web Site: http://www.lasvegasair.net
Sales Range: $1-9.9 Million
Emp.: 8
Heating & Air Conditioning Repair & Replacement Services
N.A.I.C.S.: 238220

BAUM TEXTILE MILLS INC.

812 Jersey Ave, Jersey City, NJ 07310
Tel.: (201) 659-0444　　　　**NY**
Web Site:
　http://www.baumtextile.com
Year Founded: 1949

Sales Range: $10-24.9 Million
Emp.: 50
Piece Goods & Notions
N.A.I.C.S.: 424310
Stanley Krueger (Pres)
Emanuel Krueger (Treas & VP)
Nicole Hah (Mgr-Production)

BAUMAN OIL DISTRIBUTORS INC.

1503 Commercial Blvd, Herculaneum, MO 63048
Tel.: (636) 937-3412
Web Site:
　https://www.baumanoil.com
Sales Range: $10-24.9 Million
Emp.: 20
Petroleum Bulk Stations
N.A.I.C.S.: 424710
Paul F. Bauman (Pres)

BAUMANN & SONS BUSES, INC.

3355 Veterans Memorial Hwy, Ronkonkoma, NY 11779-7626
Tel.: (631) 471-4600
Web Site:
　http://www.abatransportation.com
Sales Range: $10-24.9 Million
Emp.: 450
School Bus Transportation Services
N.A.I.C.S.: 485410
Ronald Baumann (Pres)
Constance Gilman (Sec)
Richard Baumann Jr. (VP)

BAUMANN CHRYSLER-JEEP-DODGE

2577 W State St, Fremont, OH 43420-1444
Tel.: (419) 455-1253
Web Site:
　https://www.baumannchrysler.com
Year Founded: 2001
Sales Range: $10-24.9 Million
Emp.: 34
Car Whslr
N.A.I.C.S.: 441110
Michael Hoelzer (Gen Mgr)

BAUMANN PROPERTY COMPANY INC.

217 Clarkson Executive Park, Saint Louis, MO 63011
Tel.: (636) 227-0012
Web Site:
　https://www.baumannproperty.com
Rev.: $12,000,000
Emp.: 88
Apartment Building Operator
N.A.I.C.S.: 531110
Herbert J. Baumann (Pres)

BAUMER FOODS INC.

2424 Edenborn Ave Ste 510, Metairie, LA 70001-1845
Tel.: (504) 482-5761　　　　**LA**
Web Site:
　http://www.baumerfoods.com
Year Founded: 1923
Barbecue Sauces Mfr
N.A.I.C.S.: 311421
Terry Hanes (Exec VP & CEO)
Doug Wakefield (VP-Ops)
Laura O'Connell (Mgr-Acctg)
Michelle Holtzclaw (VP-Private Label Sls, Customer Rels & Admin)

BAUSMAN & COMPANY, INC.

1425 S Campus Ave, Ontario, CA 91761
Tel.: (909) 947-0139
Web Site:
　http://www.bausmanandco.com
Year Founded: 1971

Nonupholstered Wood Household
Furniture Mfr
N.A.I.C.S.: 337122
Robert Williams (Co-Founder)
Craig Johnson (Co-Founder, Pres &
CEO)

BAUZA & ASSOCIATES, LLC
11 Asylum St Ste 402, Hartford, CT
06103
Tel.: (860) 246-2100
Web Site:
http://www.bauzaassociates.com
Year Founded: 2001
Sales Range: $1-9.9 Million
Emp.: 16
Advertising, Consulting, Event Plan-
ning & Marketing, Merchandising,
Promotions, Public Relations, Sports
Marketing, Strategic Planning & Re-
search
N.A.I.C.S.: 541810
Hector Bauza (Pres & CEO)
Wilson Camelo (Principal & CMO)
Luis Ramos (Dir-Creative)

BAVARIAN MEAT PRODUCTS,
INC.
2934 Western Ave, Seattle, WA
98121
Tel.: (206) 448-3540
Web Site:
http://www.bavarianmeats.com
Year Founded: 1961
Sales Range: $1-9.9 Million
Emp.: 18
Meat Processing Services
N.A.I.C.S.: 311612
Lyla Ridgeway (Treas & Sec)
Lynn Hofstatter (Pres)

BAVARIAN MOTOR TRANS-
PORT INC.
3681 Okemos Rd Ste 500, Okemos,
MI 48864
Tel.: (517) 349-3011
Web Site: http://www.pmtghome.com
Sales Range: $10-24.9 Million
Emp.: 500
Automobiles, Transport & Delivery
N.A.I.C.S.: 484230
Dallas Knepp (VP)

BAVARIAN SPECIALTY FOODS
LLC
11450 Sheldon St, Sun Valley, CA
91352-1121
Tel.: (310) 212-6199
Rev.: $12,250,000
Emp.: 100
Bread, Cake & Related Products
N.A.I.C.S.: 311812

BAWLA CONSULTING INC.
4 New Hyde Park Rd, Franklin
Square, NY 11010
Tel.: (212) 812-2117
Web Site: http://www.bawlainc.com
Year Founded: 2014
Sales Range: $10-24.9 Million
Emp.: 2
Human Resource Consulting Ser-
vices
N.A.I.C.S.: 541612
Naeem Bawla (Founder)

BAXTER AUTO GROUP
17950 Burt St, Omaha, NE 68118
Tel.: (402) 493-7800
Web Site:
https://www.baxterauto.com
Year Founded: 1957
New & Used Car Dealerships
N.A.I.C.S.: 441110
Mickey Anderson (Pres)

BAXTER AUTO PARTS INC.
9444 N Whitaker Rd, Portland, OR
97217
Tel.: (503) 285-2548   OR
Web Site:
https://www.baxterautoparts.com
Year Founded: 1936
Sales Range: $10-24.9 Million
Emp.: 300
Automotive Parts & Repairs
N.A.I.C.S.: 441330
Terry Anderson (Mgr)

BAXTER HODELL DONNELLY
PRESTON INC.
302 W 3rd St Ste 500, Cincinnati, OH
45202
Tel.: (513) 271-1634   OH
Web Site: https://www.bhdp.com
Year Founded: 1960
Sales Range: $75-99.9 Million
Emp.: 70
Architectural Services
N.A.I.C.S.: 541310
Michael J. Habel (CEO)
Richard Krzyminski (CFO)
Pam McDonel (Co-CFO)

BAY & BAY TRANSFER COM-
PANY INC.
3686 140th St E, Rosemount, MN
55068
Tel.: (651) 480-7991
Web Site: http://www.bayandbay.com
Rev.: $16,000,000
Emp.: 2
Trucking Except Local
N.A.I.C.S.: 484121
Sam Anderson (Pres & CEO)

BAY ACQUISITION CORP.
420 Lexington Ave Ste 2320, New
York, NY 10170
Tel.: (212) 661-6800
Web Site: http://www.secure-logic.net
Year Founded: 1997
Software Development Services
N.A.I.C.S.: 513210
Shalom Dolev (VP-Security Sys)
Michael Klein (VP-Automated Sys)
Gary Koren (CEO)

BAY ADVANCED TECHNOLO-
GIES LLC
8100 Central Ave, Newark, CA
94560-3449
Tel.: (510) 857-0900
Web Site: https://www.bayat.com
Year Founded: 1963
Sales Range: $25-49.9 Million
Emp.: 100
Automation & Control Equipment Mfr
N.A.I.C.S.: 334512
Roy Blankenship (Pres)
Michael R. Stimson (VP-Fin)
Peter H. Madison (VP-Sls & Mktg)

Subsidiaries:

Bay Advanced Technologies LLC -
Austin   (1)
8200 Cross Park Dr, Austin, TX 78754
Tel.: (512) 929-5400
Web Site: http://www.bayat.com
Sales Range: $10-24.9 Million
Emp.: 90
Automation & Control Equipment Mfr
N.A.I.C.S.: 333998
Matt Griffith (Dir-Bus Dev & Global Acct
Mgr)

BAY ALARM COMPANY INC.
5130 Commercial Cir, Concord, CA
94596
Tel.: (925) 935-1100
Web Site: http://www.bayalarm.com
Year Founded: 1946
Security System Services

N.A.I.C.S.: 561621
Matt Westphal (Co-Pres)

Subsidiaries:

Evergreen Security, Inc.   (1)
8115 Broadway, Everett, WA 98203
Tel.: (425) 348-3850
Security Systems & Services
N.A.I.C.S.: 561621
William Murray (Pres)

BAY AREA BUILDING SOLU-
TIONS, INC.
3565 126th Ave N, Clearwater, FL
33762
Tel.: (727) 528-8301
Web Site:
http://www.bayareabuildings.com
Year Founded: 2005
Sales Range: $10-24.9 Million
Emp.: 11
Building Construction
N.A.I.C.S.: 236220
Christopher T. Duncan (Co-Founder
& Pres)
F. Pate Clements (Principal)
Mark Wilson (Mgr-Pre-Construction
Svcs)
Eric Lanctot (Mgr-Bus Dev)
Stanton Cowen (Project Mgr)
John Vrabec (Principal-Ops)

BAY AREA COMMUNITY
HEALTH
40910 Fremont Blvd, Fremont, CA
94538
Tel.: (510) 770-8133   CA
Web Site: http://www.tri-cityhealth.org
Year Founded: 1970
Sales Range: $10-24.9 Million
Emp.: 261
Healtcare Services
N.A.I.C.S.: 622110
Brenda Quillan (Sec)
Louis Chicoine (Treas)
Jagat Sheth (CFO)
Marc Gannon (COO)
Harsha Ramchandani (Chief Medical
Officer)
Johnny O'Brien (Chief Strategic Dev
Officer)
Zettie D. Page III (CEO)

Subsidiaries:

Foothill Community Health
Center   (1)
2670 S White Rd Ste 200, San Jose, CA
95148
Tel.: (408) 729-9700
Web Site: http://www.sjffcc.org
Sales Range: $10-24.9 Million
Emp.: 210
Community Health Care Services
N.A.I.C.S.: 621498
Bindu Chandran (Dir-Medical)
Shilpa Mehta (Dir-Dental)
Michael Victor (CFO)
Neil Kozuma (Officer-Compliance)
Salvador Chavarin (CEO)

BAY AREA COMMUNITY RE-
SOURCES INC.
171 Carlos Dr, San Rafael, CA
94903-2005
Tel.: (415) 444-5580   CA
Web Site: https://www.bacr.org
Year Founded: 1976
Sales Range: $25-49.9 Million
Emp.: 1,951
Community Development Services
N.A.I.C.S.: 624190
Martin Weinstein (CEO)
Lissa Franklin (Pres)
Robert Davisson (Sec)
David Wight (Dir-Development)
Cathleen Campbell (CFO)
Spencer Bolles (Dir-Information Tech-
nology)

BAY AREA DISTRIBUTING
COMPANY
1061 Factory St, Richmond, CA
94801
Tel.: (510) 232-8554
Web Site:
http://www.bayareadist.com
Year Founded: 1972
Sales Range: $10-24.9 Million
Emp.: 50
Beer & Ale Whslr
N.A.I.C.S.: 424810
Michael Bosnich (VP-Sls)

BAY AREA ECONOMICS
2600 10th St, Berkeley, CA 94710
Tel.: (510) 547-9380   CA
Web Site:
http://www.bayareaeconomics.com
Year Founded: 1986
Sales Range: $1-9.9 Million
Emp.: 16
Real Estate Economics & Develop-
ment Advisory Services
N.A.I.C.S.: 541620
Janet Smith-Heimer (Founder & Mng
Principal)
David Shiver (Principal)
Lisa Loneon (Mgr-Mktg)

BAY AREA HEART CENTER,
INC.
5398 Park St N, Saint Petersburg, FL
33709
Tel.: (727) 544-1441   FL
Web Site: https://www.bahc.com
Year Founded: 1982
Sales Range: $1-9.9 Million
Emp.: 50
Radiology Services
N.A.I.C.S.: 621111
David M. Mokotoff (Founder)

BAY AREA HIGH REACH, INC.
22390 Thunderbird Pl, Hayward, CA
94545
Tel.: (510) 276-9211   CA
Web Site:
https://www.bayareahighreach.com
Year Founded: 1970
Sales Range: $1-9.9 Million
Emp.: 33
Construction Contractor
N.A.I.C.S.: 236220
Brian Burns (Pres & Gen Mgr)

BAY AREA INDUSTRIAL SER-
VICES INC.
824 12th Ave W, Bradenton, FL
34205
Tel.: (941) 721-4560
Web Site:
https://www.bayareaindustrial.com
Sales Range: $1-9.9 Million
Emp.: 11
Packaging Distr & Custom Box Mfr
N.A.I.C.S.: 424120
George Dabbiero (Pres)

BAY AREA INSURANCE SER-
VICES
4730 State Rd 64 E, Bradenton, FL
34208
Tel.: (941) 746-4107
Web Site:
http://www.serviceinsuranceco.com
Sales Range: $10-24.9 Million
Emp.: 30
Property & Liability; Personal & Com-
mercial Lines
N.A.I.C.S.: 524126
Carol A. Johnson (VP-IT)
David C. Cruikshank (Pres & CEO)
Timothy Flynn (VP-Underwriting &
Mktg)
Diane Weaver (VP-Clients)

Bay Area Oil Supply Inc.—(Continued)

BAY AREA OIL SUPPLY INC.
Ste 104 1500 Fashion Blvd, San Mateo, CA 94404-1556
Tel.: (650) 259-9506
Web Site: http://www.baosinc.com
Rev.: $23,607,791
Emp.: 15
Service Station Supplies, Petroleum
N.A.I.C.S.: 424720
Alex Gaviola (Gen Mgr)

BAY ASSOCIATES INC.
1432 Front Ave, Lutherville Timonium, MD 21093
Tel.: (410) 825-6616
Web Site:
https://www.bayassociates.com
Year Founded: 1974
Sales Range: $10-24.9 Million
Emp.: 10
Aircraft Equipment & Supplies
N.A.I.C.S.: 423860
Barry Peltzer (VP)
Robin Ewell (Asst VP)
Paul Baker (Pres)
Donald A. Greenwalt Jr. (Chm)

BAY BRIDGE FOOD AND PRODUCE COMPANY
3550 S Harlan St Ste 284, Denver, CO 80235
Tel.: (720) 385-8381   DE
Year Founded: 2013
Fruits & Vegetables Producer
N.A.I.C.S.: 111419
Andrew Duke (Pres, CEO, CFO, Principal Acctg Officer, Treas & Sec)

BAY CAPITAL MORTGAGE CORPORATION
801 Compass Way Ste 208, Annapolis, MD 21401
Tel.: (410) 974-6044
Web Site:
http://www.baycapitalmortgage.com
Year Founded: 1994
Sales Range: $25-49.9 Million
Emp.: 50
Mortgage Lender
N.A.I.C.S.: 522310
Leo Dunn (CEO)
Daniel Spotts (Pres)
Brad Watkins (COO)
Chris Nieberlein (Sr VP-Lending)
Patrick Moylan (VP & Branch Mgr)
Clint Anuszewski (Asst VP)
Jason Nader (VP)

BAY CHEVROLET
240-02 Northern Blvd, Little Neck, NY 11363
Tel.: (718) 224-4400
Year Founded: 1925
Sales Range: $10-24.9 Million
Emp.: 35
Car Whslr
N.A.I.C.S.: 441110
Robert Benjamin (Pres)

BAY CHEVROLET, INC.
2900 Government Blvd, Mobile, AL 36606
Tel.: (251) 476-8080
Year Founded: 1982
Sales Range: $25-49.9 Million
Emp.: 100
Car Whslr
N.A.I.C.S.: 441110
John S. Moses (Pres)

BAY CITIES APPLIANCE INC.
3107 Santa Monica Blvd, Santa Monica, CA 90404
Tel.: (310) 393-3771

Web Site:
http://www.baycitiesinc.com
Year Founded: 1945
Sales Range: $10-24.9 Million
Emp.: 11
Household Appliance Stores
N.A.I.C.S.: 449210
Joseph Haffid (Pres)

BAY CITY CABINETS
4335 E Hillsborough Ave, Tampa, FL 33610
Tel.: (813) 621-2198
Sales Range: $1-9.9 Million
Emp.: 9
Wood Kitchen & Bathroom Cabinet Retailer
N.A.I.C.S.: 459999
Carl L. Dunbar (Pres)

BAY COMPUTING GROUP
2300 Clayton Rd Ste 1450, Concord, CA 94520
Tel.: (925) 459-8500
Web Site: http://www.baymcp.com
Year Founded: 1999
Sales Range: $1-9.9 Million
Emp.: 20
Computer System Design Services
N.A.I.C.S.: 541512
Kirk Harding (Founder & CEO)
Jon Lee (Dir-Client Svcs)
Anne Chen (Dir-HR)

BAY CORRUGATED CONTAINER INC.
1655 W 7th St, Monroe, MI 48161
Tel.: (734) 243-5400
Web Site: https://www.baycorr.com
Sales Range: $25-49.9 Million
Emp.: 165
Boxes Corrugated: Made From Purchased Materials
N.A.I.C.S.: 322211
Jim Goins (Mgr-HR)
Keith Wagner (Plant Mgr)

BAY COVE HUMAN SERVICES, INC.
66 Canal St, Boston, MA 02114
Tel.: (617) 371-3000   MA
Web Site: http://www.baycove.org
Year Founded: 1973
Emp.: 2,000
Individual & Family Support Services
N.A.I.C.S.: 624190
Hilary Croach (CIO & VP-Tech)
Jim Laprade (Sr VP-Ops)
Nancy Mahan (Sr VP-Program Svcs)
Ronnie Springer (VP-Addiction Svcs)
Greg Buscone (Treas)
Mike Lento (Chm)
Bill Sprague (Pres & CEO)
Candace Chang (Dir-Child & Family Svcs)
Charles Hollins (Dir-Advocacy)
Jamie Rihbany (VP & Controller)
Julie Battisti (Dir-New Initiatives)
Lou Fackert (Dir-Trng)
Ajay Chadha (Vice Chm)
Emma Concepcion (VP-HR)
Mary Jo Cooper (VP-Developmental Disabilities Svcs)
David Hirschberg (VP-Dev)
Carley Lubarsky (VP-Mental Health Svcs)
Kerry Ollen (CFO & Sr VP-Fin)

BAY CRANE SERVICE, INC.
1102 43rd Ave, Long Island City, NY 11101
Tel.: (718) 392-0800   NY
Web Site: http://www.baycrane.com
Year Founded: 1956
Sales Range: $1-9.9 Million
Emp.: 46

Heavy Construction Equipment Rental
N.A.I.C.S.: 532412
Gregg Barry (VP)
John Hagerstrom (VP)

Subsidiaries:

Capital City Group, Inc.   (1)
2299 Performance Way, Columbus, OH 43207
Tel.: (614) 278-2120
Web Site: http://www.ccgroup-inc.com
Sales Range: $10-24.9 Million
Emp.: 80
Crane & Other Heavy Equipment Leasing Services
N.A.I.C.S.: 532490
Brian Gibson (Pres)
Bill Lorenz (VP-Field Ops)
Gerald Duda (Mgr-Equipment)
Jim Albert (Mgr-Coshocton)
Nick Salvatore (Mgr-Toledo)
Bob Blank (Mgr-Ottawa)
Travis Wilson (Mgr-Morgantown)

BAY ELECTRIC COMPANY, INC.
627 36th St, Newport News, VA 23607
Tel.: (757) 595-2300
Web Site:
https://www.bayelectricco.com
Year Founded: 1964
Sales Range: $75-99.9 Million
Emp.: 160
Electronic Services
N.A.I.C.S.: 238210
Carolyn J. Luckadoo (CFO)
Mark Biagas (Mgr-Bus Dev)
Daryl Lanouette (Dir-Electrical Construction)
John F. Biagas (Owner, Pres & CEO)

BAY EQUITY, LLC.
770 Tamalpais Dr Ste 207, Corte Madera, CA 94925
Tel.: (415) 632-5150
Web Site:
https://www.bayequityhome.com
Year Founded: 2007
Sales Range: $25-49.9 Million
Emp.: 502
Financial Services
N.A.I.C.S.: 523999
Brett McGovern (Founder & CEO)
Casey McGovern (Co-Founder, Pres, Mng Dir & Chief Production Officer)
Chad Santander (Sr Exec VP-Capital Markets)
Sue Melnick (COO & Chief Compliance Officer)
Paul Chevez (Sr Exec VP-Fin)
John Cady (Exec VP-Retail)
Philip Mikolaj (Exec VP-Tech)
John Marler (Exec VP-Mktg & Comm)

BAY FOODS INC.
1021 Noell Ln, Rocky Mount, NC 27802
Tel.: (252) 937-2000   NC
Web Site: http://www.bneinc.com
Year Founded: 1972
Sales Range: $10-24.9 Million
Emp.: 13,000
Fast-Food Restaurant, Chain
N.A.I.C.S.: 722513
William L. Boddie (Pres & CEO)
Craig Worthy (CFO)

BAY GROVE CAPITAL LLC
423 Washington St 7th Fl, San Francisco, CA 94111
Tel.: (415) 229-7953
Web Site: http://www.bay-grove.com
Sales Range: $25-49.9 Million
Emp.: 6
Privater Equity Firm
N.A.I.C.S.: 523999

Kevin Marchetti (Mng Dir)
Adam Forste (Mng Dir)
Kristina Hentschel (Dir-Ops)
David Brandes (Mng Dir)

Subsidiaries:

Lineage Logistics Holdings LLC   (1)
46500 Humboldt Dr, Novi, MI 48337
Tel.: (800) 678-7271
Web Site: http://www.lineagelogistics.com
Holding Company; Warehousing & Logistics Services
N.A.I.C.S.: 551112
Mike McClendon (Pres-Ops-Intl & Exec VP-Network Optimization)
Jason E. Burnett (Gen Counsel & Sr VP)
Greg Bryan (Sr VP-Transportation Solutions)
Jeff Rivera (COO-Global)
Tim Smith (Exec VP-Sls & Bus Dev)
Sudarsan Thattai (CIO)
Sean Vanderelzen (Chief HR Officer)
Brian McGowan (Sr VP-Lean Enterprise)
Robert C. Crisci (CFO)
W. Gregory Lehmkuhl (Pres & CEO)
Harld Peters (Sr VP-Europe)
Brooke Miller (Pres-Asia Pacific)

Subsidiary (Domestic):

Consolidated Distribution Corp LLC   (2)
333 E Butterfield Rd Ste 830, Lombard, IL 60148   (100%)
Tel.: (630) 633-6300
Web Site: http://www.cdcsupply.com
Rev.: $3,100,000
Emp.: 100
Distributes Food Products to Restaurants
N.A.I.C.S.: 424490
J. Mitchell Rader (CEO)
Tim Ward (CFO)

Holding (Domestic):

Emergent Cold LP   (2)
2950 N Harwood St Ste 1510, Dallas, TX 75201
Web Site: http://www.emergentcold.com
Cold Storage, Warehousing & Refrigerated Transportation Services
N.A.I.C.S.: 493120
Neal Rider (CEO)
Tom Casey (CFO)
David Palfenier (Pres-Latin America)
Chris Jamroz (Chm)

Subsidiary (Non-US):

Finlay Cold Storage (Pvt) Limited   (3)
309/6 Negombo Road, Welisara, Colombo, Sri Lanka
Tel.: (94) 114828400
Cold Storage Services
N.A.I.C.S.: 493120
Gihan S. Jayasinghe (CEO & Head-Country)

Holding (Domestic):

Flint River Services Inc.   (2)
1011 Worth St, Albany, GA 31705
Tel.: (229) 883-1912
Web Site: http://www.flintriverservices.com
Refrigerated Warehousing & Storage
N.A.I.C.S.: 493120
Lem Griffin (Pres & CEO)

Lineage Logistics - Algona   (2)
502 10th Ave N, Algona, WA 98001
Tel.: (253) 272-0900
Web Site: http://lineagelogistics.com
Refrigerated Warehousing & Storage
N.A.I.C.S.: 493120
Brian Gogerty (Gen Mgr)

Branch (Domestic):

Lineage Logistics - Midwest Regional Office   (2)
13030 Pierce St, Omaha, NE 68144
Tel.: (402) 896-6600
Refrigerated Warehousing & Storage
N.A.I.C.S.: 493120
Cathy Mertz (Mgr-Cash)
Jammie Morris (Mgr-IT)
Merle Lemmen (Pres-Midwest)

Subsidiary (Domestic):

Lineage Logistics, LLC (2)
46500 Humboldt Dr, Novi, MI 48377
Tel.: (800) 678-7271
Web Site: http://www.lineagelogistics.com
Logistics & Supply Chain
N.A.I.C.S.: 541614
Greg Lehmkuhl (Pres & CEO)

Subsidiary (Domestic):

Hanson Cold Storage, LLC (3)
440 Renaissance Dr, Saint Joseph, MI
49085-9085
Tel.: (269) 982-1390
Web Site: http://www.hansonlogistics.com
Refrigerated Warehousing & Storage
N.A.I.C.S.: 493120
Ken Whah (Pres & CEO)

**Perishable Shipping Solutions,
LLC** (3)
1130 Performance Pl, Youngstown, OH
44502
Web Site: http://www.goperishable.com
Sales Range: $1-9.9 Million
Transportation & Storage Services
N.A.I.C.S.: 484220
Mark Nelson (CEO)
Stephanie Riffell (COO)
Danny Catullo (Co-Founder & Chief Customer Officer)
Ruben Garcia (Co-Founder & Chief Strategy Officer)
Anna Alexander (Mgr-Customer Success)

Subsidiary (Non-US):

**VersaCold International
Corporation** (3)
316 Aviva Park Dr, Vaughan, L4L 9C7, ON,
Canada
Tel.: (604) 255-4656
Web Site: http://www.versacold.com
Refrigerated Warehousing & Logistics Services
N.A.I.C.S.: 493120
Michele Arcamone (Pres & CEO)

Subsidiary (Domestic):

Coastal Pacific Xpress Inc. (4)
105-5355 152nd Street, Surrey, V3S 5A5,
BC, Canada
Tel.: (604) 575-4200
Web Site: http://www.cpx.ca
Emp.: 550
Trucking Service
N.A.I.C.S.: 484110
Jeff Scott (Pres)

Holding (Domestic):

Terminal Freezers, Inc. (2)
410 S Spruce St, Burlington, WA 98233
Tel.: (360) 755-9015
Web Site: http://www.terminalfreezers.com
Refrigerated Warehousing & Storage Services
N.A.I.C.S.: 493120

Preferred Freezer Services Inc. (1)
1 Main St 3rd Fl, Chatham, NJ 07928
Tel.: (973) 820-4040
Web Site: http://www.preferredfreezer.com
Refrigerated Warehousing & Storage
N.A.I.C.S.: 493120
Daniel DiDonato (Exec VP-Sls)
John Ingrassia (Regional Dir-Sls-East)
Brian Beattie (Pres)
Samuel Hensley (CFO)
Lawrence Abbott (Mgr-Sls)
Timothy McLellan (Mng Dir-Bus Dev-Intl)
Adrian Sinay (Gen Mgr)
Ron Viola (Mgr-Sls)
Paddy Sellino (Dir-Office Ops-US)
Aaron Hinderer (Dir-Sls & Ops Midwest)
Jesse Gross (Dir-Health & Safety)
Larry Faschan (Dir-HR Dept)
James Gladis (VP-Fin)
Marc Vendome (VP-Ops)
Bob Walsh (Mgr-Corp Facilities)
Rich Williams (VP-Ops)
Eric Wolf (Asst Dir-Food Safety & Quality)

Subsidiary (Domestic):

**Preferred Freezer Services Miami,
Inc.** (2)

12855 NW 113th Ct, Miami, FL 33178
Tel.: (305) 885-2200
Web Site: http://www.preferredfreezer.com
Sales Range: $10-24.9 Million
Refrigerated Warehousing & Storage
N.A.I.C.S.: 493120
Jason Szczutkowski (Gen Mgr)
Jo Sanders (Office Mgr)
Rod Armesto (Mgr-Sls)
Gilbert Perez (Mgr-Ops)
Hugo Cordova (Mgr-Ops)
Janet Cuenca (Office Mgr)

Subsidiary (Non-US):

**Preferred Freezer Services of Ho Chi
Minh City** (2)
163 Nguyen Van Quy Khu Pho 1 Phuong
Phu Thuan Quan 7 TP, Ho Chi Minh City,
Vietnam (100%)
Tel.: (84) 8 3773 3303
Web Site: http://www.preferredfreezer.com
Refrigerated Warehousing
N.A.I.C.S.: 493120
Tim McLellan (Mng Dir)
Tien Vu (Sr Mgr-Sls)
Vien Nguyen (Sls Mgr)
Le Hong Nhung (Office Mgr)
Van Thuy Nguyen (Fin Dir)

**Preferred Freezer Services of Lin-
gang Logistics Park** (2)
211 Jiexing Road Lingang New City,
Shanghai, 201308, China (100%)
Tel.: (86) 139 1781 6902
Web Site: http://www.preferredfreezer.com
Refrigerated Warehousing
N.A.I.C.S.: 493120

Subsidiary (Domestic):

**Preferred Freezer Services of Perth
Amboy, LLC** (2)
536 Fayette St, Perth Amboy, NJ 08861
Tel.: (732) 324-2000
Web Site: http://www.preferredfreezer.com
Refrigerated Warehousing & Storage
N.A.I.C.S.: 493120
John Kennedy (Gen Mgr)
Peter Soto (Mgr-Sls)

Subsidiary (Non-US):

**Preferred Freezer Services of Wai
Gao Qiao** (2)
2 Hua Jing Road Waigaoqiao Free Trade
Zone, Shanghai, Waigaoqiao,
China (100%)
Tel.: (86) 139 1781 6902
Web Site: http://www.preferredfreezer.com
Refrigerated Warehousing
N.A.I.C.S.: 493120

BAY HUMAN SERVICES
PO Box 741, Standish, MI 48658
Tel.: (989) 846-9631 MI
Year Founded: 1980
Sales Range: $10-24.9 Million
Emp.: 723
Disability Assistance Services
N.A.I.C.S.: 624120
James Pilot (Exec Dir)

BAY INDUSTRIES INC.
2929 Walker Dr, Green Bay, WI
54311-8312
Tel.: (920) 406-4000 WI
Web Site:
http://www.baycompanies.com
Sales Range: $125-149.9 Million
Emp.: 700
Insulation Sub-Contractor
N.A.I.C.S.: 423330
Daniel Schmidt (Pres)
Ronn Kleinschmidt (CFO & VP-Fin)
Kathleen Jadin (Controller)
Mark Berg (Coord-ERP)
Kristy Wylie (Mgr-Accts Receivable)
Karen Herlich (Mgr-Gen Ledger
Acctg)
Dave Smits (Mgr-Ops)

Mark Novak (Reg Mgr)
Tim Lewis (Mgr-Fin)
Lisa Oudenhoven (Plant Mgr)

Subsidiaries:

Backer Rod Manufacturing Inc. (1)
4244 Broadway, Denver, CO 80216-4902
Tel.: (303) 308-0363
Web Site: http://www.bayindustries.com
Sales Range: $10-24.9 Million
Emp.: 6
Fabricated Structural Metal Mfr
N.A.I.C.S.: 332312
C. Bergel (Gen Mgr)

Bay Converting Inc. (1)
1330 Elizabeth St, Green Bay, WI 54302
Tel.: (920) 431-9110
Label Coating Services
N.A.I.C.S.: 561910

**Bay Industries Inc. - Fabricated Insu-
lation Division** (1)
2929 Walker Dr, Green Bay, WI 54308
Tel.: (920) 406-4300
Insulated Product Mfr
N.A.I.C.S.: 326140

Subsidiary (Domestic):

Bay Fabrication Inc. (2)
2929 Walker Dr, Green Bay, WI 54308
Tel.: (920) 406-4300
Thermal Insulation Panel System Mfr
N.A.I.C.S.: 326140

Bay Insulation (1)
7043 S 190th St, Kent, WA
98032-1059 (100%)
Tel.: (425) 251-6750
Web Site: http://www.bayindustries.com
Sales Range: $10-24.9 Million
Emp.: 22
Sub-contractors
N.A.I.C.S.: 423330
Don Gleason (Dir-Ops)

Bay Insulation (1)
2929 Walker Dr, Green Bay, WI 54311
Tel.: (920) 406-4200
Web Site: http://www.bayindustries.com
Sales Range: $10-24.9 Million
Emp.: 100
Mfr of Insulation
N.A.I.C.S.: 423330

**Bay Insulation Supply of Colorado
Inc.** (1)
14200 E 33rd Pl, Aurora, CO 80011
Tel.: (303) 371-0505
Insulation Material Whslr
N.A.I.C.S.: 423330

**Bay Insulation Supply of
Columbus** (1)
2245 Westbelt Dr, Columbus, OH 43228
Tel.: (614) 345-0804
Web Site: http://www.bayindustries.com
Sales Range: $10-24.9 Million
Emp.: 5
Insulation Material Whslr
N.A.I.C.S.: 423330
Mitchell Davis (Gen Mgr)

**Bay Insulation Supply of
Milwaukee** (1)
823R1 S 60th St, Milwaukee, WI 53214
Tel.: (414) 258-9333
Insulation Material Whslr
N.A.I.C.S.: 423330

**Bay Insulation Supply of Nevada
Inc** (1)
3555 Ponderosa Way Unit E, Las Vegas,
NV 89118
Tel.: (702) 891-5333
Insulation Material Whslr
N.A.I.C.S.: 423330

Bay Insulation Supply of Ohio (1)
4755 W 150th St Ste E, Cleveland, OH
44135
Tel.: (216) 362-7338
Web Site:
http://www.bayinsulationsupply.com
Insulation Material Whslr
N.A.I.C.S.: 423330

**Bay Insulation Supply of San Diego
Inc.** (1)

7949 Stromesa Ct Ste T, San Diego, CA
92126
Tel.: (858) 530-0414
Web Site: http://www.bayindustries.com
Sales Range: $10-24.9 Million
Emp.: 3
Insulation Material Whslr
N.A.I.C.S.: 423330
Chris Prebay (Gen Mgr)

**Bay Insulation Supply of
Spokane** (1)
1017 N Bradley Rd Ste B, Spokane Valley,
WA 99212
Tel.: (509) 893-3411
Web Site:
http://www.bayinsulationsupply.com
Insulation Material Whslr
N.A.I.C.S.: 423330

Bay Insulation Systems, Inc. (1)
2929 Walker Dr, Green Bay, WI 54308
Tel.: (920) 406-4700
Metal Building Insulation Material Mfr
N.A.I.C.S.: 332999

Bay Insulation of Arizona Inc. (1)
800 W Fairmont Dr Ste 2, Tempe, AZ
85282
Tel.: (480) 966-2266
Web Site: http://www.bayindustries.com
Emp.: 6
Insulation Material Whslr
N.A.I.C.S.: 423330
Arnold W. Schmidt (CEO)

Bay Insulation of Illinois Inc. (1)
6750 S Sayre Ave, Bedford Park, IL 60638-
4725
Tel.: (708) 728-9141
Thermal Insulation Panel System Mfr
N.A.I.C.S.: 326140
Sceve Nicinh (Gen Mgr)

**Bay Insulation of Kansas City
Inc.** (1)
5201E Front St, Kansas City, MO 64120
Tel.: (816) 920-5900
Insulation Material Whslr
N.A.I.C.S.: 423330

Bay Insulation of Missouri Inc. (1)
1170 Central Industrial Dr, Saint Louis, MO
63110
Tel.: (314) 776-2002
Building Material Dealers
N.A.I.C.S.: 444180

Bay Insulation of Tennessee Inc. (1)
8472 Industrial Dr, Olive Branch, MS 38654
Tel.: (662) 893-2400
Metal Building Insulation Mfr
N.A.I.C.S.: 332311

Bay Insulation of Texas Inc. (1)
4411B Darien St, Houston, TX 77028
Tel.: (713) 675-1811
Insulation Product Whslr
N.A.I.C.S.: 423330

Expi-Door Systems Inc. (1)
3146 Yeager Dr, Green Bay, WI 54311
Tel.: (920) 393-4028
Building Material Dealers
N.A.I.C.S.: 444180
Brian Smith (Project Mgr-Sls Svc)

FrontLine Bldg. Products Inc. (1)
610 Jensen Dr, Medford, WI 54451
Tel.: (800) 223-4792
Web Site: http://www.frontlinebldg.biz
Building Material Mfr & Whslr
N.A.I.C.S.: 444180

Midco-Bay Insulation Inc. (1)
W226N758 Eastmound Dr, Waukesha, WI
53186
Tel.: (262) 797-6675
Building Material Supplier
N.A.I.C.S.: 444180

BAY INN, INC.
800 Vanderbilt Beach Rd, Naples, FL
34108
Tel.: (239) 597-8777
Web Site:
https://www.innatpelicanbay.com
Year Founded: 1993
Sales Range: $1-9.9 Million

Bay Inn, Inc.—(Continued)
Emp.: 75
Hotel Operations
N.A.I.C.S.: 721110
Steven Gyorkos *(Dir-Sls)*
Steven Dorcy *(Gen Mgr)*
Fred Hirschovits *(Owner)*

BAY LAKES COOPERATIVE
720 N Main St, Oconto Falls, WI
54154-9301
Tel.: (920) 846-3461
Web Site: http://www.baylakes.com
Year Founded: 1935
Sales Range: $10-24.9 Million
Emp.: 80
Provider of Farm Supplies
N.A.I.C.S.: 424910
Steve Wery *(CEO)*

BAY MANUFACTURED HOMES INC.
10916 N Nebraska Ave, Tampa, FL
33612
Tel.: (813) 977-7300   FL
Web Site:
    https://www.baymanufactured.com
Year Founded: 1956
Sales Range: $1-9.9 Million
Emp.: 5
Manufactured Mobile Homes Retailer
N.A.I.C.S.: 459930
Patricia Rew *(Pres)*

BAY MECHANICAL INC.
2696 Reliance Dr Ste 200, Virginia
Beach, VA 23452-7832
Tel.: (757) 468-6700   VA
Web Site:
    https://www.baymechanical.com
Year Founded: 1980
Sales Range: $25-49.9 Million
Emp.: 200
Plumbing, Heating & Air Conditioning
Service Contractors
N.A.I.C.S.: 238220
B. R. Rod Rodriguez *(Owner & Pres)*
James Snell *(Project Mgr-Coatings Div)*

BAY MICROSYSTEMS, INC.
2055 Gateway Pl Ste 650, San Jose,
CA 95110
Tel.: (408) 437-0400
Web Site:
    http://www.baymicrosystems.com
Year Founded: 2000
Sales Range: $10-24.9 Million
Emp.: 50
Processor Routing & Switching
Equipment Developer
N.A.I.C.S.: 334413
Michael D. McDonald *(CFO)*
Gerry Jankauskas *(CTO)*
Robert Lawrentz *(Pres & CEO)*
Robert Smedley *(Sr VP-Sys Engrg)*
Jonatan Schmidt *(Chief Strategy Officer)*
Russel Davis *(COO & Exec VP-Emerging Solutions)*

BAY MUTUAL FINANCIAL, LLC
1453 3rd St Ste 490, Santa Monica,
CA 90401-4030
Tel.: (310) 586-3222   CA
Web Site: http://www.baymutual.com
Securities Brokerage & Investment
Advisory Services
N.A.I.C.S.: 523150
Martin W. Pernoll *(CEO & Sr Mng Dir)*
Tom Demko *(Pres)*

BAY N GULF INC.

4520 8th Ave S, Saint Petersburg, FL
33711
Tel.: (727) 321-0425
Web Site:
    http://www.saveonseafood.com
Year Founded: 1980
Sales Range: $25-49.9 Million
Emp.: 100
Seafoods
N.A.I.C.S.: 445250
Gilbert Migliano *(Pres)*
Rob Frost *(Controller)*

BAY OIL COMPANY INC.
2201 Frozen, Dickinson, TX 77539-
5161
Tel.: (281) 337-4671
Web Site: http://www.bayoilfuel.com
Year Founded: 1991
Sales Range: $10-24.9 Million
Emp.: 40
Producer of Petroleum Products
N.A.I.C.S.: 424720
Link Smith *(Co-Owner)*

BAY PRODUCTS, INC.
17800 15 Mile Rd, Fraser, MI 48026
Tel.: (586) 296-7130
Web Site:
    https://www.bayproductsinc.com
Year Founded: 1985
Industrial Machinery Mfr
N.A.I.C.S.: 333248

BAY RAG CORPORATION
6250 NW 35th Ave, Miami, FL 33147
Tel.: (305) 693-6868
Web Site:
    http://www.bayragcorporation.com
Sales Range: $10-24.9 Million
Emp.: 36
Knit Fabrics
N.A.I.C.S.: 424340
Abraham Salstein *(Pres)*
Howard Salstein *(VP)*

BAY RIDGE AUTOMOTIVE GROUP
6401 6th Ave, Brooklyn, NY 11220
Tel.: (718) 439-7888
Web Site:
    http://www.bayridgetoyota.com
Year Founded: 1968
Sales Range: $50-74.9 Million
Emp.: 102
Car Dealer
N.A.I.C.S.: 441110
Carmelo Giuffre *(Pres)*

BAY RIDGE PREP
8101 Ridge Blvd, Brooklyn, NY 11209
Tel.: (718) 833-9090
Web Site:
    https://www.bayridgeprep.org
Year Founded: 1998
Educational Support Services
N.A.I.C.S.: 611710

BAY RIDGE SUBARU
1819 Cropsey Ave, Brooklyn, NY
11214
Tel.: (718) 234-7960
Web Site:
    http://www.bayridgeautos.com
Rev.: $21,400,000
Emp.: 22
New Car Dealers
N.A.I.C.S.: 441110
Tom Ruggiero Jr. *(Pres)*

BAY RIDGE VOLVO-AMERICAN INC.
8919 4th Ave, Brooklyn, NY 11209
Tel.: (718) 833-7070
Web Site:
    http://www.bayridgecars.com

Sales Range: $200-249.9 Million
Emp.: 120
New & Used Automobiles
N.A.I.C.S.: 441110
Arthur Gottlieb *(Pres)*

BAY SHIP & YACHT CO
2900 Main St Ste 2100, Alameda, CA
94501
Tel.: (510) 337-9122
Web Site: https://www.bay-ship.com
Sales Range: $25-49.9 Million
Emp.: 285
Structural Steel Erection
N.A.I.C.S.: 238120
Anthony Del Gavio *(Mgr-Bus Dev)*
Mike Stoecker *(Acct Mgr)*

Subsidiaries:

Svendsen's Boat Works, Inc.   (1)
1851 Clement Ave, Alameda, CA 94501
Tel.: (510) 522-2886
Web Site: http://www.svendsens.com
Boat Building
N.A.I.C.S.: 336612
Josie Tucci *(Dir-Mktg-North America)*

BAY STAGE LIGHTING COMPANY, INC.
4008 W Alva St, Tampa, FL 33614
Tel.: (813) 877-1089
Web Site:
    http://www.baystagelighting.com
Year Founded: 1957
Sales Range: $1-9.9 Million
Emp.: 15
Electrical Apparatus & Equipment,
Wiring Supplies & Related Equipment
Merchant Whslr
N.A.I.C.S.: 423610
Yvonne Felicione Justo *(Pres)*
Michele Tunstall *(Coord-Admin)*
Greg Utley *(VP-Creative Svcs)*
Nicole Justo Idziak *(VP-Bus Dev)*
Danielle Justo Sherwin *(VP-Admin)*

BAY STATE COMPUTERS INC.
4201 Northview Dr Ste 408, Bowie,
MD 20716-2670
Tel.: (301) 352-7878
Web Site: http://www.bayst.com
Sales Range: $10-24.9 Million
Emp.: 30
Computer Repair & Support Services
N.A.I.C.S.: 423430
Patricia Hill *(Chm & CEO)*

BAY STATE ENVELOPE INC.
440 Chauncy St, Mansfield, MA
02048
Tel.: (508) 337-8900
Web Site:
    http://www.baystateenvelope.com
Sales Range: $10-24.9 Million
Emp.: 30
Mfr & Sales of Envelopes
N.A.I.C.S.: 323111
Russell Frizzell *(Pres)*
Cindy Roche *(Mgr-Admin & Mgr-HR)*
Dave Luongo *(VP)*

BAY STATE MILLING COMPANY
100 Congress St, Quincy, MA 02169-
0906
Tel.: (617) 328-4400   MA
Web Site:
    https://www.baystatemilling.com
Year Founded: 1899
Sales Range: $150-199.9 Million
Emp.: 344
Flour Mill Operator
N.A.I.C.S.: 311211
Peter F. Levangie *(Pres & CEO)*
Walker Humphries *(VP-Strategic Planning)*

Douglas J. Dewitt *(VP-Sales-Customer Dev)*
Jennifer Robinson *(VP-Corp Quality Assurance)*
Keith Adams *(VP & Gen Mgr-Core Milling)*

Subsidiaries:

Bay State Milling Company   (1)
400 Platte St, Platteville, CO 80651-1110
Tel.: (970) 785-2794
Web Site: http://www.baystatemilling.com
Flour Milling Services
N.A.I.C.S.: 311211
Carmen Poland *(Office Mgr & Mgr-Quality Assurance)*

T.J. Harkins Basic Commodity Brokers, Inc   (1)
279 Beaudin Blvd, Bolingbrook, IL 60440
Tel.: (630) 427-3400
Web Site: http://www.tjharkins.com
Sales Range: $25-49.9 Million
Emp.: 41
Natural & Organic Food Ingredients Supplier
N.A.I.C.S.: 311999
Jeff Koonce *(Controller)*

BAY STATE PHYSICAL THERAPY
26 S Main St, Randolph, MA 02368
Tel.: (781) 961-9200
Web Site: http://baystatept.com
Year Founded: 1995
Hospital & Healthcare Services
N.A.I.C.S.: 622310
Steven Windwer *(Pres & CEO)*

BAY STATE POOL SUPPLIES INC.
691 Concord Ave, Cambridge, MA
02138
Tel.: (617) 547-9145
Web Site:
    http://www.baystatepools.com
Sales Range: $25-49.9 Million
Emp.: 25
Swimming Pools, Equipment & Supplies
N.A.I.C.S.: 423910
Charles P. Arakelian *(Founder & Pres)*
Charles Hamilton *(VP-Fin)*
Joe Toro *(Mgr-Natl Sls)*

BAY STATE SAVINGS BANK
28 Franklin St, Worcester, MA 01608
Tel.: (508) 890-9000
Web Site:
    http://www.baystatesavingsbank.com
Year Founded: 1895
Sales Range: $10-24.9 Million
Commercial Banking
N.A.I.C.S.: 522110
Diane M. Giampa *(Sr VP-HR, Mktg & Retail Banking)*
Thomas J. Belton *(Sr VP-IT)*
Jeffrey B. Locke *(VP & Branch Mgr)*
Veronika Tovanyan *(VP & Branch Mgr)*
Osman K. Acheampong *(Officer-Credit Admin)*
Jayme D. Burdett *(Asst VP & Branch Mgr)*
Janet L. Jones *(VP-Retail Ops)*
Lucas J. Miller *(Gen Counsel & Sr VP-Compliance)*
William L. Martin *(Officer-Comml Loan)*
Heather L. Belair *(Virtual Branch Mgr)*
Lemonia Mironidis *(Asst VP & Branch Mgr)*
Francis Dauphinais *(CFO & Sr VP)*
Jeanie Connolly *(Sr VP-Comml Lending)*
Emiljano Beqo *(Mgr-Retail Loan Servicing & Collections)*

BAY TEK GAMES, INC.
1077 E Glenbrook Dr, Pulaski, WI 54162
Tel.: (920) 822-3951
Web Site:
http://www.baytekgames.com
Year Founded: 1977
Coin Operated Game Equipment Mfr
N.A.I.C.S.: 335999
Larry Treankler (*Founder & Chm*)
Bob Rupp (*CEO*)
Jon Moreau (*CFO*)
Jim Keane (*Pres*)
Pat Scanlan (*Dir-Product Dev*)
Shannon Herbst (*Dir-Ops*)
Rick Rochetti (*Dir-Sls*)
Mark Lenske (*Acct Mgr*)
Molly Van Lannen (*Mgr-Inside Sls*)
Holly Hampton (*Dir-Innovation*)
Ryan Cravens (*Mgr-Bus Dev*)
Sammy Harrison (*Mgr-Mktg*)
Mike Pantalone (*Mgr-Parts & Svcs*)
Dan Jahnke (*Mgr-Svc*)

BAY TO BAY PROPERTIES, LLC
600 2nd St, Safety Harbor, FL 34695
Tel.: (727) 483-9512
Web Site:
http://www.baytobayproperties.com
Sales Range: $10-24.9 Million
Emp.: 20
Commercial & Residential Construction
N.A.I.C.S.: 236220
Joseph W. Faw (*Co-Owner*)
Jerome A. Ciliento (*Co-Owner*)
John J. Downes (*Partner*)

BAY TOOL & SUPPLY INC.
1001 Yosemite Dr, Milpitas, CA 95035
Tel.: (408) 383-9266
Web Site: http://www.baytools.com
Rev.: $10,803,286
Emp.: 30
Construction Hand Tools
N.A.I.C.S.: 423710
Anton Oehlert (*VP-Fin & Controller*)

BAY VIEW FOOD PRODUCTS COMPANY
2606 N Huron Rd, Pinconning, MI 48650
Tel.: (989) 879-3555
Web Site:
https://www.bayviewfoods.com
Year Founded: 1946
Sales Range: $10-24.9 Million
Emp.: 450
Pickle Mfr
N.A.I.C.S.: 311421
Joseph Janicke (*Pres*)
Sharon Janicke (*VP-Acct Payable & Receivable*)
Randy Hugo (*VP-Agriculture*)
Jaime Dobyne (*Mgr-HR*)

BAY VILLAGE OF SARASOTA, INC.
8400 Vamo Rd, Sarasota, FL 34231
Tel.: (941) 966-5611   FL
Web Site: https://www.bayvillage.org
Year Founded: 1972
Sales Range: $10-24.9 Million
Emp.: 373
Assisted Living Facility Services
N.A.I.C.S.: 623312
Sally Seeger (*Sec*)
Kevin Hicks (*Chm*)
Thomas Combs (*Vice Chm*)
Thomas Taylor (*Treas*)
John F. McClellan (*Exec Dir*)

BAY-DOVER INC.

3301 East Rancier Ave Bldg B, Killeen, TX 76543
Tel.: (254) 699-0868
Sales Range: $1-9.9 Million
Emp.: 70
Grocery Stores
N.A.I.C.S.: 445110
John Benson (*Owner*)
Ronnie Jaro (*Owner*)

BAY-HOUSTON TOWING CO
2243 Milford St, Houston, TX 77098
Tel.: (713) 529-3755
Web Site:
https://www.bayhouston.com
Rev.: $35,800,000
Emp.: 20
Towing Of Boats
N.A.I.C.S.: 424910
Milow Klein (*CFO*)
Scott Shorkey (*Mgr-IT*)

BAY-VANGUARD, M.H.C.
7114 N Point Rd, Baltimore, MD 21219
Tel.: (410) 477-5000
Web Site:
http://www.bayvanguard.com
Mutual Holding Company
N.A.I.C.S.: 551112
Edmund T. Leonard (*Chm*)
David Flair (*Pres*)

Subsidiaries:

BV Financial, Inc.   **(1)**
7114 N Point Rd, Baltimore, MD
21219   **(86.55%)**
Tel.: (410) 477-5000
Web Site: http://www.bayvanguard.com
Rev.: $23,165,000
Assets: $815,565,000
Liabilities: $741,544,000
Net Worth: $74,021,000
Earnings: $7,645,000
Emp.: 34
Fiscal Year-end: 12/31/2020
Bank Holding Company
N.A.I.C.S.: 551111
Edmund T. Leonard (*Chm*)
David M. Flair (*Co-Pres & Co-CEO*)
Jeffrey S. Collier (*Sr VP-Lending*)
Kim C. Liddell (*Chm*)
Michael J. Dee (*CFO & Exec VP*)
Timothy L. Prindle (*Co-Pres & Co-CEO*)
Gregory J. Olinde (*Chief Credit Officer, Pres-Market & Exec VP*)
Michael L. Snyder (*Sec*)
Kim C. Liddell (*Chm*)

Subsidiary (Domestic):

Bay-Vanguard Federal Savings
Bank   **(2)**
7114 N Point Rd, Baltimore, MD 21219
Tel.: (410) 477-5000
Web Site: http://www.bayvanguard.com
Sales Range: $50-74.9 Million
Emp.: 15
Federal Savings Bank
N.A.I.C.S.: 522180
David M. Flair (*Pres & CEO*)
Denise M. Kuhar (*VP-Savings Ops*)
Rose M. Searcy (*VP-Personnel*)
Claudia L. Kraft (*Controller*)
Frieda McWilliams (*Sr VP-Comml Lending*)
Glenda Szyl (*Sr VP-Ops*)

MB Bancorp, Inc.   **(2)**
1920 Rock Spring Rd, Forest Hill, MD 21050
Tel.: (410) 420-9600
Web Site: http://www.mbofmd.com
Rev.: $5,585,000
Assets: $150,349,000
Liabilities: $117,385,000
Net Worth: $32,964,000
Earnings: $2,307,000
Emp.: 23
Fiscal Year-end: 12/31/2018
Bank Holding Company
N.A.I.C.S.: 551111
Philip P. Phillips (*Pres & CEO*)

Subsidiary (Domestic):

Madison Bank of Maryland   **(3)**
1920 Rock Spring Rd, Forest Hill, MD 21050
Tel.: (410) 420-9600
Web Site: http://www.mbofmd.com
Banking Services
N.A.I.C.S.: 522110
John Melvin Wright (*CFO & Exec VP*)
Lisa M. McGuire-Dick (*Sr VP*)

BAYADA HOME HEALTH CARE, INC.
4300 Haddonfield Rd Ste 120, Pennsauken, NJ 08109
Tel.: (856) 663-1622   DE
Web Site: https://www.bayada.com
Year Founded: 1975
Women Healthcare Services
N.A.I.C.S.: 621610
J. Mark Baiada (*Founder*)
David Baiada (*CEO*)
Scott R. Milford (*Chief People Officer*)

BAYBRENT CONSTRUCTION CORP.
1637 Sycamore Ave, Bohemia, NY 11716
Tel.: (631) 563-4500
Web Site: https://www.baybrent.com
Sales Range: $10-24.9 Million
Emp.: 50
Floor Laying Services
N.A.I.C.S.: 238330
Richard Hoshino (*Pres*)

BAYBRIDGE PHARMACY CORP.
208-48 Cross Island Pkwy, Bayside, NY 11360
Tel.: (718) 751-9911
Web Site:
http://www.baybridgepharmacy.com
Year Founded: 2015
Sales Range: $10-24.9 Million
Emp.: 27
Pharmaceutical Product Mfr & Distr
N.A.I.C.S.: 325412
Greg Savino (*Founder & CEO*)
Lucinda Lam (*VP-Ops*)
Michael O'Leary (*Mgr-Delivery*)
Alex Ruiz (*Asst Mgr-Delivery*)
Amir Ahmed (*Asst Mgr-Delivery*)

BAYBUTT CONSTRUCTION CORP.
25 Avon St, Keene, NH 03431
Tel.: (603) 352-6846
Web Site: http://www.baybutt.com
Year Founded: 1964
Sales Range: $10-24.9 Million
Emp.: 100
Commercial & Institutional Building Construction Services
N.A.I.C.S.: 236220
Fred Baybutt (*Pres*)
John Baybutt (*Mgr-Safety*)

BAYCARE HEALTH SYSTEM INC.
2985 Drew St, Clearwater, FL 33759
Tel.: (727) 519-1200
Web Site: https://www.baycare.org
Year Founded: 1997
Sales Range: $500-549.9 Million
Emp.: 30,000
Hospital & Other Healthcare Facilities Owner & Operator
N.A.I.C.S.: 622110
Tommy Inzina (*Pres & CEO*)
Janice Polo (*CFO & Exec VP*)
Nishant Anand (*Chief Medical Officer & Exec VP*)
Glenn Waters (*COO & Exec VP*)
William Walders (*CIO*)
Tim Thompson (*Chief Admin Officer*)

Subsidiaries:

Bartow Regional Medical Center
Inc.   **(1)**
2200 Osprey Blvd, Bartow, FL 33831
Tel.: (863) 533-8111
Web Site: http://www.baycare.org
Hospital Services
N.A.I.C.S.: 622110
Tommy Inzina (*CEO*)
Glenn Waters (*Pres*)

BayCare Alliant Hospital   **(1)**
601 Main St, Dunedin, FL 34698
Tel.: (727) 736-9999
Hospital
N.A.I.C.S.: 622110
Karen Duffy (*Dir-Patient Care Svcs*)

HealthPoint Medical Group   **(1)**
4902 Eisenhower Blvd Ste 300, Tampa, FL 33634-6344
Tel.: (813) 636-2000
Web Site:
http://www.baycaremedicalgroup.com
Physicians Office
N.A.I.C.S.: 621111
Lee Kirkman (*Pres*)

Morton Plant Mease Health Care   **(1)**
300 Pinellas St, Clearwater, FL 33756-3804
Tel.: (727) 462-7000
Web Site: http://www.mpmhealth.com
Sales Range: $500-549.9 Million
Emp.: 6,900
General Medical & Surgical Hospital Services
N.A.I.C.S.: 622110
Darlene Ferenz (*Sec*)
Marion R. Rich (*Pres*)
Bill Fisher (*Vice Chm*)
Sydney E. Niewierski (*Treas*)

Subsidiary (Domestic):

Mease Countryside Hospital   **(2)**
3231 McMullen Booth Rd, Safety Harbor, FL 34695
Tel.: (727) 725-6111
Sales Range: $125-149.9 Million
Emp.: 1,500
Hospital
N.A.I.C.S.: 622110
Lou Galdieri (*COO*)
Tony Schuster (*VP-Physician Svcs*)

Mease Dunedin Hospital   **(2)**
601 Main St, Dunedin, FL 34698
Tel.: (727) 733-1111
Web Site: http://www.baycare.org
Sales Range: $50-74.9 Million
Emp.: 700
Hospital
N.A.I.C.S.: 622110
Lou Galdieri (*COO*)
Tony Schuster (*VP-Physician Svcs*)

Morton Plant Hospital   **(2)**
300 Pinellas St, Clearwater, FL 33756
Tel.: (727) 462-7000
Web Site: http://www.mpmhealth.com
Hospital
N.A.I.C.S.: 622110
Matt Novak (*Dir-Ops*)

Morton Plant North Bay Hospital   **(2)**
6600 Madison St, New Port Richey, FL 34652
Tel.: (727) 842-8468
Hospital
N.A.I.C.S.: 622110
John Haffner (*Dir-Physician Svcs*)
Sarah Naumowich (*Pres*)

St. Anthony's Hospital   **(1)**
1200 7th Ave N, Saint Petersburg, FL 33705
Tel.: (727) 825-1100
Web Site: http://www.stanthonys.com
Hospital
N.A.I.C.S.: 622110
Mary McNally (*VP-Mission*)

St. Joseph's-Baptist Health Care   **(1)**
3001 W Dr Martin Luther King Jr Blvd, Tampa, FL 33607
Tel.: (813) 870-4000
Web Site: http://www.sjbhealth.org
Hospital
N.A.I.C.S.: 622110

BayCare Health System Inc.—(Continued)

Isaac Mallah (Pres & CEO)
Mark Vaaler (Chief Medical Officer)
Kris Kirasich (Coord-Nuclear Medicine)
Chris Jenkins (CTO & VP-Infrastructure)
Dave Davenport (Mgr-Rehabilitation, Wound Care, Hyperbaric, & Infusion Svcs)
Shannon L. James (Supvr-CT & MPM)

Subsidiary (Domestic):

South Florida Baptist Hospital (2)
301 N Alexander St, Plant City, FL 33563
Tel.: (813) 757-1200
Hospital
N.A.I.C.S.: 622110
Steve Nierman (COO)

St. Joseph's Children's Hospital (2)
8001 W Dr Martin Luther King Jr Blvd, Tampa, FL 33607
Tel.: (813) 554-8500
Web Site: http://www.baycare.org
Hospital
N.A.I.C.S.: 622110
Kimberly Guy (COO)
Deborah A. Kotch (Pres)
Kate Reed (Pres)

St. Joseph's Hospital (2)
3001 W Dr Martin Luther King Jr Blvd, Tampa, FL 33607
Tel.: (813) 870-4000
Web Site: http://www.baycare.org
Emp.: 3,000
Hospital
N.A.I.C.S.: 622110
Ann Lumia (Mgr-Clinical & Coord-Residency)
Rick Sosteri (Coord-Respiratory Care Svcs)
David Miller (Mgr-Facilities)
William Holcomb (Mgr-Facility Sys)
Samir Akach (Chief Medical Officer & VP)

St. Joseph's Hospital-North (2)
4211 VanDyke Rd, Lutz, FL 33558
Tel.: (813) 443-7000
Web Site: http://www.baycare.org
Emp.: 1,000
Hospital
N.A.I.C.S.: 622110
Paula McGuiness (COO)
Jennifer Soden (Mgr-Food & Nutrition Svcs)

St. Joseph's Women's Hospital (2)
3030 W Dr Martin Luther King Jr Blvd, Tampa, FL 33607
Tel.: (813) 879-4730
Web Site: http://www.baycare.org
Hospital
N.A.I.C.S.: 622110
Kimberly Guy (Sr VP)
Sarah Naumowich (Pres)

BAYER CONSTRUCTION COMPANY, INC.
120 Deep Creek Rd, Manhattan, KS 66502-9305
Tel.: (785) 776-8839
Web Site:
   https://www.bayerconst.com
Year Founded: 1935
Sales Range: $25-49.9 Million
Emp.: 120
Water & Sewer Line Structures Construction Services
N.A.I.C.S.: 237110
Leslie Briggs (Pres)
Neil Horton (VP)

BAYER MOTOR CO. INC.
218 E Grand Ave, Comanche, TX 76442
Tel.: (325) 356-2541
Web Site: http://www.bayermotor.com
Sales Range: $25-49.9 Million
Emp.: 32
Automobiles, New & Used
N.A.I.C.S.: 441110
Charles J. Bayer III (Pres)

BAYFAIR QUALITY BUILDERS, LLC
1318 W Swann Ave, Tampa, FL 33606
Tel.: (813) 875-3800
Web Site: https://www.bayfair.com
Year Founded: 1989
Sales Range: $1-9.9 Million
Emp.: 20
Residential Construction
N.A.I.C.S.: 236115
J. Michael Morris (Pres)

BAYHILL THERAPEUTICS, INC.
1804 Embarcadero Rd Ste 201, Palo Alto, CA 94303
Tel.: (650) 320-2800   DE
Sales Range: $1-9.9 Million
Emp.: 39
Biopharmaceutical Researcher & Mfr
N.A.I.C.S.: 325412
Robert S. King (VP-Mfg)

BAYLAND BUILDINGS, INC.
PO Box 13571, Green Bay, WI 54307-3571
Tel.: (920) 498-9300
Web Site:
   http://www.baylandbuildings.com
Sales Range: $10-24.9 Million
Emp.: 165
Commercial & Institutional Building Construction Services
N.A.I.C.S.: 236220
Steve Ambrosius (Pres)
Abraham Farley (COO)
Dan Verhagen (CFO)
Chad Calmes (VP-Ops)

BAYLEY CONSTRUCTION INC.
8005 SE 28th St, Mercer Island, WA 98040
Tel.: (206) 621-8884
Web Site: https://www.bayley.net
Rev.: $140,000,000
Emp.: 30
Commercial & Office Building, New Construction
N.A.I.C.S.: 236220
Ron Bayley (Pres & CEO)
Chris Bull (Project Mgr)
Steve Grasso (Pres)
Warren Johnson (VP-Bus Dev)

BAYLOFF STAMPED PRODUCTS, INC.
5910 Belleville Rd, Belleville, MI 48111
Tel.: (734) 397-9116
Web Site: https://www.bayloff.com
Year Founded: 1948
Metal Tooling, Stamping & Finishing
N.A.I.C.S.: 333514

Subsidiaries:

Bayloff Stamped Products Detroit, Inc. (1)
8700 Belleville Rd, Belleville, MI 48111
Tel.: (734) 856-2033
Web Site: http://www.bayloff.com
Tooling & Stamping Mfr
N.A.I.C.S.: 333517

BAYLOR HEALTH CARE SYSTEM
3500 Gaston Ave, Dallas, TX 75246
Tel.: (214) 820-0111   TX
Web Site:
   http://www.baylorhealth.com
Year Founded: 1981
Sales Range: $1-4.9 Billion
Emp.: 19,736
Hospital Owner & Operator
N.A.I.C.S.: 622110
Kristi Sherrill Hoyl (Chief Policy & Community Officer)

David J. Ballard (Chief Quality Officer)
Frederick Savelsbergh (CFO)
Rowland Robinson (Pres-Baylor Health Care System Foundation)
Norm Bagwell (Chm)
Matthew Chambers (CIO)
Tony W. Johnson (Sr VP-Supply Chain & Logistics)
Pete McCanna (Pres)
Robert Michalski (Chief Compliance Officer)
Nikki Moll (Sr VP-Mktg & PR)
Robert Probe (Chief Medical Officer & Exec VP)

BAYLOR SCOTT & WHITE HOLDINGS
3500 Gaston Ave, Dallas, TX 75246-2017
Tel.: (844) 279-3627   TX
Web Site: http://www.bswhealth.com
Holding Company
N.A.I.C.S.: 551112

Subsidiaries:

Baylor Scott & White Health (1)
3500 Gaston Ave, Dallas, TX 75246-2017
Tel.: (844) 279-3627
Web Site: http://www.bswhealth.com
Health Care Srvices
N.A.I.C.S.: 621999
John McWhorter (COO)

BAYMARK PARTNERS
Granite Park II 5700 Granite Pkwy Ste 435, Plano, TX 75024
Tel.: (972) 991-5457
Web Site:
   https://www.baymarkpartners.com
Privater Equity Firm
N.A.I.C.S.: 523999
David J. Hook (Mng Dir)
Tony Ludlow (Mng Dir)

Subsidiaries:

Computer Integrated Services Company of New York, LLC (1)
561 7th Ave 13th Fl, New York, NY 10018
Tel.: (212) 577-6033
Web Site: http://www.cisus.com
Sales Range: $10-24.9 Million
Emp.: 80
Information Technology, Infrastructure Integration & Support Services
N.A.I.C.S.: 541519
Anthony Fama (Dir-Infrastructure Security)
Denise Rowe (Mgr-Svc)
James Walsh (CTO)
Rob Rawson (Dir-Identity Mgmt)
Dennis Gambow (CEO)
Richard Swinyard (CFO)
Steven Waine (Dir-Procurement)
Todd Hershman (Co-Founder & Head-Sls & Mktg)
Thomas Horne (Co-Founder & COO)
Marc Rosenthal (Dir-Engrg)

Subsidiary (Domestic):

Shmitt Technologies LLC (2)
19 W 44th St Ste 1100, New York, NY 10036
Tel.: (212) 679-5727
Web Site: http://www.shmitt.net
Computer Network & Systems Design & Maintenance
N.A.I.C.S.: 541519
Laura Roche (CFO)
Daniel Shmitt (CEO)

Denver Glass Interiors, Inc. (1)
1600 W Evans Ave Ste A, Englewood, CO 80110
Tel.: (303) 744-0350
Web Site:
   http://www.denverglassinteriors.com
Sales Range: $1-9.9 Million
Emp.: 43
Building Material Dealers
N.A.I.C.S.: 444180
David Uhey (Pres)

Subsidiary (Domestic):

Bel Shower Door Corp. (2)
13300 James E Casey Ave Ste 800, Englewood, CO 80112
Tel.: (303) 788-0828
Web Site: http://www.belshowerdoor.com
Sales Range: $1-9.9 Million
Emp.: 44
Glass Product Mfr Made of Purchased Glass
N.A.I.C.S.: 327215
Bill Sain (Pres)

BAYOU CITY EXPLORATION, INC.
1151 Old Porter Pike, Bowling Green, KY 42103
Tel.: (270) 282-8544   NV
Web Site: http://www.bycex.com
Sales Range: $1-9.9 Million
Emp.: 1
Oil & Gas Exploration Services
N.A.I.C.S.: 211120
Stephen C. Larkin (Pres, CEO & CFO)
Travis N. Creed (Chm & Sr VP)

BAYOU STATE OIL CORPORATION
1115 Hawn Ave, Shreveport, LA 71107-6609
Tel.: (318) 222-0737   LA
Year Founded: 1926
Sales Range: $1-9.9 Million
Emp.: 37
Crude Oil Extraction Services
N.A.I.C.S.: 211120
Charles Brown (Chm)
Vicki Cromer (Treas)

BAYRU LLC
8230 Austin Ave, Morton Grove, IL 60053
Tel.: (847) 983-4564
Web Site: http://www.dostami.ru
Year Founded: 2007
Sales Range: $10-24.9 Million
Emp.: 120
Cross Border Shopping Site
N.A.I.C.S.: 459999
Aaron Block (CEO)

BAYSHORE CENTER AT BIVALVE
2800 High St, Port Norris, NJ 08349
Tel.: (856) 785-2060   NJ
Web Site:
   https://www.bayshorecenter.org
Year Founded: 1988
Sales Range: $1-9.9 Million
Emp.: 28
Riverfront Corridor Redevelopment Services
N.A.I.C.S.: 541320
Meghan Wren (Exec Dir)
Gary Stiegler (Chm)
Tony Klock (Vice Chm)
Divid Hergert (Sec)

BAYSHORE FORD TRUCK SALES INC.
4003 N Dupont Hwy, New Castle, DE 19720
Tel.: (302) 656-3160
Web Site:
   https://www.bayshoreford.com
Rev.: $27,200,000
Emp.: 120
Pickups, New & Used
N.A.I.C.S.: 441110
Gerry C. Turnauer (VP)
Dale Brewer (Pres)

BAYSHORE HEALTH & HOMEMAKER SERVICES, INC.
2430 W Bay Dr, Largo, FL 33770

Tel.: (727) 586-0044   FL
Web Site:
    https://www.bayshorehomecare.com
Year Founded: 1986
Sales Range: $10-24.9 Million
Emp.: 240
Women Healthcare Services
N.A.I.C.S.: 621610
Suzanne Johnson *(Co-Owner)*
Todd Atkinson *(Co-Owner)*

BAYSHORE INTERNATIONAL TRUCKS
24353 Clawiter Rd, Hayward, CA 94545
Tel.: (510) 264-5200
Web Site:
    http://www.bayshorenational.com
Sales Range: $10-24.9 Million
Emp.: 35
Trucks, Tractors & Trailer Sales
N.A.I.C.S.: 441227
Craig Peterson *(Pres)*
Todd Reddfield *(Controller)*

BAYSHORE SOLUTIONS INC.
600 N Westshore Blvd Ste 700, Tampa, FL 33609
Tel.: (813) 902-0141
Web Site:
    http://www.bayshoresolutions.com
Year Founded: 1996
Sales Range: $1-9.9 Million
Emp.: 56
Web Marketing Solutions
N.A.I.C.S.: 541890
Kevin Hourigan *(Pres & CEO)*
Doug Pace *(COO & Exec VP)*
Jay Wiley *(VP)*
Kimberley McCormick *(Dir-Corp Mktg)*
Keith Neubert *(Sr VP)*
Cordes Owen *(VP)*
Erin Gray *(VP)*
Michael Sapp *(Controller)*
David Stout *(Dir-Digital Mktg)*
Jay Donaldson *(VP-Corp Mktg)*
Becki Dilworth *(VP)*
Liz Turner *(VP)*

BAYSHORE SUPPLY & LIGHTS
501 Industrial Rd, San Carlos, CA 94070
Tel.: (650) 596-8899
Web Site:
    http://www.bayshoresupply.com
Rev.: $11,315,487
Emp.: 15
Plumbing Fittings & Supplies
N.A.I.C.S.: 423720
Jack Tseng *(Pres)*

BAYSIDE CHRYSLER JEEP DODGE INC.
21219 Northern Blvd, Bayside, NY 11361
Tel.: (929) 442-2904
Web Site:
    https://www.baysidechryslerjeep.net
Sales Range: $10-24.9 Million
Emp.: 56
Owner & Operator of Car Dealerships
N.A.I.C.S.: 441110
Michael Campanelle *(Owner)*

BAYSIDE ENGINEERING, INC.
2000 E 11th Ave Ste 300, Tampa, FL 33605
Tel.: (813) 314-0314   FL
Web Site: http://www.baysideng.com
Year Founded: 1994
Sales Range: $1-9.9 Million
Emp.: 1,500
Civil Engineering & Surveying Services
N.A.I.C.S.: 237990

Kimberlee DeBosier *(VP)*
Robert Dvorak *(VP)*

BAYSIDE FUEL OIL DEPOT CORPORATION
1776 Shore Pkwy, Brooklyn, NY 11214-6546
Tel.: (718) 372-9800   NY
Web Site:
    https://www.baysidedepot.com
Year Founded: 1965
Sales Range: $75-99.9 Million
Emp.: 49
Fuel Oil Whslr
N.A.I.C.S.: 424710
Vincent Allegretti *(VP)*

BAYSIDE MACHINE CORP.
2257 American Blvd, De Pere, WI 54115
Tel.: (920) 330-9972   WI
Web Site:
    https://www.baysidemachine.com
Year Founded: 2002
Sales Range: $1-9.9 Million
Emp.: 38
General Machine Shop
N.A.I.C.S.: 332710
Paul Fritsch *(Pres)*
Tracy Burbey *(VP)*

BAYSIDE PET RESORT & SPA, INC.
8154 N Tamiami Trl, Sarasota, FL 34243
Tel.: (941) 351-0730
Web Site:
    https://www.baysidepetresort.com
Sales Range: $10-24.9 Million
Emp.: 30
Pet Care Services
N.A.I.C.S.: 812910
Bob Huff *(Owner)*

BAYSIDE SOLUTIONS, INC.
6210 Stoneridge Mall Rd Ste 200, Pleasanton, CA 94588
Tel.: (925) 460-8270
Web Site:
    http://www.baysidesolutions.com
Year Founded: 2001
Sales Range: $10-24.9 Million
Emp.: 50
Staffing Services
N.A.I.C.S.: 561311
Robert Klotz *(CEO)*
David Rampa *(Pres-IT&C)*
Linda Koeplin *(CFO)*
Kurt Decker *(Mgr-Help Desk)*

BAYSTAR HOTEL GROUP, LLC
500 N Westshore Blvd Ste 740, Tampa, FL 33609
Tel.: (813) 849-0001
Web Site:
    http://www.baystarhotels.com
Year Founded: 2000
Sales Range: $25-49.9 Million
Emp.: 100
Hotel Development, Acquisition, Operation & Sales
N.A.I.C.S.: 721110
George E. Glover *(Chm & CEO)*
Ford B. Smith *(Pres & Principal)*
J. Norman Giovenco *(CFO & Principal)*

BAYSTATE FINANCIAL SERVICES, LLC
200 Clarendon St 19th Fl, Boston, MA 02116
Tel.: (617) 585-4500   DE
Web Site:
    https://www.baystatefinancial.com
Year Founded: 1901
Sales Range: $25-49.9 Million

Emp.: 310
Insurance Agents, Brokers & Service
N.A.I.C.S.: 524210
Michael Yoken *(Partner)*
Jill Constantine *(Dir-Mktg)*
Christopher McIntosh *(CMO)*

BAYSTATE HEALTH SYSTEM, INC.
759 Chestnut St, Springfield, MA 01199-1001
Tel.: (413) 794-0000   MA
Web Site:
    http://www.baystatehealth.org
Year Founded: 1983
Sales Range: $500-549.9 Million
Emp.: 12,000
Wealth Management Services
N.A.I.C.S.: 561110
Peter A. Lyons *(VP-Fin Support Svcs)*
Evan M. Benjamin *(Chief Quality Officer & Sr VP-Quality & Population Health)*
Mark A. Keroack *(Pres & CEO)*
Jane Albert *(Sr VP-Mktg, Comm & External Rels)*
Anne M. Paradis *(Chm)*
Jean Ahn *(Chief Strategy Officer & Sr VP)*
Jo-Ann W. Davis *(Chief Admin Officer & Sr VP)*
Raymond McCarthy *(CFO & Treas)*
Kevin Conway *(Chief Info & Digital Officer & Sr VP)*
Sam Skura *(Pres-Baystate Medical Center & Sr VP-Hospital Ops)*
Marion McGowan *(COO & Exec VP)*

Subsidiaries:

Baystate Medical Education & Research Foundation Inc.   (1)
759 Chestnut St, Springfield, MA 01199-1001
Tel.: (413) 784-0000
Web Site: http://www.baystatehealth.com
Sales Range: $75-99.9 Million
Emp.: 2,000
Noncommercial Research Organization
N.A.I.C.S.: 622110
Evan M. Benjamin *(Chief Quality Officer & Sr VP-Quality & Population Health)*

BAYVIEW ASSET MANAGEMENT, LLC
4425 Ponce de Leon Blvd, Coral Gables, FL 33146
Tel.: (305) 854-8880   MD
Web Site:
    http://www.bayviewassets.com
Year Founded: 1993
Sales Range: $10-24.9 Million
Emp.: 100
Mortgage Investment Services
N.A.I.C.S.: 531390
Richard O'Brien *(Pres & CEO)*
John H. Fischer *(CFO)*
David Ertel *(Chm)*

BAYVIEW ELECTRIC COMPANY, LLC.
12230 Dixie St, Redford, MI 48239
Tel.: (313) 255-5252
Web Site:
    https://www.bayelectric.com
Year Founded: 2004
Sales Range: $10-24.9 Million
Emp.: 75
Electrical Contractor
N.A.I.C.S.: 238210
Bob Davies *(Co-Owner & CEO)*
Rob Davies *(Co-Owner & COO)*

BAYVIEW FINANCIAL, L.P.
4425 Ponce de Leon Blvd 4th Fl, Coral Gables, FL 33146
Tel.: (305) 854-8880   DE

Web Site:
    http://www.bayviewfinancial.com
Year Founded: 1978
Sales Range: $1-4.9 Billion
Emp.: 1,000
Real Estate Loans; Home Mortgages
N.A.I.C.S.: 523150
Ross Aronovitz *(VP)*
Elva Neumann *(First VP-Real Estate)*
Michael Sorenson *(Sr VP)*
Timothy Barnes *(Mgr-Residential Asset)*

Subsidiaries:

Bayview Financial Small Business Funding LLC   (1)
4425 Ponce De Leon Blvd Fl 4, Coral Gables, FL 33146
Tel.: (305) 854-8880
Web Site: http://www.bayviewfinancial.com
Sales Range: $50-74.9 Million
Emp.: 150
Financial Mortgages
N.A.I.C.S.: 523150

BAYVIEW LIMOUSINE SERVICE, INC.
15701 Nelson Pl S, Seattle, WA 98188
Tel.: (425) 453-6200   WA
Web Site:
    https://www.bayviewlimo.com
Year Founded: 1990
Sales Range: $1-9.9 Million
Emp.: 78
Limousine Transportation
N.A.I.C.S.: 485320
Catherine Lewan *(Co-Owner & VP)*
Rob Hansen *(Co-Owner & Pres)*

BAYWAY LINCOLN-MERCURY INC.
12333 Gulf Fwy, Houston, TX 77034
Tel.: (281) 810-9270
Web Site:
    https://www.baywaylincoln.com
Rev.: $56,400,000
Emp.: 200
Automobiles, New & Used
N.A.I.C.S.: 441110
Nathan Dawson *(Dir-Pre-Owned Ops)*
Joe Hyde *(Mgr-New Car Sls)*
James Blair *(COO)*

BAZAR GROUP INC.
793 Waterman Ave, East Providence, RI 02914
Tel.: (401) 434-2595
Web Site: http://www.bruce.com
Rev.: $22,800,000
Emp.: 100
Jewelry
N.A.I.C.S.: 339910
Banice C. Bazar *(Chm)*

BB&B CONSTRUCTION SERVICES OF FLORIDA, INC.
12244 Treeline Ave Ste 10, Fort Myers, FL 33913
Tel.: (239) 437-5781
Web Site:
    http://www.bbconstruction.com
Year Founded: 1972
Sales Range: $1-9.9 Million
Commercial & Industrial Construction Services
N.A.I.C.S.: 236220
Carolyn Bowe *(Co-Founder & Pres)*
David Bowe *(Co-Founder & VP)*

BBAM LLC
50 California St 14th Fl, San Francisco, CA 94111
Tel.: (415) 267-1600   DE
Web Site: http://www.bbam.com
Year Founded: 1991

BBAM LLC—(Continued)

Commercial Aircraft Sales Financing & Leasing Services
N.A.I.C.S.: 522220
Steven Zissis (CEO)
Rob Tomczak (CFO)
Vincent Cannon (COO & Gen Counsel)

BBC INTERNATIONAL LLC
1515 N Federal Hwy Ste 206, Boca Raton, FL 33432
Tel.: (561) 417-7474
Web Site: https://www.bbcint.com
Year Founded: 1975
Sales Range: $25-49.9 Million
Emp.: 80
Distributing Shoes
N.A.I.C.S.: 424340
Donald Wilborn (Pres)
Robert B. Campbell (Chm & CEO)

BBC STEEL CORP.
2001 S Township Rd, Canby, OR 97013-9734
Tel.: (503) 263-6343
Web Site: https://www.bbcsteel.com
Year Founded: 1969
Sales Range: $10-24.9 Million
Emp.: 50
Steel Products Mfr
N.A.I.C.S.: 331513
Tony Boyer (Owner)

BBCK ENTERPRISES INC.
3005 El Camino Real, Redwood City, CA 94061
Tel.: (650) 364-8544
Web Site: https://www.klwines.com
Sales Range: $10-24.9 Million
Emp.: 150
Winery
N.A.I.C.S.: 445320
Todd F. Zucker (Pres)
Scott Beckerley (Head-In-Store Tastings Section)
Trey Beffa (VP-Domestic Wine Buyer)
Steve Berg (Mgr-Ops)
Brian Keating (Mgr-Ops)
Brian Zucker (VP)
Linda Zucker (Mgr-Mailing List)
Amy Monroe (Mgr-Store)
Chris Puppione (Editor)
James Knight (Editor)
Jason Marwedel (Gen Mgr)
Kate Soto (Editor)
Sarah Covey (Mgr-Store)
Sara Jenkins (Editor)
Clyde Beffa Jr. (VP, Dir-Sls & Editor-Wine News)

BBE SOUND INC.
5381 Production Dr, Fullerton, CA 92831
Tel.: (714) 897-6766
Web Site: http://www.bbesound.com
Rev.: $17,000,000
Emp.: 16
Musical Instruments
N.A.I.C.S.: 339992
John C. McLaren (Chm & CEO)
Paul Gagon (VP-Tech)
David C. McLaren (Exec VP)

Subsidiaries:

G&L Music Sales Inc.   (1)
2548 Fender Ave, Fullerton, CA 92831
Tel.: (714) 897-6766
Web Site: http://www.glguitars.com
Electric Guitar Mfr
N.A.I.C.S.: 339992
John C. McLaren (Founder)

BBEX INC.
5550 Glades Rd Ste 500, Boca Raton, FL 33431
Web Site:
https://www.bbexmarketing.com
Sales Range: $1-9.9 Million
Internet Marketing Consulting Services
N.A.I.C.S.: 541613
Nate Aloni (Owner)

BBG COMMUNICATIONS, INC.
1658 Gailes Blvd Ste B, San Diego, CA 92154
Tel.: (619) 661-6661   DE
Web Site:
https://www.bbgcommunication.com
Year Founded: 1996
Operated-Assisted Call Services
N.A.I.C.S.: 517121
Gregorio Galicot (Pres & CEO)
Rafael Galicot (VP)
Clara Martinez (Mgr-AP)
Ruben G. Gonzalez (VP-Engrg)

Subsidiaries:

BBG Global AG   (1)
Bahnhof Park #4, CH-6340, Baar, Switzerland
Tel.: (41) 41 768 1075
Web Site: http://www.bbgcommch.com
Sales Range: $200-249.9 Million
Emp.: 600
Operated-Assisted Call Services
N.A.I.C.S.: 517121

Subsidiary (Non-US):

0800 Reverse Limited   (2)
35 New Bridge Street, London, EC4V 6BW, United Kingdom
Tel.: (44) 2075912292
Web Site: http://www.0800reverse.co.uk
Sales Range: $25-49.9 Million
Emp.: 50
Reverse Charge Phone Services
N.A.I.C.S.: 517121

BBG INC.
8343 Douglas Ave Ste 700, Dallas, TX 75225
Tel.: (214) 739-0700   TX
Web Site: http://www.bbgres.com
Year Founded: 1992
Emp.: 100
Real Estate Valuation, Advisory & Assessment Services
N.A.I.C.S.: 531390
Chris Roach (CEO)
Chris Belknap (CFO)
Patrick Walsh (Dir-IT)
Kenneth Konrath (Sr Mng Dir)
Rodman Schley (Sr Mng Dir)
Grant Griffin (Pres-Valuation)
Marc G. Nassif (Sr Mng Dir)
Mary Ann Barnett (Sr Mng Dir-Affordable Multifamily Practice Leader)
Dennis Cruise (Mng Dir-Energy Assessment)
Scott Beebe (Sr Mng Dir-Sacramento)
Brian T. Bryant (Sr Mng Dir-Charlotte)
Jon A. DiPietra (Sr Mng Dir-New York)
Susan Kominski (Sr Mng Dir)
Eric Haims (Mng Dir-Litigation Support-New York)
Louis Yorey (Sr Mng Dir-New Jersey)
Louis S. Izenberg (Mng Dir-New Jersey)
Paul E. Ping (Sr Mng Dir)
Frank Catlett (Dir-Tampa)
Kyle Catlett (Dir-Tampa)
Will Childs (Exec VP-Alternative Practice Groups)

Subsidiaries:

Catlett & Company Inc.   (1)
3800 Bay to Bay Blvd Ste 23, Tampa, FL 33629-6844
Tel.: (813) 254-5700

Web Site: http://www.triggcatlett.com
Offices of Real Estate Appraisers
N.A.I.C.S.: 531320
Heather L. Fuentes (Sec & Office Mgr)

Crown Appraisal Group   (1)
355 E Campus View Blvd, Columbus, OH 43235
Tel.: (614) 431-3332
Web Site: http://www.crownappraisal.com
Sales Range: $1-9.9 Million
Emp.: 35
Offices of Real Estate Appraisers
N.A.I.C.S.: 531320

Izenberg Appraisal Associates, Inc.   (1)
205 Main St, Chatham, NJ 07928
Tel.: (973) 515-4700
Web Site: http://www.izenbergappraisal.com
Lessors of Residential Buildings & Dwellings
N.A.I.C.S.: 531110

Jerome Haims Realty, Inc.   (1)
112 Madison Ave 11th Fl, New York, NY 10016
Tel.: (212) 687-0154
Web Site:
http://www.jeromehaimsrealty.com
Real Estate Appraisal & Consulting Services
N.A.I.C.S.: 531390
Eric P. Haims (Mng Dir)

BBJ RENTALS INC.
6125 W Howard St, Niles, IL 60714
Tel.: (847) 329-8400
Web Site: http://www.bbjlinen.com
Rev.: $12,000,000
Emp.: 300
Party Supplies Rental Services
N.A.I.C.S.: 532289
Judy Goldberg (Owner & Chm)
Kimberly Bibb McDonald (Mgr-Sls)
Bonnie Dannen (Pres)
Brooke Marino (Exec Mgr-Sls)
Rob Millman (CIO)
Tina Williams (Sr Mgr-Sls-Opdenbrouw)

BBN NETWORKS, INC.
1304 Concourse Dr Ste 120, Linthicum, MD 21090
Tel.: (410) 694-9333
Web Site:
http://www.bbnnetworks.com
Year Founded: 2008
Sales Range: $1-9.9 Million
Emp.: 12
Advertising Related Services
N.A.I.C.S.: 541890
Selcuk Ozturk (Sr VP-Tech)

BBQ BLUES TEXAS LTD.
8041 Walnet Hill Ln Ste 820, Dallas, TX 75231
Tel.: (972) 869-4042
Web Site: http://www.rhnb.com
Year Founded: 1988
Sales Range: $10-24.9 Million
Emp.: 200
Owners of Barbecue Restaurants
N.A.I.C.S.: 722511
Craig Collins (Pres)
Juan Chavez (Dir-Ops)

BBQ GUY'S MANUFACTURING, LLC
6620 Greenwell Springs Rd, Baton Rouge, LA 70805
Web Site: http://www.blazegrills.com
Year Founded: 2012
Sales Range: $25-49.9 Million
Design & Outdoor Grill Product Mfr
N.A.I.C.S.: 332323
Jason Thompson (Sls Dir)

BBS TECHNOLOGIES, INC.
802 Lovett Blvd, Houston, TX 77006
Tel.: (713) 862-5250   TX

Year Founded: 2000
Sales Range: $10-24.9 Million
Emp.: 177
Managing, Securing, Auditing & Backing Up Critical Windows & Linux Servers
N.A.I.C.S.: 541512
Hythem El-Nazer (Chm)
Randy Jacops (CEO)
Chris Smith (CQO)
Heidi Farris (VP-Mktg)
Trey Chambers (CFO)

Subsidiaries:

R1Soft   (1)
America Tower 2929 Allen Pkwy Ste 3200, Houston, TX 77019-7112
Tel.: (713) 344-0047
Web Site: http://www.r1soft.com
Backup Software
N.A.I.C.S.: 513210

BC PARTNERS LENDING CORPORATION
650 Madison Ave, New York, NY 10022
Tel.: (212) 891-2880   MD
Year Founded: 2017
Rev.: $9,273,000
Assets: $109,473,000
Liabilities: $60,701,000
Net Worth: $48,772,000
Earnings: $2,543,000
Emp.: 381
Fiscal Year-end: 12/31/22
Investment Services
N.A.I.C.S.: 523999
Edward Goldthorpe (Chm, Chm, CEO & CEO)
Jason T. Roos (CFO, Treas & Sec)

BC STEEL BUILDINGS, INC.
9900 NW 10th St, Oklahoma City, OK 73127
Tel.: (405) 324-5100
Web Site: https://www.bcsteel.com
Year Founded: 1973
Sales Range: $10-24.9 Million
Emp.: 65
Fabricated Structural Metal Mfr
N.A.I.C.S.: 332312
Rodney Laubach (Pres)

BCA (BRIAN CRONIN & ASSOCIATES INC.)
315 Madison Ave Ste 702, New York, NY 10017-6503
Tel.: (212) 286-9300
Year Founded: 1984
Sales Range: $10-24.9 Million
Emp.: 10
Advetising Agency
N.A.I.C.S.: 541810
James M. Cronin (Pres)
Evelyn Galli (COO)
Kelly DeChiaro (Dir-Digital Svcs)
Susanna Gahan (Comptroller)
Erin Leitten (Art Dir)
Katherine Rup (Acct Exec)

BCB HOMES INC.
3696 Enterprise Ave Ste 100, Naples, FL 34104
Tel.: (239) 643-1004
Web Site:
https://www.bcbhomes.com
Sales Range: $10-24.9 Million
Emp.: 100
Residential Construction
N.A.I.C.S.: 236115
Joe Smallwood (Pres & CEO)
Scott Weidle (COO)
Chuck Rainey (VP)
Eric Morris (VP-Field Ops)

Travis Smith *(VP)*
Greg Brisson *(VP)*
Barbie Rogers Kellam *(Dir-Sls)*

BCB INTERNATIONAL INC.
1010 Niagara St, Buffalo, NY 14213
Tel.: (716) 884-1554
Web Site:
　https://www.bcbinternational.com
Year Founded: 1981
Sales Range: $10-24.9 Million
Emp.: 26
Freight Forwarding Services
N.A.I.C.S.: 488510
David W. Odden *(Pres)*
Peter K. Vaccaro *(CEO)*
Barbara Carman *(Gen Mgr-Customs Ops)*

BCBG MAX AZRIA GROUP, INC.
2761 Fruitland Ave, Vernon, CA 90058
Tel.: (323) 589-2224
Web Site:
　http://www.bcbgmaxazriagroup.com
Year Founded: 1989
Rev.: $236,224,027
Emp.: 600
Women's Clothing Store
N.A.I.C.S.: 458110
Max Azria *(Chm & CEO)*
Glenda Light *(VP-Global Mdse Plng & Allocation)*
Miguel Campos *(Dir-Logistics)*
Muriel Messica *(Dir-Customer Svc)*
Tita Macaspac *(VP & Mgr-Collection)*
Anne Buchanan *(Dir-HR)*
Richard Chang *(Sr Mgr-Inventory Control)*
Sandra Fava *(Mgr-Color & Print Dev)*
Jacqueline Fowler *(Mgr-Transportation)*
Meghan Gibson *(Brand Mgr)*
Matthew Wallace *(Dir-IT)*
Polina Karaseva *(Mgr-Fabric R&D)*
Jack Chiang *(Sr Mgr-Tax)*
Billie Parsons *(Treas & Sr VP-Fin)*
Lesli Fonte *(Asst Mgr-Trim R&D)*
Sarah Layland *(Dir-Art)*
Michael Song *(Engr-Sys)*
Amador Gonzalez-Basilio *(Mgr-DC)*
William Ma *(Mgr-FP&A)*
Emily Hanson *(Mgr-Production Ops)*
Marita Marshall *(Mgr-Tech Fabrics)*
Sasha Cuevas *(Mgr-Visual Traffic & Comm)*
Jennifer Tan *(Sr Mgr-Mktg)*
Kim Afflerbach *(VP & Controller-Retail)*
Etienne Capgras *(VP-Distr)*
Anthony Murguia *(Reg Mgr-Asset Protection)*

BCC INVESTMENT CORP.
200 Clarendon St, Boston, MA 02116
Tel.: (617) 516-2000　　　　Ky
Year Founded: 2021
Investment Services
N.A.I.C.S.: 523999
Jeffrey Robinson *(Chm)*
Olof Bergqvist *(CEO)*
Sally F. Dornaus *(CFO)*
Matthew Evans *(Treas & VP)*

BCCH, LLC
100 Four Paws, Maumelle, AR 72113-6554
Tel.: (501) 851-0002　　　　AR
Web Site:
　http://www.claudiascanine.com
Sales Range: $10-24.9 Million
Emp.: 103
Dog & Cat Food Mfr
N.A.I.C.S.: 311111

BCCI CONSTRUCTION COMPANY
1160 Battery St Ste 250, San Francisco, CA 94111
Tel.: (415) 817-5100
Web Site: https://www.bcciconst.com
Year Founded: 1986
Sales Range: $100-124.9 Million
Emp.: 90
Nonresidential Construction Services
N.A.I.C.S.: 236220
Cynthia Gage *(Dir-Mktg)*
Michael Scribner *(Pres)*

BCCU INC.
5242 S College Dr, Murray, UT 84123
Tel.: (801) 397-4000　　　　UT
Year Founded: 1991
Sales Range: $10-24.9 Million
Emp.: 371
Elderly Housing Services
N.A.I.C.S.: 624229
Dee R. Bangerter *(Pres & Sec)*

BCDVIDEO
3170 MacArthur Blvd, Northbrook, IL 60062
Tel.: (847) 205-1922
Web Site: http://www.bcdvideo.com
Year Founded: 1999
Sales Range: $25-49.9 Million
Emp.: 26
Computer Peripheral Equipment Mfr
N.A.I.C.S.: 334118
Jeff Burgess *(Pres)*

BCER ENGINEERING, INC.
5420 Ward Rd Ste 200, Arvada, CO 80002
Tel.: (303) 422-7400　　　　CO
Web Site: https://www.bcer.com
Year Founded: 1994
Sales Range: $10-24.9 Million
Emp.: 70
Engineering, Architectural Design & Technology Consultancy Services
N.A.I.C.S.: 541330
Marc Espinoza *(Chm, Pres & Principal)*
Dick Matthies *(Principal)*
Mike Cordero *(Sec & Principal)*
Steve Rondinelli *(Principal)*

Subsidiaries:

Rimrock Group, Inc.　　　　　(1)
10807 New Allegiance Dr Ste 400, Colorado Springs, CO 80921
Tel.: (719) 533-1112
Web Site: http://www.bcer.com
Sales Range: $1-9.9 Million
Emp.: 20
Technology Systems Engineering Consultancy Services
N.A.I.C.S.: 541690
John Thompson *(Founder & Pres)*

BCF
4500 Main St Ste 600, Virginia Beach, VA 23462
Tel.: (757) 497-4811
Web Site:
　http://www.boomyourbrand.com
Year Founded: 1980
Rev.: $30,000,000
Emp.: 53
Advetising Agency
N.A.I.C.S.: 541810
Art Webb *(Pres & CEO)*
Keith Ireland *(Partner, VP & Dir-Creative)*
Ginny Petty *(Sr Dir-Art)*
Greg Ward *(Partner & Acct Grp Dir)*
Jacinthe Pare *(Partner & Acct Grp Dir)*
Katherine Kivlighan Taylor *(Dir-Media)*

John Runberg *(Dir-Interactive Media)*
Mary Pannullo *(Dir-New Bus)*
Chris McCarley *(Acct Supvr)*

BCF SOLUTIONS, INC.
14325 Willard Rd Ste 107, Chantilly, VA 20151
Tel.: (703) 717-9912
Web Site:
　https://www.bcfsolutions.com
Year Founded: 2003
Sales Range: $1-9.9 Million
Emp.: 250
Professional Services to Government & Commercial Customers
N.A.I.C.S.: 561499
Brady C. Foster *(CEO & Chief Strategy Officer)*
Chand N. Gupta *(Pres & CFO)*
Spencer Curtis *(Dir-Triad Div-Arlington, Virginia & France)*
Jack Nebb *(VP & Dir-Contracts)*
Franco Deangelis *(CTO)*

BCFORWARD
9777 N College Ave, Indianapolis, IN 46280
Tel.: (317) 493-2000
Web Site: https://www.bcforward.com
Emp.: 3,000
Consulting Services
N.A.I.C.S.: 541611
Douglas R. Heath *(VP)*
Greg Goodin *(Dir-Recruiting-Global)*
Greg Jack *(Dir-Stafforward)*
Jen Franklin *(Dir-Svc Delivery)*
Joe Forestal *(Dir-Solutions Delivery)*
Katie Nagy *(Dir-Fin & Acctg)*
Satish Ramadenu *(Dir-Offshore Ops)*
Darrianne P. Christian *(Founder)*
Justin P. Christian *(Pres & CEO)*

Subsidiaries:

Global Networkers, Inc.　　　　(1)
11520 North Community House Rd, Charlotte, NC 28277
Tel.: (704) 343-0094
Web Site: http://www.globalnetworkers.com
Emp.: 15
Human Resources & Executive Search Consulting Services
N.A.I.C.S.: 541612
William Haygood *(Pres)*

BCI AIRCRAFT LEASING, INC
330 N Wabash Ave Ste 2801, Chicago, IL 60611
Tel.: (312) 329-1700
Web Site: http://www.bciaircraft.com
Year Founded: 1997
Rev.: $85,000,000
Emp.: 20
Commercial Aircraft Operating Leasing Services
N.A.I.C.S.: 532411
Craig Papayanis *(Mng Dir)*
Brian Hollnagel *(Pres & CEO)*

BCI HOLDING, INC.
9500 W Flamingo Rd Ste 205, Las Vegas, NV 89147
Tel.: (800) 581-1522　　　　NV
Web Site:
　http://www.assetprotections.com
Year Founded: 2010
Estate Planning & Asset Protection Services
N.A.I.C.S.: 525920
Jean Yves Gicque *(CEO & CFO)*

BCM CONSTRUCTION COMPANY INC.
2990 California 32, Chico, CA 95973-8649
Tel.: (530) 342-1722
Web Site:
　https://www.bcmconstruction.com

Sales Range: $10-24.9 Million
Emp.: 13
Industrial Buildings Construction
N.A.I.C.S.: 236210
Kurtis Carman *(Pres)*
Nancy Chinn *(CFO & Treas)*
Matt Bowman *(VP)*
Scott January *(VP-Agricultural Construction)*
Nick Starnes *(Project Mgr)*
Cole Spohr *(Project Mgr)*
Gary Graves *(Dir-Design & Build)*
Marc Madsen *(Project Mgr)*
Greg January *(Project Mgr)*

BCM ENERGY PARTNERS, INC.
5005 Riverway Ste 350, Houston, TX 77056
Tel.: (713) 623-2003
Web Site: http://www.bcmenergy.com
Year Founded: 2004
Sales Range: Less than $1 Million
Drilling Oil & Gas Wells
N.A.I.C.S.: 213111
David M. Beach *(CEO)*
James McCuistion *(VP-Land & Legal)*

BCP INC.
1101 Isaac Shelby Dr, Shelbyville, KY 40066-8171
Tel.: (502) 633-0650
Web Site:
　http://www.blazeproducts.com
Year Founded: 1998
Sales Range: $25-49.9 Million
Emp.: 85
Holding Company
N.A.I.C.S.: 551112
Amy Jo Condo *(Pres)*

Subsidiaries:

BLAZE Products Corporation　　(1)
1101 Isaac Shelby Dr, Shelbyville, KY 40065
Tel.: (502) 633-0650
Web Site: http://www.blazeproducts.com
Sales Range: $10-24.9 Million
Emp.: 30
Alcohol Based Chafing Dish Fuels Mfr
N.A.I.C.S.: 325193
Amy Jo Condo *(Pres)*
Bob O'Donnell *(Controller-AAPER)*

BCP TECHNICAL SERVICE, INC.
PO Box 6876, New Orleans, LA 70174
Tel.: (504) 361-4236　　　　FL
Web Site:
　http://www.bcpengineers.com
Year Founded: 1981
Sales Range: $1-9.9 Million
Emp.: 18
Nuclear Engineering Service & Technical Support
N.A.I.C.S.: 541690
Ronald L. Rowley *(Pres)*
Nuria Rowley *(CEO)*

BCR ENVIRONMENTAL CORPORATION
3740 St Johns Bluff Rd S Ste 21, Jacksonville, FL 32224
Tel.: (904) 819-9170
Web Site: http://www.bcrenv.com
Year Founded: 2003
Sales Range: $1-9.9 Million
Emp.: 30
Wastewater Treatment Systems Mfr
N.A.I.C.S.: 221310
Aaron F. Zahn *(Pres & CEO)*
Jim Flanary *(COO & VP-Ops)*
Fredrick D. Zahn *(CFO & VP-Fin & Admin)*

BCR Environmental Corporation—(Continued)

BCS CALLPROCESSING, INC.
55 Accord Park Dr, Rockland, MA 02370
Tel.: (781) 871-0700
Web Site:
http://www.bcscallprocessing.com
Year Founded: 2011
Sales Range: $10-24.9 Million
Information Technology Management Services
N.A.I.C.S.: 541618
Roy Abiyounes (CEO)

BCS PROSOFT
118 W Nakoma Dr, San Antonio, TX 78216
Tel.: (210) 361-2177
Web Site:
https://www.bcsprosoft.com
Year Founded: 1986
Sales Range: $1-9.9 Million
Emp.: 26
Computer & Software Stores
N.A.I.C.S.: 449210
William Vespe (Pres & COO)
Sally Craig (Exec VP)

Subsidiaries:

Steward Consulting Inc. (1)
715 W Main St Ste A, Jenks, OK 74037-3553
Tel.: (918) 299-7514
Web Site: http://www.stewardconsulting.com
Electronics Stores
N.A.I.C.S.: 449210
Darin Steward (Pres)

BCS WEST LLC
5975 Lusk Blvd, San Diego, CA 92121
Tel.: (858) 638-7508
Web Site: http://www.budget.com
Rev.: $83,000,000
Emp.: 35
Automobiles, Used Cars Only
N.A.I.C.S.: 441120

BCS, LLC
8920 Stephens Rd, Laurel, MD 20723-1486
Tel.: (410) 997-7778
Web Site: http://www.bcs-hq.com
General Management Consulting Services
N.A.I.C.S.: 541611
Kenneth W. Boras (CEO)

Subsidiaries:

Allegient Defense Inc. (1)
4401 N Fairfax Dr Ste 321, Arlington, VA 22203
Tel.: (703) 294-6235
Web Site: https://allegientdefense.com
Information Technology Services
N.A.I.C.S.: 541519

BCT CONSULTING, INC.
440 W Fallbrook Ave Ste 111, Fresno, CA 93711
Tel.: (559) 322-1989
Web Site:
http://www.bctconsulting.com
Year Founded: 1996
Sales Range: $1-9.9 Million
Emp.: 49
Web Design & Other Technology Services
N.A.I.C.S.: 541618
Eric G. Rawn (Founder & Pres)
Christopher Rawn (VP-Ops)

Subsidiaries:

TeleDynamic Communications Inc. (1)
3501 Breakwater Ave, Hayward, CA 94545
Tel.: (510) 785-2480

Web Site: http://www.teledynamic.com
Rev.: $4,995,000
Emp.: 15
Wired Telecommunications Carriers
N.A.I.C.S.: 517111
Randy Kremlacek (Pres)

BCT INTERNATIONAL, INC.
3000 NE 30th Pl 5th Fl, Fort Lauderdale, FL 33306-1957
Tel.: (954) 563-1224 DE
Web Site: http://www.bct-net.com
Year Founded: 1975
Sales Range: $10-24.9 Million
Emp.: 15
Retailer of Printed Products
N.A.I.C.S.: 533110
William A. Wilkerson (Chm & CEO)
Peter Posk (Pres)
Bob Dolan (VP-Sls)

BD&A REALTY & CONSTRUCTION
821 Ocean Trl Ste 4, Corolla, NC 27927
Tel.: (252) 453-3600
Web Site: http://www.bdahomes.com
Year Founded: 1987
Sales Range: $10-24.9 Million
Emp.: 25
Construction of Single-Family Houses
N.A.I.C.S.: 236115
Eric Avery (Pres)
Raju V. Uppalapati (CEO)
Jan Morgan (Controller)

BDG ARCHITECTS LLP
100 S Ashley Dr Ste 100, Tampa, FL 33602
Tel.: (813) 323-9233
Web Site: http://www.bdgllp.com
Sales Range: $1-9.9 Million
Emp.: 60
Architectural Services
N.A.I.C.S.: 541310
Chris Kirschner (Pres)
Gregg Holdsworth (Sr VP-Architecture)
Mickey Jacob (Chief Mktg Officer)
Brian Hammond (Sr VP-Architecture)
Jeff Mendenhall (VP-Architecture)
Deighton Babis (VP-Architecture)
David Sicca (VP-Program Mgmt)
Anita Shumaker (Dir-Interior Design)
Lisa Gabler (Mgr-Bus Dev & Mktg)
Donnally Bailey (Mgr-Program)
Brad La Tourette (Mgr-Program)
Gary Szpicek (VP-Architecture)
Philip Kennedy (COO)
Peter Hauerstein (VP-Architecture)

Subsidiaries:

Fleischman & Garcia Architects & Planners, AIA (1)
324 Hyde Park Ave Ste 300, Tampa, FL 33606
Tel.: (813) 251-4400
Web Site: http://www.fleischmangarcia.com
Sales Range: $1-9.9 Million
Emp.: 130
Architectural Services
N.A.I.C.S.: 541310
John Cutler Kelly (Pres)
Kevin S. Smith (Sr VP)
Stan L. Loper (Exec VP)
Sol J. Fleischman Jr. (Founder, Chm & CEO)

BDG MEDIA, INC.
315 Park Ave S 11th Fl, New York, NY 10010
Tel.: (917) 551-6510 DE
Web Site: https://www.bdg.com
Year Founded: 2013
Online Media Publisher
N.A.I.C.S.: 513199

Bryan Goldberg (Founder & CEO)
Jason Wagenheim (Pres & Chief Revenue Officer)
Tyler Love (CTO)
Kate Robinson (Sr VP-Bus Dev & Video)
Emily DeSear (VP-Creative & Mktg)
Trisha Dearborn (Chief People Officer)

Subsidiaries:

Flavorpill Productions LLC (1)
594 Broadway Ste 1212, New York, NY 10012
Tel.: (212) 253-9309
Web Site: http://www.flavorpill.com
Online Media Services & Publisher
N.A.I.C.S.: 513199

BDI-BEARING DISTRIBUTORS, INC.
8000 Hub Pkwy, Cleveland, OH 44125
Tel.: (216) 642-9100
Web Site: http://www.bdi-usa.com
Year Founded: 1935
Rev.: $395,900,000
Emp.: 850
Bearing Distr
N.A.I.C.S.: 332991
Samantha Pijor (Mgr-Sourcing)

BDK HOLDINGS, INC.
2255 N Ontario St, Burbank, CA 91504
Tel.: (818) 260-4800 DE
Year Founded: 1992
Sales Range: $75-99.9 Million
Emp.: 500
Piece Goods & Notions
N.A.I.C.S.: 424310

Subsidiaries:

Barth & Dreyfuss of California Inc. (1)
2255 N Ontario St Ste 300, Burbank, CA 91504-3191
Tel.: (818) 260-4800
Sales Range: $10-24.9 Million
Emp.: 100
Household Furnishings
N.A.I.C.S.: 314120
Marc Espinoza

BDK USA
2660 E 37th St, Vernon, CA 90058
Tel.: (323) 585-4949
Web Site: http://www.bdkauto.com
Year Founded: 1990
Sales Range: $10-24.9 Million
Emp.: 6
Motor Vehicle Parts Whslr
N.A.I.C.S.: 423140
Ken Chau (COO)

BDO PUERTO RICO, P.S.C.
1302 Avenida Juan Ponce de Leon, San Juan, PR 00907
Tel.: (787) 754-3436 PR
Web Site: http://www.bdopr.com
Year Founded: 2000
Emp.: 211
Accounting & Consulting Services
N.A.I.C.S.: 541211
Fernando Scherrer (Co-Founder, Mng Partner & Head-Bus Advisory Div)
Gabriel Hernandez (Co-Founder, Partner & Head-Tax Div)
Ryan Marin (Partner)
Sigfredo Velez (Partner)
Patricia Wangen (Partner)
Carlos Vazquez-Rodriguez (Partner)
Luis Torres-Llompart (Partner)
Wallace Rodriguez Parissi (Partner)
Alina Rivera (Partner-Bus Advisory Practice)
Dialy M. Otero (Partner)
Wigberto Marcano-Vazquez (Partner)

Harry E. Aleman-Quinones (Partner)
Juan Jose Diaz (Partner)
Aida Escribano (Partner)

BDO USA, LLP
330 N Wabash Ave Ste 3200, Chicago, IL 60611
Tel.: (312) 856-9100 DE
Web Site: http://www.bdo.com
Year Founded: 1910
Rev.: $2,000,000,000
Emp.: 9,647
Accounting, Tax, Financial Advisory & Consulting Services
N.A.I.C.S.: 541211
Wayne Berson (CEO)
Michael Horwitz (Exec Dir-Alliance)
Christopher Orella (Mng Partner-Operations-Assurance Natl)
Stephen Ferrara (COO)
Todd Simmens (Mng Partner-Tax-Risk Management-Natl)
Adam Brown (Mng Partner-Accounting-Auditing-Natl)
William Eisig (Mng Partner-Assurance-Natl)
Scott Hendon (Partner-Intl Liaison)
Angela J. Newell (Deputy Mng Partner-Accounting-Natl)
Catherine Moy (Chief HR Officer)
Brooke Anderson (Mng Principal)
Brian Miller (Partner-Audit Data Analytics & Emerging Methods-Natl)
Matthew Dyment (Mng Partner-State & Local Tax)
Daniel Newton (Partner-Tax-Natl)
Deneen Akture (CMO & Chief Comm Officer)
Russ Ahlers (CIO)
Jeff Bilsky (Partner)
Judith Grimmer (Deputy Gen Counsel)
Bryan Martin (Mng Partner-Assurance Tech-Natl)
Carrie Shagat (Partner-Assurance)
Eskander Yavar (Mng Partner-Advisory-Natl)
Demetrios Frangiskatos (Mng Partner-Assurance)
Christopher Tower (Mng Partner-Sustainability & ESG)
Hoon Lee (Mng Partner-Tax)
Matthew K. Becker (Mng Partner-Tax-Natl)
Anthony Lawrence (Mng Partner-Assurance)
Kevin Karo (Mng Partner-Assurance)
Lori Langholz (Chief Bus Dev Officer)
Matthew DeMong (Mng Partner-Tax)
Kelly Johnson (Chm)
Steven Shill (Mng Partner-Assurance Market)
Natalie Kotlyar (Mng Partner-Industry Groups-Natl)
Tiffany Prudhomme (Mng Partner-Quality in Markets-Industry-Assurance Natl)
Maria Karalis (Mng Partner-Assurance Market)
Monika Loving (Mng Partner-Tax Svcs)
John Marquardt (Mng Partner-Tax)
Clark Schweers (Mng Partner)
Jesus Socorro (Mng Partner-Mgmt Consulting)
Michael Williams (Partner-Income Tax Provision)
Michael Masciangelo (Partner-Tax)
John Nuckolls (Sr Dir-Private Client Svcs Natl Technical & Mng Dir)
Scott Smith (Mng Dir)
Joan Vines (Mng Dir)
Keith McGowan (Partner-Assurance)
Kevin Bianchi (Partner-Assurance)
Megan Condon (Partner)
Jordan Argiz (Partner)

Mark Houston *(Mng Dir)*
Anthony Ferguson *(Partner-Assurance)*
Kacy Lutrick *(Partner-Assurance)*
Aaron Raddock *(Partner)*
Amy Thorn *(Partner)*
Brad Boyd *(Mng Dir-Mgmt Consulting)*
Karen Fitzsimmons *(Partner-Assurance)*
Imran Makda *(Partner-Assurance-Insurance)*
Peter Popo *(Partner-Assurance-Insurance)*
Todd Berry *(Partner-Assurance)*
Lance Minor *(Principal)*
Bill Pellino *(Partner-Tax)*
Clark Sackschewsky *(Mng Principal-Tax)*
Andrea Espinola Wilson *(Mng Partner)*
Frank Landefeld *(Principal)*
Matt Segal *(Partner-PE Assurance-Natl)*
Verenda Graham *(Partner)*
Jim Clayton *(Principal-Mgmt Consulting)*
Robert Littman *(Mng Partner-Northeast Ohio)*
Ian Shapiro *(Partner)*
Lisa Haffer *(Partner-Tax)*
Gary Sturisky *(Mng Partner-Natl)*
Blake Wilson *(Chief Compliance & Ethics Officer)*
Phillip Austin *(Mng Partner-Professional Practice-Auditing-Natl)*
Chris Swanson *(Mng Partner-Assurance Special Ops-Natl)*
Michael Becker *(Partner-Assurance Learning-Natl)*
Patricia Bottomly *(Mng Partner-Audit Methodology-Consultations-Natl)*
James Gerace *(Partner-Expansion & Alliance-Private Company Approach-Natl)*
Timothy Kviz *(Mng Partner-SEC Svcs-Natl)*
Steve Maniaci *(Mng Partner-Tax-Accounting-Auditing-Natl)*
Amy Rojik *(Mng Partner-Governance-Emerging Issues-External Comm-Natl)*
Sergey Starysh *(Partner-Global Support Svcs-Natl)*
Jim Weber *(Partner-Engagement Team Support-Issuer Remediation-Natl)*
Jennifer Puterman *(Chief Risk Officer)*
Jeff Ward *(Mng Partner-Third-Party Attestation/SOC-IS Assurance-Natl)*
Nanda Gopal *(Mng Partner-West-Southwest Regional & Mng Partner-Technical)*
Jeffrey Keene *(Mng Partner-Technical-Northeast)*
John McKay *(Mng Partner-Technical-Central-Atlantic-Southeast)*
Lillian Ceynowa *(Partner-Audit Quality)*
Lisa Snyder *(Mng Partner-Independence-Natl)*
Todd Tosti *(Mng Partner-Inspections-Natl)*
John Rod *(Mng Partner-Assurance Quality Mgmt-Natl)*
Kim Bolte *(Principal-People-Culture)*
Cathy Rozanski McNamara *(Partner-Corporate Planning)*
Bernadette Pieters *(Chief Diversity, Equity & Inclusion Officer & Principal-People-Culture)*
Roland Reimink *(CFO)*

Subsidiaries:

Anton Collins Mitchell, LLP **(1)**
303 E 17th Ave Ste 600, Denver, CO 80203
Tel.: (303) 830-1120
Web Site: http://www.acmllp.com
Accounting, Financial & Business Services
N.A.I.C.S.: 541211
Greg Anton *(Chm & CEO)*
Tim Watson *(Partner-Tax-Boulder)*
Lisa Modglin *(Sr Mgr-Tax-Boulder)*

BDO Capital Advisors, LLC **(1)**
2 International Pl 4th Fl, Boston, MA 02110
Tel.: (617) 422-7576
Web Site: http://www.bdocap.com
Investment Advisory & Corporate Consulting Services
N.A.I.C.S.: 523940
Valentina Midura *(Mng Dir)*
Kevin Sendlenski *(Mng Dir)*
Robert A. Snape *(Pres)*

BDO Digital, LLC **(1)**
1420 Kensington Rd Ste 110, Oak Brook, IL 60523
Tel.: (630) 572-0240
Web Site: https://www.bdodigital.com
Information Technology Consulting Services
N.A.I.C.S.: 541690
Adam Ferguson *(Mng Partner)*
Michael Lee *(Dir-Infrastructure Solutions & Principal)*
Bob Compere *(Principal-Solution Development)*

DemandGen International, Inc. **(1)**
9000 Crow Canyon Rd Ste 180, Danville, CA 94506
Tel.: (925) 678-2511
Web Site: http://www.demandgen.com
Sales Range: $1-9.9 Million
Emp.: 28
Marketing Automation & Customer Relationship Management Consulting Systems
N.A.I.C.S.: 541613
David Lewis *(Founder & CEO)*
Tiffanie Lewis *(Dir-Mktg)*
Christina Yozallinas *(Dir-Svc Ops)*
Gaea Connary *(Dir-Consulting Svcs)*
John Bokelmann *(Dir-Managed Svcs)*
Tom Svec *(Dir-Mktg Tech Svcs)*
Greg Carver *(COO)*
Rob Bonham *(VP-SIs)*

Subsidiary (Non-US):

DemandGen AG **(2)**
Willy-Brandt-Allee 2, 82041, Munich, Germany **(100%)**
Tel.: (49) 8920321040
Web Site: http://www.demandgen.de
Emp.: 25
Marketing Consulting Services
N.A.I.C.S.: 541613
Reinhard Janning *(CEO)*

DemandGen Australia Pty Ltd. **(2)**
L7 390 St Kilda Rd, Melbourne, 3004, VIC, Australia **(100%)**
Tel.: (61) 407 077 388
Web Site: http://www.demandgen.com.au
Business Marketing Consulting Services
N.A.I.C.S.: 541613
John Paola *(Mng Dir)*

DemandGen International **(2)**
25 Broadway Ave Ste 2203, M4T 1P7, Toronto, ON, Canada **(100%)**
Tel.: (416) 302-0231
Web Site: http://www.demandgen.com
Marketing Consulting Services
N.A.I.C.S.: 541613

DemandGen UK **(2)**
Kingsgate House 12-50 Kingsgate Rd, Kingston, KT2 5AA, Surrey, United Kingdom **(100%)**
Tel.: (44) 20 8547 4031
Web Site: http://www.demandgen.com
Marketing Consulting Services
N.A.I.C.S.: 541613

Morrison, Brown, Argiz & Farra, LLC **(1)**
1450 Brickell Ave 18th Fl, Miami, FL 33131
Tel.: (305) 373-5500
Web Site: http://www.mbafcpa.com
Sales Range: $75-99.9 Million
Emp.: 473
Accounting, Tax, Audit & Consulting Services
N.A.I.C.S.: 541211

Sandra Sarria *(Dir-Tax & Acctg Dept)*
Steven Morrison *(Principal-Audit Dept)*
Erbin J. Ramirez *(Principal-Audit Dept)*
Alexander E. Binelo *(Principal)*
Hernando Gomez *(Dir-Mgmt Advisory Svcs Dept)*
Christian Kutscherauer *(CTO)*
Miguel G. Farra *(Chm-Tax & Acctg)*
Marc Freeman *(Principal-Tax & Acctg)*
Aura Rodriguez *(Dir-Audit Dept)*
Diana Rivera *(Principal-Audit Dept)*
Lazaro Gutierrez *(Dir-Audit Dept)*
Keith Urtel *(Principal)*
Wolfgang Pinther *(Dir-Mktg)*
Kashyap Bakhai *(Principal)*
Ed Blum *(Principal)*
Marc S. Dickler *(Principal)*
Monte Kane *(Principal)*
Stuart C. Rosenberg *(Principal)*
Ira Rubenstein *(Principal)*
Emilio Escandon *(Principal)*
Lisette Rodriguez *(Principal-Audit Dept)*
Ileana Salort-Horta *(COO & Principal)*
Brian Schlang *(Principal-Tax & Acctg Dept)*
Andre N. Chammas *(Mng Principal-Orlando)*

BDP INTERNATIONAL INC.
510 Walnut St Fl 2A, Philadelphia, PA 19106-3621
Tel.: (215) 629-8900 **PA**
Web Site:
http://www.bdpinternational.com
Year Founded: 1972
Sales Range: $75-99.9 Million
Emp.: 900
Freight Transportation Arrangement Services
N.A.I.C.S.: 488510
Arnie F. Bornstein *(Exec Dir-Mktg & Corp Comm)*
Michael Ford *(Chief Compliance Officer)*
Terry Derr *(Dir-Ops-Houston)*
Adrian Kornmacher *(Mgr-Argentina)*
Ricardo Gelain *(Mgr-Brazil)*
Enrico Benedetti *(Mgr-Colombia)*
Amy O'Brien *(Mgr-Mktg)*
Mehul Bhanushali *(Mgr-Sls-India-Natl)*
Gerry Fama *(VP-Sls-Europe)*
Katherine Harper *(CFO)*
Richard Bolte Jr. *(Chm & CEO)*

Subsidiaries:

BDP (Malaysia) SDN BHD **(1)**
Block B-809 Jalan 16/11, 46350, Petaling Jaya, Selangor, Malaysia
Tel.: (60) 3 7954 2001
Emp.: 300
Logistics Consulting Servies
N.A.I.C.S.: 541614
Ng Karkit *(Gen Mgr)*

BDP Asia Pacific Limited **(1)**
4201-07 Tower One MetroPlaza 223 Hing Fong Street, Kwai Chung, China (Hong Kong)
Tel.: (852) 2485 0061
Logistics Consulting Servies
N.A.I.C.S.: 541614

BDP Asia Pacific Pte Ltd. **(1)**
11F No 35 Guangfu S Rd, Songshan District, Taipei, 105, Taiwan
Tel.: (886) 2 2742 5555
Web Site: http://www.bdpinternational.com
Emp.: 60
Logistics Consulting Servies
N.A.I.C.S.: 541614
Weiheng Chen *(Gen Mgr)*

BDP Canada ULC **(1)**
10 Carlson Court Ste 801, Etobicoke, L4W 5B2, ON, Canada
Tel.: (905) 602-0200
Web Site: http://www.bdpinternational.com
Logistics Consulting Servies
N.A.I.C.S.: 541614
Gerry Dickie *(Gen Mgr)*

BDP Chile Ltda. **(1)**
401 Monsenor sotero Sanz 161, Providencia, Santiago, Chile
Tel.: (56) 2 964 46 50

Web Site: http://www.bdpinternational.com
Emp.: 25
Logistics Consulting Servies
N.A.I.C.S.: 541614
Ricardo Koahn *(Gen Mgr)*

BDP Global Logistics (India) Private Limited **(1)**
304 Connection Point Building Airport Exit Road, Bengaluru, 560017, India
Tel.: (91) 8041258126
Web Site: http://www.bdpinternational.com
Emp.: 2
Logistics Consulting Servies
N.A.I.C.S.: 541614
Pavithran M. Kallada *(Mng Dir)*

BDP International BV **(1)**
Reykjavikweg 2 Schiphol SouthEast, 1118 LK, Amsterdam, Netherlands
Tel.: (31) 20 654 4040
Web Site: http://www.bdpinternational.com
Emp.: 15
Logistics Consulting Servies
N.A.I.C.S.: 541614
Jamal Boukidid *(Gen Mgr)*

BDP International Ltd. **(1)**
Room 604 China Youth Plaza No 19 North Road of East 3rd Ring Road, Chaoyang District, Beijing, 100020, China
Tel.: (86) 10 6581 4080
Web Site: http://www.bdpint.com
Emp.: 12
Logistics Consulting Servies
N.A.I.C.S.: 541614
Amanda Qiu *(Gen Mgr)*

BDP International Mexico, S.A. de C.V. **(1)**
Prol Blvd Campestre N 2509 Col Refugio Campestre, Leon, 37156, Mexico
Tel.: (52) 477 10 42 234
Emp.: 100
Logistics Consulting Servies
N.A.I.C.S.: 541614

BDP International NV **(1)**
Braderijstraat 11, Antwerp, 2000, Belgium
Tel.: (32) 3 234 5711
Web Site: http://www.bdpinternational.com
Emp.: 160
Logistics Consulting Servies
N.A.I.C.S.: 541614
Yves Letange *(Mng Dir-Europe)*

Division (Domestic):

BDP International NV - Airfreight Division **(2)**
Bedrijvenzone Machelen Cargo 729/2, Machelen, 1830, Belgium
Tel.: (32) 2 753 0362
Logistics Consulting Servies
N.A.I.C.S.: 541614

BDP International Spain, S.A **(1)**
Avda Ports d'Europa 100 - 2 Planta Edificio Service Center, 08040, Barcelona, Spain
Tel.: (34) 932633324
Web Site: http://www.bdpinternational.com
Emp.: 20
Logistics Consulting Servies
N.A.I.C.S.: 541614

BDP International UK Limited **(1)**
Corinthian House Galleon Boulevard, Dartford, DA2 6QE, Kent, United Kingdom
Tel.: (44) 1322388870
Web Site: http://www.bdpinternational.com
Emp.: 25
Logistics Consulting Servies
N.A.I.C.S.: 541614

BDP Italia S.P.A **(1)**
Via Di Gonfienti 5/C/54, Prato, 59100, Italy
Tel.: (39) 0574 583 244
Logistics Consulting Servies
N.A.I.C.S.: 541614

BDP Kanoo Chemical Logistics Co Ltd **(1)**
PO Box 37, Dammam, 31411, Saudi Arabia
Tel.: (966) 38328601
Logistics Consulting Servies
N.A.I.C.S.: 541614

BDP Logistics Korea Limited **(1)**
10th Fl Mijee Bldg 141-4 Changjun-Dong, Mapo-ku, Seoul, 121881, Korea (South)

BDP International Inc.—(Continued)

Tel.: (82) 2 3703 6400
Web Site: http://www.bdpint.com
Emp.: 56
Logistics Consulting Servies
N.A.I.C.S.: 541614
J. D. Ko (Gen Mgr)

BDP South America Ltda. (1)
Rua Geraldo Flausino Gomes 78-5o Andar,
Sao Paulo, 04575-060, Brazil
Tel.: (55) 11 5504 3400
Web Site: http://www.bdp.com.br
Emp.: 500
Logistics Consulting Servies
N.A.I.C.S.: 541614

BDP Transport, LLC (1)
510 Walnut St, Philadelphia, PA 19106-
3601
Tel.: (215) 629-8900
Web Site: http://www.bdpinternational.com
Sales Range: $10-24.9 Million
Emp.: 50
Ocean Transportation Intermediary
N.A.I.C.S.: 541611

DJS International Services Inc. (1)
4215 Gateway Dr Ste 100, Colleyville, TX
76034
Tel.: (972) 929-8433
Web Site: http://www.djsintl.com
Rev.: $3,000,000
Emp.: 25
Freight Transportation Arrangement
N.A.I.C.S.: 488510
David Meyer (Pres & COO)
Martha Sekin (Controller)
Melissa Meyer (VP-Fin)
Paul Sekin (VP-Sls & Mktg)

BDR TRANSPORT, INC.
7994 US Rte 5, Westminster, VT
05158
Tel.: (802) 463-0606
Web Site:
http://www.bdrtransport.com
Year Founded: 1970
Sales Range: $10-24.9 Million
Emp.: 35
LTL Trucking Services
N.A.I.C.S.: 484122
Greg Gay (Pres)
Doug Gay (VP)

BDS MARKETING, LLC
10 Holland, Irvine, CA 92618   CA
Web Site: http://www.bdsmktg.com
Year Founded: 1984
Advetising Agency
N.A.I.C.S.: 541810
Ken Kress (CEO)
Jim Fulk (Pres)
Tracy Neff (Sr VP-Ops & Client Svc)
David Tranberg (Sr VP-Client Dev)
Randy Schrock (Sr VP-Strategic
Svcs)

Subsidiaries:

The Michael Alan Group (1)
22 W 38th St 8th Fl, New York, NY 10018
Tel.: (212) 563-7656
Web Site: http://www.michael-alan.com
Advetising Agency
N.A.I.C.S.: 541810

**BDT CAPITAL PARTNERS,
LLC**
401 N Michigan Ave Ste 3100, Chi-
cago, IL 60611
Tel.: (312) 660-7300   DE
Web Site: https://bdtmsd.com
Privater Equity Firm
N.A.I.C.S.: 523999
Ben Sher (Partner)

Subsidiaries:

Alliance Laundry Holdings LLC (1)
Shepard St, Ripon, WI 54971-0990
Tel.: (920) 748-3121
Web Site: http://alliancelaundry.com

Holding Company; Commercial Laundry
Equipment Mfr
N.A.I.C.S.: 551112
Michael D. Schoeb (CEO)
Richard L. Pyle (Chief Comml Officer &
Pres)
Scott Chiavetta (CIO)
Gary Luckow (Chief Value Enhancement
Officer)
Robert Macklin (Chief Legal Officer, Sec &
VP)
Joe Michels (VP-Global HR)
Robert A. Habura (CFO)
Justin Tripp (Pres-Global Retail)

Subsidiary (Domestic):

Alliance Laundry Systems LLC (2)
Shepard St, Ripon, WI 54971
Tel.: (920) 748-3121
Web Site: http://alliancelaundry.com
Commercial Laundry Equipment Mfr
N.A.I.C.S.: 333310
Craig Dakauskas (Sr VP-North America
Comml)
Michael D. Schoeb (CEO)
Haresh Shah (CFO & VP)
Jan Vleugels (COO-Intl & Sr VP)
Samantha Hannan (Gen Counsel)
Richard Baazi (VP-Product & Tech Strat-
egy)
Amanda Kopetsky (VP-Global HR)
Cody Masluk (VP-North America Residen-
tial)
Mick Mancuso (VP-Ops-North America)

Subsidiary (Domestic):

Commercial & Coin Laundry Equip-
ment Co. (3)
1626 Tradewinds Dr, Gulf Breeze, FL
32563
Tel.: (850) 932-8348
Sales Range: $1-9.9 Million
Emp.: 24
Coin-Operated Laundry
N.A.I.C.S.: 812310

Dynamic Laundry Systems, Inc. (3)
12910 NE 125th Way 3B, Kirkland, WA
98034
Tel.: (425) 823-4300
Web Site: http://www.dynamicss.com
Sales Range: $1-9.9 Million
Emp.: 10
Service Establishment Equipment & Sup-
plies Merchant Whslr
N.A.I.C.S.: 423850
Daniel Danhof (Founder & Pres)
Julie Johnson (Office Mgr)

Subsidiary (Domestic):

PWS Inc. (2)
6500 Flotilla St, Los Angeles, CA 90040-
1714
Tel.: (323) 721-8832
Web Site: http://www.pwslaundry.com
Sales Range: $10-24.9 Million
Emp.: 55
Develops, Refurbishes, Brokers & Finances
Laundries & Distributes Laundry Products
N.A.I.C.S.: 423850
Brad Pollack (Pres)
Brad Pollack (Pres)

Commercial Credit, Inc. (1)
277 W Trade St Ste 1450, Charlotte, NC
28202
Tel.: (704) 944-2770
Web Site:
http://www.commercialcreditinc.com
Sales Range: $25-49.9 Million
Emp.: 120
Holding Company; Commercial Equipment
Financing
N.A.I.C.S.: 551112
Daniel McDonough (Chm, Pres & CEO)
E. Roger Gebhart (CFO & Sr VP)
Kevin McGinn (Sr VP-Natl Waste)
Donald Pokorny (Sr VP-Midwest)
Angelo Garubo (Sr VP & Sec)
Robert Qulia (Gen Counsel & VP)
Rebecca Sabo (Chief Acctg Officer & VP)
Mark Lempko (Sr VP-NE US & Canada)
Paul Bottiglio (Treas)

Subsidiary (Domestic):

Commercial Credit Group Inc. (2)

227 W Trade St Ste 1450, Charlotte, NC
28202
Tel.: (704) 731-0031
Web Site:
http://www.commercialcreditgroup.com
Emp.: 40
Commercial Equipment Finance & Leasing
Services
N.A.I.C.S.: 522220
Dan McDonough (Pres & CEO)
Kevin McGinn (Sr VP-Natl Waste)
Don Pokorny (Sr VP-Central & West Div)
E. Roger Gebhart (CFO & Sr VP)
Paul Bottiglio (Treas)
Chris Evered (VP-Canada)
Angelo G. Garubo (Sec & Sr VP)
Brett Goodman (Sr VP-Southeast Div)
Mark Lempko (Sr VP-Northeast & Canada
Div)
Rebecca Sabo (Chief Acctg Officer & VP)

Division (Domestic):

Manufacturers Capital (3)
227 W Trade St Ste 1450, Charlotte, NC
28202
Tel.: (866) 375-2999
Web Site: http://www.mfrscapital.com
Miscellaneous Intermediation
N.A.I.C.S.: 523910
David Goose (Sr VP-Machine Tool Div)
Chris Richardson (VP)
Bill Moore (VP)
Troy Martz (Reg Sls Mgr)
Janna North (Reg Sls Mgr)
Stefanie Leedy (Coord-Transaction)

Subsidiary (Domestic):

Keystone Equipment Finance
Corp. (2)
433 New Park Ave, West Hartford, CT
06110
Web Site: http://www.keystoneefc.com
General Rental Centers
N.A.I.C.S.: 532310
Harold Katz (Controller)
Todd Kaufman (Pres)

Culligan International Company (1)
9399 W Higgins Rd Ste 1100, Rosemont, IL
60018-4940
Tel.: (847) 430-2800
Web Site: http://www.culligan.com
Water Conditioning & Purification Equip-
ment & Related Products Mfr
N.A.I.C.S.: 333310
Samuel Allen Hamood (Pres & Chief Admin
& Fin Officer)
Sheila M. Rutt (Chief HR Officer)
Tim Sewell (Mgr-Mktg & Sls)
Samuel Allen Hamood (Pres & Chief Admin
& Fin Officer)
Sheila M. Rutt (Chief HR Officer)

Subsidiary (Non-US):

AquaVenture Holdings Limited (2)
Commerce House Wickhams Cay 1, PO
Box 3140, Road Town, VG1110, Virgin Is-
lands (British)
Tel.: (284) 8138558636
Web Site: http://www.aquaventure.com
Rev.: $203,487,000
Assets: $797,581,000
Liabilities: $397,994,000
Net Worth: $399,587,000
Earnings: ($20,075,000)
Emp.: 780
Fiscal Year-end: 12/31/2019
Water Purification Solution Provider
N.A.I.C.S.: 562910
Lee S. Muller (CFO, Treas,Sec & Sr VP)
Brian Miller (Gen Counsel & Sr VP)

Culligan Australia Pty Ltd. (2)
Unit 10 8-10 Dympna Street Cromer, 2099,
Sydney, NSW, Australia
Tel.: (61) 401077245
Web Site:
http://www.culliganaustralia.com.au
Water Conditioning & Purification Equip-
ment & Related Products Mfr
N.A.I.C.S.: 333310

Culligan Espana S.A. (2)
Calle Trepadella 12, Castellbisbal, 08173,
Barcelona, Spain
Tel.: (34) 935653300
Web Site: http://www.culligan.es

Water Conditioning & Purification Equipment & Related Products Mfr
N.A.I.C.S.: 333310

Culligan France (2)
2 rue Rene Caudron, 78960, Voisins-le- (100%)
Bretonneux, France
Tel.: (33) 130162323
Web Site: http://www.culligan.fr
Water Conditioning & Purification Equip-
ment & Related Products
N.A.I.C.S.: 333310

Culligan Italiana S.p.A. (2)
Via Gandolfi 6, Cadriano Di Granarolo
Emilia, 40057, Bologna, Italy
Tel.: (39) 0516017111
Web Site: http://www.culligan.it
Water Conditioning & Purification Equip-
ment & Related Products
N.A.I.C.S.: 333310

Branch (Domestic):

Culligan Water (2)
3450 Kossuth St, Lafayette, IN 47905-4797
Tel.: (765) 248-0917
Web Site:
http://www.culliganwaterindiana.com
Water Softener Service
N.A.I.C.S.: 561990

Culligan Water Indiana (2)
9220 Corporation Dr, Indianapolis, IN 46256
Tel.: (317) 420-2686
Web Site:
http://www.culliganwaterindiana.com
Water Purification Equipment Supplier
N.A.I.C.S.: 423420

Subsidiary (Domestic):

Paragon Water Systems, Inc. (3)
13805 Monroes Park, Tampa, FL 33635
Tel.: (727) 538-4704
Web Site: http://www.paragonwater.com
Water Filtration Products Design & Mfr
N.A.I.C.S.: 333310
George L. Lutich (Founder & CEO)

Subsidiary (Domestic):

Quench USA, Inc. (2)
630 Allendale Rd Ste 200, King of Prussia,
PA 19406
Tel.: (833) 203-1352
Web Site: https://quenchwater.com
Filtered Water Coolers Mfr
N.A.I.C.S.: 339999
Anthony A. Ibarguen (CEO)
Tony Ibarguen (CEO)
Todd Peterson (COO)
Tom Breslin (CFO)
John Whalen (Sr VP-Sls, Mktg & Customer
Svc)
Chris Turano (Sr VP-Field Svc & Supply
Chain)
Jeff Doughty (VP-Natl Accounts)
Michael Thomas (VP-Natl Accounts)
Dan Duffy (VP & Controller)
Mort Goldman (VP-IT)
Ted Hertz (VP-Product Mgmt)
Patrick White (VP-Sls-West)
Michael Nosek (VP-Sls-East)
Chermei Wong (VP-IT Svcs)
Trevor Owens (VP-IT Architecture)

Subsidiary (Domestic):

Carolina Pure Water Systems
LLC (3)
4267 US Hwy 701 S, Four Oaks, NC
27524-9168
Tel.: (919) 993-3526
Web Site: http://www.carolinapure.com
All Other Specialty Food Stores
N.A.I.C.S.: 445298
Steve Cole (Founder)

Mirex Aquapure Solutions, LP (3)
2105 Silber Rd Ste 101, Houston, TX
77055
Tel.: (713) 682-3000
Water Filtration Services
N.A.I.C.S.: 339999

Pure Health Solutions, Inc. (3)
475 Half Day Rd Ste 450, Lincolnshire, IL
60069
Tel.: (224) 215-2401
Web Site: http://www.purewatertech.com

Sales Range: $1-9.9 Million
Emp.: 19
Filtered Water Coolers Distr & Mfr
N.A.I.C.S.: 339999

Pure Water Tech of San Diego (3)
4683 Mission Gorge Pl, San Diego, CA 92120
Tel.: (619) 564-8500
Web Site:
    http://www.purewatertechsandiego.com
Business Support Services
N.A.I.C.S.: 561499
Rosa Palacios (Mgr)

Do Outdoors, LLC (1)
3031 N Martin, Springfield, MO 65803
Tel.: (417) 881-5397
Sporting & Athletic Goods Mfr
N.A.I.C.S.: 339920

Subsidiary (Domestic):

SP Company, Inc. (2)
2 Humminbird Ln, Eufaula, AL 36027
Tel.: (334) 687-5758
Sporting & Athletic Goods Mfr
N.A.I.C.S.: 339920

Strike King Lure Co. (2)
466 Washington St, Collierville, TN 38017
Tel.: (901) 853-1455
Web Site: http://www.strikeking.com
Sales Range: $1-9.9 Million
Emp.: 50
Sporting & Athletic Goods Mfr
N.A.I.C.S.: 339920
Douglas Minor (Mgr-Sls)
Mary Cozart (Mgr-HR)
Chris Brown (Mgr-Customer Svc)

Weber Inc. (1)
1415 S Roselle Rd, Palatine, IL 60067   (71.56%)
Tel.: (847) 934-5700
Rev.: $1,982,406,000
Assets: $1,550,992,000
Liabilities: $1,672,337,000
Net Worth: ($121,345,000)
Earnings: $47,726,000
Emp.: 2,534
Fiscal Year-end: 09/30/2021
Holding Company
N.A.I.C.S.: 551112
Alan D. Matula (CEO)
Guenther Weber (Founder)
Hans-Jurgen Herr (Sr VP-Global Brand & Consumer Experience)
Michael G. Jacobs (COO)
Mary A. Sagripanti (CMO)
Phil Zadeik (Gen Counsel & Sec)
Marla Yvonne Kilpatrick (Interim CFO)
Alan Matula (Interim CEO & CTO)
Erik W. Chalut (Corp Counsel)

Subsidiary (Domestic):

June Life, Inc. (2)
649 Front St, San Francisco, CA 94111
Tel.: (415) 799-5863
Web Site: https://www.juneoven.com
Household Appliance Distr
N.A.I.C.S.: 449210
Matt Horn (CEO & Co-Founder)
Nikhil Bhogal (Co-Founder & CTO)

Subsidiary (Non-US):

Weber-Stephen Nordic ApS (2)
Bogildsmindevej 23, 9400, Norresundby, Denmark
Tel.: (45) 9 936 3010
Kitchen Accessory Mfr
N.A.I.C.S.: 332215

Weber-Stephen Osterreich GmbH (2)
Kienzlstrasse 17/Top 404, 4600, Wels, Austria
Tel.: (43) 724 289 0135
Kitchen Accessory Mfr
N.A.I.C.S.: 332215

Weber-Stephen Products Belgium BVBA (2)
Blarenberglaan 6 B4, Industriezone Noord B6, 2800, Mechelen, Belgium
Tel.: (32) 1 528 3099
Kitchen Accessory Mfr
N.A.I.C.S.: 332215

Weber-Stephen Products LLC (1)
200 E Daniels Rd, Palatine, IL 60067-6266
Tel.: (847) 934-5700
Web Site: http://www.weber.com
Sales Range: $200-249.9 Million
Emp.: 1,155
Gas & Charcoal Grill & Accessories Mfr; Restaurant Operator
N.A.I.C.S.: 335220
Brooke Jones (Dir-Mktg)

BE ACTIVE CORP.
41 W 33rd St, New York, NY 10001
Tel.: (212) 244-6444   NY
Web Site:
    https://www.activestaffing.com
Industrial Staffing & Recruitment Services
N.A.I.C.S.: 561311
Elliot Elzweig (Pres & CEO)
Tina Acker (VP-Reg Ops & Corp Support)
Seth Dinsky (VP-Admin)
Benjamin Elzweig (Dir-Strategic Dev)
Matt Kaplan (Dir-Acctg Ops)
Mike Breit (Exec VP)

BE FOUND ONLINE
3304 N Lincoln Ave, Chicago, IL 60657
Tel.: (773) 904-1342
Web Site:
    https://www.befoundonline.com
Year Founded: 2008
Sales Range: $1-9.9 Million
Emp.: 17
Online Digital Marketing
N.A.I.C.S.: 541613
Dan Golden (Co-Founder & Pres)
Steve Krull (Co-Founder & CEO)

BEACH AUTOMOTIVE GROUP
851 Jason Blvd, Myrtle Beach, SC 29577-6743
Tel.: (843) 626-3666
Web Site:
    http://www.beachautomotive.com
Year Founded: 1995
Sales Range: $25-49.9 Million
Emp.: 85
Car Whslr
N.A.I.C.S.: 441110
Wes Grubbs (Owner)

Subsidiaries:

Keffer of Little River, LLC (1)
3740 Hwy 9 E, Little River, SC 29566
Tel.: (843) 399-4400
Web Site: http://www.judkuhnchevrolet.com
Sales Range: $1-9.9 Million
Emp.: 30
New Car Dealers
N.A.I.C.S.: 441110

BEACH COMPANY INC.
211 King St Ste 300, Charleston, SC 29401
Tel.: (843) 722-2615
Web Site:
    http://www.thebeachcompany.com
Year Founded: 1945
Sales Range: $25-49.9 Million
Emp.: 500
Subdividing & Developing Services
N.A.I.C.S.: 237210
John Darby (Pres)
J. D. Reyna (CFO & VP)
Pat McDermott (Treas & Controller)
Charles S. Way Jr. (Chm)

BEACH FORD
1600 N Main St, Suffolk, VA 23434
Tel.: (757) 539-1595
Web Site: http://www.beachford.com
Year Founded: 1978
Sales Range: $10-24.9 Million
Emp.: 38
Automobiles, New & Used

N.A.I.C.S.: 441110
Bob Harris (Dir-Comml Sls)
Chris Bryan (Mgr-Sls)
Jeff Tuell (Mgr-Quality Control)

BEACH FORD SUFFOLK
1600 N Main St, Suffolk, VA 23434
Tel.: (757) 539-1595
Web Site:
    http://www.beachfordsuffolk.com
Year Founded: 1980
Sales Range: $10-24.9 Million
Emp.: 42
New Car Whslr
N.A.I.C.S.: 441110
Matt Dungan (Gen Mgr)

BEACH FORD, INC.
2717 Virginia Beach Blvd, Virginia Beach, VA 23452
Tel.: (757) 486-2717
Web Site:
    http://www.beachfordvirginia.com
Year Founded: 1955
Sales Range: $50-74.9 Million
Emp.: 216
New Car Whslr
N.A.I.C.S.: 441110
Bob Barton (Pres-Beach Ford Lincoln-Mercury)

BEACH OIL COMPANY INC.
631 Hwy 76, Clarksville, TN 37043
Tel.: (931) 358-9303
Web Site: https://www.beachoil.com
Sales Range: $10-24.9 Million
Emp.: 15
Convenience Store
N.A.I.C.S.: 445131
William N. Beach (Owner)

BEACH PATROL INC.
Apt 2 3771 Lockland Dr, Los Angeles, CA 90008-3538
Tel.: (310) 522-2700   DE
Web Site:
    http://www.beachpatrolinc.com
Year Founded: 1987
Sales Range: $100-124.9 Million
Emp.: 167
Women's Swimwear & Beachwear
N.A.I.C.S.: 424350

BEACH PRODUCTS, INC.
3010 W De Leon, Tampa, FL 33609
Tel.: (813) 839-6565   FL
Year Founded: 1958
Sales Range: $75-99.9 Million
Emp.: 300
Pharmaceuticals Mfr
N.A.I.C.S.: 325412
Richard B. Jenkins (Chm, Pres & CEO)
Richard S. Jenkins (Exec VP)
Betty Jo Jenkins (Treas & Sec)
Carol Jenkins (Mgr-Sls)
David Thomas (Controller)

Subsidiaries:

Pharmaceutical Associates, Inc. (1)
201 Delaware St, Greenville, SC 29605-5823   (100%)
Tel.: (864) 277-7282
Web Site: http://www.paipharma.com
Sales Range: $25-49.9 Million
Emp.: 225
Mfr of Pharmaceuticals
N.A.I.C.S.: 325412
Jane C. Hicks (COO)
Myers Turner (Mgr-Engrg)
BSmith Smith (Mgr-Maintenance)

BEACH TO BAY CONSTRUCTION INC.
5702 Marina Dr, Holmes Beach, FL 34217
Tel.: (941) 778-8658

Web Site:
    http://www.beachtobayliving.com
Sales Range: $1-9.9 Million
Emp.: 6
Residential Construction
N.A.I.C.S.: 236115
Shawn Kaleta (Co-Owner)
Scott Eason (Co-Owner)
Emily Wettstein (Office Mgr)

BEACHBODY, LLC
3301 Exhibition Blvd, Santa Monica, CA 90404
Tel.: (323) 904-5600
Web Site: http://www.beachbody.com
Year Founded: 1998
Sales Range: $75-99.9 Million
Emp.: 400
Fitness Videos & DVDs Producer, Marketer & Distr
N.A.I.C.S.: 512110
Carl Daikeler (Co-Founder, Chm & CEO)
Jon Congdon (Co-Founder & CMO)
Robert K. Gifford (COO)
Bryan Carney (Sr Mgr-Employee Experience)
Jonathan Gelfand (Chief Legal Officer & Sr VP-Bus Dev)
Helene Klein (Chief People Officer)
Bryan Muehlberger (CIO)
Robert K. Gifford (COO)
Jean-Michel Fournier (Pres-Global Partnerships & Corp Dev)

BEACHNER GRAIN INC.
2600 Slynn Dr, Parsons, KS 67357
Tel.: (620) 820-8600
Web Site:
    http://www.beachnergrain.com
Year Founded: 1986
Sales Range: $10-24.9 Million
Emp.: 130
Grain & Field Beans Distr
N.A.I.C.S.: 424510
Daniel Allen (Dir-Loss Control)

BEACHSIDE CAPITAL PARTNERS
43 North Ave, Bridgeport, CT 06606-5120
Tel.: (203) 610-8269
Year Founded: 1971
Sales Range: $10-24.9 Million
Emp.: 4
Investment Holding Companies
N.A.I.C.S.: 551112
James R. McManus (Chm)
Ed McGill (Mng Partner)
Jonathan D'Agostino (COO)

BEACON ACQUISITION PARTNERS INC.
721 Waverly Rd, Ridgewood, NJ 07450
Tel.: (201) 447-2486   Ca
Web Site:
    https://www.beaconacquisition.com
Year Founded: 2007
Sales Range: $1-9.9 Million
Investment Services
N.A.I.C.S.: 523999
Robert Philip Mather (Chm, Pres & CEO)

BEACON APPLICATION SERVICES CORPORATION
959 Concord St Ste 250, Framingham, MA 01701
Tel.: (508) 663-4433
Web Site:
    http://www.beaconservices.com
Year Founded: 1990
Rev.: $14,200,000
Emp.: 80

Beacon Application Services
Corporation—(Continued)
Professional, Scientific & Technical
Services
N.A.I.C.S.: 541990
Madeline Osit *(Principal)*
David Eddy *(VP)*

BEACON ASSOCIATES, INC.
900-A S Main St Ste 102, Bel Air, MD
21014
Tel.: (410) 638-7279
Web Site:
   http://www.beaconassociates.net
Year Founded: 2001
Sales Range: $10-24.9 Million
Emp.: 100
Management Consulting Services
N.A.I.C.S.: 541618
Carol Koffink *(Pres & CEO)*
Ann M. Bryant *(Sr VP)*
Amy Pfaff *(VP-Ops)*

BEACON AVIATION INSUR-ANCE SERVICES, INC.
126 S Osprey Ave Ste 200, Sarasota,
FL 34236
Tel.: (941) 953-5390
Web Site: http://www.beaconais.com
Sales Range: $1-9.9 Million
Emp.: 10
Aviation Industry Insurance Services
N.A.I.C.S.: 524294
Raymond M. Neff *(Chm & VP)*
Robert E. McManus *(COO)*
John B. Cunningham *(Pres)*

BEACON BAY AUTO WASH
1600 Sunflower Ave Ste 110, Costa
Mesa, CA 92626
Tel.: (714) 427-1100
Web Site: http://www.beaconbay.com
Rev.: $29,400,000
Emp.: 225
Gasoline Stations
N.A.I.C.S.: 457120
Linda Kendell *(Treas & VP)*
Kathryn S. Utt *(Sec & VP)*
Patrick C. Shea *(Pres)*

BEACON COMMUNICATIONS LLC
2900 Olympic Blvd, Santa Monica,
CA 90404
Tel.: (310) 260-7000   DE
Web Site:
   http://www.beaconpictures.com
Year Founded: 1990
Sales Range: $50-74.9 Million
Emp.: 30
Develops, Products, Distributes &
Finances Film & Television
N.A.I.C.S.: 512110
Suzann Ellis *(Pres-Beacon Pictures)*

BEACON COMMUNITIES LLC
2 Center Plz Ste 700, Boston, MA
02108
Tel.: (617) 574-1100
Web Site:
   https://www.beaconcommunity.com
Real Estate Firm
N.A.I.C.S.: 236116
Howard Cohen *(Chm)*
Tim Cowles *(CFO)*
David Greenblatt *(Sr VP-Fin)*
Mercedes Farrando *(Dir-Design Svcs)*
Mary Corthell *(Sr VP-Asset Mgmt)*
Ellen Morreale *(Sr VP & Controller)*
Frank Alvarez *(Sr VP-Operations)*

BEACON CONTAINER CORPO-RATION
700 W 1st St, Birdsboro, PA 19508-
2128
Tel.: (610) 582-2222   PA

Web Site:
   https://www.beaconcontainer.com
Year Founded: 1957
Sales Range: $25-49.9 Million
Emp.: 180
Mfr of Corrugated Shipping Contain-
ers
N.A.I.C.S.: 322211

BEACON CREDIT UNION
586 S Wabash St, Wabash, IN 46992
Tel.: (260) 563-7443   IN
Web Site: https://www.beaconcu.org
Year Founded: 1931
Credit Union
N.A.I.C.S.: 522130
Dustin Cuttriss *(Pres & CEO)*

BEACON ELECTRIC SUPPLY
9630 Chesapeake Dr, San Diego, CA
92123
Tel.: (858) 279-9770
Web Site:
   http://www.beaconelectric.com
Sales Range: $25-49.9 Million
Emp.: 75
Electrical Construction Materials
N.A.I.C.S.: 423610
Diana Timm *(Project Mgr)*

BEACON ELECTRONIC ASSO-CIATES, INC.
5887 Glenridge Dr NE Ste 130, At-
lanta, GA 30328
Tel.: (404) 256-9640
Web Site:
   http://www.beaconelectronics.com
Year Founded: 1963
Sales Range: $10-24.9 Million
Emp.: 30
Electrical Apparatus & Equipment
N.A.I.C.S.: 423690
Brian Sims *(Mgr-HR)*
Pam Cuviello *(Mgr-Acctg)*
Mark West *(Pres)*
John Gollner *(VP)*
Rita Hall *(Coord-Distr)*

BEACON HEALTH HOLDINGS LLC
200 State St, Boston, MA 02109
Tel.: (781) 994-7500   DE
Holding Company
N.A.I.C.S.: 551112
Elizabeth Pattullo *(Chm)*
Timothy Murphy *(CEO)*
Bill Fandrich *(COO & Exec VP)*

Subsidiaries:

Beacon Health Strategies, LLC   (1)
200 State St, Boston, MA 02109
Tel.: (781) 994-7500
Web Site:
   http://www.beaconhealthstrategies.com
Behavioral Health Care Management Ser-
vices
N.A.I.C.S.: 524114
Brian Wheelan *(Exec VP-Corp Dev)*
Dale Seamans *(Dir-Corp Comm)*
Timothy Murphy *(CEO)*
Anup Vidyarthy *(CIO & Sr VP)*

Subsidiary (Domestic):

ValueOptions, Inc.   (2)
240 Corporate Blvd, Norfolk, VA 23502
Tel.: (757) 459-5100
Web Site: http://www.valueoptions.com
Sales Range: $1-4.9 Billion
Emp.: 4,400
Healtcare Services
N.A.I.C.S.: 621498
Nancy Lane *(Reg Sr VP-Pub Sector)*
Sunny Sonner *(Exec VP-HR)*
Bob Esposito *(COO & Exec VP)*
John Tadich *(Exec VP-Pub Sector &
Emerging Markets)*
Daniel Santmyer *(Sr VP-Data Analytics &
Reporting Svcs)*
Knute Rotto *(CEO-Connecticut)*

Division (Domestic):
ValueOptions, Inc.   (3)
3800 Paramount Pkwy Ste 300, Morrisville,
NC 27560-6901
Tel.: (919) 379-9060
Web Site: http://www.valueoptions.com
Sales Range: $25-49.9 Million
Emp.: 175
Job Counseling
N.A.I.C.S.: 621111
Bob Esposito *(COO)*
Tom Warburton *(Dir-Mktg)*
Carolyn Brockmann *(Mgr-Value Options
Acct)*
Wilton Hollins *(Dir-HR-ValueOptions)*
Tom James *(Dir-Health & Performance So-
lutions ValueOptions)*
Michael W. Wood *(Sr Dir-Bus Dev)*

BEACON HEALTH SYSTEM, INC.
615 N Michigan St, South Bend, IN
46601
Tel.: (574) 647-1000   IN
Web Site:
   https://www.beaconhealthcare.org
Year Founded: 2012
Sales Range: $800-899.9 Million
Emp.: 7,300
Non-Profit Healthcare Organization;
Hospitals, Clinics & Other Healthcare
Facilities Operator
N.A.I.C.S.: 813920
Daniel A. Morrison *(Chm)*
Jeff Costello *(CFO)*
Steven Eller *(Chief HR Officer)*
Diane Maas *(VP-Managed Care &
Bus Dev)*
Kreg Gruber *(CEO)*
Danielle A. Gagliano *(Chief Strategy
Officer & Chief Plng Officer)*
Mark Warlick *(CIO)*
Lori Turner *(CMO, Chief Innovation &
Customer Experience Officer)*

Subsidiaries:

Elkhart General Hospital, Inc.   (1)
600 East Blvd, Elkhart, IN 46514
Tel.: (574) 294-2621
Web Site: http://www.ehg.org
Healthcare Professional Organization; Hos-
pital, Clinic & Other Healthcare Facilities
Operator
N.A.I.C.S.: 813920
Carl Risk II *(Pres)*

Memorial Hospital of South Bend,
Inc.   (1)
615 N Michigan St, South Bend, IN
46601   (100%)
Tel.: (574) 647-1000
Web Site: http://www.qualityoflife.org
Healthcare Professional Organization; Hos-
pital Operator
N.A.I.C.S.: 813920
Larry Tracy *(Pres)*

BEACON HILL STAFFING GROUP LLC
152 Bowdoin St, Boston, MA 02108
Tel.: (617) 326-4000
Web Site:
   https://www.beaconhillstaffing.com
Year Founded: 2000
Sales Range: $25-49.9 Million
Emp.: 500
Staffing Services
N.A.I.C.S.: 561320
Jeff McLaren *(Mng Dir & Exec VP)*
Charles J. Cain *(Mng Dir & Exec VP)*
Andrew Wang *(CEO)*
Aaron Mace *(Mng Dir & CFO)*
John David Tarbox *(Mng Dir & Exec
VP)*
Tim Bolduc *(Mgr-Div)*
Amy Van Sicklin *(Mng Dir & Exec
VP)*
Jim Demone *(Controller & Dir-Acctg)*
Jennifer Patterson *(Dir-Admin & FSO)*

Megan Conroy *(Dir-Div)*
Caitlin Antosz *(Mgr-Mktg)*
Stephen Lavoie *(Mgr-Tech & Ops)*
Ken Cole *(Sr Mgr-Recruiting)*
Michael A. Chiappardi *(Mgr-VMS &
Cash App)*
Joanna Foulk *(Mng Dir & Exec VP)*
Kathleen Keliher *(Mng Dir & Exec
VP)*
Ryan Pirnat *(Mng Dir & Exec VP)*
Charles S. Sullivan III *(CIO)*

Subsidiaries:

Beacon Hill Associates   (1)
152 Bowdoin St, Boston, MA 02108
Tel.: (617) 326-4000
Web Site: http://www.beaconhillstaffing.com
Sales Range: $10-24.9 Million
Emp.: 150
Staffing Services
N.A.I.C.S.: 541612
Charles J. Cain *(Mng Dir & Exec VP)*

Beacon Hill Financial   (1)
152 Bowdoin St, Boston, MA 02108
Tel.: (617) 326-4000
Sales Range: $25-49.9 Million
Emp.: 100
Staffing Services
N.A.I.C.S.: 541612
Amy Van Sicklin *(Mng Dir)*

Beacon Hill Financial   (1)
111 W Washington St Ste 1410, Chicago, IL
60602
Tel.: (312) 759-1500
Web Site: http://www.beaconhillstaffing.com
Sales Range: $10-24.9 Million
Emp.: 20
Staffing Services
N.A.I.C.S.: 541612
Michael Pickens *(Mng Dir)*

Beacon Hill HR   (1)
152 Bowdoin St, Boston, MA 02108
Tel.: (617) 326-4000
Web Site:
   http://www.beaconhillstaffinggroup.com
Sales Range: $25-49.9 Million
Emp.: 100
Staffing Services
N.A.I.C.S.: 541612
Jen McDon *(Office Mgr)*

Beacon Hill Legal   (1)
152 Bowdoin St, Boston, MA 02108
Tel.: (617) 326-4000
Web Site: http://www.beaconhillfg.com
Sales Range: $25-49.9 Million
Emp.: 100
Staffing Services
N.A.I.C.S.: 541612
John David Tarbox *(Mng Dir)*

Beacon Hill Technologies   (1)
152 Bowdoin St, Boston, MA 02108
Tel.: (617) 326-4000
Web Site: http://www.beaconhillstaffing.com
Sales Range: $25-49.9 Million
Emp.: 300
IT Staffing Services
N.A.I.C.S.: 541612
Jeff McLaren *(Mng Dir & Exec VP)*

BEACON INDUSTRIES, INC.
549 Cedar St, Newington, CT 06111
Tel.: (860) 594-5200   CT
Web Site: https://www.beacongp.com
Aircraft Components Mfr
N.A.I.C.S.: 336412
Don Lopardo *(Controller)*

BEACON OCCUPATIONAL HEALTH & SAFETY SER-VICES, INC.
800 Cordova St, Anchorage, AK
99501
Tel.: (907) 222-7612
Web Site:
   http://www.beaconohss.com

Year Founded: 1999
Sales Range: $10-24.9 Million
Emp.: 300
Safety Consulting Services
N.A.I.C.S.: 541620
Holly Hylen *(Pres)*
Mark Hylen *(VP)*
Tony French *(VP-Ops)*
Kevin Luppen *(Dir-Health Svcs)*

BEACON POINTE HOLDINGS, LLC

24 Corporate Plz Ste 150, Newport Beach, CA 92660
Tel.: (949) 718-1600   CA
Web Site: http://www.bpadvisors.com
Year Founded: 2002
Emp.: 56
Holding Company; Investment Advisory & Wealth Management Services
N.A.I.C.S.: 551112
Shannon F. Eusey *(Co-Founder, Pres & Partner)*
Garth Flint *(Co-Founder, CEO & Partner)*
Mollie Rosing *(Partner & Head-HR)*
Douglas Allison *(Partner)*
Matthew Cooper *(Partner & Pres-Beacon Pointe Wealth Advisors)*
Felix Lin *(Partner)*
Graham Pierce *(Partner)*
Commie Stevens *(Partner & Head-Strategic & Fin Plng)*
Diane Peck *(CFO)*
Steven Beals *(Mng Dir & Head-Client Svcs & Ops)*
Ellie Chizmarova *(Mng Dir & Head-Investment Res)*
Allison Hillgren *(Dir & Head-Mktg & Comm)*
Catherine Prentice *(Dir-Compliance)*
Michele Sarna *(Mng Dir & Partner)*

Subsidiaries:

Beacon Pointe Advisors, LLC   **(1)**
24 Corporate Plz Dr Ste 150, Newport Beach, CA 92660
Tel.: (949) 718-1600
Web Site: http://www.bpadvisors.com
Emp.: 55
Investment Advisory & Management Services
N.A.I.C.S.: 523940
Shannon F. Eusey *(Co-Founder, Pres & CEO)*
Garth Flint *(Co-Founder, CEO & Partner)*
Mollie Rosing *(Partner & Head-HR)*
Commie Stevens *(Partner & Head-Strategic & Fin Plng)*
Douglas Allison *(Partner)*
Felix Lin *(Partner-Institutional Consulting Svcs Grp)*
Graham Pierce *(Partner)*
Steven Beals *(Mng Dir & Head-Client Svcs & Ops)*
Ellie Chizmarova *(Mng Dir & Head-Investment Res)*
Diane Peck *(CFO)*
Allison Hillgren *(Dir & Head-Mktg & Comm)*
Catherine Prentice *(Dir-Compliance)*
Mike Breller *(Mng Dir-Institutional Consulting Svcs)*
Kathy Sharp *(Office Mgr)*
Wanda Ho *(Dir-Private Client Svcs)*

Beacon Pointe Wealth Advisors, LLC   **(1)**
610 Newport Ctr Dr Ste 280, Newport Beach, CA 92660
Tel.: (949) 720-9980
Web Site: http://www.bpadvisors.com
Wealth Management Services
N.A.I.C.S.: 523940
Brian Coughlan *(Mng Dir & Partner-Arizona)*
Landen Lunsway *(Mng Dir & Partner-Arizona)*
Chris Palermo *(Mng Dir & Partner-Arizona)*
Andrew Reinhardt *(Mng Dir & Partner-Arizona)*
Matthew Cooper *(Pres & Partner)*
Karisa Diephouse *(Dir-Practice Integration & Strategy)*

Chitra Staley *(Mng Dir & Partner-Massachusetts)*
Carolyn Smith *(Mgr-Private Client Svcs)*
Lauren Meixel *(Mgr-Private Client Svcs)*
Sue Fritts *(Mgr-Private Client Svcs)*

Subsidiary (Domestic):

Walden Capital Advisors, LLC   **(2)**
2 Bala Plz Ste 401, Bala Cynwyd, PA 19004-1513
Tel.: (610) 664-6100
Investment Advice
N.A.I.C.S.: 523940

Wealth Design, LLC   **(2)**
50 W San Fernando St Ste 405, San Jose, CA 95113
Tel.: (408) 558-1660
Web Site: http://www.wealthdesignllc.com
Investment Advice
N.A.I.C.S.: 523940
Gene Ka *(Partner)*

BEACON SALES ACQUISITION INC.

50 Webster Ave, Somerville, MA 02143-4117
Tel.: (617) 666-2800
Web Site:
    http://www.beaconsales.com
Year Founded: 1997
Sales Range: $10-24.9 Million
Emp.: 97
Provider of Roofing, Siding & Insulation
N.A.I.C.S.: 423330
Andrew Logie *(Mgr)*
Katie Sposato *(Mgr-HR)*
Martin Gorman *(Reg Dir-Sls)*

Subsidiaries:

Quality Roofing Supply Company Inc.   **(1)**
2700 Cumberland St, Lebanon, PA 17042
Tel.: (717) 277-0800
Web Site:
    http://www.qualityroofingsupply.com
Sales Range: $10-24.9 Million
Emp.: 5
Provider of Roofing, Siding & Insulation
N.A.I.C.S.: 423330

BEAD INDUSTRIES INC.

11 Cascade Blvd, Milford, CT 06460
Tel.: (203) 301-0270   CT
Web Site:
    http://www.beadindustries.com
Year Founded: 1914
Sales Range: $50-74.9 Million
Emp.: 24
Bead Chains & Custom-Designed Contact Pins Mfr
N.A.I.C.S.: 332999
Ron Andreoli *(Pres)*
Jill Mayer *(Chm)*

Subsidiaries:

Bead Industries Inc - Bead Chain Division   **(1)**
11 Cascade Blvd, Milford, CT 06460
Tel.: (203) 301-0270
Web Site: http://www.beadchain.com
Bead Chain Mfr
N.A.I.C.S.: 332323
Ken Bryant *(Chm & CEO)*
Ron Andreoli *(Pres)*
Bob Halkowicz *(Mgr-National Sls)*
Jim Balazsi *(Sr Engr)*
Jill Mayer *(Controller-Fin)*

Bead Industries Inc - Bead Electronics Division   **(1)**
11 Cascade Blvd, Milford, CT 06460
Tel.: (203) 301-0270
Web Site: http://www.beadelectronics.com
Solid-Wire & Electronic Equipment Mfr
N.A.I.C.S.: 334419
Ron Andreoli *(Dir-Special Projects)*
Bob Halkowicz *(Mgr-Natl Sls)*
Jim Balazsi *(Sr Engr)*
Jerry Weglinski *(Engr-Mfg)*

Lou Guerci *(Pres)*
Alana Montano *(Supvr-Production)*
Sylvia Pessin *(Mgr-ERP)*
Phil Rejeski *(Dir-Ops)*

McGuire Manufacturing   **(1)**
60 Grandview Ct, Cheshire, CT 06410-1261   **(100%)**
Tel.: (203) 699-1801
Web Site: http://www.mcguiremfg.com
Sales Range: $10-24.9 Million
Emp.: 22
Plumbing Supplies Mfr
N.A.I.C.S.: 332913

Sturge Industries   **(1)**
Blackbrook Business Pk, Narrowboat Way, Dudley, DY2 0XQ, United Kingdom   **(100%)**
Tel.: (44) 1384 455 426
Web Site: http://www.sturge.co.uk
Sales Range: $25-49.9 Million
Mfr of Ball & Bead Chain Products
N.A.I.C.S.: 332991
Jon Kendrick *(Mgr-Ops)*

BEAL FINANCIAL CORPORATION

6000 Legacy Dr, Plano, TX 75024
Tel.: (469) 467-5000
Web Site: http://www.bealbank.com
Year Founded: 1993
Sales Range: $100-124.9 Million
Emp.: 400
Bank Holding Company
N.A.I.C.S.: 522180
Andrew Beal *(Founder, Chm & CEO)*

Subsidiaries:

Beal Bank Inc.   **(1)**
6000 Legacy Dr, Plano, TX 75024
Tel.: (469) 467-5000
Web Site: http://www.bealbank.com
Savings Bank
N.A.I.C.S.: 522180
Andrew Beal *(Founder & Chm)*

Beal Bank USA   **(1)**
1970 Village Center Cir Ste 1, Las Vegas, NV 89134
Tel.: (702) 598-3500
Web Site: http://www.bealbank.com
Commercial Banking Services
N.A.I.C.S.: 522110
D. Andrew Beal *(Founder & Chm)*

Subsidiary (Domestic):

New Harquahala Generating Co, LLC   **(2)**
2530 N 491st Ave, Tonopah, AZ 85354
Tel.: (928) 372-3200
Sales Range: $1-9.9 Million
Emp.: 16
Management Consulting Services
N.A.I.C.S.: 541618

BEAL GROUP

221 Felch Ste 6, Ann Arbor, MI 48103
Tel.: (734) 662-6133
Web Site: http://www.gobeal.com
Year Founded: 2006
Sales Range: $1-9.9 Million
Emp.: 15
Holding Company: Construction, Development & Property Management
N.A.I.C.S.: 551112
Stewart W. Beal *(Pres)*

BEALL MANUFACTURING, INC.

421 N Shamrock St, East Alton, IL 62024-1174
Tel.: (618) 259-8154   IL
Web Site: http://www.supertuf.com
Year Founded: 1984
Sales Range: $25-49.9 Million
Emp.: 35
Farm Machinery & Equipment
N.A.I.C.S.: 333111

Mark Speciale *(Owner)*
Jim Speciale *(Controller)*
Art Fultz *(Dir-Corp Sls & Mktg)*

Subsidiaries:

Cutting Specialists, Inc.   **(1)**
25570 Hwy 22, McKenzie, TN 38201-5270
Tel.: (731) 352-5351
Web Site: http://www.supertuf.com
Sales Range: $10-24.9 Million
Mower Blade Mfr
N.A.I.C.S.: 333515

BEALL'S, INC.

1806 38th Ave E, Bradenton, FL 34208-4708
Tel.: (941) 747-2355   FL
Web Site: http://www.beallsinc.com
Year Founded: 1915
Sales Range: $1-4.9 Billion
Emp.: 4,700
Department Stores
N.A.I.C.S.: 455110
Tianne Doyle *(Pres)*
Dan Doyle *(Chief HR Officer)*
Justin MacIntyre *(Reg Mgr-Loss Prevention)*
Ryan Barthel *(Mgr-Field Trng & Dev)*
Stephen Hall *(Dir-Loss Prevention)*
Lance Lee *(Coord-Loss Prevention Trng & Audit)*
Robert M. Beall II *(Chm)*

Subsidiaries:

Beall's Dept. Stores   **(1)**
1806 38th Ave E, Bradenton, FL 34208-4708   **(100%)**
Tel.: (941) 747-2355
Web Site: http://www.bealls.com
Sales Range: $25-49.9 Million
Emp.: 250
Department Stores
N.A.I.C.S.: 455110
Gwen Bennett *(VP-E-Commerce)*

Beall's Outlet Inc.   **(1)**
1806 38th Ave E, Bradenton, FL 34208-4708   **(100%)**
Tel.: (941) 747-2355
Web Site: http://www.beallsinc.com
Sales Range: $25-49.9 Million
Emp.: 100
Retail of Clothing
N.A.I.C.S.: 458110
Dave Alves *(Pres)*

Beall's Westgate Corporation   **(1)**
1806 38th Ave E, Bradenton, FL 34208-4700
Tel.: (941) 747-2355
Retail Store Operator
N.A.I.C.S.: 459999
Jim Simpson *(VP-Real Estate)*

Burke's Outlet Stores   **(1)**
700 13th Ave E, Bradenton, FL 34208
Tel.: (941) 747-2355
Web Site: http://www.burkesoutlet.com
Discount Department Stores
N.A.I.C.S.: 455110

Burkes Westgate Corporation   **(1)**
1806 38th Ave E, Bradenton, FL 34208
Tel.: (941) 747-2355
Web Site: http://www.burkesoutlet.com
Retail Store Operator
N.A.I.C.S.: 459999

BEALS CUNNINGHAM STRATEGIC SERVICES

2333 E Britton Rd, Oklahoma City, OK 73131-3526
Tel.: (405) 478-4752
Web Site:
    http://www.bealscunningham.com
Year Founded: 1957
Rev.: $20,000,000
Emp.: 30
N.A.I.C.S.: 541810
Jon Lundeen *(Treas, Sec & Exec VP)*
Michael Cunningham *(Chm)*

Beals Cunningham Strategic Services—(Continued)

Nick Cunningham *(Pres-Beals Cunningham Strategic Svcs)*
Phil Tomey *(Dir-Art)*
Larry Grizzle *(Mgr-Mdsg)*
Will Arnett *(Dir-Multimedia)*
Kelly McCubbin *(Dir-Art)*
Michael Hayes *(VP-Bus Dev)*
Michelle Howard *(Media Dir)*
Makk Short *(Art Dir)*
Lyndsay Bayne *(Dir-Video)*
Joi Marcum *(VP-Bus Dev)*
Lucja Hecksher *(Dir-Art)*
Ricardo Herrera *(Dir-Art)*
Deborah Hamlin *(Comptroller)*
Adrienne Fox *(Mgr-Office)*

BEAM CONSTRUCTION CO. INC.
601 E Main St, Cherryville, NC 28021-3416
Tel.: (704) 435-3206   NC
Web Site:
https://www.beamconstruction.com
Year Founded: 1925
Sales Range: $10-24.9 Million
Emp.: 125
Nonresidential Construction
N.A.I.C.S.: 236220
Susan B. Lewis *(Pres)*
Robert Browne *(Exec VP)*
Marshall A. Bailes *(VP)*
Steven A. Williams *(Project Mgr)*

BEAM MACK SALES & SERVICE, INC.
2674 W Henrietta Rd, Rochester, NY 14623
Tel.: (585) 424-4860
Web Site: http://www.beammack.com
Year Founded: 1951
Sales Range: $25-49.9 Million
Emp.: 250
Retailer of Trucks
N.A.I.C.S.: 423120
Tom Conway *(Pres)*
Dave Pyfrom *(Acct Mgr-Comml)*
Matt Sommers *(CFO)*
Tim Zornow *(Mgr-Used Truck)*
Ben Clarry *(Mgr-Svc)*
Gabriel Smith *(Gen Mgr)*

Subsidiaries:

Conway Beam Leasing Inc.   **(1)**
2654 W Henrietta Rd, Rochester, NY 14623
Tel.: (585) 424-1250
Truck Rental & Leasing Services
N.A.I.C.S.: 532120
John Bourbonnais *(Acct Mgr-Lease)*
Robert Kaczmarski *(Mgr-Svc-Buffalo)*
Susan Shaffer *(Office Mgr & Coord-Rental)*

Empire Bus Sales, LLC   **(1)**
2654 W Henrietta Rd, Rochester, NY 14623
Tel.: (585) 424-1250
Web Site: http://www.empirebus.com
Bus Transportation Services
N.A.I.C.S.: 485210
Rob Maloney *(Mgr-Sls)*

BEAMAN AUTOMOTIVE GROUP
1525 Broadway, Nashville, TN 37203-3121
Tel.: (615) 251-8400   TN
Web Site:
http://www.beamanauto.com
Year Founded: 1945
Sales Range: $200-249.9 Million
Emp.: 400
Automobile Dealership
N.A.I.C.S.: 441110
Lee Beaman *(Owner)*
Ruthie Keene *(CFO)*
Douglas McClanahan *(COO)*
Ann Eaden *(VP-Cust Rels)*

BEAN BOX, INC.
5050 1st Ave S Ste 103, Seattle, WA 98134
Web Site: http://www.beanbox.com
Year Founded: 2014
Sales Range: $1-9.9 Million
Coffee Product Distr
N.A.I.C.S.: 445298
Ryan Fritzky *(Co-Founder)*
Matthew Berk *(Co-Founder)*

BEAN CREATIVE, INC.
2213 Mt Vernon Ave, Alexandria, VA 22301
Tel.: (703) 684-5945
Web Site:
http://www.beancreative.com
Year Founded: 1997
Sales Range: $1-9.9 Million
Emp.: 10
Interactive Web Design
N.A.I.C.S.: 541890
Layla Masri *(Pres)*
Keith Soares *(VP)*
Bill Setzer *(Dir-Design & Dev)*
Amy Warnke *(Project Dir)*

BEAN DRYWALL, INC.
23011 N 15 Ln, Phoenix, AZ 85027
Tel.: (623) 516-2500
Web Site:
https://www.beandrywall.com
Year Founded: 1980
Sales Range: $25-49.9 Million
Emp.: 250
Plastering Services
N.A.I.C.S.: 238310
Michael N. Bean *(Pres)*

BEAN GROUP
2 International Dr Ste 301, Portsmouth, NH 03801
Tel.: (603) 766-1980
Web Site: http://www.beangroup.com
Sales Range: $10-24.9 Million
Emp.: 12
Real Estate Development Services
N.A.I.C.S.: 531390
Michael Bean *(Founder & CEO)*
Andrew Werry *(COO)*
Fred Doleac *(Dir-Online Svcs)*
Mark Miller *(Dir-Creative)*
Andrea Spiegel *(Controller)*
Lia Hoffmann *(Coord-Mktg)*
Pam Kirby *(Dir-Trng)*
Candice Krans *(Mgr-Agent Svcs)*
Randi Hoppe *(Office Mgr-NEXC)*
Ellen Wood *(Supvr-Title Ops)*

BEAN'S BEST LLC
1240 Jewett Ave, Ann Arbor, MI 48104
Tel.: (734) 585-4634
Metal Products Mfr
N.A.I.C.S.: 332721

BEAR & SON CUTLERY, INC.
1111 Bear Blvd SW, Jacksonville, AL 36265
Tel.: (256) 435-2227   DE
Web Site:
http://www.bearandsoncutlery.com
Rev.: $4,000,000
Emp.: 50
Knives Mfr & Marketer
N.A.I.C.S.: 332215
Kenneth Griffey *(Owner)*

BEAR CONSTRUCTION CO., INC.
1501 Rohlwing Rd, Rolling Meadows, IL 60008
Tel.: (847) 222-1900
Web Site: https://www.bearcc.com
Year Founded: 1984
Sales Range: $50-74.9 Million

Emp.: 193
General Contractors
N.A.I.C.S.: 236115
Nicholas Wienold *(Co-Owner & Pres)*
George Wienold *(Co-Owner)*
James Wienold *(Co-Owner & Exec VP)*
Scott Kurinsky *(Exec VP)*
H. Dennis Hill *(Sr VP)*

BEAR MOUNTAIN FOREST PRODUCTS, INC.
5 NE Cramblett Way, Hood River, OR 97014
Tel.: (503) 334-1558
Web Site:
http://bearmountainforestprod.com
Year Founded: 1988
Sales Range: $75-99.9 Million
Emp.: 70
Wood Products Mfr
N.A.I.C.S.: 321999
Bob Sourek *(Chm & Owner)*
Rolf Anderson *(CEO)*
Stan Doi *(Plant Mgr)*
Stan Elliot *(Mgr-Sls & Mktg)*
Eric Laurance *(Mgr-Fiber Procurement)*
Angie Powell *(Office Mgr)*
Gabriel Salvador *(Asst Mgr-Plant)*

BEAR REPUBLIC BREWING CO., INC.
110 Sandholm Ln, Cloverdale, CA 95425
Tel.: (707) 894-2722
Web Site:
https://www.bearrepublic.com
Sales Range: $10-24.9 Million
Emp.: 140
Brewery Mfr
N.A.I.C.S.: 312120
Richard R. Norgrove *(CEO)*
Tami Norgrove *(CFO)*
Sandy Norgrove *(Office Mgr)*
Jonathan Williman *(Mgr-Sls)*
Marcin Furmankiewicz *(Mgr-Restaurant)*

BEAR STEWART CORPORATION
1025 N Damen Ave, Chicago, IL 60622
Tel.: (773) 276-0400
Web Site:
https://www.bearstewart.com
Rev.: $10,000,000
Emp.: 35
Mfr of Foods & Flavorings
N.A.I.C.S.: 311421
Clifford Brooks *(Pres)*
Michael Hoffman *(VP)*
Jason Brooks *(COO)*

BEAR'S PLUMBING INC.
1900 Trade Center Way, Naples, FL 34109
Tel.: (239) 597-2951
Web Site:
https://www.bearsplumbing.com
Year Founded: 1982
Rev.: $14,500,000
Emp.: 90
Plumbing, Heating & Air-Conditioning Contractors
N.A.I.C.S.: 238220
Daniel Anderman *(Pres)*
Allan Steelman *(VP)*

BEARD EQUIPMENT CO. INC.
2480 E I-65 Service Rd N, Mobile, AL 36617
Tel.: (850) 476-0277   FL
Web Site:
https://www.beardequipment.com
Year Founded: 1970

Sales Range: $25-49.9 Million
Emp.: 200
Rental of Construction & Mining Machinery
N.A.I.C.S.: 423810
Brad Beard *(Pres)*

BEARD HARDWOODS, INC
2801 Thurston Rd, Greensboro, NC 27406
Tel.: (336) 378-1265
Web Site: https://www.enbeard.com
Year Founded: 1932
Sales Range: $10-24.9 Million
Emp.: 38
Timber Product Mfr
N.A.I.C.S.: 423310
John Beard *(Pres)*
Derick Shular *(Exec VP)*

BEARD IMPLEMENT CO.
216 Frederick St, Arenzville, IL 62611
Tel.: (217) 997-5514
Web Site:
https://www.beardimplement.com
Sales Range: $10-24.9 Million
Emp.: 50
Farm Implements
N.A.I.C.S.: 423820
Jerry Beard *(CEO)*

BEARING SALES CORPORATION
4153 N Kostner Ave, Chicago, IL 60641
Tel.: (773) 282-8686
Web Site:
https://www.bearingsales.com
Year Founded: 1977
Rev.: $10,000,000
Emp.: 35
Bearings
N.A.I.C.S.: 423840
John Hilton *(Chm)*
James B. White *(Pres)*

BEARING SERVICE & SUPPLY INC.
1327 N Market St, Shreveport, LA 71107
Tel.: (318) 424-1447
Web Site: https://www.bearserco.com
Year Founded: 1972
Sales Range: $10-24.9 Million
Emp.: 120
Industrial Supplies
N.A.I.C.S.: 423840
John Scott Harkey *(Pres-Fluid Power Div)*

BEARING SERVICE COMPANY
630 Alpha Dr RIDC Park, Pittsburgh, PA 15238-2802
Tel.: (412) 963-7710   PA
Web Site: https://www.bearing-service.com
Year Founded: 1933
Sales Range: $50-74.9 Million
Emp.: 140
Mfr & Distr of Ball & Roller Bearings
N.A.I.C.S.: 423840
William J. Banks *(Pres)*

Subsidiaries:

Southern Industrial Technologies Inc.   **(1)**
4810 Technology Dr Ste 2, Martinez, GA 30907
Tel.: (706) 210-8798
Bearing Whslr
N.A.I.C.S.: 423840

BEARING SERVICE INC.
13400 Newburgh Rd, Livonia, MI 48150
Tel.: (734) 591-0400   MI

Web Site:
http://www.bearingservice.com
Year Founded: 1943
Sales Range: $10-24.9 Million
Emp.: 55
Distr of Bearings & Power Transmission Products
N.A.I.C.S.: 423840
Douglas Savage (Pres)
Lee Critchfield (Dir-Pur)
Chris Sweeney (Sr Acct Mgr)
Leroy Burcroff (VP-Sls)

BEARING SPECIALTY COMPANY INC.
50 Energy Dr, Canton, MA 02021
Tel.: (781) 989-2222
Web Site: http://www.bearings-specialty.com
Sales Range: $10-24.9 Million
Emp.: 58
Bearings
N.A.I.C.S.: 423610
Peter Fitzpatrick (VP)
James J. Fitzpatrick Jr. (Pres)

BEARING SUPPLY CO. OF ODESSA
3411 N County Rd W, Odessa, TX 79764
Tel.: (432) 366-8855
Web Site:
https://www.bearingsupplyco.com
Rev.: $14,400,000
Emp.: 50
Bearings
N.A.I.C.S.: 423840
Bonnie Eason (Treas)

BEARINGPOINT, INC.
Tyson's Tower 1676 International Dr, McLean, VA 22102-4832
Tel.: (703) 747-3000   DE
Web Site:
http://www.bearingpoint.com
Year Founded: 1999
Sales Range: $1-4.9 Billion
Emp.: 17,100
Business Consulting & Systems Integration Services
N.A.I.C.S.: 541611
Peter N. Mockler (Mng Partner)
Charles White (Sr Mgr)
Rob Staples (Partner)
Chetan Rangaswamy (Partner)
Kiumars Hamidian (Mng Partner)
Alexander Bock (Mgr-Comm-Global)

Subsidiaries:

BearingPoint (Asia Pacific) Pte.
Ltd.   (1)
8 Temasek Blvd 22 01 Suntec Twr 3, Singapore, 38988, Singapore   (100%)
Tel.: (65) 63338001
Sales Range: $10-24.9 Million
Emp.: 30
Provider of Business Consulting & Systems Integration Services
N.A.I.C.S.: 541611

BearingPoint Information Technologies (Shanghai) Ltd.   (1)
Unit 3101 31F CITIC Square 1168 West Nanjing Road, Shanghai, 200041, China   (100%)
Tel.: (86) 2152925392
Sales Range: $75-99.9 Million
Emp.: 300
Provider of Business Consulting & Systems Integration Services
N.A.I.C.S.: 541611

BearingPoint Information Technology N.V.   (1)
Kaya Flamboyan 7, Willemstad, Curacao
Tel.: (599) 97343200
Sales Range: $75-99.9 Million
Management Consulting & IT Services
N.A.I.C.S.: 541611
Peter Grootens (Gen Mgr)

BearingPoint Management Consulting N.V.   (1)
Kaya Flamboyan 7, Willemstad, Curacao
Tel.: (599) 97325300
Sales Range: $10-24.9 Million
Emp.: 27
Provider of Business Consulting & Systems Integration Services
N.A.I.C.S.: 541611

BearingPoint OOO   (1)
Bolshaya Ordynka 40, 119017, Moscow, Russia
Tel.: (7) 4959374466
Web Site: http://www.bearingpoint.com
Sales Range: $75-99.9 Million
Emp.: 115
Provider of Business Consulting & Systems Integration Services
N.A.I.C.S.: 541611

BearingPoint Pte. Ltd.   (1)
8 Temasek Blvd, 22 01 Suntec Tower Three, Singapore, 38988, Singapore   (100%)
Tel.: (65) 63338001
Sales Range: $10-24.9 Million
Emp.: 50
Provider of Business Consulting & Systems Integration Services
N.A.I.C.S.: 541611

BearingPoint SRL   (1)
Str Izvor nr 80 et 4 Sector 5, 050564, Bucharest, Romania
Tel.: (40) 21 315 25 46
Information Technology Consulting Services
N.A.I.C.S.: 541512

BearingPoint South East Asia LLC   (1)
Rm 6105 6107 61st Fl The Center, 99 Queens Rd, Central, China (Hong Kong)   (100%)
Tel.: (852) 29018200
Sales Range: $75-99.9 Million
Provider of Business Consulting & Systems Integration Services
N.A.I.C.S.: 541611

INFONOVA GmbH   (1)
Seering 6, Unterpremstaetten, 8141, Graz, Austria
Tel.: (43) 316 8003
Web Site: http://www.infonova.com
Emp.: 350
Business Management Consulting Services
N.A.I.C.S.: 541611
Thomas Kutschi (VP-Alliances)

BEARINGS LIMITED
2100 Pacific St, Hauppauge, NY 11788
Tel.: (631) 273-8200
Web Site:
https://www.bearingslimited.com
Rev.: $12,200,000
Emp.: 100
Bearings
N.A.I.C.S.: 423840
Martin Granowitz (Pres)
Jeff Feldman (Sr VP)
Larry Ansel (Sr VP)
Mark Magray (Sr VP)

BEARTOOTH BILLINGS CLINIC
2525 N Broadway, Red Lodge, MT 59068
Tel.: (406) 446-2345   MT
Web Site:
https://www.beartoothbillings.org
Year Founded: 1948
Sales Range: $10-24.9 Million
Emp.: 124
Emergency Care Services
N.A.I.C.S.: 624230
Sharon Norby (Chief Quality Officer)
William George (Dir-Medical)
Katie Nordstrom (Dir-HR)
Sara Urbanik (Exec Dir-Foundation)
Clay Cummins (Treas & Sec)
Kelly Miner (Pres)
Deborah Agnew (CEO)

Kelley Evans (Chief Admin Officer)
George Clow (Chm)
Mitzi Vorachek (Vice Chm)

BEARWARE, INC.
7160 Chagrin Rd Ste 210, Chagrin Falls, OH 44023
Tel.: (440) 893-2327
Web Site:
http://www.bearwareinc.com
Year Founded: 1987
Software Developer for Mobile Solutions
N.A.I.C.S.: 513210
Eric Merkys (Sr Engr-Sys)
Robert Brooks III (Pres & COO)

BEASLEY-WILSON, INCORPORATED
3000 Interstate 35 S, Waco, TX 76706
Tel.: (254) 662-3610   TX
Web Site:
http://www.movetomiller.com
Year Founded: 1984
Sales Range: $10-24.9 Million
Emp.: 52
New & Used Car Dealer
N.A.I.C.S.: 441110
Rogers Wilson (Founder)
Jerry Miller (Pres)

BEATLEY GRAVITT COMMUNICATIONS
9A W Grace St, Richmond, VA 23220
Tel.: (804) 355-9151
Year Founded: 1981
Sales Range: $10-24.9 Million
Emp.: 10
Advetising Agency
N.A.I.C.S.: 541810
Ed Lacy (VP)
Beth Johnson (Project Mgr)
Chuck Lindsay (Sr Art Dir)
Mike Shackelford (Creative Dir)
John Oat (Sr Art Dir)
Chris Williams (Dir-Bus Dev-Big Creative Studio)

BEATON BROTHERS FLOORING, INC.
45 7th St, Lakewood, NJ 08701
Tel.: (732) 363-3360   NJ
Web Site:
http://www.beatonbrothers.com
Year Founded: 1982
Sales Range: $10-24.9 Million
Emp.: 18
Floor Coverings
N.A.I.C.S.: 423220
David Beaton (CEO)

BEATON INC.
4250 Glass Rd NE Ste 100, Cedar Rapids, IA 52402-2513
Tel.: (319) 378-1127   IA
Year Founded: 1984
Sales Range: $25-49.9 Million
Emp.: 500
Eating Place
N.A.I.C.S.: 722513
Perry T. Beaton (Pres)
Kathy Frerichs (Controller)
Travis Stovie (Mng Dir)

BEATTIE FARMERS UNION COOPERATIVE ASSOCIATION
203 Hamilton St, Beattie, KS 66406
Tel.: (785) 353-2237   KS
Web Site:
http://www.beattiecoop.com
Year Founded: 1915
Sales Range: Less than $1 Million
Emp.: 29
Production of Grain & Field Beans
N.A.I.C.S.: 424510

Larry Preuss (Gen Mgr)

BEATTY MACHINE & MFG. COMPANY
940 150th St, Hammond, IN 46327-1805
Tel.: (219) 931-3000
Web Site:
https://www.beattymachine.com
Year Founded: 1917
Rev.: $5,000,000
Emp.: 50
Hydraulic Presses, Punches & Shears, Quickwork Rotary Shears & Stamping Trimmers
N.A.I.C.S.: 332710
W.C. Beatty (Pres)

Subsidiaries:

Bemcor Inc.   (1)
940 150th St, Hammond, IN 46327
Tel.: (219) 937-1660
Web Site: http://www.bemcor.com
Sales Range: $10-24.9 Million
Emp.: 45
Mill & Equipment Repair
N.A.I.C.S.: 333519
Debbie-Jim Wilson (Asst Treas)

Quickwork Div.   (1)
940-150th St, Hammond, IN 46327
Tel.: (219) 931-3000
Web Site: http://www.beattymachine.com
Emp.: 20
Metal Parts Stamping
N.A.I.C.S.: 332119
Brian Beatty (Gen Mgr)

BEATY CHEVROLET COMPANY
9615 Parkside Dr, Knoxville, TN 37922
Tel.: (865) 693-7718
Web Site:
https://www.beatychevrolet.com
Sales Range: $50-74.9 Million
Emp.: 110
New Car Retailer
N.A.I.C.S.: 441110
Ronnie Shelley (Dir-Svc)
Ronnie Dillinger (Mgr-Sls)
Glen McGee (Mgr)
Jamie Dickerson (Mgr-Fleet)
Danny Ballinger (Mgr)
Ladonna Ballinger (Asst Mgr)
Josh Griffin (Mgr-Internet Sls)

BEAU DELICIOUS! INTERNATIONAL LLC
456 Charnelton St, Eugene, OR 97401
Web Site:
https://www.cafeyumm.com
Year Founded: 1997
Sales Range: $10-24.9 Million
Emp.: 235
Healthy Fast Food Franchise
N.A.I.C.S.: 722511
Mark Beauchamp (Co-Founder)
Mary Ann Beauchamp (Co-Founder)

BEAU TOWNSEND FORD INC.
1020 W National Rd, Vandalia, OH 45377
Tel.: (937) 898-5841
Web Site: http://www.btford.com
Sales Range: $75-99.9 Million
Emp.: 500
Sales of New & Used Automobiles
N.A.I.C.S.: 441110
Beau Townsend (Pres)
Larry Talyor (VP)
Kevin Berger (Mgr-Fin)

BEAU TOWNSEND FORD LINCOLN, INC.
1020 W National Rd, Vandalia, OH 45377

BEAU TOWNSEND FORD LINCOLN, INC.

Beau Townsend Ford Lincoln, Inc.—(Continued)

Tel.: (937) 410-0808
Web Site: https://www.btford.com
Year Founded: 1976
Sales Range: $25-49.9 Million
Emp.: 500
New Car Whslr
N.A.I.C.S.: 441110
Jamie Spencer *(Gen Mgr)*
Larry Taylor *(Owner)*

BEAU TOWNSEND NISSAN, INC.

1050 W National Rd, Vandalia, OH 45377
Tel.: (937) 898-6200
Web Site: https://www.btnissan.com
Year Founded: 2002
Sales Range: $10-24.9 Million
Emp.: 33
New Car Whslr
N.A.I.C.S.: 441110
Bob Dull *(Treas)*
Jamie Spencer *(Gen Mgr)*

BEAUCHAMP DISTRIBUTING COMPANY

1911 S Santa Fe Ave, Compton, CA 90221
Tel.: (310) 639-5320
Web Site:
  https://www.beauchampdist.com
Year Founded: 1971
Sales Range: $75-99.9 Million
Emp.: 99
Distr & Retailer of Beer & Wine
N.A.I.C.S.: 424810
Peter Gumpert *(Controller)*

BEAUFORT-JASPER WATER & SEWER AUTHORITY

6 Snake Rd, Okatie, SC 29909
Tel.: (843) 987-9200
Web Site: https://www.bjwsa.org
Sales Range: $10-24.9 Million
Emp.: 168
Water Supply
N.A.I.C.S.: 221310
Mike Jones *(Mgr-Revenue & Billing)*
Jeffrey Boss *(Deputy Gen Mgr)*
Ed Saxon *(Gen Mgr)*

BEAULIEU GROUP, LLC

1502 Coronet Dr, Dalton, GA 30722
Tel.: (706) 278-6666
Web Site:
  http://www.accessbeaulieu.com
Year Founded: 1978
Sales Range: $1-4.9 Billion
Emp.: 7,000
Mfr of Carpets & Rugs
N.A.I.C.S.: 314110
Brenten Bailey *(VP-Western Territory)*
Dallas Chapman *(Exec VP-Sls)*

Subsidiaries:

Beaulieu Canada (1)
335 Rue De Roxton, Acton Vale, J0H 1A0, QC, Canada (100%)
Tel.: (450) 546-5000
Web Site: http://www.beaulieucanada.ca
Sales Range: $150-199.9 Million
Emp.: 1,400
Mfr of Tufted Carpet
N.A.I.C.S.: 314110

BEAUMIER, TROGDON, ORMAN, HURD & VIEGAS, PLLP

227 W First St Ste 610 Missabe Bldg, Duluth, MN 55802
Tel.: (218) 722-1000
Web Site: https://btolawyers.com
Law firm
N.A.I.C.S.: 541110

Matthew Beaumier *(Mng Partner)*
Michael E. Orman *(Partner)*
Katrina M. Viegas *(Partner)*
Jeremy M. Hurd *(Partner)*

Subsidiaries:

Orman, Nord & Hurd, P.L.L.P. (1)
1301 Miller Trunk Hwy, Duluth, MN 55811
Tel.: (218) 722-1000
Web Site: http://www.onslaw.com
Law firm
N.A.I.C.S.: 541199
Michael Orman *(Partner)*

BEAUMONT COCA-COLA REFRESHMENTS

11450 Eastex Fwy, Beaumont, TX 77708-0900
Tel.: (409) 899-5080
Year Founded: 1907
Sales Range: $25-49.9 Million
Emp.: 170
Soft Drinks Mfr
N.A.I.C.S.: 312111
Pat Hamilton *(Mgr-HR)*

BEAUMONT HEALTH

3601 W 13 Mile Rd, Royal Oak, MI 48073
Tel.: (248) 898-2000
Web Site: https://www.beaumont.org
Year Founded: 2014
Sales Range: $1-4.9 Billion
Emp.: 35,000
Non Profit Healthcare Organization & Health Care Services
N.A.I.C.S.: 813910
Christopher Blake *(Chm)*
David Wood *(Chief Medical Officer & Exec VP)*
Margaret Cooney Casey *(Chief Dev Officer & Sr VP)*
Sam Flanders *(Chief Quality & Safety Officer & Sr VP)*
Dawn Geisert *(Chief Compliance Officer & Sr VP)*
Susan Grant *(Chief Nursing Officer & Exec VP)*
Paul LaCasse *(Exec VP-Post-Acute Care Div & Diversified Bus Ops)*
Subra Sripada *(CIO, Chief Transformation Officer & Exec VP)*
Carolyn Wilson *(COO & Exec VP)*
Mary Zatina *(Sr VP-Govt Rels & Community Affairs)*
Laura Glenn *(Sr VP & Exec Dir)*
Malcolm Henoch *(Sr VP-Acute Care)*
William Isenstein *(Sr VP)*
Leslie Rocher *(Chief Academic & Clinical Officer & Sr VP)*
David Walters *(Sr VP)*
Mark Bohen *(Chief Mktg & Comm Officer & Sr VP)*
Aaron Gillingham *(Chief HR Officer & Sr VP)*
John T. Fox *(Pres & CEO)*
John Kerndl *(CFO & Exec VP)*
Michael Rebock *(Chief Medical Officer-Farmington Hills)*
Jonathan Kaper *(Chief Medical Officer/Sr VP-Trenton)*
Anne Stewart *(Chief Nursing Officer-Grosse Pointe)*
Maureen Bowman *(Chief Nursing Officer-Royal Oak)*
Debra Guido-Allen *(Chief Nursing Officer-Troy)*
Jane E. Jordon *(Gen Counsel & Sr VP)*
E. D. Hardin *(Sr VP)*
Nancy Susick *(COO-Acute & Post-Acute Svcs)*
Benjamin Schwartz *(Pres)*

Subsidiaries:

Beaumont Home Medical Equipment (1)

30943 Woodward Ave, Royal Oak, MI 48073
Tel.: (248) 743-9100
Sales Range: $10-24.9 Million
Medical Equipment Rental
N.A.I.C.S.: 456199
Phil Corsi *(Gen Mgr)*

Beaumont Mobile Medicine (1)
26150 Northline Northline Rd, Taylor, MI 48180
Tel.: (248) 304-6012
Web Site:
  http://www.beaumontmedicaltransport.org
Ambulance Service
N.A.I.C.S.: 621910
Greg Beauchemin *(Pres)*

Community Emergency Medical Service, Inc. (1)
25400 W 8 Mile Rd, Southfield, MI 48034
Tel.: (248) 356-3900
Web Site: http://www.communityems.org
Sales Range: $10-24.9 Million
Emp.: 390
Ambulance Service
N.A.I.C.S.: 621910
Gregory Beauchemin *(Pres & CEO)*

Parastar, Inc. (1)
25400 W 8 Mile Rd, Southfield, MI 48034
Web Site: http://www.parastar.net
Professional, Scientific & Technical Services
N.A.I.C.S.: 541990
Michelle Boal *(Supvr-Front End)*

The Beaumont Foundation (1)
3711 W 13 Mile Rd, Royal Oak, MI 48073
Tel.: (248) 551-5330
Web Site: http://www.beaumont.org
Sales Range: $1-9.9 Million
Emp.: 65
Grantmaking Foundations
N.A.I.C.S.: 813211
Geoffrey L. Hockman *(Chm)*
Warren Elliot Rose *(Treas)*
Margareth Cooney Casey *(Pres)*
Shane Cerone *(Sr VP)*
Donna Hoban *(Sr VP)*
James P. Lynch *(Sr VP)*
Leslie L. Rocher *(Sr VP)*
Richard P. Swaine *(Sr VP)*
Donna Zuk *(VP-Fin Ops)*
David Wood Jr. *(Exec Dir)*

William Beaumont Hospital (1)
3601 W 13 Mile Rd, Royal Oak, MI 48073
Tel.: (248) 898-5000
Web Site: http://www.beaumont.edu
Non-Profit Healthcare Organization; Hospital Operator & Other Health Care Services
N.A.I.C.S.: 813920
Gordon Walker *(Chief Legal Officer)*
John Keuten *(CFO)*
Debbie Guido-Allen *(Interim Pres)*

BEAUREGARD ELECTRIC COOPERATIVE, INC.

1010 E 1st St, Deridder, LA 70634
Tel.: (337) 463-6221
Web Site: https://www.beci.org
Rev.: $46,000,000
Emp.: 126
Distr of Electric Power
N.A.I.C.S.: 221122
Kevin Turner *(Gen Mgr)*
Freddy Campbell *(Mgr-Pur & Warehouse)*
Kay Fox *(VP-Mktg & Member Svcs)*
Lesile Williams *(Mgr-HR)*
Scott Deshotel *(VP-Ops)*

BEAUREGARD EQUIPMENT INC.

28 Jasper Mine Rd, Colchester, VT 05446-7358
Tel.: (802) 893-1555
Web Site:
  https://www.beauregardequip.com
Year Founded: 1968
Sales Range: $10-24.9 Million
Emp.: 40
Mfr And Distributor of Construction & Mining Machinery
N.A.I.C.S.: 423810

Carl Beauregard *(Co-Owner)*
John Beauregard *(Co-Owner)*
Jim Carpenter *(Gen Mgr)*

BEAUTECH POWER SYSTEMS, LLC

1920 McKinney Ave Ste 920, Dallas, TX 75201
Tel.: (214) 764-4131
Web Site: http://www.beautech.aero
Year Founded: 2011
Sales Range: $75-99.9 Million
Emp.: 14
Aircraft Engine Repair & Maintenance Services
N.A.I.C.S.: 811198
Lee Beaumont *(Pres & CEO)*
Tobias Konrad *(COO)*
Brad Forsyth *(Mng Dir & CFO)*
Brian Ceelen *(Sr VP-Sls)*
Carl Kelley *(VP-Sls)*

BEAUTI-VUE PRODUCTS CORP.

8555 194th Ave, Bristol, WI 53104-9543
Tel.: (262) 857-2306
Web Site: https://www.beautivue.com
Blind & Shade Mfr
N.A.I.C.S.: 337920
Stormy Grumbeck *(Owner)*

BEAUTIFUL RESTAURANT INC.

2218 Cascade Rd SW, Atlanta, GA 30311
Tel.: (404) 758-3883
Web Site:
  http://www.beautifulrestaurant-atlanta.com
Rev.: $11,600,000
Emp.: 60
Grocery Stores, Independent
N.A.I.C.S.: 812320
Ron Williams *(Pres)*

BEAUTY BAKERIE COSMETICS BRAND LLC

1640 Camino Del Rio N Ste 344, San Diego, CA 92108
Web Site:
  http://www.beautybakerie.com
Year Founded: 2011
Sales Range: $1-9.9 Million
Emp.: 30
Cosmetic Product Distr
N.A.I.C.S.: 456120
Cashmere Nicole *(Founder)*

BEAUTY BARRAGE, LLC

4340 Von Karman Ave Ste 240, Newport Beach, CA 92660
Tel.: (949) 771-3399
Web Site:
  http://www.beautybarrage.com
Year Founded: 2015
Sales Range: $1-9.9 Million
Emp.: 250
Beauty Parlour Training Services
N.A.I.C.S.: 611511
Sonia Summers *(Founder & CEO)*
Kirk Summers *(COO)*
Heather Forcari *(VP-Learning & Dev)*
Rebekah Von Der Hellen *(VP-Sls Dev)*
Alissa Spencer *(Acct Dir)*

BEAUTY BAZAR INC.

36 Stanford Shopping Ctr, Palo Alto, CA 94304
Tel.: (650) 326-8522
Web Site:
  http://www.labelledayspas.com
Year Founded: 1976
Beauty Shops
N.A.I.C.S.: 812112

Tiffany Schneider Collins *(Dir-Corp Comm)*

BEAUTY BRANDS INC.
4600 Madison Ave Ste 400, Kansas City, MO 64112
Tel.: (816) 531-2266   MO
Web Site:
   http://www.beautybrands.com
Year Founded: 1995
Sales Range: $100-124.9 Million
Emp.: 2,000
Toiletries, Cosmetics & Perfumes Retailer
N.A.I.C.S.: 456120
Lisa Green *(Sr VP-Mdse)*
Caryn Lerner *(CEO)*
Lyn Kirby *(Chm)*
Doug Barnes *(Dir-Loss Prevention)*

BEAUTY ENTERPRISES INC.
150 Meadow St, Hartford, CT 06114-1505
Tel.: (860) 296-9303   CT
Web Site:
   http://www.beautyenterprises.com
Year Founded: 1969
Sales Range: $100-124.9 Million
Emp.: 190
Ethnic Hair Care & Skin Product Distr
N.A.I.C.S.: 424210
Robert H. Cohen *(Founder)*

Subsidiaries:

Southern Beauty Enterprises   **(1)**
165 Goodrich Dr Unit 115, Birmingham, AL 35217-1465   **(100%)**
Tel.: (205) 854-2330
Web Site: http://www.beautyenterprises.com
Sales Range: $10-24.9 Million
Emp.: 40
Ethnic Hair & Skin Care Distributors
N.A.I.C.S.: 423850

BEAUTY MANAGEMENT IN-CORPORATED
270 S Beavercreek Rd Ste 100, Oregon City, OR 97045
Tel.: (503) 723-3200
Web Site:
   http://www.perfectlooksalons.com
Sales Range: $10-24.9 Million
Emp.: 500
Owner & Operator of Beauty Shops
N.A.I.C.S.: 812112
Michael Clark *(Pres)*
Jack Holewa *(VP)*

BEAUTY MANUFACTURING SOLUTIONS CORP.
13525 Denton Dr, Dallas, TX 75234
Tel.: (972) 241-9665
Web Site:
   http://www.beautymanufacture.com
Year Founded: 1922
Sales Range: $10-24.9 Million
Emp.: 110
Cosmetic, Beauty & Personal Care Product Mfr
N.A.I.C.S.: 456120
Peter Song *(VP)*
Jin Song *(Founder & CEO)*
Bennet Samani *(Engr-Matls)*

BEAVER BUILDERS, INC.
3130 47th Ave, Rock Island, IL 61201-7049
Tel.: (309) 786-1491
Web Site:
   http://www.beaverbuilders.com
Year Founded: 1976
Sales Range: $10-24.9 Million
Emp.: 45
New Multifamily Housing Construction Services
N.A.I.C.S.: 236116
Bob Buker *(Pres)*

BEAVER DAM COMMUNITY HOSPITALS, INC.
707 S University Ave, Beaver Dam, WI 53916
Tel.: (920) 887-7181   WI
Web Site: https://www.bdch.com
Year Founded: 1972
Sales Range: $100-124.9 Million
Emp.: 1,145
Health Care Srvices
N.A.I.C.S.: 622110
David Corso *(COO)*
Doug Mathison *(Treas)*
Sue Sutter *(Vice Chm)*
Jim Kirsh *(Chm)*
Kim Miller *(Pres & CEO)*
Marsha Borling *(Sec)*
John Moser *(VP)*

BEAVER EXPRESS SERVICE, LLC
4310 Oklahoma Ave, Woodward, OK 73802
Tel.: (580) 256-6460
Web Site:
   http://www.beaverexpress.com
Year Founded: 1943
Sales Range: $25-49.9 Million
Emp.: 309
General Freight Trucking
N.A.I.C.S.: 484121
Misty Comstock *(Office Mgr)*
Troy Hemminger *(Mgr-MIS)*
Brian Stone *(Mgr-Claims)*
Ricky Frech *(VP-Ops)*
Mike R. Stone *(Pres)*
David Myer *(Dir-Safety)*
Tina Kline *(VP-Fin)*

BEAVER STREET FISHERIES, INC.
1741 W Beaver St, Jacksonville, FL 32209
Tel.: (904) 354-8533   FL
Web Site:
   https://www.beaverstreetfisheries.com
Year Founded: 1955
Sales Range: $450-499.9 Million
Emp.: 400
Provider of Processed Seafoods & Frozen Foods
N.A.I.C.S.: 424420
Benjamin P. Frisch *(Pres)*
Lathun Brigman *(Gen Mgr)*

BEAVER VALLEY SUPPLY CO. INC.
21366 Highway 36, Atwood, KS 67730
Tel.: (785) 626-3251
Web Site:
   https://www.beavervalleysupply.com
Sales Range: $10-24.9 Million
Emp.: 37
Agricultural Machinery & Equipment
N.A.I.C.S.: 423820
Frank A. Chvatal *(Pres)*

BEAVERTON TOYOTA COM-PANY INC.
4300 SW Murray Blvd, Beaverton, OR 97005-2566
Tel.: (503) 626-7200
Web Site:
   https://www.beavertontoyota.com
Sales Range: $25-49.9 Million
Emp.: 175
New Car Whslr
N.A.I.C.S.: 441110

BEAVERTOWN BLOCK CO. INC.
3612 Paxtonville Rd, Middleburg, PA 17842
Tel.: (570) 837-1744

Web Site:
   https://www.beavertownblock.com
Year Founded: 1922
Sales Range: $10-24.9 Million
Emp.: 95
Concrete Block & Brick
N.A.I.C.S.: 327331
David L. Kline *(Pres)*
Logan Myers *(Mgr-Sls)*
Wanda Stuck *(Controller)*

BEAVEX
800 Corporate Row, Cromwell, CT 06416-2072
Tel.: (203) 234-2250
Web Site: http://www.beavex.com
Rev.: $17,822,538
Emp.: 49
Courier Services, Except By Air
N.A.I.C.S.: 492110
Mark Tuchmann *(Founder)*
Scott McDade *(COO)*
Terry Carter *(CEO)*

BEBER SILVERSTEIN GROUP
89 NE 27th St Ste 119, Miami, FL 33137
Tel.: (305) 856-9800   FL
Web Site: http://www.thinkbsg.com
Year Founded: 1972
Sales Range: $50-74.9 Million
Emp.: 50
Advetising Agency
N.A.I.C.S.: 541810
Elaine Silverstein *(Chm)*
Jennifer Beber *(Pres)*
Joe Perz *(Dir-Creative)*
Victoria Penn *(Dir-Media)*
Mitch Shapiro *(Partner & Gen Mgr)*
Bruce Noonan *(Pres-Travel Grp)*
Christine Bucan *(Exec VP-PR)*
Ann Marie Drozd *(VP-Brand Dev)*
Leslie V. Pantin Jr. *(Pres-PR Grp)*

BEC INC.
26079 Schoenherr Rd, Warren, MI 48089
Tel.: (586) 758-6000   MI
Web Site: http://www.becinc.net
Year Founded: 1962
Sales Range: $125-149.9 Million
Emp.: 100
Holding Company; General Contractor of Industrial & Commercial Buildings
N.A.I.C.S.: 551112
Mary L. Brickel *(Chm)*
Chuck Brickel *(VP)*

Subsidiaries:

Brencal Contractors Inc.   **(1)**
26079 Schoenherr Rd, Warren, MI 48089
Tel.: (313) 365-4300
Web Site: http://www.brencal.net
Sales Range: $10-24.9 Million
Emp.: 40
General Contractors
N.A.I.C.S.: 561110
Brian Brickel *(Pres)*
Karen Lassiter *(Dir-DP)*
Chuck Brickel *(VP)*

BECCA & BEN LLC
4000 Haslet Roanoke Rd Ste 26, Roanoke, TX 76262
Tel.: (817) 637-3069
Web Site: http://www.kikilarue.com
Year Founded: 2013
Sales Range: $1-9.9 Million
Emp.: 13
Women Clothing Mfr & Distr
N.A.I.C.S.: 315250
Becka Clark *(CEO)*

BECCO CONTRACTORS, INC.
PO Box 9159, Tulsa, OK 74157
Tel.: (918) 445-2684

Web Site: http://www.beccousa.com
Year Founded: 1998
Sales Range: $75-99.9 Million
Emp.: 350
Highway & Street Construction Services
N.A.I.C.S.: 237310
Ed Smith *(VP)*
Dwayne Jantz *(Project Mgr)*

BECHARD GROUP, INC.
17 Park Pl Ste 100, Appleton, WI 54914
Tel.: (920) 738-7100   WI
Web Site:
   http://www.bechardgroup.com
Year Founded: 1992
Sales Range: $1-9.9 Million
Emp.: 28
Real Estate Broker
N.A.I.C.S.: 531210
Jerold J. Bechard *(Pres)*

BECHTEL DESIGNS, INC.
1400 Thurman Ave, Lynchburg, VA 24501
Tel.: (434) 847-2004
Year Founded: 2012
Sawmill Services
N.A.I.C.S.: 321113
Andy Bechtel *(Pres)*

BECHTEL GROUP, INC.
50 Beale St, San Francisco, CA 94105-1813
Tel.: (415) 768-1234   DE
Web Site: http://www.bechtel.com
Year Founded: 1898
Sales Range: $25-49.9 Billion
Emp.: 42,500
Engineering, Construction & Project Management
N.A.I.C.S.: 541330
Keith Hennessey *(CFO)*
Michael C. Bailey *(Gen Counsel)*
Bill Dudley *(Vice Chm)*
Anette Sparks *(Controller)*
Walker Kimball *(Sr VP)*
Brendan Bechtel *(Chm & CEO)*
Craig Albert *(Pres & COO)*
John Howanitz *(Pres-Nuclear, Security & Environmental)*
Shaun Kenny *(Pres-Infrastructure Global Bus)*
Ailie MacAdam *(Pres-Mining & Metals & Sr VP)*
Paul Marsden *(Pres-Energy)*
Catherine Hunt Ryan *(Pres-Mfg & Tech)*
Tarek Amine *(Chief Supply Chain Officer)*
Kevin Edwards *(Chief Diversity & Inclusion Officer)*
Rayna V. Farrell *(Mgr-Corp Comm)*
Paul Gibbs *(Mgr-Corp Bus Dev)*
Stuart Jones *(Pres-Regions & Corp Rels)*
Vikas Joshi *(Mgr-EPC Functions)*
Emad Khedr *(Mgr-Comml)*
Justin Zaccaria *(Chief HR Officer)*

Subsidiaries:

Bechtel Bettis Inc.   **(1)**
814 Pittsburgh McKeesport Blvd, West Mifflin, PA 15122-2849
Tel.: (412) 476-6000
Sales Range: $450-499.9 Million
Emp.: 3,000
Research & Development in the Social Sciences & Humanities
N.A.I.C.S.: 541720

Bechtel Canada Co.   **(1)**
1500 University St Ste 910, Montreal, H3A 3S7, QC, Canada   **(100%)**
Tel.: (514) 871-1711
Web Site: http://www.bechtel.com

Bechtel Group, Inc.—(Continued)

Sales Range: $50-74.9 Million
Emp.: 500
Engineering & Construction Company
N.A.I.C.S.: 237990

Bechtel Chile Ltda. (1)
Apoquindo 4001 P8 Las Condes, CP
6650185, Santiago, Chile
Tel.: (56) 26751000
Web Site: http://www.bechtel.com
Sales Range: $350-399.9 Million
Emp.: 3,000
Engineering & Construction Services
N.A.I.C.S.: 237990

Bechtel Civil, Inc. (1)
50 Beale St, San Francisco, CA
94105-1813 (100%)
Tel.: (415) 768-1234
Web Site: http://www.bechtel.com
Engineeering Services
N.A.I.C.S.: 541330

Bechtel Construction Company, Inc. (1)
3000 Post Oak Blvd, Houston, TX 77056-6501
Tel.: (713) 235-2000
Web Site: http://www.bechtel.com
Sales Range: $10-24.9 Million
Emp.: 30
Industrial Buildings New Construction
N.A.I.C.S.: 236220

Bechtel Enterprises, Inc. (1)
50 Beale St, San Francisco, CA 94105-1813
Tel.: (415) 768-1234
Web Site: http://www.bechtel.com
Sales Range: $100-124.9 Million
Emp.: 1,600
Engineeering Services
N.A.I.C.S.: 541330
Jaime Guillen (Executives)
Bill Caudle (Pres)

Bechtel Financing Services, Inc. (1)
50 Beale St, San Francisco, CA 94105-1813
Tel.: (415) 768-1234
Web Site: http://www.bechtel.com
Sales Range: $100-124.9 Million
Emp.: 600
Investment Services
N.A.I.C.S.: 523940
Jaime Guillen (Executives)

Bechtel India Private Limited (1)
244-245 Udyog Vihar Phase- IV, Gurgaon, 122015, Haryana, India
Tel.: (91) 1244098000
Web Site: http://www.bechtel.com
Engineeering Services
N.A.I.C.S.: 237990

Bechtel International Inc. (1)
388 Sukhumvit Rd 13th Fl Exchange Tower
Klong Toey, Bangkok, 101100, Thailand
Tel.: (66) 25457000
Web Site: http://www.bechtel.com
Sales Range: $10-24.9 Million
Emp.: 100
Engineeering Services
N.A.I.C.S.: 237990

Bechtel International Inc. (1)
Fuji Bldg Room 410 2-3 Marunouchi
3-chome Chuo-ku, Tokyo, 100-0005, Japan
Tel.: (81) 332144481
Web Site: http://www.bechtelgroup.com
Sales Range: $10-24.9 Million
Emp.: 400
Engineeering Services
N.A.I.C.S.: 237990
Takehiko Miyazaki (Gen Mgr)

Bechtel International Inc. (1)
Bestekarsevki Bey Sok Enka Bldg 3 Fl -1, Balmumcu, 34349, Istanbul, Turkiye
Tel.: (90) 2123761616
Web Site: http://www.bechtel.com
Sales Range: $10-24.9 Million
Emp.: 2
Engineeering Services
N.A.I.C.S.: 237990
John Weaver (Mgr-Branch)

Bechtel Jacobs Company LLC (1)
Hwy 58, Oak Ridge, TN 37831

Tel.: (865) 576-4006
Sales Range: $350-399.9 Million
Emp.: 3,000
Facilities Support Services & Environmental
Engineering & Management Support
N.A.I.C.S.: 237990

Bechtel Ltd. (1)
FC 200 2 Lakeside Dr Park Royal London,
PO Box 739, London, NW10 7FQ, United
Kingdom (100%)
Tel.: (44) 2088465111
Sales Range: $100-124.9 Million
Emp.: 1,500
Engineering & Construction Services
N.A.I.C.S.: 237990

Bechtel Malaysia Inc. (1)
Suite 16 2 16th Floor Menara Weld, Kuala
Lumpur, 50200, Malaysia
Tel.: (60) 320782050
Sales Range: $10-24.9 Million
Emp.: 11
Engineeering Services
N.A.I.C.S.: 237990

Bechtel National, Inc. (1)
50 Beale St, San Francisco, CA 94105-1813
Tel.: (415) 768-1234
Web Site: http://www.bechtel.com
Sales Range: $100-124.9 Million
Emp.: 1,448
Engineering, Startup, Operations & Major
Maintenance of Industrial Manufacturing
Facilities, Electronics Plants, Nuclear Fuel
Cycle Facilities, Hazardous Waste & Other
Non-Nuclear Facilities
N.A.I.C.S.: 541330
Lorne Parker (Sr VP)

Division (Domestic):

Bechtel Hanford Inc. (2)
2435 Stevens Ctr Pl, Richland, WA
99354-1874 (100%)
Tel.: (509) 371-2000
Web Site: http://www.bechtel.com
Engineeering Services
N.A.I.C.S.: 541330
Frank Russo (Dir)

Bechtel Power Corporation (1)
5275 Westview Dr, Frederick, MD
21703-8306 (100%)
Tel.: (301) 228-6000
Web Site: http://www.bechtel.com
Sales Range: $100-124.9 Million
Emp.: 2,000
Engineering Construction Procurement
Management Operations
N.A.I.C.S.: 541330
Dave Walker (Pres)
Ann D. Murtlow (Executives)
Michael Levy (Engr-Civil)
Steve Loll (Engr-Quality)
Ron Beck (Project Mgr)
Basant Dilodare (Project Mgr)

**Bechtel Services (Australia) Pty
Ltd** (1)
540 Wickham St Fortitude Valley, Brisbane,
4006, QLD, Australia
Tel.: (61) 731675000
Engineeering Services
N.A.I.C.S.: 237110

**Bechtel do Brasil Construcoes
Ltda.** (1)
Praia de Botafogo 440, CEP 22250-040,
Rio de Janeiro, RJ, Brazil
Tel.: (55) 2125792400
Sales Range: $10-24.9 Million
Emp.: 4
Engineering & Construction Services
N.A.I.C.S.: 237990

IPSI L.L.C. (1)
3000 Post Oak Blvd, Houston, TX 77056-6501
Tel.: (713) 235-2903
Web Site: http://www.ipsi.com
Sales Range: $10-24.9 Million
Emp.: 25
Consulting Engineer
N.A.I.C.S.: 541330
Jame Yao (VP)
Riley Bechtel (Chm)

**Pacific Engineers & Constructors,
Ltd.** (1)

11F No 325 Tun Hwa South Road, Taipei,
Taiwan
Tel.: (886) 2 27032880
Web Site: http://www.pecl.com.tw
Civil Engineering Services
N.A.I.C.S.: 541330
Steven Katzman (Co-Chm)
Edward H. C. Lee (Pres)
Si-Min Chang (Co-Chm)

BECK & HOFER CONSTRUC-TION, INC.
618 E Maple St, Sioux Falls, SD
57104-0910
Tel.: (605) 336-0118
Web Site:
  https://www.beckandhofer.com
Sales Range: $10-24.9 Million
Emp.: 50
Nonresidential Construction Services
N.A.I.C.S.: 236220
Dick Beck (Owner)
John Beck (Pres)

BECK AG
17542 Jones St, Omaha, NE 68118
Web Site: http://www.beckag.com
Year Founded: 1997
Sales Range: $1-9.9 Million
Emp.: 90
Developer of Marketing Processes for
Agricultural Industries
N.A.I.C.S.: 926140
John Finegan (Founder)
Stephanie Liska (CEO)
Margaret W. Oldham (Dir-Innovation
& Opportunity)
Vernon Benes (Dir-Bus Dev)

BECK CHEVROLET CO. INC.
561 Central Park Ave, Yonkers, NY
10704
Tel.: (914) 965-2400
Web Site: http://www.beckauto.com
Rev.: $25,000,000
Emp.: 45
New & Used Car Dealers
N.A.I.C.S.: 441110
Leon Geller (Pres)
Russell Geller (VP)

BECK COMPANY
1323 Jamestown Rd Ste 101, Wil-liamsburg, VA 23185
Tel.: (757) 565-4100
Web Site:
  http://www.beckcompanyhotels.com
Sales Range: $10-24.9 Million
Emp.: 5
Hotel
N.A.I.C.S.: 721199
Robert G. Beck (Pres)

BECK OIL, INC.
16640 D St, Victorville, CA 92395-3169
Tel.: (760) 245-3477
Web Site: https://www.beckoilinc.com
Year Founded: 1967
Rev.: $30,000,000
Emp.: 60
Petroleum Products
N.A.I.C.S.: 424710
Glenn A. Beck (Pres)

BECK PROPERTIES INC.
3114 W Hammer Ln, Stockton, CA
95209-2720
Tel.: (209) 957-0331
Year Founded: 1985
Sales Range: $50-74.9 Million
Emp.: 40
Housing Construction Services
N.A.I.C.S.: 531120
Mel Ratto (Pres)
Jim Ferguson (VP)

BECK SUPPLIERS, INC.
1000 N Front St, Fremont, OH 43420
Tel.: (419) 332-5527   OH
Web Site: http://www.beckoil.com
Year Founded: 1963
Sales Range: $75-99.9 Million
Emp.: 400
Petroleum Delivery Services; Pro-pane Supplier & Car Wash Systems
Sales & Installation
N.A.I.C.S.: 424710

BECK TOTAL OFFICE INTERI-ORS
5300 Eagle Rock Ave NE Ste A, Al-buquerque, NM 87113
Tel.: (505) 883-6471
Web Site: http://www.becktoi.com
Year Founded: 1983
Sales Range: $10-24.9 Million
Emp.: 10
Mfr of Office Furniture
N.A.I.C.S.: 423210
Greg King (Co-Owner & Principal)
Lori Addison (Co-Owner & Principal)
Brent Aldridge (VP & Interior De-signer)
Scott Hutchinson (Project Mgr)
Robert Turner (Mgr-Installation)

BECKER & POLIAKOFF, P.A.
1 E Broward Blvd Ste 1800, Fort Lau-derdale, FL 33301
Tel.: (954) 987-7550   FL
Web Site:
  http://www.beckerlawyers.com
Year Founded: 1973
Emp.: 114
Law firm
N.A.I.C.S.: 541110
Pamela J. Anselmo (Atty)
Evan B. Berger (Atty)
Marni Becker-Avin (Dir-Pro Dev &
Client Svcs)
Alan S. Becker (Atty)
Michelle C. Ammendola (Atty)
Marcie Oppenheimer Nolan (Atty)
Edward C. Lohrer (Partner)
George Burgess (COO)
Karen Skyers (Atty)
Jordan Blumenthal (Atty-Washington)
Curtis B. Hunter (Atty-Corp & Securi-ties Practice Grp)
Bert Gomez (Sr Dir-Corp & Govt
Rels-Washington)

Subsidiaries:

Taylor & Carls, P.A. (1)
150 N Westmonte Dr, Altamonte Springs,
FL 32714
Tel.: (407) 660-1040
Law firm
N.A.I.C.S.: 541110

BECKER BUICK INC.
E 636 Sprague Ave, Spokane, WA
99202-2191
Tel.: (509) 455-3550
Web Site:
  http://www.beckerbuick.com
Year Founded: 1958
Rev.: $17,200,000
Emp.: 60
Automobiles, New & Used
N.A.I.C.S.: 441110
Dale Cornwell (Owner)
Wayne Cornwell (Pres)

BECKER COMMUNICATIONS, INC.
9419 Corporate Lake Dr, Tampa, FL
33634
Tel.: (813) 249-1020   FL
Web Site: https://www.bcifl.net
Year Founded: 1999
Sales Range: $1-9.9 Million

Emp.: 30
Electronic Parts & Equipment Merchant Whslr
N.A.I.C.S.: 423690
Grant Becker (Pres)

BECKER GLOVE INTERNATIONAL INC.

4240 Rider Trl N, Earth City, MO 63045-1105
Tel.: (314) 298-9810
Web Site:
   http://www.beckerglove.com
Rev.: $10,000,000
Emp.: 15
Glove & Mitten Mfr
N.A.I.C.S.: 315990
Winnie Bahr (Mgr)
Jon Flom (Pres)

BECKER HOLDING CORPORATION

1701 Hwy A1A Ste 204, Vero Beach, FL 32963
Tel.: (772) 234-5234
Web Site:
   http://www.beckerholding.com
Year Founded: 1983
Sales Range: $10-24.9 Million
Emp.: 9
Crop Planting & Protection Services
N.A.I.C.S.: 115112

Subsidiaries:

Becker Tree Farm & Nursery,
Inc.   (1)
2400 SE Bridge Rd, Hobe Sound, FL 33455
Tel.: (772) 546-3541
Web Site: http://www.beckertreefarm.com
Plant & Tree Production Services
N.A.I.C.S.: 111421

BECKER LLC

354 Eisenhower Pkwy Plz II Ste 1500, Livingston, NJ 07039
Tel.: (973) 422-1100
Web Site: https://www.becker.legal
Law firm
N.A.I.C.S.: 541110
Martin L. Borosko (Mng Partner)
David J. Sprong (Partner)
Timothy J. Szuhaj (Partner)
David G. Tomeo (Partner)
Allen J. Underwood (Partner)
Michael A. Bartels (Chief Dev Officer)
Joseph G. Harraka Jr. (Partner)

BECKER MARKETING SERVICES INC.

115 Davis St, Monroe, GA 30655
Tel.: (770) 266-7659
Web Site:
   http://www.bmsipackaging.com
Sales Range: $10-24.9 Million
Emp.: 11
Packaging Materials
N.A.I.C.S.: 424990
Donald Becker (Pres)

BECKER MOTORS INC.

4155 State Rte 5 and 20, Canandaigua, NY 14424
Tel.: (585) 393-9500
Web Site:
   https://www.beckermotors.com
Rev.: $17,000,000
Emp.: 9
Automobiles, New & Used
N.A.I.C.S.: 441110
Bonnie Rex (Office Mgr)

BECKER TIRE & TREADING INC.

904 Washington St, Great Bend, KS 67530
Tel.: (620) 793-5414

Web Site: http://www.beckertire.com
Sales Range: $10-24.9 Million
Emp.: 100
Tires & Tubes
N.A.I.C.S.: 423130
Bob Harris (VP)
Staci Bownes (Mgr-Adv)
Sondra Uhrich (Mgr-HR)
Gary Albright (Pres & CEO)
Tammy Hayden (Mgr-Credit)
Jeanie Radke (VP-Acctg)
Willy Allen (Exec VP)
Steve Burhenn (Exec VP)
Brett Foster (VP & Reg Mgr)
Paul Doll (Sr VP)

BECKER'S SCHOOL SUPPLIES, INC.

1500 Melrose Hwy, Pennsauken, NJ 08110
Tel.: (856) 792-9292
Web Site:
   https://www.shopbecker.com
Sales Range: $25-49.9 Million
Emp.: 65
School Supplies & Teacher Resources
N.A.I.C.S.: 423490
George J. Becker (Pres)

BECKERLE LUMBER SUPPLY CO., INC.

3 Chestnut St, Spring Valley, NY 10977
Tel.: (845) 356-1600
Web Site:
   http://www.beckerlelumber.com
Sales Range: $10-24.9 Million
Emp.: 100
Lumber & Other Building Materials
N.A.I.C.S.: 423310
Larry Beckerle (Pres)

BECKERMAN GROUP

1 University Plz Ste 507, Hackensack, NJ 07601
Tel.: (201) 465-8000
Web Site:
   http://www.beckermanpr.com
Year Founded: 1990
Sales Range: $10-24.9 Million
Emp.: 60
Public Relations Agency
N.A.I.C.S.: 541820
Christa Segalini (VP & Head-Real Estate)
Keith Zakheim (CEO)
Denyse Dabrowski (Sr VP)
Naomi Decter (Sr VP)
Ryan Smith (VP)
Jerry Schranz (Dir-Media Strategy)
Jessica Orsini (Mgr-HR)
Desiree Santiago (Supvr-Acct)

Subsidiaries:

Antenna Group, Inc.   (1)
135 Main St Ste 800, San Francisco, CA 94105-8110
Tel.: (415) 896-1800
Web Site: http://www.antennagroup.com
Sales Range: $10-24.9 Million
Emp.: 22
Public Relations Agency
N.A.I.C.S.: 541820
Anna Cahill Leonard (Pres)
Keith Zakheim (CEO)
Eric Schoenberg (COO)
Jake Rozmaryn (Chief Growth Officer)
Christa Segalini (Chief Client Officer)
Marisa Long (Sr VP-Climate & Energy)
Kristin Ford-Glencross (VP-Climate & Mobility)
Paul Newton (Exec VP-Integration & Innovation)

BECKETT & BECKETT, INC.

1051 E Altadena Dr, Altadena, CA 91001-2040

Tel.: (626) 791-7954   CA
Web Site: http://www.beckettadv.com
Year Founded: 1967
Emp.: 10
Advertising Services
N.A.I.C.S.: 541810
G. Edward Beckett (Founder & Chief Creative Officer)
Kevin McLaughlin (VP & Controller)

Subsidiaries:

Beckett & Beckett, Inc.   (1)
2712 E Grace St, Richmond, VA 23223
Tel.: (804) 562-2256
Web Site: http://www.beckettadv.com
Sales Range: Less than $1 Million
Emp.: 3
Advertising Services
N.A.I.C.S.: 541870

BECKETT AIR INC.

37850 Beckett Pkwy, North Ridgeville, OH 44039
Tel.: (440) 327-9999
Web Site: https://www.beckettair.com
Year Founded: 1988
Sales Range: $10-24.9 Million
Emp.: 130
Mfr of Blower Wheels
N.A.I.C.S.: 333413
Chuck Visocky (Pres & CEO)

BECKETT MEDIA LLC

4635 McEwen Rd, Dallas, TX 75244
Tel.: (972) 991-6657
Web Site:
   http://www.beckettmedia.com
Year Founded: 1984
Sales Range: $25-49.9 Million
Emp.: 300
Magazine Publisher
N.A.I.C.S.: 513120
James Beckett (CEO)
Jane Lathen (Mgr-HR)
Brian Gulledge (Pres)
Nick Singh (Sr VP-Newsstand & Ops)
Mike Obert (Sr VP-Adv Sls)
Erin Masercola (Dir-Editorial Bus Unit)
Tim Clevenger (Dir-IT)
Pual Graff (VP-Creative Design)
Al Muir (Editor-Hockey)

BECKLEY AUTOMALL, INC.

3934 Robert C Byrd Dr, Beckley, WV 25801-7105
Tel.: (304) 252-3300
Web Site:
   http://www.beckleyautomall.com
Sales Range: $10-24.9 Million
Emp.: 46
New Car Retailer
N.A.I.C.S.: 441110
Andrew Hudson (Mgr)

BECKMAN & GAST CO. INC.

282 W Kremer Hoying Rd, Saint Henry, OH 45883
Tel.: (419) 678-4195
Web Site:
   https://www.beckmangast.com
Sales Range: $1-9.9 Million
Emp.: 15
Canned Green Beans & Tomatoes
N.A.I.C.S.: 311422
Paul Moorman (Treas & Sec)

BECKMANN CONVERTING, INC.

14 Park Dr, Amsterdam, NY 12010-0390
Tel.: (518) 842-0073
Web Site:
   https://www.beckmannconver
ting.com
Sales Range: $75-99.9 Million
Emp.: 25

Laminating & Fabric Coating Services
N.A.I.C.S.: 326130
Peter Piusz (Gen Mgr)

BECKNELL WHOLESALE I LP

504 E 44th St, Lubbock, TX 79404
Tel.: (806) 747-3201
Web Site: https://www.becknell.com
Rev.: $15,000,000
Emp.: 50
Hardware
N.A.I.C.S.: 423710
Eugene Becknell (Pres)

BECKS BOOKSTORES INC.

4520 N Broadway St 22, Chicago, IL 60640
Tel.: (773) 784-7963
Web Site:
   http://www.becksbooks.com
Sales Range: $10-24.9 Million
Emp.: 50
Book Stores
N.A.I.C.S.: 459210
Robert L. Beck (Chm)

BECKS FURNITURE INC.

11840 Folsom Blvd, Rancho Cordova, CA 95742
Tel.: (916) 353-5000
Web Site:
   https://www.becksfurniture.com
Sales Range: $10-24.9 Million
Emp.: 130
Furniture Retailer
N.A.I.C.S.: 449110
Robert S. Beckinger (Pres)

BECKSTROM ELECTRIC

37277 E Richardson Ln, Purcellville, VA 20132
Tel.: (540) 338-2344
Web Site:
   https://www.beckstromelectric.com
Year Founded: 1989
Rev.: $31,800,000
Emp.: 180
Electrical Contractor
N.A.I.C.S.: 238210
Ken Beckstrom (Founder & CEO)
Mick Beckstrom (Co-Owner & Pres)
Rob Kizer (Co-Owner & VP)
Kenneth Beckstrom (Owner)
Rob Kizer (VP)

BECKWITH ELECTRIC CO. INC.

6190 118th Ave, Largo, FL 33773-3724
Tel.: (727) 544-2326
Web Site:
   https://www.beckwithelectric.com
Year Founded: 1967
Rev.: $15,441,157
Emp.: 124
Relays & Industrial Controls
N.A.I.C.S.: 335314
Laurie E. Tudor (CFO)
Thomas R. Beckwith (CEO)
Murty V. V. S. Yalla (Pres)
Hugo Monterrubio (Dir-Mktg)
Thai Chong Li (Dir-Engrg)
Kevin Gerrish (VP-Ops)
Wayne Hartmann (VP-Ops)

BECKY'S CARD & GIFTS INC.

221 McLaws Cir, Williamsburg, VA 23185
Tel.: (757) 220-6772
Year Founded: 1978
Sales Range: $10-24.9 Million
Emp.: 170
Greeting Cards
N.A.I.C.S.: 459420
Peggy Sims (Office Mgr)
Francis Norsworthy Jr. (Pres)

Becmar Sprinkler Systems, Inc.—(Continued)

BECMAR SPRINKLER SYS-TEMS, INC.

2620 Bridge Ln, Woodstock, IL 60098
Tel.: (815) 356-1467
Web Site:
 http://www.becmarsprinkler.com
Year Founded: 1988
Sales Range: $10-24.9 Million
Emp.: 100
Water Supply & Irrigation System
Maintenance Services
N.A.I.C.S.: 221310
Rosemary Farver (Pres)

BECO ENGINEERING COM-PANY

2077 SE Talbot Pl, Stuart, FL 34997-5692
Tel.: (412) 828-6080   PA
Year Founded: 1973
Sales Range: $50-74.9 Million
Emp.: 6
Custom Design of Air Pollution Control Equipment for Industrial Purposes
N.A.I.C.S.: 333413
Bernard J. Lerner (Pres & CEO)

BECOMING INDEPENDENT

1455 Corporate Ctr Pkwy, Santa Rosa, CA 95407
Tel.: (707) 524-6600   CA
Web Site:
 https://www.becomingindependent.org
Year Founded: 1980
Sales Range: $10-24.9 Million
Emp.: 728
Developmental Disability Assistance Services
N.A.I.C.S.: 624120
Luana Vaetoe (CEO)

BECORE

1652 Mateo St, Los Angeles, CA 90021
Tel.: (213) 747-3123
Web Site: https://www.becore.com
Year Founded: 1999
Sales Range: $10-24.9 Million
Emp.: 30
Event Marketing & Planning & Consulting Services
N.A.I.C.S.: 711310
Mark Billik (Founder & CEO)
Kelly Vaught (Partner)
Jen Fisch (Dir-Creative)
Ryan Vaught (Dir-Fin)

BEDDING GALLERY

606 Albert Pike Rd, Hot Springs, AR 71913
Tel.: (501) 623-4619
Sales Range: $10-24.9 Million
Emp.: 12
Bedding
N.A.I.C.S.: 449110
Clifton Crooks (Pres)

BEDERSON & COMPANY LLP

100 Passaic Ave Ste 310, Fairfield, NJ 07004
Tel.: (973) 736-3333
Web Site: https://www.bederson.com
Sales Range: $10-24.9 Million
Emp.: 70
Accounting Services
N.A.I.C.S.: 541219
Edward P. Bond (Partner)
Steven P. Bortnick (Partner)
Seymour Bressler (Partner)
Timothy J. King (Partner)
Mark A. Mazza (Partner)
James H. Ruitenberg (Partner)
Matthew Schwartz (Partner)

Jules Schneider (Partner)
Kenneth E. Winslow (Partner)
Jeffrey E. Callahan (Partner)
Charles S. Lunden (Partner)
Charles N. Persing (Partner)
Sean Raquet (Partner)
Toni Klimowicz (Partner)

BEDFORD ADVERTISING INC.

1718 Trinity Vly Dr Ste 200, Carrollton, TX 75006
Tel.: (972) 458-1150   TX
Web Site: http://www.bedfordads.com
Year Founded: 1980
Sales Range: $10-24.9 Million
Emp.: 20
Advertising Services
N.A.I.C.S.: 541810
Jeff Jutte (Pres)
John Adams (Dir-Art)

BEDFORD FUNDING

10 New King St Ste 104, White Plains, NY 10604
Tel.: (914) 287-4880
Web Site:
 https://www.bedfordfunding.com
Privater Equity Firm
N.A.I.C.S.: 523999
Charles Snowden Jones (Founder & Mng Partner)
Larry Kaplan (Mng Dir & CFO)
Jonathan D. Salon (Mng Dir & Gen Counsel)
George M. Regnery (Principal)
Doug A. Ring (Principal)
Gwen A. Weiss (Controller)

BEDFORD INDUSTRIES, INC.

1659 Rowe Ave, Worthington, MN 56187-0039
Tel.: (507) 376-4136   SD
Web Site: https://www.bedford.com
Year Founded: 1966
Sales Range: $200-249.9 Million
Emp.: 190
Twist-Tie & Tag Mfr
N.A.I.C.S.: 326199
Norma J. Cook (Mgr-Mktg & Admin)
Steve Bermimg (Coord-Pur)
Jeff Tschetter (Gen Mgr)
Colin O'Donnell (Mgr-Engrg & Quality)
Chad Mammen (Mgr-Fin)
Anthony Bui (Acct Coord)

Subsidiaries:

Bedford Technology, LLC   (1)
2424 Armour Rd, Worthington, MN 56187-0609
Tel.: (507) 372-5558
Web Site: http://www.bedfordtech.com
Plastic Lumber Mfr & Sales
N.A.I.C.S.: 326199
Brian Larsen (Founder)
Jeff Breitzman (Pres & CEO)
Jesse Hooge (Sr Dir-Multi-X & Sls Sys)
Dan Greve (CFO)
Steve Colvin (Mgr-Territory Dev)
Lynn Osmera (Mktg Mgr)
Blake Hoffman (Mgr-Customer Svc & Key Acct)
Mike Nesdahl (VP-Sls & Mktg)
Jeff Turner (Chm)

BEDFORD NISSAN INC.

18115 Rockside Rd, Bedford, OH 44146
Tel.: (440) 345-8822
Web Site:
 https://www.bedfordnissan.com
Sales Range: $25-49.9 Million
Emp.: 30
Car Dealership
N.A.I.C.S.: 441110
Jeffrie Greenberg (Pres)

BEDFORD REINFORCED PLASTICS

1 Corporate Dr Ste 106, Bedford, PA 15522
Tel.: (814) 623-8125
Web Site:
 https://www.bedfordreinforced.com
Year Founded: 1974
Rev.: $41,100,000
Emp.: 300
Plastics Product Mfr
N.A.I.C.S.: 326199
Mike A. Beaupre (VP-Ops)
Ken Morris (Mgr-Pur)

BEDFORD VALLEY PETRO-LEUM CORP

10228 Lincoln Hwy, Everett, PA 15537
Tel.: (814) 623-5151
Web Site:
 https://www.bvpetroleum.com
Sales Range: $10-24.9 Million
Emp.: 36
Petroleum Products Mfr
N.A.I.C.S.: 424720
Candie Calhoun (Dir-Logistic)

BEDFORD WEAVING MILLS INC.

Monroe St, Bedford, VA 24523
Tel.: (540) 586-8235   VA
Web Site:
 https://www.bedfordweaving.com
Year Founded: 1982
Sales Range: $10-24.9 Million
Emp.: 100
Broadwoven Fabric Mills
N.A.I.C.S.: 313210
Philip J. Garbarini Jr. (Pres)

BEDGEAR LLC

110 Bi-County Blvd Ste 101, Farmingdale, NY 11735
Tel.: (631) 414-7758
Web Site: http://www.bedgear.com
Year Founded: 2008
Sales Range: $25-49.9 Million
Emp.: 62
Pillowcases & Mattress Mfr
N.A.I.C.S.: 313210
Eugene Alletto (Founder & CEO)
Nicolas Dopico (Engr-Logistics)
Justin Gannon (Dir-Sls)
Todd Merker (VP-Intl Sls)
Tom Sakry (Sr Acct Mgr)
Lori Ellis (Dir-Sls Ops)
Daniel Reppe (Dir-Mktg & Sls)
Leslie Clay (VP-Mktg & Sls)
Erin Cohen (Mgr-Sls Acct)
Ross Stuart (Acting Pres-Asia Pacific)

BEDROCK INDUSTRIES GP, LLC

1530 Wilson Rd Ste 113, Arlington, VA 22209
Tel.: (786) 650-0074   DE
Web Site: http://www.bi15.com
Holding Company
N.A.I.C.S.: 551112
David Cheney (Pres)
Alan Kestenbaum (Chm & CEO)

Subsidiaries:

Stelco Inc.   (1)
386 Wilcox Street, Hamilton, L8L 8K5, ON, Canada
Tel.: (905) 577-4434
Web Site: http://www.stelcocanada.com
Steel Products Mfr
N.A.I.C.S.: 331221
Alan Kestenbaum (Chm & CEO)
Sujit Sanyal (COO)

BEDROCK LOGISTICS LLC

2501 N Harwood St Ste 2600, Dallas, TX 75201
Tel.: (214) 347-8219
Web Site:
 https://www.bedrocklogistics.com
Sales Range: $10-24.9 Million
Freight Transportation Services
N.A.I.C.S.: 488510
Robert J. Schlegel (Chm)

BEDROCK TECHNOLOGY PARTNERS

451 B St, San Diego, CA 92101
Tel.: (408) 673-4040
Web Site: https://www.bedrock-tech.com
Year Founded: 2007
Sales Range: $50-74.9 Million
Emp.: 20
IT Consultancy & Systems Integrator on Architecture Implementation for Various Companies
N.A.I.C.S.: 519290
Dean Cappellazzo (CEO)
Mark Burbrink (CFO)
Ravi Poddar (CTO)
Tom Holt (Sr VP-Sls)

BEE AGRICULTURAL COM-PANY INC.

1004 S Washington St, Beeville, TX 78102-3929
Tel.: (361) 358-3470   TX
Year Founded: 1969
Sales Range: $10-24.9 Million
Emp.: 27
Grain & Field Beans
N.A.I.C.S.: 424510
Kenneth Schauer (VP)
Fred R. Schauer III (Pres & CEO)

BEE DARLIN', INC.

1854 E 22nd St, Los Angeles, CA 90058
Tel.: (213) 749-2116   CA
Sales Range: $10-24.9 Million
Emp.: 46
Dresses
N.A.I.C.S.: 315250
Steve Namm (Pres)
Andy Schwarz (Controller)
Johnny Slm (Mgr-Import)
Victor Felix (Mgr-Production)

BEE LINE, INC.

955 Busse Rd, Elk Grove Village, IL 60007
Tel.: (847) 378-8758
Web Site:
 http://www.beelineimage.com
Year Founded: 2008
Sales Range: $1-9.9 Million
Emp.: 10
Janitorial Services
N.A.I.C.S.: 561720
Jamie Van Vuren (Pres)
Andre Van Vuren (COO)
Nancy Hernandez (Mgr-HR)

Subsidiaries:

Bee Line Construction L.L.C.   (1)
955 Busse Rd, Elk Grove Village, IL 60007   (100%)
Tel.: (847) 378-8758
Web Site: http://www.beelineimage.com
New Construction, Tenant Improvements & Vacancy Preparations
N.A.I.C.S.: 236116
Danny Perkins (Mgr-Ops)

BEE MINE PRODUCTS INC.

PO Box 15951, Clearwater, FL 33766-5951
Tel.: (941) 921-5581
Web Site:
 http://www.beemineproducts.com
Sales Range: $10-24.9 Million
Emp.: 105
Air Conditioning System Installation Services

N.A.I.C.S.: 238220
Charles Blum *(Mgr)*

BEE SALES COMPANY
6330 W Touhy Ave, Niles, IL 60714
Tel.: (773) 989-9008
Web Site: http://www.beesales.com
Year Founded: 1983
Sales Range: $10-24.9 Million
Emp.: 85
Whslr of Beauty Salon & Barber
Shop Equipment & Supplies
N.A.I.C.S.: 423850
Yong Kim *(Pres)*
Steve Ahn *(Gen Mgr)*

BEE STREET HOLDINGS LLC
425 S Financial Pl 3100, Chicago, IL
60605
Tel.: (312) 553-3653   DE
Holding Company
N.A.I.C.S.: 551112
James G. Gidwitz *(Owner)*

Subsidiaries:

Riverbend Industries Inc.   **(1)**
110 N Wacker Dr Ste 3300, Chicago, IL
60606   **(100%)**
Tel.: (312) 541-7200
Web Site:
   https://www.riverbendindustries.com
Rev.: $113,276,000
Assets: $89,983,000
Liabilities: $54,794,000
Net Worth: $35,189,000
Earnings: ($13,899,000)
Emp.: 460
Fiscal Year-end: 12/28/2019
Natural Resources Mining; Construction
Materials, Gas Wall Furnaces, Evaporative
Coolers & Fan Coil Systems Mfr
N.A.I.C.S.: 327320
James G. Gidwitz *(Chm & CEO)*
Brian Kobylinski *(Pres & CEO)*
Noah Mineo *(CFO)*
Craig Knot *(Gen Counsel & Dir-Compliance)*
Jim Woss *(VP-Information Technology)*
Matt Blue *(VP-Marketing & Innovation)*
David Ryan *(Treas & Controller-Corp)*
Ryan Spilman *(Engr-Lead Sys)*
Robert Krueger *(Dir-Fin Due Diligence & Bus Ops Support)*
Santa Sorrentino *(Mktg Mgr)*

Subsidiary (Domestic):

Castle Concrete Company   **(1)**
7250 Allegheny Dr, Colorado Springs, CO
80919
Tel.: (719) 475-0700
Sales Range: $25-49.9 Million
Emp.: 30
Distribution of Sand, Gravel & Limestone
N.A.I.C.S.: 212321
Jerry Schnabel *(Pres)*

Continental Copper, Inc.   **(2)**
200 S Wacker Dr Ste 4000, Chicago, IL
60606-5821
Tel.: (312) 876-5000
Sales Range: Less than $1 Million
Emp.: 10
Copper Mining
N.A.I.C.S.: 212230
James G. Gidwitz *(Chm & CEO)*

Subsidiary (Domestic):

Continental Catalina, Inc.   **(3)**
200 S Wacker Dr Ste 4000, Chicago, IL
60606
Tel.: (312) 541-7200
Mining Operations
N.A.I.C.S.: 212220
James G. Gidwitz *(Chm & CEO)*
Mark S. Nichter *(Sec)*

Subsidiary (Domestic):

Edens Industrial Park, Inc.   **(2)**
200 S Wacker Dr 4000, Chicago, IL 60606
Tel.: (312) 541-7200
Sales Range: $150-199.9 Million
Emp.: 10
Commercial Real Estate Services

N.A.I.C.S.: 531390
Joseph J. Sum *(VP)*
Mark S. Nichter *(Sec & Controller)*

In-O-Vate Technologies, Inc.   **(2)**
810 Saturn St Ste 20, Jupiter, FL 33477-4456
Tel.: (561) 743-8696
Web Site: http://www.inovate.com
Construction Products Mfr & Retailer
N.A.I.C.S.: 423390
Rick Harpenau *(Founder)*
James Ortiz *(VP-Ops)*
Todd Peach *(VP-Mktg)*
Clifford Budnick *(Pres)*
Josh Goldstone *(Controller)*
Frank Ambrose *(Natl Sls Mgr)*
Missy Clark *(Office Mgr-Bus)*
Ryan Stromik *(Sr Acct Mgr)*
Bobby Chisholm *(Acct Mgr)*
Matt Rinehart *(Acct Mgr)*
Ben Fleming *(Acct Mgr)*
Jackie Lopopolo *(Coord-Office)*
Steven Langston *(Mgr-Digital Mktg)*

McKinney Door and Hardware,
Inc.   **(2)**
2700 N Freeway, Pueblo, CO 81003
Tel.: (719) 543-3124
Web Site: http://www.mckinneydoor.com
Emp.: 25
Hardware & Metal & Wood Doors Mfr &
Distr
N.A.I.C.S.: 332321
Bob Zinanti *(Mgr-Sls)*
Mark Zinanti *(Project Mgr)*
Robert Willard *(Project Mgr)*
Mike Musso *(Project Mgr)*
Brian Cadena *(Project Mgr)*
Greg Lopez *(Project Mgr)*
Isaac Benavidez *(Project Mgr)*
Kyle Rayburn *(Project Mgr)*
Nick Zinanti *(Project Mgr)*
Oscar Olson *(Sls Mgr)*
Ethan Bronner *(Project Mgr)*
Mike Robinson *(Project Mgr)*
Craig Waller *(Project Mgr)*
Matt Williams *(Project Mgr)*
Robert Chillino *(Project Mgr)*

Phoenix Manufacturing, Inc.   **(2)**
3655 E Roeser Rd, Phoenix, AZ 85040-3968
Tel.: (602) 437-1034
Web Site:
   http://www.phoenixmanufacturing.com
Sales Range: $50-74.9 Million
Emp.: 150
Evaporative Air Cooling Equipment Mfr
N.A.I.C.S.: 333415

TMOP Legacy Company   **(2)**
2596 Howard 96 E, Pueblo, CO
81005-9769   **(100%)**
Tel.: (719) 561-8350
Web Site: http://transitmix.net
Ready Mix Concrete, Building Supplies,
Sand & Gravel Mfr
N.A.I.C.S.: 327320

Williams Furnace Co.   **(2)**
250 W Laurel St, Colton, CA 92324-1744
Tel.: (909) 825-0993
Web Site:
   http://www.williamscomfortprod.com
Sales Range: $125-149.9 Million
Emp.: 310
Heating & Ventilating Equipment Mfr
N.A.I.C.S.: 333414

BEE WINDOW INCORPORATED
115 Shadowlawn Dr, Fishers, IN
46038-2432
Tel.: (317) 283-8522
Web Site:
   https://www.beewindow.com
Year Founded: 1983
Sales Range: $10-24.9 Million
Emp.: 75
Windows, Plastics
N.A.I.C.S.: 326199
George Faerber *(Pres)*
Charlie Hill *(CFO)*

BEE-ALIVE INC.

7 New Lake Rd, Valley Cottage, NY
10989
Tel.: (845) 268-0960
Web Site: http://www.beealive.com
Year Founded: 1984
Rev.: $13,300,000
Emp.: 50
Vitamins & Minerals
N.A.I.C.S.: 424210
Jason Balletta *(Pres & CEO)*
Kimberly McCord-Russo *(Dir-Fin Ops)*
Rae Anne Gross *(Mgr-Mktg)*

BEE-LINE COMMUNICATIONS
100 E Cook Ave Ste 200, Libertyville,
IL 60048
Tel.: (224) 207-4320
Web Site:
   http://www.beecommunications.com
Year Founded: 2006
Sales Range: $1-9.9 Million
Emp.: 20
Strategic Global Marketing & Com-
munications
N.A.I.C.S.: 541613
Stacey McClenathan *(Founder & CEO)*
Hillary Chapple *(Mgr-HR)*

BEEBE MEDICAL CENTER
424 Savannah Rd, Lewes, DE 19958
Tel.: (302) 645-3300   DE
Web Site:
   https://www.beebehealthcare.org
Year Founded: 1916
Sales Range: $250-299.9 Million
Emp.: 1,946
Health Care Services
N.A.I.C.S.: 622110
Paul T. Cowan *(Treas)*
Jeffrey M. Fried *(Sec)*
Jacquelyn O. Wilson *(Vice Chm)*
William Swain Lee *(Chm)*

BEEBY CLARK + MEYLER
1 Bridge St Ste 30, Irvington, NY
10533
Tel.: (914) 693-1003
Web Site:
   http://www.beebyclarkmeyler.com
Year Founded: 2005
Sales Range: $25-49.9 Million
Emp.: 16
Management Consulting Services
N.A.I.C.S.: 541613
Michael K. Clark *(Principal)*
Stuart H. Meyler *(Principal)*
Thomas Beeby *(Principal & Exec Dir-Creative)*

BEECHMONT AUTOMOTIVE GROUP
8667 Beechmont Ave, Cincinnati, OH
45255-4709
Tel.: (513) 388-3800   OH
Web Site:
   http://www.beechmonttoyoto.com
Year Founded: 1980
Sales Range: $125-149.9 Million
Emp.: 300
Dealer, Sales & Service of New &
Used Cars
N.A.I.C.S.: 441110
Jim Woodall *(VP)*
Bob Wilder *(Mgr-Parts)*
Bill F. Woeste Jr. *(Pres)*

Subsidiaries:

Beechmont Isuzu   **(1)**
7636 Beechmont Ave, Cincinnati, OH
45255-4202   **(100%)**
Tel.: (513) 624-1150
Sales Range: $10-24.9 Million
Emp.: 10
Isuzu Franchise Dealer
N.A.I.C.S.: 441110

Beechmont Toyota   **(1)**
8667 Beechmont Ave, Cincinnati, OH
45245   **(100%)**
Tel.: (513) 388-3800
Web Site: http://www.beechmonttoyota.com
Sales Range: $50-74.9 Million
Emp.: 100
Auto Dealership
N.A.I.C.S.: 425120
Ron Behymer *(Gen Mgr-Sls)*
Troy Tidwell *(Asst Gen Mgr-Sls)*
Don Buescher *(Mgr-Svcs)*
Josh Caupp *(Mgr-Internet)*
Myron Heggood *(Mgr-New Car Sls)*
Terri Hopkins *(Asst Mgr-Svcs)*
Randy Johnson *(Mgr-Fin)*
Adam Lester *(Mgr-New Car Sls)*
Bob Wilder *(Mgr-Parts)*
Bill Woeste Jr. *(Pres)*

Honda East   **(1)**
529 Ohio Pike, Cincinnati, OH
45255-3338   **(100%)**
Tel.: (513) 528-8000
Web Site: http://www.hondaeastcincy.com
Rev.: $34,000,000
Emp.: 100
Auto Dealership
N.A.I.C.S.: 441110
Bill Woeste *(Pres)*
Neil Pambrick *(Gen Mgr)*

BEECHMONT FORD INC.
600 Ohio Pike, Cincinnati, OH 45245
Tel.: (513) 685-6510   OH
Web Site:
   https://www.beechmontford.com
Year Founded: 1970
Car Dealership Owner & Operator
N.A.I.C.S.: 441110
Mark Williams *(Pres)*
Jeff Fithen *(Gen Mgr)*
Charlie Watson *(Dir-Mktg)*
Brad Houk *(Gen Mgr-Sls)*
Greg Kien *(Mgr-New Car)*
Cliff McCord *(Mgr-Used Car)*
Michael Mikles *(Mgr-Used Car)*
Bob Galvin *(Mgr-Parts)*
Robyn Rapp *(Mgr-Svc)*
Carol Mansfield *(Mgr-Body Shop)*
Danny VanWinkle *(Mgr-Fin)*
Ralph Todd *(Mgr-Fin)*
Tony Tambash *(Mgr-Fin)*
Nick Howell *(Dir-IT)*

BEECHMONT MOTORS, INC
646 Mount Moriah Dr, Cincinnati, OH
45245
Tel.: (513) 752-0088
Web Site: http://www.zoomtown.com
Year Founded: 1979
Rev.: $16,000,000
Emp.: 40
Motorcycle & Car Dealers
N.A.I.C.S.: 441227
Thomas Bellamy *(Pres)*
Dennis Homan *(Controller)*

BEECHUM FINANCIAL CORP.
12 S Grant St, Roseville, CA 95678
Tel.: (916) 781-9999
Web Site: https://www.lend2me.com
Mortgage Bankers & Loan Corre-
spondents
N.A.I.C.S.: 522310
Craig Beechum *(Owner)*

BEECHWOOD CREATIVE, INC.
200 Robbins Ln Ste D-1, Jericho, NY
11753
Tel.: (516) 935-5555
Web Site:
   http://www.beechwoodhomes.com
Year Founded: 2001
Sales Range: $1-9.9 Million
Emp.: 4
In House Advertising Agency
N.A.I.C.S.: 541810
Kathy Sheck *(Sr VP)*

Beecken Petty O'Keefe & Company, LLC—(Continued)

BEECKEN PETTY O'KEEFE & COMPANY, LLC

131 S Dearborn St Ste 2800, Chicago, IL 60603
Tel.: (312) 435-0300   DE
Web Site: http://www.bpoc.com
Year Founded: 1996
Healthcare Industry Equity Investment Firm
N.A.I.C.S.: 523999
John W. Kneen *(CFO, COO & Partner)*
Dave Cooney *(Partner)*
Ann Koerner *(VP & Controller)*
David Poss *(VP)*
Debbie Wahl *(Office Mgr)*

Subsidiaries:

Examination Management Services, Inc.   (1)
3050 Regent Blvd Ste 100, Irving, TX 75063
Tel.: (214) 689-3600
Web Site: http://www.emsinet.com
Medical Risk Management & Investigative Services
N.A.I.C.S.: 561499
James Calver *(CEO)*
Anthony Mustoe *(CIO)*
Brian Vidrik *(Gen Counsel & Sec)*
Burt Wolder *(CMO)*
Denisa Bravenec *(Chief People Officer & Sr VP)*
Greg James *(COO)*
William Keys *(CFO)*

Subsidiary (Domestic):

Bi-State Professional Services, Inc.   (2)
17838 Chesterfield Airport Rd, Chesterfield, MO 63005
Tel.: (636) 537-3200
Web Site: http://www.emsi-bistate.com
Emp.: 3
Paramedical Support Services
N.A.I.C.S.: 561499
Iris Hardy *(Pres & CEO)*

Branch (Domestic):

Examination Management Services, Inc. - National Service Center   (2)
3050 Regent Blvd Ste 400, Irving, TX 75063
Tel.: (214) 689-3600
Web Site: http://www.emsinet.com
Call Center
N.A.I.C.S.: 561421
Shelia Baker *(Mgr)*

Home Care Delivered, Inc.   (1)
11013 West Br St 4th Fl, Glen Allen, VA 23060
Tel.: (804) 354-1578
Web Site: http://www.homecaredelivered.com
Rev.: $4,900,000
Emp.: 30
Medical, Dental & Hospital Equipment & Supplies Merchant Whslr
N.A.I.C.S.: 423450
Gordon L. Fox *(Chm)*

Network Packaging Group LLC   (1)
2180 N Pointe Dr, Warsaw, IN 46582
Tel.: (574) 377-7151
Web Site: http://www.networkpartners.com
Management Consulting & Packaging Risk Management
N.A.I.C.S.: 541618
Tim Early *(Founder & CEO)*

Subsidiary (Domestic):

The FlexPro Group, LLC   (2)
620 W Germantown Pike Ste 260, Plymouth Meeting, PA 19462
Tel.: (484) 674-7838
Web Site: http://www.theflexprogroup.com
Distribution & Logistics consultancy Services
N.A.I.C.S.: 541614

Rose Cook *(Co-Founder & CEO)*
Lynn Faughey *(VP)*

BEEF CORPORATION OF AMERICA

1703 N College Ave, Bloomington, IN 47404
Tel.: (812) 332-4838
Year Founded: 1986
Sales Range: $25-49.9 Million
Emp.: 30
Fast-Food & Chain Restaurants Retailer
N.A.I.C.S.: 722513
Stephen M. Huse *(CEO)*
Thomas Browne *(Pres)*
Jill Garner *(VP-Fin)*
Craig Trulock *(VP-Ops)*
Bryn Jones *(Dir-Mktg)*
Jennifer Todd *(Dir-HR)*

BEELMAN TRUCK CO. INC.

6639 SR 15, Saint Libory, IL 62282
Tel.: (618) 768-4411   DE
Web Site: http://www.beelman.com
Year Founded: 1945
Sales Range: $25-49.9 Million
Emp.: 700
Local Trucking Services
N.A.I.C.S.: 327320
Sam Beelman *(Pres)*

BEEMER PRECISION, INC.

230 New York Dr, Fort Washington, PA 19034-0980
Tel.: (215) 646-8440
Web Site: http://www.beemerprecision.com
Industrial Supplies Mfr
N.A.I.C.S.: 423840
George White *(VP-Engrg)*

BEENVERIFIED.COM

307 5th Ave 16th Floor, New York, NY 10016
Web Site: https://www.beenverified.com
Year Founded: 2008
Sales Range: $10-24.9 Million
Emp.: 20
Affordable & Easy Access to Public Record Information
N.A.I.C.S.: 561499
Josh Levy *(Co-Founder & CEO)*

BEER CAPITOL DISTRIBUTING, LAKE COUNTRY, LLC

W 222 N 5700 Miller Way, Sussex, WI 53089-3988
Tel.: (262) 932-2337
Web Site: http://www.beercapitol.com
Year Founded: 1976
Alcoholic Beverages Distr
N.A.I.C.S.: 424810
Michael Merriman *(Pres)*
Aldo Madrigrano *(Chm)*

BEER NUTS, INC.

103 N Robinson St, Bloomington, IL 61701-5424
Tel.: (309) 585-6159   DE
Web Site: https://www.beernuts.com
Year Founded: 1953
Sales Range: $75-99.9 Million
Emp.: 100
Nut Products Mfr & Distr
N.A.I.C.S.: 311911
Cindy Shirk *(Branch Mgr)*

BEERE PRECISION PRODUCTS INC.

4915 21St, Racine, WI 53406
Tel.: (262) 632-0472
Web Site: http://www.beere.com
Sales Range: $10-24.9 Million
Emp.: 25

Machine Shop, Jobbing & Repair
N.A.I.C.S.: 332710
Richard F. Beere *(Chm)*
Kitty Charo *(Gen Mgr)*
Crystal Gillmore *(Mgr-Accts Payable)*

BEERS & HOFFMAN, LTD.

55N Water St, Lititz, PA 17543
Tel.: (717) 625-0400
Web Site: https://www.beershoffman.com
Year Founded: 1982
Rev.: $1,200,000
Emp.: 100
Architectural Services
N.A.I.C.S.: 541310
Scott Shonk *(Principal)*
Peter Kerekgyarto *(Principal)*
Michele J. Wierman *(Principal)*
C. Bruce Christman Jr. *(Principal)*

Subsidiaries:

Diversified Design Inc.   (1)
1104 Bridge St, New Cumberland, PA 17070
Tel.: (717) 774-7450
Web Site: http://www.diversified-design.com
Emp.: 50
Interior Design Services
N.A.I.C.S.: 541410
Michele J. Wierman *(Principal-Bus Dev)*

BEESON HARDWARE CO. INC.

201 Sheffield St, High Point, NC 27260
Tel.: (336) 821-2100
Web Site: http://www.beesonhardware.com
Sales Range: $25-49.9 Million
Emp.: 85
Building Materials, Interior
N.A.I.C.S.: 423310
A. Ed Spivey *(Chm & Pres)*
Jim Kinney *(VP & Gen Mgr-Indus)*
Pete Vitola *(VP & Gen Mgr-Hardware & Lumber)*

BEFUN INC.

14964 Slover Ave, Fontana, CA 92337
Tel.: (909) 829-7100
Web Site: http://www.tossware.com
Year Founded: 2014
Sales Range: $1-9.9 Million
Emp.: 15
Drink Product Mfr
N.A.I.C.S.: 312111
Benson Liu *(CEO & Partner)*

BEGINAGAIN, INC.

PO Box 2265, Fort Collins, CO 80524
Tel.: (970) 372-0522
Web Site: http://www.beginagaintoys.com
Toy & Game Mfr
N.A.I.C.S.: 339930
David Bowen *(Co-Founder & Designer)*
Chris Clemmer *(Co-Founder & Designer-Industrial)*
Katie Dugan *(VP-Sls)*

BEGLEY COMPANY

1850 Bryant Rd Ste 400, Lexington, KY 40555-5910
Tel.: (859) 422-4800   KY
Web Site: https://www.concordcustomcleaners.com
Year Founded: 1994
Sales Range: $75-99.9 Million
Emp.: 1,100
Drycleaning Plants, Except Rugs
N.A.I.C.S.: 812320
John M. Schacht *(Pres)*

Subsidiaries:

B&B Equipment & Supply Company Inc.   (1)
183 A Brock McVey Dr, Lexington, KY 40509
Tel.: (859) 422-4800
Rev.: $2,000,000
Emp.: 25
Service Establishment Equipment
N.A.I.C.S.: 423850

BEGLEY LUMBER COMPANY INC.

24 Sealey Rd, London, KY 40743-2800
Tel.: (606) 877-1228   KY
Web Site: http://www.begleylumber.com
Year Founded: 1973
Sales Range: $10-24.9 Million
Emp.: 150
Sawmill & Planting Mill Services
N.A.I.C.S.: 321113
George Begley *(Pres)*

BEHAN COMMUNICATIONS, INC.

86 Glen St, Glens Falls, NY 12801
Tel.: (518) 792-3856
Web Site: https://www.behancommunications.com
Year Founded: 1988
Sales Range: $1-9.9 Million
Emp.: 15
Public Relations Agency
N.A.I.C.S.: 541820
Troy P. Burns *(Chief Creative Officer, Partner & VP)*
Joan F. Gerhardt *(VP)*
Mik Bondy *(Media Buyer)*
Kathy Messina *(Controller)*
Bill Richmond *(VP)*
Marilyn Reisch *(Project Mgr & Media Buyer)*
Andrea MacDougall *(Controller)*
Colleen Potter *(Office Mgr)*
Bill Callen *(VP)*
Mark L. Behan *(Pres)*
John H. Brodt Jr. *(Partner & VP)*

BEHAVIORAL CONSULTING OF TAMPA BAY INC.

6951 Pistol Range Rd Ste 101, Tampa, FL 33635
Tel.: (813) 814-2000
Web Site: https://www.bcotb.com
Sales Range: $1-9.9 Million
Emp.: 48
Behavioral Services
N.A.I.C.S.: 621112
Kelley Prince *(Founder & Pres)*
Catherine Ganem *(Dir-Program)*
Fred Ullrich *(Office Mgr)*

BEHAVIORAL HEALTH GROUP

5001 Spring Vly Rd Ste 600 E, Dallas, TX 75244
Tel.: (214) 365-6100
Web Site: http://www.bhgrecovery.com
Year Founded: 2006
Sales Range: $25-49.9 Million
Emp.: 240
Opiate Addiction Treatment Services
N.A.I.C.S.: 623220
Kelly J. Clark *(Chief Medical Officer)*
Jean Williams *(Dir-Clinical)*
Mary Pat Angelini *(CEO)*
Grace Hanlon *(Chm)*

BEHAVIORAL HEALTH SERVICES NORTH, INC.

22 US Oval Ste 218, Plattsburgh, NY 12903
Tel.: (518) 563-8206   NY

Web Site: https://www.bhsn.org
Year Founded: 1874
Sales Range: $10-24.9 Million
Behavioral Healthcare Services
N.A.I.C.S.: 621420
Mark Lukens (CEO)
Jerome McGovern (Vice Chm)
Deanne Price (Sec)
Casey Gould (Chm)
Magen Renadette (Treas)

BEHAVIORAL HEALTHCARE CORPORATION
822 Marietta Ave, Lancaster, PA 17603
Tel.: (717) 399-8288
Web Site: http://www.bhc-pa.com
Year Founded: 2002
Mental Health Care Services
N.A.I.C.S.: 621420
Eric Eshleman (CEO)
Charlene Eshleman (CFO)
Catherine Minnerly (Dir-HR)
Tom Kennedy (Dir-Admin Ops)
Marge Moriarty (Dir-Outpatient Clinic)

BEHAVIORAL HEALTHCARE PARTNERS OF CENTRAL OHIO, INC.
PO Box 4670, Newark, OH 43058-4670
Tel.: (740) 522-8477   OH
Web Site: http://www.bhcpartners.org
Year Founded: 1955
Sales Range: $10-24.9 Million
Emp.: 219
Behavioral Healthcare Services
N.A.I.C.S.: 623220

BEHIND THE SCENES MARKETING
90 Windsor Dr, Pine Brook, NJ 07058
Tel.: (973) 276-9472
Web Site:
    http://www.behindthescenes.com
Year Founded: 2003
Sales Range: Less than $1 Million
Emp.: 5
Advertising Agencies, Advertising Specialties
N.A.I.C.S.: 541810
Michael Adams (Owner & Founder)
Tina Wang (VP)

BEHIND THE SCENES, INC
9888 Waples St, San Diego, CA 92121
Tel.: (858) 638-1400   CA
Web Site: https://www.btscenes.com
Year Founded: 1999
Sales Range: $1-9.9 Million
Emp.: 210
Eating Place
N.A.I.C.S.: 722320
John D. Crisafulli (Pres)
Kelly Fagan McElroy (Mgr-Special Projects)

BEHLEN MFG. CO.
4025 E 23rd St, Columbus, NE 68601-8501
Tel.: (402) 564-3111   NE
Web Site: http://www.behlenmfg.com
Year Founded: 1936
Sales Range: $350-399.9 Million
Emp.: 800
Industrial Machinery & Equipment Whslr
N.A.I.C.S.: 423830
Richard F. Casey (Sr VP-Fin)
Steve Becker (Gen Mgr)
Phil Raimondo (Chm & CEO)
Tony Raimondo (Vice Chm)

Subsidiaries:

BMC Transportation Co.   (1)

4025 E 23rd St, Columbus, NE 68601
Web Site: http://www.bmctrans.com
Transportation & Logistics Services
N.A.I.C.S.: 488490

Behlen Custom Fabrication   (1)
4025 E 23rd St, Columbus, NE 68602
Tel.: (402) 564-3111
Web Site: http://www.behlencf.com
Steel Fabrication Services
N.A.I.C.S.: 331110
Phil Raimondo (CEO)

Behlen Mfg. Co. - Behlen Building Systems Unit   (1)
4025 E 23rd St, Columbus, NE 68601
Tel.: (402) 564-3111
Web Site:
    http://www.behlenbuildingsystems.com
Pre-engineered Metal Building & Component Mfr
N.A.I.C.S.: 332311

Behlen Mfg. Co. - Behlen Country Division   (1)
PO Box 569, Columbus, NE 68602-0569
Web Site: http://www.behlencountry.com
Farm & Ranch Equipment Mfr
N.A.I.C.S.: 333111
Mark Prososki (Mgr-Mfg)
Nathan Blaser (Coord-Shipping)
Phil Raimondo (Pres & CEO)

Behlen Mfg. Co. - East Coast Distribution Center   (1)
101 Rosser-Wyatt Rd, Huntingdon, TN 38344-0466
Tel.: (800) 447-2751
Steel Fabrication Services
N.A.I.C.S.: 331110

Behlen Mfg. Co. - WEST COAST PLANT   (1)
4000 23rd St, Baker City, OR 97814
Tel.: (541) 523-8661
Web Site: http://www.behlenmfg.com
Steel Fabrication Services
N.A.I.C.S.: 331110

Distefano Technology & Manufacturing   (1)
3838 S 108th St, Omaha, NE 68144
Tel.: (402) 451-1796
Industrial Machinery & Equipment Whslr
N.A.I.C.S.: 423830
Brian Turner (Gen Mgr)

Trident Building Systems, Inc.   (1)
2812 Tallevast Rd, Sarasota, FL 34243-3914
Tel.: (941) 755-7073
Web Site:
    http://www.tridentbuildingsystems.com
Prefabricated Metal Building & Component Mfr
N.A.I.C.S.: 332311
Carl S. Petrat (Pres)

BEHNKE NURSERIES CO.
11300 Baltimore Ave, Beltsville, MD 20705
Tel.: (301) 937-1100   MD
Web Site: http://www.behnkes.com
Year Founded: 1930
Sales Range: $10-24.9 Million
Emp.: 30
Operator of Full-Service Garden Centers
N.A.I.C.S.: 444240
Alfred Millard (Pres)

BEHRINGER HARVARD HOLDINGS, LLC
14675 Dallas Pkwy Ste 600, Dallas, TX 75254
Tel.: (214) 655-1600
Web Site:
    http://www.behringerinvestments.com
Sales Range: $25-49.9 Million
Emp.: 200
Real Estate Investment Trust Investment Advisory & Portfolio Management Services
N.A.I.C.S.: 551112

M. Jason Mattox (COO)
Michael D. Cohen (Pres & CEO)
Bradley D. Behringer (Exec VP)
Stanton P. Eigenbrodt (Chief Legal Officer)
David Aisner (Chief Investment Officer)
Scott W. Fordham (Chief Acctg Officer & Sr VP)

Subsidiaries:

Behringer Securities LP   (1)
15601 Dallas Pkwy Ste 600, Addison, TX 75001
Tel.: (214) 655-1600
Web Site:
    http://www.behringerinvestments.com
Emp.: 150
Securities Brokerage
N.A.I.C.S.: 523150
Karen Mitchell (Mgr-HR)

BEHRMAN BROTHERS MANAGEMENT CORP.
126 E 56th St 27th Fl, New York, NY 10022
Tel.: (212) 980-6500   DE
Web Site:
    http://www.behrmancap.com
Year Founded: 1991
Privatez Equity Firm
N.A.I.C.S.: 523999
Gary K. Dieber (CFO & Chief Compliance Officer-Behrman Capital)
William M. Matthes (Mng Partner)
Jeffrey S. Wu (Partner)
Simon P. Lonergan (Mng Partner)
Mark P. Visser (Partner)
Robert E. Flaherty (Operating Partner)
Tammy Orellana (Mgr-Fin & Admin)
Michael Rapport (Principal)
Vincent M. Buffa (Operating Partner)
Calvert Thomas (VP)
Grant Behrman (Mng Partner)

Subsidiaries:

Atherotech, Inc.   (1)
201 London Pkwy, Birmingham, AL 35211
Tel.: (205) 871-8344
Web Site: http://www.atherotech.com
Medical Laboratory & Testing
N.A.I.C.S.: 621511
Robert Shufflebarger (Co-COO)
Michael E. Cobble (Chief Medical Officer)
James McClintic (Pres & CEO)
Michael Tarwater (CTO)
Gerard Abate (Chief Clinical Officer)
Robert Flaherty (Chm)
Les Hric (Chief Compliance Officer)
Kris Kulkarni (VP-Res & Dev)

George Industries LLC   (1)
1 S Page Ave, Endicott, NY 13760
Tel.: (607) 748-3371
Web Site: http://www.georgeindustries.com
Metal Product Machining, Fabrication & Brazing Services
N.A.I.C.S.: 332999
Matt Greene (Gen Mgr-Endicott)
Chris Schick (Gen Mgr-Wheeling)
Jan Mathiesen (CEO)

Subsidiary (Domestic):

Alexander Machine & Tool Company, Inc.   (2)
49R High St, Woburn, MA 01801
Tel.: (781) 935-0010
Web Site:
    http://www.alexandermachine.com
Special Die & Tool, Die Set, Jig & Fixture Mfr
N.A.I.C.S.: 333514
Tammy Soper (Pres)

Numerical Precision, Inc.   (2)
2200 Foster Ave, Wheeling, IL 60090-6509
Tel.: (847) 394-3610
Web Site:
    http://www.numericalprecision.com
All Other Miscellaneous Fabricated Metal Product Mfr

N.A.I.C.S.: 332999

Hillside Plastics Inc.   (1)
262 Millers Falls Rd, Turners Falls, MA 01376
Tel.: (413) 863-2222
Web Site: http://www.hillsideplastics.com
Plastics Bottle Mfr
N.A.I.C.S.: 326160
Jim Sicard (Mgr-Warehouse & Distr)

Inter-Med, Inc.   (1)
2200 Northwestern Ave, Racine, WI 53404
Tel.: (262) 636-9755
Web Site: http://www.vista-dental.com
Sales Range: $1-9.9 Million
Emp.: 35
Dental Equipment & Supplies Mfr
N.A.I.C.S.: 339114
Gary Pond (Pres & CEO)

Micross Components, Inc.   (1)
7725 N Orange Blossom Trl, Orlando, FL 32810-2696
Tel.: (407) 298-7100
Web Site: http://www.micross.com
Mfr & Distr of Chip Components for Microelectronics Industry
N.A.I.C.S.: 334419
Richard Gibbs (Mng Dir & Pres-France)
Valerie Thomas (Mgr-Mktg)
Christine Ortiz (VP-HR)
Vincent Buffa (Chm & CEO)

Subsidiary (Domestic):

Chip Supply Inc.   (2)
7725 N Orange Blossom Trl, Orlando, FL 32810-2696
Tel.: (407) 298-7100
Web Site: http://www.chipsupply.com
Sales Range: $350-399.9 Million
Emp.: 1,300
Processor & Packager of Semiconductor Chips
N.A.I.C.S.: 334413
Scott Smith (Dir-Sls)
F. Michael Pisch (Sec)
Brad Buser (VP & Treas)

Unit (Domestic):

Micross Components, Inc. - Electro-Mechanical Services, Hatfield   (2)
2294 N Penn Rd, Hatfield, PA 19440
Tel.: (215) 997-3200
Web Site: http://www.micros.com
Sales Range: $1-9.9 Million
Emp.: 60
Electro-Mechanical Services
N.A.I.C.S.: 334419
Steve Bahmueller (Controller)

Subsidiary (Domestic):

Micross Manchester   (2)
1050 Perimeter Rd, Manchester, NH 03103
Tel.: (603) 893-9900
Web Site: http://www.corfin.com
Semiconductor & Related Device Mfr
N.A.I.C.S.: 334413
Christine Seuss (Supvr-Sls Support)

Semi Dice, LLC   (2)
10961 Bloomfield St PO Box 3002, Los Alamitos, CA 90720
Tel.: (562) 594-4631
Web Site: http://www.semidice.com
Wafer & Die Products Mfr
N.A.I.C.S.: 541990
Dan Cormack (CEO)
Laura Margeson (VP & Gen Mgr)
Jerry Flynt (Founder & Pres)

The Emmes Company, LLC   (1)
401 N Washington St Ste 700, Rockville, MD 20850
Tel.: (301) 251-1161
Web Site: http://www.emmes.com
Emp.: 336
Professional Training Services
N.A.I.C.S.: 611430
Brian P. Hochheimer (CFO)

Tresys Technology LLC   (1)
8840 Stanford Blvd Ste 2100, Columbia, MD 21045
Tel.: (410) 290-1411
Web Site: http://www.tresys.com
Emp.: 45
Software Development Services

Behrman Brothers Management Corp.—(Continued)

N.A.I.C.S.: 541511
Peter Pace *(Chm)*
Robert Stalick *(CEO)*
Anthony Corbi *(CFO)*
Art Wilson *(VP-Tech)*
Ken Walker *(VP-Products)*
Jackson Kemper *(Sr VP-Bus Dev & Sls)*
Gregg Carlen *(VP-Svcs)*
Charlie Zaloom *(VP-Comml)*

BEI CONSTRUCTION, INC.
1829 Clement Ave, Alameda, CA 94501
Tel.: (510) 521-3792   CA
Web Site:
    http://www.beiconstruction.com
Year Founded: 1988
Sales Range: $1-9.9 Million
Emp.: 25
Electrical Contractor
N.A.I.C.S.: 237130
David Rantz *(VP)*

BEIER RADIO LLC
1150 N Causeway Blvd, Mandeville, LA 70471
Tel.: (504) 341-0123
Web Site: http://www.beierradio.com
Year Founded: 1945
Marine Electronics Mfr
N.A.I.C.S.: 811210
Karl A. Beier *(Pres)*
Ben Todd *(COO & VP)*
David Lirette *(VP-Mfg)*
Laura Weinstein *(CFO)*

Subsidiaries:

South Coast Electric Systems, LLC   (1)
13061 Rd D, Bay Saint Louis, MS 39520
Tel.: (228) 533-0002
Emp.: 100
Commercial & Machinery Equipment Repair & Maintenance Services
N.A.I.C.S.: 811310
Ralph Lindfors *(VP)*

BEISSER LUMBER COMPANY
3705 SE Beisser Dr, Grimes, IA 50111
Tel.: (515) 986-4422   IA
Web Site:
    https://www.beisserlumber.com
Year Founded: 1953
Sales Range: $10-24.9 Million
Emp.: 130
Lumber & Other Building Materials
N.A.I.C.S.: 423310
Kim David Beisser *(Pres)*

BEITERS INC.
560 Montgomery Pike, South Williamsport, PA 17702
Tel.: (570) 326-2073   PA
Web Site: https://www.beiters.com
Year Founded: 1966
Sales Range: $10-24.9 Million
Emp.: 140
Home Products & Services
N.A.I.C.S.: 449110
Steve Sholder *(VP)*

BEITLER & ASSOCIATES INC.
825 S Barrington Ave, Los Angeles, CA 90049
Tel.: (310) 820-2955
Web Site: http://www.beitler.com
Sales Range: $10-24.9 Million
Emp.: 55
Real Estate Broker
N.A.I.C.S.: 531210
Marjan Khonsari *(Art Dir)*

BEITZEL CORPORATION
12072 Bittinger Rd, Grantsville, MD 21536

Tel.: (301) 245-4107
Web Site:
    https://www.beitzelcorp.com
Year Founded: 1978
Sales Range: $10-24.9 Million
Emp.: 180
Fabricated Plate Work (Boiler Shop)
N.A.I.C.S.: 236220
Olen J. Beitzel *(Pres)*
Jim Fratz *(Mgr-Fin)*
Dave Callis *(Project Mgr)*
Michael Shamblen *(Dir-HR)*
Todd Schneider *(Dir-Safety)*
Ray Guthriee *(Mgr-Tool)*
Ray Guthre *(Mgr-Tools)*

BEJAC CORPORATION
569 S Van Buren St, Placentia, CA 92870
Tel.: (714) 528-6224
Web Site: https://www.bejac.com
Sales Range: $10-24.9 Million
Emp.: 66
Industrial Machinery & Equipment
N.A.I.C.S.: 423830
Ron Barlet *(Pres)*

BEKINS MOVING & STORAGE CO.
6501 216th St SW, Mountlake Terrace, WA 98043
Tel.: (425) 775-8950
Web Site:
    http://www.bekinsmovingco.com
Year Founded: 1903
Relocation & Storage Services
N.A.I.C.S.: 484210
Jillian Ihly *(Exec VP)*
Steve Suhre *(VP-Ops)*
Rob Schmidt *(VP-Sls & Mktg)*

Subsidiaries:

Clancy's Transfer & Storage, Inc. (1)
841 N 6th Ave, Walla Walla, WA 99362
Tel.: (509) 529-2022
Web Site: http://www.clancysmoving.com
Relocation & Storage Services
N.A.I.C.S.: 484210
Randy Kaping *(Owner)*

BEKINS MOVING SOLUTIONS, INC.
2025 Gillespie Way, San Diego, CA 92121
Tel.: (619) 873-1040
Web Site:
    http://www.mybekinsa1.com
Rev.: $20,000,000
Emp.: 25
Moving & Storage Services
N.A.I.C.S.: 484110
Scott Harvey *(Mgr)*
Tom Smith *(Gen Mgr)*

BEL USA LLC
12610 NW 115th Ave, Medley, FL 33178
Tel.: (305) 593-0911   DE
Web Site:
    http://www.discountpromos.com
Year Founded: 2012
Sales Range: $50-74.9 Million
Emp.: 540
Promotional Items Supplier & Distr
N.A.I.C.S.: 541890
Amin R. Ramjee *(Pres)*

Subsidiaries:

Branders.com Inc. (1)
171 Main St Ste 277, Los Altos, CA 94022
Tel.: (650) 292-2752
Web Site: http://www.branders.com
Sales Range: $1-9.9 Million
Online Retailer of Promotional Products
N.A.I.C.S.: 455219
David Hey *(Sr Acct Exec)*
Stephanie Leiva *(Mgr-Acct)*

DiscountMugs.com (1)
12610 NW 115th Ave, Medley, FL 33178   (100%)
Tel.: (305) 406-9507
Web Site: http://www.discountmugs.com
Sales Range: $75-99.9 Million
Offers A Variety of Promotional Items With or Without Personalization
N.A.I.C.S.: 541890
Julie O'Neal *(Mgr-Mktg)*

BEL-AQUA POOL SUPPLY INC.
20 Commerce Dr, New Rochelle, NY 10801
Tel.: (914) 235-2200
Web Site: https://www.bel-aqua.com
Rev.: $17,454,071
Emp.: 34
Swimming Pools, Equipment & Supplies
N.A.I.C.S.: 459999
Shanna Leuchter *(Mgr-Mktg)*

BELAIR BUILDERS INC.
2200 Old Hwy 8 NW, Saint Paul, MN 55112
Tel.: (651) 786-1300
Web Site:
    http://www.belairexcavating.com
Sales Range: $25-49.9 Million
Emp.: 75
Industrial Building Construction Services
N.A.I.C.S.: 236220
Mark D. Murlowski *(CEO)*
Tracey Dabrowski *(CFO)*
David Smart *(Project Mgr)*

BELAIR INSTRUMENT COMPANY LLC
36 Commerce St, Springfield, NJ 07081
Tel.: (973) 912-8900   NJ
Year Founded: 1970
Sales Range: $1-9.9 Million
Emp.: 20
Repair Services, Nec, Nsk
N.A.I.C.S.: 811210
David Patterson *(Pres)*

Subsidiaries:

Marston Technical Services (1)
11576 Goldcoast Dr, Cincinnati, OH 45249
Tel.: (513) 563-8100
Web Site: http://www.marstontechnical.com
Sales Range: $1-9.9 Million
Emp.: 11
Electronic & Precision Equipment Repair & Maintenance
N.A.I.C.S.: 811210
Mike McDonald *(Mgr-Svc)*
Steve Giuliani *(Mgr-Sls & Mktg)*

BELAIR ROAD SUPPLY COMPANY INC.
7750 Pulaski Hwy, Baltimore, MD 21237
Tel.: (410) 687-4200   MD
Web Site:
    https://www.belairroadsupply.com
Year Founded: 1923
Sales Range: $10-24.9 Million
Emp.: 50
Whslr of Lumber, Plywood & Millwork Products
N.A.I.C.S.: 423310
Jeff Wheeler *(VP)*
Thurston R. Adams Jr. *(Pres)*

BELAM INC.
63 Grand Ave Ste 230, River Edge, NJ 07661
Tel.: (201) 488-2500
Web Site: https://www.belam.com
Rev.: $16,683,625
Emp.: 8
Telephone Equipment

N.A.I.C.S.: 423690
Dmitry Krupnikov *(Pres)*

BELASCO PETROLEUM CO. INC.
PO Box 8, Cookstown, NJ 08511
Tel.: (609) 758-2800
Web Site: http://www.belascoil.com
Rev.: $15,508,800
Emp.: 13
Gasoline
N.A.I.C.S.: 424720

BELAY, INC.
885 Woodstock Rd Ste 430-365, Roswell, GA 30075-2274
Web Site:
    http://www.belaysolutions.com
Year Founded: 2010
Sales Range: $1-9.9 Million
Human Resource Consulting Services
N.A.I.C.S.: 541612
Tricia Sciortino *(CEO)*
Lisa Zeeveld *(CFO & COO)*
Shannon Miles *(Founder & Chm)*
Krisha Buehler *(VP-HR)*
Lisa Seal *(VP-Revenue)*

Subsidiaries:

Scale Finance LLC (1)
PO Box 110404, Durham, NC 27709
Tel.: (919) 484-8424
Web Site: http://www.scalefinance.com
Sales Range: $1-9.9 Million
Emp.: 25
Integrated Financial Solutions to Entrepreneurial Companies
N.A.I.C.S.: 525990
Gary Hayes *(Co-Founder, COO & Mng Dir)*
Tom Livingston *(CFO & Partner)*
David V. Gilroy *(Co-Founder & Mng Dir)*

BELCAM INC.
27 Montgomery St, Rouses Point, NY 12979
Tel.: (518) 297-3366
Web Site:
    https://www.belcamshop.com
Sales Range: $25-49.9 Million
Emp.: 200
Toilet Preparations Mfr & Whslr
N.A.I.C.S.: 325620
Michael Bellm *(Pres)*
Huguette Deschenes *(Brand Mgr)*
Robert Barry *(Engr-Dev)*

Subsidiaries:

Delagar Division (1)
27 Montgomery St, Rouses Point, NY 12979
Tel.: (518) 297-3366
Web Site: http://www.delagar.com
Sales Range: $10-24.9 Million
Emp.: 50
Fragrances, Toiletry & Body Care Products Mfr & Whslr
N.A.I.C.S.: 325620
John Knot *(Pres)*

Denco Division (1)
27 Montgomery St, Rouses Point, NY 12979
Tel.: (518) 297-3366
Web Site: http://www.belcamshop.com
Sales Range: $25-49.9 Million
Emp.: 80
Personal Care Products Supplier
N.A.I.C.S.: 456199
Gail Hekkema *(VP-Sls)*

BELCARO GROUP, INC.
5575 Dtc Pkwy Ste 300, Greenwood Village, CO 80111
Tel.: (303) 843-0302
Web Site:
    http://www.shopathome.com
Year Founded: 1986
Sales Range: $75-99.9 Million
Emp.: 100

Online & Printable Grocery, Restaurant & Retail Coupons
N.A.I.C.S.: 513199
Claudia Braunstein (Co-Founder)
Marc Braunstein (Co-Founder)

BELCHER OIL CO. INC.
109 Old Concord Rd, Murray, KY 42071
Tel.: (270) 753-0212
Web Site:
http://www.berkshirestore.com
Sales Range: $10-24.9 Million
Emp.: 14
Petroleum Bulk Stations
N.A.I.C.S.: 424710
J. Bradford Belcher (Pres)

BELCHER PHARMACEUTI-CALS, LLC
6911 Bryan Dairy Rd, Largo, FL 33777
Tel.: (727) 471-0850
Web Site:
http://www.geopharmainc.com
Sales Range: $150-199.9 Million
Pharmaceuticals Product Mfr
N.A.I.C.S.: 325412
Prabhu Peesapati (Mgr-Calibrations)
Mandeep Taneja (Gen Counsel & VP)

BELCO COMMUNITY CREDIT UNION
449 Eisenhower Blvd, Harrisburg, PA 17111
Tel.: (717) 232-3526   PA
Web Site: http://www.belco.org
Year Founded: 1939
Rev.: $24,327,569
Assets: $613,628,375
Liabilities: $34,329,186
Net Worth: $579,299,189
Earnings: $4,539,353
Emp.: 182
Fiscal Year-end: 12/31/18
Credit Union
N.A.I.C.S.: 522130
Jason Allen (Sr VP-Lending)
Robert Hoke (VP-Corp Support)
Amey Sgrignoli (Pres & CEO)
Stephanie F. Miller (Treas)
Beverly A. Lilley (Sec)
Richard Myxter (Vice Chm)
Samuel Glesner (Sr VP-Corp Support)
Rebeka Landon (VP-Fin)
Marti Speck (VP-HR & Trng)
Michael Wolfe (VP-Lending)
Paul Perini III (Sr VP-Retail)

BELCO INDUSTRIES INC.
9138 W Belding Rd, Belding, MI 48809
Tel.: (616) 794-0410
Web Site: https://www.belcoind.com
Sales Range: $10-24.9 Million
Emp.: 60
Paint Baking & Drying Ovens
N.A.I.C.S.: 333994
Thomas F. Kohn (CEO)
Mike T. Kohn (Pres)
Jim Holderman (Plant Mgr)

BELCO INDUSTRIES, INC.
1001 31st St, Kenosha, WI 53140-1926
Tel.: (262) 654-3516
Web Site:
https://www.famcomachine.com
Sales Range: $1-9.9 Million
Emp.: 30
Mfr of Metal Fabricating Equipment
N.A.I.C.S.: 333517
Michael T. Kohn (Pres)

Subsidiaries:
Belco Industries, Inc. - Famco Machine Division   (1)
1001 31st St, Kenosha, WI 53140-1926
Tel.: (262) 654-3516
Web Site: http://www.famcomachine.com
Sales Range: $1-9.9 Million
Emp.: 28
Air, Arbor, Foot Presses; Power Squaring Shears; Foot Shears; Engraving Machines
N.A.I.C.S.: 333517
William Blasi (Pres)

Subsidiary (Domestic):
Milwaukee Slide and Spindle   (2)
1001 31st St, Kenosha, WI 53140   (100%)
Tel.: (262) 654-3516
Web Site: http://www.famcomachine.com
Mfr of Precision Slides for the Machine Tool Industry
N.A.I.C.S.: 333517
William Blasi (Pres)

BELCO PACKAGING SYS-TEMS INC.
910 S Mountain Ave, Monrovia, CA 91016
Tel.: (626) 357-9566
Web Site:
https://www.belcopackaging.com
Sales Range: $10-24.9 Million
Emp.: 25
Plastics Materials, Nec
N.A.I.C.S.: 424610
A. Michael Misik (Pres)
Tom Misik (VP-Sls)
James Howell (Engr-Design)
Denice Myers (Mgr-Ops)

BELCORP INC.
2100 Walnut St, Kansas City, MO 64108-1813
Tel.: (816) 474-3250
Web Site: http://www.belcorpinc.com
Year Founded: 1984
Sales Range: $25-49.9 Million
Emp.: 275
Provider of Building Installation Equipment
N.A.I.C.S.: 238290

Subsidiaries:
Belger Cartage Service, Inc.   (1)
2100 Walnut St, Kansas City, MO 64108-1813
Tel.: (816) 474-3250
Web Site: http://www.belger.net
Sales Range: $10-24.9 Million
Emp.: 20
Provider of Building Installation Equipment
N.A.I.C.S.: 238290
Clay Chenoweth (Mgr-Kansas City Reg)
Jessica Gochenour (Office Mgr)
Amy Barnhart (Office Mgr)
Evelyn Belger (Pres & CEO)
C. Richard Belger (Chm)

Belger Realty Co. Inc.   (1)
2100 Walnut St, Kansas City, MO 64108-1813
Tel.: (816) 474-3250
Web Site: http://www.belgerartscenter.org
Sales Range: $10-24.9 Million
Emp.: 1
Provider of Nonresidential Building Operator Services
N.A.I.C.S.: 531120

Belway Insurance Service, Inc.   (1)
2100 Walnut St, Kansas City, MO 64108-1885
Tel.: (816) 474-3250
Sales Range: $25-49.9 Million
Emp.: 1
Insurance Agents, Brokers & Services
N.A.I.C.S.: 524210
Richard Belger (Pres)

BELDEN BRICK & SUPPLY CO. INC.
620 Leonard St NW, Grand Rapids, MI 49504
Tel.: (616) 459-8367   MI
Web Site:
https://www.beldenbricksupply.com
Year Founded: 1885
Sales Range: $10-24.9 Million
Emp.: 20
Supplier of Bricks, Fireplaces & Wood Stoves
N.A.I.C.S.: 444180
Patricia Conkright (Controller)
Robert F. Belden (Pres)

BELDEN'S SUPER MARKET INC.
99 Bracewood Sq, Houston, TX 77096
Tel.: (713) 723-5670
Rev.: $10,700,000
Emp.: 3
Supermarket
N.A.I.C.S.: 445110
Richard A. Belden (Pres)

BELDON ENTERPRISES, INC.
5039 West Ave, San Antonio, TX 78213-2711
Tel.: (210) 341-3100
Web Site: https://www.beldon.com
Year Founded: 1985
Sales Range: $75-99.9 Million
Emp.: 595
Provider of Roofing, Siding & Sheetmetal Work
N.A.I.C.S.: 238160
Bea Gunderman (VP-Customer Care)
Michael D. Beldon (Chm)
Pat Franks (COO-LeafGuard by Beldon & VP)
Chris C. Edelen (Pres-LeafGuard by Beldon)
Danny Mendez (VP-Production)

Subsidiaries:
Beldon Roofing Company   (1)
5039 W Ave, San Antonio, TX 78213-2711
Tel.: (210) 341-3100
Web Site: http://www.beldon.com
Sales Range: $25-49.9 Million
Emp.: 200
Provider of Roofing, Siding & Sheetmetal Work
N.A.I.C.S.: 238160
Brad Beldon (Pres & CEO)

BELFONTE DAIRY DISTRIBU-TION INC.
1625 Cleveland, Kansas City, MO 64127
Tel.: (816) 231-2000
Web Site: https://belfontedairy.com
Sales Range: $25-49.9 Million
Emp.: 50
Milk
N.A.I.C.S.: 424430
David Belfonte (Gen Mgr)

Subsidiaries:
Belfonte Ice Cream, Inc.   (1)
1625 Cleveland, Kansas City, MO 64127   (100%)
Tel.: (816) 483-9070
Web Site: http://www.belfonteicecream.com
Ice Cream & Ice Milk
N.A.I.C.S.: 311520
David Belfonte (Pres)

BELFOR USA GROUP, INC.
185 Oakland Ave Ste 300, Birmingham, MI 48009
Tel.: (248) 594-1144
Web Site: http://www.us.belfor.com
Sales Range: $700-749.9 Million
Emp.: 7,000
Storm, Fire & Water Damage Repair Services
N.A.I.C.S.: 238990

Bernd Elsner (Chm)

Subsidiaries:
Belfor (Canada) Inc.   (1)
7972 Enterprise Street, Vancouver, V5A 1V7, BC, Canada
Tel.: (604) 432-1123
Web Site: http://www.ca.belfor.com
Sales Range: $10-24.9 Million
Emp.: 120
Storm, Fire & Water Damage Repair Services
N.A.I.C.S.: 562910
Will Cook (Pres)

Branch (Domestic):
Belfor (Canada) Inc.   (2)
7677 D 132nd Street, Surrey, V3W 4M8, BC, Canada
Tel.: (604) 599-9980
Web Site: http://www.belforcanada.com
Emp.: 75
Special Trade Contractors Nec
N.A.I.C.S.: 238990

BELGARDE ENTERPRISES
7841 Wayzata Blvd Ste 111, Minneapolis, MN 55426-1452
Tel.: (952) 546-2000
Web Site: https://www.belgarde.com
Year Founded: 1965
Sales Range: $50-74.9 Million
Emp.: 100
Apartment Building Operation Services
N.A.I.C.S.: 531110
Charles Belgarde (Pres)

BELGIOIOSO CHEESE INC.
4200 Main St, Green Bay, WI 54311-9614
Tel.: (920) 863-2123
Web Site: http://www.belgioioso.com
Rev.: $22,600,000
Emp.: 60
Natural Cheese
N.A.I.C.S.: 311513
Errico Auricchio (Pres)
Mike Hermans (Supvr-Maintenance)
Scott Terrien (Supvr)
Gaetano Auricchio (Exec VP)

BELHEALTH INVESTMENT PARTNERS LLC
401 E Las Olas Blvd Ste 2360, Fort Lauderdale, FL 33301
Tel.: (954) 636-3685
Web Site: http://www.belhealth.com
Year Founded: 2011
Healthcare Private Equity Firm
N.A.I.C.S.: 523999
Harold S. Blue (Founder & Mng Partner)
Dennis Drislane (Mng Partner)
Joseph P. Wynne (CFO & Chief Admin Officer)
Inder Tallur (VP-Fin)
Scott Lee (Mng Partner)
Alan Kamienny (VP-Fin)

Subsidiaries:
Gemini Bio-Products, LLC   (1)
930 Riverside Pkwy 50, West Sacramento, CA 95605
Tel.: (800) 543-6464
Web Site: http://www.gembio.com
Sales Range: $1-9.9 Million
Biological Product Mfr
N.A.I.C.S.: 325414
Brian Parker (CEO)
Ed Mendham (CFO)
Robert Perry (Chief Scientific Officer)
Justin Henson (CMO & Chief Strategy Officer)
Jay Hertweck (Chief Comml Officer)
Patricia Cazcarro (VP-Ops)

Subsidiary (Domestic):
E.I. Spectra, LLC   (2)

BelHealth Investment Partners LLC—(Continued)

260 Northwood Way, Ketchum, ID 83340
Tel.: (855) 879-6694
Web Site: http://www.orflo.com
General Purpose Machinery Mfr
N.A.I.C.S.: 333998
Ted Ayliffe (Owner & CTO)

Geritrex Corp.   (1)
144 E Kingsbridge Rd, Mount Vernon, NY 10550
Tel.: (914) 668-4003
Sales Range: $1-9.9 Million
Emp.: 35
Topical Generic OTC Products & Pharmaceuticals Mfr & Distr
N.A.I.C.S.: 325412

Subsidiary (Domestic):

Unipack, Inc.   (2)
3253 Old Frankstown Rd B, Pittsburgh, PA 15239
Tel.: (724) 733-7381
Web Site: http://www.unipackinc.com
Pharmaceutical Preparation Mfr
N.A.I.C.S.: 325412

BELIN & ASSOCIATES, INC.

2438 Windmill Dr, Richmond, TX 77406
Tel.: (281) 633-8201
Web Site: http://www.bentwater.com
Year Founded: 1971
Sales Range: $50-74.9 Million
Emp.: 500
Provider of Subdivision & Developer Services
N.A.I.C.S.: 237210
Dawn Cleboski (Gen Mgr)

BELK FORD INC.

447 Hwy 6 W, Oxford, MS 38655-9068
Tel.: (662) 234-4661
Web Site: http://www.belkford.com
Sales Range: $10-24.9 Million
Emp.: 50
New Car Dealers
N.A.I.C.S.: 441110
Frank W. Belk III (Pres)
Rick Petillo (Mgr-Sls)

BELL & ASSOCIATES CONSTRUCTION, LP.

255 Wilson Pike Cir, Brentwood, TN 37027
Tel.: (615) 373-4343
Web Site: http://www.balp.com
Year Founded: 1970
Sales Range: $25-49.9 Million
Emp.: 425
Commercial & Institutional Building Construction Services
N.A.I.C.S.: 236220
Keith Pyle (Pres & Partner)
Darek Bell (Partner & VP)
Jody Evans (CFO & Partner)
Steve Hoover (Partner & VP-Transportation)
Chip Greene (Partner & Sr Project Mgr)
John David Goolesby (Sr Project Mgr)
Brad Bell (Partner)
Elvis Butler (Partner & VP-Corrections)
Kevin Keller (Partner & Sr Project Mgr)
Jeremy Michell (Partner & Project Mgr)
John Thayer (Partner & Sr Project Mgr)
Buffy Wilson (CFO)

BELL & BELL BUICK PONTIAC GMC ISUZU TRUCKS, INC.

2491 Hwy 9 E, Little River, SC 29566-6803
Tel.: (843) 399-8300
Sales Range: $10-24.9 Million
Emp.: 52
Car Whslr
N.A.I.C.S.: 441110
William C. Bell (Pres)
Tammy Floyd (Principal)

BELL & EVANS

154 W Main St, Fredericksburg, PA 17026
Tel.: (717) 865-1121
Web Site: https://www.bellandevans.com
Sales Range: $150-199.9 Million
Emp.: 1,050
Poulty Production, Processing & Retail
N.A.I.C.S.: 311615
Scott I. Sechler (Owner)

BELL AND MCCOY INC.

4613 Valwood Farmers Branch, Carrollton, TX 75244
Tel.: (469) 574-0300
Web Site: http://www.bellandmccoy.com
Rev.: $11,100,000
Emp.: 32
Electrical Supplies
N.A.I.C.S.: 334419
Jason Binyon (Principal)
Chris Coursey (Principal)
Nancy Brown (VP-Sls Ops)
Tina Howard (Mgr-Inside Sls)
David Stanton (Mgr-IT)

BELL AVIATION INC.

2404 Edmund Hwy, West Columbia, SC 29170-1930
Tel.: (803) 822-4114   SC
Web Site: http://www.bellaviation.com
Year Founded: 1990
Sales Range: $75-99.9 Million
Emp.: 20
Aircraft Sales
N.A.I.C.S.: 441227
Don J. Bell (Pres)
Angie Tindal (Dir-Adv)
Tonya Breedlove (Controller)
Cary Friedman (Mgr-Sls-Aircraft)

BELL BROTHERS OIL CO. INC.

118 S 50 W, Coalville, UT 84017
Tel.: (435) 336-4411
Sales Range: $10-24.9 Million
Emp.: 100
Owner & Operator of Convenience Stores & Gas Stations
N.A.I.C.S.: 445131
Bryce A. Bell (Pres)
David Bell (Treas & Sec)

BELL CONCRETE INCORPORATED

2130 W Williams Dr, Phoenix, AZ 85027
Tel.: (623) 434-5781   AZ
Year Founded: 1967
Sales Range: $10-24.9 Million
Emp.: 40
Concrete Work
N.A.I.C.S.: 238110
James Bell (Pres)

BELL CORP. OF ROCHESTER

1340 Lexington Ave, Rochester, NY 14606
Tel.: (585) 277-1000
Web Site: https://www.thebellcompany.com
Sales Range: $125-149.9 Million
Emp.: 100

Commercial & Office Building Contractors
N.A.I.C.S.: 236220
Joseph M. Bell (Chm)

Subsidiaries:

Bell BCI Company   (1)
1340 Lexington Ave, Rochester, NY 14606
Tel.: (585) 277-1000
Web Site: http://www.thebellcompany.com
Rev.: $79,143,000
Emp.: 30
Mechanical Contractor
N.A.I.C.S.: 238220
Steven Ruether (Pres & CEO)
Michael J. Benulis (Exec VP)
Andrew P. Carayiannis (Exec VP)

Bell Constructors Inc.   (1)
1340 Lexington Ave, Rochester, NY 14606
Tel.: (585) 277-1000
Rev.: $51,600,000
Commercial & Office Building Contractor
N.A.I.C.S.: 236220
Joseph Bell (CEO)

BELL ELECTRICAL SUPPLY INC.

316 Mathew St, Santa Clara, CA 95050
Tel.: (408) 727-2355
Web Site: https://www.bell-electrical.com
Sales Range: $10-24.9 Million
Emp.: 32
Whslr of Electrical Supplies
N.A.I.C.S.: 423610

BELL FLAVORS & FRAGRANCES, INC.

500 Academy Dr, Northbrook, IL 60062-2497
Tel.: (847) 291-8300   IL
Web Site: https://www.bellff.com
Year Founded: 1912
Sales Range: $10-24.9 Million
Emp.: 120
Flavors, Fragrances & Aromatics Mfr
N.A.I.C.S.: 325199
Karen Graves (Dir-Sensory)
Karen Clint (Mgr-Mktg)
Aaron Graham (VP-Technical Svcs-Flavors)
Simon Poppelsdorf (VP-Technical Svcs-Fragrances-Global)
Ron Stark (Pres & COO)
William M. Bell (Founder)

Subsidiaries:

Bell Flavors & Fragrances Duft und Aroma GmbH   (1)
Schimmelstr 1, Leipzig, 4205, Miltitz, Germany   (100%)
Tel.: (49) 34194510
Web Site: http://www.bell-europe.com
Mfr of Flavors & Fragrances
N.A.I.C.S.: 311930
Raymond Heinz (Pres)
Michael Heinz (VP)

Subsidiary (Non-US):

Bell Flavors & Fragrances Duft und Aroma GmbH   (2)
Kapka Ball Nael Oreitel, BG 1202, Sofia, Bulgaria
Tel.: (359) 29311992
Web Site: http://www.bell-europe.com
Sales of Flavors & Fragrances
N.A.I.C.S.: 424490

Bell Flavors & Fragrances Duft und Aroma GmbH   (2)
Skolkovskoye Shosse 23, 121353, Moscow, Russia
Tel.: (7) 4954475230
Web Site: http://www.bell-europe.com
Sales of Flavors & Fragrances
N.A.I.C.S.: 424490

Bell Flavors & Fragrances, Inc. - Fragrance Manufacturing Facility   (1)
12 Sprague Ave, Middletown, NY 10940

Tel.: (845) 342-1233
Food & Beverage Fragrance Mfr
N.A.I.C.S.: 311999

Bell Flavors and Fragrances do Brasil Industria   (1)
Rua Eli Walter Cesar 180, 06612-130, Jandira, Sao Paulo, Brazil
Tel.: (55) 11 4789 2314
Web Site: http://www.bellff.com
Emp.: 100
Food Flavor & Fragrance Mfr & Distr
N.A.I.C.S.: 311930
Paulo Darros (Gen Mgr)

BELL FOODS, LLC

134 Brookhollow Esplanade, Harahan, LA 70123
Tel.: (504) 837-2355
Web Site: http://www.bellfoods.net
Year Founded: 1985
Rev.: $5,700,000
Emp.: 20
Miscellaneous Food Mfr
N.A.I.C.S.: 311999
John Bellini III (Co-Owner & Dir-Ops)
Shane Nicaud Sr. (Co-Owner & Dir-Sls)

BELL FORK LIFT INC.

34660 Centaur Dr, Clinton Township, MI 48035
Tel.: (586) 415-5200
Web Site: https://www.bellforklift.com
Sales Range: $10-24.9 Million
Emp.: 110
Lift Trucks & Parts
N.A.I.C.S.: 423830
Wayne Bell (Founder, Pres & CEO)
Ziggy Quentin Zielinski (Mgr-Used Truck)

BELL FUELS INC.

5041 W 39th St, Cicero, IL 60804-4544
Tel.: (773) 286-0200   NV
Web Site: https://www.bellfuels.com
Year Founded: 1898
Sales Range: $25-49.9 Million
Emp.: 165
Petroleum Services
N.A.I.C.S.: 424720
Joe Jams (CEO)

BELL GAS, INC.

1811 SE Main St, Roswell, NM 88203-5919
Tel.: (575) 622-4800   NM
Web Site: http://www.cookietree.com
Year Founded: 1950
Sales Range: $25-49.9 Million
Emp.: 300
Petroleum Bulk Stations; Filling Stations; Automobile Tires & Tubes
N.A.I.C.S.: 457120

BELL LABORATORIES, INC.

3699 Kinsman Blvd, Madison, WI 53704
Tel.: (608) 241-0202
Web Site: http://www.belllabs.com
Year Founded: 1974
Emp.: 400
Pesticides Mfr & Distr
N.A.I.C.S.: 325320
Steve Levy (Pres & CEO)
Patrick Lynch (VP-Sls-US & Canada)
Dan Schlegel (Mgr-West)
Scott Smith (Mgr-Southwest)
Sara Knilans (Mgr-Midwest)
Rod Smith (Mgr-Florida)
Sheila Haddad (VP-East & Southeast)

BELL PARTNERS, INC.

300 N Greene St Ste 1000, Greensboro, NC 27401-2173
Tel.: (336) 232-1900

Web Site:
http://www.bellpartnersinc.com
Year Founded: 1976
Sales Range: $50-74.9 Million
Emp.: 1,500
Real Estate Investment & Management
N.A.I.C.S.: 531210
Steven D. Bell (Chm)
Jonathan D. Bell (Pres)
Lili F. Dunn (Chief Investment Officer)
John E. Tomlinson (CFO)
B. Kevin Thompson (Sr VP-Mktg)
Erin O. Ditto (Sr VP-Asset Mgmt)
E. Durant Bell (Principal & Exec VP-Ops)
Nickolay Bochilo (Exec VP)
Joseph F. Cannon (Sr VP-Investments)
Kristin L. Stanton (Sr VP-Ops)
Rebecca Shaffrey (Sr VP-Ops)
J. Zachary Maggart (Sr VP-Construction Svcs)
Anne Ossewaarde (Sr VP-Asset & Portfolio Mgmt)
Christie Jordan (VP-New Bus Dev)
Cindy Clare (COO)
Angela Gibbons (Sr VP-HR)
Laurann Stepp (Sr VP-IR)

BELL PROCESSING INCORPORATED
1326 Burkburnett Rd, Wichita Falls, TX 76306
Tel.: (940) 322-8621
Web Site:
http://www.bellprocessing.net
Sales Range: $10-24.9 Million
Emp.: 63
Iron & Steel (Ferrous) Products
N.A.I.C.S.: 423510
Lavonne Bell (Pres)

BELL PRODUCTS, INC.
722 Soscol Ave, Napa, CA 94559-3014
Tel.: (707) 255-1811
Web Site:
https://www.bellproducts.com
Sales Range: $10-24.9 Million
Emp.: 74
Plumbing Services
N.A.I.C.S.: 238220
Stan Foltz (Mgr-Sls-New Car)
Paul Irwin (Pres)

BELL PUMP SERVICE COMPANY
29 Lafayette St, Hartford, CT 06106
Tel.: (860) 246-6775
Web Site: http://www.bellsimons.com
Year Founded: 1940
Sales Range: $50-74.9 Million
Emp.: 400
Heating & Cooling Equipment
N.A.I.C.S.: 423720
Dennis C. Redden Jr. (Pres)

BELL RECRUITMENT ADVERTISING
606 Liberty Ave Ste 201, Pittsburgh, PA 15222-3412
Tel.: (412) 281-5180
Web Site: http://www.bellrecruit.com
Year Founded: 1977
Sales Range: $10-24.9 Million
Emp.: 5
Recruitment
N.A.I.C.S.: 541810
Nancy Cadwallader (VP)
Diana Hartman (Owner)

BELL SUPPLY CO.
7221 N Crescent Blvd, Pennsauken, NJ 08110-1597
Tel.: (856) 663-3900

Web Site:
https://www.bellsupplyinc.com
Year Founded: 1946
Sales Range: $10-24.9 Million
Emp.: 65
Drywall, Metal Stud & Commercial Insulation Supplier
N.A.I.C.S.: 423320
Robert Clark (Pres)
Mike Vittese (Gen Mgr)
Mike Battaglini (Mgr-Pur & Credit)
Wayne Sanders (Mgr-Sls)

BELL TRADING INCORPORATED
593 Jerusalem Ave, Uniondale, NY 11553
Tel.: (516) 483-3444
Year Founded: 2000
Sales Range: $25-49.9 Million
Emp.: 8
Whslr of Cigarettes
N.A.I.C.S.: 424940
Arlington Filler (Pres)
Jesal Shah (Comptroller)

BELL'S BREWERY, INC.
8938 Krum Ave, Galesburg, MI 49053
Tel.: (269) 382-2338   MI
Web Site: http://www.bellsbeer.com
Year Founded: 1983
Emp.: 550
Brewery
N.A.I.C.S.: 312120
Larry Bell (Co-Owner)
Matt Moberly (VP-Mktg & Sls)
Mike Fuerst (Supvr-Pkg)
Patrick Rolfe (Mgr-IT)
Laura Bell (Co-Owner)

BELL'S FOOD MARKET INC.
995 Hawthorne Ave, Athens, GA 30606-2175
Tel.: (706) 548-1307   GA
Year Founded: 1955
Sales Range: $10-24.9 Million
Emp.: 350
Grocery Stores
N.A.I.C.S.: 445110
Fred R. Bell (Pres)
Russ Bell (Dir-IT)
Ralph Costa (Dir-Ops)

Subsidiaries:

Bell's of Athens Inc.   (1)
995 Hawthorne Ave, Athens, GA 30606-2175
Tel.: (706) 548-1307
Sales Range: $10-24.9 Million
Emp.: 53
Grocery Stores
N.A.I.C.S.: 445110

BELL-ANDERSON INSURANCE, INC.
600 SW 39th St Ste 200, Renton, WA 98057
Tel.: (425) 291-5200
Web Site: https://www.bell-anderson.com
Rev.: $12,600,000
Emp.: 170
Insurance Agencies & Brokerages
N.A.I.C.S.: 524210
Jeffrey Vanbishler (Dir-IT)
Dwight Newman (Dir-Mktg)

BELL-CARTER FOODS, INC.
3742 Mt Diablo Blvd, Lafayette, CA 94549-3682
Tel.: (925) 284-5933   CA
Web Site: http://www.bellcarter.com
Year Founded: 1930
Sales Range: $100-124.9 Million
Emp.: 300
Olive Processor
N.A.I.C.S.: 311421

Ron Kerr (Dir-Ops)
Robert Rugeroni (Dir-IT)
Torrey Lowder (Mgr-Acctg)
Doug Reifsteck (Exec VP-Ops)
Tim T. Carter (CEO)
Paul Adcock (CFO)
Tom Rickard (VP-Sls)
James Thomas (VP-Strategy & Mktg)

Subsidiaries:

Bell-Carter Foods, Inc. - Corning Plant   (1)
1012 2nd St, Corning, CA 96021
Tel.: (888) 522-3557
Table Olive Mfr
N.A.I.C.S.: 311423

Bell-Carter Packaging   (1)
4207 Finch Rd, Modesto, CA 95357-4101
Tel.: (209) 549-5939
Distr of Bell-Carter Foods
N.A.I.C.S.: 311421

BELL-MARK CORPORATION
331 Changebridge Rd, Pine Brook, NJ 07058
Tel.: (973) 882-0202
Web Site: https://www.bell-mark.com
Sales Range: $75-99.9 Million
Emp.: 100
Coding, Printing & Marking Solutions for Packaging & Converting Industries Designer & Mfr
N.A.I.C.S.: 423830
John Marozzi (Pres)
James Pontrella (CFO)
Bob Batesko (Project Mgr)
Tom Pugh (VP)
Doug Duch (Mgr-Mktg)

BELLA FRESH, LLC
420 N 52nd Ave Ste #1, Phoenix, AZ 85043
Tel.: (602) 415-1882
Web Site: http://www.bellafresh.com
Year Founded: 1993
Fruit & Vegetable Distr
N.A.I.C.S.: 424480
Tim Unick (Exec VP)

BELLA GROUP
PO Box 190816, San Juan, PR 00919-0816
Tel.: (787) 620-7010   PR
Web Site:
http://www.bellainternational.com
Year Founded: 1963
Sales Range: $150-199.9 Million
Emp.: 500
Automobile Sales
N.A.I.C.S.: 423110
Jeronimo Esteve-Abril (Chm)
Carlos A. Lopez-Lay (Pres & CEO)
Maria I. Esteve (Owner)
Jose Carlos Villares (VP-Wholesale)
William Cuebas (VP-HR & Admin)

BELLA VISTA GROUP, INC.
6495 Transit Rd, Bowmansville, NY 14026-1049
Tel.: (716) 684-9000   NY
Web Site:
https://www.bellavistagroup.com
Year Founded: 1987
Sales Range: $10-24.9 Million
Emp.: 15
Subdividers & Developers
N.A.I.C.S.: 236115
Joseph A. Cipolla (Pres & Gen Mgr)
Pasquale F. Cipolla (CFO)
Paul Kinmartin (Controller)
Derek Malke (Mgr-Residential Property)

BELLA VISTA VILLAGE PROPERTY OWNERS ASSOCIATION

98 Clubhouse Dr, Bella Vista, AR 72715
Tel.: (479) 855-8000   AR
Web Site:
https://www.bellavistapoa.com
Year Founded: 1965
Sales Range: $10-24.9 Million
Emp.: 426
Property Owner Association
N.A.I.C.S.: 813990
Tom Judson (COO)

BELLACOR INC.
251 1st ave N Ste 600, Minneapolis, MN 55401
Tel.: (651) 294-2500   MN
Web Site: https://www.bellacor.com
Year Founded: 2000
Sales Range: $1-9.9 Million
Emp.: 50
Decorative Furniture Accessories Retailer
N.A.I.C.S.: 449129
Chris Fowler (Dir-Marketing)

BELLAIR EXPEDITING SERVICE INC.
3713 25th Ave, Schiller Park, IL 60176
Tel.: (847) 928-2500
Web Site: https://www.bellair.com
Year Founded: 1968
Sales Range: $10-24.9 Million
Emp.: 25
Freight Forwarding Services
N.A.I.C.S.: 488510
Edward M. Becht (Pres)
Joseph Becht (Co-Owner)
Richard Lindcren (Treas)

Subsidiaries:

Bellair Expediting Northwest, Inc. (1)
17800 Des Moines Memorial Dr Ste C, Burien, WA 98148
Tel.: (206) 241-7710
Web Site: http://www.bellair.com
Emp.: 10
Freight Forwarding
N.A.I.C.S.: 488510
Kelly Sutton (Mgr-Ops)

BELLAMY STRICKLAND CHEVROLET GMC AND PONTIAC INC.
145 Industrial Blvd, McDonough, GA 30253
Tel.: (770) 957-6631
Web Site:
http://www.bellamystrickland.com
Sales Range: $75-99.9 Million
Emp.: 200
Automobiles; New & Used
N.A.I.C.S.: 441110
William Strickland (Pres)
Bob Pickins (Gen Mgr)
Moushir Shata (Controller)

BELLAVIA CHEVROLET BUICK
Route 17 & Union Ave, East Rutherford, NJ 07073
Tel.: (201) 939-6800
Web Site:
https://www.bellaviachevy.com
Sales Range: $25-49.9 Million
Emp.: 35
Car Whslr
N.A.I.C.S.: 441110
Peter Baca (Mgr-Internet Sls)

BELLBOY CORPORATION
2220 Florida Ave S, Minneapolis, MN 55426-2839
Tel.: (952) 544-7791   MN
Web Site:
http://www.bellboycorp.com
Year Founded: 1973

519

Bellboy Corporation—(Continued)

Sales Range: $10-24.9 Million
Emp.: 100
Food, Beverage & Tobacco Distr
N.A.I.C.S.: 424420
Martin Bell *(Pres & Treas)*

Subsidiaries:

American Food Services International
Inc.   **(1)**
2220 Florida Ave S, Minneapolis, MN
55426-2839
Tel.: (952) 544-7791
Packaged Frozen Goods
N.A.I.C.S.: 445110

Bellboy Bar Supply   **(1)**
6005 Golden Vly Rd, Golden Valley, MN
55422-4439
Tel.: (952) 544-7791
Alcoholic Beverages Whslr
N.A.I.C.S.: 424820
Alan Tenenholtz *(Gen Mgr)*

Bellboy Cigars   **(1)**
2220 Florida Ave S, Minneapolis, MN 55422
Tel.: (800) 554-4700
Web Site: http://www.bellboycorp.com
Emp.: 50
Tobacco Product Distr
N.A.I.C.S.: 424940
Martin Bell *(Owner)*

BELLE TIRE DISTRIBUTOR INC.
3500 Enterprise Dr, Allen Park, MI
48101-3530
Tel.: (313) 271-9400   **MI**
Web Site: http://www.belletire.com
Year Founded: 1922
Sales Range: $200-249.9 Million
Emp.: 350
Whslr & Retailer of Tires & Accessories
N.A.I.C.S.: 441340
Robert Barnes *(CEO)*
Daniel T. Light *(Treas & Sec)*
Vivek Saran *(CMO)*
Don Barnes III *(Pres)*

BELLE TIRE DISTRIBUTORS, INC.
45875 Ford Rd, Canton, MI 48187
Tel.: (734) 844-6001
Web Site: http://www.belletire.com
Sales Range: $1-9.9 Million
Emp.: 13
Tire Dealers
N.A.I.C.S.: 441340
Don Barnes III *(Pres)*

Subsidiaries:

Tireman Auto Service Centers
Ltd.   **(1)**
1549 Campbell St, Toledo, OH 43607
Tel.: (419) 724-8473
Web Site: http://www.thetireman.com
Rev.: $12,488,065
Emp.: 230
Automotive Tires
N.A.I.C.S.: 441340
Randy Jones *(Pres)*

BELLEAIR DEVELOPMENT GROUP, INC.
6654 78th Ave N, Pinellas Park, FL
33781
Tel.: (727) 536-8686
Web Site:
   https://www.belleairgroup.com
Year Founded: 1997
Sales Range: $1-9.9 Million
Emp.: 6
Real Estate Development & Investment
N.A.I.C.S.: 237210
Carlos Yepes *(Pres & CEO)*
Christian Yepes *(VP-Dev & Acq)*

BELLEFAIRE JCB
1 Pollock Cir 22001 Fairmount Blvd,
Cleveland, OH 44118
Tel.: (216) 932-2800   **OH**
Web Site:
   https://www.bellefairejcb.org
Year Founded: 1868
Sales Range: $25-49.9 Million
Emp.: 733
Behavioral Healthcare Services
N.A.I.C.S.: 623220
Thomas Browne *(CFO)*
Jeffrey Lox *(COO)*

BELLETETE'S INC.
51 Peterborough St, Jaffrey, NH
03452-5865
Tel.: (603) 532-7716   **NH**
Web Site: https://www.belletetes.com
Year Founded: 1964
Sales Range: $25-49.9 Million
Emp.: 135
Producer of Lumber & Other Building
Materials
N.A.I.C.S.: 423310
Jack Belletete *(Pres)*
Mark Thompson *(Mgr)*
Andy Bergeron *(Mgr-IT)*
Susan Peterson *(Mgr-HR & Safety)*

BELLEVUE HOLDING COMPANY INC.
909 Delaware Ave, Wilmington, DE
19806
Tel.: (302) 655-1818
Web Site:
   https://bellevuerealtyco.com
Rev.: $21,640,352
Emp.: 15
Nonresidential Construction Services
N.A.I.C.S.: 236220
Carl Cantera *(Gen Mgr)*

BELLEVUE PHILHARMONIC ORCHESTRA INC.
10900 NE 4th St #2300, Bellevue,
WA 98004
Tel.: (425) 455-4171
Web Site: http://www.bellevuephil.org
Year Founded: 1967
Sales Range: $1-9.9 Million
Emp.: 65
Symphony Orchestra
N.A.I.C.S.: 711130
Kirsten G. James *(Principal)*
Fusao Kajima *(Dir-Music)*

BELLMAN OIL CO. INC.
550 E 2nd St, Bremen, IN 46506
Tel.: (574) 546-2342
Web Site: https://www.bellmanoil.com
Rev.: $20,000,000
Emp.: 20
Gasoline
N.A.I.C.S.: 424720
James W. Bellman *(Pres)*
Thomas Fair *(Acct Mgr)*

BELLWEST MANAGEMENT CORPORATION
902 Broadway 13th Fl, New York, NY
10010-6033
Tel.: (212) 243-9090   **NY**
Year Founded: 1973
Sales Range: $25-49.9 Million
Low Income Housing Services
N.A.I.C.S.: 624229
Adam Weinstein *(Pres & CEO)*
Brian Bricker *(Treas)*
Matthew Kelly *(VP)*
Michael Wadman *(VP)*
James Robert Pigott Jr. *(Sec & VP)*

BELLWETHER ASSET MANAGEMENT, INC.
200 Pacific Coast Hwy Ste 1400, El
Segundo, CA 90245
Tel.: (310) 525-3022
Web Site:
   http://www.bellwetheram.com
Year Founded: 2013
Sales Range: $10-24.9 Million
Emp.: 37
Real Estate Asset Management Services
N.A.I.C.S.: 531390
Dennis Grzeskowiak *(Principal)*
Joe Mossotti *(Principal)*
Michael Baracco *(Principal)*
Ben Easton *(VP)*
Patrick Foley *(VP)*

BELLWETHER COMMUNITY CREDIT UNION
425 Hooksett Rd, Manchester, NH
03104
Tel.: (603) 645-8181   **NH**
Web Site: http://www.bccu.org
Year Founded: 1921
Sales Range: $10-24.9 Million
Emp.: 95
Credit Union
N.A.I.C.S.: 522130
Nancy D. Nadeau *(Chief Admin Officer)*
Paul D. Roy *(CFO & Sr VP)*
John Gunther *(VP-Risk Mgmt)*
Nathan Saller *(Pres & CEO)*
William Zafirson *(Chief Lending Officer & Sr VP)*
Lori Holmes *(VP-Mktg)*
Jeff Benson *(COO)*
Tamatha Laramie *(Officer-Bus Dev)*
Sue Beaubien *(VP-Retail)*
Kelly Barry *(VP-HR)*

BELLWETHER FINANCIAL GROUP, INC.
201 Shipyard Way Ste D, Newport
Beach, CA 92663
Tel.: (949) 723-7788
Web Site:
   http://www.bellwetherfinancial.com
Year Founded: 1997
Capital Investments
N.A.I.C.S.: 523999
Joe Ueberroth *(Pres & CEO)*

Subsidiaries:

Bellingham Marine Industries
Inc.   **(1)**
1323 Lincoln St, Bellingham, WA 98229
Tel.: (360) 676-2800
Web Site: http://www.bellingham-marine.com
Sales Range: $75-99.9 Million
Emp.: 18
Design, Manufacture & Construction of Marinas & Related Products & Services
N.A.I.C.S.: 236210
J. Everett Babbitt *(Pres & CEO)*
Joseph Ueberroth *(Chm)*
Rob Rasmussen *(Gen Mgr-Northwest)*
Jim Engen *(Mgr-Project Dev-Northwest)*
Bruce Birtwistle *(Gen Mgr-New Zealand)*
John Spragg *(Pres-Australasia & Middle East)*
Crystal Greear *(CFO)*

Division (Domestic):

Florida Floats Inc.   **(2)**
1813 Dennis St, Jacksonville, FL 32204
Tel.: (904) 358-3362
Sales Range: $50-74.9 Million
Emp.: 50
Design, Manufacture & Construction of Marinas & Related Products & Services
N.A.I.C.S.: 236210
Steve Ryder *(Mgr-Project Dev)*

BELLWETHER HOUSING
1651 Bellevue Ave, Seattle, WA
98122

Tel.: (206) 623-0506
Web Site:
   http://www.bellwetherhousing.org
Year Founded: 1980
Sales Range: $10-24.9 Million
Affordable Housing Solutions
N.A.I.C.S.: 925110
Susan Boyd *(CEO)*
Sue Selman *(Dir-Property Mgmt)*
Carole Williams *(Dir-HR)*
Gabriel F. Grant *(Vice Chm)*
Harry Matsumoto *(Chm)*
Duane T. Leonard *(Treas)*
Deva Hasson *(Sec)*
Amy Besunder *(Dir-Fund Dev & Comm)*

BELMARK INC.
600 Heritage Rd, De Pere, WI 54115
Tel.: (920) 336-2848
Web Site: https://www.belmark.com
Rev.: $107,000,000
Emp.: 900
Commercial Printing
N.A.I.C.S.: 323111
Bruce A. Bell *(Founder, Chm & Pres)*

BELMAY, INC.
1 Odell Plz, Yonkers, NY 10701-6806
Tel.: (914) 376-1515   **NY**
Year Founded: 1935
Fragrance Mfr & Developer
N.A.I.C.S.: 325620
Joanne Obergfell *(Mgr-Creative Mktg)*

BELMONT GROUP INC.
2999 Turtle Creek Blvd, Dallas, TX
75219
Tel.: (214) 520-7171
Web Site: http://belmontgroup.com
Rev.: $10,000,000
Emp.: 31
Investment Counselors
N.A.I.C.S.: 523940
Harold W. Lehrmann *(Pres)*
Nita Melcher *(VP-Employee Benefits)*

Subsidiaries:

Vantage Management Co., Inc.   **(1)**
2999 Turtle Creek Blvd, Dallas, TX 75219
Tel.: (214) 521-4777
Rev.: $370,000
Emp.: 6
Commercial & Industrial Building Operation
N.A.I.C.S.: 531120
Pittman Haynore *(Pres)*

BELMONT HOUSING RESOURCES FOR WNY
1195 Main St, Buffalo, NY 14209-
2196
Tel.: (716) 884-7791   **NY**
Web Site:
   http://www.belmonthousingwny.org
Year Founded: 1977
Sales Range: $1-9.9 Million
Emp.: 119
Community Housing Services
N.A.I.C.S.: 624229
Aaron Hejmowski *(CFO)*
Pamela Berger *(VP-Property Ops)*
Michael Riegel *(Pres)*

BELMONT METALS, INC.
330 Belmont Ave, Brooklyn, NY
11207-4000
Tel.: (718) 342-4900   **NY**
Web Site:
   https://www.belmontmetals.com
Year Founded: 1896
Sales Range: $25-49.9 Million
Emp.: 75
Non-Ferrous Metals
N.A.I.C.S.: 331410

Theodore W. Henning *(Treas)*
Richard G. Henning *(Pres)*
Herbert Doyl *(Dir-Sls & Mktg)*
Robert V. Henning Jr. *(Sec)*

BELMONT SOFTWARE SERVICES

1305 Clinton St Ste 220, Nashville, TN 37203
Tel.: (615) 340-7744
Web Site: http://www.belmont-ss.com
Year Founded: 2006
Sales Range: $1-9.9 Million
Emp.: 25
Software Development Services
N.A.I.C.S.: 541511
Peter Hermann *(Co-Founder & Mng Partner)*
Wilkie McKelvey *(Co-Founder, Partner & Mgr-Automation Grp)*
Brian Baril *(Mgr-Automation Grp)*
Joe Doherty *(Dir-Bus Dev)*
William Thackrey *(Mgr-Advanced Solutions Grp)*

BELMONT TRADING COMPANY

9000 Corporate Grove Dr, Buffalo Grove, IL 60089
Tel.: (847) 412-9690
Web Site: http://www.belmont-trading.com
Sales Range: $10-24.9 Million
Emp.: 50
Sales of Used Computers
N.A.I.C.S.: 423690
Igor Boguslavsky *(Pres)*
Kerri Lauritsen *(Sr Acct Mgr-Sls)*

Subsidiaries:

Belmont Technology Remarketing **(1)**
Davy House Davy Ave The Quadrant, Birchwood Park, Warrington, WA36SW, Cheshire, United Kingdom
Tel.: (44) 925242000
Web Site: http://www.belmont-trading.com
Sales of Used Computers
N.A.I.C.S.: 541512

Subsidiary (Domestic):

Datec Technologies, Ltd. **(2)**
1 Byreho Pl, W Byreho Industrial Est, Kilwinning, KA136LD, United Kingdom **(100%)**
Tel.: (44) 001294556581
Web Site: http://www.datectech.co.uk
Sales of Used Computers
N.A.I.C.S.: 541512
Douglas Noris *(Mng Dir)*

Belmont Technology Remarketing **(1)**
30944 San Clemente St, Hayward, CA 94544
Tel.: (510) 475-5502
Web Site: http://www.belmont-trading.com
Sales Range: $10-24.9 Million
Emp.: 25
Sales of Used Computers
N.A.I.C.S.: 423690
Moena Cameron *(Pres & CEO)*

BELOIT BEVERAGE CO. INC.

4059 W Bradley Rd, Brown Deer, WI 53209-1769
Tel.: (414) 362-5000
Year Founded: 1938
Sales Range: $10-24.9 Million
Emp.: 5
Provider & Distributor of Beer
N.A.I.C.S.: 424810
Ralph Morello *(Pres)*
Brian Morello *(Sec)*
Donald Morello *(VP)*

BELOIT HEALTH SYSTEM, INC.

1969 W Hart Rd, Beloit, WI 53511

Tel.: (608) 364-5011 **WI**
Web Site: https://www.beloithealthsystem.org
Year Founded: 1965
Sales Range: $100-124.9 Million
Health Care Srvices
N.A.I.C.S.: 622110
Thomas McCawley *(VP)*
Kenneth Klein *(VP)*
Timothy McKevett *(Pres & CEO)*
Sharon Cox *(Chief Nursing Officer & VP)*

Subsidiaries:

Beloit Regional Hospice **(1)**
655 Third St Ste 200, Beloit, WI 53511 **(100%)**
Tel.: (608) 363-7421
Web Site: http://www.beloitregionalhospice.com
Rev.: $1,225,000
Emp.: 50
Quality of Life Care for Patients & Caregivers & Grief Support Services
N.A.I.C.S.: 622310
Deidre Bennett *(Exec Dir)*

BELTING CO. OF CINCINNATI INC.

737 W 6th St, Cincinnati, OH 45203-1729
Tel.: (513) 621-9050
Web Site: http://www.cbtcompany.com
Year Founded: 1975
Sales Range: $10-24.9 Million
Emp.: 120
Provider of Electrical Apparatus & Equipment
N.A.I.C.S.: 423610
James E. Stahl Jr. *(Pres & Treas)*

Subsidiaries:

CBT Co. **(1)**
301 S Stolle Ave, Sidney, OH 45365
Tel.: (937) 498-2104
Web Site: http://www.cbtcompany.com
Electrical Apparatus & Equipment, Wiring Supplies & Related Equipment Merchant Whslr
N.A.I.C.S.: 423610

BELTING INDUSTRIES CO. INC.

20 Boright Ave, Kenilworth, NJ 07033
Tel.: (908) 272-8591
Web Site: http://www.beltingindustries.com
Rev.: $10,500,000
Emp.: 50
Mfr of Industrial Hoses, Belting & Packing
N.A.I.C.S.: 423840
Scott Cooper *(Pres)*
Paul West *(Controller)*
Rita Kae *(Mgr-Market Dev)*
Ray Kaufman *(Mgr-Inside Sls)*

BELTMANN GROUP INC.

2480 Long Lake Rd, Roseville, MN 55113-2534
Tel.: (651) 760-0816 **MN**
Web Site: https://www.beltmann.com
Year Founded: 1925
Sales Range: $75-99.9 Million
Emp.: 1,076
Household, Commercial, High Value, Local & Long Haul Trucking
N.A.I.C.S.: 484121
Dan Battina *(Pres & CEO)*
Mike Peshut *(Gen Mgr)*
Mick Douglas *(VP-Logistics Ops-Chicago)*
Shelly Kennedy-Schenk *(Gen Mgr)*
Glen Jenkins *(Gen Mgr-Atlanta)*
Jean Titus *(Gen Mgr)*
Brock Soutendijk *(Gen Mgr)*

BELTON INDUSTRIES, INC.

1205 Hamby Rd, Honea Path, SC 29654
Tel.: (864) 338-5711 **DE**
Web Site: https://www.beltonindustries.com
Year Founded: 1916
Sales Range: $100-124.9 Million
Emp.: 200
Specialty Fabrics Mfr
N.A.I.C.S.: 314999
Keith Crocker *(Mgr-Pur)*
Linda Clinkscales *(Dir-Info Svcs)*
Carroll B. Hart Sr. *(Pres)*
Carroll B. Hart Jr. *(VP)*

BELTRAM EDGE TOOL SUPPLY CORP

6800 N Florida Ave, Tampa, FL 33604
Tel.: (813) 239-1136
Web Site: https://www.beltram.com
Sales Range: $25-49.9 Million
Emp.: 80
Restaurant Equipment & Supplies
N.A.I.C.S.: 423440
Daniel G. Beltram *(Chm)*

BELTRAME LEFFLER ADVERTISING

708 Massachusetts Ave, Indianapolis, IN 46204
Tel.: (317) 916-9930
Web Site: http://www.bladv.com
Year Founded: 1999
Sales Range: $10-24.9 Million
Emp.: 5
Full Service
N.A.I.C.S.: 541810
Mike Beltrame *(Co-Owner)*
K.C. Leffler *(Co-Owner)*

BELTRAMI ELECTRIC COOPERATIVE, INC.

4111 Technology Dr NW, Bemidji, MN 56601
Tel.: (218) 444-2540 **MN**
Web Site: http://www.beltramielectric.com
Year Founded: 1940
Sales Range: $50-74.9 Million
Electronic Services
N.A.I.C.S.: 221118
Sid Sletten *(Dir-Fin & Member Svcs)*
Sam Mason *(Mgr-Energy Svcs & Facilities)*
Dan Edens *(Mgr-Ops)*
Judy Honer *(Treas)*
Rick Coe *(Chm)*
Murl Nord *(Sec)*
Rich Riewer *(Mgr-Engrg)*
John Lund *(Vice Chm)*
Arlene Hogquist *(Dir-Strategy & Corp Svcs)*
Jolene Kallroos *(Mgr-Member Svcs)*
Chris Kelsey *(Mgr-Info Tech)*
Randy Dahle *(Line Superintendent)*
Jared Echternach *(CEO & Gen Mgr)*

BELTSERVICE CORPORATION

4143 Rider Trl N, Earth City, MO 63045-1102
Tel.: (314) 344-8500 **MO**
Web Site: http://www.beltservice.com
Year Founded: 1969
Industrial Supplies Distributors
N.A.I.C.S.: 423840
Dick Engelsmann *(Pres)*
Armando Garcia *(Dir-Intl Ops)*
Kerry Mosher *(Dir-Corp Ops)*

BELTWAY BUICK INC.

1819 Cropsey Ave, Brooklyn, NY 11214
Tel.: (718) 256-1414
Rev.: $19,172,119

Emp.: 22
New & Used Automobiles
N.A.I.C.S.: 441110

BELTWAY CAPITAL PARTNERS, LLC

7312 Parkway Dr, Hanover, MD 21076
Tel.: (443) 285-9843
Web Site: http://www.beltwaycapital.com
Year Founded: 2001
Privater Equity Firm
N.A.I.C.S.: 523999
Scott W. Gray *(Founding Partner)*
Stephen V. Rieger *(Sr VP)*

BELTWAY INTERNATIONAL TRUCKS, INC.

1800 Sulphur Spring Rd, Baltimore, MD 21227
Tel.: (410) 247-5700
Web Site: http://www.beltwaycompanies.com
Rev.: $55,670,712
Emp.: 68
Sales & Service of Trucks, Tractors & Trailers
N.A.I.C.S.: 441110
Jack Saum Sr. *(Pres)*

BELUGA VENTURES, LLC.

PO Box 369, Springville, UT 84663-0369
Tel.: (801) 491-3113
Web Site: http://www.siselinternational.com
Sales Range: $10-24.9 Million
Emp.: 112
Dry, Condensed & Evaporated Dairy Product Mfr
N.A.I.C.S.: 311514
Luis Arriscorreta *(Mgr-Regulatory Affairs)*
Tara Prestwich *(Mgr)*
Caroline Roberts *(Mgr-HR)*
Kathy Martin *(Dir-HR)*

BELVEDERE CORPORATION

1125 W 8th St Ste 200, Cincinnati, OH 45203
Tel.: (513) 241-8725
Web Site: http://www.cbcreliantrealty.com
Sales Range: $10-24.9 Million
Emp.: 50
Commercial & Industrial Building Operation Services
N.A.I.C.S.: 531120
James Bastin *(Pres)*
Kelly Gerrein *(Mgr-Property)*

BELVEDERE, LLC

1 Belvedere Blvd, Belvidere, IL 61008-8596
Tel.: (815) 544-3131 **DE**
Web Site: https://www.belvedere.com
Year Founded: 1927
Sales Range: $100-124.9 Million
Emp.: 300
Beauty & Barber Furniture & Equipment Mfr
N.A.I.C.S.: 337127
Barry Sanders *(Pres)*
Horst Ackermann *(Owner)*

BELVERON REAL ESTATE PARTNERS, LLC

268 Bush St Ste 3534, San Francisco, CA 94104
Tel.: (415) 273-6800 **DE**
Web Site: http://www.belveron.com
Investment Services
N.A.I.C.S.: 523999
Paul Odland *(Founder)*

Belveron Real Estate Partners, LLC—(Continued)

Subsidiaries:

Conifer Realty, LLC (1)
1000 University Ave Ste 500, Rochester, NY 14607
Tel.: (585) 324-0500
Web Site: http://www.coniferllc.com
Emp.: 276
Real Estate Management & Development Services
N.A.I.C.S.: 531390
Andrew I. Crossed (Principal & Exec VP)
Joan Hoover (Pres & CEO)
Richard J. Crossed (Chm & Mng Partner)
Thomas Johnson (CFO, Principal & Exec VP)
Charles M. Lewis (Sr VP)
Cheryl Stulpin (VP)
Jessica Zuniga (VP)
Barbara Ross (VP-HR & Employee Dev)
Mark Benotti (VP-Shared Svcs)
Scott Dueker (Dir-Dev Design)
Lisa Kaseman (VP-Dev Ops)
Danielle Crary (Coord-Mktg & Comm)

BELVOIR PUBLICATIONS INC.
535 Connecticut Ave, Norwalk, CT 06854
Tel.: (203) 857-3100
Web Site: http://www.belvoir.com
Year Founded: 1971
Sales Range: $25-49.9 Million
Emp.: 348
Publisher of Books, Videos & Web Sites
N.A.I.C.S.: 513120
Robert Englander (Chm, CEO & Principal)
Tom Canfield (Principal & VP-Circulation)
Timothy H. Cole (Exec VP)
Ron Goldberg (CFO)
Greg King (Sr VP-Circulation)

BELWITH PRODUCTS, LLC
3100 Broadway Ave SW, Grandville, MI 49418
Tel.: (616) 247-4000
Web Site: http://www.belwith.com
Year Founded: 1893
Sales Range: $50-74.9 Million
Emp.: 100
Decorative & Functional Hardware Mfr
N.A.I.C.S.: 332510
Tim Emmitt (Pres)

Subsidiaries:

Belwith Products, LLC - First Watch Security Division (1)
3100 Broadway Ave SW, Grandville, MI 49418-1581
Tel.: (800) 235-9484
Web Site: http://www.belwithproducts.com
Emp.: 60
Home Security Product Mfr & Distr
N.A.I.C.S.: 334290
Tim Emmitt (Gen Mgr)

Belwith Products, LLC - Hickory Hardware Division (1)
3100 Broadway Ave SW, Grandville, MI 49418
Tel.: (616) 247-4000
Web Site: http://www.hickoryhardware.com
Hardware Product Mfr & Distr
N.A.I.C.S.: 332510
Regenia Robb (Mgr-Customer Svc)

Belwith Products, LLC - Keeler Division (1)
3100 Broadway Ave SW, Grandville, MI 49418
Web Site: http://www.keelerproducts.com
Hardware Product Mfr
N.A.I.C.S.: 332510
Jerry Lloyd (Dir-Bus Dev)

BELZ ENTERPRISES
100 Peabody Pl Ste 1400, Memphis, TN 38103-3648

Tel.: (901) 260-7348
Web Site: https://www.belz.com
Year Founded: 1940
Sales Range: $200-249.9 Million
Emp.: 260
Real Estate Development & Management
N.A.I.C.S.: 531120
Martin S. Belz (COO)

Subsidiaries:

Peabody Hotel Group, Inc. (1)
5118 Park Ave Ste 245, Memphis, TN 38117
Tel.: (901) 762-5400
Web Site: http://www.peabodyhotelgroup.com
Sales Range: $10-24.9 Million
Emp.: 200
Motel, Franchised
N.A.I.C.S.: 721110
Merilyn G. Mangum (Chief Admin Officer & Exec VP)

BEMCO ASSOCIATES, INC.
2720 S River Rd Ste 130, Des Plaines, IL 60018-4110
Tel.: (800) 747-1066
Web Site: http://www.bemco.com
Year Founded: 1956
Mattress Mfr & Licensing
N.A.I.C.S.: 337910

BEMCO INC.
2255 Union Pl, Simi Valley, CA 93065
Tel.: (805) 583-4970
Web Site: https://www.bemcoinc.com
Year Founded: 1951
Sales Range: $10-24.9 Million
Emp.: 26
Environmental Test Equipment & Space Simulation Systems Mfr
N.A.I.C.S.: 334516
Barry Bruskrud (Pres)
Mike Hodan (Mgr)
Dick Behrendt (Engr-Sls)

BEMIDJI CHRYSLER CENTER, LLC.
755 Paul Bunyan Dr NW, Bemidji, MN 56601-2438
Tel.: (218) 407-6164
Web Site: https://www.bemidjichrysler.com
Sales Range: $10-24.9 Million
Emp.: 35
Car Whslr
N.A.I.C.S.: 441110
Daryl Clink (Mgr-Parts)

BEMIDJI WOOLEN MILLS
301 Irvine Ave NW, Bemidji, MN 56601-0279
Tel.: (218) 751-5166
Web Site: https://www.bemidjiwoolenmills.com
Year Founded: 1920
Sales Range: $50-74.9 Million
Emp.: 50
Woolen Apparel
N.A.I.C.S.: 458110
Bill Batchelder (Pres)

BEMIS ASSOCIATES INC.
1 Bemis Way, Shirley, MA 01464
Tel.: (978) 425-6500
Web Site: https://www.bemisworldwide.com
Sales Range: $10-24.9 Million
Emp.: 200
Adhesives
N.A.I.C.S.: 325520
Stephen Howard (Pres & CEO)

Subsidiaries:

Bemis Hong Kong Ltd. (1)
7th Floor East Warwick House Taikoo Place

979 Kings Road, Quarry Bay, China (Hong Kong)
Tel.: (852) 2785 5155
Web Site: http://www.bemisworldwide.com
Thermoplastic Adhesive Mfr
N.A.I.C.S.: 325211
Germany Cheung (Asst Mgr-Sls)
Alison Lam (Sr Mgr-Sls)
Adrian Lui (Mgr-Technical Sls)

Poly Visions, Inc. (1)
25 Devco Dr, Manchester, PA 17345
Tel.: (717) 266-3031
Web Site: http://www.polyvisions.com
Sales Range: $10-24.9 Million
Emp.: 15
PlasticAdditives Mfr
N.A.I.C.S.: 326121
David Altland (Dir-Ops)
Cathy Johnson (Office Mgr)
Scott B. Howard (CEO)

BEMIS MANUFACTURING COMPANY
300 Mill St, Sheboygan Falls, WI 53085
Tel.: (920) 467-4621
Web Site: http://www.bemismfg.com
Sales Range: $125-149.9 Million
Emp.: 2,200
Molded Finished Plastics Products Mfr
N.A.I.C.S.: 326199
Pete Probe (Controller)
Norman Giertz (COO & Pres-Proprietary Grp)
Bob Davis (Mgr-Mktg)
Patrick Mulvey (VP-Sls-Plumbing Products-North America)
Vesla Hoeschen (Chm)
Jeff Lonigro (CEO)

BEN ARNOLD CO., INC.
300 Plaza Dr, Vestal, NY 13850
Tel.: (607) 729-9331
Year Founded: 1965
Emp.: 2
Suspended Furnace Arches
N.A.I.C.S.: 333414
Burton Koffman (Pres & Treas)
David Koffman (VP)

BEN B. BLISS COMPANY, INC.
191 Dunwoodie St, Yonkers, NY 10704-1835
Tel.: (914) 478-1201
Year Founded: 1946
Sales Range: Less than $1 Million
Emp.: 5
N.A.I.C.S.: 541810
Ben B. Bliss (Pres, Creative Dir & Acct Exec)
William Bennett (Media Dir)
Steven Jeffrey (Dir-Mktg)
Peter Scott (Dir-Brdcst)
Flora Mae Meister (Acct Exec)

BEN E. KEITH COMPANY
601 E 7th St, Fort Worth, TX 76102
Tel.: (817) 877-5700
Web Site: https://www.benekeith.com
Year Founded: 1906
Sales Range: Less than $1 Million
Emp.: 5,600
General Line Grocery Merchant Wholesalers
N.A.I.C.S.: 424410
Robert Hallam (COO)
David Werner (Sr VP-Independent Sls & Mktg)
Aimee Lakotas (VP-Mktg)
Flint Prewitt (Pres-Beverage)
Casey Dorrill (Asst Gen Mgr-Southeast)
Mike Sweet (Pres)

Subsidiaries:

Ben E. Keith Foods of Oklahoma (1)
14200 N Santa Fe Ave, Edmond, OK 73013 (100%)
Tel.: (405) 753-7600
Web Site: http://www.benekeith.com
Sales Range: $25-49.9 Million
Emp.: 400
Frozen Foods
N.A.I.C.S.: 424420
Keith Causey (Mgr-Protein Pur)
Cathi Shive (Coord-Rebate & Bid)

Kelley Foods of Alabama, Inc. (1)
1697 Lowr Curtis Rd, Elba, AL 36323
Tel.: (334) 897-5761
Web Site: http://www.kelleyfoods.com
General Line Grocery Merchant Whslr
N.A.I.C.S.: 424410
Eddie Kelley (Pres & CEO)

Orrell's Food Service, Inc. (1)
9827 S NC Hwy 150, Linwood, NC 27299
Tel.: (336) 752-2114
Web Site: http://www.orrellsfoodservice.com
Sales Range: $25-49.9 Million
Emp.: 82
Meats & Meat Products
N.A.I.C.S.: 424470
Tony Ray Orrell (Pres)
Keith Swan (Gen Mgr)

BEN ELIAS INDUSTRIES CORP
550 7th Ave 12th Fl, New York, NY 10018
Tel.: (212) 354-8300
Web Site: https://www.benelias.com
Year Founded: 1945
Sales Range: $75-99.9 Million
Emp.: 500
Provider of Women's & Children's Clothing
N.A.I.C.S.: 424350
Stanley Elias (Chm)
Butch Elias (Pres & COO)

BEN HILL GRIFFIN INC.
700 S Scenic Hwy, Frostproof, FL 33843
Tel.: (863) 635-2251
Year Founded: 1943
Sales Range: $450-499.9 Million
Emp.: 300
Citrus Fruits
N.A.I.C.S.: 111320
Jon Clayton (Dir-IT)
Craig Prine (Dir-Occupational Health & Safety)
Mike Roberts (Dir-Sls & Mktg)
Chad Hadden (Mgr-Fin & Admin)
Donna Respress (Sec)
William Lay (VP-HR)
Ben Hill Griffin IV (Pres)
Ben Hill Griffin III (Chm & CEO)

BEN HUR CONSTRUCTION CO. INC.
3783 Rider Trl S, Earth City, MO 63045-1114
Tel.: (314) 298-8007
Web Site: http://www.benhurconstruction.com
Year Founded: 1909
Sales Range: $10-24.9 Million
Emp.: 50
Provider of Construction Services
N.A.I.C.S.: 238120
John Vogt (Pres)
Mark Douglas (VP-Cincinnati & Mgr-Steel Construction Div-Cincinnati)
Scott Bullerdick (Mgr-Steel Construction Div)
R. Philip Stupp (Chm)

BEN LEWIS PLUMBING, HEATING & AIR CONDITIONING, INC.

23407 Frederick Rd, Clarksburg, MD 20871
Tel.: (301) 428-3900
Web Site:
https://www.benlewisplumbing.com
Sales Range: $10-24.9 Million
Emp.: 170
Plumbing, Heating & Air-Conditioning Services
N.A.I.C.S.: 238220
Matt Goundry (Pres)
Mike Bowersox (VP)
Dick Clinton (Mgr-Sys)
Steve Norris (Treas)
Dalton Cevallos (Mgr-Pur)
Chris Blair (Mgr-Production-Residential)
William Martinez (Project Mgr)
Earl Rockwood (Mgr-Svc-Columbus)
Alfonso Camacho (Mgr-Warehouse)
Tammy Hopkins (Office Mgr)
Danny Hurley (Project Mgr)

BEN LOMAND RURAL TELEPHONE CO-OP, INC.
311 N Chancery St, McMinnville, TN 37110
Tel.: (931) 668-4131
Web Site: http://www.blomand.net
Sales Range: $10-24.9 Million
Emp.: 135
Local Telephone Communications
N.A.I.C.S.: 517121
Lisa Cope (CEO)

BEN MYNATT MEGASTORE
PO Box 1390, Concord, NC 28026-1390
Tel.: (704) 788-2121
Web Site: http://www.benmynatt.com
Year Founded: 1976
Sales Range: $25-49.9 Million
Emp.: 40
Used Car Whslr
N.A.I.C.S.: 441120
Cynthia L. Mynatt (Pres)
Lynn Steen (Comptroller)
Ethan Tucker (Mgr-Svc)

BEN S. LOEB, INC.
25 Pier Ln W, Fairfield, NJ 07004-2572
Tel.: (973) 882-9022
Web Site: https://www.bsloeb.com
Year Founded: 1907
Sales Range: $10-24.9 Million
Emp.: 55
Apparel Product Whslr
N.A.I.C.S.: 424990
Todd Becker (Partner)

BEN TAYLOR INC.
2122 W Roosevelt Hwy, Shelby, MT 59474
Tel.: (406) 434-5546
Web Site: http://www.bentaylor.com
Rev.: $11,595,503
Emp.: 50
Farm Supplies, True Value Hardware
N.A.I.C.S.: 444130
Gregory B. Taylor (Pres)

BEN TIRE DISTRIBUTORS LTD. INC.
203 E Madison, Toledo, IL 62468-0158
Tel.: (217) 849-3516   DE
Web Site: http://www.bentire.com
Year Founded: 1997
Sales Range: $50-74.9 Million
Emp.: 300
Tire & Tube Services
N.A.I.C.S.: 423130

Terry Carlon (Pres)
Dave Dillier (Dir-Pur & Inventory Control)
John Floyd (Dir-Wholesale)
April Nance (Mgr-HR)

BEN WEITSMAN & SON INC.
15 W Main St, Owego, NY 13827
Tel.: (607) 687-2780
Web Site:
http://upstateshredding.com
Rev.: $11,823,792
Emp.: 150
Scrap & Waste Materials
N.A.I.C.S.: 424690
Adam Weitsman (Pres)

BEN'S ASPHALT & SEAL COATING INC.
2200 S Yale St, Santa Ana, CA 92704-4427
Tel.: (714) 540-1700
Web Site:
https://www.bensasphalt.com
Year Founded: 1961
Sales Range: $10-24.9 Million
Emp.: 125
Masonry Services
N.A.I.C.S.: 238990
Bill Skeffington (Pres & CEO)

BENAKA, INC.
7 Lawrence St, New Brunswick, NJ 08901
Tel.: (732) 246-7060
Web Site:
https://www.benakainc.com
Year Founded: 1994
Sales Range: $10-24.9 Million
Emp.: 6
Commercial & Institutional Building Construction Services
N.A.I.C.S.: 236220
Amit Deshmukh (Project Mgr & Engr-Quality Control)

BENAROYA RESEARCH INSTITUTE AT VIRGINIA MASON
1201 9th Ave, Seattle, WA 98101-2795
Tel.: (206) 342-6500   WA
Web Site:
https://www.benaroyaresearch.org
Year Founded: 1956
Sales Range: $50-74.9 Million
Emp.: 312
Medical Research Services
N.A.I.C.S.: 541715
Cheryl Weaver (Dir-Clinical Res Admin)
Holly Chase (Dir-Human Resources)
Bolong Cao (Dir-Business Development)
Jane Buckner (Pres)
Margaret McCormick (Chief Admin Officer)
Michael Labosier (CFO)

BENAY-HAT CO.
4710 Roanoke Ave, Newport News, VA 23607-2339
Tel.: (757) 244-0807   VA
Year Founded: 1992
Sales Range: $75-99.9 Million
Emp.: 21
Hats Mfr
N.A.I.C.S.: 315990
Stanley Molin (Gen Mgr)
Jeff Jacobs (Pres)

BENCHMARC DISPLAY INC.
1001 Woodlands Pkwy, Vernon Hills, IL 60061
Tel.: (847) 541-2828
Web Site: http://www.benchmarc.com
Rev.: $11,320,438

Emp.: 39
Displays & Cutouts, Window & Lobby
N.A.I.C.S.: 339950
Marc Modlin (Mgr-Product Dev)
Mike Glisch (VP-Sls)
Martha Beck (Project Mgr)

BENCHMARK BRANDS INC.
5250 Triangle Pkwy Ste 200, Norcross, GA 30092
Tel.: (901) 365-4032
Web Site:
http://www.benchmarkbrands.com
Sales Range: $25-49.9 Million
Emp.: 25
Cosmetics & Perfumes, Mail Order & Shoe Insoles
N.A.I.C.S.: 424210
Alan Beychok (Pres & CEO)
David Rogalski (CFO)

BENCHMARK CAPITAL
2965 Woodside Rd, Woodside, CA 94062
Tel.: (650) 854-8180
Web Site: http://www.benchmark.com
Sales Range: $25-49.9 Million
Emp.: 25
Privater Equity Firm
N.A.I.C.S.: 523999
Robert C. Kagle (Gen Partner)
Bruce W. Dunlevie (Gen Partner)
Jill Jarrett (CFO)
Peter H. Fenton (Gen Partner)
J. William Gurley (Gen Partner)

Subsidiaries:

Benchmark Capital   (1)
12 Auvaeven, PO BOX 039, Herzliya Pituach, 46725, Israel
Tel.: (972) 99617600
Web Site: http://www.benchmark.com
Sales Range: $50-74.9 Million
Emp.: 10
Privater Equity Firm
N.A.I.C.S.: 523999

BENCHMARK CIVIL ENGINEERING SERVICES INC.
1727 Jonathan St, Allentown, PA 18104
Tel.: (610) 776-6700
Web Site: https://www.bencivil.com
Year Founded: 1994
Sales Range: Less than $1 Million
Emp.: 7
Civil & Traffic Engineering Services
N.A.I.C.S.: 541330
Peter A. Terry (Pres)
Bernie Telatovich (VP-Engrg)
Sharon Colon (Office Mgr)

BENCHMARK CONSTRUCTION COMPANY, INC.
4121 Oregon Pike, Brownstown, PA 17508
Tel.: (717) 626-9559   DE
Web Site:
https://www.benchmarkgc.com
Year Founded: 1985
Sales Range: $25-49.9 Million
Emp.: 140
Nonresidential Construction
N.A.I.C.S.: 236220
Michael K. Callahan (Pres)
Christopher Smith (VP-Ops)
Walter Taylor (Dir-Estimating-West Earl Township Lancaster County)
Christian Recknagel (VP-Leadership & Culture)
Steve Conway (VP-Sr Living & Higher Education)
Skylar Gingrich (Project Mgr-Lancaster County)
Jeff Moderacki (CFO)
Robert A. Brandt III (Pres)

BENCHMARK DISPLAYS
44311 Monterey Ave, Palm Desert, CA 92260
Tel.: (760) 775-2424   CA
Web Site:
http://www.benchmarkdisplays.com
Year Founded: 1985
Sales Range: $1-9.9 Million
Emp.: 4
Custom Display Production Services
N.A.I.C.S.: 541820
Joanne Frohman (Pres)
Bonnie Miller (VP-Sls)

BENCHMARK FINANCIAL GROUPS, LLC
65 Enterprise, Aliso Viejo, CA 92656
Tel.: (949) 716-2100
Year Founded: 1999
Sales Range: $10-24.9 Million
Emp.: 35
Equipment Leasing Financing Services
N.A.I.C.S.: 525990
Marcus Davin (Pres & CEO)

BENCHMARK HOMES INC.
2266 Fairburn Rd, Douglasville, GA 30135
Tel.: (770) 949-3006
Web Site:
https://www.benchmarkatlanta.com
Sales Range: $10-24.9 Million
Emp.: 25
Land Subdividers & Developers, Commercial
N.A.I.C.S.: 237210
Larry Boggs (Pres)
Michelle Bostwick (Office Mgr)

BENCHMARK HOSPITALITY INTERNATIONAL INC.
4 Waterway Sq Ste 300, The Woodlands, TX 77380
Tel.: (281) 367-5757
Web Site:
http://www.benchmarkhospitality.com
Sales Range: $1-9.9 Million
Emp.: 6,300
Management & Marketing Services for Resorts, Conference Centers, Conference Hotels & Golf Clubs
N.A.I.C.S.: 541611
Kim Nugent (VP-Revenue Mgmt)
Greg Champion (Pres-Pyramid Luxury & Lifestyle & COO-Pyramid Luxury & Lifestyle)
Alex Cabanas (CEO)
John Davies (VP-Mktg)
Ted Davis (Chief Sls & Mktg Officer)
Eric Gavin (Chief Sls Officer)
Andrew Finn (VP-Grp Sls)
Todd M. Felsen (Sr VP-Ops)
Calvin J. Banks (Dir-Trng & Dev)
Karen DiFulgo (Chief People Officer)
Jackie Allee (Dir-Comm)
Kirk Jones (CFO)
Humberto Cabanas (Chm)
Todd Parmelee (VP-Food & Beverage)
Susan Benshoff (Reg Dir-Revenue Mgmt)
Molly Fierro-Preston (Dir-Procurement)
Jay Rocha (VP-Ops)
Fatima Molina (Dir-Revenue Support Center-Global)
Gary Harnist (VP-Design & Construction-Technical Svcs)
Jackie Humes (VP-Fin & Ops)
Tony Gaeta (VP-IT)

Benchmark Hospitality International
Inc.—(Continued)
Lisa Stice (VP-Online Mktg-Global)
Cedric Fasbender (VP-Ops)
Paul D'Andrea (VP-Ops)
Nour Asfari (Dir-Revenue-Orlando)
Rikki Boparai (VP-Ops)
Nicole Di Maio (Dir-Revenue Mgmt-
New Jersey)
Evan Crawford (Dir-Field Mktg Sup-
port)
Chris Audia (Dir-Mktg)
Lisa Fasbender (Acting Gen Mgr)
John Annicchiarico (VP-Sls Ops)
Sam Johnson (VP-Ops-Pyramid
Luxury & Lifestyle)

Subsidiaries:

Gemstone Hotels & Resorts,
LLC   (1)
1912 Sidewinder Dr Ste 105, Park City, UT
84060
Tel.: (435) 658-1594
Web Site: http://www.gemstoneresorts.com
Hotel & Resort Operators
N.A.I.C.S.: 721110
William Parris (Dir-Natl Sls)
Debbie Batt (VP-Sls & Mktg)
Thomas Prins (Partner)
Jeff McIntyre (Partner)
Brett Atkinson (CFO)
Jan McCormick (VP-Ops)
Greg Merrick (VP-HR)

BENCHMARK INDUSTRIAL, INC.
950 Claycraft Rd, Gahanna, OH
43230
Tel.: (937) 325-1001
Web Site:
http://www.benchmarkindustrial.com
Sales Range: $10-24.9 Million
Emp.: 20
Industrial Product Distr
N.A.I.C.S.: 423840
Mary P. Walling (CFO)
Jim Reid (Pres)

Subsidiaries:

Donby Shippers Supply, Co.   (1)
4607 Spring Rd, Cleveland, OH 44131
Tel.: (216) 741-1819
Web Site: http://www.donby.com
Sales Range: $1-9.9 Million
Emp.: 11
Packaging & Warehouse Supply Services
N.A.I.C.S.: 561910
Eric Blumenthal (Pres)

BENCHMARK INDUSTRIES
630 Hay Ave, Brookville, OH 45309-
1908
Tel.: (937) 833-4091   OH
Year Founded: 1946
Sales Range: $75-99.9 Million
Emp.: 70
Industrialized Housing Mfr
N.A.I.C.S.: 321992
George Kirby (VP-Production)
Debbie Maxson (Controller)
David Sowers (VP-Pur)

BENCHMARK INTERNET GROUP, LLC
3636 S. Geyer Rd, Ste 100,, St
Louis, MO 63127
Web Site:
http://www.benchmarkemail.com
Online Marketing Services
N.A.I.C.S.: 541613
Curt Keller (CEO)

BENCHMARK REALTY LLC
11941 W 48th Ave, Wheat Ridge, CO
80033
Tel.: (303) 341-0077

Web Site:
http://www.benchmarkrealtyllc.com
Year Founded: 2006
Offices of Real Estate Agents & Bro-
kers
N.A.I.C.S.: 531210
Mark Marati (Mgr)

BENCHMARK REHAB PARTNERS
6397 Lee Hwy Ste 300, Chattanooga,
TN 37421
Tel.: (423) 238-7217
Web Site: http://www.bmrp.com
Year Founded: 1995
Sales Range: $50-74.9 Million
Emp.: 733
Physical & Occupational Therapy
Services
N.A.I.C.S.: 621340
Jeff Londis (Mng Partner)
Harvey Hillyer (Owner)

BENCHMARK SENIOR LIVING, LLC
201 Jones Rd Ste 300 W, Waltham,
MA 02451
Tel.: (781) 489-7100
Web Site:
http://www.benchmarkseniors.com
Sales Range: $250-299.9 Million
Emp.: 3,000
Continuing Care Retirement Services
N.A.I.C.S.: 623311
Thomas Grape (Founder, Chm &
CEO)
Jayne Sallerson (Exec VP-Sls & Ops)
Linda Amir (Dir-Senior Care Fin Svcs)
Tasha Thomas (Dir-Harbor Care-New
Pond Village Community)
Terry Hornikel (Exec Dir-Sturges
Ridge of Fairfield)
John Quevillon (Exec Dir)
Fatima Oliveira (Exec Dir)
Denise McQuaide (Pres/COO-
Benchmark Wellness Mgmt Div)
Heather Frahm (CMO & Exec VP)
Missy Ebner (Dir-Resident Care-
Northeast)
Allyson Sweeney (Exec Dir-The
Atrium-Rocky Hill)
Jerry Liang (CFO & Exec VP)
John Hartmayer (COO & Exec VP)

Subsidiaries:

Southfarm LP   (1)
645 Saybrook Rd, Middletown, CT 06457
Tel.: (860) 342-8033
Sales Range: $10-24.9 Million
Emp.: 45
Continuing Care Retirement Services
N.A.I.C.S.: 623311
Norma Walberg (Mgr-Bus Office)

BENCHMARK SERVICES, INC.
308 Maltbie St Ste 102, Syracuse,
NY 13204
Tel.: (315) 295-2233   NY
Web Site:
http://www.benchmarksvcs.com
Year Founded: 2016
Gas Brokerage & Consulting Services
N.A.I.C.S.: 523160
Mark Tackley (Founder & Pres)
Dave French (VP-Ops)

BENCHMARK USA
25 Skycrest, Mission Viejo, CA 92692
Tel.: (949) 380-9400
Year Founded: 1987
Sales Range: $1-9.9 Million
Emp.: 4
Sales Promotion
N.A.I.C.S.: 541810
Anita Depauw (Pres)

BENCHWORKS, INC.

954 High St, Chestertown, MD
21620-3909
Tel.: (410) 810-8862
Web Site:
http://www.benchworks.com
Year Founded: 1991
Sales Range: $1-9.9 Million
Emp.: 50
Marketing Services
N.A.I.C.S.: 541810
Thad Bench (Founder & CEO)
Amanda Skilling (VP-Fin & Admin)
Sally Reed (VP-Digital Svcs)
Jake King (VP & Grp Dir-Creative)
Chuck Heinz (Exec Dir-Strategic
Plng)
Lisa Wolfington (Dir-Health Sys Mktg)
Angelina Sciolla (Exec Creative Dir)

Subsidiaries:

Safe Chain Solutions, LLC   (1)
822 Chesapeake Dr, Cambridge, MD
21613-9408
Tel.: (443) 205-4558
Web Site:
http://www.safechainsolutions.com
Sales Range: $1-9.9 Million
Process, Physical Distribution & Logistics
Consulting Services
N.A.I.C.S.: 541614
Charles Boyd (Pres)

BENCO DENTAL SUPPLY CO. INC.
295 Centerpoint Blvd, Pittston, PA
18640
Tel.: (570) 602-7781   DE
Web Site: https://www.benco.com
Year Founded: 1930
Sales Range: $300-349.9 Million
Emp.: 850
Dental Supplies & Equipment
N.A.I.C.S.: 423450
Lawrence E. Cohen (Chm)
Charles Cohen (Pres)
Richard Cohen (Sr VP)
Mike McElaney (VP-Sls & Branch
Ops)

BENDCARE, LLC
2255 Glades Rd Ste 228W, Boca Ra-
ton, FL 33431
Web Site: http://www.bendcare.com
Year Founded: 2015
Sales Range: $150-199.9 Million
Emp.: 37
Health Care Srvices
N.A.I.C.S.: 621610
Andrew Ripps (Chm & CEO)
Jake Spruit (Exec VP-Fin)
Kathi Garrett (Exec VP-Practice
Transformation)
Patrick Stewart (Sr VP-Product Inno-
vation)
Michael Chavez (VP)

BENDER LUMBER COMPANY INC.
611 W 11th ST, Bloomington, IN
47404-2872
Tel.: (812) 339-9737
Web Site:
http://www.benderlumber.com
Year Founded: 1962
Sales Range: $25-49.9 Million
Emp.: 230
Lumber & Other Building Materials
Mfr
N.A.I.C.S.: 423310
John Bender (CEO)

BENDER WAREHOUSE CO.
345 Parr Cir, Reno, NV 89512
Tel.: (775) 788-8800
Web Site:
http://www.bendergroup.com
Year Founded: 1945

Sales Range: $10-24.9 Million
Emp.: 180
General Warehousing
N.A.I.C.S.: 493110
Chris Bender (Owner)

BENDERSON DEVELOPMENT COMPANY, LLC
7978 Cooper Creek Blvd, University
Park, FL 34201
Tel.: (941) 359-8303   NY
Web Site: http://www.benderson.com
Year Founded: 1957
Sales Range: $300-349.9 Million
Emp.: 280
Real Estate Development & Manage-
ment
N.A.I.C.S.: 237210
Randall Benderson (CEO)

BENDIGO PARTNERS, LLC
535 5th Ave 30th Fl, New York, NY
10017
Tel.: (212) 867-4490
Web Site:
http://www.bendigopartners.com
Year Founded: 2009
Financial Services
N.A.I.C.S.: 523999
Peter de Florio (Partner)

Subsidiaries:

Hazeltree Fund Services Inc   (1)
150 W 30th St 11th Fl, New York, NY
10001
Tel.: (212) 727-0883
Treasury Management & Portfolio Finance
Services
N.A.I.C.S.: 523940
Stephanie D. Miller (CEO)
Sameer Shalaby (Pres)
Scott Metro (Chief Info Security Officer)
Richard Winter (CTO)

Subsidiary (Domestic):

ENSO Financial Management,
LLP   (2)
450 Park Ave S 3rd, New York, NY 10016
Tel.: (212) 819-2858
Web Site: http://www.ensofinancial.com
Financial Services
N.A.I.C.S.: 522320
Paul Busby (Head-Global)

BENDITO RESOURCES INC.
6490 S McCarran Blvd Bldg E Ste
121, Reno, NV 89509
Tel.: (775) 340-2719
Web Site:
https://benditoresources.com
Emp.: 100
Mining & Exploration Services
N.A.I.C.S.: 212220

Subsidiaries:

Mt. Hamilton, LLC   (1)
4251 Kipling St Ste 390, Wheat Ridge, CO
80033
Tel.: (303) 534-1030
Gold Ore Mining Services
N.A.I.C.S.: 212220

BENEDEK INVESTMENT GROUP, LLC
145 W 57th St 14th Fl, New York, NY
10019
Tel.: (212) 586-8444
Web Site: http://www.benedek.com
Privater Equity Firm
N.A.I.C.S.: 523999
A. Richard Benedek (Chm & Mng Dir)
Stephen D. Benedek (Mng Dir)

Subsidiaries:

Broadcast Interactive Media,
LLC   (1)
122 W Washington Ave Ste 350, Madison,
WI 53703

Tel.: (608) 255-8155
Web Site: http://www.broadcast-interactive.com
Web Content Development Services
N.A.I.C.S.: 518210
Timur Yarnall (Founder)
Julie Moses (Sr VP-Natl Sls)
Richard Sullivan (Sr VP-Publr Dev)
Heidi Steffen (VP-Licensed Application Sls)
Mick Rinehart (Pres-Data Svcs)
Pat Liegel (COO)
Mike Schuch Jr. (VP-Local Sls)

Unit (Domestic):

TitanTV.com   (2)
300 Collins Rd NE Ste 200, Cedar Rapids, IA 52402
Tel.: (319) 365-5597
Web Site: http://www.titantv.com
Sales Range: $10-24.9 Million
Emp.: 16
Online Television Programming Schedule Publisher
N.A.I.C.S.: 516210
Mick Rinehart (VP-Product Dev)

BENEDICT ADVERTISING

640 N Peninsula Dr, Daytona Beach, FL 32118-3829
Tel.: (386) 255-1222   FL
Web Site:
   http://www.benedictadvertising.com
Year Founded: 1974
Rev.: $48,000,000
Emp.: 26
Advetising Agency
N.A.I.C.S.: 541810
Chris LeBlanc (Dir-Creative)
Pam Moss (VP-Acct Service)
Brenda Sidoti (Dir-Media)
Michael Benedict (Pres)
Christine Byelick (Mgr-Production)
Kym Zurstadt (Art Dir)
Julie Coln (Mgr-Media)
Juan Vasquez (Acct Coord)
Annika Elston (Acct Exec)
Ashley Kelly (Acct Exec)
Joey Ramos (Art Dir)
Bud Hanson (Dir-Strategy & Consumer Insights)
Kellen Wohlford (Dir-Fin)
Adam Bunke (Graphic Designer)
Lori Murray (Coord-Media)
Sonja Munafo (Office Mgr)
Darin Duehl (Sr Acct Exec)
Joseph Yelvington (Sr Acct Exec)

BENEDICT REFRIGERATION SERVICE, INC.

1003 Harlem St, Altoona, WI 54720
Tel.: (715) 834-3191   WI
Web Site:
   http://www.benedictrefrigerator.com
Year Founded: 1968
Sales Range: $1-9.9 Million
Emp.: 35
Plumbing/Heating/Air Cond Contractor Refrigeration Service/Repair
N.A.I.C.S.: 238220
Tim Benedict (Owner & Pres)

Subsidiaries:

Schomburg Refrigeration Co, Inc.   (1)
1815 Caledonia St, La Crosse, WI 54603
Tel.: (608) 781-6614
Commercial Refrigeration Services, Equipment, Repair & Maintenance
N.A.I.C.S.: 333415

BENEFICIAL STATE FOUNDATION

1438 Webster St Ste 300, Oakland, CA 94612
Tel.: (510) 663-2253   DE
Web Site:
   http://www.beneficialstate.org
Year Founded: 2006
Sales Range: $10-24.9 Million

Community Enrichment Organization
N.A.I.C.S.: 813219
Kat Taylor (Co-Founder)
Tom Steyer (Co-Founder)
Salvador Menjivar (Exec Dir)
Erin Kilmer Neel (Chief Impact Officer & Deputy Dir)
Annie Claybaugh (Dir-Ops)

Subsidiaries:

Beneficial State Bancorp, Inc. (1)
1438 Webster St Ste 100, Oakland, CA 94612   (100%)
Web Site:
   http://www.beneficialstatebank.com
Bank Holding Company
N.A.I.C.S.: 551111
Kat Taylor (Co-CEO)
Daniel Skaff (Pres & Co-CEO)

Subsidiary (Domestic):

Beneficial State Bank   (2)
1438 Webster St Ste 100, Oakland, CA 94612-3229   (100%)
Tel.: (510) 550-8400
Web Site:
   http://www.beneficialstatebank.com
Sales Range: $10-24.9 Million
Emp.: 150
Commericial Banking
N.A.I.C.S.: 522110
Kat Taylor (Founder & CEO)
Cem Bolkan (Chief Credit Officer & Sr VP)
Madison Le (Chief Admin Officer & Exec VP)
Jann W. Wallach (Sr VP-Compliance & BSA)
Randell Leach (Pres & COO)
Thu Nguyen (CFO & Sr VP)
Daniel Lawrence Skaff (Vice Chm)
Grant Word (Exec VP & Dir-Comml & Bus Banking)
Monique Johnson (Sr VP & Dir-Client & Treasury Mgmt)
Sherri Arnold (Chief People Officer & Sr VP)
Steve Goodrich (Exec VP & Head-Consumer & Microlending)
Tyson Smith (CTO & Exec VP)

BENEFIS HEALTH SYSTEM

1101 26th St S, Great Falls, MT 59405
Tel.: (406) 455-5000   MT
Web Site: https://www.benefis.org
Year Founded: 2008
Sales Range: $50-74.9 Million
Emp.: 222
Health Insurance Services
N.A.I.C.S.: 524114
John Goodnow (CEO)
Deb McCracken (Chief Compliance Officer & Chief Risk Officer)
Terry Olinger (Pres)
Forrest Ehlinger (CFO & Chief Resources Officer)
Carl Bruesch (Dir-Fin & Fin Analysis-Medical Grp)
Paul Dolan (Chief Medical Info Officer)
Rayn Ginnaty (VP-Nursing-Hospitals)
Peter Gray (Exec Dir-Senior Care)
Greg Hilpert (Dir-Radiology & Lab)
Julie Wall (VP-Sys, Quality & Safety)
David Richards (Chm)
Mike Milburn (Vice Chm)
J. W. Bloemendaal (Sec)
Terry Preite (Pres-Reg Relationships)
Greg Tierney (Chief Medical Officer)
Casey Buckingham (VP-HR)
Joe Lo Duca (Chief Admin Officer-Cancer & Heart)
Kathy Hill (COO)
Mark Simon (CIO & Sr VP-Sys)

BENEFIT ADMINISTRATION COMPANY LLC

1200 5th Ave Ste 1100, Seattle, WA 98101
Tel.: (206) 625-1800   WA

Web Site:
   http://www.benefitadminco.com
Year Founded: 1980
Sales Range: $1-9.9 Million
Emp.: 31
Benefits Administration & Consulting
N.A.I.C.S.: 541612
Terrence G. Atkins (Principal & CFO)
Tim C. Hill (Mng Principal & CEO)
Janet K. Schott (Dir-Client Ops)
Bryan Hill (Dir-Grp Benefits)

BENEFIT ADVISORS, INC.

741 NE 3rd St, Ocala, FL 34470
Tel.: (352) 479-0944
Web Site: http://www.benefit-advisors.com
Sales Range: $1-9.9 Million
Emp.: 20
Employee Benefit Consulting Services
N.A.I.C.S.: 541611
Angela Branch (Reg Dir)
Brandon Whiteman (Acct Mgr)
Claire Heller (Acct Mgr)
Raymond N. Strickland Jr. (Pres & CEO)

BENEFIT SOURCE, INC.

1627 E North St, Greenville, SC 29607
Tel.: (864) 370-0711   SC
Web Site: http://www.yoursca.com
Year Founded: 1990
Sales Range: $1-9.9 Million
Emp.: 17
Insurance Agents, Brokers & Benefit Services
N.A.I.C.S.: 524298
Robert Harling (Pres)

BENEFITS NETWORK INC.

115 Vip Dr 120, Wexford, PA 15090
Tel.: (724) 940-9400
Web Site:
   http://www.benefitsnetwork.biz
Rev.: $1,700,000
Emp.: 10
Administrative Management & General Management Consulting Service
N.A.I.C.S.: 541611
David Straight (Exec Dir)

Subsidiaries:

VCS Group Inc.   (1)
118 W Main St Ste 301, Somerset, PA 15501-2007
Tel.: (814) 445-4943
Web Site: http://www.vcsgroup.net
Insurance Agencies & Brokerages
N.A.I.C.S.: 524210
Glenn E. Miller Jr. (Pres)

BENES SERVICE CO.

3195 County Rd B, Valparaiso, NE 68065
Tel.: (402) 784-3581
Sales Range: Less than $1 Million
Emp.: 20
Farm Implements & Chemicals
N.A.I.C.S.: 423820
Leonard Benes (Pres)

BENESYS, INC.

700 Tower Dr Ste 300, Troy, MI 48098-2808
Tel.: (248) 813-9800
Web Site: https://www.benesys.com
Year Founded: 1979
Trust Fund Administrative Services
N.A.I.C.S.: 524292
David Sauro (CFO)
Sherry Verstraete (Mgr-HR)
Edward Wolyniec (CEO)
Jim Lareau (COO)
Bonnie Maraia (Pres-Ops-West Coast)

Chuck Wytrychowski (VP-Sls)
Jay Kolker (CIO)
Matthew Morbello (Chief Compliance Officer)

BENETECH INVESTMENTS CORP

2245 Sequoia Dr Ste 300, Aurora, IL 60506
Tel.: (630) 844-1300
Web Site:
   https://www.benetechglobal.com
Year Founded: 1983
Sales Range: $10-24.9 Million
Emp.: 61
Chemicals & Allied Products
N.A.I.C.S.: 424690
Ronald W. Pearson (Pres)

Subsidiaries:

Bentech S.A. (Pty) Ltd.   (1)
1 B Stevenson Street Ext 25, 1035, Witbank, South Africa
Tel.: (27) 1127136974617
Chemicals & Allied Products
N.A.I.C.S.: 424690

Servicios Benetech C.A.   (1)
Calle La Joya Edificio Cosmos Oficina 8-, Chacao, Caracas, Venezuela
Tel.: (58) 21226446686171
Chemicals & Allied Products
N.A.I.C.S.: 424690

BENEVA FLOWERS AND GIFTS INC.

6980 Beneva Rd, Sarasota, FL 34238
Tel.: (941) 308-5151
Web Site: https://www.beneva.com
Sales Range: $1-9.9 Million
Emp.: 40
Florists
N.A.I.C.S.: 459310
Arthur Conforti (Pres)
Tina Rivkin (VP-Sls)

BENFIELD ELECTRIC COMPANY, INC.

400 Hickery Dr Ste 200, Aberdeen, MD 21001
Tel.: (410) 879-1485
Web Site:
   https://www.benfieldinc.com
Year Founded: 1968
Sales Range: $10-24.9 Million
Emp.: 115
General Electrical Contractor
N.A.I.C.S.: 238210
Greg Benfield (Pres)

BENFORD CAPITAL PARTNERS, LLC

121 W Wacker Ste 650, Chicago, IL 60601
Tel.: (312) 932-0200
Web Site:
   http://www.benfordcapital.com
Privater Equity Firm
N.A.I.C.S.: 523999
Edward H. Benford (Founder & Mng Dir)
Benjamin R. Riefe (Mng Dir)
Brendan Green (Principal)

Subsidiaries:

Animix, LLC   (1)
W7104 County KW, Juneau, WI 53039
Tel.: (920) 386-5657
Web Site: http://www.animix.net
Sales Range: $1-9.9 Million
Emp.: 18
Animal Feed Mfr
N.A.I.C.S.: 311119
Ronelle Blome (Pres)
Sherry Jones (Gen Mgr-Pur)
Joe Grosskopf (Controller)
Dave Wood (Dir-Sls & Technical Svcs)

Benford Capital Partners, LLC—(Continued)

Legacy Bakehouse, LLC (1)
N8 W22100 Johnson Dr, Waukesha, WI 53186
Tel.: (262) 547-2447
Web Site: http://nerdydata.com
Sales Range: $1-9.9 Million
Emp.: 35
Potato Chips, Corn Chips & Similar Snacks
N.A.I.C.S.: 311919
Chris Pinahs (Pres)

Subsidiary (Domestic):

Angelic Bakehouse, Inc. (2)
3275 E Layton Ave, Cudahy, WI 53110
Tel.: (414) 312-7300
Food & Beverage Mfg
N.A.I.C.S.: 311999

SACO Foods Inc. (1)
1845 Deming Way, Middleton, WI 53562
Tel.: (608) 662-2662
Web Site: http://www.sacofoods.com
Sales Range: $10-24.9 Million
Baking Items & Chocolate
N.A.I.C.S.: 311351
Charles Olins (VP-Sls & Mktg)
Tom Walzer (CEO)

Subsidiary (Domestic):

California Sun Dry Foods, Inc. (2)
1845 Deming Way, Middleton, WI 53562
Tel.: (925) 743-9973
Web Site: https://www.calsundry.com
Dried & Dehydrated Food Mfr
N.A.I.C.S.: 311423

SOLO Foods, LLC (2)
PO Box 990, Burgaw, NC 28425-0990
Tel.: (910) 259-9407
Sales Range: $1-9.9 Million
Emp.: 6
Specialty Baking Ingredient Products Mfr
N.A.I.C.S.: 424450
Tim Kelly (Gen Mgr)

U.S. Underwater Services, LLC (1)
123 Sentry Dr, Mansfield, TX 76063-3601
Tel.: (817) 447-7321
Web Site: http://www.usunderwaterservices.com
Commercial Diving & Underwater Inspection Services
N.A.I.C.S.: 561990
Michael Hale (CFO)
Ashley Johnson (Mgr-Admin & Fin)

BENGAL MACHINE
61 Depot St, Buffalo, NY 14206
Tel.: (716) 855-1555
Web Site: https://bengalmachine.com
Year Founded: 1928
Reduction Equipment Designer & Mfr
N.A.I.C.S.: 333612
Martin Berardi (CEO)

Subsidiaries:

CM Recycling Equipment Solutions (1)
1920 Whitfield Ave, Sarasota, FL 34243-3921
Tel.: (941) 755-2621
Web Site: http://www.cmshredders.com
High Volume Tire Shredders
N.A.I.C.S.: 332710
Charles Astafan (Gen Mgr)
Richard Colyar (Mgr-Sls)

BENGAL TRANSPORTATION SERVICES, LLC.
37156 Hwy 30, Geismar, LA 70734
Tel.: (225) 677-8890
Web Site: https://www.bengaltransport.com
Year Founded: 1995
Sales Range: $10-24.9 Million
Emp.: 98
General Freight Trucking, Long-Distance, Truckload
N.A.I.C.S.: 484121

John Austin (Pres)
Jeff Cronan (VP-Transportation)
Ben Fromenthal (Dir-Sls & Mktg)
Bryan Vige (VP-Crane)

BENHAVEN, INC.
187 Half Mile Rd, North Haven, CT 06473
Tel.: (203) 239-6425 CT
Web Site: https://www.benhaven.org
Year Founded: 1967
Sales Range: $10-24.9 Million
Emp.: 334
Developmental Disability Assistance Services
N.A.I.C.S.: 623210
Tacie Lowe (Dir-Family-Individual Support)
Linda Grimm (Dir-Benhaven's Learning Network)
Stephen Simonson (Dir-Residential)

BENICIA FOUNDRY & IRON WORKS INC.
2995 Bayshore Rd, Benicia, CA 94510
Tel.: (707) 745-4645
Web Site: http://www.beniciafoundry.com
Rev.: $12,000,000
Emp.: 30
Metal Household Furniture Mfr
N.A.I.C.S.: 337126
Mary Anne Sanchez (Pres)

BENJAMIN FOODS, LLC.
1001 S York Rd, Hatboro, PA 19040
Tel.: (215) 437-5000
Web Site: http://www.benjaminfoods.com
Year Founded: 2008
Sales Range: $50-74.9 Million
Emp.: 62
Food Products Distr
N.A.I.C.S.: 424420
Howard Klayman (Pres & CEO)
David Salib (Exec VP)
Mark Oltman (CFO)
Makis Fazen (Mgr-Facilities)
Laura Cartwright (Coord-Bid)
John Hindman (Acct Exec)
Mindy Schley (Coord-Customer Svc)
Peggy Corcoran-Magis (VP-Equipment & Supply)
Judy Hummel (Controller)
Michael Cheeks (VP-HR)
Mitch Cohen (Asst Coord-Bid)
Barb Schaarschmidt (Mgr-Credit)

BENJAMIN FRANKLIN PLUMBING
13551 Method St, Dallas, TX 75243
Tel.: (214) 989-4919
Web Site: http://www.punctualplumbers.com
Year Founded: 2000
Sales Range: $10-24.9 Million
Emp.: 75
Plumbing Services
N.A.I.C.S.: 332913
Keresa Richardson (Pres & Owner)

BENJAMIN MACFARLAND COMPANY, LLC
424 Park Pl, West Palm Beach, FL 33401
Tel.: (561) 686-3161 FL
Web Site: http://www.bmacre.com
Year Founded: 2006
Sales Range: $10-24.9 Million
Commercial Real Estate Broker
N.A.I.C.S.: 531210
Christopher DeVaughn (Exec Dir-Business Development)
Benjamin S. Macfarland III (Founder & Mng Partner)

Subsidiaries:

Calidus Holdings, LLC (1)
400 N Congress Ave Ste 100, West Palm Beach, FL 33401
Tel.: (561) 686-3161
Web Site: http://www.calidus.co
Commercial Real Estate Investment Holding Company
N.A.I.C.S.: 551112
Jonathan Cameron-Hayes (CEO)
Frank Miller (CFO)
Oliver Cameron-Hayes (COO)
Farah Abdulla (Controller)
John Judd (Dir-Dev & Construction)
Benjamin S. Macfarland III (Chief Investment Officer)

Elite Stor Capital Partners, LLC (1)
324 Datura St Ste 338, West Palm Beach, FL 33401
Tel.: (561) 412-4719
Web Site: http://www.elitestorcapitalpartners.com
Emp.: 60
Self-Storage Facilities Investment Holding Company
N.A.I.C.S.: 551112
Donald Toler (COO)
Beau Raich (Gen Counsel)
Wallace Cascio (Dir-Acq)
Jacqueline Hall (Dir-Mktg)
John Judd (Dir-Dev & Construction)
Adam Kessler (Dir-Bus Dev)
Sheila Reinken (CFO)
Rob Consalvo (Pres & CTO)
Jim Jenkins (Principal)
Sidney Kohl (Principal)
Benjamin S. Macfarland III (CEO & Mng Partner)

Holding (Domestic):

Storage Rentals of America (2)
185 Westridge Dr, Danville, KY 40422
Web Site: http://www.storagerentalsofamerica.com
Emp.: 1
Self-Storage Unit Leasing Services
N.A.I.C.S.: 531130

BENJAMIN MICHAEL & ASSOCIATES, INC.
PO Box 41, Coram, NY 11727
Tel.: (631) 944-6730 DE
Web Site: http://www.mycollectionagency.info
Year Founded: 1998
Sales Range: $10-24.9 Million
Emp.: 5
Debt Collection Services
N.A.I.C.S.: 561440
Michael Hess (Sr VP-Sls)

BENJAMIN OBDYKE, INC.
400 Babylon Rd Ste A, Horsham, PA 19044-1232
Tel.: (215) 672-7200 DE
Web Site: http://www.benjaminobdyke.com
Year Founded: 1868
Sales Range: $200-249.9 Million
Emp.: 40
Provider of Building Construction Products
N.A.I.C.S.: 423730
George Caruso (COO)
Karl Feucht (Mgr-Market Dev)
Joe Holcombe (Sls Mgr-Natl)
David A. Campbell (Pres & CEO)

BENJAMIN STEEL COMPANY INC.
777 Benjamin Dr, Springfield, OH 45502-8846
Tel.: (937) 322-8600 OH
Web Site: https://www.benjaminsteel.com
Year Founded: 1947
Sales Range: $25-49.9 Million
Emp.: 175
Supplier of Metal Services

N.A.I.C.S.: 423510
Nick Demana (Co-Owner)
Dan Kelly (Exec VP)
Dominic Demana (Chm & CEO)

BENKO PRODUCTS, INC.
5350 Evergreen Pkwy, Sheffield Village, OH 44054
Tel.: (440) 934-2180 OH
Web Site: https://www.benkoproducts.com
Year Founded: 1983
Sales Range: $1-9.9 Million
Emp.: 70
Material Handling Equipment Mfr
N.A.I.C.S.: 333248
Bob Becka (Mgr-Ops)
Holly Benko Monchein (Mgr-Mktg)
Doug Ingram (Mgr-Bus Dev)

BENMAR MARINE ELECTRONICS, INC.
PO Box 4007, Idyllwild, CA 92549
Tel.: (714) 540-5120 CA
Web Site: http://www.benmarmarine.com
Year Founded: 1959
Sales Range: $25-49.9 Million
Emp.: 35
Marine Autopilot Systems & Marine Fuel Management Systems
N.A.I.C.S.: 334511
Robert Edwards (Owner)
Darrel Stucky (Controller)

BENNER-NAWMAN INC.
3450 Sabin Brown Rd, Wickenburg, AZ 85390
Tel.: (928) 684-2813
Web Site: https://www.bnproducts.com
Sales Range: $10-24.9 Million
Emp.: 15
Telephone Booths; Except Wood
N.A.I.C.S.: 337126
Ed Kientz (Pres)
Mel Kientz (Sr VP)
Lon Brown (Sr VP-Mfg)

BENNETT & BROSSEAU ROOFING INC.
535 Anderson Dr, Romeoville, IL 60446
Tel.: (630) 759-0009
Web Site: https://www.bennettbrosseau.com
Sales Range: $10-24.9 Million
Emp.: 100
Roofing Contractors
N.A.I.C.S.: 238160
James Brosseau (Owner)
George Peterson (Pres)
Chris Eheart (VP)
Susan Lee (Treas)

BENNETT & PLESS, INC.
47 Perimeter Ctr E Ste 500, Atlanta, GA 30346
Tel.: (678) 990-8700
Web Site: http://www.bennett-pless.com
Engineeering Services
N.A.I.C.S.: 541330
Patrick Valent (Dir-Betacom)
Melinda Parrish Brumfield (Dir-Strategy & Bus Dev-Natl)
Ed Gazzola (CEO)

Subsidiaries:

LHC Structural Engineers, PC (1)
5430 Wade Park Blvd Ste 400, Raleigh, NC 27607
Tel.: (919) 832-5587
Web Site: http://www.lhcengineers.com
Rev.: $1,863,000
Emp.: 9
Engineeering Services

N.A.I.C.S.: 541330
Bobby Lasater (Pres)
Rob Stevenson (VP)

Linton Engineering LLC (1)
46090 Lk Ctr Plz Ste 309, Sterling, VA 20165-5879
Tel.: (571) 323-0320
Web Site: http://www.lintonengineering.com
Engineeering Services
N.A.I.C.S.: 541330
David E. Linton (Principal)

BENNETT AUTO SUPPLY INC.
3141 SW Tenth St, Pompano Beach, FL 33069-4828
Tel.: (954) 335-8700   FL
Web Site:
    http://www.bennettauto.com
Year Founded: 1957
Sales Range: $50-74.9 Million
Emp.: 400
Provider of Auto Parts
N.A.I.C.S.: 423120
Harold Bennett (Co-Owner)
Barry Bennett (Co-Owner)

BENNETT AUTOMOTIVE GROUP
4800 W Tilghman St, Allentown, PA 18104
Tel.: (610) 841-5700
Web Site:
    http://www.bennettcars.com
Sales Range: $10-24.9 Million
Emp.: 100
New & Used Car Dealers
N.A.I.C.S.: 441110
Robert Bennett (Owner & Pres)

BENNETT BROTHERS, INC.
30 E Adams St, Chicago, IL 60603-5610
Tel.: (312) 263-4800   IL
Web Site:
    http://www.bennettbrothers.com
Year Founded: 1906
Sales Range: $75-99.9 Million
Emp.: 100
Jewelry & Electric Devices Sales
N.A.I.C.S.: 423940
Bob Switalla (VP-Adv)
Rick Brest (Acct Mgr)
G. Kirk Bennett Jr. (Treas & VP)

Subsidiaries:

Bennett Brothers, Inc.   (1)
30 E Adams St, Chicago, IL 60603-5610   (100%)
Tel.: (312) 263-4800
Web Site: http://www.bennettbrothers.com
Sales Range: $10-24.9 Million
Emp.: 30
Building Management Company For Commercial Properties
N.A.I.C.S.: 531190

BENNETT BUICK GMC
651 S Ohio St, Salina, KS 67401
Tel.: (785) 823-6372
Web Site:
    http://www.bennettbuickgmc.com
Sales Range: $10-24.9 Million
Emp.: 40
New & Used Car Dealer
N.A.I.C.S.: 441110
Ralph Bennett (Owner & Pres)

BENNETT CAPITAL PARTNERS, LLC
901 N Washington St Ste 602, Alexandria, VA 22314
Tel.: (202) 629-2185   DE
Web Site:
    http://www.bennettcapital.com
Privater Equity Firm
N.A.I.C.S.: 523999
Tim Bennett (Operating Partner)
Jane Bennett (Operating Partner)

BENNETT CONTRACTING, INC.
6029 33rd St E, Bradenton, FL 34203
Tel.: (941) 756-8200
Web Site:
    http://www.bennettcontracting.com
Year Founded: 2000
Sales Range: $1-9.9 Million
Emp.: 20
Site Preparation Contractor
N.A.I.C.S.: 238910
Jason Bennett (Pres)
Alisa S. Bennett (VP)
Jim Hunter (Project Mgr)
Connie Shoemaker (Office Mgr)

BENNETT ENTERPRISES INC.
27476 Holiday Ln, Perrysburg, OH 43551-3345
Tel.: (419) 874-1933
Web Site: https://www.bennett-enterprises.com
Year Founded: 1960
Sales Range: $50-74.9 Million
Emp.: 1,500
Provider of Hotel & Motel Services
N.A.I.C.S.: 721110
Rob Armstrong (CEO)

BENNETT EUBANKS OIL COMPANY
17410 Main St N, Blountstown, FL 32424
Tel.: (850) 674-8219
Sales Range: $10-24.9 Million
Emp.: 80
Petroleum Products
N.A.I.C.S.: 424720
Bennett Eubanks III (Pres)

BENNETT INTERNATIONAL GROUP, INC.
1001 Indus Pkwy, McDonough, GA 30253-7330
Tel.: (770) 957-1866   GA
Web Site: http://www.bennettig.com
Year Founded: 1993
Sales Range: $10-24.9 Million
Emp.: 200
Transportation Services
N.A.I.C.S.: 484121
Marcia G. Taylor (Owner, Chm, Pres & CEO)
Lynette Alt (VP-Mktg & Supplier Diversity)
David Pittman (CFO & Co-COO)
Tim Hadden (CIO)
Lee Gentry (Exec VP)
Phil Hibbs (VP)
David Lowry (VP)
Danny Lowry (VP)
Regina Auletta (VP-Admin & HR)
Paul Molnar (VP-Safety & Bennett Intl Grp)
Jodi Penn (VP-Quality, Customer Svc & Bennett Intl Grp)
Peter L. Costello (Co-COO)

Subsidiaries:

American Eagle Logistics, LLC   (1)
1247 Petrolum Pkwy, Broussard, LA 70518
Tel.: (337) 288-7944
Web Site: http://www.aeagle.net
Sales Range: $10-24.9 Million
Emp.: 100
Refrigerated Trucking Services
N.A.I.C.S.: 484230
David L. Lippman (Mgr)

Bennett Building Systems, LLC   (1)
1660 Dixon Airline Rd, Augusta, GA 30906
Tel.: (877) 498-8069
Web Site: http://www.bennettbuildings.com
Prefabricated Metal Building Mfr
N.A.I.C.S.: 332311
Danny Lowry (Pres)

Bennett Distribution Services, LLC   (1)
2340 Doug Barnard Pkwy, Augusta, GA 30906
Tel.: (706) 772-4729
Web Site:
    http://www.bennettdistributionservices.com
Logistics Consulting Servies
N.A.I.C.S.: 541614

Bennett International Transport Inc.   (1)
1001 Industrial Pkwy, McDonough, GA 30253
Tel.: (770) 957-1866
Web Site: http://www.bennettig.com
Sales Range: $10-24.9 Million
Provider of Freight Transportation Arrangements
N.A.I.C.S.: 488510
Marcia G. Taylor (CEO)
Lee Gentry (Exec VP)

Bennett Motor Express Inc.   (1)
1001 Industrial Pkwy, McDonough, GA 30253-7330
Tel.: (770) 957-1866
Web Site: http://www.bennettig.com
Provider of Trucking, Except Local
N.A.I.C.S.: 484121
Virgina Auletta (Office Mgr)

Bennett Truck Transport   (1)
1001 Industrial Pkwy, McDonough, GA 30253
Tel.: (770) 957-1866
Web Site: http://www.bennetig.com
Rev.: $37,000,000
Emp.: 100
Trucking
N.A.I.C.S.: 484121
Marcia Taylor (Pres)

Transport Services, Inc.   (1)
2700 Broening Hwy, Baltimore, MD 21222-4190
Tel.: (410) 284-6214
Web Site: http://www.bds-solutions.com
Sales Range: $10-24.9 Million
Emp.: 30
Provider of Trucking Services
N.A.I.C.S.: 484121
Marcia G. Taylor (Pres)

BENNETT KUHN VARNER, INC.
3390 Peachtree Rd 10th Fl, Atlanta, GA 30326
Tel.: (404) 233-0332
Web Site: http://www.bkv.com
Year Founded: 1981
Rev.: $60,000,000
Emp.: 150
N.A.I.C.S.: 541810
Maribett Varner (Pres-Atlanta)
Virginia Doty (Exec VP & Dir-Mktg)
Jamie Turner (Dir-Consumer Insights)
Jana Ferguson (Exec VP & Dir-Client Svcs)
Jerelle Gainey (CTO & VP)
Michelle Gunn (VP & Creative Dir)
Angela Hilton (Sr VP & Dir-Acct)
Kimberly Honore (VP & Dir-Search Engine Mktg)
Mai Huynh (VP & Controller)
David Randolph (Chief Strategy Officer & Sr VP)
Bree Roe (Sr VP & Dir-Exec Media)

BENNETT LUMBER COMPANY
111 Old Ladiga Rd, Piedmont, AL 36272
Tel.: (256) 447-9663
Web Site:
    http://www.bennettlumber.com
Rev.: $15,000,000
Emp.: 86
Mfr of Lumber, Plywood & Millwork
N.A.I.C.S.: 423310
Lee Hubbard (CFO)
Jeremy Calvert (Office Mgr)

BENNETT PACKAGING OF KANSAS CITY

220 NW Space Center Cir, Lees Summit, MO 64064
Tel.: (816) 379-5001
Web Site: https://www.bpkc.com
Year Founded: 1972
Sales Range: $10-24.9 Million
Emp.: 130
Corrugated Boxes, Partitions, Display Items, Sheets & Pad
N.A.I.C.S.: 322211
Doug Bennett (Co-Owner & VP)
Don Daly (Dir-Sls & Mktg)
Mark Edwards (Controller)

BENNETT THRASHER
3300 Riverwood Pkwy Ste 700, Atlanta, GA 30339-6403
Tel.: (770) 396-2200
Web Site: http://www.bennett-thrasher.com
Emp.: 200
Offices of Certified Public Accountants
N.A.I.C.S.: 541211
Kenneth L. Thrasher (Partner)
Jenna Walker (Partner)
Raygan J. Evans (Partner)
John Cummings (Dir-Bus Dev)
Jeffrey A. Eischeid (Mng Partner)
Betsi Barrett (Partner)
Ben Miller (Partner)
Alana Mueller (Partner)
Michael Thrasher (Partner)
Vijay Vaswani (Partner-Transaction Advisory Svcs Practice)
Kelly Smith (Partner-Real Estate Hospitality Tax Practice)
Mike Hostinsky (Partner-Risk Advisory Svcs Practice)
Brian Hamm (Partner-Fin Reporting & Assurance Practice)
Bridget Dunk (Partner-Intl Personal Fin Svcs Tax Practice)
Stephen Bradshaw (Partner-State & Local Tax Practice)
Peter G. Stathopoulos (Partner)
Melisa Cook (Chief HR Officer)
Courtney Edwards (CIO)
Jeff Call (Mng Partner)

Subsidiaries:

Excelsia Investment Advisors   (1)
15 Lake St # 100, Savannah, GA 31411
Tel.: (912) 598-4032
Web Site: http://www.draughnpartners.com
Rev.: $2,010,000
Emp.: 5
Investment Banking & Securities Dealing
N.A.I.C.S.: 523150
Cliff Draughn (Owner)
Troy Gayle (Chief Investment Officer)

BENNETT TOYOTA
1951 Lehigh St, Allentown, PA 18103
Tel.: (610) 437-6711
Web Site:
    https://www.bennettcars.com
Year Founded: 1955
Rev.: $16,500,000
Emp.: 200
Automobile Dealers
N.A.I.C.S.: 441120
Chris Hendershot (Mgr-Parts)
Chris Zerfass (Mgr-Gen Sls)
Jeremey Miller (Mgr-Svc)
Jim Stinner (Mgr-Svc)

BENNETT, BRICKLIN & SALTZBURG LLC
1601 Market St 16th Fl, Philadelphia, PA 19103
Tel.: (215) 561-4300   PA
Web Site: http://www.bbs-law.com
Year Founded: 1946
Emp.: 54

Bennett, Bricklin & Saltzburg LLC—(Continued)

Law firm
N.A.I.C.S.: 541110
Charity C. Hyde *(Atty)*
Louis E. Bricklin *(Atty)*
Michael Saltzburg *(Atty)*
John F. Barrett *(Partner & Atty)*
Paul F. Lantieri *(Partner & Atty)*
Warren F. Sperling *(Mng Atty)*

BENNETTS OIL CO.
810 E Sheldon St, Prescott, AZ
86301
Tel.: (928) 445-1181
Web Site: http://www.bennettoil.com
Year Founded: 1962
Sales Range: $75-99.9 Million
Emp.: 47
Whslr of Petroleum Products
N.A.I.C.S.: 424710
Lenora Nelson *(Pres)*
Brad Nelson *(Mgr-Ops)*
Karla Green *(Controller)*

BENNING CONSTRUCTION COMPANY INC.
4695 S Atlanta Rd SE, Smyrna, GA
30339
Tel.: (404) 792-1911
Web Site: http://www.benningnet.com
Year Founded: 1953
Sales Range: $10-24.9 Million
Emp.: 80
Provider of Nonresidential Construction
N.A.I.C.S.: 236220
T. R. Benning *(Chm)*
Allen V. George *(Treas)*
Kevin T. Jenny *(Asst VP)*
Ryce Elliott *(VP)*

Subsidiaries:

English American Constructors
Inc. **(1)**
4695 S Atlanta Rd SE, Smyrna, GA
30080-7001 **(100%)**
Tel.: (404) 792-1911
Web Site: http://www.benningnet.com
Sales Range: $10-24.9 Million
Emp.: 60
Provider of Nonresidential Construction
N.A.I.C.S.: 236220

BENNY'S INC.
340 Waterman Ave, Smithfield, RI
02917
Tel.: (401) 231-1000
Web Site:
    http://www.hellobennys.com
Sales Range: $25-49.9 Million
Emp.: 150
Auto & Home Supply Stores
N.A.I.C.S.: 441330
John Monti *(Controller)*

BENOIST BROS. SUPPLY CO. INC.
107 N 16th St, Mount Vernon, IL
62864-4318
Tel.: (618) 242-0345
Web Site: https://www.benoist.com
Year Founded: 1928
Rev.: $12,200,000
Emp.: 57
Warm Air Heating & Air Conditioning
N.A.I.C.S.: 423730
Jack Benoist *(CEO)*
Karla Rector *(Controller)*
Merele Shurtz *(Coord-Mktg)*
Jackie Weems *(Mgr-Credit)*

BENOIT PREMIUM THREAD-ING, LLC
3400 Industrial Park Dr, Houma, LA
70363
Tel.: (985) 879-2487

Web Site: https://www.benoit-inc.com
Year Founded: 1943
Sales Range: $25-49.9 Million
Emp.: 200
Oilfield Downhole Accessories Mfr &
Tubing Threading Services
N.A.I.C.S.: 333132
Mike Arceneaux *(Project Coord)*
Ron Pederson *(CEO)*

BENOY MOTOR SALES, INC.
1790 S Eastwood Dr, Woodstock, IL
60098-4657
Tel.: (815) 338-5100
Web Site:
    http://www.benoymotor.com
Sales Range: $10-24.9 Million
Emp.: 17
Car Whslr
N.A.I.C.S.: 441110
Raymond C. Benoy *(Pres)*

BENSATA CORPORATION
2500 City W Blvd Ste 300, Houston,
TX 77042
Tel.: (713) 267-2361
Web Site:
    http://www.helpinventit.com
Year Founded: 2007
Online Inventors' Social Network
N.A.I.C.S.: 513210
Kim Kim *(Chm & CEO)*
Valerie Grant *(Sec)*

BENSON AUTOMOTIVE COMPANY
100 Sandau Rd Ste 210, San Antonio, TX 78216
Tel.: (210) 349-6200
Web Site:
    http://www.walkeracura.com
Rev.: $10,600,000
Emp.: 3
Sales of New & Used Cars
N.A.I.C.S.: 441110

BENSON CHRYSLER PLYM-OUTH INC.
400 W Wade Hampton Blvd, Greer,
SC 29651
Tel.: (864) 877-0161
Web Site:
    http://www.bensonchrysler.com
Sales Range: $50-74.9 Million
Emp.: 80
Car Whslr
N.A.I.C.S.: 441110
Chris Bensch *(Gen Mgr)*
James H. Benson *(Owner)*

BENSON LINCOLN MERCURY CORPORATION
4800 Clairton Blvd, Pittsburgh, PA
15236
Tel.: (412) 881-7000
Web Site:
    http://www.bensonlincoln.com
Year Founded: 1968
Sales Range: $25-49.9 Million
Emp.: 55
Car Whslr
N.A.I.C.S.: 441110
George Benson *(Pres)*

BENSON LINCOLN MERCURY INC.
4800 Clairton Blvd, Pittsburgh, PA
15236
Tel.: (412) 881-7000
Web Site:
    http://www.bensonmercury.com
Year Founded: 1968
Rev.: $32,000,000
Emp.: 55
Owner & Operator of Car Dealerships
N.A.I.C.S.: 441110

Terry Lahoff *(Controller)*

BENSON LUMBER & HARD-WARE INC.
6 Martin St, Derry, NH 03038-2311
Tel.: (603) 432-2531
Web Site:
    https://www.bensonslumber.com
Sales Range: $10-24.9 Million
Emp.: 120
Lumber & Other Building Materials
Mfr
N.A.I.C.S.: 423310
Bradley Benson *(Pres)*

BENSON MOTORS CORPORA-TION
3727 Veterans Blvd, Metairie, LA
70002
Tel.: (504) 456-3727
Web Site: http://www.mbofno.com
Year Founded: 1956
Sales Range: $500-549.9 Million
Emp.: 1,500
Car Dealer
N.A.I.C.S.: 441110
Tom Roddy *(Pres)*
Don Zander *(Sr VP & Controller)*

Subsidiaries:

Renson Enterprises **(1)**
100 Sandau Rd Ste 210, San Antonio, TX
78216-3635
Tel.: (210) 349-6200
Web Site: http://www.bensonmotor.com
Retailer of New & Used Automobiles
N.A.I.C.S.: 541611

BENSON'S, INC.
134 Elder St, Bogart, GA 30622
Tel.: (770) 725-5711
Web Site:
    http://www.bensonsbakery.com
Year Founded: 1918
Sales Range: $25-49.9 Million
Emp.: 250
Commercial Bakeries
N.A.I.C.S.: 311812
Larry R. Benson *(Owner)*

BENSUR CREATIVE MARKET-ING GROUP
1062 Brown Ave Ste 300, Erie, PA
16502
Tel.: (814) 461-9436
Web Site: http://www.bensur.com
Sales Range: $10-24.9 Million
Emp.: 8
Advetising Agency
N.A.I.C.S.: 541810
Daniel J. Bensur *(Owner)*
Bill Berger *(Dir-Creative)*
Kevin Seeker *(Acct Dir)*
Eric Armbruster *(Sr Dir-Art)*

BENSUSSEN-DEUTSCH & AS-SOCIATES INC.
15525 Woodinville Redmond Rd NE,
Woodinville, WA 98072-6977
Tel.: (425) 492-6111
Web Site: https://www.bdainc.com
Year Founded: 1984
Sales Range: $25-49.9 Million
Emp.: 219
Custom Branded Merchandise Design & Distribution Services
N.A.I.C.S.: 423990
Jay Deutsch *(Co-Founder & CEO)*
Steve Avanessian *(VP-Client Services)*
Barry Deutsch *(Chief Sls Officer)*
Jared Collinge *(CFO)*

BENTECH INC.
4135-4165 N 5th St, Philadelphia, PA
19140

Tel.: (215) 225-8955
Web Site:
    https://www.bentechinc.com
Rev.: $12,000,000
Emp.: 35
Fabricated Pipe & Fittings
N.A.I.C.S.: 332996

BENTEX KIDDIE CORPORA-TION
34 W 33rd St 2nd Fl, New York, NY
10001-2914
Tel.: (212) 594-4250
Web Site: http://www.bentex.com
Year Founded: 1970
Sales Range: $75-99.9 Million
Emp.: 100
Provider of Children's Clothing
N.A.I.C.S.: 424350
Ronald Benun *(Pres)*
Joseph Benun *(VP)*
Eli Benun *(CFO)*
Morris Dweck *(Sr VP)*
Morris Benun *(Controller)*

BENTHALL BROTHERS, INC.
15 Read St, Evansville, IN 47710
Tel.: (812) 424-0413
Web Site:
    https://www.benthallbros.com
Year Founded: 1943
Sales Range: $10-24.9 Million
Emp.: 25
Lumber, Plywood, Millwork & Wood
Panel Whslr
N.A.I.C.S.: 423310
Greene Benthall *(Co-Founder)*
Fred Benthall *(Co-Founder)*

BENTLEY FORBES GROUP, LLC
10250 Constellation Blvd Ste 2300,
Los Angeles, CA 90067-6223
Tel.: (310) 282-8000
Web Site:
    http://www.bentleyforbes.com
Year Founded: 1993
Rev.: $282,000,000
Emp.: 20
Real Estate Investors, Except Property Operators
N.A.I.C.S.: 523999
C. Frederick Wehba *(Chm)*
C. Frederick Wehba II *(Pres & CEO)*

BENTLEY TRUCK SERVICES, INC.
7777 Essington Ave, Philadelphia, PA
19153
Tel.: (215) 937-1044
Web Site:
    http://www.bentleytruckservices.com
Year Founded: 1991
Sales Range: $10-24.9 Million
Emp.: 47
New Car Retailer
N.A.I.C.S.: 441110
Donna Bentley *(Owner & CFO)*

BENTON & BROWN INC.
5626 Hwy 528, Minden, LA 71055
Tel.: (318) 377-8720
Sales Range: $25-49.9 Million
Emp.: 50
Highway & Street Paving Contractor
N.A.I.C.S.: 237310
John B. Benton III *(Pres)*

BENTON & PARKER CO. INC.
703 Medical Park Ln NE, Gainesville,
GA 30501
Tel.: (770) 536-8340
Web Site:
    https://www.bentonandparker.com
Year Founded: 1985
Sales Range: $10-24.9 Million

Emp.: 20
Insurance Agency Services
N.A.I.C.S.: 524210
Frank L. Parker (Co-Founder)
David Benton (Co-Founder)

BENTON ENTERPRISES IN-CORPORATED

5508 W Hwy 290 Ste 201, Austin, TX 78735
Tel.: (512) 891-7711   TX
Web Site: http://www.mcdonalds.com
Year Founded: 1973
Sales Range: $25-49.9 Million
Emp.: 400
Franchise Owner of Fast-Food Restaurants
N.A.I.C.S.: 722513
James Mike Benton (Pres)
Diane Benton (VP)
Becki Benton Russell (CFO)

BENTON RURAL ELECTRIC ASSOCIATION

402 7th St, Prosser, WA 99350
Tel.: (509) 786-2913
Web Site: http://www.bentonrea.com
Sales Range: $10-24.9 Million
Emp.: 73
Distribution, Electric Power
N.A.I.C.S.: 221122
Clint Gerkensmeyer (Gen Mgr)
Virgil Boyle (Pres)
John Porter (Mgr-Fin & Admin)
Michael Bradshaw (Mgr-Special Svcs)

BENTON'S EQUIPMENT & CONSTRUCTION, INC.

4590 Chester Portie Rd, Sulphur, LA 70665
Tel.: (337) 583-4943
Web Site: https://www.becpipe.com
Sales Range: $10-24.9 Million
Emp.: 100
Other Heavy & Civil Engineering Construction Services
N.A.I.C.S.: 237990
Clay Benton (Pres)
Tim Benton (VP)
Judd Benton (Mgr-Construction)

BENTON-GEORGIA, INC.

7760 Bankhead Hwy, Douglasville, GA 30134
Tel.: (770) 942-8180
Web Site: http://www.benton-georgia.com
Year Founded: 1988
Sales Range: $300-349.9 Million
Emp.: 356
Underground Utilities Contractor
N.A.I.C.S.: 237110
Bruce Freniere (Mgr-Claims)
Greg Lawson (Dir-Ops)
Scott Bailey (Mgr-Construction)

BENTZEL MECHANICAL INC.

2880 Scherer Dr N Ste 860, Saint Petersburg, FL 33716
Tel.: (727) 572-7767
Web Site:
    http://www.bentzelmechanical.com
Year Founded: 1989
Sales Range: $1-9.9 Million
Emp.: 10
Mechanical Contractor
N.A.I.C.S.: 238220
Thomas Bentzel (CEO)

BENZ CONNECTION OF NAPLES INC.

3126 Davis Blvd, Naples, FL 34104
Tel.: (239) 774-9290
Web Site:
    https://www.thebenzconnection.net

Sales Range: $1-9.9 Million
Automotive Repair & Maintenance
N.A.I.C.S.: 811198
Paula Studzinski (Pres)

BENZEL-BUSCH MOTOR CAR CORP.

28 Grand Ave, Englewood, NJ 07631-3560
Tel.: (201) 567-1400
Web Site: http://www.benzel-busch.com
Year Founded: 1975
Sales Range: $25-49.9 Million
Emp.: 205
Sales of New & Used Cars
N.A.I.C.S.: 441110
Joseph Agresta (Pres)
Charles Bond (Controller)
Phil Battagligno (Mgr-Pre-Owned Sls)
Benzel Busch (VP)
Justin Pooler (Mgr-Parts)
Willy Aramayo (Mgr-Client Rels)

BENZER PHARMACY HOLD-ING LLC

125 W Country Club Dr, Tampa, FL 33612
Tel.: (813) 304-2221   FL
Web Site:
    http://www.benzerpharmacy.com
Holding Company; Pharmacies & Drug Stores Owner, Operator & Franchisor
N.A.I.C.S.: 551112
Alpesh Patel (Co-Owner)
Manish Patel (Co-Owner)

Subsidiaries:

Rx Care Specialty Pharmacy LLC   (1)
125 W Country Club Dr, Tampa, FL 33612
Tel.: (813) 304-2221
Web Site:
    http://www.benzerspecialtypharmacy.com
Specialty Pharmacies Operator
N.A.I.C.S.: 456110
Michael LaBrecque (VP)
Ryan Rushing (Dir-New Bus Dev-340B Program)
Ruidvin Ragunath (Mgr-Compliance)
Ricque Gonder (Mgr-Payer Rels & Reimbursement)

BEOCARE GROUP, INC.

1905 International Blvd, Hudson, NC 28638-8638
Tel.: (828) 728-7300
Web Site: https://www.beocare.net
Emp.: 125
Leather Goods Mfr
N.A.I.C.S.: 315210
Peter Vanderbruggen (Chm & CEO)
Jim Verberg (Pres-North America)
Craig Wood (VP-Sls & Mktg)
Patsy Smith (VP-Customer Rels)
Willy Van Waeyenberghe (VP-Sls & Mktg-Europe)

Subsidiaries:

Shelby Elastics of North Carolina, LLC   (1)
639 N Post Rd, Shelby, NC 28150-8150
Tel.: (704) 487-4301
Web Site: http://www.shelbyelastics.com
Fabric Mills
N.A.I.C.S.: 313220
Craig Wood (Pres)

BEOWULF ENERGY LLC

100 NW St, Easton, MD 21601
Tel.: (410) 770-9500
Web Site:
    http://www.beowulfenergy.com
Sales Range: $10-24.9 Million
Emp.: 25
Energy Investments
N.A.I.C.S.: 523999

Paul Prager (Pres & CEO)
Douglas Halliday (Exec VP)
Michael R. Enright (Mng Dir)

Subsidiaries:

Bicent Power LLC   (1)
100 North West St, Easton, MD 21601
Tel.: (410) 770-9500
Electric Power Services
N.A.I.C.S.: 221122
Paul Prager (Chm & CEO)
Douglas Halliday (COO & Exec VP)
Nazar Khan (Sr VP-Dev & Acq)

Subsidiary (Domestic):

Centennial Power, Inc.   (2)
1930 Burntboat Dr, Bismarck, ND 58503
Tel.: (701) 222-7989
Power Company
N.A.I.C.S.: 221118

Colorado Energy Management, LLC   (2)
2575 Park Ln Ste 200, Lafayette, CO 80026
Tel.: (303) 442-5112
Web Site: http://www.coloradoenergy.com
Emp.: 17
Electrical Power Plant
N.A.I.C.S.: 221118
Elizabeth Strothman (Gen Mgr-Ledger)

BEPCO, INC.

219 Junia Ave, Winston Salem, NC 27103
Tel.: (336) 760-0740   NC
Web Site: http://www.bepco.biz
Sales Range: $75-99.9 Million
Emp.: 120
Remanufacturer of Air Brake Components for Heavy Duty Equipment
N.A.I.C.S.: 333415
Susan Marshall (VP)

BEPEX INTERNATIONAL, LLC

333 Taft St NE, Minneapolis, MN 55413-2810
Tel.: (612) 400-8745
Web Site: https://www.bepex.com
Year Founded: 1976
Sales Range: $50-74.9 Million
Emp.: 45
Food & Chemical Processing Equipment Mfr
N.A.I.C.S.: 333241
Warren White (CFO)
Dale Roberts (Chm)
Ken Eckel (Mgr-Info Svcs)
Kaitlin Carter (Mgr-Mktg Comm)
Scott Halvorsen (Dir-Intl)
Tom Brion (Mgr-Engrg)
Andrei Bortnov (Engr-Laboratory)

Subsidiaries:

Bepex Asia Limited   (1)
A-11 10 Floor Tonic Industrial Center 26 Kai Cheung Road, Kowloon Bay, Kowloon, China (Hong Kong)
Tel.: (852) 2318 0898
Web Site: http://www.bepex.asia
Sales Range: $10-24.9 Million
Emp.: 3
Industrial Equipment Sales & Maintenance Services
N.A.I.C.S.: 423830
Ricky Shum (Gen Mgr)

BERAT CORPORATION

1230 Blackwood Clementon Rd, Clementon, NJ 08021
Tel.: (856) 627-6501
Web Site: http://www.shoprite.com
Sales Range: $200-249.9 Million
Emp.: 2,000
Grocery Stores, Independent
N.A.I.C.S.: 445110

BERBER FOOD MANUFAC-TURING INC.

425 Hester St, San Leandro, CA 94577-1025
Tel.: (510) 553-0444
Sales Range: $10-24.9 Million
Emp.: 150
Tortilla Mfr
N.A.I.C.S.: 311830
Robert Berber (Treas & Sec)
Manuel Berber (Pres)
Marlon Buitrago (Mgr)

BERBERIAN BROS INC.

10777 Trinity Pkwy, Stockton, CA 95219
Tel.: (209) 944-5511
Web Site:
    http://www.berberianmotors.com
Rev.: $14,624,728
Emp.: 14
New & Used Car Dealers
N.A.I.C.S.: 551112
Ronald Berberian (Pres)
Mike Berberian (Treas & Sec)

BERBERIAN ENTERPRISES INC.

5315 Santa Monica Blvd, Los Angeles, CA 90029-1105
Tel.: (323) 460-4646
Web Site:
    https://www.jonsmarketplace.com
Year Founded: 1977
Sales Range: $250-299.9 Million
Emp.: 1,000
Provider of Grocery Services
N.A.I.C.S.: 445110
Andy Meechan (VP-Operations)

BERCHTOLD EQUIPMENT COMPANY

330 E 19th St, Bakersfield, CA 93305
Tel.: (661) 323-7817
Web Site: http://www.berchtold.com
Rev.: $15,990,903
Emp.: 40
Farm Machinery
N.A.I.C.S.: 459999
Charlie Jorgensen (Mgr-Sls-Delano)
Kevin Klugow (Mgr-Svc-Delano)
Mike McGinley (Mgr-Sls-Santa Maria)

BERCO RESOURCES LLC

100 Fillmore St Ste 400, Denver, CO 80206-4921
Tel.: (303) 825-1188
Sales Range: $25-49.9 Million
Emp.: 4
Oil & Gas Exploration
N.A.I.C.S.: 211120
William S. Bergner (Pres)

BERDON LLP

360 Madison Ave Fl 8, New York, NY 10017
Tel.: (212) 832-0400
Web Site: http://www.berdonllp.com
Year Founded: 1917
Sales Range: $25-49.9 Million
Emp.: 400
Full Service Accounting & Advisory Services
N.A.I.C.S.: 541211
Saul Brenner (Partner-Intl Tax)
Scott T. Ditman (Partner)
Meyer Mintz (Partner)
William Saya (Partner)
Marc Fogel (Partner-Audit)
Frank J. Vitale (CMO-Manhattan & Jericho)
Clifford Forrester (CIO)
Mark G. Bosswick (Mng Partner)
Bonnie Mann Falk (Partner-Quality Control)

BERENSON & COMPANY, INC.

Berenson & Company, Inc.—(Continued)

667 Madison Ave, New York, NY
10065
Tel.: (212) 935-7676
Web Site:
http://www.berensonco.com
Privater Equity Firm
N.A.I.C.S.: 523999
MOhammed M. Ansari *(Pres)*
Robert H. Clymer *(Mng Dir)*
Amir Hegazy *(Mng Dir)*
Michael Lewis *(CFO & Chief Com-
plaince Officer)*
Jeffrey L. Berenson *(Founder & CEO)*

Subsidiaries:

Berenson & Company, LLC   (1)
667 Madison Ave Fl 22, New York, NY
10021
Tel.: (212) 935-7676
Web Site: http://www.berensonco.com
Sales Range: $1-9.9 Million
Emp.: 28
Investment Banking & Securities Dealing
N.A.I.C.S.: 523150
Jonathan Newcomb *(Mng Dir)*
Jeffrey Sechrest *(Pres)*

Interactive Digital Solutions, Inc.   (1)
14701 Cumberland Rd 400, Noblesville, IN
46060
Tel.: (317) 770-3500
Web Site: http://www.e-idsolutions.com
Rev.: $10,000,000
Emp.: 18
Wired Telecommunications Carriers
N.A.I.C.S.: 517111
Tracy Mills *(Founder & Pres)*
Chris Apple *(VP-Engrg)*
Brad Ballentine *(VP-Customer Svc)*
Zac Cook *(VP-Enterprise Sls)*
Rick Dawson *(VP-Healthcare Sls)*
John Hess *(VP-Ops)*
David Fetterolf *(Exec Chm)*

Skience LLC   (1)
580 Herndon Pkwy, Herndon, VA 20170
Tel.: (866) 754-3623
Web Site: https://skience.com
Cloud-Based Wealth Management Services
N.A.I.C.S.: 518210
Kripa Shety *(Chief Admin Officer)*

BEREXCO INC.
2020 N Bramblewood St, Wichita, KS
67206-1094
Tel.: (316) 265-3311
Web Site: https://www.berexco.com
Rev.: $48,000,000
Emp.: 100
Crude Petroleum & Natural Gas Pro-
vider
N.A.I.C.S.: 211120
Robert M. Beren *(Pres)*

BERG & BERG ENTERPRISES, INC.
10050 Bandley Dr, Cupertino, CA
95014
Tel.: (408) 725-7200   CA
Year Founded: 1979
Investment Holding Company
N.A.I.C.S.: 551112
Carl E. Berg *(Pres & CEO)*

Subsidiaries:

Berg & Berg Enterprises, LLC   (1)
10050 Bandley Dr, Cupertino, CA 95014
Tel.: (408) 725-0700
Sales Range: $1-9.9 Million
Investment Management Service
N.A.I.C.S.: 523940
Kara Berg *(Mgr)*

BERG COMPANY, LLC.
2160 Industrial Dr, Madison, WI
53713
Tel.: (608) 221-4281   WI
Web Site:
http://www.bergliquorscontrols.com
Sales Range: $1-9.9 Million

Emp.: 16
Measuring & Dispensing Pump Mfr
N.A.I.C.S.: 333914
Micheal Keating *(Reg Mgr)*

BERG EAST IMPORTS INC.
120 E Gloucester Pike, Barrington,
NJ 08007-1330
Tel.: (908) 354-5252
Web Site:
http://www.bergfurniture.com
Year Founded: 1984
Rev.: $10,400,000
Emp.: 47
Juvenile Furniture Retailer
N.A.I.C.S.: 561499
Larry Newman *(Controller)*

BERG ELECTRIC CORPORA-TION
5650 W Centinela Ave, Los Angeles,
CA 90045-1501
Tel.: (310) 337-1377   CA
Web Site:
http://www.bergelectric.com
Year Founded: 1946
Sales Range: $200-249.9 Million
Emp.: 600
Electrical Contracting Services
N.A.I.C.S.: 238210
John R. Briscoe *(CEO)*
Don L. Briscoe *(Pres)*
Ed Billig *(VP)*
Bill Winering *(Sr VP)*

BERG EQUIPMENT CORPO-RATION
2700 W Veterans Pkwy, Marshfield,
WI 54449
Tel.: (715) 384-2151   WI
Web Site:
https://www.bergequipment.com
Year Founded: 1919
Sales Range: $10-24.9 Million
Emp.: 25
Barn Cleaners & Barn Equipment,
Manure Pumps, Automatic Feeding
Equipment & Barn Ventilation
N.A.I.C.S.: 333111
Robert Augustine *(Coord-Adv)*
Vernon R. Berg Jr. *(Pres)*

Subsidiaries:

Sand Mark Corporation   (1)
2700 W Weterens Pkwy, Marshfield, WI
54449
Tel.: (715) 384-2151
Web Site: http://www.bergequipment.com
Manufactures, Designs & Markets Products
for Agricultural & Industrial Use
N.A.I.C.S.: 115116
Vernon R. Berg Jr. *(Pres)*

BERG MILL SUPPLY COM-PANY INC.
5900 Wilshire Blvd Ste 2350, Los An-
geles, CA 90036-5007
Tel.: (323) 939-4300
Web Site: http://www.bergmill.com
Year Founded: 1962
Sales Range: $50-74.9 Million
Emp.: 35
Supplier of Scrap & Waste Materials
N.A.I.C.S.: 423930
Daniel Marks *(CEO)*

BERGAN PAULSEN & COM-PANY PC
100 East Park Ave, Waterloo, IA
50703
Tel.: (319) 234-6885
Web Site: http://www.bpccpa.com
Rev.: $3,000,000
Emp.: 40
Other Accounting Services
N.A.I.C.S.: 541219

Becky Miller *(Mgr-Acctg)*
Becky Morgan *(Mgr)*

Subsidiaries:

Kern Dewenter Viere, Ltd.   (1)
220 Park Ave S, Saint Cloud, MN 56301
Tel.: (320) 251-7010
Web Site: http://www.kdv.com
Rev.: $3,200,000
Emp.: 75
Accounting Services
N.A.I.C.S.: 541219
Lorne Viere *(Principal)*

BERGEN REGIONAL MEDICAL CENTER
230 E Ridgewood Ave, Paramus, NJ
07652
Tel.: (201) 967-4000
Web Site:
https://www.bergenregional.com
Year Founded: 1991
Emp.: 1,196
Health Care Srvices
N.A.I.C.S.: 621610
Serge Dumay *(Chief Medical Officer
& VP-Quality & Outcomes Mgmt)*
John Regina *(Sr VP-HR)*
Susan Mendelowitz *(Pres)*
Ehud Fried *(Vice Chm & Exec VP)*
Joseph S. Orlando *(Chm)*
Tom McCloskey *(CFO & VP)*

BERGER BROS INC.
154 N Aspan Ave, Azusa, CA 91702
Tel.: (626) 334-2699
Web Site: https://www.bergerbro.com
Sales Range: $10-24.9 Million
Emp.: 300
Plastering Plain or Ornamental
N.A.I.C.S.: 238310
Brad Berger *(CEO)*
Michael Berger *(Pres-Southern Cali-
fornia)*

BERGER CHEVROLET, INC.
2525 28th St SE, Grand Rapids, MI
49512-1616
Tel.: (616) 949-5200
Web Site:
https://www.bergerchevy.com
Sales Range: $25-49.9 Million
Emp.: 140
Car Whslr
N.A.I.C.S.: 441110
Matthew S. Berger *(Pres)*
Leonard George *(Coord-Customer
Care)*

BERGER COMPANY
104 N 6th St Ste 10, Atchison, KS
66002
Tel.: (913) 367-3700
Web Site:
https://www.bergercompany.com
Sales Range: $10-24.9 Million
Emp.: 10
Leather Goods, Except Footwear,
Gloves, Luggage, Belting
N.A.I.C.S.: 424990
Richard N. Berger *(Pres)*

BERGER FAMILY DEALER-SHIP
Susquehanna Blvd, Hazleton, PA
18202
Tel.: (570) 454-0856
Web Site:
http://www.bergerfamilydealers.com
Year Founded: 1921
Sales Range: $50-74.9 Million
Emp.: 65
Car Whslr
N.A.I.C.S.: 441110
Edward Butkiewicz *(Mgr-Parts)*

BERGER ORGANIZATION, LLC

50 Park Pl, Newark, NJ 07102
Tel.: (973) 623-3300
Web Site: https://www.bergerorg.com
Rev.: $35,038,056
Emp.: 220
Real Estate Development
N.A.I.C.S.: 531210
Benjamin Berger *(Pres-Berger &
Berger)*
Miles Berger *(Chm, COO & CEO)*
Bruce Berger *(Pres)*
Brendan Berger *(VP)*

BERGER SINGERMAN PA.
350 E Las Olas Blvd Ste 1000, Fort
Lauderdale, FL 33301
Tel.: (954) 525-9900
Web Site:
http://www.bergersingerman.com
Year Founded: 1985
Sales Range: $25-49.9 Million
Emp.: 120
Law firm
N.A.I.C.S.: 541110
C. Shelton James *(Partner-Govt &
Regulatory Team)*
Paul Steven Singerman *(Co-Chm)*
Mitchell W. Berger *(Co-Chm)*
James L. Berger *(Mng Dir)*
Mario Rumasuglia *(Dir-Admin)*
Philip A. Sanchez *(Dir-IT)*
Isaac Marcushamer *(Partner)*
Jeffrey S. Wertman *(Partner)*
Paul A. Avron *(Partner)*
Gavin C. Gaukroger *(Partner)*
Paul Figg *(Partner)*
David Black *(Partner)*
Pamela Cothran Marsh *(Partner)*
Michel O. Weisz *(Partner)*
Nancy K. Watkin *(Partner)*
Colin Mark Roopnarine *(Partner-Govt
& Regulatory)*
Jeffrey S. Bartel *(Partner)*
Jodi Maier *(Dir-Mktg & Recruitment)*
Matthew Nelles *(Partner-Dispute
Resolution Team)*
Jordi Guso *(Partner)*
Andrew B. Zelman *(Partner)*

BERGER TRANSFER & STOR-AGE, INC.
2950 Long Lk Rd, Saint Paul, MN
55113-1050
Tel.: (651) 639-2260   MN
Web Site: http://www.berger-
transfer.com
Year Founded: 1910
Sales Range: $150-199.9 Million
Emp.: 500
Moving & Storage Services
N.A.I.C.S.: 488510
Tom Boehme *(CFO)*
Chuck Speth *(Dir-Mktg)*
John DeWitt *(VP)*
Richard Goffin *(CIO)*
Angie Karlson *(Mgr-Customer Svc)*
Don Schrooten *(VP-Svcs)*

BERGERON PROPERTIES & INVESTMENT CORP.
19612 SW 69th Pl, Pembroke Pines,
FL 33332
Tel.: (954) 680-0223
Web Site:
http://www.bergeronland.com
Year Founded: 1963
Sales Range: $25-49.9 Million
Emp.: 300
Owner & Developer of Real Estate
N.A.I.C.S.: 212321
Ronald M. Bergeron *(Founder)*

Subsidiaries:

Bergeron Land Development Inc.   (1)
19612 SW 69th Pl, Fort Lauderdale, FL
33332-1618

Tel.: (954) 680-6100
Web Site: http://www.bergeronlanddev.com
Sales Range: $50-74.9 Million
Emp.: 50
Provider of Heavy Construction Services
N.A.I.C.S.: 236210
Ronald M. Bergeron (Founder)
Phil Desai (CFO)
Brian Landis (Mgr-Construction-Projects)
Brian Wetherington (VP)

BERGEYS INC.
462 Harleysville Pike, Souderton, PA 18964
Tel.: (215) 723-6071　　　　DE
Web Site: https://www.bergeys.com
Year Founded: 1924
Rev.: $108,819,871
Emp.: 800
New & Used Car Dealerships & Service Centers
N.A.I.C.S.: 441110
Norman Lester Bergey (Founder)
Henry Bergey (VP)
Wayne Derstine (Gen Mgr)
Paul Yothers (Gen Mgr-Sls)

Subsidiaries:

Bergey's Chevrolet　　　　(1)
518 Bethlehem Pike 610, Colmar, PA 18915-9604
Tel.: (215) 855-9041
Sales Range: $25-49.9 Million
Emp.: 150
New & Used Car Dealer Services
N.A.I.C.S.: 441110
Ken Long (Mgr-Sls)
Brain Derstine (Gen Mgr)

GMC Bergeys Inc.　　　　(1)
462 Harleysville Pike, Souderton, PA 18964
Tel.: (215) 723-6071
Rev.: $64,067,886
Emp.: 119
Automobiles, New & Used
N.A.I.C.S.: 441110

RBL Leasing Corp.　　　　(1)
446 Harleysville Pike, Souderton, PA 18964
Tel.: (215) 723-6071
Rev.: $18,812,881
Emp.: 1
Truck Leasing, Without Drivers
N.A.I.C.S.: 532120

BERGGRUEN HOLDINGS, INC.
304 S Broadway 550, Los Angeles, CA 90013
Tel.: (213) 430-2350
Web Site:
　　https://www.berggruenholdings.com
Privater Equity Firm
N.A.I.C.S.: 523999
Nicolas Berggruen (Chm)

Subsidiaries:

Berggruen Holdings, Ltd.　　　　(1)
9 11 Grosvenor Gardens, London, SW1W OBD, United Kingdom
Tel.: (44) 207 861 0980
Equity Investment Services
N.A.I.C.S.: 523999

Holding (Domestic):

Celloglas Ltd.　　　　(2)
12C Exeter Way, Theale Commercial Estate, Reading, RG7 4AW, Berkshire, United Kingdom
Tel.: (44) 1189167300
Web Site: http://www.celloglas.co.uk
Sales Range: $50-74.9 Million
Print Finishing Services
N.A.I.C.S.: 322220
Peter Clayton (Dir-Fin)
Richard Gilgrass (Mng Dir)
Steve Middleton (Dir-Sls-Leicester)
Gill Grafs (Mng Dir)

Nicolas Berggruen Holdings GmbH　　　　(1)
Wilhelm-Kabus-Strasse 42/44 house 6 3, 10829, Berlin, Germany
Tel.: (49) 3025939960
Web Site: http://www.berggruenholdings.de

Privater Equity Firm
N.A.I.C.S.: 523999
Samuel Czarny (Mng Dir)

Transport Labor Contract/Leasing　　　　(1)
6160 Summit Dr N Ste 500, Brooklyn Center, MN 55430
Tel.: (763) 585-7000
Web Site: http://www.tlccompanies.com
Professional Employer Organizations
N.A.I.C.S.: 561330

BERGHORST FOODS SERVICES INC.
2896 Dormax St SW, Grandville, MI 49418
Tel.: (616) 531-8530
Sales Range: $10-24.9 Million
Emp.: 40
Whslr of Meats & Meat Products
N.A.I.C.S.: 424470
Scott Rawlings (Controller)
Keith Littlepage (Gen Mgr)

BERGKAMP INC.
3040 Emulsion Dr, Salina, KS 67401
Tel.: (785) 825-1375
Web Site:
　　http://www.bergkampinc.com
Year Founded: 1977
Sales Range: $10-24.9 Million
Emp.: 75
Construction Machinery Mfr
N.A.I.C.S.: 333120

BERGLUND CONSTRUCTION COMPANY
8410 S Chicago Ave, Chicago, IL 60617
Tel.: (773) 374-1000
Web Site:
　　https://www.berglundco.com
Rev.: $111,500,000
Emp.: 375
Commercial & Institutional Building Construction
N.A.I.C.S.: 236220
Kevin Geshwender (CFO & Exec VP)
Fred Berglund (Pres)
Eric Dexter (Project Mgr-Restoration)
Tim Vanderbilt (Mgr-Ops)
Julia Randles (Mgr-Preconstruction)
Chad Todhunter (Sr Project Mgr)
Thomas L. Sicinski (Sr VP)
Joe Hirsch (Dir-Bus Dev)
JoAnna Baum (Sr Mgr-Creative Svcs)
Larry Wiley (VP)
Tony Baca (VP-Safety)
Wayne Ziemer (VP)
Dennis M. Kulick Jr. (Mgr-Preconstruction)

BERGLUND OAK RIDGE TOYOTA
3000 Wards Rd, Lynchburg, VA 24502
Tel.: (434) 528-3202
Web Site:
　　http://www.oakridgetoyota.com
Rev.: $16,600,000
Emp.: 52
New & Used Car Dealers
N.A.I.C.S.: 441110
Joel Sodikoff (Gen Mgr-Sls)
Robert Tucker (Mgr-Used Car)
Tom Gilber (Gen Mgr)

BERGMAN ASSOCIATES
511 W 25th St Ste 804, New York, NY 10001
Tel.: (212) 645-1911　　　　NY
Web Site:
　　http://www.bergassociates.com
Year Founded: 1991
Sales Range: $10-24.9 Million
Emp.: 12

Advetising Agency
N.A.I.C.S.: 541810
Robert Bergman (Owner)
Michael Bogan (Acct Dir)

BERGMANN ASSOCIATES, ARCHITECTS, ENGINEERS, LANDSCAPE ARCHITECTS & SURVEYORS, D.P.C.
28 E Main St 200 1st Federal Plz, Rochester, NY 14614
Tel.: (585) 232-5135　　　　NY
Web Site:
　　http://www.bergmannpc.com
Year Founded: 1980
Rev.: $41,000,000
Emp.: 248
Engineering, Architectural & Surveying Services
N.A.I.C.S.: 541330
James Buckley (CFO)
Thomas C. Mitchell (Exec VP-Client Rels & Bus Dev)
John R. Murray Jr. (VP)
Janet Romanic (Mgr-Retail & Comml-SE)
Wayne Kiefer (Sr Project Mgr-Comml & Retail-Philadelphia)
Pietro Giovenco (Pres & CEO)
Robert Switala (Mgr-Energy Supply)
Steve Boisvert (Reg Mgr)
Rick Chelotti (Reg Mgr)
Kevin Miller (Reg Mgr)
Mick Stuebben (Reg Mgr)
Douglas J. Cohen (Sr Program Mgr)
Timothy McDowell (Asst Project Mgr-Comml & Retail-Philadelphia)
Jeff Ledy (VP-Midwest)
Sean O'Rourke (VP-Atlantic Buildings)

BERGMANN'S INC.
2147 Lee Hwy, Arlington, VA 22201
Tel.: (703) 247-7600
Web Site: http://www.bergmanns.com
Sales Range: $10-24.9 Million
Emp.: 600
Drycleaning Plants, Except Rugs
N.A.I.C.S.: 812320
Larry M. Bergmann (VP-Sls & Mgr-Ops)
Jeffrey R. Bergmann (Exec VP)

Subsidiaries:

Bergmann's Cleaning Inc.　　　　(1)
2147 Lee Hwy, Arlington, VA 22201
Tel.: (703) 247-7600
Web Site: http://www.bergmanns.com
Rev.: $9,637,656
Emp.: 160
Drycleaning Plants, Except Rugs
N.A.I.C.S.: 812320

G&G Beverages Inc.　　　　(1)
2147 Lee Hwy, Arlington, VA 22201
Tel.: (202) 737-5400
Rev.: $460,000
Emp.: 6
Liquor Stores
N.A.I.C.S.: 445320

BERGSTROM CORP.
1 Neenah Ctr, Neenah, WI 54956
Tel.: (920) 725-4444
Web Site:
　　http://www.bergstromauto.com
Year Founded: 1974
Sales Range: $25-49.9 Million
Emp.: 1,400
Car Dealership Owner & Operator
N.A.I.C.S.: 441110
John F. Bergstrom (Chm & CEO)
Tim Bergstrom (Pres & COO)

Subsidiaries:

Bergstrom Cadillac of Madison　　　　(1)
1200 Applegate Rd, Madison, WI 53713
Tel.: (866) 462-6412

Web Site: http://www.madisoncadillac.com
New & Used Automobiles
N.A.I.C.S.: 441110

Cliff Wall Automotive LLC　　　　(1)
1988 E Mason St, Green Bay, WI 54302
Tel.: (920) 468-8898
Web Site: http://www.cliffwallcars.com
Automotive Repair & Maintenance
N.A.I.C.S.: 811198
Martha Litkey (Office Mgr)

BERGSTROM ELECTRIC INC.
3100 N Washington St, Grand Forks, ND 58203
Tel.: (701) 775-8897
Web Site:
　　http://www.bergstromele.com
Rev.: $11,040,484
Emp.: 100
General Electrical Contractor
N.A.I.C.S.: 238210
Vernon W. Thingvold (Project Mgr)

BERGSTROM INC.
2390 Blackhawk Rd, Rockford, IL 61125
Tel.: (815) 874-7821　　　　IL
Web Site:
　　https://www.bergstrominc.com
Year Founded: 1960
Sales Range: $25-49.9 Million
Emp.: 400
Supplier of Motor Vehicle Parts & Accessories
N.A.I.C.S.: 336320
Jim Elliott (Chief Quality & Program Dev Officer)
Jack Shaffer (Pres & CEO)
Steven Rosella (Mng Dir-Truck, Bus & Military Markets-North America)
John Ventimiglia (Mgr-Acct)
Graham Cook (Pres-Europe & Bus-Intl)
John Bracey (VP-Global Engrg)
Joe Kirby (Gen Mgr-Sls-Truck)
Bill Gordon (Pres-Parts)
Gus Anton (Pres-North America Div)
Dan Giovannetti (CFO)
Aaron Potter (VP-Fin Plng & Analysis)
Nicole Murphy (Coord-Sls)
Joe Nett (Dir-Sls-Bergstrom)
Tom Fisher (Mgr-Acct-Off-Highway)
George Lamoureux (Dir-New & Advance Product Introduction)
Mark Meegan (Chief Procurement Officer)
Terry Zeigler (VP-Electrified Sys)
Forrest Fields (Dir-Bus Air Conditioning)
Larry Landreth (Mng Dir-BSP, Bus Air Conditioning & Solar)

BERICO HEATING AND AIR CONDITIONING, INC.
2200 E Bessemer Ave, Greensboro, NC 27405
Tel.: (336) 273-8663　　　　NC
Web Site: https://www.berico.com
Year Founded: 1924
Fuel Oil Dealers
N.A.I.C.S.: 457210
John W. Fuquay (Chm)
Tom Berry (Pres)
J. B. Reid (VP)

BERICO TECHNOLOGIES LLC
1501 Lee Hwy Ste 303, Arlington, VA 22209
Tel.: (703) 224-8300
Web Site:
　　http://www.bericotechnologies.com
Year Founded: 2006
Sales Range: $10-24.9 Million
Emp.: 70

Berico Technologies LLC—(Continued)

Analytical Software Development
Services
N.A.I.C.S.: 541511
Jeremy Glesner (CTO)

BERING HOME CENTER INC.
6102 Westheimer Rd, Houston, TX
77057
Tel.: (713) 785-6400
Web Site: http://www.bering.com
Rev.: $25,711,881
Emp.: 100
Gifts & Novelties
N.A.I.C.S.: 459420
August C. Bering IV (Chm)

**BERING STRAITS NATIVE
CORPORATION**
110 Front St Ste 300, Nome, AK
99762
Tel.: (907) 443-5252
Web Site:
	https://www.beringstraits.com
Year Founded: 1972
Rev.: $76,200,000
Emp.: 162
Support Activities for Metal Mining
N.A.I.C.S.: 213114
Henry Ivanoff (Chm)
Eugene Asicksik (Asst Sec)
Roy Ashenfelter (Sec)
Clara Langton (Treas)
Stephen Ivanoff (Asst Treas)
Laura L. Edmondson (CFO & Sr VP)
Krystal M. Nelson (COO)
Lee Ryan (Vice Chm)
Richard Foster (Exec VP)
Dan Graham (Interim Pres & Interim
CEO)
Ana Grayson (Assoc Dir-Comm)

Subsidiaries:

Alaska Industrial Hardware Inc.		(1)
2192 Viking Dr, Anchorage, AK 99501
Tel.: (907) 276-7201
Web Site: http://www.aih.com
Insulated Food Service System for Hospital
Correctional Facility & Institution Mfr
N.A.I.C.S.: 423710
Terry Shurtleff (Pres & CEO)
Chris Hines (Dir-IT)

Division (Domestic):

AIH Tool Repair Center		(2)
2192 Viking Dr, Anchorage, AK 99501
Tel.: (907) 276-7201
Web Site: http://www.aih.com
Tools & Equipment Repair Services
N.A.I.C.S.: 812990

BERINGER ASSOCIATES, INC.
612 E Woodlawn Ave Ste 200, Maple
Shade, NJ 08052
Tel.: (856) 325-2800
Web Site: http://www.beringer.net
Year Founded: 1993
Data Processing, Hosting & Related
Services
N.A.I.C.S.: 518210
Craig Beringer (Pres & CEO)
Greg Belza (Mgr-Mktg)

Subsidiaries:

DeckerWright Corporation		(1)
628 Shrewsbury Ave, Tinton Falls, NJ
07701-4932
Tel.: (732) 747-9373
Web Site: http://www.deckerwright.com
Electronics Stores
N.A.I.C.S.: 449210
Marshall Wright (Owner)

**BERK WIPER CONVERTING &
PACKAGING, LLC**
400 E 2nd St, Boyertown, PA 19512
Tel.: (215) 412-8181

Web Site: http://www.berkwiper.com
Sales Range: $10-24.9 Million
Emp.: 37
Disposable Wiping Cloth Mfr
N.A.I.C.S.: 313230
Larry Berk (CEO)
Jeff Berk (Pres)

**BERK WIPER INTERNATIONAL
LLC**
707 N Valley Forge Rd, Lansdale, PA
19446
Tel.: (215) 412-8181
Web Site: http://www.berkwiper.com
Year Founded: 2000
Sales Range: $10-24.9 Million
Emp.: 40
Disposable Wiping Cloths
N.A.I.C.S.: 322291
Jeff Berk (Pres)

**BERKADIA COMMERCIAL
MORTGAGE LLC**
Norristown Rd Ste 300, Ambler, PA
19002
Tel.: (215) 328-3458
Web Site: http://www.berkadia.com
Year Founded: 1994
Sales Range: $25-49.9 Million
Emp.: 275
Real Estate Lending Services
N.A.I.C.S.: 522310
Randall L. Jenson (CFO)
Mark E. McCool (Exec VP & Head-
Servicing)
Thomas Miraglia (Gen Counsel &
Exec VP)
Ernie Katai (Exec VP & Head-
Production)
Justin R. Wheeler (CEO)
Darren Wesemann (Chief Innovation
Officer)
Mitchell Thurston (Sr Mng Dir-Comml
& Multifamily Financing)
Gemma Geldmacher (Sr Dir-FHA &
Affordable Housing)
Kyle Stevenson (Mng Dir-Hotel Bro-
kerage Expert)
Marc Possick (Sr Dir-New York)
Hilary Provinse (Exec VP & Head-
Mortgage Banking)
Robert Wrzosek (Mng Dir-Affordable
Housing Team-New York)
Tom Genetti (Mng Dir-Mortgage
Banking)
Richard Levine (Sr Mng Dir)
Warren Higgins (Exec VP & Head-
Production Tech)
Keith Misner (Sr VP & Head-
Investment Sls)
Michael N. Weinberg (Mng Dir-
Orlando)
Rebecca Van Reken (Mng Dir-
Orlando)
Mary Cosmides (Mgr-PR)
David Leopold (Sr VP & Head-
Affordable Housing)

**BERKEL & COMPANY CON-
TRACTORS INC.**
2649 S 142nd St, Bonner Springs,
KS 66012
Tel.: (913) 422-5125
Web Site:
	https://www.berkelandcompany.com
Sales Range: $75-99.9 Million
Emp.: 460
Foundation & Footing Contractor
N.A.I.C.S.: 238110
David Weatherer (VP & Mgr)

**BERKELEY ASPHALT COM-
PANY**
699 Virginia St, Berkeley, CA 94710

Tel.: (510) 526-1611
Rev.: $11,100,000
Emp.: 20
Asphalt & Asphaltic Paving Mixtures
N.A.I.C.S.: 324121

**BERKELEY COUNTY WATER
& SANITATION AUTHORITY**
212 Oakley Plantation Dr, Moncks
Corner, SC 29461
Tel.: (843) 761-8817
Web Site: http://www.bcwsa.com
Sales Range: $10-24.9 Million
Emp.: 240
Water Supply Treatment & Potable
Water Distr
N.A.I.C.S.: 221310
Jerri Christmas (Mgr-IT)
Karen Jones (Project Coord)
Josh Hawkins (Superintendent)
Christy Davis (Dir-Procurement)
Alan Roberts (Superintendent-Solid
Waste)
Sarah McCarthy-Smith (Coord-
Recycling)
Nick Bruno (Vice Chm)
Elizabeth Davis (Sec)

**BERKELEY ELECTRIC COOP-
ERATIVE INC.**
414 N Hwy 52, Moncks Corner, SC
29461-1234
Tel.: (843) 761-8200			SC
Web Site:
	http://www.berkeleyelectric.coop
Year Founded: 1940
Sales Range: $25-49.9 Million
Emp.: 210
Provider of Electric Services
N.A.I.C.S.: 221122
Harry A. Brunson (Chm)

**BERKELEY FLORIST SUPPLY
CO, INC.**
2360 NW 23rd St, Miami, FL 33142
Tel.: (786) 540-8400			FL
Web Site:
	https://www.berkeleyflorists.com
Year Founded: 1947
Sales Range: $1-9.9 Million
Emp.: 35
Flower, Nursery Stock & Florists'
Supplies Merchant Whslr
N.A.I.C.S.: 424930
Morey Moss (Pres)
Mauricio Astudillo (Mgr-Supply)
George Perez (Mgr-Export)
Jose Norori (Mgr-Warehouse & Re-
ceiving)

**BERKELEY FORGE & TOOL
INC.**
1331 Eastshore Hwy, Berkeley, CA
94710
Tel.: (510) 526-5034
Web Site: https://www.berkforge.com
Sales Range: $10-24.9 Million
Emp.: 64
Provider of Tools & Forgings
N.A.I.C.S.: 332111
Peter Bierwith (Founder)

**BERKELEY NUCLEONICS
CORP.**
2955 Kerner Blvd D, San Rafael, CA
94901
Tel.: (415) 453-9955
Web Site:
	http://www.berkeleynucleonics.com
Rev.: $2,299,000
Emp.: 15
Electromedical & Electrotherapeutic
Apparatus Mfr
N.A.I.C.S.: 334510

John Yee (Mgr-Applications)
Kristin Geertsema (Dir-Ops)
Mel Brown (CFO & Founder)

Subsidiaries:

Directed Energy, Inc.		(1)
135 12th St SW, Loveland, CO 80537
Tel.: (970) 493-1901
Web Site: http://directedenergy.com
Electronics Mfr; Solar Handheld Technology,
Solar Circuit Boards & Computer Compo-
nents
N.A.I.C.S.: 334419

**BERKELEY RESEARCH
GROUP LLC**
2200 Powell St Ste 1200, Emeryville,
CA 94608-1833
Tel.: (510) 285-3300
Administrative Management & Gen-
eral Management Consulting Ser-
vices
N.A.I.C.S.: 541611
David J. Teece (Founder & Chm)
Eric Miller (Gen Counsel & Sr VP)
Michael Slattery (Mng Dir)
Michael Athanason (Mng Dir)
Jeffrey H. Cramer (Mng Dir-Global
Investigations & Strategic Intelligence
Practice)
Constantine Korologos (Mng Dir-
Capital Markets Svcs Practice-New
York)
Kenneth Segal (Mng Dir-Capital Mar-
kets Svcs)
Daniel Galante (Mng Dir-Chicago)
Marvin Tenenbaum (Sr VP)
Ariel Ramirez (Mng Dir-Global Inves-
tigations & Strategic Intelligence
Practice)
Rebecca Li Bo-lan (Dir-Global Investi-
gations & Strategic Intelligence
Practice-Hong)
Janice G. Jacobs (Mng Dir-
Healthcare Corp Compliance & Risk
Mgmt Practice)
Edward J. Buthusiem (Mng Dir-Health
Analytics Practice-Philadelphia)
Naomi Bowman (Mng Dir-Fin Svcs
Practice-EMEA)
Steven Shi (Dir-Beijing)
Stuart Witchell (Mng Dir)
Allen D. Applbaum (Mng Dir)
Richard D. Gregorie (Mng Dir-Global
Investigations & Strategic Intelligence
Practice)
Tri MacDonald (Pres & CEO)
Mark Laber (Head-Corp Fin-New
York)
Bob Duffy (Mng Dir & Co-Head-Corp
Fin)
Christopher Kearns (Co-Head-Corp
Fin)
Dan Troy (Mng Dir-Health Analytics
Practice)
Jerry Lewandowski (Mng Dir-Health
Analytics Practice)
Orlando L. Alvarez Jr. (Mng Dir-
Healthcare Performance Improve-
ment Practice)

**BERKELEY SYMPHONY OR-
CHESTRA**
1942 University Ave Ste 207, Berke-
ley, CA 94704
Tel.: (510) 841-2800
Web Site:
	https://www.berkeleysymphony.org
Sales Range: $10-24.9 Million
Emp.: 45
Symphony Orchestra
N.A.I.C.S.: 711130
Ming Luke (Dir-Education)
Joana Carneiro (Dir-Music)
Kathleen G. Henschel (VP-
Governance)
Rene Mandel (Exec Dir)

BERKERY, NOYES & CO., LLC

245 Park Ave 16th Fl, New York, NY 10167
Tel.: (212) 668-3022
Web Site:
   https://www.berkerynoyes.com
Year Founded: 1983
Sales Range: $1-9.9 Million
Emp.: 25
Investment Banking & Securities Dealing
N.A.I.C.S.: 523150
Jonathan Krieger *(Mng Dir)*
Peter Yoon *(Mng Dir)*
John D. Guzzo *(Mng Dir)*
Thomas P. O'Connor *(Mng Dir)*
Richard W. O'Donnell *(Mng Dir)*
Peter B. Ognibene *(Mng Dir)*
Jeffrey Smith *(Mng Dir)*
Mary Jo Zandy *(Mng Dir)*
Vineet Asthana *(Mng Dir)*
Elizabeth Granville-Smith *(Mng Dir)*
Greg Bell *(Founder & CEO)*
Howard Reba *(CFO)*
Jinsoo Kim *(Founder & CEO)*
Kenny Hargis *(Owner & CEO)*
Michael Fram *(Mng Dir)*
Paul Watnes *(Pres & CEO)*
Stephen Margrett *(Co-Founder & CEO)*
Martin Magida *(Mng Dir)*
Sameer Pal *(Mng Dir)*

BERKLEY MEDICAL RE-SOURCES INC.

700 Mountain View Dr, Smithfield, PA 15478
Tel.: (724) 564-5002
Rev.: $30,000,000
Emp.: 100
Surgical & Medical Instruments
N.A.I.C.S.: 339112
John R. Berkley *(Owner)*
Joseph Siba *(VP)*
Dean Dennis *(Mgr-Pur & IT)*
Ed Kolencik *(Supvr-Customer Svc)*

Subsidiaries:

Berkley Medical Resources Inc.   **(1)**
PO Box 3285, Palm Beach, FL 33480
Tel.: (561) 841-7254
Rev.: $12,200,000
Emp.: 20
Surgical & Medical Instruments
N.A.I.C.S.: 339112

BERKLY ENTERPRISES INC.

2342 S Bridge St, Brady, TX 76825-3541
Tel.: (325) 597-5201
Rev.: $10,000,000
Emp.: 7
Convenience Store
N.A.I.C.S.: 445131
Ray Hawkins *(Owner)*
Prabin Raj Ghimire *(Owner)*

BERKOT LTD. INC.

20005 Wolf Rd, Mokena, IL 60448
Tel.: (708) 479-7411
Web Site:
   https://www.berkotfoods.com
Sales Range: $10-24.9 Million
Emp.: 1,000
Grocery Stores, Independent
N.A.I.C.S.: 445110
John Kotara *(Pres)*

BERKOWITZ DEVELOPMENT GROUP, INC.

2665 S Bayshore Dr Ste 1200, Miami, FL 33133
Tel.: (305) 854-2800   **FL**
Web Site:
   https://www.berkowitzdev.com
Year Founded: 1986
Sales Range: $1-9.9 Million

Emp.: 12
Land Subdivision, Property Development & Management
N.A.I.C.S.: 237210
David Singer *(CEO & CFO)*
Jeffrey Berkowitz *(Founder & Pres)*
Michael R. Berkowitz *(VP)*
Andrew Berkowitz *(VP)*
Ann M. O'Hare *(Dir-Construction Svcs)*
David S. Markowitz *(Mgr-Property)*

BERKOWITZ POLLACK BRANT

200 S Biscayne Blvd 7th & 8th Fl, Miami, FL 33131-5310
Tel.: (305) 379-7000
Web Site: http://www.bdpb.com
Year Founded: 1980
Sales Range: $10-24.9 Million
Emp.: 170
Accounting & Advisory Services
N.A.I.C.S.: 541211
Barry M. Brant *(Dir-Tax, Consulting & Intl Svcs)*
Richard A. Berkowitz *(Founder, Chm & CEO)*
Scott M. Bouchner *(Dir-Forensic & Bus Valuation Svcs)*
Andreea Cioara Schinas *(Dir-Tax Svcs)*
Joseph L. Saka *(CEO)*
James W. Spencer *(Dir-Tax Svcs-Intl)*
David E. Kolan *(Dir-Audit & Attest Svcs Practice)*
Robert Aldir *(Dir-Audit & Attest Svcs Practice)*
Arthur J. Lieberman *(Dir-Tax Svcs)*
Shea Smith *(Dir-Audit & Attest Svcs)*
Cherry Laufenberg *(Assoc Dir-Tax Svcs)*
J. Stephen Nouss *(Chief Consulting Officer)*
John G. Ebenger *(Dir-Real Estate Tax Svcs)*
Edward N. Cooper *(Dir-Tax Svcs)*
Joel Glick *(Dir-Forensics & Bus Valuation Svcs)*
Arthur J. Dichter *(Dir-Tax-Intl)*
Lewis Taub *(Dir-Tax Svcs-New York City)*
Ken Vitek *(Dir-Intl Tax Svcs Practice)*
Laurence Bernstein *(Dir-Tax Svcs Practice)*
Andrew Leonard *(Dir-Intl Tax Svcs Practice)*
Timothy R. Larson *(Dir-Tax Svcs Practice)*

BERKS COUNTY CENTER FOR INDEPENDENT LIVING

210 N 5th St, Reading, PA 19601
Tel.: (610) 376-0010   **PA**
Web Site:
   https://www.abilitiesinmotion.org
Year Founded: 1990
Sales Range: $25-49.9 Million
Emp.: 50
Disability Assistance Services
N.A.I.C.S.: 624120
Ralph Trainer *(Exec Dir)*

BERKS HOME DESIGN BUILD

3335 Morgantown Rd, Mohnton, PA 19540
Tel.: (610) 628-0441
Web Site:
   https://www.bhdesignbuild.com
Sales Range: $25-49.9 Million
Emp.: 62
Housing Construction Services
N.A.I.C.S.: 236117
Jonathan Detwiler *(Partner)*

BERKSHIRE ASSET MANAGE-MENT, LLC

46 Public Sq Ste 700, Wilkes Barre, PA 18701-2609
Tel.: (570) 825-2600   **PA**
Web Site:
   https://www.berkshireasset.com
Year Founded: 1999
Sales Range: $25-49.9 Million
Emp.: 6
Financial Consultant & Asset Management Services
N.A.I.C.S.: 523999
Gerard Mihalick *(VP)*
Greg Weaver *(VP)*
Kenneth J. Krogulski *(Pres, CEO, Mng Partner & Chief Investment Officer)*
Marilyn D. Millington *(Chief Compliance Officer & VP)*

BERKSHIRE BANCORP INC.

4 E 39th St, New York, NY 10016
Tel.: (212) 802-1000   **DE**
Web Site: https://www.berkbank.com
Year Founded: 1979
BERK–(OTCIQ)
Rev.: $30,586,000
Assets: $684,856,000
Liabilities: $518,703,000
Net Worth: $166,153,000
Earnings: $6,259,000
Emp.: 110
Fiscal Year-end: 12/31/19
Bank Holding Company
N.A.I.C.S.: 551111
Isabelle Baball-Khan *(VP)*
Richard E. Rooney *(VP)*
Ramon Santiago *(VP)*
Chani Simchon *(VP)*
Allison Stroh *(VP)*
Karen Trapani *(VP)*

Subsidiaries:

The Berkshire Bank   **(1)**
4 E 39th St, New York, NY 10016 **(100%)**
Tel.: (212) 802-1000
Web Site: http://www.berkbank.com
Sales Range: $1-9.9 Million
Emp.: 15
Personal & Commercial Banking Services
N.A.I.C.S.: 522110
David Lukens Jr. *(CFO & Exec VP)*
Allison M. Powell *(COO & Sr VP)*
Avram J. Gutmann *(VP)*
Dan Kimchi *(VP)*
Ira Mermelstein *(VP)*
Frank Pugliese *(VP)*

BERKSHIRE FARM CENTER AND SERVICES FOR YOUTH

13640 State Route 22, Canaan, NY 12029
Tel.: (518) 781-4567   **NY**
Web Site:
   https://www.berkshirefarm.org
Year Founded: 1886
Sales Range: $25-49.9 Million
Emp.: 910
Child Care & Development Services
N.A.I.C.S.: 624110
Nancy McGuire *(Sec)*
Timothy Giacchetta *(Pres & CEO)*
Robert A. Kandel *(Chm)*
Deanna Harrington *(Sec)*

BERKSHIRE FASHIONS INC.

10 Woodbridge Ctr Dr Ste 600, Woodbridge, NJ 07095-1181
Tel.: (732) 287-9300
Web Site:
   http://www.berkshireinc.com
Year Founded: 1944
Sales Range: $10-24.9 Million
Emp.: 25
Mfr of Womens, Childrens & Infants Clothing
N.A.I.C.S.: 424350
Angelica Garcia *(Coord-Production-Fashion)*

BERKSHIRE FINANCIAL SER-VICES, INC.

75 Park St, Lee, MA 01238
Tel.: (413) 243-0117
Web Site: http://www.leebank.com
Year Founded: 1992
Bank Holding Company
N.A.I.C.S.: 551111
Chuck Leach *(Pres-Lee Bank)*

Subsidiaries:

Lee Bank   **(1)**
75 Park St, Lee, MA 01238
Tel.: (413) 243-0117
Web Site: http://www.leebank.com
Commercial Banking
N.A.I.C.S.: 522110
Chuck Leach *(Pres)*

BERKSHIRE GROUP, LLC

1 Beacon St Ste 1500, Boston, MA 02108
Tel.: (617) 646-2300   **DE**
Web Site: http://www.berkshire-group.com
Year Founded: 1969
Rev.: $6,200,000,000
Emp.: 120
Real Estate Investment Management Services
N.A.I.C.S.: 531390
Christopher M. Nichols *(Mng Dir & Chief Operating & Admin Officer)*
Mary Beth Bloom *(Mng Dir, Chief Compliance Officer & Gen Counsel)*
David J. Olney *(Mng Dir & Chief Investment Officer-Multifamily Investments)*
George Krupp *(Co-Founder & Chm)*
Michael Coffey *(Sr VP-Client Rels)*
John Bottomley *(Mng Dir & Head-Client Rels)*
Jed Gates *(Sr VP-Client Rels)*
David Doherty *(Mng Dir & Head-Portfolio Performance Reporting)*
Eric Draeger *(Mng Dir & Head-Multifamily Equity & Debt Investments)*
Larry Ellman *(Mng Dir & Head-Venture Investments)*
Alan King *(Pres-Communities, Mng Dir & Head-Multifamily Property Ops)*
Jason Grossman *(Mng Dir-Venture Investments)*
Jack Dent *(Mng Dir & Mgr-Portfolio)*
Stephen Parthum *(Mng Dir & Mgr-Portfolio)*

Subsidiaries:

Berkshire Income Realty LLC   **(1)**
1 Beacon St, Boston, MA 02108
Tel.: (617) 523-7722
Web Site:
   http://www.berkshireincomerealty.com
Rev.: $82,181,108
Assets: $521,672,570
Liabilities: $510,998,995
Net Worth: $10,673,575
Earnings: $123,508,112
Fiscal Year-end: 12/31/2014
Real Estate Investment Trust
N.A.I.C.S.: 525990
Mary Beth Bloom *(Sec & Sr VP)*
David E. Doherty *(CFO & Sr VP)*
Jack Dent *(VP)*
Elvira Hadzihasanovic *(VP)*

BERKSHIRE MOUNTAIN SPRING WATER

772 Norfolk Rd, Southfield, MA 01259
Tel.: (413) 229-2086
Web Site:
   http://www.berkshiresprings.com
Year Founded: 1970
Sales Range: $10-24.9 Million
Emp.: 5
Bottled Water Mfr & Distr
N.A.I.C.S.: 312112

Berkshire Mountain Spring Water—(Continued)

Dale C. Bosworth (*Owner*)
Janis Graham-Jones (*Gen Mgr*)
Pamela Bosworth (*Treas*)
Tara White (*CEO*)

BERKSHIRE PARTNERS LLC

200 Clarendon St 35th Fl, Boston,
MA 02116
Tel.: (617) 227-0050   MA
Web Site:
    http://www.berkshirepartners.com
Year Founded: 1986
Private Equity Investments
N.A.I.C.S.: 523999
Kevin T. Callaghan (*Mng Dir*)
Ross M. Jones (*Mng Dir*)
Chris Hadley (*Mng Dir*)
Lawrence S. Hamelsky (*Mng Dir*)
Michael C. Ascione (*Mng Dir*)
Joshua L. Lutzker (*Mng Dir*)
Elizabeth L. Hoffman (*Mng Dir*)
Marni F. Payne (*Mng Dir*)
E. J. Whelan (*Mng Dir*)
Richard K. Lubin (*Mng Dir*)
Elizabeth Liacos (*Dir-Ops*)
Raleigh A. Shoemaker (*Mng Dir-IR*)
Sharlyn C. Heslam (*Mng Dir & Gen Counsel*)
Matthew A. Janchar (*Mng Dir-Capital Markets*)
Gary Giordano (*VP-Tax*)
David Bordeau (*Mng Dir*)
Robert Joshua Small (*Mng Dir*)
Reuben Ackerman (*Chief Compliance Officer*)
Elizabeth A. Chang (*Partner-Capital Markets*)
Christopher W. Dacey (*Operating Partner-Portfolio Support*)
Blake L. Gottesman (*Mng Dir*)
Joshua B. Johnson (*Principal*)
Whitney M. Kelly (*VP*)
Benjamin D. Levy (*Principal*)
John A. Nelson (*VP*)
Jonathan D. Nuger (*Principal*)
Nii Amaah K. Ofosu-Amaah (*Principal-Bus Dev*)
Greg J. Pappas (*Mng Dir*)
Ted Rainaud (*Mng Dir*)
Amelia E. Random (*VP*)
Howard M. Singer (*VP*)
Samuel W. Spirn (*Principal*)
Andrew C. Walker (*Principal*)
Joe Delaney (*Dir-Advisory*)
Matthew B. Gooch (*Dir-Bus Dev*)
Chuck Ball (*Dir-Advisory*)
Carol Vallone (*Dir-Advisory*)
Javier Vlez-Bautista (*CEO-El Dorado Foods*)
Rick Michaux (*Dir-Advisory*)

Subsidiaries:

AHEAD, LLC   (1)
150 S Wacker Dr Ste 2500, Chicago, IL
60606
Tel.: (312) 329-7880
Web Site: http://www.thinkahead.com
Sales Range: $125-149.9 Million
Emp.: 150
Information Technology Consulting Services
N.A.I.C.S.: 541512
Daniel Adamany (*Founder & CEO*)
Tim Frank (*VP-Sls*)
Eric Kaplan (*CTO*)
Michael Hoehne (*Chief People Officer*)

Subsidiary (Domestic):

Computer Design & Integration,
LLC   (2)
1111 Metropolitan Ave Ste 1070, Charlotte,
NC 28204
Tel.: (704) 716-0010
Web Site: http://www.cdillc.com
Sales Range: $25-49.9 Million
Emp.: 28
Software Development Services

N.A.I.C.S.: 541511
Brian Reid (*CFO*)
David A. Brown (*Pres-CDI Southeast*)
Eric Bakker (*Co-Founder & Pres*)
Frank Romano (*Pres-Engrg*)
Trish Bakker (*Co-Founder & CEO*)
Will Huber (*Dir-Advanced Svcs Grp*)
Jason Kalvesmaki (*Chief Revenue Officer*)
Rich Falcone (*Pres-Sls Ops*)
Matt Biringer (*Sr Acct Exec-Emerging Tech*)
Dan Ryan (*VP-Sls & Ops-Southeast*)
Matt Long (*Mgr-Pro Svcs Grp*)
Rob Sienrukos (*VP-Managed Svcs.Sls*)
Alyssa Hall (*VP-Mktg & Bus Dev*)
Vince Collado (*COO*)
George Gosselin (*CIO*)
Mido Hajaji (*Dir-Sls-Pub Sector*)
Rosemary Pron (*Assoc VP-SLED*)

Subsidiary (Domestic):

PlanB Technologies, Inc.   (3)
185 Admiral Cochrane Dr Ste 150, Annapolis, MD 21401
Tel.: (301) 860-1006
Web Site: http://www.planbtech.net
Rev.: $23,800,000
Emp.: 40
Computer Integrated Systems Design
N.A.I.C.S.: 541511
Bill Monaghan (*Dir-Inside Sls*)
Katie Mish (*Dir-Mktg*)
Curtis C. Eshelman (*Dir-Enterprise Sls*)
Stephen Taylor (*CTO*)
June Eshelman (*CFO*)
Donald W. Downs (*Pres & CEO*)

Subsidiary (Domestic):

Mbx Systems   (2)
7699 Golf Channel Dr, Orlando, FL 32819-8923
Tel.: (321) 354-2000
Web Site: http://www.mbx.com
Advertising Material Distribution Services
N.A.I.C.S.: 541870
John Sullivan (*Mgr*)

vCORE Technology Partners
LLC   (2)
17744 Skypark Cir Ste 260, Irvine, CA
92614-4475
Web Site: http://www.vcoretec.com
Computer Related Services
N.A.I.C.S.: 541519
Mike Koski (*Sr Acct Exec*)

Accela Inc.   (1)
2633 Camino Ramon Ste 500, San Ramon,
CA 94583
Tel.: (925) 659-3200
Web Site: http://www.accela.com
Software Devolpment
N.A.I.C.S.: 541810
Jeffrey C. Tung (*COO*)
Max Schnoedl (*Chief Strategy Officer*)
Khaled Jaouni (*Mng Dir-Intl*)
Dani Chehak (*Chief HR Officer*)
Jonathon Knight (*Chief Customer Officer*)
Srini Kakkera (*CTO*)
Troy Coggiola (*Chief Product Officer*)
Heidi Lorenzen (*VP-Mktg*)
Dennis Michalis (*Chief Revenue Officer*)
Tom Nieto (*VP-Ops & Strategy*)
Dave Rusconi (*Sr VP-Cloud Ops*)
Max Schnoedi (*Pres & Gen Mgr-Springbook*)
Dennis W. Alpert (*Head-Govt Affairs*)

Access Information Information Managed Information Shared Services LLC   (1)
500 Unicorn Park Dr, Woburn, MA 01801
Tel.: (925) 583-0100
Web Site: http://www.accesscorp.com
Records Storage Services
N.A.I.C.S.: 334112
John Chendo (*Founder & Pres*)
Chad Bevington (*Exec VP-Client Success*)
Timothy Walker (*Mgr-Landisville*)
Todd Seman (*Mgr-Denver*)
Brian Quinn (*VP-Conversion Svcs*)
Cheryl Pearson (*Gen Mgr-Sacramento*)
Shaun Stevens (*Mgr-Acct-Natl*)
Steve Engdahl (*Chief Product Officer*)
Ted Kenney (*CIO*)
Tony Skarupa (*CFO & COO*)
Jeremy Benedict (*Chief People & Strategy Officer*)
Kendall B. Davis (*CEO*)

Subsidiary (Domestic):

Archives Corp.   (2)

3401 Nevada Ave N, Minneapolis, MN
55427
Tel.: (763) 533-0612
Web Site: http://www.archivescorp.com
Sales Range: $1-9.9 Million
Emp.: 48
Special Warehse/Storage Business Services Mfg Corrugated/Fiber Box Information Retrieval Sv
N.A.I.C.S.: 493190

Central Files, Inc.   (2)
922 S Main St, South Bend, IN 46601
Tel.: (574) 289-3000
Web Site: http://www.centralfilesinc.com
Document Storage & File Management Services
N.A.I.C.S.: 334112
Jim Lender (*Gen Mgr*)

Data Logic Services Corp   (2)
5333 Westheimer Rd Ste 100, Houston, TX
77056
Tel.: (713) 840-8282
Data Processing Services
N.A.I.C.S.: 518210

Document Storage Corporation.   (2)
2021 E Locust Ct, Ontario, CA 91761
Tel.: (888) 947-9428
Web Site:
    http://www.documentstoragecorp.com
Records Management Services
N.A.I.C.S.: 493190

IntegBusiness Services, Inc.   (2)
98-736 Moanalua Loop, Aiea, HI 96701
Tel.: (808) 673-3200
Web Site: http://www.integbusiness.com
Information Management Outsourcing Services
N.A.I.C.S.: 519290
Chris Harris (*Reg VP-Pacific*)
Azia McCord (*Branch Mgr*)

International Data Depository   (2)
3450 NW 112th St, Miami, FL 33166
Tel.: (305) 477-7388
Web Site: http://www.intdd.com
Sales Range: $1-9.9 Million
Emp.: 50
Special Warehouse/Storage
N.A.I.C.S.: 493190

Tindall Record Storage Ltd.   (2)
630 N Freeway, Fort Worth, TX 76102
Tel.: (817) 870-3677
Web Site: http://www.tindallrecord.com
General Warehousing & Storage
N.A.I.C.S.: 493110
Steve Stamp (*Pres*)

Affordable Care, Inc.   (1)
5430 Wade Park Blvd Wade II Ste 310, Raleigh, NC 27607
Tel.: (919) 851-3996
Web Site:
    http://www.affordabledentures.com
Dental Laboratories
N.A.I.C.S.: 339116
Adam Siegal (*CMO*)
Matt Wells (*CIO*)
Randy Ammons (*VP-HR & Legal*)
Gene Kirtser (*CEO*)

Catalina Marketing Corporation   (1)
200 Carillon Pkwy, Saint Petersburg, FL
33716
Tel.: (727) 579-5000
Web Site: http://www.catalinamarketing.com
Sales Range: $650-699.9 Million
Digital Marketing Solutions
N.A.I.C.S.: 541890
Tricia Manning (*Exec VP-Global Ops*)
Shelly Schaffer (*CFO*)
David Glogoff (*Chief Admin Officer & Chief Legal Officer*)
Kevin Hunter (*Chief Product Officer*)
Marshall Stanton (*Exec VP-Ops-Global*)
Marta Cyhan (*CMO*)
Wes Chaar (*Chief Data & Analytics Officer*)
Jerry Sokol (*Pres & CEO*)
Michael Bailey (*CTO*)

Subsidiary (Non-US):

Catalina Marketing Deutschland
GmbH   (2)
Saalburgstrasse 157, 61350, Bad Homburg,
Germany

Tel.: (49) 6172 7898 1 0
Web Site: http://www.catalinamarketing.de
Marketing Consulting Services
N.A.I.C.S.: 541613

Catalina UK Ltd.   (2)
Pinnacle House 20 Tudor Road, Reading,
RG1 1NH, United Kingdom
Tel.: (44) 118 902 7900
Web Site:
    http://www.catalinamarketing.co.uk
Emp.: 50
Marketing Consulting Services
N.A.I.C.S.: 541613
Steve Lane (*Mng Dir*)

Subsidiary (Domestic):

Cellfire, Inc.   (2)
2890 Zanker Rd, San Jose, CA 95134
Tel.: (408) 324-1000
Web Site: http://www.cellfire.com
Emp.: 25
Digital Coupon Services
N.A.I.C.S.: 513210
Frank Careccia (*CTO & VP-Engrg*)
Robert Drescher (*CEO*)
Wes Horvath (*VP-Sls & Bus Dev*)

Citizens of Humanity LLC   (1)
95 5th Ave, New York, NY 10003   (63%)
Tel.: (212) 242-1829
Web Site:
    http://www.citizensofhumanity.com
Sales Range: $100-124.9 Million
Clothing Store Operator
N.A.I.C.S.: 458110
Jerome Dahan (*Founder*)

Crossfit, Inc.   (1)
3196 Willow Creek Rd, Prescott, AZ 86301-6689
Tel.: (928) 445-9739
Web Site: http://www.crossfit.com
Rev.: $1,000,000
Emp.: 2
Independent Artists, Writers & Performers
N.A.I.C.S.: 711510
Don Faul (*CEO*)
Alison Andreozzi (*CFO*)
Annette Reavis (*Chief People Officer*)

FoodChain ID Group, Inc.   (1)
504 N 4th St, Fairfield, IA 52556
Tel.: (641) 209-4500
Web Site: https://www.foodchainid.com
Holding Company; Food Safety & Testing
N.A.I.C.S.: 551112
Conor Kearney (*CEO*)

Subsidiary (Domestic):

FoodChain ID Technical Services,
Inc   (2)
504 N 4th St, Fairfield, IA 52556
Tel.: (641) 469-6181
Web Site: https://www.foodchainid.com
Food Safety Technical & Testing Services
N.A.I.C.S.: 541990
Brad Riemenapp (*CEO*)

Subsidiary (Domestic):

Decernis LLC   (3)
1250 Ct Ave NW Ste 200, Washington, DC
20036-0000
Tel.: (240) 428-1800
Web Site: http://www.decernis.com
Technology Enabled Global Risk Management
N.A.I.C.S.: 541690
Andrew Waldo (*CEO*)

Implus Footcare, LLC   (1)
2001 TW Alexander Dr, Durham, NC
27709-3925
Tel.: (919) 313-9031
Web Site: http://www.implus.com
Footwear & Other Sporting Goods Accessories Mfr & Distr
N.A.I.C.S.: 316210
Michael B. Polk (*CEO*)
Ryan Cruthirds (*Chief Global Category & Brand Development Officer*)
Dannie Pratt (*Sr Dir-Ops*)
Jeff Payne (*Dir-Ops*)
Jennifer Payne (*VP-HR*)
Kyle Macemore (*CFO*)
Lori O'Sullivan (*Chief HR Officer*)

Alexander Crispin Baker (COO)
Gwen Moilanen (CIO)
Drew Davies (Chief Comml Officer-Americas)

Subsidiary (Domestic):

32 North Corp. (2)
16 Pomerleau St, Biddeford, ME 04005
Tel.: (207) 284-5010
Footwear Mfr
N.A.I.C.S.: 316210

Rocktape, Inc. (2)
2001 TW Alexander Dr, Drive Durham, NC 27709 USA, Durham, NC 27709
Tel.: (408) 912-7625
Web Site: http://www.rocktape.com
Sales Range: $50-74.9 Million
Sports Goods Distr
N.A.I.C.S.: 459110

Masergy Communications, Inc. (1)
2740 N Dallas Pkwy Ste 260, Plano, TX 75093
Tel.: (214) 442-5700
Web Site: http://www.masergy.com
Software Defined Networking Services
N.A.I.C.S.: 513210
Robert Bodnar (CFO & Exec VP)
Chris MacFarland (Chm & CEO)
Tim Naramore (CTO & Exec VP)
John Dumbleton (Sr VP-Bus Dev)
Bill Madison (VP-Global Channel Dev Program)
Chuck Ward (VP-Global Channels)
Jeff Walker (Gen Counsel & Sec)
Keith Hatley (Sr VP-Global Channel Sls)
Todd Lechtenberg (Sr VP-Global Ops)
Brian Norton (Sr VP-Direct Sls-North America)
Terry Traina (Sr VP-Engrg)
Ethan Blodgett (VP-Network Ops)
Vikesh Gumpalli (VP-Sls Strategy & Ops)

Subsidiary (Non-US):

Masergy Communications UK Limited (2)
29 Finsbury Circus Salisbury House 5th Floor, London, EC2M 5QQ, United Kingdom
Tel.: (44) 2071736900
Web Site: http://www.masergy.com
Corporate Communication Network Builder
N.A.I.C.S.: 517810
Nick Rattey (Acct Dir)

National Carwash Solutions, Inc. (1)
1500 SE 37th St, Grimes, IA 50111-2172
Tel.: (515) 986-3700
Web Site: http://www.ncswash.com
Automated Car Wash Equipment & Accessories Mfr
N.A.I.C.S.: 333310
Michael Gillen (CEO)

Subsidiary (Domestic):

Hill & Foss, Inc. (2)
5995 Financial Dr, Norcross, GA 30071
Tel.: (770) 449-3630
Service Establishment Equipment & Supplies Merchant Whslr
N.A.I.C.S.: 423850

PT Holdings, LLC (1)
1200 Greenbriar Dr, 60101, Addison, IL
Tel.: (800) 438-8898
Holding Company
N.A.I.C.S.: 551112
David Wenger (Pres)

Subsidiary (Domestic):

Greenwich, Inc. (2)
1377 N Brazos St, San Antonio, TX 78207
Tel.: (210) 735-2811
Web Site:
    http://www.commercialkitchen.com
Electronic & Precision Equipment Repair & Maintenance
N.A.I.C.S.: 811210
Brock W. Coleman (Pres)

Parts Town LLC (2)
1200 Greenbriar Dr, Addison, IL 60101-1001
Tel.: (630) 263-4900
Web Site: http://www.partstown.com
Rev.: $18,100,000
Emp.: 35

Equipment Merchant Whslrs
N.A.I.C.S.: 423830
Steve Snower (Pres & CEO)
Laura Hugger (Sr Mgr-Ops)
Miron Washington (Chief Digital Officer)

Subsidiary (Domestic):

Dayton Appliance Parts Co. Inc. (3)
122 Sears St, Dayton, OH 45402
Tel.: (937) 224-3531
Web Site: http://www.partwizard.com
Sales Range: $10-24.9 Million
Emp.: 150
Household Appliance Parts
N.A.I.C.S.: 423620
James E. Houtz (Pres)
Greg Bossart (Mgr-Warehouse)
Henry Wolf (Mgr-Ops)
Bryan Leininger (Mgr-Logistics)
Bub Houtz (VP)

Food Equipment Services Co. (3)
1209 S Watkins St, Chattanooga, TN 37404
Tel.: (423) 624-3381
Web Site: http://www.fesco-tenn.com
Emp.: 15
Foodservice Equipment Mfr
N.A.I.C.S.: 423440
David Hahn (Pres)

General Parts, LLC (3)
11311 Hampshire Ave S, Bloomington, MN 55438
Tel.: (952) 944-5800
Web Site: http://www.generalparts.com
Sales Range: $1-9.9 Million
Emp.: 140
Electronic & Precision Equipment Repair & Maintenance
N.A.I.C.S.: 811210
Jeff Weber (VP-Sls)
Gary Schermann (VP-Ops)

Whaley Foodservice, LLC (3)
137 Cedar Rd, Lexington, SC 29073
Tel.: (803) 996-9900
Web Site:
    http://www.whaleyfoodservice.com
Emp.: 500
Foodservice Equipment Part Distr Restaurant Equipment Maintenance & Repair Services
N.A.I.C.S.: 423440
Lee Knight (Branch Mgr-Columbus)
Chuck Anderson (Area Mgr-Columbia & Augusta)
Terry Humphries (Area Mgr-Raleigh)
Keith Tomlinson (Area Mgr-Greensboro & Winston-Salem)
Mick Jackson (Area Mgr-Charlotte)
Kevin Cahill (Branch Mgr-Springfield)
Brett Marshall (Area Mgr-Wilmington)
Sandi Halcomb (Area Mgr-Ocala)

Vi-Jon, Inc. (1)
8515 Page Ave, Saint Louis, MO 63114-6014
Tel.: (314) 427-1000
Web Site: http://www.vijon.com
Sales Range: $75-99.9 Million
Beauty Product Mfr
N.A.I.C.S.: 325620
Eduardo Alves (Chief Sls & Mktg Officer)
Darren Baker (COO)
Tim Spihlman (CEO)
Alice Clark (Chief HR Officer)
Keith Grypp (Gen Counsel & VP)
Matt Harper (CFO)

Plant (Domestic):

Vi-Jon, Inc. (2)
1 Swan Dr, Smyrna, TN 37167-2099
Tel.: (615) 459-8900
Web Site: http://www.vijon.com
Sales Range: $100-124.9 Million
Mfr of Personal Care Products for the Store Brand Market, Health
N.A.I.C.S.: 325620

BERKSHIRE TACONIC COMMUNITY FOUNDATION, INC.
800 N Main St, Sheffield, MA 01257-9503
Tel.: (413) 229-0370   CT
Web Site:
    https://www.berkshiretaconic.org

Year Founded: 1987
Sales Range: $10-24.9 Million
Emp.: 20
Fundraising Services
N.A.I.C.S.: 813211
Peggy Gearity (Controller)
A. J. Pietrantone (VP-Fin & Admin)
Jill Cancellieri (Dir-Philanthropic Svcs)
Justin Burke (Dir-Mktg & Comm)
Peter Taylor (Pres)

BERKSHIRE-WESTWOOD GRAPHICS GROUP
20 Hadley Mill Rd, Holyoke, MA 01040
Tel.: (413) 532-1735
Year Founded: 1980
Sales Range: $25-49.9 Million
Emp.: 59
Printing Trades Machinery, Equipment & Supplies
N.A.I.C.S.: 423830
Michael Sullivan (Pres)
Lew Shouse (Ops Mgr-Sls)

BERLANDS INC.
600 Oak Creek Dr, Lombard, IL 60148
Tel.: (630) 627-9090
Rev.: $14,007,071
Emp.: 70
Power Handtools
N.A.I.C.S.: 423710
Dwight Sherman (Pres & CEO)

BERLINE
423 N Main St Ste 300, Royal Oak, MI 48067
Tel.: (248) 593-7402   MI
Web Site: https://www.berline.com
Year Founded: 1982
Rev.: $70,000,000
Emp.: 20
Advetising Agency
N.A.I.C.S.: 541810
Shane Wright (Assoc Dir-Creative)

BERLINER SPECIALTY DISTRIBUTORS, INC.
5101 Buchanan St, Hyattsville, MD 20781
Tel.: (301) 531-5957   MD
Web Site:
    https://www.berlinerfoods.com
Year Founded: 1973
Ice Cream & Specialty Foods Distr
N.A.I.C.S.: 445298
Sandra Griffin (Mgr-Customer Sls)
Guy Berliner (Pres)
Jason Medina (Supvr-Distr)

BERMCO ALUMINUM
3230 Messer Airport Hwy, Birmingham, AL 35222
Tel.: (502) 867-4498
Web Site: https://www.bermco.com
Sales Range: $50-74.9 Million
Emp.: 100
Ferrous Metal Scrap & Waste
N.A.I.C.S.: 423930
Steve Weinstein (Pres & CEO)
Mitchell Skipper (CFO)
Jeri Berman-Davis (Owner & VP)
Dennis Shellenbarger (Mgr)

BERMIL INDUSTRIES CORP.
461 Doughty Blvd, Inwood, NY 11096-1344
Tel.: (516) 371-4400
Web Site: http://www.laundrylux.com
Sales Range: $75-99.9 Million
Emp.: 70
Laundry Equipment Mfr
N.A.I.C.S.: 423850

Neal Milch (CEO)
Archie Abrams (CFO)
Howard Herman (VP-Mktg & Sls)
David Milch (VP)

BERMO ENTERPRISES INC.
12033 US 131, Schoolcraft, MI 49087-0426
Tel.: (269) 679-2580   MI
Web Site:
    http://www.bermoenterprises.com
Year Founded: 1973
Sales Range: $25-49.9 Million
Emp.: 245
Family Clothing Stores
N.A.I.C.S.: 458110
Edward Bernard (Pres)
Tony Peters (VP-Sls)

BERMO INCORPORATED
4501 Ball Rd NE, Circle Pines, MN 55014-1818
Tel.: (763) 786-7676   MN
Web Site: https://www.bermo.com
Year Founded: 1947
Sales Range: $75-99.9 Million
Emp.: 150
Mfr of Metal Stampings For Trades & Injection Molded Finished Plastic Products
N.A.I.C.S.: 332119
Daniel M. Berdass (Chm)
Margo Berdass (Treas)
Nancy J. Hartman (CEO)
Steve Smith (VP-Customer Svcs)
Tom Johnson (CFO)
David A. Berdass (Pres)

Subsidiaries:

Bermo Scotland, Ltd (1)
Westwood Park Glover Road, Glenrothes, KY7 4UH, Scotland, United Kingdom   (100%)
Tel.: (44) 1592662300
N.A.I.C.S.: 332119

BERNARD & SONS INC.
4011 Jewett Ave, Bakersfield, CA 93301
Tel.: (661) 327-4431
Web Site:
    http://www.bernardandsons.com
Sales Range: $10-24.9 Million
Emp.: 33
Fresh Meats
N.A.I.C.S.: 424470

BERNARD BUILDING CENTER INC.
395 S Washington M-65, Hale, MI 48739
Tel.: (989) 728-2211
Web Site:
    https://www.bernardbuilding.com
Sales Range: $10-24.9 Million
Emp.: 60
Lumber & Other Building Materials
N.A.I.C.S.: 423310
Bryon Bernard (Pres & CEO)
Bruce Bernard (VP)
Daryn Bernard (VP-Store Ops)

BERNARD CHAUS, INC.
530 7th Ave, New York, NY 10018
Tel.: (212) 354-1280   NY
Web Site: http://www.bcibrands.com
Year Founded: 1975
Sales Range: $400-449.9 Million
Women's Apparel Designer, Mfr & Marketer
N.A.I.C.S.: 315250
Judith Leech (VP-Design)
Jackie Muldowney (VP-Mdsg)
Ken Christmann (VP-Logistics)
Ariel Chaus (CEO)

Bernard Chaus, Inc.—(Continued)

BERNARD FOOD INDUSTRIES INC.
1125 Hartrey Ave, Evanston, IL 60204
Tel.: (847) 869-5222
Web Site:
http://www.bernardfoods.com
Sales Range: $10-24.9 Million
Emp.: 25
Dried & Dehydrated Fruits, Vegetables & Soup Mixes
N.A.I.C.S.: 311423
Steven F. Bernard (Pres & CEO)
Ann Paige (Gen Mgr)
Bill Sliwa (Controller)

BERNARD KARCHER INVESTMENTS INC.
1631 Market St Ste B, Corona, CA 92860
Tel.: (951) 272-6277
Web Site: http://www.bkiinc.com
Sales Range: $10-24.9 Million
Emp.: 9
Fast-Food Restaurant, Chain
N.A.I.C.S.: 722513
Carlos Torres (VP-Ops)

BERNARD KLEIN INC.
450 Nepperhan Ave, Yonkers, NY 10701
Tel.: (914) 968-2222
Web Site:
http://www.crownproducts.com
Sales Range: $10-24.9 Million
Emp.: 50
Industrial & Personal Service Paper
N.A.I.C.S.: 424130
Peter Mollo (Pres)

BERNARD ROBINSON & COMPANY, L.L.P.
1501 Highwoods Blvd Ste 300, Greensboro, NC 27410
Tel.: (336) 294-4494
Web Site: https://www.brccpa.com
Year Founded: 1947
Emp.: 160
Offices of Certified Public Accountants
N.A.I.C.S.: 541211
James Connolly (Principal)
Tim Hooks (Partner)
Sandy P. Newell (Partner-Assurance)
Ron Kuyath (Partner-Tax)
Patrick Flanagan (Mgr-Tax)
Andy Harding (Dir-Bus Dev)
Kyle Corum (Principal)
Ben Ripple (Partner)
Courtney Coker (Partner)
Jeremy S. Bass (Partner-Tax)
Daniel G. Hayes (Partner)
Sherry S. Johnson (Partner)
Erica B. Vernon (Partner)
David McClure (Partner)
Tracey Flynn Martin (Partner)
Wade Pack (Mng Partner)
Genie Petrangeli (Partner)
Freddy H. Robinson (Partner)
Ben Hunter III (Mgr-Advisory Svcs)

BERNARD WILLIAMS & CO.
6001 Chatham Center Dr Ste 100, Savannah, GA 31405
Tel.: (912) 234-4476
Web Site:
http://www.thepoweroftheshield.com
Year Founded: 1934
Sales Range: $1-9.9 Million
Emp.: 31
Insurance Brokerage Services
N.A.I.C.S.: 524210
Alan S. Williams (Sr VP)
Richard D. Williams (Pres & CEO)

BERNARDI AUTOMALL TRUST
1626 Worcester Rd Route 9 E, Framingham, MA 01702
Tel.: (508) 466-5421
Web Site:
https://www.bernarditoyota.com
Sales Range: $25-49.9 Million
Emp.: 90
New Car Retailer
N.A.I.C.S.: 441110
Bernie Geddry (Dir-Parts)
Bill Joyce (Asst Mgr-Parts)
Eric Anderson (Mgr-Wholesale Parts)
Joseph Chang (Gen Mgr-Sls)
Mike Gugino (Dir-Variable Ops)
Keith Monnin (Gen Mgr)
Howie Charnitsky (Mgr-Gen Sls)
Kham Dam (Mgr-Sls)
Alfredo Lopez (Mgr-Svc-Columbus)

BERNARDI HONDA
960 Worcester St, Natick, MA 01760
Tel.: (508) 651-3033
Web Site:
https://www.bernardiautogroup.com
Year Founded: 1966
Sales Range: $125-149.9 Million
Emp.: 120
Sales of New & Used Automobiles
N.A.I.C.S.: 441110
Joel Richards (Gen Mgr)
Seth Marshall (Gen Mgr)
Adam Shapiro (Dir-Svc)

BERNARDI'S HONDA
960 Worcester St, Natick, MA 01760
Tel.: (508) 651-3033
Web Site:
http://www.bernardihonda.com
Sales Range: $25-49.9 Million
Emp.: 120
New Car Retailer
N.A.I.C.S.: 441110
Joel E. Richards (Gen Mgr)

BERNARDS BROS, INC.
610 Ilex St, San Fernando, CA 91340
Tel.: (818) 898-1521
Web Site: http://www.bernards.com
Year Founded: 1974
Sales Range: $75-99.9 Million
Emp.: 180
Civil Engineering Services
N.A.I.C.S.: 237310
Douglas Bernards (Chm, Pres & CEO)

BERNARDS BROTHERS, INC.
555 1st St, San Fernando, CA 91340-3403
Tel.: (818) 898-1521   CA
Web Site: https://www.bernards.com
Year Founded: 1974
Sales Range: $125-149.9 Million
Emp.: 180
Provider of Contracting & Construction Services
N.A.I.C.S.: 236210
Douglas Bernards (Chm, Pres & CEO)
Gregory Bernards (Exec VP)
Jeffrey Bernards (Sec & VP)
Gregory C. Simons (Exec VP)

BERNATELLOS PIZZA INC.
220 Congress St, Maple Lake, MN 55358
Tel.: (320) 963-6191
Web Site: http://www.bernatellos.com
Sales Range: $25-49.9 Million
Emp.: 200
Pizza, Frozen
N.A.I.C.S.: 311412
William Ramsay (Pres)
Jim Cousin (Gen Mgr)
Dwayne Ebert (Controller)

BERND GROUP INC.
1251 Pinehurst Rd, Dunedin, FL 34698
Tel.: (727) 733-0122
Web Site:
https://www.berndgroup.com
Year Founded: 1989
Sales Range: $50-74.9 Million
Emp.: 65
Industrial Machinery & Equipment
N.A.I.C.S.: 423830
Pilar Ricaurte-Bernd (Founder & Pres)

BERNE APPAREL CORP
2501 E 850 N, Ossian, IN 46777
Web Site:
http://www.berneapparel.com
Year Founded: 1915
Sales Range: $10-24.9 Million
Emp.: 200
Work Apparel
N.A.I.C.S.: 315990
Ronald Nussbaum (Pres)

BERNE COOPERATIVE ASSOCIATION INC.
158 W Main St, Ute, IA 51060
Tel.: (712) 885-2249
Web Site:
http://www.bernecoopassoc.com
Rev.: $11,500,000
Emp.: 50
Gasoline Stations
N.A.I.C.S.: 457120
Dennis Holdsworth (Pres)

BERNHARD BROTHERS MECHANICAL CONTRACTORS, LLC.
13641 Airline Hwy, Baton Rouge, LA 70817
Tel.: (225) 752-0785
Web Site:
http://www.bernhardbros.com
Sales Range: $10-24.9 Million
Emp.: 85
Plumbing Services
N.A.I.C.S.: 238220
Travis Bernhard (Mgr)
Barry L. Bernhard (Principal)
Eric Randy Bernhard (Principal)
William F. Bernhard III (Principal)

BERNHARD CAPITAL PARTNERS MANAGEMENT, LP
400 Convention St 10th Fl, Baton Rouge, LA 70802
Tel.: (225) 228-2500
Web Site:
http://www.bernhardcapital.com
Year Founded: 2013
Privater Equity Firm
N.A.I.C.S.: 523999
Lucie Kantrow (Gen Counsel)
Christopher Ringswald (VP)
Jeffrey Koonce (Partner)
Luther C. Kissam IV (Partner)
Mark Spender (Mng Dir)
Brian K. Ferraioli (Operating Partner)

Subsidiaries:

ATC Group Services LLC   (1)
221 Rue De Jean 3rd Fl, Lafayette, LA 70508
Tel.: (337) 234-8777
Web Site: http://www.atcassociates.com
Emp.: 1,900
Environmental Consulting, Industrial Hygiene, Geotechnical Engineering, Construction Materials Testing & Inspection Services
N.A.I.C.S.: 541620
Don Beck (Sr VP-North Reg)
Robert Toups (CEO)
Paul Grillo (CFO)
John Mollere (Chief Admin Officer)
Ashley Foti (Gen Counsel)

Kevin Sommers (Sr VP-South Reg)
Chris Phillips (Sr VP-West Reg)
Dave Paholak (Sr VP-Midwest Reg)
Alan Agadoni (Sr VP-Natl Programs)
Bob Sorvillo (Exec VP)

Subsidiary (Domestic):

Sage ATC Environmental Consulting LLC   (2)
4611 Bee Caves Rd Ste 100, Austin, TX 78746
Tel.: (512) 327-0288
Web Site:
http://www.sageenvironmental.com
Environmental Consulting Services
N.A.I.C.S.: 541620

White Environmental Consultants, Inc.   (2)
731 I St Ste 201, Anchorage, AK 99501
Tel.: (907) 258-8663
Business Consulting Services
N.A.I.C.S.: 541690

Allied Power Holdings, LLC   (1)
2600 Citiplace Drive Suite 250, Baton Rouge, LA 70808
Tel.: (225) 412-6455
Web Site: https://www.alliedpwr.com
Power Plant Services
N.A.I.C.S.: 237130

Subsidiary (Domestic):

Dominion Engineering, Inc.   (2)
12100 Sunrise Valley Dr Ste 220, Reston, VA 20191
Tel.: (703) 437-1155
Web Site: http://www.domeng.com
Rev.: $8,382,500
Emp.: 40
Engineeering Services
N.A.I.C.S.: 541330
David J. Gross (Officer-Bus)

Radiation Safety & Control Services, Inc.   (2)
91 Portsmouth Ave Ste B, Stratham, NH 03885
Tel.: (603) 778-2871
Web Site: http://www.radsafety.com
Sales Range: $1-9.9 Million
Emp.: 50
Scientific & Technical Consulting Services
N.A.I.C.S.: 541690

Ascension Wastewater Treatment   (1)
37458 Cornerview Rd, Geismar, LA 70734
Tel.: (225) 673-3156
Sewage Treatment Facilities
N.A.I.C.S.: 221320

BEM Systems, Inc.   (1)
100 Passaic Ave, Chatham, NJ 07928-2848
Tel.: (908) 598-2600
Web Site: http://www.bemsys.com
Sales Range: $10-24.9 Million
Emp.: 45
Environmental Consulting & Industrial Hygiene Services
N.A.I.C.S.: 561210
Mark Nardolillo (CEO)
Dave Leonard (CIO)
Andrew Crabb (Mgr-Application Dev)
Mark Murset (CFO)

Branch (Domestic):

BEM Systems - Newport News   (2)
11815 Fountain Way One City Ctr Ste 300, Newport News, VA 23606   (100%)
Tel.: (757) 591-9466
Web Site: http://www.bemsys.com
Sales Range: $10-24.9 Million
Emp.: 3
Environmental Consulting & Industrial Hygiene Services
N.A.I.C.S.: 561210

BEM Systems - Orlando   (2)
3101 Maguire Blvd Ste 265, Orlando, FL 32803-3713   (100%)
Tel.: (407) 894-9900
Web Site: http://www.bemsys.com
Sales Range: $10-24.9 Million
Emp.: 3
Environmental Consulting & Industrial Hygiene Services

N.A.I.C.S.: 561210

BEM Systems - Phoenix (2)
7500 N Dreamy Draw Dr, Phoenix, AZ
85020   (100%)
Tel.: (602) 266-2011
Web Site: http://www.bemsys.com
Sales Range: $10-24.9 Million
Emp.: 10
Environmental Consulting & Industrial Hy-
giene Services
N.A.I.C.S.: 541618

Brown & Root Industrial Services,
LLC (1)
2600 Citiplace Dr Ste 500, Baton Rouge,
LA 70808   (50%)
Tel.: (225) 778-7655
Web Site: https://www.brownandroot.com
Emp.: 1,600
Industrial Services, Including Engineering,
Construction & Maintenance
N.A.I.C.S.: 541330
Charlie Heath *(CFO)*
Brandon Politz *(Gen Counsel)*
Crista Stokes Wynne *(VP-Finance)*
Mary Bihlmeyer *(VP-, , and)*
Jerry Redden *(VP-, Safety, and)*
Mike Firmin *(Pres-)*
Jack Penley *(Pres-Engineering &)*
Grant Landry *(Pres)*
Ross Campesi *(Pres-)*
Donnie Hopkins *(Pres-)*
Katie Richardson *(VP-Human Resources)*
Shannon Wild *(VP-, Technology, and)*

Subsidiary (Domestic):

Maintenance Enterprises LLC (2)
52410 Clark Rd, White Castle, LA 70788
Tel.: (225) 545-3970
Web Site: http://maintenanceenterprise.com
Renovation, Remodeling & Repairs: Indus-
trial Buildings
N.A.I.C.S.: 236220

Petrin Corp. (2)
1405 Commercial Dr, Port Allen, LA 70767-
0330
Tel.: (225) 343-0471
Web Site: https://www.petrinllc.com
Sales Range: $50-74.9 Million
Emp.: 670
Industrial Insulation Services
N.A.I.C.S.: 238310
Bob Hall *(Mgr-Northern Div)*
Kenny Freeman *(Pres)*
Michael Shipp *(Exec VP)*

Affiliate (Domestic):

Scaffolding Rental & Erection Ser-
vices, LLC (3)
1423 Commercial Dr, Port Allen, LA 70767
Tel.: (225) 339-0871
Web Site: http://www.scaffold-rental.com
Emp.: 350
Scaffolding Rental & Erection Services
N.A.I.C.S.: 532490
Mike Shipp *(Exec VP)*
Sonny Jordan *(Gen Mgr)*
Richard Trisler *(Dir-Safety & Health)*

Duotech Services, Inc (1)
245 Industrial Park Road, Franklin, NC
28734
Tel.: (828) 369-5411
Web Site: http://www.duotechservices.com
Rev.: $2,333,333
Emp.: 25
Other Electronic Component Mfr
N.A.I.C.S.: 334419
Daniel Rogers *(VP)*
Chris Ott *(Sys Engr-Software)*
Brett Rogers *(VP)*

Elos Environmental, LLC (1)
43177 E Pleasant Rdg Rd, Hammond, LA
70403-0403
Tel.: (985) 662-5501
Web Site: http://www.elosenv.com
Environmental Consulting Services
N.A.I.C.S.: 541620
Jay Prather *(VP)*

Epic Piping, LLC (1)
9489 Interline Ave, Baton Rouge, LA 70809
Tel.: (844) 760-6682
Web Site: http://www.epicpiping.com
Fabricated Pipe & Pipe Fitting Mfr

N.A.I.C.S.: 332996
Remi Bonnecaze *(CEO)*

Subsidiary (Domestic):

BendTec, Inc. (2)
366 Garfield Ave, Duluth, MN 55802
Tel.: (218) 722-0205
Web Site: http://www.bendtec.com
Sales Range: $1-9.9 Million
Emp.: 67
Bending & Fabrication Services
N.A.I.C.S.: 333517
Jon Rairdon *(Mgr-Safety)*
David Meierhoff *(Dir-Ops)*

Grace Hebert Curtis Architects,
LLC (1)
501 Government St Ste 200, Baton Rouge,
LA 70802
Tel.: (225) 338-5569
Web Site: https://ghc-arch.com
Architectural Services
N.A.I.C.S.: 541310
Jerry Hebert *(CEO)*

Subsidiary (Domestic):

BSSW Architects, Inc. (2)
1500 Jackson St Ste 200, Fort Myers, FL
33901
Tel.: (239) 278-3838
Web Site: https://www.bsswarchitects.com
Sales Range: $1-9.9 Million
Emp.: 15
Architectural Services
N.A.I.C.S.: 541310
Kevin Williams *(Partner)*
Ron Weaver *(Partner)*
Dan Summers *(Pres)*

Bullock Tice Associates, Inc. (2)
909 E Cervantes St Ste B, Pensacola, FL
32501
Tel.: (850) 434-5444
Web Site: https://bullocktice.com
Sales Range: $1-9.9 Million
Emp.: 43
Architectural Services
N.A.I.C.S.: 541310
Douglas Ashley *(VP)*
John Tice *(CEO)*

K C Harvey Environmental LLC (1)
376 Gallatin Park Dr, Bozeman, MT 59715-
7909
Tel.: (406) 585-7402
Web Site: http://www.kcharvey.com
Environmental Consulting Services
N.A.I.C.S.: 541620
Kevin Harvey *(Pres & CEO)*

United Utility Services, LLC (1)
13850 Ballantyne Corporate Pl Ste 500,
Charlotte, NC 28277
Tel.: (704) 887-4925
Web Site: http://www.unitedutility.com
Transmission & Distribution Services
N.A.I.C.S.: 335311
Ali Azad *(CEO)*

Subsidiary (Domestic):

Bartlett Holdings, Inc. (2)
97 Libbey Industrial Pkwy Fl 4, Weymouth,
MA 02189
Tel.: (508) 746-6464
Web Site: http://www.bhienergy.com
Turbine & Generator Equipment Mainte-
nance, Nuclear Power Generation & Staff-
ing Services
N.A.I.C.S.: 811310
Robert Decensi *(CEO)*
Mike Kaveney *(COO-Energy Industrial*
Svcs)
Paul Rubin *(COO-Energy Power Generation*
Svcs)
Nick DiMascio *(Pres-Radiation Protection*
Svcs)
Charles Harvey *(CFO)*
Juanita Biasini *(Chief Admin Officer)*
Ken Loynes *(Pres-Transmission & Distr Div)*

Subsidiary (Domestic):

BHI Energy I Power Services
LLC (3)
110 Prosperity Blvd, Piedmont, SC 29673
Tel.: (864) 375-9030
Web Site: http://www.bhienergy.com

Specialty Mechanical & Maintenance Ser-
vices
N.A.I.C.S.: 541330
Steve Stewart *(Ops Mgr-Wind Div)*
Victor Ferraro *(VP-Bus Dev & Alliances)*
Paul Rubin *(Pres-MMC Svcs)*
Mike Kaveney *(COO-Power Svcs)*

BHI Energy I Specialty Services
LLC (3)
2005 Newpoint Pkwy, Lawrenceville, GA
30043
Tel.: (678) 205-1025
Web Site: http://www.bhienergy.com
Welding Contract Services
N.A.I.C.S.: 238190
Steve Smith *(Sr VP & Gen Mgr)*

D & D Power Inc. (3)
16 Hemlock St, Latham, NY 12110
Tel.: (518) 869-2221
Electric Power Installation Services
N.A.I.C.S.: 238210
Kevin Symons *(VP-Ops)*
Philip A. Utter *(Mgr-Safety & Environmental*
Compliance)
Ken Loynes *(COO)*
Darren Donohue *(Founder, Pres & CEO)*

SUN Technical Services, Inc. (3)
5490 Longley Ln Ste B, Reno, NV 89511
Tel.: (775) 829-2499
Web Site: http://www.bhienergy.com
Temporary Staffing Services
N.A.I.C.S.: 561320
Nadine Luty *(Project Mgr)*

Subsidiary (Domestic):

W.A. Chester, LLC (2)
4200 Parliament Pl Ste 400, Lanham, MD
20706
Tel.: (240) 487-1940
Web Site: http://www.wachester.com
Cable Transmission & Distributions Systems
Installation, Repair & Maintenance Services
Contractor
N.A.I.C.S.: 237130
Frank Musick *(Pres)*

BERNHARDT FURNITURE
COMPANY
1839 Morganton Blvd, Lenoir, NC
28645-5338
Tel.: (828) 758-9811   NC
Web Site: https://www.bernhardt.com
Year Founded: 1889
Sales Range: $350-399.9 Million
Emp.: 2,000
Wood & Upholstered Dining Room,
Living Room & Bedroom Furniture
Importer, Mfr & Distr
N.A.I.C.S.: 337122
William B. Collett *(Exec VP & Gen*
Mgr-Bernhardt Residential Case-
goods)
J. Rountree Collett *(Pres-Bernhardt*
Ventures)

Subsidiaries:

Bernhardt Furniture Company - Bern-
hardt Hospitality Division (1)
1839 Morganton Blvd, Lenoir, NC 28645
Tel.: (828) 759-6532
Furniture Whslr
N.A.I.C.S.: 423210

BERNICK COMPANIES
801 Sundial Dr, Waite Park, MN
56387
Tel.: (320) 252-6441
Web Site: https://www.bernicks.com
Year Founded: 1916
Sales Range: $75-99.9 Million
Emp.: 700
Soft Drinks: Malt Beverage: & Vend-
ing
N.A.I.C.S.: 424490
John Torgerson *(COO)*
Jesse Westrup *(VP-Ops-Bernick's*
Beverages & Vending)

Subsidiaries:

Bernick Companies - Bemidji
Plant (1)
959 Industrial Park Dr SE, Bemidji, MN
56601
Tel.: (218) 751-5752
Beverages Mfr
N.A.I.C.S.: 312111

Bernick Companies - Brainerd
Plant (1)
1916 10th St S, Brainerd, MN 56425
Tel.: (218) 829-3156
Beverages Mfr
N.A.I.C.S.: 312111
John Torgerson *(CEO)*

Bernick Companies - Dresser
Plant (1)
690 Kelly Ave, Dresser, WI 54009
Tel.: (715) 755-2100
Web Site: http://www.bernick.com
Emp.: 50
Beverages Mfr
N.A.I.C.S.: 312111

Bernick Companies - Duluth
Plant (1)
4301 W Michigan St, Duluth, MN 55807
Tel.: (218) 628-0276
Web Site: http://www.bernick.com
Beverages Mfr
N.A.I.C.S.: 312111

Bernick Companies - Twin Cities
Plant (1)
6820 Shingle Creek Pkwy Ste 16, Brooklyn
Center, MN 55430
Tel.: (612) 789-9377
Beverages Mfr
N.A.I.C.S.: 312111

Bernick Companies - Willmar
Plant (1)
2400 19th Ave SW, Willmar, MN 56201
Tel.: (320) 235-1370
Web Site: http://www.bernicks.com
Emp.: 15
Beverages Mfr
N.A.I.C.S.: 312111
Dean Bernick *(CEO)*

Bernicks Pepsicola Inc. (1)
801 Sundial Dr, Waite Park, MN 56387
Tel.: (320) 252-6441
Web Site: http://www.bernicks.com
Sales Range: $10-24.9 Million
Emp.: 500
Soft Drinks
N.A.I.C.S.: 424490
John Torgerson *(COO)*
Kelly Walz *(Dir-HR)*
Jason Bernick *(Dir-Corp Affairs)*
Scott Oeffling *(VP-Beer)*
Jason Hinnenkamp *(VP-Fin & IT)*
Jill Kampa *(VP-Sls & Mktg)*
Reed Stevens *(Mgr-Fountain Sls)*
Jesse Westrup *(VP-Ops)*
John Ampe III *(VP-Bernick's Twin Cities)*

BERNING MARKETING, LLC
710 Papworth Ave, Metairie, LA
70005
Tel.: (504) 834-8811
Web Site:
   http://www.berningmarketing.com
Sales Range: $10-24.9 Million
Emp.: 16
Advertising Agencies
N.A.I.C.S.: 541810
Robert Berning *(Founder & Pres)*
Elizabeth Schindler *(Mgr-Social Me-*
dia)
Matt Mistretta *(Dir-Media)*

BERNINI INC.
10401 Venice Blvd, Los Angeles, CA
90034
Tel.: (310) 815-1786
Web Site: http://www.bernini.com
Sales Range: $50-74.9 Million
Emp.: 35
Men's & Boy's Clothing Stores
N.A.I.C.S.: 458110

Bernini Inc.—(Continued)

BERNSTEIN MANAGEMENT CORPORATION
5301 Wisconsin Ave Ste 500, Washington, DC 20015
Tel.: (202) 363-6301
Web Site:
http://www.bernsteinmgmt.com
Year Founded: 1953
Sales Range: $50-74.9 Million
Emp.: 140
Real Estate Management
N.A.I.C.S.: 531210
Joshua B. Bernstein (CEO)
Daniel Porter (Dir-Residential Projects)
David Batlan (VP-Fin)
Fred Underwood (Sr VP)
Randi Killen (Dir-HR)
William Aleshire (Dir-Comml Projects)

BERNSTEIN-REIN ADVERTISING, INC.
4600 Madison Ave Ste 1500, Kansas City, MO 64112-3016
Tel.: (816) 756-0640
Web Site: https://www.b-r.com
Year Founded: 1964
Rev.: $409,821,557
Emp.: 227
Advetising Agency
N.A.I.C.S.: 541810
Steve Bernstein (Pres)
David A. Lubeck (Exec Dir)
Bryan Michurski (Grp Dir-Creative)
Chris Perkins (Mng Dir)
Lara Wyckoff (Exec Dir-Creative)

BERNTSEN BRASS & ALUMINUM FOUNDRY INC.
2334 Pennsylvania Ave, Madison, WI 53704
Tel.: (608) 249-9233
Web Site: http://www.berntsen-foundry.com
Sales Range: $10-24.9 Million
Emp.: 90
Foundry Services
N.A.I.C.S.: 331529
Steven Tomlin (Pres)
Jim Dudley (VP)
Terry Sherven (Mgr-QA)

BERONIO LUMBER CO
2525 Marin St, San Francisco, CA 94124
Tel.: (415) 824-4300
Web Site: https://www.beronio.com
Rev.: $34,553,733
Emp.: 70
Lumber Products
N.A.I.C.S.: 444110
Mike Casassa (Pres)
Chris Cassidy (Mgr-Credit)
Tim Sullivan (Gen Mgr-Millwork Div)
Sean O'Neill (Mgr-Fin & Acctg)

BERRENDA MESA WATER DISTRICT
14823 Hwy 33, Lost Hills, CA 93249-9734
Tel.: (661) 797-2671
Web Site: https://www.bmwd.org
Year Founded: 1963
Sales Range: $10-24.9 Million
Emp.: 10
Water Distribution Or Supply Systems For Irrigation
N.A.I.C.S.: 221310
Joe MacIlvaine (Pres)
Timothy Long (Treas)
George Logan (Gen Counsel)

BERRICLE LLC
141-07 20th Ave Ste 401, Whitestone, NY 11357
Web Site: http://www.berricle.com
Year Founded: 2006
Sales Range: $1-9.9 Million
Emp.: 11
Silver & Fashion Jewelry
N.A.I.C.S.: 458310
Kevin Chen (Pres)

BERRIDGE MANUFACTURING COMPANY INC.
6515 Fratt Rd, San Antonio, TX 78218
Tel.: (210) 650-3050
Web Site: http://www.berridge.com
Year Founded: 1971
Sales Range: $10-24.9 Million
Emp.: 145
Architect Metal Roofing
N.A.I.C.S.: 332322
Patrick Berridge (Owner)

BERRY COMPANIES, INC.
3223 N Hydraulic Ave, Wichita, KS 67219-3803
Tel.: (316) 832-0171
Web Site: http://www.berrycompaniesinc.com
Year Founded: 1957
Sales Range: $200-249.9 Million
Emp.: 500
Construction & Industrial Equipment Leasing & Sales
N.A.I.C.S.: 423810
Walter T. Berry (Pres & CEO)
Stephanie Farley (Chief People Officer)
Jared Halderson (Mgr-Safety)
Greg Joerg (CFO)
Fred F. Berry Jr. (Chm)

Subsidiaries:

Berry Material Handling, Inc. **(1)**
3769 McCormick, Wichita, KS 67277
Tel.: (316) 945-0101
Web Site: http://www.berrymaterial.com
Material Handling Equipment Distr
N.A.I.C.S.: 423830
Joe Wilson (Pres)
Brian Zimmerman (Mgr-Parts)
Judy Naramore (Mgr-Credit)
Curtis Haynes (Mgr-Trng)
Todd Williams (Mgr-Svc)
Heather Rey (Mgr-Credit)

Berry Tractor & Equipment Co **(1)**
930 S West St, Wichita, KS 67213
Tel.: (316) 943-4246
Web Site: http://www.berrytractor.com
Sales Range: $10-24.9 Million
Emp.: 50
Construction Equipment Dealer
N.A.I.C.S.: 423830
Steve Thomas (Mgr-Product Support)
Bill Simmon (Mgr-Used Equipment)
Dianna Hofflinger (Mgr-Credit)
Randy Spear (Gen Mgr-Sls)

Bobcat of Houston, Inc. **(1)**
18340 Northwest Freeway, Houston, TX 77065
Tel.: (281) 477-8646
Web Site: http://www.bobcatofhouston.com
Emp.: 50
New & Used Construction Equipment Dealer
N.A.I.C.S.: 423810
Jonathan Tarpey (Pres)
Paul Moriarty (Mgr-Sls)

Bobcat of the Rockies, LLC **(1)**
15680 W 6th Ave, Golden, CO 80401
Tel.: (303) 216-1402
Web Site:
http://www.bobcatoftherockies.com
Sales Range: $1-9.9 Million
Emp.: 22
Construction Equipment Distr
N.A.I.C.S.: 423810
Pat Kelleher (Mgr-Sls)

KC Bobcat Inc. **(1)**

2209 W 40 Hwy, Blue Springs, MO 64015
Tel.: (816) 229-4006
Web Site: http://www.kcbobcat.com
Rev.: $17,000,000
Emp.: 36
Construction Equipment Distr
N.A.I.C.S.: 423810
Dawn Carnahan (Mgr-Credit)

SB Manufacturing, Inc. **(1)**
3707 W McCormick, Wichita, KS 67213
Tel.: (316) 941-9591
Web Site: http://www.superiorbroom.com
Sales Range: $10-24.9 Million
Emp.: 100
Commercial Sweeping Equipment Mfr
N.A.I.C.S.: 333310
Tom McBride (Pres)
Tom Cox (VP-Product Support)
Eric Anderson (Mgr-Parts)
Nick Vidrios (Mgr-Production)
Kristina Rubalcaba (Office Mgr)

White Star Machinery & Supply Co. **(1)**
3223 N Hydraulic, Wichita, KS 67219
Tel.: (316) 838-3321
Web Site:
http://www.whitestarmachinery.com
New & Used Construction Equipment Dealer
N.A.I.C.S.: 423810
Glenn Engels (Mgr-Branch)
Nick Clay (Mgr-Rental)
Brent Hurst (Mgr-Credit)
Jeff Sperry (Mgr-Rental)
Jim Brennan (Mgr-Sls-Kansas)
Russell Crone (Branch Mgr)
Paul Hall (Branch Mgr)
Travis Krueger (Branch Mgr)

BERRY CONTRACT INC.
1414 Valero Way, Corpus Christi, TX 78409
Tel.: (361) 693-2100
Web Site: https://www.bayltd.com
Sales Range: $400-449.9 Million
Emp.: 2,800
Civil Engineering Services
N.A.I.C.S.: 237310
Ed Martin (CEO)

BERRY CONTRACTING L.P.
1414 Valero Way, Corpus Christi, TX 78409
Tel.: (361) 693-2100
Web Site: https://www.bayltd.com
Year Founded: 1962
Sales Range: $300-349.9 Million
Emp.: 2,800
Merit Shop General Contractor Services
N.A.I.C.S.: 237120
Jim Bliss (CIO & VP)

Subsidiaries:

Bay International Canada, ULC **(1)**
910 640 - 5th Ave SW, Calgary, T2P 3N3, AB, Canada
Tel.: (403) 817-5764
Web Site: http://www.bayintlcanada.com
Industrial Building Construction Services
N.A.I.C.S.: 236210

Subsidiary (Domestic):

Bay Tank & Vessel Canada, Ltd. **(2)**
2100 140 - 4th Ave SW, Calgary, T2P 3N3, AB, Canada
Tel.: (403) 457-2144
Web Site: http://www.bayintlcanada.com
Industrial Building Construction Services
N.A.I.C.S.: 236210
Darren Glover (Exec VP)

Berry Contracting L.P. - Belle Chasse Facility **(1)**
219 WPA Rd, Belle Chasse, LA 70037
Tel.: (504) 394-7013
Industrial Building Construction Services
N.A.I.C.S.: 236210

Berry Contracting L.P. - Colombia Facility **(1)**
Carrera 2 1F-149 Zona Franca, Barran-

quilla, Colombia
Tel.: (57) 5 3704754
Web Site: http://www.baycolombia.com
Industrial Building Construction Services
N.A.I.C.S.: 236210

Berry Contracting L.P. - Houston Facility **(1)**
4406 Rex Rd, Friendswood, TX 77546
Tel.: (281) 648-7000
Industrial Building Construction Services
N.A.I.C.S.: 236210

Berry Contracting L.P. - Mexico Facility **(1)**
Bosque De Duraznos 127 Piso 8 Colonia Bosques De Las Lomas, Case Postale 11700, Delegacion Miguel Hidalgo, Mexico, Mexico
Tel.: (52) 55 5010 2300
Industrial Building Construction Services
N.A.I.C.S.: 236210

Berry Contracting L.P. - Montana Facility **(1)**
2450 S 32nd St W, Billings, MT 59102
Tel.: (406) 294-9850
Web Site: http://www.bayltd.com
Emp.: 20
Industrial Building Construction Services
N.A.I.C.S.: 236210
Ken Luhan (Pres)
Diane DeCou (CFO, Treas & VP)
Jack Dill (Sr VP-Houston Ops)

Berry Contracting L.P. - Morgan City Facility **(1)**
430 Ford Industrial Rd, Amelia, LA 70340
Tel.: (985) 631-4600
Industrial Building Construction Services
N.A.I.C.S.: 236210

Berry Contracting L.P. - Redfish Bay Terminal Facility **(1)**
Beasley Rd Ocean Dr, Aransas Pass, TX 78336
Tel.: (361) 758-3201
Industrial Building Construction Services
N.A.I.C.S.: 236210

BERRY ECKE ASSOCIATES
93 Spring St, Newton, NJ 07860
Tel.: (973) 984-3100
Web Site:
http://www.berryassociates.com
Year Founded: 1972
Sales Range: $1-9.9 Million
Public Relations Agency
N.A.I.C.S.: 541820
Richard A. Ecke (Pres)
Tom Rice (Dir-Design)
Laura Squier (VP-Fin)
Lori Malvey (Acct Exec)
Susan Scutti (Acct Exec)
Scott Olson (Dir-Design)

BERRY ENTERPRISES INC.
E Main St, Chilhowie, VA 24319
Tel.: (276) 646-5333
Web Site:
http://www.berryhomecenter.com
Sales Range: $25-49.9 Million
Emp.: 100
Building Materials, Interior
N.A.I.C.S.: 423310
Thomas B. Bishop (Pres)

BERRY INVESTMENTS INC.
3055 Kettering Blvd, Dayton, OH 45439-1989
Tel.: (937) 293-0398
Year Founded: 1983
Sales Range: $200-249.9 Million
Emp.: 234
Holding Company
N.A.I.C.S.: 551112
William T. Lincoln (Pres)
John W. Berry Jr. (CEO)

BERRYMAN PRODUCTS, INC.
3800 E Randol Mill Rd, Arlington, TX 76011-5437

Tel.: (817) 640-2376   NJ
Web Site:
    https://www.berrymanproducts.com
Year Founded: 1918
Sales Range: $50-74.9 Million
Emp.: 45
Automotive Chemicals, Fuel Condi-
tioners, Carburetor Cleaner, Parts
Cleaners, Degreasers, Aerosol Lubri-
cants & Tire Sealers
N.A.I.C.S.: 424690
Cheri Lee *(Controller)*
Eddie Torres *(Plant Mgr)*
Doreen McCarthy *(Mgr-Natl Sls)*

BERSCHAUER PHILLIPS CON-STRUCTION CO

2823 29th Ave SW Ste A, Tumwater,
WA 98512
Tel.: (360) 754-5788
Web Site: http://www.bp-
    construction.com
Rev.: $74,000,000
Emp.: 50
New Construction Of Commercial &
Industrial Buildings
N.A.I.C.S.: 236220
Jace Munson *(Pres & CEO)*

BERT HAZEKAMP & SON, INC.

3933 S Brooks Rd, Muskegon, MI
49444-9721
Tel.: (231) 773-6425
Sales Range: $10-24.9 Million
Emp.: 110
Prepared Meat Mfr
N.A.I.C.S.: 311612
David Hazekamp *(Pres)*

BERT NASH COMMUNITY MENTAL HEALTH CENTER, INC.

200 Maine St, Lawrence, KS 66044
Tel.: (785) 843-9192   KS
Web Site: https://www.bertnash.org
Year Founded: 1971
Sales Range: $10-24.9 Million
Emp.: 201
Community Mental Health Services
N.A.I.C.S.: 621420
Dave Johnson *(Chm)*

BERT R HUNCILMAN & SON INC.

115 Security Pkwy, New Albany, IN
47150
Tel.: (812) 945-3544
Web Site:
    https://www.huncilman.com
Sales Range: $10-24.9 Million
Emp.: 40
Sheet Metalwork
N.A.I.C.S.: 332322
Gordon L. Huncilman *(Pres & CEO)*

BERT SMITH AUTOMOTIVE

3800 34th St N US 19, Saint Peters-
burg, FL 33714
Tel.: (727) 527-1111
Web Site: http://www.bertsmith.com
Sales Range: $25-49.9 Million
Emp.: 130
New & Used Car Dealership Owner &
Operator
N.A.I.C.S.: 441110
E.W. Smith III *(Pres & CEO)*

BERT SMITH OLDSMOBILE, INC.

3800 34th St N, Saint Petersburg, FL
33714
Tel.: (727) 565-1001
Web Site:
    http://www.bertsmithvw.com
Sales Range: $75-99.9 Million
Emp.: 120

New Car Dealers
N.A.I.C.S.: 441110
Will E. Smith *(Pres)*
Larry A. Graner *(Sec & Treas)*

BERT WOLFE AUTOMOTIVE GROUP

1900 Patrick St Plz, Charleston, WV
25387
Tel.: (304) 344-1601
Web Site: http://www.bertwolfe.com
Sales Range: $50-74.9 Million
Emp.: 200
New Car Retailer
N.A.I.C.S.: 441110
Parke Wolfe *(Owner)*
Jeff Boster *(Gen Mgr)*
Steve Lilly *(Mgr-Parts & Svc)*
Will Patterson *(Mgr-Toyota)*
Randy Baiely *(Mgr-Pre-Owned)*
Joe Beach *(Mgr-Sls-Ford)*
Brian Craft *(Mgr-Sls-Toyota)*
Greg Ellis *(Mgr-Fin-Toyota)*
Phil Parsons *(Mgr-Customer & PR)*
Dustin Resler *(Mgr-Svc-Audi)*
Scott Rooper *(Mgr-Fin-Ford)*
Derek Tingler *(Mgr-Sls-Pre-Owned)*
James Birthisel *(Mgr-Svc-Toyota)*
Joel Bloss *(Mgr-Svc-Ford)*
P. J. Wolfe *(Pres)*

BERT WOLFE FORD

1900 Patrick St Plz, Charleston, WV
25387
Tel.: (304) 344-1601
Web Site: http://www.bertwolfe.com
Sales Range: $50-74.9 Million
Emp.: 200
Car Whslr
N.A.I.C.S.: 441110
Barrie Warwick *(Sec)*

BERTCH CABINET MANUFAC-TURING INC.

4747 Crestwood Dr, Waterloo, IA
50702-4543
Tel.: (319) 296-2987   IA
Web Site: http://www.bertch.com
Year Founded: 1977
Sales Range: $100-124.9 Million
Emp.: 1,200
Wood Kitchen Cabinets & Accesso-
ries
N.A.I.C.S.: 337110
Gary Bertch *(Pres & Owner)*

BERTECH-KELEX, INC.

640 Maple Ave, Torrance, CA 90503
Tel.: (310) 787-8346
Web Site: https://www.bertech.com
Year Founded: 1983
Sales Range: $1-9.9 Million
Emp.: 6
Mfr of Electronic Parts & Equipment
N.A.I.C.S.: 423690
Munir Moon *(Pres & CEO)*

BERTELKAMP AUTOMATION INC.

6321 Baum Dr, Knoxville, TN 37919
Tel.: (865) 588-7691
Web Site: http://www.bertelkamp.com
Year Founded: 1975
Sales Range: $10-24.9 Million
Emp.: 32
Distr Of Hydraulic Systems Equip-
ment & Supplies
N.A.I.C.S.: 423830
Bert Bertelkamp *(Pres)*
Henry F. Bertelkamp Jr. *(CEO)*

BERTHEL FISHER & COM-PANY INC.

4201 42nd St SE Ste 100, Cedar
Rapids, IA 52402-0609
Tel.: (319) 447-5700

Web Site: https://www.berthel.com
Year Founded: 1985
Sales Range: $10-24.9 Million
Emp.: 80
Security Broker Services
N.A.I.C.S.: 523150
Thomas J. Berthel *(Co-Founder, Chm, Pres & CEO)*
Brian M. Rupp *(VP & Controller)*
Joanna M. Schaul *(Sec & Sr VP-Admin)*
Ronald O. Brendengen *(CFO, COO & Treas)*
Fred P. Fisher *(Co-Founder)*
Rick Murphy *(Pres)*
Brittany M. Noethen *(CTO)*
Shelley R. Davenport *(VP-Legal & Regulatory Matters)*
Randy A. Wilcox *(Chief Compliance Officer)*

Subsidiaries:

Berthel Fisher & Co Leasing   (1)
701 Tama St Bldg B, Marion, IA 52302
Tel.: (319) 447-5700
Web Site: http://www.berthel.com
Rev.: $589,768
Emp.: 60
Provider of Equipment Rental & Leasing
N.A.I.C.S.: 532490

Berthel Fisher & Co. Financial
Services   (1)
4201 42nd St NE Ste 100, Cedar Rapids,
IA 52402-0609
Tel.: (319) 447-5700
Web Site: http://www.berthel.com
Rev.: $15,324,300
Emp.: 60
Brokers Security
N.A.I.C.S.: 523150
Brian M. Rupp *(CFO & Treas)*
Joanna M. Schaul *(Chief Admin Officer)*
Tom Berthel *(Pres)*
Andrew J. Christofferson *(Pres & CEO)*
Paige N. Swartzendruber *(Chief Bus Dev Officer)*
Julie K. Driscoll *(Exec VP & Mgr-Special Projects)*
Erin Burke *(Chief Compliance Officer)*
Steve C. Hannah *(CIO)*

Berthel Fisher & Co. Management
Corp.   (1)
701 Tama St, Marion, IA 52302
Tel.: (319) 447-5700
Web Site: http://www.berthel.com
Sales Range: $1-9.9 Million
Emp.: 65
Nonresidential Building Operators
N.A.I.C.S.: 531120
Thomas J. Berthel *(Pres & CEO)*
Ron Brendengen *(CFO & COO)*

Berthel Fisher Investments Inc   (1)
701 Tama St, Marion, IA 52302
Tel.: (319) 447-5700
Rev.: $82,000
Emp.: 60
Security Brokers & Dealers
N.A.I.C.S.: 523150
Thomas J. Berthel *(Pres)*

BERTHOD MOTORS INC.

2914 S Grand Ave, Glenwood
Springs, CO 81602
Tel.: (970) 945-7466
Web Site: http://www.berthod.com
Sales Range: $25-49.9 Million
Emp.: 59
Automobiles, New & Used
N.A.I.C.S.: 441110
Calvin L. Gerbaz *(Pres)*
Fred Flohr *(Mgr-Fleet & Comml)*
Greg Hire *(Mgr-Sls)*
Liz Velasquez *(Office Mgr)*

BERTHOLD FARMERS ELEVA-TOR CO.

1 Main St S, Berthold, ND 58718
Tel.: (701) 453-3431

Web Site:
    https://www.bertholdfarmers.com
Sales Range: $25-49.9 Million
Emp.: 10
Grain Elevators
N.A.I.C.S.: 424510
Les Simons *(Gen Mgr)*
Dan DeRouchey *(Gen Mgr)*
Dee Dee Sauer *(Office Mgr)*

BERTKE INVESTMENTS, INC.

1645 Blue Rock St, Cincinnati, OH
45223
Tel.: (513) 542-2350
Web Site: https://www.bertke.com
Sales Range: $10-24.9 Million
Emp.: 150
Electrical Wiring Services
N.A.I.C.S.: 238210
Kevin Bertke *(Pres)*

BERTLING LOGISTICS INC.

19054 Kenswick Dr, Humble, TX
77338
Tel.: (281) 774-2300
Web Site: http://www.bertling.com
Sales Range: $10-24.9 Million
Emp.: 55
International Freight Forwarding Ser-
vices
N.A.I.C.S.: 488510
Thomas Ott *(Pres)*
John Hark *(Reg Dir-Mng)*
Colin MacIsaac *(CEO)*
Steve Walter *(Gen Mgr-Houston)*

BERTRAM ASSOCIATES

1325 Morris Ave, Union, NJ 07083
Tel.: (908) 688-7711
Rev.: $14,400,000
Emp.: 15
Operative Builders
N.A.I.C.S.: 236117

BERTRAM CAPITAL MANAGE-MENT, LLC

950 Tower Ln Ste 1000, Foster City,
CA 94404
Tel.: (650) 358-5000   CA
Web Site:
    http://www.bertramcapital.com
Year Founded: 2006
Privater Equity Firm
N.A.I.C.S.: 523999
Jeffrey M. Drazan *(Mng Partner)*
Ryan Craig *(Partner)*
Jared Ruger *(Partner)*
Kevin Yamashita *(Partner)*
Tom Beerle *(Partner)*
Tim Heston *(Partner)*
David Hellier *(Partner)*
Brian Wheeler *(Partner)*
Michelle Chao *(VP)*
Alex Goldscher *(VP)*

Subsidiaries:

AFC Industries, Inc.   (1)
3795 Port Union Rd, Fairfield, OH 45014
Tel.: (513) 874-7456
Web Site: http://www.afcind.com
Industrial Fastening Components Distr
N.A.I.C.S.: 423840
Kevin Godin *(CEO)*
Steve Davis *(CFO)*

Subsidiary (Domestic):

Cline Tool & Service Company   (2)
1415 E 19th St N, Newton, IA 50208
Tel.: (641) 792-7081
Web Site: http://www.clinetool.com
General Purpose Machinery Mfr
N.A.I.C.S.: 333998
Todd Tool *(VP-Mfg)*
Jim Long *(Pres)*

Subsidiary (Domestic):

Davis Tool Inc.   (3)
3740 NW Aloclek Pl, Hillsboro, OR 97124

Bertram Capital Management, LLC—(Continued)

Tel.: (503) 648-0936
Web Site: http://www.davistl.com
Machine Shops
N.A.I.C.S.: 332710
Ron Davis (CEO)
M. Lopez (Engr-Software)
Robert Methven (Mgr-Sls)
Kevin Viner (Mgr-Mfg)
Jim Scheradella (Engr-Mechanical-PE)
Alton Crousser (Plant Mgr-Swing Shift)
Chris House (Project Mgr)

Subsidiary (Domestic):

Dell Fastener Corporation (3)
1901 Mayview Rd Unit 8, Bridgeville, PA
15017
Tel.: (412) 344-2200
Web Site: http://www.afcholdings.com
Emp.: 25
Stainless Steel Fasteners Distr
N.A.I.C.S.: 444140
Doug Kortyna (Gen Mgr)

Eckart & Finard, Inc. (2)
80 Weston St, Hartford, CT 06120
Tel.: (860) 246-7411
Web Site: http://www.eckart-finard.com
Industrial Supply Whslr
N.A.I.C.S.: 423840
Richard Jones (Pres & CEO)

The Boulder Company (2)
4045 East 16th St, Des Moines, IA 50313
Tel.: (515) 264-8900
Web Site: http://www.thebboulderco.com
Sales Range: $10-24.9 Million
Emp.: 17
Industrial Fasteners
N.A.I.C.S.: 423840
Mike Hood (Mgr-Pur)
Jeff Conner (Pres)
John Bruntz (CEO)

BearCom Inc. (1)
4009 Distribution Dr Ste 200, Garland, TX
75041
Tel.: (214) 340-8876
Web Site: https://www.bearcom.com
Sales Range: $50-74.9 Million
Emp.: 500
Retailer of Electronic Parts & Equipment
N.A.I.C.S.: 423690
Jerry Denham (Founder & CEO)
Jerry Noonan (CFO)
Paul Moore (Dir-Eastern Reg)
Mark Kroh (Pres)

Subsidiary (Domestic):

BearCom Inc. - Cleveland (2)
900 Resource Dr Ste 8, Brooklyn Heights,
OH 44131-1884
Tel.: (216) 642-1670
Web Site: http://bearcom.com
Wireless Services
N.A.I.C.S.: 517112

Bearcom Wireless (2)
5235 NW 33rd Ave Ste 106, Fort Lauder-
dale, FL 33309-6345
Tel.: (954) 733-2327
Retailer of Electronic Parts & Equipment
N.A.I.C.S.: 423690
Jerry Denham (Pres)
Mark Parmelee (Gen Mgr)
Brent Bisnar (Founder & Exec VP)
Nader Mortazavi (VP-Sls)
Jerry Noonan (CFO)

Cogency Global Inc. (1)
225 W 34th St Ste 910, New York, NY
10122
Tel.: (212) 947-7200
Web Site: http://www.nationalcorp.com
Sales Range: $1-9.9 Million
Emp.: 100
Commercial Nonphysical Research
N.A.I.C.S.: 541910
Bruce Jacoby (CEO)

Subsidiary (Domestic):

Tax Guard, Inc. (2)
1750 14th St Ste 201, Boulder, CO 80302
Web Site: http://www.tax-guard.com
Sales Range: $1-9.9 Million
Emp.: 40
Tax Preparation Services

N.A.I.C.S.: 541213
Hansen Rada (Founder & CEO)
Jason Peckham (VP-Resolutions)
David Bohrman (VP-Mktg)
Rachel Sexton (Dir-Product)
Anurag Amatya (COO)
Peter Leenhouts (VP-Sls)
Darin Manica (VP-Engrg)

KSC Studio, LLC (1)
3850 N 29th Ter Ste 101, Hollywood, FL
33020
Tel.: (954) 322-7600
Web Site: http://www.onekreate.com
Advertising Agencies; Photography
N.A.I.C.S.: 541810
Brad Tuckman (Founder)
Steve Bondurant (COO)

Sanare, LLC (1)
3660 Enterprise Way, Miramar, FL 33025
Tel.: (305) 438-9696
Web Site: http://www.sanare.com
Diabetes Supplies Distr
N.A.I.C.S.: 423450
Tim Hargarten (Chm & CEO)

Subsidiary (Domestic):

Doctor Diabetic Supply, Inc. (2)
101 NW 24 St, Miami, FL 33127
Tel.: (305) 476-6006
Online Supplier & Shipper of Diabetic Sup-
plies
N.A.I.C.S.: 456199

OMNIS Health, LLC (2)
535 Enterprise Ave, Conway, AR 72032
Tel.: (501) 450-9063
Web Site: http://www.omnishealth.com
Emp.: 20
Medical Dental & Hospital Equipment &
Supplies Merchant Whslr
N.A.I.C.S.: 423450

Trademark Global, LLC (1)
7951 W Erie Ave, Lorain, OH 44053
Tel.: (440) 960-6200
Web Site: http://www.trademarkglobal.com
Online Retailing Services
N.A.I.C.S.: 551112
Dan Sustar (Co-Founder & CEO)
Eric Rolnicki (CTO)
Jason Pavlik (Dir-Art & Licensing)
Jim Sustar (Co-Founder & Pres)
Paul Hervey (Exec VP-Sourcing & Product
Dev)
Vince Tuttolomundo (Plant Mgr-Warehouse
Ops)
Jeff Marshall (CFO & Chief Admin Officer)
Jason Dietz (Controller)
Eric Dickens (Dir-Category Mgmt)
Shawn Gilleece (Sr Dir-Fulfillment Ops)
John Snowden (CEO)
Abdul Khan (CIO)

Subsidiary (Domestic):

Bolton Furniture Inc. (2)
133 Gallery Ln, Morrisville, VT 05661
Tel.: (408) 205-6255
Web Site: http://www.boltonfurniture.biz
Furniture Retailer
N.A.I.C.S.: 449110
Geoff Jackson (Founder)

Tyden Group Inc. (1)
28181 River Dr, Circleville, OH 43113
Tel.: (740) 420-6777
Web Site: http://www.tydengroup.com
Emp.: 100
Security, Identification, Traceability & Utility
Product Mfr
N.A.I.C.S.: 334519
Ashot Mesropyan (CEO)

Subsidiary (Domestic):

Brooks Utility Products Group (2)
23847 Industrial Park Dr, Farmington Hills,
MI 48335-2860
Tel.: (248) 477-0250
Web Site: http://www.ekstrom-metering.com
Sales Range: $10-24.9 Million
Emp.: 100
Metering Equipment Mfr
N.A.I.C.S.: 334519
Karl Loehr (Mgr-Quality)

Telesis Technologies Inc. (2)
28181 River Dr, Circleville, OH 43113

Tel.: (740) 477-5000
Web Site: http://www.telesistech.com
Emp.: 125
Laser Marking System Mfr
N.A.I.C.S.: 334419
Ashot Mesropyan (Pres)

**TydenBrooks Security Products
Group** (2)
2727 Paces Ferry Rd, Atlanta, GA 30339
Web Site: http://www.tydenbrooks.com
Sales Range: $25-49.9 Million
Plastic/Metal Security Seals & Locking De-
vices Mfr
N.A.I.C.S.: 332510

Subsidiary (Non-US):

Precintia International, S.A. (3)
Vic St 26-28, E 08120, Barcelona, La Lla-
gosta, Spain
Tel.: (34) 935446450
Web Site: http://www.precintia.com
Sales Range: $10-24.9 Million
Seals, Locking Devices, Security Bags &
Modular Mail Sorting Products Retail & Mfr
N.A.I.C.S.: 561621

**Tyden (Suzhou) Security Seal Co.,
Ltd.** (3)
Bldg 11 Workshop Wujiang Export Process-
ing Zone, 215200, Wujiang, Jiangsu, China
Tel.: (86) 51263496166
Web Site: http://www.tydenbrooks.com
Plastic/Metal Security Seals & Locking De-
vices Mfr
N.A.I.C.S.: 332510

Unit (Domestic):

**TydenBrooks Security Products
Group** (3)
409 Hoosier Dr, Angola, IN 46703
Tel.: (260) 665-3178
Web Site: http://www.tydenbrooks.com
Sales Range: $10-24.9 Million
Cargo Security Seal Mfr
N.A.I.C.S.: 332510

Subsidiary (Domestic):

**TydenBrooks Stoffel Seals
Corporation** (3)
400 High Ave, Nyack, NY 10960
Tel.: (845) 353-3800
Web Site: http://www.stoffel.com
Sales Range: $50-74.9 Million
Security Seals, Printed Packaging Materi-
als, Promotional Products, Identification
Cards & Badges Mfr
N.A.I.C.S.: 322220

Webex, Inc. (1)
1035 Breezewood Ln, Neenah, WI 54956
Tel.: (920) 729-6666
Web Site: http://www.webexinc.com
Sales Range: $25-49.9 Million
Web Handling & Converting Industry Cus-
tom Rollers, Machinery & Components Mfr
N.A.I.C.S.: 332114
Pete Eggen (Product Mgr-Rollers)
Frank Pozar (VP-REM Products)
Gary Edwards (CEO)
Terry Edwards (Pres)
Mark Fulcer (Dir-Site Ops)

BERTRAM CORPORATION
300 Industrial Dr, Random Lake, WI
53075
Tel.: (920) 351-1023
Web Site:
http://www.bertramwireless.com
Year Founded: 1991
Wireless Broadband Internet Services
N.A.I.C.S.: 517112
James Bertram (Pres & CEO)

**BERTUCCI CONTRACTING
CORPORATION**
7 River Rd, Jefferson, LA 70121
Tel.: (504) 835-0303
Web Site:
https://www.bertuccicorp.com
Rev.: $36,000,000
Emp.: 40
Heavy Construction

N.A.I.C.S.: 236210
Nolan Simoneaux (VP-Ops)
Anthony Zelenka (Pres)
Eugene Simon (Controller)

BERWICK ELECTRIC CO.
3450 N Neveda Ave Ste 100, Colo-
rado Springs, CO 80907
Tel.: (719) 632-7683
Web Site:
https://www.berwickelectric.com
Year Founded: 1921
Sales Range: $100-124.9 Million
Emp.: 300
Water & Sewer Line Structures Con-
struction Services
N.A.I.C.S.: 237110
Jim Peterson (Founder)
Doug Berwick (Pres)
Tim Prime (VP)
Ellie Capek (Treas & Sec)
Will Krueger (Mgr-Warehouse)
Buddy Lowther (Project Mgr)
James Rockhill (Project Mgr)
Bill Tuten (Mgr-Safety)
Tony Cerciello (Mgr-Ops)
Daniel Mondragon (Project Mgr)

BERWIN INC.
3501 Commerce Pkwy, Miramar, FL
33025
Tel.: (954) 785-3212
Web Site: https://www.jcwhite.com
Sales Range: $25-49.9 Million
Emp.: 100
Office Furniture
N.A.I.C.S.: 423210
Joanna Bray (Mgr-Ops)

BERWIND CORPORATION PA
3000 Centre Sq W 1500 Market St,
Philadelphia, PA 19102
Tel.: (215) 563-2800
Web Site: http://www.berwind.com
Year Founded: 1886
Sales Range: $1-4.9 Billion
Emp.: 3,500
Privater Equity Firm
N.A.I.C.S.: 523999
Van Billet (CFO & VP)
Pamela I. Lehrer (Gen Counsel)
Tim Callahan (Pres & CEO)
C. Graham Berwind Jr. (Chm)

Subsidiaries:

**Berwind Natural Resources
Corporation** (1)
1500 Market St, Philadelphia, PA 19102-
2100
Tel.: (215) 563-2800
Web Site: http://www.berwind.com
Sales Range: $25-49.9 Million
Emp.: 2
Management of Mining & Coal Lands Leas-
ing Services
N.A.I.C.S.: 212114

Subsidiary (Domestic):

**Kentucky Berwind Land
Company** (2)
300 Summers St Ste 1050, Charleston, WV
25301-1642 (100%)
Tel.: (304) 346-0569
Sales Range: $25-49.9 Million
Leasing Coal Lands
N.A.I.C.S.: 325998
Bryan Ronck (Pres)

Reitz Coal Company LLC (2)
509 15th St, Windber, PA 15963-1603
Tel.: (814) 467-4519
Web Site: http://www.berwind.com
Sales Range: $25-49.9 Million
Mines Bituminous Coal
N.A.I.C.S.: 325998

Wilmore Coal Company (2)
509 15th St, Windber, PA
15963-1603 (100%)
Tel.: (814) 467-4519

Sales Range: $25-49.9 Million
Leases Coal Lands
N.A.I.C.S.: 325998

Berwind Property Group, Ltd. (1)
1500 Market St, Philadelphia, PA 19102-2100
Tel.: (215) 496-0400
Web Site: http://www.bpgltd.com
Sales Range: $10-24.9 Million
Emp.: 40
Real Estate
N.A.I.C.S.: 531210

CRC Industries, Inc. (1)
885 Louis Dr, Warminster, PA 18974-0586
Tel.: (215) 674-4300
Web Site: http://www.crcindustries.com
Sales Range: $125-149.9 Million
Emp.: 150
Petroleum Mfr
N.A.I.C.S.: 324191
Ken Cantwell *(Dir-Strategic Accts)*
Wayne King *(Pres-Americas)*
Alan Cantor *(Mgr-Bus Dev)*
Chris Sieto *(Mgr-Mktg)*
Glenn Rice *(Mgr-Oil & Gas Market)*
Jack Rolfe *(Dir-Sls)*
Mike Hoban *(VP-Sls & Mktg)*
Brian Murtaugh *(CFO)*
Perry Cozzone *(CEO-Global)*

Subsidiary (Domestic):

ChemFree Corporation (2)
8 Meca Way, Norcross, GA 30093-2919
Tel.: (770) 564-5580
Web Site: http://www.chemfree.com
Emp.: 60
Bioremediating Parts Washers Mfr
N.A.I.C.S.: 333310
Thomas McNally *(VP & Gen Mgr)*

Weld-Aid Products, Inc. (2)
14650 Dequindre St, Detroit, MI 48212
Tel.: (313) 883-6977
Web Site: http://www.weldaid.com
Sales Range: $1-9.9 Million
Emp.: 25
Welding Chemical Product Mfr
N.A.I.C.S.: 325998
James Centella *(Dir-HR)*
Steven Smith *(Pres)*

Colorcon, Inc. (1)
275 Ruth Rd, Harleysville, PA 19438
Tel.: (215) 256-7700
Web Site: http://www.colorcon.com
Sales Range: $75-99.9 Million
Emp.: 399
Pharmaceutical Products Medical Equipment Rental Mfr
N.A.I.C.S.: 325412

Subsidiary (Non-US):

Colorcon Ltd. (2)
Flagship House Victory Way Crossways, Dartford, DA2 6QD, Kent, United Kingdom
Tel.: (44) 1322293000
Web Site: http://www.colorcon.com
Sales Range: $25-49.9 Million
Emp.: 230
Film Coating Mfr
N.A.I.C.S.: 322220
Raj Singh *(Controller-Fin)*

Division (Domestic):

Colorcon, Inc. - North America Headquarters (2)
420 Moyer Blvd, West Point, PA 19486
Tel.: (215) 699-7733
Web Site: http://www.colorcon.com
Sales Range: $75-99.9 Million
Emp.: 350
Dispersed Edible Color System Mfr
N.A.I.C.S.: 325412
Ali Rajabi-Siahboomi *(Chief Scientific Officer & VP)*
Sam Benner *(Dir-Contract Svcs)*
Tom Farrell *(Dir-Knowledge Mgmt & IP)*
Pankaj Rege *(Dir-Market Dev)*
Jamison Bell *(Dir-West Point Site)*
Alexander Klemp *(Engr-Support Plant)*
Kurt Fegely *(Gen Mgr-Alliance Products)*
Kamlesh Oza *(Gen Mgr-Brand Enhancement Svcs)*
Steven Yoder *(Mgr-Brand Enhancement Svcs)*

Ajay Reddy *(Mgr-Bus Applications)*
Paula Trevino *(Mgr-Bus Dev)*
Kenneth Bowers *(Mgr-Data Center & Sys Admin)*
Gus LaBella *(Mgr-Formulation Tech)*
Yagna Madasu *(Mgr-Global Applications Dev)*
Dave Ashworth *(Mgr-Global Applications Svcs)*
Rita Steffenino *(Mgr-Global Market & Patent Res)*
Charles Vesey *(Mgr-New Product Dev)*
Ron Tarewicz *(Mgr-Scientific Affairs)*
Frank Nuneviller *(Principal & Mgr-Tech)*
Ankur K. Chokshi *(Reg Mgr-Sls)*
Ngoc Do *(Sr Mgr-Tech & Product Dev)*

Maxcess International Corporation (1)
1211 W 22nd St Ste 804, Oak Brook, IL 60523
Tel.: (405) 755-1600
Web Site: http://www.maxcessintl.com
Process Control Instruments Mfr
N.A.I.C.S.: 334513
Francesco Cristante *(Mgr-Sls & Mktg-Europe)*
Greg Jehlik *(CEO)*
Dave Knudtson *(Dir-Supply Chain)*
Gary Edwards *(Chm)*

Subsidiary (Domestic):

Componex Corporation (2)
10200 N County Rd F, Edgerton, WI 53534
Tel.: (608) 884-2201
Web Site: http://www.componex.net
Aluminum Extruded Product Mfr
N.A.I.C.S.: 331318

Magnetic Power Systems Inc. (2)
1626 Manufacturers Dr, Fenton, MO 63026
Tel.: (404) 755-1600
Web Site: http://www.maxcessintl.com
Sales Range: $1-9.9 Million
Emp.: 75
Power Transmission Equipment Mfr
N.A.I.C.S.: 333613

Tidland Corporation (2)
2305 SE 8th Ave, Camas, WA 98607
Tel.: (360) 834-2345
Web Site: http://www.maxcessintl.com
Sales Range: $10-24.9 Million
Slitting & Winding Products Developer
N.A.I.C.S.: 333243
Sean Craig *(Gen Mgr)*

Valley Roller Company, Inc. (2)
N257 Stoney Brook Rd, Appleton, WI 54915-9444
Tel.: (920) 733-1991
Web Site: http://www.valleyroller.com
Sales Range: $1-9.9 Million
Plastics Material & Resins Mfr
N.A.I.C.S.: 325211
Ken Pennings *(Mgr-Quality)*

Oliver Products Company Inc. (1)
3236 Wilson Dr NW, Walker, MI 49534
Tel.: (616) 356-2950
Web Site: http://www.oliverproducts.com
Sales Range: $75-99.9 Million
Emp.: 500
Food & Medical Products Packaging Materials Mfr
N.A.I.C.S.: 322220
Jeff Murak *(VP-Sls & Mktg)*

Perfect Equipment Company, LLC (1)
1435 Heil Quaker Blvd, La Vergne, TN 37086-3520 (100%)
Tel.: (615) 641-1950
Web Site: https://www.perfectequipment.com
Sales Range: $25-49.9 Million
Emp.: 140
Wheel Balance Weights Mfr
N.A.I.C.S.: 336390
Jeff Waecther *(Pres & CEO)*

Perfect Equipment Company, LLC (1)
1435 Heil Quaker Blvd, La Vergne, TN 37086-3520 (100%)
Tel.: (615) 641-1950
Web Site: https://www.perfectequipment.com

Sales Range: $25-49.9 Million
Emp.: 140
Wheel Balance Weights Mfr
N.A.I.C.S.: 336390
Jeff Waecther *(Pres & CEO)*

Plant (Domestic):

Perfect Equipment Co., LLC - Murfreesboro (2)
1715 Joe B Jackson Pkwy, Murfreesboro, TN 37127
Tel.: (615) 893-0643
Web Site: http://www.perfectequipment.com
Sales Range: $50-74.9 Million
Wheel Balance Weight Mfr
N.A.I.C.S.: 336390

Division (Domestic):

Perfect Equipment Co., LLC - Snugl Manufacturing Division (2)
1498 Kleppe Ln, Sparks, NV 89431-6428
Tel.: (775) 359-4200
Web Site: https://www.perfectequipment.com
Sales Range: $25-49.9 Million
Emp.: 13
Wheel Balance Equipment Mfr
N.A.I.C.S.: 336390

Perfect Equipment Company, LLC (1)
1435 Heil Quaker Blvd, La Vergne, TN 37086-3520 (100%)
Tel.: (615) 641-1950
Web Site: https://www.perfectequipment.com
Sales Range: $25-49.9 Million
Emp.: 140
Wheel Balance Weights Mfr
N.A.I.C.S.: 336390
Jeff Waecther *(Pres & CEO)*

Perfect Equipment Company, LLC (1)
1435 Heil Quaker Blvd, La Vergne, TN 37086-3520 (100%)
Tel.: (615) 641-1950
Web Site: https://www.perfectequipment.com
Sales Range: $25-49.9 Million
Emp.: 140
Wheel Balance Weights Mfr
N.A.I.C.S.: 336390
Jeff Waecther *(Pres & CEO)*

Plant (Domestic):

Perfect Equipment Co., LLC - Murfreesboro (2)
1715 Joe B Jackson Pkwy, Murfreesboro, TN 37127
Tel.: (615) 893-0643
Web Site: http://www.perfectequipment.com
Sales Range: $50-74.9 Million
Wheel Balance Weight Mfr
N.A.I.C.S.: 336390

Division (Domestic):

Perfect Equipment Co., LLC - Snugl Manufacturing Division (2)
1498 Kleppe Ln, Sparks, NV 89431-6428
Tel.: (775) 359-4200
Web Site: https://www.perfectequipment.com
Sales Range: $25-49.9 Million
Emp.: 13
Wheel Balance Equipment Mfr
N.A.I.C.S.: 336390

BERYL CORPORATION
141 Cheshire Ln N Ste 100, Minneapolis, MN 55441
Tel.: (763) 449-9699
Year Founded: 1946
Rev.: $26,700,000
Emp.: 25
Cellophane Adhesive Tape: Made From Purchased Materials
N.A.I.C.S.: 322220

BESCAST, INC.
4602 E 355th St, Willoughby, OH 44094
Tel.: (440) 946-5300

Web Site: https://www.bescast.com
Year Founded: 1945
Sales Range: $10-24.9 Million
Emp.: 127
Steel Investment Foundry Services
N.A.I.C.S.: 331512
Russell Gallagher *(VP-Engrg)*
Lee Watson *(Co-Pres)*
George Brown Sr. *(Founder)*

BESCHE OIL COMPANY, INC.
3045 Old Washington Rd, Waldorf, MD 20601-3122
Tel.: (301) 645-7061   MD
Web Site: http://www.bescheoil.com
Year Founded: 1948
Sales Range: $75-99.9 Million
Emp.: 85
Operator of Petroleum Bulk Stations, Filling Stations & Convenience Stores
N.A.I.C.S.: 457120
Michael Besche *(Owner & Pres)*
John Hartline *(Sr VP)*
Melvin Williams *(Treas & Sec)*
Ron Sweeney *(VP-Admin)*

BESHENICH MUIR & ASSOCIATES, LLC
121A Cherokee St, Leavenworth, KS 66048
Tel.: (913) 904-1800
Web Site: http://www.bma-1.com
Sales Range: $1-9.9 Million
Emp.: 75
Defense & Homeland Security Services
N.A.I.C.S.: 611699
George Beshenich *(Founder)*

BESHORE & KOLLER INC.
4370 N George St, Manchester, PA 17345
Tel.: (717) 266-3651
Web Site: https://www.beshorekollerford.com
Sales Range: $10-24.9 Million
Emp.: 50
Car Whslr
N.A.I.C.S.: 441110
Craig G. Schaffner *(Treas)*

BESSEMER INVESTMENT PARTNERS LLC
630 5th Ave 27th Fl, New York, NY 10111
Tel.: (212) 708-9200
Web Site: http://www.bessemerinvestors.com
Privater Equity Firm
N.A.I.C.S.: 523940
Amit Singh *(VP)*

Subsidiaries:

Bessemer Investors LLC (1)
630 5th Ave 27th Fl, New York, NY 10111
Tel.: (212) 708-9200
Web Site: http://www.bessemerinvestors.com
Privater Equity Firm
N.A.I.C.S.: 523940
David A. Barr *(Mng Dir)*

Holding (Domestic):

Leonard Valve Company (2)
1360 Elmwood Ave, Cranston, RI 02910
Tel.: (401) 461-1200
Web Site: http://www.leonardvalve.com
Other Metal Valve & Pipe Fitting Mfr
N.A.I.C.S.: 332919
Rick Cota *(VP & Dir-Technical Svcs)*
E. Niles Wilcox *(Pres)*

BESSEMER VENTURE PARTNERS
1865 Palmer Ave Ste 104, Larchmont, NY 10538
Tel.: (914) 833-9100

Bessemer Venture Partners—(Continued)

Web Site: http://www.bvp.com
Year Founded: 1911
Sales Range: $25-49.9 Million
Emp.: 90
Equity Investment Firm Services
N.A.I.C.S.: 523999
Robert P. Goodman *(Partner)*
J. Edmund Colloton *(Partner)*
Adam Fisher *(Partner)*
Sandy Grippo *(Partner & CFO)*
Robert P. Goodman *(Partner)*
Jeremy S. Levine *(Partner)*
Scott Ring *(Partner & Gen Counsel)*
Nancy Straface *(VP-Ops)*
Alex Ferrara *(Partner)*
Byron B. Deeter *(Partner)*
Robert M. Stavis *(Partner)*
Amit Karp *(Partner)*
Charles Birnbaum *(Partner)*
Kristina Shen *(Partner)*
Talia Goldberg *(Partner)*
Ethan Kurzweil *(Partner)*
David Cowan *(Partner)*
Andy Geisse *(Operating Partner)*
Chini Krishnan *(Operating Partner)*
Scott Smith *(Operating Partner)*
Mayo Stuntz *(Operating Partner)*
Jeff Epstein *(Operating Partner)*
Jeffrey E. Epstein *(Operating Partner)*

BESSER COMPANY
801 Johnson St, Alpena, MI 49707-
1870
Tel.: (989) 354-4111   MI
Web Site: https://www.besser.com
Year Founded: 1904
Sales Range: $75-99.9 Million
Emp.: 1,000
Concrete Block Machinery & Product
Handling Equipment
N.A.I.C.S.: 333248
Kevin L. Curtis *(Pres & CEO)*
John Reedy *(Dir-Sls-Americas)*
Scott Foerstner *(CFO)*
Larry Dutkiewicz *(Controller)*
Janet Behnke *(Dir-HR)*
Tim Farley *(Dir-Engrg)*
Doug Rozema *(Dir-Curing & Installa-
tions)*
Brian Siegert *(VP-Mfg)*
Duane Rondeau *(Exec Dir-Sls-
Masonry & Hardscape)*
Jason Rensberry *(Controller)*
Ryan Suszek *(VP-Pipe & Precast)*

Subsidiaries:

Besser Co.   (1)
2121 E Del Amo Blvd, Compton, CA 90220
Tel.: (310) 537-5171
Web Site: http://www.besser.com
Sales Range: $10-24.9 Million
Emp.: 35
Designer & Mfr of Molds for Concrete Ma-
sonry & Hardscape
N.A.I.C.S.: 333511
John Reedy *(Dir-Sls-Americas)*
Brian Siegert *(VP-Mfg)*
Janet Behnke *(Dir-HR)*
Ryan Suszek *(Dir-Pipe & Precast)*
Tim Farley *(Dir-Engrg)*
Scott Foerstner *(CFO)*
Candie Guthrie *(Mgr-Corp Comm)*
Jason Rensberry *(Controller)*
Duane A. Rondeau *(Dir-Intl Sls & Applica-
tions Engrg)*
Mike Munro *(Mgr-Sls-Intl)*

Besser Proneq, Inc.   (1)
765 Sicard, Mascouche, J7K 3L7, QC,
Canada   (60%)
Tel.: (450) 966-3000
Web Site: http://www.besser.com
Sales Range: $10-24.9 Million
Emp.: 31
Special Industry Machinery
N.A.I.C.S.: 333310
Assad Nader *(Gen Mgr)*

International Pipe Machinery
Corp.   (1)

111 S George St, Sioux City, IA
51103-4801   (100%)
Tel.: (712) 277-8111
Web Site: http://www.besser.com
Sales Range: $10-24.9 Million
Emp.: 30
Mfr of Equipment for the Concrete Industry
N.A.I.C.S.: 333998
Gary Ericson *(Dir-Sls)*

Division (Domestic):

Besser Quinn Machine &
Foundry   (2)
1518 12th St, Boone, IA 50036-2309
Tel.: (515) 432-3553
Web Site: http://www.besser.com
Manufactures Cast Iron to Mold Concrete
N.A.I.C.S.: 333120

**BESSETTE DEVELOPMENT
CORPORATION**
3025 Lake St, Lake Charles, LA
70601
Tel.: (337) 474-3132
Web Site:
     http://www.bessettedev.com
Year Founded: 1982
Sales Range: $10-24.9 Million
Emp.: 85
Commercial & Institutional Building
Construction Services
N.A.I.C.S.: 541310
Harvey Bessette *(CEO)*
Therese Bourgue *(Project Mgr)*
Tobie Hodgkins *(Pres)*
Zane Long *(Project Mgr)*

BESSEY MOTOR SALES, INC.
209 Main St, South Paris, ME 04281-
1647
Tel.: (207) 393-2570
Web Site:
     https://www.besseymotor.com
Year Founded: 1967
Sales Range: $10-24.9 Million
Emp.: 50
Car Whslr
N.A.I.C.S.: 441110
Eugene Benner *(Pres)*
Douglas Van Durme *(Mgr-Sls)*

**BESSOLO DESIGN GROUP,
INC.**
556 Central Ave, Saint Petersburg,
FL 33701
Tel.: (727) 894-4453   FL
Web Site: http://www.bessolo.com
Year Founded: 1987
Sales Range: $1-9.9 Million
Emp.: 47
Architectural, Engineering & Interior
Design Services
N.A.I.C.S.: 541310
Kevin J. Bessolo *(Pres)*
Dan Jones *(Project Mgr)*
Debra Curry *(Project Coord)*
Christopher Hill *(Mgr-BIM & IT)*

BEST BUY TIRE CENTER, INC.
12932 Pioneer Blvd, Norwalk, CA
90650
Tel.: (562) 868-7724
Web Site:
     https://www.bestbuytirepros.com
Year Founded: 1981
Sales Range: $10-24.9 Million
Auto And Home Supply Stores, Nsk
N.A.I.C.S.: 441330
Andy Kasbarian *(Pres)*

BEST CHAIRS INC.
PO Box 158, Ferdinand, IN 47532-
0158
Tel.: (812) 367-1761   IN
Web Site: http://www.bestchairs.com
Year Founded: 1962
Sales Range: $75-99.9 Million

Emp.: 1,000
Furniture Mfr & Distr
N.A.I.C.S.: 337121
Julie Hauser *(Mgr-Employment)*

BEST CHEVROLET INC.
128 Derby St, Hingham, MA 02043-
4200
Tel.: (781) 749-1950   DE
Web Site:
     http://www.thebestchevy.com
Year Founded: 1957
Sales Range: $10-24.9 Million
Emp.: 108
New & Used Car Dealers
N.A.I.C.S.: 441110
Scott Shulman *(Owner)*
Peter Brazauskas *(Controller)*
Michael Volonino *(Mgr-Sls)*
Faith Bermingham *(Office Mgr)*
Andrea Downey *(Mgr-Collision Shop)*

**BEST CONTRACTING SER-
VICES INC.**
19027 S Hamilton Ave, Gardena, CA
90248
Tel.: (310) 328-6969
Web Site:
     https://www.bestcontracting.com
Sales Range: $25-49.9 Million
Emp.: 100
Roofing Contractors
N.A.I.C.S.: 238160
Bob Mars *(COO)*
Moji Taba *(Pres)*
John McClain *(VP)*
Kenn Daku *(Project Mgr)*
Lita Pablo *(Mgr-Acctg)*
Gary Sdao *(VP)*

BEST CUTTING DIE CO.
8080 McCormick Blvd, Skokie, IL
60076-2919
Tel.: (847) 675-5522   IL
Web Site:
     https://www.bestcuttingdie.com
Year Founded: 1966
Sales Range: $10-24.9 Million
Emp.: 147
Special Dies, Tools, Jigs & Fixtures
Mfr
N.A.I.C.S.: 333514
Gary Porento *(VP)*

**BEST DEAL FOOD COMPANY,
INC.**
760 N Yosemite Ave, Oakdale, CA
95361
Tel.: (209) 845-3888
Sales Range: $25-49.9 Million
Emp.: 150
Grocery Stores
N.A.I.C.S.: 445110

Subsidiaries:

Best Deal Food Company Inc.   (1)
255 W Main St, Turlock, CA 95380
Tel.: (209) 667-8641
Rev.: $18,000,000
Emp.: 50
Grocery Stores
N.A.I.C.S.: 445110

BEST DISTRIBUTION
829 Graves St, Kernersville, NC
27284
Tel.: (336) 992-0288   NC
Year Founded: 1987
Sales Range: $10-24.9 Million
Emp.: 65
Operates Local Trucking & Tempera-
ture Controlled Storage Services
N.A.I.C.S.: 484110
David W. Reich Jr. *(Owner)*

BEST DRIVERS

3008 Topside Business Park Dr Suite
D, Louisville, TN 37777
Tel.: (865) 977-9326
Web Site: http://www.bestdrivers.com
Year Founded: 1988
Sales Range: $10-24.9 Million
Emp.: 540
Class A & Class B Commercial Truck
Drivers Throughout the Southeast for
Both Long & Short-Term Assignments
N.A.I.C.S.: 488510
Brad Smith *(Founder & CEO)*

BEST EDGE SEO, INC.
6171 Bahia Del Mar Blvd Ste 215,
Saint Petersburg, FL 33715
Tel.: (727) 278-6295
Web Site:
     https://www.bestedgeseo.com
Sales Range: $1-9.9 Million
Emp.: 52
Sear Engine Optimization & Internet
Marketing
N.A.I.C.S.: 541890
Colin Carney *(Dir-Search Engine
Optimization-Internet Mktg)*

BEST EXPRESS FOODS, INC.
2105 Grandin Rd, Cincinnati, OH
45208
Tel.: (513) 531-2378
Web Site:
     http://www.bestexpressfoods.com
Year Founded: 1998
Sales Range: $10-24.9 Million
Emp.: 60
Packaged Frozen Food Whslr
N.A.I.C.S.: 424420
Allan Berliant *(Pres & CEO)*

BEST FACILITY SERVICES
305 N E Loop 820 Ste 106, Hurst, TX
76053
Tel.: (817) 595-0002
Web Site:
     http://www.bestfacilityservices.com
Year Founded: 2004
Sales Range: $1-9.9 Million
Emp.: 6
Customized Janitorial Management &
Cleaning Services
N.A.I.C.S.: 561720
Freda Wingate *(Area Mgr)*
Jesse Galarza *(Area Mgr)*
Steve Nobles *(Co-Founder)*
Mark Borge *(Principal)*

**BEST FRIENDS ANIMAL SOCI-
ETY**
5001 Angel Canyon Rd, Kanab, UT
84741-5000
Tel.: (435) 688-2327   UT
Web Site: https://www.bestfriends.org
Year Founded: 1984
Sales Range: $50-74.9 Million
Emp.: 728
Animal Care Services
N.A.I.C.S.: 813312
Julie Castle *(CEO)*
Francis Battista *(Co-Founder & Chm)*
Judah Battista *(Co-Founder)*
Silva Battista *(Co-Founder)*
Gregory Castle *(Co-Founder)*
Gabriel DePeyer *(Co-Founder)*
Jana DePeyer *(Co-Founder)*
Steven Hirano *(Co-Founder)*
Anne Mejia *(Co-Founder)*
Cyrus Mejia *(Co-Founder)*

BEST HEALTH, INC.
3163 Kennedy Blvd, Jersey City, NJ
07306
Tel.: (201) 217-4173   FL
Year Founded: 1992
Sales Range: Less than $1 Million
Emp.: 2

Contact Lens Cleaning Device Mfr
N.A.I.C.S.: 339115
Robert Gilbert *(Pres, CEO & CFO)*

BEST HOMES TITLE AGENCY, LLC

23938 Research Dr Ste 100, Farmington Hills, MI 48335
Tel.: (248) 286-3800   MI
Web Site:
https://www.besthomestitle.com
Year Founded: 2006
Title Insurance Agency
N.A.I.C.S.: 524210
Neil Sherman *(Pres)*
Peter M. Schneiderman *(Founder & Sr VP)*
Dwayne Ruszala *(Sr VP-Ops)*
Tracie McRae *(Mgr-Western Div)*
Christy Jessop *(VP-Ops-Southern Div)*
Kisha Dallas *(Mgr-Escrow-Southeastern)*

BEST INTERIORS INC.

2100 E Via Burton, Anaheim, CA 92806
Tel.: (714) 490-7999
Web Site:
https://www.bestinteriors.net
Year Founded: 1986
Sales Range: $10-24.9 Million
Emp.: 280
Mfr of Drywall & Acoustical Ceilings
N.A.I.C.S.: 238310
Mike Herrig *(CFO)*
Dennis Ayres *(Pres)*
Mark Barlow *(Mgr-Ops)*
Tony Maraia *(Superintendent)*

BEST IPRODUCTS.COM LLC

111 N Ridgewood Ave, Edgewater, FL 32132
Tel.: (386) 402-7800
Sales Range: $1-9.9 Million
Computer Product Mfr
N.A.I.C.S.: 334118
Robert Skelton *(Pres & CEO)*

BEST LINE LEASING INC.

140 Hawbaker Industrial Dr, State College, PA 16803
Tel.: (814) 237-9050
Web Site: http://www.bestlineinc.com
Year Founded: 1985
Sales Range: $10-24.9 Million
Emp.: 100
Heavy Construction Equipment Rental
N.A.I.C.S.: 532412
Michael Houseknecht *(Pres)*
Mike Getz *(COO)*

BEST LOGISTICS GROUP, INC.

829 Graves St, Kernersville, NC 27284-3209
Tel.: (800) 849-1818   NC
Web Site: https://shipwithbest.com
Year Founded: 1985
Transportation, Logistics & Storage
N.A.I.C.S.: 541614
David Reich III *(VP-Sales)*

Subsidiaries:

Best Cartage Inc.   **(1)**
829 Graves St, Kernersville, NC 27284
Tel.: (336) 992-0288
Web Site: http://www.shipwithbest.com
Local Trucking & Long Distance Trucking Services
N.A.I.C.S.: 484110
Dave Reich *(Pres)*

C & S Carpet Distribution, Inc.   **(1)**
220 Cross Plains Blvd, Dalton, GA 30721
Tel.: (706) 277-9556
Distribution & Logistics Services
N.A.I.C.S.: 541614

Reich Logistics Services Inc.   **(1)**
829 Graves St, Kernersville, NC 27284
Tel.: (336) 993-6339
Web Site: http://www.bestcartage.com
Rev.: $13,387,255
Emp.: 10
Transportation Agents & Brokers
N.A.I.C.S.: 488510
David W. Reich Jr. *(Pres & CEO)*

BEST MEDICAL INTERNATIONAL, INC.

7643 Fullerton Rd, Springfield, VA 22153
Tel.: (703) 451-2378
Web Site: https://www.teambest.com
Year Founded: 1977
Sales Range: $75-99.9 Million
Emp.: 250
Diagnostic & Therapeutic Services & Products
N.A.I.C.S.: 334510
Krishnan Suthanthiran *(Founder & Pres)*
Lauri Luxton *(Atty)*
Jessie Girgenti *(Office Mgr)*

Subsidiaries:

ATV Productions Ltd.   **(1)**
207 W Hastings St Ste 501, Vancouver, V6B 1H7, BC, Canada
Tel.: (604) 681-3327
Web Site: http://www.atvproductions.ca
Sales Range: $10-24.9 Million
Emp.: 25
Television & Film Production
N.A.I.C.S.: 516120

Best Medical Canada, Ltd.   **(1)**
413 March Rd, Ottawa, K2K 0E4, ON, Canada
Tel.: (613) 591-2100
Web Site:
http://www.bestmedicalcanada.com
Sales Range: $10-24.9 Million
Emp.: 8
Diagnostic & Therapeutic Services & Products
N.A.I.C.S.: 334510
Krishnan Suthanthiran *(Founder & Pres)*

Best Nomos Radiation Oncology   **(1)**
1 Best Dr, Pittsburgh, PA 15202
Tel.: (724) 741-8200
Web Site: http://www.nomos.com
Sales Range: $25-49.9 Million
Emp.: 45
Radiation Therapy Systems Mfr & Supplier
N.A.I.C.S.: 339112
Krishnan Suthanthiran *(Pres)*

Best Vascular, Inc.   **(1)**
4350 International Blvd, Norcross, GA 30093
Tel.: (770) 717-0904
Web Site: http://www.bestvascular.com
Sales Range: $10-24.9 Million
Emp.: 12
Vascular Brachytherapy Therapy Products Supplier
N.A.I.C.S.: 423450
Krishnan Suthanthiran *(Pres)*

CNMC Company, Inc.   **(1)**
865 Easthagan Dr, Nashville, TN 37217
Tel.: (615) 391-3076
Web Site: http://www.cnmcco.com
Sales Range: $10-24.9 Million
Emp.: 20
Radiation Dosimetry Products Supplier
N.A.I.C.S.: 423450
Thomas Kraus *(VP-R&D)*

Huestis Machine Corp.   **(1)**
68 Buttonwood St, Bristol, RI 02809-0718
Tel.: (401) 253-5500
Web Site: http://www.huestis.com
Sales Range: $10-24.9 Million
Emp.: 40
Radiotherapy Equipment Mfr & Diagnostic Imaging Equipment Remanufacturer
N.A.I.C.S.: 334510
Fred Correira *(Gen Mgr)*

BEST MOULDING CORP

100 Alameda Rd NW, Albuquerque, NM 87114
Tel.: (505) 898-6770
Web Site:
http://www.bestmoulding.com
Sales Range: $10-24.9 Million
Emp.: 35
Moldings Wood Unfinished & Prefinished
N.A.I.C.S.: 321918
Joe Rise *(VP)*
Frank Demott *(Pres)*

BEST OIL COMPANY

30 8th St N, Cloquet, MN 55720
Tel.: (218) 879-4666
Web Site:
http://www.bestoilcompany.com
Rev.: $53,800,000
Emp.: 50
Petroleum Bulk Stations & Terminals
N.A.I.C.S.: 424710
John Mckinney *(Pres)*

BEST ONE TIRE & SERVICE OF MID AMERICA, INC.

5999 Meijer Dr 606, Milford, OH 45150
Tel.: (513) 248-3900   OH
Web Site: http://bestonetire.com
Year Founded: 1948
Sales Range: $10-24.9 Million
Emp.: 50
Tires & Tubes
N.A.I.C.S.: 423130
Jim Ebbing *(Gen Mgr)*

BEST PERSONALIZED BOOKS, INC.

Best Plz 4201 Airborn Dr, Addison, TX 75001
Tel.: (972) 250-1000
Sales Range: $10-24.9 Million
Emp.: 100
Book Publishers
N.A.I.C.S.: 513130
Jack Kalisher *(Pres)*
Wendy Kalisher *(Treas & Sec)*

BEST PLUMBING TILE & STONE INC.

3333 Crompond Rd Ste 1, Yorktown Heights, NY 10598
Tel.: (914) 736-2468
Web Site: http://www.bestplg.com
Rev.: $19,900,000
Emp.: 100
Plumbing & Hydronic Heating Supplies
N.A.I.C.S.: 423720
Melvin Weiner *(Founder & Pres)*
Patricia Clark *(Supvr-Showroon)*
Pete Kolesar *(Asst Mgr-Warehouse)*

Subsidiaries:

Best Plumbing Tile & Stone Inc.   **(1)**
830 Central Ave, Scarsdale, NY 10583
Tel.: (914) 723-2002
Web Site: http://www.bestplg.com
Mfrs Tile & Plumbing Products
N.A.I.C.S.: 423720

Best Plumbing Tile & Stone Inc.   **(1)**
1989 W Main St, Stamford, CT 06902
Tel.: (203) 975-9448
Web Site: http://www.bestplg.com
Mfrs Tile & Plumbing Products
N.A.I.C.S.: 423720

BEST PROVISION CO., INC.

144 Avon Ave, Newark, NJ 07108-1936
Tel.: (973) 242-5000   NJ
Web Site:
http://www.bestprovision.com
Year Founded: 1938
Sales Range: $75-99.9 Million
Emp.: 115

Provider of Beef Frankfurters, Meat & Deli Products
N.A.I.C.S.: 311612
Leonard Karp *(Treas & VP)*
Richard Dolinko *(Co-Owner)*

BEST RESTAURANT EQUIPMENT & DESIGN CO.

4020 Business Park Dr, Columbus, OH 43204
Tel.: (614) 488-2378
Web Site:
https://www.bestrestaurant.com
Year Founded: 1987
Sales Range: $10-24.9 Million
Emp.: 55
Design & Marketing of Restaurants
N.A.I.C.S.: 423440
James V. Hanson *(Pres)*
Michael Sasko *(VP)*

BEST TRANSPORTATION OF ST. LOUIS

8531 Page Ave Ste 160, Saint Louis, MO 63114
Tel.: (314) 989-1500
Web Site:
http://www.besttransportation.com
Year Founded: 2002
Sales Range: $1-9.9 Million
Emp.: 91
Transportation Services
N.A.I.C.S.: 488999
Christopher Doerhoff *(Dir-Airport Ops)*
Kim J. Garner *(Co-Owner)*
Debbie Rudawsky *(Co-Owner)*
Lori Edwards *(Dir-Ops)*

BEST UPON REQUEST CORPORATE, INC.

8170 Corporate Park Dr Ste 300, Cincinnati, OH 45242
Tel.: (513) 605-7800   OH
Web Site:
https://www.bestuponrequest.com
Year Founded: 1994
Sales Range: $10-24.9 Million
Emp.: 105
On-Site Concierge Services for Businesses
N.A.I.C.S.: 812990
Tillie Hidalgo Lima *(CEO)*
William Mills *(Pres & COO)*
Jessica Lima Bollin *(VP-Mktg & Comm)*
Katie Stout *(Controller)*

BEST VALUE TECHNOLOGY, INC. (BVTI)

15855 Parnell Ct, Haymarket, VA 20169
Tel.: (703) 229-4200
Web Site: http://www.bvti.com
Year Founded: 2002
Sales Range: $10-24.9 Million
Emp.: 125
Business, Program Management, Acquisitions & Critical Infrastructure Services to Federal Government Customers
N.A.I.C.S.: 921190
Daniel L. Zimmerman *(Founder, Pres & CEO)*
Scott McCrae *(VP-Ops)*
Cheryl Warner *(VP-Bus Dev & Mgr-Contract-Level Program)*
Scott Deibler *(VP-HR & Security)*

BEST WAY OF INDIANA INC.

2577 Kentucky Ave, Indianapolis, IN 46221
Tel.: (317) 484-3365
Web Site: https://www.bestway-disposal.com
Sales Range: $10-24.9 Million

Best Way of Indiana Inc.—(Continued)
Emp.: 40
Recycling, Waste Materials
N.A.I.C.S.: 562920
John Balkema (Pres)

BEST WELL SERVICES, LLC (BWS)
5727 S Lewis Ave Ste 550, Tulsa, OK 74105
Tel.: (918) 392-9350
Web Site: http://www.bestwell.com
Year Founded: 2007
Sales Range: $25-49.9 Million
Emp.: 250
Services & Support for Gas & Oil Operations
N.A.I.C.S.: 213112
Timothy R. Cargile (CEO)
J. Douglas Janes (CFO)
Tony R. McKaig (Founder & Pres)
T. Bruce Blackman (Exec VP-Ops)

BEST WESTERN INTERNATIONAL, INC.
6201 N 24th Pkwy, Phoenix, AZ 85016-2023
Tel.: (602) 957-4200
Web Site: http://www.bestwestern.com
Year Founded: 1946
Lodging Chain Motor Inns, Hotels, Resorts
N.A.I.C.S.: 561599
David Kong (Pres & CEO)
Suzi Yoder (Sr VP-Intl Ops)
Mark Straszynski (CFO & Sr VP)
Lawrence Cuculic (Gen Counsel & Sr VP)
Wendy Ferrill (VP-Worldwide Sls)
Greg Adams (Chief Digital Officer & VP)
Bruce Wienberg (VP-Ops)
Tammy Lucas (VP-Mktg)
Michael Morton (VP-Owner Rels)
Ron Pohl (COO & Sr VP)
Anthony Klok (Treas & Sec)
James Cosgrove (Vice Chm)
Harold Dibler (VP-Tech Mgmt)
Jay Pricher (VP-Legal)
Graham Perry (Mng Dir-Australasia)

Subsidiaries:

AutoClerk, Inc. **(1)**
1990 N California Blvd Ste 20 PMB 1139, Walnut Creek, CA 94596
Tel.: (925) 284-1005
Web Site: http://www.autoclerk.com
Custom Computer Programming Services
N.A.I.C.S.: 541511

B-W Advertising Agency, Inc. **(1)**
6201 N 24th Pkwy, Phoenix, AZ 85016-2023
Tel.: (602) 957-5854
Web Site: http://www.bestwestern.com
Advertising Services
N.A.I.C.S.: 541810
David Aong (Pres)

BWI Denmark, Inc. **(1)**
Trommesalen 5 Sal 5Mf, 1614, Copenhagen, Denmark
Tel.: (45) 35393313
Web Site: http://www.bestwestern.dk
Home Management Services
N.A.I.C.S.: 721110

Prince Ocala, Ltd. **(1)**
3701 SW 38th Ave, Ocala, FL 34474
Tel.: (352) 237-4848
Web Site: http://www.bestwestern-ocala.com
Hotels (except Casino Hotels) & Motels
N.A.I.C.S.: 721110

Space Shuttle Inn **(1)**
3455 Cheney Hwy, Titusville, FL 32780
Tel.: (321) 269-9100
Web Site: http://www.bestwestern.com
Hotels & Motels

N.A.I.C.S.: 721110

BEST YET MARKET INCORPORATED
1 Lexington Ave, Bethpage, NY 11714-3121
Tel.: (516) 570-5300
Web Site: http://www.bestyetmarket.com
Sales Range: $50-74.9 Million
Emp.: 465
Grocery Stores
N.A.I.C.S.: 445110
Joe D'Angelo (Mgr-East Northport)
Tony Dominioni (Dir-Deli)
John Rowan (Dir-Bakery)
John Sender (Dir-Adv & Mktg)
Heather Bozza (Dir-HR)
Brian Kix (VP-Store Ops)

BEST-WAY MOTOR LINES INC.
14020 US Hwy 20 A, Montpelier, OH 43543
Tel.: (419) 485-8373
Web Site: https://www.bryansystems.com
Year Founded: 1948
Sales Range: $10-24.9 Million
Emp.: 20
Trucking Except Local
N.A.I.C.S.: 484121
Ronald W. Dean (Chm)

BESTGOFER INC.
401 Ryland St Ste 200-A, Reno, NV 89502
Tel.: (801) 243-5661
Year Founded: 2017
Assets: $19,456
Liabilities: $8,600
Net Worth: $10,856
Earnings: ($7,294)
Emp.: 1
Fiscal Year-end: 11/30/21
Express Delivery Services
N.A.I.C.S.: 492110
Mohammad Hasan Hamed (Pres, CEO, CFO, Principal Acctg Officer, Treas & Sec)

BESTIGE HOLDINGS LLC
1887 Gold Dust Ln, Park City, UT 84060
Tel.: (480) 267-1574
Privater Equity Firm
N.A.I.C.S.: 523940
Nathan Richey (Founder & Mng Partner)

Subsidiaries:

National Waste Partners, LLC **(1)**
2538 E University Dr Ste 165, Phoenix, AZ 85034
Tel.: (833) 254-6864
Commercial & Industrial Waste Compactors
N.A.I.C.S.: 562998
Gary Brooks (VP-Sls)

Subsidiary (Domestic):

GK Industrial Refuse Systems **(2)**
3207 C St NE, Auburn, WA 98002
Tel.: (253) 735-5543
Web Site: http://www.gk-irs.com
Recycling & Solid Waste Compaction Services
N.A.I.C.S.: 924110
Bruce Gustavason (Gen Mgr)

BESTIT CORP.
3724 N 3rd St, Phoenix, AZ 85012
Tel.: (602) 667-5613
Web Site: http://www.bestit.com
Year Founded: 2004
Rev.: $6,500,000
Emp.: 50
Computer System Design Services
N.A.I.C.S.: 541512

Harry Curtin (CEO)

BESTNEST, INC.
4000 Mcmann Rd, Cincinnati, OH 45245-1904
Tel.: (513) 232-4225
Web Site: https://www.bestnest.com
Year Founded: 1990
Sales Range: $1-9.9 Million
Emp.: 20
Backyard Wildlife & Outdoor Decor Products Retailer & Whslr
N.A.I.C.S.: 459999

BESTOW, INC.
750 N Saint Paul St Ste 1900, Dallas, TX 75201
Web Site: http://www.bestow.com
Insurance Services
N.A.I.C.S.: 524298
Melbourne O'Banion (Co-Founder & CEO)
Jonathan Abelmann (Co-Founder & Pres)

Subsidiaries:

Centurion Life Insurance Company **(1)**
800 Walnut St, Des Moines, IA 50309
Tel.: (515) 557-7321
Insurance Management Services
N.A.I.C.S.: 524298

BESTPASS, INC.
500 N Karner Rd, Albany, NY 12205
Tel.: (888) 410-9696
Web Site: https://bestpass.com
Year Founded: 2001
Emp.: 167
Truck Transportation
N.A.I.C.S.: 488999
Tom Fogarty (CEO)

Subsidiaries:

Fleetworthy Solutions, Inc. **(1)**
4600 American Pkwy Ste 300, Madison, WI 53718
Tel.: (608) 230-8200
Web Site: http://www.fleetworthy.com
Sales Range: $1-9.9 Million
Emp.: 51
Management Consulting Services
N.A.I.C.S.: 541614
Dixie J. Burbank (COO & VP)
John Vosters (Chief Sls Officer)
Becky J. Schowalter (Mgr-Acctg)
Philip Haven (CTO)
Michael Precia (Pres & CEO)

Subsidiary (Domestic):

Eclipse Software Systems LLC **(2)**
3400 W 16th St Bldg 1, Greeley, CO 80634
Tel.: (252) 227-7013
Web Site: http://www.rapidlog.com
Data Processing, Hosting & Related Services
N.A.I.C.S.: 518210
Larry Steinbecker (Founder & CEO)

BESTWAY ENTERPRISES INC.
3877 Luker Rd, Cortland, NY 13045-9385
Tel.: (607) 753-8261
Web Site: https://www.bestwaylumber.com
Year Founded: 1980
Sales Range: $25-49.9 Million
Emp.: 130
Lumber & Building Products Distr
N.A.I.C.S.: 423310
Jeff Tinkham (Mgr-Sales)

Subsidiaries:

Bestway South, Inc. **(1)**
165 Halyburton Rd, Stony Point, NC 28678
Tel.: (704) 585-6373
Emp.: 14
Pressure Treated Lumber Mfr

N.A.I.C.S.: 321113
Rick Petrovich (Gen Mgr)

Bestway of New England, Inc. **(1)**
840 Sterling Rd, South Lancaster, MA 01561 **(100%)**
Tel.: (978) 368-7667
Sales Range: $10-24.9 Million
Emp.: 10
Wood Preserving
N.A.I.C.S.: 321114

Bestway of Pennsylvania, Inc. **(1)**
3870 Route 191/390, Cresco, PA 18326
Tel.: (570) 595-0185
Emp.: 25
Pressure Treated Lumber Mfr
N.A.I.C.S.: 321113
Richard Currie (Gen Mgr)

Builders Best DeWitt Centers Inc. **(1)**
3798 Luker Rd, Cortland, NY 13045-9385
Tel.: (607) 756-7871
Web Site: http://www.buildersbest.dewittbest.com
Sales Range: $10-24.9 Million
Emp.: 35
Lumber & Other Building Materials
N.A.I.C.S.: 423310
Treber Norman (Office Mgr)

BESTWAY RECYCLING COMPANY INC.
2268 Firestone Blvd, Los Angeles, CA 90002
Tel.: (323) 588-8157
Web Site: http://www.bestwayrecycling.com
Year Founded: 1970
Rev.: $14,000,000
Emp.: 52
Waste Paper
N.A.I.C.S.: 423930

BESTWAY REFRIGERATED SERVICE, INC.
2994 Orange Ave, Apopka, FL 32703
Tel.: (407) 889-9726
Web Site: http://www.bestwayrefrigerated.com
Sales Range: $10-24.9 Million
Emp.: 50
Provider of Freight Transportation Services
N.A.I.C.S.: 488510
Ed Campbell (Owner)
Larry Roberts (Controller)
Ricky Wise (VP)

BESTWAY, INC.
2703 Telecom Pkwy Ste 180, Richardson, TX 75082
Tel.: (214) 630-6655
Web Site: http://www.bestwayrto.com
Year Founded: 1993
Sales Range: $1-9.9 Million
Emp.: 45
Rent-to-Own Chain
N.A.I.C.S.: 532420
R. Brooks Reed (Chm)
Beth A. Durrett (CFO)
David A. Kraemer (CEO)

BETA INTERNATIONAL & AFFILIATES
13860 Ballantyne Corporate Pl Ste 240, Charlotte, NC 28277-3167
Tel.: (704) 399-8331
Web Site: http://www.betaintl.com
Sales Range: $350-399.9 Million
Emp.: 90
Fabricated Structural Metal
N.A.I.C.S.: 332312
Jim Anderson (Mgr-Opers)

Subsidiaries:

Lynchburg Steel & Specialty Co. **(1)**
275 Francis Ave, Monroe, VA 24574
Tel.: (434) 929-0951

Steel Foundries, NEC
N.A.I.C.S.: 332312
Andy Anderson *(Founder & COO)*
Doug Anderson *(COO)*

Southern Steel Company LLC (1)
13860 Ballantyne Corporate Pl Ste 240,
Charlotte, NC 28277-3167
Tel.: (704) 399-8331
Web Site: http://www.betaintl.com
Fabricated Structural Metal
N.A.I.C.S.: 332312

BETA MUSIC GROUP, INC.
7100 Biscayne Blvd, Miami, FL
33138
Tel.: (212) 249-4900   FL
Web Site:
   http://www.betamusicgroupinc.com
Year Founded: 2006
Sales Range: Less than $1 Million
Emp.: 1
Musician Management Services
N.A.I.C.S.: 711410
Jim Ennis *(Pres)*
Elizabeth Karwowski *(CEO)*

BETA SOFT SYSTEMS, INC.
42808 Ste 101 Christy St, Fremont,
CA 94538
Tel.: (510) 744-1700
Web Site:
   http://www.betasoftsystems.com
Year Founded: 2005
Sales Range: $25-49.9 Million
Emp.: 250
Information Technology Services
N.A.I.C.S.: 541512
Ritu Mangla *(Founder, Pres & CEO)*
Amrita Ghatak *(Mgr-HR)*
Ashwin Das *(Dir-Bus Strategy)*
Vivek Kumar Singh *(Dir-HRD & Admin)*

BETA SQUARED LITHOGRAPHY, INC.
940 Federal Rd, Brookfield, CT
06804
Tel.: (203) 775-4242   CT
Web Site:
   https://www.betasquared.com
Year Founded: 1985
Sales Range: $75-99.9 Million
Emp.: 15
Semiconductor Equipment Distr
N.A.I.C.S.: 423690
Horst Burandt *(VP-Ops)*
Anthony Santospirito *(Mgr-Sls & Mktg)*

Subsidiaries:

Beta Squared Lithography Singapore
Pte Ltd.   (1)
Novena Lodge 2 Jalan Merlimau Unit 02-
17, Singapore, 308728, Singapore
Tel.: (65) 6250 1505
Electronic Equipment Supplier
N.A.I.C.S.: 423690

BETCO CORPORATION
1001 Brown Ave, Toledo, OH 43607-
3942
Tel.: (419) 241-2156   OH
Web Site: http://www.betco.com
Year Founded: 1986
Sales Range: $25-49.9 Million
Emp.: 160
Chemicals, Equipment, Programs &
Processes for Institutional Cleaning &
Maintenance Applications
N.A.I.C.S.: 325998
Tony Lyons *(CFO)*

Subsidiaries:

The Atlas Companies, Inc.   (1)
1001 Brown Ave, Toledo, OH 43607
Tel.: (515) 288-0231
Web Site: http://www.basiccoatings.com

Sales Range: $10-24.9 Million
Emp.: 50
Hardwood Floor Coatings Mfr
N.A.I.C.S.: 325510

BETCO INC.
228 Commerce Blvd, Statesville, NC
28625
Tel.: (704) 872-2999   DE
Web Site: https://www.betcoinc.com
Year Founded: 1984
Sales Range: $10-24.9 Million
Emp.: 125
Provider of Prefabricated Metal Buildings
N.A.I.C.S.: 332311
Scott Dunlap *(Dir-Mgmt Info Sys)*
Shara Gilreath *(Mgr-Pur)*

BETE FOG NOZZLE INC.
50 Greenfield St, Greenfield, MA
01301
Tel.: (413) 772-0846
Web Site: https://www.bete.com
Year Founded: 1950
Rev.: $13,000,000
Emp.: 130
Nozzles, Spray: Aerosol, Paint, Or
Insecticide
N.A.I.C.S.: 332319
Jonathan Hall *(Supvr-Quality)*
Noah Wallace *(Engr-Applications)*
Douglas Dziadzio *(VP-Mfg)*
Jeffrey Krawczynski *(Mgr-Mfg Engrg)*
Laurie Byrne *(Supvr-Customer Svc)*
Michael Pascoe *(Engr-Design)*

BETH ISRAEL LAHEY HEALTH INC
109 Brookline Ave, Boston, MA
02215
Tel.: (978) 283-4000
Web Site: https://bilh.org
Year Founded: 2019
Emp.: 2,494
Hospitals & Health Care
N.A.I.C.S.: 621610
Kevin Tabb *(Pres & CEO)*

Subsidiaries:

Exeter Health Resources, Inc.   (1)
5 Alumni Dr, Exeter, NH 03833
Tel.: (603) 778-7311
Web Site: http://www.exeterhospital.com
Sales Range: $300-349.9 Million
Emp.: 2,300
Healtcare Services
N.A.I.C.S.: 923150
Kevin J. Callahan *(Pres & CEO)*
Glenn McKenzie *(Chm)*
Constance D. Sprauer *(Sec)*
Kevin J. O'Leary *(Treas)*
William Schleyer *(Vice Chm)*

BETH SHOLOM LIFECARE COMMUNITY
1600 John Rolfe Pkwy, Richmond,
VA 23238
Tel.: (804) 750-2183   VA
Web Site:
   http://www.bethsholomcampus.org
Year Founded: 1945
Sales Range: $10-24.9 Million
Emp.: 458
Lifecare Retirement Community Operator
N.A.I.C.S.: 623311
Mark W. Finkel *(CEO & Exec VP)*
John Bellotti *(CFO)*
Deirdre Arnowitz *(Dir-Social Work Svcs)*
Vickie Brown *(Dir-Nursing)*
Will McCauley *(Dir-Physical Ops)*

BETHANNA INC.
1030 2nd St Pike, Southampton, PA
18966-3976
Tel.: (215) 355-6500

Web Site: https://www.bethanna.org
Year Founded: 1934
Rev.: $16,032,429
Emp.: 206
Individual & Family Residential Care
Services
N.A.I.C.S.: 623990
William J. Maguire *(Dir-Dev Office)*
Laurie Dash *(Dir-HR)*
Mace Cooper-Drew *(Dir-Community Treatment Svcs)*
Tina Burkholder *(Dir-Permanency Svcs)*
John Chase *(CIO)*
Rein Clabbers *(Pres)*

BETHANY CHRISTIAN SERVICES
901 Eastern Ave NE, Grand Rapids,
MI 49503
Tel.: (616) 224-7550
Web Site: https://www.bethany.org
Year Founded: 2000
Sales Range: $75-99.9 Million
Emp.: 1,519
Child & Family Welfare Services
N.A.I.C.S.: 624190
Chris Palusky *(Pres & CEO)*

BETHANY FOR CHILDREN & FAMILIES
1830 6th Ave, Moline, IL 61265
Tel.: (309) 797-7700   IL
Web Site: http://www.bethany-qc.org
Year Founded: 1900
Sales Range: $1-9.9 Million
Emp.: 64
Child & Family Care Services
N.A.I.C.S.: 624190
Joscelyn Stone *(Mgr-Comm)*
Pam Garcia *(Office Mgr)*
Bill Steinhauser *(Pres & CEO)*
Gretchen Hagen *(Mgr-Acctg & Personnel)*
Tom Tallman *(VP-Fin & Support Svcs)*
Patricia Castro *(Sec)*
Ron Edwards *(Vice Chm)*
Jenny Hager *(VP-Mktg & Fund Dev)*
Kevin L. Koski *(Treas)*
Lance Willett *(Chm)*

Subsidiaries:

Bridgeview Community Mental Health
Center   (1)
1320 19th Ave NW, Clinton, IA 52732
Tel.: (563) 243-5633
Web Site: http://www.bridgeviewcmhc.com
Sales Range: $1-9.9 Million
Emp.: 56
Behavioral Healthcare Services
N.A.I.C.S.: 623220
Marcia Christiansen *(Exec Dir)*
Ghada Hamdan-Allen *(Dir-Medical)*
Paul Blair *(Exec Dir)*
Deb Olson *(VP)*

BETHANY HOME SOCIETY OF SAN JOAQUIN COUNTY, INC.
930 W Main St, Ripon, CA 95366
Tel.: (209) 599-4221   CA
Web Site:
   https://www.bethanyripon.org
Year Founded: 1963
Sales Range: $10-24.9 Million
Emp.: 296
Elder Care Services
N.A.I.C.S.: 623312
Lori Van Duyn *(Mgr-Independent Living)*
Adam Hutchins *(Dir-HR)*
Larry Stocks *(Dir-Plant Ops)*
Susan Winters *(Sec)*
Al Grimm *(Dir-Info Sys)*
Rob Wagner *(Dir-Dev & Comm)*
Sandi Wolfe *(Dir-Nursing)*
Vonnie Van Dyken *(Accountant)*

BETHANY ST. JOSEPH CORPORATION
2501 Shelby Rd, La Crosse, WI
54601
Tel.: (608) 788-5700   WI
Web Site: https://www.bsjcorp.com
Year Founded: 1976
Sales Range: $10-24.9 Million
Emp.: 889
Elder Care Services
N.A.I.C.S.: 623312
Craig Ubbelohde *(Exec Dir)*

BETHEL MILLS, INC.
40 Marsh Meadow Rd, Bethel, VT
05032-9002
Tel.: (802) 234-9951   VT
Web Site: http://www.bethelmills.com
Year Founded: 1781
Sales Range: $75-99.9 Million
Emp.: 50
Retail Sales of Lumber & Building
Materials
N.A.I.C.S.: 423310
John Durfee *(Chm, Pres & Treas)*
J.Lang Durfee *(Owner & VP-Sls)*
Tom Tucker *(Mgr-Store)*

Subsidiaries:

Bethel Mills Kitchen & Bath   (1)
40 Marsh Meadow Rd, Bethel, VT
05032-0061   (100%)
Tel.: (802) 234-9951
Web Site: http://www.bethelmills.com
Sales Range: $10-24.9 Million
Emp.: 2
Kitchen & Bath Cabinet Distr
N.A.I.C.S.: 423310
John Durfee *(Pres)*

BETHEL WOODS CENTER FOR THE ARTS, INC.
PO Box 222, Liberty, NY 12754   NY
Web Site:
   http://www.bethelwoodscenter.org
Year Founded: 2011
Sales Range: $10-24.9 Million
Emp.: 483
Arts Promotion Services
N.A.I.C.S.: 711310
Alan Gerry *(Chm)*

BETHEL-ECKERT ENTERPRISES INC.
1300 Lebanon Rd, Collinsville, IL
62234-0298
Tel.: (618) 345-1138
Web Site: http://www.bethel-eckert.com
Sales Range: $75-99.9 Million
Emp.: 15
Dry, Chilled & Frozen Grocery Products Distribution to the Military
N.A.I.C.S.: 424410
Larry Eckert *(Pres)*
James Eckert *(VP)*

BETHESDA COUNTRY CLUB
7601 Bradley Blvd, Bethesda, MD
20817
Tel.: (301) 365-1700   MD
Web Site:
   https://www.bethesdacountry.org
Year Founded: 1947
Sales Range: $10-24.9 Million
Emp.: 283
Country Club Operator
N.A.I.C.S.: 713910
Brad Cance *(COO & Gen Mgr)*

BETHESDA FOUNDATION
15475 Gleneagle Dr, Colorado
Springs, CO 80921
Tel.: (719) 481-5481   NE
Web Site:
   https://www.bethesdaseniors.com

Bethesda Foundation—(Continued)
Year Founded: 1959
Sales Range: $10-24.9 Million
Emp.: 1,093
Elder Care Services
N.A.I.C.S.: 623312
Rick G. Summers (VP-Ops)
Larry W. Smith (Pres)
Michelle Cox Ingerson (VP-Health Svcs)
Angela Urbaczewski (VP-Sls & Mktg)

BETHESDA INVESTMENT HOLDING CO., INC.

10400 Auto Pk Ave, Bethesda, MD 20817-1006
Tel.: (301) 469-6600
Web Site:
  http://www.jimcolemancadillac.com
Year Founded: 1989
Sales Range: $75-99.9 Million
Emp.: 170
Car Dealership Holding Company
N.A.I.C.S.: 441110
James R. Coleman (Pres)
William H. Coleman Jr. (VP)

Subsidiaries:

Jim Coleman Cadillac Inc.   (1)
10400 Auto Park Ave, Bethesda, MD 20817-1006
Tel.: (301) 469-6600
Web Site:
  http://www.jimcolemancadillac.com
Sales Range: $25-49.9 Million
Emp.: 156
Automobiles
N.A.I.C.S.: 441110
James R. Coleman (Pres)

Jim Coleman Toyota, Inc.   (1)
10400 Auto Park Ave, Bethesda, MD 20817-1006   **(100%)**
Tel.: (301) 469-7100
Web Site: http://www.jimcolemantoyota.com
Sales Range: $25-49.9 Million
Emp.: 107
New & Used Car Dealers
N.A.I.C.S.: 441110
James R. Coleman (Pres)

BETHESDA MINISTRIES

15475 Gleneagle Dr, Colorado Springs, CO 80921
Tel.: (719) 481-0100
Web Site:
  http://www.businessbeneveolce.org
Year Founded: 1989
Sales Range: $10-24.9 Million
Child & Youth Care Services
N.A.I.C.S.: 624190
Sean P. Rice (Asst Sec)

BETHLEHEM CONSTRUCTION INC.

5505 Titchenal Way, Cashmere, WA 98815
Tel.: (509) 782-1001
Web Site:
  http://www.bethlehemc.com
Year Founded: 1978
Sales Range: $10-24.9 Million
Emp.: 75
General Contractor; Pre-Casted; & Pre-Stressed Construction
N.A.I.C.S.: 236220
Michael J. Addleman (Pres)
Tom Pattison (Mgr-Construction)

BETHLEHEM ENDOSCOPE CENTER

5325 Northgate Dr Ste 101, Bethlehem, PA 18017
Tel.: (610) 866-5008
Web Site:
  http://www.thebigeye105.com
Sales Range: $1-9.9 Million
Emp.: 15

General Medical Services
N.A.I.C.S.: 621493
Karen Fioriglil (Mgr)

BETHLEN HOME OF THE HUNGARIAN REFORMED FEDERATION OF AMERICA

125 Kalassay Dr, Ligonier, PA 15658
Tel.: (724) 238-2235
Web Site: https://www.bethlen.com
Year Founded: 1929
Sales Range: $10-24.9 Million
Emp.: 351
Elder Care Services
N.A.I.C.S.: 623312
Imre Bertalan (Exec Dir)

BETRAS USA, INC.

2525 Chesnee Hwy, Spartanburg, SC 29307-4121
Tel.: (864) 599-0855
Web Site: http://www.betras.com
Year Founded: 1983
Sales Range: $100-124.9 Million
Emp.: 200
Mfr of Promotional Plastic Drinkware, Thermos Mugs & Sports Bottles
N.A.I.C.S.: 326199
Joe Betras (Pres & CEO)
Henya Betras (Exec VP)
Brandi Ligon (Mgr- Mktg-Customer Svc)

BETSILL BROTHERS CONSTRUCTION, INC.

635 Kenolio Rd, Kihei, HI 96753
Tel.: (808) 879-5375
Web Site:
  http://www.betsillbuilder.com
Year Founded: 1993
Sales Range: $10-24.9 Million
Emp.: 80
New Single Family Housing Construction Services
N.A.I.C.S.: 236115
Dwayne Betsill (Founder)
Steve Betsill (Founder)
Randy Betsill (Founder)
Doyle Betsill Jr. (Founder)

BETSY & ADAM LTD.

1400 Broadway Fl 6, New York, NY 10018
Tel.: (212) 302-3750
Web Site:
  http://www.betsyandadam.com
Rev.: $36,000,000
Emp.: 50
Women's & Misses' Blouses & Shirts Mfr & Distr
N.A.I.C.S.: 315250
Martin Sklar (Pres)

BETSY ANN CANDIES, INC.

322 Perry Hwy, Pittsburgh, PA 15229
Tel.: (412) 931-4288
Web Site: http://www.betsyann.com
Year Founded: 1938
Sales Range: $10-24.9 Million
Emp.: 60
Candy Mfr
N.A.I.C.S.: 311352
James D. Paras (Pres & CEO)
Karen Paras (VP)

BETT-A-WAY TRAFFIC SYSTEMS, INC.

110 Sylvania Pl, South Plainfield, NJ 07080
Tel.: (908) 222-2500
Web Site: http://www.bett-a-way.com
Rev.: $37,104,171
Emp.: 65
Truck Transportation Brokers
N.A.I.C.S.: 488510
Betty Vaccaro (Founder & Pres)

BETTE & CRING, LLC

22 Century Hill Dr Ste 201, Latham, NY 12110
Tel.: (518) 213-1010
Web Site: https://www.bettecring.com
Year Founded: 1999
Industrial Buildings & Warehouses
N.A.I.C.S.: 236220
Matthew Bette (Owner)

BETTEN AUTO CENTER, INC.

810 Robbins Rd, Grand Haven, MI 49417-2604
Tel.: (616) 842-5750
Web Site:
  http://bettenautocenter.com
Sales Range: $10-24.9 Million
Emp.: 38
Car Whslr
N.A.I.C.S.: 441110
Joseph Betten (Pres)
Lorie Woodhams (Controller)

BETTEN IMPORTS

5901 28th St SE, Grand Rapids, MI 49546
Tel.: (616) 301-2100
Web Site:
  https://www.bettenimports.com
Sales Range: $10-24.9 Million
Emp.: 65
Sales of Automobiles
N.A.I.C.S.: 441110
Greg Betten (Owner)
Holly Mcgavin (Controller)
Eric Mock (Gen Mgr-Sls)

BETTENDORF ENTERPRISES INC.

4545 W End Rd, Arcata, CA 95518-4689
Tel.: (707) 822-8271
Web Site:
  https://www.bettendorftrucking.com
Sales Range: $25-49.9 Million
Emp.: 290
Trucking Service
N.A.I.C.S.: 484121
Ron Borges (CEO)

BETTENHAUSEN AUTOMOTIVE

17514 Oak Park Ave, Tinley Park, IL 60477-3905
Tel.: (708) 532-2665
Web Site:
  http://www.bettenhausenauto.com
Sales Range: $10-24.9 Million
Emp.: 44
Car Whslr
N.A.I.C.S.: 441110
Alec Bettenhausen (Dir-ECommerce)
Chip Brauer (Mgr-Parts)
Jan Disney (Mgr-Acctg)
Joe Handzik (Dir-Parts)
John Doolin (Dir-Mktg)
Lisa Castillo (Gen Mgr-Sls)
Mike Sorensen (Gen Mgr-Sls)
Ray Rossi (Dir-Svc)
Rocky Latorre (Dir-Svc)
Sherry Carroll (Dir-HR)

BETTER BACKERS INC.

1122 Hwy 411 S, Chatsworth, GA 30705
Tel.: (706) 695-7371
Sales Range: $25-49.9 Million
Emp.: 65
Finishers Of Tufted Carpets & Rugs
N.A.I.C.S.: 314110
Jack C. Jones (Pres)
Sid Frost (Controller)
Darrell Dobbins (Mgr-Production)

BETTER BAKED FOODS, INC.

56 Smedley St, North East, PA 16428-1632
Tel.: (814) 725-8778
Web Site:
  http://www.betterbaked.com
Year Founded: 1970
Sales Range: $50-74.9 Million
Emp.: 300
Frozen Pizza, Bread & Bakery Products Mfr & Distr
N.A.I.C.S.: 311412
Robert Miller (Chm)
Chris Miller (CEO)
Joseph Pacinelli (Pres & COO)

BETTER BEVERAGES, INC.

10624 Midway Ave, Cerritos, CA 90703
Tel.: (562) 924-8321
Web Site: https://www.betbev.com
Year Founded: 1969
Sales Range: $10-24.9 Million
Emp.: 40
Beverage Bases
N.A.I.C.S.: 311999
H. Ronald Harris (Pres)

BETTER FOOD SYSTEMS INCORPORATION

101 W Columbus Ave, Bellefontaine, OH 43311
Tel.: (937) 593-9015
Rev.: $14,000,000
Emp.: 10
Fast-Food Restaurant, Chain
N.A.I.C.S.: 722513
D. James Hilliker (VP)

BETTER HEADS LLC

9973 FM 521 Rd, Rosharon, TX 77583
Tel.: (281) 595-2400
Web Site:
  http://www.betterheadsllc.com
Year Founded: 2005
Sales Range: $1-9.9 Million
Emp.: 4
Gas & Electric Trimmer Head Attachments & Accessories Mfr
N.A.I.C.S.: 333112
Mike Watts (Pres)

BETTER HEALTH

42875 Grand River Ave, Novi, MI 48375
Tel.: (248) 735-8100
Web Site:
  http://www.thebetterhealthstore.com
Sales Range: $25-49.9 Million
Emp.: 150
Health Foods
N.A.I.C.S.: 456191
Tedd Handelsman (Pres)

BETTER LIVING INC.

Rte 29 N, Charlottesville, VA 22906
Tel.: (434) 973-4333
Web Site: http://www.btrlvg.com
Year Founded: 1893
Sales Range: $25-49.9 Million
Emp.: 100
Retail Building Materials & Household Furnishings
N.A.I.C.S.: 423310
John Nunley (Pres)
Charles E. Haney (VP)
Pat Mete (Dir-Adv, Mktg & Sls)

BETTER MADE SNACK FOODS INC.

10148 Gratiot Ave, Detroit, MI 48213
Tel.: (313) 925-4774
Web Site:
  http://www.bettermadesnacks.com
Year Founded: 1930
Sales Range: $10-24.9 Million

Emp.: 150
Potato Chips & Other Potato-Based Snacks
N.A.I.C.S.: 311919
Salvatore Cipriano *(Owner)*

BETTER MERCHANT RATES INC.

125 Fairfield Way Ste 230, Bloomingdale, IL 60108
Web Site:
http://www.loanpaymentpro.com
Year Founded: 2011
Sales Range: $1-9.9 Million
Emp.: 12
Payment Processing Services
N.A.I.C.S.: 522320
James Celli *(Founder & CEO)*

BETTER ROADS INC.

1910 Seward Ave, Naples, FL 34109
Tel.: (239) 597-2181
Web Site:
https://www.betterroads.net
Year Founded: 1920
Sales Range: $50-74.9 Million
Emp.: 150
Highway, Street & Bridge Construction
N.A.I.C.S.: 237310
Joan Johnson *(Sec)*
Dan Kelly *(Treas)*
Joseph Bonness III *(Chm & CEO)*

BETTER WORLD BOOKS

55740 Currant Rd, Mishawaka, IN 46545
Tel.: (574) 968-9701
Web Site:
https://www.betterworldbooks.com
Year Founded: 2002
Sales Range: $50-74.9 Million
Emp.: 326
Reseller of New & Used Books Online & Funds Literacy Programs Worldwide
N.A.I.C.S.: 424920
Dustin Holland *(VP-Global Sls & Mktg)*
Kreece Fuchs *(Founder & VP-Logistics)*
Jeff Baer *(VP-Finance)*

BETTERMENT LLC

247 Centre St 5th Fl, New York, NY 10013
Tel.: (212) 228-1328
Web Site: http://www.betterment.com
Online Investment, Wealth Management & Financial Advisory Data Services
N.A.I.C.S.: 522320
Kiran Keshav *(CTO)*
Jonathan Stein *(Founder)*
Sarah Kirshbaum Levy *(CEO)*

BETTEROADS ASPHALT CORP

Marginal 65 Infanteria Ave, San Juan, PR 00928
Tel.: (787) 760-1050
Web Site: http://www.emdi.net
Sales Range: $125-149.9 Million
Emp.: 215
Highway & Street Paving Contractor
N.A.I.C.S.: 237310
Arturo Diaz Jr. *(Pres)*

BETTERWORLD TELECOM, LLC

11951 Freedom Dr 13th Fl, Reston, VA 20190-5640
Tel.: (703) 797-1750
Web Site:
http://www.betterworldtelecom.com
Year Founded: 2002

Sales Range: $1-9.9 Million
Emp.: 10
Telecommunication Servicesb
N.A.I.C.S.: 517111
David O'Leary *(Dir-IT)*
Glenn Powell *(Dir-Ops)*
John McCormick *(Co-Founder & Dir-Sls)*
James F. Kenefick *(Chm)*
Matt Bauer *(Founder)*
Ali Gunertem *(Co-Founder & Dir-Customer Ops)*
Salem Kimble *(Mgr-Online Strategies)*
Pamela Sorensen *(Dir-Bus Dev)*

BETTIOL FUEL SERVICE INC.

4966 State Hwy 23 Ste 1, Oneonta, NY 13820-4506
Tel.: (607) 432-9274
Year Founded: 1965
Sales Range: $10-24.9 Million
Emp.: 7
Convenience Store
N.A.I.C.S.: 445131
Eugene Bettiol Sr. *(CEO)*

BETTS INDUSTRIES INC.

1800 Pennsylvania Ave W, Warren, PA 16365-1932
Tel.: (814) 723-1250
Web Site:
http://www.bettsindustries.com
Year Founded: 1901
Sales Range: $10-24.9 Million
Emp.: 245
Valves & Pipe Fittings
N.A.I.C.S.: 332919
Paul Wood *(Mgr-Pur)*
Gregory Stenta *(Mgr-Quality Assurance)*

BETTS SPRING COMPANY, INC.

2843 S Maple Ave, Fresno, CA 93725
Tel.: (559) 498-3304
Web Site:
https://www.bettsspring.com
Year Founded: 1980
Sales Range: $10-24.9 Million
Emp.: 180
Mfr of Steel Springs
N.A.I.C.S.: 332613
Joe Devany *(Dir-Ops)*
Randy George *(Coord-Mktg)*

BETTY JEAN KERR PEOPLES HEALTH CENTERS

5701 Delmar Blvd, Saint Louis, MO 63112
Tel.: (314) 367-7848   MO
Web Site: https://www.phcenters.org
Year Founded: 1979
Sales Range: $10-24.9 Million
Emp.: 275
Health Care Srvices
N.A.I.C.S.: 622110
Mark Sanford *(Exec VP)*
Dwayne Butler *(Pres & CEO)*
Karen Richardson *(Dir-Dental)*

BETTY LOU'S, INC.

750 SE Booth Bend Rd, McMinnville, OR 97128
Tel.: (503) 434-5205
Web Site:
http://www.bettylousinc.com
Year Founded: 1978
Sales Range: $10-24.9 Million
Emp.: 80
Snack Food Mfr
N.A.I.C.S.: 311919
Sheyla Wulf *(Mgr-Pur)*
Cheri Drake *(Office Mgr-Sls)*

Betty Lou Carrier *(Owner)*
Vicky McKinney *(Dir-Pur)*
Richard K. Patton *(Sec)*

BEUCKMAN FORD INC.

15675 Manchester Rd, Ellisville, MO 63011-2242
Tel.: (636) 227-5700   MO
Web Site: http://www.gotobo.com
Year Founded: 1970
Sales Range: $25-49.9 Million
Emp.: 100
New & Used Car Dealers
N.A.I.C.S.: 441110
Fred Beuckman *(Pres)*
Larry Perez *(Gen Mgr)*
Jim Helms *(Dir-Svc)*

BEUERMAN MILLER FITZGER-ALD, INC.

748 Camp St, New Orleans, LA 70130
Tel.: (504) 524-3342
Year Founded: 1926
Rev.: $13,000,000
Emp.: 10
N.A.I.C.S.: 541810
Laura Lee Killeen *(Exec VP-Mktg & Adv)*
Greg Beuerman *(Founder & Partner)*
Virginia Miller *(Owner)*
Ronald J. Thompson *(Pres-Mktg & Adv)*

BEUTLER HEATING & AIR CONDITIONING INC.

4700 Lang Ave, McClellan, CA 95662
Tel.: (916) 646-2222   CA
Web Site: http://www.beutler.com
Year Founded: 1947
Sales Range: $450-499.9 Million
Emp.: 1,000
Provider of Residential & Commercial Heating, Ventilating, Air Conditioning & Sheet Metal Fabricating Service & Repair
N.A.I.C.S.: 238220
Gary Beutler *(Chm)*
Scott Sahota *(VP-Field Ops & Construction)*
Rob Penrod *(Chief Engr & VP-Tech)*
Rick Wylie *(Pres)*
Jeffrey Starsky *(VP-Legal & Govt Affairs)*
Scot Williams *(CFO & VP)*

BEUTLICH PHARMACEUTI-CALS LP

1541 S Shields Dr, Waukegan, IL 60085-8304
Tel.: (847) 473-1100   IL
Web Site: http://www.beutlich.com
Year Founded: 1954
Sales Range: $50-74.9 Million
Emp.: 25
Pharmaceutical Products
N.A.I.C.S.: 325412
Jack Beutlich *(Owner)*

BEVERAGE MARKETING CORPORATION

2670 Commercial Ave, Mingo Junction, OH 43938
Tel.: (740) 598-4133
Web Site:
http://www.beveragemarketing.com
Sales Range: $10-24.9 Million
Emp.: 15
Beer & Wine Wholesalers
N.A.I.C.S.: 424810
Michael C. Bellas *(Chm & CEO)*
Andrew Standarsi *(Editor)*
Beverly Carey *(Dir-Ops)*

BEVERAGE MARKETING USA INC.

222 Bloomingdale Rd, White Plains, NY 10605
Tel.: (914) 597-7900
Sales Range: $50-74.9 Million
Emp.: 1,000
Other Grocery & Related Products Merchant Wholesalers
N.A.I.C.S.: 424490
Domenick J. Vultaggio *(Chm)*
Michael C. Bellas *(Chm)*

BEVERAGE WORKS NY INC.

1800 State Route 34 n Ste 203, Wall, NJ 07719
Tel.: (732) 938-7600
Web Site:
http://www.thebeverageworks.com
Rev.: $11,500,000
Emp.: 300
Beverage Concentrates
N.A.I.C.S.: 424490
Mark Ponsiglione *(Pres)*

BEVERLY CAPITAL LLC

630 Davis St Ste 201, Evanston, IL 60201
Tel.: (847) 961-9210
Web Site: https://beverly-capital.com
Emp.: 100
Investment Services
N.A.I.C.S.: 523999

BEVERLY HILLS SHOE INC.

5951 Skylab Rd, Huntington Beach, CA 92647
Tel.: (714) 899-8049
Sales Range: $10-24.9 Million
Emp.: 50
Men Shoe Stores
N.A.I.C.S.: 458110
Antonio Sanchez *(Pres)*
Katherine Baddorsf *(CFO)*

BEVERLY HILLS TEDDY BEAR COMPANY

24625 Railroad Ave, Newhall, CA 91321
Tel.: (800) 996-2327
Web Site:
https://www.bhteddybear.com
Year Founded: 1994
Sales Range: $10-24.9 Million
Emp.: 20
Toy Mfr & Distr
N.A.I.C.S.: 339930
David Socha *(CEO)*

BEVERLY HILLS TRANSFER & STORAGE CO.

15500 S Main St, Gardena, CA 90248
Tel.: (310) 532-1121
Web Site:
http://www.beverlyhillstransfer.com
Year Founded: 1924
Sales Range: $25-49.9 Million
Emp.: 100
Local Trucking with Storage
N.A.I.C.S.: 484110
Frank R. Rolapp *(Pres)*
Ronie Antonio *(CFO)*

BEVERLY J. SEARLES FOUNDATION

3555 Sweetwater Rd, Duluth, GA 30096
Tel.: (678) 467-6861   GA
Web Site:
http://www.bjsfoundation.org
Year Founded: 2007
Sales Range: $1-9.9 Million
Elder Care Services
N.A.I.C.S.: 624120

Beverly J. Searles Foundation—(Continued)

Philip E. Searles (Pres)
Richard D. Searles (Exec Dir)
David S. Searles Jr. (Treas)

BEVILACQUA RESEARCH CORPORATION
4901 Corporate Dr Ste B, Huntsville, AL 35805
Tel.: (256) 882-6229
Web Site: https://www.brc2.com
Year Founded: 1992
Rev.: $5,800,000
Emp.: 83
Technical Research
N.A.I.C.S.: 541511
Jeri Bevilacqua (CEO)
Andy Bevilacqua (Pres)
Renee Richardson (Mgr-HR)

BEVSOURCE, INC.
219 Little Canada Rd E Ste 100, Saint Paul, MN 55117
Tel.: (651) 766-5281   MN
Web Site: http://www.bevsource.com
Year Founded: 2002
Outsourced Beverage Manufacturing & Support Services
N.A.I.C.S.: 561499
Janet Johanson (CEO)
Todd Geisness (Pres)
Thomas Hartman (VP-Ops)

BEYER BROS. CORP.
109 Broad Ave Routes 1 & 9, Fairview, NJ 07022-1500
Tel.: (201) 943-3100
Web Site: https://www.beyerbros.com
Year Founded: 1914
Sales Range: $10-24.9 Million
Emp.: 69
New Car Retailer
N.A.I.C.S.: 441110
Emil Beyer (CEO)
Willie Hunt (Mgr-Parts)
Jeff Oltar (Mgr-Svc)
Guy Montaina (Mgr-Sls)
Michael Beyer (Mgr-Govt Sls)
Steve Church (Asst Mgr-Parts)

BEYER CONSTRUCTION LTD.
3080 S Calhoun Rd, New Berlin, WI 53151
Tel.: (262) 789-6040
Web Site: http://www.beyer.com
Rev.: $15,000,000
Emp.: 70
Commercial & Institutional Building Construction
N.A.I.C.S.: 236220
George M. Beyer (Pres)

BEYER MECHANICAL, LTD.
4711 Broom St, San Antonio, TX 78217
Tel.: (210) 656-9027
Web Site: http://www.beyerboys.com
Sales Range: $10-24.9 Million
Emp.: 75
Plumbing, Heating & Air-Conditioning Services
N.A.I.C.S.: 238220
Patrick Beyer (Co-Owner)
Jeffery Beyer (Co-Owner)

BEYOND BREAD
6260 E Speedway Blvd, Tucson, AZ 85712
Tel.: (520) 747-7477
Web Site:
https://www.beyondbread.com
Year Founded: 1998
Sales Range: $25-49.9 Million
Emp.: 175
Bread & Pastry Mfr
N.A.I.C.S.: 311812

Shelby Collier (Co-Owner)
Randie Collier (Co-Owner)
Dean Schwemmer (Dir-Pur)

BEYOND COMPONENTS OF MASS INC.
5 Carl Thompson Rd, Westford, MA 01886
Tel.: (978) 392-9191
Web Site: https://www.beyondc.com
Sales Range: $25-49.9 Million
Emp.: 100
Electrical Fittings & Construction Materials
N.A.I.C.S.: 423610
Louis D. Dinkel (Pres & CEO)

BEYOND HOME PRODUCTIONS
942 Elliot Ave W, Seattle, WA 98119
Tel.: (206) 501-3054
Web Site: http://www.b47studios.com
Year Founded: 2001
Sales Range: $1-9.9 Million
Emp.: 13
Media Production Services
N.A.I.C.S.: 512110
Kevin Maude (Founder & CEO)
RuthAnn Taylor Lopez (Mgr-Production)
Matt Reese (Editor)
Graeme Lowry (Editor)

BEYOND LIMITS, INC.
400 North Brand Boulevard, Glendale, CA 91204
Tel.: (619) 308-5227   DE
Web Site: https://www.beyond.ai
Year Founded: 2014
Emp.: 200
Artificial Intelligence
N.A.I.C.S.: 513210
AJ Abdallat (Founder & CEO)

Subsidiaries:
Altec Products Inc.   (1)
23422 Mill Creek Dr Ste 225, Laguna Hills, CA 92653
Tel.: (949) 727-1248
Web Site: http://www.altec-inc.com
Sales Range: $10-24.9 Million
Emp.: 60
Telemarketing Services
N.A.I.C.S.: 561422
Brandt Morrell (Pres & COO)
Mark Ford (CEO)
Bill Brown (Exec VP-Sls)
April Blankenship (Dir-Mktg)
Cathy Champlin (Mgr-Customer Support Svcs)
Frank Sansone (CFO)
Jessica Quintanilla (Dir-Pro Svcs)
Kathleen Geriak (Dir-HR)
Kevin Dudevoir (Dir-Sls)
Mark Wood (Dir-Software Dev)
Merri Jo Cleair (Product Mgr)
Whitney Lewis (Dir-Print Sls)

BEYOND SPOTS & DOTS INC.
1034 5th Ave Ste 100, Pittsburgh, PA 15219
Tel.: (412) 281-6215
Web Site:
https://www.beyondspotsdots.com
Year Founded: 2006
Sales Range: $1-9.9 Million
Emp.: 10
Multi-Channel Advertising Agency with Global Capabilities
N.A.I.C.S.: 541810
Melanie Querry (Pres)
Andreas Beck (CFO)

BEYOND THE OFFICE DOOR, LLC
623 Washington St, Wausau, WI 54403

Web Site:
http://www.beyondtheofficedoor.com
Year Founded: 2006
Sales Range: $1-9.9 Million
Emp.: 4
Ergonomic Office Furniture Mfr & Distr
N.A.I.C.S.: 337214
Gregory Knighton (Pres & Owner)

BEYOND.COM, INC.
1060 1st Ave Ste 100, King of Prussia, PA 19406
Tel.: (610) 878-2800
Web Site: http://www.beyond.com
Year Founded: 1998
Sales Range: $10-24.9 Million
Emp.: 70
Online Career Database & Directory
N.A.I.C.S.: 561311
James John (COO)
Marla R. Milgram (Gen Counsel, Sec & Exec VP)
Mark Karsch (CFO)
Steven L. Kraut (VP-Bus Dev)
Michael J. Owsiany (VP-Strategy & Execution)
Alex Murphy (Sr VP-Bus Dev & Traffic)
Joe Stubblebine (VP-Talent Solutions)

BEYONDROI, LLC
4855 Technology Way Ste 710, Boca Raton, FL 33431
Tel.: (954) 456-5000
Web Site: http://www.beyondroi.com
Year Founded: 2002
Sales Range: $1-9.9 Million
Emp.: 30
Marketing Consulting Services
N.A.I.C.S.: 541613
Richard J. Pollack (Founder)
Clinton Melton (Mng Partner-Enterprise Architecture)
Emi Nakamura (Mng Partner-DMO)
Preston Zimmerman (VP-Sls-Agency Partnerships)
Salman Lakhani (VP-Tech)

BEZAIRE ELECTRIC INC.
8889 E Via Linda, Scottsdale, AZ 85258
Tel.: (480) 368-8500
Web Site:
http://www.bezaireelectric.com
Rev.: $30,000,000
Emp.: 60
Electrical Contractor
N.A.I.C.S.: 238210
Denise Anteri (Controller)

BEZEMA BUICK CORPORATION
401 Boston Providence Tpke, Norwood, MA 02062
Tel.: (781) 769-4700
Web Site:
http://www.bezemamotors.com
Sales Range: $10-24.9 Million
Emp.: 38
Car Whslr
N.A.I.C.S.: 441110
Donna Miller (Mgr-Customer Rels)

BF ENTERPRISES, INC.
100 Bush St Ste 1730, San Francisco, CA 94104-3919
Tel.: (415) 989-6580   DE
Year Founded: 1986
Sales Range: $1-9.9 Million
Emp.: 5
Real Estate Development & Investment
N.A.I.C.S.: 237210

Brian P. Burns (Chm & CEO)
Paul Woodberry (Exec VP)
Stuart B. Aronoff (Sr VP-Ops & Asst Sec)
S. Douglas Post (CFO, Chief Acctg Officer, Treas, VP & Controller)
Brian P. Burns Jr. (Pres)

BF SOUTH INC.
3309 Collins Ln, Louisville, KY 40245
Tel.: (502) 254-7130
Sales Range: $10-24.9 Million
Emp.: 10,000
Fast-Food Restaurant, Chain
N.A.I.C.S.: 722513
Gladdis Barkley (Controller)
Shawn Kemper (Controller & Office Mgr)
Ulysses Lee Bridgeman Jr. (Owner, Pres & CEO)

BFPE INTERNATIONAL INC.
7512 Connelley Dr, Hanover, MD 21076
Tel.: (410) 768-2200   MD
Web Site: https://www.bfpe.com
Year Founded: 1970
Sales Range: $25-49.9 Million
Emp.: 320
Provider of Fire Protection & Security Systems
N.A.I.C.S.: 561621
Pamela A. Boyer (Pres)
William Jenkins (Controller)
Michael Beatty (Gen Mgr-York)
Jeff Davis (Asst Mgr-Ops)

BFS BUSINESS PRINTING INC.
76 South St, Boston, MA 02111-2868
Tel.: (617) 426-1160
Web Site: http://www.bfsprinters.com
Year Founded: 1965
Sales Range: $10-24.9 Million
Emp.: 125
Offset Printing
N.A.I.C.S.: 323111
Benjamin Franklin Smith (Chm & CEO)
John Merrill (CFO)
Richard Smith (Pres)

BG PICTURES LLC
5318 Bob White Dr, Holiday, FL 34690
Tel.: (727) 946-1000
Web Site: http://www.bgpictures.com
Sales Range: Less than $1 Million
Emp.: 1
Photography Shop
N.A.I.C.S.: 541922
Bryan Gynn (Owner)

BG PRODUCTS, INC.
740 S Wichita St, Wichita, KS 67213
Tel.: (316) 265-2686
Web Site: https://www.bgprod.com
Year Founded: 1971
Sales Range: $300-349.9 Million
Emp.: 300
Fuel Additives, Lubricating Oils & Greases Mfr
N.A.I.C.S.: 324191
Ron Garcia (CFO)
Darin Greseth (Pres)
Danielle Wallace (Mgr-Content Strategy)
Lisa Chamness (Mgr-Event)
Chris Whittington (Dir-Creative)
John Cheek (Mgr-Proving Ground Engrg)
Cody Lyons (Mgr-Proving Ground Technical Svc)
Evan Martens (Coord-Accts Payable)

BGI USA, INC.

10216 Werch Dr., Ste. 103,
Woodridge, IL 60517
Tel.: (630) 783-2618
Web Site:
   http://www.bgiusaonline.com
Year Founded: 1995
Industrial Machinery & Equipment
Merchant Whslr
N.A.I.C.S.: 423830

BGP CORP.
630 Central Ave, New Providence, NJ
07974
Tel.: (908) 673-0000
Web Site: http://bgp.he.net
Year Founded: 1986
Sales Range: $10-24.9 Million
Emp.: 150
Reprographics
N.A.I.C.S.: 561110
Mike Brown *(Pres)*
Tania Hurst *(Mgr-Corp Affiliates)*
Thomas Bach *(Mgr-MDM)*
Liz Marshton *(Mgr-Content Ops)*
Erin M. Downs *(Mgr-Quality Assurance)*

Subsidiaries:

BGP Corp.   (1)
3 Main St., Georgetown, Cayman Islands
Tel.: (345) 543 7589
Sales Range: $10-24.9 Million
Emp.: 14
Reprographics
N.A.I.C.S.: 541810
Tania Hurst *(Dir-Corp Affiliates)*
Erin M. Downs *(Mgr-QA)*
Kev Gavrio *(Mgr-M&A)*
Eric Leman *(Mgr-Specialty Practice)*
Christian Borrot *(Mgr-Operation Effectiveness)*

BGR INC.
6392 Gano Rd, West Chester, OH
45069-4809
Tel.: (513) 755-7100   OH
Web Site: http://www.bgrinc.com
Year Founded: 1972
Sales Range: $10-24.9 Million
Emp.: 100
Wholesale Distributor of Packaging
Supplies
N.A.I.C.S.: 424130
Roger Neilheisel *(Pres)*
Dean Backschelder *(VP)*
Allen Backschelder *(VP)*

BGW CPA, PLLC
1616 Camden Rd Ste 510, Charlotte,
NC 28203
Tel.: (704) 552-0553
Web Site: https://www.trustbgw.com
Accounting Firm
N.A.I.C.S.: 541219
Larry Wagner *(Partner)*

Subsidiaries:

Hawkins Conrad & Co., PLLC   (1)
1616 Camden Rd Ste 510, Charlotte, NC
28203
Tel.: (704) 552-0553
Certified Public Accountants Services
N.A.I.C.S.: 541211
Blaine Hawkins *(Mgr)*

BH CAPITAL PARTNERS, LLC
1200 Ponce de Leon Blvd, Coral
Gables, FL 33134
Tel.: (305) 372-0822
Web Site:
   http://www.bhcapitalpartners.com
Year Founded: 1994
Rev.: $171,300,000
Emp.: 120
Real Estate Developers
N.A.I.C.S.: 236116
Omar Hernandez *(Pres)*

BH MANAGEMENT SERVICES, LLC
5420 LBJ Freeway Ste 530, Dallas,
TX 75240
Tel.: (515) 244-2622
Web Site:
   http://www.bhmanagement.com
Year Founded: 1993
Sales Range: $10-24.9 Million
Emp.: 1,000
Property Management
N.A.I.C.S.: 531110
Harry Bookey *(Owner & CEO)*
Tasha Krawiec *(VP-North Reg)*
Laurie Lyons *(Founder)*

BHARCAP ACQUISITION CORP.
2 Stamford Plz 281 Tresser Blvd Ste
1003, Stamford, CT 06901
Tel.: (704) 451-0979   DE
Year Founded: 2021
Emp.: 5
Investment Services
N.A.I.C.S.: 523999
Bharath Srikrishnan *(Chm & CEO)*
Ethan Wang *(CFO)*

BHARCAP PARTNERS, LLC
165 Mason St 2nd Fl., Greenwich,
CT 06830
Tel.: (203) 489-7770
Web Site: https://bharcap.com
Year Founded: 2021
Private Investment Firm
N.A.I.C.S.: 523999

Subsidiaries:

Francis David Corporation   (1)
5005 Rockside Rd Ph 100, Independence,
OH 44131
Tel.: (216) 524-0900
Web Site: https://www.emscorporate.com
Credit Card Sales & Issuing Services
N.A.I.C.S.: 522210
Shawn Silver *(Chief Revenue Officer)*

Subsidiary (Domestic):

PaymentCloud Inc.   (2)
15165 Ventura Blvd Ste 245, Sherman
Oaks, CA 91403
Web Site: http://www.paymentcloudinc.com
Sales Range: $1-9.9 Million
Credit Card Processing Services
N.A.I.C.S.: 522320
Neal Hamou *(CTO)*
Michael Wright *(COO & Chief Sls Officer)*
Amanda Delzer *(Fin Dir)*
B. Carolina *(Ops Mgr)*

BHB INC.
260 N Main St, Brigham City, UT
84302
Tel.: (435) 734-2345
Rev.: $12,900,000
Emp.: 75
Grocery Stores, Independent
N.A.I.C.S.: 445110
Kent Beckstrum *(Pres)*

BHHH COMPANIES INC.
500 E Polk St, Burnet, TX 78611
Tel.: (512) 756-6041
Sales Range: $10-24.9 Million
Emp.: 2
Heavy Construction Equipment
Rental & Retail Lumber
N.A.I.C.S.: 532412
John Hoover *(Pres)*
Danna Hoover *(VP)*

Subsidiaries:

Hamilton Valley Management,
Inc.   (1)
209 SW St, Burnet, TX 78611
Tel.: (512) 756-6809
Web Site: http://www.hamiltonvalley.com

Sales Range: $10-24.9 Million
Real Estate Managers
N.A.I.C.S.: 531210
Dennis Hoover *(Pres)*

Hoover Building Supply Inc.   (1)
500 E Polk St, Burnet, TX 78611
Tel.: (512) 756-2138
Lumber: Rough, Dressed & Finished
N.A.I.C.S.: 423310
John W. Hoover *(Pres)*

BHI ENERGY
97 Libbey Industrial Pkwy, Weymouth, MA 02189
Tel.: (800) 225-0385   MA
Web Site: http://www.bhienergy.com
Year Founded: 1979
Emp.: 8,500
Business Consulting & Staff Augmentation Services
N.A.I.C.S.: 541690
Mary R. Barletta *(COO-Corp Support Svcs)*
Mike Kaveney *(COO)*
Paul Rublin *(Pres)*
Jim Cootes *(Exec VP-Strategy & Dev)*

Subsidiaries:

Bartlett, Inc.   (1)
7633 E 63rd Pl Ste 400, Tulsa, OK 74133-
1272
Tel.: (918) 252-9111
Sales Range: $75-99.9 Million
Personnel Support & Services for Nuclear
Safety
N.A.I.C.S.: 561320

BHI SENIOR LIVING, INC.
5415 Bearberry Ln, Indianapolis, IN
46268
Tel.: (317) 873-3371   IN
Web Site:
   https://www.bhiseniorliving.org
Year Founded: 1903
Sales Range: $25-49.9 Million
Emp.: 641
Elder Care Services
N.A.I.C.S.: 623312
Harry H. Kennerk *(Chm)*
Jane A. Seigel *(Sec)*
John Dattilo *(Pres & CEO)*
Roger E. Weideman II *(CFO & VP)*

BHMS INVESTMENTS LP
152 W 57th 46th Fl, New York, NY
10019
Tel.: (646) 481-6214
Web Site:
   http://www.bhmsinvestments.com
Year Founded: 2010
Rev.: $50,000,000
Emp.: 25
Private Investment Firm
N.A.I.C.S.: 523999
Kevin L. Angelis *(Co-Founder & Mng Partner)*
Robert L. Salamon *(Co-Founder & Mng Partner)*

Subsidiaries:

Osmotics Corp.   (1)
1444 Wazee St Ste 210, Denver, CO 80202
Tel.: (303) 534-1800
Web Site: http://www.osmotics.com
Sales Range: $10-24.9 Million
Emp.: 24
Anti-Aging Technologies Mfr
N.A.I.C.S.: 456120
Stephanie Arnold *(VP-Ops)*
Francine Edmund Porter *(Pres)*

BHS SPECIALTY CHEMICALS
2320 Indiana Ave, Salt Lake City, UT
84104
Tel.: (801) 973-8232
Web Site:
   http://www.bhsmarketing.com

Sales Range: $10-24.9 Million
Emp.: 96
Specialty Chemicals Services & Marketing
N.A.I.C.S.: 325180
Bruce Schechinger *(Pres & CEO)*

Subsidiaries:

Steam Engineering, Inc.   (1)
204 NE 117th Ave, Vancouver, WA 98684
Tel.: (360) 260-8655
Web Site: http://www.steamengineering.com
Engineeering Services
N.A.I.C.S.: 541330
Bill Stanwood *(Pres)*
Bill Moir *(Mgr-Engrg)*

BHVT MOTORS INC.
701 W Bell Rd, Phoenix, AZ 85023
Tel.: (602) 789-9771
Web Site: https://www.bellhonda.com
Sales Range: $25-49.9 Million
Emp.: 100
New & Used Car Dealers
N.A.I.C.S.: 441110
Robby Motz *(Gen Mgr)*

BHW SHEET METAL COMPANY
113 Johnson St, Jonesboro, GA
30236
Tel.: (770) 471-9303
Web Site: http://www.bhwsm.com
Year Founded: 1959
Sales Range: $10-24.9 Million
Emp.: 200
Roofing Services
N.A.I.C.S.: 238160
Keith Harris *(Pres)*

BHX INC.
555 Commerical Pkwy, Dover, OH
44622
Tel.: (330) 343-5553
Sales Range: $10-24.9 Million
Emp.: 163
Local Trucking without Storage
N.A.I.C.S.: 484121

Subsidiaries:

Shopco Leasing Inc   (1)
555 Commercial Pkwy, Dover, OH 44622
Tel.: (330) 343-5553
Rev.: $1,400,000
Emp.: 16
Industrial Truck Rental
N.A.I.C.S.: 532490

BI ACQUISITION CORP.
600 Brickell Ave Ste 1500, Miami, FL
33131
Tel.: (786) 650-0074   DE
Year Founded: 2019
Emp.: 2
Investment Services
N.A.I.C.S.: 523999
Alan Kestenbaum *(Chm)*
David Cheney *(CEO)*

BI CONSULTING GROUP
860 Blue Gentian Rd Ste 290, Eagan, MN 55121
Tel.: (651) 403-6500
Web Site:
   http://www.biconsultinggroup.com
Sales Range: $10-24.9 Million
Emp.: 56
Software Enhancement Services
N.A.I.C.S.: 513210
Amy Mayer *(Founder & Pres)*
Mike Zajec *(VP-Sls & Mktg)*
Brent Kardell *(Dir-Sls-West)*

BI-CON SERVICES, INC.
10901 Clay Pike Rd, Derwent, OH
43733
Tel.: (740) 685-2542

Bi-Con Services, Inc.—(Continued)

Web Site: https://www.bi-conservices.com
Year Founded: 1959
Emp.: 288
Engineeering Services
N.A.I.C.S.: 541330
Stephen Warner (Gen Mgr-Estimating & Bus Dev)
Joel Gebhart (Project Mgr)
Michael Cole (VP)

BI-LINK METAL SPECIALTIES INC.
391 Glen Ellyn Rd, Bloomingdale, IL 60108-2176
Tel.: (630) 858-5900
Web Site: http://www.bi-link.com
Year Founded: 1979
Sales Range: $10-24.9 Million
Emp.: 210
Provider of Metal Stampings
N.A.I.C.S.: 332119
Ray Ziganto (Pres)
Mike Giammarino (Mgr-Engrg)
Roy Spangler (Pres & CEO)
Mirlo Villarreal (Mgr-Quality)

BI-MART ACQUISITION CORP.
220 S Seneca Rd, Eugene, OR 97402
Tel.: (541) 344-0681
Web Site: http://www.bimart.com
Sales Range: $200-249.9 Million
Emp.: 3,200
General Stores; Discount Retailers
N.A.I.C.S.: 455219
Marty Smith (Chm & CEO)
Dave Zintara (Chm & CFO)
Don Leber (Dir-Adv)

Subsidiaries:

Bi-Mart Corporation **(1)**
220 S Seneca Rd, Eugene, OR 97402-0199
Tel.: (541) 344-0681
Web Site: http://www.bimart.com
Sales Range: $300-349.9 Million
Emp.: 2,700
Variety Store Services
N.A.I.C.S.: 455211
Marty Smith (Chm & CEO)
Dan Chin (Controller)
Rich Truett (Pres & CEO)

BI-PETRO, INC.
3150 Executive Park Dr, Springfield, IL 62794-9246
Tel.: (217) 535-0181
Web Site: https://www.bipetro.com
Rev.: $50,000,000
Emp.: 21
Petroleum Terminal
N.A.I.C.S.: 424710
Skip Homeier (Pres)
Charley Woods (Treas)

BI-RITE COMPANY INC.
6608 E Adamo Dr, Tampa, FL 33619
Tel.: (813) 623-5461
Web Site: http://www.buddyrents.com
Year Founded: 1961
Sales Range: $25-49.9 Million
Emp.: 400
Rent-To-Own Home Furnishings
N.A.I.C.S.: 532310
Joseph Gazzo (Pres)

BI-RITE SERVICE FOOD CO.
123 S Hill Dr, Brisbane, CA 94005
Tel.: (415) 656-0254
Web Site: http://www.biritefoodservice.com
Year Founded: 1966
Sales Range: $100-124.9 Million
Emp.: 250

Whslr of Groceries & Restaurant Equipment
N.A.I.C.S.: 424410
William Barulich (CEO)
Steve Barulich (Pres)

BIAGGIS RISTORANTE ITALIANO
1705 Clearwater Ave, Bloomington, IL 61704
Tel.: (309) 664-2148
Web Site: https://www.biaggis.com
Year Founded: 1998
Sales Range: $50-74.9 Million
Emp.: 1,500
Retail Bakeries
N.A.I.C.S.: 311811
Carolyn Evans (Controller)

BIAGI BROS INC.
787 Airpark Rd, Napa, CA 94558-7515
Tel.: (707) 251-9990
Web Site: https://www.biagibros.com
Year Founded: 1977
Sales Range: $25-49.9 Million
Emp.: 420
Provider of Trucking Services
N.A.I.C.S.: 484121
Fred Biagi (Co-Founder)
Greg Biagi (Co-Founder)
Aaron Jordan (Mgr-Store-Retail)
Pamela Quezada (Sr Mgr-Human Resources)

BIANCHI HONDA
8430 Peach St, Erie, PA 16509
Tel.: (814) 868-9678
Web Site: http://www.bianchihonda.com
Year Founded: 1982
Sales Range: $75-99.9 Million
Emp.: 100
Car Whslr
N.A.I.C.S.: 441110
Heather Cloutier (Mgr-Fin)
Holly Wurst (Mgr-Inventory)

BIANCHI LAND CO.
PO Box 190, Merced, CA 95348
Tel.: (209) 722-8134
Sales Range: $10-24.9 Million
Emp.: 3
Farm Land Leasing
N.A.I.C.S.: 531190
John Bianchi (Pres)
Bette Apland (Office Mgr)

BIANCHI PUBLIC RELATIONS INC.
888 W Big Beaver Rd Ste 777, Troy, MI 48084
Tel.: (248) 269-1122
Web Site: http://www.bianchipr.com
Year Founded: 1992
Sales Range: $1-9.9 Million
Emp.: 8
Public Relations Agency
N.A.I.C.S.: 541820
James A. Bianchi (Pres)
Leslie Dagg (Acct Supvr)

BIANCHI U.S.A., INC.
2536A Barrington Ct, Hayward, CA 94545-1650
Tel.: (510) 264-1001
Web Site: http://www.bianchiusa.com
Sales Range: $100-124.9 Million
Emp.: 12
Bicycles, Clothing & Accessories Mfr & Distr
N.A.I.C.S.: 336991
Rodney Jewett (Pres)
David Reed (VP)

BIBBERO SYSTEMS INC.

1300 N McDowell Blvd, Petaluma, CA 94954
Tel.: (707) 778-3131
Web Site: http://www.bibbero.com
Year Founded: 1953
Sales Range: $10-24.9 Million
Emp.: 200
Offset & Photolithographic Printing Services
N.A.I.C.S.: 323111
Michael J. Buckley (Pres)
Don Buckely (VP)

BIBLE BROADCASTING NETWORK
11530 Carmel Commons Blvd, Charlotte, NC 28226
Tel.: (704) 523-5555
Web Site: https://www.bbnradio.org
Year Founded: 1971
Sales Range: $10-24.9 Million
Emp.: 85
Radio Broadcasting Stations
N.A.I.C.S.: 516110
Lowell Davey (Pres)

BIBLE STUDY FELLOWSHIP
19001 Huebner Rd, San Antonio, TX 78258-4019
Tel.: (210) 492-4676
Web Site: https://www.bsfinternational.org
Year Founded: 1961
Sales Range: $10-24.9 Million
Emp.: 84
Bible Teaching Services
N.A.I.C.S.: 611699
Robert A. Birkeneder (COO)
Richard S. Mazur (CFO)

BICK CO.
9333 Dielman Industrial Dr, Saint Louis, MO 63132
Tel.: (314) 993-3355
Web Site: http://www.bickgroup.com
Sales Range: $25-49.9 Million
Emp.: 80
Civil Engineering Services
N.A.I.C.S.: 237310
James P. Bick (Pres)

BICK GROUP, INC.
3140 Riverport Tech Center Dr, Maryland Heights, MO 63043
Tel.: (314) 993-3355
Web Site: http://www.bickgroup.com
Sales Range: $100-124.9 Million
Emp.: 65
IT Strategy Services
N.A.I.C.S.: 518210
Tad Davies (Sr VP)
Karl Lederman (Sr VP & Gen Mgr)
Gianna Favignano (Dir-Design Svcs)
Aref Ali (CFO)

BICKERDIKE REDEVELOPMENT CORPORATION
2550 W North Ave, Chicago, IL 60647
Tel.: (773) 278-5669
Web Site: https://www.bickerdike.org
Year Founded: 1942
Sales Range: $1-9.9 Million
Emp.: 85
Community Housing Services
N.A.I.C.S.: 624229
Joy Aruguete (CEO)
Gregory Bork (Pres)
Raul Morales (Sec)

Subsidiaries:

Rockwell Community Development, Inc. **(1)**
2550 W North Ave Fl 2, Chicago, IL 60647-5216
Tel.: (773) 278-5669

Real Estate Subdivision Services
N.A.I.C.S.: 237210

BICKFORD SENIOR LIVING GROUP, LLC
13795 S Mur-len Rd Ste 301, Olathe, KS 66062
Tel.: (913) 782-3200
Web Site: http://www.enrichinghappiness.com
Emp.: 2,400
Holding Company; Senior Living Facilities Operator
N.A.I.C.S.: 551112
Andy Eby (Co-Pres)
Joe Eby (Co-Pres)
Mike Eby (Co-Pres)
Alan Fairbanks (Exec VP-Ops)

Subsidiaries:

Bickford of Alpharetta, LLC **(1)**
4125 N Point Pkwy, Alpharetta, GA 30022-4100
Tel.: (678) 366-7700
Web Site: http://www.enrichinghappiness.com
Assisted Living Facility Operator
N.A.I.C.S.: 623312
Jeanette Rodgers (Exec Dir)

BICKFORD'S FAMILY RESTAURANTS
1330 Soldiers Field Rd, Brighton, MA 02135-1020
Tel.: (617) 782-4010
Web Site: http://www.bickfordsrestaurants.com
Sales Range: $10-24.9 Million
Emp.: 5
Operator of Restaurants
N.A.I.C.S.: 722511
Bernard Driscoll (Controller)

BICOASTAL MEDIA, LLC
1 Blackfield Dr Ste 333, Tiburon, CA 94920
Tel.: (415) 789-5035
Web Site: http://www.bicoastal.media
Sales Range: $75-99.9 Million
Emp.: 400
Holding Company; Radio Broadcasting Stations
N.A.I.C.S.: 551112
Mike Wilson (Pres & COO)
Kevin Mostyn (CTO & VP)

Subsidiaries:

Bicoastal Media - Albany **(1)**
2840 Marion St SE, Albany, OR 97322-3978
Tel.: (541) 926-8628
Web Site: http://www.bicoastalmedia.com
Sales Range: $10-24.9 Million
Emp.: 25
Radio Broadcasting Stations
N.A.I.C.S.: 516110
Larry Rogers (Gen Mgr)

Bicoastal Media - Centralia **(1)**
1635 S Gold St, Centralia, WA 98531-8950
Tel.: (360) 736-3321
Web Site: http://www.bicoastalmedia.com
Sales Range: $10-24.9 Million
Emp.: 12
Radio Broadcasting Stations
N.A.I.C.S.: 516110
Victoria Bennington (Gen Mgr-Sls)
Levi Gebeke (Mgr-Web Svcs)
Gary Grossman (Reg VP & Mgr-Market)
Phil Jimenez (Mgr-Market)
Kevin Mostyn (Chief Engr)
Larry Rogers (Mgr-Market)
Rene Shanle-Hutzell (Mgr-Market)
Mike Wilson (Pres & COO)

Bicoastal Media - Crescent City **(1)**
1345 Northcrest Dr, Crescent City, CA 95531
Tel.: (707) 464-9561
Web Site: http://www.bicoastalmedia.com

Sales Range: $10-24.9 Million
Emp.: 10
Radio Broadcasting Stations
N.A.I.C.S.: 516110
Rene Shanle-Hutzell (Gen Mgr)

Bicoastal Media - Eureka (1)
5640 S Broadway, Eureka, CA 95503
Tel.: (707) 442-2000
Web Site: http://www.bicoastalmedia.com
Sales Range: $10-24.9 Million
Emp.: 15
Radio Broadcasting Stations
N.A.I.C.S.: 516110
Laurie Tite (Gen Mgr)

Bicoastal Media - Medford (1)
3624 Avion Dr, Medford, OR 97504-4011
Tel.: (541) 772-4170
Web Site: http://www.bicoastalmedia.com
Sales Range: $10-24.9 Million
Emp.: 40
Radio Broadcasting Stations
N.A.I.C.S.: 516110
Karen Eding (Bus Mgr)

Bicoastal Media - Ukiah-Lakeport (1)
140 N Main St, Lakeport, CA 95453
Tel.: (707) 263-6113
Web Site: http://www.bicoastalmedia.com
Sales Range: $10-24.9 Million
Emp.: 8
Radio Broadcasting Stations
N.A.I.C.S.: 516110
Mike Wilson (Pres & COO)

BICYCLE CASINO

7301 Eastern Ave, Bell Gardens, CA 90201
Tel.: (562) 806-4646   CA
Web Site: http://www.thebike.com
Year Founded: 1984
Sales Range: $300-349.9 Million
Emp.: 1,665
Casino
N.A.I.C.S.: 713210
John Tian (Mgr)
Robert Gilbert (Owner)

BID4ASSETS, INC.

8757 Georgia Ave Ste 1330, Silver Spring, MD 20910-3758
Tel.: (301) 650-9193
Web Site: http://www.bid4assets.com
Professional, Scientific & Technical Services
N.A.I.C.S.: 541990
Richard Hayman (Pres)

BID4FLOORS.COM

5405 Bandera Rd Ste 104, San Antonio, TX 78238
Tel.: (210) 824-1957
Web Site: http://www.bid4floors.com
Year Founded: 2004
Flooring Resellers
N.A.I.C.S.: 449121
Jason Tristan (Owner & Pres)

Subsidiaries:

Broadway Floors, Inc.   (1)
5405 Bandera Rd #104, San Antonio, TX 78238
Tel.: (210) 824-1957
Web Site: http://www.broadway-floors.com
Floor Covering Stores
N.A.I.C.S.: 449121
Jason Tristan (Owner & Pres)

BIDDINGFORGOOD INC.

100 Cambridgepark Dr 110, Cambridge, MA 02140-2369
Tel.: (617) 252-6400
Web Site:
   http://www.biddingforgood.com
Emp.: 300
Online Auction Platform Services
N.A.I.C.S.: 541519
Greg Salls (VP-Engrg)

BIDDLE SAWYER CORPORATION

505 8th Ave Ste 1500, New York, NY 10018-6505
Tel.: (212) 736-1580   DE
Web Site:
   https://www.biddlesawyer.com
Year Founded: 1948
Sales Range: $75-99.9 Million
Emp.: 75
Chemicals, Oils & Enzymes Distr
N.A.I.C.S.: 424690
Wallace Chavkin (Chm)
Robert Chavkin (Pres & COO)
Neil L. Chavkin (Exec VP)

BIDPAL, INC.

8440 Woodfield Crossing Blvd Ste 500, Indianapolis, IN 46240
Tel.: (888) 729-0399
Web Site:
   http://www.bidpalnetwork.com
Year Founded: 2008
Sales Range: $10-24.9 Million
Emp.: 90
Helps Nonprofits With Online Fundraising, Consulting Services, Automated Auctions, Payment Processing & Event Management Solutions
N.A.I.C.S.: 561499
Rachael Clark (VP-Product & Tech)
Karrie Wozniak (VP-Mktg)
James Rischar (VP-Ops & Events)
Steve Johns (CEO)
Joshua Meyer (Dir-Mktg)
Rick Siefert (Dir-Ops)
Joe Duca (Dir-Support)
Terri Summers (Mgr-Acctg)
John Miller (Mgr-Ops)
Courtney Bader (Mgr-Release)
Jonathan Runes (Mgr-Tech R&D)
Kris Ghosh Johnson (VP-North Central Reg)
Parrish Snyder (VP-Sls)
Mark McCorkle (CTO)
Mark Ward (CFO)

BIDWELL INDUSTRIAL GROUP, INC.

2055 S Main St, Middletown, CT 06457-6151
Tel.: (860) 346-9283   CT
Web Site: http://www.bidwellinc.com
Year Founded: 1948
Sales Range: $50-74.9 Million
Emp.: 25
Holding Company
N.A.I.C.S.: 334514
Donald Bidwell Sr. (Pres & CEO)

Subsidiaries:

Blu-Ray Div.   (1)
2055 S Main St, Middletown, CT 06457-6151
Tel.: (860) 343-5353
Web Site: http://www.bidwellinc.com
Sales Range: $10-24.9 Million
Mfr of Whiteprint Copiers & X-ray Duplicators
N.A.I.C.S.: 334514
Donald Bidwell Jr. (Pres)

Contemporary Products, LLC   (1)
2055 S Main St, Middletown, CT 06457-6151
Tel.: (860) 343-1100
Web Site:
   http://www.contemporaryproducts.com
Respiratory Product Mfr
N.A.I.C.S.: 339113

Magnagrip   (1)
2055 S Main St, Middletown, CT 06457-6151
Tel.: (860) 343-5350
Web Site: http://www.bidwellinc.com
Mfr Organizational Magnetic Holders
N.A.I.C.S.: 334514

Power-Dyne   (1)
2055 S Main St, Middletown, CT 06457-6151   (100%)

Tel.: (860) 343-6640
Web Site: http://www.powerdyne.com
Sales Range: $10-24.9 Million
Emp.: 10
Mfr of Wrenches
N.A.I.C.S.: 334514
Donald Bidwell (Pres & CEO)

Rapid Print   (1)
2055 S Main St, Middletown, CT 06457-6151
Tel.: (860) 346-9283
Web Site: http://www.bidwellinc.com
Time & Date Stamps Mfr
N.A.I.C.S.: 334514

BIEDERMANN & SONS, INC.

190 Northfield Rd, Northfield, IL 60093
Tel.: (847) 446-8150
Web Site:
   http://www.biedermannandsons.com
Sales Range: $1-9.9 Million
Emp.: 14
Candle Mfr
N.A.I.C.S.: 459999
Martin Biedermann (Pres)
Michael Kopach (VP-Sls & Mktg)
Amalfi Tenorio-Cohen (Mgr-Warehouse)

BIEDERMANN MANUFACTURING INDUSTRIES

4500 Preslyn Dr, Raleigh, NC 27616
Tel.: (919) 878-7776
Web Site: http://www.bmi-inc.com
Sales Range: $1-9.9 Million
Emp.: 25
Screw Machine Products
N.A.I.C.S.: 332721
John Biedermann (Pres)
Holly Borowy (Gen Mgr)

BIEHL INTERNATIONAL CORPORATION

5200 Hollister Rd Ste 300, Houston, TX 77040-6298
Tel.: (713) 690-7200   LA
Web Site: http://www.biehlco.com
Year Founded: 1972
Sales Range: $25-49.9 Million
Emp.: 300
Provider of Freight Transportation Arrangement Services
N.A.I.C.S.: 488510
Sid Gaudet (CFO)

Subsidiaries:

Biehl & Co. L.P.   (1)
5200 Hollister St, Houston, TX 77040-6298
Tel.: (713) 690-7200
Web Site: http://www.biehlco.com
Sales Range: $10-24.9 Million
Emp.: 70
Freight Transportation Arrangement
N.A.I.C.S.: 488510
Leigh Phillips (Pres-Sls)
Thomas Springer (CEO)

Carolina Shipping Co. Inc.   (1)
1064 Gardner Rd Ste 312, Charleston, SC 29407-5746   (100%)
Tel.: (843) 769-5531
Web Site: http://www.carolinashipping.com
Sales Range: $10-24.9 Million
Emp.: 8
Freight Transportation Arrangement
N.A.I.C.S.: 488510
Lee McDonald (CFO)
Dennis Forsberg (Pres)

BIELY & SHOAF CO.

4616 25th Ave NE PMB 706, Seattle, WA 98105
Tel.: (877) 957-0940
Web Site: http://bielyshoaf.com
Gift & Stationary Mfr
N.A.I.C.S.: 322299
Tom Shoaf (Principal)

Subsidiaries:

Oatmeal Studios, Inc.   (1)
35 Town Road, Rochester, VT 05767
Tel.: (802) 767-3171
Web Site: http://www.oatmealstudios.com
Rev.: $3,666,666
Emp.: 15
Other Commercial Printing
N.A.I.C.S.: 323111
Craig Wiggett (Mgr-Ops)
Joseph Massimino (Pres)

BIENER AUTO GROUP, INC.

795 Northern Blvd, Great Neck, NY 11021
Tel.: (516) 829-2834   NY
Web Site: http://www.biener.com
Year Founded: 1929
Rev.: $90,000,000
Emp.: 100
New & Used Auto Dealers
N.A.I.C.S.: 441110
James Dychkowski (Mgr-Sls)
Stanley Weinstock (Pres)

BIENVENIDOS

316 W 2nd St Ste 800, Los Angeles, CA 90012
Tel.: (213) 785-5906   CA
Web Site: http://www.bienvenidos.org
Year Founded: 1986
Sales Range: $10-24.9 Million
Emp.: 223
Child Care & Development Services
N.A.I.C.S.: 624110
Diana Buehler (COO)
Ritchie L. Geisel (Pres & CEO)
Miriam Gonzalez (Chief Program Officer)
Lizbeth Nevarez (Treas)
Cara Valentini (Chm)
Wayne Guzman (Sec)
Dunn Crutcher Gibson (Vice Chm)

BIENVIVIR SENIOR HEALTH SERVICES

2300 McKinley St, El Paso, TX 79930
Tel.: (915) 562-3444
Web Site: https://www.bienvivir.org
Year Founded: 1988
Sales Range: $100-124.9 Million
Emp.: 400
Provider of Hospital & Medical Service Plan Services
N.A.I.C.S.: 524114
Rosemary Castillo (CEO)
Irene Garcia (Supvr-Acctg)
Nina King (Sec)
Rosa Monge (Supvr-LVN Home Health Field)
Barbara Green (Sec)
Art Lopez (Treas)
Delia Gutierrez (Dir-Medical)
James Baca (VP-Ops-Center)

BIERLEIN COMPANIES INCORPORATED

2000 Bay City Rd, Midland, MI 48642
Tel.: (989) 496-0066
Web Site: http://www.bierlein.com
Sales Range: $50-74.9 Million
Emp.: 500
Demolition, Buildings & Other Structures
N.A.I.C.S.: 238910
Mike Dobis (Mgr-Fleet & Facilities)
Keith Dodd (Project Mgr)

BIERSCHBACH EQUIPMENT & SUPPLY CO.

1101 S Lyons Ave, Sioux Falls, SD 57106
Tel.: (605) 332-4466
Web Site:
   http://www.bierschbach.com
Sales Range: $10-24.9 Million

Bierschbach Equipment & Supply Co.—(Continued)
Emp.: 45
Construction & Mining Machinery
N.A.I.C.S.: 423810
Rick Bierschbach (VP)

BIFLEX INTIMATE GROUP, LLC
180 Madison Ave 6th FL, New York, NY 10016
Tel.: (212) 696-3432
Sales Range: $1-9.9 Million
Emp.: 110
Intimate Apparel Mfr
N.A.I.C.S.: 315120
Kevin Coll (VP-Sls)

BIG 2 TOYOTA
1250 S Gilbert Rd, Chandler, AZ 85286
Tel.: (480) 302-4650
Web Site:
https://www.bigtwotoyota.com
Sales Range: $75-99.9 Million
Emp.: 225
Automobiles; New & Used
N.A.I.C.S.: 441110
Brian Mouffe (Dir-Fin)
Ron Riggins (Dir-Used Car)
Wally Henkel (Gen Mgr)
Brett Henkel (Asst Gen Mgr)
Trish Fox (Mgr-Guest Svc)
Rusty Anderson (Mgr-Sls)
Jason Briggs (Dir-Svc)
Lynn Young (Mgr-Used Car)
Shawn Oliver (Office Mgr-Bus)
Sandi Nickel (Comptroller)
Sean Booth (Mgr-Svc-Columbus)

BIG APPLE CAR INC.
169 Bay 17th St, Brooklyn, NY 11214
Tel.: (718) 236-8765
Web Site:
https://www.bigapplecar.com
Sales Range: $10-24.9 Million
Emp.: 75
Limousine Rental, With Driver
N.A.I.C.S.: 485320
Diana Clemente (Pres)
Paul Radovsky (Controller & Dir-IT)
Jill Spero (Sec)

BIG ARROW CONSULTING GROUP, LLC
584 Broadway Ste 1210, New York, NY 10012
Tel.: (212) 414-5650
Web Site:
http://www.bigarrowgroup.com
Sales Range: $10-24.9 Million
Emp.: 12
N.A.I.C.S.: 541810
Michael Marino (Principal)
Katherine Burton (Acct Dir)

BIG B LUMBERTERIA
6600 Brentwood Blvd, Brentwood, CA 94513
Tel.: (925) 634-2442
Web Site:
https://www.bigblumber.com
Sales Range: $10-24.9 Million
Emp.: 45
Home Center Operator
N.A.I.C.S.: 444110
Mark Balfrey (Pres)
Oscar Hernandez (Mgr-Store)

BIG BANK PRODUCTIONS, INC.
PO Box 27233, Golden Valley, MN 55427
Tel.: (952) 994-0033
Sales Range: $25-49.9 Million
Emp.: 150

Real Estate Manangement Services
N.A.I.C.S.: 531210
Miguel R. Deleon (Pres)

BIG BARN HARLEY-DAVIDSON, INC.
81 NW 49th Pl, Des Moines, IA 50313
Tel.: (515) 265-4444
Web Site: http://www.bigbarnhd.com
Year Founded: 1981
Sales Range: $10-24.9 Million
Emp.: 40
Motorcycles & Motorcycle Parts Dealer
N.A.I.C.S.: 441227
Keith Zoellner (Controller)
Amy Shane (Mgr-Apparel Sls)
Rlick Zimney (Mgr-Rider Svcs)

BIG BEAM EMERGENCY SYSTEMS, INC.
290 E Prairie St, Crystal Lake, IL 60014
Tel.: (815) 459-6100
Web Site: https://www.bigbeam.com
Year Founded: 1938
Sales Range: $75-99.9 Million
Emp.: 80
Portable & Emergency Lighting Equipment
N.A.I.C.S.: 335139
Nick Shah (Pres)
Steve Loria (Controller)

BIG BEAR STORES INC.
2618 King Ave W, Billings, MT 59102
Tel.: (406) 652-5777
Web Site:
http://www.bigbearsports.com
Sales Range: $10-24.9 Million
Emp.: 100
Sports Apparel
N.A.I.C.S.: 458110
Rodger S. Wilson (Chm & Pres)
Judy Steiner (Controller)

BIG BEN REALTY, INC.
5338 1st Ave N, Saint Petersburg, FL 33710
Tel.: (727) 381-6683
Web Site:
http://www.bigbenrealty.com
Sales Range: $1-9.9 Million
Real Estate Broker
N.A.I.C.S.: 531210
Ben G. Friedlander (Owner)

BIG BEND ELECTRIC COOPERATIVE, INC.
1373 N Hwy 261, Ritzville, WA 99169-0348
Tel.: (509) 659-1700
Web Site: https://www.bbec.org
Year Founded: 1939
Sales Range: $25-49.9 Million
Electric Power Distr
N.A.I.C.S.: 221122
Shannon Phillips (Mgr-Fin & Admin)
Yvette Armstrong (CEO & Gen Mgr)
Kenneth Story (Sec)
Curtis Dahl (Pres)
Duane Johnson (Mgr-Ops-Mesa Center)
Jon Schuh (Superintendent-Operations)

BIG BEND TELEPHONE COMPANY, INC.
808 N 5th St, Alpine, TX 79830
Tel.: (432) 364-1000
Web Site: http://www.bigbend.net
Year Founded: 1960
Sales Range: $10-24.9 Million
Telecommunication Servicesb
N.A.I.C.S.: 517111

Justin Haynes (Pres)

BIG BOY RESTAURANTS INTERNATIONAL, LLC
4199 Marcy St, Warren, MI 48091
Tel.: (586) 759-6000 MI
Web Site: http://www.bigboy.com
Year Founded: 1938
Sales Range: $300-349.9 Million
Emp.: 1,000
Restaurant
N.A.I.C.S.: 722511
Debra Murphy (VP-HR)
Keith E. Sirois (CEO)
Marc Matlen (VP)

BIG BRAND TIRE & SERVICE
809 Calle Plano, Camarillo, CA 93012
Tel.: (805) 650-3290
Web Site:
http://www.bigbrandtire.com
Sales Range: $1-9.9 Million
Emp.: 12
Tire & Tube Merchant Whslr
N.A.I.C.S.: 423130

Subsidiaries:

Robertson Tire Co. Inc. (1)
4370 S Mingo Rd, Tulsa, OK 74146
Tel.: (918) 664-2211
Web Site: http://www.robertson-tire.com
Sales Range: $10-24.9 Million
Emp.: 8
Automotive Tires
N.A.I.C.S.: 441340
Rick Robertson (VP)
Mark Roberston (Pres & COO)
Aaron Beers (Mgr-Stores)

BIG BROTHERS BIG SISTERS OF AMERICA
230 N 13th St, Philadelphia, PA 19107
Tel.: (215) 567-7000 PA
Web Site: http://www.bbbs.org
Year Founded: 1977
Sales Range: $25-49.9 Million
Emp.: 1,977
Child & Youth Care Services
N.A.I.C.S.: 624110
Mary Flores (Sr VP-HR)
Kelly D. Williams (Sr VP-Mktg & Comm)
Jeff Engle (CEO-Southwest Washington)
Artis Stevens (Pres & CEO)
Dvon Williams (Chief Comm Officer)
Lowell W. Perry Jr. (Chief Diversity Officer & Sr VP-Community & Corp Engagement)

BIG BUCK BREWERY & STEAKHOUSE, INC.
550 S Wisconsin Ave, Gaylord, MI 49735-1742
Tel.: (989) 732-5781 MI
Web Site: http://www.bigbuck.com
Year Founded: 1995
Sales Range: $10-24.9 Million
Emp.: 111
Restaurant
N.A.I.C.S.: 722410
Joel R. Flowers (COO)

BIG C CORPORATION
600 Coolidge Rd, Lafayette, TN 37083-2306
Tel.: (615) 666-9102
Sales Range: $50-74.9 Million
Emp.: 40
General Trading Company
N.A.I.C.S.: 561990
Coy L. Groves (Pres & Mgr)

BIG C LUMBER CO. INC.

50860 Princess Way, Granger, IN 46530
Tel.: (574) 277-4550
Web Site:
https://www.bigclumber.com
Year Founded: 1921
Rev.: $60,000,000
Emp.: 40
Lumber & Other Building Materials Distr
N.A.I.C.S.: 423310
Bill Wallace (COO)
Bridget Brady (CFO)
Nick Brady (VP-HR)
Andy Tolch (Mgr-La Porte)
Brian Voorde (Mgr-Elkhart)
Gregg Pudell (Mgr-Adrian)
Scott Foley (Mgr-Eau Claire)

BIG CAT ADVERTISING
27 Commercial Blvd Ste C, Novato, CA 94949
Tel.: (415) 884-3501
Web Site:
http://www.bigcatadvertising.com
Year Founded: 1986
Sales Range: Less than $1 Million
Emp.: 4
Advetising Agency
N.A.I.C.S.: 541810
Gayle Peterson (Dir-Creative)
Marty Rubino (Pres, Principal & Chief Acct Exec)
Terri Thornton (Project Coord)

BIG CAT RESCUE CORP.
12802 Easy St, Tampa, FL 33625
Tel.: (813) 920-4130
Web Site:
https://www.bigcatrescue.org
Year Founded: 1992
Sales Range: $1-9.9 Million
Animal Rescue
N.A.I.C.S.: 813312
Carole Baskin (Founder & CEO)
Howard Baskin (CFO, Treas & Sec)
Chelsea Feeny (Dir-Program)
Gale Ingham (Ops Mgr)
Honey Wayton (Mgr-Store)
Jenn Leon (Dir-Outreach)
Lauren Buckingham (Dir-Res)
Karma Hurworth (Asst Mgr)
Barbara Stairs (Mgr-Records)
Susan Bass (Dir-Public Rels)

BIG CEDAR LODGE
612 Devil's Pool Rd, Ridgedale, MO 65739
Tel.: (417) 335-2777
Web Site: http://www.big-cedar.com
Sales Range: $10-24.9 Million
Emp.: 450
Hotel & Motel Operating Services
N.A.I.C.S.: 721110
John Morris (Owner)
Jamie Keys (Dir-Ops)
Debbie Bennett (Gen Mgr)

BIG CHIEF DISTRIBUTING CO. INC.
114 E Ave D, Killeen, TX 76541
Tel.: (254) 634-5421
Sales Range: $1-9.9 Million
Emp.: 9
Petroleum Products Distr
N.A.I.C.S.: 424710
John Gilmore (Office Mgr)

BIG COUNTRY ELECTRIC COOP
1010 W South 1st St, Roby, TX 79543
Tel.: (325) 776-2244
Web Site:
https://www.bigcountry.coop
Sales Range: $10-24.9 Million

Emp.: 25
Distribution, Electric Power
N.A.I.C.S.: 221122
Fredda Buckner *(CEO & Gen Mgr)*

BIG CREEK CONSTRUCTION, LTD.
1617 Old Temple Rd, Lorena, TX 76655
Tel.: (254) 857-3200
Web Site:
https://www.bigcreekconstruct.com
Year Founded: 1997
Sales Range: $10-24.9 Million
Emp.: 150
Highway, Street & Bridge Construction Services
N.A.I.C.S.: 237310
John Miller *(Co-Founder)*
Wade Miller *(Co-Founder)*

BIG CREEK LUMBER CO. INC.
3564 Hwy 1, Davenport, CA 95017
Tel.: (831) 457-5015
Web Site: http://www.big-creek.com
Rev.: $26,800,000
Emp.: 235
Manufacture, Wholesale & Retail Lumber
N.A.I.C.S.: 444110
Bob Berlage *(Dir-Comm)*

BIG DEE AUTO SALES INC.
499 Old Tarrytown Rd, White Plains, NY 10603-2617
Tel.: (914) 682-1515   NY
Web Site:
http://www.bigdeevolvo.com
Year Founded: 1946
Sales Range: $10-24.9 Million
Emp.: 35
Sales New & Used Car Dealers
N.A.I.C.S.: 441110
David Somma *(Dir-Svc)*
Eloy Sanchez *(Acct Mgr)*
Ken Bryce *(Mgr-Parts)*
Peter Teller *(Mgr-Used Car)*
Tom McAllister *(Bus Mgr)*
Tony Martinez *(Mgr-Sls)*
Victor D. Bellavia *(Gen Mgr)*

BIG E ENTERPRISES INC.
5118 Cumberland Rd, Fayetteville, NC 28306
Tel.: (910) 485-2443
Sales Range: $10-24.9 Million
Emp.: 151
Lawn & Garden Equipment
N.A.I.C.S.: 333112
Jim Klemish *(Pres)*
Kim Klemish *(Treas)*

BIG FRESH MEDIA, INC.
2219 Rimland Dr Ste 110, Bellingham, WA 98226
Tel.: (360) 752-3304   WA
Year Founded: 2002
Information Technology Services
N.A.I.C.S.: 519290
Troy Wright *(Owner)*

Subsidiaries:

HCF Holdings Inc.   (1)
2120 Grant St #6, Bellingham, WA 98225
Tel.: (360) 399-1847
Web Site: http://www.handcrankfilms.com
Motion Picture & Video Production Services
N.A.I.C.S.: 512110
Micah Bobbink *(Pres & Mng Partner)*
Angie Wright *(Partner)*
Troy Wright *(Partner)*
Caleb Young *(Creative Dir)*

BIG GAIN INC.
416 Mathews St, Mankato, MN 56001
Tel.: (507) 387-7971
Web Site: https://www.biggain.com

Sales Range: $25-49.9 Million
Emp.: 75
Livestock Feeds
N.A.I.C.S.: 311119
Doug Jackson *(Controller)*

BIG GEYSER INC.
5765 48th St, Maspeth, NY 11378-2015
Tel.: (718) 821-2200   DE
Web Site: https://www.biggeyser.com
Year Founded: 1986
Sales Range: $25-49.9 Million
Emp.: 200
Alcoholic Beverages Mfr
N.A.I.C.S.: 424490
Irving Hershkowitz *(Founder)*
Lewis Hershkowitz *(Pres & CEO)*
Jerry Reda *(COO)*
Mike Wodiska *(VP-New York City Bus Div)*

BIG HONKIN' IDEAS (B.H.I.)
1424 Lincoln Blvd, Santa Monica, CA 90401
Tel.: (310) 656-0557   CA
Web Site:
http://www.bighonkinideas.com
Year Founded: 1997
Sales Range: Less than $1 Million
Emp.: 5
Brand Development, Business-To-Business, E-Commerce, Environmental, Financial, Magazines, Newspaper, Out-of-Home Media, Outdoor, Radio, Seniors' Market, Trade & Consumer Magazines, Travel & Tourism
N.A.I.C.S.: 541810
Larre Johnson *(Partner & Dir-Creative)*
Karl Kristkeitz *(Owner)*

BIG HORN COOPERATIVE MARKETING ASSOCIATION
4784 Hwy 310, Greybull, WY 82426-2242
Tel.: (307) 765-2061   WY
Web Site:
https://www.bighorncoop.com
Year Founded: 1923
Sales Range: $75-99.9 Million
Emp.: 80
Provider of Agricultural Products & Services
N.A.I.C.S.: 424910
Darrell Horton *(Pres)*
Chris Bullinger *(Treas & Sec)*
Gary Petrich *(VP)*

BIG IDEA TECHNOLOGY, LLC
450 Seventh Ave Ste 1003, New York, NY 10123
Tel.: (646) 277-9700
Web Site:
http://www.bigideatech.com
Year Founded: 2015
Sales Range: $1-9.9 Million
Emp.: 20
Information Technology Services
N.A.I.C.S.: 541512
Ben Brukner *(CEO)*

BIG IDEA, INC.
320 Billingsly Ct Ste 30, Franklin, TN 37067-4707
Tel.: (615) 224-2200
Web Site: http://www.bigidea.com
Year Founded: 1993
Rev.: $34,300,000
Emp.: 172
Family Media Services
N.A.I.C.S.: 512110
Ron Eddy *(Dir-Design)*

BIG IMAGINATION GROUP

3603 Hayden Ave, Culver City, CA 90232
Tel.: (310) 204-6100
Web Site: http://www.bigla.com
Year Founded: 1987
Rev.: $11,000,000
Emp.: 10
Full Service
N.A.I.C.S.: 541810
Susan Tom-Nellis *(Dir-Creative)*
Orlando Cabalo *(Comptroller)*
Colette Brooks *(Chief Imagination Officer)*
Brian Dolen *(Dir-Art)*
Julie Hough Torres *(VP-Creative Svcs)*
C. Casper Casparian *(VP-Client Strategy)*
Jamie Greenberg *(Dir-Art)*

BIG INK PR & MARKETING
1409 S Lamar Ste 214, Dallas, TX 75215
Tel.: (214) 485-7300
Web Site: http://www.biginkpr.com
Sales Range: $10-24.9 Million
Emp.: 12
Crisis Communications, Event Planning & Marketing
N.A.I.C.S.: 541820
Jeffrey Yarbrough *(CEO & Founder)*

BIG J ENTERPRISES LLC
8440 Washington St NE, Albuquerque, NM 87113
Tel.: (505) 821-1500
Web Site: http://www.bigjllc.com
Rev.: $42,000,000
Emp.: 200
Plumbing Contractor
N.A.I.C.S.: 238220
Pete Boyd *(Mgr-Pur & Asset)*
Steve Lyle *(Project Mgr)*

BIG L CORPORATION
620 S Main St, Sheridan, MI 48884
Tel.: (989) 291-3232
Web Site: http://www.big-l-lumber.com
Year Founded: 1966
Sales Range: $10-24.9 Million
Emp.: 46
Lumber & Other Building Materials Mfr
N.A.I.C.S.: 423310
Kim Lehman *(Pres)*
Bonnie Smith *(Office Mgr)*
Jeff Feazel *(Mgr-IT)*

BIG LAKE LUMBER, INC.
791 Rose Dr NW, Big Lake, MN 55309
Tel.: (763) 263-3400   MN
Web Site:
http://www.biglakelumber.com
Year Founded: 1976
Sales Range: $10-24.9 Million
Emp.: 13
Lumber & Other Building Materials Mfr
N.A.I.C.S.: 423310
Ronald L. Klindworth *(Pres)*

BIG M ON DIXIE, LLC.
704 N Dixie Blvd, Radcliff, KY 40160
Tel.: (270) 351-4454
Web Site:
https://www.bigmchevy.com
Year Founded: 1986
Sales Range: $10-24.9 Million
Emp.: 35
Car Whslr
N.A.I.C.S.: 441110
Rodney Chancey *(Gen Mgr)*

BIG M, INC.

5901 West Side Ave, North Bergen, NJ 07047
Tel.: (201) 868-6220   NJ
Web Site: http://www.mandee.com
Year Founded: 1951
Sales Range: $300-349.9 Million
Emp.: 3,500
Women's Clothing Retailer
N.A.I.C.S.: 458110
Alan Mandelbaum *(Chm & Owner)*
David Faircloth *(COO)*
George Wegner *(Mgr)*
Kimberly Rembis *(Mgr-HR & Benefits)*
Lisa Firestone *(Asst Mgr-Facilities)*
Gerry Paolello *(Dir-DP)*
Jill Monogan *(Mgr-Store)*
Joel Seibert *(VP-Real Estate)*
Sunita Persaud *(Mgr-Store)*
Caryl Paez *(CIO)*
Antonietta Gencarelli *(Coord-Mktg)*
Renee Knapik *(CMO-Mandee)*
Jan Harvey *(Dir-Mktg-Annie Sez)*

BIG NIGHT ENTERTAINMENT GROUP
3 Boylston Pl 3rd Fl, Boston, MA 02116
Tel.: (617) 338-4343
Web Site: http://www.bneg.com
Year Founded: 2006
Sales Range: $10-24.9 Million
Emp.: 243
Nightlife Event Management Services
N.A.I.C.S.: 711310
Ed Kane *(Principal)*
Joe Kane *(Principal)*
Kevin Long *(Partner)*
Christie Leigh Bellany *(Dir-Sls & Mktg)*
Christine Roane *(Dir-HR)*
Lynn Scheufler *(CFO)*
Mark Desfosses *(Dir-Inventory & Facilities)*
Randy Greenstein *(Principal)*

BIG RED EXPRESS TRUCKING LLC
1501 Lake Ave SE, Largo, FL 33771
Tel.: (727) 601-4171   FL
Web Site:
http://bigredexpresstrucking.com
Sales Range: Less than $1 Million
Freight Shipping & Trucking Company
N.A.I.C.S.: 484110

BIG RED FASTENERS, INC.
608 N Walnut Ave, Broken Arrow, OK 74012
Tel.: (918) 251-7291
Web Site:
http://www.bigredfasteners.com
Year Founded: 2001
Sales Range: $10-24.9 Million
Emp.: 18
Whol Industrial Supplies
N.A.I.C.S.: 423840
Shawna Clark *(Pres)*

BIG RED INC.
2014 Jacksonville Rd, Charleston, SC 29405
Tel.: (843) 566-9982
Web Site:
http://www.bigredincorporated.com
Rev.: $10,000,000
Emp.: 60
Lift Trucks & Parts
N.A.I.C.S.: 423830
Neil Webb *(Gen Mgr)*

BIG RED KENO LTD.
11248 John Galt Blvd, Omaha, NE 68137-2320
Tel.: (402) 339-1200   NE

Big Red Keno Ltd.—(Continued)

Web Site:
https://www.bigredkeno.com
Year Founded: 1991
Sales Range: $10-24.9 Million
Emp.: 45
Amusement & Recreation
N.A.I.C.S.: 713290
Dan Pankow *(Pres & CEO)*
Gary Vanderwood *(Treas)*

BIG RED SPORTS IMPORTS, INC.
418 N Interstate Dr, Norman, OK 73072-4747
Tel.: (405) 364-4400
Web Site:
https://www.bigredsports.com
Sales Range: $10-24.9 Million
Emp.: 90
Car Whslr
N.A.I.C.S.: 441110
Chris Mayes *(Owner)*
Richard Roby *(Sec & Treas)*

BIG RIVER CYPRESS & HARDWOOD, INC.
19431 State Rte 71 N, Blountstown, FL 32424
Tel.: (850) 674-5991
Web Site:
http://www.bigrivercypress.com
Year Founded: 1992
Sales Range: $1-9.9 Million
Emp.: 35
Cypress & Hardwoods Mfr
N.A.I.C.S.: 321211
Harry Rogers *(Pres)*

BIG RIVER OIL COMPANY INC.
1920 Orchard Ave, Hannibal, MO 63401-6036
Tel.: (573) 221-0226
Web Site: https://www.bigriveroil.com
Year Founded: 1972
Sales Range: $10-24.9 Million
Emp.: 20
Distr of Petroleum Products
N.A.I.C.S.: 424720
William Craigmiles *(Co-Founder)*
Stewart Mcintyre *(Controller & Gen Mgr)*
Ruth Craigmiles *(Co-Founder)*

Subsidiaries:

Big River Propane Service LLC **(1)**
2631 Market St, Hannibal, MO 63401
Tel.: (573) 221-0226
Propane Fuel Field Operating Services
N.A.I.C.S.: 324110

BIG RIVER RESOURCES WEST BURLINGTON, LLC
211 N Gear Ste 200, West Burlington, IA 52655
Tel.: (319) 753-1100
Web Site:
https://www.bigriverresources.com
Year Founded: 2002
Emp.: 183
Livestock Whslr
N.A.I.C.S.: 424520
Raymond E. Defenbaugh *(Chm, Pres & CEO)*
Andy Brader *(VP)*
Les Allen *(Treas)*
Pat Edmonds *(Sec)*
Jim Leiting *(COO)*
Brian Schasel *(Mgr-Safety)*
David Zimmerman *(Mgr-HR)*
Terry Manchester *(Plant Mgr)*

BIG RIVER TELEPHONE COMPANY LLC
24 S Minnesota St, Cape Girardeau, MO 63703
Tel.: (573) 651-3373
Web Site:
http://www.bigrivertelephone.com
Sales Range: $10-24.9 Million
Emp.: 80
Local & Long Distance Telephone Communications
N.A.I.C.S.: 517121
John F. Jennings *(CFO)*
Kevin Keaveny *(VP-Ops & Engrg)*
Kevin Cantwell *(Pres)*

BIG RIVERS ELECTRIC CORPORATION
201 3rd St, Henderson, KY 42420
Tel.: (270) 827-2561
Web Site: https://www.bigrivers.com
Year Founded: 1961
Emp.: 621
Eletric Power Generation Services
N.A.I.C.S.: 221118
Mark A. Bailey *(Pres & CEO)*
Michael W. Chambliss *(VP-Sys Ops)*

BIG SANDY FURNITURE INC.
8375 Gallia Pike, Franklin Furnace, OH 45629
Tel.: (740) 574-2113
Web Site:
http://www.bigsandysuperstore.com
Sales Range: $75-99.9 Million
Emp.: 300
Owner & Operator of Furniture Stores
N.A.I.C.S.: 449110
Don Stewart *(Controller)*
Robert Vanhoose *(CEO)*

BIG SANDY RECC
504 11th St, Paintsville, KY 41240
Tel.: (606) 789-4095
Web Site:
https://www.bigsandyrecc.com
Sales Range: $10-24.9 Million
Emp.: 40
Electronic Services
N.A.I.C.S.: 221118
David A. Estepp *(Pres & Gen Mgr)*
Kelly Shepherd *(Sec)*
Danny Wallen *(Chm)*

BIG SEA, INC.
136 4th St N Ste 238, St. Petersburg, FL 33701
Tel.: (727) 386-8031
Web Site: https://www.bigsea.co
Year Founded: 2005
Emp.: 100
Marketing & Advertising Services
N.A.I.C.S.: 541613
Rob Kane *(Pres)*
Andi Graham *(CEO)*

Subsidiaries:

Sparxoo, LLC **(1)**
514 N Franklin St #202, Tampa, FL 33602
Tel.: (813) 402-0208
Web Site: http://www.sparxoo.com
Sales Range: $10-24.9 Million
Emp.: 6
Advetising Agency
N.A.I.C.S.: 541810
David Capece *(Founder & CEO)*
Adrienne Morgan *(VP-Strategic Growth)*
Joey Baird *(VP-Digital Mktg)*
Nick Ferry *(Sr Dir-Accounts)*

BIG SHOULDERS CAPITAL LLC
105 Revere Dr Ste D, Northbrook, IL 60062
Tel.: (224) 927-5330
Web Site:
https://www.bigshoulderscap.com
Privater Equity Firm
N.A.I.C.S.: 523940

David Muslin *(Chm)*
Brian Schroeder *(VP-Equity Investments)*

Subsidiaries:

Anderson Manufacturing Co., Inc. **(1)**
19800 86th St, Bristol, WI 53104
Tel.: (262) 857-7056
Web Site: http://www.andersonmfg.com
Bolt & Washer Mfr
N.A.I.C.S.: 332722

Design Molded Plastics Inc. **(1)**
8220 Bavaria Rd, Macedonia, OH 44056
Tel.: (330) 963-4400
Web Site: http://www.designmolded.com
Sales Range: $1-9.9 Million
Emp.: 120
Custom Injected Molded Products Mfr
N.A.I.C.S.: 326199
Jerry J. Honsaker *(Pres)*
Diane Hanson *(Treas)*

BIG SKY COMMUNICATIONS, INC.
2001 Gateway Pl Ste 130W, San Jose, CA 95110
Tel.: (541) 322-6240
Web Site: http://www.bigskypr.com
Year Founded: 1994
Rev.: $1,400,000
Emp.: 13
Fiscal Year-end: 12/31/06
Collateral, Corporate Communications, Crisis Communications, Media Relations, Public Relations, Strategic Planning/Research
N.A.I.C.S.: 541810
Katy Boos *(VP-PR Client Svcs)*
Coleen Muller Padnos *(Pres)*
Eddie Miller *(Exec VP)*

BIG SKY GROWTH PARTNERS, INC.
1201 Western Ave Ste 406, Seattle, WA 98101
Tel.: (206) 890-3572
Year Founded: 2020
Investment Services
N.A.I.C.S.: 523999
Mark C. Vadon *(Chm & CEO)*
Paul Ferris *(Pres)*
Lauren Neiswender *(CFO & Chief Legal Officer)*

BIG SPRINGS INC.
2700 Meridian St, Huntsville, AL 35801
Tel.: (256) 533-9450
Web Site: http://www.coca-cola.com
Sales Range: $25-49.9 Million
Emp.: 175
Bottled & Canned Soft Drink Mfr
N.A.I.C.S.: 312111
Jim Sentell *(Mgr-HR)*
Rusty Isoem *(Sr VP-Mktg)*
Wanda Moon *(Acct Mgr)*
Paul Fowler *(Pres)*

BIG STATE ELECTRIC LTD.
8923 Aero St, San Antonio, TX 78217
Tel.: (210) 735-1051
Web Site:
https://www.bigstateelectric.com
Year Founded: 1966
Sales Range: $10-24.9 Million
Emp.: 150
Electrical Wiring Services
N.A.I.C.S.: 238210
Vincent Real *(Pres)*

BIG STREET CONSTRUCTION, INC.
1685 Richardson Hwy, North Pole, AK 99705
Tel.: (907) 590-9915

Web Site:
http://www.bigstreetconstruction.com
Year Founded: 2005
Sales Range: $1-9.9 Million
Emp.: 28
Commercial Building Construction & Restoration Services
N.A.I.C.S.: 541330
Patty Flemming *(Co-Owner & Pres)*
Brian Flemming *(Co-Owner & CEO)*

BIG SUR TECHNOLOGIES, INC.
4631 Woodland Corporate Blvd Ste 110, Tampa, FL 33614
Tel.: (813) 269-9145
Web Site:
https://www.bigsurtech.com
Year Founded: 1999
Sales Range: $1-9.9 Million
Emp.: 11
IT Services & Computer Distr
N.A.I.C.S.: 541519
Sam Sandusky *(Pres & CEO)*
Jennifer Parmley *(Dir-Fin & Admin)*
Charles Love *(Dir-Svc Ops)*
John Gessman *(Gen Mgr)*

BIG TEN ACADEMIC ALLIANCE
1819 S Neil St Ste D, Champaign, IL 61820-7271
Tel.: (217) 333-8475
Web Site: http://www.btaa.org
Year Founded: 1958
Sales Range: $1-9.9 Million
Academic Professional Association
N.A.I.C.S.: 813920
Karen Hanson *(Chm)*
Keith A. Marshall *(Exec Dir)*

BIG TEN CONFERENCE
5440 Park Pl, Rosemont, IL 60018
Tel.: (847) 696-1010
Web Site: http://www.bigten.org
Year Founded: 1987
Sales Range: $300-349.9 Million
Emp.: 50
Athlete Support Services
N.A.I.C.S.: 813990
Tony Buyniski *(Dir-Video Svcs)*
Brenda Hilton *(Dir-Building Svcs)*
Brandon Winbush *(Dir-IT)*
Kimberly Smith *(Dir-HR)*
Omar Brown *(Chief People & Culture Officer)*
Jon Schwartz *(Sr VP-Comm, Mktg, Digital & Social Media)*
Rebecca Pany *(Sr VP-Sports Admin)*
Scott Dolson *(VP-Intercollegiate Athletics & Dir-Intercollegiate Athletics)*

BIG THREE RESTAURANTS, INC.
9085 Charles E Limpus Rd, Orlando, FL 33836
Tel.: (516) 375-6649
Year Founded: 2009
Sales Range: Less than $1 Million
Emp.: 2
Holding Company
N.A.I.C.S.: 551112
Jackson L. Morris *(Sec)*
Kenneth L. Shartz *(VP-Retail Sls)*
John V. Whitman Jr. *(Chm & CEO)*
William R. VanHook Jr. *(CFO)*

BIG TREE GROUP, INC.
28325 UTICA RD, ROSEVILLE, MI 48066
Tel.: (321) 216-7500
N.A.I.C.S.: 339930

BIG TRUCK RENTAL, LLC
1039 S 50th St, Tampa, FL 33619
Tel.: (813) 261-0820

Web Site:
http://www.bigtruckrental.com
Sales Range: $1-9.9 Million
Emp.: 5
Refuse Truck Rental Services
N.A.I.C.S.: 532120
Robert Mecchi *(Pres)*
Scott Kanne *(VP)*
Scott Dols *(CEO)*

BIG V SUPERMARKET INC.

122 N Hwy 169, Smithville, MO
64089
Tel.: (816) 532-0883
Sales Range: $10-24.9 Million
Emp.: 150
Owner & Operator of Grocery Stores
N.A.I.C.S.: 445110
William E. Parks *(Owner & Gen Mgr)*

BIG VALLEY RANCHERIA

2726 Mission Rancheria Rd, Lakeport, CA 95453
Tel.: (707) 263-3924   CA
Web Site: http://www.big-valley.net
Year Founded: 1994
Sales Range: $10-24.9 Million
Emp.: 178
Gambling & Casino Services
N.A.I.C.S.: 713290
John Cruz *(Supvr-Ops)*

BIG Y FOODS, INC.

2145 Roosevelt Ave, Springfield, MA
01102-7840
Tel.: (413) 784-0600   MA
Web Site: https://www.bigy.com
Year Founded: 1936
Sales Range: $1-4.9 Billion
Emp.: 12,000
Supermarkets & Other Grocery Retailers (except Convenience Retailers)
N.A.I.C.S.: 445110
Donald H. D'Amour *(Co-Founder)*
Gerald E. D'Amour *(Co-Founder)*
Guy McFarlane *(Sr VP-Sls & Mktg)*
Charles L. D'Amour *(Pres, Pres, CEO & CEO)*
Michael P. D'Amour *(COO & Exec VP)*
Michael Galat *(VP-Employee Svcs)*
Nicole D'Amour Schneider *(VP-Supermarket Ops)*
Eric A. Swensen *(VP-Fresh Foods)*
Jim Wilson *(Dir-Workforce Mgmt)*
Samarra DeJesus *(Sls Mgr-Bakery-Southwick)*
Trista Sabin *(Sls Mgr-Deli-Lee)*
Colin M. D'Amour *(Sr Dir-Express Gas & Convenience Stores)*
Jason Corriveau *(Dir-Center Store)*
Shaun-Robert Burbank *(Mgr-Meat & Seafood Sls-North Adams)*
Richard Bossie *(Sr VP-Ops & Customer Experience)*
David E. Murphy *(Dir-Massachusetts Stores)*
Sarah Steven *(Sr Dir-Mktg)*
Stephen M. Creed *(Sr Dir-Distr & Logistics)*
Theresa Jasmin *(CFO)*
Michael Cormier *(VP-Center Store-New England)*
Christian D'Amour *(Dir-E-Commerce)*
Thomas Christensen Jr. *(Sls Mgr-Meat & Seafood-Rocky Hill)*

Subsidiaries:

Table & Vine, Inc.   **(1)**
1119 Riverdale St Route 5, West Springfield, MA 01089   **(100%)**
Tel.: (413) 736-4694
Web Site: http://www.tableandvine.com
Sales Range: $10-24.9 Million
Emp.: 10
Wine & Alcoholic Beverage Distr

N.A.I.C.S.: 424820

BIG-D CONSTRUCTION COR-PORATION

404 W 400 S, Salt Lake City, UT
84101
Tel.: (801) 415-6000
Web Site: http://www.big-d.com
Sales Range: $300-349.9 Million
Emp.: 700
Construction Services
N.A.I.C.S.: 236210
Jack D. Livingood *(Chm)*
Larry Worrell *(CFO)*
Dale R. Satterwaite *(Sr VP)*
Rich Hazel *(VP)*
Jana Cochell *(Mgr-Subcontractor)*
Chris Grzybowski *(VP-Ops)*
Jason Dunlop *(VP)*
Oscar Yousefi *(VP)*
Will Hopkins *(VP-Jackson)*
Ken Braun *(VP-Project Dev)*
Cory Schubert *(VP-Ops)*
Cory Moore *(CEO)*

BIGBEE STEEL & TANK COM-PANY

4535 Elizabethtown Rd, Manheim, PA
17545
Tel.: (717) 664-0600
Web Site:
http://www.highlandtank.com
Rev.: $20,000,000
Emp.: 130
Tanks, Standard Or Custom Fabricated: Metal Plate
N.A.I.C.S.: 332420
Charles Frey Jr. *(Pres)*

BIGBY COMPANIES

429 S Muskogee Ave, Tahlequah, OK
74464
Tel.: (918) 456-1781
Sales Range: $10-24.9 Million
Emp.: 30
Convenience Stores, Independent
N.A.I.C.S.: 445131
Gilbert S. Bigby *(Partner)*

BIGCOMMERCE, INC.

2711 W Anderson Ln, Austin, TX
78757
Tel.: (512) 758-7588
Web Site:
http://www.bigcommerce.com
Year Founded: 2009
Sales Range: $25-49.9 Million
Emp.: 243
eCommerce Software & Services
N.A.I.C.S.: 513210
Robert Alvarez *(CFO & COO)*
Scott Baker *(VP-IT, Security & Technical Ops)*
Russell Klein *(Chief Dev Officer)*
Cheri Winterberg *(VP-Comm)*
Debbie Shotwell *(Sr VP-People & Culture)*
Leo Castro *(VP-Product Mktg & Brand)*
Jimmy Duvall *(Chief Product Officer)*
Brian Dhatt *(CTO)*
Tod Klubnik *(Sr VP-Global Sls)*
Brian Parks *(VP-Mid Market & Channel Sls)*
Lisa Pearson *(Chief Mktg Officer)*
Jim Herbert *(VP & Gen Mgr-Europe, Middle East & Africa)*
Marc Ostryniec *(Chief Sls Officer)*
Brent Bellm *(CEO)*
Rob Kaloustian *(Chief Svcs Officer)*

BIGELOW HOMES, LLC.

4057 28th St NW Ste 100, Rochester, MN 55901-7946
Tel.: (507) 529-1161

Web Site:
https://www.bigelowhomes.net
Sales Range: $10-24.9 Million
Emp.: 25
Housing Construction Services
N.A.I.C.S.: 236117
Mike Paradise *(Pres)*

BIGELOW LABORATORY FOR OCEAN SCIENCES

60 Bigelow Dr, East Boothbay, ME
04544
Tel.: (207) 315-2567   ME
Web Site: http://www.bigelow.org
Year Founded: 1974
Rev.: $13,105,622
Assets: $51,185,244
Liabilities: $16,604,274
Net Worth: $34,580,970
Earnings: ($719,055)
Emp.: 75
Fiscal Year-end: 06/30/19
Ocean Science Research & Development Services
N.A.I.C.S.: 541715
Jennifer Cutshall *(VP-Advancement)*
Deborah Bronk *(Pres & CEO)*
Chris Cash *(Officer-Advancement)*
Kevin Guay *(Dir-IT)*
Margaret McDiarmid *(Dir-HR)*
John McKown *(Mgr-Grants)*
Tim Pinkham *(Mgr-Laboratory)*
Steven Profaizer *(Chief Comm Officer)*
Chris Vooght *(Accountant)*
Matthew Wade *(Asst Mgr-Laboratory)*
David Whitt *(CFO)*
Dana Wilson *(Mgr-Advancement)*

BIGGE CRANE & RIGGING COMPANY

10700 Bigge St, San Leandro, CA
94577-1032
Tel.: (510) 277-4747   CA
Web Site: https://www.bigge.com
Year Founded: 1916
Sales Range: $10-24.9 Million
Emp.: 130
Installing Building Equipment Services
N.A.I.C.S.: 238290
Weston Settlemier *(Pres)*

Subsidiaries:

Bigge Crane and Rigging Co.   **(1)**
221 30th St NE, Auburn, WA
98002-1709   **(100%)**
Tel.: (206) 443-8500
Web Site: http://www.bigge.com
Sales Range: $10-24.9 Million
Emp.: 10
Heavy hauling Trucking
N.A.I.C.S.: 484230
John Palmer *(Branch Mgr)*

Bigge Development Corporation   **(1)**
10700 Bigge St, San Leandro, CA
94577-1032   **(100%)**
Tel.: (510) 638-8100
Web Site: http://www.bigge.com
Crane
N.A.I.C.S.: 237210
Cherri Rushing *(Gen Mgr)*

Bigge Equipment Co.   **(1)**
14800 Jersey Shore Dr, Houston, TX 77047
Tel.: (713) 434-0995
Web Site: http://www.bigge.com
Emp.: 200
Crane Rental Services
N.A.I.C.S.: 532412
Brian Noga *(VP)*

Bigge Power Constructors   **(1)**
10700 Bigge St, San Leandro, CA 94577
Tel.: (510) 638-8100
Construction Engineering Services
N.A.I.C.S.: 541330

The Empire Crane Company,
LLC   **(1)**

7021 Performance Dr, North Syracuse, NY
13212
Tel.: (315) 458-4101
Sales Range: $1-9.9 Million
Emp.: 12
Construction & Mining (except Oil Well) Machinery & Equipment Merchant Whslr
N.A.I.C.S.: 423810
Paul Lonergan *(Co-Founder & Pres)*
Luke Lonergan *(Co-Founder, CEO & VP)*
Karl Pitre *(Mgr-New Jersey)*

BIGGER MITSUBISHI

1325 E Chicago St, Elgin, IL 60120-4715
Tel.: (847) 282-4846
Web Site:
https://www.biggersmitsubishi.com
Sales Range: $10-24.9 Million
Emp.: 45
New Car Whslr
N.A.I.C.S.: 441110
Brian Schwartz *(Dir-Svc)*

BIGGS PONTIAC

1197 US Hwy 17 S, Elizabeth City,
NC 27909-7630
Tel.: (252) 338-2131   DE
Year Founded: 1971
Sales Range: $10-24.9 Million
Emp.: 65
Car Whslr
N.A.I.C.S.: 441110
Bruce A. Biggs *(Pres)*

BIGHAM CABLE CONSTRUC-TION INC.

132 Leade Dr, Piedmont, SC 29673
Tel.: (864) 269-4058
Web Site:
https://www.bighamcable.com
Year Founded: 1977
Sales Range: $10-24.9 Million
Emp.: 75
Cable Television Line Construction Services
N.A.I.C.S.: 237130
Margaret Bigham *(Pres)*

BIGLER, LP

1920 N Memorial Way Ste 201,
Houston, TX 77007
Tel.: (713) 864-3303
Year Founded: 1998
Sales Range: $25-49.9 Million
Emp.: 40
Petroleum Products Merchant Whslr
N.A.I.C.S.: 424720
Joel E. Herger *(Pres & CEO)*
Smith E. Howland *(Gen Mgr)*
Seth Barron *(Treas)*

BIGRENTZ, INC.

1063 McGaw Ave, Irvine, CA 92614
Tel.: (855) 253-1369
Web Site: http://www.bigrentz.com
Year Founded: 2012
Sales Range: $25-49.9 Million
Online Construction Equipment Rental Services
N.A.I.C.S.: 238910
Dallas Imbimbo *(Chm)*
George Abdelmassieh *(Sr Engr-Software)*
Danny Adams *(Coord-Rental)*
Noemi Benitez *(Mgr-Bus Dev)*
Chris Bernardo *(Reg Mgr-Supply)*
Tamara Burton *(Coord-Rental)*
Scott Cannon *(CEO)*
Daniel Cavic *(Dir-Bus Dev)*
Paul Chang *(Mgr-Rental Ops)*
Monique Clark *(Coord-Strategic Accts)*
Maryjane Clark *(Engr-Software)*
Shelby Collopy *(Engr-Software)*
Michelle Crockett *(Coord-Rental)*
Kevin Dickinson *(Sr Engr-Software)*

BigRentz, Inc.—(Continued)

Billy Ernst *(Coord-Rental)*
Neda Etemad *(VP-Fin & Ops)*
Gigiolla Etzel *(Coord-Rental)*
Matthew Evans *(Sr Engr-Software)*
Rudy Falcon *(Mgr-Bus Dev)*
Justin Flores *(Coord-Rental)*
Jennifer Gulbransen *(Mgr-Bus Dev)*
Jade Gutierrez *(Coord-Rental)*
Keith Hansen *(Dir-Software Engrg)*
David Hoffman *(Sr Mgr-IT)*
Keith Holmes *(VP-Ops)*
Brett Howard *(Mgr-Product Dev)*
Eric Esquivel *(Dir-Ops)*

Subsidiaries:

Equipment Management Group,
LLC   (1)
1180 West Peachtree St NW Ste 850, Atlanta, GA 30309
Tel.: (404) 876-7998
Web Site: http://www.equipmentmg.com
Dumpster Distr
N.A.I.C.S.: 423390
Spencer Thomas *(Acct Coord)*

Lizzy Lift, Inc.   (1)
3333 Mount Prospect Rd, Franklin Park, IL
60131-1337
Tel.: (630) 834-8900
Web Site: http://www.lizzylift.com
Sales Range: $1-9.9 Million
Emp.: 7
Construction Equipment Rental Services
N.A.I.C.S.: 532412
Jennifer DuBose-Lombard *(Sr VP)*

BIGSTON CORPORATION USA
1590 Touhy Ave, Elk Grove Village, IL
60007
Tel.: (847) 439-3500
Web Site: http://www.bigston.com
Sales Range: $25-49.9 Million
Emp.: 50
Radio Repair Shop
N.A.I.C.S.: 811210
Tom Sekiguchi *(Pres)*
Takeshi Kusumoto *(CEO)*
Rob Findlay *(VP-Ops)*

BIGVISIBLE SOLUTIONS, INC.
470 Atlantic Ave 4th Fl, Boston, MA
02210
Web Site: http://www.bigvisible.com
Year Founded: 2006
Sales Range: $1-9.9 Million
Emp.: 30
Coaches & Trains Companies & Employees for Organizational Agility &
Transformation.
N.A.I.C.S.: 611430
Giora Morein *(Co-Founder)*
George Schlitz *(Co-Founder)*
Jim Cundiff *(Co-Founder & Principal)*

BIJOUX INTERNATIONAL INC.
131 W 33rd St, New York, NY 10001
Tel.: (212) 564-3276   NY
Web Site: http://www.eastsport.com
Year Founded: 1982
Sales Range: $10-24.9 Million
Emp.: 50
Mfr of Bagpacks
N.A.I.C.S.: 424350
Arthur Grayer *(VP)*
Angela Han *(Pres)*
Sal LaRosa *(VP-Sls & Plng)*

BIJOUX TERNER, INC.
6950 NW 77th Ct, Miami, FL 33166
Tel.: (305) 500-7500   FL
Web Site:
    http://www.bijouxterner.com
Year Founded: 1974
Rev.: $1,900,000
Emp.: 39
Fiscal Year-end: 12/31/06
Holding Companies

N.A.I.C.S.: 551112
Gabriel Bottazzi *(Pres & CEO)*

**BIKINIS SPORTS BAR &
GRILL**
6901 N IH-35, Austin, TX 78752
Tel.: (512) 454-2247
Web Site:
    http://www.bikinissportsbar.com
Year Founded: 2006
Sales Range: $10-24.9 Million
Emp.: 500
Sports Bar & Restaurant
N.A.I.C.S.: 722511
Doug Guller *(Founder & CEO)*
Matthew Beck *(Asst Gen Mgr)*
Laura Manrique *(Mgr)*
Domenic Battelli *(Mgr)*
Marcus Garza *(Head-Coach)*
R. D. Norris *(Mgr)*
Joey Martinez *(Gen Mgr)*

BIL-JAC FOODS INC.
3337 Medina Rd, Medina, OH 44256
Tel.: (330) 722-7888   OH
Web Site: http://www.biljac.com
Year Founded: 1947
Sales Range: $10-24.9 Million
Emp.: 90
Mfr & Seller of Dry Foods
N.A.I.C.S.: 311111
Jim Kelly *(VP-Mktg)*
Ray Kelly *(VP-Logistics)*
Jeff Dimmerling *(Controller)*
Joanne Duncan *(CFO)*
Robert Kelly *(Pres)*

BIL-RAY GROUP
344 Long Beach Rd, Island Park, NY
11558
Tel.: (516) 442-2125
Year Founded: 1949
Sales Range: $125-149.9 Million
Emp.: 140
Provider of Home Improvement Services
N.A.I.C.S.: 238170
Charles G. LePorin *(CEO)*

Subsidiaries:

Bil-Ray Home Improvements   (1)
214 W Park Ave, Long Beach, NY 11561-
3212
Tel.: (516) 442-2125
Rev.: $30,683,770
Emp.: 50
Siding Contractors
N.A.I.C.S.: 236220

BILD & COMPANY
3608 Shady Ln, Tampa, FL 34683
Web Site: http://www.bildandco.com
Year Founded: 1999
Sales Range: $1-9.9 Million
Emp.: 15
Consulting, Marketing, Recruiting,
Leadership Coaching & Sales
N.A.I.C.S.: 541611
Traci Bild *(Founder)*
Seth Garber *(Pres & CEO)*

BILL ALEXANDER FORD LINCOLN MERCURY, INC.
801 E 32nd St, Yuma, AZ 85365
Tel.: (928) 344-2200   AZ
Web Site:
    http://www.billalexander.com
Sales Range: $50-74.9 Million
Emp.: 166
New & Used Car Dealer
N.A.I.C.S.: 441110
Ryan Hancock *(Owner & Pres)*
Jeff Fritz *(CFO & Treas)*
Everett Dawson *(Gen Mgr)*
Chad Pierson *(Gen Mgr-Sls)*

BILL BARNES

---

812 Moorefield Park Dr Ste 102,
Richmond, VA 23236
Tel.: (804) 320-2296
Sales Range: Less than $1 Million
Emp.: 6
Fast Food Restaurant Operator
N.A.I.C.S.: 722513
Bill Barnes *(Pres)*

BILL BARTH FORD, INC.
3334 Memorial Hwy, Mandan, ND
58554-4643
Tel.: (701) 667-9999
Web Site:
    http://www.billbarthford.com
Sales Range: $10-24.9 Million
Emp.: 70
Car Whslr
N.A.I.C.S.: 441110
Ryan Barth *(Gen Mgr)*
Bill Barth *(Owner)*

BILL BARTMANN ENTERPRISES
2488 E 81st St Ste 500, Tulsa, OK
74137
Tel.: (918) 394-3950
Web Site: http://www.cfstwo.com
Year Founded: 2005
Sales Range: $10-24.9 Million
Emp.: 180
Credit Card Debt Collection
N.A.I.C.S.: 561440
Bill Bartmann *(Co-Founder)*

BILL BLACK CHEVROLET CADILLAC INC.
601 E Bessemer Ave, Greensboro,
NC 27405-6904
Tel.: (336) 944-6555   NC
Web Site:
    https://www.billblackauto.com
Year Founded: 1955
Sales Range: $100-124.9 Million
Emp.: 100
Car Dealership Owner & Operator
N.A.I.C.S.: 441110
Ronald E. McKinney *(Controller)*
Michelle Conaway *(Mgr-HR)*

BILL BLASS GROUP, LLC
236 5th Ave 5th Fl, New York, NY
10001
Tel.: (212) 689-8957   NY
Web Site: http://www.billblass.com
Year Founded: 1970
Women's & Men's Fashion Apparel
Designer, Licensor & Retail Franchisor
N.A.I.C.S.: 533110
Stuart M. Goldblatt *(Pres)*
Simon Yom *(VP)*

BILL BRITT MAZDA
5208 Jefferson Davis Hwy, Fredericksburg, VA 22408
Tel.: (540) 898-1600
Web Site: http://www.rosnerauto.com
Sales Range: $10-24.9 Million
Emp.: 80
Car Whslr
N.A.I.C.S.: 441110
Shawn Kloppman *(Gen Mgr)*
Adam Dunn *(Gen Mgr)*

BILL BUCK CHEVROLET INC.
2324 Tamiami Trl S, Venice, FL
34293
Tel.: (941) 493-5000
Web Site:
    http://www.billbuckchevrolet.com
Rev.: $16,900,000
Emp.: 62
New Car Dealers
N.A.I.C.S.: 441110

Matt Brogan *(Mgr-Svc)*
Ben Lewis *(Gen Mgr)*

**BILL BUTLER CHRYSLER
DODGE PLYMOUTH JEEP,
INC.**
2817 Watson Blvd, Warner Robins,
GA 31093
Tel.: (478) 971-7777
Web Site: http://www.billbutler.com
Sales Range: $10-24.9 Million
Emp.: 60
Car Whslr
N.A.I.C.S.: 441110
Charles Cantrell *(Owner)*
Bobby Cramer *(Mgr-Ops)*
Jeremy Shauganessy *(Gen Mgr)*
Beverly Wooten *(Mgr-Customer Rels)*

BILL CLARK HOMES LLC
200 E Arlington Blvd Ste A, Greenville, NC 27858
Tel.: (252) 355-5805
Web Site:
    http://www.billclarkhomes.com
Year Founded: 1977
Sales Range: $50-74.9 Million
Emp.: 65
Single-Family Houses Builder
N.A.I.C.S.: 236115
Dan Koch *(Dir-IT)*
Maggie Wade *(Coord-Sls & Design)*
Kathy Smith *(CFO)*
William H. Clark Sr. *(Pres)*

BILL CURRIE FORD INC.
5815 N Dale Mabry Hwy, Tampa, FL
33614
Tel.: (813) 872-5555
Web Site: http://www.billcurrie.com
Year Founded: 1960
Rev.: $161,690,464
Emp.: 300
Automobiles, New & Used
N.A.I.C.S.: 441110
Jennifer Currie *(VP)*
Al Diaz *(Controller)*
Gary Phillips *(Mgr-Quick Lane)*
Bruce Slusher *(Mgr-Fleet)*
Wayne Rudzewicz *(Dir-HR)*
Wilmer E. Currie III *(Pres)*

BILL DE NOON LUMBER CO.
571 County Rd Rte 164, Bergholz,
OH 43908-7961
Tel.: (740) 768-2597
Web Site: http://www.denoon.com
Year Founded: 1963
Sales Range: $10-24.9 Million
Emp.: 100
Sawmills & Planing Mills, General
N.A.I.C.S.: 321113
Bill De Noon *(Pres)*
Richard Smith *(Dir-Sls)*

**BILL DELORD AUTOCENTER
INC.**
917 Columbus Ave, Lebanon, OH
45036
Tel.: (513) 932-3000
Web Site: http://www.billdelord.com
Sales Range: $25-49.9 Million
Emp.: 51
New & Used Automobiles
N.A.I.C.S.: 441110
William Delord *(Pres)*
Dale Boreing *(Mgr-Fixed Ops)*
Don Lawder *(Mgr-Customer Dev)*

BILL DODGE AUTO GROUP
1 Saunders Way, Westbrook, ME
04092
Tel.: (207) 854-3200
Web Site:
    https://www.billdodgeautogroup.com
Sales Range: $10-24.9 Million

Emp.: 25
New & Used Automobiles
N.A.I.C.S.: 441110
William Dodge *(Pres)*
Stacy Chandler *(VP)*
Amanda Herrman *(Coord-Bus Dev Center)*
Chris Marcisso *(Mgr-Fin)*
Chris Chase *(Mgr-Comml & Fleet Sls)*

BILL DORAN COMPANY
619 W Jefferson St, Rockford, IL 61103
Tel.: (815) 965-6042
Web Site: http://www.billdoran.com
Sales Range: $25-49.9 Million
Emp.: 450
Whslr of Flowers
N.A.I.C.S.: 424930
William Lafever *(Pres)*
Brian VanDeMark *(Mgr)*

BILL EDWARDS PRESENTS, INC.
6090 Central Ave, Saint Petersburg, FL 33707
Tel.: (727) 343-1840
Web Site:
https://www.billedwardspresent.com
Performing Arts Promoter
N.A.I.C.S.: 711310
Bill Edwards *(Chm & CEO)*

Subsidiaries:

The Club at Treasure Island   (1)
400 Treasure Island Cswy, Treasure Island, FL 33706
Tel.: (727) 367-4511
Web Site: http://www.theclubti.com
Country Club & Resort
N.A.I.C.S.: 713910
Bill Edwards *(Owner)*
Yvonne Vanderlaan *(Dir-Special Events)*
Kolby Kucyk *(Mgr-Mktg)*
Jeff Davis *(Dir-Tennis)*

BILL FAIR & CO.
478 N 1950 Rd, Lecompton, KS 66050-4124
Tel.: (785) 887-6900
Web Site: http://www.billfair.com
Year Founded: 1989
Sales Range: $1-9.9 Million
Emp.: 5
In House Advertising Agency
N.A.I.C.S.: 541810
Kathleen Gentry *(Owner)*
Bill Fair *(Pres)*

BILL GATTON ACURA MAZDA SATURN
2909 N Roan St, Johnson City, TN 37601
Tel.: (423) 418-6034
Web Site:
https://www.johnsoncityacura.com
Rev.: $21,200,000
Emp.: 60
New Car Dealers
N.A.I.C.S.: 441110
William Gatton *(Pres)*
Chris Lee *(Chm)*
Jesse Ford *(Gen Mgr)*

BILL GRAY VOLVO
2897 Washington Rd, McMurray, PA 15317
Tel.: (724) 949-1555
Web Site: http://www.billgray.com
Sales Range: $25-49.9 Million
Emp.: 85
Sales of New & Used Automobiles
N.A.I.C.S.: 441110
Joe Gusky *(Mgr-Fin)*
William L. Gray Jr. *(Pres & Treas)*

BILL HANKS LUMBER CO.
2655 Piney Grove Rd, Danbury, NC 27016
Tel.: (336) 593-2022
Web Site: http://www.bhlumber.com
Sales Range: $10-24.9 Million
Emp.: 85
Lumber: Rough, Dressed & Finished
N.A.I.C.S.: 423310
Jeff Hanks *(Pres)*

BILL HEARD ENTERPRISES, INC.
200 Brookstone Ctr Pkwy Ste 205, Columbus, GA 31904-4563
Tel.: (706) 323-1111   GA
Web Site: http://www.billheard.com
Year Founded: 1919
Sales Range: $1-4.9 Billion
Emp.: 3,100
New & Used Automobiles
N.A.I.C.S.: 441110
Ronald A. Feldner *(CFO)*

BILL HESSER ENTERPRISES INC.
2009 Milton Ave, Janesville, WI 53545
Tel.: (608) 754-7754
Web Site:
http://www.hessertoyota.com
Sales Range: $10-24.9 Million
Emp.: 40
Automobiles, New & Used
N.A.I.C.S.: 441110
William H. Hesser *(Pres)*
Barb Stankes *(Controller)*

Subsidiaries:

Hesser Toyota Inc.   (1)
1811 Humes Rd, Janesville, WI 53545
Tel.: (608) 754-7754
Web Site: http://www.hessertoyota.com
Automobiles, New & Used
N.A.I.C.S.: 441110
William H. Hesser *(Principal)*

BILL HOOD FORD INC.
1500 N Morrison Blvd, Hammond, LA 70401
Tel.: (985) 345-1590
Web Site:
http://www.billhoodford.dealer.com
Sales Range: $25-49.9 Million
Emp.: 65
New & Used Automobile Dealer
N.A.I.C.S.: 441110
Bill Hood *(Pres)*
Chris Forbes *(Mgr-Sls)*

BILL HUDSON & ASSOCI-ATES, INC., ADVERTISING & PUBLIC RELATIONS
1701 W End Ave, Nashville, TN 37203
Tel.: (615) 259-9002   TN
Year Founded: 1964
Sales Range: $25-49.9 Million
Emp.: 20
Advetising Agency
N.A.I.C.S.: 541810
Wayne Edwards *(Pres & CEO)*
John Bolger *(Controller)*
Carole Murphy *(Media Dir)*
Steve Travis *(Exec VP)*

BILL JACKSON, INC.
9501 US Hwy 19 N, Pinellas Park, FL 33782
Tel.: (727) 576-4169   FL
Web Site:
https://www.billjacksons.com
Year Founded: 1946
Sales Range: $1-9.9 Million
Emp.: 45
Sporting Goods Store

N.A.I.C.S.: 459110
Douglas Jackson *(Co-Owner)*
William Jackson *(Co-Owner)*

BILL JACOBS MOTORSPORT INC.
2495 Aurora Ave, Naperville, IL 60540
Tel.: (630) 357-1200
Web Site: http://www.billjacobs.com
Year Founded: 1987
Sales Range: $25-49.9 Million
Emp.: 70
Sales of Automobiles, New & Used
N.A.I.C.S.: 441110
William Jacobs *(Pres)*

BILL JARRETT FORD, INC.
1305 Us Hwy 27 N, Avon Park, FL 33825
Tel.: (863) 453-3117   FL
Web Site: http://www.jarrett-ford.com
Rev.: $15,000,000
Emp.: 53
New Car Dealers
N.A.I.C.S.: 441110
Bruce Anderson *(Mgr-Bus)*
Dennis Crews *(Mgr-Sls)*
Thomas Lamorte *(Mgr-Body Shop)*
Doug Gentry *(Mgr)*
Eddie Fitch *(Mgr-Sls)*
Tim Massey *(Mgr-Svc)*

BILL JOHNSONS RESTAU-RANT
2906 W Fairmount Ave, Phoenix, AZ 85017
Tel.: (602) 264-5565
Web Site:
http://www.billjohnsons.com
Sales Range: $10-24.9 Million
Emp.: 12
Barbecue Restaurant
N.A.I.C.S.: 722511
Jim Rich *(Dir-Ops)*

BILL L. DOVER INC.
Hwy 96 S, Jasper, TX 75951
Tel.: (409) 384-8900
Rev.: $21,000,000
Emp.: 16
Petroleum Products
N.A.I.C.S.: 424720
K. Bebney *(Controller)*
Wade Dover *(Pres)*

BILL LEWIS MOTORS INC.
404 N Jefferson St, Lewisburg, WV 24901
Tel.: (304) 645-2424
Web Site:
http://www.billlewismotors.com
Sales Range: $10-24.9 Million
Emp.: 41
Car Whslr
N.A.I.C.S.: 441110
Charles Lewis *(Principal)*

BILL LUKE CHRYSLER JEEP & DODGE, INC.
2425 W Camelback Rd, Phoenix, AZ 85015
Tel.: (602) 249-1234
Web Site: http://www.billluke.com
Year Founded: 1939
Sales Range: $25-49.9 Million
Emp.: 160
Car Whslr
N.A.I.C.S.: 441110
Kim Carter *(Gen Mgr)*
Donald Lawrence Luke *(Pres)*

BILL LYNCH ASSOCIATES, LLC
308 Lenox Ave, New York, NY 10027
Tel.: (212) 283-7515

Web Site: http://www.bill-lynch.com
Year Founded: 1999
Rev.: $2,300,000
Emp.: 15
Construction Services
N.A.I.C.S.: 423730
Bill Lynch *(Founder & Chm)*
Karen Torres *(Office Mgr)*
Luther A. Smith *(Pres)*

BILL MACINTYRE CHEVRO-LET BUICK
10 E Walnut St, Lock Haven, PA 17745
Tel.: (570) 748-4068
Web Site:
https://www.billmacintyre.com
Sales Range: $25-49.9 Million
Emp.: 50
New & Used Car Dealer
N.A.I.C.S.: 441110
Richard Smith *(Mgr-Sls)*
Barry Jones *(Mgr-Sls)*
Shane Hartle *(Bus Mgr)*
Donald Stewart *(Mgr-Svc)*
William P. MacIntyre Jr. *(Owner)*
William MacIntyre III *(VP)*
Boyd Musser Jr. *(Mgr-Parts)*

BILL MARKVE & ASSOCIATES GROUP
625 Sioux Point Rd, Dakota Dunes, SD 57049
Tel.: (605) 232-3333
Web Site:
http://www.billmarkveassociates.com
Year Founded: 1980
Sales Range: $10-24.9 Million
Emp.: 13
Insurance Agency & Brokerage Services
N.A.I.C.S.: 524210
Bill Markve *(Pres & CEO)*
Carolyn Anderson *(Mgr-Svc)*
Kim Snell *(Mgr-Customer Svc)*
Cheryl Stevens *(Office Mgr)*
Lori Whitman *(Mgr-Customer Svc)*

BILL MARSH AUTO MALL
1655 S Garfield Ave, Traverse City, MI 49686-4335
Tel.: (231) 941-4141
Web Site: https://www.billmarsh.com
Sales Range: $25-49.9 Million
Emp.: 150
New Car Whslr
N.A.I.C.S.: 441110
Bill Marsh *(Dir-Mktg)*

BILL MCCURLEY CHEVROLET
PO Box 2698, Pasco, WA 99302
Tel.: (509) 547-5555
Web Site:
http://www.billmccurley.com
Sales Range: $25-49.9 Million
Emp.: 120
New Car Retailer
N.A.I.C.S.: 441110
Henry Field *(Gen Mgr)*
Craig Cavanaugh *(Gen Mgr-Sls)*

BILL MILLER EQUIPMENT SALES
10200 Parkersburg Rd, Eckhart Mines, MD 21528
Tel.: (301) 689-1013
Web Site:
https://www.bmillerequipment.com
Sales Range: $10-24.9 Million
Emp.: 100
Construction & Mining Machinery
N.A.I.C.S.: 423810
William M. Miller *(Pres, Co-Owner & Mgr)*
Marie Miller *(Treas & Sec)*
Lee Murdy *(Controller)*

Bill Miller Equipment Sales—(Continued)

BILL NAITO COMPANY
2701 NW Vaughn St, Portland, OR
97210
Tel.: (503) 488-5000
Web Site: http://www.billnaito.com
Year Founded: 1921
Sales Range: $1-9.9 Million
Emp.: 18
Commercial, Office, Retail & Rental
Properties
N.A.I.C.S.: 531210
Doug Campbell *(Owner)*
William W. Barendrick *(CEO)*
Diane McMahon *(CEO)*

BILL PAGE HONDA
6715 Arlington Blvd, Falls Church, VA
22042-2799
Tel.: (703) 533-9700
Web Site:
https://www.billpagehonda.com
Year Founded: 1950
Sales Range: $10-24.9 Million
Emp.: 70
Car Whslr
N.A.I.C.S.: 441110
Brian Kanyan *(Gen Mgr)*
William J. Page *(Pres)*

BILL PAGE IMPORTS INC.
6715 Arlington Blvd, Falls Church, VA
22042-2728
Tel.: (703) 533-9700
Web Site:
https://www.billpagehonda.com
Sales Range: $25-49.9 Million
Emp.: 70
Automobiles, New
N.A.I.C.S.: 441110
William J. Page *(Pres)*
Bryan Canyan *(CFO & Sec)*

BILL PEARCE MOTORS INC.
11555 S Virginia St, Reno, NV 89511-
9307
Tel.: (775) 826-2100
Web Site:
https://www.billpearcemotors.com
Sales Range: $10-24.9 Million
Emp.: 55
Automobiles, New & Used
N.A.I.C.S.: 441110
Mike Frietas *(Gen Mgr)*
Sandy Raffealli *(Owner)*

BILL PENNEY TOYOTA
4808 University Dr NW, Huntsville,
AL 35816-1847
Tel.: (256) 837-1111
Web Site:
https://www.billpenneytoyota.com
Sales Range: $25-49.9 Million
Emp.: 100
Car Whslr
N.A.I.C.S.: 441110
Jerre F. Penney *(CEO)*
Buddy Watkins *(Asst Mgr-Svc)*
Ron Hammon *(Dir-IT)*
Victor Callahan *(Mgr-Sls)*

BILL PLEMMONS INC.
6725 University Pkwy, Rural Hall, NC
27045
Tel.: (336) 377-2213
Web Site:
https://www.billplemmonsrv.com
Sales Range: $25-49.9 Million
Emp.: 56
Recreational Vehicle Whslr
N.A.I.C.S.: 441210

BILL RAPP SUPERSTORE
3449 Burnet Ave, Syracuse, NY
13206
Tel.: (315) 437-2501

Web Site: https://www.billrapp.com
Year Founded: 1954
Sales Range: $10-24.9 Million
Emp.: 120
Car Whslr
N.A.I.C.S.: 441110
Rich Bourque *(Mgr-Digital Inventory)*

BILL RAY NISSAN, INC.
2724 N US Hwy 17 92, Longwood,
FL 32750-3782
Tel.: (407) 831-1318
Web Site:
https://www.billraynissan.com
Sales Range: $100-124.9 Million
Emp.: 80
Provider of New & Used Automobile
Sales & Service
N.A.I.C.S.: 441110
Mike Frank *(Gen Mgr)*
Herb Macaya *(Mgr-Sls)*
Suzanne LaFlesh *(Controller)*
Philip Copeland *(Dir-Fin)*

**BILL ROBERTSON & SONS
INCORPORATED**
6525 Santa Monica Blvd, Hollywood,
CA 90038
Tel.: (323) 466-7191
Web Site: http://www.honda4u.com
Rev.: $54,838,102
Emp.: 35
Automobiles, New & Used
N.A.I.C.S.: 441110
Donald Robertson *(Owner)*

**BILL SEIDLE AUTOMOTIVE
GROUP**
2724 NW 36th St, Miami, FL 33142
Tel.: (305) 638-8000
Web Site:
http://billseidleautogroup.com
Sales Range: $25-49.9 Million
Emp.: 150
New Car Whslr
N.A.I.C.S.: 441110
Bill Oster *(VP)*
Ariel Perera *(Mgr-Svc)*

BILL SELIG FORD, INC.
801 Bloomfield Ave, Windsor, CT
06095
Tel.: (860) 688-3651
Web Site:
https://www.mitchellseligford.com
Year Founded: 1970
Sales Range: $10-24.9 Million
Emp.: 35
Car Whslr
N.A.I.C.S.: 441110
Mark Mitchell *(Pres)*

**BILL SHULTZ CHEVROLET,
INC.**
4200 S US Hwy 1, Fort Pierce, FL
34982
Tel.: (772) 461-4800
Sales Range: $10-24.9 Million
Emp.: 70
Car Whslr
N.A.I.C.S.: 441110
John Shepherd *(Mgr-Svc)*
E. Shultz *(Mgr-Site)*

BILL SMITH INCORPORATED
1651 Fowler St 1850, Fort Myers, FL
33901
Tel.: (239) 334-1121
Web Site: http://www.billsmithinc.com
Sales Range: $25-49.9 Million
Emp.: 50
Household Appliance Stores
N.A.I.C.S.: 449210
Earl Smith *(Pres)*
Mike Vinci *(Acct Mgr)*
Bob Hanley *(Acct Mgr)*

BILL SNETHKAMP INC.
16430 Woodward Ave, Lansing, MI
48911
Tel.: (313) 868-3300
Web Site:
http://www.billsnethkamp.com
Year Founded: 1926
Sales Range: $25-49.9 Million
Emp.: 100
Sales of New & Used Automobiles
N.A.I.C.S.: 441110
Mark Snethkamp *(Owner-Dealership)*

Subsidiaries:

Bill Snethkamp Lansing Dodge   (1)
6131 S Pennsylvania Ave, Lansing, MI
48911
Tel.: (517) 394-1200
Web Site: http://www.snethkampdodge.com
Rev.: $40,388,548
Emp.: 40
New & Used Automobiles
N.A.I.C.S.: 441110
Tony Sasso *(Gen Mgr)*

BILL SPURLOCK DODGE INC.
351 4th Ave, Huntington, WV 25701
Tel.: (304) 427-6331
Web Site:
https://www.billspurlockauto.com
Year Founded: 1984
Sales Range: $10-24.9 Million
Emp.: 11
Car Whslr
N.A.I.C.S.: 441110
William S. Spurlock *(Pres)*

BILL STASEK CHEVROLET
700 W Dundee Rd, Wheeling, IL
60090
Tel.: (847) 537-7000
Web Site:
https://www.stasekchevrolet.com
Sales Range: $10-24.9 Million
Emp.: 100
New Car Retailer
N.A.I.C.S.: 441110
Brent Baker *(Mgr-Corvette)*
Bob Stasek *(Gen Mgr)*
Jeremy Stasek *(Mgr-Used Car)*
Randy Carlson *(Mgr-Svc)*
Karen Pradun *(Mgr-Customer Rels)*
Scott Wiscomb *(Mgr-Fleet & Comml)*
Dean Witter *(Mgr-Fixed Ops)*
Jennifer Ferrel *(Asst Mgr-Body Shop)*
Jeff Principio *(Mgr-Fin)*
Andy Miodynski *(Mgr-Gen Sls)*
Kim Novak *(Mgr-Inventory)*
Jack Beery *(Mgr-Sls)*

BILL TERPENING INC.
936 S Central Ave, Medford, OR
97501
Tel.: (541) 773-7311
Web Site:
http://www.medfordfuel.com
Sales Range: $10-24.9 Million
Emp.: 7
Whslr of Petroleum Products
N.A.I.C.S.: 424210
William Terpening *(Pres)*
Karen Ferguson *(VP)*

BILL UTTER FORD
4901 S Interstate 35 E, Denton, TX
76210
Tel.: (940) 321-7400
Web Site:
https://www.billutterford.com
Year Founded: 1956
Sales Range: $25-49.9 Million
Emp.: 150
New Car Whslr
N.A.I.C.S.: 441110
Carl Anderson *(Gen Mgr-Sls)*
Craig Bowen *(Gen Mgr)*

**BILL WALSH AUTOMOTIVE
GROUP**
1752 E Norris Dr, Ottawa, IL 61350
Tel.: (815) 431-6181
Web Site: https://www.billwalsh.com
Sales Range: $25-49.9 Million
Emp.: 125
Car Dealership
N.A.I.C.S.: 441110
William J. Walsh *(Owner & Pres)*
Glenn Corrie *(CFO)*
K. C. Murphy *(VP-Grp Ops)*
William Walsh Jr. *(Gen Mgr)*

Subsidiaries:

Bill Walsh Chevrolet   (1)
1752 E Norris Dr, Ottawa, IL 61350
Tel.: (815) 552-1425
Web Site: http://www.billwalshchevy.com
Sales Range: $25-49.9 Million
Trucks, Commercial
N.A.I.C.S.: 423110
William J. Walsh *(Pres)*
Glen Corrie *(CFO)*

Bill Walsh Ford Lincoln Mercury
Kia   (1)
4001 N Columbus St, Ottawa, IL 61350
Tel.: (815) 434-4800
Web Site: http://www.billwalsh.com
Rev.: $13,000,000
Emp.: 32
New Car Dealers
N.A.I.C.S.: 441110
Mike Bannos *(Mgr-Fin & Insurance)*
Shannon Ingram *(Gen Mgr)*
Donna Moore *(Office Mgr)*
Jason Sears *(Mgr-Parts)*
Joe Arteaga *(Mgr-Sls)*

Sierra Volkswagen Inc.   (1)
510 E Norris Dr, Ottawa, IL 61350
Tel.: (815) 434-2323
Web Site: http://www.sierravw.com
Sales Range: $125-149.9 Million
Emp.: 30
New & Used Automobiles
N.A.I.C.S.: 441110
William Walsh Sr. *(Pres)*

**BILL WHITE VOLKSWAGEN
AUDI INC.**
3510 S Zero St, Fort Smith, AR
72908-6848
Tel.: (479) 648-3510
Web Site:
https://www.billwhitevw.com
Rev.: $17,400,000
Emp.: 25
New Car Dealers
N.A.I.C.S.: 441110
Bill White *(Pres)*
Larry White *(Exec VP)*

BILL WILLIAMS TIRE CENTER
1500 Rankin Hwy, Midland, TX
79701
Tel.: (432) 682-1671
Web Site:
https://www.billwilliamstire.com
Rev.: $24,438,401
Emp.: 100
Automotive Tires
N.A.I.C.S.: 441340
Billy Williams *(Pres)*

BILL WRIGHT TOYOTA
5100 Gasoline Alley Dr, Bakersfield,
CA 93313-3200
Tel.: (661) 398-8697
Web Site:
https://www.billwrighttoyota.com
Sales Range: $25-49.9 Million
Emp.: 168
Car Whslr
N.A.I.C.S.: 441110
Andy Pappas *(Dir-Svc)*
Larry Puryear *(Gen Mgr)*
Summer Hankins *(Bus Mgr)*

BILLBOARD CENTRAL
419 Main St Ste 16, Huntington
Beach, CA 92648
Tel.: (714) 960-5106   CA
Web Site:
https://www.billboardcentral.com
Year Founded: 1996
Sales Range: Less than $1 Million
Emp.: 2
Out-of-Home Media Solutions
N.A.I.C.S.: 541810
Dave Lindsey *(Owner)*

BILLBOARD CONNECTION
400 Perimeter Ctr Terrace NE Ste
900, Atlanta, GA 30346
Tel.: (770) 391-8528
Web Site:
http://www.billboardconnection.com
Year Founded: 1997
Sales Range: $1-9.9 Million
Media Planning, New Product Development, Out-of-Home Media
N.A.I.C.S.: 541830

BILLCO MOTORS INC.
Rt 19, Wexford, PA 15090
Tel.: (724) 940-1000
Web Site: http://www.cochran.com
Year Founded: 1950
Sales Range: $10-24.9 Million
Emp.: 38
Car Whslr
N.A.I.C.S.: 441110
Rob Cochran *(Owner & Pres)*

BILLEO, INC
2933 Bunker Hill Ln Ste 140, Santa
Clara, CA 95054   DE
Year Founded: 2003
Sales Range: $1-9.9 Million
Custom Computer Programming Services
N.A.I.C.S.: 541511

BILLER REINHART STRUCTURAL GROUP INC.
3434 Colwell Ave Ste 100, Tampa, FL
33614
Tel.: (813) 908-7203
Web Site:
https://www.billerreinhart.com
Year Founded: 2001
Sales Range: $10-24.9 Million
Emp.: 10
Structural Engineering Services
N.A.I.C.S.: 541330
Michael H. Biller *(Pres)*
Robert J. Reinhart *(VP)*

BILLIAN PUBLISHING INC.
2100 Riveredge Pkwy Ste 1200, Atlanta, GA 30328-4666
Tel.: (770) 955-8484
Sales Range: $25-49.9 Million
Emp.: 55
Consumer Magazines, Trade Magazines, Databases & Directories
N.A.I.C.S.: 513120
Steven Prazak *(Mgr-Mktg Res)*
Bradley Meier *(CEO & CFO)*
Louise Billian *(Sec)*

BILLING SERVICES GROUP, LLC
7411 John Smith Dr Ste 1500, San
Antonio, TX 78229
Tel.: (210) 949-7000
Web Site:
http://www.bsgclearing.com
Sales Range: $25-49.9 Million
Emp.: 67
Outsourced Telecommunication Billing Solutions
N.A.I.C.S.: 561499

Norman M. Phipps *(CFO)*
Kelli P. Cubeta *(Gen Counsel)*

Subsidiaries:

Avery Holdings, Inc.   (1)
2700 Patriot Blvd Ste 150, Glenview, IL
60025
Tel.: (312) 832-0077
Provider of Outsourced Billing, Customer
Care & Collection Services
N.A.I.C.S.: 517810

BILLINGSLEY RANCH OUTFITTERS
PO Box 768, Glasgow, MT 59230
Tel.: (406) 367-5577
Web Site:
http://www.billingsleyoutfitters.com
Sales Range: $10-24.9 Million
Emp.: 5
Livestock Product Whslr
N.A.I.C.S.: 424520
Jack Billingsley *(Mgr)*

BILLION MOTORS, INC.
600 W 41st St, Sioux Falls, SD
57105-6404
Tel.: (605) 334-2020   SD
Web Site: https://www.billionauto.com
Rev.: $14,500,000
Emp.: 300
Holding Company; New & Used Car
Dealerships Owner & Operator
N.A.I.C.S.: 551112
David H. Billion *(Pres & CEO)*
David R. Billion *(VP)*
Jen Ruter *(Controller)*

Subsidiaries:

Billion CC, Inc.   (1)
3401 W 41st St, Sioux Falls, SD 57106
Tel.: (605) 362-3420
Web Site: http://www.billionauto.com
Sales Range: $10-24.9 Million
Emp.: 1,200
Automobile Body Repair & Paint Shop
N.A.I.C.S.: 811121
David H. Billion *(Pres)*

Billion Honda of Iowa City   (1)
2641 Mormon Trek Blvd, Iowa City, IA
52240-4311   (100%)
Tel.: (319) 337-6100
Web Site: http://www.billionauto.com
Sales Range: $10-24.9 Million
Emp.: 80
New & Used Cars Dealer
N.A.I.C.S.: 441110
David Billion *(Pres)*

Billion Motors - Chrysler Dodge Jeep
Fiat   (1)
5910 S Louise Ave, Sioux Falls, SD 57108
Tel.: (605) 336-1700
Web Site: http://www.billionauto.com
Sales Range: $25-49.9 Million
Emp.: 125
New & Used Car Dealer
N.A.I.C.S.: 441110
Duane Mellema *(Gen Mgr)*

Billion Motors - GMC Buick Kia   (1)
600 W 41st St, Sioux Falls, SD 57105-6404
Tel.: (605) 334-2020
Web Site: http://www.billionauto.com
Sales Range: $25-49.9 Million
Emp.: 120
New & Used Car Dealer
N.A.I.C.S.: 441110
Dave Billion *(Owner)*

Billion Southtown, Inc.   (1)
47025 SD Hwy 44, Worthing, SD 57077
Tel.: (605) 372-4000
Web Site: http://www.billionauto.com
Sales Range: $1-9.9 Million
Emp.: 20
New Car Retailer
N.A.I.C.S.: 441110
David H. Billion *(Pres)*

BILLS ELECTRIC, INC.

1716 Falcon St, Webb City, MO
64870-9501
Tel.: (417) 624-6660
Web Site: https://www.beijoplin.com
Year Founded: 1940
Sales Range: $10-24.9 Million
Emp.: 200
Electrical Contracting Services
N.A.I.C.S.: 238210
Bill Endicott *(Branch Mgr)*

BILLUPS, INC.
340 Oswego Pointe Dr Ste 101, Lake
Oswego, OR 97034
Tel.: (503) 454-0714
Web Site: http://www.billupsww.com
Year Founded: 2004
Sales Range: $10-24.9 Million
Emp.: 86
Outdoor Advertising; Out-of-Home
Media
N.A.I.C.S.: 541830
Benjamin Billups *(Founder, Mng Partner & CEO)*
Rick Robinson *(Chief Strategy Officer)*
Beth Schissler *(Dir-Media)*
Matt Leible *(CMO)*
Suzie Lopez *(Dir-Bus-Austin)*
Simone Davis *(Dir-Seattle)*
Shabnam Irilian *(Mng Dir)*
David Krupp *(CEO-Americas)*
Jeff Jan *(Head-Growth)*

BILLY BENDER CHEVROLET INC.
10355 Mount Savage Rd NW, Cumberland, MD 21502
Tel.: (301) 895-5115
Web Site:
http://www.billybenderchevrolet.com
Sales Range: $10-24.9 Million
Emp.: 26
New & Used Car Dealers
N.A.I.C.S.: 441110
William S. Bender *(Pres)*

BILLY GENE IS MARKETING, INC.
1133 Columbia St Ste 102, San Diego, CA 92101
Web Site:
http://www.billygeneismarketing.com
Year Founded: 2015
Sales Range: $1-9.9 Million
Emp.: 24
Media Advertising Services
N.A.I.C.S.: 541840
Billy Gene Shaw *(Founder & CEO)*
Daniel Flores *(CFO & COO)*
Reena Ayoub *(CMO)*
Ashley Bairan *(Chief Compliance Officer)*
Rheya Green *(Dir-Campaign)*

BILLY GRAHAM EVANGELISTIC ASSOCIATION
1 Billy Graham Pkwy, Charlotte, NC
28201
Tel.: (704) 401-2432   MN
Web Site:
https://www.billygraham.org
Year Founded: 1950
Sales Range: $100-124.9 Million
Emp.: 959
Christian Ministry Services
N.A.I.C.S.: 813110
Billy Graham *(Chm)*
William Franklin Graham IV *(VP)*

BILLY HOWELL FORD-LINCOLN
1805 Atlanta Hwy, Cumming, GA
30040
Tel.: (770) 887-2311

Web Site:
https://www.howellford.com
Year Founded: 1977
Sales Range: $25-49.9 Million
Emp.: 80
New Car Retailer
N.A.I.C.S.: 441110
Bill Howell *(VP)*
Dan Hayward *(Mgr-New Car Sls)*
Jerry McDonald *(Mgr-Pre-Owned Car)*
Gary LaDue *(Gen Mgr-Sls)*
Dudley Bentle *(Mgr-Fin)*
Denis Howell *(Mgr-Body Shop)*
Justin Murphy *(Mgr-Detail)*
Lisa Myers *(Office Mgr)*
Sandra Roberts *(Mgr-Rental)*
Larry Waters *(Mgr-Parts)*
Diane Clackum *(Coord-Svc)*
David Stiles *(Mgr-Quick Lane)*
Glenn Spayde *(Mgr-Svc-Columbus)*

BILLY REID, INC.
114 North Court St, Florence, AL
35630
Tel.: (256) 767-4692
Web Site: http://www.billyreid.com
Emp.: 100
Clothing Mfr & Distr
N.A.I.C.S.: 424350
Billy Reid *(Chief Designer)*
Kieran Mcneill *(Partner)*
John Paul Rowan *(COO)*

Subsidiaries:

Knot Standard, LLC   (1)
1123 Broadway Ste 307, New York, NY
10010
Web Site: http://www.knotstandard.com
Sales Range: $1-9.9 Million
Emp.: 50
Online Apparel Distr
N.A.I.C.S.: 424350
John Ballay *(Co-Founder)*
Matthew Mueller *(Co-Founder)*

BILMAR BEACH RESORT
10650 Gulf Blvd, Treasure Island, FL
33706
Tel.: (727) 360-5531
Web Site:
https://www.bilmarbeachresort.com
Emp.: 100
Hotel Operations
N.A.I.C.S.: 721110
Clyde Smith *(Gen Mgr)*

BILOTTA CONSTRUCTION CORP.
296 Purchase St, Rye, NY 10580-
2102
Tel.: (914) 967-2944
Sales Range: $10-24.9 Million
Emp.: 15
Excavation & Grading Services
N.A.I.C.S.: 238910
Joseph Bilotta *(Pres)*
Michael Wagner *(Superintendent)*

BILT RITE SCAFFOLD CO
12126 Roxie Dr, Austin, TX 78729
Tel.: (512) 918-0800
Web Site:
https://www.scaffoldingaustintx.com
Year Founded: 2006
Sales Range: $1-9.9 Million
Emp.: 80
Scaffolding Distr
N.A.I.C.S.: 423810
Chris Kelley *(CEO)*
Jeff Kelley *(VP)*

BILTMORE CONSTRUCTION CO. INC.
1055 Ponce De Leon Blvd, Belleair,
FL 33756
Tel.: (727) 585-2084

Biltmore Construction Co. Inc.—(Continued)

Web Site:
https://www.biltmoreconstruct.com
Sales Range: $25-49.9 Million
Emp.: 50
Commercial & Office Building, New
Construction
N.A.I.C.S.: 236220
Travis Parker (VP)
Edward A. Parker Jr. (Pres)

**BILTMORE ESTATE WINE
COMPANY**
1 N Pack Sq, Asheville, NC 28801
Tel.: (828) 255-1776
Web Site: https://www.biltmore.com
Year Founded: 1985
Sales Range: $10-24.9 Million
Emp.: 1,800
Mfr of Wines
N.A.I.C.S.: 312130
Steve Watson (CFO & Sr VP-Fin &
IT)
William A. V. Cecil Jr. (Pres & CEO)

**BILTMORE HOLDING ARI-
ZONA L.L.C.**
7600 E Redfield Rd Ste 180, Scotts-
dale, AZ 85260
Tel.: (602) 324-5340
Web Site:
http://www.biltmoreholdings.com
Year Founded: 1994
Sales Range: $10-24.9 Million
Emp.: 45
Real Estate Investment Trust
N.A.I.C.S.: 551112
Richard J. Lund (Pres)

BIMECO GROUP INC.
200 Kelly Dr Ste A, Peachtree City,
GA 30269
Tel.: (770) 631-7761
Web Site:
https://www.bimecogroup.com
Year Founded: 2007
Sales Range: $10-24.9 Million
Emp.: 20
Medical, Dental & Hospital Equipment
& Supplies
N.A.I.C.S.: 423450
Mark Jungers (VP)
Sandra Jungers (Pres)

BIMEDA, INC.
460 NW Pkwy Rd, Kansas City, MO
64150-9576
Tel.: (630) 928-0361
Web Site: http://www.bimedaus.com
Drugs & Druggists' Sundries Mer-
chant Whslr
N.A.I.C.S.: 424210
Robert Hinckley (Pres)

Subsidiaries:

Texas Vet Lab Inc.   (1)
1702 North Bell St, San Angelo, TX 76903
Tel.: (325) 653-4505
Web Site: http://www.texasvetlab.com
Pet Care, except Veterinary, Services
N.A.I.C.S.: 812910

BIMINI TECHNOLOGIES, LLC
8400 Belleview Dr Ste 125, Plano,
TX 75024
Tel.: (858) 348-8050
Web Site:
https://biminihealthtech.com
Medical Equipment Manufacturing
N.A.I.C.S.: 339112
Bradford Conlan (CEO)

Subsidiaries:

Ideal Implant, Inc.   (1)
5005 Lyndon B Johnson Freeway, Dallas,
TX 75244-6172

Tel.: (972) 716-9909
Web Site: http://www.idealimplant.com
Offices of Dentists
N.A.I.C.S.: 621210
Kevin Morano (CFO)
Gabe Walters (VP-Sls)

BIN TO BOTTLE, LLC
110 Camino Oruga Napa, Napa, CA
94558-4558
Tel.: (707) 307-4501   CA
Web Site: http://www.bintobottle.com
Year Founded: 2006
Emp.: 100
Wineries
N.A.I.C.S.: 312130
John Wilkinson (Mng Partner)

**BINARY DEFENSE SYSTEMS,
LLC**
600 Alpha Pkwy, Stow, OH 44224
Tel.: (330) 777-4300
Web Site:
http://www.binarydefense.com
Year Founded: 2014
Sales Range: $1-9.9 Million
Emp.: 64
Cyber Security Consulting Services
N.A.I.C.S.: 541690
Bob Meindl (CEO)
Mike Valentine (Founder & Chm)
Dave Kennedy (Co-Founder & CTO)
Dave DeSimone (Chief Security Offi-
cer)
Mike Hofherr (CFO & COO)
Ryan Burnheimer (VP-Bus Dev)

BINARY TREE, INC.
1 Gateway Ctr 25th Fl, Newark, NJ
07102
Tel.: (908) 309-3992   DE
Web Site: http://www.binarytree.com
Year Founded: 1993
Sales Range: $10-24.9 Million
Emp.: 65
Software Manufacturer
N.A.I.C.S.: 541511
Carl Baumann (VP-Sls & Mktg)
Steven Pivnik (Founder & Chm)
Ryan Niemann (Chief Revenue Offi-
cer & Sr VP)
Vadim Gringolts (CTO)
Deni Llambiri (Dir-Dev)
Pete Caldecourt (Mgr-Product Mgmt)
Nick Wilkinson (CEO)
Francois deCourtivron (Co-CFO)
Stacie Wolf (CFO)

BINDAGRAPHICS INC.
2701 Wilmarco Ave, Baltimore, MD
21223-3352
Tel.: (410) 362-7200
Web Site:
https://www.bindagraphics.com
Year Founded: 1974
Sales Range: $10-24.9 Million
Emp.: 220
Post-Press Services
N.A.I.C.S.: 323120
Martin Anson (Pres, CEO & Owner)

Subsidiaries:

Bindagraphics South, Inc.   (1)
100 N Pendleton St, High Point, NC 27260
Tel.: (336) 431-6200
Book Binding Services
N.A.I.C.S.: 323117

The Colad Group, Inc.   (1)
801 Exchange St, Buffalo, NY 14210-1434
Tel.: (716) 961-1776
Web Site: http://www.colad.com
Sales Range: $10-24.9 Million
Emp.: 90
Custom Office Supply Mfr
N.A.I.C.S.: 323111
Todd Hatcher (Controller)
Todd Anson (Pres)
Tim Towne (Acct Exec-Dallas & Fort Worth)

BINDTECH LLC
1232 Antioch Pike, Nashville, TN
37211
Tel.: (615) 834-0404
Web Site:
https://www.bindtechinc.com
Emp.: 100
Book Mfr, Bookbinding & Printing
Services
N.A.I.C.S.: 323117
John Helline (CEO)

Subsidiaries:

Eckhart & Company, Inc.   (1)
4011 W 54th St, Indianapolis, IN 46254-
4789
Tel.: (317) 347-2665
Web Site: http://eckhartandco.com
Rev.: $6,400,000
Emp.: 75
Tradebinding & Related Work
N.A.I.C.S.: 323120
Cari Medaris (Mgr-Acctg & Office)
Gary Neidlinger (Mgr-Plant)
Chris Eckhart (Pres)

BINEX LINE CORP.
19515 S Vermont Ave, Torrance, CA
90502
Tel.: (310) 416-8600
Web Site: https://www.binexline.com
Rev.: $14,000,000
Emp.: 40
Deep Sea Foreign Transportation Of
Freigh
N.A.I.C.S.: 483111
David Paek (Pres)
Katie An (Mgr-Import)
Jay Hahn (Asst Mgr)

**BING CONSTRUCTION COM-
PANY INC.**
2930 S Telegraph Rd, Bloomfield
Hills, MI 48302
Tel.: (248) 338-4033   MI
Year Founded: 1963
Sales Range: $10-24.9 Million
Emp.: 10
Residential Construction
N.A.I.C.S.: 236115

**BING ENERGY INTERNA-
TIONAL, LLC**
2051 E Paul Dirac Dr, Tallahassee,
FL 32310
Tel.: (850) 597-7431
Web Site:
http://www.bingenergyinc.com
Sales Range: $1-9.9 Million
Emp.: 15
Fuel Cell Mfr
N.A.I.C.S.: 335311
Yung Chen (Chm & CEO)
Harry Chen (CTO)
Richard Hennek (VP-Bus Dev)
Dean Minardi (CFO)

**BINGAMAN & SON LUMBER,
INC.**
1195 Creek Mountain Rd, Kreamer,
PA 17833
Tel.: (570) 374-1108   PA
Web Site:
https://www.bingamanlumber.com
Year Founded: 1968
Sales Range: $10-24.9 Million
Emp.: 100
Lumber Plywood & Millwork
N.A.I.C.S.: 423310
Max E. Bingaman (Owner)
Scott Hurst (CFO)
Chris Bingaman (Owner & VP-Sls-
USA & Canada)
Brad Bingaman (Dir-Domestic Sls)
David Whitten (Dir-Exports)
Michael Worrell (Dir-HR)

BINGHAM COOPERATIVE INC.
477 W Hwy 26, Blackfoot, ID 83221
Tel.: (208) 785-3440
Web Site:
http://www.binghamcoop.com
Sales Range: $50-74.9 Million
Emp.: 40
Fertilizer & Fertilizer Materials
N.A.I.C.S.: 424910
Michael Jensen (Gen Mgr)
Janice Fehringer (Dir-HR)

**BINGHAM GREENEBAUM
DOLL LLP**
2700 Market Tower 10 W Market St,
Indianapolis, IN 46204-4900
Tel.: (317) 635-8900   DE
Web Site: http://www.bgdlegal.com
Year Founded: 1914
Law firm
N.A.I.C.S.: 541110
Jeffrey T. Bennett (Partner-
Indianapolis)
Sue A. Beesley (Partner-Indianapolis)
David A. Adams (Partner-
Indianapolis)
Steven R. Wilson (Partner-
Louisville/Cincinnati & Co-Head-
Estate, Trust & Fiduciary)
William Scott Croft (Partner-
Louisville)
W. Tobin McClamroch (Mng Partner)
James R. Irving (Mng Partner-
Louisville Office)
Jared A. Cox (Partner-Louisville)
John S. Lueken (Partner-Louisville &
Chm-Estate Plng Dept)
Brad R. Maurer (Partner-Indianapolis)
Rene R. Savarise (Partner-Louisville)
Benjamin J. Lewis (Partner-Louisville
& Chm-Fiduciary Litigation Practice
Grp)
Jeffrey A. McKenzie (Partner & Chm-
Corp Svcs Dept)
Mark A. Loyd (Partner-Louisville &
Chm-Tax & Employee Benefits Dept)
Christopher W. D. Jones (Partner-
Louisville & Chm-Private
Equity/Mergers & Acq Practice)
Raja J. Patil (Partner-Louisville &
Chm-Banking Practice Grp)
Daniel E. Fisher (Partner-Louisville &
Chm-Health Care Practice Grp)
Melissa Norman Bork (Partner-
Louisville & Chm-Bus Litigation Prac-
tice Group)
J. Mark Grundy (Partner-Louisville &
Chm-Litigation Dept)
Courtney Wright (Dir-Mktg Ops)
Matthew Price (Mng Partner-
Indianapolis Office)
Timothy W. Dunn (Mng Partner-
Lexington Office)
James M. Hinshaw (Partner-
Indianapolis & Chm-Litigation Dept)
Philip Sicuso (Partner-Indianapolis &
Chm-Economic Dev Dept)
William J. Kaiser Jr. (Partner-Jasper
& Chm-Corp Svcs Dept)
C. W. Raines III (COO)

**BINGHAM MEMORIAL HOSPI-
TAL**
98 Poplar St, Blackfoot, ID 83221
Tel.: (208) 785-4100   ID
Web Site:
https://www.binghammemorial.org
Year Founded: 2006
Sales Range: $75-99.9 Million
Emp.: 838
Health Care Srvices
N.A.I.C.S.: 622110
Shandra Averett (Dir-Quality)
Josh Maynard (Dir-Engrg)
Carolyn Hansen (Chief Nursing Offi-
cer)

Jake Erickson (CEO)
Joe Cannon (Chm)
Dave Lowry (COO)
John Fullmer (CFO)

BINGO NATION, INC.

6440 Sky Pointe Dr Ste 140/149, Las Vegas, NV 89131
Year Founded: 2006
Television Services
N.A.I.C.S.: 516120
Dave Matheson (Pres & CEO)

BINKELMAN CORPORATION

2601 Hill Ave, Toledo, OH 43607
Tel.: (419) 537-9333
Web Site: http://www.binkelman.com
Sales Range: $10-24.9 Million
Emp.: 35
Power Transmission Equipment & Apparatus
N.A.I.C.S.: 423840
Daniel Kazmierczak (Pres & CEO)
Brad Fitzgerald (Gen Mgr)
Rich Reed (Mgr)
Dave Popkin (Acct Mgr)
Brian Frey (Acct Mgr)
Dave Grana (VP-Ops)

BINS CORPORATION

737 Ponce De Leon Ave NE, Atlanta, GA 30306
Tel.: (404) 872-1109
Web Site:
   http://www.greensbeverages.com
Rev.: $10,000,000
Emp.: 30
Beer & Wine Whslr
N.A.I.C.S.: 445320
Jeff Greenbaum (Pres)

BINSONS HOSPITAL SUPPLIES INC.

26834 Lawrence, Center Line, MI 48015
Tel.: (586) 755-2300
Web Site: https://www.binsons.com
Rev.: $25,400,000
Emp.: 130
Hospital Equipment & Supplies
N.A.I.C.S.: 459999
James Binson (Pres)
Mary Uhrig (Co-Dir-Reimbursement)

BINSWANGER MANAGEMENT CORP.

2 Logan Sq, Philadelphia, PA 19103
Tel.: (215) 448-6000   PA
Web Site:
   http://www.binswanger.com
Year Founded: 1931
Sales Range: $1-4.9 Billion
Emp.: 5,200
Real Estate Investment, Development & Management Services
N.A.I.C.S.: 531210
David R. Binswanger (Pres)
John J. Dues (Vice Chm)
Christopher J. Hall (Pres-Appraisal)
Charles S. Pawlak (Mng Dir-Tech Grp & VP)
Larry M. Spinelli (Pres-Natl Grp)
Eric Dienstbach (Sr VP)
Andrew Harris (Sr VP-Advisory Svcs)
Marc Policarpo (Sr VP)
Daniel Yentz (VP-Mgmt Svcs)
Brett J. Dedeaux (Dir-Binswanger & Realty Advisory Grp)
Douglas M. Faris (Sr VP-Realty Grp-South)
Edwin Hernandez (Mng Dir-Binswanger Puerto Rico)
Fernando Gimenez Zapiola (Pres)
Helder Molina (Pres-Binswanger Brazil)
James A. Medbery (Sr VP)

Rodrigo Fuenzalida (Mng Dir-Fuenzalida Mujica Binswanger)
Rafael Florez-Estrada (Mng Dir-Peru)
Daniel Stubbs (Sr VP)
David R. Barber (Sr VP)
Michael M. Reid (Sr VP)
Ron Link (Sr VP-Supply Chain & Logistics)
Frank J. Cullen (Pres-Realty Grp-East)
Jason A. Kramer (Partner & Sr VP)
Josh Haber (Partner & Sr VP)
Robert Corr (Sr VP)
Owen Murphy (Sr VP-Mktg)

Subsidiaries:

Binswanger International Ltd.   (1)
2 Logan Sq, Philadelphia, PA 19103
Tel.: (215) 448-6000
Web Site: http://www.binswanger.com
Holding Company; Real Estate Investment, Development & Management Services
N.A.I.C.S.: 551112
David R. Binswanger (Pres & CEO)

BIO ESSENCE HERBAL ESSENTIALS INC.

12 Chrysler Unit B, Irvine, CA 92618
Tel.: (800) 538-1333
Web Site:
   https://www.bioessence.com
Emp.: 100
Health Supplement Mfr & Retailer
N.A.I.C.S.: 325412

BIO MEDIC CORPORATION

1 Silas Rd, Seaford, DE 19973
Tel.: (302) 628-4100   DE
Web Site: http://www.bmds.com
Sales Range: $10-24.9 Million
Emp.: 13
Laboratory Animal Housing & Care Equipment
N.A.I.C.S.: 423490
George S. Gabriel (CEO)

Subsidiaries:

Lab Products, Inc.   (1)
742 Sussex Ave, Seaford, DE 19973-2057
Tel.: (302) 628-4300
Web Site: http://www.labproductsinc.com
Sales Range: $10-24.9 Million
Laboratory Animal Housing Care Equipment Mfr
N.A.I.C.S.: 541990
Neil Campbell (Pres)

Affiliate (Domestic):

Bio Medic Data Systems Inc   (2)
1 Silas Rd, Seaford, DE 19973-2061
Tel.: (302) 628-4100
Web Site: http://www.bmds.com
Laboratory Animal Identification Equipment Mfr
N.A.I.C.S.: 334419

Subsidiary (Domestic):

Harford Systems, Inc.   (2)
2225 Pulaski Hwy, Aberdeen, MD 21001
Tel.: (410) 272-3400
Web Site: http://www.harfordsystems.com
Research Animal Cage Systems; Design Consultants; Manufacturing & Leasing of Contract Special Metals, Walk-In Coolers & Freezers
N.A.I.C.S.: 332322

Maryland Plastics, Inc.   (2)
251 E Central Ave, Federalsburg, MD 21632
Tel.: (410) 754-5566
Web Site: http://www.marylandplastics.com
Plastic Cutlery, Plastic Laboratory Equipment & Custom Molded Products Mfr
N.A.I.C.S.: 326199
Ida Giles (Mgr-Customer Svc)
Lynn Irwin (Mgr-Engrg)
John Soper (Pres)

BIO SOIL ENHANCERS, INC.

1161 James St, Hattiesburg, MS 39401
Tel.: (601) 582-4000
Web Site: http://www.sumagrow.org
Year Founded: 2007
Sales Range: $1-9.9 Million
Emp.: 20
Mfr of Products Containing Suma-Grow Proprietary Blend Microbes to Increase Crop Yields
N.A.I.C.S.: 115112
Chuck Grantham (Dir-Field Svcs)
Janiece Rawalt (Dir-Quality Control)

BIO-SERV CORPORATION

1130 Livernois Rd, Troy, MI 48083
Tel.: (248) 588-1005
Web Site:
   https://www.rosepestsolutions.com
Sales Range: $10-24.9 Million
Emp.: 20
Pest Control Services
N.A.I.C.S.: 561710
H. Russell Ives (Pres)
John Bohrer (CFO)

BIOAUTHORIZE HOLDINGS, INC.

15849 N 71st St Ste 216, Scottsdale, AZ 85254
Tel.: (928) 300-5965   NV
Web Site:
   http://www.bioauthorize.com
Year Founded: 1999
Sales Range: $50-74.9 Million
Emp.: 5
Holding Company; Mobile Applications
N.A.I.C.S.: 551112
Jeffrey R. Perry (CFO, COO, Sec & VP)
Yada Schneider (Pres, CEO & CTO)

BIOCARE MEDICAL, LLC

60 Berry Dr, Pacheco, CA 94553
Tel.: (925) 603-8000   CA
Web Site: https://www.biocare.net
Year Founded: 1997
Sales Range: $10-24.9 Million
Emp.: 150
Cancer Diagnosis Technologies
N.A.I.C.S.: 325412
Roy Paxton Yih (Co-Founder & CEO)
Gene J. Castagnini (COO & Exec VP)
Nicolas M. Barthelemy (Chm)

BIOCENTRIC HEALTH INC.

700 Indian Springs Dr, Lancaster, PA 17601
Tel.: (877) 880-7800
Web Site:
   http://www.biocentrichealth.com
Year Founded: 2005
Sales Range: $1-9.9 Million
Emp.: 4
Develops, Manufactures & Sells Nutritional Supplements Directly to Consumers
N.A.I.C.S.: 456191
Floyd Taub (Chm)

BIODERM INC.

12320 73rd Ct N, Largo, FL 33773
Tel.: (727) 507-7655
Web Site:
   http://www.mensliberty.com
Sales Range: $1-9.9 Million
Emp.: 50
Men's Urinary Incontinence Medical Device Mfr
N.A.I.C.S.: 339112
Jim Terpstra (Mgr-Natl Sls)
John Debella (Gen Mgr)
Steve Babb (VP-Tech)
David Underwood (Dir-IT)

Jake Snee (VP-Sls & Mktg)
Gaet Tyranski (Pres & CEO)
Colleen Kennedy (VP-Direct-to-Consumer Sls & Mktg)
Alicia Lance (Sr Dir-Compliance)

BIODTECH, INC.

2100 SouthBridge Pkwy Ste 650, Birmingham, AL 35209
Tel.: (205) 414-7586
Web Site:
   http://www.biodtechinc.com
Year Founded: 2003
Pharmaceutical & Biotechnology Distr
N.A.I.C.S.: 424210
Paul Castella (Chm)
Alan Dean (Pres)
Keith Champion (Dir-Ops)

BIOELEMENTS, INC.

3502 E Boulder St, Colorado Springs, CO 80909-6608
Tel.: (719) 260-0297
Web Site:
   https://www.bioelements.com
Year Founded: 1985
Sales Range: $10-24.9 Million
Emp.: 60
Mfr of Cosmetic Preparations
N.A.I.C.S.: 325620
Barbara Salomone (Founder & Pres)
Bob Schatz (VP)
Ron Lucero (CFO & Controller)
Adrienne Schatz (Treas)
Kelly Melvin (Sls Dir-Natl)

BIOFINA, INC.

1915 Mark Court Ste 110, Concord, CA 94520
Tel.: (925) 288-2935
Web Site:
   http://www.biofinagroup.com
Year Founded: 2010
Sales Range: $1-9.9 Million
Emp.: 50
Bio-Renewable Plastics Mfr
N.A.I.C.S.: 325211
Domenico F. De Luca (Co-Founder & CEO)
Drew Roth (Co-Founder & COO)
Mark Knoll (Founder & Partner)

BIOFUELS ENERGY, LLC

2210 Encinitas Blvd Ste P, Encinitas, CA 92024
Tel.: (760) 944-4572   DE
Web Site:
   https://www.biofuelsenergyllc.com
Year Founded: 2007
Emp.: 100
Biomethane Gas Extraction & Distr
N.A.I.C.S.: 211130

BIOFUELS POWER CORP.

20202 Hwy 59 N Ste 210, Humble, TX 77338
Tel.: (281) 364-7590
Year Founded: 2004
Assets: $2,213,603
Liabilities: $8,415,921
Net Worth: ($6,202,318)
Earnings: ($908,305)
Emp.: 4
Fiscal Year-end: 12/31/15
Renewable Energy Services
N.A.I.C.S.: 221114
Robert Wilson (VP-Fin)

BIOGAS ENERGY SOLUTIONS, LLC

40 Tower Ln 1st Fl, Avon, CT 06001
Tel.: (860) 678-7537   DE
Web Site: http://www.besch4.com
Sales Range: $10-24.9 Million
Emp.: 60

Biogas Energy Solutions, LLC—(Continued)
Develops, Owns & Operates Landfill Gas for Alternative Energy Projects
N.A.I.C.S.: 221118
Steve Laliberty (Pres)
Mary Lou Kachnowski (Sec)
Cathrine Parent (Controller)

Subsidiaries:

UK Energy Systems, Ltd. (1)
Knapton Generating Station, East Knapton, Malton, YO17 8JF, N Yorkshire, United Kingdom
Tel.: (44) 1944758746
Natural Gas Distr
N.A.I.C.S.: 221210

BIOGROUPUSA, INC.
1059 Broadway Ste F, Palm Harbor, FL 34698
Tel.: (727) 789-1646
Web Site: http://www.biobagusa.com
Sales Range: $1-9.9 Million
Biodegradable Compostable Bag Mfr
N.A.I.C.S.: 322220
Dave Williams (Pres)
Mark Williams (VP-Sls)

BIOHABITATS, INC.
2081 Clipper Park Rd, Baltimore, MD 21211
Tel.: (410) 554-0156　　　MD
Web Site:
　https://www.biohabitats.com
Sales Range: $25-49.9 Million
Emp.: 60
Ecological Restoration, Conservation Planning & Regenerative Design Services
N.A.I.C.S.: 813312
Keith Bowers (Founder & Pres)
John Herchl (Sr Project Mgr-Great Lakes & Ohio River Bioregions)

Subsidiaries:

Natural Systems International, LLC (1)
3600 Cerrillos Rd Ste 1102, Santa Fe, NM 87507-2687　　　(100%)
Tel.: (505) 988-7453
Web Site: http://www.biohabitats.com
Sales Range: $1-9.9 Million
Emp.: 12
Applied Biotechnology & Ecological Engineering Services
N.A.I.C.S.: 813312

BIOIVT, LLC
123 Frost St, Westbury, NY 11590
Tel.: (516) 483-1196　　　DE
Web Site: http://www.bioivt.com
Year Founded: 1981
Biological Product Mfr
N.A.I.C.S.: 325414
Richard Haigh (CEO)

Subsidiaries:

Biological Specialty Company LLC (1)
2165 N Line St, Colmar, PA 18915
Tel.: (833) 464-2873
Web Site: http://www.biospecialty.com
Rev.: $7,700,000
Emp.: 35
Drugs & Druggists' Sundries Merchant Whslr
N.A.I.C.S.: 424210
Aileen Widdoss (VP)

Optivia Biotechnology Inc. (1)
3010 Kenneth St, Santa Clara, CA 95054
Tel.: (650) 324-3177
Web Site: http://www.bioivt.com
Transporter Assay Services
N.A.I.C.S.: 541380
Dominique Bridon (COO & Exec VP)
Yong Huang (Founder, Pres & CEO)

PrecisionMed, LLC (1)

132 N Acacia Ave, Solana Beach, CA 92075-1104
Tel.: (858) 847-0117
Web Site: http://www.precisionmed.com
Voluntary Health Organizations
N.A.I.C.S.: 813212
Eric Leach (CEO)

Tennessee Blood Services Corp. (1)
807 Poplar Ave, Memphis, TN 38105
Tel.: (901) 526-0293
Web Site:
　http://www.tennesseebloodservices.com
Ambulatory Health Care Services
N.A.I.C.S.: 621999
Bob Rice (Mgr-Laboratory)

XenoTech, LLC (1)
1101 W Cambridge Circle Dr, Kansas City, KS 66103
Tel.: (913) 438-7450
Web Site: https://www.xenotech.com
Chemical Products Mfr
N.A.I.C.S.: 325998
Elizabeth Jackson (Mgr-Sales-Operations-Strategic)
David Buckley (Chief Scientific Officer)
Cindy Rewerts (Acct Mgr)
Holly Stefl (Acct Mgr)
Christian Darabant (VP)
Jason Neat (COO)
Joe Saltta (CFO)
Yasuhisa Adachi (CEO)
Darren Warren (Pres & CEO)

BIOLIFE, LLC
8163 25th Ct E, Sarasota, FL 34243
Tel.: (941) 360-1300
Web Site: https://www.biolife.com
Year Founded: 1999
Sales Range: $1-9.9 Million
Emp.: 39
Pharmaceutical Preparation Mfr
N.A.I.C.S.: 325412
Tim Kelly (Exec VP)
Claudia Masselink (VP-Quality Assurance & Regulatory Affairs)
Kelly Keene (VP-R&D)
Gloria DiPuma (CFO, Chief Strategic Officer & VP)
Stuart Jones (Pres & CEO)

BIOLOGICS DEVELOPMENT SERVICES, LLC
5670 W Cypress St Ste D, Tampa, FL 33607
Tel.: (813) 520-9073
Web Site: http://www.bdscro.com
Sales Range: $10-24.9 Million
Emp.: 12
Biological Researcher & Developer
N.A.I.C.S.: 541715
Alan Breau (COO)

BIOMARK, INC.
703 S Americana Blvd, Boise, ID 83702
Tel.: (208) 275-0011
Web Site: http://www.biomark.com
Year Founded: 1990
Sales Range: $1-9.9 Million
Emp.: 22
Radio Frequency Idenification Transmitter Mfr
N.A.I.C.S.: 334419
Dean Park (CEO)
Steve Anglea (Dir-Tech & Applied Svcs)
Scott Gary (VP-Sls & Mktg)

BIOME MAKERS INC.
202 Cousteau Pl Ste 100, Davis, CA 95618
Tel.: (916) 378-8580
Web Site: https://biomemakers.com
Year Founded: 2015
Biotechnology Research & Development Services
N.A.I.C.S.: 541714

BIOMEDICAL RESEARCH FOUNDATION OF NORTH-WEST LOUISIANA
2031 Kings Hwy, Shreveport, LA 71103
Tel.: (318) 716-4100　　　LA
Web Site: http://www.biomed.org
Year Founded: 1986
Sales Range: $10-24.9 Million
Emp.: 51
Biomedical Research Services
N.A.I.C.S.: 541715
Kris Ypya (Mgr-Bus)
James D. Dean (COO & Exec VP)
Malcolm Murchison (Chm)
Lennis S. Elston (Treas)
Arthur Thompson (Vice Chm)
John F. George (Pres & CEO)
Jay D. Meyers (VP-External Affairs)
Vassia Roulia (VP-R&D & Admin)
Willie C. White III (Sec)

BIOMEDICAL RESEARCH INSTITUTE OF NEW MEXICO
1501 San Pedro SE 151-B - Bldg 14, Albuquerque, NM 87108
Tel.: (505) 260-1033　　　NM
Web Site: https://www.brinm.org
Year Founded: 1989
Sales Range: $10-24.9 Million
Emp.: 119
Health Care Srvices
N.A.I.C.S.: 622110
Donna Wilt (Exec Dir)

BIOMETICS INTERNATIONAL, INC.
1170 Avenida Acaso, Camarillo, CA 93012
Tel.: (805) 383-3535　　　CA
Web Site: http://www.biometics.com
Year Founded: 1993
Sales Range: $10-24.9 Million
Nutritional Supplement Products Mfr & Distr
N.A.I.C.S.: 325411
Chris Sanchez (Pres)

BIONEUTRAL GROUP, INC.
211 Warren St, Newark, NJ 07103
Tel.: (973) 577-8003　　　NV
Web Site: http://www.bioneutral.com
Sales Range: Less than $1 Million
Emp.: 3
Chemical Biotechnology Product Developer & Mfr
N.A.I.C.S.: 325998
Andrew Kielbania (CEO & Chief Scientific Officer)
Mark Lowenthal (Pres & CEO)

BIONOVATE TECHNOLOGIES CORP
3651 Lindell Rd Ste D1141, Las Vegas, NV 89103
Tel.: (208) 231-1606　　　NV
Year Founded: 2012
Liabilities: $503,209
Net Worth: ($503,209)
Earnings: ($106,544)
Fiscal Year-end: 06/30/21
LED Lighting Solutions
N.A.I.C.S.: 334413
Aleksander Vucak (Pres, CEO, CFO, Treas & Sec)

BIONUMERIK PHARMACEUTICALS, INC.
8122 Datapointe Dr Ste 1250, San Antonio, TX 78229
Tel.: (210) 641-1701
Web Site: http://www.bionumerik.com
Sales Range: $1-9.9 Million
Emp.: 43
Cancer Drug Mfr

N.A.I.C.S.: 541720

BIONUTRITIONAL RESEARCH GROUP, INC.
6 Morgan Ste 100, Irvine, CA 92618-2206
Tel.: (714) 427-6990
Web Site:
　http://www.powercrunch.com
Rev.: $15,000,000
Emp.: 8
Food & Nutritional Supplements Distr
N.A.I.C.S.: 456191
Kevin Lawrence (Pres & CEO)
Ken Braunstein (VP-Sls)
Curtis Steinhaus (CFO)
Karen Lawrence Stensby (Treas & Sec)

BIOONE
21 Dupont Cir NW Ste 800, Washington, DC 20036
Tel.: (202) 296-1605
Web Site: https://www.bioone.org
Year Founded: 1999
Sales Range: $10-24.9 Million
Online Journal Publisher
N.A.I.C.S.: 513120
Susan Skomal (CEO)
Nicole Colovos (Sr Dir-Mktg Comm)
Lauren Kane (COO)
Mark Kurtz (Sr Dir-Strategic Dev)
Maeg Keane (Designer-Graphic)
Kent E. Holsinger (Chm)
Joni Blake (Sec)
Catherine Murray-Rust (Treas)
Danessa Itaya (Pres)

BIOPHARMA MANUFACTURING SOLUTIONS, INC.
1443 Merion Way, Seal Beach, CA 90740
Tel.: (562) 244-9785　　　DE
Year Founded: 2011
Sales Range: Less than $1 Million
Biopharmaceutical Mfr
N.A.I.C.S.: 325412
Gary Riccio (CEO)

BIOPLUS SPECIALTY PHARMACY SERVICES, LLC
376 Northlake Blvd, Altamonte Springs, FL 32701
Tel.: (407) 830-8820
Web Site: http://www.bioplusrx.com
Year Founded: 1989
Sales Range: $500-549.9 Million
Emp.: 150
Health Care Srvices
N.A.I.C.S.: 621498

BIOPSY SCIENCES, LLC
4900 Creekside Dr Ste C, Clearwater, FL 33760
Tel.: (727) 290-9825
Web Site: http://www.hydromark.com
Sales Range: $1-9.9 Million
Medical Device Mfr
N.A.I.C.S.: 339112
John Fisher (Co-Founder & CEO)
Fred Ahari (Co-Founder & CTO)
James C. Gibson (Co-Founder & Mgr-Legal, Acctg, Insurance & Tax)

BIOSAFE SYSTEMS, LLC
22 Meadow St, East Hartford, CT 06108
Tel.: (860) 290-8890　　　CT
Web Site:
　https://www.biosafesystems.com
Sales Range: $1-9.9 Million
Emp.: 30
Biodegradeable Disease-Control Products Mfr
N.A.I.C.S.: 325320

Tammy Raymond *(Dir-Mktg & PR)*
Robert Larose *(Pres & CEO)*
Donna Bishel *(Dir-Tech)*
Vijay Choppakatla *(Dir-Res)*
Frank Pennington *(Mgr-Crop Protection, Water Treatment & Post Harvest Market)*

BIOSECTOR 2
450 W 15th St 6th Fl, New York, NY 10011
Tel.: (212) 845-5600
Web Site: http://www.biosector2.com
Year Founded: 2002
Rev.: $2,000,000
Emp.: 20
Fiscal Year-end: 12/31/06
Brand Development & Integration, Collateral, Communications, Corporate Communications, Crisis Communications, Industrial, Media Relations
N.A.I.C.S.: 541810
Ellen Miller *(Principal)*
Lisa Stockman *(Mng Dir)*

BIOSPECTRA INC.
Rockdale Lane, Stroudsburg, PA 18360
Tel.: (570) 476-2710
Web Site: http://www.biospectra.us
Sales Range: $10-24.9 Million
Emp.: 100
Pharmaceutical Preparation Mfr
N.A.I.C.S.: 325412
Richard Mutchler *(Pres)*
Joseph Mastrobattista *(Officer-Corp & VP-Fin)*
Dora Meissner *(Officer-Corp & VP-Regulatory Affairs)*

Subsidiaries:

Polydex Pharmaceuticals Limited **(1)**
421 Comstock Road, Toronto, M1L 2H5, ON, Canada
Tel.: (416) 755-2231
Web Site: http://www.polydex.com
Rev.: $5,141,000
Assets: $7,184,000
Liabilities: $1,203,000
Net Worth: $5,981,000
Earnings: $250,000
Emp.: 23
Fiscal Year-end: 01/31/2020
Pharmaceuticals Product Mfr
N.A.I.C.S.: 325412

Subsidiary (Domestic):

Dextran Products Limited **(2)**
421 Comstock Road, Toronto, M1L 2H5, ON, Canada **(100%)**
Tel.: (416) 755-2231
Web Site: http://www.dextran.ca
Sales Range: $1-9.9 Million
Pharmaceuticals Mfr
N.A.I.C.S.: 325412
David P. M. Jamestee *(CFO)*

BIOSPLICE THERAPEUTICS, INC.
9360 Towne Ctr Dr, San Diego, CA 92121
Tel.: (858) 926-2900   DE
Web Site: https://biosplice.com
Year Founded: 2021
Biopharmaceutical Development Services
N.A.I.C.S.: 325412

BIOSTAR ANGEL STEM CELL CORPORATION
419 Hindry Ave Ste E, Inglewood, CA 90301
Tel.: (424) 227-9568   DE
Year Founded: 2017
Management Consulting Services
N.A.I.C.S.: 541611
Keewon Ra *(CEO, CFO & Sec)*

BIOSTAT INTERNATIONAL, INC.
14506A University Point Pl, Tampa, FL 33613
Tel.: (813) 979-1619
Web Site:
http://biostatinternational.com
Year Founded: 1994
Sales Range: $1-9.9 Million
Emp.: 15
Contract Research Focusing on Biostatistics, Data Management & Clinical Management Services
N.A.I.C.S.: 541714
Maureen R. Lyden *(Pres & CEO)*
Susanne C. Panzera *(Mgr-Clinical & Quality Affairs)*

BIOTECH INVESTMENT GROUP LLC
11011 Torreyana Rd, San Diego, CA 92121
Tel.: (858) 622-2900   DE
Web Site: http://www.bioinv.com
Year Founded: 2006
Healthcare Services Private Equity Firm
N.A.I.C.S.: 523999
Masood Tayebi *(Co-Founder & Chm)*
Massih Tayebi *(Co-Founder)*

BIOTHERA HOLDING CORP.
3388 Mike Collins Dr, Eagan, MN 55121
Tel.: (651) 675-0300   MN
Web Site: http://www.biothera.com
Year Founded: 2013
Holding Company; Immunotherapy Pharmaceutical & Biotechnology Research & Development
N.A.I.C.S.: 551112
Richard Mueller *(Chm & CEO)*
William Gacki *(CFO)*
Myra Patchen *(Chief Scientific Officer)*
James Horstmann *(Sr VP-Fin)*
Steven Karel *(Chief Admin Officer)*
Nancy Herbeck *(Dir-IR)*
David Walsh *(Sr VP-Mktg & Comm)*
Barry A. Labinger *(CEO-Biothera Pharmaceutical Inc.)*
Jose Iglesias *(CMO)*

Subsidiaries:

Biothera, Inc. **(1)**
3388 Mike Collins Dr A, Saint Paul, MN 55121
Tel.: (651) 675-0300
Web Site: http://www.biothera.com
Emp.: 63
Immunotherapy Biotechnology Research & Development
N.A.I.C.S.: 541714
Richard Mueller *(Pres & CEO)*
Steven Karel *(Chief Admin Officer)*
James Horstmann *(Sr VP-Fin)*

BIOTIX INC.
9880 Mesa Rim Rd, San Diego, CA 92121
Tel.: (858) 875-7696
Web Site: http://www.biotix.com
Sales Range: $25-49.9 Million
Emp.: 500
Life Science Research Services
N.A.I.C.S.: 541715
Paul Nowak *(CEO)*
Celia Reyes-Hoke *(VP-HR)*
Ron Perkins *(COO)*
Arta Motadel *(Founder & CTO)*

BIOURJA TRADING, LLC
1080 Eldridge Pkwy Ste 1175, Houston, TX 77077-2582
Tel.: (832) 775-9000
Web Site: https://www.biourja.com
Year Founded: 2006

Petroleum & Petroleum Products Merchant Whslr
N.A.I.C.S.: 424720
Lisa Bromiley *(CFO)*
Amit Bhandari *(Chm & CEO)*
Shek Jain *(COO & Gen Counsel)*
Arpita Bhandari *(VP-HR)*
Dushyant Kansara *(Chief Acctg Officer)*
Louis Stroms *(CTO)*
Jordan Fife *(Head-Ethanol Trading)*
Steve Lewis *(Head-Trading)*
Pritesh Pratangia *(Head-Asia & Offshore Svcs)*
Arun Eamani *(Head-Power Trading)*
Casey Carmodi *(Head-Comml Ops)*
Casey Carmody *(Gen Mgr)*
Darin Hanson *(Pres)*

BIOVENTUS LLC
4721 Emperor Blvd Ste 100, Durham, NC 27703
Tel.: (919) 474-9194
Web Site: https://www.bioventus.com
Year Founded: 2012
Emp.: 1,200
Healthcare Equipment Distr
N.A.I.C.S.: 423450
Anthony James *(Sr VP-Ops & Quality)*
David Varner *(VP-Mktg-Active Healing Therapies)*
Anthony Dadamio *(Gen Counsel & Sr VP)*
Katrina Church *(Chief Compliance Officer)*
Alessandra Pavesio *(Chief Science Officer & Sr VP)*
Andrew Hosmer *(VP-Sls-Bioventus Surgical & Gen Mgr-Surgical Solutions)*
Robert Claypoole *(CEO)*
Mark Singleton *(CFO & Sr VP)*
Helen Leupold *(Chief HR Officer & Sr VP)*
Kellie Stefaniak *(VP-Global Regulatory & Quality)*
Mike Growe *(Sr VP-Operations)*

BIOWORLD MERCHANDISING, INC.
2111 W Walnut Hill Ln, Irving, TX 75038
Tel.: (972) 488-0655
Web Site:
http://www.bioworldcorp.com
Fashion Designers
N.A.I.C.S.: 458110
David D. Reynolds *(CFO)*
Raj Malik *(Pres, CEO & Founder)*

Subsidiaries:

Nolan Originals, LLC **(1)**
22 W 38th St 6th Fl, New York, NY 10018 **(100%)**
Tel.: (212) 239-0426
Web Site: http://nolanglove.com
Other Apparel Accessories & Other Apparel Mfr
N.A.I.C.S.: 315990
Michael Nolan *(VP)*

Vandor, LLC **(1)**
165 S Main St Ste 400, Salt Lake City, UT 84111
Tel.: (801) 972-2888
Web Site: http://www.vandorproducts.com
Houseware Products & Gifts Mfr & Distr
N.A.I.C.S.: 459420
Sarah DeVoll *(CEO)*

BIOZYME INCORPORATED
6010 Stockyards Expy, Saint Joseph, MO 64504
Tel.: (816) 238-3326
Web Site:
https://www.biozymeinc.com

Year Founded: 1997
Rev.: $12,800,000
Emp.: 60
Livestock Feeds
N.A.I.C.S.: 311119
Bob Norton *(Pres)*
Kevin Glaubius *(Dir-Nutrition & Regulatory Support)*
Josh Brockman *(Coord-Show Products Mktg & Growth)*
Elishia Carrillo *(Dir-Intl Sls)*
Barry Christie *(Mgr-Dairy Bus)*
Casie Greenwood *(Coord-Dealer Assurance)*
Howard Jensen *(Mgr-Dairy Bus)*
Jamie Miller *(Coord-Online & Data Mgmt)*
John Sylvester *(Dir-R&D)*
Jeremy Roberts *(Mgr-Sls-Montana)*
Mike Wadle *(Dir-Sls-Natl)*

BIP OPPORTUNITIES FUND, LP
Piedmont Ctr 3575 Piedmont Rd Bldg 15 Ste 730, Atlanta, GA 30305
Tel.: (404) 495-5230
Web Site: http://www.bipfund.com
Emp.: 12
Investment Services
N.A.I.C.S.: 523999
Mark A. Buffington *(Partner)*
H. Scott Pressly *(Partner)*

Subsidiaries:

Tropical Smoothie Franchise Development Corp. **(1)**
12598 US Hwy 98 W Ste 200, Destin, FL 32550
Tel.: (850) 269-9850
Web Site: http://www.tropicalsmoothie.com
Sales Range: $10-24.9 Million
Emp.: 33
Restaurant Franchisor; Intangible Assets Lessor
N.A.I.C.S.: 722513
Mike Rotondo *(CEO)*
Rob Collins *(CMO)*
Pete Ward *(Gen Counsel)*
Paul Marsden *(CFO)*
Cheryl Fletcher *(VP-Franchise Dev)*
Kristi Kingery *(Sr VP-Supply Chain & Quality Assurance)*

BIP VENTURES EVERGREEN BDC
3575 Piedmont Rd NE Bldg 15 Ste 730, Atlanta, GA 30305
Tel.: (404) 410-6476   DE
Web Site:
https://www.bipevergreenfunds.com
Year Founded: 2022
Investment Management Service
N.A.I.C.S.: 523999

BIPARTISAN POLICY CENTER
1225 Eye St NW Ste 1000, Washington, DC 20005
Tel.: (202) 204-2400   DE
Web Site:
http://www.bipartisanpolicy.org
Year Founded: 2002
Sales Range: $10-24.9 Million
Emp.: 129
Public Policy Services
N.A.I.C.S.: 813410
Blaise Misztal *(Dir-Natl Security)*
Janet M. Marchibroda *(Dir-Health and Innovation)*
Lisel Loy *(VP-Programs)*
Robert Traynham *(VP-Comm)*
Julie Anderson *(Sr VP)*
Jason Grumet *(Co-Founder & Pres)*
William G. Hoagland *(Sr VP)*
Elena Muehlenbeck *(VP-Fin & Admin)*
Tom Daschle *(Co-Founder)*

BIR HOLDINGS, LLC

BIR Holdings, LLC—(Continued)

5523 Birchdale Rd, Brainerd, MN 56401
Tel.: (218) 824-7220
Holding Company
N.A.I.C.S.: 551112
Kristi Copham *(Owner)*
Jed Copham *(Owner)*

Subsidiaries:

Brainerd International Raceway (1)
5523 Birchdale Rd, Brainerd, MN 56401-6848
Tel.: (218) 824-7220
Web Site:
  http://www.brainerdracewayandresort.com
Sales Range: $10-24.9 Million
Emp.: 100
Operates a Motor Race Facility
N.A.I.C.S.: 711212
Kristi Copham *(Co-Owner)*
Jed Copham *(Co-Owner)*

BIRCH FAMILY SERVICES, INC.
104 West 29th St 3rd Fl, New York, NY 10001
Tel.: (212) 616-1800
Web Site:
  http://www.birchfamilyservices.org
Year Founded: 1975
Sales Range: $50-74.9 Million
Emp.: 1,169
Education, Habilitation & Residential Services
N.A.I.C.S.: 611710
Lisa Gilday *(COO)*
Matthew Sturiale *(Pres & CEO)*

BIRCH SWING CAPITAL LLC
1 Irving Pl, New York, NY 10003
Tel.: (646) 701-1019
Web Site:
  https://www.birchswing.com
Year Founded: 2016
Private Equity
N.A.I.C.S.: 523999
Ford Schumacher *(Co-Founder & Mng Dir)*

Subsidiaries:

Scrubs On Wheels (1)
1730 Gateway Ct, Elkhart, IN 46514
Tel.: (574) 970-0382
Web Site: http://www.scrubsonwheels.com
Other Clothing Stores
N.A.I.C.S.: 458110
Monica Palicki *(Coord-Social Media)*
Dennis Carrico *(Pres)*

BIRD CONSTRUCTION COMPANY, INC.
Urb Altamesa 1307 San Alfonso Ave, San Juan, PR 00921-3622
Tel.: (787) 721-6630
Web Site:
  http://www.birdconstruction.com
Year Founded: 1964
Sales Range: $50-74.9 Million
Emp.: 200
Nonresidential Construction
N.A.I.C.S.: 236220
Francisco Guevara *(Treas & Comptroller)*
Manuel Deliz *(VP)*
Miguel Sabater Jr. *(Pres)*

BIRD ROCK SYSTEMS, INC.
9605 Scranton Rd Ste 160, San Diego, CA 92121
Tel.: (858) 777-1617
Web Site:
  https://www.birdrockusa.com
Year Founded: 2004
Sales Range: $1-9.9 Million
Emp.: 14

Security, IP Communications, Network Infrastructure, Installation, Storage & Network Management Services
N.A.I.C.S.: 541618
James Matteo *(CEO & Gen Mgr)*
David Vorce *(Reg Mgr-Sls)*

BIRD TECHNOLOGIES GROUP INC.
30303 Aurora Rd, Solon, OH 44139-2743
Tel.: (440) 248-1200
Web Site: http://www.birdrf.com
Year Founded: 1942
Rev.: $44,175,000
Emp.: 6
Radio Frequency Equipment Mfr
N.A.I.C.S.: 334515
Mark Lacy *(Mgr-Product)*
Ed Sliwinski *(Mgr-Matls)*

BIRDBRAIN, INC.
52 E Cross St, Ypsilanti, MI 48198
Tel.: (734) 483-4536
Web Site: http://www.birdbrain.com
Sales Range: $10-24.9 Million
Emp.: 27
Other Animal Food Mfr
N.A.I.C.S.: 311119
Christine King *(CEO)*

BIRDDOG SOFTWARE CORPORATION
8277 S Walker Ave, Oklahoma City, OK 73139
Tel.: (405) 794-5950
Web Site: https://www.birddogsw.com
Year Founded: 2001
Sales Range: $1-9.9 Million
Emp.: 15
Computer Software
N.A.I.C.S.: 513210
Robin Zwirtz *(Pres)*

BIRDDOG SOLUTIONS, INC.
10 New England Business Center Dr Ste 202, Andover, MA 01810
Tel.: (978) 688-8400
Web Site: http://www.birddog.com
Year Founded: 1997
Sales Range: $10-24.9 Million
Emp.: 135
Transportation Logistics
N.A.I.C.S.: 541614
Joel L. Sitak *(Pres & CEO)*

BIRDEYE, INC.
3101 Park Blvd, Palo Alto, CA 94306
Web Site: http://www.birdeye.com
Year Founded: 2012
Sales Range: $1-9.9 Million
Software Development Services
N.A.I.C.S.: 541511
Naveen Gupta *(Co-Founder & CEO)*
Neeraj Gupta *(Co-Founder & Chief Customer Officer)*
David Lehman *(Pres & COO)*
Yang Chao *(CFO)*
Sunil Madan *(CIO)*
Sarah Bennett *(Sr VP-Sls)*

BIRDS BARBERSHOP
1107 E 6th St, Austin, TX 78702
Tel.: (512) 457-0400
Web Site:
  https://www.birdsbarbershop.com
Year Founded: 2006
Sales Range: $1-9.9 Million
Emp.: 130
Barbershops with Arcades, Art & Music
N.A.I.C.S.: 812111
Michael Portman *(Co-Founder)*
Beth Schindler *(Gen Mgr)*

Jayson Rapaport *(Co-Founder & Co-Owner)*
Jeremy Nguyen *(Mgr-Mktg)*

BIRDSALL INTERACTIVE, INC.
111 Myrtle St 3rd Fl, Lafayette, CA 94607-2525
Tel.: (925) 284-5900
Web Site:
  http://www.birdsallinteractive.com
Year Founded: 1991
Sales Range: $10-24.9 Million
Emp.: 15
Web Development, E-Mail Marketing & Flash Demonstrations
N.A.I.C.S.: 541810
David Ford *(Project Mgr)*

BIRDSONG CORPORATION
612 Madison Ave, Suffolk, VA 23434-4028
Tel.: (757) 539-3456
Year Founded: 1911
Sales Range: $450-499.9 Million
Emp.: 570
Nuts & Nut By-Products
N.A.I.C.S.: 424590
George Y. Birdsong *(CEO)*

BIRDSONG GREGORY INC.
715 N Church St Ste 101, Charlotte, NC 28202
Tel.: (704) 332-2299
Web Site:
  https://www.birdsonggregory.com
Year Founded: 2001
Sales Range: $1-9.9 Million
Emp.: 10
Shopper Marketing & Advertising Agency Services
N.A.I.C.S.: 541810
Leslie Kraemer *(Principal)*

BIRK MANUFACTURING, INC.
14 Capitol Dr, East Lyme, CT 06333
Tel.: (860) 739-4170
Web Site: http://www.birkmfg.com
Year Founded: 1989
Sales Range: $10-24.9 Million
Emp.: 140
Machine Tool, Metal Forming Types, Mfr
N.A.I.C.S.: 333517
Norman Birk *(Founder)*
Mike Mattox *(Pres)*
Stacey Stevens *(Mgr-Customer Svc)*

BIRKENSTOCK USA, LP
8171 Redwood Blvd, Novato, CA 94945-1403
Tel.: (415) 884-3315
Web Site:
  http://www.birkenstock.com
Year Founded: 1966
Comfort Footwear Distr
N.A.I.C.S.: 424340
Scott Radcliffe *(VP-Marketing-Americas)*

BIRKEY'S FARM STORE INC.
1120 Veterans Pkwy, Rantoul, IL 61866
Tel.: (217) 892-8255
Web Site: http://www.birkeys.com
Year Founded: 1954
Rev.: $60,149,478
Emp.: 360
Suppliers of Farm & Garden Machinery
N.A.I.C.S.: 423820
Michael Hedge *(Pres & CEO)*
Mike Carley *(Reg Mgr & VP)*
Jeff Hedge *(Reg Mgr & VP)*
Steve Waibel *(CFO)*

BIRKITT ENVIRONMENTAL

SERVICES, INC.
110 S Edison Ave, Tampa, FL 33606
Tel.: (813) 259-1085
Web Site: http://www.birkitt.com
Year Founded: 1996
Sales Range: $1-9.9 Million
Emp.: 8
Environmental Consulting Services
N.A.I.C.S.: 541620
Beverly F. Birkitt *(Pres)*
Abbey Naylor *(VP)*

BIRMINGHAM BARONS, LLC
1401 1st Ave S, Birmingham, AL 35233
Tel.: (205) 988-3200
Web Site: http://www.barons.com
Sales Range: $50-74.9 Million
Emp.: 15
Minor-League Baseball Franchise
N.A.I.C.S.: 711211
Jonathan Nelson *(Gen Mgr)*

BIRMINGHAM FASTENER & SUPPLY INC.
931 Ave W, Birmingham, AL 35214-6255
Tel.: (205) 595-3511
Web Site: https://www.bhamfast.com
Year Founded: 1980
Sales Range: $10-24.9 Million
Emp.: 118
Mfr & Distributor of Fasteners
N.A.I.C.S.: 423840
Howard P. Tinney *(Pres & CFO)*

Subsidiaries:

Birmingham Fastener & Supply Inc. -
B-Fast Bolt & Supply Division (1)
1910 Ave C, Mobile, AL 36615
Tel.: (251) 438-7833
Web Site: http://www.bhamfast.com
Emp.: 8
Bolt Mfr
N.A.I.C.S.: 332722
Frank Haas *(Gen Mgr)*

Dallas Fastener, Inc. (1)
1825 Westpark Dr Ste 200, Grand Prairie, TX 75050
Tel.: (972) 623-0011
Web Site: http://www.bmfast.com
Emp.: 25
Fastener Whslr
N.A.I.C.S.: 423710
Steve Burley *(Gen Mgr)*

Huntsville Fastener & Supply Inc. (1)
100 Skylab Dr, Huntsville, AL 35806
Tel.: (256) 859-6707
Web Site: http://www.huntfast.com
Sales Range: $10-24.9 Million
Emp.: 35
Resale of screw & bolt washer Whslr
N.A.I.C.S.: 423710

Omaha Fastener, Inc. (1)
8840 S 137th Cir, Omaha, NE 68138
Tel.: (402) 861-8463
Fastener Whslr
N.A.I.C.S.: 423710

Prosouth Fastener (1)
1116 N Edgewood Ave, Jacksonville, FL 32254
Tel.: (904) 378-3107
Emp.: 10
Fastener Whslr
N.A.I.C.S.: 423710
Mike Bethel *(Gen Mgr)*

BIRMINGHAM HIDE & TALLOW COMPANY INC.
2700 1st Ave N, Birmingham, AL 35203-3901
Tel.: (205) 252-1197
Web Site: http://www.bhtonline.com
Year Founded: 1904
Sales Range: $10-24.9 Million
Emp.: 126
Provide Fat & Oil Renderering Distr

N.A.I.C.S.: 424590
T. Owen Vickers *(Pres & CEO)*
Michael S. Glenn *(CFO & VP)*
Micah Salsman *(Gen Counsel)*

Subsidiaries:

Birmingham Hide & Tallow Company
Inc. - Aberdeen Division **(1)**
Prairie Industrial Park, Aberdeen, MS 39730
Tel.: (662) 369-4413
Web Site: http://www.bhtonline.com
Animal Feed Mfr
N.A.I.C.S.: 311119

Birmingham Hide & Tallow Company
Inc. - Arley Division **(1)**
350 Oak Ln, Arley, AL 35541
Tel.: (205) 387-2529
Animal Feed Mfr
N.A.I.C.S.: 311119

Birmingham Hide & Tallow Company
Inc. - Bessemer Division **(1)**
5430 Johns Rd, Bessemer, AL 35023
Tel.: (205) 425-1711
Animal Feed Mfr
N.A.I.C.S.: 311119

Birmingham Hide & Tallow Company
Inc. - Huntsville Division **(1)**
192 Saint Clair Ln, Huntsville, AL 35811
Tel.: (256) 852-6511
Animal Feed Mfr
N.A.I.C.S.: 311119

Birmingham Hide & Tallow Company
Inc. - Loxley Division **(1)**
28360 County Rd 66 N, Loxley, AL 36551
Tel.: (334) 964-5069
Animal Feed Mfr
N.A.I.C.S.: 311119

Birmingham Hide & Tallow Company
Inc. - Montgomery Division **(1)**
3353 Birmingham Hwy, Montgomery, AL 36108
Tel.: (334) 263-4309
Emp.: 10
Animal Feed Mfr
N.A.I.C.S.: 311119
Robert Owens *(Gen Mgr)*

Birmingham Hide & Tallow Company
Inc. - Panama City Division **(1)**
PO Box 1245, Panama City, FL 32466-1245
Tel.: (850) 913-0089
Animal Feed Mfr
N.A.I.C.S.: 311119

Birmingham Hide & Tallow Company
Inc. - Ringgold Division **(1)**
1212 Yates Spring Rd, Ringgold, GA 30736
Tel.: (706) 965-4945
Web Site: http://www.bhtonline.com
Animal Feed Mfr
N.A.I.C.S.: 311119

BIRMINGHAM JEFFERSON CONVENTION COMPLEX
2100 Richard Arrington Jr Blvd, Birmingham, AL 35203
Tel.: (205) 458-8400
Web Site: https://www.bjcc.org
Year Founded: 1965
Sales Range: $50-74.9 Million
Emp.: 130
Convention Center
N.A.I.C.S.: 721110
Tad Snider *(Office Mgr)*

BIRMINGHAM RAIL LOCOMOTIVE CO.
5205 5th Ave N, Bessemer, AL 35020
Tel.: (205) 424-7245
Web Site: http://www.bhamrail.com
Sales Range: $10-24.9 Million
Emp.: 85
Railroad Equipment & Supplies
N.A.I.C.S.: 332618
Monroe Jones *(Pres)*
Barry Hillgartner *(Dir-Spike Ops)*
Jo Ann Cary *(Gen Mgr)*
Carlisle Jones Sr. *(Chm)*

BIRMINGHAM VENDING COMPANY
540 2nd Ave N, Birmingham, AL 35204
Tel.: (205) 324-7526
Web Site: https://www.bhmvending.com
Year Founded: 1931
Sales Range: $10-24.9 Million
Emp.: 20
Coin-Operated Vending Machines
N.A.I.C.S.: 423440
Jerry Spiegel *(VP)*

BIRNBACH COMMUNICATIONS, INC.
20 Devereux St Ste 3A, Marblehead, MA 01945-3051
Tel.: (781) 639-6701
Web Site: https://www.birnbachcom.com
Year Founded: 2001
Sales Range: Less than $1 Million
Emp.: 10
Public Relations Agency
N.A.I.C.S.: 541820
Norman Birnbach *(Founder)*

BIRNS TELECOMMUNICATIONS INC.
233 W 17th St, New York, NY 10011
Tel.: (212) 807-6000
Web Site: http://www.birns.net
Rev.: $10,000,000
Emp.: 37
Telephone Equipment & Systems
N.A.I.C.S.: 449210
Sol Birnbaum *(Pres)*
Moshe Kravips *(Controller)*
Donovan LeBoeuf *(Supvr-Dynalink Customer Svc Tech)*

BIS DIGITAL, INC.
1350 NE 56 St Ste 300, Fort Lauderdale, FL 33334
Tel.: (800) 834-7674
Web Site: http://www.bisdigital.com
Digital Recording & Integrated Audio Visual Technology Solutions Services
N.A.I.C.S.: 334610
Steve Coldren *(Founder & Pres)*

Subsidiaries:

Office Business Systems, Inc. **(1)**
1 Chapin Rd, Pine Brook, NJ 07058
Tel.: (973) 575-6550
Web Site: http://www.obsinc.com
Rev.: $9,200,000
Emp.: 60
Fiscal Year-end: 12/31/2006
Digital Recording & Integrated Audio Visual Technology Solutions Services
N.A.I.C.S.: 334610
Douglas Smith *(Pres)*

BISCAYNE CONTRACTORS INCORPORATED
5845 Richmond Hwy Ste 500, Alexandria, VA 22303-1872
Tel.: (703) 562-5660
Web Site: http://www.biscayne-contractors.com
Rev.: $13,000,000
Emp.: 26
Commercial & Office Building, New Construction
N.A.I.C.S.: 236220
Gerardo Omeechevarria *(CEO)*
Alberto C. Omeechevarria *(Pres)*
Frank Zawitoski *(VP & Mgr)*

BISCOMERICA CORP.
565 W Slover Ave, Rialto, CA 92377
Tel.: (909) 877-5997
Web Site: https://www.biscomericacorp.com
Year Founded: 1980

Sales Range: $50-74.9 Million
Emp.: 250
Cookie & Cracker Mfr
N.A.I.C.S.: 311821
Nadi Soltan *(CEO)*
Stacy Augustine *(Plant Mgr)*
Rosalind McAdoo *(Mgr-Quality Control)*
Ayad Adeeb Fargo *(Pres)*

BISCUITVILLE, INC.
1414 Yanceyville St Ste 300, Greensboro, NC 27405-1753
Tel.: (336) 229-6671
Web Site: http://www.biscuitville.com
Year Founded: 1966
Sales Range: $125-149.9 Million
Emp.: 750
Food Service Chain
N.A.I.C.S.: 722513
Maurice Jennings *(Founder)*
Burney Jennings *(CEO)*
Kellie Hicks *(Dir-Brand Dev & Mktg)*
Connie Bennett *(COO)*
Kevin Bennett *(CFO)*
Kathie S. Niven *(Pres)*
Kristie Mitchell *(VP-Brand & Mktg)*
Lisa Weaver *(Dir-Mktg Svcs)*
Blake Jennings *(Dir-Dev)*
John Young *(VP-Tech & Transformation)*
Jeff Linville *(VP-Ops)*

BISH'S RV, INC.
3911 N 5th E, Idaho Falls, ID 83401
Tel.: (208) 529-4386
Web Site: http://www.bishs.com
Year Founded: 1959
Sales Range: $10-24.9 Million
Emp.: 70
Recreational Vehicle Whslr
N.A.I.C.S.: 441210
Troy Jenkins *(Owner & Mgr)*

Subsidiaries:

Haylett Auto Company, Inc. **(1)**
891 E Chicago St, Coldwater, MI 49036
Tel.: (517) 278-5196
Web Site: http://www.haylettnorthcountry.com
Sales Range: $10-24.9 Million
Emp.: 30
New & Used Car & RV Dealer & Service & Parts
N.A.I.C.S.: 441120
David Haylett *(Owner & Pres)*
Ron Van Kersen *(Controller)*
Jeff Knapp *(Mgr-Sls & Fin)*

BISHOP & ASSOCIATES, INC.
1111 W Cass St, Tampa, FL 33606
Tel.: (813) 250-1820
Web Site: http://www.bishopassoc.com
Year Founded: 2000
Sales Range: $1-9.9 Million
Commercial Real Estate Acquisition, Disposition & Sales
N.A.I.C.S.: 531390
Robin Bishop *(Owner)*

BISHOP & BROGDON, INC.
790 B Great SW Pkwy, Atlanta, GA 30336
Tel.: (404) 494-4333
Sales Range: $10-24.9 Million
Emp.: 20
Eletric Power Generation Services
N.A.I.C.S.: 221118
Richard N. Lathem *(CFO & Sec)*

BISHOP BUSINESS EQUIPMENT CO.
4125 S 94th St, Omaha, NE 68127
Tel.: (402) 537-8000
Web Site: https://www.bbec.com
Rev.: $11,014,981

Emp.: 45
Photocopy Machines
N.A.I.C.S.: 423420
David Bishop *(Pres)*
Jodi Hauptman-Drannen *(Exec VP)*

BISHOP DISTRIBUTING CO.
5200 36th St SE, Grand Rapids, MI 49512
Tel.: (616) 942-9734
Web Site: http://www.bishopdistributing.com
Year Founded: 1959
Sales Range: $10-24.9 Million
Emp.: 35
Distr of Carpets & Floor Coverings
N.A.I.C.S.: 423220
Bill Morrison *(Pres)*
Jane Bosch *(Mgr-Credit & Collection)*
Cynthia Marshall *(CFO & VP-Ops)*

BISHOP ENERGY SERVICES, L.L.C.
1152 James Savage Rd, Midland, MI 48640
Tel.: (989) 631-1536
Web Site: https://www.bishopenergy.com
Year Founded: 1999
Sales Range: $10-24.9 Million
Emp.: 4
Natural Gas Distr
N.A.I.C.S.: 221210
Jacob Bishop *(Mgr-Bus Dev)*

BISHOP FIXTURE AND MILLWORK
101 Eagle Dr, Balsam Lake, WI 54810
Tel.: (715) 485-9312
Web Site: https://www.bishopfixtures.com
Sales Range: $10-24.9 Million
Emp.: 200
Store Fixtures, Wood
N.A.I.C.S.: 337212
Morgan Nelson *(Gen Mgr)*
Mark Call *(Gen Mgr)*

BISHOP INTERNATIONAL, INC.
224 N Corinth St, Dallas, TX 75203
Tel.: (214) 426-6449
Web Site: https://www.bishopengine.com
Sales Range: $10-24.9 Million
Emp.: 109
Motor Vehicle Supply & New Part Whslr
N.A.I.C.S.: 423120
Jeff Bishop *(Owner & Principal)*
Mark Flannery *(VP)*

BISHOP MUSEUM
1525 Bernice St, Honolulu, HI 96817
Tel.: (808) 847-3511
Web Site: https://www.bishopmuseum.org
Year Founded: 1889
Sales Range: $10-24.9 Million
Emp.: 200
Museums
N.A.I.C.S.: 712110
Allison Holt Gendreau *(Chm)*

BISHOP ROSEN & CO. INC.
100 Broadway Fl 16, New York, NY 10005
Tel.: (212) 285-5500
Web Site: http://www.bishoprosen.com
Year Founded: 1964
Sales Range: $10-24.9 Million
Emp.: 67
Security Brokers
N.A.I.C.S.: 523150

Bishop Rosen & Co. Inc.—(Continued)

Robert Rosen (Pres & CEO)
Isaac Schlesinger (COO & VP)
Thomas Murphy (VP)

BISK EDUCATION, INC.
9417 Princess Palm Ave, Tampa, FL
33619-8348
Tel.: (813) 621-6200
Web Site: http://www.bisk.com
Year Founded: 1971
Sales Range: $75-99.9 Million
Emp.: 750
Online Education Services
N.A.I.C.S.: 611710
Nathan M. Bisk (Founder)
Michael D. Bisk (CEO)
Alison L. Bisk (VP)
Ravi Seepersad (Chief Strategy Officer)
Chad Bandy (VP-Client Engagement)
Carl Hixson (GTO)
Ted Kulawiak (VP-Enrollment Svcs)
Misty Brown (Chief People Officer)
Srini Medi (Chief Legal Officer)
Rustam Irani (Sr VP-Mktg)
William Geary III (CFO)

BISMARCK HONDA NISSAN HYUNDAI
1025 E Bismarck Expy, Bismarck, ND
58504-6616
Tel.: (701) 258-1944
Web Site:
　http://www.bismarckmotorco.com
Year Founded: 2001
Sales Range: $10-24.9 Million
Emp.: 38
Car Whslr
N.A.I.C.S.: 441110
Janell Johnson (Office Mgr)

BISON CAPITAL ASSET MANAGEMENT, LLC
780 3rd Ave 30th Fl, New York, NY
10017
Tel.: (704) 433-4898　　　　DE
Web Site:
　http://www.bisoncapital.com
Year Founded: 2003
Investment Advice
N.A.I.C.S.: 523940
Jason Strife (Owner)

Subsidiaries:

Lapmaster Group Holdings LLC　(1)
501 W Algonquin Rd, Mount Prospect, IL
60056-5705
Tel.: (224) 659-7101
Web Site: http://www.lapmaster.com
Emp.: 600
Industrial Machinery Mfr
N.A.I.C.S.: 333248
Chelsea A. Grayson (Chm)

Subsidiary (Non-US):

Lapmaster Wolters GmbH　(2)
Buesumer Strasse 96, 24768, Rendsburg,
Germany
Tel.: (49) 43314580
Web Site: http://www.lapmaster-wolters.de
Precision Machine Tools & Systems Mfr
N.A.I.C.S.: 333248
Sebastian Jessen (Dir-Sls Admin)

Subsidiary (Non-US):

Lapmaster India Private Limited　(3)
Plot 55 1st Floor 2nd Street Samayapuram
Main Road, Karambakkam Porur, Chennai,
600 116, Tamil Nadu, India
Tel.: (91) 4465356555
Web Site: http://www.lapmasterindia.com
Precision Machine Tool & System Mfr
N.A.I.C.S.: 333515

Subsidiary (US):

Lapmaster Wolters LLC　　　(3)

14 High St, Plainville, MA 02762
Tel.: (508) 695-7151
Web Site: http://www.lapmaster-wolters.de
Emp.: 15
Precision Machine Tool & System Mfr
N.A.I.C.S.: 333248
Scott Schuster (Product Mgr-Fine Grinding Products)

Subsidiary (Non-US):

Lapmaster Wolters Limited　(3)
Lee Mill Industrial Estate Unit 1 North Road,
Ivybridge, Devon, PL21 9EN, United King-
dom
Tel.: (44) 1752893191
Web Site: http://www.lapmaster.co.uk
Precision Machine Tools & Systems Mfr &
Distr
N.A.I.C.S.: 333248
Kevin M. Hook (Mgr-Quality)
Martin Nicholas (Mgr-Technical)

Peter Wolters Japan Co., Ltd.　(3)
Daisho Bldg 6th Floor Room 601 12-28
Esaka-cho 1-chome, Suita, 564-0063,
Osaka, Japan
Tel.: (81) 668217024
Web Site: http://www.peter-wolters.com
High Precision Machine Tools & Systems
Mfr
N.A.I.C.S.: 333515
Keiko Hoshikawa (Mgr-Acctg)
Kosaku Matsuno (Sr Mgr-Bus Dev)

BISON INVESTMENTS INC.
3225 S MacDill Ave Ste 129 #236,
Tampa, FL 33629
Tel.: (813) 832-6359
Web Site:
　http://www.bisoninvestments.com
Rev.: $25,000,000
Private Equity
N.A.I.C.S.: 523999
C. Birge Sigety (CEO)

BISON OPTICAL DISC INC.
803 S Orlando Ave Ste J, Winter
Park, FL 32789
Tel.: (407) 770-6900
Web Site: https://www.bisondisc.com
Sales Range: $10-24.9 Million
Emp.: 10
DVD & CD Duplication & Custom
Packaging Services
N.A.I.C.S.: 334610
John Cleeveley (Mgr-Product Acct)

BISSELL HOMECARE, INC.
2345 Walker Ave NW, Grand Rapids,
MI 49544-2516
Tel.: (833) 470-1876　　　　MI
Web Site: http://www.bissell.com
Year Founded: 1955
Emp.: 100
Carpet Sweepers, Vacuum Cleaners,
Home Care Devices, Chemical Floor
Scrubbers, Rug Shampooers & Home
Cleaning Chemical Specialties Mfr
N.A.I.C.S.: 335210
Mark J. Bissell (CEO)

Subsidiaries:

Bissell Australia Pty Ltd　　(1)
42 Rocco Drive, Scoresby, 3179, VIC, Aus-
tralia
Tel.: (61) 392372500
Web Site: http://www.bissell.com.au
Home Appliance Mfr
N.A.I.C.S.: 335210
Chris Egan (CEO)

Bissell Canada Corp.　　　(1)
6934 Kinsmen Ct, PO Box 1003, Niagara
Falls, L2E 6S5, ON, Canada　(100%)
Tel.: (905) 356-1531
Web Site: http://www.bissell.ca
Sales Range: $10-24.9 Million
Emp.: 20
Distr & Marketer of Carpet Sweepers, Rug
& Upholstery Shampoo & Vacuum Cleaners
N.A.I.C.S.: 449210

Bissell Homecare (Overseas)
Inc.　　　　　　　　　　　　(1)
Ground Floor 226 Berwick Avenue, Slough,
SL1 4QT, Berkshire, United Kingdom
Tel.: (44) 844 888 6644
Web Site: http://www.bisselldirect.co.uk
Home Appliance Mfr
N.A.I.C.S.: 335210

Electrolux Canada Corp.　　(1)
5855 Terry Fox Way, Mississauga, L5V
3E4, ON, Canada
Tel.: (800) 265-8352
Web Site: http://www.electrolux.ca
Home Appliance Distr
N.A.I.C.S.: 423620

Electrolux Home Care Products,
Inc.　　　　　　　　　　　　(1)
10200 David Taylor Dr, Charlotte, NC
28262-8060　　　　　　　　(100%)
Tel.: (980) 236-2000
Web Site: http://www.eureka.com
Sales Range: $50-74.9 Million
Emp.: 200
Floor Care Products, Upright & Canister
Vacuum Cleaners & Lightweight Cleaners
Mfr
N.A.I.C.S.: 325612

Unit (Domestic):

Electrolux Central Vacuum
Systems　　　　　　　　　(2)
1700 W 2nd St, Webster City, IA 50595-
0788
Tel.: (515) 832-4620
Web Site: http://www.beamvac.com
Sales Range: $50-74.9 Million
Emp.: 170
Control Vacuum Systems Mfr
N.A.I.C.S.: 335210

Subsidiary (Non-US):

Electrolux Home Care Products
Canada　　　　　　　　　(2)
5855 Terry Fox Way, Mississauga, L5V
3E4, ON, Canada　　　　　(100%)
Tel.: (905) 813-7700
Web Site: http://www.electroluxca.com
Sales Range: $50-74.9 Million
Emp.: 120
Household & Commercial Appliances, Out-
door Products & Industrial Products Mfr
N.A.I.C.S.: 335220

Electrolux Home Products, Inc.　(1)
2715 Washington Rd, Augusta, GA
30909　　　　　　　　　　(100%)
Tel.: (706) 651-1751
Web Site:
　http://www.electroluxappliances.com
Sales Range: $100-124.9 Million
Emp.: 400
Indoor Home Appliances Mfr & Distr
N.A.I.C.S.: 335220

Plant (Domestic):

Electrolux Home Products, Inc. -
Anderson　　　　　　　　(2)
101 Masters Blvd, Anderson, SC 29626
Tel.: (864) 224-5264
Web Site:
　http://www.electroluxappliances.com
Refrigerator Mfr
N.A.I.C.S.: 335220.

Electrolux Home Products, Inc. -
Saint Cloud　　　　　　　(2)
701 33rd Ave N, Saint Cloud, MN 56303
Tel.: (320) 253-1212
Web Site: http://www.electroluxusa.com
Household Freezers Mfr
N.A.I.C.S.: 335220
Terry Anthony (Mgr)

Branch (Domestic):

Electrolux Home Products, Inc. -
Webster City　　　　　　(2)
400 Des Moines St, Webster City, IA 50595
Tel.: (515) 832-5334
Web Site:
　http://www.electroluxappliances.com
Home Laundry Appliances Mfr
N.A.I.C.S.: 335220

BISTRO MANAGEMENT
5803 Mariemont Ave, Cincinnati, OH
45227-4217
Tel.: (513) 271-2349　　　　OH
Web Site:
　http://www.cunamutual.com
Year Founded: 1989
Sales Range: $50-74.9 Million
Emp.: 2,200
Management of Restaurants
N.A.I.C.S.: 722511
Robert Conway (Chm)
Tom Clark (Treas)

BIT BROKERS INTERNATIONAL, LTD.
5568 Logan Rd, West Frankfort, IL
62896
Tel.: (618) 435-5811
Web Site: https://www.bitbrokers.com
Year Founded: 1988
Sales Range: $1-9.9 Million
Emp.: 15
Rock Drill Bit Supplier
N.A.I.C.S.: 423830
Tim Thomas (Pres)

BIT-WIZARDS INFORMATION TECHNOLOGY SOLUTIONS, INC.
13 Memorial Pkwy SW, Fort Walton
Beach, FL 32548
Tel.: (850) 226-4200
Web Site: http://www.bitwizards.com
Year Founded: 2000
Computer System Design Services
N.A.I.C.S.: 541512
Vincent W. Mayfield (Co-Founder & CEO)
Ryder W. Diviney (Lead Engr-Software)
John M. Jackson (Dir-Tech)
Matthew J. Parry-Hill (Sr Engr-Software)
Samuel O. Blowes (Dir-IT)
Tabitha R. Erickson (Dir-Fin)
Candace R. Mitchell (Dir-Mktg)
Michael N. Morris (Dir-Client Svcs)
Alexandra Morrow (Dir-Solution Consulting)
Dave J. Perkins (Chief Architect-Enterprise)
Mallory Whalen (Dir-HR)
Michael T. Whalen (Dir-Digital Strategy)
Keith C. Telle (Sr Engr-Software)
Scott M. Baldric (Engr-Software)
Russell E. Davis (Engr-Software)
Anthony M. Fuller (Engr-Software)
Randy S. Schumann (Architect-Cloud)
Louis J. Erickson Jr. (Co-Founder & COO)

BIT9, INC.
266 Second Ave, Waltham, MA
02451
Tel.: (617) 393-7400
Web Site: http://www.bit9.com
Sales Range: $10-24.9 Million
Emp.: 120
Security Software Developer
N.A.I.C.S.: 513210
Patrick M. Morley (Pres & CEO)
Di Hall (VP-Svcs)
Eric Schurr (CMO)
Harry Sverdlove (CTO)
Eric Pyenson (Gen' Counsel & VP)
Roman Brozyna (Chief Info Security Officer)
Mark Sullivan (CFO)

BITCENTRAL INC.
4340 VonKarman Ste 410, Newport
Beach, CA 92660

Tel.: (949) 474-1900
Web Site: http://www.bitcentral.com
Year Founded: 1981
Sales Range: $10-24.9 Million
Emp.: 70
Communication Equipment Mfr &
Distr
N.A.I.C.S.: 423690
John King (VP-Engrg)
Michael Petersen (VP-Product Mgmt)
Ron Rosentha (VP-Global Sls &
Mktg)
Mike Healey (Controller)
David Hemingway (Sr Product Mgr-
New Ventures)
Camille Jayne (Pres)

Subsidiaries:

Bitcentralcom Inc. (1)
4340 Von Karman Ave Ste 400, Newport
Beach, CA 92660-2085
Tel.: (949) 253-9000
Web Site: http://www.bitcentral.com
Rev.: $18,000,000
Emp.: 57
Communications Equipment
N.A.I.C.S.: 423690
Frederic Fourcher (CEO)

BITCOIN BRANDS INC.
215 Dino Dr, Ann Arbor, MI 48103
Tel.: (623) 738-5792   DE
Year Founded: 1997
Sales Range: Less than $1 Million
Emp.: 1
Investment Services
N.A.I.C.S.: 523999
Peter Klamka (Chm, Pres, CEO,
Treas & Sec)

Subsidiaries:

Legend Credit, Inc. (1)
100 Chacey Ln, Columbus, OH 43085
Tel.: (614) 846-4212
Sales Range: $125-149.9 Million
Credit Issuing Services
N.A.I.C.S.: 522210

Legend Studios, Inc. (1)
5530 S Valley View Blvd, Las Vegas, NV
89118
Tel.: (702) 795-2012
Sales Range: $200-249.9 Million
Radio Station Owner & Operator
N.A.I.C.S.: 516110

BITEC INC.
2 Industrial Park Dr, Morrilton, AR
72110
Tel.: (501) 354-8585
Web Site: https://www.bi-tec.com
Sales Range: $25-49.9 Million
Emp.: 40
Sales of Roofing Felts & Cements
N.A.I.C.S.: 324122
Larry Easterling (Mgr-South Central
Reg)
David G. Allen (VP-Ops)
Jeff Hough (VP-Fin)

BITNER GOODMAN
2101 NE 26th St, Fort Lauderdale, FL
33305
Tel.: (954) 730-7730   FL
Web Site:
     http://www.bitnergoodman.com
Year Founded: 1980
Sales Range: $10-24.9 Million
Emp.: 17
Public Relations & Advertising Agen-
cies
N.A.I.C.S.: 541820
Gary E. Bitner (Founder)
Beth Zuckerkorn (Sr VP-Graphic
Comm)
Mayra Hernandez (VP-Multicultural
Mktg)

Scott Dobroski (Acct Supvr)
Elizabeth Senk-Moss (Acct Supvr)
Nichole Teixeira (Acct Exec)

Subsidiaries:

Bitner Hennessy (1)
3707 Edgewater Dr, Orlando, FL 32804
Tel.: (407) 290-1060
Web Site: http://www.bitner.com
Sales Range: Less than $1 Million
Emp.: 7
Public Relations Agency
N.A.I.C.S.: 541820
Kimbra Hennessy (Partner)
Minnie Escudero Morris (Acct Supvr &
Coord-Hispanic Mktg)
Nancy Glasgow (VP & Acct Supvr)

BITTERROOT INTERNA-
TIONAL SYSTEMS, LTD.
500 Taylor, Missoula, MT 59808-9056
Tel.: (406) 541-7320   MT
Year Founded: 1982
Sales Range: $10-24.9 Million
Emp.: 220
Trucking
N.A.I.C.S.: 484121

BITTNER VENDING, INC.
1120 Miller Picking Rd, Davidsville,
PA 15928
Tel.: (814) 479-3100
Web Site:
     http://www.bittnervending.com
Year Founded: 1979
Sales Range: $25-49.9 Million
Emp.: 75
Vending Machine Rental & Leasing
Services
N.A.I.C.S.: 445132
John Jones (Dir-Ops & Sls)
Tom Hayduk (Dir-Ops & Logistics)
Gary Monnich (Gen Mgr)
Charles Barron (VP)
Kim Bittner (Pres)
Tim Allison (Mgr-Shop)
Denise Carey (Mgr-Water)
Pam Brydon (Office Mgr)

BITUMINOUS ROADWAYS,
INC.
1520 Commerce Dr, Mendota
Heights, MN 55120
Tel.: (651) 686-7001   MN
Web Site: https://www.bitroads.com
Year Founded: 1946
Sales Range: $75-99.9 Million
Emp.: 95
Asphalt Paving Services
N.A.I.C.S.: 324121
Kent D. Peterson (Co-Owner &Co-
CEO)
John Kittleson (Co-Owner & Co-CEO)

Subsidiaries:

Bituminous Roadways, Inc. - Inver
Grove Heights Plant (1)
11201 Rich Valley Blvd, Inver Grove
Heights, MN 55077
Tel.: (651) 686-7001
Housing Construction Services
N.A.I.C.S.: 236116

Bituminous Roadways, Inc. - Minne-
apolis Plant (1)
2828 Longfellow Ave S, Minneapolis, MN
55407
Tel.: (612) 721-2451
Emp.: 3
Housing Construction Services
N.A.I.C.S.: 236116
Todd Smedshammer (Plant Mgr)

Bituminous Roadways, Inc. - Shako-
pee Plant (1)
6898 Hwy 101 E, Shakopee, MN 55379
Tel.: (952) 233-1660
Web Site: http://www.bitroads.com
Housing Construction Services
N.A.I.C.S.: 236116

BITWISE BITCOIN ETP TRUST
300 Brannan St Ste 201, San Fran-
cisco, CA 94107   DE
Investment Services
N.A.I.C.S.: 523999
Hunter Horsley (CEO)
Paul Fusaro (Pres)

BIXBY INTERNATIONAL CORP.
1 Preble Rd, Newburyport, MA 01950
Tel.: (978) 462-4100   MA
Web Site: https://www.bixbyintl.com
Sales Range: $75-99.9 Million
Emp.: 55
Box Toes, Counter Materials, Adhe-
sives & Extruded Plastic Sheeting Mfr
N.A.I.C.S.: 326130
Kenneth S. Hughes (Acct Mgr)
Dennis Lauzon (VP-Sls)

BIZBASH MEDIA INC.
115 W 27th St, New York, NY 10001
Tel.: (646) 638-3600
Web Site: http://www.bizbash.com
Year Founded: 2000
Rev.: $8,900,000
Emp.: 56
Trade Media for the Event Industry
N.A.I.C.S.: 513120
David Levine (CFO)
David Adler (Founder & CEO)
Richard Aaron (Pres)
Grazia Mohren (VP-Mktg)
David Wilkes (VP-Sls)
Sue Babin (Publr-Chicago)
Ann G. Keusch (Publr-Florida)
Beth Kormanik (Exec Editor)
Matt Lima (CTO)
Nicole Peck (Exec VP)
Rebecca Pappas (VP-Audience Dev)
Jonathan Adler (Chm)
Kim Romano (Dir-Events)
Vincent Murphy (VP-Sls-Canada)
Mandana Mondi Nahed (VP-Sls-West
Coast)

BIZCENTRAL USA, INC.
2151 Consulate Dr Ste 13, Orlando,
FL 32837
Tel.: (407) 857-9002
Web Site:
     http://www.bizcentralusa.com
Year Founded: 2004
Sales Range: $1-9.9 Million
Emp.: 25
Business Support & Consulting Ser-
vices
N.A.I.C.S.: 561499
Efrain Rodriguez (Founder & CEO)
Felix Zapata (Dir-Ops)
Melanie Swift (Dir-Non-Profit Svcs)

BIZCHAIR.COM
4350 Ball Ground Hwy, Canton, GA
30144
Tel.: (770) 721-8200
Web Site: http://www.bizchair.com
Year Founded: 2001
Sales Range: $10-24.9 Million
Emp.: 40
Furniture Retailer
N.A.I.C.S.: 423210
Sean Belnick (CEO)
Gary Glazer (Owner)
Bob Henry (Dir-Mktg)

BIZCOM WEB SERVICES, INC.
5711 6 Forks Rd Ste 211, Raleigh,
NC 27609
Tel.: (919) 855-8399
Web Site: http://www.bizcomweb.com
Sales Range: $1-9.9 Million
Emp.: 10
Website Development & Other Com-
puter Related Services
N.A.I.C.S.: 541519

Mark Wiener (Pres & CEO)
Don Rodger (VP-Web Solutions)
Jay Allred (Dir-Network Engrg)

BIZLAB, INC.
N56 W13365 Silver Spring Rd,
Menomonee Falls, WI 53051
Tel.: (262) 437-2300
Web Site: http://www.BizLab.com
Year Founded: 2003
Sales Range: $10-24.9 Million
Holding Company; Online Marketing
& Management Support Services
N.A.I.C.S.: 551112
Jeff Hughes (Pres)
Jodi Brunner (Dir-Ops)

Subsidiaries:

Rocket Clicks (1)
N56 W 13365 Silver Spring Rd, Menom-
onee Falls, WI 53051   (100%)
Tel.: (262) 253-2435
Web Site: http://www.rocketclicks.com
Internet Marketing Agency With Focus on
Pay Per Click Advertising
N.A.I.C.S.: 541613
Jeff Hughes (CEO & Partner)

BIZRATE.COM
12200 W Olympic Blvd Ste 300, Los
Angeles, CA 90064
Tel.: (310) 571-1235
Web Site: http://www.bizrate.com
Year Founded: 1996
Sales Range: $100-124.9 Million
Emp.: 300
E-Commerce Search Services
N.A.I.C.S.: 541910
Blythe Holden (Gen Counsel)

BIZSTREAM, INC.
11480 53rd Ave Ste A, Allendale, MI
49401
Web Site: http://www.bizstream.com
Year Founded: 2001
Sales Range: $1-9.9 Million
Emp.: 31
Software Development Services
N.A.I.C.S.: 541511
Mark Schmidt (Founder)
Brian Mckeiver (Owner)
Dave Valko (Dir-Sls & Mktg)
Mike Kren (Project Mgr)
Caleb Compston (Project Mgr)

BIZTECH SOLUTIONS
21 Waterway Ave Ste 300, The
Woodlands, TX 77380
Tel.: (281) 362-2713
Web Site:
     https://www.biztechsolinc.com
Year Founded: 2001
Sales Range: $1-9.9 Million
Emp.: 50
Consulting Services Across Multiple
Practice Areas
N.A.I.C.S.: 541612
Krishna Hari (CEO)
Rajee Hari (Dir-Ops)
Priya Subramanian (Sr Mgr-
Recruiting)
Shoba Prabhakaran (Dir-HR)
Bulki Bartz (VP-Sls-North America)

BIZVIZ AUDIENCE ANALYT-
ICS, INC.
2 Bala Plz Ste 300, Bala Cynwyd, PA
19004
Tel.: (610) 505-9189
Web Site: http://www.bizviz.com
Year Founded: 2002
Sales Range: $1-9.9 Million
Software Publisher
N.A.I.C.S.: 513210
Roxanne Christensen (VP-Client
Svcs)

BizViz Audience Analytics, Inc.—(Continued)

Russell Perkins *(Chm)*
Stephen Lee *(Pres & CEO)*
George Lindsey *(CFO)*

BIZXCHANGE INCORPO-RATED

3600 136th Pl SE Ste 270, Bellevue, WA 98006
Tel.: (206) 447-9933
Web Site: http://www.bizx.com
Year Founded: 2002
Rev.: $2,900,000
Emp.: 36
Business Products & Services
N.A.I.C.S.: 323111
Bob Bagga *(Pres & CEO)*
Chris Haddawy *(COO)*
Raj Kapoor *(CFO)*

BIZZOOM INC.

505 S Orange Ave Ste 101, Sarasota, FL 34236
Tel.: (941) 953-3777
Web Site: http://www.bizzoom.com
Year Founded: 2012
Sales Range: $25-49.9 Million
Emp.: 12
Privater Equity Firm
N.A.I.C.S.: 523999
James Abrams *(CEO)*
Terry Nicholson *(Pres)*
Sean Abrams *(Partner)*
Connie Mattis *(CFO)*
Matt DiMauro *(VP-Sls & Mktg)*

BIZZUKA, INC.

105 Chapel Dr, Lafayette, LA 70506
Tel.: (337) 216-4423
Web Site: https://www.bizzuka.com
Sales Range: $1-9.9 Million
Emp.: 20
Website Design Services & Content Management Services
N.A.I.C.S.: 541511
John Munsell *(Co-Founder & CEO)*
Babette Lastrapes *(Mgr-Acctg)*

BJ ELECTRIC SUPPLY, INC.

805 Plaenert Dr, Madison, WI 53713
Tel.: (608) 257-4777
Web Site: http://www.bjelectric.com
Sales Range: $10-24.9 Million
Emp.: 52
Wholesale Distributor of Electrical Supplies
N.A.I.C.S.: 423610
Keith Topp *(CEO)*
Maureen Barsema *(CFO & VP)*
Kimberly McNabb *(Mgr-Sls)*

BJ SERVICES, INC.

11211 FM 2920, Tomball, TX 77375
Tel.: (281) 408-2361 DE
Web Site: http://www.bjservices.com
Year Founded: 2017
Emp.: 2,600
Pressure Pumping Service Provider
N.A.I.C.S.: 238110
Warren M. Zemlak *(Pres & CEO)*
Caleb J. Barclay *(COO & Exec VP)*
John R. Bakht *(Chief Compliance Officer, Gen Counsel, Sec & Exec VP)*
Charles S. Leykum *(Chm)*
Andrea Osmond *(Dir-Comm & Mktg)*
Malcolm O'Neal *(VP-HR)*
Jim Collins *(Exec VP-EHS&Q)*

BJC HEALTH SYSTEM

4901 Forest Park Ave Ste 1200, Saint Louis, MO 63108
Tel.: (314) 286-2000 MO
Web Site: http://www.bjc.org
Year Founded: 1993
Sales Range: $1-4.9 Billion
Emp.: 27,000

Hospitals & Healthcare Facilities Operator
N.A.I.C.S.: 561110
Joan R. Magruder *(Grp Pres)*
Claiborne Dunagan *(Chief Clinical Officer & Sr VP)*
Kelvin R. Westbrook *(Chm)*
David R. Aplington *(Gen Counsel & VP)*
Richard Liekweg *(CEO)*
Matthew Modica *(Chief Info Security Officer & VP)*
Nick Barto *(Pres & Pres-Eastern Reg)*
John R. Beatty *(Chief HR Officer & Sr VP)*
Jason Purnell *(VP-Community Health Improvement)*
Julie Quirin *(Pres-Western Reg)*
Jerry Fox Jr. *(CIO & Sr VP)*

Subsidiaries:

Saint Luke's Health System, Inc. **(1)**
901 E 104th St, Kansas City, MO 64031
Tel.: (816) 932-2000
Web Site:
　http://www.saintlukeshealthsystem.org
Sales Range: $75-99.9 Million
Emp.: 610
Health Care Srvices
N.A.I.C.S.: 622110
Chuck Robb *(CFO & Sr VP-Fin & Admin)*
Bob Bonney *(Sr VP-Non & Bus Dev-Acute Svcs)*
Dawn Murphy *(Sr VP-HR)*
Julie Quirin *(Sr VP-Hospital Ops)*

BJJ COMPANY INC.

2431 E Mariposa Rd, Stockton, CA 95205
Tel.: (209) 941-8361
Web Site: http://Www.bjjco.net
Sales Range: $10-24.9 Million
Emp.: 110
Contract Haulers
N.A.I.C.S.: 484121
James E Blincoe *(Pres)*

BJK INDUSTRIES INC.

945 S 15th St, Louisville, KY 40210
Tel.: (502) 581-1800
Web Site:
　http://www.bjkindustries.com
Year Founded: 1977
Sales Range: $25-49.9 Million
Emp.: 75
Plastics Film & Sheet Mfr
N.A.I.C.S.: 326113
Brian Krein *(CEO)*
Lisa Moore *(Mgr-Customer Svc)*
Milo Kalis *(Plant Mgr)*
Fred Howell *(Mgr-Quality)*

BJM AND ASSOCIATES INC.

190 W Lowry Ln Ste 120, Lexington, KY 40503
Tel.: (859) 223-3000
Web Site: http://www.bjmstaffing.com
Sales Range: $10-24.9 Million
Emp.: 1,000
Temporary Help Service
N.A.I.C.S.: 561320
Barbara Jane Moores *(Pres)*

BJT INC.

2233 Capital Blvd, Raleigh, NC 27604
Tel.: (919) 828-3842
Web Site:
　https://www.mutualdistributing.com
Year Founded: 1946
Sales Range: $100-124.9 Million
Emp.: 650
Winery
N.A.I.C.S.: 424820
William Kennedy *(Chm)*
Mark Bennet *(VP-Ops)*
Jimmy Enzor *(VP-Mktg)*

BK PLASTICS INDUSTRY, INC.

13414 Byrd Dr, Odessa, FL 33556
Tel.: (813) 920-3628 FL
Web Site: http://www.bkplastics.com
Year Founded: 1995
Sales Range: $1-9.9 Million
Emp.: 16
Plastics Product Molding & Mfr
N.A.I.C.S.: 326199
Bruce Knecht *(Pres)*
Robin Knecht *(VP)*

BKCW, L.P.

2100 Trimmier Rd Ste 100, Killeen, TX 76541
Tel.: (254) 699-7100 TX
Web Site: https://www.bkcw.com
Year Founded: 1952
Sales Range: $10-24.9 Million
Insurance Agents
N.A.I.C.S.: 524210
William Kliewer *(Pres)*

Subsidiaries:

Greater Texas Insurance Managers & Agency, Inc. **(1)**
9809 Anderson Mill Rd, Austin, TX 78750
Tel.: (512) 250-5055
Web Site: http://www.greatertexasins.com
Sales Range: $1-9.9 Million
Emp.: 25
Insurance Services
N.A.I.C.S.: 524210
Kenneth McLain *(Pres)*
Melissa Muniz *(Mgr-Acct-Comml Lines)*

BKD, LLP

910 E St Louis St Ste 400, Springfield, MO 65806
Tel.: (417) 831-7283
Web Site: http://www.bkd.com
Year Founded: 1923
Sales Range: $400-449.9 Million
Emp.: 2,000
Accounting & Advisory Services
N.A.I.C.S.: 541211
Brad Buehler *(CFO)*
Ted Dickman *(CEO)*
David Tate *(Mng Partner)*
Brian Mischel *(Partner)*
Eric Hansen *(COO)*
Jason Buschert *(Mng Dir)*
Mitch Caddell *(Mng Dir)*
Michael Burlew *(Mng Partner)*
Marvin Brown *(Partner)*
Donna Bruce *(Partner)*
John Bruce *(Partner)*
Timothy Burns *(Partner)*
David Kottak *(Partner)*
Mary McKinley *(Partner)*
Jim Regnier *(Partner)*
Joseph Vande Bosche *(Partner)*
Gary A. Edwards *(Partner)*
Andrea Hecht *(Mng Dir-Cincinnati)*
Nicholas Romanelli *(Dir-Chicago)*
Martin Martinez *(Partner-Intl tax)*
Todd Kenney *(Partner)*
Kori Zey *(Mgr-Tax)*
Jason Seaton *(Sr Mgr-Audit)*
Dustin Redger *(Mgr-Audit)*
L. Toug Plilar *(Partner)*
Gordon Dobner *(Partner)*
Christopher Salandra *(Mng Dir)*
Anthony Pasternak *(Partner)*
Tim Wilson *(Mng Partner-Nebraska Practice)*
Brian Pavona *(Mng Dir-Health Care Practice-Chicago)*
Russell Romanelli *(Mng Partner-Chicago)*
Julia Dodson *(Dir-Audit Dept)*
Megan Adams *(Dir-Audit Dept)*
Jennifer Wold *(Partner-Audit Dept)*
Brenda Benning *(Sr Mgr-Tax Dept)*

Subsidiaries:

BKD Corporate Finance, LLC **(1)**

910 E Saint Louis St Ste 200, Springfield, MO 65806 **(100%)**
Tel.: (417) 869-8588
Web Site:
　http://www.bkdcorporatefinance.com
Sales Range: $10-24.9 Million
Emp.: 100
Corporate Financial Advisory Services
N.A.I.C.S.: 541611
Steve Blumreich *(Pres)*
Brad Purifoy *(Sr VP)*
Jason Corson *(Sr VP)*
Tony Giordano *(Pres & Mng Dir)*
Gregory Lafin *(Mng Dir)*
Tony Schneider *(Mng Dir)*
Barry Adamson *(Partner)*
Jeffrey Balyeat *(Partner)*
Jeff Beach *(Partner)*
Jeff Allen *(Partner)*
James Anderson *(Partner)*
Lyle Alexander *(Partner)*
Tim Adler *(Partner)*

BKD Insurance, LLC **(1)**
901 E St Louis St Ste 200, Springfield, MO 65801 **(100%)**
Tel.: (417) 866-5822
Web Site: http://www.bkd.com
Sales Range: $50-74.9 Million
Emp.: 230
Insurance Services
N.A.I.C.S.: 524298

BKD Wealth Advisors, LLC **(1)**
910 E Saint Louis St, Springfield, MO 65801 **(100%)**
Tel.: (417) 866-5822
Web Site:
　http://www.bkdwealthadvisors.com
Sales Range: $50-74.9 Million
Emp.: 100
Investment Advisory & Management Services
N.A.I.C.S.: 523940
Jeffrey A. Layman *(Chief Investment Officer & Principal)*

BKD, LLP - Indianapolis **(1)**
201 N Illinois St Ste 700, Indianapolis, IN 46204-4224
Tel.: (317) 383-4000
Web Site: http://www.bkd.com
Sales Range: $25-49.9 Million
Emp.: 250
Accounting, Auditing & Bookkeeping
N.A.I.C.S.: 541211
Robert J. Pruitt *(Chief Practice Officer)*
Troy Gilstorf *(Partner)*
Gary Farrar *(Chief Innovation & Tech Officer)*
Tony Giordano *(Pres & Mng Dir-BKD Corp Fin)*
Lea Geiser Hayler *(Mng Dir)*
John Gernand *(Mng Dir-Bloomington)*
John Phipps *(Coord-Tech)*

Wolf & Company, P.C. **(1)**
99 High St, Boston, MA 02110
Tel.: (617) 439-9700
Web Site: http://www.wolfandco.com
Sales Range: $25-49.9 Million
Emp.: 140
Accounting & Business Consulting Services
N.A.I.C.S.: 541211
Mark A. O'Connell *(Pres & CEO)*
Scott C. Baranowski *(Dir-Internal Audit Svcs Grp)*
Jean M. Joy *(Dir-Fin Institutions Grp)*
Stephen R. King *(Dir-Regulatory Compliance Grp)*
Matthew J. Putvinski *(Dir-IT Assurance Svcs Grp)*
Michael C. Stravin *(Officer-Engagement-Comml Tax Grp)*
Michael J. Tetrault *(Principal & Dir-Tax Svcs Grp)*
Charles J. Frago *(Principal)*
Daniel F. Morrill *(Principal)*
Gary S. Lafond *(Principal)*
Michael J. Rowe *(Principal)*
William J. Nowik *(Principal)*
Erica Torres *(Principal-Regulatory Compliance Grp)*
James McGough *(Principal)*
Ryan Rodrigue *(Principal-IT Assurance Svsc Grp)*
Derek Graves *(Principal)*
Cecilia M. Frerotte *(Principal)*
Matthew P. Foley *(Principal)*

Matthew C. Vaughn (*Principal*)
Meredith F. Piotti (*Principal*)
Michael E. Kanarellis (*Principal*)
Piro D. Sassa (*Principal*)
Ryan P. Brunell (*Principal*)
Scott M. Goodwin (*Principal*)
Gary J. Emond Jr. (*Principal*)

BKM CAPITAL PARTNERS, L.P.

1701 Quail St Ste 100, Newport Beach, CA 92660
Tel.: (949) 566-8800   DE
Web Site:
   http://www.bkmcapitalpartners.com
Year Founded: 2013
Sales Range: $10-24.9 Million
Emp.: 66
Real Estate Investment Services
N.A.I.C.S.: 531210
Brian Malliet (*Co-Founder & CEO*)
Nima Taghavi (*Co-Founder*)
Barbara Rea (*COO*)
Kelly Blair (*CFO*)
Rob Sistek (*Exec Mng Dir-Investments*)

BKM OFFICEWORKS

4780 Eastgate Mall Ste 100, San Diego, CA 92121
Tel.: (858) 569-4700
Web Site:
   https://www.bkmofficeworks.com
Sales Range: $25-49.9 Million
Emp.: 250
Total Office Solutions
N.A.I.C.S.: 337214
William Kuhnert (*CEO*)

Subsidiaries:

bkm of California   (1)
6959 Bandini Blvd, Commerce, CA 90040
Tel.: (323) 726-2900
Web Site: http://www.bkmoffice.com
Sales Range: $25-49.9 Million
Emp.: 7
Retail Office & Public Building Furniture
N.A.I.C.S.: 423210
William Kuhnert (*CEO*)
James Skidmore (*COO*)

BKM TOTAL OFFICE TEXAS LP

9755 Clifford Dr No 100, Dallas, TX 75220
Tel.: (214) 902-7200
Web Site: http://www.bkmtexas.com
Sales Range: $10-24.9 Million
Emp.: 80
Mfr & Selling Office Furniture
N.A.I.C.S.: 449110
Carol Roehrig (*Pres*)
Carlene Wilson (*Owner*)
Curtis Gilmore (*CFO*)
Trey Harris (*Dir-Architecture & Design*)

BKT ENTERPRISES INC.

701 N Mettlebrook Rd, Waukesha, WI 53188
Tel.: (262) 542-8800
Rev.: $22,500,000
Emp.: 60
Grocery Stores, Independent
N.A.I.C.S.: 445110
Bob Fleming (*Owner*)

BKV TELLOS, INC.

161B Pleasant St, Lynn, MA 01901
Tel.: (617) 567-0830
Web Site:
   http://www.tellowfashion.com
Sales Range: $10-24.9 Million
Emp.: 100
Women's Ready-To-Wear Apparel
N.A.I.C.S.: 458110
Kirk Vitello (*Pres*)

BLACH CONSTRUCTION

469 El Camino Real Ste 120, Santa Clara, CA 95050-4372
Tel.: (408) 244-7100
Web Site: http://www.blach.com
Sales Range: $25-49.9 Million
Emp.: 75
Industrial Building Construction Services
N.A.I.C.S.: 236210
Michael J. Blach (*Chm*)
Kate Blocker (*Dir-Mktg*)
Daniel L. Rogers (*Pres*)
Keith Craw (*VP-Ops*)

BLACHLY-LANE COUNTY CO-OPERATIVE ELECTRIC ASSOCIATION

90680 Hwy 99 N, Eugene, OR 97402
Tel.: (541) 688-8711   OR
Web Site:
   https://www.blachlylane.coop
Year Founded: 1937
Sales Range: $10-24.9 Million
Emp.: 26
Electric Power Transmission Services
N.A.I.C.S.: 221122
Curtis Short (*Vice Chm*)
Marlene Northrup (*Chm*)
Cliff Kelley (*Treas & Sec*)

BLACK & COMPANY

1717 E Garfield Ave, Decatur, IL 62526-5076
Tel.: (217) 428-4424   IL
Web Site:
   https://www.blackandco.com
Year Founded: 1920
Sales Range: $10-24.9 Million
Emp.: 300
Wholesale Distr of Hardware & Industrial Machine Tools
N.A.I.C.S.: 423840
Jeffrey S. Black (*Chm*)
Bradley Kent (*Pres*)
Val Roberts (*Mgr-Illinois*)
Brian Simpson (*Mgr-Illinois*)
Carole McHugh (*Sec*)

BLACK & DEW

1959 Sloan Ste 220, North Saint Paul, MN 55117
Tel.: (651) 777-4900
Web Site: http://www.black-dew.com
Sales Range: $10-24.9 Million
Emp.: 25
Construction Contractors & Engineering Services
N.A.I.C.S.: 236220
Sterling Black (*CEO*)
Jim French (*COO*)
John Opheim (*VP-Ops & Sr Project Mgr*)
Robert Dew (*Pres*)
Steve Meyenburg (*Project Mgr-Civil*)
Dan Weinmeyer (*Exec VP-Bus Dev & Mktg*)

BLACK & VEATCH HOLDING COMPANY

11401 Lamar Ave, Overland Park, KS 66211
Tel.: (913) 359-1622   DE
Web Site: https://www.bv.com
Year Founded: 1991
Sales Range: $1-4.9 Billion
Emp.: 12,000
Offices of Other Holding Companies
N.A.I.C.S.: 551112
Timothy W. Triplett (*Gen Counsel & Sec*)
Cindy L. Wallis-Lage (*Mng Dir-Technical Solutions*)
John Chevrette (*Pres-Mgmt Consulting*)
Martin G. Travers (*Pres-Telecom*)
Mike Orth (*Exec Mng Dir-Water Bus-Americas*)
Rajiv Menon (*Mng Dir-India*)
Marc Walch (*Dir-Client-North Florida*)
Bruce Duff (*Mng Dir-Design-Build-Water Bus-Toronto Metro Area*)
Joe Lauria (*VP/Dir-Plng & Growth-Water Bus-Americas*)
Jim Doull (*Exec VP-Engrg, Procurement & Construction-Power Bus-Americas*)
Mario Azar (*Chm & CEO*)
Patty Corcoran (*Chief HR Officer*)
Chris Murphy (*CTO*)
Shibu Cherian (*Chief Security Officer*)
John Janchar (*Pres-Strategic Growth Organization-Global*)
Michael Williams (*CFO*)
Narsingh Chaudhary (*Pres-Asia Pacific*)
Irvin Bishop Jr. (*Exec VP*)

Subsidiaries:

Black & Veatch Construction, Inc   (1)
11401 Lamar Ave, Overland Park, KS 66211
Tel.: (913) 458-2000
Web Site: http://www.bv.com
Sales Range: $50-74.9 Million
Emp.: 900
Construction Engineering Services
N.A.I.C.S.: 237990
James D. Byrd (*Sr VP & Dir-Global Construction*)
J. J. Mauk (*Dir-Bus Dev*)
Neil Riddle (*Pres*)
Scean Cherry (*VP-Labor Rels*)
Shelby Barbier (*Sr VP*)

Black & Veatch Corporation   (1)
11401 Lamar Ave, Overland Park, KS 66211
Tel.: (913) 458-2000
Web Site: http://www.bv.com
Sales Range: $300-349.9 Million
Emp.: 2,700
Human Resources, Legal, Financial & Administration Services
N.A.I.C.S.: 541612
Timothy W. Triplett (*Gen Counsel*)
Stephanie Hasenbos-Case (*Pres & Chief HR Officer*)

Subsidiary (Non-US):

Black & Veatch Ltd.   (2)
Grosvenor House 69 London Road, Redhill, RH1 1LQ, Surrey, United Kingdom
Tel.: (44) 1737774155
Web Site: http://www.bvl.bv.com
Sales Range: $100-124.9 Million
Emp.: 250
Water-Related Project Engineering Services
N.A.I.C.S.: 541330
Emma WhiteOwn (*Dir-Fin*)
Arthur Close (*Dir-Sls-Energy Bus*)
Dean Oskvig (*Pres & CEO-Global Energy Bus*)
Rob Joyce (*Dir-Fin*)

Subsidiary (Domestic):

Overland Contracting Inc.   (2)
587 Sigman Rd NE Ste 100, Conyers, GA 30013   (100%)
Tel.: (678) 806-1049
Sales Range: $50-74.9 Million
Emp.: 40
Electric Utility Substations, Power Plants, Water & Wastewater Facilities, Telecommunication Wireless Sites, Gas, Oil & Chemical Facilities Construction
N.A.I.C.S.: 236210

Black & Veatch International Company   (1)
8400 Ward Pkwy, Kansas City, MO 64114
Tel.: (913) 458-2000
Construction & Engineering Management Services
N.A.I.C.S.: 237990
Mike Orth (*Exec VP-Water Bus*)

BLACK & WHITE ADVERTISING, INC.

3646 Highlands Pkwy, Smyrna, GA 30082
Tel.: (770) 818-0303
Web Site: http://www.discoverbw.com
Year Founded: 1999
Sales Range: Less than $1 Million
Emp.: 9
Advetising Agency
N.A.I.C.S.: 541810
Keith White (*Pres & CEO*)
Lisa Blacker (*COO & VP*)

BLACK BALLOON PUBLISHING, LLC

1140 Broadway Ste 704, New York, NY 10001
Tel.: (323) 839-6204
Web Site:
   http://www.blackballoonpublishing.com
Book Publishing
N.A.I.C.S.: 513130
Leigh Newman (*Co-Founder & Editor-in-Chief*)
Elizabeth Koch (*Co-Founder & Editor*)
Julie Buntin (*Editor*)

Subsidiaries:

Counterpoint, LLC   (1)
2560 9th St Ste 318, Berkeley, CA 94710
Tel.: (510) 704-0230
Web Site: http://www.counterpointpress.com
Book Publishers
N.A.I.C.S.: 513130
Megan Fishmann (*Assoc Publr & Dir-Publicity*)

Division (Domestic):

Soft Skull Press   (2)
1140 Broadway Ste 704, New York, NY 10001
Tel.: (510) 704-0230
Web Site: http://www.softskull.com
Emp.: 8
Book Publishers
N.A.I.C.S.: 513130

BLACK BELT SOLUTIONS LLC

12423 Bristol Commons Cir, Tampa, FL 33626
Tel.: (813) 325-9676
Web Site:
   http://www.blackbeltsolutions.us
Year Founded: 2020
Emp.: 100
Software Development Services
N.A.I.C.S.: 513210
Kevin Schaal (*Pres*)

Subsidiaries:

Imagetech Systems Inc.   (1)
3913 Hartzdale Dr Ste 1300, Camp Hill, PA 17011-7845
Tel.: (717) 761-5900
Web Site: http://www.imagetechsys.com
Emp.: 100
Custom Computer Programming Services
N.A.I.C.S.: 541511
R. J. Oommen (*CEO*)

BLACK BOOK MARKET RESEARCH LLC

3030 N Rocky Point Dr W Ste 150, Tampa, FL 33607
Tel.: (727) 222-5656
Web Site:
   http://www.blackbookmarketresearch.com
Year Founded: 2011
Sales Range: $1-9.9 Million
Emp.: 50
Information Technology Consulting Services
N.A.I.C.S.: 541512
Douglas Brown (*Founder*)

BLACK CANYON CAPITAL LLC

2000 Ave of the Stars 11th Fl, Los Angeles, CA 90067

Black Canyon Capital LLC—(Continued)

Tel.: (310) 272-1800
Web Site:
http://www.blackcanyoncapital.com
Year Founded: 2004
Privater Equity Firm
N.A.I.C.S.: 523999
Bradley Spencer (CFO & Chief Compliance Officer)
Mark W. Lanigan (Co-Founder & Mng Dir)
Michael K. Hooks (Co-Founder & Mng Dir)

BLACK COACH NETWORK, INC.

1184 San Mateo Ave, South San Francisco, CA 94080　　CA
Web Site: http://www.urbanbcn.com
Year Founded: 2013
Sales Range: $1-9.9 Million
Emp.: 20
Travel Agency Services
N.A.I.C.S.: 561510
David Uziel (CEO)

BLACK CONTRACTORS ASSOCIATION OF SAN DIEGO, INC.

6125 Imperial Ave, San Diego, CA 92114-4213
Tel.: (619) 263-9791　　CA
Web Site: https://www.bcasd.org
Year Founded: 1983
Sales Range: $1-9.9 Million
Emp.: 4
Grantmaking Services
N.A.I.C.S.: 813219
Abdur Rahim Hameed (Founder & Pres)
C. Black (Treas)
Najor Hameed (Sec)
Mike Travis (VP)

BLACK CREEK GROUP, LLC

518 17th St Ste 1700, Denver, CO 80202
Tel.: (303) 869-4600　　CO
Web Site:
http://www.blackcreekgroup.com
Year Founded: 1993
Sales Range: $1-9.9 Million
Emp.: 80
Holding Company; Real Estate Investment, Development & Property Management Services
N.A.I.C.S.: 551112
John A. Blumberg (Principal)
Rajat Dhanda (CEO)
Jeff Taylor (Sr VP)
Heather Grubbs (Mng Dir & CMO)
Dwight L. Merriman III (CEO-Industrial)

Subsidiaries:

Ares Real Estate Income Trust Inc.　　(1)
1 Tabor Ctr 1200 17th St Ste 2900, Denver, CO 80202
Tel.: (303) 228-2200
Web Site: https://areswmsresources.com
Rev: $299,223,000
Assets: $4,174,724,000
Liabilities: $2,980,857,000
Net Worth: $1,193,867,000
Earnings: ($39,979,000)
Fiscal Year-end: 12/31/2022
Real Estate Investment Services
N.A.I.C.S.: 523999
Jay W. Glaubach (Co-Pres & Partner)
Amber Ingram (Principal)
Brendan McCurdy (Mng Dir)
Casey Galligan (Partner)
Christina Adamson (Partner)
Jill Mozer (Partner)
Kelly Briden (Mng Dir)
Carlin Calcaterra (Mng Dir & Principal)
Kristina Tunick (Principal & Reg Dir)

Taylor M. Paul (Mng Dir, CFO & Treas)
Bridgette Lococo (VP)
Christopher Gilpin (VP & Reg Dir)
Connor Ervin (VP & Reg Dir)
Ellie Knott (Principal)
Haley Sorensen (Principal & Reg Dir)
Logan Woehl (Principal & Reg Dir)
Tyler Wilson (Principal)

Black Creek Capital Markets, LLC　　(1)
518 17th St 17 Fl, Denver, CO 80202
Tel.: (303) 869-4600
Web Site: http://www.blackcreekgroup.com
Real Estate Investment Services
N.A.I.C.S.: 531390
Sydney Hare (VP)
Steve Stroker (CEO)
Christina Adamson (VP-Institutional Sls)
Casey Galligan (Mgr-Natl Sls)
John Norris (Mgr-Natl Sls)
Tom Pellowe (Dir-Natl Accts)

BLACK CREEK INTEGRATED SYSTEMS CORPORATION

2900 Crestwood Blvd, Irondale, AL 35210
Tel.: (205) 949-9900　　AL
Web Site:
https://www.blackcreekisc.com
Year Founded: 2001
Sales Range: $10-24.9 Million
Emp.: 35
Security System Mfr
N.A.I.C.S.: 513210
Ike Newton (Pres)

Subsidiaries:

TSI PRISM　　(1)
15575 N 83rd Way Ste 4, Scottsdale, AZ 85260
Tel.: (480) 998-7700
Web Site: http://www.tsiprism.com
RFID Security Applications Mfr
N.A.I.C.S.: 561621
Dan Jackson (Project Mgr)

BLACK DAVIS & SHUE AGENCY INC.

2019 Market St, Harrisburg, PA 17103
Tel.: (717) 233-8461
Sales Range: $25-49.9 Million
Emp.: 16
Insurance Agents, Brokers & Service
N.A.I.C.S.: 524210
Suzy Black (Treas)
Timothy J. Black Sr. (Pres)
Thomas C. Black Jr. (Chm)

BLACK DIAMOND ASSOCIATES, LLC

123 W Bloomingdale Ave Ste 402, Brandon, FL 33511
Tel.: (813) 785-9768
Web Site: https://www.the-black-diamond.com
Sales Range: $1-9.9 Million
Business Consulting Services
N.A.I.C.S.: 541611
Lisa Huetteman (Co-Founder & Mng Partner)
Mary Owens (Co-Founder & Mng Partner)

BLACK DIAMOND CAPITAL HOLDINGS, LLC

One Sound Shore Dr Ste 200, Greenwich, CT 06830
Tel.: (203) 552-0888　　DE
Web Site: http://www.bdcm.com
Year Founded: 1995
Holding Company; Alternative Investment & Asset Management Services
N.A.I.C.S.: 551112
Stephen H. Deckoff (Founder & Mng Principal)
Mounir Nahas (Principal & COO)
Leslie Meier (Principal)

Subsidiaries:

Black Diamond Capital Management, LLC　　(1)
1 Sound Shore Dr Ste 200, Greenwich, CT 06830
Tel.: (203) 552-0888
Web Site: http://www.bdcm.com
Rev.: $11,000,000,000
Emp.: 25
Alternative Investment & Asset Management Services
N.A.I.C.S.: 523999
Ethan Auerbach (Sr Mng Dir/Portfolio Mgr-Non Control Distressed Investments)
Mounir Nahas (COO & Principal)
Stephen Deckoff (Founder & Mng Principal)
Leslie Meier (Principal)

Holding (Domestic):

BD White Birch Paper Investment LLC　　(2)
80 Field Point Rd, Greenwich, CT 06830-6416
Tel.: (203) 661-3344
Web Site: http://www.whitebirchpaper.com
Holding Company; Newsprint, Paperboard & Pulp Mills Operator & Products Distr
N.A.I.C.S.: 551112
Peter M. Brant (Chm & CEO)
Christopher M. Brant (Pres & COO)
Jean Blais (Sr VP-Ops)
Timothy Butler (Treas, Sec & VP)

Subsidiary (Domestic):

Bear Island Paper WB L.P.　　(3)
10026 Old Rdg Rd, Ashland, VA 23005
Tel.: (804) 227-3394
Web Site: http://www.whitebirchpaper.com
Newsprint Mill & Pulp Recycling Services
N.A.I.C.S.: 322120

Subsidiary (Non-US):

FF Soucy WB L.P.　　(3)
191 Rue Delage, CP 490, Riviere-du-Loup, G5R 3Z1, QC, Canada
Tel.: (418) 862-6941
Web Site: http://www.whitebirch.com
Newsprint Mill
N.A.I.C.S.: 322120

Papier Masson WB L.P.　　(3)
2 Montreal Road West, Gatineau, J8M 2E1, QC, Canada
Tel.: (819) 986-4300
Web Site: http://www.papiermasson.com
Newsprint & Pulp Mill
N.A.I.C.S.: 322120

Stadacona WB L.P.　　(3)
10 Boulevard des Capucins, CP 1487, Quebec, G1K 7H9, QC, Canada
Tel.: (418) 525-2500
Newsprint & Paperboard Mill
N.A.I.C.S.: 322120

Subsidiary (Non-US):

Black Diamond Capital Management Limited　　(2)
68 Pall Mall 4th Floor, London, SW1Y 5ES, United Kingdom
Tel.: (44) 20 7968 3600
Web Site: http://www.bdcm.com
Sales Range: $25-49.9 Million
Emp.: 6
Private Equity Services
N.A.I.C.S.: 523999
Martin Ward (Mng Dir)

Branch (Domestic):

Black Diamond Capital Management, LLC - Greenwich Office　　(2)
1 Sound Shore Dr Ste 200, Greenwich, CT 06830
Tel.: (203) 552-0888
Web Site: http://www.bdcm.com
Sales Range: $75-99.9 Million
Emp.: 60
Alternative Investment & Asset Management Services
N.A.I.C.S.: 523999
Stephen H. Deckoff (Founder & Mng Principal)
Philip Raygorodetsky (Mng Dir-Distressed & Private Equity)

Jean Fleischhacker (Sr Mng Dir-Bus Dev)
Michael Moreno (Principal & Head-Mktg & IR)
Jerome Shapiro (Mng Dir & Portfolio Mgr-Structured Product)
Samuel Farahnak (Dir-Private Equity Bus)
Todd Arden (Sr Mng Dir & Chief Credit Officer)

Joint Venture (Domestic):

CTI Foods, LLC　　(2)
22303 Hwy 95, Wilder, ID 83676
Tel.: (208) 482-7844
Web Site: http://www.ctifoods.com
Sales Range: $700-749.9 Million
Emp.: 2,000
Processed Food Mfr & Supplier
N.A.I.C.S.: 311999
Bobby Horowitz (CEO)
Ben Badiola (VP-Ops)
Sam Rovit (Pres & CEO)

Plant (Domestic):

CTI Foods, LLC - Carson Plant　　(3)
20644 S Fordyce Ave, Carson, CA 90810
Tel.: (310) 637-0900
Sales Range: $50-74.9 Million
Emp.: 300
Prepared Food Mfr
N.A.I.C.S.: 311991
Jeff Golangco (VP-Supply Chain)

Subsidiary (Domestic):

Liguria Foods, Inc.　　(3)
1515 15th St N, Humboldt, IA 50548
Tel.: (515) 332-4121
Web Site: http://www.liguriafood.com
Emp.: 200
Processed Meat Mfr
N.A.I.C.S.: 311612
Mark Majewski (Sr VP & Gen Mgr)
Joe Christopherson (VP-Ops)

Holding (Domestic):

InSight Health Services Holdings Corp.　　(2)
26250 Enterprise Ct Ste 100, Lake Forest, CA 92630
Tel.: (949) 282-6000
Web Site: http://www.insighthealth.com
Sales Range: $150-199.9 Million
Emp.: 1,094
Holding Company; Diagnostic Medical Imaging Services
N.A.I.C.S.: 551112
Patricia R. Blank (Exec VP-Bus Process Mgmt)
Rick Long (COO)

Subsidiary (Domestic):

InSight Health Corp.　　(3)
26250 Enterprise Ct Ste 100, Lake Forest, CA 92630
Tel.: (949) 282-6000
Web Site: http://www.insighthealth.com
Sales Range: $350-399.9 Million
Emp.: 2,500
Owns & Operates Imaging Centers; Provides Radiology Management & Diagnostic Imaging Under Service Contracts
N.A.I.C.S.: 621511
Patricia R. Blank (Exec VP-Bus Process Mgmt)

Holding (Domestic):

PTC Alliance Corp.　　(2)
6051 Wallace Rd Ext Ste 200, Wexford, PA 15090
Tel.: (412) 299-7900
Web Site: http://www.ptcalliance.com
Sales Range: $200-249.9 Million
Cold Drawn Buttweld & Electric Weld Mechanical Steel Tubing Marketer & Mfr
N.A.I.C.S.: 331210
Warren MacKenzie (VP-Mktg & Sls)
Cary Hart (Chm, Pres & CEO)

Subsidiary (Domestic):

Enduro Industries, Inc.　　(3)
2001 Orchard Ave, Hannibal, MO 63401
Tel.: (573) 248-2084
Web Site: http://www.enduroindustries.com

Sales Range: $10-24.9 Million
Emp.: 85
Steel Plating & Polishing Services
N.A.I.C.S.: 332813

Subsidiary (Non-US):

Wiederholt GmbH (3)
Vincents Wiederholt Plz Str 1, Holzwickede,
59439, Germany (100%)
Tel.: (49) 02301800
Web Site: http://www.wiederholt.com
Sales Range: $50-74.9 Million
Emp.: 700
Tubes Mfr
N.A.I.C.S.: 331210

Holding (Domestic):

Valley Joist, LLC (2)
3019 Gault Ave N, Fort Payne, AL 35968
Tel.: (256) 845-2330
Web Site: http://www.valleyjoist.com
Steel Joists Mfr
N.A.I.C.S.: 332312
Jonathan Dooley *(Mgr-Environment Health & Safety)*

Joint Venture (Domestic):

Vertellus Specialties Inc. (2)
201 N Illinois St Ste 1800, Indianapolis, IN 46204
Tel.: (317) 247-8141
Web Site: http://www.vertellus.com
Sales Range: $500-549.9 Million
Specialty Chemicals Mfr
N.A.I.C.S.: 325199
Robert McNeeley *(Chm)*
Scott Dearing *(Controller)*
James Keay *(Bus Dir)*
Linda Hicks *(VP)*
Richard V. Preziotti *(Pres & CEO)*
Bentley Park *(Pres-Agriculture & Nutrition Bus)*
John Washuta *(VP-Global Ops & Supply Chain)*

Subsidiary (Domestic):

Vertellus Agriculture & Nutrition Specialties LLC (3)
201 N Illinois St Ste 1800, Indianapolis, IN 46204
Tel.: (317) 247-8141
Web Site: http://www.vertellus.com
Sales Range: $200-249.9 Million
Pyridine, Picolines & Vitamin B-3 Mfr
N.A.I.C.S.: 325199

Vertellus Health & Specialty Products LLC (3)
201 N Illinois St Ste 1800, Indianapolis, IN 46204
Tel.: (317) 247-8141
Web Site: http://www.vertellus.com
Sales Range: $100-124.9 Million
Specialty Pyridine Derivatives, Sulfones, DEET & Reducing Agents Mfr
N.A.I.C.S.: 325998

Plant (Domestic):

Vertellus Health & Specialty Products LLC - Delaware Water Gap (4)
PO Box 730, Delaware Water Gap, PA 18327
Tel.: (570) 420-3900
Web Site: http://www.vertellus.com
Sales Range: $50-74.9 Million
High Purity Organic & Inorganic Salts
N.A.I.C.S.: 325199

Vertellus Health & Specialty Products LLC - Elma (4)
4800 State Rte 12, Elma, WA 98541
Tel.: (360) 482-4350
Emp.: 75
Sodium Borohydride Mfr
N.A.I.C.S.: 325180

Vertellus Health & Specialty Products LLC - Zeeland (4)
215 N Centennial St, Zeeland, MI 49464-1309
Tel.: (616) 772-2193
Web Site: http://www.vertellus.com
Sales Range: $25-49.9 Million
Specialty Chemicals Mfr
N.A.I.C.S.: 325998

Ken Walits *(Mgr-Quality & Regulatory Affairs)*
Leeann Karabelski *(Engr-HSSE)*

Subsidiary (Domestic):

Vertellus Performance Materials, Inc. (3)
2110 High Point Rd, Greensboro, NC 27403-2642
Tel.: (336) 292-1781
Web Site: http://www.vertellus.com
Sales Range: $50-74.9 Million
Emp.: 70
Castor Oil, Shea Butter & Citrate Derivatives
N.A.I.C.S.: 325199
Ben Stewart *(Gen Mgr)*

Subsidiary (Non-US):

Vertellus Specialties Asia Pacific (3)
Room 1602 16th Floor No 66 Hua Yuan Shi Qiao Rd, BEA Finance Tower, Shanghai, 200120, China
Tel.: (86) 21 38993000
Chemical Products Mfr
N.A.I.C.S.: 325998

Vertellus Specialties UK Ltd. (3)
Seal Sands Rd, Seal Sands, Middlesbrough, TS2 1UB, United Kingdom
Tel.: (44) 1642546546
Web Site: http://www.vertellus.com
Sales Range: $25-49.9 Million
Performance-Enhancing Synthetic Organic Fine Chemicals
N.A.I.C.S.: 325199
Mike Driver *(Dir-Bus & Biomaterials)*

BLACK DIAMOND ENERGY, INC.
29 Stage Trail Rd, Buffalo, WY 82834
Tel.: (307) 684-2910 **WY**
Web Site:
 https://www.blackdiamond.com
Coal Methane Drilling
N.A.I.C.S.: 213111
Eric D. Koval *(Dir-Marketing-East Coast & Pres)*

BLACK DIAMOND FINANCIAL GROUP, LLC
1610 Wynkoop St Ste 400, Denver, CO 80202
Tel.: (303) 893-2334
Web Site: https://www.bdfin.com
Private Investment Firm
N.A.I.C.S.: 523999
Patrick W. M. Imeson *(Mng Dir)*

Subsidiaries:

EASTERN RESOURCES, INC. (1)
1610 Wynkoop St Ste 400, Denver, CO 80202
Tel.: (604) 687-4450
Web Site:
 http://www.easternresourcesinc.com
Sales Range: Less than $1 Million
Emp.: 11
Precious Metal Mining Services
N.A.I.C.S.: 212220
Patrick W. M. Imeson *(Chm & CEO)*
Robert Trenaman *(Pres & COO)*
Eric Michael Altman *(CFO, Treas & VP-Fin)*
Timothy G. Smith *(VP-Ops & Gen Mgr-Montana Tunnels)*
Shane Hanninen *(Mgr-Mine Ops-Golden Dream)*

BLACK DIAMOND GROUP, INC.
6925 S 6th St Ste 100, Oak Creek, WI 53154
Tel.: (414) 762-8050
Web Site:
 http://www.blackdiamondgrp.com
Year Founded: 1959
Sales Range: $10-24.9 Million
Emp.: 45
Surfacing & Paving
N.A.I.C.S.: 237310

Deborah A. Teglia *(Pres)*
Joe Teglia *(VP)*
Brian Cooper *(Project Mgr)*

BLACK DIAMOND MEDIA
574 Heritage Rd Ste 201A, Southbury, CT 06488
Tel.: (203) 262-0588
Web Site: https://www.b-d-m.com
Sales Range: $1-9.9 Million
Emp.: 8
Media Buying Solutions
N.A.I.C.S.: 541830
Brian Mahoney *(Owner)*

BLACK DIAMOND PLUMBING & MECHANICAL, INC.
1400 Miller Pkwy, McHenry, IL 60050
Tel.: (815) 444-0979
Web Site:
 https://www.blackdiamondtoday.com
Year Founded: 1999
Rev.: $1,752,000
Emp.: 12
HVAC Contractors
N.A.I.C.S.: 333415
Rick Sperando *(Owner)*

Subsidiaries:

Axberg Heating (1)
3548 35th St, Rockford, IL 61109-2765
Tel.: (815) 873-6003
Web Site: http://axbergtoday.com
Heating, Air Conditioning, Electrical & Plumbing Contractor
N.A.I.C.S.: 238220

BLACK DRAGON CAPITAL LLC
6365 Collins Ave Ste 3001, Miami Beach, FL 33141
Tel.: (978) 640-5010
Web Site: http://blackdragoncap.com
Privater Equity Firm
N.A.I.C.S.: 523999
Sarah Buonfiglio *(Mgr-IR & Project Mgr)*
Louis Hernandez Jr. *(Founder, Chm & CEO)*

Subsidiaries:

Grass Valley Canada (1)
3499 Douglas-B-Floreani, Montreal, H4S 2C6, QC, Canada
Tel.: (514) 333-1772
Web Site: http://www.grassvalley.com
Media & Television Equipment Distr
N.A.I.C.S.: 334118
Christian Bernard *(Sr VP-Ops)*
Tim Ordaz *(Sr VP-Svcs & Support)*
Timothy Shoulders *(Pres)*
Michael Cronk *(VP-Core Tech)*
Ian Fletcher *(Designer-Applications)*
Eve Dery Hodnett *(VP-Legal)*
Sydney Lovely *(Sr VP-Products & Tech)*
Chuck Meyer *(CTO-Live)*
Neil Maycock *(Sr VP-Strategic Mktg & Playout)*

Subsidiary (Non-US):

Grass Valley Australia Pty Ltd (2)
Unit 8 372 Eastern Valley Way, Chatswood, 2067, Australia
Tel.: (61) 385403600
Cable Product Distr
N.A.I.C.S.: 423510
Wenjun Hong *(Accountant)*

Grass Valley Belgium NV (2)
Avenue Mozartlaan 2, Drogenbos, 1620, Belgium
Tel.: (32) 23349033
Emp.: 5
Cable Product Distr
N.A.I.C.S.: 423510

Subsidiary (Domestic):

Grass Valley Canada, Inc. (2)
3499 Douglas-B-Floreani, Montreal, H4S 2C6, QC, Canada

Tel.: (514) 333-1772
Web Site: http://www.grassvalley.com
Cable Product Distr
N.A.I.C.S.: 423510

Subsidiary (Non-US):

Grass Valley China Co. Ltd. (2)
Room 503 Tower A Technology Fortune Centre 8 Xueqing Road, Haidian District, Beijing, 100192, China
Tel.: (86) 1082731515
Cable Product Distr
N.A.I.C.S.: 423510

Grass Valley France S.A. (2)
32 rue Pierre Grenier, 92100, Boulogne-Billancourt, France (100%)
Tel.: (33) 173299659
Networking Equipment Distr
N.A.I.C.S.: 423690

Grass Valley France SAS (2)
5-7 Avenue de Paris, Vincennes, 94300, France
Tel.: (33) 155095560
Television Production & Broadcasting Equipment Mfr
N.A.I.C.S.: 334220

Grass Valley Germany GmbH (2)
Brunnenweg 9, 64331, Weiterstadt, Germany
Tel.: (49) 6150104782
Teleproduction & Broadcasting Services
N.A.I.C.S.: 512191

Grass Valley India Pte. Ltd. (2)
1A/1 5th Fl SB Towee Sector 16A, Noida, 201301, Uttar Pradesh, India
Tel.: (91) 1204804961
Cable Product Distr
N.A.I.C.S.: 423510
A. S. Prakash *(Mgr-Technical)*

Grass Valley Italia S.R.L. (2)
Via Di Quarto Peperino 22, Rome, 00188, Italy
Tel.: (39) 0687203523
Cable Product Distr
N.A.I.C.S.: 423510
Daniele Rossini *(Acct Mgr-Technical)*

Grass Valley Malaysia SDN BHD (2)
Suite 1-2 Lower Level 1 The Horizon Annexe Avenue 7, Bangsar South No 8 Jalan Kerinchi, 59200, Kuala Lumpur, Malaysia
Tel.: (60) 322471898
Cable Product Distr
N.A.I.C.S.: 423510

Grass Valley Nederland B.V. (2)
Bergschot 69, 4817 PA, Breda, Netherlands
Tel.: (31) 763032100
Cable Product Distr
N.A.I.C.S.: 423510
Andreas Nederveen *(Mgr-Fin)*

Subsidiary (US):

Grass Valley USA, LLC (2)
1600 NE Compton Dr Ste 100, Hillsboro, OR 97006
Tel.: (818) 729-7706
Web Site: http://www.grassvalley.com
Sales Range: $500-549.9 Million
Emp.: 110
Broadcasting Equipment Mfr & Distr
N.A.I.C.S.: 334220

Subsidiary (Non-US):

Grass Valley do Brasil Comercio e Servicos de Equipamentos de Telecomunicacoes Ltda (2)
Rua Surubim 577 - 4 Andar Cidade Moncoes, Sao Paulo, 04571-050, Brazil
Tel.: (55) 1140581513
Cable Product Distr
N.A.I.C.S.: 423510

Green Valley - United Kingdom (2)
Turnpike Road Newbury, Reading, RG14 2NX, Berkshire, United Kingdom
Tel.: (44) 1635569777
Web Site: http://www.grassvalley.com
Communication Equipment Mfr
N.A.I.C.S.: 334290

BLACK ELECTRICAL SUPPLY

Black Electrical Supply—(Continued)

203 Westfield St, Greenville, SC
29601
Tel.: (864) 233-4142
Web Site:
http://www.blackelectricalsupply.com
Sales Range: $10-24.9 Million
Emp.: 44
Electrical Distr
N.A.I.C.S.: 423610
Robert C. Hamilton *(Owner)*

BLACK ELK ENERGY
3100 S Gessner Rd Ste 215, Houston, TX 77063
Tel.: (281) 598-8600
Web Site:
http://www.blackelkenergy.com
Year Founded: 2007
Sales Range: $300-349.9 Million
Emp.: 152
Oil & Gas Exploration Services
N.A.I.C.S.: 213112
John Hoffman *(Pres & CEO)*
Arthur Garza *(CTO)*
Gary Barton *(Interim CFO)*

BLACK ELK ENERGY OFF-SHORE OPERATIONS, LLC
3100 S Gessner Ste 210, Houston, TX 77063
Tel.: (832) 973-4230   **TX**
Web Site:
http://www.blackelkenergy.com
Year Founded: 2007
Oil & Natural Gas Exploration Services
N.A.I.C.S.: 213112
James Hagemeier *(CFO)*
Bubba Broussard *(Supvr-Ops)*

BLACK EQUIPMENT CO. INC.
1187 Burch Dr, Evansville, IN 47725
Tel.: (812) 477-6481
Web Site:
http://www.blackequipment.com
Sales Range: $10-24.9 Million
Emp.: 64
Materials Handling Equipment
N.A.I.C.S.: 423830
Becky Ernst *(Coord-Sls)*
Troy Fuqua *(Supvr-Shop)*

BLACK FAMILY DEVELOPMENT, INC.
2995 E Grand Blvd, Detroit, MI 48202
Tel.: (313) 758-0150   **MI**
Web Site:
https://www.blackfamilydev.org
Year Founded: 1978
Sales Range: $10-24.9 Million
Emp.: 102
Family Welfare Services
N.A.I.C.S.: 624190
Jane Fernanders *(CFO)*
Alice G. Thompson *(CEO)*
Kenyatta Stephens *(COO)*

BLACK FOREST BUILDING COMPANY
16570 E 12 Mile Rd, Roseville, MI 48066
Tel.: (586) 954-4800
Web Site:
http://www.ajbellomostudios.com
Sales Range: $10-24.9 Million
Emp.: 7
General Remodeling, Single-Family Houses
N.A.I.C.S.: 236118
A. J. Bellomo *(Pres)*

BLACK FOREST INDUSTRIES
1000 E Chatham St, Cary, NC 27511
Tel.: (919) 468-5400

Web Site:
https://www.blackforestindustries.com
Year Founded: 2001
Sales Range: $1-9.9 Million
Emp.: 12
Automobile Repair, Service & After Market Parts
N.A.I.C.S.: 811198
Joseph Flaherty *(Owner)*

BLACK GOLD POTATO SALES INC.
4320 18th Ave S, Grand Forks, ND 58201
Tel.: (701) 772-2620
Web Site:
http://www.blackgoldpotato.com
Rev.: $24,618,434
Emp.: 50
Production & Marketing of Potatoes
N.A.I.C.S.: 424410
Eric Halverson *(CEO)*

BLACK HILLS BENTONITE LLP
55 S Salt Creek Hwy, Casper, WY 82601
Tel.: (307) 265-3740
Web Site:
http://www.bhbentonite.com
Sales Range: $10-24.9 Million
Emp.: 100
Bentonite Mining
N.A.I.C.S.: 212323
Thomas A. Thorson *(Founder)*
Sherry Gray *(Mgr-HR)*
Bob Perry *(Superintendent-Mine)*
Tammy Keeran *(Controller)*

BLACK IPO, INC.
6125 Imperial Ave, San Diego, CA 92114
Tel.: (619) 527-1668
Web Site: http://www.blackipocm.com
Year Founded: 2000
Sales Range: $1-9.9 Million
Emp.: 25
Engineering & Construction Management Services
N.A.I.C.S.: 541330
Wendell Stemley *(CEO)*

BLACK KNIGHT SPORTS & ENTERTAINMENT LLC
1701 Vlg Ctr Cir, Las Vegas, NV 89134
Tel.: (702) 790-2663   **DE**
Year Founded: 2016
Holding Company; Professional Hockey Team & Arena Owner & Operator
N.A.I.C.S.: 551112
William P. Foley II *(Owner-Majority, Exec Chm & CEO)*

Subsidiaries:

The Las Vegas Golden Knights   **(1)**
1701 Vlg Ctr Cir, Las Vegas, NV 89134
Tel.: (702) 790-2663
Web Site: http://www.nhl.com
Professional Hockey Team
N.A.I.C.S.: 711211
George McPhee *(Pres-Hockey Ops & Alternate Governor)*
Kelly McCrimmon *(Gen Mgr)*

Subsidiary (Domestic):

Black Knight Sports Arena LLC   **(2)**
3780 Las Vegas Blvd S, Las Vegas, NV 89109
Tel.: (702) 692-1515
Web Site: http://www.t-mobilearena.com
Sports & Entertainment Arena Operator
N.A.I.C.S.: 711310
Darren Eliot *(Grp VP-Hockey Programming & Facility Ops)*

BLACK LAKE CAPITAL, LLC
1524 Belford Ct,, Evergreen, CO 80439
Tel.: (303) 327-9701
Web Site: https://blacklakecap.com
Year Founded: 2013
Private Equity
N.A.I.C.S.: 523999
Charles Scripps *(Mng Partner)*

Subsidiaries:

Spinnaker SCA   **(1)**
2590 Welton St, Ste 200 PMB 1257, Denver, CO 80205
Tel.: (213) 443-8308
Web Site: https://spinnakersca.com
Emp.: 107
Business Consulting & Services
N.A.I.C.S.: 541618
John Sharkey *(CEO)*

Subsidiary (Domestic):

Accelogix LLC   **(2)**
8000 Regency Pkwy Ste 515, Cary, NC 27518
Tel.: (919) 346-4544
Web Site: http://www.accelogix.com
Sales Range: $1-9.9 Million
Business Support Services
N.A.I.C.S.: 561499
Ryan Kirklewski *(COO)*
Paul Patin *(Chief Customer Officer)*
Brian Krueger *(VP-Fin & Admin)*
Chris Positano *(Dir-Consulting Svcs)*
Bert Perrizo *(Dir-Consulting Svcs)*
Mark Miller *(Dir-Technical)*
Claire Amos *(Dir-HR)*
Seth Hamm *(Dir-Consulting Svcs)*
Harvey Cohen *(Partner-Client)*

BLACK LOTUS COMMUNICATIONS
1 Sansome St Suite 1500, San Francisco, CA 94104
Tel.: (866) 477-5554
Web Site: http://www.blacklotus.net
Year Founded: 1999
Sales Range: $1-9.9 Million
Emp.: 12
Delivers DDoS Protection for Websites & Servers
N.A.I.C.S.: 541519
Warren Dewar *(CFO)*
Shawn Merck *(Chief Security Officer)*

BLACK LUMBER CO. INC.
1710 S Henderson St, Bloomington, IN 47401
Tel.: (812) 332-7208
Web Site:
https://www.myblacklumber.com
Rev.: $14,500,000
Emp.: 40
Lumber & Other Building Materials
N.A.I.C.S.: 423310
Thomas R. Black Jr. *(Pres)*

BLACK MILLWORK CO., INC.
220 W Crescent Ave, Allendale, NJ 07401
Tel.: (201) 934-0100   **DE**
Web Site:
http://www.blackmillwork.com
Year Founded: 1938
Sales Range: $100-124.9 Million
Emp.: 30
Distr of Windows & Doors
N.A.I.C.S.: 423310
Marc McKeon *(Mgr-Ops)*

BLACK MOUNTAIN SOFTWARE, LLC
830 Shoreline Dr, Polson, MT 59860
Tel.: (406) 883-4819   **MT**
Web Site:
http://www.blackmountains.com
Year Founded: 1988
Sales Range: $1-9.9 Million
Emp.: 35

Custom Computer Programming Services
N.A.I.C.S.: 541511
Allison Green *(Dir)*
Donna Hislop *(Bus Mgr-HR)*

Subsidiaries:

Fiscalsoft Corp.   **(1)**
1139 Tatesbrook Dr, Lexington, KY 40517-3029
Tel.: (606) 584-1119
Web Site: http://www.fiscalsoft.com
Electronics Stores
N.A.I.C.S.: 449210
Howard Chandler Jr. *(Pres)*

BLACK RETAIL
219 N 2nd St Ste 333, Minneapolis, MN 55401
Tel.: (612) 377-7377
Web Site: http://www.blackretail.us
Year Founded: 2005
Sales Range: $1-9.9 Million
Emp.: 15
Branding & Marketing Services for the Retail Sector
N.A.I.C.S.: 541613
Tina Wilcox *(CEO & Creative Dir)*
Wayne Talley *(Pres & Creative Dir)*
Renae Debates *(CFO)*

BLACK RIVER COMPUTER, LLC
440 4th St NW, Barberton, OH 44203
Tel.: (440) 327-7999   **OH**
Web Site: http://www.blackriver.com
Year Founded: 1989
Rev.: $3,200,000
Emp.: 14
Fiscal Year-end: 12/31/06
Whol Computers/Peripherals Computer Maintenance/Repair
N.A.I.C.S.: 423430
Bill McChesney *(Pres)*
Greg Brumbaugh *(CEO)*
Ron Pollard *(VP)*

Subsidiaries:

Peripheral Company, Inc.   **(1)**
101 Medford Mt Holly Rd, Medford, NJ 08055
Tel.: (609) 654-5555
Web Site: http://www.pecoinc.com
Computers, Peripherals, And Software, Nsk
N.A.I.C.S.: 423430
Donald Hory *(Pres)*

BLACK RIVER ELECTRIC CO-OP
2600 Hwy 67, Fredericktown, MO 63645
Tel.: (573) 783-3381
Web Site: https://www.brec.coop
Sales Range: $25-49.9 Million
Emp.: 75
Electronic Services
N.A.I.C.S.: 221118
Steve Rohan *(Asst Mgr-Line Distr)*

BLACK RIVER ELECTRIC CO-OP., INC.
1121 N Pike W, Sumter, SC 29153
Tel.: (803) 469-8060
Web Site: https://www.blackriver.coop
Sales Range: $50-74.9 Million
Emp.: 65
Distribution, Electric Power
N.A.I.C.S.: 221122
Betty Welsh *(VP)*
Charlie Allen *(CEO)*
Rowland Alston *(Vice Chm)*
Lee Sigler *(Mgr-Warehouse)*

BLACK RIVER MEMORIAL HOSPITAL
711 W Adams St, Black River Falls, WI 54615
Tel.: (715) 284-5361   **WI**
Web Site: https://www.brmh.net
Year Founded: 1966
Sales Range: $25-49.9 Million
Emp.: 352
Health Care Srvices
N.A.I.C.S.: 622110
Mary Beth White-Jacobs *(CEO)*
Robert Daley *(VP-Fiscal & Info Svcs)*

BLACK SPECTACLES, LLC
222 Merchandise Mart Ste 1212, Chicago, IL 60654
Tel.: (312) 884-9091
Web Site:
    http://www.blackspectacles.com
Year Founded: 2012
Sales Range: $1-9.9 Million
Emp.: 12
Educational Support Services
N.A.I.C.S.: 611710
Marc Teer *(Founder & CEO)*

BLACK STAR NETWORKS, INC.
15679 N 83rd Way, Scottsdale, AZ 85260-1820
Year Founded: 2006
Sales Range: $1-9.9 Million
Emp.: 28
Electronic Parts & Equipment Merchant Whslr
N.A.I.C.S.: 423690
Ryan Miller *(Pres)*
Deborah Miller *(Treas & Sec)*

BLACK TIE TRANSPORTATION LLC
7080 Commerce Dr, Pleasanton, CA 94588-8021
Tel.: (925) 847-0747   **CA**
Web Site:
    https://www.blacktietrans.com
Year Founded: 1986
Sales Range: $10-24.9 Million
Emp.: 110
Travel Agencies; Ground Transportation
N.A.I.C.S.: 561510
Bill Wheeler *(CEO)*
Debbie Moore *(VP-Ops)*

BLACK-HAAK HEATING, INC.
N967 Quality Dr, Greenville, WI 54942
Tel.: (920) 202-5584
Web Site: http://www.black-haak.com
Year Founded: 1956
Sales Range: $1-9.9 Million
Emp.: 200
Air Conditioning System Installation Services
N.A.I.C.S.: 238220
Noreen Haak *(Owner)*

BLACKALL ASSOCIATES INC.
20 Stimson Ave, Providence, RI 02906
Tel.: (401) 427-1022
Web Site:
    http://www.masterpiecedolls.com
Rev.: $12,000,000
Emp.: 1
Dolls Mfr & Whslr
N.A.I.C.S.: 339930
Shirley Blackall *(Pres)*

BLACKBERN PARTNERS LLC
590 Madison Ave Fl 14, New York, NY 10022
Tel.: (646) 948-3500   **DE**

Web Site:
    http://www.blackbernpartners.com
Equity Investment Firm
N.A.I.C.S.: 523999
G. Jonathan Bernstein *(Partner)*

Subsidiaries:

Westfall Technik, Inc.   (1)
3883 Howard Hughes Ste 590, Las Vegas, NV 89169
Tel.: (702) 659-9898
Web Site: http://www.westfall-technik.com
Holding Company; Plastic Products Mfr
N.A.I.C.S.: 551112
Rick Shaffer *(Mng Dir-SW Europe)*
Merritt Williams *(Chief Comml Officer)*
Mark Gomulka *(CEO)*

Subsidiary (Domestic):

10 Day Parts, Inc.   (2)
235 Citation Cir, Corona, CA 92880-2523
Tel.: (951) 279-4810
Web Site: http://www.10dayparts.com
Plastics Products, Nec, Nsk
N.A.I.C.S.: 326199

AMS Plastics, Inc.   (2)
1530 Hilton Head Rd Ste 205, El Cajon, CA 92019-4655
Tel.: (619) 713-2000
Web Site: http://www.amsplastics.com
Plastics Product Mfr
N.A.I.C.S.: 326199
Scott Modic *(VP-Sls & Mktg)*

Carolina Precision Plastics LLC   (2)
111 CPP Global Dr, Mocksville, NC 27028
Tel.: (336) 283-4700
Web Site: http://www.cppglobal.com
Sales Range: $10-24.9 Million
Emp.: 135
Injection Molding Of Plastics
N.A.I.C.S.: 326199
Brian Tauber *(CEO)*

Delta Pacific Products, Inc.   (2)
33170 Central Ave, Union City, CA 94587
Tel.: (510) 487-4411
Plastics Product Mfr
N.A.I.C.S.: 326199

Subsidiary (Domestic):

Prism Plastics Products, Inc.   (3)
1544 Hwy 65, New Richmond, WI 54017
Tel.: (715) 246-7535
Web Site: http://www.prismplasticsinc.com
Sales Range: $1-9.9 Million
Emp.: 40
Custom Injection Molding Plastic Products Mfr
N.A.I.C.S.: 326199
Kevin Larson *(Mgr-Quality)*
Mark Fagerland *(Pres)*
Mike Brinkman *(Gen Mgr)*
Tom Schweitzer *(Mgr-Engrg)*

Subsidiary (Domestic):

Fairway Injection Molds, Inc.   (2)
20109 Paseo Del Prado, Walnut, CA 91789
Tel.: (909) 595-2201
Web Site: http://www.fairwaymolds.com
Injection Mould Mfr
N.A.I.C.S.: 333511
Steven Bilderain *(Mgr-Engrg)*

Integrity Mold, Inc.   (2)
905 W Alameda Dr, Tempe, AZ 85282
Tel.: (480) 829-3899
Web Site: http://www.intmold.com
Industrial Mold Mfr
N.A.I.C.S.: 333511
Mike Friend *(VP & Gen Mgr)*
Dan Joseph *(Partner & VP)*

Mold Craft, Inc.   (2)
200 Stillwater Rd, Willernie, MN 55090
Tel.: (651) 426-3216
Web Site: http://www.mold-craft.com
Mfg Dies/Tools/Jigs/Fixtures
N.A.I.C.S.: 333511

Zentech Manufacturing, Inc.   (1)
6800 Tudsbury Rd, Baltimore, MD 21244
Tel.: (443) 348-4500
Web Site: http://www.zentech.com
Contract Bare Printed Circuit Board Mfr
N.A.I.C.S.: 334412

Charlene Wright *(VP-Fin & HR)*
Clint Fleming *(VP-Program Mgmt & Supply Chain)*
Waleid Jabai *(VP-Tech)*
John Vaughan *(VP-Sls & Mktg)*
Steve Pudles *(Pres & CEO)*

Subsidiary (Domestic):

Zentech Dallas, LLC   (2)
1717 Firman Dr Ste 200, Richardson, TX 75081
Tel.: (972) 907-2727
Web Site: http://www.zentech.com
Bare Printed Circuit Board Mfr
N.A.I.C.S.: 334412
Charles Capers *(Pres)*
Mark Mccrocklin *(VP-Sls & Mktg)*

Zentech Fredericksburg LLC   (2)
3361 Shannon Airport Cir, Fredericksburg, VA 22408
Tel.: (540) 372-6500
Web Site: http://www.zentech.com
Contract Bare Printed Circuit Board Mfr
N.A.I.C.S.: 334412
Dave Forrest *(VP-Mfg)*
Cindy Snellings *(VP-Admin)*

BLACKBURN'S PHYSICIANS PHARMACY, INC.
301 Corbet St, Tarentum, PA 15084
Tel.: (724) 224-9100   **PA**
Web Site:
    https://www.blackburnsmed.com
Year Founded: 1936
Sales Range: $10-24.9 Million
Emp.: 100
Medical Equipment & Supplies Pharmacy
N.A.I.C.S.: 423450
Charles R. Blackburn *(Chm & Principal)*
Tom Blackburn *(VP)*
Ronald Rukas *(Pres & Principal)*

BLACKBURN-RUSSELL CO. INC.
157 Railroad St, Bedford, PA 15522
Tel.: (814) 623-5181
Web Site:
    http://www.blackburnrussell.com
Sales Range: $10-24.9 Million
Emp.: 43
Groceries
N.A.I.C.S.: 424410

BLACKCRAFT CULT, INC.
2890 E Via Martens, Anaheim, CA 92806
Tel.: (949) 547-5916   **NV**
Web Site:
    https://www.blackcraftcult.com
Year Founded: 2011
BLCK—(OTCBB)
N.A.I.C.S.: 458110
James Somers *(Pres & Dir)*

BLACKEAGLE PARTNERS, LLC
6905 Telegraph Rd Ste 119, Bloomfield Hills, MI 48301
Tel.: (313) 647-5340
Web Site:
    https://www.blackeaglepartners.com
Sales Range: $25-49.9 Million
Emp.: 10
Privater Equity Firm
N.A.I.C.S.: 523999
Michael D. Madden *(Mng Partner)*
Jason G. Runco *(Founder & Partner)*
Kimberly Lawrence *(Office Mgr)*
Eugene M. Matalene Jr. *(Chief Admin Officer)*

Subsidiaries:

InStar Services Group, LP   (1)
1743 Maplelawn Dr, Troy, MI 48084
Tel.: (248) 203-7714
Web Site: http://www.instarservices.com

Sales Range: $25-49.9 Million
Disaster Response & Restoration & Reconstruction Services
N.A.I.C.S.: 238990

Subsidiary (Domestic):

Oakwood Construction & Restoration Services, Inc.   (2)
4955 E Hunter Ave, Anaheim, CA 92807
Web Site: http://www.oakwoodteam.com
Sales Range: $25-49.9 Million
Emp.: 100
Commercial & Institutional Building Construction
N.A.I.C.S.: 236220
Todd Benson *(Pres & Corp Counsel)*

Rockford Products, LLC   (1)
707 Harrison Ave, Rockford, IL 61104-7162
Tel.: (815) 397-6000
Web Site: http://www.rockfordproducts.com
Chassis & Suspension Components Mfr
N.A.I.C.S.: 332722
Rosanna Ray *(Mgr-Tooling Ops)*
Roger Bauer *(Plant Mgr)*

Waste Associates, LLC   (1)
1790 Darbytown Rd, Richmond, VA 23231
Tel.: (804) 328-0093
Web Site:
    http://www.wasteassociatesllc.com
Holding Company; Landfill Operator & Other Waste Management Services
N.A.I.C.S.: 551112

BLACKFIN MARKETING GROUP
5780 Lincoln Dr Ste 170, Edina, MN 55436
Tel.: (952) 303-3093
Web Site:
    http://www.blackfinmarketing.com
Sales Range: Less than $1 Million
Emp.: 3
Business-To-Business, Communications, Local Marketing
N.A.I.C.S.: 541810
Jim Gresham *(Pres)*
John Fischer *(Partner)*

BLACKFOOT TELEPHONE COOPERATIVE, INC.
1221 N Russell St, Missoula, MT 59802-1805
Tel.: (406) 541-5000   **MT**
Web Site: https://www.blackfoot.com
Year Founded: 1954
Sales Range: $25-49.9 Million
Emp.: 170
Telephone Communication Services
N.A.I.C.S.: 517121
Stacey Mueller *(CFO)*
Jason Williams *(CEO)*
Dave Martin *(CTO)*
J. P. Violette *(VP-Sls & Mktg)*

Subsidiaries:

BTC Holdings Inc.   (1)
1221 N Russell St, Missoula, MT 59808-1805
Tel.: (406) 541-2121
Web Site: http://www.blackfoot.com
Sales Range: $25-49.9 Million
Emp.: 155
Electronic Parts & Equipment
N.A.I.C.S.: 423690

Blackfoot Communications Inc.   (1)
1221 N Russell St, Missoula, MT 59808-1805
Tel.: (406) 541-5000
Web Site: http://www.blackfoot.net
Sales Range: $10-24.9 Million
Emp.: 130
Telephone Communications
N.A.I.C.S.: 517121
Geoff Wilson *(Vice Chm)*
Cindy Lewis *(Treas)*
Tom Eggensperger *(Chm)*

Blackwood Communications   (1)
1221 N Russell St, Missoula, MT 59808-1805

Blackfoot Telephone Cooperative, Inc.—(Continued)
Tel.: (406) 541-5000
Web Site: http://www.blackfoot.com
Sales Range: $10-24.9 Million
Emp.: 130
Radio & Telephone Communication
N.A.I.C.S.: 517112
William Squires (Sr VP & Gen Counsel)

BLACKFORD CAPITAL LLC
190 Monroe Ave NW Ste 600, Grand
Rapids, MI 49503
Tel.: (616) 233-3161
Web Site:
https://www.blackfordcapital.com
Year Founded: 2000
Emp.: 2,000
Privater Equity Firm
N.A.I.C.S.: 523999
Martin Stein (Founder & Mng Dir)
Jeffrey Johnson (Mng Dir)
Carmen Evola (Mng Dir)
Dennis Dunn (Partner-Operating)
Allen Palles (Partner-Operating)
Steve Parker (Partner-Operating)

Subsidiaries:

Artificial Turf Supply LLC   (1)
83013 A1A N Ste 160, Ponte Vedra Beach,
FL 32082
Tel.: (706) 659-4513
Web Site: http://www.artificialturfsupply.com
Artificial, Synthetic Fibers & Filaments Mfr
N.A.I.C.S.: 325220
Fred A. Espinosa (Dir-Sls)

Boston Trade Interior Solutions   (1)
476 Brighton Dr, Bloomingdale, IL 60108
Tel.: (630) 543-2323
Web Site: http://www.bostontrade.com
Hospitality Industry Home Furnishings Inte-
rior Design, Procurement & Logistics Man-
agement Services
N.A.I.C.S.: 423220
Greg Kadens (CEO)
Dipak Kapadia (Pres)

Subsidiary (Domestic):

Design Enviroments, Inc.   (2)
95 Chastain Rd NW, Kennesaw, GA 30144
Tel.: (770) 429-3200
Web Site:
http://www.designenvironments.com
Rev.: $2,100,000
Emp.: 27
Automatic Environmental Control Manufac-
turing for Residential, Commercial & Appli-
ance Use
N.A.I.C.S.: 334512
Donna Deluca (Principal)

Davalor Mold Company, LLC   (1)
46480 Continental, Chesterfield, MI 48047-
8047
Tel.: (586) 598-0100
Web Site: http://www.davalor.com
Plastics Product Mfr
N.A.I.C.S.: 326199
William Werling (Controller)
John Boeschenstein (CEO)

Subsidiary (Domestic):

Industrial Molding Corporation   (2)
616 E Slaton Rd, Lubbock, TX 79404
Tel.: (806) 474-1000
Plastic Injection Molding Mfr
N.A.I.C.S.: 326199

Grand Transformers Inc.   (1)
1500 Marion Ave, Grand Haven, MI 49417
Tel.: (616) 842-5430
Web Site: http://www.gtipower.com
Sales Range: $10-24.9 Million
Emp.: 80
Transformer Mfr
N.A.I.C.S.: 335311
Kent Kiley (CFO)
Nick Hoiles (Pres)
Stephen A. Paul (CEO)
Steve Parker (Chm)

Subsidiary (Domestic):

Warner Power, LLC   (2)

---

40 Depot St, Warner, NH 03278
Tel.: (603) 456-3111
Web Site: http://www.warnerpower.com
Emp.: 100
Engineered Power Conversion Products
N.A.I.C.S.: 335999
Scott Rogers (CFO & Sec)
Souheil Benzerrouk (CTO & VP-Engrg)
Kevin Shannon (VP-Product Mktg & Strate-
gic Accts)
Nick Holles (Pres & CEO)

Subsidiary (Domestic):

Warner Power Conversion, LLC   (3)
40 Depot St, Warner, NH 03278
Tel.: (603) 456-3111
Web Site: http://www.warnerpower.com
Power, Distribution & Specialty Transformer
Mfr
N.A.I.C.S.: 335311
Andrew Northrop (Mgr-Testing Svcs)

Paciv, Inc.   (1)
807 Avenida Fernandez Juncos, San Juan,
PR 00907
Tel.: (787) 721-5290
Web Site: http://www.paciv.com
Ambulatory Health Care Services
N.A.I.C.S.: 621999
Shawn Perkins (Dir-Engrg Svcs)
Rick Straw (Pres & Co-Founder)
Douglas Garrote (CFO & VP-Admin)

Subsidiary (Domestic):

Data Science Automation, Inc.   (2)
375 Valleybrook Rd Ste 106, Canonsburg,
PA 15317-3370
Tel.: (724) 942-6330
Web Site: http://www.dsautomation.com
Engineeering Services
N.A.I.C.S.: 541330
Richard Brueggman (Founder & CEO)

Starfire Direct, Inc.   (1)
42168 Remington Ave, Temecula, CA
92590
Web Site: http://www.starfiredirect.com
Concrete Products Mfr
N.A.I.C.S.: 327390
Jonathan Burlingham (Founder & CEO)
Wes Chyrchel (COO)

BLACKFRIARS CORP.
555 Skokie Blvd Ste 555, Northbrook,
IL 60062
Tel.: (818) 991-9000   DE
Holding Company
N.A.I.C.S.: 551112
Keith W. Colburn (Chm, Pres & CEO)

Subsidiaries:

Amari Plastics plc   (1)
Holmes House 24 30 Baker St, Weybridge,
KT13 8AU, Surrey, United Kingdom
Tel.: (44) 1932835000
Web Site: http://www.amariplastics.com
Sales Range: $150-199.9 Million
Emp.: 20
Industrial Plastic Product Mfr
N.A.I.C.S.: 326199
Andy Carroll (Mng Dir)

Subsidiary (Non-US):

Vink Kunststoffen B.V.   (2)
Bergvredestraat 7, 6942 GK, Didam,
Netherlands   (100%)
Tel.: (31) 6298911
Web Site: http://www.vinkkunststoffen.nl
Sales Range: $50-74.9 Million
Plastics Product Mfr
N.A.I.C.S.: 326199
Henk Abma (Gen Dir)

Subsidiary (Non-US):

Vink A/S   (3)
Kristrup Engvej 9, 8900, Randers,
Denmark   (100%)
Tel.: (45) 89110100
Web Site: http://www.vink.dk
Sales Range: $25-49.9 Million
Emp.: 100
Plastics Product Mfr
N.A.I.C.S.: 326199
Walter Blunck (COO-Northern Europe)

Subsidiary (Non-US):

Vink Finland OY   (4)
Silokalliontie 6, Kerava, 4250, Finland
Tel.: (358) 207444300
Web Site: http://www.vink.fi
Sales Range: $100-124.9 Million
Emp.: 70
Plastic Component Mfr
N.A.I.C.S.: 326199
Reijo Asikainen (Mng Dir)

Vink Norway AS   (4)
Bjornerudveien 8, Oslo, 1266,
Norway   (100%)
Tel.: (47) 22766000
Web Site: http://www.vink.no
Sales Range: $100-124.9 Million
Emp.: 38
Plastics Product Mfr
N.A.I.C.S.: 326199
Reidar Nesje (CEO)

Subsidiary (Non-US):

Vink Kunststoffe GmbH & Co.
KG   (3)
Tackenweide 48, 46446, Emmerich am
Rhein, Germany   (100%)
Tel.: (49) 28226060
Web Site: http://www.vinkkunststoffe.de
Sales Range: $25-49.9 Million
Emp.: 40
Plastics Product Mfr
N.A.I.C.S.: 326199
Rals Hullmann (Gen Mgr)

Vink N.V.   (3)
Industrie Park 7, Heist-op-den-Berg, 2220,
Belgium   (100%)
Tel.: (32) 15259711
Web Site: http://www.vink.be
Sales Range: $50-74.9 Million
Emp.: 140
Plastics Product Mfr
N.A.I.C.S.: 326199
Eric Muys (COO-Western Europe)

Consolidated Electrical Distributors,
Inc.   (1)
1920 Westridge Dr, Irving, TX 75038
Web Site: http://www.cedcareers.com
Sales Range: $1-4.9 Billion
Emp.: 7,500
Electrical Supplies & Equipment Whslr &
Distr
N.A.I.C.S.: 423610
Frank Gonzalez (Mgr-Location)
David Whitaker (District Mgr)

Subsidiary (Domestic):

All-Phase Electric Supply Co.   (2)
3905 M 139 Ste 101, Saint Joseph, MI
49085
Tel.: (269) 429-1700
Sales Range: $500-549.9 Million
Emp.: 1,550
Electrical Supplies Whslr
N.A.I.C.S.: 531120

Lappin Electric Company   (2)
W 229 N 1420th Westwood Dr Unit A,
Waukesha, WI 53188
Tel.: (262) 547-5500
Sales Range: $25-49.9 Million
Emp.: 22
Distr & Retailer of Electrical Equipment &
Lighting Fixtures
N.A.I.C.S.: 423610

Port Plastic Inc.   (2)
6312 Airport Fwy, Fort Worth, TX 76117
Tel.: (817) 834-7678
Web Site: http://www.portplastics.com
Rev.: $1,640,000
Emp.: 10
All Other Plastics Product Mfr
N.A.I.C.S.: 326199
David Bonjouklian (Gen Mgr)
Tony Adams (Mgr)

Raybro Electric Supplies   (2)
4910 A Adamo Dr, Tampa, FL 33605-5920
Tel.: (813) 248-6699
Web Site:
http://www.cedtampa.portalced.com
Sales Range: $25-49.9 Million
Emp.: 18

Distr of Electric Equipment, Appliances,
Lighting Fixtures, Generators & Wiring De-
vices
N.A.I.C.S.: 423610
Larry Padron (Mgr)

Stusser Electric Company   (2)
411 E 54th Ave, Anchorage, AK 99518
Tel.: (907) 561-1061
Web Site:
http://www.stusserak.shopced.com
Sales Range: $25-49.9 Million
Emp.: 50
Retailer of Electrical Parts & Equipment
N.A.I.C.S.: 423610

U.S. Electrical Services, Inc.   (2)
701 Middle St, Middletown, CT 06457
Tel.: (860) 522-3232
Web Site: http://www.usesi.com
Sales Range: $50-74.9 Million
Emp.: 350
Electrical Supplies & Equipment Whslr &
Distr
N.A.I.C.S.: 423610
John Marshall (Pres-Metro DC)
Randy Eddy (Pres & CEO)

Subsidiary (Domestic):

Monarch Electric Company Inc.   (3)
30 Plymouth St, Fairfield, NJ 07004-6713
Tel.: (973) 227-4151
Web Site: http://www.monarchelectric.com
Sales Range: $25-49.9 Million
Emp.: 40
Electrical Supplies & Equipment Whslr &
Distr
N.A.I.C.S.: 423610

Standard Electric Supply Co.   (3)
14 Jewel Dr, Wilmington, MA 01887
Tel.: (978) 658-5050
Web Site: http://www.standardelectric.com
Sales Range: $100-124.9 Million
Emp.: 75
Electrical Supplies
N.A.I.C.S.: 423610
Ted Glugolecki (Pres & CEO)

Branch (Domestic):

Standard Electric Co.   (4)
170 Pond View Dr, Meriden, CT 06450
Tel.: (203) 237-8944
Web Site:
http://www.standardelectricco.com
Sales Range: $75-99.9 Million
Emp.: 30
Whslr & Distributor of Electrical Products to
Industrial, Commercial & Residential Mar-
kets
N.A.I.C.S.: 423610
William H. Gray (Pres)

Standard Electric Co.   (4)
103 N Beacon St, Allston, MA 02134
Tel.: (617) 782-1237
Web Site: http://www.standardelectric.com
Electrical Supplies
N.A.I.C.S.: 423610

Standard Electric Co.   (4)
345 Central St, Leominster, MA 01453
Tel.: (978) 466-3806
Sales Range: $75-99.9 Million
Emp.: 4
Electrical Supplies
N.A.I.C.S.: 423610

Standard Electric Co.   (4)
960 Massachusetts Ave, Boston, MA 02118
Tel.: (617) 442-1000
Web Site: http://www.standardelectric.com
Sales Range: $75-99.9 Million
Emp.: 15
Electrical Supplies
N.A.I.C.S.: 423610

Standard Electric Co.   (4)
615 Broadway, Chelsea, MA 02150
Tel.: (617) 884-6616
Web Site: http://www.standardelectric.com
Sales Range: $75-99.9 Million
Emp.: 3
Electrical Supplies
N.A.I.C.S.: 423610

Standard Electric Co.   (4)
1 Heritage Way, Gloucester, MA 01930
Tel.: (978) 281-1933

Web Site: http://www.standardelectric.com
Sales Range: $75-99.9 Million
Emp.: 6
Electrical Supplies
N.A.I.C.S.: 423610

Standard Electric Co. (4)
5 Foundry Industrial Pk, Lowell, MA 18525-5129
Tel.: (978) 452-8985
Web Site: http://www.standardelectric.com
Sales Range: $75-99.9 Million
Emp.: 5
Electrical Supplies
N.A.I.C.S.: 423610
John Nappa (Gen Mgr)

Standard Electric Co. (4)
20 Kearney Rd, Needham, MA 02494
Tel.: (781) 449-7767
Web Site: http://www.standardelectric.com
Sales Range: $75-99.9 Million
Emp.: 3
Electrical Supplies
N.A.I.C.S.: 423610
Fred Forsgard (Sr VP)
Ted Dlugolecki (Pres)

Standard Electric Co. (4)
40 Reservoir Park Dr, Rockland, MA 02370
Tel.: (781) 681-9354
Sales Range: $75-99.9 Million
Emp.: 3
Electrical Supplies
N.A.I.C.S.: 423610
Michael Lips (Branch Mgr)

Standard Electric Co. (4)
1339 Main St, Waltham, MA 02451
Tel.: (781) 890-1050
Web Site: http://www.standardelectric.com
Sales Range: $75-99.9 Million
Emp.: 11
Electrical Supplies
N.A.I.C.S.: 449129

Standard Electric Co. (4)
14 Jewel Dr, Wilmington, MA 01887
Tel.: (978) 658-5050
Web Site: http://www.standardelectric.com
Electrical Supplies
N.A.I.C.S.: 423610

Subsidiary (Domestic):

Wiedenbach-Brown Co. Inc. (3)
10 Skyline Dr, Hawthorne, NY 10532
Tel.: (914) 235-4500
Web Site: http://www.wblight.com
Sales Range: $50-74.9 Million
Emp.: 55
Electrical Contracting Services & Speciality Lighting Distr
N.A.I.C.S.: 423610
Christopher Brown (CEO)
Elisabeth Brown-Daley (VP)
Jeffrey Codd (Sr VP-Ops)
Rodger S. Cherry (Pres)
Ron Doyle (VP-Bus Dev)
Christine DeRosa (Dir-Project Ops)
Lara Cordell (Dir-Tech)
Gary Popovics (Dir-MRO)

Subsidiary (Domestic):

Vegas Electric Supply (2)
3655 W Sunset Rd Ste F, Las Vegas, NV 89118
Tel.: (702) 367-0980
Web Site: http://www.vegaselesupply.com
Sales Range: $25-49.9 Million
Emp.: 20
Retailer of Electrical Appliances
N.A.I.C.S.: 423610

Hajoca Corporation (1)
1209 E Welsh Rd, Lansdale, PA 19446-0109
Tel.: (215) 699-4884
Web Site: http://www.hajoca.com
Plumbing Heating & Industrial Supply Distr
N.A.I.C.S.: 423720
Rick Klau (Chm)

Subsidiary (Domestic):

Able Distributing Co. Inc. (2)
2727 W Grovers Ave, Phoenix, AZ 85053
Tel.: (602) 993-1140
Web Site: http://www.abledistributing.com

Sales Range: $25-49.9 Million
Emp.: 125
Plumbing & Hydronic Heating Supplies Distr
N.A.I.C.S.: 423720

Subsidiary (Non-US):

EMCO Corporation (2)
1108 Dundas St, London, N5W 3A7, ON, Canada
Tel.: (519) 453-9600
Sales Range: $800-899.9 Million
Emp.: 85
Plumbing HVAC Waterwork & Industrial Product Distr
N.A.I.C.S.: 423720
Rick Fantham (Pres)

Subsidiary (Domestic):

EMCO Corporation - British Columbia (3)
11 Burbidge Street, Coquitlam, V3K 7B2, BC, Canada
Tel.: (604) 468-2727
Web Site: http://www.emcobc.ca
Plumbing, HVAC, Waterworks & Industrial Products Distr
N.A.I.C.S.: 423720

Division (Domestic):

Independent Supply Company Inc. (3)
2808 Ingleton Avenue, Burnaby, V5C 6G7, BC, Canada
Tel.: (604) 298-4472
Web Site: https://ischvacr.com
Refrigeration, Heating, Ventilation & Air Conditioning Parts Distr
N.A.I.C.S.: 423740
David Sevcik (Mgr-Saint Catharines)
Ray Spencer (Mgr-North Bay)

Waterworks Supplies & Services Limited (3)
18 Bruce Street, Mount Pearl, A1N 4T4, NL, Canada
Tel.: (709) 747-2626
Sales Range: $25-49.9 Million
Emp.: 15
Plumbing Supplies Distr
N.A.I.C.S.: 423720
Clarence Brown (Mgr)

Westlund (3)
1130 34th Ave Bay 1 Nisku, Edmonton, T9E 1K7, AB, Canada
Tel.: (780) 463-7473
Web Site: http://www.westlundpvf.com
Sales Range: $25-49.9 Million
Emp.: 25
Industrial Pipe, Valves & Fittings Distr
N.A.I.C.S.: 423840
Kevin O'Reilly (VP & Gen Mgr)

Branch (Domestic):

Hajoca Corp. - Costa Mesa (2)
3170 Airway Ave, Costa Mesa, CA 92626
Tel.: (714) 638-4442
Web Site: http://www.hajocacostamesa.com
Plumbing & Hydronic Heating Supplies
N.A.I.C.S.: 423720

Hajoca Corp. - Hawthorne (2)
14701 Inglewood Ave, Hawthorne, CA 90250-6717
Tel.: (310) 970-0007
Web Site: http://www.hajocahawthorne.com
Plumbing Fittings & Supplies Distr
N.A.I.C.S.: 423720
Shad Peck (Gen Mgr)

Hajoca Corp. - Los Angeles (2)
2275 S Carmelina Ave, Los Angeles, CA 90064
Tel.: (310) 231-1111
Web Site: http://www.hajocalosangeles.com
Emp.: 6
Plumbing & Hydronic Heating Supplies
N.A.I.C.S.: 423720
Carlo Noble (Branch Mgr)

Hajoca Corp. - Stroudsburg (2)
163 N 2nd St, Stroudsburg, PA 18360-2523
Tel.: (570) 421-8050
Web Site: http://www.hajocastroudsburg.com
Emp.: 4

Plumbing, Heating & Industrial Supplies Whslr
N.A.I.C.S.: 423720
Daren Handelong (Mgr)

Subsidiary (Domestic):

Kelly's Pipe & Supply Co. (2)
2124 Industrial Rd, Las Vegas, NV 89102-4627
Tel.: (702) 382-4957
Web Site: http://www.kellyspipe.com
Sales Range: $10-24.9 Million
Emp.: 18
Plumbing Fixture Equipment & Supply
N.A.I.C.S.: 423720
Chris Dresch (Gen Mgr)

Unit (Domestic):

European Bath, Kitchen, Tile & Stone (3)
4050 S Decatur Blvd, Las Vegas, NV 89103-5810
Tel.: (702) 873-8600
Web Site: http://www.europeanlv.com
Sales Range: $10-24.9 Million
Emp.: 3
N.A.I.C.S.: 444180
Chris Thresch (Gen Mgr)

Laird Plastics, Inc. (1)
14350 NW 56 Ct Ste 103, Opa Locka, FL 33054
Tel.: (305) 626-9800
Web Site: http://www.lairdplastics.com
Rev.: $101,000,000
Emp.: 500
Plastic Material Distr
N.A.I.C.S.: 424610

Metal Manufactures Pty Limited (1)
27-29 Federal Street North, Hobart, 7000, TAS, Australia
Tel.: (61) 362346999
Electrical Services & Distr
N.A.I.C.S.: 238210

Subsidiary (Domestic):

Crane Distribution Limited (2)
Virginia Business Centre, Locked Bag 71, Virginia, 4014, QLD, Australia
Tel.: (61) 732609777
Web Site: https://tradelink.com.au
Building Supplies Distr
N.A.I.C.S.: 423390

Modern Plastics Inc. (1)
88 Long Hill Cross Rd, Shelton, CT 06484
Tel.: (203) 333-3128
Web Site: http://www.modernplastics.com
Sales Range: $25-49.9 Million
Emp.: 100
Distr of Plastic Sheet, Rod, Tube & Film Materials
N.A.I.C.S.: 424610
David A. Altieri (VP-Corp Sls)
Bing J. Carbone (Pres)
Vince Griffin (Mgr-Global Sls)
Juan Hernandez (Mgr-Warehouse Production)
Chris M. Acosta (Gen Mgr-Pur)
Julio Alfonso (Dir-Plastics Fabrication)
Kevin Daly (Dir-Certified Quality Control)

Nu-Lite Electrical Wholesalers, Inc. (1)
850 Edwards Ave, Harahan, LA 70123-3123
Tel.: (504) 733-3300
Web Site: http://www.nulite.com
Sales Range: $75-99.9 Million
Emp.: 80
Distr of Electrical Apparatus & Equipment
N.A.I.C.S.: 423610
Gary Corales (VP)
Joe Impastato (Gen Mgr)
Richard Zimmerman (Mgr-Credit)
Allen Pertuit (Branch Mgr)
Derek Guilbeau (Branch Mgr)
Brenda Crutchfield (Branch Mgr)
Rick Corales (Pres)
Nick Rogers (Controller)
Nappy Naquin (Mgr-Counter Sls)
Allen Pierre (Branch Mgr)
Jennifer Gray (Coord-Mktg)
Robbie Young (Mgr-Bridgeport)

Polymershapes LLC (1)

10130 Perimeter Pkwy Ste 500, Charlotte, NC 28216
Tel.: (866) 437-7427
Web Site: http://www.polymershapes.com
Plastics Product Mfr
N.A.I.C.S.: 424610
Trevor Lee (Dir-Reg)

BLACKHAWK COUNTRY CLUB
599 Blackhawk Club Dr, Danville, CA 94506
Tel.: (925) 736-6500   **CA**
Web Site:
   https://www.blackhawkcc.org
Year Founded: 1988
Sales Range: $10-24.9 Million
Emp.: 370
Country Club
N.A.I.C.S.: 713910
Julianne Yee (Dir-HR)
Morisha Dechter (Dir-Membership & Mktg)
Ashlie Miller (Dir-Tennis)
Dustin Wade (Controller)
Kevin Dunne (COO & Gen Mgr)
Kirk Philippou (Mgr-Clubhouse)
Mary Clancy (Asst Controller)
Jessica Hood-Samayoa (Mgr-Food & Beverage)

BLACKHAWK MODIFICATIONS INC.
7601 Karl May Dr, Waco, TX 76708
Tel.: (254) 755-6711
Web Site:
   https://www.blackhawk.aero
Year Founded: 1999
Engine Performance Solutions; Aircraft Engine Maintenance & Repair Services
N.A.I.C.S.: 441330
Jim Allmon (Pres & CEO)
Matt Shieman (Chm)
Lynnette Allmon (Exec VP & Mgr-HR)
Edwin Black (Sr VP-Global Sls & Mktg)
Chris Dunkin (Reg Sls Mgr-Eastern US)
Bobby Patton (VP-Intl Sls)
Donnie Holder (VP-Mktg)
Lindzie Lane (Coord-Sls)
Micky Bitcon (CFO)
Cisca De Lange (Reg Sls Mgr-Africa)
Mauricio Melro (Reg Sls Mgr-South America)
Amber Dunkin (Dir-Sls Support)
Charles Aybar (Sls Mgr-Aircraft)
Linda Hill (Coord-Aircraft Sls)
Don Moore (Dir-Global Customer Support)
Lindsay Allmon (Coord-Mktg)
Bob Kromer (Sr VP-Engrg)

BLACKHAWK MOLDING CO. INC.
120 W Interstate Rd, Addison, IL 60101
Tel.: (630) 543-3900
Web Site:
   https://www.blackhawkmolding.com
Rev.: $18,400,000
Emp.: 160
Caps, Plastics
N.A.I.C.S.: 326199
Richard Hogan (Controller)
Bob Komperda (Engr-Plastics)
Jeff Davis (Dir-Ops)
Roberto Castro (Dir-HR)
Juan Tapia (Mgr-HR)

BLACKHAWK NEFF INC.
805 Northgate Cir, New Castle, PA 16105
Tel.: (724) 658-8186

Blackhawk Neff Inc.—(Continued)

Web Site:
   https://www.blackhawkneff.com
Sales Range: $10-24.9 Million
Emp.: 35
General Electrical Contractor
N.A.I.C.S.: 238210
Greg Al Hogue *(VP)*
Robert W. Neff *(VP)*
Michael D. Robinson Sr. *(CEO)*

BLACKHAWK STEEL CORP
4500 W 47th St, Chicago, IL 60632
Tel.: (773) 778-4100
Rev.: $27,000,000
Emp.: 100
Steel
N.A.I.C.S.: 423510
Mark Herman *(Pres)*

BLACKLIDGE EMULSIONS, INC.
12251 Bernard Pkwy Ste 200, Gulf-port, MS 39503
Tel.: (228) 863-3878
Web Site:
   http://www.blacklidgeemulsions.com
Year Founded: 1990
Sales Range: $10-24.9 Million
Emp.: 100
Asphalt Paving Mixture & Block Mfr
N.A.I.C.S.: 324121
Kimberly Lewis *(Dir-Fin)*
David Vaught *(Plant Mgr)*

BLACKLINE SYSTEMS
21300 Victory Blvd 12th Fl, Woodland Hills, CA 91367
Tel.: (818) 223-9008
Web Site: https://www.blackline.com
Year Founded: 2001
Sales Range: $10-24.9 Million
Emp.: 75
Enterprise Software Designer & Mfr
N.A.I.C.S.: 513210
Mario Spanicciati *(Chief Strategy Officer)*
David Adler *(Dir-Implementations)*
Chris Murphy *(Chief Revenue Officer)*
David Downing *(CMO)*
Therese Tucker *(CEO)*
Max Solonski *(Chief Security Officer)*
Karen Flathers *(Chief Customer Officer)*

BLACKMAN PLUMBING SUP-PLY CO. INC.
900 Sylvan Ave, Bayport, NY 11705
Tel.: (516) 579-2000   NY
Web Site: http://www.blackman.com
Year Founded: 1921
Rev.: $70,200,000
Emp.: 350
Plumbing Fixtures, Equipment & Sup-plies
N.A.I.C.S.: 423720
Robert Mannheimer *(Chm, Pres & CEO)*
Sean Mulderig *(VP-Sls-East)*
Diane C. Nardone *(Chief Legal Officer)*
Kathleen Neglia *(VP-Fin & Acctg)*
Erich Liendo *(CTO)*

Subsidiaries:

Blackman Plumbing Supply Co. Inc.   **(1)**
50 Hazel St, Hicksville, NY 11801
Tel.: (516) 931-6144
Web Site: http://www.blackman.com
Sales Range: $10-24.9 Million
Emp.: 50
Plumbing Fixtures, Equipment & Supplies
N.A.I.C.S.: 423720

Blackman Plumbing Supply Co. Inc.   **(1)**

348 Broadway, Lynbrook, NY 11563-3908
Tel.: (516) 593-3100
Web Site: http://www.blackman.com
Sales Range: $10-24.9 Million
Emp.: 50
Plumbing Fixtures, Equipment & Supplies
N.A.I.C.S.: 423720

Blackman Plumbing Supply Co. Inc.   **(1)**
940 W Main St, Riverhead, NY 11901-2820
Tel.: (631) 727-4800
Web Site: http://www.blackman.com
Sales Range: $10-24.9 Million
Emp.: 5
Plumbing Fixtures, Equipment & Supplies
N.A.I.C.S.: 423720
Joe Perez *(Branch Mgr)*

Blackman Plumbing Supply Co. Inc.   **(1)**
3480 Sunrise Hwy, Wantagh, NY 11793-4028
Tel.: (516) 785-6000
Web Site: http://www.blackman.com
Plumbing Fixture & Equipment Distr
N.A.I.C.S.: 423720

Blackman Plumbing Supply Co. Inc.   **(1)**
134 07 Northern Blvd, Flushing, NY 11354-4004
Tel.: (718) 939-7200
Web Site: http://www.blackman.com
Sales Range: $10-24.9 Million
Emp.: 22
Plumbing Fixtures, Equipment & Supplies
N.A.I.C.S.: 423720
Andy Rothenbucher *(Gen Mgr)*

Blackman Plumbing Supply Co. Inc.   **(1)**
240 Broadway, Huntington Station, NY 11746-1403
Tel.: (631) 760-2050
Web Site: http://www.blackman.com
Sales Range: $25-49.9 Million
Emp.: 60
Plumbing Fixtures, Equipment & Supplies
N.A.I.C.S.: 423720
Paul Monahan *(Branch Mgr-Blackman Mineola)*

Blackman Plumbing Supply Co. Inc.   **(1)**
2700 Rte 112, Medford, NY 11763-2553
Tel.: (631) 475-3170
Web Site: http://www.blackman.com
Sales Range: $10-24.9 Million
Emp.: 18
Plumbing Fixtures Equipment & Supplies
N.A.I.C.S.: 423720
Tony Piliero *(Office Mgr)*

Blackman Plumbing Supply Co. Inc.   **(1)**
217 68 Hempstead Ave, Queens Village, NY 11429
Tel.: (718) 479-5533
Web Site: http://www.blackman.com
Sales Range: $10-24.9 Million
Emp.: 7
Plumbing Fixtures, Equipment & Supplies
N.A.I.C.S.: 423720
Andrew Rothenbucher *(Branch Mgr-Blackman Flushing)*

Blackman Plumbing Supply Co. Inc.   **(1)**
444 County Rd 39A, Southampton, NY 11968-5257
Tel.: (631) 283-2176
Web Site: http://www.blackman.com
Plumbing Fixtures, Equipment & Supplies
N.A.I.C.S.: 423720
Robert Manheimer *(CEO)*

Blackman Plumbing Supply Co. Inc., Mineola Branch   **(1)**
208 Herricks Rd, Mineola, NY 11501-2207   **(100%)**
Tel.: (516) 742-1011
Web Site: http://www.blackman.com
Sales Range: $10-24.9 Million
Emp.: 15
Plumbing Fixtures, Equipment & Supplies
N.A.I.C.S.: 423720
Paul Manahan *(Branch Mgr)*

BLACKPOINT IT SERVICES, INC.

20435 72nd Ave S Ste 200, Kent, WA 98032
Tel.: (206) 575-9511   WA
Web Site: http://www.blackpoint-it.com
Year Founded: 1977
Information Technology Consulting Services & Computer Repair Services
N.A.I.C.S.: 541690
James R. Watson *(CEO)*
Lesleigh Watson *(Co-Owner & COO)*

Subsidiaries:

Copper State Communications, Inc.   **(1)**
2820 N 36th Ave, Phoenix, AZ 85009
Tel.: (602) 272-2800
Web Site: http://www.copper-state.com
Voice, Data & Business Communications
N.A.I.C.S.: 517810
Steven Sutton *(Co-Founder & Pres)*
Karen Roberts *(Mng Dir)*

BLACKRAPID, INC.
517 Aloha St, Seattle, WA 98109
Tel.: (206) 402-4905
Web Site: http://www.blackrapid.com
Year Founded: 2008
Sales Range: $1-9.9 Million
Emp.: 20
Designs & Retails Camera Accessories, Including the R-Strap Worn Diagonally Across the Body, Reducing Neck Strain
N.A.I.C.S.: 423410
Ron Henry *(Founder & CEO)*
Todd Spraetz *(CFO)*
Marc Gottula *(Dir-Sls-Natl & Intl)*
Joe Zagorski *(Mgr-Global Sls)*
Lillian Zagorski *(Bus Mgr)*

BLACKSANDS PETROLEUM, INC.
4833 Front St B405, Castle Rock, CO 80104
Tel.: (720) 536-5824   NV
Year Founded: 2004
Oil & Gas Exploration Services
N.A.I.C.S.: 211120
Mark Spoone *(CEO)*

BLACKSTONE AUDIO, INC.
31 Mistletoe Rd, Ashland, OR 97520
Tel.: (541) 482-9239   OR
Web Site:
   http://www.blackstoneaudio.com
Year Founded: 1987
Book Stores
N.A.I.C.S.: 459210
Josh Stanton *(CEO)*
Greg Boguslawski *(Dir-Sls & Mdsg)*

Subsidiaries:

The Audio Partners, Inc.   **(1)**
131 E Placer St, Auburn, CA 95603
Tel.: (530) 888-7801
Web Site: http://www.audioeditions.com
Direct to Consumer Audiobook Retailer
N.A.I.C.S.: 459210
Grady Hesters *(CEO)*

BLACKSTONE CALLING CARD, INC.
11600 NW 34th St, Doral, FL 33178
Tel.: (305) 639-9590   FL
Web Site:
   http://www.blackstoneonline.com
Year Founded: 1995
Sales Range: $350-399.9 Million
Emp.: 180
Telecommunications Resellers
N.A.I.C.S.: 517121
Carlos Rodriguez *(Pres)*

BLACKSTRATUS, INC.
1551 S Washington Ave, Piscataway, NJ 08854

Tel.: (732) 393-6000
Web Site:
   http://www.blackstratus.com
Year Founded: 1999
Sales Range: $1-9.9 Million
Emp.: 41
Cloud-Based Security Information & Event Management Software Solutions
N.A.I.C.S.: 513210
Dennis Cline *(Vice Chm)*
Dale W. Cline *(CEO)*
Philip Rugani *(Chief Revenue Officer)*
Mike Maxwell *(Chief Security Officer)*
Charles Johnson *(Dir-Security Ops Center-Stamford)*
Roland Cloutier *(Chief Security Officer & VP)*
Rich Murphy *(VP-Products)*

BLACKSTREET CAPITAL HOLDINGS LLC
7250 Woodmont Ave Ste 210, Bethesda, MD 20814
Tel.: (240) 223-1330
Web Site: http://bchhold.com
Year Founded: 2015
Holding Company
N.A.I.C.S.: 551112
Murry Gunty *(Founder, CEO & Mgr)*

Subsidiaries:

Black Bear Sports Group, Inc.   **(1)**
7250 Woodmont Ave Ste 210, Bethesda, MD 20814
Tel.: (240) 223-1330
Web Site:
   http://www.blackbearsportsgroup.com
Ice Skating Rink Management Services
N.A.I.C.S.: 611620
Murry N. Gunty *(Founder & CEO)*
Robert Dragonette *(CFO)*

Subsidiary (Domestic):

Center Ice Delmont, LLC   **(2)**
100 Ctr Ice Dr, Delmont, PA 15626-1686
Tel.: (724) 468-1100
Web Site: http://www.centericearena.com
Fitness & Recreational Sports Centers
N.A.I.C.S.: 713940
Mindy Ulyas *(Mgr)*

Ice Land Associates, LP   **(2)**
6 Tennis Ct, Trenton, NJ 08619
Tel.: (609) 588-6672
Web Site: http://www.ice-land.com
Fitness & Recreational Sports Centers
N.A.I.C.S.: 713940

Milford Ice Pavilion   **(2)**
291 Sub Way, Milford, CT 06461-3057
Tel.: (203) 878-6516
Web Site: http://www.milfordice.com
Promoters of Performing Arts, Sports & Similar Events with Facilities
N.A.I.C.S.: 711310

Twin Ponds East Arena   **(2)**
3904 Corey Rd, Harrisburg, PA 17109-5929
Tel.: (717) 558-7663
Web Site: http://www.twinponds.com
Fitness & Recreational Sports Centers
N.A.I.C.S.: 713940
Diane Heckendorn *(Mgr)*

Cartesian, Inc.   **(1)**
6405 Metcalf Ave Ste 417, Overland Park, KS 66202
Tel.: (913) 234-3300
Web Site: http://www.cartesian.com
Sales Range: $50-74.9 Million
Management & Consulting Services to Communications Industry
N.A.I.C.S.: 541611
Ron Angner *(Sr VP-Network & Ops)*
Jim Serafin *(CEO)*

Subsidiary (Non-US):

Cartesian Ltd.   **(2)**
Descartes House 8 Gate Street, London, WC2A 3HP, United Kingdom
Tel.: (44) 2076435555
Web Site: http://www.cartesian.com

Business Management Software Programming Services
N.A.I.C.S.: 541511.
Tim Jacks *(Principal)*

Farncombe France SARL   (2)
243 Rue de Vaugirard, Paris, 75015,
France
Tel.: (33) 607375127
Television Design Services
N.A.I.C.S.: 334220

BLACKSTREET CAPITAL MANAGEMENT, LLC

5425 Wisconsin Ave Ste 701, Chevy
Chase, MD 20815
Tel.: (240) 223-1330   DE
Web Site:
  http://www.blackstreetcapital.com
Year Founded: 2003
Sales Range: $150-199.9 Million
Privater Equity Firm
N.A.I.C.S.: 523999
Murry N. Gunty *(Mng Partner)*
David A. Hartman *(Principal-Portfolio Fin)*
Kevin Kuby *(Mng Dir-Restructuring)*
Ryan J. Hammon *(VP-Ops)*
Robert Dragonette *(CFO)*
Ryan Scott *(VP)*

Subsidiaries:

AWE Acquisition, Inc.   (1)
2501 Seaport Dr Ste 410-Sh, Chester, PA
19013-2252
Tel.: (610) 833-6400
Web Site: http://www.awelearning.com
Custom Computer Programming Services
N.A.I.C.S.: 541511
Karl D. Thornton *(Pres)*

Rauch Industries, Inc.   (1)
3800 Little Mountain Rd Ste A, Gastonia,
NC 28056
Tel.: (704) 867-5333
Web Site: http://www.rauchindustries.com
Sales Range: $75-99.9 Million
Mfr of Christmas Ornaments & Novelties
N.A.I.C.S.: 327215

ThinkDirect Marketing Group,
Inc.   (1)
8285 Bryan Dairy Rd Ste 150, Largo, FL
33777
Tel.: (727) 369-2900
Web Site: http://www.tdmg.com
Customer Acquisition Services
N.A.I.C.S.: 541860
Dennis A. Cahill *(Chm & CEO)*
Robert Paolillo *(COO & Sec)*

Western Capital Resources, Inc.   (1)
11550 I St Ste 150, Omaha, NE 68137
Tel.: (402) 551-8888
Web Site:
  https://www.westerncapitalresources.com
Rev.: $164,145,268
Assets: $116,197,672
Liabilities: $38,040,021
Net Worth: $78,157,651
Earnings: $10,306,735
Emp.: 950
Fiscal Year-end: 12/31/2021
Consumer Loan Broker
N.A.I.C.S.: 522310
John Quandahl *(Pres, CEO & COO)*
Angel Donchev *(CFO & Chief Investment Officer)*
Steve Irlbeck *(Sec & Dir-Acctg & Acctg)*

BLACKTHORNE PARTNERS LTD.

375 Bishops Way Ste 222, Brookfield, WI 53005
Tel.: (262) 786-5100   WI
Web Site:
  http://www.blackthornepartners.com
Year Founded: 2006
Privater Equity Firm
N.A.I.C.S.: 523999
John F. Syburg *(Founder & Mng Dir)*
Steve Balistreri *(Mng Dir)*

Subsidiaries:

Design Specialties, Inc.   (1)
11100 W Heather Ave, Milwaukee, WI
53224
Tel.: (414) 371-1200
Web Site:
  http://www.glassfireplacedoors.com
Sales Range: $1-9.9 Million
Emp.: 24
Glass Fireplace Door Mfr & Whslr
N.A.I.C.S.: 327215
Michael Draves *(Pres)*

BLACKTIE LLC

1660 S Albion St Ste 1025, Denver,
CO 80222
Tel.: (303) 832-2903
Web Site: http://www.blacktie-colorado.com
Sales Range: $1-9.9 Million
Online Event Planning & Communications Tools for Members
N.A.I.C.S.: 711310
Kenton Kuhn *(Founder & CEO)*
Robb Stenman *(VP-Mktg)*

Subsidiaries:

Blacktie-San Antonio   (1)
3210 Limestone Trail, San Antonio, TX
78253   (100%)
Tel.: (210) 319-5020
Web Site: http://www.blacktie-sanantonio.com
Online Event Planning
N.A.I.C.S.: 711310

BLACKTON, INC.

1714 Alden Rd, Orlando, FL 32803
Tel.: (407) 898-2661
Web Site: http://www.blacktoninc.com
Year Founded: 1954
Sales Range: $10-24.9 Million
Emp.: 63
Flooring & Roofing Contractor & Supplier
N.A.I.C.S.: 238330
Michael Blackton *(CEO)*
Bruce Blacton *(COO)*
Sean Monett *(Pres)*
Aubrie Blackton Smith *(Mgr-Mktg)*

Subsidiaries:

Blackton Interiors of Orlando   (1)
1714 Alden Rd, Orlando, FL 32803
Tel.: (407) 898-2661
Web Site: http://www.blacktoninteriors.com
Flooring Contractor & Retailer
N.A.I.C.S.: 238330

BLACKWATCH INTERNATIONAL CORP.

1430 Spring Hill Rd Ste 205,
McLean, VA 22102
Tel.: (571) 395-8403
Web Site:
  http://www.blackwatchintel.com
Year Founded: 2010
Cyber Security & IT Systems Operations & Maintenance
N.A.I.C.S.: 561621
Allen Morningstar *(Exec Dir)*
Clifford Webster *(Pres)*
David Wolf *(Sr VP-Ops & Capture)*

Subsidiaries:

FutureWorld Technologies, Inc.   (1)
5740 Windmill Way Ste 12, Carmichael, CA
95608
Tel.: (916) 481-3156
Web Site: http://www.futureworld.biz
Computer Related Services
N.A.I.C.S.: 541512
Chris Michels *(Engrg-Software)*

BLACKWELL CAPITAL GROUP LLC

1440 W Dean Rd, River Hills, WI
53217

Tel.: (414) 331-2766
Web Site:
  http://blackwellcapitalgroup.com
Privater Equity Firm
N.A.I.C.S.: 523999
Steve Balistreri *(Founder & Mng Dir)*

Subsidiaries:

Custom Production Grinding, Inc.   (1)
N56 W13500 Silver Spg, Menomonee Falls,
WI 53051
Tel.: (262) 783-5770
Web Site:
  http://www.customproductiongrind.com
Sales Range: $1-9.9 Million
Emp.: 39
Mfr Industrial Machinery
N.A.I.C.S.: 332710
Christine Marx *(VP)*
Greg Schoepke *(CFO)*
Michael Marx *(Mgr-Sls & Mktg)*

BLACKWELL CO-OP

410 N Main St, Blackwell, OK 74631
Tel.: (580) 363-0515
Web Site: http://www.blackwell.com
Sales Range: $10-24.9 Million
Emp.: 35
Grains
N.A.I.C.S.: 424510
Rian Thomas *(Mgr)*

BLACKWELL LAND, LLC

1340 7th St, Wasco, CA 93280
Tel.: (661) 393-7238
Web Site:
  https://www.blackwellco.com
Agricultural Production; Crops
N.A.I.C.S.: 111335

BLACKWOLF INC.

2802 Saint Lawrence St, Riverside,
CA 92504
Tel.: (909) 785-1500
Web Site: http://www.blackwolf.net
Sales Range: $10-24.9 Million
Emp.: 44
Computers, Peripherals & Software
N.A.I.C.S.: 423430

BLADE CHEVROLET

1100 Freeway Dr, Mount Vernon, WA
98273
Tel.: (360) 424-3231
Web Site: http://www.bladechevy.com
Sales Range: $10-24.9 Million
Emp.: 60
New Car Retailer
N.A.I.C.S.: 441110
Zane Morrison *(Mgr-Fleet & Comml Sls)*
Ryan Stevens *(Mgr-Parts)*

BLADE ENERGY PARTNERS, LTD.

2600 Network Blvd Ste 550, Frisco,
TX 75034
Tel.: (972) 712-8407   TX
Web Site: https://www.blade-energy.com
Year Founded: 2000
Sales Range: $10-24.9 Million
Emp.: 85
Business Consultants
N.A.I.C.S.: 541618
David Lewis *(Pres)*
Ravi Krishnamurthy *(Exec VP)*
Sriram Vasantharajan *(Exec VP)*
Jim Wooten *(Exec VP)*
Bob Pilko *(Dir-Strategic Relationship)*

BLADE HQ, LLC

400 S 1000 E Ste E, Lehi, UT 84043
Tel.: (801) 768-0232
Web Site: http://www.bladehq.com
Year Founded: 2002
Rev.: $2,400,000
Emp.: 40

Military, Law Enforcement & Collectible Knife Whlsr
N.A.I.C.S.: 423990
Cameron Hughes *(CEO)*
Ammon Padeken *(Mgr-Order Fulfillment)*
Jim Brown *(Co-Founder & CTO)*
Mark Christensen *(Mgr-Mktg)*

BLADE-TECH INDUSTRIES, INC.

5530 184th St E, Puyallup, WA
98375
Tel.: (253) 655-8059
Web Site: http://www.blade-tech.com
Year Founded: 1988
Sales Range: $10-24.9 Million
Emp.: 50
Plastic Material Whslr
N.A.I.C.S.: 424610
Bryce Wegner *(Pres)*
Lilly Nieto *(Mgr-Production)*
Tara Clarkson *(Office Mgr)*
Josh Crawford *(Mgr-Production)*
Micah Galbraith *(Engr-Design)*
Chris Thomas *(Mgr-Inventory)*
Tricia Fisk *(Mgr-HR)*
Dallas Farquhar *(Controller & Mgr-Acctg)*

BLADES CO. INC.

750 Nicholas Blvd, Elk Grove Village,
IL 60007
Tel.: (847) 439-2126
Web Site:
  https://www.bladesmachinery.com
Rev.: $10,900,000
Emp.: 37
Industrial Machinery & Equipment
N.A.I.C.S.: 423830
Alex Shore *(Pres)*
Bill Neil *(VP)*

Subsidiaries:

Blades Machinery Co Inc   (1)
750 Nicholas Blvd, Elk Grove Village, IL
60007
Tel.: (847) 439-2126
Web Site: http://www.bladesmachinery.com
Rev.: $5,000,000
Plastic Products Machinery Rebuilder &
Parts Distr
N.A.I.C.S.: 423830
Alex Shore *(Pres)*

BLAIN SUPPLY, INC.

3507 E Racine St, Janesville, WI
53546
Tel.: (608) 754-2821
Web Site:
  http://www.farmandfleet.com
Year Founded: 1955
Sales Range: $10-24.9 Million
Emp.: 4,000
Retailers Stores
N.A.I.C.S.: 423820
Jane Blain Gilbertson *(Owner & Pres)*
Monica Bonamego *(CFO)*
Kristin Stewart *(Chief Mktg Officer)*
Paul Miller *(Chief Mdsg Officer)*
Dennis Armstrong *(Chief HR Officer)*

Subsidiaries:

Woodstock Farm & Fleet Inc.   (1)
11501 US Hwy 14, Woodstock, IL 60098
Tel.: (815) 338-2549
Web Site: http://www.farmandfleet.com
Automotive Accessories Distr; Car Tire
Store & Auto Repair Shop
N.A.I.C.S.: 441330
Jane Blain Gilbertson *(Pres)*
Gary Hilt *(VP-Loss Prevention)*

BLAINE CONVENTION SERVICES

114 S Berry St, Brea, CA 92821-4826
Tel.: (714) 522-8270

Blaine Convention Services—(Continued)
Web Site:
http://blaineconventionservices.com
Year Founded: 1972
Sales Range: $25-49.9 Million
Emp.: 18
Exhibit Construction By Industrial
Contractors
N.A.I.C.S.: 561990
Jacob Ruppert *(Mgr-Sls)*
Lola Alvitre *(Mgr-Exhibitor Svc)*
Thomas W. Blaine Sr. *(CEO)*

BLAINE LARSEN FARMS INC.
2379 E 2300 N, Hamer, ID 83425-
5025
Tel.: (208) 662-5501
Web Site:
http://www.larsenfarms.com
Year Founded: 1966
Sales Range: $25-49.9 Million
Emp.: 460
Provider of Grains, Fruits & Veg-
etables
N.A.I.C.S.: 311423
Blaine Larsen *(Pres)*
Bart Larsen *(Pres)*

BLAINE WARREN ADVERTIS-ING LLC
7120 Smoke Ranch Rd, Las Vegas,
NV 89128
Tel.: (702) 435-6947
Web Site:
http://www.blainewarren.com
Sales Range: $10-24.9 Million
Advertising Services
N.A.I.C.S.: 541810
Sterling Martell *(Owner)*
Michael Sabatier *(CFO)*
Sabrina Granati *(Acct Mgr)*

BLAIR & ASSOCIATES, LTD.
11333 E 60th Pl, Tulsa, OK 74146
Tel.: (918) 254-6337
Web Site:
http://www.vcientertainment.com
Sales Range: $1-9.9 Million
Emp.: 50
Video & DVD Producer & Distr
N.A.I.C.S.: 512120
Robert A. Blair *(Pres)*

BLAIR COMPANIES, INC.
5107 Kissell Ave, Altoona, PA 16601
Tel.: (814) 949-8287
Web Site:
http://www.blaircompanies.com
Year Founded: 1951
Sales Range: $50-74.9 Million
Emp.: 400
Architectural Services
N.A.I.C.S.: 541310
Jim Nations *(VP-Ops)*
Joe DeLeo *(VP-Project Mgmt)*
Philip Devorris *(Pres & CEO)*
Robert Burns *(Dir-Automotive
Imaging-Troy)*
Rick Sanchez *(VP-Chicago)*
Scott Rizzo *(VP-Philadelphia)*
Jerry Gillham *(VP-Tampa)*
Bradley A. Alford *(VP-Architectural
Imaging)*

BLAIR CONSTRUCTION INC.
23020 US Hwy 29 S, Gretna, VA
24557
Tel.: (434) 656-6243
Web Site:
http://www.blairbuildsbetter.com
Year Founded: 1911
Sales Range: $25-49.9 Million
Industrial & Commercial Construction
Services
N.A.I.C.S.: 236220

Timothy J. Clark *(VP)*
Bobby Adkins *(Project Mgr)*
Ken BeCraft *(VP-Estimation)*
J. Matthew Doss *(CFO)*
Brian Nichols *(Project Mgr)*
Jason Richardson *(Project Mgr)*
Brandon Simpkins *(Dir-Safety)*
Michael Trent *(Asst Project Mgr)*

BLAIR SERVICES OF AMERICA INC.
1121 Walt Whitman Rd Ste 204, Mel-
ville, NY 11747-3083
Tel.: (631) 385-8700
Sales Range: $25-49.9 Million
Emp.: 32
Mortgage Banker
N.A.I.C.S.: 522292
Frank B. Wigley *(Pres)*

BLAIREX LABORATORIES, INC.
1600 Brian Dr, Columbus, IN 47202
Tel.: (812) 378-1864   IN
Web Site: https://www.blairex.com
Year Founded: 1976
Sales Range: $75-99.9 Million
Emp.: 130
Retailer of Medical Products: Respi-
ratory, Eye, Cough & Cold & Wound
Care Products
N.A.I.C.S.: 424210
Anthony J. Moravec *(Pres)*

BLAKE & PENDLETON INC.
200 Cherry St Ste 402, Macon, GA
31201
Tel.: (478) 746-7645
Web Site:
https://www.blakeandpendleton.com
Year Founded: 1971
Sales Range: $25-49.9 Million
Emp.: 100
Compressed Air & Gas Equipment,
Pumping Equipment, Heat Transfer
Equipment & Vacuum Systems
N.A.I.C.S.: 423830
Allen King *(CEO)*
Denna Ochs *(CEO)*
Roy Barrineau *(Mgr-Ops)*
Michael Bazemore *(Mgr-Sys)*
Mark Joubert *(Mgr)*

BLAKE EQUIPMENT COM-PANY INC.
4 New Park Rd, East Windsor, CT
06088
Tel.: (860) 243-1491   CT
Web Site:
http://www.blakegroupholding.com
Year Founded: 1965
Sales Range: $10-24.9 Million
Emp.: 115
Mfr of Plumbing Fixtures; Equipment
& Supplies; Bolter Service & Sales
N.A.I.C.S.: 423820
Fred Cuda *(Pres)*
David Birdsey *(VP)*

BLAKE H BROWN INC.
1300 W Artesia Blvd, Compton, CA
90220
Tel.: (310) 764-0110
Web Site: http://www.jtillman.com
Rev.: $24,800,000
Emp.: 110
Safety Equipment
N.A.I.C.S.: 339113
Blake Brown *(Owner & Pres)*

BLAKE INTERNATIONAL USA RIGS, LLC
410 S Van Ave, Houma, LA 70363
Tel.: (985) 274-2200

Web Site:
https://www.blakeinternational.com
Year Founded: 2008
Emp.: 191
Oil Well Drilling Services
N.A.I.C.S.: 213111
Nicole Boquet *(VP-Fin)*
Ronnie Haydel *(VP-Admin)*
Jeff Kessler *(VP-Sls & Mktg)*
Michael Blake Jr. *(Pres & CEO-US &
Mexico)*

BLAKE REAL ESTATE, INC.
1150 Connecticut Ave NW Ste 900,
Washington, DC 20036
Tel.: (202) 778-0400   DC
Web Site: https://www.blakereal.com
Year Founded: 1945
Sales Range: $200-249.9 Million
Emp.: 750
Real Estate Services
N.A.I.C.S.: 531210
David S. Bender *(Chm)*
Stephen F. Lustgarten *(Pres & CEO)*
Neil Simon *(VP-Leasing)*
Donald P. Silverstein *(Sr VP)*
Mark Benedetti *(VP-Property Mgmt)*
William Clark *(VP-Ops)*
Desmona Harris *(Controller)*
Mary K. Kave *(Sec)*
Reagan Moseley *(Asst Mgr-Dev)*
Owen Billman *(VP-Leasing)*
Debra Wood *(Coord-Ops & Asset)*

BLAKE WILLSON GROUP, LLC
2311 Wilson Blvd Ste 620, Arlington,
VA 22201
Tel.: (703) 552-4541
Web Site:
http://www.blakewillsongroup.com
Year Founded: 2013
Sales Range: $1-9.9 Million
Emp.: 17
Professional Consultancy Services
N.A.I.C.S.: 541690
Robert J. Blake *(Founder, Pres &
CEO)*
Andrew H. Griffin *(Sr VP)*
Jennifer Hughes *(VP-Ops)*
James Moreland *(VP-Bus Dev)*

BLAKE'S LOTABURGER LLC
3205 Richmond Dr NE, Albuquerque,
NM 87107-1922
Tel.: (505) 884-2160   NM
Web Site: https://www.lotaburger.com
Year Founded: 1954
Sales Range: $125-149.9 Million
Emp.: 800
Fast Food
N.A.I.C.S.: 722513
Brian Rule *(Pres)*

BLAKEFORD AT GREEN HILLS
11 Burton Hills Blvd, Nashville, TN
37215
Tel.: (615) 665-9505   TN
Web Site: https://www.blakeford.com
Year Founded: 1992
Sales Range: $10-24.9 Million
Emp.: 293
Lifecare Retirement Community Op-
erator
N.A.I.C.S.: 623311
Doug Smith *(CFO)*
Allison Griffith *(Chief Admin Officer)*
Sarah Bishop *(Dir-Sls & Mktg)*
Van Cluck *(CEO)*

BLAKEMORE CONSTRUCTION CORP.
1201 Old Francis Rd, Glen Allen, VA
23059
Tel.: (804) 262-1233

Web Site:
http://www.blakemoreconstruct.com
Emp.: 80
Highway & Street Paving Contracting
Services
N.A.I.C.S.: 237310
David Houser *(Pres)*
John A. Blakemore Jr. *(Chm & CEO)*

BLAKESLEE ADVERTISING
916 N Charles St, Baltimore, MD
21201
Tel.: (410) 727-8800
Web Site:
http://www.blakesleeadv.com
Advertising Services
N.A.I.C.S.: 541810
Duane Levine *(Pres)*
Trudy Setree *(VP)*
Tom Wilson *(VP & Dir-Creative)*
Mark Fischer *(CEO)*

Subsidiaries:

Blakeslee Advertising - Park City   (1)
1790 Bonanza Dr Ste 275, Park City, UT
84060
Tel.: (410) 727-8800
Web Site: http://www.blakesleeadv.com
Advertising Services
N.A.I.C.S.: 541810

BLAKESLEE ARPAIA CHAP-MAN INC.
200 N Branford Rd, Branford, CT
06405
Tel.: (203) 433-7029
Web Site: https://www.bac-inc.com
Rev.: $19,357,860
Emp.: 100
Highway & Street Construction
N.A.I.C.S.: 237310
David Chapman *(Pres)*
John Fucci *(VP-Marine Div)*
Carl Arpaia *(VP-Estimating & Engrg)*
James Cooke *(VP-Heavy Construc-
tion)*
Keith Dolyak *(Sec & VP-Fin)*

BLAKESLEE PRESTRESS INC.
Rt 139 at Mc Dermott Rd, Branford,
CT 06405
Tel.: (203) 481-5306
Web Site:
https://www.blakesleeprestress.com
Rev.: $21,900,000
Emp.: 300
Prestressed Concrete Products
N.A.I.C.S.: 327390
Vincent A. Gambardella *(CFO &
VP-Finance)*

BLAKLEY CORPORATION
8060 E 88th St, Indianapolis, IN
46256
Tel.: (317) 842-9600
Web Site: https://www.blakleys.com
Rev.: $50,000,000
Emp.: 175
Exterior Cleaning, Including Sand-
blasting
N.A.I.C.S.: 238990
Curt Fankhauser *(CEO)*
Chris Rambis *(Project Mgr)*
Jeff Blakley *(Project Mgr)*

BLALOCK WALTERS P.A.
802 11th St W, Bradenton, FL 34205
Tel.: (941) 748-0100
Web Site:
https://www.blalockwalters.com
Sales Range: $1-9.9 Million
Emp.: 40
Law firm
N.A.I.C.S.: 541110
Mark P. Barnebey *(Principal)*
Melanie Luten *(Principal)*

Stephen G. Perry *(Principal)*
Matthew R. Plummer *(Principal)*
Scott E. Rudacille *(Principal)*
Robert G. Blalock *(Principal)*
Jonathan D. Fleece *(Mng Partner & Principal)*
Mary Fabre LeVine *(Principal)*
Fred E. Moore *(Principal)*
Anthony D. Bartirome *(Principal)*
Robert S. Stroud *(Principal)*
Jenifer S. Schembri *(Principal)*
Anne Chapman *(Principal)*
Clifford L. Walters III *(Principal)*
William C. Robinson Jr. *(Principal)*
Charles F. Johnson III *(Principal)*

BLANC INDUSTRIES, INC.
88 King St, Dover, NJ 07801
Tel.: (973) 537-0090   NJ
Web Site: http://www.blancind.com
Year Founded: 1997
Sales Range: $10-24.9 Million
Emp.: 55
Sign Mfr
N.A.I.C.S.: 339950
Didier Blanc *(Pres)*

BLANCHARD EQUIPMENT CO. INC.
138 State Hwy 80 W, Waynesboro, GA 30830
Tel.: (706) 554-2158
Web Site:
https://www.blancharddequip ment.com
Sales Range: $10-24.9 Million
Emp.: 37
Farm & Garden Machinery
N.A.I.C.S.: 423820
Phillip Blanchard *(Pres)*

BLANCHARD SCHAEFER ADVERTISING & PUBLIC RELATIONS
1521 N Cooper St Ste 600, Fort Worth, TX 76104
Tel.: (817) 226-4332
Web Site:
http://www.schaeferadvertising.com
Year Founded: 1985
Sales Range: $10-24.9 Million
Emp.: 11
Advertising Services
N.A.I.C.S.: 541810
Ken Schaefer *(Owner)*
Kim McRee *(VP-Acct Svc)*
Laura Carroll *(Mgr-Production)*

BLANCHARD SYSTEMS, INC.
1100 Poydras St Ste 1230, New Orleans, LA 70163
Tel.: (504) 529-8869
Web Site:
http://www.blanchardsystems.com
Sales Range: $1-9.9 Million
Emp.: 15
Computer Software
N.A.I.C.S.: 513210
Charles Blanchard *(Pres & CEO)*
Keith Zibilich *(COO & VP)*
Gary Dolgins *(Dir-Sls & Mktg)*
Jessie Williams *(Dir-Software Dev)*

BLANCHARD VALLEY FARMERS CO-OP
6566 County Rd 236, Findlay, OH 45840
Tel.: (419) 423-2611
Web Site: http://www.bvfcoop.com
Rev.: $70,743,603
Emp.: 100
Distribution Of Grains
N.A.I.C.S.: 424510
Michael Tobe *(Asst Mgr)*
Jamie Pratt *(Mgr-IT)*

BLANCHARD VALLEY HEALTH SYSTEM
1900 S Main St, Findlay, OH 45840
Tel.: (419) 423-4500
Web Site:
http://www.bvhealthsystem.org
Health Care Outpatient Services
N.A.I.C.S.: 621498
Scott Malaney *(Pres & CEO)*

Subsidiaries:

Findlay Surgery Center, Ltd.   **(1)**
1709 Medical Blvd, Findlay, OH 45840
Tel.: (419) 429-0409
Web Site:
http://www.findlaysurgerycenter.com
Outpatient Care Centers
N.A.I.C.S.: 621498
Julie Steiner *(Dir-Surgical Svcs & Nurses)*

BLANCHARDVILLE COOP OIL ASSOCIATION
314 S Main St, Blanchardville, WI 53516
Tel.: (608) 523-4294
Sales Range: $10-24.9 Million
Emp.: 35
Petroleum Bulk Stations
N.A.I.C.S.: 424710
Dave Erickson *(Pres)*
Ladd Tettit *(Gen Mgr)*

BLAND FARMS
1126 Raymond D Bland Rd, Glennville, GA 30427
Tel.: (912) 654-1426
Web Site:
https://www.blandfarms.com
Sales Range: $10-24.9 Million
Emp.: 25
Sale Of Sweet Onions
N.A.I.C.S.: 424480
Delbert Bland *(Owner & Pres)*
Troy Bland *(Dir-Quality Control)*
Bryce Edmonson *(CEO)*

BLANK ROME LLP
1 Logan Sq 130 N 18th St, Philadelphia, PA 19103-6998
Tel.: (215) 569-5500   PA
Web Site: http://www.blankrome.com
Year Founded: 1946
Sales Range: $300-349.9 Million
Emp.: 1,001
Law firm
N.A.I.C.S.: 541110
Leon R. Barson *(Partner)*
Arthur Bachman *(Partner)*
Yelena M. Barychev *(Partner)*
Lawrence J. Beaser *(Partner)*
Patrick O. Cavanaugh *(COO)*
Karen M. Jablonski *(Sr Dir-Atty & Client Svcs)*
Laurence Liss *(CTO)*
John M. Sperger *(Sec)*
Samuel H. Becker *(Partner)*
Daniel R. Blickman *(Partner)*
Simon J. K. Miller *(Partner)*
Alan J. Hoffman *(Chm)*
Frank M. Kaplan *(Partner)*
Rick Antonoff *(Partner)*
Jeremy Herschaft *(Partner)*
John Adkins *(Partner)*
Jason E. Reisman *(Partner)*
Michelle M. Gervais *(Partner)*
Richard E. Berman *(Partner)*
David Houston *(Partner-Washington)*
Michael C. Cohen *(Partner-Corp, M&A & Securities Grp-Los Angeles)*
Sophia Lee *(Partner-Energy, Environment & Mass Torts Practice Grp)*
Susan B. Flohr *(Partner)*
Julie Dressing *(Chief HR Officer-Washington)*
Ronald W. Frank *(Partner-Corp, Securities & Merger & Acq Grp-Pittsburgh)*

Alan H. Lieblich *(Chm-Corp, Securities & Merger & Acq Practice Grp)*
Lisa M. Campisi *(Partner-Insurance Coverage Grp-New York)*
James R. Murray *(Partner & Chm-Insurance Recovery Practice Grp)*
Samuel D. Levy *(Partner-Corp Litigation Grp-New York)*
Harris N. Cogan *(Chm-Corp Litigation Grp)*
Ira L. Herman *(Partner-Fin, Restructuring & Bankruptcy-New York)*
Robert Wessely *(Partner)*
Amy Barrette *(Partner)*
Jeremy Mercer *(Partner)*
James J. Barnes *(Partner-Corp, Merger & Acq, Securities Grp & Admin-Pittsburgh)*
Brendan Delany *(Partner-Fin, Restructuring & Bankruptcy Grp-Washington)*
Jonathan M. Harris *(Partner)*
Keith A. Rutherford *(Chm-Intellectual Property & Tech Grp)*
David Moise *(Partner)*
Elizabeth E. Klingensmith *(Partner-Corp Litigation Grp-Houston)*
Laura Reathaford *(Partner)*
Martin Teckler *(Partner-Fin Grp-Washington)*
Daniel R. Peterson *(Partner)*
Nicole M. Vorrasi *(Partner-Tax, Benefits & Private Client Grp)*
Omid Safa *(Partner-Insurance Recovery Practice)*
Saminaz Akhter *(Partner-Corp, Merger & Acq Securities Grp)*
Jeffrey N. Rosenthal *(Partner)*
Scott E. Wortman *(Partner-Consumer Fin Litigation Grp-New York)*
Wayne Streibich *(Chm-Fin Institutions Litigation & Regulatory Compliance Practice Grp)*
Andrew K. Fletcher *(Partner-Comml Litigation Grp-Pittsburgh)*
Charles S. Marion *(Partner-Comml Litigation Grp)*
Louis Meng *(Partner-Corp, Merger & Acq & Securities Grp-Shangai & Head)*
Mike Margolis *(Chm-Asia & Partner)*
Luke W. Meier *(Partner-Govt Contracts Grp-Washington)*
David M. Nadle *(Chm-Govt Contracts Grp)*
Grant S. Palmer *(CEO & Mng Partner)*
Peter Schnur *(Chm-Corp, Merger & Acq & Securities Practice Grp)*
Terrence A. Everett *(Partner-Corp, Merger & Acq & Securities Grp-Los Angeles)*
Ryan Craig *(Partner-Washington)*
Ariel Glasner *(Partner-Washington)*
Robert L. Kahan *(Partner-Transactions)*
Andrew T. Hambelton *(Partner)*
Joshua A Huber *(Partner)*
Adam V. Orlacchio *(Partner)*
Jim Stapleton *(Chief Bus Dev & Mktg Officer-Washington)*
Dominique Casimir *(Partner-Govt Contracts Grp-Washington)*
Shawn M. Wright *(Partner)*
Seth Lamden *(Partner-Insurance Recovery Grp-Chicago)*
Cynde H. Munzer *(Partner-Fin, Restructuring & Bankruptcy Grp-Chicago)*
David Kronenberg *(Partner-Fin, Restructuring & Bankruptcy Grp- Washington, D.C & Cincinnati)*
Cassandra Mott *(Partner-Fin, Restructuring & Bankruptcy Grp-Houston)*

Sarah Frazier *(Partner-Fin, Restructuring & Bankruptcy Grp-Houston)*
Kenneth Ottaviano *(Partner-Fin & Restructuring-Chicago & Chm-Chicago)*
R. Colgate Selden *(Partner-Fin Institutions Litigation & Regulatory Compliance Practice-Washington DC)*
Lawrence F. Flick II *(Chm-Fin Svcs Industry Team)*

BLANTON CONSTRUCTION
550 Turner Blvd, Saint Peters, MO 63376
Tel.: (636) 928-4444
Web Site:
https://www.blantonconstruction.com
Year Founded: 2002
Sales Range: $10-24.9 Million
Emp.: 70
Civil Engineering Services
N.A.I.C.S.: 237310
Jeff Blanton *(Principal)*
David Sampl *(Sr Mgr-Construction)*

BLASCHAK ANTHRACITE CORPORATION
1166 W Ctr St, Mahanoy City, PA 17948
Tel.: (570) 773-2113
Web Site:
https://www.blaschakanthracite.com
Year Founded: 1937
Rev.: $9,000,000
Emp.: 40
Bituminous Coal Underground Mining
N.A.I.C.S.: 212115
Boyd Kreglow *(CEO)*

BLASE MANUFACTURING COMPANY
60 Watson Blvd, Stratford, CT 06615
Tel.: (203) 375-5646
Web Site: http://www.blasemfg.com
Year Founded: 1947
Rev.: $10,000,000
Emp.: 120
Metal Stampings, Nec
N.A.I.C.S.: 332119

BLASER DIE CASTING CO.
5700 3rd Ave S, Seattle, WA 98108
Tel.: (206) 767-7800
Year Founded: 1957
Sales Range: $25-49.9 Million
Zinc Die Casting Services
N.A.I.C.S.: 331523
Kevin Callan *(Controller)*

BLASER'S USA, INC.
1858 Hwy 63, Comstock, WI 54826
Tel.: (715) 822-2437
Web Site: http://www.blasersusa.com
Year Founded: 1998
Sales Range: $1-9.9 Million
Emp.: 55
Specialty Cheese Manufacturing
N.A.I.C.S.: 311513
Joe Hines *(Superintendent-Plant)*
John Freyholtz *(Mgr-Ops)*

BLASS MARKETING
17 Drowne Rd, Old Chatham, NY 12136-3006
Tel.: (518) 766-2222
Web Site:
https://www.blassmarketing.com
Year Founded: 1969
Advertising Services
N.A.I.C.S.: 541810
Kenneth L. Blass *(Pres & CEO)*

BLATT BILLIARDS CORP.
809 Broadway, New York, NY 10003
Tel.: (212) 674-8855

Blatt Billiards Corp.—(Continued)

Web Site:
http://www.blattbilliards.com
Year Founded: 1923
Rev.: $6,500,000
Emp.: 50
Mfr, Engineer & Supplier of Billiards
Furniture & Gaming Accessories
N.A.I.C.S.: 339930
Ronald Blatt (Pres)
John Chermack (CIO)
Steve Receder (Dir-Mktg)

BLATT GROUP
8 Tube Dr, Reading, PA 19605
Tel.: (610) 916-9828
Web Site: https://theblattgroup.com
Year Founded: 1987
Sales Range: $1-9.9 Million
Emp.: 45
Commercial & Industrial General
Contracting, Facility Maintenance,
Plant Services & Rapid Response
Services
N.A.I.C.S.: 238290
Larry J. Blatt (Pres & Founder)
Jim Blatt (Office Mgr)

Subsidiaries:

Blatt Construction Inc. **(1)**
8 Tube Dr, Reading, PA 19605 **(100%)**
Tel.: (610) 916-9828
Web Site: http://www.blattgroup.com
Commercial & Industrial Construction Services
N.A.I.C.S.: 236220
Timothy Blatt (VP & Head)

Blatt Industrial Services Inc. **(1)**
8 Tube Dr, Reading, PA 19605 **(100%)**
Tel.: (610) 916-9828
Web Site: http://www.blattgroup.com
Commercial & Industrial Services
N.A.I.C.S.: 541420
James Blatt (VP & Office Mgr)

Blatt Welding and Fabrication,
Inc. **(1)**
8 Tube Dr, Reading, PA 19605 **(100%)**
Tel.: (610) 916-9828
Web Site: http://www.blattgroup.com
Welding & Fabrication Services
N.A.I.C.S.: 236210
Josh Blatt (VP & Head)

BLAUER MANUFACTURING COMPANY, INC.
20 Aberdeen St, Boston, MA 02215
Tel.: (617) 536-6606   **MA**
Web Site: https://www.blauer.com
Year Founded: 1936
Sales Range: $25-49.9 Million
Emp.: 550
Men's & Women's Uniform Outerwear
N.A.I.C.S.: 315250
Charles L. Blauer (Chm)
Stephen J. Blauer (Sr VP-Sls & Mktg)
Bill Blauer (Mgr-Natl Sls)

BLAYLOCK ROBERT VAN LLC
350 Frank Ogawa Plz 10th Fl, Oakland, CA 94612
Tel.: (510) 208-6100
Web Site: http://www.brv-llc.com
Year Founded: 1991
Sales Range: $25-49.9 Million
Emp.: 60
Investment Advisory & Management
Services
N.A.I.C.S.: 523150
Eric Van Standifer (Pres)
Steven Singleton (Exec VP & Dir-Res)
Alan Jones (Sr VP-Sls & Trading)
William Crabbe (Sr VP)
John Engles (Sr VP-Municipal Sls & Trading)
Garth Griffiths (Sr VP-Pub Fin)
Alex Palmieri (Sr VP)

Osee Pierre (Sr VP)
Manny Small (Exec VP & Mgr-Sls-Natl)
Karen Nazzareno (Sr VP & Controller)
Alex Ciulla (Sr VP-Fin Ops)
Judith Ashworth (Sr VP-Admin)
Richard Hanley (Sr VP-Compliance)
Kevin Wood (CTO & Sr VP)
Ed Tollefsen (Sr VP-Sls & Trading)
Earl Manns (Sr VP)
Gail Schaeffer (Sr VP-Institutional Banking & Sls)
Carlton Martin (Exec VP & Dir-Res)
David Womack (Sr VP-Pub Fin)

Subsidiaries:

Blaylock Robert Van LLC **(1)**
600 Lexington Ave 3rd Fl, New York, NY 10022
Tel.: (212) 715-6600
Sales Range: $50-74.9 Million
Emp.: 50
Investment Advisory & Management Services
N.A.I.C.S.: 523150
Eric Van Standifer (Founder, Pres & CEO)
John Anderson (Sr VP)
Gordon L. Armstrong (Sr VP-Sls & Trading)
Wendell Bristol (Sr VP-Capital Markets)
Louis DeCaro (Sr VP & Head-Banking)
Tarrell Gamble (Sr VP-Capital Markets)
William J. Guilshan (Sr VP-Sls & Trading)
Aquacena Lopez (Sr VP)
Michael McNally (Sr VP-Sls & Trading)
Edward R. Moore (Sr VP-Sls & Trading)
Timothy O'Brien (Exec VP-Sls & Trading)

BLAYLOCK, THREET, PHILLIPS & ASSOCIATES, INC.
1510 S Broadway St, Little Rock, AR 72202-4848
Tel.: (501) 224-3922
Year Founded: 1948
Sales Range: $10-24.9 Million
Emp.: 6
Engineeering Services
N.A.I.C.S.: 541330
Carl J. Meurer (Pres)

BLAZER INDUSTRIES INC.
945 Olney St, Aumsville, OR 97325
Tel.: (503) 749-1900
Web Site: https://www.blazerind.com
Year Founded: 1976
Sales Range: $100-124.9 Million
Emp.: 150
Prefabricated Wood Buildings, Modular Structures
N.A.I.C.S.: 321992
Marvin R. Shetler (Pres)
Charlie Nichols (Project Mgr)
Jeffrey Swanborough (Mgr-Warranty)

BLB RESOURCES, INC.
16845 Von Karman Ste 100, Irvine, CA 92606
Tel.: (949) 261-9492
Web Site:
http://www.blbresources.com
Emp.: 119
Property Management Services
N.A.I.C.S.: 531312
Susie Gaston (Owner & Pres)
Rod Gaston (CEO)

BLDD ARCHITECTS, INC.
100 Merchant St, Decatur, IL 62523
Tel.: (217) 429-5105
Web Site: http://www.bldd.com
Emp.: 100
Architectural Services
N.A.I.C.S.: 541310
Tom Mulligan (Superintendent)

Subsidiaries:

Dickinson Hussman Architects,
P.C. **(1)**

7777 Bonhomme Ave, Saint Louis, MO 63105
Tel.: (314) 727-8500
Web Site: http://www.dharch.com
Rev.: $1,963,000
Emp.: 13
Architectural Services
N.A.I.C.S.: 541310

BLDG MANAGEMENT INC.
417 5th Ave 4th Fl, New York, NY 10016
Tel.: (212) 557-6700
Sales Range: $250-299.9 Million
Emp.: 50
Residential Building Investors
N.A.I.C.S.: 531120
Donald Olenik (Gen Counsel & Sr VP-Comml Real Estate)

BLDG.WORKS-USA, INC.
2108 Hurd Dr Ste 300, Irving, TX 75038
Tel.: (972) 756-9320   **TX**
Web Site:
http://www.bldgworksusa.com
Rev.: $20,500,000
Emp.: 60
Franchises, Selling Or Licensing
N.A.I.C.S.: 926150
Peggie Householder (Office Mgr)

BLEACH GROUP, INC.
347 Fifth Ave Ste 1402, New York, NY 10016
Tel.: (646) 205-8124   **DE**
Web Site:
http://www.bleachgroupinc.com
Sales Range: $25-49.9 Million
Emp.: 78
Women's Clothing & Accessories Mfr,
Distr & Retailer
N.A.I.C.S.: 315250
Harry Hodge (Chm)
Mark Byers (Pres & CEO)
Kristopher Black (CFO)
Tim Morris (COO)

BLEACHER RESTORATORS OF COLORADO, LLC
11676 Shaffer Pl Unit 406, Littleton, CO 80127
Tel.: (303) 973-4517
Web Site: http://www.brocllc.com
Year Founded: 1982
Sales Range: $1-9.9 Million
Emp.: 15
Spectator Seating Installation Services
N.A.I.C.S.: 238390
Rick Baker (Founder)

BLEACHER SALES COMPANY INC.
1617 Enid St, Houston, TX 77009
Tel.: (713) 869-3491
Web Site: http://www.scaffold.com
Rev.: $15,000,000
Emp.: 247
Scaffolds, Mobile Or Stationary: Metal
N.A.I.C.S.: 531210
William E. Gilbreath (Pres)
Jay Rosen (VP)

BLEDSOE TELEPHONE CO-OPERATIVE CORPORATION
338 Cumberland Ave, Pikeville, TN 37367
Tel.: (423) 447-2121
Web Site: https://www.bledsoe.net
Rev.: $10,600,000
Emp.: 50
Telecommunications Resellers
N.A.I.C.S.: 517121
John Lee Downey (Pres)
Robin Rothwell (Controller)
Gregory L. Anderson (Gen Mgr)

BLEIGH CONSTRUCTION CO. INC.
9037 Hwy 168, Palmyra, MO 63461-3102
Tel.: (573) 221-2247   **MO**
Web Site: http://www.bleigh.com
Year Founded: 1950
Sales Range: $25-49.9 Million
Emp.: 250
Nonresidential Construction Contractors
N.A.I.C.S.: 237110
Tom Bleigh (VP)

BLEND IMAGES, LLC
501 E Pine St # 200, Seattle, WA 98122-2310
Tel.: (206) 749-9394
Web Site:
http://www.blendimages.com
Sales Range: $10-24.9 Million
Emp.: 15
Multicultural Photography Services
N.A.I.C.S.: 541922
Rick Becker-Leckrone (Founder)
Sarah Fix (CEO)
Jasmine Hartsook (VP-Ops)
Stacey Lester (Mgr-Distr)
Jerome Montalto (Mgr-Submission & Content)
Jennifer Engel (Mgr-Royalty & Channel)
Brock Jones (Dir-Sls)
Terry Vine (Mgr-LLC)
Jamie Grill (Mgr-LLC)
Rick Leckrone (CEO)

Subsidiaries:

RGB Ventures LLC **(1)**
6620 Southpoint Dr S Ste 501, Jacksonville, FL 32216
Tel.: (904) 565-0066
Web Site: http://www.superstock.com
Motion Picture & Video Production
N.A.I.C.S.: 512110
Tom Sheeter (Acct Mgr)

BLENDEX COMPANY
11208 Electron Dr, Louisville, KY 40299
Tel.: (502) 267-1003
Web Site: https://www.blendex.com
Year Founded: 1975
Sales Range: $10-24.9 Million
Emp.: 100
Spice & Extract Mfr
N.A.I.C.S.: 311942
Ronald Pottinger (CEO)
Jacquelyn Bailey (Pres)
Tony Jessee (Exec VP)
Ron Carr (VP-Sls)
Jordan Stivers (VP-R&D)

BLENKO GLASS COMPANY INC.
9 Bill Blenko Dr, Milton, WV 25541
Tel.: (304) 743-9081
Web Site:
http://www.blenkoglass.com
Year Founded: 1922
Sales Range: $75-99.9 Million
Emp.: 50
Glassware
N.A.I.C.S.: 327212
Christy Gibson (Office Mgr)

BLETHEN CORPORATION
1201 3rd Ave Ste 2200, Seattle, WA 98109-5321
Tel.: (206) 464-2471   **WA**
Year Founded: 1956
Sales Range: $300-349.9 Million
Newspapers
N.A.I.C.S.: 513110
Frank A. Blethen (Pres)

Subsidiaries:

Seattle Times Company **(1)**
1000 Denny Way, Seattle, WA
98109 **(50.5%)**
Tel.: (206) 464-2111
Web Site: http://company.seattletimes.com
Sales Range: $500-549.9 Million
Emp.: 3,020
Newspaper Publishers
N.A.I.C.S.: 513110
Frank A. Blethen (CEO & Publr)
Alan Fisco (Pres)
Sharon Pian Chan (VP-Innovation, Product & Dev)
Levi Pulkkinen (Editor-Bus)

Subsidiary (Domestic):

Rotary Offset Press **(2)**
6600 S 231st St, Kent, WA 98032-1847
Tel.: (253) 813-9900
Web Site: http://www.rotaryoffsetpress.com
Sales Range: $75-99.9 Million
Emp.: 215
Lithographic Commercial Printing
N.A.I.C.S.: 323111
Ken Hatch (Gen Mgr)

Walla Walla Union Bulletin Inc. **(1)**
112 S 1st Ave, Walla Walla, WA 99362-3011 **(100%)**
Tel.: (509) 525-3300
Web Site: http://www.union-bulletin.com
Sales Range: $1-9.9 Million
Emp.: 120
Newspapers
N.A.I.C.S.: 513110
Mike Cibart (Mgr-Circulation)
Brian Hunt (Publr)
James Blethen (Supvr-Ad Production)
Steven Butcher (Mgr-HR)
Matthew Nelson (Coord-Sls)
Jim Seiner (Mgr-Press & Distr)
Dian Ver Valen (Editor)
Vicki Hillhouse (Editor-News)

BLETHEN, GAGE & KRAUSE, PLLP

100 Warren St Ste 400, Mankato, MN 56001
Tel.: (507) 345-1166
Web Site: http://www.bgklaw.com
Year Founded: 1896
Emp.: 17
Law firm
N.A.I.C.S.: 541110
Richard J. Corcoran (Atty)
James H. Turk (Co-Partner)
Randall C. Berkland (Atty)
Michael C. Karp (Co-Partner)
Bailey W. Blethen (Atty)
Julia Ketcham Corbett (Co-Partner & Atty)
Silas L. Danielson (Co-Partner & Atty)
Ben D. McAninch (Co-Partner & Atty)
Christopher M. Roe (Co-Partner & Atty)
Beth A. Serrill (Co-Partner & Atty)
Roger H. Hippert (Atty)

Subsidiaries:

Nierengarten & Hippert Ltd. **(1)**
11 N Minnesota St, New Ulm, MN 56073
Tel.: (507) 359-2991
Web Site: http://www.nhltdlaw.com
Law firm
N.A.I.C.S.: 541110
Hugh T. Nierengarten (Partner)

BLEVINS INC.

421 Hart Ln, Nashville, TN 37216-2026
Tel.: (615) 228-2616 **TN**
Web Site: https://www.blevinsinc.com
Year Founded: 1971
Sales Range: $10-24.9 Million
Emp.: 230
Part & Accessory for Mobile Home RV Distr
N.A.I.C.S.: 423730

Brad Blevins (Pres)
Tim Kentner (CFO)
Jim Eades (Sr VP-Ops)
Jim Carper (VP-Pur)
Rick Silvia (VP-Sls & Bus Dev)

BLEVINS WORK SHOP INC.

7258 United States Hwy 21 S, Glade Valley, NC 28627
Tel.: (336) 363-2216
Web Site:
  http://www.blevinsbuildinginc.com
Sales Range: $10-24.9 Million
Emp.: 13
Lumber & Other Major Building Materials
N.A.I.C.S.: 423310
Peggy Blevin (Treas & Sec)
Bill G. Blevins Sr. (Pres)

BLEWETT'S FOOD, INC.

218 N 2nd St, Ishpeming, MI 49849
Tel.: (906) 485-1027 **MI**
Sales Range: $10-24.9 Million
Emp.: 25
Independent Grocery Store
N.A.I.C.S.: 445110
James R. Blewett (Pres)

BLEYHL FARM SERVICE INC.

940 E Wine Country Rd, Grandview, WA 98930-1387
Tel.: (509) 882-2248 **WA**
Web Site: https://www.bleyhl.com
Year Founded: 1964
Rev.: $26,293,672
Emp.: 80
Farm Supplies Specializing in Orchard & Vinyard
N.A.I.C.S.: 424910
Greg Robertson (Gen Mgr)
William Nolt (Mgr-Store)
Nick Friend (Controller)

BLICKMAN HEALTH INDUSTRIES, INC.

500 US Hwy 46 E, Clifton, NJ 07011-3808
Tel.: (973) 330-0557
Web Site: https://www.blickman.com
Year Founded: 1975
Sales Range: $50-74.9 Million
Emp.: 80
Stainless Steel Hospital Furniture & Food Equipment
N.A.I.C.S.: 332312
Paul D. Freedman (CFO)
Robert J. Freedman (Pres)

BLIFFERT LUMBER & FUEL CO. INC.

6826 S 13th St, Oak Creek, WI 53154
Tel.: (414) 762-9090 **WI**
Web Site:
  https://www.bliffertlumber.com
Year Founded: 1904
Millwork & Lumber
N.A.I.C.S.: 444110
Eli Bliffert (VP)
Chris Hegeman (Mgr-Morgan Avenue)
Josh Brown (VP-Sls)

Subsidiaries:

Chase Lumber & Fuel Company, Inc. **(1)**
2175 McCoy Rd, Sun Prairie, WI 53590
Tel.: (608) 837-5101
Web Site: https://www.chaselumber.com
Rev.: $22,811,289
Emp.: 30
Lumber & Other Building Materials
N.A.I.C.S.: 423310
Valerie Stiener (Pres)

Portage Lumber Company, Inc. **(1)**

1009 E Wisconsin St, Portage, WI 53901
Tel.: (608) 742-7186
Sales Range: $1-9.9 Million
Emp.: 39
Ret Lumber/Building Materials Ret Hardware Ret Floor Covering
N.A.I.C.S.: 423310
Dennis Dorn (CEO)
Doreen Herbert (Mgr-Home Decor)
Gil Kuzera (Controller)
Kimberly Dorn (Dir-Mktg & Mgr-HR)
Ron Dorn (Pres)
Vicky Binder (Mgr-Paint Dept)
Jacob Joranger (Mgr-Rental)
Ryan Geissler (Mgr-Retail)

BLIGHT OIL COMPANY

4530 E Lansing Rd, Bancroft, MI 48414
Tel.: (989) 634-5513
Web Site:
  http://www.blightpropane.com
Rev.: $10,000,000
Emp.: 5
Petroleum Bulk Stations
N.A.I.C.S.: 424710

BLIMPIE INTERNATIONAL INC.

6300 Powers Ferry Rd Ste 400, Atlanta, GA 30339-2900
Tel.: (770) 937-0100 **NJ**
Web Site: https://www.blimpie.com
Year Founded: 1964
Sales Range: $25-49.9 Million
Emp.: 110
Fast Food Restaurants Franchisor
N.A.I.C.S.: 722513
Jeff Smit (Pres)
Matt Harper (Owner)

Subsidiaries:

Blimpie Subs & Salads **(1)**
145 Huguenot St Ste 410, New Rochelle, NY 10801 **(100%)**
Tel.: (914) 576-1006
Web Site: http://www.blimpie.com
Sales Range: $10-24.9 Million
Emp.: 70
Franchisor of Blimpie Fast Food Restaurants
N.A.I.C.S.: 722513

Maui Tacos International, Inc. **(1)**
2001 Palmer Ave Ste 105, Larchmont, NY 10538 **(73%)**
Tel.: (914) 576-7601
Web Site: http://www.mauitacos.com
Sales Range: $10-24.9 Million
Emp.: 5
Franchisor of Maui Tacos & Smoothie Island
N.A.I.C.S.: 541618
Jeff Endervelt (Pres & CEO)
Alfonso Navarro (VP)
Mark Ellman (Founder)

BLINC INC.

1141 S Rogers Cir Ste 7, Boca Raton, FL 33487
Tel.: (561) 300-2727
Web Site: https://www.blincinc.com
Year Founded: 1999
Rev.: $4,300,000
Emp.: 15
Pharmaceuticals Distr & Whslr
N.A.I.C.S.: 424210

BLIND INDUSTRIES & SERVICES OF MARYLAND

3345 Washington Blvd, Baltimore, MD 21227-1602
Tel.: (410) 737-2600
Web Site: https://www.bism.org
Year Founded: 1908
Sales Range: $50-74.9 Million
Emp.: 640
Rehabilitation Services
N.A.I.C.S.: 622310
William E. Hadlock (Sec)
Jim Berens (Treas)
Walter Brown (Vice Chm)

Don Morris (Chm)
Frederick J. Puente (Pres)
Michael L. Gosse (Treas)

BLIND SUPPLY, LLC

6063 FM 535, Cedar Creek, TX 78612
Tel.: (512) 835-5333
Web Site: http://www.blind-supply.com
Sales Range: $10-24.9 Million
Emp.: 20
Venetian Blinds & Window Coverings Mfr & Distr
N.A.I.C.S.: 337920
Ray Hicks (Gen Mgr)
Devin James (Owner & Pres)

BLINDS CHALET

4320 E Brown Rd #112, Mesa, AZ 85205
Tel.: (480) 633-7840
Web Site:
  http://www.blindschalet.com
Year Founded: 2006
Sales Range: $1-9.9 Million
Emp.: 20
Custom Blinds & Window Coverings Mfr & Installation Guidelines
N.A.I.C.S.: 449122
Ron Manwaring (Owner)

BLINDS TO GO INC.

101 E State Rte 4, Paramus, NJ 07652
Tel.: (732) 321-5000
Web Site:
  https://www.blindstogo.com
Year Founded: 1999
Sales Range: $50-74.9 Million
Emp.: 600
Window Covering Parts & Accessories
N.A.I.C.S.: 423220
Nkere Udofia (Vice Chm)
Antoine Filion (Mgr-Production & Dev-Montreal)
Meetu Mehra (Gen Mgr-Toronto)
Rachel Smith (Gen Mgr-Long Island)
Stephanie Carson (Mgr-Sls & Dev-Montreal)

Subsidiaries:

Blinds To Go (Canada) Inc. **(1)**
3510 St-Joseph Blvd E, Montreal, H1X 1W6, QC, Canada
Tel.: (514) 255-4000
Web Site: http://www.blindstogo.com
Mfr & Retailer of Window Blinds
N.A.I.C.S.: 337920
David J. Shiller (Founder)

BLINDS.COM

10555 Richmond Ave, Houston, TX 77042
Web Site: http://www.blinds.com
Year Founded: 1996
Sales Range: $50-74.9 Million
Emp.: 110
Window Treatment Installation Services
N.A.I.C.S.: 449122

BLINNPR

39 W 14th St Ste 506, New York, NY 10011
Tel.: (212) 675-4777
Web Site: http://www.blinnpr.com
Year Founded: 1996
Sales Range: $1-9.9 Million
Emp.: 12
Public Relations Agency
N.A.I.C.S.: 541820
Steven Blinn (Pres & CEO)
Bill Stephenson (CFO)

BLISH-MIZE CO.

Blish-Mize Co.—(Continued)
223 S 5th St, Atchison, KS 66002-
0249
Tel.: (913) 367-1250   **KS**
Web Site: https://www.blishmize.com
Year Founded: 1871
Sales Range: $300-349.9 Million
Emp.: 250
Hardware, Tools, Plumbing & Ventila-
tion Components, Electrical Compo-
nents, Paint, Housewares, Industrial
Supplies, Lawn & Garden Supplies
Distr
N.A.I.C.S.: 423710
Jonathan D. Mize (Pres & CEO)
Greg Lutz (Exec VP-Ops)
Don Miller (Dir-Customer Svc)
Blish Connor (Dir-Comm)
Lydia E. Funk (CFO & Exec VP)
Amy Knoch (Sec & VP-HR)
Clay Uhrmacher (VP-Sls & Mktg)
John H. Mize Jr. (Chm)

BLISS INTEGRATED COMMU-
NICATION
500 5th Ave Ste 1010, New York, NY
10110
Tel.: (212) 840-1661
Web Site: http://blissintegrated.com
Communications, Media Relations,
Media Training, Public Relations,
Strategic Planning/Research Agency
N.A.I.C.S.: 541810
Elizabeth Sosnow (Mng Dir)
Meg Wildrick (Mng Dir)
Cortney Rhoads Stapleton (Exec VP)
Vicky Aguiar (VP)
Nathan Burgess (Acct Supvr)
Nicole Cassidy (Acct Supvr)
Liz DeForest (Acct Supvr)
Dani Mckie (Office Mgr)
Patrick Ruppe (VP-Fin Svcs Practice)
Julia Mellon (Acct Dir)
Morgan Fine (Sr Acct Exec)
Reed Handley (Acct Dir)
Gregory Hassel (Acct Dir)
Evan Stisser (Acct Supvr)
Megan Tuck (Sr Acct Exec)
Alexis Odesser (VP)
Sally Slater (VP)

Subsidiaries:

BlissPR   (1)
17 N State St Ste #1700, Chicago, IL
60602
Tel.: (312) 252-7314
Web Site: http://www.blisspr.com
Public Relations Firm
N.A.I.C.S.: 541820

BLISTEX, INC.
1800 Swift Dr, Oak Brook, IL 60523-
1574
Tel.: (630) 571-2870   **IL**
Web Site: https://www.blistex.com
Year Founded: 1947
Sales Range: $125-149.9 Million
Emp.: 200
Oral Care & Skin Care Products Mfr
N.A.I.C.S.: 325620
Michael J. Donnantuono (Pres &
COO)
Mike Wojcik (VP-Tech)
Brian Satre (VP-Mktg)
Scott Halliday (VP-Ops)
David C. Arch (Chm & CEO)

Subsidiaries:

Blistex Limited   (1)
5915 Airport Road Suite 805, Mississauga,
L4V 1T1, ON, Canada   (100%)
Tel.: (905) 678-2521
Web Site: http://www.blistex.com
Sales Range: $10-24.9 Million
Emp.: 8
Mktg. & Sales of Ointments, Lotions, Lip
Balms

N.A.I.C.S.: 325412
Steve Terry (Dir-Sls)

BLITZ AGENCY
6080 Center Dr Ste 260, Los Ange-
les, CA 90045
Tel.: (310) 551-0200
Web Site: http://www.blitzagency.com
Year Founded: 2001
Sales Range: $10-24.9 Million
Emp.: 93
Develops, Markets & Brands Prod-
ucts & Companies for Various Clients
N.A.I.C.S.: 541613
Ivan Todorov (Co-Founder & CEO)
Ken Martin (Co-Founder)
Tim Richards (Exec VP-Strategy)
Eric Perez (Dir-Creative Grp)
Chris Morabito (Exec Dir-Experience)
Noah Gedrich (VP-Tech)
Wanda Shapiro (Dir-Delivery)
Celeste DeMartis (Dir-Experience)
John Liu (Dir-Search)
Kevin Wright (Dir-Social)
Amy Call (Exec VP-Brand Leadership
& Gen Mgr)
Andy Sullivan (Sr VP-New Bus)
Peter Apple (VP-Strategy)

BLITZ MEDIA, INC.
203 Crescent St, Waltham, MA
02453-3436
Tel.: (781) 247-7100
Web Site: http://www.blitzmedia.com
Year Founded: 1986
Sales Range: $1-9.9 Million
Advertising Services
N.A.I.C.S.: 541870
Sarah McAuley (Dir-Brdcst)
Beth Ringer (Dir-Digital Media & Ana-
lytics)
Pat Lacroix (Dir-Innovation)
Melissa Lea (Pres & CEO)
Kerryann Driscoll (Dir-Mktg)
Francis Ferrara (CFO)
Ellen Comley (Chief Media Officer)

BLOCK & COMPANY, INC.
1111 Wheeling Rd, Wheeling, IL
60090-5795
Tel.: (847) 537-7200
Web Site:
    http://www.blockandcompany.com
Year Founded: 1934
Sales Range: $25-49.9 Million
Emp.: 250
Mfr of Metal Stampings
N.A.I.C.S.: 332119
Mitchell Block (Founder)
Larry Greenberg (Dir-Sls & Mktg-
MMF POS)

BLOCK & DECORSO
3 Claridge Dr, Verona, NJ 07044-
3000
Tel.: (973) 857-3900
Web Site:
    http://www.blockdecorso.com
Year Founded: 1931
Rev.: $14,000,000
Emp.: 25
N.A.I.C.S.: 541810
Bill Decorso (Pres)
David Cannon (Copywriter)
Carol Cennamo (Production Mgr)
Ruth Digiorgio (Media Dir)
John Murray (Sr Art Dir)
David Block (CEO)
Carla Dean (Sr Acct Exec)
John Romano (Dir-Internets)
Jay Baumann (Creative Dir)
Bob Lettiere (Dir-Bus Plng)

BLOCK COMMUNICATIONS,
INC.

405 Madison Ave Ste 2100, Toledo,
OH 43604
Tel.: (419) 724-6212   **OH**
Web Site:
    http://www.blockcommunication.com
Year Founded: 1900
Newspaper Publisher; Television
Broadcasting; Advertising Distr
N.A.I.C.S.: 513110
Allan Block (Chm)
Diana Block (Exec VP)

Subsidiaries:

Buckeye Cablevision   (1)
5566 Southwyck Blvd, Toledo, OH 43614-
1536
Tel.: (419) 724-9800
Web Site:
    http://www.buckeyecablesystem.com
Sales Range: $10-24.9 Million
Emp.: 60
Cable Television
N.A.I.C.S.: 516210

Buckeye TeleSystem, Inc.   (1)
4818 Angola Rd, Toledo, OH 43615
Tel.: (419) 724-9898
Web Site: http://www.buckeye-
telesystem.com
Voice & Internet Service Provider
N.A.I.C.S.: 517810
John Martin (Pres)

CCS   (1)
1140 Corporate Dr, Holland, OH 43528-
9591
Tel.: (419) 867-2020
Producer & Distributor of Advertising Material
N.A.I.C.S.: 455219

Erie County Cablevision   (1)
409 E Market St, Sandusky, OH 44870
Tel.: (419) 627-0800
Web Site: http://www.the-cablesystem.com
Sales Range: $10-24.9 Million
Emp.: 45
Cable Television Services Including Installa-
tion & Retransmission
N.A.I.C.S.: 516210

Idaho Independent Television,
Inc.   (1)
PO Box 1212, Nampa, ID
83653-1211   (100%)
Tel.: (208) 466-1200
Web Site: http://www.ktrv.com
Sales Range: $10-24.9 Million
Emp.: 16
Independent Television Station
N.A.I.C.S.: 516120
Ken Hunter (Pres & Gen Mgr)

Independence Television Co.   (1)
624 W Muhammad Ali Blvd, Louisville, KY
40203   (100%)
Tel.: (502) 584-6441
Web Site: http://www.wdrb.com
Sales Range: $25-49.9 Million
Emp.: 200
Television Station
N.A.I.C.S.: 516120
Bill Lamb (Pres & Gen Mgr)
Ray Foushee (Dir-Mktg)
Kim Bauerla (Dir-HR)
David Callan (Dir-Production)
Rick Burrice (Mgr-Sls)
Marti Hazel (VP & Dir-Sls)
Ken Logsdon (Mgr-IT)

Lima Communications Corp. WLIO
Television   (1)
1424 Rice Ave, Lima, OH 45805
Tel.: (419) 228-8835
Web Site: http://www.hometownstations.com
Sales Range: $10-24.9 Million
Emp.: 75
Network-Affiliated Television Station
N.A.I.C.S.: 516120
Sherral Garlock (Sec)
Kevin Creamer (Gen Mgr)
Jayson Geiser (Dir-Sports)

MaxxSouth Broadband   (1)
1901 Jackson Ave W Ste B, Oxford, MS
38655
Web Site: http://www.maxxsouth.com

Cable & Broadband Network Service Provider
N.A.I.C.S.: 516120

Monroe Cablevision Inc.   (1)
1034 N Monroe St, Monroe, MI 48162-3113
Tel.: (734) 241-2225
N.A.I.C.S.: 513110

PG Publishing Company   (1)
34 Blvd Of The Allies, Pittsburgh, PA 15222-
1204
Tel.: (412) 263-1100
Web Site: http://www.post-gazette.com
Sales Range: $100-124.9 Million
Emp.: 1,250
Newspaper Publishing
N.A.I.C.S.: 513110
John Robinson Block (Publr & Editor-in-
Chief)
Keith Burris (Exec Editor & Dir-Editorial)

The Blade Co.   (1)
541 N Superior St, Toledo, OH
43660-1000   (100%)
Tel.: (419) 724-6000
Web Site: http://www.toledoblade.com
Sales Range: $50-74.9 Million
Emp.: 650
Newspaper Publishing
N.A.I.C.S.: 513110
Dave Murray (Mng Editor)
Heather Dennis (Editor-Copy)
Tony Durham (Editor-News)
Alan Ponzio (Editor-Copy)
Todd Wetzler (Editor-Copy)
Mark Peddicord (Mgr-Mktg)
William Southern (Pres & Gen Mgr)
Steve Dolley (Controller)
Bettyann Cole (Sr Mgr-IT)
John Fedderke (Dir-Mktg)
Annie Cieslukowski (Asst Dir-Mktg)
Ken Burkett (Dir-Adv Ops)
Mike Merem (Dir-Production)
Marion Jaeger (Sr Mgr-Adv Ops)
Kim Przybylski (Asst Mgr-Retail Adv)
Keith Burris (Dir-Editorial)

WAND Television, Inc.   (1)
904 W S Side Dr, Decatur, IL 62521-4022
Tel.: (217) 424-2500
Web Site: http://www.wandtv.com
Sales Range: $25-49.9 Million
Emp.: 80
Television Station Services
N.A.I.C.S.: 516120
Ricky Joseph (Pres & Gen Mgr)
Clay Koenig (VP & Dir-Sls)

BLOCK ELECTRIC CO. INC.
7107 N Milwaukee Ave, Niles, IL
60714-4424
Tel.: (847) 647-4030   **IL**
Web Site:
    https://www.blockelectric.com
Year Founded: 1920
Sales Range: $25-49.9 Million
Emp.: 200
Electrical Work Contractors
N.A.I.C.S.: 238210
Jack G. Block (Pres)
Michael Block (Project Mgr)

BLOCK INDUSTRIES INC.
6101 Oakton St, Skokie, IL 60077
Tel.: (847) 966-3000
Web Site: https://www.blocksteel.com
Sales Range: $50-74.9 Million
Emp.: 80
Metals Service Center
N.A.I.C.S.: 423510
Larry J. Wolfson (Chm)
Donald R. Morgan (VP)
Steve Wysocke (VP-Fin)
Joe Block (Pres)
Bruce Cotton (Acct Mgr)
Dave Balboa (Acct Mgr)
Bryan Withrow (Coord-Matls)
Aron Funes (Coord-Production)
Melvin Malone (Coord-Slitting)
William Mula (Dir-Steel Sourcing)
Glen Rutherford (Mgr-Production)
Tony Stuart (Mgr-Quality)
John Pfeifer (Plant Mgr)
Michael Quandt (VP)

BLOCK INSTITUTE
376 Bay 44th St, Brooklyn, NY 11214
Tel.: (718) 906-5400   NY
Web Site:
   https://www.blockinstitute.org
Year Founded: 1977
Sales Range: $10-24.9 Million
Emp.: 303
Disability Assistance Services
N.A.I.C.S.: 624120
Jeffrey Dold *(Dir-Fin)*
Mary Ellen O'Driscoll *(Dir-HR)*
Brian Riley *(Dir-IT)*
Scott L. Barkin *(Exec Dir)*

BLOCKCHAIN OF THINGS, INC.
747 3rd Ave, New York, NY 10017
Tel.: (646) 926-2268   DE
Web Site:
   http://www.blockchainofthings.com
Year Founded: 2015
Rev.: $2,024,137
Assets: $2,255,634
Liabilities: $12,276,880
Net Worth: ($10,021,246)
Earnings: $1,706,912
Emp.: 4
Fiscal Year-end: 12/31/21
Software Development Services
N.A.I.C.S.: 541511
Andre De Castro *(Pres & CEO)*
Deborah de Castro *(CFO, Treas, Sec & VP-Ops)*

BLOCKCHAIN SOLUTIONS INC.
319 Clematis St Ste 714, West Palm Beach, FL 33401
Tel.: (561) 249-6511   NV
Year Founded: 2014
Investment Services
N.A.I.C.S.: 523999

BLOCKCHAINS, LLC
610 Waltham Way, Sparks, NV 89434
Tel.: (775) 432-0000
Web Site:
   http://www.blockchains.com
Year Founded: 2014
Digital Asset Custody & Management;
Blockchain Connectivity & Digital
Identity Software Developer
N.A.I.C.S.: 541511
Jeffrey Berns *(Founder & CEO)*

BLOCKHOUSE COMPANY, INC.
3285 Farmtrail Rd, York, PA 17406
Tel.: (717) 764-5555   PA
Web Site:
   https://www.blockhouse.com
Year Founded: 1971
Sales Range: $50-74.9 Million
Emp.: 90
Mfr of Institutional Furniture
N.A.I.C.S.: 337127
Douglas P. Mihalak *(Dir-Natl Sls)*
Robin Volker *(Controller-Mfg)*

BLOCKSOM & CO.
450 St John Rd Ste 710, Michigan City, IN 46360-7351
Tel.: (219) 874-3231
Web Site: http://www.blocksom.com
Filtered Products & Bridge Vents Mfr
N.A.I.C.S.: 314999

BLODGETT OIL COMPANY, INC.
PO Box 39, Mount Pleasant, MI 48804-0039
Tel.: (989) 773-3878   MI
Web Site:
   http://www.blodgettfoodmarts.com

Year Founded: 1958
Sales Range: $25-49.9 Million
Emp.: 190
Mfr of Petroleum Products
N.A.I.C.S.: 424720
Ross Blodgett *(Pres)*

BLOEDORN LUMBER COMPANY INC.
201 W 21st Ave, Torrington, WY 82240
Tel.: (307) 532-2151
Web Site:
   http://www.bloedornlumber.com
Sales Range: $25-49.9 Million
Emp.: 200
Millwork & Lumber ; Hardware Home Centers
N.A.I.C.S.: 444110
Mark Yung *(Treas & Sr VP)*
Gregory George *(Pres)*
Mark Young *(VP)*

BLOOD BANK OF HAWAII
2043 Dillingham Blvd, Honolulu, HI 96819
Tel.: (808) 845-9966   HI
Web Site: http://www.bbh.org
Year Founded: 1941
Sales Range: $10-24.9 Million
Emp.: 173
Blood Bank Operator
N.A.I.C.S.: 621991
Albert Yoza *(CFO)*
Lori Kaneshige *(Dir-Clinical Svc)*
Gary A. Okamoto *(VP)*
Jill F. Shimokawa Higa *(VP)*
Patrick D. Ching *(Treas)*
John T. Komeiji *(Sec & VP)*
Kim-Anh T. Nguyen *(Pres & CEO)*
Lori L. McCarney *(Chm)*

BLOOD-HORSE PUBLICATIONS
3101 Beaumont Centre Cir, Lexington, KY 40513
Tel.: (859) 278-2361
Web Site: http://www.bloodhorse.com
Sales Range: $10-24.9 Million
Emp.: 105
Periodical Publishers
N.A.I.C.S.: 513120
Albert M. Stall *(Owner)*
Stuart S. Janney *(Chm)*
Evan I. Hammonds *(Mng Editor)*
Claire Novak *(Editor-BloodHorse Daily)*
John K. Keitt *(Exec Dir)*

BLOOM ELECTRIC SERVICES, INC.
9525 W Reno Ave, Oklahoma City, OK 73127-2963
Tel.: (405) 495-7500   OK
Web Site: http://www.bloomok.com
Year Founded: 1950
Sales Range: $50-74.9 Million
Emp.: 100
Designer, Builder & Servicer of Electric Systems for Industrial & Commercial Buildings & Oil Drilling Industry;
Motor & Generator Repair
N.A.I.C.S.: 811310
David B. Bloom *(Treas)*
Richard A. Bloom *(Gen Mgr-Sls & Mktg)*

BLOOM EQUITY PARTNERS MANAGEMENT, LLC
11 E 44th St Ste 1501, New York, NY 10017
Tel.: (212) 984-2478   DE
Web Site:
   https://www.bloomequitypartner.com
Year Founded: 2020

Privater Equity Firm
N.A.I.C.S.: 523999
Bart Macdonald *(Founder & Mng Partner)*

Subsidiaries:

GRC International Group plc   (1)
Unit 3 Clive Court Bartholomews Walk
Cambridgeshire Business Park, Ely, CB7
4EA, Cambridgeshire, United Kingdom
Tel.: (44) 3309990222
Web Site: http://www.grci.group
Rev.: $15,966,787
Assets: $20,314,207
Liabilities: $10,937,792
Net Worth: $9,376,414
Earnings: ($3,490,698)
Emp.: 149
Fiscal Year-end: 03/31/2021
Information Technology Management Services
N.A.I.C.S.: 541512
Alan Philip Calder *(CEO)*
Christopher John Hartshorne *(Fin Dir)*

Subsidiary (Domestic):

Data Quality Management Group
Limited   (2)
Oakridge House Wellington Road, Cressex
Business Park, High Wycombe, HP12 3PR,
Buckinghamshire, United Kingdom
Tel.: (44) 1494442900
Web Site: https://www.dqmgrc.com
Software Development Services
N.A.I.C.S.: 541511

GRC Elearning Limited   (2)
Unit 3 Clive Court Bartholomew's Walk,
Cambridgeshire Business Park, Ely, CB7
4EA, Cambridgeshire, United Kingdom
Tel.: (44) 3309002002
Web Site: https://www.grcelearning.com
Learning Services
N.A.I.C.S.: 611710

Vigilant Software Ltd.   (2)
Unit 3 Clive Court Bartholomew's Walk
Cambridgeshire Business Park, Ely, CB7
4EA, Cambridgeshire, United Kingdom
Tel.: (44) 3337001700,
Web Site: https://www.vigilantsoftware.co.uk
Software Development Services
N.A.I.C.S.: 541511

BLOOM HOLDCO LLC
PMBS 1387 1000 Brickell Ave Ste 715, Miami, FL 33131
Tel.: (850) 660-7301   DE
Year Founded: 2017
Assets: $9,532,000
Liabilities: $42,043,000
Net Worth: ($32,511,000)
Earnings: ($4,090,000)
Fiscal Year-end: 09/30/23
Holding Company
N.A.I.C.S.: 551112

BLOOMBERG L.P.
731 Lexington Ave, New York, NY 10022
Tel.: (212) 318-2000   DE
Web Site: http://www.bloomberg.com
Year Founded: 1981
Sales Range: $5-14.9 Billion
Emp.: 25,000
Fiscal Year-end: 12/31/23
Holding Company; Multimedia Business & Financial Information Services
N.A.I.C.S.: 551112
Michael Rubens Bloomberg *(Co-Founder & Owner)*
Thomas F. Secunda *(Co-Founder)*
Elizabeth Mazzeo *(COO)*
Justin B. Smith *(CEO-Media)*
Patricia E. Harris *(CEO-Bloomberg Philanthropies)*
Mary L. Schapiro *(Founder, Chm & Vice Chm-Public Policy-Global)*
John Micklethwait *(Editor-in-Chief)*
Karin M. Klein *(Founding Partner-Bloomberg Beta)*

Anne Riley Moffat *(Sr Editor-Energy & Commodities-News)*
Nikki Naik *(Editor-Social Media)*
Tim O'Brien *(Exec Editor-Opinion)*
Patti Roskill *(CFO)*
Vladimir Kliatchko *(CEO)*

Subsidiaries:

Bloomberg BusinessWeek   (1)
731 Lexington Ave, New York, NY 10022
Tel.: (212) 318-2000
Web Site: http://www.businessweek.com
Sales Range: $50-74.9 Million
Emp.: 200
Business Magazine
N.A.I.C.S.: 513120
David Rocks *(Sr Editor)*
Marc Miller *(Deputy Copy Editor)*
Ronnie Weil *(Dir-Photo)*
Kathleen Moore *(Sr Photo Editor)*
Susan Fingerhut *(Dir-Editorial Ops)*
Christian Corser *(Dir-Sls Dev-Special Ad Sections)*
Robert Vargas *(Dir-Creative)*
Pat Regnier *(Editor)*
Bret Begun *(Editor-Etc)*
Amanda Kolson Hurley *(Sr Editor)*
Danielle Sacks *(Editor-Features)*

Bloomberg Television   (1)
731 Lexington Ave, New York, NY 10022-1331
Tel.: (212) 318-2000
Web Site: http://www.bloomberg.com
Business, Financial & News Television Broadcasting Services
N.A.I.C.S.: 516210
Gary Groenheim *(Dir-Comml-Asia Pacific Reg)*
Claudia Milne *(Head-Live TV)*
Amol Maheshwari *(Head-Natl Sls)*
Lavneesh Gupta *(COO-India)*
Alok Nair *(Exec VP-India)*

Bloomberg Tradebook LLC   (1)
731 Lexington Park Ave, New York, NY 10022
Tel.: (212) 893-5555
Web Site:
   http://www.bloombergtradebook.com
Sales Range: $800-899.9 Million
Emp.: 5,000
Stock & Fund Management Broker Services
N.A.I.C.S.: 523150
Josh Schwartz *(Dir-Brokerage Tech Partnerships)*
Tom Keene *(Editor)*
Beth Mazzeo *(COO)*
Gia Freireich *(Acct Exec)*
Alex Goodman *(Acct Mgr)*
Mike Jay *(Dir-Television)*
Jake Kimble *(Mgr-Acct-Trading Sys & Sls)*
Vipul Nagrath *(CIO-Enterprise Solutions)*
Minnie Park *(Acct Mgr-Intl Banks Team)*
Sara Piaseczynski *(Head-Ad Traffic)*
Mani Ramezani *(Engr-Fin Applications)*
Jonathan Seva *(Engr-Data Center & Network Infrastructure)*
Yurij Baransky *(Head-Product Dev-Global)*
Gerald E. Burke *(CFO)*
Sabrina Gagliotta *(Head-Trading & Execution Consulting-Global)*
David Loffredo *(COO)*
Liron Mandelbaum *(CMO)*
Robert Shapiro *(Chief Risk Officer)*
Joseph Zangri *(Head-Compliance-Global)*

Broadway Technology, LLC   (1)
11 Broadway, New York, NY 10004
Tel.: (646) 912-6450
Web Site:
   http://www.broadwaytechnology.com
Rev.: $1,000,000
Emp.: 17
Software Publisher
N.A.I.C.S.: 513210
Claudia Cantarella *(Gen Counsel)*
David Meeker *(Exec VP-Engrg)*
Bruce Boytim *(COO)*
Dan Romanelli *(Head-Relationships)*

The Bureau of National Affairs, Inc.   (1)
1801 S Bell St, Arlington, VA 22202
Tel.: (703) 341-3000
Web Site: http://www.bna.com
Sales Range: $300-349.9 Million
Emp.: 1,506

Bloomberg L.P.—(Continued)

Print, Electronic News, Analysis & Reference Products Publisher
N.A.I.C.S.: 513110
Paul N. Wojcik (Chm)
Gregory C. McCaffery (CEO)
Margret S. Hullinger (VP & Publr-Book Div Grp)
Lisa A. Fitzpatrick (VP & Gen Mgr-Tax & Acctg)
Ken Crutchfield (VP-Software)
Daniel M. Fine (Co-COO)
Joe Breda (Exec VP-Product)
Mike MacKay (Pres-Cross Platform)
Peter Sherman (Gen Counsel)
David Perla (Pres-Legal)
Christina Correira (Chief HR Officer)
Kevin Colangelo (VP-Strategic Accts)
Baker Evans (VP & Gen Mgr-Corp & Transactional)
Scott Falk (VP & Gen Mgr-Health Care & Litigation)
Brian Houk (VP & Head-Sls-Legal)
Linda Kaufman (VP-Client Success)
Darin Ohlandt (VP-Corp Mktg)
Victoria Roberts (VP & Gen Mgr-Labor, Employment, Benefits & HR)
Rich Thompson (CTO)
Darren P. McKewen (Pres-Tax & Specialty)
Richard A. Montella Jr. (Exec VP-Comml Ops)

Subsidiary (Non-US):

BNA International Inc.　　　　　　(2)
1st Floor 38 Threadneedle Street, London, EC2R 8AY, United Kingdom　(100%)
Tel.: (44) 2078475800
Web Site: http://www.bnai.com
Sales Range: $25-49.9 Million
Emp.: 18
Financial Publishing
N.A.I.C.S.: 513120
Nick Gallehawk (Dir-Mktg)

Division (Domestic):

BNA PLUS　　　　　　　　　　(2)
1801 S Bell St, Arlington, VA 22202
Tel.: (703) 341-3000
Web Site: http://www.bna.com
Sales Range: $75-99.9 Million
Emp.: 700
Custom Research & Document Delivery Online Services; Book Publishing; Conferences & Seminars on Current Aspects of Labor Relations, Various Areas of Legal Practice, Business & Government
N.A.I.C.S.: 921190

Subsidiary (Domestic):

McArdle Printing Co., Inc.　　　(2)
800 Commerce Dr, Upper Marlboro, MD 20774-8792　　　　　　　(100%)
Tel.: (301) 390-8500
Web Site: http://www.mcardlesolutions.com
Sales Range: $25-49.9 Million
Emp.: 100
Commercial Printing; Miscellaneous Publishing
N.A.I.C.S.: 323111
Lisa Arsenault (Pres)
Jeff Emerson (VP-Ops)
Jeff Gomes (Mgr-Production)
Chris Carlucci (Mgr-Mail)
Steve McKenzie (Mgr-Quality Control)
Terry Dorsey (Mgr-Estimating)
Dan Boger (Mgr-Logistics)
Silvia Edwards (Mgr-BBNA Production)
Kan Cratty (Mgr-Cross Channel Ops)

Tax Management, Inc.　　　　　　(2)
1801 S Bell St, Arlington, VA 22202　　　　　　　　　　　(100%)
Tel.: (703) 341-3500
Web Site: http://www.bnatax.com
Publisher of Information Services on Legalities of Tax System
N.A.I.C.S.: 513199

Division (Domestic):

BNA Software　　　　　　　　(3)
1801 S Bell St, Arlington, VA 22202-4506
Tel.: (202) 728-7962
Web Site: http://www.bnasoftware.com
Sales Range: $25-49.9 Million
Emp.: 70

Publisher of PC-based Software Applications for Tax & Financial Professionals
N.A.I.C.S.: 513210
Michael T. Smith (VP & Gen Mgr)
Rashid Nur (Dir-Project Mgmt Office)

BLOOMER CANDY CO.
2200 Linden Ave, Zanesville, OH 43702
Tel.: (740) 452-7501
Web Site:
　http://www.bloomercandy.com
Rev.: $19,000,000
Emp.: 40
Confectionery Mfr
N.A.I.C.S.: 424450
Jerry Nolder (CEO)

BLOOMER PLASTICS, INC.
1710 N Industrial Dr, Bloomer, WI 54724
Tel.: (715) 568-5775　　　　　　WI
Web Site:
　http://www.bloomerplastics.com
Sales Range: $25-49.9 Million
Emp.: 60
Unlaminated Plastics Film & Sheet Mfr
N.A.I.C.S.: 326113
Debbie Poirier (Mgr-IT)
Rich Koehler (Dir-Engrg Staff)
Jerry Kolanczyk (Dir-Sls)
Carl J. Kubas (Sec)
Neil P. Lundgren (Pres)
Jason Rothbauer (Dir-Pur)

Subsidiaries:

Optimum Plastics, Inc.　　　　　(1)
1188 S Houk Rd, Delaware, OH 43015
Tel.: (740) 369-2770
Web Site: http://www.optimumplastics.com
Sales Range: $1-9.9 Million
Emp.: 40
Plastic/Coated Paper Mfr
N.A.I.C.S.: 322220
Bill Wright (VP-Tech & Innovation)
Kevin Fee (VP-Sls & Mktg)
Jerry Kolanczyk (VP-Sls & Mktg)
Terrance Smith (COO)

BLOOMERANG, LLC
9120 Otis Ave, Indianapolis, IN 46216
Tel.: (866) 332-2999
Web Site: https://bloomerang.co
Emp.: 100
Software Publr
N.A.I.C.S.: 513210
Dennis Fois (CEO)

Subsidiaries:

Qgiv, Inc.　　　　　　　　　　(1)
53 Lake Morton Dr, Lakeland, FL 33801
Tel.: (863) 687-0110
Web Site: http://www.qgiv.com
Sales Range: $1-9.9 Million
Emp.: 14
Online Fundraising Software
N.A.I.C.S.: 513210
John Baylis (CEO)
Jennifer Mansfield (Dir-Customer Svc)
Peter Rudden (Dir-Mktg)

BLOOMING COLOR, INC.
230 Eisenhower Ln N, Lombard, IL 60148
Tel.: (630) 517-4195
Web Site:
　https://www.bloomingcolor.com
Sales Range: $1-9.9 Million
Prepress Services
N.A.I.C.S.: 323120
John Lehman (Owner)

Subsidiaries:

Graphics Plus, Inc.　　　　　　(1)
1808 Ogden Ave, Lisle, IL 60532
Tel.: (630) 968-9073
Web Site: http://www.gpdelivers.com
Other Commercial Printing
N.A.I.C.S.: 323111

BLOOMINGTON OFFSET PROCESS
1705 S Veterans Pkwy, Bloomington, IL 61701
Tel.: (309) 662-3395
Web Site: https://www.bopi.com
Sales Range: $10-24.9 Million
Emp.: 72
Offset Printing
N.A.I.C.S.: 323111
Thomas G. Mercier (Pres & CEO)
Jeff Fritzen (Exec VP)

BLOOMNATION, INC.
1316 3rd St Ste 301, Santa Monica, CA 90401
Tel.: (210) 405-5050
Web Site:
　http://www.bloomnation.com
Year Founded: 2010
Sales Range: $50-74.9 Million
Emp.: 48
Software Development Services
N.A.I.C.S.: 541511
Farbod Shoraka (Co-Founder & CEO)
Gregg Weisstein (Co-Founder & COO)

BLOOMREACH, INC.
82 Pioneer Way, Mountain View, CA 94041
Tel.: (888) 263-3917
Web Site:
　https://www.bloomreach.com
Year Founded: 2009
Web Search Services for Online Retailers & Commerce Sites
N.A.I.C.S.: 541519
Raj De Datta (Co-Founder & CEO)
Christina Augustine (COO)
Xun Wang (CTO)
Brian Walker (Chief Strategy Officer)

Subsidiaries:

BloomReach B.V.　　　　　　　(1)
Fred. Roeskestraat 109, 1076 EE, Amsterdam, Netherlands
Tel.: (31) 205224466
Web Site: http://www.bloomreach.com
Computer Software Designer; Web Search Services
N.A.I.C.S.: 541519
Tjeerd Brenninkmeijer (Exec VP-EMEA)

BLOOMSBURG CARPET INDUSTRIES INC.
4999 Columbia Blvd, Bloomsburg, PA 17815-8854
Tel.: (570) 784-9188　　　　　　PA
Web Site:
　http://www.bloomsburgcarpet.com
Year Founded: 1998
Sales Range: $10-24.9 Million
Emp.: 230
Mfr of Carpets & Rugs
N.A.I.C.S.: 314110
Martin Bowman (VP)
Tom Habib (Pres)
Lorraine Carey (Mgr-Personnel)

BLOOMSBURG MILLS INC.
111 W 40th St Fl 10, New York, NY 10018-2506
Tel.: (212) 221-6114　　　　　　PA
Year Founded: 1890
Sales Range: $100-124.9 Million
Emp.: 600
Mfr of Textiles
N.A.I.C.S.: 313210
James P. Marion (Pres & CEO)
Frederick J. Shaw (Exec VP-Sls)
Todd Moyer (Treas & VP)
James P. Marion Jr. (Chm)

BLOSSOM FARM PRODUCTS CO.
545 Rt 17 S, Ridgewood, NJ 07450
Tel.: (201) 493-2626
Sales Range: $10-24.9 Million
Emp.: 5
Distr of Dairy Products
N.A.I.C.S.: 424430

BLOUNT FINE FOODS CORPORATION
383 Water St, Warren, RI 02885
Tel.: (401) 245-8800　　　　　　RI
Web Site:
　http://www.blountseafood.com
Year Founded: 1946
Sales Range: $25-49.9 Million
Emp.: 200
Fresh & Frozen Packaged Soups
N.A.I.C.S.: 311710
Todd Blount (Pres & CEO)
Robert Sewall (Exec VP-Sls & Mktg)
William Bigelow (Chief Innovation Officer)
Todd W. Brown (VP-Food Safety & Quality Assurance)
Jeff Wirtz (Sr Dir-Culinary Dev)
David Vittorio (Sr Dir-Mktg)

BLOUNT SMALL SHIP ADVENTURES, INC.
461 Water St, Warren, RI 02885
Tel.: (401) 247-0955　　　　　　DE
Web Site:
　http://www.blountsmallship.com
Year Founded: 1966
Rev.: $9,000,000
Emp.: 65
Small Ship Cruise Trip Services
N.A.I.C.S.: 487210
Nancy Blount (Pres)
Cassandra Doyle (Mgr-Ops)
Lisa Pontarelli (Dir-Cruise)

BLOWER DEMPSAY CORPORATION
4042 W Garry Ave, Santa Ana, CA 92704-5140
Tel.: (714) 557-7420
Web Site: http://www.pakwest.com
Year Founded: 1973
Sales Range: $25-49.9 Million
Emp.: 200
Industrial & Personal Service Paper
N.A.I.C.S.: 424130
James F. Blower (Pres)
Serge Poirier (Controller)
James Fleming (COO)

Subsidiaries:

Coats-Warner Corporation　　　(1)
14731 Keswick St, Van Nuys, CA 92405
Tel.: (818) 994-4505
Web Site: http://www.coatswarner.com
Industrial Machinery Mfr
N.A.I.C.S.: 333248

Pacific Conveyor Systems, Inc.　(1)
1535 E Edinger Ave, Santa Ana, CA 92705
Tel.: (714) 258-1810
Web Site: http://www.pacificconveyor.net
Sales Range: $1-9.9 Million
Conveyor Mfr
N.A.I.C.S.: 333922

Pacific Western Container Corp.　(1)
4044 W Garry Ave, Santa Ana, CA 92704
Tel.: (714) 547-9266
Web Site: http://www.pacificwestern.com
Emp.: 90
Plastic Container Whslr
N.A.I.C.S.: 423840
Ken Ilt (Gen Mgr)

Pak West Paper & Packaging LLC　　　　　　　　　　　　(1)
4042 W Garry Ave, Santa Ana, CA 92704-6404
Tel.: (714) 557-7420
Web Site: http://www.pakwest.com

Sales Range: $25-49.9 Million
Emp.: 115
Printing & Writing Paper
N.A.I.C.S.: 424130
James F. Blower (Pres)
Serge Poirier (Controller)

BLR/FURTHER
3000 Meadow Brook Lake Dr Ste 11,
Birmingham, AL 35242
Tel.: (205) 324-8005
Web Site: http://www.blrfurther.com
Year Founded: 1986
Rev.: $17,000,000
Emp.: 22
N.A.I.C.S.: 541810
Cary Bynum (Pres)
Kelly Davis (Dir-Media)
Dana Stephens-Travis (Sr Acct Mgr)
Marc Stricklin (Dir-Creative)
Brian Lawrence (Dir-Bus Dev)

BLS LIMOUSINE SERVICE
1820 Steinway St, Astoria, NY 11105
Tel.: (718) 267-4760
Web Site: http://www.blslimo.com
Rev.: $18,427,651
Emp.: 10
Limousine Rental, With Driver
N.A.I.C.S.: 485320
Michael Okon (Owner)
Chrystal Colon (Mgr-Billing)
Marilyn Hornik (Dir-Global Acct Mgmt
& Customer Svc & Mgr-Acctg)

BLT ENTERPRISES
501 Spectrum Cir, Oxnard, CA 93030
Tel.: (805) 278-8220
Web Site: http://www.blt-
enterprises.com
Year Founded: 1943
Sales Range: $25-49.9 Million
Emp.: 60
Recycling, Waste Materials
N.A.I.C.S.: 562920
Bernard Huberman (Pres)
Dan Rosenthal (Vice Chm)
Lisa Tamayo (Mgr-Dev)
Mario Quezada (Mgr-Corp Safety &
HR)

BLU DOT DESIGN & MANU-
FACTURING, INC.
1323 Tyler St NE, Minneapolis, MN
55413-1530
Tel.: (612) 782-1844   MN
Web Site: http://www.bludot.com
Year Founded: 1996
Sales Range: $10-24.9 Million
Emp.: 200
Furniture Mfr
N.A.I.C.S.: 337121
John Christakos (CEO & Co-
Founder)
Maurice Blanks (Co-Founder & COO)

BLU-ALLIANCE LIFESCIENCE
6801 Wayzata Blvd Ste 3, Saint
Louis Park, MN 55426
Tel.: (952) 545-4000
Web Site: http://www.blu-
alliance.com
Year Founded: 1998
Sales Range: $1-9.9 Million
Emp.: 53
Executive Recruiting & Consulting for
the Life Science Industry
N.A.I.C.S.: 561312
Susan St. James (Pres & CEO)
Mike A. Steinke (VP-Ops)

BLUDAU FABRICATION INC.
431 County Road 187, Hallettsville,
TX 77964
Tel.: (361) 798-4339
Sales Range: $10-24.9 Million
Emp.: 40

Building Components, Structural
Steel
N.A.I.C.S.: 332312
Anthony Bludau (Pres)

BLUDWORTH MARINE, LLC
3502 Broadway, Houston, TX 77017
Tel.: (713) 644-1595   TX
Web Site:
    https://www.vesselrepair.com
Year Founded: 1984
Sales Range: $10-24.9 Million
Emp.: 155
Machine Repair Services
N.A.I.C.S.: 811310
Richard Bludworth (Owner)
Leonard Warren Eitelbach (Project
Mgr)

BLUE & ASSOCIATES, INC.
15602 Patrica St Ste 200, Austin, TX
78728
Tel.: (512) 670-9310   TX
Web Site:
    https://www.blueconstruction.com
Year Founded: 1999
Sales Range: $10-24.9 Million
Emp.: 16
Commercial Building Construction
N.A.I.C.S.: 236220
Donald J. Jay (Chm & COO)
Thomas R. Jay (Pres & CEO)
J. Gib Jones (Exec VP)

BLUE & CO. LLC
12800 N Meridian St Ste 400, Car-
mel, IN 46032
Tel.: (317) 848-8920
Web Site:
    https://www.blueandco.com
Year Founded: 1970
Sales Range: $10-24.9 Million
Emp.: 72
Certified Public Accountants & Busi-
ness Advisors
N.A.I.C.S.: 541211
Bradley A. Shaw (Mng Dir)
Julie DiFrancesco (Principal)
Thomas Skoog (Principal)
Dennis Klocke (Sr Mgr-Fin Institutions
Practice)

BLUE ARMOR SECURITY SER-
VICES, INC.
10515 Gulfdale Dr Ste 109, San An-
tonio, TX 78216
Tel.: (210) 495-4610
Web Site:
    https://www.bluearmorsecurity.com
Year Founded: 2003
Sales Range: $1-9.9 Million
Emp.: 115
Residential & Commercial Security
Services
N.A.I.C.S.: 561612
Willie Ng (Owner & Pres)

BLUE BAKER
201 Dominik Dr, College Station, TX
77840
Tel.: (979) 696-5055
Web Site: https://www.bluebaker.com
Year Founded: 2001
Rev.: $3,700,000
Emp.: 88
Food & Beverage Services
N.A.I.C.S.: 722511
Dave Fox (Owner)

BLUE BEACON INTERNA-
TIONAL, INC.
500 Graves Blvd, Salina, KS 67401-
4306
Tel.: (785) 825-2221   KS
Web Site:
    http://www.bluebeacon.com

Year Founded: 1973
Sales Range: $100-124.9 Million
Emp.: 3,000
Truck & RV Washing Operations
N.A.I.C.S.: 811192
Trace Walker (Pres)
Mike Walker (VP)
Morrie Foderberg (CFO)

Subsidiaries:

Blue Beacon Truck Wushea   (1)
500 Graves Blvd, Salina, KS 67401-4306
Tel.: (785) 825-2221
Web Site: http://www.bbi-inc.com
Sales Range: $10-24.9 Million
Emp.: 30
Provider of Equipment Rental & Leasing
N.A.I.C.S.: 532411
Trace Walker (Pres)

Green Lantern, Inc.   (1)
500 Graves Blvd, Salina, KS 67401-4306
Tel.: (785) 825-2221
Sales Range: $25-49.9 Million
Emp.: 100
Grocery Stores
N.A.I.C.S.: 445131

Lighthouse Properties, LLC   (1)
500 Graves Blvd, Salina, KS 67401
Tel.: (785) 826-8222
Web Site:
    http://www.lighthousepropertieshotels.com
Hotel Manager
N.A.I.C.S.: 721110

Subsidiary (Domestic):

The Raphael Hotel   (2)
325 Ward Pkwy, Kansas City, MO 64112-
2111
Tel.: (816) 756-3800
Web Site: http://www.raphaelkc.com
Sales Range: $10-24.9 Million
Emp.: 100
Hotel
N.A.I.C.S.: 721110
Timothy Brice (Dir-Sls)
Deanna Brazil (Dir-Food & Beverage)
Bill Carter (Gen Mgr)
David Rabinovitz (Mgr-Night)

BLUE BELL ADVERTISING AS-
SOCIATES
1101 S Bluebell Rd, Brenham, TX
77833
Tel.: (979) 836-7977   TX
Web Site: https://www.bluebell.com
Year Founded: 1985
Sales Range: $1-9.9 Million
Emp.: 4,000
In House Advertising Agency
N.A.I.C.S.: 541810
Jim R. Hayhurst (Mgr-Adv)
Karen Krnavek (Coord-Production)
Joe Robertson (Mgr-Pub Rels)

BLUE BELL CREAMERIES,
L.P.
1101 S Blue Bell Rd, Brenham, TX
77833
Tel.: (979) 836-7977   DE
Web Site: https://www.bluebell.com
Year Founded: 1907
Sales Range: $1-4.9 Billion
Emp.: 2,400
Ice Cream & Frozen Desserts Mfr
N.A.I.C.S.: 311520
Jim Kruse (Chm)
Ricky Dickson (Pres)

Subsidiaries:

Blue Bell Creameries   (1)
1123 Military Pkwy, Mesquite, TX 75149-
4126
Tel.: (979) 830-2190
Sales Range: $25-49.9 Million
Emp.: 45
Ice Cream Treats Mfr
N.A.I.C.S.: 311520

Blue Bell Creameries   (1)
2211 Karbach St, Houston, TX 77092-8001

Tel.: (713) 686-3468
Web Site: http://www.bluebell.com
Sales Range: $25-49.9 Million
Emp.: 80
Mfr of Ice Cream
N.A.I.C.S.: 424430
Rob Hungate (Branch Mgr)
Andy Richardson (Mgr-Sls)

BLUE BENEFITS CONSULTING
INC.
12800 N Meridian St Ste 400, Car-
mel, IN 46032
Tel.: (317) 848-8920   IN
Web Site:
    https://bluebenefitsonline.com
Employee Benefit Plans & Retirement
Plan Design
N.A.I.C.S.: 525110
Stephen Canter (Mgr)

Subsidiaries:

Indiana Benefits Inc.   (1)
400 W 7th St Ste 200, Bloomington, IN
47404
Tel.: (812) 334-3122
Web Site: http://www.indianabenefits.com
Insurance & Retirement Benefits
N.A.I.C.S.: 525110
Terri Gould (Sec)

BLUE CABOOSE INC.
4650 N Port Washington Rd, Milwau-
kee, WI 53212
Tel.: (414) 203-8060
Web Site:
    http://www.hunterbusiness.com
Sales Range: $10-24.9 Million
Emp.: 40
Whslr of Personal Computers
N.A.I.C.S.: 423430
Victor L. Hunter (Pres)
Leslie Wyrowski (Controller)

BLUE CANOE BODYWEAR
390 A Lk Benbow Dr, Garberville, CA
95542
Tel.: (707) 923-1373
Web Site: http://www.bluecanoe.com
Year Founded: 1991
Sales Range: $25-49.9 Million
Emp.: 20
Women's Bodywear Mfr
N.A.I.C.S.: 424350
Laurie Dunlap (Pres)

BLUE CANOPY INC.
11710 Plaza America Dr Ste 950,
Reston, VA 20190
Tel.: (703) 896-4000
Web Site:
    http://www.bluecanopy.com
Year Founded: 1998
Sales Range: $1-9.9 Million
Emp.: 82
Information Technology Management
Services
N.A.I.C.S.: 541513
Mike Harris (Partner)
Eric Husebo (Partner)
Bradley Schwartz (Pres & CEO)
Sheryl Schwartz (COO, Chief Admin
Officer & Mng Partner)

BLUE CANYON PARTNERS,
INC.
1603 Orrington Ave Ste 1200, Evan-
ston, IL 60201
Tel.: (847) 967-0801
Web Site:
    http://www.bluecanyonpartners.com
Sales Range: $1-9.9 Million
Emp.: 25
Business & Marketing Consulting
N.A.I.C.S.: 541611
David Hartman (Mng Dir-China)
Axel Leichum (Mgr-Engagement)
Atlee Valentine Pope (Co-Founder)

Blue Canyon Partners, Inc.—(Continued)

BLUE CANYON TECHNOLO-GIES LLC
2550 Crescent Dr, Lafayette, CO 80026
Tel.: (720) 458-0703 **CO**
Web Site:
http://www.bluecanyontech.com
Year Founded: 2008
Engineering Services
N.A.I.C.S.: 541330
Steve Schneider (COO)
Matthew Beckner (Founder)
Karen McConnell (Exec Dir-Smallsats)
Jeffrey Schrader (Pres)

Subsidiaries:

Antenna Development Corporation (1)
151 S Walnut St Ste B6, Las Cruces, NM 88001
Tel.: (575) 541-9319
Radio, Television Broadcasting & Wireless Communications Equipment Mfr
N.A.I.C.S.: 334220
Bruce Blevins (Chief Technical Officer)

BLUE CASA COMMUNICA-TIONS, INC.
114 E Haley St Ste A, Santa Barbara, CA 93101
Tel.: (805) 966-1801
Web Site: https://www.bluecasa.com
Year Founded: 2003
Emp.: 50
Telecommunication Servicesb
N.A.I.C.S.: 517121
Jeff Compton (Pres & CEO)

Subsidiaries:

TNCI Operating Company, LLC (1)
114 E Haley St Ste A, Santa Barbara, CA 93101
Tel.: (805) 966-1801
Telecommunication Servicesb
N.A.I.C.S.: 517810
Jeff Compton (Pres & CEO)
Bill Farwell (CFO)
Victor Flores (VP-Network Ops)

Subsidiary (Domestic):

Impact Telecom, Inc. (2)
9000 E Nichols Ave Ste 230, Englewood, CO 80112
Tel.: (301) 610-4354
Web Site: http://www.impacttelecom.com
Telecommunications Resellers
N.A.I.C.S.: 517121
Robert Beaty (Pres)
Chuck Griffin (CEO)
Doug Funsch (Chief Revenue Officer)
Brian McClintock (CFO)
Patrick Reilly (VP-Carrier Svcs)
Jason Welch (Exec VP-Carrier Svcs)
Bob Imhoff (VP-Bus Dev-Intl)

Subsidiary (Domestic):

AmericaTel Corporation (3)
11300 Rockville Pike Ste 900, Rockville, MD 20855
Tel.: (800) 221-3020
Web Site: http://www.americatel.com
Telecommunication Servicesb
N.A.I.C.S.: 517810

Matrix Telecom, LLC (3)
433 E Las Colinas Blvd Ste 500, Irving, TX 75039
Tel.: (866) 728-7490
Web Site: http://www.matrixbt.com
Business Voice, Data & Internet Telecommunications Services
N.A.I.C.S.: 517112

Subsidiary (Domestic):

Excel Telecommunications (4)
433 Las Colinas Blvd Ste 500, Irving, TX 75039
Tel.: (972) 910-1900

Web Site: http://www.excel.com
Voice & Data Communication Products & Services
N.A.I.C.S.: 517810
Don Eben (Sr Dir-Network Plng)

Division (Domestic):

TNCI (2)
2 Charlesgate W, Boston, MA 02215
Tel.: (617) 369-1000
Web Site: http://www.tncii.com
Telecommunication Servicesb
N.A.I.C.S.: 517810

BLUE CAST DENIM CO. INC.
215 W 40th St, New York, NY 10018
Tel.: (212) 719-1182
Web Site: http://hydraulicjeans.com
Sales Range: $10-24.9 Million
Emp.: 10
Mfr of Womens Clothing
N.A.I.C.S.: 315250
Steven Brandis (Chm)

BLUE CHIP CAPITAL GROUP, INC.
69 S Beverly Dr Ste 373, Beverly Hills, CA 90212
Tel.: (402) 960-6110 **NV**
Year Founded: 2019
Assets: $91,333
Liabilities: $169,265
Net Worth: ($77,932)
Earnings: ($345,868)
Fiscal Year-end: 05/31/24
Asset Management Services
N.A.I.C.S.: 523999

BLUE CHIP VENTURE COM-PANY, LTD
1308 Race St Ste 200, Cincinnati, OH 45202
Tel.: (513) 723-2300
Web Site: http://www.bcvc.com
Rev.: $1,100,000
Emp.: 14
Commodity Contracts Dealing
N.A.I.C.S.: 523160

BLUE CLOVER
425 Soledad St Ste 500, San Antonio, TX 78205
Tel.: (210) 223-5409
Web Site: http://www.blueclover.com
Year Founded: 2003
Sales Range: $10-24.9 Million
Emp.: 15
Full Service
N.A.I.C.S.: 541810
Jose B. Sena (Pres & CEO)
Juan Barrera (Exec Dir-Creative)
Chris Gilbert (Dir-Fin)
John Innotti (Dir-Tech)
Alison Zulaica (Office Mgr)

BLUE COD TECHNOLOGIES, INC.
295 Donald Lynch Blvd, Marlborough, MA 01752
Tel.: (508) 970-0170
Web Site: http://www.bluecod.com
Year Founded: 2001
Sales Range: $75-99.9 Million
Emp.: 165
Custom Computer Programming Services
N.A.I.C.S.: 541511
Robert Bruce (Pres & COO)

BLUE CORONA
7595 Rickenbacker Dr, Gaithersburg, MD 20879
Web Site:
https://www.bluecorona.com
Year Founded: 2007
Sales Range: $1-9.9 Million
Emp.: 20

Online Marketing, Analytics & Optimization Services
N.A.I.C.S.: 541613
Ben Landers (Pres & CEO)

BLUE CREEK INVESTMENT PARTNERS
100 Church St Ste 500, Huntsville, AL 35801
Tel.: (866) 730-6944
Web Site:
http://www.bluecreekip.com
Sales Range: $1-9.9 Million
Emp.: 63
Investment Banking & Securities Dealing
N.A.I.C.S.: 523150
Robert Mayes (CEO)
Lyle Minton (Chief Investment Officer)

Subsidiaries:

Keel Point Advisors, LLC (1)
8065 Leesburg Pike Ste 300, Vienna, VA 22182
Tel.: (703) 807-2020
Web Site: http://www.keelpoint.com
Emp.: 20
Financial Investment Activities
N.A.I.C.S.: 523999
David M. Parks (Founder)
Steven L. Skancke (CIO)
Miriam Boysen (Chief Wealth Officer)
G. Matthew Thomett (Principal)
Christopher J. Cook (Chief-Compliance Officer)
Alan L. Bagwell (COO)
Scott Copeland (Dir-Corp Svcs)
Dawn Daniel (Mgr-Ops)
Kate Knight (Dir-Acctg)
Christine Leyva (Mgr-Client Relationship)
Martha Maples (Dir-Client Svcs)
Robert Mayes (CEO)
Lyle Minton (Chief Investment Officer)
Sandra Stephens (CFO)
Scott Jenkins (Dir-IT)

Subsidiary (Domestic):

Demoss Capital Inc. (2)
25 E Main St Ste 201, Chattanooga, TN 37408-1231
Tel.: (423) 756-4800
Web Site: http://www.demosscapital.com
Investment Advice
N.A.I.C.S.: 523940
John De Moss (Pres)

BLUE CROSS & BLUE SHIELD ASSOCIATION
225 N Michigan Ave, Chicago, IL 60601-7601
Tel.: (312) 297-6000 **IL**
Web Site: http://www.bcbs.com
Year Founded: 1929
Sales Range: $200-249.9 Million
Emp.: 850
Health Insurance Hospital & Medical Plans
N.A.I.C.S.: 533110
Kim A. Keck (Pres & CEO)
Maureen E. Sullivan (Chief Strategy & Innovation Officer)
Jennifer Vachon (Exec VP)
Paul Markovich (Pres/CEO-California)
Robert Kolodgy (CFO & Exec VP)
William A. Breskin (Sr VP-Govt Programs)
Justine Handelman (Sr VP-Office of Policy & Representation)
Kari Hedges (Sr VP-Comml Markets & Enterprise Data Solutions)
Scott Nehs (Gen Counsel, Sec & Sr VP)
David L. Holmberg (Chm)

Subsidiaries:

Blue Cross & Blue Shield Association Government Relations (1)
1310 G St NW, Washington, DC 20005 (100%)

Tel.: (202) 626-4780
Web Site: http://www.bcbs.com
Sales Range: $75-99.9 Million
Emp.: 275
Health Insurance & Lobbyist
N.A.I.C.S.: 524292
Ellisa Fox (Sr VP-Govt Rels)

BLUE CROSS & BLUE SHIELD OF ALABAMA
450 Riverchase Pkwy E, Birmingham, AL 35298-0001
Tel.: (205) 220-5400
Web Site: http://www.bcbsal.org
Year Founded: 1936
Sales Range: $150-199.9 Million
Emp.: 3,700
Health & Medical Insurance Carrier
N.A.I.C.S.: 524114
James Priest (Sr VP-External Affairs)
Michael Patterson (Chief Legal Officer & Sr VP)
Ashley Mosko (VP-Health Mgmt)
Michael Velezis (VP-Legal Svcs)
Darrel Weaver (Chief Medical Officer, VP-Network Svcs & Dir-Medical)
Kipp Keown (VP-Mktg)
Charles DeCroes (VP-Tech Support)
Sheila Herringdon (VP-Bus Dev)
Mary Smith (VP-Treasury Ops)
Timothy Vines (Pres & CEO)

BLUE CROSS & BLUE SHIELD OF ARIZONA, INC.
2444 W Las Palmaritas Dr, Phoenix, AZ 85021-4860
Tel.: (602) 864-4400 **AZ**
Web Site: https://www.azblue.com
Year Founded: 1939
Sales Range: $550-599.9 Million
Emp.: 1,350
Health Insurance Plan
N.A.I.C.S.: 524114
Richard L. Boals (Pres & CEO)
Richard M. Hannon (Sr VP-Mktg)
Susan H. Navran (Exec VP-Internal Ops)

BLUE CROSS & BLUE SHIELD OF KANSAS CITY, INC.
2301 Main St, Kansas City, MO 64108
Tel.: (816) 395-2222 **MO**
Web Site: https://www.bluekc.com
Year Founded: 1938
Sales Range: $700-749.9 Million
Emp.: 1,000
Hospital & Medical Service Plans
N.A.I.C.S.: 524114
Rusty Doty (VP-Ops & Individual Sls)
Matt All (Pres & CEO)
Scott Raymond (Gen Counsel & VP-Legal Svcs)
Sunee N. Mickle (VP-Govt & Community Rels)
Keith E. Kapp (CIO & VP-IT & Svcs)

Subsidiaries:

Cobalt Ventures LLC (1)
PO Box 1509, Louisville, KY 40201-3222
Tel.: (502) 589-8280
Web Site: http://www.cobaltventures.com
Real Estate Management Services
N.A.I.C.S.: 531390
Todd L. Blue (Chm & CEO)
Dianna W. Green (Office Mgr & Accountant)

Subsidiary (Domestic):

Premier WorkComp Management, L.L.C. (2)
9393 W 110th St Ste 200, Overland Park, KS 66210
Tel.: (913) 685-6370
Administrative Management Consulting Services
N.A.I.C.S.: 541611

Preferred Health Professionals, Inc. (1)
9393 W 110th St Ste 200, Overland Park, KS 66210
Tel.: (913) 685-6300
Web Site: http://www.phpkc.com
Sales Range: $50-74.9 Million
Emp.: 65
Hospital & Medical Service Plans
N.A.I.C.S.: 524298
Joe Intfen (CFO)
Sherry Patton (Mgr-Claims)
Mindy Purkeypile (Dir-Ops)
Hali Smith (Dir-Fin & Corp Procurement)
Michelle Tagg (Exec Dir-Network Client Svcs)

BLUE CROSS & BLUE SHIELD OF MASSACHUSETTS, INC.
101 Huntington Ave Ste 1300, Boston, MA 02199-7611
Tel.: (617) 246-5000   MA
Web Site: http://www.bcbsma.com
Year Founded: 1937
Sales Range: $1-4.9 Billion
Emp.: 3,500
Health Insurance Carrier
N.A.I.C.S.: 524114
Linda M. Williams (Chief Risk & Audit Officer & Sr VP)
Andrew Dreyfus (Pres & CEO)

BLUE CROSS & BLUE SHIELD OF MISSISSIPPI
3545 Lakeland Dr, Flowood, MS 39232
Tel.: (601) 664-4590   MS
Web Site: http://www.bcbsms.com
Year Founded: 1947
Sales Range: $200-249.9 Million
Emp.: 1,200
Hospital & Medical Service Plan
N.A.I.C.S.: 524114

Subsidiaries:

Bluebonnet Life Insurance Company (1)
PO Box 1043, Flowood, MS 39215-1043   (100%)
Tel.: (601) 664-4218
Web Site: http://www.bcbsms.com
Sales Range: $75-99.9 Million
Emp.: 3
Life Insurance
N.A.I.C.S.: 524113

BLUE CROSS & BLUE SHIELD OF NEBRASKA
1919 Aksarben Dr, Omaha, NE 68180-0001
Tel.: (402) 982-7000
Web Site: http://www.nebraskablue.com
Year Founded: 1939
Sales Range: $25-49.9 Million
Emp.: 1,400
Health Care Srvices
N.A.I.C.S.: 524114
Lewis E. Trowbridge (COO)
Steven H. Grandfield (Pres & CEO)
Andy Williams (VP-Pharmacy & Risk Adjustment)
Leslie R. Anderson (Chief Acctg Officer, Treas & VP)
George G. Beattie (Chm)
Daniel Alm (Chief Underwriting Officer & VP-Underwriting)
Russell Collins (Chief Legal Officer)
Debra Esser (Chief Medical Officer)
Rama Kolli (CIO & VP-Information Svcs)
Timothy McGill (Chief Sls Officer & Chief Mktg Officer)
Gretchen Twohig (Gen Counsel & VP)
Jennifer Richardson (Officer-Compliance & VP-Compliance & Ethics)

Joann Schaefer (Exec VP-Health Delivery Engagement)
Susan Courtney (Exec VP-Ops, Bus Process & Shared Svcs)
James R. Englese (Gen Counsel, Sec & Sr VP)
Joseph C. Muenzen (Sr VP-Underwriting & Product Dev)

BLUE CROSS & BLUE SHIELD OF NORTH CAROLINA INC
4615 University Dr, Durham, NC 27707
Tel.: (919) 765-4600   NC
Web Site:
   http://www.bluecrossnc.com
Year Founded: 1968
Sales Range: $5-14.9 Billion
Emp.: 4,000
Hospital & Medical Service Plan Services
N.A.I.C.S.: 524114
John T. Roos (Chief Sls, Mktg & Comm Officer & Sr VP)
Gerald Petkau (COO & Sr VP)
Mitch Perry (CFO & Sr VP)
Fara M. Palumbo (COO & Exec VP)
King N. Prather (Gen Counsel, Sec & Sr VP)
Patrick Conway (Pres & CEO)
Jo Abernathy (CIO)
Lisa Cade (Chief Svc Ops Officer)
Patrick Getzen (Chief Data & Analytics Officer & Sr VP)
Danielle C. Gray (Chief Legal Officer, Sec & VP)
Rahul Rajkumar (Chief Growth Officer & Sr VP)
Frank B. Holding Jr. (Chm)

BLUE CROSS & BLUE SHIELD OF RHODE ISLAND
500 Exchange St, Providence, RI 02903-3206
Tel.: (401) 459-1000   RI
Web Site: http://www.bcbsri.org
Year Founded: 1939
Sales Range: $1-4.9 Billion
Emp.: 1,100
Healthcare Insurance
N.A.I.C.S.: 524114
Michele B. Lederberg (Chief Admin Officer, Gen Counsel & Exec VP)
Gus Manocchia (VP & Chief Medical Officer-Provider Rels)
Mark Waggoner (Sr VP-Care Integration & Mgmt)
Michael Marrone (VP-Fin)
Chris Bush (VP-Network Mgmt)
Melissa Cummings (Chief Customer Officer & Sr VP)
Mark Stewart (CFO & Sr VP)
Christine Musial (VP-Shared Svc Ops)
Rena Sheehan (VP-Clinical Integration)
Martha L. Wofford (Pres & CEO)

BLUE CROSS & BLUE SHIELD OF SOUTH CAROLINA
I-20 E at Alpine Rd, Columbia, SC 29219-0001
Tel.: (803) 788-3860   SC
Web Site: http://www.bcbssc.com
Year Founded: 1946
Rev.: $535,361,000
Emp.: 1,000
Hospital & Medical Service Plans
N.A.I.C.S.: 524114
Ed Sellers (Chm, Pres & CEO)
Phil Dunn (Asst VP-Tech Support)
Susan Black (Dir-Medical Svcs)
Sean King (Mgr-Info Sys)
Mark Rish (Mgr-IT & Network Infrastructure)
Steve Austin (Mgr-Key Accts)

Edwin Green (Project Mgr)
Sandy Cartledge (VP-Grp & Individual Ops)
Dwaine Rogers (Engr-Network)
Bill Winslow (Asst VP-ICT Host Tech Support)
Brenetta Richards (Mgr-HR)
Bryanne Curry (Dir-IT)
Judy Davis (Chief Lending Officer & Exec VP)
Kim Wellman (Asst VP-Corp Mktg Comm)
Mary Tandberg (Mgr)
Louis McElveen (VP-Fin)
Martha Perry (Asst VP)
Myra Miracle (VP)
Tony Cirrincione (Mgr-IS Audit)
Daniel Claas (Asst VP-Grp & Individual Underwriting)
Kay Earles (Acct Mgr)
Karen Price (Mgr-IT)
Paula Ingram (Project Mgr)

Subsidiaries:

Alpine Agency Inc. (1)
1023 W Delkab St, Camden, SC 29020
Tel.: (803) 432-4960
Web Site: http://www.alpineagency.com
Rev.: $480,000
Emp.: 9
Hospital & Medical Service Plans
N.A.I.C.S.: 524114

Blue Choice Health Plan (1)
4101 Percival, Columbia, SC 29223
Tel.: (803) 786-8466
Web Site: http://www.bluechoicesc.com
Sales Range: $100-124.9 Million
Emp.: 350
Hospital & Medical Service Plans
N.A.I.C.S.: 524114
Mary Mazzola Spivey (Pres & COO)
Dionne Robinson (Project Coord)

Companion Life Insurance Company (1)
7909 Parklane Rd Ste 200, Columbia, SC 29223-5666
Tel.: (803) 735-1251
Web Site: http://www.companionlife.com
Sales Range: $200-249.9 Million
Emp.: 90
Life Insurance
N.A.I.C.S.: 524113
Trescott N. Hinton (Pres)
F. David Wythe (Mgr-Compliance)
Harvey Myer (VP-Underwriting)
James E. Thompson (Dir-Fin Svcs)
Stephen P. Carter (VP-Actuarial Svcs)
Merri J. Bradley (Mgr-Mktg Comm)
J. C. Preas (VP-Field Mktg)
Karl Kemmerlin (CFO & VP)
Ida Myers (VP-Claims & Admin)
Tim Benefield (Dir-Fin)
Jeff Brown (Mgr-Fin)
Diane Fischer (CFO & VP)
Phil Gardham (VP-Specialty Markets)
Hollie Henderson (Mgr-Compliance)
Wayne Jones (VP-Bus Dev)
Carmelita Knight (Dir-Claims Ops)
Chenille Marshall (Mgr-Claims)
Debbie Padgett (Mgr-Mktg Sls)
Cheryl Peppers (Mgr-Dental Claims)

Palmetto GBA, LLC (1)
AG-903 17 Technology Cir, Columbia, SC 29203
Tel.: (803) 735-1034
Web Site: http://www.palmettogba.com
Sales Range: $100-124.9 Million
Health Care Technology, Training, Finance & Customer Service Solutions
N.A.I.C.S.: 541511
Donna Keese (Dir-Program Changes)
David Pankau (Chm)
Joe Johnson (Pres & CEO)
Mike Barlow (VP-Ops-Specialty Contracts)
Neal Burkhead (VP-Shared Svcs)
Elaine Garrick (VP-Support Ops)

Planned Administrators Inc. (1)
17 Technology Cir Ste E2AG, Columbia, SC 29203
Tel.: (803) 462-0151
Web Site: http://www.paisc.com
Rev.: $5,072,000

Emp.: 300
Insurance Agent Broker & Service
N.A.I.C.S.: 524210
David J. Huntington (Pres & COO)
Barbara Windham (CFO)
T. Clayton Kelley (Dir-Sls)
P. J. Rescigno (Asst VP-Sls & Mktg)
Suzanne Miller (Officer-Compliance)

Preferred Health Systems Inc. (1)
51 Clemson Rd, Columbia, SC 29229-6543
Tel.: (803) 788-0222
Web Site:
   http://www.southcarolinablues.com
Health Care Srvices
N.A.I.C.S.: 524114

BLUE CROSS BLUE SHIELD OF MICHIGAN
600 E Lafayette Blvd, Detroit, MI 48226-2998
Tel.: (313) 225-9000   MI
Web Site: http://www.bcbsm.com
Year Founded: 1939
Rev.: $29,330,000,000
Assets: $16,059,000,000
Liabilities: $10,186,000,000
Net Worth: $5,873,000,000
Earnings: $566,000,000
Fiscal Year-end: 12/31/18
Healthcare Insurance
N.A.I.C.S.: 524114
Daniel J. Loepp (Pres & CEO)
Mark R. Bartlett (CFO & Exec VP)
Thomas L. Simmer (Co-Chief Medical Officer & Sr VP)
Elizabeth R. Haar (Pres-Emerging Markets & Exec VP)
F. Remington Sprague (Vice Chm)
Susan L. Barkell (Sr VP-Hospital Contracting, Provider Engagement & Pharmacy Svcs)
Kenneth R. Dallafior (Pres-Health Plan Bus & Exec VP)
Darrell E. Middleton (COO & Exec VP)
Lynda M. Rossi (Exec VP-Strategy, Govt & Pub Affairs)
Tricia A. Keith (Chief Admin Officer & Exec VP)
James Grant (Co-Chief Medical Officer & Sr VP)
Michele A. Samuels (Sr VP)
Jeffrey L. Connolly (Pres-West Michigan & Upper Peninsula & Sr VP)
William M. Fandrich (CIO & Sr VP)
Todd Van Tol (Sr VP-Health Care Value)
Paul L. Mozak (Chief Risk Officer & Sr VP-Fin)
Waymond E. Harris (Treas & VP)
Laurine Symula Parmely (Gen Counsel & Sr VP)

Subsidiaries:

Accident Fund Holdings, Inc. (1)
200 N Grand Ave, Lansing, MI 48901-7990
Tel.: (517) 342-4200
Web Site: http://www.accidentfund.com
Employee Benefit Services
N.A.I.C.S.: 525120
Frank H. Freund (CFO & Exec VP-Corp Performance)
Becky Holnagel (VP-Actuarial Svcs)
Jeffrey Austin White (Dir-Innovation)
Linda Barnes (VP)
Al Gileczek (Sr VP-Reg Ops & Bus Dev)
Lisa Riddle (VP-Claims & Medical Ops)
Mike Seling (Sr VP-Reg Ops & Bus Dev)

Blue Care Network of Michigan (1)
611 Cascade W Pkwy SE, Grand Rapids, MI 49546   (100%)
Tel.: (616) 957-5057
Sales Range: $1-4.9 Billion
Emp.: 1,400
Processing Of Claims
N.A.I.C.S.: 524114
Kevin Klobucar (Exec VP-Healthcare Value)
Tiffany Albert (Pres & CEO)

Blue Cross Blue Shield of Michigan—(Continued)

Subsidiary (Domestic):

Blue Cross Blue Shield of Michigan
Foundation (2)
600 E Lafayette Blvd, Detroit, MI 48226-
2998
Tel.: (313) 225-8706
Web Site: http://www.bcbsm.com
Sales Range: $10-24.9 Million
Emp.: 5
Health Care Srvices
N.A.I.C.S.: 813212
Thomas L. Simmer (Chief Medical Officer &
Sr VP)
Audrey J. Harvey (CEO & Exec Dir)
Joel I. Ferguson (Vice Chm)
Susan Shelton (Sec)

LifeSecure Insurance Company (1)
10559 Citation Dr Ste 300, Brighton, MI
48116
Tel.: (866) 582-7701
Web Site: http://www.yourlifesecure.com
General Insurance Services
N.A.I.C.S.: 524210
Sara Hogan (Sec & Sr Dir-Corp Admin)
Brian Vestergaard (VP-Sls & Mktg)
Joseph Radtka (VP-Fin)
Kevin Stutler (Pres, CEO & VP-Ancillary
Products)

BLUE CROSS COMPLETE OF
MICHIGAN
600 E Lafayette Blvd, Detroit, MI
48226
Tel.: (313) 225-9000 MI
Web Site:
http://www.bluecrosscomplete.com
Year Founded: 2002
Sales Range: $100-124.9 Million
Health & Welfare Services
N.A.I.C.S.: 525120

BLUE CROSS LABORATORIES
20950 Ctr Point Pkwy, Saugus, CA
91350-2621
Tel.: (661) 255-0955 CA
Web Site: http://www.bc-labs.com
Year Founded: 1951
Sales Range: $75-99.9 Million
Emp.: 100
Household Cleaning Product Mfr
N.A.I.C.S.: 325612
Darrell Mahler (Pres & Mgr-Sls &
Adv)

BLUE CROSS-BLUE SHIELD
WYOMING
4000 House Ave, Cheyenne, WY
82001
Tel.: (307) 634-1393
Web Site: https://www.bcbswy.com
Rev.: $187,976,407
Emp.: 185
Health Insurance Carrier
N.A.I.C.S.: 524114
Rick Schum (Pres & CEO)

BLUE DAISY MEDIA
2906 S Douglas Rd Ste 201, Coral
Gables, FL 33134
Tel.: (305) 442-4229
Web Site:
http://www.bluedaisymedia.com
Year Founded: 2001
Sales Range: $10-24.9 Million
Emp.: 4
Media Buying Services
N.A.I.C.S.: 541810
Diana Fleming (Partner)

BLUE DANUBE INCORPO-
RATED
201 S Johnson Rd Ste 303, Houston,
PA 15342-1351
Tel.: (724) 746-9550
Web Site: https://www.barges.us
Year Founded: 1967

Sales Range: $25-49.9 Million
Emp.: 450
Towing & Tugboat Service
N.A.I.C.S.: 488330

Subsidiaries:

C&C Marine Maintenance
Company (1)
1500 State St N, Clairton, PA 15025-3952
Tel.: (412) 233-4124
Rev.: $6,700,000
Emp.: 70
Shipbuilding & Repairing
N.A.I.C.S.: 336611
Greg Bucci (Gen Mgr)

BLUE DELTA CAPITAL PART-
NERS LLC
1751 Pinnacle Dr Suite #1125,
McLean, VA 22102
Tel.: (703) 989-4829
Web Site:
https://bluedeltacapitalpartners.com
Year Founded: 2009
Emp.: 100
Private Equity
N.A.I.C.S.: 523940
Mark A. Frantz (Co-Founder & Gen
Partner)

Subsidiaries:

Acclaim Technical Services (1)
7777 Center Ave Ste 690, Huntington
Beach, CA 92648
Tel.: (714) 596-8704
Web Site: http://www.acclaimtechnical.com
Sales Range: $25-49.9 Million
Emp.: 231
Translation Services & IT Consulting &
Staffing
N.A.I.C.S.: 561311
Nancy Sherman (Co-Founder)
Trever Neves (Co-Founder)
Jon Grund (CFO)
Mark Poirier (Gen Mgr-Intelligence Ops
Bus)
Dave Cerne (CEO)
Yvonne Vervaet (Chief Growth Officer)

Subsidiary (Domestic):

Alder Technology, Inc. (2)
4732 Glass Mtn Way, Haymarket, VA
20169-8146
Tel.: (540) 352-2168
Web Site: http://www.aldertechnology.com
Computer System Design Services
N.A.I.C.S.: 541512

BLUE DIAMOND GROWERS
1802 C St, Sacramento, CA 95811-
1010
Tel.: (916) 442-0771 CA
Web Site:
http://www.bluediamondgrower.com
Year Founded: 1910
Rev.: $19,000,000
Emp.: 1,000
Almonds, Macadamias, Hazelnuts,
Pistachios & Almond Butter; Operator
of Almond Research Center
N.A.I.C.S.: 111335
Kristen Arakaki (Asst Mgr-Mktg)
Kai Bockmann (Pres & CEO)
Dan Cummings (Chm)
Lynn Machon (Dir-Corp Comm)

Subsidiaries:

Blue Diamond Growers - Global In-
gredients Division (1)
1802 C St, Sacramento, CA 95811
Tel.: (916) 446-8500
Web Site: http://www.bdingredients.com
Almond Distr
N.A.I.C.S.: 424490
Mark D. Jansen (Pres & CEO)
Bill Morecraft Jr. (Sr VP-Global)

BLUE EAGLE LITHIUM INC.
2831 St Rose Pky Ste 200, Henderson, NV 89052

Tel.: (702) 899-3369 NV
Web Site:
http://www.blueeaglelithium.com
Year Founded: 2009
Assets: $15,618
Liabilities: $210,910
Net Worth: ($195,292)
Earnings: ($46,790)
Fiscal Year-end: 04/30/18
Lithium Exploration & Development
Company
N.A.I.C.S.: 212290

BLUE EARTH VALLEY COM-
MUNICATIONS
123 W 7th St, Blue Earth, MN 56013
Tel.: (507) 526-2822
Web Site: http://www.bevcomm.net
Year Founded: 1939
Sales Range: $10-24.9 Million
Emp.: 85
Internet, Telecommunications & Cable
Services
N.A.I.C.S.: 517112
William V. Eckles (Pres & CEO)

Subsidiaries:

Blue Earth Valley
Communications (1)
N3767 4th St, Weyerhaeuser, WI 54895-
0228
Tel.: (715) 353-2434
Web Site: http://www.bevcomm.net
Sales Range: $10-24.9 Million
Emp.: 10
Telephone Communications
N.A.I.C.S.: 517121

Hector Communications
Corporation (1)
Tel.: (507) 354-2500
Holding Company; Local Telecommunica-
tion Services
N.A.I.C.S.: 551112

Subsidiary (Non-US):

Eagle Valley Telephone
Company (2)
Tel.: (218) 756-2312
Web Site: http://www.eaglevalleytel.net
Sales Range: $10-24.9 Million
Emp.: 1
Telecommunications & Internet Services
N.A.I.C.S.: 517121

Pine Island Telephone Company (2)
Tel.: (507) 356-8302
Web Site: http://www.pitel.net
Sales Range: $10-24.9 Million
Emp.: 12
Telephone Services
N.A.I.C.S.: 517111

Sleepy Eye Telephone Company (2)
Tel.: (507) 794-3361
Sales Range: $10-24.9 Million
Emp.: 20
Telephone Services
N.A.I.C.S.: 517121

BLUE EARTH-NICOLLET CO-
OPERATIVE ELECTRIC ASSO-
CIATION
20946 549th Ave, Mankato, MN
56001
Tel.: (507) 387-7963
Web Site: https://www.benco.org
Sales Range: $10-24.9 Million
Emp.: 35
Electronic Services
N.A.I.C.S.: 221118
Wade Hensel (Gen Mgr)
Sandy Sowieja (Office Mgr)

BLUE ENGINE MESSAGE &
MEDIA, LLC
1140 Connecticut Ave NW Ste 800,
Washington, DC 20036-4010
Tel.: (202) 331-0110
Web Site: http://www.sevenletter.com

Year Founded: 2006
Administrative Management & Gen-
eral Management Consulting Ser-
vices
N.A.I.C.S.: 541611
Erik Smith (Co-Founder & Partner)
Trevor Francis (Co-Founder & Part-
ner)
Thomas P. O'Neill III (Partner)

Subsidiaries:

JDA Frontline, Inc. (1)
438 King St Ste B, Charleston, SC 29403-
6200
Tel.: (843) 722-9670
Web Site: http://www.jdafrontline.com
Information Services
N.A.I.C.S.: 519290
Adam Temple (VP-Pub Affairs)
Kelly Cushman (Exec VP)
Laurie Rossbach (VP)

O'Neill and Associates, LLC (1)
31 New Chardon St, Boston, MA 02114
Tel.: (617) 646-1000
Web Site: http://www.oneillandassoc.com
Public Relation & Consulting Services
N.A.I.C.S.: 541611
Krista Robinson (Sr Acct Exec)
Todd Tiahrt (Sr VP-Federal Rels Practice)
Cayenne Isaksen (Dir-Comm)
Matthew Irish (Vice Chm & Mng Dir-Govt
Rels Practice)
Christopher Tracy (Sr Dir-Community Rels
& Govt Affairs Practice-New England)
Shelly O'Neill (COO)
Thomas P. O'Neill III (CEO)

BLUE EQUITY, LLC
101 S 5th St Ste 3800, Louisville, KY
40202
Tel.: (502) 589-8181
Web Site: http://www.blueequity.com
Year Founded: 2004
Privater Equity Firm
N.A.I.C.S.: 523999
Jonathan S. Blue (Chm & Mng Dir)
David M. Roth (Vice Chm)
Juan Reffregor (COO & Exec VP)
Cordt Huneke (VP)
Edward Harrison (Dir-Bus Dev)

Subsidiaries:

Napoli Management Group (1)
8844 W Olympic Blvd Ste 100, Beverly
Hills, CA 90211-3697
Tel.: (310) 385-8222
Web Site: http://www.tvtalent.com
Employment Placement Agencies
N.A.I.C.S.: 561311
Mendes Napoli (Founder & Pres)

BLUE FLAME THINKING
55 W Monroe St 1550, Chicago, IL
60603
Tel.: (312) 382-9000
Web Site:
http://blueflamethinking.com
Year Founded: 1965
Advetising Agency
N.A.I.C.S.: 541810
Lynne Gallegos (Pres)

BLUE GECKO, LLC
1408 4th Ave Ste 200, Seattle, WA
98101
Tel.: (206) 686-3349
Web Site: http://www.bluegecko.net
Year Founded: 2001
Sales Range: $1-9.9 Million
Emp.: 17
Administration of Database Environ-
ments
N.A.I.C.S.: 541519
Sarah Novotny (Founder)

BLUE GLOBAL MEDIA
7144 E Stetson Dr Ste 300, Scottsdale, AZ 85251
Tel.: (480) 365-0335

Web Site:
http://www.blueglobalmedia.com
Year Founded: 2005
Sales Range: $10-24.9 Million
Emp.: 13
Internet Advertising & Marketing
N.A.I.C.S.: 541890
Chris Kay *(Founder & CEO)*
Abdu El-Shaarawy *(Pres)*
Evette Cecena *(Dir-Mktg)*

BLUE GOOSE GROWERS, LLC.
9901 Okeechobee Rd, Fort Pierce, FL 34945
Tel.: (772) 461-3020
Web Site:
http://www.bluegoosegrowers.com
Year Founded: 1963
Sales Range: $25-49.9 Million
Emp.: 125
Planting & Cultivation Services
N.A.I.C.S.: 115112
Tim Dooley *(VP & Gen Mgr-Farming Div)*

BLUE GRASS COMMUNITY FOUNDATION
499 E High St Ste 112, Lexington, KY 40507
Tel.: (859) 225-3343   KY
Web Site: http://www.bgcf.org
Year Founded: 1967
Sales Range: $75-99.9 Million
Emp.: 12
Grantmaking Services
N.A.I.C.S.: 813211
Lisa Adkins *(Pres & CEO)*
Brian Dineen *(Sr VP-Fin & Admin)*
Jonathan Barker *(Treas)*
Fran Taylor *(Sec)*
Madonna Turner *(Vice Chm)*
Arthur Salomon *(Chm)*
Barbara Fischer *(Dir-Nonprofit Svcs)*
Maddie Booher *(Dir-Acctg)*
Scott Fitzpatrick *(VP-Advancement)*

BLUE GRASS DAIRY & FOOD LLC
1117 Cleveland Ave, Glasgow, KY 42141
Tel.: (270) 651-2146
Web Site:
http://www.bluegrassdairy.com
Rev.: $38,000,000
Emp.: 125
Dry, Condensed & Evaporated Dairy Products
N.A.I.C.S.: 311514
Billy Joe Williams *(CEO)*

BLUE GRASS PROVISION COMPANY
2645 Commerce Dr, Crescent Springs, KY 41017-1503
Tel.: (859) 331-7100   KY
Year Founded: 1867
Sales Range: $75-99.9 Million
Emp.: 100
Mfr & Distributor of Meat
N.A.I.C.S.: 311612
David Kegley *(VP-Sls)*
Gary Bork *(Mgr-Quality Assurance)*
Paul Rice *(Pres & CEO)*
Pat Voet *(CFO)*

BLUE GRASS SHOWS, INC.
2032 S 51st St, Tampa, FL 33619
Tel.: (813) 247-4431
Web Site:
http://www.mightybluegrass.com
Year Founded: 1974
Sales Range: $1-9.9 Million
Emp.: 100
Recreational Services
N.A.I.C.S.: 713990

Jerry Murphy *(Pres)*

BLUE HARBOUR GROUP, L.P.
646 Steamboat Rd, Greenwich, CT 06830
Tel.: (203) 422-6540
Web Site:
http://www.blueharbourgroup.com
Investment Services
N.A.I.C.S.: 523999
Clifton S. Robbins *(CEO)*
David Silverman *(Mng Dir)*
Jose Claxton *(Mng Dir-IR)*
Todd Marcy *(Mng Dir)*
John P. Ernenwein *(CFO)*

BLUE HAVEN POOLS NATIONAL INC.
636 Broadway Ste 310, San Diego, CA 92101-5410
Tel.: (619) 233-3522   CA
Web Site: http://www.bluehaven.com
Year Founded: 1992
Sales Range: $25-49.9 Million
Emp.: 50
Specialty Trade Contractors
N.A.I.C.S.: 238990

BLUE HILL DATA SERVICES, INC.
2 Blue Hill Plz, Pearl River, NY 10965
Tel.: (845) 620-0400   NY
Web Site:
http://www.bluehilldata.com
Year Founded: 1994
Emp.: 85
Data Processing, Hosting & Related Services
N.A.I.C.S.: 518210
John M. Lalli *(COO & Mng Dir)*
Peter Piasentini *(Dir-Network Svcs)*
Rosary De Filippis *(CMO & Exec Dir-Bus Dev)*
Thomas Laudati *(CTO & Exec Dir-Svc Delivery)*
Robert Miesieski *(Chief Applications Officer)*

Subsidiaries:

Xybernet, Inc.   (1)
10640 Scripps Ranch Blvd, San Diego, CA 92131
Tel.: (858) 530-1900
Web Site: http://www.xyber.net
Automobile Component Distr
N.A.I.C.S.: 423120
Ellen M. Myers *(Owner)*

BLUE HORIZON SOFTWARE HOLDINGS LLC
50 E Washington St Ste 400, Chicago, IL 60602
Tel.: (312) 759-5000   DE
Web Site:
http://www.bluehorizonsoftware.com
Investment Services
N.A.I.C.S.: 523999
Jeff Galowich *(CEO)*

Subsidiaries:

Synthesis Technology Corp.   (1)
135 S LaSalle St Ste 2025, Chicago, IL 60603
Tel.: (312) 948-4949
Web Site: http://www.snth.com
Custom Computer Programming Services
N.A.I.C.S.: 541511
Cheryl Gelfond *(VP-Ops)*
Noel Rodolfo *(Mgr-Product)*
Mark Gilson *(Project Mgr)*
John R. Toepfer *(Founder & CEO)*
Julia Kessler *(Project Mgr)*
Adam Childs *(Dir-Software Engrg)*
Robert Juergens *(VP-Engrg)*
Emilie Totten *(Head-Mktg)*

BLUE HORSESHOE SOLUTIONS, INC.
11939 N Meridian St Ste 300, Carmel, IN 46032-6954
Tel.: (317) 573-2583   IN
Web Site:
http://www.bhsolutions.com
Year Founded: 2001
Sales Range: $1-9.9 Million
Emp.: 302
Business Consulting Services
N.A.I.C.S.: 541618
Brian Cason *(COO)*
Kevin Paul *(Chief Strategy Officer)*
John Foster *(CTO)*
Chris Cason *(CEO)*
Chad Edge *(CIO)*
Monica Bolt *(CFO)*

Subsidiaries:

Transtech Consulting, Inc.   (1)
600 N Cleveland Ave Ste 190, Westerville, OH 43082
Tel.: (614) 751-0575
Web Site:
http://www.transtechconsulting.com
Rev.: $4,800,000
Emp.: 15
Management Consulting Services
N.A.I.C.S.: 541614
Jeff Cook *(Sr VP)*

BLUE ICEBERG, LLC
146 W 29th St Studio 11W, New York, NY 10001
Tel.: (212) 337-9920
Web Site: http://www.blue-iceberg.com
Sales Range: $1-9.9 Million
Emp.: 50
Interactive Advertising Services
N.A.I.C.S.: 541810
Richard Cacciato *(Partner & Chief Strategist)*
Natalie Yates *(Partner & Exec Producer)*
Sean Phillips *(Sr Developer)*

BLUE INTERACTIVE AGENCY
608 SW 4th Ave, Fort Lauderdale, FL 33315
Tel.: (954) 779-2801
Web Site:
http://www.blueinteractive.com
Year Founded: 2003
Sales Range: $1-9.9 Million
Emp.: 15
Designs, Develops, Implements & Supports Business Development, Sales & Marketing Strategies
N.A.I.C.S.: 541890
Peter Brooke *(CEO)*
Samantha Jerabek *(Mgr-Digital Mktg)*

BLUE LAKE FINE ARTS CAMP
300 E Crystal Lake Rd, Twin Lake, MI 49457
Tel.: (231) 894-1966   MI
Web Site: https://www.bluelake.org
Year Founded: 1922
Sales Range: $10-24.9 Million
Art Support Services
N.A.I.C.S.: 611610
James Chick *(Bus Mgr)*
Adrian Cook *(Dir-Camp)*
Paul Boscarino *(Gen Mgr-WBLU)*
Duane Wright *(Mgr-Site & Production)*
Heidi Stansell *(VP-Fin & Ops)*
Fritz Stansell *(Pres)*
Tim Kleaveland *(Dir-Food Svc)*
Dave Myers *(VP-Brdcst & Dev)*
Sandra Sheroky *(Sec-Intl Program)*

BLUE MARBLE MEDIA INC.
704 Berkeley Ave Ste B, Atlanta, GA 30318

Tel.: (404) 982-9552
Web Site:
http://www.bluemarblemedia.com
Year Founded: 1995
Sales Range: $1-9.9 Million
Emp.: 11
Film & Video Production
N.A.I.C.S.: 512110
Cara Barineau *(Pres)*
Alaina Voerg *(Project Mgr)*

BLUE MEDIUM, INC.
20 W 22nd St Ste 807, New York, NY 10010
Tel.: (212) 675-1800
Web Site:
http://www.bluemedium.com
Sales Range: Less than $1 Million
Emp.: 10
Arts, Communications
N.A.I.C.S.: 541810
John Melick *(Pres)*
Antoine Vigne *(VP)*
Elizabeth Reina *(Acct Exec)*
Ozgur Gungor *(Acct Coord)*
Deirdre Maher *(Acct Coord)*

BLUE MOON WORKS, INC.
1512 Larimer St Ste 270, Denver, CO 80202
Tel.: (303) 565-1100
Web Site:
http://www.bluemoonworks.com
Sales Range: $1-9.9 Million
Emp.: 15
Digital Marketing Agency Services
N.A.I.C.S.: 541613
Mindy Phillips *(VP-Emerging Media & New Product Innovation)*

BLUE OCEAN PRESS, INC.
6299 NW 27th Way, Fort Lauderdale, FL 33309
Tel.: (954) 973-1819   FL
Web Site:
https://www.blueoceanpress.com
Year Founded: 1984
Sales Range: $1-9.9 Million
Emp.: 45
Printing & Graphic Design Services
N.A.I.C.S.: 323111
Tom Mounce *(Founder & Pres)*
Michael Nelson *(Plant Mgr)*

BLUE OWL CREDIT INCOME CORP.
399 Park Ave, New York, NY 10022
Tel.: (212) 419-3000   MD
Web Site: https://www.orcic.com
Year Founded: 2020
Rev.: $666,813,000
Assets: $11,036,362,000
Liabilities: $5,786,609,000
Net Worth: $5,249,753,000
Earnings: $346,851,000
Fiscal Year-end: 12/31/22
Investment Services
N.A.I.C.S.: 523940
Craig W. Packer *(Pres & CEO)*
Bryan Cole *(CFO & Chief Acctg Officer)*

BLUE OWL TECHNOLOGY FINANCE CORP.
399 Park Ave, New York, NY 10022
Tel.: (212) 419-3000   MD
Web Site: https://www.blueowl.com
Year Founded: 2018
Rev.: $494,845,000
Assets: $6,663,369,000
Liabilities: $3,276,004,000
Net Worth: $3,387,365,000
Earnings: $273,243,000
Emp.: 1
Fiscal Year-end: 12/31/22
Financial Investment Services

Blue Owl Technology Finance Corp.—(Continued)
N.A.I.C.S.: 523940
Craig W. Packer (Founder, Pres & CEO)

BLUE PHOENIX MEDIA, INC.
265 Canal St Ste 509, New York, NY 10013
Web Site:
https://www.bluephoenixmedia.com
Sales Range: $1-9.9 Million
Emp.: 10
Customer Acquisition & Interactive Lead Generation Network
N.A.I.C.S.: 541890
Amy Sheridan (CEO)
Malaika Schmidt (COO)

BLUE PLATE CATERING, LTD.
1061 W Van Buren, Chicago, IL 60607
Tel.: (312) 421-6666
Web Site:
http://www.blueplatechicago.com
Year Founded: 1983
Emp.: 226
Merchandise Store Operator
N.A.I.C.S.: 459510
Jim Horan (Founder & CEO)

BLUE POINT CAPITAL PARTNERS, LLC
127 Public Sq Ste 5100, Cleveland, OH 44114-1312
Tel.: (216) 535-4700   DE
Web Site:
http://www.bluepointcapital.com
Year Founded: 2000
Private Equity Firm
N.A.I.C.S.: 523999
Jim Marra (Dir-Bus Dev)
Chip Chaikin (Partner-Cleveland/Shanghai)
John LeMay (Partner)
Sean Ward (Partner)
Juli Marley (Partner-Charlotte)
Charley Geiger (Principal)
Michelle Drago (Dir-Tax)
Colleen Greenrod (CFO & Chief Compliance Officer)
Dennis Wu (Mng Dir-Shanghai)
Brian Castleberry (Principal-Charlotte)
Jonathan Pressnell (Partner)
Jeff Robich (Partner)
Tom Pitera (Operating Partner)
Grant H. Beard (Sr Exec Operating Partner)

Subsidiaries:

Country Pure Foods, Inc.   (1)
681 W Waterloo Rd, Akron, OH 44314-1587
Tel.: (330) 848-6875
Web Site: http://countrypure.com
Fruit Drinks Producer
N.A.I.C.S.: 311421
Rid Moses (HR Mgr)

Europa Eyewear   (1)
255 Corporate Woods Pkwy, Vernon Hills, IL 60061
Tel.: (800) 621-4108
Web Site: https://europaeye.com
Apparel & Fashion Mfg.
N.A.I.C.S.: 315990

Subsidiary (Domestic):

EyeBobs, LLC   (2)
1401 Glenwood Ave, Minneapolis, MN 55405
Web Site: http://www.eyebobs.com
Optical Goods Stores
N.A.I.C.S.: 456130
Julie Allinson (Pres)

FM Sylvan, Inc.   (1)
815 Auburn Ave, Pontiac, MI 48342-3309
Tel.: (248) 836-2200
Web Site: http://www.fmsylvan.com

Plumbing, Heating & Air-Conditioning Contractor
N.A.I.C.S.: 238220
Matthew Panconi (Sr VP)
Robert H. Metz (Partner & CEO)
Terry McKinnon (Sr VP)
Ed Musbach (CFO)
Thomas Bach (VP-Ops)
Ken Giacobbe (Sr VP)
Bill Proctor (Gen Mgr & Sr VP)
Jeff Mckinnon (VP)
Don Wilber (VP)
Curtis Lyons (VP & Mgr-Construction)
James T. Metz III (VP)

Subsidiary (Domestic):

Great Lakes Mechanical Corp.   (2)
3800 Maple St, Dearborn, MI 48126
Tel.: (313) 581-1400
Web Site:
http://www.greatlakesmechanical.com
Sales Range: $50-74.9 Million
Emp.: 150
Provider of Mechanical Contracts
N.A.I.C.S.: 238220
Harold J. Perpich (CEO)
Mark H. Perpich (Pres)
Thomas Wheaton (VP-Svcs)

Fire & Life Safety America, Inc.   (1)
8827 Staples Mill Rd, Richmond, VA 23228
Tel.: (800) 252-5069
Web Site: http://www.flsamerica.com
Fire Protection System Design & Installation Services
N.A.I.C.S.: 922160
Jeffrey Cannon (CIO)
Jack M. Medovich (VP-Ops & Trng)
Thomas York (Pres & CEO)
Tom Coulbourn (Sr VP-Svc Sls)
Jason Gilmore (CFO)
Susan Shelburne Hunt (Chief HR Officer)
Jeremiah Hazzard (Reg VP)
Kevin Grat (Sr VP-Svc Ops)
John McDade (VP-Alarms & Special Hazards)
Manny Ortiz (Reg VP)

Branch (Domestic):

Fire and Life Safety America, Inc.   (2)
2280 Old Lake Mary Rd, Sanford, FL 32771
Tel.: (407) 688-1949
Web Site: http://flsamerica.com
Fire Protection Contractor
N.A.I.C.S.: 238220
Peter Amato (Mgr-District)

Subsidiary (Domestic):

Integrated Fire Protection LLC   (2)
4487 Park Dr Ste A1, Norcross, GA 30093
Tel.: (770) 458-8828
Web Site:
http://www.integratedfireprotection.com
Fire & Safety Solutions & Services
N.A.I.C.S.: 922160
John Bennett (Pres)

Italian Rose Garlic Products, Inc.   (1)
1380 W 15th St, West Palm Beach, FL 33404
Tel.: (561) 863-5556
Web Site: http://www.italian-rose.com
Sales Range: $1-9.9 Million
Emp.: 50
Salsas, Dips, Sauces & Spreads Mfr
N.A.I.C.S.: 311941
Kenneth J. Berger (Founder & Pres)

J. America, Inc.   (1)
1200 Mason Ct, Webberville, MI 48892
Tel.: (517) 521-2525
Web Site:
http://www.jamericasportswear.com
Sales Range: $1-9.9 Million
Emp.: 100
Designer & Distr of Licensed & Blank Apparel & Headwear Products
N.A.I.C.S.: 315250
Jeff Fenech (Co-Founder)
Peter Ruhala (Pres)
Nate Holmes (VP-Product & Brand Dev)

Mattco Forge, Inc.   (1)
16443 Minnesota Ave, Paramount, CA 90723
Tel.: (562) 634-8635

Web Site: http://www.mattcoforge.com
Aluminum High Temperature & Steel Forgings Mfr
N.A.I.C.S.: 332112
Rob Lewis (Pres & CEO)

National Safety Apparel, Inc.   (1)
15825 Industrial Pkwy, Cleveland, OH 44135
Web Site: http://www.thinknsa.com
Accessories & Other Apparel Mfr
N.A.I.C.S.: 315990
Annette K. (Mgr-Intl Customer Svc)
Rich Gojdics (Sr VP-Indus Sls)
Chuck Grossman (CEO)
Mike Enright (Pres)

Subsidiary (Domestic):

Forum Industries, Inc.   (2)
1903 Hormel Dr, San Antonio, TX 78219
Tel.: (210) 225-9600
Web Site: https://www.forumindustries.com
Sales Range: $1-9.9 Million
Emp.: 75
Support Services
N.A.I.C.S.: 561990
Thomas McKown (Pres & CEO)
Delton Scholwinski (Controller)
Cindy Hamilton (Mgr-Matls)

Wild Things, LLC   (2)
184 Business Park Dr Ste 205, Virginia Beach, VA 23462
Tel.: (828) 421-4349
Web Site: https://www.wildthingsgear.com
Sporting & Athletic Goods Mfr
N.A.I.C.S.: 339920
Amy Coyne (CEO)

Packers Sanitation Services, Inc.   (1)
3681 Prism Ln, Kieler, WI 53812
Web Site: http://www.pssi.co
Emp.: 17,000
Cleaning & Sanitation Services
N.A.I.C.S.: 561720
Amy Lowe (VP-HR)
Dan Taft (CEO)
Craig Hart (CFO)
Doug White (Sr VP-West Reg)
John Neuhalfen (Sr VP-Midwest Reg)
Josh Kuepers (Sr VP-East Reg)
Monty Christenberry (Sr VP-Central Reg)
Doug Sharp (Pres)
Tom Eckmann (VP-Ops)

Premier Needle Arts, Inc.   (1)
501 N 400 W, North Salt Lake, UT 84054
Tel.: (801) 292-7988
Web Site: http://www.premierneedlearts.com
Emp.: 250
Holding Company
N.A.I.C.S.: 551112
Mark Hyland (CEO)

Subsidiary (Domestic):

Crafts Americana Group Inc.   (2)
13118 NE 4th St, Vancouver, WA 98684
Tel.: (360) 260-8900
Web Site: http://www.craftsamericana.com
Craft Store Retailer
N.A.I.C.S.: 459130
Matt Petkun (Pres & CEO)

Ritus Corp.
7900 N 73rd St, Milwaukee, WI 53223
Tel.: (414) 586-3535
Web Site: http://www.ritus.com
Fabricated Rubber Products, Nec, Nsk
N.A.I.C.S.: 326299

Russell Food Equipment Limited   (1)
1255 Venables St, Vancouver, V6A 3X6, BC, Canada
Tel.: (604) 253-6611
Web Site: https://www.russellfood.ca
Food Equipment Services
N.A.I.C.S.: 335220
Don Russell (Pres)

Subsidiary (Domestic):

Hendrix Hotel & Restaurant Equipment & Supplies Ltd.   (2)
3011 Highway 29 North, Brockville, K6V 5V2, ON, Canada
Tel.: (613) 342-0616
Web Site: http://www.russellhendrix.com
Commercial Food Service Equipment & Supplies Whslr

N.A.I.C.S.: 423850

Branch (Domestic):

Hendrix London   (3)
812 Dundas Street, London, N5W 2Z7, ON, Canada
Tel.: (519) 679-9350
Web Site: http://www.hendrixequip.com
Sales Range: $10-24.9 Million
Emp.: 40
Food Service Equipment Supplier
N.A.I.C.S.: 423850
Larry Vander Baaren (Pres)

SASE Company, LLC   (1)
2475 Stock Creek Blvd, Rockford, TN 37853
Tel.: (800) 522-2606
Web Site: http://www.sasecompany.com
Construction & Mining Machinery Equipment Mfr, Distr & Rental Services
N.A.I.C.S.: 333120
Jim Weder (Pres)

Transtar Holding Company   (1)
7350 Young Dr, Walton Hills, OH 44146
Web Site: http://www.transtarholding.com
Holding Company
N.A.I.C.S.: 551112
Chris Bodh (Grp Pres-General Repair Businesses-NexaMotion Group)
Neil Sethi (Pres & CEO)
Joseph Levanduski (CFO, COO & Exec VP)
Ben DePompei (Pres-Mfg & TAT)
Tom DeMille (VP-Sls & Mktg-Transtar Distr)
Kevin Rozsa (VP-Supply Chain-Transtar Distr)
Maggie McNamara (Mgr-Comm)
Chip Chaikin (Chm)

Subsidiary (Domestic):

Arch Auto Parts Corp.   (2)
181-02 Jamaica Ave, Hollis, NY 11423-2326
Tel.: (718) 657-9600
Web Site: https://www.archautoparts.com
Rev.: $15,000,000
Emp.: 50
Automotive Supplies & Parts
N.A.I.C.S.: 423120

C & M Auto Parts, Inc.   (2)
1104 Martin Luther King, Trenton, NJ 08638
Tel.: (609) 396-5086
Web Site: http://www.cmautoparts.net
Sales Range: $1-9.9 Million
Emp.: 38
Motor Vehicle Supplies & New Parts Merchant Whslr
N.A.I.C.S.: 423120
Glenn Morreale (Pres)

Transtar Industries, Inc.   (2)
7350 Young Dr, Walton Hills, OH 44146-5357
Tel.: (440) 232-5100
Web Site: http://www.transtar1.com
Sales Range: $500-549.9 Million
Automotive Transmission Kits & Accessories Distr
N.A.I.C.S.: 423120
Monte Ahuja (Chm)
Neil Sethi (CEO)
Ben Depompei (Pres-Mfg Ops)
Segi Quinones (Gen Mgr-Transmart)
Joe Levanduski (CFO & Exec VP)
Anna Gluck (VP-HR)
Chris Osos (VP-Mktg)
Tom DeMille (Exec VP-Sls & Mktg)

Subsidiary (Domestic):

Axiom Automotive Technologies, Inc.   (3)
6550 Hamilton Ave, Pittsburgh, PA 15206
Tel.: (412) 441-7353
Rev.: $55,000,000
Motor Vehicle Supplies & Transmission Replacement Parts Distr
N.A.I.C.S.: 423120
Bob Fitzsimmons (Pres)

ETX Holdings, Inc.   (3)
2000 Michigan Ave, Alma, MI 48801
Tel.: (989) 463-1151
Web Site: http://www.almaproducts.com
Holding Company
N.A.I.C.S.: 551112
Alan Gatlin (Pres & CEO)

Holding (Domestic):

ATCO Products, Inc. (4)
601 S Interstate 45, Ferris, TX 75125
Tel.: (972) 842-8178
Web Site: http://www.atcomall.com
Emp.: 200
Air Conditioning, Cooling & Power Steering
Assemblies & Components Mfr & Supplier
N.A.I.C.S.: 336330
Alan Gatlin (Pres & Gen Mgr)

Alma Products Company (4)
2000 Michigan Ave, Alma, MI 48801
Tel.: (989) 463-1151
Web Site: http://www.almaproducts.com
Emp.: 250
Air Conditioning Compressors, Torque Con-
verters, Clutch & Disc Assemblies& Trans-
missions Mfr & Distr
N.A.I.C.S.: 336350
Alan Gatlin (Pres)

DACCO, Inc. (4)
741 Dacco Dr, Cookeville, TN
38506 (100%)
Tel.: (931) 528-7581
Web Site: http://www.daccoinc.com
Sales Range: $25-49.9 Million
Mfr & Rebuilder of Auto Parts & Automatic
Transmissions for Auto Aftermarket
N.A.I.C.S.: 336390
Sam Lugo (Sr Dir-Fin)

Branch (Domestic):

Dacco Detroit of Ohio, Inc. (5)
3316 Refugee Rd, Columbus, OH
43232-4810 (100%)
Tel.: (614) 237-2322
Sales Range: $25-49.9 Million
Emp.: 5
Retail of Automotive Supplies & Parts
N.A.I.C.S.: 423120
Mike Snodgrass (Gen Mgr)

Division (Domestic):

Nickels Performance Warehouse (3)
293 Industrial Park Rd, Piney Flats, TN
37686-4418
Tel.: (423) 391-0032
Web Site:
http://www.nickelsperformance.com
Sales Range: $25-49.9 Million
Motor Vehicle Supplies & Parts
N.A.I.C.S.: 423120
Scott Peer (Asst Mgr-Warehouse)

Subsidiary (Domestic):

**Transtar Autobody Technologies,
Inc.** (3)
2040 Heiserman Dr, Brighton, MI 48114-
8969
Tel.: (810) 220-3000
Web Site: http://www.tat-co.com
Sales Range: $25-49.9 Million
Automotive Refinishing
N.A.I.C.S.: 325612
Alberto Castillo (Dir-Intl Sls)

**United Transmission Exchange,
Inc.** (3)
21 Ramah Cir S, Agawam, MA 01001
Tel.: (413) 789-4340
Web Site: http://www.deantransmission.com
Sales Range: $10-24.9 Million
Emp.: 40
Sales of Automotive Supplies & Parts
N.A.I.C.S.: 423120
Dean Curtis (VP-Tech Support)
Bill Maroni (VP-Ops)
Donna Lofgren (Office Mgr)

Weaver Leather, LLC (1)
7540 CR 201, Mount Hope, OH 44660
Tel.: (330) 674-1782
Web Site: http://www.weaverleather.com
Leather Goods Mfr
N.A.I.C.S.: 316990
Paul Weaver (Chm)
Chris Weaver (Exec VP)
Jason Weaver (Pres & CEO)
Carlos Mullet (CFO)

**BLUE RIBBON FARM DAIRY
INC.**

827 Exeter Ave, West Pittston, PA
18643
Tel.: (570) 655-5579
Web Site:
https://www.blueribbondairy.com
Year Founded: 1945
Sales Range: $10-24.9 Million
Emp.: 25
Dairy & Icecream Product Whlsr &
Distr
N.A.I.C.S.: 424490
Ken Sorick (Pres)

BLUE RIBBON MEATS INC.
3316 W 67th Pl, Cleveland, OH
44102-5243
Tel.: (216) 631-8850 OH
Web Site:
https://www.blueribbonmeats.com
Year Founded: 1948
Meats & Meat Products Distr
N.A.I.C.S.: 424470
Albert J. Radis (Founder)

**BLUE RIBBON TRANSPORT,
INC.**
5752 Wheeler Rd, Indianapolis, IN
46216
Tel.: (317) 897-0138
Web Site:
http://www.blueribbontransport.com
Freight Transportation, Warehousing
& Supply Chain Services
N.A.I.C.S.: 488510
Philip J. Caito (Pres)
Alex Miller (Coord-Dedicated Logis-
tics)

**BLUE RIDGE ACQUISITION
CO. LLC**
1546 Progress Rd, Ellijay, GA 30540
Tel.: (706) 276-2001
Web Site:
http://www.blueridgecarpet.com
Sales Range: $10-24.9 Million
Emp.: 260
Mfr of Carpets & Rugs
N.A.I.C.S.: 314110
Mike Gallman (Pres & CEO)
David Westmoreland (Controller)
Gary Anderson (CFO)

BLUE RIDGE ARSENAL INC.
14725-K Flint Lee Rd, Chantilly, VA
20151-0151
Tel.: (703) 818-0230
Web Site:
http://www.blueridgearsenal.com
Amusement & Recreation Industries
N.A.I.C.S.: 713990
Earl Curtis (Pres & CEO)

**BLUE RIDGE BANCSHARES
INC.**
c/o Blue Ridge Bank 17 W Main St,
Luray, VA 22835
Tel.: (540) 743-6521
Year Founded: 1990
Bank Holding Company
N.A.I.C.S.: 551111

Subsidiaries:

Blue Ridge Bank and Trust Co. (1)
4200 Little Blue Pkwy, Independence, MO
64057
Tel.: (816) 358-5000
Web Site: http://www.blueridgebank.net
Sales Range: $25-49.9 Million
Emp.: 50
Commericial Banking
N.A.I.C.S.: 522110
William C. Esry (Pres & CEO)
G. L. Thomas (Chm)
David Kyle (VP-Comml Loans)
Tara Sturtevant (Asst VP)
Adam Hubbard (VP)
Marla Mullen (Asst VP)

Yvonne Hall (Exec VP-Retail & Treasury
Svcs)
Patrick Campbell (Exec VP-Comml Svcs)
Sidney Stecker (Asst VP & Mgr-North 7
Highway Blue Springs)
Matthew Brown (VP-Comml Lending)

**BLUE RIDGE BEHAVIORAL
HEALTHCARE**
301 Elm Ave SW, Roanoke, VA
24016
Tel.: (540) 345-9841
Web Site: https://www.brbh.org
Sales Range: $10-24.9 Million
Emp.: 400
Mental Health Care Services
N.A.I.C.S.: 621420
Bruce N. Thomasson (Treas)
Helen Lang (Officer-Continuous Qual-
ity Improvement)
Debbie Bonniwell (CEO)
David Wells (Chm)

**BLUE RIDGE BEVERAGE
COMPANY INCORPORATED**
4446 Barley Dr, Salem, VA 24153
Tel.: (540) 380-2000
Web Site:
https://www.blueridgebeverage.com
Sales Range: $100-124.9 Million
Emp.: 170
Beer & Other Fermented Malt Liquors
N.A.I.C.S.: 424810
Lee Blair (Office Mgr)
Bob Archer (Pres)
Jacqueline L. Archer (Pres & COO)

BLUE RIDGE CAPITAL, LLC
660 Madison Ave 20th Fl, New York,
NY 10065
Tel.: (212) 446-6200 NY
Year Founded: 1996
Sales Range: $25-49.9 Million
Emp.: 60
Privater Equity Firm
N.A.I.C.S.: 523999
John A. Griffin (Pres & Mng Partner)

**BLUE RIDGE ELECTRIC CO-
OPERATIVE INC.**
734 W Main St, Pickens, SC 29671-
0277
Tel.: (864) 878-6326 SC
Web Site: http://www.blueridge.com
Year Founded: 1940
Sales Range: $200-249.9 Million
Emp.: 150
Provider of Electricity Distribution
N.A.I.C.S.: 221118
Charles E. Dalton (Pres & CEO)

Subsidiaries:

Blue Ridge Security Systems (1)
1212 N Fant St, Anderson, SC
29621-5710 (100%)
Web Site:
http://www.blueridgesecuritysystems.com
Sales Range: $10-24.9 Million
Emp.: 35
Installation of Security Monitoring Systems
N.A.I.C.S.: 561621

**BLUE RIDGE ELECTRIC MEM-
BERSHIP CORPORATION**
1216 Blowing Rock Blvd NE, Lenoir,
NC 28645-3619
Tel.: (828) 758-2383 NC
Web Site:
https://www.blueridgeenergy.com
Year Founded: 1936
Sales Range: $150-199.9 Million
Emp.: 165
Electric Utility Services
N.A.I.C.S.: 221122
Doug Johnson (CEO & Exec VP)
Kenneth Greene (Pres)
Jeff Joines (VP-Caldwell District)

Brad Shields (CTO & Sr VP)
Susan Simmons (Mgr-Comm)
Jeff Benfield (Mgr-Ops)
Sandra Hicks (Dir-Member Svcs)
Renee Whitener (Dir-PR)
Joy B. Coffey (Treas & Sec-Watauga
District)
Julie O'Dell-Michie (Chief Admin Offi-
cer & Sr VP)
Robert Kent (Dir-Ops)
Susan Jones (District Mgr-Watauga)
Dee Strickland (Gen Mgr-Acctg)
Grey Scheer (Dir-Community Rels)
Ralph Seamon (Mgr-Engrg)
Mike Kincaid (Mgr-Ops)
Karen Warlick (Mgr-HR)
Kelly Huffman (Mgr-Safety)
Lynn Heatherly (Mgr-Cost Acct)
Katie Woodle (CFO, Sec & Sr VP)
Alan Merck (COO & Sr VP)

Subsidiaries:

Blue Ridge Energies, Inc. (1)
110 Nuway Cir NE, Lenoir, NC
28645-3699 (100%)
Tel.: (828) 758-4401
Web Site: http://www.blueridgenergies.com
Sales Range: $10-24.9 Million
Emp.: 20
Propane Appliance Sales & Service; Com-
mercial Gasoline Sales
N.A.I.C.S.: 424720
Doug Johnson (Chm, Pres & CEO)
Glenda Christian (COO & Sr VP)
Katie Woodle (Vice Chm & CEO)

RidgeLink, LLC (1)
1216 Blowing Rock Blvd NE, Lenoir, NC
28645
Tel.: (800) 451-5474
Broadband & Telecommunication Services
N.A.I.C.S.: 517810
Brad Shields (COO)

BLUE RIDGE FOODS LLC.
PO Box 679, Allenwood, NJ 08720
Tel.: (718) 307-7793
Sales Range: $10-24.9 Million
Emp.: 90
Frozen Specialty Food Mfr
N.A.I.C.S.: 311412
Saly Ammach (Controller-Fin)
Paul Prusiensky (Controller-Fin)
Wanda Simon (Mgr-HR)

BLUE RIDGE GROUP INC.
632 Adams St Ste 700, Bowling
Green, KY 42101
Tel.: (270) 842-2421
Web Site:
http://www.blueridgegroup.com
Sales Range: $10-24.9 Million
Emp.: 15
Oil & Gas Exploration
N.A.I.C.S.: 213111
Kim Flora (Office Mgr)
Stephen C. Larkin (Pres & CEO)
Jon Paul (Dir-Comm)

Subsidiaries:

Blueridge Group (1)
632 Adams St Ste 700, Bowling Green, KY
42101
Tel.: (270) 781-8596
Web Site: http://www.blueridgegroup.com
New Construction, Single-Family Houses
N.A.I.C.S.: 236115

BLUE RIDGE HOSPICE
333 W Cork St Ste 405, Winchester,
VA 22601
Tel.: (540) 536-5210 VA
Web Site:
http://www.blueridgehospice.org
Year Founded: 1981
Sales Range: $10-24.9 Million
Hospice Care Services
N.A.I.C.S.: 621610

Blue Ridge Hospice—(Continued)

Bethanne Berman (Sec)
Mary Ann Kaplan (Vice Chm)
Nancy Picklap (Treas)
Paul Delmerico (Chm)
Ernest J. Carnevale Jr. (Pres & CEO)

BLUE RIDGE INDUSTRIES, INC.

300 N Greene St Ste 2100, Greensboro, NC 27401
Tel.: (336) 275-7002　　NC
Web Site:
　http://www.blueridgeindustries.com
Year Founded: 2005
Sales Range: Less than $1 Million
Industrial Holding Company
N.A.I.C.S.: 551112
Russell R. Myers (Founder & CEO)
Pamela Streeter (Controller)

BLUE RIDGE KNIVES, INC.

314 Lee Highway, Marion, VA 24354
Tel.: (276) 783-6143
Web Site:
　https://www.blueridgeknives.com
Wholesale Dist.
N.A.I.C.S.: 423710

Subsidiaries:

Ontario Knife Company　　(1)
26 Empire St, Franklinville, NY 14737
Tel.: (716) 676-5527
Web Site: https://ontarioknife.com
Knife Mfr & Distr
N.A.I.C.S.: 332215
Dave Fenske (VP & Gen Mgr)

BLUE RIDGE LOG CABINS, LLC

625 E Frontage Rd, Campobello, SC 29322
Tel.: (864) 457-7343　　SC
Web Site:
　https://www.blueridgelogcabins.com
Year Founded: 2004
Sales Range: $10-24.9 Million
Emp.: 80
Residential Log Home Mfr
N.A.I.C.S.: 321992
Doug Terrell (VP-Mfg)
Carol Pritchard (Mgr-HR)
Catherine Brusk (Coord-Fin)
Greg Altizer (Mgr-Sls)
Greg Barnes (Mgr-Engrg)
Julie Phillips (Coord-Sls)
Marlene Goode (Controller)
Sarah Smith (Dir-Mktg)
Donn Dack (CFO)
Milton A. Smith Jr. (Owner & Pres)

BLUE RIDGE MOUNTAIN SPORTS LTD

24 Conestoga Way, Troy, VA 22974
Web Site: http://www.brms.com
Sales Range: $10-24.9 Million
Emp.: 200
Backpacking Equipment
N.A.I.C.S.: 459110
Jeffrey C. Smith (Pres)

BLUE RIDGE PRESSURE CASTINGS, INC.

PO Box 208, Lehighton, PA 18235-0208
Tel.: (610) 377-2510　　PA
Web Site:
　http://www.blueridgediecasting.net
Year Founded: 1946
Sales Range: $75-99.9 Million
Emp.: 150
Mfr of Brass Zinc & Aluminum Die Castings
N.A.I.C.S.: 331523
Andrew D. Behler (VP-Engrg)
James Martinez (Engr-Tooling)

BLUE RIDGE PRINTING CO., INC.

544 Haywood Rd, Asheville, NC 28806-3556
Tel.: (828) 254-1000　　NC
Web Site:
　https://www.blueridgeprinting.com
Year Founded: 1974
Commercial Printing
N.A.I.C.S.: 323111
Bruce Fowler (Pres)

BLUE RIVER GROUP, LLC.

1950 N Park Pl SE Bldg 600, Atlanta, GA 30339
Tel.: (770) 953-3133
Web Site:
　http://www.thebluerivergroup.com
Sales Range: $10-24.9 Million
Emp.: 8
Residential Remodeling Services
N.A.I.C.S.: 236118
Jonathan Charles Clay (Pres)
Wayne Bradley (Superintendent)
Ernest Mendoza (Superintendent)
Doreen Leroux (Office Mgr)
Brandan Mote (Superintendent)
Ben Thrift (Superintendent)
Tony Watson (Superintendent)
Kelly Clay (VP)

BLUE ROAD MANAGEMENT, L.P.

570 Lexington Ave 32nd Fl, New York, NY 10022
Tel.: (212) 822-9710
Web Site: https://www.blueroad.com
Private Equity
N.A.I.C.S.: 523940
Clifford Leung (VP)

Subsidiaries:

NS Brands Ltd　　(1)
2338 N Loop 1604, San Antonio, TX 78248-4523
Web Site: http://www.naturesweet.com
Fresh Fruit & Vegetable Merchant Whslr
N.A.I.C.S.: 424480

BLUE ROCK OF MAINE

737 Spring St, Westbrook, ME 04092
Tel.: (207) 772-6770
Web Site:
　https://www.bluerockmaine.com
Sales Range: $10-24.9 Million
Emp.: 121
Masonry Contracting Services
N.A.I.C.S.: 238140
David Lamb (Gen Mgr-Sls)

BLUE ROCK PARTNERS, LLC

5650 Breckenridge Park Dr Ste 302, Tampa, FL 33610
Tel.: (813) 620-0800
Web Site:
　http://www.bluerockpartnersllc.com
Sales Range: $25-49.9 Million
Emp.: 60
Real Estate Investment & Management
N.A.I.C.S.: 531311
Reuven Oded (Partner)
Pam Armocida (Exec VP-Ops)

BLUE SAGE CAPITAL, L.P.

114 W 7th St Ste 820, Austin, TX 78701
Tel.: (512) 536-1900　　DE
Web Site: http://www.bluesage.com
Emp.: 8
Privater Equity Firm
N.A.I.C.S.: 523999
Peter Huff (Co-Founder)
Jim McBride (Co-Founder)

Jonathan Pearce (Partner)
Eric Weiner (Partner)
Alan Mire (Controller)

Subsidiaries:

All-State Industries Inc.　　(1)
520 S 18th St, West Des Moines, IA 50265-5532
Tel.: (515) 223-5843
Web Site: http://www.all-stateind.com
Sales Range: $25-49.9 Million
Emp.: 200
Industrial Supplies Mfr & Whslr
N.A.I.C.S.: 423840
Robert G. Pulver (Chm, Pres & CEO)
Scott Pulver (Dir-Sls & Mktg)

Subsidiary (Domestic):

dB Engineering, Inc.　　(2)
1936 Lone Star Rd, Mansfield, TX 76063
Tel.: (817) 453-1100
Web Site: http://www.800nonoise.com
Rev.: $3,108,000
Emp.: 8
Hardware Stores
N.A.I.C.S.: 444140
Mike Gibson (Owner)

Impact Floord of Texas, LLC　　(1)
3700 Pipestone, Dallas, TX 75212
Tel.: (214) 951-9462
Web Site:
　https://impactpropertysolutions.com
Sales Range: $1-9.9 Million
Emp.: 40
Floor Laying Services
N.A.I.C.S.: 238330

Subsidiary (Domestic):

Interior Concepts, Inc.　　(2)
4444 S 34th St, Phoenix, AZ 85040
Tel.: (480) 967-1384
Web Site:
　http://www.interiorconceptsaz.com
Rev.: $1,800,000
Emp.: 15
Flooring Contractors
N.A.I.C.S.: 238330
John M. Doughty (Pres)

BLUE SEA CAPITAL MANAGEMENT LLC

222 Lakeview Ave Ste 1700, West Palm Beach, FL 33401
Tel.: (561) 655-8400　　DE
Web Site:
　http://www.blueseacapital.com
Year Founded: 2013
Privater Equity Firm
N.A.I.C.S.: 523999
Mark J. Silk (Operating Partner)
Adam P. Klein (CFO)
Richard J. Wandoff (Mng Partner)
T. Andrew Boswell (Partner)
Scott R. Kirkendall (Partner)
Jennifer L. Toothman (Coord-Mktg)
James R. Davis Jr. (Mng Partner)
J. Thomas Bowler Jr. (Partner-Human Capital)

Subsidiaries:

Krueger-Gilbert Health Physics, Inc.　　(1)
809 Gleneagles Court Ste 100, Towson, MD 21286
Tel.: (410) 339-5447
Web Site: http://www.kruegergilbert.com
Professional, Scientific & Technical Services
N.A.I.C.S.: 541990
Keith N. Burns (Pres)
Michele F. Loscocco (Dir-Tech Ops)
Jessica Perovic (Dir-Fin & Client Svcs)
Michael Curry Jr. (CEO)

ProSource LLC　　(1)
3 Independence Pointe Ste 101, Greenville, SC 29615
Tel.: (864) 565-8880
Web Site: https://prosourcesupply.com
Plumbing & Heating Equipment & Supplies Whslr
N.A.I.C.S.: 423720
Drew Roberts (CEO)

Subsidiary (Domestic):

Morehouse-Huber, Inc.　　(2)
160 George Patton St, Orangeburg, SC 29115
Tel.: (803) 534-8025
Sales Range: $1-9.9 Million
Emp.: 10
Plumbing & Heating Equipment & Supplies Merchant Whslr
N.A.I.C.S.: 423720
Robbie Huber (Pres)

RESA Power, LLC　　(1)
8300 Cypress Creek Pkwy Ste 225, Houston, TX 77070
Tel.: (832) 900-8340
Web Site: http://www.resapower.com
Power System Testing & Engineering Services
N.A.I.C.S.: 335999
Monte Roach (CEO)

Subsidiary (Domestic):

Crews Electrical Testing, Inc.　　(2)
6148 Tim Crews Rd, Macclenny, FL 32063
Tel.: (904) 653-1900
Web Site: http://www.cetestinginc.com
Sales Range: $1-9.9 Million
Emp.: 12
Electrical Testing Services
N.A.I.C.S.: 811114
Carolyn Crews (Sec)

Halco Service Corp.　　(2)
5773 Venice Blvd, Los Angeles, CA 90019
Tel.: (323) 933-9431
Web Site: http://www.halco.net
Sales Range: $1-9.9 Million
Emp.: 20
Electrical Work, Nsk
N.A.I.C.S.: 238210
Harold Orum (Pres)

Rhino Tool House　　(1)
7575 Westwinds Blvd NW, Concord, NV 28027
Tel.: (888) 727-7882
Web Site: https://rhinotoolhouse.com
Emp.: 100
Automation Machinery Mfr
N.A.I.C.S.: 333310
Dan Brooks (CEO)

Subsidiary (Domestic):

Bomar Pneumatics, Inc.　　(2)
5785 W 74th St, Indianapolis, IN 46278
Tel.: (317) 216-7606
Web Site: http://www.bomarpneumatics.com
Sales Range: $1-9.9 Million
Emp.: 6
Industrial Machinery & Equipment Whslr
N.A.I.C.S.: 423830
Blair Brimmer (Pres)

Spectrum Vision Partners LLC　　(1)
825 E Gate Blvd, Garden City, NY 11530
Tel.: (516) 804-5200
Web Site:
　https://www.spectrumvisionpartners.com
Medical Practice
N.A.I.C.S.: 621111

Joint Venture (Domestic):

Crossroads Eye Care Associates, Ltd.　　(2)
4160 Washington Rd, McMurray, PA 15317
Tel.: (724) 941-1466
Web Site:
　http://www.crossroadseyecare.com
Offices of Physicians (except Mental Health Specialists)
N.A.I.C.S.: 621111
Shelley Butti (Mgr-Optical)

Fishman Center For Total Eye Care　　(2)
9229 Queens Blvd Ste 2I, Rego Park, NY 11374-1072
Tel.: (718) 261-7007
Offices of Physicians (except Mental Health Specialists)
N.A.I.C.S.: 621111
Allen Fishman (Pres)

BLUE SHIELD OF CALIFORNIA

50 Beale St, San Francisco, CA
94105-1808
Tel.: (415) 229-5000   CA
Web Site:
   http://www.blueshieldca.com
Year Founded: 1939
Sales Range: $5-14.9 Billion
Emp.: 6,800
Health Care Service Plans
N.A.I.C.S.: 524114
Seth A. Jacobs *(Gen Counsel, Sec & Sr VP)*
Amy Yao *(Chief Actuary & Sr VP)*
Jeff Smith *(VP-Individual & Family Plans)*
David Fields *(Exec VP-Markets)*
Shayna Schulz *(VP-Customer Care)*
Doug Busch *(Chm)*
Lisa M. Davis *(CIO & Exec VP)*
Don Antonucci *(Sr VP-Employer Markets)*
Jeffrey Bailet *(Exec VP-Health Care Quality & Affordability)*
Sandra Clarke *(CFO & Sr VP)*
Terry Gilliland *(Chief Health Officer & Sr VP)*
Mimi Kokoska *(Sr VP-Strategic Partnerships & Innovation)*
Elizabeth Mitchell *(Sr VP-Healthcare & Community Health Transformation)*
Mark Morgan *(Sr VP-Consumer Markets)*
Mary O'Hara *(Chief HR Officer & Sr VP)*
Armine Papouchian *(Sr VP-Provider Contracting, Rels, Compliance & Analytics)*
Jeffrey Robertson *(CMO & Sr VP)*
Jeffrey Semenchuk *(Chief Innovation Officer & Sr VP)*
Peter Long *(Exec VP-Strategy & Health Solutions)*
Krishna Ramachandran *(Sr VP-Health Transformation & Provider Adoption)*
Kristina M. Leslie *(Chm)*

Subsidiaries:

Blue Shield of California   (1)
6300 Canoga Ave, Woodland Hills, CA
91367-2555   **(100%)**
Tel.: (818) 598-8000
Web Site: http://www.blueshieldca.com
Sales Range: $50-74.9 Million
Emp.: 500
Hospital & Medical Insurance
N.A.I.C.S.: 524128
Brent Hitchings *(VP-Broker Sls)*

Blue Shield of California - Large
Group Business Unit   (1)
100 N Sepulveda Blvd 20th Fl, El Segundo,
CA 90245
Tel.: (310) 744-2580
Web Site: http://www.blueshieldca.com
Sales Range: $50-74.9 Million
Emp.: 200
Health Insurance Services
N.A.I.C.S.: 524114
Rob Geyer *(Sr VP-Customer Quality)*

Blue Shield of California Life & Health
Insurance Company   (1)
50 Beale St, San Francisco, CA
94105-1808   **(100%)**
Tel.: (415) 229-5000
Web Site: http://www.bscalife.com
Sales Range: $50-74.9 Million
Emp.: 500
Life & Health Insurance Services
N.A.I.C.S.: 524113

BLUE SKY AGENCY
950 Lowery Blvd Ste 30, Atlanta, GA
30318
Tel.: (404) 876-0202
Web Site:
   http://www.blueskyagency.com
Year Founded: 1994
Rev.: $30,000,000

Emp.: 30
Advetising Agency
N.A.I.C.S.: 541810
Stacy Scott *(VP-Fin & Ops)*
Rob Farinella *(Founder & Pres)*
Mike Bevil *(Mng Dir & Sr VP)*
Matthew Richardson *(Dir-Art)*
Ryan Kellogg *(Assoc Creative Dir-Interactive)*
Eileen Goodyear *(Dir-Acct Svc)*

BLUE SKY ENERGY
2598 Fortune Way Ste K, Vista, CA
92081-8442
Tel.: (760) 597-1642
Web Site:
   http://www.blueskyenergyinc.com
Heating Equipment Mfr
N.A.I.C.S.: 333414
Ahmed Said *(Pres & CEO)*
Kenny Choi *(Corp Sec)*

Subsidiaries:

Sonoro Energy Iraq B.V.   (1)
Prinses Margrietplnts 76, Hague, 2595 BR,
Netherlands
Tel.: (31) 38 420 9860
Asphalt Exploration Services
N.A.I.C.S.: 213115

BLUE SKY EXHIBITS
125 Church St Ste 320, Marietta, GA
30068
Tel.: (678) 331-3800
Web Site:
   https://www.blueskyexhibits.com
Year Founded: 2003
Rev.: $6,100,000
Emp.: 15
Business Services
N.A.I.C.S.: 561990
Don B. Keller *(CEO)*
Michael A. Darby *(Project Mgr)*
Jeff Sasser *(Project Mgr)*
Lori Wager *(Acct Dir-Mgmt)*
Geralyn Virostek *(Controller & Dir-HR)*
Darryl Peterson *(Dir-Ops)*
Tim Kelley *(COO)*
Debra Crawford *(VP-Bus Dev & Mktg)*
Brett Clark *(Mgr-Production)*

BLUE SKY GROUP HOLD-INGS, INC.
8017 Glenview Dr Ste A, North Richland Hills, TX 76180
Tel.: (817) 616-3651   DE
Web Site:
   http://www.blueskymortgages.com
Year Founded: 2016
Mortgage Banking Services
N.A.I.C.S.: 522292
Chirag Patel *(Chm, Pres, CEO & Treas)*
Cyrus Sajna *(CFO)*

BLUE SKY IT PARTNERS CORPORATION
2429 Bissonnet Ste 483, Houston, TX
77005
Tel.: (713) 929-0950   TX
Web Site:
   http://www.blueskyitpartners.com
Year Founded: 2010
Sales Range: $1-9.9 Million
Emp.: 10
Information Technology Management
Services
N.A.I.C.S.: 541512
Meg Toups *(Founder & CEO)*

BLUE SKY MD
317 N King St, Hendersonville, NC
28792
Tel.: (828) 693-9199

Web Site:
   https://www.blueskymd.com
Year Founded: 2008
Sales Range: $1-9.9 Million
Emp.: 30
Weight Loss Programs, Hormone
Therapy & Cosmetic Skincare Procedures
N.A.I.C.S.: 812191
David LaMond *(Dir-Medical)*
Kristen Hunter *(Program Dir)*

Subsidiaries:

Blue Sky MD   (1)
1998 Hendersonville Rd Unit 51, Asheville,
NC 28803   **(100%)**
Tel.: (828) 651-0450
Web Site: http://www.blueskymd.com
Emp.: 15
Weight Loss Programs, Hormone Therapy
& Cosmetic Skincare Procedures
N.A.I.C.S.: 812191
David LaMond *(Medical Dir)*

BLUE SKY NETWORK, LLC
16559 N 92nd St Ste 101, Scottsdale, AZ 85260
Tel.: (858) 551-3894
Web Site:
   http://www.blueskynetwork.com
Emp.: 100
Satellite & Communication Equipment
Distr
N.A.I.C.S.: 423690
Jon S. Gilbert *(Founder)*
Lillie Cheung *(Exec VP)*
Joel Goron *(VP-Channel Dev)*
Heng Wang *(VP-Hardware Engrg)*
Wade E. Worthington *(VP-Software Dev)*
Kambiz Aghili *(CEO)*
Gregoire Demory *(Pres)*
David Thoreau *(Mgr-PR)*

Subsidiaries:

NAL Research Corp.   (1)
9385 Discovery Blvd Ste 300, Manassas,
VA 20109-3992
Tel.: (703) 392-1136
Web Site: http://www.nalresearch.com
Search, Detection, Navigation, Guidance,
Aeronautical & Nautical System & Instrument Mfr
N.A.I.C.S.: 334511

BLUE SKY SCRUBS LLC
1906 W Koenig Ln, Austin, TX 78756
Tel.: (512) 420-9018
Web Site:
   https://www.blueskyscrubs.com
Year Founded: 2006
Sales Range: $1-9.9 Million
Emp.: 7
Medical Scrubs & Uniforms
N.A.I.C.S.: 458110
Shelby Marquardt *(Founder)*

BLUE SPRIG PEDIATRICS, INC.
7500 San Felipe St Ste 990, Houston, TX 77063
Tel.: (832) 742-0001   DE
Web Site:
   http://bluesprigpediatrics.com
Year Founded: 2017
Applied Behavior Therapy Services
N.A.I.C.S.: 621999
Sharyn Kerr *(Chief Clinical & Admin Officer)*
Jason Owen *(Pres & CEO)*
Kristy Rohwedder *(COO)*
Michael Ames *(CFO)*
Lance Carlson *(Chief Acctg Officer)*

BLUE STAR GAS
880 N Wright Rd, Santa Rosa, CA
95407
Tel.: (707) 546-1400

Web Site:
   https://www.bluestargas.com
Sales Range: $10-24.9 Million
Emp.: 70
Provider of Gas Transmission & Distribution Services
N.A.I.C.S.: 457210
Jeff Stewart *(Pres)*
Chris Mastrup *(Dir-Safety & Trng)*
Darren Engle *(Mgr-Mktg)*
Bill Stewart *(Chm)*

BLUE STAR GROWERS INC.
200 Blue Star Rd, Cashmere, WA
98815
Tel.: (509) 782-2922
Rev.: $37,000,000
Emp.: 400
Refrigerated Warehousing & Storage
N.A.I.C.S.: 493120
Terry Twitchell *(Pres-Board)*
Dan Kenoyer *(Gen Mgr)*

BLUE STAR JETS, INC.
805 3rd Ave Fl 16, New York, NY
10022
Tel.: (212) 446-9037
Web Site:
   http://www.bluestarjets.com
Sales Range: $200-249.9 Million
Emp.: 25
Private Jet Services
N.A.I.C.S.: 541990
Todd Rome *(Pres)*
Richard Sitomer *(CEO)*
Mauric Loga *(Coord-Paris)*

BLUE STAR PARTNERS LLC
660 La Salle Pl, Highland Park, IL
60035
Tel.: (847) 780-4214
Web Site:
   http://www.bluestarpartners.com
Year Founded: 2003
Sales Range: $1-9.9 Million
Emp.: 5
Business Consultants
N.A.I.C.S.: 561499
Rob Malench *(Founder & Mng Partner)*
Dana Kirchman *(Partner)*
Bob Matoesian *(Mng Partner)*
Anh McCormick *(Mgr-Shared Svcs)*
Jamal Baggett *(Principal)*

BLUE STAR WEBBING CORP.
45 Fairchild Ave, Plainview, NY
11803
Tel.: (516) 346-4636
Web Site:
   https://www.nationalwebbing.com
Sales Range: $10-24.9 Million
Emp.: 18
Webbing, Woven
N.A.I.C.S.: 313220
Edward Glassgold *(Pres)*
Robert Kaye *(Controller)*

BLUE SUN BIODIESEL
1687 Cole Blvd, Lakewood, CO
80401
Tel.: (303) 865-7700
Web Site: http://www.gobluesun.com
Year Founded: 2003
Sales Range: $10-24.9 Million
Emp.: 55
Blended Biodiesel Fuel Products
N.A.I.C.S.: 424720
Jean Lafferty *(Founder & VP-Tech & Strategy)*
Jerry Washburn *(CFO & VP)*

BLUE TECH, INC.
4025 Hancock St Ste100, San Diego,
CA 92110

Blue Tech, Inc.—(Continued)

Tel.: (619) 497-6060
Web Site: https://www.bluetech.com
Year Founded: 1984
Sales Range: $25-49.9 Million
Emp.: 20
IT Consulting Services
N.A.I.C.S.: 541690
Susan Stone (*Co-Founder & CEO*)
Guy Stone (*Co-Founder & Pres*)

BLUE TEE CORPORATION

250 Park Ave S, New York, NY 10003
Tel.: (212) 598-0880   DE
Web Site: http://www.bluetee.com
Year Founded: 1986
Sales Range: $300-349.9 Million
Emp.: 1,000
Mfr & Distr of Water Well Rigs & Related Equipment
N.A.I.C.S.: 333132
David P. Alldian (*Pres & CFO*)
Thomas Caruso (*Asst Sec & Controller*)
Annette Marino D'Arienzo (*Asst Sec & Exec Dir-Benefit Plans*)

Subsidiaries:

Azcon Corp.   (1)
13733 S Ave O, Chicago, IL 60633-1547
Tel.: (312) 559-3100
Web Site: http://www.azcon.net
Rev.: $100,000,000
Emp.: 200
Ferrous Scrap
N.A.I.C.S.: 423510
Ronnie Hirsch (*Sr VP*)
Rich Secrist (*Pres*)

Brown-Strauss Steel   (1)
2495 Uraban St, Aurora, CO 80011-8108
Tel.: (303) 371-2200
Web Site: http://www.brown-strauss.com
Sales Range: $10-24.9 Million
Emp.: 60
Ferrous Scrap
N.A.I.C.S.: 423510
Robert Beall (*Gen Mgr-Phoenix*)
Rick Geller (*Mgr-Ops-Denver*)
Matt McClain (*Mgr-Sls-Denver*)
Chris Gunderson (*Gen Mgr-Kansas City*)
Nelson Smith (*Mgr-Ops-Kansas City*)
Matt Staab (*Mgr-Ops-Kansas City*)
Paul Whiton (*Mgr-Sls-Longview*)
Mike Gilbert (*Gen Mgr-Ops-Los Angeles*)
Scott McClain (*Mgr-Ops-Los Angeles*)

BLUE TORCH CAPITAL, LP

150 East 58th St 18th Fl, New York, NY 10155
Tel.: (212) 503-5850
Web Site: https://bluetorchcapital.com
Emp.: 100
Privater Equity Firm
N.A.I.C.S.: 523940
Kevin P. Genda (*Founder & CEO*)

Subsidiaries:

Blue Torch Finance LLC   (1)
150 E 58th St 39th Fl, New York, NY 10155
Tel.: (212) 503-5850
Investment Services
N.A.I.C.S.: 523999

Subsidiary (Domestic):

Near Intelligence, Inc.   (2)
1096 Keeler Ave, Berkeley, CA 94708
Tel.: (650) 246-9907
Rev.: $9,306,887
Assets: $107,433,910
Liabilities: $119,641,248
Net Worth: ($12,207,338)
Earnings: $5,032,569
Emp.: 4
Fiscal Year-end: 12/31/2022
Investment Services
N.A.I.C.S.: 523999

BLUE VICTORY HOLDINGS, INC.

4400 Ambassador Caffery Pkwy Ste A, Lafayette, LA 70508
Tel.: (337) 981-1447   DE
Web Site: http://www.bluevictoryholdings.com
Year Founded: 2009
Real Estate Properties & Restaurants
Manager & Owner
N.A.I.C.S.: 531312
Fred Alexander (*VP-Bus Dev*)
Owen P. Thompson (*Dir-Ops-Restaurants*)

BLUE WATER PETROLEUM CORP.

729 Main St, Canon City, CO 81212
Tel.: (720) 383-0651
Oil & Gas Exploration Services
N.A.I.C.S.: 213112
Jose Kreidler (*Pres*)
Alexander Dekhtyar (*Chm & CEO*)
Andrew Osidchuk (*CFO, Treas & Sec*)

BLUE WATER SHIELD LLC

5620 Sheridan St, Hollywood, FL 33021
Tel.: (561) 463-6090
Web Site: https://www.bluewatershield.com
Management Consulting Services
N.A.I.C.S.: 541618

BLUE WAVE MICRO

26895 Aliso Creek Rd Ste B751, Aliso Viejo, CA 92656
Tel.: (949) 297-3877
Web Site: http://www.bluewavemicro.com
Year Founded: 2000
Sales Range: $1-9.9 Million
Emp.: 12
Computer Hardware & Software Resellers & Distr
N.A.I.C.S.: 423430
Keith Andrews (*CEO*)

BLUE WHALE WEB SOLUTIONS, INC.

12230 Forest Hill Blvd Ste 300, Wellington, FL 33414
Tel.: (561) 753-0776
Web Site: http://www.bluewhalews.com
Sales Range: $1-9.9 Million
Emp.: 10
Mobile Applications
N.A.I.C.S.: 513210
Greg Weiss (*Founder & CEO*)
Joshua Jaffe (*VP*)
Christine Morrow (*Mgr-Client Relationship*)

BLUE WOLF CAPITAL PARTNERS LLC

1 Liberty Plz 52nd Fl 165 Broadway, New York, NY 10006
Tel.: (212) 488-1340   DE
Web Site: http://www.bluewolfcapital.com
Year Founded: 2005
Privater Equity Firm
N.A.I.C.S.: 523999
Eve G. Mongiardo (*CFO & Chief Compliance Officer*)
Adam Blumenthal (*Chm & Mng Partner*)
Charles Miller (*Partner*)
Jeremy Kogler (*Mng Partner*)
Aakash Patel (*Principal*)
Percy C. Tomlinson Jr. (*Operating Partner*)
Bennet Grill (*Principal*)
Vijay Nandwani (*VP*)

Marina Suhanitski (*Controller*)
Jason Kamm (*Operating Partner*)
Rick Tattersfield (*Operating Partner*)

Subsidiaries:

Blue Wolf Capital Management LLC   (1)
1 Liberty St, New York, NY 10006-1402
Tel.: (212) 488-1340
Web Site: http://www.blue-wolf.com
Private Equity Portfolio Management Services
N.A.I.C.S.: 523940
Adam Blumenthal (*Mng Partner*)
Ralph Wright (*Partner-Operating*)
Michael Ranson (*Partner*)
Charles P. Miller (*Partner*)
Aakash Patel (*Principal*)
Andrew Schwartz (*VP*)
Dana Halasz (*Chief Admin Officer*)
Joshua Cherry-Seto (*CFO*)
Michael Musuraca (*Mng Dir*)
Rob Groberg (*VP*)
Victor Caruso (*Mng Dir*)

Channel Technologies Group, Inc.   (1)
879 Ward Dr, Santa Barbara, CA 93111
Tel.: (805) 967-0171
Web Site: http://www.channeltechgroup.com
Sales Range: $75-99.9 Million
Emp.: 250
Piezoelectric Ceramic Products, Transducers, Sonar Equipment & Electro-Optical Test & Calibration Device Mfr
N.A.I.C.S.: 334419
Christopher E. Holmes (*CEO*)

Subsidiary (Domestic):

Sonatech Inc.   (2)
879 Ward Dr, Santa Barbara, CA 93111-2920
Tel.: (805) 683-1431
Web Site: http://www.sonatech.com
Navigation & Sonar Equipment Mfr
N.A.I.C.S.: 334511
Mark Shaw (*VP-Sonar & Transducer Sys*)
Brent Febo (*Dir-Bus Dev-Washington*)

Extreme Plastics Plus, LLC   (1)
360 Epic Cir Dr, Fairmont, WV 26554
Tel.: (304) 534-3600
Web Site: http://www.extremeplasticsplus.com
Environmental Lining & Drilling Support Services
N.A.I.C.S.: 213112
Jeff Anderson (*Mgr-Reg Ops*)
Wade Holt (*Pres*)
Jay Minmier (*CEO*)

Great Lakes Home Health Services, Inc.   (1)
900 Cooper St, Jackson, MI 49202
Tel.: (517) 780-9500
Web Site: http://www.greatlakescaring.com
Home Health Care & Hospice Care Services
N.A.I.C.S.: 621610
Eric Mynster (*Dir-Tech & Infrastructure*)

Logistec Corporation   (1)
Tel.: (514) 844-9381
Web Site: http://www.logistec.com
Rev.: $473,045,498
Assets: $623,775,209
Liabilities: $387,862,247
Net Worth: $235,912,962
Earnings: $25,649,397
Emp.: 2,715
Fiscal Year-end: 12/31/2020
Cargo Handling Services
N.A.I.C.S.: 488320
Madeleine Paquin (*Pres & CEO*)
Ingrid Stefancic (*Sec & VP-Corp & Legal Svcs*)
Suzanne Paquin (*VP*)
Nicole Paquin (*VP-Information Sys*)
George Di Sante (*VP-Bulk Market Dev*)
Alain Pilotte (*VP-Strategic Initiatives*)
Rodney Corrigan (*Pres-Logistec Stevedoring Inc*)
Marie-Chantal Savoy (*VP-Strategy*)
Trip Bailey (*VP-Ops*)
Dany Trudel (*VP*)
Frank Robertson (*VP-Operations*)
Martin Ponce (*CIO*)

Michel Brisebois (*VP*)
Philip O'Brien (*VP-Business Development*)
Sean Pierce (*CEO*)
Russell Stevens (*CFO*)
John Rosen (*CIO*)
Katia Reyburn (*VP-Communications & Public Affairs*)
Patrick Burgoyne (*Chief Strategy Officer*)
Cleidy Liborio Fernandes (*Chief Comml Officer*)
Eric Sauvageau (*Exec VP*)
Lukas Loeffler (*Dir*)
Jane Skoblo (*Dir*)

Subsidiary (Domestic):

FER-PAL Construction Ltd.   (2)
171 Fenmar Drive, Toronto, M9L1M7, ON, Canada
Tel.: (416) 742-3713
Trenchless Technology Services
N.A.I.C.S.: 238910

Subsidiary (US):

LOGISTEC Gulf Coast LLC   (2)
2327 S Dock St, Palmetto, FL 34221
Tel.: (941) 417-7953
Web Site: http://www.gc.logistec.com
Material Handling Equipment Whslr
N.A.I.C.S.: 423830
Richard Tager (*Pres*)
James Williams (*Mgr-Terminal*)

Subsidiary (Domestic):

Lakehead Shipping Company Limited   (2)
100 Main St Ste 300, Thunder Bay, P7B 6R9, ON, Canada   (100%)
Tel.: (807) 345-1494
Web Site: http://www.logistec.com
Sales Range: $25-49.9 Million
Emp.:
Shipping Services
N.A.I.C.S.: 488320
Jennifer Bennett (*Mgr-Agency*)

Logistec Marine Agencies Inc.   (2)
360 Rue Saint-Jacques 1500, Montreal, H2Y 1P5, QC, Canada
Tel.: (514) 844-9381
Web Site: http://www.logistec.com
Sales Range: $125-149.9 Million
Emp.: 35
Marine Shipping Services
N.A.I.C.S.: 488320
Madeleine Paquin (*CEO*)

Logistec Stevedoring Inc.   (2)
360 Saint Jacques St Ste 1500, Montreal, H2Y 1P5, QC, Canada   (100%)
Tel.: (514) 844-9381
Web Site: http://www.logistec.com
Sales Range: $50-74.9 Million
Emp.: 70
Marine Cargo Handling; Port & Harbor Operations
N.A.I.C.S.: 488320
Nicole Paquin (*VP-Information Sys*)
Rodney Corrigan (*Exec VP-Ops*)

Subsidiary (Domestic):

Forest Products Terminal Corporation Ltd. (Forterm)   (3)
12 King St W, PO Box 518, Saint John, E2M 7Y5, NB, Canada   (100%)
Tel.: (506) 635-1910
Web Site: http://www.logistec.com
Rev.: $50,086,464
Emp.: 15
Stevedoring Services
N.A.I.C.S.: 488320

Logistec Stevedoring (Atlantic) Inc.   (3)
10 Kings Street West Unit 8, Saint John, E2M 7Y5, NB, Canada
Tel.: (506) 635-1910
Sales Range: $25-49.9 Million
Emp.: 2
Marine Handling Services
N.A.I.C.S.: 488320
Bruce Harding (*Gen Mgr*)

Logistec Stevedoring (New Brunswick) Inc.   (3)
10 King Street West Unit 8, PO Box 3518, Saint John, E2M 7Y5, NB, Canada (100%)

Tel.: (506) 635-1940
Web Site: http://www.logistec.com
Sales Range: $25-49.9 Million
Emp.: 20
Stevedoring Services
N.A.I.C.S.: 488320

Logistec Stevedoring (Nova Scotia) Inc. (3)
1096 Marginal Rd, PO Box 264, Halifax, B3J 2N7, NS, Canada (100%)
Tel.: (902) 422-7483
Web Site: http://www.logistic.com
Sales Range: $25-49.9 Million
Emp.: 8
Stevedoring Services
N.A.I.C.S.: 488320

Unit (Domestic):

Logistec Stevedoring (Nova Scotia) Inc. - Sydney (4)
1139 Grand Lake Road, Sydney, B1M 1A2, NS, Canada
Tel.: (902) 563-4460
Cargo Handling Services
N.A.I.C.S.: 488320

Subsidiary (Domestic):

Logistec Stevedoring (Ontario) Inc. (3)
100 Main St Ste 360, Thunder Bay, B7B 6R9, ON, Canada (100%)
Tel.: (807) 344-1393
Sales Range: $25-49.9 Million
Emp.: 2
Stevedoring Services
N.A.I.C.S.: 488320
Vaso Popovic (Mgr-Ops)

Unit (Domestic):

Logistec Stevedoring Inc. - Churchill (3)
PO Box 307, Churchill, MB, Canada
Tel.: (204) 675-2414
Web Site: http://www.logistec.com
Sales Range: $25-49.9 Million
Emp.: 2
Stevedoring Services
N.A.I.C.S.: 488320

Logistec Stevedoring Inc. - Contrecoeur (3)
1920 Marie-Victorin Road, Contrecoeur, J0L 1C0, QC, Canada
Tel.: (450) 587-2073
Web Site: http://www.logistec.com
Sales Range: $25-49.9 Million
Emp.: 45
Stevedoring Services
N.A.I.C.S.: 488320

Logistec Stevedoring Inc. - Montreal, Laurier Terminal (3)
360 St Jacques Street Suite 1500, Montreal, H2Y 1P5, QC, Canada
Tel.: (514) 844-9381
Web Site: http://www.logistec.com
Sales Range: $25-49.9 Million
Stevedoring Services
N.A.I.C.S.: 488320

Logistec Stevedoring Inc. - Quebec (3)
2 rue Nouvelle France, Quebec, G1K 8P7, QC, Canada
Tel.: (418) 522-7161
Web Site: http://www.logistec.com
Sales Range: $25-49.9 Million
Emp.: 2
Stevedoring Services
N.A.I.C.S.: 488320

Logistec Stevedoring Inc. - Sept-Iles (3)
400 Chemin De La Pointe Noire Ct 149, Sept-Iles, G4R 5C7, QC, Canada
Tel.: (418) 962-7638
Web Site: http://www.logistec.com
Sales Range: $1-9.9 Million
Emp.: 6
Stevedoring Services
N.A.I.C.S.: 488320

Logistec Stevedoring Inc. - Trois-Rivieres (3)
2075 Notre Dame Centre, Trois Rivieres,

G9A 4Y7, QC, Canada
Tel.: (819) 379-0811
Web Site: http://www.logistec.com
Sales Range: $1-9.9 Million
Emp.: 5
Stevedoring Services
N.A.I.C.S.: 488320

Affiliate (Domestic):

Termont Montreal Inc. (3)
Section 68 Port de Montreal, Montreal, H1N 3K9, QC, Canada (100%)
Tel.: (514) 254-0526
Web Site: http://www.termont.com
Sales Range: $25-49.9 Million
Emp.: 30
Stevedoring Services
N.A.I.C.S.: 488320
Julien Dubreuil (Gen Mgr)
Emeric Doutriaux (Mgr-IT & Project)

Subsidiary (US):

Logistec USA Inc. (2)
225 Newcastle St, Brunswick, GA 31520-8571
Tel.: (912) 264-4044
Web Site: http://www.logistec.com
Sales Range: $25-49.9 Million
Emp.: 30
Multi-Purpose Terminal; Cargo Handling
N.A.I.C.S.: 488320

Subsidiary (Domestic):

BalTerm, L.L.P. (3)
2001 E McComas St, Baltimore, MD 21230
Tel.: (410) 752-9981
Web Site: https://www.balterm.com
Magazine & Tissue Paper Mfr
N.A.I.C.S.: 322299
Morgan Bailey (Pres)
Ron Cooper (Gen Mgr-Terminal Ops)

CrossGlobe Transport, Ltd. (3)
2500-D Warwick Blvd, Newport News, VA 23607 (100%)
Tel.: (804) 412-4518
Web Site: http://www.crossglobegroup.com
Sales Range: $10-24.9 Million
Emp.: 20
Marine Cargo Handling & Port Logistics Services
N.A.I.C.S.: 488320

Subsidiary (Domestic):

CrossGlobe Distribution Services, Inc. (4)
2500-D Warwick Blvd, Newport News, VA 23607
Tel.: (757) 244-8169
Web Site: http://www.crossglobegroup.com
Warehousing & Distribution Services
N.A.I.C.S.: 493110

CrossGlobe Express, LLC (4)
2500-D Warwick Blvd, Newport News, VA 23607
Tel.: (757) 244-8169
Web Site: http://www.crossglobegroup.com
Drayage & Asset-Based Transportation & Logistics Services
N.A.I.C.S.: 541614

Subsidiary (Domestic):

Gulf Stream Marine Inc. (3)
10000 Manchester St Ste C, Houston, TX 77012-2412
Tel.: (713) 926-7611
Web Site: https://www.gulfstreammarine.com
Marine Cargo Handling & Loading
N.A.I.C.S.: 488320
Tony Jaworski (Reg VP)
Shelby Herrera (VP-HR)
Michel Miron (Exec VP)
Wojciech Rutkowski (Reg VP)
Rocky Picard (Reg Controller)
Tim Kulcsar (Gen Mgr-Manchester Terminal)
Alex Montoya (Gen Mgr-Freeport Terminal)
Robert McNew (Mgr-Cedar Port Terminal)
Lynn Loftis (Gen Mgr-Corpus Christi Terminal)
David Harrington (Gen Mgr-South Central Terminal)
Ricardo Quiroga (Gen Mgr-Brownsville Terminal)

Unit (Domestic):

Logistec USA Inc. - Port Manatee (3)
Port Manatee 300 Tampa Bay Way Ste 2, Palmetto, FL 34221
Tel.: (941) 721-7209
Web Site: http://www.logistec.com
Marine Cargo Handling, Warehousing & Port Logistics Services
N.A.I.C.S.: 488320

Subsidiary (Domestic):

MtlLINK Multimodal Solutions Inc. (2)
10 000 Sherbrooke St East, East Montreal, H1B 1B4, QC, Canada
Tel.: (514) 645-6297
Web Site: https://www.mtllink.com
Logistic Services
N.A.I.C.S.: 488510
Michel Paquette (Gen Mgr)
Geoffry Lewis (Mgr-Sls & Logistics)

Ramsey Greig & Co. Ltd. (2)
2 Nouvelle France, Quebec, G1K 8T7, QC, Canada (100%)
Tel.: (418) 525-8171
Web Site: http://www.ramsey-greg.com
Sales Range: $25-49.9 Million
Emp.: 10
Mooring & Stevedoring Services
N.A.I.C.S.: 488320
Jean-Francois Bealieu (Mng Dir)

Sanexen Environmental Services Inc. (2)
9935 de Chateauneuf Street Entrance 1 Suite 200, Brossard, J4Z 3V4, QC, Canada (100%)
Tel.: (450) 466-2123
Web Site: http://www.sanexen.com
Sales Range: $150-199.9 Million
Emp.: 400
Environmental Services Specializing in Site Remediation & Water Main Rehabilitation
N.A.I.C.S.: 541620
Kevin Bourbonnais (Pres)
Madeleine Paquin (Chm)

Subsidiary (Domestic):

Niedner Inc. (3)
675 Merrill Street, Coaticook, J1A 2S2, QC, Canada
Tel.: (819) 849-2751
Web Site: http://www.niedner.com
Sales Range: $75-99.9 Million
Emp.: 140
Fire Hose & Water Main Liner Mfr
N.A.I.C.S.: 326220

Branch (Domestic):

Sanexen Environmental Services Inc. - Toronto (3)
Bldg 52 Marine Terminal 8 Unwind Ave, Toronto, M5A 1A1, ON, Canada
Tel.: (416) 622-5011
Web Site: http://www.sanexen.com
Sales Range: $25-49.9 Million
Emp.: 2
Environmental Services
N.A.I.C.S.: 541620

Subsidiary (Domestic):

Sorel Maritime Agencies Inc. (2)
201 Rue Montcalm St, Sorel, J3R 1B9, QC, Canada (100%)
Tel.: (450) 743-3585
Web Site: http://www.sorel-maritime.qc.ca
Sales Range: $50-74.9 Million
Emp.: 6
Marine Cargo Handling
N.A.I.C.S.: 488320

Sydney Coal Railway Inc. (2)
1139 Grand Lake Road, Sydney, B1M 1A2, NS, Canada
Tel.: (902) 563-8430
Sales Range: $25-49.9 Million
Emp.: 40
Warehousing & Transportation Services
N.A.I.C.S.: 493110
Robert Kazamel (Gen Mgr)

Transport Nanuk Inc. (2)
Port Of Montreal Bldg Wing No 2 St 2060,

Montreal, H3C 3R5, QC, Canada (100%)
Tel.: (514) 597-0186
Web Site: http://www.neas.ca
Sales Range: $25-49.9 Million
Emp.: 14
Navigational Services
N.A.I.C.S.: 488320
Suzanne Paquin (Pres)

National Home Health Care Corp. (1)
136 Berlin Road, Cromwell, CT 06416
Tel.: (800) 286-6300
Web Site: http://www.nhhc.net
Emp.: 7,200
Women Healthcare Services
N.A.I.C.S.: 621610
Stan Dennis (CEO)

Subsidiary (Domestic):

Accredited Health Services, Inc. (2)
235 Moore St, Hackensack, NJ 07601-4410
Tel.: (201) 342-8844
Web Site: http://www.accreditedhs.com
Home Health Agency
N.A.I.C.S.: 621610
Melissa Eschert (Pres)

Health Acquisition Corp (2)
70 00 Austin St, Forest Hills, NY 11373
Tel.: (718) 657-2966
Web Site: http://www.allenhealth.com
Women Healthcare Services
N.A.I.C.S.: 621610
Marie Andreacchio (Pres)

New England Home Care, Inc. (2)
136 Berlin Rd, Cromwell, CT 06416
Tel.: (800) 950-1004
Web Site: http://www.newenglandhomecare.com
Women Healthcare Services
N.A.I.C.S.: 621610
Kimberly Nystrom (Pres)

RHA Health Services Inc. (1)
17 Church St, Asheville, NC 28801-3303
Tel.: (828) 232-6844
Web Site: http://www.rhahealthservices.org
Sales Range: $25-49.9 Million
Emp.: 1,400
Management Services
N.A.I.C.S.: 561110
Jeanne Duncan (Pres)

Recipharm Hoganas AB (1)
Sporthallsvagen 6, 263 34, Hoganas, Sweden
Tel.: (46) 86025200
Pharmaceuticals Product Mfr
N.A.I.C.S.: 325412

Recipharm Karlskoga AB (1)
Bjorkbomsvagen 5, Box 410, 691 27, Karlskoga, Sweden
Tel.: (46) 58668200
Pharmaceuticals Product Mfr
N.A.I.C.S.: 325412

Recipharm OT Chemistry AB (1)
Virdings alle 18, 754 50, Uppsala, Sweden
Tel.: (46) 766148739
Pharmaceuticals Product Mfr
N.A.I.C.S.: 325412
Jonas Malmstrom (Project Mgr)

Recipharm Parets SL (1)
C/Ramon y Cajal 2, 08150, Parets del Valles, Spain
Tel.: (34) 934629800
Pharmaceuticals Product Mfr
N.A.I.C.S.: 325412

Recipharm Pessac S.A.S. (1)
11 Avenue Gustave Eiffel, Parc Industriel Bersol I, 33608, Pessac, Cedex, France
Tel.: (33) 557260770
Pharmaceuticals Product Mfr
N.A.I.C.S.: 325412

Recipharm Pharmaceutical Development AB (1)
Gardsvagen 10, 169 70, Solna, Sweden
Tel.: (46) 86025200
Pharmaceuticals Product Mfr
N.A.I.C.S.: 325412

Recipharm Strangnas AB (1)
Mariefredsvagen 35, 645 41, Strangnas, Sweden

Blue Wolf Capital Partners LLC—(Continued)
Tel.: (46) 86025200
Pharmaceuticals Product Mfr
N.A.I.C.S.: 325412

Standex Air Distribution Products, Inc. (1)
7601 State Rd, Philadelphia, PA 19136
Tel.: (215) 338-2850
Web Site: http://www.snappyco.com
Sales Range: $75-99.9 Million
Galvanized Metal Heating, Ventilation & Air
Conditioning Pipe & Pipe Fittings Mfr &
Distr
N.A.I.C.S.: 332996
Thomas H. Smid (Pres & COO)
Cal Douglas (VP-Ops)
George Judd (CEO)
David Hillman (CFO)
Allison Dodson (Mgr-Pur)
Valentin Sanchez (Dir-IT)

Plant (Domestic):

Standex Air Distribution Products, Inc. - Georgia (2)
3365 Florence Rd, Lithia Springs, GA 30127
Tel.: (770) 222-0788
Web Site: http://www.snappyco.com
Sales Range: $25-49.9 Million
Galvanized Metal Heating, Ventilation & Air
Conditioning Pipe & Pipe Fittings Mfr &
Distr
N.A.I.C.S.: 332996
Brad Torrey (Plant Mgr)

BLUE-GRACE LOGISTICS, LLC
2846 S Falkenburg Rd, Riverview, FL 33578-2563
Tel.: (813) 641-0357   FL
Web Site:
http://www.mybluegrace.com
Year Founded: 2009
Transportation & Logistics Services
N.A.I.C.S.: 488510
Randy Collack (Chief Strategy Officer)
Mike Dolski (CFO)
Adam Blankenship (COO)
Robert Beckmann (Gen Counsel)
Justin Belcher (CIO)
Sean Butler (Chief HR Officer)
Bobby Harris (Founder & CEO)
Mark Ford (COO-Transportation)
Carly Bly (Sr Dir-Carrier Rels)
Bryce Williford (Sr VP-3PL Svcs)

BLUE-GRASS ENERGY COOPERATIVE
1201 Lexington Rd, Nicholasville, KY 40356
Tel.: (859) 885-4191
Web Site: https://www.bgenergy.com
Sales Range: $25-49.9 Million
Emp.: 55
Electronic Services
N.A.I.C.S.: 221118
Jody Hughes (Chm)
Michael I. Williams (Pres & CEO)
Roy Honican (Coord-Residential Svcs)

BLUE-WHITE INDUSTRIES LTD
5300 Business Dr, Huntington Beach, CA 92649
Tel.: (714) 893-8529
Web Site: http://www.bluwhite.com
Year Founded: 1957
Rev.: $11,316,929
Emp.: 90
Water Meters
N.A.I.C.S.: 334514
Robin Gledhill (CEO)
David Koch (Mgr-Sls & Mktg)
Jennifer Tsuyuki (Engr-Mechanical)
Bill McDowell (VP-Ops)

BLUE1USA, LLC

3040 White Horse Rd, Greenville, SC 29611
Tel.: (864) 385-7030
Web Site:
http://www.blue1energyequip
ment.com
Diesel Exhaust Fluid Storage & Dispensing Equipment Mfr & Distr
N.A.I.C.S.: 333132

BLUEBERRY FORD MERCURY INC.
241 Dublin St, Machias, ME 04654
Tel.: (207) 255-4747
Web Site:
http://www.blueberryford.dealer
connection.com
Rev.: $14,000,000
Emp.: 15
New Car Dealers
N.A.I.C.S.: 441110
Norm Howe (Mgr-Parts)
Rachel Smith (Mgr-Fin)
Stan VanDunk (Mgr-Parts)

BLUEBIRD INTERACTIVE
1300 Valley House Dr Ste 100-27, Rohnert Park, CA 94928
Tel.: (707) 266-6686
Web Site: http://www.bluebird.io
Sales Range: $1-9.9 Million
Interactive Marketing & Consulting
N.A.I.C.S.: 541613
Mark Beyak (CFO)

BLUEBONNET ELECTRIC CO-OP, INC.
155 Electric Ave, Bastrop, TX 78602
Tel.: (512) 376-8244   TX
Web Site:
https://www.bluebonnetelectric.coop
Year Founded: 1939
Sales Range: $1-9.9 Million
Emp.: 247
Electronic Services
N.A.I.C.S.: 221122
Mark Rose (CEO & Gen Mgr)
Johnny Sanders (Mgr-Community & Economic Dev)
Elizabeth Kana (CFO)
Leslie Barrios (Mgr-IT)
Matt Bentke (COO)
Eric Kocian (Officer-Sys Ops)
Rachel Ellis (Chief Admin Officer)
Grant Gutierrez (CIO & Controller)
Sarah Newman-Altamirano (Gen Counsel)
Melissa Segrest (Mgr-Comm)
Wesley Brinkmeyer (Mgr-Energy Programs)
Jennifer Foery (Mgr-HR)
Barbara Seilheimer (Mgr-Member Svcs)
Will Holford (Mgr-Pub Affairs)

BLUEBONNET NUTRITION, CORP.
12915 Dairy Ashford Rd, Sugar Land, TX 77478
Tel.: (281) 240-3332   TX
Web Site:
http://www.bluebonnetnutrition.com
Year Founded: 1991
Sales Range: $10-24.9 Million
Emp.: 100
Natural Nutritional Supplements Mfr & Distr
N.A.I.C.S.: 325411
Gary Barrows (Founder & Pres)
R.L. Burrows (CEO)
Joyce Burrows (CFO)
Steve Burrows (VP-Production & Distr)
Chris Burrows (Dir-IT)
Mindy Burrows (Mgr-Key Accts)
Bob Barrows Jr. (VP-Sls & Mktg)

BLUECAVA, INC.
131 Innovation Dr Ste 250, Irvine, CA 92617
Tel.: (949) 483-9494
Web Site: http://www.bluecava.com
Year Founded: 2010
Computer Software Development Services
N.A.I.C.S.: 513210
Phil Myers (Chm)
Bill Varga (Chief Revenue Officer)

BLUECOTTON, INC.
250 Mitch McConnell Way, Bowling Green, KY 42101
Tel.: (270) 796-8801   KY
Web Site:
https://www.bluecotton.com
Year Founded: 1998
Rev.: $3,500,000
Emp.: 37
Custom Screen Printing Services
N.A.I.C.S.: 323113
Tom Dolan (Mgr-Product)
Michael Coffey (Founder & CEO)
Warren Guyer (CFO)
Brad Wayland (VP-Bus Dev)

BLUECREST CAPITAL FINANCE CORP.
225 W Washington St 2nd Fl, Chicago, IL 60606
Tel.: (312) 368-4970
Investment Services
N.A.I.C.S.: 523999
William DeMars (Chm, Pres, CEO & Sec)
Robert Nagy (Chief Compliance Officer)

BLUEDOT COMMUNICATIONS
2174 NW Aspen Ave, Portland, OR 97210
Tel.: (503) 702-6811
Web Site: http://www.gobluedot.com
Sales Range: Less than $1 Million
Emp.: 3
N.A.I.C.S.: 541810
John Mazzocco (Principal)

BLUEDOT MEDICAL, INC.
10345 Nations Ford Rd Ste A, Charlotte, NC 28273
Tel.: (704) 344-0700
Web Site: http://www.bluedotmed.net
Year Founded: 2002
Sales Range: $1-9.9 Million
Emp.: 30
Medical & Mobility Equipment for the Healthcare Industries
N.A.I.C.S.: 339112
Jimmy Clonaris (VP-Supply)
Tri Smith (VP)
Kevin Bilderback (Owner)

BLUEFIN PAYMENT SYSTEMS
1050 Crown Pointe Parkway Suite 720, Atlanta, GA 30338
Tel.: (678) 894-2638
Web Site: http://www.bluefin.com
Year Founded: 2007
Sales Range: $50-74.9 Million
Emp.: 30
Customized & Secure Payment Services
N.A.I.C.S.: 525990
John M. Perry (CEO)
Ruston Miles (Chief Innovation Officer)
Patrick Burke (COO)
Tim Barnett (CIO)
Ron Rois (VP-Ops)
Jeannine Gates (VP-New Acct Ops)

Stephanie Myers (VP-Relationship Mgmt)
Huib Dekker (CFO)
Philip M. Dolan (Chief Mktg Officer)

BLUEFIN SEAFOOD CORP
617 E Washington St, Louisville, KY 40202
Tel.: (502) 587-1505
Web Site:
http://www.bluefinseafood.com
Sales Range: $10-24.9 Million
Emp.: 35
Fish & Seafoods
N.A.I.C.S.: 424460
Ken Berry (Pres)

BLUEFIRE EQUIPMENT CORP.
1113 Vine St Ste 125, Houston, TX 77002   DE
Web Site:
http://www.bluefireequipment.com
Year Founded: 2008
Sales Range: Less than $1 Million
Emp.: 1
Oilfield Equipment
N.A.I.C.S.: 333132
William Blackwell (Chm, CEO & CFO)
Anatoli Borissov (Pres & COO)

BLUEGLASS INTERACTIVE, INC.
4343 Anchor Plaza Pkwy Ste 230, Tampa, FL 33634
Tel.: (813) 487-9900
Web Site: http://www.blueglass.com
Sales Range: $10-24.9 Million
Emp.: 85
Digital Marketing Services
N.A.I.C.S.: 541890
Michael Bonfils (VP-Global Markets)

Subsidiaries:

BlueGlass Interactive AG (1)
Tellstrasse 31, CH-8004, Zurich, Switzerland
Tel.: (41) 44 542 00 00
Digital Marketing Services
N.A.I.C.S.: 541810

BlueGlass Interactive UK Ltd. (1)
45 Leather Lane, London, EC1N 7TJ, United Kingdom
Tel.: (44) 207 242 0142
Web Site: http://www.blueglass.co.uk
Digital Marketing Services
N.A.I.C.S.: 541890
Chelsea Blacker (Dir-Digital Acct)
Kevin Gibbons (Founder & CEO)
Irma Hunkeler (Head-Content)
Clarissa Sajbl (Mgr-Mktg & Bus Dev)
Claudia Donia (Project Mgr)
Joey Peters (Head-Paid Media)
Ben Hitchens (Dir-Performance)
David Iwanow (Dir-Strategy)

BLUEGRASS SUPPLY CHAIN SERVICES
350 Scottys Way, Bowling Green, KY 42101
Tel.: (270) 282-2211
Web Site: http://www.bluegrass-
scs.com
Year Founded: 2004
Sales Range: $10-24.9 Million
Emp.: 137
Product Delivery & Transportation Services
N.A.I.C.S.: 492110
John Higgins (Pres)

BLUEGRASS TOOL WAREHOUSE INC.
2433 Fortune Dr, Lexington, KY 40509
Tel.: (859) 281-6146

Web Site:
http://www.jiffyfastening.com
Sales Range: $10-24.9 Million
Emp.: 33
Distr of Power Handtools
N.A.I.C.S.: 423710
Barry Miller *(Mgr-Pur)*

BLUEGRASS.ORG, INC.

1351 Newtown Pike Bldg 1, Lexington, KY 40511-1217
Tel.: (859) 253-1686   KY
Web Site: http://www.bluegrass.org
Year Founded: 1965
Sales Range: $150-199.9 Million
Emp.: 2,156
Intellectual & Developmental Health
Care Services
N.A.I.C.S.: 623210
Steve Garrison *(Dir-Facilities, Pur & Environmental Safety)*
Christopher Whitsell *(Dir-Children's Svcs)*
Scott Gould *(Treas)*
Constance Morgan *(Sec)*
Peggy Tudor *(Chm)*
Lora Adams *(Officer-Corp Compliance & Privacy)*
Don Rogers *(Chief Clinical Officer)*
Della Tuttle *(Chief IDD Officer)*
Dana Royse *(CFO)*
Nathan Millay *(Controller-Fin)*
Kent Miller *(Mgr-HR)*
Crystal Meece *(Office Mgr)*
Paul R. Beatrice *(Pres & CEO)*
Cory McGlone *(Dir-IT)*
Bethany Langdon *(Dir-Mktg & Comm)*
Sarah Bell *(Reg Dir-Intellectual & Dev Disabilities Ops)*
Melissa Hill *(Office Mgr)*
Nina Begley *(Dir-Children's Review Program)*
Don Putnam *(Vice Chm)*

BLUEGROUND US INC

106 W 32nd St., New York, NY 10001
Tel.: (917) 259-1222
Web Site:
https://www.theblueground.com
Year Founded: 2013
Real Estate
N.A.I.C.S.: 531390
Aneesa Arshad *(CEO)*
Alex Chatzieleftheriou *(Co-Founder & CEO)*

Subsidiaries:

Travelers Haven, LLC   (1)
950 S Cherry St Ste 1000, Denver, CO 80246
Tel.: (720) 833-5333
Web Site: http://www.mytravelershaven.com
Sales Range: $10-24.9 Million
Emp.: 18
Affordable, Quality Corporate & Temporary
Housing Solutions
N.A.I.C.S.: 531190
Jordan Epstein *(Sr Acct Mgr)*
Troy Shaffer *(VP-Acct Mgmt)*
Carlos Abisambra *(Chief Strategy Officer)*
Daniel Jagd *(VP-Strategic Rels)*
Ellis Hugunin *(VP-Ops)*
Jay Triplett *(VP-Sls)*
Mike Scarborough *(CTO)*

BLUEJAY CAPITAL PARTNERS, LLC

1909 3rd St N, Jacksonville Beach, FL 32250
Tel.: (904) 571-3609
Web Site: https://bluejay-capital.com
Logistics & Transportation Services
N.A.I.C.S.: 488999
Josh Putterman *(Founding Partner)*

Subsidiaries:

Best Warehousing & Transportation
Center Inc.   (1)

125 Villanova Dr SW Ste B, Atlanta, GA 30336
Tel.: (404) 344-1121
Web Site: http://www.bestwtc.com
Farm Product Warehousing & Storage
N.A.I.C.S.: 493130
Howard Shope *(Sr VP)*
Winston McDonald Jr. *(Pres & CEO)*

Subsidiary (Domestic):

International Express Trucking,
Inc.   (2)
4901 Larkmoore Ct, Charlotte, NC 28208
Tel.: (704) 424-5454
Web Site: https://intexpr.com
Rev.: $1,500,000
Emp.: 24
General Freight Trucking, Local
N.A.I.C.S.: 484110

BLUELINE

25 Central Way Ste 400, Kirkland, WA 98033
Tel.: (425) 216-4051
Web Site:
https://www.thebluelinegroup.com
Year Founded: 2003
Sales Range: $1-9.9 Million
Emp.: 24
Civil Engineering Services
N.A.I.C.S.: 541330
Brian J. Darrow *(Co-Founder, Pres & Principal)*
Geoff Tamble *(Co-Founder & Principal)*
Todd Oberg *(Co-Founder & Principal)*
Ken Lauzen *(Principal)*

BLUELINE PARTNERS, LLC

3480 Buskirk Ave Ste 214, Pleasant Hill, CA 94523
Tel.: (925) 236-9790   CA
Web Site:
http://www.bluelinepartners.com
Year Founded: 2002
Sales Range: $25-49.9 Million
Emp.: 10
Privater Equity Firm
N.A.I.C.S.: 523999
Bob Rebitz *(Partner)*
Scott A. Shuda *(Mng Dir)*

BLUEPEAK TECHNOLOGY SOLUTIONS, LLC

3631 Warren Way Ste A, Reno, NV 89509
Tel.: (775) 284-7100
Web Site: http://www.bluepeak.io
Year Founded: 2008
Sales Range: $1-9.9 Million
Emp.: 5
Information Technology Services
N.A.I.C.S.: 541512
Brian Gifford *(Pres)*

BLUEPEARL VETERINARY PARTNERS LLC

3000 Busch Lake Blvd, Tampa, FL 33614
Tel.: (813) 933-8944
Web Site:
https://www.bluepearlvet.com
Year Founded: 1996
Sales Range: $100-124.9 Million
Emp.: 1,350
Veterinary Services
N.A.I.C.S.: 541940
Darryl Shaw *(Co-Founder & CEO)*
Jennifer Welser *(Chm & Chief Medical Officer)*
Angela Calderone *(VP-People & Organization)*

BLUEPOINT DATA, INC.

791 Park of Commerce Blvd Ste 200, Boca Raton, FL 33487
Tel.: (561) 417-0324

Web Site:
http://www.bluepointdata.com
Year Founded: 2000
Sales Range: $1-9.9 Million
Emp.: 20
Data Processing, Hosting & Related Services
N.A.I.C.S.: 518210
Vance Kistler *(CFO & Corp Sec)*
Edwin Hernandez *(Sr VP-Managed Svc & Chief Architect)*
Dale Borchardt *(VP-Customer Svc & Mgr-Cloud Svc)*

BLUEPRINT HEALTH MERGER CORP.

200 Exchange St, Providence, RI 02903
Tel.: (347) 687-6360   DE
Year Founded: 2021
Investment Services
N.A.I.C.S.: 523999
Rajiv Kumar *(CEO)*
Mathew Farkash *(Pres)*
Brad Weinberg *(CFO & COO)*
Richard J. Harrington *(Chm)*

BLUEPRINT VENTURES, LLC

201 Post St 11Fl Ste 1140, San Francisco, CA 94108
Tel.: (415) 901-4000
Web Site:
http://www.blueprintventures.com
Year Founded: 1999
Sales Range: $25-49.9 Million
Emp.: 11
Privater Equity Firm
N.A.I.C.S.: 523999
Jim Huston *(Mng Dir)*

BLUEROCK ENERGY, INC.

432 N Franklin St Ste 20, Syracuse, NY 13204
Tel.: (315) 701-1549
Web Site:
http://www.bluerockenergy.com
Year Founded: 2006
Sales Range: $25-49.9 Million
Emp.: 31
Electric Power & Natural Gas Distribution Services
N.A.I.C.S.: 221122
Jon M. Gipson *(COO)*
Jerry Schavone *(Dir-Bus Dev)*
Jim Nichols *(Dir-Wholesale Ops)*
Jon Collins *(Mgr-Risk)*
Tammy Maule *(Dir-Customer Admin)*
Jason Starzyk *(Dir-Sls Ops)*
Wendy DeFazio *(Dir-Sls & Comm)*
Jason Klaben *(CFO & VP)*
Phil Van Horne *(Pres & CEO)*
Michael Francis *(Gen Mgr-Solar Div)*

BLUERUN VENTURES

545 Middlefield Rd Ste 250, Menlo Park, CA 94025
Tel.: (650) 462-7250
Web Site: https://www.brv.com
Sales Range: $25-49.9 Million
Emp.: 15
Privater Equity Firm
N.A.I.C.S.: 523999
John Malloy *(Gen Partner)*
Jonathan Ebinger *(Gen Partner)*
Kwan Yoon *(Gen Partner)*
Jeff Tannenbaum *(Principal)*
Cheryl Cheng *(Partner)*

Subsidiaries:

AppCentral, Inc.   (1)
575 Florida St #125, San Francisco, CA 94110
Tel.: (415) 513-5428
Web Site: http://www.appcentral.com
Mobile Applications
N.A.I.C.S.: 513210
Spencer Shearer *(VP-Svcs)*

BLUESKY RESOURCE SOLUTIONS, LLC

1010 Huntcliff Ste 1250, Atlanta, GA 30350
Tel.: (470) 395-7359
Web Site: http://www.blueskyrs.com
Year Founded: 2013
Sales Range: $1-9.9 Million
Emp.: 98
Recruitment Consulting Services
N.A.I.C.S.: 541612
Christian Dominick *(Pres)*

BLUESNAP, INC.

800 South St Ste 640, Waltham, MA 02453
Tel.: (781) 790-5013   CA
Web Site: https://www.bluesnap.com
Year Founded: 2002
Emp.: 110
eCommerce Programming Services
N.A.I.C.S.: 541511
Bill Sobo *(CFO)*
Ralph Dangelmaier *(CEO)*
Manny Pansa *(Sr VP-Support & Acct Mgmt)*
Jeff Coppolo *(Sr VP-Bus Dev)*
Susan Madden *(Sr VP-Bus Ops)*
Faouzi Kassab *(Sr VP-Engrg)*
Peter Caparso *(Chief Comml Officer)*
Meir Gefen *(Gen Mgr)*
Paul Savage *(Sr VP-Sls)*
Scott Fitzgerald *(Sr VP-Mktg)*
Terry Monteith *(Sr VP-Payments)*
Brad Hyett *(Mng Dir-Europe)*
Michael Misasi *(Dir-Integrated Partnerships)*

BLUESPHERE ADVISORS LLC

2108 Dekalb Pike, East Norriton, PA 19401
Tel.: (610) 277-1515
Web Site:
http://www.bluesphereadvisors.com
Financial Planning & Consultation Services
N.A.I.C.S.: 523940
Sanjay K. Pawar *(Pres & CEO)*

Subsidiaries:

Empowering Financial Solutions,
Inc.   (1)
3591 Sacramento Dr Ste 120, San Luis Obispo, CA 93401-7258
Tel.: (805) 541-5105
Web Site: http://www.empoweringfinancial
solutions.com
Investment Advice
N.A.I.C.S.: 523940

BLUESQUARE RESOLUTIONS, LLC.

14500 N Blvd 200, Scottsdale, AZ 85260
Tel.: (602) 732-4405
Web Site:
http://www.getbluesquare.com
Year Founded: 2009
Sales Range: $10-24.9 Million
Emp.: 14
Financial Payment Services
N.A.I.C.S.: 522320
Sabin Burrell *(Owner)*

BLUESTAR ALLIANCE LLC

240 Madison Ave Ste 1500, New York, NY 10016
Tel.: (212) 290-1370   NY
Web Site:
http://www.bluestaralliance.com
Year Founded: 2007
Sales Range: $100-124.9 Million
Emp.: 50
Brand Management & Investment Holding Company
N.A.I.C.S.: 551112

Bluestar Alliance LLC—(Continued)

Joseph Gabbay *(CEO)*
Ralph Gindi *(COO)*

Subsidiaries:

Brookstone Company, Inc. **(1)**
1 Innovation Way, Merrimack, NH 03054-4873
Tel.: (603) 880-9500
Web Site: http://www.brookstone.com
Sales Range: $450-499.9 Million
Emp.: 1,214
Specialty Products Retailer
N.A.I.C.S.: 459420
Stephen A. Gould *(VP & Gen Counsel)*
Steven H. Schwartz *(Chief Mdsg Officer)*
Piau Phang Foo *(Chm)*
Valen Tong *(CFO & VP)*
Jim Ferguson *(Sr VP-Retail)*
Frank Hu *(VP-Ops)*
Scott Schultz *(VP-Ecommerce)*
Steven Goldsmith *(Pres & CEO)*
Kenneth Boremi *(VP-Retail)*

Hurley International LLC **(1)**
1945 G Placentia Ave, Costa Mesa, CA 92627
Tel.: (949) 548-9375
Sales Range: $200-249.9 Million
Emp.: 200
Clothing Mfr
N.A.I.C.S.: 315250

Subsidiary (Non-US):

Hurley Australia Pty. Ltd. **(2)**
Unit 5 16222 Cross Street, Brookvale, Manly, 2100, Australia
Tel.: (61) 289667500
Web Site: http://www.hurley.com
Emp.: 20
Sporting Goods Mfr
N.A.I.C.S.: 339920
Jason Amg *(Gen Mgr)*

Liz Lange **(1)**
c/o The Cherokee Group 5990 Sepulveda Blvd Suite 600, Sherman Oaks, CA 91411
Tel.: (818) 908-9868
Web Site: http://www.lizlange.com
Sales Range: $25-49.9 Million
Emp.: 30
Maternity & Baby Clothing Retailer
N.A.I.C.S.: 458110

Scotch & Soda B.V. **(1)**
Keizersgracht 22, 1015 CR, Amsterdam, Netherlands
Tel.: (31) 205141060
Web Site: http://www.scotch-soda.com
Clothing Store Operator
N.A.I.C.S.: 458110
Ari Hoffman *(CEO-US)*
Geert Van Iwaarden *(CFO)*
Frederick Lukoff *(CEO)*

BLUESTAR INDUSTRIES, LLC
3801 Watman Ave, Memphis, TN 38118
Tel.: (901) 365-8767　　　　**TN**
Web Site: http://www.bluestar-ind.com
Year Founded: 1964
Sales Range: $10-24.9 Million
Emp.: 20
Pneumatic Tools & Equipment Distr
N.A.I.C.S.: 423830

BLUESTAR MARKETING, INC.
915 Jenkintown Rd, Elkins Park, PA 19027-1633
Tel.: (215) 886-4002
Web Site:
　https://www.betterbybluestar.com
Sales Range: $10-24.9 Million
Emp.: 5
Promotional Products Distr
N.A.I.C.S.: 541870
Fran Sheppard *(Dir-Sls)*
Hal Sheppard *(Pres)*

BLUESTEM BRANDS, INC.

6509 Flying Cloud Dr, Eden Prairie, MN 55344
Tel.:
　http://www.bluestembrands.com　　**DE**
Web Site:
　http://www.bluestembrands.com
Sales Range: $1-4.9 Billion
Emp.: 3,900
General Merchandise Retailer, E-commerce & Catalog Mail Order
N.A.I.C.S.: 455219
Chidambaram A. Chidambaram *(Chief Revenue Officer & Exec VP)*
Mark P. Wagener *(CFO & Exec VP)*
Erica C. Street *(Chief Legal Officer & Exec VP)*
Vince Jones *(COO, Chief Digital Officer & Exec VP)*
Shawn Moren *(Sr VP-HR)*
Jim Slavik *(Pres-Credit Svcs & Exec VP)*

Subsidiaries:

Appleseed's, Inc. **(1)**
35 Vlg Rd, Middleton, MA 01949
Tel.: (800) 546-4554
Web Site: http://www.appleseeds.com
Women's Apparel Retailer
N.A.I.C.S.: 458110
Wendy Gamache *(VP-Mktg)*

Blair, LLC **(1)**
220 Hickory St, Warren, PA 16366
Tel.: (800) 821-5744
Web Site: http://www.blair.com
Men & Women's Apparel Retailer
N.A.I.C.S.: 458110

Drapers & Damons, LLC **(1)**
9 Pasteur Ste 200, Irvine, CA 92628
Tel.: (800) 843-1174
Web Site: http://drapers.blair.com
Women's Clothing Retailer; Catalog & Mail-Order Services
N.A.I.C.S.: 458110

Norm Thompson Outfitters Inc. **(1)**
3188 NW Aloclek Dr, Hillsboro, OR 97124
Tel.: (877) 718-7899
Web Site:
　http://www.normthompson.blair.com
Men & Women's Apparel Retailer; Catalog & Mail-Order Services
N.A.I.C.S.: 424350

The Tog Shop **(1)**
PO Box 126, Jessup, PA 18434
Tel.: (877) 718-7902
Web Site: http://togshop.blair.com
Women's Apparel Catalog & On-Line Retailer
N.A.I.C.S.: 458110

BLUESTEM EQUITY, LTD.
12800 NW Fwy, Houston, TX 77040
Tel.: (713) 452-7616　　　　**TX**
Web Site:
　https://www.bluestemequity.com
Year Founded: 2021
Privater Equity Firm
N.A.I.C.S.: 523999
Todd Fisk *(Mng Partner)*

Subsidiaries:

Ditch Witch of South Texas **(1)**
337 Flato Rd, Corpus Christi, TX 78405
Tel.: (361) 400-2507
Web Site: https://dwsouthtexas.com
Industrial Machinery & Equipment Merchant Whslr
N.A.I.C.S.: 423830

Subsidiary (Domestic):

Ditch Witch of Houston **(2)**
6807 W Little York, Houston, TX 77040-4807
Tel.: (713) 462-8866
Web Site: http://www.dwhouston.com
Construction & Mining Machinery Distr
N.A.I.C.S.: 423810
Mike Craig *(VP)*

BLUESTEM FARM & RANCH SUPPLY, INC.

2611 W Hwy 50, Emporia, KS 66801
Tel.: (620) 342-5502
Web Site:
　https://www.bluestemfarmranch.com
Year Founded: 1961
Rev.: $13,600,000
Emp.: 60
Hardware & Home Improvement Supply Whslr
N.A.I.C.S.: 423620
Kenneth Bruner *(Pres)*

BLUESTONE INVESTMENT PARTNERS, LLC
7900 Westpark Dr Ste T405, McLean, VA 22102
Tel.: (703) 462-5600
Web Site:
　http://www.bluestoneinv.com
Privater Equity Firm
N.A.I.C.S.: 523999
Kevin M. Phillips *(Partner)*
John Allen *(Co-Founder & Mng Partner)*
Bill Strang *(Co-Founder & Mng Partner)*
Mike Ivey *(Mng Dir)*

Subsidiaries:

Chesapeake Technology International Corp. **(1)**
44427 Airport Rd Ste 100, California, MD 20619-2011
Tel.: (301) 862-2726
Web Site:
　http://www.chesapeaketechnology.com
Custom Computer Programming Services
N.A.I.C.S.: 541511
Mike Kepferle *(Pres)*

Continental Mapping Consultants, Inc. **(1)**
100 QBE Way Ste 1225, Sun Prairie, WI 53590
Tel.: (608) 834-9823
Web Site:
　http://www.continentalmapping.com
Rev.: $1,738,000
Emp.: 11
Engineering Services
N.A.I.C.S.: 541330
David Hart *(CEO)*
Andy Dougherty *(Pres)*

Subsidiary (Domestic):

Geographic Information Services, Inc. **(2)**
216 Aquarius Dr Ste 312, Birmingham, AL 35209
Tel.: (205) 941-0442
Web Site: http://www.gisinc.com
Sales Range: $1-9.9 Million
Emp.: 30
Prepackaged Software
N.A.I.C.S.: 513210
Dan Levine *(CTO & Program Mgr-Range)*
Jeff Vreeland *(Mgr-Mktg)*
Brad Epker *(Chief Revenue Officer)*
Dale Dunham *(Founder & Chm)*

TSG Solutions, Inc. **(2)**
2701 Loker Ave W Ste 100, Carlsbad, CA 92010
Tel.: (760) 827-7087
Web Site: https://www.aximgeo.com
Sales Range: $25-49.9 Million
Computer Technology Development Services
N.A.I.C.S.: 541511

DCS Consulting, Inc. **(1)**
9435 Lorton Market St Ste 720, Lorton, VA 22079-3474
Tel.: (703) 690-5730
Web Site: http://www.cbeyondata.com
Custom Computer Programming Services
N.A.I.C.S.: 541511
Dyson Richards *(CEO)*
David Schmidtknecht *(Co-Founder & Chief Solutions Officer)*

Subsidiary (Domestic):

Alta Via Consulting, LLC **(2)**

525 Tanasi Cir, Loudon, TN 37774
Tel.: (708) 448-4059
Web Site: http://www.altavia.com
Custom Computer Programming Services
N.A.I.C.S.: 541511
Christopher Jackiw *(Principal)*
Dawn Sedgley *(Principal)*
Anton Van Der Merwe *(Principal)*

Summit2Sea Consulting, LLC **(2)**
6222 21st St N, Arlington, VA 22205-2037
Tel.: (703) 582-3665
Web Site: http://www.sum2sea.com
Custom Computer Programming Services
N.A.I.C.S.: 541511
Bryan Eckle *(Pres)*

BLUESTONE PARTNERS LLC
4708 N FM 1417, Sherman, TX 75092-6602
Tel.: (903) 813-1415
Web Site: http://www.bluestone.com
Single-Family Housing
N.A.I.C.S.: 236115
Kyle Boothe *(Owner)*

BLUEWARE, INC.
1825 Riverview Dr, Melbourne, FL 32901
Tel.: (321) 953-5999
Web Site: http://www.blueware.us
Year Founded: 1993
Sales Range: $1-9.9 Million
Emp.: 31
Software Publisher
N.A.I.C.S.: 513210
Rose Harr *(Pres & CEO)*

BLUEWATER DEFENSE, INC.
BO Cibuco Rd 159 Km 13 5 Corozal Industrial Zone, Corozal, PR 00783
Tel.: (787) 746-5020
Web Site:
　https://www.bluewaterdefense.com
Sales Range: $25-49.9 Million
Emp.: 400
Deployment Ready Tactical Gear Mfr
N.A.I.C.S.: 314910
Eric Sparky *(Pres)*

BLUEWATER MEDIA LLC
14375 Myerlake Cir, Clearwater, FL 33760
Tel.: (813) 944-2926
Web Site:
　http://www.bluewatermedia.tv
Year Founded: 2000
Emp.: 50
Branded Direct Response, Brand Integration & Advertising
N.A.I.C.S.: 541890
Andy Latimer *(Founder & CEO)*
Mark Henning *(Partner & Dir-Post Production)*
Gina Pomponi *(COO)*
Michael Weinstein *(Pres-Digital Div)*
Beth Rugg *(CFO)*
Colleen Ferrier *(Chief Mktg Officer)*
Dave Shimkus *(Dir-Bus Dev)*
Adam Warfield *(VP-Sls & Strategic Partnerships)*
Loralie Parrish *(VP-Mktg)*
Rob Fallon *(CEO)*

Subsidiaries:

DNA Response, Inc. **(1)**
411 1st Ave S Ste 205, Seattle, WA 98104　　　　　　　　　**(100%)**
Tel.: (206) 995-8080
Web Site: http://www.dnaresponse.com
Online Commerce Solutions
N.A.I.C.S.: 519290

BLUEWATER TECHNOLOGIES INC.
24050 Northwestern Hwy, Southfield, MI 48075
Tel.: (248) 356-4399

Web Site:
http://www.bluewatertech.com
Year Founded: 1985
Sales Range: $50-74.9 Million
Emp.: 142
Audio & Visual Equipment Rental &
Video Conferencing Services
N.A.I.C.S.: 532490
Tom Battaglia (CEO)
Kim Hale (Dir-Mktg)
Bob Marsh (Exec VP)
Braden Graham (VP-Client Svcs-
Grand Rapids)

BLUEWATER TRADING INC.
8633 Ellard Dr, Alpharetta, GA 30022
Tel.: (770) 642-5458
Sales Range: $10-24.9 Million
Emp.: 3
General Merchandise
N.A.I.C.S.: 424990
Dan Alford (Pres)

BLUEWAVE COMPUTING LLC
2251 Corporate Pl Pkwy, Smyrna,
GA 30080
Tel.: (770) 980-9283
Web Site: http://www.bluewave-
computing.com
Year Founded: 1997
Sales Range: $1-9.9 Million
Emp.: 120
Custom Computer Programming Ser-
vices
N.A.I.C.S.: 541511
Steve Vicinanaza (Founder & CEO)
Todd Merry (Dir-Sls)
Cathy Pruett (Acct Mgr)
Joel Hardee (Engr-Sys-II)
Sean Vojtasko (Exec VP)
Ben Balsley (Co-Founder & CEO)

**BLUEWAVE TECHNOLOGY
GROUP, LLC**
1719 NJ Ste 222, Parsippany, NJ
07054
Tel.: (800) 962-7752
Web Site: https://bluewave.net
Year Founded: 2021
Communication & Information Tech-
nology Solutions
N.A.I.C.S.: 541512
Seth Penland (Founder & CEO)

Subsidiaries:

J.I.L. Communications, Inc.   (1)
610 Willowhurst Pl, Louisville, KY 40223-
3367
Tel.: (502) 400-5000
Web Site: http://www.jilcommunications.com
Telecommunications
N.A.I.C.S.: 517810
Charlie Booth (Pres & CEO)

BLUEWOLF, INC.
11 E 26th St Fl 21, New York, NY
10010-1413
Tel.: (212) 308-4220
Web Site: http://www.bluewolf.com
Year Founded: 2000
Sales Range: $25-49.9 Million
Emp.: 350
Software Publisher, Computer Con-
sulting & IT Staffing
N.A.I.C.S.: 513210
Eric Berridge (Co-Founder & CEO)
Michael Kirven (Co-Founder)
Corinne Sklar (VP-Mktg)
Mark Loveless (Sr Dir-Sls)
Shane Sarty (Mng Dir-Enterprise
Acct)
Shane Sugino (Dir-Higher Education)

Subsidiaries:

Bluewolf UK   (1)
1 Poultry, London, EC2R 8JR, United Kingdom

Tel.: (44) 207 643 2749
Emp.: 45
Software Publisher, Computer Consulting &
IT Staffing
N.A.I.C.S.: 513210

BLUFF CITY BEER COMPANY
450R Siemers Dr, Cape Girardeau,
MO 63701
Tel.: (573) 651-6228
Web Site:
http://www.bluffcitybeer.com
Sales Range: $10-24.9 Million
Emp.: 14
Beer & Other Fermented Malt Liquors
N.A.I.C.S.: 424810
Doug Sanders (Mgr-Sls)

**BLUFF CITY DISTRIBUTING
CO., INC.**
3339 Fontaine Rd, Memphis, TN
38116-3503
Tel.: (901) 345-9500   TN
Web Site:
https://bluffcityelectronicsinc.com
Year Founded: 1938
Sales Range: $75-99.9 Million
Emp.: 83
Whslr of Electronic Parts & Entertain-
ment Products
N.A.I.C.S.: 423690
Alfred L. Cowles III (Pres & CFO)

BLUFF EQUIPMENT, INC.
290 US Hwy 40, Vandalia, IL 62471
Tel.: (618) 283-3277   IL
Web Site:
http://www.bluffequipment.net
Year Founded: 1949
Sales Range: $10-24.9 Million
Emp.: 22
Tractor & Other Farm Equipment
Dealer
N.A.I.C.S.: 423820
John Britt (Pres)
Lisa Lange (Mgr-Receivables)

**BLUFF POINT ASSOCIATES
CORP.**
274 Riverside Ave, Westport, CT
06880-4823
Tel.: (203) 557-9450   DE
Web Site: http://www.bluffpt.com
Emp.: 10
Privater Equity Firm
N.A.I.C.S.: 523999
Neil Q. Gabriele (Mng Dir)
John P. Gilliam (Mng Dir)
Thomas E. McInerney (Co-Founder &
CEO)
Paula G. McInerney (Co-Founder &
Pres)
Kevin P. Fahey (Mng Dir)
John L. McInerney (Mng Dir)
Erin Letizia (Office Mgr)

**BLUM CAPITAL PARTNERS,
L.P.**
909 Montgomery St, San Francisco,
CA 94133-4625
Tel.: (415) 434-1111   CA
Web Site:
https://www.blumcapital.com
Year Founded: 1975
Sales Range: $25-49.9 Million
Emp.: 55
Privater Equity Firm
N.A.I.C.S.: 523999
Murray J. McCabe (Mng Partner)
Verett A. Mims (CFO)

Subsidiaries:

Suntron Corporation   (1)
2401 W Grandview Rd, Phoenix, AZ 85023-
3112
Tel.: (602) 282-5059
Web Site: http://www.suntroncorp.com

Sales Range: $300-349.9 Million
Electronic Manufacturing Services for Origi-
nal Equipment Manufacturers; Joint Venture
of Thayer Capital Partners L.P. & BLUM
Capital Partners, L.P.
N.A.I.C.S.: 423690

Division (Domestic):

Suntron Gulf Coast Operations   (2)
1113 Gillingham Ln, Sugar Land, TX 77478-
2865
Tel.: (281) 243-5000
Web Site: http://www.suntroncorp.com
Sales Range: $25-49.9 Million
Electronics Mfr
N.A.I.C.S.: 334419

Suntron Northeast Express   (2)
300 Griffin Brook Dr, Methuen, MA 01844-
1873
Tel.: (603) 627-9556
Web Site: http://www.suntroncorp.com
Sales Range: $10-24.9 Million
Circuit Board Mfr
N.A.I.C.S.: 334412

Suntron Northeast Operations   (2)
104 Glenn St, Lawrence, MA 01843-1022
Tel.: (978) 747-2000
Web Site: http://www.suntroncorp.com
Sales Range: Less than $1 Million
Emp.: 40
Printed Circuit Board Mfr
N.A.I.C.S.: 334412

Xtralis Pty. Ltd.   (1)
4 North Drive Virginia Park 236-262 East
Boundary Road, Bentleigh, 3165, VIC, Aus-
tralia
Tel.: (61) 399367000
Web Site: http://www.xtralis.com
Sales Range: $75-99.9 Million
Smoke Detection Fire Protection & Security
Equipment Mfr
N.A.I.C.S.: 561621
Samir Samhourhi (CEO)

Subsidiary (Non-US):

VSK Electronics N.V.   (2)
Venetielann 39, B 8530, Harelbeke, Bel-
gium
Tel.: (32) 56241951
Web Site: http://www.vsk.be
Sales Range: $25-49.9 Million
Intrusion Detection & Home Security Sys-
tems Mfr
N.A.I.C.S.: 561621
Robert Verwee (Mgr-Sls)
Rik Debruyckere (Gen Mgr)

Xtralis UK Ltd.   (2)
Peoplebuilding Ground Floor Maylands Av-
enue, Hemel Hempstead, HP2 4NW, United
Kingdom
Tel.: (44) 1442 242330
Web Site: http://www.xtralis.com
Emp.: 50
Smoke Detection, Fire Protection & Security
Equipment Mfr
N.A.I.C.S.: 561621
Mick Goodfellow (VP-Sls)

Subsidiary (US):

Xtralis, Inc.   (2)
175 Bodwell St, Avon, MA 02322
Tel.: (781) 616-1125
Sales Range: $25-49.9 Million
Emp.: 30
Smoke Detection, Fire Protection & Security
Equipment Mfr
N.A.I.C.S.: 561621
Fred Coons (Dir-Comm)

**BLUM, SHAPIRO & COMPANY,
P.C.**
29 S Main St, West Hartford, CT
06107
Tel.: (860) 561-4000
Web Site:
http://www.blumshapiro.com
Sales Range: $1-9.9 Million
Emp.: 300
Certified Public Accountants & Busi-
ness Consultanting Services
N.A.I.C.S.: 541618

Andrew Lattimer (Partner)
Janet Prisloe (Partner)
Michelle Hatch (Partner)
Shannon Crowley (Mgr)
Kevin White (Partner)
Lori M. Budnick (Partner)
Luke S. Ebersold (Mng Partner-
Rhode Island)
Jonathan H. Fink (Partner)
Michael L. Hanna (Partner)
Christopher P. Hines (Partner)
Gerald Paradis (Partner)
Rick Parmelee (Partner)
Brian Renstrom (Mng Partner-
Advisory Grp)
Reed Risteen (Partner)
David Rosenthal (Partner)
Vanessa E. Rossitto (Partner)
Jay A. Sattler (Mng Partner)
John D. Spatcher (Partner)
Anthony Switajewski (Partner)
William L. Inchoco (Dir-Tax-Intl Tax
Svcs)
Alan Osmolowski (Partner)
Thomas DeVitto (CMO)
Joseph Kask (CEO)
James J. Krouse (Partner-Tax Dept-
Shelton)
Frank E. Rudewicz (Sr Partner)
Francis J. Nemia (Partner-Advisory
Svcs Grp-Boston)

Subsidiaries:

Cowan, Bolduc, Doherty & Company,
LLC   (1)
231 Sutton St, North Andover, MA 01845
Tel.: (978) 620-2000
Web Site: http://www.cbdcpa.com
Business, Financial & Client Accounting
Services
N.A.I.C.S.: 541219
Joshua A. Pfeil (Principal)
Stephen J. Doherty (Partner)

BLUMBERG INDUSTRIES INC.
5772 Miami Lks Dr E, Miami Lakes,
FL 33014
Tel.: (305) 821-3850
Web Site:
http://www.fineartlamps.com
Year Founded: 1941
Sales Range: $25-49.9 Million
Emp.: 200
Residential Electric Lighting Fixture
Manufacturing
N.A.I.C.S.: 335131
Max Blumberg (Chm)
Laura Goldblum (CFO)

BLUMBERGEXCELSIOR INC.
16 Court St, Brooklyn, NY 11241
Tel.: (212) 431-5000
Web Site: http://www.blumberg.com
Sales Range: $10-24.9 Million
Emp.: 75
Mail Order House, Nec
N.A.I.C.S.: 459410
Robert H. Blumberg (Pres)

**BLUMENTHAL PERFORMING
ARTS**
130 N Tryon St, Charlotte, NC 28202
Tel.: (704) 372-1000   NC
Web Site:
https://www.blumenthalarts.org
Year Founded: 1987
Sales Range: $10-24.9 Million
Emp.: 511
Arts Promotion Services
N.A.I.C.S.: 711310
Tom Gabbard (Pres)
Jeffrey Hay (Sec)
Kristin Hills Bradberry (Chm)

BLUNT ENTERPRISES LLC

Blunt Enterprises LLC—(Continued)

9440 Pennsylvania Ave Ste 200, Upper Marlboro, MD 20772
Tel.: (240) 492-2001
Web Site: http://www.essex-llc.com
Year Founded: 1979
Sales Range: $10-24.9 Million
Emp.: 11
General Construction Contractor
N.A.I.C.S.: 236220
Roger R. Blunt *(Chm, Pres & CEO)*
Jonathan Blunt *(Exec VP)*

Subsidiaries:

Essex Construction, LLC   (1)
9440 Pennsylvania Ave Ste 200, Upper Marlboro, MD 20772
Tel.: (240) 492-2001
Web Site: http://www.essex-llc.com
Sales Range: $10-24.9 Million
Commercial, Institutional & High Rise Residential Construction
N.A.I.C.S.: 236220
Roger R. Blunt *(Pres & CEO)*
Jonathan Blunt *(Exec VP)*
Jayaprakash Swamy *(Mgr-Acctg)*
Howard Johnson *(Partner)*
Anthony Moore *(VP-Ops)*
Kirk Saunders *(CFO)*

Tyroc Construction, LLC   (1)
9440 Pennsylvania Ave Ste 200, Upper Marlboro, MD 20772
Tel.: (240) 492-2001
Web Site: http://www.essex-llc.com
Sales Range: $10-24.9 Million
Single-Family Housing Construction
N.A.I.C.S.: 236115
Roger R. Blunt *(Pres & CEO)*
Jonathan Blunt *(Exec VP & CCO)*
Iman Newman *(Office Mgr)*
DeRosette Blunt *(Treas & Sec)*

BLVD COMPANIES
745 Merchant St, Los Angeles, CA 90021
Tel.: (213) 568-4715
Web Site:
   http://www.blvdcompanies.com
Year Founded: 2009
Hospitality Focused Venture & Holdings Company
N.A.I.C.S.: 551112
Jon Blanchard *(Co-Founder)*
Nicolo Rusconi *(CO-Founder)*

Subsidiaries:

The Georgian Hotel   (1)
1415 Ocean Ave, Santa Monica, CA 90401
Tel.: (310) 395-9945
Web Site: http://www.georgianhotel.com
Hotels (except Casino Hotels) & Motels
N.A.I.C.S.: 721110
Everardo Choza *(Chief Engr)*

BLVD SUITES CORPORATE HOUSING, INC.
1880 Arapahoe St, Denver, CO 80202
Tel.: (303) 433-1423
Web Site: http://www.blvdsuites.com
Year Founded: 2003
Housing Solutions & Services
N.A.I.C.S.: 624229
Angie Renteria *(Dir-Sls)*
Jason Luther *(Pres)*
Sally Davis *(VP-Ops)*
Nicole Hollenbeck *(VP-Fin & Acctg)*
Charley Muste *(Dir-Training & Special Ops)*
Kim Krollman *(Dir-Sls)*
Darrin Kerby *(Dir-Sls-Indiana, Ohio & Kentucky)*
Greg Reitz *(Mgr-Bus Dev-Michigan)*
Christy Walker *(Gen Mgr-Indiana, Ohio & Kentucky)*
Kristy Wisdom *(Gen Mgr-Kansas, Omaha & Lincoln)*
Genna Edmonds *(Acct Mgr)*

Linda Johnson *(Acct Mgr)*
Toni Vanicelli *(Sr Mgr-Inside Sls)*
Linda Harris *(Sr Mgr-Inside Sls)*
DeAn Lowery *(Mgr-Market Svc)*
Charlotte Winter *(Bus Mgr-UK-EMEA)*
Sara Duderstadt *(Coord-Guest Svcs)*
Elliott Krueger *(Coord-Guest Svcs)*
Carl Spencer *(Mgr-Ops-Mountain Reg)*
Mike Dunklee *(Founder & Partner)*
Maria Schmitt *(VP-Supply Chain)*

BLYTHE DEVELOPMENT CO.
1415 E Westinghouse Blvd, Charlotte, NC 28273
Tel.: (704) 588-0023
Web Site:
   https://www.blythedevelopment.com
Sales Range: $50-74.9 Million
Emp.: 850
Grading
N.A.I.C.S.: 237310
L. Jack Blythe *(Co-Founder & Co-Owner)*
Joey Dodson *(CFO & Mgr-IT)*
Dave Tolley *(Project Mgr)*
Frank Blythe *(Co-Founder & Co-Owner)*
Mike Weiss *(Project Mgr)*
Luke Blythe *(VP-Ops)*
Richard Kirkman *(Mgr-Bridge Div)*

BLYTHECO, LLC
23161 Mill Creek Dr Ste 200, Laguna Hills, CA 92653
Tel.: (949) 583-9500
Web Site: http://www.blytheco.com
Year Founded: 1980
Sales Range: $10-24.9 Million
Emp.: 125
Computer System Design Services
N.A.I.C.S.: 541512
Stephen P. Blythe *(CEO)*
Anne Alario *(Fin Dir)*
Phil Sim *(VP-Pro Svcs)*
Lori Seal *(COO)*
Apryl Hanson *(Sr Dir-Customer & Partner Strategy)*

BLYTHEDALE CHILDREN'S HOSPITAL
95 Bradhurst Ave, Valhalla, NY 10595
Tel.: (914) 592-7555
Web Site: https://www.blythedale.org
Year Founded: 1891
Sales Range: $150-199.9 Million
Emp.: 509
Child Health Care Services
N.A.I.C.S.: 622310
Maureen Desimone *(Chief Admin Officer)*
John Canning *(CFO)*
Larry Levine *(Pres & CEO)*
Adam Herbst *(Chief HR Officer)*
Jane MacDonald *(Chief Medical Officer)*
Susan Murray *(Chief Dev Officer)*

BLYTHEWOOD OIL CO. INC.
4118 US Hwy 21 S, Ridgeway, SC 29130
Tel.: (803) 754-3319
Rev.: $27,000,000
Emp.: 25
Distr of Petroleum Products
N.A.I.C.S.: 424720
Cristy Trogdon *(CFO)*
Larry H. Sharpe Jr. *(Owner)*
Larry Sharpe Sr. *(Pres)*

BM MIAMI INC.
10401 NW 36th St, Miami, FL 33178
Tel.: (305) 592-3234
Rev.: $14,006,238
Emp.: 6

Electronics & Appliances Import & Export Services
N.A.I.C.S.: 423620
Bharat M. Nebhrajani *(Pres)*

BMB ENTERPRISES
11240 Business Park Blvd, Jacksonville, FL 32256
Tel.: (904) 880-7925
Web Site: https://www.bmb-enterprisesinc.com
Sales Range: $1-9.9 Million
Emp.: 15
Air Conditioning Equipment Whslr
N.A.I.C.S.: 333415
Cathy Humphrey *(Pres)*
Mitch Morris *(Exec VP)*
Brandon Davis *(VP-HVAC Support Sls)*
Butch Lee *(VP-Filtration Sls)*
Curtis Humphrey *(CFO)*

BMC ADVERTISING
4025 E 23rd St, Columbus, NE 68601-8501
Tel.: (402) 564-3111   NE
Web Site: http://www.behlenmfg.com
Year Founded: 1984
Sales Range: $200-249.9 Million
Emp.: 900
In House Advertising Agency
N.A.I.C.S.: 541810
Mike Krzycki *(Mgr-Adv)*
Kirk Nelson *(Mgr-Mktg-Ag Prods)*
Matt Schumann *(Mgr-Mktg-Behlen Country)*

BMC CAPITAL, INC.
3267 Bee Caves Rd Ste 107-122, Austin, TX 78746
Tel.: (512) 553-6785   NV
Web Site:
   http://www.bmchardassets.com
Year Founded: 2009
Emp.: 4
Rare Coins, Precious Metals & Antiquities
N.A.I.C.S.: 423940
Christian Briggs *(Chm, Pres & CEO)*
Thomas J. Gingerich *(CFO & Sec)*
Delfino Galindo *(Chief Creative Officer)*

BMG METALS, INC.
950 Masonic Ln, Richmond, VA 23223
Tel.: (804) 226-1024   VA
Web Site: http://www.bmgmetals.com
Year Founded: 1963
Sales Range: $25-49.9 Million
Emp.: 150
Metals Service Centers & Offices
N.A.I.C.S.: 423510
Corey Calder *(Mgr-Pur)*
Andrew Gay *(Branch Mgr)*
Chip Gay *(Product Mgr)*
Kathy Kelley *(Mgr-Credit)*
Wayne Galleher *(Mgr-Facilities/Logistics)*
Kingsbery W. Gay Jr. *(Pres)*

BMH CORP.
11 Forbes Rd, Woburn, MA 01801-2103
Tel.: (781) 933-8300   MA
Web Site:
   http://www.admiralmetals.com
Year Founded: 1950
Sales Range: $50-74.9 Million
Emp.: 120
Holding Company; Metal Services; Metals Distributor
N.A.I.C.S.: 423510
Dave Pastucci *(CFO)*

Subsidiaries:

Admiral Metals Servicenter Company Inc.   (1)
11 Forbes Rd, Woburn, MA 01801-2103
Tel.: (781) 933-8300
Web Site: http://www.admiralmetals.com
Sales Range: $10-24.9 Million
Metal Supply Service & Distr
N.A.I.C.S.: 423510
James Burstein *(Pres & CEO)*
Dave Pascucci *(CFO)*

M. Burstein Co. Inc.   (1)
12 Mear Rd, Holbrook, MA
02343-1339   (100%)
Tel.: (781) 986-0012
Sales Range: $10-24.9 Million
Emp.: 15
Provider of Scrap & Waste Material Services
N.A.I.C.S.: 423930

BMI ELITE, INC.
1095 Broken Sound Pkwy NW Ste 300, Boca Raton, FL 33487
Tel.: (561) 330-6666
Web Site: http://www.bmielite.com
Sales Range: $1-9.9 Million
Emp.: 50
Advetising Agency
N.A.I.C.S.: 541810
Branden Rosen *(CEO)*
Dan Lansman *(COO)*
Mike Schweiger *(CFO)*
Fred Zuckerman *(CMO)*

BMI FINANCIAL GROUP, INC.
8950 SW 74th Ct, Miami, FL 33156
Tel.: (305) 443-2898   FL
Web Site: http://www.bmicos.com
Sales Range: $200-249.9 Million
Emp.: 100
Holding Company; Financial & Insurance Services
N.A.I.C.S.: 524210
Antonio M. Sierra *(Founder & Chm)*
David Sierra *(CMO & Exec VP)*
Brent Bush *(Vice Chm & COO)*
Anthony Sierra *(Pres & CEO)*

Subsidiaries:

Business Mens Insurance Corporation   (1)
8950 SW 74 Ct Fl 24, Miami, FL 33156-2926
Tel.: (305) 443-2898
Web Site: http://www.bmicos.com
Sales Range: $50-74.9 Million
Insurance Agents
N.A.I.C.S.: 524210
Antonio M. Sierra *(Chm & Founder)*
Brent Bush *(Vice Chm & COO)*
Anthony Sierra *(Pres & CEO)*
David Sierra *(Exec VP & CMO)*
Manuel Pelati *(VP & CFO)*
Andrew Sierra *(VP, Treas & Chief Compliance Officer)*

BMI IMAGING SYSTEMS INC.
1115 E Arques Ave, Sunnyvale, CA 94085
Tel.: (408) 736-7444
Web Site:
   https://www.bmiimaging.com
Sales Range: $10-24.9 Million
Emp.: 75
Microfilm Equipment
N.A.I.C.S.: 423420
Janice Harrison *(Treas & Controller)*
Bill Whitney *(Pres & CEO)*
Brad Penfold *(VP-Sls)*
Jim Modrall *(VP-Tech Svcs)*
Jim Detrick *(VP & Sr Acct Exec)*
Mike Aufranc *(VP)*

BMI SYSTEMS CORPORATION
913 N Broadway, Oklahoma City, OK 73102-5810
Tel.: (405) 232-1264   OK

Web Site:
   http://www.bmisystems.com
Year Founded: 1956
Sales Range: $200-249.9 Million
Emp.: 450
Holding Company; Digital Sign & Display Consulting Services
N.A.I.C.S.: 551112
Thomas L. Russell *(Dir)*
Les Samuel *(VP-Service)*

Subsidiaries:

ImageNet Consulting, LLC   **(1)**
913 N Broadway, Oklahoma City, OK 73102-5810
Tel.: (800) 937-2647
Web Site:
   https://www.imagenetconsulting.com
Digital Sign & Display Consulting Services
N.A.I.C.S.: 541690

Subsidiary (Domestic):

The IT Guys, LLC   **(2)**
913 N Broadway, Oklahoma City, OK 73102
Tel.: (405) 748-0808
Web Site: http://www.okcitguys.com
Computer System Design Services
N.A.I.C.S.: 541512

BMJ FOODS PR INC.
PO Box 4963, Caguas, PR 00726-4963
Tel.: (787) 286-7040
Year Founded: 1993
Sales Range: $50-74.9 Million
Emp.: 1,350
Provider of Dining Services
N.A.I.C.S.: 722511
Samuel Jove *(Pres)*

BMS CAT, INC.
5718 Airport Freeway, Haltom City, TX 76117
Web Site: http://www.bmscat.com
Residential Remodeler
N.A.I.C.S.: 236118
Mark Rocco *(Sr VP)*

Subsidiaries:

Drymaster Restoration   **(1)**
3401 Glendale Blvd Ste A, Los Angeles, CA 90039-1814
Tel.: (323) 212-5836
Residential Remodeler
N.A.I.C.S.: 236118
Carlos Ramirez *(CEO)*

HJM Enterprises, Inc.   **(1)**
1035 Executive Dr, Gibsonia, PA 15044
Tel.: (412) 487-3332
Web Site: http://www.firedexpgh.com
Residential Remodeler
N.A.I.C.S.: 236118
David Hood *(VP)*

Jarvis Painting, Inc.   **(1)**
41800 Executive Dr, Harrison Township, MI 48045
Tel.: (586) 954-4700
Web Site: http://www.jarvisconstruction.com
Sales Range: $1-9.9 Million
Emp.: 80
Residential Remodeler
N.A.I.C.S.: 236118
Chris Smith *(Mgr)*
Bill Jarvis *(Pres)*
Matt Jarvis *(VP)*

BMS ENTERPRISES INC.
308 Arthur St, Fort Worth, TX 76107
Tel.: (817) 810-9200
Web Site:
   http://www.blackmonmooring.com
Rev.: $10,000,000
Emp.: 20
Carpet & Furniture Cleaning On Location
N.A.I.C.S.: 561740
Tom Head *(Pres)*

BMT COMMODITY CORPORATION
530 5th Ave 24th Fl, New York, NY 10036-5101
Tel.: (212) 302-4200   NY
Web Site: http://www.bmtny.com
Year Founded: 1959
Rev.: $40,000,000
Emp.: 30
Nondurable Goods
N.A.I.C.S.: 424990
Robert Ganz *(Chm, Co-Pres & CEO)*
Shannon Keegan *(VP-Fibers)*
Joe Viggiani *(Mgr-Logistics)*

Subsidiaries:

Delca Distributors Inc.   **(1)**
Mercado Central Zona Portuaria, Puerto Nuevo, PR 00922   **(100%)**
Tel.: (809) 792-9600
Web Site: http://www.bmtny.com
Sales Range: $10-24.9 Million
Emp.: 3
Fish & Seafood Distr
N.A.I.C.S.: 424460

BMW NORTHWEST INC.
4011 20th St E, Tacoma, WA 98424
Tel.: (253) 517-2524
Web Site:
   https://www.bmwnorthwest.com
Rev.: $20,000,000
Emp.: 65
New Car Dealers
N.A.I.C.S.: 441110
Manfred Scharmach *(Owner)*
Allen Deen *(Gen Mgr-Sls)*
Bryan Nelson *(Mgr-Sls)*
Jesse Case *(Dir-IT & Network)*
Susan Grissom *(Dir-Fin)*
Jimmy Barber *(Mgr-Internet)*
Mark Rauschert *(Mgr-Internet)*
James Barlow *(Mgr-Parts-Columbus)*
Eddie Bang *(Mgr-Sls)*

BMW OF AUSTIN
7011 McNeil Dr, Austin, TX 78729
Tel.: (512) 343-3500
Web Site:
   http://www.bmwofaustin.com
Rev.: $31,200,000
Emp.: 120
Automobiles, New & Used
N.A.I.C.S.: 441110
Chris Markey *(Mgr-Sls)*

BMW OF BAYSIDE
24721 Northern Blvd, Douglaston, NY 11363
Tel.: (718) 229-4400
Web Site:
   http://www.bmwbayside.com
Sales Range: $10-24.9 Million
Emp.: 80
New & Used Car Dealer
N.A.I.C.S.: 441110

BMW OF DARIEN
140 Ledge Rd, Darien, CT 06820-4423
Tel.: (203) 656-1804
Web Site: http://www.bmwdarien.com
Sales Range: $25-49.9 Million
Emp.: 50
New Car Dealers
N.A.I.C.S.: 441110
Anthony Martinez *(Mgr-Fin & Insurance)*
Tom Samperi *(Mgr-Pre-Owned)*

BMW OF ESCONDIDO
1555 Auto Park Way, Escondido, CA 92029
Tel.: (760) 745-3000
Web Site:
   http://www.bmwofescondido.com
Year Founded: 1985

Sales Range: $25-49.9 Million
Emp.: 100
Car Whslr
N.A.I.C.S.: 441110
Tom Brecht *(Owner)*

BMW OF MACON
4785 Riverside Dr, Macon, GA 31210-1841
Tel.: (478) 757-7000
Web Site:
   https://www.bmwofmacon.com
Year Founded: 1993
Sales Range: $25-49.9 Million
Emp.: 39
New Car Whslr
N.A.I.C.S.: 441110
Scott Smith *(Gen Mgr)*
Raul Ibarra *(Mgr-Parts)*

BMWC GROUP INC.
1740 W Michigan St, Indianapolis, IN 46222
Tel.: (317) 267-0400
Web Site: https://www.bmwc.com
Sales Range: $25-49.9 Million
Holding Company
N.A.I.C.S.: 551112
Brian Acton *(Chm & CEO)*
Mike Keller *(CFO)*
Chris Buckman *(Pres & COO)*
Tony Kanaly *(Pres-Western Reg)*

Subsidiaries:

BMWC Constructors, Inc.   **(1)**
1740 W Michigan St, Indianapolis, IN 46222-3855
Tel.: (317) 267-0400
Web Site: http://www.bmwc.com
Sales Range: $50-74.9 Million
Emp.: 765
General Industrial Construction Contractor
N.A.I.C.S.: 237990
John Manta *(VP-Mktg & Sls)*
Mike Keller *(CFO)*
Chris Buckman *(Pres & CEO)*
Kevin Kohart *(Corp Counsel & Mgr-Risk)*
Brian Acton *(Chm)*
Keith Brennan *(Gen Mgr-Indianapolis)*

Subsidiary (Domestic):

BMWC Constructors, Inc. - Seattle   **(2)**
14615 NE N Woodinville Way Ste 207, Woodinville, WA 98072
Tel.: (425) 251-9091
Web Site: http://www.bmwc.com
Industrial Construction Services
N.A.I.C.S.: 236220
Tony Kanaly *(Pres-Western)*

BN MEDIA LLC
999 Waterside Dr Ste 1900, Norfolk, VA 23510
Tel.: (757) 228-1722
Web Site: http://www.bnmediallc.com
Media Holding Company
N.A.I.C.S.: 551112
Steve Halliday *(CEO)*

Subsidiaries:

Beliefnet, Inc.   **(1)**
303 Park Ave S PO Box 1062, New York, NY 10010
Tel.: (917) 286-8390
Web Site: http://www.beliefnet.com
Sales Range: $1-9.9 Million
Emp.: 30
Religion-Based Website
N.A.I.C.S.: 513199

Subsidiary (Domestic):

Patheos, Inc.   **(2)**
4700 S Syracuse St Ste 400, Denver, CO 80237
Tel.: (303) 909-7939
Web Site: http://www.patheos.com
Internet Publishing & Broadcasting & Web Search Portals
N.A.I.C.S.: 516210

Leo Brunnick *(Founder)*
Cathie Brunnick *(COO)*

BNBUILDERS, INC.
2601 4th Ave Ste 350, Seattle, WA 98121
Tel.: (206) 382-3443   WA
Web Site: http://www.bnbuilders.com
Year Founded: 2000
Sales Range: $25-49.9 Million
Emp.: 300
Commercial & Institutional Building Construction
N.A.I.C.S.: 236220
Bradley Bastian *(Co-Founder)*
Jeffrey Nielsen *(Co-Founder)*
Rick Philipovich *(Dir-Ops)*
Chris Bae *(Mgr-Preconstruction)*

BNC INSURANCE AGENCY, INC.
90 S Ridge St, Rye Brook, NY 10573
Tel.: (914) 937-1230
Web Site:
   https://www.bncagency.com
Insurance Agency & Brokerages
N.A.I.C.S.: 524210
Brian M. Colby *(Pres & Principal)*
John Cofini *(Principal)*
R. Todd Rockefeller *(Principal)*
Paul G. Sohigian *(Principal)*

BNC REAL ESTATE
13151 Emily Rd Ste 250, Dallas, TX 75240
Tel.: (972) 437-9900
Web Site:
   http://www.bncrealestate.com
Year Founded: 1977
Sales Range: $10-24.9 Million
Emp.: 100
Real Estate Services
N.A.I.C.S.: 523999
Barry S. Nussbaum *(Founder, Pres & CEO)*

BNH FINANCIAL
62 Pleasant St, Laconia, NH 03246
Tel.: (603) 524-1212
Web Site: https://www.banknh.com
Year Founded: 1998
Sales Range: $50-74.9 Million
Emp.: 271
Bank Holding Company
N.A.I.C.S.: 551111

Subsidiaries:

Bank of New Hampshire   **(1)**
62 Pleasant St, Laconia, NH 03246
Tel.: (603) 524-1212
Web Site: http://www.banknh.com
Sales Range: $10-24.9 Million
Federal Savings Bank
N.A.I.C.S.: 522180
Bruce D. Clow *(Chm)*
Claudette L. Ayotte *(Vice Chm)*
Paul C. Nee *(CIO & Sr VP)*
Gayle E. Price *(Chief HR Officer & Sr VP)*
Vickie Routhier *(Chief Retail Banking & Mktg Officer & Exec VP)*
Cydney Shapleigh-Johnson *(Chief Wealth Mgmt Officer & Exec VP)*
Lindsay D. Cota-Robles *(VP)*
John E. Swenson *(Chief Bank Ops Officer & Sr VP)*
Bill Zafirson *(Chief Mortgage & Retail Lending Officer & Sr VP)*
Frank H. Anderson *(Officer-Private Banking & Sr VP)*
Kathleen Crane *(VP-Wealth Mgmt Team)*
Arlene C. Folsom *(Officer-Fiduciary & Sr VP-Wealth Mgmt)*
Charles P. Mathews *(Officer-Private Banking Investment & Sr VP)*
Dona G. Murray *(Officer-Investment & VP)*
Paul Falvey *(Pres & CEO)*
Aaron Gill *(VP-Comml Banking)*
Elin Leonard *(Asst VP-Bedford)*
Carolyn B. Peverly *(Officer-Retail Banking & Sr VP)*

BNH Financial—(Continued)

Cecile M. Chase *(Sr VP-Retail Sls & Dev)*
Christopher J. Logan *(Chief Admin Officer & Exec VP)*
Debra L. Davis *(Officer-Retail Banking & Sr VP)*
Edwin K. Killam *(Sr VP)*
Eric C. Carter *(Sr VP & Mgr-Electronic Banking)*
Evelyn M. Whelton *(Sr VP & Mgr-Retail Lending Sls)*
Jeremy C. Deering *(Sr VP)*
Michael J. St. Onge *(Officer-Investment & Sr VP)*
Nobo Sircar *(CFO & Exec VP)*
Robert A. Magan *(Officer-Private Banking Investment & Sr VP)*
Ross W. Bartlett *(Sr VP & Dir-Credit)*
Tania L. Baert *(Officer-Comml Credit & Sr VP)*

BNI PUBLICATIONS, INC.
990 Park Center Dr Ste E, Vista, CA 92081-8352
Tel.: (714) 517-0970   DE
Web Site: https://www.bnibooks.com
Year Founded: 1946
Construction Books & Other Reference Materials Publisher
N.A.I.C.S.: 513130
William Mahoney *(Pres)*

Subsidiaries:

Construction Book Express   (1)
990 Park Ctr Dr Ste E, Vista, CA 92081
Tel.: (760) 734-1113
Web Site: http://www.constructionbook.com
Emp.: 11
Online & Mail-Order Construction Professional Trade Book & Materials Retailer
N.A.I.C.S.: 459210
William Mahoney *(Pres)*

Design Cost Data   (1)
990 Park Ctr Dr Ste E, Vista, CA 92081
Web Site: http://www.dcd.com
Design & Construction Industry Cost Estimation Trade Journal Publisher
N.A.I.C.S.: 513120
Barbara Castelli *(Pres & Publr)*
David Castelli *(VP)*
Patty Owens *(Mgr-Data Svcs)*

BNL TECHNOLOGIES INC.
20525 Manhattan Pl, Torrance, CA 90501
Tel.: (310) 320-7272
Web Site: http://www.micronet.com
Year Founded: 1988
Rev.: $24,000,000
Emp.: 30
Data Storage Technology Holding Company
N.A.I.C.S.: 423430
Behzad Eshghieh *(Pres)*

Subsidiaries:

Fantom Drives   (1)
20525 Manhattan Pl, Torrance, CA 90501-1102
Tel.: (310) 320-7272
Web Site: http://www.fantomdrives.com
Sales Range: $10-24.9 Million
Emp.: 25
Mfr of High Performance Data Storage
N.A.I.C.S.: 423430
Nasser Ahdout *(CFO)*

MicroNet Technology   (1)
20525 Manhattan Pl, Torrance, CA 90501-1102   (100%)
Tel.: (310) 320-7272
Web Site: http://www.micronet.com
Mfr of High Performance Data Storage
N.A.I.C.S.: 423430
Nasser Ahdout *(CFO)*

BNP MEDIA, INC.
2401 W Big Beaver Rd Ste 700, Troy, MI 48084
Tel.: (248) 362-3700   MI
Web Site: https://www.bnpmedia.com

Year Founded: 1926
Sales Range: $100-124.9 Million
Emp.: 400
Business-to-Business Magazines, Internet Resources, Trade Shows & Conventions
N.A.I.C.S.: 513120
Taggart Henderson *(Co-CEO)*
Mitchell Henderson *(Co-CEO)*
Kaylee Hendrick *(Coord-Event Mktg)*
Rebecca Martin *(Coord-Event Mktg)*
Elizabeth Parker *(Coord-Online Support)*
Catherine Ronan *(Mgr-Audience Audit)*
Kristine Wyatt *(Mgr-Audience Mktg)*
Jennesa Kreiner *(Mgr-Mktg)*
Andrea Camp *(Mgr-Payroll)*
Scott Hilling *(Sr Dir-Art)*
Kevin Hackney *(Sr Mgr-Mktg)*
Beth Skinner *(Supvr-Credit)*
Samantha Meux *(Assoc Editor)*
Ashley Ludwig *(Coord-Multimedia)*
Lauren Kastman *(Coord-Multimedia)*
Kristin Overbeck *(Coord-Online Events)*
Molly Bogits *(Coord-Online Support)*
Dave Brown *(Dir-IT)*
Eric Fish *(Editor)*
Tom Watts *(Editor)*
Jill Buchowski *(Mgr-Audience Dev)*
Kathleen Koval *(Mgr-Audience Dev)*
Lindsey Bryant *(Mgr-Events Mktg)*
Drew Matthews *(Mgr-Mktg)*
Brooke Geisz *(Mgr-Mktg & Promos)*
Lisa Thomas *(Mgr-Online Dev)*
Karen Talan *(Mgr-Production)*
Wendy Zaremba-Just *(Sr Dir-Art)*

Subsidiaries:

Architectural Record   (1)
350 5th Ave Ste 6000, New York, NY 10118
Tel.: (646) 849-7100
Web Site: http://www.archrecord.com
Monthly Print & Online Publication
N.A.I.C.S.: 513120
Elisabeth Broome *(Mng Editor)*
Cathleen McGuigan *(Editor-in-Chief)*
Josephine Minutillo *(Editor-Features)*
Joann Gonchar *(Sr Editor)*
Linda C. Lentz *(Sr Editor)*
Julie Taraska *(Editor-Product)*
Anna Fixsen *(Editor-News)*
Miriam Sitz *(Editor-Web)*

BNP Media   (1)
155 Pfingsten Rd Ste 205, Deerfield, IL 60015
Tel.: (847) 405-4030
Web Site: http://www.bnpevents.com
Sales Range: $25-49.9 Million
Emp.: 65
Food, Beverage & Packaging Magazines, Internet Resources, Trade Shows & Conferences
N.A.I.C.S.: 513120

Engineering News-Record Magazine   (1)
2401 W Big Beaver Rd Ste 700, Troy, MI 48084-3333   (100%)
Tel.: (248) 362-3700
Web Site: http://www.enr.com
Emp.: 20
Construction Magazines
N.A.I.C.S.: 513120
Timothy J. Grogan *(Sr Editor)*
Gary J. Tulacz *(Sr Editor)*
Aileen Cho *(Sr Editor)*
Scott Lewis *(Assoc Editor)*
Janice L. Tuchman *(Editor in Chief)*
Justin Rice *(Editor-ENR-MidAtlantic & New England)*
Scott Judy *(Editor-ENR-Southeast)*
Mark Shaw *(Editor-ENR Mountain States & Contractor Business Quarterly)*
Louise Poirier *(Editor-ENR Texas & Louisiana)*
John Guzzon *(Editor-ENR Southwest)*
Pam Hunter McFarland *(Editor-ENR Florida)*
Alisa Zevin *(Editor-ENR New York)*
Mike Anderson *(Editor-Equipment & ENR Midwest)*

Luke Abaffy *(Assoc Editor)*
Jeff Rubenstone *(Editor-Product News)*
Jordan Bowens *(Reg Dir-Art)*
Scott Hilling *(Dir-Art)*
Kaela Torres *(Dir-Art)*
Scott Wolters *(Dir-Conference & Event)*

BNX SHIPPING INC.
910 E 236th St, Carson, CA 90745
Tel.: (310) 764-0999
Web Site: https://www.bnxinc.com
Sales Range: $25-49.9 Million
Emp.: 35
Freight Forwarding
N.A.I.C.S.: 488510
Daniel Kim *(Pres)*
Jane Lin *(Mgr-Accts)*

BNZ MATERIALS, INC.
6901 S Pierce St Ste 260, Littleton, CO 80128-7205
Tel.: (303) 978-1199   CO
Web Site:
   http://www.bnzmaterials.com
Year Founded: 1987
Sales Range: $10-24.9 Million
Emp.: 75
Mfr of Clay Refractories; High Temapature Insulation Boards
N.A.I.C.S.: 327120
John Fischer *(Vice Chm)*
Ken Hunter *(Pres)*
Larry Peterson *(CFO)*

Subsidiaries:

BNZ Materials, Inc. - Billerica Plant   (1)
400 Iron House Park, North Billerica, MA 01862
Tel.: (978) 663-3401
Web Site: http://www.bnzmaterials.com
Insulating Panel Mfr
N.A.I.C.S.: 332618
Lee Kinnon *(Plant Mgr)*

BNZ Materials, Inc. - Insulating Fire Brick Plant   (1)
191 Front St, Zelienople, PA 16063
Tel.: (724) 452-8650
Insulating Fire Brick Mfr
N.A.I.C.S.: 327120
Ken Hunter *(Pres)*

BNZ s.a.   (1)
Les Landelles, BP 9, 22210, Plemet, France
Tel.: (33) 296256101
Insulating Fire Brick Mfr
N.A.I.C.S.: 327120

BO TECHNOLOGY INCORPORATED
142 W 36 St Ste 1001, New York, NY 10018
Tel.: (212) 967-4477
Web Site:
   http://www.botechnology.com
Year Founded: 2002
Rev.: $2,300,000
Emp.: 25
IT Consulting Services
N.A.I.C.S.: 541618
Thierry Duclay *(Pres)*
Veronica Duclay *(Dir-Admin)*

BO'S FOOD STORES
301 N Pine St, Lumberton, NC 28358
Tel.: (910) 739-5137
Web Site: http://bosfoodstores.com
Rev.: $40,000,000
Emp.: 10
Owner of Grocery Store
N.A.I.C.S.: 445110
Bo Abbott Jr. *(Pres)*

BOAN CONTRACTING CO. INC.
498 Merriweather Ln, Greenville, AL 36037
Tel.: (334) 382-6558

Web Site: http://www.boanco.com
Sales Range: $10-24.9 Million
Emp.: 70
Water & Sewer Line Construction
N.A.I.C.S.: 237110
Patsy Nall *(Project Mgr)*

BOARDMAN FOODS INC.
13500 SW 72nd Ave, Portland, OR 97223
Tel.: (503) 968-2300
Web Site:
   http://www.boardmanfoodsinc.com
Rev.: $14,700,000
Vegetables, Quick Frozen & Cold Pack, Excluding Potato Products
N.A.I.C.S.: 311411
Tom Flaherty *(VP-Sls)*

BOARDMAN INDUSTRIES INC.
15810 Chatham Wood Dr, Austin, TX 78717
Tel.: (512) 248-8120
Web Site:
   http://www.benergypartners.com
Sales Range: $10-24.9 Million
Emp.: 13
Custom Engineered Finishing Solutions.
N.A.I.C.S.: 424610

BOARDROOM INCORPORATED
281 Tresser Blvd, Stamford, CT 06901
Tel.: (203) 973-5900
Web Site:
   http://www.bottomlinepublishing.com
Year Founded: 1971
Rev.: $12,500,000
Emp.: 80
Periodicals, Publishing
N.A.I.C.S.: 513120
Brian Kurtz *(Exec VP)*

BOARDWALK VOLKSWAGEN
300 N Central Expy, Richardson, TX 75080-7409
Tel.: (214) 453-5000
Year Founded: 2000
Sales Range: $10-24.9 Million
Emp.: 55
New Car Whslr
N.A.I.C.S.: 441110
Clay Cooley *(Owner)*

BOARMAN KROOS VOGEL GROUP INC.
222 N 2nd St, Minneapolis, MN 55401-1457
Tel.: (612) 339-3752
Web Site: http://www.bkvgroup.com
Year Founded: 1978
Sales Range: $10-24.9 Million
Emp.: 100
Architectural Services
N.A.I.C.S.: 541310
Jack Boarmen *(Pres & CEO)*
Julie Lux *(Dir-Pre-Dev Svcs)*

BOAT TREE INC.
4370 Carraway Pl, Sanford, FL 32771-8522
Tel.: (407) 322-1610
Web Site: https://www.boattree.com
Rev.: $36,354,829
Emp.: 48
Motor Boat Dealers
N.A.I.C.S.: 441222
Joe Pozo Jr. *(Pres)*

BOATARAMA INC.
915 NE 3rd Ave Ste 5, Fort Lauderdale, FL 33304-1921
Tel.: (954) 783-8080
Sales Range: $10-24.9 Million

Emp.: 15
Motor Boat Dealers
N.A.I.C.S.: 441222
Lynn Bost (Treas)

BOATHOUSE CAPITAL MANAGEMENT, LLC
353 W Lancaster Ave Ste 200, Wayne, PA 19087
Tel.: (610) 688-6314   PA
Web Site:
http://www.boathousecapital.com
Rev.: $350,000,000
Privater Equity Firm
N.A.I.C.S.: 523999
Ken Jones (Gen Partner)
Bill Dyer (Gen Partner)
Steve Gord (Gen Partner)
Chong Moua (Gen Partner)
Brian Adamsky (CFO)
Andrew Olsen (Principal)
Colin Raws (Dir-Bus Dev)

Subsidiaries:

Accurate Background, Inc.   (1)
6 Orchard Ste 200, Lake Forest, CA 92630
Tel.: (949) 609-2206
Sales Range: $1-9.9 Million
Background Checks & Security Products
N.A.I.C.S.: 928110
Dave Dickerson (Founder)
Aaron Charbonnet (Sr VP-Client Dev)
Debbie Klarfeld (VP-Product Mgmt)
Connie Suoo (CTO)
Tim Dowd (CEO)
Scott Hebert (Chief Revenue Officer)
Bon Idziak (Chief Compliance Officer)
Carlos Hernandez (VP-Continuous Improvement & Project Mgmt)
Mandy Schaniel (Sr VP-Customer Success)
Paul Reyor (Sr VP-Ops)
Sherri Davis (VP-HR)
Kristen Whitt (Sr VP-Ops)
Cheryl Cerkoske (VP-Sls)
Dan Shoemaker (Sr VP-Bus Dev)
Stacey Torrico (Chief HR Officer)
Rashid Ismail (COO)

Subsidiary (Domestic):

CareerBuilder Employment Screening, LLC   (2)
Atrium Corporate Ctr 3800 Golf Rd Ste 120, Rolling Meadows, IL 60008
Tel.: (847) 255-1852
Web Site:
http://www.screen.careerbuilder.com
Background Check Investigation Services
N.A.I.C.S.: 561611
Ben Goldberg (CEO)
Laura Randazzo (VP-Compliance)
Mary Delaney (Chm)

Orange Tree Employment Screening LLC   (2)
7301 Ohms Ln Ste 600, Minneapolis, MN 55439
Tel.: (952) 941-9040
Web Site:
http://www.orangetreescreening.com
Sales Range: $1-9.9 Million
Emp.: 53
Help Supply Services
N.A.I.C.S.: 561320
Craig Vinje (Mng Partner)
Steve Mihalik (VP-Solutions)
Renee Ernste (CEO)

Subsidiary (Domestic):

Info Cubic LLC   (3)
116 Inverness Dr E Ste 206, Englewood, CO 80112
Tel.: (303) 220-0169
Web Site: https://infocubic.net
Pre-employment Screening & Drug Testing Services
N.A.I.C.S.: 561311
Justin Den (CEO)

Mediafly, Inc.   (1)
150 N Michigan Ave Ste 2000, Chicago, IL 60601
Tel.: (312) 281-5175
Web Site: http://www.mediafly.com

Content Management
N.A.I.C.S.: 513210
Carson Conant (Founder & CEO)
Jason Shah (CTO)
John Evarts (CFO & COO)
Matt Suggs (Exec VP-Sls)
Tony Kavadas (Exec VP-Global Sls & Alliances)

Subsidiary (Domestic):

Alinean, Inc.   (2)
127 W Fairbanks Ave Ste 401, Winter Park, FL 32789
Tel.: (407) 382-0005
Web Site: http://www.alinean.com
Marketing Software Publisher
N.A.I.C.S.: 513210
Tom Pisello (Founder & CEO)
Dan Sixsmith (VP)
Betty McNeil (VP)

Navint Partners, LLC   (1)
5569 W Henrietta Rd, West Henrietta, NY 14586
Web Site: http://www.navint.com
Consulting & Techonlogy Firm
N.A.I.C.S.: 541611
Jim Martindale (Mng Dir)

Subsidiary (Domestic):

Statera, Inc.   (2)
5619 DTC Pkwy Ste 900, Greenwood Village, CO 80111
Tel.: (720) 346-0070
Web Site: http://www.statera.com
Rev.: $26,000,000
Emp.: 201
Computer System Design Services
N.A.I.C.S.: 541512
Brent LaBier (Exec VP)
Bill Gilbert (Exec VP-Tech & Integration)
Brad Weydert (Pres)
Carl R. Fitch (CFO)
Karey Brown (VP-Recruiting)
Dan Fox-Gliessman (CIO)
Lori Sanders (VP-Bus Applications)
Dennis Shipman (VP-Bus Transformation)
Mike Volpi (VP-Sls & Digital Transformation)
Nam Le (Dir-Sls)

BOATHOUSE GROUP INC.
260 Charles St 4th Fl, Waltham, MA 02453-3826
Tel.: (781) 663-6600
Web Site:
http://www.boathouseinc.com
Sales Range: $10-24.9 Million
Emp.: 35
N.A.I.C.S.: 541810
John Connors (Founder & CEO)

BOATNER CONSTRUCTION CO INC.
114 Hickman St, Rainbow City, AL 35906
Tel.: (256) 442-3820
Web Site:
http://www.cecobuildings.com
Rev.: $15,000,000
Emp.: 50
Commercial & Institutional Building Construction
N.A.I.C.S.: 236220
John Nolen (VP)
Dock Graham (Pres)
Linda Petty (Treas & Sec)

BOATRACS LLC
11610 Iberia Pl Ste 100, San Diego, CA 92128
Tel.: (858) 458-8100
Web Site: http://www.boatracs.com
Sales Range: $10-24.9 Million
Emp.: 20
Communications, Satellite Transmission Technology & Video Compression Products
N.A.I.C.S.: 519290
Irwin Rodrigues (Chm & CEO)
Claudette Anderson (Mgr-Client Care)

BOATRIGHT RAILROAD COMPANIES, INC.
31 Inverness Ctr Pkwy Ste 120, Birmingham, AL 35242
Tel.: (205) 298-7279   AL
Web Site:
http://www.boatrightcompanies.com
Year Founded: 1989
Sales Range: $10-24.9 Million
Emp.: 200
Railroad Maintenance
N.A.I.C.S.: 488210
Rush Shane Boatright (Pres & CEO)
John Steven Bookout (CFO & VP)

BOB ALLEN FORD
9239 Metcalf Ave, Overland Park, KS 66212
Tel.: (913) 381-3000
Web Site:
https://www.boballenford.com
Sales Range: $25-49.9 Million
Emp.: 120
Sell Automobiles, New & Used & Service Department
N.A.I.C.S.: 441110
John Iegers (Owner)
Larry Brown (Dir-Internet)
Jason Hensley (Dir-Fin)

BOB ALLEN MOTOR MALL
725 Maple Ave, Danville, KY 40422
Tel.: (859) 236-3217
Web Site:
http://www.boballengmc.com
Year Founded: 1985
Sales Range: $10-24.9 Million
Emp.: 80
Car Whslr
N.A.I.C.S.: 441110
Bob Allen (Pres)
Gary Dupray (Mgr-Used Car)
Joe Henderson (Gen Mgr-Sls)

BOB ALLEN-CHRYSLER PLYMOUTH DODGE
725 Maple Ave, Danville, KY 40422
Tel.: (859) 236-3217
Web Site:
http://www.boballenchrysler.com
Sales Range: $10-24.9 Million
Emp.: 80
Car Whslr
N.A.I.C.S.: 441110
Kathy Allen (Treas, Sec & VP)
Gary Dupray (Mgr-Used Car)
Joe Henderson (Mgr-Sls)
Fred Sizemore (Dir-Svc)

BOB BAKER AUTO GROUP
591 Camino De La Reina Ste 1100, San Diego, CA 92108-3113
Tel.: (619) 297-1001   CA
Web Site: http://www.bobbaker.com
Sales Range: $200-249.9 Million
Emp.: 500
Automobile Dealership
N.A.I.C.S.: 441110
Robert H. Baker (Pres)

BOB BARBOUR, INC.
3300 S Memorial Dr, Greenville, NC 27834-6731
Tel.: (252) 231-3293
Web Site:
https://www.barbourhendrick.com
Sales Range: $10-24.9 Million
Emp.: 50
Car Whslr
N.A.I.C.S.: 441110
Guy Wade (Gen Mgr)

BOB BARKER COMPANY, INC.
PO Box 429, Fuquay Varina, NC 27526
Tel.: (919) 552-3431   NC

Web Site: http://www.bobbarker.com
Year Founded: 1972
Sales Range: $25-49.9 Million
Emp.: 220
Law Enforcement & Detention Center Equipment & Supplies
N.A.I.C.S.: 424310
Robert J. Barker (Pres)
Bob Barker (Chm)
David Sears (VP-Ops)

BOB BAY & SONS INC.
1215 N Memorial Dr, Lancaster, OH 43130
Tel.: (740) 687-1495
Web Site:
http://www.carnivalfoodsohio.com
Rev.: $33,000,000
Emp.: 178
Grocery Stores, Independent
N.A.I.C.S.: 445110
Dan Bay (Pres)

BOB BOAST VOLKSWAGEN
4827 14th St W, Bradenton, FL 34207
Tel.: (941) 755-8585
Web Site: https://www.boastvw.com
Rev.: $20,000,000
Emp.: 14
New Car Dealers
N.A.I.C.S.: 441110
Steve Bierwirth (Pres)
Joanne Boast (Owner)
Mike Shaughnessy (Mgr-Sls)

BOB BRADY DODGE INC.
4025 E Boyd Rd, Decatur, IL 62521
Tel.: (217) 876-3800
Web Site:
http://www.bobbradydodge.com
Rev.: $17,500,000
Emp.: 100
New Car Dealers
N.A.I.C.S.: 441110
Bob Brady (Pres)
Angie Manns (Mgr-Bus Dev)
Rick Hazelrigg (Mgr-Customer Rels)

BOB BROCKLAND BUICK GMC
580 Old State Rte 3, Columbia, IL 62236-2626
Tel.: (618) 332-2277
Web Site: https://www.brockland.com
Sales Range: $10-24.9 Million
Emp.: 47
Automobiles, New & Used
N.A.I.C.S.: 441110
Robert Brockland (Pres)

BOB BROWN CHEVROLET INC.
3600 111th St, Urbandale, IA 50322
Tel.: (515) 278-7800   IA
Web Site:
http://www.bobbrownauto.com
Year Founded: 1961
Sales Range: $25-49.9 Million
Emp.: 150
New & Used Automobiles Sls
N.A.I.C.S.: 441110
Tim Manning (Gen Mgr-Sls)

BOB CALDWELL CHRYSLER JEEP DODGE RAM
1888 Morse Rd, Columbus, OH 43229
Tel.: (614) 888-2331
Web Site:
https://www.caldwellchrysler.com
Year Founded: 1956
Sales Range: $10-24.9 Million
Emp.: 65
New Car Dealers
N.A.I.C.S.: 441110

Bob Caldwell Chrysler Jeep Dodge
Ram—(Continued)

Joe Reichley *(Mgr-Sls-New Vehicle)*
Steve Staub *(Mgr-Fin)*
Tom Dean *(Asst Mgr)*
Ike Eversole *(Mgr-Body Shop)*
Justin Harmon *(Gen Mgr)*
Cheryl Linscott *(Office Mgr)*
Mark Regan *(Dir-Parts)*
Lori Lawarre *(Controller)*
J. K. Sheasby *(Mgr-F&I Funding)*
Tom Endicott *(Mgr-Fin)*
Tim Ryan *(Mgr-Gen Sls)*
Andrea Heaton *(Mgr-HR)*
Jack Bowshier *(Mgr-Sls)*
Dennis Ward *(Mgr-Sls)*
Shane Cawley *(Mgr-Svc-Columbus)*
Brad Kaasa *(Mgr-Svc-Columbus)*

BOB DAVIDSON FORD LINCOLN

1845 E Joppa Rd, Parkville, MD
21234-2794
Tel.: (410) 661-6400
Web Site:
   http://www.bobdavidsonauto.com
Sales Range: $25-49.9 Million
Emp.: 100
Car Whslr
N.A.I.C.S.: 441110
John Marusiodis *(Mgr-Svc)*
Joe Mcneal *(Partner & VP)*
Bruce L. Schindler *(Owner & Pres)*

BOB DEAN SUPPLY, INC.

2624 Hanson St, Fort Myers, FL
33901
Tel.: (239) 332-1131
Web Site:
   https://www.bobdeansupply.com
Year Founded: 1947
Sales Range: $10-24.9 Million
Emp.: 60
Industrial Supplies Merchant Whslr
N.A.I.C.S.: 423840
Michael Gibbons *(Mgr-Sls Staff)*
Rosemary Schmidt *(VP)*

Subsidiaries:

Bob Dean Supply Inc.   (1)
1310 Evercane Rd, Clewiston, FL 33440
Tel.: (863) 983-6131
Web Site: http://www.bobdeansupply.com
Sales Range: $1-9.9 Million
Emp.: 5
Industrial Supplies Merchant Whslr
N.A.I.C.S.: 423840

BOB DUNN HYUNDAI SUBARU

801 E Bessemer Ave, Greensboro,
NC 27405
Tel.: (336) 275-9761
Web Site:
   http://www.bobdunnhyundai.com
Sales Range: $25-49.9 Million
Emp.: 100
Car Whslr
N.A.I.C.S.: 441110
Rick Powell *(Gen Mgr)*

BOB FISHER CHEVROLET, INC.

4111 Pottsville Pike, Reading, PA
19605-1203
Tel.: (610) 370-6683
Web Site:
   https://www.bobfisherchev.com
Sales Range: $50-74.9 Million
Emp.: 62
New Car Dealers
N.A.I.C.S.: 441110
Tom Cotter *(Bus Mgr-Elite)*
Andrew Geoghegan *(Mgr-Svc)*
Frank Perricone *(Mgr-Fin)*

BOB FOWLER & ASSOCIATES

1710 Mossbach Cir, Fresno, TX
77545
Tel.: (281) 431-9166
Sales Range: Less than $1 Million
Emp.: 3
N.A.I.C.S.: 541810
Bob Fowler *(Pres)*
Trish Jacquin *(Coord-Admin)*

BOB GOLD & ASSOCIATES

2780 Skypark Dr Ste 295, Torrance,
CA 90505
Tel.: (310) 784-1040   CA
Web Site: http://www.bobgoldpr.com
Sales Range: $10-24.9 Million
Emp.: 15
Advetising Agency
N.A.I.C.S.: 541810
Bob Gold *(Pres)*
Irene Simaono *(Office Mgr)*

BOB GRIMM CHEVROLET INC.

2271 S Main St, Morton, IL 61550
Tel.: (309) 263-2241
Web Site:
   http://www.bobgrimmchevrolet.com
Sales Range: $25-49.9 Million
Emp.: 51
Automobiles, New & Used
N.A.I.C.S.: 441110
Chuck Hart *(Pres)*
Gary Rassi *(CFO)*

BOB HALL INC.

5600 SE Crain, Upper Marlboro, MD
20772
Tel.: (301) 627-1900   MD
Year Founded: 1961
Sales Range: $25-49.9 Million
Emp.: 100
Distr of Beer & Alcoholic Products
N.A.I.C.S.: 424810
Evalina S. Mitchell *(Owner)*
Clarence Hall *(Controller)*
Eric Best *(Gen Mgr)*

BOB HEMBREE MOTOR COMPANY INC.

11982 US Hwy 431, Guntersville, AL
35976
Tel.: (256) 582-5603
Web Site:
   http://www.bobhembree.com
Rev.: $12,200,000
Emp.: 45
New Car Dealers
N.A.I.C.S.: 441110
Giselle Hembree *(Treas & Sec)*
R.L. Hembree Jr. *(Pres)*

BOB HOOK CHEVROLET

4144 Bardstown Rd, Louisville, KY
40218
Tel.: (502) 694-4460
Web Site: https://www.bobhook.com
Sales Range: $25-49.9 Million
Emp.: 110
New Car Retailer
N.A.I.C.S.: 441110
Bob Hook Jr. *(Pres)*
Bob Hook III *(Gen Mgr)*

BOB HOOK OF SHELBYVILLE

700 Taylorsville Rd, Shelbyville, KY
40065
Tel.: (502) 583-5727
Year Founded: 1980
Sales Range: $10-24.9 Million
Emp.: 20
Home Supply Whslr
N.A.I.C.S.: 441330
Richard Goss *(Gen Mgr)*

BOB HOPE AIRPORT

2627 N Hollywood Way, Burbank, CA
91505
Tel.: (818) 840-8840
Web Site:
   http://www.hollywoodairport.com
Sales Range: $10-24.9 Million
Emp.: 100
Airport
N.A.I.C.S.: 488119
Scott R. Smith *(Dir-Fin Svcs)*
Victor Gill *(Dir-Pub Affairs & Comm)*
Tom Janowitz *(Supvr-Ops)*
Ed Kochendarfer *(Supvr-Maintenance Electrical)*
Marco Rodriguez *(Supvr-Fleet)*
Carlos Villaneda *(Supvr-Comm Center)*
Kimberley Parker-Polito *(Dir-IT)*

BOB HOWARD DOWNTOWN DODGE INC.

9240 S Memorial, Tulsa, OK 74133
Tel.: (918) 584-1481
Web Site:
   http://www.southpointecjd.com
Rev.: $23,000,000
Emp.: 80
Car Dealership Owner & Operator
N.A.I.C.S.: 441110
Chris Sloan *(Mgr-Parts)*

BOB KING AUTO MALL

5115 New Centre Dr, Wilmington, NC
28403-1629
Tel.: (910) 782-2982
Web Site: https://www.bobking.com
Year Founded: 1978
Sales Range: $25-49.9 Million
Emp.: 175
Car Whslr
N.A.I.C.S.: 441110
Del Eaves *(Mgr-Svc)*
J. Phil Hardee *(VP)*
Robert King *(Pres)*
Jessie Thompson *(Mgr-Customer Rels)*
Richard Trask *(Gen Mgr)*

BOB KING, INC.

1601 Silas Creek Pkwy, Winston Salem, NC 27127
Tel.: (336) 295-1055
Web Site:
   https://www.bobkinghyundai.com
Sales Range: $10-24.9 Million
Emp.: 52
Car Whslr
N.A.I.C.S.: 441110
Rob King *(Pres)*

BOB MASSIE TOYOTA

12204 Rte 30, North Huntingdon, PA
15642
Tel.: (412) 678-6679
Web Site: http://www.bobmassie.com
Rev.: $18,300,000
Emp.: 40
Automobile Dealership
N.A.I.C.S.: 441110
Jason Massie *(Mgr-Sls)*
Les Mitchell *(Mgr-Inventory)*
Mark Carlson *(Gen Mgr)*
Robert Massie Jr. *(VP)*

BOB MAXEY FORD, INC.

1833 E Jefferson Ave, Detroit, MI
48207
Tel.: (313) 757-4698
Web Site:
   https://www.bobmaxeyford.com
Sales Range: $25-49.9 Million
Emp.: 100
Automobiles, New & Used
N.A.I.C.S.: 441110
Cheryl Staples *(Mgr-Fin)*
Kurt Limburg *(Mgr-Svcs)*

Subsidiaries:

Bob Maxey Ford, Inc-Bob Maxey Lincoln Mercury   (1)
16901 Mack Ave, Detroit, MI
48224   (100%)
Tel.: (313) 885-4000
Web Site: http://www.bobmaxeyford.com
Sales Range: $10-24.9 Million
Emp.: 60
New & Used Automobile Retailer
N.A.I.C.S.: 423110

BOB MILLS FURNITURE CO. INC.

3600 W Reno Ave, Oklahoma City,
OK 73107
Tel.: (405) 947-6500
Web Site:
   https://www.bobmillsfurniture.com
Rev.: $10,026,279
Emp.: 94
Furniture Retailer
N.A.I.C.S.: 449110
Robert L. Mills *(Pres)*
Jeff Barnes *(Mgr-Warehouse)*

BOB MOORE CADILLAC INC.

13000 N Broadway Ext, Oklahoma
City, OK 73114
Tel.: (405) 749-9000
Web Site: http://www.bobmoore.com
Rev.: $94,000,000
Emp.: 1,000
Automobiles, New & Used
N.A.I.C.S.: 441110
Mark Moore *(Pres)*

BOB MOORE DODGE, LLC.

7420 NW Expy, Oklahoma City, OK
73132
Tel.: (405) 546-2241
Web Site:
   https://www.bobmoorechrysler.com
Year Founded: 1970
Sales Range: $10-24.9 Million
Emp.: 100
Car Whslr
N.A.I.C.S.: 441110
Craig Newman *(Dir-Fin)*
Jason Akers *(Gen Mgr)*
Justin Fifield *(Dir-Fin)*

BOB NEILL INC.

691 Jonestown Rd, Winston Salem,
NC 27103
Tel.: (336) 760-4580
Web Site:
   https://www.mbwinstonsalem.com
Sales Range: $10-24.9 Million
Emp.: 100
Automobiles, New & Used
N.A.I.C.S.: 441110
David Neill *(Pres)*
Tim Cooper *(Gen Mgr)*
Lee Reavis *(Sls Mgr)*

BOB NOVICK AUTO MALL

808 N Pearl St, Bridgeton, NJ 08302
Tel.: (856) 451-0095
Web Site:
   https://www.bridgetonautomall.com
Year Founded: 1972
Sales Range: $10-24.9 Million
Emp.: 48
Car Whslr
N.A.I.C.S.: 441110
Debby Novick *(Gen Mgr)*

BOB PARKS REALTY LLC

8119 Isabella Ln Ste 105, Brentwood,
TN 37027
Tel.: (615) 370-8669
Web Site: http://www.bobparks.com
Sales Range: $10-24.9 Million
Emp.: 75
Real Estate Brokers & Agents
N.A.I.C.S.: 531210

Bob Parks *(Owner)*
Laura Crist *(Mgr-Relocation)*
Mary Catherine McAnulty *(Office Mgr)*

BOB PARRETT CONSTRUC-TION INC.
1226 W Barkley, Orange, CA 92868
Tel.: (714) 288-9108
Web Site:
http://www.bobparrettconstruc
tion.com
Rev.: $26,740,278
Emp.: 18
Industrial Buildings & Warehouses
N.A.I.C.S.: 236220
Bob Parrett *(Pres & CEO)*
Mike McCracken *(Project Mgr)*
Rich Zajic *(Project Mgr)*

BOB PROPHETER CON-STRUCTION LLC
18573 Pennington Rd, Sterling, IL 61081
Tel.: (815) 625-3077
Sales Range: $125-149.9 Million
Emp.: 15
General Contractor, Highway & Street Construction
N.A.I.C.S.: 237310
Florence Propheter *(Exec Dir)*

BOB RICHARDS, INC.
5512 Jefferson Davis Hwy, Beech Island, SC 29842-8544
Tel.: (803) 279-8400
Web Site:
http://www.bobrichardstoyota.com
Sales Range: $10-24.9 Million
Emp.: 72
Car Whslr
N.A.I.C.S.: 441110
Jo Griggs *(Mgr-Customer Rels)*
Terry Lambert *(Gen Mgr)*
Bob Richards *(Pres)*
Jeffrey F. Richards *(VP)*

BOB RIDINGS FORD INC.
931 W Springfield Rd, Taylorville, IL 62568
Tel.: (217) 824-2207
Web Site:
https://www.bobridings.com
Sales Range: $25-49.9 Million
Emp.: 110
Owner & Operator of Car Dealerships
N.A.I.C.S.: 441110
Robert Ridings *(Pres)*
Helen Ridings *(VP)*

BOB ROHRMAN MOTORS IN-CORPORATED
3900 South St, Lafayette, IN 47905
Tel.: (765) 448-1000
Web Site: http://www.rohrman.com
Sales Range: $10-24.9 Million
Emp.: 50
Sales of New & Used Automobiles
N.A.I.C.S.: 441110
Robert V. Rohrman *(Owner & Pres)*
Tom Hamlin *(Controller)*

BOB ROSS BUICK, INC.
85 Loop Rd, Dayton, OH 45459
Tel.: (937) 433-0990
Web Site:
http://www.bobrossauto.com
Sales Range: $50-74.9 Million
Emp.: 100
New Car Dealers
N.A.I.C.S.: 441110
Butch Spencer *(Gen Mgr)*
Kathleen Mayer *(Mgr-Bus & New Ve-hicle Sls)*
Bill Klapper *(Mgr-Pre-Owned Sls)*
Richard Knipp *(Mgr-Fleet)*
Randy Schuyler *(Asst Mgr-Parts)*

Barry Sullivan *(Dir-Fixed Ops)*
Soliel Verse *(Mgr-Internet Sls)*
Alfa Romeo *(Mgr-FIAT Sls)*
Vauni Blaut *(Mgr-Govt & Fleet Sls)*
Doug Glaser *(Mgr-HR)*
Michael Johnston *(Mgr-Parts-Columbus)*
Tyrone Kemp *(Mgr-Pre-Owned Bus)*

BOB SCHMITT HOMES INC.
9095 Gatestone Rd, North Ridgeville, OH 44039
Tel.: (440) 327-9495
Web Site:
https://www.bobschmitthomes.com
Rev.: $13,049,528
Emp.: 15
New Construction, Single-Family Houses
N.A.I.C.S.: 236115
Joe Mnolnar *(Exec VP)*
Michael P. Schmitt *(Pres & CEO)*
Scott T. Kubit *(VP)*
Edward A. Schmitt *(Chm)*

BOB SIGHT FORD INC.
610 NW Blue Pkwy, Lees Summit, MO 64063
Tel.: (816) 524-6550
Web Site: https://www.bobsight.com
Rev.: $63,100,000
Emp.: 100
New & Used Car Dealers
N.A.I.C.S.: 441110
Zach Sight *(CEO)*

BOB STALL CHEVROLET
7601 Alvarado Rd, La Mesa, CA 91942-8211
Tel.: (619) 460-1311
Web Site: https://www.bobstall.com
Year Founded: 1948
Sales Range: $25-49.9 Million
Emp.: 110
Car Whslr
N.A.I.C.S.: 441110
Vicki Dillingham *(CFO & Controller)*

BOB SUMEREL TIRE CO., INC.
1257 Cox Ave, Erlanger, KY 41018-1003
Tel.: (859) 341-2728   OH
Web Site:
https://www.bobsumereltire.com
Year Founded: 1968
Sales Range: $25-49.9 Million
Emp.: 200
Auto & Home Supply Services
N.A.I.C.S.: 441110
Robert B. Sumerel *(Chm & CEO)*
Tom Sumerel *(Pres & Head-Comml Sls)*

BOB SWOPE FORD, INC.
1307 N Dixie Ave, Elizabethtown, KY 42701
Tel.: (270) 737-1000
Web Site:
https://www.bobswopeford.com
Year Founded: 1975
Sales Range: $25-49.9 Million
Emp.: 40
Car Whslr
N.A.I.C.S.: 441110
Harry Partington *(Mgr)*
Bob F. Swope *(Pres)*
Carl Swope *(VP)*

BOB TAYLOR CHEVROLET INC.
5665 N Airport Rd, Naples, FL 34109
Tel.: (239) 591-0991
Web Site:
http://www.bobtaylorchevy.com
Rev.: $30,000,000
Emp.: 70

Car Dealership
N.A.I.C.S.: 441110
Michael Curtis *(Gen Mgr)*

BOB TOMES FORD, INC.
950 S Central Expy, McKinney, TX 75072
Tel.: (214) 544-5000
Web Site: https://bobtomesford.com
Sales Range: $25-49.9 Million
Emp.: 128
Car Whslr
N.A.I.C.S.: 441110
Ernie Smith *(Mgr-Ops)*
Bob Tomes *(Pres)*
Brandon Tomes *(VP)*

BOB TRACEY INC.
4744 University Blvd, Moon Town-ship, PA 15108
Tel.: (412) 269-9999
Web Site:
http://www.worldofcycles.com
Sales Range: $10-24.9 Million
Emp.: 37
Sales of Motorcycles
N.A.I.C.S.: 441227
Gregory Michel *(Pres)*

BOB UTTER FORD
2525 Texoma Pkwy, Sherman, TX 75090
Tel.: (903) 771-0100
Web Site:
https://www.bobutterford.net
Sales Range: $10-24.9 Million
Emp.: 90
New Car Whslr
N.A.I.C.S.: 441110
Bob Utter *(Owner & Mgr)*
Mike Martin *(Mgr-Parts)*

BOB WAGNER'S MILL CAR-PET INC.
4531 W Lincoln Hwy, Downingtown, PA 19335
Tel.: (610) 269-7808
Web Site: http://www.bobwagner.com
Sales Range: $10-24.9 Million
Emp.: 90
Owner & Operator of Floor Covering Stores
N.A.I.C.S.: 449121
Matt Wagner *(Owner)*

BOB WARD & SONS INCOR-PORATED
3015 Paxson St, Missoula, MT 59801
Tel.: (406) 728-3220
Web Site: https://www.bobwards.com
Sales Range: $50-74.9 Million
Emp.: 60
Sporting Goods & Bicycle Shops
N.A.I.C.S.: 459110
Keith I. Ward *(Pres)*
Mark Anderson *(Mgr-Ops)*

BOB WONDRIES FORD
400 S Atlantic Blvd, Alhambra, CA 91801
Tel.: (626) 231-0198
Web Site:
https://www.bobwondriesford.com
Year Founded: 1968
Sales Range: $25-49.9 Million
Emp.: 97
Owner & Operator of Car Dealerships
N.A.I.C.S.: 441110
Paul Wondries *(Owner)*

BOB WOODRUFF FOUNDA-TION
4628 Vernon Blvd Ste 531, Long Is-land, NY 11101
Tel.: (646) 341-6879   NY

Web Site:
http://www.bobwoodrufffoun
dation.org
Year Founded: 2007
Rev.: $7,868,581
Assets: $6,174,404
Liabilities: $326,483
Net Worth: $5,847,921
Earnings: $3,149,071
Emp.: 10
Fiscal Year-end: 12/31/13
Veteran Support Services
N.A.I.C.S.: 813410
Kevin Dougherty *(Fin Dir & Dir-Ops)*
Anne Marie Dougherty *(Exec Dir)*
Megan Bunce *(Mgr-Charitable Invest-ments Program)*
Sam Kille *(Mgr-Comm)*
Brett Morash *(Dir-Ops & Fin)*

BOB ZIMMERMAN FORD INC.
4001 1st Ave SE, Cedar Rapids, IA 52402
Tel.: (319) 366-4000
Web Site:
http://www.gozimmerman.com
Sales Range: $50-74.9 Million
Emp.: 127
Car Dealership
N.A.I.C.S.: 441110
R. Mark Zimmerman *(Pres)*
Bill Miller *(CFO)*

BOB'S BARRICADES INC.
921 Shotgun Rd, Sunrise, FL 33326-1910
Tel.: (954) 423-2627
Web Site:
https://www.bobsbarricades.com
Year Founded: 1975
Sales Range: $25-49.9 Million
Emp.: 225
Equipment Rental & Leasing
N.A.I.C.S.: 532490
Alan Chesler *(Pres & Partner)*
Happy Alter *(Owner & CEO)*
Gabriel Amarazeanu *(Mgr-Area Ops)*
Joe Alter *(Sr VP)*
John Baldwin *(VP-Sls & Mktg-South Florida)*

BOB'S DISCOUNT INC.
1750 Lisbon St, Lewiston, ME 04240
Tel.: (207) 689-2189
Rev.: $10,000,000
Emp.: 30
Variety Stores
N.A.I.C.S.: 455219

BOB'S KWIK SHOP FOODS CO
620 E 25th St, Kearney, NE 68847
Tel.: (308) 233-3000
Web Site:
http://www.bobssuperstore.com
Rev.: $10,699,471
Emp.: 115
Grocery Stores
N.A.I.C.S.: 445110
Robert B. Wilson Jr. *(Pres)*

BOB'S MARKETS, INC.
N of Bridge on Hwy 7, Jasper, AR 72641
Tel.: (870) 446-2381   AR
Year Founded: 1967
Sales Range: $10-24.9 Million
Emp.: 30
Grocery Stores, Independent
N.A.I.C.S.: 445110
Richard Matlock *(Gen Mgr)*

BOB'S PROCESSING, INC.
70705 16th Ave, South Haven, MI 49090
Tel.: (269) 637-5739
Web Site: https://www.bobsmeat.com

Bob's Processing, Inc.—(Continued)

Sales Range: $10-24.9 Million
Emp.: 3
Meat Processing Services
N.A.I.C.S.: 311612
Robert Filbrandt (Pres)

BOB'S RED MILL NATURAL FOODS, INC.
13521 SE Pleasant Ct, Milwaukie, OR 97222
Tel.: (503) 654-3215
Web Site:
http://www.bobsredmill.com
Sales Range: $25-49.9 Million
Emp.: 400
Mfr of Natural Food Products
N.A.I.C.S.: 311211
Robert Moore (Founder)
Dennis Gilliam (Owner)
Bryan Emerson (CIO)
Nancy Flint (Controller)
Dennis Vaughn (COO & Sr VP-Ops)
Richard Jones (Coord-Environmental Health & Safety)
Julia Person (Mgr-Sustainability)
Allyson Borozan (Sr VP-Mktg)
Trey Winthrop (CEO)

BOB'S SUPER SAVER INC
624 W Main St PO Box 323, Gardner, KS 66030-9627
Tel.: (913) 856-6610
Rev.: $11,300,000
Emp.: 116
Gasoline Stations with Convenience Stores
N.A.I.C.S.: 457110
Craig Dickey (VP-Pur)
Larry Good (Chm)

BOB'S TRANSPORT STORAGE CO
7980 Tar Bay Dr, Jessup, MD 20794
Tel.: (410) 796-2706
Web Site:
http://www.bobstransport.com
Sales Range: $10-24.9 Million
Emp.: 100
Trucking & Storage Services
N.A.I.C.S.: 484121
Robert Pfeffer Jr. (Pres)

BOB-BOYD LINCOLN OF COLUMBUS
2445 Billingsley Rd, Columbus, OH 43235
Tel.: (614) 759-3390
Web Site:
https://www.lincolnofcolumbus.com
Sales Range: $10-24.9 Million
Emp.: 100
Car Dealership
N.A.I.C.S.: 441110
Bob Dawes (Co-Owner)
Steve Skeldon (Gen Mgr-Sls-New Cars)
Tim Clark (Gen Mgr-Sls)
Steve Kessler (Gen Mgr-Sls)
Dave Wilson (Mgr-Fin)
John Dillon (Mgr-Sls-Internet)
Randy Ott (Mgr-Parts)
Betsy Newell-VanKirk (Mgr-Sls)
Wilbur Williams (Mgr-Body Shop)
Julie Brozie (Mgr-Customer Svc Lane)
Darrell Havener (Asst Mgr-Body Shop)

Subsidiaries:

Bob-Boyd Ford Mazda Dodge Inc.   (1)
2840 N Columbus St, Lancaster, OH 43130
Tel.: (740) 654-1122
Web Site: http://www.bobboyd.com
Rev.: $19,600,000

Emp.: 53
New & Used Car Dealers
N.A.I.C.S.: 441110
Robert L. Dawes (Owner)
Boyd Flacker (Owner)

BOBACK COMMERCIAL GROUP
10561 Ben C Pratt/6 Mile Cypress Pkwy Ste 116, Fort Myers, FL 33966
Tel.: (239) 466-7770
Web Site:
https://www.bobackcommercial.com
Sales Range: $1-9.9 Million
Emp.: 4
Commercial Real Estate Broker
N.A.I.C.S.: 531210
Jim Boback (Owner)

BOBAK SAUSAGE COMPANY
5275 S Archer Ave, Chicago, IL 60632
Tel.: (773) 735-5334
Web Site: http://www.bobak.com
Year Founded: 1967
Sales Range: $50-74.9 Million
Emp.: 150
Sausages & Related Products, From Purchased Meat
N.A.I.C.S.: 311612
Michael Phalen (Controller)
Stanley Bobak (Owner & Pres)

BOBB AUTOMOTIVE INC.
4639 W Braod St, Columbus, OH 43228
Tel.: (614) 853-3000
Web Site:
https://www.bobbsaysyes.com
Year Founded: 1945
Sales Range: $125-149.9 Million
Emp.: 900
Car Dealership Owner & Operator
N.A.I.C.S.: 441110
Jeff May (Pres)

BOBBIE BABY, INC.
1500 Castro St, San Francisco, CA 94114
Tel.: (415) 854-2500
Web Site: https://www.hibobbie.com
Year Founded: 2018
Organic Infant Products Mfr
N.A.I.C.S.: 311511
Laura Modi (CEO & Co-Founder)
Sarah Hardy (Co-Founder)

Subsidiaries:

Nature's One, LLC   (1)
8754 Cotter St, Lewis Center, OH 43035
Tel.: (740) 548-0135
Web Site: http://www.naturesone.com
Emp.: 26
Organic Baby Products Mfr
N.A.I.C.S.: 424210
Leslie VonKaenel (Asst Mgr-Medical Sls)
Jay Highman (Pres & CEO)

BOBBY COX COMPANIES, INC.
5000 Overton Plz, Fort Worth, TX 76109
Tel.: (817) 377-6200
Web Site: https://www.bobbycox.com
Year Founded: 1961
Sales Range: $200-249.9 Million
Emp.: 4,000
Restaurant
N.A.I.C.S.: 722513
Bobby D. Cox (Founder)

BOBBY DODD INSTITUTE
2120 Marietta Blvd NW, Atlanta, GA 30318
Tel.: (678) 365-0071   GA
Web Site: https://www.bobbydodd.org

Year Founded: 1989
Rev.: $21,028,293
Assets: $15,296,950
Liabilities: $1,384,885
Net Worth: $13,912,065
Earnings: $4,120,195
Emp.: 275
Fiscal Year-end: 06/30/18
Social Advocacy Services
N.A.I.C.S.: 813319
Wayne McMillan (Pres & CEO)
John Ralls (Chm)
David Essary (Vice Chm)
Leah Davenport (Treas)
Ron Shah (Sec)

BOBBY HENARD TIRE SERVICE
308 E Cypress, Brinkley, AR 72021
Tel.: (870) 734-1044
Web Site:
http://www.bobbyhenardtire.com
Year Founded: 1967
Sales Range: $10-24.9 Million
Emp.: 18
Tire & Tube Whslr
N.A.I.C.S.: 423130
Bobby Henard (CEO)
Jacquelyn H. Geisler (Pres)

BOBBY LAYMAN CADILLAC GMC, INC.
3733 Claypool St NW, Carroll, OH 43112
Tel.: (740) 654-9560   OH
Web Site:
http://www.bobbylaymancars.net
Sales Range: $1-9.9 Million
New & Used Car Dealer
N.A.I.C.S.: 441110
Bobby Layman (Owner)

BOBBY MURRAY TOYOTA
943 N Wesleyan Blvd, Rocky Mount, NC 27804-1786
Tel.: (252) 977-0224
Web Site:
http://www.bmurraytoyota.com
Year Founded: 1983
Sales Range: $10-24.9 Million
Emp.: 45
New Car Whslr
N.A.I.C.S.: 441110
J. Brent King (Sec)
Tim Martin (Gen Mgr)

BOBBY RAHAL AUTO GROUP
15035 Perry Hwy, Wexford, PA 15090
Tel.: (724) 940-3411
Web Site:
https://www.bobbyrahal.com
Year Founded: 1999
Sales Range: $10-24.9 Million
Emp.: 80
Car Whslr
N.A.I.C.S.: 441110
Perry Black (Owner)

BOBBY RAHAL HONDA
6696 Carlisle Pike, Mechanicsburg, PA 17050
Tel.: (717) 610-0330
Web Site:
https://www.bobbyrahalhonda.com
Sales Range: $10-24.9 Million
Emp.: 60
New Car Retailer
N.A.I.C.S.: 441110
Ben Shipp (Asst Gen Mgr)
Rob Bowersox (Mgr-Parts)
Calvin Dutton (Mgr-Svc)
Mark Feschuk (Mgr-Customer Rels)
Aaron McAdoo (Asst Mgr-Svc)
Linda Moore (Coord-Shipping & Receiving)

Adam Crouse (Mgr-Fin)
Matt Cole (Gen Mgr-Sls)
Rick Kunkle (Mgr-Sls)

BOBCAT ENTERPRISES INC.
9605 Princeton-Glendale Rd, Hamilton, OH 45011
Tel.: (513) 874-8945
Web Site: http://www.bobcat-ent.com
Sales Range: $10-24.9 Million
Emp.: 100
General Construction Machinery & Equipment
N.A.I.C.S.: 423810
Tim Riley (Branch Mgr-KY-Louisville)
Jeff Brandner (Mgr-Parts)
Kimberly Trapp (Gen Mgr)
Tom Bruecken (Branch Mgr)
Tim Cannon (Mgr-Field Sls-Ohio)
Arlen Swenson (Mgr-Sls)
Jon Schell (Branch Mgr)

BOBCAT OF BOSTON, INC.
20 Concord St, North Reading, MA 01864-2602
Tel.: (978) 664-3727
Web Site:
https://www.bobcatboston.com
Sales Range: $10-24.9 Million
Emp.: 45
Construction Equipment Sales, Service & Rental
N.A.I.C.S.: 423810
Steven Arsenault (Pres)
Guido Lonzana (Pres)

BOBCAT OF CONNECTICUT INC.
54 Alna Ln, East Hartford, CT 06108
Tel.: (860) 282-2648
Web Site: https://www.bobcatct.com
Sales Range: $10-24.9 Million
Emp.: 50
General Construction Machinery & Equipment
N.A.I.C.S.: 423810
Ed Reeves (VP)

BOBCAT OF NEW YORK INC.
24 Industrial Blvd, Medford, NY 11763
Tel.: (631) 447-2228
Web Site:
https://www.bobcatzone.com
Rev.: $15,000,000
Emp.: 40
Heavy Construction Equipment Rental
N.A.I.C.S.: 532412
Gary Angelino (Mgr)
Rob Sonnick (VP-Sls)

BOBCO INC.
1700 Starita Rd, Charlotte, NC 28206
Tel.: (704) 596-8900
Web Site:
https://www.charlottetractor.com
Year Founded: 1966
Sales Range: $25-49.9 Million
Emp.: 60
Whslr & Retailer of General Construction Machinery & Equipment
N.A.I.C.S.: 423810
Bobby Cockerham (Pres)
Tommy Overcash (Mgr-Svc)
Tim N. Cockerham (VP)
Tony Carter (Mgr-Parts)

Subsidiaries:

Charlotte Tractor Company   (1)
1700 Starita Rd, Charlotte, NC 28206
Tel.: (704) 596-8900
Web Site: http://www.charlottetractor.com
Sales Range: $10-24.9 Million
Emp.: 19
Whslr & Retailer of General Construction Machinery & Equipment

N.A.I.C.S.: 423810
Bobby Cockerham *(Gen Mgr)*

Greensboro Tractor Company (1)
2820 S Elm Eugene St, Greensboro, NC 27406
Tel.: (336) 273-3606
Web Site: http://www.charlottetractor.com
Sales Range: $10-24.9 Million
Emp.: 17
Whslr & Retailer of General Construction Machinery & Equipment
N.A.I.C.S.: 423810
Larry Hobbs *(Gen Mgr & Mgr-Sls)*
Tony Carter *(Mgr-Parts)*
Tim Cockerham *(VP)*

Lake Norman Tractor Company (1)
18309 Statesville Rd, Cornelius, NC 28031
Tel.: (704) 892-6750
Web Site: http://www.charlottetractor.com
Sales Range: $25-49.9 Million
Emp.: 25
Whslr & Retailer of General Construction Machinery & Equipment
N.A.I.C.S.: 444240
Dan Swanger *(Gen Mgr)*

Winston Tractor Company (1)
3859 N Patterson Ave, Winston Salem, NC 27105
Tel.: (336) 744-7000
Web Site: http://www.winstontractor.com
Sales Range: $10-24.9 Million
Emp.: 15
Whslr & Retailer of General Construction Machinery & Equipment
N.A.I.C.S.: 423820
Greg Barnett *(Gen Mgr)*

BOBIT BUSINESS MEDIA INC.
3520 Challenger St, Torrance, CA 90503
Tel.: (310) 533-2400   DE
Web Site: http://www.bobit.com
Year Founded: 1961
Sales Range: $100-124.9 Million
Emp.: 170
Business Magazine Publishing Services
N.A.I.C.S.: 513120
Christine Strain *(Dir-Acctg)*
Michelle Mendez *(Dir-Events)*
Kelly Bracken *(Dir-Production)*
Sherb Brown *(Pres & Chief Revenue Officer)*
Cyndy Drummey *(COO)*
Paul Andrews *(CMO)*
Tim Sendelbach *(VP)*
Brian O'Rourke *(Pres-New Beauty, Health & Wellness Div-Buffalo Grove)*
Tim Chambers *(Mktg Dir)*
Colin Sutherland *(CEO)*

BOBOLI INTERNATIONAL, LLC
3439 Brookside Rd Ste 104, Stockton, CA 95219
Tel.: (209) 473-3507   CA
Web Site: http://www.boboli-intl.com
Year Founded: 1986
Sales Range: $10-24.9 Million
Emp.: 75
Frozen Baked Goods Mfr & Marketer
N.A.I.C.S.: 311412
Donna Liddiard *(Office Mgr)*
Kym Gervais *(Office Mgr)*

Subsidiaries:

Bakery Van Diermen BV (1)
Handelsweg 1, Postbus 116, Bunschoten, 3751 LR, Netherlands
Tel.: (31) 332995045
Web Site: http://www.vandiermen.nl
Sales Range: $10-24.9 Million
Emp.: 120
Bakery
N.A.I.C.S.: 311812
Jan Van Diermen *(CEO)*

BOBRICK WASHROOM EQUIPMENT, INC.

6901 Tujunga Ave, North Hollywood, CA 91605-6213
Tel.: (818) 764-1000   CA
Web Site: https://www.bobrick.com
Year Founded: 1906
Sales Range: $300-349.9 Million
Emp.: 500
Commercial Hand Dryer Soap Dispenser & Washroom Accessory Mfr
N.A.I.C.S.: 332999
Mark Louchheim *(Pres)*

Subsidiaries:

Bobrick Washroom Equipment Limited (1)
2 The Hangar Perseverance Works, 38 Kingsland Road, London, E2 8DD, United Kingdom
Tel.: (44) 20 8366.1771
Web Site: http://www.bobrick.co.uk
Sales Range: $10-24.9 Million
Emp.: 2
Washroom Equipment Mfr
N.A.I.C.S.: 333310
Philippe Sukyas *(Mgr-Ops)*

Koala Kare Products (1)
6982 S Quentin St, Centennial, CO 80112 (100%)
Tel.: (303) 539-8300
Web Site: http://www.koalabear.com
Sales Range: $25-49.9 Million
Emp.: 50
Baby Diaper-Changing Stations, Child Seating & Activity Products Mfr
N.A.I.C.S.: 339930
Brendan Cherry *(VP & Gen Mgr)*
Bonnie Yatkeman *(Mgr-Mktg Category)*

BOC INTERNATIONAL, INC.
23 Drydock Ave 5th Fl, Boston, MA 02210
Tel.: (617) 345-0050   MA
Web Site: http://www.bocintl.com
Year Founded: 1993
Rev.: $20,700,000
Emp.: 36
Deep Sea Freight Transportation
N.A.I.C.S.: 483111
Brian Kilduff *(Co-Founder, Co-Owner & Pres)*
Patrick Fay *(Co-Founder, Co-Owner & VP)*

BOCA RATON TRAVEL & CRUISES, INC.
225 E Palmetto Park Rd, Boca Raton, FL 33432
Tel.: (561) 395-1414   FL
Web Site: https://www.bocaratontravel.com
Year Founded: 1989
Sales Range: $10-24.9 Million
Emp.: 15
Travel Agency
N.A.I.C.S.: 561510
Lisa Le Brun *(Dir-Corp Travel)*

BOCA SYSTEMS, INC.
1065 S Rogers Cir, Boca Raton, FL 33487
Tel.: (561) 998-9600
Web Site: https://www.bocasystems.com
Year Founded: 1980
Sales Range: $10-24.9 Million
Emp.: 135
Computer Peripheral Equipment Mfr
N.A.I.C.S.: 334118
Joseph Gross *(Pres)*
Larry Gross *(CFO & Treas)*
Robert Kohn *(VP-Sls & Mktg)*

BOCA THEATER & AUTOMATION, INC.
9020 Kimberly Blvd, Boca Raton, FL 33434
Tel.: (561) 999-9024   FL

Web Site: http://www.bocatheater.com
Year Founded: 2001
Sales Range: $1-9.9 Million
Emp.: 20
Installation of Home Entertainment Systems
N.A.I.C.S.: 811210
Jeffrey Galea *(Pres)*

BOCA WEST COUNTRY CLUB INC.
20583 Boca W Dr, Boca Raton, FL 33434
Tel.: (561) 488-6990
Web Site: http://www.bocawest.org
Year Founded: 1971
Rev.: $32,582,419
Emp.: 300
Operator of Country Club
N.A.I.C.S.: 713910
Matthew Linderman *(COO & Gen Mgr)*
Arthur Charwat *(Pres)*
William Simmons *(Treas)*
Howard Liebman *(Chm)*
Brad Friend *(Dir-Golf)*

BOCK COMMUNICATIONS, INC.
610 Loretta Dr, Laguna Beach, CA 92651-4126
Tel.: (714) 540-1030   CA
Web Site: http://www.bockpr.com
Year Founded: 1995
Rev.: $1,700,000
Emp.: 16
Fiscal Year-end: 12/31/06
Advetising Agency
N.A.I.C.S.: 541810

BOCK CONSTRUCTION INC.
1900 E 28th St, Chattanooga, TN 37407
Tel.: (423) 698-5250
Web Site: http://www.bockco.com
Sales Range: $10-24.9 Million
Emp.: 130
Drywall Products Mfr
N.A.I.C.S.: 238310
George Bock *(Pres)*

BOCKER CHEVROLET BUICK GMC CADILLAC
801 E South St, Freeport, IL 61032
Tel.: (815) 235-2121
Web Site: http://www.bockerautogroup.com
Sales Range: $10-24.9 Million
Emp.: 75
New Car Retailer
N.A.I.C.S.: 441110
Delbert Bunker *(Owner)*
Chuck Hayes *(Mgr-New Car)*
Steve Stiefel *(Mgr-Used Car)*
Robert Robb *(Mgr-Svc)*
Mike Haffele *(Bus Mgr)*
Steve Burris *(Mgr-Collision Center Shop)*
Gretchen Cross *(Office Mgr-Collision Center)*
Gary McGuire *(Asst Mgr-Svc)*
Denny Rackow *(Mgr-Parts)*
Greg Tremble *(Mgr-Leasing)*
Danny Stark *(Bus Mgr)*

BODDEN PARTNERS
102 Madison Ave 8th Fl, New York, NY 10016-7417
Tel.: (212) 328-1111   NY
Web Site: http://www.boddenpartners.com
Year Founded: 1975
Sales Range: $100-124.9 Million
Emp.: 60
Advertising Agencies

N.A.I.C.S.: 541810
Marty Mitchell *(CMO)*
Chris Bodden *(Pres & Exec Dir-Creative)*
Bill Cuff *(VP & Dir-Strategic Partners)*

Subsidiaries:

Hamilton Public Relations (1)
102 Madison Ave 7th Fl, New York, NY 10016
Tel.: (212) 328-5201
Web Site: http://www.getpr.com
Sales Range: $10-24.9 Million
Emp.: 5
Public Relations
N.A.I.C.S.: 541820
John H. Frew *(Pres)*
Kevin Sniffen *(VP)*

BODDIE-NOELL ENTERPRISES, INC.
1021 Noell Ln, Rocky Mount, NC 27804
Tel.: (252) 937-2000   NC
Web Site: https://www.bneinc.com
Year Founded: 1962
Sales Range: $1-4.9 Billion
Emp.: 10,000
Restaurant Franchise
N.A.I.C.S.: 722511
William L. Boddie *(Co-Pres & Co-CEO)*
Michael W. Boddie *(Co-Pres & Co-CEO)*
Michael Hancock *(Exec VP)*
Jerry Allsbrook *(CMO)*

Subsidiaries:

BNE Land & Development Co. (1)
1021 Noel Ln, Rocky Mount, NC 27802-1908
Tel.: (252) 937-2000
Web Site: http://www.bneinc.com
Sales Range: $25-49.9 Million
Emp.: 6
Acquisition & Development of Residential & Commercial Real Estate
N.A.I.C.S.: 237210
Mayo Boddie *(Chm)*

BODDINGTON LUMBER CO
4220 Mark Dabling Blvd, Colorado Springs, CO 80907
Tel.: (719) 528-6000
Web Site: http://www.boddingtonlumberco.com
Sales Range: $10-24.9 Million
Emp.: 25
Lumber: Rough, Dressed & Finished
N.A.I.C.S.: 423310
Robert Jordan *(VP)*
Mervin G. Humphries *(VP)*

BODEANS BAKING COMPANY LLC
2375 Industrial Rd SW, Le Mars, IA 51031
Tel.: (712) 548-4422
Web Site: http://www.bodeansbaking.com
Sales Range: $10-24.9 Million
Emp.: 70
Sugar Cones Mfr
N.A.I.C.S.: 311340
Dean Jacobson *(Co-Owner)*
Bo Jacobson *(Co-Owner)*

BODEANS WAFER COMPANY, LLC
1790 21st St SW, Le Mars, IA 51031-8860
Tel.: (712) 548-4422
Web Site: https://www.bodeansbaking.com
Sales Range: $10-24.9 Million
Emp.: 200
Cookie & Cracker Mfr
N.A.I.C.S.: 311821

Bodeans Wafer Company, LLC—(Continued)

Angela Kneip *(CFO)*
John Wilhelm *(COO)*

BODELL CONSTRUCTION COMPANY INC.
586 Fine Dr, Salt Lake City, UT 84115-4244
Tel.: (801) 261-4343   UT
Web Site:
    https://www.bodellconstruction.com
Year Founded: 1972
Sales Range: $25-49.9 Million
Emp.: 250
General Contractors
N.A.I.C.S.: 236220
Michael J. Bodell Sr. *(Pres & CEO)*
Michael J. Bodell II *(Exec VP)*

Subsidiaries:

Bodell Construction Company Inc. - Hawaii Division   (1)
550 Paiea St Ste 228, Honolulu, HI 96819
Tel.: (808) 537-1826
Industrial Building Construction Services
N.A.I.C.S.: 236210

BODEN STORE FIXTURES INC.
5335 NE 109th Ave, Portland, OR 97220
Tel.: (503) 252-4728
Web Site: http://www.boden.com
Sales Range: $10-24.9 Million
Emp.: 100
Store & Office Display Cases & Fixtures
N.A.I.C.S.: 337212
Benjamin Boden *(Pres)*
Rosely Ayers *(CFO)*

BODENSTEINER IMPLEMENT COMPANY
24125 Highway 13, Elkader, IA 52043
Tel.: (563) 245-2470   IA
Web Site: https://www.bodimp.com
Year Founded: 1982
Farm Equipment Retailer
N.A.I.C.S.: 423820
Robert Bodensteiner *(Pres)*
Luther Koenig *(Sls Mgr)*
Jeff Reierson *(Mgr-Part)*
Craig Heying *(Mgr-Svc)*

BODIN CONCRETE LP
4810 Boyd Blvd, Rowlett, TX 75088-3935
Tel.: (972) 475-8118   TX
Web Site:
    https://www.bodinconcrete.com
Year Founded: 1962
Sales Range: $25-49.9 Million
Emp.: 25
Ready-Mixed Concrete Products & Sales
N.A.I.C.S.: 327320
Cynthia Kelley *(COO)*
Charlotte Bodin *(Owner)*
Michelle Ragland *(Controller & Dir-HR)*

BODINE AND COMPANY, LLC
8544 Hickory Hill Dr Ste 2, Poland, OH 44514
Tel.: (330) 333-4000   OH
Web Site:
    https://www.bodinecompany.com
Accounting Services
N.A.I.C.S.: 541219
Matthew Bodine *(Founder)*

Subsidiaries:

Cerimele, Meyer & Wray, LLC   (1)
727 E Western Reserve Rd Unit D, Poland, OH 44514
Tel.: (330) 629-7520

Web Site: http://www.cmwcpa.com
Accounting Services
N.A.I.C.S.: 541219
John Wray *(Partner)*

BODINE ELECTRIC COMPANY
201 Northfield Rd, Northfield, IL 60093-3311
Tel.: (773) 478-3515   IL
Web Site: https://www.bodine-electric.com
Year Founded: 1905
Sales Range: $100-124.9 Million
Emp.: 200
Electric FHP Motors, Gearmotors & Motion Control Systems
N.A.I.C.S.: 335312
Michael Gschwind *(VP-Sls & Mktg)*
Gary Janecek *(Coord-Sample)*
Steve Zgoba *(Sr Engr-Electrical)*
Pao Han *(Sr Engr-Mechanical)*

BODIS, LLC
1133 Broadway Ste 706, New York, NY 10010
Tel.: (877) 263-4744
Web Site: http://www.bodis.com
Year Founded: 2007
Sales Range: $1-9.9 Million
Domain Name Registration, Hosting & Parking Services
N.A.I.C.S.: 518210
Matt Wegrzyn *(Founder & CEO)*

BODKIN ASSOCIATES, INC.
1555 W Oak St Ste 100, Zionsville, IN 46077-1959
Tel.: (877) 263-5468
Web Site:
    http://www.teambodkin.com
Year Founded: 1990
Sales Range: Less than $1 Million
Emp.: 5
Advetising Agency
N.A.I.C.S.: 541810
Clyde Bodkin *(Owner)*
Steve Miller *(Designer)*
Barbara Putz *(Dir-Opers)*

BODON INDUSTRIES INC.
400 Old Reading Pke Ste 100, Pottstown, PA 19464-3781
Tel.: (610) 323-0700   PA
Web Site:
    http://www.universalconcrete.com
Year Founded: 1981
Sales Range: $10-24.9 Million
Emp.: 100
Mfr Architectural Pre-Cast Concrete Products
N.A.I.C.S.: 327390
Donald L. Faust Jr. *(Pres)*

Subsidiaries:

Universal Concrete Products Corporation   (1)
400 Old Reading Pike Ste 100, Pottstown, PA 19464-3781   (100%)
Tel.: (610) 323-0700
Web Site: http://www.universalconcrete.com
Sales Range: $10-24.9 Million
Emp.: 25
Concrete Products
N.A.I.C.S.: 327390

Universal Concrete Products of New Jersey Inc.   (1)
400 Old Reading Pike Ste A100, Pottstown, PA 19464-3781
Tel.: (609) 704-9400
Sales Range: $1-9.9 Million
Emp.: 45
Mfr of Concrete Products
N.A.I.C.S.: 327390

BODWELL CHRYSLER-JEEP-DODGE

169 Pleasant St, Brunswick, ME 04011-2215
Tel.: (207) 729-3375
Web Site:
    http://www.bodwellauto.com
Sales Range: $25-49.9 Million
Emp.: 45
New Car Dealers
N.A.I.C.S.: 441110
William E. Bodwell *(Pres & Treas)*

BODY BASICS FITNESS EQUIPMENT
10912 Prairie Brook Rd, Omaha, NE 68144
Tel.: (402) 397-8866
Web Site:
    https://www.bodybasics.com
Sales Range: $1-9.9 Million
Emp.: 10
Fitness Equipment Store Operator
N.A.I.C.S.: 459110
David Kutler *(Founder, Owner & Pres)*
Buddy Vincent *(Mgr-Comml Sls)*

BODY BASICS, INC.
10912 Prairie Brook Rd, Omaha, NE 68144
Tel.: (402) 397-8866   NE
Web Site: http://www.bodybasics.com
Year Founded: 1986
Sales Range: $1-9.9 Million
Emp.: 10
Body Fitness Equipment Supplies
N.A.I.C.S.: 459110
David Kutler *(Founder, Owner & Pres)*
Buddy Vincent *(Mgr-Comml Sls)*
Joe Rauth *(Mgr-Store & Buyer)*

BODY WAVES INC.
12362 Knott St, Garden Grove, CA 92841
Tel.: (714) 898-9900
Web Site: http://www.bodywaves.com
Sales Range: $25-49.9 Million
Emp.: 100
Mfr of Dresses
N.A.I.C.S.: 561990
Au Peng *(Mgr-Ops)*

BODY WISE INTERNATIONAL INC.
1701 Armstrong Ave Ste 101, Irvine, CA 92614
Tel.: (714) 505-6121
Web Site: http://www.bodywise.com
Rev.: $40,000,000
Emp.: 20
Organic & Diet Food
N.A.I.C.S.: 424490
William F. Farley *(CEO)*
Rolando Weissenberg *(Dir-IT)*

BODYGUARDZ
2600 Executive Pkwy Ste 140, Lehi, UT 84043
Tel.: (801) 495-3514
Web Site:
    http://www.bodyguardz.com
Year Founded: 2002
Sales Range: $1-9.9 Million
Emp.: 40
Mfr Protection Products to Mobile Device Users
N.A.I.C.S.: 517112
Kirk Feller *(Pres & CEO)*
Whitney Pye *(Dir-ECommerce)*
Lyndsay Kirkham *(Mgr-Natl Trng)*

BODYHEALTH.COM LLC
707 Cleveland St, Clearwater, FL 33755
Web Site: http://www.bodyhealth.com
Year Founded: 2000

Sales Range: $1-9.9 Million
Medical Product Retailer
N.A.I.C.S.: 456110
Chris Alexander *(Mgr)*

BODYSHOPBIDS, INC.
1 N Dearborn Ste 600, Chicago, IL 60602
Tel.: (312) 906-7038
Web Site:
    http://www.snapsheetclaims.com
Year Founded: 2010
Sales Range: $25-49.9 Million
Emp.: 497
Mobile Application Development Services
N.A.I.C.S.: 541511
Brad Weisberg *(Co-Founder, Chm & CEO)*
Jamie Yoder *(Pres)*
C. J. Przybyl *(Co-Founder & Chief Strategy Officer)*
Dan Colomb *(CTO)*
Susan Sell *(CFO)*

BOEKEL INDUSTRIES INC.
855 Pennsylvania Blvd, Feasterville Trevose, PA 19053
Tel.: (215) 396-8200
Web Site: https://www.boekelsci.com
Sales Range: $10-24.9 Million
Emp.: 36
Laboratory Apparatus & Furniture
N.A.I.C.S.: 334516
Leo Synnestvedt *(Chm & CEO)*
Steve Christie *(Pres & COO)*
Brian Canna *(Dir-Natl Sls)*

BOELTER + LINCOLN MARKETING COMMUNICATIONS
222 E Erie Ste 400, Milwaukee, WI 53202
Tel.: (414) 271-0101
Web Site:
    http://www.boelterlincoln.com
Year Founded: 1975
Advetising Agency
N.A.I.C.S.: 541810
Jill Brzeski *(Pres & CEO)*
Dawn Agacki *(COO & VP)*
H. Andrew Larsen *(VP & Dir-PR)*
Lisa Huebner *(VP & Dir-Media)*
Wendy Appelbaum *(Dir-Fin Svcs)*
Steve Roneid *(Mgr-Acctg)*
Garth Cramer *(Dir-Creative)*
Scott Winklebleck *(Mgr-Interactive)*
Brian Stefanik *(Assoc Dir-Creative)*
Katie Vieau *(Mgr-Production)*
Shannon Novotny *(Acct Dir)*
Mary Wienkers *(VP & Dir-Media)*

BOENNING & SCATTERGOOD, INC.
4 Tower Bridge, West Conshohocken, PA 19428
Tel.: (610) 832-1212
Web Site:
    http://www.boenningscattergood.com
Year Founded: 1914
Sales Range: $25-49.9 Million
Emp.: 100
Stock Brokers & Dealers
N.A.I.C.S.: 523150
Michael A. Galantino *(Mng Dir-Private Client Grp)*
Jeff Stannard *(Mng Dir & Head-Private Client Grp)*
Michael Mara *(Pres)*
Jennifer Weintraub *(Mgr-Mktg & Corp Comm)*
Lynn Niedrowski *(Chief HR Officer)*
Dan Cardenas *(Dir-Equity Res)*
Ryan Connors *(Dir-Res)*
Harold F. Scattergood Jr. *(Chm & CEO)*
Henry D. Boenning Jr. *(Founder)*
Anthony A. Latini Jr. *(Mng Dir)*

BOERNER TRUCK CENTER
3620 E Florence Ave, Huntington
Park, CA 90255-5905
Tel.: (323) 560-3882   CA
Web Site:
   http://www.boernertrucks.com
Year Founded: 1926
Sales Range: $10-24.9 Million
Emp.: 86
Dealer of Commercial Trucks
N.A.I.C.S.: 441110

Subsidiaries:

Fleet Lease Inc.   (1)
3620 E Florence Ave, Huntington Park, CA
90255-5905
Tel.: (323) 560-3882
Web Site: http://www.rwcgroup.com
Sales Range: $10-24.9 Million
Emp.: 4
Truck Rental & Leasing Services
N.A.I.C.S.: 532120
Gloria Mada (CEO)

BOGATI URNS COMPANY
4431 Independence Ct, Sarasota, FL
34234
Tel.: (941) 351-3382
Web Site: http://www.bogatiurns.com
Sales Range: $1-9.9 Million
Urn Distr & Retailer
N.A.I.C.S.: 423990
Andrea Bogard (Founder)
Jim Knake (Creative Dir)
Michelle Matson (Dir-Sls & Mktg)

BOGDANA CORPORATION
421 S Lafayette Pk Pl 513, Los Ange-
les, CA 90057
Tel.: (213) 365-0144
Web Site:
   http://www.bogdanavitamins.com
Distribution Of Nutritional Products &
Perfumes
N.A.I.C.S.: 325620
Bogda Gruber (Pres)

BOGER CONCRETE
202 N Railroad St, Annville, PA
17003
Tel.: (717) 867-3992
Web Site:
   https://www.bogerconcrete.com
Sales Range: $10-24.9 Million
Emp.: 80
Dealers of Ready-Mixed Concrete
N.A.I.C.S.: 327320
Randy Peiffer (Mgr)

BOGNER CONSTRUCTION COMPANY
305 W Mulberry St, Wooster, OH
44691
Tel.: (330) 262-6730
Web Site:
   https://www.bognergroup.com
Year Founded: 1897
Sales Range: $10-24.9 Million
Emp.: 75
Commercial & Institutional Building
Construction Services
N.A.I.C.S.: 236220
Theodore R. Bogner (Pres & CEO)
Robert E. Bogner (Treas & VP)
Brian Bogner (Dir-Costing & Estimat-
ing)
Michael Bogner (Dir-Procurement)
Adam Bogner (Project Mgr)
Barry Cochran (Project Mgr)
Chris Curtis (Mgr-Warehouse)
Kathy Horst (Mgr-Acctg)
Ted Luc (Project Mgr)
Randy Robinson (Project Mgr)
Vickie Shriver (Dir-Acctg)
William Studenic (Project Mgr)
Tim Bogner (Dir-Field Ops)

BOGOPA ENTERPRISES INC.
650 Fountain Ave, Brooklyn, NY
11208
Tel.: (718) 257-7801
Web Site: http://www.bogopausa.com
Sales Range: $10-24.9 Million
Emp.: 11
Groceries, General Line
N.A.I.C.S.: 424410
Hee Whril (Pres & CEO)
James Y. Chung (COO & Sr VP)

Subsidiaries:

37th Ave Market Inc.   (1)
35-60 Junction Blvd, Corona, NY 11368
Tel.: (718) 396-6454
Grocery Stores
N.A.I.C.S.: 445110

BOGOTA LATIN BISTRO
141 5th Ave, Brooklyn, NY 11217
Tel.: (718) 230-3805
Web Site:
   https://www.bogotabistro.com
Year Founded: 2005
Sales Range: $1-9.9 Million
Emp.: 60
Restaurant Featuring Colombian-
Style Dishes & Drinks
N.A.I.C.S.: 722511
Farid Ali Lancheros (Partner)
George Constantinou (Co-Owner)
Maya H. Warren (Mgr-Admin)

BOGOTA SAVINGS BANK
60 E Main St, Bogota, NJ 07603
Tel.: (201) 862-8260
Web Site:
   https://www.bogotasavingbank.com
Sales Range: $10-24.9 Million
Emp.: 30
Banking Services
N.A.I.C.S.: 522180
Diane Scriveri (Chief Lending Officer)
Adam Friedberg (Mgr-Bridgeport)
Laura Labetti (Mgr-Bridgeport)
Brian Kohles (VP-Residential & Mgr-
Loan)
Kevin Pace (Pres & CEO)
Michael A. Catania Sr. (Officer-Loan,
VP & Mgr-Sls)

BOGRAD BROTHERS INC.
81 Hamburg Tpke, Riverdale, NJ
07457
Rev.: $10,419,944
Emp.: 33
Furniture Retailer
N.A.I.C.S.: 449110
Joseph Bograd (Pres)

BOH BROS. CONSTRUCTION CO., LLC
730 S Tonti St, New Orleans, LA
70119-7551
Tel.: (504) 821-2400   LA
Web Site: https://www.bohbros.com
Year Founded: 1909
Sales Range: $75-99.9 Million
Emp.: 85
Heavy Construction Contracting Ser-
vices
N.A.I.C.S.: 237310
Jacques Saucier (Project Mgr)
Robert S. Boh (Chm & CEO)
Stephen Boh (Pres & Chief Admin
Officer)
Edward A. Scheuermann (COO)
Robert Senior (CFO)
G.J. Schexnayder (Mgr-Heavy Con-
struction)

BOHL CRANE INC.
534 W Laskey Rd, Toledo, OH 43612
Tel.: (419) 476-7525
Web Site: http://www.bohlco.com

Year Founded: 1927
Sales Range: $10-24.9 Million
Emp.: 30
Industrial Crane Sales
N.A.I.C.S.: 423830
Douglas E. Bohl (Pres)
Steve Bohl (VP)
Curtis Dickason (Mgr-Svcs)
Troy Willett (Product Mgr-Engineered
Lifting Dev)
Dave Klopping (Project Mgr-Engrg)

BOHL EQUIPMENT CO.
534 W Laskey Rd, Toledo, OH 43612
Tel.: (419) 476-7525
Web Site: https://www.bohlco.com
Year Founded: 1950
Sales Range: $10-24.9 Million
Emp.: 70
Materials Handling Machinery; Fork-
lifts Whslr
N.A.I.C.S.: 423830

BOHME
9783 S 600 W, Sandy, UT 84070
Tel.: (801) 266-2002
Web Site: https://www.bohme.com
Year Founded: 2008
Sales Range: $10-24.9 Million
Emp.: 239
Fashion Retailer of Women's Clothing
N.A.I.C.S.: 458110
Fernanda Bohme (Co-Founder)
Vivien Bohme (Co-Founder)

BOHN BROTHERS TOYOTA
3800 Lapalco Blvd, Harvey, LA 70058
Tel.: (504) 341-3300
Web Site:
   http://www.bohnbrostoyota.com
Year Founded: 1986
Sales Range: $10-24.9 Million
Emp.: 115
Car Whslr
N.A.I.C.S.: 441110
Jim Smith (Gen Mgr)
Tony LaRosa (Gen Mgr)

BOHREN'S MOVING & STOR-AGE INC.
3 Applegate Dr, Robbinsville, NJ
08691
Tel.: (609) 208-1470
Web Site:
   https://www.bohrensmoving.com
Rev.: $21,115,182
Emp.: 26
Local Trucking, Moving Without Stor-
age,
N.A.I.C.S.: 484121
Ted W. Froehlich (Chm)
Denise Hewitt (Pres)
Robert Abbenante (Controller)
Louise Froelich (VP)

BOICE ENTERPRISES, INC.
700 Pearl St, New Albany, IN 47150
Tel.: (502) 271-2100
Web Site: http://www.boice.net
Year Founded: 1994
Sales Range: $10-24.9 Million
Emp.: 46
Information Technology Solutions
N.A.I.C.S.: 541511
Bill Hall (Pres & CEO)

BOIES SCHILLER FLEXNER LLP
575 Lexington Ave 7th Fl, New York,
NY 10022
Tel.: (212) 446-2300   NV
Web Site: http://www.bsfllp.com
Year Founded: 1997
Law firm
N.A.I.C.S.: 541110

Jonathan D. Schiller (Mng Partner)
David Barrett (Partner)
Eric Brenner (Partner)
Nicholas Gravante (Partner)
Damien Marshall (Partner)
Lee Wolosky (Partner)
Harlan Levy (Partner)
Christopher Belelieu (Partner)
Ilana Miller (Partner)
Sean O'Shea (Partner)

Subsidiaries:

Caldwell Leslie & Proctor PC   (1)
725 S Figueroa St 31st Fl, Los Angeles, CA
90017-5524
Tel.: (213) 629-9040
Web Site: http://www.bsfllp.com
Lawyers & Legal Services
N.A.I.C.S.: 541110
Christopher G. Caldwell (Partner)
Andrew A. Esbenshade (Partner)
Robyn C. Crowther (Partner)
Arwen Johnson (Partner)
Kelly Perigoe (Partner)

BOILING SPRINGS SAVINGS BANK INC.
25 Orient Way, Rutherford, NJ 07070
Tel.: (201) 939-5000   NJ
Web Site: http://www.bssbank.com
Year Founded: 1939
Sales Range: $50-74.9 Million
Emp.: 135
State Savings Bank
N.A.I.C.S.: 522110
Carmen Addeo (Mgr-Rutherford-
Orient Way)
Joanne Salvio (Mgr-Clifton)

BOISE HOUSING CORPORA-TION
PO Box 108, Boise, ID 83701
Tel.: (208) 343-6438   ID
Web Site:
   http://www.boisehousingcorp.com
Year Founded: 2000
Sales Range: $10-24.9 Million
Housing Assistance Services
N.A.I.C.S.: 624229
Patrick McKeegan (VP)
Shan Miller (Treas & Sec)
James R. Tomlinson (Pres)
Fred Shoemaker (Atty)

BOISE PETERBILT, INC.
6633 S Federal Way, Boise, ID
83716
Tel.: (208) 344-8515
Web Site:
   http://www.peterbiltofidaho.com
Rev.: $21,443,033
Emp.: 35
New & Used Car Dealers
N.A.I.C.S.: 441120
Blake Jackson (Owner)

BOISE SALES CO
1445 Commerce Ave, Boise, ID
83705
Tel.: (208) 345-4600
Sales Range: $50-74.9 Million
Emp.: 100
Winery
N.A.I.C.S.: 424820
John Hayden (Pres)

BOKARA RUG CO., INC.
50 Enterprise N, Secaucus, NJ 07094
Tel.: (201) 601-0040   NY
Web Site: https://www.bokara.com
Year Founded: 1975
Sales Range: $10-24.9 Million
Emp.: 20
Whol Homefurnishings
N.A.I.C.S.: 423220
Jan Soleimani (Owner)

Bokara Rug Co., Inc.—(Continued)

BOKU, INC.
735 Battery St, San Francisco, CA 94111
Tel.: (415) 375-3160
Web Site: http://www.boku.com
Year Founded: 2008
Emp.: 51
Online Mobile Payment Services
N.A.I.C.S.: 522320
Mark Britto *(Chm)*
Jon Prideaux *(CEO)*
Stuart Neal *(CFO)*

BOLAND MALONEY ENTERPRISES INC.
4010 Collins Ln, Louisville, KY 40245-1644
Tel.: (502) 426-6121   **KY**
Web Site:
    http://www.bolandmaloney.com
Year Founded: 1937
Sales Range: $50-74.9 Million
Emp.: 108
Retailers of Lumber & Other Building Materials
N.A.I.C.S.: 444110
Bernie Koontz *(Controller)*
Gerry Boland *(VP)*

Subsidiaries:

Boland-Maloney Lumber Company Inc.   **(1)**
4010 Collins Ln, Louisville, KY 40245-1644   **(100%)**
Tel.: (502) 426-6121
Web Site: http://www.bolandmaloney.com
Sales Range: $10-24.9 Million
Emp.: 45
Retailer of Lumber, Plywood & Millwork
N.A.I.C.S.: 423310
Barney Koochs *(Gen Mgr)*

Boland-Maloney Realty Co.   **(1)**
4010 Collins Ln, Louisville, KY 40245-1644
Tel.: (502) 426-6121
Web Site: http://www.bolandmaloney.com
Sales Range: $10-24.9 Million
Emp.: 5
Nonresidential Building Operators
N.A.I.C.S.: 423310
Richard Boland *(Pres)*

BOLAND TRANE SERVICES INC.
30 W Watkins Mill Rd, Gaithersburg, MD 20878
Tel.: (240) 306-3000
Web Site: https://www.boland.com
Rev.: $20,900,000
Emp.: 300
Water Heaters, Except Electric
N.A.I.C.S.: 423720
James M. Boland *(Pres)*
Jerry Scanlan *(VP-Sls)*
Sarah Heitkemper *(VP-HR)*
Louis J. Boland Jr. *(Exec VP)*

BOLD HARDWARE CO.
12852 Earhart Ave #106, Auburn, CA 95602
Tel.: (530) 885-1400
Web Site:
    http://www.drawerslides.com
Year Founded: 2006
Sales Range: $1-9.9 Million
Emp.: 10
Home Hardware Sales
N.A.I.C.S.: 444140
Nick Giovanni *(VP-Software Dev)*

BOLD ORANGE COMPANY, LLC
100 Washington Ave S Ste 750, Minneapolis, MN 55401
Tel.: (612) 354-2832   **DE**
Web Site: http://www.boldorange.com
Year Founded: 2018

Consulting Services
N.A.I.C.S.: 541611
Margaret Murphy *(Founder & CEO)*
Jim Specht *(Chief Experience Officer)*
Dave Woodbeck *(Eexc VP & Mng Dir)*

Subsidiaries:

Great Lakes Scrip Center, LLC   **(1)**
PO Box 8158, Kentwood, MI 49518-8158
Tel.: (800) 727-4715
Web Site: http://www.shopwithscrip.com
Shopping Support Services
N.A.I.C.S.: 561990
Margaret Murphy *(Pres & CEO)*
Jill Whalen *(VP-Retail Partnerships)*
Brian Snodgrass *(Dir-IT)*
Emily Ploeg *(Dir-Ops)*
Jim Specht *(Chief Experience Officer)*

Three Deep, Inc.   **(1)**
289 5th St E 2nd Fl, Saint Paul, MN 55101
Tel.: (651) 789-7701
Web Site:
    http://www.threedeepmarketing.com
Online Brokerage Services
N.A.I.C.S.: 524210
Dave Woodbeck *(Co-Founder & Pres)*
Dan Derosier *(VP)*

BOLDATA TECHNOLOGY, INC.
48363 Fremont Blvd, Fremont, CA 94538-6580
Tel.: (510) 490-8296
Web Site: http://www.boldata.com
Year Founded: 1984
Sales Range: $10-24.9 Million
Emp.: 60
Computer Systems, Servers, Notebooks & Peripherals
N.A.I.C.S.: 334111
Eugene Kiang *(Pres)*

Subsidiaries:

Crown Micro Inc.   **(1)**
48351 Fremont Blvd, Fremont, CA 94538-6580
Tel.: (510) 445-8800
Sales Range: $10-24.9 Million
Emp.: 50
Electronic Computers
N.A.I.C.S.: 334111
Eugene Kiang *(Pres)*

BOLDFACE GROUP, INC.
1945 Euclid St, Santa Monica, CA 90404
Tel.: (310) 450-4501   **NV**
Web Site:
    http://www.boldfacegroup.com
Year Founded: 2007
Sales Range: $1-9.9 Million
Emp.: 6
Beauty Product Mfr
N.A.I.C.S.: 456120
John C. LaBonty *(Pres & CEO)*
Ashumi Kothary Shippee *(CFO & Sec)*

BOLEK INC.
1284 W Henri De Tonti Blvd, Springdale, AR 72762
Tel.: (479) 756-2707
Web Site: http://www.Wheelsrv.net
Sales Range: $10-24.9 Million
Emp.: 22
Recreational Vehicle Dealers
N.A.I.C.S.: 441210
Mark Kersey *(Treas)*
Judy Bolek *(Sec)*
Heath Bolek *(VP)*

BOLER VENTURES LLC
500 Park Blvd Ste 1010, Itasca, IL 60143
Tel.: (630) 773-9111
Web Site: http://www.hendrickson-intl.com
Sales Range: $10-24.9 Million

Emp.: 40
Nonferrous Forgings
N.A.I.C.S.: 332112
Matthew Boler *(Pres & CEO)*
Mark Slingluff *(Dir-Mktg)*

BOLEY CENTERS, INC.
445 31st St N, Saint Petersburg, FL 33713
Tel.: (727) 545-7278   **FL**
Web Site:
    http://www.boleycenters.org
Year Founded: 1970
Sales Range: $10-24.9 Million
Emp.: 440
Mental Health Services
N.A.I.C.S.: 621420
Jeri Flanagan *(Dir-Dev)*
Jim Miller *(CIO)*
Tom Eckman *(Dir-Quality Improvement)*
Marcy Macmath *(Dir-Trng)*
Carol Miele *(Dir-Day Svcs)*
Jack Humburg *(Dir-Housing Dev & ADA Svcs)*
Kevin Marrone *(VP-Community & Homeless Svcs & Dir-Program & Svc)*

BOLEY TOOL & MACHINE WORKS
1044 Spring Bay Rd, East Peoria, IL 61611
Tel.: (309) 694-2722
Web Site: https://www.boleytool.com
Sales Range: $10-24.9 Million
Emp.: 110
Parts & Accessories, Internal Combustion Engines
N.A.I.C.S.: 333618
Frank D. Boley *(Controller)*
Eldon Beever *(Mgr-IT)*
Steve Summa *(Mgr-Pur)*

BOLGER & ASSOCIATES, INC.
8340 Plainfield Rd, Cincinnati, OH 45236
Tel.: (513) 793-6267
Year Founded: 1987
Sales Range: $10-24.9 Million
Emp.: 5
Accounting & Auditing Services
N.A.I.C.S.: 541211
John P. Bolger *(Owner)*

BOLGER ADVERTISING
56 Niles Ave, Madison, NJ 07940
Tel.: (973) 377-1634   **NJ**
Year Founded: 1972
Sales Range: $10-24.9 Million
Emp.: 5
Advertising Agencies
N.A.I.C.S.: 541810
Michael Triano *(Sr Dir-Art)*
John Bolger *(CEO)*

BOLIN MARKETING & ADVERTISING
2523 Wayzata Blvd Ste 300, Minneapolis, MN 55405
Tel.: (612) 374-1200   **MN**
Web Site:
    http://www.bolinmarketing.com
Year Founded: 1950
Sales Range: $10-24.9 Million
Emp.: 18
Advertising Agencies
N.A.I.C.S.: 541810
Scott Bolin *(Dir-Creative)*
Todd Bolin *(Pres & CEO)*
Kathy Gladfelter *(VP-Media)*
Tom Carbonneau *(CFO & Exec VP)*

BOLIVAR FARMERS EXCHANGE

112 W Jefferson St, Bolivar, MO 65613
Tel.: (417) 326-5231   **MO**
Web Site: http://www.bolivar.com
Year Founded: 1920
Sales Range: $10-24.9 Million
Emp.: 50
Farm Supplies
N.A.I.C.S.: 424910
Steve Austin *(Mgr)*

BOLIVAR MINING CORP.
215 Dino Dr, Ann Arbor, MI 48103
Tel.: (604) 687-7492
Year Founded: 1999
Metal Mining Services
N.A.I.C.S.: 212290
Peter Klamka *(Pres & CEO)*

BOLIVAR READY MIX & MATERIAL, INC.
1601 Killingsworth Ave., Bolivar, MO 65613-2283
Tel.: (417) 326-5532
Web Site:
    https://bolivarreadymix.com
Year Founded: 1987
Sales Range: Less than $1 Million
Emp.: 7
Readymix Concrete Mfr
N.A.I.C.S.: 327320

BOLL & BRANCH LLC
1 Prospect St, Summit, NJ 07901
Web Site:
    http://www.bollandbranch.com
Year Founded: 2014
Sales Range: $50-74.9 Million
Emp.: 45
Home Furnishing Distr
N.A.I.C.S.: 423220
Scott Tannen *(Co-Founder)*
Missy Tannen *(Co-Founder)*

BOLLER CONSTRUCTION COMPANY, INC.
3045 Washington St, Waukegan, IL 60085-4843
Tel.: (847) 662-5566
Web Site:
    http://www.bollerconstruction.com
Sales Range: $10-24.9 Million
Emp.: 90
Nonresidential Construction Services
N.A.I.C.S.: 236220
Bob Boller *(Owner)*

BOLLES MOTORS, INC.
84 W Rd, Ellington, CT 06029-3722
Tel.: (860) 875-2595
Web Site:
    https://www.bollesmotors.com
Sales Range: $10-24.9 Million
Emp.: 45
Car Whslr
N.A.I.C.S.: 441110
Brian Bolles *(Gen Mgr)*

BOLLINGER SHIPYARDS, INC.
8365 LA-308, Lockport, LA 70374-3954
Tel.: (985) 532-2554   **LA**
Web Site:
    https://www.bollingershipyards.com
Year Founded: 1946
Sales Range: $350-399.9 Million
Emp.: 1,800
Marine Repairs, Conversions, Construction & Machine Shop Services
N.A.I.C.S.: 336611
Benjamin G. Bordelon *(Pres & CEO)*
Craig P. Roussel *(Chief Admin Officer & Exec VP)*
Darren Savoye *(VP-Bus Dev & Engrg)*
Tim Martinez *(Exec VP-Repair)*

Eric Bollinger *(VP-Sls)*
Andrew J. St. Germain *(CFO, Treas & Exec VP)*
Christian Pierce *(Dir-Engrg)*

Subsidiaries:

Bollinger Algiers LLC **(1)**
434 Powder St, New Orleans, LA 70114-2350
Tel.: (504) 362-7960
Web Site: http://www.bollingershipyards.com
Sales Range: $10-24.9 Million
Emp.: 30
Ship & Boat Builders, Marine Repairs, Machine Shop
N.A.I.C.S.: 336611

Bollinger Amelia Repair, LLC **(1)**
PO Box 2628, Morgan City, LA 70381
Tel.: (985) 631-2020
Web Site: http://www.bollingershipyards.com
Sales Range: $10-24.9 Million
Emp.: 45
Ship & Boat Builders, Marine Repairs, Machine Shop
N.A.I.C.S.: 336611
Corey Phelps *(Gen Mgr)*

Bollinger Fourchon, LLC **(1)**
106 Norman Doucet Dr, Golden Meadow, LA 70357-5618 **(100%)**
Tel.: (985) 396-2366
Web Site: http://www.bollingershipyards.com
Sales Range: $10-24.9 Million
Emp.: 9
Ship & Boat Builders, Marine Repairs, Machine Shop
N.A.I.C.S.: 336611
Jon Degruise *(Asst Mgr-Ops)*
Paul Bailleaux *(VP-Repair-Southern Div)*

Bollinger Marine Fabricators, LLC **(1)**
8365 Hwy 308 S, Lockport, LA 70374-1609
Tel.: (985) 631-5300
Web Site: http://www.bollingershipyards.com
Sales Range: $25-49.9 Million
Emp.: 300
Ship & Boat Builders, Marine Repairs, Machine Shop
N.A.I.C.S.: 336611
Charlotte A. Bollinger *(Sec & Exec VP)*
Eric Bollinger *(VP-Sls)*
Benjamin G. Bordelon *(Pres & CEO)*
Tim Martinez *(Exec VP-Repair)*
Craig P. Roussel *(Chief Admin Officer & Exec VP)*
Marc L. Stanley *(Exec VP)*

Bollinger Morgan City, LLC **(1)**
PO Box 2628, Morgan City, LA 70381-2628
Tel.: (985) 631-2020
Web Site: http://www.bollingershipyards.com
Sales Range: $50-74.9 Million
Emp.: 500
Ship & Boat Builders, Marine Repairs, Machine Shop
N.A.I.C.S.: 336611
Corey Phelps *(Gen Mgr)*

Bollinger Quick Repair **(1)**
615 Destrehan Ave, Harvey, LA 70058-2739
Tel.: (504) 340-0621
Web Site: http://www.bollingershipyards.com
Sales Range: $25-49.9 Million
Emp.: 200
Ship & Boat Builders, Marine Repairs, Machine Shop
N.A.I.C.S.: 336611
Allen Stein *(Gen Mgr)*

Bollinger RGS **(1)**
434 Powder St, New Orleans, LA 70114
Tel.: (504) 362-7960
Web Site: http://www.bollingershipyards.com
Sales Range: $10-24.9 Million
Emp.: 40
Ship & Boat Builders, Marine Repairs, Machine Shop
N.A.I.C.S.: 336611
Elvin Cheremia *(Mgr)*

Bollinger Shipyard Lockport, LLC **(1)**
8365 Hwy 308 S, Lockport, LA 70374-0250
Tel.: (985) 532-2554
Web Site: http://www.bollingershipyard.com
Sales Range: $50-74.9 Million
Emp.: 900

Ship & Boat Builders, Marine Repairs, Machine Shop
N.A.I.C.S.: 336611
Benjamin Bordelon *(CEO)*

Subsidiary (Domestic):

VT Halter Marine, Inc **(2)**
900 Bayou Casotte Pkwy, Pascagoula, MS 39581
Tel.: (228) 696-6888
Web Site: http://www.vthaltermarine.com
Ship Building & Repair Services
N.A.I.C.S.: 336611
Norman D. Ballinger *(CFO)*
Richard A. Zubic *(Exec VP-Shipbuilding)*
Robert D. Mullins *(Sr VP-Strategy)*
L. Walker Foster *(VP-Govt Contracts)*
Harry Bell *(VP-Sls & Mktg)*
Pawan Agrawal *(VP-Repair)*
Phil Adams *(Sr VP)*
Bill Landay *(Chm)*
Robert A. Socha *(Sr VP-Bus Dev & Estimating)*
Robert L. Merchent *(Pres & CEO)*

Bollinger Texas City, LP **(1)**
2201 Dock Rd Dock 42, Texas City, TX 77590
Tel.: (409) 945-0770
Ship Building & Repairing Services
N.A.I.C.S.: 336611
Monty Bludworth *(Gen Mgr)*

Chand, LLC **(1)**
157 Hwy 654, Mathews, LA 70375-2009 **(100%)**
Tel.: (985) 532-2512
Web Site: http://www.chand.com
Sales Range: $25-49.9 Million
Emp.: 60
Ship & Boat Builders, Marine Repairs, Machine Shop
N.A.I.C.S.: 423860
Mark Landry *(Mgr-Sustainment)*
Chas Guidry *(Editor-Tech)*
Dick Savoie *(Project Coord)*
Darin Richard *(Mgr-Procurement)*
Thad Angelloz *(Editor-Tech)*

BOLLMAN HAT CO.
110 E Main St, Adamstown, PA 19501-0517
Tel.: (717) 484-4361 **PA**
Web Site:
  https://www.bollmanhats.com
Year Founded: 1868
Sales Range: $200-249.9 Million
Emp.: 500
Mfr of Hats
N.A.I.C.S.: 315990
Don Rongione *(Pres & CEO)*
Chris Fitterling *(Sec & Exec VP-Admin)*
Dave Huber *(CFO & COO)*
Jeffrey M. Clair *(Exec VP-Global Sls)*

Subsidiaries:

Bailey Hats Company **(1)**
3800 Sandshell Dr, Fort Worth, TX 76137-2429
Tel.: (817) 232-9707
Web Site: http://www.baileyhats.com
Sales Range: $10-24.9 Million
Emp.: 4
Hats Mfr
N.A.I.C.S.: 315990

Betmar Hats, Inc. **(1)**
411 5th Ave, New York, NY 10016-2203
Tel.: (212) 684-8080
Web Site: http://www.betmarhats.com
Sales Range: $10-24.9 Million
Emp.: 12
Mfr of Ladies Millinery
N.A.I.C.S.: 424350

BOLLO CONSTRUCTION, INC.
852 Northport Dr Ste 105, West Sacramento, CA 95691-2167
Tel.: (916) 372-6266
Sales Range: $10-24.9 Million
Emp.: 40
Civil Engineering Services
N.A.I.C.S.: 237310

Mark Bollinger *(Pres)*

BOLOCO
1080 Boylston St, Boston, MA 02215
Tel.: (617) 369-9087
Web Site: https://www.boloco.com
Year Founded: 1986
Sales Range: $10-24.9 Million
Emp.: 295
Full-Service Restaurants
N.A.I.C.S.: 722511
Michael Harder *(Pres & COO)*
Patrick Renna *(VP)*
Brian Keith *(Reg Mgr)*
Christina Rowley *(Mgr-HR)*
Matt Taylor *(Area Mgr)*

BOLOGNUE HOLDINGS INC.
1450 Firestone Pkwy Ste D, Akron, OH 44301-1655
Tel.: (330) 724-5444
Sales Range: Less than $1 Million
Emp.: 10
Dried Or Canned Foods
N.A.I.C.S.: 424490
Joseph T. Bolognue *(Pres)*
Michael Bolognue *(VP)*

BOLT EXPRESS LLC
7255 Crossleigh Ct, Toledo, OH 43617 **OH**
Web Site: https://www.bolt-express.com
Year Founded: 2001
Sales Range: $25-49.9 Million
Emp.: 95
Transportation & Logistics
N.A.I.C.S.: 488510
Derek Bodden *(Mgr-Ops-Truckload)*

BOLT MOBILITY CORP.
936 SW 1st Avenue Suite 993, Miami, FL 33130
Web Site:
  http://www.micromobility.com
Motor Vehicle Parts Mfr
N.A.I.C.S.: 423110
Ignacio Tzouma *(CEO)*

Subsidiaries:

Gotcha Mobility, LLC **(1)**
7 Radcliffe St Ste 200, Charleston, SC 29403
Tel.: (843) 647-7342
Web Site: http://www.ridegotcha.com
Transport Services
N.A.I.C.S.: 485999
Anne Morgan *(CMO)*

BOLTEX INC.
4901 Oates Rd, Houston, TX 77013
Tel.: (713) 675-9433
Web Site: https://www.boltex.com
Rev.: $23,000,000
Emp.: 120
Flange Facing Machines
N.A.I.C.S.: 333517
Frank Bernobich *(Pres)*
Franco Geremia *(Plant Mgr)*

BOLTON & MENK, INC.
1960 Premiere Dr, Mankato, MN 56001-5900
Tel.: (507) 625-4171
Web Site: https://www.bolton-menk.com
Year Founded: 1949
Sales Range: $10-24.9 Million
Emp.: 500
Professional Engineering & Surveying Services
N.A.I.C.S.: 541370
Bruce Firkins *(VP & Mgr-Civil Engrg)*
Bradley DeWolf *(Pres & CEO)*
Kreg Schmidt *(VP)*
Mike Waltman *(Engr)*
Dan Sarff *(Sr Engr)*

Aaron Warford *(Engr-Transportation)*
Andrew Budde *(Project Mgr)*
Jason Femrite *(Engr)*
Josh Eckstein *(Engr-Design)*
Ron Roetzel *(Principal)*
Brian Malm *(Engr-City)*

BOLTON EMERSON AMERICAS, LLC
410 Blount Ave W, Knoxville, TN 37920
Tel.: (603) 219-0055 **MA**
Web Site: https://www.boltonemerson
  americas.com
Year Founded: 1905
Industrial & Coating Equipment Mfr
N.A.I.C.S.: 333243

BOLTON FORD INC.
1500 E College St, Lake Charles, LA 70607
Tel.: (337) 474-0070 **LA**
Web Site: https://www.boltonford.com
Year Founded: 1976
Sales Range: $10-24.9 Million
Emp.: 80
Automobile Dealer of New & Used Cars
N.A.I.C.S.: 441110
Joseph S. Bolton *(Pres)*
Jordan LeLeux *(Controller)*
Chadd Cutsinger *(Mgr-Internet Sls)*

BOLTON OIL CO. LTD
1316 54th St, Lubbock, TX 79412
Tel.: (806) 747-1629
Web Site: https://www.boltonoil.com
Rev.: $12,525,043
Emp.: 80
Automobile Maintenance Services
N.A.I.C.S.: 811198
Charles Bolton *(Pres)*

BOMAC INC.
6477 Ridings Rd, Syracuse, NY 13206
Tel.: (315) 433-9181
Web Site: https://www.bomacinc.com
Sales Range: $1-9.9 Million
Emp.: 15
Industrial Electric Controls & Control Accessories
N.A.I.C.S.: 335314
Kevin Knecht *(Pres)*

BOMAN KEMP BASEMENT WINDOW SYSTEMS
2393 S 1900 W, Ogden, UT 84401-3215
Tel.: (801) 731-0615 **UT**
Web Site: https://www.boman-kemp.com
Year Founded: 1967
Sales Range: $75-99.9 Million
Emp.: 95
Holding Company; Fabricated Structural Metal
N.A.I.C.S.: 332312
Melvin T. Kemp *(Pres & CEO)*
Dave Boydston *(Mgr-Western Sls)*

Subsidiaries:

Bowman & Kemp Rebar **(1)**
2397 S 1900 W, Ogden, UT 84401-3215
Tel.: (801) 731-0615
Web Site: http://www.boman-kemp.com
Sales Range: $25-49.9 Million
Mfr of Steel Rebar
N.A.I.C.S.: 332312

Bowman & Kemp Steel & Supply Company **(1)**
2393 S 1900 W, Ogden, UT 84401-3215 **(100%)**
Tel.: (801) 731-0615
Web Site: http://www.boman-kemp.com

Boman Kemp Basement Window
Systems—(Continued)

Sales Range: $10-24.9 Million
Emp.: 175
Fabricated Structural Metal; Steel
N.A.I.C.S.: 332312
Melvin T. Kemp (Pres)

BOMAR EXO LLC

200 B Wood Ave, Middlesex, NJ
08846
Tel.: (732) 356-7787　　　**NJ**
Web Site:
　https://www.bomarcrystal.com
Holding Company; Electronics Components Mfr
N.A.I.C.S.: 551112
Ermina Lirio (Gen Mgr)
David Miskov (CTO)

Subsidiaries:

Bomar Crystal Company　　　(1)
200 B Wood Ave, Middlesex, NJ 08846
Tel.: (732) 356-7787
Web Site: http://www.bomarcrystal.com
Electronic Components Mfr
N.A.I.C.S.: 334419
Ermina Lirio (Gen Mgr)
David Miskov (CTO)

BOMARKO, INC.

1955 N Oak Dr, Plymouth, IN 46563-
3412
Tel.: (574) 936-9901　　　**IN**
Web Site: https://www.bomarko.com
Year Founded: 1950
Sales Range: $50-74.9 Million
Emp.: 150
Mfr of Wax & Coated Papers
N.A.I.C.S.: 322220
Gaza Verik (Pres)

BOMBAY PALACE COMPANY

8690 Wilshire Blvd, Beverly Hills, CA
90211
Tel.: (310) 659-9944
Web Site:
　https://www.bombaypalace.com
Restaurant Operators
N.A.I.C.S.: 722511
Mohan Ahluwalia (Gen Mgr)

BOMBERGERS STORE INC.

555 Furnace Hills Pike, Lititz, PA
17543
Tel.: (717) 626-3333
Web Site:
　http://www.bombergersstore.com
Sales Range: $10-24.9 Million
Emp.: 150
Floor Covering; Lawn & Gardening;
Hardware; Sporting Goods; Cabinets;
Housewares
N.A.I.C.S.: 449121
Wilma Eberly (Controller)
Roy Bomberger (Gen Mgr)
Roy L. Bomberger Jr. (Treas & Sec)

BOMBSHELL ACCESSORIES INC.

248 W 35th St Rm 601, New York,
NY 10001
Tel.: (212) 279-4655
Web Site: http://www.metalmafia.com
Year Founded: 2004
Sales Range: $1-9.9 Million
Emp.: 14
Body Piercing & Costume Jewelry
N.A.I.C.S.: 339910
Vanessa Nornberg (Pres)

BOMEL CONSTRUCTION CO. INC.

96 Corporate Park, Irvine, CA 92606
Tel.: (714) 921-1660
Web Site:
　https://www.bomelconstruction.com
Rev.: $17,500,000
Emp.: 96
Industrial Buildings & Warehouses
N.A.I.C.S.: 236220
Robert C. Matranga (Chm & CEO)
Lisa Mcginnis (Controller)
Kent Matranga (Pres)

BOMGAARS SUPPLY INC.

1805 Zenith Dr, Sioux City, IA 51103-
5208
Tel.: (712) 226-5000　　　**IA**
Web Site: https://www.bomgaars.com
Year Founded: 1944
Sales Range: $75-99.9 Million
Emp.: 1,000
Department Stores
N.A.I.C.S.: 455110
Roger Bomgaars (Pres)
Jane Bomgaars (VP)
Dave Meyer (Gen Mgr-Ops)
Torrey Wingert (CFO)

BOMMARITO AUTOMOTIVE GROUP

15736 Manchester Rd, Ellisville, MO
63011-2206
Tel.: (636) 391-7200　　　**DE**
Web Site:
　http://www.bommaritoautos.com
Year Founded: 1952
Emp.: 936
Automobile Dealership
N.A.I.C.S.: 441110
Frank Bommarito (CEO)
Betty Ellis (Controller)
John Bommarito (Pres)
Chuck Wallis (VP & Gen Mgr)

BOMMARITO CHEVROLET MAZDA INC.

6127 S Lindbergh Blvd, Saint Louis,
MO 63123-7020
Tel.: (314) 487-9800　　　**MO**
Web Site:
　https://bommaritomazdasouth.com
Year Founded: 2001
Sales Range: $10-24.9 Million
Emp.: 84
Car Whslr
N.A.I.C.S.: 441110
John Bommarito (Pres)
Mike Jordan (Gen Mgr)

BOMMER INDUSTRIES, INC.

19810 Asheville Hwy, Landrum, SC
29356-9027
Tel.: (864) 457-3301　　　**SC**
Web Site: https://www.bommer.com
Year Founded: 1876
Sales Range: $100-124.9 Million
Emp.: 200
Lavatory Hardware, Spring Hinges &
Mail Receptacles
N.A.I.C.S.: 332510
Charles A. Martin (Pres, COO & Treas)
Ed Pruitt (Dir-Builders Hardware)
Tony Ballenger (Engr-Mfg)
Digit Laughridge (Dir-Sls & Mktg)
James Bond (Mgr-Engrg)
Peter Frohlich (Owner)
Randy Searcy (Mgr-Admin)
Thomas Fortune (Dir-Fin & Admin)

Subsidiaries:

Bommer Industries, Inc. - GAFFNEY
PLANT　　　(1)
584 Peachoid Rd, Gaffney, SC 29341
Tel.: (864) 487-3504
Hinge Mfr
N.A.I.C.S.: 332510

BON CHEF INC.

205 NJ-94, Lafayette, NJ 07848
Tel.: (973) 383-8848
Web Site: https://www.bonchef.com
Rev.: $22,000,000
Emp.: 75
Painting, Coating & Hot Dipping
N.A.I.C.S.: 332812
Salvatore Torre (Owner & Pres)
Amy Passafaro (Dir-Sls Ops)
Diane Manna (Mgr-Customer Svc)
Eva Sher (Exec Dir-Design & Concept)
Paul McGreevy (Mgr-Ops)
William Chan (Mgr)

BON JOUR CAPITAL

499 7th Ave 11th Fl, New York, NY
10018
Tel.: (212) 398-1000　　　**NY**
Web Site:
　https://www.bonjourcapital.com
Sales Range: $100-124.9 Million
Real Estate Investment & Development Services
N.A.I.C.S.: 531390
Zev Friedman (CFO)

Subsidiaries:

Bon Jour International Licensing
Division　　　(1)
1400 Broadway Fl 22, New York, NY
10018-3402
Tel.: (212) 398-1000
Sales Range: $10-24.9 Million
Emp.: 11
Licensing
N.A.I.C.S.: 926150

BON MANAGEMENT INC.

4500 E Thousand Oaks Blvd Ste
104, Thousand Oaks, CA 91362
Tel.: (805) 496-0357
Year Founded: 1983
Rev.: $15,000,000
Emp.: 3
Property Management Services
N.A.I.C.S.: 531210
Chuck Nester (Chm)

BON SECOUR FISHERIES INC.

17449 Country Rd 49 S, Bon Secour,
AL 36511
Tel.: (251) 949-7411　　　**AL**
Web Site:
　https://www.bonsecourfisheries.com
Year Founded: 1896
Sales Range: $25-49.9 Million
Emp.: 200
Fish & Seafoods Processor & Distr
N.A.I.C.S.: 311710
John Ray Nelson (Co-Owner)
Christopher Nelson (Co-Owner & VP)
Melanie Parker (CFO, Treas & Sec)
Pam Skinner (Mgr-Credit)
David Nelson (Co-Owner & VP)

Subsidiaries:

Bon Secour Boats Inc.　　　(1)
17449 County Rd 49 S, Bon Secour, AL
36511
Tel.: (251) 949-7411
Sales Range: $1-9.9 Million
Emp.: 170
Shellfish
N.A.I.C.S.: 114112

Bon Secour Marine Supply Inc.　　　(1)
17449 County Rd 49 S, Bon Secour, AL
36511
Tel.: (251) 949-7411
Sales Range: Less than $1 Million
Emp.: 1
Boat Dealers
N.A.I.C.S.: 441222

BON SECOURS MERCY HEALTH, INC.

1701 Mercy Health Pl, Cincinnati, OH
45237

Tel.: (513) 952-5000
Web Site: http://www.bsmhealth.org
Health Care Srvices
N.A.I.C.S.: 621610
Brian Smith (COO)
Wael Haidar (Chief Clinical Officer)
David Cannady (Chief Strategy Officer)
Michael A. Bezney (Chief Legal Officer)
Deborah Bloomfield (CFO)
John M. Starcher Jr. (Pres & CEO)

Subsidiaries:

Bon Secours Health System, Inc.　　　(1)
2000 W Baltimore St, Baltimore, MD 21223
Tel.: (416) 362-3000
Web Site: http://www.bonsecours.com
Rev.: $2,305,000,000
Emp.: 25,000
Hospital & Nursing Home Operator
N.A.I.C.S.: 622110
Mark Nantz (Exec VP-Enterprise Strategic Initiatives)
Samuel L. Ross (CEO-Baltimore Health Sys)

Subsidiary (Non-US):

Bon Secours Health System Ltd　　　(2)
College Road, Cork, Ireland
Tel.: (353) 214542807
Web Site: http://www.bonsecours.ie
Health Care Srvices
N.A.I.C.S.: 621999
Peter Lacy (Chm)
Jim O'Shaughnessy (CFO)
Harry Canning (Mgr-Hospital)

Emporia Hospital Corporation　　　(1)
727 N Main St, Emporia, VA 23847
Tel.: (434) 348-4400
Web Site: http://www.svrmc.com
Health Care Srvices
N.A.I.C.S.: 622110

Franklin Hospital Corporation　　　(1)
100 Fairview Dr, Franklin, VA 23851
Tel.: (757) 569-6100
Web Site: http://www.smhfranklin.com
Health Care Srvices
N.A.I.C.S.: 622110

Mercy Health　　　(1)
14528 S Outer Forty Ste 100, Chesterfield,
MO 63017
Tel.: (314) 364-3381
Web Site: http://www.mercy.net
Health Care Services Organization
N.A.I.C.S.: 813910
Michael McCurry (COO & Exec VP)
Shannon Sock (CFO & Exec VP)
Daryle Voss (Pres-Ardmore)
Ryan Gehrig (Pres-Fort Smith)
Eric Ammons (Pres-Jefferson)
Eric Pianalto (Pres-Northwest Arkansas)
Jeff Johnston (Pres-East Communities)
Eric Eoloff (Pres-Washington)
Tim Moyer (Dir-Environmental Svcs)
Brandon Mencini (CEO)

Subsidiary (Domestic):

Oncology/Hematology Care, Inc.　　　(2)
5053 Wooster Rd, Cincinnati, OH
45226　　　(100%)
Tel.: (812) 537-1911
Web Site: http://www.ohcare.com
Emp.: 1,000
Specialized Treatment for Cancer & Blood
Disorders
N.A.I.C.S.: 621111
Rich Schiano (CEO)
Kathy Blair-Johnson (CFO)
E. Randolph Broun (Chm & Pres)

Petersburg Hospital Company,
LLC　　　(1)
801 S Adams St, Petersburg, VA 23803-
5149
Tel.: (804) 765-5000
Web Site: http://www.srmconline.com
General Medical & Surgical Hospitals
N.A.I.C.S.: 622110
Trent Erik Nobles (CEO)

BON TOOL COMPANY

4430 Gibsonia Rd, Gibsonia, PA 15044
Tel.: (724) 443-7080
Web Site: https://www.bontool.com
Year Founded: 1958
Sales Range: $10-24.9 Million
Emp.: 78
Hand & Edge Tool Mfr
N.A.I.C.S.: 332216
Carl A. Bongiovanni (Pres)
Paula Wight (Mgr-PR)
John Wight (VP-Sls)

BON-AIRE INDUSTRIES INC.

873 E Citation Ct, Boise, ID 83716
Tel.: (208) 336-2666
Web Site: https://www.bon-aireindustries.com
Rev.: $11,424,715
Emp.: 8
Motor Vehicle Parts & Accessories
N.A.I.C.S.: 336390
Robert L. Bonzer (Pres)
Treva Hahn (Office Mgr)
Steve Bragg (Dir-Art)

BONA VISTA PROGRAMS, INC.

1220 E Laguna St, Kokomo, IN 46904-2496
Tel.: (765) 457-8273   IN
Web Site: https://www.bonavista.org
Year Founded: 1958
Sales Range: $10-24.9 Million
Emp.: 881
Child & Adult Care Services
N.A.I.C.S.: 624110
Christy Barker (Exec VP-Community Living)
Shannon Collins (CFO & Exec VP)
Beth Barnett (VP-Early Childhood Svcs)
Grace Miller (VP-HR)
Brittnee Smith (VP-Therapies & Dev)
Kevin O-Keefe (Atty)
Brianne Boles (Pres & CEO)

BONADENT DENTAL LABO-RATORIES

2465 BonaDent Dr, Seneca Falls, NY 13148
Tel.: (315) 539-8875
Web Site: https://www.bonadent.com
Year Founded: 1950
Sales Range: $10-24.9 Million
Emp.: 225
Dental Implant & Denture Mfr
N.A.I.C.S.: 339116
Bruce H. Bonafiglia (Pres)
Daniele Bonafiglia-Wirth (VP)
Cathy Johnson (Coord-Lab)
Frank Belle (Mgr-Fixed Dept Team)
Mario Agnello (Mgr-Fixed Dept Team)
Daniele Bonafiglia Wirth (VP)
Mike Alessio (Mgr-Fixed Dept Team)

BONADIO & CO. LLP

171 Sullys Trl, Pittsford, NY 14534
Tel.: (585) 381-1000   NY
Web Site: http://www.bonadio.com
Year Founded: 1978
Sales Range: $50-74.9 Million
Emp.: 380
Accounting, Tax, Payroll & Consulting Services
N.A.I.C.S.: 541211
Thomas F. Bonadio (Founder, CEO & Mng Partner)
Robert J. Enright (COO)
Carl Cadregari (Exec VP)
Robert Pickering (Sr Exec VP)
Rafael Vidal (Pres)
Joseph Peresan (Principal)
Thomas Landers (Partner)
Lisa Palladino (Principal)
Stephen Turner (Principal-Comml)

Scott Donnelly (Mgr-Comml)
Kenneth McGivney (Partner)
Richard Bigham (Partner)
Tom Gianatasio (Mng Partner-Albany & Partner)
Janine Mangione (Partner)
Jim Wetzold (Partner)
Angela LaTerra (Mgr-Mktg)
Kevin Testo (Partner)
Joseph Romanello (Dir-Sls-Enterprise Risk Mgmt Practice)
S. Taylor Brodell (Mgr-HR & Benefits-Rochester)
David Snyder (Partner-Small Bus Advisory Div)
Christopher Abram (Principal)
Jason Acker (Principal)
Ariel Ammirato (Principal)
Christopher Anderson (Partner)
Jennifer Arbore (Partner)
Tim Ball (Principal)
Regina Bass (Principal)
John Bevilacqua (Partner)
Mark Blazek (Principal)
Kait Bloss (Principal)
Mary Ellen Bott (Principal)
Heather Briggs (Principal)
Thomas Bruckel (Partner)
Jack Capron (Principal)
Samuel Capuano (Principal)
Jean Close (Partner)
Jamie Cote (Principal)
Jeffrey Couchman (Partner)
Nancy Cox (Partner)
June Crawford (Principal)
Jamie Crosley (Principal)
Paula Deckman (Principal)
Kelley DeMonte (Partner)
Jeffrey Dieso (Principal)
R. J. Genovese (Partner)
Joseph Heroux (Principal-Govt Compliance Div)
Blair Wang (Mgr-Healthcare & Tax Exempt Practice)
Jeffrey Audi (Mgr-Tax Team)
Mallory Conway (Principal-Internal Audit Div-Albany & Rutland)
Robin Brand (Principal-Buffalo)
Robert Urban (Mng Partner)

BONAMOUR, INC.

2301 Cedar Springs Rd Ste 450, Dallas, TX 75201
Tel.: (214) 855-0808   CO
Web Site: http://bonamour.com
Year Founded: 2002
Sales Range: Less than $1 Million
Health & Beauty Products Developer & Distr
N.A.I.C.S.: 424210
Nathan W. Halsey (Pres, CEO & Sec)

BONANDER PONTIAC INC.

231 S Ctr St, Turlock, CA 95380
Tel.: (209) 632-8871
Web Site: https://www.bonanderauto.com
Rev.: $23,872,999
Emp.: 60
New & Used Car Dealers-Buick, Oldsmobile & GMC
N.A.I.C.S.: 441110
Donald E. Bonander (Pres)

BONANZA FOODS & PROVI-SIONS INC.

2716 E Vernon Ave, Los Angeles, CA 90058-1823
Tel.: (323) 582-5513
Web Site: http://www.bonanzafood.com
Sales Range: $10-24.9 Million
Emp.: 35
Beef, Pork, Lamb, Seafood, Deli Meats, Dairy Products Butcher & Restaurant Supplies Distr

N.A.I.C.S.: 722310
Hilario Navarro (Pres)

BONANZA OIL AND GAS, INC.

3417 Mercer Ste D, Houston, TX 77027
Tel.: (713) 333-5808   NV
Year Founded: 2002
Sales Range: Less than $1 Million
Emp.: 2
Oil & Gas Exploration Services
N.A.I.C.S.: 211120
William Wiseman (Chm, Pres & CEO)
Robert Teague (VP-Ops)

BONAVENTURE CAPITAL LLC

820 Shades Creek Pkwy Ste 1200, Birmingham, AL 35209
Tel.: (205) 639-1679
Web Site:
    http://www.bonaventurecapital.net
Sales Range: $10-24.9 Million
Emp.: 5
Private Investment Firm
N.A.I.C.S.: 523999
Steve Dauphin (Co-Founder)
Williamr E. Reiser (Co-Founder)
Billy Harbert (Partner)
James Rein (Partner)
Dennis Hilton (Dir-Investments)

Subsidiaries:

Time Domain Corp.   (1)
Cummings Research Park 4955 Corporate Dr Ste 101, Huntsville, AL 35805
Tel.: (256) 922-9229
Web Site: http://www.timedomain.com
Ultra Wideband Ranging Radio & Radar Sensors Mfr
N.A.I.C.S.: 334220
Anthony Buszka (Treas & Controller)
Rachel Reinhardt (CEO)
Brandon Dewberry (CTO)
Kevin E. Davis (Dir-Strategic Bus Dev)
John Stein (Chm)

BONAVENTURE CO, LLC

1147-G Saint Marks Church Rd, Burlington, NC 27215
Tel.: (336) 584-7530   NC
Web Site:
    http://www.ricracandruffles.com
Year Founded: 2013
Children Clothes Mfr
N.A.I.C.S.: 315250

BONAVIA FOODS LLC.

15 White St, Rochester, NY 14608
Tel.: (585) 546-8910
Sales Range: $10-24.9 Million
Emp.: 32
Flour & Grain Product Mfr
N.A.I.C.S.: 311211
Yogesh Nauida (Pres)

BOND AUTO PARTS INC.

272 Morrison Rd, Barre, VT 05641
Tel.: (802) 479-0571   VT
Web Site: http://www.bondauto.com
Year Founded: 1956
Sales Range: $10-24.9 Million
Emp.: 30
Sales of Automotive Supplies & Parts
N.A.I.C.S.: 423120
Adam Metzler (Mgr-Pur Dept)
Mark Harper (Mgr-Pur Dept)
Tom Hanchett (Mgr-Pur Dept)
Shawn Broe (Mgr-Pur Dept)
Mark Mast (VP-Mktg)

BOND COMMUNITY HEALTH CENTER, INC.

1720 S Gadsden St, Tallahassee, FL 32301
Tel.: (850) 576-4073   FL
Web Site: https://www.bondchc.com
Year Founded: 1984

Sales Range: $10-24.9 Million
Emp.: 168
Health Care Srvices
N.A.I.C.S.: 622110
Temple Robinson (Interim Exec Dir)
Gabriel Otuonye (Chief Compliance Officer & Mgr-Risk)

BOND PHARMACY, INC.

18451 Dallas Pkwy Ste 150, Dallas, TX 75287
Tel.: (601) 988-1700   MS
Web Site: http://aiscaregroup.com
Year Founded: 1998
Advanced Nusing Solutions
N.A.I.C.S.: 621610
Simon Castellanos (CEO)
Charles R. Bell Jr. (Founder & Pres)

Subsidiaries:

Hunt Valley Pharmacy, LLC   (1)
10 Warren Rd Ste 220, Cockeysville, MD 21030
Tel.: (410) 667-6246
Pharmacies & Drug Stores
N.A.I.C.S.: 456110
Tim Askew (Pres)

BOND PLUMBING SUPPLY IN-CORPORATED

1250 NW 23rd St, Miami, FL 33142
Tel.: (305) 634-0656
Web Site:
    https://www.bondsupply.com
Rev.: $21,417,934
Emp.: 36
Plumbing & Hydronic Heating Supplies
N.A.I.C.S.: 423720
Tracy Bond (Owner)

BOND, SCHOENECK & KING, PLLC

1 Lincoln Center 110 W Lafayette St, Syracuse, NY 13202-1355
Tel.: (315) 218-8000   NY
Web Site: https://www.bsk.com
Year Founded: 1897
Emp.: 400
Law firm
N.A.I.C.S.: 541110
Clifford G. Tsan (Partner)
Kathleen M. Bennett (Partner)
Kevin M. Bernstein (Partner)
Christopher Charles Canada (Partner)
Ronald C. Berger (Partner)
Jean M. Hay (Dir-IT)
Kathleen B. Leach (Dir-Mktg)
David Otte (COO)

BONDED CARRIERS INC.

1014 MidAtlantic Pkwy, Martinsburg, WV 25404
Tel.: (304) 263-0884
Web Site:
    http://www.bondedcarriers.com
Sales Range: $10-24.9 Million
Emp.: 120
General Freight Trucking, Long-Distance & Truckload
N.A.I.C.S.: 484121

BONDS COMPANY, INC.

Walker Switch & US 72, Iuka, MS 38852
Tel.: (662) 427-9581
Sales Range: $10-24.9 Million
Emp.: 87
Highway, Street & Bridge Construction Services
N.A.I.C.S.: 237310
Phillip L. Bonds (Sec)
Larry R. Bonds (Pres)
Dennis R. Bonds (VP)

BONDYS FORD INC.

Bondys Ford Inc.—(Continued)

3615 Ross Clark Cir NW, Dothan, AL
36303
Tel.: (334) 792-5171
Web Site:
   http://www.fordalabama.com
Sales Range: $1-9.9 Million
Emp.: 150
Car Dealership
N.A.I.C.S.: 441110
Robert Stahlecker (Mgr-Parts)

BONEAL INCORPORATED
6962 US Hwy 460, Means, KY 40346
Tel.: (606) 768-3620
Web Site: https://www.boneal.com
Year Founded: 1980
Rev.: $20,300,000
Emp.: 90
Industrial Machinery & Equipment Mfr
N.A.I.C.S.: 333922
David B. Ledford (Pres)
Georgetta Hollon Gannon (CFO)
John Karaus (VP)

BONEL BUILDING CORPORA-TION INC.
30802 Gunn Hwy, Tampa, FL 33618
Tel.: (813) 962-4019
Web Site:
   https://www.bonelbuilding.com
Sales Range: $1-9.9 Million
Emp.: 7
Residential Remodeler
N.A.I.C.S.: 236118
Juli Papka (Office Mgr)
Richard Noble (Pres)
Shantell McLean (VP)

BONES TOYOTA, INC.
1615 E 10th St, Roanoke Rapids, NC
27870-4103
Tel.: (252) 537-6161
Web Site:
   http://www.bonestoyota.com
Sales Range: $10-24.9 Million
Emp.: 30
Car Whslr
N.A.I.C.S.: 441110
Troy Lee Bone Jr. (Pres)

BONEY'S FARM STORE, INC.
2201 SE 3rd St, Aledo, IL 61231
Tel.: (309) 582-5395
Web Site:
   http://www.boneysfarmstoreinc.com
Year Founded: 1949
Sales Range: $10-24.9 Million
Emp.: 20
Farm Supply Whslr
N.A.I.C.S.: 424910
Carol Ann Boney (Pres)
Drue E. Baugher (Sec)

BONGARDS CREAMERIES
250 Lake Dr E, Chanhassen, MN
55317
Tel.: (952) 277-5500   MN
Web Site: https://www.bongards.com
Year Founded: 1908
Sales Range: $200-249.9 Million
Emp.: 250
Mfr & Processor of Cheese
N.A.I.C.S.: 311514
Daryl Larson (Pres & CEO)
Subsidiaries:

Bongards South LLC.   (1)
3001 US Hwy 45 Bypass W, Humboldt, TN
38343
Tel.: (731) 784-7978
Cheese Mfr
N.A.I.C.S.: 311513

BONGO JAVA ROASTING CO.

2007 Belmont Blvd, Nashville, TN
37212
Tel.: (615) 385-5282
Web Site:
   https://www.bongojava.com
Year Founded: 1993
Sales Range: $25-49.9 Million
Emp.: 40
Roasted Coffee Mfr
N.A.I.C.S.: 311920
Bob Bernstein (Owner)

BONIFACE-HIERS INSURANCE AGENCY, INC.
880 S Apollo Blvd, Melbourne, FL
32901
Tel.: (321) 951-9595
Web Site:
   http://www.bonifacehierskia.com
Rev.: $22,700,000
Emp.: 40
New Car Dealers
N.A.I.C.S.: 441110
A. J. Hiers (Co-Owner)
Bernard Boniface (Co-Owner)
Neil Huhta (CFO)

BONITA BAY CLUB
26660 Country Club Dr, Bonita
Springs, FL 34134
Tel.: (239) 495-0200   FL
Web Site:
   https://www.bonitabayclub.net
Year Founded: 2009
Sales Range: $10-24.9 Million
Emp.: 469
Country Club Operator
N.A.I.C.S.: 713910
Dan Miles (Gen Mgr)

BONITA BAY PROPERTIES, INC.
9990 Coconut Rd Ste 200, Bonita
Springs, FL 34135-8488
Tel.: (239) 495-1000
Web Site:
   http://www.bonitabaygroup.com
Sales Range: $100-124.9 Million
Emp.: 30
Land Subdivider & Developer
N.A.I.C.S.: 237210
David Lucas (Chm)
Subsidiaries:

Bonita Bay Marina   (1)
27598 Marina Pointe Dr SW, Bonita
Springs, FL 34134
Tel.: (239) 495-3222
Web Site: http://www.bonitabaymarina.net
Marinas
N.A.I.C.S.: 713930
Tibe Larson (Mgr-Marina)

Resource Conservation Systems,
LLC   (1)
9990 Coconut Rd Ste 102, Bonita Springs,
FL 34135
Tel.: (239) 495-5805
Web Site: http://www.rcsirrigation.com
Emp.: 4
Water Supply & Irrigation
N.A.I.C.S.: 221310
Vince Barraco (Gen Mgr)

Sweetwater Landing   (1)
16991 State Rd 31, Fort Myers, FL 33905
Tel.: (239) 694-3850
Web Site: http://www.sweetwaterlanding.net
Emp.: 6
Marinas
N.A.I.C.S.: 713930
Brandon Mayer (Owner)

BONITA SPRINGS UTILITIES INC.
11900 E Terry St, Bonita Springs, FL
34135
Tel.: (239) 992-0711
Web Site: https://www.bsu.us

Year Founded: 1970
Sales Range: $10-24.9 Million
Emp.: 107
Waste Treatment Services
N.A.I.C.S.: 221310
Robert Bachman (VP)
Andy Koebel (Dir-Ops)
James Strecansky (Pres)
David McKee (Treas)
Henry Hochstetler (Sec)

BONITAS INTERNATIONAL LLC
12383 Kinsman Rd, Newbury, OH
44065
Web Site:
   http://www.bonitasinternational.com
Year Founded: 2003
Sales Range: $1-9.9 Million
Emp.: 15
Jewelry Mfr & Distr
N.A.I.C.S.: 339910
Kimberly Martinez (Co-Founder &
CEO)

BONITZ INC.
645 Rosewood Dr, Columbia, SC
29201-4603
Tel.: (803) 799-0181   SC
Web Site: http://www.bonitz.com
Year Founded: 1953
Sales Range: $100-124.9 Million
Emp.: 500
Plastering, Drywall, Insulation Ser-
vices & Sub Contracting
N.A.I.C.S.: 238310
George William Rogers (Founder &
Chm)
Steve Jordan (VP)
Pete Larmore (Pres & CEO)
Doug Dozier (CFO)
William Huckaby (Mng Partner-
Winston-Salem)
Clay Chapman (Mng Partner-
Knoxville)
Rhett Seel (Sr VP)
Jared Culler (Mng Partner)
Subsidiaries:

Bonitz Contracting Company   (1)
232A Industrial Way Dr, Kernersville, NC
27284
Tel.: (336) 996-9900
Web Site: http://www.bonitz.com
Sales Range: $10-24.9 Million
Emp.: 115
Floor Laying & Floor Work
N.A.I.C.S.: 238310

Bonitz Contracting Company,
Inc.   (1)
645 Rosewood Dr, Columbia, SC 29201-
4603
Tel.: (803) 799-0181
Web Site: http://www.bonitz.com
Sales Range: $50-74.9 Million
Emp.: 450
Plastering, Drywall & Insulation
N.A.I.C.S.: 238310

Bonitz Flooring Group, Inc.   (1)
645 Rosewood Dr, Columbia, SC 29201-
4603
Tel.: (803) 799-0181
Web Site: http://www.bonitz.com
Sales Range: $50-74.9 Million
Plastering, Drywall & Insulation
N.A.I.C.S.: 238330
George William Rogers (Chm)
Harold Chapman (Pres & CEO)

Bonitz Inc. - Roofing Systems
Division   (1)
823-B Purser Dr, Raleigh, NC 27603
Tel.: (919) 779-2055
Web Site: http://www.bonitz.com
Emp.: 15
Roof Contracting Services
N.A.I.C.S.: 238160
Jim Leverieg (Gen Mgr)

Bonitz Insulation Company, Inc.   (1)

645 Rosewood Dr, Columbia, SC 29201-
4603
Tel.: (803) 799-0181
Web Site: http://www.bonitz.com
Sales Range: $1-9.9 Million
Emp.: 400
Roofing, Siding & Sheetmetal Work
N.A.I.C.S.: 238160

BONLAND INDUSTRIES, INC.
50 Newark Pompton Tpke, Wayne,
NJ 07470-6635
Tel.: (973) 694-3211   NJ
Web Site:
   https://www.bonlandhvac.com
Year Founded: 1956
Sales Range: $125-149.9 Million
Emp.: 250
Provider of Sheet Metal Services
N.A.I.C.S.: 238220
Andrew Boniface (Exec VP)
Nicolas Scheidel (VP)
Linda West (VP)
William Boniface (Pres & CEO)

BONNER CHEVROLET CO. INC.
694 Wyoming Ave, Kingston, PA
18704
Tel.: (570) 763-8253
Web Site:
   https://www.bonnerchevrolet.com
Sales Range: $10-24.9 Million
Emp.: 45
Sales of New & Used Automobiles
N.A.I.C.S.: 441110
Richard F. Crossin (Pres)

BONNER FOODS INC.
6504 Taylor St, Bonners Ferry, ID
83805
Tel.: (208) 267-3203
Web Site:
   http://www.tradingcostores.com
Sales Range: $10-24.9 Million
Emp.: 140
Supermarket
N.A.I.C.S.: 445110
Paul Matejovsky (Pres)
Gary Morgan (VP)
Subsidiaries:

Trading Co. Stores, Food & Drug   (1)
PO Box 1296, Bonners Ferry, ID 83805
Tel.: (208) 267-3203
Web Site: http://www.tradingcostores.com
Sales Range: $200-249.9 Million
Supermarket
N.A.I.C.S.: 445410
Paul Matejovsky (Co-Owner)

BONNETTE PAGE & STONE CORP.
91 Bisson Ave, Laconia, NH 03246
Tel.: (603) 524-3411
Web Site: https://www.bpsnh.com
Year Founded: 1969
Sales Range: $25-49.9 Million
Emp.: 57
Industrial Building Construction Ser-
vices
N.A.I.C.S.: 236210
Randy Remick (Pres)
Keith McBey (VP)

BONNEVILLE & SON INC.
625 Hooksett Rd, Manchester, NH
03104-2642
Tel.: (603) 624-9280   NH
Web Site:
   https://www.bonnevilleandson.com
Year Founded: 1963
Sales Range: $25-49.9 Million
Emp.: 120
New & Used Car Dealers
N.A.I.C.S.: 441110
Edward Bonneville (Pres & Treas)
John Berry (Gen Mgr)

BONNEVILLE BILLING & COL-LECTIONS

6026 Fashion Point Dr, Ogden, UT
84403
Tel.: (801) 621-7880
Web Site: http://www.bonncoll.com
Sales Range: $10-24.9 Million
Emp.: 100
Collection Agency, Except Real Estate
N.A.I.C.S.: 561440
Dave Toller (Pres)

BONNEVILLE CANNING COCA COLA

2269 S 3270 W, Salt Lake City, UT
84119-1111
Tel.: (801) 816-5450
Sales Range: $25-49.9 Million
Emp.: 200
Bottled & Canned Soft Drink Mfr
N.A.I.C.S.: 312111
Christy Bennett (Mgr-Quality Control)
Curt Sisler (VP-Engrg)
Vijaya Paulraj (Mgr-Quality Control)
Russell Smart (Mgr-IT)
Jeff Sanborn (Mgr-Sls)
Kurt P. Fiedler (VP-Mfg)
Randy Gustaveson (Mgr-Production)
Tyson Fiedler (Mgr-Pur)
Paul Paulraj (Mgr-Quality Assurance)
Richard Smith (Mgr-IT)
Chris Pollock (Mgr-Maintenance)

BONNEVILLE COMMUNICA-TIONS

55 N 300 W, Salt Lake City, UT
84101-3502
Tel.: (801) 237-2488   UT
Web Site: http://www.bonneville.com
Year Founded: 1967
Rev.: $25,000,000
Emp.: 30
Broadcast, Consumer Marketing, Direct Marketing,
Government/Political/Public Affairs,
Production, Radio, T.V.
N.A.I.C.S.: 541810
Stephen R. Wunderli (Dir-Creative)
Bruce T. Reese (Pres & CEO)

BONNEVILLE POWER ADMIN-ISTRATION

905 NE 11th Ave, Portland, OR
97232-4169
Tel.: (503) 230-3000
Web Site: http://www.bpa.gov
Year Founded: 1937
Sales Range: $1-4.9 Billion
Emp.: 1,126
Electric Power Administration Organization
N.A.I.C.S.: 926130
John L. Hairston (Chief Admin Officer)
Claudia R. Andrews (COO)
Mark O. Gendron (Sr VP-Power Svcs)
John Lahti (VP-Transmission Field Svcs)
Richard Shaheen (Sr VP-Transmission Svcs)
Mary Jensen (Gen Counsel)
Michelle Manary (CFO & Exec VP)
Joel Cook (Sr VP-Power Svcs)
Tina Ko (VP-Transmission Svcs Mktg & Sls)
Kim Thompson (VP-Requirements Mktg-Northwest)

BONNEY FORGE CORPORA-TION

14496 Croghan Pike, Mount Union,
PA 17066
Tel.: (814) 542-2545   DE

Web Site:
   https://www.bonneyforge.com
Year Founded: 1984
Sales Range: $150-199.9 Million
Emp.: 400
Pipe Fittings & Valves
N.A.I.C.S.: 332111
John A. Leone (CEO)
Doug Holmes (VP-Bus Dev-Canada & Mgr-Sls)
Ken O'Connell (VP-Bus Dev-Eastern Reg & Mgr-Sls)
Rob Stephens (Mgr-Bus Dev & Sls-Midwest Canada)
Steve Thomas (VP-Valve Products & Bus Dev-Southwest Reg)
Mark Slayton (VP-Bus Dev-Midwest Reg & Mgr-Sls)
Jason Schirf (Mgr-Quality)
Jamie Hicks (Mgr-Sls Admin)
Mary Park (Supvr-Quality)
Rex Casner (Supvr-Shipping Warehouse)
Paul Heald (VP-Product Engrg, Specialties & China Ops)

Subsidiaries:

Bonney Forge Corporation - RP & C Valve Division   **(1)**
14496 Croghan Pike, Mount Union, PA 17066
Tel.: (888) 231-0655
Web Site: http://www.rpc-valve.com
Forged Steel Valve Mfr
N.A.I.C.S.: 332911

WFI International, Inc.   **(1)**
4407 Haygood St, Houston, TX 77022-3505
Tel.: (713) 695-3633
Web Site: http://www.wfi-intl.com
Sales Range: $25-49.9 Million
Emp.: 169
Mfr of Ferrous & Nonferrous Machinery Forgings
N.A.I.C.S.: 332919
Victor Ortega (Mgr-Maintenance)
Stan Tewell (Mgr-Engrg)
Bill Licarione (Mgr-Valve Products)
Donna Davis (Mgr-Comml Sls)
Sue Leone (Exec VP)

BONNEY LAKE FOOD BANK

24015 State Rte 410, Buckley, WA
98321
Tel.: (253) 303-5909
Web Site:
   http://www.bonneylakefoodbank.org
Civic & Social Organization
N.A.I.C.S.: 813410
Stacey Crnich (CEO)

BONSAI OUTLET

914 S Main St, Bellingham, MA
02019
Tel.: (877) 806-3200
Web Site:
   https://www.bonsaioutlet.com
Nursery, Garden Center & Farm Supply Stores
N.A.I.C.S.: 444240

Subsidiaries:

New England Bonsai Gardens   **(1)**
914 S Main St, Bellingham, MA 02019-1846
Tel.: (508) 883-2842
Web Site: http://www.nebonsai.com
Nursery, Garden Center & Farm Supply Stores
N.A.I.C.S.: 444240

BONTERRA CONSULTING

3 Hutton Centre Dr Ste 200, Santa
Ana, CA 92707
Tel.: (626) 351-2000   CA
Web Site:
   http://www.bonterraconsulting.com
Year Founded: 1996
Sales Range: $10-24.9 Million
Emp.: 60

Environmental Planning Consulting
Services
N.A.I.C.S.: 541620
Kristin L. Starbird (Sr Project Mgr)
Tracy E. Zucker (Controller)
Melissa A. Howe (Assoc Principal)
Christina L. Andersen (Principal)
Ann M. Johnston (Principal)
Kathleen Brady (Principal)

BONUS CROP FERTILIZER, INC.

5903 Hwy 66, Greenville, TX 75401
Tel.: (903) 455-9439   TX
Web Site:
   http://www.bcfproducts.com
Year Founded: 1982
Fertilizer Mfr & Distr
N.A.I.C.S.: 325314
W. D. Barton Jr. (CEO)

BONWORTH INC.

40 Francis Rd, Hendersonville, NC
28792
Tel.: (828) 697-2216
Web Site: http://www.bonworth.com
Year Founded: 1971
Sales Range: $25-49.9 Million
Emp.: 2,500
Women's Apparel Mfr & Retailer
N.A.I.C.S.: 458110
Craig Goodman (Mgr-Pur)
Marie Roach (Mgr-Production & Resource)

BONZI TECHNOLOGY INC.

18765 SW Boones Ferry Rd Ste 125,
Tualatin, OR 97062
Tel.: (503) 691-9860
Web Site:
   http://www.bonzicentral.com
Software Publisher
N.A.I.C.S.: 513210
Amy Pate (COO)
Anthony Pate (CTO)

BOOK WORLD INC.

1000 S Lynndale Dr, Appleton, WI
54914
Tel.: (920) 830-7897
Web Site:
   http://www.bookworldstores.com
Sales Range: $10-24.9 Million
Emp.: 200
Book Stores
N.A.I.C.S.: 459210
William Streur (Pres)

BOOKAZINE COMPANY, INC.

75 Hook Rd, Bayonne, NJ 07002-5006
Tel.: (201) 339-7777   NY
Web Site:
   https://www.bookazine.com
Year Founded: 1928
Sales Range: $125-149.9 Million
Emp.: 170
Book & Catalog Publisher
N.A.I.C.S.: 424920
Robert Kallman (Pres & CEO)
Cindy Raiton (VP-Sls)
Allan Davis (VP-Distr)
Andrew Collings (VP-Mdsg)

BOOKE & COMPANY, INC.

600 3rd Ave, New York, NY 10016
Tel.: (212) 490-9095
Web Site:
   http://www.bookeandco.com
Year Founded: 1958
Sales Range: $10-24.9 Million
Emp.: 4
Public Relations Agency
N.A.I.C.S.: 541820
Gerald Amato (Pres)

BOOKER TRANSPORTATION SERVICES, INC.

7601 Canyon Dr, Amarillo, TX 79110
Tel.: (806) 335-3330
Web Site:
   http://www.bookertransportation.com
Rev.: $18,500,000
Emp.: 12
Local Trucking without Storage
N.A.I.C.S.: 484110
Denis Cowley (Pres)

BOOKKEEPERS.COM, LLC

3011 Sutton Gate Dr Ste 210, Suwanee, GA 30024
Tel.: (678) 541-8000
Web Site:
   http://www.bookkeepers.com
Year Founded: 2015
Sales Range: $1-9.9 Million
Emp.: 8
Business Management Services
N.A.I.C.S.: 541611
Ben Robinson (Founder)
Kelly Perry (COO)
Jamie Rodriguez (Dir-Student Success)
Darlene Peacock (Mktg Mgr)
Faith Spradling (Mgr-Affiliate)

BOOKPAL, L.L.C.

18101 Von Karman Ave Ste 1240,
Irvine, CA 92612
Tel.: (949) 333-4872
Web Site: http://www.book-pal.com
Year Founded: 2005
Sales Range: $1-9.9 Million
Emp.: 7
Sells Books of Any Genre in Quantities of 25 or More Copies Per Title to
Businesses, Associations, Educational Institutions, Religious Groups &
Government Organizations
N.A.I.C.S.: 513199
Anthony DiCortanzo (Founder & Pres)

BOOKRAGS, INC.

999 3rd Ave Ste 700, Spokane, WA
98104
Tel.: (216) 519-7910
Web Site: http://www.bookrags.com
Year Founded: 1999
On-Demand Online Educational Resources
N.A.I.C.S.: 513199

BOOKS INCORPORATED

1501 Vermont St, San Francisco, CA
94107-3250
Tel.: (415) 643-3400
Web Site: http://www.booksinc.net
Sales Range: $10-24.9 Million
Emp.: 200
Book Stores
N.A.I.C.S.: 459210
Michael Tucker (Pres, Co-Owner & CEO)
Margie Scott-Tucker (Co-Owner)
Kwok Chan (Controller)

BOOKS-A-MILLION, INC.

402 Industrial Ln, Birmingham, AL
35211
Tel.: (205) 942-3737   DE
Web Site:
   http://www.booksamillioninc.com
Year Founded: 1917
Sales Range: $450-499.9 Million
Emp.: 2,400
Book Retailer
N.A.I.C.S.: 459210
Clyde B. Anderson (Chm)
Terrance G. Finley (CEO)
R. Todd Noden (Pres)

Books-A-Million, Inc.—(Continued)

Subsidiaries:

American Wholesale Book Company
Inc. (1)
4350 Bryson Blvd, Florence, AL 35630-
7317
Tel.: (256) 766-3789
Web Site: http://www.booksamillioninc.com
Sales Range: $150-199.9 Million
Emp.: 400
Book Distr
N.A.I.C.S.: 424920
Clyde Anderson (Pres)

BOOKSTORE1SARASOTA

12 South Palm Ave, Sarasota, FL
34236
Tel.: (941) 365-7900
Web Site:
http://www.bookstore1sarasota.com
Sales Range: $1-9.9 Million
Emp.: 8
Book Retailer
N.A.I.C.S.: 459210
Georgia Court (Owner)

BOOKSY INC.

1011 E Touhy Ave Ste 140, Des
Plaines, IL 60018
Tel.: (312) 548-0085
Web Site: http://www.booksy.com
Year Founded: 2014
Sales Range: $1-9.9 Million
Emp.: 500
Beauty Salon Services
N.A.I.C.S.: 812112
Stefanee Horwitch (Dir-HR)
Stefan Batory (Co-Founder & CEO)

Subsidiaries:

Genbook, Inc. (1)
548 Market St Ste 71035, San Francisco,
CA 94104
Tel.: (415) 227-9903
Web Site: http://www.genbook.com
Ambulatory Health Care Services
N.A.I.C.S.: 621999
Rody Moore (Founder & CEO)
Philipp Liver (CEO)

BOOMERANG DIRECT MAR-KETING, LLC

8005 S Chester St Ste 175, Centen-
nial, CO 80112
Tel.: (303) 997-7047
Web Site:
http://www.boomerangdm.com
Year Founded: 2010
Sales Range: $1-9.9 Million
Emp.: 10
Real Estate Agency Services
N.A.I.C.S.: 531210
Michael Zak (Founder & CEO)
Jayne Jansen (Mgr-Production &
Dev)
Elizabeth Parker (Sls Mgr)

BOOMERANG SYSTEMS, INC.

30 A Vreeland Rd Ste 150, Florham
Park, NJ 07932
Tel.: (973) 538-1194   DE
Web Site:
http://www.boomerangsystems.com
Year Founded: 2006
Sales Range: $1-9.9 Million
Automated Parking & Storage Sys-
tems Developer
N.A.I.C.S.: 812930
Christopher Mulvihill (Founder)
James V. Gelly (CEO)
Stephen G. Marble (CFO)

BOOMM MARKETING & COM-MUNICATIONS

17 N Catherine Ave, La Grange, IL
60525

Tel.: (708) 352-9700   IL
Web Site: http://www.boomm.com
Year Founded: 1998
Sales Range: $1-9.9 Million
Emp.: 10
Advetising Agency
N.A.I.C.S.: 541810
Gary Mattes (CEO)
Fred Gaede (Chief Creative Officer)
Lisa Ryan (Partner)
Randy Mitchell (Dir-Creative)

BOOMTOWN, LLC

1505 King St Ext Ste 101, Charles-
ton, SC 29403   SC
Web Site:
https://www.boomtownroi.com
Year Founded: 2006
Sales Range: $1-9.9 Million
Emp.: 38
Web-Based Software Solutions for
Real Estate
N.A.I.C.S.: 513210
Cooper Bane (Founder & VP-Product
Dev)
Lwando Marambana (Acct Dir)
Lisa Snymanc (Acct Mgr-Port Eliza-
beth)
Andrew MacKenzie (Mng Dir)
Grier Allen (Co-Founder & CEO)

BOONE & DARR, INC.

4465 S State St, Ann Arbor, MI,
48108
Tel.: (734) 665-0648
Web Site: https://www.boone-
darr.com
Sales Range: $10-24.9 Million
Emp.: 60
Plumbing, Heating & Air-Conditioning
Services
N.A.I.C.S.: 238220
John Kipfmiller (Mgr-Bus Dev)
Jeff Darr (Project Mgr)
Anna Marie Weller (Project Mgr)

BOONE & SONS INC.

5550 The Hills Plz, Chevy Chase,
MD 20815
Tel.: (301) 657-2144
Web Site:
https://www.booneandsons.com
Rev.: $17,029,404
Emp.: 50
Jewelry, Precious Stones & Precious
Metals
N.A.I.C.S.: 458310
Darryl J. Boone (Pres)

BOONE DELEON COMMUNI-CATIONS, INC.

3100 S Gessner Rd Ste 110, Hous-
ton, TX 77063
Tel.: (713) 952-9600
Web Site:
http://www.boonedeleon.com
Year Founded: 1947
Sales Range: $10-24.9 Million
Emp.: 8
N.A.I.C.S.: 541810
Ron Lucas (Media Dir & Acct Exec)
Patty Morris (Office Mgr)

BOONE FORD LINCOLN MER-CURY, INC.

300 New Market Blvd, Boone, NC
28607
Tel.: (828) 264-6111
Web Site:
http://www.boonefordlincoln.com
Year Founded: 2003
Sales Range: $10-24.9 Million
Emp.: 48
Car Whslr
N.A.I.C.S.: 441110
Alfred Glover (Pres)

BOONE MEMORIAL HOSPITAL

701 Madison Ave, Madison, WV
25130
Tel.: (304) 369-1230   WV
Web Site: https://www.bmh.org
Year Founded: 2010
Sales Range: $25-49.9 Million
Emp.: 224
Health Care Srvices
N.A.I.C.S.: 622110
Randell D. Foxx (CFO)
Robert Brown (Pres)
Virgil Underwood (CEO)
David Gresham (Chief Dev Officer)
Mark Linville (COO)
Terri Castle (Chief Nursing Officer)

BOONEOAKLEY

1445 S Mint St, Charlotte, NC 28203
Tel.: (704) 333-9797
Web Site:
https://www.booneoakley.com
Year Founded: 2000
Rev.: $59,400,000
Emp.: 18
N.A.I.C.S.: 541810
David Oakley (Dir-Creative & Pres)
Claire Oakley (Dir-Acct Svcs)
Jim Mountjoy (Dir-Eye)

BOOSE CHEVROLET CO., INC.

575 Arlington Rd, Brookville, OH
45309
Tel.: (937) 833-4011
Web Site:
http://www.boosechevrolet.com
Sales Range: $10-24.9 Million
Emp.: 32
Car Whslr
N.A.I.C.S.: 441110

BOOST PAYMENT SOLU-TIONS, INC.

767 3rd Ave, New York, NY 10017
Tel.: (212) 750-7771
Web Site: http://www.boostb2b.com
Year Founded: 2009
Sales Range: $1-9.9 Million
Emp.: 32
Online Payment Services
N.A.I.C.S.: 522320
Dean M. Leavitt (Founder, Chm &
CEO)
Gordon Elliot (COO)
James Lister (Exec VP-Product &
Tech)
Jesse H. Davis (CIO)
Lou Longhi (Chief Revenue Officer)

BOOST TECHNOLOGIES, LLC

811 E 4th St Ste B, Dayton, OH
45402
Tel.: (800) 324-9756
Web Site: http://www.recognition.com
Year Founded: 2007
Sales Range: $1-9.9 Million
Emp.: 50
Holding Company: Online Rewards
Program
N.A.I.C.S.: 551112
Anita Emoff (Pres)

Subsidiaries:

Boost Rewards (1)
811 E Fourth St Suite B, Dayton, OH 45402
Tel.: (800) 324-9756
Web Site: http://www.boostrewards.com
Sales Range: $1-9.9 Million
Emp.: 60
Online Rewards & Recognition Programs
N.A.I.C.S.: 541613
Anita Emoff (Pres)
Michael Emoff (Partner)
Joe Drayer (VP-Boost Rewards & Ignite)

BOOT CREEK ROYALTY LTD.

400 W Illinois Ste 1070, Midland, TX
79701
Tel.: (432) 685-9005
Year Founded: 2011
Sales Range: $25-49.9 Million
Oil & Gas Support Services
N.A.I.C.S.: 213112
Armand Smith (Pres)

BOOTH & LADUKE MOTORS, INC.

880 S Main St, Colville, WA 99114
Tel.: (509) 684-8404
Web Site:
http://www.boothladuke.com
Year Founded: 1981
Sales Range: $10-24.9 Million
Emp.: 50
New Car Dealers
N.A.I.C.S.: 441110
Tony Booth (Co-Owner)
Dave Laduke (Co-Owner)
Cory Fitzgerald (Mgr)
Kris Lecaire (Mgr-Internet Sls)
Dan Anders (Mgr-Svc)

BOOTH CREEK MANAGE-MENT CORPORATION

950 Red Sand Stone Rd Ste 43, Vail,
CO 81657
Tel.: (970) 476-4030   DE
Year Founded: 1994
Investment Holding Company
N.A.I.C.S.: 551112
George N. Gillett Jr. (Founder &
Chm)
Jeffrey J. Joyce (CFO)
Alex Gillett (Mng Dir-Automotive Plat-
form)

Subsidiaries:

Booth Creek Ski Holdings, Inc. (1)
11025 Pioneer Trl Ste 100, Truckee, CA
96161-0249
Tel.: (530) 550-7112
Web Site: http://www.boothcreek.com
Sales Range: $75-99.9 Million
Holding Company; Ski Resort Owner &
Operator
N.A.I.C.S.: 551112
George N. Gillett Jr. (Chm & CEO)
Brian J. Pope (VP-Fin & Acctg)

Subsidiary (Domestic):

Mount Cranmore Ski Resort, Inc. (2)
239 Skimobile Rd, North Conway, NH
03860-5364
Tel.: (603) 356-5544
Web Site: http://www.cranmore.com
Sales Range: $10-24.9 Million
Emp.: 100
Skiing & Snowboarding Resort
N.A.I.C.S.: 713920
Becca Deschenes (Dir-Mktg)

Richard Petty Motorsports LLC (1)
7065 Zephyr Pl, Concord, NC 28027
Tel.: (704) 743-5420
Web Site:
http://www.richardpettymotorsports.com
Sales Range: $25-49.9 Million
Professional Stock Car Motorsports Team
N.A.I.C.S.: 711211
Richard Lee Petty (Partner)
Sammy Johns (VP-Ops)
Lance Brown (VP-Mktg Svcs & Comm)
Jim Hannigan (VP-Licensing & Mdsg)
Mike Hargrave (CMO & Exec VP)
Brian Moffitt (CEO)
Andrew Murstein (Co-Owner)

Summit Automotive Partners,
LLC (1)
5299 DTC Blvd Ste 1050, Greenwood Vil-
lage, CO 80111
Tel.: (303) 209-3965
Web Site: http://www.summit-ap.com
Sales Range: $100-124.9 Million
Emp.: 12
Holding Company; New & Used Car Dealer-
ships Owner & Operator
N.A.I.C.S.: 551112

William Carmichael *(CEO)*
Andrew Bradford *(CFO)*
Rob Meador *(VP-Dealer Ops)*
Tamila Bauer *(CMO)*
Alexander Gillett *(Mng Dir)*
Yegor Malinovskii *(VP-Dealer Ops)*

Group (Domestic):

Berlin City Auto Group   (2)
485 Main St, Gorham, NH 03581
Tel.: (603) 752-6644
Web Site: http://www.berlincity.com
Holding Company; New & Used Car Dealerships Operator
N.A.I.C.S.: 551112
Yegor Malinovskii *(VP-Stores)*
Gary Poirier *(Mgr-Parts)*
Phil Cooutier *(Mgr-Parts)*

Subsidiary (Domestic):

Berlin City Ford, Inc.   (3)
485 Main St, Gorham, NH 03581
Tel.: (603) 752-6644
Web Site: http://www.berlincity.com
Sales Range: $50-74.9 Million
Emp.: 100
New & Used Car Dealer
N.A.I.C.S.: 441110
Ed Watson *(Gen Mgr)*
Allen Binette *(Mgr-Ford Sls)*

Berlin City's Chevrolet Buick, Inc.   (3)
545 Main St, Gorham, NH 03581
Tel.: (603) 752-3700
Web Site: http://www.berlincitygm.com
Sales Range: $1-9.9 Million
Emp.: 32
New & Used Car Dealer
N.A.I.C.S.: 441110
Bobby Hill *(Mgr-Sls)*

Subsidiary (Domestic):

NTAN, LLC   (2)
307 Thompson Ln, Nashville, TN 37211
Tel.: (615) 200-1899
Web Site: http://www.actionnissan.com
Sales Range: $25-49.9 Million
New & Used Car Dealer Distr
N.A.I.C.S.: 441110
Ashley Davis *(Mgr-Fin)*
Chris Jensen *(Mgr-Sls)*
Ray Pritchard *(Mgr-New Car Sls)*
Jamie Thompson *(Dir-Svc)*
Steve Totok *(Mgr-Sls)*
Kevin Winningham *(Gen Mgr)*

BOOTH WALTZ ENTERPRISES, INC.
42 Rumsey Rd, East Hartford, CT 06108-1133
Tel.: (860) 289-7800
Web Site: http://www.ghberlin.com
Year Founded: 1920
Sales Range: $10-24.9 Million
Emp.: 45
Lubricants Whslr
N.A.I.C.S.: 424720
David Fenderson *(Pres)*

Subsidiaries:

G. H. Berlin-Windward   (1)
1064 Goffs Falls Rd, Manchester, NH 03103-6128
Tel.: (603) 222-2900
Web Site: http://www.ghberlinwindward.com
Petroleum, Lubricating Oils & Specialty Products Mfr
N.A.I.C.S.: 424720
Stephen Eldred *(Pres)*
Meg Fenderson *(Dir-Mgmt Info Svcs)*
David Fenderson *(Sr VP-Mktg)*
John Scanlon *(VP-Sls)*
Bret Waltz *(VP-Ops)*
Al Tetu *(Dir-Fin)*
Kevin Barbeau *(Dir-Industrial Products)*
Mike Kumpulanian *(Mgr-Pricing)*
Erik Strout *(Sls Mgr)*
Rob Funkhouser *(Sls Mgr)*
Justin Johnson *(Sls Mgr)*
Rich Flaherty *(Sls Mgr)*

Division (Domestic):

Windward Petroleum   (2)

10 Mecaw Rd, Hampden, ME 04401
Tel.: (207) 990-1100
Web Site:
http://www.windwardpetroleum.com
Petroleum Lubricating Oils & Specialty
Products Distr
N.A.I.C.S.: 424720

BOOTHEEL PETROLEUM COMPANY
623 N State Rt 25, Dexter, MO 63841
Tel.: (573) 624-4160
Web Site:
https://www.bootheelpetroleum.com
Sales Range: $10-24.9 Million
Emp.: 25
Petroleum Bulk Stations
N.A.I.C.S.: 424710
Jay Barbour *(VP)*

BOOTS SMITH OILFIELD SERVICES, LLC
2501 Airport Dr, Laurel, MS 39440-4719
Tel.: (601) 649-1220   MS
Web Site: http://www.bootssmith.net
Year Founded: 1954
Sales Range: $50-74.9 Million
Emp.: 500
Pipeline Construction, Oil & Gas Drilling & Production Support Services
N.A.I.C.S.: 237120
Jason Smith *(Pres)*

BOOTSTRAP SOFTWARE PARTNERS, LLC
300 Constitution Ave Ste 200, Portsmouth, NH 03801
Tel.: (603) 610-6111
Web Site: http://www.politemail.com
Year Founded: 2006
Sales Range: $1-9.9 Million
Emp.: 28
Software Development Services
N.A.I.C.S.: 541511
Michael DesRochers *(Founder)*

BOOTZ MANUFACTURING COMPANY
PO Box 18010, Evansville, IN 47719-1010
Tel.: (812) 423-5401
Web Site: http://www.bootz.com
Sales Range: $10-24.9 Million
Emp.: 50
Bathtubs: Enameled Iron, Cast Iron, Or Pressed Metal
N.A.I.C.S.: 332999
Pete Desotio *(Pres)*
Bill Weidman *(VP-Fin)*

BOOYAH NETWORKS, INC.
11030 Cir Point Rd Ste 350, Westminster, CO 80020
Tel.: (303) 345-6600
Web Site:
http://www.booyahnetworks.com
Year Founded: 2001
Sales Range: $10-24.9 Million
Emp.: 30
Internet Services
N.A.I.C.S.: 541519
Michael Shehan *(Chm)*
Steve Swoboda *(CFO)*

Subsidiaries:

The Booyah Agency   (1)
11030 Circle Point Rd Ste 350, Westminster, CO 80020
Tel.: (303) 345-6600
Web Site: http://www.thebooyahagency.com
Sales Range: $10-24.9 Million
Emp.: 27
N.A.I.C.S.: 541810

BORA BORA INC.

5A Tabonuco St, Guaynabo, PR 00968
Tel.: (787) 781-1368
Sales Range: $10-24.9 Million
Emp.: 270
Clothing, Sportswear, Men's & Boys' Beachware
N.A.I.C.S.: 458110

BORAN CRAIG BARBER ENGEL CONSTRUCTION CO., INC.
3570 Enterprise Ave Ste 200, Naples, FL 34104
Tel.: (239) 643-3343
Web Site: http://www.bcbe.com
Year Founded: 1972
Sales Range: $50-74.9 Million
Emp.: 45
Multi-Family Dwellings & Commercial Construction & Remodeling
N.A.I.C.S.: 236116
Melvin Engel *(Pres & CEO)*
Harry Engel *(VP-Field Ops)*
Brian Mayotte *(VP)*
Bryan Trtan *(Project Mgr)*
Denise Fernandez *(Coord-Finishing Touches)*
Gary Smith *(Project Mgr)*
Jessica E. Lynch *(Coord-Finishing Touches)*
Joe Krastel *(Project Mgr)*
Scott Wagner *(Project Mgr)*

BORCHERDING BUICK GMC, INC.
9737 Kings Auto Mall Rd, Cincinnati, OH 45249
Tel.: (513) 677-9200
Web Site:
https://www.borcherding.com
Sales Range: $10-24.9 Million
Emp.: 72
Car Whslr
N.A.I.C.S.: 441110
Kim Borcherding *(Pres)*

BORDER FOODS, INC.
5425 Boone Ave N, New Hope, MN 55428
Tel.: (763) 559-7338
Web Site:
https://www.borderfoods.com
Sales Range: $75-99.9 Million
Fast-Food Restaurant, Chain
N.A.I.C.S.: 722513
Lee Engler *(Co-Owner)*
Jennifer Bang *(Mgr-Ops Svcs)*
Jeff Engler *(Co-Owner)*
Carol Williams *(VP-Ops)*
Sharla Hennek *(Mgr-Training)*

BORDER GRILL
1145 W Washington St, Marquette, MI 49855
Tel.: (906) 228-5228
Web Site: https://www.bordergrill.net
Year Founded: 1997
Sales Range: $1-9.9 Million
Emp.: 85
Mexican Restaurant
N.A.I.C.S.: 722511
Cailey Herman *(Gen Mgr)*

BORDER INTERNATIONAL
12283 Rojas Dr, El Paso, TX 79936
Tel.: (915) 858-4644
Web Site: https://www.borderint.com
Sales Range: $10-24.9 Million
Emp.: 300
Car Whslr
N.A.I.C.S.: 441110
Steve Thummel *(Principal)*

BORDER INTERNATIONAL TRUCKS

12283 Rojas Dr, El Paso, TX 79936
Tel.: (915) 858-4644
Web Site: http://www.borderintl.com
Sales Range: $10-24.9 Million
Emp.: 50
New Car Dealers
N.A.I.C.S.: 441110
William Jarvis *(Mgr-Fixed Ops)*
Ami Knight *(Dir-Fin)*

BORDER STATES INDUSTRIES, INC.
105 25th St N, Fargo, ND 58102-4002
Tel.: (701) 293-5833   ND
Web Site: http://www.bseweb.com
Year Founded: 1952
Sales Range: $650-699.9 Million
Emp.: 240
Wholesale Distr of Plumbing & Electrical Supplies
N.A.I.C.S.: 423610
Tammy J. Miller *(CEO)*
Lex Silbernagel *(VP-Strategic Alliances)*
Jason Stein *(COO)*
Jason Seger *(Sr VP-Supply Chain)*
Patrick Novak *(VP-Mktg)*
Jeremy Welsand *(CFO)*
Gary Daniel *(VP-SC Reg)*
Don Masters *(VP-SE Reg)*
James Sipe *(VP-Strategy Enablement)*

Subsidiaries:

Border States Electric Supply LLC   (1)
105 25th St N, Fargo, ND 58102-4002   (100%)
Tel.: (701) 293-5834
Web Site:
http://www.borderstateselectric.com
Sales Range: $25-49.9 Million
Emp.: 150
Holding Company
N.A.I.C.S.: 423610
Tammy Miller *(Chm)*
Jason Seger *(Pres)*
Jason Stein *(Exec VP-Sls & Mktg)*
Kelly Rudolf *(Sr Mgr-IT Infrastructure)*
Ryan Stall *(Sr VP-IT, Ops & Strategy Enablement)*
Greg Hallfielder *(Mgr-Ops-Northeast Reg)*
Victor Harding *(Mgr-Bus Dev-Southwest Reg)*
Brad Kvalheim *(VP-Northwest Reg)*
David Held *(Sr Mgr-Mktg Svcs & Digital Mktg)*
Adam Guderian *(Sr Mgr-IT Applications)*
Shane Kerska *(VP-Northeast Reg)*
Jeremy Welsand *(CFO)*
Pat Nolte *(Mgr-Ops-South Central Reg)*
Mike Busch *(Sr VP-HR & Organizational Dev)*
Lyla Ableidinger *(Mgr-Organizational Change)*
Neil Gartin *(Dir-Inventory & Pur)*
Tony Serati *(Dir-Sourcing & Pricing)*
AnnaLisa Nash *(Gen Counsel)*
David White *(CEO)*
Geoff Murphy *(VP-Vendor Rels)*

Border States Industries, Inc.   (1)
502 N Bryant Blvd, San Angelo, TX 76903-5200
Tel.: (325) 655-9163
Web Site:
http://www.borderstateselectric.com
Sales Range: $25-49.9 Million
Electrical Supplies Distr
N.A.I.C.S.: 423610
Scott Dugger *(Branch Mgr)*

Border States Industries, Inc. - UtiliCor Division   (1)
1645 N Pkwy, Jackson, TN 38301
Tel.: (731) 423-0071
Web Site: http://www.borderstates.com
Emp.: 10
Electrical Component Distr
N.A.I.C.S.: 423610
Joel Wright *(Pres)*

Border States Industries, Inc.—(Continued)

Bush Supply Company (1)
1101 W Jackson St, Harlingen, TX 78550
Tel.: (956) 428-1613
Sales Range: $50-74.9 Million
Emp.: 7
Electrical Supplies Distr
N.A.I.C.S.: 423610
Greg Evrard (Mng Dir)

Harris Electric Supply Co., Inc. (1)
656 Wedgewood Ave, Nashville, TN 37203
Tel.: (615) 255-4161
Web Site:
http://www.harriselectricsupply.com
Sales Range: $10-24.9 Million
Emp.: 80
Electrical Supplies
N.A.I.C.S.: 423610

Sequel Electrical Supply, LLC (1)
14 Hughes St NE, Fort Walton Beach, FL 32548-4405
Tel.: (601) 483-4903
Web Site:
http://www.sequelelectricalsupply.com
Electrical Apparatus & Related Equipment Merchant Whslr
N.A.I.C.S.: 423610
Lee Moseley (Pres)

Shealy Electrical Wholesalers, Inc. (1)
120 Saxe Gotha Rd, West Columbia, SC 29172
Tel.: (803) 227-0599
Web Site: http://www.borderssstate.com
Sales Range: $200-249.9 Million
Emp.: 115
Electrical Equipment Whslr
N.A.I.C.S.: 423610
John A. Wilson (Dir-Mgmt Info Sys)
Steve Freiburger (VP-Sls-Engineered Products)
Bill Hurd (VP-Sls-Lighting & Controls)

Western Extralite Company (1)
1470 Liberty St, Kansas City, MO 64102
Tel.: (816) 421-8404
Web Site: http://www.borderstates.com
Sales Range: $125-149.9 Million
Emp.: 250
Electrical Supplies Distr
N.A.I.C.S.: 423610
Gene Baker (Acct Mgr)
Leith Winsor (Mgr-Sls-Construction & Indus)
Sharon Todd (Supvr-Pur)

BORDER STATES PAVING, INC.
4101 32nd St N, Fargo, ND 58102
Tel.: (701) 237-4860   ND
Web Site:
https://www.borderstatespaving.com
Year Founded: 1967
Sales Range: $25-49.9 Million
Emp.: 250
Asphalt Paving & Concrete Construction Services
N.A.I.C.S.: 237310
Dan Thompson (Pres)
Nancy Slotten (Treas & Exec VP)

BORDER VALLEY TRADING LTD
604 E Mead Rd, Brawley, CA 92227
Tel.: (760) 344-6700
Web Site:
https://www.bordervalley.com
Rev.: $25,000,000
Emp.: 10
Hay Grower & Distributor
N.A.I.C.S.: 424910
Greg Braun (Owner)

BORDERLESS HOLDINGS, INC.
10045 Red Run Blvd Ste 140, Owings Mills, MD 21117
Tel.: (855) 545-0251   DE
Web Site:
http://www.borderlessholdings.com
Year Founded: 2013

Gold Jewelry Sales
N.A.I.C.S.: 423940
David Mathias (Sec)

BORDERPLEX REALTY LLC
2015 E Griffin Pkwy, Mission, TX 78572
Tel.: (956) 682-3131
Web Site: http://www.bplexhome.com
Sales Range: $25-49.9 Million
Emp.: 20
Real Estate Agents & Managers
N.A.I.C.S.: 531210
Mario Baez (Pres)

BORDERS PERRIN NORRANDER INC.
520 SW Yamhill St Ste 950, Portland, OR 97204-2400
Tel.: (503) 227-2506   OR
Web Site: http://www.bpninc.com
Year Founded: 1977
Sales Range: $10-24.9 Million
Emp.: 35
Advertising Services
N.A.I.C.S.: 541810
Andrea Mitchell (Dir-Media)

BORDIER'S NURSERY INC
7231 Irvine Blvd, Irvine, CA 92618-1199
Tel.: (949) 559-4221
Year Founded: 1951
Rev.: $27,500,000
Emp.: 620
Ornamental Tress & Shrubs Whslr
N.A.I.C.S.: 111421
Richard Rehm (Owner)
George Gutman (Gen Mgr-Tech & Regulatory Svc)

BORE TECH UTILITIES & MAINTENANCE INC.
19025 SW 194 Ave, Miami, FL 33187
Tel.: (786) 345-3345
Web Site: http://www.bore-tech.net
Year Founded: 2011
Sales Range: $1-9.9 Million
Emp.: 52
Business Management Consulting Services
N.A.I.C.S.: 541611
Santy Fernandez (Co-Founder, Principal & Dir-Construction)
Kleimer Cruz (Co-Founder, Principal & Dir-Projects)
Wendy Cabral (Dir-Engrg)

BORG COMPRESSED STEELE
1032 N Lewis Ave, Tulsa, OK 74110
Tel.: (918) 587-2511
Web Site: https://www.yaffeco.net
Sales Range: $10-24.9 Million
Emp.: 80
Mfr of Ferrous Metal Scrap & Waste
N.A.I.C.S.: 423930
Sharla McAfee (Controller)
Chuck Cale (Pres)

BORG INDAK INC.
701 Enterprise Dr, Delavan, WI 53115-1313
Tel.: (262) 728-5531   WI
Web Site: http://www.borgindak.com
Year Founded: 1994
Sales Range: $25-49.9 Million
Emp.: 100
Mfr of Clocks & Parts, Circuit Boards, Switches
N.A.I.C.S.: 334519
Martin Cobb (Chm)
Bob Meincke (Program Mgr & Supvr-Mechanical Engrg)
Jeffrey Katzenberger (Supvr-IT)
Patty Paschke (VP)

BORGHESE, INC.
10 E 34th St Fl 3, New York, NY 10016-4327
Tel.: (212) 659-5300   DE
Web Site: http://www.borghese.com
Sales Range: $50-74.9 Million
Emp.: 140
Cosmetics & Fragrances Mfr
N.A.I.C.S.: 424210
Frank Palladino (CFO)
Maria Monastersky (Mgr-HR & Payroll)
Maureen Perry (Bus Mgr)
Cheryl Tilders (Dir-Ops)

BORGHESI BUILDING & ENGINEERING CO., INC.
2155 E Main St, Torrington, CT 06790
Tel.: (860) 482-7613
Web Site:
https://www.borghesibuilding.com
Year Founded: 1942
Sales Range: $10-24.9 Million
Emp.: 25
Civil Engineering Services
N.A.I.C.S.: 237310
Jeff Borghesi (Pres)

BORGMAN CAPITAL LLC
111 E Kilbourn Ave Ste 2600, Milwaukee, WI 53202
Tel.: (414) 975-4629
Web Site:
https://www.borgmancapital.com
Investment Firm
N.A.I.C.S.: 523999
David Bartelme (Mng Dir)
Sequoya S. Borgman (Founder & Mng Dir)

Subsidiaries:

Skinner & Cook, Inc. (1)
611 Springfield Rd, Kenilworth, NJ 07033
Tel.: (908) 241-0152
Industrial Buildings And Warehouses
N.A.I.C.S.: 236210
Eileen Perretta-Blum (Pres)

BORGMAN FORD MAZDA
3150 28th St SW, Grandville, MI 49418-1111
Tel.: (616) 534-7651
Web Site:
http://www.borgmanfordmazda.com
Year Founded: 1960
Sales Range: $25-49.9 Million
Emp.: 110
Car Whslr
N.A.I.C.S.: 441110
John F. Borgman (Pres)
Joe Kaldor (Mgr-Inventory)
Sundew Prindle (Accts Mgr & Coord-Internet)

BORING & TUNNELING CO. OF AMERICA
515 S Loop W, Houston, TX 77054
Tel.: (832) 204-8741
Web Site: http://www.bortunco.com
Sales Range: $10-24.9 Million
Emp.: 80
Water Main Construction
N.A.I.C.S.: 237110
Dale Kornegay (Pres & CEO)
Bob Gowens (CFO)
Joe Gibbs (VP & Controller)

BORING BUSINESS SYSTEMS, INC.
950 E Main St, Lakeland, FL 33801
Tel.: (863) 686-3167   FL
Web Site: https://www.boring.com
Year Founded: 1924
Sales Range: $1-9.9 Million
Emp.: 44

Miscellaneous Retail Stores
N.A.I.C.S.: 459999
Dean Boring (Pres & CEO)
Carol Catanzarite (Controller)
Mike Phillips (Mgr-Svc)
Jessica Lewis (Dir-HR)
Mary Jo (Coord-Network Svcs)

BORINQUEN CONTAINER CORP.
800 El Mangotin Bo Carrizales, Hatillo, PR 00659
Tel.: (787) 898-5000
Web Site:
http://www.borinquengroup.com
Year Founded: 1969
Sales Range: $25-49.9 Million
Emp.: 243
Mfr of Corrugated & Solid Fiber Boxes
N.A.I.C.S.: 322211
Lezette Gonzalez (Pres)

Subsidiaries:

Borinquen Fiber Drums (1)
PO Box 145170, Arecibo, PR 00614-5170
Tel.: (787) 898-5000
Web Site: http://www.borinquengroup.com
Sales Range: $10-24.9 Million
Emp.: 20
Fiber Cans, Drums & Similar Products
N.A.I.C.S.: 322219
Edgar Rivadeneyra (Mgr-Production)
Milton Rosa (VP-Mfg)

Hatillo Paper Board Corp. (1)
PO Box 145170, Arecibo, PR 00614-5170
Tel.: (787) 898-5000
Web Site: http://www.borinquengroup.com
Sales Range: $1-9.9 Million
Paperboard Mills
N.A.I.C.S.: 322130
Livette Gonzalez (Pres & CEO)

BORIS FX, INC.
65 Franklin St Ste 400, Boston, MA 02110
Tel.: (617) 451-9900
Web Site: https://www.borisfx.com
Year Founded: 1995
Sales Range: $1-9.9 Million
Emp.: 50
Developer of Visual Effects, Titling, Video Editing & Workflow Tools for Broadcast, Post-Production & Film Professionals
N.A.I.C.S.: 513210
Ross Shain (Chief Product Officer)
Boris Yamnitsky (Founder & Pres)
Jessie E. Petrov (Dir-Mktg)

Subsidiaries:

GenArts, Inc. (1)
65 Franklin St, Boston, MA 02114 (100%)
Tel.: (617) 492-2888
Web Site: http://www.genarts.com
Video Effects Software Development Services
N.A.I.C.S.: 541511
Gary Oberbrunner (CTO)
Daniel Sims (Sr Dir-Mktg & Bus Dev)
George Naspo (Pres & CEO)
George Finnegan (VP-Fin & Controller)

BORKHOLDER CORPORATION
786 United States 6 W, Nappanee, IN 46550
Tel.: (574) 773-3144
Web Site: http://www.borkholder.com
Sales Range: $10-24.9 Million
Emp.: 150
Sales of Building Materials
N.A.I.C.S.: 423310
Freeman D. Borkholder (Pres)
Brandon Myers (Controller)

BORLAND BENEFIELD, P.C.

2101 Highland Ave S Ste 500, Birmingham, AL 35205
Tel.: (205) 802-7212   AL
Web Site:
http://www.borlandbenefield.com
Year Founded: 1922
Accounting Services
N.A.I.C.S.: 541219
Jeffrey D. Chandler *(Pres & Mng Dir)*
John M. Wilson *(Exec VP)*

BORMAN MOTOR COMPANY
470 W Boutz Rd, Las Cruces, NM 88005
Tel.: (575) 525-4500
Web Site:
http://www.bormanmotorco.com
Sales Range: $25-49.9 Million
Emp.: 145
Car Whslr
N.A.I.C.S.: 441110
Liz Altuna *(Mgr)*

BORNQUIST INC.
7050 N Lehigh Ave, Chicago, IL 60646
Tel.: (773) 774-2800
Web Site: https://www.bornquist.com
Sales Range: $25-49.9 Million
Emp.: 60
Industrial Machinery & Equipment
N.A.I.C.S.: 423830
David Everhart *(Mgr-Sls)*
Dan Watkins *(Engr-Sls)*
John Berg *(CEO)*

BORNS GROUP, INC.
1610 14th Ave SE, Watertown, SD 57201-5324
Tel.: (605) 226-3356   SD
Web Site:
https://www.bornsgroup.com
Year Founded: 1991
Sales Range: $10-24.9 Million
Emp.: 52
Commercial Printing & Direct Mail Services
N.A.I.C.S.: 541860
Virgil Borns *(Pres)*
Lee Borns *(VP)*
Carl Perry *(VP-Bus Analytics)*

BORNSTEIN SEAFOODS INC.
1001 Hilton Ave, Bellingham, WA 98225
Tel.: (360) 734-7990
Web Site: https://www.bornstein.com
Rev.: $20,700,000
Emp.: 80
Fish, Fresh & Prepared
N.A.I.C.S.: 311710
Myer J. Bornstein *(Pres)*
Vic Christianson *(Mgr-Export Sls)*

BORO CONSTRUCTION
400 Seheley Dr, King of Prussia, PA 19406
Tel.: (610) 272-7400
Web Site:
https://www.boroconstruction.com
Sales Range: $75-99.9 Million
Emp.: 185
Nonresidential Construction Services
N.A.I.C.S.: 236220
Fred Shapiro *(Principal)*

BORO-WIDE RECYCLING CORP.
3 Railroad Pl, Maspeth, NY 11378
Tel.: (718) 416-1656   NY
Web Site: https://www.borowide.com
Year Founded: 1992
Sales Range: $1-9.9 Million
Emp.: 45
Recycling Services
N.A.I.C.S.: 562920

Michael A. Cristina *(COO, Treas & Sec)*
Robert S. Cristina *(Pres & CEO)*
Tom Salzano *(Sr Mgr-Sls)*
Betsy Singh *(Mgr-Billing & Collection)*
Victor Zabicki *(Mgr-Dispatch)*
Fatima Cristina *(Mgr-Accts Payable)*
Domingo Lopez *(Mgr-Fleet Maintenance)*
Jose Cortes *(Coord-Route)*

BOROWIAK'S IGA FOODLINER, INC.
13 N 5th St, Albion, IL 62806
Tel.: (618) 302-2032
Web Site:
https://www.borowiaksonline.com
Year Founded: 1972
Grocery Store Operator
N.A.I.C.S.: 445110
Greg Uhls *(Mgr-Store)*

BORRELL ELECTRIC CO INC.
3601 N Nebraska Ave, Tampa, FL 33603
Tel.: (813) 223-2727
Web Site:
http://www.borrellelectric.com
Sales Range: $10-24.9 Million
Emp.: 150
Electrical Work
N.A.I.C.S.: 238220
James W. Smith *(Pres & CEO)*
Carlos Menendez *(Owner)*

BORTEK INDUSTRIES INC.
4713 Old Gettysburg Rd, Mechanicsburg, PA 17055
Tel.: (717) 737-7162   PA
Web Site:
http://www.bortekindustries.com
Supplier of Janitors' Equipment & Products
N.A.I.C.S.: 423850
Patty Miller *(Dir-Acctg)*

BORTON VOLVO, INC.
905 Hampshire Ave S, Golden Valley, MN 55426
Tel.: (612) 827-3666
Web Site: https://www.borton.com
Year Founded: 1957
Sales Range: $10-24.9 Million
Emp.: 81
Car Whslr
N.A.I.C.S.: 441110
Kjell Bergh *(Chm & CEO)*

BORTON, LC.
21 des Moines, South Hutchinson, KS 67505
Tel.: (620) 669-8211   KS
Web Site: http://www.borton.biz
Year Founded: 1960
Sales Range: $50-74.9 Million
Emp.: 350
Contractors of Industrial Buildings & Warehouses
N.A.I.C.S.: 236220
Jim Tadtman *(Chm)*
John Kretzer *(Pres)*
Brian Augustine *(CFO)*

BOS STAFFING
651 W Broad St, Athens, GA 30601-2507
Tel.: (706) 353-3030
Web Site: https://www.bosstaff.com
Year Founded: 1979
Sales Range: $1-9.9 Million
Emp.: 150
Temporary & Direct Hire Employees
N.A.I.C.S.: 561311
Nathan Carmack *(Pres & CEO)*

BOSAK MOTORS OF HIGHLAND INC.
9800 Indianapolis Blvd, Highland, IN 46322
Tel.: (219) 595-9333
Web Site:
https://www.bosakhighland.com
Rev.: $22,800,000
Emp.: 40
New Car Dealers
N.A.I.C.S.: 441110
Theresa Bosak *(VP)*
Cary C. Bosak *(Treas & Sec)*
Gregory C. Bosak *(Pres)*

BOSC REALTY ADVISORS
6905 Telegraph Ste 340, Bloomfield Hills, MI 48301
Tel.: (248) 792-5075   DE
Web Site: http://www.bosc.com
Sales Range: $25-49.9 Million
Emp.: 10
Commercial Real Estate Acquisition & Development
N.A.I.C.S.: 237210
Najwa S. Nadhir *(Chm & CEO)*
Waad Nadhir *(Mgr-Property)*

BOSCH MOTORS
1201 E Winnemucca Blvd, Winnemucca, NV 89445
Tel.: (775) 623-2551
Web Site:
http://www.boschmotors.com
Sales Range: $10-24.9 Million
Emp.: 35
New & Used Car Dealers
N.A.I.C.S.: 441110
Herbert L. Bosch Jr. *(Pres)*

BOSCO OIL, INC.
785 Yuba Dr, Mountain View, CA 94041
Tel.: (650) 967-2253   CA
Web Site: https://www.valleyoil.com
Year Founded: 1947
Fuel, Lubricant & Oil Products Dealer
N.A.I.C.S.: 457210
Robert Christiansen *(Co-Owner & Pres)*
Robert Buck *(Co-Owner & VP)*
Mike Eyre *(CFO)*
Mike Taft *(Plant Mgr)*

BOSCOV'S INC.
4500 Perkiomen Ave, Reading, PA 19606-3200
Tel.: (610) 779-2000
Web Site: http://www.boscovs.com
Sales Range: $250-299.9 Million
Emp.: 5,000
Holding Company
N.A.I.C.S.: 455110

Subsidiaries:

Boscov's Department Store, LLC **(1)**
4500 Perkiomen Ave, Reading, PA 19606-3202
Tel.: (610) 779-2000
Web Site: http://www.boscovs.com
Department Stores
N.A.I.C.S.: 455110
Kenneth S. Lakin *(Dir-Ops)*
Burton Krieger *(Co-Pres & Chief Mdsg Officer)*
Ed Elko *(Sr VP-HR)*
Edward McKeaney *(Sr Exec VP-Mdse & Adv)*
Dean Sheaffer *(Chief Compliance Officer & Sr VP-Fin Svcs)*
Sam Flamholz *(Co-Pres)*
Russell C. Diehm *(Chief Acctg Officer & Sr VP-Fin)*
Toni Miller *(CFO, Chief Admin Officer & Sr Exec VP)*
Gary Boyer *(Chief Stores Officer & Sr Exec VP)*
T. J. Javier *(Sr VP & Gen Mgr-Mdse-Shoes, Lingerie & Accessories)*

Brian Nugent *(Sr VP & Gen Mgr-Mdse-Men's)*
Joe McGrath *(Sr VP & Gen Mgr-Mdse-Housewares, Small Appliances & Tabletop)*
Jim Boscov *(Chm & CEO)*
Jon Holmquist *(Sr VP-Direct Mktg)*

BOSE CORPORATION
100 Mountain Rd, Framingham, MA 01701-9168
Tel.: (508) 879-7330   DE
Web Site: https://www.bose.com
Year Founded: 1964
Sales Range: $1-4.9 Billion
Emp.: 6,000
Audio & Video Equipment Manufacturing
N.A.I.C.S.: 334310
Bob Maresca *(Chm)*
Phil Hess *(Pres)*
Lila J. Snyder *(CEO)*
Katherine Kountze *(CIO-Global & VP)*
Raza S. Haider *(Chief Product & Supply Chain Officer)*

Subsidiaries:

Bose A/S **(1)**
Industriazej 7, 2605, Brondby, Denmark **(100%)**
Tel.: (45) 43437777
Web Site: http://www.bose.dk
Sales Range: $10-24.9 Million
Emp.: 20
Stereo Speaker Equipment, Professional Sound Systems & Home Theater Systems Mfr
N.A.I.C.S.: 334310

Representative Office (Non-US):

Bose A/S - Norway Representative Office **(2)**
Kongsvinger Festning, 2213, Kongsvinger, Norway
Tel.: (47) 62821560
Web Site: http://www.bose.no
Electronic Product Whslr
N.A.I.C.S.: 423690

Bose A/S - Sweden Representative Office **(2)**
Bifrostgatan 38, 431 44, Molndal, Sweden
Tel.: (46) 770930100
Web Site: http://www.bose.se
Electronic Product Whslr
N.A.I.C.S.: 449210

Bose AG **(1)**
Hauptstrasse 134, CH 4450, Sissach, Switzerland **(100%)**
Tel.: (41) 619757733
Web Site: http://www.bose.ch
Sales Range: $10-24.9 Million
Emp.: 16
Loudspeakers & Accessories Sales
N.A.I.C.S.: 449210

Bose B.V. **(1)**
Nijverheidstraat 8, 1135 GE, Edam, Netherlands **(100%)**
Tel.: (31) 299390111
Web Site: http://www.bose.nl
Sales Range: $10-24.9 Million
Emp.: 100
Stereo Speaker Equipment, Professional Sound Systems & Home Theater Systems Mfr
N.A.I.C.S.: 334514
Collette Burke *(VP)*

Bose Corporation India Private Limited **(1)**
4th Floor Shriram Bharatiya Kala Kendra, 1 Copernicus Marg, New Delhi, 110001, India
Tel.: (91) 1123073825
Web Site: http://www.boseindia.com
Audio Equipment Mfr & Sales
N.A.I.C.S.: 334310
Ratish Pandey *(Gen Mgr & Country Mgr)*

Bose Electronics (Shanghai) Co. Limited **(1)**
36F West Gate Tower 1038 West Nanjing Road Meilongzhen Plaza, Shanghai, 200041, China
Tel.: (86) 21 6271 3800

Bose Corporation—(Continued)

Web Site: http://www.bose.cn
Sound System Mfr
N.A.I.C.S.: 334310

Bose Ges.m.b.H. (1)
Wienerbergstrasse 11/12a, 1100, Vienna,
Austria
Tel.: (43) 1604043452
Web Site: http://www.bose.at
Electronic Product Whslr
N.A.I.C.S.: 449210

Bose GmbH (1)
Max-Planck-Strasse 36, 61381, Frie-
drichsdorf, Germany (100%)
Tel.: (49) 69667786790
Web Site: http://www.bose.de
Sales Range: $10-24.9 Million
Emp.: 95
Stereo Speaker Equipment Professional
Sound System & Home Theater System Mfr
N.A.I.C.S.: 334310

Division (Domestic):

**Bose GmbH - Consumer Direct
Division** (2)
Neuenhauser Strasse 73, 48527, Nordhorn,
Germany
Tel.: (49) 800 267 34 44
Electronic Product Whslr
N.A.I.C.S.: 423690

Bose K.K. (1)
Sumitomo Fudosan Shibuya Garden Tower
5F 16-17 Nanpeidai-cho, Shibuya-ku, To-
kyo, 150-0036, Japan (100%)
Tel.: (81) 354890955
Web Site: http://www.bose.co.jp
Emp.: 100
Stereo Speaker Equipment, Professional
Sound Systems & Home Theater Systems
Mfr
N.A.I.C.S.: 334310

Bose Limited (1)
Room 905 9F No131 Min Sheng East Road
Section 3, Taipei, 10596, Taiwan
Tel.: (886) 2 2514 7676
Sales Range: $10-24.9 Million
Emp.: 50
Electronic Product Whslr
N.A.I.C.S.: 423690

Bose Ltd. (1)
280 Hillmount Road Unit 5, Markham, L6C
3A1, ON, Canada (100%)
Tel.: (905) 886-9123
Web Site: http://www.bose.ca
Sales Range: $10-24.9 Million
Emp.: 40
Electric Appliances Mfr
N.A.I.C.S.: 335999

Bose N.V. (1)
Limesweg 2, Tongeren, 3700,
Belgium (100%)
Tel.: (32) 12390800
Web Site: http://www.bosebelgium.be
Sales Range: $25-49.9 Million
Emp.: 150
Stereo Speaker Equipment, Professional
Sound Systems & Home Theater Systems
Mfr
N.A.I.C.S.: 334310
Patrick Perrin *(Mng Dir)*

Bose Pty. Ltd. (1)
3/2 Holker St, PO Box 6461, Newington,
2127, NSW, Australia (100%)
Tel.: (61) 287379999
Web Site: http://www.bose.com.au
Emp.: 50
Stereo Speaker Equipment Professional
Sound System & Home Theater System Mfr
N.A.I.C.S.: 334310
Andrew Cron *(Gen Mgr)*

Bose S.A. de C.V. (1)
Av Miguel de la Madrid y Calle de la Indus-
tria, Parque Industria San Luis Rio, 83450,
Sonora, Mexico (100%)
Tel.: (52) 6535340140
Web Site: http://www.bose.com
Sales Range: $75-99.9 Million
Emp.: 1,000
Stereo Speaker Equipment, Professional
Sound System & Home Theater Systems
Mfr

N.A.I.C.S.: 334310

Bose S.A.R.L. (1)
26-28 avenue de Winchester, 78100, Saint
Germain-en-Laye, France
Tel.: (33) 130616363
Web Site: http://www.bose.fr
Sales Range: $10-24.9 Million
Emp.: 50
Stereo Speaker Equipment Professional
Sound System & Home Theater System Mfr
N.A.I.C.S.: 334310

Bose S.p.A. (1)
Via Spadolini 5, 20141, Milan, Italy
Tel.: (39) 0232060600
Web Site: http://www.bose.it
Stereo Speaker Equipment Professional
Sound System & Home Theater System Mfr
N.A.I.C.S.: 334310

Bose Sp. z o.o. (1)
ul Woloska 12 lok 274, 02-675, Warsaw,
Poland
Tel.: (48) 22 8522928
Web Site: http://www.bose.pl
Electronic Product Whslr
N.A.I.C.S.: 449210

Bose Systems Corporation (1)
100 The Mountain, Framingham, MA 01701
Tel.: (508) 879-7330
Web Site: http://www.bose.com
Audio Equipment Mfr
N.A.I.C.S.: 334310

Group (Domestic):

**Bose Systems Corporation - Electro-
Force Systems Group** (2)
10250 Vly View Rd Ste 113, Eden Prairie,
MN 55344
Tel.: (952) 278-3070
Testing Instrument Mfr
N.A.I.C.S.: 334513
Anita Moulton *(Controller)*

Bose U.K., Ltd. (1)
Quayside Chatham Maritime, Chatham,
ME4 4QZ, Kent, United Kingdom (100%)
Tel.: (44) 3333000112
Web Site: http://www.bose.co.uk
Sales Range: $10-24.9 Million
Emp.: 40
High Fidelity Equipment Distr
N.A.I.C.S.: 449210
Philip Carpenter *(Gen Mgr)*

Bose UAE Trading LLC (1)
Office No102A 1st Floor Sama Tower
Sheikh Zayed Road, Dubai, United Arab
Emirates
Tel.: (971) 4 4172000
Web Site: http://www.bose.ae
Electronic Product Whslr
N.A.I.C.S.: 449210
Ratish Pandey *(Gen Mgr)*

BOSKOVICH FARMS INC.
711 Diaz Ave, Oxnard, CA 93030
Tel.: (805) 487-2299 **CA**
Web Site:
https://www.boskovichfarms.com
Year Founded: 1915
Rev.: $85,000,000
Emp.: 220
Growers, Shippers & Packers of
Fresh Vegetables & Fruits
N.A.I.C.S.: 111219
Don Hobson *(VP-Sales-Marketing)*

BOSP BANCSHARES, INC.
228 E Main St, Sun Prairie, WI 53590
Tel.: (608) 837-4511 **WI**
Web Site:
http://www.bospbancshares.com
Sales Range: $10-24.9 Million
Bank Holding Company
N.A.I.C.S.: 551111
Thomas A. Tubbs *(Chm)*
Alan Sebranek *(CFO & Exec VP)*
Ron Blawusch *(Chief Lending Officer
& Sr VP)*
Dave Suchomel *(Chief Credit Officer
& Sr VP)*
Cher Breunig *(VP & Comptroller)*

Anne Pingry *(Sr VP-Compliance)*
Michelle Hahn *(VP & Mgr-Residential
Lending)*
Kurt Kniess *(Sr VP-Wealth Mgmt)*
Jimmy Kauffman *(Pres & CEO)*
Deb Krebs *(Officer-Mktg)*
John Loeffler *(Sr VP & Dir-Retail
Banking)*
Vince Hartmann *(VP-Bus Lending)*
Larry Schwenn *(VP-IT)*
Kim Klinkner *(Asst VP & Sr Mgr-
Bank)*
Kim Lantta *(Asst VP & Sr Mgr-Bank)*
Bill Niebuhr *(Asst VP & Mgr-Loan Ad-
min)*
Mary Kay Weston *(Asst VP-Bus
Lending)*
Audrey Ballweg *(Ops Mgr)*
Ashley Herro *(Mgr-Payment Solu-
tions)*
Candy Heyroth *(Mgr-Retail Training &
Ops)*
Dan Hines *(Officer-Fin & Security)*
Dave Petrie *(Officer-Network Admin)*

Subsidiaries:

Bank of Sun Prairie (1)
228 E Main St, Sun Prairie, WI 53590
Tel.: (608) 837-4511
Web Site: http://www.bankofsunprairie.com
Sales Range: $10-24.9 Million
Commericial Banking
N.A.I.C.S.: 522110
Jimmy Kauffman *(Chm, Pres & CEO)*

BOSS CHAIR, INC.
5353 Jillson St, Commerce, CA
90040
Tel.: (323) 262-1919
Web Site: http://www.bosschair.com
Year Founded: 1990
Rev.: $21,176,000
Emp.: 50
Chairs
N.A.I.C.S.: 488999
William Huang *(CEO)*
Darren Abe *(Pres)*

BOSS CREATIVE
1723 N Loop 1604 E Ste #21, San
Antonio, TX 78232-1672
Tel.: (800) 969-5707
Web Site: http://www.thisisboss.com
Year Founded: 2005
Rev.: $30,000,000
Emp.: 25
Media Agency
N.A.I.C.S.: 541830
Joe Flores *(Pres, Partner & Dir-
Creative)*
Charles Pilkilton *(CEO)*

BOSS ENTERPRISES INC.
147 Commercial St Ne Ste 4, Salem,
OR 97301-3418
Tel.: (503) 585-1366
Sales Range: $10-24.9 Million
Emp.: 12
Fast-Food Restaurant, Chain
N.A.I.C.S.: 722513
Robert Bruce Boss *(Pres)*

BOSS OFFICE PRODUCTS
5353 Jillson St, Commerce, CA
90040
Tel.: (323) 262-1919
Web Site: http://www.bosschair.com
Sales Range: $150-199.9 Million
Emp.: 100
Wood Office Furniture Mfr
N.A.I.C.S.: 337211
William Huang *(CEO)*
Darren Abe *(Pres)*

**BOSSE MATTINGLY CON-
STRUCTORS, INC.**

2116 Plantside Dr, Louisville, KY
40299
Tel.: (502) 671-0995
Web Site:
https://bosseconstruction.com
Year Founded: 2000
Sales Range: $10-24.9 Million
Emp.: 38
Commercial & Institutional Building
Construction Services
N.A.I.C.S.: 236220
Boyd Bosse *(VP)*
Craig Mooney *(CFO)*

BOSSELMAN ENERGY INC.
3123 W Stolley Park Rd, Grand Is-
land, NE 68801
Tel.: (308) 381-6900
Web Site: http://www.bosselman.com
Rev.: $193,386,861
Emp.: 1,100
Petroleum Products
N.A.I.C.S.: 424720
Chuck Bosselman *(VP)*
Stephanie Keezer *(Mgr-Mktg)*
Mike Daniels *(Division Mgr)*
Mary Gordon *(District Mgr)*
Wayne Davis *(Division Mgr)*
Big Grandma *(Asst Mgr)*
Bob Schverman *(Dir -HR)*

**BOSSHARDT REALTY SER-
VICES, INC.**
5542 NW 43rd St, Gainesville, FL
32653
Tel.: (352) 275-5630 **FL**
Web Site:
http://www.bosshardtrealty.com
Year Founded: 1987
Sales Range: $10-24.9 Million
Emp.: 50
Real Estate Broker
N.A.I.C.S.: 531210
Carol R. Bosshardt *(CEO)*
Aaron Bosshardt *(Owner & Pres)*
Gene Anne McKay *(Sr VP)*
Chris Handy *(VP)*
Garry Griffin *(Pres-Bosshardt Prop-
erty Mgmt)*
Beverly Anderson *(VP)*
Ken Cornell *(Sr VP)*
Dan Drotos *(VP)*
Martha Jane Green *(Sr VP)*
Perry McDonald *(VP)*
Henry Rabell *(Sr VP)*
Bruce Rider *(VP)*
Michael Ryals *(Sr VP)*
Susan Baird *(Sr VP)*
Davonda Brown *(VP)*
Angela Cornell *(Sr VP)*
Linda Rabell *(VP)*

**BOSSONG HOSIERY MILLS,
INC.**
840 W Salisbury St, Asheboro, NC
27203
Tel.: (336) 625-2175 **DE**
Web Site:
http://www.bossongmills.com
Year Founded: 1927
Sales Range: $10-24.9 Million
Emp.: 220
Panty Hose
N.A.I.C.S.: 315120
F. Huntley Bossong *(Pres)*

BOST, INC.
PO Box 11495, Fort Smith, AR 72917
Tel.: (479) 478-5600 **AR**
Web Site: http://www.bost.org
Year Founded: 1980
Sales Range: $25-49.9 Million
Emp.: 1,054
Developmental Disability Assistance
Services
N.A.I.C.S.: 624120

Lesa A. Fuller *(Dir-Clinical Svcs)*

BOSTLEMAN CORP.
7142 Nightingale Dr Ste 1, Holland, OH 43528-7822
Tel.: (419) 724-7000
Web Site: http://bostleman.com
Year Founded: 1946
Sales Range: $50-74.9 Million
Emp.: 50
Nonresidential Construction Services
N.A.I.C.S.: 236220
Bill Bostleman *(Pres)*
Jack Colbath *(Mgr-Ops)*
John Novaczyk *(Controller)*
Kevin X. Smith *(VP-Bus Dev)*

BOSTOCK COMPANY, INC.
175 Titus Ave, Warrington, PA 18976
Tel.: (215) 343-7040
Web Site: http://www.snapcabs.com
Sales Range: $1-9.9 Million
Emp.: 45
Customized Elevator Interior Systems
N.A.I.C.S.: 333921
Glenn Bostock *(Pres)*

BOSTON AGREX INC.
295 Washington St, Norwell, MA 02061-1721
Tel.: (781) 659-0330   MA
Web Site:
   http://www.bostonagrex.com
Year Founded: 1981
Sales Range: $10-24.9 Million
Emp.: 11
Packaged Frozen Goods
N.A.I.C.S.: 424420
Larry Lieberman *(Pres)*

BOSTON ATHLETIC ASSOCIATION
40 Trinity Pl 4th Fl, Boston, MA 02116
Tel.: (617) 236-1652   MA
Web Site: http://www.baa.org
Year Founded: 1887
Sales Range: $10-24.9 Million
Emp.: 23
Athletic Event Management Services
N.A.I.C.S.: 813990
Marc Davis *(Mgr-Comm)*
David McGillivray *(Dir-Race)*
Barbara Sicuso *(Dir-Registration Svcs)*
Jack Fleming *(Dir-Mktg & Comm)*

BOSTON BALLET INC.
130 Black Bear Dr Unit 1326, Waltham, MA 02451-0224
Tel.: (617) 695-6950
Web Site: http://www.bostonballet.org
Year Founded: 1963
Sales Range: $10-24.9 Million
Emp.: 115
Ballet Production
N.A.I.C.S.: 711120
Benjamin J. Phillips *(Mgr-Production & Dir-Technical)*
Valerie Wilder *(Exec Dir)*
Craig Margolis *(Mgr-Production Stage)*
Rachel Yurman *(Dir-Foundation & Govt Rels)*
Nate Noce *(Asst Mgr-Production)*
Gabby Rossi *(Coord-Special Events)*
Linda Jones *(Dir-Corp Partnership & Events)*
Melanie Sheffield *(Dir-Dev)*
Zakiya Thomas *(Dir-Education & Community Initiatives)*
Jennifer M. Rodts *(Dir-HR)*
Meredith Max Hodges *(Exec Dir-Admin)*
Rachael Rosselli *(Sr Mgr-Annual Giving)*

Sarah McKitterick *(Sr Mgr-Community Rels)*
Eula Lee *(Sr Mgr-Corp Rels)*

BOSTON BASKETBALL PARTNERS LLC
226 Causeway St, Boston, MA 02114
Tel.: (617) 523-6050
Sales Range: $75-99.9 Million
Emp.: 50
Holding Company; Professional Basketball Franchise Owner & Operator
N.A.I.C.S.: 551112
Wycliffe Grousbeck *(Mng Partner & CEO)*
Robert Epstein *(Mng Partner)*
H. Irving Grousbeck *(Mng Partner)*
Stephen G. Pagliuca *(Mng Partner)*

Subsidiaries:

Boston Celtics Limited Partnership   (1)
226 Causeway St, Boston, MA 02114
Tel.: (617) 523-6050
Web Site: http://www.celtics.com
Sales Range: $10-24.9 Million
Professional Basketball Franchise Operator
N.A.I.C.S.: 711211
Wycliffe Grousbeck *(Mng Partner & CEO)*
Stephen G. Pagliuca *(Co-Owner-Boston Celtics basketball franchise & Mng Gen Partner)*
Rich Gotham *(Pres)*
Jay Wessel *(VP-Tech)*
Patrick Lynch *(Sr Dir-Acctg & Ops)*
Matt Griffin *(VP-Strategic Mktg & Bus Ops)*
Bill Reissfelder *(CFO & Sr VP)*
Barbara Reed *(Sr Dir-HR & Investor Svcs)*
Tim Rath *(VP & Controller)*
Jeffrey Twiss *(VP-Media Rels & Alumni Rels)*
Shawn Sullivan *(CMO)*
Keith Sliney *(Creative Dir)*
Duane Johnson *(Dir-Ticket Ops)*
Paul Cacciatore *(Sr Dir-Bus Ops)*
Austin Ainge *(Dir-Player Personnel)*
Frank Burke *(Dir-Basketball Admin)*
Tessa Caffrey *(Sr Dir-Corp Partnerships)*
Ted Dalton *(Sr VP-Corp Partnerships & Bus Dev)*
Sean Sullivan *(Sr Dir-Event Presentation)*
Heather Walker *(Sr Dir-PR)*
David Lewin *(Dir-Scouting)*
Andrew Mannix *(Mgr-Basketball Facilities)*
Kathleen Nimmo *(Mgr-Team Svcs)*
Katherine Perry *(Dir-Partnership Sls)*
Siobhan Sherbovich *(Dir-Corp Partnerships)*
Richie Smith *(Mgr-Analytics & Strategy)*
David Sparks *(Dir-Basketball Analytics)*
Jake Spiak *(Mgr-Corp Partnerships)*

BOSTON BENEFIT PARTNERS, LLC
177 Milk St 3rd Fl, Boston, MA 02109
Tel.: (617) 570-9100
Web Site: https://www.bosben.com
Year Founded: 1998
Human Resouce Services
N.A.I.C.S.: 541612
John Brouder *(Partner)*
Kathryn H. Tolan *(Partner)*
Carol Chandor *(CEO & Mng Dir)*
Piper McNealy *(Partner)*
Donna Denaro *(Office Mgr)*

BOSTON CAR SERVICE, INC.
28 Marshall St, Canton, MA 02021-2478
Tel.: (617) 267-2100
Web Site: http://www.bostoncar.com
Year Founded: 1988
Sales Range: $10-24.9 Million
Emp.: 92
Transportation Services
N.A.I.C.S.: 485999
Brett Barenholtz *(CEO)*

BOSTON CENTERLESS INC.
11 Presidential Way, Woburn, MA 01801

Tel.: (781) 994-5000
Web Site:
   https://www.bostoncenterless.com
Year Founded: 1958
Rev.: $12,100,000
Emp.: 125
Machine Shop, Jobbing & Repair
N.A.I.C.S.: 332710
David Mersereau *(Gen Mgr)*
Rich Morneweck *(Mgr-Sls Ops)*
Larry Salvucci *(Mgr-IT)*

BOSTON COMMON ASSET MANAGEMENT, LLC
200 State St 7th Fl, Boston, MA 02109
Tel.: (617) 720-5557
Web Site:
   https://www.bostoncommon.com
Rev.: $1,000,000
Emp.: 10
Industrial Building Construction
N.A.I.C.S.: 236210
Matt Zalosh *(CIO)*
Marykelly Smith *(Controller)*
Kristina Eisnor *(Chief Compliance Officer)*
Geeta Aiyer *(Founder & Pres)*
Ashley Lyon *(VP)*
Brian Chiappinelli *(Sr VP & Dir-Bus Dev)*
Lauren Compere *(Dir-Shareowner Engagement)*
Sharon Flynn *(Office Mgr)*
Steven Heim *(Dir-Esg Res)*

BOSTON FINANCIAL MANAGEMENT, INC.
255 State St 6th Fl, Boston, MA 02109
Tel.: (617) 338-8108
Web Site:
   https://www.bostonfinancial.com
Year Founded: 1976
Rev.: $1,800,000,000
Emp.: 40
Portfolio Management
N.A.I.C.S.: 523940
Susan G. Zimmerman *(Mng Dir)*
Geoffry Juviler *(Mng Dir)*
Alisa O'Neil *(Dir-Estate & Fin Plng)*
Carol A. Cusson *(Controller)*
Bradford A. Gardner *(Vice Chm & Mng Dir)*
Dana F. Clark *(Mng Dir)*
Richard H. Morse *(Founder & Chm)*
Michael L. Brown *(Mng Dir & Vice Chm)*
Charles J. Zambri *(COO, Chief Compliance Officer & Dir-Client Svc)*
Jonathan D. Lynch *(Mng Dir)*
Stacy Austin Reinhart *(Mng Dir)*
Brian J. Walsh *(Mgr-Wealth)*
Abigail M. Psyhogeos *(Mng Dir)*
Brad M. Weafer *(Chief Investment Officer)*
Edward F. Glesmann Jr. *(Mng Dir)*
Clarence H. King III *(Mng Dir)*

BOSTON HARBOR CRUISES
One Long Wharf, Boston, MA 02110-3602
Tel.: (617) 227-4321   MA
Web Site:
   http://www.bostonharborcruises.com
Year Founded: 1926
Sales Range: $10-24.9 Million
Cruise Operator
N.A.I.C.S.: 561520
Chris Nolan *(Principal)*
Abigail Stephens *(Dir-Event Sls)*

BOSTON HARLEY-DAVIDSON
1760 Revere Beach Pkwy Rte 16 E, Everett, MA 02149
Tel.: (617) 389-8888   MA

Web Site:
   http://www.bostonharley.com
Year Founded: 1998
Sales Range: $10-24.9 Million
Emp.: 50
Sales of Motorcycles, Clothing & Accessories
N.A.I.C.S.: 441227
Jamie Budny *(Mgr-Svc)*
Dan Stay *(Pres)*

BOSTON HEALTH CARE FOR THE HOMELESS PROGRAM
780 Albany St, Boston, MA 02118
Tel.: (857) 654-1000   MA
Web Site: https://www.bhchp.org
Year Founded: 1985
Sales Range: $25-49.9 Million
Emp.: 443
Health Care Srvices
N.A.I.C.S.: 622110
Agnes Leung *(CFO)*
Jim O'Connell *(Pres)*
Barry Bock *(CEO)*

BOSTON INC.
1015 Commonn Cir, Stevens Point, WI 54467
Tel.: (715) 344-7700
Web Site:
   http://www.furnitureappliances.com
Rev.: $10,800,000
Emp.: 150
Furniture Retailer
N.A.I.C.S.: 449110
Bill Fonti *(Pres & COO)*
Jon Gadbois *(Dir-Adv & Mktg Comm)*

BOSTON IRRIGATION SUPPLY CO
60 Stergis Way, Dedham, MA 02026
Tel.: (781) 461-1560
Web Site: http://www.gobisco.com
Sales Range: $10-24.9 Million
Emp.: 60
Sprinkler Systems
N.A.I.C.S.: 423850
John P. Ramey *(Pres)*
Randy Baker *(Branch Mgr-Connecticut Div)*
Megan Laloy *(Mgr-Mktg)*
Megan Lally *(Mgr-Mktg)*

BOSTON KITCHEN DIST. INC
215 S Main St, Middleton, MA 01949
Tel.: (978) 733-0900
Web Site:
   http://www.bostonkitchen.com
Sales Range: $10-24.9 Million
Emp.: 60
Cabinet Building & Installation
N.A.I.C.S.: 238130
George Menihtas *(Pres)*
Maria Menihtas *(Acct Mgr)*

BOSTON MARKET CORPORATION
14103 Denver W Pkwy, Golden, CO 80401-3116
Tel.: (303) 278-9500   DE
Web Site:
   http://www.bostonmarket.com
Year Founded: 1985
Sales Range: $800-899.9 Million
Emp.: 13,000
Restaurant Operators
N.A.I.C.S.: 722513
Randy Miller *(Pres)*
Eric Wyatt *(COO)*
Christopher Mukhar *(Mgr-Loss Prevention)*
Caryn Doyle *(CFO)*
Jay Pandya *(Chm)*

BOSTON METAL PRODUCTS CORPORATION

Boston Metal Products Corporation—(Continued)

400 Riverside Ave, Medford, MA
02155-4949
Tel.: (781) 395-7417
Web Site:
    http://www.bostonretail.com
Rev.: $26,211,165
Emp.: 140
Architectural Metalwork
N.A.I.C.S.: 332323
Frank Quartarone (Mgr-Sls-Americas)
Subsidiaries:

Boston Metal Products Corporation,
Home Center Merchandising
Division   (1)
400 Riverside Ave, Medford, MA 02155
Tel.: (781) 395-7417
Web Site: http://www.bostonretail.com
Sales Range: $25-49.9 Million
Architectural Metalwork
N.A.I.C.S.: 332323

**BOSTON MUTUAL LIFE IN-
SURANCE COMPANY**
120 Royall St, Canton, MA 02021-
1028
Tel.: (781) 828-7000   MA
Web Site:
    https://www.bostonmutual.com
Year Founded: 1891
Sales Range: $250-299.9 Million
Insurance Company
N.A.I.C.S.: 524113
Clifford A. Lange (CFO & Exec VP)
Linda Izzo (VP-Individual Insurance
Ops)
Dave Cirulis (VP-Sls-Illinois)
Grant Ward (Gen Counsel, Sec-
Legal, Compliance & HR & Exec VP)
James Dawson (Sr Dir-Sls-Florida)
Joseph W. Sullivan (Chief Risk Offi-
cer & Exec VP)
Jim Jacobsen (Exec VP-Distr & Un-
derwriting)
Nicholas K. Barishian (VP-Sls & Gen-
eral Agencies)
David Mitchell (Exec VP-External Af-
fairs & Corp Comm)
John Flores (Gen Counsel, Sec &
VP)
Mary Tillson (Exec VP-legacy Ops)
Doug Rosburg (Sls Dir-Heartland)
Marie Lackey (Sr Dir-Sls-
Southeastern Reg)
Christine Williams (Chief Compliance,
Privacy & Anti-Money Laundering Of-
ficer)
Lesley Schafer (Sr Dir-Sls-Central)
Brendan Sharpe (Sr Sls Dir-Tri State)
Marie Loughran (VP-Sls Ops-Distr &
Underwriting Strategic Bus Center)
David Martin (CIO & VP)
Jennifer Helms (Exec VP-Customer
Experience, Innovation, Projects &
Tech)
Howard V. Neff Jr. (CIO & Sr VP)
Paul A. Quaranto Jr. (Chm, Pres &
CEO)

Subsidiaries:

Life Insurance Company of Boston &
New York   (1)
4300 Camp Rd, Athol Springs, NY 14010
Web Site: http://www.lifeofboston.com
Fire Insurance Company
N.A.I.C.S.: 524210
Paul E. Petry (Chm)
Christine T. Coughlin (Treas)
John R. Flores (Gen Counsel, Sec & VP)
Susan J. Gardner (Controller)
Nora E. Hoffman (Asst Treas)
Clifford A. Lange (CFO, Chief Actuary &
Exec VP)
David C. Mitchell (VP-Strategic Plng &
Comm)
Howard V. Neff (Chief Investment Officer &
Sr VP)

Charles R. Mabry (VP-Workplace Solutions)
Frederick C. Thurston (Chief Compliance
Officer)
Peter S. Connolly (Dir-Medical)
James E. Jacobsen (Exec VP-Distr)
Paul A. Quaranto Jr. (Pres)

**BOSTON PROFESSIONAL
HOCKEY ASSOCIATION, INC.**
100 Legends Way, Boston, MA
02114-1390
Tel.: (617) 624-1900   MA
Web Site:
    http://www.bostonbruins.com
Year Founded: 1924
Sales Range: $50-74.9 Million
Emp.: 100
Professional Hockey Franchise
N.A.I.C.S.: 711211
Matt Chmura (VP-Mktg & Comm)
Jeremy M. Jacobs Sr. (Owner &
Governor)

**BOSTON RESTAURANT ASSO-
CIATES, INC.**
6 Kimball Ln Ste 210, Lynnfield, MA
01940
Tel.: (339) 219-0466   DE
Web Site:
    http://www.pizzeriaregina.com
Year Founded: 1926
Sales Range: $10-24.9 Million
Emp.: 425
Pizzerias & Full-Service Italian Res-
taurants Owner & Franchiser
N.A.I.C.S.: 722511

**BOSTON SEMI EQUIPMENT
LLC**
Federal St 3 Burlington Woods Dr,
Billerica, MA 01821
Tel.: (781) 273-0090
Web Site:
    http://www.bostonsemiequip
    ment.com
Semiconductor Equipment Mfr
N.A.I.C.S.: 333242
Colin P. Scholefield (Founder & Co-
CEO)
Gary Romano (Co-CEO & Pres-Fin &
Admin)
Dan Griffin (VP-Svc Ops-Global)
Larry Stuckey (VP-Sls)
Scott Kroeger (Sr VP-Mktg & Sls)

Subsidiaries:

Probe Specialists Inc.   (1)
2161 OToole Ave Ste 20, San Jose, CA
95131
Tel.: (408) 456-0900
Web Site: http://www.probespecialists.com
Emp.: 25
Wafer Probing Equipment Mfr
N.A.I.C.S.: 334413
Jim Lennon (Mgr-Parts)
Joe Garcia (Mgr-Procurement & Compli-
ance)

**BOSTON TECHNOLOGIES,
INC.**
610 E Landis Ave, Vineland, NJ
08360
Tel.: (856) 692-4958
Web Site:
    https://www.bostontech.com
Sales Range: $1-9.9 Million
Emp.: 6
Software Reproducing Services
N.A.I.C.S.: 334610
John Garavento, (Gen Mgr)

**BOSTON TECHNOLOGY COR-
PORATION**
33 Boston Post Rd W Ste 160, Marlborough, MA 01752
Tel.: (781) 583-1144

Web Site: http://www.boston-
technology.com
Year Founded: 2004
Sales Range: $1-9.9 Million
Emp.: 40
Software, Consulting & Mobile Appli-
cation Development Services
N.A.I.C.S.: 513210
Ken Jeff (Engr)
Jayas Damodaran (CEO)
Nithin Rao (Pres)

**BOSTON VA RESEARCH IN-
STITUTE, INC.**
150 S Huntington Ave Room 11B 60,
Boston, MA 02130
Tel.: (617) 738-1313   MA
Web Site: http://www.bvari.org
Year Founded: 1990
Sales Range: $10-24.9 Million
Emp.: 165
Medical Research Services
N.A.I.C.S.: 541715
Jeffrey Burd (Gen Counsel)
Daniel Burke (Mgr-Ops)
Janyce Sarmaniote (Dir-Fin)
Nancy Watterson-Diorio (CEO)
Helen Bril (Dir-HR)
Amy Kimball (COO)

**BOSTONBEAN COFFEE CO.,
INC.**
23 Draper St, Woburn, MA 01801
Tel.: (781) 935-3100
Web Site:
    https://www.bostonbeancoffee.com
Year Founded: 1949
Sales Range: $10-24.9 Million
Emp.: 70
Coffee & Tea Mfr
N.A.I.C.S.: 311920
Ralph Parsons (Acct Exec)
Steve Serino (Mgr-Sls)

BOSTWICK-BRAUN COMPANY
7349 Crossleigh Ct, Toledo, OH
43617-3108
Tel.: (419) 259-3600
Web Site: https://www.bostwick-
braun.com
Sales Range: $75-99.9 Million
Emp.: 250
Hardware Distr
N.A.I.C.S.: 423710
George Thiel (VP-Info Sys)

BOSWELL ENGINEERING
330 Phillips Ave, South Hackensack,
NJ 07606-1717
Tel.: (201) 641-0770
Web Site:
    https://www.boswellengineering.com
Year Founded: 1924
Sales Range: $25-49.9 Million
Emp.: 250
Design & Construction Management
Services
N.A.I.C.S.: 541330
John E. Cassetta (Sr VP)
Bruce Boswell (VP)
Christopher J. Nash (VP)
James D. Kelly (Exec VP)
Kevin J. Boswell (VP)
Stephen T. Boswell (Pres & CEO)
Peter C. Ten Kate (VP-Municipal
Svcs)
Michael J. Ganas (VP-Underwater &
Marine Engrg)

Subsidiaries:

Boswell Engineering   (1)
799 Madison Ave, Albany, NY
12208-2718   (100%)
Tel.: (518) 436-6310
Web Site:
    http://www.boswellengineering.com

Sales Range: $10-24.9 Million
Emp.: 40
Engineering Services
N.A.I.C.S.: 541330
Bruce D. Boswell (VP)
Christopher J. Nash (VP-Transportation)
Peter C. Ten-Kate (VP-Municipal Svcs)

Boswell McClave Engineering   (1)
330 Phillips Ave, South Hackensack, NJ
07606-1717   (100%)
Tel.: (201) 641-0770
Web Site:
    http://www.boswellengineering.com
Engineering Services
N.A.I.C.S.: 541330
Stephen T. Boswell (Pres & CEO)

Boswell Underwater Engineering   (1)
330 Phillips Ave, South Hackensack, NJ
07606-1717
Tel.: (201) 641-0770
Web Site:
    http://www.boswellengineering.com
Sales Range: $25-49.9 Million
Emp.: 210
Engineering Services
N.A.I.C.S.: 541330
Stephen T. Boswell (Pres & CEO)

BOSWORTH PAPERS INC.
10425 Okanella St Ste 600, Houston,
TX 77041
Tel.: (713) 460-5060
Web Site:
    http://www.bosworthpapers.com
Rev.: $33,000,000
Emp.: 100
Printing Paper
N.A.I.C.S.: 424110
Joseph T. Jordan (Pres)

**BOSWORTH STEEL EREC-
TORS, INC.**
4001 Jaffee St, Dallas, TX 75216-
4023
Tel.: (214) 371-3700
Web Site:
    https://www.bosworthsteel.com
Year Founded: 1995
Sales Range: $300-349.9 Million
Emp.: 300
Structural Steel Erection Services
N.A.I.C.S.: 236220
John Bosworth (Pres & CEO)
Micah Conrad (VP & Mgr-Safety)
Cindy Lott (VP-Fin)
Vincent Bosworth (COO & VP)
Carl Williams (Dir-Preconstruction &
Engrg)
Matt Shiery (Project Mgr)

**BOTANICA INTERNATIONAL
FLORIST, INC.**
1713 W Cypress St, Tampa, FL
33606
Tel.: (813) 831-0965
Web Site:
    http://www.botanicaflorist.com
Year Founded: 1989
Sales Range: $10-24.9 Million
Emp.: 11
Florists
N.A.I.C.S.: 459310
Ian Prosser (Co-Owner)
Athena Valle (Mgr-Production)
Fiona Prosser (Co-Owner & Dir-Fin)
Zoe Gallina (Dir-Creative)

**BOTKIN LUMBER COMPANY,
INC.**
1901 Progress Dr, Farmington, MO
63640
Tel.: (573) 756-2400   MO
Web Site:
    https://www.botkinlumber.com
Lumber & Lumber Products Whslr
N.A.I.C.S.: 423310
Jennifer Cleve Blum (Sls Mgr)
Brian Groves (Mgr-Pur & Portland
Sls)
Juan Diaz (Mgr-Intl Bus Dev)

BOTSFORD & GOODFELLOW, INC.

8440 SE Sunnybrook Blvd, Clacka-
mas, OR 97015-9740
Tel.: (503) 653-9930   OR
Web Site:
   https://www.botsfordgoodfellow.com
Year Founded: 1970
Sales Range: $10-24.9 Million
Emp.: 20
Fresh Fruits & Vegetables Sales
N.A.I.C.S.: 424480

BOTT RADIO NETWORK

10550 Barkley St Ste 100, Overland
Park, KS 66212
Tel.: (913) 642-7770   KS
Web Site:
   https://www.bottradionetwork.com
Year Founded: 1996
Sales Range: $10-24.9 Million
Emp.: 151
Radio Broadcasting Services
N.A.I.C.S.: 516210
Thomas J. Holdeman (CFO)
Don Boyd (Mgr-Station)

BOTTINI FUEL COMPANY

2785 W Main St, Wappingers Falls,
NY 12590
Tel.: (845) 297-5580
Web Site: https://www.bottinifuel.com
Sales Range: $10-24.9 Million
Emp.: 60
Fuel & Oil Services
N.A.I.C.S.: 457210
Anthony R. Bottini (Pres)
Dan Brosnan (Mgr-Sls)
Matt Feldman (Mgr-Propane)
Marty Brundage (Mgr-Fleet)
Mark Caprara (Comptroller)
Steve King (Mgr-Propane Sls)
Dave Wood (Mgr-Corp Ops)
Rosa McSwegan (Mgr-Credit)
Tammy Osterhoudt (Mgr-Customer
Svc)
Alan Proper (Mgr-Sls)

BOTTOM LINE EQUIPMENT, L.L.C.

10260 Airline Hwy, Saint Rose, LA
70087
Tel.: (504) 464-6755
Web Site: http://www.bottomlineequip
   ment.com
Year Founded: 2005
Construction, Mining, Forestry Ma-
chinery, Equipment Rental & Leasing
N.A.I.C.S.: 532412
Kimberly Degueyter (Founder, Owner
& CEO)
Corey Gauthier (VP-Rentals, Sls &
Ops)

BOTTOM LINE PROCESS TECHNOLOGIES, INC.

10360 72nd St N Ste 817, Largo, FL
33777
Tel.: (727) 548-6484
Web Site: http://www.blt-inc.com
Year Founded: 1993
Sales Range: $1-9.9 Million
Emp.: 7
Food & Beverage Processing Equip-
ment Mfr
N.A.I.C.S.: 333241
John Vessa (Pres)
Kim Vessa (VP)

BOU BANCORP, INC.

2605 Washington Blvd, Ogden, UT
84401
Tel.: (801) 409-5000   UT
Web Site: http://www.bankofutah.com
Year Founded: 1952
Rev.: $77,268,000

Assets: $1,425,023,000
Liabilities: $1,250,723,000
Net Worth: $174,300,000
Earnings: $23,423,000
Fiscal Year-end: 12/31/18
Bank Holding Company
N.A.I.C.S.: 551111
Frank W. Browning (Chm)
Douglas L. DeFries (Pres & CEO)
Nathan L. DeFries (Treas)
Benjamin F. Browning (Vice Chm &
VP)

Subsidiaries:

Bank of Utah   (1)
2605 Washington Blvd, Ogden, UT 84401-
3626
Tel.: (801) 409-5000
Web Site: http://www.bankofutah.com
Sales Range: $25-49.9 Million
Emp.: 350
Commericial Banking
N.A.I.C.S.: 522110
Frank W. Browning (Chm)
Douglas L. DeFries (Pres & CEO)
K. Darrel May (Sr VP-HR)
Roger G. Shumway (Chief Credit Officer &
Exec VP)
Menah C. Strong (Chief Admin Officer & Sr
VP)
Branden P. Hansen (CFO & Exec VP)
Taft G. Meyer (Chief Lending Officer & Exec
VP)
T. Craig Roper (Chief Deposit Officer & Sr
VP)
Brian S. Stevens (Sr VP-IT)
Charly Owens (VP & Mgr-Treasury Mgmt
Relationship)
Roger L. Christensen (Sr VP-Bus Dev &
Comm)
Bret J. Wall (Sr VP-Residential Lending)
Colby J. Dustin (Sr VP-Enterprise Risk)

BOUCHER CHEVROLET, INC.

1421 E Moreland Blvd, Waukesha,
WI 53186-3960
Tel.: (262) 347-4314
Web Site:
   https://www.boucherchevrolet.com
Year Founded: 1990
Sales Range: $10-24.9 Million
Emp.: 60
New & Used Car Dealer
N.A.I.C.S.: 441110
Christian Rano (Gen Mgr)
Gordie Boucher Jr. (Owner)

BOULDER CHEVROLET BUICK, INC.

1825 W Main St, Salem, IL 62881-
5839
Tel.: (618) 740-4306
Web Site:
   https://www.boulderchevrolet.com
Sales Range: $10-24.9 Million
Emp.: 12
Car Whslr
N.A.I.C.S.: 441110
Tal Brauneker (Owner)

BOULDER CITY HOSPITAL

901 Adams Blvd, Boulder City, NV
89005
Tel.: (702) 293-4111   NV
Web Site: https://www.bchcares.org
Year Founded: 1954
Sales Range: $10-24.9 Million
Emp.: 259
Health Care Srvices
N.A.I.C.S.: 622110
Thomas E. Maher (CEO)
Frey Belete (Controller)
Andre Pastian (Chief Nursing Officer)

BOULDER CREEK BUILDERS

712 Main St, Louisville, CO 80027
Tel.: (303) 544-5857
Web Site:
   https://www.liveouldercreek.com

Year Founded: 2006
Sales Range: $25-49.9 Million
Emp.: 24
General Real Estate Services
N.A.I.C.S.: 531390
David Sinkey (Co-Founder & Pres)
Steven Erickson (Co-Founder & VP)
Michael Sinkey (Co-Founder & VP
Quality Control)
David Oyler (Exec VP)
Debbie Barker (Dir-Admin)
Jessica Champlin (Dir-Mktg)
Kacey Funari (Dir-Fin)
Lisa Mason (Mgr-Acctg)
Drew Kell (Mgr-Community)
Karen Sanders (Mgr-Community)
Brian Fink (VP-Sls)

BOULDER DAM CREDIT UNION

530 Avenue G, Boulder City, NV
89006-1530
Tel.: (702) 293-7777   NV
Web Site:
   https://www.boulderdamcu.org
Year Founded: 1940
Sales Range: $10-24.9 Million
Emp.: 46
Credit Union
N.A.I.C.S.: 522130
Eric Estes (Pres & CEO)
Le-Chen Cheng (CFO)

BOULDER PHILHARMONIC ORCHESTRA

2590 Walnut St, Boulder, CO 80302
Tel.: (303) 449-1343
Web Site: http://www.boulderphil.org
Year Founded: 1958
Sales Range: Less than $1 Million
Emp.: 150
Orchestra
N.A.I.C.S.: 711130
Michael Butterman (Dir-Music)
Kim Peoria (Mgr-Orchestra Person-
nel)
Kevin Shuck (Exec Dir)

BOULDER SCIENTIFIC COM-PANY

598 3rd St, Mead, CO 80542
Tel.: (970) 535-4494   CO
Web Site: http://www.bouldersci.com
Year Founded: 1972
Sales Range: $10-24.9 Million
Emp.: 90
Organic Chemical Product Mfr
N.A.I.C.S.: 325199
John M. Birmingham (Founder)
Roy Isiminger (CFO)
Scott Birmingham (CEO)

BOULDINCORP.

195 Mount View Industrial Dr, Morri-
son, TN 37357
Tel.: (931) 815-8520
Web Site:
   https://www.bouldincorp.com
Year Founded: 1959
Sales Range: $10-24.9 Million
Emp.: 55
Farm Supply Whslr
N.A.I.C.S.: 424910
Floyd Bouldin (Pres)

BOULEVARD AUTO SALES INC.

20579 N Dupoint Blvd, Georgetown,
DE 19947
Tel.: (302) 856-2561
Web Site:
   http://www.boulevardauto.com
Sales Range: $10-24.9 Million
Emp.: 70
Sales of New & Used Automobiles
N.A.I.C.S.: 441110

James Blecki (Gen Mgr)

BOUMA CORPORATION

4101 Roger B Chaffee Blvd SE,
Grand Rapids, MI 49548
Tel.: (616) 538-3600
Web Site:
   http://www.boumaconructions.com
Sales Range: $75-99.9 Million
Emp.: 250
Drywall
N.A.I.C.S.: 238310
Joe Driver (Project Mgr)

BOUND TO STAY BOUND BOOKS INC.

1880 W Morton Ave, Jacksonville, IL
62650-2619
Tel.: (217) 245-5191   DE
Web Site: https://www.btsb.com
Year Founded: 1920
Sales Range: $25-49.9 Million
Emp.: 200
Bookbinding & Related Work
N.A.I.C.S.: 323120
Robert Sibert (Pres)
Steve Flynn (CFO)
Steve Glenn (Controller)

BOUNDARY SYSTEMS, LTD

7055 Engle Rd Ste 601, Cleveland,
OH 44130
Web Site:
   http://www.boundarysys.com
Year Founded: 2005
Sales Range: $1-9.9 Million
Emp.: 18
Software Providing Service
N.A.I.C.S.: 513210
Ian Kimbrell (Pres)
Wade Moravek (Dir-Engrg)
Mike Kanczak (Dir-Sls)
Mike Denno (Acct Mgr)
Tony Graue (Acct Mgr)

BOUNDLESS IMMIGRATION INC.

2101 4th Ave Ste 850, Seattle, WA
98121
Tel.: (855) 286-6353
Web Site: http://www.boundless.com
Year Founded: 2017
Immigrant Information & Support Ser-
vices
N.A.I.C.S.: 519290
Xiao Wang (Co-Founder & CEO)

Subsidiaries:

RapidVisa Inc.   (1)
6145 Spring Mountain Rd Ste 100, Las Ve-
gas, NV 89146
Tel.: (702) 988-8454
Web Site: http://www.rapidvisa.com
Sales Range: $1-9.9 Million
Emp.: 4,545
Online Immigration Support Services
N.A.I.C.S.: 928120
Rick Whitaker (Mgr-Immigration Svcs)

BOUNDLESS NETWORK

200 E 6th St Ste 300, Austin, TX
78701
Tel.: (512) 472-9200
Web Site:
   http://www.boundlessnetwork.com
Sales Range: $25-49.9 Million
Emp.: 49
Promotional Products Distr
N.A.I.C.S.: 423990
Pat Barry (Exec VP-Sls)
Jason Broadhead (CFO)
Mark Lopez (VP-Tech & Svcs)
Henrik Johansson (Co-Founder &
CEO)

Boundless Network—(Continued)

Scott Stewart (Dir-Enterprise Sls & Customer Satisfaction)
Jennifer Purcell (VP-Mktg)

BOUNTEOUS, INC.
4115 N Ravenswood Ave Ste 101, Chicago, IL 60613
Web Site: http://www.bounteous.com
Year Founded: 2003
Sales Range: $25-49.9 Million
Emp.: 342
Information Technology Development Services
N.A.I.C.S.: 541512
Keith Schwartz (Founder & CEO)
Chris Westall (Sr VP-Strategy)
Dave Mankowski (Chief Growth Officer)
Marc Blanchard (Chief Experience Officer)
Melinda Ramos (VP-Learning & Diversity)
Leah Weyandt (Chief People Officer)
Jaspreet Singh (Chief Strategy & Insights Officer)
Mike Brown (Chief Client Officer)
Sheena Banton (Sr VP-Customer Mktg)
Jillian Tate (Sr VP-Media)
Michael McLaren (Pres-North America)
Michael Twedell (Sr VP-Slsforce Growth)
Larry Hinz (CFO)

Subsidiaries:

Hathway Inc. (1)
81 Higuera St Ste 220, San Luis Obispo, CA 93401
Tel.: (805) 265-6863
Web Site: http://www.WeAreHathway.com
Online Advertising & Marketing Services
N.A.I.C.S.: 518210
Jesse Dundon (CEO)
Kevin Rice (Co-Founder & Chief Mktg Officer)

BOUNTYJOBS INC.
230 W 41st St, New York, NY 10036
Tel.: (212) 660-3960
Web Site: http://www.bountyjobs.com
Year Founded: 2006
Sales Range: $10-24.9 Million
Emp.: 35
Online National Network Connecting Employers & Headhunters
N.A.I.C.S.: 561320
Jason Putnam (Sr VP-Sls)
Stacey Steiger (VP-Product Mktg)

BOUNTYLAND PETROLEUM INC.
5038 S Hwy 11, Westminster, SC 29693
Tel.: (864) 647-7282
Web Site: http://mybountyland.com
Sales Range: $25-49.9 Million
Emp.: 11
Petroleum Bulk Stations
N.A.I.C.S.: 424710
R. David Land (Pres & CEO)

BOUQUET COLLECTION, INC.
2750 NW 79th Ave, Doral, FL 33122
Tel.: (305) 594-4981
Sales Range: $10-24.9 Million
Emp.: 100
Malt Mfr
N.A.I.C.S.: 311213
Javier Mesa (Pres)
Stephanie Fernandes (Mgr)
Rafael Marino (Mgr)

BOURDEAUS BROS OF MIDDLEBURY

88 Seymour St, Middlebury, VT 05753
Tel.: (802) 388-7000
Web Site: http://www.bourdeaubrothers.com
Sales Range: $10-24.9 Million
Emp.: 60
Farm Supply Whslr
N.A.I.C.S.: 424910
Jim Bushey (Owner)

BOURGET BROS. BUILDING MATERIALS
1636 11th St, Santa Monica, CA 90404
Tel.: (310) 450-6556
Web Site: https://www.bourgetbros.com
Sales Range: $10-24.9 Million
Emp.: 74
Lumber & Other Building Materials
N.A.I.C.S.: 423310
John Bourget (Owner)

BOURLAND & LEVERICH HOLDING COMPANY
11707 Hwy 152 W, Pampa, TX 79065
Tel.: (806) 665-0061
Web Site: http://www.bl-supply.com
Year Founded: 1935
Sales Range: $1-9.9 Million
Emp.: 50
Oil Drilling Tubular Goods
N.A.I.C.S.: 423510
Bob Dvorak (CFO)

Subsidiaries:

Bourland & Leverich Supply Co. Inc. (1)
11707 Hwy 152 W, Pampa, TX 79065
Tel.: (806) 665-0061
Web Site: http://www.bl-supply.com
Emp.: 30
Wholesale & Lease Steel Tubular Products
N.A.I.C.S.: 423510
Bob Dvorak (CEO)

BOURNIVAL INC.
2355 Lafayette Rd, Portsmouth, NH 03801
Tel.: (603) 259-4937
Web Site: http://www.bournivalgroup.com
Sales Range: $10-24.9 Million
Emp.: 85
Car Dealership
N.A.I.C.S.: 441110
Alissa Bournival (Pres)

BOURNS, INC.
1200 Columbia Ave, Riverside, CA 92507-2129
Tel.: (951) 781-5690
Web Site: https://www.bourns.com
Year Founded: 1947
Sales Range: $300-349.9 Million
Emp.: 5,400
Electronic Components Mfr
N.A.I.C.S.: 334515
Gordon L. Bourns (CEO)

Subsidiaries:

Bourns (Xiamen) Ltd. (1)
4F & 5F Guangyao Bldg Torch Hi-Tech Industrial Development Zone, Xiamen, 361006, Fu Jen, China
Tel.: (86) 592 603 8880
Electronic Component Mfr & Whslr
N.A.I.C.S.: 334413

Bourns AG (1)
Zugerstrasse 74, CH 6340, Baar, Switzerland (100%)
Tel.: (41) 417685555
Web Site: http://www.bourns.com
Sales Range: $10-24.9 Million
Emp.: 50
Sales/European Distributor

N.A.I.C.S.: 449210
Bourns Asia Pacific Inc. (1)
Belle International Plaza Room 1701 No 928 Liuzhou Road, Xuhui district, Shanghai, 200235, China
Tel.: (86) 21 6482 1250
Sales Range: $10-24.9 Million
Emp.: 20
Electronic Components Mfr
N.A.I.C.S.: 334419
Kevin Lin (Gen Mgr)

Bourns Electronics (Taiwan) Ltd. (1)
1 Kung 6th Road The 2nd Industrial Zone Lin-Kou Shiang, Hsien, Taipei, Taiwan
Tel.: (886) 2 2601 3748
Electronic Component Mfr & Whslr
N.A.I.C.S.: 334419

Bourns Electronics, Ltd. (1)
Mahon Industrial Estate, Blackrock, Cork, Ireland (100%)
Tel.: (353) 214515221
Sales Range: $350-399.9 Million
Emp.: 5,000
Electronic Parts Sales
N.A.I.C.S.: 423690

Bourns Kft. (1)
Harsfa u 9, 8400, Ajka, Hungary
Tel.: (36) 88520214
Web Site: http://bourns.hu
Automotive Product Supplier
N.A.I.C.S.: 441330
Istvan Bulyaki (Plant Mgr)
Jozsef Goger (Mgr-Worldwide Lab)
Krisztian Szavel (Mgr-HR)
Attila Sarkany (Mgr-Quality)
Karoly Kovacs (Mgr-Production)

Bourns Ltd. (1)
East Site Manton Lane, Bedford, MK41 7BJ, United Kingdom (100%)
Tel.: (44) 1234 223001
Web Site: http://www.bourns.com
Emp.: 120
Electronic Components Mfr
N.A.I.C.S.: 334419
Erik Meijer (Pres)

Bourns Sensors GmbH (1)
Robert Bosch Str 14, 82054, Sauerlach, Germany
Tel.: (49) 8104 646 0
Electrical Engineering Services
N.A.I.C.S.: 541330

Bourns Trading (Shanghai) Co., Ltd. (1)
Belle International Plaza Room 1701 No 928 Liuzhou Road, Xuhui district, Shanghai, 200235, China
Tel.: (86) 21 6482 1250
Electronic Component Mfr & Whslr
N.A.I.C.S.: 423690

Bourns de Mexico S de RL de CV (1)
Blvd Aqua Caliente 4006 Local 13, Centro Industrial Barranquita, 22400, Tijuana, BC, Mexico
Tel.: (52) 6646086800
Web Site: http://www.bourns.ttieurope.com
Sales Range: $25-49.9 Million
Emp.: 800
Mfr of Electronic Components
N.A.I.C.S.: 334416

Division (Domestic):

Bourns de Mexico, S. de R.L. de C.V. - Automotive Division (2)
Avenida Victor Hugo 310 Chihuahua Industrial Complex, 31109, Chihuahua, Mexico
Tel.: (52) 614 442 9700
Web Site: http://www.bourns.com
Emp.: 500
Electrical Equipment Mfr & Distr
N.A.I.C.S.: 423610
Sergio Valencia (Gen Mgr)

Bourns, Inc. - Automotive Division (1)
1660 N Opdyke Ste 200, Auburn Hills, MI 48326
Tel.: (248) 926-4088
Web Site: http://www.bourns.com
Automotive Part Whslr
N.A.I.C.S.: 423120

Linda Exum (Coord-Admin Svcs)
Jerry Baldridge (Coord-Engrg Lab)
Jerry Durand (VP-Worldwide Automotive Sls & Engrg)
Gordon Bourns (CEO)

Bourns, Inc. - Circuit Protection Division (1)
1200 Columbia Ave, Riverside, CA 92507-2129
Tel.: (951) 781-5690
Electrical Equipment Mfr & Distr
N.A.I.C.S.: 423610

BOURY ENTERPRISES
808 National Rd, Wheeling, WV 26003-6439
Tel.: (304) 233-1300
Year Founded: 1912
Sales Range: $10-24.9 Million
Emp.: 100
Holding Company; Restaurants, Wholesale Prepared Foods; Retailer of Commercial Appliances
N.A.I.C.S.: 493190

Subsidiaries:

T.J.'s Sports Garden Restaurant (1)
808 National Rd, Wheeling, WV 26003
Tel.: (304) 232-9555
Sales Range: $10-24.9 Million
Emp.: 60
Restaurant & Sports Bar
N.A.I.C.S.: 722410
T. J. Radevski (Pres)

BOUTIQUE HOTEL MANAGEMENT GROUP, LLC
Fl 4 783 Madison Ave, New York, NY 10021-6144
Tel.: (212) 967-9929
Web Site: http://www.boutiquehotelsgroup.com
Year Founded: 1999
Rev.: $10,100,000
Emp.: 50
Hotels & Motels
N.A.I.C.S.: 541611
William Howell (Chm)
Gerald K. Cappello (Dir)
Marideth Post (Dir-Pub Rel)

BOUTIQUE TERE, INC.
1167 3rd St S Ste 207, Naples, FL 34102
Tel.: (239) 262-6994
Web Site: http://www.marissacollections.com
Year Founded: 1975
Sales Range: $10-24.9 Million
Emp.: 40
Women's Clothing, Accessories, Shoes, Cosmetics & Jewelry Retailer
N.A.I.C.S.: 458110
Burt Hartington (Pres)

BOUTWELL OWENS & CO. INC.
251 Authority Dr, Fitchburg, MA 01420
Tel.: (978) 343-3067
Web Site: http://www.boutwellowens.com
Sales Range: $10-24.9 Million
Emp.: 150
Offset Printing
N.A.I.C.S.: 323111
Ward W. McLaughlin (Owner & CEO)
Bill Hodges (VP-Sls)

BOVEDA INC.
10237 Yellow Circle Dr, Minnetonka, MN 55343
Tel.: (952) 745-2900
Web Site: https://bovedainc.com
Emp.: 100
Herbal Medicine, Tobacco & Wood Instruments Packaging Solutions

N.A.I.C.S.: 561910
Sean Knutsen *(CEO)*

Subsidiaries:

Freshstor Inc.   **(1)**
2693 Whispering Pines Dr, Grayson, GA
30017-2859
Web Site: http://www.freshstor.com
Metal Kitchen Cookware, Utensil, Cutlery &
Flatware Mfr
N.A.I.C.S.: 332215
Gary Swanson *(Principal)*

BOW AND ARROW MANOR INC.

111 Prospect Ave, West Orange, NJ
07052
Tel.: (973) 731-2360
Web Site:
   https://www.manorrestaurant.com
Sales Range: $10-24.9 Million
Emp.: 75
Independent Family Restaurant
N.A.I.C.S.: 722511
Barbara Loria *(Dir-HR)*
Harry Knowles Jr. *(Pres)*

BOW RIVER ASSET MANAGE-MENT CORP.

205 Detroit St Ste 800, Denver, CO
80206
Tel.: (303) 861-8466
Web Site:
   http://www.bowrivercapital.com
Privater Equity Firm
N.A.I.C.S.: 523999
Blair Richardson *(CEO)*
Rick Pederson *(Vice Chm & Chief
Strategy Officer)*
David A. Ettenger *(Mng Dir-IR)*
Greg J. Hiatrides *(Mng Dir-Private
Equity)*
Matt Warta *(Mng Dir-Software Growth
Equity)*
John Raeder *(Mng Dir & Head-
Software Investments)*

Subsidiaries:

Veris Consulting, Inc.   **(1)**
11710 Plz America Dr 300, Reston, VA
20190
Tel.: (703) 654-1400
Web Site: http://www.verisconsulting.com
Rev.: $5,000,000
Emp.: 40
Administrative Management & General
Management Consulting Service
N.A.I.C.S.: 541611
Larry Johnson *(Chm & CEO)*
Brandon Hubbard *(Dir-IT)*
Cristie Lucas *(Dir-Recruiting)*
Ed Buttner *(Sr Mng Dir)*
John Lucca *(Mng Dir & CFO)*
Jonathan Couchman *(Mng Dir)*
Kent Barrett *(Sr Mng Dir)*
Kevin Tullier *(Mng Dir)*
Michelle Avery *(Mng Dir & Exec VP)*

BOW STREET, LLC

1140 Ave of Americas 10th Fl, New
York, NY 10036
Tel.: (212) 554-5700   DE
Web Site:
   http://www.bowstreetllc.com
Investment Management Service
N.A.I.C.S.: 523940
Bryan Murray *(Dir-Investor Relations)*
A. Akiva Katz *(Mng Partner)*

BOW TIE CINEMAS, LLC

641 Danbury Rd, Ridgefield, CT
06877
Tel.: (203) 659-2600
Web Site:
   https://www.bowtiecinemas.com
Year Founded: 1900
Motion Picture Theater
N.A.I.C.S.: 512131

Ben Moss *(Owner & CEO)*
Jared Milgram *(VP-Film & Mktg)*

BOW-BOECK ENTERPRISES LLC

5017 Bristol Industrial Way, Buford,
GA 30518
Tel.: (800) 537-0669   GA
Web Site: http://www.reach-
   technologies.com
Year Founded: 1983
Office Equipment Supplier
N.A.I.C.S.: 423420
Kevin Boeckman *(Pres & CEO)*

Subsidiaries:

Murfreesboro Business Machines,
Inc.   **(1)**
620 NW Broad St, Murfreesboro, TN 37130
Tel.: (615) 890-6498
Office Equipment Supplier
N.A.I.C.S.: 423420

BOWDEN FORD LINCOLN MERCURY, INC.

2265 E Main St, Alice, TX 78332
Tel.: (361) 664-9541   TX
Web Site:
   http://www.bowdenford.com
Sales Range: $10-24.9 Million
Emp.: 49
New & Used Car Dealer
N.A.I.C.S.: 441110
Lamar Bowden *(Pres)*
Cindy Pawelek *(Controller)*

BOWE INDUSTRIES INC.

88-36 77th Ave, Glendale, NY 11386
Tel.: (718) 441-6464
Web Site:
   https://www.changesonline.com
Rev.: $14,604,727
Emp.: 80
Men's & Boys' Apparel
N.A.I.C.S.: 315250
Marek Kiyashka *(VP)*

BOWEN AGENCY INC.

1372 N Suquehanna Trl, Selinsgrove,
PA 17870
Tel.: (570) 743-2165
Web Site:
   http://www.thebowenagency.com
Rev.: $19,000,000
Emp.: 28
Real Estate Agent, Commercial &
Residential Rental & Appraisal
N.A.I.C.S.: 531210
Arthur F. Bowen *(Pres)*

BOWEN ENGINEERING COR-PORATION

8802 N Meriodian St, Indianapolis, IN
46260
Tel.: (317) 842-2616
Web Site:
   https://www.bowenengineering.com
Year Founded: 1967
Sales Range: $25-49.9 Million
Emp.: 250
Waste Water, Sewage Treatment
Plant & General Construction Ser-
vices
N.A.I.C.S.: 237110
Scot Evans *(CFO & Sr VP)*
Doug Bowen *(Pres & CEO)*
John Dettman *(VP-Ops)*
Aaron Purdue *(VP-Ops)*

BOWEN INDUSTRIAL CON-TRACTORS

8250 N Luke Dr, El Paso, TX 79907
Tel.: (915) 598-9100
Web Site:
   http://www.bowencontractors.com
Sales Range: $10-24.9 Million

Emp.: 75
Mechanical Contractor
N.A.I.C.S.: 238220
Jodie Bowen *(CEO)*
Nate Soltero *(Mgr-IT)*

BOWEN JUICES INTERNA-TIONAL

500 Firetower Rd, Haines City, FL
33844
Tel.: (863) 439-1139
Rev.: $13,000,000
Emp.: 1
Beverage Concentrates
N.A.I.C.S.: 424490
Maristela Ferrari *(Pres & CEO)*

BOWEN PETROLEUM INC.

364 Taft Ave, Pocatello, ID 83201
Tel.: (208) 232-1131
Web Site:
   http://www.bowenpetroleum.com
Sales Range: $50-74.9 Million
Emp.: 35
Petroleum Bulk Stations
N.A.I.C.S.: 424710
Clair Bowen *(Pres & CEO)*

BOWEN SCARFF FORD SALES, INC.

1157 Central Ave N, Kent, WA 98032
Tel.: (253) 852-1480
Web Site:
   http://www.bowenscarffford.com
Year Founded: 1958
Sales Range: $50-74.9 Million
Emp.: 130
New Car Dealers
N.A.I.C.S.: 441110
Mark Scarff *(Gen Mgr)*
Bowen Scarff *(Owner)*

BOWEN TRAVEL SERVICES INC.

4905 W State St, Tampa, FL 33609
Tel.: (813) 289-8344
Web Site:
   https://www.bowentravel.com
Year Founded: 1924
Sales Range: $10-24.9 Million
Emp.: 20
Travel Agency
N.A.I.C.S.: 561510
Willis Vazquez *(Pres)*
Don Oneal Jr. *(CEO)*

BOWEN, MICLETTE & BRITT, INC.

1111 N Loop W Ste 400, Houston, TX
77008
Tel.: (713) 880-7100   TX
Web Site: http://www.bmbinc.com
Year Founded: 1980
Rev.: $16,300,000
Emp.: 142
Insurance Services
N.A.I.C.S.: 524210

BOWERS ENTERPRISES, LLC

1430 Gadsden Hwy Ste 116 Unit 110,
Birmingham, AL 35235
Web Site: http://www.dropified.com
Year Founded: 2015
Sales Range: $1-9.9 Million
Emp.: 30
Online Shopping Services
N.A.I.C.S.: 441330
Chase Bowers *(Founder & Co-CEO)*
Lowell Rempel *(Co-CEO)*

BOWERS FIBERS INC.

4001 Yancey Rd, Charlotte, NC
28217-1735
Tel.: (704) 523-5323   NC
Web Site:
   http://www.bowersfibers.com

Year Founded: 1944
Sales Range: $10-24.9 Million
Emp.: 100
Scrap & Waste Material Services
N.A.I.C.S.: 423930
John F. Braxton *(CFO)*

BOWERY RESIDENTS' COM-MITTEE, INC.

131 W 25th St, New York, NY 10001
Tel.: (212) 803-5700   NY
Web Site: https://www.brc.org
Year Founded: 1973
Sales Range: $50-74.9 Million
Emp.: 764
Community Housing Services
N.A.I.C.S.: 624229
Muzzy Rosenblatt *(Exec Dir)*
David Tatum *(Chief Program Officer)*

BOWES CONSTRUCTION, INC.

2915 22nd Ave S, Brookings, SD
57006-4521
Tel.: (605) 693-3557
Web Site:
   https://bowesconstruction.com
Sales Range: $10-24.9 Million
Emp.: 100
Highway & Street Construction Ser-
vices
N.A.I.C.S.: 237310
Miranda Bowes-Peterson *(Pres)*

BOWIE RESOURCES LLC

6100 Dutchmans Ln, Louisville, KY
40205
Tel.: (502) 584-6022
Web Site:
   http://www.bowieresources.com
Emp.: 55
Coal Mining
N.A.I.C.S.: 212115
Carlos Pons *(CEO)*

Subsidiaries:

Canyon Fuel Company, LLC   **(1)**
6955 Union Park Ctr Ste 540, Midvale, UT
84047-4188
Tel.: (801) 539-4700
Coal Mining
N.A.I.C.S.: 212115

BOWIE-SIMS-PRANGE INC.

2400 Worthington Dr, Denton, TX
76207-3449
Tel.: (972) 245-6505   TX
Web Site: http://www.bspgroup.com
Year Founded: 1975
Sales Range: $10-24.9 Million
Emp.: 30
Distr & Processor of Lumber, Ply-
wood & Millwork
N.A.I.C.S.: 423310
David Lautzenheiser *(VP-Pur)*

Subsidiaries:

Bowie-Sims-Prange Treating
Corp.   **(1)**
2400 Worthington Dr, Denton, TX
76207-3449   **(100%)**
Tel.: (972) 446-1150
Web Site: http://www.bspgroup.com
Sales Range: Less than $1 Million
Wood Preserving
N.A.I.C.S.: 423310

BOWL NEW ENGLAND INC.

215 Mtn View Dr, Colchester, VT
05446
Tel.: (802) 655-3468
Web Site: http://bowlne.com
Sales Range: $10-24.9 Million
Emp.: 40
Ten Pin Center
N.A.I.C.S.: 713950

BOWLEN SPORTS, INC.

Bowlen Sports, Inc.—(Continued)

13655 Broncos Pkwy, Englewood, CO 80112-4150
Tel.: (303) 649-9000   **AZ**
Emp.: 200
Holding Company; Professional Football Franchise Owner & Operator
N.A.I.C.S.: 551112
Pat D. Bowlen (Owner)
Joe Ellis (Pres & CEO)
Rich Slivka (Gen Counsel & Exec VP)
Justin Webster (CFO)

Subsidiaries:

Denver Broncos Football Club   **(1)**
13655 Broncos Pkwy, Englewood, CO 80112-4150
Tel.: (303) 649-9000
Web Site: http://www.denverbroncos.com
Emp.: 1,000
Professional Football Franchise
N.A.I.C.S.: 711211
Joe Ellis (Pres & CEO)
Rich Slivka (Gen Counsel & Exec VP-Admin)
Rick Seifert (Chief Engr-Comm)
Chip Conway (VP-Ops)
Cindy Galloway Kellogg (VP-Community Dev)
Dianne Sehgal (Controller)
Mac Freeman (Sr VP-Bus Dev)
Fred Fleming (Dir-Special Svcs-Pro Scouting)
Chris Valenti (Mgr-Equipment)
Billy Thompson (Dir-Community Outreach)
Fred Krebs (Mgr-Cash Mgmt & Treasury)
Brady Kellogg (VP-Corp Partnerships)
Sandy Bretzlauf Young (Dir-Partnership Mktg)
Bobby Mestas (Dir-Youth & High School Football)
Derek Thomas (Dir-Corp Partnerships)
John Karpan (Mgr-Facilities)
Dennis Moore (VP-Mktg & Sls)
Howard Brown (Ops Mgr-Facility)
Scott Bliek (Asst Gen Mgr-Stadium Mgmt)
Clark Wray (Dir-Ticket & Database Ops)
John Elway (Exec VP-Football Ops & Gen Mgr)
Justin Webster (CFO)
Mark Thewes (VP-Team Admin)
Keith Bishop (VP-Security)
Russ Trainor (VP-IT)
Darren O'Donnell (VP-Bus Dev)
Patrick Smyth (VP-PR)
Nancy Svoboda (Sr VP-HR)
Erich Schubert (Sr Mgr-Media Rels)
Liz Mannis (Mgr-Community Dev)
Brittany Bowlen (VP-Strategic Initiatives)

BOWLES CORPORATE SERVICES INC.
555 8th Ave 7th Fl, New York, NY 10018
Tel.: (212) 629-9201
Web Site: http://www.bcs.ws
Sales Range: $500-549.9 Million
Emp.: 2,500
Security Guards & Patrol Services
N.A.I.C.S.: 561612
Angel Dufore (Exec VP-Ops)
Roger Hawkins (VP)
Roger Harwood (Acct Mgr)
Eduardo Arroyo (Acct Mgr)
Alan Bowles (Founder & Principal)

BOWLING GREEN FREIGHT INC.
581 Hardison Rd, Woodburn, KY 42170
Tel.: (270) 781-0197
Web Site: http://www.bgfreight.com
Sales Range: $10-24.9 Million
Emp.: 130
Trucking Service
N.A.I.C.S.: 484121
Anthony W. Thornton (Pres)
Toni Thornton (Owner)
Eldon Isenberg (Dir-HR)

BOWMAN ANDROS PRODUCTS, LLC
10119 Old Valley Pike, Mount Jackson, VA 22842-9565
Tel.: (540) 217-4100   **VA**
Web Site: https://www.androsna.com
Year Founded: 1939
Sales Range: $25-49.9 Million
Emp.: 200
Canned Fruits & Specialties
N.A.I.C.S.: 311421
Thierry Jean (CEO)

BOWMAN CONSTRUCTORS, INC.
552 Moosehead Trl, Newport, ME 04593
Tel.: (207) 368-2405
Web Site:
   https://www.bowmanconstructors.com
Year Founded: 1987
Sales Range: $10-24.9 Million
Emp.: 35
Commercial & Institutional Building Construction Services
N.A.I.C.S.: 236220
Kevin Bowman (Co-Owner & Pres)
Brian Bowman (Co-Owner & VP)

BOWMAN ENTERPRISES INC.
2934 Fish Hatchery Rd, Madison, WI 53713-5015
Tel.: (608) 271-6870   **WI**
Year Founded: 1969
Sales Range: $25-49.9 Million
Emp.: 150
Operate Grocery Stores & Gasoline Service Stations
N.A.I.C.S.: 445131

Subsidiaries:

Bowman Farms Inc.   **(1)**
2934 Fish Hatchery Rd Ste 222, Madison, WI 53713-3175
Tel.: (608) 271-6870
Sales Range: $25-49.9 Million
Emp.: 20
Operate Grocery Stores
N.A.I.C.S.: 445131

BOWMAN GROUP LLP
10228 Governor Ln Blvd, Williamsport, MD 21795-4064
Tel.: (301) 582-1555   **MD**
Web Site:
   http://www.bowmangroupllp.com
Year Founded: 1987
Sales Range: $25-49.9 Million
Emp.: 700
Property Management Services
N.A.I.C.S.: 531312
Cindy J. Joiner (CFO)

Subsidiaries:

Bowman Development Corporation   **(1)**
10228 Governor Ln Blvd, Williamsport, MD 21795-4033
Tel.: (301) 582-1555
Web Site:
   http://www.bowmandevelopment.com
Rev.: $920,000
Emp.: 13
Nonresidential Building Operators
N.A.I.C.S.: 531120
Jeff Tedrick (Project Mgr)

Bowman Logistics   **(1)**
10228 Governor Lane Blvd Ste 3006, Williamsport, MD 21795
Tel.: (301) 223-1007
Web Site: http://www.bowmanlogistics.com
Emp.: 400
Logistics Consulting Servies
N.A.I.C.S.: 541614
Don Bowman (Owner & Chm)
Jim Ward (Pres & CEO)

Jeff Huff (Mgr-Logistics)
David Ebner (Mgr-Bus Dev)
Ron Trackwell (Mgr-Logistics-Indiana)

Bowman Sales & Equipment Inc. **(1)**
10233 Governor Ln Blvd, Williamsport, MD 21795
Tel.: (301) 582-1793
Web Site: http://www.bowmanleasing.com
Rev.: $510,000
Emp.: 20
Utility Trailer Rental
N.A.I.C.S.: 532120
Todd Bowman (Pres)
Mike Straliper (Branch Mgr)

Bowman Truck Leasing, LLC **(1)**
10038 Governor Lane Blvd, Williamsport, MD 21795
Web Site:
   http://www.bowmantruckleasing.com
Truck Leasing Services
N.A.I.C.S.: 532120

D.M. Bowman Incorporated **(1)**
10228 Governor Lane Blvd Ste 3006, Williamsport, MD 21795
Tel.: (301) 223-6900
Web Site: http://www.dmbowman.com
Rev.: $68,573,422
Emp.: 250
Transportation, Warehousing & Logistics Services
N.A.I.C.S.: 484121
Dave Wine (VP-Sls)
Jim Ward (Pres & CEO)
Donald Meckley (Dir-Ops)
Mike Boarman (Dir-Maintenance)
Robert Dragonette (CFO)
Anthony Triggs (Dir-Ops)
Barry L. Wertz (Dir-Risk Mgmt & Safety)

BOWMAN HOLLIS MANUFACTURING, INC.
2925 Old Steele Creek Rd, Charlotte, NC 28208
Tel.: (704) 374-1500
Web Site:
   https://www.bowmanhollis.com
Emp.: 54
Industrial Supplies Distr
N.A.I.C.S.: 423830
Ann Bowman (Treas)

Subsidiaries:

Bowman Hollis Manufacturing Co., Inc. - LaGrange   **(1)**
1606 Orchard Hill Rd, LaGrange, GA 30240
Tel.: (706) 882-6483
Web Site: http://www.bowmanhollis.com
Sales Range: $1-9.9 Million
Emp.: 18
Industrial Supplies Distr
N.A.I.C.S.: 423840
Mark Houghton (Mgr-Shop)
Jeff Buchanan (Mgr)

BOWMAN INC.
8301 University Ave, Lubbock, TX 79423
Tel.: (806) 745-9701
Sales Range: $10-24.9 Million
Emp.: 65
Homecenter; Millwork & Lumber
N.A.I.C.S.: 444110
Donald L. Smith Sr. (Chm)
Donald Smith Jr. (Pres)

BOXABL INC.
5345 E North Belt Rd, Las Vegas, NV 89115
Tel.: (702) 500-9000
Web Site: https://www.boxabl.com
Emp.: 100
Portable Building Systems Design & Mfr
N.A.I.C.S.: 236116
Paolo Tiramani (Founder)

Subsidiaries:

500 Group Inc.   **(1)**
700 Canal St Ste 11, Stamford, CT 06902-5937

Tel.: (203) 357-9000
Web Site: http://www.500group.com
Emp.: 100
Marketing Research & Public Opinion Polling
N.A.I.C.S.: 541910

BOXCEIPTS.COM, INC.
5711 W 157th Ter, Overland Park, KS 66223
Tel.: (913) 232-2290   **NV**
Web Site: http://www.boxceipts.com
Year Founded: 2010
Online Receipt Services
N.A.I.C.S.: 513199
Geoffrey T. Farwell (Chm & Pres)
Mark W. DeFoor (CEO, CFO & Chief Acctg Officer)

BOXER PROPERTY MANAGEMENT CORPORATION
720 N Post Oak Rd Ste 500, Houston, TX 77024
Tel.: (713) 777-7368   **TX**
Web Site:
   http://www.boxerproperty.com
Year Founded: 1992
Sales Range: $25-49.9 Million
Emp.: 156
Nonresidential Building Operators
N.A.I.C.S.: 531120
Andrew Segal (Founder, Chm & CEO)
John Rentz (VP)
Justin Segal (Pres)
Michael T. Pariza (Pres-Boxer Retail-Resorts)

BOXERCRAFT INCORPORATED
7131 Discovery Blvd, Mableton, GA 30126
Tel.: (404) 355-9994
Web Site: http://www.boxercraft.com
Sales Range: $10-24.9 Million
Emp.: 25
Women's, Children's & Infants' Clothing & Accessories Merchant Whslr
N.A.I.C.S.: 424350
Shelley Foland (CEO)

Subsidiaries:

Jones & Mitchell Sportswear   **(1)**
1880 College Blvd Ste 400, Overland Park, KS 66210
Tel.: (913) 324-2700
Web Site: http://www.jonesmitchell.com
Sales Range: $10-24.9 Million
Emp.: 45
Sportswear Mfr
N.A.I.C.S.: 424350

BOXLIGHT INC.
151 State Hwy 300 Ste A, Belfair, WA 98528
Tel.: (360) 464-2119
Web Site: http://www.boxlight.com
Year Founded: 1985
Sales Range: $50-74.9 Million
Emp.: 15
Audio-Visual Equipment & Supplies
N.A.I.C.S.: 459999
Sunshine Nance (Dir-Mktg)
Hank Nance (Pres)

BOXOFFICETICKETSALES.COM
17 E Monroe St #217, Chicago, IL 60603
Tel.: (855) 514-5629
Web Site:
   http://www.boxofficeticketsales.com
Year Founded: 2007
Sales Range: $10-24.9 Million
Emp.: 20
Premium Event Seating & Ticketing Services

N.A.I.C.S.: 711310
Jonathan Poppas *(Mgr-Sales)*

BOXUNION HOLDINGS LLC
1755 Ocean Ave, Santa Monica, CA 90401
Tel.: (310) 882-5508
Web Site: http://www.boxunion.com
Fitness Services
N.A.I.C.S.: 713940
Todd Wadler *(Founder & CEO)*
Felicia Alexander *(Founder & Chief Revenue Officer)*

Subsidiaries:

TBC International LLC   (1)
5360 College Blvd Ste 120, Overland Park, KS 66211
Tel.: (734) 531-6250
Web Site: http://www.titleboxingclub.com
Fitness & Recreational Sports Centers
N.A.I.C.S.: 713940
Gerry Weir *(Mgr)*

BOXWOOD PARTNERS LLC
11 S 12th St Ste 400, Richmond, VA 23219-4035
Tel.: (804) 343-3300
Web Site:
   http://www.boxwoodpartnersllc.com
Privater Equity Firm
N.A.I.C.S.: 523999
Patrick Galleher *(Partner)*
Bobby Morris *(Partner)*
Chris Deel *(Partner)*

BOXY CHARM, INC.
880 SW 145th Ave, Pembroke Pines, FL 33027
Tel.: (305) 705-3752
Web Site: http://www.boxycharm.com
Year Founded: 2013
Sales Range: $125-149.9 Million
Emp.: 90
Cosmetic Product Distr
N.A.I.C.S.: 456120
Yosef Martin *(Founder & CEO)*

BOY SCOUTS OF AMERICA
1325 W Walnut Hill Ln, Irving, TX 75038-3008
Tel.: (972) 580-2219   TX
Web Site: https://www.scouting.org
Year Founded: 1911
Rev.: $244,000,000
Emp.: 1,000
National Council of Boy Scouts
N.A.I.C.S.: 541211
Jeff Issac *(CEO-Chicagoland & Northwest Indiana)*
Robert M. Gates *(Pres)*
Robert M. Gates *(Pres)*

Subsidiaries:

Boys' Life Magazine   (1)
271 Madison Ave Ste 401, New York, NY 10016-1001
Tel.: (212) 532-0985
Web Site: http://www.boyslife.org
Rev.: $15,000,000
Emp.: 400
Magazine Operations
N.A.I.C.S.: 513120
Barry Brown *(Dir-Adv)*
Lisa Hott *(Mgr-Print & Production)*
Judy Bramlett *(Mgr-Circulation)*
Paula Murphey *(Mng Editor)*
Bryan Wursten *(Editor-Online)*
W. Garth Dowling *(Dir-Photography)*
Myla Johnson *(Mgr-Media Sls-Midwest)*
Leah Myers *(Mgr-Print & Production)*
Eric Ottinger *(Dir-Design)*
Reva Stark *(Mgr-Media Sls-West)*

BOYCE LUMBER CO.
1410 S Russell St, Missoula, MT 59801
Tel.: (406) 728-7100

Web Site:
   https://www.boycelumber.com
Rev.: $15,271,504
Emp.: 34
Lumber & Other Building Materials
N.A.I.C.S.: 423310
Bob A. Boyce *(Pres)*

BOYD AUTOMOTIVE
1025 Martin Luther King Jr Ave, Oxford, NC 27565-3657
Tel.: (919) 693-7196
Web Site: https://www.boydauto.com
Year Founded: 1978
Sales Range: $10-24.9 Million
Emp.: 43
New Car Whslr
N.A.I.C.S.: 441110
Maurice A. Boyd *(Pres)*

BOYD CHEVROLET INC.
517 N Main St, Emporia, VA 23847
Tel.: (434) 634-5134
Web Site:
   http://boydchevroletofemporia.com
Sales Range: $10-24.9 Million
Emp.: 34
Automobiles, New & Used
N.A.I.C.S.: 441110

BOYD COUNTY FORD
2119 Greenup Ave, Ashland, KY 41101
Tel.: (606) 329-2120
Web Site:
   http://www.boydcountyford.net
Sales Range: $10-24.9 Million
Emp.: 54
Car Whslr
N.A.I.C.S.: 441110
Todd Clagg *(Mgr-F&I)*
Tim Conley *(Mgr-New Car Sls)*
Tom Casto *(Gen Mgr)*

BOYD INSURANCE & INVESTMENT SERVICES, INC.
717 Manatee Ave W Ste 300, Bradenton, FL 34205
Tel.: (941) 745-8300   FL
Web Site:
   https://www.boydinsurance.com
Year Founded: 1974
Sales Range: $1-9.9 Million
Emp.: 24
Insurance Brokerage & Investment Services
N.A.I.C.S.: 524210
James E. Boyd *(CEO)*
L. Pat Osburn *(Pres)*
Richard G. Gross *(Dir-Bus Dev)*
Kristin D. Smith *(VP-Client Rels)*
Phillip B. Baker *(VP)*
Russ Dozeman *(Dir-Sls)*
Nicholas J. Zec Jr. *(VP-Fin Svcs & Employee Benefits)*

BOYD LIGHTING
30 Liberty Ship Way Ste 3150, Sausalito, CA 94965
Tel.: (415) 778-4300
Web Site:
   http://www.boydlighting.com
Rev.: $12,500,000
Emp.: 75
Commercial Industrial & Institutional Electric Lighting Fixture Mfr
N.A.I.C.S.: 335132
John S. Sweet *(Pres)*
John Stone *(VP)*

BOYD MANAGEMENT
1324 Old River Rd, Camden, SC 29020
Tel.: (803) 419-6556
Web Site:
   http://www.boydmanagement.com

Sales Range: $800-899.9 Million
Emp.: 200
Housing Construction Services
N.A.I.C.S.: 236117
Barbara Jaco *(Mgr)*

BOYD METALS, INC.
600 S 7th St, Fort Smith, AR 72902
Tel.: (479) 782-9060
Web Site:
   https://www.boydmetals.com
Year Founded: 1991
Rev.: $31,800,000
Emp.: 100
Metal Service Centers & Other Metal Merchant Whslr
N.A.I.C.S.: 423510
Ron Tabor *(Territory Mgr)*
Tom Kennon *(Pres)*
Steve Harvey *(VP & Gen Mgr)*
Audie Dennis *(VP & Gen Mgr)*
Brian Newman *(VP & Dir-Pur)*
Stephen Crane *(Asst Gen Mgr)*
Elisabeth Presson *(Dir-HR)*
Jack Quinn *(Mgr-Quality Assurance)*
Ronny Testa *(VP & Gen Mgr)*
Larry Smith *(Mgr-Warehouse)*
Paul Culwell *(Mgr-Sls)*
Tracy Lowe *(Mgr-Acct)*
Tye Throneberry *(Mgr-Sls)*
Caleb Williamson *(Mgr-Acct)*
Chad Wilson *(Mgr-Acct)*
Ken Boyd *(VP-Fin & Controller)*
David Lyman *(VP & Gen Mgr)*
Richard Schultz *(VP & Gen Mgr)*

Subsidiaries:

Boyd Metals of Joplin, Inc   (1)
1027 Byers Ave, Joplin, MO 64801
Tel.: (417) 626-2693
Web Site: http://www.boydmetals.com
Sales Range: $10-24.9 Million
Emp.: 30
Metal Service Centers & Other Metal Merchant Whslr
N.A.I.C.S.: 423510
Ken Boyd *(Controller)*
Brian Newman *(VP & Dir-Pur)*
Robin Archer *(Mgr-HR)*
Steve Kindle *(Mgr-Corp Ops)*
Elisabeth Presson *(Asst Mgr-Acctg)*
Mike Rowland *(VP-Bus Dev)*
Brenda Schneider *(Mgr-Accts Payable)*

BOYD TAMNEY CROSS INC.
994 Old Eagle School Rd Ste 1015, Wayne, PA 19087-1802
Tel.: (610) 293-0500   PA
Year Founded: 1980
Rev.: $24,000,000
Emp.: 20
Advertising Agencies, Business-To-Business, Collateral, Financial, Full Service, Leisure, Planning & Consultation, Public Relations, Sales Promotion, Strategic Planning/Research, Travel & Tourism
N.A.I.C.S.: 541810
Raymond J. Hoffman *(VP)*
Christy Hoffman *(Controller)*
Tom Cancelmo *(CEO)*
David Culver *(VP-PR)*
Mandi Zola *(Sr Dir-Art)*
Chris Murray *(Exec VP)*

BOYDEN & YOUNGBLUTT ADVERTISING & MARKETING
120 W Superior St, Fort Wayne, IN 46802
Tel.: (260) 422-4499
Web Site: http://www.b-y.net
Year Founded: 1990
Sales Range: $25-49.9 Million
Emp.: 32
Consumer Marketing, Education, Financial, Health Care, Medical
N.A.I.C.S.: 541810

Jerry Youngblutt *(VP)*
Andy Boyden *(Owner)*
Clayton James *(Pres & Exec Dir-Creative)*

BOYDEN WORLD CORPORATION
3 Manhattanville Rd Ste 104, Purchase, NY 10577
Tel.: (914) 747-0093
Web Site: http://www.boyden.com
Year Founded: 1946
Sales Range: $25-49.9 Million
Emp.: 500
Executive Search Service
N.A.I.C.S.: 541612
Trina D. Gordon *(Pres & CEO)*
Daniela Ossikovska *(Mng Partner-Bulgaria)*
James N. J. Hertlein *(Mng Partner-Houston)*
Paul W. Schmidt *(Mng Partner-Chicago)*
Trevor M. Pritchard *(Partner-San Francisco)*
Breck Armstrong *(CIO)*
Jorg Kasten *(Chm-World Corp & Mng Partner-Germany)*
Finn Krogh Rants *(Mng Partner-Denmark)*
Brian G. Bachand *(Partner)*
Gary Claus *(Partner-Pittsburgh)*
Thomas Flannery *(Mng Partner-Pittsburgh)*
Antonio Sanchez *(Mng Partner-Colombia)*
Kenneth Vinther Mortensen *(Mng Partner-Denmark)*
Pedro del Valle *(Mng Partner-Argentina)*
Allan Marks *(Mng Partner-Australia)*
Andreas Hruschka *(Mng Partner-Austria)*
Andreas Landgrebe *(Mng Partner-Austria)*
Helga Rantasa *(Mng Partner-Austria)*
Kerstin Roubin *(Mng Partner-Austria)*
Nina Plattner *(Mng Partner-Austria)*
Aurea Imai *(Mng Partner-Brazil)*
William Penney *(Mng Partner-Brazil)*
Kalina Petkova *(Mng Partner-Bulgaria)*
Jim Harmon *(Mng Partner-Canada)*
Kevin Gormely *(Mng Partner-Canada)*
Michael Naufal *(Mng Partner-Canada)*
Roger T. Duguay *(Mng Partner-Canada)*
B. O. Eske Nielsen *(Mng Partner-Denmark)*
Jesper Broeckner Nielsen *(Mng Partner-Denmark)*
Carita Lahti *(Mng Partner-Finland)*
Erkki Panula *(Mng Partner-Finland)*
Jussi Eranen *(Mng Partner-Finland)*
Anne Raphael *(Mng Partner-France)*
Caroline Golenko *(Mng Partner-France)*
Michele Marchesan *(Principal-Milan)*
Anders Lindholm *(Mng Partner-Italy)*
Victor Escandon *(CFO & COO)*
Chip Novick *(Partner)*
Fanny Gimenez *(Mng Partner-Belgium)*
Koen Vandenberghe *(Mng Partner-Luxembourg)*
Paul Maertens *(Mng Partner-Brussels)*
Kerry Moynihan *(Partner-Washington, D.C.)*
Craig Stevens *(Mng Partner-Washington, D.C.)*
Chris Swee *(CMO)*
Petter Kleppe *(Partner-Norway)*
Joao Guedes Vaz *(Head-Leadership Consulting-Global)*

Boyden World Corporation—(Continued)

Katia Pina (*Sr Dir-Leadership Consulting Center of Excellence-Global*)

BOYDS MEN'S STORE
1818 Chestnut St, Philadelphia, PA 19103
Tel.: (215) 564-9000
Web Site: https://boydsphila.com
Sales Range: $25-49.9 Million
Emp.: 130
Women's Wear Whslr
N.A.I.C.S.: 458110
Gerald Gushner (*Pres*)

BOYER AND RITTER LLC
211 House Ave, Camp Hill, PA 17011
Tel.: (717) 761-7210
Web Site: https://www.cpabr.com
Year Founded: 1926
Accounting Firm
N.A.I.C.S.: 541211
Robert J. Murphy (*CEO*)
Paul D. Fisher (*Principal*)
Thomas J. Taricani (*Principal*)
Daniel P. Thompson (*Principal*)
Diane C. Grove (*Mgr-Support Svcs*)
Fina Salvo (*Dir-Mktg*)
Kathleen A. Walters (*Dir-Fin*)

BOYER CANDY COMPANY INC.
821 17th St, Altoona, PA 16602
Tel.: (814) 944-9401   DE
Web Site:
   https://www.boyercandies.com
Year Founded: 1936
Sales Range: $75-99.9 Million
Emp.: 64
Confectionery Products
N.A.I.C.S.: 311352
Jim Lidwell (*Plant Mgr*)

BOYER'S FOOD MARKETS INC.
301 S Warren St, Orwigsburg, PA 17961-0249
Tel.: (570) 366-1477   PA
Web Site:
   https://www.boyersfood.com
Year Founded: 1949
Sales Range: $50-74.9 Million
Emp.: 610
Grocery Store Services
N.A.I.C.S.: 445110
Matt Kase (*VP-Finance*)

BOYETT CONSTRUCTION INC.
2404 Tripaldi Way, Hayward, CA 94545-5017
Tel.: (510) 264-9100
Web Site:
   https://www.boyettconstruction.com
Rev.: $13,919,190
Emp.: 100
Drywall & Door Installation
N.A.I.C.S.: 238310
Vernon Boyett (*Pres*)
Jim Roberts (*COO*)

BOYETT PETROLEUM
601 McHenley Ave, Modesto, CA 95350
Tel.: (209) 577-6000
Web Site: https://www.boyett.net
Year Founded: 1962
Sales Range: $10-24.9 Million
Emp.: 80
Petroleum Product Distr
N.A.I.C.S.: 424720
Scott Castle (*Pres*)
Ken Berns (*VP-Wholesale*)
John Kruse (*CFO*)
Dale Boyett (*CEO*)
Kristie Olson (*Dir-HR*)
Terry Just (*Mgr-Wholesale Credit*)

Katie Hollowell (*Chief Legal Officer*)
Samantha Falk (*Coord-Wholesale Sls & Mktg*)
Michelle Gill (*Dir-Mktg & Events*)
Benjamin Frizzell (*Mgr-Acctg Svcs*)
Kim Castillo (*Mgr-Fleet Fueling Credit*)
Mark Goularte (*Mgr-Fuel Dispatch*)
David Zellman (*Mgr-IT*)
Clark Nakamura (*VP-Supply & Wholesale*)

BOYKIN CONTRACTING, INC.
167 Lott Ct, West Columbia, SC 29169
Tel.: (803) 926-4930
Sales Range: $10-24.9 Million
Emp.: 62
Electrical Wiring Services
N.A.I.C.S.: 238210
Cory Adams (*Pres*)

BOYKIN MANAGEMENT COMPANY, LLC
8015 W Kenton Cir Ste 220, Huntersville, NC 28078
Tel.: (704) 896-2880   OH
Web Site: https://www.boykin.com
Year Founded: 1958
Sales Range: $10-24.9 Million
Emp.: 7
Hotel Property Development & Management
N.A.I.C.S.: 531312
Robert Boykin (*CEO*)
Richard Longo (*Pres & CFO*)

Subsidiaries:

Pink Shell Beach Resort & Marina   **(1)**
275 Estero Blvd, Fort Myers Beach, FL 33931
Tel.: (239) 463-6181
Web Site: http://www.pinkshell.com
Emp.: 200
Resort
N.A.I.C.S.: 721110
Robert Boykin (*Chm & CEO*)

BOYLAN SALES INC.
607 N Main St, Plainwell, MI 49080
Tel.: (269) 685-6828
Web Site:
   http://www.boylansales.com
Sales Range: $10-24.9 Million
Emp.: 45
Golf Carts
N.A.I.C.S.: 423860
Patrick Boylan (*Pres*)

BOYLAND HONDA
6141 S 27th St, Greenfield, WI 53221
Tel.: (414) 281-2700
Web Site:
   http://www.boylandhonda.com
Sales Range: $10-24.9 Million
Emp.: 50
New Car Retailer
N.A.I.C.S.: 441110
Rob Eberwein (*Gen Mgr*)
Pete Stein (*Mgr-Sls*)
Terry Searcy (*Bus Mgr*)
Chris Williams (*Mgr-Internet*)

BOYLE BUICK GMC
3015 Emmorton Rd, Abingdon, MD 21009-2002
Tel.: (410) 670-7468
Web Site:
   https://www.boylebuickgmc.com
Year Founded: 1968
Sales Range: $10-24.9 Million
Emp.: 60
Car Whslr
N.A.I.C.S.: 441110
Linda Berry (*Controller*)
Page Boyle (*VP & Dir-Mktg*)

Christopher Boyle (*Pres & Principal-Dealer*)
Blake Boyle (*Corp Sec & Dir-Svc*)
Randy Boyle (*VP & Gen Mgr-Sls*)

BOYLE CONSTRUCTION INC.
1209 Hausman Rd Ste B, Allentown, PA 18104-9300
Tel.: (484) 223-0726
Web Site:
   https://www.boyleconstruction.com
Year Founded: 1977
Sales Range: $25-49.9 Million
Emp.: 45
Commercial & Institutional Building Construction
N.A.I.C.S.: 236220
Ken R. Duerholz (*VP*)
Sean Boyle (*Chm & Pres*)
Anthony J. Boyle (*Founder*)
Beverly Boger (*Accountant*)
Karen Cooney Duerholz (*VP-Bus Dev*)
Shane Follweiler (*Superintendent-Projects*)
Joe Klocek (*Mgr-Projects*)
Ed Refsnider (*Sr Mgr-Projects*)
Michael A. Spano (*Dir-Safety & Sr Mgr-Projects*)
Dave Kepler (*VP-New Bus Dev*)

BOYLE INVESTMENT COMPANY
5900 Poplar Ave, Memphis, TN 38119
Tel.: (901) 767-0100
Web Site: https://www.boyle.com
Sales Range: $10-24.9 Million
Emp.: 100
Commercial Real Estate
N.A.I.C.S.: 236220
Russell Bloodworth (*Exec VP*)
Cary Whitehead (*Exec VP*)
Debbie Shelton (*Asst Treas*)
Mark J. Halperin (*COO & Exec VP*)
Theresa Locastro (*Asst Sec & Dir-HR*)
Kathy Jones Pampuro (*Sr VP*)
Gary Thompson (*VP*)
Joel A. Fulmer (*Sr VP*)
John B. Doherty (*VP*)
John Faquin (*VP*)
Paul Boyle (*Chm*)
Tom Hutton (*VP*)
Les Binkley (*VP*)
Bayard Morgan (*Vice Chm*)
Jason Walters (*Mgr-Dev-Land Dev Dept*)
Matt Hayden (*Pres & CEO*)
Phil Fawcett (*Partner*)
Henry Morgan Jr. (*Vice Chm*)

BOYLE TRANSPORTATION INC.
15 Riverhurst Rd, Billerica, MA 01821-3425
Tel.: (978) 670-3499
Web Site:
   https://www.boyletransport.com
Rev.: $15,350,000
Emp.: 24
Transportation Protective Services, Hazardous Materials, Secure Cold Chain & Small Shipments Services
N.A.I.C.S.: 562112
Benjamin T. Curtis (*Mgr-Fleet*)
Marc Boyle (*Pres & CEO*)
Michael J. Collins (*Mgr-Ops*)
Nancy Haskell (*Dir-Admin*)
Scott Ryan (*VP-Ops*)
Andrew T. Boyle (*CFO & Exec VP*)
Enrique A. Araniz (*Dir-Ops-Central & Western United States*)
Steve Norbeck (*Mgr-Safety*)

BOYLES MOTOR SALES INCORPORATED
7919 Oak Orchard Rd, Batavia, NY 14020
Tel.: (585) 343-2860   NY
Web Site:
   http://www.boylesmotor.com
Year Founded: 1967
Sales Range: $10-24.9 Million
Emp.: 35
Sales of New & Used Trucks, Tractors & Trailers
N.A.I.C.S.: 441110
James J. Fanara (*Pres & Principal*)
Heidi S. Marshall (*Controller*)

BOYNE CAPITAL MANAGEMENT, LLC
3350 Virginia St Ste 400, Miami, FL 33133
Tel.: (305) 856-9500   DE
Web Site:
   http://www.boynecapital.com
Year Founded: 2006
Privater Equity Firm
N.A.I.C.S.: 523999
Derek McDowell (*Founder & Mng Partner*)
Valerie Barrett (*VP & Controller*)
Adam Herman (*COO*)
Jessica Anaya (*Coord-HR Office*)
Jon Goldsher (*CFO & Chief Compliance Officer*)
Alexis Mendel (*VP-Human Capital*)
Rob Regan (*VP-Bus Dev*)

Subsidiaries:

A.S.A.P. Industries Manufacturing, LLC   **(1)**
908 Blimp Rd, Houma, LA 70363
Tel.: (985) 851-7272
Web Site: http://www.asapind.net
Machine Tools Mfr
N.A.I.C.S.: 333517
Timothy Deroche (*CEO*)

Adapt Laser Systems, LLC   **(1)**
1218 Guinotte Ave, Kansas City, MO 64120
Tel.: (816) 466-5855
Web Site: http://www.adapt-laser.com
Laser Cleaning Solutions
N.A.I.C.S.: 334413
Georg Heidelmann (*Founder*)
Ralph Contzen (*CEO*)
Nathan Jonjevic (*Dir-Logistics*)
Steve Silva (*CTO*)

Evolution Lighting LLC   **(1)**
16200 NW 59th Ave Ste 101, Miami Lakes, FL 33014-7541
Tel.: (305) 558-4777
Web Site:
   http://www.evolutionlightingllc.com
Sales Range: $75-99.9 Million
Emp.: 200
Light Fixture Mfr & Distr
N.A.I.C.S.: 335132
A. Corydon Meyer (*Pres & CEO*)
Anthony Cirocco (*CFO*)
John Hartnett (*VP-Sls*)
Grace Bonnelly (*Product Mgr*)

Subsidiary (Non-US):

Evolution Lighting Canada   **(2)**
185 Courtney Pk Dr E, Dorval, L5T 2T6, QC, Canada   **(100%)**
Tel.: (905) 795-9995
Web Site:
   http://www.evolutionlightingllc.com
Sales Range: $100-124.9 Million
Lighting Product Distr
N.A.I.C.S.: 423610

Subsidiary (Domestic):

Evolution Lighting LLC-Tupelo   **(2)**
2214 S Green St, Tupelo, MS 38804
Tel.: (662) 407-0204
Sales Range: $25-49.9 Million
Lighting Equipment Distr
N.A.I.C.S.: 493190

Fresh Alternatives, LLC   **(1)**

1476 Town Center Dr Ste 219, Lakeland, FL 33803
Tel.: (410) 123-4567
Holding Company
N.A.I.C.S.: 551112

Holding (Domestic):

Crispers, LLC (2)
1476 Town Ctr Dr Ste 219, Lakeland, FL 33803
Tel.: (863) 646-2102
Web Site: http://www.crispers.com
Fast Food Restaurants
N.A.I.C.S.: 722513
Jami Julius (Mgr-Catering)
Don Voss (CEO)
Calvin C. Sellers III (CFO)

Galleher Lumber Co. (1)
1384 S Signal Dr, Pomona, CA 91766-5462
Tel.: (909) 623-5888
Web Site: https://galleherind.com
Other Building Material Dealers
N.A.I.C.S.: 444180
David Dowden (Owner)

Subsidiary (Domestic):

Fleet Parts & Service, Inc. (2)
590 Belleville Tpke, Kearny, NJ 07032
Tel.: (201) 997-1441
Web Site: http://www.fleetpartsonline.com
Sales Range: $1-9.9 Million
Emp.: 16
Motor Vehicle Supplies And New Parts
N.A.I.C.S.: 423120
Richard Lebowitz (Pres)
Lorraine Burns (Mgr-Accts)

Greenrise Technologies, LLC (1)
525 Barker Rd, Readyville, TN 37130
Tel.: (615) 907-7460
Web Site: http://greenrisetech.com
Environmental Services; Stormwater Management & Green Roof Installation
N.A.I.C.S.: 562998
Ray Derbecker (CEO)

Subsidiary (Domestic):

Southern Nurseries, Inc. (2)
3738 Dickerson Pike, Nashville, TN 37207
Tel.: (615) 333-4444
Web Site: http://www.southernnurseries.com
Engineered Soils Mfr & Supplier
N.A.I.C.S.: 115112
Kathy Garfield (Pres)

Pilot Power Group, Inc. (1)
8910 Univ Ctr Ln Ste 520, San Diego, CA 92122
Tel.: (858) 678-0118
Web Site: http://www.pilotpowergroup.com
Electric Power Generation
N.A.I.C.S.: 221111
Ian Middleton (Founder & COO)
Denis Vermette (Pres)

Ryan Construction Co. Inc (1)
2061 Wilroy Rd, Suffolk, VA 23434-2309
Tel.: (757) 538-8013
Web Site: http://www.ryanconstruction.us
Commercial & Institutional Building Construction
N.A.I.C.S.: 236220
Brink Nelms (Owner)

BOYNE USA RESORTS INC.
1 Boyne Mountain Rd, Boyne Falls, MI 49713-9642
Tel.: (231) 549-6040   MI
Web Site:
    http://www.boyneresorts.com
Year Founded: 1947
Sales Range: $800-899.9 Million
Emp.: 3,000
Operator of Ski & Golf Resorts
N.A.I.C.S.: 721110
Stephen Kircher (Owner & Pres-Eastern Ops)
Julie Ard (Dir-Mktg)
Trisha Olach (Mgr-Sls-Natl Accts)
Tracy Russold (Mgr-Sls)
Erin Ernst (Mgr-PR)
John Kircher (Pres-Western Ops)
Roland Andreasson (CFO)

Subsidiaries:

Bay Harbor Golf Club Inc. (1)
5800 Coastal Rdg Dr, Petoskey, MI 49770-8590
Tel.: (231) 439-4028
Web Site: http://www.bayharbour.com
Sales Range: $10-24.9 Million
Emp.: 75
Hotel & Golf Resort
N.A.I.C.S.: 713940

Big Sky Resort (1)
1 Lone Mtn Trl, Big Sky, MT 59716   (100%)
Tel.: (406) 995-5000
Web Site: http://www.bigskyresort.com
Rev.: $6,294,000
Emp.: 900
Resort
N.A.I.C.S.: 721110
John Kircher (CEO & Owner)
Taylor Middleton (Gen Mgr)
Brandon Bang (Dir-Sls)
Dax Schieffer (Mgr-HR)

Boyne Highlands Resort (1)
600 Highland Dr, Harbor Springs, MI 49740   (100%)
Tel.: (231) 526-3000
Web Site: http://www.boyne.com
Sales Range: $75-99.9 Million
Emp.: 628
Resort
N.A.I.C.S.: 721110
Erin Ernst (Mgr-PR)

Boyne Mountain Resort (1)
1 Boyne Mountain Rd, Boyne Falls, MI 49713-0019   (100%)
Tel.: (231) 549-6000
Web Site: http://www.boyne.com
Sales Range: $25-49.9 Million
Emp.: 500
Resort
N.A.I.C.S.: 721110
Matt Alagna (Dir-Sls)
Colin Riviere (Area Mgr)
Brenda Haight (Mgr-Sls)
Brie Kear (Mgr-Sls)
Laura McFarren (Dir-Convention Svcs)
Heather Pelton (Coord-Event)
Joe Arnold (Mgr-Sls Golf)
Jaclyn Wingate (Coord-Event)
Kristina Sherwood (Coord-Event)
Trisha Olach (Asst Dir-Sls)
Tracy Russold (Mgr-Sls)

Brighton Ski Resort (1)
12601 E Big Cottonwood Canyon, Brighton, UT 84121   (100%)
Tel.: (801) 532-4731
Web Site: http://www.brightonresort.com
Sales Range: $10-24.9 Million
Emp.: 40
Ski Resort
N.A.I.C.S.: 721110
John Kircher (Pres)

Crooked Tree Golf Club Inc. (1)
600 Crooked Tree Dr, Petoskey, MI 49770-8545   (100%)
Tel.: (231) 439-4030
Web Site: http://www.boyne.com
Sales Range: $10-24.9 Million
Emp.: 5
Golf Club & Real Estate Development Services
N.A.I.C.S.: 713910

Sugarloaf/USA (1)
5092 Access Rd, Carrabassett Valley, ME 04947-9799   (51%)
Tel.: (207) 237-2000
Web Site: http://www.sugarloaf.com
Sales Range: $25-49.9 Million
Emp.: 200
Operators of Sugarloaf Mountain Ski Resort
N.A.I.C.S.: 713920
Ethan Austin (Mgr-Comm)
Nancy Peabbles (Controller)
Rich Wilkinson (VP-Mountain Ops)
Leah Stevens (Dir-Sls)
Brent Larson (Dir-Lifts)
Tom Butler (Dir-Skier Svcs)
Karl Strand (Gen Mgr)

Sunday River Skiway Corp. (1)
15 S Ridge Rd, Newry, ME 04261
Tel.: (207) 824-3000

Web Site: http://www.sundayriver.com
Sales Range: $150-199.9 Million
Emp.: 1,800
Resort & Ski Area Operator
N.A.I.C.S.: 713920
Nick Lambert (VP-Sls & Mktg)
Karolyn Castaldo (Dir-Comm)

BOYS & GIRLS CLUBS OF BOSTON
200 High St Ste 3B, Boston, MA 02110
Tel.: (617) 994-4700
Web Site: https://www.bgcb.org
Year Founded: 1893
Youth Organization Services
N.A.I.C.S.: 813410

BOZ ELECTRICAL CONTRACTORS, INC.
6 Warren Dr, Vernon, NJ 07462
Tel.: (973) 764-2800
Web Site:
    https://www.bozelectricnj.com
Year Founded: 1991
Sales Range: $1-9.9 Million
Emp.: 25
Electrical Contractor
N.A.I.C.S.: 238210
Dorianne Struck (Mgr-Fin)
John V. Bosma (Pres)

BOZARD FORD CO.
540 Outlet Mall Blvd, Saint Augustine, FL 32084
Tel.: (904) 824-1641
Web Site:
    https://www.bozardford.com
Rev.: $10,700,000
Emp.: 140
New Car Dealers
N.A.I.C.S.: 441110
Leddi Bozard (Owner)

BOZELL & JACOBS, LLC
1022 Leavenworth, Omaha, NE 68102-2944
Tel.: (402) 965-4300   NE
Web Site: http://www.bozell.com
Year Founded: 1921
Sales Range: $10-24.9 Million
Emp.: 50
Advetising Agency
N.A.I.C.S.: 541810
Robin Donovan (Pres)
Kim Mickelsen (CEO)
Tom Giitter (Mgr-PR)
Heather McCain (Sr Dir-Art)
Tracy Koeneke (Dir-Media)
David Moore (Dir-Creative)
Laura Spaulding (Mgr-Corp Comm)
Nathan Anderson (Dir-Digital Creative)
Tim Young (Dir-Creative)
Alex Maltese (Dir-Acct Svc)
Justin Henriksen (Dir-Digital Creative)
Kayla Eggenberg (Coord-PR)
Jenna Kruntorad (Acct Coord)
Jackie Miller (Chief Mktg Officer)

BOZEMAN FORD
2900 N 19th St, Bozeman, MT 59718
Tel.: (406) 587-1221
Web Site:
    http://www.bozemanford.com
Year Founded: 1954
Sales Range: $25-49.9 Million
Emp.: 40
Car Whslr
N.A.I.C.S.: 441110
Jan Curry (Mgr-Customer Rels)

BOZZUTO'S INC.
275 Schoolhouse Rd, Cheshire, CT 06410
Tel.: (203) 272-3511   CT
Web Site: https://www.bozzutos.com

Year Founded: 1945
Sales Range: Less than $1 Million
Emp.: 3,500
General Line Grocery Merchant Wholesalers
N.A.I.C.S.: 424410
Michael A. Bozzuto (Chm, Pres & CEO)

BP ENERGY PARTNERS, LLC
2911 Turtle Creek Blvd. Ste 400, Dallas, TX 75219
Tel.: (214) 265-8473
Web Site:
    https://www.bpenergypartners.com
Year Founded: 2012
Emp.: 100
Private Equity
N.A.I.C.S.: 523999

Subsidiaries:

American Industrial Machine (1)
3401 N County Rd, Odessa, TX 79764-6404
Tel.: (432) 366-3516
Web Site: http://www.aimodessa.com
Machine Shops
N.A.I.C.S.: 332710

BP MICROSYSTEMS, L.P.
15000 NW Fwy, Houston, TX 77040
Tel.: (713) 688-4600   TX
Web Site: https://www.bpmmicro.com
Year Founded: 1985
Semiconductor Programming Systems Mfr
N.A.I.C.S.: 333242
William H. White (Founder & CEO)

BPA INTERNATIONAL
1 Old Country Rd Ste 330, Carle Place, NY 11514
Tel.: (516) 295-3620
Web Site: http://www.bpaquality.com
Year Founded: 1988
Sales Range: $1-9.9 Million
Emp.: 95
Remote Call Monitoring, Benchmarking & Mystery Shopping
N.A.I.C.S.: 459999
David Blackwell (Owner)
Lisa Renda (Pres)
Gladys Belson (Supvr-HR)
Robert Grogan (Mgr)

BPI BY-PRODUCT INDUSTRIES
612 S Trenton Ave, Pittsburgh, PA 15221
Tel.: (412) 371-8554
Web Site:
    https://www.bpiminerals.com
Year Founded: 1982
Sales Range: $10-24.9 Million
Emp.: 35
Minerals & Oxidizers Distr
N.A.I.C.S.: 325998

BPI INFORMATION SYSTEMS OF OHIO, INC.
6055 W Snowville Rd, Brecksville, OH 44141
Tel.: (440) 717-4112
Web Site: http://www.bpiohio.com
Sales Range: $10-24.9 Million
Emp.: 50
Computer Maintenance & Repair
N.A.I.C.S.: 813910
Gary Ellis (Pres)
George Stoll (VP)

BPM INC.
200 W Front St, Peshtigo, WI 54157
Tel.: (715) 582-4551   WI
Web Site: http://www.bpmpaper.com
Year Founded: 1929
Sales Range: $25-49.9 Million

BPM Inc.—(Continued)
Emp.: 120
Specialty Papers & Flexible Packaging Products Mfr
N.A.I.C.S.: 322120
James S. Koronkiewicz (Gen Mgr)
Rebecca Schoenebeck (Coord-Mktg)

BPO SYSTEMS INC.
2099 Mt Diablo Blvd Ste 205, Walnut Creek, CA 94596
Tel.: (925) 478-4299
Web Site:
  https://www.bposystems.com
Year Founded: 2001
Rev.: $2,700,000
Emp.: 50
Computer Software Services
N.A.I.C.S.: 513210
Bill Brown (Dir-Staffing Svcs)
Rambabu Yarlagadda (Pres & CEO)
Harold Rhineberger (VP-Mgmt)

BPR-RICO EQUIPMENT INC.
691 W Liberty, Medina, OH 44256-2225
Tel.: (330) 723-4050
Web Site:
  http://www.ricoequipment.com
Year Founded: 1986
Rev.: $20,000,000
Emp.: 70
Provider of Material Handling Services
N.A.I.C.S.: 333924
Steve Shuck (Pres)
Kent Stelmasczuk (CFO)

BQE SOFTWARE, INC.
3825 Del Amo Blvd, Torrance, CA 90503
Tel.: (310) 530-3065   CA
Web Site: http://www.bqe.com
Year Founded: 1995
Sales Range: $1-9.9 Million
Emp.: 95
Project Management Software
N.A.I.C.S.: 513210
Shafat Qazi (Founder & CEO)
Steven Burns (Chief Creative Officer)
Irfan Qazi (VP-Customer Svcs & Support)
Aumil Manzoor (VP-Res & Dev)
Bob Dias (Sr Product Dir)
Ikhlaq Bhat (Mgr-Mktg)
Mark Khurshid (VP-Trng)
Robert Guiler (VP-Sls)
Rueen Andrabi (COO)
Matt Cooper (Chief Revenue Officer)

BR ASSOCIATES, INC.
4201 Mannheim Rd Ste A, Jasper, IN 47546-9618
Tel.: (812) 482-3212   IN
Web Site: http://www.brsidal.com
Year Founded: 1971
Sales Range: $50-74.9 Million
Emp.: 3,200
Fast-Food Restaurant Chain
N.A.I.C.S.: 722513
Jason Kelly (CFO)

BR HOMEBUILDING GROUP, L.P.
211 E 7th St Ste 620, Austin, TX 78701-3218
Tel.: (214) 763-5742
Year Founded: 2010
Holding Company
N.A.I.C.S.: 551112
Bobby Ray (Founder & Pres)

Subsidiaries:
Scott Felder Homes, LLC   (1)
6414 River Pl Blvd Ste 100, Austin, TX 78730

Tel.: (512) 418-5400
Web Site: http://www.scottfelderhomes.com
Sales Range: $125-149.9 Million
Residential Building Construction Services
N.A.I.C.S.: 236115
Scott Felder (Co-Founder)
Steve Krassoff (Co-Founder & Pres)

BR PRINTERS, INC.
665 Lenfest Road, San Jose, CA 95133
Tel.: (408) 582-5100
Web Site: http://www.brprinters.com
Rev.: $1,500,000
Emp.: 115
Other Commercial Printing
N.A.I.C.S.: 323111
Adam DeMaestri (Pres)
Carina Follante (VP-Fin)
David Gall (Dir-Ops)
Kathryn Torre (Dir-HR)
Wade Walker (Sr Mgr-Product)

Subsidiaries:
Content Management
Corporation   (1)
4287 Technology Dr, Fremont, CA 94538
Tel.: (510) 505-1100
Web Site: http://cmcondemand.com
Sales Range: $1-9.9 Million
Emp.: 28
Commercial Lithographic Printing
N.A.I.C.S.: 323111
David Wang (Gen Mgr)

BRA SMYTH OF CALIFORNIA, INC.
100 N Winchester Blvd, Santa Clara, CA 95050
Tel.: (408) 261-9560
Web Site: http://www.brasmyth.com
Year Founded: 1991
Sales Range: $75-99.9 Million
Emp.: 5
Women's Intimate Apparel Retailer & Mail Order
N.A.I.C.S.: 458110
Rebecca Simon (Pres)
Sandi Simon (Principal)

BRAAVOS, INC.
160 Gilbert St, San Francisco, CA 94103
Tel.: (888) 788-2547
Web Site:
  http://www.bannerman.com
Year Founded: 2013
Emp.: 15
Security Guard Services
N.A.I.C.S.: 561612
Johnny Chin (Co-Founder & CEO)
Matt Voska (COO)

BRABENDERCOX, LLC
Market Stn 108 S St 3rd Fl, Leesburg, VA 20175
Tel.: (703) 896-5300   VA
Web Site:
  http://www.brabendercox.com
Political Advertising Agency
N.A.I.C.S.: 541810
Craig Etheridge (VP-Strategic Dev)
Robert Aho (Partner)

Subsidiaries:
BrabenderCox, LLC - Pittsburgh   (1)
1218 Grandview Ave, Pittsburgh, PA 15211
Tel.: (412) 434-6320
Web Site: http://www.brabendercox.com
Political Advertising Agency
N.A.I.C.S.: 541810
John Brabender (Pres)
Julie Didiano (Production Mgr)

BRABHAM OIL CO. INC.
525 Midway St, Bamberg, SC 29003
Tel.: (803) 245-2471
Web Site: http://www.brabhamoil.com

Sales Range: $50-74.9 Million
Emp.: 300
Petroleum Bulk Stations
N.A.I.C.S.: 424710
Joe James (Dir-Ops)

BRABNER & HOLLON, INC.
3053 Cotton St, Mobile, AL 36607
Tel.: (251) 479-5408
Web Site:
  https://www.brabnerhollon.com
Year Founded: 1954
Emp.: 30
Hardware Merchant Whslr
N.A.I.C.S.: 423710
Ronda Parker (Mgr-Pur)
Tim DeLong (CFO)
Burl Barbour (Detailing Mgr)
Michael L. Priesgen (Estimating Mgr)
Jay Hollon (Sls Mgr)
Ron Lins (Estimating Mgr)
Brian Spann (Asst Controller)
Terry Wood (Field Mgr)
M. Denison Crocker Jr. (COO)
James I. Hollon III (CEO)

BRACALENTE MANUFACTURING CO., INC.
20 W Creamery Rd, Trumbauersville, PA 18970-8970
Tel.: (215) 536-4844
Web Site: http://www.bracalente.com
Machine Shops
N.A.I.C.S.: 332710
James White (Engr-Quality)

Subsidiaries:
Millennium Manufacturing, Inc.   (1)
130d Penn Am Dr, Quakertown, PA 18951
Tel.: (215) 536-3006
Web Site:
  http://www.millenniummanufacturing.com
Rev.: $1,100,000
Emp.: 10
Precision Turned Product Mfr
N.A.I.C.S.: 332721
David B. Fricke (CEO)

BRACEWELL & GIULIANI LLP
711 Louisiana St Ste 2300 Pennzoil Pl - S Tower, Houston, TX 77002-2770
Tel.: (713) 223-2300   TX
Web Site: http://www.bracewell.com
Year Founded: 1945
Sales Range: $300-349.9 Million
Emp.: 860
Legal Advisory Services
N.A.I.C.S.: 541110
Jay R. Aldis (Partner)
Charles L. Almond (Partner)
Jessica Nolley Adkins (Partner)
Jane H. Macon (Partner-San Antonio)
Michael D. Bernard (Partner-San Antonio)
Blakely L. Fernandez (Partner-San Antonio)
William T. Avila (Partner-San Antonio)
Douglas F. Stewart (Partner-Seattle)
Edward Cavazos (Mng Partner-Austin)
Clint Steyn (Partner-Dubai)
Patrick C. Oxford (Chm)
Gregory M. Bopp (Mng Partner)
Christopher L. Dodson (Partner)
Jason M. Jean (Partner)
Robert A. Jacobson (Partner-Tax)
Gavin E. Hill (Partner)
Sean Gorman (Partner)
Alan D. Albright (Partner)
Sara M. Burgin (Partner-Environment & Natural Resources Practice)
Kevin Collins (Partner-Environment & Natural Resources Practice)
Matt Paulson (Partner-Environment & Natural Resources Practice)

Whit Swift (Partner-Environment & Natural Resources Practice)
Daniel S. Connolly (Mng Partner-New York)
Dale Smith (Partner)
Annette L. Tripp (Partner)
Jason Fox (Mng Partner-London)
Fernando J. Rodriguez Marin (Partner-Project Fin Team-New York)
Nicolai J. Sarad (Partner-Project Fin Team-New York)
Oliver Irwin (Partner-Fin-London)
Todd W. Eckland (Partner-Corp & Securities Grp-New York)
Liam Julius Stoker (Partner)
Phillip L. Sampson Jr. (Partner)

BRACEY'S SUPERMARKET INC.
921 Drinker Tpke, Moscow, PA 18444
Tel.: (570) 842-7461
Web Site: http://www.shoprite.com
Sales Range: $25-49.9 Million
Emp.: 300
Grocery Stores Owner & Operator
N.A.I.C.S.: 445110
William G. Bracey (Owner & Pres)

BRACING SYSTEMS INC.
4 N 350 Old Gary Ave, Hanover Park, IL 60133
Tel.: (630) 665-2732
Web Site:
  https://www.bracingsystems.com
Year Founded: 1972
Sales Range: $10-24.9 Million
Emp.: 70
Construction Equipment Repair
N.A.I.C.S.: 811210
Robert Williams (Pres)
John Williams (VP)

BRACKEN ENGINEERING, INC
2701 W Busch Blvd Ste 200, Tampa, FL 33618
Tel.: (813) 243-4251
Web Site:
  http://www.brackenengineering.com
Year Founded: 1996
Sales Range: $1-9.9 Million
Emp.: 30
Construction Engineering Services
N.A.I.C.S.: 541330
William C. Bracken (CEO)
Stephen R. Towne (Sr Project Mgr)
Phillip Hinton (VP-IT)
Gregg Golson (Dir-Mktg & Strategic Plng)

BRACY TUCKER BROWN & VALANZANO
1615 L St NW Ste 520, Washington, DC 20036-5608
Tel.: (202) 429-8855
Web Site: http://www.btbv.com
Year Founded: 1981
Sales Range: $1-9.9 Million
Emp.: 15
Public Relations Agency
N.A.I.C.S.: 541820
James P. Brown (Partner & COO)
Terrence L. Bracy (Pres & CEO)
Michael M. Bracy (Partner)
Tracy P. Tucker (Partner & VP)
Anthony Valanzano (Partner)
Clara Pratte (VP)

BRAD DEERY MOTORS, INC.
112 N 2nd St, Maquoketa, IA 52060
Tel.: (563) 652-4900
Web Site: https://www.braddeery.com
Year Founded: 1985
Sales Range: $10-24.9 Million
Emp.: 42
Car Whslr
N.A.I.C.S.: 441110

Nick Mc Cutcheon *(Gen Mgr)*
Bradford Deery *(Principal)*
Val Wherry *(Controller)*

BRAD LANIER OIL CO. INC.

611 W Roosevelt Ave, Albany, GA
31701-2150
Tel.: (229) 436-0131   **GA**
Year Founded: 1988
Sales Range: $10-24.9 Million
Emp.: 70
Provider of Petroleum Bulk Station &
Terminal Services
N.A.I.C.S.: 424710
Hans Pomeroy *(Pres)*
Donald Stull *(Mgr-Ops)*

BRAD!BRYAN MULTIMEDIA INC.

PO Box 15981, Sarasota, FL 34277
Tel.: (941) 539-3315
Web Site: https://www.bradbryan.com
Sales Range: $1-9.9 Million
Video Production Services
N.A.I.C.S.: 512110
Brad Ryan *(Pres)*

BRADBURY COMPANY, INC.

1200 E Cole Air Industrial Park,
Moundridge, KS 67107
Tel.: (620) 345-6394   **KS**
Web Site:
   https://www.bradburygroup.com
Year Founded: 1959
Sales Range: $75-99.9 Million
Emp.: 225
Rollforming Equipment & Tooling
Equipment Mfr
N.A.I.C.S.: 333519
David Bradbury *(Chm & Pres)*
Donald L. Koehn *(Treas, Sec & Exec VP)*
David Cox *(Gen Mgr)*
Mike Meuli *(Mgr-Engrg Project)*
Ben Bigham *(Mgr-Mechanical Engrg)*
Caner Dogruyol *(Mgr-Bus Dev-Kuopio)*

BRADBURY STAMM CONSTRUCTION, INC.

7110 2nd St NW, Albuquerque, NM
87107
Tel.: (505) 765-1200   **NM**
Web Site:
   https://www.bradburystamm.com
Year Founded: 1930
Sales Range: $125-149.9 Million
Emp.: 250
General Construction Of Commercial
& Multi Family Housing & Civil Engi-
neering Services
N.A.I.C.S.: 236220
Cynthia Schultz *(CEO)*
John Brown *(Dir-Safety)*
Lawrence Peterson *(Sr VP-Bus Dev & HR)*
Amy Brown *(CFO)*

BRADCO INC.

107 11th Ave, Holbrook, AZ 86025
Tel.: (928) 524-3976
Web Site: http://www.bradcoinc.com
Year Founded: 1936
Petroleum Products & Services
N.A.I.C.S.: 457210
John Bradley *(Pres)*

BRADDOCK METALLURGICAL, INC.

14600 Duval Pl W, Jacksonville, FL
32218
Tel.: (904) 741-4777   **FL**
Web Site:
   https://www.braddockmt.com
Year Founded: 1953
Sales Range: $1-9.9 Million

Emp.: 46
Metal Heat Treating
N.A.I.C.S.: 332811
Stephen Braddock *(CEO)*
George Gieger *(Pres)*
Cynthia Earl *(CFO)*
Griff Braddock *(Gen Mgr-Tampa)*
William Schultz *(Gen Mgr)*
Tim Waters *(Gen Mgr)*
Mark Yost *(Gen Mgr)*
Jeff Young *(Gen Mgr)*

Subsidiaries:

Braddock Caribe Metallurgical,
Corp.   (1)
Industrial Luchetti, Bayamon, PR 00960
Tel.: (787) 787-1919
Web Site: http://www.braddockmt.com
Emp.: 13
Metal Heat Treating
N.A.I.C.S.: 332811
Clayton Braddock *(Gen Mgr)*

Braddock Heat Treating Co., Inc. (1)
123 Chimney Rock Rd, Bridgewater, NJ
08807
Tel.: (732) 356-2906
Web Site: http://www.braddockmt.com
Emp.: 19
Metal Heat Treating
N.A.I.C.S.: 332811
William Schultz *(Gen Mgr)*

Braddock Metallurgical - Atlanta (1)
1590 Huber St NW, Atlanta, GA 30318
Tel.: (404) 355-6952
Web Site: http://www.braddockmt.com
Emp.: 20
Metal Heat Treating
N.A.I.C.S.: 332811
Tim Waters *(Gen Mgr)*

Braddock Metallurgical - Daytona (1)
400 Fentress Blvd, Daytona Beach, FL
32114
Tel.: (386) 323-1500
Web Site: http://www.braddockmt.com
Sales Range: $10-24.9 Million
Emp.: 20
Metal Heat Treating
N.A.I.C.S.: 332811
Jeff Young *(Gen Mgr)*
Bill Braddock *(Exec VP)*

Braddock Metallurgical -
Jacksonville   (1)
14600 Duval Pl W, Jacksonville, FL 32218
Tel.: (904) 741-4777
Web Site: http://www.braddockempty.com
Emp.: 13
Metal Treat Heating
N.A.I.C.S.: 332811
Mitch Evans *(Gen Mgr)*

Braddock Metallurgical - Tampa (1)
6502 S 78th St, Riverview, FL 33578
Tel.: (813) 672-7722
Web Site: http://www.braddock.com
Emp.: 15
Metal Heat Treating
N.A.I.C.S.: 332811
Griff Braddock *(Gen Mgr)*

Braddock Metallurgical Aerospace -
Boynton Beach   (1)
507 Industrial Way, Boynton Beach, FL
33426
Tel.: (561) 622-2200
Web Site: http://www.braddockmt.com
Emp.: 9
Metal Heat Treating
N.A.I.C.S.: 332811
Steve Hutchinson *(Gen Mgr)*

BRADDOCKMATTHEWS-BARRETT, LLC

28 W 44th St Ste 914, New York, NY
10036
Tel.: (212) 257-4422
Web Site:
   https://www.braddockmatthews.com
Emp.: 100
Asset Management & Financial Ser-
vices; Staffing & Recruiting Services
N.A.I.C.S.: 561311

David Barrett *(Partner)*

Subsidiaries:

David Barrett Partners LLC.   (1)
230 Park Ave Ste 450, New York, NY
10169
Tel.: (212) 710-8840
Web Site:
   http://www.davidbarrettpartners.com
Human Resource Consulting Services
N.A.I.C.S.: 541612
Darryl Adachi *(Co-Founder)*
David Barrett *(Co-Founder)*

BRADEN PARTNERS L.P

773 San Marin Dr Ste 2230, Novato,
CA 94945
Tel.: (415) 893-1518
Web Site: http://www.ppsc.com
Year Founded: 1978
Home Oxygen & Respiratory Medica-
tions Equipment & Services
N.A.I.C.S.: 621610
Tia Myers *(Ops Mgr)*

BRADENTON FUEL OIL

6116 21st St E, Bradenton, FL
34203-5005
Tel.: (941) 746-0342
Web Site:
   http://www.bradentonfueloil.com
Rev.: $10,300,000
Emp.: 10
Heating Oil Dealers
N.A.I.C.S.: 457210
David Baumgartner *(Mgr)*
Sally Baumgartner *(Co-Owner)*

BRADFORD BANCORP, INC.

100 E College Ave, Greenville, IL
62246
Tel.: (618) 664-2200   **DE**
Web Site:
   https://www.bradfordbank.com
Year Founded: 1867
Sales Range: $10-24.9 Million
Emp.: 65
Bank Holding Company
N.A.I.C.S.: 522110
James C. Keaster *(VP-HR)*
Robert D. Tompkins *(VP)*
Randy Alderman *(VP-Community Rels)*
Frank R. Joy Jr. *(CEO)*
Cathy Eyman *(VP-DP)*
Pennie Slatton *(Asst VP-Consumer Lending)*
Richard Knebel *(Sr VP)*
Renee Fuller *(Asst Mgr-Marine Branch)*
Janet Renko *(VP-Ops)*
Mike Ennen *(Sr VP)*

Subsidiaries:

The Bradford National Bank of
Greenville   (1)
100 E College Ave, Greenville, IL
62246-1144   (100%)
Tel.: (618) 664-2200
Web Site: http://www.bradfordbank.com
Sales Range: $25-49.9 Million
Emp.: 50
Commericial Banking
N.A.I.C.S.: 522110
James C. Keaster *(Sec & Sr VP)*
Terrance Barth *(VP)*
Robert D. Tompkins *(VP)*
Randy Alderman *(Asst VP & Dir-Community Rels)*

BRADFORD COMPANY

13500 Quincy St, Holland, MI 49424-
9460
Tel.: (616) 399-3000   **MI**
Web Site: http://www.bradfordco.com
Year Founded: 1924
Sales Range: $100-124.9 Million
Emp.: 175

Mfr of Packaging Products & Materi-
als Handling Systems
N.A.I.C.S.: 322211
Mark Feenstra *(Engrg Dir & Mfg)*
Judson A. Bradford *(CEO)*

Subsidiaries:

Bradford Systems Malaysia Sdn.
Bhd.   (1)
2013 Solok Perusahaan 3 Kawasan MIEL,
13600, Prai, Penang, Malaysia
Tel.: (60) 4 640 3998
Packaging Products Mfr
N.A.I.C.S.: 326112

Bradford de Mexico, S. de R.L. de
C.V   (1)
Parque Industrial Kalos Platon No 110, Apo-
daca, 66603, Nuevo Leon, Mexico
Tel.: (52) 81 8748 9100
Web Site: http://www.bradfordcompany.com
Packaging Products Mfr
N.A.I.C.S.: 326112

BRADFORD EQUITIES MANAGEMENT, LLC

360 Hamilton Ave, White Plains, NY
10601
Tel.: (914) 922-7171
Web Site:
   http://www.bradfordequities.com
Sales Range: Less than $1 Million
Emp.: 2
Fiscal Year-end: 12/31/15
Investor
N.A.I.C.S.: 541820
Neil J. Taylor *(CFO & Principal)*
Richard A. Rudolph *(Mng Dir)*

BRADFORD FAIRWAY SALES & LEASING INC.

472 E Main St, Bradford, PA 16701
Tel.: (814) 368-7166
Web Site:
   https://www.bradfordfairwayford.com
Sales Range: $10-24.9 Million
Emp.: 35
Car Whslr
N.A.I.C.S.: 441110
Len A. Toy *(Pres)*

BRADFORD INDUSTRIAL SUPPLY

120 NE Hill St, Oklahoma City, OK
73154
Tel.: (405) 525-8855
Web Site:
   http://www.bradfordsupply.com
Year Founded: 1963
Sales Range: $10-24.9 Million
Emp.: 40
Air Conditioning Equipment
N.A.I.C.S.: 423730
Robert H. Bradford *(Owner)*
Mike Simons *(Pres)*
Dick Giles *(Mgr-Sls)*
Marge Thomas *(Treas & Sec)*
Frank Jarvis *(Mgr-Pur)*

BRADFORD MARINE, INC.

8020 Landers Rd, North Little Rock,
AR 72117
Tel.: (501) 835-1735   **AR**
Web Site:
   https://www.bradfordmarine.com
Year Founded: 1971
Sales Range: $10-24.9 Million
Emp.: 50
Boat Dealers
N.A.I.C.S.: 441222

BRADFORD OIL COMPANY, INC.

530 Wates River Rd, Bradford, VT
05033
Tel.: (802) 333-9984   **VT**
Web Site: http://www.bradfordoil.com

Bradford Oil Company, Inc.—(Continued)

Year Founded: 1969
Sales Range: $75-99.9 Million
Emp.: 4
Producer & Retailer of Petroleum Products; Operator of Service Stations
N.A.I.C.S.: 424720
Hazel Pratt (Controller)

Subsidiaries:

P&H Transportation (1)
PO Box 443, North Haverhill, NH 03774-0458 (100%)
Tel.: (603) 787-2085
Web Site:
http://www.pandhtransportation.com
Sales Range: $10-24.9 Million
Trucking Carrier
N.A.I.C.S.: 484230
George Pratt (Owner)
Gene Pushee (Pres)

BRADFORD PRODUCTS, LLC.

2101 Enterprise Dr NE, Leland, NC 28451
Tel.: (910) 791-2202
Web Site:
https://www.bradfordproducts.com
Sales Range: $10-24.9 Million
Emp.: 100
Specialty Trade Contractors
N.A.I.C.S.: 238910
Michael Brodeur (Principal)

BRADFORD SUPPLY COMPANY

801 E Main St, Robinson, IL 62454
Tel.: (618) 544-3171
Web Site:
https://www.bradfordsupplycompany.com
Year Founded: 1961
Sales Range: $10-24.9 Million
Emp.: 85
Oil Refining Machinery, Equipment & Supplies Distr
N.A.I.C.S.: 423830
David L. McDaniel (Exec VP)
Jon R. Chamblin (Pres)
Charles J. Miller (Dir-Safety)
Janice V. Wagy (Comptroller)
R. J. Rains (VP-Sls)
Marleen Benson (Office Mgr)
David Chamblin (Exec VP)
David Coughlin (Mgr-Salem)
Brian Melton (Asst Mgr)
Randy Bell (Mgr)
Brett Hartrich (Mgr)
Mike Pickel (Mgr)
Chad Smith (Mgr)

BRADFORD-WHITE CORPORATION

725 Talamore Dr, Ambler, PA 19002-1815
Tel.: (215) 641-9400 DE
Web Site:
https://www.bradfordwhitecorporation.com
Year Founded: 1881
Sales Range: $10-24.9 Million
Emp.: 1,100
Water Heaters For Residential, Commercial & Industrial Applications; Available In Gas, Electric, Oil & Solar Power Mfr
N.A.I.C.S.: 333414
Bruce Carnevale (CEO)
F. D. Vattimo (Dir-Mktg)
Eric Lannes (Gen Mgr)
Ken Mitchell (Controller)

Subsidiaries:

Heat-Flo, Inc. (1)
15 Megan Ct, Uxbridge, MA 01569

Tel.: (508) 422-9880
Web Site: http://www.heat-flo.com
Rev.: $1,500,000
Emp.: 15
Plate Work Mfr
N.A.I.C.S.: 332313
Stephen Ross (Gen Mgr)
George Celorier (Pres)

Keltech, Inc. (1)
729 S Grove St, Delton, MI 49046
Tel.: (269) 623-6395
Web Site: http://www.keltech-inc.com
Sales Range: $1-9.9 Million
Emp.: 16
Water Heating Solutions Services
N.A.I.C.S.: 423620
Brandon Lorenz (Product Mgr)
John Gingrass (Mgr-Sls-Reg)
Jon Dommisse (Dir-Product Dev)
Kris Alderson (Sr Mgr-Mktg)
Susan Manley (Mgr-Customer Svc)

LAARS Heating Systems Co. (1)
20 Industrial Way, Rochester, NH 03867
Tel.: (603) 335-6300
Web Site: http://www.laars.com
Emp.: 160
Hydronic Boiler Mfr
N.A.I.C.S.: 332410
Cindy Taylor (Mgr-Pur)
Mark Hughes (Mgr-Svc-Natl)

BRADLEY & MONTGOMERY ADVERTISING

1 Monument Cir 2F, Indianapolis, IN 46204
Tel.: (317) 423-1745
Web Site: http://www.bamideas.com
Year Founded: 1999
Advertising Agencies
N.A.I.C.S.: 541810
Mark Bradley (Principal)
Scott Montgomery (Principal)

BRADLEY ARANT BOULT CUMMINGS LLP

1819 5th Ave N, Birmingham, AL 35203
Tel.: (205) 521-8000
Web Site: http://www.babc.com
Year Founded: 1871
Emp.: 550
Intellectual Property Rights Legal Services
N.A.I.C.S.: 541110
Scott E. Adams (Partner)
Hal Albritton (Partner)
Dana C. Lumsden (Partner)
Jon H. Patterson (Partner)
Colin G. Moorhouse (Partner)
John Mark Goodman (Partner)
Jason R. Bushby (Partner)
Luke D. Martin (Partner)
Nicholas J. Landau (Partner)
Edmund S. Sauer (Partner)
Keith S. Anderson (Partner)
C. Jason Avery (Partner)
Kyle C. Hankey (Partner)
Stuart M. Maxey (Partner)
Michael F. Walker (Partner)
Ryan L. Beaver (Partner)
Johanna L. Jumper (Partner)
Susan A. Weber (Partner)
Phillip Walker (Partner-Nashville)
Alysa J. Ward (Partner)
Edwin G. Rice (Partner)
Robert C. Rasmussen (Partner)
Mark A. Hanley (Partner)
Sharon Docherty Danco (Partner)
Michael B. Colgan (Partner)
Timothy A. Andreu (Partner)
Jeffery Beatrice (Partner-Washington)
Heather Cain Hutchings (Partner)
Haydn J. Richards (Partner)
A. Michelle Canter (Partner)
J. Mark Hendrick (CIO)
Lela Hollabaugh (Mng Partner-Nashville)
Elizabeth Ferrell (Partner)

J. Thomas Richie (Partner)
Ginger Carroll Gray (Partner)
Tiffany J. deGruy (Partner)
Whitt Steineker (Partner)
Brad Robertson (Partner)
Craig Mayfield (Mng Partner-Tampa)
Corby O. Anderson (Partner-Charlotte)
Christopher C. Lam (Partner-Charlotte)
Matthew S. DeAntonio (Sr Atty-Charlotte)
Zachary A. Madonia (Sr Atty)
Brian O'Neill (Sr Atty-Washington)
Patrick L. Alexander (Partner)
Paul A. Alexis (Partner)
Danielle Decker (Sec)
Debra Jones (Sec)
Denise DeArman (Sec)
Emily Powell (Sec)
Gina Wilhite (Sec)
Lisa Davis (Sec)
Patti Burns (Sec)
Sherry Barber (Sec)
Julia Gruenewald Bernstein (Partner-Real Estate, Banking & Fin Svcs)
Andrew S. Nix (Partner-Corp & Securities)
Timothy W. Gregg (Partner-Corp & Securities)
Walter Little (Partner-Tampa)
Trisha A. Culp (Sr Atty)
Maggie Johnson Cornelius (Partner)
Kane Burnette (Partner)
C. Meade Hartfield (Partner)
Nicholas A. Danella (Partner)
Stephen Hinton (Partner)
B. Radcliff Menge (Partner)
Mark S. Wierman (Partner)
Jose D. Vega (Partner)
Avery Simmons (Partner)
Troy M. Carnrite (Partner)
S. David Smith (Partner)
Lee Birchall (Partner)
Thomas A. Wilson (Partner)
Jonathan M. Skeeters (Chm & Mng Partner)
Dawn Helms Sharff (Mng Partner)
Richard A. Sayles (Partner-Dallas)
John M. Perry Jr. (Partner)
Charles B. Hill III (Partner)
Edward S. Sledge IV (Partner)
James E. Long Jr. (Partner)
George H. Cate III (Partner)
William T. Thistle II (Partner)
T. Parker Griffin Jr. (Partner)
James W. Porter III (Partner)
Charles A. Roberts Jr. (Partner)

BRADLEY BANCORP, INC.

200 N 10th St, Centerville, IA 52544
Tel.: (641) 437-4500 IA
Web Site: http://www.iowatrust.bank
Year Founded: 1974
Sales Range: $1-9.9 Million
Bank Holding Company
N.A.I.C.S.: 551111
Jeffrey T. Young (Chm, Pres & CEO)

Subsidiaries:

Iowa Trust and Savings Bank (1)
200 N 10th St, Centerville, IA 52544
Tel.: (641) 437-4500
Web Site: http://www.iowatrust.bank
Sales Range: $1-9.9 Million
Emp.: 31
Commercial Banking
N.A.I.C.S.: 522110
Jeffrey T. Young (Chm)
Tracy Alexander (Officer-Trust & VP-Fin Svcs)
Mary Craver (VP-Ops)
David Yahnke (Sr VP-Lending)
Dustin Harvey (Officer-Mktg & Sls)
Xaviera Scott (Officer-Loan)

BRADLEY BANCSHARES, INC.

104 S Main St, Warren, AR 71671
Tel.: (870) 226-2601 AR
Year Founded: 1981
Sales Range: $1-9.9 Million
Emp.: 32
Bank Holding Company
N.A.I.C.S.: 551111
Freddie Mobley (Pres)
Mary Haynes (Asst VP)

Subsidiaries:

First State Bank of Warren (1)
104 S Main St, Warren, AR 71671
Tel.: (870) 226-2601
Web Site: http://www.firststatewarren.com
Rev.: $9,000,000
Emp.: 30
Commericial Banking
N.A.I.C.S.: 522110
Hugh A. Quimby (Exec VP)

BRADLEY CALDWELL, INC.

200 Kiwanis Blvd, Hazleton, PA 18201
Tel.: (570) 455-7511
Web Site:
https://www.bradleycaldwell.com
Year Founded: 1930
Sales Range: $1-9.9 Million
Emp.: 400
Veterinary & Gardening Supplies Sales
N.A.I.C.S.: 444240
Ed Swoboda (Mgr)

BRADLEY CHEVROLET INC.

711 N Lake Havasu Ave, Lake Havasu City, AZ 86403
Tel.: (928) 302-2787
Web Site:
https://www.bradleychevrolet.com
Sales Range: $10-24.9 Million
Emp.: 40
Owner & Operator of Car Dealerships
N.A.I.C.S.: 441110

BRADLEY COATING INC.

410 38th Ave, Saint Charles, IL 60174
Tel.: (630) 443-8424
Web Site:
http://www.bradleygroupcoatings.com
Year Founded: 1984
Sales Range: $10-24.9 Million
Emp.: 100
Adhesives
N.A.I.C.S.: 325520
John Bradley (Pres)

BRADLEY COUNTY MEDICAL CENTER

404 S Bradley St, Warren, AR 71671
Tel.: (870) 226-3731 AR
Web Site:
https://www.bradleymedical.com
Year Founded: 1996
Sales Range: $10-24.9 Million
Emp.: 284
Community Health Care Services
N.A.I.C.S.: 621498
Clayton Winters (Dir-Matls Mgmt)
Ladonna Goodwin (Dir-Respiratory Therapy)
Tammy Hensley (Dir-Home Health)
Keith Wright (Dir-Maintenance)
Tiffany Holland (Chief Nursing Officer)
Lathan Hairston (Vice Chm)
Gingy Cuthbertson (Sec)
Freddie Mobley (Chm)
Brandon Gorman (CFO)
Rex Jones (CEO)
Charlotte Laster (Dir-Radiology)
Mitzy Sullivan (Sr Dir-Care Program)
Suzette Russell (Dir-Social Svcs)

BRADLEY EXCAVATING, INC.

2220 Busch Ave, Colorado Springs, CO 80904
Tel.: (719) 685-9755
Web Site:
https://www.bradleyexcavating.com
Year Founded: 2003
Sales Range: $1-9.9 Million
Emp.: 20
Excavation & Construction
N.A.I.C.S.: 238910
Bradley Grubaugh (Pres & CEO)
Jonathan Thorne (Gen Mgr)

BRADLEY HARDWARE INC.
6930 Arlington Rd, Bethesda, MD 20814-5206
Tel.: (301) 654-5688
Web Site:
https://www.strosniders.com
Year Founded: 1953
Sales Range: $10-24.9 Million
Emp.: 125
Hardware Retailer
N.A.I.C.S.: 326199
Chuck Kelley (Mgr-Store)

BRADLEY INVESTMENTS, INC.
1690 Industrial Blvd, Lake Havasu City, AZ 86403
Tel.: (928) 855-1191
Web Site:
https://www.bradleyford.com
Year Founded: 1991
Sales Range: $10-24.9 Million
Emp.: 75
New Car Retailer
N.A.I.C.S.: 441110
Michael J. Bradley (Pres)

BRADLEY REPRESENTATIVES
PO Box 1014, Saint Charles, IL 60174
Tel.: (630) 587-0909
Rev.: $20,000,000
Emp.: 7
Electronic Parts
N.A.I.C.S.: 423690
Diane Bradley (Pres)

BRADMARK TECHNOLOGIES INC.
4265 San Felipe St 700, Houston, TX 77027
Tel.: (713) 621-2808
Web Site: http://www.bradmark.com
Rev.: $10,000,000
Emp.: 25
Utility Computer Software
N.A.I.C.S.: 513210
C. Bradley Tashenberg (Founder, Pres & CEO)
John Avery (Mgr-Mktg-Bradmark Technologies)
William Smith (VP-Worldwide Ops)
Steve Capelli (Chm)

BRADSBY GROUP
1700 Broadway Ste 1500, Denver, CO 80290
Tel.: (303) 813-8100
Web Site:
https://www.bradsbygroup.com
Sales Range: $10-24.9 Million
Emp.: 60
Employment Agencies
N.A.I.C.S.: 561311
Greg Peay (Founder)

BRADSHAW ADVERTISING
811 NW 19th Ave, Portland, OR 97209-1401
Tel.: (503) 221-5000   OR
Web Site:
https://www.bradshawads.com
Year Founded: 1986
Sales Range: $10-24.9 Million

Emp.: 15
Advertising Agencies
N.A.I.C.S.: 541810
Emilie Timmer (Dir-Media)

BRADSHAW AUTOMOTIVE GROUP, INC.
14000 E Wade Hampton Blvd, Greer, SC 29651
Tel.: (864) 879-7111
Sales Range: $25-49.9 Million
Emp.: 110
Car Whslr
N.A.I.C.S.: 441110
William Bradshaw (Pres)

BRADSHAW CONSTRUCTION CORP
175 W Liberty Rd, Eldersburg, MD 21784-9381
Tel.: (410) 970-8300
Web Site:
https://www.bradshawcc.com
Sales Range: $10-24.9 Million
Emp.: 60
Underground Utilities Contractor
N.A.I.C.S.: 237110
Joe D. Bradshaw (VP)
J. Twomey (Mgr-HR)
Eric Eisold (Area Mgr)
Andrea Harrison (Mgr-Accts Payable)

BRADSHAW INTERNATIONAL, INC.
9409 Buffalo Ave, Rancho Cucamonga, CA 91730-6012
Tel.: (909) 476-3884   CA
Web Site: http://www.goodcook.com
Year Founded: 1966
Sales Range: $125-149.9 Million
Emp.: 350
Retailer of Kitchenware
N.A.I.C.S.: 423220
Brett Bradshaw (Pres-Bradshaw Holdings)
Jeff Megorden (COO)
Sandip Grewal (CFO)

Subsidiaries:

Clean Ones Corporation   (1)
122 SW 3rd Ave, Portland, OR 97204
Tel.: (503) 224-5211
Web Site: http://www.cleanones.com
Rev.: $1,900,000
Emp.: 7
Develops & Manufactures Gloves for a Variety of Industries
N.A.I.C.S.: 458110
Scott Pitts (Dir-Sls)
Rob Michaelson (Pres)

BRADY DISTRIBUTING COMPANY INC.
2708 Yorkmont Rd, Charlotte, NC 28208-7324
Tel.: (704) 357-6284   NC
Web Site: http://www.bradydist.com
Year Founded: 1944
Sales Range: $25-49.9 Million
Emp.: 80
Vending Machine & Other Coin Operated Amusement Equipment Distr & Maintenance Services
N.A.I.C.S.: 423850
Jon P. Brady (Pres)

BRADY ENTERPRISES, INC.
167 Moore Rd, East Weymouth, MA 02189-2332
Tel.: (781) 337-5000
Web Site:
https://bradyenterprises.com
Year Founded: 1964
Dry Food Products Mixing & Packaging Services; Stuffing & Seasonings Mfr
N.A.I.C.S.: 311942

Paul Lenihan (Sr VP-Contract Mfg)
Chuck Kozubal (Pres & CEO)

BRADY FARMS INC.
14786 Winans St, West Olive, MI 49640
Tel.: (616) 842-3916
Web Site: http://www.bradyfarms.com
Year Founded: 1961
Sales Range: $10-24.9 Million
Emp.: 112
Blueberry Product Whslr
N.A.I.C.S.: 111334
Erickson Lee (Office Mgr)
Sanjuana Chavez (Mgr)

BRADY MARKETING COMPANY
153 S Ave, Alamo, CA 94507
Tel.: (925) 676-1300   CA
Web Site:
http://www.bradymarketing.com
Year Founded: 1976
Sales Range: $75-99.9 Million
Emp.: 25
Marketing & Consulting Services
N.A.I.C.S.: 541613
Frank Brady (Pres & CEO)

BRADY TRANE SERVICE, INC.
1915 N Church St, Greensboro, NC 27405-5631
Tel.: (336) 378-0680   NC
Web Site:
http://www.bradyservices.com
Year Founded: 1966
Sales Range: $10-24.9 Million
Emp.: 450
Refrigeration Service & Repair
N.A.I.C.S.: 811412
Donald J. Brady (Chm)
Jim Brady (Pres)
Al Kuhnemann (VP-Sls-Indirect)
Jeff Smith (VP-Ops-Svc)
Patrick Tonker (VP-Energy Svcs)
Brad Resler (VP)
Wendy Alexander (VP)
Brian Simpson (CFO)
Raynor Smith (COO & VP)

BRADY WARE & SCHOEN-FELD INC.
One South Main St, Dayton, OH 45402
Tel.: (937) 223-5247
Web Site: http://www.bradyware.com
Rev.: $10,000,000
Emp.: 100
Other Accounting Services
N.A.I.C.S.: 541219

Subsidiaries:

GrossDukeNelson & Co., P.C.   (1)
11175 Cicero Dr Ste 300, Alpharetta, GA 30022
Tel.: (770) 458-5000
Web Site: http://www.bradyware.com
Offices of Certified Public Accountants
N.A.I.C.S.: 541211
Teresa Snyder (Partner)

BRAEBURN INC.
450 Plymouth Rd Ste 400, Plymouth Meeting, PA 19462
Tel.: (610) 467-8680   DE
Web Site: https://braeburnrx.com
Year Founded: 2012
Pharmaceuticals Product Mfr
N.A.I.C.S.: 325412
Michael M. Derkacz (Pres & CEO)
Paul Johnson (Chief Comml Officer)
Richard Malamut (Chief Medical Officer)
Susan Franks (Sr VP & Head-Regulatory Affairs)
Ted Buckley (VP-Govt Affairs)
Seth L. Harrison (Chm)

BRAEGER COMPANY OF WISCONSIN INC.
4100 S 27th St, Milwaukee, WI 53221-1831
Tel.: (414) 281-5000   WI
Web Site: http://www.braeger.com
Year Founded: 1985
Sales Range: $25-49.9 Million
Emp.: 150
Dealer of New & Used Vehicles
N.A.I.C.S.: 441110
Todd M. Reardon (Pres)

Subsidiaries:

Braeger Chevrolet Inc.   (1)
4100 S 27th St, Milwaukee, WI 53221-1830
Tel.: (414) 281-5000
Web Site: http://www.braeger-parts.com
Sales Range: $25-49.9 Million
Emp.: 60
New & Used Car Dealership
N.A.I.C.S.: 441110
Todd M. Reardon (Pres)

Braeger Ford Inc.   (1)
4201 S 27th St, Milwaukee, WI 53221-1831   (100%)
Tel.: (414) 282-5300
Web Site: http://www.braeger.com
Sales Range: $10-24.9 Million
Emp.: 55
New & Used Car Dealerships
N.A.I.C.S.: 811111
Todd M. Reardon (Pres)

BRAEMONT CAPITAL MANAGEMENT LLC
3963 Maple Ave Ste 490, Dallas, TX 75219
Tel.: (214) 833-8880
Web Site: https://braemont.com
Privater Equity Firm
N.A.I.C.S.: 523940

Subsidiaries:

Loenbro, Inc.   (1)
409 14th St SW, Great Falls, MT 59404
Tel.: (406) 453-1542
Web Site: http://www.loenbro.com
Engineering & Industrial Construction Services
N.A.I.C.S.: 541330
Jon Leach (VP)

Subsidiary (Domestic):

Power Controls, Inc.   (2)
1205 W Center Ave, Denver, CO 80223
Tel.: (303) 777-3100
Web Site: http://www.powercontrols.com
Engineering & Industrial Construction Services
N.A.I.C.S.: 541330
Deb Nelson (Office Mgr-Acctg)
Jim Welch (Pres-Outside Sls)

BRAES CAPITAL LLC
6116 Skyline Dr Ste 108, Houston, TX 77057
Tel.: (713) 830-6094
Web Site: http://www.braescapital.net
Holding Company
N.A.I.C.S.: 551112
Alex Clary (Principal)

Subsidiaries:

Siege Technologies, LLC   (1)
540 N Commercial St, Manchester, NH 03101
Tel.: (603) 747-9800
Web Site: http://www.siegetechnologies.com
Research & Development in the Physical, Engineering & Life Sciences
N.A.I.C.S.: 541715
Jason Syversen (Co-Founder & CEO)
Joe Sharkey (CTO & VP)
Samuel Corbitt (Co-Founder & CFO)

BRAFTON, INCORPORATED
1 Winthrop Square Floor 5, Boston, MA 02110
Tel.: (617) 206-3040

Brafton, Incorporated—(Continued)

Web Site: http://www.brafton.com
Year Founded: 2007
Sales Range: $10-24.9 Million
Emp.: 184
Full-Spectrum Content Marketing Services to Increase Brand Authority, Website Traffic & Leads
N.A.I.C.S.: 541613
Katherine Griwert *(Dir-Mktg)*
Francis Ma *(VP-Content)*
Sarah Cugini *(Chief Client Officer)*
Meredith Farley *(VP-Product)*
Richard Pattinson *(CEO)*
Christine Rose *(Chief Comml Officer)*
Irene Manian *(VP-Fin)*
Paul Banas *(Founder)*
Stewart Snow *(CTO)*

BRAGG CRANE & RIGGING

6251 N Paramount Blvd, Long Beach, CA 90805
Tel.: (562) 984-2400
Web Site:
   http://www.braggnorcal.com
Sales Range: $10-24.9 Million
Emp.: 99
Heavy Construction Equipment Rental
N.A.I.C.S.: 238220
Gary Fowler *(Sls Mgr)*

BRAGG INVESTMENT COMPANY, INC.

6251 N Paramount Blvd, Long Beach, CA 90805-3714
Tel.: (562) 984-2400   **CA**
Web Site:
   http://www.braggcrane.com
Year Founded: 1946
Sales Range: $75-99.9 Million
Emp.: 1,000
Holding Company
N.A.I.C.S.: 561990
Mary Ann Pool *(Treas & Sec)*
Subsidiaries:

Bragg Crane & Rigging   **(1)**
6242 N Paramount Blvd, Long Beach, CA 90805
Tel.: (562) 984-2473
Web Site: http://www.braggcrane.com
Crane Operation & Rigging Services
N.A.I.C.S.: 541990
Gary Fowler *(Sls Mgr)*

Bragg Crane Service   **(1)**
6251 Paramount Blvd, Long Beach, CA 90805
Tel.: (562) 984-2400
Web Site: http://www.braggcrane.com
Crane Rental Services
N.A.I.C.S.: 532412
Mike Roy *(Exec VP)*

Heavy Transport, Inc.   **(1)**
6251 Paramount Blvd, Long Beach, CA 90805
Tel.: (562) 984-2448
Web Site: http://www.braggcrane.com
Specialty Oversized, Multi-Dimensional & Large Capacity Trucking Services
N.A.I.C.S.: 484230
Bob Weyers *(Gen Mgr)*

BRAILLE INSTITUTE OF AMERICA

741 N Vermont Ave, Los Angeles, CA 90029
Tel.: (323) 663-1111   **CA**
Web Site:
   http://www.brailleinstitute.org
Year Founded: 1961
Sales Range: $25-49.9 Million
Emp.: 301
Visually Impaired Care Services
N.A.I.C.S.: 623990

Peter A. Mindnich *(Pres)*
Anthony Joji Taketa *(Gen Counsel, Sec & VP)*
Rezaur Rahman *(VP-Fin)*
Gene M. Mathiowetz *(VP-Reg Programs)*
David L. Burkhardt *(VP-Philanthropy)*
Nancy N. Niebrugge *(VP-Program Content)*
George E. Thomas *(Chm)*
David McCaslin *(Dir-Library Svcs)*
Sergio Oliva *(VP-Programs & Svcs)*

BRAILSFORD & DUNLAVEY

1140 Connecticut Ave NW Ste 400, Washington, DC 20036
Tel.: (202) 289-4455
Web Site:
   http://www.programmanagers.com
Year Founded: 1993
Sales Range: $10-24.9 Million
Emp.: 84
Program Management Services for Governmental Agencies & Private-Sector Organizations
N.A.I.C.S.: 541618
Paul Brailsford *(Co-Founder & CEO)*
Chris Dunlavey *(Pres)*
William Bannister *(Controller)*
Chris McCay *(Dir-IT)*
Brad Noyes *(Sr VP)*
Matthew Bohannon *(Reg VP-West Coast)*
Doug Kotlove *(VP-Bus Dev & Mktg)*
Andrew Perez *(Project Mgr)*
Ann Pak *(Mgr-HR)*
Bill Mykins *(VP)*
Deisy Brangman *(Project Mgr)*
Joyce Fasano *(VP)*
Kevin Keegan *(VP)*
Luke Mitchell *(Project Mgr)*
Mahboud Nobakht *(Project Mgr)*
Sam Jung *(Project Mgr)*

BRAIN POWER INC.

4470 SW 74th Ave, Miami, FL 33155
Tel.: (305) 264-4465
Web Site: https://www.callbpi.com
Year Founded: 1970
Sales Range: $10-24.9 Million
Emp.: 40
Optical Product Mfr
N.A.I.C.S.: 339112
Herbert Wertheim *(Chm & CEO)*
Phil Bartick *(Mgr-IT)*
Subsidiaries:

Brain Power International Ltd.   **(1)**
One Prospect Way, Rugby, CV21 3UU, Warwickshire, United Kingdom
Tel.: (44) 1788 568686
Web Site: http://www.callbpi.com
Emp.: 6
Optical Product Mfr
N.A.I.C.S.: 333310
Herbert Wertheim *(Chm)*

BRAINERD COMMUNICATORS, INC.

521 5th Ave 8th Fl, New York, NY 10175
Tel.: (212) 986-6667   **DE**
Year Founded: 1994
Rev.: $3,100,000
Emp.: 30
Fiscal Year-end: 06/30/06
Advetising Agency
N.A.I.C.S.: 541810
Diana Brainerd *(Pres)*
Anthony Herrling *(Mng Dir)*
Jeff Majtyka *(Mng Dir)*
Christian Plunkett *(Mng Dir)*
Michael Smargiassi *(Mng Dir)*
Joseph LoBello *(Mng Dir)*
Raymond Yeung *(Mng Dir)*
Denise Roche *(Sr VP)*
Corey Kinger *(Sr VP)*

Scott Cianciulli *(Sr VP)*
Brad Edwards *(VP)*
Nancy Zakhary *(Sr VP)*
Giovanni Garcia *(CFO)*
Maggie Duquin *(VP)*
Anna Yen *(Mng Dir)*

BRAINIUM INC.

66 Hanover St Ste 101, Manchester, NH 03101
Tel.: (603) 624-2800
Web Site:
   http://www.brainiumevents.com
Year Founded: 2000
Sales Range: Less than $1 Million
Emp.: 6
N.A.I.C.S.: 541810
Kathryn Conway *(Partner)*
Pete Lecours *(Partner)*

BRAINLAB INC.

3 Westbrook Corp Ctr, Westchester, IL 60154
Tel.: (708) 409-1343   **CA**
Web Site: http://www.brainlab.com
Year Founded: 1861
Sales Range: $10-24.9 Million
Emp.: 450
Medical Equipment & Supplies Distr
N.A.I.C.S.: 423430
Stefan Vilsmeier *(Founder, Pres & CEO)*
Tim Koopman *(Dir-Fin)*
Ann Marie *(Mgr-Mktg Comm)*
Subsidiaries:

BrainLAB France   **(1)**
Tour Ariane, 5 Pl De La Pyramide, 92088, Paris, France   **(100%)**
Tel.: (33) 00155681075
Web Site: http://www.brainlab.com
Sales Range: $10-24.9 Million
Emp.: 10
Disbributor of Medical Equipment & Supplies
N.A.I.C.S.: 456199

BRAINS ON FIRE, INC.

148 River St Ste 100, Greenville, SC 29601
Tel.: (864) 676-9663   **SC**
Web Site:
   http://www.brainsonfire.com
Year Founded: 1982
Sales Range: $1-9.9 Million
Advetising Agency
N.A.I.C.S.: 541810
Robbin Phillips *(Pres-Courageous)*
Greg Ramsey *(Designer)*
Greg Cordell *(Chief Inspiration Officer)*
Jack Welch *(Media Strategist)*
Alison Quarles *(Graphic Designer)*
Cathy Harrison *(Acct Mgr)*
Geno Church *(Officer-Word of Mouth Inspiration)*
Megan Byrd *(Dir-Traffic & Production)*
Brandy Amidon *(CFO)*
Mary Susan Henderson *(Office Mgr)*
Sean Madden *(Creative Dir & Sr Designer)*
Laura Garvin *(Mgr-Community)*
Moe Rice *(Mgr-Community)*
Subsidiaries:

Brains on Fire, Inc. - Los Angeles   **(1)**
1800 S Brand Blvd Ste 122, Los Angeles, CA 91204-2903
Tel.: (818) 638-2617
Web Site: http://www.brainsonfire.com
Advetising Agency
N.A.I.C.S.: 541810
Benjamin Hart *(Principal & Strategist-Design)*

BRAINSELL TECHNOLOGIES, LLC

458 Boston St Fl 2 Ste 1, Topsfield, MA 01983
Tel.: (978) 887-3870
Web Site: http://www.brainsell.net
Year Founded: 1994
Emp.: 4
Engineering Services
N.A.I.C.S.: 541330
Kellie Pitt *(VP-ERP Practice)*
Jacqueline White *(Gen Counsel)*
Sonja Fridell *(Pres)*
Ross Jones *(VP-Sls Engrg)*
Deven Pearson *(Mgr-Bus Dev)*
Michelle Batchelder *(Controller)*
Cat Stone *(Dir-Mktg)*
Theresa Conway *(COO)*
Kevin Cook *(Exec VP)*
Subsidiaries:

Aether Consulting Inc.   **(1)**
8369 Windstone Ct, Goodrich, MI 48438
Tel.: (586) 939-5869
Web Site: http://www.aetherconsulting.com
Software & Technology Development Services
N.A.I.C.S.: 513210
Jerry Eisinger *(Founder & Pres)*
Theresa Ziegler *(Project Mgr)*

BRAINSTORM CORPORATION

241 S 3rd Ave Ste 1, La Puente, CA 91746
Tel.: (626) 330-0636
Web Site:
   https://www.brainstormco.com
Year Founded: 2005
Sales Range: $10-24.9 Million
Emp.: 20
Sales of Name-Brand Consumer Electronic Products & Accessories
N.A.I.C.S.: 449210

BRAINSTORMUSA LLC

8800 Roswell Rd Ste 200, Atlanta, GA 30350
Tel.: (770) 587-5880
Web Site:
   http://www.brainstormusa.com
Sales Range: $10-24.9 Million
Emp.: 50
Educational Aids & Electronic Training Materials
N.A.I.C.S.: 423430
Joe Galluccio *(Pres & CEO)*
Brauch Pappo *(CFO)*
Luis Nunez *(Dir-Creative)*
Umberto Aguilar *(Mgr-Call Center)*

BRAINTREE ELECTRIC LIGHT DEPARTMENT

150 Potter Rd, Braintree, MA 02184
Tel.: (781) 348-2353
Web Site: https://www.beld.com
Year Founded: 1892
Sales Range: $150-199.9 Million
Emp.: 500
Electric, Internet & Cable Television Service Supplier
N.A.I.C.S.: 221122
James P. Regan *(Vice Chm)*

BRAINWARE, INC.

20110 Ashbrook Pl Ste 150, Ashburn, VA 20147
Tel.: (703) 948-5800
Web Site: http://www.brainware.com
Sales Range: $10-24.9 Million
Emp.: 100
High-Volume Document Processing & Data Extraction Services
N.A.I.C.S.: 518210
Stuart Neale *(Acct Exec)*

BRAKE-O-RAMA INC.

145 US Hwy 46 W, Lodi, NJ 07644
Tel.: (973) 779-7743

Web Site: http://www.brake-o-
rama.com
Year Founded: 1949
Sales Range: $10-24.9 Million
Emp.: 35
Automotive Repair & Maintenance
Services; Tire Distr
N.A.I.C.S.: 811111
Eugene De Angelo *(Owner & Pres)*

Subsidiaries:

Brake-O-Rama   (1)
234 Scotland Rd, Orange, NJ 07050-1424
Tel.: (973) 678-8473
Web Site: http://brake-o-rama.com
Sales Range: $10-24.9 Million
Emp.: 3
Automotive Repair & Maintenance Services;
Tire Distr
N.A.I.C.S.: 811111

BRAKEBUSH BROTHERS INC.
N4993 6th Dr, Westfield, WI 53964-
8200
Tel.: (608) 296-2121   **WI**
Web Site:
https://www.brakebush.com
Year Founded: 1925
Sales Range: $10-24.9 Million
Emp.: 100
Poultry Slaughtering & Processing
N.A.I.C.S.: 311615
Carl Brakebush *(Pres)*
Rob Caradonna *(Dir-Bus Dev)*
Dan Caron *(Mgr-Sls-Northeast)*
Glenn Jenisch *(Mgr-Bus Dev)*

BRAKEQUIP, LLC
3143 Regal Dr, Alcoa, TN 37701
Tel.: (865) 251-9193
Web Site: https://www.brakequip.com
Year Founded: 2002
Sales Range: $1-9.9 Million
Emp.: 12
Mfr of Automotive Hoses & Tubes,
Including all Brake & Clutch Hoses
N.A.I.C.S.: 326220
Fred Anderson *(Owner)*

BRAKES PLUS CORPORA-TION
6911 S Yosemite St, Englewood, CO
80112
Tel.: (303) 221-8600
Web Site: http://www.brakesplus.com
Sales Range: $25-49.9 Million
Emp.: 500
Brake Repair, Automotive
N.A.I.C.S.: 811114
Larry F. Pisciotta *(Founder & Chm)*
Dean P. Pisciotta *(Pres)*
Mark Pisciotta *(VP-Mktg)*
R. J. Pisciotta *(VP-Sls & Ops)*

BRAMAN IMPORTS, INC.
2060 Biscayne Blvd 2nd Fl, Miami,
FL 33137
Tel.: (305) 266-9900
Year Founded: 1980
Sales Range: $25-49.9 Million
Emp.: 133
Car Whslr
N.A.I.C.S.: 441110
Norman Braman *(Chm)*

BRAMAN MOTORS, INC.
2060 Biscayne Blvd, Miami, FL
33137
Tel.: (786) 577-5220   **FL**
Web Site:
https://www.bramanmotorsbmw.com
Year Founded: 1976
Sales Range: $200-249.9 Million
Emp.: 500
New & Used Car & Truck Dealer
N.A.I.C.S.: 441110

Norman Braman *(Owner)*
Ken Harte *(Gen Mgr)*
Bryan Innocent *(Supvr-
Reconditioning)*
Russ Bennett *(Mgr-Sls)*

Subsidiaries:

Braman Cadillac Inc.   (1)
2020 Biscayne Blvd, Miami, FL 33137
Tel.: (305) 576-6900
Web Site: http://www.braman.com
Rev.: $18,600,000
Emp.: 60
Automobiles, New & Used
N.A.I.C.S.: 441100
Norman Braman *(Owner)*
Vebra Allena *(Mgr-Mktg)*

BRAMCO INC.
1801 Watterson Trl, Louisville, KY
40232
Tel.: (502) 491-4000   **KY**
Web Site: https://www.bramco.com
Year Founded: 1923
Sales Range: $125-149.9 Million
Emp.: 450
Provides Construction & Mining Ser-
vices & Equipment
N.A.I.C.S.: 423810
Charles Leis *(Vice Chm)*
Michael Brennan *(Pres & COO)*
Charles Paradis *(VP-HR & Compli-
ance)*
Mike Paradis *(CFO & Exec VP)*

Subsidiaries:

Bramco Inc. - Certified Rental
Division   (1)
1801 Watterson Trl, Louisville, KY 40299
Tel.: (502) 491-4000
Web Site: http://www.certifiedrental.com
Emp.: 4
Construction Equipment Rental Services
N.A.I.C.S.: 532412
Steve Feelbach *(Branch Mgr)*

Bramco-MPS   (1)
PO Box 32230, Louisville, KY 40232-9970
Tel.: (502) 491-4000
Web Site: http://www.bramcomps.com
Emp.: 35
Construction Engineering Services
N.A.I.C.S.: 541330
Bill Corrie *(Gen Mgr)*

Brandeis Machinery & Supply
Company   (1)
1801 Watterson Trl, Louisville, KY
40299-2431   (100%)
Tel.: (502) 493-4300
Web Site:
http://www.brandeismachinery.com
Emp.: 62
Construction & Mining Equipment
N.A.I.C.S.: 423810
Gene Snowden Jr. *(Pres & COO)*
Lee Heffley *(VP & Mgr-Reg Sls)*
Bob Bisig *(Mgr-Parts)*
Mike Krow *(Mgr-Svc)*
Steve Seelbach *(Reg Mgr)*

BRAME SPECIALTY COM-PANY INC.
949 Wahington St, Durham, NC
27701
Tel.: (919) 598-1500   **NC**
Web Site: http://www.brameco.com
Year Founded: 1924
Sales Range: $25-49.9 Million
Emp.: 240
School Products
N.A.I.C.S.: 424130
James R. Garrison *(CFO)*
Randal A. Brame *(Pres)*
Ginnie Redd *(Dir-HR)*
Mercer Stanfield *(Sec & VP-Sls)*
Jan Moore *(Dir-Ops-School Products)*
Steve Somerville *(Mgr-Office Prod-
ucts)*
James B. Brame Jr. *(Chm & CEO)*

BRAMMER ENGINEERING INC.
400 Texas St Ste 600, Shreveport,
LA 71101
Tel.: (318) 429-2345
Web Site: http://www.brammer.com
Year Founded: 1968
Sales Range: $25-49.9 Million
Emp.: 55
Gas Field Services
N.A.I.C.S.: 213112
Keith J. Evans *(Pres)*
Fred Weeks *(Dir-Health, Safety &
Environment)*
Sherry Garrett *(Mgr-Acctg)*
Peyton Giddens *(Mgr-Safety)*

BRAN-ZAN CO. INC.
1631 Barclay Blvd, Buffalo Grove, IL
60089
Tel.: (847) 342-0000
Web Site: http://www.branzan.com
Rev.: $20,000,000
Emp.: 15
Potato Products, Dried & Dehydrated
N.A.I.C.S.: 311423
Steven Marlowe *(Pres)*

BRANAGH INC.
750 Kevin Ct, Oakland, CA 94621
Tel.: (510) 638-6455
Web Site:
https://www.branaghinc.com
Rev.: $33,997,388
Emp.: 30
Commercial & Office Building; New
Construction
N.A.I.C.S.: 236220
Rick Newacheck *(VP)*
Chris Nelson *(Controller)*

BRANCE KRACHY COMPANY, INC.
4411 Navigation Blvd, Houston, TX
77011-1035
Tel.: (713) 225-6661   **TX**
Web Site:
http://www.brancekrachy.com
Year Founded: 1932
Sales Range: $75-99.9 Million
Emp.: 100
Mfr & Retailer of Power Transmission
Equipment
N.A.I.C.S.: 423840
Brent Bertrand *(VP)*

Subsidiaries:

AC&C Companies, Inc.   (1)
4255 S Buckley Rd, Aurora, CO 80013
Tel.: (303) 680-7858
Web Site: http://www.rustnomor.com
Emp.: 6
Cathodic Protection Equipment Mfr
N.A.I.C.S.: 335999

JA Electronics Company   (1)
13715 N Promenade Blvd, Stafford, TX
77477
Tel.: (281) 879-9903
Web Site: http://www.jaelectronics.com
Emp.: 20
Electronic Components Mfr
N.A.I.C.S.: 334419
Michael Grace *(Mgr-Ops)*
C. M. Nelson *(VP)*

BRANCH CAPITAL PARTNERS LP
3340 Peachtree Rd NE Ste 600, At-
lanta, GA 30326
Tel.: (404) 832-8900
Web Site:
http://www.branchprop.com
Sales Range: $10-24.9 Million
Emp.: 20
Commercial Real Estate
N.A.I.C.S.: 531120

Nicholas B. Telesca *(Pres)*
Richard H. Lee *(Exec VP)*

BRANCH PROPERTIES, INC.
PO Box 940, Ocala, FL 34478
Tel.: (352) 732-4143
Sales Range: $10-24.9 Million
Emp.: 97
Animal Feed Mfr
N.A.I.C.S.: 311119
Gregory Croswell Branch *(Chm &
Pres)*
Christine Gledden *(Office Mgr)*
Greg Allen *(VP-Fin & Sec)*
Richard D. Simone *(VP)*

BRANCO ENTERPRISES INC.
1640 Hwy 64 W, Asheboro, NC
27203
Tel.: (336) 629-1090
Web Site:
http://www.brancoenterprises.com
Year Founded: 1968
Sales Range: $10-24.9 Million
Emp.: 42
Women's Ready-To-Wear Apparel
N.A.I.C.S.: 458110
Larry W. McKenzie *(Pres)*

BRAND BANKING COMPANY
141 Hurricane Shoals Rd, Lawrence-
ville, GA 30046
Tel.: (770) 972-4153
Web Site:
http://www.thebrandbank.com
Rev.: $29,114,000
Emp.: 300
Banking Services
N.A.I.C.S.: 522110
Shirley Wiley *(Sr VP)*

BRAND FX BODY COMPANY
2800 Golden Traingle Blvd, Fort
Worth, TX 76177
Tel.: (817) 431-1131
Web Site:
https://www.brandfxbody.com
Sales Range: $100-124.9 Million
Emp.: 100
Mfr of Fiberglass, Line Bodies, Top-
pers & Inserts
N.A.I.C.S.: 336211
Gary Heisterkamp *(Pres)*

Subsidiaries:

GemTop Manufacturing, Inc.   (1)
36600 Industrial Way, Sandy, OR 97055-
7375
Tel.: (503) 659-3733
Sales Range: $10-24.9 Million
Emp.: 28
Mfr of Steel Caps & Lids for Light Trucks
N.A.I.C.S.: 441330

BRAND INDUSTRIAL SER-VICES, INC.
1325 Cobb International Dr Ste A-1,
Kennesaw, GA 30152
Tel.: (800) 558-4772   **DE**
Web Site: http://www.beis.com
Year Founded: 1966
Sales Range: $1-4.9 Billion
Emp.: 15,000
Scaffold & Industrial Construction
Contracting Services
N.A.I.C.S.: 238990
Paul T. Wood *(Chm & CEO)*
Joseph A. Sadowski *(Pres-Technical
Svcs & Bus Dev)*
Stephen F. Tisdall *(Pres-Americas
Forming & Shoring)*
David J. Witsken *(Pres-Aluma Sys-
tems Indus & Intl Ops)*
Mark Neas *(Pres-Brand Energy Solu-
tions)*
Jason Fisher *(CIO)*
James R. Billingsley Jr. *(Gen Counsel
& Exec VP)*

Brand Industrial Services, Inc.—(Continued)

Subsidiaries:

All-American Scaffold, LLC (1)
51 Washington Ave, Des Moines, IA 50314-3642
Tel.: (515) 282-9633
Web Site:
http://www.allamericanscaffold.com
Heavy Construction Equipment Supplier & Rental Services
N.A.I.C.S.: 532412

Aluma Enterprises, Inc. (1)
55 Costa Road, Concord, L4K 1M8, ON, Canada
Tel.: (905) 669-5282
Web Site: http://www.beis.com
Sales Range: $50-74.9 Million
Concrete Construction & Industrial Scaffold Contracting Services
N.A.I.C.S.: 238110
Stephen F. Tisdall (Pres-Infrastructure Svcs)

Subsidiary (Domestic):

Aluma Systems (2)
345 Saint Clair Street, Sarnia, N7T 7H8, ON, Canada
Tel.: (519) 336-8200
Web Site: http://www.aluma.com
Sales Range: $50-74.9 Million
Emp.: 200
Scaffolding, Civil & General Contracting Services
N.A.I.C.S.: 238990
Ian Steer (Gen Mgr)

Big City Access, Inc. (1)
5922 Centralcrest St, Houston, TX 77092
Tel.: (713) 680-8888
Web Site: http://bigcityaccess.com
Sales Range: $1-9.9 Million
Emp.: 26
Specialty Trade Contractors
N.A.I.C.S.: 238990
Barbara Roberts (Pres)
James Evanicky (Gen Mgr & Mgr-Sls)

Brace Industrial Group, Inc. (1)
14950 Heathrow Forest Pkwy Ste 150, Houston, TX 77032
Tel.: (281) 749-1020
Web Site: http://www.brace.com
Industrial Services
N.A.I.C.S.: 541420
Lee Barnett (CFO)
Mark Talley (Exec VP)
Todd Rouw (Exec VP)
Mark Gottlich (VP-Health, Safety & Environmental)
Bobby Gould (VP-Sls & Mktg)
Danny Saenz (Pres-BRACE Integrated Svcs)
DeWayne Harmon (Pres-BRACE Integrated Svcs S Central)
Rick Swindle (Pres-BRACE Integrated Svcs-Southeast)
Ron Bourgoin (Pres-Brace Integrated Svcs-Northeast)
Willie Westmoreland (Pres-PLATINUM Scaffolding Svcs)
Sam Morasca (Chm)

Brand Energy & Infrastructure Services Australia Pty Ltd (1)
Unit B 49 Boundary Road, Rocklea, 4106, QLD, Australia
Tel.: (61) 737133333
Sales Range: $50-74.9 Million
Construction Services & Industrial Maintenance Services
N.A.I.C.S.: 532412
David Kidd (Mgr-HR)

Subsidiary (Domestic):

Brand Energy & Infrastructure Services (Gladstone) Pty. Ltd. (2)
20 Neil Street, Gladstone, 4680, QLD, Australia
Tel.: (61) 749786606
Web Site: http://www.harsco-i.com.au
Sales Range: $50-74.9 Million
Emp.: 40
Construction Services & Industrial Maintenance Services
N.A.I.C.S.: 532412
Jason Mills (Branch Mgr)

Brand Energy & Infrastructure Services (Hunter Valley) Pty. Ltd. (2)
6 Strathmore Road, Hunter Valley, Muswellbrook, 2333, NSW, Australia
Tel.: (61) 265411381
Web Site: http://www.harsco-i.com.au
Sales Range: $50-74.9 Million
Construction Services & Industrial Maintenance Services
N.A.I.C.S.: 532412
Kryston Baker (Office Mgr)

Brand Energy & Infrastructure Services B.V. (1)
George Stephensohnweg 15, 3133 KJ, Vlaardingen, Netherlands
Tel.: (31) 10 445 5444
Web Site: http://www.beis.com
Construction & Industrial Maintenance Services
N.A.I.C.S.: 238990
John Simpson (Gen Mgr)

Subsidiary (Domestic):

Brand Energy & Infrastructure Services (2)
George Stephensonweg 15, 3133 KJ, Vlaardingen, Netherlands
Tel.: (31) 104455444
Web Site: http://www.beis.com
Emp.: 150
Industrial Maintenance Services
N.A.I.C.S.: 541990
Peter van den Bent (Mng Dir)

Harsco Infrastructure Construction Services B.V. (2)
George Stephensonweg 15, Vlaardingen, 3133KJ, Netherlands
Tel.: (31) 10 445 5444
Web Site: http://www.harsco-i.nl
Emp.: 31
Construction Services
N.A.I.C.S.: 236210
Peter van den Bent (Office Mgr)

Harsco Infrastructure Logistic Services B.V. (2)
George Stephensonweg 15, 3133 KJ, Vlaardingen, Netherlands
Tel.: (31) 10 445 5444
Logistics Management Consulting Services
N.A.I.C.S.: 541614

Brand Energy & Infrastructure Services GmbH (1)
Rehhecke 80, 40885, Ratingen, Germany
Tel.: (49) 21 02 937 0
Web Site: http://www.beis-deutschland.de
Construction Services & Industrial Maintenance Services
N.A.I.C.S.: 532412
Ralf Tytko (Mng Dir)

Subsidiary (Domestic):

Gerustbau Muehlhan GmbH (2)
Rubbertstrasse 31, 21109, Hamburg, Germany
Tel.: (49) 407560950
Ship Building & Repairing Services
N.A.I.C.S.: 336611

Brand Energy & Infrastructure Services NV/SA (1)
Mannheimweg 1 - Kaai 242, 2030, Antwerp, Belgium
Tel.: (32) 37708991
Web Site: http://www.beis.com
Sales Range: $25-49.9 Million
Industrial Services & Non-Residential Building Constructing Services
N.A.I.C.S.: 236210
Venoalsa Tom (Mgr)

Brand Energy & Infrastructure Services-Hazel Crest (1)
17315 Ashland Ave, Hazel Crest, IL 60429
Tel.: (708) 957-1010
Web Site: http://www.beis.com
Sales Range: $25-49.9 Million
Emp.: 35
Scaffolding Sales & Contracting Services
N.A.I.C.S.: 238990
Bill Kuhn (Branch Mgr)

Brand Energy Solutions (1)
2309 W Mulberry, Angleton, TX 77515

Tel.: (713) 427-5400
Web Site: http://www.beis.com
Sales Range: $75-99.9 Million
Industrial Insulation, Painting, Scaffolding, Fireproofing & Other Protective Contracting Services
N.A.I.C.S.: 238990
Lindsey Hebert (VP-Ops)

Brand France S.A.S. (1)
Allee de Fetan 256, BP 130, 1601, Trevoux, France
Tel.: (33) 474089050
Web Site: http://www.brandfrance.fr
Construction Services & Industrial Maintenance Services
N.A.I.C.S.: 532412

Brand Insulation Services (1)
740 Veterans Dr, Swedesboro, NJ 08085
Tel.: (856) 467-2850
Web Site: http://www.beis.com
Sales Range: $10-24.9 Million
Emp.: 20
Industrial & Commercial Insulation Contracting Services
N.A.I.C.S.: 238990
Aric Drnevich (Gen Mgr)

Brand Italia S.p.A. (1)
Via Isonzo 9, 22078, Turate, Como, Italy
Tel.: (39) 02969731
Web Site: http://www.beis-italia.it
Construction Services & Industrial Maintenance Services
N.A.I.C.S.: 532412

Brand Scaffolding Services (1)
15450 S Outer 40 Rd Ste 250, Chesterfield, MO 63017-2066
Tel.: (636) 519-1000
Web Site: http://www.beis.com
Scaffolding Sales & Contracting Services
N.A.I.C.S.: 238990
Paul T. Wood (Pres & CEO)

Forming Concepts, Inc. (1)
185 Industrial Dr, Gilberts, IL 60136-9753
Tel.: (847) 426-4400
Web Site: http://www.formingconcepts.com
Concrete Forming Products & Systems Mfr & Distr
N.A.I.C.S.: 327390
Norton Baum (Founder)

Harsco Infrastructure (1)
1 Mack Centre Dr, Paramus, NJ 07652-3908
Tel.: (201) 261-5600
Web Site: http://www.harsco-i.us
Sales Range: $50-74.9 Million
Steel & Aluminum Scaffolding, Shoring & Forming Equipment Mfr & Distr
N.A.I.C.S.: 423810

Subsidiary (Non-US):

Harsco Infrastructure Group Limited (2)
Harsco House Regent Park, 299 Kingston Road, Leatherhead, KT22 7SG, Surrey, United Kingdom
Tel.: (44) 1372381300
Web Site: http://www.beis.com
Sales Range: $50-74.9 Million
Emp.: 180
Access Design, Engineering & Installation Support Services
N.A.I.C.S.: 541330
Jeff Butler (Mng Dir)

Huennebeck GmbH (1)
Rehhecke 80, 40885, Ratingen, Germany
Tel.: (49) 21029370
Web Site: http://www.huennebeck.com
Sales Range: $25-49.9 Million
Scaffold & Formwork Products Distr
N.A.I.C.S.: 332311
Martin Hemberger (Mng Dir)

Subsidiary (Domestic):

Huennebeck Deutschland GmbH (2)
Rehhecke 80, D-40885, Ratingen, Germany
Tel.: (49) 21029371
Web Site: http://www.huennebeck.de
Sales Range: $10-24.9 Million
Formwork & Scaffolding Services
N.A.I.C.S.: 237990

Martin Hemberger (Chm-Mgmt Bd & Mng Dir)
Markus Kehren (Member-Mgmt Bd)

Hunnebeck Romania SRL (1)
Capusu Mare nr 310, 407154, Cluj-Napoca, Romania
Tel.: (40) 264504270
Web Site: http://www.huennebeck.ro
Emp.: 120
Scaffold & Formwork Products Distr
N.A.I.C.S.: 332311
Jerold Schonthaler (Head-Mktg)

J A Electronic Manufacturing Co, Inc. (1)
13715 N Promenade Blvd, Stafford, TX 77477
Tel.: (281) 879-9903
Web Site: http://www.jaelectronics.com
Sales Range: $1-9.9 Million
Emp.: 20
Electronic Components Mfr
N.A.I.C.S.: 334419
John Abramski (Pres)

MATCOR, Inc. (1)
101 Liberty Ln, Chalfont, PA 18914
Tel.: (215) 348-2974
Web Site: http://www.matcor.com
Electric Equipment Mfr
N.A.I.C.S.: 335999
Eileen Jacob (VP-Fin & Admin)
Glenn Shreffler (Exec VP-Engrg)
Carlos Fuentes (Plant Mgr)
Rebecca Haring (Mgr-Safety & Compliance)
Kevin Pitts (Pres)
Kris Rubino (VP-Svcs)
Ted Huck (VP-Intl)
Kevin Groll (Reg Mgr-Northeast)
Geoff Rhodes (Mgr-Proposal & Engr)

National Coating & Lining Co. (1)
29885 2nd St, Lake Elsinore, CA 92532
Tel.: (951) 674-1030
Web Site: http://www.socal-pacific.com
Rev.: $2,500,000
Emp.: 25
Wood Container & Pallet Mfr
N.A.I.C.S.: 321920
Anton Anstett (Pres)

Protherm Services Group, LLC (1)
1830 Jasmine Dr, Pasadena, TX 77503-3222
Tel.: (713) 667-9361
Sales Range: $25-49.9 Million
Coatings, Insulation, Scaffolding, Fireproofing & Tank Lining Services
N.A.I.C.S.: 238990
Chuck Bouboulis (Controller)

SGB Aluma Malaysia Sdn. Bhd. (1)
No 3A-01 & 3A-02 Level 3A Menara Maxisegar, Jalan Pandan Indah 4/2, 55100, Kuala Lumpur, Malaysia
Tel.: (60) 342965455
Web Site: http://www.sgb-aluma.my
Formwork & Shoring Systems
N.A.I.C.S.: 532412
Luis Alvarez (Gen Mgr-UAE)
Sandy Maxwell (Mng Dir-Middle East India & Africa)

SGB Aluma Singapore Pte. Ltd. (1)
23 Gul Road, Singapore, 629356, Singapore
Tel.: (65) 68626122
Web Site: http://www.industrial.sgb-aluma.sg
Emp.: 20
Construction Services & Industrial Maintenance Services
N.A.I.C.S.: 532412
Barry Bolt (Dir)

SafeWorks, LLC (1)
365 Upland Dr, Seattle, WA 98188
Tel.: (206) 575-6445
Web Site: http://www.safeworks.com
Powered Suspended Access & Safety Solutions
N.A.I.C.S.: 333120
Greg Crew (VP-Global Product Mgmt)
John Sotiroff (VP & Gen Mgr-Spider Ops)
Michael Moritz (Gen Mgr)
Colby Hubler (VP-Global Sis-POwer Climber & Power Climber Wind)

Safway Atlantic LLC (1)

700 Commercial Ave, Carlstadt, NJ 07072
Tel.: (201) 636-5500
Web Site: http://www.safwayatlantic.com
Construction Engineering Services
N.A.I.C.S.: 541330

Subsidiary (Domestic):

Engel Holdings Incorporated (2)
14754 Ceres Ave, Fontana, CA 92335
Tel.: (866) 950-9862
Web Site: http://www.cabrillohoist.com
Cranes & Aerial Lift Equipment Sales &
Rental
N.A.I.C.S.: 532412
Matthew Engel *(CEO)*
Randy Prusik *(VP)*
Dave Brooks *(Sls Mgr-Northern CA)*
John McCormack *(Sls Mgr-Southern CA)*
Monica Jackson *(Gen Mgr-Ops)*
James Ivicevic *(Controller)*
Hector Melgar *(Mgr-Safety)*

Swing Staging LLC (1)
25-20 Borden Ave, Long Island City, NY
11101
Tel.: (718) 361-2861
Web Site: http://www.swingstaging.com
Scaffolding Rental Services
N.A.I.C.S.: 532412

BRAND INNOVATION GROUP
8902 Airport Dr Ste A, Fort Wayne,
IN 46809
Tel.: (260) 469-4060
Web Site: https://www.gotobig.com
Year Founded: 1995
Sales Range: $25-49.9 Million
Emp.: 24
Advertising Agencies
N.A.I.C.S.: 541810
Chad Stuckey *(Chief Compliance Officer)*
Scott Stuckey *(Sr Dir-Art)*
Mark Felger *(Dir-Fin Ops)*
Greg Becker *(Sr Dir-Art)*
John Crilly *(Acct Dir)*
Craig Crook *(Dir-Client Dev)*
Christina Egts *(Acct Dir)*
Brady Wieland *(CEO)*
Eric Hall *(Dir-Digital)*

Subsidiaries:

AccessPoint (1)
8653 Bash St, Indianapolis, IN 46256-1202
Tel.: (317) 525-8441
Web Site: http://www.xspt.com
Emp.: 12
Advertising Agencies
N.A.I.C.S.: 541810
Tom Downs *(Owner)*

BRAND STORY EXPERTS INC.
1911 Manatee Ave E Ste 101,
Bradenton, FL 34208
Tel.: (941) 650-0407
Web Site:
    http://www.brandstoryexperts.com
Sales Range: $1-9.9 Million
Advetising Agency
N.A.I.C.S.: 541810
Kelly Keenan *(Founder)*

BRAND UP, LLC
9950 Research Dr, Irvine, CA 92653
Tel.: (949) 542-7000
Web Site: http://www.brand-up.com
Year Founded: 2004
Sales Range: $1-9.9 Million
Emp.: 15
Digital Strategy & Marketing Services
N.A.I.C.S.: 541613
Rob Goodyear *(Mng Partner)*
Bryan MacGillivray *(Mng Partner)*

BRAND VELOCITY ACQUISITION CORP.
62 Magnolia Ave, Larchmont, NY
10538
Tel.: (203) 930-1000
Year Founded: 2021

Investment Services
N.A.I.C.S.: 523999
Stephen Lebowitz *(Chm & CEO)*
Drew Sheinman *(Pres & CMO)*
Austin Ramos *(CFO & COO)*

BRAND VELOCITY PARTNERS
200 Park Ave Ste 1700, New York,
NY 10166
Tel.: (203) 930-1000
Web Site:
    http://brandvelocitypartners.com
Year Founded: 2019
Privater Equity Firm
N.A.I.C.S.: 523999
Steve Lebowitz *(Mng Partner)*
Eli Manning *(Partner)*
Drew Sheinman *(Partner)*
Austin Ramos *(Partner)*

Subsidiaries:

American Soccer Company, Inc. (1)
726 E Anaheim St, Wilmington, CA 90744
Tel.: (310) 830-6161
Web Site: http://www.scoresports.com
Sales Range: $50-74.9 Million
Emp.: 300
Sports Uniforms Mfr
N.A.I.C.S.: 339920
Jill Menzel *(Founder)*

ShoppersChoice.com, LLC (1)
8151 Airline Hwy, Baton Rouge, LA 70815
Tel.: (225) 296-0043
Web Site: http://www.shopperschoice.com
Rev.: $17,800,000
Emp.: 50
Retail Misc Homefurnishings
N.A.I.C.S.: 449129
Marc Broussard *(Mgr-BBQ Category-Bus Dev)*
Ladina Hackley *(CFO)*
Jason Stutes *(Dir-Analytics & Design-Mktg)*
Corey Tisdale *(COO)*
Mike Hackley *(Pres)*

The Original Footwear Co. (1)
5968 Commerce Blvd, Morristown, TN
37814
Tel.: (209) 234-4200
Web Site: http://www.originalswat.com
Footwear Mfr & Whslr
N.A.I.C.S.: 316210
Kevin D. Cole *(Founder)*
Brett Weitl *(Mktg Dir)*
Mark Cavanaugh *(CEO)*

Unit (Domestic):

Altama Footwear (2)
1821 Industrial Dr, Stockton, CA 95206
Tel.: (209) 234-4200
Web Site: http://www.altama.com
Emp.: 25
Military & Police Boots Designer & Mfr
N.A.I.C.S.: 316210
Kevin Cole *(Pres)*

BRAND-NU LABORATORIES INC.
377 Research Pkwy, Meriden, CT
06450
Tel.: (203) 235-7989
Web Site: http://www.brandnu.com
Year Founded: 1956
Rev.: $15,000,000
Emp.: 30
Chemical Preparations, Nec
N.A.I.C.S.: 325998
Paul Lombardo *(VP-Mfg)*
John J. Gorman III *(Pres)*

BRANDED ENTERTAINMENT NETWORK, INC.
710 2nd Ave Ste 640, Seattle, WA
98104
Tel.: (206) 373-6000
Web Site:
    http://www.productplacement.com
Year Founded: 1989
Sales Range: $100-124.9 Million
Emp.: 300

Customer Computer Programming
Commercial Photography
N.A.I.C.S.: 523999
Gary Richard Shenk *(Founder & Chm)*
Kristin Glushon *(Exec VP-Client Dev-Los Angeles)*
Tamra Knepfer *(Sr VP-Greenlight)*
Maria Teresa Hernandez *(VP-Client Dev)*
Ricky Ray Butler *(CEO)*
Nicolas Bertagnolli *(Principal-Data Scientist)*
Khudor Annous *(Sr VP-Influencer Client Dev)*
Megan Savitt *(VP-Influencer Client Svcs)*
Vanessa McCullers *(VP-Diversity, Equity & Inclusion & Strategy)*

Subsidiaries:

Branded Entertainment Network, Inc.
- New York Office (1)
170 Varick St Ste 1002, New York, NY
10013
Tel.: (212) 777-6200
Web Site:
    http://www.ben.productplacement.com
Emp.: 100
Photo Studio
N.A.I.C.S.: 561990
Ryan Kernan *(Sr Dir-Mdse Licensing)*

BRANDED GROUP, INC.
222 S Harbor Blvd Ste 500, Anaheim,
CA 92805
Tel.: (323) 940-1444
Web Site: http://www.branded-group.com
Year Founded: 2014
Sales Range: $10-24.9 Million
Emp.: 76
Construction Management Services
N.A.I.C.S.: 236220
Michael Kurland *(Founder & CEO)*

BRANDENBURG INDUSTRIAL SERVICE COMPANY INC.
2625 S Loomis St, Chicago, IL
60608-5400
Tel.: (312) 326-5800
Web Site:
    https://www.brandenburg.com
Year Founded: 1968
Sales Range: $50-74.9 Million
Emp.: 550
Demolitions Experts
N.A.I.C.S.: 236220
Thomas J. Little *(Pres)*
Lynn Jasinowski *(Controller)*
Dale Morrison *(Mgr-Quality & Database)*

Subsidiaries:

Bradenburg Industrial Service Company Inc.-Bethlehem, PA (1)
2217 Stillman Dr, Bethlehem, PA 18015
Tel.: (610) 691-1800
Web Site: http://www.brandenburg.com
Sales Range: $25-49.9 Million
Emp.: 150
Building Demolition Services
N.A.I.C.S.: 237310

BRANDENBURG PROPERTIES
1122 Willow St Ste 200, San Jose,
CA 95125
Tel.: (408) 279-5200
Web Site: https://www.brandenburg-properties.com
Real Estate Investment & Development
N.A.I.C.S.: 523999
Eric Brandenburg *(Partner)*
William B. Baron *(Partner)*

BRANDENBURG TELEPHONE COMPANY
200 Telco Dr, Brandenburg, KY
40108
Tel.: (270) 422-2121
Web Site: http://www.bbtel.com
Rev.: $19,641,100
Emp.: 70
Local Telephone Communications
N.A.I.C.S.: 517121
Joseph D. Tobin Jr. *(Pres)*

BRANDEXTRACT, LLC
7026 Old Katy Rd Ste 210, Houston,
TX 77024
Tel.: (713) 942-7959
Web Site:
    http://www.brandextract.com
Year Founded: 2005
Sales Range: $10-24.9 Million
Emp.: 30
Marketing Consulting Services
N.A.I.C.S.: 541613
Bo Bothe *(Pres & CEO)*
Jonathan Fisher *(Chm)*
Malcolm Wolter *(Partner & VP-Digital)*
Donovan Buck *(Partner & VP-Software Engrg)*
Greg Weir *(VP-Digital Mktg & Analytics)*
Cynthia Stipeche *(Dir-User Experience)*
Ashley Horne *(Brand Mgr)*
Leigh Anne Bishop *(Mgr-Digital Project)*
Sherrill Baggett *(Mgr-Support)*
Julia Rice *(Office Mgr)*
Rachelle Sifuentes *(Project Mgr)*
Sharon Lenert *(Project Mgr)*
Daren Guillory *(Dir-Creative)*
Margo Lunsford *(Dir-Art)*
Kyle Smith *(Mgr-Digital Mktg)*

BRANDICORP
7346 Beechmont Ave, Cincinnati, OH
45230
Tel.: (513) 232-2233
Sales Range: $10-24.9 Million
Emp.: 5
Sandwiche & Submarine Shop
N.A.I.C.S.: 722513

BRANDIMAGE DESGRIPPES & LAGA
990 Skokie Blvd, Northbrook, IL
60062
Tel.: (847) 291-0500
Web Site: http://www.laga.com
Year Founded: 1971
Sales Range: $10-24.9 Million
Emp.: 300
Brand Development & Integration,
Graphic Design, Internet/Web Design,
Package Design
N.A.I.C.S.: 541810
Joel Desgrippes *(Owner)*
Howard Alport *(Principal)*

BRANDMAN CENTERS FOR SENIOR CARE
7150 Tampa Ave, Reseda, CA 91335
Tel.: (818) 774-8444
Web Site:
    https://www.brandmanseniorcare.org
Year Founded: 2008
Sales Range: $10-24.9 Million
Emp.: 36
Senior Care Services
N.A.I.C.S.: 623312
Susie Fishenfeld *(Exec Dir)*
Ed Schneider *(Chm)*
Joyce Brandman *(Vice Chm)*
Scott Weiss *(Sec)*
Mary M. Forrest *(Pres & CEO)*

BRANDMIND

brandMIND—(Continued)

996 Bryans Place Rd, Winston Salem, NC 27104-5006
Tel.: (336) 721-2049
Year Founded: 1997
Rev.: $21,000,000
Emp.: 15
Advertising Agencies
N.A.I.C.S.: 541810
Dave Tambling (CEO & Chief Strategist)
Jeff Tambling (Pres & Dir-Results)
Lori Soper (Lead Mktg Strategist)

BRANDMUSCLE, INC.
233 S Wacker Dr Ste 4400, Chicago, IL 60606
Tel.: (312) 235-5700
Web Site: http://www.centiv.com
Year Founded: 2000
Emp.: 700
Marketing Programs
N.A.I.C.S.: 423430
Philip Alexander (CEO)

BRANDOM CABINETS
404 Hawkins St, Hillsboro, TX 76645-3224
Tel.: (254) 580-1200
Web Site: http://www.brandom.com
Sales Range: $10-24.9 Million
Emp.: 150
Mfr of Custom Wood Kitchen Cabinets
N.A.I.C.S.: 337110
Maretta Fry (Controller)
Charles Gideon (VP-Sls)
Timothy Bear (VP-Mfg)
Nora Parrack (Dir-HR)
Michael Drybola (Engr-Mfg)
John Wisenbaker Sr. (Founder & CEO)

BRANDON & CLARK INC.
3623 Interstate 27, Lubbock, TX 79404
Tel.: (806) 747-3861
Web Site:
http://www.brandonclark.com
Sales Range: $10-24.9 Million
Emp.: 250
Power Transmission Equipment, Electric
N.A.I.C.S.: 811310
Gary Clark (VP)

BRANDON ADVERTISING, INC.
3023 Church St, Myrtle Beach, SC 29577
Tel.: (843) 916-2000
Web Site:
http://www.thebrandonagency.com
Year Founded: 1959
Sales Range: $10-24.9 Million
Emp.: 100
Advetising Agency
N.A.I.C.S.: 541810
Scott Brandon (CEO)
Barry Sanders (Dir-New Bus)
Tyler Easterling (Pres & COO)
Andy Kovan (Dir-Acct Plng & Dev)
Shelby Greene (VP & Dir-Media)
Jan Suchanek (CFO)
Missy Thompson (Dir-Acct)
Stephen Childress (Chief Creative Officer)
Alex Childress (Editor)

BRANDON COMPANY
401 N Vine St, North Little Rock, AR 72114
Tel.: (501) 374-1271
Web Site:
https://www.brandonco.com
Rev.: $12,099,490
Emp.: 35

Floor Covering Distribution
N.A.I.C.S.: 423220
Steve Willmon (Pres)
Ray Cahoon (Mgr-Comml)

BRANDON CONSTRUCTION COMPANY, INC.
557 Alt 19 N, Palm Harbor, FL 34683
Tel.: (727) 784-6378
Web Site:
http://www.brandonconstruction.com
Year Founded: 1983
Sales Range: $10-24.9 Million
Emp.: 12
Construction Services
N.A.I.C.S.: 236115
David L. Brandon (Pres)
Robert Carr (VP)
Mark Malloy (VP & Project Mgr)
Dan Downes (Project Mgr)
Jenny Smith (Controller)

BRANDON INTERNATIONAL
2221 W Camden Rd, Milwaukee, WI 53209-3709
Tel.: (626) 960-4981
Web Site:
http://www.brandondiecutting.com
Rev.: $20,774,596
Emp.: 54
Paper Die-Cutting
N.A.I.C.S.: 322299

BRANDORCHARD
34 State St, Pittsford, NY 14534
Tel.: (585) 419-7060
Sales Range: Less than $1 Million
Emp.: 10
N.A.I.C.S.: 541810
Michael Stone (Founder & Mng Dir)
Bridget G. Stone (Dir-Fin Svcs)
Anne Sheehan (Founder & Assoc Dir-Creative)

BRANDPOINT SERVICES, INC.
820 Adams Ave Ste 130, Trooper, PA 19403
Web Site:
http://www.brandpointservices.com
Year Founded: 2003
Sales Range: $1-9.9 Million
Emp.: 200
Construction Services
N.A.I.C.S.: 236210
Steve Hearon (Pres)
Michael Hersh (CEO)
Jason Seward (CFO)
Will Nelson (COO)
Dave Knoche (Exec VP-Sls)
David Moura (VP-Client Rels)

Subsidiaries:

Progroup Network Inc.   (1)
4 Lambeth Park Dr, Fairhaven, MA 02719-4734
Web Site: http://www.progroupnetwork.com
Drywall & Insulation Contractors
N.A.I.C.S.: 238310

BRANDS, LLC
101 McAlister Farm Rd, Portland, ME 04103
Web Site:
http://www.brickellmensproduct.com
Year Founded: 2014
Sales Range: $10-24.9 Million
Emp.: 35
Skin Care Product Mfr
N.A.I.C.S.: 325620
Josh Meyer (Co-Founder)
Matt Bolduc (Co-Founder)

BRANDSMART USA
3200 SW 42nd St, Hollywood, FL 33312-6813
Tel.: (954) 797-4000   FL

Web Site:
http://www.brandsmartusa.com
Year Founded: 1977
Sales Range: $900-999.9 Million
Emp.: 1,000
Radio & Television & Electronic Products Retailer
N.A.I.C.S.: 449210
Robert Perlman (Founder)

BRANDSPA LLC
215 Glenridge Ave, Montclair, NJ 07042-3562
Tel.: (973) 509-2728
Web Site: http://www.brandspa.net
Year Founded: 1986
Sales Range: Less than $1 Million
Emp.: 4
Brand Development, Health Care, Strategic Planning/Research
N.A.I.C.S.: 541810
Allan Gorman (CEO & Dir)
Suzanne Giovanetti (Dir-Art)

BRANDSPINS, LLC
1301 S Jones Blvd, Las Vegas, NV 89146
Tel.: (702) 878-0959
Web Site: http://www.brandspins.com
Digital Music Stores & Music Player Apps
N.A.I.C.S.: 459140
Daniel Waibel (CFO)

Subsidiaries:

Music Dealers, LLC   (1)
3540 W Sahara Ave Ste 311, Las Vegas, NV 89102
Tel.: (888) 584-0005
Web Site: http://www.musicdealers.com
Music Recording Services
N.A.I.C.S.: 512250

BRANDSPRING SOLUTIONS LLC
14500 Martin Dr Ste 1000, Eden Prairie, MN 55344-2075
Tel.: (952) 345-7260   MN
Web Site:
http://www.brandspringsolution.com
Year Founded: 1975
Sales Range: $1-9.9 Million
Emp.: 12
Advertising Agency
N.A.I.C.S.: 541810
David F. Maiser (Pres)
Carl Halverson (VP-Interactive Div)
Jay Thomas (VP-Client Svcs)
Lindsay Beckstein (Asst Acct Mgr)
Sean Mosley (Sr Dir-Art)
Tara Beyer (Project Mgr)
Bud Grimes (Acct Exec)

BRANDT & HILL INC.
3306 Longhorn Blvd No 111, Austin, TX 78758
Tel.: (512) 834-0456
Rev.: $23,067,235
Emp.: 52
Materials Handling Machinery
N.A.I.C.S.: 423830
Bob Hill (Founder & Pres)

BRANDT BOX & PAPER CO INC
6 W Crisman Rd, Columbia, NJ 07832
Tel.: (908) 496-4500
Web Site:
https://www.brandtboxnj.com
Sales Range: $10-24.9 Million
Emp.: 9
Boxes, Paperboard & Disposable Plastic
N.A.I.C.S.: 424130
Robert Brandt (Pres)

BRANDT CO., INC.
PO Box 118, Brawley, CA 92227
Tel.: (760) 344-3430   CA
Year Founded: 1975
Sales Range: $10-24.9 Million
Emp.: 60
Cattle Feedlots
N.A.I.C.S.: 112112
Bill Brandt (Owner)

BRANDT CONSOLIDATED, INC.
2935 S Koke Mill Rd, Springfield, IL 62711
Tel.: (217) 547-5800   IL
Web Site:
http://www.brandtconsolidated.co
Year Founded: 1959
Sales Range: $100-124.9 Million
Emp.: 325
Fertilizer & Other Farm Chemical Mfr
N.A.I.C.S.: 325314
Albert Allen (Mgr-Dealer Support)
Bill Engel (Exec VP)
Rick C. Brandt (Pres & CEO)
Tim McArdle (COO & Exec VP)
Joe Brummel (CFO & Exec VP)
Karl Barnhart (Chief Mktg Officer & Exec VP)
Kenny Tate (Plant Mgr-Raymond)

Subsidiaries:

Monterey Chemical Company Inc.   (1)
3654 S Willow Ave, Fresno, CA 93725-9009   (100%)
Tel.: (559) 499-2100
Web Site:
http://www.montereyagresources.com
Rev.: $40,000,000
Emp.: 65
Distr, Packager & Formulator of Agricultural Chemicals
N.A.I.C.S.: 325320
John Salmonson (Pres & CEO)

BRANDT HOLDINGS COMPANY
4650 26th Ave S Ste E, Fargo, ND 58104
Tel.: (701) 237-6000
Web Site:
https://www.brandtholdings.com
Sales Range: $75-99.9 Million
Emp.: 500
Investment Holding Company
N.A.I.C.S.: 551112
Ace A. Brandt (Pres & CEO)
Michael Vannett (Sr VP & CFO)
Cindy Keller (Controller)
Jon Kram (Gen Mgr-Entertainment Div)

Subsidiaries:

Hunter Equipment Inc   (1)
501 Main St, Hunter, ND 58048
Tel.: (701) 874-2168
Web Site:
http://www.hunterequipmentinc.com
Sales Range: $25-49.9 Million
Emp.: 33
Farm & Garden Machinery & Equipment Merchant Whslr
N.A.I.C.S.: 423820
Lonnie Nelson (Mgr)

Branch (Domestic):

Hunter Equipment   (2)
207 Preirie Ave, Galesburg, ND 58035
Tel.: (701) 488-2238
Web Site:
http://www.hunterequipmentinc.com
Sales Range: $25-49.9 Million
Emp.: 15
Farm & Garden Machinery & Equipment Merchant Whslr
N.A.I.C.S.: 423820
Lonnie Nelson (Mgr)

James River Equipment, Co.   (1)

23484 455th Ave 1340, Madison, SD 57042
Tel.: (605) 256-4575
Web Site: http://www.jre.net
Sales Range: $25-49.9 Million
Emp.: 20
Farm Equipment Whslr
N.A.I.C.S.: 423820

Kibble Equipment Inc. (1)
3099 Hwy 7 SW, Montevideo, MN 56265
Tel.: (320) 269-6466
Web Site: http://www.kibbleeq.com
Farm Equipment Sales & Services
N.A.I.C.S.: 423820
Dan DeBaere (Sls Mgr)
Chad Arends (Mgr-Integrated Solutions)
Mark DeBeer (Mgr-Parts)
Craig Krysan (Sls Mgr-Blue Earth)
Kory Newman (Mgr-Svc-Blue Earth)
Jim Nauman (Mgr-Parts-Blue Earth)

Branch (Domestic):

Kibble Equipment (2)
1381 W Hwy Ave, Bird Island, MN 55310
Tel.: (320) 365-3445
Web Site: http://www.kibbleeq.com
Sales Range: $25-49.9 Million
Emp.: 20
Farm & Garden Machinery & Equipment
Merchant Whslr
N.A.I.C.S.: 423820
Matt Kramer (Gen Mgr)

Northstar Power LLC (1)
7301 SE Northstar Dr, Ankeny, IA 50021
Tel.: (515) 964-6100
Web Site: http://www.northstarpowerco.com
Gasoline Engine & Engine Parts Mfr
N.A.I.C.S.: 336510
Becky Leer (Controller)
Aaron Poland (Mgr-Svc)
Troy Kaney (Mgr-Sls)

SE Equipment, Inc. (1)
670 Buffington Rd, Spartanburg, SC 29303
Tel.: (864) 342-9003
Web Site: http://www.seequipinc.com
Sales Range: $25-49.9 Million
Emp.: 38
Heavy Construction Equipment Rental
N.A.I.C.S.: 423830

BRANDT INFORMATION SERVICES, INC.
501 N Duval St, Tallahassee, FL 32301
Tel.: (850) 577-4900
Web Site: http://www.brandtinfo.com
Year Founded: 1985
Sales Range: $1-9.9 Million
Computer Software Developer & Market Research Services
N.A.I.C.S.: 513210
John Thomas (CEO)

BRANDT TRUCK LINE INC.
1619 S Morrisy Ave, Bloomington, IL 61701
Tel.: (309) 662-3341
Rev.: $13,513,348
Emp.: 250
Trucking Except Local
N.A.I.C.S.: 484121
John Brandt (Owner)
Steven Kubsch (Pres & CEO)

BRANDTRUST, INC.
444 N Michigan Ave Ste 3100, Chicago, IL 60611
Tel.: (312) 440-1833   IL
Web Site: https://www.brandtrust.com
Year Founded: 1982
Sales Range: $1-9.9 Million
Emp.: 38
Advetising Agency
N.A.I.C.S.: 541810
Daryl Travis (Founder, Pres & CEO)
Ed Jimenez (Creative Dir)
Carmie Stornello (Dir-People Ops)
Beth Wozniak (Dir-Fin)

BRANDVIA ALLIANCE, INC.

2159 Bering Dr, San Jose, CA 95131
Tel.: (408) 955-0500
Web Site: https://www.brandvia.com
Sales Range: $1-9.9 Million
Emp.: 138
Promotional Marketing Services
N.A.I.C.S.: 541890
Jim Childers (Pres)
Amy Noel (Partner-Strategic Acct)
Shirley Doxtad (Acct Exec)

BRANDYWINE AUTO PARTS INC.
14000 Crain Hwy, Brandywine, MD 20613
Tel.: (301) 372-1000
Web Site: https://www.brandywineparts.com
Sales Range: $25-49.9 Million
Emp.: 40
Motor Vehicle Parts, Used
N.A.I.C.S.: 541611
Judy McFaden (Dir-HR)
Kevin Squires (Mgr-Recycling)
Woody Meinhart (Owner)

BRANDYWINE CONSTRUCTION & MANAGEMENT
1521 Locust St, Philadelphia, PA 19102
Tel.: (215) 557-9800
Web Site: http://www.brandywinemanagement.com
Rev.: $12,600,000
Emp.: 70
Land Subdividers & Developers, Commercial
N.A.I.C.S.: 237210
Adam Kauffman (Pres)
Mark Berman (VP)
Edward E. Cohen (Chm)

BRANDYWINE SPORTS, INC.
2200 Concord Pike, Wilmington, DE 19803
Tel.: (302) 426-3938   DE
Sales Range: $75-99.9 Million
Emp.: 9
Provider of Real Estate Management
N.A.I.C.S.: 531120

BRANFORD CASTLE, INC.
150 E 58th St 37th Fl, New York, NY 10155
Tel.: (212) 317-2004   DE
Web Site: http://www.branfordcastle.com
Year Founded: 1986
Holding Company; Private Equity Investment Services
N.A.I.C.S.: 551112
David B. Pittaway (Vice Chm, Sr Mng Dir, CFO & VP)
John K. Castle (Chm)
John S. Castle (Pres & CEO)
David Castle (Mng Partner)
James Reddington (CFO)
Eric Korsten (Sr Mng Dir)
Laurence Lederer (Sr Mng Dir)
Darby Blaker (Mgr-Office)

Subsidiaries:

Branford Castle Partners, L.P. (1)
150 E 58th St 37th Fl, New York, NY 10155-0002
Tel.: (212) 317-2004
Web Site: http://www.branfordcastle.com
Emp.: 10
Privater Equity Firm
N.A.I.C.S.: 523999
David B. Pittaway (Vice Chm & Chief Compliance Officer)
John S. Castle (Pres & CEO)
John K. Castle (Chm)
David Castle (Mng Partner)
Eric Korsten (Sr Mng Dir)

Laurence Lederer (Sr Mng Dir)
James Reddington (CFO)
Camille Pena (Controller)

Holding (Domestic):

ABC Industries Inc. (2)
301 Kings Hwy, Winona Lake, IN 46590
Tel.: (574) 267-5166
Web Site: http://www.abc-industries.net
Sales Range: $10-24.9 Million
Emp.: 90
Ventilating Products
N.A.I.C.S.: 333413
Paul Nutter (Mgr-Product-Indus Ventilation Ducting)
Vicki Cook (Dir-HR & IT)
Jennifer Kussmaul (Mgr-Natl Sls)

Clean Solutions Group, Inc. (2)
119 Poplar Pointe Dr, Ste C, Mooresville, NC 28117
Tel.: (704) 394-2111
Web Site: https://cleangrp.com
Chemicals Mfr
N.A.I.C.S.: 325998
Keith White (CEO)

Subsidiary (Domestic):

Fibrix LLC (3)
119-C Polar Pointe Dr, Mooresville, NC 28117
Tel.: (704) 394-2111
Web Site: https://fibrixfiltration.com
Filtration Products Mfr
N.A.I.C.S.: 313230

Subsidiary (Domestic):

Americo Manufacturing Co., Inc. (4)
6224 N Main St, Acworth, GA 30101-3330
Tel.: (770) 974-7000
Web Site: http://www.americomfg.com
Sales Range: $10-24.9 Million
Emp.: 200
Mfr & Distributor of Janitorial Supplies
N.A.I.C.S.: 327910
Richard L. Rones (Pres)
David M. Rones (VP-Matting Div)
Lenny Shutzberg (CEO)

HDK Industries, Inc. (4)
100 Industrial Park Dr, Rogersville, TN 37857
Tel.: (423) 272-7119
Web Site: http://hdkind.com
Nonwoven Fabric Mill Operator
N.A.I.C.S.: 313230

Holding (Domestic):

Earthlite, LLC (2)
990 Joshua Way, Vista, CA 92081
Tel.: (760) 599-1112
Web Site: http://www.earthlite.com
Massage Tables & Related Products Mfr
N.A.I.C.S.: 337127
Tomas Nani (Founder)
Tara Grodjesk (VP-Consumables Div & Chief Wellness Officer)

Subsidiary (Domestic):

Tara Spa Therapy, Inc. (3)
990 Joshua Way, 92081, Vista, CA
Tel.: (309) 734-1232
Web Site: https://www.taraspatherapy.com
Health, Wellness & Aromatherapy Services
N.A.I.C.S.: 812990
Tara Donna Grodjesk (Founder)

Subsidiary (Domestic):

Handi Quilter, Inc. (2)
501 N 400 W, North Salt Lake, UT 84054
Tel.: (801) 292-7988
Web Site: http://www.handiquilter.com
Quilting Machinery, Applications & Supplies Mfr
N.A.I.C.S.: 333248
Darren Denning (CEO)
Laurel Barrus (Founder)

Holding (Domestic):

Lafayette Instrument Company, Inc. (2)
3700 Sagamore Pkwy N, Lafayette, IN 47904-1066
Tel.: (765) 423-1505

Web Site: http://www.lafayetteinstrument.com
Measuring & Controlling Device Mfr
N.A.I.C.S.: 334519
Mike Greene (Mgr-Ops)
Terry Echard (VP-Life Sciences & Gen Mgr)
Chris Fausett (VP & Gen Mgr-Polygraph)
Brent Smitley (Mgr-Engrg)
Todd Hooker (Mgr-Facilities & Shipping)
Greg Prescott (Mng Dir)
Jennifer Rider (Pres & CEO)
Julie Gledhill (Mgr-Acctg)
Steve Rider (Mgr-Info Sys)

Vitrek Corporation (2)
12169 Kirkham Rd, Poway, CA 92064
Tel.: (858) 689-2755
Web Site: http://www.vitrek.com
Mfg Electrical Measuring Instruments
N.A.I.C.S.: 334515
Kevin Clark (CEO)
Bob D'Amico (Mgr-Sls Team-East)

Subsidiary (Domestic):

MTI Instruments Inc. (3)
325 Washington Ave Ext, Albany, NY 12205-5505
Tel.: (518) 218-2550
Web Site: http://www.mtiinstruments.com
Sales Range: $10-24.9 Million
Electronics Instrument Mfr
N.A.I.C.S.: 334519
Don Welch (Dir-New Bus Dev)
Ken Ameika (Gen Dir-Sls-Turbomachinery)
Moshe Binyamin (Pres & CEO)
Peter Opela (Engr-Product Innovation)

BRANHAVEN CHRYSLER JEEP DODGE RAM
348 W Main St, Branford, CT 06405
Tel.: (203) 488-6351
Web Site: https://www.branhaven.com
Year Founded: 1970
Sales Range: $10-24.9 Million
Emp.: 41
Car Whslr
N.A.I.C.S.: 441110
Robert Lavallee Jr. (Pres)

BRANNAN PAVING COMPANY, LTD.
111 Elk Dr, Victoria, TX 77904
Tel.: (361) 573-3130
Web Site: https://www.brannanpaving.com
Year Founded: 1954
Sales Range: $300-349.9 Million
Emp.: 90
Highway, Street & Bridge Construction Services
N.A.I.C.S.: 237310
Brian Lindsey (VP)

BRANNAN SAND & GRAVEL CO. LLC
2500 E Brannon Way, Denver, CO 80229
Tel.: (303) 534-1231
Web Site: http://www.brannan1.com
Year Founded: 1906
Highway & Street Paving Contractor
N.A.I.C.S.: 237310
Stephanie Ziegler (Controller)

Subsidiaries:

Boral Construction Materials LLC (1)
5775 Franklin St, Denver, CO 80216
Tel.: (303) 292-1771
Web Site: http://www.boralcolorado.com
Construction Materials Mfr & Distr
N.A.I.C.S.: 327331

Subsidiary (Domestic):

Ready Mixed Concrete Co. (2)
4395 Washington St, Denver, CO 80216
Tel.: (303) 292-1771
Ready Mixed Concrete
N.A.I.C.S.: 327320

Brannen Banks of Florida, Inc.—(Continued)

BRANNEN BANKS OF FLORIDA, INC.
320 Hwy 41 S, Inverness, FL 34450
Tel.: (352) 726-1221   FL
Web Site:
https://www.brannenbanks.com
Year Founded: 1926
Sales Range: $50-74.9 Million
Emp.: 200
Bank Holding Company
N.A.I.C.S.: 522110
Joseph S. Brannen (Vice Chm)
G. Matt Brannen (Pres)

Subsidiaries:

Brannen Bank   (1)
200 W Main St, Inverness, FL 34450-4956
Tel.: (352) 726-8435
Web Site: http://www.brannenbanks.com
Rev.: $9,700,000
Emp.: 6
State Commercial Banks
N.A.I.C.S.: 522110
Michael T. Fitzpatrick (CFO)
Walter D. Connors III (CIO, CTO & Chief Info Security Officer)
Jerry M. Martin Jr. (Chief Lending Officer)

Brannen Bank Services Inc.   (1)
320 US Hwy 41 S, Inverness, FL 34450
Tel.: (352) 726-6995
Web Site: http://www.brannenbank.com
Rev.: $2,787,881
Emp.: 25
Data Processing & Preparation
N.A.I.C.S.: 518210

BRANOM INSTRUMENT CO. INC.
5500 4th Ave S, Seattle, WA 98108
Tel.: (206) 762-6050
Web Site: http://www.branom.com
Rev.: $10,876,788
Emp.: 45
Measuring & Testing Equipment, Electrical
N.A.I.C.S.: 423830

BRANSCUM CONSTRUCTION COMPANY, INC.
90 Key Village Rd, Russell Springs, KY 42642-4511
Tel.: (270) 866-5107
Web Site:
https://www.branscumconstruction.com
Sales Range: $10-24.9 Million
Emp.: 80
Civil Engineering Services
N.A.I.C.S.: 237310
Steve Branscum (Pres & CEO)
Michelle Pettey (Coord-Mktg)

BRANT PUBLICATIONS, INC.
110 Greene St 2nd Fl, New York, NY 10012-3230
Tel.: (212) 941-2800   DE
Year Founded: 1922
Sales Range: $75-99.9 Million
Emp.: 100
Magazine Publisher
N.A.I.C.S.: 513120
Jennifer Norton (Publr-The Magazine Antiques)
Debbie Blasucci (CFO)
Peter M. Brant (Owner)
Cynthia Zabel (Publr-Art in America)

BRASADA CAPITAL MANAGEMENT LP
3200 Southwest Freeway, Houston, TX 77027-7524
Tel.: (713) 630-8390
Web Site:
http://www.brasadacapital.com
Year Founded: 2008

Process, Physical Distribution & Logistics Consulting Services
N.A.I.C.S.: 541614
Mark McMeans (CEO)

Subsidiaries:

Globescan Capital Inc.   (1)
2650 Fountain View Dr, Houston, TX 77057-7619
Tel.: (713) 789-4121
Web Site: http://www.globescancapital.com
Investment Banking & Securities Dealing
N.A.I.C.S.: 523150
Pas Sadhukhan (Pres)

BRASFIELD & GORRIE, LLC
3021 7th Ave S, Birmingham, AL 35233
Tel.: (205) 328-4000   DE
Web Site:
https://www.brasfieldgorrie.com
Year Founded: 1922
Sales Range: $1-4.9 Billion
Emp.: 3,741
Commercial & Institutional Building Construction
N.A.I.C.S.: 236220
Randall J. Freeman (CFO)
Jeffrey I. Stone (COO)
Tom Garrett (CIO)
Charles Grizzle (Gen Counsel)
Rob Taylor (Pres-East Reg)
Jill V. Deer (Chief Admin Officer)
Magnus James Gorrie (Bd of Dirs, Pres, Pres & CEO)

BRASHE ADVERTISING, INC.
420 Jericho Tpke, Jericho, NY 11753-1344
Tel.: (516) 935-5544
Web Site: http://www.brashe.com
Year Founded: 1977
Rev.: $10,209,000
Emp.: 5
Recruitment
N.A.I.C.S.: 541810
Ronnie Stein (VP & Media Dir)
Jeffrey Cherkis (Pres & Acct Dir)

BRASS ARMADILLO INC.
106 SW Linden Ste 1 D, Ankeny, IA 50021
Tel.: (515) 965-8375
Web Site:
http://www.brassarmadillo.com
Rev.: $24,000,000
Emp.: 100
Antiques
N.A.I.C.S.: 459510
David Briddle (VP)

BRASS MEDIA INC.
987 NW Cir Blvd, Corvallis, OR 97330
Tel.: (541) 753-8546
Web Site:
http://www.brassMEDIA.com
Year Founded: 2003
Rev.: $3,900,000
Emp.: 31
Periodical Publishers
N.A.I.C.S.: 513120
Bryan Sims (Co-Founder)
Steve Sims (Co-Founder & CEO)
Harry Reich (Mgr-Facilities)
Sara Krainik (Dir-Creative)
Jeff Horton (Dir-Partnership)
Liz Baker (Dir-Customer Rels)

BRASS RING CAPITAL INC.
826 N Plankinton Ste 500, Milwaukee, WI 53203
Tel.: (414) 225-0228
Web Site:
http://www.brassringcapital.com
Privater Equity Firm
N.A.I.C.S.: 523999

Steven D. Peterson (Mng Dir)
Steve Laczniak (Principal)

Subsidiaries:

Portu-Sunberg & Associates Inc.   (1)
50 S 10th St Ste 550, Minneapolis, MN 55403-2022
Tel.: (612) 455-2130
Web Site: http://www.portu-sunberg.com
Sales Range: $25-49.9 Million
Emp.: 50
Retail & Vendor Marketing Consulting Services
N.A.I.C.S.: 541613
David Sunberg (Pres)
Teresa Christenson (VP-Sls & Food)
Jennifer Stone (Chief HR Officer)

BRASTILE INC.
110 NE 179th St, Miami, FL 33162
Tel.: (305) 653-8337
Web Site: https://www.brastile.com
Rev.: $11,600,000
Emp.: 40
Tile & Marble Products
N.A.I.C.S.: 423320
Joseph Battat (Pres)

BRASWELL MILLING COMPANY
105 Cross St, Nashville, NC 27856
Tel.: (259) 459-2143
Web Site:
http://www.braswellfoods.com
Year Founded: 1942
Sales Range: $10-24.9 Million
Holding Company: Organic Feed Mfr
N.A.I.C.S.: 551112
Russ Powell (VP-Feed Div)
Scott Braswell (Pres)
Sean C. Bennett (CFO & Strategic Officer)
Lisa Lewis (VP-Fin)
Ronald Scott Braswell III (Exec VP)

Subsidiaries:

Braswell Foods   (1)
105 Cross St, Nashville, NC 27856   (100%)
Tel.: (252) 459-2143
Web Site: http://www.braswellfoods.com
Producer & Marketer of Feed & Egg Products
N.A.I.C.S.: 112310
Scott Braswell (Owner)
Lisa Lewis (VP-Acctg Stewardship & Controller)
Trey Braswell (Pres)

Carolina Egg Companies, Inc.   (1)
105 E Cross St, Nashville, NC 27856-1360
Tel.: (252) 451-2111
Web Site: http://www.braswellfoods.com
Sales Range: $1-9.9 Million
Emp.: 19
Poultry & Poultry Product Whslr
N.A.I.C.S.: 424440
Wayne Boseman (Dir-Ops & Procurement)

Glenwood Foods, L.L.C.   (1)
20850 Jackson Lane, Jetersville, VA 23083
Tel.: (804) 561-3447
Chicken Egg Production
N.A.I.C.S.: 112310
Scott Akom (Gen Mgr)

BRATTAIN INTERNATIONAL TRUCKS, INC.
61 NE Columbia Blvd, Portland, OR 97211
Tel.: (503) 285-9300
Web Site: http://www.brattain.com
Sales Range: $10-24.9 Million
Emp.: 100
Sales of Auto & Truck Equipment & Parts
N.A.I.C.S.: 441330
Creed V. Brattain (Founder & Owner)

BRATTLEBORO RETREAT

1 Anna Marsh Ln, Brattleboro, VT 05301
Tel.: (802) 258-3737   VT
Web Site:
https://www.brattlebororetreat.org
Year Founded: 1834
Sales Range: $50-74.9 Million
Emp.: 918
Mental Health & Addiction Treatment Services
N.A.I.C.S.: 621420
Jeffrey Corrigan (VP-HR)
Gerri Cote (VP-Ops)
Konstantin von Krusenstiern (VP-Strategy & Dev)
Frederick Engstrom (Dir-Medical-Intensive Care Svcs)
Elizabeth Catlin (Chm)
Mark McGee (Chief Medical Officer)
Louis Josephson (Pres & CEO)
Arthur W. Nichols (CFO & Exec VP)
Meghan Baston (Chief Nursing Officer)

BRATTON CORPORATION
2801 E 85th St, Kansas City, MO 64132
Tel.: (816) 363-1014
Web Site:
http://www.brattonsteel.com
Rev.: $23,555,876
Emp.: 45
Structural Steel Erection
N.A.I.C.S.: 238120
Robert D. Long (Pres)

BRATTON MASONRY INC.
2763 N Argyle Ave, Fresno, CA 93727
Tel.: (559) 291-9423
Sales Range: $50-74.9 Million
Emp.: 100
Masonry & Other Stonework
N.A.I.C.S.: 238140
James A. Bratton (Pres)
Kevin McElroy (Controller)
Billy Wells (VP)

BRAUER MATERIAL HANDLING SYSTEMS, INC.
226 Molly Walton Dr, Hendersonville, TN 37075
Tel.: (615) 859-2930
Web Site:
https://www.braueronline.com
Sales Range: $10-24.9 Million
Emp.: 40
Materials Handling Machinery
N.A.I.C.S.: 423830
Jeffrey L. Brauer (Pres)
Bret Looney (Mgr-IT)
Jason Duke (Acct Mgr)
Jon Pond (Mgr-Ops & Svc)
Nicole Bess (Coord-Sls)

BRAUER SUPPLY COMPANY
1218 S Vandeventer Ave, Saint Louis, MO 63110-3808
Tel.: (314) 534-7150
Web Site:
https://www.brauersupply.com
Sales Range: $10-24.9 Million
Emp.: 50
Warm Air Heating Equipment & Supplies
N.A.I.C.S.: 423730
James L. Truesdell (Pres)
Robert Quam (Mgr-Info Sys)

BRAUM'S ICE CREAM & DAIRY STORES INC.
3000 NE 63rd St, Oklahoma City, OK 73121-1202
Tel.: (405) 478-1656   OK
Web Site: http://www.braums.com
Year Founded: 1968
Sales Range: $150-199.9 Million
Emp.: 8,500
Ice Cream Mfr & Retailer

N.A.I.C.S.: 445298
Terry Holden (Dir-Mktg)
Drew Braum (Pres & CEO)
James Deaton (Controller)
Mark Godwin (CFO)

BRAUN & BUTLER CONSTRUCTION, INC.
8130 N Lamar Blvd, Austin, TX 78753
Tel.: (512) 837-2882
Web Site: http://www.braun-butler.com
Year Founded: 1982
Sales Range: $10-24.9 Million
Emp.: 30
Nonresidential Construction Services
N.A.I.C.S.: 236220
John Braun (Principal)

BRAUN ELECTRIC COMPANY INCORPORATED
3000 E Belle Ter, Bakersfield, CA 93307
Tel.: (661) 633-1451
Web Site: https://www.braunelec.com
Year Founded: 1945
Sales Range: $25-49.9 Million
Emp.: 300
General Electrical Contractor
N.A.I.C.S.: 238210
John A. Braun (Pres)
Kevin Coghlin (VP)

BRAUN INTERTEC CORPORATION
11001 Hampshire Ave S, Minneapolis, MN 55438
Tel.: (612) 688-4132
Web Site: https://www.braunintertec.com
Year Founded: 1957
Sales Range: $25-49.9 Million
Emp.: 200
Engineering & Business Consulting Services
N.A.I.C.S.: 541690
George D. Kluempke (VP)
Daniel R. Holte (CFO)
Kimberly Simmons (Project Mgr-NDE)
Jim Bird (VP-Tech)
Richard McGuire (Sr Engr-Building Sciences Grp)
Charles Cadenhead (Principal & Dir-Transportation Div-Minnesota)
Jon Carlson (CEO)
Robert Janssen (Pres)
Carmen Borgeson (CFO)
John McCormick (COO)
Bridget O'Brien (Chief People Officer)
Jennifer Clayson Kraus (Gen Counsel)

BRAUNS EXPRESS INC.
10 Tandem Way, Hopedale, MA 01747
Tel.: (508) 473-8405
Web Site: https://www.braunsexpress.com
Rev.: $10,575,204
Emp.: 50
Trucking Except Local
N.A.I.C.S.: 484121
David Normandin (Pres)
Stephanie Connolly (Mgr-AR, Credit & Freight Claims)
John Erickson (Mgr-Acctg)
Chris Rafferty (Mgr-Safety)

BRAUNS ONLINE MEDIA INC.
93 Winthrop St, Cambridge, MA 02138
Tel.: (617) 497-5100
Web Site: http://www.mergernetwork.com
Year Founded: 1995

Sales Range: $1-9.9 Million
Online Database Featuring Businesses For Sale
N.A.I.C.S.: 425120
Robert Brauns (Chm & CEO)

BRAUNSCHWEIGER BROS., INC.
33 S St, Morristown, NJ 07960-4137
Tel.: (973) 538-2189
Web Site: https://www.braunschweiger.com
Year Founded: 1947
Emp.: 40
Jewelry Retailer
N.A.I.C.S.: 458310
Greg Kettle (Mgr)
Kristy Braunschweiger-Smith (Pres)

BRAVE ASSET MANAGEMENT INC.
47 Summit Ave, Summit, NJ 07901
Tel.: (908) 522-8822
Rev.: $186,836,391
Emp.: 3
Investment Management Service
N.A.I.C.S.: 523940
David G. Bunting (Chm, Sec, Treas & Principal)
T. Brett Haire Jr. (Chief Compliance Officer & Principal)

BRAVE NEW WORLD
506 New York Ave, Point Pleasant Beach, NJ 08742
Tel.: (732) 899-9874
Web Site: https://www.bravesurf.com
Sales Range: $10-24.9 Million
Emp.: 80
Sports Apparel
N.A.I.C.S.: 458110
William Lammers (Pres)

BRAVE SPIRITS LLC
111 Forrest Ave Rear Annex, Narberth, PA 19072
Tel.: (610) 667-3270
Web Site: http://www.bravespirits.com
Year Founded: 2007
Sales Range: $10-24.9 Million
Emp.: 1
Spirit Mfr
N.A.I.C.S.: 312140
Powell Arms (COO)
Jamie Clark (Mgr-Bar)

BRAVO CHEVROLET CADILLAC
1601 S Main St, Las Cruces, NM 88005
Tel.: (575) 527-3800
Web Site: https://www.bravolascruces.com
Year Founded: 2004
Sales Range: $25-49.9 Million
Emp.: 120
New Car Retailer
N.A.I.C.S.: 441110
Felipe Molina (Gen Mgr)

BRAVO RESTAURANTS INC.
600 W Jackson Blvd Ste 200, Chicago, IL 60661-5636
Tel.: (312) 463-1210   DE
Web Site: http://www.featuredfoods.com
Year Founded: 1994
Sales Range: $10-24.9 Million
Emp.: 300
Restaurant Operators
N.A.I.C.S.: 722513
Ivan Himmel (Chm)
Jeffrey Himmel (Pres)

Subsidiaries:

Edwardo's Restaurant, Inc.   (1)
600 W Jackson Blvd Ste 200, Chicago, IL 60661-5636
Tel.: (815) 758-2677
Sales Range: $10-24.9 Million
Emp.: 5
Eating Place
N.A.I.C.S.: 561110

BRAWER BROS INC.
375 Diamond Bridge Ave, Hawthorne, NJ 07506
Tel.: (973) 238-1800
Web Site: http://www.brawerbros.com
Sales Range: $10-24.9 Million
Emp.: 12
Yarns, Nec
N.A.I.C.S.: 424990
John Italia (Dir-Mgmt Info Sys)
Skip Smith (CEO)
Adolfo Castillo (Controller)
David Dreeben (Mgr-Credit)

BRAXTON RESOURCES INC.
7558 W Thunderbird Rd #1-486, Peoria, AZ 85381
Tel.: (602) 509-2822   NV
Year Founded: 2012
Gold Mining
N.A.I.C.S.: 212220
Charles Irizarry (Pres, CEO, CFO, Treas & Sec)

BRAXTON STRATEGIC GROUP
54 Westbrook Rd, Westfield, NJ 07090
Tel.: (908) 209-3331
Web Site: https://www.braxtonstrategic.com
Year Founded: 2003
Sales Range: $1-9.9 Million
Emp.: 3
Media Buying Services, Media Planning
N.A.I.C.S.: 541830
Reatha Braxton (Dir-Media)

BRAY & SCARFF INC.
8610 Cherry Ln, Laurel, MD 20707
Tel.: (301) 317-0400
Web Site: https://www.brayandscarff.com
Sales Range: $10-24.9 Million
Emp.: 200
Electric Household Appliances
N.A.I.C.S.: 449210
R. Kenneth Dodson (Pres)
Jon Lardy (Mgr-IT)
Wayne Powell (VP-Ops)

BRAY ASSOCIATES ARCHITECTS INC.
829 S 1st St, Milwaukee, WI 53204
Tel.: (414) 226-0200
Web Site: http://www.brayarch.com
Year Founded: 1962
Rev.: $2,500,000
Emp.: 40
Architectural Services
N.A.I.C.S.: 541310
Matthew Wolfert (Pres & Principal)
Ryan Sands (VP-Architect)
Clint Selle (VP-Architect)

Subsidiaries:

Bracke Hayes Miller Mahon, Architects LLP   (1)
1465 41st St Ste 10, Moline, IL 61265
Tel.: (309) 762-0511
Rev.: $1,057,000
Emp.: 7
Architectural Services
N.A.I.C.S.: 541310
Mark Miller (Partner)

BRAY INTERNATIONAL, INC.
13333 Westland E Blvd, Houston, TX 77041-1219
Tel.: (281) 894-5454   TX
Web Site: https://www.bray.com
Year Founded: 1986
Rev.: $41,600,000
Emp.: 200
Flow Control Equipment Mfr
N.A.I.C.S.: 332911

Subsidiaries:

Bray Controls (UK) Ltd.   (1)
16/18 Fountain Crescent Inchinnan Business Park, Inchinnan, PA4 9RE, United Kingdom
Tel.: (44) 141 812 5199
Industrial Valve Mfr
N.A.I.C.S.: 332911

Bray Controls Andina Ltda.   (1)
Calle 106 57-23 Oficina 409 Edificio Square 106, Bogota, Colombia
Tel.: (57) 1226 6173
Industrial Valve Mfr
N.A.I.C.S.: 332911

Bray Controls Canada Corporation   (1)
3299 Boulevard Jean Baptiste Deschamps Lachine, Lachine, H8T 3E4, QC, Canada
Tel.: (514) 344-2729
Web Site: http://www.bray.com
Emp.: 25
Industrial Valve Mfr
N.A.I.C.S.: 332911
James Henderson (Gen Mgr)

Bray Controls France S.A.R.L   (1)
Centre d affaires La Fontaine Entree G Boulevard Moliere, Maubeuge, 59600, France
Tel.: (33) 3 27 59 41 89
Industrial Valve Mfr
N.A.I.C.S.: 332911

Bray Controls Pacific Pty. Ltd.   (1)
8 Phoenix Court, Braeside, 3195, VIC, Australia
Tel.: (61) 3 8541 2555
Web Site: http://www.bray.com
Emp.: 23
Industrial Valve Mfr
N.A.I.C.S.: 332911

Bray Controls Peru S.A.C   (1)
Calle los Gorriones 130B Urb La Campina, Chorrillos, Lima, Peru
Tel.: (51) 1 251 0251
Industrial Valve Mfr
N.A.I.C.S.: 332911

Bray Controls S.A.   (1)
Centro de Empresas Flexcenter Avda Lo Boza 8395 Modulo B-25, Pudahuel, 33178, Santiago, Chile
Tel.: (56) 2 739 29 66
Emp.: 20
Industrial Valve Mfr
N.A.I.C.S.: 332911

Bray Controls Southeast Asia Pte Ltd   (1)
10 Ubi Crescent Lobby C 04-47 Ubi Techpark, Singapore, 408564, Singapore
Tel.: (65) 6742 1428
Emp.: 2
Industrial Valve Mfr
N.A.I.C.S.: 332911
Ken Shoff (Gen Mgr)

Bray Controls Vietnam Company Ltd.   (1)
No 52 Road No 2 Quarter 5 An Phu Ward District 2, 790000, Ho Chi Minh City, Vietnam
Tel.: (84) 8 6281 8821
Industrial Valve Mfr
N.A.I.C.S.: 332911

Bray International, Inc. - Bray Controls Benelux Division   (1)
Joulestraat 8, 1704 PK, Heerhugowaard, Netherlands
Tel.: (31) 725721410
Web Site: http://www.bray.nl
Emp.: 15
Industrial Valve Mfr

Bray International, Inc.—(Continued)
N.A.I.C.S.: 332911
Jaap Jonker (Office Mgr)

Bray International, Inc. - Bray Controls Indonesia Division (1)
Talavera Office Park 28th Floor JI TB Simatupang Kav 22-26, Jakarta, 12430, Indonesia
Tel.: (62) 21 7599 9937
Industrial Valve Mfr
N.A.I.C.S.: 332911

Bray International, Inc. - Bray Controls Poland Division (1)
ul Fabryczna 10, 32 600, Oswiecim, Poland
Tel.: (48) 33 842 19 68
Web Site: http://www.bray.com
Emp.: 10
Industrial Valve Mfr
N.A.I.C.S.: 332911
Janusz Brzozowski (Gen Mgr)

Bray International, Inc. - Bray Controls S. Korea Division (1)
16/F Gangnam B/D 1321-1 Seocho-dong, Seocho-gu, Seoul, 137 070, Korea (South)
Tel.: (82) 2 2190 3809
Industrial Valve Mfr
N.A.I.C.S.: 332911

Bray Sales Southern California Inc. (1)
461 S Dupont Ave, Ontario, CA 91761-1504 (100%)
Tel.: (909) 937-1624
Web Site: http://www.bray.com
Sales Range: $10-24.9 Million
Emp.: 10
Industrial Supplies
N.A.I.C.S.: 423830

Bray Technical Services India Pvt. Ltd. (1)
D1 3rd Floor MSM Plaza 114/115 Outer Ring Road, Banaswadi, Bengaluru, 560043, Karnataka, India
Tel.: (91) 80 30081111
Industrial Valve Mfr
N.A.I.C.S.: 332911

Bray Valvulas de Mexico S.A. de C.V. (1)
Juan Gil Preciado 2450 Nave 10 Ecopark Col El Tigre, Zapopan, 45203, Jalisco, Mexico
Tel.: (52) 33 3836 4460
Emp.: 40
Industrial Valve Mfr
N.A.I.C.S.: 332911
Javier Padilla (Gen Mgr)

Flow-Tek Industria e Comercio de Valvulas Ltda (1)
Av Madrid 500 Paulinia Cascade, Sao Paulo, 13146 038, Brazil
Tel.: (55) 19 3517 5555
Industrial Valve Mfr
N.A.I.C.S.: 332911

Intermountain Valve & Controls Inc. (1)
7003 E 47th Ave Ste 600A, Denver, CO 80216-3458 (100%)
Tel.: (303) 322-7979
Web Site: http://www.bray.com
Sales Range: $10-24.9 Million
Emp.: 8
Industrial Supplies Distributor
N.A.I.C.S.: 423830
Kris Johnson (Gen Mgr)

RitePro Corporation (1)
10200 Boulevard Parkway, Montreal, H1J 2K4, QC, Canada
Tel.: (514) 324-8900
Web Site: http://www.ritepro.com
Emp.: 45
Industrial Valve Mfr
N.A.I.C.S.: 332911
Michael Glamour (Mgr-Ops)

Valvtronic S.A. (1)
Acceso Sur Km 13 5 Lujan de Cuyo, Mendoza, M5507ADA, Argentina
Tel.: (54) 261 498 6022
Web Site: http://www.valvtronic.com
Industrial Valve Mfr
N.A.I.C.S.: 332911

BRAY MEDIA, LLC
100 Rocking Arrow Rd, Many, LA 71449
Tel.: (225) 767-8600
Year Founded: 1987
Sales Range: $1-9.9 Million
Emp.: 4
Media Buying Agency
N.A.I.C.S.: 541810
Bonnie Bray (Owner)
Penny George (Mgr-Bus)

BRAY TRUCKING INC.
7000 Thelma Lee Dr Ste 200, Alexandria, KY 41001
Tel.: (859) 635-5680
Rev.: $11,000,000
Emp.: 57
Provider of Dump Truck Haulage & Excavation Services
N.A.I.C.S.: 484220
Dallas E. Bray (Pres)
Bill Ice (Mgr-Dispatch)

BRAYMAN CONSTRUCTION CORPORATION
1000 John Roebling Way, Saxonburg, PA 16056
Tel.: (724) 443-1533
Web Site:
    http://www.braymanconstruc-
    tion.com
Year Founded: 1948
Construction Services
N.A.I.C.S.: 237310
Stephen M. Muck (Chm & CEO)
Jason Booher (Project Mgr)
Bill Coury (Project Mgr)
Frank Piedimonte (Pres & COO)
Evan Ring (Project Mgr)
Jim Messenger (Superintendent)
Chad LeViere (CFO)
Brent Conklin (Superintendent)
Chris Cortese (Superintendent-Bridge)
Tom Puzniak (Mgr-Bus Dev)
Mike Gedman (Superintendent)
Rich Mannarino (VP-Estimating)

Subsidiaries:

Brayman Foundations LLC (1)
1000 John Roebling Way, Saxonburg, PA 16056
Tel.: (724) 443-1533
Web Site:
    http://www.braymanconstruction.com
Geotechnical Foundation Construction Contractor
N.A.I.C.S.: 238110
Stephen M. Muck (Pres & CEO)

BRAZEWAY INC.
2711 E Maumee St, Adrian, MI 49221-3534
Tel.: (517) 265-2121
Web Site: https://www.brazeway.com
Year Founded: 1946
Sales Range: $25-49.9 Million
Emp.: 365
Provider of Aluminum Products
N.A.I.C.S.: 331318
Saumin S. Mehta (Dir-Sls & Bus Dev)

BRAZORIA TELEPHONE CO
314 W Texas St, Brazoria, TX 77422
Tel.: (979) 798-2121
Web Site: https://www.btel.com
Sales Range: $10-24.9 Million
Emp.: 60
Local Telephone Communications
N.A.I.C.S.: 517121
John H. Greenberg (CFO)
Gilbert Rasco (VP)
Jonathan Champagne (Controller)
Kenneth Goolsby (VP-Plant)

BRAZOS ELECTRIC POWER

COOPERATIVE, INC.
2404 La Salle Ave, Waco, TX 76706-3928
Tel.: (254) 750-6500
Web Site:
    http://www.brazoselectric.com
Year Founded: 1941
Sales Range: $300-349.9 Million
Emp.: 355
Producer & Retailer of Electricity
N.A.I.C.S.: 221118
Michael Galler (Supvr-Pur)
Ruben Padilla (Controller-Sys)
Timothy Hartz (Mgr-Engrg)

BRAZOS HIGHER EDUCATION SERVICE CORPORATION
2600 Washington Ave, Waco, TX 76710
Tel.: (254) 753-0915
Web Site: http://www.bhesc.org
Year Founded: 1975
Sales Range: $125-149.9 Million
Emp.: 80
Personal Credit Institutions
N.A.I.C.S.: 522299
Ricky Turman (CFO & Exec VP)
Debbie Urias (VP)

BRAZOS PRIVATE EQUITY PARTNERS, LLC
100 Crescent Ct Ste 1777, Dallas, TX 75201-7862
Tel.: (214) 301-4201
Web Site:
    https://www.brazospartners.com
Sales Range: $25-49.9 Million
Emp.: 27
Private Equity Investment Firm
N.A.I.C.S.: 551112
Randall S. Fojtasek (Co-Founder, Co-CEO & Partner)
Patrick K. McGee (Co-Founder & Partner)
Jeff S. Fronterhouse (Co-Founder, Co-CEO & Partner)
Glenn Askew (Mng Dir-Bus Dev)
Lucas T. Cutler (Mng Dir)
Douglas L. Kennealey (Mng Dir)
Jason D. Sutherland (Mng Dir)

Subsidiaries:

Flint Trading, Inc. (1)
115 Todd Ct, Thomasville, NC 27360
Tel.: (336) 475-6600
Web Site: http://www.ennisflint.com
Sales Range: $450-499.9 Million
Paint & Coatings Mfr
N.A.I.C.S.: 325510
Bryce Anderson (Chm)
Steve Vetter (Pres & CEO)
Matt Soule (CFO)
Dan Lang (VP-Mktg & Bus Dev)
Zina Brooks (Dir-Mktg)

Subsidiary (Domestic):

Ennis Paint Inc. (2)
1509 S Kaufman St, Ennis, TX 75119
Tel.: (214) 874-7200
Sales Range: $75-99.9 Million
Paint & Coatings Mfr
N.A.I.C.S.: 325510
Bryce Anderson (Chm)
Andrew Liebert (Sr VP-Sls & Mktg)

BRB CONTRACTORS, INC.
3805 NW 25th St, Topeka, KS 66618
Tel.: (785) 232-1245
Web Site:
    https://www.brbcontractors.com
Year Founded: 1959
Sales Range: $50-74.9 Million
Emp.: 250
Heavy Construction
N.A.I.C.S.: 237110
Mike Laird (Pres)
Ken Johnson (VP-Estimating)

BRC RUBBER & PLASTICS INC.
589 S Main St, Churubusco, IN 46723
Tel.: (260) 693-2171
Web Site: http://www.brcrp.com
Year Founded: 1973
Sales Range: $50-74.9 Million
Emp.: 500
Automotive Rubber Goods Mfr
N.A.I.C.S.: 326291
Susan Ikerd (Mgr-Accts Receivable)

BREAKAWAY COMMUNICATIONS LLC
381 Park Ave S Ste 1216, New York, NY 10016
Tel.: (212) 616-6010
Web Site:
    https://www.breakawaycom.com
Year Founded: 2002
Sales Range: Less than $1 Million
Emp.: 5
Full-Service Technology Public Relations & Communications Services
N.A.I.C.S.: 541820
Pamela F. Preston (Mng Partner-New York)
Kelly Fitzgerald (Mng Partner-New York)
Barbara Hagin (Mng Partner-San Francisco)

Subsidiaries:

Breakaway Communications LLC (1)
300 Broadway Ste 14, San Francisco, CA 94133
Tel.: (415) 358-2480
Web Site: http://www.breakawaycom.com
Sales Range: $25-49.9 Million
Full-Service Technology Public Relations
N.A.I.C.S.: 541820
Barbara Hagin (Mng Partner)

BREAKAWAY HONDA
330 Woodruff Rd, Greenville, SC 29607
Tel.: (864) 234-6632
Web Site:
    https://www.breakawayhonda.com
Sales Range: $25-49.9 Million
Emp.: 99
Car Whslr
N.A.I.C.S.: 441110
Dale Ward (Mgr-New Car Sls)
Robby Upton (Gen Mgr-Sls)

BREAKERS UNLIMITED INC.
15241 Stony Creek Way, Noblesville, IN 46060
Tel.: (317) 776-8817
Web Site:
    https://www.breakersunlimited.com
Year Founded: 1986
Sales Range: $10-24.9 Million
Emp.: 41
Whslr of Circuit Breakers
N.A.I.C.S.: 335313
Joseph A. Wendel (Pres)
Jim Jakobe (COO)

Subsidiaries:

Breakers Unlimited (1)
100 Petty Rd Ste F, Lawrenceville, GA 30043
Tel.: (770) 237-8923
Web Site: http://www.breakersunlimited.com
Sales Range: $10-24.9 Million
Emp.: 8
Circuit Breakers
N.A.I.C.S.: 423610

BREAKTHROUGH MANAGEMENT GROUP, INC.
1200 17th St Ste 180, Denver, CO 80202

Tel.: (303) 827-0010
Web Site: http://www.bmgi.com
Year Founded: 1999
Sales Range: $25-49.9 Million
Emp.: 150
Management Consulting
N.A.I.C.S.: 541611
David Silverstein *(Pres & CEO)*

BREAKTHROUGH PHYSICAL THERAPY MARKETING LLC

680 S Cache St Unit 100-9149, Jackson, WY 83001 **WY**
Web Site: http://www.breakthroughpt
  marketing.com
Year Founded: 2014
Sales Range: $1-9.9 Million
Emp.: 8
General Marketing Services
N.A.I.C.S.: 541613
Carl Mattiola *(Co-Founder)*
Chad Madden *(Co-Founder)*

BREAKTHROUGH T1D

Tel.: (212) 479-7551 **PA**
Web Site:
  https://www.breakthrought1d.org
Year Founded: 1970
Sales Range: $200-249.9 Million
Emp.: 923
Type 1 Diabetes Research Funding Services
N.A.I.C.S.: 813219
Mark Fischer-Colbrie *(Treas)*
Peter Cleary *(VP-Comm)*
Richard A. Insel *(Chief Scientific Officer-Res)*
John Vranas *(VP-Fundraising Programs)*
Gerri Feemster Bostick *(Chief HR Officer & Asst Sec)*
James Szmak *(COO)*
Diana Gray *(VP-West Div)*
Patrick McKenna *(VP-East Div)*
Linda C. Saulnier *(VP-Central Div)*
Tracy Bennett Smith *(Exec Dir-Alabama)*
Denise Nicastro *(Dir-Dev)*
Bonnie Bergstein *(VP-Pub Outreach)*
Samaa Haridi *(Treas)*
Tara Lee *(Mgr-Dev)*
Scott Minor *(VP-Govt Rels)*
Grant T. Murray *(Pres-New York Chapter)*
David Alleva *(Dir-Discovery Res)*
Vincent Crabtree *(Dir-Res Bus Dev)*
Kristin DiFoglio *(Exec Dir)*
Steven Griffen *(VP-Translational Dev)*
Michael Mayberry *(Dir-Dev)*
Gabriela Mogrovejo *(Mgr-Fin)*
Helen Dawn Nickerson *(Dir-Translational Dev)*
Jit Patel *(VP-Res Bus Dev)*
Andrew Rakeman *(Dir-Discovery Res)*
Christopher Rucas *(Dir-PR-Natl)*
Richard T. Hewlett *(Pres-Metro Detroit & Southeast Michigan)*

BREAKTHRU BEVERAGE GROUP, LLC

60 E 42nd St Ste 1915, New York, NY 10165
Tel.: (708) 298-3333
Web Site:
  https://www.breakthrubev.com
Year Founded: 1944
Sales Range: $5-14.9 Billion
Emp.: 7,000
Offices of Other Holding Companies
N.A.I.C.S.: 551112
Julian Burzynski *(COO)*
Raymond Herrmann *(Chm)*
Gene Luciana *(CFO)*
Rich Ostermann *(Controller)*
Charles Merinoff *(Vice Chm)*

Ann Giambusso *(Exec VP-HR)*
Dennis DiMaggio *(Dir-Bus Dev)*
Paul Fipps *(VP-Bus Svcs)*
Andrew Crisses *(Exec VP-Strategy & Corp Affairs)*
Gerald L. Baxter *(VP-Natl Accts)*
Arlyn Miller *(Gen Counsel & Exec VP)*
Bob Catalani *(Exec VP-Sls & Mktg)*
Kristen Bareuther *(VP-Dev)*
Joseph Bruhin *(CIO & Sr VP)*
Kevin Roberts *(Chief Comml Officer)*
Tom Bene *(Pres & CEO)*

Subsidiaries:

Alliance Beverage Distributing Company, LLC **(1)**
1115 N 47th Ave, Phoenix, AZ 85043
Tel.: (602) 760-5500
Web Site: http://www.alliance-beverage.com
Sales Range: $150-199.9 Million
Emp.: 700
Beer, Wine & Liquor Distr
N.A.I.C.S.: 424820
Gary Letter *(Exec VP)*

Bacchus Importers, Ltd. **(1)**
1817 Portal St, Baltimore, MD 21224
Tel.: (410) 633-0400
Web Site:
  http://www.bacchusimportersltd.com
Sales Range: $10-24.9 Million
Emp.: 80
Wine & Liquor Distr
N.A.I.C.S.: 424810
Bruce Gearhart *(Pres)*
Jennifer Hess *(Coord-Sls)*
Michael Baker *(Mgr-IT)*
Anita Totty *(Mgr-Fin)*
Bryant Cuppett *(Mgr-Warehouse)*
Donna Haifley *(Controller)*
Lou Zwirlein *(VP-Sls)*
Russell Benson *(Mng Dir & Dir-Sls)*
Shannon Breedlove *(Project Coord-Mdsg)*
Steve Rock *(Dir-Fine Wine)*
Steve Beck *(Mng Dir & Sls Mgr-Field)*

Beverage Distributors Company, LLC **(1)**
14200 E Moncrieff Pl Ste E, Aurora, CO 80011
Tel.: (303) 371-3421
Web Site: http://www.beveragedistr.com
Sales Range: $200-249.9 Million
Emp.: 400
Beer, Wine & Distilled Spirits Distr
N.A.I.C.S.: 424820
Justin Voigts *(CFO)*
John Johnson *(VP & Gen Mgr-Ops)*
Jeff Ryckman *(VP-IT)*
John Slater *(Mgr-Pur)*
Melissa Scott *(Dir-HR)*

Breakthru Beverage Illinois **(1)**
3333 S Laramie Ave, Cicero, IL 60804
Tel.: (708) 298-3333
Web Site: http://www.breakthrubev.com
Beer & Liquor Distr
N.A.I.C.S.: 424810

Breakthru Beverage Minnesota **(1)**
489 Prior Ave N, Saint Paul, MN 55104
Tel.: (651) 646-7821
Web Site: http://www.breakthrubev.com
Beer & Liquor Distr
N.A.I.C.S.: 424810

Breakthru Beverage Nevada **(1)**
1849 W Cheyenne Ave, North Las Vegas, NV 89032
Tel.: (702) 699-8880
Web Site: http://www.breakthrubev.com
Beer & Liquor Distr
N.A.I.C.S.: 424810

Breakthru Beverage Wisconsin **(1)**
500 W N Shore Dr, Hartland, WI 53045
Tel.: (262) 821-0600
Web Site: http://www.breakthrubev.com
Beer & Liquor Distr
N.A.I.C.S.: 424810

Connecticut Distributors, Inc. **(1)**
333 Lordship Blvd, Stratford, CT 06615-7100
Tel.: (203) 377-1440
Web Site: http://www.ctdist.com

Emp.: 276
Wine & Liquor Distr
N.A.I.C.S.: 424820
Brian Albenze *(Pres)*

Efficiency Enterprises Inc. **(1)**
4601 SW 30th St, Davie, FL 33314
Tel.: (561) 752-8510
Web Site: http://www.efficiencyleasing.com
Truck Leasing Services
N.A.I.C.S.: 532120
Joseph Martarella Sr. *(Pres & CEO)*

Empire Merchants North, LLC **(1)**
16 Houghtaling Rd, West Coxsackie, NY 12192
Tel.: (518) 731-5200
Web Site: http://www.empirenorth.com
Sales Range: $25-49.9 Million
Emp.: 200
Wine & Distilled Beverage Distr
N.A.I.C.S.: 424820
Carol G. Brown *(Exec Dir-HR)*
John Devin *(Pres & CEO)*
Patrick Arlantico *(COO)*

Empire Merchants, LLC **(1)**
19-50 48th St, Astoria, NY 11105
Tel.: (718) 726-2500
Web Site: http://www.empiremerchants.com
Sales Range: $100-124.9 Million
Emp.: 1,800
Wholesale Liquor Distr
N.A.I.C.S.: 424820
E. Lloyd Sobel *(CEO)*

Branch (Domestic):

Empire Merchants, LLC - Brooklyn **(2)**
16 Bridgewater St, Brooklyn, NY 11222-3804
Tel.: (718) 383-5500
Web Site: http://www.empiremerchants.com
Rev.: $1,270,000,000
Emp.: 1,600
Wine & Distilled Beverages Mfr
N.A.I.C.S.: 424820
E. Lloyd Sobel *(Pres & CEO)*
Terreence A. Arlotta *(CFO)*
Stephen E. Meresman *(Sec)*

Premier Beverage Company, LLC **(1)**
9801 Premier Pkwy, Miramar, FL 33025
Tel.: (954) 436-9200
Web Site: http://www.premier-bev.com
Sales Range: $50-74.9 Million
Emp.: 500
Wine & Liquor Distr
N.A.I.C.S.: 424810

Prestige Wines Distributors, LLC **(1)**
525 Progress Dr Ste K, Linthicum Heights, MD 21090-2250
Tel.: (704) 969-9463
Web Site: http://www.prestigewines.com
Wine & Liquor Distr
N.A.I.C.S.: 424820

R&R Marketing, LLC **(1)**
10 Patton Dr, West Caldwell, NJ 07006
Tel.: (973) 228-5100
Web Site: http://www.rrmarketing.com
Sales Range: $50-74.9 Million
Emp.: 240
Wine & Spirits Distr
N.A.I.C.S.: 424820
Dennis M. Portsmore *(CFO & VP)*
Dennis A. Resnick *(Dir-Sls & Mktg)*
Jon Maslin *(Pres & CEO)*
Douglas Siegel *(VP-Ops)*

Reliable Churchill, LLP **(1)**
7621 Energy Pkwy, Baltimore, MD 21226
Tel.: (410) 439-5000
Web Site: http://www.reliable-churchill.com
Sales Range: $25-49.9 Million
Emp.: 200
Wine & Liquor Distr
N.A.I.C.S.: 424810
Jim Smith *(Chm & CEO)*
Kevin Dunn *(Pres & COO)*

The Ben Arnold-Sunbelt Beverage Company of South Carolina, L.P. **(1)**
101 Beverage Blvd, Ridgeway, SC 29130
Tel.: (803) 337-3500
Web Site: http://www.benarnold-sunbelt.com

Sales Range: $200-249.9 Million
Emp.: 250
Wine & Distilled Spirits Distr
N.A.I.C.S.: 424820
Mike Sisk *(CFO & Exec VP)*
Sean O'Connor *(Pres)*
Martin Fettig *(VP-Mktg)*
Robert Gist *(VP-Ops)*
Frank Parks *(VP-HR)*

Washington Wholesale Liquor Company, LLC **(1)**
2800 V St NE Unit E, Washington, DC 20018
Tel.: (202) 832-5600
Web Site: http://www.washington-wholesale.com
Sales Range: $10-24.9 Million
Emp.: 100
Wine & Liquor Distr
N.A.I.C.S.: 424820
Kevin Dunn *(Pres)*

Wine Warehouse, LLC **(1)**
6550 E Washington Blvd, Los Angeles, CA 90040
Web Site: http://www.winewarehouse.com
Beer, Wine & Liquor Stores
N.A.I.C.S.: 445320
James P. Myerson *(Chm & CEO)*
Greg Akins *(Acting Exec VP)*

BREATHOMETER, INC.

330 Primrose Rd Ste 407, Burlingame, CA 94010
Tel.: (415) 425-9980
Web Site:
  http://www.breathometer.com
Sales Range: $10-24.9 Million
Emp.: 13
Smartphone Breathalyzer
N.A.I.C.S.: 513210
Charles Michael Yim *(Founder & CEO)*
Matt Sammons *(VP-Sls)*
Joe Xue *(Engr-Lead Mobile)*
Alex Yim *(Engr-Web Software)*
Jonathan Gallagher *(Sr Engr-Hardware)*
Kenton Ngo *(Engr-Sr Project)*
Larry Arne *(Sr Dir-Hardware)*
Michael Golomb *(CFO)*
Royal Wang *(Sr Engr-R&D)*
Russ Harris *(COO)*
Tim Ratto *(CTO)*
Val Valentine *(Dir-Hardware Engrg)*
Gary Kaplan *(COO)*

BREAUX MART INC.

2904 Severn Ave, Metairie, LA 70002
Tel.: (504) 885-9022
Web Site:
  https://www.breauxmart.com
Sales Range: $25-49.9 Million
Emp.: 220
Owner & Operator of Grocery Stores
N.A.I.C.S.: 445110
Jimmie Johnson *(Head-Cashier)*

BREAZEALE, SACHSE & WILSON, LLP.

1 American Pl 301 Main St Ste 2300, Baton Rouge, LA 70801
Tel.: (225) 387-4000
Web Site: https://www.bswllp.com
Year Founded: 1928
Sales Range: $10-24.9 Million
Emp.: 190
Law firm
N.A.I.C.S.: 541110
Scott N. Hensgens *(Mng Partner-Baton Rouge)*
Jeanne C. Comeaux *(Partner-Baton Rouge)*
John A. Moore *(COO)*
David R. Cassidy *(Partner-Baton Rouge)*
Clay J. Countryman *(Partner-Baton Rouge)*
John W. Barton Jr. *(Partner-Baton Rouge)*

Brechbuhler Scales Inc.—(Continued)

BRECHBUHLER SCALES INC.
1424 Scales St SW, Canton, OH
44706
Tel.: (330) 453-2424   OH
Web Site:
 https://www.brechbuhler.com
Year Founded: 1929
Sales Range: $10-24.9 Million
Emp.: 200
Provider of Weighing Equipment
N.A.I.C.S.: 423440
Kraig Brechbuhler (Pres)

**BRECKENRIDGE HOLDING
COMPANY**
471 Kalamath St, Denver, CO 80204
Tel.: (303) 623-2739
Web Site: http://www.breckenridge
 brewery.com
Sales Range: $10-24.9 Million
Emp.: 200
Holding Company
N.A.I.C.S.: 551112
B. J. Langton (Controller)
Edward A. Cerkovnik (Founder, Pres
 & Co-CEO)

Subsidiaries:

BBD Acquisition Co   (1)
2220 Blake St, Denver, CO 80205
Tel.: (303) 297-3644
Web Site: http://www.breckbrew.com
Sales Range: $1-9.9 Million
Emp.: 37
Beer (Alcoholic Beverage)
N.A.I.C.S.: 312120
Ed Cerkovnik (Pres)

BRECKENRIDGE IS, INC.
245 Town Park Dr Ste 200, Kenne-
saw, GA 30144
Tel.: (678) 322-3536
Web Site: http://www.breckis.com
Insurance Services
N.A.I.C.S.: 524298
Bill Chesley (Exec VP-Fin & Ops)
James Robertson (Exec VP-Bus Dev)
Dick Eichhorn (Founder)

Subsidiaries:

Breckenridge Insurance Services (1)
3870 S Lindbergh Ste 100, Saint Louis, MO
63127
Tel.: (314) 725-8394
Web Site: http://www.breckis.com
Sales Range: $25-49.9 Million
Emp.: 25
Insurance Services
N.A.I.C.S.: 524210
John N. Harmon (VP-Middle Market Broker-
 age)
Jean M. Regan (VP-Acctg)
Jino Masone (COO)
Sonya O'Malley (VP-HR)
Chris Mitchell (CTO)
Alan Lewis (VP-Wholesale Brokerage)
Pete Feeney (Pres-Brokerage)
Ron Boudreaux (Exec VP-Natl Accts)
Victoria Dearing (Sr VP-Wholesale Broker-
 age Team)
Trevor Pierce (VP-Wholesale Brokerage
 Team-South & East)
Kristopher Parsons (Sr VP-Sr Broker)

BRECKINRIDGE HEALTH, INC.
1011 Old Hwy 60, Hardinsburg, KY
40143
Tel.: (270) 756-7000   KY
Web Site:
 http://www.breckinridgehealth.org
Year Founded: 1947
Sales Range: $10-24.9 Million
Emp.: 264
Community Health Care Services
N.A.I.C.S.: 621498
Angela Portman (CEO)

BRECO HOLDINGS, INC

7941 Katy Fwy Ste 529, Houston, TX
77024-1924
Tel.: (713) 869-0900   TX
Investment Holding Company
N.A.I.C.S.: 551112
Alfredo Brener (Pres)

Subsidiaries:

Numero Uno Markets   (1)
701 E Jefferson Blvd, Los Angeles, CA
90011
Tel.: (323) 846-5842
Web Site:
 http://www.numerounomarkets.com
Supermarket Operator
N.A.I.C.S.: 445110
Douglas Minor (CEO)

**BREDEMANN CHEVROLET
INC.**
1401 W Dumpster, Park Ridge, IL
60068
Tel.: (847) 698-1234
Web Site:
 http://www.bredemannchevy.com
Sales Range: $1-9.9 Million
Emp.: 47
Automobiles, New & Used
N.A.I.C.S.: 441110
John Bredemann (CEO)
Duey Schroeder (Mgr-Fleet & Comml
 Vehicles)
Marty Bredemann (Gen Mgr-Lexus)
Joseph J. Bredemann Sr. (Pres)

BREED & CO. INC.
718 W 29th St, Austin, TX 78705
Tel.: (512) 474-6679
Web Site:
 https://www.breedandco.com
Rev.: $10,000,000
Emp.: 45
Hardware Stores
N.A.I.C.S.: 444140
Truman Breed (Pres)
Dave Barker (Pres)

BREEN'S MARKET, INC.
611 E Main St, Palmyra, NY 14522
Tel.: (315) 597-9509   NY
Web Site:
 http://www.breensmarket.com
Year Founded: 1908
Sales Range: $25-49.9 Million
Supermarket Owner & Operator
N.A.I.C.S.: 445110
Michael Breen (Pres & CEO)

BREEZY POINT LP
34555 Chagrin Blvd, Chagrin Falls,
OH 44022
Tel.: (440) 247-5400
Sales Range: $10-24.9 Million
Emp.: 60
Land Subdividers & Developers,
Residential & Golf Course Commu-
nity
N.A.I.C.S.: 237210
Rob Benjamin (VP)

**BREHM COMMUNICATIONS
INC.**
16644 W Bernardo Dr Ste 300, San
Diego, CA 92127-1901
Tel.: (858) 451-6200   DE
Web Site:
 https://www.brehmcommuni
 cations.com
Year Founded: 1919
Sales Range: $50-74.9 Million
Emp.: 100
Newspaper Publishers
N.A.I.C.S.: 323111
Bill Brehm Jr. (Pres & CEO)

Subsidiaries:

Auburn Journal Inc.   (1)

1030 High St, Auburn, CA 95603-4707
Tel.: (530) 885-5656
Web Site: http://www.auburnjournal.com
Sales Range: $10-24.9 Million
Newspapers
N.A.I.C.S.: 513110

Auburn Trader   (1)
1115 Grass Valley Hwy, Auburn, CA 95603-
3439
Tel.: (530) 888-7653
Web Site: http://www.auburntrader.com
Sales Range: $10-24.9 Million
Emp.: 5
Publisher of Daily Except Saturday News-
 paper
N.A.I.C.S.: 513110

Brehm Communications Inc. - Gold
Country Printing Division   (1)
1030 High St, Auburn, CA 95603
Tel.: (530) 852-0279
Web Site: http://www.goldcountryprint.com
Commercial Printing Services
N.A.I.C.S.: 323111
Jim Easterly (Gen Mgr)
Sandy Stockton (Mgr-Bus Ops)
Cesar Gomez (Mgr-Pressroom)
Randy Jaworski (Mgr-Mailroom)
Jeff Royce (Mgr-Sls)

Daily Republican Register   (1)
115 E 4th St, Mount Carmel, IL
62863-2110   (100%)
Tel.: (618) 262-5144
Web Site: http://www.tristate-media.com
Sales Range: $10-24.9 Million
Emp.: 8
Newspaper Publishers
N.A.I.C.S.: 513110
William Brehm (Pres)
Phillip Summers (Publr)

Hi-Desert Publishing Co. Inc.   (1)
56445 29 Palms Hwy, Yucca Valley, CA
92284
Tel.: (760) 365-3315
Web Site: http://www.hidesertstar.com
Sales Range: $25-49.9 Million
Emp.: 70
Publisher of Newspapers
N.A.I.C.S.: 513110
Cindy Melland (Mgr-Adv & Publr)

Lincoln News Messenger   (1)
553 F St, Lincoln, CA 95648-1849 (100%)
Tel.: (916) 645-7733
Web Site:
 http://www.lincolnnewsmessenger.com
Sales Range: $10-24.9 Million
Emp.: 7
Weekly Newspaper Publisher
N.A.I.C.S.: 513110
Deth O'Brian (Gen Mgr)

MT. CARMEL REGISTER
COMPANY   (1)
117 E 4th St, Mount Carmel, IL 62863
Tel.: (618) 262-5144
Publication Services
N.A.I.C.S.: 513110

News West Publishing Company
Inc.   (1)
2435 Miracle Mile, Bullhead City, AZ
86442-7311   (100%)
Tel.: (928) 763-2505
Web Site: http://www.mohavedailynews.com
Sales Range: $10-24.9 Million
Daily Except Saturday Paper Publisher
N.A.I.C.S.: 513110
Gary Milks (Pres & Publr)

Princeton Publishing Co.   (1)
100 N Gibson St, Princeton, IN 47670-1855
Tel.: (812) 385-2525
Web Site: http://www.pdclarion.com
Sales Range: $10-24.9 Million
Emp.: 42
Newspaper Publishers
N.A.I.C.S.: 513110
Greg Burney (Publr)

The Democrat Co.   (1)
1226 Avenue H, Fort Madison, IA 52627-
4544
Tel.: (319) 372-6421
Web Site: http://www.dailydem.com
Sales Range: $10-24.9 Million
Emp.: 40
Newspapers

N.A.I.C.S.: 513110

The Press-Tribune   (1)
188 Cirby Way, Roseville, CA 95678-6420
Tel.: (916) 786-8746
Web Site: http://www.rosevillept.com
Sales Range: $10-24.9 Million
Emp.: 10
Publisher of Daily Newspapers
N.A.I.C.S.: 513110
Erin Mezzetti (Bus Mgr)

The Richfield Reaper   (1)
65 W Center, Richfield, UT
84701-2546   (100%)
Tel.: (435) 896-5476
Web Site: http://www.richfieldreaper.com
Sales Range: $10-24.9 Million
Emp.: 30
Weekly Newspaper Publisher
N.A.I.C.S.: 513110
Chuck Hawley (Publr)
David Anderson (Editor)

WINE COUNTRY PUBLICATIONS,
INC.   (1)
669 Broadway Ste B, Sonoma, CA 95476
Tel.: (707) 938-3494
Web Site:
 http://www.winecountrythisweek.com
Magazine Publisher
N.A.I.C.S.: 513120
Mike Giangreco (Publr)
Chandra Grant (Editor)
Cathy Gore (Editor-Calendar & Office Mgr)
Jeff Burgess (Dir-Circulation & Distr)

Warrick Publishing Co. Inc.   (1)
204 W Locust St, Boonville, IN 47601-1594
Tel.: (812) 897-2330
Web Site: http://www.tristate-media.com
Sales Range: $10-24.9 Million
Emp.: 9
Newspaper Publishers
N.A.I.C.S.: 513110
Gary Neal (Publr)

BREHOB CORPORATION
1334 S Meridian St, Indianapolis, IN
46225
Tel.: (317) 231-8080
Web Site: http://www.brehob.com
Rev.: $30,380,000
Emp.: 180
Motors, Electric
N.A.I.C.S.: 423610
Allen Bland (Mgr-Svcs)
Michael Dottery (Dir-HR)
Rob Grizzle (Dir-Sls)

**BREIHOLZ CONSTRUCTION
CO**
1527 Main St, Des Moines, IA 50314
Tel.: (515) 288-6077
Web Site: https://www.breiholz.com
Sales Range: $25-49.9 Million
Emp.: 70
Industrial Buildings, New Construction
N.A.I.C.S.: 236210
Steve Ferguson (Pres)
Patrick Deal (Controller)

**BREITLING ENERGY CORPO-
RATION**
1910 Pacific Ave Ste 12000, Dallas,
TX 75201
Tel.: (214) 716-2600   NV
Web Site:
 http://www.breitlingenergy.com
Sales Range: $25-49.9 Million
Emp.: 50
Onshore Oil & Gas Properties Explo-
ration & Development
N.A.I.C.S.: 211120
Chris R. Faulkner (Founder, Chm,
 Pres & CEO)
Jeremy S. Wagers (COO, Chief Com-
 pliance Officer, Gen Counsel & Sec)
Thomas Miller (VP-Comm)

BRELIAN, INC.

7830 Westpark Dr, Houston, TX
77063
Tel.: (713) 532-1111   TX
Web Site:
    http://www.salonwholesaler.com
Year Founded: 1985
Rev.: $19,562,315
Emp.: 10
Salon & Spa Equipment & Furniture
Whslr
N.A.I.C.S.: 423850
Frank Tavakoli *(Pres)*

BREMEN CASTINGS, INC.
500 N Baltimore St, Bremen, IN
46506
Tel.: (574) 546-2411
Web Site:
    http://www.bremencastings.com
Year Founded: 1939
Sales Range: $50-74.9 Million
Emp.: 240
Metal Casting Services
N.A.I.C.S.: 331523

BREMEN-BOWDON INVEST-MENT CO
141 Commerce St, Bowdon, GA
30108
Tel.: (770) 258-3315
Sales Range: $25-49.9 Million
Emp.: 375
Tailored Suits & Formal Jackets
N.A.I.C.S.: 315250
Dan Buttiemer *(Chm & Pres)*

BREMER FINANCIAL CORPO-RATION
380 Saint Peter St Ste 500, Saint
Paul, MN 55102   MN
Web Site: http://www.bremer.com
Year Founded: 1943
Sales Range: $350-399.9 Million
Emp.: 2,000
Bank Holding Company
N.A.I.C.S.: 551111
Jeanne H. Crain *(Pres & CEO)*
Ann H. Hengel *(Chief Risk Officer &
Exec VP)*

Subsidiaries:

Bremer Bank, N.A.   (1)
372 Saint Peter St, Saint Paul, MN 55102
Tel.: (651) 288-3751
Web Site: http://www.bremer.com
Federal Savings Bank
N.A.I.C.S.: 522180
Lauren Beecham Henry *(VP-Community Mktg)*
Dan Flaningan *(Chief Strategy Officer)*
Stacy Childers *(Mgr-Municipal Solutions)*

Bremer Business Finance
Corporation   (1)
445 Minnesota St Ste 2000, Saint Paul, MN
55101-2135   (100%)
Tel.: (651) 227-7621
Sales Range: $10-24.9 Million
Emp.: 50
Corporate Lending Services
N.A.I.C.S.: 522291

Bremer Financial Services, Inc.   (1)
445 Minnesota St Ste 2000, Saint Paul, MN
55101-2135   (100%)
Tel.: (651) 227-7621
Web Site: http://www.bremer.com
Investment Management & Trust Services
N.A.I.C.S.: 523940

Bremer Insurance Agencies, Inc.   (1)
445 Minnesota St Ste 2000, Saint Paul, MN
55101   (100%)
Tel.: (651) 734-4426
Sales Range: $50-74.9 Million
Emp.: 100
Insurance Brokerage Services
N.A.I.C.S.: 524210

BRENCO MARKETING CORP

3704 S College Ave, Bryan, TX
77801
Tel.: (979) 260-3835
Web Site:
    http://www.brencomarketing.com
Sales Range: $50-74.9 Million
Emp.: 55
Petroleum Products Sales
N.A.I.C.S.: 424720
Donald H. Broach *(Pres)*
Selvin Kelley Broach *(CEO)*
Nancy Broach *(VP)*

BRENDAN TECHNOLOGIES, INC.
2236 Rutherford Rd Ste 107, Carls-bad, CA 92008
Tel.: (760) 929-7500   NV
Web Site: http://www.brendan.com
Year Founded: 1961
Sales Range: Less than $1 Million
Emp.: 14
Software Mfr
N.A.I.C.S.: 334610

BRENDEN THEATRE CORPO-RATION
4321 W Flamingo Rd, Las Vegas, NV
89103
Tel.: (702) 507-4849
Web Site:
    https://www.brendentheatres.com
Sales Range: $25-49.9 Million
Emp.: 850
Motion Picture Theater Operator
N.A.I.C.S.: 512131

BRENHAM BANCSHARES, INC.
2211 S Day St, Brenham, TX 77833
Tel.: (979) 836-4571   TX
Web Site: http://www.bnbank.com
Sales Range: $10-24.9 Million
Emp.: 3
Bank Holding Company
N.A.I.C.S.: 551111
T. H. Dippel *(Chm)*
Douglas Borchardt *(CFO)*

Subsidiaries:

The Brenham National Bank   (1)
2211 S Day St, Brenham, TX 77833
Tel.: (979) 836-4571
Web Site: http://www.bnbank.bank
Sales Range: $25-49.9 Million
Emp.: 55
National Commercial Banks
N.A.I.C.S.: 522110
T. H. Dippel *(Chm)*

BRENHAM CHRYSLER JEEP DODGE
1880 Highway 290 W, Brenham, TX
77833-5216
Tel.: (979) 451-6727
Web Site:
    https://www.brenhamcjd.com
Year Founded: 1925
Sales Range: $10-24.9 Million
Emp.: 45
Car Whslr
N.A.I.C.S.: 441110
Gregg Appel *(Pres)*
John Jeff Appel *(VP)*
Jeff Hazlewood *(Owner)*
Ruth Lorenz *(Office Mgr)*
Walter Phillips *(Mgr)*

BRENNAN BEER GORMAN ARCHITECTS LLP
161 Avenue of The Americas 3rd Fl,
New York, NY 10013
Tel.: (212) 888-7663
Web Site: http://www.hok.com
Year Founded: 1984
Sales Range: $10-24.9 Million

Emp.: 160
Provider of Architectural Services
N.A.I.C.S.: 541310
Heather Hughes *(Dir-Comm)*
Rebecca Snyder *(Dir-Mktg)*

BRENNAN INDUSTRIES INC.
6701 Cochran Rd, Cleveland, OH
44139
Tel.: (440) 248-1880
Web Site: http://www.brennaninc.com
Sales Range: $25-49.9 Million
Emp.: 300
Supplier of Hydraulic Fittings &
Adapters
N.A.I.C.S.: 423830
David D. Carr *(Pres)*
Thomas Levicky *(Controller)*
John Dewey *(Dir-IT)*
Bill Jarrell *(VP)*
Jeff Worobel *(Dir-Fin)*
Matt Kontur *(Dir-Supply Chain Mgmt)*
Michael Lombardo *(Mgr)*
Angela Sebesy *(Mgr-HR)*
Melissa Veloff *(Mgr-ISO Compliance)*

BRENNAN INVESTMENT GROUP, LLC
9450 Bryn Mawr Ave Ste 750, Rose-mont, IL 60018-5253
Tel.: (847) 257-8800   IL
Web Site:
    http://www.brennaninvestments.com
Sales Range: $10-24.9 Million
Industrial Real Estate Investment
Firm
N.A.I.C.S.: 531390
Scott McKibben *(Chief Investment
Officer & Mng Principal)*
Thomas F. Philbin *(Sr VP-Asset
Mgmt)*
Chris Massey *(Sr VP-Acq)*
Kevin Brennan *(Founder & Mng
Principal-Midwest)*
Michael W. Brennan *(Chm & Mng
Principal)*
W. Troy MacMane *(Mng Principal)*
Robert G. Vanecko *(Mng Principal)*
Tim Gudim *(Mng Principal)*
Robert J. Krueger *(Mng Principal)*
Tod Greenwood *(Mng Principal)*
Allen Crosswell *(Mng Principal)*
Brad O'Halloran *(Mng Principal &
Exec Dir-IR)*
Samuel A. Mandarino *(Gen Counsel)*
Michael Martin *(Sr VP)*
Brian Roach *(Mng Principal)*
John Torp *(VP-Denver)*
Doug Lance *(Sr VP)*
Sharon Fields *(VP-Property Mgmt)*
Amanda Moore *(VP-Property Mgmt)*
Kevin Carlson *(VP-Capital Markets)*
CJ Stempeck *(VP-Capital Markets)*

BRENNER OIL COMPANY INC.
12948 Quincy St, Holland, MI 49424-9262
Tel.: (616) 399-0919   MI
Web Site: http://www.brenneroil.com
Year Founded: 1968
Sales Range: $10-24.9 Million
Emp.: 65
Producer of Petroleum Products
N.A.I.C.S.: 484220
Brad Bartels *(Controller)*

BRENT INDUSTRIES, INC.
695 S Scottsville Rd, Brent, AL 35034
Tel.: (205) 926-4801   AL
Web Site: http://www.brentind.com
Year Founded: 1977
Sales Range: $10-24.9 Million
Emp.: 150
Safety Glove Supply
N.A.I.C.S.: 812332
Royce Earl Willie *(CEO)*

BRENT SCARBROUGH & COMPANY, INC.
155 Robinson Dr, Fayetteville, GA
30214
Tel.: (770) 461-8603
Web Site:
    http://www.brentscarbrough.com
Year Founded: 1985
Sales Range: $25-49.9 Million
Emp.: 210
Water & Sewer Line Structures Con-struction Services
N.A.I.C.S.: 237110
Brent Scarbrough *(Founder)*

BRENTHAVEN
321 3rd Ave S Ste 403, Seattle, WA
98104
Tel.: (360) 733-5608
Web Site:
    https://www.brenthaven.com
Year Founded: 1994
Sales Range: $1-9.9 Million
Emp.: 18
Computer & Equipment Dealers
N.A.I.C.S.: 449210
Scott Armstrong *(CEO)*
David McLeod *(CFO)*

BRENTWOOD ASSOCIATES
11150 Santa Monica Blvd Ste 1200,
Los Angeles, CA 90025
Tel.: (310) 477-6611   CA
Web Site: http://www.brentwood.com
Year Founded: 1972
Emp.: 100
Privater Equity Firm
N.A.I.C.S.: 523999
William M. Barnum Jr. *(Partner)*
Steve W. Moore *(Partner)*
Eric G. Reiter *(Partner)*
Rahul Aggarwal *(Partner)*
Toros Yeremyan *(Mng Dir-Capital
Markets)*
Jonathan Berkowitz *(Operating
Partner-Tech)*
Jay Sung *(Operating Partner-Mktg)*
Craig Milius *(Partner)*
Bill Barnum *(Partner)*
Jonathan Ang *(Mng Dir)*
Ryan Foltz *(Mng Dir)*
Chris Scherer *(VP)*
Chris Reekie *(Mng Dir)*
Alan Chen *(VP)*
Peter Edelson *(VP)*
Patrick McGrorey *(VP)*
Randolph Brown *(Operating Partner-Fin)*
Katherine Mossman *(Industry
Partner-Beauty & Wellness)*
Drew Nations *(Dir-Cybersecurity & IT)*
Sheri Nemeth *(Operating Partner-Ops
& Supply Chain)*

Subsidiaries:

Boston Proper LLC   (1)
1155 Broken Sound Pkwy NW, Boca Raton,
FL 33487
Tel.: (800) 243-4300
Web Site: http://www.bostonproper.com
Online Clothing Retailer
N.A.I.C.S.: 458110
Sheryl Clark *(CMO)*

Excelligence Learning
Corporation   (1)
20 Ryan Ranch Road Ste 200, Monterey,
CA 93940
Tel.: (831) 333-2000
Web Site: http://www.excelligence.com
Educational Products Developer, Mfr & Re-tailer
N.A.I.C.S.: 611710
Dipak Golechha *(COO)*
Eric Reiter *(Chm)*
Anupam Martins *(CEO)*

Brentwood Associates—(Continued)

Subsidiary (Domestic):

Discount School Supply　(2)
20 Ryan Ranch Rd Ste 200, Monterey, CA 93940
Tel.: (800) 627-2829
Web Site:
http://www.discountschoolsupply.com
Early Childhood Educational Books, Toys, Games & Software Online Retailer
N.A.I.C.S.: 459120
Kelly Crampton (CEO)

Frog Street Press, Inc.　(2)
800 Industrial Blvd Ste 100, Grapevine, TX 76051
Web Site: http://www.frogstreet.com
Sales Range: $1-9.9 Million
Emp.: 35
Early Childhood Educational Programs & Publishers
N.A.I.C.S.: 923110
Ron Chase (CEO)
Bill Hunt (Dir-Ops)
Brenda Claborn (CFO)
Sharon Burnett (Dir-Conferences & Special Projects)
Charles Pierson (Pres)

Really Good Stuff, LLC　(2)
448 Pepper St, Monroe, CT 06468
Tel.: (203) 261-1920
Web Site: http://www.reallygoodstuff.com
Early Childhood Programs & Educational Products Distr
N.A.I.C.S.: 611710
Jon Sorneborn (Co-Owner)
Jim Bennett (Co-Owner, Pres & CEO)
Jennifer Garcia (Mktg Dir)

K-Mac Enterprises, Inc.　(1)
1820 S Zero St, Fort Smith, AR 72901
Tel.: (479) 646-2053
Web Site: http://www.kmaccorp.com
Sales Range: $100-124.9 Million
Holding Company; Franchise Fast-Food Restaurants Owner & Operator
N.A.I.C.S.: 551112
Virgil Samuel Fiori (CEO)
Tina Reagan (Pres & COO)

Affiliate (Domestic):

Golden Partners Inc.　(2)
5151 Glenwood Ave, Raleigh, NC 27612
Tel.: (919) 781-9310
Web Site: http://www.goldencorral.com
Sales Range: $25-49.9 Million
Family Restaurant Operator Services
N.A.I.C.S.: 722511

Marshall Retail Group LLC　(1)
3755 W Sunset Rd Ste A, Las Vegas, NV 89118-2368
Tel.: (702) 385-5233
Web Site:
http://www.marshallretailgroup.com
Sales Range: $25-49.9 Million
Emp.: 160
Casino Resort Specialty Retailer
N.A.I.C.S.: 459999

Sea Island Clothiers, LLC　(1)
236-250 Greenpoint Ave Bldg 6 2nd Fl, Brooklyn, NY 11222
Tel.: (718) 532-9000
Web Site: http://www.jmclaughlin.com
Family Fashion & Accessories Retailer
N.A.I.C.S.: 458110

Simply Southern Restaurant Group LLC　(1)
2810 Paces Ferry Rd SE 310, Atlanta, GA 30339
Tel.: (470) 558-0090
Web Site: http://www.chickensaladchick.com
Restaurant Operators
N.A.I.C.S.: 722511
Scott Deviney (Pres & CEO)
Stacy Brown (Founder)
Terry A. McKee (Chief Dev Officer)
Tom Carr (CMO)
Jim Thompson (COO)
Patti Evanosky (Dir-Trng & Dev)
David Ostrander (CFO)
Larissa Allsup (Dir-Franchise Development)
Mary Lou Atkins (VP-HR)
Ryles Dodd (CIO)
Mark Verges (VP-Franchise Development)

Subsidiary (Domestic):

Piece of Cake, Inc　(2)
3215 Roswell Rd NE, Atlanta, GA 30305-1840
Tel.: (404) 351-2253
Web Site: http://www.pieceofcakeinc.com
Commercial Bakeries
N.A.I.C.S.: 311812
Melissa Bunnen (Owner)

Sundance Catalog Co., Ltd.　(1)
3865 W 2400 S, Salt Lake City, UT 84120-7212
Tel.: (801) 973-2711
Web Site: http://www.sundancecatalog.com
Sales Range: $75-99.9 Million
Catalog & Mail-Order Houses
N.A.I.C.S.: 424350
Matey Erdos (Pres & CEO)
Neil Hymas (CFO)
Trish Robinson (VP-Design & Product Dev)
Rick Turek (VP-IT)
Jessica Bassin Fehn (Dir-Mktg)

BRENTWOOD BANK

411 McMurray Rd, Bethel Park, PA 15102
Tel.: (412) 409-9000
Web Site:
http://www.brentwoodbank.com
Sales Range: $10-24.9 Million
Emp.: 85
Federal Savings & Loan Associations
N.A.I.C.S.: 522180
Thomas Bailey (Pres & CEO)
Jeffrey R. Skocik (Chief Lending Officer & Sr VP)
Vincent L. Cassano (VP & Mgr-Residential & Consumer Lending)
Joseph P. Verduci (VP-Relationship Banking)
John C. Nave (Asst VP-Residential Lending)
Brad J. Pascarella (Asst VP-Comml Lending)
Clayton E. Kinlan (Asst VP-Relationship Banking)

BRENTWOOD BIOMEDICAL RESEARCH INSTITUTE, INC.

PO Box 25027, Los Angeles, CA 90025
Tel.: (310) 312-1554　CA
Year Founded: 1988
Sales Range: $1-9.9 Million
Biomedical Research Services
N.A.I.C.S.: 541715
Kenneth Hickman (Exec Dir)
Thoyd Ellis (CFO)
Matthew Rettig (Chm)
Sydney Finegold (Sec)
Robert Baker (Treas)

BRENTWOOD INDUSTRIES INC.

610 Morgantown Rd, Reading, PA 19611-2012
Tel.: (610) 374-5109　PA
Web Site:
http://www.brentwoodindustries.com
Year Founded: 1975
Sales Range: $25-49.9 Million
Emp.: 450
Mfr of Plastic Products
N.A.I.C.S.: 326199
Michael Whittemore (VP-Water Tech)
Jason Eric Evans (CEO)

Subsidiaries:

Brentwood Industries Inc. - NRG Products Division　(1)
621 Brentwood Dr, Reading, PA 19611
Tel.: (484) 651-1300
Plastics Product Mfr
N.A.I.C.S.: 326199
Henry Ramsay (Mgr-Production)

Polychem Systems　(1)
621 Brentwood Dr, Reading, PA 19611-2014
Tel.: (484) 651-1300
Web Site: http://www.polychemsys.com
Sales Range: $10-24.9 Million
Emp.: 30
Mfr of Industrial Plastics
N.A.I.C.S.: 326199
Antonia Barrasse (Coord-Customer Care)
Mike Walker (Dir-Ops)
Vladimir Mekeda (Engr-Design)
Pat Schuster (Gen Mgr)
Sharon Platt (Mgr-Sls-After Market)
Fred Irvin (Reg Mgr)
Michael Whittemore (VP-Water Tech Grp)

BRENTWOOD VENTURE MANAGEMENT, LLC

11150 Santa Monica Blvd Ste 1200, Los Angeles, CA 90025
Tel.: (310) 477-7678
Web Site: http://www.redpoint.com
Year Founded: 1982
Sales Range: $1-9.9 Million
Emp.: 20
Venture Capital Investment Services
N.A.I.C.S.: 523999
Lars Pedersen (Partner & CFO)
Brad Jones (Founder & Partner)
Ryan Sarver (Partner)
Andy Rubin (Venture Partner)
Annie Kadavy (Partner)

Subsidiaries:

Redpoint Ventures　(1)
3000 Sand Hill Rd Bldg 2 Ste 290, Menlo Park, CA 94025
Tel.: (650) 926-5600
Web Site: http://www.redpointventures.com
Sales Range: $1-9.9 Million
Emp.: 40
Investment Advisory Services
N.A.I.C.S.: 523940
Lars Pedersen (Partner & CFO)
Ryan Sarver (Partner)
Tomasz Tunguz (Partner)
Jamie Davidson (VP-Product)

Redpoint Ventures　(1)
1539 Nanjing Road West Kerry Center Tower 2 Suite 1801, Tower 2 Suite 3205, Shanghai, 200040, China　(100%)
Tel.: (86) 2162887757
Web Site: http://www.redpoint.com
Emp.: 9
Investment Services
N.A.I.C.S.: 523940
Kyle Liu (Principal)
Nancy Shi (CFO)
Alex Zhang (Principal)
Reggie Zhang (Partner)
Timothy M. Haley (Founder & Mng Dir)

BRETFORD MANUFACTURING INC.

11000 Seymour Ave, Franklin Park, IL 60131
Tel.: (847) 678-2545
Web Site: https://www.bretford.com
Rev.: $61,600,000
Emp.: 450
Office Furniture, Except Wood
N.A.I.C.S.: 334310
David Chris Petrick (CEO)

BRETHREN HOME COMMUNITY WINDBER

277 Hoffman Ave, Windber, PA 15963
Tel.: (814) 467-5505　PA
Web Site: http://www.cbrethren.com
Year Founded: 1921
Sales Range: $10-24.9 Million
Emp.: 279
Nursing Care Services
N.A.I.C.S.: 621610
Thomas Reckner (CEO)
Emily Reckner (Dir-Social Svcs)
Susan Haluska (Dir-Activities)

BRETHREN RETIREMENT COMMUNITY

750 Chestnut St, Greenville, OH 45331
Tel.: (937) 547-8000　OH
Web Site: https://www.bhrc.org
Year Founded: 1902
Sales Range: $10-24.9 Million
Emp.: 554
Retirement Community Care Services
N.A.I.C.S.: 623311
John L. Warner (Pres & CEO)
Janet E. Julian (COO & Sr VP)
Kara Allread (Chief Admin Officer & VP)
James E. Roe (VP-Admin)

BRETHREN VILLAGE

3001 Lititz Pike, Lititz, PA 17543
Tel.: (717) 569-2657　PA
Web Site: https://www.bv.org
Year Founded: 1897
Sales Range: $25-49.9 Million
Emp.: 677
Retirement Community Operator
N.A.I.C.S.: 623311
Mark Tedford (Dir-Pastoral Svcs)
Nancy Eshleman (Dir-HR)
John N. Snader (Pres & CEO)
David Rayha (VP-Health Svcs)
Carol D. Hess (Vice Chm)
David L. Hawthorne (Sec)
F. Barry Shaw (Co-Chm)
Steven L. Edris (Asst Treas & Asst Sec)
Steven L. Faus (Co-Chm)
Scott Wissler (Dir-Mktg)
J. Eric Brubaker (Treas & Asst Sec)

BRETMOR HEADWEAR, INC.

10525 S Crater Rd, Petersburg, VA 23805
Tel.: (804) 530-8222
Web Site: http://www.bretmor.com
Sales Range: $1-9.9 Million
Hat Distr
N.A.I.C.S.: 424350
Brian Rennecker (Mgr-Acct-Midwest)

BRETZ, INC.

640 W Long, Dighton, KS 67839
Tel.: (620) 397-5329
Web Site:
http://www.agcocorpdealers.com
Sales Range: $1-9.9 Million
Emp.: 10
Boat Dealers
N.A.I.C.S.: 441222
Russell Bretz (Pres)
Austin Bretz (VP)

Subsidiaries:

Bretz Capital Sports Sales, Inc.　(1)
9900 Fairview Ave, Boise, ID 83704
Tel.: (208) 323-1500
Web Site: http://www.capitalsportssales.com
Sales Range: $1-9.9 Million
Emp.: 6
New & Used Boat Dealer
N.A.I.C.S.: 441222
Doug Quinn (Mgr-Svc)

BREVARD FAMILY PARTNERSHIP

2301 W Eau Gallie Blvd Ste 104, Melbourne, FL 32935
Tel.: (321) 752-4650　FL
Web Site: http://www.brevardfp.org
Year Founded: 2001
Sales Range: $10-24.9 Million
Emp.: 40
Community Care Services
N.A.I.C.S.: 624190

BREW

530 University Ave SE, Minneapolis, MN 55414
Tel.: (612) 331-7700

Web Site: http://www.brew-creative.com
Year Founded: 2006
Sales Range: Less than $1 Million
Emp.: 10
Advertising, Production (Ad, Film, Broadcast), Production (Print), T.V., Web (Banner Ads, Pop-ups, etc.)
N.A.I.C.S.: 541810
Michelle Fitzgerald *(Strategist)*
Ned Sundby-Munson *(Art Dir)*

BREWER & COMPANY OF WEST VIRGINIA, INC.

3601 7th Ave, Charleston, WV 25387
Tel.: (304) 744-5314
Web Site:
http://www.brewersprinkler.com
Sales Range: $10-24.9 Million
Emp.: 79
Fire Sprinkler System Installation
N.A.I.C.S.: 238220

BREWER DIRECT, INC.

507 S Myrtle Ave, Monrovia, CA 91016-2813
Tel.: (626) 359-1015
Web Site:
http://www.brewerdirect.com
Year Founded: 2004
Direct Marketing Agency & Fundraising Consulting Services
N.A.I.C.S.: 541613
Randy W. Brewer *(Pres & CEO)*
Brian Hackler *(VP-Ops & Client Support)*
Shellie Speer *(Exec VP-Client Strategic Dev)*
Lolly Colombo *(VP-Client Svc)*
Matt Sommer *(VP & Creative Dir)*
Phil Stolberg *(Exec VP & Gen Mgr)*
Anna Wooton *(Controller)*
Lori Vernon *(Office Mgr)*
David Stolberg *(Acct Strategist)*
Matthew Rayburn *(Acct Strategist)*
Mindy Sherfy *(Account Strategist)*
Rhonda Moore *(Account Strategist)*
Sarah Wallin-Wightman *(Dir-Associate Creative)*
Mindy Bortz *(Designer)*
Stephanie Tippitt *(VP-Digital Strategy & Optimazation)*
Mindy Vanderhoeven *(Mgr-Digital Optimization & Analytics)*
Alison Devriendt *(Project Mgr)*
Carol Li *(Sr Project Mgr)*

BREWER OIL CO.

2701 Candelaria NE, Albuquerque, NM 87107
Tel.: (505) 884-2040   NM
Web Site: https://www.breweroil.com
Year Founded: 1970
Sales Range: $200-249.9 Million
Emp.: 500
Petroleum & Petroleum Products
N.A.I.C.S.: 445131
Charles Brewer *(Pres)*

BREWER SCIENCE, INC.

2401 Brewer Dr, Rolla, MO 65401-7003
Tel.: (573) 364-0300   MO
Web Site:
https://www.brewerscience.com
Year Founded: 1981
Sales Range: $25-49.9 Million
Emp.: 300
Thin Film Polymer Coatings Supplier
N.A.I.C.S.: 325510
Terry Brewer *(Pres & CEO)*
Tony D. Flaim *(CTO)*
Alan Gerson *(Chief Legal Officer & Exec Dir-HR & Facilities)*

Subsidiaries:

Brewer Science Japan, G.K.   (1)
618 MG Meguro Ekimae Bldg 2-15-19, Kami Osaki Shinagawa, Tokyo, 141 0021, Japan
Tel.: (81) 3 4540 1084
Paint & Coating Mfr
N.A.I.C.S.: 325510

Brewer Science Limited   (1)
North Mill 2nd Floor Darley Abbey Mills Darley Abbey, Wyvern Business Park, Derby, DE21 1DZ, United Kingdom   (100%)
Tel.: (44) 1332545888
Web Site: http://www.brewerscience.com
Sales Range: $10-24.9 Million
Emp.: 6
Bonding Technology Mfr
N.A.I.C.S.: 325180
Gianna Murray *(Mgr-Global Office)*

Brewer Science, Inc.   (1)
1743 S Redrock St, Gilbert, AZ 85234-5818
Tel.: (480) 963-0480
N.A.I.C.S.: 325510

Brewer Science, Inc.   (1)
240 Washington Ave Ext Ste 504, Albany, NY 12203
Tel.: (518) 608-6616
Sales Range: $10-24.9 Million
Emp.: 2
Produce Protective Coatings for Semiconductor Manufacturing
N.A.I.C.S.: 325510
Joe Raposo *(Acct Mgr)*

Brewer Science, Inc.   (1)
150 9020 N Capital of Texas Hwy Ste 1, Austin, TX 78759
Tel.: (512) 535-5210
N.A.I.C.S.: 325510

BREWER SEWING SUPPLIES CO

3702 Prairie Lake Ct, Aurora, IL 60504
Tel.: (630) 820-5695
Web Site:
https://www.brewersewing.com
Rev.: $23,472,969
Emp.: 100
Sewing Machines, Household: Electric
N.A.I.C.S.: 424310
Dennis Bromberek *(Mgr-Pur)*

BREWER-GARRETT CO

6800 Eastland Rd, Middleburg Heights, OH 44130
Tel.: (440) 243-3535
Web Site: https://www.brewer-garrett.com
Sales Range: $10-24.9 Million
Emp.: 150
Heating & Air Conditioning Contractors
N.A.I.C.S.: 238220
Lou Joseph *(Pres & CEO)*

BREWER-HENDLEY OIL CO

207 N Forest Hills Rd, Marshville, NC 28103
Tel.: (704) 233-2600
Web Site:
http://www.brewerhendleyoilco.com
Year Founded: 1981
Sales Range: $25-49.9 Million
Emp.: 20
Petroleum Products, Nec
N.A.I.C.S.: 424720
Sharon Scurry *(Mgr-Ops)*
Pat O'Hagan *(CFO)*

BREWSTER DAIRY INC.

800 S Wabash Ave, Brewster, OH 44613
Tel.: (330) 767-3492
Web Site:
https://www.brewstercheese.com
Year Founded: 1964

Sales Range: $25-49.9 Million
Emp.: 200
Producers of Natural & Processed Cheese
N.A.I.C.S.: 311513
Fritz Leeman *(CEO)*
Doug Linhart *(Coord-Safety & Hygiene)*
Emil Alecusan *(CFO & VP)*
Lonnie Via *(Mgr-Facility)*
Mike Reneker *(Supvr-Maintenance)*
Jim Barnard *(Dir-Ops)*
Mike Walpole *(Mgr-Sls-Natl)*

BREWSTER WALLPAPER CORP.

67 Pacella Park Dr, Randolph, MA 02368
Tel.: (781) 963-4800   MA
Web Site: https://www.brewsterwallcovering.com
Year Founded: 1935
Sales Range: $25-49.9 Million
Emp.: 150
Wallcovering, Wallpaper & Related Products Mfr & Distr
N.A.I.C.S.: 423220
Ken Grandberg *(Pres)*

Subsidiaries:

Brewster Wallcovering International Trade (Shanghai) Ltd.   (1)
186 Hedan Rd, Pudong, Shanghai, 201108, China
Tel.: (86) 21 6497 6060
Wallpaper & Wallcovering Distr
N.A.I.C.S.: 424950

Fine Decor Wallcoverings Limited   (1)
Victoria Mill Macclesfield Rd, Holmes Chapel, Crewe, CW4 7PA, Cheshire, United Kingdom
Tel.: (44) 1477536100
Web Site: http://www.fine-decor.com
Emp.: 120
Wallcoverings Mfr
N.A.I.C.S.: 444120
Anthony Garnett *(Mng Dir)*

Provincial Wallcoverings Ltd.   (1)
5659 McAdam Rd, Mississauga, L4Z 1N9, ON, Canada
Tel.: (905) 890-2834
Wallpaper & Wallcovering Distr
N.A.I.C.S.: 424950

BRG PETROLEUM CORPORATION

7134 S Yale Ave Ste 600, Tulsa, OK 74136
Tel.: (918) 496-2626
Web Site: http://www.brgpcorp.com
Rev.: $12,562,159
Emp.: 25
Crude Petroleum Production
N.A.I.C.S.: 211120
B. J. Reid *(Pres & CEO)*
Mike W. Burkhart *(Exec VP)*

BRH & ASSOCIATES

3415 Wake Forest Rd, Raleigh, NC 27609
Tel.: (919) 872-2323
Web Site: http://www.hilton.com
Rev.: $12,900,000
Emp.: 200
Hotel Operations
N.A.I.C.S.: 531120
Connie Wren *(Controller)*

BRI INC.

1550 Larkin Williams Rd, Fenton, MO 63026
Tel.: (636) 227-2535
Web Site: http://www.bri-inc.com
Sales Range: $10-24.9 Million
Emp.: 150
Industrial Machinery & Equipment

N.A.I.C.S.: 423830

BRIABE MEDIA INC.

634 A Venice Blvd, Venice, CA 90291
Tel.: (310) 710-2380
Web Site:
http://www.briabemedia.com
Sales Range: Less than $1 Million
Emp.: 8
Mobile Marketing
N.A.I.C.S.: 541810
James Briggs *(CEO & Mng Dir)*

BRIAN BEMIS AUTOMOTIVE GROUP, LTD.

1875 Dekalb Ave, Sycamore, IL 60178
Tel.: (815) 991-2704   IL
Web Site: http://www.brianbemis.com
Holding Company; New Car Dealerships Owner & Operator
N.A.I.C.S.: 551112
Brian J. Bemis *(Pres & CEO)*

Subsidiaries:

Brian Bemis Auto World, Inc.   (1)
1875 Dekalb Ave, Sycamore, IL 60178
Tel.: (815) 895-8105
Web Site: http://www.hondaofsycamore.com
Sales Range: $10-24.9 Million
Emp.: 65
New Car Dealers
N.A.I.C.S.: 441110
Brian J. Bemis *(Pres)*
Chad Bemis *(VP)*
Joe Emerich *(Mgr-Svc-Imports)*
Keith Krabbe *(Mgr-Body Shop)*
Bobby Weeks *(Mgr-Parts)*

Brian Bemis, Inc.   (1)
1380 Dekalb Ave, Sycamore, IL 60178-3105
Tel.: (815) 895-4584
Web Site: http://www.sycamoreford.com
Sales Range: $10-24.9 Million
New Car Dealers
N.A.I.C.S.: 441110
Brian J. Bemis *(Pres)*

BRIAN CORK HUMAN CAPITAL

1055 Canton St Studio 220, Roswell, GA 30075
Tel.: (770) 569-5103
Web Site:
http://briancorkhumancapital.com
Year Founded: 2002
Sales Range: $10-24.9 Million
Emp.: 12
Key Executive Search & Coaching Services
N.A.I.C.S.: 561311
Brian Patrick Cork *(Founder & CEO)*

BRIAN TAYLOR INTERNATIONAL LLC

100 Cheshire Dr, Griffin, GA 30223
Tel.: (770) 294-4653
Web Site: https://www.btillc.com
Year Founded: 2004
Rev.: $2,800,000
Emp.: 10
Support Services
N.A.I.C.S.: 561990
Brian Taylor *(Principal)*

BRIAN TRADING CO. INC.

6440 W 20th Ave, Hialeah, FL 33016
Tel.: (305) 651-5020
Web Site:
http://www.briantrading.com
Sales Range: $10-24.9 Million
Emp.: 20
Home Furnishing Whslr
N.A.I.C.S.: 423220
Brian Sherriton *(Owner)*

BRIAN UNLIMITED DISTRIBUTION COMPANY, INC.

Brian Unlimited Distribution Company, Inc.—(Continued)

13700 Oakland St, Highland Park, MI 48203-3173
Tel.: (313) 957-5100   MI
Web Site: http://www.budco.com
Year Founded: 1982
Sales Range: $75-99.9 Million
Emp.: 100
Provider of Marketing & Distribution Services
N.A.I.C.S.: 518210
Michael R. Pavan (VP-Sls)
Michael Watson (Sr VP-Sls)
Annette Watts (VP-HR & Trng)
Glenn Fontane (VP-Sls)

BRIARWOOD CONTINUING CARE RETIREMENT COMMUNITY

65 Briarwood Cir, Worcester, MA 01606
Tel.: (508) 852-2670   MA
Web Site: https://www.briarwoodretirement.com
Year Founded: 1974
Sales Range: $10-24.9 Million
Emp.: 280
Continuing Care Retirement Community Operator
N.A.I.C.S.: 623311
Paul F. Bowler (CEO)
Marla Prestone (Dir-Assisted Living)
Anita Thomas (Dir-PR & Community Outreach)
Daria Meshenuk (Dir-Resident Svcs)
Alice Eriksen (Dir-Mktg & Dev)
Robert Evans (Pres)
Stephen Pitcher (Treas)
Robert Chase Sr. (VP)

BRIARWOOD FORD, INC.

7070 E Michigan Ave, Saline, MI 48176
Tel.: (734) 429-5478
Web Site: http://www.briarwoodford.com
Sales Range: $125-149.9 Million
Emp.: 150
New Car Dealers
N.A.I.C.S.: 441110
Jeff Russel (Mgr-New Car Sls)
Tom Bicknell (Mgr-New Car Sls)
Karl Swan (Mgr-Pre-Owned Sls)
Paul Holstein (Mgr-Value Center)
Dawn Tatu (Mgr-Bus)

BRICE ENVIRONMENTAL SERVICES CORPORATION

301 Cushman St, Fairbanks, AK 99701-3520
Tel.: (907) 452-2512
Web Site: http://www.briceinc.com
Year Founded: 1961
Sales Range: $10-24.9 Million
Emp.: 30
Provider of Earthmoving Contracting Services
N.A.I.C.S.: 562910

BRICK AND TILE CORP. OF LAWRENCEVILLE

16052 Governor Harrison Pkwy, Lawrenceville, VA 23868
Tel.: (434) 848-3151
Web Site: http://www.lawrencevillebrick.co
Sales Range: $25-49.9 Million
Emp.: 150
Brick & Structural Clay Tile
N.A.I.C.S.: 327120
Marvin H. Thomas Jr. (Pres)

BRICK INVESTMENT PARTNERS LLC

20 Vesey St, New York, NY 10007
Tel.: (212) 655-9537
Web Site: http://www.brickipllc.com
Holding Company
N.A.I.C.S.: 551112
David R. Hobbs (Mng Partner)

BRICKELL BANK

1395 Brickell Ave, Miami, FL 33131-3012
Tel.: (305) 347-8300   FL
Web Site: http://www.brickellbankmiami.com
Year Founded: 1973
Sales Range: $10-24.9 Million
Emp.: 95
Investment Banking & Financial Advisory Services
N.A.I.C.S.: 523150
Carlos M. Modia (Co-CFO)
Martin G. Prego (Chief Compliance Officer & Sr VP)
G. Frederick Reinhardt (Chm & CEO)
M. Andrew Methven (COO)
Aydin Koymen (Treas)
Evelyn Santana Buonsante (Sr VP-HR)
Elliot Nunez (Co-CFO)
Aida Galvez (Chief Credit Officer & Sr VP)
Alina M. Robau (Chief Lending Officer & Sr VP)

Subsidiaries:

Brickell Global Markets, Inc.   (1)
1395 Brickell Ave, Miami, FL 33131-3012   (84.15%)
Tel.: (305) 347-8300
Web Site: http://www.brickellbankmiami.com
Investment Advisory & Wealth Management Services
N.A.I.C.S.: 523940

BRICKHOUSE SECURITY

980 Avenue of the Americas 3rd Fl, New York, NY 10018
Tel.: (212) 643-7449
Web Site: http://www.brickhousesecurity.com
Year Founded: 2005
Sales Range: $10-24.9 Million
Emp.: 34
Security & Surveillance Products
N.A.I.C.S.: 561621
Bryan M. Parola (Dir-R&D)
Anthony Rios (Acct Mgr-Client)
Robb Jeter (Sr Acct Exec-B2B)

BRICKNER MOTORS, INC.

16450 County Hwy A, Marathon, WI 54448-9599
Tel.: (715) 842-5611   WI
Web Site: http://www.bricknerfamily.com
Year Founded: 1945
Sales Range: $25-49.9 Million
Emp.: 50
New & Used Car Dealers
N.A.I.C.S.: 441110
Darin Weiks (Sls Mgr)

Subsidiaries:

Brickner   (1)
3000 E Main St, Merrill, WI 54452
Tel.: (715) 536-2833
Web Site: http://www.bricknersparkcity.net
Emp.: 30
New & Used Car Dealer
N.A.I.C.S.: 441110

Brickner Chrysler Center   (1)
2525 Grand Ave, Wausau, WI 54403-6921
Tel.: (715) 842-4646
Web Site: http://www.bricknerfamily.com
Sales Range: $25-49.9 Million
New & Used Car Dealers
N.A.I.C.S.: 441110
Cindy Anderson (Gen Mgr)

Brickners of Antigo   (1)
123 E State Hwy 64, Antigo, WI 54409-2959
Tel.: (715) 623-3935
Web Site: http://www.bricknersofantigo.com
Rev.: $6,986,078
Emp.: 35
Dealers of New & Used Cars
N.A.I.C.S.: 441110

BRICKSTREET INSURANCE

400 Quarrier St, Charleston, WV 25301
Tel.: (304) 941-3049
Web Site: http://www.brickstreet.com
Year Founded: 2006
Emp.: 319
Laboratory Testing Services
N.A.I.C.S.: 541380
J. Christopher Howat (CFO, Treas & Sr VP)
Thomas J. Obrokta Jr. (COO, Gen Counsel & Sec)

BRICKTOWN RESTAURANT GROUP, INC.

14504 Hertz Quail Springs Pkwy, Oklahoma City, OK 73134
Tel.: (405) 285-5362   OK
Web Site: http://www.bricktownbrewery.com
Year Founded: 2014
Rev.: $28,105,402
Assets: $8,328,615
Liabilities: $18,017,910
Net Worth: ($9,689,295)
Earnings: ($1,263,676)
Emp.: 894
Fiscal Year-end: 12/31/18
Restaurant Management Services
N.A.I.C.S.: 722511
W. G. Buck Warfield (Pres & CEO)

BRICKYARD BANCORP

6676 N Lincoln, Lincolnwood, IL 60712
Tel.: (847) 679-2265
Web Site: https://www.brickyardbank.net
Sales Range: $25-49.9 Million
Emp.: 29
Bank Holding Company
N.A.I.C.S.: 522110
Mimi Sallis (Pres & CEO)

Subsidiaries:

Brickyard Bank   (1)
6676 N Lincoln Ave, Lincolnwood, IL 60712
Tel.: (847) 679-2265
Web Site: http://www.brickyardbank.net
Sales Range: $25-49.9 Million
Emp.: 25
Provider of Banking Services
N.A.I.C.S.: 522110
Mimi Sallis (Pres & CEO)

BRIDGE GROWTH PARTNERS, LLC

510 Madison Ave 8th Fl, New York, NY 10022
Tel.: (212) 560-1170
Web Site: http://www.bridgegrowthpartner.com
Year Founded: 2013
Investment Advice
N.A.I.C.S.: 523930
Joseph M. Tucci (Founder & Chm)
Nicholas Thomas Long (Mng Partner)
Sander Morton Levy (Co-Founder & Mng Principal)
Nicholas T. Long (Mng Partner)
Yves C. de Balmann (Exec Partner)
Alok Singh (Co-Founder & CEO)
Tom Manley (Chief Admin Officer & Sr Principal)
Christopher J. Chu (VP)
Fletcher Gregory (Mng Dir)
Robert Jones (VP)

Alison Catchpole (CFO & Chief Compliance Officer)
Brad Weckstein (Mng Dir)
Don Callahan (Exec Partner)
Jack Welch (Exec Partner)
Rob Ashe (Exec Partner)
Steve Mills (Exec Partner)
Steve Pusey (Exec Partner)
William J. Teuber Jr. (Sr Principal-Operating)

Subsidiaries:

Active Internet Technologies, Inc.   (1)
655 Winding Brook Dr, Glastonbury, CT 06033
Tel.: (860) 289-3507
Web Site: http://www.finalsite.com
Web Software & Services
N.A.I.C.S.: 541511
Rob Dimartino (Dir)
Angelo Otterbein (Chief Innovation Officer)
Jon Moser (Founder & CEO)

BackOffice Associates, LLC   (1)
75 Perseverance Way, Hyannis, MA 02601
Tel.: (508) 430-7100
Web Site: http://www.syniti.com
Software Developing Services
N.A.I.C.S.: 541511
Alex Berry (Pres-North America)
William D. Green (Chm)
Stephen Webber (CFO & COO)
Kevin Campbell (CEO)
Suzanne Barth (Chief People Officer & Exec VP)
Alok Singh (Owner)
Kate Reed (CMO)

Subsidiary (Non-US):

360Science Ltd.   (2)
15-17 The Crescent, Leatherhead, KT22 8DY, United Kingdom
Tel.: (44) 1372 360 070
Web Site: http://www.360science.com
Data Processing, Hosting & Related Services
N.A.I.C.S.: 518210

Subsidiary (US):

360Science, Inc.   (3)
560 S Winchester Blvd, San Jose, CA 95128
Tel.: (408) 236-7489
Web Site: http://www.helpit.com
Sales Range: $1-9.9 Million
Emp.: 20
Custom Computer Programming Services
N.A.I.C.S.: 541511
Steve Tootill (CEO)
Ben Gallagher (Dir-Sys Dev)
Christina Shaw (Dir-Mktg)
Graham Clark (Dir-Sls)
Josh Buckler (Dir-Bus Dev)
Simon Swan (VP-Bus Dev)

Salient Federal Solutions, Inc.   (1)
4000 Legato Rd Ste 600, Fairfax, VA 22033-2893
Tel.: (703) 891-8200
Web Site: http://www.salientcrgt.com
Emp.: 1,600
Government Agency IT & Engineering Services
N.A.I.C.S.: 541512
Keith Hoback (VP-Benefits & Security Solutions)
Kay R. Curling (Chief HR Officer & Sr VP)
Charles Sowell (Sr VP-Natl Security & Syber Solutions)
J. D. Kuhn (CFO & Sr VP)
Larry Rose (Sr VP-Comml Ops)
Tom Ferrando (Pres & CEO)
PC Manning (Sr VP-C4US Urgent Solutions)
Mark Colturi (Sr VP-Federal Modernization of Sys & Svcs)
Manoj Gandhi (Sr VP-Enterprise Solutions Grp)
Linda Harris (Sr VP-Responsive Mission Support Solutions)
Ken Raffel (Sr VP-Data Analytics & Bus Solutions)
Phil Nolan (Chm)
John Anderson (Pres-Defense & Intel Agencies Div)

Rebecca Miller *(Pres-Health & Civilian Agencies Div)*
Atacan Donmez *(Sr VP-Civilian Svcs Grp)*
Rory Schultz *(Exec Dir-Strategic Programs-Civilian Svcs Grp)*

Subsidiary (Domestic):

Command Information, Inc.   **(2)**
2034 Eisenhower Ave Ste 222, Alexandria, VA 22314
Tel.: (703) 224-2866
Sales Range: $10-24.9 Million
Computer Network Design & Information Technology Support Services
N.A.I.C.S.: 541512

Subsidiary (Domestic):

AnviCom-Command Federal, Inc.   **(3)**
2034 Eisenhower Ave, Alexandria, VA 22314
Tel.: (703) 224-2866
Web Site: http://www.anvi.com
Computer Network Design & Information Technology Support Services to the U.S. Department of Defense
N.A.I.C.S.: 541512

Subsidiary (Domestic):

LIST Innovative Solutions, Inc.   **(2)**
13921 Park Center Rd Ste 500, Herndon, VA 20171
Tel.: (703) 467-0100
Web Site: http://www.listinc.com
Sales Range: $10-24.9 Million
Emp.: 90
Application Software Solutions
N.A.I.C.S.: 541690

BRIDGE HOLDINGS USA, LLC
1170 Lee Wagener Blvd Ste 203, Fort Lauderdale, FL 33315
Tel.: (954) 314-0940
Web Site:
  http://www.skyhopglobal.com
Year Founded: 2014
Sales Range: $10-24.9 Million
Emp.: 400
Transportation Support Services
N.A.I.C.S.: 485999
Kristine Scotto *(Owner)*

BRIDGE LOGISTICS, INC.
5 Circle Fwy, Cincinnati, OH 45246
Tel.: (513) 874-7444
Web Site:
  http://www.bridgelogisticsinc.com
Year Founded: 2003
Sales Range: $1-9.9 Million
Emp.: 30
Third-Party Logistics Providing Transportation Services Throughout the U.S & Canada
N.A.I.C.S.: 484121
Jim Campbell *(Pres)*

BRIDGE PARTNERS CONSULTING
3240 Eastlake Ave E Suite 200, Seattle, WA 98102
Tel.: (206) 219-5634
Web Site: http://www.bridgepartners
  consulting.com
Year Founded: 2007
Business Consultancy Offering Technology, Marketing, Business Transformation & Sales Strategies for Companies
N.A.I.C.S.: 541618
Jerry Leishman *(Dir)*
Tim Gunderson *(Mgr-Mktg)*
Michael P. McDonald *(Mgr-Advanced Analytics)*
Ksenija Pergar *(Mgr)*
Matt Hansink *(Sr Mgr)*
Matthew Albert *(Mng Dir)*
Curtis Metz *(Sr Mgr)*
Cynthia Larowe *(Dir-Practice)*
Danita Cain *(Sr Mgr)*

Jim Leff *(Principal)*
Christine King *(Mng Dir-Talent)*
Frank Myers *(Mgr-Payroll)*
Kathy Chung *(Mgr)*
John Tribble *(Mng Dir)*
Todd Vold *(Partner)*
Jennifer Kerns *(Mgr)*
Rachel Evans *(Mgr-HR)*
Zac Lysen *(CFO)*
Rebecca Jones *(Partner & Chief Customer Officer)*

BRIDGE PRIVATE LENDING, LP
4639 Falls Rd # 2, Baltimore, MD 21209-4914
Tel.: (410) 538-1990   **MD**
Sales Range: $1-9.9 Million
Emp.: 3
Business Lending Services
N.A.I.C.S.: 522310
David Borinsky *(Mng Member)*

BRIDGE PUBLICATIONS INC.
5600 E Olympic Blvd, Los Angeles, CA 90022
Tel.: (323) 888-6200
Web Site: https://www.bridgepub.com
Rev.: $13,000,000
Emp.: 65
Book Publishing
N.A.I.C.S.: 513130
Don Arnow *(Dir-Sls)*

BRIDGE TECHNICAL SOLUTIONS
2730 S County Trl, East Greenwich, RI 02818
Tel.: (401) 398-1900
Web Site: http://www.bridgetechnical
  solutions.com
Year Founded: 2002
Sales Range: $1-9.9 Million
Emp.: 80
Information Technology Staffing Services
N.A.I.C.S.: 561311
Joe Devine *(Partner)*
Mike Mollo *(Mgr-Recruiting & Tech)*

BRIDGE TECHNOLOGY INC
9025 Ctr Pt Dr Ste 400, West Chester, OH 45069
Tel.: (513) 763-8210
Web Site:
  http://www.contactbridge.com
Sales Range: $10-24.9 Million
Emp.: 60
Computer Services
N.A.I.C.S.: 541519
Jeff Lee *(CFO)*

BRIDGECOM LLC
3810 Wabash Dr, Mira Loma, CA 91752-1143
Tel.: (951) 361-7100   **CA**
Web Site: http://www.abgraphics.com
Year Founded: 1955
Sales Range: $25-49.9 Million
Emp.: 44
Printing & Information Management Solutions
N.A.I.C.S.: 323111
Jenny Brown *(Office Mgr)*
Ken Patrick *(Mgr-EDI & ERP)*

BRIDGEMAN'S RESTAURANTS INC.
6201 Brooklyn Blvd, Brooklyn Center, MN 55429-4035
Tel.: (763) 971-2947   **MN**
Web Site:
  http://www.bridgmans.com
Year Founded: 1932
Sales Range: Less than $1 Million
Emp.: 4

Ice Cream Parlors & Soda Fountains Operator
N.A.I.C.S.: 722513
Steve Lampi *(Pres & COO)*

BRIDGEPOINT SYSTEMS
4282 S 590 W, Salt Lake City, UT 84123-2522
Tel.: (801) 261-1282
Web Site:
  https://www.bridgepoint.com
Rev.: $22,524,650
Emp.: 120
Carpet & Rug Cleaning Equipment & Supplies, Commercial
N.A.I.C.S.: 423850
Rob Hanks *(Pres)*
Dave Hanks *(VP)*
John Sirrine *(CFO)*
Steve Johnson *(Mgr-Sls)*

BRIDGEPOINT TECHNOLOGIES
1111 W 22nd St Ste 245, Oak Brook, IL 60523
Tel.: (630) 368-2981
Web Site:
  http://www.mybridgepoint.com
Year Founded: 2004
Rev.: $6,600,000
Emp.: 52
Computer System Design Services
N.A.I.C.S.: 541512
Michael Millhouse *(Pres & CEO)*
Brian Sharp *(CFO & VP)*
John Gavilan *(CTO)*
Laura Barker *(COO)*

BRIDGEPORT EQUIPMENT & TOOL
500 Hall St Ste 2, Bridgeport, OH 43912
Tel.: (740) 635-1129
Web Site:
  https://www.bridgeportequip.com
Year Founded: 1995
Sales Range: $1-9.9 Million
Emp.: 50
Equipment & Tool Rental Services
N.A.I.C.S.: 532289
Thomas Knight *(Owner)*

BRIDGEPORT PARTNERS LP
220 Fifth Ave 18th Fl, New York, NY 10001
Tel.: (650) 385-8776
Web Site:
  https://www.bgptpartners.com
Emp.: 100
Investment Services
N.A.I.C.S.: 523999
Frank G. D'Angelo *(Partner)*

BRIDGER COAL COMPANY
932 9 Mile Rd, Point of Rocks, WY 82942
Tel.: (307) 922-7600
Rev.: $64,900,000
Emp.: 360
Bituminous Coal & Lignite Surface Mining
N.A.I.C.S.: 212114
John Brown *(Gen Mgr)*

BRIDGER INSURANCE AGENCY, INC.
389 S Ferguson Ave Ste 210, Bozeman, MT 59718
Tel.: (406) 922-5110
Web Site:
  https://www.bridgerinsurance.com
Year Founded: 2005
Insurance Agencies & Brokerages
N.A.I.C.S.: 524210
Chris Harrison *(Founder)*

BRIDGER PHOTONICS, INC.
2310 University Way Bldg 4-4, Bozeman, MT 59715
Tel.: (406) 585-2774
Web Site:
  https://www.bridgerphotonics.com
Year Founded: 2006
Sales Range: $1-9.9 Million
Emp.: 15
Laser Product Mfr
N.A.I.C.S.: 334510
Peter Roos *(Co-Founder & CEO)*
Chris Wilson *(Engr-Mechanical)*

BRIDGER VALLEY ELECTRIC ASSOCIATION, INC.
40014 Business Loop I-80, Lyman, WY 82937
Tel.: (307) 786-2800   **WY**
Web Site: https://www.bvea.coop
Year Founded: 1938
Sales Range: $1-9.9 Million
Emp.: 35
Electric Power Distr
N.A.I.C.S.: 221122
Gary Nix *(VP)*

BRIDGER, LLC.
6100 W Plano Pkwy Ste 1600, Plano, TX 75093
Tel.: (214) 722-6960
Web Site:
  http://www.bridgergroup.com
Year Founded: 2009
Sales Range: $1-4.9 Billion
Emp.: 50
Logistic Consulting & Transportation Services
N.A.I.C.S.: 541614
Jeremy H. Gamboa *(COO & Exec VP)*
Otis Randle *(Dir-Environmental & Regulatory Compliance)*
Les Patterson *(Sr VP-Pipelines & Terminals)*
Guillermo Grossi *(VP-Mktg-Crude Oil)*
Todd Soiefer *(CFO & Exec VP)*
Julio E. Rios II *(Pres & CEO)*

BRIDGES & COMPANY, INC.
1300 Brighton Rd, Wexford, PA 15233-1630
Tel.: (412) 321-5400   **PA**
Web Site: http://www.bridgespbt.com
Year Founded: 1983
Sales Range: $125-149.9 Million
Emp.: 150
Provider of Commercial Construction Services
N.A.I.C.S.: 236220
Paul R. Bridges *(Founder & Principal)*
Mark A. Davis *(Principal)*
Paul A. Marquart *(Pres)*
Steve Breuner *(Founder)*

BRIDGESTONE MULTIMEDIA GROUP
300 N Mckemy Ave, Chandler, AZ 85226
Tel.: (866) 774-3774
Web Site: http://www.gobmg.com
Christian Media Distr
N.A.I.C.S.: 512120
David Austin *(Exec VP-Sls & Ops)*
Patrick Smith *(CFO)*

BRIDGEVINE, INC.
2770 Indian River Blvd Ste 400, Vero Beach, FL 32960
Tel.: (470) 719-4535
Web Site: http://www.bridgevine.com
Year Founded: 2003
Sales Range: $25-49.9 Million
Emp.: 95
Web Marketing Services
N.A.I.C.S.: 519290

Bridgevine, Inc.—(Continued)

Mark Weibel *(Chief Acquisition Officer)*
Mark Wilkinson *(Sr VP-Enterprise Client Svcs)*
Sean Barry *(CEO)*
Chris Lefebvre *(Exec VP-Bus Dev)*
John Pumpelly *(CFO)*
John Caplinger *(Chief Customer Officer)*

BRIDGEWATER RESOURCES CORPORATION

N 10905 Prospect Dr, Bessemer, MI 49911-9711
Tel.: (906) 663-0260　　　　**TX**
Year Founded: 1982
Sales Range: $300-349.9 Million
Emp.: 600
Holding Company: Lumber, Logs, Flooring Hardwood
N.A.I.C.S.: 551112
Lori J. Poulos *(CEO)*

Subsidiaries:

Connor Forest Industries, Inc.　　(1)
N 10905 Prospect Dr, Bessemer, MI 49911-9711
Tel.: (906) 663-0260
Sales Range: $10-24.9 Million
Emp.: 3
Logging & Sawmills
N.A.I.C.S.: 561110

BRIDGEWATER SAVINGS BANK

756 Orchard St, Raynham, MA 02767
Tel.: (508) 884-3300
Web Site:
http://www.bridgewatersavings.com
Year Founded: 1872
Sales Range: $10-24.9 Million
Emp.: 100
Fiscal Year-end: 12/19/14
Federal Savings Bank
N.A.I.C.S.: 522180
Glenn Silverberg *(VP)*
John Moran *(Officer-Comml Loan & VP)*
Peter Dello Russo *(Pres & CEO)*
Richard Fisher *(COO & Exec VP)*

BRIDGEWAY REHABILITATION SERVICES

615 N Broad St, Elizabeth, NJ 07208
Tel.: (908) 355-7886　　　　**NJ**
Web Site:
http://www.bridgewayrehab.com
Year Founded: 1972
Sales Range: $10-24.9 Million
Emp.: 291
Behavioral Healthcare Services
N.A.I.C.S.: 622010
Cory Storch *(Exec Dir)*
Lisa Vara *(Dir-Program For Assertive Community Treatment)*
Dave D'Antonio *(Program Dir)*

BRIDGEWELL INC.

10 Dearborn St, Peabody, MA 01960
Tel.: (781) 593-1088　　　　**MA**
Web Site: https://www.bridgewell.org
Year Founded: 1958
Sales Range: $25-49.9 Million
Emp.: 1,400
Disability Assistance Services
N.A.I.C.S.: 624120
John Hyland *(Dir-IT)*
Laura K. McNamara *(Dir-Program Ops)*
Inge Peters *(Dir-HR)*
Elaine White *(Dir-Housing)*
Rita McAteer *(Dir-Dev & Mktg)*
James F. Low *(CFO)*
Christopher Tuttle *(Interim CEO)*
Robin Sutherland *(Chm)*

BRIDGEWELL INCOME TRUST INC.

710 Vassar St, Orlando, FL 32804　　FL
Year Founded: 2012
Real Estate Investment Trust
N.A.I.C.S.: 525990
Lindsay T. Parrett *(Pres, CEO, CFO & Treas)*

BRIDGEWEST GROUP, INC.

7310 Miramar Rd Ste 500, San Diego, CA 92126
Tel.: (858) 412-2027
Web Site: http://bridgewestgroup.com
Privater Equity Firm
N.A.I.C.S.: 523999
Massih Tayebi *(Co-Founder, Chm & Partner)*
Masood Tayebi *(Co-Founder, CEO & Partner)*
Kevin Russell *(Chief Legal Officer & Partner)*
Saum Vahdat *(Dir-Fin & Corp Strategy)*
Chandima Mendis *(Portfolio Mgr)*
Aja Harbert *(Dir-HR)*
Chris Wendle *(Controller)*
Tom Giffin *(Mng Dir-Bridgewest Fin)*
Kathryn L. Munro *(Principal)*

BRIDGTON HOSPITAL

10 Hospital Dr, Bridgton, ME 04009
Tel.: (207) 647-6000　　　　**ME**
Web Site:
http://www.bridgtonhospital.org
Year Founded: 1917
Sales Range: $50-74.9 Million
Emp.: 414
Healtcare Services
N.A.I.C.S.: 622110
Andrey J. MacIntyre *(Sec)*
Peter Wright *(Pres)*

BRIECHLE-FERNANDEZ MARKETING SERVICES INC.

625 Industrial Way W Ste 7, Eatontown, NJ 07724
Tel.: (732) 982-8222
Web Site:
http://www.bfmarketing.com
Year Founded: 1984
Sales Range: $10-24.9 Million
Emp.: 21
Advertising Agencies
N.A.I.C.S.: 541810
Lorenzo Fernandez *(Pres)*
Art Guns *(Dir-Art)*
Christian Fernandez *(Exec VP)*
Richard Lomonaco *(Dir-Creative)*

BRIEFING.COM, INC.

401 N Michigan Ste 2950, Chicago, IL 60611
Tel.: (650) 347-2220　　　　**DE**
Web Site: http://www.briefing.com
Rev.: $6,500,000
Emp.: 40
Online Stock Market Analysis
N.A.I.C.S.: 522320
Dick Green *(Founder & Chm)*
Penny Green *(Pres & CEO)*

BRIEN MOTORS INC.

5200 Evergreen Way, Everett, WA 98203-3632
Tel.: (425) 353-7171　　　　**WA**
Web Site: http://www.brienford.com
Year Founded: 1971
Sales Range: $75-99.9 Million
Emp.: 140
New & Used Car Dealers
N.A.I.C.S.: 441110
Casey Salz *(VP)*
Brian Millhuff *(Dir-Svc)*
Caleb Schramer *(Mgr-New Car)*
Kelleigh Johnson *(Mgr-Quick Lane)*

Mike Ryan *(Mgr-Fleet)*
Chad Anderson *(Asst Mgr-Parts)*
Mark Brown *(Mgr-Fin)*
Ken Fisher *(Mgr-Fin)*
Michael Rider *(Mgr-Gen Sls)*
Isaiah Washington *(Mgr-Internet Sls)*
Paul Wilbur *(Mgr-Internet Sls)*
Alex Tiran *(Mgr-Parts-Columbus)*
Jake Wittke *(Mgr-Special Fin)*
Stephan Campbell *(Mgr-Used Car)*

BRIESS MALT & INGREDIENTS CO.

625 S Irish Rd, Chilton, WI 53014-1733
Tel.: (920) 849-7711
Web Site: https://www.briess.com
Year Founded: 1876
Sales Range: $10-24.9 Million
Emp.: 165
Malts & Brewing Ingredients Mfr
N.A.I.C.S.: 311213
Bob Hansen *(Mgr-Tech Svcs)*
Vincent Coonce *(Dir-Ops)*
Ryan Otoole *(Pres & COO)*
Cynthia Kopesky *(CFO)*

BRIGADE CAPITAL MANAGEMENT, LLC

399 Park Ave 16th Fl Ste 1600, New York, NY 10022
Tel.: (212) 745-9700
Web Site:
http://www.brigadecapital.com
Scientific & Technical Consulting Services
N.A.I.C.S.: 541690
Patrick William Kelly *(COO)*

BRIGANDI & ASSOCIATES, INC. MARKETING COMMUNICATIONS

1918 N Mendell Ste 200, Chicago, IL 60642
Tel.: (773) 278-9911　　　　**IL**
Web Site: http://www.brigandi.com
Year Founded: 1991
Sales Range: $1-9.9 Million
Emp.: 22
Advetising Agency
N.A.I.C.S.: 541810
Karen Kolodzey *(Exec VP)*
Margie Alicea *(Sr VP-Fin)*
Bill Forsberg *(VP-Production + IT Svcs)*
Jennifer Perucca *(Acct Mgr)*
Iris Alicea *(Exec VP-Creative)*
Jerry Campbell *(Sr Copy Dir)*

BRIGANTINE ACQUISITION CORP.

4 Embarcadero Ctr Ste 2100, San Francisco, CA 94111
Tel.: (415) 780-9975　　　　**DE**
Year Founded: 2021
Investment Services
N.A.I.C.S.: 523999
Rufina A. Adams *(CFO & Sec)*
James H. Greene Jr. *(Chm & CEO)*

BRIGGS & CALDWELL

9801 Westheimer Rd Ste 701, Houston, TX 77042
Tel.: (713) 532-4040
Web Site:
https://www.briggscaldwell.com
Year Founded: 2005
Sales Range: $10-24.9 Million
Emp.: 6
Media Planning Agency
N.A.I.C.S.: 541830
Chris Caldwell *(Partner)*
Kellie Briggs *(Pres)*

BRIGGS & STRATTON CORPORATION

12301 W. Wirth St, Wauwatosa, WI 53222
Tel.: (414) 259-5333　　　　**WI**
Web Site: http://www.basco.com
Year Founded: 1909
Rev.: $1,836,605,000
Assets: $1,551,431,000
Liabilities: $1,104,711,000
Net Worth: $446,720,000
Earnings: ($54,083,000)
Emp.: 5,251
Fiscal Year-end: 06/30/19
Gasoline Engines for Outdoor Power Equipment
N.A.I.C.S.: 333611
William H. Reitman *(Pres-Support & Sr VP)*
Harold L. Redman *(Pres-Turf-Global & Consumer Products Grp & Sr VP)*
David J. Rodgers *(Pres-Engines & Power & Sr VP)*
Andrea L. Golvach *(Treas & VP)*
Randall R. Carpenter *(VP-Corp Mktg)*
Joseph T. Liotine *(Pres & CEO)*
Mark A. Schwertfeger *(CFO & Sr VP)*
Jeffrey M. Zeiler *(VP-Product Innovation)*
Kathryn M. Buono *(Gen Counsel, Sec & VP)*
David A. Frank *(VP-Sls-Comml Engines & Power)*
Michelle A. Kumbier *(Pres-Turf & Consumer Products Bus & Sr VP)*
Thomas H. Rugg *(Pres-Job Site/Standby & VP)*

Subsidiaries:

Allmand Bros., Inc.　　(1)
1502 W 4th Ave, Holdrege, NE 68949-8949
Tel.: (308) 995-4495
Web Site: http://www.allmand.com
Power Equipment Mfr & Distr
N.A.I.C.S.: 333912

Billy Goat Industries, Inc.　　(1)
1803 SW Jefferson, Lees Summit, MO 64082
Tel.: (816) 524-9666
Web Site: http://www.billygoat.com
Turf Machinery Mfr & Distr
N.A.I.C.S.: 333111
Will Coates *(Pres)*

Branco Motores Ltda.　　(1)
Rua Tenente Benedito Nepomuceno 153, Bairro Estacao, Araucaria, 83705-190, Parana, Brazil
Tel.: (55) 4132114040
Web Site: http://www.branco.com.br
Gasoline Engine Mfr
N.A.I.C.S.: 333618

Briggs & Stratton (Malaysia) Sdn. Bhd.　　(1)
No 21 Jalan Teknologi 3/3A Surian Industrial Park, Kota Damansara, 47810, Petaling Jaya, Selangor Darul Ehsan, Malaysia
Tel.: (60) 361414889
Gasoline Engine Mfr
N.A.I.C.S.: 333618
Steven Ho Wei Siang *(Mgr-Technical Services)*

Briggs & Stratton (Shanghai) International Trading Co., Ltd.　　(1)
Qingpu Industrial Zone Block A32, Qingpu, Shanghai, 201707, China　　(100%)
Tel.: (86) 2169212133
Web Site: http://www.briggsandstratton.com
Engine Equipment Mfr
N.A.I.C.S.: 333618

Briggs & Stratton Australia Pty. Limited　　(1)
8 Dan Sue Ct, PO Box 048, Dandenong, Hallam, 3803, VIC, Australia　　(100%)
Tel.: (61) 397964900
Web Site:
http://www.briggsandstratton.com.au
Sales Range: $25-49.9 Million
Emp.: 40
Distribution of Lawn Mowers

Briggs & Stratton CZ, s.r.o. (1)
Pekarska 14, 155500, Prague, 5, Czech
Republic (100%)
Tel.: (420) 222995222
Web Site: http://www.briggsandstratton.com
Industrial Machinery & Equipment Mfr
N.A.I.C.S.: 811310

Briggs & Stratton Canada Inc. (1)
6500 Tomken Rd, Mississauga, L5T 2E9,
ON, Canada
Tel.: (905) 565-0265
Web Site: http://www.murray.com
Sales Range: $10-24.9 Million
Emp.: 20
Lawn & Garden Power Equipment & Active
Outdoor Product Retailer
N.A.I.C.S.: 333112

**Briggs & Stratton France
S.A.R.L.** (1)
43 Avenue des 3 Peuples, 78180,
Montigny-le-Bretonneux, France (100%)
Tel.: (33) 892462777
Sales Range: $25-49.9 Million
Emp.: 15
Service & Distribution of Lawn Mowers
N.A.I.C.S.: 423820

**Briggs & Stratton Germany
GmbH** (1)
Max Born Str 2 4, D 68519, Viernheim,
Germany (100%)
Tel.: (49) 620460010
Web Site: http://www.briggsandstratton.com
Sales Range: $1-9.9 Million
Emp.: 16
Distribution of Lawn Mowers
N.A.I.C.S.: 423820

**Briggs & Stratton India Private
Limited** (1)
No 37/1-C Palladam Road Pappam Patti
Privu, Ondipudur, Coimbatore, 641016,
India
Tel.: (91) 4223008555
Gasoline Engine Mfr
N.A.I.C.S.: 333618

**Briggs & Stratton International Hold-
ing BV** (1)
Bijsterhuizen 3171, 6604 LV, Nijmegen,
Netherlands
Tel.: (31) 243723620
Web Site: http://www.briggsandstratton.com
Emp.: 40
Holding Company
N.A.I.C.S.: 551112

**Briggs & Stratton International
Sales** (1)
12301 W Wirth St, Wauwatosa, WI 53222-
2110
Tel.: (414) 259-5333
Web Site: http://www.briggsandstratton.com
Sales Range: $125-149.9 Million
Outdoor Power Equipment, Parts & Acces-
sories
N.A.I.C.S.: 333618

Briggs & Stratton Japan KK (1)
591 Asagoi-cho, Omihachiman, 523-0817,
Shiga, Japan
Tel.: (81) 748 33 3621
Web Site: http://www.briggsandstratton.co.jp
Emp.: 17
Engine Equipment Mfr
N.A.I.C.S.: 333618

**Briggs & Stratton Netherlands
B.V.** (1)
Schepersweg 4C, 6049 CV, Herten,
Netherlands (100%)
Tel.: (31) 475 40 83 83
Web Site: http://www.briggsandstratton.nl
Sales Range: $25-49.9 Million
Emp.: 70
Power Engine Equipments Mfr
N.A.I.C.S.: 333618

**Briggs & Stratton New Zealand
Limited** (1)
54 Apollo dr, PO Box 65155, Rosedale,
Auckland, 0632, New Zealand (100%)
Tel.: (64) 94770827
Web Site:
http://www.briggsandstratton.co.nz

Sales Range: $25-49.9 Million
Emp.: 15
Service & Distribution of Lawn Mowers
N.A.I.C.S.: 423820

**Briggs & Stratton Power Products
Group, LLC** (1)
3300 N 124th St, Wauwatosa, WI 53222
Tel.: (414) 259-5333
Web Site: http://www.briggsandstratton.com
Generators & Pressure Washer Mfr
N.A.I.C.S.: 335312

Unit (Domestic):

**Briggs & Stratton Power Products
Group, LLC - McDonough** (2)
535 Macon St, McDonough, GA 30253
Tel.: (770) 954-2500
Web Site: http://www.snapper.com
Sales Range: $200-249.9 Million
Emp.: 450
Lawn & Garden Equipment Mfr
N.A.I.C.S.: 333112

Subsidiary (Domestic):

Simplicity Manufacturing, Inc. (2)
500 N Spring St, Port Washington, WI
53074-1752
Tel.: (262) 377-5450
Web Site: http://www.simplicitymfg.com
Sales Range: $150-199.9 Million
Emp.: 550
Mfr of Outdoor Power Equipment
N.A.I.C.S.: 333112

**Briggs & Stratton RSA (Proprietary)
Limited** (1)
Unit 4 1510 Zeiss Road Lazer Park, Gau-
teng, Honeydew, South Africa
Tel.: (27) 117948190
Web Site:
http://www.briggsandstratton.co.za
Lawn & Garden Tractor Equipment Mfr
N.A.I.C.S.: 333112

**Briggs & Stratton Representacao de
Motores e Productos de Forca do
Brasil Ltda.** (1)
Av Coronel Marcos Konder 1207 sala 56,
Itajai, 88301-303, Brazil
Tel.: (55) 47 3248 9776
Web Site: http://www.briggs.com.br
Sales Range: $10-24.9 Million
Emp.: 5
Engine Equipment Mfr
N.A.I.C.S.: 333618

Briggs & Stratton Sweden AB (1)
Rotebergssvagen 2, 19278, Sollentuna,
Sweden
Tel.: (46) 8 449 56 30
Web Site: http://www.briggsandstratton.com
Emp.: 7
Engine Equipment Mfr
N.A.I.C.S.: 333618

Briggs & Stratton U.K. Limited (1)
Rd 4 Winsford Industrial Estate, Winsford,
CW7 3QN, Cheshire, United
Kingdom (100%)
Tel.: (44) 1606862182
Sales Range: $25-49.9 Million
Emp.: 20
Distribution of Lawn Mowers
N.A.I.C.S.: 423820
Enian Small (Mgr-Mktg)
Kristina A. Cerniglia (CFO & Sr VP)

**Daihatsu Briggs & Stratton Co.,
Ltd.** (1)
722 Kagami Ryuo Cho, Shiga, 520 2573,
Japan
Tel.: (81) 748582151
Sales Range: $50-74.9 Million
Emp.: 92
Overhead Valve Engines Mfr
N.A.I.C.S.: 336412

BRIGGS & VESELKA CO.
9 Greenway Plz 1700, Houston, TX
77046
Tel.: (713) 667-9147
Web Site: https://www.bvccpa.com
Year Founded: 1973
Accounting, Tax & Business Consult-
ing Services

N.A.I.C.S.: 541211
Ilse Rew (COO)

BRIGGS CORP.
4900 University Ave Ste 200, West
Des Moines, IA 50266
Tel.: (515) 327-6400
Web Site: http://www.briggscorp.com
Sales Range: $25-49.9 Million
Emp.: 225
Medical Documentation Systems,
Training Materials & Professional
Reference Products; Durable & Dis-
posable Medical Products
N.A.I.C.S.: 423450
Tom Young (CFO)
Bruce Dan (Chm & Pres)

Subsidiaries:

Briggs Healthcare (1)
1931 Norman Dr S, Waukegan, IL 60085
Tel.: (800) 526-4753
Web Site: http://www.mabisdmi.com
Emp.: 320
Medical Equipment & Supplies Distr
N.A.I.C.S.: 423450
Bruce Dan (CEO)
Tim Caver (VP-Sls & Bus Dev)

BRIGGS ELECTRIC INC.
14381 Franklin Ave, Tustin, CA 92780
Tel.: (714) 544-2500
Web Site:
https://www.briggselectric.com
Sales Range: $25-49.9 Million
Emp.: 175
Electrical Work
N.A.I.C.S.: 238210
Thomas J. Perry (Pres)
Jeff Perry (VP)
Frank Gandara (Dir-Preconstruction)
Ron Calkins (Project Mgr)
Lisa Cutts (Controller)

BRIGGS INC.
14549 Grover St, Omaha, NE 68144
Tel.: (402) 330-3400
Web Site: http://www.briggsinc.com
Sales Range: $10-24.9 Million
Emp.: 75
Plumbing & Hydronic Heating Sup-
plies
N.A.I.C.S.: 423720
John Ellsworth (CEO)
David Crider (Controller)
Barb Ganey (Mgr-Corp Showroom)
Randy Hassenstab (Asst Controller &
Mgr-Credit)

BRIGHT EQUIPMENT INC.
2935 Bluff Rd, Indianapolis, IN 46225
Tel.: (317) 787-2201 IN
Web Site:
http://www.bobcatofindy.com
Year Founded: 1947
Sales Range: $10-24.9 Million
Emp.: 22
Sales of General Construction Equip-
ment
N.A.I.C.S.: 423810
Joseph Bright (Pres)
John Falk (Controller)

BRIGHT KEY
9050 Jct Dr, Annapolis Junction, MD
20701
Tel.: (301) 604-3305 MD
Web Site: https://www.brightkey.net
Year Founded: 1988
Sales Range: $10-24.9 Million
Emp.: 300
Information Processing & Distribution
& Fulfillment Services
N.A.I.C.S.: 488510
Rita Hope Counts (Pres)
George Abunassar (CIO)
David Elam (COO)

BRIGHT MARKET, LLC
11 W Victoria St Ste 207A, Santa
Barbara, CA 93101
Tel.: (805) 409-9008
Web Site: http://www.fastspring.com
Year Founded: 2005
Sales Range: $100-124.9 Million
Emp.: 20
E-Commerce Merchandising & Fulfill-
ment Solutions
N.A.I.C.S.: 513210
Ken White (Founder)
Michael Ventrella (Sr VP-Worldwide
Sls)
Michael Smith (CTO)
Christina O'Toole (Dir-Mktg)
Brian Howard (Dir-Fin)
Michele Johannes (Dir-Customer
Success)
Scott Halstead (Sr VP-Bus Dev &
Mktg)
Andrea Nelson (VP-People & Culture)
David Nachman (CEO)
Kurt Smith (VP-Product-FastSpring)
Sarah Bottorff (VP-Mktg-FastSpring)
Mark Lambert (CFO)

**BRIGHT SHEET METAL COM-
PANY, INC.**
4212 W. 71st Street Suite A, India-
napolis, IN 46268
Tel.: (317) 291-7600
Web Site:
https://www.brightsheetmetal.com
Emp.: 100
Plumbing, Heating & Air-Conditioning
Contractors
N.A.I.C.S.: 238220

BRIGHT WOOD CORP.
335 NW Hess St, Madras, OR 97741
Tel.: (541) 475-2234 OR
Web Site:
https://www.brightwood.com
Year Founded: 1960
Sales Range: $200-249.9 Million
Emp.: 1,200
Remanufacturer of Lumber
N.A.I.C.S.: 321911
Daryl Booren (Dir-Personnel)

Subsidiaries:

Pioneer Cut Stock Inc. (1)
1941 NW Industrial Park Rd, Prineville, OR
97754
Tel.: (541) 447-5962
Web Site: http://www.pioneercutstock.com
Emp.: 27
Millwork & Flooring
N.A.I.C.S.: 321918
Chris Davis (Gen Mgr)

BRIGHTBOX, INC.
4747 S Pinemont Ste 100, Houston,
TX 77041
Tel.: (281) 252-0979
Web Site:
http://www.brightboxonline.com
Sales Range: $1-9.9 Million
Emp.: 27
Creative Brand Marketing Design
Providers
N.A.I.C.S.: 541512
Kimberley Harrison (Acct Mgr)
Casey Dunn (Acct Mgr)

**BRIGHTEDGE TECHNOLO-
GIES, INC.**
999 Bakerway Ste 500, San Mateo,
CA 94404
Tel.: (650) 627-3500
Web Site: http://www.brightedge.com
Sales Range: $1-9.9 Million
Emp.: 115
Search Engine Optimization Software
N.A.I.C.S.: 513210

BrightEdge Technologies, Inc.—(Continued)

Jim Yu (CEO)
Lemuel Park (CTO)
Joshua Crossman (VP-Client Svcs & Strategy)
Albert Gouyet (VP-Ops)
Tom Ziola (VP-Bus Dev)
Jim Emerich (CFO)

BRIGHTFIELDS, INC.
801 Industrial St, Wilmington, DE 19801
Tel.: (302) 656-9600
Web Site: https://www.brightfieldsinc.com
Year Founded: 2003
Business Consulting Services
N.A.I.C.S.: 541690
Marian Young (Co-Founder & Pres)
Mark Lannan (Co-Founder & Principal)
Matt Jones (Project Mgr)
Cheryl Titcher (Mgr-Mktg)
Gregg Crystall (Sr Program Mgr)
Kathy Stiller (Sr Program Mgr)
Jenna Harwanko (VP & Program Mgr)
Ken Hannoh (Program Mgr)

BRIGHTFLOW.AI, INC.
440 N Barranca Ave Ste 6084, Covina, CA 91723
Tel.: (415) 625-3485   DE
Web Site: https://brightflow.ai
Year Founded: 2019
Financial Consulting Services
N.A.I.C.S.: 522320
Robbie Bhathal (Founder & CEO)

Subsidiaries:

CircleUp Network Inc.   (1)
1300 N Bristol Ste 100, Newport Beach, CA 92660
Tel.: (949) 955-1915
Web Site: http://www.circleup.com
Software Publisher
N.A.I.C.S.: 513210
Rory Eakin (Co-Founder)
Jake Cabala (Head-Institutional Bus)
Ryan Caldbeck (Co-Founder)

BRIGHTFOCUS FOUNDATION
22512 Gateway Center Dr, Clarksburg, MD 20871
Tel.: (301) 948-3244   DC
Web Site: https://www.brightfocus.org
Year Founded: 1973
Sales Range: $10-24.9 Million
Emp.: 40
Scientific Research Funding for Age-Related & Degenerative Diseases
N.A.I.C.S.: 813319
Dave Marks (VP-Fin & Admin)
Diana Campbell (Dir-Strategic Partnerships)
Preeti Subramanian (Dir-Scientific Programs-Vision Science)
Keith Whitaker (Dir-Scientific Programs-Neuroscience)

BRIGHTLANE ACQUISITION CORP.
101 Marketplace Ave Ste 404-128, Miami, FL 32081
Tel.: (904) 509-4227   DE
Investment Holding Company
N.A.I.C.S.: 551112
Peter Hellwig (CEO)

Subsidiaries:

Brightlane Corp.   (1)
1600 W Loop S, Houston, TX 77056
Tel.: (404) 419-6040
Web Site: http://www.brightlanecorp.com
Sales Range: Less than $1 Million
Emp.: 3
Real Estate Services

N.A.I.C.S.: 531190
David Over (CEO)
Erwin Vahlsing Jr. (CFO)

BRIGHTON AGENCY, INC.
231 S Bemiston Ste 1000, Saint Louis, MO 63105
Tel.: (314) 726-0700   MO
Year Founded: 1989
Rev.: $31,294,972
Emp.: 35
N.A.I.C.S.: 541810
Roger E. Yount (Pres & CEO)
Sandra L. Coons (Dir-HR)
Leo Madden (Dir-Adv Svcs)
Mary Roddy Sawyer (Dir-PR)
Amanda Hassler (Acct Exec-PR)
Scott McLure (VP-Agriculture Strategy)
Jared Macke (Dir-Innovation & Analytics)
Mary Barber (Dir-Comm & PR)
Mallory Gnaegy (Mgr-PR Acct)
Chris Yost (Asst Editor-Multimedia)
Kim Gorsek (Acct Exec)
Reigan Massey (Asst Acct Exec-PR)
Madison Molho (Asst Acct Exec)
Jenny Dibble (VP-Engagement & Insights)
Jason Keeven (Dir-Creative)
Richard Labonte (Sr VP-Audience Engagement)
Chris Young (Assoc Acct Exec)
Brittany Phillips (Assoc Acct Exec)
Kristin Rohlfing (Dir-Integrated Media)
Gina Presley (Acct Mgr)
Molly Weber (VP & Dir-Acct Mgmt & Strategic Plng)

BRIGHTON BANK
7101 Highland Dr, Salt Lake City, UT 84121
Tel.: (801) 943-6500
Web Site: http://www.brightonbank.com
Sales Range: $10-24.9 Million
Emp.: 75
State Commercial Banks
N.A.I.C.S.: 522110
Kent A. Nelson (Sr VP & Branch Mgr)
Eric Tadje (VP)

BRIGHTON COLLECTIBLES, INC.
14022 Nelson Ave, City of Industry, CA 91746
Tel.: (800) 628-7687   DE
Web Site: http://www.brighton.com
Year Founded: 1991
Mfr of Apparel & Belts
N.A.I.C.S.: 315990
Jerry Kohl (Co-Founder & Pres)
Terri Kravitz (Co-Founder)

BRIGHTON COMMUNITY HOSPITAL ASSOCIATION
1600 Prairie Center Pkwy, Brighton, CO 80601
Tel.: (303) 498-1600   CO
Web Site: http://www.pvmc.org
Year Founded: 1958
Sales Range: $75-99.9 Million
Emp.: 750
Health Care Srvices
N.A.I.C.S.: 622110
Eric Strim (Dir-Pharmacy)
John Hicks (Pres & CEO)
Tim Brannigan (Dir-IT)

BRIGHTON FORD-MERCURY INC.
8240 W Grand River Ave, Brighton, MI 48114
Tel.: (810) 893-7771
Web Site: https://www.brightonford.com

Sales Range: $150-199.9 Million
Emp.: 130
Sales of New & Used Automobiles
N.A.I.C.S.: 441110
Todd Spilter (CEO)
Chris Boring (Mgr-Internet Sls)
Jeremiah Alvarado (Mgr-Fin)

BRIGHTON HOMES
13111 NW Freeway Ste 200, Houston, TX 77040
Tel.: (713) 460-0264
Year Founded: 1976
Sales Range: $10-24.9 Million
Emp.: 144
Operative Builder Services
N.A.I.C.S.: 236117
John C. Rose (Chief Legal Officer-Houston Div)

BRIGHTON HOMES LTD.
13111 NW Fwy Ste 200, Houston, TX 77040
Tel.: (713) 460-0264
Web Site: http://www.brightonhomes.com
Rev.: $19,600,000
Emp.: 144
Speculative Builder, Single-Family Houses
N.A.I.C.S.: 236115
David Orlando (Pres)

BRIGHTON MANAGEMENT LLC
1901 Main St Ste 150, Irvine, CA 92614
Tel.: (949) 390-6888
Web Site: http://www.brightonmgtllc.com
Year Founded: 1994
Sales Range: $10-24.9 Million
Emp.: 20
Hotel Management
N.A.I.C.S.: 531390
Joseph Fan (Pres)
Michael Schaefer (Exec VP)
Stacy Morris (VP-HR)
James Hsu (Sr VP-Real Estate)
Victor Dollar (Sr VP-Sls)

Subsidiaries:

Ventura Beach Marriott   (1)
2055 Harbor Blvd, Ventura, CA 93001
Tel.: (805) 643-6000
Web Site: http://www.marriott.com
Sales Range: $1-9.9 Million
Hotel
N.A.I.C.S.: 721110

BRIGHTON MAZDA
8282 Grand River Rd, Brighton, MI 48114
Tel.: (810) 227-1100   MI
Web Site: http://www.brightonmazdausa.com
Year Founded: 1987
Car Dealership
N.A.I.C.S.: 441110
Richard Mcintyre (Pres)
Robert Justice (Gen Mgr)

BRIGHTON PARK CAPITAL MANAGEMENT, L.P.
330 Railroad Ave 2nd Fl, Greenwich, CT 06830
Tel.: (203) 542-0750
Web Site: http://www.brightonparkcap.com
Investment Services
N.A.I.C.S.: 523940
Michael P. Gregoire (Partner)
Mark F. Dzialga (Mng Partner)
Mike Gregoire (Partner)
Erica Blob (Partner, COO & Chief Compliance Officer)
Zachary Gut (Partner)

Jeff Machlin (Partner)
Kevin Magan (Principal)
Sam Kentor (Principal)

BRIGHTON PARTNERS, LLC
1201 Peachtree St 400 Colony Sq Ste 530, Atlanta, GA 30361
Tel.: (404) 565-2800   GA
Web Site: http://www.bpequity.com
Year Founded: 2002
Privater Equity Firm
N.A.I.C.S.: 523999
Daniel G. Broos (Founder)

BRIGHTON-BEST INTERNATIONAL, INC.
5855 Obispo Ave, Long Beach, CA 90805
Tel.: (562) 808-8000
Web Site: https://www.brightonbest.com
Year Founded: 1925
Rev.: $3,349,000
Emp.: 17
Metal Coating, Engraving, except Jewelry & Silverware & Allied Services to Manufacturers
N.A.I.C.S.: 332812
Steve Andrasik (VP-Sls)

BRIGHTROCK GOLD CORP.
3872 SW Ridley St, Port Saint Lucie, FL 34953
Tel.: (206) 337-3867
Year Founded: 1995
Gold Mining Services
N.A.I.C.S.: 212220
Mac Shashavar (Chm, CEO & Dir-Acctg)

BRIGHTSOURCE ENERGY, INC.
1999 Harrison St Ste 2150, Oakland, CA 94612
Tel.: (510) 550-8161   DE
Web Site: https://www.brightsourceenergy.com
Year Founded: 2004
Sales Range: $10-24.9 Million
Emp.: 350
Solar Power Generating Plant Mfr
N.A.I.C.S.: 221118
Israel Kroizer (Exec VP-Engrg & Ops)
Daniel T. Judge (Gen Counsel & Sec)
Joe Desmond (Sr VP-Mktg Govt Affairs)
Mathew Brett (Sr VP-Bus Dev)
Steven Goers (Sr VP-Ops)
David Ramm (Chm)

BRIGHTSTAR CAPITAL PARTNERS, L.P.
650 5th Ave 29th Fl, New York, NY 10019
Tel.: (212) 430-2500   DE
Web Site: http://www.brightstarcapital.com
Year Founded: 2015
Rev.: $3,400,000,000
Privater Equity Firm
N.A.I.C.S.: 523999
Matthew Allard (Partner)
Andrew S. Weinberg (Founder, CEO & Mng Partner)
Renee Noto (Pres & Partner)
Reidar Brekke (Partner)
Jarrett Arkin (Principal)
Joseph Bartek (Partner & CFO)
Roger Bulloch (Partner)
Jeremy Mallinckrodt (Controller)
Millie Tutlam (VP-Tax)
Shana Bochinis (VP-Ops)
Gary Hokkanen (Partner)

Subsidiaries:

Amerit Fleet Solutions, Inc.   (1)

1331 N California Blvd Ste 150, Walnut Creek, CA 94596
Tel.: (949) 595-4400
Web Site:
  http://www.ameritfleetsolutions.com
Sales Range: $100-124.9 Million
Emp.: 1,387
Automotive Repair Services
N.A.I.C.S.: 811111
Matthew Allard (Vice Chm)
Dan Williams (Co-Founder & CEO)
Bob Brauer (Pres)
Mireille Duclos (VP-HR)
Gary Herbold (Chm)
Ron Green (VP-Bus Integration)
Amein Punjani (Co-Founder & COO)

Brightstar Corp.   (1)
9725 NW 117th Ave Ste 3105, Miami, FL 33178
Tel.: (305) 421-6000
Web Site: http://www.brightstarcorp.com
Wireless Distribution & Supply Chain Management Services
N.A.I.C.S.: 541614
Rod Millar (CEO)
Marcelo Claure (Founder)
Catherine R. Smith (Chief Admin Officer, Gen Counsel, Sec & Exec VP)
Joe Kalinoski (CFO)
Ray Roman (Chief Comml Officer & Pres-Device Protection-Global)
Michael Singer (Chief Strategy Officer & Sr VP)
Rafael M. de Guzman III (Sr VP-Strategic Initiatives)

Subsidiary (Non-US):

Beetel Teletech Limited   (2)
1st Floor Plot No 16 Udyog Vihar Phase IV, Gurgaon, 122 002, Haryana, India
Tel.: (91) 24 4823500
Web Site: http://www.beetel.in
Mobile & Telecommunications Equipment Mfr & Whslr
N.A.I.C.S.: 334220
Bunty Rohatgi (Head-Consumer Bus)
Alok Shankar (Mng Dir)
Puneet Khanna (CFO)
Mukesh Kapoor (Controller)

Brightstar 20:20 Mobile   (2)
Weston Rd, Crewe, CW1 6BU, Cheshire, United Kingdom
Tel.: (44) 1270412020
Web Site: http://www.brightstar.com
Sales Range: $100-124.9 Million
Emp.: 400
Cellular & Wireless Parts Mfr
N.A.I.C.S.: 517112
German Lopez (Pres-Europe)
Jim Michel (Mng Dir-UK)
Elan Elton (Head-Accessories Div)
Adam McCormick (Dir-Channel)
Trevor Molley (Head-B2B)
John-Daniel Whyte (Mgr-Propositions)
Ian Gale (Acct Dir-Hardware Sls)

Subsidiary (Non-US):

Brightstar 20:20 Mobile   (3)
Osterogatan 1, PO Box 50, SE-164 94, Kista, Sweden
Tel.: (46) 86327300
Web Site: http://www.brightstar-2020.se
Emp.: 75
Telecommunication Equipment Distr
N.A.I.C.S.: 423690
Hans Mussbichler (CFO & Dir-Fin)
Fredrik Rudberg (CEO)

Subsidiary (Non-US):

Brightstar Argentina, S.A.   (2)
Estomba 243, 1427, Buenos Aires, Argentina   (100%)
Tel.: (54) 40168100
Sales Range: $10-24.9 Million
Emp.: 30
Telephone Equipment Distr
N.A.I.C.S.: 517112
Giampaolo Guarino (Reg Dir)

Brightstar Colombia Ltda.   (2)
Carrera 13 No 98-70 Piso 6, Officina 604 Barrio Chico, Bogota, Colombia
Tel.: (57) 1 404 6919
Sales Range: $10-24.9 Million
Emp.: 90
Wireless Telecommunications Distr

N.A.I.C.S.: 517112

Brightstar Dominicana S.A.   (2)
Elrecodo 2 Building Monte Mirador Bella Vista, Santo Domingo, Dominican Republic
Tel.: (809) 5601277
Web Site: http://www.brightstarcorp.com
Wireless Telecommunications Distr
N.A.I.C.S.: 334210
Neil Rodriguez (Sls & Product Mgr)

Brightstar Logistics Pty. Ltd.   (2)
Level 5 607 Bourke St, Melbourne, 3000, VIC, Australia
Tel.: (61) 386230300
Web Site: http://www.Brightstar.com
Sales Range: $10-24.9 Million
Emp.: 100
Distr of Wireless Phones, Devices & Accessories
N.A.I.C.S.: 541614

Brightstar Mexico S.A. de C.V.   (2)
Industria No 8, 54075, Tlalnepantla, Mexico   (100%)
Tel.: (52) 5553667150
Web Site: http://www.brightstar.com.mx
Sales Range: $25-49.9 Million
Emp.: 850
Wireless Telecommunications Distr
N.A.I.C.S.: 517112
Richardo Wolff (VP)

Brightstar Paraguay S.R.L.   (2)
Madre Teresa de Calcula y Mencia de Sanabria, Asuncion, Paraguay   (100%)
Tel.: (595) 21550506
Web Site: http://www.brightstar.com
Sales Range: $10-24.9 Million
Emp.: 11
Wireless Communications Distr
N.A.I.C.S.: 517112

Brightstar Proceedor de Soluciones Tecnologicas S.A.   (2)
Av Enrique Finot No 190, Zona Equipetrol, Santa Cruz, Bolivia   (100%)
Tel.: (591) 33121448
Web Site: http://www.brightstar.com
Sales Range: $10-24.9 Million
Emp.: 9
Wireless Telecommunications
N.A.I.C.S.: 517112

Subsidiary (Domestic):

Brightstar Puerto Rico, Inc.   (2)
Carr 189 Interior Lote 3 Edificio 2 Bo Martin Gonzalez, Carolina, PR 00987
Tel.: (787) 653-5000
Web Site: http://www.brightstar.com
Emp.: 21
Telephone Equipment
N.A.I.C.S.: 517111

LetsTalk.com Inc.   (2)
410 Townsend St Ste 100, San Francisco, CA 94105
Tel.: (817) 258-6200
Web Site: http://www.letstalk.com
Cellular & Other Wireless Telecommunications
N.A.I.C.S.: 517112

Douglas Products & Packaging Company LLC   (1)
1550 E Old State Route 21, Liberty, MO 64068
Tel.: (816) 781-4250
Web Site: http://www.douglasproducts.com
Sales Range: $1-9.9 Million
Emp.: 20
Miscellaneous Chemical Product & Preparation Mfr
N.A.I.C.S.: 325998
Gerald McCaslin (Pres)
Hunter Dance (Mgr-Bus Dev)
Wes Long (CEO)
Vince Adams (Chief Bus Dev Officer)

InfraServ US, LLC   (1)
401 W Outer Rd, Valley Park, MO 63088
Tel.: (636) 225-2900
Web Site: http://www.infraservus.com
Industrial Equipment Merchant Whslr
N.A.I.C.S.: 423810

Subsidiary (Domestic):

Gateway Bobcat, LLC   (2)

401 W Outer Rd, Valley Park, MO 63088-2031
Tel.: (636) 225-2900
Web Site: http://www.bobcatofstl.com
Construction & Mining Machinery & Equipment Merchant Whslr
N.A.I.C.S.: 423810
Rob Graeler (Mgr-Svc)
Mike Allen (CEO)

Subsidiary (Domestic):

Miramar Bobcat, Inc.   (3)
9370 Miramar Rd, San Diego, CA 92126
Tel.: (858) 566-4600
Web Site: http://www.bobcatsouthwest.com
Sales Range: $1-9.9 Million
Emp.: 28
Construction & Mining Machinery & Equipment Merchant Whslr
N.A.I.C.S.: 423810
John DeGour (Gen Mgr-Ops)

Novae Corporation   (1)
1 Novae Pkwy, Markle, IN 46770-9087
Tel.: (260) 758-9838
Web Site: http://www.novaecorp.com
Tow Trailers & Lawn Mower Attachments Mfr
N.A.I.C.S.: 532120
Matthew Allard (Chm)
Steve Bermes (Founder & CEO)
Amy Moreland (Controller)
Chris Storie (Pres & COO)
Mark Kundo (Mgr-Matls)
Veronica Garrison (Mgr-HR)
Mark Yde (Dir-Bus Dev)
Oliver Reelsen (Dir-IT)

BRIGHTSTAR CORPORATION
13575 Lynam Dr, Omaha, NE 68138
Tel.: (402) 597-9770
Web Site:
  http://www.brightstaraccessory.com
Year Founded: 1997
Emp.: 6,100
Wireless Accessories Distr
N.A.I.C.S.: 423990
Matthew Allard (Partner)

BRIGHTSTAR FRANCHISING, LLC
1125 Tri State Pkwy, Gurnee, IL 60031
Tel.: (866) 777-7110   IL
Web Site:
  http://www.brightstarcare.com
Sales Range: $75-99.9 Million
Emp.: 88
Home Healthcare Services Franchisor
N.A.I.C.S.: 533110
Steve Schildwachter (CMO)
Tom Lehr (CFO)
Thom Gilday (Pres & COO)

BRIGHTWAY INSURANCE, INC.
3733 W University Blvd Ste 100, Jacksonville, FL 32217
Tel.: (904) 764-9554   FL
Web Site:
  http://www.brightwayinsurance.com
Year Founded: 2003
Sales Range: $250-299.9 Million
Emp.: 350
Insurance Brokerage Services
N.A.I.C.S.: 524210
David C. Miller (Co-Founder & Vice Chm)
Michael A. Miller (Founder)
Kristine Azar (VP-Customer Experience)
Courtney Heidelberg (Mgr-PR & Comm)
Chinikqua Maddox (VP-Strategic Initiatives)
Scott Pollard (VP-Agency Growth & Dev)

Chip Hyers (VP-Sls)
Rick Fox (Chief Revenue Officer)
Mark Cantin (Pres & CEO)

BRIGHTWING
431 Stephenson Hwy, Troy, MI 48083
Tel.: (248) 585-4750
Web Site:
  https://www.gobrightwing.com
Year Founded: 1973
Sales Range: $25-49.9 Million
Emp.: 349
Staffing, Recruiting, Training & Employee Development
N.A.I.C.S.: 541612
Aaron Chernow (CEO)
Adam Conrad (VP-Bus Ops)
David Chernow (Chief Mktg Officer)
George Albert Opitz (Pres)

BRIGHTWOOD CAPITAL ADVISORS, LLC
810 7th Ave 26 Fl, New York, NY 10019
Tel.: (646) 957-9525
Web Site:
  http://www.brightwoodlp.com
Holding Company
N.A.I.C.S.: 523999
Damien Dwin (Founder & CEO)
Cornelia Cheng (Mng Dir-Investments)

Subsidiaries:

Vertellus Specialties Inc.   (1)
201 N Illinois St Ste 1800, Indianapolis, IN 46204
Tel.: (317) 247-8141
Web Site: http://www.vertellus.com
Sales Range: $500-549.9 Million
Specialty Chemicals Mfr
N.A.I.C.S.: 325199
Robert McNeeley (Chm)
Scott Dearing (Controller)
James Keay (Bus Dir)
Linda Hicks (VP)
Richard V. Preziotti (Pres & CEO)
Bentley Park (Pres-Agriculture & Nutrition Bus)
John Washuta (VP-Global Ops & Supply Chain)

Subsidiary (Domestic):

Vertellus Agriculture & Nutrition Specialties LLC   (2)
201 N Illinois St Ste 1800, Indianapolis, IN 46204
Tel.: (317) 247-8141
Web Site: http://www.vertellus.com
Sales Range: $200-249.9 Million
Mfr of Pyridine, Picolines & Vitamin B-3
N.A.I.C.S.: 325998

Vertellus Health & Specialty Products LLC   (2)
201 N Illinois St Ste 1800, Indianapolis, IN 46204
Tel.: (317) 247-8141
Web Site: http://www.vertellus.com
Sales Range: $100-124.9 Million
Mfr of Specialty Pyridine Derivatives, Sulfones, DEET & Reducing Agents
N.A.I.C.S.: 325998

Plant (Domestic):

Vertellus Health & Specialty Products LLC - Delaware Water Gap   (3)
PO Box 730, Delaware Water Gap, PA 18327
Tel.: (570) 420-3900
Web Site: http://www.vertellus.com
Sales Range: $50-74.9 Million
High Purity Organic & Inorganic Salts
N.A.I.C.S.: 325199

Vertellus Health & Specialty Products LLC - Elma   (3)
4800 State Rte 12, Elma, WA 98541
Tel.: (360) 482-4350
Emp.: 75
Sodium Borohydride Mfr
N.A.I.C.S.: 325180

Brightwood Capital Advisors, LLC—(Continued)

Vertellus Health & Specialty Products LLC - Zeeland (3)
215 N Centennial St, Zeeland, MI 49464-1309
Tel.: (616) 772-2193
Web Site: http://www.vertellus.com
Sales Range: $25-49.9 Million
Mfr of Specialty Chemicals
N.A.I.C.S.: 325998
Ken Walits (Mgr-Quality & Regulatory Affairs)
Leeann Karabelski (Engr-HSSE)

Subsidiary (Domestic):

Vertellus Performance Materials, Inc. (2)
2110 High Point Rd, Greensboro, NC 27403-2642
Tel.: (336) 292-1781
Web Site: http://www.vertellus.com
Sales Range: $50-74.9 Million
Emp.: 70
Castor Oil, Shea Butter & Citrate Derivatives
N.A.I.C.S.: 325199
Ben Stewart (Gen Mgr)

Subsidiary (Non-US):

Vertellus Specialties Asia Pacific (2)
Room 1602 16th Floor No 66 Hua Yuan Shi Qiao Rd, BEA Finance Tower, Shanghai, 200120, China
Tel.: (86) 21 38993000
Chemical Products Mfr
N.A.I.C.S.: 325998

Vertellus Specialties UK Ltd. (2)
Seal Sands Rd, Seal Sands, Middles-brough, TS2 1UB, United Kingdom
Tel.: (44) 1642546546
Web Site: http://www.vertellus.com
Sales Range: $25-49.9 Million
Performance-Enhancing Synthetic Organic Fine Chemicals
N.A.I.C.S.: 325199
Mike Driver (Dir-Bus & Biomaterials)

BRIGHTWORK REAL ESTATE, INC.
3708 W Swann Ave Ste 200, Tampa, FL 33609
Tel.: (813) 874-1700
Web Site:
https://www.brightworkre.com
Sales Range: $1-9.9 Million
Commercial Real Estate Development, Acquisition, Management & Brokerage Services
N.A.I.C.S.: 237210
Brad Douglas (Partner)
Henry Hilsman (Partner)
T. Austin Simmons (Partner)
Ashley Guyton (CFO)
Matt Britten (Partner-Reg)
Ross Kirchman (Partner-Reg)

BRIGHTWORKS SUSTAIN-ABILITY LLC
1125 NW Couch St Ste 470, Portland, OR 97209
Tel.: (503) 290-3000
Web Site:
https://www.brightworks.net
Year Founded: 2001
Management Consulting Services
N.A.I.C.S.: 541618

BRILLIANT DIGITAL ENTER-TAINMENT, INC.
12711 Ventura Blvd Ste 210, Studio City, CA 91604-2434
Tel.: (818) 386-2180   DE
Web Site:
http://www.brilliantdigital.com
Year Founded: 1996
Sales Range: $1-9.9 Million
Emp.: 8

Entertainment Content, Internet Tools & Technology
N.A.I.C.S.: 334610
Anthony Rose (CTO)
Anthony Neumann (VP-Bus Dev)
Lee Jaffe (Chief Creative Officer)
Kevin Bermeister (Chm, Pres & CEO)

Subsidiaries:

Global File Registry, Inc. (1)
14011 Ventura Blvd Ste 501, Sherman Oaks, CA 91423
Tel.: (818) 386-2179
Web Site: http://www.globalfileregistry.com
Database Management Services
N.A.I.C.S.: 561499

BRILLIANT ENVIRONMENTAL SERVICES, LLC
1A Executive Dr, Toms River, NJ 08755
Tel.: (732) 818-3380
Web Site: http://www.brilliantenviron-mental.com
Sales Range: $1-9.9 Million
Emp.: 25
Consulting & Contracting Services
N.A.I.C.S.: 541611
Philip I. Brilliant (Owner)
Anthony S. Belfield (Mgr-Pennsylvania)
Jonathan A. Libourel (Reg Mgr)
Barbara Bish (Dir-Fin & Office Mgr)
Robert Boehler (Dir-Ops-Natl)
Donald Finnegan (Project Mgr)
Mark Marotta (Project-Mgr)

BRILLIANT TELECOMMUNICA-TIONS, INC.
307 Orchard City Dr, Campbell, CA 95008
Tel.: (408) 866-1896
Sales Range: $10-24.9 Million
Emp.: 10
Network Timing, Management & Synchronization Solutions.
N.A.I.C.S.: 513210
Don Patton (Mgr-Ops)
Erik Wahlstrom (Mgr-Engrg Svcs)

BRILLIENT CORPORATION
1893 Metro Ctr Dr Ste 210, Reston, VA 20190
Tel.: (703) 994-4232
Web Site: http://www.brillient.net
Year Founded: 2003
Sales Range: $1-9.9 Million
Emp.: 57
Online Business Management Consulting Services
N.A.I.C.S.: 513199
Sukumar R. Iyer (Founder & Chm)
Paul Strasser (CEO)
R. J. Kolton (Chief Growth Officer)
Richard Jacik (Gen Mgr-Health)

BRIMAR WOOD INNOVA-TIONS, INC.
2108 Eisenhower Dr N, Goshen, IN 46526-8836
Tel.: (574) 535-0024
Web Site:
https://www.brimarwood.com
Year Founded: 2004
Sales Range: $1-9.9 Million
Emp.: 52
Wood Product & Services
N.A.I.C.S.: 337211
Brian Roe (Pres)

BRIMMER, BUREK & KEELAN, LLP
5601 Mariner St Ste 200, Tampa, FL 33609
Tel.: (813) 282-3400
Web Site: https://www.bbkm.com

Year Founded: 1961
Sales Range: $1-9.9 Million
Emp.: 27
Certified Public Accountants
N.A.I.C.S.: 541211
Brian Burek (Mng Partner)
John Keelan (Partner)
Donald Keyes (Partner)
Kara Keyes (Partner)
Frank Lagor (Partner)
Heather Kovalsky (Partner)

BRIMROSE CORPORATION OF AMERICA
19 Loveton Cir Hunt Valley Loveton Center, Sparks, MD 21152-9201
Tel.: (410) 472-7070
Web Site: https://www.brimrose.com
Year Founded: 1989
Rev.: $20,000,000
Emp.: 50
Search & Navigation Equipment
N.A.I.C.S.: 334511
Ronald G. Rosemeier (Pres & CEO)
Jolanta Soos (Mgr-Mktg)
Angelina Hartini (Engr-Applications)
Sergey Vishnyakov (Engr-Electronic)
Daniel Yang (Mgr-Sls & Mktg-Asia Pacific)
Feng Jin (Product Mgr-Dev)
Sue Kutcher (Mgr-R&D)

Subsidiaries:

Brimrose-Acousto Optic Components Division (1)
19 Loveton Cir, Baltimore, MD 21152-9201
Tel.: (410) 472-7070
Web Site: http://www.brimrose.com
Sales Range: $10-24.9 Million
Emp.: 45
Search & Navigation Equipment
N.A.I.C.S.: 334511
Jolanta Soos (Mgr-Mktg)
Dave Chaffe (Mgr-Mktg)

Brimrose-NIR Process Analysis Division (1)
19 Loveton Cir Hunt Valley Loveton Ctr, Sparks, MD 21152
Tel.: (410) 472-7070
Web Site: http://www.brimrose.com
Sales Range: $10-24.9 Million
Emp.: 10
Search & Navigation Equipment
N.A.I.C.S.: 334511
Vladimir Stanislavsky (Dir-Ops)

BRIMSTONE ACQUISITION HOLDINGS CORP.
500 S Pointe Dr Ste 240, Miami Beach, FL 33139
Tel.: (786) 482-6333   DE
Year Founded: 2021
Investment Services
N.A.I.C.S.: 523999
Michael F. Goss (Chm, Pres & CEO)
Robert A. E. Franklin (COO)
Desiree DeStefano (CFO, Treas & Sec)

BRIN FINANCIAL CORPORA-TION
455 Short St, South Boston, VA 24592
Tel.: (434) 572-4544
Web Site:
http://www.brinfinancial.com
Sales Range: $10-24.9 Million
Emp.: 5
Equipment Rental & Leasing Consulting
N.A.I.C.S.: 532490
Joseph Gasperini (Pres)
Wayne Hughes (VP)

BRIN NORTHWESTERN GLASS COMPANY INC.

2300 N 2nd St, Minneapolis, MN 55411-2209
Tel.: (612) 529-9671
Web Site: https://www.bringlass.com
Year Founded: 1912
Sales Range: $25-49.9 Million
Emp.: 200
Flat Glass Product Whslr & Distr
N.A.I.C.S.: 327211
Bill Spiess (Mgr-Svc Sls)
Chris Streeter (Mgr-Ops)

Subsidiaries:

Hentges Glass Company Inc. (1)
626 1st Ave SW, Rochester, MN 55902-3305
Tel.: (507) 282-1769
Sales Range: $10-24.9 Million
Emp.: 8
Residential & Commercial Glass Products Whslr
N.A.I.C.S.: 238150

Piltz Glass and Mirror, Inc. (1)
1011 Vernon St, Altoona, WI 54720-2223   (100%)
Tel.: (715) 835-3144
Sales Range: $10-24.9 Million
Emp.: 6
Glass Contracting Services
N.A.I.C.S.: 238150
Tanya Sheehan (Office Mgr)

St. Germain's Glass Co. (1)
212 N 40th Ave W, Duluth, MN 55807-2835
Tel.: (218) 628-0221
Web Site: http://www.stgermainsglass.com
Sales Range: $10-24.9 Million
Emp.: 30
Glass Products Whslr; Glazing Services
N.A.I.C.S.: 238150
Douglas M. Nelson (Pres)
Rob McCabe (Gen Mgr)
Gary Johnson (Controller)

BRINDLEY BEACH VACA-TIONS & SALES
1023 Ocean Trl, Corolla, NC 27927
Tel.: (252) 453-3000
Web Site:
https://www.brindleybeach.com
Year Founded: 2003
Rev.: $2,600,000
Emp.: 10
Travel Agencies
N.A.I.C.S.: 561510
Kelly B. Hanig (Treas & Sec)
Douglas R. Brindley (Pres)
Dart Neher (Mgr-Sls)

BRINDLEY CONSTRUCTION, LLC.
747 W College St, Pulaski, TN 38478
Tel.: (931) 363-4544
Web Site:
https://www.brindleyconst.com
Year Founded: 1960
Sales Range: $10-24.9 Million
Emp.: 75
Commercial & Institutional Building Construction Services
N.A.I.C.S.: 236220
Ronnie Brindley (Pres)
Kathy T. Pigg (Exec VP)

BRINK CONSTRUCTORS, INC.
2950 N Plaza Dr, Rapid City, SD 57702-9323
Tel.: (605) 342-6966
Web Site: https://www.brinkred.com
Year Founded: 1946
Transmission & Fibre Optics Contractors
N.A.I.C.S.: 238210
Zane Brink (Pres)
Brent Voorhees (VP)

BRINKER CAPITAL HOLDINGS INC.

1055 Westlakes Dr Ste 250, Berwyn, PA 19312-2410
Tel.: (610) 407-5500
Web Site:
https://clients0.brinkercapital.com
Rev.: $14,400,000
Emp.: 110
Investment Advisory Services
N.A.I.C.S.: 523940
Charles Widger *(Co-Founder & Chm)*
Noreen D. Beaman *(CEO)*
Mitchell J. Mellen *(Reg VP)*
Thomas K. R. Wilson *(Sr VP & Head-Wealth Advisory)*
Ed Kelly *(Exec VP-Natl Sls)*
Roddy P. Marino *(Exec VP-Natl Accounts & Distr)*
Jeff Raupp *(Chief Investment Officer)*
Christopher P. Hart *(Sr VP)*
Brian Ferko *(Chief Compliance Officer)*
Brendan McConnell *(COO)*
Jason Moore *(Chief Admin Officer)*
Avery Cook *(Sr VP-Managed Products & Solutions)*
Amy Magnotta *(Sr VP & Head-Discretionary Portfolios)*
David Hall *(Sr VP & Head-Quantitative Strategy)*
Timothy Holland *(Sr VP-Investment Strategist-Global)*
David A. Ix *(Sr VP)*
John E. Coyne III *(Co-Founder)*
Philip F. Green Jr. *(CFO)*

BRINKLEY FINANCIAL GROUP
2815 Coliseum Centre Dr Ste 100, Charlotte, NC 28217
Tel.: (704) 423-9690
Web Site:
http://www.brinkleyfinancial.com
Sales Range: $25-49.9 Million
Emp.: 5
Financial Advisors
N.A.I.C.S.: 523940
Lynn Connor *(Office Mgr)*
David C. Brinkley Sr. *(Owner, Chm & Pres)*
David C. Brinkley Jr. *(Mgr-Insurance)*

BRINKMAN INTERNATIONAL GROUP, INC.
167 Ames St, Rochester, NY 14611
Tel.: (585) 235-4545
Web Site:
https://www.brinkmanig.com
Sales Range: $10-24.9 Million
Emp.: 100
Machine Tools Mfr
N.A.I.C.S.: 333515
Robert Brinkman *(Owner)*
Ella Gardner *(CFO)*
Liberato Pietrantoni *(Product Mgr & Mgr-Acct-Natl)*
Michael Mineti *(Mgr-IT)*

Subsidiaries:

Brinkman Products Inc **(1)**
167 Ames St, Rochester, NY 14611-1701
Tel.: (585) 235-4545
Web Site: http://www.brinkmanig.com
Sales Range: $10-24.9 Million
Emp.: 75
Mfr of Machine Tools, Metal Cutting Types
N.A.I.C.S.: 333517
Robert Brinkman *(Chm)*
Andy Laniak *(Pres & COO)*

BRINKMANN CORP.
4215 McEwen Rd, Dallas, TX 75244-5202
Tel.: (972) 387-4939
Web Site: http://www.brinkmann.net
Year Founded: 1981
Sales Range: $25-49.9 Million
Emp.: 500
Lighting Equipment Mfr & Distr

N.A.I.C.S.: 335139
J. Baxter Brinkmann *(Pres & CEO)*
Martin Donoghue *(CFO)*
Suzette Hall *(Dir-Customer Ops)*

Subsidiaries:

Dallas Manufacturing Company Inc. **(1)**
4215 McEwen Rd, Dallas, TX 75244-5202
Tel.: (972) 770-8503
Sales Range: $25-49.9 Million
Emp.: 150
Mfr of Industrial Equipment
N.A.I.C.S.: 339999

Smoke'N Pit Corporation **(1)**
4215 McEwen Rd, Dallas, TX 75244-5202
Tel.: (972) 387-4939
Web Site: http://www.brinkmann.net
Rev.: $4,500,000
Emp.: 75
Household Cooking Equipment
N.A.I.C.S.: 335221
J. Baxter Brinkmann *(Chm & Pres)*

BRINKMERE CAPITAL PARTNERS LLC
One Independent Dr Ste 2208, Jacksonville, FL 32202
Tel.: (904) 437-4560
Web Site: http://www.brinkmere.com
Emp.: 2
Privater Equity Firm
N.A.I.C.S.: 523999
Russell Beard *(Mng Dir)*

Subsidiaries:

Certified Power Inc. **(1)**
970 Campus Dr, Mundelein, IL 60060
Tel.: (847) 573-3800
Web Site: http://www.certifiedpower.com
Sales Range: $100-124.9 Million
Power Train Components Mfr; Hydraulic, Pneumatic, Electronic & Drive Train Components Distr for Industrial & Mobile Applications
N.A.I.C.S.: 423830
Scott Rosenzweig *(CEO)*

Division (Domestic):

Certified Power Inc. - Driveline Division **(2)**
390 Koopman Ln, Elkhorn, WI 53121
Tel.: (262) 723-2944
Torque Transfer Equipment Mfr
N.A.I.C.S.: 336350

Subsidiary (Domestic):

Cirus Control LLC **(2)**
7165 Boone Ave N Suite 190, Minneapolis, MN 55428 **(100%)**
Tel.: (763) 493-9380
Web Site: http://www.ciruscontrols.com
Rev.: $4,606,000
Emp.: 7
Hydraulics, Controls, Telematics & Related Accessories for Winter Maintenance Equipment & Snow Removal
N.A.I.C.S.: 811310
Paul Mortell *(CEO)*

Master Mechanic Mfg. Co. **(2)**
970 Campus Dr, Mundelein, IL 60060
Tel.: (847) 573-3812
Web Site: http://www.certifiedpower.com
Sales Range: $25-49.9 Million
Hydraulic & Fluid Power Products & Accessories Distr for Marine & Heavy Equipment Applications
N.A.I.C.S.: 423830

BRINLEY'S GRADING SERVICE, INC.
3611 Cessna Ln, Garner, NC 27529-8588
Tel.: (919) 771-1997
Web Site:
https://www.brinleysgrading.com
Sales Range: $10-24.9 Million
Emp.: 101
Excavation Services
N.A.I.C.S.: 238910

Thomas E. Brinley Sr. *(Comptroller)*

BRINSON AUTO GROUP
2970 Hwy 31 E, Athens, TX 75752
Tel.: (903) 675-5753
Web Site: http://www.brinsonford.com
Year Founded: 1992
Sales Range: $10-24.9 Million
Emp.: 47
New & Used Automobiles
N.A.I.C.S.: 441110
David Brinson *(Pres)*

BRINX RESOURCES LTD.
c/o Dill Dill Carr Stonbraker & Hutchings PC 455 Sherman St Ste 300, Denver, CO 80203
Tel.: (505) 250-9992   NV
Web Site:
http://www.brinxresources.com
Year Founded: 1998
Sales Range: Less than $1 Million
Oil & Gas Exploration Services
N.A.I.C.S.: 213112
Kenneth A. Cabianca *(Pres)*

BRIOSCHI PHARMACEUTICALS INTERNATIONAL, LLC
19-01 Pollitt Dr, Fair Lawn, NJ 07410-2827
Tel.: (201) 796-4226   NJ
Year Founded: 1880
Rev.: $2,000,000
Emp.: 14
Antacid Preparations Mfr
N.A.I.C.S.: 325412
Patrick Duncan *(CEO)*

Subsidiaries:

Brioschi International Corp. **(1)**
19-01 Pollitt Dr, Fair Lawn, NJ 07410
Tel.: (201) 796-4226
Sales Range: $10-24.9 Million
Emp.: 11
Antacid Mfr
N.A.I.C.S.: 325412

BRISCO APPAREL CO. INC.
637 Patterson Grove Rd, Ramseur, NC 27316
Tel.: (800) 283-9490
Web Site:
http://www.briscoapparel.com
Year Founded: 1996
Emp.: 100
Men & Women's Apparel Mfr & Retailer
N.A.I.C.S.: 315250
Scott Gartner *(Pres & CEO)*

BRISTLECONE ADVISORS
999 3rd Ave Ste 600, Seattle, WA 98104
Tel.: (206) 664-2500
Web Site:
http://www.bristleconeadvisors.com
Year Founded: 1999
Sales Range: $1-9.9 Million
Emp.: 17
Investment Advisory Services
N.A.I.C.S.: 523940
Kevin S. Berry *(Partner)*
Tony Waltier *(Partner)*
Ashley Mooney *(Mgr-Compliance & Ops)*
Piper Hanson *(Mgr-Client)*
Larry Kinner *(Partner)*
Kevin McCandlish *(Partner)*
Jeff Parker *(Partner)*
Joseph Winkler *(Partner)*
Stephanie B. Fox *(Mgr-Client)*
Joelle Wade *(Mgr-Client)*
Christopher J. Taylor *(Partner)*
Adam Guenther *(Principal-Investment Mgmt)*

BRISTOL BAY ECONOMIC DEVELOPMENT CORPORATION
Po Box 1464, Dillingham, AK 99576
Tel.: (907) 842-4370   AK
Web Site: http://www.bbedc.com
Year Founded: 1992
Sales Range: $25-49.9 Million
Emp.: 67
Economic Development Services
N.A.I.C.S.: 541720
Staci Fieser *(CFO)*
Chris Napoli *(Chief Admin Officer)*
Gary Cline *(Dir-Reg Fisheries)*
Alice Ruby *(Dir-Economic Dev-Brokerage)*
Robert Heyano *(Treas)*
H. Robin Samuelsen Jr. *(Chm)*

BRISTOL BAY NATIVE CORPORATION
111 W 16th Ave Ste 400, Anchorage, AK 99501-5109
Tel.: (907) 278-3602   AK
Web Site: http://www.bbnc.net
Year Founded: 1972
Emp.: 100
Holding Company
N.A.I.C.S.: 551112
Greta L. Goto *(Vice Chm)*
Russell S. Nelson *(Chm)*
Nancy S. Schierhorn *(Chief Dev Officer & Exec VP)*
Scott Torrison *(COO & Exec VP)*
Ryan York *(CFO & Exec VP)*
Ethan Schutt *(Gen Counsel & Exec VP)*
Jason Metrokin *(Pres & CEO)*

Subsidiaries:

Aerostar SES LLC **(1)**
11181 St Johns Industrial Pkwy N, Jacksonville, FL 32246
Tel.: (904) 565-2820
Web Site: http://www.aerostar.net
Emp.: 80
Environmental Engineering Services
N.A.I.C.S.: 541330
Basil Skelton *(Pres)*
Roy Hoekstra *(Gen Mgr)*
Leon J. Carrero *(Sr Program Mgr)*
Tiffany Seibt *(Sr Program Mgr)*
M. Chris McNees *(Sr Program Mgr)*
Kevin Seaway *(Sr Program Mgr)*
Frank Redway *(Sr Project Mgr)*
G. Scott Hughes *(Mgr-Ops-Jacksonville)*

Badger Technical Services, LLC **(1)**
111 W 16th Ave Ste 400, Anchorage, AK 99501
Tel.: (210) 477-2450
Web Site: http://www.badger-tech.com
Emp.: 30
Environmental Consulting Services
N.A.I.C.S.: 541620
John Reeder *(Gen Mgr)*

Bristol Bay Resource Solutions, LLC **(1)**
111 W 16th Ave, Anchorage, AK 99501
Tel.: (907) 793-9200
Web Site: http://www.bbrs-llc.com
Administrative Management Consulting Services
N.A.I.C.S.: 541611
Amy Hastings *(Sr Mgr-Mktg & Comm)*
Rhonda Lamp *(Sr Mgr-HR)*
Michael Redmond *(Sr Mgr-HR-Field Support)*
Beth Poisson *(Mgr-Contracts Admin & Svcs)*
Niel Smith *(Mgr-IT)*

Bristol Environmental Engineering Services Corporation **(1)**
111 West 16th Ave Ste 301, Anchorage, AK 99501 **(100%)**
Tel.: (907) 563-0013
Sales Range: $10-24.9 Million
Emp.: 50
Environmental & Engineering Services
N.A.I.C.S.: 541690
Travis Woods *(CEO)*

Bristol Bay Native Corporation—(Continued)

Bristol Fuel Systems, LLC (1)
1072 NC Hwy 210 Ste C, Sneads Ferry,
NC 28460-9605
Tel.: (910) 327-9204
Construction Engineering Services
N.A.I.C.S.: 541330

Bristol General Contractors, LLC (1)
1101 NW Pamela Blvd Ste B, Grain Valley,
MO 64029-7803
Tel.: (816) 443-5292
Web Site: http://www.bristol-companies.com
Emp.: 2
Industrial Building Construction Services
N.A.I.C.S.: 236210

**Business Resource Solutions
LLC** (1)
7067 Madison Pike, Huntsville, AL 35806
Tel.: (256) 726-4701
Web Site: http://www.brs-llc.com
Administrative Management Consulting Services
N.A.I.C.S.: 541611
Patrick Patterson (CEO)
Jim Oakes (Dir-HR)
Pam Metcalf (Dir-Payroll)

CCI Group, LLC (1)
111 W 16th Ave Ste 400, Anchorage, AK
99501
Tel.: (207) 620-7172
Investment Management Service
N.A.I.C.S.: 523940

CCI Industrial Services, LLC (1)
5015 Business Park Blvd Ste 4000, Anchorage, AK 99503-7146
Tel.: (907) 258-5755
Web Site: http://www. cciindustrial.com
Sales Range: $10-24.9 Million
Emp.: 13
Specialized Services for Facility & Infrastructure Businesses
N.A.I.C.S.: 562112

CCI Solutions, LLC (1)
51 3rd St Ste 5, Shalimar, FL 32579
Tel.: (850) 613-6456
Web Site: http://www.ccialliance.com
Industrial Building Construction Services
N.A.I.C.S.: 236210
Laura Lawrence (Dir-Mktg)

Clipper Seafoods Ltd. (1)
641 W Ewing St, Seattle, WA 98119-8119
Tel.: (206) 284-1162
Web Site: https://bristolwaveseafoods.com
Seafood Product Preparation & Packaging
N.A.I.C.S.: 311710
Kathy Lee (Sr VP-Sls)
Joel Peterson (Pres)

Eagle Applied Sciences, LLC. (1)
1826 N Loop 1604 W Ste 350, San Antonio, TX 78248
Tel.: (210) 477-9242
Web Site: http://www.eagle-app-sci.com
Emp.: 2
Medical Laboratory Testing Services
N.A.I.C.S.: 541380
George Gisin (Pres & CEO)
Charles Miffleton (VP-Fin)

Herman Construction Group, Inc. (1)
10366 Roselle St Ste A, San Diego, CA
92121-1543
Tel.: (858) 277-7100
Web Site: http://www.hermancg.com
Commercial & Institutional Building Construction
N.A.I.C.S.: 236220
Lars C. Herman (Pres & CEO)

Kakivik Asset Management, LLC (1)
5015 Business Park Blvd Ste 4000, Anchorage, AK 99503-4161
Tel.: (907) 770-9400
Web Site: http://www.kakivik.com
Asset Management Services
N.A.I.C.S.: 523940
Ben Schlossman (Pres & CEO)

Katmailand, Inc. (1)
4125 Aircraft Dr, Anchorage, AK 99502
Web Site: http://www.katmailand.com
Emp.: 14
Travel & Lodging Accomodations Operator
N.A.I.C.S.: 561510

MedPro Technologies, LLC (1)
1826 N Loop 1604 W Ste 350, San Antonio, TX 78248
Tel.: (210) 477-2418
Web Site:
　http://www.medprotechnologies.com
Emp.: 1
Information Technology Consulting Services
N.A.I.C.S.: 541512
Ken Chandler (Gen Mgr)

PetroCard, Inc. (1)
730 Central Ave S, Kent, WA 98032
Tel.: (253) 852-2777
Web Site: http://www.petrocard.com
Gasoline Service Stations
N.A.I.C.S.: 457120
Aaron Redding (Sr VP)
Scott Walters (COO)

Subsidiary (Domestic):

Masco Petroleum, Inc (2)
110 Commerce St, Aberdeen, WA 98520
Tel.: (360) 537-9744
Web Site: http://www.mascopetroleum.com
Petroleum & Petroleum Products Merchant
Wholesalers, except Bulk Stations & Terminals
N.A.I.C.S.: 424720
James C. Mason (Owner & Pres)

Division (Domestic):

PetroCard Systems Inc. - Fuel & Lubricant Division (2)
N 220 Haven St, Spokane, WA 99202
Tel.: (509) 534-5040
Petroleum Product Whslr
N.A.I.C.S.: 424720

**PetroCard Systems Inc. - Fuel
Division** (2)
12900 Avon Allen Rd, Burlington, WA 98233
Tel.: (360) 428-0905
Petroleum Product Whslr
N.A.I.C.S.: 424720

**PetroCard Systems Inc. - Lubricant
Division** (2)
6405 172nd NE, Arlington, WA 98223
Tel.: (360) 435-1848
Petroleum Product Whslr
N.A.I.C.S.: 424720

**SES Construction and Fuel Services
LLC** (1)
1006 Floyd Culler Ct, Oak Ridge, TN 37830
Tel.: (865) 481-7837
Web Site: http://www.scf-llc.com
Industrial Building Construction Services
N.A.I.C.S.: 236210
Jim Madaj (Gen Mgr)
Basil Skelton (Pres & CEO)

**SpecPro Environmental Services
LLC** (1)
1006 Floyd Culler Ct, Oak Ridge, TN 37830
Tel.: (865) 481-7837
Web Site: http://www.specproenv.com
Environmental Consulting Services
N.A.I.C.S.: 541620
Doug Hodson (Gen Mgr)

**SpecPro Technical Services,
LLC** (1)
1077 Central Pkwy S Bldg A Ste 100, San
Antonio, TX 78232
Tel.: (210) 477-1818
Web Site: http://www.specpro-tech.com
Emp.: 40
Investment Management Service
N.A.I.C.S.: 523940
Dennis Hopkins (CEO)

Specpro Inc. (1)
4815 Bradford Dr Ste 201, Huntsville, AL
35805　　　　　　　　　　　**(100%)**
Tel.: (256) 726-4701
Web Site: http://www.specpro-inc.com
Specialty Trade Contractors
N.A.I.C.S.: 562910

TekPro Services, LLC (1)
12500 San Pedro Ave Ste 650, San Antonio, TX 78216
Tel.: (210) 245-2080
Web Site: http://www.tkpro.us

Technical Consulting Services
N.A.I.C.S.: 541690
Regina Monroe (Gen Mgr)
Laurie Grams (Mgr-Ops)

**Vista International Operations,
Inc.** (1)
1479 Gillespie St Bldg 131 Ste 309, Rock
Island, IL 61201
Tel.: (563) 323-3968
Web Site: http://www.viops.com
Information Technology Consulting Services
N.A.I.C.S.: 541512

BRISTOL BROADCASTING
CO. INC.
PO Box 1389, Bristol, VA 24203-1389
Tel.: (276) 669-8112
Web Site:
　http://www.bristolbroadcasting.com
Rev.: $10,200,000
Emp.: 60
Radio Broadcasting Stations
N.A.I.C.S.: 516110
Lisa Hale (Pres)
Nikki Thomas (Program Dir)
Jason Reed (Mgr-Ops)

BRISTOL COUNTY SAVINGS
BANK
35 Broadway, Taunton, MA 02780
Tel.: (508) 828-5300　　　　　　MA
Web Site:
　http://www.bristolcountysavings.com
Year Founded: 1846
Sales Range: $50-74.9 Million
Emp.: 29
Banking Services
N.A.I.C.S.: 522180
Stephen F. Hardy (Sr VP-Comml
Lending-Attleboro)
Dennis F. Leahy (CFO, Treas & Exec
VP)
Peter E. Selley (Sr VP-Comml
Lending-Taunton & Southcoast)
Jann M. Alden (Officer-Reg Banking
& VP)
Robert J. DeMoura (CIO & Exec VP)
Julie D. S. Chapman (COO & Exec
VP)
Paul M. Lenahan (Exec VP)
Kevin M. McCarthy (Sr VP)
Donna M. Oliveira (Sr VP-Indirect
Lending)
Nelson J. Braga (Sr VP-Residential
Lending-NMLS)
Mark A. Borkman (VP-Rhode Island)
Roger Cabral (VP-Fall River)
Paul A. Camille (VP-Attleboro Reg)
Michael J. Chatwin (VP-Taunton)
Richard Farmer (VP-Fall River)
William D. Lewis (VP-Taunton)
Jack McCarthy (VP-Attleboro Reg)
Linda Sternfelt (VP-Taunton)
Richard D. Terry (VP-Attleboro Reg)
Hollie B. Lussier (Chief Risk Officer,
Gen Counsel & Exec VP)
Timothy A. Chaves (VP-Taunton)
John Silva (Sr VP-Comml Lending-
Rhode Island)
Lisa Lassiter (VP & Controller)
Jeffrey Kolarik (Sr VP)
Brian Hunter (VP)
Joan M. Medeiros (VP-Fall River)
Denise Murphy (VP)
Michael Patacao (VP-Fall River)
Nancy F. Pimentel (VP)
Michele L. Roberts (Officer-
Community Rels & Exec VP)
David C. Tipping (VP)
Todd Zoppo (Mgr-Pawtucket)
Amy Briggs (Asst VP & Mgr-
Raynham Center)
Marlene C. Lira (Mgr-Ashley Boule-
vard)
Francine Ferguson (Sr VP)

Michael E. Coppolino (VP & Mgr-
Risk)
Isaura Tavares (Asst VP-Cash Mgmt)
Patrick J. Murray Jr. (Pres & CEO)
Steve Sherman Jr. (VP & Sr Mgr-
Cash Mgmt)

Subsidiaries:

Anawon Trust (1)
130 Pleasant St, Attleboro, MA 02703
Tel.: (508) 223-5200
Web Site:
　http://www.bristolcountysavingsbank.com
Emp.: 10
Investment Advisory Services
N.A.I.C.S.: 523940

Freedom National Bank (1)
584 Putnam Pike, Greenville, RI 02828-
1498
Tel.: (401) 244-6600
Web Site:
　http://www.freedomnationalbank.com
Commercial Banking
N.A.I.C.S.: 522110
Anthony Botelho (CEO)

BRISTOL DEVELOPMENT LLC
325 Seaboard Ln Ste 190, Franklin,
TN 37067
Tel.: (615) 369-9009
Web Site:
　http://www.bristoldevelopment.com
Sales Range: $1-9.9 Million
Emp.: 20
Property Leasing, Management &
Investment
N.A.I.C.S.: 531110
Ashlyn Hines Meneguzzi (Founder &
Principal)
Dan Daniel (Principal)
Sam Yeager (Founder & Principal)
Charles Carlisle (CEO)
Glen Bartosh (Chief Dev Officer)
David Hancrow (Chief Investment
Officer)
Bryan Jacobs (CFO)
Andrea Sullivan (Controller-Fin)
Kayla Bates (Dir-Mktg)
Jay Duncan (Mgr-Dev)
Amy Thompson (Sr Project Mgr)
Lisa Gunderson (VP-Asset Mgmt)

BRISTOL FIBERLITE INDUS-
TRIES
401 Goetz Ave, Santa Ana, CA 92707
Tel.: (714) 540-8950
Web Site: http://www.bristolite.com
Rev.: $12,300,000
Emp.: 200
Skylights Manufacturer
N.A.I.C.S.: 326199
Randolph Heartfield (Owner)

BRISTOL ID TECHNOLOGIES,
INC.
1370 Rochester St, Lima, NY 14485
Tel.: (412) 279-2480
Web Site: http://www.bristolid.com
Rev.: $8,200,000
Emp.: 50
Photographic Equipment & Supplies
Merchant Whslr
N.A.I.C.S.: 423410
Keith Yeates (CEO)

Subsidiaries:

**Plastic Printing Professionals,
Inc.** (1)
151 Park Ln, Brisbane, CA 94005
Tel.: (415) 585-9600
Plastics Product Mfr
N.A.I.C.S.: 322219
Mike Caulley (Pres)

BRISTOL INVESTMENTS, LTD.
3422 Old Capitol Trl Ste 784, Wilmington, DE 19808

Tel.: (978) 874-5434
Web Site:
http://www.bristolinvestments.com
Private Investment Capital
N.A.I.C.S.: 523999
Franklin B. Levin *(Gen Counsel & VP)*
Philip N. Burgess Jr. *(Chm & CEO)*

Subsidiaries:

MicroBilt Corporation **(1)**
1640 Airport Rd Ste 115, Kennesaw, GA 30144
Tel.: (770) 218-4400
Web Site: http://www.microbilt.com
Sales Range: $10-24.9 Million
Emp.: 47
Risk Management & Business Consulting Services
N.A.I.C.S.: 541611
Walt Wojciechowski *(CEO)*
Sheri Jouas *(VP-Sls)*
John Hambrick *(Sr VP-Bus Dev)*
Sean Albert *(CMO & Sr VP)*

Subsidiary (Domestic):

MicroBilt Collection Agency, Inc. **(2)**
1640 Airport Rd Ste 115, Kennesaw, GA 30144 **(100%)**
Tel.: (770) 218-4400
Web Site: http://www.microbilt.com
Collection Services
N.A.I.C.S.: 561440
Walt Wojciechowski *(CEO)*

BRISTOL VIRGINIA UTILITIES

15022 Lee Hwy, Bristol, VA 24202
Tel.: (276) 669-4112
Web Site: https://www.bvu-optinet.com
Year Founded: 1945
Sales Range: $25-49.9 Million
Emp.: 165
Electric, Water, Wastewater & Telecommunication Services Administration Organization
N.A.I.C.S.: 926130
Brigitte Grenier *(Sr VP & Portfolio Mgr-Comml)*
Jacob Kojalo *(Officer-Comml Loan & Sr VP)*
Melissa Maranda *(Sr VP-Wealth Mgmt Div)*
Michael J. Bovenzi *(Officer-Comml Loan & Sr VP)*
William F. Greene *(Officer-Risk & Sr VP)*
Martin F. Connors Jr. *(Pres & CEO)*

BRIT MEDIA, INC.

550 Sutter St, San Francisco, CA 94102
Tel.: (415) 923-8878 DE
Web Site: http://www.brit.co
Instructional Media Platform & Website Publisher
N.A.I.C.S.: 541511
Annette Cardwell *(VP-Editorial)*
Adam Goldband *(Sr VP-Technology)*
Alex Miller *(Mgr-Partnerships)*
Alonna Morrison *(Dir-Art & Video)*
Alyssa Asadoorian *(Sr Mgr-Acct)*
Amy Keroes *(Gen Counsel)*
Anita Maiella *(Sr VP-Brand Partnerships)*
Anjelika Temple *(Chief Creative Officer & Founding Partner)*
Anna Monette Roberts *(Editor-Food)*
Ashley Fischer Stern *(Dir-Branded Partnerships)*
Ashley Perlman *(Dir-Creative Production)*
Allison Takeda *(Exec Editor-New + Buzz)*
Alicia Winding *(Mgr-Brand Partnerships)*
Ayaz Manji *(VP-Fin)*
Jill Braff *(Pres)*

BRITE COMPUTERS

7647 Main St Fishers, Victor, NY 14564
Tel.: (585) 869-6000
Web Site:
https://www.britecomputers.com
Year Founded: 1983
Sales Range: $10-24.9 Million
Emp.: 37
Electronic Products Mfr
N.A.I.C.S.: 334111
Lindsey Sengle *(Mgr-Pub Safety Acct)*

BRITESKIES, LLC

Rockside Square Office Park 6155 Rockside Rd Ste 110, Independence, OH 44131
Tel.: (216) 369-3600
Web Site: http://www.briteskies.com
Year Founded: 2000
Sales Range: $1-9.9 Million
Emp.: 60
Application Development, Technical Support, Web Design & Development
N.A.I.C.S.: 513210
Michael Berlin *(Founder & Mng Dir)*
William Onion *(Mng Dir)*
Stefanie Rhine *(Mgr-Bus Continuity)*

BRITISH MOTOR CAR DISTRIBUTORS LTD.

901 Van Ness Ave, San Francisco, CA 94109
Tel.: (415) 776-7700
Year Founded: 1951
Sales Range: $75-99.9 Million
Emp.: 125
New & Used Car Sales
N.A.I.C.S.: 441110
Kjell Qvale *(Founder)*
Nancy Bong *(Sec)*
Donald Endo *(CFO)*
Vincent Golde *(Gen Mgr)*
John Wolbertus *(Dir-Parts)*
Jeffrey Qvale *(Owner)*

BRITT MOBILE HOMES INC.

1343 N Lamar Blvd, Oxford, MS 38655
Tel.: (662) 234-4889
Sales Range: $10-24.9 Million
Emp.: 5
Mobile Home Dealers
N.A.I.C.S.: 459930
Rickey Britt *(Pres)*
Greg Dykes *(Office Mgr)*

BRITT RICE ELECTRIC LP.

3002 Longmire Dr Ste D, College Station, TX 77845
Tel.: (979) 693-4076
Web Site: https://www.briceco.net
Rev.: $26,000,000
Emp.: 195
Electrical Contractor
N.A.I.C.S.: 238210
James Boren *(Mgr-Pur)*
Leonard Dannhaus *(Office Mgr)*
David Moore *(Mgr-IT)*
Larry Patton *(Gen Mgr)*
Britt L. Rice *(Partner)*
Chris Wright *(Office Mgr)*

BRITT'S HOME FURNISHINGS, INC.

3293 Hwy 78 W, Snellville, GA 30078-6856
Tel.: (770) 972-2808
Web Site:
http://www.brittshomefurnishing.com
Year Founded: 1972
Sales Range: $10-24.9 Million
Emp.: 35
Floor Coverings Whslr
N.A.I.C.S.: 449121

Matt Britt *(Mgr)*
Tony Britt *(Owner & Pres)*

BRITTANICA HOME FASHIONS INC.

214 W 39th St Rm 1203, New York, NY 10018-5523
Tel.: (212) 764-3851
Year Founded: 1977
Sales Range: $10-24.9 Million
Emp.: 50
Mfr of Homefurnishings
N.A.I.C.S.: 423220
Harry Gross *(CEO)*
Manny Monge *(CFO)*

BRITTANY DYEING & PRINTING CORPORATION

1357 E Rodney French Blvd, New Bedford, MA 02744-2124
Tel.: (508) 999-3281 MA
Web Site:
https://www.brittanyusa.com
Year Founded: 1939
Sales Range: $100-124.9 Million
Emp.: 300
Cotton Broadwoven Fabrics Dyeing & Printing; Circular Knit Fabrics Dyeing & Finishing
N.A.I.C.S.: 313310
Kenneth Joblon *(Pres & CEO)*
Michelle Ostiguy *(Controller)*
Jane Ostrowsky *(Mgr-HR)*

BRITTANY STAMPING, LLC

16000 Commerce Park Dr, Cleveland, OH 44142
Tel.: (216) 574-4808 OH
Year Founded: 1978
Sales Range: $125-149.9 Million
Emp.: 1,170
Metal Stampings; Gray Iron Castings; Thermoformed Finished Plastic Products; Stoneware Pottery Products
N.A.I.C.S.: 332119
Charles P. Bolton *(Chm)*
Jeff Lezan *(Controller)*
Janet M. Tilton *(Treas)*

Subsidiaries:

Great Lakes Castings Corporation **(1)**
800 N Washington Ave, Ludington, MI 49431-2724 **(100%)**
Tel.: (231) 843-2501
Web Site: http://www.glccadv.com
Sales Range: $25-49.9 Million
Emp.: 300
Mfr of Gray Iron Castings
N.A.I.C.S.: 331511

The Payne Investment Company **(1)**
PO Box 609490, Cleveland, OH 44109 **(100%)**
Tel.: (216) 574-4808
Sales Range: $10-24.9 Million
Emp.: 12
Holding Company: Precision Gaskets & Tool Die
N.A.I.C.S.: 551112

Subsidiary (Domestic):

Flow Dry Technology Ltd **(2)**
379 Albert Rd, Brookville, OH 45309 **(100%)**
Tel.: (937) 833-2161
Web Site: http://www.flowdry.com
Emp.: 100
Non-Metallic Gaskets, Sealing Devices & Automotive Air Conditioning Product Mfr
N.A.I.C.S.: 339991
Rahul Deshmukh *(Pres)*

Robinson-Ransbottom Pottery Company **(2)**
Ste 4000 50 Public Sq, Cleveland, OH 44113-2202 **(100%)**
Tel.: (740) 697-7355
Mfr of Pottery
N.A.I.C.S.: 327110

BRITZ & COMPANY

1302 9th St, Wheatland, WY 82201
Tel.: (307) 322-4040
Web Site: https://www.britzco.com
Sales Range: $10-24.9 Million
Emp.: 30
Cages, Wire
N.A.I.C.S.: 332618
William E. Britz Jr. *(Pres, CEO & Treas)*

BRIVO SYSTEMS, LLC

7700 Old Georgetown Rd Ste 300, Bethesda, MD 20814
Tel.: (301) 664-5242 DE
Web Site: http://www.brivo.com
Year Founded: 1999
Sales Range: $10-24.9 Million
Emp.: 195
Cloud & Data Security Services
N.A.I.C.S.: 518210
Steve Van Till *(Founder, Pres & CEO)*
John Szczygiel *(COO & Exec VP)*
Dave Williams *(VP-Strategic Accts)*
Eric Wagner *(Sr VP-Engrg & Ops)*
Bill Yesnick *(VP-Sls)*
Dean Drako *(Owner & Chm)*
Nathan Scott *(VP-Fin & Admin)*
JuliAnn Tuleya *(Sr Mgr-Mktg)*
Mike Voslow *(CFO)*
Kelly Bond *(VP-Dealer Dev)*
Mary Clark *(CMO)*
Ingo Meijer *(Reg Dir-Europe)*

BRIX CORPORATION

30591 Schoolcraft, Livonia, MI 48150
Tel.: (313) 965-0000
Web Site:
https://www.brixcorporation.com
Year Founded: 1998
Sales Range: $10-24.9 Million
Emp.: 25
Civil Engineering Services
N.A.I.C.S.: 237310
Ije C. Osuagwu *(Pres)*

BRIX HOLDINGS, LLC

2811 McKinney Ave Ste 354, Dallas, TX 75204
Tel.: (631) 615-6711 TX
Year Founded: 2013
Holding Company; Pizzerias & Non-Alcoholic Beverage Bars Franchisor & Operator
N.A.I.C.S.: 551112
Miguel Foegal *(Pres-RedBrick Pizza & Smoothie Factory)*
John F. Antioco *(Chm)*
Christopher Pfau *(VP-Restaurant Ops)*
Sal Rincione *(VP-Real Estate & Construction)*
Robert DiBartolomeo *(Dir-Franchising-Natl)*
Scott McIntosh *(Dir-Franchise Dev)*
Richard Jensrud *(CFO)*
Jim Notarnicola *(CMO & VP-Franchise Dev)*
Luke Mandola Jr. *(VP-Franchise Sls & Dev)*
Sherif Mityas *(CEO)*

Subsidiaries:

Red Brick Pizza LLC **(1)**
2811 McKinney Ave Ste 354, Dallas, TX 75204
Tel.: (214) 302-5939
Web Site: http://www.redbrickpizza.com
Pizzerias Franchisor & Operator
N.A.I.C.S.: 722513
Miguel Foegal *(Pres)*

Red Mango, LLC **(1)**
2811 McKinney Ave Ste 18, Dallas, TX 75204
Tel.: (631) 615-7909
Web Site: http://www.redmangousa.com

BRIX Holdings, LLC—(Continued)

Frozen Yogurt & Non-Alcoholic Beverage Bars Franchisor & Operator
N.A.I.C.S.: 722515
Daniel J. Kim (Founder)
Lindsay Carreker (Dir-Art & Brand Mgr)
Mitzi Brown (Chief Legal Officer)
Richard Jensrud (CFO)

Souper Salad, LLC (1)
2811 McKinney Ave Ste 354, Dallas, TX 75204
Tel.: (210) 495-9644
Web Site: http://www.soupersalad.com
Buffet-Style Restaurants Franchisor & Operator
N.A.I.C.S.: 722513
Dan Hernandez (Pres)
Jackie Hernandez (VP-Fin)
Jeff Farnell (VP-Ops)
Richard Jensrud (VP-Fin)

The Smoothie Factory, Inc. (1)
11910 Greenville Ave Ste 220, Dallas, TX 75243
Tel.: (214) 792-9359
Web Site: http://www.smoothiefactory.net
Fruit Smoothie Beverage Bars Franchisor & Operator
N.A.I.C.S.: 722515
Miguel Foegal (Pres)

BRIXEY & MEYER, INC.
2991 Newmark Dr, Miamisburg, OH 45342
Tel.: (937) 291-4110 OH
Web Site:
    https://www.brixeyandmeyer.com
Year Founded: 2002
Accounting, Tax, Audit & Business Advisory Services; Private Equity Investment Services
N.A.I.C.S.: 541211
Jeff Kujawa (Dir-Tax Svcs)
David Brixey (Co-Founder, Partner & Mng Dir)
Douglas L. Meyer (Co-Founder, Partner & Mng Dir)
Kevin Weckesser (Dir-Assurance & Bus Valuation Svcs)
Jeff Bruner (Dir-CFO Svcs)
Tom Petrovic (Dir-Audit & Assurance Svcs)

Subsidiaries:

Brixey & Meyer Capital LLC (1)
2991 Newmark Dr, Miamisburg, OH 45342
Tel.: (937) 291-4110
Web Site:
    http://www.brixeyandmeyercapital.com
Emp.: 100
Privater Equity Firm
N.A.I.C.S.: 523999
David Brixey (CEO & Mng Dir)
Patrick Odell (Principal)
John Handelsman (Partner-Ops)
H. Pat Hobby (Dir-Shared Svcs)

Holding (Domestic):

3 Sigma Corp. (2)
1985 W Stanfield Rd, Troy, OH 45373
Tel.: (937) 440-3400
Web Site: http://www.3sigma.cc
Sales Range: $1-9.9 Million
Emp.: 80
Surgical Appliance & Supplies Mfr
N.A.I.C.S.: 339113
Tony Rowley (Pres)

Access Control Systems, LLC (2)
2617 Grissom Dr, Nashville, TN 37204-2820
Tel.: (615) 255-4466
Web Site: http://www.acs-llc.com
Electrical Contractor
N.A.I.C.S.: 238210
Chad Colony (CEO)

City Dash, LLC (2)
949 Laidlaw Ave, Cincinnati, OH 45237
Tel.: (513) 562-2000
Web Site: http://www.citydash.com
Courier Service
N.A.I.C.S.: 492110

Jim Bush (Founder)

Hamlett Engineering Sales Company (2)
28838 Van Dyke Ave, Warren, MI 48093
Tel.: (586) 978-7200
Web Site: http://www.hesco-mi.com
Sales Range: $1-9.9 Million
Waste Water Treatment Equipment Installation Services
N.A.I.C.S.: 562998
Kevin S. Livingston (Pres)
Kip Koszewski (Engr-Sls)
Heather Brawner (Project Mgr)
Dee Livingston (Controller)
Kari Stuart (Dir-Mktg)
Dave Burkel (Mgr-Field Svc)

Patriot Converting, Inc. (2)
12698 Industrial Blvd, Elk River, MN 55330
Tel.: (763) 427-5710
Web Site: http://www.patriotconverting.com
Coated & Laminated Paper Mfr
N.A.I.C.S.: 322220
Brian Stilwell (CEO)
Annette Payne (Mgr-Fin)
Michael Stilwell (Exec VP)
Dale Carlson (Dir-Sls)
Jerry Ebersole (Mgr-Ops)
Chris Goral (Mgr-Customer Svc)

Stillwater Technologies, LLC (2)
1040 S Dorset Rd, Troy, OH 45373
Tel.: (937) 440-2500
Web Site:
    http://www.stillwatertechnologies.com
Sales Range: $10-24.9 Million
Emp.: 90
Special Dies & Tools
N.A.I.C.S.: 333514
Wanda Lukens (VP-Fin)
Joe McDowell (Engr-Sls)
Steve Young (Mgr-Applications)
Michael van Haaren (Pres & CEO)
Bill Diederich (CEO)

Unistructural Support Systems, Ltd. (2)
1275 Hill Smith Dr, Cincinnati, OH 45233
Tel.: (513) 321-2502
Web Site: https://www.unistrut.biz
Structural Steel & Precast Concrete Contractors
N.A.I.C.S.: 238120
Mark Ellis (Pres)

BRIXTON GROUP INC.
310 Arlington Ave, Charlotte, NC 28203
Tel.: (704) 376-2700
Web Site: http://www.brixton.net
Year Founded: 1998
Sales Range: $10-24.9 Million
Emp.: 7
It Consulting
N.A.I.C.S.: 541690
Brendan Sobel (Dir-Recruiting)

BRK, INC.
411 Eastgate Rd Ste A, Henderson, NV 89011
Tel.: (702) 572-8050 NV
Year Founded: 2008
BRKK—(OTCBB)
Rev.: $2,797,000
Assets: $95,000
Liabilities: $2,137,000
Net Worth: ($2,042,000)
Earnings: $2,059,000
Fiscal Year-end: 04/30/19
Investment Services
N.A.I.C.S.: 523999

BRMI
5525 Adams Ridge Rd, Chevy Chase, MD 21029
Tel.: (202) 449-3763
Web Site: http://www.brmi.com
Year Founded: 2004
Sales Range: $1-9.9 Million
Emp.: 50

Business, Information & Technology Management Services to Federal Government & Commercial Sector Clients
N.A.I.C.S.: 519290
Michael Battle (Pres)
Jennifer Yang (Sr VP)
Anita Lynn (Sr VP)
Eric Crowe (CFO)

BRO RETAIL GROUP INC.
14644 N 74th St Ste 101, Scottsdale, AZ 85260
Tel.: (480) 948-8955
Sales Range: $25-49.9 Million
Emp.: 60
Owner & Operator of Convenience Stores
N.A.I.C.S.: 445131
Kent D. Bro (Pres)
Todd Bro (VP)
Dan Smith (Dir-Mdsg)

BROACH & COMPANY
520 S Elm St, Greensboro, NC 27406
Tel.: (336) 373-0811 NC
Year Founded: 1983
Sales Range: Less than $1 Million
Emp.: 6
Advetising Agency
N.A.I.C.S.: 541810
J. Allen Broach (Pres & CEO)
Norman F. Brame (Acct Exec)

BROAD ACRES NURSING HOME ASSOCIATION
1883 Shumway Hill Rd, Wellsboro, PA 16901
Tel.: (570) 724-3913 PA
Web Site:
    http://www.broadacresnursing.com
Year Founded: 1977
Sales Range: $10-24.9 Million
Emp.: 255
Nursing Care Services
N.A.I.C.S.: 623110
Sara Roupp (VP)

BROAD STREET MEDIA, LLC
2512 Metropolitan Dr, Trevose, PA 19053
Tel.: (215) 354-3000 NJ
Web Site: http://www.bsmphilly.com
Community Newspaper & Internet Publisher
N.A.I.C.S.: 513110
Darwin Oordt (CEO)
Perry Corsetti (Publr)
Gail Bruno (Acct Exec)
Pearl Harta (Dir-Circulation)
Brandon Chamberlain (Gen Mgr-Bus)
Don Russell (Editor-in-Chief)

Subsidiaries:

Broad Street Media, LLC - Cherry Hill (1)
915 N Lenola Rd, Moorestown, NJ 08057
Tel.: (856) 779-3800
Web Site: http://www.bsmphilly.com
Sales Range: $25-49.9 Million
Emp.: 50
Community Newspaper & Internet Publisher
N.A.I.C.S.: 513110

Philadelphia Weekly (1)
1617 JFK Blvd Ste 1005, Philadelphia, PA 19103
Tel.: (215) 563-7400
Web Site:
    http://www.philadelphiaweekly.com
Sales Range: $1-9.9 Million
Emp.: 25
Newspaper Publishers
N.A.I.C.S.: 513110
Anastasia Barbalios (Mng Editor)
Kelsey Lee (Acct Exec)
Donna Mackey (Designer-Graphic)

Holly Siemon (Mgr-Production)
Jay Sterin (Gen Mgr)
Katharine Wamser (Mgr-Bus)

BROAD STREET REALTY, LLC
7250 Woodmont Ave Ste 350, Bethesda, MD 20814
Tel.: (301) 828-1200 MD
Web Site:
    http://www.broadstreetllc.net
Commercial Real Estate Services
N.A.I.C.S.: 531210
Thomas M. Yockey (Founder & Dir)
Michael Z. Jacoby (Chm & CEO)

Subsidiaries:

Broad Street Realty, Inc. (1)
11911 Freedom Dr, Reston, VA 20190
Tel.: (301) 828-1200
Web Site: https://www.broadstreetrealty.com
Rev.: $32,951,000
Assets: $402,286,000
Liabilities: $363,541,000
Net Worth: $38,745,000
Earnings: ($15,291,000)
Emp.: 42
Fiscal Year-end: 12/31/2022
Acquisition Company; Real Estate
N.A.I.C.S.: 523999
Michael Z. Jacoby (Co-Founder, Chm & CEO)
Thomas M. Yockey (Co-Founder)
Alexander Topchy (CFO & Sec)
Lucas Aguilar (Asst Mgr-Property)
Terry Burka (VP-Asset Mgmt)
Telita Campbell (Mgr-Office Admin)
Colin Clancy (VP)
David Cravedi (Sr VP)
Toni Fitzgerald (Coord-Property)
Holly Gray (VP-Acctg)
Kena Hodges (VP-HR & Admin)
Aras Holden (VP-Acquisitions & Dev)
Kimberly Johnson (Asst VP-Lease Admin)
Marisa Michnick (VP-Retail Leasing)
James Rayborn (Sr VP)
Michael Spector (VP-Retail Leasing)
Vanessa Thomas (Mgr-Acctg)
Chad Knoth (VP)
Mylisha Palmer (Coord-Mktg)
Mark Strauss (Sr VP-Tenant Representation Svcs)
Dawn Thompson (Sr Mgr-Property)
Tina Weathersbee (Mgr-AP/AR)
Barry Weber (Supvr-Maintenance)
Sean Mays (Sr Mgr-Asset)
Nicholas Nguyen (Asst Mgr-Asset)
Keir Hogan (Sr Mgr-Property)
Stacy Rukavishnikov (Sr Mgr-Property)
Dane Tekin (Sr VP-Retail Leasing Brokerage)
Halina Druz (Controller)
Terri Levin (Coord)
Tracy Williams (VP-Fin Reporting)

BROADBAND ACCESS NETWORKING GROUP, INC.
70 Wilbur St Ste 1, Lowell, MA 01851
Tel.: (978) 937-3036
Year Founded: 1998
Sales Range: $10-24.9 Million
Emp.: 100
Computer System Design Services
N.A.I.C.S.: 541512
Walter Casey (Pres)

BROADBAND SPECIALIST
100 1700 S Peachtree Rd, Mesquite, TX 75180-1110
Tel.: (972) 329-1280
Web Site: http://www.bsicable.com
Rev.: $10,100,000
Emp.: 50
Telephone & Telephone Equipment Installation
N.A.I.C.S.: 238210
Ramona Locke (VP)
Gerard M. Locke Sr. (Pres & CEO)

BROADCAST ELECTRONICS, INC.
4100 N 24th St, Quincy, IL 62305-7749

Tel.: (217) 224-9600
Web Site: https://www.bdcast.com
Year Founded: 1959
Supplier of Radio & T.V. Communications Equipment
N.A.I.C.S.: 334220

BROADCAST SUPPLY WORLDWIDE, INC.
2237 S 19th St, Tacoma, WA 98405
Tel.: (253) 565-2301   **WA**
Web Site: https://www.bswusa.com
Year Founded: 1973
Audio Communication Equipment Retailer
N.A.I.C.S.: 423690
Tim Schweiger *(Pres)*
Kathy Thatcher *(VP-Ops)*
Tom Roalkvam *(COO)*

BROADCAST TIME, INC.
91 Blackheath Rd, Lido Beach, NY 11561-4807
Tel.: (516) 431-2215   **NY**
Web Site:
    https://www.broadcasttime.com
Year Founded: 1981
Sales Range: $25-49.9 Million
Emp.: 8
Advertising Services
N.A.I.C.S.: 541810
Bruce Kuperschmid *(Pres)*
Peter Kuperschmid *(Exec VP)*

BROADCASTER, INC.
353 Bel Marin Keys Blvd #14, Novato, CA 94949-5641
Tel.: (415) 883-5641   **DE**
Year Founded: 1982
Sales Range: $1-9.9 Million
Emp.: 4
Mobile Entertainment Services
N.A.I.C.S.: 517112
Blair Mills *(CFO)*

BROADCASTMED, INC.
195 Farmington Ave, Farmington, CT 06032
Tel.: (860) 760-4202
Web Site:
    https://www.broadcastmed.com
Year Founded: 1994
Digital Medical Broadcasting
N.A.I.C.S.: 516210
Ross Joel *(Co-Founder & CEO)*
Peter Gailey *(Co-Founder & Pres)*

Subsidiaries:

Or-Live, Inc.   (1)
195 Farmington Ave, Farmington, CT 06032
Tel.: (860) 953-2900
Web Site: http://www.orlive.com
Sales Range: $1-9.9 Million
Emp.: 15
On-Line & Video-Based Communication Solutions for Healthcare Industry
N.A.I.C.S.: 519290
Ross Joel *(CEO)*
Peter Gailey *(Co-Founder & Pres)*
Ron Obston *(VP-Brdcst Ops)*
William White *(VP-IT)*

BROADCASTSTORE.COM
9420 Lurline Ave Unit C, Chatsworth, CA 91311
Tel.: (818) 998-9100
Web Site:
    http://www.broadcaststore.com
Rev.: $13,868,895
Emp.: 3
Communications Equipment
N.A.I.C.S.: 423690
J. P. Claude *(Pres)*

BROADDUS & ASSOCIATES, INC.
1301 S Capital of Texas Hwy Ste A

302, Austin, TX 78746
Tel.: (512) 329-8822   **TX**
Web Site:
    http://www.broaddusassociates.com
Year Founded: 2000
Sales Range: $75-99.9 Million
Emp.: 85
Construction Management & Consulting Services
N.A.I.C.S.: 541330
James A. Broaddus *(Founder & Pres)*
David J. Bowlin *(Exec VP)*
Gilbert O. Gallegos *(Sr VP)*
Scott A. Broaddus *(VP)*
Donna K. Wells *(Exec Dir)*
Hyde Griffith *(VP & Area Mgr)*
Gerald Akin *(VP)*
Rick Johnson *(VP)*
Sam Sprouse *(VP)*

Subsidiaries:

FJW Construction, LLC   (1)
905 W Mitchell St, Arlington, TX 76013
Tel.: (512) 306-7975
Web Site: http://www.fjwcc.com
Sales Range: $10-24.9 Million
Emp.: 3
Healthcare, Financial, Religious & Aviation Facilitiy Contstruction
N.A.I.C.S.: 236220
J. Patrick Messer *(Exec VP)*
Hank Stogner *(VP)*
Michael N. Heid *(Exec VP)*
James A. Broaddus *(CEO)*
Bobby Whatley *(Exec VP)*

BROADFIELD DISTRIBUTING INC.
179 Liberty Ave, Mineola, NY 11501
Tel.: (516) 676-2378   **NY**
Web Site: http://www.broadfield.com
Year Founded: 1982
Sales Range: $10-24.9 Million
Emp.: 15
Distr of Video Editing & Production Equipment
N.A.I.C.S.: 423690
Philip Bettan *(Pres)*
Jim Bask *(Dir-Adv)*
Kim Serravalle *(Mgr-Ops)*

BROADGATE INC
830 Kirts Blvd Ste 400, Troy, MI 48084
Tel.: (248) 918-0110
Web Site:
    https://www.broadgateinc.com
Year Founded: 2006
Sales Range: $1-9.9 Million
Emp.: 60
IT Consulting & Staffing
N.A.I.C.S.: 541690
Swaroopa Kotha *(Pres)*
Satish Reddy *(Mgr-Bus Dev)*

BROADHEAD + CO., INC.
123 N 3rd St Ste 400, Minneapolis, MN 55401
Tel.: (612) 623-8000
Web Site:
    http://www.broadheadco.com
Year Founded: 2001
Advetising Agency
N.A.I.C.S.: 541810
Dean Broadhead *(CEO)*
Dee Weeda *(Sr Mgr-Pub Rel)*
Beth Burgy *(COO)*
Troy Schroeder *(Assoc VP)*
Linda Romander *(Sr Mgr-PR)*
Clifford Owen *(Acct Dir)*
Tom DiBacco *(Dir-Consumer Pub Rel)*
John Walker *(Dir-Creative)*
Lannie Dawson *(VP-Engagement)*
Lana Olson *(Sr Acct Exec)*
Sarah Zanger Perron *(VP-Bus Dev)*
Steve Renier *(Sr VP-Talent)*

Subsidiaries:

Kohnstamm Communications   (1)
400 Robert St N Ste 1450, Saint Paul, MN 55101
Tel.: (651) 228-9141
Web Site: http://www.kohnstamm.com
Advertising Agencies
N.A.I.C.S.: 541810
Josh Kohnstamm *(Founder & CEO)*
Aaron Berstler *(VP-Bus & Dir-Agency Sys)*
Allan Newbold *(VP-Consumer & Dir-Brand & Client Svcs)*
Rebecca Zanger *(Mgr-Client Admin & Coord-talent)*

BROADLINE COMPONENTS, LLC
1780 102nd Ave N St, Saint Petersburg, FL 33716
Tel.: (813) 333-2312
Web Site:
    http://www.broadlinecomponent.com
Year Founded: 2008
Sales Range: $1-9.9 Million
Emp.: 10
Electronic Components Distr
N.A.I.C.S.: 449210
Gary Banlowe *(Pres & CEO)*
Juan Guillermo Lopez *(Sls Dir)*
Nancy Conn *(Office Mgr)*
Cassandra Laviani *(Sls Mgr)*

BROADNET TELESERVICES
1805 Shea Ctr Dr Ste 160, Littleton, CO 80129-2253
Tel.: (303) 268-5500
Web Site: http://www.Broadnet.us
Year Founded: 2004
Sales Range: $10-24.9 Million
Emp.: 22
Online Business Communications Solutions
N.A.I.C.S.: 517810
Stephen Patterson *(CEO)*
Torbjorn Krovel *(COO)*

BROADREACH MEDICAL RESOURCES, INC.
1350 Broadway, New York, NY 10018
Tel.: (212) 220-0080
Web Site: http://www.bmr-inc.com
Year Founded: 2004
Sales Range: $1-9.9 Million
Health Care Srvices
N.A.I.C.S.: 621610
Timothy N. Teen *(Pres)*
Michael Fendrich *(Dir-Analytical Svcs)*
Beth MacKnight *(Dir-Ops)*
Elliot Berkovitz *(Dir-Clinical Svcs)*
Joe Moran *(Dir-Corp Dev)*

BROADSTONE REAL ESTATE, LLC
800 Clinton Sq, Rochester, NY 14604
Tel.: (585) 287-6500
Web Site:
    https://www.broadstone.com
Year Founded: 2006
Sales Range: $50-74.9 Million
Emp.: 55
Real Estate Services
N.A.I.C.S.: 531390
John Maguire *(Mgr-Property)*
Ryan Albano *(VP-Fin)*
Molly Wiegel *(VP-HR)*
Christopher J. Czarnecki *(Pres & CFO)*

BROADSTREET PRODUCTIONS, LLC
242 W 30 St Fl 2, New York, NY 10010
Tel.: (212) 780-5700
Web Site:
    http://www.broadstreet.com

Year Founded: 1981
Sales Range: $10-24.9 Million
Emp.: 25
Advertising Related Services
N.A.I.C.S.: 541890
Mark Baltazar *(CEO & Mng Partner)*
Ed Gibbons *(CFO & Partner)*
Claudia Tressler *(Sr VP-Production)*

BROADTREE PARTNERS, LLC
101 S. Tryon Street, Ste 2700, Charlotte, NC 28280
Tel.: (704) 228-1262
Web Site:
    http://broadtreepartners.com
Year Founded: 2016
Privater Equity Firm
N.A.I.C.S.: 523999
Bryan da Frota *(Principal & Operating Partner)*
Sean Mahon *(CEO-ASAP Site Services)*
Johannes Zwick *(Mng Partner)*

Subsidiaries:

Joint Research & Development, Inc.   (1)
50 Tech Pkwy Ste 209, Stafford, VA 22556-1803
Tel.: (540) 288-3132
Web Site: http://www.jrad.us
Research & Development in the Physical, Engineering & Life Sciences
N.A.I.C.S.: 541715
Peter Christensen *(VP-Ops-Edgewood)*
Terri Hague *(Pres)*

List Engage, Inc.   (1)
5 Edgell Rd Ste 20, Framingham, MA 01701
Tel.: (508) 935-2275
Web Site: http://www.listengage.com
Computer Related Services
N.A.I.C.S.: 541519
Altaf M. Shaikh *(Founder & CEO)*
Bryan da Frota *(COO)*

Sayres & Associates, LLC   (1)
55 M St SE Ste 200, Washington, DC 20003
Tel.: (202) 355-0922
Web Site: https://broadtreepartners.com
Space & Defense Equipment Manufacturing
N.A.I.C.S.: 336419
Tim Reardon *(CEO)*

Subsidiary (Domestic):

Global Systems Technologies, Inc.   (2)
109 Floral Vale Blvd, Yardley, PA 19067
Tel.: (215) 579-8200
Web Site: http://www.gstpa.com
Sales Range: $1-9.9 Million
Emp.: 80
Engineeering Services
N.A.I.C.S.: 541330
Achintya Bhattacharjee *(Pres)*
Ozzie Gerald *(Mgr-Sls)*

Seanair Machine Co., Inc.   (1)
95 Verdi St, Farmingdale, NY 11735
Tel.: (631) 694-2820
Web Site: http://www.seanairmachine.com
Sales Range: $1-9.9 Million
Emp.: 18
Machine Shops
N.A.I.C.S.: 332710
Avi Das *(CEO)*

Triage Partners, LLC   (1)
210 S Lincoln Ave, Tampa, FL 33609
Tel.: (813) 801-9869
Web Site: http://www.triage-partners.com
Sales Range: $1-9.9 Million
Emp.: 24
Employment Agency And Computer Related Consulting
N.A.I.C.S.: 561311
Patricia Dominguez *(Pres & CEO)*

BROADUS OIL CORP. OF ILLINOIS

Broadus Oil Corp. of Illinois—(Continued)

201 Dannys Dr Ste 5, Streator, IL
61364-1191
Tel.: (815) 673-5515
Web Site: http://www.broadusoil.com
Sales Range: $10-24.9 Million
Emp.: 3
Engine Fuels & Oils; Owner of Pit
Stop Convenience Stores
N.A.I.C.S.: 424720
Steven P. Broadus (Pres)

BROADVIEW GROUP HOLD-INGS, LLC

7676 Forsyth Ste 2210, St. Louis,
MO 63105
Tel.: (314) 366-3240
Web Site:
https://www.broadviewgroup.com
Private Equity
N.A.I.C.S.: 523940

Subsidiaries:

Certified Recycling, Inc.   (1)
555 S Rose St., Anaheim, CA 92805
Tel.: (714) 635-2181
Web Site:
https://certifiedwastesolutions.com
Environmental Services
N.A.I.C.S.: 562998

BROADVOICE, INC.

20847 Sherman Way, Winnetka, CA
91306
Tel.: (888) 332-8036
Web Site: http://www.broadvoice.com
Hosted Voice & Data Services
N.A.I.C.S.: 518210
Jim Murphy (CEO)
George Mitsopoulos (COO)
Tessley Smith (VP-Channel)
Sam Ghahremanpour (Pres)
Ryan Ficken (Mgr-Channel)
Eric Dagg (Dir-Solutions Architecture)
Todd Scarborough (Mgr-Channel-Texas)
Vinit Ahooja (VP-Ops)
Kevin Connor (CFO)
Rebecca Rosen (VP-Mktg)
Cathy Banks (Mgr-Channel-Midwest)
Erald Lika (Mgr-Channel-Northeast)
Brian Kelly (Mgr-Channel-Southeast)
Robert Sanchez (Mgr-Channel-Mountain West)
Joseph Galluzzi (Mgr-Channel-Northeast)
Kim McLachlan (Sr VP-Sls & Mktg)
Kimberly Way (Mktg Mgr-Email)
Lauri Martinez (VP-Channel Mktg)

Subsidiaries:

DSLExtreme.com Inc.   (1)
9221 Corbin Ave Ste 260, Northridge, CA
91324
Tel.: (818) 902-4821
Web Site: http://www.dslextreme.com
High-Speed Internet Services
N.A.I.C.S.: 517810

BROADWAY BANCSHARES, INC.

1177 NE Loop 410, San Antonio, TX
78209-1517
Tel.: (210) 283-6500
Web Site: http://www.broadway.bank
Year Founded: 1981
Rev.: $70,000,000
Emp.: 600
Bank Holding Company
N.A.I.C.S.: 551111
Joe C. McKinney (Vice Chm)
David Bohne (Pres & CEO)
Karen Mawyer (Sr Exec VP)
Joshua Loden (Exec VP & Mgr-Comml Lending)
Jeffrey S. Nelson (Chief Investment
Officer & Exec VP-Investment Mgmt
Grp)

Subsidiaries:

Broadway National Bank   (1)
1177 NE Loop 410, San Antonio, TX 78209-1517
Tel.: (210) 283-6500
Web Site: http://www.broadwaybank.com
Sales Range: $50-74.9 Million
Emp.: 293
National Commercial Banks
N.A.I.C.S.: 522110
James D. Goudge (CEO & Chm)
David Bohne (Pres & CEO)
John Ensminger (CTO & Exec VP)
Kelly A. Colotla (Sr VP & Portfolio Mgr-Investment Mgmt Grp)
Ken Herring (Sr VP)
Matt Delgado (Sr VP-Comml Banking)
Michelle Pair (Sr VP)
Roger D. Bott (Sr VP)
Sherry Gonzalez (Sr VP)
William E. Dieterle (Exec VP-Comml Banking)
Alyssa Hartlage (Sr VP-Comml Real Estate)
Annette McClintock (Sr VP-Bus Dev Specialist)
Brian R. Korb (Sr VP & Portfolio Mgr-Investment Mgmt Grp)
Bruce McMillan (Sr VP-Comml Banking)
Casey Friesenhahn (Sr VP-Comml Real Estate)
Cliff Bandy (Sr VP)
Danny Van De Walle (Sr VP)
Jeffrey S. Nelson (Chief Investment Officer
& Exec VP-Investment Mgmt Grp)
John Cruz (Sr VP-Comml Banking)
John Justin (Sr VP)
Karen Mawyer (Sr Exec VP)

BROADWAY ELECTRIC SERVICE CORPORATION

1800 N Central St, Knoxville, TN
37917
Tel.: (865) 524-1851
Web Site: https://www.besco.com
Year Founded: 1950
Sales Range: $75-99.9 Million
Emp.: 480
Electrical Contractor
N.A.I.C.S.: 238210

BROADWAY ENTERPRISES, INC.

2700 S Ashland Ave, Green Bay, WI
54304-5303
Tel.: (920) 498-6666
Year Founded: 1916
Sales Range: $100-124.9 Million
Emp.: 350
Holding Company; New & Used Car
Dealerships & Passenger Car Rental
Franchises Owner & Operator
N.A.I.C.S.: 551112
David M. Cuene (VP)
Kevin Cuene (Pres)
Michael Cuene (Sec & VP)

Subsidiaries:

Broadway Automotive-Green Bay,
Inc.   (1)
2700 S Ashland Ave, Green Bay, WI
54304-5303   (100%)
Tel.: (920) 498-6666
Web Site:
http://www.broadwayautomotive.com
Sales Range: $25-49.9 Million
Emp.: 300
New & Used Car Dealer
N.A.I.C.S.: 441110
Jef Franken (Gen Mgr)

Broadway Rental Cars, Inc.   (1)
2700 Ashland Ave, Green Bay, WI 54304
Tel.: (920) 498-7733
Rev.: $1,772,145
Emp.: 10
Passenger Car Rental Franchises Operator
N.A.I.C.S.: 532111
Karen Vanxistine (Gen Mgr)

BROADWAY SERVICES, INC.

3709 E Monument St, Baltimore, MD
21205

Tel.: (410) 563-6900
Web Site:
https://www.broadwayservices.com
Year Founded: 1984
Sales Range: $1-9.9 Million
Emp.: 1,400
Provider of Building Maintenance
Services
N.A.I.C.S.: 561720
Robert Biemiller (VP-Security, Parking & Transportation)
Peter Seidl (Pres & CEO)
P. Michael Kastendike (CFO & VP-Finance)

BROADWAY TRUCK CENTERS

1501-1506 S 7th St, Saint Louis, MO
63104
Tel.: (314) 241-9140
Web Site:
http://www.broadwaytruck.com
Year Founded: 1964
Sales Range: $25-49.9 Million
Emp.: 98
Commercial & Personal Truck Sales
N.A.I.C.S.: 441330
Ell R. Linton (Pres)
Jim Cavanagh (Gen Mgr-Rental & Leasing)
Jack L. Garland (VP & Gen Mgr)

BROADWAY VIDEO INC.

1619 Broadway 4th Fl, New York, NY
10019-7412
Tel.: (212) 265-7600
Web Site:
http://www.broadwayvideo.com
Year Founded: 1979
Sales Range: $25-49.9 Million
Emp.: 300
Motion Picture, Video Production &
Post Production
N.A.I.C.S.: 512110
Lorne Michaels (Founder & Chm)

Subsidiaries:

Broadway Sound   (1)
1619 Broadway Fl 4, New York, NY 10019-7412
Tel.: (212) 333-0700
Web Site: http://www.broadwayvideo.com
Sales Range: $10-24.9 Million
Emp.: 27
Television Post Production
N.A.I.C.S.: 512110
Kim Seit (Gen Mgr)

BROADWING COMMUNICA-TIONS, INC.

1025 Eldorado Blvd, Broomfield, CO
80021
Tel.: (720) 888-2518
Telecommunication Servicesb
N.A.I.C.S.: 517810
Thomas A. Schilling (CFO)

BROASTER COMPANY

2859 Cranston Rd, Beloit, WI 53511
Tel.: (608) 365-0193
Web Site: http://www.broaster.com
Sales Range: $10-24.9 Million
Emp.: 65
Manufacturing, Commercial Cooking
Equipment
N.A.I.C.S.: 551112
Richard Schrank (Pres & COO)
Derek Fellows (VP-Mfg)
Randy McKinney (VP-New Product &
Program Dev)
Bill Loeffelhoz (Mgr-Export, Govt &
Special Accts)

Subsidiaries:

Broaster Company LLC   (1)
2855 Cranston Rd, Beloit, WI 53511
Tel.: (608) 365-0193
Web Site: http://www.broaster.com

Sales Range: $10-24.9 Million
Food Products Machinery
N.A.I.C.S.: 333241

BROCE MANUFACTURING CO. INC.

1460 S 2nd Ave, Dodge City, KS
67801
Tel.: (620) 227-8811
Web Site:
https://www.brocebroom.com
Sales Range: $10-24.9 Million
Emp.: 60
Street Sweeper Mfr & Sales
N.A.I.C.S.: 336120
Terry Wimer (VP-Sls & Ops)
Alan Vance (CEO)
Dave Krason (Mgr-Sls-Northeastern)
Jim Grasse (Mgr-Sls-Northwestern)
John Morton (Mgr-Sls-Southeastern)

BROCK & COMPANY INC.

257 Great Valley Pkwy, Malvern, PA
19355
Tel.: (610) 647-5656
Web Site: https://www.brockco.com
Sales Range: $25-49.9 Million
Emp.: 520
Contract Food Services
N.A.I.C.S.: 722310
Lynmar Brock Jr. (Founder & Vice Chm)

BROCK INSURANCE AGENCY

823 Chickamauga Ave, Rossville, GA
30741
Tel.: (706) 866-3394
Web Site: https://www.brockins.com
Year Founded: 1963
Sales Range: $10-24.9 Million
Emp.: 25
Insurance Brokerage Services
N.A.I.C.S.: 524210
Dana Davis (VP)

BROCK INVESTMENTS INC.

2591 Hiram Acworth Hwy, Dallas, GA
30157
Tel.: (770) 947-8770
Sales Range: $10-24.9 Million
Emp.: 10
Convenience Stores, Independent
Grands Food Stores
N.A.I.C.S.: 445131
Charles Brock (Pres)

BROCKTON NEIGHBORHOOD HEALTH CENTER

63 Main St, Brockton, MA 02301
Tel.: (508) 559-6699
Web Site: https://www.bnhc.org
Year Founded: 1992
Sales Range: $25-49.9 Million
Emp.: 459
Health Care Srvices
N.A.I.C.S.: 622110
Benjamin Lightfoot (Dir-Medical)
Melvin Benson (CFO)
Linda Gabruk (COO)
Susan Joss (CEO)

BROCKTON VISITING NURSE ASSOCIATION

500 Belmont St Ste 200, Brockton,
MA 02301-4985
Tel.: (508) 587-2121
Web Site:
https://www.brocktonvna.org
Year Founded: 1910
Sales Range: $10-24.9 Million
Emp.: 154
Horse Association
N.A.I.C.S.: 813920

Lawrence Baker (VP-Fin)
Philip J. Tarallo (Chm)
Scott Sanborn (Treas)
Robert Ford (Pres)

BROCKWAY MORAN & PARTNERS, INC.
225 NE Mizner Blvd Ste 700, Boca Raton, FL 33432
Tel.: (561) 750-2000
Web Site:
https://www.brockwaymoran.com
Year Founded: 1998
Sales Range: $1-4.9 Billion
Emp.: 25
Private Equity Firm Services
N.A.I.C.S.: 523999
Michael E. Moran (Mng Partner)
Peter W. Klein (Partner & Gen Counsel)
H. Randall Litten (Partner-Advisory)
Ari M. Zur (Partner)
B. Jay Anderson (CFO)
Peter C. Brockway (Mng Partner)

Subsidiaries:

MD Now Medical Centers, Inc.   (1)
2007 Palm Beach Lakes Blvd, West Palm Beach, FL 33409
Tel.: (561) 420-8555
Web Site: http://www.mymdnow.com
Urgent Care Facilities
N.A.I.C.S.: 621111

BROCO, INC.
400 S Rockefeller Ave, Ontario, CA 91761
Tel.: (909) 483-3222
Web Site: https://www.broco-rankin.com
Welding & Exothermic Cutting Equipment Mfr
N.A.I.C.S.: 333992
Lee Baker (Dir-Sls)
Richard Ferry (Pres & CEO)

Subsidiaries:

Rankin Industries, Inc.   (1)
8745 Production Ave Site A, San Diego, CA 92121-2261
Tel.: (858) 684-5000
Welding Equipment Mfr
N.A.I.C.S.: 333992

Ready Welder Corporation   (1)
811 E G St Ste A, Wilmington, CA 90744
Tel.: (310) 834-3321
Web Site: http://www.readywelder.com
Sales Range: Less than $1 Million
Emp.: 5
Welding Equipment Mfr
N.A.I.C.S.: 333992
Theodore Holstein (Chm, Pres, CEO & CFO)
Karen M. Leavitt (Sec)
Suzie Charney (Gen Mgr)

BRODART CO.
500 Arch St, Williamsport, PA 17701-7809
Tel.: (570) 326-2461   NJ
Web Site: https://www.brodart.com
Year Founded: 1940
Sales Range: $450-499.9 Million
Emp.: 800
Automated Library Information System Book & Book Services Library Equipment & Furniture Distr
N.A.I.C.S.: 424920
Gretchen Herman (VP-Books & Automation Div)

Subsidiaries:

Brodart Co. - Books & Library Services Division   (1)
500 Arch St, Williamsport, PA 17701
Tel.: (570) 326-2461
Web Site: http://www.brodartbooks.com
Book & Library Services

N.A.I.C.S.: 519210
Robert McAndrew (Pres)

Brodart Co. - Contract Furniture Division   (1)
280 N Rd Clinton County Industrial Park, McElhattan, PA 17748-0280
Tel.: (570) 769-7412
Web Site: http://www.brodartfurniture.com
Furniture Mfr
N.A.I.C.S.: 337214
Chris Frantz (Mgr-Sls)

Brodart Co. - Supplies & Furnishings Division   (1)
500 Arch St, Williamsport, PA 17701
Tel.: (570) 326-2461
Web Site: http://www.shopbrodart.com
Emp.: 150
Furniture Whslr
N.A.I.C.S.: 423210
Ryan Hickey (Supvr-Mktg)

Brodart Company   (1)
109 Roy Blvd Braneida Industrial Pk, Brantford, N3R 7K1, ON, Canada   (100%)
Tel.: (519) 759-4350
Web Site: http://www.brodart.ca
Sales Range: $1-9.9 Million
Emp.: 15
Distribution of Library Supplies & Equipment
N.A.I.C.S.: 459410

The Entwistle Co - Danville Facility   (1)
1940 Halifax Rd, Danville, VA 24543
Tel.: (434) 799-6186
Machine Tools Mfr
N.A.I.C.S.: 333515

BRODEUR CARVELL INC.
13499 S Cleveland Ave Ste 185, Fort Myers, FL 33907
Tel.: (239) 931-4000
Web Site:
https://www.brodeurcarvell.com
Year Founded: 2003
Sales Range: $1-9.9 Million
Emp.: 6
Men's & Women's Clothing Store
N.A.I.C.S.: 458110
Ron Brodeur (Co-Owner)
Rob Carvell (Co-Owner)

BRODIE BUICK MITSUBISHI KIA
2213 Jacksboro Hwy, Wichita Falls, TX 76301
Tel.: (940) 642-8584
Web Site: http://www.motorplace.com
Rev.: $23,000,000
Emp.: 50
Automobiles, New & Used
N.A.I.C.S.: 441110
Jeff L. Koontz (Pres)

BRODIE CONTRACTORS INC.
3901 Computer Dr, Raleigh, NC 27609
Tel.: (919) 782-2482
Web Site: https://www.brodiecon.com
Year Founded: 1978
Sales Range: $10-24.9 Million
Emp.: 150
Masonry Contracting Services
N.A.I.C.S.: 238140
Calvin Brodie (Pres)
Douglas Gray (Project Mgr)
Ingrid Kenner (Project Mgr)

BRODIE TOYOTA-LIFT
10 Ballard Rd, Lawrence, MA 01843
Tel.: (978) 682-6300
Web Site:
https://www.brodietoyotalift.com
Year Founded: 1948
Rev.: $22,000,000
Emp.: 100
Lift Trucks & Parts
N.A.I.C.S.: 423830
Ronald C. Mccluskey (Pres)
Larry Snook (VP-Sls)

Bob Harron (VP-Ops)
Jeff Wiklund (Mgr-Rental & Used Equipment)
Dave Carter (VP-Sls)

BROETJE ORCHARDS
1111 Fishook Park Rd, Auburn, WA 99348
Tel.: (509) 749-2217
Web Site:
http://www.broetjeorchards.com
Year Founded: 1968
Sales Range: $50-74.9 Million
Emp.: 1,100
Apple Orchards
N.A.I.C.S.: 111331
Jim Hazen (Bus Mgr)
Joe Shelton (Mgr-Field)

BROGAN & PARTNERS CONVERGENCE MARKETING
325 S Old Woodward Ave, Birmingham, MI 48009
Tel.: (248) 341-8200   MI
Web Site: http://www.brogan.com
Year Founded: 1984
Sales Range: $50-74.9 Million
Emp.: 55
N.A.I.C.S.: 541810
Marcie Brogan (CEO)
Bonnie Folster (Partner & Exec Dir-Creative)
David Ryan (Partner & Assoc Dir-Creative)
Maria Marcotte (CEO & Partner)
Deidre Bounds (Mng Partner)
Ellyn Davidson (Mng Partner)
Jim Tobin (Partner)
Vong Lee (Assoc Dir-Creative)
Laurie Hix (Partner & Dir-Creative)
Julia Shea (Partner & Dir-Healthcare)
Lauren Zuzelski (Acct Dir)

Subsidiaries:

Brogan & Partners Convergence Marketing   (1)
14600 Western Pkwy Ste 300, Cary, NC 27513
Tel.: (919) 653-2580
Web Site: http://www.brogan.com
Emp.: 25
Advertising Agencies, Collateral, Full Service, Public Relations
N.A.I.C.S.: 541810
Jim Tobin (Partner)
Julia Mastropallo (Partner & Dir-Healthcare Div)
Marcie Brogan (CEO)
Maria Marcotte (Partner & CEO)
Bonnie Folster (Partner & Exec Dir-Creative)
Deidre Bounds (Mng Partner)
Ellyn Davidson (Mng Partner)

BROGAN TENNYSON GROUP, INC.
2245 US Hwy 130 Ste 102, Dayton, NJ 08810-2420
Tel.: (732) 355-0700   NJ
Web Site:
https://www.brogantennyson.com
Year Founded: 1982
Sales Range: $10-24.9 Million
Emp.: 24
Advertising Services
N.A.I.C.S.: 541810
Bill Quinn (Pres)
Howard Kenworthy (Sr VP)
Kim Shargay (Production Dir)
Wendy Scheutz (Acct Dir)
Shirlene Soos (CFO)

Subsidiaries:

Brogan Tennyson   (1)
887 W Marietta St NW Studio T-102, Atlanta, GA 30318-5295
Tel.: (404) 816-0094
Web Site: http://www.brogantennyson.com

Advertising Services
N.A.I.C.S.: 541810
Stacy McCarron (Dir-Mktg)
Wendy Schuetz (Exec VP)

BROKEN ARROW ELECTRIC SUPPLY INC.
2350 W Vancouver St, Broken Arrow, OK 74012
Tel.: (918) 258-3581
Web Site: https://www.baes.com
Year Founded: 1977
Sales Range: $10-24.9 Million
Emp.: 100
Electrical Apparatus & Equipment
N.A.I.C.S.: 423610
Joe Banfield (CTO)
Michael Leibold (Gen Mgr-Sls)
Bruce Garner (Pres)
David Edkins (COO)

BROKEN ARROW INCORPORATED
8960 Hwy 40, Tooele, UT 84074
Tel.: (435) 882-3942
Web Site:
http://www.brokenarrowusa.com
Rev.: $18,954,882
Emp.: 130
Excavation & Grading, Building Construction
N.A.I.C.S.: 238910
Stephen Bunn (Pres)
Scott Maxfield (VP)

BROKEN SOUND CLUB, INC.
2401 Willow Springs Blvd, Boca Raton, FL 33496
Tel.: (561) 241-6800
Web Site:
https://www.brokensoundclub.org
Sales Range: $10-24.9 Million
Emp.: 120
Country Club
N.A.I.C.S.: 713910
John Crean (CEO)
Dave Payne (Dir-Facilities Maintenance)
Dianne Hart (Dir-Fin)
Tim Nelson (Dir-Food & Beverage)
Maureen Schreiber (Dir-Membership)

BROKER GENIUS, INC.
228 Park Ave S PMB 42630, New York, NY 10003
Tel.: (866) 626-2847
Web Site: https://automatiq.com
Automated Ticketing Solutions
N.A.I.C.S.: 541511
Sam Sherman (CEO)

BROKER ONLINE EXCHANGE LLC
400 Rella Blvd, Suffern, NY 10901
Tel.: (817) 350-4880   DE
Web Site:
http://www.brokeronlinexchange.com
Year Founded: 2013
Sales Range: $1-9.9 Million
Emp.: 25
Energy Consulting Services
N.A.I.C.S.: 541690
Arthur Gruen (CEO)
Benji Coomer (VP)
Jason Bear (Dir-Ops)
Lauren Johnson (Sls Dir)
Dana Netel (Mgr-Commissions)

BROKER SOLUTIONS, INC.
14511 Myford Rd Ste 100, Tustin, CA 92780
Web Site:
https://www.newamericanfunding.com
Year Founded: 2003
Sales Range: $25-49.9 Million
Emp.: 330

Broker Solutions, Inc.—(Continued)

Mortgage Lender
N.A.I.C.S.: 522310
Rick Arvielo (Co-Founder & CEO)
Patty Arvielo (Co-Founder & Pres)
Christy Bunce (COO)
Frank Fuentes (VP-Multicultural Lending-Natl)
Anthony Ramirez (Mgr-Sls-San Diego)
Baron O'Brien (VP-Talent Acq)
Kevin Gibbs (Mgr-Missouri)
Chris MacNaughton (VP-Builder & Bus Dev-Northern California)
Kelly Allison (VP-Southeast)
Joe Smith (Mgr-Sls-Arizona)
Milt Karavites (Reg VP)
Zeeda Daniele (Mgr-Community Lending-Orange)
Scott Bristol (Sr VP & Mgr-Sls-Natl)
Virginia Martinez (Mgr-Sls)
Candy Buzan (Mgr-Austin)
Max Leaman (Sr Officer-Loan & Mgr-Austin)
Justin Brown (Mgr-Glendora)
Scott Groves (Mgr-Los Angeles West)
Patricia L. Arvielo (Co-Founder & Pres)

BROKERAGE CONCEPTS INC.
801 Lakeview Dr Ste 301, Blue Bell, PA 19422
Tel.: (610) 337-6103
Web Site: http://www.bcitpa.com
Year Founded: 1977
Emp.: 172
Health Care Srvices
N.A.I.C.S.: 621610
Julie R. Snyder (Dir-Corp Rels)
Margaret Anderson (Exec VP-Bus Dev)

BROKERS CONSOLIDATED, INC.
201 E Saint George Blvd, Saint George, UT 84770
Tel.: (435) 628-1606
Web Site: https://www.erabrokers.com
Year Founded: 1982
Real Estate Brokerage & Property Management Agency
N.A.I.C.S.: 531210
Neil Walter (CEO)
Fafie Moore (Exec VP)
Matt Walter (CTO)

Subsidiaries:

ERA Brokers Consolidated - Las Vegas   (1)
1735 Village Ctr Cir, Las Vegas, NV 89134
Tel.: (702) 873-4500
Web Site: http://www.erabrokers.com
Real Estate Brokerage & Property Management Agency
N.A.I.C.S.: 531210
Jeff Moore (Principal)

ERA Brokers Consolidated - Mesquite   (1)
599 W Mesquite Blvd Ste 100, Mesquite, NV 89027-5156
Tel.: (702) 346-7200
Web Site: http://www.mesquiteera.com
Real Estate Brokerage & Property Management Agency
N.A.I.C.S.: 531210
Natalie Hafen (VP & Broker)

BROKERS LOGISTICS, LTD.
1000 Hawkins Blvd, El Paso, TX 79915
Tel.: (915) 778-7751
Web Site: https://www.brokerslogistics.com
Sales Range: $10-24.9 Million
Emp.: 100

Provider of Trucking & Logistics Services
N.A.I.C.S.: 493110
Jerry Wright (CEO)

BROMIUM, INC.
20813 Stevens Creek Blvd Ste 150, Cupertino, CA 95014
Tel.: (408) 598-3623
Web Site: http://www.bromium.com
Sales Range: $10-24.9 Million
Emp.: 75
Software Publisher
N.A.I.C.S.: 513210
Simon Crosby (Co-Founder & CTO)
Ian Pratt (Co-Founder)
Manish Kalia (Sr VP-Product Mgmt)
Brent Remai (CMO)
Earl Charles (CFO)
David Weier (Sr VP-Worldwide Sls)
Jan Kang (Gen Counsel & VP)
Ravi Khatod (COO)
Bob Maus (Sr VP-Bus Dev)
Gregory Webb (CEO)
Kevin Mosher (Chief Revenue Officer)

BROMWELL FINANCIAL FUND, LIMITED PARTNERSHIP
505 Brookfield Dr, Dover, DE 19901
Year Founded: 1999
Investment Services
N.A.I.C.S.: 523999
Michael Pacult (Pres)

BRONCO MOTORS INC.
9250 W Fairview Ave, Boise, ID 83704
Tel.: (208) 376-8510
Web Site: https://www.broncomotors.com
Rev.: $35,489,000
Emp.: 45
Automobiles, Used Cars Only
N.A.I.C.S.: 441110
Jan Cliff (Dir-HR)
Grant Petersen Jr. (Pres & CEO)

BRONCO WINE COMPANY
6342 Bystrum Rd, Ceres, CA 95307
Tel.: (209) 538-3131
Web Site: https://www.broncowine.com
Sales Range: $25-49.9 Million
Emp.: 200
Winery
N.A.I.C.S.: 312130
Daniel J. Leonard (Pres & CEO)

Subsidiaries:

Rosenblum Cellars   (1)
10 Clay St Ste 100, Oakland, CA 94607
Tel.: (510) 601-2200
Web Site: http://www.rosenblumcellars.com
Vineyard & Winery
N.A.I.C.S.: 312130

BRONCUS MEDICAL, INC
1400 N Shoreline Blvd Ste A8, Mountain View, CA 94043
Tel.: (650) 428-1600
Web Site: http://www.broncus.com
Medical Device Mfr
N.A.I.C.S.: 334510
Henky Wibowo (VP-Imaging-Navigation)

Subsidiaries:

Uptake Medical Corp.   (1)
1173 Warner Ave, Tustin, CA 92780
Tel.: (949) 440-1800
Web Site: http://www.uptakemedical.com
Medical Research Facility
N.A.I.C.S.: 541715
Norma Lowe (VP-RA & QA)

BRONDES FORD TOLEDO
5545 Secor Rd, Toledo, OH 43623-1932
Tel.: (567) 702-2336
Web Site: https://www.brondesfordtoledo.com
Year Founded: 1953
Sales Range: $25-49.9 Million
Emp.: 91
New Car Whslr
N.A.I.C.S.: 441110
Deb Peters Layout (VP)
Andy Shambarger (Sec)
John Stedcke (Gen Mgr)
Phil Brondes Jr. (Pres)

BRONDOW, INC.
68 Marbledale Rd, Tuckahoe, NY 10707-3420
Tel.: (914) 961-9026
Web Site: http://www.brondow.com
Year Founded: 1947
Sales Range: $50-74.9 Million
Emp.: 120
Mfr of Household Cleaners, Disinfectants & Deodorizers
N.A.I.C.S.: 325612
Timothy E. Kelley (Pres)

BRONER GLOVE COMPANY INC.
1750 Harmon Rd, Auburn Hills, MI 48326-1548
Tel.: (248) 391-5000
Web Site: http://www.broner.com
Year Founded: 1933
Sales Range: $10-24.9 Million
Emp.: 50
Hat & Glove Distr
N.A.I.C.S.: 424350
Donna Preston (CEO)
Bob Broner (Pres)

BRONIEC ASSOCIATES INC.
4855 Peachtree Industrial Blvd Ste 245, Norcross, GA 30092-3014
Tel.: (770) 729-9664
Web Site: https://www.broniec.com
Year Founded: 1972
Sales Range: $10-24.9 Million
Emp.: 100
Auditing Services
N.A.I.C.S.: 541211
Gerry Conheady (Pres & CEO)
Frank G. Broniec (CEO)
Paul M. Broniec (CFO)
Pam Ancil (Dir-HR)
Tim Stewart (VP & Reg Mgr-Ops)
Robert Cebula (VP & Reg Mgr-Ops)
Bob Sheppard (CTO)
Matt Broniec (Dir-Mgmt Info Sys)
Scott Levine (VP-Audit Dev)

BRONNER BROTHERS INC.
2141 Powers Ferry Rd, Marietta, GA 30067
Tel.: (770) 988-0015
Web Site: http://www.bronnerbros.com
Sales Range: $10-24.9 Million
Emp.: 150
Hair Preparations, Including Shampoos
N.A.I.C.S.: 325620
Bernard Bronner (Pres)

BRONSON & BRATTON INC
220 Shore Dr, Burr Ridge, IL 60527
Tel.: (630) 986-1815
Web Site: http://www.brons.com
Year Founded: 1948
Rev.: $15,000,000
Emp.: 135
Special Dies & Tools
N.A.I.C.S.: 333514

Mark Bronson (Pres)
Steve McClary (Controller)
Gary Steves (Engr-Sls)

BRONSON HEALTHCARE GROUP, INC.
601 John St, Kalamazoo, MI 49007
Tel.: (269) 341-7654
Web Site: https://www.bronsonhealth.com
Emp.: 7,700
Hospital Owner & Operator
N.A.I.C.S.: 622110
Donald R. Parfet (Chm)
John T. Hayden (Chief HR Officer & Sr VP)
Scott D. Larson (Chief Medical Officer & Sr VP-Medical Affairs)
Denise J. Neely (Chief Nursing Officer & VP)
Sue Birch (Chief Strategy Officer & Sr VP-Strategy & Comm)
Christine Sangalli (Chief Compliance Officer & VP)
Michael S. Way (Sr VP-Supply Chain, Facilities & Real Estate)
Barbara L. James (Treas)
Neil Nyberg (Sec)
Nelson Karre (Vice Chm)
Randall W. Eberts (Vice Chm)
Becky East (CFO & Sr VP)
Ashutosh Goel (Chief Medical Information Officer & VP)
Katie Harrelson (Sr VP-Hospital Svcs & Post Acute Care)
Susan Watts (VP-Comm & Pub Affairs)
Nancy Vannest (VP-Contracting & Clinically Integrated Network)
Terry Morrow (VP-Dev & Community Health)
Ken Buechele (VP-IT)
Marijo Snyder (VP-Medical Staff Dev & Clinical Engagement)
Rebecca Trella (VP-Post-Acute Network)
Cheryl L. Knapp (Chief Quality Officer & VP)
Deb Rozewicz (CEO-Bronson Behavioral Health Hospital)
Bill Manns (Pres & CEO)
James B. Falahee Jr. (Sr VP-Legal & Legislative Affairs)
John L. Jones Jr. (Sr VP-Physician Hospital Org)

Subsidiaries:

Bronson Athletic Club   (1)
6789 Elm Vly Dr, Kalamazoo, MI 49009-7476
Tel.: (269) 544-3200
Web Site: http://www.bronsonathleticclub.com
Sales Range: $1-9.9 Million
Emp.: 200
Fitness & Recreational Sport Center Operating Services
N.A.I.C.S.: 713940
Michael Rowe (Exec Dir)
Deborah Peck (Coord-Mktg)
Sheri Shon (Dir-Grp Exercise)
Cynthia Baranowski (Dir-Membership Sls)
Char Heckaman (Mgr-Shop)

Bronson Battle Creek Hospital   (1)
300 N Ave, Battle Creek, MI 49017-3424
Tel.: (269) 966-8000
Web Site: http://www.bronsonhealth.com
Emp.: 7,100
Hospital Operator
N.A.I.C.S.: 622110
Cheryl L. Knapp (VP-Sys Quality Standards)
James E. McKernan (COO & Sr VP)

BRONX HONDA
2543 E Tremont Ave, Bronx, NY 10461
Tel.: (718) 892-3300

Web Site:
http://www.bronxhonda.com
Sales Range: $10-24.9 Million
Emp.: 75
Car Dealership
N.A.I.C.S.: 441110
Ira Lange *(VP)*
Marcie Jacob *(Chief Compliance Officer)*
Izzy Wahba *(Gen Sls Mgr)*

BROOK FURNITURE RENTAL, INC.
100 N Field Dr Ste 220, Lake Forest, IL 60045-2598
Tel.: (847) 810-4000   IL
Web Site: http://www.bfr.com
Year Founded: 1979
Sales Range: $50-74.9 Million
Emp.: 350
Equipment Rental & Leasing
N.A.I.C.S.: 532289
Rob Pruim *(Dir-Operations-Natl)*

BROOK LANE
13218 Brook Ln Dr, Hagerstown, MD 21742
Tel.: (301) 733-0330   MD
Web Site: http://www.brooklane.org
Year Founded: 1949
Sales Range: $10-24.9 Million
Emp.: 334
Behavioral Health Services
N.A.I.C.S.: 623220
Sharon Gladfelter *(Dir-Health Info Svcs)*
J. Emmet Burke *(Dir-Clinical)*
Jason Allen *(Dir-Patient Care Svcs)*

BROOK MAYS MUSIC COMPANY INC.
5756 LBJ Freeway, Dallas, TX 75240
Tel.: (214) 905-8614   TX
Web Site: http://www.brookmays.com
Year Founded: 1901
Sales Range: $25-49.9 Million
Emp.: 800
Musical Instrument Stores
N.A.I.C.S.: 459140
Carl Bolin *(Treas & Sec)*

BROOKE CHASE ASSOCIATES, INC.
1543 2nd St Ste 201, Sarasota, FL 34236
Tel.: (941) 358-3111
Web Site:
http://www.brookechase.com
Year Founded: 1980
Sales Range: $1-9.9 Million
Emp.: 10
Executive Search & Recruitment
N.A.I.C.S.: 561312
Joseph McElmeel *(Chm & CEO)*
Josh Mosier *(Mgr-Pur & Matls-Advanced Mobility)*
Daniel Millard *(Sls Mgr-Midwest)*
Ram Sridhar *(Assoc Product Mgr-Eemax-Midwest)*
Brian Eason *(Gen Mgr-Rugby Architectural Building Products-Southeast)*

BROOKE DISTRIBUTORS INC.
16250 NW 52nd Ave, Miami, FL 33014
Tel.: (305) 624-9752   FL
Web Site: http://www.brookedist.com
Year Founded: 1949
Sales Range: $10-24.9 Million
Emp.: 25
Provider of Electrical Appliance Services
N.A.I.C.S.: 423620
Glenn Kipilman *(Mgr-Sls-Miami Reg)*

BROOKE PRIVATE EQUITY

ASSOCIATES MANAGEMENT LLC
20 Custom House St Ste 610, Boston, MA 02110
Tel.: (617) 227-3160   DE
Web Site: http://www.brookepea.com
Year Founded: 2002
Sales Range: $25-49.9 Million
Emp.: 10
Private Equity Firm
N.A.I.C.S.: 523999
Peter Brooke *(Co-Founder)*
John F. Brooke *(Founder & Mng Dir)*
Christopher M. Austen *(Mng Dir)*
Laurie Callicutt *(VP-Fin & Admin)*

Subsidiaries:

Candescent SoftBase, LLC   (1)
20 Fall Pippin Ln Ste 202, Asheville, NC 28803
Tel.: (828) 670-9900
Web Site: http://www.softbase.com
Sales Range: $1-9.9 Million
Software Testing & Support Services
N.A.I.C.S.: 541519
Stephen Woodard *(CEO)*
Jim Spires *(Dir-Dev)*
Teresa Turbyfill *(Controller & Dir-HR)*

BROOKESIDE VENTURES INC.
524 Main St, Acton, MA 01720
Tel.: (978) 266-9876
Web Site: http://www.brookeside.com
Year Founded: 2000
Rev.: $5,600,000
Emp.: 19
Business Services
N.A.I.C.S.: 561499
Tom Cates *(Principal)*
Alex Horovitz *(VP)*
Rick Bierwagen *(VP)*

BROOKFIELD AUTO WRECKERS INC.
280 Lamont St, Elmsford, NY 10523
Tel.: (914) 592-5250
Web Site:
http://www.brookfieldco.com
Sales Range: $10-24.9 Million
Emp.: 80
Recycler of Scrap Materials
N.A.I.C.S.: 423930

BROOKHAVEN MEDICAL, INC.
3424 Peachtree Rd Ste 1150, Atlanta, GA 30326
Tel.: (404) 205-8282
Web Site:
http://www.brookhavenmed.com
Medical Products Research & Development & Mfr
N.A.I.C.S.: 339112
Steve Johnson *(Pres & COO)*
John Feltman *(Chm & CEO)*
Robert E. Atenbach *(Gen Counsel & Sec)*
Ross DeDeyn *(CFO)*
Ken Snider *(Exec Dir)*
David DePoyster *(Mng Partner & VP-Dev)*
Marc Morin *(Co-CFO)*
Scott Jones *(Co-COO)*
Grace Powers *(VP-Regulatory Affairs)*

Subsidiaries:

CreatiVasc Medical, LLC   (1)
330 E Coffee St, Greenville, SC 29601-2804
Tel.: (864) 242-4700
Web Site: http://www.creativasc.com
Medical Products Research & Development
N.A.I.C.S.: 541715
Tim Reed *(Mgr)*

FutureMatrix Interventional, Inc.   (1)
1605 Enterprise St, Athens, TX 75751
Tel.: (903) 677-9166
Web Site: http://www.fmxi.net
Emp.: 340

Surgical & Medical Instrument Mfr
N.A.I.C.S.: 339112
David Nichols *(Dir-Engrg)*

BROOKHILL GROUP INC.
501 Madison Ave Fl 18, New York, NY 10022-5613
Tel.: (212) 753-3123
Web Site: http://www.brookhillre.com
Year Founded: 1977
Sales Range: $10-24.9 Million
Emp.: 30
Real Estate Services
N.A.I.C.S.: 531210
Charles Kramer *(Pres)*

BROOKHURST, INC.
107 W Carob St, Compton, CA 90220-5206
Tel.: (310) 604-7300   CA
Year Founded: 1889
Sales Range: $100-124.9 Million
Emp.: 300
Mfr of Uniforms
N.A.I.C.S.: 315250

BROOKLAWN INC.
3121 Brooklawn Campus Dr, Louisville, KY 40218
Tel.: (502) 451-5177   KY
Web Site: http://www.brooklawn.net
Year Founded: 1991
Sales Range: $10-24.9 Million
Emp.: 307
Child & Family Care Services
N.A.I.C.S.: 624229
Bruce Ferguson *(Chm)*
Janet Sims *(Sec)*
David Graffy *(Treas)*
Linda Heitzman *(Vice Chm)*

BROOKLYN ACADEMY OF MUSIC, INC.
30 Lafayette Ave, Brooklyn, NY 11217
Tel.: (718) 636-4100   NY
Web Site: https://www.bam.org
Year Founded: 1861
Sales Range: $75-99.9 Million
Emp.: 898
Art Event Promoter
N.A.I.C.S.: 711310
William I. Campbell *(Vice Chm)*
Karen Brooks Hopkins *(Pres)*
James I. McLaren *(Treas)*
Alice Bernstein *(Exec VP)*
Matthew Bregman *(VP)*
Stephanie Hughley *(VP)*
David Binder *(Dir-Artistic)*

BROOKLYN BOTANIC GARDEN CORPORATION
1000 Washington Ave, Brooklyn, NY 11225
Tel.: (718) 623-7200   NY
Web Site: http://www.bbg.org
Year Founded: 1977
Sales Range: $10-24.9 Million
Emp.: 370
Botanical Garden
N.A.I.C.S.: 712130
Sonal Bhatt *(VP-Education)*
Tracey Faireland *(VP-Plng, Design & Construction)*
Leslie Findlen *(Sr VP-Institutional Advancement)*
Melanie Sifton *(VP-Horticulture & Facilities)*
Dorota Rashid *(CFO & VP-Fin)*
Samantha Campbell *(VP-Visitor Experience & Mktg)*
Adrian Benepe *(Pres & CEO)*

BROOKLYN BOTTLING CO. OF MILTON, NY
143 S Rd, Milton, NY 12547

Tel.: (845) 795-2171   NY
Web Site:
http://www.brooklynbottling.com
Year Founded: 1992
Sales Range: $25-49.9 Million
Emp.: 110
Provider of Beverage Bottling Services
N.A.I.C.S.: 312111
Eric Miller *(Pres)*
Miguel Duarte *(Mgr-Bulk)*

BROOKLYN BREWERY CORPORATION
79 N 11th St, Brooklyn, NY 11249
Tel.: (718) 486-7422
Web Site:
http://www.brooklynbrewery.com
Year Founded: 1987
Sales Range: $25-49.9 Million
Emp.: 50
Beer & Ale
N.A.I.C.S.: 424810
Steve Hindy *(Co-Founder & Pres)*
Eric Ottaway *(Gen Mgr)*
Debra Bascome *(Controller)*
Robin Ottaway *(VP-Sls)*

Subsidiaries:

International Beverages Inc.   (1)
79 N 11th St, Brooklyn, NY 11211-1913
Tel.: (781) 767-9600
Web Site: http://www.brooklynbrewery.com
Rev.: $4,600,000
Emp.: 17
Beer & Other Fermented Malt Liquors
N.A.I.C.S.: 424810

BROOKLYN CHILDREN'S MUSEUM INC.
145 Brooklyn Ave, Brooklyn, NY 11213
Tel.: (718) 735-4400
Web Site:
https://www.brooklynkids.org
Year Founded: 1899
Sales Range: $10-24.9 Million
Emp.: 100
Children's Museum
N.A.I.C.S.: 712110
William D. Rifkin *(Chm)*
Stephanie Hill Wilchfort *(Pres & CEO)*
Daniela Fifi *(VP-Programs & Education)*

BROOKLYN ELEVATOR INC.
143 W Front St, Brooklyn, IA 52211
Tel.: (641) 522-7521
Web Site:
http://www.brooklynelevator.com
Rev.: $13,370,416
Emp.: 5
Grains
N.A.I.C.S.: 424510

BROOKLYN FORD
10405 Brooklyn Rd, Brooklyn, MI 49230
Tel.: (517) 592-2112
Web Site:
http://www.guyonthesign.com
Sales Range: $10-24.9 Million
Emp.: 22
Automobiles, New & Used
N.A.I.C.S.: 441110
Cole Guthrie *(Pres)*

BROOKLYN INDUSTRIES
70 Front St, Brooklyn, NY 11201
Tel.: (718) 797-4240
Web Site:
http://www.brooklynindustries.com
Year Founded: 2000
Sales Range: $10-24.9 Million
Emp.: 60
Specialty Garment Distr
N.A.I.C.S.: 315250

Brooklyn Industries—(Continued)

Lexy Funk *(Co-Founder, Pres & CEO)*
Meagan Buis *(Mgr-Design)*
Nicole Musto *(Mgr-Production)*
Alexis Held *(Mgr-Store)*
Ryleigh Morrissey *(Mgr-Store)*
Jason Zwickl *(Mgr-Tech Design)*
Damian Torres *(Mgr-Store)*
Lauren Thomas *(Mgr-Store)*

BROOKLYN INSTITUTE OF ARTS AND SCIENCES
200 Eastern Pkwy, Brooklyn, NY 11238-6052
Tel.: (718) 638-5000   NY
Web Site:
   https://www.brooklynmuseum.org
Year Founded: 1893
Sales Range: $50-74.9 Million
Emp.: 452
Museum Operator
N.A.I.C.S.: 712110
Judith Frankfurt *(Asst Treas)*

BROOKMAN-FELS ASSOCIATES INCORPORATED
11382 Prosperity Farms Rd Ste 222, Palm Beach Gardens, FL 33410-3463
Tel.: (954) 455-2700
Sales Range: $10-24.9 Million
Emp.: 8
New Construction, Single-Family Houses
N.A.I.C.S.: 236115

BROOKRIDGE FUNDING CORP.
26 Mill Plain Rd, Danbury, CT 06811-5111
Tel.: (203) 790-7301   DE
Web Site:
   https://www.brookridgefunding.com
Year Founded: 1995
Sales Range: $25-49.9 Million
Emp.: 10
Purchase Order Funding & Accounts Receivable Factoring
N.A.I.C.S.: 522299

BROOKS & BROOKS SERVICES INC.
1227 Good Hope Rd SE, Washington, DC 20020
Tel.: (202) 678-7762
Web Site:
   http://www.brooksandbrooks.com
Sales Range: $10-24.9 Million
Emp.: 10
Water Quality Monitoring & Control Systems
N.A.I.C.S.: 561210
Larry R. Brooks *(Pres)*

BROOKS & FREUND, LLC
5661 Independence Cir Ste 1, Fort Myers, FL 33912
Tel.: (239) 939-5251
Web Site:
   https://www.brooksandfreund.com
Year Founded: 2000
Sales Range: $25-49.9 Million
Emp.: 21
Commercial & Institutional Building Construction
N.A.I.C.S.: 236220
Richard Freund *(Founder & Mgr)*
Jack Jamme *(Sr Project Mgr)*
Jim Grubb *(Project Mgr)*
Michelle Wise *(Comptroller)*
Jesse Olsovsky *(Dir-Field Ops & Sr Mgr-Project)*
David Lawless *(Project Mgr)*
Rose McCurry *(Dir-Ops)*

BROOKS ASSOCIATES INC.
300 Long Water Dr, Norwell, MA 02061
Tel.: (781) 871-3400
Web Site:
   http://www.brooksmachinery.com
Sales Range: $10-24.9 Million
Emp.: 11
Machine Tools & Accessories
N.A.I.C.S.: 423830
Joe Klier Jr. *(Pres)*

BROOKS AUTO SUPPLY INC.
402 Peterson Ave, Douglas, GA 31533-5250
Tel.: (912) 384-7818   GA
Year Founded: 1952
Sales Range: $100-124.9 Million
Emp.: 400
Provider of Motor Vehicle Supplies & Services
N.A.I.C.S.: 551112
Terry Moore *(Treas & Sec)*
Wayne Marsh *(VP-Ops)*
Elton D. Brooks Jr. *(Pres)*

BROOKS BIDDLE AUTOMOTIVE
17909 Bothell Way NE, Bothell, WA 98011-1915
Tel.: (425) 486-1212
Web Site:
   https://www.brooksbiddle.com
Year Founded: 1959
Sales Range: $25-49.9 Million
Emp.: 40
New Car Retailer
N.A.I.C.S.: 441110
JoAnn Poor *(Controller)*

BROOKS BROTHERS, INC.
346 Madison Ave, New York, NY 10017
Tel.: (800) 274-1815   DE
Web Site:
   http://www.brooksbrothers.com
Year Founded: 1818
Sales Range: $400-449.9 Million
Clothing Retailer
N.A.I.C.S.: 458110
Tiffany Wimbish *(Reg Mgr-Loss Prevention)*
Jessie Alvarez *(Reg Mgr-Loss Prevention)*
Ken Ohashi *(Pres)*
Michael Bastian *(Creative Dir-Men's & Women's)*

Subsidiaries:

Carolee LLC   (1)
88 Hamilton Ave Ste 3, Stamford, CT 06902
Tel.: (800) 227-6533
Web Site: http://www.carolee.com
Sales Range: $10-24.9 Million
Jewelry Mfr
N.A.I.C.S.: 339910
Joel Fivis *(Co-Pres)*
Theresa Jaeger *(VP-Sls)*
Nancy Risdon *(Dir-Mktg)*
Jill Maier *(Co-Pres)*
M. J. Racey *(Mgr-Sls)*

Subsidiary (Domestic):

Alexis Bittar, LLC   (2)
86 34th St 3rd Fl Section DS, Brooklyn, NY 11232
Tel.: (877) 680-9017
Web Site: http://www.alexisbittar.com
Premium Fashion Jewelry Designer, Mfr & Distr
N.A.I.C.S.: 339910

BROOKS CONSTRUCTION COMPANY
6525 Ardmore Ave, Fort Wayne, IN 46809
Tel.: (260) 478-1990

Web Site: https://www.brooks1st.com
Rev.: $52,502,450
Emp.: 262
Highway & Street Paving Contractor
N.A.I.C.S.: 237310
Andrew Brooks *(Pres)*
Steve Koble *(VP-Ops)*
Cindy Riebersal *(CFO)*

BROOKS INCORPORATED
1900 W Main St, Sun Prairie, WI 53590
Tel.: (608) 837-5141   WI
Web Site:
   https://www.brookstractor.com
Year Founded: 1948
Sales Range: $25-49.9 Million
Emp.: 80
Sell & Lease Industrial Equipment
N.A.I.C.S.: 423830
Lewis R. Brooks *(Pres)*
Mark Pilgrim *(Controller)*

Subsidiaries:

Brooks Tractor Incorporated   (1)
1900 W Main St, Sun Prairie, WI 53590-2521
Tel.: (608) 837-5141
Web Site: http://www.brookstractor.com
Sales Range: $10-24.9 Million
Emp.: 50
Construction & Mining Machinery
N.A.I.C.S.: 423810
Mary Kay Brooks *(Gen Mgr)*

BROOKS MEMORIAL HOSPITAL
529 Central Ave, Dunkirk, NY 14048
Tel.: (716) 366-1111   NY
Web Site:
   http://www.brookshospital.org
Year Founded: 1898
Sales Range: $25-49.9 Million
Emp.: 513
Health Care Srvices
N.A.I.C.S.: 622110
Virginia S. Horvath *(Sec)*
Christopher Lanski *(Chm)*
Louis Dipalma *(Treas)*
Mary E. LaRowe *(Pres & CEO)*
Joanna Banach *(Treas)*
Jeffrey H. Morgan *(CFO & VP-Fin)*
Lisa Muldowney *(Pres)*
Maria Orosz *(VP)*

BROOKS MUFFLER & BRAKE CENTER
11405 Pulaski Hwy, White Marsh, MD 21162-1511
Tel.: (410) 335-4828
Web Site:
   http://www.brooksramseyrv.com
Year Founded: 1953
Sales Range: $1-9.9 Million
Emp.: 20
Automotive Exhaust System Maintenance Services
N.A.I.C.S.: 811114
William Ramsey *(Pres)*

BROOKS RESOURCES CORPORATION
409 NW Franklin Ave, Bend, OR 97703
Tel.: (541) 382-1662   OR
Web Site:
   http://www.brooksresources.com
Year Founded: 1969
Sales Range: $75-99.9 Million
Emp.: 50
Real Estate Development
N.A.I.C.S.: 531210
Kirk Schueler *(Pres & CEO)*
Lynda Lyons *(Mktg Dir)*
Rick Hayes *(Dir-Real Estate Dev)*

Subsidiaries:

Awbrey Glen Golf Club, Inc.   (1)
2500 NW Awbrey Glen Dr, Bend, OR 97703
Tel.: (541) 385-6011
Web Site: http://www.awbreyglen.com
Sales Range: $1-9.9 Million
Private Golf Club
N.A.I.C.S.: 713910
Barbara Hess *(Sec)*
Mark Amberson *(Gen Mgr)*

Brooks Resources Sales Corp.   (1)
409 NW Franklin Ave, Bend, OR 97701   (100%)
Tel.: (541) 382-1662
Sales Range: $10-24.9 Million
Emp.: 10
Real Estate Brokerage
N.A.I.C.S.: 237210

Mount Bachelor Village Drive   (1)
19717 Mount Bachelor Dr, Bend, OR 97702-1901   (100%)
Tel.: (541) 389-5900
Web Site: http://www.mtbachelorvillage.com
Sales Range: $10-24.9 Million
Real Estate Development
N.A.I.C.S.: 721199
Diane Wilcox *(Gen Mgr)*

BROOKS RESTAURANTS INC.
3221 Behrman Pl, New Orleans, LA 70114
Tel.: (504) 363-0210
Web Site:
   http://www.brooksrestaurants.com
Sales Range: $10-24.9 Million
Emp.: 850
Limited-Service Restaurants
N.A.I.C.S.: 722513
Patricia Brooks *(Treas, Sec & VP)*
Eugene Brooks *(Pres)*
Luis Malespin *(Mgr-Louisiana District)*

BROOKSHIRE BROTHERS, LTD.
1201 Ellen Trout Dr, Lufkin, TX 75904-1233
Tel.: (936) 634-8155   MN
Web Site:
   https://www.brookshirebrothers.com
Year Founded: 1921
Sales Range: $800-899.9 Million
Emp.: 7,000
Supermarkets & Other Grocery Retailers (except Convenience Retailers)
N.A.I.C.S.: 445110
Clay Oliver *(CFO)*

BROOKSHIRE GROCERY COMPANY
2020 Roseland Blvd, Tyler, TX 75701   TX
Web Site:
   https://www.brookshires.com
Year Founded: 1928
Sales Range: Less than $1 Million
Emp.: 19,000
Supermarkets & Other Grocery Retailers (except Convenience Retailers)
N.A.I.C.S.: 445110
Bradley W. Brookshire *(Chm, Chm, Chm, CEO, CEO & CEO)*
Pete Leung *(Sr VP-Category Mgmt)*
Mike Terry *(Exec VP-Retail Ops)*
Jim Cousineau *(Sr VP-Pharmacy Ops)*
Lisa Glorioso *(VP-Pharmacy Ops)*
Carolyn Hutson *(CFO & Exec VP)*
Scott Reily *(Sr VP-Logistics)*
Don Gilbreath *(VP-Transportation Logistics)*
Kyle McCoy *(CFO & Exec VP)*
Ray Harrison *(VP-Center Store)*
Holly Shotts *(VP & Controller)*
Cindy Murphy *(VP-IT)*
Curtis Wiggins *(VP-IT)*

Mark Simmons *(VP)*
Lynette Hatley *(Dir-Store-Super 1 Foods)*
Suzanne Osbourn *(VP-Partner Rels & Dev)*
Jason Cooper *(VP-Corp Dev & Real Estate)*

BROOKSIDE CAPITAL, INC.
2269 Chestnut St Ste 400, San Francisco, CA 94123
Tel.: (415) 233-4640
Web Site:
http://www.brooksidecapital.com
Investor Portfolio Management Services
N.A.I.C.S.: 523940
James T. Rea *(Pres)*

BROOKSIDE ENTERPRISES, LLC
7703 N Lamar Blvd Ste 280, Austin, TX 78752
Tel.: (512) 537-0597   TX
Web Site:
http://www.brooksideus.com
Year Founded: 2015
Communication Service
N.A.I.C.S.: 517112
Mike Dance *(CEO)*

BROOKSIDE EQUIPMENT SALES
7707 Mosley Rd, Houston, TX 77017
Tel.: (713) 943-7100
Web Site:
http://www.brooksideusa.com
Rev.: $24,118,921
Emp.: 30
Lawn & Garden Equipment & Tractors
N.A.I.C.S.: 444230
C. A. Bielamowicz *(Pres)*
Antonio Vasquez *(Branch Mgr)*

BROOKSIDE INTERNATIONAL INCORPORATED
201 Tresser Blvd, Stamford, CT 06901
Tel.: (203) 618-0202
Web Site:
http://www.brooksidegroup.com
Sales Range: $25-49.9 Million
Emp.: 20
Investment Services
N.A.I.C.S.: 523999
Don Kolodz *(VP-Bus Dev)*
Michael Sawka *(Founder & Principal)*

Subsidiaries:

Brookside Equity Partners LLC   (1)
1 Stamford Forum 201 Tresser Blvd Ste 320, Stamford, CT 06901
Tel.: (203) 595-4520
Web Site: http://www.brooksideequity.com
Privater Equity Firm
N.A.I.C.S.: 523999
Raymond F. Weldon *(Mng Dir)*
Richard T. Dell'Aquila *(Mng Dir)*
Brian Piacentino *(VP)*
Donald L. Hawks III *(Pres & Mng Dir)*

Holding (Domestic):

Hillsdale Furniture LLC   (2)
3901 Bishop Ln, Louisville, KY 40218
Tel.: (502) 562-0000
Web Site: http://www.hillsdalefurniture.com
Sales Range: $1-9.9 Million
Furniture Designer, Importer & Marketer
N.A.I.C.S.: 337126
Jim Theilmann *(VP-Fin)*
Danny Glick *(Exec VP)*
Jessica Powers *(Mgr-Web Content)*
Bill Howard *(VP-Sls)*
Jack Elting *(VP-Internet Sls & Mgr-Pur)*
Doug Devine *(Pres-NE Kids Div)*

Hillside Capital Incorporated   (1)
80 Fields Point Rd, Greenwich, CT 06830

Tel.: (212) 935-6090
Web Site: http://www.brooksidegrp.com
Sales Range: $25-49.9 Million
Emp.: 10
Investment Services
N.A.I.C.S.: 523999

BROOKSIDE LUMBER COMPANY
500 Logan Rd, Bethel Park, PA 15102
Tel.: (412) 835-7610
Web Site:
https://www.brooksidelumber.com
Year Founded: 1936
Sales Range: $10-24.9 Million
Emp.: 64
Building Materials Whslr
N.A.I.C.S.: 444180
Peter Edwards Jr. *(Pres)*

BROOKSTONE HOLDINGS, INC.
2180 Sand Hill Rd Ste 340, Menlo Park, CA 94025
Tel.: (650) 233-7110   NV
Year Founded: 1980
Sales Range: $75-99.9 Million
Holding Company
N.A.I.C.S.: 551112
Michael Uytengsu *(Pres)*
Candice Hamilton *(VP, Controller & Dir)*
David Hurd *(VP-Fin)*
Donna Brownell *(Controller)*

BROOME OLDSMOBILE CADILLAC INC.
11911 E 40 Hwy, Independence, MO 64055
Tel.: (816) 358-2500
Sales Range: $25-49.9 Million
Emp.: 50
Car Whslr
N.A.I.C.S.: 441110
Paul Broome *(Principal)*

BROOMFIELD LABORATORIES INC.
164 Still River Rd, Bolton, MA 01740-1073
Tel.: (978) 368-0931
Web Site:
http://www.broomfieldusa.com
Other Building Material Dealers
N.A.I.C.S.: 444180
Thomas Broomfield *(Pres)*
Andrew Broomfield *(VP)*

Subsidiaries:

Thermoplastics Engineering Corporation   (1)
11 Spruce St, Leominster, MA 01453
Tel.: (978) 537-8135
Web Site:
http://www.thermoplasticseng.com
Rev.: $4,920,000
Emp.: 40
All Other Miscellaneous Fabricated Metal Product Mfr
N.A.I.C.S.: 332999
Paul Dacey *(Mgr-Ops)*

BROPFS CORPORATION
3707 Veterans Memorial Pkwy, Saint Charles, MO 63303
Tel.: (636) 946-6399
Web Site: http://www.brofps.com
Rev.: $20,000,000
Emp.: 9
Mobile Home Dealers
N.A.I.C.S.: 423120
Michael Bross *(Pres)*

BROS MANAGEMENT INC.
2501 E Magnolia Ave, Knoxville, TN 37914

Tel.: (865) 523-2157
Sales Range: $25-49.9 Million
Emp.: 1,500
Franchise Owner of Fast-Food Restaurants
N.A.I.C.S.: 722513
Josephine Cochran *(Owner)*
Tom Cockran *(Pres)*
Gary McGee *(Controller)*

BROTHER'S BROTHER FOUNDATION
1200 Galveston Ave, Pittsburgh, PA 15233
Tel.: (412) 321-3160   OH
Web Site:
https://www.brothersbrother.org
Year Founded: 1958
Sales Range: $250-299.9 Million
Emp.: 20
Medical & Educational Support Services
N.A.I.C.S.: 611710
Robert Miller *(Mgr-Warehouse)*
Karen Dempsey *(VP-Dev & Admin)*
William Davis *(VP-Fin)*
Austin P. Henry *(Sec)*
Charles J. Stout *(Chm)*
Deborah K. McMahon *(Dir-Medical)*
Joseph T. Senko *(Treas)*
Luke L. Hingson *(Pres)*
Ozzy Samad *(COO)*

BROTHERHOOD'S RELIEF AND COMPENSATION FUND
2150 Linglestown Rd, Harrisburg, PA 17110
Tel.: (717) 657-1890   PA
Web Site: http://www.brcf.org
Year Founded: 1914
Sales Range: $10-24.9 Million
Emp.: 19
Employee Welfare Fund Services
N.A.I.C.S.: 525120
J. E. Taylor *(Treas & Sec)*

BROTHERS & CO.
4860 S Lewis Ave Ste 100, Tulsa, OK 74105-5171
Tel.: (918) 743-8822   OK
Year Founded: 1974
Rev.: $16,000,000
Emp.: 25
Fiscal Year-end: 12/31/03
N.A.I.C.S.: 541810
Paul Brothers *(Pres & Sr Dir-Creative)*
Eric Barnes *(Sr VP)*
Eric West *(Acct Exec)*
Tommy Campbell *(VP & Dir-Creative)*
John Dunlap *(Copywriter & Producer)*
Mike Seiler *(CFO)*
Alan McGuckin *(Dir-Media Rels)*
Jeff Tolle *(Sr VP)*
Dave Thomas *(VP-Acct Plng)*
Alicia Hale Abele *(Mgr-Media)*
Tyler Allen *(Copywriter)*
Danya Brown *(Acct Exec)*
Buddy Pinneo *(Copywriter)*
Todd Pyland *(Assoc Dir-Creative)*
Kristjan Olson *(Sr Acct Supvr)*

BROTHERS INTERNATIONAL CORP
100 Bush St Ste 218, San Francisco, CA 94104
Tel.: (415) 986-0647
Web Site: http://www.brother.com
Rev.: $10,000,000
Emp.: 10
Commercial & Industrial Building Operation
N.A.I.C.S.: 531120
Toshikazu Koike *(Pres)*

BROTHERS INTERNATIONAL

DESSERTS, INC.
1682 Kettering, Irvine, CA 92614
Tel.: (949) 655-0080   CA
Web Site:
http://www.brothersdesserts.com
Year Founded: 1984
Sales Range: $1-9.9 Million
Emp.: 80
Mfg Ice Cream/Frozen Desert
N.A.I.C.S.: 311520
Gary Winkler *(Pres)*
Richard Lewin *(Controller)*
Keith Williams *(Mgr-Maintenance)*
Stacy Jackson *(Mgr-Quality Control)*

Subsidiaries:

Schoep's Ice Cream Co., Inc.   (1)
2070 Helena St, Madison, WI 53704
Tel.: (608) 249-6411
Web Site: http://www.schoepsicecream.com
Sales Range: Less than $1 Million
Emp.: 150
Mfr of Ice Cream
N.A.I.C.S.: 311520
Eric Thomsen *(Dir-Food Safety)*
Vickie Nebl *(Mgr-HR)*
Allen Thomsen *(Pres)*

BROTHERS TRADING CO. INC.
400 Victory Dr, Springboro, OH 45066
Tel.: (937) 746-1010
Web Site: http://www.vwg.com
Year Founded: 1979
Rev.: $52,300,000
Emp.: 200
Groceries
N.A.I.C.S.: 424410
David Kantor *(Pres)*
Scott Mattis *(VP)*

Subsidiaries:

Food Marketing Group Inc.   (1)
1700 E Putnam Ave Ste208A, Greenwich, CT 06870
Tel.: (203) 352-7840
Web Site:
http://www.foodmarketinggroup.com
Sales Range: $10-24.9 Million
Emp.: 20
Grocery Services
N.A.I.C.S.: 424410
Michael Pappas *(Mgr-Ops)*

BROTMAN WINTER FRIED COMMUNICATIONS
1651 Old Meadow Rd Ste 500, McLean, VA 22102
Tel.: (703) 748-0300   DC
Web Site: http://www.bwfcom.com
Year Founded: 1969
Sales Range: $1-9.9 Million
Emp.: 12
Public Relations Agency
N.A.I.C.S.: 541820
Steve Winter *(Pres)*
Kenny Fried *(Exec VP)*
Kerry Lynn Bohen *(VP)*
Brian Bishop *(VP)*

BROULIMS SUPER MARKET INC.
182 N State St, Rigby, ID 83442-1444
Tel.: (208) 745-9201
Web Site: http://www.broulims.com
Year Founded: 1966
Sales Range: $125-149.9 Million
Emp.: 1,000
Grocery Sales
N.A.I.C.S.: 445110

BROUSSARD POCHE LEWIS BREAUX LLC
4112 W Congress St, Lafayette, LA 70596-1400
Tel.: (337) 988-4930

Broussard Poche Lewis Breaux LLC—(Continued)

Web Site: http://www.bplb.com
Year Founded: 1953
Rev.: $18,384,748
Emp.: 66
Accounting, Auditing & Bookkeeping
N.A.I.C.S.: 541219
John L. Istre *(Partner)*

BROWARD BEHAVIORAL HEALTH COALITION, INC.
1715 SE 4th Ave, Fort Lauderdale, FL 33316
Tel.: (954) 622-8121   FL
Web Site: http://www.bbhcflorida.org
Year Founded: 2011
Sales Range: $25-49.9 Million
Emp.: 7
Behavioral Healthcare Services
N.A.I.C.S.: 621420
Silvia Quintana *(CEO)*
Danica Mamby *(Dir-Administration)*
Kerline Robinson *(Office Mgr)*
Nan Rich *(Vice Chm)*

BROWARD HEALTH
1600 South Andrew Ave, Fort Lauderdale, FL 33316
Tel.: (954) 355-4400
Web Site:
    http://www.browardhealth.org
Year Founded: 1938
Sales Range: $900-999.9 Million
Emp.: 8,190
Medical Health Network
N.A.I.C.S.: 622110
Dennis L. Stefanacci *(Pres-Broward Health Foundation)*
Jasmin Shirley *(VP-Community Health Svcs)*
Alice Taylor *(CEO-Imperial Point)*
Ronaldo Montmann *(VP-IT)*
Maria Panyi *(VP)*
Alan D. Goldsmith *(CFO)*
Peter Nyamora *(Sr VP)*
Beth A. Cherry *(VP-Physician Svcs)*
Jennifer S. Cohen *(Assoc VP-Benefits & Wellness)*
Andrew K. Ta *(Chief Medical Officer)*
Kiera Page *(Chief HR Officer)*
Jorge F. Hernandez *(Chief Procurement Officer & VP-Supply Chain)*
Tory Y. Drakeford *(VP-HR)*
Jared M. Smith *(CEO-Coral Springs)*
Paul C. Schwarzkopf *(CFO-Broward Health Medical Center)*
Shane Strum *(CEO)*
Nancy Gregoire *(Chm)*
Arthur Wallace III *(Treas & VP-Fin)*

BROWN & BIGELOW, INC.
345 Plato Blvd E, Saint Paul, MN 55107-1211
Tel.: (651) 293-7316   DE
Web Site:
    http://www.brownandbigelow.com
Year Founded: 1896
Sales Range: $100-124.9 Million
Emp.: 225
Mfr of Calendars & Advertising Specialties
N.A.I.C.S.: 541890
William D. Smith Jr. *(Pres & CEO)*
Gary Tuchler *(VP-South Reg)*
Herb Hemenway *(VP-IT)*
Daron Johnson *(CFO)*
Cindy Smith *(Exec VP)*

Subsidiaries:

Hotline Products   **(1)**
345 Plato Blvd E, Saint Paul, MN 55107-1211   **(100%)**
Tel.: (651) 293-7000
Web Site: http://www.hotlineproducts.com

Sales Range: $25-49.9 Million
Mfr of Calendars & Sales of Advertising Specialty Products
N.A.I.C.S.: 541890
William Smith Sr. *(Pres)*

BROWN & GAY ENGINEERS, INC.
10777 Westheimer Rd Ste 400, Houston, TX 77042
Tel.: (281) 558-8700
Web Site: http://www.bginc.com
Year Founded: 1975
Sales Range: $25-49.9 Million
Emp.: 206
Engineeering Services
N.A.I.C.S.: 541330
Ronnie Mullinax *(Chm)*
L. S. Brown *(Founder)*
Larry Milberger *(VP)*
Bob Arroyave *(VP)*
Lee Lennard *(Pres & CEO)*
Kerry R. Gilbert *(Dir-Land Plng Svcs)*

BROWN & HALEY
3500 20th St E Ste C, Fife, WA 98424
Tel.: (253) 620-3000   WA
Web Site: https://www.brown-haley.com
Year Founded: 1912
Sales Range: $100-124.9 Million
Emp.: 275
Candy & Confectionery Product Mfr
N.A.I.C.S.: 311340
Clarence Guimond *(CFO & Exec VP)*
Al Hlas *(Controller)*
Pierson Clair *(Vice Chm & CEO)*
John Melin *(Pres & COO)*

Subsidiaries:

Almond Roca International   **(1)**
1940 E 11th St, Tacoma, WA 98421-3301
Tel.: (253) 620-3011
Sales Range: $25-49.9 Million
Emp.: 150
Confection Manufacturing & Importing
N.A.I.C.S.: 424450

BROWN & JOSEPH LTD.
1701 Golf Rd Tower 2 Ste 100, Rolling Meadows, IL 60008
Tel.: (847) 758-3000
Web Site:
    http://www.brownandjoseph.com
Rev.: $20,000,000
Emp.: 80
Adjustment & Collection Services
N.A.I.C.S.: 561440
Kevin Walsh *(Pres)*
Chris Cappuccilli *(CEO)*
Dennis Falletti *(Exec VP-Insurance)*
Jessica Schneider *(Comptroller)*
David Trout *(Sr VP-Insurance Programs)*
John Whyte *(VP-Bus Dev)*
Mykhaylo Storozhuk *(CTO)*
Stacy Affatigato *(Dir-Intl Claims & Litigation)*

BROWN & SAENGER
711 W Russell St, Sioux Falls, SD 57104
Tel.: (605) 336-1960
Web Site: http://www.brown-saenger.com
Sales Range: $10-24.9 Million
Emp.: 80
Furniture Sales
N.A.I.C.S.: 449110
Lyle D. Dabbert *(Owner)*
Joel Eiesland *(Dir-HR)*
Mike Severson *(Mgr-Printing Div)*
Dale Bloem *(Mgr)*

BROWN & WOOD, INC.

329 Greenville Blvd SW, Greenville, NC 27834
Tel.: (877) 318-7898
Web Site: https://www.brown-wood.net
Emp.: 100
Car Dealer
N.A.I.C.S.: 441110
Bill Brown *(Owner)*
Jeff Stein *(Gen Mgr)*

BROWN AND CALDWELL
201 N Civic Dr, Walnut Creek, CA 94596-3864
Tel.: (925) 937-9010   CA
Web Site:
    http://www.brownandcaldwell.com
Year Founded: 1947
Sales Range: $150-199.9 Million
Emp.: 1,315
Environmental Consulting & Engineering Services
N.A.I.C.S.: 541330
Paula Spurlock *(Corp Librarian)*
Nancy Ringer *(Mgr-Risk Mngmt)*
Craig Goehring *(Chm)*
Richard D'Amato *(CEO)*
Leofwin Clark *(VP-Integrated Project Delivery-Denver)*
Steve Dills *(Sr VP-Digital Svcs)*
Kati Bell *(Mng Dir)*
Wendy Broley *(VP)*
Martha Bixby *(VP-Health & Safety)*
Marc Damikolas *(Dir-Ops)*
Carey Allen *(Sr VP)*
Adam Evans *(VP)*

BROWN APPLIANCE PARTS COMPANY
857 N Central St, Knoxville, TN 37917
Tel.: (865) 525-9363
Web Site: http://www.tribles.com
Rev.: $18,300,000
Emp.: 45
Appliance Parts, Household
N.A.I.C.S.: 423620
Treston Tribles *(Pres)*

BROWN AUTOMOTIVE GROUP, INC.
5625 W Central Ave, Toledo, OH 43615
Tel.: (419) 531-0151
Web Site:
    http://www.brownmazda.com
Year Founded: 1926
Sales Range: $100-124.9 Million
Emp.: 130
New Car Dealers
N.A.I.C.S.: 441110
Steve Yoos *(Gen Mgr)*
Randy Robbins *(Bus Mgr)*
Chris Sundermeier *(Mgr-Sls)*

BROWN BROS. CADILLAC, INC.
728 S 4th St, Louisville, KY 40202
Tel.: (502) 583-9771
Web Site:
    http://www.brownbroscad.com
Year Founded: 1946
Sales Range: $25-49.9 Million
Emp.: 90
Car Whslr
N.A.I.C.S.: 441110
Gary Brown *(Pres)*

BROWN BROTHERS HARRIMAN & CO.
140 Broadway, New York, NY 10005-1101
Tel.: (212) 483-1818   DE
Web Site: http://www.bbh.com
Year Founded: 1818
Sales Range: $5-14.9 Billion

Emp.: 2,400
Banking Services
N.A.I.C.S.: 523150
Landon Hilliard *(Partner)*
Michael W. McConnell *(Partner)*
Lawrence Cole Tucker *(Gen Partner)*
Taylor S. Bodman *(Partner)*
William Tyree *(Mng Partner)*
William J. Whelan *(Partner)*
Maroa C. Velez *(Partner)*
Charles O. Izard *(Partner)*
Jeffrey B. Meskin *(Partner)*
Ivan A. Pirzada *(Mng Dir & Principal-Private Banking)*
Jonathan A. Vickery *(Mng Dir-Investor Svcs)*
Shawn R. McNinch *(Mng Dir-Investor Svcs)*
Michael Kim *(Partner & Mgr)*
Michael McGovern *(Head-Investor Svcs Fintech Offerings)*
Geoffrey Cook *(Partner & Head-Investment Ops & Tech Svcs)*
Brian Condon *(Co-Head-Tech)*
Lorrie Gordon *(Co-Head-Tech)*
Ross Connell *(Sr VP-Investor Svcs)*
Christopher W. McChesney *(Sr VP-Investor Svcs)*
Joe Pennini *(Sr VP-Investor Svcs)*
Christian M. Brunet *(Mng Dir-Private Banking)*
Christopher C. Remondi *(Partner)*
Daniel Becker *(Mng Dir)*
Dario Galindo *(Partner)*
Haluk S. Akdemir *(Mng Dir-Investor Svcs)*
Hilary M. Capay *(Mng Dir-Investor Svcs)*
Hugh B. Bolton *(Mng Dir-Investor Svcs)*
Jean-Marc Crepin *(Partner)*
Kathryn C. George *(Partner)*
Mark Balcom *(Mng Dir-Investor Svcs)*
Radford W. Klotz *(Partner)*
Suzanne Brenner *(Mng Dir-Private Wealth Mgmt & Private Banking)*
Thomas E. Berk *(Partner)*
William E. Rosensweig *(Partner-Investor Svcs)*
Thomas Davis *(Partner)*
Kathryn George *(Partner)*
Randall P. Ayer Jr. *(Mng Dir-Private Wealth Mgmt)*

Subsidiaries:

Brown Brothers Distribution Limited   **(1)**
Robjohns Road Widford Trading Estate, Chelmsford, CM1 3AF, Essex, United Kingdom   **(100%)**
Tel.: (44) 1245 266736
Web Site: http://www.brownbrothers.com
Sales Range: $75-99.9 Million
Emp.: 130
National Distr to the UK Vehicle Refurbishment Industry
N.A.I.C.S.: 423120

Brown Brothers Harriman (Hong Kong) Ltd.   **(1)**
Unit 1507 Level 15 International Comm Ctr 1 Austin Rd W, Central, China (Hong Kong)   **(100%)**
Tel.: (852) 28773222
Web Site: http://www.bbh.com
Sales Range: $75-99.9 Million
Emp.: 9
Brokerage & Financial Advisory Services
N.A.I.C.S.: 523940
Scott McLaren *(Head-Relationship Mgmt & Sls-Asia)*

Brown Brothers Harriman (Luxembourg) S.A.   **(1)**
Route d'Esch, L-1470, Luxembourg, Luxembourg   **(100%)**
Tel.: (352) 4740661
Web Site: http://www.brownbrothers.com
Sales Range: $100-124.9 Million
Emp.: 230

Global Custody & Fund Administration Services
N.A.I.C.S.: 524292
Hacken Berg (Mng Dir)

Brown Brothers Harriman (Poland) Sp. z o.o. (1)
ul Klimeckiego 1, Orange Office Park, 30-705, Krakow, Poland
Tel.: (48) 123406000
Web Site: http://www.bbh.com
Sales Range: $50-74.9 Million
Emp.: 300
Investment Management Service
N.A.I.C.S.: 523940
Michael J. McDonald (Mng Dir)

Brown Brothers Harriman Fund Administration Services (Ireland) Limited (1)
30 Herbert Street, Dublin, Ireland
Tel.: (353) 1 603 6200
Web Site: http://www.bbh.com
Sales Range: $50-74.9 Million
Emp.: 220
Transfer Agency Services
N.A.I.C.S.: 522320
Hugh B. Bolton (Mng Dir)

Brown Brothers Harriman Investors Services Incorporated (1)
Toranomon Kotohira Tower 15F 1 2 8 Toranomon, Minato Ku, Tokyo, 105 0014, Japan (100%)
Tel.: (81) 363616300
Sales Range: $75-99.9 Million
Emp.: 50
Brokerage & Financial Advisory Services
N.A.I.C.S.: 523940
Yukinori Nagahisa (Partner)

Brown Brothers Harriman Securities (Japan) Inc. (1)
1-2-8 Toranomon, Minato-ku, Tokyo, 105-0001, Japan
Tel.: (81) 363616500
Web Site: http://www.bbh.com
Emp.: 100
Investment Management Service
N.A.I.C.S.: 523940

Brown Brothers Harriman Services AG (1)
Baerengasse 25, 8001, Zurich, Switzerland (100%)
Tel.: (41) 12271818
Web Site: http://www.bbh.com
Sales Range: $75-99.9 Million
Emp.: 50
Investment Brokerage & Financial Advisory Services
N.A.I.C.S.: 523910

Brown Brothers Harriman Trust Co. (Cayman) Ltd. (1)
18 Forum Lane Camana Bay, PO Box 2330, Georgetown, KY1-1106, Grand Cayman, Cayman Islands (100%)
Tel.: (345) 945 2719
Web Site: http://www.bbh.com
Trust & Fiduciary Services
N.A.I.C.S.: 523991

Brown Brothers Harriman Trust Co., LLC (1)
140 Broadway, New York, NY 10005-1101 (100%)
Tel.: (212) 483-1818
Web Site: http://www.bbh.com
Sales Range: $250-299.9 Million
Emp.: 2,000
Trust Company
N.A.I.C.S.: 523150
Becky Love (Controller)
William Mears Jr. (Exec VP)

Brown Brothers Harriman Trust Company of Delaware, N. A. (1)
919 N Market St Ste 420, Wilmington, DE 19801
Tel.: (302) 552-4040
Sales Range: $25-49.9 Million
Emp.: 10
Financial Management Services
N.A.I.C.S.: 523999

Brown Brothers Harriman Trust Company, N. A. (1)
40 Water Str, Boston, MA 02109-3661

Tel.: (617) 742-1818
Web Site: http://www.bbh.com
Investment Management Service
N.A.I.C.S.: 523999

Brown Brothers Harriman Trustee Services (Ireland) Limited (1)
Styne House Uppr Half St, Dublin, 2, Ireland (100%)
Tel.: (353) 4757840
Web Site: http://www.bbh.com
Sales Range: $100-124.9 Million
Emp.: 140
Securities Custody & Financial Advisory Services
N.A.I.C.S.: 523991

DynaGrid Construction Group, LLC (1)
725 E Jones St, Lewisville, TX 75077-2608
Tel.: (972) 829-6021
Web Site: http://www.dynagrid.com
Power & Communication Line Construction
N.A.I.C.S.: 237130
Diane Ferrara (Pres)
Charlie Ferrara (Co-Founder & CEO)
Kendrew Witt (CFO)

Quest Media & Supplies Inc. (1)
9000 Foothills Blvd Ste 100, Sacramento, CA 95747-3071
Tel.: (916) 338-7070
Web Site: http://www.questsys.com
Sales Range: $10-24.9 Million
Emp.: 80
Computer & Software Stores
N.A.I.C.S.: 541512
Barbara Klide (Dir-Mktg)

Subsidiary (Domestic):

Lanlogic, Inc. (2)
248 Rickenbacker Cir, Livermore, CA 94551
Tel.: (925) 273-2333
Web Site: http://www.lanlogic.com
Computer System Design Services
N.A.I.C.S.: 541512
Marcus Solorio (Gen Mgr)
Wilma Smith (CFO)
Dan Ferguson (Pres & CEO)
Amy Thomatis (Dir-Managed Svcs)
Karen Fernandez (Mgr-Technical Program)

BROWN BUILDERS INC.
1619 Jimmie Davis Hwy, Bossier City, LA 71112-4513
Tel.: (318) 746-0211
Web Site:
https://www.brownbuilders.com
Year Founded: 1971
Sales Range: $10-24.9 Million
Emp.: 70
Provider of Commercial Contracting Services
N.A.I.C.S.: 236220
B. Wayne Brown (Chm)
C. David Dumas (Exec VP)

BROWN CHEMICAL CO., INC.
302 W Oakland Ave, Oakland, NJ 07436-1309
Tel.: (201) 337-0900   NJ
Web Site:
http://www.brownchem.com
Year Founded: 1936
Sales Range: $10-24.9 Million
Emp.: 20
Chemicals Distribution
N.A.I.C.S.: 424690
Doug Blum (Office Mgr)
Doug Brown (Pres & COO)
Patrick Brown (VP-Sls & Mktg)
Dave Lyle (VP-Fin & Ops)
Rob Eckert (Mgr-Info Sys)
Tony Gulli (Mgr-Sls)
Dennis Tetradis (Plant Mgr)

BROWN CHEVROLET CO. INC.
340 IH 35 S, Devine, TX 78016
Tel.: (830) 665-4435
Web Site: http://www.browncar.com
Sales Range: $75-99.9 Million
Emp.: 75

New & Used Car Dealers
N.A.I.C.S.: 441110
Jim Gardner (Comptroller)
Ronnie Harrell (Gen Mgr)

BROWN CRAIG TURNER
100 N Charles St Ste 1800, Baltimore, MD 21201-3817
Tel.: (410) 837-2727
Web Site:
http://www.brownandcraig.com
Architectural Services
N.A.I.C.S.: 541310
Bryce A. Turner (Pres & CEO)
Robert C. Northfield (Principal)
Janet Meyer (Principal)
Scot Foster (Principal)
Pedro Sales (Principal)
Christopher Holler (Principal)

Subsidiaries:

Development Design Group Inc. (1)
3700 Odonnell St, Baltimore, MD 21224
Tel.: (410) 962-0505
Web Site: http://www.ddg-usa.com
Rev.: $9,000,000
Emp.: 75
Architectural Services
N.A.I.C.S.: 541310
Brandon Diamond (Partner)
Rajesh Gulati (Partner & Dir-Plng)

BROWN DERBY STORES INC.
2023 S Glenstone Ave, Springfield, MO 65804
Tel.: (417) 883-4066
Web Site:
https://www.brownderby.com
Sales Range: $10-24.9 Million
Emp.: 100
Hard Liquor
N.A.I.C.S.: 445320
Russ Smith (Mgr)

BROWN DISTRIBUTING COMPANY
8711 Johnny Morris Rd, Austin, TX 78724
Tel.: (512) 478-9353
Web Site: http://www.austinbud.com
Rev.: $62,800,000
Emp.: 300
Beer & Other Fermented Malt Liquors
N.A.I.C.S.: 424810
J. Dan Brown (Owner)

BROWN DISTRIBUTING COMPANY, INCORPORATED
7986 Villa Park Dr, Richmond, VA 23228-5805
Tel.: (804) 266-7645   VA
Web Site:
http://www.browndistributing.com
Year Founded: 1951
Sales Range: $25-49.9 Million
Emp.: 230
Distr of Beer & Ale
N.A.I.C.S.: 424810
Reid Brown (Pres)

BROWN ENTERPRISES
511 Couch Dr Ste 300, Oklahoma City, OK 73102-2250
Tel.: (405) 232-1158
Year Founded: 1987
Sales Range: $10-24.9 Million
Emp.: 4
Distr of Bottled & Canned Soft Drinks
N.A.I.C.S.: 312111
Stephen B. Brown (CEO)

BROWN FOODSERVICE, INC.
500 E Clayton Lane, Louisa, KY 41230
Tel.: (606) 638-1139
Web Site:
http://www.brownfoodservice.com

Year Founded: 1939
Sales Range: $50-74.9 Million
Emp.: 150
Whslr of Packaged Frozen Foods, Canned Goods, Bakery Supplies, Dressings & Spices, Cleaning Supplies, Paper Products & Equipment & Supplies
N.A.I.C.S.: 424410
Wayne Brown (Pres)
Laura Kegley (Controller)
Darrell Hopson (Mgr-Transportation)
Ralph Gilliam (Dir-Ops)
Mark Qualls (VP-Procurement)

BROWN HARRIS STEVENS, LLC
770 Lexington Ave Fl 3, New York, NY 10065
Tel.: (212) 508-7200
Web Site:
http://www.brownharrisstevens.com
Year Founded: 1997
Sales Range: $1-9.9 Million
Emp.: 50
Offices of Real Estate Agents & Brokers
N.A.I.C.S.: 531210
David Burris (Principal)
Joel Burris (Mng Dir)
Erin Boisson Aries (Mng Dir & Sr VP)
Robert M. Nelson (Sr Mng Dir)
Philip Gutman (Exec VP)
Bess Freedman (CEO)
Hall Willkie (Pres)
Pablo Marvel (CMO)

Subsidiaries:

Brown Harris Stevens, LLC - Coconut Grove Office (1)
2665 S Bayshore Dr Ste 100, Miami, FL 33133
Tel.: (305) 666-1800
Web Site: http://www.bhsmiami.com
Real Estate Broker
N.A.I.C.S.: 531210
Vivian Z. Dimond (Pres)

Zilbert Realty Group (1)
605 Lincoln Rd Ste 230, Miami Beach, FL 33139-2934
Tel.: (305) 726-0100
Web Site: http://www.zilbert.com
Offices of Real Estate Agents & Brokers
N.A.I.C.S.: 531210
Mark Zilbert (Pres)

BROWN IMPORTS INC.
5625 W Central Ave, Toledo, OH 43615
Tel.: (419) 536-6200
Web Site:
http://www.brownautomotive.com
Year Founded: 1974
Sales Range: $25-49.9 Million
Emp.: 120
Sales of Automobiles, New & Used
N.A.I.C.S.: 441110
Rob Brown (Pres)

BROWN INDUSTRIES, INC.
205 W Industrial Blvd, Dalton, GA 30722-1103
Tel.: (706) 277-1977   GA
Web Site:
http://www.brownindustries.com
Year Founded: 1958
Sales Range: $400-449.9 Million
Emp.: 600
Sales Aids for Carpet Industry; Processing Carpet Swatches; Printing Labels & Business Forms Mfr
N.A.I.C.S.: 323111
Samuel Shon (VP-Sls)
Jason Neil (Mgr-Engrg)
Stuart Nelson (Pres)
Tim Holt (Mgr-HR)

Brown Industries, Inc.—(Continued)

BROWN INTERNATIONAL CORP.
333 Ave M NW, Winter Haven, FL 33881-2405
Tel.: (626) 966-8361
Web Site: http://www.brown-intl.com
Rev.: $13,100,000
Emp.: 15
Food Products Machinery
N.A.I.C.S.: 333241
Charles Gagliano *(CEO)*
Bob Hudson *(Mgr-Pur)*
Helvert Obando *(Mgr-Sls Engrg)*
Peter DeVito *(Sr VP-Sls & Svcs)*
John Cox *(VP)*
Greg St. Maria *(Controller)*
Victor Onchi *(Sr VP-Sls & Svc-LA)*
Roger Waters *(VP-Process Engrg)*

BROWN LUMBER & SUPPLY COMPANY
1701 S Airport Rd W, Traverse City, MI 49686
Tel.: (231) 946-4361
Web Site: http://www.brownlumber.com
Rev.: $24,992,600
Emp.: 80
Lumber & Other Building Materials
N.A.I.C.S.: 423310
Scott E. Williams *(Pres)*

BROWN LUMBER SALES COMPANY
Ste 101 123 Madison St, Denver, CO 80206-5417
Tel.: (303) 320-4704
Sales Range: $10-24.9 Million
Emp.: 3
Lumber: Rough, Dressed & Finished
N.A.I.C.S.: 423310
Charles H. Kurtz *(Pres)*

BROWN METALS COMPANY
8635 White Oak Ave, Rancho Cucamonga, CA 91730
Tel.: (909) 484-3124
Web Site: https://www.brownmetals.com
Rev.: $10,900,000
Emp.: 43
Metal Service Centers & Other Metal Merchant Whslr
N.A.I.C.S.: 423510
Justin Lasley *(CIO)*

BROWN MOTORS INC.
39 Beacon St, Greenfield, MA 01301
Tel.: (413) 772-2111
Web Site: http://www.brownfivestar.com
Rev.: $12,000,000
Emp.: 23
New & Used Car Dealers
N.A.I.C.S.: 441110
Darci Brown *(Owner)*

BROWN MOTORS, INC.
2170 N US 31, Petoskey, MI 49770
Tel.: (231) 439-9660
Web Site: https://www.brownmotors.com
Year Founded: 1898
Sales Range: $75-99.9 Million
Emp.: 50
Sales of New & Used Automobiles
N.A.I.C.S.: 441110
J. Steven Brown *(Pres)*
Rick Kline *(Dir-Svc)*

BROWN OIL CO.
205 E Spring St, Monroe, GA 30655
Tel.: (770) 267-5011
Sales Range: $10-24.9 Million
Emp.: 5

Petroleum Product Mfr & Distr
N.A.I.C.S.: 424710
John Alan Brown *(CFO)*
Donna B. Sisk *(Sec)*
Mark W. Sisk *(CEO)*

BROWN PACKAGING
1990 W Corporate Way, Anaheim, CA 92801
Tel.: (714) 300-0650
Web Site: https://www.brownpackaging.com
Packaging Products Mfr & Distr
N.A.I.C.S.: 424130
Mike Turfanda *(CEO)*
Carlos Samayoa Sr. *(Pres)*

BROWN PACKING CO., INC.
116 Willis St, Gaffney, SC 29341
Tel.: (864) 489-5723
Web Site: https://www.brownpacking.com
Year Founded: 1947
Sales Range: $25-49.9 Million
Emp.: 200
Meat Processing & Packaging Services
N.A.I.C.S.: 311612
Sloan Bradford *(Dir-Pur & Safety)*
Reed Brown *(VP)*
David Brown *(VP)*
Steven Blanton *(Controller)*

BROWN PACKING COMPANY INC.
1 Dutch Valley Dr, South Holland, IL 60473
Tel.: (708) 849-7990
Web Site: http://www.casereadyveal.com
Sales Range: $10-24.9 Million
Emp.: 60
Veal Processing Services
N.A.I.C.S.: 311611
John A. Oedzes *(Pres)*
Brian Oedzes *(VP & Mgr)*
Bryan Scott *(VP & Dir-Opers)*

BROWN PALACE HOTEL ASSOCIATES L.P.
321 17th St, Denver, CO 80202
Tel.: (303) 297-3111
Web Site: http://www.brownpalace.com
Year Founded: 1892
Sales Range: $25-49.9 Million
Emp.: 440
Luxury Hotel Operator
N.A.I.C.S.: 721110
Renae Willer *(Coord-Sls)*
Ryan Pratt *(Mgr-Rooms Div)*
Lorena Toland *(Dir-Trng)*

BROWN PAPER COMPANY INC.
67 Holly Hill Ln, Greenwich, CT 06830-6072
Tel.: (203) 661-0001
Web Site: http://www.brownpaper.com
Year Founded: 1985
Sales Range: $10-24.9 Million
Emp.: 20
Distr of Printing & Writing Paper
N.A.I.C.S.: 424110
Douglas Brown *(Pres & Treas)*
Phil Digennaro *(CFO)*
Mike Burdi *(Mgr-Sls-Chicago)*
Frank Grippo *(Mgr-Credit)*
Brian McEnaney *(Mgr-Sls-Greenwich)*
Karina Pirone *(Mgr)*
George Stockbridge *(Dir-Intl Sls)*
Susan Thompson *(Mgr-Sls Admin)*
Carin Triozzi *(Mgr)*

BROWN PAPER GOODS COMPANY
3530 Birchwood Dr, Waukegan, IL 60085-8334
Tel.: (847) 688-1450
Web Site: http://www.brownpapergoods.com
Year Founded: 1918
Sales Range: $75-99.9 Million
Emp.: 125
Mfr of Paper & Foil Bags
N.A.I.C.S.: 322220
Allen Mons *(Pres)*
Will Jefferson *(VP-Fin)*
P. Luthy *(VP-Sls)*

BROWN PARKER & DEMARINIS ADVERTISING INC.
1825 NW Corporate Blvd Ste 250, Boca Raton, FL 33431
Tel.: (561) 276-7701
Web Site: http://www.bpdadvertising.com
Year Founded: 2002
Sales Range: $25-49.9 Million
Emp.: 46
Advertising Agency Services
N.A.I.C.S.: 541810
Jason Brown *(CEO & Chief Strategy Officer)*
Ward Parker *(Founder & Partner)*
Susan Barbosa *(Co-Pres & Office Mgr)*
Vince DeMarinis *(Partner)*
Jessica Schmidt *(Co-Pres)*
Guillermo Tragant *(Co-Chief Creative Officer)*
Mindy Adams *(Co-Chief Creative Officer)*
Loren Kronemeyer *(CFO)*

BROWN PONTIAC AUTOMOTIVE GROUP LP
4300 S Georgia St, Amarillo, TX 79110
Tel.: (806) 353-7211
Web Site: http://www.brownpontiacgmc.com
Sales Range: $50-74.9 Million
Emp.: 60
Automobiles, New & Used
N.A.I.C.S.: 441110
Bryan L. Brown *(Pres)*
Charles Cooksey *(Gen Mgr-Sls)*

BROWN RUDNICK LLP
One Financial Ctr, Boston, MA 02111
Tel.: (617) 856-8200
Web Site: http://www.brownrudnick.com
Year Founded: 1948
Sales Range: $150-199.9 Million
Emp.: 184
Law firm
N.A.I.C.S.: 541110
Mary D. Bucci *(Partner-Fin)*
Alejandro Fiuza *(Chm-Latin American Practice Grp)*
Greg Sampson *(Partner)*
Guillermo Christensen *(Partner-Cybersecurity, Data Privacy & Enterprise Risk Mgmt)*
Benjamin Chew *(Partner-Litigation & Arbitration)*
Philip Watkins *(Partner-London)*
Mark Dorff *(Chm-Intl Corp)*
Anupreet Amole *(Partner-White Collar Crime-London)*
Kenneth Aulet *(Partner-Bankruptcy & Corp Restructuring-New York)*
Zachary D. Hyde *(Partner-Intellectual Property)*
Chelsea Mullarney *(Partner-Commercial Litigation-New York)*
Brown Rudnick *(Chm)*

William R. Baldiga *(CEO)*
Peter Willsey *(Partner-Intellectual Property Practice Grp/Chm-Global Trademark)*

BROWN SMITH WALLACE LLC
1050 N Lindbergh Blvd, Saint Louis, MO 63132
Tel.: (314) 983-1200
Web Site: http://www.bswllc.com
Year Founded: 1972
Sales Range: $10-24.9 Million
Emp.: 200
Accounting, Auditing & Tax Services
N.A.I.C.S.: 541211
David Hudson *(Dir-IT Svcs)*
Joanne Kearbey *(Mgr-Insurance Advisory Svcs)*
Janet Beckmann *(Principal)*
Jeff Gusdorf *(Principal-Advisory Svcs)*
David Heilich *(Partner)*
Darla Hemmann *(Partner-Tax Svcs)*
Larry Newell *(Mgr-Risk Svcs)*
Jason Oesterlei *(Mgr-Benefit Plans Plus)*
Matthew Powell *(Partner-Audit Svcs)*
Janet Ramey *(Mgr-Not For Profit)*
Steve Ronquest *(Mgr-Tax Svcs)*
William Wagnon *(Mgr-Benefit Plans Plus)*
Harvey N. Wallace *(Partner)*
Kelly Weis *(Partner-Audit Svcs)*
Dave Winkler *(Mgr-Bus Intelligence)*
Ann L. Holtshouser *(Partner)*
Robert Haggerty *(Partner)*
Joe Montes *(Mgr-Advisory Svcs)*
Keenan McKinney *(Mgr-Advisory Svcs)*
Katie Zahner *(Mgr-Audit Svcs)*
Megan McDonald *(Mgr-Tax Practice)*
Todd Reich *(Mgr-Tax Svcs)*
Pamela Sigmund *(Mgr-Entrepreneurial Svcs Grp)*
Holly Manwaring *(Mgr-Advisory Svcs)*
Lincoln Gray *(Partner)*
Ron Present *(Partner)*
Ron Steinkamp *(Partner-Advisory Svcs)*
Lauren Sanders *(Mgr-HR)*
Reza Montasser *(Mgr-Advisory Svcs)*
Laura Simmons *(Coord-HR)*
Amy Ribick *(Principal-Advisory Svcs)*
Lindsay Bowling *(Mgr-Tax Svcs)*
Kyle Dodwell *(Mgr-Insurance Advisory Svcs)*
Jennifer Vacha *(Principal-Tax Svcs)*
Dan Ward *(Principal-Audit Svcs)*
Vicki Swider *(Mgr-Entrepreneurial Svcs Grp)*
Barb Gruzeski *(Mgr-Acctg)*
Wendy Shireman *(Principal-Entrepreneurial Svcs Grp)*
Joel Schraier *(Partner-Entrepreneurial Svcs Grp)*
Ira Bergman *(Partner-Entrepreneurial Svcs Grp)*
Katheryn Schroeder *(Principal-Entrepreneurial Svcs Grp)*
Ellen Norrenberns *(Principal-Audit Svcs)*
Paul Krussel *(Principal-Entrepreneurial Svcs Grp)*
Ben Morgan *(Mgr-Transaction Advisory & Litigation Support)*
Melinda Diesselhorst *(Coord-Practice & Entrepreneurial Svcs)*
Sean McKenzie *(Principal-Tax Svcs)*
Richie Kingree *(Principal-Tax Svcs)*
Kevin Boeving *(Principal-Tax Svcs)*
Emily Sill *(Mgr-Tax Svcs)*
Bianca Sarrach *(Principal-Advisory Svcs)*
Chelle Schneider *(Mgr-Tax Svcs)*
Casey Pelech *(Mgr-Tax Svcs)*
Scott Ngo *(Mgr-Tax Svcs)*

Jonathan Steur *(Mgr-Audit Svcs)*
Stephanie Hardt *(Mgr-Audit Svcs)*
Cory Metz *(Mgr-Advisory Svcs)*
Alan DeVaughan *(Mgr-Advisory Svcs)*
Jennifer Cassidy *(Mgr-Advisory Svcs)*
Matt Hans *(Mgr-Tax Svcs)*
Natalie Mamrenko *(Mgr-Entrepreneurial Svcs)*
Deborah Vandeven *(Principal-Tax Svcs)*
Bernard Ottenlips *(Principal-State & Local Tax Svcs)*

BROWN SPRINKLER CORPORATION
4705 Pinewood Rd, Louisville, KY 40218
Tel.: (502) 968-6274
Web Site:
    http://www.brownsprinkler.com
Rev.: $14,650,414
Emp.: 65
Fire Sprinkler System Installation
N.A.I.C.S.: 238220
Richard R. Brown *(Pres)*
Danny Ledford *(Office Mgr)*

BROWN STEVENS ELMORE & SPARRE
655 University Ave Ste 225, Sacramento, CA 95825-6747
Tel.: (916) 929-0262
Web Site:
    https://www.brownstevens.com
Year Founded: 2002
Sales Range: $10-24.9 Million
Emp.: 8
Real Estate Development Services
N.A.I.C.S.: 531210
Franklin Brown *(Principal)*
Tom Harry *(Partner)*

BROWN SUGAR BAKERY & CAFE, INC.
328 E 75th St, Chicago, IL 60619
Tel.: (773) 224-6262
Web Site:
    http://www.brownsugarbakery.com
Pastry & Restaurant
N.A.I.C.S.: 311813
Stephanie Hart *(Founder)*

Subsidiaries:

Cupid Candies, Inc.   (1)
7637 South Western Ave, Chicago, IL 60620
Tel.: (773) 925-8191
Web Site: http://www.cupidcandies.com
Confectionery Manufacturing from Purchased Chocolate
N.A.I.C.S.: 311352

BROWN TRANSFER COMPANY
911 E 11th St, Kearney, NE 68847
Tel.: (308) 237-2244
Web Site:
    http://www.browntransfer.com
Rev.: $11,748,622
Emp.: 60
Local Trucking without Storage
N.A.I.C.S.: 484110
Dwayne Brown *(Pres)*
Dean Aden *(Treas & Sec)*

BROWN TRUCK LEASING CORP
2525 E Euclid Ave Ste 214, Des Moines, IA 50317
Tel.: (515) 265-9951
Web Site:
    http://www.brownnationalease.com
Sales Range: $10-24.9 Million
Emp.: 200
Truck Leasing, Without Drivers
N.A.I.C.S.: 532120

Thomas D. Brown *(Pres)*

BROWN'S CHICKEN & PASTA, INC.
489 W Fullerton Ave, Elmhurst, IL 60126
Tel.: (630) 617-8800   IL
Year Founded: 1949
Sales Range: $50-74.9 Million
Emp.: 12
Fast Food Services
N.A.I.C.S.: 722513
Toni Portillo *(Owner)*
Mark Smith *(Dir-Mktg)*

BROWN'S FAIRFAX NISSAN
11010 Fairfax Blvd, Fairfax, VA 22030
Tel.: (703) 591-8009
Web Site:
    https://www.fairfaxnissan.com
Year Founded: 1983
Sales Range: $10-24.9 Million
Emp.: 95
Car Whslr
N.A.I.C.S.: 441110
Aaron Spicer *(Gen Mgr)*

BROWN, GIBBONS, LANG & COMPANY, LLC
1 Cleveland Ctr 1375 E 9th St Ste 2500, Cleveland, OH 44114
Tel.: (216) 241-2800   OH
Web Site: http://www.bglco.com
Year Founded: 1996
Investment Bank & Financial Advisory Firm
N.A.I.C.S.: 523150
Elizabeth R. Rozsypal *(Mgr-Mktg)*
Clifford M. Sladnick *(Mng Dir)*
Rebecca A. Dickenscheidt *(Dir-Res)*
Andrew K. Petryk *(Mng Dir)*
Anthony D. Delfre *(Mng Dir)*
Joyce E. Murphy *(VP-Admin)*
Lynn Basconi *(VP-Fin)*
Wendy S. Neal *(VP-Mktg)*
Ethan Goodson *(VP-Healthcare & Life Sciences Grp-Chicago)*
Brett Kornblatt *(VP-Metals Grp)*
E. Robert Kent III *(Mng Dir)*

BROWN, MITCHELL & ALEXANDER, INC.
401 Cowan Rd Ste A, Gulfport, MS 39507
Tel.: (228) 864-7612
Web Site:
    http://www.bmaengineers.com
Year Founded: 1967
Engineering Firm
N.A.I.C.S.: 541330
Dax Alexander *(Pres)*
Bill Mitchell *(VP)*
Benjamin Smith *(VP)*
Chris William *(Engr)*
Kevin Mullen *(Engr)*
Grady Martin *(Engr)*
Nick Gant *(Engr)*
Lucas Lizana *(Engr-Graduate)*
Keith Dern *(Mgr-CADD Production)*
Lorrie McCampbell *(Bus Mgr)*

BROWN-CAMPBELL COMPANY
11800 Investment Dr, Shelby, MI 48315-1794
Tel.: (586) 884-2123
Web Site: https://www.brown-campbell.com
Rev.: $21,120,570
Emp.: 13
Steel
N.A.I.C.S.: 423510
Murdoch T. Campbell *(Pres)*

BROWN-DAUB INC.

3903 Hecktown Rd, Easton, PA 18045
Tel.: (610) 991-7356   PA
Web Site: https://www.browndaub.net
Year Founded: 1936
Holding Company; New & Used Car Dealerships Owner & Operator
N.A.I.C.S.: 551112
Shane Remaley *(Gen Mgr)*
Chris Andreas *(Gen Sls Mgr)*
Stephanie Keeler *(Mgr-Internet Sls)*
Rich Wilson *(Sls Mgr)*
Ashley Ohlin *(Sls Mgr)*
Andy Taylor *(Fin Mgr)*
David Graves *(Fin Mgr)*
Joey Hoagland *(Mgr-Lease Retention)*
Mark Porcaro *(Mgr-Svc)*
Dave Ferri *(Mgr-Parts)*

BROWN-MINNEAPOLIS TANK, CO.
8301 Broadway Blvd SE, Albuquerque, NM 87105
Tel.: (505) 873-0160
Web Site: http://www.bmt-tank.com
Year Founded: 2001
Sales Range: $50-74.9 Million
Emp.: 65
Metal Fuel Tank Mfr
N.A.I.C.S.: 332420
Charles Travelstead *(Pres & CEO)*
Mark Demoss *(VP-Risk Mgmt, Engrg Improvement, HR & Ops)*
Mike Morris *(Sr VP)*

Subsidiaries:

Brown-Minneapolis-Rocky Mountain, LLC   (1)
520 W 2000 S, Orem, UT 84058
Tel.: (801) 373-8520
Metal Fuel Tank Mfr
N.A.I.C.S.: 332420

BROWN-WILBERT INC.
2280 Hamline Ave N, Saint Paul, MN 55113
Tel.: (651) 631-1234
Web Site: http://www.wilbertvault.com
Rev.: $19,000,000
Emp.: 150
Concrete Products
N.A.I.C.S.: 327390
Don Vomhof *(CFO)*
Jack Ascheman *(VP-Ops)*

BROWNBOOTS INTERACTIVE, INC.
108 S Main St, Fond Du Lac, WI 54935
Tel.: (920) 906-9175
Web Site:
    http://www.brownboots.com
Sales Range: Less than $1 Million
Emp.: 7
N.A.I.C.S.: 541810
Alan Hathaway *(Owner & Pres)*
Heather Biro *(Acct Exec)*
Jim Quackenboss *(Mgr-Sys & Developer)*
Danelle Smit *(Mgr-Bus Dev)*

BROWNELL & COMPANY, INC.
423 E Haddam Moodus Rd, Moodus, CT 06469-1025
Tel.: (860) 873-8625   CT
Web Site: http://www.brownellco.com
Year Founded: 1825
Mfr of Textiles
N.A.I.C.S.: 314994
Cynthia Stackowitz *(Sec)*
Thomas Ferraz *(Pres)*

BROWNING CHEVROLET
157 S Penn Ave, Eminence, KY 40019

Tel.: (502) 845-4212
Web Site: http://www.thinkgm.com
Year Founded: 1971
Sales Range: $10-24.9 Million
Emp.: 32
Used Car Whslr
N.A.I.C.S.: 441120
Jeff Browning *(Gen Mgr)*
Marlyn Browning *(Pres)*

BROWNING PRODUCTIONS & ENTERTAINMENT, INC.
2821 SW 23rd Ter Unit 8, Fort Lauderdale, FL 33312
Tel.: (305) 926-1917
Web Site:
    http://www.browningproductions.com
Television Broadcasting Services
N.A.I.C.S.: 334220
William Browning *(CEO)*

BROWNLEE JEWELERS OF THE CAROLINAS
4147 Park Rd, Charlotte, NC 28209
Tel.: (704) 527-1717
Web Site:
    https://www.brownleejewelers.com
Year Founded: 1974
Sales Range: $10-24.9 Million
Emp.: 48
Jewelry, Precious Stones & Precious Metals
N.A.I.C.S.: 458310
Harold W. Rousso *(Owner)*
Liba Roussu *(Controller)*

BROWNMED, INC.
4435 Main St Ste 820, Kansas City, MO 64111
Tel.: (712) 336-4395
Web Site:
    https://www.brownmed.com
Year Founded: 1965
Sales Range: $1-9.9 Million
Emp.: 60
Orthopedic Products Developer, Mfr & Whslr
N.A.I.C.S.: 339112
Ivan E. Brown *(Pres & CEO)*
Brian Miller *(VP-Info Svcs)*
Tony Poncelet *(VP-Fin)*
Brandon Rodriguez *(VP-Bus Dev)*
Janet Greene Brown *(VP-HR)*
Kylia Garver *(VP-Clinical Innovation)*
Matt Garver *(VP-Mktg)*
Cindy Chadwick *(VP-Sls)*

BROWNS BROOKLAWN INC.
Rte 130 Browning Rd, Brooklawn, NJ 08030
Tel.: (856) 742-8700
Web Site: http://www.shopright.com
Rev.: $43,100,000
Emp.: 200
Supermarkets, Chain
N.A.I.C.S.: 459310
Jeffrey N. Brown *(Pres)*

BROWNS ELECTRICAL SUPPLY CO.
1415 Spar Ave, Anchorage, AK 99501
Tel.: (907) 272-2259
Rev.: $15,000,000
Emp.: 60
Electrical Supplies Distr
N.A.I.C.S.: 423610
Leon T. Brown Jr. *(Owner)*

BROWNS JEEP EAGLE CHRYSLER PLYMOUTH
483 Medford Ave, Patchogue, NY 11772
Tel.: (631) 289-8500
Web Site:
    http://www.brownsjeepdodge.com

Browns Jeep Eagle Chrysler
Plymouth—(Continued)

Sales Range: $10-24.9 Million
Emp.: 65
Car Whslr
N.A.I.C.S.: 441110
Gary Brown (Pres)

BROWNS SALES & LEASING INC.
202 Hwy 52 S, Guttenberg, IA 52052
Tel.: (563) 276-3427   IA
Web Site: https://www.brownssl.com
Sales Range: $10-24.9 Million
Emp.: 30
Sales of New & Used Automobile
N.A.I.C.S.: 441110
David Brown (Pres)

BROWNS SUPER STORES INC.
700 Delsei Dr, Westville, NJ 08093
Tel.: (856) 933-7000
Web Site: http://www.shoprite.com
Sales Range: $500-549.9 Million
Emp.: 2,300
Supermarkets, Chain
N.A.I.C.S.: 445110
Jeffrey Brown (Pres)
Paul Brauer (VP-Ops)

Subsidiaries:

Browns Cheltenham LLC   (1)
2385 W Cheltenham Ave, Philadelphia, PA 19150
Tel.: (215) 887-7300
Web Site: http://www.shoprite1.com
Rev.: $32,300,000
Emp.: 300
Supermarkets, 66,000 - 99,000 Square Feet
N.A.I.C.S.: 458210
Paul Brown (Owner)

BROWNSTEIN GROUP
215 S Broad St, Philadelphia, PA 19107-5325
Tel.: (215) 607-2088   DE
Web Site:
     http://www.brownsteingroup.com
Year Founded: 1964
Rev.: $50,000,000
Emp.: 60
Advetising Agency
N.A.I.C.S.: 541810
Marc A. Brownstein (Pres & CEO)
Berny Brownstein (Chm & Chief Creative Officer)
Carol Petro (CFO & Exec VP)
Erin Allsman (Mng Dir)
Aimee Cicero (Mgr-Agency Comm)
Laura Emanuel (Dir-PR)
Terry Dukes (VP & Dir-Client Svcs)
Sean Carney (Dir-Content)
Kyle Harty (Grp Dir-Social Media)

Subsidiaries:

The Brownstein Group   (1)
1752 NW Market St #612, Seattle, WA 98107
Tel.: (425) 274-0820
Web Site: http://www.brownsteingroup.com
Emp.: 7
N.A.I.C.S.: 541810
Adam Deringer (Sr VP & Chief Digital Officer)

BROWNSTEIN HYATT FARBER SCHRECK, LLP.
Tel.: (303) 223-1100
Web Site: http://www.bhfs.com
Year Founded: 1968
Sales Range: $125-149.9 Million
Emp.: 214
Legal Advisory Services
N.A.I.C.S.: 541199
Adam Agron (Co-Mng Partner)
Rich Benenson (Mng Partner)

Carmencita N. M. Whonder (Dir-Policy & Lobbying)
Barbara Mica (COO)
Lara Day (Chief Culture & Comm Officer)
Carolynne White (Partner & Co-Chm-Real Estate Dept)
Aaron M. Hyatt (Partner & Co-Chm-Real Estate Dept)
Margaux Trammell (CTO & Dir-Pro Dev)
Norman Brownstein (Founder & Chm)
Nancy Crawford (Chief HR Officer)
John P. Huber (CFO)
Andrew R. Johnson (CIO)
Susan Erlenborn (Dir-Communications)
Larry E. McDonald (Dir-Information Technology)
Melissa Santiago (Sr Dir-Business Development)
Aaron T. Schneider (Dir-eDiscovery Svcs & Litigation Support)
Kevin Twomey (Dir-Fin Reporting & Analysis)
Ray Colas (Dir-Policy)
Joan Coplan (Dir-Policy)
Michael J. Stratton (Sr Dir-Policy)
Gino A. Maurelli (Partner)
Christopher L. Ottele (Partner)
Elizabeth D. Paulsen (Partner)
Jonathan G. Pray (Partner)
Airina L. Rodrigues (Partner)
Christine A. Samsel (Partner)
Jay Spader (Partner)
David M. Spaulding (Partner)
Nicole R. Ament (Partner)
Sarah Auchterlonie (Partner)
Douglas J. Friednash (Partner)

BROWNSTOWN ELECTRIC SUPPLY CO. INC.
PO Box L, Brownstown, IN 47220-0312
Tel.: (812) 358-4555
Web Site:
     http://www.brownstown.com
Year Founded: 1970
Sales Range: $10-24.9 Million
Emp.: 55
Provider of Electrical Apparatus & Equipment
N.A.I.C.S.: 423610
Gregg Deck (Pres & CEO)
Jon Robison (Dir-Pur)
Ken Horton (Treas & Sec)

BROWNSVILLE PUBLIC UTILITIES BOARD
1425 Robinhood Dr, Brownsville, TX 78520
Tel.: (956) 983-6100
Web Site: https://www.brownsville-pub.com
Sales Range: $100-124.9 Million
Emp.: 500
Electric, Waste & Water Services
N.A.I.C.S.: 221118
John S. Bruciak (CEO & Gen Mgr)
Nick Shah (Chm)

BROWNWOOD ACRES FOODS, INC.
4819 US Hwy 31 N, Eastport, MI 49627
Tel.: (231) 599-3101
Web Site:
     http://www.brownwoodacres.com
Year Founded: 1945
Sales Range: $1-9.9 Million
Emp.: 6
Specialty Health Food Mfr
N.A.I.C.S.: 456191
Stephen De Tar (Owner & Pres)

BROX INDUSTRIES INC.
1471 Methuen St, Dracut, MA 01826-5439
Tel.: (978) 454-9105   MA
Web Site:
     https://www.broxindustries.com
Year Founded: 1947
Sales Range: $10-24.9 Million
Emp.: 130
Provider of Construction Materials & Services
N.A.I.C.S.: 324121
Steven Brox (Pres)
Vic Goulet (Dir-Safety)
David Rousseau (Mgr-IT)
Erik Stevenson (Project Mgr)
Joe Russo (Mgr-Corp Credit)
Mark Nikitas (Mgr-Sls)

BRPH COMPANIES, INC.
5700 N Habourcity Blvd Ste 400, Melbourne, FL 32940
Tel.: (321) 254-7666
Web Site: https://www.brph.com
Sales Range: $50-74.9 Million
Emp.: 180
Commercial & Office Building New Construction
N.A.I.C.S.: 541310
Randall Thron (Sr VP)
Ana Flores (Engr-Electrical)
Art Waite (Dir-Aerospace)
Jessica Roddenberry (Dir-Design)
Raul E. Aviles Jr. (Pres-Engrg & Architecture)
Brian Curtin (Chm & CEO)

BRRH CORPORATION
800 Meadows Rd, Boca Raton, FL 33486
Tel.: (561) 955-7100   FL
Web Site: https://www.brrh.com
Year Founded: 1984
Sales Range: $25-49.9 Million
Emp.: 25
Healtcare Services
N.A.I.C.S.: 561110
Christine E. Lynn (Chm)
Mindy Sloane Shikiar (VP-Ops)
Mindy Raymond (VP-HR)
Jerry Fedele (Pres & CEO)
Dawn Javersack (CFO & VP)
Melissa Durbin (Chief Nursing Officer & VP)
Charles Posternack (CMO)
Karen Poole (COO & VP)
Amy M. Cole (Pres)
Thomas Chakurda (VP-Mktg & Comm)
Warren Orlando (Vice Chm)

Subsidiaries:

BRCH Home Health Service Inc.   (1)
640 Glades Rd, Boca Raton, FL 33431-2301   (100%)
Tel.: (561) 393-4040
Web Site: http://www.brch.org
Sales Range: $10-24.9 Million
Women Healthcare Services
N.A.I.C.S.: 621610
Jenny Watts (Dir-Home Health)

BRS MEDIA INC.
55 New Montgonery St Ste 622, San Francisco, CA 94105
Tel.: (415) 677-4027
Web Site: http://www.brsmedia.fm
Sales Range: $10-24.9 Million
Emp.: 400
Internet E-Commerce
N.A.I.C.S.: 517810
George T. Bundy (Founder, Chm & CEO)

BRT INC.
813 N Octorara Trl, Parkesburg, PA 19365

Tel.: (610) 857-9216
Web Site:
     https://www.brtransport.com
Year Founded: 1980
Sales Range: $10-24.9 Million
Emp.: 95
Hauler of Petroleum Products
N.A.I.C.S.: 484220
Daniel Mast (VP)

BRUBAKER GRAIN & CHEMICAL INC.
2918 Quaker Trace Rd, West Alexandria, OH 45381
Tel.: (937) 839-4636
Web Site:
     https://www.brubakergrain.com
Year Founded: 1976
Sales Range: $10-24.9 Million
Emp.: 45
Selling Grains
N.A.I.C.S.: 424510
Gary Brubaker (Pres)

BRUBAKER, INC.
1284 Roherstown Rd, Lancaster, PA 17601
Tel.: (717) 299-5643
Web Site:
     https://www.brubakerinc.com
Sales Range: $10-24.9 Million
Emp.: 100
Plumbing Services
N.A.I.C.S.: 238220
Gerald Brubaker (VP)
Bruce Baker (Treas & Sec)
Erik Weiss (Mgr)

BRUCE CAVENAUGH'S AUTOMART
6321 Market St, Wilmington, NC 28405
Tel.: (910) 399-3480
Web Site:
     http://www.brucecavenaugh.com
Year Founded: 1990
Sales Range: $10-24.9 Million
Emp.: 100
New Car Retailer
N.A.I.C.S.: 441110
Matt Cavenaugh (Mgr-Sls)
Robbie Pennington (Bus Mgr)

BRUCE CLAY, INC.
2245 1st St Ste 101, Simi Valley, CA 93065
Tel.: (805) 517-1900   CA
Web Site: http://www.bruceclay.com
Year Founded: 1996
Sales Range: $1-9.9 Million
Emp.: 30
Search Engine Optimization & Internet Marketing ServicesSearch Engine Optimization & Internet Marketing Services
N.A.I.C.S.: 541890
Bruce Clay (Founder & Pres)

Subsidiaries:

Bruce Clay Australia Pty Ltd   (1)
Export House 22 Pitt Street, Sydney, 2000, NSW, Australia
Tel.: (61) 2 9252 1700
Web Site: http://www.bruceclay.com
Search Engine Optimization & Internet Marketing
N.A.I.C.S.: 541890

Bruce Clay Europe   (1)
Via San Gottardo 61, 6828, Balerna, Switzerland
Tel.: (41) 91 682 95 83
Web Site: http://www.bruceclay.com
Search Engine Optimization & Internet Marketing
N.A.I.C.S.: 541890
Alessandro Agostini (Mng Dir)

Bruce Clay India Pvt Ltd   (1)

Suite 611 6th Floor DLF City Court DLF City, Sikanderpur, Gurgaon, 122022, Haryana, India
Tel.: (91) 124 414 3291
Web Site: http://www.bruceclay.com
Search Engine Optimization & Internet Marketing
N.A.I.C.S.: 541890
Siddharth Lal (Mng Dir)

Bruce Clay Japan, Inc.   (1)
7F Kotobuki Dougenzaka Bldg 1-19-11 Dougenzaka, Shibuya, Tokyo, 150-0043, Japan
Tel.: (81) 3 5456 4201
Web Site: http://www.bruceclay.co.jp
Search Engine Optimization & Internet Marketing
N.A.I.C.S.: 541890

BRUCE COMPANY OF WISCONSIN, INC.
2830 Parmenter St, Middleton, WI 53562
Tel.: (608) 836-7041
Web Site:
https://www.brucecompany.com
Rev.: $36,860,072
Emp.: 500
Landscape Contractors & Retail
N.A.I.C.S.: 561730

Subsidiaries:

Landscape Care Co.   (1)
4026 Pacheco Blvd, Martinez, CA 94553-2224
Tel.: (925) 372-7973
Web Site: http://www.landscapecare.net
Landscaping Services
N.A.I.C.S.: 561730
Don Nielsen (Pres)

BRUCE FOODS CORPORATION
Hwy 182 W, Cade, LA 70519
Tel.: (337) 365-8101   LA
Web Site: http://www.brucefoods.com
Year Founded: 1928
Sales Range: $200-249.9 Million
Emp.: 900
Canned Vegetables, Seasonings, Mexican Food & Hot Sauce Mfr & Whslr
N.A.I.C.S.: 311999
Virginia Brown (Branch Mgr)
John McGinley (Plant Mgr)
Byron Vidrine (Mgr-Safety & Night)
Darren Stroud (Mgr-Ops)
Virginia Forestier (Mgr-Mktg)

BRUCE FOX INC.
1909 McDonald Ln, New Albany, IN 47150
Tel.: (812) 945-3511
Web Site: https://www.brucefox.com
Rev.: $10,000,000
Emp.: 120
Trophies
N.A.I.C.S.: 339910
Dave Miller (VP-Sls)
Angela Brinkworth (Mgr-Relationship)
David H. Morrison (Pres)

BRUCE LOWRIE CHEVROLET INC.
711 SW Loop 820, Fort Worth, TX 76134-1299
Tel.: (817) 293-5811
Web Site:
http://www.brucelowrie.com
Rev.: $89,821,445
Emp.: 150
Automobiles, New & Used
N.A.I.C.S.: 441110
Bruce W. Lowrie (Pres)
Karen Peterson (Comptroller)
Terry Peterson (Mgr-Body Shop)

BRUCE WILLIAMS HOMES, INC.
456 12th St W, Bradenton, FL 34205
Tel.: (941) 748-8834
Web Site: http://www.bwhomes.com
Year Founded: 1969
Sales Range: $1-9.9 Million
Residential Construction
N.A.I.C.S.: 236115
Britt Williams (Pres)
Judy Chadwick (Mgr-Design)
Patricia Martino (Coord-Land Dev)

BRUCETON FARM SERVICE, INC.
1768 Mileground Rd, Morgantown, WV 26505-3753
Tel.: (304) 291-6980   WV
Web Site:
http://www.bfscompanies.com
Year Founded: 1974
Sales Range: $10-24.9 Million
Emp.: 350
Holding Company
N.A.I.C.S.: 445131

Subsidiaries:

BFS Foods Inc.   (1)
1768 Mileground Rd, Morgantown, WV 26505-3753
Tel.: (304) 291-6980
Web Site: http://www.bfscompanies.com
Rev.: $29,400,000
Emp.: 30
Gasoline Service Stations & Convenience Stores
N.A.I.C.S.: 457120

Bruceton Ag-Services Inc.   (1)
1768 Mileground Rd, Morgantown, WV 26505-3753   (100%)
Tel.: (304) 291-6980
Web Site: http://www.bsscompany.com
Rev.: $4,362,545
Emp.: 30
Farm Supplies
N.A.I.C.S.: 459999

Bruceton Petroleum Co. Inc.   (1)
1768 Mileground Rd, Morgantown, WV 26505-3753   (100%)
Tel.: (304) 291-6980
Web Site: http://www.bfscompanies.com
Rev.: $28,052,194
Emp.: 5
Petroleum Products
N.A.I.C.S.: 424720
Marshall Bishop (Pres)

BRUCKMANN, ROSSER, SHERRILL & CO., LLC
126 E 56th St 29th Fl, New York, NY 10022-3613
Tel.: (212) 521-3700   DE
Web Site: https://www.brs.com
Year Founded: 1995
Sales Range: $1-4.9 Billion
Emp.: 20
Private Equity Investment Firm
N.A.I.C.S.: 523999
Bruce C. Bruckmann (Mng Dir)
Thomas J. Baldwin (Mng Dir)
Stephen C. Sherrill (Founder & Mng Dir)
Rashad Rahman (Mng Dir)

Subsidiaries:

DTLR Holding, Inc.   (1)
1300 Mercedes Dr, Hanover, MD 21076
Tel.: (410) 850-5911
Web Site: http://www.dtlr.com
Rev.: $181,484,598
Assets: $92,673,057
Liabilities: $97,337,228
Net Worth: ($4,664,171)
Earnings: $5,125,692
Emp.: 377
Fiscal Year-end: 02/02/2013
Holding Company; Retailer of Men's Footwear, Apparel & Accessories
N.A.I.C.S.: 551112

Bruce C. Bruckmann (Chm)
Michelle Holmes (Dir-HR)
Phillip F. Villari (CFO)
Scott V. Collins (Chief Mdsg Officer)
Frank M. Long (Dir-Ops)
Todd S. Kirssin (Mgr-Gen Mdse)
Elena Mencos (Mgr-Asset Protection)

Daisy Manufacturing Company   (1)
1700 N 2nd St, Rogers, AR 72756-2411
Tel.: (479) 636-1200
Web Site: http://www.daisy.com
Sales Range: $50-74.9 Million
B-B Guns, Pistols, Targets, CO-2 Gas Operated & Toy Play Guns Mfr
N.A.I.C.S.: 332994
Joe Murfin (Dir-Mktg)

Subsidiary (Domestic):

Crosman Corporation   (2)
7629 Routes 5 20, Bloomfield, NY 14469
Tel.: (585) 657-6161
Web Site: https://www.crosman.com
Air Guns, Paint Ball Guns & Accessories Mfr
N.A.I.C.S.: 339920

Gamo Outdoor USA, Inc.   (1)
3911 SW 47th Ave Ste 914, Fort Lauderdale, FL 33314
Tel.: (954) 581-5822
Web Site: http://www.gamousa.com
Hunting Equipment & Supplies Mfr
N.A.I.C.S.: 332994
Jordi Riera (Dir-Mktg)
Norvin Hornberger (VP-Sls)

New Archery Products, Inc.   (1)
7500 Industrial Dr, Forest Park, IL 60130
Tel.: (708) 488-2500
Web Site: http://www.newarchery.com
Sales Range: $1-9.9 Million
Archery Products Mfr
N.A.I.C.S.: 339920
Andy Simo (Pres)
Brady Arview (VP-Sls & Mktg)
David Speelman (Controller)

BRUCKNER TRUCK SALES, INC.
9471 Interstate 40 E, Amarillo, TX 79118
Tel.: (806) 376-6273   TX
Web Site:
http://www.brucknertruck.com
Year Founded: 1932
Sales Range: $50-74.9 Million
Emp.: 480
Truck Dealership
N.A.I.C.S.: 441227
Chip McCampbell (Dir-HR)
Victor Brown (Mgr)
Tyson Smith (Mgr-Rental)
Brian Murphy (VP-Sls)
Brian Bruckner (Pres)
Chris Bruckner (VP)

Subsidiaries:

Bruckner Leasing Co. Inc.   (1)
9471 I 40 E, Amarillo, TX 79118   (100%)
Tel.: (806) 376-6273
Web Site: http://www.brucknertrucks.com
Sales Range: $1-9.9 Million
Emp.: 200
Truck Rental & Leasing
N.A.I.C.S.: 532120
Chris Bruckner (Pres)

Bruckner Truck Sales   (1)
3611 Irving Blvd, Dallas, TX 75247
Tel.: (214) 631-4770
Web Site: http://www.brucknertruck.com
Rev.: $19,900,000
Emp.: 100
New & Used Truck Tractor & Trailer Distr
N.A.I.C.S.: 441227
Dennis DeLong (Mgr-Leasing Sls)
Bruce Meador (Gen Mgr)
Allan Fite (Mgr-Parts)

Shipley Motor Equipment Company   (1)
324 S Bloomington St, Lowell, AR 72745
Tel.: (479) 770-6040
Web Site: http://www.shipleymack.com

Truck Tractors
N.A.I.C.S.: 423110
Carl Shipley (Pres)
David Bass (VP)

BRUDERMAN & CO., LLC
119 Birch Hill Rd, Locust Valley, NY 11560
Tel.: (212) 244-1460
Web Site:
https://www.bruderman.com
Emp.: 100
Holding Company; Investment Services
N.A.I.C.S.: 551112
James M. Bruderman (Pres)

Subsidiaries:

H M S Productions, Inc.   (1)
250 W 39th St, New York, NY 10018
Tel.: (212) 719-9190
Web Site: http://www.hmsproductions.nyc
Women's & Girls' Cut & Sew Other Outerwear Mfr
N.A.I.C.S.: 315250

BRUIN CAPITAL HOLDINGS, LLC
7 Renaissance Sq 2nd Fl, White Plains, NY 10601
Tel.: (914) 849-0900
Web Site: https://bruincptl.com
Investment Services
N.A.I.C.S.: 523999
George Pyne (CEO & Founder)

Subsidiaries:

Proof of the Pudding   (1)
6400 Sugarloaf Pkwy, Duluth, GA 30097-7419
Tel.: (404) 249-6400
Web Site: http://www.proofpudding.com
Caterers
N.A.I.C.S.: 722320
Larry Larsen (Mgr)
Laurie Smith (Gen Mgr-Off Premise Div)
Aaron Barba (Dir-Facilities & Logistical Ops)
Jay Bethel (Mgr-Special Projects & Warehouse)

BRUIN PLASTICS COMPANY, INC.
61 Joslin Rd, Glendale, RI 02826
Tel.: (401) 568-3081
Web Site:
https://www.bruinplastics.com
Year Founded: 1964
Sales Range: $10-24.9 Million
Emp.: 50
Mfr of Laminated & Coates Fabrics
N.A.I.C.S.: 313320
Dennis E. Angelone (Pres)
Kevin Pettit (Controller)

BRUINS SPORTS CAPITAL, LLC
7 Renaissance Sq 2nd Fl, White Plains, NY 10601
Tel.: (914) 849-0900
Web Site:
http://bruinsportscapital.com
Year Founded: 2015
Privater Equity Firm
N.A.I.C.S.: 523999
George Pyne (Founder & CEO)
David Arbutyn (Partner)

Subsidiaries:

Deltatre SpA   (1)
Via Francesco Millio 41, Turin, 10141, Italy
Tel.: (39) 0117543
Web Site: http://www.deltatre.com
Information Technology & Services
N.A.I.C.S.: 513199
Giampiero Rinaudo (Co-founder & CEO)

Subsidiary (Non-US):

Massive Interactive, Inc.   (2)
Media House 3 Palmerston Road, London,

Bruins Sports Capital, LLC—(Continued)
SW19 1PG, United Kingdom
Tel.: (44) 2076365585
Web Site:
    http://www.massiveinteractive.com
Internet Protocol-Based Video & Media
Management, Delivery & Streaming
N.A.I.C.S.: 541511
Andrea Marini (Dir)

Soulsight, LLC   (1)
205 W Wacker Dr Ste 400, Chicago, IL
60606
Tel.: (312) 982-2400
Web Site: http://www.soulsight.com
Graphic Design Services
N.A.I.C.S.: 541430
George Argyros (CEO & Partner)
Justin Berglund (Exec Creative Dir)
Laura DeGroot (Exec VP-Strategy & Sr VP-
Strategy)
Jim Pietruszynski (Partner & CMO)

BRUMFIELD OIL COMPANY INC.
500 Pearl River Ave, McComb, MS
39648
Tel.: (601) 684-3341
Rev.: $13,700,000
Emp.: 65
Petroleum Bulk Stations
N.A.I.C.S.: 424710
Ann Brumfield (Treas & Sec)
Pat H. Brumfield Jr. (Pres)

BRUMIT OIL CO. INC.
1101 Osage St, Leavenworth, KS
66048
Tel.: (913) 682-0275
Sales Range: $10-24.9 Million
Emp.: 40
Gasoline Mfr
N.A.I.C.S.: 325120

BRUMIT RESTAURANT GROUP
40 Seminole St, Asheville, NC 28803
Tel.: (828) 274-5835
Web Site: http://www.ncarbys.com
Sales Range: $10-24.9 Million
Emp.: 700
Franchise Owner of Fast-Food Res-
taurants
N.A.I.C.S.: 722513
Joe Brumit (Owner)
Greg Catevenis (Controller)

BRUNA BROS IMPLEMENT LLC
1128 Pony Express Hwy, Marysville,
KS 66508
Tel.: (785) 562-5304
Web Site:
    https://www.brunaimplementco.com
Sales Range: $10-24.9 Million
Emp.: 15
Agricultural Machinery & Equipment
N.A.I.C.S.: 423820
Alan W. Bruna (Pres)
Doug Bruna (Vice Chm)

BRUNDAGE ASSOCIATES IN-CORPORATED
555 Goffle Rd, Ridgewood, NJ 07450
Tel.: (610) 393-9497
Web Site: https://www.brundage-
    inc.com
Rev.: $15,000,000
Emp.: 6
Air Conditioning & Ventilation & Duct
Work Contractor
N.A.I.C.S.: 423730
Edward Schwehm (Pres & Mgr-Natl
Sls)

BRUNDAGE MANAGEMENT COMPANY

254 Spencer Ln, San Antonio, TX
78201
Tel.: (210) 735-9393
Rev.: $11,921,351
Emp.: 59
Miniwarehouse, Warehousing
N.A.I.C.S.: 531130
Gerald A. Griffin (CEO)
Thomas Brundage (Pres)
Hugh Doherty (VP & Dir-Ops)
Randy Kelly (Mgr-Special Projects)
Rochelle Cuff (VP & Controller)

BRUNER MOTORS, INC.
1515 W Southloop, Stephenville, TX
76401
Tel.: (254) 968-2135   TX
Web Site: http://www.brunerauto.com
Sales Range: $50-74.9 Million
Emp.: 115
New & Used Car Dealer
N.A.I.C.S.: 441110
Greg Bruner (VP & Gen Mgr)
Dwain Bruner (Pres)
Mike Melton (Controller)
Karma Watson (Mgr-Accts Payable &
Accts Receivable)
Sammie Vaughn (Mgr-Acctg)
Mike Waters (Mgr-Comml & Fleet)

Subsidiaries:

Bruner Auto Group   (1)
224 Early Blvd, Early, TX 76802
Tel.: (325) 200-4143
Web Site: http://www.brunerautogroup.com
Sales Range: $25-49.9 Million
New & Used Car Dealer
N.A.I.C.S.: 441110
Janice Burt (Office Mgr)
Brian Lee (Dir-Svc)
Irma Castillo (Mgr-Bus)
Rick Newton (Mgr-Sls)

BRUNING GRAIN & FEED CO. INC.
417 W Railway, Bruning, NE 68322
Tel.: (402) 353-4785
Web Site:
    http://www.bruninggrain.com
Sales Range: $10-24.9 Million
Emp.: 20
Grains
N.A.I.C.S.: 424510
Darreld Domeier (Mgr)

BRUNK INDUSTRIES, INC.
1225 Sage St, Lake Geneva, WI
53147
Tel.: (262) 248-8873
Web Site:
    http://www.brunkindustries.com
Year Founded: 1960
Sales Range: $25-49.9 Million
Emp.: 32
Metal Stamping
N.A.I.C.S.: 332119
Lars E. Brunk (Pres)
Michael S. Black (VP-Fin)
Bertil E. Brunk (Chm & CEO)
Ulla E. Brunk (CFO & Treas)
Nancy Vecchio (Mgr-HR)

BRUNNER
11 Stanwix St 5th Fl, Pittsburgh, PA
15222-1312
Tel.: (412) 995-9500   PA
Web Site:
    https://www.brunnerworks.com
Year Founded: 1989
Rev.: $220,000,000
Emp.: 210
Advetising Agency
N.A.I.C.S.: 541810
Scott Morgan (Pres)
Rick Gardinier (Chief Digital Officer)
Jeff Maggs (Chief Client Officer)
Rob Schapiro (Chief Creative Officer)

Louis Sawyer (Chief Strategy Officer
& Sr VP)
Kelly Larkin (Acct Mgr)
Ashley Jones (Mgr-PR Content)
Marissa Rayes (Coord-Agency Svcs)
John Ganovsky (VP-Co-Innovation)
Drew Wirfel (Dir-Digital Ops)
David Sladack (Sr VP & Dir-Bus
Strategy)
Eric Perz (Dir-Data Science & Deci-
sion Analytics)
Justin Bowman (Engr-DevOps)
Ashlee Bartko (Acct Mgr-Search-
Paid)
Lindsay Grystar (Project Mgr-Digital)

Subsidiaries:

Brunner   (1)
260 Peachtree St NW Ste 1100, Atlanta,
GA 30303
Tel.: (404) 479-2200
Web Site: http://www.brunnerworks.com
Emp.: 70
Advetising Agency
N.A.I.C.S.: 541810
Louis Sawyer (Chief Strategy Officer)
Rich Fabritius (Mng Dir-Atlanta)
Michael Brunner (Chm & CEO)
Jeff Maggs (Mng Dir & Chief Client Officer)
Petra Arbutina (Exec VP, Dir-Contact-
Strategy & Partner)
Mary Kay Modaffari (Exec VP, Mng Dir-
Pittsburgh & Partner)
Jay Giesen (Exec Dir-Creative)
Scott Morgan (Pres & Partner)
Rick Gardinier (Sr VP & Chief Digital Offi-
cer)
Matt Blackburn (VP & Dir-Creative)
Randall Hooker (Dir-Creative)

BRUNNER MANUFACTURING CO. INC.
1025 Parker Dr, Mauston, WI 53948
Tel.: (608) 847-6667
Web Site: http://www.brunner-
    inc.com
Rev.: $14,100,000
Emp.: 280
Fasteners
N.A.I.C.S.: 339993
Ronald E. Brunner (Pres)
Paul Arbanas (VP-Sls & Mktg)
Mark Skiba (CFO)

BRUNO INDEPENDENT LIVING AIDS, INC.
1780 Executive Dr, Oconomowoc, WI
53066
Tel.: (262) 567-4990
Web Site: http://www.bruno.com
Sales Range: $75-99.9 Million
Emp.: 300
Mfr of Motorized Lifts & Platform Lifts
& Other Accessibility & Mobility Prod-
ucts
N.A.I.C.S.: 423450
Mike Krawczyk (Mgr-Mktg)
Alan Karch (Mgr-Mfg Plant)
Kristopher Lampe (Engr-Electrical)
Jeff Marcheske (Engr-Mfg)
Jay Schroeter (VP-Fin)
Kris Kreutzmann (Asst Mgr-Customer
Care)

BRUNO, DIBELLO & CO., LLC
785 Totowa Rd Ste 2, Totowa, NJ
07512
Tel.: (973) 790-8800   NJ
Web Site:
    https://www.brunodibello.com
Year Founded: 1983
Sales Range: $1-9.9 Million
Emp.: 20
Accounting Firm
N.A.I.C.S.: 541211
Patricia Cuviello (Gen Mgr)

BRUNS, CONNELL, VOLLMAR

& ARMSTRONG, LLC
40 N Main St Ste 2010, Dayton, OH
45423
Tel.: (937) 999-6261   OH
Web Site: https://www.bcvalaw.com
Year Founded: 2016
Law firm
N.A.I.C.S.: 541110
Thomas B. Bruns (Partner)
Kevin C. Connell (Partner)
Adam C. Armstrong (Partner)
T. Andrew Vollmar (Partner)

BRUNS-PAK INC.
999 New Durham Rd, Edison, NJ
08817-2253
Tel.: (732) 248-4455   NJ
Web Site: https://www.bruns-pak.com
Year Founded: 1980
Rev.: $75,000,000
Emp.: 85
Engineeering Services
N.A.I.C.S.: 541330
Mark S. Evanko (Pres)
Paul Evanko (Dir-Sls & Mktg)
Bob Kennedy (Project Dir)
Joshua Tiner (Dir-Ops)

BRUNSELL BROTHERS LTD.
4611 W Beltline Hwy, Madison, WI
53711
Tel.: (608) 275-7171
Web Site: https://www.brunsell.com
Rev.: $27,198,968
Emp.: 150
Lumber & Other Building Materials
N.A.I.C.S.: 423310
Craig Brunsell (COO)

BRUNSWICK AUTO MART, INC.
3031 Ctr Rd, Brunswick, OH 44212
Tel.: (330) 273-3300   OH
Web Site:
    http://www.brunswickautomart.com
Year Founded: 1990
Sales Range: $25-49.9 Million
Emp.: 200
New & Used Car Dealer
N.A.I.C.S.: 441110
Gary Panteck (Owner, Pres & CEO)
Eric Avondet (Mgr-Wholesale Parts)
Jacob Kash (Mgr-Used Car Sls)
Jonathan Sero (Mgr-Wholesale)
Michele Miller (Asst Mgr-Svc)

BRUNSWICK ELECTRIC MEM-BERSHIP CORPORATION
795 Ocean Hwy 17 W, Supply, NC
28462
Tel.: (910) 754-4391
Web Site: https://www.bemc.org
Year Founded: 1939
Sales Range: $75-99.9 Million
Emp.: 135
Electric Power Distr
N.A.I.C.S.: 221122
Bobby Davis (VP-Tech Ops)
Hubert Brittain (Pres)
Moses C. Herring (Treas & Asst Sec)
JoAnn B. Simmons (VP)

BRUNSWICK MEDIA SER-VICES LLC
214 Lincoln Blvd, Middlesex, NJ
08846
Tel.: (732) 599-0022
Year Founded: 2003
Sales Range: Less than $1 Million
Emp.: 2
Audio/Visual, Industrial
N.A.I.C.S.: 541810
Michael J. Conaty (Pres)

BRUSH MASTERS, INC.

11775 95th Ave N, Maple Grove, MN
55369-5521
Tel.: (763) 478-3232
Web Site:
https://www.brushmasters.com
Sales Range: $10-24.9 Million
Emp.: 110
Plastering Services
N.A.I.C.S.: 238310
Paul Luedemann (Owner & Pres)
Todd Polifka (Principal)
Debbie Scully (Office Mgr)

**BRUSH RESEARCH MANU-
FACTURING COMPANY**
4642 E Floral Dr, Los Angeles, CA
90022
Tel.: (323) 261-2193   CA
Web Site:
https://www.brushresearch.com
Year Founded: 1958
Sales Range: $50-74.9 Million
Emp.: 50
Mfr of Industrial Brushes
N.A.I.C.S.: 339994
Tara Rands (Pres & CEO)
Robert G. Fowlie (Exec VP-Ops)
Don Didier (Gen Mgr)
Mike Miller (Mgr-Sls)

**BRUSTER'S REAL ICE
CREAM, INC.**
730 Mulberry St, Bridgewater, PA
15009
Tel.: (724) 774-4250   PA
Web Site:
http://www.brustersicecream.com
Year Founded: 1989
Sales Range: $1-9.9 Million
Ice Cream Parlors
N.A.I.C.S.: 311520
James Sahene (CEO)
Dave Guido (Sr VP-Ops)
Gregg McMillan (VP-Fin)
Bruce Reed (Founder)
Corey Bradley (VP-Franchise Dev)
Jennifer Brinker (VP-Mktg)
Kathy Kemerer (Dir-HR & Mgr-Legal)
Bob Bryant (Reg VP)
Marcie Chong (Reg VP)
Sean Krings (Reg VP-Ops)
Jason Selesky (Dir-Pur)
Tricia DeLisle (Mktg Dir)
Gina Negley (Creative Dir)
Diane Fleming (Mktg Mgr-Design
Production)
Thomas J. Tranel (VP-Real Estate)
Kim Ellis (VP-Franchise Dev)

BRUTGER EQUITIES, INC.
100 4th Ave S, Saint Cloud, MN
56301
Tel.: (320) 252-6262   MN
Web Site:
http://www.brutgerequities.com
Year Founded: 1990
Sales Range: $50-74.9 Million
Emp.: 15
Operation of Apartments & Hotels
N.A.I.C.S.: 721110
Larry Brutger (Pres & CEO)
Tom S. Etienne (VP-HR)
Laura Pfenstein (CFO)

**BRUTOCO ENGINEERING &
CONSTRUCTION, INC.**
14801 Slover Ave, Fontana, CA
92337
Tel.: (909) 350-3535
Web Site: http://www.brutoco.net
Year Founded: 1967
Sales Range: $25-49.9 Million
Emp.: 200
Highway, Street & Bridge Construc-
tion Services
N.A.I.C.S.: 237310

Michael J. Murphy (Pres)
Donald D. Brake (CFO)

BRUZZONE SHIPPING, INC.
224 Buffalo Ave, Freeport, NY 11520
Tel.: (516) 239-7120
Web Site: https://www.bruzzone.com
Rev.: $50,000,000
Emp.: 20
Freight Forwarding
N.A.I.C.S.: 488510
Ana Datena (Coord-Import)

Subsidiaries:

Ovair Freight Service, Inc.   (1)
530 Burnside Ave, Inwood, NY
11096   (100%)
Tel.: (516) 239-7120
Freight Forwarding
N.A.I.C.S.: 488510

**BRYAN BUSH CONSTRUC-
TION COMPANY, INC.**
PO Box 14649, Baton Rouge, LA
70898
Tel.: (225) 766-8284
Sales Range: $10-24.9 Million
Emp.: 13
Nonresidential Construction Services
N.A.I.C.S.: 236220
Bryan E. Bush III (Pres)

BRYAN CAVE LLP
1 Metropolitan Sq 211 N Broadway
Ste 3600, Saint Louis, MO 63102-
2750
Tel.: (314) 259-2000
Web Site: http://www.bryancave.com
Year Founded: 1873
Sales Range: $550-599.9 Million
Emp.: 2,000
Legal Advisory Services
N.A.I.C.S.: 541110
Don G. Lents (Sr Partner)
Lisa Demete Martin (Chief Diversity
Officer)
Judith L. Harris (Chief Library & Res
Svcs Officer)
Ketrina G. Bakewell (Partner)
Dan H. Ball (Partner)
Fred W. Bartelsmeyer (Partner)
Steven M. Baumer (Partner)
Brian W. Berglund (Partner)
Trevor A. Jenkins (Partner-Kansas
City)
Daniel T. Rockey (Partner-San Fran-
cisco)
Harold A. Hagen (Partner-San Fran-
cisco)
Stephanie Moll (Partner)
Jason DeJonker (Partner)
Andrew Schoulder (Partner-
Bankruptcy, Restructuring & Creditors
Rights Grp)
Allison Eckstrom (Partner)
Kristin Yemm (Partner)
Jason Kempf (Partner)
Christopher Blaesing (Partner)
Taavi Annus (Partner)
Jorge J. Perez (Partner)
Tracy Talbot (Partner)
Michelle Masoner (Partner)
Vanessa Sunshine (Partner)
Broderick D. Johnson (Partner)
Benjamin F. Sidbury (Mng Partner-
Charlotte)
Brian A. Sher (Mng Partner-Chicago)
Bryce A. Suzuki (Mng Partner-
Phoenix)
C. Ryan Reetz (Mng Partner-Miami)
Carol R. Osborne (Mng Partner-
London)
Diana M. Vuylsteke (Mng Partner-
Jefferson City)
Douglas A. Thompson (Mng Partner-
Los Angeles)

Eckart Budelmann (Mng Partner-
Hamburg)
G. Patrick Watson (Mng Partner-
Atlanta)
Holly Lopez (Mng Partner-Irvine)
Kristi L. Swartz (Mng Partner-Hong
Kong)
LaDawn Naegle (Mng Partner-
Washington)
Mark W. Weakley (Mng Partner-
Boulder)
Paul Lopach (Mng Partner-Denver)
Remy Blain (Mng Partner-Paris)
Robin R. Dubas (Mng Partner-Dallas)
Seth M. Frederiksen (Mng Partner-
San Francisco)
Steve Stimell (Mng Partner-New
York)
Steven B. Smith (Mng Partner-
Colorado Springs)
Tobias Fenck (Mng Partner-Frankfurt)
William Perry Brandt (Mng Partner-
Kansas City & Overland Park)
Zhongdong Zhang (Mng Partner-
Shanghai)
Richard E. Finneran (Partner)
Liz Blackwell (Partner-Comml Litiga-
tion & Product Liability Groups)
Mark Leadlove (Partner)
Leslie Leader Brooks (Mgr-Pub Rels)
Ryan Davis (Mng Partner)

BRYAN CHEVROLET INC.
8213-8701 Airline Dr, Metairie, LA
70003-6852
Tel.: (504) 466-6000
Web Site:
http://www.bryanchevy.com
Sales Range: $50-74.9 Million
Emp.: 80
New & Used Car Dealers
N.A.I.C.S.: 441110
Jay Bryan (Owner & Pres)
Keith Treuting (Gen Mgr-Sls)
Jim Davies (Gen Mgr)

**BRYAN CONSTRUCTION COM-
PANY**
1007 N Earl Rudder Fwy, Bryan, TX
77802
Tel.: (979) 776-6000
Web Site:
http://bryanconstruction.com
Year Founded: 1957
Sales Range: $10-24.9 Million
Emp.: 100
Nonresidential Construction Services
N.A.I.C.S.: 236220
Dave Ridgway (Dir-Safety)
Larry Ridgway (Pres)

BRYAN EASLER TOYOTA
1409 Spartanburg Hwy, Henderson-
ville, NC 28792
Tel.: (828) 693-7261
Web Site:
https://www.bryaneaslertoyota.com
Year Founded: 1990
Sales Range: $10-24.9 Million
Emp.: 70
Car Whslr
N.A.I.C.S.: 441110
Bryan Easler (Owner & Pres)
Alex Long (Mgr-Sls)
Leo Luna (Mgr-Sls)

**BRYAN HONDA-
FAYETTEVILLE**
4104 Raeford Rd, Fayetteville, NC
28304
Tel.: (910) 483-1234
Web Site:
https://www.bryanfayetteville.com
Sales Range: $75-99.9 Million
Emp.: 90
New & Used Automobiles

N.A.I.C.S.: 441110
David Bryan (Sec & VP)
Rico Glover (Mgr-Internet Sls)
Norwood E. Bryan Jr. (Pres)

BRYAN IMPORTS INC.
3100 Briarcrest Dr, Bryan, TX 77802
Tel.: (979) 776-7600
Web Site:
http://www.garlynsheltonbryan.com
Rev.: $40,000,000
Emp.: 300
Automobiles, New & Used
N.A.I.C.S.: 441110
Garlyn O. Shelton (Pres)

**BRYAN LGH MEDICAL CEN-
TER INC.**
1600 S 48th St, Lincoln, NE 68506-
1227
Tel.: (402) 489-0200
Web Site: http://www.bryanlgh.org
Year Founded: 1926
Sales Range: $750-799.9 Million
Emp.: 3,000
Medical & Surgical Hospital Services
N.A.I.C.S.: 622110
Samantha Collier (VP-Medical Affairs)
Matt Reimer (Controller)
Kimberly Russell (Pres & CEO)
Carolyn Cudy (VP-Medical Affairs)

BRYANT & WELBORN L.L.P.
2335 Oak Alley, Tyler, TX 75703
Tel.: (903) 561-4041
Web Site:
https://www.bryantwelborncpas.com
Year Founded: 1974
Sales Range: $1-9.9 Million
Emp.: 14
Accounting, Auditing & Bookkeeping
Services
N.A.I.C.S.: 541211
Jerry Garrett (Partner)

**BRYANT DISTRIBUTING COM-
PANY**
1201 E 18th St, Owensboro, KY
42303
Tel.: (270) 684-2326
Sales Range: $25-49.9 Million
Emp.: 21
Wine & Beer Distr
N.A.I.C.S.: 424820
John Albert Carpenter (Chm)

BRYANT RESTAURANTS INC.
3105 Glenwood Ave Ste 103, Ra-
leigh, NC 27612
Tel.: (919) 787-0036
Sales Range: $10-24.9 Million
Emp.: 2
Fast-Food Restaurant, Chain
N.A.I.C.S.: 722513
Richard Bryant (Pres)

BRYANT RUBBER CORP
1112 Lomita Blvd, Harbor City, CA
90710
Tel.: (310) 530-2530
Web Site:
http://www.bryantrubber.com
Rev.: $15,900,000
Emp.: 140
Hard Rubber & Molded Rubber Prod-
ucts
N.A.I.C.S.: 326299
Steven Bryant (Owner & CEO)
Rafael Radillo (Mgr-Quality)
Stephen Rookey (VP-Tech)
Sue Mangione (Mgr-Customer Svc)

**BRYANT-DURHAM ELECTRIC
CO., INC.**

Bryant-Durham Electric Co., Inc.—(Continued)

5102 Neal Rd, Durham, NC 27705-2363
Tel.: (919) 383-2526   NC
Web Site:
   https://www.bryantdurham.com
Year Founded: 1976
Sales Range: $25-49.9 Million
Emp.: 370
Industrial Commercial Electrical Installation
N.A.I.C.S.: 238210

Subsidiaries:

Bradburn Plumbing Co. Inc.   (1)
4603 Hillsborough Rd Ste H, Durham, NC 27705-2343
Tel.: (919) 384-9283
Sales Range: $10-24.9 Million
Emp.: 30
Plumbing, Heating & Air-Conditioning Services
N.A.I.C.S.: 238220

Bryant-Durham Alarm Co. Inc.   (1)
5102 Neal Rd, Durham, NC 27705-2363   (100%)
Tel.: (919) 383-2526
Web Site: http://www.bryantdurham.com
Sales Range: $10-24.9 Million
Emp.: 30
Security Alarm Services
N.A.I.C.S.: 561621
James E. Beasley (Pres)
Stephen Brown (VP)
Stephen Fanney (VP)
Donald Martin (VP)
Marie Schrift (Sec)

Bryant-Durham Electric Co., Inc.
Eastern Division   (1)
1596 Catherine Lake Rd Hwy 111, Jacksonville, NC 28540
Tel.: (910) 324-7759
Electrical Engineering Services
N.A.I.C.S.: 541330

Bryant-Durham Services Inc.   (1)
5102 Neal Rd, Durham, NC 27705-2363
Tel.: (919) 383-9227
Web Site: www.bryantdurham.com
Sales Range: $25-49.9 Million
Emp.: 85
Electrical Work
N.A.I.C.S.: 238210
Andy Clark (Gen Mgr)

BRYCE CORPORATION
4505 Old Lamar Ave, Memphis, TN 38118
Tel.: (901) 369-4400   TN
Web Site: https://www.brycecorp.com
Year Founded: 1969
Sales Range: $400-449.9 Million
Emp.: 1,000
Plastic Packaging Film Mfr
N.A.I.C.S.: 326112
Thomas J. Bryce (Chm & CEO)
Martha Babb (Coord-Facilities)
Greg Barnett (Sr Mgr-Dev)
Maria Cowart (Mgr-Pur)
Len Swett (Mgr-HR)
David Lindberg (VP-Sls)

Subsidiaries:

Adlam Films   (1)
62 CR 520, Shannon, MS 38868
Tel.: (662) 823-1345
Web Site: http://www.adlamfilms.com
Sales Range: $10-24.9 Million
Emp.: 60
Plastics Lamination
N.A.I.C.S.: 326199
Terry Goggans (CFO)
John Bryce (CEO)

Johnson Bryce Inc   (1)
276SPkwy W, Memphis, TN 38109
Tel.: (901) 942-6500
Web Site: http://www.johnsonbryce.com
Sales Range: $10-24.9 Million
Emp.: 72
Plastic Packaging Film Mfr

N.A.I.C.S.: 322220
Brandy Ray (Mgr-Demand Plng & Logistics)
Darrell Kellner (Sr Mgr-R&D & Quality)
Rich Henry (Mgr-Quality)
Sherry Akins (Controller)
Steve Fitzgerald (Mgr-Graphics & Press)
Scott Mitchell (Mgr-Sls & Customer Svc)

BRYCON CORP
134 Rio Rancho Blvd NE, Rio Rancho, NM 87124
Tel.: (505) 892-6163
Web Site: https://www.brycon.com
Sales Range: $75-99.9 Million
Emp.: 651
Industrial Buildings & Warehouses
N.A.I.C.S.: 236220
Bryant Lemon (CEO)
Phil Casaus (CFO)
Tommy Robinson (Mgr-NM Advanced Tech Div)
Steve Garcia (Dir-Bus Dev-Mexico)
Aaron Johnson (Mgr-Ops-New Mexico General Contracting Div)

BRYNWOOD PARTNERS MANAGEMENT LLC
8 Sound Shore Dr, Greenwich, CT 06830-6471
Tel.: (203) 622-1790   DE
Web Site:
   http://www.brynwoodpartners.com
Year Founded: 1984
Sales Range: $10-24.9 Million
Emp.: 10
Privater Equity Firm
N.A.I.C.S.: 523999
Ian B. MacTaggart (Pres, CFO & COO)
Kevin C. Hartnett (Mng Dir)
Christian M. Conley (Principal)
Guy Einav (Chief Compliance Officer, VP & Controller)
David A. Eagle (Mng Dir)
John LeBoutillier (Mng Dir)
Vipul B. Soni (Mng Dir)
Wyley C. Scherr (Mng Dir)
Peter B. Wilson (Mng Dir)
David J. West (Principal)
Hendrik J. Hartong III (Chm & CEO)

Subsidiaries:

De Wafelbakkers, LLC   (1)
PO Box 13570, Little Rock, AR 72113-0570
Tel.: (501) 791-3320
Web Site: http://www.dewafelbakkers.com
Food Mfr
N.A.I.C.S.: 311999
Dumas Garrett (Pres)

Harvest Hill Beverage Company   (1)
1 High Ridge Park 2nd Fl, Stamford, CT 06905
Tel.: (203) 914-1620
Web Site: http://www.harvesthill.co
Holding Company
N.A.I.C.S.: 551112
David Champlain (Pres-Sls)
Bean Kingsbury (Exec VP)
John LeBoutillier (Pres & CEO)

Subsidiary (Domestic):

American Beverage Corporation   (2)
1 Daily Way, Verona, PA 15147-1135
Tel.: (412) 828-9020
Web Site: http://www.ambev.com
Sales Range: $125-149.9 Million
Emp.: 337
Mfr of Drink Cocktails, Mixers & Fruit Drinks
N.A.I.C.S.: 311411
Tim Barr (VP-Mktg)

Hometown Food Company   (1)
500 W Madison St, Chicago, IL 60661
Tel.: (312) 500-7710
Web Site:
   http://www.hometownfoodcompany.com
Baking Products Mfr
N.A.I.C.S.: 311999
Tim Young (CFO)
Tom Polke (Pres & CEO)

Subsidiary (Domestic):

Arrowhead Mills, Inc.   (2)
110 S Lawton Ave, Hereford, TX 79045
Tel.: (806) 364-0730
Web Site: http://www.arrowheadmills.com
Flour Grain Mill Products & Specialty Pasta Products Mfr
N.A.I.C.S.: 311230

Subsidiary (Domestic):

AMI Operating, Inc.   (3)
110 S Lawton Ave, Hereford, TX 79045-5802
Tel.: (806) 364-0730
Natural & Organic Food Products Mfr
N.A.I.C.S.: 311999

Newhall Laboratories, Inc.
5 High Ridge Park Ste 100, Stamford, CT 06905
Tel.: (203) 595-5228
Web Site: http://www.newhalllabs.com
Marketing Consulting Services
N.A.I.C.S.: 541613

Pearson Candy Company   (1)
2140 W 7th St, Saint Paul, MN 55116
Tel.: (651) 698-0356
Web Site: http://www.pearsonscandy.com
Chocolate Mfr
N.A.I.C.S.: 311351

Sunny Delight Beverages Co.   (1)
10300 Alliance Rd 500, Cincinnati, OH 45242
Tel.: (513) 483-3300
Web Site: http://www2.sunnyd.com
Fruit Drinks, Fruit Juices, Sweet Cider, Natural Juices & Nectars Mfr
N.A.I.C.S.: 311411
John R. Crossetti (Sr VP-Sls)
Timothy Voelkerding (Pres)
Brian Grote (CFO)
Eric Meyer (VP-Insights & Innovations)
Shawn Roberts (CIO & VP)
Kevin Singletary (VP-Mfg)
Jim Gerbo (CMO)
Joe Spinazola (Sr VP-Alternative Channel)
Greg Ogborn (Dir-Pur)
Scott Langley (Dir-HR)
Hendrick Hartong III (Chm)

BRYSTAR CONTRACTING, INC.
8385 Chemical Rd, Beaumont, TX 77705-6996
Tel.: (409) 842-6768
Web Site: http://www.brystar.com
Year Founded: 1990
Sales Range: $10-24.9 Million
Emp.: 70
Highway & Street Construction Services
N.A.I.C.S.: 237310
Bryan Phelps (Owner)

BRZZ GEAR LLC
412 Old Mill Cir, Lincolnshire, IL 60069
Tel.: (650) 965-8731   IL
Year Founded: 2012
Luggage, Backpacks & Other Outdoor & Travel Goods
N.A.I.C.S.: 316990
Bryan Kinsley (CEO)
Zee Zhuang (VP-Ops)
Rob Coughlin (Sr VP-Sls & Product Dev)

Subsidiaries:

Granite Gear, Inc.   (1)
2312 10th St, Two Harbors, MN 55616
Tel.: (218) 834-6157
Sales Range: $1-9.9 Million
Emp.: 21
Textile Bag Mills
N.A.I.C.S.: 314910

BS&B SAFETY SYSTEMS, LLC
7455 E 46th St, Tulsa, OK 74145-6379
Tel.: (918) 622-5950

Web Site:
   https://www.bsbsystems.com
Year Founded: 1931
Sales Range: $100-124.9 Million
Emp.: 225
Pressure Releasing Valves Mfr & Distr
N.A.I.C.S.: 332919
J. Kenneally (Owner)
Kamran Faruqi (Mgr-Nafta IT)
Lisa Gunther (Mgr-Sls Process)

Subsidiaries:

BS&B MID ATLANTIC   (1)
12311 Framar Dr, Midlothian, VA 23113
Tel.: (804) 302-4420
Sales Range: $10-24.9 Million
Emp.: 1
Electrical Engineering Services
N.A.I.C.S.: 541330

BS&B PRESSURE SAFETY MANAGEMENT, L.L.C.   (1)
1663 S 153rd St, Omaha, NE 68144
Tel.: (402) 905-2255
Electrical Engineering Services
N.A.I.C.S.: 541330

BS&B Safety Systems (India) Ltd.   (1)
9 Cathedral Road, Chennai, 600 686, India
Tel.: (91) 4424504000
Web Site: http://www.sanmargroup.com
Sales Range: $25-49.9 Million
Emp.: 60
Industrial Valve Mfr; Owned by Sanmar Holdings Ltd. & by BS&B Safety Systems, LLC
N.A.I.C.S.: 332911
David Roy (Acct Mgr)

BSC AMERICA
803 Bel Air Rd, Bel Air, MD 21014
Tel.: (410) 879-9956
Web Site:
   http://www.bscamerica.com
Sales Range: $25-49.9 Million
Emp.: 600
Administrative Management & General Management Consulting Services
N.A.I.C.S.: 541611
Kathy Antonelle (Sr Acct Mgr)
Laura Thacker (Sr Acct Mgr)
Raymond C. Nichols (Chm)
R. Charles Nichols (Pres)
S. Michelle Nichols (VP)
Chuck Wenzel (Dir-Sls-Specialty Div)

BSC GROUP, INC.
803 Summer St, Boston, MA 02127
Tel.: (617) 896-4300   MA
Web Site: http://www.bscgroup.com
Sales Range: $1-9.9 Million
Engineeering Services
N.A.I.C.S.: 541330
Ingeborg Hegemann (Exec VP)
Matthew von Wahlde (VP)
Sean P. O'Brien (Pres & CEO)
Lee Curtis (VP)
Jef Fasser (VP)
John Hession (VP)
Kurt Prochorena (VP)

BSC STEEL INC.
2808 E 85th St, Kansas City, MO 64132
Tel.: (816) 363-0433
Sales Range: $10-24.9 Million
Emp.: 150
Lightweight Steel Framing (Metal Stud) Installation
N.A.I.C.S.: 238130
Jay D. Patel (Pres)
William Groh (Superintendent)

BSE INDUSTRIAL CONTRACTORS
3716 29th St N, Birmingham, AL 35207

Tel.: (205) 254-8027
Web Site: http://www.bsecrane.com
Year Founded: 1972
Sales Range: $10-24.9 Million
Emp.: 30
Industrial Buildings & Warehouses
N.A.I.C.S.: 236220
Randy B. Whisonant *(Pres)*

Subsidiaries:

BSE   (1)
169 Danforth Ave, Hampton, VA 23665-2201
Tel.: (757) 865-9654
Web Site: http://www.bseak.com
Sales Range: $10-24.9 Million
Emp.: 4
Search & Navigation Equipment
N.A.I.C.S.: 334511

BSI CONSTRUCTORS, INC.
6767 Southwest Ave, Saint Louis, MO 63143
Tel.: (314) 781-7820
Web Site: https://www.bsistl.com
Year Founded: 1972
Sales Range: $50-74.9 Million
Emp.: 125
Industrial Building Construction Services
N.A.I.C.S.: 236210
Joe Shaughnessy *(Founder)*
Paul Shaughnessy *(Chm, Pres & CEO)*
Don McCall *(VP-Field Ops)*
Bruce Calvert *(Chief Safety Officer)*
Tim Hudwalker *(VP)*

BSI DIVERSIFIED LLC
RR2, Reynoldsville, PA 15851-9611
Tel.: (814) 653-7625
Year Founded: 2001
Sales Range: $10-24.9 Million
Emp.: 8
Holding Company
N.A.I.C.S.: 561110

Subsidiaries:

Brookville Glove Manufacturing Company, Inc.   (1)
98 Service Ctr Rd Ste B, Brookville, PA 15825
Tel.: (814) 849-7324
Web Site: http://www.brookvilleglove.com
Sales Range: $10-24.9 Million
Mfr of Work & Garden Gloves, Rainwear, Safety Items & Personal Protective Equipment
N.A.I.C.S.: 315990

Utilities & Industries   (1)
1995 Industrial Blvd, Reynoldsville, PA 15851   **(100%)**
Tel.: (814) 653-8269
Sales Range: $10-24.9 Million
Repair of Residential & Industrial Gas Meters
N.A.I.C.S.: 811210
Brian Dougherty *(CEO)*

BSI ENGINEERING, INC.
300 E-Business Way Ste 300, Cincinnati, OH 45241
Tel.: (513) 201-3100
Web Site: https://www.bsiengr.com
Year Founded: 2007
Sales Range: $1-9.9 Million
Emp.: 100
Engineering Services
N.A.I.C.S.: 541330
Phil Beirne *(Pres)*
Bill Topmiller *(Project Mgr & Mgr-Construction)*
Chad Kelly *(Project Mgr)*

BSJ BANCSHARES, INC.
307 Plank Rd, Saint Joseph, LA 71366
Tel.: (318) 766-3246   LA

Web Site: http://www.crosskeys.bank
Year Founded: 1984
Sales Range: $10-24.9 Million
Bank Holding Company
N.A.I.C.S.: 551111
Michael R. Vizard *(Chm/CEO-Cross Key Bank)*
Benjamin M. Watson *(Chm & CFO-Cross Keys Bank)*

Subsidiaries:

Cross Keys Bank   (1)
307 Plank Rd, Saint Joseph, LA 71366
Tel.: (318) 766-3246
Web Site: http://www.crosskeys.bank
Sales Range: $10-24.9 Million
Commericial Banking
N.A.I.C.S.: 522110
Michael R. Vizard *(Chm & CEO)*
Shane Bridges *(Pres & Chief Credit Officer)*
Benjamin M. Watson *(CFO & Exec VP)*
Mandy Smart *(COO & Exec VP)*
Chris Fuller *(Chief Lending Officer-Western Div, Market Pres & Exec VP)*
Walter Hillman *(Market Pres-Richland & Madison)*
Mike Thompson *(Market Pres-Tensas, Controller & Dir-HR)*

BSLC II
15475 Gleneagle Dr, Colorado Springs, CO 80921
Tel.: (719) 481-5481   NE
Web Site:
    https://www.bethesdasenior living.com
Year Founded: 2011
Sales Range: $25-49.9 Million
Senior Living Services
N.A.I.C.S.: 623311
Nathan D. Merrill *(Treas & VP)*

BSP ACQUISITION CORP.
444 Seabreeze Blvd Ste 1002, Daytona Beach, FL 32118
Tel.: (386) 238-7035   DE
Year Founded: 2014
Investment Services
N.A.I.C.S.: 523999
Sanford Miller *(Chm, Pres & CEO)*
Jeffrey D. Congdon *(CFO & VP)*
Daniel J. Miller *(Sec & VP)*

BSP MARKETING INC.
10702 Cash Rd, Stafford, TX 77477
Tel.: (281) 277-9696
Web Site:
    http://www.bspmarketing.com
Rev.: $14,000,000
Emp.: 60
General Merchandise, Non-Durable
N.A.I.C.S.: 424990
Sam Dimiceli *(Pres)*

BSP SOFTWARE LLC
1701 Golf Rd 3-604, Rolling Meadows, IL 60008
Tel.: (847) 439-0308
Web Site:
    http://www.bspsoftware.com
Sales Range: $1-9.9 Million
Emp.: 8
Software Development Services
N.A.I.C.S.: 541511
Andrew Rachmiel *(Pres)*
Andrew Weiss *(VP-Product R&D)*

BSP TRANSPORTATION INC.
2500 Liberty Dr, Londonderry, NH 03053
Tel.: (603) 432-1400
Web Site:
    https://www.bsptransinc.com
Sales Range: $10-24.9 Million
Emp.: 95
Trucking Service
N.A.I.C.S.: 484121

Jack R. Law *(Pres)*
Michael Creaney *(CFO)*

BST & CO. CPA LLP
26 Computer Dr W, Albany, NY 12205
Tel.: (518) 459-6700
Web Site: https://www.bstco.com
Accounting Services
N.A.I.C.S.: 541219
Kristen D. Berdar *(Partner)*
Judy A. Cahee *(Partner)*
James W. Cole *(Partner)*
William C. Freitag *(Partner)*
Ronald L. Guzior *(Mng Partner)*
John R. Johnson *(Sr Mng Dir)*
Joseph A. Torani *(Sr Partner)*
Katie E. Stott *(Partner)*
James A. Lozano *(Partner)*
Mary S. Mlock *(Partner)*

BST NANOCARBON LLC
16275 Technology Dr, San Diego, CA 92127
Tel.: (858) 312-1111
Web Site: http://www.bstnano.com
Emp.: 50
Advanced Composites, Nano Materials, Design, Engineering & Manufacturing, Carbon Nano Tubes & Graphene
N.A.I.C.S.: 541330
Sabrina Patterson *(VP-HR)*
Tom Preece *(Sr VP-R&D)*
Christopher Fleming *(VP-R&D-Nanocomposites)*

Subsidiaries:

Ellsworth Handcrafted Bicycles, Inc.   (1)
16275 Technology Dr, San Diego, CA 92127
Tel.: (760) 788-7500
Web Site: http://www.ellsworthbikes.com
Sales Range: $1-9.9 Million
Emp.: 25
Bicycles & Parts Mfr
N.A.I.C.S.: 336991
Tony Ellsworth *(CEO)*

BT INCORPORATED
642 S Federal Blvd, Riverton, WY 82501
Tel.: (307) 856-7480
Web Site: http://www.bonntran.com
Year Founded: 1985
Sales Range: $10-24.9 Million
Emp.: 200
Local Trucking without Storage
N.A.I.C.S.: 484110
Ron Vosika *(Owner)*

BT TRUCKING, INC.
2600 S 25th Ave #K, Broadview, IL 60155
Tel.: (708) 343-2090
Web Site: http://www.bttrucking.com
Sales Range: $10-24.9 Million
Emp.: 17
Trucking Service
N.A.I.C.S.: 488510
Michael Irwin *(Pres)*
Michael Fabrizio *(Acct Mgr-Logistics)*
Justin Dalton *(Asst Dir-Safety)*
Alex Santi *(Controller)*

Subsidiaries:

BT Brokerage, Inc.   (1)
2600 S 25th Ave Ste K, Broadview, IL 60155
Tel.: (708) 345-2581
Web Site: http://www.bttrucking.com
Brokerage & Trucking Services
N.A.I.C.S.: 523160
Michael Irwin *(Pres)*

BTA OIL PRODUCERS INC.
104 S Pecos St, Midland, TX 79701

Tel.: (432) 682-3753
Web Site: http://www.btaoil.com
Year Founded: 1970
Sales Range: $25-49.9 Million
Emp.: 68
Producer of Crude Petroleum
N.A.I.C.S.: 211120
Gregg Groves *(Controller)*
Spencer Beal *(Partner)*
Bob Davenport *(Partner)*
Laura Hanson *(Mgr-Insurance)*

BTC FINANCIAL CORPORATION
453 7th St, Des Moines, IA 50309
Tel.: (515) 245-2863
Web Site:
    http://www.bankerstrust.com
Year Founded: 2002
Bank Holding Company
N.A.I.C.S.: 551111
J. Michael Earley *(Pres & CEO)*
Kip Albertson *(CFO, Sr VP & Sr Trust Officer)*
John Ruan III *(Chm)*

Subsidiaries:

Bankers Trust Company   (1)
453 7th St, Des Moines, IA 50309
Tel.: (515) 245-2863
Web Site: http://www.bankerstrust.com
Sales Range: $75-99.9 Million
Emp.: 69
Commericial Banking
N.A.I.C.S.: 522110
Bradley E. Smith *(Founder-Credit Derivatives Bus)*
Tina Smith Fritz *(COO & Sr VP)*

BTI GROUP
1901 S Bascom Ave, Campbell, CA 95008
Tel.: (408) 246-1102   CA
Web Site: http://www.btigroupma.com
Year Founded: 1981
Sales Range: $50-74.9 Million
Emp.: 150
Merger & Acqusition Consulting Services
N.A.I.C.S.: 541618
Ian MacLachlan *(Founder & Pres)*
Greg Carpenter *(Mng Dir)*
Katrina Winkel Loftin *(Mng Dir)*
Tony Moran *(Mng Dir)*
John Mittelstet *(Mng Dir)*
G. Robert Allen *(Mng Dir)*
Donald Baum *(Mng Dir)*

BTM CO.
100 Bach Ave, New York Mills, MN 56567
Tel.: (218) 385-3777   MN
Web Site: http://www.msaanym.com
Sales Range: $10-24.9 Million
Emp.: 110
Used Car Dealer & Auction Services
N.A.I.C.S.: 441120
Robert Thompson *(CEO)*
Wendy Windels *(Dir-Transportation)*
Dee Sullivan *(Mgr-Fleet)*
Jesse Wilkowski *(Mgr-Lot)*

BTR FARMERS CO-OP
6001 60th Ave NE, Leeds, ND 58346
Tel.: (701) 466-2281
Web Site:
    http://www.btrfarmerscoop.com
Sales Range: $10-24.9 Million
Emp.: 15
Grain Elevators
N.A.I.C.S.: 424910
Randy Heck *(Gen Mgr)*

BTR INCORPORATED
31 Industrial Pkwy, Milton, PA 17847
Tel.: (570) 742-1768
Sales Range: $10-24.9 Million
Emp.: 80
Truck Rental With Drivers
N.A.I.C.S.: 484110

BTR Incorporated—(Continued)

Ray B. Bowersox (Pres)

BTV CROWN EQUITIES, INC.
2870 Gateway Oaks Dr Ste 110, Sacramento, CA 95833
Tel.: (916) 569-1900
Web Site: http://www.btvcrown.com
Sales Range: $10-24.9 Million
Emp.: 300
Commercial Real Estate Services
N.A.I.C.S.: 531390
John Brennan (Pres)

BUBBA OUSTALET INC.
246 N Broadway St, Jennings, LA 70546
Tel.: (337) 824-3673
Web Site:
http://www.bubbaoustaletford.com
Sales Range: $25-49.9 Million
Emp.: 40
Sales & Service Of New & Used Automobiles
N.A.I.C.S.: 441110
Rick Oustalet (Gen Mgr)

BUBBLEUP, LTD
719 Sawdust Rd Ste 104, The Woodlands, TX 77380
Tel.: (832) 585-0709
Web Site: http://www.bubbleup.net
Year Founded: 2004
Sales Range: $1-9.9 Million
Emp.: 30
Search Engine Optimization Services
N.A.I.C.S.: 541511
Blake Mark (Dir-Project Mgmt)
Brad Jameson (Mgr-Acct Svcs)
Coleman Sisson (Chm & CEO)
Jennifer Balzer (Sr Dir-Creative)
Mike Newman (CMO)
Steve Newman (Mgr-Client)
Tracy Goldenberg (Dir-Acct Svcs)
Chris Hester (VP-Mktg)
Lee Totten (Chief Creative Officer)
Amanda Fassett (Office Dir)

BUBLITZ MATERIAL HANDLING, INC.
703 E 14th Ave, Kansas City, MO 64116
Tel.: (816) 221-7335
Web Site:
http://www.bublitzmaterials.com
Rev.: $12,785,411
Emp.: 70
Heavy Construction Equipment Rental & Distr
N.A.I.C.S.: 532412
Jeff Bublitz (Chm)

BUCCANEER LANDSCAPE MANAGEMENT CORPORATION
1800 12th St SE, Largo, FL 33770
Tel.: (727) 209-0383
Web Site: https://www.buccanealandscape.com
Sales Range: $1-9.9 Million
Emp.: 65
Landscaping Services
N.A.I.C.S.: 561730
Christopher T. Witherington (Pres)

BUCCANEERS LIMITED PARTNERSHIP
1 Buccaneer Pl, Tampa, FL 33607
Tel.: (813) 870-2700   FL
Web Site:
http://www.buccaneers.com
Year Founded: 1973
Sales Range: $75-99.9 Million
Emp.: 175
Professional Football Franchise

N.A.I.C.S.: 711211
Malcolm Glazer (Owner & Pres)
Joel M. Glazer (Co-Chm)
Chris Bryan (Asst Dir-Video)
Dave Levy (Dir-Video)
James Sorenson (Mgr-Equipment)
Edward S. Glazer (Co-Chm)
Jon Robinson (Dir-Player Personnel)
Carey Cox (Dir-Mktg & Brand Strategy)
Joe Fada (CFO)
Jim Frevola (Chief Partnership Officer)
Jeff Ryan (Dir-Broadcast Ops)
Nelson Luis (Dir-Comm)
Amy Saxon (Dir-Grp Sls)
Kristin Houston (Dir-HR)
Ed Johnston (Dir-IT)
Deno Anagnost (Dir-Sls)
David Cohen (Gen Counsel)
Jason Licht (Gen Mgr)
Bryan G. Glazer (Co-Chm)

BUCHALTER, NEMER, FIELDS & YOUNGER LLP
1000 Wilshire Blvd Ste 1500, Los Angeles, CA 90017-1730
Tel.: (213) 891-0700
Web Site: https://www.buchalter.com
Year Founded: 1933
Law firm
N.A.I.C.S.: 541110
Adam Bass (Pres & CEO)

BUCHANAN & EDWARDS INC.
1400 Key Blvd Ste 1000, Arlington, VA 22209
Tel.: (703) 535-5511
Web Site: http://www.buchanan-edwards.com
Year Founded: 1997
Sales Range: $10-24.9 Million
Emp.: 81
Management Consulting & information Technology Services
N.A.I.C.S.: 541618
Jay Smith (VP-Ops)
Tom Peter (Dir-Ops)
Michael Innella (COO)
Christopher Kelly (Project Mgr)
Darren Earley (Project Mgr)
Tony Parchment (Co-Founder)
Carter Wood (CFO)
Brian Karlisch (Co-Founder & Chm)
Sean Gleason (VP-Bus Dev)
Mary Tabb Howard (Dir-Strategic Capture)
Chris Rochester (Dir-Bus Dev)
Timothy Healy (Dir-Govt Svcs Contractor-Security Bus-Natl)
Katie Mooshian (Dir-Foreign Affairs)
Eric Olson (Dir)
Mohamed Elansary (VP-Ops-Global)
Dennis J. Kelly Jr. (Pres)

BUCHANAN HARDWOODS INC.
PO Box 424, Aliceville, AL 35442
Tel.: (205) 373-8717
Web Site:
http://www.buchananhardwood.com
Year Founded: 1960
Sales Range: $450-499.9 Million
Emp.: 500
Provider of Sawmill & Planing Mill Services
N.A.I.C.S.: 238330
Butch Ousley (Mgr-Sales)
Debbie Sawyer (Mgr-Credit)

BUCHANAN INGERSOLL & ROONEY PC
1 Oxford Ctr 301 Grant St 20th Fl, Pittsburgh, PA 15219-1410
Tel.: (412) 562-8800

Web Site: http://www.bipc.com
Year Founded: 1850
Emp.: 400
Law firm
N.A.I.C.S.: 541110
Lynn J. Alstadt (Atty)
Margaret B. Angel (Atty)
Nolan W. Kurtz (COO)
Philip Casale (CIO)
Randy P. Vulakovich (Chief Admin Officer)
Megan McAteer (Sr Atty-Tampa)
Melissa Croteau (Chief Bus Dev Officer-Washington)
Joseph A. Dougherty (CEO & Mng Dir)
Lloyd Freeman (Chief Diversity & Inclusion Officer)

Subsidiaries:

Ratner & Prestia PC   **(1)**
1235 Westlakes Dr Ste 301, Valley Forge, PA 19482
Tel.: (610) 407-0700
Web Site: http://www.ratnerprestia.com
Emp.: 26
Law firm
N.A.I.C.S.: 541110
Lawrence E. Ashery (Atty)
Joshua L. Cohen (Atty)
Rex A. Donnelly (Atty)
Jack J. Jankovitz (Atty)
Jacques J. Etkowicz (Atty)

BUCHANAN OIL CORPORATION
PO Box 1220, Grundy, VA 24614
Tel.: (276) 498-4522
Rev.: $24,000,000
Emp.: 22
Distr of Petroleum Products
N.A.I.C.S.: 424710
Bill Ray Lester (Pres)

BUCHANAN SALES CO INC
4088 Alpha Dr, Allison Park, PA 15101
Tel.: (412) 487-8090
Year Founded: 1956
Sales Range: $1-9.9 Million
Emp.: 9
Stampings, Metal
N.A.I.C.S.: 423510
Frank Hueske (Owner)

BUCHANAN STREET PARTNERS, INC.
620 Nwport Ctr Dr Ste 850, Newport Beach, CA 92660
Tel.: (949) 721-1414   CA
Web Site:
http://www.buchananstreet.com
Year Founded: 1998
Sales Range: $10-24.9 Million
Emp.: 35
Miscellaneous Financial Investment Activities
N.A.I.C.S.: 523999
Robert S. Brunswick (Co-Founder & CEO)
Timothy Ballard (Co-Founder & Pres)
Dominicci J. Petrucci (COO & CFO)

Subsidiaries:

Almeda Mall, Inc.   **(1)**
555 Almeda Mall, Houston, TX 77075-3509
Tel.: (713) 944-1010
Web Site: http://www.almedamall.com
Sales Range: $1-9.9 Million
Emp.: 10
Nonresidential Building Operators
N.A.I.C.S.: 531120

BUCHBINDER TUNICK & COMPANY LLP
1 Pennsylvania Plz Ste 5335, New York, NY 10119
Tel.: (212) 695-5003

Web Site:
https://www.buchbinder.com
Year Founded: 1978
Emp.: 100
Accounting Firm
N.A.I.C.S.: 541211
Harry Wendroff (Mng Partner)
Andrea Gianni (Partner-Bethesda)

BUCHHEIT INC.
33 Perry County Rd 540, Perryville, MO 63775-8757
Tel.: (573) 547-1010   MO
Web Site:
http://www.buchheitonline.com
Year Founded: 1934
Home Improvement Store
N.A.I.C.S.: 423310
Tim Buchheit (Pres)
Reid Willen (CFO & Sec)
Doug Buchheit (VP-Mdse)
Dave Danker (Gen Mgr)

BUCK & KNOBBY EQUIPMENT CO.
6220 Sterns Rd, Ottawa Lake, MI 49267
Tel.: (734) 856-2811
Web Site:
http://www.buckandknobby.com
Rev.: $16,379,800
Emp.: 40
Heavy Construction Equipment Rental
N.A.I.C.S.: 532412
Ray Cordrey (Pres)

BUCK KNIVES, INC.
660 S Lochsa St, Post Falls, ID 83854-5200
Tel.: (208) 262-0500   CA
Web Site: http://www.buckknives.com
Year Founded: 1902
Sales Range: $100-124.9 Million
Emp.: 200
Outdoor Cutlery Mfr
N.A.I.C.S.: 332215
C. J. Buck (Chm & CEO)
Trent Malone (CFO)
Joseph Piedmont (COO)
Lane A. Tobiassen (Pres)

BUCK LA
515 W 7th St 4th Fl, Los Angeles, CA 90014
Tel.: (213) 623-0111   CA
Web Site: http://www.buckla.com
Year Founded: 2003
Emp.: 10
Advertising Agencies
N.A.I.C.S.: 541890
Ryan Honey (Exec Dir-Creative)
Jeff Ellermeyer (Mng Dir)
Joe Mullen (Dir-Creative)
Jenny Ko (Assoc Dir-Art)
Robert Bisi (Creative Dir)

Subsidiaries:

Buck NY   **(1)**
31 Howard St, New York, NY 10013
Tel.: (212) 668-0111
Web Site: http://www.buck.tv
Advertising Agencies
N.A.I.C.S.: 541890
Orion Tait (Principal & Dir-Creative)

BUCK'S INC.
7315 Mercy Rd, Omaha, NE 68124
Tel.: (402) 558-9860   NE
Year Founded: 1982
Sales Range: $50-74.9 Million
Emp.: 500
Gasoline Station Services
N.A.I.C.S.: 457120
Steve Buchanan (Pres)
Leanne Noble (Mgr-PR)
Keil Brumit (CFO)

BUCKELEW'S FOOD SERVICE EQUIPMENT CO.

1715 Spring St, Shreveport, LA 71101
Tel.: (318) 424-6673
Sales Range: $10-24.9 Million
Emp.: 27
Restaurant Equipment & Supplies
N.A.I.C.S.: 423440
C. Henry Hunsicker *(Pres)*
Milton Kelley *(Controller)*
Mark Hines *(Engr)*

BUCKEYE BOXES INC.

601 N Hague Ave, Columbus, OH 43204
Tel.: (614) 274-8484
Web Site:
https://www.buckeyeboxes.com
Sales Range: $10-24.9 Million
Emp.: 80
Corrugated Boxes
N.A.I.C.S.: 322211
Craig R. Hoyt *(Pres & CEO)*
Fred Bridger *(Area Mgr-Corrugated Sls & Design)*
Mike Capron *(Acct Mgr)*
Duane Wood *(Engr-Maintenance)*

BUCKEYE CHECK CASHING INC.

6785 Bobcat Way Ste 200, Dublin, OH 43016-8238
Tel.: (614) 798-5900
Web Site: http://www.ccfi.com
Sales Range: $450-499.9 Million
Emp.: 5,000
Provider of Check Cashing Services
N.A.I.C.S.: 522390
Ted Saunders *(CEO)*

BUCKEYE CORRUGATED INC.

275 Springside Dr Ste 200, Akron, OH 44333-4551
Tel.: (330) 576-0590   DE
Web Site:
http://www.buckeyecorrugated.com
Year Founded: 1958
Sales Range: $350-399.9 Million
Emp.: 450
Packaging Material, Corrugated Boxes, Inner Packaging, Foam Packaging, In-Store Displays & High Quality Graphics Mfr
N.A.I.C.S.: 322211
Mark A. Husted *(CFO & Exec VP)*
Doug Bosnik *(Pres & CEO)*

Subsidiaries:

All Size Corrugated   (1)
3950 Continental Dr, Columbia, PA 17512   (100%)
Tel.: (717) 684-6921
Web Site: http://www.allsizecorrugated.com
Sales Range: $10-24.9 Million
Emp.: 40
Mfr of Corrugated Boxes
N.A.I.C.S.: 322211

Buckeye Container   (1)
3350 Long Rd, Wooster, OH 44691-0016   (100%)
Tel.: (330) 264-6336
Web Site: http://www.bcipkg.com
Sales Range: $10-24.9 Million
Emp.: 100
Corrugated Box Mfr
N.A.I.C.S.: 322211
Terri Wall *(Controller)*

CRA-WAL   (1)
4001 S High School Rd, Indianapolis, IN 46241-6448
Tel.: (317) 856-3701
Web Site: http://www.cra-wal.com
Sales Range: $10-24.9 Million
Emp.: 100
Mfr of Corrugated Containers
N.A.I.C.S.: 322211

Concord Specialty Corrugated   (1)
101 Industrial Dr, Batesville, AR 72501   (100%)
Tel.: (870) 793-1100
Sales Range: $1-9.9 Million
Emp.: 35
Corrugated Containers Mfr
N.A.I.C.S.: 322211

Dakota Corrugated Box Company   (1)
4501 N 2nd Ave, Sioux Falls, SD 57104
Tel.: (605) 332-3501
Packaging Paper Box Mfr
N.A.I.C.S.: 322212

Empire State Container Inc   (1)
151 Midler Park Dr, Syracuse, NY 13206
Tel.: (315) 437-1181
Web Site: http://www.bcppkg.com
Emp.: 50
Packaging Paper Box Mfr
N.A.I.C.S.: 322212
Boba Barish *(Production Mgr)*

Hawkeye Corrugated Box Co   (1)
725 Ida St, Cedar Falls, IA 50613
Tel.: (319) 268-0407
Web Site: http://www.hawkeyebox.com
Emp.: 34
Packaging Paper Box Mfr
N.A.I.C.S.: 322212
Matt Highland *(Pres-Div)*

Koch Container   (1)
797 Old Dutch Rd, Victor, NY 14564-8972   (100%)
Tel.: (585) 924-1600
Rev.: $9,400,000
Emp.: 50
Corrugated Boxes
N.A.I.C.S.: 322211
Robert Harris *(COO)*

Tennessee Packaging   (1)
2300 Hwy 11 N Longmeadow Rd, Sweetwater, TN 37874   (100%)
Tel.: (423) 337-3527
Web Site: http://www.tnpkg.com
Sales Range: $25-49.9 Million
Emp.: 70
Corrugated Boxes
N.A.I.C.S.: 322211
Scott Winfield *(Gen Mgr)*

BUCKEYE DRUGS

315 N Cumberland St, Lebanon, TN 37087-2720
Tel.: (615) 444-2999
Web Site:
https://www.buckeyedrugs.com
Year Founded: 1981
Sales Range: $10-24.9 Million
Emp.: 5
Pharmacy & Drug Product Distr
N.A.I.C.S.: 456110
John A. Tuner *(Owner)*

BUCKEYE FIRE EQUIPMENT COMPANY

110 Kings Rd, Kings Mountain, NC 28086
Tel.: (704) 739-7415
Web Site: https://www.buckeyef.com
Rev.: $26,000,000
Emp.: 356
Mfr of Portable Fire Extinguishers
N.A.I.C.S.: 332999
Mike Patti *(Mgr-Tooling)*

BUCKEYE FORD, INC.

110 US Route 42, London, OH 43140
Tel.: (740) 852-3673
Web Site:
https://www.buckeyefordlondon.com
Year Founded: 1986
Sales Range: $25-49.9 Million
Emp.: 45
Car Whslr
N.A.I.C.S.: 441110
James Hunt *(Pres)*
Jason Hunt *(Principal)*

BUCKEYE INTERNATIONAL INC.

2700 Wagner Pl, Maryland Heights, MO 63043-3422
Tel.: (314) 291-1900   MO
Web Site:
http://www.buckeyenational.com
Year Founded: 1844
Sales Range: $25-49.9 Million
Emp.: 250
Specialty Cleaning Chemicals
N.A.I.C.S.: 325612
John Ehrhard *(CFO)*
Justin Freistein *(Reg Mgr-Reflections Sls)*
Sue Spaihoward *(Office Mgr)*
Tina Meier *(Office Mgr-Ops)*

BUCKEYE NISSAN INC.

3820 Pkwy Ln, Hilliard, OH 43026-1217
Tel.: (614) 771-2345   OH
Web Site:
https://www.buckeyenissan.com
Year Founded: 1980
Sales Range: $350-399.9 Million
Emp.: 90
Car Dealership Owner & Operator
N.A.I.C.S.: 441110
Gerald Spires *(Pres)*
Sean Kenney *(COO & VP)*
Patrick Shepherd *(Mgr-New Car Sls)*

BUCKEYE POWER SALES COMPANY INC

6850 Commerce Ct Dr, Blacklick, OH 43004
Tel.: (614) 861-6000
Web Site:
https://www.buckeyepowersale.com
Sales Range: $25-49.9 Million
Emp.: 75
Sales of Lawn Mowers
N.A.I.C.S.: 423610
Donald E. Bohls *(Pres)*
Tom Bohls *(Pres)*
Greg Bohls *(VP)*
Vince Campise *(Mgr-Mktg)*

BUCKEYE READY-MIX LLC

7657 Taylor Rd SW, Reynoldsburg, OH 43068
Tel.: (614) 575-2132
Web Site:
https://www.buckeyereadymix.com
Year Founded: 1999
Sales Range: $10-24.9 Million
Emp.: 110
Ready Mixed Concrete
N.A.I.C.S.: 327320
Gary Conley *(Controller)*
Larry Randles *(VP-Ops)*
Cress Jenkins *(Mgr-Transportation)*
Dan Hunt *(Mgr-Quality Control)*
Jeff Young *(VP)*
Randy Painter *(Mgr-Sls)*

BUCKEYE RUBBER & PACKING CO.

23940 Mercantile Rd, Cleveland, OH 44122
Tel.: (216) 464-8900
Web Site:
https://www.buckeyerubber.com
Year Founded: 1937
Rev.: $15,795,319
Emp.: 55
Provider of Industrial Seals & Packaging Services
N.A.I.C.S.: 423840
Bob Hurst *(Mgr-Quality)*
Bill Bauer *(Engr-Sls)*

BUCKEYE STATE BANCSHARES, INC.

9494 Wedgewood Blvd, Powell, OH 43065
Tel.: (614) 796-4747   OH
Web Site: https://www.joinbsb.com
Year Founded: 2018
Bank Holding Company
N.A.I.C.S.: 551111
Shawn Keller *(Pres & CEO)*
John Kirksey *(CFO & Exec VP)*

Subsidiaries:

Buckeye State Bank   (1)
9494 Wedgewood Blvd, Powell, OH 43065
Tel.: (614) 796-4747
Web Site: http://www.joinbsb.com
Sales Range: $1-9.9 Million
Emp.: 23
Commericial Banking
N.A.I.C.S.: 522110
Shawn Keller *(Pres & CEO)*
John Kirksey *(CFO & Exec VP)*
Gene Spurbeck *(Chief Credit Officer & Sr VP)*

BUCKEYE STATE MUTUAL INSURANCE CO.

1 Heritage Pl, Piqua, OH 45356
Tel.: (937) 778-5000
Web Site: https://www.buckeye-ins.com
Year Founded: 1879
Sales Range: $50-74.9 Million
Emp.: 40
Fire, Marine & Casualty Insurance Carriers
N.A.I.C.S.: 524126
John Brooks *(CEO)*

BUCKINGHAM & COMPANY

6856 Loop Rd, Dayton, OH 45459
Tel.: (937) 435-2742   OH
Year Founded: 1987
Sales Range: $10-24.9 Million
Holding Company
N.A.I.C.S.: 551112
Jay A. Buckingham *(Founder, Pres & CEO)*
Monica Romero *(Mgr-Bus Office)*

Subsidiaries:

Buckingham Financial Group, Inc.   (1)
6856 Loop Rd, Dayton, OH 45459
Tel.: (937) 435-2742
Web Site:
http://www.buckinghamfinancial.com
Investment Advisory & Management, Financial Planning, Tax & Insurance Brokerage Services
N.A.I.C.S.: 523991

Subsidiary (Domestic):

Buckingham Capital Management, Inc.   (2)
6856 Loop Rd, Dayton, OH 45459
Tel.: (937) 435-2742
Web Site: http://www.bcminvest.com
Sales Range: $50-74.9 Million
Emp.: 20
Investment Advisory & Management Services
N.A.I.C.S.: 523940
Linda S. Parenti *(Pres)*

BUCKINGHAM CAPITAL, LLC

950 Third Ave 19th Fl, New York, NY 10022
Tel.: (212) 752-0500   NY
Web Site:
http://www.buckinghamcapital.com
Privater Equity Firm
N.A.I.C.S.: 523999
Shail Sheth *(Mng Partner)*
Albert Naggar *(Mng Partner)*

Subsidiaries:

Aerovox Corp.   (1)
167 John Vertente Blvd, New Bedford, MA 02745

Buckingham Capital, LLC—(Continued)

Tel.: (508) 910-3500
Web Site: http://www.aerovox.com
Emp.: 100
AC Capacitors, Custom & Pulse Power Capacitors, AC Power Line Filters, DC Film Capacitors & Aluminum Electrolytic Capacitors
N.A.I.C.S.: 335999
Marco Castillo (Mgr-Sls-Intl)

CPAC, Inc. (1)
2364 Leicester Rd, Leicester, NY 14481
Tel.: (585) 382-3223
Web Site: http://www.cpac.com
Sales Range: $25-49.9 Million
Emp.: 10
Medical Equipment Distr
N.A.I.C.S.: 423450
William Smith (CEO)

Subsidiary (Non-US):

CPAC Africa (Pty.) Ltd. (2)
Zandpark Richardsbay Avenue, Pretoria, 0084, South Africa
Tel.: (27) 123720671
Web Site: http://www.kioskksa.co.za
Sales Range: $1-9.9 Million
Emp.: 25
Sales of Specialty Chemicals & Chemical & Equipment Alternatives
N.A.I.C.S.: 325998
Thomas N. Hendrickson (Mng Dir)

CPAC Asia Imaging Products Limited (2)
112 Moo 9 Bangna Trad Hwy Km 36, Bangkok, 24180, Thailand
Tel.: (66) 385709669
Web Site: http://www.opacasia.com
Sales Range: $1-9.9 Million
Mfr of Specialty Chemicals & Chemical & Equipment Alternatives
N.A.I.C.S.: 325998
Stanley H. Gulbin (Co-Pres)
James Pembroke (Chief Acctg Officer)
Thomas J. Weldgen (CFO & VP-Fin)

Subsidiary (Domestic):

CPAC Equipment, Inc. (2)
2364 Leicester Rd, Leicester, NY 14481
Tel.: (585) 382-3223
Web Site: http://www.cpacequipment.com
Sales Range: $25-49.9 Million
Emp.: 10
Imaging Chemicals Mfr & Distr
N.A.I.C.S.: 333310
William Smith (CEO)

Subsidiary (Non-US):

CPAC Europe N.V. (2)
Industriepark Klein Gent, Saffierstraat 3, 2200, Herentals, Belgium
Tel.: (32) 14232451
Web Site: http://www.cpac.be
Mfr of Photographic Processing Chemicals & Distributor of Silver Recovery Equipment
N.A.I.C.S.: 333310

CPAC Italia S.r.l (2)
Via Carlo Porta 49 56, 20064, Gorgonzola, MI, Italy
Tel.: (39) 0295300952
Sales Range: $10-24.9 Million
Produces Processing Chemicals for Photographic, Medical & Graphic Arts Industries
N.A.I.C.S.: 333310

BUCKINGHAM FOUNDATION
941 N Meridian St, Indianapolis, IN 46204
Tel.: (317) 554-6830   IN
Web Site:
     https://www.buckinghamfoundationinc.org
Year Founded: 2006
Sales Range: $1-9.9 Million
Emp.: 1
Philanthropic Services
N.A.I.C.S.: 813211
Theresa Farrington Rhodes (Exec Dir)

BUCKINGHAM FOUNTAIN LP

200 N Columbus Dr, Chicago, IL 60601
Tel.: (312) 565-8000
Web Site: http://www.fairmont.com
Sales Range: $50-74.9 Million
Emp.: 730
Holding Company: Hotels & Resorts
N.A.I.C.S.: 551112
Jennifer Fox (Pres-Fairmont Hotels & Resorts)

BUCKLE AGENCY LLC
1040 W Marietta St NW Ste S2, Atlanta, GA 30318
Tel.: (404) 476-8224
Web Site: http://www.buckleup.com
Insurance Services
N.A.I.C.S.: 524298
Dustin Walsey (Co-Founder & CEO)
Marty Young (Co-CEO & Co-Founder)

Subsidiaries:

Gateway Insurance Company (1)
1401 S Brentwood Blvd Ste 925, Saint Louis, MO 63144
Tel.: (314) 373-3333
Web Site: http://www.gicauto.com
Automobile & Specialty Contractor Insurance Products & Services
N.A.I.C.S.: 524126

BUCKLEY & COMPANY INC.
3401 Moore St, Philadelphia, PA 19145-1005
Tel.: (215) 334-7500   PA
Year Founded: 1926
Sales Range: $10-24.9 Million
Emp.: 50
Highway & Street Construction Services
N.A.I.C.S.: 237310
Robert R. Buckley (Pres & CEO)

BUCKLEY & KALDENBACH
3810 N Upland St, Arlington, VA 22207
Tel.: (703) 533-9805
Web Site:
     http://www.buckleykaldenbach.com
Sales Range: Less than $1 Million
Emp.: 2
Media Relations, Public Affairs, Litigation Communications, Coalition Management & Public Education Campaigns
N.A.I.C.S.: 541820
Robin Buckley (Co-Founder)
Isabel Kaldenbach (Co-Founder & Counsel)

BUCKLEY ASSOCIATES INC.
385 King St, Hanover, MA 02339
Tel.: (781) 878-5000
Web Site:
     https://www.buckleyonline.com
Year Founded: 1970
Sales Range: $10-24.9 Million
Emp.: 130
Warm Air Heating Equipment & Supplies
N.A.I.C.S.: 423730
Tom McNamara (Dir-HR)
James Westfall (Engr-Sls)
Mark Persechini (Engr-Sls)
Vincent Maccarrone (VP)

BUCKLEY INDUSTRIES INC.
1850 E 53rd St N, Wichita, KS 67219
Tel.: (316) 744-7587
Web Site:
     https://www.buckleyind.com
Sales Range: $25-49.9 Million
Emp.: 100
Distribution of Thermal Insulation
N.A.I.C.S.: 424690
Linda West (Mgr-Matl)

BUCKLEY OIL COMPANY INC.
1809 Rock Island St, Dallas, TX 75207
Tel.: (214) 421-4147
Web Site: https://www.buckleyoil.com
Sales Range: $10-24.9 Million
Emp.: 28
Petroleum Bulk Stations
N.A.I.C.S.: 424710
R. E. Dodson (Owner)

BUCKLEY POWDER CO.
42 Inverness Dr E, Englewood, CO 80112-5403
Tel.: (303) 790-7007   CO
Year Founded: 1921
Blasting Supplies Services & Product Mfr
N.A.I.C.S.: 325920
Scott Harman (Bus Mgr)
Dave Dannenberger (Mgr-Sls)
Jay Pumphrey (Partner & VP)

BUCKLEYSANDLER LLP.
1250 24th St NW Ste 700, Washington, DC 20037
Tel.: (202) 349-8000
Web Site:
     http://www.buckleysandler.com
Year Founded: 2009
Sales Range: $75-99.9 Million
Emp.: 201
Legal Advisory Services
N.A.I.C.S.: 541110
Jeremiah S. Buckley (Partner-Washington)
Jeffrey P. Naimon (Partner-Washington)
Margo H. K. Tank (Partner-Washington)
Joseph M. Kolar (Partner-Washington)
John P. Kromer (Partner-Washington)
Walter E. Zalenski (Partner-Washington)
David Baris (Partner-Washington)
Manley Williams (Partner-Washington)
Christopher M. Witeck (Partner-Washington)
Fredrick S. Levin (Partner-Los Angeles)
Clinton R. Rockwell (Partner-Los Angeles)
Elizabeth E. McGinn (Partner-Washington)
Matthew P. Previn (Partner-New York)
Andrew W. Schilling (Partner-New York)
John C. Redding (Partner-Los Angeles, CA)
Douglas F. Gansler (Partner-Washington)
Amanda Raines Lawrence (Partner-Washington)
Andrew R. Louis (Partner-Washington)
Aaron C. Mahler (Partner-Washington)
Adam Miller (Partner-Washington)
Benjamin B. Klubes (Partner-Washington)
Benjamin K. Olson (Partner-Washington)
Caitlin M. Kasmar (Partner-Washington)
David S. Krakoff (Partner-Washington)
Melissa Klimkiewicz (Partner-Washington)
Ross E. Morrison (Partner-New York)
Preston Burton (Partner)
Andrew L. Sandler (Chm & Partner)
Heather Russell (Partner-Fin Institutions Regulation, Supervision & Tech Practice)

Jonice Gray Tucker (Founder)
Andrea K. Mitchell (Partner-Washington)

BUCKMAN'S INC.
105 Airport Rd, Pottstown, PA 19464
Tel.: (610) 495-7495
Web Site:
     https://www.buckmansinc.com
Year Founded: 1975
Sales Range: $10-24.9 Million
Emp.: 85
Whslr of Pool Supplies & Sporting Equipment
N.A.I.C.S.: 424690
Jeffrey Buckman (Pres)
Nancy Buckman (Owner)
Josh Fenton (Controller)

BUCKO'S INC.
1923 Myrtle St, Sarasota, FL 34234
Tel.: (941) 355-7644
Web Site: http://www.buckos.net
Year Founded: 1959
Sales Range: $1-9.9 Million
Emp.: 7
Office Furniture & Equipment Dealer
N.A.I.C.S.: 423210
William P. Barrineau (Pres)

BUCKS COUNTY COFFEE COMPANY
730 E Elm St Ste 300, Conshohocken, PA 19428-2375
Tel.: (215) 741-1855
Web Site:
     http://www.buckscountycoffee.com
Year Founded: 1982
Sales Range: $25-49.9 Million
Emp.: 300
Retailer & Mail Order of Coffee & Coffee Products
N.A.I.C.S.: 445298
Barbara Patty (VP-Opers)

BUCKS COUNTY FREE LIBRARY
150 S Pine St, Doylestown, PA 18901-4932
Tel.: (215) 348-9081   PA
Web Site: http://www.buckslib.org
Year Founded: 1956
Rev.: $9,717,197
Assets: $14,667,809
Liabilities: $396,917
Net Worth: $14,270,892
Earnings: $647,456
Fiscal Year-end: 12/31/14
Library Operator
N.A.I.C.S.: 519210
Martina Kominiarek (Exec Dir)
Lawrence D. Jones (Pres)
Roberta Foerst (VP)
Constance Moore (Sec)
Richard D. Rogers (Treas)

BUCKS COUNTY WATER & SEWER AUTHORITY
1275 Almshouse Rd, Warrington, PA 18976
Tel.: (215) 343-2538
Web Site: https://www.bcwsa.net
Year Founded: 1962
Sales Range: $25-49.9 Million
Emp.: 100
Water Supply, Sewer
N.A.I.C.S.: 221310
Benjamin W. Jones (CEO)
Norman F. Stainthorp (Chm)
Arthur Haas (CFO)
Dennis Cowley (Pres)
Dick Weaver (Treas)

BUD BROWN VOLKSWAGEN
925 N Rawhide Dr, Olathe, KS 66061
Tel.: (913) 254-0100   KS

Web Site:
http://www.budbrownvw.com
Year Founded: 1949
Sales Range: $25-49.9 Million
Emp.: 80
New & Used Car Dealership
N.A.I.C.S.: 441110
Philip J. Brown *(Pres & CEO)*
Bud Brown *(Chm)*
David Kugler *(Treas & Sec)*

BUD CLARY CHEVROLET CADILLAC INC.
1030 Commerce Ave, Longview, WA 98632
Tel.: (360) 200-4105
Web Site:
http://www.budclarychevrolet.com
Rev.: $34,700,000
Emp.: 120
New Car Dealers
N.A.I.C.S.: 441110
Ira E. Clary *(Treas)*
Clara A. Clary *(VP)*
James E. Clary *(Pres)*
Jerry Reitsch *(Sec)*

BUD CLARY TOYOTA OF YAKIMA
2230 Longfibre Ave, Yakima, WA 98903
Tel.: (509) 575-4868
Web Site:
http://www.toyotaofyakima.com
Year Founded: 2002
Sales Range: $25-49.9 Million
Emp.: 59
Car Whslr
N.A.I.C.S.: 441110
Jeff Matson *(Principal)*

BUD DAVIS CADILLAC, INC.
5433 Poplar Ave, Memphis, TN 38119-3634
Tel.: (901) 881-0177   TN
Web Site:
http://www.buddaviscadillac.com
Year Founded: 1975
Sales Range: $125-149.9 Million
Emp.: 125
Retailer of New & Used Automobiles
N.A.I.C.S.: 441110
John Creel *(Mgr-Used Car)*
Jon Neal *(Dir-Fin)*

BUD INDUSTRIES, INC.
4605 E 355th St, Willoughby, OH 44094-4629
Tel.: (440) 946-3200   OH
Web Site: https://www.budind.com
Year Founded: 1928
Sales Range: $75-99.9 Million
Emp.: 120
Electronic Enclosures & Accessories Mfr
N.A.I.C.S.: 332119
Blair K. Haas *(Pres)*

Subsidiaries:

Bud Industries   (1)
2226 W Northern Ave Ste C130, Phoenix, AZ 85021-4951
Tel.: (602) 870-8377
Web Site: http://www.budind.com
Sales Range: $10-24.9 Million
Emp.: 10
Electronic Enclosures & Accessories
N.A.I.C.S.: 484110

BUD KOUTS CHEVROLET COMPANY
2801 East Michigan Ave, Lansing, MI 48912
Tel.: (517) 374-0900
Web Site:
http://www.budkoutschevy.com
Sales Range: $25-49.9 Million

Emp.: 100
Automobiles, New & Used
N.A.I.C.S.: 441110
Richard Iding *(Pres)*
Pat Iding *(Mgr-New Car)*
Ralph Garza *(Mgr-Parts)*
Steve Jackson *(Mgr-Sls)*

BUD SHELL FORD INC.
613 N State Route 25, Dexter, MO 63841
Tel.: (573) 624-7476
Web Site:
https://www.budshellford.com
Year Founded: 1944
Rev.: $13,600,000
Emp.: 50
Automobile Dealers
N.A.I.C.S.: 441110
Jason Caldwell *(Mgr-Svc)*
Patti Bishop *(Office Mgr)*
John Shell *(Mgr-Fin)*
Robert Shell *(Mgr-Sls)*
Philip Pounds *(Mgr-Internet Sls)*

BUD'S BEST COOKIES, INC.
2070 Pkwy Office Cir, Birmingham, AL 35244
Tel.: (205) 987-4840
Web Site:
https://www.budsbestcookies.com
Year Founded: 1991
Sales Range: $10-24.9 Million
Emp.: 100
Cookie & Cracker Mfr
N.A.I.C.S.: 311821
Al Cason *(Pres)*
Bud Cason *(Owner, Chm & CEO)*

BUDCO CREATIVE SERVICES
13700 Oakland Ave, Highland Park, MI 48203
Tel.: (313) 957-5100
Web Site: http://www.budco.com
Year Founded: 1982
Rev.: $12,000,000
Emp.: 25
N.A.I.C.S.: 541810
Thom Gulock *(Dir-Creative)*
Annette Watts *(VP-HR, Trng & Dev)*
Pete King *(VP-Sls)*
Michael Pavan *(VP-Sls)*
Michael T. Watson *(Sr VP)*
Bud Brian *(Chm)*
John Gregory *(Dir-IT)*
Robert K. Hyman *(Exec VP)*
Glenn Fontaine *(VP-Client Svcs)*
Jeff Sierra *(VP-Mktg & Product Dev)*
Terry Niles *(Pres)*
Mike Sederberg *(CFO)*
Sue Barber *(Dir-Mktg)*
Jim Suddendorf *(Exec VP-Sls & Mktg)*
Steve Gough *(Dir-Sls)*
Don McKenzie *(Vice Chm)*
William Rozek *(Chm)*
Daryl Minor *(CIO)*

BUDCO GROUP, INC.
1100 Gest St, Cincinnati, OH 45202
Tel.: (513) 621-6111   OH
Web Site: https://www.parsecinc.com
Year Founded: 1949
Sales Range: $150-199.9 Million
Emp.: 1,500
Convention Decorating Services; Piggyback Ramping Services; Equipment Leasing; Real Estate Development
N.A.I.C.S.: 532490
Brian Schwartz *(Controller)*

Subsidiaries:

George E. Fern Company   (1)
645 Linn St, Cincinnati, OH 45203-1114
Tel.: (513) 333-7060
Web Site: http://www.fernexpo.com

Sales Range: $25-49.9 Million
Emp.: 25
Event Support Services
N.A.I.C.S.: 561499

BUDCO, INC.
2004 N Yellowood Ave, Broken Arrow, OK 74012
Tel.: (918) 252-3420   OK
Web Site:
https://www.budcocable.com
Sales Range: $10-24.9 Million
Emp.: 15
Mail-Order Houses
N.A.I.C.S.: 444140
D. Nicholas Allen *(Supvr-Customer Svc)*
Marty Roberson *(CFO)*
Melissa Moore *(Supvr-Customer Svc)*

BUDD BAER
71 Murtland Ave, Washington, PA 15301
Tel.: (724) 222-0700
Web Site: https://www.buddbaer.com
Year Founded: 1947
Sales Range: $10-24.9 Million
Emp.: 72
New Car Retailer
N.A.I.C.S.: 441110
Mark Baer *(Owner)*
Gregg Cron *(Gen Mgr-Sls)*
Joe Moreno *(Mgr-Sls-Subaru)*
Greg McVicker *(Mgr-Collision Center)*
Tom Austin *(Mgr-Sls-Mazda)*
Susan Bresso *(Mgr-Fin & Insurance)*
Bill Chase *(Bus Mgr)*
Kevin Lane *(Mgr-Parts)*
Charlie Lloyd *(Mgr-Fleet)*
Tom Marquis *(Dir-Svc)*
Jan Slaiman *(Gen Mgr-Sls)*
Ashley Matusky *(Mgr-Bus Dev)*

BUDD VAN LINES, INC.
24 Schoolhouse Rd, Somerset, NJ 08873
Tel.: (732) 627-0600   NJ
Web Site:
https://www.buddvanlines.com
Sales Range: $25-49.9 Million
Emp.: 150
Household Goods Transport
N.A.I.C.S.: 484210
Kim Budd *(Sr VP)*
Arlene Yanogacio *(CFO)*
Gary M. Grund *(Sr VP-Sls-Natl)*
Marcella S. Budd *(VP-Corp Rels)*
David W. Budd Sr. *(Chm & CEO)*

BUDDY SQUIRREL, LLC
1801 E Bolivar Ave, Saint Francis, WI 53235
Tel.: (414) 483-4500
Web Site: http://www.qcbs.com
Year Founded: 1916
Rev.: $12,300,000
Emp.: 100
Chocolate & Confectionery Mfr from Cacao Beans
N.A.I.C.S.: 311351
Karin Frontczak *(Mgr-Retail Store)*

BUDDY'S CARPET AND FLOORING LLC
3160 S Tech Blvd, Miamisburg, OH 45342
Tel.: (937) 743-7700
Web Site:
http://www.buddyscarpet.com
Sales Range: $10-24.9 Million
Emp.: 15
Asphalted-Felt-Base Floor Coverings: Linoleum, Carpet
N.A.I.C.S.: 326199

BUDDYTV

190 Queen Anne Ave N Ste 250, Seattle, WA 98109
Tel.: (206) 859-4180
Web Site: http://www.buddytv.com
Year Founded: 2005
Sales Range: $1-9.9 Million
Emp.: 20
Television & Entertainment Website
N.A.I.C.S.: 517810
David Niu *(Co-Founder & Pres)*
Andy Liu *(Co-Founder & CEO)*
Bill Baxter *(CTO)*

BUDGE INDUSTRIES INC.
1690 Sumneytown Pike Ste 250, Lansdale, PA 19446-4882
Tel.: (267) 263-0600
Web Site:
http://www.budgeindustries.com
Sales Range: $10-24.9 Million
Emp.: 50
Automotive Covers & Accessories
N.A.I.C.S.: 423120
Charles Simon *(Pres)*
Lance Bunch *(Mgr-Natl Sls)*

BUDGET LIGHTING INC.
15275 Minnetonka Blvd, Minnetonka, MN 55345
Tel.: (952) 933-4146
Web Site:
http://www.budgetlighting.com
Rev.: $11,100,000
Emp.: 35
Distr Lighting Fixtures
N.A.I.C.S.: 423610
Jess Coykendall *(VP-Sls & Mktg)*

BUDGET MOTELS INC.
10605 Gaskins Way, Manassas, VA 20109
Tel.: (703) 361-6202
Web Site:
http://www.budgetmotelsinc.com
Year Founded: 1973
Sales Range: $10-24.9 Million
Emp.: 6
Hotel
N.A.I.C.S.: 721110
William Liddle *(Dir-Ops)*

BUDGET NATIONAL FINANCE CO.
1849 Sawtelle Blvd Ste 700, Los Angeles, CA 90025
Tel.: (310) 696-4050
Web Site: http://www.bfcloans.com
Sales Range: $10-24.9 Million
Emp.: 50
Consumer Finance Companies
N.A.I.C.S.: 522291
Sheldon J. Cohn *(Pres)*

BUDNEY INDUSTRIES
40 New Park Dr, Berlin, CT 06037
Tel.: (860) 828-1950
Web Site: https://www.budney.com
Year Founded: 1940
Emp.: 133
Aircraft Engine Mfr
N.A.I.C.S.: 336412
Daniel Darmoros *(Mgr-Quality)*
Fadi Salamour *(Mgr-Engrg)*
Jake Ventrella *(Engr-Quality)*
Michael Jordan *(Mgr-Production Control)*
Mark Zarek *(Gen Mgr)*

BUDWAY ENTERPRISES INC.
13600 NAPA St, Fontana, CA 92335
Tel.: (909) 463-0500
Web Site: http://www.budway.net
Sales Range: $10-24.9 Million
Emp.: 75
Local Trucking with Storage
N.A.I.C.S.: 484121

Budway Enterprises Inc.—(Continued)

Craig Davis *(Supvr-Harbor)*
Michael Van Houtte *(Mgr-Terminal)*
Vincent McLeod III *(Pres)*

BUECHEL STONE CORPORATION
W3639 Hwy H, Chilton, WI 53014
Tel.: (920) 849-9361
Web Site:
http://www.buechelstone.com
Sales Range: $10-24.9 Million
Emp.: 150
Rock Quarrying Services
N.A.I.C.S.: 212319
Timothy A. Buechel *(Pres)*
Scott Buechel *(Co-Owner & Exec VP)*
April Dowland *(Mgr-HR)*

BUEHLER FOOD MARKETS INC.
1401 Old Nancefield Rd, Wooster, OH 44691-0196
Tel.: (330) 264-4355   OH
Web Site: http://www.buehlers.com
Year Founded: 1929
Sales Range: $250-299.9 Million
Emp.: 2,500
Grocery Store Operator
N.A.I.C.S.: 445110
Cindy McVey *(Mgr-Food Svc)*
Michele Vick *(Mgr-Food Svc)*
Verne Mounts *(Dir-Pharmacy & Health Svcs)*
Deb Wilcox *(Dir-Comm)*
Dan Shanahan *(Chm)*
Mike Davidson *(Pres & CEO)*
Peter O'Donnell *(CFO & Treas)*

BUEHLER MOTOR INC.
860 Aviation Pkwy, Morrisville, NC 27560
Tel.: (919) 380-3333
Web Site:
http://www.buehlermotor.com
Sales Range: $50-74.9 Million
Emp.: 150
Motors, Electric
N.A.I.C.S.: 335312
Ray Welterlin *(Pres-Ops-North America)*

BUENA VIDA CONTINUING CARE & REHABILITATION CENTER
48 Cedar St, Brooklyn, NY 11221
Tel.: (718) 455-6200   NY
Web Site:
http://www.buenavidacenter.org
Year Founded: 1994
Sales Range: $10-24.9 Million
Emp.: 403
Continuing Care Retirement Community Operator
N.A.I.C.S.: 623311
Barbara McFadden *(Pres)*
Evelyn Conner *(Dir-Food & Nutrition Svcs)*
Ovidiu Calin *(Dir-Facilities Mgmt)*
Judy Griffith *(VP-Resident Care Svcs)*
Anita Harvey-Edwards *(VP-HR)*

BUENA VISTA HOSPITALITY GROUP
6675 Westwood Blvd Ste 170, Orlando, FL 32821
Tel.: (407) 352-7161
Web Site: http://www.bvhg.com
Year Founded: 1986
Sales Range: $10-24.9 Million
Emp.: 7
Hospitality & Golf Management Services
N.A.I.C.S.: 721110

Michael Frost *(Founder, Pres & Partner)*
Colin Wright *(Partner & Exec VP)*
Chad Martin *(VP)*
David Fletcher *(Dir-Fin)*

BUENO OF CALIFORNIA INC.
13607 Orden Dr, Santa Fe Springs, CA 90670-6354
Tel.: (562) 623-4000
Rev.: $23,000,000
Emp.: 22
Handbags
N.A.I.C.S.: 424350
Joe Pagliaro *(Pres)*

BUERKLE AUTOMOTIVE GROUP
3360 Hwy 61 N, Saint Paul, MN 55110
Tel.: (651) 490-6600
Web Site: http://www.buerkle.com
New Car Dealers
N.A.I.C.S.: 441110
David A. Buerkle *(Pres)*

Subsidiaries:

Buerkle Honda   (1)
3360 Hwy 61 N, Saint Paul, MN 55110-5212
Tel.: (651) 484-0231
Web Site: http://www.buerklehonda.com
Sales Range: $125-149.9 Million
Emp.: 137
New & Used Dealership
N.A.I.C.S.: 441110
David Buerkle *(Co-Owner)*
Mary Buerkle Grant *(Co-Owner)*
Steve Gorr *(Controller)*

Buerkle Hyundai   (1)
3350 Hwy 61 N, White Bear Lake, MN 55110-5293
Tel.: (651) 484-0231
Web Site: http://www.buerklehyundai.com
Sales Range: $25-49.9 Million
Emp.: 135
Car Whslr
N.A.I.C.S.: 441110
Gabe Monsivias *(Mgr-Fin & Insurance)*
Jim Bonney *(Mgr-Hyundai Svc)*
Justin Sederski *(Mgr-Fin & Insurance)*
Juston Anderson *(Gen Mgr-Sls)*
Patti Adams *(Mgr-Continuous Improvement)*
Toulong Yang *(Mgr-Fin & Insurance)*

BUESCHER INTERESTS LP
2591 Dallas Pkwy Ste 501, Frisco, TX 75034
Tel.: (972) 668-9000
Rev.: $10,213,357
Emp.: 70
Speculative Builder, Single-Family Houses
N.A.I.C.S.: 236115

BUESO & FORMAN, INC.
8824 Urbana Church Rd, Frederick, MD 21704
Tel.: (301) 694-5460
Web Site:
http://www.dynamicautomotive.net
General Automotive Repair
N.A.I.C.S.: 811111

Subsidiaries:

Twin Ridge Auto and Light Truck Service, Inc.   (1)
1006 Rising Rdg Rd, Mount Airy, MD 21771-5799
Tel.: (301) 829-6100
Web Site: http://www.twinridgeauto.com
Automotive Repair & Maintenance
N.A.I.C.S.: 811198

BUFF WHELAN CHEVROLET & GEO, INC.
40445 Van Dyke Ave, Sterling Heights, MI 48313-3736
Tel.: (586) 939-7300   MI

Web Site: http://www.buffwhelan.com
Year Founded: 1970
Sales Range: $75-99.9 Million
Emp.: 108
Provider of Automobile Sales, Service & Leasing
N.A.I.C.S.: 441110
Jack Bos *(Gen Mgr)*
Kerry Whelan *(Pres)*

BUFFALO AND ERIE COUNTY WORKFORCE DEVELOPMENT CONSORTIUM, INC.
726 Exchange St Ste 630, Buffalo, NY 14210
Tel.: (716) 819-9845   NY
Web Site: http://www.wdcinc.org
Year Founded: 2000
Sales Range: $10-24.9 Million
Emp.: 82
Employment Placement Services
N.A.I.C.S.: 561311
Russell J. Sferlazza *(Dir-Finance)*

BUFFALO BAYOU PARTNERSHIP, INC.
1113 Vine St Ste 215, Houston, TX 77002
Tel.: (713) 752-0314   TX
Web Site:
http://www.buffalobayou.org
Year Founded: 1986
Sales Range: Less than $1 Million
Emp.: 14
Natural Resource Conservation Services
N.A.I.C.S.: 813312
Robby Robinson *(Mgr-Field Ops)*
Leigh McBurnett *(Dir-Dev)*
Anne Olson *(Pres)*
Thomas Fish *(Chm)*

BUFFALO BILL MEMORIAL ASSOCIATION
720 Sheridan Ave, Cody, WY 82414
Tel.: (307) 587-4771   WY
Year Founded: 1917
Sales Range: $10-24.9 Million
Emp.: 235
Historical Museum
N.A.I.C.S.: 712110
Charles T. Roberson *(Dir-Dev)*
Lynn P. Rodgers *(CFO)*
Bruce B. Eldredge *(CEO & Exec Dir)*

BUFFALO BILLS, INC.
1 Bills Dr, Orchard Park, NY 14127-2237
Tel.: (716) 648-1800   NY
Web Site: http://www.buffalobills.com
Year Founded: 1960
Sales Range: $75-99.9 Million
Emp.: 300
Professional Football Franchise
N.A.I.C.S.: 711211
Bill Munson *(VP-Govt Rels & External Affairs)*
Marc Honan *(Sr VP-Media & Content)*
Jim Overdorf *(Sr VP-Football Admin)*
Dan Evans *(Exec Dir-IT)*
Gretchen Geitter *(VP-Community Rels)*
Greg Estes *(Dir-Video)*
Stephen Asposto *(Sr Dir-Brdcst Engrg)*
Julie Lantaff *(Dir-Bus Ops)*
Gregg Pastore *(Dir-Digital & Social Media Strategy)*
Chris Holland *(Asst Dir-Ticket Sls)*
Chris Costanzo *(Dir-Premium Seating)*
Sharon Hart *(Mgr-Acct Svc)*
Debbi Cummins *(Dir-Ticket Sys)*
David Wheat *(Chief Admin Officer)*

Pat Mathews *(Asst Dir-Customer Svc)*
Joe Frandina *(Dir-Construction Mgmt)*
Marty McLaughlin *(Mgr-Security)*
Neal McMullen *(Dir-Sls)*
Andy Major *(VP-Ops & Guest Experience)*
Chris Jenkins *(Exec Dir-Media Rels)*
Christopher Clark *(Sr Dir-Security)*
Bob Schatz *(Asst Dir-Stadium Ops)*
Chris Colleary *(Exec Dir-Ticket Sls & Svcs)*
Bruce Popko *(Exec VP-Bus Dev-PSE)*
Marlon Kerner *(Dir-Alumni)*
Leslie Bisson *(Dir-Medical)*
Michael Lyons *(Dir-Analytics)*
Shaun Handley *(Mgr-IT)*
Sondra Bridge *(Mgr-Payroll)*
Terry Pegula *(Owner & CEO)*
Derek Boyko *(VP-Comm)*
Brandon Beane *(Gen Mgr)*
Terrance Gray *(Dir-Player Personnel)*
Brian Gaine *(Asst Gen Mgr)*
Dennis Lock *(Sr Dir-Football Res)*
Matt Worswick *(Dir-Team Admin)*

BUFFALO DENTAL MANUFACTURING CO., INC.
159 LaFayette Dr, Syosset, NY 11791-0678
Tel.: (516) 496-7200   NY
Web Site:
https://www.buffalodental.com
Sales Range: $10-24.9 Million
Emp.: 35
Dental Products Mfr
N.A.I.C.S.: 339114
Donald Nevin *(Pres & CEO)*

BUFFALO EXCHANGE LTD.
203 E Helen St, Tucson, AZ 85705
Tel.: (520) 622-2711
Web Site:
http://www.buffaloexchange.com
Year Founded: 1974
Sales Range: $25-49.9 Million
Emp.: 600
Clothing, Secondhand
N.A.I.C.S.: 459510

BUFFALO FUEL CORP.
4870 Packard Rd, Niagara Falls, NY 14304
Tel.: (716) 278-2000
Web Site: http://www.buffalofuel.com
Sales Range: $10-24.9 Million
Emp.: 80
Trucking Service
N.A.I.C.S.: 484121
Paul Kulawik *(Dir-Safety)*

BUFFALO HOSPITAL SUPPLY CO., INC.
4039 Genesee St, Buffalo, NY 14225-1904
Tel.: (716) 626-9400   NY
Web Site:
http://www.buffalohospital.com
Year Founded: 1977
Sales Range: $75-99.9 Million
Emp.: 105
Medical & Surgical Supplies Whslr
N.A.I.C.S.: 423450
Ryan M. Burke *(CEO)*

BUFFALO LODGING ASSOCIATES, LLC
3000 Davenport Ave Ste 101, Canton, MA 02021
Tel.: (781) 344-4435
Web Site:
http://www.buffalolodging.com
Year Founded: 1996
Sales Range: $125-149.9 Million
Emp.: 1,500

Hotel Construction & Management
N.A.I.C.S.: 721110
Ronald R. Kendall *(Pres)*
Richard Schroen *(VP-Ops-Midwest Reg)*
Vernon Varela *(VP-Construction & Engrg)*

BUFFALO LUMBER CO
1588 Murfreesboro Rd, Woodbury, TN 37190-6150
Web Site: https://www.buffalo-lumber.com
Year Founded: 2005
Rev.: $2,100,000
Emp.: 8
Home Center Operator
N.A.I.C.S.: 444110
Chris Buffalo *(Owner)*

BUFFALO NIAGARA MEDICAL CAMPUS
640 Ellicott St, Buffalo, NY 14203
Tel.: (716) 854-2662   **NY**
Web Site: http://www.bnmc.org
Year Founded: 1990
Sales Range: $1-9.9 Million
Emp.: 23
Biomedical Research Services
N.A.I.C.S.: 541715

BUFFALO OPTICAL COMPANY INC.
280 Delaware Ave, Buffalo, NY 14202
Tel.: (716) 854-1620
Web Site:
    http://www.buffalooptical.com
Year Founded: 1895
Sales Range: Less than $1 Million
Emp.: 15
Opticians & Optical Retail
N.A.I.C.S.: 456130
G. H. Schneggenburger *(Treas & VP)*
Joseph Gugliuzza *(Pres)*

BUFFALO ROCK COMPANY
111 Oxmoor Rd, Birmingham, AL 35209
Tel.: (205) 942-3435   **AL**
Web Site: http://www.buffalorock.com
Year Founded: 1901
Sales Range: $5-14.9 Billion
Emp.: 2,500
Bottler of Soft Drinks
N.A.I.C.S.: 312111
Mary B. Allums *(Sec)*
Adriene Jones *(Employee Benefits Mgr)*
Bill Moore *(Risk Mngmt Mgr)*
Jim Woods *(DP Mgr)*
Matthew Dent *(Pres & COO)*
Warren Austin *(VP-Field Execution)*
Scott Parks *(VP-Product Fulfillment, Facilities, Fleet & Safety)*
Bruce Parsons *(CFO & Exec VP)*
James C. Lee III *(Chm & CEO)*

BUFFALO TRUCK CENTER
271 Dingens St, Buffalo, NY 14206-2355
Tel.: (716) 821-9911   **NY**
Web Site:
    http://www.buffalotruckcenter.com
Year Founded: 1968
Sales Range: $75-99.9 Million
Emp.: 36
Provider of Sales & Service of Trucks
N.A.I.C.S.: 441110
Thomas Krug *(Pres & CEO)*

BUFFALO WIRE WORKS CO., INC.
1165 Clinton St, Buffalo, NY 14206-2825
Tel.: (716) 826-4666   **DE**

Web Site:
    https://www.buffalowire.com
Year Founded: 1869
Sales Range: $1-9.9 Million
Emp.: 80
Wire Cloth; Vibrator Screen Replacements; Perforated Plate; Custom Cut Plate
N.A.I.C.S.: 332618
Joseph Abramo *(CEO)*
Dominic Nasso *(Exec VP-Sls)*
Erich Steadman *(VP-Engrg)*
Rick Zimmer *(COO)*
George Ulrich *(CFO)*

BUFFALO'S EXPERT SERVICE TECHNICIANS, INC.
3003 Genesee St, Buffalo, NY 14225
Tel.: (716) 893-6464
Web Site:
    https://www.buffaloexpert.com
Year Founded: 1984
Sales Range: $1-9.9 Million
Emp.: 12
Electronic & Precision Equipment Repair & Maintenance Services
N.A.I.C.S.: 811210
Chuck Kotarski *(Treas & Sec)*

BUFFELEN WOODWORKING COMPANY
1901 Taylor Way, Tacoma, WA 98421-4113
Tel.: (253) 627-1191   **WA**
Web Site:
    http://www.buffelendoor.com
Year Founded: 1913
Sales Range: $100-124.9 Million
Emp.: 250
Mfr of Wooden Doors
N.A.I.C.S.: 321911
Marylene Rosier *(Mgr-Customer Svc)*

BUFORD WHITE LUMBER COMPANY
603 E Independence St, Shawnee, OK 74804
Tel.: (405) 275-4900
Web Site: http://www.whiteace.com
Sales Range: $10-24.9 Million
Emp.: 75
Lumber & Other Building Materials
N.A.I.C.S.: 423310
Buford W. White *(CEO)*

BUG BUSTERS USA, INC.
6775 Hwy 92, Woodstock, GA 30189
Tel.: (770) 517-0990
Web Site: http://bugbustersusa.com
Year Founded: 1984
Pest Control Services
N.A.I.C.S.: 561710
Daphne Betholf *(CEO)*

Subsidiaries:

Scott Exterminating Co   **(1)**
864 S Central Ave, Hapeville, GA 30354
Tel.: (404) 767-2847
Rev.: $1,326,000
Emp.: 17
Exterminating & Pest Control Services
N.A.I.C.S.: 561710

BUG BUSTERS, INC.
6950 146th St W Ste 104, Saint Paul, MN 55124
Tel.: (952) 432-2221   **MN**
Year Founded: 1986
Sales Range: $1-9.9 Million
Emp.: 25
Exterminating & Pest Control Services
N.A.I.C.S.: 561710
Steve Devine *(VP)*

BUGGSI, INC.

8440 SW Holly Ln, Wilsonville, OR 97070
Tel.: (503) 783-5222
Sales Range: $1-9.9 Million
Emp.: 13
Hotel & Motel Operating Services
N.A.I.C.S.: 721110
Rajendra J. Patel *(Sec)*
Bakulesh G. Patel *(Pres)*

BUHL INDUSTRIES INC.
30 Ruta Ct, South Hackensack, NJ 07606
Tel.: (201) 296-0600   **NJ**
Web Site: http://www.buhl-ind.com
Year Founded: 1953
Sales Range: $10-24.9 Million
Emp.: 100
Projectors Mfr & Distr
N.A.I.C.S.: 423690

BUHLER DODGE, INC.
105 Hwy 36, Eatontown, NJ 07724
Tel.: (732) 747-0040
Year Founded: 1987
Sales Range: $10-24.9 Million
Emp.: 45
Car Whslr
N.A.I.C.S.: 441110
Pat Buhler *(Mgr)*
Donald Buhler *(Pres)*

BUIKEMAS ACE HARDWARE HOME CENTER
1030 N Washington St, Naperville, IL 60563-2700
Tel.: (630) 355-0077
Web Site:
    https://www.acehardware.com
Rev.: $10,900,000
Emp.: 200
Hardware Stores
N.A.I.C.S.: 444140
C. Jay Buikema *(Owner)*
Kyle Buikema *(Owner)*
Kim Novak *(Controller)*

BUILD GROUP, INC.
457 Minna St, San Francisco, CA 94103
Tel.: (415) 367-9399
Web Site: http://www.buildgc.com
Sales Range: $10-24.9 Million
Emp.: 160
Building Construction Services
N.A.I.C.S.: 236210
Scott Brauninger *(COO)*
Nathan Rundel *(Pres-Northern California Reg)*
Todd C. Pennington *(Pres-Ops-Southern California)*
Simon Bowden *(VP-Oakland)*
Peter Read *(Reg VP)*
Ron Marano *(CFO)*
Cody Bedell *(Pres-Ops-Silicon Valley)*
Eric Horn *(Co-Founder & Chm)*
Ron Yen *(Pres-Div & Head-Signature Spaces)*

Subsidiaries:

Bulild SJC   **(1)**
1210 Coleman Ave, Santa Clara, CA 95050
Tel.: (408) 986-8711
Web Site: http://www.sjconstruction.com
Commercial & Non Commercial Construction Services
N.A.I.C.S.: 236220
John Meyers *(VP)*
John Di Manto *(Pres & CEO)*
Jean Di Manto *(CFO)*
Erin Di Manto Conte *(Chief Admin Officer)*
Fran Conte *(Exec VP)*
Cody Bedell *(Sr Project Mgr)*

BUILD LLC
5611 University Way NE 100B, Seattle, WA 98105

Tel.: (206) 382-0401
Web Site: http://www.buildllc.com
Sales Range: $1-9.9 Million
Architectural Services
N.A.I.C.S.: 541310
Kevin Eckert *(Founder & Partner)*
Andrew van Leeuwen *(Partner)*
Bart Gibson *(Project Mgr)*

Subsidiaries:

Special Projects Division LLC   **(1)**
5611 University Way NE 100B, Seattle, WA 98105
Tel.: (206) 382-0401
Web Site:
    http://www.specialprojectsdivisionllc.com
Cabinet & Furniture Mfr
N.A.I.C.S.: 337110
David Hentzel *(Partner)*

BUILDASIGN.COM
11525A Stonehollow Dr Ste 100, Austin, TX 78758
Tel.: (512) 374-9850
Web Site: http://www.buildasign.com
Sales Range: $25-49.9 Million
Emp.: 169
Web Design Services
N.A.I.C.S.: 541511
Dan Graham *(Co-Founder)*
Nick Swerdfeger *(COO)*
Kit Mellem *(CFO)*
Chelsea Woodhead *(Chief People Officer)*
David House *(Dir-Sls)*
Jeff Novak *(Sr Dir-Digital Mktg)*
Kara Leal *(Dir-HR)*
Jason Kendrick *(Dir-Home Decor)*
Joe Licata *(Sr Dir-Ops)*
Christian Orawetz *(Dir-Tech)*
Dom Granato *(Sr Dir-Customer Experience)*
Bryan Kranik *(CEO)*

BUILDER HOMESITE, INC.
11900 Ranch Rd 620 N, Austin, TX 78750-1345
Tel.: (512) 371-3800
Web Site:
    https://www.builderhomesite.com
Year Founded: 2000
Sales Range: $25-49.9 Million
Emp.: 63
Building & Construction Industry Information & Marketing Services
N.A.I.C.S.: 541613
Tim Costello *(Chm, Pres & CEO)*
Greg Miller *(CFO, Treas & VP)*
Krishna Murthy *(CTO & VP)*

Subsidiaries:

EX2 Solutions, Inc.   **(1)**
11900 Ranch Rd 620 N, Austin, TX 78750-1345
Tel.: (512) 371-7842
Web Site: http://www.exsquared.com
Software Developer
N.A.I.C.S.: 513210

Subsidiary (Domestic):

RockSauce Studios, LLC   **(2)**
11900 Ranch Rd 620 N, 78750, Austin, TX
Tel.: (512) 410-7679
Web Site: http://www.rocksaucestudios.com
Software Devolement
N.A.I.C.S.: 513210

New Home Technologies, LLC   **(1)**
11900 Ranch Rd 620 N, Austin, TX 78750-1345
Tel.: (512) 371-3800
Sales Range: $10-24.9 Million
Emp.: 100
Building Information Services
N.A.I.C.S.: 518210

BUILDERS CARPET INC.
5600 Queens Ave NE, Otsego, MN 55376

Builders Carpet Inc.—(Continued)
Tel.: (763) 497-4407
Web Site:
http://www.focalpointflooring.com
Sales Range: $10-24.9 Million
Emp.: 150
Floor Coverings
N.A.I.C.S.: 423220
Katie Smith *(VP)*

BUILDERS CONCRETE SER-VICES LLC
31 Wt330 Schoger Dr, Naperville, IL 60564
Tel.: (630) 851-0789
Web Site: http://www.builders-concrete.com
Rev.: $10,000,000
Emp.: 75
Concrete Work
N.A.I.C.S.: 238110
Sebastian Palumbo *(Pres)*

BUILDERS DESIGN & LEAS-ING INC.
7601 Lindbergh Dr, Gaithersburg, MD 20879
Tel.: (301) 590-1100
Web Site:
https://www.buildersdesign.com
Year Founded: 1976
Sales Range: $10-24.9 Million
Emp.: 56
Interior Design; Furniture Rental
N.A.I.C.S.: 541410
Mark Nash *(Chm)*
Joe Duffus *(Pres)*
Randy Smith *(Comptroller)*
Kayla Jones *(Reg Mgr-Mktg)*
Donna Freitag *(Dir-New Client Dev & Reg Mgr-Mktg)*
Jon Nash *(Reg Mgr-Mktg)*

BUILDERS FENCE COMPANY INC.
8937 San Fernando Rd, Sun Valley, CA 91352
Tel.: (818) 768-5500
Web Site:
https://www.buildersfence.com
Rev.: $24,000,000
Emp.: 160
Fencing, Wood
N.A.I.C.S.: 423310
Marshall K. Frankel *(Pres)*

BUILDERS GENERAL SUPPLY COMPANY
15 Sycamore Ave, Little Silver, NJ 07739
Tel.: (732) 747-0808
Web Site:
https://www.buildersgeneral.com
Year Founded: 1931
Sales Range: $25-49.9 Million
Emp.: 170
Sells Lumber & Building Supplies
N.A.I.C.S.: 444110
Timothy J. Shaheen *(Pres)*

BUILDERS INC.
1081 S Glendale St, Wichita, KS 67218
Tel.: (316) 684-1400   **KS**
Web Site:
https://www.buildersinc.com
Year Founded: 1941
Sales Range: $50-74.9 Million
Emp.: 120
Apartment & Non-Residential Building Operator & Subdivider & Developer
N.A.I.C.S.: 531110
Bradley K. Smisor *(Exec VP)*
Josh Turner *(Supvr-Property)*

Subsidiaries:

Builders Development Inc.   (1)
1081 S Glendale, Wichita, KS 67208   (100%)
Tel.: (316) 684-1400
Web Site: http://www.buildersinc.com
Sales Range: $10-24.9 Million
Emp.: 20
Real Estate Development Services
N.A.I.C.S.: 237210
Brad Smisor *(Mgr)*

BUILDERS SAND & CEMENT CO., INC.
3636 W River Dr, Davenport, IA 52802
Tel.: (563) 322-1757
Web Site: http://buildersrmg.com
Sales Range: $10-24.9 Million
Emp.: 47
Readymix Concrete Mfr
N.A.I.C.S.: 327320
Brian Hahn *(Pres)*
Wayne Lawson *(VP-Ops)*
Brian Nagle *(VP-Sls)*
Karen VanDeWostine *(CFO)*

BUILDERS SPECIALTIES & HARDWARE
5145 Fisher Pl, Cincinnati, OH 45217
Tel.: (513) 641-2424
Commercial Doors, Hardware & Bath-room Accessories Distr
N.A.I.C.S.: 444140

BUILDERS SUPPLY COMPANY INC.
611 Godfrey Ave Se, Fort Payne, AL 35967
Tel.: (256) 845-1451
Web Site: http://www.bsupply.net
Sales Range: $10-24.9 Million
Emp.: 110
Lumber & Other Building Materials
N.A.I.C.S.: 423310
George Weather *(Gen Mgr)*

BUILDERS SURPLUS, INC.
1800 E Dyer Rd, Santa Ana, CA 92705
Web Site:
https://www.builderssurplus.net
Rev.: $12,500,000
Emp.: 25
Lumber Plywood Millwork & Wood Panel Merchant Whslr
N.A.I.C.S.: 423310
Kenneth Drake *(Pres)*
Daryl Drake *(Founder, Treas & Sec)*

BUILDERS TRUSS INC
2800 Hunter St, Fort Myers, FL 33916
Tel.: (239) 332-1753
Rev.: $25,800,000
Emp.: 65
Lumber: Rough, Dressed & Finished
N.A.I.C.S.: 423310
Cora Gilbert *(Pres)*

BUILDERS' HARDWARE & SUPPLY CO.
1516 15th Ave W, Seattle, WA 98119
Tel.: (206) 281-3700
Web Site: https://www.builders-hardware.com
Sales Range: $10-24.9 Million
Emp.: 102
Builders' Hardware
N.A.I.C.S.: 423710
Greg Lunde *(Chm)*

BUILDERTREND SOLUTIONS INC.
11818 I St, Omaha, NE 68137-3700
Tel.: (402) 905-2506

Web Site:
http://www.buildertrend.com
Year Founded: 2006
Computer Related Services
N.A.I.C.S.: 541519
Clint Johanek *(Mgr-S|s-Intl)*
Dan Houghton *(Co-Founder & CEO)*
Steve Dugger *(Co-Founder)*
Jeff Dugger *(Co-Founder)*

Subsidiaries:

CoConstruct, LLC   (1)
1807 Seminole Trl Ste 203, Charlottesville, VA 22901
Tel.: (800) 213-3392
Web Site: http://www.co-construct.com
Software Development Services
N.A.I.C.S.: 541511
Donny Wyatt *(Founder & CEO)*

BUILDFIRE, INC.
1760 The Alameda Ste 300, San Jose, CA 95126
Tel.: (949) 899-8224
Web Site: https://buildfire.com
Mobile App Development Services
N.A.I.C.S.: 513210
Daniel Hindi *(Founder & COO)*

Subsidiaries:

Bizness Apps, Inc.   (1)
1645 California St, San Francisco, CA 94109
Web Site: http://www.biznessapps.com
Sales Range: $1-9.9 Million
Emp.: 70
Software Development Services
N.A.I.C.S.: 541512
Andrew Gazdecki *(CEO)*
Zach Cusimano *(COO)*
Stephen Heisserer *(VP-Product)*
James Ransom *(VP-Engrg)*
Sam Schnaible *(VP-Bus Dev)*

BUILDING CONTROLS & SO-LUTIONS
2241 Valwood Pkwy Ste 200, Farm-ers Branch, TX 75234
Tel.: (214) 390-6900
Web Site:
https://www.buildingcontrols.com
Emp.: 100
Building Automation, Building Con-trols, Gas Detection & Energy Man-agement Services
N.A.I.C.S.: 541990
Eric Chernik *(CEO)*

Subsidiaries:

Activelogix LLC   (1)
710 Peninsula Ln Ste E, Charlotte, NC 28273-5981
Tel.: (704) 553-8510
Web Site: http://www.activelogix.com
Software Publisher
N.A.I.C.S.: 513210
Robert Palmer *(Mgr-Tech Support)*

Minvalco, Inc.   (1)
3340 Gorham Ave, Minneapolis, MN 55426
Tel.: (952) 920-0131
Web Site: http://www.minvalco.com
Whol Heating Air Conditioning Refrigeration Controls & Supplies
N.A.I.C.S.: 423720
Mary Delmore *(Pres)*
Daniel Sinn *(Gen Mgr)*

BUILDING CRAFTS INC.
2 Rosewood Dr, Wilder, KY 41076
Tel.: (859) 781-9500
Web Site:
https://www.buildingcrafts.com
Sales Range: $25-49.9 Million
Emp.: 100
Waste Water & Sewage Treatment Plant Construction
N.A.I.C.S.: 237110
Ken Ashcraft *(Mgr-Fleet)*
Darryl R. Geiman *(VP)*

Daniel Breetz *(Project Mgr)*
Tim Dunlevy *(Dir-Safety)*
Rick Blank *(Mgr-Bus Dev)*
Brad Miller *(VP & Project Mgr)*
Shannon Stallmeyer *(Mgr-HR)*

BUILDING ENGINES, INC.
33 Arch St 32nd Fl, Boston, MA 02110
Tel.: (781) 290-5300   **DE**
Web Site:
http://www.buildingengines.com
Year Founded: 1999
Property Management & Commercial Real Estate Software Developer
N.A.I.C.S.: 513210
Tim Curran *(Exec Mng Dir)*
Mahesh Nair *(CTO)*
Daniel Russo *(Chief Product Officer)*
Brendan Cournoyer *(VP-Mktg)*

Subsidiaries:

Real Data Management Inc.   (1)
1400 Broadway, 22nd fl, New York, NY 10018
Tel.: (212) 213-8190
Industrial Design Services
N.A.I.C.S.: 541420

BUILDING EQUITY SOONER FOR TOMORROW
301 E Camperdown Way, Greenville, SC 29601
Tel.: (864) 355-1160   **SC**
Year Founded: 2004
Sales Range: $25-49.9 Million
School Construction & Renovation Services
N.A.I.C.S.: 236220
Doug Webb *(Sec)*
Joseph F. Sullivan *(Vice Chm)*
James W. Blakely Jr. *(Chm)*

BUILDING ERECTION SER-VICES CO.
15585 S Keeler St, Olathe, KS 66062
Tel.: (913) 764-5560
Web Site: http://www.builderec.com
Rev.: $32,000,000
Emp.: 148
Commercial & Office Building Con-struction
N.A.I.C.S.: 236220
Toby Green *(Project Mgr)*

BUILDING FASTENERS OF MINNESOTA INC.
7100 Sunwood Drive NW, Ramsey, MN 55303
Tel.: (763) 252-2300
Web Site:
https://www.bffastenersupply.com
Rev.: $18,700,000
Emp.: 100
Mfr Bolts, Nuts & Screws
N.A.I.C.S.: 423710
Loren O'Brien *(CEO)*
Todd Boone *(Exec VP)*

Subsidiaries:

Northern States Supply Inc.   (1)
600 Industrial Dr SW, Willmar, MN 56201
Tel.: (320) 235-0555
Web Site:
http://www.northernstatessupply.com
Sales Range: $10-24.9 Million
Emp.: 50
Industrial Supplies
N.A.I.C.S.: 423840
Tina Ertendach *(CEO)*

BUILDING INDUSTRY PART-NERS LLC
301 Commerce St Ste 3025, Fort Worth, TX 76102
Tel.: (214) 550-0405
Web Site: http://www.buildingip.com

Year Founded: 2008
Privater Equity Firm
N.A.I.C.S.: 523999
Matt Ogden *(Founder & Mng Partner)*
Zach Coopersmith *(Mng Partner)*
Steve Shaffer *(Operating Partner)*
Robert Lane *(VP)*
Toni Burke *(Head-Strategic & IR)*

Subsidiaries:

Haywood Builders Supply
Company **(1)**
PO Box 187, Waynesville, NC 28786
Tel.: (828) 456-6051
Web Site: http://www.haywoodbuilders.com
Building Material Dealers
N.A.I.C.S.: 444180
Tim Freeman *(Mgr-Ops)*

North American Specialty Lamina-
tions, LLC **(1)**
51149 Whitetail Rd, Osseo, WI 54758
Tel.: (715) 597-6525
Web Site: https://northamericanlam.com
Lamination, Fabrication & Finishing Solu-
tions Mfr
N.A.I.C.S.: 238990
Doug Rende *(CEO)*
Zach Wiedenhoeft *(Pres & COO)*

Subsidiary (Domestic):

Midwest Prefinishing
Incorporated **(2)**
2310 Pinehurst Dr, Middleton, WI 53562
Tel.: (608) 836-3667
Web Site: http://prefinishing.com
Sales Range: $1-9.9 Million
Emp.: 30
Wood Window & Door Mfr
N.A.I.C.S.: 321911
Mark Larson *(Pres)*

West Coast Lumber, Inc. **(1)**
465 Alta Rd, San Diego, CA 92179
Tel.: (619) 436-1490
Web Site: https://westcoastlumber.com
Lumber & Building Materials Distr
N.A.I.C.S.: 423310
Joe Lawrence *(CEO)*
Jason Walsh *(VP-Component Mfg)*

Subsidiary (Domestic):

Stone Truss Company, Inc. **(2)**
507 Jones Rd, Oceanside, CA 92054
Tel.: (760) 967-6171
Web Site: https://stonetruss.com
Sales Range: $1-9.9 Million
Emp.: 35
Roof & Floor Truss Mfr
N.A.I.C.S.: 321215
Steve Hall *(CTO)*
Richard Thomas *(Pres)*
Charlie Signorino *(VP)*

BUILDING MAINTENANCE & SUPPLY
716 Bank St, Wallace, ID 83873
Tel.: (208) 556-1164
Web Site:
https://www.nwminesupply.com
Sales Range: $10-24.9 Million
Emp.: 31
Mining Machinery & Equipment, Ex-
cept Petroleum
N.A.I.C.S.: 423810
Donald Berger *(Pres)*
John Hull *(Dir-Sls)*

BUILDING MATERIAL DIS-TRIBUTORS
225 Elm Ave, Galt, CA 95632
Tel.: (209) 745-3001
Web Site: https://www.bmdusa.com
Sales Range: $10-24.9 Million
Emp.: 175
Building Materials; Exterior
N.A.I.C.S.: 423310
Cindy Thompson *(Controller)*
Mike Reilly *(Dir-IT)*

BUILDING PLASTICS, INC.

3263 Sharpe Ave, Memphis, TN
38111-3729
Tel.: (901) 744-6200   TN
Web Site:
http://www.bpidecosurf.com
Year Founded: 1962
Sales Range: $75-99.9 Million
Emp.: 400
Whslr of Building Materials & Floor
Coverings
N.A.I.C.S.: 423220
Wallace R. McAlexander Jr. *(CFO)*

BUILDING PRODUCTS CORP.
950 Freeburg Ave, Belleville, IL
62220
Tel.: (618) 233-4427
Web Site:
https://www.buildingproducts.com
Sales Range: $1-9.9 Million
Emp.: 13
Concrete Blocks
N.A.I.C.S.: 327331
Paul Mueth *(Pres)*

BUILDING PRODUCTS INC.
405 1st Ave NE, Watertown, SD
57201-2701
Tel.: (605) 886-3495   SD
Web Site:
http://www.buildingproductsinc.com
Year Founded: 1957
Sales Range: $125-149.9 Million
Emp.: 250
Distr of Building Products
N.A.I.C.S.: 423320
Jim Walz *(VP-Pur)*
Lee E. Schull *(CEO)*
Darrell Lindner *(Branch Mgr)*
Cas Rangel *(CTO)*
Paul Maassen *(CFO)*
Vince Welch *(COO)*

Subsidiaries:

Building Products Inc. of Iowa **(1)**
PO Box 210, Waterloo, IA
50704-0210 **(100%)**
Tel.: (319) 233-7476
Web Site: http://www.bpi.build
Sales Range: $10-24.9 Million
Emp.: 100
Distr of Building Products
N.A.I.C.S.: 423310
J. J. Robson *(Mgr)*

Building Products Inc. of S.D. **(1)**
1500 N Industrial Ave, Sioux Falls, SD
57104-0258 **(100%)**
Tel.: (605) 336-3460
Sales Range: $25-49.9 Million
Emp.: 75
Wholesale Building Materials
N.A.I.C.S.: 423310
Chris Fischer *(Branch Mgr)*

BUILDING SECURITY SER-VICES, INC.
20 Valley St Ste 340, South Orange,
NJ 07079
Tel.: (973) 414-1111
Web Site:
https://www.buildingsecurity.com
Year Founded: 1982
Sales Range: $10-24.9 Million
Emp.: 470
Management Consulting Services
N.A.I.C.S.: 541618
Joseph Di Ferdinando *(Pres)*
Susan Ferdinando *(Exec VP)*

BUILDING SERVICE INDUS-TRIAL SUPPLY CO.
1710 S 106th St, Milwaukee, WI
53214
Tel.: (414) 258-6929
Web Site:
https://www.acoustechsupply.com
Sales Range: $10-24.9 Million

Emp.: 21
Insulation Materials
N.A.I.C.S.: 812990
Thomas E. Popalisky *(Pres)*

BUILDING SOLUTIONS, LLC.
248 King St, Oxford, ME 04270
Tel.: (207) 539-8787
Web Site:
https://www.buildingsolutions.com
Year Founded: 2001
Sales Range: $10-24.9 Million
Emp.: 35
Architectural Services
N.A.I.C.S.: 541310
Joseph J. Casalinova *(Pres)*
John Boehnlein *(VP & Dir-Construction)*

BUILDING SYSTEMS TRANS-PORTATION CO.
460 E High St, London, OH 43140
Tel.: (740) 852-9700
Web Site: http://www.bsttrucking.com
Sales Range: $25-49.9 Million
Emp.: 150
Trucking Except Local
N.A.I.C.S.: 484121
Jerry Alcott *(Owner)*
David Beickman *(Controller)*
Victor Robertson *(Mgr-Flatbed & Sls)*

BUILDINGSTARS
33 Worthington Access Dr, Maryland
Heights, MO 63043
Tel.: (314) 991-3356   MO
Web Site:
https://www.buildingstars.com
Year Founded: 1994
Sales Range: $10-24.9 Million
Emp.: 100
Patent Owners And Lessors
N.A.I.C.S.: 561210
Chris Blase *(Owner)*
Derec Bieri *(Owner-Franchise)*
Chris Horstman *(VP-Fin)*

BUILDPOINT CORPORATION
2200 Bridge Pkwy Ste 102, Redwood
City, CA 94065
Web Site: http://www.buildpoint.com
Rev.: $10,900,000
Emp.: 70
Internet Connectivity Services
N.A.I.C.S.: 517810

BULAB HOLDINGS, INC.
1256 N McLean Blvd, Memphis, TN
38108-1241
Tel.: (901) 278-0330   TN
Web Site: http://www.buckman.com
Year Founded: 1945
Emp.: 1,733
Holding Company; Industrial Organic
& Inorganic Chemicals Mfr
N.A.I.C.S.: 551112
Lela Gerald *(VP-Global Mktg)*
David Rosenthal *(CFO)*
Junai Maharaj *(Pres & CEO)*
Chrales W. Westbrook *(VP-HR)*
Jonathan Scharff *(Gen Counsel, Sec & VP)*
James W. Fitzhenry *(VP-Global Product Tech)*
Brad Walden *(VP-Global Supply Chain)*
Robert P. Shannon *(Chm)*
Tony Rindone *(COO)*
Rahul Goturi *(CIO & VP)*
Narasimha Rao *(Chief Digital Officer)*

Subsidiaries:

Buckman Laboratories International,
Inc. **(1)**
1256 N McLean Blvd, Memphis, TN 38108-
1241

Tel.: (901) 278-0330
Web Site: http://www.buckman.com
Sales Range: $350-399.9 Million
Emp.: 1,733
Holding Company; Commercial Chemical
Research, Development & Products Mfr
N.A.I.C.S.: 551112
Edson P. Peredo *(Pres)*
Robin H. Luck *(VP-Mktg)*
Steve Buckman *(Owner)*

Subsidiary (Non-US):

Buckman Laboratories (Asia) PTE
LTD. **(2)**
33 Tuas South Street 1, Singapore,
638038, Singapore
Tel.: (65) 68919200
Web Site: http://www.buckman.com
Chemical Testing Services
N.A.I.C.S.: 541380
Rain Zhang *(Gen Mgr-Ops)*

Buckman Laboratories (India) Private
Limited **(2)**
Ega Trade Centre 11th Floor Block A & B
#809 Poonamalle High Road, Kilpauk,
Chennai, 600010, Tamil Nadu, India
Tel.: (91) 4426480220
Web Site: http://www.buckman.com
Laboratory Testing Services
N.A.I.C.S.: 541380
Ramamurthy Ashok *(Gen Mgr)*

Buckman Laboratories (Shanghai)
Chemicals Co., LTD. **(2)**
8500 Songze Avenue Qingpu Industrial
Zone, 201707, Shanghai, China
Tel.: (86) 2169210188
Web Site: http://www.buckman.com
Laboratory Testing Services
N.A.I.C.S.: 541380
Ming Zhang *(Gen Mgr)*
Shen Paul *(Area Mgr)*
Chen David *(Mgr-Div)*
Ma Kevin *(Reg Mgr)*

Buckman Laboratories PTY LTD. **(2)**
Buckman Boulevard Hammarsdale Sterk-
spruit, Hammarsdale, 3700, South Africa
Tel.: (27) 317368800
Web Site: http://www.buckman.com
Specialty Chemicals Mfr
N.A.I.C.S.: 325998
Martin Connor *(Mng Dir)*

Buckman Laboratories Pty. Ltd. **(2)**
Office Building 2 280 Byrnes Road, PO Box
1396, Wagga Wagga, 2650, NSW, Australia
Tel.: (61) 269235888
Web Site: https://www.buckman.com
Specialty Chemical Whslr
N.A.I.C.S.: 424690
Rod Taylor *(Dir-Sls-Australia & New Zea-
land)*

Buckman Laboratories of Canada,
Ltd. **(2)**
Laboratoires Buckman du Canada ltee.
Vaudreuil-Dorion, J7Z 5V5, QC, Canada
Tel.: (450) 424-4404
Sales Range: $10-24.9 Million
Emp.: 72
Laboratory Testing Services
N.A.I.C.S.: 541380
Ihab Wassef *(Gen Mgr-Ops)*
Davor Mehes *(Gen Mgr-Sls)*
Rosemary Ghaly *(Treas)*

Subsidiary (Domestic):

Buckman Laboratories, Inc. **(2)**
1256 N Mclean Blvd, Memphis, TN 38108-
1241
Tel.: (901) 278-0330
Web Site: http://www.buckman.com
Specialty Chemicals Mfr
N.A.I.C.S.: 325199
Michael Alpert *(Dir-Sls Ops)*
Patricia Browning *(VP-Strategic Plng)*
Lela Gerald *(Dir-Global Mktg Comm)*
Christine Staples *(VP-Water-Global)*
Junai Maharaj *(Pres & CEO)*
Anthony Rindone *(COO)*
Naraimha Rao *(Chief Digital Officer)*
Rahul Goturi *(CIO)*

Subsidiary (Non-US):

Buckman Laboratories, K.K. **(2)**

Bulab Holdings, Inc.—(Continued)

Taisay Yaesu Bldg 9F 2-8-8 Yaesu, Chuo-ku, 104-0028, Tokyo, Japan
Tel.: (81) 362021515
Web Site: http://www.buckman.com
Specialty Chemicals Mfr
N.A.I.C.S.: 325998

Buckman Laboratories, N.V. (2)
Wondelgemkaai 159, 9000, Gent, Belgium
Tel.: (32) 92579211
Web Site: http://www.buckman.nl
Specialty Chemicals Mfr
N.A.I.C.S.: 325998
Martin Connor (Mng Dir)

Buckman Laboratories, S.A. de C.V. (2)
Paseo Cuauhnahuac Km 13 5 Col Progreso, Jiutepec, CP 62550, Morelos, Mexico
Tel.: (52) 7773293740
Web Site: http://www.buckman.com
Laboratory Testing Services
N.A.I.C.S.: 541380
Paulo Sergio Oliveira Beltrao (Gen Mgr)

Buckman Laboratorios Chile LTDA. (2)
Coyancura 2241 oficina 73, Santiago, 750-0759, Chile
Tel.: (56) 229461000
Web Site: http://www.buckman.com
Laboratory Testing Services
N.A.I.C.S.: 541380
Paulo Sergio Oliveira Beltrao (Gen Mgr)

Laboratorios Buckman S.A. (2)
Av San Isidro 4602 1o piso, 1429, Buenos Aires, Argentina
Tel.: (54) 1147016415
Web Site: http://www.buckman.com
Laboratory Testing Services
N.A.I.C.S.: 541380
Nelson Roberto Tomys (Bus Mgr)

Bulab Realty of Missouri, LLC (1)
14664 E State Hwy 47, Cadet, MO 63630
Tel.: (901) 278-0330
Rev.: $2,000,000
Emp.: 307
Equipment Rental & Leasing; Nonresidential Building Operators
N.A.I.C.S.: 532490

Bulab Realty of Tennessee, LLC (1)
1256 N Mclean Blvd, Memphis, TN 38108
Tel.: (901) 278-0330
Web Site: http://www.buckman.com
Sales Range: $125-149.9 Million
Equipment Rental & Leasing; Nonresidential Building Operators
N.A.I.C.S.: 532490

BULBMAN INC
630 Sunshine Ln, Reno, NV 89502
Tel.: (775) 788-5661
Web Site: http://www.bulbman.com
Sales Range: $10-24.9 Million
Emp.: 38
Light Bulbs
N.A.I.C.S.: 423610
Larry Reis (Controller)

BULBS.COM INCORPORATED
243 Stafford St, Worcester, MA 01603
Tel.: (508) 363-2800   DE
Web Site: https://www.bulbs.com
Year Founded: 1999
Sales Range: $10-24.9 Million
Emp.: 40
Lighting Fixture Bulb Replacement Online Retailer
N.A.I.C.S.: 444180
Michael Connors (CEO)
Donald Walker (Chm)
Chris Weber (VP-Mdsg)

BULBTRONICS INC.
45 Banfi Plz N, Farmingdale, NY 11735
Tel.: (631) 249-2272

Web Site:
https://www.bulbtronics.com
Sales Range: $10-24.9 Million
Emp.: 68
Light Bulbs & Related Supplies
N.A.I.C.S.: 423610
Andrew Zinzi (CFO)
Evelyn Arena (Mgr-Export Sls)
Elaine Scoppetti (Mgr-HR)
Hugh McDermott (CIO)
Jaclyn Brady (Mgr-Sls)
Celeste McLaren (Controller)
Lee Vestrich (Sr VP)
Litzy Lebett (Dir-Sls & Mktg)
Bruce R. Thaw (Pres & CEO)

BULK CHEMICAL SERVICES, LLC
1303 Boyd Ave NW, Atlanta, GA 30318
Tel.: (404) 350-8404
Web Site:
http://www.bulkchemicalservice.com
Sales Range: $1-9.9 Million
Emp.: 10
Specialty Chemicals Mfr
N.A.I.C.S.: 325998
Harry D. Colley (Dir-Sls & Mktg)

Subsidiaries:

Bulk Chemical Services, LLC - Sandersville Plant (1)
726 Industrial Dr, Sandersville, GA 31082
Tel.: (478) 552-1337
Web Site:
http://www.bulkchemicalservices.com
Specialty Chemicals Mfr
N.A.I.C.S.: 325998
Mark Gardner (Plant Mgr)

BULK MATERIALS INTERNATIONAL CO.
153 S Main St, Newtown, CT 06470
Tel.: (203) 270-1416
Web Site:
http://www.bulkmaterials.net
Year Founded: 1986
Sales Range: $25-49.9 Million
Emp.: 25
Cement Services & Products
N.A.I.C.S.: 327310
Peter D'Amico (Pres & CEO)
Matt D'Amico (Mgr)
Steve Conte (CFO)

BULK REEF SUPPLY
672 Mendelssohn Ave N, Golden Valley, MN 55427
Tel.: (763) 432-9691
Web Site:
http://www.bulkreefsupply.com
Year Founded: 2007
Sales Range: $1-9.9 Million
Emp.: 30
Saltwater & Reef Aquarium Supplies
N.A.I.C.S.: 459910
Andrew Duneman (Co-Founder)

BULK STORAGE SOFTWARE, INC.
10790 Glengate Loop, Highlands Ranch, CO 80130
Tel.: (303) 862-6857   CO
Year Founded: 2007
Emp.: 1
Software Publisher
N.A.I.C.S.: 513210
Geoffrey Gibbs (Pres, CFO, Chief Acctg Officer, Treas & Sec)
Matthew Milonas (CEO & COO)

BULK TRANSIT CORPORATION
7177 Industrial Pkwy, Plain City, OH 43064
Tel.: (614) 873-4632   TX

Web Site:
https://www.bulktransit.com
Year Founded: 1972
Sales Range: $10-24.9 Million
Emp.: 40
General Freight Trucking, Long-Distance, Truckload
N.A.I.C.S.: 484121
Ronald DeWolf (Pres)
Gloria D. Wolf (Sec)
Randy Wolf (Gen Mgr)

BULK TRANSPORTATION
415 S Lemon Ave, Walnut, CA 91789
Tel.: (909) 594-2855
Web Site: http://www.bulk-dti.com
Sales Range: $10-24.9 Million
Emp.: 49
Bulk & Liquid Commodities Transport Services
N.A.I.C.S.: 484121
Jeff MacHado (VP-Ops)
Gabriel Parra (Mgr)
Brett Richardson (COO & Exec VP)
Susan Duffield (Sec)
Frank Cutter (VP-Safety & HR)

BULK-PACK INC.
1900 N 18 Ste 802, Monroe, LA 71201
Tel.: (318) 387-3260
Web Site: https://www.bulk-pack.com
Sales Range: $10-24.9 Million
Emp.: 350
Corrugated & Solid Fiber Boxes
N.A.I.C.S.: 322211
Thomas O. Bancroft (Chm)
Will Mintz (Pres)

BULKMATIC TRANSPORT COMPANY INC.
2001 N Cline Ave, Griffith, IN 46319-1008
Tel.: (219) 972-7630   IN
Web Site: https://www.bulkmatic.com
Year Founded: 1965
Sales Range: $75-99.9 Million
Emp.: 1,300
Provider of Trucking Services
N.A.I.C.S.: 484121
Albert Bingham (Pres)
Kimberly Rasberry (Mgr-Inside Sls)
Steve Kirk (Asst VP-Sls)
Stacy Friedericks (Mgr-Fleet)

BULL BROS., INC.
401 Herkimer Ave, Utica, NY 13502
Tel.: (315) 797-7760   NY
Year Founded: 1958
Sales Range: $50-74.9 Million
Emp.: 380
Own & Operate Convenience Stores
N.A.I.C.S.: 551112
Larry E. Bull (Pres & CEO)
Anthony Tomaselli (CFO)

BULL ENGINEERED PRODUCTS, INC.
12001 Steele Creek Rd, Charlotte, NC 28273
Tel.: (704) 504-0300
Web Site: https://www.bullep.com
Year Founded: 2001
Sales Range: $1-9.9 Million
Emp.: 33
Injection-Molded Plastics Mfr
N.A.I.C.S.: 326199
Gary Dickison (Pres & Owner)
Matt Herr (Mgr-Programs)

BULLARD CONSTRUCTION INC.
4371 Lindbergh Dr, Addison, TX 75001
Tel.: (972) 661-8474

Web Site:
http://www.bullardconstruction.com
Sales Range: $10-24.9 Million
Emp.: 20
Commercial & Office Building Construction
N.A.I.C.S.: 236220
Ralph Bullard (Pres)

BULLARD RESTAURANTS INC.
1901 N Pine St, Lumberton, NC 28358
Tel.: (910) 738-7183
Web Site:
http://www.bullardrestaurants.com
Year Founded: 1983
Sales Range: $10-24.9 Million
Emp.: 1,500
Fast-Food Restaurant, Chain
N.A.I.C.S.: 722513
Drew Bullard (COO)
Clifford Earl Bullard Jr. (CEO)

BULLDOG BATTERY CORPORATION
98 E Canal St, Wabash, IN 46992
Tel.: (260) 563-0551
Web Site: http://www.bulldog-battery.com
Year Founded: 1977
Sales Range: $10-24.9 Million
Emp.: 90
Storage Batteries
N.A.I.C.S.: 335910
Norman Benjamin (Pres)
Rick Glassburn (COO)

BULLDOG DRUMMOND, INC.
2741 4th Ave, San Diego, CA 92103
Tel.: (619) 528-8404
Web Site:
http://www.bulldogdrummond.com
Year Founded: 1997
Sales Range: $10-24.9 Million
Emp.: 25
N.A.I.C.S.: 541810
Shawn E. Parr (CEO)
Annie J. Buchanan (CFO)
Catharine Berry (VP-Ops)
Erin Kaplan (VP-Consumer Intelligence & Common Sense)
Megan Langel (VP-Creative & Strategy)
Christopher Trementozzi (Dir-Production)

BULLDOG MARINE
1740 Hudson Bridge Rd Ste 1012, Stockbridge, GA 30281
Tel.: (251) 650-1195
Web Site:
http://www.bulldogmarine.biz
Year Founded: 2003
Rev.: $8,900,000
Emp.: 360
Engineeering Services
N.A.I.C.S.: 541330
BL Hall (Pres)

BULLDOG MEDIA GROUP, INC.
114 N Egan Ave, Madison, SD 57042
Tel.: (605) 256-9103   SD
Web Site:
http://www.bulldogmediagroup.com
Year Founded: 2000
Sales Range: $1-9.9 Million
Emp.: 25
Online Marketing Services
N.A.I.C.S.: 541613
Todd Knodel (CEO)
Darin Namken (Pres)
Camelyn Sims (Mgr-Ops)
Scott Delzer (Dir-Dev-Infusion Strategies)

Lisa Robson *(Dir-Dev-Commission Soup)*

Joel Molascon *(Mgr-Web Production)*

BULLDOG MOVERS, INC.
4194 Northeast Expy, Atlanta, GA 30340
Tel.: (770) 333-8100
Web Site:
http://www.bulldogmovers.net
Year Founded: 1999
Sales Range: $25-49.9 Million
Emp.: 27
Local Trucking with Storage
N.A.I.C.S.: 484210
Erik D. Christensen *(Pres)*

BULLDOG OFFICE PRODUCTS INC.
500 Glass Rd, Pittsburgh, PA 15205
Tel.: (412) 787-3333
Web Site: http://www.bulldogop.com
Year Founded: 1979
Rev.: $15,000,000
Emp.: 100
Stationery & Office Supplies
N.A.I.C.S.: 424120
Christine Fera *(CEO)*
Michele Liberatore *(Pres)*
Jodi Fera *(Treas)*
Marisa Stevenson *(Sec)*

BULLEY & ANDREWS, LLC
1755 W Armitage Ave, Chicago, IL 60622-1163
Tel.: (773) 235-2433   IL
Web Site: https://www.bulley.com
Year Founded: 1891
Sales Range: $125-149.9 Million
Emp.: 200
General Contractors
N.A.I.C.S.: 236220
Mark Evans *(Pres-Construction & Client Solutions)*
Michael Sudol *(CFO & VP-Fin & Admin)*
Donna Borgerding *(Mgr-Bus Dev-Indianapolis)*
Patrick J. Healy *(VP-Bus Dev)*
Timothy Puntillo *(Pres)*
Allan E. Bulley Jr. *(Co-Chm)*
Allan E. Bulley III *(Co-Chm & CEO)*

Subsidiaries:

B&A Telecom   (1)
1755 W Armitage Ave, Chicago, IL 60622-1163
Tel.: (773) 235-2433
Web Site: http://www.bulley.com
Sales Range: $25-49.9 Million
Emp.: 20
General Contractor Specializing in Telecommunications Construction
N.A.I.C.S.: 236220
Allan E. Bulley *(Chm & CEO)*
Paul R. Hellerman *(COO)*
Stephen K. Sever *(VP)*

Bulley & Andrews Concrete Restoration   (1)
1755 W Armitage Ave, Chicago, IL 60622
Tel.: (773) 235-2433
Web Site: http://www.takaonagai.com
Concrete Restoration Services
N.A.I.C.S.: 237990

BULLOCH & BULLOCH, INC.
309 Cash Memorial Blvd, Forest Park, GA 30297
Tel.: (404) 762-4047
Web Site:
http://www.jphallexpress.com
Year Founded: 1988
Freight Trucking Services
N.A.I.C.S.: 484230
Steve Norsworthy *(Dir-Safety & Compliance)*
Shawn Tolbert *(Mgr-Customer Svc)*
Tom Schmitt *(Chm, Pres & CEO)*

BULLOCKS EXPRESS TRANSPORTATION
510 E 51st Ave, Denver, CO 80216
Tel.: (303) 296-0302
Rev.: $29,874,408
Emp.: 200
Contract Haulers
N.A.I.C.S.: 484121
Bruce Bullock *(Owner)*

BULLSEYE DATABASE MARKETING LLC
5546 S 104th E Ave, Tulsa, OK 74146-6508
Tel.: (918) 587-1731
Web Site:
http://www.bullseyedm.com
Year Founded: 1989
Rev.: $7,050,000
Emp.: 12
Fiscal Year-end: 12/31/04
Advertising Agencies, Consulting, Consumer Marketing, Direct Marketing, E-Commerce, Financial, Strategic Planning
N.A.I.C.S.: 541810
Mark Jennemann *(Pres)*
Barbara Lacey *(VP)*
Pauline Dugger *(Controller)*

BULLYAN TRAILER SALES INC.
4956 Miller Trunk Hwy, Duluth, MN 55811
Tel.: (218) 729-9111
Web Site: https://www.bullyanrvs.com
Sales Range: $10-24.9 Million
Emp.: 40
Mfr Motor Homes
N.A.I.C.S.: 441210
Joe Bullyan *(Pres)*

BULOVA TECHNOLOGIES GROUP, INC.
1501 Lk Ave SE, Largo, FL 33771
Tel.: (727) 536-6666   FL
Web Site:
http://www.bulovatechgroup.com
Year Founded: 1979
Rev.: $25,150,112
Assets: $20,293,319
Liabilities: $46,314,521
Net Worth: ($26,021,202)
Earnings: ($500,296)
Fiscal Year-end: 09/30/17
Holding Company; Military & Industrial Products Distr & Services
N.A.I.C.S.: 551112
Stephen L. Gurba *(Chm, Pres & CEO)*
Michael J. Perfetti *(CFO)*
Anthony Pelliccio *(Dir-Logistics & Customer Svc)*

Subsidiaries:

BT-Twiss Transport LLC   (1)
1501 Lake Ave SE, Largo, FL 33771
Tel.: (866) 584-1585
Web Site: http://www.twisstransport.com
Emp.: 200
Freight Shipping
N.A.I.C.S.: 484121
Nick Damico *(Gen Mgr)*

Subsidiary (Domestic):

Twiss Transport, Inc.   (2)
1501 Lake Ave SE, Largo, FL 33771
Tel.: (727) 584-1585
Web Site: http://www.twisstransport.com
Freight Trucking Services
N.A.I.C.S.: 484121

Subsidiary (Domestic):

Twiss Cold Storage, Inc.   (3)
6422 Harney Rd, Tampa, FL 33610
Tel.: (813) 247-7111
Web Site: http://www.twisscoldstorage.com

Lessors of Miniwarehouses & Self-Storage Units
N.A.I.C.S.: 531130
Rick White *(Mgr)*

Twiss Logistics Inc.   (3)
860 1st St S, Winter Haven, FL 33880-3666
Tel.: (863) 291-0300
Web Site: http://www.bt-twisstransport.com
Freight Transportation Arrangement
N.A.I.C.S.: 488510
George Calza *(Mgr)*

Bulova Technologies Machinery LLC   (1)
1501 Lake Ave SE, Largo, FL 33771
Tel.: (727) 536-6666
Web Site: http://www.bulovatech.com
Emp.: 3
Industrial Machinery Distr
N.A.I.C.S.: 423830
Gary L. Shapiro *(Pres)*
Michael J. Perfetti *(CFO & VP-Ops)*

BUMGARNER OIL CO. INC.
2004 Highland Ave NE, Hickory, NC 28601
Tel.: (828) 322-4377
Web Site:
https://www.bumgarneroil.com
Sales Range: $25-49.9 Million
Emp.: 15
Fuel Oil
N.A.I.C.S.: 424720
Glenn A. Bumgarner *(Pres)*
David Bumgarner *(VP)*

BUMPERDOC INC.
10731 Treena St Ste 200, San Diego, CA 92131
Tel.: (858) 505-0770   CA
Web Site: http://www.bumperdoc.com
Year Founded: 1998
Automotive Repair & Maintenance Shops Owner, Operator & Franchisor
N.A.I.C.S.: 811111
Triston Miller *(CEO & Founder)*
Ray Wahoff *(Pres & COO)*
Richard Perez *(Dir-Marketing-Operations)*
Buddy Guyette *(Dir-Franchise Support)*

BUN PENNY INC.
6442 Lochridge Rd, Columbia, MD 21044-4033
Tel.: (410) 730-4100
Rev.: $10,400,000
Emp.: 70
Delicatessen Operator
N.A.I.C.S.: 445110
Jeff P. Ditter *(Pres)*

BUNCH TRANSPORT INC.
3325 Hill Park Dr, North Charleston, SC 29418
Tel.: (843) 207-5100
Web Site:
http://www.bunchtransport.com
Year Founded: 1984
Rev.: $11,000,000
Emp.: 90
Trucking Except Local
N.A.I.C.S.: 484121
Paula Long *(Mgr-Acctg)*

BUNGOBOX
305 Ryder Ln Ste 1325, Casselberry, FL 32707
Tel.: (407) 261-5531
Web Site: http://www.bungobox.com
Year Founded: 2009
Sales Range: $1-9.9 Million
Emp.: 7
Reusable Moving Box Rental Services
N.A.I.C.S.: 532289
Tom Cannon *(Co-Founder & CEO)*
Bob Cannon *(Co-Founder & Pres)*

BUNKER CORPORATION
1131 Via Callejon, San Clemente, CA 92673
Tel.: (949) 361-3935
Web Site:
http://www.energysuspension.com
Rev.: $12,000,000
Emp.: 140
Motor Vehicle Body Components & Frame
N.A.I.C.S.: 336390
Don Bunker *(Pres)*

Subsidiaries:

Urethane Engineering Inc.   (1)
960 Calle Amanecer Ste B, San Clemente, CA 92673
Tel.: (949) 492-0265
Web Site:
http://www.energysuspension.com
Rev.: $1,500,000
Emp.: 4
Custom Compound Purchased Resins
N.A.I.C.S.: 325991

BUNKER HILL CAPITAL LP
260 Franklin St Ste 1860, Boston, MA 02110
Tel.: (617) 720-4030
Web Site:
http://www.bunkerhillcapital.com
Sales Range: $25-49.9 Million
Emp.: 10
Private Equity Investment Firm
N.A.I.C.S.: 523999
Mark H. DeBlois *(Co-Founder & Mng Partner)*
Jason H. Hurd *(Co-Founder & Partner)*
Angela Jajko *(Office Mgr)*
Robert L. Clark Jr. *(Founder & Mng Partner)*

Subsidiaries:

ImportLA, Inc.   (1)
315 Cloverleaf Dr Ste K, Baldwin Park, CA 91706
Tel.: (626) 336-8118
Web Site: http://www.importla.com
Sales Range: $10-24.9 Million
Emp.: 15
Enables Small-to Medium-Sized Companies to Source Products & Services
N.A.I.C.S.: 541614
Michael Chen *(Founder & Mng Dir)*

BUNKOFF GENERAL CONTRACTORS
1041 Watervliet Shaker Rd, Albany, NY 12205
Tel.: (518) 869-0981
Sales Range: $10-24.9 Million
Emp.: 35
Nonresidential Construction Services
N.A.I.C.S.: 236220
Richard Bunkoff *(Pres)*

BUNN-O-MATIC CORPORATION
1400 Stevenson Dr, Springfield, IL 62703-4228
Tel.: (217) 529-6601   DE
Web Site:
http://www.bunnomatic.com
Year Founded: 1952
Sales Range: $150-199.9 Million
Emp.: 400
Coffee Brewing Equipment; Iced Tea Brewers, Coffee Grinders, Hot Water Machines; Coffee & Tea Filters; Water Conditioners
N.A.I.C.S.: 333310
Arthur H. Bunn *(Pres & CEO)*

Subsidiaries:

Bunn-O-Matic Corp. of Canada Ltd.   (1)
280 Industrial Pkwy S, Aurora, L4G 3T9,

Bunn-O-Matic Corporation—(Continued)

ON, Canada **(100%)**
Tel.: (905) 841-2866
Web Site: http://www.bunnomatic.com
Sales Range: $25-49.9 Million
Emp.: 170
Mfr of Coffee Makers
N.A.I.C.S.: 335210
Ken Cox *(VP-Sls & Mktg)*

BUNTING BEARINGS CORP.
1001 Holland Park Blvd, Holland, OH
43528-9287
Tel.: (419) 866-7000
Web Site:
  http://www.buntingbearings.com
Year Founded: 1855
Sales Range: $50-74.9 Million
Emp.: 170
Bronze, Plastic, Powdered Metal, Aluminum Bearings & Solid Bars Mfr
N.A.I.C.S.: 331529
George Mugford *(Pres)*

BUNTING CONSTRUCTION CORPORATION
32996 Lighthouse Rd, Selbyville, DE
19975
Tel.: (302) 436-5124
Web Site:
  https://www.buntingconstruction.com
Year Founded: 1971
Sales Range: $10-24.9 Million
Emp.: 18
New Single Family Housing Construction Services
N.A.I.C.S.: 236115
C. Coleman Bunting Jr. *(Pres)*

BUNTING MAGNETICS CO.
500 S Spencer Rd, Newton, KS
67114-4109
Tel.: (316) 284-2020
Web Site:
  https://www.buntingmagnetics.com
Year Founded: 1959
Sales Range: $10-24.9 Million
Emp.: 140
Magnetic Conveyors, Magnetic Separators & Filters, Cast Magnets, Ceramic Holding Magnets, Printing Cylinders Mfr
N.A.I.C.S.: 327110
Robert J. Bunting Sr. *(Pres & CEO)*

Subsidiaries:

Bunting Magnetics Co. **(1)**
1150 Howard St, Elk Grove Village, IL
60007-2210
Tel.: (847) 593-2060
Web Site: http://www.buntingmagnetics.com
Magnets & Magnet-Related Equipment for Material Handling, Magnetic Separation, Metal Detection & Printing
N.A.I.C.S.: 213114
Robert J. Bunting *(Gen Mgr-Magnet Matls)*

Bunting Magnetics Europe
Limited **(1)**
Northbridge Road, Berkhamsted, HP4 1EH,
Herts, United Kingdom
Tel.: (44) 1442 875081
Web Site: http://www.buntingeurope.com
Sales Range: $10-24.9 Million
Emp.: 30
Magnet Product Mfr
N.A.I.C.S.: 332999
Simon Ayling *(Mng Dir)*

Subsidiary (Domestic):

MagDev Limited **(2)**
Unit 23 Ash Industrial Estate Kembrey Park,
Swindon, SN2 8UN, Wiltshire, United
Kingdom **(100%)**
Tel.: (44) 1793425600
Web Site: http://www.magdev.co.uk
Sales Range: $25-49.9 Million
Emp.: 20
Magnetic Materials Distr
N.A.I.C.S.: 423690

Dave Richards *(Mgr-Technical)*
Yvonne Mills *(Gen Mgr & Dir-Fin)*
Andy Hayling *(Mgr-Technical)*
Alex Tremlett *(Mgr-Sls)*

Magnet Applications Inc. **(1)**
12 Industrial Dr, Du Bois, PA 15801
Tel.: (814) 375-9145
Web Site:
  http://www.magnetapplications.com
Emp.: 22
Magnetic Assembly Mfr
N.A.I.C.S.: 334610
Donald Lindstrom *(Gen Mgr)*

BUNTING MANAGEMENT GROUP, INC.
2677 Willakenzie Rd Ste 3, Eugene,
OR 97401
Tel.: (541) 344-0028
Web Site:
  https://www.buntingmanagement.com
Rev.: $11,314,455
Emp.: 6
Real Estate Investment Services
N.A.I.C.S.: 531210
Brandt Bunting *(Pres)*

BUQUET & LE BLANC INC.
18145 Petroleum Dr, Baton Rouge,
LA 70809-6125
Tel.: (225) 753-4150
Web Site: https://www.buquet-leblanc.com
Year Founded: 1945
Sales Range: $25-49.9 Million
Emp.: 87
Provider of Contracting Services
N.A.I.C.S.: 236220
Gary D. Noel *(Owner & Mgr-Quality Assurance)*
Randy G. Roussel *(Sr Project Mgr)*
William T. Firesheets II *(Pres)*
Robert Bogan III *(Treas)*

BUQUET & LEBLANC CONTRACTORS, INC.
18145 Petroleum Dr, Baton Rouge,
LA 70809
Tel.: (225) 753-4150
Web Site: https://www.buquet-leblanc.com
Year Founded: 1946
Sales Range: $10-24.9 Million
Emp.: 87
Civil Engineering Services
N.A.I.C.S.: 237310
Gary D. Noel *(Owner & Mgr-Quality Assurance)*

BUQUET DISTRIBUTING COMPANY, INC.
100 Eagle Nest Ct, Houma, LA 70360
Tel.: (985) 853-3100
Web Site:
  http://www.abwholesaler.com
Rev.: $13,600,000
Emp.: 64
Beer & Ale Merchant Whslr
N.A.I.C.S.: 424810
Glenny L. Buquet *(Treas & Sec)*
James J. Buquet III *(Pres & CEO)*

BURCH FOOD SERVICE INC.
108 Stallcup Dr, Sikeston, MO
63801-2834
Tel.: (573) 471-3003
Web Site: https://www.burchfood.com
Year Founded: 1972
Sales Range: $10-24.9 Million
Emp.: 100
Provider of Vending Services
N.A.I.C.S.: 445132
Steven H. Burch *(Pres)*

BURCH MANAGEMENT CO., INC.

10723 Composite Dr, Dallas, TX
75220
Tel.: (214) 358-0055
Web Site: http://www.babydolls.com
Sales Range: $25-49.9 Million
Emp.: 1,450
Office Administrative Services
N.A.I.C.S.: 561110
Steven W. Craft *(VP)*
Kathie K. Golden *(VP)*
Gene Leclaire *(VP)*
Bert Stair *(Sec & VP)*
Duncan Burch *(Pres)*

BURD & FLETCHER COMPANY
5151 E Geospace Dr, Independence,
MO 64056-3321
Tel.: (816) 257-0291 **MO**
Web Site:
  https://www.burdfletcher.com
Year Founded: 1886
Sales Range: $25-49.9 Million
Emp.: 300
Mfr of Folding Cartons
N.A.I.C.S.: 322212
Peter A. Young *(Sec & Exec VP)*
John A. Young III *(Chm & CEO)*

Subsidiaries:

The ALC Group **(1)**
219 W 18th St, Kansas City, MO 64108
Tel.: (816) 421-8335
Web Site: http://www.artlithocraft.com
Emp.: 60
Commercial Printing Services
N.A.I.C.S.: 323111
Byron Pendleton *(Pres)*
Brenda Frick *(VP-Sls)*

BURDEN SALES COMPANY
1015 W O St, Lincoln, NE 68528
Tel.: (402) 474-5167 **NE**
Web Site:
  https://www.surpluscenter.com
Year Founded: 1967
Sales Range: $10-24.9 Million
Emp.: 45
Mail Order Sales of Farm Machinery
N.A.I.C.S.: 459999
David P. Burden *(Pres)*
Chris Cole *(VP-Sls)*

Subsidiaries:

Surplus Center **(1)**
1015 W O St, Lincoln, NE 68528
Tel.: (402) 474-4055
Web Site: http://www.surpluscenter.com
Emp.: 50
Wholesale Compressors, Power Plants, Hydraulics & Electronic Components
N.A.I.C.S.: 423490
David P. Burden *(Pres)*
Chris Cole *(VP-Sls)*
John Burden *(VP)*

BURDICK PLUMBING & HEATING CO
1175 N 20th St, Decatur, IL 62525
Tel.: (217) 429-2385
Web Site:
  http://www.burdickplumbing.com
Sales Range: $10-24.9 Million
Emp.: 32
Plumbing Contractor
N.A.I.C.S.: 238220
Doug Burdick *(Chm & Pres)*
Jeffery Burdick *(VP)*
Mike Braye *(Project Mgr)*
Rhonda Moyer *(Office Mgr)*

BURDICK TOYOTA
5947 E Cir Dr, Cicero, NY 13039
Tel.: (315) 458-7590
Web Site:
  http://toyota.driversvillage.com
Sales Range: $10-24.9 Million
Emp.: 45

Car Whslr
N.A.I.C.S.: 441110
Kevin Burdick *(Owner)*
Keith Naples *(Mgr-Fin)*

BURDITCH MARKETING COMMUNICATIONS
6240 Trimross Ave, Los Angeles, CA
90068
Tel.: (323) 932-6262
Web Site: http://www.burditchmc.com
Sales Range: $10-24.9 Million
Emp.: 20
Advetising Agency
N.A.I.C.S.: 541810
Paul Burditch *(Pres)*
Brian Garrido *(Owner)*
Carrol Gettko *(Sr VP)*
Dan Howard *(VP-Los Angeles)*

BURFORD CAPITAL LLC
350 Madison Ave, New York, NY
10017
Tel.: (212) 235-6820
Web Site:
  http://www.burfordcapital.com
Rev.: $424,977,000
Assets: $2,318,982,000
Liabilities: $955,828,000
Net Worth: $1,363,154,000
Earnings: $317,577,000
Emp.: 120
Fiscal Year-end: 12/31/18
Financial Services
N.A.I.C.S.: 523999
Peter Benzian *(Mng Dir)*
Ernest J. Getto *(Mng Dir)*
Elizabeth O'Connell *(Chief Strategy Officer)*
Aviva O. Will *(Co-COO)*
Christopher Bogart *(CEO)*
Leslie Paster *(Controller-Fin)*
Leah Guggenheimer *(Mng Dir & Chief Innovation Officer)*
Jim Ballan *(Head-IR)*
Craig Batchelor *(Sr VP)*
Philip Braverman *(Mng Dir-Tax & HR)*
Christopher Catalano *(Mng Dir)*
Suzanne Grosso *(VP)*
Joshua Harris *(VP)*
Mark Klein *(Chief Admin Officer & Gen Counsel)*
John Lazar *(Mng Dir)*
G. Andrew Lundberg *(Mng Dir)*
David Perla *(Co-COO)*
Kenneth A. Brause *(CFO)*

BURGER CHRYSLER-JEEP
2600 S 3rd St, Terre Haute, IN 47802
Tel.: (812) 645-3039
Web Site:
  http://www.burgerchryslerjeep.net
Sales Range: $10-24.9 Million
Emp.: 60
New Car Retailer
N.A.I.C.S.: 441110
Kevin Caldweel *(Owner)*

BURGER STREET INCORPORATED
10903 Alder Cir, Dallas, TX 75238
Tel.: (214) 349-9600
Web Site:
  http://www.burgerstreet.com
Rev.: $10,900,000
Emp.: 6
Grills Eating Places
N.A.I.C.S.: 722513
Liwei Waugh *(Chm)*

BURGERBUSTERS INC.
2242 W Great Neck Rd, Virginia
Beach, VA 23451
Tel.: (757) 412-0112
Sales Range: $10-24.9 Million
Emp.: 25

Mexican Restaurant
N.A.I.C.S.: 722511
Tassos Paphites *(Pres)*
Debora Fitzgerald *(Mgr-HR)*

BURGESS & NIPLE, INC.

5085 Reed Rd, Columbus, OH 43220
Tel.: (614) 459-2050 OH
Web Site:
 http://www.burgessniple.com
Year Founded: 1912
Sales Range: $50-74.9 Million
Emp.: 400
Engineering & Architectural Services
N.A.I.C.S.: 541330
Ed Muccillo *(Co-Owner & Chm)*
Mark Bernhardt *(Co-Owner, Pres & CEO)*
Rachel Headings *(Dir-Mktg Comm)*

Subsidiaries:

Burgess & Niple, Inc. (1)
1500 N Priest Dr Ste 102, Tempe, AZ 85281
Tel.: (602) 244-8100
Web Site: http://www.burgessniple.com
Sales Range: $10-24.9 Million
Emp.: 10
Engineers & Architects
N.A.I.C.S.: 541330
Ed Muccillo *(Dir-Arizona)*
Mark Bernhardt *(Co-Owner & Chm)*

Burgess & Niple, Inc. - Chantilly (1)
4160 Pleasant Vly Rd, Chantilly, VA 20151-1226
Tel.: (703) 631-9630
Web Site: http://www.burgessniple.com
Emp.: 25
Engineeering Services
N.A.I.C.S.: 541330
Dennis M. Thomas *(Reg Dir)*

Burgess & Niple, Inc. - Forth Worth (1)
3950 Fossil Creek Blvd Ste 210, Fort Worth, TX 76137
Tel.: (817) 306-1444
Web Site: http://www.burgessniple.com
Engineering & Architectural Services
N.A.I.C.S.: 541330
Billy Wendland *(Dir)*

Burgess & Niple, Inc. - Painesville (1)
100 W Erie St, Painesville, OH 44077
Tel.: (440) 354-9700
Web Site: http://www.burgessniple.com
Engineering & Architectural Services
N.A.I.C.S.: 541330
Mark Hutson *(Reg Dir)*

BURGESS CARRIAGE HOUSE INC.

8921 US Hwy 19 N, Pinellas Park, FL 33782
Tel.: (727) 576-7207
Web Site:
 http://www.hhinteriors.com
Sales Range: $10-24.9 Million
Emp.: 40
Furniture Retailer
N.A.I.C.S.: 449110
James M. Burgess *(Pres)*

BURGESS CIVIL, LLC

7816 Professional Pl, Tampa, FL 33637
Tel.: (813) 906-1350
Web Site:
 http://www.burgesscivil.com
Year Founded: 2014
Sales Range: $10-24.9 Million
Emp.: 55
Sewage & Drainage Construction Services
N.A.I.C.S.: 237990
Ben Burgess *(Owner)*

BURGESS COMPUTER DECISIONS, INC.

3170 Macarthur Blvd, Northbrook, IL 60062
Tel.: (847) 205-1922
Web Site: http://www.bcdvideo.com
Year Founded: 1999
Sales Range: $25-49.9 Million
Emp.: 23
Computer Products Reseller
N.A.I.C.S.: 423430
Jeffrey Burgess *(Pres)*
Elizabeth Cikowski *(Exec VP)*
Tom Larson *(Dir-Sls & Engrg)*
Nana Mintah *(Mgr-Fin)*
Joe Silva *(Dir-Ops)*
Alexander Burgess *(Mgr-Supply Chain Ops)*
Eugene Kozlovitser *(Dir-Tech)*
Kristen Costello *(Mgr-Mktg)*

BURGESS LIGHTING & DISTRIBUTING CO.

3601 Forestville Rd, Forestville, MD 20747
Tel.: (301) 568-8000
Web Site:
 https://www.burgesslighting.com
Rev.: $10,961,445
Emp.: 40
Lighting Fixtures, Residential
N.A.I.C.S.: 445110
Thomas Early *(Pres)*

BURGESS PIGMENT COMPANY

525 Beck Blvd, Sandersville, GA 31082
Tel.: (478) 552-2544 GA
Web Site:
 https://www.burgesspigment.com
Year Founded: 1948
Sales Range: $150-199.9 Million
Emp.: 162
Processor of Kaolin & Alumina
N.A.I.C.S.: 327992
Robert S. Burgess *(Pres)*
Malcolm S. Burgess *(Founder)*

Subsidiaries:

Burgess Pigment Company (1)
525 Beck Blvd, Sandersville, GA 31082
Tel.: (478) 552-2544
Web Site: http://www.burgesspigment.com
Aluminum Silicates Producer
N.A.I.C.S.: 325998
Robert S. Burgess *(Exec VP)*

BURGESS STEEL PRODUCTS CORP

200 W Forest Ave, Englewood, NJ 07631
Tel.: (201) 871-3500
Web Site:
 https://www.burgesssteel.com
Year Founded: 1976
Sales Range: $25-49.9 Million
Emp.: 70
Fabricated Structural Metal
N.A.I.C.S.: 523999
Brian Krug *(Project Mgr)*

BURIEN TOYOTA

15025 1st Ave S, Burien, WA 98148
Tel.: (206) 243-0700
Web Site:
 https://www.burientoyota.com
Year Founded: 1983
Sales Range: $25-49.9 Million
Emp.: 97
New Car Dealers
N.A.I.C.S.: 441110
Alan Anderson *(Pres)*
Pat Dillon *(Gen Mgr)*
Dean Anderson *(Owner)*

BURK ADVERTISING & MARKETING

302 N Market Ste 400, Dallas, TX 75202
Tel.: (214) 953-0494 TX
Web Site: http://www.wambam.com
Year Founded: 1991
Sales Range: $1-9.9 Million
Emp.: 7
Fiscal Year-end: 12/31/01
Advetising Agency
N.A.I.C.S.: 541810
B. Bailey Burk *(Partner & VP)*
Gene Hardon *(CFO)*

BURK ROYALTY CO.

PO Box 94903, Wichita Falls, TX 76308-2829
Tel.: (940) 397-8600 TX
Web Site: http://www.burkroyalty.com
Year Founded: 1934
Sales Range: $125-149.9 Million
Emp.: 50
Oil Production
N.A.I.C.S.: 211120
David A. Kimbell *(Pres)*
Mike Elyea *(Treas & Sr VP-Fin)*
Stephen R. Stults *(Sr VP-Ops)*
Dustan Mathews *(VP-Acctg)*
Pat Hensley *(Sec)*
Tammie Henderson *(VP-Admin)*
Stan Kimbell *(Sr VP-Environmental & Real Estate)*
David Kimbell Jr. *(Mgr)*
G. T. Kimbell II *(Sr VP-South Texas & Mgr)*

Subsidiaries:

Kibo Compressor Corp. (1)
PO Box 94903, Wichita Falls, TX 76308-0903
Tel.: (940) 397-8600
Web Site: http://www.burkroyalty.com
Sales Range: $25-49.9 Million
Emp.: 45
Transmission of Natural Gas
N.A.I.C.S.: 213112
David A. Kimbell *(Chm & Pres)*

BURKE & HERBERT BANK & TRUST COMPANY

100 S Fairfax St, Alexandria, VA 22314
Tel.: (703) 684-1655
Web Site:
 http://www.burkeherbertbank.com
Year Founded: 1852
Rev.: $120,088,000
Assets: $3,432,644,000
Liabilities: $3,047,767,000
Net Worth: $384,877,000
Earnings: $26,499,000
Emp.: 399
Fiscal Year-end: 12/31/20
Commericial Banking
N.A.I.C.S.: 522110
Christopher A. Tomasino *(VP)*
Noble W. Rubenstein *(VP)*
Jeffrey L. Stryker *(CFO & Sr Exec VP)*
Teresa M. DeMarco *(VP-Loan Ops)*
Joseph P. Collum *(Exec VP-Branch & Bus Banking & Dir-Branch & Bus Banking)*
Emily S. Debeniotis *(Sr VP-HR & Dir-HR)*
E. Hunt Burke *(Chm)*
S. Laing Hinson *(Vice Chm)*
Terry Cole *(CMO & Exec VP-Mktg)*
Shannon B. Rowan *(Exec VP-Trust & Wealth Mgmt Svcs & Dir-Wealth Mgmt & Trust Svcs)*
Jeffrey A. Welch *(Chief Credit Officer & Exec VP)*
Nicholas Greksouk *(Sr VP-Fin)*
Jennifer P. Schmidt *(VP-Compliance)*
Nicholas J. Fitzgerald *(VP-Project Mgmt)*

Daniel E. Adamson *(Branch Mgr-Vienna)*
Dawn N. Boynton *(VP)*
Noemie C. Cam *(VP)*
Kripa Subramanian *(VP)*
Erik J. Darm *(VP)*
Nancy Hong *(VP)*
Shon B. Koly *(VP)*
David F. Wallace *(VP-Learning & Dev)*
Penelope M. Barnett *(VP)*
Joseph D. Bonaccorsy *(VP-Consumer Lending)*
John W. Hill *(VP-Comml & Industrial Lending)*
Marina Lubbers *(VP)*
Jane Petty Lichter *(VP)*
Mary S. Edwards *(VP-Comml Credit)*
Adriana C. Johnson *(VP)*
John Woolfolk Burke *(Co-Founder)*
Arthur Herbert *(Co-Founder)*
David P. Boyle *(Pres & CEO)*
Matthew T. Tikoyan *(VP)*
Erica K. Swanton *(VP)*
Dean Sosa *(VP)*
Iwona Saoudi *(VP)*
Matthew W. Rucker *(VP)*
Elizabeth L. Ray *(VP)*
Hector D. Ochoa *(VP)*
Ann Marie Moore *(VP)*
Christine M. McNamara *(VP)*
Brian T. Lawrence *(VP)*
Cheryle L. Mack *(VP)*
Michael J. Giles *(VP)*
Ahmed Hachim *(VP)*
James W. Harper *(VP)*
Victoria A. Hatfield *(VP)*
Lenny X. Hesser *(VP)*
Travis H. Clarke *(VP)*
Karen M. Clinton *(VP)*
Gregory P. Mellors *(Sr VP-Comml & Industrial Banking)*
Kendrick Smith *(Exec VP-Ops)*
Jeffrey M. Aleshire *(Sr VP-Comml Real Estate Lending)*
Alexis F. Santin *(Sr VP-Treasury Mgmt)*
Araba A. Brobbey *(VP-Branch Banking)*
Derrick M. Copeland *(VP-Corp Security)*
Carl A. Ford *(VP-IT)*
Yvette M. Golladay *(VP-Mktg)*
Philip J. Harvilla *(VP-Comml Credit)*
K. C. Ramita *(VP-Branch Banking)*
Daniel S. Kendle *(VP-Acctg)*
Joseph R. Matusek *(VP-Ops)*
Debra L. Mills *(VP-Project Mgmt)*
John E. Osborn *(VP-Comml Credit)*
Lee Pugh *(VP-Comml & Industrial Lending)*
Leonid Rann *(VP-Comml & Industrial Lending)*
Jeffrey Rouse *(VP-Comml & Industrial Lending)*
Catherine E. Slepitza *(VP-Ops)*
John A. Tomasello *(VP-Consumer Mortgage)*
Sandra N. Vasquez *(VP-Branch Banking)*
Khalil Y. Abu-Ghannam *(VP)*
Daniel A. Andryszak *(VP)*
Suman Barua *(VP)*
Josefina M. Beck *(VP)*
John Dan Convery Jr. *(VP)*
Edward W. Kraemer Jr. *(VP)*
Henry B. Swoope V *(VP-Private Banking)*

Subsidiaries:

Burke & Herbert Financial Services Corp. (1)
Tel.: (703) 684-1655
Web Site:
 https://www.burkeandherbertbank.com
Emp.: 800

Burke & Herbert Bank & Trust
Company—(Continued)

Bank Holding Company
N.A.I.C.S.: 551111

BURKE BROTHERS INC.
519 Stone Harbor Blvd, Cape May,
NJ 08210
Tel.: (609) 465-8200
Web Site:
https://www.burkemotorgroup.com
Rev.: $12,100,000
Emp.: 90
Automobiles, New & Used
N.A.I.C.S.: 441110
Ray Burke *(Pres)*

BURKE ENGINEERING COMPANY
9700 Factorial Way, South El Monte,
CA 91733-1799
Tel.: (626) 579-0039   CA
Year Founded: 1949
Sales Range: $75-99.9 Million
Emp.: 115
Automatic Controls For Heating, Air
Conditioning & Refrigeration
N.A.I.C.S.: 423720
Kelly M. Burke *(CFO)*

BURKE FOUNDATION
320 E Buffalo St Ste 600, Milwaukee,
WI 53202
Tel.: (414) 477-5933   WI
Web Site:
https://www.theburkefoundation.org
Year Founded: 1995
Sales Range: $1-9.9 Million
Educational Support Services
N.A.I.C.S.: 611710
Deanna Singh *(Exec Dir)*

BURKE HANDLING SYSTEMS, INC.
431 Hwy 49 S, Jackson, MS 39218
Tel.: (601) 939-6600
Web Site:
http://www.burkehandling.com
Sales Range: $10-24.9 Million
Emp.: 50
Industrial Machinery & Equipment
Whslr
N.A.I.C.S.: 423830
Robert O. Burke *(Owner & CEO)*
Leonard Sharp *(Mgr-Svc)*
James Graham *(VP-Sls)*
Ted Gray *(VP-Sls)*
S. T. Ray *(Mgr-Allied Sls)*

BURKE INC.
500 W 7th St, Cincinnati, OH 45203
Tel.: (513) 241-5663
Web Site: https://www.burke.com
Sales Range: $25-49.9 Million
Emp.: 202
Market Analysis or Research
N.A.I.C.S.: 541910
Jeff Miller *(Pres & CEO)*
Diane Surette *(Chief Client Officer)*
Tara Marotti *(Sr VP & Head-Client Svcs)*
John Thomas *(Mng Dir-Healthcare & Sr VP)*

BURKE INC.
1800 Merriam Ln, Kansas City, KS
66106
Tel.: (913) 722-5658
Web Site:
https://www.pacesaver.com
Rev.: $12,000,000
Emp.: 70
Mfr of Motor Scooters & Related
Parts
N.A.I.C.S.: 336991

DuWayne Kramer *(Pres)*
Patty Luikart *(Office Mgr)*
Bob Dulle *(Plant Mgr)*

BURKE MARKETING CORPORATION
1516 S D Ave, Nevada, IA 50201
Tel.: (507) 434-6374
Web Site: https://www.burkecorp.com
Sales Range: $50-74.9 Million
Emp.: 350
Frozen Meats From Purchased Meat
N.A.I.C.S.: 311612
Thomas R. Burke *(VP-Pur)*
Chad A. Randick *(Pres)*
Douglas B. Cooprider *(VP-Sls & Mktg)*
Casey B. Frye *(VP-R&D)*
David J. Weber *(Sr VP-Ops)*

BURKE OIL CO., INC.
2097 Hwy 70, Connelly Springs, NC
28612
Tel.: (828) 397-3421   NC
Year Founded: 1963
Sales Range: $10-24.9 Million
Emp.: 120
Provider of Petroleum Products; Distributor of Home Heating Oil, Kerosene & Gasoline to Convenience
Stores
N.A.I.C.S.: 424720
Jerald N. Baker Jr. *(Pres)*

BURKE SUPPLY COMPANY INC.
255 US Hwy, Jersey City, NJ 07306
Tel.: (718) 643-2875
Web Site:
http://www.burkesupply.com
Year Founded: 1950
Sales Range: $1-9.9 Million
Emp.: 50
Distr of Janitorial, Chemical, Foodservice, Packaging, Paper, Cleaning &
Safety Supplies
N.A.I.C.S.: 424130
Robert Tillis *(Pres)*

BURKETT RESTAURANT EQUIPMENT, CO.
3011 Council St, Toledo, OH 43606
Tel.: (419) 242-7377
Web Site:
http://www.basequipment.com
Year Founded: 1987
Sales Range: $10-24.9 Million
Emp.: 45
Restaurant Equipment & Supplies
N.A.I.C.S.: 423440
Aicha Burkett *(Co-Pres)*
Jameel Burkett *(Co-Pres)*

BURKEY CONSTRUCTION CO. INC.
506 Morgantown Rd, Reading, PA
19611
Tel.: (610) 375-8591
Web Site: http://www.burkeynet.com
Sales Range: $10-24.9 Million
Industrial Building Construction Services
N.A.I.C.S.: 236210
Gregory Bechtel *(Dir-Estimating-LEED Accredited Pro)*
Eric G. Burkey *(Pres)*
Matthew Forrer *(Project Mgr-LEED Accredited Pro)*
Joan Wolf *(Project Mgr-LEED Accredited Pro)*
Franklin D. Watts *(Project Mgr-Registered Architect)*
John Frank *(Treas & Controller)*
Richard J. McDougall *(VP & Dir-Bus Dev)*

BURKHARDT EXCAVATING
30 North 40th St, Allentown, PA
18104
Tel.: (610) 395-4837
Sales Range: $10-24.9 Million
Emp.: 250
Excavation Work
N.A.I.C.S.: 238910

BURKHARDT LTD.
22 E 49th St 7th Fl/Media Logic, New
York, NY 10017
Tel.: (917) 328-2614   NY
Rev.: $10,310,000
Emp.: 13
N.A.I.C.S.: 541810
Luke Scott *(Copywriter & Specialist-Web)*
Dave Miranda *(CMO & Dir-Strategy)*
Susan Hello *(Mgr-Bus)*
Robert Billings *(Assoc Dir-Creative)*
Marcie Kovac *(Dir-Art & Designer)*
Cubby West *(Graphic Designer)*
Judy Salmon *(Mgr-Print Production)*
Jeff Devlin *(Dir-Brdcst Production)*
Ronald Burkhardt *(CEO & Dir-Creative)*

BURKHART DENTAL SUPPLY CO. INC.
2502 S 78th St, Tacoma, WA 98409-
9053
Tel.: (253) 474-7761   WI
Web Site:
https://www.burkhartdental.com
Year Founded: 1891
Sales Range: $10-24.9 Million
Emp.: 100
Dental Supplies & Equipment Distr
N.A.I.C.S.: 423450
Greg Biersack *(VP-Ops)*
Jim Lout *(Branch Mgr-TX-Austin)*
Jeff Reece *(VP-Sls)*
Lori Burkhart Isbell *(Pres)*
Anneene French *(Controller)*
Bill Sundheimer *(Dir-Mdse)*
Bret Leach *(Dir-Sls-Southern)*
Judi Griffin *(Dir-Logistics)*
Margaret Boyce-Cooley *(Dir-Practice Support Team)*
Michael Norton *(Dir-Equipment & Tech)*
Robb Marshall *(Mgr-Pur)*
Ron DeLaura *(Dir-IT)*
Shannon Bruil *(Dir-Exceptional Client Experience)*

BURKHOLDER'S HEATING & AIR CONDITIONING, INC.
383 Minor St, Emmaus, PA 18049
Tel.: (610) 816-6889
Web Site: https://www.burkholders-hvac.com
Sales Range: $10-24.9 Million
Emp.: 80
Heating & Air Conditioning Sales,
Service & Installation
N.A.I.C.S.: 238220
Robert Burkholder *(Pres)*
Dave Wieder *(VP)*
Don Miller *(Dir-Ops)*
Jamie Wiley *(Coord-Mktg)*

BURKMANN INDUSTRIES INC.
1111 Perryville Rd, Danville, KY
40422
Tel.: (859) 236-0400
Web Site: https://www.burkmann.com
Sales Range: $10-24.9 Million
Emp.: 40
Livestock Feeds
N.A.I.C.S.: 311119
David B. Williams *(Co-Founder & Pres)*
Shane Mason *(Dir-IT)*

BURLAGE HOTEL ASSOCIATES LLC
8th & Atlantic 701, Virginia Beach, VA
23451
Tel.: (757) 425-6439
Sales Range: $10-24.9 Million
Emp.: 70
Operative Builders
N.A.I.C.S.: 236117
L.C. Burlage Jr. *(Chm)*

BURLAN CORPORATION
2740 W Franklin Blvd, Gastonia, NC
28052
Tel.: (704) 867-3548
Web Site: http://www.burlan.com
Year Founded: 1971
Sales Range: $25-49.9 Million
Emp.: 200
Industrial Belting Reinforcement Fabric Mfr
N.A.I.C.S.: 314994
David Devan *(CFO)*
Tim Adams *(Mgr-Filament Div)*
Alice Auten *(Controller)*
Tammy Norman *(Mgr-Logistics)*
Lucy Scott *(Mgr-Laminate Tech)*
Gwin Hilton *(Mgr-Tech Sls)*
David Hinson *(VP-Ops)*

BURLESON'S INC.
301 Peters St, Waxahachie, TX
75165-2855
Tel.: (972) 937-4810   TX
Web Site: https://www.burlesons-honey.com
Year Founded: 1907
Sales Range: $75-99.9 Million
Emp.: 30
Honey & Honey Related Products Mfr
N.A.I.C.S.: 311999
T. E. Burleson Jr. *(Pres)*

BURLINGAME INDUSTRIES, INCORPORATED
3546 N Riverside Ave, Rialto, CA
92377-3802
Tel.: (909) 822-6000   CA
Year Founded: 1969
Sales Range: $75-99.9 Million
Emp.: 1,000
Mfr of Structural Clay Products
N.A.I.C.S.: 327120
Rich Jones *(COO)*
Rich Duquette *(Controller)*

BURLINGTON BASKET CO.
1404 W Mt Pleasant Rd, West Burlington, IA 52655
Tel.: (319) 754-6508   IA
Web Site:
http://www.burlingtonbasket.com
Year Founded: 1888
Sales Range: $25-49.9 Million
Emp.: 75
Fiber Products & Household Accessories Mfr
N.A.I.C.S.: 337126
Steve Thompson *(Exec VP)*
Rick Thompson *(CEO)*

Subsidiaries:

Burlington Timber   **(1)**
1404 W Mt Pleasant St, West Burlington, IA
52655   **(100%)**
Tel.: (319) 754-6508
Web Site: http://www.burlingtonbasket.com
Wicker Fiber Mfr
N.A.I.C.S.: 321999

Joanne Plastics   **(1)**
1418 West Mount Pleasant St, West Burlington, IA 52655-1020   **(100%)**
Tel.: (319) 752-1164
Sales Range: $50-74.9 Million
Emp.: 17
N.A.I.C.S.: 314910

Thompson Machines   (1)
1418 W Mount Pleasant St, West Burling-
ton, IA 52655-1020   (100%)
Tel.: (319) 754-6508
Web Site: http://www.burlingtonbasket.com
Sales Range: $1-9.9 Million
Emp.: 50
Basket Manufacturer
N.A.I.C.S.: 314910

BURLINGTON CAPITAL LLC

1 Burlington Pl 1004 Farnam St Ste
400, Omaha, NE 68102
Tel.: (402) 444-1630   DE
Web Site:
    https://burlingtoncapital.com
Year Founded: 1994
Rev.: $4,400,000
Emp.: 55
Fiscal Year-end: 12/31/06
Investment Banking & Real Estate
Management Services
N.A.I.C.S.: 523150
Lisa Y. Roskens (Chm, Pres & CEO)
Craig S. Allen (CFO)

BURLINGTON CAPITAL PART-
NERS, LLC

33 S Aberdeen Ste 304, Chicago, IL
60607-0000
Web Site:
    https://www.burlingtoncp.us
Private Equity
N.A.I.C.S.: 523999
Michael Baldwin (Partner)

Subsidiaries:

Martin Pallet, Inc.   (1)
1414 Industrial Ave SW, Massillon, OH
44647
Tel.: (330) 832-5309
Web Site: http://www.martinpallet.com
Sales Range: $1-9.9 Million
Emp.: 21
Wood Container & Pallet Mfr
N.A.I.C.S.: 321920
Judith Miller (VP)

BURLINGTON CHEMICAL
COMPANY INC.

8646 W Market St Ste 116, Greens-
boro, NC 27409-9447
Tel.: (336) 584-0111   NC
Web Site: http://www.burco.com
Year Founded: 1954
Sales Range: $10-24.9 Million
Emp.: 7
Chemicals & Allied Products
N.A.I.C.S.: 424690
Carolyn Ozment (Controller)

BURLINGTON HEALTHCARE
PROVIDERS, INC.

12425 Knoll Rd Ste 120, Elm Grove,
WI 53132
Tel.: (414) 858-2401
Web Site: http://www.bhpdoctors.com
Year Founded: 2002
Hospitals, Clinics & Other Medical
Facilities Temporary Staffing Services
N.A.I.C.S.: 561320
Matt Bratz (Pres)

BURLINGTON MOTORS, INC.

2920 S Church St, Burlington, NC
27215-5123
Tel.: (336) 584-4870   NC
Year Founded: 1964
Sales Range: $50-74.9 Million
Emp.: 97
New & Used Car Dealers
N.A.I.C.S.: 441110
Daryl Ingold (Owner)

BURLINGTON VERMONT CITY
ELECTRIC

585 Pine St, Burlington, VT 05401

Tel.: (802) 865-7300   VT
Web Site:
    https://www.burlingtonelectric.com
Year Founded: 1905
Sales Range: $25-49.9 Million
Emp.: 121
Provider of Electric Services
N.A.I.C.S.: 221118
Daryl J. Santerre (CFO)

BURMA BIBAS INC.

597 5th Ave Fl 10, New York, NY
10017
Tel.: (212) 750-2500
Web Site:
    http://www.burmabibas.com
Sales Range: $50-74.9 Million
Emp.: 10
Men's Sportswear & Boy's Neckwear
N.A.I.C.S.: 315990
Mortimer Klaus (CEO)
Robert Vinagray (CIO & Dir-IT)
Bob Parisi (Dir-Design)
George W. Camacho (VP-Sls)

BURMAX COMPANY INC.

28 Barretts Ave, Holtsville, NY 11742
Tel.: (631) 447-8700
Web Site: https://www.burmax.com
Year Founded: 1948
Barber Shop Equipment & Supplies
N.A.I.C.S.: 423850
Marc Centomini (VP)

Subsidiaries:

Product Club, Inc.   (1)
28 Barretts Ave, Holtsville, NY 11742
Tel.: (973) 664-0565
Web Site: http://www.productclub.com
Sales Range: $10-24.9 Million
Emp.: 10
Non-Durable Goods Whslr
N.A.I.C.S.: 424990
Eric B. Polesuk (Pres)

BURNAM HOLDING COMPA-
NIES INC

2407 Rangeline St, Columbia, MO
65202
Tel.: (573) 449-0091
Web Site: http://www.storage-
mart.com
Sales Range: $125-149.9 Million
Emp.: 500
Lessors Of Piers, Docks, Associated
Buildings & Facilities
N.A.I.C.S.: 531120
Mike Burnam (CEO)
Cris Burnam (Pres & COO)
Steve Dulle (CFO)

BURNETT & CO. INC.

1300 Post Oak Blvd Ste 700, Hous-
ton, TX 77056
Tel.: (713) 243-4300
Web Site: http://www.bcoinc.com
Sales Range: $25-49.9 Million
Emp.: 8
Insurance Agents, Brokers & Service
N.A.I.C.S.: 524210
John Burke Jr. (Pres)

BURNETT DAIRY COOP ASSO-
CIATION

11631 State Rd 70, Grantsburg, WI
54840
Tel.: (715) 689-2468
Web Site:
    https://www.burnettdairy.com
Sales Range: $50-74.9 Million
Emp.: 200
Natural Cheese
N.A.I.C.S.: 457210

BURNETT MEDICAL CENTER

257 W Saint George Ave, Grantsburg, WI 54840

Tel.: (715) 463-5353   WI
Web Site:
    https://www.burnettmedical.com
Year Founded: 1957
Sales Range: $10-24.9 Million
Emp.: 275
Health Care Srvices
N.A.I.C.S.: 622110
Charles Faught (CFO)
Gordon Lewis (CEO)

BURNETTE FOODS INC.

701 US Hwy 31, Elk Rapids, MI
49629
Tel.: (231) 264-8116
Web Site:
    https://www.burnettefoods.com
Rev.: $34,900,000
Emp.: 60
Fruit, Vegetable & Other Food Can-
ning & Whslr
N.A.I.C.S.: 311421
Ken Hoffman (Mgr-Ops)
Jennifer Boyer (Mgr-Quality)

BURNHAM ASSET MANAGE-
MENT CORP.

1325 6th Ave Fl 26, New York, NY
10019
Tel.: (212) 262-3100
Web Site:
    http://www.burnhamfunds.com
Rev.: $13,800,000
Emp.: 130
Money Market Mutual Funds
N.A.I.C.S.: 525910
Jon Burnham (Chm)
Debra Hyman (VP)
Steven Kapen (Mng Dir)
Mortimer Sullivan III (Portfolio Mgr-
Fixed Income)

BURNHAM BENEFITS INSUR-
ANCE SERVICES, INC.

2211 Michelson Dr Ste 1200, Irvine,
CA 92612
Tel.: (949) 833-2983
Web Site:
    https://www.burnhambenefits.com
Year Founded: 1995
Sales Range: $1-9.9 Million
Emp.: 38
General Insurance Services
N.A.I.C.S.: 524210
Kristen Mauger Allison (Pres & CEO)
Darin Gibson (Exec VP)
Scott Aston (VP)
Dan Exceen (VP)
Patrick Lowry (VP)
Doug Ramsthel (VP)
Melanie Thomas (VP)
Richard P. Asensio (VP & Dir-
Compliance)
Helen Vits (VP)
Bryan Bate (VP-Client Svcs)
Alicia Bergsto (Acct Mgr)
Ann Marie Estrada (VP)
Debra Farmer (VP)
Catherine Seitz (VP)
Vanessa Scarbo (Dir-HR & Ops)
Lorena Chavez (Supvr-Acct)
Stephanie Cregger (Supvr-Acct)
Sydney Dougherty (Supvr-Acct)
Allison Bliesner (VP)
Nooshin George (VP)
Corrine Choi (Sr Acct Mgr)
Raymond Tunnell (Sr VP)
Chris Krusiewicz (VP)
Mary Garcia (VP)
Rachel Aleknavicius (VP)
Steve Vilas (CFO & Partner)
Rosa White (Mgr-Mktg)
Nathan Ackeret (Mng Dir-LA Office &
VP)
Cathy Gee (VP)
Luis Milla (Chief Strategy Officer)
Margie Spear (VP)

BURNHAM INDUSTRIAL CON-
TRACTORS INC.

3229 Babcock Blvd, Pittsburgh, PA
15237
Tel.: (412) 366-6622
Web Site:
    http://www.burnhamins.com
Sales Range: $10-24.9 Million
Emp.: 25
Building Insulation Contracting Ser-
vices
N.A.I.C.S.: 238310
James P. Burnham Sr. (Pres)

BURNHAM RICHARDS AD-
VERTISING

2020 Riverside Dr, Green Bay, WI
54301
Tel.: (920) 406-1663
Sales Range: $10-24.9 Million
Emp.: 7
Advetising Agency
N.A.I.C.S.: 541810
David Richards (Owner & Dir-
Creative)

BURNING MAN PROJECT

660 Alabama St, San Francisco, CA
94110-2008
Tel.: (415) 865-3800   CA
Web Site: http://www.burningman.org
Year Founded: 2011
Sales Range: $1-9.9 Million
Emp.: 3
Cultural Promotion Services
N.A.I.C.S.: 541720
Doug Robertson (Fin Dir)
Charlie Dolman (Dir-Event Ops)
Elizabeth Scarborough (Assoc Dir-Art
Mgmt)
Glenda Solis (Mgr-Material Culture)
Wilfredo Sanchez Vega (Mgr-Black
Rock Ranger Ops)
Crimson Rose (Founder)
Jennifer Raiser (Treas)
Larry Harvey (Founder)
Marian Goodell (Founder & CEO)
Michael Mikel (Founder)
Will Roger Peterson (Founder &
Chm)

Subsidiaries:

Black Rock Arts Foundation   (1)
660 Alabama, San Francisco, CA 94110
Tel.: (415) 626-1248
Web Site: http://www.blackrockarts.org
Agents & Managers for Artists, Athletes,
Entertainers & Other Public Figures
N.A.I.C.S.: 711410

BURNIPS EQUIPMENT COM-
PANY

3260 142nd Ave, Dorr, MI 49323
Tel.: (616) 896-9190
Web Site: http://www.burnips.com
Emp.: 20
Agricultural Machinery & Equipment
N.A.I.C.S.: 423820
Carl VanderKolk (Gen Mgr-Dorr)
Gail VanderKolk (Gen Mgr-Dorr)
Craig Vander Kolk (Mgr-Sls)
Dave Smith (Mgr-Parts)
Susan Ostrom (Gen Mgr-
Coopersville)
Tom Healy (Mgr-Svc-Big Rapids)
Christy Mills (Gen Mgr-Hudson)
Jason Mills (Mgr-Svc-Hudson)
Jeff Bouman (Mgr-Svc-Dorr)
Matt Raterink (Mgr-Parts-
Coopersville)
Tory Bishop (Mgr-Parts-Hudson)

BURNS & MCDONNELL, INC.

9400 Ward Pkwy, Kansas City, MO
64114-3319
Tel.: (816) 333-9400   MO

Burns & McDonnell, Inc.—(Continued)

Web Site: https://www.burnsmcd.com
Year Founded: 1898
Emp.: 14,000
Engineeering Services
N.A.I.C.S.: 541330
Steve Linnemann (VP & Gen Mgr)
Doug Riedel (Sr VP-Water Solutions)
Ed Anello (VP-Houston)
John Olander (COO)
Chris Courtright (VP)
Don Chase (VP-Canada)
Brett Williams (Pres/Gen Mgr-New England)
Woody E. McOmber (VP)
Ray Kowalik (Chm, Chm, CEO & CEO)
Rick Halil (Gen Mgr-Energy)
Scott Clark (VP)
Paul Odum (VP)
Dan Korinek (VP & Dir-National Water Supply)
Jamie Butler (VP)
Greg Carlson (VP)
Craig Casey (VP)
Steven Schmidt (Mgr-Transportation Dept)
Jon Schwartz (Principal)
Oko Buckle (Principal)
Mahmoud Khalifa (Principal)
Parker Gregg (Dir-Bus Dev, Sls & Mktg-Oil, Gas & Chemical Grp-Houston)
Terry Cole (Mgr-Strategic Comm-Water Div-Atlanta)
Rich Miller (VP & Dir-IT)
Koi Morford (Principal)
Rob Rainbolt (Principal)
Kerrie Greenfelder (Project Mgr-Water Div)
Lori Top (Principal)
Wes Hardin (Principal)
Karen Bray (Principal)
Chris Cambridge (Mgr-Engrg)
Jose J. Rodriguez (Mgr-Transmission & Distr Project-Orlando)
Denys Stavnychyi (Mgr-Pipeline Project-Houston)
Randy Griffin (Gen Mgr-CDM Div)
Steve Nalefski (VP & Gen Mgr-Environmental Svcs)
Dotun Famakinwa (Principal)
Gene Sieve (VP)
Stephen Kane (VP-California)
Mark Lichtwardt (Sr VP)
Ken Gerling (VP)
Allen Xi (Sr VP)
Bret Pilney (VP-Aviation)
Yvonne Bilshausen (Sr Project Mgr-Natl & Intl Aviation-Chicago)
Amy Lewis (Mgr-Fin Project)
Joel DeBoer (VP)
Mal Warrick (Mgr-Bus Dev)
Renee Gartelos (Dir-HR)
Steven Beam (Bus Mgr)
Wayne Keller (Project Mgr)
Tami Anderson (Assoc Engr-Transmission Plng)
Robert Healy (Mgr-Renewable Energy Grp-Phoenix)
Steve Adcock (Sr Project Mgr-Houston)
Jeremy Wilkerson (Sr Project Mgr-Houston)
Kirsten Glesne (Sr Project Mgr-Denver)
Chris McFarland (Sr Project Mgr-Denver)
Matthew Kapusta (Mgr-Orlando)
Jose Rodriguez Alvarez (Mgr-Electrical Transmission & Distr-Atlanta)
Misam Taherbhai (Asst Mgr-Substation)

Patricia Scroggin (Reg Mgr-Energy Grp-Chicago)
Lana Tullis (Sr Engr-Staff)
Jim Coll (Sr Project Mgr-Natl Water Projects)
Don Schriber (Mgr-Bus Dev-Environmental Grp-Wallingford)
Jerome Farquharson (Principal & Mgr-Compliance & Infrastructure Protection Grp)
Tim Faber (VP)
Paul Callahan (Principal & Reg Grp Mgr)
Erica Bowyer-Grason (Project Mgr-Northeast)
Paul Sherman (Project Mgr)
Dave Barr (VP & Dir-Federal Projects)
Chris Baxter (VP)
Darin Brickman (VP)
Jon Wright (VP-Food & Consumer Products)
Leslie Duke (Pres-Houston)
Scott Newland (Sr VP & Gen Mgr-Chicago)
Rick Cramer (Mgr-Environmental Technologies)
Chris Dowdell (Project Mgr-Decommissioning & Demolition-Environmental Svcs)
Rafael Pagan (Project Mgr-Transmission & Distr-Washington)
Travis Blair (Project Mgr-Construction-Comml Design Build Grp)
Gregory Stribling (Project Mgr-Construction-Comml Design Build Grp)
Kristine Sutherlin (Mgr-Client)
Trevor Hoiland (Mgr-Design-Comml Design Build Grp)
Gene Khislavskiy (Sr Engr-Electrical-Atlanta)
Nathan Sims (Project Mgr-Aviation Sys)
Rafat Elahi (Sr Engr-Instrument & Controls-Houston)
Sam Allen (Mgr-Dept)
Scott Hungerford (Sr Engr-Instrument & Controls-Food & Consumer Products Grp)
Mike Thomas (Mgr-Environmental-Denver)
Holly Fults (Project Mgr-Environmental Svcs)
Morgan Lilly (Engr-Mechanical)
Jason Li (Engr-Instrument & Controls)
Anthony Paresa (Project Mgr-Federal Grp-Honolulu)
Jason Mayyak (Mgr-Transmission & Distr-Rocky Mountain & Pacific Northwest)
Chris Underwood (VP & Gen Mgr-Bus & Tech Solutions Grp)
Jeff Sittner (Dir-Bus Dev-Comml Design Build Grp)
Brett Pugh (Project Mgr-Denver)
Kelli Haden (Principal)
Julie Lorenz (Principal)
Todd Hunt (Principal)
Jason Turner (Principal)
Bryan Hawthorne (Principal)
Seth Hanebutt (Principal)
Meghan Calabro (Principal)
Pasanthi Vidyasagara (Principal)
Tyler Lamb (Sr Engr-Civil-Transmission & Distr-Phoenix)
Robert Bonar (Principal)
Dana Book (Principal)
Jeff DeWitt (Principal)
Dana Steph (Principal)
Michael Hathorne (Assoc Engr-Mechanical)
Mike Roush (Project Mgr-Energy Grp-Columbus)

Matthew Olearczyk (Project Mgr-Utility Consulting)
Chris Perrin (Mgr-Dev-Bus & Tech Solutions Grp)
Kevin Norman (Mgr-Strategic Partnerships-Bus & Tech Solutions Grp)
Robb Montgomery (Project Mgr-Bus & Tech Solutions Grp)
Jeff Kopp (Mgr-Utility Consulting Dept)
Steve Dresie (Mgr-Software & Tech Consulting)
Kevin Fuller (Mgr-Security Consulting-Bus & Tech Solutions Grp)
Max Dodge (Mgr-Bus Dev)
Dana Houston Jackson (Mgr-Project & Change-Bus & Tech Solutions Grp)
David Kinchen (Mgr-Water-Global Practice-Southwest)
Rich Mahaley (Mgr-Orlando)
Stacy Price (Principal)
Greg Fay (Product Mgr-Software Solutions Grp)
Phil Voegtle (Project Mgr-Global Facilities Grp-Denver)
Alissa Schuessler (VP & Dir-Acctg)
Laron Evans (Dir-Bus Diversity-Transmission & Distr Grp)
Tyler Shannon (Engr-Commissioning)
Jim Kirschbaum (Project Mgr-Aviation)
Peter Aarons (Dir-Aviation Dev-California)
Jeff Williamson (Mgr-Bus Dev)
Beth Freymiller (Project Mgr-Environmental-Minneapolis)
Rick Mena (Mgr-Oil, Gas & Chemical Consulting)
Jerry Price (Mgr-Oil, Gas & Chemical Consulting)
Christine Wood (Principal)
Cary Gallaway (Principal)
Mark Gaddy (Mgr-Commissioning-Southeast)
Mike DeBacker (VP & Gen Mgr-Transportation Grp)
Jon Conway (Project Dir-Transmission & Distr Grp)
Amanda Olson (Dir-Engrg-Transmission & Distr Grp)
Zach Herrington (Natl Dir-Construction-The Water Grp & Project Dir-Kansas City)
Agnes Otto (Dir-Transportation)
Kevin Syphard (Mng Dir-Chemical Bus)
Jason Hetherington (Mng Dir-Logistics & Midstream)
Dave Nispel (Mng Dir-Refining)
Meaghan McCaffrey (Mng Dir-Renewables & Emerging Markets-Oil, Gas & Chemical Grp)
Patricia Scroggin-Wicker (Dir-Process Tech-Energy Grp)
Cameron Garner (Project Mgr-Construction)
Dan Richards (Project Mgr-Mining Grp)
Tara McCullen (Principal)
Mark Jansen (Project Mgr-Aviation & Federal Grp-Florida)
Eric Perry (Sr Engr-Electrical)
Justin Sobol (Mgr-Water Grp-Southeast)
Todd Wicker (Sr Engr-Mechanical)

Subsidiaries:

AZCO Inc.   **(1)**
1025 E South River St, Appleton, WI 54915
Tel.: (920) 734-5791
Web Site: http://www.azco-inc.com
Emp.: 250
Industrial General Contractor & Fabricator
N.A.I.C.S.: 238220

John Trottier (Pres & CEO)
Christopher Muller (Dir-IT-AZCO Construction)
Greg A. Stock (CFO, Treas & VP)
David Recker (VP-Fabrication)
Scott Kennedy (Dir-Bus Dev)
Jenny Morrow (Gen Counsel & VP)
Steve Dreger (Mgr-Bus Dev-Field Svcs)
Al King (Gen Mgr-Minnesota Office)
Dan Ferris (Gen Mgr-Western Div)
Scott Koval (VP-Ops)
Dale Coenen (VP-Ops)
Robert Brockington (VP-Estimating & Bus Dev)

Harrington & Cortelyou, Inc.   **(1)**
911 Main St Ste 1900, Kansas City, MO 64105
Tel.: (816) 421-8386
Web Site: http://www.hcbridges.com
Sales Range: $10-24.9 Million
Emp.: 27
Engineeering Services
N.A.I.C.S.: 237990
Kevin Eisenbeis (Dir-Bridges)

BURNS & SCALO ROOFING CO., INC.
22 Rutgers Rd, Pittsburgh, PA 15205
Tel.: (412) 921-1962
Web Site: https://www.burns-scalo.com
Sales Range: $25-49.9 Million
Emp.: 300
Roofing Contractors
N.A.I.C.S.: 238160
Jack Scalo (Pres & CEO)
Mark Heckathorne (COO & Exec VP-Sls & Ops)
John F. Scalo Jr. (Project Mgr-Sheet Metal, Repair & Maintenance)

Subsidiaries:

Burns & Scalo North Carolina, Inc.   **(1)**
White Oak Business Park 151 Sigma Dr, Garner, NC 27529
Tel.: (919) 662-1622
Web Site: http://www.burns-scalo.com
Roofing Contractors
N.A.I.C.S.: 238160

Burns & Scalo Ohio, Inc.   **(1)**
22 Rutgers Rd Ste 200, Pittsburgh, PA 15205-2565
Tel.: (330) 759-4675
Web Site: http://www.burns-scalo.com
Sales Range: $10-24.9 Million.
Emp.: 18
Roofing Contractors
N.A.I.C.S.: 238160
Bill Ludwig (VP-Ops)
Brian Exline (VP & Gen Mgr)

Voegele Co., Inc.   **(1)**
200 Bridge St, Pittsburgh, PA 15223
Tel.: (412) 781-0940
Web Site: http://www.voegeleco.com
Other Building Finishing Contractors
N.A.I.C.S.: 238390

BURNS BROS. CONTRACTORS, INC.
400 Leavenworth Ave, Syracuse, NY 13204-1414
Tel.: (315) 422-0261   **NY**
Web Site:
https://www.bbcontractors.com
Year Founded: 1948
Sales Range: $10-24.9 Million
Emp.: 38
Commercial Mechanical Contractor; Hvac Systems; Plumbing; Heating
N.A.I.C.S.: 238220
Karl Engelbrecht (Pres)

BURNS BROS., INC.
4949 SW Meadows Rd Ste 330, Lake Oswego, OR 97035
Tel.: (503) 697-0666   **OR**
Web Site: http://www.burnsbros.com
Year Founded: 1946

Emp.: 60
Commercial Real Estate Development & Property Management Services
N.A.I.C.S.: 531390
Bruce E. Burns (Chm, Pres & CEO)
Stephen Gross (CFO)

BURNS BUICK-GMC-HYUNDAI-HONDA
500 W Route 70, Marlton, NJ 08053
Tel.: (856) 452-0330
Web Site:
https://www.burnsbuickgmc.com
Year Founded: 1970
Sales Range: $10-24.9 Million
Emp.: 100
Car Whslr
N.A.I.C.S.: 441110
Peter Lanzavecchia (Principal)

BURNS CONTROLS COMPANY
13735 Beta Rd, Dallas, TX 75244
Tel.: (972) 233-6712
Web Site:
https://www.burnscontrols.com
Year Founded: 1971
Sales Range: $10-24.9 Million
Emp.: 50
Pneumatic Tools & Equipment
N.A.I.C.S.: 423830
Patrick J. Burns Sr. (Pres)

BURNS FORD INC.
188 N Broadway Ave, Burns, OR 97720
Tel.: (541) 573-6014
Web Site:
https://www.burnsfordinc.com
Sales Range: $10-24.9 Million
Emp.: 30
New & Used Automobiles
N.A.I.C.S.: 441110

BURNS INDUSTRIAL EQUIPMENT, INC.
1050 Rico Rd, Monroeville, PA 15146
Tel.: (412) 242-2800
Web Site:
http://www.yalepittsburgh.com
Sales Range: $10-24.9 Million
Emp.: 200
Industrial Trucks Distr
N.A.I.C.S.: 423110
Christopher J. Burns (Pres)

BURNS MCCLELLAN, INC.
257 Park Ave S 15th Fl, New York, NY 10010
Tel.: (212) 213-0006   NY
Web Site: http://www.burnsmc.com
Year Founded: 1998
Rev.: $2,400,000
Emp.: 20
Fiscal Year-end: 12/31/06
Communications, Corporate Communications, Health Care, Investor Relations, Local Marketing, Public Relations, Strategic Planning/Research
N.A.I.C.S.: 541810
Lisa Burns (Pres & CEO)
Justin W. Jackson (Exec VP & Dir-East Coast Life Sciences Practice)
Kathy L. Jones Nugent (Sr VP-Life Sciences Practice)
Carney Noensie (VP-IR)
Juliane Snowden-Andrew (Sr VP-IR)
Catherine Watts Collier (VP-Pub Rels)

BURNS MOTOR FREIGHT INC.
PO Box 149, Marlinton, WV 24954
Tel.: (304) 799-6106
Web Site:
http://www.burnsmotorfreight.com
Sales Range: $10-24.9 Million

Emp.: 106
Trucking Except Local
N.A.I.C.S.: 484121
Larry L. Burns (Vice Chm)
Douglas L. Burns (Dir-Safety & & Recruiting)
Rhonda Withers (Dir-HR)
Samuel McNeel (CFO)
John Burns (Pres)
Mike Burns (VP)
Rebecca Puffenbarger (Mgr-Acctg)
Fred C. Burns Jr. (CEO)

BURNS360
8144 Walnut Hill Ln Ste 310, Dallas, TX 75231
Tel.: (214) 692-2042
Web Site: http://www.burns-360.com
Year Founded: 1989
Business-to-Business Communications
N.A.I.C.S.: 541820
Michael A. Burns (Founder & Pres)
Jennifer Green-Moneta (Exec VP & Mng Partner)
Lois Weaver (Dir-Creative)
Jeff Green (Dir-Operations-Supervisor-Acct)
Raleigh Kung (Mgr-Digital Mktg)

BURNSTAD BROTHERS, INC.
701 E Clifton St, Tomah, WI 54660-2633
Tel.: (608) 372-6335   WI
Web Site:
http://www.burnstadsmarket.com
Year Founded: 1969
Sales Range: $100-124.9 Million
Emp.: 125
Operator of Supermarkets
N.A.I.C.S.: 445110

BURNSTEAD CONSTRUCTION COMPANY
11980 NE 24th St Ste 200, Bellevue, WA 98005-1516
Tel.: (425) 454-1900   WA
Web Site: https://www.burnstead.com
Sales Range: $1-9.9 Million
Emp.: 50
Builder of Single Family Homes
N.A.I.C.S.: 236115
Mary Jane Slye (Pres)
Jolyn Davis (VP-Mktg)

Subsidiaries:

Rick Burnstead Construction LLC   (1)
11980 NE 24th St Unit 200, Bellevue, WA 98005
Tel.: (425) 454-1900
Sales Range: $1-9.9 Million
Emp.: 30
Housing Construction Services
N.A.I.C.S.: 236115
Rick Burnstead (Gen Mgr)

BURR & FORMAN LLP
420 N 20th St Ste 3400, Birmingham, AL 35203
Tel.: (205) 251-3000
Web Site: https://www.burr.com
Year Founded: 1905
Sales Range: $100-124.9 Million
Emp.: 503
Legal Advisory Services
N.A.I.C.S.: 541110
Douglas L. Anderson (Partner-Mobile)
Jeffrey T. Baker (Partner)
Brad A. Baldwin (Partner-Atlanta)
Bryan O. Balogh (Partner)
Matthew W. Barnes (Partner)
Jeffrey U. Beaverstock (Partner)
Howard E. Bogard (Partner)
Edward H. Brown (Partner-Atlanta)
Scott Brown (Partner-Tampa)
John P. Browning (Partner-Mobile)

S. Greg Burge (Partner)
Martin E. Burke (Partner)
Jennifer M. Busby (Partner-Birmingham)
Ron Poole (CIO)
Jon M. Gumbel (Partner-Atlanta)
Ellen T. Mathews (Partner-Birmingham)
Ronald D. Williams (Partner-Birmingham)
Ty G. Roofner (Partner-Orlando)
William Lee Thuston (Mng Partner)
Laurence S. Litow (Mng Partner-Fort Lauderdale)
Eric S. Golden (Partner-Orlando, Florida)
Andrew Demers (Partner-Ft. Lauderdale, Florida)
Joshua A. Ehrenfeld (Partner)
J. Matthew Kroplin (Partner)
Zachary D. Miller (Partner)
Brian A. Watson (Partner)
Justin H. Kelly (Partner)
Jacqueline Simms-Petredis (Partner-Tampa)
Erich N. Durlacher (Pres & Mng Partner-Atlanta)
Erin C. Hewitt (Partner-Real Estate, Corp, Tax Grp-Atlanta)
Ryan Corbett (Partner)
Chris Strohmenger (Partner)
Timothy May (Partner)
John Ibach (Partner)
Sims Rhyne (Atty)
Jennifer Moseley (Partner-Atlanta)
Gary M. London (Mng Partner-Birmingham)
Gregory F. Lunny (Mng Partner-Jacksonville)
Warren C. Matthews (Mng Partner-Montgomery)
Kerry Mattox (Pres)
Richard A. Robinson (Mng Partner-Wilmington)
Jonathan Sykes (Partner-Orlando)
Chris Thompson (Partner-Orlando)
Russell Rutherford (Partner)
Alex Little (Partner-Nashville)
Emily Mack (Partner-Nashville)
Brent David Hitson (Partner)
James H. Haithcock III (Partner)

Subsidiaries:

Mcnair Law Firm P.A.   (1)
1221 Main St Ste 1800, Columbia, SC 29211
Tel.: (803) 799-9800
Web Site: http://www.mcnair.net
Law firm
N.A.I.C.S.: 541110
O. Wayne Corley (Atty)
Durham Thomas Boney (Atty)
Michael McNulty Beal (Atty)
Elizabeth Bowe Anders (Atty)
Carl Benton Carruth (Atty)

BURR, PILGER & MAYER LLP
600 California St Ste 1300, San Francisco, CA 94108
Tel.: (415) 421-5757
Web Site: https://www.bpm.com
Sales Range: $50-74.9 Million
Emp.: 411
Accounting & Consulting Services
N.A.I.C.S.: 541211
Jan Adams (Mgr-Tax)
Tom Benton (Dir-Private Client Svcs)
Elizabeth Lukaszewicz (Mgr-Fin)
Maria Melo (Mgr-Assurance)
Henry Pilger (Co-Founder)
Yun Zhou (Mgr-Tax)
Jim Wallace (CEO)

BURRELL CENTER
1300 Bradford Pkwy, Springfield, MO 65804
Tel.: (417) 761-5000   MO

Web Site:
https://www.burrellcenter.com
Year Founded: 1976
Sales Range: $25-49.9 Million
Emp.: 1,038
Behavioral Healthcare Services
N.A.I.C.S.: 623220
Todd Schaible (Pres & CEO)
Sabrina Wilford (VP-HR)
Jim Rives (VP-Corp Dev)
Sherri Viland (VP-Fin & Admin)
Allyson Ashley (VP-Fin & Admin)
Cheryl Groves (VP-Developmental Svcs)
Becky Millard (VP)
Megan Steen (VP-Res & Quality Assurance)

BURRELL MINING PRODUCTS INC.
2400 Leechburg Rd Ste 221, New Kensington, PA 15068
Tel.: (724) 339-2511
Web Site: http://www.burrellinc.com
Sales Range: $10-24.9 Million
Emp.: 200
Concrete & Cinder Block
N.A.I.C.S.: 423320
Charles H. Booth Jr. (CEO)

Subsidiaries:

Burrell Mining Products Inc. Utah   (1)
75 W 3450 S, Price, UT 84501
Tel.: (435) 637-1155
Web Site: http://www.burrellmining.com
Rev.: $1,600,000
Emp.: 11
Concrete & Cinder Block
N.A.I.C.S.: 423320

BURRELLE'S INFORMATION SERVICES LLC
75 E Northfield Rd, Livingston, NJ 07039-4501
Tel.: (973) 992-6600   NJ
Web Site: http://www.burrelles.com
Year Founded: 1888
Sales Range: $75-99.9 Million
Emp.: 1,300
Information Services
N.A.I.C.S.: 561990
Robert C. Waggoner (Chm & CEO)
Steve Blaha (Controller)
Daniel Schaible (Sr VP-Content Mgmt)
Cathy Del Colle (Pres)

Subsidiaries:

BurellesLuce   (1)
44 W 1st Ave, Mesa, AZ
85210-1356   (100%)
Tel.: (480) 834-2889
Web Site: http://www.burrellesluce.com
Rev.: $160,000
Emp.: 1,200
Information Services
N.A.I.C.S.: 519290
Gail Nelson (Sr VP-Mktg)
Steve Shannon (Exec VP)

BURRIS LOGISTICS
501 SE 5th St, Milford, DE 19963-2022
Tel.: (302) 422-4531   DE
Web Site:
https://www.burrislogistics.com
Year Founded: 1939
Sales Range: $350-399.9 Million
Emp.: 2,000
Packaged Frozen Food Merchant Wholesalers
N.A.I.C.S.: 424420
Jennifer Gallagher (Gen Mgr)
Maggie Owens (Dir-Mktg)
Donnan R. Burris (Pres & CEO)
Jeffrey M. Swain (Co-Chm)

Burris Logistics—(Continued)

Subsidiaries:

Honor Foods, Inc.   (1)
1801 N 5th St, Philadelphia, PA 19122
Tel.: (215) 236-1700
Web Site: http://www.honorfoods.com
Food Products Distr
N.A.I.C.S.: 424490
Ann Polites (Dir-HR)
Emory Pepper (Dir-Fin)
Joe Adams (VP-Sls & Pur)
Walt Tullis (Pres)

BURROUGHS & CHAPIN CO. INC.
611 Burroughs & Chapin Blvd Ste 100, Myrtle Beach, SC 29577
Tel.: (843) 448-5123
Web Site:
   http://www.burroughschapin.com
Sales Range: $25-49.9 Million
Emp.: 275
Subdivision Developers
N.A.I.C.S.: 237210
J. Egerton E. Burroughs (Chm)
Tony K. Cox (Exec VP-Real Estate)
Patrick J. Walsh (Sr VP-Asset Mgmt & Comml Leasing)

BURROW GLOBAL, LLC
6200 Savoy Dr Ste 800, Houston, TX 77036
Tel.: (713) 963-0930
Web Site:
   http://www.burrowglobal.com
Year Founded: 2009
Sales Range: $150-199.9 Million
Emp.: 974
Engineeering Services
N.A.I.C.S.: 541330
Michael L. Burrow (Chm & CEO)
Gary Knight (Pres-Burrow Global Construction & Burrow Global Automation)
Nigel James (Chief Strategy Officer)
Buster Burnett (VP-Buildings Construction)
Mark Vise (CFO & COO)
Jason Savoie (Exec VP-Automation)
David Hartman (Mgr-Ops-Deer Park & Angleton Automation)
Alicia Dutton (Mgr-Mktg Media)
Steve Sock (Mgr-Bus Dev)
Matt Smith (Sr Mgr-Construction)

Subsidiaries:

Demar Ltd   (1)
6200 Savoy Dr Ste 800, Houston, TX 77036
Tel.: (713) 963-0930
Web Site: http://www.demar-ltd.com
Sales Range: $10-24.9 Million
Emp.: 50
Commercial & Office Building, New Construction
N.A.I.C.S.: 236220
Dennis Knoop (CEO & Principal)
Steve Maricelli (Principal & Pres)
James D. Weaver (VP-Architecture)
Richard Hart (Dir-Safety & Mgr-Sls)
Fred Flesch (VP-Pro Svcs)
E. Edward Halderman Jr. (VP-Construction)

BURROWS PAPER CORPORATION
501 W Main St, Little Falls, NY 13365-1817
Tel.: (315) 823-2300   NY
Web Site:
   http://www.burrowspaper.com
Year Founded: 1919
Sales Range: $150-199.9 Million
Emp.: 900
Mfr of Specialty Packaging Paper
N.A.I.C.S.: 322120
Dwayne Judd (VP-Sls-Paper Div)
Eric Deutschman (Reg Mgr-Sls)

Michael McCormick (Mgr-Energy Svcs)
Mary Trombley (Dir-SAP)

Subsidiaries:

Burrows Netherlands B.V.   (1)
Klarenanstelerweg 7, 6468 EP, Kerkrade, Netherlands
Tel.: (31) 45 56 78 600
Web Site: http://www.burrows.nl
Emp.: 140
Industrial Paper Mfr
N.A.I.C.S.: 322120
Raymonds Nuijens (Plant Mgr)
Wilbert Schocke (Mgr-Sls)

BURRTEC WASTE INDUSTRIES, INC.
9890 Cherry Ave, Fontana, CA 92335
Tel.: (909) 429-4200
Web Site: http://www.burrtec.com
Year Founded: 1978
Sales Range: $250-299.9 Million
Emp.: 1,350
Mfr of Refuse Systems
N.A.I.C.S.: 562111
Cole Burr (Pres & CEO)
Diana Guzman (Mgr-Customer Svc)
John French (Supvr-Shop)
Ramon Rodriguez (Mgr-Ops)

Subsidiaries:

Avco Disposal Inc.   (1)
17080 Stoddard Wells Rd, Victorville, CA 92394
Tel.: (760) 245-8607
Web Site: http://www.avco.com
Sales Range: $10-24.9 Million
Emp.: 100
Provider of Refuse Systems
N.A.I.C.S.: 236210
Edward G. Burr (Owner)

Monte Vista Disposal, Inc.   (1)
9890 Cherry Ave, Fontana, CA 92335-5202
Tel.: (909) 429-4200
Sales Range: $25-49.9 Million
Emp.: 850
Provider of Refuse Systems
N.A.I.C.S.: 562111
Edward G. Burr (Chm)

Rancho Disposal Service, Inc.   (1)
9820 Cherry Ave, Fontana, CA 92335-5202
Tel.: (909) 429-4200
Web Site: http://www.burrtech.com
Sales Range: $10-24.9 Million
Emp.: 25
Provider of Refuse Systems
N.A.I.C.S.: 562211

West Valley Recycling & Transfer LLC   (1)
13373 Napa St, Fontana, CA 92335-5202
Tel.: (909) 899-0911
Web Site: http://www.burrtech.com
Sales Range: $10-24.9 Million
Emp.: 30
Provider of Refuse Systems
N.A.I.C.S.: 562111
Edward G. Burr (Owner)

BURRUS & MATTHEWS, INC.
2221 Vanco Dr, Irving, TX 75061-8817
Tel.: (972) 438-8881   TX
Web Site: http://www.b-m.com
Year Founded: 1937
Sales Range: $25-49.9 Million
Emp.: 200
Mfr of Electrical Apparatus & Equipment
N.A.I.C.S.: 423610
Galen Hollar (Pres)

BURRUS INVESTMENT GROUP INC.
401 Veterans Memorial Blvd, Metairie, LA 70005
Tel.: (504) 455-7600

Web Site: http://www.burrusgroup.com
Rev.: $29,200,000
Emp.: 20
Manager of Investments
N.A.I.C.S.: 523999
David R. Burrus (Co-Founder & Chm)
George J. Newton III (Co-Founder, Pres & CEO)

BURRY FOODS
1750 E Main St Ste 260, Saint Charles, IL 60174
Tel.: (630) 584-2754
Web Site:
   https://www.burryfoods.com
Year Founded: 2003
Rev.: $5,900,000
Emp.: 4
Sales of Frozen & Non-Frozen Products to the Foodservice, Convenience Stores, Vending & In-Store Bakery Industries
N.A.I.C.S.: 311813
Gary Gittleson (Pres)
Gerard Mitchell (VP-Ops)
Dave Phillips (CFO)

BURSCH TRAVEL AGENCY, INC.
324 Broadway, Alexandria, MN 56308
Tel.: (320) 762-1544
Web Site:
   https://www.burschtravel.com
Year Founded: 1956
Scenic & Sightseeing Transportation
N.A.I.C.S.: 487990
W. Gretchen (Dir-Sales-Marketing)
G. John (Dir-Grp-Corp Svcs)
H. Lee (Exec VP)
L. Mozelle (Dir-Operations)
P. Sue (CFO)

Subsidiaries:

Bursch Travel - Sheridan   (1)
150 S Main St, Sheridan, WY 82801-4224
Tel.: (307) 672-2481
Web Site: http://www.burschtravel.com
Travel Agencies
N.A.I.C.S.: 561510
Peg Martin (Mgr)

BURSICH ASSOCIATES, INC.
2129 E High St, Pottstown, PA 19464
Tel.: (610) 323-4040
Web Site: https://www.bursich.com
Year Founded: 1972
Sales Range: $1-9.9 Million
Emp.: 30
Site/Civil Engineering & Full-Service Surveying
N.A.I.C.S.: 541330
Dane K. Moyer (Pres)
Nicholas E. Feola (VP)

Subsidiaries:

Bursich Associates, Inc.   (1)
706 Lakeside Dr, Southampton, PA 18966   (100%)
Tel.: (215) 364-2520
Web Site: http://www.bursich.com
Transportation, Civil Engineering, Site Surveys & Land Development
N.A.I.C.S.: 237990
Dane K. Moyer (VP-Ops & Surveying)

BURST COMMUNICATIONS INC.
8200 S Akron St Ste 108, Centennial, CO 80112
Tel.: (303) 649-9600
Web Site: http://www.burstvideo.com
Sales Range: $10-24.9 Million
Emp.: 20
Radio & Television Equipment & Parts
N.A.I.C.S.: 423690

Greg Gorian (Engr-Sls)
Barry Samuels (Engr-Sls)
Tom Smith (Engr-Sls)
Chris Nicholson (Engr-Sls)
Don Rooney (VP-Engrg)

BURT BROTHERS TIRE & SERVICE, INC.
737 N 400 W, North Salt Lake, UT 84054
Tel.: (801) 335-8013
Web Site:
   http://www.burtbrothers.com
Year Founded: 1991
Emp.: 156
Tire Distr
N.A.I.C.S.: 441340
Ron Burt (Co-Founder)
Wendel Burt (Co-Founder)

BURT LEWIS INTERNATIONAL CORP
875 N Michigan Ave Ste 2720, Chicago, IL 60611-1827
Tel.: (312) 640-8899
Web Site: https://www.blintl.net
Rev.: $80,000,000
Emp.: 6
Dairy Products Distr
N.A.I.C.S.: 424430
Dermit Collins (Pres)
Yeseian Garcia (Office Mgr)

BURT PROCESS EQUIPMENT INC.
100 Overlook Dr, Hamden, CT 06514
Tel.: (203) 287-1985
Web Site:
   https://www.burtprocess.com
Year Founded: 1970
Sales Range: $25-49.9 Million
Emp.: 50
Pump Distribution & Waste Treatment
N.A.I.C.S.: 332913
Stephen Burt (Pres)
Alan Speckhart (VP)

BURTCO, INC.
185 Route 123, Westminster Station, VT 05159
Tel.: (802) 722-3358   VT
Web Site:
   https://www.burtcoselfstorage.com
Sales Range: $50-74.9 Million
Emp.: 25
Self-Storage Facilities Operator
N.A.I.C.S.: 531130

BURTIS MOTOR COMPANY, INC.
601 W Kansas Ave, Garden City, KS 67846-5150
Tel.: (620) 412-4104
Web Site: http://www.burtismotor.com
Sales Range: $25-49.9 Million
Emp.: 40
Car Whslr
N.A.I.C.S.: 441110
Jack Kirchoff (Pres)

BURTNESS CHEVROLET, INC.
802 Genesis Dr, Orfordville, WI 53576
Tel.: (608) 879-2931   WI
Web Site:
   http://www.burtnesschevy.com
Year Founded: 1967
Sales Range: $10-24.9 Million
Emp.: 45
New & Used Car Dealerships Owner & Operator
N.A.I.C.S.: 441110
John B. Bowditch Jr. (Owner & Pres)
Debbie Speich (Office Mgr)
Matt Nenneman (Mgr-Svc)

Subsidiaries:

Burtness Chevrolet of
Whitewater   **(1)**
1389 W Main St, Whitewater, WI 53190
Tel.: (262) 473-2522
Web Site: http://www.burtnesschevrolet.com
Sales Range: $10-24.9 Million
Emp.: 15
New & Used Car Dealer
N.A.I.C.S.: 441110
John B. Bowditch Jr. *(Pres)*

BURTON BANCSHARES, INC.

515 N Main, Burton, TX 77835
Tel.: (979) 289-3151
Web Site: http://www.burtonbank.com
Bank Holding Company
N.A.I.C.S.: 551111
E. J. Muehlbrad *(Chm)*

Subsidiaries:

Burton State Bank   **(1)**
515 N Main, Burton, TX 77835
Tel.: (979) 289-3151
Web Site: http://www.burtonbank.com
Sales Range: $1-9.9 Million
Emp.: 11
State Commercial Banks
N.A.I.C.S.: 522110
Donna Kunkel *(VP)*

BURTON BROTHERS GENERAL CONTRACTORS LC

23516 Telegraph Rd, Southfield, MI
48034
Tel.: (248) 357-7000
Web Site:
   http://www.burtonbrothers.net
Sales Range: $10-24.9 Million
Emp.: 50
Provider of Building Contracting Services
N.A.I.C.S.: 236220
Ken Christenson *(Partner)*
Don Teiper *(Gen Mgr)*
Savannah VanKeuren *(Dir-Mktg & Project Mgr)*

BURTON CAROL MANAGEMENT, LLC

4832 Richmond Rd Ste 200, Cleveland, OH 44128
Tel.: (216) 464-5130
Web Site:
   https://www.burtoncarol.com
Year Founded: 2010
Sales Range: $25-49.9 Million
Emp.: 150
Property Management
N.A.I.C.S.: 531312
David King *(Gen Counsel)*
Rob G. Risman *(Pres & CEO)*
Joy Anzalone *(COO & Exec VP)*
Roger Katz *(CFO & Corp Counsel)*
John Petryshin *(VP & Dir-Property Ops-Ohio)*
Joseph W. Kincaid *(VP & Dir-Property Ops-Michigan)*
Marcia Hayward *(VP & Dir-Property Ops-Florida)*

BURTON ENERGY GROUP

3650 Mansell Rd Ste 350, Alpharetta, GA 30022
Web Site:
   http://www.burtonenergygroup.com
Year Founded: 2001
Sales Range: $1-9.9 Million
Emp.: 20
Designs & Manages Energy Plans for
Multi-Site Businesses
N.A.I.C.S.: 541490
Brent Burton *(Mng Partner)*
Mark Breuker *(Mng Partner)*
Jason Hamby *(VP-Ops & Tech)*
Kristen Murphy *(VP-Energy Supply & Risk Mgmt)*

Banks Quarles *(Dir-Fin)*
Henry Kelley *(CFO)*
Douglas Latulippe *(Dir-Demand Side Programs)*
Bob Valair *(Dir-Energy & Environmental Mgmt)*

BURTON F CLARK INC.

41155 State Hwy 10, Delhi, NY
13753
Tel.: (607) 746-2727
Web Site: http://www.sportsedge.net
Sales Range: $10-24.9 Million
Emp.: 65
Nonresidential Construction
N.A.I.C.S.: 236220
B. Scott Clark *(Pres)*

BURTON INDUSTRIES INC.

9821 Cedar Falls Rd, Hazelhurst, WI
54531
Tel.: (715) 356-5767
Web Site:
   http://www.burtonindustries.com
Rev.: $12,000,000
Emp.: 15
Printed Circuit Boards
N.A.I.C.S.: 334412
Janet Lehman *(Pres)*
Mark Lehman *(Mgr-Ops)*

BURTON LUMBER & HARDWARE CO.

1170 S 4400 W, Salt Lake City, UT
84104
Tel.: (801) 952-3800
Web Site:
   https://www.burtonlumber.com
Sales Range: $150-199.9 Million
Emp.: 375
Lumber & Other Building Materials
N.A.I.C.S.: 423310
Robert T. Burton *(Chm)*
Daniel Burton *(Owner)*
JoAnn Hall *(CFO & Controller)*
Jeff Burton *(VP-Sls)*

BURTON LUMBER CORP.

835 Wilson Rd, Chesapeake, VA
23324
Tel.: (757) 545-4613
Web Site: http://www.burton-lumber.com
Rev.: $15,983,137
Emp.: 33
Lumber: Rough, Dressed & Finished
N.A.I.C.S.: 423310

BURTON SIGNWORKS, INC.

609 Junction St, Mount Airy, NC
27030
Tel.: (336) 789-0090
Web Site:
   http://www.burtonsignworks.com
Sales Range: $10-24.9 Million
Emp.: 55
Specialty Trade Contractors
N.A.I.C.S.: 238910
T. J. Payne *(Pres)*
Angela Marion *(Program Mgr & Project Mgr)*

BURTON SNOWBOARD COMPANY

80 Industrial Pkwy, Burlington, VT
05401-5434
Tel.: (802) 660-3200   VT
Web Site: http://www.burton.com
Year Founded: 1977
Sales Range: $125-149.9 Million
Emp.: 650
Snowboard Related Items Seller &
Mfr
N.A.I.C.S.: 339920
Jake Burton Carpenter *(Founder)*
Donna Carpenter *(Owner & Chm)*

John Lacy *(CEO)*
Kelly Murnaghan *(Sr VP-Mktg-Global)*
Adrian Josef Margelist *(Exec Creative Dir)*

Subsidiaries:

Gravis Footwear Inc.   **(1)**
8659 Research Dr Ste 100, Irvine, CA
92618
Tel.: (949) 789-1800
Sales Range: $10-24.9 Million
Emp.: 20
Footwear
N.A.I.C.S.: 424340

BURTONS INC.

2370 Hwy 77, Gadsden, AL 35907
Tel.: (256) 442-1063
Year Founded: 1982
Sales Range: $10-24.9 Million
Emp.: 25
Independent Grocery Store
N.A.I.C.S.: 445110
Harold L. Burton *(Pres)*

BURTRONICS BUSINESS SYSTEMS, INC.

216 S Arrowhead Ave, San Bernardino, CA 92408
Tel.: (909) 885-7576   CA
Web Site: http://www.burtronics.com
Year Founded: 1985
Rev.: $14,308,440
Emp.: 30
Sales & Service of Copying Equipment
N.A.I.C.S.: 423420
Tom Thompson *(Pres & CEO)*
Greg Gray *(VP-Svc)*
Troy Mast *(Mgr-Svc)*
Rock Janecek *(Mgr-Svc)*
Randy Hlebasko *(VP-Sls)*

BURWOOD GROUP INC.

20 N Clark St 125 S Walker Dr Ste
2950, Chicago, IL 60606
Tel.: (312) 327-4600
Web Site: http://www.burwood.com
Year Founded: 1997
Sales Range: $50-74.9 Million
Emp.: 104
Technology Consulting Services
N.A.I.C.S.: 541690
Kevin Stewart *(CTO & VP)*
Mark Theoharous *(CEO)*
Jim Hart *(Pres)*
Tim Needham *(Exec Dir-Healthcare Solutions)*
Joanna L. Robinson *(Sr VP-Tech)*
Chris Pond *(Pres-Cloud Svcs)*
Phillip Hodge *(VP-Sls)*
Jennifer Courtney *(VP-Pro Svcs)*
Colleen Barry *(Dir-Mktg Comm)*
Russel Buetow *(Dir-Sls-West)*

BUS SUPPLY COMPANY, INC.

2084 Hwy 98 E, McComb, MS 39648
Tel.: (601) 684-2900
Web Site: https://www.bussupply.com
Sales Range: $10-24.9 Million
Emp.: 40
Recreational Vehicle Whslr
N.A.I.C.S.: 441210
John McCommon *(Pres)*

BUSCH DISTRIBUTORS INC.

7603 State Route 270, Pullman, WA
99163
Tel.: (208) 882-3021
Web Site: http://www.buschdist.com
Year Founded: 1963
Rev.: $17,299,135
Emp.: 20
Gasoline, Heating Oil & Lubricants
Distr
N.A.I.C.S.: 424710

Eric Busch *(VP-Fin)*
Jess Scourey *(VP-Sls)*

BUSCHE PERFORMANCE GROUP, INC.

1563 E State Rd 8, Albion, IN 46701
Tel.: (260) 636-7030
Web Site:
   http://www.buschegroup.com
Year Founded: 1997
Sales Range: $125-149.9 Million
Emp.: 750
CNC Machining Services
N.A.I.C.S.: 332710
Nick Busche *(CEO)*
Tom Keller *(Dir-Quality)*
Cory Ryner *(VP-Engrg & Bus Dev-Automotive Grp)*
Lori Busche *(Mgr-HR)*
Daniel Dressler *(VP-Procurement)*

Subsidiaries:

Busche Southfield, Inc.   **(1)**
26290 W 8 Mile Rd, Southfield, MI 48033-
3050
Tel.: (248) 357-2483
Emp.: 387
Machined Components & Assemblies Mfr
N.A.I.C.S.: 332999
Matt Roberts *(VP-Sls & Mktg)*
Dennis Thornburg *(Mgr-Sls)*
Dan Minor *(CEO)*

BUSCHS INC.

2240 S Main St, Ann Arbor, MI 48103
Tel.: (734) 998-2666
Web Site: https://www.buschs.com
Year Founded: 1975
Rev.: $155,601,640
Emp.: 1,200
Supermarkets, Chain
N.A.I.C.S.: 445110
John J. Busch *(Co-Founder)*
Tina Scrupsky *(CFO)*
Eric Aguirre *(Head-Cleaning)*
Ethan Allen *(Dir-Sys Support)*
Tony Hall *(VP-Store Support)*
Mike Brooks *(Pres & CEO)*
Charlie Mattis *(Co-Founder)*

BUSCO INC.

720 E Norfolk Ave, Norfolk, NE
68701
Tel.: (402) 371-3850
Web Site:
   http://www.arrowstagelines.com
Sales Range: $10-24.9 Million
Emp.: 375
Bus Charter Service, Except Local
N.A.I.C.S.: 485510
Gene Wordekemper *(Dir-Maintenance)*
Lynn Marinkovic *(Mgr-Sls-Denver)*
Steve Busskohl *(CEO)*
Darlene Mullins *(Mgr-Sls-Nevada)*
Jamie Meyer *(Asst Mgr-Sls-North Iowa)*
Jolene Webb *(Mgr-Sls-North Iowa)*
Kim Weaver *(Mgr-Sls-Arizona)*

BUSH AUTO PLACE INC.

1850 Rombach Ave, Wilmington, OH
45177-1993
Tel.: (937) 382-2542   OH
Web Site: http://www.bushauto.com
Year Founded: 1985
Sales Range: $10-24.9 Million
Emp.: 70
New & Used Car Dealers
N.A.I.C.S.: 441110
Mark Bush *(Pres)*
Andrea Bush *(Controller)*
Amy Wilson *(Office Mgr)*
Gary Lachey *(Pres)*

BUSH BROTHERS & COMPANY

Bush Brothers & Company—(Continued)

PO Box 52330, Knoxville, TN 37950-
2330
Tel.: (865) 588-7685   **TN**
Web Site: http://www.bushbeans.com
Year Founded: 1908
Sales Range: $200-249.9 Million
Emp.: 700
Edible Bean Mfr & Distr
N.A.I.C.S.: 311422
Jim Ethier (Chm)
Phil Perkins (Sr VP-Innovation & R&D)
Rich Clark (Mgr-Product & Tech Solutions)
Steve Savell (Dir-Info Svcs)
Lynne Farmer (Mgr)
Michael Lowe (Mgr-Transportation & Warehouse)
Subsidiaries:

Bush Brothers & Company Plant   (1)
600 S Bush Brothers Dr, Augusta, WI
54722-7205
Tel.: (715) 286-2211
Sales Range: $25-49.9 Million
Emp.: 130
Canned Products Mfr & Distr
N.A.I.C.S.: 311421

BUSH COMMUNICATIONS, LLC
25 N Washington St 4th Fl, Rochester, NY 14614
Tel.: (585) 244-0270
Web Site:
    http://www.bushcommunication.com
Year Founded: 2000
Sales Range: Less than $1 Million
Emp.: 5
N.A.I.C.S.: 541810
Jim Bush (Pres)
Geoff Baumbach (Dir-New Media)
Nadine Ball (Dir-Creative)

BUSH EQUITIES
14 Yarmouth Jct, Yarmouth, ME
04096
Tel.: (207) 761-0201   **ME**
Web Site:
    http://www.cuddledown.com
Year Founded: 1973
Sales Range: $10-24.9 Million
Emp.: 100
Mfr & Retailer of Certified Safe Fabrics, Bedding & Home Furnishings
N.A.I.C.S.: 449129
Norma Wilkins-Gross (Pres)

BUSH INC.
2581 Hickory Blvd SE, Lenoir, NC
28645
Tel.: (828) 728-4222
Web Site:
    http://www.roosterbush.com
Rev.: $17,000,000
Emp.: 38
New & Used Car Sales
N.A.I.C.S.: 441110
Barbara Bush (Pres)

BUSH O'DONNELL & CO., INC.
101 S Hanley Rd Ste 1250, Saint
Louis, MO 63105
Tel.: (314) 727-4555   **MO**
Web Site:
    http://www.bushodonnell.com
Year Founded: 1988
Sales Range: $50-74.9 Million
Emp.: 15
Holding Company; Investment Advisory & Asset Management Services
N.A.I.C.S.: 551112
Subsidiaries:

Bush O'Donnell Investment Advisors,
Inc.   (1)

101 S Hanley Rd Ste 1250, Saint Louis,
MO 63105   **(100%)**
Tel.: (314) 727-4555
Web Site: http://www.bushodonnell.com
Investment Advisory & Asset Management
Services
N.A.I.C.S.: 523940
John F. Brown (Mng Dir)
William H. T. Bush (Chm)
James V. ODonnell (Pres)

BUSHWICK STUYVESANT HEIGHTS HOME ATTENDANTS, INC.
992 Gates Ave, Brooklyn, NY 11221
Tel.: (718) 453-8400   **NY**
Year Founded: 1983
Sales Range: $1-9.9 Million
Emp.: 578
Home Attendant Services
N.A.I.C.S.: 623210
Judy Jones (Treas)
Barbara Williams (Sec)
Narcissus Frett-Moses (Chm)

BUSINESS & LEGAL RESOURCES INC.
141 Mill Rock Rd E, Old Saybrook,
CT 06475-4217
Tel.: (860) 510-0100   **CT**
Web Site: http://www.blr.com
Year Founded: 1977
Sales Range: $25-49.9 Million
Emp.: 150
Magazine Publishing Services
N.A.I.C.S.: 513120
Peggy Cretella (Project Mgr)

BUSINESS BROKERS OF SAN ANTONIO
1777 NE Loop 410 Ste 615, San Antonio, TX 78217
Tel.: (210) 348-8989
Web Site: https://www.bbofsa.com
Document Preparation Services
N.A.I.C.S.: 561410
Bob Howells (Mgr)

BUSINESS CARD SERVICE INC.
3200 143rd Cir, Burnsville, MN 55306
Tel.: (952) 894-4904
Web Site: https://www.bcsinet.com
Year Founded: 1954
Sales Range: $10-24.9 Million
Emp.: 112
Business Form & Card Printing,
Lithographic
N.A.I.C.S.: 323111
James Marchessault (Pres)
Brian Nelson (Mgr-Info Tech)
Heather Moss (Acct Coord)

BUSINESS COMMUNICATIONS MANAGEMENT, INC
521 5th Ave 14th Fl, New York, NY
10175
Tel.: (800) 543-4226   **NY**
Web Site: http://www.bcm1.com
Year Founded: 1992
Sales Range: $1-9.9 Million
Emp.: 90
Telecommunication Management
Services
N.A.I.C.S.: 541618
John Cunningham (CEO)
Frank Ahearn (Pres)
Jay Monaghan (Partner)
Geoff Bloss (CIO)

BUSINESS COMMUNICATIONS, INC.
442 Highland Colony Pkwy, Ridgeland, MS 39157
Tel.: (601) 427-4185

Web Site:
    https://www.bcianswers.com
Year Founded: 1983
Sales Range: $25-49.9 Million
Emp.: 90
Designs, Installs & Maintains Information Technology Systems
N.A.I.C.S.: 541519
Tony Bailey (Owner)

BUSINESS CONSULTING GROUP, INC.
707 S Lafayette St Ste G, Shelby,
NC 28150
Tel.: (704) 487-0638   **NC**
Web Site:
    https://www.bcgroupinc.com
Year Founded: 1974
Business Consulting Services
N.A.I.C.S.: 541618
Robby Reynolds (Pres)
Barbara Earl (Client Svc Mgr-Acctg)
Tracy Harper (Client Svcs Mgr)

BUSINESS CONTROL SYSTEMS LP
16415 Addison Rd Ste 150, Addison,
TX 75001
Tel.: (972) 241-8392
Web Site: https://www.bcsmis.com
Rev.: $24,269,398
Emp.: 20
Provider of Computer Related Consulting Services
N.A.I.C.S.: 541512
Bernie Francis (Co-Founder & CEO)
Dianne Ferguson (Pres)

BUSINESS DEVELOPMENT ASIA LLC
1270 Ave of Americas Ste 2310, New
York, NY 10020
Tel.: (212) 265-5300
Web Site:
    http://www.bdcpartners.com
Year Founded: 1996
Sales Range: $10-24.9 Million
Emp.: 65
Management Consulting Services
N.A.I.C.S.: 541611
Andrew Huntley (Sr Mng Dir-London & Dubai)
Euan Rellie (Co-Founder & Sr Mng Dir-New York)
Charles Maynard (Co-Founder & Sr Mng Dir-London)
Kumar Mahtani (Mng Dir-Mumbai)
Jeffrey Wang (Mng Dir & Co-Head-Shanghai)
Mark Webster (Mng Dir & Co-Head-Shanghai)
Karen Cheung (Mng Dir-Hong Kong)
Simon Kavanagh (Mng Dir-Hong Kong)
Matthew Doull (Mng Dir-New York & Hong Kong)
Howard Lee (Mng Dir-Seoul)
Anthony Siu (Mng Dir-Shanghai)
Paul DiGiacomo (Mng Dir-Singapore)
Jeff Acton (Mng Dir-Tokyo)
Koichiro Yasuda (Mng Dir-Tokyo)
Abhishek Agarwal (VP-Mumbai)
Alexander Ditchfield (VP-New York)
Yougyeong Kwon (VP-Seoul)
Dorothy Cai (VP-Shanghai)
Kevin Song (VP-Shanghai)
Jonathan Fein (VP-Singapore)
Shinya Kimura (VP-Tokyo)

BUSINESS DEVELOPMENT SALES
2430 Enterprise Dr, Saint Paul, MN
55120-1143
Tel.: (651) 688-8000
Web Site:
    https://www.bdslaundry.com

Sales Range: $10-24.9 Million
Emp.: 50
Laundry Equipment & Supplies
N.A.I.C.S.: 423850
David Demarsh (Pres)

BUSINESS ELECTRONICS SOLDERING TECHNOLOGIES
3603 Edison Pl, Rolling Meadows, IL
60008
Tel.: (847) 797-9250
Web Site: https://www.solder.net
Year Founded: 1997
Rev.: $3,400,000
Emp.: 30
Rework Repair Services
N.A.I.C.S.: 811198
Bob Wettermann (Pres & CEO)
Gary Lynch (Mgr-SMT Engrg & Prototype Dev)

BUSINESS FURNITURE LLC
8421 Bearing Dr Ste 200, Indianapolis, IN 46268
Tel.: (317) 216-1600   **IN**
Web Site:
    http://www.businessfurniture.net
Year Founded: 1922
Sales Range: $50-74.9 Million
Emp.: 160
Office Furniture Distr
N.A.I.C.S.: 423210
Richard Oakes (Chm)
Mary Meredith (VP-Client Svcs)
Heather Moore (Mgr-Design)
Terry Richard (COO)
Suzanne Bentley (Pres)

BUSINESS FURNITURE, INC.
133 Rahway Ave, Elizabeth, NJ
07202
Tel.: (908) 355-3400   **NJ**
Web Site: https://www.bfionline.com
Year Founded: 1948
Sales Range: $50-74.9 Million
Emp.: 45
Office Furniture Distr
N.A.I.C.S.: 423210
Paul Gold (CEO)
Daniel Morley (Pres)
Scott Carlson (VP & Gen Mgr-Ohio Markets)

BUSINESS IMPACT GROUP LLC
2411 Galpin CT Ste 120, Chanhassen, MN 55317
Tel.: (952) 278-7800
Web Site:
    http://www.impactgroup.com
Year Founded: 2003
Emp.: 100
Business Consulting Services
N.A.I.C.S.: 541611
Carol Overman (Mgr-Acctg)
Louise Anderson (VP-Recognition Sls)
Subsidiaries:

Anderson Performance Improvement
Company, Inc.   (1)
12181 Margo Ave S Ste 210, Hastings, MN
55033-9437
Tel.: (612) 636-0529
Web Site:
    http://www.andersonperformance.com
Emp.: 35
Business Consulting Services
N.A.I.C.S.: 541611
Louise Anderson (CEO)

BUSINESS INDUSTRIAL NETWORK
2 Cityplace Dr Ste 200, Saint Louis,
MO 63141
Tel.: (573) 547-5630
Web Site: http://www.bin95.com

Year Founded: 1995
On-Site & On-Line Industrial, Mainte-
nance, Engineering & Technical
Training Services
N.A.I.C.S.: 611699
Donald Fitchett (Pres & Owner)

Subsidiaries:

Koldwater Technologies LLC   (1)
136 Elm St, Mannford, OK 74044
Tel.: (573) 547-5630
Web Site: http://www.koldwater.com
Technical Training Software Developer
N.A.I.C.S.: 513210
Stan Kaltwasser (Owner)

BUSINESS INTEGRA TECH-
NOLOGY SOLUTIONS, INC.
7229 Hanover Pkwy Ste D, Green-
belt, MD 20817
Tel.: (301) 474-9600
Web Site:
  http://www.businessintegra.com
Year Founded: 2001
Sales Range: $10-24.9 Million
Emp.: 140
IT Staffing & Recruitment Services
N.A.I.C.S.: 561320
Prathiba Ramadoss (Founder, Pres &
CEO)
Selva Jayaraman (COO & Exec VP)
Padma Shinde (VP-Fin & Ops)
Ray Leshynski (Sr VP-Bus Dev &
Federal Grp)
Trent Martin (VP-Tech)
Lee Ann Anderson (Pres-Federal So-
lutions Grp)

BUSINESS INTEGRATORS
INC.
3130 Rogerdale Rd Ste 100, Hous-
ton, TX 77042
Tel.: (713) 425-4500
Sales Range: $10-24.9 Million
Emp.: 20
Computer & Software Stores
N.A.I.C.S.: 423430

BUSINESS INTERIORS INC.
2309 5th Ave, Birmingham, AL 35233
Tel.: (205) 939-1008
Web Site:
  https://www.businteriors.com
Year Founded: 1986
Rev.: $22,475,992
Emp.: 170
Sales of Office & Public Building Fur-
niture
N.A.I.C.S.: 423210
Alan Pizzitola (Pres)
Lee Moody (Project Mgr-Field)
Jack Womack (CFO)
Richie Hamer (Partner)

Subsidiaries:

Office Furniture USA   (1)
107A W Clinton Ave, Huntsville, AL 35801
Tel.: (205) 939-1008
Web Site: http://www.businteriors.com
Sales Range: $10-24.9 Million
Emp.: 30
Office Furniture
N.A.I.C.S.: 449110
Bryan Mullins (Mgr-Sls)

BUSINESS INTERIORS OF SE-
ATTLE NORTH WEST INC.
10848 E Marginal Way S, Seattle,
WA 98168
Tel.: (206) 762-8818   WA
Web Site: http://www.binw.com
Year Founded: 1982
Sales Range: $10-24.9 Million
Emp.: 125
Full Service Office Furniture Dealer-
ship
N.A.I.C.S.: 449110

Sean O'Brien (Pres)
Don King (VP-Sls)

BUSINESS LEADER MEDIA
2 Penn Plz Ste 1500, New York, NY
10121
Tel.: (866) 963-6118
Periodical Publishers
N.A.I.C.S.: 513120
Michael Plotnik (Mng Dir)

Subsidiaries:

South Florida Business Leader   (1)
299 SE 1st St Ste 601, Miami, FL 33131
Tel.: (305) 379-1118
Magazine
N.A.I.C.S.: 513120

BUSINESS NETWORK CON-
SULTING, LTD.
450 E 17th Ave Ste 300, Denver, CO
80203
Tel.: (303) 782-9090
Web Site:
  https://www.bncsystems.com
Year Founded: 1997
Sales Range: $1-9.9 Million
Emp.: 40
Computer Consulting Services
N.A.I.C.S.: 541618
Joe Kelly (Pres)

BUSINESS OFFICE SUITE
SERVICES, INC.
3225 McLeod Dr Ste 100, Las Vegas,
NV 89121
Tel.: (702) 214-1100   NV
Web Site:
  http://www.andersonadvisorslv.com
Year Founded: 1994
Sales Range: $1-9.9 Million
Emp.: 35
Business Consulting Services
N.A.I.C.S.: 541618
Andrew Toby Mathis (Pres)
Steven Kalt (Pres-Anderson Tax Advi-
sors)
Dorothy Bunker (Pres-Anderson Reg-
istered Agents)

BUSINESS OFFICE SYSTEMS
INC.
501 S Garry Ave, Roselle, IL 60172
Tel.: (630) 773-7777
Web Site: https://www.bos.com
Year Founded: 1948
Office Furniture
N.A.I.C.S.: 423210
George Pfeiffer (CEO)
Gretchen Kuzas (VP-Project Mgmt)
John Fredericks (VP)
Jeff Warner (CFO)
Brent Weibel (CIO)
Carla Schroeder (VP-Design)
Glenn Basgall (Principal)
Vince Russett (VP)
Kimberly Sullivan (VP)
Darrin Weidman (VP)
Arlene Martinez (Pres-Market)
Denny Bowman (Principal)
Georgia Dobbelaere (Pres)
George Lucas Pfeiffer (CMO)

Subsidiaries:

Florida Business Interiors Inc.   (1)
200 Technology Park, Lake Mary, FL 32746
Tel.: (407) 805-9911
Web Site: http://www.4fbi.com
Emp.: 24
Office Furniture Sales
N.A.I.C.S.: 423210
Denny Bowman (Pres)

Branch (Domestic):

Florida Business Interiors - Tampa
Bay   (2)

1600 E 8th Ave Ste C-201, Tampa, FL
33605
Tel.: (813) 549-7310
Web Site: http://www.fbitampa.com
Office Furniture Sales
N.A.I.C.S.: 423210
Kevin Baker (Owner & Pres)
Chrisanne Schock (Dir-Design)
Angelena Robinson (Designer)
Farah Deeb (Designer)
Cari Bennett (Acct Mgr)
Jennifer Presley (Acct Mgr)
Debbie Manikis (Dir-Acctg)
Diane Casey (Dir-Ops)
Kenny Dodds (Project Mgr)
Toni Olmsted (Project Mgr)
Leon Ferguson (Mgr-Warehouse)

Kayhan International Limited   (1)
1475 E Woodfield Rd Ste 104, Schaum-
burg, IL 60173
Tel.: (847) 843-5060
Web Site: http://www.shop.bos.com
Provider of Architectural Design, Interior
Design, Contract Furniture, Warehousing,
Delivery Services & Furniture Installation
N.A.I.C.S.: 493110
Ken Bylsma (CEO)

BUSINESS RECORDS MAN-
AGEMENT, INC.
401 Commerce Blvd, Oldsmar, FL
34677
Tel.: (727) 447-3199   FL
Web Site: http://www.brm-inc.com
Year Founded: 1972
Sales Range: $10-24.9 Million
Emp.: 75
Records Storage & Document Imag-
ing Services
N.A.I.C.S.: 493190
Thomas G. Seibert (VP)

BUSINESS SECURITY CON-
SULTANTS, INC.
4309 Robins Ridge Dr, Las Vegas,
NV 89129
Tel.: (928) 202-8459
Security Consulting Services
N.A.I.C.S.: 541618
Lawrence E. Schreiber (Pres, CEO,
CFO, Treas & Sec)

BUSINESS SENSE SOLU-
TIONS
2805 W Busch Blvd Ste 201, Tampa,
FL 33618
Tel.: (813) 220-1981
Web Site: http://www.businesssense
  solutions.com
Sales Range: $1-9.9 Million
Business Consulting & Advisory Ser-
vices
N.A.I.C.S.: 541611
Jerry Hurley (Pres)

BUSINESS SOFTWARE, INC.
420 Technology Pkwy Ste 100,
Peachtree Corners, GA 30092
Tel.: (770) 449-3200
Web Site: https://www.bsi.com
Rev.: $6,900,000
Emp.: 75
Software Publisher
N.A.I.C.S.: 513210
Ralph Rindik (Pres & CEO)

BUSINESS STRATEGIES & BE-
YOND LLC
1512 Fox Trail Ste B1, Mountainside,
NJ 07092
Tel.: (908) 232-5977
Web Site:
  http://www.bizstratbeyond.com
Year Founded: 1985
Sales Range: $1-9.9 Million
Emp.: 3
Public Relations Branding & Market-
ing Consultants

N.A.I.C.S.: 541820
Gail Steckler (Principal & Chief Strat-
egy Officer)
Danielle Gnichtel (Mng Dir)

BUSINESS TECHNOLOGY
SERVICES, INC.
1150 1st Ave, King of Prussia, PA
19406
Tel.: (610) 592-0600
Web Site: http://www.biztech.com
Year Founded: 2001
Rev.: $17,300,000
Emp.: 59
Business Consulting Services
N.A.I.C.S.: 541618
Michael Lennon (Mng Partner)
Kyle Snyder (Mng Partner)
Lee Tsao (Partner)
Thomas Connolly (CEO)
Margot G. McDonnell (VP-Sls)
Marsha Edgell (Dir-Applications
Practice-Chesapeake)

BUSINESS TRAINING LI-
BRARY
285 Chesterfield Business Pkwy,
Chesterfield, MO 63005
Tel.: (636) 534-1000   MO
Web Site: http://www.bizlibrary.com
Year Founded: 1996
Business Training Programs
N.A.I.C.S.: 611430
Dean Pichee (Founder & CEO)
Les Wight (CTO)
Debbie Williams (VP-Content Dev)

BUSINESS-TO-BUSINESS
MARKETING COMMUNICA-
TIONS
900 Ridgefield Dr Ste 270, Raleigh,
NC 27609-8524
Tel.: (919) 872-8172   NC
Web Site:
  http://www.btbmarketing.com
Year Founded: 1989
Rev.: $7,000,000
Emp.: 22
Fiscal Year-end: 12/31/03
N.A.I.C.S.: 541810
Chris Burke (VP-Acct Svcs)
George Bournazian (VP-Acct Svcs)
Geoff Dunkak (VP-Creative Svcs)
Deborah Jaques (Dir-Media)
Patricia Staino (Dir-Writing Svcs &
Mgr-PR Acct)

BUSINESSONLINE INC.
701 B St Ste 1000, San Diego, CA
92101
Tel.: (619) 699-0767
Web Site: http://www.businessol.com
Year Founded: 1996
Sales Range: $1-9.9 Million
Emp.: 37
Interactive Marketing
N.A.I.C.S.: 541890
Thad Kahlow (CEO)
Richard Roberts (Sr VP)
Todd Cohen (Sr VP-Client Svcs)
Matthew Lee (VP-Pro Svcs)

BUSLINK MEDIA
440 Cloverleaf Dr, Baldwin Park, CA
91706
Tel.: (626) 336-1888
Web Site: https://www.buslink.com
Rev.: $3,100,000
Emp.: 10
Administrative Management & Gen-
eral Management Consulting Ser-
vices
N.A.I.C.S.: 541611
James Djen (CEO)
Jie Zhu (Sec)

Buss Ford LLC—(Continued)

BUSS FORD LLC
111 S Ste 31, McHenry, IL 60050
Tel.: (815) 385-2000
Web Site: http://www.bussford.com
Sales Range: $50-74.9 Million
Emp.: 45
Car Dealership Owner & Operator
N.A.I.C.S.: 441110
Steven Buss *(Owner)*
Edward Buss *(Co-Owner)*
Drew Buss *(Gen Mgr)*
Dave Wickenkamp *(Mgr-Sls)*
Ivan Romero *(Mgr-Fin)*
Gary Morowski *(Mgr-Internet Sls)*
Robert Loudon *(Mgr-Parts)*
Bob Kouba *(Mgr-Svc)*

BUSS FORD SALES
111 S Route 31, McHenry, IL 60050-
0516
Tel.: (815) 669-1384
Web Site: https://www.bussford.com
Year Founded: 1928
Sales Range: $10-24.9 Million
Emp.: 51
Car Whslr
N.A.I.C.S.: 441110
Edward Buss *(Partner & VP)*
Stephen Buss *(Pres & Partner)*
Robert Buss *(Sec & Partner)*

BUSSEN QUARRIES, INC.
5000 Bussen Rd, Saint Louis, MO
63129
Tel.: (314) 894-8777   MO
Web Site:
  https://www.bussenquarries.com
Year Founded: 1882
Sales Range: $25-49.9 Million
Emp.: 50
Limestone Quarry & Resource Termi-
nal Operator
N.A.I.C.S.: 212312
Mark Bussen *(Pres)*

Subsidiaries:

Bussen Quarries, Inc. - Jefferson
Barracks Quarry   **(1)**
5000 Bussen Rd, Saint Louis, MO 63129
Tel.: (314) 487-2300
Web Site: http://www.bussenquarries.com
Limestone Quarry Operator
N.A.I.C.S.: 212312
Charlie Rock *(VP)*
Dana Bussen *(VP & Dir-Safety)*
Craig Bussen *(VP-Sls)*
Mark Bussen *(VP-Sls)*
Dave Merz *(Mgr)*

Bussen Quarries, Inc. - Trautman
Quarry   **(1)**
8799 Trautman Quarry Rd, Pevely, MO
63707
Tel.: (636) 475-5555
Web Site: http://www.bussenquarries.com
Emp.: 4
Limestone Quarry Operator
N.A.I.C.S.: 212312
Curt Ruff *(VP & Superintendent)*

**BUSY BEAVER BUILDING
CENTERS, INC.**
3130 William Pitt Way, Pittsburgh, PA
15238-1360
Tel.: (412) 828-2323   PA
Web Site:
  http://www.busybeaver.com
Year Founded: 1962
Sales Range: $200-249.9 Million
Emp.: 450
Retail Home Improvement
N.A.I.C.S.: 444110
Mike Slobodnik *(VP-Mdsg)*
Dave Miller *(VP-Sls & Ops)*

BUSY BEE CABINETS, INC.

2845 Commerce Pkwy, North Port,
FL 34289
Tel.: (941) 426-5656   FL
Web Site:
  http://www.busybeecabinets.com
Year Founded: 1982
Sales Range: $1-9.9 Million
Emp.: 15
Cabinetry Mfr
N.A.I.C.S.: 337110
Matt Uebelacker *(Co-Owner & Pres)*
Diana Uebelacker *(VP)*
Glenn Miller *(Gen Mgr)*

**BUSY BODY FITNESS IN MO-
TION**
2330 Apollo Cir, Carrollton, TX 75006
Tel.: (972) 416-7200
Web Site:
  http://www.busybodytx.com
Year Founded: 1987
Sales Range: $10-24.9 Million
Emp.: 100
Apparel Whslr
N.A.I.C.S.: 424350
Gary Glanger *(Gen Mgr)*
Trevor Glanger *(Pres)*
Norm Gremont *(Controller)*

**BUTCH OUSTALET CHEVRO-
LET CADILLAC**
4012 14th St, Pascagoula, MS
39567-2406
Tel.: (800) 293-8114
Web Site:
  http://www.bigochevycadillac.com
Sales Range: $10-24.9 Million
Emp.: 45
New Car Dealers
N.A.I.C.S.: 441110
Phillip Pogue *(Gen Mgr)*

**BUTCH OUSTALET FORD LIN-
COLN**
9274 Highway 49 N, Gulfport, MS
39503-4256
Tel.: (228) 863-5525   MS
Web Site:
  http://www.butchoustalet.com
Year Founded: 1985
Sales Range: $25-49.9 Million
Emp.: 70
Sales of New & Used Automobiles &
Pickups
N.A.I.C.S.: 441110
A.J.M. Butch Oustalet *(Pres)*
Larry Clark *(VP)*
Tommy Wittmann *(Controller)*

**BUTCHER & BAECKER CON-
STRUCTION CO., INC.**
3885 Industrial Dr, Rochester Hills,
MI 48309
Tel.: (248) 852-2323
Web Site:
  https://www.bbconstruction.com
Year Founded: 1977
Sales Range: $10-24.9 Million
Emp.: 80
Masonry Services
N.A.I.C.S.: 238140
Stephan F. Slavik *(Pres)*

**BUTCHER DISTRIBUTORS
INC.**
101 Boyce St, Broussard, LA 70518
Tel.: (337) 243-3503
Web Site: https://www.butcherac.com
Sales Range: $10-24.9 Million
Emp.: 40
Heating & Air Conditioning
N.A.I.C.S.: 423730
Thomas P. Butcher *(CEO)*
Bill Colvin *(Controller)*
Liz Hebert *(Mgr-Credit)*

**BUTCHER VENTURE CAPITAL
COMPANY**
15 E Uwchlan Ave Ste 404, Exton,
PA 19341
Tel.: (484) 875-4140   DE
Year Founded: 1910
Sales Range: $150-199.9 Million
Emp.: 5
Capital Investment Services
N.A.I.C.S.: 523999
Jonathan Butcher *(Pres)*

BUTECH BLISS
550 S Ellsworth Ave, Salem, OH
44460-3067
Tel.: (330) 337-0000   OH
Web Site:
  https://www.butechbliss.com
Year Founded: 1985
Sales Range: $100-124.9 Million
Emp.: 200
Industrial Machinery Mfr
N.A.I.C.S.: 333517
Ed Leclerc *(Dir-Automation)*
Justin Seguin *(Engr-Application)*
Paul Satolli *(Engr-Electrical)*
Theodore Bricker *(Mgr-Pur)*
Jason Cuff *(Product Mgr-Coil Pro-
cessing Lines)*
Steve Malone *(Engr-Proposal)*
Brian Meeks *(Supvr-Maintenance)*
Scott Thomas *(Mgr-Press Sls)*
Al Waigand *(VP-Sls & Mktg)*
Ray Dombrosky *(Mgr-Sls)*
Larry Pigza *(Engr-Mechanical)*
Raymond Hudran *(Engr-Sls)*
Christopher Gorence *(Mgr-Spare
Parts & Sls)*

BUTERA FINER FOODS INC.
1 Clock Tower Plz, Elgin, IL 60120-
6918
Tel.: (847) 741-1010   IL
Web Site:
  http://www.buteramarket.com
Year Founded: 1968
Sales Range: $75-99.9 Million
Emp.: 500
Food Store
N.A.I.C.S.: 445110
Joseph Butera *(Pres)*
Paul Butera Jr. *(VP)*
Paul Butera Sr. *(CEO)*

**BUTLER & BUTLER INVEST-
MENTS**
4464 Lone Tree Way Ste 620, Anti-
och, CA 94531-7413
Tel.: (925) 706-2100
Year Founded: 1985
Sales Range: $10-24.9 Million
Emp.: 5
Real Estate Development Services
N.A.I.C.S.: 531110
Jeffrey Butler *(Owner)*

BUTLER AMERICA, INC.
2 Trap Falls Rd Ste 204, Shelton, CT
06484
Tel.: (203) 926-2700   MD
Web Site: https://www.butler.com
Year Founded: 1985
Sales Range: $300-349.9 Million
Emp.: 3,600
Technical Outsourcing Service Solu-
tions
N.A.I.C.S.: 561311
Christine Ciocca *(Pres)*
James Elsner *(VP-UTC & Comml
Verticals)*
Chris Hamel *(Sr VP-Bus Dev)*
Jim Heun *(Sr VP-Lockheed Martin &
Defense Verticals)*

Subsidiaries:

Butler Design Services, Inc.   **(1)**

110 Summit Ave, Montvale, NJ
07645-1712   **(100%)**
Tel.: (201) 573-8000
Web Site: http://www.butlerdesign.com
Sales Range: $25-49.9 Million
Emp.: 60
Off-site Design & Drafting Services
N.A.I.C.S.: 561320

Butler Fleet Services, Inc.   **(1)**
110 Summit Ave, Montvale, NJ 07645
Tel.: (201) 573-8000
Web Site: http://www.butler.com
Sales Range: $550-599.9 Million
Emp.: 2,000
Provides Maintenance for Vehicles in the
Telecommunications Industry
N.A.I.C.S.: 561320

Butler Service Group, Inc.   **(1)**
3820 State St Ste A, Santa Barbara, CA
93105-3182   **(100%)**
Tel.: (201) 573-8000
Web Site: http://www.butler.com
Sales Range: $75-99.9 Million
Contract Technical Services
N.A.I.C.S.: 561320

Subsidiary (Domestic)

Butler Service Group - U.K. Ltd.   **(2)**
3820 State St Ste A, Santa Barbara, CA
93105-3182   **(100%)**
Tel.: (201) 573-8000
Web Site: http://www.butler.com
Sales Range: $10-24.9 Million
Emp.: 60
N.A.I.C.S.: 561330

Butler Technical Services India Pri-
vate Limited   **(1)**
6th Floor West Wing Block I My Home Hub,
Madhapur, Hyderabad, 500081,
India   **(100%)**
Tel.: (91) 40 3071 7171
Web Site: http://www.butler.com
Technical Services Including Staff Augmen-
tation, Managed Services & Project Man-
agement Solutions
N.A.I.C.S.: 541612
Bharani K. Aroll *(VP-Ops)*

Butler Technology Solutions, Inc.   **(1)**
110 Summit Ave, Montvale, NJ
07645-1712   **(100%)**
Tel.: (203) 926-2700
Web Site: http://www.butler.com
Sales Range: $25-49.9 Million
Emp.: 100
Technology Solutions
N.A.I.C.S.: 561320

Butler Utility Service, Inc.   **(1)**
110 Summit Ave, Montvale, NJ
07645-1712   **(100%)**
Tel.: (201) 307-1600
Web Site: http://www.butler.com
Sales Range: $75-99.9 Million
Provider of Outsourcing & Project Manage-
ment Services
N.A.I.C.S.: 561320

BUTLER AUTOMATIC, INC.
41 Leona Dr, Middleboro, MA 02346-
1404
Tel.: (508) 923-0544   DE
Web Site:
  https://www.butlerautomatic.com
Year Founded: 1956
Sales Range: $25-49.9 Million
Emp.: 100
Machinery for the Printing & Packag-
ing Industries Mfr
N.A.I.C.S.: 333248
Dave Ewan *(Specialist-Svc)*
Lou Pelnar *(Dir-Sls-East)*
Phil Johnson *(VP-Sls & Mktg)*
Mark Austin *(Dir-Sls-West)*
Loris Medart *(Dir-Sls-EMEA)*
David Steines *(Mgr-Technical Sls-
Europe)*

Subsidiaries:

Hydralign   **(1)**
41 Leona Dr, Middleboro, MA 02346-1404
Tel.: (508) 923-0544

Emp.: 40
Electronic Web Guide Systems, Mechanical Core Chucks, Winding & Unwinding Machines Mfr
N.A.I.C.S.: 339999
Andrew P. Butler (Pres & CEO)
Daniel Killory (Sls Mgr)

BUTLER AUTOMOTIVE GROUP INC.
1977 Hwy 99 N, Ashland, OR 97520-9651
Tel.: (541) 482-2521
Sales Range: $10-24.9 Million
Emp.: 53
New Car Whslr
N.A.I.C.S.: 441110
Rob Butler (Pres)

BUTLER BROS, INC.
2001 Lisbon St, Lewiston, ME 04243-1375
Tel.: (207) 784-6875
Web Site: https://www.butlerbros.com
Year Founded: 1952
Box & Tractor Trailer Trucks Fleet Operator
N.A.I.C.S.: 488490
Ronald Cote (VP-Sls)

BUTLER CARPET COMPANY INC.
10815 US Hwy 19 N, Clearwater, FL 33764
Tel.: (727) 571-9998   FL
Web Site: http://www.bobscarpet.com
Year Founded: 1969
Sales Range: $25-49.9 Million
Emp.: 100
Carpets & Hardwood Floors
N.A.I.C.S.: 449121
Lori Smith (VP)
Robin Farley (Treas & Sec)
Robert H. Butler III (Pres)

BUTLER ENTERPRISES
3217 SW 35th Blvd, Gainesville, FL 32608
Tel.: (352) 372-6060
Web Site: http://www.butlerplaza.com
Sales Range: $10-24.9 Million
Emp.: 50
Shopping Center, Property Operation Only
N.A.I.C.S.: 531120
Deborah Butler (Owner & Pres)
Jerry Jones (Mgr-Property)
Corey A. Presnick (Controller)
Terry Harrison (Mgr-Ops)
Mary Reichardt (Dir-Mktg-Neighborhoods At Butler Project)

BUTLER FOODS OF PENSACOLA INC.
3311 Hwy 29 S, Cantonment, FL 32533
Tel.: (850) 478-2363
Web Site: https://www.butler-foods.com
Sales Range: $10-24.9 Million
Emp.: 36
Dairy Products Distr
N.A.I.C.S.: 424430
Ann Ward (Office Mgr)
Steven Butler (Pres)

BUTLER HOME PRODUCTS, INC.
311 Hopping Brook Rd, Holliston, MA 01746-1456
Tel.: (508) 429-8100   MA
Year Founded: 1969
Sales Range: $75-99.9 Million
Emp.: 145
Mfr of Mops, Brooms, Brushes, Sponges & Dust Pans

N.A.I.C.S.: 339994
Mark Michelson (Dir-Sls)

BUTLER INDUSTRIES INC.
3243 Whitfield St, Macon, GA 31204
Tel.: (478) 745-0878
Web Site: http://www.partscentral.net
Sales Range: $10-24.9 Million
Emp.: 75
Automotive Supplies & Parts
N.A.I.C.S.: 423120
Milton Butler (CEO)

BUTLER MACHINERY COMPANY
3401 33rd St SW, Fargo, ND 58104
Tel.: (701) 232-0033
Web Site: http://www.butler-machinery.com
Rev.: $167,042,539
Emp.: 80
Construction & Mining Machinery
N.A.I.C.S.: 423810
Dan Butler (Pres)

BUTLER PETROLEUM CORPORATION
824 Butler Rd, Kittanning, PA 16201-1907
Tel.: (724) 285-4111   PA
Web Site: http://www.reedoil.com
Year Founded: 1936
Sales Range: $10-24.9 Million
Emp.: 15
Petroleum Product Distr
N.A.I.C.S.: 424710
Ken Jones (Pres)
William R. Preston (VP)

BUTLER SNOW LLP
1020 Highland Colony Pkwy Ste 1400, Ridgeland, MS 39157
Tel.: (601) 948-5711   DE
Web Site: http://www.butlersnow.com
Year Founded: 1954
Emp.: 247
Law firm
N.A.I.C.S.: 541110
P. Ryan Beckett (Atty)
Rance Sapen (COO)
Tommie S. Cardin (Atty)
Dan H. Elrod (Atty)
Michael E. McWilliams (Atty)
Benjamin W. Roberson (Atty)
Timothy Kemp (Partner)
R. Barry Cannada (Chm-Bus Dept)
Gregg C. Gumbert (Atty)
Stephen Weyl (Atty)
Kimbrely Dandridge (Atty)
Steve Groom (Principal-Butler Snow Advisory Services)
Susan Davis Egger (Chief HR Officer)
Benjamin Whitehouse (Atty)
Eric J. R. Nichols (Atty)
Cedric E. Evans (Atty-Pharmaceutical, Medical Device & Health Care Litigation Grp)
Christopher R. Cowan (Atty)
Keith C. Mier (Atty-Labor & Employment Grp)
Scott K. Field (Atty)
Thomas A. Forbes (Partner)
Jones Wilson Luna (Atty)
A. La'Verne Edney (Partner-Litigation)
Donald Clark Jr. (Corp Counsel)
Orlando R. Richmond Sr. (Atty)

BUTLER SUPPLY INC.
965 Horan Dr, Saint Louis, MO 63026
Tel.: (636) 349-9000
Web Site:
   https://www.butlersupply.com
Sales Range: $50-74.9 Million
Emp.: 300

Distribute Electrical Apparatus & Equipment
N.A.I.C.S.: 423610
William Kuempel (Pres)
Bill Immer (VP)
Tina Jett (VP-HR)
David Gault (Reg VP)
Randy Kunkel (Mgr)
Mick Portell (Controller)
Kim Johnston (Dir-Mktg)
Russ Braunseis (Dir-Pur)
Dennis McCarthy (Exec VP)
Don Ault (Mgr-Bridgeport)
Thomas Litty (Mgr-Bus Dev)
Glenn Lohse (Mgr-Credit)
Mike Haley (Mgr-Electrical Pur)
Marvin Shaffrey (Mgr-Electrical Pur)
Pat Grawitch (Mgr-Plumbing Pur)
Pete Cummings (Reg VP)

BUTLER TIRE COMPANY INCORPORATED
106 Powers Ferry Rd SE, Marietta, GA 30067
Tel.: (404) 751-1608
Web Site: https://www.butlertire.com
Rev.: $13,671,442
Emp.: 70
Tires, Used: Retail Only
N.A.I.C.S.: 423140
Alan Dobrin (COO)
Gary Port (Gen Mgr)

BUTLER TRUCKING COMPANY
142 Owens Rd, Woodland, PA 16881
Tel.: (814) 857-7644
Sales Range: $10-24.9 Million
Emp.: 100
Trucking Except Local
N.A.I.C.S.: 484121
D. Stephen Butler (Pres)

BUTLER WHOLESALE PRODUCTS, INC.
1067 State Rd, North Adams, MA 01247-3034
Tel.: (413) 743-3885   MA
Year Founded: 1915
Sales Range: $75-99.9 Million
Emp.: 65
Foodservice Distr
N.A.I.C.S.: 424410

BUTLER'S ELECTRIC SUPPLY
2013 Castle St, Wilmington, NC 28403
Tel.: (910) 762-3345
Web Site:
   https://www.butlerselectrics.com
Year Founded: 1948
Rev.: $10,000,000
Emp.: 85
Whslr of Electrical Supplies
N.A.I.C.S.: 423610
James Butler (Owner)
Johnson Butler (VP-Butler's Electric & Co-Owner-DiscountLightingSale.com)
Susan Butler (Co-Owner)
Subsidiaries:
DiscountLightingSale.com   (1)
2013 Castle St, Wilmington, NC 28403   (100%)
Tel.: (888) 402-0688
Web Site:
   http://www.discountlightingsale.com
Discount Lighting Products
N.A.I.C.S.: 335131
Johnson Butler (Co-Owner)

BUTLER, SHINE, STERN & PARTNERS
20 Liberty Ship Way, Sausalito, CA 94965-3312
Tel.: (415) 331-6049   CA

Web Site: http://www.bssp.com
Year Founded: 1993
Rev.: $100,000,000
Emp.: 150
Advetising Agency
N.A.I.C.S.: 541810
Greg Stern (Founder & CEO)
Patrick Kiss (Pres)
Amy Clawson (Dir-HR & Ops)
Tom Coates (Dir-Creative)
John Butler (Chm)
Greg Stern (Founder & CEO)
Cristiano Alburitel (Dir-New Bus)
Mark Krajan (Dir-Creative)
Keith Cartwright (Exec Dir-Creative)
David Eastman (COO)
Amanda Mobley (Dir-Strategy)
Tracey Faux-Pattani (CEO)
Sinan Dagli (Exec Creative Dir)

BUTLER-JOHNSON CORPORATION
2200 Zanker Rd Ste 130, San Jose, CA 95133
Tel.: (408) 259-1800   CA
Web Site: http://www.butler-johnson.com
Year Founded: 1960
Sales Range: $10-24.9 Million
Emp.: 50
Retail of Household Items
N.A.I.C.S.: 423220
Rolston Johnson (Owner & Pres)

BUTLER/TILL MEDIA SERVICES, INC.
1565 Jefferson Rd Building 200 Ste 280, Rochester, NY 14623-3178
Tel.: (585) 274-5100
Web Site: http://www.butlertill.com
Year Founded: 1998
Sales Range: $25-49.9 Million
Emp.: 102
Media Buying Services
N.A.I.C.S.: 541830
Sue Butler (Chm)
Tracy Till (Vice Chm)
Sue Belias (Controller)
Andria DiFelice (Dir-Acct Grp)
Karen Sharp (Dir-Acct)
Peter Infante (Chief Strategy Officer)
Kelly Kilpatrick (Assoc Dir-Media)
Michael Charles Deichmiller (Acct Dir)
Melissa Palmer (CFO & COO)
Kimberly Jones (Pres)
Amy Moyer (Dir-HR)
Jill Tobin (Office Mgr)
Kristin Lennarz (Dir-Digital Strategy)
Amanda DeVito (VP-Engagement)
Carrie Riby (Dir-Strategic Plng)
Cathi Perkins (Mgr-PMO)
David Grome (Acct Dir)
Robin Miller (Mgr-Traffic)
Sara Wallace (Acct Dir)
Stacie Smith (Acct Mgr)
Tricia Beggs (Project Mgr)
Keith Betz (VP-Client Svcs)
Stacey Barlow (VP-Media Investment)
Gabrielle Bedewi (Chief Analytics Officer)

Subsidiaries:

Brand Cool Marketing Inc.   (1)
2300 East Ave, Rochester, NY 14610-2564
Tel.: (585) 381-3350
Web Site: http://www.brandcool.com
Advertising & Marketing Services
N.A.I.C.S.: 541810
Sue Kochan (CEO)
Sarah Gibson (VP-Client Svcs)
Kristin Clauss (Dir-Fin & Ops)
Amanda DeVito (VP-Engagement)
Holly Barrett (VP-Agency Svcs)
Kimberly Jones (Pres)

Digital Hyve Marketing LLC   (1)

Butler/Till Media Services, Inc.—(Continued)

126 N Salina St, Syracuse, NY 13202
Tel.: (315) 412-0988
Web Site: http://www.digitalhyve.com
Digital Marketing Services
N.A.I.C.S.: 541810
Jake Tanner (Co-Founder)
Jeff Knauss (Co-Founder & CEO)
Sarah Mastrangelo (VP-Ops)
Christy Leroy (Dir-Analytics & Res)
Connor Dehaan (Art Dir)

BUTTE COUNTY RICE GROW-ERS ASSOCIATION
1193 Richvale Hwy, Richvale, CA 95974
Tel.: (530) 882-4261
Web Site: https://www.bucra.com
Sales Range: $10-24.9 Million
Emp.: 25
Rice Growing & Marketing Services
N.A.I.C.S.: 424910
Carl Hoff (Pres)
Susan Ricketts (VP)

BUTTE GLASS
840 S Utah, Butte, MT 59701
Tel.: (406) 723-3792
Web Site:
https://www.butteglass.com
Sales Range: $10-24.9 Million
Emp.: 10
Glass & Glazing Work
N.A.I.C.S.: 238150
Chris Blom (Pres)
Diana Blom (Treas & Sec)

BUTTER KRUST BAKING COMPANY
249 N 11th St, Sunbury, PA 17801
Tel.: (570) 286-5845
Web Site: http://www.butter-krust.com
Rev.: $37,800,000
Emp.: 210
Bakery
N.A.I.C.S.: 311812
James G. Apple (Pres)

BUTTERFIELD TRAIL VIL-LAGE, INC.
1923 E Joyce Blvd, Fayetteville, AR 72703-5205
Tel.: (479) 442-7220
Web Site:
http://www.butterfieldtrailvillage.com
Year Founded: 1986
Sales Range: $10-24.9 Million
Emp.: 200
Property Management Services
N.A.I.C.S.: 531110
Patricia Poertner (Principal-Admin)
Renee King (Dir-Nursing)
Quintin Trammell (Pres & CEO)
Renee Ting (Dir-Nursing)
Jay Green (Dir-Health Care Svcs)
Kelly Syer (Dir-Mktg)

BUTTERFLY EFFECTS INC
500 Fairway Dr Ste 102, Deerfield Beach, FL 33441
Tel.: (954) 603-7885
Web Site:
http://www.butterflyeffects.com
Year Founded: 2005
Sales Range: $1-9.9 Million
Emp.: 450
Comprehensive Care for Individuals With Complex Medical Conditions
N.A.I.C.S.: 621420
Martin Mosley (COO)
Neal Shapiro (Dir-Bus Dev)
Jennifer Rivera (Dir-Hiring & Mgr-Recruiting Dept)

BUTTERFLY EQUITY LP

9595 Wilshire Blvd Ste 510, Beverly Hills, CA 90212
Tel.: (310) 409-4994   DE
Web Site:
http://www.butterflyequity.com
Privater Equity Firm
N.A.I.C.S.: 523999
Vishal Patel (Partner)
Adam Waglay (Co-Founder & Co-CEO)
Dustin Beck (Co-Founder & Co-CEO)
Bill Allen (Operating Partner)
Peter Tang (Mng Dir & CFO)

Subsidiaries:

Chosen Foods LLC   (1)
1747 Hancock St, San Diego, CA 92101
Tel.: (877) 674-2244
Web Site: http://www.chosenfoods.com
Online Nourish Food Retailer
N.A.I.C.S.: 455110
Carsten Hagen (Founder)
George R. Todd (Pres)
Gabriel Perez Krieb (CEO)

Orgain, LLC   (1)
16631 Millikan Ave, Irvine, CA 92606
Tel.: (888) 881-4246
Web Site: http://www.orgain.com
Ready-to-Drink Organic Nutritional Drinks
N.A.I.C.S.: 456191
Andrew Abraham (Founder & CEO)

Pete & Gerry's Organics, LLC   (1)
140 Buffum Rd, Monroe, NH 03771
Tel.: (603) 638-2827
Web Site: http://www.peteandgerrys.com
Sales Range: $1-9.9 Million
Emp.: 30
Miscellaneous Food Mfr
N.A.I.C.S.: 311999
Jesse Laflamme (CEO)

Wm. Bolthouse Farms, Inc.   (1)
7200 E Brundage Ln, Bakersfield, CA 93307-3016
Tel.: (661) 366-7207
Web Site: http://www.bolthouse.com
Sales Range: $800-899.9 Million
Emp.: 2,200
Carrot Farming, Processing, Packaging & Marketing; Fruit Beverage & Dressing Bottler & Whslr
N.A.I.C.S.: 424480
Tracy Marchant Saiki (Gen Counsel)
Jorge Rodriguez (Mgr-Farm)
Mike Illum (Sr VP-Retail Sls & Mdsg)
Scott LaPorta (Pres & Gen Mgr)

BUTTON MOTORS, INC.
1220 E Blvd, Kokomo, IN 46902
Tel.: (765) 252-4447
Web Site:
https://www.buttondodge.com
Year Founded: 1932
Sales Range: $10-24.9 Million
Emp.: 100
Car Whslr
N.A.I.C.S.: 441110
Judith A. Weaver (Mgr-Admin)
Don Button (Pres)
Rex Gingerich (Gen Mgr)

BUTTON TRANSPORTATION INC.
8034 Schroeder Rd, Dixon, CA 95620
Tel.: (707) 678-1983
Web Site: http://www.buttontrans.com
Sales Range: $10-24.9 Million
Emp.: 50
Trucking Except Local
N.A.I.C.S.: 484121
Robert Button (Pres)
Chris Reading (Controller)

BUTZ ENTERPRISES, INC.
840 Hamilton St Ste 600, Allentown, PA 18105-0509
Tel.: (610) 395-6871   PA
Web Site: https://butz.com
Year Founded: 1978
Sales Range: $200-249.9 Million

Emp.: 75
Construction Management Services
N.A.I.C.S.: 236220
Lee A. Butz (Chm)
Greg L. Butz (Pres & CEO)
Raymond Federici (Sec)

Subsidiaries:

Alvin H. Butz, Inc.   (1)
840 Hamilton St Ste 600, Allentown, PA 18105
Tel.: (610) 395-6871
Web Site: http://www.butz.com
Sales Range: $250-299.9 Million
Construction Management Firm
N.A.I.C.S.: 541618
Lee A. Butz (Chm)
Greg L. Butz (Pres & CEO)
Michael D. Weber (Mgr-Property Damage Repair & Restoration Svcs)
Matthew Mengel (Project Mgr)
James Messick (Project Mgr)

Subsidiary (Domestic):

L.V.H. Inc.   (2)
840 Hamilton St, Allentown, PA 18101
Tel.: (610) 395-6871
Sales Range: $10-24.9 Million
Emp.: 30
Air Transportation, Scheduled
N.A.I.C.S.: 481111

Shoemaker Construction Co.   (1)
1 Tower Bridge 100 Frnt St Ste 365, West Conshohocken, PA 19428-2876
Tel.: (610) 941-5500
Web Site: http://www.shoemakerco.com
Emp.: 24
General Contractor & Construction Management Services
N.A.I.C.S.: 236210
Maura Hesdon (Gen Mgr)

Subsidiary (Domestic):

Alexander Building Construction LLC   (2)
315 Vaughn St, Harrisburg, PA 17110
Tel.: (717) 234-7041
Web Site: http://www.alexanderbuilding.com
Nonresidential Construction Services
N.A.I.C.S.: 236220
Richard J. Seitz (Pres)

Shoemaker Construction   (2)
100 Front St Ste 365 W, Conshohocken, PA 19428
Tel.: (610) 941-5500
Web Site: http://www.shoemakerco.com
Sales Range: $1-9.9 Million
Emp.: 20
Subdividers & Developers
N.A.I.C.S.: 541618
Maura Hesdon (Gen Mgr)

BUURMA FARMS INC.
3909 Kok Rd, Willard, OH 44890-7450
Tel.: (419) 935-6411
Web Site:
https://www.buurmafarms.com
Sales Range: $10-24.9 Million
Emp.: 400
Celery Farm
N.A.I.C.S.: 111219
Nathan Buurma (Sec)
Bruce Buurma (First VP)
Ric Buurma (Pres & Mgr-Field-Michigan)
Aaron Buurma (VP & Mgr-Packing Shed)
Barbara Buurma (Office Mgr)
Bryan Buurma (VP)
Chadd Buurma (VP-Sls & Transportation)
Dan Buurma (VP & Mgr-Maintenance Shop)
Greg Buurma (VP & Mgr-Field-Michigan)
Henry Buurma (VP & Mgr-R&D)
Joel Buurma (Mgr-Food Safety)
Loren Buurma (Treas)
Mike Buurma (VP)

BUXBAUM GROUP
2780 Canwood St Ste 108, Agoura Hills, CA 91301-6088
Tel.: (818) 878-3900   CA
Web Site:
http://www.buxbaumgroup.com
Year Founded: 1998
Sales Range: $10-24.9 Million
Emp.: 20
Retail Liquidation & Appraisal Services
N.A.I.C.S.: 541618
Jim Siebersma (Exec VP & Head-Asset Appraisal)
Paul M. Buxbaum (Chm, CEO & Partner)

BUXTON ACQUISITION CO., LLC
245 Cadwell Dr, Springfield, MA 01104
Tel.: (413) 734-5900   DE
Web Site:
http://www.buxtonstyle.com
Year Founded: 1898
Personal Leather Goods Designer, Distr & Online Retailer
N.A.I.C.S.: 458320
Eric Lund (Pres)

BUXTON OIL CO. INC.
24 Charter St, Exeter, NH 03833
Tel.: (603) 772-3400
Web Site: http://www.buxtonoil.com
Year Founded: 1960
Sales Range: $10-24.9 Million
Emp.: 40
Provider of Fuel Oil Dealer Services
N.A.I.C.S.: 115112

BUY ADS DIRECT
33247 Westwood Dr, Ridge Manor, FL 33523
Tel.: (352) 397-4221
Web Site:
http://www.buyadsdirect.com
Sales Range: $1-9.9 Million
Emp.: 3
Advetising Agency
N.A.I.C.S.: 541830
Will Crawford (Pres)

BUY HAPPIER, LLC
322 S Green St Ste 208, Chicago, IL 60607
Tel.: (800) 590-0996
Web Site: http://www.buyhappier.com
Year Founded: 2009
Sales Range: $10-24.9 Million
Emp.: 32
Offers Online Shopping Channels for Household Products
N.A.I.C.S.: 449129
Jeff Mariola (CEO)

BUY-LO QUALITY FOOD STORES
32 Phillips Dr, Birmingham, AL 35228
Tel.: (205) 923-1787
Sales Range: $10-24.9 Million
Emp.: 30
Supermarket
N.A.I.C.S.: 445110
Naseem Ajlouny (Pres)

BUY-RITE FOODS INC.
1227 Military Rd Ste 1, Benton, AR 72015-2934
Tel.: (501) 570-0007
Sales Range: $10-24.9 Million
Emp.: 40
Supermarket Services
N.A.I.C.S.: 445110
John Miller (Pres)
Gale Bates (Controller)

BUYATIMESHARE.COM
32 Daniel Webster Hwy Ste 25, Merrimack, NH 03054
Tel.: (603) 883-8626   NH
Web Site:
https://www.buyatimeshare.com
Year Founded: 2000
Sales Range: $1-9.9 Million
Emp.: 200
Online Timeshare Sales & Marketing
N.A.I.C.S.: 531210
Wesley Kogelman (CEO)
Jason Dobbins (CTO)
Rosanne Luba (COO)
Chris Hand (Mgr)
Steve Luba (Chief Comm Officer)

BUYCASTINGS.COM
2411 Crosspointe Dr, Miamisburg, OH 45342
Tel.: (937) 247-9194
Web Site:
https://www.buycastings.com
Year Founded: 2000
Rev.: $7,400,000
Emp.: 11
Business Management Services
N.A.I.C.S.: 561110
Robert Dzugan (Co-Founder & Pres)
Neil Chaudhry (Co-Founder & COO)
Dave Rauen (Project Mgr)
Bob Dzugan (Co-Founder & Pres)

BUYER ADVERTISING, INC.
189 Wells Ave 2nd Fl, Newton, MA 02459
Tel.: (617) 969-4646   MA
Web Site: http://www.buyerads.com
Year Founded: 1966
Rev.: $18,000,000
Emp.: 42
Food Service, Logo & Package Design, Recruitment
N.A.I.C.S.: 541810
Betty R. Buyer (Pres)
Charles G. Buyer (Exec VP & Gen Mgr)
Ann Toll (VP, Sls Mgr & Client Svcs Dir)
Marion B. Buyer (VP)
Linda Rau (Pur Dir)
Jean Desharnais (Designer)
Kristina M. Bunce (Dir-New Bus Dev)
Jill Kushner (Internet Dir)
Loretta Lacamara (VP-Fin)
Joel Glick (VP)
Elyse Effenson (Dir-Media)
Jody Robie (Exec Dir-Bus Dev)

BUYERS EDGE PLATFORM LLC
307 Waverley Oaks Rd Ste 401, 02452, Waltham, MA
Tel.: (617) 275-8430
Web Site:
https://buyersedgeplatform.com
Year Founded: 2018
Emp.: 100
Cloud Platform, Software & Analytics Company
N.A.I.C.S.: 518210
John Davie (Owner & CEO)
Subsidiaries:
ArrowStream, Inc.   (1)
100 Lexington Dr Ste 201, 60089, Buffalo Grove, IL
Tel.: (312) 267-4400
Web Site: http://www.arrowstream.com
Industrial Building Construction
N.A.I.C.S.: 236210
Bill Michalski (Chief Solutions Officer)
Jeff Dorr (Pres)
David Maloni (Exec VP-Analytics)
Raj Badarinath (Chief Revenue Officer)
Jeff Stone (CEO)
Kate Hubbard (Mktg Dir)
Raleigh McClayton (CEO)

BUYMYTRONICS.COM
5858 Staple Pen Dr N Ste A 155, Denver, CO 80216
Tel.: (303) 955-5554
Web Site:
http://www.buymytronics.com
Sales Range: $1-9.9 Million
Emp.: 10
Electronics Products Recycling Services
N.A.I.C.S.: 423930
Brett Mosley (Owner)
Andy Hellmuth (Mgr-Customer Svcs)
Brian Bratton (Dir-Ops)

BUYONLINENOW.COM
4865 19th St NW Ste 110, Rochester, MN 55901
Tel.: (507) 281-6899
Web Site:
http://www.buyonlinenow.com
Sales Range: $1-9.9 Million
Emp.: 30
Online Store for Office Supplies & Office Furniture
N.A.I.C.S.: 424120
Robert Herman (Founder & CEO)
Jeff Kraus (Pres)

BUYRITE CLUB CORP.
7076 Spyglass Ave, Parkland, FL 33076
Tel.: (954) 599-3672   FL
Year Founded: 2008
Internet-Based Merchant Gift Card Services
N.A.I.C.S.: 513199
Judith Adelstein (Pres, CEO, CFO, Treas & Sec)

BUZICK CONSTRUCTION INC.
PO Box 98, Bardstown, KY 40004-0098
Tel.: (502) 348-6401
Web Site:
http://www.teambuzick.com
Year Founded: 1937
Sales Range: $10-24.9 Million
Emp.: 100
Commercial & Institutional Building Construction Services
N.A.I.C.S.: 236220
Thomas C. Blincoe (Chm)
Kevin Aldred (VP & Chief Engr)
Donald Blincoe (Pres & Engr-Professional)
Laura Blincoe Ganoe (Sec & VP)

BUZTRONICS, INC.
4343 W 62nd St, Indianapolis, IN 46268
Tel.: (317) 876-3413
Web Site: http://www.buzline.com
Year Founded: 1989
Sales Range: $150-199.9 Million
Emp.: 145
Electronic Blinking Buttons, Lights & Flashing Point of Purchase Signs in Celluloid, Metal & Custom Plastic for Promotional Efforts; Light Harnesses, Circuits Mfr
N.A.I.C.S.: 339999
Edward Lewis (Founder & CEO)
Alan Heideman (VP-Ops)
Dan Jarosinski (Dir-Creative)
Buzz Lewis (CEO)
Paula Thomas (Controller)

BUZZ OATES COMPANIES
555 Capitol Mall Ste 900, Sacramento, CA 95814
Tel.: (916) 379-3800   CA
Web Site: http://www.buzzoates.com
Year Founded: 1951
Sales Range: $75-99.9 Million
Emp.: 75
Real Estate Development, Construction Contracting & Asset Management
N.A.I.C.S.: 237210
Larry Allbaugh (CEO)
Kevin Ramos (Chief Investment Officer & Partner)
Brandon Lewis (Controller)
Paulina Flores (Mgr-Transaction)
Kimberly Chambers (Sr VP-Acctg & Tax Svcs)
Troy Estacio (Sr VP-Dev & Construction Svcs)
Lorri Schulte (VP & Sr Mgr-Property)
Larry E. Allbaugh (Bd of Dirs, Executives)
Subsidiaries:
Buzz Oates Construction, LP   (1)
2385 Arch Airport Rd Ste 100, Stockton, CA 95206
Tel.: (209) 982-1200
Real Estate Manangement Services
N.A.I.C.S.: 531390
Steve Sherman (Sr VP-Construction Svcs)
Denny Boom (Pres)

BUZZ PRODUCTS, INC.
4818 Kanawha Blvd E, Charleston, WV 25306
Tel.: (304) 925-4781   WV
Web Site:
http://www.buzzfoodsvc.com
Year Founded: 1938
Rev.: $11,700,000
Emp.: 47
Packaged Frozen Food Merchant Whslr
N.A.I.C.S.: 424420
Joanette V. Gould V (Sec)

BUZZSAW ADVERTISING & DESIGN INC.
19600 Fairchild Rd Ste 140, Irvine, CA 92612
Tel.: (949) 453-1393
Web Site: http://www.buzzsaw.biz
Year Founded: 1986
Sales Range: Less than $1 Million
Emp.: 4
N.A.I.C.S.: 541810
Robert Haynes (Principal)

BUZZTABLE INC.
214 W 29th St 6th Fl, New York, NY 10001
Tel.: (855) 321-2899
Web Site: http://www.buzztable.com
Sales Range: $1-9.9 Million
Restaurant & Hospitality Software
N.A.I.C.S.: 513210
Warner H. Siebert (Co-Founder & CEO)
John Brennan (Co-Founder & Pres)
Mike Cerrone (Co-Founder & Head-Mktg)
John Williams (Co-Founder & Head-Sls)

BV INVESTMENT PARTNERS, LLC
125 High St 17th Fl, Boston, MA 02110
Tel.: (617) 350-1500   DE
Web Site: http://www.bvlp.com
Year Founded: 1983
Sales Range: $500-549.9 Million
Emp.: 20
Privater Equity Firm
N.A.I.C.S.: 523999
Justin H. Harrison (Mng Dir)
Gerald S. Hobbs (Operating Partner & Mng Dir)
Matthew J. Kinsey (Mng Dir)
Maggie Carter (COO)
Carolyn Hoglund (Controller)
Roy F. Coppedge III (Co-Founder)
Sean Wilder (Principal)
Jonathan Holmes (CFO)
Stuart Brown (Partner)
Subsidiaries:
Homepages, LLC   (1)
915 E Lincoln Hwy, Dekalb, IL 60115
Tel.: (815) 756-2840
Web Site:
http://www.homepagesdirectories.com
Directory Publishing Services
N.A.I.C.S.: 513140
Abram Andrzejewski (Founder & CEO)
Petty Holdings LLC   (1)
311 Branson Mill Rd, Randleman, NC 27317
Tel.: (336) 495-6643
Web Site: http://www.pettys-garage.com
Sales Range: $250-299.9 Million
Emp.: 500
Holding Company; Professional Motorsports & Driving Experience Organization
N.A.I.C.S.: 551112
Barry Baker (Mng Dir)
David F. Zucker (CEO)
Subsidiary (Domestic):
Richard Petty Driving Experience, Inc.   (2)
6022 Victory Ln, Concord, NC 28027
Tel.: (704) 455-9443
Web Site: http://www.drivepetty.com
Sales Range: $25-49.9 Million
Motorsports Driving Instruction & Entertainment Services
N.A.I.C.S.: 611620
Bryan Flynn (Pres & CEO)
Joint Venture (Domestic):
Richard Petty Motorsports LLC   (2)
7065 Zephyr Pl, Concord, NC 28027
Tel.: (704) 743-5420
Web Site:
http://www.richardpettymotorsports.com
Sales Range: $25-49.9 Million
Professional Stock Car Motorsports Team
N.A.I.C.S.: 711211
Richard Lee Petty (Partner)
Sammy Johns (VP-Ops)
Lance Brown (VP-Mktg Svcs & Comm)
Jim Hannigan (VP-Licensing & Mdsg)
Mike Hargrave (CMO & Exec VP)
Brian Moffitt (CEO)
Andrew Murstein (Co-Owner)
Resource Innovations, LLC   (1)
719 Main St, Half Moon Bay, CA 94019
Tel.: (650) 678-9154
Web Site: http://www.resource-innovations.com
Environmental Services & Energy Consulting Firm
N.A.I.C.S.: 541620
Lauren Casentini (CEO)
Subsidiary (Domestic):
Nexant, Inc.   (2)
101 2nd St Ste 1000, San Francisco, CA 94105-3672
Tel.: (415) 369-1000
Web Site: http://www.nexant.com
Energy Conservation Consultant
N.A.I.C.S.: 541990
Basem Sarandah (Founder)
Bruce Burke (Sr VP)
Arjun Gupta (Chm)
Richard Sleep (Sr VP)
Marcos Nogueira Cesar (VP)
Michael Sullivan (Sr VP-Utility Svcs)
Stephen George (Sr VP-Utility Svcs)
Peter Noland (VP-Bus Dev)
John Gustafson (CEO)
Anish Shah (CFO)
Henri van Rensburg (Principal)
Matthew S. Mendis (Sr VP-Govt Svcs)
Patrick Burns (Sr VP-Strategy & Plng)
Bob Streich (VP)
Josh Bode (VP)
Josh Schellenberg (VP)
Luther Dow (VP)
Manuel Asali (VP)
Karen Del Barrio Neuendorff (VP-HR-Global)
Tanya Shepherd (VP-Product Mgmt & Mgr-Revenue)
Sunil Bhardwaj (CFO)

BVB General Contractors, LLC—(Continued)

BVB GENERAL CONTRAC-
TORS, LLC
1289 S 4th Ave, Brighton, CO 80601-6808
Tel.: (303) 637-0981
Web Site: https://www.bvgci.com
Year Founded: 2003
Sales Range: $10-24.9 Million
Emp.: 18
Commercial Construction Services
N.A.I.C.S.: 236220
James Vigesaa (Co-Owner)
Dan Brown (Co-Owner)

BVB PROPERTIES
4508 E Independence Blvd Ste 207, Charlotte, NC 28205-7499
Tel.: (704) 532-0028
Web Site:
http://www.bvbproperties.com
Year Founded: 1980
Sales Range: $25-49.9 Million
Emp.: 11
Land Subdividing Services
N.A.I.C.S.: 237210
Tammy Belk (Coord-Customer Care)
Mark Derek (Principal)
B. V. Belk III (Owner)

BVI DOUBLE DRIVE-THRU
INC.
3020 Bardstown Rd 173, Louisville, KY 40205
Tel.: (502) 266-5325
Sales Range: $10-24.9 Million
Emp.: 500
Fast Food Restaurants
N.A.I.C.S.: 722513

BVK, INC.
250 W Coventry Ct, Milwaukee, WI 53217-3972
Tel.: (414) 228-1990   WI
Web Site: https://www.bvk.com
Year Founded: 1984
Rev.: $282,000,000
Emp.: 158
Advetising Agency
N.A.I.C.S.: 541810
Michael Voss (Pres & CEO)
Gary Mueller (Mng Partner & Creative Dir)
Joel English (Mng Partner-Bus Dev)
David Kelly (VP & Dir-Media)
Bret Stasiak (Mng Partner-Acct Svc & Plng)
Mike Czerwinski (VP-Mktg Analytics)
Mike Eaton (Sr VP)
Matt Herrmann (VP-Mktg Analytics)
Jeremy Whitt (Sr VP)
Mary DeLong (Sr VP & Dir-Tourism)

Subsidiaries:

BVK Direct, Inc.   (1)
5740 Fleet St Ste 260, Carlsbad, CA 92008-4703
Tel.: (760) 804-8300
Web Site: http://www.bvkdirect.com
Sales Range: $10-24.9 Million
Emp.: 13
Advertising Material Distr
N.A.I.C.S.: 541870
Julie Morgans (Dir-Ops)
Ron Kendrella (Exec VP)
Brandon Haan (Dir-Internet Svcs)
Todd Aubol (VP-Client Svcs)

BlueFin Imaging Group, LLC   (1)
250 W Coventry Ct Ste 300, Milwaukee, WI 53217   (100%)
Tel.: (414) 247-2100
Web Site: http://www.bluefininc.com
Sales Range: $10-24.9 Million
Emp.: 3
N.A.I.C.S.: 541810
Debbie Sherman (Dir-Customer Svc)

BW GAS & CONVENIENCE
HOLDINGS, LLC
7745 Office Plz Dr N Hawthore Bldg Ste 150, West Des Moines, IA 50266
Tel.: (978) 468-3076
Web Site: http://yesway.com
Convenience Store
N.A.I.C.S.: 445131
Thomas Nicholas Trkla (Chm & CEO)

Subsidiaries:

Allsup's Convenience Stores Inc.   (1)
2112 N Thornton St, Clovis, NM 88101-4130
Tel.: (575) 769-2311
Web Site: http://www.allsups.com
Sales Range: $25-49.9 Million
Emp.: 50
Retail Convenience Stores; Gasoline Service Stations; Wholesale Commercial Machines & Equipment
N.A.I.C.S.: 445131
Barbara Allsup (Co-Founder)
Mark Allsup (Co-Founder & Pres)

BWAB, INC.
475 17th St Ste 1390, Denver, CO 80202
Tel.: (303) 295-7444
Web Site: http://www.bwab.com
Diversified Holding Company
N.A.I.C.S.: 551112
Steven A. Roitman (Chm & CEO)
David Roitman (COO)
William G. Mills II (VP-Land)

Subsidiaries:

The Industrial Group, LLC   (1)
9781 S Meridian Blvd Ste 105, Englewood, CO 80112
Tel.: (303) 799-9099
Web Site: http://www.industrialgroupco.com
Construction & Industrial Supplies Whslr
N.A.I.C.S.: 423390

BWAY.NET, INC.
568 Broadway Ste 404, New York, NY 10012-3265
Tel.: (212) 982-9800   DE
Web Site: http://www.bway.net
Year Founded: 1995
Sales Range: $10-24.9 Million
Emp.: 10
Internet Dial-Up & Broadband, Web Hosting & Design & Computer Training & Consulting Services
N.A.I.C.S.: 541511
George Rosen (Dir-Sales)

BWC TERMINALS LLC
1111 Bagby St Ste 1800, Houston, TX 7702
Tel.: (832) 699-4001
Web Site:
https://www.bwcterminals.com
Liquid Storage Services
N.A.I.C.S.: 493190
Mike Suder (CEO)
Adam Smith (Pres & COO)

Subsidiaries:

IMTT-Gretna   (1)
1145 4th St, Harvey, LA 70058
Tel.: (504) 368-2560
Chemical Products Distr
N.A.I.C.S.: 424690

BWI COMPANIES INC.
1355 N Kings Hwy, Nash, TX 75569
Tel.: (903) 838-8561
Web Site:
http://www.bwicompanies.com
Sales Range: $10-24.9 Million
Emp.: 20
Farm Supplies
N.A.I.C.S.: 424910

James S. Bunch (Pres & CEO)
Melissa Evans (Mgr-Customer Service)

BWI, INC.
5711 Corsa Ave, Westlake Village, CA 91362
Tel.: (818) 991-6644
Web Site: https://www.bwi-imports.com
Sales Range: $10-24.9 Million
Emp.: 16
Dried & Dehydrated Food Mfr
N.A.I.C.S.: 311423
John Bamberger (CFO)
Kerry Bamberger (Owner)

BY APPOINTMENT ONLY, INC.
100 Brickstone Sq Ste 501, Andover, MA 01810-1428
Tel.: (781) 323-7000
Web Site: http://www.baoinc.com
Year Founded: 1997
Rev.: $20,000,000
Emp.: 176
Management Consulting Services
N.A.I.C.S.: 541611
John Bomba (VP-IT)
Linda Metzger (VP-HR & Admin)
Brian Giguere (VP & Gen Mgr)
Derek Gray (VP & Gen Mgr)
Jessica Pilat (VP-Mktg)
Suzanne Higgins (Founder)
Michael Farrell (COO)
Jim Higgins (CEO)

BY DESIGN LLC
1450 Broadway 24th Fl, New York, NY 10018
Tel.: (212) 500-4400
Web Site:
http://www.lovebydesign.com
Year Founded: 1994
Sales Range: $1-9.9 Million
Emp.: 40
Importing of Women's, Childrens' & Infants' Clothing
N.A.I.C.S.: 424350
Jaylee Choi (Owner)

BY-LO MARKETS INC.
217 Western Ave, Morristown, TN 37814
Tel.: (423) 587-2047
Sales Range: $10-24.9 Million
Emp.: 125
Convenience Store Operator
N.A.I.C.S.: 445131
Tim Taylor (Pres)
Marilyn Pinkston (Controller)

BY-LO OIL COMPANY INC.
2799 Wadhams Rd, Kimball, MI 48074
Tel.: (810) 982-1451   MI
Web Site:
http://www.speedyqmarkets.com
Year Founded: 1980
Sales Range: $10-24.9 Million
Emp.: 45
Gasoline Service Station Operator
N.A.I.C.S.: 457120

BYER CALIFORNIA
66 Potrero Ave, San Francisco, CA 94103-4837
Tel.: (415) 626-7844   CA
Web Site: http://www.byer.com
Year Founded: 1964
Sales Range: $400-449.9 Million
Emp.: 1,000
Womens & Girls Apparel Mfr
N.A.I.C.S.: 315250

Sandi Sebastian (VP-Tech Design)
Todd McCormack (Controller)
Tracey Lewis (Mgr-Imports Logistics)
Miguel Varela (Mgr-Shipping)

Subsidiaries:

Byer California - Los Angeles Factory   (1)
1201 Rio Vista, Los Angeles, CA 90023
Tel.: (323) 266-4561
Web Site: http://www.byer.com
Emp.: 500
Women Apparel Mfr
N.A.I.C.S.: 315250
Gerson Galdamez (Mgr)

BYERLY FORD-NISSAN INC.
4041 Dixie Hwy, Louisville, KY 40216-3807   KY
Web Site: http://www.byerlyford.com
Year Founded: 1944
Sales Range: $100-124.9 Million
Emp.: 130
Provider of New & Used Automobile Sales, Parts, Service & Leasing
N.A.I.C.S.: 441110
John R. Daunhauer (Chm)
John Paul Daunhauer (Exec VP)

BYERS ENGINEERING COM-
PANY
6285 Barfield Rd, Atlanta, GA 30328-4303
Tel.: (404) 843-1000   GA
Web Site: https://www.byers.com
Year Founded: 1971
Sales Range: $75-99.9 Million
Emp.: 1,000
Data Processing & Preparation
N.A.I.C.S.: 518210
Denise C. Demick (CFO)
Dan Clark (VP-Business Development)
Charles Mayberry (VP-Atlantic)
Timothy H. Parker (COO)
C. Frank Roberson (VP-Spatial)
Tom Moore (VP-Support)
Alan Anthony (VP-MW Reg)
Kenneth G. Byers Jr. (Founder & Pres)

Subsidiaries:

SpatialAge Solutions Division   (1)
6285 Barfield Rd, Atlanta, GA 30328-4303
Tel.: (404) 497-1518
Data Processing Services
N.A.I.C.S.: 518210

Telespan Network Services, LLC   (1)
3888 State St Ste 204, Santa Barbara, CA 93105
Tel.: (480) 905-8689
Telecommunication Servicesb
N.A.I.C.S.: 517810

BYRD COOKIE CO.
6700 Waters Ave, Savannah, GA 31406
Tel.: (912) 355-1716
Web Site:
http://www.byrdcookiecompany.com
Cookie & Cracker Mfr
N.A.I.C.S.: 311821
Benny H. Curl (Co-Owner)
Kay Curl (Co-Owner)

Subsidiaries:

Selma's Cookies, Inc.   (1)
2230 E Semoran Blvd, Apopka, FL 32703
Tel.: (407) 884-9433
Web Site: http://www.selmas.com
Cookie & Cracker Mfr
N.A.I.C.S.: 311821
Selma Sayin (Pres)

BYRDS MOBILE HOME SALES
INC.

624 S US Hwy 17, San Mateo, FL 32187
Tel.: (386) 328-1020
Sales Range: $10-24.9 Million
Emp.: 8
Mobile Home Dealers
N.A.I.C.S.: 459930
William D. Byrd Jr. *(Pres)*

BYRNE DAIRY INC.
2394 US Route 11, Lafayette, NY 13084
Tel.: (315) 475-2111   NY
Web Site:
https://www.byrnedairy.com
Year Founded: 1933
Sales Range: $75-99.9 Million
Emp.: 400
Dairy & Ice-Cream Products Mfr & Supplier
N.A.I.C.S.: 311511
Carl V. Byrne *(Pres)*
Mark Byrne *(Treas & Exec VP)*

Subsidiaries:

Fourth Group Inc.   (1)
PO Box 176, La Fayette, NY 13084
Tel.: (315) 475-2111
Web Site: http://www.brynedairy.com
Rev.: $500,000
Emp.: 60
Mfr of Dairy Products
N.A.I.C.S.: 424430

BYRNE ELECTRICAL SPE-CIALISTS, INC.
320 Byrne Industrial Dr, Rockford, MI 49341
Tel.: (616) 866-3461
Web Site: http://www.byrne-electrical.com
Year Founded: 1970
Sales Range: $10-24.9 Million
Emp.: 200
Harness Assemblies
N.A.I.C.S.: 334419

Subsidiaries:

Byrne Tool & Die Inc.   (1)
316 Byrne Industrial Dr, Rockford, MI 49341
Tel.: (616) 866-4479
Web Site: http://www.byrne-tool.com
Sales Range: $10-24.9 Million
Emp.: 20
Tool & Die Shop
N.A.I.C.S.: 332710
Jackie Overley *(Office Mgr)*
Andy Baker *(Mgr-Strategic Acct)*

Wee Folk Rockford Child Center, Inc.   (1)
723 Byrne Industrial Dr, Rockford, MI 49341
Tel.: (616) 866-4740
Web Site:
http://www.weefolkchildcenter.com
Sales Range: $10-24.9 Million
Emp.: 14
Child Day Care Services
N.A.I.C.S.: 624410
Kathy Scudder *(Founder & Exec Dir)*
Michelle Norton *(Dir-Ops)*
Lindsey Annerino *(Coord-Program)*
Chris Kaiser *(Coord-Curriculum)*

BYRNE, RICE & TURNER, INC.
1172 Camp St, New Orleans, LA 70130
Tel.: (504) 525-7137
Web Site: https://www.brtmarine.com
Year Founded: 1947
Sales Range: $10-24.9 Million
Emp.: 10
Transportation Equipment & Supplies Whslr
N.A.I.C.S.: 423860
John B. Rice *(Pres)*

BYRNES & KIEFER COMPANY
131 Kline Ave, Callery, PA 16024
Tel.: (724) 538-5200   PA

Web Site:
https://www.bkcompany.com
Year Founded: 1902
Sales Range: $75-99.9 Million
Emp.: 50
Mfr of Bakery, Candy & Confectionery Products, Flavoring Extracts & Syrups
N.A.I.C.S.: 424490
Edward G. Byrnes *(CEO)*
Jay Thier *(Pres)*

Subsidiaries:

B&K Manufacturing   (1)
131 Kline Ave, Callery, PA 16024
Tel.: (724) 538-5200
Web Site: http://www.bkcompany.com
Sales Range: $1-9.9 Million
Mfr Food Ingredients & Products
N.A.I.C.S.: 424490

Charlie's Specialties Inc.   (1)
2500 Freedland Rd, Hermitage, PA 16148-9022   (100%)
Tel.: (724) 346-2350
Web Site: http://www.bkcompany.com
Sales Range: $10-24.9 Million
Frozen Cookie Manufacturer
N.A.I.C.S.: 311821
Jay Thier *(Pres)*

Chefmaster   (1)
501 Airpark Dr, Fullerton, CA 95825
Tel.: (714) 554-4000
Web Site: http://www.bkcompany.com
Sales Range: $10-24.9 Million
Emp.: 40
Packager & Blender of FD & C Colors
N.A.I.C.S.: 311930
Ed Larrarte *(Controller)*

BYRNES CONSULTING, LLC
24 Fox Den Rd, Kingston, MA 02364
Tel.: (832) 429-7637
Web Site:
https://www.byrnesconsulting.com
Year Founded: 2008
Sales Range: $1-9.9 Million
Emp.: 3
Business Consulting Services
N.A.I.C.S.: 541611
Kevin M. Feehily *(VP)*
Michael W. Byrnes Jr. *(Founder & Pres)*

BYRON E. TALBOT CONTRAC-TOR
301 Main Project Rd, Schriever, LA 70395
Tel.: (985) 447-5764
Web Site:
https://www.byronetalbot.com
Rev.: $14,694,491
Emp.: 100
Water, Sewer & Utility Lines
N.A.I.C.S.: 237110
Stan Arceneaux *(CFO)*
Nick Grabert *(Project Mgr)*

C & B DEVELOPMENT, INC.
430 State Pl, Escondido, CA 92029
Tel.: (760) 745-3311
Web Site:
http://www.cbdevelopmentinc.com
Sales Range: $300-349.9 Million
Emp.: 3
Residential Construction Services
N.A.I.C.S.: 236118
Charles E. Signorimo II *(Pres)*

C & C FORD SALES, INCOR-PORATED
1100 Easton Rd Route 611, Horsham, PA 19044
Tel.: (215) 315-7671
Web Site:
https://www.chapmannewcars.com
Sales Range: $25-49.9 Million
Emp.: 120
Car Whslr

N.A.I.C.S.: 441110
Michael Chapman *(Pres)*

C & C TOURS, INC.
2157 S Lincoln St, Salt Lake City, UT 84106
Tel.: (801) 323-2395   WY
Year Founded: 1989
Assets: $324
Liabilities: $318,797
Net Worth: ($318,473)
Earnings: ($30,109)
Fiscal Year-end: 12/31/22
Investment Advisory Services
N.A.I.C.S.: 523940
Brett D. Taylor *(Pres, CEO, CFO & Chief Acctg Officer)*
J. William Peters *(Treas & Sec)*

C & I ENGINEERING, LLC
369 Falcon Ridge St, Richland, WA 99352
Tel.: (509) 628-2885
Web Site: http://www.cni-engr.com
Year Founded: 1999
Sales Range: $10-24.9 Million
Emp.: 5
Management, Technical & Engineer-ing Solutions
N.A.I.C.S.: 541330
Michael Cabrera *(CEO)*

C & K SYSTEMS, INC.
648 Independence Pkwy Ste 400, Chesapeake, VA 23320
Tel.: (757) 482-6343
Web Site: http://www.cksystem.com
Year Founded: 1989
Sales Range: $1-9.9 Million
Emp.: 50
Software Services
N.A.I.C.S.: 449210
Kevin Bowden *(Pres & CEO)*
Mary Fawley *(Controller)*

C & L SERVICES LLC
350 Faraday Ave, Jackson, NJ 08527
Tel.: (732) 886-1940
Web Site: http://sweeping.com
Year Founded: 1971
Street Sweeping & Pavement Mainte-nance Services
N.A.I.C.S.: 237310
Gabe Vitale Jr. *(Sls Mgr)*

Subsidiaries:

Knipfing Asphalt Solutions, Inc.   (1)
381 Cranberry Rd, Farmingdale, NJ 07727
Tel.: (732) 308-2323
Web Site: http://www.knipfingasi.com
Sales Range: $1-9.9 Million
Emp.: 9
Construction & Mining (except Oil Well) Machinery & Equipment Merchant Whslr
N.A.I.C.S.: 423810
Albert Knipfing *(Pres)*

C & R MECHANICAL CO.
12825 Pennridge Dr, Bridgeton, MO 63044
Tel.: (314) 739-1800
Web Site:
https://www.crmechanical.com
Year Founded: 1950
Sales Range: $25-49.9 Million
Emp.: 200
Plumbing, Heating & Air-Conditioning Services
N.A.I.C.S.: 238220
George Edinger *(Chm & CEO)*
Tim Decker *(Pres & COO)*
Mike Adkinson *(VP-Fin)*
Vito Nicastri *(VP-Engrg)*
Tom Beyer *(VP-Construction Ops)*

Cory Hall *(VP-Sheet Metal Fabrica-tion)*
Todd McFall *(VP-Construction Ops)*
Chuck Schuermann *(VP-Sheet Metal Fabrication)*

C & R SYSTEMS, INC.
1835 Capital St, Corona, CA 92878
Tel.: (951) 270-0255
Web Site: https://www.crsys.net
Sales Range: $10-24.9 Million
Emp.: 100
Electronic Services
N.A.I.C.S.: 238210
Tim Potts *(Gen Mgr)*
Pam Mosbaugh *(Mgr-Acctg)*
Diana Grady *(Mgr-Billing)*
Todd Gharring *(Mgr-Sls & Mktg)*
Martha Cardenas *(Mgr-Monitoring)*
Luis Estrada *(Mgr-Customer Svc)*

C BENNETT BUILDING SUP-PLY INC.
1700 W Terra Ln, O'Fallon, MO 63366
Tel.: (636) 379-9886
Web Site: https://www.cbennett.net
Year Founded: 1980
Sales Range: $10-24.9 Million
Emp.: 60
Plumbing & Heating Equipment Sup-ply Whslr
N.A.I.C.S.: 423720
Bruce Colbert *(Mgr-Field)*

C F STINSON, INC.
2849 Product Dr, Rochester Hills, MI 48309
Tel.: (248) 299-3800   MI
Web Site: http://www.cfstinson.com
Year Founded: 1952
Sales Range: $1-9.9 Million
Emp.: 52
Piece Goods, Notions & Other Dry Goods Merchant Whslr
N.A.I.C.S.: 424310
Bill Diedrich *(Gen Mgr)*
Anna Stinson *(Sr Mgr-Acct)*

Subsidiaries:

Anzea Textiles, Inc.   (1)
901 Foch St, Fort Worth, TX 76107
Tel.: (817) 336-2310
Web Site: http://www.anzea.com
Sales Range: $1-9.9 Million
Emp.: 10
Piece Goods, Notions & Other Dry Goods Merchant Whslr
N.A.I.C.S.: 424310
Bruce Doeren *(Co-Founder, Partner & Prin-cipal)*
Mitzi Mills *(Co-Founder, Principal & Creative Dir)*

C I HOST
2300 Valley View Ln, Irving, TX 76021
Tel.: (817) 868-9931
Web Site: http://www.cihost.com
Year Founded: 1995
Sales Range: $25-49.9 Million
Emp.: 202
Web Hosting & Related Services
N.A.I.C.S.: 517810
Rebecca Laird *(VP)*
Van Stout *(CFO)*

C LAZY U RANCH, INC.
3640 Colorado Hwy 125, Granby, CO 80446
Tel.: (970) 887-3344
Web Site: https://www.clazyu.com
Year Founded: 1988
Sales Range: $10-24.9 Million
Emp.: 20
Hotel Operator
N.A.I.C.S.: 721110

C Lazy U Ranch, Inc.—(Continued)
David Craig (Gen Mgr)
Cody Arnold (Asst Mgr-Ops)

C PRODUCTS DEFENSE, INC.
6115 31st St E, Bradenton, FL 34203
Tel.: (941) 727-0009
Web Site:
http://www.cproductsdefense.com
Sales Range: $1-9.9 Million
Emp.: 30
Firearm Component Mfr
N.A.I.C.S.: 332999
Adel Jamil (CEO)

C S & W CONTRACTORS
6135 N 7th St Ste 105, Phoenix, AZ
85014
Tel.: (602) 266-7000
Web Site:
http://www.cswcontractors.com
Year Founded: 1982
Sales Range: $50-74.9 Million
Emp.: 309
Excavation Contractor
N.A.I.C.S.: 238910
Robert Meyers (CEO)

C T R SYSTEMS INC.
555 Keystone Dr, Warrendale, PA
15086
Tel.: (724) 772-2400
Web Site: http://www.ctrsystems.com
Year Founded: 1964
Sales Range: $25-49.9 Million
Emp.: 248
Building Equipment Installation Services
N.A.I.C.S.: 238290
Doug Duffy (Owner)

C&A MARKETING, INC.
114 Tived Ln E, Edison, NJ 08837
Tel.: (848) 244-2000
Web Site:
http://www.camarketing.com
Consumer Products Marketer & Retailer
N.A.I.C.S.: 449210
Chaim Pikarski (Exec VP)
Harry Klein (Pres & CEO)
Abe Berkowitz (CFO)
Yoel Holtzman (VP-Sls & Bus Dev)
Moshe Isaacson (VP-Mktg)

Subsidiaries:

C&A Marketing, Inc. - Ritz Camera &
Image Division   (1)
114 Tived Ln E, Edison, NJ 08837
Tel.: (848) 244-2000
Web Site: http://www.ritzcamera.com
Photographic & Video Equipment Retailer
N.A.I.C.S.: 449210
Eric Moseson (Exec VP)
Michael Roth (Mng Dir)
Shirley Czerwinski (Natl Sls Mgr)

Saris Cycling Group, Inc.   (1)
5253 Verona Rd, Madison, WI 53711
Tel.: (608) 274-6550
Web Site: http://www.sariscyclinggroup.com
Sales Range: $1-9.9 Million
Emp.: 80
Motorcycle, Bicycle & Parts Mfr
N.A.I.C.S.: 336991
Christopher Fortune (Pres)

Skymall Holdings, LLC   (1)
2 Bergen Tpke, Ridgefield Park, NJ 07660
Tel.: (201) 881-1900
Web Site: http://www.skymall.com
Specialty Gifts Retailer
N.A.I.C.S.: 459420
Harry Klein (Pres & CEO)

C&B DISTRIBUTORS INC.
201 S Main St, Lowell, NC 28098
Tel.: (704) 824-8515

Web Site:
http://www.candbdistributors.com
Sales Range: $10-24.9 Million
Emp.: 15
Tobacco & Tobacco Products
N.A.I.C.S.: 424940
Judy Zilchrist (Office Mgr)
Pam Reynolds (Office Mgr)
Harold G. Clemmer Jr. (Pres)

C&B OPERATIONS LLC
30965 US Hwy 212, Gettysburg, SD
57442
Tel.: (605) 765-2434
Web Site:
https://www.deerequipment.com
Year Founded: 1988
Sales Range: $25-49.9 Million
Emp.: 200
Provider of Agricultural Machinery &
Equipment
N.A.I.C.S.: 811310
Scott Lunke (Controller)
Cindy Frost (Mgr-Acctg & HR)

C&B WAREHOUSE DISTRIB-UTING
101 1st Ave S, Virginia, MN 55792
Tel.: (218) 741-3103
Sales Range: $10-24.9 Million
Emp.: 100
Petroleum Bulk Stations & Terminals
N.A.I.C.S.: 424710
Phil Troutwine (Pres)
David Troutwine (VP)

C&C FLORAL INC.
1245 W Washington Blvd, Chicago,
IL 60607
Tel.: (312) 666-8400
Sales Range: $10-24.9 Million
Emp.: 10
Artificial Flowers
N.A.I.C.S.: 424930
Brett Clamage (Pres)

C&C HOLDING INC.
301 Industrial Dr, Birmingham, AL
35211-4443
Tel.: (205) 945-1300   KY
Year Founded: 1982
Sales Range: $75-99.9 Million
General Construction Machinery &
Equipment
N.A.I.C.S.: 423810
James Cowin (Pres & Owner)

Subsidiaries:

Cowin Equipment Company Inc   (1)
2238 Pinson Vly Pkwy, Birmingham, AL
35217
Tel.: (205) 841-6666
Web Site: http://www.cowin.com
Sales Range: $50-74.9 Million
General Construction Machinery & Equip-ment Mfr & Distr
N.A.I.C.S.: 333120
James P. Cowin (Pres)
Rod Drake (VP)
Tim Gann (VP & Gen Mgr-Sls)
George Tickle (Treas & VP-Admin)
Mike Andrews (Mgr-Product Support)
Dale Clark (Mgr-Parts)
Hugh Dobbs (Mgr-Svc)
Trent Davis (Mgr-Product Support)
Joe DeGrado (Mgr-Product Support)
Jimmy Kearns (Mgr-Rental)
Curtis Jackson (Gen Mgr-Rental)
Matt MacDonald (Mgr-Rental)
Randy Rockwell (VP-South Alabama & Mgr-Sls-Florida)
John Edwards (Mgr-Governmental Sls)
Matt McGowan (Mgr-Mktg)
Justin Aaron (Mgr-Rental)
Jeff Beasley (Mgr-Svc)
Richard Brennan (Mgr-Credit)
Robin McKinney (Mgr-Parts-Gulf Coast)

C&C HYDRAULICS, INC.

116 Wolcott Rd, Terryville, CT 06786
Web Site:
https://www.cchydraulics.com
Rev.: $2,000,000
Emp.: 16
Industrial Machinery & Equipment
Merchant Whslr
N.A.I.C.S.: 423830
Mary L. Brodeur (Office Mgr)

C&C METAL PRODUCTS CORP
456 Nordhoff Pl, Englewood, NJ
07631
Tel.: (201) 569-7300
Web Site: http://www.ccmetal.com
Sales Range: $10-24.9 Million
Emp.: 60
Mfr of Fasteners
N.A.I.C.S.: 339993
Matthew Naatkal (VP)
Neal Liber (VP)

C&C MILLWRIGHT MAINTE-NANCE CO.
311 Old Knoxville Hwy Ste 1, Green-eville, TN 37743
Tel.: (423) 639-0131
Web Site:
https://www.ccmillwright.com
Year Founded: 1973
Sales Range: $10-24.9 Million
Emp.: 113
Installing Building Equipment
N.A.I.C.S.: 238290
Jerry Fortner (Pres)
Fred Blake (VP)
Kenny Rednour (Project Mgr)
Rick Greene (VP-Construction)

C&C ORGANIZATION INC.
8651 Madrone Ave, Rancho Cu-camonga, CA 91730
Tel.: (909) 981-5771
Web Site:
https://www.caskncleaver.com
Sales Range: $10-24.9 Million
Emp.: 35
Holding Company; Restaurant Man-agement
N.A.I.C.S.: 551112
Charles Keagle (Founder)
Brady Main (Pres)
Carlos Rivas (Controller)

Subsidiaries:

Cask 'n Cleaver   (1)
8689 9th St, Rancho Cucamonga, CA
91730   (100%)
Tel.: (909) 982-7108
Web Site: http://www.caskncleaver.com
Restaurant & Banquet Services
N.A.I.C.S.: 722511
Peter Reuther (Gen Mgr)

Cask 'n Cleaver   (1)
1333 University Ave, Riverside, CA
92507   (100%)
Tel.: (951) 682-4580
Web Site: http://www.caskncleaver.com
Emp.: 15
Restaurant & Banquet Services
N.A.I.C.S.: 722511
Dave Hara (Gen Mgr)

Cask 'n Cleaver   (1)
125 N Village Court, San Dimas, CA
91773   (100%)
Tel.: (909) 592-1646
Web Site: http://www.caskncleaver.com
Banquet Facilities & Restaurant Dining
N.A.I.C.S.: 722511
Derek Downing (Gen Mgr)

C&D FRUIT & VEGETABLE CO., INC.
16505 State Rd 64 E, Bradenton, FL
34212
Tel.: (941) 744-0505   FL

Web Site: http://www.cdveg.com
Year Founded: 1978
Sales Range: $25-49.9 Million
Emp.: 20
Vegetable & Melon Farm Crop Prepa-ration
N.A.I.C.S.: 424480
Thomas O'Brien (Pres)
John Cucci (Gen Mgr)

C&D INSULATION, INC.
333 Perry St Ste 210, Castle Rock,
CO 80104
Tel.: (303) 681-9099
Web Site: http://cdinsulation.com
Year Founded: 1992
Commercial & Industrial Insulation
Contractors
N.A.I.C.S.: 238310
Chad Habegger (Founder, Partner &
Gen Mgr)
Israel Sanchez (Partner & VP-Ops)
Marc Wood (Partner & VP)
Ryan Barker (Partner & Pres)
Ace Cowan (Dir-Estimating)
Donna Overby (Office Mgr)
John Byes (Dir-Safety)

Subsidiaries:

Colorado Scaffolding & Equipment
Co Inc.   (1)
4540 E 60th Ave, Commerce City, CO
80022
Tel.: (303) 287-3333
Web Site:
http://www.coloradoscaffolding.com
Scaffolding Erection & Dismantle Services
N.A.I.C.S.: 238990

C&D PRODUCTION SPECIAL-ISTS CO., INC.
14090 Hwy 1, Cut Off, LA 70345
Tel.: (985) 693-4880
Web Site: http://www.cdind.com
Rev.: $12,000,000
Emp.: 100
Contractor of Oil Field Services
N.A.I.C.S.: 213112
Ruth Bagge (VP & Branch Mgr)

C&D SEMICONDUCTOR SER-VICES, INC.
2031 Concourse Dr, San Jose, CA
95131-1727
Tel.: (408) 383-1888
Web Site: https://www.cdsemi.com
Rev.: $14,223,417
Emp.: 45
Semiconductors & Related Devices
N.A.I.C.S.: 334413
Dong Nguyen (Pres & CEO)
Loi Lam (Mgr)

C&D TRADING INC.
125 Coachmans Ln, North Andover,
MA 01845
Tel.: (978) 777-6653
Rev.: $30,000,000
Emp.: 2
Bond Brokers
N.A.I.C.S.: 424410
Darryl Mochrie (Pres)

C&E SERVICES INC.
1950 Old Gallows Rd Ste 550, Vi-enna, VA 22182
Tel.: (703) 506-1960
Web Site:
https://www.chemengineering.com
Year Founded: 1984
Sales Range: $10-24.9 Million
Emp.: 15
Water Purification Equipment Whslr
N.A.I.C.S.: 423720
Carl L. Biggs (Owner, Pres & Gen
Mgr)
Jim Biggs (Mgr-Area)

Dorene Shaffer (*VP-Fin & Acctg*)
Douglas B. Pickering (*Sr VP-Engrg*)
James M. Roenick (*VP*)
Jossie P. Biggs (*VP-HR*)

Subsidiaries:

C&E Services Inc. Washington   (1)
1224 W St SE, Washington, DC 20020
Tel.: (202) 678-0532
Web Site:
   http://www.cneswchemengineering.com
Rev.: $260,000
Emp.: 12
Water Treating Compounds
N.A.I.C.S.: 325998
Peter Baum (*Mgr-Watergate Central Plant*)

C&F ENTERPRISES, INC.
819 BlueCrab Rd, Newport News, VA
23606-4220
Tel.: (757) 873-5688   VA
Web Site: https://www.cnfei.com
Year Founded: 1976
Sales Range: $10-24.9 Million
Emp.: 130
Importer & Wholesaler of Textiles
N.A.I.C.S.: 423220
Carol S. Fang (*Pres*)
Jimmy Fang (*VP*)
Nelson Chow (*VP-Sls*)
Connie Lowe (*Mgr-Shipping, Receiving & Logistics*)
Nathan Boettcher (*Supvr-Warehouse*)

C&F FOODS INC.
15620 E Vly Blvd, City of Industry,
CA 91744
Tel.: (626) 723-1000
Web Site: http://www.cnf-foods.com
Sales Range: $25-49.9 Million
Emp.: 60
Agricultural Services
N.A.I.C.S.: 424510
Manuel G. Fernandez (*CEO*)
Luis Faura (*Pres*)
Alberto Vazquez (*Mgr-Pkg*)

C&F WORLDWIDE AGENCY CORP.
Carr 848 Km 32 Carolina, Trujillo
Alto, PR 00983
Tel.: (787) 750-0450
Web Site:
   http://www.harryheinsen.com
Rev.: $10,000,000
Emp.: 100
Freight Consolidation
N.A.I.C.S.: 488510
Jose Del Cueto (*Pres*)

C&G FOOD BROKERAGE INC.
4595 Parkbreeze Ct, Orlando, FL
32808
Tel.: (407) 578-5959
Web Site:
   http://www.cgfoodbroker.com
Sales Range: $10-24.9 Million
Emp.: 10
Bond Brokers
N.A.I.C.S.: 424410
Pat Clifford (*Pres*)
Kandie Price (*Owner*)

C&G PARTNERS, LLC.
116 E 16th St 10th Fl, New York, NY
10003
Tel.: (212) 532-4460
Web Site:
   http://www.cgpartnersllc.com
Rev.: $1,700,000
Emp.: 22
Fiscal Year-end: 12/31/06
Brand Development & Integration,
Environmental, Exhibit/Trade Shows,
Graphic Design, Identity Marketing,

Internet/Web Design, Logo & Package Design, Multimedia, Print, Strategic Planning/Research
N.A.I.C.S.: 541810
Steff Geissbuhler (*Partner*)
Keith Helmetag (*Partner*)
Jonathan Alger (*Partner*)
Maya Kopytman (*Partner*)
Amy Siegel (*Partner*)
Scott Plunkett (*Assoc Partner*)
Red DeLeon (*Dir-Tech*)
Daniel Fouad (*Dir-Design*)
Daniel Guillermo Rodriguez (*Dir-Design*)
Laura Grady (*Dir-Project Mgmt*)

C&I HOLDINGS INC.
1100 Central Industrial Dr, Saint
Louis, MO 63110
Tel.: (314) 771-6600
Web Site:
   http://www.interconchemical.com
Year Founded: 1990
Sales Range: $10-24.9 Million
Emp.: 100
Holding Company
N.A.I.C.S.: 551112
James A. Epstein (*Pres*)
William Biddle (*COO*)

Subsidiaries:

Continental Research
Corporation   (1)
1180 Central Industrial Dr, Saint Louis, MO
63110-2306
Tel.: (314) 776-0410
Web Site: http://www.crcorp.com
Sales Range: $10-24.9 Million
Emp.: 20
Specialty Chemical Products & Durable
Goods Mfr & Distr
N.A.I.C.S.: 424690
Thomas W. Epstein (*Chm*)
William Biddle (*CFO*)
Brian Taylor (*Controller*)

Intercon Chemical Company   (1)
1100 Central Industrial Dr, Saint Louis, MO
63110
Tel.: (314) 771-6600
Web Site: http://www.interconchemical.com
Polish, Sanitation Good, Soap & Detergent
Mfr
N.A.I.C.S.: 325612
James A. Epstein (*Pres*)
William M. Biddle (*CFO & VP-Fin*)

C&K MARKET, INC.
850 O'Hare Pkwy Ste 100, Medford,
OR 97504
Tel.: (541) 469-3113   OR
Web Site: https://www.ckmarket.com
Year Founded: 1956
Sales Range: $250-299.9 Million
Emp.: 2,500
Operator of Supermarkets
N.A.I.C.S.: 445110
Rocky Campbel (*VP-Ops*)
Karl V. Wissmann (*Pres & CEO*)
David D. Doty (*CFO*)
Jon Wissman (*VP-Perishable Mktg*)

C&K PETROLEUM PRODUCTS
3790 State Rte 7, New Waterford,
OH 44445
Tel.: (330) 482-3340
Sales Range: $50-74.9 Million
Emp.: 10
Gasoline
N.A.I.C.S.: 424720
Scott McCray (*CEO*)

C&K PROPERTIES
675 3rd Ave Ste 2400, New York, NY
10017
Tel.: (212) 279-9000
Web Site:
   http://www.candkproperties.com
Year Founded: 1984

Sales Range: $10-24.9 Million
Emp.: 50
Real Estate Investment & Property
Management Services
N.A.I.C.S.: 531390
Meir Cohen (*Co-Founder*)
Ben Korman (*Co-Founder & Principal*)
Kevin Collins (*CFO*)

C&L DISTRIBUTING
1020 Industrial Dr S, Sauk Rapids,
MN 56379
Tel.: (320) 251-7375
Web Site:
   http://www.abwholesaler.com
Rev.: $16,100,000
Emp.: 50
Distr of Beer
N.A.I.C.S.: 424810
Bernadette Perryman (*Pres*)
Mike Bengtson (*CFO & Controller*)
Russ Goldstein (*Supvr-Sls*)
Shane Vasek (*Mgr-Ops*)

C&L ELECTRIC CO-OPERATIVE
900 Church St, Star City, AR 71667
Tel.: (870) 628-4221
Web Site: https://www.clelectric.com
Sales Range: $10-24.9 Million
Emp.: 100
Electronic Services
N.A.I.C.S.: 221118
C. B. Leonard (*Dir-Field Engrg*)
Jay P. Frizzell (*Mgr-Ops*)
Greg S. Smith (*Mgr-Fin & Admin*)

C&L MANAGEMENT INC.
427 Lincoln Blvd, Middlesex, NJ
08846-2440
Tel.: (732) 667-2000
Web Site: http://www.mcrirents.com
Sales Range: $10-24.9 Million
Emp.: 20
Computer Rental & Leasing
N.A.I.C.S.: 532420
Cindy M. Lange (*CEO*)

C&L SUPPLY INC.
335 S Vann, Vinita, OK 74301
Tel.: (918) 256-6411
Web Site:
   https://www.clsupplyinc.com
Sales Range: $25-49.9 Million
Emp.: 100
Electrical Appliances, Major
N.A.I.C.S.: 423620
Tom Lewis (*Mgr-Nevada*)
Kelly Charles (*Mgr-Springdale*)
Wes Forgey (*Mgr-Grove*)

C&M CORPORATION
51 S Walnut St, Wauregan, CT
06387
Tel.: (860) 774-4812   CT
Web Site:
   http://www.cmcorporation.com
Year Founded: 1964
Sales Range: $50-74.9 Million
Emp.: 200
Insulated Wire, Cable & Retractable
Cords Mfr
N.A.I.C.S.: 335921
John Laskowsky (*Pres & CEO*)
Monte Haymon (*Chm*)
Eileen Harvey (*Mgr-Indus Bus*)
Gordon Stryker (*Mgr-Sls-Eastern
Reg*)
Nick Toscas (*Mgr-Sls-Western Reg*)
Steven DeFrancesco (*VP-Sls & Mktg*)

C&N GROUP INC.
3712 Old Denton Rd, Carrollton, TX
75007-2821
Tel.: (972) 939-8871

Web Site:
   http://www.colonnadehomesdfw.com
Sales Range: $10-24.9 Million
Emp.: 10
Single-Family Housing Construction
N.A.I.C.S.: 236115
Doyle Nix (*CEO*)
Wendy Hall (*Coord-Mktg*)

C&O FOOD SERVICES INC.
3200 Sunset Ave Ste 209, Asbury
Park, NJ 07712
Tel.: (732) 776-8822
Sales Range: $10-24.9 Million
Emp.: 7
Eggs
N.A.I.C.S.: 424440
Boyce Overstreet (*Pres & CEO*)
Nicki Brandimarte (*Controller*)

C&R RESEARCH, INC.
500 N Michigan Ave Ste 1100, Chicago, IL 60611
Tel.: (312) 828-9200
Web Site: http://www.crresearch.com
Rev.: $15,100,000
Emp.: 120
Market Analysis & Research
N.A.I.C.S.: 541910
Sharon Seidler (*Exec VP*)
Paul Metz (*Sr VP*)

C&R STEAKS INC.
2113 1 2 W Britton Rd, Oklahoma
City, OK 73120
Tel.: (405) 755-8761
Rev.: $13,217,929
Emp.: 320
Steak Restaurant
N.A.I.C.S.: 722511
Mackie W. McNear (*Pres*)
Kelly Pindel (*Office Mgr*)

C&S CAPITAL MANAGEMENT
1316 N Hills Blvd, North Little Rock,
AR 72114
Tel.: (501) 376-9971
Sales Range: $10-24.9 Million
Emp.: 150
Provider of Management & Investment Services
N.A.I.C.S.: 493130
Joseph J. Senna (*Mng Partner*)

C&S CONTRACTORS INC.
1160 Kenwood Rd, Cincinnati, OH
45242
Tel.: (513) 530-9844
Sales Range: $10-24.9 Million
Emp.: 15
Commercial & Office Building, New
Construction
N.A.I.C.S.: 236220
Raymond A. Conn (*Pres*)

C&S INC.
300 W 1st St, Portales, NM 88130
Tel.: (575) 356-4495
Web Site: https://candsoil.com
Sales Range: $10-24.9 Million
Emp.: 30
Petroleum Brokers
N.A.I.C.S.: 424720
Mike Stratton (*Pres*)

C&S INC.
2001 Main St, Tell City, IN 47586
Tel.: (812) 547-6435
Sales Range: $75-99.9 Million
Emp.: 280
Convenience Stores, Independent
N.A.I.C.S.: 445131
Jonathan Smith (*Pres*)
Sandy Spencer (*Controller*)

C&S Inc.—(Continued)

C&S INSURANCE AGENCY, INC.
190 Chauncy St, Mansfield, MA 02048
Tel.: (508) 339-2951   **MA**
Web Site: https://www.candsins.com
Year Founded: 1959
Insurance Agents
N.A.I.C.S.: 524210
Keith J. Signoriello *(Owner & Principal)*
Ben Cavallo *(Owner & Principal)*
Tim Kane *(Partner & Exec VP)*
Paul A. Marks *(Exec VP & Partner)*

Subsidiaries:

Francis M. Walley Insurance Agency, Inc.   **(1)**
475 High St, Dedham, MA 02026-2838
Tel.: (781) 326-8383
Web Site: http://www.walleyinsurance.com
Insurance Agencies
N.A.I.C.S.: 524210
F. M. Walley III *(Principal)*

C&S MOTORS, INC.
113 S Dort Hwy, Flint, MI 48503-2842
Tel.: (810) 234-5686   **MI**
Web Site: https://www.tricotruck.com
Year Founded: 1980
Sales Range: $10-24.9 Million
Emp.: 60
Whslr of Trucks, Truck Parts & Repair Services
N.A.I.C.S.: 423110

Subsidiaries:

Idealease of Flint Inc.   **(1)**
113 S Dort Hwy, Flint, MI 48503-2842   **(100%)**
Tel.: (810) 234-5686
Web Site: http://www.tricotruck.com
Sales Range: $10-24.9 Million
Emp.: 20
Truck Rental & Leasing Services
N.A.I.C.S.: 532120
Annette Sraccalossi *(Office Mgr)*

Tri-County International Trucks Inc.   **(1)**
5701 Wyoming St, Dearborn, MI 48126-2355   **(100%)**
Tel.: (313) 584-7090
Web Site: http://www.tricotruck.com
Rev.: $40,126,396
Emp.: 50
Heavy-Duty Truck Sales
N.A.I.C.S.: 423110
Henry Fracalossi *(Owner & Chm)*

C&S PACKAGING GROUP INC.
1300 Commerce Dr, Coraopolis, PA 15108
Tel.: (412) 604-5141
Sales Range: $25-49.9 Million
Emp.: 22
Packaging Materials
N.A.I.C.S.: 424990

C&S WHOLESALE GROCERS, INC.
7 Corporate Dr, Keene, NH 03431
Tel.: (808) 682-3312   **VT**
Web Site: https://www.cswg.com
Year Founded: 1918
Sales Range: $15-24.9 Billion
Emp.: 15,000
General Line Grocery Merchant Wholesalers
N.A.I.C.S.: 424410
Richard B. Cohen *(Founder & Exec Chm)*
Ron Wright *(Sr VP-Logistics)*
Bob Palmer *(CEO)*
Kevin Francis McNamara *(CFO)*
Miriam Ort *(Chief HR Officer)*
Lauren La Bruno *(VP-Comm, Change Mgmt & Community Rels)*

Eric Winn *(COO)*
Bill Boyd *(Chief Legal Officer)*
Michael Papaleo *(Chief Procurement Officer & Exec VP)*
Andrew Connell *(Sr VP-Center Store Procurement)*
Christine Curtis *(Sr VP & Gen Mgr-Comml)*
Alona Florenz *(Sr VP-Corp Dev, Fin Plng & Analysis)*
Bryan Granger *(Sr VP-Ops, Law & Compliance)*
Sudhakar Lingineni *(CIO)*
Mark McGowan *(Sr VP-Retail)*
Greg Patch *(Sr VP-Ops)*
Anthony Sattler *(Sr VP-Fresh Procurement & Mdsg)*

Subsidiaries:

Freshko Produce Services, LLC   **(1)**
2155 E Muscat Ave, Fresno, CA 93725
Tel.: (559) 497-7000
Web Site: http://www.freshkoproduce.com
Rev.: $5,000,000
Emp.: 21
Fruit & Vegetable Markets
N.A.I.C.S.: 445230
Ali Haggagi *(Gen Mgr)*

Grocers Supply International, Inc.   **(1)**
3131 E Holcomb Blvd, Houston, TX 77021-2199
Tel.: (713) 749-9386
Web Site: http://www.gscapps1.grocerybiz.com
Emp.: 10,000
Wholesale Food Distr
N.A.I.C.S.: 424410

Olean Wholesale Grocery Cooperative Inc.   **(1)**
1587 Haskell Rd, Olean, NY 14760-9229
Tel.: (716) 372-2020
Web Site: http://www.oleanwholesale.com
Sales Range: $25-49.9 Million
Emp.: 245
Distribute & Warehouse Groceries
N.A.I.C.S.: 445110
James Ried *(Pres & CEO)*
Brian Bowen *(Gen Mgr)*
Eric Holmberg *(Dir-Wholesale Acctg)*
Cal O'Rourke *(Dir-HR)*

Subsidiary (Domestic):

Eden Shur-Fine   **(2)**
8081 N Main St, Eden, NY 14057-1118   **(100%)**
Tel.: (716) 992-9210
Web Site: http://www.wholesupply.org
Sales Range: $1-9.9 Million
Emp.: 40
Grocery Stores
N.A.I.C.S.: 445110
Fred Bossert *(Mgr)*

Shur-Market Development Co., Inc.   **(2)**
1587 Haskell Rd, Olean, NY 14760-9229
Tel.: (716) 372-2020
Sales Range: $25-49.9 Million
Nonresidential Building Operators
N.A.I.C.S.: 531120
David Winnicki *(VP)*

Piggly Wiggly Midwest, LLC   **(1)**
2215 Union Ave, Sheboygan, WI 53083
Tel.: (920) 457-4433
Web Site: http://www.shopthepig.com
Supermarket Retailer & Grocery Whslr
N.A.I.C.S.: 445110
Paul Butera Sr. *(Founder & Pres)*
Gary J. Suokko *(COO)*
Michael G. Isken *(CFO)*
Barb Pike *(Mgr-HR)*
Thomas Johnson *(Controller)*
Richard Saaman *(Dir-Adv)*
Bill Bell *(CIO)*
Jim Lecy *(Dir-Logistics)*

Piggly Wiggly, LLC   **(1)**
7 Corporate Dr, Keene, NH 03431
Tel.: (603) 354-7000
Web Site: http://www.pigglywiggly.com
Brand Supermarket Franchisor
N.A.I.C.S.: 533110

Robesonia Logistics LLC   **(1)**
336 E Penn Ave, Robesonia, PA 19551
Tel.: (610) 693-3161
Groceries Whslr
N.A.I.C.S.: 424410
Geoffrey McVey *(Sr Mgr-HR)*

Southern Family Markets LLC   **(1)**
800 Lakeshore Pkwy, Birmingham, AL 35211
Tel.: (205) 940-9400
Sales Range: $25-49.9 Million
Supermarket Operator
N.A.I.C.S.: 445110

C&T AFFILIATES INC.
1000 Hagey Rd, Souderton, PA 18964
Tel.: (215) 721-1000
Rev.: $11,500,000
Emp.: 20
Commercial & Industrial Building Operation
N.A.I.C.S.: 532490

C&T CONSULTING SERVICES LLP
14012 Marathon Rd, Austin, TX 78717
Tel.: (512) 502-1031
Web Site: http://www.ctconsult.com
Sales Range: $10-24.9 Million
Emp.: 15
Data Processing Consultant
N.A.I.C.S.: 541512
Roger Conway *(Pres)*

C&W ACQUISITION CORP.
225 W Wacker Dr Ste 3000, Chicago, IL 60606
Tel.: (312) 470-1800   **Ky**
Year Founded: 2021
Investment Services
N.A.I.C.S.: 523999
Adam L. Stanley *(Pres)*
Brett White *(Chm)*
Nathaniel Robinson *(CEO)*

C&W TRUCKING INC.
703 Hennis Rd, Winter Garden, FL 34787
Tel.: (407) 877-2600
Web Site: http://www.candwtrucking.com
Sales Range: $25-49.9 Million
Emp.: 250
Local Trucking without Storage
N.A.I.C.S.: 484110
Kris Creeden *(Pres)*
Kevin Creeden *(Treas & Sec)*

C-A-L RANCH STORES
665 E Anderson St, Idaho Falls, ID 83401-2020
Tel.: (208) 523-3431   **ID**
Web Site: http://www.calranch.com
Year Founded: 1959
Sales Range: $10-24.9 Million
Emp.: 130
Farm Supplies
N.A.I.C.S.: 424910
Randy Holmes *(Reg Mgr)*

C-D UTILITY CONSTRUCTION INC.
103 Deer Tree Dr, Lafayette, LA 70507
Tel.: (337) 234-7334
Sales Range: $10-24.9 Million
Emp.: 20
Cable Laying Construction
N.A.I.C.S.: 237130

C-FLEX BEARING CO., INC.
104 Industrial Dr, Frankfort, NY 13340-1139
Tel.: (315) 895-7454
Web Site: https://www.c-flex.com

Year Founded: 1993
Sales Range: $10-24.9 Million
Emp.: 8
Turbine Component Mfr
N.A.I.C.S.: 333613
Wayne Smith *(VP)*

C-LINE PRODUCTS, INC.
1100 Bus Ctr Dr, Mount Prospect, IL 60056-6053
Tel.: (847) 827-6661   **IL**
Web Site: http://www.c-lineproducts.com
Year Founded: 1949
Sales Range: $100-124.9 Million
Emp.: 155
Mfr of Plastic Storage, Identification & Organization Products
N.A.I.C.S.: 326199
James Krumwiede *(Chm, Pres & CEO)*
Judi Krumwiede *(VP-Employee & Customer Rels)*
Susan Travis *(Controller)*
Paul Chasnoff *(Dir-Product Mgmt)*

C-SYSTEMS INTERNATIONAL CORPORATION
6930 San Tomas Rd, Elkridge, MD 21075-6227
Tel.: (703) 768-1800
Web Site: http://www.csystemsinc.com
Year Founded: 1992
Rev.: $10,700,000
Emp.: 115
General Freight Trucking Services
N.A.I.C.S.: 484110
Howard Ulep *(CEO)*
Tom Dannessa *(Gen Mgr)*

C-W VALLEY CO-OP
PO Box 69, Wolverton, MN 56594
Tel.: (218) 995-2565
Web Site: http://www.cwvalley.com
Sales Range: $10-24.9 Million
Emp.: 11
Fertilizer & Fertilizer Materials
N.A.I.C.S.: 424910

C. A. CURTZE COMPANY INC.
1717 E 12th St, Erie, PA 16511-1723
Tel.: (814) 452-2281   **PA**
Web Site: https://www.curtze.com
Year Founded: 1968
Rev.: $80,000,000
Emp.: 300
Groceries, General Line
N.A.I.C.S.: 424410
David Boyd *(VP-Sls)*
James Snyder *(Plant Mgr)*
Randy Work *(Dir-Sls & Mktg)*
Bruce Kern II *(Pres)*

C. A. PERRY & SON INC.
4033 Virginia Rd, Hobbsville, NC 27946
Tel.: (252) 221-4463
Web Site: https://www.caperryandson.com
Sales Range: $10-24.9 Million
Emp.: 80
Trucking Services & Outerwear Distr
N.A.I.C.S.: 455219
Sidney Perry *(Pres)*

C. BREWER & CO. LTD.
26-238 Hawaii Belt Rd, Hilo, HI 96720
Tel.: (808) 969-1826   **HI**
Year Founded: 1826
Sales Range: $50-74.9 Million
Emp.: 3
Agriculture & Real Estate
N.A.I.C.S.: 111335

John W.A. Buyers *(Chm)*
J. Alan Kugle *(CEO-Real Estate)*

Subsidiaries:

HT&T Company **(1)**
PO Box 1826, Papaikou, HI
96781-1826 **(100%)**
Tel.: (808) 933-7700
Sales Range: $25-49.9 Million
Trucking & Storage
N.A.I.C.S.: 441110

Mauna Kea Agribusiness Co.,
Inc. **(1)**
PO Box 15, Papaikou, HI
96781-0015 **(100%)**
Tel.: (808) 964-1013
Sales Range: $10-24.9 Million
Macadamia Nuts
N.A.I.C.S.: 531190

Wailuku Agribusiness Co., Inc. **(1)**
255 E Waiko Rd, Wailuku, HI
96793-9355 **(87.7%)**
Tel.: (808) 244-7079
Sales Range: $10-24.9 Million
Wholesale of Macadamia Nuts
N.A.I.C.S.: 111335

C. COAKLEY RELOCATION SYSTEMS, INC.
1300 N 4th St, Milwaukee, WI 53212
Tel.: (414) 272-4040   WI
Web Site: http://www.ccoakley.com
Year Founded: 1999
Sales Range: $1-9.9 Million
Emp.: 55
Moving, Storage & Warehousing Services
N.A.I.C.S.: 484110
Chris Coakley *(Pres)*
Robert Isnard *(Exec VP)*

C. COWLES & CO.
83 Water St, New Haven, CT 06511
Tel.: (203) 865-3117
Web Site: http://www.ccowles.com
Year Founded: 1838
Sales Range: $10-24.9 Million
Emp.: 220
Stamped Metal Mfr
N.A.I.C.S.: 336390
Larry Moon *(Pres)*
Rich Lyons *(VP-Sls & Mktg)*
Tony Amenta *(VP-Mfg)*

Subsidiaries:

Hydrolevel Company **(1)**
126 Bailey Rd, North Haven, CT 06473
Tel.: (203) 776-0473
Web Site: http://www.hydrolevel.com
Rev.: $12,000,000
Emp.: 75
Injection Molding Of Plastics
N.A.I.C.S.: 332919
Lawrence C. Moon *(Pres)*
Russell Spector *(VP & Controller)*

C. ERICKSON & SONS INC.
2200 Arch St Ste 200, Philadelphia, PA 19103
Tel.: (215) 568-3120   PA
Web Site: https://www.cerickson.com
Year Founded: 1953
Sales Range: $10-24.9 Million
Emp.: 100
Provider of Nonresidential Construction Services
N.A.I.C.S.: 236220
Charles G. Erickson *(Pres)*
Michael G. Erickson *(Exec VP)*

C. G. BRETTING MANUFACTURING CO., INC.
3401 Lake Park Rd, Ashland, WI 54806
Tel.: (715) 682-5231
Web Site: https://www.bretting.com
Year Founded: 1966
Sales Range: $25-49.9 Million

Emp.: 500
Mfr of Paper Converting Equipment
N.A.I.C.S.: 333243

Subsidiaries:

Bretting Development Corp., Inc. **(1)**
3401 Lake Park Rd, Ashland, WI 54806-2522
Tel.: (715) 682-5231
Web Site: http://www.bretting.com
Sales Range: $25-49.9 Million
Emp.: 400
Provider of Building Maintenance Services
N.A.I.C.S.: 561720
David Bretting *(Pres)*

S&S Specialty Systems, LLC **(1)**
68150 Front St, Iron River, WI 54847
Tel.: (715) 372-8988
Web Site:
http://www.ssspecialtysystems.com
Sales Range: $1-9.9 Million
Industrial Supplies Whslr
N.A.I.C.S.: 423840

T & T Manufacturing, LLC **(1)**
700 Industrial Blvd, Spooner, WI 54801
Tel.: (715) 635-8421
Web Site: https://www.ttmfg.com
Machining & Fabrication Services
N.A.I.C.S.: 332312
Steve Sundeen *(Pres & CEO)*
Ryan LaPorte *(Coord-Engrng)*
Tony Rust *(Supvr)*
Patty Tallant *(Office Mgr)*
Jack Johnson *(Quality Assurance Mgr)*
Diane Zeien *(Dir-HR)*
Tucker McCumber *(Dir-IT)*

C. H. LANGMAN & SONS INC.
220 34th Ave, Rock Island, IL 61201
Tel.: (309) 786-8885
Rev.: $15,000,000
Emp.: 60
Highway & Street Construction
N.A.I.C.S.: 237310

C. HAGER & SONS HINGE MANUFACTURING COMPANY INC.
139 Victor St, Saint Louis, MO 63104-4724
Tel.: (314) 772-4400   MO
Web Site: https://www.hagerco.com
Year Founded: 1849
Sales Range: $25-49.9 Million
Emp.: 929
Provider of Hardware
N.A.I.C.S.: 332510
August W. Hager III *(Chm)*
Ralph Hager II *(Pres)*

C. MARTIN COMPANY, INC.
3395 W Cheyenne Ave Ste 102, North Las Vegas, NV 89032
Tel.: (702) 656-8080
Web Site: https://www.cmartin.com
Year Founded: 1974
Sales Range: $25-49.9 Million
Emp.: 475
Commercial & Institutional Building Construction Services
N.A.I.C.S.: 236220
Laura A. Craig *(Pres)*
John C. Martin *(Founder, Partner & VP)*
Harold J. Huge *(VP-Tech Ops)*

C. O. CHRISTIAN & SONS COMPANY, INC.
2139 Canady Ave, Nashville, TN 37211-2003
Tel.: (615) 254-3491
Web Site:
https://www.cochristian.com
Year Founded: 1967
Sales Range: $10-24.9 Million
Emp.: 75
Electronic Services
N.A.I.C.S.: 238210

Janice Christian *(Sec)*
C. Oakley Christian Jr. *(Pres)*
C. Oakley Christian III *(VP)*

C. OVERAA & CO.
200 Parr Blvd, Richmond, CA 94801
Tel.: (510) 234-0926
Web Site: https://www.overaa.com
Year Founded: 1907
Sales Range: $50-74.9 Million
Emp.: 150
Industrial Building Construction Services
N.A.I.C.S.: 236210
Jerry Overaa *(CEO)*
Christopher Manning *(Pres)*
Larry Etcheverry *(VP-Estimating)*
Jeff Naff *(VP-Municipal Infrastructure)*
Dale Jackson *(VP-Ops & Superintendent)*
Erin Overaa Dissman *(Sec & Dir-IT)*
Kara Overaa Gragg *(Dir-Mktg)*
Ellen Hoffman *(CFO)*
Carl Overaa *(VP-Bus Dev)*
Colby Powell *(VP & Project Dir)*
Kevin Smith *(Dir-Project)*
Don Stock *(Dir-Project)*
Maggie White *(Dir-HR & Trng)*
Mike Conrad *(Dir-Project)*
Vinson Heine *(Dir-Project)*

C. RENNER PETROLEUM
110 D St, Crescent City, CA 95531
Tel.: (707) 465-1776
Web Site: https://www.c-renner.com
Rev.: $11,034,273
Emp.: 25
Gasoline
N.A.I.C.S.: 424720
C. Renner *(Pres)*

C. SPECK MOTORS
61 E Allen Rd, Sunnyside, WA 98944
Tel.: (509) 293-4791
Web Site:
https://www.cspeckmotors.com
Year Founded: 1912
Sales Range: $10-24.9 Million
Emp.: 56
New Car Retailer
N.A.I.C.S.: 441110
Carlos Munguia *(Gen Mgr)*
Angel Castaneda *(Mgr-Svc)*
Angel Garza *(Mgr-Sls)*
Miguel Lepez *(Mgr-Fin)*

C. STEIN, INC.
5408 Northeast 88th St Ste B101, Vancouver, WA 98665
Tel.: (360) 693-8251
Web Site: http://www.csteindist.com
Year Founded: 1990
Sales Range: $25-49.9 Million
Emp.: 240
Holding Company
N.A.I.C.S.: 551112
Craig Stein *(Owner)*

Subsidiaries:

Stein Distributing Inc. **(1)**
5408 NE 88th St Ste B101, Vancouver, WA 98665
Tel.: (360) 693-8251
Web Site: http://www.steindist.com
Sales Range: $25-49.9 Million
Emp.: 80
Beer & Other Fermented Malt Liquors
N.A.I.C.S.: 424810
Craig Stein *(Pres)*

C. THORREZ INDUSTRIES INC.
4909 W Michigan Ave, Jackson, MI 49201
Tel.: (517) 750-3160
Web Site: https://www.thorrez.com
Rev.: $45,000,000

Emp.: 15
Screw Machine Products
N.A.I.C.S.: 332721
Camiel E. Thorrez *(Pres)*
Al Thorezz *(VP)*

C. VARGAS & ASSOCIATES, LTD.
8808 Arlington Expy, Jacksonville, FL 32211
Tel.: (904) 722-2294
Web Site: https://www.cvaltd.com
Year Founded: 1978
Rev.: $15,200,000
Emp.: 10
Environmental Engineering Services
N.A.I.C.S.: 541330
Clark C. Vargas *(Principal & Exec VP)*

C. W. DRIVER, INC.
468 N Rosemead Blvd, Pasadena, CA 91107
Tel.: (626) 351-8800
Web Site: https://www.cwdriver.com
Year Founded: 1919
Sales Range: $25-49.9 Million
Emp.: 300
Commercial & Institutional Building Construction Services
N.A.I.C.S.: 236220
Dana Roberts *(CEO)*
Mike Castillo *(VP)*
John Janacek *(VP)*
Carl Lowman *(CFO)*

C. WATTS AND SONS CONSTRUCTION INC.
1305 S Rockwell, Oklahoma City, OK 73128
Tel.: (405) 787-2377
Web Site: http://cwattsandsons.com
Sales Range: $75-99.9 Million
Emp.: 100
Excavation Work
N.A.I.C.S.: 238910
Calvin L. Watts *(Chm)*
Larry Smith *(Exec Dir)*

C. WILLIAM HETZER, INC.
9401 Sharpsburg Pike, Hagerstown, MD 21740
Tel.: (301) 733-7300
Web Site:
https://www.cwilliamhetzer.com
Rev.: $12,071,000
Emp.: 100
Roadway, Piping & Land Protection Engineering & Construction Services
N.A.I.C.S.: 237310
Cary Donley *(Asst Controller)*
Earle Rose *(Project Mgr)*
Greg Eckard *(Project Mgr)*
Tony Kerns *(Project Mgr)*

C.A. LINDMAN INC.
10401 Guilford Rd, Jessup, MD 20794
Tel.: (301) 470-4700
Web Site:
https://www.calindman.com
Sales Range: $50-74.9 Million
Emp.: 250
Commercial & Office Buildings; Renovation & Repair
N.A.I.C.S.: 236220
Robert G. Pusheck *(Co-Founder)*
Jeff Procter *(Co-Founder)*

C.A. LITZLER CO., INC.
4800 W 160th St, Cleveland, OH 44135-2689
Tel.: (216) 267-8020
Web Site: https://www.calitzler.com
Sales Range: $10-24.9 Million
Emp.: 40

C.A. Litzler Co., Inc.—(Continued)

Oven & Drying Equipment Processes
N.A.I.C.S.: 333994
Matt Litzler *(Pres)*

C.A. MURREN & SONS COMPANY

2275 Loganville Hwy, Grayson, GA 30017
Tel.: (770) 682-2940
Web Site: https://www.camurren.com
Sales Range: $10-24.9 Million
Emp.: 50
Water, Sewer & Utility Lines
N.A.I.C.S.: 237110
Perry Taggart *(Mgr-Equipment)*
Charles A. Murren III *(Pres)*

C.A. RASMUSSEN, INC.

28548 Livingston Ave, Valencia, CA 91355
Tel.: (661) 367-9040
Web Site:
   https://www.carasmussen.com
Year Founded: 1964
Sales Range: $100-124.9 Million
Emp.: 200
General Engineering Contractor
N.A.I.C.S.: 237310
Charles A. Rasmussen *(Pres)*
Lisa Punches *(Sec)*

C.A. SCHROEDER COMPANY, INC.

1318 1st St, San Fernando, CA 91340
Tel.: (818) 365-9561   **CA**
Web Site: http://www.cal-flex.com
Year Founded: 1969
Sales Range: $1-9.9 Million
Emp.: 46
Mineral Wool Mfr
N.A.I.C.S.: 327993
Clifford Schroeder *(Pres)*

C.B. RAGLAND COMPANY

2720 Eugenia Ave, Nashville, TN 37211
Tel.: (615) 259-4622   **TN**
Web Site: http://www.cbragland.com
Year Founded: 1919
Sales Range: $10-24.9 Million
Emp.: 7
Real Estate Services
N.A.I.C.S.: 531390
J. Michael Hayes *(CEO)*
Ryan Finley *(Controller)*
Mike Hayes *(Chm)*

C.B. STRAIN & SON INC.

417 Manchester Rd, Poughkeepsie, NY 12603-2572
Tel.: (845) 454-0600   **NY**
Web Site: http://www.cbstrain.com
Year Founded: 1919
Sales Range: $10-24.9 Million
Emp.: 100
Plumbing, Heating & Air-Conditioning
N.A.I.C.S.: 238220
Richard C. Strain *(Pres & Treas)*

C.C. BORDEN CONSTRUCTION, INC.

1019 Rosselle St, Jacksonville, FL 32204
Tel.: (904) 354-3458
Web Site: https://www.ccborden.com
Year Founded: 1988
Sales Range: $10-24.9 Million
Emp.: 25
Commercial & Institutional Building Construction Services
N.A.I.C.S.: 236220
Camille C. Borden *(Founder & Pres)*

C.C. CLARK, INC.

501 Academy Rd, Starkville, MS 39759-4047
Tel.: (662) 323-4317   **MS**
Web Site: http://www.ccclark.com
Year Founded: 1903
Sales Range: $100-124.9 Million
Emp.: 700
Holding Company; Bottled & Canned Soft Drink Mfr
N.A.I.C.S.: 551112
Albert C. Clark *(Pres, CEO & Treas)*
Morgan E. Clark *(Sec)*
Harold N. Clark *(VP-Mississippi)*
Dallas Clark *(CFO-Kentucky)*

Subsidiaries:

Clark Beverage Group, Inc.   **(1)**
1235 Scott St Senatobia, Southaven, MS 38668
Tel.: (662) 280-8540
Beer & Ale Distr
N.A.I.C.S.: 424810
Rodney Henderson *(Mgr-Sls)*

Clark Distributing Company, Inc.   **(1)**
300 Oakland Flatrock Rd, Oakland, KY 42159-9766
Tel.: (270) 563-4735
Web Site: http://www.ccclark.com
Sales Range: $25-49.9 Million
Emp.: 140
Distr of Beer & Ale
N.A.I.C.S.: 424810
George P. Clark *(Pres)*

Branch (Domestic):

Clark Distributing Company, Inc. - Paducah   **(2)**
330 Locust Dr, Paducah, KY 42003
Tel.: (270) 443-7386
Web Site: http://www.ccclark.com
Emp.: 21
Beer & Ale Merchant Whslr
N.A.I.C.S.: 424810

Northeast Mississippi Coca-Cola Bottling Co., Inc.   **(1)**
110 Miley Rd, Starkville, MS 39759-8977   **(100%)**
Tel.: (662) 338-3400
Web Site: http://www.ccclark.com
Rev.: $18,800,000
Emp.: 150
Bottled & Canned Soft Drinks Distr
N.A.I.C.S.: 312111

Western Kentucky Coca-Cola Bottling Co., Inc.   **(1)**
300 Oakland-Flatrock Rd, Oakland, KY 42159   **(100%)**
Tel.: (270) 563-4735
Web Site: http://www.ccclark.com
Rev.: $770,000
Emp.: 135
Bottled & Canned Soft Drinks Distr
N.A.I.C.S.: 312111
William D. Clark Jr. *(Pres)*

all3sports, Inc.   **(1)**
8601 Dunwoody Pl Ste 420, Atlanta, GA 30350
Tel.: (770) 587-9994
Web Site: http://www.all3sports.com
Emp.: 12
Bicycle Whslr
N.A.I.C.S.: 459110
Ed Crossman *(Gen Mgr)*

C.C. JOHNSON & MALHOTRA, P.C.

1025 Connecticut Ave NW Ste 1201, Washington, DC 20036-5414
Tel.: (202) 363-0350
Web Site: https://www.ccjm.com
Rev.: $7,500,000
Emp.: 68
Engineeering Services
N.A.I.C.S.: 541330
L. David Chang *(Sr VP-Washington)*
Albert R. Posthuma *(VP)*
Kumar S. Malhotra *(Pres & Treas)*

C.C. MYERS, INC.

3286 Fitzgerald Rd, Rancho Cordova, CA 95742-6811
Tel.: (916) 635-9370   **CA**
Web Site: http://www.ccmyers.com
Year Founded: 1977
Sales Range: $200-249.9 Million
Emp.: 200
Heavy Engineering & Bridge Contracting Services
N.A.I.C.S.: 237310
Linda Clifford *(CFO)*
Steve Francis *(Sec)*
Bill Kidwell *(Mgr-Engrg)*

C.D. SMITH CONSTRUCTION INC.

889 E Johnson St, Fond Du Lac, WI 54936
Tel.: (920) 924-2900
Web Site: http://www.cdsmith.com
Rev.: $218,700,000
Emp.: 440
Commercial & Institutional Building Construction
N.A.I.C.S.: 236220
Thomas D. Baker *(Chm)*
Steve Schmitz *(VP-Field Ops)*
Robert Baker *(Treas)*
Patrick Smith *(Dir-Safety)*
Michael Krolczyk *(Exec VP)*
Justin Smith *(Pres & CEO)*
Robert Seibel *(Treas)*
Darin Garbisch *(Sr Project Mgr)*
Greg Sabel *(VP)*
Tricia Muellenbach *(Dir-Strategic Initiatives)*

C.D.S. OFFICE TECHNOLOGY CORP

612 S Dirksen Pkwy, Springfield, IL 62703-2111
Tel.: (217) 528-8936   **IL**
Web Site:
   https://www.cdsofficetech.com
Year Founded: 1971
Sales Range: $25-49.9 Million
Emp.: 180
Retail Sales & Service of Officer Equipment
N.A.I.C.S.: 423420
John Bolser *(VP-Sls)*

C.E. NIEHOFF & CO.

2021 Lee St, Evanston, IL 60202
Tel.: (847) 866-6030
Web Site: https://www.ceniehoff.com
Sales Range: $25-49.9 Million
Emp.: 450
Automotive Alternators
N.A.I.C.S.: 336320
George Buhrfeind *(Pres)*
Paul Cacciapore *(Mgr-Sls)*
Stan Rosenbloom *(CFO)*

Subsidiaries:

Goodman Ball Inc.   **(1)**
3639 Haven Ave, Menlo Park, CA 94025
Tel.: (650) 363-0113
Web Site: http://www.goodmanball.com
Sales Range: $10-24.9 Million
Emp.: 40
Spare Military Equipment Mfr
N.A.I.C.S.: 332710

C.E. SHEPHERD COMPANY LP

2221 Canada Dry St, Houston, TX 77023
Tel.: (713) 924-4300
Web Site:
   https://www.ceshepherd.com
Rev.: $22,000,000
Emp.: 215
Plastics Film & Sheet
N.A.I.C.S.: 326113
Maury Shepherd *(Chm, Pres & CEO)*

C.E. SUNDBERG COMPANY INC.

5852 W 51st St, Chicago, IL 60638
Tel.: (773) 723-2700
Web Site: http://www.appliance-parts.com
Year Founded: 1912
Sales Range: $10-24.9 Million
Emp.: 90
Electric Household Appliances
N.A.I.C.S.: 423620
Bob Burke *(Pres)*

C.E. TAYLOR OIL INC.

215 NW 3rd St, Washington, IN 47501
Tel.: (812) 254-2248
Web Site:
   http://www.chucklesstores.com
Rev.: $17,000,000
Emp.: 300
Owner & Operator of Convenience Stores; Distributor of Oil Products
N.A.I.C.S.: 445131
Charles E. Taylor *(Pres)*
Margaret Taylor *(VP)*

C.E. THURSTON & SONS INCORPORATED

3335 Croft St, Norfolk, VA 23513-4903
Tel.: (757) 855-7700   **VA**
Web Site: http://www.cethurston.com
Year Founded: 1919
Sales Range: $25-49.9 Million
Emp.: 110
Special Trade Contracting Services
N.A.I.C.S.: 238990
Linda R. Ashley *(Sec)*

Subsidiaries:

C.E. Thurston & Sons Distributing, LLC   **(1)**
5300 Lewis Rd, Sandston, VA 23150
Tel.: (804) 592-3183
Industrial Equipment & Supplies Distr
N.A.I.C.S.: 423830
John Perkins *(VP-Admin)*
Douglas A. Sims Jr. *(Pres)*

C.E. Thurston & Sons Inc. - Empire Industrial Products   **(1)**
3550 Virginia Beach Blvd, Norfolk, VA 23502
Tel.: (757) 222-9200
Emp.: 85
Industrial Supplies Distr
N.A.I.C.S.: 423840
Jim Topping *(Mgr-Creative Innovations)*

C.E.F.S. ECONOMIC OPPORTUNITY CORPORATION

1805 S Banker St, Effingham, IL 62401-0928
Tel.: (217) 342-2193   **IL**
Web Site: https://www.cefseoc.org
Year Founded: 1965
Sales Range: $10-24.9 Million
Emp.: 403
Community Action Services
N.A.I.C.S.: 624190
Kevin Bushur *(CEO)*

C.F. BEAN, LLC

619 Engineer Rd, Belle Chasse, LA 70037
Tel.: (504) 587-8600
Web Site: http://www.cfbean.com
Year Founded: 1952
Sales Range: $10-24.9 Million
Emp.: 275
Provider of Heavy Construction Services
N.A.I.C.S.: 541620
Arthur Burgoyne *(Mgr-Estimating)*
Sandra Viallon *(Sec)*
Jorge Martinez *(CFO)*
James Bean Jr. *(Chm, Pres & CEO)*

Subsidiaries:

Bean Dredging, L.L.C.   **(1)**
619 Engineers Rd, Belle Chasse, LA 70037
Tel.: (504) 587-8600
Web Site: http://www.cfbean.com
Heavy Construction Services
N.A.I.C.S.: 237990
James W. Bean (CEO)

Bean Horizon Corp.   **(1)**
PO Box 237, Belle Chasse, LA 70037-0237
Tel.: (504) 587-8600
Web Site: http://www.cfbean.com
Provider of Heavy Construction Services
N.A.I.C.S.: 237110

C.F. BURGER CREAMERY COMPANY

8101 Greenfield Rd, Detroit, MI
48228-2220
Tel.: (313) 584-4040   MI
Web Site: https://www.cfburger.com
Sales Range: $75-99.9 Million
Emp.: 65
Producers of Dairy Specialties
N.A.I.C.S.: 424430
Chris Angott (VP-Sls)
Dean Angott (Pres)

C.F. HAGLIN & SONS, INC.

3939 W 69th St, Edina, MN 55435
Tel.: (952) 920-6123   MN
Year Founded: 1873
Sales Range: $10-24.9 Million
Emp.: 60
Contracting Services
N.A.I.C.S.: 237990
Thomas B. Roberts (CEO)
Gary G. Gunderson (Pres)
Doris A. Fritzen (Controller)
Tom Goering (Project Mgr)

C.F. JORDAN L.P.

7700 CF Jordan Dr, El Paso, TX
79912-8802
Tel.: (915) 877-3333   TX
Web Site: http://www.cfjordan.com
Year Founded: 1988
Sales Range: $25-49.9 Million
Emp.: 500
Industrial Buildings & Warehouse
Management Services
N.A.I.C.S.: 236220
Paul Bauer (COO-Comml)
Darren Woody (CEO)
Jennifer Green (CFO)
Leland Rocchio (Pres-Comml)
Roy Raines (Pres-Multifamily)
John Goodrich (Pres-Infrastructure &
Concrete)
C. F. Jordan III (Founder)

Subsidiaries:

C.F. Jordan Construction LLC   **(1)**
7700 C F Jordan Dr, El Paso, TX 79912-
8802
Tel.: (915) 877-3333
Web Site: http://www.cfjordan.com
Sales Range: $25-49.9 Million
Emp.: 245
Industrial Buildings & Warehouses
N.A.I.C.S.: 551112
Matt Hardison (Project Mgr)

C.F. Jordan Residential
Incorporated   **(1)**
7700 C F Jordan Dr, El Paso, TX 79912-
8802
Tel.: (915) 877-3333
Web Site: http://www.westerngas.com
Sales Range: $50-74.9 Million
Emp.: 7
Residential Construction
N.A.I.C.S.: 236116

C.F. MARTIN & CO., INC.

510 Sycamore St, Nazareth, PA
18064-1000
Tel.: (610) 759-2837   NY

Web Site:
http://www.martinguitar.com
Year Founded: 1833
Sales Range: $25-49.9 Million
Emp.: 700
Acoustic Guitars, Musical Strings &
Related Accessories Producer
N.A.I.C.S.: 339992
Thomas Ripsam (CEO)
Christian Frederick Martin IV (Chm)

C.F. SCHWARTZ MOTOR COMPANY, INC.

1536 N DuPont Hwy, Dover, DE
19901
Tel.: (302) 734-5748
Web Site:
https://www.cfschwartztoyota.com
Sales Range: $10-24.9 Million
Emp.: 36
Car Whslr
N.A.I.C.S.: 441110
Robert A. Schwartz (Pres)

C.G. ENTERPRISES INC.

12001 Guilford Rd, Annapolis Junc-
tion, MD 20701-1201
Tel.: (410) 792-9400
Web Site:
http://www.cgenterprises.biz
Year Founded: 1920
Sales Range: $25-49.9 Million
Emp.: 500
Highway & Street Construction
N.A.I.C.S.: 237310

Subsidiaries:

Corman Construction Inc.   **(1)**
12001 Guilford Rd, Annapolis Junction, MD
20701   **(100%)**
Tel.: (410) 792-9400
Web Site:
http://www.cormanconstruction.com
Sales Range: $50-74.9 Million
Emp.: 50
Highway & Street Construction
N.A.I.C.S.: 237310
William G. Cox (Pres)
David Gates (Mgr-Estimating)

Corman Marine Construction,
Inc.   **(1)**
711 E Ordnance Rd Ste 715, Baltimore, MD
21226
Tel.: (410) 424-1870
Web Site: http://www.cormanmarine.com
Marine Construction Services
N.A.I.C.S.: 237990
F. Xavier McGeady (Chief Engr)
Martin Corcoran (Gen Mgr)

C.G. SCHMIDT INC.

11777 W Lk Park Dr, Milwaukee, WI
53224-3047
Tel.: (414) 577-1177
Web Site: http://www.cgschmidt.com
Year Founded: 1920
Sales Range: $50-74.9 Million
Emp.: 370
Provider of Construction Contracting
Services
N.A.I.C.S.: 236220
Richard L. Schmidt (Pres & CEO)
Mark Lillesand (VP)
Sarah Dunn (Dir-Client Strategies)
Allison Zahn (Coord-Mktg)

C.H. BRIGGS COMPANY

2047 Kutztown Rd, Reading, PA
19605
Tel.: (610) 929-6969   PA
Web Site: http://www.chbriggs.com
Year Founded: 1969
Sales Range: $50-74.9 Million
Emp.: 158
Wholesale Distr of Products & Infor-
mation to Cabinet Manufacturing, Re-
modeling & Decorative Surfacing
Industries

N.A.I.C.S.: 444180
Julia Klein (Chm & CEO)
Bob Spangler (Chief Sls Officer)
Luis Arias (CMO)
Scott Withers (CIO)
Timothy Keane (CFO)
Jonathan W. Peters (Pres & COO)
Mike Strauss (Chief Supply Chain
Officer)

C.H. CARPENTER LUMBER COMPANY

6160 Summit Dr N Ste 125, Minne-
apolis, MN 55430
Tel.: (763) 560-7576
Sales Range: $10-24.9 Million
Emp.: 75
Lumber & Other Building Materials
N.A.I.C.S.: 423310

C.H. COAKLEY & CO.

2151 N Dr Martin Luther King Dr, Mil-
waukee, WI 53212
Tel.: (414) 372-7000
Web Site: https://www.chcoakley.com
Sales Range: $10-24.9 Million
Emp.: 50
Moving & Storage Services
N.A.I.C.S.: 493110
Kathleen Coakley (Mng Partner)
Dean Tandeski (VP-American Micro-
graphics)
Ezekiel Gipson (Mgr-Sls & Customer
Svc-Retention & Micrographics Div)

C.H. FENSTERMAKER & AS-SOCIATES, INC.

135 Regency Sq, Lafayette, LA
70508
Tel.: (337) 237-2200
Web Site:
http://www.fenstermaker.com
Rev.: $10,454,727
Emp.: 80
Surveying Wells
N.A.I.C.S.: 541370
Alan Day (VP-IT)
Charles Fenstermaker (Pres)
Travis Bodin (VP-Survey & Mapping)
Charles Howard Fenstermaker Jr.
(Founder)

C.H. GUERNSEY & COMPANY, INC.

5555 N Grand Blvd, Oklahoma City,
OK 73112
Tel.: (405) 416-4054
Web Site: http://www.guernsey.us
Year Founded: 1928
Emp.: 127
Consulting & Management Services
N.A.I.C.S.: 541611
Suhas Patwardhan (Pres & CEO)
Phil Dean (VP & Mgr-Power Engrg)
Richard Hinkle (Sr VP)
Ray Kilway (VP)
Sheldon Hunt (VP)

C.H. HOLDERBY CO.

150 12th Ave, Seattle, WA 98122
Tel.: (206) 622-6646
Web Site:
https://www.chholderby.com
Sales Range: $10-24.9 Million
Emp.: 5
Industrial Machinery & Equipment
Merchant Whslr
N.A.I.C.S.: 423830
Earnest Allen (Owner)
Loretta Rombauer (Controller)

C.H. HOLDINGS, USA INC.

10733 Sunset Office Dr, Saint Louis,
MO 63127-1018
Tel.: (314) 984-8484   MO
Web Site: http://www.enclos.com

Year Founded: 1999
Sales Range: $25-49.9 Million
Emp.: 500
Glass Contractor
N.A.I.C.S.: 238150
David Coleman (CFO)
Greg Shage (Owner)

Subsidiaries:

Enclos Corp.   **(1)**
2770 Blue Water Rd, Eagan, MN 55121-
1887
Tel.: (651) 796-6100
Web Site: http://www.enclos.com
Sales Range: $25-49.9 Million
Emp.: 80
Designer & Builder of Outside Curtain Wall
N.A.I.C.S.: 238150
Gregg Sage (Pres)

C.H. JAMES RESTAURANT HOLDINGS, LLC

1020 N Milwaukee Ave Ste 360,
Deerfield, IL 60015
Tel.: (847) 215-0190   DE
Web Site: http://www.chjamesco.com
Year Founded: 1883
Fast Food Restaurant Holding Com-
pany
N.A.I.C.S.: 551112
Robert Klinke (VP-Acctg)
Charles H. James III (Owner, Chm &
CEO)

C.H. MARTIN, INC.

156 Port Richmond Ave, Staten Is-
land, NY 10302-1335
Tel.: (718) 273-2350
Web Site: http://www.chmartin.com
Year Founded: 1964
Sales Range: $25-49.9 Million
Emp.: 150
Variety Stores
N.A.I.C.S.: 455219
Charles Goldman (Pres)

C.H. POWELL COMPANY

75 Shawmut Rd, Canton, MA 02021-
1408
Tel.: (410) 609-2580
Web Site: http://www.chpowell.com
Year Founded: 1919
Sales Range: $25-49.9 Million
Emp.: 175
Customhouse Brokers
N.A.I.C.S.: 488510
Peter H. Powell (CEO)

C.H. SPENCER & COMPANY

1075 S Pioneer Rd, Salt Lake City,
UT 84104
Tel.: (801) 975-0300
Web Site: http://www.chspencer.com
Sales Range: $10-24.9 Million
Emp.: 25
Mfr & Distributor of Power Plant Ma-
chinery
N.A.I.C.S.: 423830
Jim Beck (Owner & Pres)
Ailisa Wheeler (Mgr-Accts Receivable
& Credit)
Mahmod Awadalla (Controller)

C.I. CONSTRUCTION, LLC

1210 Broadway St, Alexandria, MN
56308
Tel.: (320) 763-2998
Web Site:
http://www.ciconstruction.com
Rev.: $12,000,000
Emp.: 10
Commercial & Office Building Con-
tractors
N.A.I.C.S.: 236220
Robert Thompson (Pres & CEO)

C.I. VISIONS INC.

C.I. Visions Inc.—(Continued)

281 Ave C Ste 9A, New York, NY 10009
Tel.: (212) 477-4755
Web Site: https://www.civisions.com
Sales Range: $1-9.9 Million
Emp.: 20
Public Relations & Marketing
N.A.I.C.S.: 541820
Carol A. Ientile (Founder)

C.J. BETTERS CORPORATION
3468 Brodhead Rd Ctr, Monaca, PA 15061
Tel.: (724) 773-0444
Rev.: $21,700,000
Emp.: 200
Mechanical Contractor
N.A.I.C.S.: 238220
Charles J. Betters (Pres)

C.J. ERICKSON PLUMBING CO.
4141 W 124th Pl, Alsip, IL 60803-1809
Tel.: (708) 371-4900
Web Site: https://www.cjerickson.com
Sales Range: $10-24.9 Million
Emp.: 130
Plumbing Services
N.A.I.C.S.: 238220
Matthew Erickson (CEO)

C.J. MILLER LLC
3514 Basler Rd, Hampstead, MD 21074
Tel.: (410) 239-8006
Web Site: https://www.cjmillerllc.com
Year Founded: 1970
Sales Range: $75-99.9 Million
Emp.: 400
Construction Services
N.A.I.C.S.: 237310

C.J. SEGERSTROM & SONS, LLC
3315 Fairview Rd, Costa Mesa, CA 92626
Tel.: (714) 546-0110
Sales Range: $200-249.9 Million
Emp.: 300
Commercial Real Estate Development & Investment
N.A.I.C.S.: 531390
Mark L. Heim (CFO)
Nancy West (Dir-HR)

C.K. SMITH & COMPANY INC.
99 Crescent St, Worcester, MA 01615
Tel.: (508) 753-1475
Web Site: https://www.cksmithsuperior.com
Rev.: $19,900,000
Emp.: 30
Petroleum Bulk Stations
N.A.I.C.S.: 424710
Anthony Santoro (Gen Mgr)

C.L. BARNES FURNITURE CO.
6717 B Spring Mall Rd, Springfield, VA 22150
Tel.: (703) 780-7444
Web Site: http://www.barnesfurniture.com
Year Founded: 1943
Sales Range: $25-49.9 Million
Emp.: 250
Furniture Retailer
N.A.I.C.S.: 449110
Renny Barnes (Owner & CEO)

C.L. FRATES AND COMPANY
5005 N Lincoln Blvd, Oklahoma City, OK 73105
Tel.: (405) 290-5600

Web Site: http://www.clfrates.com
Rev.: $11,300,000
Emp.: 75
Insurance Services
N.A.I.C.S.: 524210
Rodman Frates (Pres & CEO)
Rick Franklin (CEO-Health Svcs)

C.L. PRESSER COMPANY
4224 Market St, Philadelphia, PA 19104
Tel.: (215) 222-1800
Web Site: http://www.clpresser.com
Year Founded: 1900
Rev.: $11,700,000
Emp.: 20
General Construction Machinery & Equipment
N.A.I.C.S.: 423810
Harry Presser (Pres)

C.L. SMITH COMPANY INC.
1311 S 39th St, Saint Louis, MO 63110-2535
Tel.: (314) 771-1202 MO
Web Site: http://www.clsmith.com
Year Founded: 1972
Sales Range: $10-24.9 Million
Emp.: 75
Mfr & Distributor of Containers
N.A.I.C.S.: 423840
Clarence L. Smith (Owner)
Nancy Newby (Pres)

C.L. THOMAS, INC.
9701 US Hwy 59 N, Victoria, TX 77905
Tel.: (361) 582-5100 TX
Web Site: http://www.thomaspetro.com
Year Founded: 1980
Holding Company; Convenience Stores Owner & Operator; Fuels, Lubricants & Chemicals Wholesale Distr
N.A.I.C.S.: 551112
Jeff Johanson (Pres)
Lourdes Fric (Mgr-Risk)
Paul Hermansen (Dir-Tech)

Subsidiaries:

Speedy Stop Food Stores, LLC (1)
9701 US Hwy 59 N, Victoria, TX 77905
Tel.: (361) 573-7662
Web Site: http://www.speedystop.com
Convenience Store Operator
N.A.I.C.S.: 445131

C.M. ALMY & SON, INC.
3 American Ln, Greenwich, CT 06831
Tel.: (203) 552-7600
Web Site: http://www.almy.com
Year Founded: 1892
Rev.: $12,000,000
Emp.: 40
Clergy Vestments & Textiles for Churches
N.A.I.C.S.: 315250
Stephen Fendler (Co-Owner & Pres)
Michael Fendler (Co-Owner & VP)
Michael Mcallen (Controller)

C.M. HOLTZINGER FRUIT CO. INC.
1312 N 6th Ave, Yakima, WA 98902
Tel.: (509) 457-5115 WA
Web Site: http://www.holtzingerfruit.com
Year Founded: 1955
Sales Range: $75-99.9 Million
Emp.: 125
Producer of Fresh Fruits & Vegetables
N.A.I.C.S.: 424480
Scott Hanses (Dir-Sls)

C.N. BROWN COMPANY INC.

1 CN Brown Way, South Paris, ME 04281-1600
Tel.: (207) 743-9212 VT
Web Site: https://www.cnbrown.com
Year Founded: 1970
Rev.: $150,000,000
Emp.: 1,000
Producer of Petroleum Products
N.A.I.C.S.: 424720
Harold D. Jones (CEO & Gen Mgr)
Jinger Duryea (Pres)

C.O. BIGELOW CHEMISTS, INC.
414 6th Ave, New York, NY 10011
Tel.: (212) 533-2700
Web Site: http://www.cobigelowchemists.com
Year Founded: 1838
Sales Range: $1-9.9 Million
Emp.: 40
Essential Oils, Perfume, Soap, Facial Care, Hair Care, Body Care, Remedies, Oral Hygiene, Formularies & Various other Personal Care Products Retailer
N.A.I.C.S.: 456120
Ian Ginsberg (Pres)

C.P. BAKER & COMPANY, LTD
280 Summer St Fl 9, Boston, MA 02210-1131
Tel.: (617) 439-0770
Web Site: http://www.cpbaker.com
Sales Range: $10-24.9 Million
Emp.: 6
Management Consulting & Corporate Finance Services
N.A.I.C.S.: 541611
Christopher P. Baker (Mng Partner)

C.P. RICHARDS CONSTRUCTION CO., INC.
2654 Dekalb Medical Pkwy, Lithonia, GA 30058-4866
Tel.: (678) 244-1450 GA
Web Site: http://www.cprichardsconstruction.com
Year Founded: 1949
Sales Range: $10-24.9 Million
Nonresidential Construction Services
N.A.I.C.S.: 236220
Charles P. Richards Jr. (Pres)

Subsidiaries:

ABCO Builders, Inc. (1)
2821 Lackland Rd, Fort Worth, TX 76117
Tel.: (817) 569-0330
Web Site: http://www.abcobuilders.com
Sales Range: $10-24.9 Million
Emp.: 4
Provider of Contracting Services
N.A.I.C.S.: 236220

C.R. CALDERON CONSTRUCTION, INC.
5104 Branchville Rd, College Park, MD 20740
Tel.: (301) 614-0715
Rev.: $5,000,000
Emp.: 100
Commercial & Institutional Building Construction
N.A.I.C.S.: 236220
Ana P. Calderon (VP)
Juanita Vinas (Mgr)
Carlos Calderon (Pres)

C.R. DANIELS, INC.
3451 Ellicott Center Dr, Ellicott City, MD 21043
Tel.: (410) 461-2100 NY
Web Site: https://www.crdaniels.com
Year Founded: 1918
Sales Range: $200-249.9 Million
Emp.: 450
Truck Baskets & Hampers

N.A.I.C.S.: 314910
Andy Szulinski (VP-Sls & Mktg)
Lee Smith (Gen Mgr-Natl Accounts)
Don Godfrey (VP)
Kevin Abel (Sr VP)

C.R. ENGLAND, INC.
4701 W 2100 S, Salt Lake City, UT 84120
Tel.: (801) 972-2712 UT
Web Site: https://www.crengland.com
Year Founded: 1920
Sales Range: $250-299.9 Million
Emp.: 4,500
Refrigerated Cargo Transport
N.A.I.C.S.: 484230
Corey England (Exec VP-Ops Support)

Subsidiaries:

England Logistics, Inc. (1)
1325 S 4700 W, Salt Lake City, UT 84104-1223 (100%)
Tel.: (801) 972-2712
Web Site: http://www.englandlogistics.com
Sales Range: $100-124.9 Million
Emp.: 500
Integrated Freight Transportation Logistics Services
N.A.I.C.S.: 488510
Joel Ashby (Gen Mgr-Mexico)
Jason Beardall (Pres)
Cold Chain (VP-Sls & Mktg)
Ryan Lavigne (VP-England Carrier Svcs)
Shaun Beardall (VP-Logistics Svcs)
Justin Smith (VP-Fin & Admin Support)
Wendy Barclay (VP-Mktg & PR)

C.R. FEDRICK, INC.
23000 Meadow Ln Ste C, Twain Harte, CA 95383
Tel.: (707) 887-0734 CA
Web Site: http://www.crfedrick.com
Year Founded: 1948
Sales Range: $25-49.9 Million
General Engineering Contractor
N.A.I.C.S.: 237990
Robert J. Fedrick (Pres & CEO)

C.R. JACKSON INC.
100 Independence Blvd, Columbia, SC 29210
Tel.: (803) 750-6070
Web Site: https://www.crjackson.com
Year Founded: 1972
Sales Range: $10-24.9 Million
Emp.: 100
Highway & Street Construction
N.A.I.C.S.: 237110
Charles R. Jackson (Founder & CEO)
Bruce Sproles (VP-Insurance & Personnel)
Clarke Dehart (VP)
Mike Fowke (CFO & Controller)

C.R. LOUGHEAD
755 S Chester Rd, Swarthmore, PA 19081
Tel.: (610) 328-1500
Web Site: http://www.loughead.com
Sales Range: $25-49.9 Million
Emp.: 25
New & Used Automobile Sales
N.A.I.C.S.: 441110
Ted Loughead (Owner)

C.R. MEYER & SONS COMPANY INC.
895 W 20th Ave, Oshkosh, WI 54902
Tel.: (920) 235-3350
Web Site: https://www.crmeyer.com
Year Founded: 1985
Sales Range: $25-49.9 Million
Emp.: 300
Construction of Industrial Buildings & Warehouses
N.A.I.C.S.: 236220

Phillip J. Martini (CEO)
John Longworth (Superintendent)
Markus Manderfield (Project Coord)
Dan Lynch (Pres)

C.S. GENERAL INC.
905 Industrial Way, Sparks, NV
89431-6009
Tel.: (775) 355-8500   NV
Web Site:
   http://www.clarksullivan.com
Year Founded: 1985
Sales Range: $25-49.9 Million
Emp.: 50
Holding Companies
N.A.I.C.S.: 551112
B. J. Sullivan (Chm & CEO)
Jarrett Rosenau (Pres-NV Ops)
Kevin Stroupe (CEO & CFO)
Ted Foor (Pres-CA Ops)

Subsidiaries:

Clark & Sullivan Constructors
Inc.   (1)
905 Industrial Way, Sparks, NV 89431-6009
Tel.: (775) 355-8500
Web Site: http://www.clarksullivan.com
Nonresidential Construction
N.A.I.C.S.: 236220
B. J. Sullivan (Pres)

C.S. MCCROSSAN, INC.
7865 Jefferson Hwy, Maple Grove,
MN 55369-4900
Tel.: (763) 425-4167   MN
Web Site:
   https://www.mccrossan.com
Year Founded: 1953
Sales Range: $25-49.9 Million
Emp.: 325
Provider of Highway & Street Con-
struction Services
N.A.I.C.S.: 237310

Subsidiaries:

Midwest Pipe Coating Inc.   (1)
925 Kennedy Ave, Schererville, IN
46375-1325   (100%)
Tel.: (219) 322-4564
Web Site: http://www.midwestpiperebar.com
Sales Range: $25-49.9 Million
Emp.: 130
Provider of Special Trade Contracting Ser-
vices
N.A.I.C.S.: 238990
Joel Chermak (Gen Mgr)

C.S. WO & SONS LTD.
702 S Beretania St, Honolulu, HI
96813-2581
Tel.: (808) 543-5388
Web Site:
   http://www.cswoandsons.com
Year Founded: 1982
Rev.: $40,000,000
Emp.: 270
Furniture Store Owner & Operator
N.A.I.C.S.: 449110
Robert W. Wo Jr. (Owner, Pres &
CEO)
C. Scott Wo (Founder & Owner)

Subsidiaries:

Advantage Inc.   (1)
702 S Beretania St, Honolulu, HI 96813-
2581
Tel.: (808) 545-5966
Sales Range: $10-24.9 Million
Emp.: 7
Furniture Retailer
N.A.I.C.S.: 449110

HomeWorld   (1)
702 S Beretania St, Honolulu, HI 96813
Tel.: (808) 543-5300
Web Site: http://www.homeworld.com
Furniture Retailer
N.A.I.C.S.: 449110
Mark Kantor (Mgr-Warehouse)

Security Loan Inc.   (1)
702 S Beretania St, Honolulu, HI 96813-
2581
Tel.: (808) 545-5966
Sales Range: $25-49.9 Million
Emp.: 7
Personal Credit Institutions
N.A.I.C.S.: 522310

SlumberWorld   (1)
702 S Beretania St, Honolulu, HI 96813
Tel.: (808) 545-3555
Web Site:
   http://www.slumberworldhawaii.com
Mattress Retailer
N.A.I.C.S.: 449110

Van's Inc.   (1)
702 S Beretania St, Honolulu, HI 96813-
2581
Tel.: (808) 545-5966
Sales Range: $10-24.9 Million
Emp.: 8
Nonresidential Building Operators
N.A.I.C.S.: 531120

C.S.B. BANCSHARES, INC.
155 8th St, Somerville, TX 77879
Tel.: (979) 596-1421
Web Site: http://www.csbtx.com
Bank Holding Company
N.A.I.C.S.: 551111
Aaron K. Fletcher (Pres & CEO)

Subsidiaries:

Citizens State Bank   (1)
155 8th St, Somerville, TX 77879
Tel.: (979) 596-1421
Banking Services
N.A.I.C.S.: 522110
Aaron K. Flencher (Pres & CEO)

C.U. TRANSPORT INC.
19885 Harrison Ave, City of Industry,
CA 91789-2849
Tel.: (909) 895-8388
Web Site: http://www.cutrans.com
Year Founded: 1997
Sales Range: $10-24.9 Million
Emp.: 20
International Transportation, Domestic
Freight, Customs Brokerage, Ware-
housing, Distribution, Packaging, For-
eign Trade & Insurance Brokerage
Services
N.A.I.C.S.: 488390
Larry Li (Pres)

C.V. STARR & CO., INC.
399 Park Ave Ste 1700, New York,
NY 10022
Tel.: (646) 227-6300   DE
Web Site:
   http://www.starrcompanies.com
Year Founded: 1950
Holding Company
N.A.I.C.S.: 551112
Geoffrey G. Clark (Sr Mng Dir-Starr
Investment Holdings)
Leilani M. Brown (CMO)
Howard I. Smith (Vice Chm-Fin)
Danielle Wilson (Head-Mgmt Liability-
London)
Robert McTaggart (Head-Pro
Indemnity-London)
Liz Ilott (Chief Underwriting Officer-
Fin Lines)
Colin Buchanan (Head-Casualty-Intl)
Laura Owen (Head-Accident &
Health)
Dave Fitzgerald (Chief Claims
Officer-Global)
Nehemiah E. Ginsburg (Sr VP &
Deputy Gen Counsel)
Conan Dolce (Reg VP)
Carmella Capitano (Sr VP-Primary &
Excess Energy Casualty)
Andrew Murray (Mgr-Profit Center-
Primary Construction)

Subsidiaries:

Starr Investment Holdings LLC   (1)
399 Park Ave Ste 1700, New York, NY
10022
Tel.: (212) 230-5050
Web Site: http://www.starrcompanies.com
Holding Company
N.A.I.C.S.: 551112
Geoffrey G. Clark (Pres)

C.W. BROWN FOODS, INC.
161 Kings Hwy, Mount Royal, NJ
08061
Tel.: (856) 423-3700
Web Site:
   https://www.bottosausage.com
Year Founded: 1887
Sales Range: $10-24.9 Million
Emp.: 30
Pork Sausage Mfr
N.A.I.C.S.: 311615
Domenic Botto (VP-Mktg)
Robert Botto (Assoc Mgr)

C.W. HAYDEN CO., INC.
556 Kittyhawk Ave, Auburn, ME
04210
Tel.: (207) 783-2054
Web Site:
   https://www.cwhaydenonline.com
Year Founded: 1948
Sales Range: $10-24.9 Million
Emp.: 24
Industrial Supplies Whslr
N.A.I.C.S.: 423840
Jeff Brackett (Gen Mgr)

C.W. MATTHEWS CONTRACT-
ING COMPANY, INC.
1600 Kenview Dr, Marietta, GA
30060-1086
Tel.: (770) 422-7520   GA
Web Site:
   https://www.cwmatthews.com
Year Founded: 1946
Sales Range: $50-74.9 Million
Emp.: 500
Bridge, Tunnel, Elevated Highway &
Roadway Construction
N.A.I.C.S.: 237310
Michael D. Bell (CFO)
Chris Rountree (Coord-Utility)

C.W. SUTER SERVICES
1800 11th St, Sioux City, IA 51101
Tel.: (712) 252-3007
Web Site: https://www.cwsuter.com
Year Founded: 1926
Sales Range: $10-24.9 Million
Emp.: 85
Plumbing, Heating & Air-Conditioning
Contracting Services
N.A.I.C.S.: 238220
John Baker (Pres & CEO)

C.W. WRIGHT CONSTRUC-
TION CO., INC.
11500 Ironbridge Rd, Chester, VA
23831-8220
Tel.: (804) 768-1054   VA
Web Site: http://www.cwwright.com
Year Founded: 1968
Sales Range: $25-49.9 Million
Emp.: 450
Utility Construction Services
N.A.I.C.S.: 237130
Joan Fitzpatrick (Mgr-HR)

C/F DATA SYSTEMS INC.
220 Libbey Pkwy, East Weymouth,
MA 02189
Tel.: (781) 337-9900
Web Site:
   http://www.cfdatasystems.com
Year Founded: 1979
Sales Range: $1-9.9 Million

Emp.: 15
Custom Computer Programming Ser-
vices
N.A.I.C.S.: 541511
Eric Goldstein (Pres)
Dennis Coleman (CEO)

C2 SOLUTIONS GROUP, INC.
1600 Tysons Blvd 8 Fl, McLean, VA
22102
Web Site: http://www.c2sginc.com
Year Founded: 2005
Sales Range: $1-9.9 Million
Emp.: 17
Information Technology Services
N.A.I.C.S.: 519290
Gary E. Shumaker (Pres & CEO)
W. David Murphy (Dir-Svc Delivery)
Teresa Waitzman-Bannister (VP-Corp
Dev)

C2 TECHNOLOGIES, INC.
1921 Gallows Rd Ste 200, Vienna,
VA 22182
Tel.: (703) 448-7900
Web Site: https://www.c2ti.com
Sales Range: $25-49.9 Million
Emp.: 230
Business Consulting Services
N.A.I.C.S.: 561110
Dolly Oberoi (Founder & Chief Learn-
ing Officer)
Curtis Cox (Pres)
Michael Maraghy (CFO)
Manik K. Rath (CEO)
LeNaye Willis-Lloyd (VP-Contracts)

C2C OUTDOOR
353 Lexington Ave Ste 204, New
York, NY 10016
Tel.: (212) 209-1519
Web Site: http://www.c2c-
outdoor.com
Year Founded: 2007
Sales Range: $10-24.9 Million
Emp.: 7
Advertising & Marketing Services
N.A.I.C.S.: 541810
Michael Palatnek (Founder, Pres &
CEO)

C2C SOLUTIONS, INC.
301 W Bay St 6th Fl, Jacksonville, FL
32202-4914
Tel.: (904) 224-7396
Web Site: http://www.c2cinc.com
Sales Range: $10-24.9 Million
Emp.: 450
Third Party Administration of Insur-
ance & Pension Funds
N.A.I.C.S.: 524292
Lisa A. Hanson (Sec)
Jeff Peterson (Pres)

C2DESIGN
8228 Mayfield Rd Ste 6B Rear,
Cleveland, OH 44026
Tel.: (440) 461-1201
Web Site: https://www.c2design.com
Year Founded: 1992
Interior Design Services
N.A.I.C.S.: 541410

C2F, INC.
6600 SW 111th Ave, Beaverton, OR
97008
Tel.: (503) 643-9050
Web Site: http://www.c2f.com
Sales Range: $10-24.9 Million
Emp.: 75
Art Goods & Supplies
N.A.I.C.S.: 424990
Todd Richmond (Mgr-Inside Sls)

C2SNOW

C2Snow—(Continued)

PO Box 2050, Olympic Valley, CA 96146
Tel.: (530) 412-0863
Web Site: http://www.c2snow.com
Year Founded: 2004
Sales Range: Less than $1 Million
Event Promotions
N.A.I.C.S.: 541810
Meg Kiihne (Owner)

C3 BANCORP

850 S Coast Hwy 101, Encinitas, CA 92024
Tel.: (760) 759-1130   CA
Web Site: http://www.c3bank.com
Year Founded: 2015
Bank Holding Company
N.A.I.C.S.: 551111
Michael Archie Persall (Chm, Pres & CEO)
Adam J. Moyer (Pres/CEO-C3bank)

Subsidiaries:

C3bank, National Association   (1)
850 S Coast Hwy 101, Encinitas, CA 92024
Tel.: (760) 759-1130
Web Site: http://www.c3bank.com
Sales Range: $10-24.9 Million
Emp.: 36
Savings Bank
N.A.I.C.S.: 522180
Adam J. Moyer (CEO)

C3 CAPITAL PARTNERS, LP

1511 Baltimore Ave Ste 500, Kansas City, MO 64108
Tel.: (816) 756-2225   MO
Web Site: https://www.c3cap.com
Emp.: 12
Privater Equity Firm
N.A.I.C.S.: 523999
Baron Cass (Partner)
Patrick Curran (Partner)
Patrick Healy (Partner)
Robert Smith (Partner)
Steven Swartzman (Partner)

Subsidiaries:

Laclede Chain Manufacturing Company, LLC   (1)
1549 Fenpark Dr, Fenton, MO 63026
Tel.: (636) 680-2320
Web Site: http://www.lacledechain.com
Emp.: 19
Metal Chain Mfr
N.A.I.C.S.: 332618
Jim Riley (Pres & CEO)
Robert Nupp (Mgr-IT)

Plant (Domestic):

Laclede Chain Manufacturing Co., LLC - Maryville   (2)
2500 E 1st St, Maryville, MO 64468-3122
Tel.: (660) 562-2160
Web Site: http://www.lacledechain.com
Chain Mfr
N.A.I.C.S.: 332618

C3 COMPUTER CORPORATION

3010 LBJ Freeway Ste 1200, Dallas, TX 75234
Tel.: (469) 254-1996
Web Site:
    http://www.c3corporation.com
Year Founded: 1999
Sales Range: $10-24.9 Million
Emp.: 65
Information Technology Services & Consulting
N.A.I.C.S.: 541512
Xavier Mottley (Chm)

C3 CONSULTING LLC

2963 Sidco Dr, Nashville, TN 37204
Tel.: (615) 371-8612   TN
Web Site: http://www.c3-consult.com

Year Founded: 2005
Sales Range: $10-24.9 Million
Emp.: 90
Business Consulting Services
N.A.I.C.S.: 541611
Helen Lane (Exec VP)
Brian Bowman (Exec VP)
Katherin M. McElroy (Exec VP)
Beth R. Chase (CEO)
Mark Cappellino (VP)
Kevin Cowherd (VP)
Vicki Estrin (Partner & VP)
Janet McDonald (Partner & VP)
Meg Underwood (VP)

C3 EVENT MANAGEMENT, INC.

9846 Bailey Rd, Cornelius, NC 28031
Tel.: (704) 519-7494   DE
Year Founded: 2011
Event Planning
N.A.I.C.S.: 561920
Charity Helms (Pres, CEO, Treas & Sec)

C3 INTEGRATED SOLUTIONS INC.

1001 19th St N Ste 1200, Arlington, VA 22209
Tel.: (571) 384-7950
Web Site: http://www.c3isit.com
Year Founded: 2008
Sales Range: $1-9.9 Million
Information Technology Management Services
N.A.I.C.S.: 541512
Jason Ingalls (Chief Cybersecurity Officer)
Bill Wootton (Founder & CEO)

Subsidiaries:

Ingalls Information Security LLC   (1)
5615F Jackson St Ext Ste C, Alexandria, LA 71303-2304
Web Site: http://www.iinfosec.com
Computer Related Services
N.A.I.C.S.: 541519

C3 CUSTOMER CONTACT CHANNELS & HOLDINGS L.P.

1200 S Pine Is Rd Ste 200, Plantation, FL 33324
Tel.: (954) 849-9548
Web Site: http://www.c3connect.com
Year Founded: 2004
Emp.: 1,132
Business Process Outsourcing Services
N.A.I.C.S.: 561499
Richard Ferry (Pres & COO)
Tony Macaione (CFO & Sr VP-Fin)
Kenneth Epstein (Exec VP-Global Sls & Mktg)
Bob Tenzer (Sr VP-HR)
Curt Gooden (CIO & Sr VP)
David Epstein (Chm & Co-CEO)
Mark Gordon (Chm)
Miguel Ramos (Pres-Performance Optimization)
Richard Mondre (Vice Chm & Co-CEO)

C3G, L.P.

3001 Knox St Ste 405, Dallas, TX 75205
Tel.: (214) 828-2284
Holding Company
N.A.I.C.S.: 551112
Christopher Cole (Founder & Pres)

Subsidiaries:

Cole + Co.   (1)
1254 Round Table Dr, Dallas, TX 75247
Tel.: (214) 828-2284
Web Site: http://www.vanitybath.com

Sales Range: $1-9.9 Million
Emp.: 8
Vanities & Bathroom Accessories Mfr
N.A.I.C.S.: 327110

C4 INCORPORATED

6746 E 12th St, Tulsa, OK 74112
Tel.: (918) 835-2323
Web Site:
    http://www.c4industrial.com
Year Founded: 1972
Sales Range: $10-24.9 Million
Emp.: 30
Industrial Tools
N.A.I.C.S.: 423840
Scott Eastwood (Mgr-Svc)
Edward F. Raschen III (Pres)
Ed Raschen IV (VP & Mgr-Sls)

C5 WEALTH MANAGEMENT, LLC

746 Walker Rd Ste 26, Great Falls, VA 22066
Tel.: (703) 759-7007
Web Site:
    http://www.dcmetro.unitedcp.com
Year Founded: 2006
Sales Range: $1-9.9 Million
Emp.: 15
Private Investment Consulting
N.A.I.C.S.: 523940
Paul C. Bennett (Mng Partner)
Mark E. Weber (Mng Partner)
Adam Morgan (Mng Partner)
Stanley B. Corey Jr. (Mng Partner)
James Russell Juncker II (Head-Ops)

CAANES, LLC.

4200 Osuna Rd NE Ste 3-300, Albuquerque, NM 87109
Tel.: (505) 217-9422
Web Site: http://www.caanes.com
Year Founded: 2006
Sales Range: $1-9.9 Million
Emp.: 75
Network Security Management Services
N.A.I.C.S.: 541512
Ryyan Bentley (Dir-HR)

CAB INCORPORATED

5411 Cole Rd, Buford, GA 30518
Tel.: (678) 745-2100   GA
Web Site: https://www.cabinc.com
Year Founded: 1982
Castings, Forgings, Metal Fabrications & Flanges Mfr
N.A.I.C.S.: 332999
Terri Jondahl (CEO)
Mike Vanderbosch (Pres)
Carey Herron (CFO)

Subsidiaries:

CAB Incorporated - Texas Mfg. & Distr. Facility   (1)
2306 S Rayburn Dr, Nacogdoches, TX 75961
Tel.: (936) 569-9430
Web Site: http://www.cabinc.com
Castings, Forgings, Metal Fabrications & Flanges Mfr, Whslr & Distr
N.A.I.C.S.: 332999
Brian Payne (VP-Supply Chain & Quality Assurance-Asia & Ops Mgr-Texas)
Allen Owens (Plant Mgr)

CABANA HOLDINGS LLC

220 S School Ave, Fayetteville, AR 72701
Tel.: (479) 442-6464
Web Site:
    https://thecabanagroup.com
Holding Company; Investment Advisory Services
N.A.I.C.S.: 551112
G. Chadd Mason (CEO)
Daniel Snover (Dir-Institutional Sls)

CABELA'S CREDIT CARD MASTER NOTE TRUST

4800 NW 1st St, Lincoln, NE 68521
Tel.: (402) 323-5958   DE
Credit Financial Support Services
N.A.I.C.S.: 522210
Thomas A. Feil (Pres)

CABELA'S MASTER CREDIT CARD TRUST

4800 NW 1st St, Lincoln, NE 68521
Tel.: (402) 323-5958   NY
Credit Financial Support Services
N.A.I.C.S.: 522210
Thomas A. Feil (Pres)

CABELL HUNTINGTON HOSPITAL, INC.

1340 Hal Greer Blvd, Huntington, WV 25701
Tel.: (304) 526-2000   WV
Web Site:
    https://www.cabellhuntington.org
Year Founded: 1956
General Hospital Operator
N.A.I.C.S.: 622110
Kevin Fowler (Pres & CEO)
Monte Ward (CFO, Chief Acq Officer & Sr VP)
Dennis Lee (CIO & VP)
Hoyt Burdick (Chief Medical Officer & Sr VP)
Joy Pelfrey (Chief Nursing Officer & VP)
Paul English Smith (Gen Counsel & VP)
Bradley Burck (VP-Foundation)
Tim Martin (VP-Hospital Ops & ECCC)
Lisa Chamberlin Stump (VP-Strategic Mktg, Plng & Bus Dev)

Subsidiaries:

Pleasant Valley Hospital, Inc.   (1)
2520 Vly Dr, Point Pleasant, WV 25550
Tel.: (304) 675-4340
Web Site: http://www.pvalley.org
Hospital Operator
N.A.I.C.S.: 622110
Jeff Noblin (CEO)
Jim Lockhart (Chm)
Emily Gaskins (Dir-HR)

St. Mary's Medical Center, Inc.   (1)
2900 1st Ave, Huntington, WV 25702
Tel.: (304) 526-1234
Web Site: http://www.st-marys.org
Emp.: 2,600
Hospital Operator
N.A.I.C.S.: 622110
Angie Swearingen (CFO & VP-Fin)
Libby Bosley (Chief Nursing Officer & VP-Patient Svcs)
Diane Bushee (VP-Mission Integration)
Lee Taylor (VP-Medical Affairs)
Susan Beth Robinson (VP-HR & Corp Compliance)
David Sheils (Pres-Foundation)
Tim Parnell (VP-Support Svcs, Plng & Dev)
Vera Rose (VP-Oncology Svcs)
Joey Trader (VP-Schools of Nursing & Health Pros)
Doug Korstanje (VP-Mktg & Community Rels)

CABI DEVELOPERS, LLC

19950 W Country Club Dr, Miami, FL 33180
Tel.: (305) 466-1810
Year Founded: 2001
Sales Range: $1-9.9 Million
Emp.: 10
Land Subdivision
N.A.I.C.S.: 237210
Elias Cababie (Principal)

CABINET DISCOUNTERS INC.

9500 Berger Rd, Columbia, MD 21046

Tel.: (301) 621-8062
Web Site:
https://www.cabinetdiscounters.com
Rev.: $13,675,000
Emp.: 22
Cabinets, Kitchen
N.A.I.C.S.: 444180
John Mikk (Pres, CFO & COQ)
Elaine Mikk (VP)
Lois Elliott (Mgr)

CABINETWERKS DESIGN STUDIO, LLC.
1799 Willow Rd, Northfield, IL 60093
Tel.: (847) 572-5200
Sales Range: $50-74.9 Million
Emp.: 130
Housing Construction Services
N.A.I.C.S.: 236117
Dave Heigl (VP)
Orren Pickell (Principal)

CABINS FOR YOU, LLC
349 E Pkwy, Gatlinburg, TN 37738
Tel.: (865) 436-2109
Web Site:
http://www.cabinsforyou.com
Year Founded: 2001
Cabin Rental Business
N.A.I.C.S.: 532284
Greg Plimpton (Founder, Owner & CEO)

Subsidiaries:

Chalet Village Properties, Inc.   (1)
1441 Wiley Oakley Dr, Gatlinburg, TN 37738
Tel.: (865) 436-6800
Web Site: http://www.chaletvillage.com
Sales Range: $1-9.9 Million
Emp.: 20
Real Estate Brokerage Services
N.A.I.C.S.: 531210
Kevin White (Gen Mgr)
Nancy Winter (Owner)

CABLE CAR CAPITAL LLC
1449 Washington St. Apt 6, San Francisco, CA 94109
Tel.: (415) 857-1965
Web Site:
http://www.cablecarcapital.com
Investment Management
N.A.I.C.S.: 523999

CABLE ENTERPRISES INC.
PO Box 80, Saltsburg, PA 15681
Tel.: (724) 639-9043
Web Site:
http://www.cticoordinators.com
Rev.: $10,000,000
Emp.: 5
Local Trucking without Storage
N.A.I.C.S.: 484110
Jeffrey Cable (Pres)

Subsidiaries:

C E Ready Mix   (1)
185 N Washington Rd, Apollo, PA 15613
Tel.: (724) 727-7285
Natural Gas Production
N.A.I.C.S.: 211130

CABLE MANUFACTURING, INC.
16462 Gothard St Ste A, Huntington Beach, CA 92647
Tel.: (714) 848-5796
Web Site:
http://www.cablemanufacturing.com
Year Founded: 1998
Rev.: $3,700,000
Emp.: 12
Misc Fabricated Wire Products Mfr
N.A.I.C.S.: 332618

CABLE PLUS INC.

2012 Corporate Ln Ste 116, Naperville, IL 60563
Tel.: (630) 357-9770
Web Site:
https://www.cableplusinc.com
Sales Range: $10-24.9 Million
Emp.: 20
Communications Equipment
N.A.I.C.S.: 423690
Bob Swanson (VP & Gen Mgr)
Jerry Hiss (Controller)
Steven McDonald (Mgr-Sls)

CABLE TELEVISION LABORATORIES, INC.
858 Coal Creek Cir, Louisville, CO 80027
Tel.: (303) 661-9100
Web Site: http://www.cablelabs.com
Sales Range: $25-49.9 Million
Emp.: 180
Research Services, Except Laboratory
N.A.I.C.S.: 541910
Christopher J. Lammers (COO)
Ralph W. Brown (CTO)

CABLEAMERICA CORPORATION
11422 Schenk Dr, Maryland Heights, MO 63043
Tel.: (314) 995-4800
Web Site:
https://www.cableamerica.com
Year Founded: 1971
Rev.: $19,918,312
Emp.: 6
Subscription Television Services
N.A.I.C.S.: 516210
Alan C. Jackson (VP-Engrg)
Eric W. Jackson (VP-Internet Ops)
Christopher A. Dyrek (Pres & CEO)

CABLEORGANIZER.COM, INC.
6250 NW 27th Way, Fort Lauderdale, FL 33309
Tel.: (954) 861-2000
Web Site:
http://www.cableorganizer.com
Year Founded: 2002
Sales Range: $10-24.9 Million
Emp.: 45
Electronic Cable & Cable Organization Equipment Mfr & Distr
N.A.I.C.S.: 423690
Valerie Holstein (Co-Founder)
Paul D. Holstein (Co-Founder & COO)

CABLEREADY CORPORATION
98 E Ave, Norwalk, CT 06851
Tel.: (203) 855-7979
Web Site: http://www.cableready.net
Year Founded: 1992
Rev.: $11,600,000
Emp.: 11
Television Program Distr
N.A.I.C.S.: 423620
Gary Lico (Pres & CEO)
John Casey (VP-Fin)
Reess Kennedy (Dir-Digital Media)
Eric Benitez (VP-Ops)
Peter Delong (VP-Sls & Mktg)
Maurizio Tavares (VP & Mgr-Global Sls)

CABLES PLUS LLC
8504 Glazebrook Ave, Richmond, VA 23228
Tel.: (804) 716-9007
Web Site:
http://www.cablesplususa.com
Year Founded: 2002
Sales Range: $10-24.9 Million
Emp.: 12
Computer & Internet Cables Whslr

N.A.I.C.S.: 423610
Jack Polly (Mgr-Sls-South West)
Ann Scheller (Mgr-Sls-North East)
David Mullsteff (Owner & Pres)

CABLESANDKITS.COM
4555 Atwater Ct Ste A, Buford, GA 30518
Tel.: (678) 597-5000
Web Site:
https://www.cablesandkits.com
Year Founded: 2001
Sales Range: $10-24.9 Million
Emp.: 30
General Networking Accessories Sales
N.A.I.C.S.: 423430
Craig Haynie (CEO)
Christin Haynie (Owner)
Susan Moore (Mgr-Acctg)
Martin Dyhr (Mgr-Sls)
Gary Epp (Pres)
Jonathan Stover (Mgr-PR)

CABLEWHOLESALE.COM
1200 Voyager St, Livermore, CA 94551
Tel.: (925) 455-0800   CA
Web Site:
https://www.cablewholesale.com
Year Founded: 1996
Sales Range: $10-24.9 Million
Emp.: 27
Mfr & Marketer of Home & Business USB Cables & Specialized Products
N.A.I.C.S.: 335921
Sharon Jiang (Founder, Pres & CEO)
Michael Capone (COO)
Joe Davis (Dir-Ops)
Jaimee Trulin (Sls Mgr)

Subsidiaries:

Core Cable Corporation   (1)
Room 2221 No 2668 North Zhongshan Rd, Shanghai, 200063, Putuo District, China
Tel.: (86) 21 512 93877
Web Site: http://www.cablewholesale.com
Fiber Optics, USB Cables, Mobile Accessories Sales
N.A.I.C.S.: 335921
Sharon Jiang (CEO)

CABOT COACH BUILDER INC.
99 Newark St, Haverhill, MA 01832-1348
Tel.: (978) 374-4530   MA
Web Site:
https://www.royalelimo.com
Year Founded: 1986
Sales Range: $10-24.9 Million
Emp.: 50
Mfr of Motor Vehicles & Car Bodies
N.A.I.C.S.: 336110
Richard Portors (VP)
Jeff DeMarco (Dir-Ops)
Steve Edelmann (Dir-Sls)

CABOT LODGE SECURITIES, LLC
44 Wall St Ste 401, New York, NY 10005
Tel.: (212) 388-6200
Web Site: http://www.clsecurities.com
Sales Range: $1-9.9 Million
Investment Banking & Securities Dealing
N.A.I.C.S.: 523150
Craig Gould (Pres & CEO)

CABOT PROPERTIES, INC.
1 Beacon St Ste 1700, Boston, MA 02108
Tel.: (617) 723-7400   FL
Web Site: https://www.cabotprop.com
Year Founded: 1986
Sales Range: $1-9.9 Million
Emp.: 30

Real Estate Investment Services
N.A.I.C.S.: 523999
Robert E. Patterson (Principal)
Franz F. Colloredo-Mansfeld (Co-Founder & CEO)
Andrew D. Ebbott (Chief Investment Officer & Exec VP-Investments)
Mark A. Bechard (CFO & Exec VP-Fin)
Charles L. Forbes (Sr VP & Dir-Core Investments)
Patrick V. Ryan (Sr VP-Investments)
Stephen P. Vallarelli (Sr VP-Asset Mgmt)
Kathleen M. Reardon (Sr VP-IR)
Kelly J. Stevens (Sr VP-Asset Mgmt)
Bradford M. Otis (Sr VP-Asset Mgmt)
Justin S. Harvey (Sr VP-Investments)
Howard B. Hodgson Jr. (Vice Chm & Chief Compliance Officer)

CABRAL WESTERN MOTORS, INC.
1145 W Yosemite Ave, Manteca, CA 95337
Tel.: (209) 823-1148
Web Site:
http://www.cabralchryslerjeep.com
Year Founded: 1957
Sales Range: $10-24.9 Million
Emp.: 49
Car Whslr
N.A.I.C.S.: 441110
Don Cabral (VP)

CABS NURSING HOME COMPANY INC.
270 Nostrand Ave, Brooklyn, NY 11205
Tel.: (718) 638-0500   NY
Year Founded: 1972
Sales Range: $10-24.9 Million
Emp.: 128
Nursing Care Services
N.A.I.C.S.: 623110
Afeena Ali (Asst Dir-Nursing Svc)
Basil Alfor Douglas (Dir-Nursing Svc)
Harry W. Alford (Controller)
David Wieder (Exec VP)

CAC INDUSTRIES INC.
5408 Vernon Blvd, Long Island City, NY 11101
Tel.: (718) 729-3600
Web Site: https://www.cacindinc.com
Rev.: $17,141,225
Emp.: 150
Sewer Line Construction
N.A.I.C.S.: 237110
Michael A. Capasso (Pres)
John M. Labozza (COO & VP)
Jim McMurray (VP)
Richard E. Gavin (CFO)

CACHE CREEK FOODS, LLC.
411 N Pioneer Ave, Woodland, CA 95776
Tel.: (530) 662-1764
Web Site:
http://www.cachecreekfoods.com
Year Founded: 1993
Sales Range: $10-24.9 Million
Emp.: 19
Food Ingredient Mfr
N.A.I.C.S.: 311351
Matthew Morehart (Pres & CEO)
Pao Yang (Supvr-Quality Assurance)
Connie Stephens (Office Mgr-Accts Receivable)
Christie Myers (Mgr-Mktg)
William A. Shade (Founder)
Ana Contreras (Mgr-Production)
Sally Morehart (Co-Owner)

CACHE CREEK INDUSTRIES, LLC

Cache Creek Industries, LLC—(Continued)

10100 Santa Monica Blvd Ste 300,
Los Angeles, CA 90067
Tel.: (310) 772-2240
Web Site:
  http://www.cachecreekllc.com
Year Founded: 2015
Privater Equity Firm
N.A.I.C.S.: 523999
Jake Blumenthal *(Partner)*
Dean Douglas *(Partner)*

Subsidiaries:

Brandywine Communications,
Inc.   **(1)**
1153 Warner Ave, Tustin, CA 92780
Tel.: (714) 755-1050
Web Site: http://www.brandywinecomm.com
Engeeering Services
N.A.I.C.S.: 541330
Alyona Diachenko *(VP-Sls & Mktg)*
Jay Krutsinger *(Dir-Sls-Western Reg)*
Neil Pitman *(Dir-Sls-Asia)*
David Wright *(Dir-Sls-Europe, Middle East, Africa & Australia)*

CACHE RIVER VALLEY SEED, LLC

Hwy 226 E, Cash, AR 72421
Tel.: (870) 477-5427
Web Site: https://www.crvseed.com
Rev.: $10,799,499
Emp.: 15
Seeds: Field, Garden & Flower
N.A.I.C.S.: 424910
Randy Woodard *(CFO)*

CACHE VALLEY BANKING COMPANY

101 N Main St, Logan, UT 84321
Tel.: (435) 753-3020   **UT**
Web Site:
  https://www.cachevalleybank.com
Year Founded: 1995
Sales Range: $50-74.9 Million
Bank Holding Company
N.A.I.C.S.: 551111
J. Gregg Miller *(Pres & CEO)*
Scott Colton *(Pres-Bank)*

Subsidiaries:

Cache Valley Bank   **(1)**
101 N Main St, Logan, UT 84321
Tel.: (435) 753-3020
Web Site: http://www.cachevalleybank.com
Sales Range: $50-74.9 Million
Emp.: 220
Commericial Banking
N.A.I.C.S.: 522110
Paul Erickson *(Chief Credit Officer)*
Scott Colton *(Pres)*
J. Gregg Miller *(CEO)*

CACHE VALLEY ELECTRIC COMPANY INC.

875 N 1000 W, Logan, UT 84321-
7800
Tel.: (435) 752-6405   **UT**
Web Site: https://www.cve.com
Year Founded: 1915
Sales Range: $100-124.9 Million
Emp.: 800
Electrical Work Services
N.A.I.C.S.: 238210
James D. Laub *(Pres & CEO)*
Nathan Wickizer *(COO)*

Subsidiaries:

Cache Valley Electric Company
Inc.   **(1)**
6200 SW Arctic Dr, Beaverton, OR
97005   **(100%)**
Tel.: (503) 431-6600
Web Site: http://www.cvelectric.com
Sales Range: $25-49.9 Million
Emp.: 40
Communications & Electrical
N.A.I.C.S.: 238210

Cache Valley Electric Company Inc. -
Avtec Systems Integrator
Division   **(1)**
2345 S John Henry Dr, Salt Lake City, UT
84119
Tel.: (801) 530-1330
Electrical Contracting Services
N.A.I.C.S.: 238210

CACHET INDUSTRIES INC.

1400 Broadway Lbby 4, New York,
NY 10018
Tel.: (212) 944-2188
Sales Range: $10-24.9 Million
Emp.: 10
Retailer of Women's & Children's
Clothing
N.A.I.C.S.: 315250
David Darouvar *(Pres)*

CACIQUE, INC.

800 Royal Oaks Dr Ste 200, Monro-
via, CA 91017
Tel.: (626) 961-3399   **CA**
Web Site:
  https://www.caciquefoods.com
Year Founded: 1973
Fresh & Processed Natural Cheese
Mfr
N.A.I.C.S.: 311513
Tirso Iglesias *(Sr VP-Sls & Mktg)*

Subsidiaries:

El Sol Foods LLC   **(1)**
566 E Germann Rd Ste 109, Gilbert, AZ
85297
Tel.: (480) 857-2212
Web Site: http://www.elsolfoods.com
Homemade-style Salsas Mfr & Distr
N.A.I.C.S.: 424410
Ryan S. Bullock *(Pres)*

CACTUS

2128 15th St Ste 100, Denver, CO
80202
Tel.: (303) 455-7545
Year Founded: 1990
Rev.: $8,000,000
Emp.: 45
Fiscal Year-end: 12/31/06
Advertising, Digital/Interactive,
Graphic Design, Media Relations,
Public Relations
N.A.I.C.S.: 541810
Joseph Conrad *(Founder & CEO)*
Norm Shearer *(Partner & Dir-
Creative)*
Lauren Hudson *(Acct Exec)*
Lee Perlman *(Copywriter)*
Allie Edwards *(Dir-Art)*
Tara Childers *(Acct Exec)*
Charity Czerwinski *(Acct Coord-
STEPP)*
Chris Stirling *(Acct Supvr)*
Samantha Searles *(Acct Exec)*
Elliot Nordstrom *(Copywriter)*
Vanessa Louis *(Acct Exec)*
Ryan Moats *(Acct Exec)*
Matt Chiabotti *(Sr Dir-Art)*
Ryan Johnson *(Assoc Dir-Creative)*
Rhonda Brown *(Office Mgr)*
Gennifer Hobbs *(Acct Dir)*
Shea Tullos *(Copywriter)*
Claire Gipson *(Dir-Art)*
Jeff Strahl *(Dir-Creative)*
Andrew Baker *(Dir-Creative Tech)*

CACTUS COMMUNICATIONS, INC.

214 Carnegie Ctr Ste 102, Princeton,
NJ 08540
Tel.: (267) 332-0051
Web Site:
  https://www.cactuslifesciences.com
Year Founded: 2010
Scientific & Medical Communications
Services

N.A.I.C.S.: 541690
Oliver Dennis *(Chm)*
Elvira Dsouza *(Pres)*

Subsidiaries:

NSPM AG   **(1)**
Luzernerstrasse 36, 6045, Meggen, Swit-
zerland
Tel.: (41) 413775333
Web Site: http://www.nspm.com
Medical Communications Services
N.A.I.C.S.: 541618

CACTUS FEEDERS, INC.

2209 W 7th Ave, Amarillo, TX 79106-
6769
Tel.: (806) 373-2333   **NV**
Web Site:
  http://www.cactusfeeders.com
Year Founded: 1975
Sales Range: $650-699.9 Million
Emp.: 500
Agricultural Services
N.A.I.C.S.: 112112
Michael Engler *(Pres & CEO)*
Jack Rhoades *(Sr VP & Gen Mgr-
Feedyard Div)*
Ronny Hargis *(VP & Controller)*
Kevin Hazelwood *(VP & Dir-
Employee Dev)*
Spencer Swingle *(VP & Dir-Nutrition
& Res)*

CADD EDGE INC.

241 Boston Post Rd W 2nd Fl, Marl-
borough, MA 01752
Tel.: (508) 630-8000
Web Site: http://www.caddedge.com
Sales Range: $1-9.9 Million
Emp.: 49
Software Publisher
N.A.I.C.S.: 513210
Tim Preston *(Founder & CEO)*

CADDELL CONSTRUCTION CO., INC.

2700 Lagoon Park Dr PO Box
210099, Montgomery, AL 36109-1110
Tel.: (334) 272-7723   **AL**
Web Site: http://www.caddell.com
Year Founded: 1983
Sales Range: $250-299.9 Million
Emp.: 300
Nonresidential Construction
N.A.I.C.S.: 236220

CADDO ELECTRIC COOPERA-TIVE

3 MI W On Hwy 152, Binger, OK
73009
Tel.: (405) 656-2322
Web Site:
  http://www.caddoelectric.com
Year Founded: 1958
Sales Range: $10-24.9 Million
Emp.: 60
Electric Power Distr
N.A.I.C.S.: 221122
Bob Thomasson *(Gen Mgr)*
Oscar Codopony *(Dir-Ops)*

CADDOCK ELECTRONICS, INC.

1717 Chicago Ave, Riverside, CA
92507-2364
Tel.: (951) 788-1700   **CA**
Web Site: http://www.caddock.com
Year Founded: 1962
Sales Range: $10-24.9 Million
Emp.: 234
Precision Resistors & Resistor Net-
works Mfr
N.A.I.C.S.: 334416
Gary R. Whitehead *(VP-Ops)*
Perry Schaefer *(Supvr-Production)*

Subsidiaries:

Applied Sciences Division   **(1)**
17271 N Umpqua Hwy, Roseburg, OR
97470-9422   **(100%)**
Tel.: (541) 496-0700
Product Development
N.A.I.C.S.: 332216

Caddock Network Division   **(1)**
1717 Chicago Ave, Riverside, CA
92507-2208   **(100%)**
Tel.: (951) 788-1700
Sales Range: $10-24.9 Million
Emp.: 70
Resistive Devices Mfr
N.A.I.C.S.: 334416

Roseburg Manufacturing Division **(1)**
17271 N Umpqua Hwy, Roseburg, OR
97470-9422   **(100%)**
Tel.: (541) 496-0700
Web Site: http://www.caddock.com
Sales Range: $10-24.9 Million
Emp.: 100
Mfr & Distr of High Performance Electrical
Resistors
N.A.I.C.S.: 332216
Gary Whitehead *(VP-Ops)*

CADDY CORPORATION OF AMERICA

509 Sharptown Rd, Bridgeport, NJ
08014-0345
Tel.: (856) 467-4222
Web Site:
  https://www.caddycorp.com
Sales Range: $50-74.9 Million
Emp.: 50
Mfr of Food Service Equipment
N.A.I.C.S.: 333241
Craig A. Cohen *(CEO)*
Michael Bodine *(Mgr-Sls)*
Gary Markowski *(Reg Mgr-Sls)*
Harry Schmidt *(Pres)*
A. Scuderi *(VP-Corp Svcs)*
Janet Calligy *(Controller)*
Michael Shapiro *(Mgr-Credit)*
Brad Wallace *(Mgr-Sls-West Coast
Reg)*
Alan Hutchinson *(Mgr-Svc-Columbus)*
Phil Bailis *(VP-Sls)*

CADE, LTD.

4100 Midway Rd Ste 2115, Carroll-
ton, TX 75007
Tel.: (469) 368-6400
Web Site: http://www.burtcollect.com
Year Founded: 1979
Sales Range: $75-99.9 Million
Emp.: 40
Accounts Receivable & Other Back
Office Services
N.A.I.C.S.: 541219
Ken Bone *(Pres)*

CADECI INTERNATIONAL CORPORATION

3101 Fairlane Farms Rd Ste 5, Wel-
lington, FL 33414
Tel.: (561) 792-0026
Web Site: http://www.cadeci.com
Year Founded: 1995
Sales Range: $1-9.9 Million
Emp.: 9
Construction Equipment Whslr
N.A.I.C.S.: 423810
Mauricio Alvarez *(CEO)*

CADENA CONTRACTING, INC.

1108 W 35th St, North Little Rock,
AR 72118-4806
Tel.: (501) 771-1643   **AR**
Year Founded: 2000
Sales Range: $10-24.9 Million
Emp.: 15
Painting, Plastering, Drywall, Roofing
& Insulation Contractor
N.A.I.C.S.: 238310

Debbie Garzona *(Office Mgr)*
Jim Cross *(Project Mgr)*

CADENCE MCSHANE CORPO-RATION
5057 Keller Springs Rd, Addison, TX 75001
Tel.: (972) 239-2336
Web Site:
http://www.cadencemcshane.com
Sales Range: $10-24.9 Million
Emp.: 80
Commercial & Office Building, New Construction
N.A.I.C.S.: 236220
James A. McShane *(CEO)*
Colby Rose *(VP)*
Steven Levy *(VP-Education)*
Stephanie Fox *(VP-Fin)*
Jody Lee *(VP-Mktg)*

CADENCE RESEARCH & CON-SULTING
501-I S Reino Rd, Thousand Oaks, CA 91320
Tel.: (805) 499-8603
Web Site:
http://www.cadenceresearch.com
Year Founded: 2008
Sales Range: $1-9.9 Million
Emp.: 13
Healthcare Research & Consulting Services
N.A.I.C.S.: 541715
Sugata Biswas *(Founder & Mng Principal)*
Susanne Blassingille *(Principal)*
Sherry Danese *(Principal-Market Res)*
Daryl Twitchell *(Principal)*
Zachary Moore *(Dir-Medical Content)*
Katie Fordyce *(Sr Dir-Qualitative Res)*
Kevin Tolman *(Sr Dir-Quantitative Res)*
Allison Robbins *(Sr Dir-Strategy Consulting Practice)*

CADENT ENERGY PARTNERS, LLC
4 High Ridge Park Ste 303, Stamford, CT 06905
Tel.: (203) 638-5000
Web Site:
http://www.cadentenergy.com
Privater Equity Firm
N.A.I.C.S.: 523999
Paul G. McDermott *(Mng Partner)*
Bruce M. Rothstein *(Co-Founder & Mng Partner)*
Darin R. Booth *(Partner)*
Jennifer S. Cochran *(Chief Compliance Officer & Principal-Fin & Admin)*
Joseph R. Dee IV *(Partner)*

Subsidiaries:

Energy Services Holdings, LLC **(1)**
170 New Camilla Blvd Ste 200, Covington, LA 70433
Tel.: (985) 590-5165
Web site:
http://www.energyservicesholdings.com
Emp.: 2,000
Holding Company; Electrical & Instrumentation Services
N.A.I.C.S.: 551112
Bryan Landry *(CEO)*

Subsidiary (Domestic):

Contracting Enterprises, LLC **(2)**
2003 Russell Ave SW, Roanoke, VA 24036
Tel.: (540) 342-3175
Web Site: http://www.ceicompany.com
Rev.: $3,304,000
Emp.: 14
Electric & Telecommunications Maintenance & Construction Services
N.A.I.C.S.: 238210

Jim F Webb, Inc. **(2)**
700 S Fairgrounds Rd, Midland, TX 79701
Tel.: (432) 684-4388
Emp.: 100
Construction Services
N.A.I.C.S.: 237990
Benton Posey *(Pres)*

Richardson-Wayland Electric Company LLC **(2)**
Memorial Bridge 13th St, Roanoke, VA 24015
Tel.: (540) 344-3244
Web Site: http://www.rwec.com
Sales Range: $10-24.9 Million
Emp.: 150
Water, Sewer & Utility Lines
N.A.I.C.S.: 237110
Brian Zeppenfeld *(Pres)*

Pipeline Supply & Service Holdings, LLC **(1)**
6969 Ardmore, Houston, TX 77054
Tel.: (713) 747-0090
Web Site: http://www.pipelinesupply.com
Emp.: 75
Distr of Industrial Products & Rental Equipment to Oil & Gas Pipeline Construction Industry
N.A.I.C.S.: 532490
Chuck Dalio *(CEO)*

Subsidiary (Domestic):

North State Supply Co., Inc. **(2)**
200 Lucerne Rd, Homer City, PA 15748
Tel.: (724) 479-3511
Web Site: http://www.tsscompanies.com
Sales Range: $1-9.9 Million
Emp.: 25
Industrial Supplies Distr
N.A.I.C.S.: 423840
Scott Bandi *(Gen Mgr)*

CADIE PRODUCTS CORP.
151 E 11th St, Paterson, NJ 07524-1228
Tel.: (973) 278-8300
Web Site: https://www.cadie.com
Year Founded: 1939
Sales Range: $50-74.9 Million
Emp.: 50
Chemically Treated Specialty Polishing Cloths Mfr
N.A.I.C.S.: 325612
E.W. Meyers *(Pres)*
Kenneth D. Meyers *(Exec VP)*
Robert Appelbaum *(Treas, Sec & VP)*

CADILLAC COFFEE COMPANY
1801 Michael St, Madison Heights, MI 48071
Tel.: (248) 545-2266
Web Site:
http://www.cadillaccoffee.com
Sales Range: $10-24.9 Million
Emp.: 105
Coffee Sales
N.A.I.C.S.: 311920
Guy Gehlert *(Pres)*
John R. Gehlert *(Chm)*

CADILLAC PRODUCTS, INC.
5800 Crooks Rd Ste 200, Troy, MI 48098-2830
Tel.: (248) 879-5000   DE
Web Site:
http://www.cadillacpackaging.com
Year Founded: 1942
Sales Range: $50-74.9 Million
Emp.: 35
Mfr of Flexible Plastic Packaging, Automotive Trim, Thermal-Formed Products & Plastic Pallets
N.A.I.C.S.: 336390
Roger K. Williams *(Chief Admin Officer & Treas)*
David DeMocker *(Mgr-Mktg)*
Jim Eckl *(Mgr-Mktg)*
Robert J. Williams Jr. *(CEO)*
Michael P. Williams II *(CTO)*

Subsidiaries:

Cadillac Products Packaging Company - Dallas Plant **(1)**
271 Cadillac Pkwy, Dallas, GA 30157
Tel.: (770) 445-0015
Web Site: http://www.cadprod.com
Product Packaging Services
N.A.I.C.S.: 561910

Cadillac Products Packaging Company - Paris Plant **(1)**
2005 S Main St, Paris, IL 61944-2950
Tel.: (217) 463-1444
Product Packaging Services
N.A.I.C.S.: 561910
Mike Switzer *(Plant Mgr)*

CADILLAC UNIFORM & LINEN SUPPLY
221 Laurel Ave, Bayamon, PR 00959
Tel.: (787) 785-5757
Web Site:
http://www.cadillacuniforms.com
Rev.: $16,707,969
Emp.: 250
Industrial Launderers
N.A.I.C.S.: 812332
William Shulevitz *(Chm)*
Michael Shulevitz *(Pres)*

CADOGAN MANAGEMENT, LLC
149 5th Ave 15th Fl, New York, NY 10010
Tel.: (212) 585-1600   DE
Year Founded: 1994
Sales Range: $75-99.9 Million
Emp.: 50
Investment Management & Banking Services
N.A.I.C.S.: 523940
Lawrence M. Becerra *(Mng Dir)*
Jack Estes *(Head-Bus Dev-US)*
Paul Isaac *(Chief Investment Officer)*
Stuart N. Leaf *(Chm)*
Michael Waldron *(Chief Risk Officer)*
Jerry Bizzarro *(VP & Product Controller)*
Christina O'Kelly *(Mgr-IT)*
Joel Gantcher *(Dir-Research)*
Laura C. Grove *(VP & Mgr-Research)*
John Trammell *(CEO)*
Iris C. Gibbons-Avanzino *(VP & Product Controller)*
Heather Gibson *(VP-HR)*
Clinton B. Grady *(Dir-Quantitative Research)*
Peter Hommeyer *(Mng Dir-Research)*
Chi Hae Park *(VP-Client Svc)*
Lisa K. Preudhomme *(VP-Bus Dev-US)*
Melissa Santaniello *(Dir-Alternative Investment Strategies)*
Samir Shah *(Sr VP-Operational Risk)*
Samuel Sussman *(Mng Dir-Research)*
Sander van Stijn *(Mng Dir-Research)*
Hirsh Aronowitz *(COO)*
Shadab Shaikh *(VP & Assoc Counsel)*

CADON PLATING COMPANY
3715 11th St, Wyandotte, MI 48192-6435
Tel.: (734) 282-8100   MI
Web Site:
https://www.cadonplating.com
Year Founded: 1947
Provider Resistant Coatings
N.A.I.C.S.: 332813
Alan Ensign *(VP & Gen Mgr)*

CADWALADER, WICKERSHAM & TAFT LLP
One World Financial Ctr, New York, NY 10281

Tel.: (212) 504-6000   NY
Web Site:
http://www.cadwalader.com
Year Founded: 1792
Sales Range: $450-499.9 Million
Emp.: 1,001
Legal Advisory Services
N.A.I.C.S.: 541110
Dorothy R. Auth *(Partner-New York)*
Ingrid M. Bagby *(Partner-New York)*
James Frazier *(Partner)*
Michael S. Gambro *(Co-Chm-Capital Markets Grp)*
Stuart N. Goldstein *(Co-Chm-Capital Markets Grp)*
Jason M. Halper *(Chm-Global Litigation Grp)*
Patrick Quinn *(Mng Partner)*
Anne M. Tompkin *(Partner)*
Mark R. Haskell *(Partner-Washington)*
Andrew Alin *(Partner)*
Dorothy D. Mehta *(Partner-New York)*
Joseph V. Moreno *(Partner-Washington)*
Bonnie A. Neuman *(Partner-New York)*
Amy W. Ray *(Partner-Washington)*
Jodi L. Avergun *(Partner)*
Jonathan M. Hoff *(Partner)*
Richard M. Brand *(Partner)*
Jeremy Cross *(Partner-Fund Fin Practice-London)*
Peter C. Morreale *(Partner-Capital Markets-Washington)*
Gregory P. Patti Jr. *(Partner)*

CADY CHEESE FACTORY, INC.
126 Hwy 128, Wilson, WI 54027
Tel.: (715) 772-4218
Web Site:
http://www.cadycheese.com
Rev.: $19,900,000
Emp.: 45
Cheese Mfr
N.A.I.C.S.: 311513
Malisa Stambaugh *(Mgr-Store)*
Sandy Lee *(Mgr-Production)*
Gay Wang *(Office Mgr)*

CAE CIVIL AVIATION TRAINING SOLUTION, INC.
4908 Tampa W Blvd, Tampa, FL 33634   FL
Web Site: http://www.cae.com
Year Founded: 2000
Sales Range: $10-24.9 Million
Flight Training
N.A.I.C.S.: 611512
Nick Leontidis *(Pres)*

CAELUM RESEARCH CORPO-RATION
1700 Research Blvd Ste 250, Rockville, MD 20850
Tel.: (301) 424-8205
Web Site: http://www.caelum.com
Year Founded: 1987
Sales Range: $10-24.9 Million
Emp.: 200
Applied Sciences, Information Technology & System Engineering Services
N.A.I.C.S.: 541715
Diana Yeh *(Co-Founder & CEO)*
Marcia Mills *(Gen Counsel)*

CAELUS ENERGY LLC
8401 N Central Expressway Ste 400, Dallas, TX 75225
Tel.: (214) 368-6050
Web Site:
http://www.caelusenergy.com
Energy Management Services
N.A.I.C.S.: 221118

Caelus Energy LLC—(Continued)

James C. Musselman *(Pres & CEO)*
Kenny Goh *(COO & Founding Partner)*

Subsidiaries:

Caelus Energy Alaska LLC (1)
3700 Centre Point Dr Ste-500, Anchorage, AK 99503
Tel.: (907) 277-2700
Sales Range: $150-199.9 Million
Emp.: 55
Natural Gas Producer, Developer & Explorer
N.A.I.C.S.: 211130
Dave Hart *(Sr Mgr-Ops)*

CAERUS CORPORATION
1251 Red Fox Rd, Arden Hills, MN 55112
Tel.: (703) 474-6204
Web Site: http://caerusco.nextmp.net
Year Founded: 2015
Animal Rehabilitation Products
N.A.I.C.S.: 812910
Fariborz Boor Boor *(Pres & CEO)*

Subsidiaries:

OrthoCor Medical, Inc. (1)
1251 Red Fox Rd, Arden Hills, MN 55112
Tel.: (877) 678-7354
Web Site: http://www.orthocormedical.com
Professional Equipment & Supplies Merchant Whslr
N.A.I.C.S.: 423490
John Dinusson *(Founder & Pres)*
Keith Steichen *(VP-Sls Ops & Revenue Cycle Mgmt)*
Aneeta Babulal *(Mktg Dir)*

CAETECH INTERNATIONAL, INC.
43000 W 9 Mile Rd Ste 305, Novi, MI 48375
Tel.: (248) 522-6700
Web Site: https://www.caetech.com
Year Founded: 1989
Staffing & Information Technology Consulting Services; Engineering Services
N.A.I.C.S.: 561499
Vic Havele *(Pres)*

CAF LLC
PO Box 1121, Maple Valley, WA 98038
Tel.: (425) 433-8277
Web Site: https://www.mycaf.com
Year Founded: 2003
Sales Range: $1-9.9 Million
Emp.: 15
Environmentally Friendly Cleaning Products
N.A.I.C.S.: 325998
Perry Paganelli *(Exec VP-Sls)*
Mike Zahajko *(Pres)*

CAFE EXPRESS LLC
675 Bering Dr Ste 600, Houston, TX 77057-2128
Tel.: (713) 977-1922
Web Site: http://www.cafe-express.com
Rev.: $22,305,883
Emp.: 10
Restaurant Operators
N.A.I.C.S.: 722513
Candi Flores *(Mgr)*

CAFE RIO, INC.
2825 E Cottonwood Pkwy Ste 360, Salt Lake City, UT 84121-5053
Tel.: (801) 930-6000
Web Site: http://www.caferio.com
Year Founded: 1997
Sales Range: $25-49.9 Million
Emp.: 900
Mexican Restaurant

N.A.I.C.S.: 722513
Don Lewandowski *(Chief Dev Officer)*
Ben Craner *(CMO)*
Abe Hollands *(Chief Concept Officer)*
Andy Hooper *(Chief People Officer)*
Dave Gagnon *(CEO & COO)*
Shea Bodet *(CFO)*
Todd Whitney Smith *(Executives)*

CAFFINO INC.
4070 Nelson Ave Ste G, Concord, CA 94520-1231
Tel.: (925) 363-3200
Web Site: http://www.caffino.com
Sales Range: $10-24.9 Million
Emp.: 75
Coffee Bars
N.A.I.C.S.: 311920
Bob Biddle *(VP-Ops)*
Becky Eastman *(Dir-Fin)*
Martin Lauzze *(Pres, Co-Owner & CEO)*
Paul Keehn *(CMO & Exec VP, Co-Owner)*

CAGUAS MECHANICAL CONTRACTOR, INC.
Nebraska U 4 Caguas Norte, Caguas, PR 00725
Tel.: (787) 743-0723
Web Site: http://www.caguasmechanical.com
Sales Range: $1-9.9 Million
Emp.: 250
Plumbing Contractor
N.A.I.C.S.: 237990
Carmelo Nieves *(Pres & CEO)*

CAGWIN & DORWARD
1565 S Novato Blvd Ste B, Novato, CA 94947
Tel.: (415) 892-7710
Web Site: http://www.cagwin.com
Year Founded: 1955
Rev.: $19,783,889
Emp.: 350
Landscape Contractors
N.A.I.C.S.: 561730
Steve Glennon *(Pres, CEO & COO)*
Ken Mcpherson *(Mgr-Acct)*
Ramirez Ollie *(Mgr-Acct)*
Paul Schultz *(Mgr-Irrigation Resource)*
Devol Doug *(Mgr-Ops)*
Dan Sheehy *(Mgr-Special Projects)*
Sarah Dunia *(Reg Mgr-Sls)*
Bob Bain *(Reg Mgr-Sls)*
Charlie Thompson *(VP)*
Judy Adame *(Reg Mgr-Sls)*
Oliver Diaz *(Sr Mgr-Acct)*

CAHILL GORDON & REINDEL LLP
80 Pine St, New York, NY 10005-1702
Tel.: (212) 701-3000
Web Site: http://www.cahill.com
Year Founded: 1919
Sales Range: $300-349.9 Million
Emp.: 270
Legal Advisory Services
N.A.I.C.S.: 541110
L. Howard Adams *(Partner)*
Robert A. Alessi *(Partner)*
Helene R. Banks *(Partner)*
Landis C. Best *(Partner)*
Kevin J. Burke *(Partner)*
James J. Clark *(Partner)*
Stuart Downing *(Partner)*
Adam M. Dworkin *(Partner)*
Jennifer B. Ezring *(Partner)*
Joan Murtagh Frankel *(Partner)*
Jonathan J. Frankel *(Partner)*
Charles A. Gilman *(Partner)*
Bradley J. Bondi *(Partner)*

Pierre M. Gentin *(Partner-Litigation Practice Grp)*
Anthony K. Tama *(Partner)*
Brian Kelleher *(Partner)*
Craig M. Horowitz *(Partner)*
Corey Wright *(Partner)*
David L. Barash *(Partner)*
Douglas S. Horowitz *(Partner)*
Darren Silver *(Partner)*
Daniel J. Zubkoff *(Partner)*
Verna Diaz *(Dir-Admin)*

CAIN & BULTMAN, INC.
2145 Dennis St, Jacksonville, FL 32204
Tel.: (904) 356-4812   FL
Web Site: http://www.cain-bultman.com
Year Founded: 1924
Sales Range: Less than $1 Million
Emp.: 85
Whslr & Distr of Floor Coverings
N.A.I.C.S.: 423220
Michael Sandifer *(Chm)*
Alan Kimball *(Mgr-Ops)*
Buddy Faircloth *(Pres)*
Nick Melnyk *(VP-Pergo Div)*
Georgette Parker *(Sec)*
Marshall Konecny *(VP-Credit Div)*
Rony Smiley *(CFO)*
Kirk Sandifer *(Exec VP)*

CAIN ACQUISITION CORPORATION
350 Park Ave 14th Fl, New York, NY 10022
Tel.: (212) 607-0501   Ky
Year Founded: 2020
Investment Services
N.A.I.C.S.: 523999
Jonathan Goldstein *(Chm, CEO & CFO)*
Ellen Brunsberg *(COO)*
Nick Franklin *(Pres)*

CAIN ELECTRICAL SUPPLY CORP.
212 NE Well St, Big Spring, TX 79720
Tel.: (432) 263-8421
Web Site: http://www.cainelectrical.com
Rev.: $23,639,277
Emp.: 6
Electrical Apparatus & Equipment
N.A.I.C.S.: 423610
Donnie Branch *(Mgr-Profit Center)*

CAIN TOYOTA
6527 Whipple Ave NW, North Canton, OH 44720
Tel.: (330) 494-8855
Web Site: http://www.caintoyota.com
Sales Range: $10-24.9 Million
Emp.: 49
New Car Retailer
N.A.I.C.S.: 441110
Tim Barnes *(Mgr-Sls)*
Scot Poppe *(Mgr-Fleet)*
Ken Damis *(Mgr-Lease)*

CAIN'S PIPELINE & INDUSTRIAL SERVICES, LLC.
7663 1st St, Addis, LA 70710
Tel.: (225) 687-7080
Web Site: https://www.cainspipeline.com
Year Founded: 1981
Sales Range: $10-24.9 Million
Emp.: 70
Pipeline & Industrial Equipment Mfr
N.A.I.C.S.: 213112
Walter Cain *(Owner)*
Larry Cain *(VP)*
Elliott Hammack *(Coord-Construction)*

CAINS INCORPORATED
1400 N 12th St, Murray, KY 42071
Tel.: (270) 753-6448
Year Founded: 1950
Sales Range: $10-24.9 Million
Emp.: 32
Car Whslr
N.A.I.C.S.: 441110
Daryl Cain *(VP)*

CAIRO COOPERATIVE EQUITY EXCHANGE
100 Cairo Main St, Cunningham, KS 67035
Tel.: (620) 298-3625
Web Site: http://www.cairocoop.com
Sales Range: $10-24.9 Million
Emp.: 35
Grains
N.A.I.C.S.: 424510
Aaron Murphy *(Pres)*

CAITHNESS ENERGY, LLC
565 5th Ave No 28-29, New York, NY 10017
Tel.: (212) 921-9099   DE
Web Site: http://www.caithnessenergy.com
Year Founded: 1964
Sales Range: $1-9.9 Million
Emp.: 40
Developer & Owner of Electric Power Plants; Renewable Energy Producer
N.A.I.C.S.: 221118
James D. Bishop *(Chm & CEO)*
David V. Casale *(VP & Controller)*
Leslie Gelber *(Pres & COO)*

CAITO FOODS SERVICE INC.
8735 E 33rd St, Indianapolis, IN 46226
Tel.: (317) 897-2009
Web Site: https://www.caitofoods.com
Emp.: 500
Fruits & Vegetables Distr
N.A.I.C.S.: 424480
Matthew Caito *(Chief Acctg Officer & Exec VP)*
Robert Kirch *(Pres & CEO)*

CAJOLEBEN INC.
10820 San Sevaine Way, Mira Loma, CA 91752
Tel.: (951) 360-1211
Web Site: http://www.galassos.com
Year Founded: 1968
Sales Range: $25-49.9 Million
Emp.: 350
Bakery Products Producer & Whslr
N.A.I.C.S.: 311812
Jeanette Galasso *(Chm)*

CAJUN COMPANY
307 Wilcox St, Lafayette, LA 70508
Tel.: (337) 232-7099
Sales Range: $10-24.9 Million
Emp.: 10
Provider of Insulation Services
N.A.I.C.S.: 238310
E.F. Duhe Jr. *(Pres)*

CAJUN CONSTRUCTORS INC.
15635 Airline Hwy, Baton Rouge, LA 70817
Tel.: (225) 753-5857
Web Site: http://www.cajunusa.com
Rev.: $157,204,239
Emp.: 200
Water, Sewer & Utility Lines
N.A.I.C.S.: 237110
Ken Jacob *(Pres & CEO)*
Shane Recile *(CFO)*
William Clouatre *(Dir-Bus Dev)*

CAJUN INDUSTRIES, L.L.C.

15635 Airline Hwy, Baton Rouge, LA 70817
Tel.: (225) 753-5857
Web Site: https://www.cajunusa.com
Year Founded: 1973
Sales Range: $200-249.9 Million
Emp.: 1,500
Oil & Gas Pipeline & Related Structures Construction Services
N.A.I.C.S.: 237120
Ken Jacob *(Pres & CEO)*
William Clouatre *(VP-Corp Bus Dev)*
Mike Lavespere *(VP-Pub Works)*

CAJUN OUTBOARDS INC.
7332 Hwy 1, Addis, LA 70710
Tel.: (225) 749-5001
Web Site:
   https://www.cajunoutboards.com
Rev.: $14,800,000
Emp.: 13
Boat Dealers
N.A.I.C.S.: 441222
Michael Oncale *(Pres)*

CAKEWALK, INC.
179 Lincoln St, Boston, MA 02111
Tel.: (617) 423-9004
Web Site: http://www.cakewalk.com
Year Founded: 1987
Music Software
N.A.I.C.S.: 423430
Neil RiCharde *(Exec VP-Sls & Mktg)*

CAL DEVELOPMENT INC.
6850 Lyons Technology Cir, Coconut Creek, FL 33073
Tel.: (954) 564-0655
Web Site:
   http://www.caldevelopment.com
Sales Range: $10-24.9 Million
Emp.: 65
Commercial & Institutional Building Construction Services
N.A.I.C.S.: 236220
Patrick Keane *(Founder & Pres)*
Declan Wilmott *(COO)*

CAL NET TECHNOLOGY GROUP
9420 Topanga Canyon Blvd Ste 100, Chatsworth, CA 91311
Tel.: (818) 701-5753
Web Site: http://www.calnettech.com
Year Founded: 1995
Sales Range: $1-9.9 Million
Emp.: 49
IT Consulting Services
N.A.I.C.S.: 541512
Luca Jacobellis *(Pres & COO)*
James U. Hwang *(CEO)*
Randy Nieves *(CTO)*
Tony Shepherd *(CFO)*
Suzanne Harris *(Chief HR Officer & VP)*
Bob Deschamps *(VP-Managed Svcs)*

CAL PACIFIC PRODUCTS INC.
600 University St Ste 2328, Seattle, WA 98101-4131
Tel.: (818) 882-4280
Rev.: $13,900,000
Emp.: 40
Industrial Supplies
N.A.I.C.S.: 423840
Leonard Katz *(Pres)*

CAL PACIFIC SPECIALTY FOODS
3050 Hilltop Rd, Moss Landing, CA 95039
Tel.: (831) 722-3615
Web Site: http://www.calpacificsf.com
Year Founded: 2003
Sales Range: $50-74.9 Million
Emp.: 10

Frozen Strawberry Mfr
N.A.I.C.S.: 311411
Terry Sebastian *(CEO)*
Maria Fernandez *(Mgr-Quality Assurance)*

CAL POLY CORPORATION
Bldg 15 California Polytechnic State Univ, San Luis Obispo, CA 93407
Tel.: (805) 756-1451
Web Site:
   http://www.calpolycorporation.org
Rev.: $66,816,340
Emp.: 1,481
Academic Promotions & Educational Assistance to Faculty & Students
N.A.I.C.S.: 561110
Don Oberhelman *(Dir-Athletics)*

CAL POLY POMONA FOUNDATION, INC.
3801 W Temple Ave, Pomona, CA 91768
Tel.: (909) 869-4378
Web Site: http://www.foundation.edu
Sales Range: $800-899.9 Million
Emp.: 1,200
Book Stores
N.A.I.C.S.: 459210
Randy Townsend *(Dir-IT)*
Sandra Cain *(Asst Dir-Retail Ops)*
Joanne Casey *(Mgr-Franchise)*
Valerie Mellano *(Chm-Plant Science Dept)*

CAL RIPKEN, SR. FOUNDATION
1427 Clarkview Rd Ste 100, Baltimore, MD 21209
Tel.: (410) 823-0808   MD
Web Site:
   http://www.ripkenfoundation.org
Year Founded: 2001
Sales Range: $10-24.9 Million
Emp.: 28
Behavioral Healthcare Services
N.A.I.C.S.: 623220
Vi Ripken *(Founder & Co-Chm)*
Bill Ripken *(Co-Founder & Vice Chm)*
Joe Rossow *(Exec VP-Ops)*
Chuck Brady *(Sr VP-Strategic Initiatives)*
Maureen Desmond *(VP-Resource Dev)*
Carrie LeBow *(Exec VP-Resource Dev & Mktg)*
Joellen Malstrom *(VP-HR & Ops)*
Steve Salem *(Pres & CEO)*
Brian Wentz *(CFO)*
Cal Ripken Jr. *(Vice Chm)*

CAL SDI, INC.
1959 Mount Vernon Ave, Pomona, CA 91768
Tel.: (909) 868-6688   CA
Year Founded: 2006
Tools Mfr & Supplier
N.A.I.C.S.: 333515
Stephen Chen *(Pres)*

Subsidiaries:

Disston Company   (1)
5 Industrial Park, South Deerfield, MA 01373
Tel.: (413) 665-1262
Web Site: http://www.disstontools.com
Sales Range: $25-49.9 Million
Emp.: 300
Hacksaw Blade Hole Saw Reciprocating Saw Blade Bandsaw Blade & Wood Boring Bit Mfr
N.A.I.C.S.: 333517

CAL SPAS, INC.
1462 E 9th St, Pomona, CA 91766
Tel.: (909) 623-8781

Web Site: https://www.calspas.com
Rev.: $19,900,000
Emp.: 300
Miscellaneous Store Retailers
N.A.I.C.S.: 459999
Casey Loyd *(Pres)*

CAL THERMOPLASTICS, INC.
2660 Townsgate Rd Ste 150, Westlake Village, CA 91361-5724
Tel.: (805) 494-7144   CA
Web Site: http://www.calthermo.com
Year Founded: 1970
Sales Range: $1-9.9 Million
Emp.: 15
Plastics Materials & Raw Materials
N.A.I.C.S.: 424610
Charles A. Levy *(Pres)*

CAL-ARK INC.
12103 Interstate 30, Little Rock, AR 72209
Tel.: (501) 455-3399
Web Site: https://www.calark.com
Year Founded: 1975
Sales Range: $25-49.9 Million
Emp.: 450
General Commodities Trucking Services
N.A.I.C.S.: 484121
Tom Bartholomew *(Owner)*
Rochelle Bartholomew Gorman *(CEO)*
Jim Moore *(VP-Mktg)*
Rochelle Bartholomew *(Pres & CEO)*

CAL-CHLOR CORPORATION
627 Jefferson St, Lafayette, LA 70501
Tel.: (337) 264-1449
Web Site: https://www.cal-chlor.com
Sales Range: $10-24.9 Million
Emp.: 90
Calcium Chloride
N.A.I.C.S.: 424690
Mark S. Hanna *(CEO)*
Todd Trahan *(Pres)*
James Bellard *(Plant Mgr)*
Jan Martin *(VP)*
Wayne Wagner *(Mgr-Ops)*
Joe Leifker *(Plant Mgr)*
Brett Davis *(Mgr-Ops)*
Chris Dugan *(Asst Plant Mgr)*
Janet Rocha *(Office Mgr)*
Mike Scelsa *(Plant Mgr-Ops)*

CAL-CLEVE LIMITED
4366 E 26th St, Los Angeles, CA 90023
Tel.: (323) 780-9010
Web Site: https://www.dotline.net
Year Founded: 1985
Sales Range: $10-24.9 Million
Emp.: 100
Provider of Trucking Services
N.A.I.C.S.: 484121
Bob Brewster *(Controller)*

CAL-COAST MACHINERY, INC.
617 S Blosser Rd, Santa Maria, CA 93458
Tel.: (805) 925-0931   CA
Web Site:
   http://www.calcoastmachinery.com
Rev.: $25,251,644
Emp.: 38
Tractor & Other Farm Machinery Dealer
N.A.I.C.S.: 423820
Tsugio Hiji *(Pres)*

CAL-LIFT, INC.
13027 Crossroads Pkwy S, City of Industry, CA 91746
Tel.: (562) 566-1400
Web Site: https://www.cal-lift.com
Sales Range: $25-49.9 Million
Emp.: 85

New & Used Trucks; Tractors; & Trailers
N.A.I.C.S.: 423830
Mark T. Maechling *(Owner & Pres)*
Michael Marrs *(Mgr-Sls)*
Rex Reinhard *(Acct Mgr)*

CAL-STATE AUTO PARTS, INC.
1361 N Red Gum St, Anaheim, CA 92806
Tel.: (714) 630-5954
Web Site:
   http://www.csautoparts.com
Sales Range: $25-49.9 Million
Emp.: 91
Automotive Supplies & Parts
N.A.I.C.S.: 423120
John McMillin *(CFO & Gen Counsel)*

CAL-STATE STEEL CORP.
1801 W Compton Blvd, Compton, CA 90220
Tel.: (310) 632-2772
Web Site:
   http://www.calstatesteel.com
Year Founded: 1963
Sales Range: $10-24.9 Million
Emp.: 150
Structural Steel & Precast Concrete Contracting Services
N.A.I.C.S.: 238120
Sean Keum *(Project Mgr)*

CAL.NET, INC.
4101 Wild Chaparral Dr, Shingle Springs, CA 95682
Tel.: (530) 212-7591
Web Site: http://www.cal.net
Year Founded: 1997
Internet Service Provider
N.A.I.C.S.: 518210
John Lane *(CEO)*

Subsidiaries:

Winters Broadband LLC   (1)
455 Russell St, Winters, CA 95694-1827
Tel.: (530) 852-7990
Web Site: http://www.winters-broadband.com
Data Processing, Hosting & Related Services
N.A.I.C.S.: 518210
Brian Horn *(CEO)*

CALABRESE CONSULTING, LLC
24 N King St, Malverne, NY 11565
Tel.: (516) 993-6008
Emp.: 100
Accounting & Financial Consulting Services
N.A.I.C.S.: 541618
Christy Albeck *(Partner)*
Jennifer Calabrese *(Founder & CEO)*
Mike Rollins *(COO)*

Subsidiaries:

Albeck Financial Service Inc.   (1)
11767 Katy Fwy Ste 985, Houston, TX 77079-1782
Tel.: (281) 496-0540
Web Site: http://www.albeck.com
Emp.: 100
Custom Computer Programming Services
N.A.I.C.S.: 541511
Christy Albeck *(Founder)*

CALABRESE HUFF
5944 Luther Ln Ste 875, Dallas, TX 75225
Tel.: (214) 939-3000
Web Site:
   http://www.calabresehuff.com
Sales Range: $1-9.9 Million
Emp.: 7
Law Office
N.A.I.C.S.: 541110

Calabrese Huff—(Continued)

Carla Calabrese (Partner)
Winifred Huff (Partner)

CALAIS REGIONAL HOSPITAL
24 Hospital Ln, Calais, ME 04619
Tel.: (207) 454-7521   **ME**
Web Site:
    https://www.calaishospital.org
Year Founded: 1938
Sales Range: $25-49.9 Million
Health Care Srvices
N.A.I.C.S.: 622110
Nancy Glidden (CFO)
Michael K. Lally (CEO)

CALAMOS ASSET MANAGEMENT, INC.
2020 Calamos Ct, Naperville, IL
60563
Tel.: (630) 245-7200   **DE**
Web Site: http://www.calamos.com
Sales Range: $200-249.9 Million
Emp.: 348
Investment Management Service
N.A.I.C.S.: 523940
John Peter Calamos Sr. (Chm &
Chief Investment Officer-Global-
Calamos Investment)
Robert Behan (Pres)
John Koudounis (CEO)
Thomas E. Herman (CFO & Sr VP)

Subsidiaries:

Calamos Financial Services LLC   **(1)**
2020 Calamos Ct, Naperville, IL 60563-
2787
Tel.: (630) 245-7200
Web Site: http://www.calamos.com
Sales Range: $650-699.9 Million
Financial Management Services
N.A.I.C.S.: 523999

Calamos Investments LLC   **(1)**
2020 Calamos Ct, Naperville, IL 60563-
2787
Tel.: (630) 245-7200
Web Site: http://www.calamos.com
Investment Banking Services
N.A.I.C.S.: 523940
John Peter Calamos Sr. (Chm & Chief In-
vestment Officer-Global)
Jon Vacko (Sr VP & Sr Mgr-Portfolio)
John Hillenbrand (Co-Chief Investment Offi-
cer & Head-Asset Strategies)
Joseph Wysocki (VP)
Dino Dussias (VP & Head-Industrials)
Nick Niziolek (Co-Chief Investment Officer
& Head-Intl & Strategies)
Thomas Herman (CFO & Sr VP)
John Koudounis (Pres & CEO)
R. Matthew Freund (Co-Chief Investment
Officer & Head-Fixed Income Strategies)
Michael Grant (Sr VP)
Dan Dufresne (COO)

Calamos Investments LLP   **(1)**
62 Threadneedle Street, London, EC2R
8HP, United Kingdom
Tel.: (44) 20 3744 7010
Web Site: http://www.calamos.com
Investment Banking & Asset Management
Services
N.A.I.C.S.: 523150

Timpani Capital Management,
LLC   **(1)**
10850 W Park Pl Ste 1020, Milwaukee, WI
53224-3636
Tel.: (847) 509-1140
Web Site: http://www.timpanicapital.com
Financial Investment Activities
N.A.I.C.S.: 523999

CALANDROS SUPERMARKET, INC.
4142 Government St, Baton Rouge,
LA 70806
Tel.: (225) 383-7815
Web Site: https://www.calandros.com
Sales Range: $10-24.9 Million

Emp.: 50
Independent Supermarket
N.A.I.C.S.: 445110
Sonny Calandro (Co-Pres)
Blaise Calandro (Co-Pres)
Bryan Bass (Mgr-Warehouse)

CALBAG METALS CO.
2495 NW Nicolai St, Portland, OR
97210
Tel.: (503) 226-3441
Web Site: https://www.calbag.com
Year Founded: 1907
Sales Range: $10-24.9 Million
Emp.: 45
Metal recycling services
N.A.I.C.S.: 423930
Warren Rosenfeld (Pres)
Jason Peterson (Mgr-Bus Dev)
Mike Buckley (Sr VP & Dir-Trading)
Jim Perris (Sr VP-Ops & Fin)

Subsidiaries:

Calbag Metals Co. - Tacoma   **(1)**
1602 Marine View Dr, Tacoma, WA 98422
Tel.: (253) 572-6800
Web Site: http://www.calbag.com
Emp.: 14
Recyclable Material Merchant Whslr
N.A.I.C.S.: 423930
Steve Glucoft (Mgr)

CALCON CONSTRUCTORS, INC.
2270 W Bates Ave, Englewood, CO
80110-1215
Tel.: (303) 762-1554
Web Site: https://www.calconci.com
Year Founded: 1981
Sales Range: $50-74.9 Million
Emp.: 70
Commercial & Institutional Building
Construction Services
N.A.I.C.S.: 236220
James P. Bosshart (Co-Founder &
CEO)
Brian Mortimore (VP)
Jeff Johnson (VP)
Jim Van Zant (VP)
Jim Kohler (VP)
Calhoun W. Cox Jr. (Founder)
Joseph S. Gallion Jr. (Pres)

CALCOT, LTD.
1900 E Brundage Ln, Bakersfield, CA
93307
Tel.: (661) 327-5961   **CA**
Web Site: http://www.calcot.com
Year Founded: 1927
Sales Range: $500-549.9 Million
Raw Cotton Marketing, Compression
& Storage
N.A.I.C.S.: 424590
Claud A. Acker (Asst VP-Sls)
Mark Bagby (Dir-Comm)
Carlo Bocardo (Mgr-Export Sls)
John A. Burch (VP-Sls)
Jarral T. Neeper (Pres & CEO)
Gregory C. Wuertz (Chm)
Jeff Mancebo (Vice Chm)
Michael Brooks (Vice Chm)
Keith Deputy (Vice Chm)
Toby Robertson (Vice Chm)

Subsidiaries:

Calcot, Ltd. - The Glendale
Facility   **(1)**
5220 N 51st Ave, Glendale, AZ 85301-7002
Tel.: (623) 937-4711
Sales Range: $25-49.9 Million
Emp.: 20
Farm Product Warehousing & Storage Ser-
vices
N.A.I.C.S.: 493130

CALCULAGRAPH CO.

280 Ridgedale Ave, East Hanover,
NJ 07936
Tel.: (973) 887-9400
Web Site: https://www.cpi-nj.com
Year Founded: 1871
Sales Range: $1-9.9 Million
Emp.: 44
Waterproof & Thermal Switch Mfr
N.A.I.C.S.: 335931

Subsidiaries:

Control Products, Inc.   **(1)**
280 Ridgedale Ave, East Hanover, NJ
07936
Tel.: (973) 887-9400
Web Site: http://www.cpi-nj.com
Thermal Device & Waterproof Snap-Action
Switches Mfr
N.A.I.C.S.: 335931
Mac Stuhler (VP-Mktg & Sls)

CALDER DEVELOPMENT ASSOCIATES, INC.
812 Avis Dr, Ann Arbor, MI 48108
Tel.: (734) 622-0240   **MI**
Web Site: http://www.biotronic.com
Year Founded: 1978
Sales Range: $1-9.9 Million
Emp.: 103
Holding Company; Neurophysiologi-
cal Monitoring Services
N.A.I.C.S.: 551112
H. B. Calder (Founder)
William J. Gecsey (Pres & CEO)

Subsidiaries:

Neurowave Monitoring Inc.   **(1)**
1541 Pkwy Loop Ste H, Tustin, CA 92780
Tel.: (949) 419-6197
Web Site:
    http://www.neurowavemonitoring.com
Intra-Operative Monitoring Services
N.A.I.C.S.: 621511
Paul Sowa (Pres)

CALDWELL COUNTY BANCSHARES, INC.
201 S Davis St, Hamilton, MO 64644
Tel.: (816) 583-2154   **MO**
Web Site: http://www.banknw.com
Year Founded: 1991
Sales Range: $1-9.9 Million
Emp.: 29
Bank Holding Company
N.A.I.C.S.: 551111
James Anderson (Pres & CEO)

Subsidiaries:

Bank Northwest   **(1)**
201 S Davis St, Hamilton, MO 64644
Tel.: (816) 583-2154
Web Site: http://www.banknw.com
Sales Range: $1-9.9 Million
Commericial Banking
N.A.I.C.S.: 522110
James Anderson (Pres & CEO)

CALDWELL COUNTY HOSPITAL, INC.
100 Medical Ctr Dr, Princeton, KY
42445
Tel.: (270) 365-0300   **KY**
Web Site: http://www.cmcky.org
Year Founded: 1947
Sales Range: $1-9.9 Million
Emp.: 250
General Medical Services
N.A.I.C.S.: 622110
Charles Lovell (CEO)
Shane Whittington (CFO)

CALDWELL IMPLEMENT COMPANY
1044 Hwy 75, Burlington, KS 66839
Tel.: (620) 364-5327
Sales Range: $10-24.9 Million
Emp.: 48
Farm Implements

N.A.I.C.S.: 423820

CALDWELL IMPORTS INC.
1155 Bloomfield Ave, West Caldwell,
NJ 07006
Tel.: (973) 882-1822
Web Site: http://caldwelltoyota.com
Year Founded: 1970
Sales Range: $25-49.9 Million
Emp.: 100
Car Whslr
N.A.I.C.S.: 441110
Michael A. Cuozzo (Pres)

CALDWELL INDUSTRIES INC.
2351 New Millennium Dr, Louisville,
KY 40216
Tel.: (502) 778-6989
Year Founded: 1987
Sales Range: $50-74.9 Million
Emp.: 85
Mfr of Injection Molding Extrusted &
Die Cut Parts
N.A.I.C.S.: 339991
Edward R. Sitzler Jr. (Pres)

CALDWELL MILLING CO. INC.
504 Hwy 5, Rose Bud, AR 72137
Tel.: (501) 556-5226
Rev.: $13,770,243
Emp.: 58
Animal Prepared Feeds & Feed In-
gredients Mfr
N.A.I.C.S.: 311119
Henry G. Caldwell (Pres)

CALDWELL PLUMBING CO., INC.
821 Childs St, Wheaton, IL 60187
Tel.: (630) 588-8900
Web Site:
    https://www.caldwellplumbing.net
Rev.: $13,000,000
Emp.: 40
Plumbing, Heating & Air-Conditioning
Contractors
N.A.I.C.S.: 238220
Nick Tenerelli (Pres & Sec)

CALDWELL TANKS, INC.
4000 Tower Rd, Louisville, KY 40219-
1901
Tel.: (502) 964-3361   **KY**
Web Site:
    https://www.caldwelltanks.com
Year Founded: 1887
Sales Range: $25-49.9 Million
Emp.: 445
Storage Tank Engineering, Fabrica-
tion & Construction Services
N.A.I.C.S.: 332420
Bernard S. Fineman (Pres)
Kevin L. Gallerger (VP-Sls)

Subsidiaries:

Caldwell Tanks, Inc. - Atlanta   **(1)**
3500 Hwy 34 Ste 14, Sharpsburg, GA
30263
Tel.: (770) 253-3232
Web Site: http://www.caldwelltanks.com
Sales Range: $25-49.9 Million
Emp.: 80
Storage Tank Engineering, Fabrication &
Construction Services
N.A.I.C.S.: 332420

CALEB HALEY & CO. INC.
800 Food Ctr Dr Unit 110, Bronx, NY
10474-0016
Tel.: (718) 617-7474
Web Site: http://www.calebhaley.com
Sales Range: $25-49.9 Million
Emp.: 34
Distribution of Fresh & Frozen Sea-
food
N.A.I.C.S.: 424460
Neil Henry Smith (Pres)

CALEDONIA FARMERS EL-EVATOR COMPANY INC.
146 E Main St, Caledonia, MI 49316-9488
Tel.: (616) 891-8108　　　MI
Web Site: https://www.cfeco.com
Year Founded: 1918
Sales Range: $10-24.9 Million
Emp.: 75
Progressive Producer Owner Cooperative; Farm & Home Supplies
N.A.I.C.S.: 459999
Pat Bolling (Comptroller)

CALERA CAPITAL MANAGE-MENT, INC.
580 California St Ste 2200, San Francisco, CA 94104
Tel.: (415) 632-5200　　　DE
Web Site:
　https://www.caleracapital.com
Year Founded: 1991
Rev.: $2,800,000,000
Emp.: 27
Privater Equity Firm
N.A.I.C.S.: 523999
James T. Farrell (Mng Partner)
Kevin R. Baker (Mng Dir & Gen Counsel)
Mark N. Williamson (Mng Partner)
Paul F. Walsh (Sr Mng Dir)
James Halow (Mng Dir)
Daniel B. Dumais (CFO & Chief Compliance Officer)
Ethan E. Thurow (Mng Dir)
Michael S. Moon (Mng Dir)
Edward H. Orzetti (Operating Partner)
Robert Jaunich II (Partner)
Robert Jaunich II (Partner)

Subsidiaries:

Carnegie Fabrics, LLC　　　(1)
110 N Ctr Ave, Rockville Centre, NY 11570
Tel.: (516) 678-6770
Web Site: http://www.carnegiefabrics.com
Textile & Wallcover Designer & Mfr
N.A.I.C.S.: 424310
Cliff Goldman (Pres)

Evans Delivery Company, Inc.　(1)
100-110 W Columbia St, Schuylkill Haven, PA 17972
Tel.: (570) 385-9048
Web Site: http://www.evansdelivery.com
Truck Transportation Brokers
N.A.I.C.S.: 488510

FitzMark, Inc.　　　(1)
8188 Allison Ave, Indianapolis, IN 46268
Tel.: (317) 475-0960
Web Site: http://www.fitzmark.com
Sales Range: $10-24.9 Million
Emp.: 26
Freight Transportation Arrangement
N.A.I.C.S.: 488510
Scott Fitzgerald (CEO)
Mark Hurley (Owner)
Dave Hyman (Acct Mgr-Natl)
Jessica Crabbe (Coord-Ops)

Subsidiary (Domestic):

GTO 2000, Inc.　　　(2)
2555 Flintridge Rd, Gainesville, GA 30501
Tel.: (770) 287-9233
Web Site: http://www.gto2000.com
Freight Transportation Arrangement
N.A.I.C.S.: 488510

CALESA MOTORS INC.
Carr Ste 1 Km 27 5, Caguas, PR 00725
Tel.: (787) 747-9343
Web Site:
　http://www.calesamotors.com
Sales Range: $25-49.9 Million
Emp.: 52
Sales of Automobiles
N.A.I.C.S.: 441110
Guillermo Berrios (Pres)
Xavier Jimenez (Controller)

CALEX LOGISTICS CORP.
58 Pittston Ave, Pittston, PA 18640
Tel.: (570) 603-0180
Web Site:
　http://www.calexlogistics.com
Year Founded: 1974
Rev.: $14,356,262
Emp.: 110
Trucking Except Local
N.A.I.C.S.: 484121

Subsidiaries:

Calex Express Inc　　　(1)
58 Pittston Ave, Pittston, PA 18640
Tel.: (570) 603-0180
Web Site: http://www.calexlogistics.com
Rev.: $7,200,000
Emp.: 97
Vehicle Sealing Systems & Anti-Vibration Products Mfr
N.A.I.C.S.: 339991

Calex Truck Sales Inc　　　(1)
58 Pittston Ave, Pittston, PA 18640
Tel.: (570) 603-0180
Rev.: $160,000
Emp.: 15
Truck Equipment & Parts
N.A.I.C.S.: 441330

CALFEE COMPANY OF DAL-TON, INC.
1503 N Tibbs Rd, Dalton, GA 30720-2915
Tel.: (706) 226-4834　　　GA
Web Site: http://www.favmkt.com
Year Founded: 1989
Sales Range: $50-74.9 Million
Emp.: 800
Convenience Store
N.A.I.C.S.: 445131
Joseph Turner (CFO)

Subsidiaries:

John L. Bond Inc.　　　(1)
1503 N Tibbs Rd, Dalton, GA 30720-2915
Tel.: (706) 226-4834
Rev.: $3,600,000
Petroleum Bulk Stations & Terminals
N.A.I.C.S.: 424710

CALHOUN APPAREL INC.
150 GC Hudson Industrial Park, Calhoun City, MS 38916
Tel.: (662) 628-6636
Sales Range: $10-24.9 Million
Emp.: 25
Men's & Boy's Trousers & Slacks
N.A.I.C.S.: 315250
Bobby Steele (Pres)

CALHOUN BUILDERS INC.
917 Polk St, Mansfield, LA 71052
Tel.: (318) 872-0286
Sales Range: $10-24.9 Million
Emp.: 10
Multi-Family Dwellings, New Construction
N.A.I.C.S.: 236116

CALHOUN COUNTY ROAD COMMISSION
13300 15 Mile Rd, Marshall, MI 49068
Tel.: (269) 781-9841
Web Site:
　http://www.calhouncountyroads.com
Year Founded: 1912
Sales Range: $10-24.9 Million
Emp.: 68
Highway & Street Construction
N.A.I.C.S.: 237310
Mary Jo Crumpton (Dir-Admin Svcs)

CALHOUN ENTERPRISES INC.
4155 Lomac St Ste G, Montgomery, AL 36106
Tel.: (334) 272-4400

Web Site:
　http://www.calhounenterprises.com
Year Founded: 1984
Sales Range: $25-49.9 Million
Emp.: 200
Grocery Store Operator
N.A.I.C.S.: 445110
Greg Calhoun (Pres & CEO)
Shakenya Palhoun (Controller)

CALHOUN INTERNATIONAL, LLC
100 N Tampa St Ste 2330, Tampa, FL 33602
Tel.: (813) 222-8400
Web Site:
　http://www.calhouninternational.com
Sales Range: $1-9.9 Million
Emp.: 40
IT & Management Consulting Services
N.A.I.C.S.: 541690
Roger Swinford (Pres & CEO)

CALHOUN LIBERTY HOSPI-TAL
20370 NE Burns Ave, Blountstown, FL 32424
Tel.: (850) 674-5411　　　FL
Web Site: https://www.calhounliberty
　hospital.com
Year Founded: 1991
Sales Range: $10-24.9 Million
Health Care Srvices
N.A.I.C.S.: 622110

CALIBRE SYSTEMS INC.
6361 Walker Ln Ste 1100, Alexandria, VA 22310-3252
Tel.: (703) 797-8500
Web Site: http://www.calibresys.com
Year Founded: 1989
Sales Range: $25-49.9 Million
Emp.: 800
Information Technology Solutions
N.A.I.C.S.: 541512
Joseph A. Martore (Chm)
Craig College (Chief Strategy Officer & Exec VP)
Janice Lambert (CFO & Exec VP)
Gretchen Larsen Idsinga (Sr VP-Growth Ops)
Richard P. Formica (VP-Defense Accounts)
Dorisa Y. Harris (VP-Health & Information Mgmt)
Joseph H. Reynolds (Vice Chm)
Richard Pineda (Pres & CEO)
Hyoshin Kim (Sr VP)
Sylvester Cotton (VP-Growth-Defense Market)
Charles Onstott (CTO & VP)
Jerry Hogge (COO & Exec VP)
Teresa Albo (VP-Bus Dev)
Kristen McLeod (Sr VP-Fin & Acctg & Controller)

Subsidiaries:

IMC Global Services　　　(1)
Kapil Complex 82/1 Baner Mahalunge Rd, Pune, 411 045, India
Tel.: (91) 20 6709 1700
Web Site: http://www.imc.com
Information Technology Consulting Services
N.A.I.C.S.: 541512
Sonali Joshi (Head-HR)

CALIBURN INTERNATIONAL CORPORATION
10701 Parkridge Blvd Ste 200, Reston, VA 20191
Tel.: (703) 261-1110　　　DE
Year Founded: 2018
Emp.: 6,800
Holding Company
N.A.I.C.S.: 551112

James D. Van Dusen (CEO)
Thomas J. Campbell (Chm)
Douglas T. Lake (Vice Chm)
Gary G. Palmer (COO)
M. Victor Esposito (Exec VP)
Beth Jannery (Sr VP-Mktg & Comm)
Mike Reynolds (VP-Risk Mgmt)
James Mehta (Chief Security Officer)
William O. King III (Chief Admin Officer & Gen Counsel)

CALICO PRECISION MOLD-ING, LLC
1211 Progress Rd, Fort Wayne, IN 46808-1261
Tel.: (260) 484-4500
Web Site: http://www.calicopm.com
Year Founded: 2001
Sales Range: $10-24.9 Million
Emp.: 32
Custom Injection Molding Plastics & Rubber
N.A.I.C.S.: 326199
Ted Hayes (VP-Sls & Engrg)
Steve Welch (Engr-Process Automation)
Monte Davis (Mgr-Facility)
Calvin Shannon Jr. (Pres & CEO)

CALIFORNIA ACRYLIC INDUS-TRIES, INC.
1462 E 9th St, Pomona, CA 91766
Tel.: (909) 623-8781
Web Site: http://www.calspas.com
Sales Range: $300-349.9 Million
Emp.: 975
Home Furnishings Retailer
N.A.I.C.S.: 449129
Shiva Noble (Exec VP)

CALIFORNIA AMMONIA CO.
1776 W March Ln Ste 420, Stockton, CA 95207
Tel.: (209) 982-1000
Web Site: https://www.calamco.com
Sales Range: $50-74.9 Million
Emp.: 33
Ammonia
N.A.I.C.S.: 424690
Vanessa Harris (Controller)

CALIFORNIA ASSOCIATION OF FOOD BANKS
1624 Franklin St Ste 722, Oakland, CA 94612
Tel.: (510) 272-4435　　　CA
Web Site:
　https://www.cafoodbanks.org
Year Founded: 1995
Sales Range: $10-24.9 Million
Emp.: 21
Food Bank Association
N.A.I.C.S.: 813910
Steve Linkhart (Dir-Farm to Family Program)
Terry Garner (Dir-Member Svcs)
Stephanie Nishio (Dir-Programs)
Sue Sigler (Exec Dir)
Lisa Houston (Treas)
James Floros (Chm)

CALIFORNIA ASSOCIATION OF REALTORS
525 S Virgil Ave, Los Angeles, CA 90020-1403
Tel.: (213) 739-8376
Web Site: https://www.car.org
Emp.: 130
State Realty Association
N.A.I.C.S.: 813910
Joel Singer (CEO & Sec)
Lynette Flores (Coord-Govt Association)
Jared Martin (Pres)
Dave Walsh (Treas)

California Association of Realtors—(Continued)

Subsidiaries:

Real Estate Business Services,
Inc. **(1)**
525 S Virgil Ave, Los Angeles, CA 90020
Tel.: (213) 739-8227
Web Site: http://www.store.car.org
Sales Range: $10-24.9 Million
Real Estate Industry Publications Retailer &
Services
N.A.I.C.S.: 459210
Joel Singer *(Pres)*

CALIFORNIA BACKYARD INC.
130 Cyber Ct, Rocklin, CA 95765
Tel.: (916) 797-9700
Web Site:
   http://www.californiabackyard.com
Rev: $10,614,064
Emp.: 50
Wicker, Rattan & Reed Furniture
Sales
N.A.I.C.S.: 449129
Wilma Homsy *(Pres)*

**CALIFORNIA BANQUET COR-
PORATION**
601 Fair Oaks Ave, South Pasadena,
CA 91030-2601
Tel.: (626) 796-8866
Sales Range: $10-24.9 Million
Emp.: 400
Owner & Operator of Restaurant
N.A.I.C.S.: 722511
Henry A. Yost *(Pres)*
Deborah Hoffman *(Owner)*
Jacob Frederick *(Gen Mgr)*
Nery Buenavidez-Pompa *(Mgr-Ops)*

**CALIFORNIA BEACH RESTAU-
RANTS**
3355 Via Lido Ste H , Newport
Beach, CA 92663
Tel.: (949) 675-0575
Web Site: http://www.eatsushi.com
Sales Range: $10-24.9 Million
Emp.: 10
Eating Place
N.A.I.C.S.: 722511
Alan Redhead *(Pres)*

CALIFORNIA CAFE
700 Welch Rd, Palo Alto, CA 94304
Tel.: (650) 325-2233   **CA**
Web Site:
   http://www.californiacafe.com
Year Founded: 1986
Sales Range: $50-74.9 Million
Emp.: 50
Operates Restaurants, Family: Chain
N.A.I.C.S.: 722511
Andre Hall *(Gen Mgr)*

**CALIFORNIA CARTAGE COM-
PANY LLC**
2931 Redondo Ave, Long Beach, CA
90806
Tel.: (310) 537-1432
Web Site: http://www.calcartage.com
Sales Range: $25-49.9 Million
Emp.: 700
Warehousing & Freight Services
N.A.I.C.S.: 493110
Robert A. Curry *(Pres)*

Subsidiaries:

Brookvale International
Corporation **(1)**
20903 S Maciel Ave, Carson, CA 90810-
1027
Tel.: (310) 604-8641
Web Site: http://www.calcartage.com
Sales Range: $10-24.9 Million
Emp.: 10
General Warehousing
N.A.I.C.S.: 493110
Gary Wicks *(Gen Mgr)*

F&S Distributing, LLC **(1)**
4444 E 26th St, Vernon, CA 90058
Tel.: (323) 264-2607
Freight Forwarding Services
N.A.I.C.S.: 541614

K&R Transportation, LLC **(1)**
2401 E Pacific Coast Hwy, Wilmington, CA
90744-2920
Tel.: (562) 436-5062
Web Site: http://www.kr.com
Emp.: 50
Freight Transportation Services
N.A.I.C.S.: 488510
Marco Perez *(Mgr)*

**CALIFORNIA CASUALTY MAN-
AGEMENT COMPANY**
1875 S Grant St, San Mateo, CA
94402
Tel.: (650) 574-4000   **CA**
Web Site: http://www.calcas.com
Year Founded: 1914
Sales Range: $300-349.9 Million
Emp.: 90
Insurance Services
N.A.I.C.S.: 524113
Carl B. Brown *(Chm)*
Michael D. Bower *(Exec VP-Tech &
Investments)*
James R. Kauffman *(Sr VP-Claims)*
Patrick O. Lynch *(Sr VP-Agency
Svcs, Customer Svc & Underwriting
Ops)*
Michael A. Ray *(CFO, Treas & Exec
VP)*
Douglas A. Goldberg *(Sr VP-Grp
Rels, Bus Dev & Partner Programs)*
Barbara K. Gurnett *(Sr VP-Learning
& Website Dev)*
Hong Chen *(Sr VP & Actuary)*
Judy Jao *(Sr VP & Actuary)*
Jonathan D. Adkisson *(Pres & CEO)*
T. Michael McCormick Jr. *(CMO & Sr
VP-Sls & Mktg)*

**CALIFORNIA CEDAR PROD-
UCTS COMPANY**
2385 Arch Airport Rd Ste 500, Stock-
ton, CA 95206
Tel.: (209) 932-5001   **CA**
Web Site: http://www.calcedar.com
Year Founded: 1929
Sales Range: $100-124.9 Million
Emp.: 250
Cedar Pencil Slats, Wood/Wax Fire
Logs, Siding & Deck Products Mfr
N.A.I.C.S.: 321999
Charles Berolzheimera *(Pres)*

Subsidiaries:

California Cedar Products Company -
Palomino Brands Division **(1)**
1340 W Washington St, Stockton, CA
95203
Tel.: (866) 473-6245
Web Site: http://www.palominobrands.com
Sales Range: $10-24.9 Million
Emp.: 15
Pencil Slat Distr
N.A.I.C.S.: 321999

Pencils.com **(1)**
1340 W Washington St, Stockton, CA
95203
Web Site: http://www.pencils.com
Stationery Product Supplier
N.A.I.C.S.: 424120

Tianjin Custom Wood Processing,
Co. Ltd **(1)**
Xun Hai Lu, Dong Li District, Tianjin,
300300, China
Tel.: (86) 2224960580
Pencil Slat Mfr
N.A.I.C.S.: 321999

**CALIFORNIA COAST CREDIT
UNION**

PO Box 502080, San Diego, CA
92150-2080
Tel.: (858) 495-1600   **CA**
Web Site: https://www.calcoastcu.org
Year Founded: 1929
Sales Range: $25-49.9 Million
Emp.: 528
Credit Union
N.A.I.C.S.: 522130
Todd Lane *(Pres & CEO)*
Kathy Cady *(COO)*
Gary Atkinson *(Sec)*
Richard Knott *(Chm)*
Barbara Brooks *(Vice Chm)*

**CALIFORNIA COASTAL COM-
MUNITIES, INC.**
27271 Las Ramblas Ste 100, Mission
Viejo, CA 92691
Tel.: (949) 250-7700   **DE**
Sales Range: $25-49.9 Million
Emp.: 33
Residential Land Development &
Home Building
N.A.I.C.S.: 236220
Linda O'Brien *(Controller)*

Subsidiaries:

Hearthside Homes, Inc. **(1)**
6 Executive Cir Ste 250, Irvine, CA 92614-
6732
Tel.: (949) 250-7700
Sales Range: $25-49.9 Million
Emp.: 20
Residential Construction
N.A.I.C.S.: 236115
Sandra G. Sciutto *(CFO & Sr VP)*
Ed Mountford *(Sr VP)*

Signal Landmark **(1)**
27285 Las Ramblas Ste 210, Mission Viejo,
CA 92691
Tel.: (949) 250-7700
Web Site: http://www.woodbridgepacific.com
Sales Range: $10-24.9 Million
Land Development
N.A.I.C.S.: 812220
Raymond J. Pacini *(Pres & CEO)*

**CALIFORNIA COMMERCIAL
ASPHALT CORP.**
13025 Danielson St Ste 260, Poway,
CA 92064
Tel.: (858) 513-0611
Web Site: http://www.ccallc.com
Sales Range: $10-24.9 Million
Emp.: 25
Asphalt Paving Mixture Mfr
N.A.I.C.S.: 324121
Dana Baltzer *(VP)*
Donald Daley Jr. *(Pres)*

**CALIFORNIA COMMUNICA-
TIONS ACCESS FOUNDATION**
1333 Broadway Ste 600, Oakland,
CA 94612
Tel.: (510) 268-4754   **CA**
Web Site: http://www.ccaf.us
Year Founded: 2002
Sales Range: $10-24.9 Million
Emp.: 100
Disabled People Assistance Services
N.A.I.C.S.: 624120
David Kehn *(Mgr-Customer Contact
Ops)*
Barry Saudan *(Dir-Ops)*
Michael Walsh *(Mgr-Information
Technology)*

CALIFORNIA CREDIT UNION
701 N Brand Blvd, Glendale, CA
91203
Tel.: (800) 334-8788   **CA**
Web Site: http://www.californiacu.org
Year Founded: 1939
Credit Union
N.A.I.C.S.: 522130

Walton Greene *(Chm)*
Victor Hanson *(Treas)*
Surviva Mendoza *(Vice Chm)*
Todd Bulich *(Vice Chm)*
Rebecca Collier *(Sec)*

Subsidiaries:

North Island Credit Union **(1)**
5898 Copley Dr, San Diego, CA 92111-
7916
Tel.: (800) 334-8788
Web Site: http://www.ccu.com
Credit Union
N.A.I.C.S.: 522130
Joshua Rehhaut *(Officer-School & Commu-
nity Dev)*
Nando Bragger *(VP-Real Estate Loan Offi-
cer)*

**CALIFORNIA CUSTOM
SHAPES INC.**
9151 Imperial Hwy, Downey, CA
90242
Tel.: (714) 626-0860
Web Site:
   http://www.calcustomshapes.com
Sales Range: $10-24.9 Million
Emp.: 35
Aluminum Extruded Products
N.A.I.C.S.: 331318
Richard T. Price Jr. *(Pres)*

CALIFORNIA DAIRIES, INC.
11709 E Artesia Blvd, Artesia, CA
90702-6210
Tel.: (562) 865-1291   **CA**
Web Site:
   http://www.californiadairies.com
Year Founded: 1999
Sales Range: $75-99.9 Million
Emp.: 80
Milk Marketing & Processing Services
N.A.I.C.S.: 311511
Andrei Mikhalevsky *(Pres & CEO)*

Subsidiaries:

California Dairies, Inc. - Fresno
Plant **(1)**
755 F St, Fresno, CA 93775-1865
Tel.: (559) 233-5154
Dairy Products Mfr
N.A.I.C.S.: 311514

California Dairies, Inc. - Los Banos
Plant **(1)**
1175 Pacheco Blvd, Los Banos, CA 93635-
2198
Tel.: (209) 826-4901
Dairy Products Mfr
N.A.I.C.S.: 311514

California Dairies, Inc. - Tipton
Plant **(1)**
11894 Avenue 120, Tipton, CA 93272-0837
Tel.: (559) 752-5200
Dairy Products Mfr
N.A.I.C.S.: 311514

California Dairies, Inc. - Turlock
Plant **(1)**
475 S Tegner Rd, Turlock, CA 95380
Tel.: (209) 668-6150
Web Site: http://www.californiadairies.com
Emp.: 140
Dairy Products Mfr
N.A.I.C.S.: 311514
Greg Ouse *(Gen Mgr)*

**CALIFORNIA DELUXE WIN-
DOWS**
20735 Superior St, Chatsworth, CA
91311
Tel.: (818) 349-5566
Web Site:
   https://www.cdwindows.com
Year Founded: 1999
Rev.: $14,700,000
Emp.: 49
Wood Window & Door Mfr
N.A.I.C.S.: 321911

Aaron Adirim *(Pres)*
Patricia Kerins *(CFO)*

CALIFORNIA DENTAL ASSOCIATION
1201 K St 17th Fl, Sacramento, CA 95814
Tel.: (916) 443-0505   CA
Web Site: https://www.cda.org
Year Founded: 1973
Sales Range: $25-49.9 Million
Emp.: 161
Dental Professional Association
N.A.I.C.S.: 813920
Cathy Mudge *(VP-Community Affairs)*
Alison Sandman *(Gen Counsel)*
Peter Dubois *(CEO & Exec Dir)*
R. Del Brunner *(Sec)*
Kenneth G. Wallis *(Pres)*
Kevin M. Keating *(Treas)*
Jenn Mason *(VP-Grp Purchasing)*
Melanie Duval-Kirrene *(VP-Mktg Svcs)*

CALIFORNIA DEPARTMENT OF CONSERVATION
801 K St MS 24-01, Sacramento, CA 95814
Tel.: (916) 322-1080
Web Site:
  http://www.conservation.ca.gov
Year Founded: 1965
Sales Range: $25-49.9 Million
Emp.: 530
Government Agency Providing Conservation Services & Information
N.A.I.C.S.: 924120
Blake Rushworth *(Mgr-Enterprise IT Infrastructure)*

CALIFORNIA DIGITAL INC.
17700 Figueroa St, Gardena, CA 90248
Tel.: (310) 217-0500
Web Site: http://www.cadigital.com
Year Founded: 1973
Sales Range: $10-24.9 Million
Emp.: 62
Mainframe Computers
N.A.I.C.S.: 334118
Terry Reiter *(Owner & Pres)*

CALIFORNIA EASTERN LABORATORIES, INC.
4590 Patrick Henry Dr, Santa Clara, CA 95054-1817
Tel.: (408) 919-2500   CA
Web Site: http://www.cel.com
Year Founded: 1959
Provider of Electronic Parts & Equipment
N.A.I.C.S.: 423690
Kerry Smith *(Sec)*

CALIFORNIA EMERGENCY FOODLINK
5800 Foodlink St, Sacramento, CA 95828
Tel.: (916) 387-9000   CA
Web Site: https://www.foodlink.org
Year Founded: 1992
Sales Range: $25-49.9 Million
Emp.: 39
Community Food Services
N.A.I.C.S.: 624210
John Healey *(Chm & CEO)*
Brenda Coker *(Sec & VP-Ops & Facilities)*
Margaret Healey *(Pres & COO)*
Linda Cristian *(Controller)*
Melinda Annis *(Sr VP-Food Programs)*

CALIFORNIA EXPANDED METAL PRODUCTS COMPANY

263 N Covina Ln, City of Industry, CA 91746
Tel.: (626) 369-3564
Web Site:
  https://www.cemcosteel.com
Year Founded: 1974
Sales Range: $50-74.9 Million
Emp.: 68
Prefabricated Metal & Components Materials Used To Make Buildings
N.A.I.C.S.: 332311
Wes Westmoreland *(Gen Mgr-Sls)*
Eric Larson *(Dir-Bus Dev)*
Natalie Pitts *(Mgr-Customer Svcs)*
Shane Dollosso *(Asst Mgr-Ops)*
Sam Guerrero *(Asst Mgr-Ops)*
Carlos Rangel *(Asst Mgr-Ops)*
Jeff Shaver *(Asst Mgr-Ops)*
Cynthia Cheesman *(Dir-Customer Svc)*
Georgi Hall *(Dir-Engrg)*
Fernando Sesma *(Dir-Technical Svcs)*
Steve Farkas *(Mgr-Corp Mktg)*
Jim Larkin *(Mgr-Customer Svc)*
Justin Miller *(Mgr-Customer Svc)*
Craig Baldwin *(Mgr-Sls-South-Central)*
Garret Koleszar *(Mgr-Sls-Southern)*

CALIFORNIA FACTORS & FINANCE LP
1609A W Magnolia Blvd, Burbank, CA 91506
Tel.: (818) 842-4891
Web Site: http://www.cfgroup.net
Sales Range: $10-24.9 Million
Emp.: 8
Factors Of Commercial Paper
N.A.I.C.S.: 522299

CALIFORNIA FAMILY HEALTH COUNCIL
3600 Wilshire Blvd Ste 600, Los Angeles, CA 90010
Tel.: (213) 386-5614   CA
Web Site: http://www.cfhc.org
Year Founded: 1968
Sales Range: $25-49.9 Million
Emp.: 87
Community Health Care Services
N.A.I.C.S.: 621498
Brenda Flores *(VP-Fin & Benefits Admin)*
Ron Frezieres *(VP-Res & Evaluation)*
Amy Moy *(VP-Pub Affairs)*
Nomsa Khalfani *(VP-Programs & Strategic Initiatives)*

CALIFORNIA FARM BUREAU FEDERATION
2300 River Plaza Dr, Sacramento, CA 95833
Tel.: (916) 561-5590   CA
Web Site: https://www.cfbf.com
Year Founded: 1931
Sales Range: $10-24.9 Million
Emp.: 83
Farm Bureau Services
N.A.I.C.S.: 813910
Paul Wenger *(Pres)*

CALIFORNIA FAST FOODS SERVICES INC.
2223 Honolulu Ave, Montrose, CA 91020
Tel.: (818) 957-8400
Year Founded: 1972
Sales Range: Less than $1 Million
Emp.: 225
Owner of Restaurants
N.A.I.C.S.: 424490
Jeff Williams *(Pres)*
Tina Khalaf *(Controller)*

CALIFORNIA FAUCETS INC.

5271 Argosy Ave, Huntington Beach, CA 92649
Tel.: (714) 891-7797
Web Site: https://www.calfaucets.com
Sales Range: $10-24.9 Million
Emp.: 70
Faucets & Spigots, Metal & Plastic
N.A.I.C.S.: 332913
Jeff Silverstein *(Pres & CEO)*
Noah Taft *(Sr VP-Mktg & Sls)*
Paulette Gibson *(Controller)*
Stephany Nguyen *(Mgr-Customer Svc)*

CALIFORNIA FINANCIAL PARTNERS, INC.
505 N Brand Blvd Ste 1470, Glendale, CA 91203
Tel.: (818) 550-9955
Web Site: http://www.calfp.com
Sales Range: $25-49.9 Million
Emp.: 9
Wealth Management Services
N.A.I.C.S.: 523999
Harvey Jacobson *(Pres & CEO)*

CALIFORNIA FIRST NATIONAL BANCORP
5000 Birch St Ste 500, Newport Beach, CA 92660
Tel.: (949) 255-0500   CA
Web Site:
  https://www.calfirstbancorp.com
CFNB—(OTCIQ)
Rev.: $16,939,000
Assets: $304,944,000
Liabilities: $97,640,000
Net Worth: $207,304,000
Earnings: $7,334,000
Emp.: 98
Fiscal Year-end: 06/30/19
Offices of Bank Holding Companies
N.A.I.C.S.: 551111
Patrick E. Paddon *(Chm & CEO)*
Glen T. Tsuma *(COO)*

CALIFORNIA FORENSIC MEDICAL GROUP, INC.
2511 Garden Rd Ste A160, Monterey, CA 93940
Tel.: (831) 649-8994
Web Site: http://www.cfmg.com
Year Founded: 1983
Emp.: 1,000
Outsourced Healthcare Services
N.A.I.C.S.: 621399
Taylor Fithian *(Pres & Dir-Medical)*
Elaine Hustedt *(VP-Ops & Personnel)*
Donald Myll *(VP-Fin)*

CALIFORNIA HYDRONICS CORPORATION
2293 Tripaldi Way, Hayward, CA 94545
Tel.: (510) 293-1993
Web Site: http://www.calhydro.com
Rev.: $19,500,000
Emp.: 49
Warm Air Heating & Air Conditioning
N.A.I.C.S.: 423730
Bill Kapanen *(Mgr-Bus Dev)*

CALIFORNIA INDEPENDENT SYSTEMS OPERATOR
250 Outcropping Way, Folsom, CA 95630
Tel.: (916) 351-4400   CA
Web Site: https://www.caiso.com
Sales Range: $150-199.9 Million
Emp.: 600
Distr of Electric Power
N.A.I.C.S.: 221122
Jim Detmers *(VP-Ops)*
Stephen Berberich *(Pres & CEO)*

CALIFORNIA INDUSTRIAL

RUBBER COMPANY
2732 S Cherry Ave, Fresno, CA 93706
Tel.: (559) 485-1487
Web Site: http://www.cir.net
Rev.: $20,500,000
Emp.: 25
Hose, Belting & Packing
N.A.I.C.S.: 423840

CALIFORNIA INSTITUTE OF TECHNOLOGY
1200 E California Blvd, Pasadena, CA 91125
Tel.: (626) 395-6811
Web Site: http://www.caltech.edu
Year Founded: 1891
Graduate & Undergraduate College
N.A.I.C.S.: 611310
Mike Tyszka *(Assoc Dir-Caltech Brain Imaging Center)*
Thomas F. Rosenbaum *(Pres)*
Daw-An Wu *(Mgr-Laboratory)*
David Li Lee *(Chm)*
Doreese Norman *(Dir-Ops)*
Jenny Somerville *(Dir-Art)*
Jacqueline K. Barton *(Executives)*
Doug MacBean *(Sr Mng Dir-Investments)*

Subsidiaries:

Jet Propulsion Laboratory   (1)
4800 Oak Grove Dr, Pasadena, CA 91109-8009
Tel.: (818) 354-4321
Web Site: http://www.jpl.nasa.gov
Sales Range: $450-499.9 Million
Emp.: 5,100
Aerospace Technology Research & Development
N.A.I.C.S.: 927110
Veronica McGregor *(Mgr-Media Rels)*
Julia Bell *(Asst Mgr-Flight Projects)*

CALIFORNIA LIFE & HEALTH INSURANCE GUARANTEE ASSOCIATION
10780 Santa Monica Blvd Ste 401, Los Angeles, CA 90025
Tel.: (323) 782-0182   CA
Web Site: http://www.califega.org
Year Founded: 1991
Sales Range: $50-74.9 Million
Life & Health Insurance Association
N.A.I.C.S.: 524113
Peter C. Leonard *(Exec Dir)*

CALIFORNIA LIGHTING SALES INCORPORATED
4900 Rivergrade Rd Ste D110, Irwindale, CA 91706
Tel.: (626) 775-6000
Web Site:
  https://www.californialighting.com
Sales Range: $10-24.9 Million
Emp.: 50
Lighting Fixtures
N.A.I.C.S.: 335139
Patty Melrose *(Mgr-Quotations)*
Roger David *(Pres)*
Steve Hall *(Mgr-Ops)*
Tami Johnson *(Engr-Applications)*

CALIFORNIA MANUFACTURING CO. INC.
2270 Weldon Pkwy, Saint Louis, MO 63146-3206
Tel.: (314) 567-4404   MO
Web Site: http://www.cmcbrands.com
Year Founded: 1943
Sales Range: $25-49.9 Million
Emp.: 10
Mens & Boys Clothing
N.A.I.C.S.: 315250
Ellen Brin *(Pres)*

CALIFORNIA NANOTECH-

CALIFORNIA NANOTECH—(CONTINUED)

NOLOGIES CORP.
17220 Edwards Rd, Cerritos, CA 90703
Tel.: (562) 991-5211
Web Site:
https://www.calnanocorp.com
Concrete Material Mfr
N.A.I.C.S.: 327320
Eric Eyerman (CEO)
Sebastien Goulet (Dir)
Brian Weinstein (VP-Research & Development)
Christopher Melnyk (Dir-Business Development)
Spencer Song (VP-Operations)

CALIFORNIA NUMISMATIC INVESTMENTS INC.
525 W Manchester Blvd, Inglewood, CA 90301-1627
Tel.: (310) 674-3330
Web Site:
https://www.golddealer.com
Sales Range: $200-249.9 Million
Emp.: 13
Gold Dealer
N.A.I.C.S.: 423940
Richard J. Schwary (Pres)
Ken Edwards (VP)

CALIFORNIA NURSES ASSOCIATION
155 Grand Ave Ste 100, Oakland, CA 94612
Tel.: (510) 273-2200
Web Site:
https://www.nationalnurses.org
Year Founded: 1903
Health Care Srvices
N.A.I.C.S.: 621610

CALIFORNIA OLIVE RANCH INC.
1367 E Lassen Ave Ste A-1, Chico, CA 95965
Tel.: (530) 846-8000
Web Site:
http://www.californiaoliveranch.com
Year Founded: 1998
Sales Range: $1-9.9 Million
Emp.: 28
Extra Virgin Olive Oil Mfr
N.A.I.C.S.: 311225
Michael Perez (Mgr-Milling)
Gregg Kelley (CEO)
Jim Lipman (VP-Production Ops)
Dana Goodman (CFO)
Claude S. Weiller (VP-Sls & Mktg)

Subsidiaries:

Lucini Italia Company   (1)
1367 E Lassen Ste A-1, Chico, CA 95973
Tel.: (888) 558-2464
Web Site: http://www.lucini.com
Sauce, Soup & Dressing Mfr
N.A.I.C.S.: 311941
Meagan Cole (Dir-Mktg)

CALIFORNIA OREGON BROADCASTING INC.
125 S 1st St, Medford, OR 97501
Tel.: (541) 779-5555
Web Site: http://www.kobi5.com
Sales Range: $100-124.9 Million
Emp.: 100
Owner of Television Broadcasting Stations
N.A.I.C.S.: 516120
Patricia C. Smullin (Pres)
Bob Wise (Gen Mgr)
Roger Harris (Controller)

CALIFORNIA OUTDOOR ADVERTISING
503 32nd St Ste 110, Newport Beach, CA 92663
Tel.: (949) 723-0713
Web Site:
http://www.californiaoutdoor.com
Year Founded: 1990
Rev.: $30,000,000
Emp.: 10
Advertising Agencies, Automotive, Financial, Full Service, Hispanic Marketing, Media Buying Services, Outdoor, Out-of-Home Media, Production, Radio
N.A.I.C.S.: 541810
Brian Gurnee (Pres)

CALIFORNIA PACIFIC HOMES INC.
9828 Research Dr, Irvine, CA 92618-4310
Tel.: (949) 833-6000
Web Site:
http://www.californiapacific.com
Sales Range: $150-199.9 Million
Emp.: 55
Speculative Builder; Multi-Family Dwellings
N.A.I.C.S.: 236116
Cari Bren (Chm)

CALIFORNIA PACIFIC RESEARCH, INC.
300 Brinkby Ave Ste 200, Reno, NV 89509-4359
Tel.: (775) 829-5600
Web Site:
https://www.newgen2000.com
Sales Range: $50-74.9 Million
Emp.: 10
Hair Care Products Mfr & Whslr
N.A.I.C.S.: 325620
Robert E. Murphy (Founder)

CALIFORNIA PANEL & VENEER COMPANY
14055 Artesia Blvd, Cerritos, CA 90703-3250
Tel.: (562) 926-5834
Web Site: https://www.calpanel.com
Year Founded: 1917
Sales Range: $10-24.9 Million
Emp.: 50
Wholesale Distributor of Plywood, Veneer & Interior Building Materials
N.A.I.C.S.: 423310
John C. Fahs (Pres)
Gary Harker (Exec VP-Sls)
Kathleen R. Allen (Treas & Sec)

CALIFORNIA PAVEMENT MAINTENANCE CO., INC.
9390 Elder Creek Rd, Sacramento, CA 95829
Tel.: (916) 381-8033
Web Site:
http://www.cpmamerica.com
Rev.: $18,777,751
Emp.: 45
Highway & Street Paving Contractor
N.A.I.C.S.: 237310
Gordon L. Rayner (Pres)
Tina Seeney (Controller)

CALIFORNIA PUBLIC EMPLOYEES' RETIREMENT SYSTEM
Lincoln Plz 400 Q St, Sacramento, CA 95811
Tel.: (916) 795-3829
Web Site: http://www.calpers.ca.gov
Sales Range: $300-349.9 Million
Emp.: 2,000
Retirement & Health Services
N.A.I.C.S.: 923130
Rob Feckner (VP)
Priya Mathur (Chm)

Matthew G. Jacobs (Gen Counsel)
Mahboob Hossain (Dir-Investment)
Paul Mouchakkaa (Dir-Mng Investment)
Marlene Timberlake D'Adamo (Chief Compliance Officer)
Curtis Ishii (Dir-Mng Investment-Global Fixed Income)
Matt Flynn (Interim Chief Operating Investment Officer)
Marcie Frost (CEO)
Scott Terando (Chief Actuary-Pension Fund)
Clinton L. Stevenson (Dir-Investment-Investment Mgmt Engagement Programs)
Beth Richtman (Mng Dir-Investment-Sustainable Investment Program)
Michael Cohen (CFO)
James Sterling Gunn (Mng Dir-Investment-Trust Level Portfolio Mgmt Program)
Nicole Musicco (Chief Investment Officer)

CALIFORNIA RURAL INDIAN HEALTH BOARD, INC.
4400 Auburn Blvd 2nd Fl, Sacramento, CA 95841
Tel.: (916) 929-9761
Web Site: http://www.crihb.org
Sales Range: $25-49.9 Million
Emp.: 109
Health Care Srvices
N.A.I.C.S.: 621498
Marilyn Pollard (COO)

CALIFORNIA SCHOOL EMPLOYEES ASSOCIATION
2045 Lundy Ave, San Jose, CA 95131
Tel.: (408) 473-1000
Web Site: https://www.csea.com
Year Founded: 1927
Sales Range: $50-74.9 Million
Emp.: 304
Educational Support Services
N.A.I.C.S.: 611710
Roy Ramos (Dir-Office Svcs)
David Low (Exec Dir)
Keith Pace (Dir-Field Ops)

CALIFORNIA SERVICE TOOL INC.
3875 Bay Ctr Pl, Hayward, CA 94545
Tel.: (510) 782-1000
Web Site:
http://www.calservicetool.com
Emp.: 150
Tools, Rental & Repair Services, Seismic & Fastening Solutions, Safety Equipment & General Construction Supplies
N.A.I.C.S.: 333517
Bob LaRue (Pres)
Harold Paschal (Mgr)

CALIFORNIA SHELLFISH COMPANY
505 Beach St Ste 200, San Francisco, CA 94133
Tel.: (415) 928-7400
Rev.: $73,500,000
Emp.: 15
Fresh & Frozen Seafood Processing
N.A.I.C.S.: 311710
Eugene Bugatto (Pres)
David Zeller (CFO)

CALIFORNIA SHINGLE & SHAKE CO.
2279 Pike Ctr, Concord, CA 94520
Tel.: (925) 676-1313
Web Site: https://www.calshingle.com
Sales Range: $25-49.9 Million

Emp.: 75
Roofing & Siding Materials
N.A.I.C.S.: 423330
Leo Brutsche (Pres)
Tom Brutsche (CEO)

CALIFORNIA STATE EMPLOYEES ASSOCIATION
1108 O St, Sacramento, CA 95814
Tel.: (916) 444-8134
Web Site: http://www.calcsea.org
Year Founded: 1984
Sales Range: $25-49.9 Million
Emp.: 364
Employee Benefit Services
N.A.I.C.S.: 525120

CALIFORNIA STEEL & ORNAMENTAL SUPPLIES, INC.
2810 N Commerce St, North Las Vegas, NV 89030
Tel.: (702) 471-1102
Web Site:
http://www.californiasteellv.com
Year Founded: 1998
Steel & Iron Distr
N.A.I.C.S.: 423510
Efrain Hernandez (Pres)

CALIFORNIA SUITES INC.
4970 Windplay Dr, El Dorado Hills, CA 95762
Tel.: (916) 941-7970
Web Site:
https://www.suiteamerica.com
Year Founded: 1990
Sales Range: $25-49.9 Million
Emp.: 30
Residential Relocation Services
N.A.I.C.S.: 561990
James Masten (CEO)
Robin Masten (Pres)
Guy Cook (COO)
Shuford Bowman (Dir-Acctg & Info Systems)
Julie Mammini (Dir-Personal Transition Svcs)
Leslie Batsford (Dir-Strategic Mktg & Bus Dev)
Vanessa Reiter (Dir-Natl Sls)
Eric Funk (Dir-Western Reg Ops)

CALIFORNIA SUPERMARKET INC.
601 S Imperial Ave, Calexico, CA 92231
Tel.: (760) 357-6888
Sales Range: $10-24.9 Million
Emp.: 100
Operator of Independent Supermarket
N.A.I.C.S.: 445110
Alex Loo (Pres)
Alicia Loo (Controller)

CALIFORNIA SUPPLY, INC.
491 E Compton Blvd, Gardena, CA 90248-2016
Tel.: (310) 532-2500
Web Site: https://www.calsupply.com
Year Founded: 1975
Sales Range: $10-24.9 Million
Emp.: 100
Hangers, Poly Bags, Maintenance Supplies & Packaging Products Distr
N.A.I.C.S.: 424130
Mark Weinstein (Co-Founder)
Michael Rosson (Co-Founder)

Subsidiaries:

California Supply, Inc. - Union City   (1)
29987 Ahern Ave, Union City, CA 94587
Tel.: (510) 429-0300

Paper Products, Packaging Materials & Janitorial Supplies Distr
N.A.I.C.S.: 424130

CALIFORNIA SUPPRESSION SYSTEMS INC.
1640 Batavia St, Orange, CA 92867
Tel.: (714) 685-8100
Web Site: http://www.redhawkus.com
Year Founded: 1976
Sales Range: $25-49.9 Million
Emp.: 60
Fire Detection & Burglar Systems
N.A.I.C.S.: 561621
Sean Stovall (Gen Mgr)
Mike McWilliams (Pres)

CALIFORNIA TEACHING FELLOWS FOUNDATION
575 E Locust Ave Ste 302, Fresno, CA 93720
Tel.: (559) 224-9200   CA
Web Site: http://www.ctff.us
Year Founded: 2004
Sales Range: $10-24.9 Million
Emp.: 1,769
Educational Association
N.A.I.C.S.: 813920
Mike Snell (Exec Dir)
Donato Mireles (Treas)
Kathy Stanton (Sec)

CALIFORNIA TECHNOLOGY VENTURES, LLC
670 N Rosemead Blvd Ste 201, Pasadena, CA 91107
Tel.: (626) 351-3700
Web Site: http://ctventures.com
Venture Company
N.A.I.C.S.: 551112
Alex Suh (Mng Dir)
William Hanna (Mng Dir)
Andrea DeVita (Dir-Fin)

Subsidiaries:

MariaDB Corporation Ab   (1)
Tekniikantie 12, 02150, Espoo, Finland
Tel.: (358) 94 2597815
Web Site: http://mariadb.com
Software Vendor
N.A.I.C.S.: 513210
Michael Howard (CEO)
Michael Widenius (CTO)
Jon Bakke (Chief Revenue Officer)
Conor J. McCarthy (CFO)

Subsidiary (US):

Clustrix, Inc.   (2)
201 Mission St Ste 1400, San Francisco, CA 94105
Tel.: (415) 501-9560
Web Site: http://www.clustrix.com
Database Software Developer
N.A.I.C.S.: 513210
Mike Azevedo (CEO)

CALIFORNIA TELESERVICES INC.
10850 Wilshire Blvd. Ste 1000, Los Angeles, CA 90024
Web Site: http://www.cticrm.com
Sales Range: $1-9.9 Million
Emp.: 500
Telephony Application Programming Interface
N.A.I.C.S.: 517810
Pinky Baldos (Mgr-HR & Admin)
Jose Maria Angelo Villaroman (CTO)
Luinell Florentin (Mgr-Honduras)
Mary Ann Palaganas (Mgr-Ops)
Kent Alfie Yee (Mgr-Ops)
Destiny Lorena (Mgr-Ops)
Hani Buligon (Mgr-Quality Assurance)
Donnie Ray Baje (Mgr-Learning & Dev)
Sheryl Rose C. Guerrero (Mgr-Fin)
Ernie Mitchell (Country Mgr)

CALIFORNIA TOOL & WELDING SUPPLIES
201 N Main St, Riverside, CA 92501
Tel.: (951) 686-7822
Web Site:
http://www.califtoolweldsupp.com
Sales Range: $10-24.9 Million
Emp.: 30
Welding Machinery & Equipment
N.A.I.C.S.: 423830
Chris Craig (Gen Mgr)

CALIFORNIA TRANSPLANT DONOR NETWORK
1000 Broadway Ste 600, Oakland, CA 94607
Tel.: (510) 444-8500   CA
Web Site: http://www.ctdn.org
Year Founded: 1987
Sales Range: $50-74.9 Million
Emp.: 311
Human Organ Transplantation Services
N.A.I.C.S.: 813212
Sean Van Slyck (VP-Organ Program)
Matt Crump (VP-Tissue & Shared Svcs Programs)
Sandra Mejia (CFO)
J. T. Mason (VP-IT)
Mark Borer (VP-Quality Sys)

CALIFORNIA WASTE SOLUTIONS
1820 10th St, Oakland, CA 94607
Tel.: (510) 832-8111
Web Site: http://www.californiawaste solutions.com
Rev.: $11,400,000
Emp.: 250
Waste Management Services
N.A.I.C.S.: 562111
David Duong (CEO)
Tasion Kwamilele (Dir-Community Engagement)

CALIFORNIANS AGAINST HIGHER HEALTHCARE COSTS
455 Capitol Mall Ste 600, Sacramento, CA 95814
Tel.: (916) 442-7757   CA
Year Founded: 2012
Sales Range: $10-24.9 Million
Civic & Social Organization
N.A.I.C.S.: 813410
Thomas W. Hiltachk (Treas)

CALISE & SEDEI
501 Elm St, Ste 500, Dallas, TX 75202
Tel.: (469) 385-4790   TX
Year Founded: 2002
Rev.: $35,301,000
Emp.: 32
N.A.I.C.S.: 541810
Charles J. Calise (Pres-Calise Partners)
Don Sedei (Partner & Exec Dir-Creative)
Taylor Calise (Mgr-Online Comm-Calise Partners)
Larry Booth (CFO)
Joan Buccola (Dir-Creative Svcs)
Jill Juncker (Acct Supvr)
Robert Greenberg (Mng Dir-Calise Partners)

CALISE & SONS BAKERY INC.
2 Quality Dr, Lincoln, RI 02865
Tel.: (401) 334-3444
Web Site:
https://www.calisebakery.com
Year Founded: 1908
Rev.: $15,300,000
Emp.: 100
Bakery
N.A.I.C.S.: 311812

Michael R. Calise (Pres)
Peter Petrozelli (Controller)
Robert L. Calise (VP)
Armand Ardante (Mgr-Sls)

CALISE PARTNERS, LLC
501 Elm St Ste 500, Dallas, TX 75202
Tel.: (469) 385-4790
Web Site:
http://www.calisepartners.com
Advertising Agencies
N.A.I.C.S.: 541810
Charles Calise (Pres)

Subsidiaries:

Imaginuity Interactive, Inc.   (1)
1409 S Lamar St Ste 1500, Dallas, TX 75215
Tel.: (214) 572-3900
Web Site: http://www.imaginuity.com
Sales Range: $1-9.9 Million
Emp.: 35
Advetising Agency
N.A.I.C.S.: 541810
Corbett Guest (Pres & CEO)
Gary Hooker (VP-Bus Dev & Mktg)
Tim Langford (Exec Dir-Creative)
Frances Yllana (Exec Dir-Creative)
Debbie Potaniec (Dir-Project Mgmt)
Tony Osterhaus (VP-Ops)
Angela Sweeney (Exec Dir-Pylot)

CALKAIN COMPANIES INC.
11150 Sunset Hills Rd Ste 300, Reston, VA 20190
Tel.: (703) 787-4714
Web Site: http://www.calkain.com
Rev.: $100,000,000
Real Estate Investment & Brokerage
N.A.I.C.S.: 523999
Jonathan W. Hipp (Pres & CEO)
David Sobelman (Mng Partner & Exec VP)
Geoffrey Bobsin (CFO)
Rich Murphy (Mng Dir)
Patrick Nutt (Mng Partner)
Rick Fernandez (Sr Mng Dir)
Betty Friant (Sr Mng Dir)
Andrew Fallon (Mng Dir)

CALKINS GMC
12951 Ferguson Valley Rd, Burnham, PA 17009
Tel.: (717) 248-3901
Web Site: http://www.calkinsauto.com
Sales Range: $10-24.9 Million
Emp.: 25
Car Whslr
N.A.I.C.S.: 441110
Kim Condron (Principal)

CALL EXPERTS
1591 Savannah Hwy, Charleston, SC 29407
Tel.: (843) 724-0000
Web Site:
https://www.callexperts.com
Year Founded: 1982
Sales Range: $1-9.9 Million
Emp.: 300
Marketing & Data Entry Service
N.A.I.C.S.: 561421
Michael Leibowitz (CEO)
Abby Pearson (Pres)
Eric Smith (Dir-IT)
Joseph Pearson (Dir-R&D & Gen Mgr)
Dishell Husser (Dir-Ops)
Paige Bartlett (Acct Mgr)
Alisia Frazier (Acct Mgr)
Paul Binion (Acct Mgr)
Josh Wiggins (Dir-Employee Dev)
Kevin Gill (Gen Mgr-New Jersey)
Haley Wright (Mgr-Ops)
Andrew Kleine (Supvr-Acct)
Stephanie Wells (Supvr-Billing & Outbound)

David Van Gorder (Supvr-Call Center)
Chris Black (Mgr-Ops-Natl)
Scott Witte (Dir-Customer Svc)
Joel Sandstrom (Dir-Fin)

CALL HENRY, INC.
308 Pine St, Titusville, FL 32796
Tel.: (321) 267-9808
Web Site: http://www.callhenry.com
Year Founded: 1990
Sales Range: $25-49.9 Million
Emp.: 500
Technical & Management Consulting Services
N.A.I.C.S.: 561210
Henry Foster (Chm & Sec)
Debbie Phenicie (Office Mgr)
Hu Sneed (Dir-Bus Dev)
William Makynen (Pres)
Donald Najemnik (Mgr-Acctg & Fin)
Robert Clark (Project Mgr)
Chris Logan (Mgr-Quality Control & Safety)

CALL MANAGEMENT PRODUCTS INC.
2150 West Sixth Ave Ste D, Broomfield, CO 80020
Tel.: (800) 245-9933   CO
Web Site: https://phonesuite.com
Year Founded: 1988
Telephone Apparatus Mfr
N.A.I.C.S.: 334210
Aaron Bailey (Product Mgr)
Frank Melville (Chief Strategy Officer)
Angela Koslowski (Dir-Customer & Product Support)

CALL NOW, INC.
1 Retama Pkwy, Selma, TX 78154
Tel.: (210) 651-7145   NV
Web Site:
http://www.retamapark.com
Year Founded: 1990
Sales Range: $1-9.9 Million
Emp.: 88
Racetracks
N.A.I.C.S.: 711212
Thomas R. Johnson (Pres & CEO)

CALL-EM-ALL LLC
2611 Internet Blvd Ste 120, Frisco, TX 75034
Tel.: (972) 668-1920
Web Site: http://www.call-em-all.com
Year Founded: 2005
Sales Range: $1-9.9 Million
Emp.: 8
Automated Voice Broadcasting & Text Messaging
N.A.I.C.S.: 334210
Brad Herrmann (Co-Founder & Pres)
Hai Nguyen (Co-Founder & VP-Engrg)
Stephen Barclay (Partner)
Attila Vari (Engr-Software)

CALL2RECYCLE, INC.
1000 Parkwood Cir Ste 200, Atlanta, GA 30339
Tel.: (678) 419-9990   DE
Web Site: http://www.call2recycle.org
Year Founded: 1994
Sales Range: $10-24.9 Million
Emp.: 25
Electronic Goods Recycling Services
N.A.I.C.S.: 811210
Greg Broe (VP-Fin & Admin)
Linda Gabor (VP-Mktg & Customer Svc)
Leo Raudys (Pres & CEO)
Andrew J. Sirjord (Chm)

CALLAHAN CAPITAL PARTNERS—(Continued)

CALLAHAN CAPITAL PART-NERS
10 S Riverside Plz Ste 1250, Chicago, IL 60606
Tel.: (312) 798-6100   MD
Web Site: http://www.callahancp.com
Real Estate Investment Services
N.A.I.C.S.: 525990
Timothy H. Callahan *(Chm, Pres & CEO)*
Michael C. Colleran *(CFO & Exec VP)*
Ross G. Satterwhite *(Chief Investment Officer & Exec VP)*

CALLAHAN CHEMICAL COMPANY
Broad St & Filmore Ave, Palmyra, NJ 08065
Tel.: (856) 786-7900   NJ
Web Site: http://www.calchem.com
Year Founded: 1960
Chemical & Allied Products Merchant Whslr
N.A.I.C.S.: 424690
Tim Dooling *(Pres)*
Brenda T. Alpert *(VP-CASE Dev)*
Jack Reynolds *(VP-Sls)*
Terry Payne *(Mgr-Sls)*
John Callahan *(CEO)*

CALLAHAN FINANCIAL PLANNING COMPANY
3157 Farnam St Ste 7111, Omaha, NE 68131
Tel.: (401) 341-2000
Web Site: https://callahanplanning.com
Year Founded: 2010
Investment Management
N.A.I.C.S.: 523940
William A. Callahan *(Pres & CIO)*
Reuben J. Brauer *(Officer)*

Subsidiaries:
Gary A. Dossick & Associates, Inc.   (1)
2175 Francisco Blvd E Ste C, San Rafael, CA 94901
Tel.: (415) 455-1055
Investment Management & Tax Preparation Services
N.A.I.C.S.: 523940
Gary A. Dossick *(Founder & Pres)*

CALLAHAN INC.
80 1st St, Bridgewater, MA 02324
Tel.: (508) 279-0012
Web Site: https://www.callahan-inc.com
Sales Range: $125-149.9 Million
Emp.: 4
Commercial & Office Building Construction
N.A.I.C.S.: 236220
Dennis E. Sheehan *(CFO & VP)*
Stephen Callahan *(VP-Ops)*
Patrick Callahan *(Pres)*

CALLAHAN'S GENERAL STORE
501 Bastrop Hwy, Austin, TX 78741
Tel.: (512) 385-3452
Web Site: https://www.callahansgeneralstore.com
Sales Range: $10-24.9 Million
Emp.: 40
Feed
N.A.I.C.S.: 424910
F. Verlin Callahan *(Pres)*
Gary Viktorin *(Controller)*

CALLAWAY CAPITAL MANAGEMENT, LLC
818 18th Ave. S Ste 925, Nashville, TN 37203
Tel.: (202) 866-0901
Web Site: https://www.callawaycap.com
Year Founded: 2013
Investment Management
N.A.I.C.S.: 523999

CALLAWAY ELECTRIC COOPERATIVE
1313 Cooperative Dr, Fulton, MO 65251-0250
Tel.: (573) 642-3326   MO
Web Site: https://www.callawayelectric.com
Year Founded: 1936
Sales Range: $25-49.9 Million
Electric Power Distr
N.A.I.C.S.: 221122
Gary Crawford *(Treas)*
David Means *(Sec)*
Charles Schmid *(Pres)*
Wesley Zerr *(VP)*

CALLAWAY TEMECULA LIMITED PARTNERSHIP
32720 Rancho California Rd, Temecula, CA 92591
Tel.: (951) 676-4001
Web Site: https://www.callawaywinery.com
Sales Range: $25-49.9 Million
Emp.: 50
Investment Services
N.A.I.C.S.: 523999
Patricia Lin *(Pres)*

Subsidiaries:
Callaway Vineyard & Winery   (1)
32720 Rancho California Rd, Temecula, CA 92591
Tel.: (951) 676-4001
Web Site: http://www.callawaywinery.com
Sales Range: $10-24.9 Million
Emp.: 60
Vineyard & Winery
N.A.I.C.S.: 111332
Peter Chang *(Gen Mgr)*

CALLCOPY, INC.
530 W Spring St, Columbus, OH 43215
Tel.: (614) 340-3346
Web Site: http://www.callcopy.com
Year Founded: 2004
Sales Range: $1-9.9 Million
Emp.: 62
Business Management Services
N.A.I.C.S.: 561499
Mark Studer *(CFO)*
Raymond Bohac *(Chm & CIO)*
Jeff Canter *(Pres & CEO)*
Jonathan R. Dunham *(Exec VP-Sls & Bus Dev)*
Tarne Tassniyom *(CTO)*
Patrick Hall *(CMO)*
Susan Terry *(VP-Global Channels & Tech Alliances)*

CALLDRIP LLC
1466 Hwy 89 Ste 200, Farmington, UT 84025
Tel.: (801) 692-7830
Web Site: http://www.calldrip.com
Year Founded: 2005
Sales Range: $1-9.9 Million
Emp.: 50
Software Development Services
N.A.I.C.S.: 541512
Koby Jackson *(CEO)*
Brock Jackson *(COO)*
Aaron Parsons *(Mktg Mgr)*
Ashley Killam *(Mgr-Billing)*
Christiaan Mol *(Acct Mgr)*

CALLE & COMPANY
17992 Alta Dr, Villa Park, CA 92861
Tel.: (714) 244-9511
Year Founded: 1927
Sales Range: $200-249.9 Million
Emp.: 57
Advetising Agency
N.A.I.C.S.: 541810
Martin Calle *(Founder)*
Bill Lynch *(Sr VP-Client Svcs)*
Ellie Weld *(Sr VP-HR)*
Gabrielle Solenne-Niarcos *(Sr VP-Media & Investor Relations)*
Charles Brody *(Exec VP-New Bus Dev)*

CALLEN MANUFACTURING CORPORATION
13 E Lake St, Northlake, IL 60164-2419
Tel.: (708) 345-0400   IL
Web Site: http://www.callengroup.com
Year Founded: 1947
Sales Range: $10-24.9 Million
Emp.: 225
Aluminum Die-Castings
N.A.I.C.S.: 331523
Eugene Callen *(CEO)*
Robert Wilson *(Pres)*
Don Marsh *(VP-Sls & Mktg)*
Michael A. Callen *(Dir-Mktg)*

Subsidiaries:
Callen Die Casting LLC   (1)
725 Andrews Rd, Fountain Inn, SC 29644
Tel.: (864) 862-0050
Metal Die Casting Mfr
N.A.I.C.S.: 331523
Don Marsh *(VP-Sls & Mktg)*
Jack Admire *(VP-Sls & Engrg)*

CALLFIRE
1335 4th St Ste 200, Santa Monica, CA 90401
Tel.: (213) 221-2289
Web Site: http://www.callfire.com
Year Founded: 2004
Sales Range: $1-9.9 Million
Emp.: 15
Pay-As-You-Go Enterprise Level Telecommunication Services
N.A.I.C.S.: 517810
Vijesh Mehta *(Co-Founder)*
Punit Shah *(Co-Founder & Chief Product Officer)*
Lucas Wilson *(Chief Revenue Officer)*
Lionel Etrillard *(CFO)*
Pete Shah *(Co-Founder & Chief Product Officer)*
Michel Veys *(CEO)*

CALLICO METALS, INC.
512 Old Baptist Rd, Kingston, RI 02852
Tel.: (401) 398-8238   RI
Web Site: https://www.osterpewter.com
Lead-Free Pewter Mfr
N.A.I.C.S.: 331492

CALLIDUS CORPORATION
9788 Cheewall Ln, Parker, CO 80134
Tel.: (303) 346-8384   NV
Web Site: http://www.callidus.com
Year Founded: 2010
Protective Screens for Flat Panel Televisions & Computers Mfr & Sales
N.A.I.C.S.: 334419
Brian E. Morsch *(Chm, Pres, CEO, CFO, Treas & Sec)*

CALLITAS HEALTH INC.
187 Pavilion Pkwy Ste 200, Newport, KY 41071
Tel.: (859) 868-3131   AB
Web Site: http://www.callitas.com
Year Founded: 2003

Sales Range: Less than $1 Million
Holding Company; Pharmaceutical & Medical Products Mfr
N.A.I.C.S.: 551112
Joshua Maurice *(VP-Sls & Bus Dev)*
William A. Rodgers Jr. *(Pres & CEO-Four 12 Solutions)*

Subsidiaries:
Callitas Therapeutics, Inc.   (1)
187 Pavilion Pkwy Ste 200, Newport, KY 41071
Tel.: (859) 868-3131
Web Site: http://www.callitas.com
Pharmaceutical Developer & Mfr
N.A.I.C.S.: 325412
Brian D. Keane *(CEO)*

CALLMINER, INC.
200 West St, Waltham, MA 02451
Tel.: (781) 547-5690
Web Site: https://www.callminer.com
Year Founded: 2002
Sales Range: $1-9.9 Million
Emp.: 60
Communication Software Development Services
N.A.I.C.S.: 513210
Jeff Gallino *(Founder & CTO)*
Paul Bernard *(Pres & CEO)*
Adam Walton *(COO)*
Michael Dwyer *(VP-Res)*
Scott Kendrick *(VP-Mktg)*
Erik Strand *(VP-Innovation)*
Rob Lane *(VP-Fin & Controller)*
Dan Lawrence *(VP-Sls)*
Roderick MacQueen *(Sr VP-Product & Cloud Svcs)*
Tony Zavala *(VP-Customer Success)*

Subsidiaries:
CallMiner UK   (1)
Strelley Hall Main Street Strelley Village, Nottingham, NG8 6PE, United Kingdom
Tel.: (44) 115 906 1142
Web Site: http://www.callminer.com
Emp.: 10
Communications Software
N.A.I.C.S.: 513210

OrecX LLC   (1)
11 S LaSalle Ste 2155, Chicago, IL 60603
Tel.: (312) 895-5292
Web Site: http://www.orecx.com
Sales Range: $1-9.9 Million
Emp.: 11
Software Publishing Services
N.A.I.C.S.: 513210
Bruno Haas *(Co-Founder & CTO)*
Bruce D. Kaskey *(Co-Founder)*
Steve D. Kaiser *(Co-Founder)*
Ralph Atallah *(VP-Product Dev)*
Craig McCue *(VP-Sls & Bus Dev)*
Omar Ramsaran *(VP-Customer Support)*

CALLOGIX, INC.
8 Commerce Dr, Bedford, NH 03110
Tel.: (603) 668-2820   VA
Web Site: https://www.callogix.net
Year Founded: 1986
Sales Range: $10-24.9 Million
Emp.: 375
Call Center Operations
N.A.I.C.S.: 561421
Chrisanne Proulx *(Dir-Client Svcs)*

CALLONE
425 W Wacker Dr 8 Fl, Chicago, IL 60606
Tel.: (312) 225-5663
Web Site: http://www.callone.com
Year Founded: 1994
Rev.: $34,000,000
Emp.: 200
Telecommunication Servicesb
N.A.I.C.S.: 517121
Christopher Surdenik *(CEO)*
Paul Aliotta *(Sr Mgr-Network Engrg)*
Rob Gronko *(Mgr-Billing)*

CALLOWAY'S NURSERY, INC.
4200 Airport Fwy Ste 200, Fort Worth, TX 76117-6200
Tel.: (817) 222-1122　　　TX
Web Site: http://www.calloways.com
Year Founded: 1986
Sales Range: $25-49.9 Million
Emp.: 250
Specialty Retailer of Lawn & Garden Products
N.A.I.C.S.: 444240
Daniel Reynolds (CFO & VP)
Marce E. Ward (Pres & CEO)
Sam Weger (VP-Recruiting & Trng)
Alicia Hicks (VP-Mktg)

Subsidiaries:

Cornelius Nurseries　　　(1)
4200 Airport Frwy Ste 200, Fort Worth, TX 76117
Tel.: (713) 782-8640
Web Site:
　http://www.corneliusnurseries.com
Specialty Retailer of Lawn & Garden Products
N.A.I.C.S.: 444240

CALLSOURCE, INC.
5601 Lindero Canyon Rd Ste 210, Westlake Village, CA 91362
Tel.: (818) 673-4700
Web Site: https://www.callsource.com
Sales Range: $10-24.9 Million
Emp.: 190
Lead Management, Business Analytics, Marketing Solutions & Employee Training
N.A.I.C.S.: 541611
Elliot Leiboff (Pres)
Carey Fried (Dir-Mktg & Trng)
Kelly Bryan (Mgr-Client Rels)
Krista Thompson (VP-Strategic Programs)
Louis Lamboy (Dir-Enterprise IT)
Clint Smith (VP-Sls)
Tim Tran (Project Mgr)
Adam Kottler (Dir-Bus Dev)
Candice Weber (Chief People Officer)
Indra Chitre (CFO)
Jason Scinocca (CTO)
Ramin Adnani (VP-Client Svcs)
Robert Gallander (VP-Advisory Svcs)
Tim Gomoll (Chief Revenue Officer)
Jas Jackson (VP-Bus Dev)
Kelley Koliopoulos (Partner-Automotive & Mgr-Strategic)
Josh Oosterhof (Partner-Pro Svcs & Mgr-Strategic)
Ben Schiftan (Mgr-Strategic Partner)
Robin Schweitzer (VP-Mktg)
Brittany Theobald (VP-Product Mgmt)
Jen Weiler (Partner-Automotive & Mgr-Strategic)
Jack Price III (Mgr-Strategic Partner)

CALLTOWER INC.
10701 River Front Pkwy 4th Fl, South Jordan, UT 84095
Web Site: http://www.calltower.com
Year Founded: 2002
Streamlined Data for Web & Audio Conferencing, Telephones & Voicemail
N.A.I.C.S.: 517810
Bret L. England (Pres & CEO)
William Rubio (Chief Revenue Officer)
Brandon Watts (CTO)
Shawn Hansen (VP-Fin, HR & Training)
Jeff Schroeder (VP-Tech)
Martin Call (VP-Customer Success & Svcs)
Doug Larsen (Sr Dir-Dev & Future Products)
James Dastrup (VP-Engrg)
Sean Bailey (Controller)

Seanna Baumgartner (Dir-Mktg)
John Lodden (Dir-Telecom)
Brett Reese (Dir-Client Svcs)

Subsidiaries:

Appia Communications, Inc.　　　(1)
1030 Hastings St Ste 100, Traverse City, MI 49686
Tel.: (231) 929-0970
Telecommunication Servicesb
N.A.I.C.S.: 517121

CALMET SERVICES INC.
7202 Petterson Ln, Paramount, CA 90723
Tel.: (562) 869-0901
Web Site:
　http://www.calmetservices.com
Year Founded: 1960
Sales Range: $25-49.9 Million
Emp.: 400
Operator of Refuse Systems
N.A.I.C.S.: 562111
Bill Kalpakoff (Pres)
Enrique Vazquez (CEO)

CALNET, INC.
12359 Sunrise Valley Dr Ste 270, Reston, VA 20191-3494
Tel.: (703) 547-6800
Web Site: https://www.calnet.com
Year Founded: 1989
Sales Range: $25-49.9 Million
Emp.: 205
Defense Contractor; Telecommunications & Information Technology Support Services
N.A.I.C.S.: 541690
Kaleem Shah (Founder, Pres & CEO)
Helena Robinette (Sr VP-Tech & Language Svcs)
Anthony Scolaro (CTO)

Subsidiaries:

CALNET, Inc. of San Diego　　　(1)
9909 Mira Mesa Blvd Ste 110, San Diego, CA 92131
Tel.: (858) 592-6300
Web Site: http://www.calnet.com
Defence Contractors
N.A.I.C.S.: 541690

CALNETIX TECHNOLOGIES, LLC.
12880 Moore St, Cerritos, CA 90703
Tel.: (562) 293-1660　　　CA
Web Site: http://www.calnetix.com
Year Founded: 1998
Sales Range: $1-9.9 Million
Emp.: 40
Motor & Generator Mfr
N.A.I.C.S.: 335312
Brad Garner (Pres)
Herman Artinian (VP-Bus Dev)
Ian Hart (CFO & Mgr-HR)
Larry Hawkins (Dir-Tech)

Subsidiaries:

Vycon, Inc.　　　(1)
16323 Shoemaker Ave, Cerritos, CA 90703
Tel.: (714) 386-3800
Emp.: 22
Flywheel Energy Storage Systems Mfr
N.A.I.C.S.: 334112
Octavio Solis (Dir-Engrg)
Oliver Ulibas (Dir-Customer Svcs)
Ian Hart (CFO & Mgr-HR)

CALNUTRI, INC.
Tel.: (530) 206-0048　　　CA
Web Site: https://calnutri.com
Emp.: 100
Supply Chain & Logistics Management
N.A.I.C.S.: 541614
David Ackerman (Founder & CEO)

Subsidiaries:

Health & Nutrition Technology, Inc.　　　(1)
Tel.: (831) 624-3904
Emp.: 100
Medical, Dental & Hospital Equipment & Supplies Merchant Whslr
N.A.I.C.S.: 423450
Stephen R. Schultz (Founder & Chief Scientific Officer)

CALOLYMPIC GLOVE & SAFETY CO, INC.
1720 Delilah St, Corona, CA 92879
Tel.: (951) 340-2229
Web Site: https://www.calolysafety.com
Sales Range: $10-24.9 Million
Emp.: 30
Industrial Machinery & Equipment Whslr
N.A.I.C.S.: 423830
Laura Lang (Mgr-Customer Svc)

CALPOP.COM, INC.
600 W 7th St 3rd Fl, Los Angeles, CA 90017
Tel.: (213) 627-1937　　　CA
Web Site: http://www.calpop.com
Year Founded: 2002
Sales Range: $1-9.9 Million
Emp.: 25
Leasing of Dedicated Computer Servers
N.A.I.C.S.: 517810
Sheree Kay (Mgr-Acctg)

CALSPAN TECHNOLOGY HOLDING CORPORATION
4455 Genesee St, Buffalo, NY 14225
Tel.: (716) 632-7500　　　NY
Web Site: http://www.calspan.com
Holding Company
N.A.I.C.S.: 551112
Lou Knotts (CEO)
John Yurtchuk (Chm)
Peter Sauer (Pres & COO)

Subsidiaries:

Calspan Aero Systems Engineering, Inc.　　　(1)
358 E Fillmore Ave, Saint Paul, MN 55107-1289
Tel.: (651) 227-7515
Web Site: http://www.aerosysengr.com
Sales Range: $25-49.9 Million
Wind Tunnels, Turbine Engine Test Cells, Test Equipment Mfr & Ancillary Computer Support for Real-Time Data Acquisition & Control Systems
N.A.I.C.S.: 333998
Grant Radinzel (VP-Product Mgmt & Dev)

CALSTAR PROPERTIES LLC
27779 Homestead Rd, Laguna Niguel, CA 92677-3762
Tel.: (949) 362-2677　　　NV
Sales Range: $10-24.9 Million
Emp.: 6
Property & Real Estate Management
N.A.I.C.S.: 531210

CALSTRIP INDUSTRIES INC.
7140 Bandini Blvd, Los Angeles, CA 90040-3388
Tel.: (323) 726-1345
Web Site:
　http://www.calstripsteel.com
Sales Range: $1-9.9 Million
Emp.: 100
Cold Finishing Of Steel Shapes
N.A.I.C.S.: 331221
Thomas B. Nelis (CEO)
Doug Clark (COO)

Subsidiaries:

Calstrip Steel Corporation　　　(1)

3030 Dulles Dr, Los Angeles, CA 91752
Tel.: (323) 726-1345
Web Site: http://www.calstripsteel.com
Rev.: $9,500,000
Emp.: 25
Cold Finishing Of Steel Shapes
N.A.I.C.S.: 331221

Omega Steel Inc.　　　(1)
7140 Bandini Blvd, Los Angeles, CA 90040-3388
Tel.: (323) 726-7669
Cold Finishing Of Steel Shapes
N.A.I.C.S.: 331221

Southwest Steel Coil Inc.　　　(1)
175 Kittyhawk Blvd, Santa Teresa, NM 88008
Tel.: (575) 589-6246
Web Site: http://www.calstripsteel.com
Steel Mfrs
N.A.I.C.S.: 331513

CALTIUS CAPITAL MANAGEMENT, L.P.
11766 Wilshire Blvd Ste 850, Los Angeles, CA 90025
Tel.: (310) 996-9585　　　DE
Web Site: https://www.caltius.com
Sales Range: $25-49.9 Million
Emp.: 21
Private Equity & Corporate Investment Firm
N.A.I.C.S.: 523999
James B. Upchurch (Pres & CEO)
Greg Brackett (CFO)
Bob Morrish (Gen Counsel & Exec VP)
Melissa Gee (Asst Controller)

Subsidiaries:

Caltius Mezzanine Partners　　　(1)
11766 Wilshire Blvd Ste 850, Los Angeles, CA 90025
Tel.: (310) 996-9585
Web Site: http://www.caltius.com
Sales Range: $50-74.9 Million
Emp.: 20
Corporate Investment Services
N.A.I.C.S.: 523999
Greg Brackett (CFO)
James B. Upchurch (Pres & CEO)
Bob Morrish (Gen Counsel & Exec VP)
Alisa Frederick (Mng Dir)
Michael Kane (Mng Dir)
Greg Howorth (Mng Dir)
Gavin Bates (Principal)
Rick Shuart (Principal)
Don Jamieson (VP)
Melissa Gee (Controller)

Caltius Private Equity Partners I, L.P.　　　(1)
11766 Wilshire Blvd Ste 850, Los Angeles, CA 90025
Tel.: (310) 996-9566
Web Site: http://www.caltius.com
Sales Range: $50-74.9 Million
Emp.: 20
Privater Equity Firm
N.A.I.C.S.: 523999
James B. Upchurch (Pres & CEO)
Greg Brackett (CFO)
Bob Morrish (Gen Counsel & Exec VP)
Garrick Ahn (Mng Dir)
Jeffrey Holdsberg (Mng Dir)
Michael Morgan (Mng Dir)

CALTON & ASSOCIATES, INC.
2701 N Rocky Point Dr Ste 1000, Tampa, FL 33607
Tel.: (813) 264-0440
Web Site: http://www.calton.com
Year Founded: 1987
Rev.: $302,000,000
Emp.: 300
Security Broker & Investment Banking
N.A.I.C.S.: 523150
Dwayne K. Calton (Pres & CEO)
Rich Haydel (VP)

CALTROL, INC.

Caltrol, Inc.—(Continued)

1385 Pana Ln Ste 111, Las Vegas, NV 89119
Tel.: (702) 966-1800   CA
Web Site: https://www.caltrol.com
Year Founded: 1934
Sales Range: $75-99.9 Million
Emp.: 105
Controlling Instruments & Accessory Mfr & Distr
N.A.I.C.S.: 333515
Duane Dudley (Controller)
David Jumonville (Pres)
Joe Taormina (Pres)

Subsidiaries:

Caltrol   (1)
1385 Pama Ln Ste 111, Las Vegas, NV 89119
Tel.: (925) 846-9000
Web Site: http://www.caltrol.com
Sales Range: $25-49.9 Million
Process Instrumentation & Controls Distr
N.A.I.C.S.: 423830

Caltrol, Inc. - ESS Division   (1)
91-110 Hanua St Ste 321, Kapolei, HI 96707
Tel.: (808) 487-7717
Web Site: http://www.caltrol.com
Industrial Automation Products Mfr
N.A.I.C.S.: 333248

CALTRON CASE COMPANY
225 Black Rock Ave, Bridgeport, CT 06605-1204
Tel.: (203) 367-5766   CT
Web Site:
   http://www.calzonecase.com
Year Founded: 1976
Sales Range: $250-299.9 Million
Emp.: 100
Holding Company; Custom Case Design & Manufacturing
N.A.I.C.S.: 551112
Joe Calzone (Pres)
Stephen Bajda (CFO)
Vin Calzone (VP-Mktg & Sls)
Frank Bravico (Reg Mgr-Sls)

Subsidiaries:

Calzone Case Co., Ltd.   (1)
225 Black Rock Ave, Bridgeport, CT 06605-1204
Tel.: (203) 367-5766
Web Site: http://www.calzonecase.com
Sales Range: $10-24.9 Million
Emp.: 50
Carrying Cases Mfr
N.A.I.C.S.: 316990
Joseph Calzone (Co-Founder)
Vin Calzone (Co-Founder)

Division (Domestic):

Anvil Cases, Inc.   (2)
15730 Salt Lake Ave, City of Industry, CA 91745   (100%)
Tel.: (626) 968-4100
Web Site: http://www.anvilcase.com
Emp.: 40
Carrying & Transit Cases Mfr
N.A.I.C.S.: 316990
Stephen Bajda (CFO)
Deborah Visokay (Gen Mgr)

CALTRONICS BUSINESS SYSTEMS
10491 Old Placerville Rd Ste 150, Sacramento, CA 95827-2533
Tel.: (916) 363-2666   CA
Web Site: https://www.caltronics.net
Year Founded: 1981
Sales Range: $10-24.9 Million
Emp.: 50
Digital Network-Connected Office Products Mfr
N.A.I.C.S.: 459999
Dan Reilly (Pres)
Tony Riehl (VP)

Yolanda Gan (Reg Mgr-Sls)
Dave DeMaria (Acct Exec)
Michael Phipps (VP-Sls)

CALUMET BANCORPORATION, INC.
26 E Main St, Chilton, WI 53014
Tel.: (920) 849-9371   WI
Web Site:
   http://www.statebankofchilton.com
Year Founded: 1984
Bank Holding Company
N.A.I.C.S.: 551111
Thomas A. Bloomer (Pres & CEO)

Subsidiaries:

State Bank of Chilton   (1)
26 E Main St, Chilton, WI 53014
Tel.: (920) 849-9371
Web Site: http://www.statebankofchilton.com
Commercial Banking
N.A.I.C.S.: 522110
Thomas A. Bloomer (Chm & CEO)
Laura Hoerth (COO & Exec VP)
Damian Hoerth (Chief Lending Officer & VP)

CALUMET CARTON COMPANY
16920 State St, South Holland, IL 60473-2841
Tel.: (708) 333-6521   IL
Web Site:
   https://www.calumetcarton.com
Year Founded: 1930
Sales Range: $75-99.9 Million
Emp.: 100
Mfr of Envelopes & Folding Cartons
N.A.I.C.S.: 322211
John Inwood (Pres)
Robert Stinozzi (VP)

CALUMET DIVERSIFIED MEATS INC.
10000 80th Ave, Pleasant Prairie, WI 53158
Tel.: (262) 947-7200
Web Site:
   https://www.porkchops.com
Rev.: $25,000,000
Emp.: 125
Meat Processed from Carcasses
N.A.I.C.S.: 311612
Larry Becker (Pres)
Andrew Becker (CEO)
Joy Huskey (Exec VP-Sls & Mktg)

CALVADA SALES COMPANY INC.
450 Richards Blvd, Sacramento, CA 95814-0220
Tel.: (916) 441-6290   CA
Web Site:
   http://www.calvadafopods.com
Year Founded: 1968
Sales Range: $10-24.9 Million
Emp.: 95
Distr of Meats & Meat Products
N.A.I.C.S.: 424470

CALVARY FELLOWSHIP HOMES
502 Elizabeth Dr, Lancaster, PA 17601
Tel.: (717) 393-0711   PA
Web Site:
   https://www.calvaryhomes.org
Year Founded: 1961
Sales Range: $10-24.9 Million
Emp.: 183
Lifecare Retirement Community Operator
N.A.I.C.S.: 623311
Carol Bazzel (Dir-HR)
Kevin Mills (Bus Mgr)
Marlene Morris (Dir-Mktg)

CALVARY HOSPITAL, INC.

1740 Eastchester Rd, Bronx, NY 10461
Tel.: (718) 518-2000   NY
Web Site:
   https://www.calvaryhospital.org
Year Founded: 1899
Sales Range: $100-124.9 Million
Emp.: 1,000
Health Care Srvices
N.A.I.C.S.: 622110
Frank A. Calamari (Pres, CEO & Exec Dir)
Robert Brescia (Dir-Palliative Care)
Nancy D'Agostino (Dir-Home Care & Hospice)

CALVERLEY SUPPLY CO. INC.
6306 15 Mile Rd, Sterling Heights, MI 48312
Tel.: (586) 979-1370
Web Site:
   http://www.calverleysupply.com
Rev.: $12,100,000
Emp.: 35
Warm Air Heating Equipment & Supplies
N.A.I.C.S.: 423730
Michael A. Calverley (CEO)

CALVERT HOLDINGS, INC.
1225 Crescent Green Ste 115, Cary, NC 27518
Tel.: (919) 854-4453   DE
Web Site:
   https://www.calvertholdings.com
Sales Range: $450-499.9 Million
Emp.: 90
Holding Company; Scientific Research & Development
N.A.I.C.S.: 551112
Russ McLauchlan (Chm)
Charles B. Spainhour (Chief Scientific Officer)
Michael A. Recny (CEO)

Subsidiaries:

Calvert Research, LLC   (1)
1225 Crescent Green Ste 115, Cary, NC 27518   (100%)
Tel.: (919) 854-4453
Web Site: http://www.calvert-research.com
Sales Range: $10-24.9 Million
Emp.: 4
Non-Clinical State Pharmaceutical Research Funding
N.A.I.C.S.: 541618
Michael A. Recny (CEO)

CALVERT STREET CAPITAL PARTNERS
2330 W Joppa Rd Ste 320, Lutherville, MD 21093
Tel.: (443) 573-3700
Web Site: https://www.cscp.com
Year Founded: 1995
Sales Range: $25-49.9 Million
Emp.: 16
Privater Equity Firm
N.A.I.C.S.: 523999
Joshua M. D. Hall III (Co-Founder)

CALVERT WIRE & CABLE CORPORATION
17909 Cleveland Pkwy Ste 180, Cleveland, OH 44135
Tel.: (216) 433-7600
Web Site: http://www.calvert-wire.com
Year Founded: 1987
Sales Range: $10-24.9 Million
Emp.: 110
Distr of Electrical Apparatus & Equipment
N.A.I.C.S.: 423610
Neil Rabi (Branch Mgr)

CALVETTI FERGUSON, P.C.

1201 Louisiana, Houston, TX 77002
Tel.: (713) 957-2300   TX
Web Site:
   http://www.calvettiferguson.com
Year Founded: 2003
Accounting Services
N.A.I.C.S.: 541219
James T. Calvetti (Pres)
Jennifer Lorraine (Office Mgr)
Jason Ferguson (Partner)
Manish Seth (Partner)
Natalie Higdem (Mgr-Specialty Svcs Grp)
Kendra Pope (Mgr-Audit)
David Luke (Sr Mgr-Tax)
Jennifer Barajas (Mgr-Tax)
Jeremy Joseph (Mgr-Mktg)
Eric Teachout (Partner-Tax)
James Larkin (Partner)
Vivek Doshi (Dir-Assurance)

Subsidiaries:

Jim Oliver & Associates   (1)
17300 Henderson Pass Ste 240, San Antonio, TX 78232-1568
Tel.: (210) 344-0205
Web Site: http://www.teamoliver.com
Other Accounting Services
N.A.I.C.S.: 541219
Jim Oliver (Pres)

Larkin Ervin & Shirley, LLP   (1)
7 Grogans Park Dr Ste 7, The Woodlands, TX 77380-2402
Tel.: (281) 931-8539
Web Site: http://www.larkin-ervin.com
Offices of Certified Public Accountants
N.A.I.C.S.: 541211

Mark M. Jones & Associates P.C.   (1)
6500 W Freeway, Fort Worth, TX 76116
Tel.: (817) 735-1110
Web Site: http://www.mmj-cpas.com
Offices of Certified Public Accountants
N.A.I.C.S.: 541211
Ron Allen (Mgr)

CALVIN GROUP
5813 Washington Blvd, Culver City, CA 90232
Tel.: (310) 287-2400
Web Site:
   http://www.calvingroups.com
Year Founded: 2007
Sales Range: $1-9.9 Million
Emp.: 15
IT Personnel Recruiter
N.A.I.C.S.: 561311
Joe Abrahams (Reg Dir)

CALVIN L. WADSWORTH CONSTRUCTION CO.
5498 E Butte Canyon Dr, Cave Creek, AZ 85331
Tel.: (801) 208-1957
Web Site:
   http://www.calwadsworth.com
Sales Range: $10-24.9 Million
Emp.: 30
Commercial & Office Buildings, Renovation & Repair
N.A.I.C.S.: 236220
Calvin L. Wadsworth (Pres)

CALVIN, GIORDANO & ASSOCIATES, INC.
1800 Eller Dr Ste 600, Fort Lauderdale, FL 33316
Tel.: (954) 921-7781   FL
Web Site:
   https://www.cgasolutions.com
Year Founded: 1937
Rev.: $25,600,000
Emp.: 220
Surveying, Engineering & Construction Support Services
N.A.I.C.S.: 541330

Robert McSweeney (Dir-Construction Engrg & Quality Assurance)
Eric Czerniejewski (Dir-Traffic Engrg)

CALVO ENTERPRISES, INC.
138 Martyr St, Hagatna, GU 96910
Tel.: (671) 472-6852
Retail, Insurance & Banking Services
N.A.I.C.S.: 524210

Subsidiaries:

Tokio Marine Pacific Insurance Limited   (1)
250 Rte 4 Ste 202, Hagatna, GU 96910
Tel.: (671) 475-8671
General Insurance Services
N.A.I.C.S.: 524210

CALYPSO ST. BARTH INC.
3302 Skillman Ave 5th Fl, Long Island City, NY 11101
Tel.: (212) 625-9880
Web Site:
   http://www.calypsostbarth.com
Sales Range: $10-24.9 Million
Emp.: 7
Women's Clothing Store
N.A.I.C.S.: 458110
Jessica Langone (Coord-Production Dev)
Shernette Matthews (Dir-Distr)
Louise Marino (Mgr-Payroll)

CALYPTE BIOMEDICAL CORPORATION
15875 SW 72nd Ave, Portland, OR 97224
Tel.: (503) 726-2227   DE
Web Site: http://www.calypte.com
Year Founded: 1998
Sales Range: Less than $1 Million
Emp.: 4
Diagnostic Biopharmaceuticals Mfr
N.A.I.C.S.: 334516
Kartlos Edilashvili (CFO & Sec)

CALYX TECHNOLOGY, INC.
6475 Camden Ave Ste 207, San Jose, CA 95120
Tel.: (408) 997-5525   CA
Web Site:
   https://www.calyxsoftware.com
Year Founded: 1991
Sales Range: $10-24.9 Million
Emp.: 60
Mortgage & Lending Software Developer & Publisher
N.A.I.C.S.: 513210
Doug Chang (Founder & CEO)
Sung Park (Sr VP-Product Dev)
Patrice Power (Dir-Mktg)
Bob Dougherty (Exec VP-Bus Dev)
David McLeod (Sls Mgr-Natl)

Subsidiaries:

Calyx Technology, Inc. - Sales, Support & Training Center   (1)
3500 Maple Ave Ste 500, Dallas, TX 75219
Tel.: (214) 252-5615
Web Site: http://www.calyxsupport.com
Mortgage & Lending Institution Software
Sales & Support Services
N.A.I.C.S.: 423430

CAM CONSULTANTS, INC.
1525 Corporate Woods Pkwy Ste 100, Uniontown, OH 44685
Tel.: (330) 896-3253   OH
Web Site:
   https://www.camincorp.com
Year Founded: 1984
Sales Range: $10-24.9 Million
Emp.: 22
Commercial & Office Building, New Construction
N.A.I.C.S.: 236220

Charles A. Mockbee (Chm)
Bob Galbraith (VP-Construction)
Denise Bloom (Mgr-Property)
Gary Thewes (Project Mgr)
Jeffrey Mockbee (CEO)
Joan Mockbee (Treas)
John Kauffman (Mgr-Property)
Julie Kernan (Bus Mgr)
Rob Guld (Project Mgr)
Traci Mockbee Hunt (VP-Sls)
Michael Mockbee (VP-Client Rels)

Subsidiaries:

Cam/Rb Inc   (1)
1525 Corporate Woods Pkwy Ste 100, Uniontown, OH 44685
Tel.: (330) 896-3253
Web Site: http://www.camincorp.com
Rev.: $610,000
Emp.: 4
Fast Food Restaurants & Stands
N.A.I.C.S.: 722513
Lisa Wise-Westfall (Mgr-Ops)

CAMAC INTERNATIONAL CORPORATION
1330 Post Oak Blvd Ste 2200, Houston, TX 77056
Tel.: (713) 965-5100
Web Site: https://www.camac.com
Year Founded: 1986
Sales Range: $1-4.9 Billion
Emp.: 1,000
Oil & Gas Exploration
N.A.I.C.S.: 211120
Kamoru A. Lawal (Pres)
Rose Valenzuela (VP-Admin)
Fisoye Delano (Sr VP-Gas & Power)
Kio Clement Bestmann (Exec Dir)
Adekunle Alli (Exec Dir-Accts & Fin)
Olayide Laide Olufemi (Exec Dir-Corp Svcs)
Jude Madubugwu (Gen Mgr-Fin & Accts)
Karim Souidi (Sr VP-Bus Dev)

Subsidiaries:

Allied Energy Corporation   (1)
1330 Post Oak Blvd Ste 2200 Central Twr, Houston, TX 77056
Tel.: (713) 965-5180
Web Site: http://www.camac.com
Rev.: $370,000
Emp.: 5
Business Management Consultant
N.A.I.C.S.: 541611

Allied Energy Investment Pty. Ltd.   (1)
Block C Suite 22 Hurlingham Office Park 59 Woodlands Drive, Hurlingham, Sandton, 2196, South Africa
Tel.: (27) 11 781 2104
Oil & Gas Exploration & Production Services
N.A.I.C.S.: 213112

Allied Energy Plc.   (1)
Plot 1649 Olosa Street, Victoria Island, Lagos, Nigeria
Tel.: (234) 1 4603357 9
Oil & Gas Exploration & Production Services
N.A.I.C.S.: 213112
Adekunle Alli (Controller-Fin)
Jude Madubugwu (Deputy Gen Mgr-Fin & Accts)
Kio Bestmann (Exec Dir)
Mickey Lawal (Vice Chm)
Olayide Olufemi (Gen Mgr-HR & Admin)

CAMAC Development Services Pty. Ltd.   (1)
2nd Floor Mindpearl Building West Quay Road, V&A Waterfront, Cape Town, 8001, South Africa
Tel.: (27) 21 418 2140
Oil & Gas Exploration & Production Services
N.A.I.C.S.: 213112

CAMAC International (UK) Ltd.   (1)
SAOC Ltd 80 Park Lane, London, W1K

7TR, United Kingdom
Tel.: (44) 20 3440 2925
Oil & Gas Exploration & Production Services
N.A.I.C.S.: 213112

CAMAC Nigeria Limited   (1)
26 T Y Danjuma Street, Asokoro, Abuja, Nigeria
Tel.: (234) 803 403 0120
Oil & Gas Exploration & Production Services
N.A.I.C.S.: 213112

CAMAC TRADING, LLC   (1)
1501 W Military Hwy, Pharr, TX 78577
Tel.: (956) 994-8229
Oil & Gas Exploration & Production Services
N.A.I.C.S.: 213112

Camac International Limited   (1)
SMB Genesis Building 3rd Floor, PO Box 32338, Georgetown, Cayman Islands
Tel.: (345) 949 6611
Oil & Gas Exploration & Production Services
N.A.I.C.S.: 213112
Kamoru Lawal (Mng Dir)

CAMARENA HEALTH
344 E 6th St, Madera, CA 93638
Tel.: (559) 664-4000   CA
Web Site:
   https://www.camarenahealth.org
Year Founded: 1978
Sales Range: $10-24.9 Million
Community Health Care Services
N.A.I.C.S.: 621498
Christine Howland (COO)
Paulo Soares (CEO)
Gabriel Mejia (Dir-HR)
Margarita Medina (Dir-Fin)
Seann Garcia (Treas)
Michael Gaskin (CIO)
Monique Asenjo-Wilhite (Co-Pres)
Edgar Jimenez (Sec)
Kenneth F. Bernstein (Chief Medical Officer)

CAMARES COMMUNICATIONS INC.
515 Vly St Ste 120, Maplewood, NJ 07040
Tel.: (973) 539-6000
Web Site: http://www.camares.com
Year Founded: 1982
Sales Range: $10-24.9 Million
Emp.: 13
Advetising Agency
N.A.I.C.S.: 541810

CAMARGOCOPELAND ARCHITECTS, LLP
14755 Preston Rd Ste 845, Dallas, TX 75254
Tel.: (972) 934-7600
Web Site:
   http://www.camargocopeland.com
Year Founded: 1985
Sales Range: $1-9.9 Million
Emp.: 20
Architectural Services
N.A.I.C.S.: 541310
Ed J. Copeland (Founding Partner & Principal)
Myriam E. Camargo (Founding Partner & Principal)
Melissa Hanson (Interior Designer)

CAMBA
1720 Church Ave 2nd Fl, Brooklyn, NY 11226
Tel.: (718) 287-2600   NY
Web Site: http://www.camba.org
Year Founded: 1977
Sales Range: $150-199.9 Million
Emp.: 2,053
Community Development Services
N.A.I.C.S.: 813319

Thomas J. Dambakly (Chief Admin Officer)
Rang T. Ngo (Chief Payroll Officer)
Kathleen Ames (Gen Counsel-Legal Svcs)
Katherine O'Neill (Chm)
Daniel Ramm (Treas & Sec)
Christopher Zarra (Vice Chm)
Claire Harding-Keefe (Sr VP)
Janet Miller (Sr VP)
Joanne M. Oplustil (Pres & CEO)
Justin Nardilla (CFO)
Michael Erhard (Sr VP)
Joan McFeely (Chief Compliance Officer)
Valerie Barton Richardson (VP)
David A. Rowe (VP)

CAMBECK PETROLEUM CORP.
505 S Pearl St, Janesville, WI 53545
Tel.: (608) 754-4393
Sales Range: $25-49.9 Million
Emp.: 8
Petroleum Products
N.A.I.C.S.: 424720
Tom Warrichaiat (Controller)
James Campbell Sr. (Pres)

CAMBEY & WEST, INC.
120 N Route 9W, Congers, NY 10920
Tel.: (845) 267-3490   NY
Web Site:
   http://www.cambeywest.com
Year Founded: 1986
Sales Range: $1-9.9 Million
Emp.: 35
Subscription Fulfillment Services
N.A.I.C.S.: 518210
Jane Giles (Dir-Bus Dev)
Carrie Caruana (Jr Acct-Mgr)
Cynthia Chodrow (Acct Mgr)
Diane Cuellar (Pres)

CAMBIA HEALTH SOLUTIONS, INC.
200 SW Market St, Portland, OR 97201-5766
Tel.: (503) 725-1628   OR
Year Founded: 1941
Sales Range: $5-14.9 Billion
Emp.: 5,000
Holding Company; Medical, Dental & Life Insurance Products & Services
N.A.I.C.S.: 551112
Mohan Nair (Chief Innovation Officer & Sr VP)
Jared L. Short (Pres & CEO)
Richard Popiel (Chief Medical Officer)
Peggy Maguire (Sr VP-Corp Accountability & Performance)
Carol Kruse (CMO & Sr VP)
Mark Stimpson (Chief HR Officer & Sr VP)
Gail Baker (Sr VP-Strategic Comm)
Scott Powers (Pres-Health Plan Ops)
Laurent Rotival (CIO & Sr VP-Strategic Tech Solutions)
Rob MacNaughton (Chief Product Officer)
Steven Gaspar (Chief Actuarial Officer & Sr VP)
William Krenz (Sr VP-Govt Programs)
Scott Burton (Dir-Revenue Mgmt & Portfolio Positioning)
Zach Snyder (Dir-Govt Affairs)
Stephen Foxley (Dir-Govt Affairs-Utah)
Sean Robbins (Sr VP-Pub Affairs & Policy)
Jennifer Danielson (VP-Pub Affairs & Strategic Advocacy)
Amy Griffin (Officer-Compliance)
Deneil Patterson (Officer-Compliance)

Cambia Health Solutions, Inc.—(Continued)

Rosemary Reeve (*Chief Compliance Officer*)
Mihir Patel (*Chief Pharmacy Officer*)
Angela Dowling (*Chief Revenue Officer*)
Faraz Shafiq (*Chief Artificial Intelligence Officer*)
Tonya Adams (*Chief Health Svcs Officer & Sr VP*)
Lindsay Harris (*Chief Comml Officer*)
Vincent P. Price (*CFO & Exec VP*)

Subsidiaries:

Asuris Northwest Health **(1)**
528 E Spokane Falls Blvd Ste 301, Spokane, WA 99202
Tel.: (509) 922-8072
Web Site: http://www.asuris.com
Emp.: 17
Health Care Srvices
N.A.I.C.S.: 621999
Brady Cass (*Pres*)

HealthSparq, Inc. **(1)**
100 SW Market St M/S WW3 31, Portland, OR 97201
Web Site: http://www.healthsparq.com
Emp.: 70
Software Development Services
N.A.I.C.S.: 541511
Mark Menton (*CEO*)
Matthew E. Parker (*VP-Product*)

LifeMap Assurance Company **(1)**
PO Box 1271, Portland, OR 97207-1271
Web Site: http://www.lifemapco.com
Health Insurance Services
N.A.I.C.S.: 524114
Jim Clark (*VP-Risk Mgmt*)
Scott Wilkinson (*VP-Ops & Tech*)
Chris Blanton (*Pres & CEO*)

Regence BlueCross BlueShield of Oregon **(1)**
100 SW Market St, Portland, OR 97201
Tel.: (503) 225-5406
Web Site: http://www.regence.com
Sales Range: $1-4.9 Billion
Emp.: 2,475
Medical, Dental & Life Insurance Services
N.A.I.C.S.: 524114
Angela Dowling (*Chief Revenue Officer-Regence Health Plans*)
Richard Popiel (*Chief Medical Officer & Exec VP-Health Care Svcs*)
Andrew Over (*VP-Reg Market*)
Ian Gordon (*Sr VP-Health Insurance Ops*)

Subsidiary (Domestic):

Regence HMO Oregon, Inc. **(2)**
201 High St SE, Salem, OR 97301 **(100%)**
Tel.: (503) 375-4336
Sales Range: $600-649.9 Million
Healthcare Services Contractor
N.A.I.C.S.: 524114
Mark B. Ganz (*Pres & CEO*)

Regence Life & Health Insurance Co. **(2)**
100 SW Mkt St Ste E 3 A, Portland, OR 97201 **(100%)**
Tel.: (503) 225-6913
Sales Range: $75-99.9 Million
Emp.: 88
Life Insurance Provider
N.A.I.C.S.: 524113

Regence BlueCross BlueShield of Utah **(1)**
2890 E Cottonwood Pkwy, Salt Lake City, UT 84121
Tel.: (801) 333-2000
Web Site: http://www.regence.com
Medical Insurance Products & Services
N.A.I.C.S.: 524114
Jennifer B. Danielson (*Pres-Mktg*)
Mark D. Hiatt (*Exec Dir-Medical*)
James Swayze (*Pres-Regence Health Plans*)

Sprig Health, Inc. **(1)**
100 SW Market St, Portland, OR 97201
Tel.: (855) 697-7744
Web Site: http://www.sprighealth.com
Health Care Srvices

Marcee Chmait (*Gen Mgr*)

TailorWell Inc. **(1)**
1011 Western Ave Ste 910, Seattle, WA 98104
Tel.: (877) 293-4150
Web Site: http://www.tailorwell.com
General Insurance Services
N.A.I.C.S.: 524210
Peter Morris (*CEO*)
Joe Parr (*Dir-Tech*)

CAMBIAR INVESTORS LLC
200 Columbine St Ste 800, Denver, CO 80206
Tel.: (303) 302-9000   CO
Web Site: https://www.cambiar.com
Year Founded: 1973
Sales Range: $150-199.9 Million
Emp.: 49
Asset Management Services
N.A.I.C.S.: 523940
Brian M. Barish (*Pres & Chief Investment Officer*)
Andrew P. Baumbusch (*Principal-Investment*)
Jennifer M. Dunne (*Principal-Investment*)
Ania A. Aldrich (*Principal-Investment*)
Colin M. Dunn (*Principal-Investment*)
Todd L. Edwards (*Principal-Investment*)
Munish Malhotra (*Principal-Investment*)
Alvaro Shiraishi (*Principal-Investment*)
Christopher T. Berry (*Sr VP-Sls & Client Servicing*)
Molly D. Cisneros (*Sr VP-Sls & Client Servicing*)
Christopher Curwen (*Sr VP-Sls & Client Servicing*)
Karl R. S. Engelmann (*Sr VP-Sls & Client Servicing*)
Katie S. Frisch (*Sr VP-Sls & Client Servicing*)
Ryan J. Newton (*Sr VP-Sls & Client Servicing*)
Greg Vandervelde (*Sr VP-Sls & Client Servicing*)
John Le (*Sr VP-Mktg & Analytics*)
Evan Geldzahler (*Gen Counsel*)
Leonard J. Keating III (*Sr VP-Sls & Client Servicing*)

CAMBRAY MUTUAL HOLDING COMPANY
42 Church St, Gouverneur, NY 13642
Tel.: (315) 287-2600
Mutual Holding Company
N.A.I.C.S.: 551112
Charles VanVleet (*Pres/CEO-Gouverneur Bancorp*)
Kimberly Adams (*CFO-Gouverneur*)

Subsidiaries:

Gouverneur Bancorp, Inc. **(1)**
42 Church St, Gouverneur, NY 13642 **(57.4%)**
Tel.: (315) 287-2600
Web Site: https://www.gouverneurbank.com
Rev.: $9,337,000
Assets: $197,260,000
Liabilities: $164,495,000
Net Worth: $32,765,000
Earnings: $539,000
Emp.: 40
Fiscal Year-end: 09/30/2024
Bank Holding Company
N.A.I.C.S.: 551111
Charles C. Van Vleet Jr. (*Pres/CEO-GS&L Municipal Bank*)
Henry J. Leader (*Bd of Dirs & Sec*)
David C. McClure (*Chm, Exec VP & VP-Real Estate*)
Sadie M. Hall (*COO, Officer-Compliance & VP*)

Subsidiary (Domestic):

Citizens Bank of Cape Vincent, Inc. **(2)**

154 Broadway, Cape Vincent, NY 13618
Tel.: (315) 654-2115
Web Site: http://www.citizensbankofcapevincent.com
Sales Range: $1-9.9 Million
Emp.: 13
Commericial Banking
N.A.I.C.S.: 522110
Debra Montondo (*Mgr-Branch*)
Faye C. Waterman (*CEO & Pres*)

Gouverneur Savings & Loan Association **(2)**
42 Church St, Gouverneur, NY 13642-1416
Tel.: (315) 287-2600
Web Site: http://www.gouverneurbank.com
Savings & Loan Institution
N.A.I.C.S.: 522180
Henry J. Leader (*Sec*)
Sadie M. Hall (*COO, Officer-Compliance & VP*)
Charles Vanvleet (*Vice Chm, Pres & CEO*)
Cortney Sharpe (*Treas*)
F. Toby Morrow (*Chm*)
Faye C. Waterman (*Exec VP*)

CAMBRIA AUTOMOTIVE COMPANIES
565 Dowd Ave, Elizabeth, NJ 07201
Tel.: (908) 354-2100
Web Site: https://www.cambrias.com
Rev.: $65,000,000
Emp.: 50
Sales of Trucks
N.A.I.C.S.: 423110
Joseph S. Cambria (*CEO*)
James E. Cambria Jr. (*Chm*)

CAMBRIA SOLUTIONS, INC.
The MARRS Bldg 1050 20th St Ste 275, Sacramento, CA 95811
Tel.: (916) 326-4446   CA
Web Site:
http://www.cambriasolutions.com
Sales Range: $1-9.9 Million
Emp.: 38
Management Consulting Services
N.A.I.C.S.: 541690
Robert Rodriguez (*Founder & CEO*)
Anand Adoni (*VP*)
Edith Thacher (*Sr Mgr*)
Ashok Rout (*Dir-Tech Svcs*)
Dhiraj Talwar (*Sr Dir-Health & Human Svcs*)
Randall Kaya (*Controller-Enterprise*)
Suzanne Vitale (*Pres*)
Kari Gutierrez (*Mktg Dir*)
Blake Jeter (*Principal & Exec Dir-Strategic Growth*)

CAMBRIDGE ARIZONA INSURANCE COMPANY
333 E Osborn Rd Ste 300, Phoenix, AZ 85012-2322
Tel.: (602) 512-8132   AZ
Year Founded: 2008
Sales Range: $1-9.9 Million
Health Insurance Services
N.A.I.C.S.: 524114
Robert L. Meyer (*Pres & CEO*)
Craig McKnight (*Treas*)
Carmen Neuberger (*Sec*)
Carmen Neuberger (*Sec*)
Craig McKnight (*Treas*)
Robert L. Meyer (*Pres & CEO*)

CAMBRIDGE ASSOCIATES LLC
125 High St, Boston, MA 02110
Tel.: (617) 457-7500
Web Site:
http://www.cambridgeassociate.com
Sales Range: $50-74.9 Million
Emp.: 230
Investment Advisory Services
N.A.I.C.S.: 523940
Alex Koriath (*Head-Pensions Practice-Europe*)

Sean Hanna (*Chief Compliance Officer*)
Jason Roberts (*CTO*)
Steven Y. Quintero (*Gen Counsel*)
Deirdre D. Nectow (*Head-Global Bus Dev*)
David Thurston (*Head-Global Investment Res*)
David T. Shukis (*Head-Global Investment Svcs*)
Steven W. Nelson (*Head-Portfolio Svcs*)
David Druley (*Chm & CEO*)
Philip Walton (*Pres-Private Client Practice*)
Jeff Blazek (*Chief Investment, Officer/Mng Dir & Pension Practice*)
Sona Menon (*Head-Pensions-North America*)
Elizabeth Ramos (*Mng Dir & Head-Human Capital*)
Christie Briscoe Zarkovich (*Head-Mission Related Investing Res-Arlington*)
Noel O'Neill (*Pres & Head-Investment-Global*)
Jasmine Richards (*Sr Dir-Investment & Mgr-Diversity*)
Ashby Hatch (*Head-Pub Equities Res*)
Eric Thielscher (*Head-Pub Investment Res*)

CAMBRIDGE CAPITAL ACQUISITION CORPORATION
525 S Flagler Dr Ste 201, West Palm Beach, FL 33401
Tel.: (561) 932-1600   DE
Year Founded: 2013
Sales Range: Less than $1 Million
Emp.: 2
Investment Services
N.A.I.C.S.: 523999

CAMBRIDGE CREDIT COUNSELING CORP.
67 Hunt St Ste 305, Agawam, MA 01001
Tel.: (413) 821-8900
Web Site:
http://www.cambridgecredit.org
Year Founded: 1996
Sales Range: $25-49.9 Million
Emp.: 260
Debt Counseling; Financial Education, Credit & Debt Management Services
N.A.I.C.S.: 812990
Christopher A. Viale (*Pres & CEO*)
Damian Vincze (*Mgr-Quality Assurance*)
Jennifer Cosentini (*Dir-Housing*)
Robin Kellerman (*Mgr-Client Svcs*)

CAMBRIDGE FINANCIAL GROUP, INC.
1374 Massachusetts Ave, Cambridge, MA 02138
Tel.: (617) 441-4155
Web Site:
https://www.cambridgesavings.com
Sales Range: $100-124.9 Million
Emp.: 380
Holding Company; Business Banking & Financial Services
N.A.I.C.S.: 551111
Wayne Patenaude (*Pres & CEO*)

Subsidiaries:

Cambridge Savings Bank **(1)**
1374 Massachusetts Ave, Cambridge, MA 02138-3822
Tel.: (617) 441-4155
Web Site: http://www.cambridgesavings.com

Sales Range: $50-74.9 Million
Emp.: 300
Banking Services
N.A.I.C.S.: 522180
Douglas J. Faithfull (*Chief Lending Officer & Exec VP*)
Wayne Patenaude (*Pres & CEO*)
Mark T. Tracy (*CTO & Sr VP*)
Susan Lapierre (*Sr VP*)
Michael Gilles (*CFO, Treas & Sr VP*)
Lisa Rodriguez (*VP & Dir-Mktg*)
Stephen J. Coukos (*Gen Counsel & Exec VP*)
Keith Broyles (*Sr VP & Head-Asset-Based Lending*)
John Bobbin (*First VP*)
Carlos Osornio (*Sr VP-Svcs*)
Katie Catlender (*Chief Customer Officer & Exec VP*)
Tony Macchi (*Sr VP-Digital & Product*)
Kevin McGuire (*CIO*)

CAMBRIDGE HEALTH ALLIANCE
1493 Cambridge St, Cambridge, MA 02139
Tel.: (617) 665-1000
Web Site: https://www.challiance.org
Sales Range: $1-4.9 Billion
Emp.: 2,000
Medical Health Network
N.A.I.C.S.: 622110
Paul Allison (*Sr VP & Gen Counsel*)
Doug Bailey (*Chief Comm Officer*)
Paul Allen (*Chief Quality Officer*)
Joy Curtis (*Sr VP-HR*)
Renee Kessler (*COO & Exec VP*)
Steve Carter (*Sr VP-IT*)
Teresa Royer (*Chief Nursing Officer*)
Stephen Greene (*Dir-Patient Fin Svcs*)
John O'Hara (*VP-Primary Care Ops*)
Patrick Wardell (*CEO*)
Brian Herrick (*CIO*)

CAMBRIDGE HEALTHTECH INSTITUTE
250 1st Ave Ste 300, Needham, MA 02494
Tel.: (781) 972-5400
Web Site:
http://www.chicorporate.com
Year Founded: 1992
Sales Range: $25-49.9 Million
Emp.: 125
Life Science Information Products & Services
N.A.I.C.S.: 519290
Phillips Kuhl (*Pres*)
Edel O'Regan (*VP-Conference Production*)
Jim MacNeil (*VP-Mktg*)
Angela Parsons (*VP-Bus Dev*)
Shauna Samson (*Dir-HR*)
Janette Mandile-Harper (*Dir-Meeting Plng*)
Ben Patel (*CFO*)

Subsidiaries:

Cambridge Healthtech Media Group **(1)**
250 1st Ave Ste 300, Needham, MA 02494 **(100%)**
Tel.: (781) 972-1341
Web Site: http://www.chimediagroup.com
Sales Range: $25-49.9 Million
Emp.: 100
Life Sciences Magazine & Online Media Publisher
N.A.I.C.S.: 513120
Allison Proffitt (*Dir-Editorial*)

CAMBRIDGE INFORMATION GROUP, INC.
7200 Wisconsin Ave Ste 601, Bethesda, MD 20814-4837
Tel.: (301) 961-6700		MD
Web Site:
http://www.cambridgeinfogroup.com

Year Founded: 1971
Sales Range: $75-99.9 Million
Emp.: 2,000
Investment Holding Company; Education, Research & Information Services
N.A.I.C.S.: 551112
Andrew M. Snyder (*CEO*)
Robert N. Snyder (*Founder & Chm*)
Barbara Inkellis (*Gen Counsel & Sr VP*)
Larisa Avner Trainor (*Gen Counsel & Sr VP*)
Michael K. Chung (*CEO & COO*)
Jill Snyder Granader (*Dir-Comm*)
George Allen (*Chief Investment Officer*)

Subsidiaries:

R.R. Bowker LLC **(1)**
630 Central Ave, New Providence, NJ 07974-1541
Tel.: (908) 795-3500
Web Site: http://www.bowker.com
Sales Range: $25-49.9 Million
Emp.: 100
Database Publisher; Bibliographic Information & Searching, Analytical Promotional & Ordering Services for Booksellers, Libraries & Patrons
N.A.I.C.S.: 513130
Peter Ashekian (*Mgr-Data Sls*)
Paul Shannon (*Acct Exec*)

Subsidiary (Domestic):

SIPX, Inc. **(2)**
855 El Camino Real Bldg 4 Ste 200, Palo Alto, CA 94301
Tel.: (248) 349-7810
Web Site: http://www.sipx.com
Digital Content & Online Education Software Solutions
N.A.I.C.S.: 513210
Franny Lee (*Co-Founder & VP-Bus Dev*)

Subsidiary (Non-US):

Thorpe-Bowker **(2)**
Level One 607 St Kilda Rd, Melbourne, 3004, VIC, Australia **(100%)**
Tel.: (61) 385178333
Web Site: http://www.thorpe.com.au
Sales Range: $1-9.9 Million
Emp.: 15
Bibliogaphic Information Services for Book Professionals
N.A.I.C.S.: 513140
Kevin Mark (*Mgr-Publr Rels*)
Alexandra Parfrey (*Mgr-Data Collection*)

CAMBRIDGE INVESTMENT GROUP, INC.
1776 Pleasant Plain Rd, Fairfield, IA 52556-8757
Tel.: (641) 472-5100
Web Site: http://www.cir2.com
Portfolio Management
N.A.I.C.S.: 523940
John Tozzi (*CEO*)

Subsidiaries:

Cambridge Investment Research, Inc. **(1)**
1776 Pleasant Plain Rd, Fairfield, IA 52556
Tel.: (800) 777-6080
Web Site: http://www.joincambridge.com
Financial & Brokerage Services
N.A.I.C.S.: 523150
Amy Webber (*Pres & CEO*)
Eric v (*Chm*)
Rick Boyles (*CFO & Exec VP-HR*)

Subsidiary (Domestic):

Jordan Creek Financial Solutions **(2)**
140 S 68th St Ste 2200, West Des Moines, IA 50266
Tel.: (515) 381-0984
Web Site: http://www.jordancreekfs.com
Security Brokers & Dealers
N.A.I.C.S.: 523150

CAMBRIDGE MUTUAL FIRE

INSURANCE COMPANY
95 Old River Rd, Andover, MA 01810
Tel.: (978) 475-3300
Year Founded: 1833
Sales Range: $25-49.9 Million
Emp.: 250
Direct Property & Casualty Insurance Services
N.A.I.C.S.: 524126
Peter Anderson (*Asst VP-Claims*)
Donald F. Vose (*Sec & VP*)
Malcolm W. Brawn (*Pres & CEO*)

CAMBRIDGE SHARPE, INC.
27521 Schoolcraft Rd, Livonia, MI 48150
Tel.: (248) 613-5562
Web Site:
http://www.cambridgesharpe.com
Sales Range: $10-24.9 Million
Emp.: 100
Snack Food Mfr
N.A.I.C.S.: 311919
Richard E. Sharpe (*Pres*)

CAMBRIDGE STREET METAL CO.
82 Stevens St, East Taunton, MA 02718-1314
Web Site: https://www.csmetal.net
Year Founded: 1933
Metals & Packaging Supplies Whslr
N.A.I.C.S.: 423510
Brian O'Hara (*Gen Mgr*)
Joe Caron (*Mgr-Warehouse*)
Stacie Barbosa (*Mgr-Accts Payable*)

CAMBRIDGE UNDERWRITERS LIMITED
15415 Middlebelt Rd, Livonia, MI 48154
Tel.: (734) 525-0927
Web Site: http://www.cambridge-pc.com
Sales Range: $10-24.9 Million
Emp.: 50
Fire, Marine & Casualty Insurance Carriers
N.A.I.C.S.: 524126
Kenneth R. Hale (*Chm*)
Michael Hale (*CEO*)

CAMBRIDGE-LEE INDUSTRIES, INC.
86 Tube Dr, Reading, PA 19605
Tel.: (610) 916-7749		DE
Web Site: https://www.camlee.com
Year Founded: 1975
Sales Range: $200-249.9 Million
Emp.: 400
Mfr of Copper Products
N.A.I.C.S.: 423510

Subsidiaries:

Cambridge-Lee (Europe) Ltd. **(1)**
1 Camphill Industrial Estate, West, Byfleet, KT14 6 EW, Surrey, United Kingdom **(100%)**
Tel.: (44) 1932352511
Sales Range: $25-49.9 Million
Emp.: 10
Metal Stockholder
N.A.I.C.S.: 423510

Cambridge-Lee Canada Ltd. **(1)**
30 Intermodal Dr Ste 202, Brampton, L6T 5K1, ON, Canada **(100%)**
Tel.: (905) 455-0010
Web Site:
http://www.camleeindustrialmetals.com
Sales Range: $25-49.9 Million
Emp.: 1
Marketing & Distribution of Non Ferrous Metals
N.A.I.C.S.: 423510
Mike Klopot (*Mgr-Sls*)

Reading Tube Division **(1)**
86 Tube Dr, Reading, PA 19605

Tel.: (610) 926-4141
Web Site: http://www.readingtube.com
Sales Range: $400-449.9 Million
Mfr of Copper Tubing
N.A.I.C.S.: 331420
Andrea Funk (*Gen Mgr*)

CAMBRO MANUFACTURING COMPANY
5801 Skylab Rd, Huntington Beach, CA 92647
Tel.: (714) 848-1555		CA
Web Site: https://www.cambro.com
Year Founded: 1951
Sales Range: $100-124.9 Million
Emp.: 1,000
Mfr of Equipment for the Food Service Industry
N.A.I.C.S.: 326199
Argyle Campbell (*Owner*)
Ken French (*Mgr-New Zealand*)

CAMCARE HEALTH CORPORATION
817 Federal St, Camden, NJ 08103
Tel.: (856) 583-2400		NJ
Web Site: https://www.camcare.net
Year Founded: 1980
Sales Range: $10-24.9 Million
Emp.: 222
Health Care Srvices
N.A.I.C.S.: 622110
David L. Whaley (*CFO & VP*)
Mark K. Bryant (*Pres & CEO*)

CAMCO CHEMICAL COMPANY INC.
8150 Holton Dr, Florence, KY 41042
Tel.: (859) 727-3200
Web Site: http://www.camco-chem.com
Sales Range: $10-24.9 Million
Emp.: 140
Chemical & Oil Manufactuer
N.A.I.C.S.: 325612
Linda Meister (*Mgr-Fin*)
Dan Theissen (*VP-Pur*)
Adrian Hothem (*VP-Bus Dev*)
Richard J. Rolfes Jr. (*Pres & CEO*)

CAMCO INTERNATIONAL GROUP INCORPORATED
333 Perry St Ste 301, Castle Rock, CO 80104
Tel.: (720) 897-6677
Year Founded: 1989
Carbon Management Strategy
N.A.I.C.S.: 335991
Jim Wiest (*Mng Dir*)

CAMCO MANUFACTURING INC.
121 Landmark Dr, Greensboro, NC 27409
Tel.: (336) 668-7661
Web Site: https://www.camco.net
Year Founded: 1968
Rev.: $54,000,000
Emp.: 190
Mfr of Water Heater Controls, Antifreeze & Other RV Accessories
N.A.I.C.S.: 325998
Robert Mancari (*Project Mgr*)
David Tickle (*Mgr-Facilities*)
Craig Miller (*Mgr-Sls-Natl*)
Denise Szamier (*Mgr-Credit-AR*)
Keith Cook (*Sr VP-Sls*)
Mike Voyles (*Dir-Dealer Mktg*)
Renee Smith (*Dir-Portfolio Dev*)
Mozell Williams (*VP-Developer Association Svcs*)

CAMCOR INC.
2273 S Church St, Burlington, NC 27215
Tel.: (336) 228-0251

Camcor Inc.—(Continued)

Web Site: http://www.camcor.com
Year Founded: 1949
Sales Range: $10-24.9 Million
Emp.: 50
Distr & Retailer Of Photographic
Cameras, Projectors, Equipment &
Supplies
N.A.I.C.S.: 423410
Raymond E. Bailey *(Pres)*
Grant Hamilton *(Mgr-VA & WV Territory)*
Ray Bailey Jr. *(Mgr-Sls)*

CAMCRAFT INC.
1080 Muirfield Dr, Hanover Park, IL
60133-5469
Tel.: (630) 582-6000
Web Site: https://www.camcraft.com
Rev.: $13,600,000
Emp.: 200
Screw Machine Products
N.A.I.C.S.: 332721
Michael Bertsche *(Pres)*
Bern Bertsche *(Chm)*
Steve Olsen *(VP)*

CAMDEN IRON & METAL INC.
1500 S 6th St, Camden, NJ 08104-
1402
Tel.: (856) 365-7500
Web Site:
    http://www.camdeniron.com
Year Founded: 1988
Sales Range: $100-124.9 Million
Emp.: 145
Scrap Metal Processing
N.A.I.C.S.: 423930
Steve D'Ottavi *(Mgr-HR)*
Harry Hagan *(Dir-Marine Ops)*
John Hammerle *(Mgr-Pur)*
Cynthia McKeown *(Dir-Environmental, Health & Safety)*

Subsidiaries:

SPC Corporation-Philadelphia   (1)
2600 Penrose Ave, Philadelphia, PA 19145
Tel.: (215) 952-1500
Web Site: http://www.camdeniron.com
Sales Range: $10-24.9 Million
Emp.: 40
Scrap & Waste Metals Recyclers
N.A.I.C.S.: 423930

CAMDEN PARTNERS HOLD-INGS, LLC
500 E Pratt St Ste 1200, Baltimore,
MD 21202
Tel.: (410) 878-6800
Web Site:
    http://www.camdenpartners.com
Year Founded: 1995
Emp.: 20
Privater Equity Firm
N.A.I.C.S.: 523999
David L. Warnock *(Sr Partner)*
David L. Warnock *(Sr Partner)*
Richard M. Berkeley *(Sr Partner)*
Jason R. Tagler *(Partner)*
Sheri L. Sprigg *(Office Mgr)*
George C. Petrocheilos *(Partner)*
Meghan M. McGee *(Partner)*

Subsidiaries:

New Horizons Worldwide, Inc.   (1)
100 Four Falls Corporate Ctr Ste 408, West
Conshohocken, PA 19428-4132
Tel.: (484) 567-3000
Web Site: http://www.newhorizons.com
Sales Range: $25-49.9 Million
Holding Company; Computer Training Centers Owner & Franchisor
N.A.I.C.S.: 551112
David L. Warnock *(Chm)*
David L. Warnock *(Chm)*

Subsidiary (Domestic):

NH Learning Solutions
Corporation   (2)
14115 Farmington Rd, Livonia, MI 48154
Tel.: (734) 525-1501
Web Site:
    http://www.nhlearningsolutions.com
Computer Learning Facilities
N.A.I.C.S.: 611519
Tynan Fischer *(COO & Sr VP)*
Brian Zibricky *(VP-Mktg & Products)*
Mark A. McManus Jr. *(Pres & CEO)*

Subsidiary (Domestic):

Computer Training Associates of Chicago, Inc.   (3)
525 W Van Buren St Ste 300, Chicago, IL
60607
Tel.: (773) 693-6000
Web Site:
    http://www.nhlearningsolutions.com
Computer Training Services
N.A.I.C.S.: 611420

New Horizons Computer Learning
Center of Cleveland, LLC   (3)
1 Infinity Corporate Ctr Dr Ste 250, Garfield
Heights, OH 44125
Tel.: (216) 332-7960
Web Site: http://www.nhcleveland.com
Computer Training Center
N.A.I.C.S.: 611420
Eric Strouse *(Gen Mgr)*

New Horizons Computer Learning
Center of Metropolitan New York,
Inc.   (3)
462 Seventh Ave 6th Fl, New York, NY
10018
Tel.: (646) 695-5700
Web Site: http://www.nhls.com
Computer Training Center
N.A.I.C.S.: 611420

Subsidiary (Domestic):

New Horizons Computer Learning
Centers, Inc.   (2)
1900 S State College Blvd Ste 450, Anaheim, CA 92806
Tel.: (714) 712-1000
Web Site: http://www.newhorizons.com
Sales Range: $50-74.9 Million
Patent Owners & Lessors of Computer
Training Centers
N.A.I.C.S.: 533110

Unit (Domestic):

New Horizons Computer Learning
Center of Southern California   (3)
1900 S State College Blvd Ste 100, Anaheim, CA 92806-0101
Tel.: (714) 221-3100
Web Site: http://www.nhsocal.com
Sales Range: $1-9.9 Million
Computer Training Centers
N.A.I.C.S.: 611420
Pablo DaSilva *(Branch Mgr)*
Ryan Landry *(Branch Mgr)*

Proposal Software, Inc.   (1)
1140 US Hwy 287 Ste 400-102, Broomfield,
CO 80020
Tel.: (203) 604-6597
Web Site: http://www.proposalsoftware.com
Offices of Dentists
N.A.I.C.S.: 621210
Glenda L. Reaux *(Mng Dir-Client Svcs)*

CAMELBACK FORD
1330 E Camelback Rd, Phoenix, AZ
85014
Tel.: (602) 264-1611
Web Site:
    https://www.camelbackford.com
Year Founded: 2001
Sales Range: $75-99.9 Million
Emp.: 100
New Car Retailer
N.A.I.C.S.: 441110
Shahzad Latis *(Controller)*
Rob Hubler *(Gen Mgr)*

CAMELBACK SKI CORPORA-TION
1 Camelback Rd, Tannersville, PA
18372
Tel.: (570) 629-1661
Web Site:
    http://www.camelbeach.com
Sales Range: $10-24.9 Million
Emp.: 900
Ski Resort
N.A.I.C.S.: 713920
Brian Bossuyt *(Mgr-Ticket)*

**CAMELLIA FOOD STORES,
INC.**
1300 Diamond Spring Rd Ste 500,
Virginia Beach, VA 23455
Tel.: (757) 855-3371
Web Site: http://www.freshpride.com
Year Founded: 1938
Sales Range: $25-49.9 Million
Emp.: 500
Retail Groceries; Dairy Products &
Confectionery Products
N.A.I.C.S.: 445110
Richard A. Saunders *(Treas & Sec)*
Greg Johnson *(Dir-Maintenance)*
Dan Hopkins *(CFO)*
Wilbur Bryant *(CFO)*
James L. Harrell III *(Chm)*

Subsidiaries:

Be-Lo Markets Inc.   (1)
1300 Diamond Springs Rd Ste 500, Virginia
Beach, VA 23455   (100%)
Tel.: (757) 855-3371
Retail Grocery Stores
N.A.I.C.S.: 445110

Eastern Shore Markets, Inc.   (1)
1300 Diamond Springs Rd Ste 500, Virginia
Beach, VA 23455-1917   (100%)
Tel.: (757) 855-3371
Web Site: http://www.freshpride.com
Sales Range: $10-24.9 Million
Emp.: 15
Retail Grocery Supermarkets
N.A.I.C.S.: 445110

CAMERA CORNER INC.
529 N Monroe Ave, Green Bay, WI
54305
Tel.: (920) 435-5353
Web Site: https://www.cccp.com
Sales Range: $25-49.9 Million
Emp.: 110
Computer & Software Stores
N.A.I.C.S.: 449210
Rick Chernick *(CEO)*
Aaron Jamir *(VP-Tech Svcs & HR)*

CAMERA REPAIR INSTRU-MENT SERVICE
250 N 54th St, Chandler, AZ 85226
Tel.: (480) 940-1103
Web Site: http://www.criscam.com
Year Founded: 1984
Sales Range: $1-9.9 Million
Emp.: 14
Photographic & Digital Imaging
Equipment Repair Services
N.A.I.C.S.: 449210
Mark Treadwell *(Pres & CEO)*

CAMERON & COMPANY, INC.
9081 W Sahara Ave Ste 270, Las
Vegas, NV 89117-4806
Tel.: (702) 259-0536
Web Site: https://www.temp-pharmacist.com
Year Founded: 1970
Sales Range: $10-24.9 Million
Emp.: 50
Medical Help Service
N.A.I.C.S.: 561320
Ronald G. Cameron *(CEO)*
Patsy Rivera *(Dir-Ops)*

**CAMERON ENGINEERING &
ASSOCIATES, LLP**
100 Sunnyside Blvd, Woodbury, NY
11797
Tel.: (516) 827-4900
Web Site:
    http://www.cameronengineering.com
Year Founded: 1996
Sales Range: $1-9.9 Million
Emp.: 50
Engineeering Services
N.A.I.C.S.: 541330
John D. Cameron *(Founder & Mng
Partner)*
Kevin McAndrew *(Partner)*
Laszlo Bodak *(Exec VP)*
Michael A. Neal *(CFO)*

Subsidiaries:

Bodak-Cameron Engineering   (1)
45 W 36th St Fl 3, New York, NY 10018
Tel.: (212) 643-1444
Engineeering Services
N.A.I.C.S.: 541330
Laszlo Bodak *(VP)*

CAMERON GENERAL CORPO-RATION
140 S Dearborn St Ste 900, Chicago,
IL 60603
Tel.: (312) 263-1620
Year Founded: 1986
Rev.: $80,000,000
Emp.: 80
Insurance Agents, Brokers & Services
N.A.I.C.S.: 524210
Fred H. Pearson *(Pres & CEO)*
Kenneth Heyman *(CFO)*

Subsidiaries:

Associated Claims Enterprises
Inc.   (1)
5703 Walnut Ave, Downers Grove, IL
60516-1002
Tel.: (312) 263-1620
Rev.: $210,000
Emp.: 10
Insurance Agents, Brokers & Services
N.A.I.C.S.: 524292

CAMERON HOLDINGS COR-PORATION
1200 Prospect St Ste 325, La Jolla,
CA 92037
Tel.: (858) 551-1335
Web Site: https://www.cameron-holdings.com
Year Founded: 1978
Privater Equity Firm
N.A.I.C.S.: 523999
Lynn E. Gorguze *(Pres & CEO)*
Donald C. Metzger *(Sr Mng Dir)*
Brian A. Lovett *(Mng Dir)*

Subsidiaries:

Cameron Holdings Corporation - St.
Louis Office   (1)
13515 Barrett Pkwy Dr, Ballwin, MO 63021
Tel.: (314) 984-0700
Web Site: http://www.cameron-holdings.com
Sales Range: $50-74.9 Million
Emp.: 5
Privater Equity Firm
N.A.I.C.S.: 523999
Donald C. Metzger *(VP)*

Multi-Pack Solutions LLC   (1)
1804 W Central Rd, Mount Prospect, IL
60056
Tel.: (847) 635-6772
Web Site:
    http://www.multipacksolutions.com
Holding Company; Outsourced Consumer
Product Packaging Services
N.A.I.C.S.: 551112
Tom McLenithan *(VP-Bus Dev & Technical
Svcs)*
Steve Crass *(Exec VP-Sls & Mktg)*
Mark Maybee *(Pres & CEO)*

David Sanchez-Turner *(Ops Mgr-Wet Wipes Mfg Bus-Milwaukee)*
Joe Ervin *(VP/Gen Mgr-Milwaukee)*

Division (Domestic):

Multi-Pack - Atlanta (2)
115 Manufacturers Ct, Winder, GA 30680
Tel.: (770) 307-9688
Web Site: http://www.multipackatlanta.com
Sales Range: $25-49.9 Million
Emp.: 70
Contract Detergent & Other Liquid Consumer Products Filling Services
N.A.I.C.S.: 561910
Frank Garriott *(Mgr-Ops)*

Multi-Pack - Milwaukee (2)
8372 N Steven Rd, Milwaukee, WI 53223
Tel.: (414) 760-9000
Web Site: http://www.multi-pack.com
Sales Range: $25-49.9 Million
Emp.: 40
Contract Wet Wipe Canister & Water Soluble Pouche Packaging Services
N.A.I.C.S.: 561910
Barbara Noel *(Mgr-Sls)*

Subsidiary (Domestic):

Span Packaging Services LLC (2)
4611-A Dairy Dr, Greenville, SC 29607
Tel.: (864) 627-4155
Web Site: http://www.spanps.com
Sales Range: $25-49.9 Million
Emp.: 300
Contract Pharmaceutical & Personal Care Product Packaging Services
N.A.I.C.S.: 561910

Sinclair & Rush, Inc. (1)
111 Manufacturers Dr, Arnold, MO 63010-4727
Tel.: (636) 282-6800
Web Site: http://www.sinclair-rush.com
Sales Range: $25-49.9 Million
Emp.: 350
Industrial, Retail & Packaging Industry Plastic Molded Products Mfr
N.A.I.C.S.: 326199
Bradford Philip *(Pres & COO)*

Subsidiary (Non-US):

Sinclair & Rush Ltd. (2)
11 - 13 St Laurence Ave, Allington, Maidstone, ME16 0LL, Kent, United Kingdom
Tel.: (44) 1622620255
Web Site: http://www.sinclair-rush.co.uk
Sales Range: $25-49.9 Million
Emp.: 75
Industrial Retail & Packaging Industry Plastic Molded Product Mfr
N.A.I.C.S.: 326199
Peter Boulton *(Mng Dir)*

Subsidiary (US):

INDEPAK, Inc. (3)
2131 NE 194 Ave, Portland, OR 97230
Web Site: http://www.indepak.com
Plastics Product Mfr
N.A.I.C.S.: 326199
Dave Aho *(Founder)*

Division (Domestic):

VisiPak (2)
111 Manufacturers Dr, Arnold, MO 63010
Tel.: (800) 949-1141
Web Site: http://www.visipak.com
Clear Plastic Packaging Mfr
N.A.I.C.S.: 326112

Subsidiary (Domestic):

MasterPac Corp. (3)
8339 Bridge Ave, Saint Louis, MO 63125
Tel.: (314) 644-6060
Web Site: http://www.masterpacpackaging.com
Custom Thermoforming Services
N.A.I.C.S.: 326199
Dave Lawrence *(Owner & Pres)*

National Plastics, Inc. (3)
2050 Congressional Dr, Saint Louis, MO 63146
Tel.: (314) 983-0825
Plastics Product Mfr
N.A.I.C.S.: 326199
Frank Forst *(CEO)*

USA Tank Sales & Erection Co., Inc. (1)
5897 Hwy 59, Goodman, MO 64865
Tel.: (417) 776-2500
Web Site: http://www.usatanksales.com
Sales Range: $10-24.9 Million
Emp.: 75
Storage Tank Mfr
N.A.I.C.S.: 237110

Subsidiary (Domestic):

All State Tank Manufacturing, LLC (2)
511 Industrial Park Rd A, Grove, OK 74344
Tel.: (918) 787-2600
Web Site: http://www.allstatetanks.com
Sales Range: $1-9.9 Million
Power Boiler & Heat Exchanger Mfr
N.A.I.C.S.: 332410
Darrel Robertson *(Pres)*

CAMERON MITCHELL RESTAURANTS, LLC
515 Park St, Columbus, OH 43215
Tel.: (614) 621-3663
Web Site:
http://www.cameronmitchell.com
Year Founded: 1992
Sales Range: $50-74.9 Million
Emp.: 40
Restaurant Operators
N.A.I.C.S.: 722511
Cameron Mitchell *(Founder & CEO)*
David Miller *(Pres & COO)*
Stacey L. Connaughton *(VP-Corp Affairs)*
Chuck Davis *(VP-HR)*
Charles Kline *(Sr VP-Ops)*
Heather Leonard *(Operating Partner & VP-Mktg)*
Tracey Smith *(Sr Mgr-Mktg)*
Gretchen Moore *(Mgr-Mktg)*
Wayne A. Schick *(Sr VP-Store Plng & Procurement)*
Steve Weis *(VP-Dev)*

CAMERON REAL ESTATE SERVICES, INC.
2390 Tamiami Trl N Ste 100, Naples, FL 34103
Tel.: (239) 261-1111
Web Site: http://www.cresfla.com
Year Founded: 1991
Sales Range: $10-24.9 Million
Real Estate Broker
N.A.I.C.S.: 531210
R. Scott Cameron *(Pres)*

CAMERON SEARCH & STAFFING LLC
745 E Mulberry Ste 170, San Antonio, TX 78212
Tel.: (210) 348-7333
Web Site:
http://www.cameronmatch.com
Year Founded: 2001
Rev.: $8,100,000
Emp.: 30
Executive Search Service
N.A.I.C.S.: 561311
Patrick W. Dudley *(Pres)*

CAMETA CAMERA
55 Sea Ln, Farmingdale, NY 11735
Tel.: (631) 389-2138
Web Site: http://www.cameta.com
Year Founded: 1983
Sales Range: $75-99.9 Million
Emp.: 70
Retailer of Branded Photographic Equipment, Photo Printers & Accessories
N.A.I.C.S.: 449210
Clifford Graham *(CFO)*
William Rosinger *(Co-Owner)*
Rosinger Elaine *(Co-Owner)*

CAMGIAN MICROSYSTEMS, INC.
100 Research Blvd Ste 313, Starkville, MS 39759
Tel.: (662) 320-1000
Web Site: https://www.camgian.com
Year Founded: 2006
Sales Range: $1-9.9 Million
Emp.: 26
Information Technology Consulting Services
N.A.I.C.S.: 541512
John Reece *(CFO)*
Gary D. Butler *(Founder, Chm & CEO)*

CAMICO MUTUAL INSURANCE COMPANY
1235 Radio Rd, Redwood City, CA 94065
Tel.: (650) 802-2500
Web Site: http://www.camico.com
Sales Range: $25-49.9 Million
Emp.: 87
Professional Liability Insurance Services
N.A.I.C.S.: 524298
Louis J. Barbich *(Founder)*
Ric Rosario *(Pres & CEO)*
Andrew M. Eassa *(Chm)*
Mike Ray *(CFO)*
Shannon Comer *(VP-Claims)*

CAMILLA PECAN COMPANY
275 Industrial Blvd, Camilla, GA 31730
Tel.: (229) 336-7282
Web Site:
http://www.camillapecan.net
Sales Range: $50-74.9 Million
Emp.: 250
Nut Processor & Distr
N.A.I.C.S.: 311911
Marty Harrell *(Pres & CEO)*

CAMILLUS HOUSE, INC.
1603 NW 7th Ave, Miami, FL 33136
Tel.: (305) 374-1065   FL
Web Site: https://www.camillus.org
Year Founded: 1987
Sales Range: $10-24.9 Million
Emp.: 224
Community Housing Services
N.A.I.C.S.: 624229
Alejandro Ramirez *(CFO)*
Richard Zonderman *(Dir-Clinical)*
Karen Mahar *(VP-Strategy Mgmt)*
Sam Gil *(VP-Mktg)*

CAMINO AGAVE INC.
US Hwy 83 N, Laredo, TX 78043
Tel.: (956) 765-6856
Web Site:
http://www.caminoagave.com
Sales Range: $10-24.9 Million
Emp.: 225
Lease Tanks, Oil Field: Erecting, Cleaning & Repairing
N.A.I.C.S.: 213112
Darren Kolbe *(Pres)*
Rick Aguero *(Gen Mgr)*
Fernando Soto *(Controller)*

CAMINO REAL CHEVROLET
2401 S Atlantic Blvd, Monterey Park, CA 91754-6807
Tel.: (323) 264-3050   CA
Web Site:
http://www.caminorealchevrolet.com
Year Founded: 1976
Sales Range: $25-49.9 Million
Emp.: 60
Retail Sales & Service of New & Used Automobiles
N.A.I.C.S.: 441110

Sara McKinney *(Mgr)*
Layne Barajas *(Gen Mgr-Sls)*
Ralph Rodriguez *(Mgr-Parts)*
Gary Takamine *(Mgr-Svc)*

CAMO SOFTWARE, INC.
1 Woodbridge Ctr, Woodbridge, NJ 07095
Tel.: (732) 726-9203
Web Site: http://www.camo.com
Year Founded: 1984
Sales Range: $10-24.9 Million
Emp.: 50
Computer Consulting Services
N.A.I.C.S.: 541512
Shirley A. Henshall *(CEO)*
Liv Annike Kverneland *(CFO)*
Geir Rune Flaten *(Chief Technological Officer)*

CAMOSY CONSTRUCTION
12795 120th Ave, Kenosha, WI 53142-7326
Tel.: (262) 552-9440
Web Site: https://www.camosy.com
Year Founded: 1989
Sales Range: $300-349.9 Million
Emp.: 125
Nonresidential Construction Services
N.A.I.C.S.: 236220
John P. Camosy *(Pres, CEO & Treas)*

CAMOSY, INC.
43451 N Hwy 41, Zion, IL 60099-9455
Tel.: (847) 395-6800   IL
Web Site: https://www.camosy.com
Year Founded: 1910
Sales Range: $75-99.9 Million
Emp.: 125
Nonresidential Construction
N.A.I.C.S.: 236220
Barbara Judeika *(Mgr-HR)*
John Camosy *(CEO & COO)*
Scott Heeter *(CFO & Controller)*

CAMP BOW WOW-BROOMFIELD
1705 W 10th Ave, Broomfield, CO 80020
Tel.: (303) 469-9972
Web Site:
http://www.campbowwowusa.com
Year Founded: 2000
Sales Range: $1-9.9 Million
Emp.: 30
Dog Daycare, Overnight Camps, Pet Care Services & Behavior Buddies Dog Training
N.A.I.C.S.: 812910
Heidi Ganahl *(Founder & CEO)*

CAMP MANAGEMENT INC.
723 Olympia Dr, Trinity, TX 75862
Tel.: (936) 594-2541
Web Site:
http://www.campolympia.com
Year Founded: 1968
Rev.: $32,400,000
Emp.: 80
Summer Camp Owner & Operator
N.A.I.C.S.: 721214
Debbi Stubblefield *(Dir-PR)*

CAMP RICHARD CAMPERS ASSOCIATION, INC.
PO Box 3002, Nantucket, MA 02584
Tel.: (508) 325-2869   MA
Web Site:
http://www.camprichard.org
Year Founded: 1955
Sales Range: $1-9.9 Million
Camping Facility Provider
N.A.I.C.S.: 713990

Camp Richard Campers Association, Inc.—(Continued)

Warren Cobb *(Treas)*
Robert Graves *(Pres)*
David Murray Jr. *(Sec)*

CAMP VENTURE, INC.
25 Smith St Ste 510, Nanuet, NY 10954
Tel.: (845) 624-3860   NY
Web Site:
http://www.campventure.org
Year Founded: 1969
Sales Range: $25-49.9 Million
Emp.: 787
Developmentally Disabled People Housing Assistance Services
N.A.I.C.S.: 623210
Daniel Lukens *(Exec Dir)*

CAMP-OUT, INC.
Rte 22 W & Jefferson Ave, North Plainfield, NJ 07060
Tel.: (908) 757-1700
Web Site:
http://www.campoutinc.com
Rev.: $11,900,000
Emp.: 12
Trailers, Truck Accessories & Recreational Vehicles Rental & Leasing
N.A.I.C.S.: 532120
Tex Tyler *(Pres)*

CAMPAIGN CONSULTATION, INC.
1001 N Calvert St, Baltimore, MD 21202
Tel.: (410) 243-7979
Web Site:
http://www.campaignconsultation.com
Year Founded: 1988
Sales Range: $1-9.9 Million
Emp.: 20
Business Management Consulting Services
N.A.I.C.S.: 541618
Linda Brown Rivelis *(Pres)*
Michelle Bond *(VP)*
Demetria Barrett *(Mgr-Fin & Ops)*
Steven Rivelis *(CEO)*
Arthurine Walker *(VP)*

CAMPAIGN MAIL & DATA, INC.
1593 Spring Hill Rd Ste 400, Tysons Corner, VA 22182
Tel.: (703) 790-8676   VA
Web Site: https://www.cmdi.com
Year Founded: 1981
Sales Range: $1-9.9 Million
Emp.: 100
Data Management Solutions
N.A.I.C.S.: 518210
John Simms *(Founder & Pres)*
Bruce Pechacek *(COO & VP)*
Junho Bae *(VP-Software Dev)*

CAMPBELL & FETTER BANK
126 S Orchid St, Kendallville, IN 46755
Tel.: (260) 347-1500
Web Site:
https://www.campbellfetterbank.com
Year Founded: 1863
Sales Range: $25-49.9 Million
Emp.: 45
Commericial Banking
N.A.I.C.S.: 522110
Lawrence M. Doyle *(Chm & Pres)*
Jeffrey J. Burns *(Sr VP-Mortgage Loans)*
Megan Voss *(Controller)*
George Bennett *(Branch Mgr)*
Bradley E. Beard *(VP-Mortgage Loans)*

Christopher D. Desper *(VP-Installment Loans)*
Robert C. Marshall *(Exec VP-Comml Loans)*

CAMPBELL & SONS OIL COMPANY, INC.
608 Church St NW, Huntsville, AL 35801-5526
Tel.: (256) 534-1601   AL
Web Site:
http://www.campbellandsoil.com
Year Founded: 1969
Sales Range: $10-24.9 Million
Emp.: 8
Provider of Petroleum Products
N.A.I.C.S.: 424720
Claude H. Campbell *(Founder)*
Todd Finnerty *(VP)*
Tony D. Campbell *(Co-Owner & Pres)*
Alan Campbell *(Co-Owner)*

CAMPBELL CHRYSLER JEEP DODGE RAM
217 W Main St, Centralia, WA 98531
Tel.: (360) 736-3353
Web Site:
http://www.campbellchrysler.com
Sales Range: $10-24.9 Million
Emp.: 35
New Car Retailer
N.A.I.C.S.: 441110
Julie Bullock *(CFO)*
Robert Pehl *(VP)*

CAMPBELL CLINIC ORTHOPAEDICS
7545 Airways Blvd, Southaven, MS 38671-5806
Tel.: (901) 759-3100
Web Site:
http://www.campbellclinic.com
Offices of Physicians (except Mental Health Specialists)
N.A.I.C.S.: 621111
Linda Britt *(Office Mgr)*

Subsidiaries:

Midtown Surgery Center J.V.   (1)
255 S Pauline St, Memphis, TN 38104
Tel.: (901) 261-2804
Web Site: http://www.campbellclinic.com
Ambulatory Surgical Center
N.A.I.C.S.: 621493

CAMPBELL CONSTRUCTION INC.
1159 Blachleyville Rd, Wooster, OH 44691
Tel.: (330) 262-5186
Web Site: https://www.campbellconstruction.com
Sales Range: $10-24.9 Million
Emp.: 60
Provider of Commercial & Residential Building Contracts
N.A.I.C.S.: 236210
John A. Campbell *(Owner & Pres)*

CAMPBELL FOUNDRY COMPANY
800 Bergen St, Harrison, NJ 07029-2034
Tel.: (973) 483-5480   NJ
Web Site:
https://www.campbellfoundry.com
Year Founded: 1921
Rev.: $26,000,000
Emp.: 30
Gray & Ductile Iron Foundries
N.A.I.C.S.: 331511
Greg Campbell *(Pres)*

Subsidiaries:

Bridgestate Foundry Corporation   (1)
175 Jackson Rd, Berlin, NJ 08009-2608

Tel.: (856) 767-0400
Web Site: http://www.bridgestate.com
Sales Range: $10-24.9 Million
Emp.: 4
Gray & Ductile Iron Foundries
N.A.I.C.S.: 331511
Ed Ceil *(Gen Mgr)*

Emporia Foundry Inc.   (1)
620 Reese St, Emporia, VA 23847-1423
Tel.: (434) 634-3125
Sales Range: $10-24.9 Million
Gray & Ductile Iron Foundries
N.A.I.C.S.: 331511

CAMPBELL LODGING INC.
2050 S Santa Cruiz St Ste 2000, Anaheim, CA 92805
Tel.: (714) 256-2070   CA
Web Site: http://www.cmpm.net
Year Founded: 1982
Sales Range: $10-24.9 Million
Emp.: 3
Provider of Hotel & Motel Services
N.A.I.C.S.: 721110
Martin A. Campbell *(Chief Dev Officer & VP)*
J. Alan Campbell *(CEO & CFO)*

CAMPBELL MANUFACTURING INC.
127 E Spring St, Bechtelsville, PA 19505
Tel.: (610) 367-2107   PA
Web Site:
http://www.campbellmfg.com
Year Founded: 1915
Sales Range: $25-49.9 Million
Emp.: 70
Residential & Light Commercial Water Systems, Sewage, Effluent, Sump Pump, Water Filtration & Treatment Systems Products Mfr
N.A.I.C.S.: 237110
Emery W. Davis *(Pres)*

CAMPBELL NELSON VOLKSWAGEN
24329 Hwy 99, Edmonds, WA 98026
Tel.: (425) 778-1131
Web Site:
http://www.campbellnelsonvw.com
Rev.: $53,200,000
Emp.: 150
New Car Dealers
N.A.I.C.S.: 441110
Craig Campbell *(Owner)*
Kurt Campbell *(Owner)*
B. C. Christman *(Gen Mgr-Sls)*

CAMPBELL OIL & GAS COMPANY
1106 W Broad St, Elizabethtown, NC 28337
Tel.: (910) 862-4107
Web Site: https://www.campbelloil.net
Sales Range: $10-24.9 Million
Emp.: 45
Petroleum Bulk Stations & Terminals
N.A.I.C.S.: 424710
James Dail *(CFO)*
Dallas M. Campbell Jr. *(Owner & Pres)*

CAMPBELL SCIENTIFIC, INC.
815 W 1800 N, Logan, UT 84321-1784
Tel.: (435) 753-2342   UT
Web Site:
http://www.campbellsci.com
Year Founded: 1974
Sales Range: $75-99.9 Million
Emp.: 300
Mfr of Dataloggers, Data Acquisition Systems & Measurement & Control Products
N.A.I.C.S.: 334513
Rob Campbell *(Pres)*

Subsidiaries:

Campbell Scientific Africa (Pty) Ltd.   (1)
1A Meson Street Technopark, Stellenbosch, 7600, South Africa
Tel.: (27) 21 880 9960
Web Site: http://www.csafrica.co.za
Emp.: 4
Measuring Instruments Mfr
N.A.I.C.S.: 334513

Campbell Scientific Australia Pty Ltd   (1)
411 Bayswater Rd, PO Box 8108, Townsville, 4814, QLD, Australia
Tel.: (61) 7 4401 7700
Web Site: http://www.campbellsci.com.au
Measuring Instruments Mfr
N.A.I.C.S.: 334513

Campbell Scientific Canada Corp.   (1)
14532 - 131 Avenue NW, Edmonton, T5L 4X4, AB, Canada
Tel.: (780) 454-2505
Web Site: http://www.campbellsci.ca
Emp.: 80
Measuring Instruments Mfr
N.A.I.C.S.: 334513
Brian Day *(VP)*

Campbell Scientific Spain, S.L.   (1)
Avda Pompeu Fabra 7-9 local 1, 8024, Barcelona, Spain
Tel.: (34) 93 2323938
Web Site: http://www.campbellsci.es
Measuring Instruments Mfr
N.A.I.C.S.: 334513

Campbell Scientific do Brasil, Ltda.   (1)
Rua Apinages nbr 2018, Perdizes, 01258-000, Sao Paulo, Brazil
Tel.: (55) 11 3732 3399
Web Site: http://www.campbellsci.com.br
Measuring Instruments Mfr
N.A.I.C.S.: 334513

Juniper Systems   (1)
1132 W 1700 N, Logan, UT 84321
Tel.: (435) 753-1881
Web Site: http://www.junipersys.com
Rev.: $2,000,000
Emp.: 110
Retail Of Electrical Equipment & Supplies
N.A.I.C.S.: 334111
DeVon Labrum *(Pres & CEO)*
Simon Bowe *(Gen Mgr-Juniper Systems Limited)*
Kirk Earl *(Mgr-Mktg Comm)*

CAMPBELL SUPPLY COMPANY
1526 N Industrial Ave, Sioux Falls, SD 57104
Tel.: (605) 331-5470
Web Site:
http://www.campbellsupply.net
Rev.: $25,000,000
Emp.: 25
Hardware Stores
N.A.I.C.S.: 444140
David J. Campbell *(Chm)*

Subsidiaries:

Campbell Supply Co.   (1)
325 W 11th St, Waterloo, IA 50702-1117
Tel.: (319) 234-6613
Web Site: http://www.campbellsupplyco.com
Abrasives, Adhesives & Sealants Mfr
N.A.I.C.S.: 327910

CAMPBELL TRACTOR & IMPLEMENT CO.
2014 Franklin Blvd, Nampa, ID 83687
Tel.: (208) 466-8414
Web Site:
https://www.campbelltractor.com
Sales Range: $10-24.9 Million
Emp.: 110
Agricultural Machinery & Equipment
N.A.I.C.S.: 423820
Allen Noble *(Pres)*

CAMPBELL WHOLESALE COMPANY, INC.
6849 E 13th St, Tulsa, OK 74112
Tel.: (918) 836-8774
Web Site:
https://www.campbellwholesale.net
Year Founded: 1967
Sales Range: $10-24.9 Million
Emp.: 50
Whslr of Candy, Tobacco & Tobacco Products
N.A.I.C.S.: 424940
Maurice Ray Campbell *(Pres)*
James Stovall *(Mgr-Retail Sls)*

CAMPBELL WRAPPER CORPORATION
1415 Fortune Ave, De Pere, WI 54115
Tel.: (920) 983-7100
Web Site:
https://www.campbellwrapper.com
Year Founded: 2001
Sales Range: $10-24.9 Million
Emp.: 100
Design, Manufacturing, Sales & Servicing of Packaging System Lines
N.A.I.C.S.: 333993
Gus Skapek *(Mgr-Sls-Intl & Reg)*
Larry Leino *(Mgr-Customer Support Engrg)*
Steve Joosten *(Reg Mgr-Sls)*
John N. Dykema *(Owner, Pres & CEO)*
Graham Nice *(Reg Mgr-Sls)*
Keenan Stahl *(Reg Mgr-Sls)*

Subsidiaries:

Parsons-Eagle Packaging Systems (1)
1415 Fortune Ave, De Pere, WI 54115
Tel.: (920) 983-7100
Web Site: http://www.parsons-eagle.com
Emp.: 50
Packaging Machinery Mfr
N.A.I.C.S.: 333993
Peter Hatchell *(Pres)*

Branch (Domestic):

Parsons-Eagle Packaging Systems (2)
2100 Dennison St, Oakland, CA 94606
Tel.: (510) 533-3000
Web Site: http://www.eaglepack.net
Packaging Machinery Mfr
N.A.I.C.S.: 333993
Pierce Butler *(VP-Sls)*
Peter Hatchell *(Pres)*

CAMPBELL, HENRY & CALVIN, INC.
34375 W 12 Mile Rd, Farmington Hills, MI 48331-3375
Tel.: (248) 553-1203
Web Site:
http://www.jervisbwebb.com
Year Founded: 1966
Sales Range: Less than $1 Million
Emp.: 4
House Agencies
N.A.I.C.S.: 541810
John M. Rankin *(Media Mgr)*

CAMPBELL-HOGUE & ASSOCIATES
2223 Ste 102 112th Ave NE, Bellevue, WA 98004
Tel.: (425) 455-3879
Web Site: http://www.cambell-hogue.com
Sales Range: $10-24.9 Million
Emp.: 4
Subdividers & Developers
N.A.I.C.S.: 237210
Terry N. Campbell *(Principal)*
David G. Rae *(CFO & VP)*
James H. Hogue *(Principal)*

CAMPBELLSPORT BUILDING SUPPLY
227 W Main St, Campbellsport, WI 53010
Tel.: (920) 533-4412
Web Site:
http://www.furnishanddesign.com
Year Founded: 1985
Sales Range: $50-74.9 Million
Emp.: 137
Building Architectural Design Services
N.A.I.C.S.: 541310
Joel Fleischman *(Pres)*
Doug Carlson *(VP-Sls & Ops)*
Harry Baker *(Mgr-Acct)*
Kurt Dulmes *(Mgr-Acct)*
Tim Lindsley *(Mgr-Acct)*
Jay Enright *(Supvr-Acct)*
Chris Gagnon *(Supvr-Acct)*
Brad Groebner *(Supvr-Acct)*
Adam Kramer *(Supvr-Acct)*
Lauren Parsons *(Supvr-Acct)*
Dave Vercauteren *(Supvr-Acct)*
Mike Wertel *(Supvr-Acct)*
Keith Zitlow *(Supvr-Acct)*
Beth Pautsch *(VP-Cabinetry Sls)*

CAMPBELLSVILLE APPAREL COMPANY, LLC
1309 E Broadway, Campbellsville, KY 42718
Tel.: (270) 465-0714
Web Site: http://www.camapp.com
Year Founded: 1999
Sales Range: $10-24.9 Million
Emp.: 200
Mfr of Men's T-shirts, Sweatshirts & Underwear for the Military
N.A.I.C.S.: 315250
Chris Reynolds *(VP-Mfg)*
George Wise *(VP-HR)*

CAMPELLO BANCORP, INC.
1265 Belmont St, Brockton, MA 02301
Tel.: (508) 587-3210
Web Site:
http://www.communitybank.com
Year Founded: 1995
Bank Holding Company
N.A.I.C.S.: 551111
David W. Curtis *(Pres & CEO)*
Dennis P. Jones *(CFO & Sr VP)*

Subsidiaries:

The Community Bank (1)
1265 Belmont St, Brockton, MA 02301
Tel.: (508) 587-3210
Web Site: http://www.communitybank.com
Sales Range: $10-24.9 Million
Emp.: 80
State Commercial Banks
N.A.I.C.S.: 522110

CAMPER CLINIC, INC.
302 W Market St, Rockport, TX 78382
Tel.: (361) 729-0031
Web Site:
https://www.camperclinic.com
Year Founded: 1983
Sales Range: $10-24.9 Million
Emp.: 35
Provider of RV Sales & Services
N.A.I.C.S.: 441330
Stacey Grosjean *(Office Mgr)*

CAMPERS INN HOLDING CORP.
146 Rte 125, Kingston, NH 03848
Tel.: (603) 642-5555
Web Site:
https://www.campersinn.com
Sales Range: $10-24.9 Million
Emp.: 15

Campers & Pickup Coaches for Mounting on Trucks
N.A.I.C.S.: 441210
Jeffrey Hirsch *(Owner)*

Subsidiaries:

Campers Inn of Kingston Inc (1)
146 State Rte 125, Kingston, NH 03848
Tel.: (603) 642-5555
Web Site: http://www.campersinn.com
Motor Homes
N.A.I.C.S.: 441210
Jeff Hirsch *(Pres)*

Campers Inn of Raynham Inc (1)
720 Church St, Raynham, MA 02767
Tel.: (508) 821-3366
Web Site: http://www.campersinn.com
Rev.: $9,613,669
Recreational Vehicle Dealers
N.A.I.C.S.: 441210
Brian Sullivan *(Gen Sls Mgr)*

CAMPFIRE
62 White St 3E, New York, NY 10013
Tel.: (212) 612-9600
Web Site:
http://www.campfirenyc.com
Rev.: $15,000,000
Emp.: 20
Advertising, Interactive, Internet/Web Design
N.A.I.C.S.: 541810
Steve Wax *(Co-Founder & Mng Partner)*
Mike Monello *(Co-Founder & Exec Dir-Creative)*
Gregg Hale *(Co-Founder)*
Sean Ganaan *(Dir-Creative)*
Jeremiah Rosen *(Pres)*
Jason Sutterfield *(COO)*
Simone Oppenheimer *(Dir-Bus Dev)*
Marianne Raphael *(Grp Acct Dir)*
Ilene Joel *(Dir-Art)*

CAMPFIRE INTERACTIVE, INC.
110 Miller Ave Garden Level Ste, Ann Arbor, MI 48104
Tel.: (734) 998-0099
Web Site: https://www.cfi2.com
Year Founded: 2000
Sales Range: $1-9.9 Million
Emp.: 35
Information Technology Services
N.A.I.C.S.: 541511
Sarvajit Sarge Sinha *(Co-Founder & CTO)*
Pradeep Seneviratne *(Co-Founder & Pres)*
Saravanan Arunachalam *(Dir-IT)*

CAMPGROUP LLC
4 New King St, White Plains, NY 10604
Tel.: (914) 997-2177
Web Site:
https://www.campgroup.com
Year Founded: 1998
Sales Range: $10-24.9 Million
Emp.: 90
Summer Camp Owner & Operator
N.A.I.C.S.: 721214
Andy Benerofe *(CEO)*
Mark Benerofe *(Pres)*

CAMPHOR TECHNOLOGIES, INC.
183 Providence New London Tpke Ste W 5, North Stonington, CT 06359-1721
Tel.: (860) 535-0241
Web Site:
http://www.camphortech.com
Sales Range: $10-24.9 Million
Emp.: 27
Mfr of Intermediates, Actives & Raw Materials
N.A.I.C.S.: 424210

Mike Creaturo *(CEO)*

CAMPION AMBULANCE SERVICE, INC.
15 W Dover St, Waterbury, CT 06706
Tel.: (203) 753-2037
Web Site:
http://www.campionambulance.com
Year Founded: 1947
Emp.: 279
Emergency Ambulance Services
N.A.I.C.S.: 621999
Ken George *(Dir-Fleet Svcs)*
Fred Rosa *(Dir-Northwest Ops)*
Connie Schmiedecke *(Coord-Trng)*
William T. Campion Jr. *(Pres & CEO)*

CAMPIONI ENTERPRISES INC.
47401 Hwy M26, Houghton, MI 49931
Tel.: (906) 482-7500
Web Site:
http://www.patsfoodsiga.com
Year Founded: 1976
Sales Range: $10-24.9 Million
Emp.: 225
Supermarket
N.A.I.C.S.: 445110
Ben Campioni *(Co-Owner)*
Joe Campioni *(Co-Owner)*

CAMPMOR INC.
400 Corporate Dr, Mahwah, NJ 07430
Tel.: (201) 335-9064
Web Site: http://www.campmor.com
Year Founded: 1977
Sales Range: $75-99.9 Million
Emp.: 100
Provider of Retail & Mail Order Equipment for Camping, Back-Packing, Bike Touring, Running & Mountain Climbing
N.A.I.C.S.: 459110
Morton Jay *(Chm)*
Dan Jay *(Pres, CEO & CFO)*
Ashley Cohen *(Asst Dir-Digital & Affiliate Mktg)*
Audrey O'Donnell *(Coord-Returns)*

CAMPO OIL COMPANY INC.
400 S Pennsylvania Ave, Fruitland, ID 83619
Tel.: (208) 452-3341
Sales Range: $10-24.9 Million
Emp.: 9
Petroleum Bulk Stations
N.A.I.C.S.: 424710
Dennis Campo *(Pres)*

CAMPORA INC.
2525 E Mariposa Rd, Stockton, CA 95205
Tel.: (209) 466-8611
Web Site: https://www.campora.com
Sales Range: $10-24.9 Million
Emp.: 13
Propane Gas, Bottled
N.A.I.C.S.: 457210
Tom Campora *(CEO)*

Subsidiaries:

Campora Wholesale Propane (1)
2537 E Mariposa Rd, Stockton, CA 95205
Tel.: (209) 466-8611
Web Site: http://www.campora.com
Rev.: $4,000,000
Emp.: 11
Butane Gas
N.A.I.C.S.: 424720

CAMPOS CREATIVE WORKS, INC.
1715 14th St, Santa Monica, CA 90404
Tel.: (310) 453-1511
Web Site: http://www.ccwla.com

Campos Creative Works, Inc.—(Continued)
Year Founded: 1991
Sales Range: $10-24.9 Million
Emp.: 20
Advetising Agency
N.A.I.C.S.: 541810
Julio Campos (Founder & Pres)
Sandra Sande (CFO)

CAMPOS, INC.
840 Pareves Line Rd, Brownsville, TX 78521
Tel.: (956) 542-6504   **TX**
Year Founded: 1983
Rev.: $25,000,000
Emp.: 5
Mexican Restaurant
N.A.I.C.S.: 722511
Tony Campos (Gen Mgr)

CAMPUS BOOK RENTALS, INC.
2805 S 1900 W, Ogden, UT 84401
Web Site:
http://www.campusbookrentals.com
Year Founded: 2007
Sales Range: $10-24.9 Million
Emp.: 118
College Textbook Rentals
N.A.I.C.S.: 532289
Alan Martin (Founder, COO & CEO)

CAMPUS LIVING VILLAGES, CENTURY
1001 Fannin Ste 1350, Houston, TX 77002
Tel.: (713) 871-5100
Web Site: https://www.campusliving villages.com
Sales Range: $75-99.9 Million
Emp.: 700
Land Subdividing Services
N.A.I.C.S.: 237210
Gary Clarke (CEO)

CAMPUS MEDIA GROUP, LLC
7760 France Ave S Ste 800, Bloomington, MN 55425
Tel.: (952) 854-3100   **MN**
Web Site:
http://www.campusmediagroup.com
Year Founded: 2002
Media Buying Services
N.A.I.C.S.: 541810
Thomas Borgerding (Pres & CEO)
Jason Bakker (Dir-Mktg & Advertising)

CAMPUS PARTNERS
3330 Healy Dr Ste 105, Winston Salem, NC 27103
Tel.: (336) 607-2000   **NC**
Web Site:
http://www.campuspartners.com
Year Founded: 1964
Sales Range: $200-249.9 Million
Emp.: 66
Student Loan Services
N.A.I.C.S.: 522310
Pattie Mastin (Acct Mgr)

CAMPUS RESEARCH CORPORATION
9070 S Rita Rd Ste 1750, Tucson, AZ 85747-6112
Tel.: (520) 382-2480   **AZ**
Year Founded: 1994
Sales Range: $10-24.9 Million
Emp.: 18
Community Welfare Services
N.A.I.C.S.: 624190
Ken Marcus (CFO)
Bruce A. Wright (Pres)
Patrick Griffin (Sec)

Fred Boice (Vice Chm)
John Carter (Chm)
Larry Lucero (Treas)

CAMPUS USA CREDIT UNION
PO Box 147029, Gainesville, FL 32614
Tel.: (352) 335-9090   **FL**
Web Site:
https://www.campuscu.com
Year Founded: 1935
Sales Range: $50-74.9 Million
Emp.: 265
Financial Support Services
N.A.I.C.S.: 522130

CAMS BLUEWIRE TECHNOLOGY, LLC
919 Milam Ste 2300, Houston, TX 77002
Tel.: (713) 358-9799
Web Site:
http://www.camsbluewiretech.com
Year Founded: 2007
Sales Range: $1-9.9 Million
Emp.: 30
IT Consulting & Development Services, Website, Database Hosting & Technology Design & Management
N.A.I.C.S.: 518210
Travis Williams (Partner, Pres & COO)
James Wyble (Partner)
Kelly King (Mgr-Tech Svcs)

CAMSING GLOBAL, LLC
8285 Bryan Dairy Rd, Largo, FL 33777
Tel.: (727) 369-5220
Web Site:
http://www.camsingglobal.com
Promotional Product Whlsr
N.A.I.C.S.: 423990
Mark Holland (VP-Mktg)
William A. Dolan II (CEO)

Subsidiaries:

Adva-Lite Inc.   (1)
8285 Bryan Dairy Rd, Largo, FL 33777-1506
Tel.: (727) 369-5220
Web Site: http://www.advalite.com
Sales Range: $25-49.9 Million
Emp.: 138
Lighting Equipment Distr
N.A.I.C.S.: 335139

Toppers LLC   (1)
8285 Bryan Dairy Rd, Largo, FL 33777
Tel.: (727) 546-5483
Web Site: http://www.toppersllc.com
Sales Range: $25-49.9 Million
Emp.: 110
Mens' & Boys' Clothing Distr
N.A.I.C.S.: 424990

CAMTERRA RESOURCES PARTNERS
2615 E 2nd Blvd S, Marshall, TX 75672
Tel.: (903) 938-9949
Sales Range: $10-24.9 Million
Emp.: 30
Oil & Gas Exploration
N.A.I.C.S.: 213112
Paul Marchand (VP)

CAMTOR COMMERCIAL REAL ESTATE LENDING, L.P.
110 E 59th St, New York, NY 10022
Tel.: (212) 915-1700
Web Site: http://www.ccre.com
Year Founded: 2010
Comercial Real Estate Finance Services
N.A.I.C.S.: 531390
Anthony Orso (CEO)
Michael May (COO)

CAN CAPITAL, INC.
2015 Vaughn Rd NW Ste 500, Kennesaw, GA 30144-7831
Web Site: https://www.cancapital.com
Year Founded: 1998
Sales Range: $150-199.9 Million
Emp.: 425
Working Capital & Data Services to Small Businesses
N.A.I.C.S.: 522299
Ray De Palma (Chief Acctg Officer)
Edward J. Siciliano (CEO)
Richard G. Irwin (CFO)

Subsidiaries:

CAN Capital, Inc.   (1)
414 W 14th St Ste 302, New York, NY 10014
Tel.: (877) 550-4731
Web Site: http://www.cancapital.com
Capital & Management Services to Small Businesses
N.A.I.C.S.: 523999
Daniel DeMeo (CEO)
James Mendelsohn (CMO)
Mandy Sebel (Chief People Officer)
Gary Johnson (Chm)
David Dart (CTO)
Kenneth Gang (Chief Risk Officer)

CAN CORPORATION OF AMERICA
326 June Ave, Blandon, PA 19510-0170
Tel.: (610) 926-3044   **PA**
Web Site:
https://www.cancorpam.com
Year Founded: 1976
Sales Range: $75-99.9 Million
Emp.: 180
Mfr of Metal Cans
N.A.I.C.S.: 332431

CAN LINES INC.
9839 Downey Norwalk Rd, Downey, CA 90241
Tel.: (562) 861-2996
Web Site: https://www.canlines.com
Sales Range: $10-24.9 Million
Emp.: 100
Canning Machinery, Food
N.A.I.C.S.: 333993
Donald H. Koplien (Co-Pres)
David Gadberry (Dir-Engrg)
Erik Koplien (VP-Ops)
Keenan Koplien (Co-Pres)
Gary Nemetz (CEO)

CANAAN PARTNERS
2765 Sand Hill Rd, Menlo Park, CA 94025
Tel.: (650) 854-8092
Web Site: https://www.canaan.com
Year Founded: 1987
Venture Capital Investment Services
N.A.I.C.S.: 523999
Daniel T. Ciporin (Gen Partner)
Richard Boyle (Partner)
Nairi Hourdajian (VP-Comm)
Brendan Dickinson (Partner-Tech Team-New York)
Michael Gilroy (Principal-Tech Team-Manhattan)
Julie Papanek Grant (Partner)
Colleen Cuffaro (Principal-Healthcare Team-San Francisco)
John V. Balen (Partner)
Maha S. Ibrahim (Gen Partner)
Hrach Simonian (Gen Partner)

CANADAY & COMPANY
3194 Airport Loop Dr Ste C2, Costa Mesa, CA 92626-3405
Tel.: (714) 327-1710
Web Site:
http://www.canadaycompany.com
Sales Range: $10-24.9 Million

Emp.: 5
New Construction, Single-Family Houses
N.A.I.C.S.: 236115
Chris Canaday (Pres)

CANADIAN FISH EXPORTERS, INC.
134 Rumford Ave Ste 202, Auburndale, MA 02466-1377
Tel.: (617) 924-8300
Web Site: http://www.cfeboston.com
Year Founded: 1972
Rev.: $23,469,491
Emp.: 25
Fish Whslr
N.A.I.C.S.: 424460
Robert Metafora (Chm & CEO)
Angel Rio (Acct Mgr)
Janelle Calamari (CFO & Treas)
Donna Metafora (Mgr-Benefits)
Raphael J. Santaella (VP-Sls & Mktg)
Lee E. Tracy (Acct Mgr)
Katherine Handscom (Coord-Transportation & Logistics)
Eric Burkhardt (Dir-Sls)
Michael Fettig (Mgr-Facilities Maintenance)
Jeffrey Long (Mgr-Import Ops)

CANADIAN RIVER MUNICIPAL WATER AUTHORITY
9875 Water Authority Rd, Sanford, TX 79078
Tel.: (806) 865-3325
Web Site: http://www.crmwa.com
Year Founded: 1953
Sales Range: $10-24.9 Million
Emp.: 44
Water Supply
N.A.I.C.S.: 221310
Kent Satterwhite (Gen Mgr)

CANADIAN VALLEY ELECTRIC CO-OP
N On Hwy 99 & IH 40, Seminole, OK 74868
Tel.: (405) 382-3680
http://www.canadianvalley.org
Rev.: $21,168,015
Emp.: 55
Distribution, Electric Power
N.A.I.C.S.: 221122
Cordis Slaughter (Mgr-Ops)
Bob Weaver (Mgr-Mktg & Economic Dev)
David Swank (Gen Mgr)

CANAL BARGE COMPANY INC.
835 Union St Ste 300, New Orleans, LA 70112
Tel.: (504) 581-2424   **LA**
Web Site: http://www.canalbarge.com
Year Founded: 1933
Sales Range: $100-124.9 Million
Emp.: 110
Independent Marine Transportation Services
N.A.I.C.S.: 483111
H. Merritt Lane III (Chm, Pres & CEO)
David M. Lane (VP-Mktg)

CANAL CAPITAL MANAGEMENT LLC
9 S 5th St, Richmond, VA 23219
Tel.: (804) 325-1450
Web Site:
http://www.canalcapitalmanagement.com
Year Founded: 2011
Sales Range: $1-9.9 Million
Emp.: 7
Financial Management Services
N.A.I.C.S.: 541611

E. Neil Gilliss *(CEO & Partner)*
Noah C. P. Greenbaum *(Partner & Dir-Investments)*
Margaret J. Smith *(Partner & Dir-Plng & Tax Svcs)*
Jarrod Feinstein *(Portfolio Mgr)*
Robin Walker *(Office Mgr)*

CANAL CORPORATION
1021 E Cary St, Richmond, VA 23219
Tel.: (804) 697-1000   VA
Web Site:
   http://www.canalcorporation.com
Holding Company; Specialty Packaging Mfr
N.A.I.C.S.: 551112
Joel K. Mostrom *(CFO & Exec VP)*
Kathryn L. Tyler *(VP & Controller)*

CANAL PARTNERS, LLC
7114 E Stetson D Ste 360, Scottsdale, AZ 85251
Tel.: (408) 264-0238
Web Site:
   http://www.canalpartners.com
Year Founded: 2008
Private Investment Firm
N.A.I.C.S.: 523999
Todd Belfer *(Mng Partner)*
Jim Armstrong *(Mng Partner)*
Wain Kellum *(Mng Partner)*
Patrick Armstrong *(Partner)*

CANAL WOOD LLC
4311d Ludgate St, Lumberton, NC 28358-2460
Tel.: (910) 739-2885
Web Site:
   https://www.canalwood.com
Year Founded: 1974
Sales Range: $10-24.9 Million
Emp.: 3
Durable Goods
N.A.I.C.S.: 423990
Allen McCall *(Pres)*
Bruce Baker *(Mgr)*
Jody Britton *(VP-Ops)*
Rudy Daughtry *(Reg Mgr)*
Cheryl Bradford *(Mgr-HR)*
Dennis Stone *(Sr VP)*
Gary McMahan *(Sr VP)*
Jeff Hughes *(Area Mgr)*
Mickey Gregory *(Mgr-Fleet)*
Ronnie Evans *(Reg Mgr)*
Carroll Harrelson *(Sr VP)*
Susan Lewis *(Supvr-Acctg)*
Matt McCall *(CFO)*

Subsidiaries:

Canal Chip, LLC   (1)
5821 US Hwy 264 Alt, Sims, NC 27880
Tel.: (252) 237-8138
Lumber Mfr
N.A.I.C.S.: 321113

Canal Wood LLC   (1)
PO Box 5566, Florence, SC 29502-5566
Tel.: (843) 669-4094
Web Site: http://www.canalwood.com
Rev.: $5,000,000
Sales of Timber
N.A.I.C.S.: 423990

Canal Wood LLC   (1)
5176 Wrightsboro Rd, Grovetown, GA 30813-2802
Tel.: (706) 650-7650
Web Site: http://www.canalwood.com
Rev.: $9,900,000
Durable Goods
N.A.I.C.S.: 423990

CANALWORKS ADVERTISING
6110 Holabird Ave, Baltimore, MD 21224
Tel.: (215) 458-6216
Year Founded: 2009
Sales Range: $10-24.9 Million
Emp.: 4

Advertising, Alternative Advertising, Cable T.V., Consumer Marketing, Co-op Advertising, Direct-to-Consumer, Email, T.V., Web (Banner Ads, Pop-ups, etc.)
N.A.I.C.S.: 541810
Edith Lever *(Dir-Adv)*
Chris Crowley *(Dir-Print & Production)*
Lauren Campbell *(Mgr-Alternate Media)*

CANARY RESOURCES, INC.
1201 Hampton St Ste 3-B, Columbia, SC 29201
Tel.: (803) 254-7861
Year Founded: 1997
Oil & Gas Exploration Services
N.A.I.C.S.: 213112
James D. Beatty *(Chm)*

CANBY TELECOM
190 SE 2nd Ave, Canby, OR 97013
Tel.: (503) 266-8111
Web Site: http://www.canbytel.com
Year Founded: 1904
Rev.: $10,000,000
Emp.: 75
Local Telephone Communications
N.A.I.C.S.: 517121
Paul Hauer *(Pres)*

CANCER CARE, INC.
275 7th Ave 22nd FL, New York, NY 10001
Tel.: (212) 712-8400   NY
Web Site: https://www.cancercare.org
Year Founded: 1955
Sales Range: $10-24.9 Million
Emp.: 154
Health Care Srvices
N.A.I.C.S.: 622110
John Rutigliano *(COO)*

CANCER CENTERS OF SOUTHWEST OKLAHOMA
104 NW 31st St, Lawton, OK 73505
Tel.: (580) 536-2121   OK
Web Site:
   http://www.cancercentersswok.com
Year Founded: 2004
Sales Range: $10-24.9 Million
Cancer Treatment Services
N.A.I.C.S.: 622310
Lane Hooton *(COO)*
William G. Wilson *(Chm)*
Randy Segler *(Pres)*
Jay Johnson *(Treas & Sec)*

CANCER DIAGNOSTICS, INC.
4300 Emperor Blvd Ste 400, Durham, NC 27703
Tel.:
Web Site:
   http://www.cancerdiagnostics.com
Surgical Appliance & Supplies Mfr
N.A.I.C.S.: 339113
Mark Seidel *(Mgr-Ops)*

Subsidiaries:

Anatech, Ltd.   (1)
1020 Harts Lake Rd, Battle Creek, MI 49037
Tel.: (269) 964-6450
Web Site: http://www.anatechltdusa.com
Sales Range: $1-9.9 Million
Emp.: 10
In-Vitro Diagnostic Substance Mfr
N.A.I.C.S.: 325413
Ada Feldman *(Sec)*

CANCER FUND OF AMERICA, INC.
2901 Breezewood Ln, Knoxville, TN 37921
Tel.: (865) 938-5281   DE
Web Site: http://www.cfoa.org
Year Founded: 1987

Sales Range: $1-9.9 Million
Emp.: 109
Fundraising Services
N.A.I.C.S.: 561499
James T. Reynolds Sr. *(Pres)*

CANCO GENERAL CONTRACTORS INC.
2502 Frontage Park Pl, Plant City, FL 33563
Tel.: (813) 750-1222
Web Site:
   http://www.cancogencon.com
Year Founded: 1986
Sales Range: $10-24.9 Million
Emp.: 32
Commercial Construction
N.A.I.C.S.: 236220
John D. Prahl *(Owner & Pres)*
Lawrence Mason *(Controller & Dir-Safety)*
Greg Gammill *(Project Mgr)*

CANCOS TILE CORP.
1085 Portion Rd, Farmingville, NY 11738
Tel.: (631) 736-0770
Web Site: http://www.cancos.com
Year Founded: 1953
Sales Range: $25-49.9 Million
Emp.: 200
Importer, Distributor & Retailer of Ceramic Tile, Marble & Granite
N.A.I.C.S.: 444180
Mark Valva *(VP)*
Berndette White *(VP)*
Jacque Purchla *(Mgr)*
Vinny Ilustre *(Mgr-Fabrication Div)*
Neil Swenning *(Mgr-Store)*
Ed Rusbarsky *(Gen Mgr)*

CANDELA CORPORATION
14420 Myford Rd Ste 100, Irvine, CA 92606-1001
Tel.: (714) 662-4900   CA
Web Site:
   http://www.candelacorp.com
Year Founded: 1986
Sales Range: $10-24.9 Million
Emp.: 35
Distribute Light Bulbs & Related Supplies
N.A.I.C.S.: 423610
Bill Baas *(Chm)*
Anthony Sinopoli *(VP-Logistics)*
Candice Williams *(Mgr-CRM)*

CANDELA SALES COMPANY INC.
1125 Pk St, Alameda, CA 94501
Tel.: (510) 747-1960
Rev.: $10,400,000
Emp.: 10
Party Favors, Balloons, Hats, Etc.
N.A.I.C.S.: 424990
Dona Candela *(Pres)*

CANDESCENT PARTNERS, LLC
2 Oliver St 10th Fl, Boston, MA 02109
Tel.: (617) 262-1480   MA
Web Site:
   https://www.candescentpartner.com
Year Founded: 2008
Equity Investment Firm
N.A.I.C.S.: 523999
Stephen M. Jenks *(Co-Founder & Mng Partner)*
Alexander S. McGrath *(Co-Founder & Mng Partner)*
Stephen A. Sahlman *(Partner)*

Subsidiaries:

Candescent SoftBase, LLC   (1)

20 Fall Pippin Ln Ste 202, Asheville, NC 28803
Tel.: (828) 670-9900
Web Site: http://www.softbase.com
Sales Range: $1-9.9 Million
Software Testing & Support Services
N.A.I.C.S.: 541519
Stephen Woodard *(CEO)*
Jim Spires *(Dir-Dev)*
Teresa Turbyfill *(Controller & Dir-HR)*

CANDID COLOR SYSTEMS, INC.
1300 Metropolitan Ave, Oklahoma City, OK 73108-2042
Tel.: (405) 947-8747
Web Site: http://www.candid.com
Year Founded: 1972
Sales Range: $10-24.9 Million
Emp.: 300
Photography Studio & Photofinishing Lab
N.A.I.C.S.: 812921
Jack E. Counts Jr. *(Pres)*

Subsidiaries:

Candid Color Photography, Inc.   (1)
1300 Metropolitan Ave, Oklahoma City, OK 73108
Tel.: (405) 951-7300
Web Site:
   http://www.candidcolorphotography.com
Photographic Services
N.A.I.C.S.: 541921

CANDLE ACQUISITION CORPORATION
18821 Bardeen Ave, Irvine, CA 92612
Tel.: (949) 852-1000
Holding Company
N.A.I.C.S.: 551112

Subsidiaries:

Candelis, Inc.   (1)
18821 Bardeen Ave, Irvine, CA 92612
Tel.: (949) 852-1000
Web Site: http://www.candelis.com
Sales Range: $25-49.9 Million
Emp.: 25
Medical Image Storage Devices
N.A.I.C.S.: 334112
Mazi Razmjoo *(VP-Sls)*

Subsidiary (Non-US):

Candelis - India   (2)
Sobha Sapphire No 15 Amruthahalli, Bengaluru, 560 092, Jakkur, India
Tel.: (91) 8023636896
Sales Range: $25-49.9 Million
Emp.: 3
Office Equipment & Computer Software
N.A.I.C.S.: 541512

CANDLE SCIENCE INC.
1717 E Lawson St, Durham, NC 27703
Tel.: (919) 226-0323
Web Site:
   http://www.candlescience.com
Year Founded: 2004
Rev.: $2,700,000
Emp.: 10
Chemical Allied Product Merchant Whslr
N.A.I.C.S.: 424690
Daniel J. Swimm *(Pres)*

CANDLE WARMERS ETC. INC.
1948 W 2425 S Ste 2, Woods Cross, UT 84087
Tel.: (801) 771-8650
Web Site:
   http://www.candlewarmers.com
Year Founded: 2000
Sales Range: $1-9.9 Million
Emp.: 35
Candle Mfr
N.A.I.C.S.: 339999

Candle Warmers Etc. Inc.—(Continued)

Brian Beesley (Dir-Product Dev)
Brent Carter (Mgr-Natl Sls)
Brett Heyland (Owner & Chief Sls
Officer)

CANDY FORD, INC.
403 Lansing St, Charlotte, MI 48813-
1654
Tel.: (517) 543-8292
Web Site: http://www.candyford.com
Year Founded: 1972
Sales Range: $10-24.9 Million
Emp.: 39
Car Whslr
N.A.I.C.S.: 441110
John Dykstra Jr. (Gen Mgr-Sls)

CANDYRIFIC LLC
108 McArthur Dr, Louisville, KY
40207
Tel.: (502) 893-3626
Web Site: https://www.candyrific.com
Year Founded: 2001
Sales Range: $10-24.9 Million
Emp.: 20
Novelty Candy Item Designer, Mfr &
Retailer
N.A.I.C.S.: 424450
Rob Auerbach (Pres & CEO)
Larry Lindenbaum (Mgr-Natl Sls)
Paul Roberts (Co-Owner)
B. J. Ruckriegel (Controller)
Matt Cameron (Sls Dir-Natl Accounts)
Kim Trask (Sls Dir-West)
Clark Taylor (Sr VP-Sls & Mktg)

CANDYWAREHOUSE.COM
2520 Mira Mar Ave, Long Beach, CA
90815
Tel.: (310) 343-4099   CA
Web Site:
    https://www.candywarehouse.com
Year Founded: 1998
Sales Range: $1-9.9 Million
Emp.: 20
Online Confectionery Store
N.A.I.C.S.: 311340
Christopher Dale Pratt (Pres)

**CANERDAY BELFSKY & AR-
ROYO ARCHITECTS INC.**
800 2nd Ave S Ste 320, Saint Peters-
burg, FL 33701
Tel.: (727) 823-0675
Web Site:
    http://www.canerdaybelfsky
    arroyo.com
Year Founded: 1984
Sales Range: $1-9.9 Million
Emp.: 8
Architectural Services
N.A.I.C.S.: 541310
Leo Arroyo (Principal)
Richard Belfsky (Principal)

**CANEY FORK ELECTRIC
COOP**
920 Smithville Hwy, McMinnville, TN
37110
Tel.: (931) 473-3116
Web Site:
    https://www.caneyforkec.com
Sales Range: $25-49.9 Million
Emp.: 86
Electronic Services
N.A.I.C.S.: 221118
William S. Rogers (Gen Mgr)
John Chisam (Dir-Member Svcs)
Donald McBee (Dir-Fin Svcs)

CANFIELD & JOSEPH, INC.
6536 E 42nd St, Tulsa, OK 74145
Tel.: (918) 663-8380

Web Site:
    https://www.canfieldjoseph.com
Sales Range: $25-49.9 Million
Emp.: 35
Foundry Products
N.A.I.C.S.: 531210
Kerry Joseph (Controller)

**CANFIELD & TACK INCORPO-
RATED**
925 Exchange St, Rochester, NY
14608
Tel.: (585) 235-7710
Web Site:
    http://www.canfieldtack.com
Sales Range: $10-24.9 Million
Emp.: 80
Offset Printing
N.A.I.C.S.: 323111
Ray Brown (Pres)

CANIDIUM, LLC
3801 Kirby Dr S456, Houston, TX
77098
Tel.: (877) 651-1837
Web Site: http://www.canidium.com
Year Founded: 2009
Sales Range: $1-9.9 Million
Emp.: 25
Sales Performance Management
Consultancy Services
N.A.I.C.S.: 541613
Michael Stus (Co-Founder & Mng
Partner)
Jason Kearns (VP-Tech Svcs)

**CANINE COMPANIONS FOR
INDEPENDENCE, INC.**
2965 Dutton Ave, Santa Rosa, CA
95407
Tel.: (707) 577-1700   CA
Web Site: http://www.cci.org
Year Founded: 1976
Sales Range: $10-24.9 Million
Emp.: 209
Guard Dog Training Services
N.A.I.C.S.: 812910
Jeanne Cooley (Dir-Dev-Southeast)
Bryan Williams (Exec Dir-Southeast)
Jack Peirce (CFO & Treas)
Kay Marquet (Interim CEO)

CANNA CORP
20200 Dexie Hghwy Ste 906, Miami,
FL 33180
Tel.: (800) 304-2657   CO
Year Founded: 2013
Rev.: $1,075,153
Assets: $1,598,026
Liabilities: $4,467,949
Net Worth: ($2,869,923)
Earnings: $1,011,919
Fiscal Year-end: 12/31/18
Cryptocurrency Mining Machines Mfr
N.A.I.C.S.: 333131

**CANNABINOID BIOSCIENCES,
INC.**
3699 Wilshire Blvd Ste 610, Los An-
geles, CA 90010
Tel.: (323) 868-6762   CA
Year Founded: 2014
Emp.: 5
Biopharmaceutical Product Mfr &
Distr
N.A.I.C.S.: 325412
Solomon Mbagwu (Chm)
Azuka L. Uzoh (Vice Chm & Gen
Counsel)
Patience C. Ogbozor (Pres & CEO)
Kareem Davis (Chief Bus Dev Officer
& VP)
Frank I. Igwealor (CFO, Treas, Sec &
VP)

**CANNABUSINESS GROUP,
INC.**
26632 Towne Centre Dr Ste 300,
Foothill Ranch, CA 92610
Real Estate Manangement Services
N.A.I.C.S.: 531210
Jeff Jiron (Chm & CEO)

CANNAMATRIX, INC.
18 Los Monteros, Monarch Beach,
CA 92629
Tel.: (949) 637-3909   NV
Year Founded: 2010
Emp.: 1
Investment Services
N.A.I.C.S.: 523999
Harrysen Mittler (Chm, Pres, CFO &
Sec)

**CANNAMED ENTERPRISES,
INC.**
391 E Brown St, Stroudsburg, PA
18301
Tel.: (949) 673-4510   DE
Year Founded: 2014
Liabilities: $64,964
Net Worth: ($64,964)
Earnings: ($25,880)
Fiscal Year-end: 12/31/18
Financial Funding Services
N.A.I.C.S.: 523940
Mikhail Artamonov (Pres, CEO, CFO
& Sec)

CANNATA'S CORPORATION
6289 W Park Ave Ste 5, Houma, LA
70364
Tel.: (985) 879-3574
Web Site:
    http://www.cannatasmarket.com
Year Founded: 1959
Sales Range: $25-49.9 Million
Emp.: 350
Grocery Stores
N.A.I.C.S.: 445110
Vincent Cannata Jr. (Pres)

Subsidiaries:

Cannata's Super Market, Inc.   (1)
1977 Prospect Blvd, Houma, LA 70363
Tel.: (985) 872-2900
Web Site: http://www.cannatasmarket.com
Sales Range: $1-9.9 Million
Emp.: 11
Grocery Stores
N.A.I.C.S.: 445110
Vincent Cannata (Pres & CEO)
Tom Hughes (Controller)

CANNDESCENT LLC
3905 State St Ste 7-537, Santa Bar-
bara, CA 93105
Tel.: (760) 205-2087
Web Site:
    http://www.canndescent.com
Year Founded: 2015
Cannabis Cultivator & Mfr
N.A.I.C.S.: 325411
Adrian Sedlin (CEO)
Rick Fisher (COO)

**CANNERY CASINO RESORTS,
LLC**
2121 E Craig Rd, North Las Vegas,
NV 89030
Tel.: (702) 507-5700   NV
Web Site:
    http://www.cannerycasinos.com
Year Founded: 2001
Holding Company; Casino, Racetrack
& Casino Hotel Owner & Operator
N.A.I.C.S.: 551112
Bill Paulos (Co-Founder, Co-Owner &
Co-CEO)
William Wortman (Co-Founder, Co-
Owner & Co-CEO)
Tom Lettero (Pres & CFO)

Xavier Walsh (COO)
Michael Day (CIO)
Guy Hillyer (Exec VP)
Dennis Shipley (Dir-HR)
Ryan Paulos (VP-Gaming Sys &
Ops)
Jennifer Nichols (Dir-Mktg Strategy)

CANNING SHOES, INC.
335 E Atlantic Ave, Delray Beach, FL
33483
Tel.: (561) 276-6570
Web Site:
    http://www.canningshoes.com
Sales Range: $1-9.9 Million
Emp.: 6
Shoe Stores
N.A.I.C.S.: 458210
Mark Denkler (Pres)

CANNIS, INC.
4760 S Pecos Rd Ste 103, Las Ve-
gas, NV 89121
Tel.: (775) 391-8588   NV
Year Founded: 2016
Assets: $29,111
Liabilities: $46,989
Net Worth: ($17,878)
Earnings: ($30,982)
Emp.: 1
Fiscal Year-end: 08/31/18
Business Management Software De-
velopment Services
N.A.I.C.S.: 541511
Aleksandr Zausaev (Pres, CEO,
CFO, Treas & Sec)

**CANNON & WENDT ELECTRIC
CO.**
4020 N 16th St, Phoenix, AZ 85016
Tel.: (602) 279-1681
Web Site: https://www.cannon-
    wendt.com
Year Founded: 1945
Sales Range: $150-199.9 Million
Emp.: 275
Electrical Wiring Services
N.A.I.C.S.: 238210
Mark A. Fjone (VP)

**CANNON AUTOMOTIVE
GROUP, INC.**
5210 S Florida Ave, Lakeland, FL
33813-5500
Tel.: (863) 646-5051
Web Site:
    http://www.cannonautos.com
Year Founded: 1949
Sales Range: $10-24.9 Million
Emp.: 70
Car Whslr
N.A.I.C.S.: 441110
Richard H. Cannon (Pres)
Terry A. Cannon (VP)
Mary Ratzel (Dir-Fin)
Jonathan Siegel (Mgr-Svc)

**CANNON COUNTY KNIT
MILLS, INC.**
237F Castlewood Dr, Murfreesboro,
TN 37129
Tel.: (615) 890-2938
Web Site:
    http://www.cckmapparel.com
Year Founded: 1959
Knit Outerwear Mills
N.A.I.C.S.: 315120
Jerry Eckstein (VP-Sls)
Brad Gibens (Chm & CEO)
Bill Perkoski (VP & CFO)

CANNON DESIGN, INC.
2170 Whitehaven Rd, Grand Island,
NY 14072-2025
Tel.: (716) 773-6800   ME

Web Site:
http://www.cannondesign.com
Year Founded: 1945
Architectural & Engineering Services, Interior Design & Construction Management
N.A.I.C.S.: 541310
Kevin L. Sticht (COO & Exec Dir-Enterprise Integration)
David M. Carlino (CFO & Exec Dir-Fin)
Bradley A. Lukanic (CEO)
Stephen Blair (Exec Dir-Science & Tech Practice)
Patricia A. Bou (Principal-Washington DC)
Joseph S. Cassata (Head-Facility Optimization Solutions)
Lynne Deninger (Principal-Boston)
Paul M. Moskal (Dir-Compliance)
Michael Pukszta (Dir-Health Practice)
Jose M. Silva (Exec Dir-Bus Strategies)
Mehrdad Yazdani (Principal-Design-Yazdani Studio)
Abbie Clary (Principal & Dir-Health Practice)
Charlene Miraglia (Dir-HR)
Swapna Sathyan (Principal/Dir-Workplace Strategy Consulting-Chicago)
Troy Hoggard (Principal-Chicago)
Megan Kindle (Assoc VP)
Margaret Bailey (Assoc VP)
Jeff Murray (Sr VP)
Juann Khoory (Sr VP-Boston)
Khanh Uong (Assoc VP)
Monica Pascatore (Assoc VP)

CANNON ENTERPRISES INC.
230 Riley Fuzzell Rd, Spring, TX 77373
Tel.: (281) 353-6868
Web Site:
https://www.cannonenterprises.com
Sales Range: $50-74.9 Million
Emp.: 30
Commercial & Office Building; New Construction
N.A.I.C.S.: 236220
Scott Eickhoff (VP)
Keith Cannon (Program Dir-Project Mgmt)
Deanna Turney (Project Coord)

CANNONBALL
8251 Maryland Ave Ste 200, Saint Louis, MO 63105
Tel.: (314) 445-6400
Web Site:
http://www.cannonballagency.com
Sales Range: $25-49.9 Million
Emp.: 42
Title Abstract & Settlement Offices
N.A.I.C.S.: 541810
Steve Hunt (Creative Dir)
Mike Binnette (Creative Dir)
Mary Jarnagin (Mgr-Bus)
Larry Israel (Sr Producer)
Stacey Goldman (Owner)

CANO CONTAINER CORP.
3920 Enterprise Ct, Aurora, IL 60504-8132
Tel.: (630) 585-7500
Web Site:
https://www.canocontainer.com
Sales Range: $10-24.9 Million
Emp.: 2
Corrugated Box Mfr
N.A.I.C.S.: 322211
Juventino Cano (Pres)

CANON RECRUITING GROUP LLC

26531 Summit Cir, Santa Clarita, CA 91350
Tel.: (661) 252-7400
Web Site:
http://www.canonrecruiting.com
Year Founded: 1980
Sales Range: $1-9.9 Million
Emp.: 400
Temporary & Permanent Staffing Services & Payroll & Consulting Solutions
N.A.I.C.S.: 561311
Tim Grayem (Pres)
Seth Kuhlman (Coord-West Coast Recruiting)

CANOOCHEE ELECTRIC MEMBERSHIP CORPORATION
342 E Brazell St, Reidsville, GA 30453
Tel.: (912) 557-4391
Web Site:
http://www.canoocheeemc.com
Sales Range: $10-24.9 Million
Emp.: 69
Electric Power Distribution
N.A.I.C.S.: 221122
Sheila Thigpen (Dir-HR)
Lou Ann Brown (CEO)

CANOPY FINANCIAL
201 Spear St, San Francisco, CA 94105
Year Founded: 2004
Sales Range: $10-24.9 Million
Emp.: 84
Financial Services
N.A.I.C.S.: 541219
Vikram Kashyap (Co-Founder & CEO)
Jeremy Blackburn (Co-Founder & Pres)
Anthony Banas (Co-Founder & CTO)
Luis Marcelo Doffo (Sr VP-Bus Dev)
Scott Hazdra (Chief Security Officer)
John Ingram (Chief Admin Officer)
Todd Rearden (VP-Product Dev)
Traci Roberts (Dir-Mktg)
Mark Wallace (VP-Prof Svcs)

CANOPY INC.
10740 Nall Ave Ste 100, Overland Park, KS 66211
Tel.: (913) 563-3500   KS
Web Site: http://www.canopykc.com
Year Founded: 1976
Sales Range: $150-199.9 Million
Emp.: 24
Health & Life Insurance
N.A.I.C.S.: 524210
Bob Zeller (Pres)

CANTECH HOLDING, INC.
109 E 17th St Ste 80, Cheyenne, WY 82001
Tel.: (626) 429-4948   NV
Web Site:
http://www.cantechholding.com
Year Founded: 2010
Emp.: 1
Investment Services
N.A.I.C.S.: 523999

CANTEEN SERVICES INC.
905 N Church St, Tekonsha, MI 49092
Tel.: (616) 956-5066   MI
Web Site:
http://www.canteenservices.com
Year Founded: 1934
Sales Range: $25-49.9 Million
Emp.: 785
Food, Commissary & Laundry Services
N.A.I.C.S.: 722310
Craig Tiggleman (CEO)

CANTERBURY CONSULTING GROUP, INC.
352 Stokes Rd Ste 200, Medford, NJ 08055
Tel.: (609) 953-0044   PA
Year Founded: 1981
Sales Range: $10-24.9 Million
Emp.: 53
Technical & Desktop Applications Software Training
N.A.I.C.S.: 611420
Stanton M. Pikus (Chm)
Kevin J. McAndrew (CEO, CFO & Treas)
Jean Zwerlein Pikus (Sec & VP)

Subsidiaries:

Canterbury Management Group, Inc.   (1)
352 Stokes Rd Ste 200, Medford, NJ 08055
Tel.: (609) 953-0044
Information Technology Services
N.A.I.C.S.: 611519

MSI/Canterbury Corp.   (1)
400 Lanidex Pl, Parsippany, NJ 07054-2722
Tel.: (973) 781-9300
Information Technology Services
N.A.I.C.S.: 561110

CANTERBURY CONSULTING INCORPORATED
660 Newport Center Dr Ste 300, Newport Beach, CA 92660
Tel.: (949) 721-9580
Web Site:
http://www.canterburyconsulting.com
Sales Range: $10-24.9 Million
Emp.: 34
Securities Brokerage
N.A.I.C.S.: 523150
Adele H. Berwanger (Mng Dir-Asset Class & Capital Mkts Res)
Debashis Chowdhury (Mng Dir)
D. Robinson Cluck (Co-Founder & Mng Dir)
Michael S. Laven (Mng Dir)
J. D. Montgomery (Mng Dir)
Ryan Quinn (Dir-Alternative Investment Res)

CANTERBURY TOWERS, INC.
3501 Bayshore Blvd, Tampa, FL 33629
Tel.: (813) 837-1083   FL
Web Site:
https://www.canterburytower.org
Year Founded: 1976
Sales Range: $1-9.9 Million
Emp.: 100
Residential Care Facilities
N.A.I.C.S.: 623990
Cary Vinas (CEO)

CANTERBURY-ON-THE-LAKE
5601 Hatchery Rd, Waterford, MI 48329
Tel.: (248) 674-9292   MI
Web Site:
http://www.canterburyonthelake.org
Year Founded: 1991
Sales Range: $10-24.9 Million
Emp.: 351
Community Health Care Services
N.A.I.C.S.: 621498
Nancy Boari (Sec)
Cindy Maxwell-Philips (Vice Chm)
William Ahlstrom (Chm)
Jim Gessner (Chm)
Phillip Hough Jr. (Treas)

CANTIN CHEVROLET, INC.
623 Union Ave, Laconia, NH 03246
Tel.: (603) 556-7070
Year Founded: 1955
Sales Range: $25-49.9 Million

Emp.: 53
Car Whslr
N.A.I.C.S.: 441110
Thomas E. Cantin (Pres)

CANTO SOFTWARE, INC.
221 Main St Ste 460, San Francisco, CA 94105
Tel.: (415) 495-6545   CA
Web Site: http://www.canto.com
Year Founded: 1990
Sales Range: $1-9.9 Million
Emp.: 15
Whol Computers/Peripherals
N.A.I.C.S.: 423430
Wain Kellum (CEO)
Nick Gerard (CFO)

Subsidiaries:

MerlinOne, Inc.   (1)
50 Braintree Hill Office Park Ste 308, Braintree, MA 02184
Tel.: (617) 328-6645
Web Site: http://www.merlinone.com
Software & Technology Development Services
N.A.I.C.S.: 513210
Shevawn Hardesty (CFO)
Andrew Forber (CTO)
Jeff Seidensticker (COO)

CANTON FOOD COMPANY
750 S Alameda St, Los Angeles, CA 90021-1624
Tel.: (213) 688-7707
Web Site:
https://www.cantonfoodco.com
Year Founded: 1971
Sales Range: $10-24.9 Million
Emp.: 106
Groceries, General Line
N.A.I.C.S.: 424410
Cho Kwan (VP)

CANTON MOTOR SALES, INC.
2255 Marietta Hwy, Canton, GA 30114
Tel.: (770) 479-1971
Sales Range: $10-24.9 Million
Emp.: 45
New Car Dealers
N.A.I.C.S.: 441110
Gene J. Moore (CEO)
Jack L. Moore (CFO & Sec)

CANTON-POTSDAM HOSPITAL
50 Leroy St, Potsdam, NY 13676
Tel.: (315) 265-3300   NY
Web Site: http://www.cphospital.org
Year Founded: 1920
Sales Range: $100-124.9 Million
Emp.: 1,028
Community Health Care Services
N.A.I.C.S.: 622110
Judy Chase (Sec)
Kathryn Mullaney (Co-Treas)
Judy Chittenden (Vice Chm)
Eric R. Burch (COO)
Steve Putman (Co-Treas)

CANTOR FITZGERALD INCOME TRUST, INC.
110 E 59th St, New York, NY 10022
Tel.: (212) 938-5000   MD
Web Site:
https://www.cfincometrust.com
Year Founded: 2016
Rev.: $72,843,136
Assets: $1,121,936,771
Liabilities: $526,607,134
Net Worth: $595,329,637
Earnings: ($5,012,221)
Fiscal Year-end: 12/31/22
Real Estate Investment Services
N.A.I.C.S.: 531210

Cantor Fitzgerald Income Trust,
Inc.—(Continued)

Howard W. Lutnick *(Chm & CEO)*
Paul M. Pion *(CFO, CFO/Treas-Cantor Fitzgerald Income Advisors & Treas)*

CANTOR FITZGERALD, L.P.
110 E 59th St, New York, NY 10022
Tel.: (212) 938-5000 DE
Web Site: http://www.cantor.com
Year Founded: 1945
Investment Banking, Market Trading & Brokerage Services
N.A.I.C.S.: 523150
Howard W. Lutnick *(Chm & CEO)*
Anshu Jain *(Pres)*
Lori Pennay *(Sr Mng Dir & Head-HR & Partnership)*
Sage Kelly *(Sr Mng Dir & Head-Investment Banking)*
Pascal Bandelier *(Head-Equities-Global)*
Jon Yalmokas *(Sr Mng Dir & Head-Prime Svcs)*
Karen Laureano-Rikardsen *(CMO, Sr Mng Dir & Head-Corp Comm)*
Michael Millard *(Head-Asset Mgmt-Global)*
Alex Englander *(Head-Institutional Equity & Prime Distribution-Global)*
Jason Chryssicas *(Head-IR)*

Subsidiaries:

CG Technology, L.P. (1)
2575 S Highland Dr, Las Vegas, NV 89109
Tel.: (702) 677-3800
Web Site: http://www.cgtglobal.com
Sportsbook Operator
N.A.I.C.S.: 713290
Lee M. Amaitis *(Pres & CEO)*
Stephen M. Merkel *(Exec Mng Dir, Gen Counsel & Secretary)*
Jeff Burge *(CFO & CTO)*
Parikshat Khanna *(COO)*
Quinton Singleton *(VP & Deputy Gen Counsel)*
Patricia Morelli *(VP-Compliance)*
Joshua A. Hanson *(CIO)*
Mark Goldman *(VP-Race & Sports Ops)*
Navarro Shepard *(VP-Race & Sports Ops)*
Jason Simbal *(VP-Risk Mgmt)*
Matthew B. Holt *(VP-Bus Dev)*

Cantor Fitzgerald & Co. (1)
110 E 59th St, New York, NY 10022
Tel.: (212) 938-5000
Web Site: http://www.cantor.com
Sales Range: $50-74.9 Million
Emp.: 40
Investment Banking & Securities Brokerage Services
N.A.I.C.S.: 523150
Paul M. Pion *(Sr Mng Dir & Chief Admin Officer)*
Steven Bisgay *(Exec Mng Dir & CFO)*
John C. Griffin *(CFO, Treas & Head-Finance-Comml Real Estate Investment Mgmt Div)*
Shawn P. Matthews *(CEO)*
Noel Kimmel *(Sr Mng Dir & Head-Prime Svcs-Global)*
Naved Khan *(Sr VP-Internet & Media Equity Res)*
Thomas Anzalone *(Sr Mng Dir & Dir-Global Ops)*
Stephen Merkel *(Exec Mng Dir, Gen Counsel & Sec)*
Lori Pennay *(Sr Mng Dir & Head-HR & Partnership-Global)*
Pascal Bandelier *(Head-Equities-Global)*
Paul Mutter *(Head-Institutional Client Coverage)*

Subsidiary (Domestic):

Cantor Futures Exchange, L.P. (2)
499 Park Ave, New York, NY 10022-1240
Tel.: (212) 829-5455
Web Site: http://www.cantorexchange.com
Securities Trading Services
N.A.I.C.S.: 523210

Howard W. Lutnick *(Chm & CEO)*
Richard Jaycobs *(Pres)*
Nolan Glantz *(COO)*
Rod Drown *(Sr Mng Dir-Global Products & Svcs)*
James Walker *(CTO)*
Benjamin Melnicki *(Chief Compliance Officer & Dir-Compliance)*

Unit (Domestic):

Cantor Ventures (2)
499 Park Ave, New York, NY 10022
Tel.: (212) 938-5000
Web Site: http://www.cantorventures.com
Venture Capital Services
N.A.I.C.S.: 523910

Subsidiary (Domestic):

Efficient Market Advisors (2)
4180 La Jolla Vlg Dr Ste 315, San Diego, CA 92037
Tel.: (888) 327-4600
Web Site: http://www.efficient-portfolios.com
Management Consulting Services
N.A.I.C.S.: 541618
Glenn A. Ambach *(Sr Portfolio Mgr)*
Clint Grady *(Portfolio Mgr & Dir)*
Samantha M. Hooper *(Dir-Investor & Advisor Ops)*
Walter Karle *(Chief Compliance Officer)*
Her W. Morgan III *(Chief Investment Officer & Sr Mng Dir)*
Jeffrey C. Anderson Jr. *(Mng Dir-Sls & Distr)*

Helix Financial Systems, L.P. (2)
110 E 59th St, New York, NY 10022
Tel.: (212) 294-7752
Financial Management Services
N.A.I.C.S.: 523940

Cantor Fitzgerald International (1)
1 America Square 17 Crosswall, London, EC3N 2LB, United Kingdom (100%)
Tel.: (44) 20 7894 7000
Web Site: http://www.cantor.com
Sales Range: $25-49.9 Million
Emp.: 800
Security Brokers & Dealers
N.A.I.C.S.: 561612
Franz Bucher *(Mng Dir)*
Dominic Curtis *(Mng Dir-Corp Fin-Europe)*
Deven Sthankiya *(Mng Dir-Debt Capital Markets-Europe)*
Caspar Kydd *(Dir-Institutional Equity Sls-Europe)*
Philip Dixon *(COO-Europe)*
Khairul Hussain *(Dir-IT)*
Jemma Broadgate *(Dir-Institutional Sls)*
Angelo Sofocleous *(CEO-Europe)*

Cantor Fitzgerald Investment Advisors, L.P. (1)
110 East 59th St, New York, NY 10022-1336
Tel.: (212) 938-5000
Web Site: http://www.cantor.com
Investment & Advisory Services
N.A.I.C.S.: 523940
Eileen Sebold *(Head-Distr)*

Subsidiary (Domestic):

Flippin, Bruce & Porter, Inc. (2)
800 Main St F 2, Lynchburg, VA 24504
Tel.: (434) 845-4900
Web Site: http://www.fbpinc.com
Investment Advice
N.A.I.C.S.: 523940
David J. Marshall *(Principal & Portfolio Mgr)*
John Hanna *(Principal & Dir-Mktg)*
Michael E. Watson *(Principal & Controller)*
Teresa L. Sanderson *(Chief Compliance Officer & Principal)*
George D. Vermilya *(Principal & Portfolio Mgr)*
J. Scott Morrell *(Principal & Portfolio Mgr)*
John T. Bruce *(Co-Founder & Portfolio Mgr)*
R. Gregory Porter III *(Co-Founder)*
Norman D. Darden III *(Principal & Portfolio Mgr)*

CANTOR GROUP, INC.
412 N Main St 100, Buffalo, WY 82834
Tel.: (307) 529-0940 WY
Year Founded: 2016

Emp.: 1
Women Apparel Mfr & Distr
N.A.I.C.S.: 315250
Iwan Kartadinata *(Pres, CEO, Treas & Sec)*

CANTU SERVICES INC.
PO Box 8325, Wichita Falls, TX 76310
Tel.: (940) 761-9720
Web Site: http://www.cantuservices.com
Sales Range: $10-24.9 Million
Emp.: 20
Provider of Food Service Contracts
N.A.I.C.S.: 722310
Ricardo Cantu *(Founder)*
David Wilkey *(Mgr-Info & Securities)*

CANTWELL-CLEARY CO., INC.
7575 Washington Blvd, Elkridge, MD 21075
Tel.: (301) 773-9800
Web Site:
https://www.cantwellcleary.com
Year Founded: 1914
Packaging Material & Equipment Distr
N.A.I.C.S.: 423850
Therese Cleary *(VP-Ops)*

CANUM CAPITAL MANAGEMENT, L.P.
1840 Washington St Ste 704, San Francisco, CA 94109
Web Site: http://www.canumcap.com
Privater Equity Firm
N.A.I.C.S.: 551112
Brandon Gregorio *(Co-Founder & Mng Partner)*
Robert Spigner *(Co-Founder & Mng Partner)*

CANUSA CORPORATION
1532 Thames St, Baltimore, MD 21231
Tel.: (410) 522-0110
Web Site:
https://www.canusacorp.com
Sales Range: $50-74.9 Million
Emp.: 22
Broker of Recycling Paper
N.A.I.C.S.: 423930
Bruce Fleming *(Founder & Pres)*
Susan Kirby *(Asst Controller)*
Michael Gajewski *(CFO)*
Mary E. Goughenour *(Mgr-A & R)*

CANUSA HERSHMAN RECYCLING, LLC
45 NE Industrial Rd, Branford, CT 06405-6801
Tel.: (203) 488-0887 MD
Web Site: http://www.chrecycling.com
Year Founded: 1887
Scrap & Waste Materials Recycling Services
N.A.I.C.S.: 562920
Ethan J. Hershman *(Co-Chm & CEO)*
Todd Laggis *(CFO)*
Bruce Fleming *(Co-Chm)*
Jonathan Sloan *(Pres)*
Michael Walter Jr. *(Gen Counsel)*

CANVAS HEALTH
7066 Stillwater Blvd N, Oakdale, MN 55128
Tel.: (651) 777-5222 MN
Web Site:
https://www.canvashealth.org
Year Founded: 1969
Sales Range: $10-24.9 Million
Emp.: 378
Mental Health Services
N.A.I.C.S.: 621420

Matt Eastwood *(COO)*
Dean Howard *(Sec)*
Jim Ellis *(Treas)*
Hilke Riechardt-Martinez *(CFO)*

CANYON CAPITAL ADVISORS LLC
2000 Avenue of the Stars 11th Fl, Los Angeles, CA 90067
Tel.: (310) 272-1000
Web Site:
http://www.canyonpartners.com
Year Founded: 1990
Emp.: 200
Privater Equity Firm
N.A.I.C.S.: 523999
Joshua S. Friedman *(Co-Founder, Co-Chm, Co-CEO & Co-CIO)*
Mitchell R. Julis *(Co-Founder, Co-Chm, Co-CEO & Co-CIO)*
Jonathan Kaplan *(Partner & Gen Counsel)*
Raj Venkataraman Iyer *(Partner)*
Doug Anderson *(Chief Compliance Officer)*
Robert Herin *(CTO)*
Christopher Heine *(Partner)*
Jonathan Heller *(Partner)*
George Jikovski *(Partner)*
Desmond Lynch *(Partner)*
Chaney M. Sheffield Jr. *(Partner & Portfolio Mgr)*
John Plaga *(Partner & CFO)*
Andy Ray *(Partner)*
Todd Lemkin *(Partner & Chief Investment Officer)*

CANYON CONSTRUCTION
925 Country Club Dr, Moraga, CA 94556
Tel.: (925) 376-3486
Web Site:
http://www.canyonconstruction.com
Year Founded: 1966
Sales Range: $25-49.9 Million
Emp.: 70
Residential & Commercial Building & Remodeling
N.A.I.C.S.: 236118
Christopher Avant *(Pres)*
Deva Rajan *(Founder & Chm)*
Dave Anderson *(CFO)*

CANYON MANUFACTURING SERVICES, INC.
523 Rinkin Rd N, Houston, TX 77073
Tel.: (281) 876-7105
Web Site: https://www.canyon-mfg.com
Year Founded: 1997
Rev.: $7,000,000
Emp.: 26
Printed Circuit Assembly Mfr
N.A.I.C.S.: 334418
Sheri Henn *(CFO)*
Kim Butler *(Mgr-HR)*
Michael Henn *(Pres)*

CANYON RANCH MANAGEMENT, LLC
8600 E Rockcliff Rd, Tucson, AZ 85750
Tel.: (520) 749-9000
Web Site:
http://www.canyonranch.com
Year Founded: 1978
Sales Range: $25-49.9 Million
Emp.: 700
Resort
N.A.I.C.S.: 721199
Kevin Coleman *(Dir-Revenue Mgmt-Global)*
Denise Bruzzone *(Dir-Sls-Global)*
Ricky Ocampo *(Dir-Food & Beverage)*

CANYON VISTA MEDICAL CENTER
5700 E Hwy 90, Sierra Vista, AZ 85635
Tel.: (520) 263-2000   AZ
Web Site: https://www.canyonvistamedical center.com
Year Founded: 1963
Emp.: 62
Health Care Srvices
N.A.I.C.S.: 622110
Randy Anderson (CEO)
Ashley Johnson (COO)
Traci L. Meyer (Dir-HR Svcs)
Bruce Dockter (Chm)
William Miller (Vice Chm)
Michelle Eason (Coord-HR)

CAP BRAND MARKETING
1962 Main St Ste 200, Sarasota, FL 34236
Tel.: (941) 953-9191
Web Site: https://www.capbrandmarketing.com
Sales Range: $1-9.9 Million
Advetising Agency
N.A.I.C.S.: 541810
Roxanne Joffe (Founder & Pres)

CAP CARPET, INC.
535 S Emerson St, Wichita, KS 67209-2161
Tel.: (316) 262-3400
Web Site: http://www.capcarpetinc.com
Year Founded: 1967
Sales Range: $25-49.9 Million
Emp.: 200
Carpet Distr
N.A.I.C.S.: 449121
Josie Barnes (Mgr-Payroll)
Rob Lindsay (Controller)
Rick Bloomer (CFO)

Subsidiaries:

Mountain Rug Mills, Inc.   (1)
609 N King St, Hendersonville, NC 28792-3778
Tel.: (828) 698-0410
Carpet & Rug Mills
N.A.I.C.S.: 314110
Gill Morgan (Pres)

CAP CITY DENTAL LAB, LLC
2189 S James Rd, Columbus, OH 43232
Web Site: http://www.capcitydentallab.com
Year Founded: 2003
Sales Range: $1-9.9 Million
Emp.: 13
Dental Equipment Mfr & Distr
N.A.I.C.S.: 339114
Chris Pendry (Pres)

CAP FOOD SERVICES CO.
4025 Delridge Way SW Ste 510, Seattle, WA 98106
Tel.: (206) 933-4850
Sales Range: $10-24.9 Million
Emp.: 3
Grocery Stores, Independent
N.A.I.C.S.: 445110

CAP LOGISTICS INC.
4120 Jackson St, Denver, CO 80216
Tel.: (303) 333-3800
Web Site: https://www.caplogistics.com
Rev.: $20,340,964
Emp.: 100
Freight Forwarding
N.A.I.C.S.: 488510
Gayle Dendinger (Pres)

CAP SERVICES, INC.

5499 Hwy 10 E Ste A, Stevens Point, WI 54482
Tel.: (715) 343-7500   WI
Web Site: http://www.capservices.org
Year Founded: 1966
Sales Range: $10-24.9 Million
Emp.: 348
Residential Support Services
N.A.I.C.S.: 623990
Mary Patoka (Pres)

CAPACITY BENEFITS GROUP, INC.
1 Blue Hill Plz, Pearl River, NY 10965
Tel.: (201) 661-2000   NJ
Web Site: http://www.capcoverage.com
Year Founded: 1980
Sales Range: $50-74.9 Million
Emp.: 242
N.A.I.C.S.:
Robert G. Lull (Mng Principal)
Carl A. Gerson (Mng Principal)
Jay Bergstein (Mng Principal)
Ron Bergstein (Mng Principal)
Laura DiPiazza (CFO)
Jon Ziman (VP-Mktg)
Gary Maier (Sr Exec VP)

CAPACITY LLC
1112 Corporate Rd, North Brunswick, NJ 08902
Tel.: (732) 745-7770
Web Site: https://www.capacityllc.com
Sales Range: $10-24.9 Million
Emp.: 204
General Warehousing & Storage Services
N.A.I.C.S.: 493110
Arlen Fish (Co-Founder & CFO)
Jeff Kaiden (Co-Founder & CEO)
Thom Campbell (Co-Founder & Chief Strategic Officer)
Anthony Ruiz (VP-Logistics)
Karim Fofana (Dir-Ops)

CAPARROS CORPORATION
18730 Crenshaw Blvd, Torrance, CA 90504
Tel.: (310) 719-2302
Web Site: http://www.caparrosshoes.com
Sales Range: $10-24.9 Million
Emp.: 12
Shoes
N.A.I.C.S.: 424340
Anavel Caparros (Founder & Pres)
Ed Amido (VP)
Jaqueline Orozco (Mgr-Admin)

CAPCO CONTRACTORS, INC.
3323 US Hwy 259 N, Henderson, TX 75652-4034
Tel.: (903) 657-2699
Web Site: https://capcocontractors.com
Sales Range: $10-24.9 Million
Emp.: 165
Construction Engineering Services
N.A.I.C.S.: 237310
Billy Torrence (Owner)

CAPCO PLASTICS INC.
297 Dexter St, Providence, RI 02907
Tel.: (401) 272-3833
Web Site: https://www.capcoplastics.com
Year Founded: 1978
Rev.: $10,000,000
Emp.: 105
Blister, Clamshell & Trifold Packaging Products
N.A.I.C.S.: 326112

Richard Capuano (Pres)
Dennis Burke (Controller)

CAPE ABILITIES INC.
895 Mary Dunn Rd, Hyannis, MA 02601
Tel.: (508) 778-5040   MA
Web Site: https://www.capeabilities.org
Year Founded: 1968
Sales Range: $10-24.9 Million
Emp.: 304
Developmentally Disabled People Training Services
N.A.I.C.S.: 623210
Carol J. Kenner (Vice Chm)
James J. Cullen (Sec)
Rosalie A. Edes (Pres & Exec Dir)
Scott Rockman (Chm)

CAPE AIR
660 Barnstable Rd, Hyannis, MA 02601
Tel.: (508) 790-3122
Web Site: http://www.capeair.com
Year Founded: 1989
Rev.: $36,000,000
Emp.: 850
Scheduled Airline Transportation
N.A.I.C.S.: 481111
Daniel Wolf (Founder & CEO)
Trish Lorino (Dir-Mktg)
Linda Markham (Pres)

CAPE ANN SAVINGS BANK
109 Main St, Gloucester, MA 01930
Tel.: (978) 283-0246
Web Site: http://www.capeannsavings.com
Year Founded: 1846
Sales Range: $10-24.9 Million
Emp.: 75
Savings Bank
N.A.I.C.S.: 522180
Marie F. Curley (VP-Ops)
Kathleen S. Purdy (VP-IT)
Marianne Smith (Treas & Sr VP)
Leo E. Bergeron (Officer-Comml Loan & VP)
Mike J. Luster (Officer-Comml Loan & VP)
Clare E. MacDonald (Officer-Compliance)
Amy L. Randazza (Officer-IT & VP)
Robert J. Gillis Jr. (Exec VP)

CAPE ASSOCIATES, INC.
345 Massasoit Rd, North Eastham, MA 02642
Tel.: (508) 255-1770
Web Site: https://www.capeassociates.com
Year Founded: 1971
Sales Range: $10-24.9 Million
Emp.: 100
Custom Builder of New Homes, Renovations, Additions & Commercial Projects on Cape Cod
N.A.I.C.S.: 236117
Matthew H. Cole (Founder, Pres & CEO)
Richard M. Bryant (VP)
Lindsay J. Cole (Office Mgr & Mgr-HR)
Mark P. Kinnane (Exec VP)
Andrea Baerenwald (Mgr-Mktg)

CAPE CLEAR SOFTWARE, INC.
2929 Campus Dr Ste 402, San Mateo, CA 94403-2537
Tel.: (781) 622-2258
Web Site: http://www.capeclear.com
Year Founded: 1999
Sales Range: $1-9.9 Million
Emp.: 85

Software
N.A.I.C.S.: 513210
Julie Bradley (CFO)
Ashley Goldsmith (Chief HR Officer)
Dave Duffield (Co-Founder & Chm)
Siobhan McFeeney (COO)
Mark Peek (Co-Pres)
Phil Wilmington (Co-Pres)
Stan Swete (CTO)
Mike Stankey (Vice Chm)
Angela Hammack (VP-Special Projects)

CAPE COD LUMBER CO. INC.
225 Groveland St, Abington, MA 02351
Tel.: (781) 878-0715
Web Site: http://www.cclco.com
Rev.: $58,069,441
Emp.: 170
Lumber & Other Building Materials
N.A.I.C.S.: 423310
Harvey Hurvitz (Owner)

CAPE FEAR CONSTRUCTION CO. INC.
1501 Starlite Dr, Lumberton, NC 28358
Tel.: (910) 738-7246
Web Site: http://www.capefearconstruction.com
Sales Range: $10-24.9 Million
Emp.: 45
Industrial Building Construction
N.A.I.C.S.: 236210
Doug Milles (Pres)

CAPE FEAR FARM CREDIT, ACA
333 E Russell St, Fayetteville, NC 28301
Tel.: (910) 323-9188   NC
Web Site: http://www.capefearfarmcredit.com
Year Founded: 1916
Rev.: $63,308,000
Assets: $958,543,000
Liabilities: $755,024,000
Net Worth: $203,519,000
Earnings: $20,191,000
Emp.: 82
Fiscal Year-end: 12/31/18
Agricultural Loans & Financial Services
N.A.I.C.S.: 522291
Jonathan Pope (Chm)
Evan J. Kleinhans (CEO)
Nash Johnson (Vice Chm)

CAPE FEAR TUTORING, INC.
3801 Wrightsville Ave, Wilmington, NC 28403
Tel.: (910) 395-6132   NC
Web Site: https://www.capefeartutoring.com
Year Founded: 1983
Sales Range: $10-24.9 Million
Emp.: 37
Child Day Care Services
N.A.I.C.S.: 624410

CAPE FOX CORPORATION
2851 S Tongass Hwy, Ketchikan, AK 99901
Tel.: (907) 225-5163
Web Site: https://www.capefoxcorp.com
Year Founded: 1973
Sales Range: $25-49.9 Million
Emp.: 237
Defense Contractor & Tour Operator
N.A.I.C.S.: 238990
Fred Lauth (Pres)
Julie Isom (Bus Mgr)
Charles Denny (Chm)

Cape Fox Corporation—(Continued)

CAPE QUALITY SEAFOOD LTD.
657 Dartmouth St, Dartmouth, MA 02748
Tel.: (508) 996-6724
Web Site: http://www.capequality.com
Rev.: $11,100,000
Emp.: 15
Fish, Fresh
N.A.I.C.S.: 424460
Norval Stanley III *(Pres)*

CAPEL INC.
831 N Main St, Troy, NC 27371
Tel.: (910) 572-7000
Web Site: http://www.capelrugs.net
Rev.: $53,173,047
Emp.: 450
Rugs, Braided & Hooked
N.A.I.C.S.: 314110
John Magee *(Pres & CEO)*
Betty Ann Williams *(Supvr-IT)*
Dree Wynkoop *(Mgr-Import)*

CAPEZIO BALLET MAKERS INC.
1 Campus Rd, Totowa, NJ 07512
Tel.: (973) 595-9000 NY
Web Site: https://www.capezio.com
Year Founded: 1887
Sales Range: $75-99.9 Million
Emp.: 500
Dance Shoes, Garments & Accessories Mfr
N.A.I.C.S.: 458210
Paul Plesh *(Sr Mgr-Product Line)*
Yolaine Aprea *(Gen Mgr-Retail)*

Subsidiaries:

Ballet Makers Australia Pty Ltd (1)
12-14 Milgate Drive, Mornington, 3931, VIC, Australia
Tel.: (61) 3 5975 0266
Web Site: http://www.capeziodanceanz.com
Dance Apparel & Accessory Retailer
N.A.I.C.S.: 458110
Graeme Taylor *(Pres)*

Ballet Makers Europe Ltd (1)
95 Whiffler Road, Norwich, NR3 2AW, Norfolk, United Kingdom
Tel.: (44) 370 350 0073
Web Site: http://www.capezioeurope.com
Dance Apparel & Accessory Retailer
N.A.I.C.S.: 458110

CAPGEN FINANCIAL GROUP LP
1185 Ave of the Americas Ste 2000, New York, NY 10036
Tel.: (212) 542-6868 DE
Web Site: http://www.capgen.com
Privater Equity Firm
N.A.I.C.S.: 523999
John W. Rose *(Principal)*
Robert B. Goldstein *(Principal)*
John Sullivan *(Mng Dir)*
Eugene Ludwig *(Mng Principal)*
Robert J. Merlino *(VP)*
Charlie Rogers *(Controller)*

Subsidiaries:

CapGen Capital Advisers LLC (1)
1185 Ave of the Americas Ste 2000, New York, NY 10036
Tel.: (212) 542-6868
Web Site: http://www.capgen.com
Private Equity Investment Advisory & Portfolio Management Services
N.A.I.C.S.: 523940
John W. Rose *(Principal)*
Robert B. Goldstein *(Principal)*
Eugene Ludwig *(Co-Founder & Mng Principal)*
John Sullivan *(Mng Dir)*
Rob Merlino *(Sr VP)*
Charlie Rogers *(CFO & Sr VP)*

CAPITA TECHNOLOGIES, INC.
17600 Gillette Ave, Irvine, CA 92614
Tel.: (949) 260-3000 DE
Web Site: http://www.capita.com
Year Founded: 1989
Rev.: $11,250,000
Emp.: 50
Advetising Agency
N.A.I.C.S.: 541810
Charles Granville *(CEO)*
Charlotte Bustle *(Controller)*
Imelda Ford *(Exec VP-Tech & Ops)*
Christian Mouritzen *(VP-Sls & Mktg)*
Lane Campbell *(Dir-eMarketing Ops)*

CAPITAL & COUNTIES USA, INC.
100 The Embarcadero Ste 300, San Francisco, CA 94105
Tel.: (415) 421-5100
Sales Range: $10-24.9 Million
Emp.: 8
Commercial & Industrial Building Operation
N.A.I.C.S.: 531120
Turner Newton *(Pres)*
John Cleary *(Chief Acctg Officer)*
Alan Zipkin *(CFO & Controller)*

CAPITAL AG PROPERTY SERVICES INC.
801 Warrenville Rd, Lisle, IL 60532-1396
Tel.: (815) 875-7418
Web Site: http://www.capitalag.com
Year Founded: 1986
Sales Range: $1-9.9 Million
Emp.: 30
Provider of Farm Management Services
N.A.I.C.S.: 531210
Royce S. Bryant *(Reg VP-Mid-South & Real Estate Broker)*
Scott D. Mason *(Exec Mgr-Mid-South & Real Estate Broker)*

CAPITAL ALIGNMENT PARTNERS, INC.
40 Burton Hills Blvd Ste 250, Nashville, TN 37215
Tel.: (615) 915-1213
Web Site: http://capfunds.com
Privater Equity Firm
N.A.I.C.S.: 523999
Burton R. Harvey *(Mng Partner)*
Mark L. McManigal *(Mng Dir)*

Subsidiaries:

Atlantis Fire Protection (1)
4550 Travis St Ste 560, Dallas, TX 75205
Tel.: (954) 599-9653
Web Site: https://atlantisfire.com
Fire Protection Services
N.A.I.C.S.: 922160
Patrick Lynch *(CEO)*

Subsidiary (Domestic):

Keller's, Inc. (2)
6750 Gordon Rd, Wilmington, NC 28411-8464
Tel.: (910) 392-7011
Web Site: http://www.kellersinc.com
Fire Protection Products Mfr
N.A.I.C.S.: 922160
Stella Black *(Pres)*

McCoy Fire & Safety, Inc. (2)
537 Temple St, Auburn, AL 36830-4019
Tel.: (334) 501-2228
Web Site: http://www.mccoyfire.com
Electrical Apparatus & Equipment, Wiring Supplies & Related Equipment Merchant Whslr
N.A.I.C.S.: 423610
Vince McCoy *(Pres)*

CAPITAL AREA COMMUNITY ACTION AGENCY, INC.
309 Office Plz Dr, Tallahassee, FL 32301
Tel.: (850) 222-2043 FL
Web Site: http://www.cacaainc.org
Year Founded: 1965
Sales Range: $10-24.9 Million
Emp.: 149
Community Action Services
N.A.I.C.S.: 624190
Roger Newsome *(Chm)*
Allen Stucks *(Treas)*

CAPITAL AREA COMMUNITY SERVICES, INC.
1301 Rensen St, Lansing, MI 48910
Tel.: (517) 393-7077 MI
Web Site: https://www.cacs-inc.org
Year Founded: 1964
Sales Range: $10-24.9 Million
Emp.: 407
Community Action Services
N.A.I.C.S.: 624190
Eric Schertzing *(Pres)*
Louis F. Goecker *(Dir-Fin)*
Gary Gosaynie *(Treas)*
Heather Pope *(Sec)*

CAPITAL AREA FOOD BANK
4900 Puerto Rico Ave NE, Washington, DC 20017
Tel.: (202) 644-9800 DC
Web Site:
https://www.capitalareafoodbank.org
Year Founded: 1979
Rev.: $71,536,596
Assets: $58,030,249
Liabilities: $7,879,187
Net Worth: $50,151,062
Emp.: 153
Fiscal Year-end: 06/30/18
Community Food Services
N.A.I.C.S.: 624210
Mark A. Jacquez *(Sr Dir-Distr Center Ops)*
Marian Barton Peele *(Sr Dir-Innovation & Food Flow)*
Jody Tick *(COO)*
Christel Allen Hair *(Sr Dir-Strategic Partnerships & Community Engagement)*
Carl L. Vacketta *(Vice Chm)*
Eric Eisenberg *(Gen Counsel)*
Peter Schnall *(Chm)*
John Huffman *(Treas)*
Diana Serrano *(Sec)*

CAPITAL AUTO & TRUCK AUCTION
1905 Brentwood Rd NE, Washington, DC 20018
Tel.: (202) 269-3361
Web Site:
https://www.capitalautoauction.com
Rev.: $10,000,000
Emp.: 25
Auctioneers, Fee Basis
N.A.I.C.S.: 561990
Mark Loesberg *(Pres)*

CAPITAL AUTO RECEIVABLES LLC
500 Woodward Ave, Detroit, MI 48226
Tel.: DE
Financial Lending Services
N.A.I.C.S.: 522390
Ryan C. Farris *(Pres)*

CAPITAL AUTOMOBILE COMPANY
2210 Cobb Pkwy S, Smyrna, GA 30080
Tel.: (770) 952-2277 GA
Web Site:
http://www.capitalcadillac.com
Year Founded: 1931
Sales Range: $50-74.9 Million

Emp.: 100
Automobile Dealership
N.A.I.C.S.: 441110
Doug Pierce *(Mgr-Svcs)*
William R. Bridges III *(Pres)*

CAPITAL AUTOMOTIVE REAL ESTATE SERVICES, INC.
8484 Westpark Dr Ste 200, McLean, VA 22102
Tel.: (703) 288-3075 DE
Web Site:
http://www.capitalautomotive.com
Year Founded: 1997
Sales Range: $200-249.9 Million
Emp.: 33
Automobile Retailing Property Investment & Management Services
N.A.I.C.S.: 525990
John M. Weaver *(Gen Counsel, Sec & Sr VP)*
Jay M. Ferriero *(Sr VP & Dir-Acq)*
Willie Beck *(VP-Acq)*
Thomas D. Eckert *(Founder)*

CAPITAL AVIONICS, INC.
3701 Hartsfield Rd, Tallahassee, FL 32303
Tel.: (850) 575-4028 FL
Web Site:
http://www.capitalavionics.com
Year Founded: 1978
Sales Range: $1-9.9 Million
Emp.: 16
Aircraft & Avionics Components Service & Repair
N.A.I.C.S.: 811210
Al Ingle *(Pres)*
Donna Ingle *(Comptroller)*
Faith Baumann *(Mgr-Stockroom)*
Tyler Gilmore *(Mgr-Depot Svcs)*

CAPITAL BEVERAGE CORPORATION
8 The Green Ste 7734, Dover, DE 19901
Tel.: (201) 679-6752 DE
Year Founded: 1995
Shell Company
N.A.I.C.S.: 551112
Rick Smith *(VP)*

CAPITAL BLUECROSS INC.
2500 Elmerton Ave, Harrisburg, PA 17110-9764
Tel.: (717) 541-7000 PA
Web Site:
http://www.capbluecross.com
Year Founded: 1938
Sales Range: $1-4.9 Billion
Emp.: 1,796
Hospital & Medical Service Plans
N.A.I.C.S.: 524114
William B. Reineberg *(Chief Compliance Officer & Sr VP-Risk Mgmt)*
David B. Skerpon *(Sr VP-Consumer Strategies & Community Impact)*
Gary D. St. Hilaire *(Pres & CEO)*
Mark A. Caron *(Exec VP-Bus Platforms & Solutions)*
Aji M. Abraham *(Sr VP-Bus & Network Dev)*
Jennifer A. Chambers *(Chief Medical Officer & Sr VP)*
Steven J. Krupinski *(Sr VP-HR Facilities)*
Donna K. Lencki *(CMO & Sr VP)*
Todd Shamash *(Gen Counsel & Sr VP)*
Scott Frank *(CIO)*
Jack Jaroh *(Sr VP-Comml Grp Sls)*
Susan Hubley *(VP-Corp Social Responsibility)*
Debbie Rittenour *(Sr VP-Govt Programs)*
Harvey Littman *(CFO, Treas & Sr VP)*

Subsidiaries:

Capital Advantage Insurance
Company   (1)
2500 Elmerton Ave, Harrisburg, PA 17110-9764
Tel.: (717) 541-7000
Web Site: http://www.capbluecross.com
Sales Range: $750-799.9 Million
Emp.: 300
Hospital & Medical Service Plans
N.A.I.C.S.: 524126
Anita M. Smith *(Pres & CEO)*
Michael R. Clearly *(VP-Fin)*
Patricia K. Wong *(Sec)*
Gary St. Hilaire *(Pres & CEO)*

Keystone Health Plan Central,
Inc.   (1)
2500 Elmerton Ave, Harrisburg, PA 17177
Tel.: (717) 541-7000
Web Site: http://www.capbluecross.com
Sales Range: $100-124.9 Million
Emp.: 468
Health & Medical Insurance Services
N.A.I.C.S.: 524114

CAPITAL BONDING CORPORATION

Ste 307 645 Penn St, Reading, PA 19601-3559
Tel.: (610) 372-8811
Web Site:
http://www.capitalbonding.com
Rev.: $38,000,000
Emp.: 70
Bail Bonding Services
N.A.I.C.S.: 812990

CAPITAL BREWERY CO., INC.

7734 Terrace Ave, Middleton, WI 53562-3163
Tel.: (608) 836-7100
Web Site: http://www.capital-brewery.com
Year Founded: 1986
Sales Range: $25-49.9 Million
Emp.: 20
Beer Mfr
N.A.I.C.S.: 312120

CAPITAL BUICK GMC

2150 Cobb Pkwy SE, Smyrna, GA 30080-7630
Tel.: (770) 872-0704
Web Site:
https://www.capitalbpg.com
Sales Range: $25-49.9 Million
Emp.: 200
New & Used Car Dealership
N.A.I.C.S.: 441110
Tony Dutton *(Mgr-Fixed Ops)*
Walter Bridges *(VP & Gen Mgr)*
Donna Bell *(Mgr-Svc)*
Greg Douthit *(Bus Mgr)*
David Parker *(Mgr-Parts)*

CAPITAL CITY AUTO AUCTION INC.

600 Winfield Rd, Saint Albans, WV 25177
Tel.: (304) 201-2270
Web Site:
https://www.capitalcityaa.com
Sales Range: $25-49.9 Million
Emp.: 100
Automobile & Other Motor Vehicle Merchant Whslr
N.A.I.C.S.: 423110
Joe Pyle *(Co-Owner)*
Charlotte A. Pyle *(Co-Owner)*
Margie Wills *(Controller)*
Ty Laughlin *(Gen Mgr)*

CAPITAL CITY CLUB INC.

7 Harris St NW, Atlanta, GA 30303
Tel.: (404) 523-8221
Web Site:
http://www.capitalcityclub.org

Sales Range: $25-49.9 Million
Emp.: 400
Country Club & Golf Club
N.A.I.C.S.: 713910
Katie Taylor *(Mgr)*
Leslie Dove *(CFO)*
Kelli Rice *(Dir-HR)*
Ted Mahoney Jr. *(Mgr-Food & Beverage)*

CAPITAL CITY COMPANIES INC.

1295 Johnson St NE, Salem, OR 97303
Tel.: (503) 362-5558   OR
Sales Range: $25-49.9 Million
Emp.: 75
Provider of Petroleum Products
N.A.I.C.S.: 484230
William Loch *(Chm)*

CAPITAL CITY CONSULTING, LLC

101 E College Ave Ste 502, Tallahassee, FL 32301
Tel.: (850) 222-9075
Web Site:
http://www.capcityconsult.com
Year Founded: 2003
Sales Range: $1-9.9 Million
Emp.: 12
Government Relations & Public Affairs Consulting
N.A.I.C.S.: 541613
Gerald Wester *(Partner)*
Nick Iarossi *(Founder & Partner)*
Ron LaFace Jr. *(Partner)*

CAPITAL CITY ENERGY GROUP, INC.

1335 Dublin Rd Ste 122-D, Columbus, OH 43215
Tel.: (614) 485-3110   NV
Web Site:
https://www.capcityenergy.com
Year Founded: 2003
CETG—(OTCBB)
Sales Range: Less than $1 Million
Oil & Gas Exploration Services
N.A.I.C.S.: 213112

Subsidiaries:

Capital City Petroleum, Inc.   (1)
1335 Dublin Rd Ste 122-D, Columbus, OH 43215
Tel.: (614) 485-3110
Management of Oil & Gas Funds
N.A.I.C.S.: 541611
Timothy S. Shear *(CEO)*

CAPITAL CITY HOME LOANS INC.

2740 Arden Way Ste 210, Sacramento, CA 95825
Tel.: (916) 489-8727
Sales Range: $25-49.9 Million
Emp.: 11
Holding Company
N.A.I.C.S.: 551112
Kelly Markey *(Pres)*

CAPITAL CITY INSURANCE CO. INC.

PO Box 212157, Columbia, SC 29221
Tel.: (803) 731-7728
Web Site: http://www.capcityins.com
Rev.: $30,462,415
Emp.: 200
Provider of Fire, Marine & Casualty Insurance Services
N.A.I.C.S.: 524126
Hinton G. Davis *(Chm)*
Patrick Naughter *(VP & Treas)*
Jim Allonier *(VP-Underwriting)*
Jack F. Grindstaff *(Sec)*

CAPITAL CITY OIL INC.

911 SE Adams St, Topeka, KS 66607
Tel.: (785) 233-8008
Web Site:
https://www.capitalcityoil.com
Sales Range: $50-74.9 Million
Emp.: 30
Petroleum Bulk Stations & Terminals
N.A.I.C.S.: 424710
Marvin Spees *(Pres)*

CAPITAL CITY PRESS

7290 Bluebonnet Blvd, Baton Rouge, LA 70810-1611
Tel.: (225) 383-1111
Web Site:
http://www.theadvocate.com
Year Founded: 1842
Sales Range: $150-199.9 Million
Emp.: 375
Morning Daily Newspaper
N.A.I.C.S.: 513110
Ralph Bender *(Chm)*
Jason Gele *(Mgr-Online Sls)*
Dean Blanchard *(Dir-Circulation)*
Connie Settle *(Mgr-Natl Adv)*
Charlene Robert *(Dir-Mktg)*
Sara Barnard *(Dir-Sls & Mktg-New Orleans)*
Fred Kalmbach *(Mng Editor)*
Gordon Russell *(Mng Editor-Investigations)*
Jay Jackson *(Mgr-Outside Sls)*
John Ballance *(Dir-Photography)*
Kyle Whitfield *(Dir-Digital)*
Lou Hudson *(Dir-Retail Sls)*
Lauren Ruello *(Mgr-Mktg)*
Megan Fambrough *(Mgr-Mktg)*
Peter Kovacs *(Editor)*
Robin Blanchard *(Dir-Classified)*
Judi Terzotis *(Publr)*

CAPITAL COMMUNICATION SERVICES, INC.

15045 Fogg St, Plymouth, MI 48170
Tel.: (734) 416-1800
Web Site: http://www.capcominc.com
Year Founded: 1986
Sales Range: $10-24.9 Million
Emp.: 48
Telephone & Telephone Equipment Installation Services
N.A.I.C.S.: 238210
David G. O'Reilly *(Founder & Pres)*
Lynne Taylor *(Controller)*

CAPITAL CONCRETE, INC.

400 Stapleton St, Norfolk, VA 23504
Tel.: (757) 627-0630
Web Site:
https://www.capitalconcreteinc.com
Rev.: $18,000,000
Emp.: 90
Ready Mixed Concrete
N.A.I.C.S.: 327320
Elizabeth A. Twohy *(Pres)*

CAPITAL CREDIT UNION

204 W Thayer Ave, Bismarck, ND 58501
Tel.: (701) 255-0042   ND
Web Site: http://www.capcu.org
Year Founded: 1936
Sales Range: $10-24.9 Million
Credit Union
N.A.I.C.S.: 522130
Vance Reinbold *(CEO)*
Scott Bullinger *(Officer-Mortgage Loan)*
Ryan Welder *(Branch Mgr)*
Loren Tollefson *(Branch Mgr)*
Lacey Hetletved *(Officer-Fin Svcs)*
Tyler Artlip *(Branch Mgr)*
Chris Nelson *(Branch Mgr)*
Sherry Doll *(Branch Mgr)*
Darcy Davidson *(Branch Mgr)*

Jim Schaefbauer *(VP-Member Svcs-East Reg)*
Corinne Hager *(Branch Mgr)*
Leanne Holzer *(Mgr-Mortgage Loan)*
Aaron Wentz *(Officer-Mortgage Loan)*
Kevin Strege *(Chief Lending Officer)*
Jillian Lagasse *(VP-Mktg)*
Kevin Kragnes *(Pres-Fargo)*

CAPITAL DEVELOPMENT CO.

3709 Griffin Ln SE, Olympia, WA 98501-2192
Tel.: (360) 491-6850   WA
Web Site: http://www.capdevco.com
Year Founded: 1960
Sales Range: $75-99.9 Million
Emp.: 20
Provider of Property Management & Development Services
N.A.I.C.S.: 237210
William A. Ehlers *(Chm)*
Burdette Chapel *(Sr VP)*
Melvin Hastings *(Treas & Sr VP)*
Jeffrey A. Blume *(VP)*
Jayna Bailey *(Mgr-Ops)*
Kevin Welsh *(Mgr-Ops)*

CAPITAL DEVELOPMENT COMPANY

3709 Griffin Ln SE, Olympia, WA 98501
Tel.: (360) 491-6850
Web Site: http://www.capdevco.com
Year Founded: 1959
Sales Range: $50-74.9 Million
Emp.: 20
Land Subdivision Services
N.A.I.C.S.: 237210
John R. Donaldson *(Sr VP)*

CAPITAL DISTRIBUTING, INC.

2910 N Stemmons Fwy, Dallas, TX 75247
Tel.: (214) 638-2681
Web Site:
https://www.capitaldistributing.com
Sales Range: $10-24.9 Million
Emp.: 70
Electrical Appliances Distr
N.A.I.C.S.: 423620
Michael J. Davis *(Pres & Sec)*

CAPITAL DISTRICT PHYSICIANS' HEALTH PLAN, INC.

500 Patroon Creek Blvd, Albany, NY 12206-1057
Tel.: (518) 641-3700   NY
Web Site: https://www.cdphp.com
Year Founded: 1984
Sales Range: $1-4.9 Billion
Emp.: 1,289
Health & Welfare Services
N.A.I.C.S.: 525120
Bruce E. Coplin *(Vice Chm)*
William P. Phelan *(Sec)*

CAPITAL DISTRICT REGIONAL OFF-TRACK BETTING CORPORATION

510 Smith St, Schenectady, NY 12305-2411
Tel.: (518) 370-5151   NY
Web Site: http://www.capitalotb.com
Year Founded: 1975
Sales Range: $25-49.9 Million
Emp.: 400
Provide Legalized Wagering-Horse Racing; Lottery Products
N.A.I.C.S.: 713290
John Signor *(Pres & CEO)*
Robert Hemsworth *(VP-Legal Affairs & Gen Counsel)*

CAPITAL ELECTRIC CONSTRUCTION COMPANY INC.

Capital Electric Construction Company
Inc.—(Continued)

600 Broadway St Ste 600, Kansas
City, MO 64105-1544
Tel.: (816) 472-9500   KS
Web Site:
     http://www.capitalelectric.com
Year Founded: 1957
Sales Range: $100-124.9 Million
Emp.: 650
Provider of Electrical Engineering
Services
N.A.I.C.S.: 238210

CAPITAL ELECTRIC COOPERATIVE, INC.
4111 State St, Bismarck, ND 58502-
0730
Tel.: (701) 223-1513   ND
Web Site:
     https://www.capitalelec.com
Year Founded: 1945
Sales Range: $25-49.9 Million
Emp.: 44
Electric Power Transmission Services
N.A.I.C.S.: 221122
Paul Fitterer (Gen Mgr)
Luke Steen (Bus Mgr)
Wes Engbrecht (Dir-Comm & PR)

CAPITAL EXCAVATION COMPANY
2967 Business Park Dr, Buda, TX
78610
Tel.: (512) 440-1717
Web Site:
     https://www.capitalexcavation.com
Year Founded: 1984
Sales Range: $50-74.9 Million
Emp.: 200
Provider of Nonresidential Construction Services
N.A.I.C.S.: 237310
Jim Bradley (Founder, Owner & CEO)
Gary Botkin (VP-Estimating & Admin)
Chris Bradley (Pres)

CAPITAL FARM CREDIT, ACA
7000 Woodway Dr, Waco, TX 76712
Tel.: (254) 776-7506
Web Site:
     https://www.capitalfarmcredit.com
Rev.: $23,600,000
Emp.: 8
Production Credit Association, Agricultural
N.A.I.C.S.: 522299
Allen Hornung (Reg Pres)
Dave Peterson (Reg Pres)
Mike Sloan (Reg Pres)
Glenn Trant (Reg Pres)
Ben R. Novosad (Pres & CEO)
Don VandeVanter (CFO & Sr VP)
Kenny S. Brown (Sr VP-Policy &
Compliance)
Mark L. Hiler (COO & Sr VP)
Patricia A. Gonzales (Sr VP-Acctg &
Admin)
Roy A. West (Reg Sr VP-Credit)
Mark Loveland (Reg Sr VP-Credit)
Jay Stewart (Chief Lending Officer &
Sr VP)
J. Scott Taylor (Sr VP & Mng Dir-
AgriBus-Austin)
Danny Parker (Vice Chm)
Phillip Munden (Chm)
Jeff Norte (Chief Credit Officer)
Stacy Bradley (Gen Counsel & Sr
VP)
Andy Smith (Officer-Credit & VP)
Jon Hutchinson (Officer-Credit & VP)
Lee Greve (Officer-Credit & VP)
Don Palm (Sr VP & Mgr-Relationship)
Scot Vidrine (VP & Mgr)
Scott Curtis (VP-Home Loans)

CAPITAL FIRST REALTY INCORPORATED
875 N Michigan Ave #3800, Chicago,
IL 60611
Tel.: (312) 202-9500
Rev.: $28,000,000
Emp.: 100
Mobile Home Site Operators
N.A.I.C.S.: 531210
Richard J. Klarcheck (Pres)
Jay Klarchek (Sr VP)
Mike Pashawitz (Treas & Mgr)

CAPITAL FORD INC.
4900 Wheel Dr, Raleigh, NC 27616
Tel.: (919) 790-4600
Web Site: http://www.capitalford.com
Rev.: $280,000,000
Emp.: 300
Automobiles, New & Used
N.A.I.C.S.: 441110
Charles Kenyon (Mgr-Comml Fin)
Glenn Lumley (Mgr-Parts)
Jerry Mosley (Gen Mgr)
Tim Mallard (Mgr-Sls)
Jerry French (Mgr-Fleet & Comml)

Subsidiaries:

Capital Chevrolet, Inc.   (1)
1820 Capital Blvd, Raleigh, NC 27604-2194
Tel.: (919) 834-6441
Web Site: http://www.capitalchevroletnc.com
Car Dealership
N.A.I.C.S.: 441110
Taylor Johnson (Mgr-F&I)
Gilbert Hay (Sls Mgr-Comml & Fleet)
Rod Mitchell (Acct Mgr-Comml & Fleet)
Wally Sheperd (Acct Mgr-Comml & Fleet)
Robert Clark (Mgr-Svc)
Pablo Figueroa (Dir-Fixed Ops)
Herb Mundt (Dir-Parts)
Jeff Bass Sr. (Asst Sls Mgr-Pre-Owned)

CAPITAL FOREST PRODUCTS INC.
111 Gibralter Ave, Annapolis, MD
21401
Tel.: (410) 280-6102
Web Site:
     http://www.capitalforest.com
Sales Range: $100-124.9 Million
Emp.: 30
Lumber: Rough, Dressed & Finished
N.A.I.C.S.: 423310
Mike L. Tichenor (Pres)
Jerome Rush (Mgr-Inventory)

CAPITAL FUNDING GROUP, INC.
1422 Clarkview Rd, Baltimore, MD
21209
Tel.: (410) 342-3155   MD
Web Site:
     https://www.capfundinc.com
Year Founded: 1993
Sales Range: $1-4.9 Billion
Emp.: 100
Financial Holding Company; Multifamily Properties & Healthcare Facilities Mortgage Financing Services
N.A.I.C.S.: 551112
John W. Dwyer (Owner & Chm)
Daniel S. Baird (COO)

Subsidiaries:

Capital Funding Bancorp, Inc.   (1)
1422 Clarkview Rd, Baltimore, MD 21209
Tel.: (410) 823-0500
Web Site:
     http://www.cfgcommunitybank.com
Emp.: 60
Bank Holding Company
N.A.I.C.S.: 551111
John W. Dwyer (Chm)

Subsidiary (Domestic):

CFG Community Bank   (2)

1422 Clarkview Rd, Baltimore, MD
21209   (100%)
Tel.: (410) 823-0500
Web Site:
     http://www.cfgcommunitybank.com
Sales Range: $50-74.9 Million
Emp.: 94
Commericial Banking
N.A.I.C.S.: 522110
Michael McClung (VP-Branch Admin)
Grace Doyle (VP-Comml Banking)
Nancy Bell (VP-Comml Banking)
Jack Dwyer (Owner)
William C. Wiedel Jr. (Pres & CEO)

Capital Finance, LLC   (2)
1422 Clarkview Rd, Baltimore, MD 21209
Tel.: (410) 342-3155
Web Site: http://www.capfundinc.com
Asset-Based Lending Services
N.A.I.C.S.: 522292

Capital Funding, LLC   (2)
1422 Clarkview Rd, Baltimore, MD 21209
Tel.: (410) 342-3155
Web Site: http://www.capfundinc.com
Loan Portfolio Management Services
N.A.I.C.S.: 523940
Patrick McGovern (Dir-Real Estate Fin)
Erik Howard (Mng Dir-Real Estate Fin)
Craig Casagrande (Dir-Real Estate Fin)
Gary Sever (Dir-Real Estate Fin)
Deborah Spangenberg (Pres)
Lauren Rexroat (Exec VP)

CAPITAL GUARDIAN LLC
1355 Greenwood Clfs Ste 250, Charlotte, NC 28204
Tel.: (704) 470-1860
Web Site:
     http://www.capitalguardianllc.com
Investment Advice
N.A.I.C.S.: 523940
Alan Boyer (CEO)

CAPITAL HEALTH SYSTEMS INC.
408 Scotch Rd, Pennington, NJ
08534
Tel.: (609) 394-4000
Web Site:
     http://www.capitalhealth.org
Sales Range: $400-449.9 Million
Emp.: 3,000
Hospital Operator
N.A.I.C.S.: 622110
Al Maghazehe (Pres & CEO)
J. Scott Clemmensen (VP-HR)
Gregory N. D'Adamo (VP-Facilities &
Pro Svcs)
Eugene Grochala (CIO)
Stephen Miller (Chief Compliance
Officer)
Nathan Bosk (VP-Supply Chain Mgmt
& Support Svcs)
Robert Remstein (VP-Accountable
Care)
Eugene J. McMahon (Chief Medical
Officer)
David K. Dafilou (Chief Admin Officer
& VP-Clinically Integrated Network)
Alexander Gladney (Chief Legal Officer & Sr VP)

CAPITAL HOLDING GROUP, INC.
700 Mokane Rd, Jefferson City, MO
65110
PO Box 21219, Columbia, SC
Tel.: (573) 635-6229
Web Site: http://www.capitalmo.com
Construction Products Mfr & Distr
N.A.I.C.S.: 423390
Drew Biddle (Controller)
Eddie Welsh (COO)

CAPITAL HOSPICE
2900 Telestar Ct, Falls Church, VA
22042
Tel.: (703) 538-2065   VA

Web Site:
     http://www.capitalcaring.org
Year Founded: 1998
Sales Range: $75-99.9 Million
Emp.: 777
Health Care Srvices
N.A.I.C.S.: 622110
Lynn Mento (Vice Chm)

CAPITAL IMPACT PARTNERS
2011 Crystal Dr Ste 750, Arlington,
VA 22202
Tel.: (703) 647-2300   DC
Web Site:
     http://www.capitalimpact.org
Year Founded: 1982
Sales Range: $25-49.9 Million
Emp.: 106
Community Development Services
N.A.I.C.S.: 624190
Scott Sporte (Chief Lending Officer)
Amy Sue Leavens (Chief Compliance
Officer, Gen Counsel & Sec)
Ellis Carr (Pres & CEO)
Carolyn Bauer (Chief Risk Officer)
Natalie Gunn (CFO)

CAPITAL INDUSTRIES, INC.
5801 3rd Ave S, Seattle, WA 98108-
3205
Tel.: (206) 762-8585   WA
Web Site: http://www.capitalind.com
Year Founded: 1953
Sales Range: $10-24.9 Million
Emp.: 120
Provider of Metal Fabrication Services
N.A.I.C.S.: 332119
Kyle Taylor (Mgr-Ops)
David Taylor (VP)
Bryan Taylor (Exec VP-Bus Dev)
Ron Taylor (Pres)
Ray Carr (Plant Mgr)
T. J. Hogan (Exec VP-Bus Dev)

CAPITAL INSIGHT PARTNERS, LLC
7328 E Deer Vly Rd Ste 105, Scottsdale, AZ 85255
Tel.: (480) 295-7100   AZ
Web Site:
     http://www.capitalinsightpartners.com
Investment Services
N.A.I.C.S.: 523999
Steven T. Nelson (Co-Founder &
CEO)
Susan C. Anastasiadis (Co-Founder
& COO)
Craig J. McCrory (Partner)
Felipe A. Arratia (Chief Investment
Officer)
Sara A. LaClair (Portfolio Mgr)
Troy Dayton (Sr Portfolio Mgr)

Subsidiaries:

Foothills Asset Management Ltd.   (1)
8767 E Via de Ventura Ste 175, Scottsdale,
AZ 85258
Tel.: (480) 777-9863
Web Site: http://www.faml.net
Investment Advice
N.A.I.C.S.: 523940

CAPITAL INSTITUTIONAL SERVICES, INC.
1601 Elm St Ste 3900, Dallas, TX
75201
Tel.: (214) 720-0055
Web Site: http://www.capis.com
Rev.: $104,748,099
Emp.: 100
Financial Services
N.A.I.C.S.: 561499
Don C. Potts (Chm)
Kristi Wetherington (CEO)
Tim R. Hall (CFO & Treas)

John P. Naudo (Sr VP & Dir-Global Trading)
Jason Christian (Chief Compliance Officer & Gen Counsel)
Dave Choate (Dir-Global Sls)
Caran Chaney (Mgr-Client Svc)

CAPITAL INVESTMENT ADVISORS, INC.
10 Glenlake Pkwy NE North Tower Ste 1000, Atlanta, GA 30328
Tel.: (404) 531-0018
Web Site:
 https://www.yourwealth.com
Year Founded: 1994
Sales Range: $1-9.9 Million
Emp.: 20
Financial Advisory & Portfolio Management Services
N.A.I.C.S.: 523940
Mike Reiner (Pres & CEO)
Holly Mallory (Mgr-Ops)
Barbara Barnett (Coord-Appointment & Prospective Client)

CAPITAL INVESTMENTS & VENTURES CORP.
30151 Tomas St, Rancho Santa Margarita, CA 92688-2125
Tel.: (949) 858-0647
Web Site: http://www.padi.com
Year Founded: 1967
Sales Range: $50-74.9 Million
Emp.: 200
Holding Company
N.A.I.C.S.: 813920
Chad Kuehn (CFO)

Subsidiaries:

PADI Americas   (1)
30151 Tomas St, Rancho Santa Margarita, CA 92688-2125
Tel.: (949) 858-7234
Web Site: http://www.padi.com
Rev.: $30,000,000
Emp.: 450
Diving Training Organization
N.A.I.C.S.: 813920
Drew Richardson (Pres & COO)

Subsidiary (Non-US):

PADI Asia Pacific Pty Ltd (2)
Unit 3 4 Skyline Place Frenchs Forest, Sydney, 2086, NSW, Australia
Tel.: (61) 2 9454 2888
Web Site: http://www.padi.com.au
Emp.: 70
Scuba Dive Training Services
N.A.I.C.S.: 611620
Henrik Nimb (Mgr)

PADI Canada Limited (2)
Unit 107 1680 Broadway St, Port Coquitlam, V3C 2M8, BC, Canada
Tel.: (604) 552-5969
Web Site: http://www.padi.com
Emp.: 5
Scuba Dive Training Services
N.A.I.C.S.: 611620
Sherri Abrahamczik (Mgr-Fin & Ops)

PADI Japan, Inc. (2)
1-20-1 Ebisu - Minami, Shibuya-Ku, Tokyo, 150-0022, Japan
Tel.: (81) 3 5721 1731
Web Site: http://www.padi.co.jp
Scuba Dive Training Services
N.A.I.C.S.: 611620

CAPITAL LIGHTING, INC.
901 Polaris Pkwy, Columbus, OH 43240-2035
Tel.: (614) 841-1200
Web Site:
 https://www.capitallightinginc.com
Year Founded: 1990
Sales Range: $10-24.9 Million
Emp.: 60
Lighting Mfr
N.A.I.C.S.: 423610

David Winks (VP)
Donnie Winks (Gen Mgr)
Michael P. Morton (Pres)

CAPITAL LUMBER COMPANY
5110 N 40th St Ste 242, Phoenix, AZ 85018-2151
Tel.: (602) 381-0709
Web Site: http://www.capital-lumber.com
Sales Range: $25-49.9 Million
Emp.: 18
Lumber: Rough, Dressed & Finished
N.A.I.C.S.: 423310
Carl Shelley (Asst Mgr-Sls-Salt Lake City)
Jeff Logue (Mgr-Healdsburg)
Asa Johnson (Mgr-Denver)
Van Vanderhoff (Mgr-Phoenix)
Grant Pearsall (Mgr-Capital Chino)
Bresha Good (Mgr-Bus-Phoenix)
Dave Harward (Mgr-Acct-Phoenix)
Jason Kelly (Mgr-Acct-Salt Lake)
Jerry Ricketts (Mgr-Acct-Salt Lake)
Stewart Hobbs (Mgr-Acct-Phoenix)
Tracy Madsen (Mgr-Salt Lake)
Michael Darby (VP-Marketing-Business Development)

CAPITAL MACHINE TECHNOLOGIES, INC.
911 U.S. Highway 301 S, Tampa, FL 33619
Tel.: (813) 621-9751
Web Site: https://capitalmachine.com
Year Founded: 1984
Machine Mfg.
N.A.I.C.S.: 332312

Subsidiaries:

Modern Machinery Company (1)
4622 Independence Sq, Indianapolis, IN 46203
Tel.: (317) 791-8290
Web Site:
 http://www.modernmachineryco.com
Sales Range: $10-24.9 Million
Emp.: 25
Retailer of Industrial Machinery & Equipment
N.A.I.C.S.: 332618
Bob Smith (Pres)
Joyan Smith (VP)

Subsidiary (Domestic):

Spokane Machinery Company (2)
4428 E Trent Ave, Spokane, WA 99220
Tel.: (509) 535-1576
Web Site: http://www.modernmachinery.com
Sales Range: $10-24.9 Million
General Construction Machinery & Equipment, Rock Crushing
N.A.I.C.S.: 423810
Kim Eickerman (Branch Mgr)

CAPITAL MANOR
1955 Salem Dallas Hwy NW Ste 1200, Salem, OR 97304
Tel.: (503) 967-3086 OR
Web Site:
 https://www.capitalmanor.com
Year Founded: 1960
Sales Range: $10-24.9 Million
Emp.: 192
Lifecare Retirement Community Operator
N.A.I.C.S.: 623311
Lisa Harisay (Dir-Nursing Svcs)
Mark Fineran (Dir-HR)
David Lewis (Exec Dir)
Cleve Knabe (Dir-Facility Svcs)

CAPITAL MARKET SERVICES LLC
350 Fifth Ave, New York, NY 10118
Tel.: (212) 563-2100
Web Site: http://www.cmsfx.com
Year Founded: 1999

Sales Range: $10-24.9 Million
Emp.: 65
Foreign Exchange Trading Services
N.A.I.C.S.: 525990
Larisa Makagon (CFO)
Nabil Zahmoul (Head-Bus Dev-Middle East Reg)
Vitaly Kalmanov (Mgr-Bus Dev)

CAPITAL MERCURY SHIRTMAKERS LLC
1385 Broadway, New York, NY 10018-7102
Tel.: (212) 704-4800 NY
Year Founded: 1960
Sales Range: $150-199.9 Million
Emp.: 2,000
Mfr of Garments, Sweaters, Shirts & Blouses
N.A.I.C.S.: 315250
Doug Pecore (Exec VP-Sls & Mktg)
John Hindon (CEO)
Howard Marks (VP)

CAPITAL MOTOR SALES INC.
5808 Lee Hwy, Chattanooga, TN 37421
Tel.: (423) 892-0661
Web Site:
 http://www.capitaltoyota.net
Rev.: $100,000,000
Emp.: 140
Automobiles, New & Used
N.A.I.C.S.: 441110
Robert Mc Kamey (Owner)
Nancy Bowling (Controller)
Jeff Mc Kamey (VP)
Karla Mc Kamey (VP)

CAPITAL NOVUS
10521 Rosehaven St Ste 300, Fairfax, VA 22030
Tel.: (703) 226-1500
Web Site:
 http://www.capitalnovus.com
Year Founded: 2002
Sales Range: $10-24.9 Million
Emp.: 186
Knowledge Management & Litigation Support Services
N.A.I.C.S.: 518210
Gita D. Shingala (Founder & Chm)
Thomas J. Skelley (Exec VP)
Dharmesh B. Shingala (Co-Founder & CEO)

CAPITAL NURSERY CO.
4700 Freeport Blvd, Sacramento, CA 95822
Tel.: (916) 455-2601
Sales Range: $10-24.9 Million
Emp.: 150
Garden Supplies & Tools
N.A.I.C.S.: 444240
Charles G. Armstrong Jr. (Founder & Pres)

CAPITAL OFFICE PRODUCTS
700 Ballough Rd 210, Daytona Beach, FL 32114
Tel.: (386) 238-1177
Web Site: http://www.cap-officeproducts.com
Sales Range: $10-24.9 Million
Emp.: 50
Office Supplies
N.A.I.C.S.: 424120
Teresa Sackmann (Dir-Ops)
Ashley Warren (Mgr-Inside Sls)
Amie Story (Mgr-Pur)
Thomas M. Patton (Pres)

CAPITAL OIL INC.
320 Carrier Blvd, Richland, MS 39218

Tel.: (601) 932-6868
Rev.: $15,896,964
Emp.: 24
Petroleum Bulk Stations
N.A.I.C.S.: 424710
G. Stanley Roberts (Pres)

CAPITAL ONE AUTO RECEIVABLES LLC
1600 Capital 1 Dr Rm 27907-B, McLean, VA 22102
Tel.: (703) 720-3148 DE
Investment Management Service
N.A.I.C.S.: 523999

CAPITAL ONE MULTI-ASSET EXECUTION TRUST
Bankers Trust Delaware E A Delle Donne Corp Ctr 1011 Ctr Rd, Wilmington, DE 19805-1266
Tel.: (302) 636-3382 DE
Asset Management Services
N.A.I.C.S.: 531390
Thomas A. Feil (Pres)

CAPITAL PARTNERS LLC
5201 Eden Ave, Ste 50, Edina, MN 55436
Tel.: (612) 431-3000
Web Site:
 https://capitalpartnersmn.com
Emp.: 600
Privater Equity Firm
N.A.I.C.S.: 523940
Peter Mork (Founding Partner)

CAPITAL PROCESSING INT'L INC.
18425 Burbank Blvd Ste 415, Tarzana, CA 91356
Tel.: (818) 996-5508
Web Site: http://www.capital-processing.com
Year Founded: 2006
Sales Range: $1-9.9 Million
Emp.: 4
Web-Based Recurring Payment Processing & Customer Relationship Management Software for Membership-Based & Subscription-Based Businesses
N.A.I.C.S.: 525990
Juan Carlos Anduiza (Dir-Risk Mgmt)

CAPITAL RECONSTRUCTION, INC.
2000 Govenors Circle Ste A, Houston, TX 77092
Tel.: (713) 681-7430
Web Site:
 http://www.capitalreconstruction.com
Year Founded: 2003
Sales Range: $1-9.9 Million
Emp.: 15
Capital Improvements, Catastrophe Restorations & High-End Interior Design Construction
N.A.I.C.S.: 236220
Peyton Welty (Pres)
Jay van Kessel (Project Mgr)
Sandi Marine (VP)

CAPITAL RESOURCE PARTNERS, L.P.
83 Walnut St Unit 10, Wellesley, MA 02481
Tel.: (617) 478-9600 DE
Web Site: https://www.crp.com
Year Founded: 1987
Sales Range: $25-49.9 Million
Emp.: 15
Equity Investment Firm
N.A.I.C.S.: 523999
Robert C. Ammerman (Mng Partner)
Jeffrey W. Potter (Gen Partner)
Andrew A. Silverman (Partner)

Capital Resource Partners, L.P.—(Continued)

Subsidiaries:

Catalog Marketplace, Inc. **(1)**
192 Paris Ave, Northvale, NJ 07647
Tel.: (201) 767-0233
Web Site: http://www.paradestore.com
Sales Range: $1-9.9 Million
Flags, Uniforms & Other Ceremonial Accessories Retailer
N.A.I.C.S.: 459999
Wendy Lazar *(Pres)*

CAPITAL RESTAURANT CONCEPTS, LTD.
1305 Wisconsin Ave NW, Washington, DC 20007-3311
Tel.: (202) 339-6800   DE
Web Site:
    http://www.capitalrestaurants.com
Year Founded: 1982
Multi-Concepted, Boutique Style Full
Service Restaurant Company
N.A.I.C.S.: 722511
Martin Craft *(CFO)*

CAPITAL RIVERS COMMERCIAL LLC
1821 Q Street, Sacramento, CA
95811
Tel.: (916) 514-5225
Web Site: https://capitalrivers.com
Emp.: 100
Real Estate
N.A.I.C.S.: 531390

Subsidiaries:

Haedrich & Co., Inc. **(1)**
358 Hartnell Ave Ste A, Redding, CA 96002
Tel.: (530) 221-1127
Web Site: http://www.haedrich.com
Offices of Real Estate Agents & Brokers
N.A.I.C.S.: 531210
Bill Haedrich *(Pres)*

CAPITAL TECHSEARCH, INC.
6800 Paragon Pl Ste 100, Richmond,
VA 23230
Tel.: (804) 282-8788
Web Site:
    http://www.capitaltechsearch.com
Year Founded: 2001
Rev.: $5,100,000
Emp.: 140
IT Staffing & Executive Search Services
N.A.I.C.S.: 561311
David A. Ingram *(Pres & CEO)*
Katie Elder Burak *(Dir-Recruiting)*
Barthe van Doorn *(Gen Mgr)*

CAPITAL TELECOMMUNICATIONS, INC.
200 W Market St, York, PA 17401
Tel.: (717) 848-8800
Web Site: http://www.captel.com
Year Founded: 1982
Sales Range: $10-24.9 Million
Emp.: 40
Long Distance Telephone Communication Services
N.A.I.C.S.: 517121
Richard Robinson *(Sr Mgr-Plng)*

CAPITAL TIRE, INC.
1001 Cherry St, Toledo, OH 43608
Tel.: (419) 241-5111   OH
Web Site: http://www.capitaltire.com
Sales Range: $25-49.9 Million
Emp.: 200
Automobile & Truck Tires & Tubes
Distr
N.A.I.C.S.: 423130
Linda Hoyt *(Controller)*
Thomas B. Geiger Sr. *(Chm)*
Thomas B. Geiger Jr. *(Pres)*

CAPITAL TOWER & COMMUNICATIONS INC
13330 Amberly Rd, Waverly, NE
68462
Tel.: (402) 786-3333
Web Site:
    https://www.capitaltower.com
Sales Range: $10-24.9 Million
Emp.: 80
Tower Bell Installation & Repair
N.A.I.C.S.: 238990
Patrick W. Reed *(Pres)*
Luke Dierking *(Dir-Ops)*

CAPITAL TRACTOR INC.
1135 Route 29, Greenwich, NY
12834
Tel.: (518) 692-9611
Web Site:
    http://www.capitaltractorinc.com
Sales Range: $10-24.9 Million
Emp.: 22
Agricultural Machinery & Equipment
N.A.I.C.S.: 423820
Jamey Gibson *(Pres)*
Kevin Armitage *(Mgr-Ops)*
John Mattison *(Mgr-Svc)*
Suzanne Neil *(Mgr-Credit)*
Stephanie Booth *(Coord-Rental & Svc)*
Paul Yakubec *(Mgr-Parts)*

CAPITAL VIDEO CORPORATION
1060 Park Ave, Cranston, RI 02910
Tel.: (401) 464-4800
Web Site: http://www.capital-video-corporation.hub.biz
Rev.: $18,909,773
Emp.: 30
Video, Disk & Tape Rentals
N.A.I.C.S.: 532282
Kenneth Guarino *(Partner)*

CAPITAL WELDING, INC.
1 Carnegie Ct, Waldorf, MD 20602
Tel.: (301) 843-7666
Web Site:
    http://www.capitalwelding.com
Sales Range: $10-24.9 Million
Emp.: 81
Fabricated Structural Metal Mfr
N.A.I.C.S.: 332312
Michael Baguley *(Project Mgr)*

CAPITAL WHOLESALE ELECTRIC CO.
1811 12th St, Sacramento, CA 95811-6508
Tel.: (916) 443-8051
Web Site: http://www.cwec.biz
Sales Range: $1-9.9 Million
Emp.: 5
Provider of Electrical Supplies
N.A.I.C.S.: 423610
William Duffy *(Pres)*

CAPITAL WHOLESALE MEATS INC.
8751 W 50th St, McCook, IL 60525-3132
Tel.: (773) 457-4097
Web Site: http://www.fontanini.com
Year Founded: 1960
Sales Range: $1-9.9 Million
Emp.: 250
Producer of Sausages & Other Prepared Meats
N.A.I.C.S.: 311612
Gene Fontanini *(Pres)*

CAPITALSOUTH CORP.
4201 Congress St Ste 360, Charlotte,
NC 28209
Tel.: (704) 376-5502

Web Site:
    http://www.capitalsouthpartners.com
Investment Services
N.A.I.C.S.: 523940
Joseph B. Alala III *(Chm & CEO)*

Subsidiaries:

BTM Company, LLC **(1)**
300 Davis Rd, Marysville, MI 48040
Tel.: (810) 364-4567
Web Site: http://www.btmcorp.com
Machine Tools Mfr
N.A.I.C.S.: 333517
Stephen Sawdon *(Dir-Mktg)*

CAPITALSPRING LLC
575 Lexington Ave 28th Fl, New York,
NY 10022
Tel.: (212) 981-0140   DE
Web Site:
    https://www.capitalspring.com
Year Founded: 2005
Emp.: 50
Private Investment Firm
N.A.I.C.S.: 523999
Richard Fitzgerald *(Founder & Mng Partner)*
Todd Foust *(Partner)*
Christina Houghton *(CFO)*
T. A. McKinney *(Chief Compliance Officer & Gen Counsel)*
Kristin Reilly *(Head-IR)*
Chad McIntyre *(Dir-Fin)*
Robin Cunningham *(Controller)*
Adrienne Misko *(Head-Shared Resources)*
Jim Balis *(Mng Dir-Strategic Ops Grp)*
Chad Spaulding *(Mng Dir-Originations)*
Chad Cohen *(Principal-Strategic Ops Grp)*
Kaivon Abrishami *(VP)*
Jason Ruiz *(VP)*
Tee Isenhour *(Principal)*
Tom Kuchler *(Mng Dir-Originations)*

Subsidiaries:

Shari's Management Corporation **(1)**
9400 SW Gemini Dr, Beaverton, OR 97008
Tel.: (503) 605-4299
Web Site: http://www.sharis.com
Restaurant Owner & Operator
N.A.I.C.S.: 722511
Allan Hartley *(VP-Fin & Employee Svcs)*
Tom Matson *(VP-IT & Facilities)*
Debbie Nelson *(Mgr-Team Rels)*
Melody Morehouse *(Mgr-Workers Compensation)*
Greta Pierce *(Mgr-Team Rels)*
Keith Wall *(CFO)*
Samuel Borgese *(Pres & CEO)*
Joe Adney *(VP-Mktg)*

CAPITALVIEW INVESTMENT PARTNERS, LLC
4800 Montgomery Lane 5th Fl,
Bethesda, MD 20814
Tel.: (301) 841-2010
Web Site:
    http://www.capitalviewip.com
Investment Services
N.A.I.C.S.: 523999

CAPITALWORKS, LLC
1100 Superior Ave 17th Fl Ste 1725,
Cleveland, OH 44114
Tel.: (216) 781-3233
Web Site: http://www.capitalworks.net
Year Founded: 1999
Privater Equity Firm
N.A.I.C.S.: 523999
W. Todd Martin *(Pres & Mng Dir)*
Mikel B. Harding *(Mng Dir & CFO)*
Andrea Zacher *(Office Mgr)*
Matthew J. Lombardo *(Principal)*
J. D. Sullivan *(Partner)*

Robert G. McCreary III *(Founder & Chm)*
Richard R. Hollington III *(CEO & Mng Dir)*
John P. Corrigan III *(Principal)*

Subsidiaries:

C&M Conveyor Inc **(1)**
4598 State Road 37, Mitchell, IN 47446
Tel.: (812) 849-5647
Web Site: http://www.cmconveyor.com
Automatic & Semi-Automatic Powered
Roller Conveyor Systems Mfr
N.A.I.C.S.: 423830
James R. Owens *(CFO)*

Capewell Components Company,
LLC **(1)**
105 Nutmeg Rd S, South Windsor, CT
06074
Tel.: (860) 610-0700
Web Site: http://www.capewell.com
Sales Range: $10-24.9 Million
Specialized Industrial, Commercial & Military Components & Tools Designer & Mfr
N.A.I.C.S.: 339999
William Ehler *(Dir-Bus Dev)*
Paul Bradick *(Sr Dir-Bus Dev-Intl)*
Bill Gorlach *(VP & Gen Mgr-Capewell Sys)*
Butch Flythe *(Mgr-Bus Dev)*
Jackie Griffin *(Mgr-Pur)*
Tom Magro *(Mgr-Quality Assurance)*
Tim Perkins *(Mgr-Bus Dev)*
Patrick J. McCarthy *(Chief Strategy Officer)*
Thomas Weidley *(CEO)*
Erin Macaluso *(CFO)*
Jack Nugent *(Chm)*

Subsidiary (Domestic):

M.H. Rhodes Cramer, LLC **(2)**
105 Nutmeg Rd S, South Windsor, CT
06074
Tel.: (860) 291-8402
Web Site: http://www.mhrhodes.com
Mechanical Timers & Switches Mfr
N.A.I.C.S.: 334513
Deborah Sage *(VP & Gen Mgr)*
Vincent Pitruzzello *(VP & Gen Mgr)*

The Ripley Company **(2)**
46 Nooks Hill Rd, Cromwell, CT 06416
Tel.: (860) 635-2200
Web Site: http://www.ripley-tools.com
Sales Range: $1-9.9 Million
Wire & Cable Preparation Tools Mfr
N.A.I.C.S.: 333515
Richard W. Salvas *(Acct Mgr-Natl-Broadband)*

Safe-Way Garage Doors LLC **(1)**
3814 E US 30, Warsaw, IN 46580
Tel.: (877) 775-1670
Web Site: https://safewaydoor.com
Garage Doors Mfr & Distr
N.A.I.C.S.: 321911
Ted Rock *(CEO)*

Subsidiary (Domestic):

First United Door Technologies,
LLC **(2)**
1016 W Geneva Dr, Tempe, AZ 85282
Tel.: (480) 705-6632
Web Site: http://www.firstudt.com
Sales Range: $10-24.9 Million
Emp.: 75
Lumber, Plywood, Millwork & Wood Panel
Merchant Whslr
N.A.I.C.S.: 423310

The Gem City Engineering Co.,
Inc. **(1)**
401 Leo St, Dayton, OH 45404-1102
Tel.: (937) 223-5544
Web Site: http://www.gemcity.com
Metalworking Machines Mfr
N.A.I.C.S.: 333248

CAPITOL AUTO GROUP
783 Auto Group Ave, Salem, OR
97301
Tel.: (503) 370-4800
Web Site:
    https://www.capitolauto.com
Sales Range: $25-49.9 Million
Emp.: 150

New Car Whslr
N.A.I.C.S.: 441110
Frank Roe *(Principal)*

CAPITOL AUTO GROUP, INC.
2855 Maple Ave, Salem, OR 97301
Tel.: (503) 585-4141   OR
Web Site: http://www.capitolauto.com
Year Founded: 1927
Sales Range: $350-399.9 Million
Emp.: 240
Holding Company; Car Dealerships
Owner & Operator
N.A.I.C.S.: 551112
Brian Schindler *(Mgr-Bus Dev)*

Subsidiaries:

Capitol Suburu   (1)
3235 Cherry Ave NE, Salem, OR 97301
Tel.: (503) 316-4294
Web Site: http://www.capitolsubaru.com
Sales Range: $25-49.9 Million
Emp.: 25
New & Used Car Dealers
N.A.I.C.S.: 441110
R. Scott Casebeer *(Pres)*

CAPITOL BEARING SERVICE
2589 Oakmont, Round Rock, TX
78665
Tel.: (512) 244-3630
Web Site:
     http://www.capitolbearing.com
Sales Range: $10-24.9 Million
Emp.: 50
Transmission Parts, Not Automotive
Related
N.A.I.C.S.: 441330
J. W. Latham *(Owner)*
Kathy Mead *(Controller)*
Carl Rushing *(Mgr-Ops)*

CAPITOL BEVERAGE SALES L.P.
6982 Hwy 65 NE, Fridley, MN 55432
Tel.: (763) 571-4115
Web Site:
     http://www.capitolbeverage.com
Beverage Mfr & Distr
N.A.I.C.S.: 424820

CAPITOL BODY SHOP INC.
102 Raymond Rd, Jackson, MS
39204
Tel.: (601) 373-4642
Web Site:
     https://www.capitolbodyshop.com
Rev.: $10,000,000
Emp.: 25
Provider of Automotive Repair Services
N.A.I.C.S.: 811121
Doug White *(Pres)*

CAPITOL BROADCASTING COMPANY, INC.
2619 Western Blvd, Raleigh, NC
27606
Tel.: (919) 890-6000   NC
Web Site:
     https://www.capitolbroadcasting.com
Year Founded: 1937
Sales Range: $150-199.9 Million
Emp.: 900
TV & Radio Broadcasting; Satellite
Services
N.A.I.C.S.: 516120
James F. Goodmon *(Chm & CEO)*
Daniel P. McGrath *(Treas & VP)*
Thomas McLaughlin *(Asst Treas)*
Steven D. Hannel *(VP & Gen Mgr)*
Jennifer B. Veenable *(Gen Counsel & VP)*
Shelly Leslie *(Gen Mgr-Audience Dev)*
Angela B. Emerline *(VP-HR)*
Michael J. Goodmon *(Sr VP)*

Jennifer B. Venable *(Gen Counsel & VP)*
George W. Habel III *(VP)*
James F. Goodmon Jr. *(Pres & COO)*

Subsidiaries:

Capitol Broadcasting Company, Inc. -
Sunrise Broadcasting Division   (1)
25 N Kerr Ave, Wilmington, NC 28405
Tel.: (910) 791-3088
Web Site:
     http://www.capitolbroadcasting.com
Emp.: 40
Radio Broadcasting Services
N.A.I.C.S.: 516110
James F. Goodmon Jr. *(VP & Gen Mgr)*

Capitol Radio Network, Inc.   (1)
2619 Western Blvd, Raleigh, NC 27606
Tel.: (919) 890-6000
Holding Company; Radio Broadcasting Stations
N.A.I.C.S.: 551112
James F. Goodmon *(Pres & CEO)*

Subsidiary (Domestic):

WRAL-FM, Inc.   (2)
3100 Highwoods Blvd Ste 140, Raleigh, NC
27604
Tel.: (919) 890-6101
Web Site: http://www.wralfm.com
Sales Range: $25-49.9 Million
Emp.: 100
Radio Broadcasting Stations
N.A.I.C.S.: 516110
Katie Phillips *(VP & Gen Mgr)*

Unit (Domestic):

WRAL Sports Fan   (3)
3100 Highwoods Blvd Ste 140, Raleigh, NC
27604-1065
Tel.: (919) 890-6299
Web Site: http://www.wralsportsfan.com
Emp.: 60
Sports Radio Network
N.A.I.C.S.: 516210

Microspace Communications
Corporation   (1)
3100 Highwoods Blvd Ste 120, Raleigh, NC
27604-1033
Tel.: (919) 850-4500
Web Site: http://www.microspace.com
Sales Range: $10-24.9 Million
Emp.: 28
Satellite Broadcasting Network
N.A.I.C.S.: 517111
Greg Hurt *(VP-Sls & Mktg)*
Karen Moss *(Mgr-Acctg)*

The Durham Bulls Baseball Club,
Inc.   (1)
409 Blackwell St, Durham, NC 27701-3972
Tel.: (919) 687-6500
Web Site: http://www.durhambulls.com
Sales Range: $10-24.9 Million
Emp.: 40
Professional Minor League Baseball Club
N.A.I.C.S.: 711211
Mike Birling *(Gen Mgr)*
Bryan Wilson *(Dir-Mdsg)*

WILM-TV   (1)
3333 Wrightsville Ave Ste G, Wilmington,
NC 28403-4183
Tel.: (910) 798-0000
Web Site: http://www.wilm-tv.com
Sales Range: $10-24.9 Million
Emp.: 11
Television Station
N.A.I.C.S.: 811210
Constance Knox *(Gen Mgr)*

WJZY-TV   (1)
3501 Performance Rd, Charlotte, NC
28214-9056
Tel.: (704) 398-0046
Web Site: http://www.wjzy.com
Sales Range: $10-24.9 Million
Emp.: 70
Television Station
N.A.I.C.S.: 811210
Anna Gay *(Sr Acct Exec)*

WRAL-TV   (1)
2619 Western Blvd, Raleigh, NC 27606-
2125

Tel.: (919) 821-8500
Web Site: http://www.wral.com
Sales Range: $10-24.9 Million
Emp.: 250
Television Station
N.A.I.C.S.: 516120
Adam Weyne *(Dir-Sls)*
Ayanna Carver *(Acct Exec)*

WRAZ-TV   (1)
2619 Western Blvd, Raleigh, NC 27606
Tel.: (919) 595-5050
Web Site: http://www.fox50.com
Sales Range: $10-24.9 Million
Emp.: 50
Television Station Services
N.A.I.C.S.: 516120
Niel Sollod *(Mgr-Sls)*
Jimmy Gamble *(Chief Engr)*

WWWB-TV   (1)
1 Julian Price Pl, Charlotte, NC 28208
Tel.: (704) 398-0046
Web Site: http://www.wjzy.com
Sales Range: $10-24.9 Million
Emp.: 70
Television Station
N.A.I.C.S.: 516120

CAPITOL BUILDERS HARD-WARE INC.
4699 24th St, Sacramento, CA 95822
Tel.: (916) 451-2821
Web Site: https://www.capitolbh.com
Sales Range: $10-24.9 Million
Emp.: 45
Finish & Trim Carpentry Hardware
Indoors
N.A.I.C.S.: 238350
Mark Harmon *(Mgr-Detention Div)*

CAPITOL CLEANING CON-TRACTORS, INC.
320 Locust St, Hartford, CT 06114
Tel.: (860) 247-6566
Web Site:
     http://www.capitolclean.com
Sales Range: $10-24.9 Million
Emp.: 800
Fiscal Year-end: 10/31/14
Provider of Industrial & Commercial
Cleaning Services
N.A.I.C.S.: 561720
Robert Symolon *(Pres & CEO)*
Bibi Khan *(Office Mgr)*
David Weintraub *(Chm & CFO)*
Greg Massalski *(Exec VP)*
John Campbell *(Sec)*
Kevin Symolon *(VP-Svcs)*

CAPITOL CLUTCH & BRAKE, INC.
3100 Duluth St, West Sacramento,
CA 95691-2208
Tel.: (916) 371-5970
Web Site:
     https://www.capitolclutch.com
Sales Range: $10-24.9 Million
Emp.: 37
Home Supply Whslr
N.A.I.C.S.: 441330
Vince Mathews *(Pres)*

CAPITOL CONCIERGE, INC.
1400 I St Nw Ste 400, Washington,
DC 20005
Tel.: (202) 223-4765
Web Site:
     http://www.capitolconcierge.com
Year Founded: 1987
Rev.: $8,400,000
Emp.: 400
Personal Services
N.A.I.C.S.: 812990
Lynda Ellis *(Owner, Pres & CEO)*
Eric Tenali *(Controller)*
Misty Tieman *(Exec VP-Dev)*
Christopher Tieman *(VP-Ops)*

CAPITOL CONSULTANTS INC.

1300 12th St Ste B, Cayce, SC
29033
Tel.: (803) 252-1087
Web Site: https://www.capconsc.com
Sales Range: $1-9.9 Million
Emp.: 10
Consulting Services
N.A.I.C.S.: 541611
Richard F. Davis *(Owner & Pres)*
Nicki S. Davis *(VP)*
Annie Wilson *(Gen Counsel & Dir-Govt Affairs)*

CAPITOL CONTRACTORS INC.
207 W Hampton Ave, Capitol
Heights, MD 20743
Tel.: (301) 808-6190
Sales Range: $10-24.9 Million
Emp.: 35
Commercial & Institutional Building
Construction
N.A.I.C.S.: 236220
Vernon J. Smith III *(Pres)*

CAPITOL DEVELOPMENT GROUP LLC
3424 Peachtree Rd NE Ste 300, At-
lanta, GA 30326
Tel.: (404) 965-3988
Web Site: http://www.capitol-
     development.com
Sales Range: $10-24.9 Million
Emp.: 15
Real Estate Development
N.A.I.C.S.: 531390

CAPITOL ENTERTAINMENT MANAGEMENT CO.
3102 Maple Ave Ste 100, Dallas, TX
75201
Tel.: (214) 855-0630
Sales Range: $25-49.9 Million
Emp.: 10
Video Disc & Tape Rental
N.A.I.C.S.: 532282
Donald Zale *(Chm)*

CAPITOL ENVIRONMENTAL SERVICES, INC.
200 Biddle Ave Ste 205, Newark, DE
19702
Tel.: (302) 652-8999
Web Site: http://www.capitol-
     environmental.com
Year Founded: 1989
Rev.: $28,700,000
Emp.: 19
Hazardous Waste Treatment & Dis-
posal
N.A.I.C.S.: 562211
Eric Palm *(Mgr)*
James M. Mraz *(Pres & CEO)*

CAPITOL FINANCIAL STRATE-GIES, LLC
1600 Wilson Blvd Ste 820, Arlington,
VA 22209
Tel.: (703) 752-5880   UT
Web Site: http://www.interlinkdc.com
Year Founded: 1994
Emp.: 15
International Trade Financing, Capital
Investment & Corporate Consulting
Services
N.A.I.C.S.: 522299
Tim Bridgewater *(Chm)*
Peter Watson *(Vice Chm)*
Alan J. Beard *(Mng Dir)*
Jozsef Szamosfalvi *(Mng Dir)*
Ravi Singh *(VP-Logistics)*
Brady Edholm *(Dir-Fin)*
Paul Chaffiotte *(VP)*

Subsidiaries:

ExWorks Capital, LLC   (1)

Capitol Financial Strategies, LLC—(Continued)

333 W Wacker Dr Ste 1620, Chicago, IL 60606
Tel.: (312) 443-8500
Web Site: http://www.exworkscapital.com
Emp.: 50
International Trade Financing, Capital Investment & Financial Advisory Services
N.A.I.C.S.: 522299
Amanda Roberts (VP-Bus Dev)
Dave Norris (Mng Dir)
Matthew Stanley (Mng Dir-Direct Origination)
Randall Abrahams (Chm)
Alan Beard (Mng Dir)
Ravi Singh V (VP-Logistics)

Branch (Domestic):

ExWorks Capital, LLC - Washington, D.C. Office   (2)
1600 Wilson Blvd Ste 1210, Arlington, VA 22209-2594
Tel.: (202) 517-0150
Web Site: http://www.exworkscapital.com
International Trade Financing, Capital Investment & Financial Advisory Services
N.A.I.C.S.: 522299
Brady Edholm (VP)
Jozsef Szamosfalvi (Dir-Emerging Market Project & Structured Fin Underwriting)
Ravi Singh (VP-Logistics)
Alan J. Beard (Mng Dir)
Juan Fronjosa (Dir-Project & Structured Trade Fin)

CAPITOL FUNDS INC.
720 S Lafayette St, Shelby, NC 28150
Tel.: (704) 487-8547
Sales Range: $10-24.9 Million
Emp.: 40
Commercial Land Subdividers & Developers
N.A.I.C.S.: 237210
Jamey Davis (CFO)

CAPITOL GROUP INC.
3125 Cockrell Ln, Springfield, IL 62704
Tel.: (217) 793-4300   IL
Web Site:
   https://www.capitolgroupinc.com
Year Founded: 1946
Sales Range: $100-124.9 Million
Emp.: 134
Whslr of Plumbing Supplies
N.A.I.C.S.: 423720
Lisa Lascody (Mgr)

CAPITOL HARDWARE COMPANY, INC.
112 Business Park Dr, Ridgeland, MS 39157
Tel.: (601) 977-9990
Web Site:
   https://www.capitolhardwareco.com
Sales Range: $10-24.9 Million
Emp.: 42
Hardware Mfr & Distr
N.A.I.C.S.: 423710
Pam Lolly (Office Mgr)
Frazure D. Stacy (VP)
Larry J. Stacy (Treas & Sec)

CAPITOL INFORMATION GROUP, INC.
7600A Leesburg Pike W Bldg Ste 300, Falls Church, VA 22043
Tel.: (703) 905-8000
Web Site:
   https://www.capinfogroup.com
Emp.: 80
Online & Print Publisher
N.A.I.C.S.: 513120
Phil Ash (Publr)
Allie Ash (Pres)

Subsidiaries:

Business Management Daily   (1)

7600A Leesburg Pike, Falls Church, VA 22043-2004
Tel.: (703) 905-8000
Web Site:
   http://www.businessmanagementdaily.com
Sales Range: $25-49.9 Million
Emp.: 75
Online Business News Services
N.A.I.C.S.: 513199
Adam Goldstein (Publr)

Investing Daily   (1)
7600A Leesburg Pike West Bldg Ste 300, Falls Church, VA 22043
Tel.: (703) 394-4931
Web Site: http://www.investingdaily.com
Newsletter Publisher & Online Financial Investment Information
N.A.I.C.S.: 513199
Robert Frick (Dir-Editorial)

CAPITOL LIGHTING
365 Rte 10, East Hanover, NJ 07936
Tel.: (973) 887-8600
Web Site:
   https://www.1800lighting.com
Year Founded: 1924
Sales Range: $25-49.9 Million
Emp.: 175
Lamps & Lamp Shades
N.A.I.C.S.: 449129
Chong Sianne (Mgr-Marketing)

Subsidiaries:

Capitol Lighting   (1)
75 S State Rte 17, Paramus, NJ 07652
Tel.: (201) 843-5353
Web Site: http://www.1800lighting.com
Sales Range: $10-24.9 Million
Emp.: 25
Lighting Fixtures
N.A.I.C.S.: 449129
Herman J. Lebersfeld (Pres)

CAPITOL MEDIA SOLUTIONS
3340 Peachtree Rd NE Ste 1050, Atlanta, GA 30326
Tel.: (404) 347-3316
Web Site:
   http://www.capitolsolutions.com
Year Founded: 2006
Sales Range: $1-9.9 Million
Emp.: 15
Advertising & Media Buying
N.A.I.C.S.: 541810
J. T. Hroncich (Pres)
Audrey Eisen (Dir-Media)
Christine Bowman (Coord-Client)
Callie Holden (Mgr-Production)
Leslie Stockton (Acct Mgr-Adv)

CAPITOL MERIDIAN PARTNERS
1601 K St NW Ste 1050, Washington, DC 20006
Tel.: (202) 742-9910
Web Site: https://capitolmeridian.com
Year Founded: 2021
Privater Equity Firm
N.A.I.C.S.: 523940
Brooke Coburn (Founding Partner)

CAPITOL NATIONAL BANK
200 Washington Sq N, Lansing, MI 48933
Tel.: (517) 484-5080
Web Site:
   http://www.capitolnational.com
Year Founded: 1982
Commericial Banking
N.A.I.C.S.: 522110
Paula D. Cunningham (Pres & CEO)
David Feldpausch (Sr VP-Comml Lending)
Lori Garcia (VP-Ops)
Ronda Thompson (VP-Comml Lending)
Pam Crossley (Sr Mgr-Customer Svc)
Art Aguirre (Chief Credit Officer)

Nick Heriford (Asst VP-Comml Lending)
Kyle Oesterle (CTO)
Steve Pricco (Dir-Govt Guaranteed Lending)
Clement Coulombe (CFO)

CAPITOL PARTNERS LLC
7454 Eye St Nw Ste 750, Washington, DC 20814
Tel.: (202) 955-7960   DE
Web Site:
   http://www.capitolpartners.com
Year Founded: 1997
Rev.: $79,000,000
Emp.: 10
Privater Equity Firm
N.A.I.C.S.: 523999
Julie Jubeir (Sr VP)
T. J. Jubeir (Mng Partner)

Subsidiaries:

Total Home Health Care, Inc.   (1)
2332 SW 67th Ave, Miami, FL 33155
Tel.: (786) 502-8188
Web Site:
   http://www.totalhomehealthcare.org
Women Healthcare Services
N.A.I.C.S.: 621610

CAPITOL PAVING OF D.C., INC.
2211 Channing St NE, Washington, DC 20018
Tel.: (202) 529-7225
Web Site:
   https://www.capitolpaving.com
Rev.: $37,600,000
Emp.: 250
Highway Street & Bridge Construction
N.A.I.C.S.: 237310
Francisco R. Neto (Pres & Treas)
Phoung D. Tran (VP)

CAPITOL PEAK PARTNERS, LLC
250 Filmore St Ste 525, Denver, CO 80206
Web Site:
   http://www.capitolpeakpartners.com
Holding Company
N.A.I.C.S.: 551112
Ed Fugger (Partner)
Gregg L. Engles (Founder & Mng Partner)
Gregg L. Engles (Founder & Mng Partner)

Subsidiaries:

Borden Dairy Company   (1)
8750 N Central Expy Ste 400, Dallas, TX 75231
Tel.: (214) 526-2653
Web Site: http://www.bordendairy.com
Holding Company; Dairy & Milk Production
N.A.I.C.S.: 551112
Lazzy Oroza (Gen Mgr)

Subsidiary (Domestic):

Borden Dairy Company of Florida   (2)
308 Avenue G SW, Winter Haven, FL 33880-3433
Tel.: (863) 297-7300
Web Site: http://www.bordenonline.com
Sales Range: $150-199.9 Million
Processing, Distribution & Sale of Milk & Dairy Products
N.A.I.C.S.: 311511
Tim Long (Controller)
Michael Lasky (Gen Mgr)

Coburg Dairy   (2)
5001 LaCross Rd, North Charleston, SC 29406
Tel.: (843) 554-4870
Web Site: http://www.bordendairy.com
Sales Range: $75-99.9 Million
Milk & Milk By-Products Processor
N.A.I.C.S.: 311511

H. Meyer Dairy   (2)
415 John St, Cincinnati, OH 45215-5481
Tel.: (513) 948-8811
Sales Range: $25-49.9 Million
N.A.I.C.S.: 311511
Tim Alger (Mgr-HR)

Milk Products, L.P.   (2)
5327 S Lamar St, Dallas, TX 75215-4972
Tel.: (214) 565-0332
Sales Range: $350-399.9 Million
Mfr of Milk & Dairy Products
N.A.I.C.S.: 311520
William Charters (CFO)

Plant (Domestic):

Borden Milk Products   (3)
71 Strandtman Cove, Austin, TX 78702-5100
Tel.: (512) 385-2100
Web Site: http://www.milkproductslp.com
Sales Range: $100-124.9 Million
Emp.: 270
Dairy Products
N.A.I.C.S.: 311511
Ruben Morales (Chief Engr)
Craig Nguyen (Mgr-Production)

CAPITOL PLYWOOD INC.
160 Commerce Cir, Sacramento, CA 95815-4208
Tel.: (916) 922-8861
Web Site:
   http://www.capitolplywood.com
Year Founded: 1957
Sales Range: $10-24.9 Million
Emp.: 32
Distr of Hardwood, Softwood & Plywood Lumber
N.A.I.C.S.: 423310
Ed Burris (Mgr-Sls)

Subsidiaries:

Capitol Plywood Inc.   (1)
1955 Timber Way, Reno, NV 89512-1617   (100%)
Tel.: (775) 329-4494
Web Site: http://www.capitolplywood.com
Sales Range: $10-24.9 Million
Emp.: 4
Hardwood, Softwood & Plywood Lumber Distr
N.A.I.C.S.: 423310
Dave Sams (Mgr)

CAPITOL SCIENTIFIC, INC.
2500 Rutland Dr, Austin, TX 78758
Tel.: (512) 836-1167   TX
Web Site:
   https://www.capitolscientific.com
Year Founded: 1963
Sales Range: $1-9.9 Million
Emp.: 32
Professional Equipment & Supplies Merchant Whslr
N.A.I.C.S.: 423490
Felix Ware (CEO)
Michael Elam (COO)

CAPITOL SUPPLY, INC.
1000 Sawgrass Corporate Pkwy Ste 452, Sunrise, FL 33323
Tel.: (954) 485-5000
Web Site:
   http://www.capitolsupply.com
Rev.: $18,176,425
Emp.: 15
Office Furniture Whslr
N.A.I.C.S.: 423210
Harry Steinman (Pres)

CAPITOL USA LLC
300 Crossplains Blvd SE, Dalton, GA 30721
Tel.: (706) 277-6241
Web Site: http://www.capitolusa.com
Sales Range: $25-49.9 Million

Emp.: 160
Floor Covering Accessories
N.A.I.C.S.: 313220
Robert Doda (VP-Ops)

CAPITOL VOLKSWAGEN, INC.
911 Capitol Expy Auto Mall, San Jose, CA 95136-1103
Tel.: (408) 265-4400
Web Site: http://www.dgdg.com
Sales Range: $10-24.9 Million
Emp.: 100
Car Whslr
N.A.I.C.S.: 441110
Tully Williams (Mgr-Ops)
Shawn Delgrande (Owner)

CAPITOL WOOD FLOORS & SUPPLIES INC.
230 Route 17, Hillburn, NY 10931
Tel.: (845) 369-3738
Web Site:
http://www.pcwoodfloors.com
Rev.: $11,330,341
Emp.: 33
Floor Installation Services
N.A.I.C.S.: 238330
Sol Weiss (Pres)

CAPONIGRO PUBLIC RELATIONS, INC.
24725 W 12 Mile Rd Ste 120, Southfield, MI 48034-8345
Tel.: (248) 355-3200
Web Site: http://www.caponigro.com
Year Founded: 1995
Sales Range: $1-9.9 Million
Emp.: 15
Public Relations Agency
N.A.I.C.S.: 541820
Jeff Caponigro (Founder)
Maribeth Farkas (Acct Supvr)

CAPP USA, INC.
201 Marple Ave, Clifton Heights, PA 19018-2414
Tel.: (610) 394-1100   PA
Web Site: https://www.cappusa.com
Year Founded: 1950
Sales Range: $50-74.9 Million
Emp.: 100
Mfr & Distributor of Automatic Controls & Valves for Temperature, Pressure, Flow & Humidity
N.A.I.C.S.: 423830
James A. Caplan (Pres)
Charles S. Yudis (Exec VP-Sls & Mktg)
David Klein (Controller)
Steven Capp (Sec & Gen Mgr)

CAPPADONNA ELECTRICAL MANAGEMENT CORPORATION
3828 Pinemont Dr, Houston, TX 77018
Tel.: (713) 681-4311   TX
Year Founded: 1984
Sales Range: $25-49.9 Million
Emp.: 250
Management Services
N.A.I.C.S.: 541611
Mitchell P. Cappadonna (Pres & CEO)

Subsidiaries:

MWMPC Corp.   (1)
3828 Pinemont Dr, Houston, TX 77018-1222
Tel.: (713) 681-0627
Web Site: http://www.mwmpc.com
Sales Range: $25-49.9 Million
Emp.: 222
Electrical Work
N.A.I.C.S.: 238210

CAPPELLI MILES (SPRING)
101 SW Main St Ste 1905, Portland, OR 97204-3227
Tel.: (503) 241-1515   OR
Year Founded: 1982
Rev.: $18,000,000
Emp.: 13
Communications, Public Relations
N.A.I.C.S.: 541810
Bruce A. Cappelli (Partner & Dir-Creative)
Rod Miles (Pres)
Darcey Price (Dir-Media)
Dianna Marshall (Coord-Production)
Bruce Eckols (Dir-Creative & Art)
Mickey Miles (Acct Exec)
Tammy Laplante (Media Buyer)
Jamie Chabot (Dir-Art)
Mark Haas (Dir-Pub Rel)
Chris L. Thompson (Broadcast Buyer)
Mark Hass (Acct Mgr)
Phil Anne Meile (Partner & Brand Strategist)
Don Schraff (Acct Mgr)

Subsidiaries:

Cappelli Miles (spring)   (1)
2260 Oakmont Way Ste 7, Eugene, OR 97401
Tel.: (541) 484-1515
N.A.I.C.S.: 541810
Rod Miles (Partner & Brand Strategist)
Bruce Cappelli (Partner & Dir-Creative)

CAPPS MANUFACTURING, INC.
2121 S Edwards St, Wichita, KS 67213-1868
Tel.: (316) 942-9351
Web Site: https://www.cappsmfg.com
Year Founded: 1984
Rev.: $22,900,000
Emp.: 130
Sheet Metal Work Mfg
N.A.I.C.S.: 332322
Barney L. Capps (Owner & Pres)
Don G. Smith (Sr Mgr-Mktg)
Ron L. Capps (CFO & VP)
Mike Irvin (Mgr-Production)

CAPPS RENT-A-CAR INC.
8555 John Carpenter Fwy, Dallas, TX 75247
Tel.: (214) 630-6555
Web Site:
http://www.cappsvanrental.com
Year Founded: 1972
Sales Range: $10-24.9 Million
Emp.: 23
Rent-A-Car Service
N.A.I.C.S.: 532111
David Capps (Pres)
David Cox (VP)
Kenneth Mawhee (VP)
Jo Fadal (Controller)

CAPPY DEVLIN INTERNATIONAL
195 N Bedford Rd, Mount Kisco, NY 10549
Tel.: (914) 241-0383
Web Site: http://www.cruises-by-net.com
Year Founded: 1973
Sales Range: $10-24.9 Million
Emp.: 5
Travel Agency
N.A.I.C.S.: 561510
Catherine F. Devlin (Pres)

Subsidiaries:

Travel-By-Net, Inc.   (1)
195 N Bedford Rd, Mount Kisco, NY 10549-1140
Tel.: (914) 241-0383
Web Site: http://www.travel-by-net.com

Online Travel Agency
N.A.I.C.S.: 561599
Catherine F. Devlin (Pres)

CAPREIT INC.
11200 Rockville Pike Ste 100, Rockville, MD 20852
Tel.: (301) 231-8700
Web Site: http://www.capreit.com
Sales Range: $10-24.9 Million
Emp.: 45
Lessors of Residential Buildings & Dwellings
N.A.I.C.S.: 531110
Richard L. Kadish (Pres)
Bruce Esposito (CFO)
Jennifer Kadish Cassell (Sr VP)
Miguel J. Gutierrez (COO)

CAPRI CAPITAL PARTNERS, LLC
875 N Michigan Ave Ste 3430, Chicago, IL 60611
Tel.: (312) 573-5300   DE
Web Site: http://www.capri.global
Year Founded: 1992
Sales Range: $25-49.9 Million
Emp.: 50
Real Estate Investment Management Services
N.A.I.C.S.: 525990

CAPRI FOODS INC.
224 E Harris Ave, Greenville, IL 62246
Tel.: (618) 664-0022
Sales Range: $10-24.9 Million
Emp.: 165
Grocery Stores, Independent
N.A.I.C.S.: 445110

CAPRICORN HOLDINGS, INC.
30 E Elm St, Greenwich, CT 06830
Tel.: (203) 861-6600
Web Site:
https://www.capricornholdings.com
Year Founded: 1988
Sales Range: $800-899.9 Million
Emp.: 8
Holding Company
N.A.I.C.S.: 311520
Herbert S. Winokur Jr. (Chm & CEO)
Dudley C. Mecum II (Gen Partner)

Subsidiaries:

Mrs. Fields' Original Cookies, Inc.   (1)
2855 E Cottonwood Pkwy Ste 400, Salt Lake City, UT 84121-7050
Tel.: (801) 736-5600
Web Site: http://www.mrsfields.com
Sales Range: $100-124.9 Million
Holding Company; Cookie, Confectionery & Frozen Yogurt Products Mfr, Retailer & Quick-Service Restaurant Owner & Franchisor
N.A.I.C.S.: 311821
Rob Streett (Sr VP-Franchise Dev/Strategic Partnerships)

Subsidiary (Domestic):

Mrs. Fields Famous Brands, LLC   (2)
2855 E Cottonwood Pkwy, Salt Lake City, UT 84121-7050
Tel.: (801) 736-5600
Web Site: http://www.mrsfieldsfranchise.com
Sales Range: $50-74.9 Million
Branded Retailer, Product Licensing & Quick-Service Restaurant Franchisor
N.A.I.C.S.: 533110
Sidney Feltenstein (Chm)

Subsidiary (Domestic):

Mrs. Fields Gifts, Inc.   (3)
1717 S 4800 W, Salt Lake City, UT 84104
Tel.: (801) 412-8803
Web Site: http://www.mrsfields.com

Sales Range: $25-49.9 Million
Gourmet Cookie & Confection Online Retailer
N.A.I.C.S.: 311821
Jeff Warner (CEO)

TCBY Systems, LLC   (3)
2855 E Cottonwood Pkwy Ste 400, Salt Lake City, UT 84121
Tel.: (801) 736-5600
Web Site: http://www.tcby.com
Frozen Yogurt Quick-Service Restaurant Franchisor
N.A.I.C.S.: 533110

CAPRIGHT PROPERTY ADVISORS, LLC
401 N Michigan Ave Ste 1750, Chicago, IL 60611
Tel.: (312) 337-9500   IL
Web Site: https://www.capright.com
Year Founded: 2007
Real Estate Appraisal & Consulting Services
N.A.I.C.S.: 531320
Jules H. Marling (CEO & Mng Principal)
Keith E. Darin (Principal)
Korin M. Arvila (Sr Dir)
Viji M. Kartha (Controller)
Jonathan B. Rivera (Dir-Real Estate)
Selina J. McCumber (Principal)
Douglas J. Ticus (Principal)
Ana C. Ribeiro Mrics (Mng Dir)
Shaun R. Oxtal (Mng Dir)
Steven J. Henderson (Mng Dir)
Ronald K. Kennedy (Sr Dir)
Felipe Cabada (Dir)
Alejandra Curry (Dir)
Melissa Brown (Dir)
Kristopher Oxtal (Dir)
Jessica E. Lore (Dir-Comm)

CAPRIOTTI'S SANDWICH SHOP
5130 S Fort Apache Rd #215-411, Las Vegas, NV 89148
Tel.: (866) 959-3737
Web Site: http://www.capriottis.com
Year Founded: 1976
Sales Range: $25-49.9 Million
Emp.: 25
Specialty Sandwich Maker
N.A.I.C.S.: 445298
Ashley Morris (CEO)
Quentin Wilson (Dir-Mktg)
Jane McPherson (Sr VP-Mktg)
David Bloom (Chief Dev Officer)
Brent Erwin (Sr VP-Fin)

CAPSONIC GROUP LLC
495 Renner Dr, Elgin, IL 60123-7008
Tel.: (847) 888-7300
Web Site:
http://www.capsonicgroup.com
Year Founded: 1968
Plastic Composite Components & High Volume Custom Composite & Insert Molding Mfr
N.A.I.C.S.: 326199
Dale White (Pres)

CAPSOURCE INC.
2009 E Windmill Ln, Las Vegas, NV 89123
Tel.: (702) 240-0977
Web Site:
http://www.capsourcenv.com
Year Founded: 1997
Rev.: $100,000,000
Emp.: 17
Real Estate Investment & Mortgage Lending Services
N.A.I.C.S.: 531390
Steve Byrne (Founder, Pres & Partner)
Andrew M. Jolley (Partner)
Suzie Bopp (VP-Ops)

CapSource Inc.—(Continued)

CAPSPIRE, INC.

620 N College Ste 204, Fayetteville, AR 72701 AR
Web Site: https://www.capspire.com
Year Founded: 2009
Sales Range: $1-9.9 Million
Emp.: 27
Energy Industry Software
N.A.I.C.S.: 513210
Mike Scharf (Co-Founder)
Jeff Hardcastle (Co-Founder)
Lance Laubach (CEO)
Dave Webb (Mng Dir)
Paul Norris (Mng Dir-Analytics-Europe)
Larry Loocke (Partner)
Rusty Robeson (Partner)
Jerry Emmert (Exec VP-Sls-Dallas)

CAPSTAN FINANCIAL CONSULTING GROUP LLC

238 S Washington Blvd, Sarasota, FL 34236
Tel.: (941) 256-9300
Web Site:
https://www.capstanfinancial.com
Year Founded: 2010
Sales Range: $1-9.9 Million
Emp.: 16
Financial Consulting Services
N.A.I.C.S.: 523940
Matthew DePalma (Mng Partner)
Nicholas Feather (Sr Partner)
Ben T. Hatcher (Partner & Dir-Client Dev)
Carrie Hulen (Partner)
Thomas M. McDonald (Sr VP)
Tiki McKelly (Dir-Branch Admin)
Jeff Baar (Asst VP-Client Dev)
Jeffrey Day (Sr VP)
Dan Hoffe (Exec VP)
Scot Jaffe (Sr VP)
Chris Jones (Exec VP)
William Marsh IV (Mng Principal)

CAPSTAN INC.

16100 S Figueroa St, Gardena, CA 90248-2617
Tel.: (310) 544-8383
Web Site:
http://www.capstanpermaflow.com
Year Founded: 1959
Sales Range: $100-124.9 Million
Emp.: 22
Fabricated Metal Products
N.A.I.C.S.: 332117
Bonnie Gonzales (Controller)
Mark Paullin (Owner & CEO)

Subsidiaries:

Capstan California (1)
16100 S Figueroa St, Gardena, CA 90248-2617
Tel.: (310) 366-5999
Web Site: http://www.capstan.com
Rev.: $290,000
Emp.: 20
Industrial Machinery
N.A.I.C.S.: 332110
Bonnie Gonzales (Controller)

CAPSTONE BROKERAGE, INC.

8681 W Sahara Ave Ste 100, Las Vegas, NV 89117
Tel.: (702) 227-5727 NV
Web Site:
https://www.capstonebrokerage.com
Year Founded: 1997
Sales Range: $10-24.9 Million
Emp.: 25
Insurance Agent/Broker
N.A.I.C.S.: 524210
Jade M. Anderson (CEO)
Mary Thompson (Pres)

CAPSTONE COMMUNITY ACTION

20 Gable Pl, Barre, VT 05641-4128
Tel.: (802) 479-1053 VT
Web Site: https://www.capstonevt.org
Year Founded: 1965
Sales Range: $10-24.9 Million
Emp.: 246
Community Care Services
N.A.I.C.S.: 624190
Paul Zabriskie (Dir-Weatherization & Energysmart of Vermont)
Rubin Bennett (Chm)
Steven Pappas (Vice Chm)
Sarah McMullen (Deputy Dir-Ops)
Colleen Lafont (CFO)

CAPSTONE CORPORATION

635 Slaters Lane Ste 100, Alexandria, VA 22314
Tel.: (703) 683-4220
Web Site:
http://www.capstonecorp.com
Year Founded: 1984
Rev.: $46,400,000
Emp.: 396
Government Services
N.A.I.C.S.: 921190
Thomas D. Madison (Owner & Vice Chm)
William J. Moore (Founder & Chm)
David Magnone (CTO)
Neal Tomblyn (Sr VP-Bus Dev, Mktg & Comm)
Lisa Carr (Dir-HR)
B. Daniel Fox (Dir-Ops)
Thomas Matthews (Dir-Ops)
Wendy H. Martin (VP-Cyber & IT Solutions)
John J. McNally III (Sr VP-Growth)

CAPSTONE FINANCIAL GROUP, INC.

26 All Souls Crescent, Asheville, NC 28803
Tel.: (843) 548-0603 NV
Web Site: https://capfg.com
Year Founded: 2012
CAPP—(OTCBB)
Sales Range: Less than $1 Million
Emp.: 4
Financial Services
N.A.I.C.S.: 523999
Carl Norman (Pres)
Chandler Kohn (VP-Investment Banking)
Tim Yoder (VP-Res)

CAPSTONE GREEN ENERGY CORPORATION

16640 Stagg St, Van Nuys, CA 91406
Tel.: (818) 734-5300 DE
Web Site:
http://www.capstoneturbine.com
Year Founded: 1988
CGRN—(NASDAQ)
Rev.: $91,219,000
Assets: $84,206,000
Liabilities: $84,993,000
Net Worth: (-$787,000)
Earnings: $7,392,000
Emp.: 101
Fiscal Year-end: 03/31/24
Microturbine Technology Solutions
N.A.I.C.S.: 333611
Darren R. Jamison (Pres & CEO)
James D. Crouse (Chief Revenue Officer)
Robert C. Flexon (Chm)
Jennifer Derstine (VP-Marketing-Distribution)
Celia Fanning (Chief Acctg Officer & Controller)
Scott W. Robinson (Treas & Sec)
John J. Juric (CFO)

Emer Higgins (VP-Ops)
Robert C. Flexon (Exec Chm, Interim Pres & Interim CEO)

Subsidiaries:

Capstone Turbine International, Inc. (1)
Shibuya Mark City W22F 1-12-1 Dougen-zaka, Shibuya-ku, Tokyo, 150-0043, Japan
Tel.: (81) 343605509
Web Site: http://www.a-p.co.jp
Sales Range: $125-149.9 Million
Microturbines Mfr
N.A.I.C.S.: 333611

CAPSTONE GROUP, INC.

1700 S MacDill Ave Ste 260, Tampa, FL 33629-5218
Tel.: (813) 253-3535
Web Site:
https://www.capstonegroup.net
Rev.: $300,000,000
Retail, Office & Industrial Property Acquisition, Development, Property Management & Construction
N.A.I.C.S.: 531390
Gordon A. McBride (Chm)
James T. Burt II (Pres, Owner & Principal)

CAPSTONE TITLE, LLC

901 S Mopac Expy Bldg II Ste 150, Austin, TX 78746
Tel.: (512) 270-4755
Web Site:
http://www.capstonetitletx.com
Year Founded: 2013
Sales Range: $1-9.9 Million
Emp.: 20
Real Estate Manangement Services
N.A.I.C.S.: 531390
J. Brad Compere (Founder, Pres & CEO)
Billy Mullens (Officer-Commercial Escrow & VP)
David Busch (CFO)
Colby Bodoin (VP-Ops)
Eddie Rodriguez (VP)

CAPSTRAT

1201 Edwards Mill Rd 1st Fl, Raleigh, NC 27607-3625
Tel.: (919) 828-0806 NC
Web Site: http://www.capstrat.com
Year Founded: 1994
Sales Range: $10-24.9 Million
Emp.: 74
Public Relations Agency
N.A.I.C.S.: 541820
Ken Eudy (Co-Founder & Chm)
Karen Albritton (Pres & CEO)
John Peterson (Exec VP)
Debbie Reed (CFO)
Todd Coats (Chief Creative Officer)
Shane Johnston (Exec VP & Dir-Client Dev)
Jonathan Wisely (Sr Dir-Art)
Angela Connor (Exec VP-Media & Audience Engagement)
Scott Ballew (Sr VP & Dir-Creative)
Kyle Sutton (VP & Dir-Digital Strategy)
Brandon Goldsworthy (Sr Dir-Art)
Mallory Pickard (Acct Exec)
Briana Beanland (Acct Coord)
Jessica Swanner (Acct Coord)
Lauren Stafford (Acct Exec)
Michelle Pickett (Acct Coord)
Elizabeth Brandt (Acct Mgr)
Brad Bennett (Acct Dir)

CAPSULINE, INC.

1889 SW 3rd St, Pompano Beach, FL 33066
Tel.: (954) 975-3363
Web Site: http://www.capsuline.com
Year Founded: 2003

Sales Range: $1-9.9 Million
Emp.: 5
Supplier of Gelatin, Vegetable & Flavored Capsule Shells for Home-Based Businesses & Small to Mid-Range Nutraceutical Manufacturers
N.A.I.C.S.: 325412
Jonathan Gilinski (Founder)
Renato Del Vecchio (VP-Ops)

CAPSYS CORP.

155 3rd St, Brooklyn, NY 11231
Tel.: (718) 403-0050
Web Site:
http://www.capsyscorp.com
Rev.: $10,000,000
Emp.: 3
Modular Homes, Prefabricated, Wood
N.A.I.C.S.: 321992
Tom O'Hara (Dir-Bus Dev)
David Parlo (Project Mgr)

CAPTAIN MARDEN'S SEAFOODS, INC.

279 Linden St, Wellesley, MA 02482
Tel.: (781) 235-0860
Web Site:
http://www.captainmardens.com
Year Founded: 1945
Sales Range: $10-24.9 Million
Emp.: 50
Seafoods
N.A.I.C.S.: 424460
Nancy Marden Goodall (VP)

CAPTECH VENTURES, INC.

1118 W Main St, Richmond, VA 23220
Tel.: (804) 355-0511
Web Site:
http://www.captechconsulting.com
Sales Range: $25-49.9 Million
Emp.: 300
Information Systems Manager, Designer & Builder; Consulting Services
N.A.I.C.S.: 541512
Slaughter Fitz-Hugh (Co-Founder, COO & Principal)
Sandy Williamson (Co-Founder & Principal)
Drew Tester (Principal-Chicago & Denver)
Errol Restelli (Principal)
Kevin McQueen (Principal)
Joanna Winston Bergeron (Chief Talent Officer)
Steve Holdych (COO)
Darrell Norton (Principal)
Vinnie Schoenfelder (CTO)
Andy Sofish (Principal)
Suzie Turner (Principal)

CAPTEX BANCSHARES, INC.

106 Hamilton St, Trenton, TX 75490
Tel.: (903) 989-2235 TX
Web Site: http://www.fnbtrenton.bank
Year Founded: 2016
Bank Holding Company
N.A.I.C.S.: 551111
George Lea (Co-Founder, Chm & CEO)
Michael R. Thomas Jr. (Co-Founder)

Subsidiaries:

The First National Bank of Trenton (1)
106 Hamilton St, Trenton, TX 75490
Tel.: (903) 989-2235
Web Site: http://www.fnbtrenton.bank
Sales Range: $1-9.9 Million
Emp.: 77
Commericial Banking
N.A.I.C.S.: 522110
Lewis H. Donaghey (Pres & CEO)

CAPTIL AUTOMOTIVE REAL ESTATE SERVICES, INC.

8484 Westpark Dr Ste 200, McLean, VA 22102
Tel.: (703) 288-3075
Web Site:
http://www.capitalautomotive.com
Year Founded: 1998
Real Estate Manangement Services
N.A.I.C.S.: 531390
Jay M. Ferriero *(Pres & CEO)*

CAPTIVA GROUP INC.
3838 Bogan Ave NE, Albuquerque, NM 87109
Tel.: (505) 872-2200
Web Site:
http://www.thecaptivagroup.com
Sales Range: $10-24.9 Million
Emp.: 100
Commercial Printing
N.A.I.C.S.: 323111
Tony Fernandez *(Pres & CEO)*
Albert Padilla *(VP-Sls)*

CAPTIVE RESOURCES, LLC
1100 N Arlington Heights Rd, Itasca, IL 60143
Tel.: (847) 781-1400
Web Site:
https://www.captiveresources.com
Year Founded: 1985
Sales Range: $1-9.9 Million
Emp.: 98
Administrative Management & General Management Consulting Services
N.A.I.C.S.: 541611
Jennifer T. Beard *(COO)*
George V. Rusu *(Founder, Chm & Co-CEO)*
Ernest Achtien *(CFO)*
Nicholas J. Hentges *(Co-CEO)*
Andrew O. Johnson *(Exec VP)*
Sam B. Meccia *(Exec VP)*
Glenn G. Carlson *(Gen Counsel)*
Jeanne Hansen *(Sr VP)*
Mike Foley *(Pres)*
John Pontin *(Sr VP-Bus Dev)*
Donna Dreuth *(Co-CFO)*
J. P. Boulus *(Chief Bus Officer)*

Subsidiaries:

Healthcare Risk Specialists, LLC **(1)**
1034 Farmington Ave, West Hartford, CT 06107
Tel.: (860) 521-8555
Web Site: http://www.myhcrs.com
Management & Consulting Services
N.A.I.C.S.: 541618
David Rossey *(Pres)*

CAPTIVE-AIRE SYSTEMS, INC.
4641 Paragon Park Rd, Raleigh, NC 27616
Tel.: (919) 882-2410
Web Site:
https://www.captiveaire.com
Year Founded: 1980
Sales Range: $75-99.9 Million
Emp.: 375
Mfr of Stainless Steel Ventilation & Fire Protection Systems for Restaurants
N.A.I.C.S.: 332322
Bob Luddy *(Pres)*
William H. Francis Jr. *(Treas & Controller)*

CAPTRUST ADVISORS, LLC
102 W Whiting St Ste 400, Tampa, FL 33602
Tel.: (813) 218-5000
Web Site:
http://www.captrustadv.com
Year Founded: 1998
Sales Range: $1-9.9 Million
Emp.: 25
Investment Consulting Services

N.A.I.C.S.: 523940
Roger E. Robson *(Co-Founder & Mng Principal)*
Eric W. Bailey *(Co-Founder & Mng Principal)*
Stephen H. Shott *(Mng Principal)*
Scott Bruin *(Dir-Wealth Svcs)*
Jeffrey Ireland *(Dir-Client Svcs)*
Heidi B. Spencer *(Dir-Client Svcs)*

CAPTURE TECHNOLOGIES, INC.
3575 Alameda Ave, Oakland, CA 94601
Tel.: (510) 534-5050
Web Site: http://www.capturet.com
Sales Range: $10-24.9 Million
Emp.: 50
Sells & Services Voice Identification Products for Security Use
N.A.I.C.S.: 459999
John Babin *(Pres)*
Chanda Brewer *(Dir-Mktg & HR)*
Robyn Blair *(Dir-Contracts)*

CAR & TRUCK RENTALS, INC.
5900 Messer Airport Hwy, Birmingham, AL 35212
Tel.: (205) 592-8901
Sales Range: $10-24.9 Million
Emp.: 80
Rent-A-Car Service
N.A.I.C.S.: 532111
Robert Klyce *(Pres)*
Tina Richardson *(Controller)*

CAR CARE CLINIC, INC.
703 Airport Rd, Flowood, MS 39232
Tel.: (601) 936-4744
Web Site:
https://www.carcareclinicjetlube.com
Rev.: $12,000,000
Emp.: 135
General Automotive Repair Shops
N.A.I.C.S.: 811111
Cindy Hannon *(Office Mgr)*
Robert R. Tewes *(Pres)*
Brian Romine *(Mgr)*

CAR CITY CHRYSLER
3100 S US Hwy 169, Saint Joseph, MO 64503
Tel.: (816) 233-9149
Web Site:
http://www.carcitymotors.com
Sales Range: $10-24.9 Million
Emp.: 80
New & Used Car Dealers
N.A.I.C.S.: 441110
Carroll Cathey *(Pres)*

CAR MONKEYS GROUP
393 Crescent Ave, Wyckoff, NJ 07481
Tel.: (201) 425-4725
Year Founded: 2010
Rev.: $779,377
Assets: $534,933
Liabilities: $61,012
Net Worth: $473,921
Earnings: ($59,156)
Emp.: 2
Fiscal Year-end: 06/30/15
Used Auto Parts Retailer
N.A.I.C.S.: 441330
Mariusz Girt *(Pres & CEO)*
Pawel Girt *(CFO)*
Marek Kudlinski *(CTO)*

CAR PARTS WAREHOUSE INC.
5200 W 130th St, Cleveland, OH 44142
Tel.: (216) 676-5100

Web Site:
http://www.carpartswarehouse.net
Rev.: $15,645,175
Emp.: 100
Sales of Automotive Supplies & Parts
N.A.I.C.S.: 423120
Tony Di Fiore *(Pres)*

CAR PROS AUTOMOTIVE GROUP, INC.
7230 S Tacoma Way, Tacoma, WA 98409
Tel.: (253) 671-2400
Web Site:
https://www.carproskia.com
Year Founded: 1993
Rev.: $42,000,000
Emp.: 100
Sales New & Used Automobiles
N.A.I.C.S.: 441120
Matthew Phillips *(CEO)*

Subsidiaries:

El Monte Auto Services LLC **(1)**
11400 Vly Blvd, El Monte, CA 91731-3230
Web Site: http://www.longotoyota.com
General Automotive Repair
N.A.I.C.S.: 811111
Try Ngoy *(Owner)*

Nick Alexander Imports, Inc **(1)**
6333 S Alameda St, Los Angeles, CA 90001-2168
Web Site: http://www.alexanderbmw.com
New Car Dealers
N.A.I.C.S.: 441110

CAR RENTAL 8, LLC
11345 Countryway Blvd, Tampa, FL 33626
Web Site: http://www.carrental8.com
Year Founded: 2008
Sales Range: $1-9.9 Million
Car Rental Services
N.A.I.C.S.: 532111
Yves Boyer *(CEO)*

CAR RENTALS INC.
1570 S Washington Ave, Piscataway, NJ 08854
Tel.: (732) 752-6800
Web Site: http://www.avisnj.com
Sales Range: $50-74.9 Million
Emp.: 35
Rent-A-Car Service
N.A.I.C.S.: 532111
Sylvester L. Sullivan *(Pres)*

CAR SOUND MAGNAFLOW
22961 Arroyo Vista, Rancho Santa Margarita, CA 92688
Tel.: (949) 858-5900
Web Site: http://www.car-sound.com
Sales Range: $100-124.9 Million
Emp.: 200
Exhaust Systems & Parts, Motor Vehicle
N.A.I.C.S.: 336390
Jerry Paolone *(Pres)*

CAR SPA INC.
4835 Lyndon B Johnson Fwy Ste 650, Dallas, TX 75244
Tel.: (469) 374-0280
Web Site: https://carspa.net
Rev.: $90,000,000
Emp.: 30
Gift Shop
N.A.I.C.S.: 459420
Alexander W. Rangos *(Founder, Chm & CEO)*
Ralph J. Guarino *(CFO & Exec VP)*

CAR STEREO CITY INC.
10136 SE Washington St, Portland, OR 97216
Tel.: (503) 256-1778
Sales Range: Less than $1 Million

Emp.: 12
Automotive Sound Equipment
N.A.I.C.S.: 441330
Bill Sanders *(Gen Mgr)*

CAR STORE INC.
63 US Rte 5 S, Norwich, VT 05055
Tel.: (802) 649-1603
Web Site:
http://www.thecarstoresubaru.com
Sales Range: $10-24.9 Million
Emp.: 35
New & Used Car Dealers
N.A.I.C.S.: 441110
Trisha Covey *(Comptroller)*
Rick MacLeay *(Pres)*

CAR TOYS INC.
20 W Galer St Ste 300, Seattle, WA 98119-3302
Tel.: (206) 443-0980
Web Site: http://www.cartoys.com
Year Founded: 1987
Sales Range: $50-74.9 Million
Emp.: 500
Retailer of Electronic Automobile Accessories
N.A.I.C.S.: 441330
Daniel Brettler *(CEO & Chm)*

CAR WASH PARTNERS, INC.
222 E 5th St, Tucson, AZ 85705
Tel.: (520) 615-4000
Web Site:
http://www.mistercarwash.com
Year Founded: 1996
Emp.: 7,000
Car Washing Services
N.A.I.C.S.: 811192
John Lai *(Pres & CEO)*
Bruce A. Schumacher *(VP-Strategic Initiatives)*
Darren Skarecky *(CFO)*
Larry Minich *(VP)*
Dave Hail *(VP-Facilities Mgmt)*
Anna Zappia *(Dir-HR)*
Joe Matheny *(Dir-Field Ops)*
Felipe Valenzuela *(Dir-Bus Ops)*
Casey Lindsay *(Dir-Fin)*
Sarah Ross *(Dir-Integration)*
Chris Northey *(Dir-Mktg)*
Mayra Chimienti *(Dir-Training & Dev)*
Joaquin Valenzuela *(Dir-Fin)*
Chris Baker *(Dir-Customer Insights)*
Beth Iacono *(Dir-Risk Mgmt)*
Bob Hoffer *(Dir-Loyalty Mktg)*
Steve Bean *(Dir-IT)*
Ben Melendez *(Mgr-Georgia, Florida, North Carolina & Alabama)*
Bill Smith *(Mgr-Houston & Tennessee)*
Derek Martin *(Mgr-Idaho, Iowa, Missouri & Washington)*
Jason Lederman *(Mgr-Colorado & Houston)*
Jeff Hoppe *(Mgr-Maryland, Pennsylvania & Utah)*
Ryan Darby *(Mgr)*
Tim Vaughn *(Mgr-Illinois, Minnesota & Wisconsin)*
Dave Craig *(Reg Mgr)*
Eric Lewis *(Gen Mgr)*

Subsidiaries:

CAR Wash Express **(1)**
13333 E Briarwood Ave, Centennial, CO 80112-0112
Tel.: (303) 799-8090
Web Site: http://www.carwashexpress.com
Car Washing Services
N.A.I.C.S.: 811192
Brett Meinberg *(Pres)*

Mister Car Wash **(1)**
1034 Gessner Dr, Houston, TX 77055-6010 **(100%)**
Tel.: (713) 467-1400

Car Wash Partners, Inc.—(Continued)
Web Site: http://www.mrcarwash.com
Rev.: $45,000,000
Emp.: 1,000
Carwash
N.A.I.C.S.: 811192
Bill Smith (Bus Mgr)
Kathy Seward (Office Mgr)
Mike Story (Supvr-Maintenance)

Mister Car Wash   (1)
5950 Fairview Ave, Boise, ID 83704-7763
Tel.: (208) 322-5950
Web Site: http://www.mistercarwash.com
Rev.: $2,600,000
Emp.: 70
Carwash
N.A.I.C.S.: 811192
John Lai (Chm, Pres & CEO)
Dave Hail (VP-Facilities Dev)
Lisa Bossard Funk (Gen Counsel)

Venture Car Wash   (1)
3510 Lakeland Dr, Flowood, MS 39232-
8888
Tel.: (769) 230-4099
Web Site: http://www.venturecarwash.com
Animal Production
N.A.I.C.S.: 112990
Patrick O'Diam (Mgr)

CAR-FRESHENER CORPORA-TION

21205 Little Tree Dr, Watertown, NY
13601-2948
Tel.: (315) 788-6250   NY
Web Site: http://www.little-trees.com
Year Founded: 1952
Sales Range: $75-99.9 Million
Emp.: 100
Mfr of Air Fresheners & Cleaning
Products for Automotive & Household
Use
N.A.I.C.S.: 325612
Betsy Tracy (Gen Mgr)

CAR-FRESHNER CORPORA-TION

21205 Little Tree Dr, Watertown, NY
13601-0719
Tel.: (315) 788-6250
Web Site: http://www.little-trees.com
Sales Range: $25-49.9 Million
Emp.: 300
Car Air Freshener Mfr
N.A.I.C.S.: 325612
Sherri Smith (Mgr-Sls)

CAR-GRAPH INC.

1545 W Elna Rae St, Tempe, AZ
85281
Tel.: (480) 894-1356
Web Site: https://www.car-graph.com
Year Founded: 1961
Sales Range: $10-24.9 Million
Emp.: 90
Aircraft Engines & Engine Parts
N.A.I.C.S.: 336412
George Lindbloom (Chm)
Charles Lindbloom (Pres)
Pat Fincher (Mgr-Pur)
Carl Murphey (Mgr-Quality)
Rhonda Hassmann (Controller)
Dave Hodges (Supvr)

CARABETTA MANAGEMENT CO., INC.

200 Pratt St, Meriden, CT 06450-
4220
Tel.: (203) 237-7400   CT
Web Site: https://www.carabetta.com
Year Founded: 1965
Rev.: $25,000,000
Emp.: 325
Real Estate & Managerial Services
N.A.I.C.S.: 531210
Joseph F. Carabetta (CEO)

CARAHSOFT TECHNOLOGY CORP.

11493 Sunset Hills Rd Ste 100, Res-
ton, VA 20190
Tel.: (703) 871-8500
Web Site: https://www.carahsoft.com
Year Founded: 2004
Sales Range: $600-649.9 Million
Emp.: 2,470
Other Computer Related Services
N.A.I.C.S.: 541519
Craig P. Abod (Founder & Pres)
Ellen Lord (Mgr-Contracts)
Karina Woods (Dir-Customer Ops
Team)
Mohammed Hamididdln (Mgr-Sls)

CARAMAGNO FOODS COM-PANY

14255 Dequindre, Detroit, MI 48212
Tel.: (313) 869-8200
Web Site:
    https://www.caramagnofoods.com
Rev.: $140,000,000
Emp.: 100
Groceries, General Line
N.A.I.C.S.: 424410
David Pieper (Controller)

CARAMOOR CENTER FOR MUSIC & THE ARTS, INC.

149 Girdle Ridge Rd, Katonah, NY
10536
Tel.: (914) 232-5035   NY
Web Site: https://www.caramoor.org
Year Founded: 1945
Sales Range: $10-24.9 Million
Music Promotion Services
N.A.I.C.S.: 711310
Jeffrey P. Haydon (CEO)
Nina Curley (Chief Dev Officer & VP)
Paul Rosenblum (Mng Dir)
Tahra Millan (CMO & VP)
Tammy Belanger (CFO & VP)

CARAN PRECISION ENGI-NEERING & MANUFACTURING

4275 N Palm St, Fullerton, CA 92835-
1045
Tel.: (714) 447-5400
Web Site:
    http://www.caranprecision.com
Sales Range: $10-24.9 Million
Emp.: 50
Metal Precision Stamping Mfr & Sup-
plier
N.A.I.C.S.: 332119
Chuck Wogman (Mgr-IT)
Ed Comber (Engr-Tooling)

CARANA CORP.

4350 Fairfax Dr, Arlington, VA 22203
Tel.: (703) 243-1701
Web Site: http://www.carana.com
Rev.: $4,590,000
Emp.: 27
Administrative Management & Gen-
eral Management Consulting Service
N.A.I.C.S.: 541611
Santiago Sedaca (Pres)
Eduardo Tugendhat (CEO)
Erin Endean (VP)
Carl Larkins (VP)
Nathan Van Dusen (Dir-Strategic Ini-
tiatives)
Peter Boone (VP)

CARAVAN TOURS, INC.

401 N Michigan Ave, Chicago, IL
60611-4255
Tel.: (312) 321-9800   IL
Web Site: https://www.caravan.com
Year Founded: 1952
Sales Range: $50-74.9 Million
Emp.: 50
Tour Operator

N.A.I.C.S.: 561520
T. Dennis Duffy (Pres & VP-Sls)
Brendan Duffy (Dir-Mktg & Sls)

CARBIDE INDUSTRIES, LLC.

4400 Bells Ln, Louisville, KY 40211-
2143
Tel.: (502) 775-4100
Web Site: https://www.carbidellc.com
Sales Range: $25-49.9 Million
Emp.: 200
Industrial Gas Mfr
N.A.I.C.S.: 325120
Greg Brasel (Mgr-Technical)
Mike Allen (Mgr-Quality)

CARBIZ AUTOS

6001 Reisterstown Rd, Baltimore, MD
21215-3440
Tel.: (410) 358-1410
Web Site: http://www.carbiz.com
Year Founded: 1997
Sales Range: $10-24.9 Million
Emp.: 40
Car Whslr
N.A.I.C.S.: 441110
Ali Macris Berney (Dir-Resolution)
Jeffrey Berney (Owner)

CARBO CERAMICS INC.

575 N Dairy Ashford Ste 300, Hous-
ton, TX 77079
Tel.: (281) 921-6400   DE
Web Site:
    http://www.carboceramics.com
Year Founded: 1987
Rev.: $161,707,000
Assets: $191,514,000
Liabilities: $152,207,000
Net Worth: $39,307,000
Earnings: ($304,201,000)
Emp.: 349
Fiscal Year-end: 12/31/19
Ceramic Proppants for the Hydraulic
Fracturing of Natural Gas & Oil Wells
N.A.I.C.S.: 333132

Subsidiaries:

Applied Geomechanics Inc   (1)
140 Chestnut St, San Francisco, CA 94111
Tel.: (415) 364-3200
Web Site: http://www.carboceramics.com
Sales Range: $10-24.9 Million
Emp.: 13
Totalizing Fluid Meter & Counting Device
Mfr
N.A.I.C.S.: 334514

CARBO Ceramics   (1)
4810 Industrial Dr, New Iberia, LA 70560
Tel.: (337) 367-6151
Web Site: http://www.carboceramics.com
Sales Range: $100-124.9 Million
Mfr & Distribution of Ceramic Proppants
Used in the Hydraulic Fracturing of Natural
Gas & Oil Wells
N.A.I.C.S.: 327910
Claude A. Krause (Dir-Bus Dev)

CARBO Ceramics   (1)
36 Arch Dr, Eufaula, AL 36027-2920
Tel.: (334) 687-7005
Sales Range: $25-49.9 Million
Emp.: 57
Mfr of Ceramic Proppants Used in the Hy-
draulic Fracturing of Natural Gas & Oil
Wells
N.A.I.C.S.: 327910
Mary Parker (Office Mgr)

CARBO Ceramics (China) Company
Ltd.   (1)
San Yuan Industry Park, Luoyang, 471031,
China
Tel.: (86) 37964121931
Oil & Gas Equipment Mfr
N.A.I.C.S.: 333131

Falcon Technologies and Services,
Inc.   (1)
201 E John Carpenter Fwy Ste 6-0, Irving,
TX 75062

Tel.: (817) 251-0525
Scientific & Technical Services
N.A.I.C.S.: 541990

CARBOLINEUM WOOD PRE-SERVING CO.

6683 N 40th St, Milwaukee, WI
53209-3049
Tel.: (414) 353-5040   WI
Web Site:
    http://www.carbolineum.com
Year Founded: 1876
Sales Range: $10-24.9 Million
Emp.: 15
Wood Coatings Mfr
N.A.I.C.S.: 325194
Frederick Leypoldt (Pres)

CARBON POWER & LIGHT, INC.

110 E Spring St, Saratoga, WY
82331
Tel.: (307) 326-5206
Web Site:
    http://www.carbonpower.com
Sales Range: $10-24.9 Million
Emp.: 27
Eletric Power Generation Services
N.A.I.C.S.: 221118
Bob Johnson (Pres)
Charles A. Larsen (Gen Mgr)
Dan Hodgkiss (Treas)
Gary Jacobsen (Sec)
Jerry Rabidue (VP)
Laurie Forster (Pres)

CARBONAIR ENVIRONMEN-TAL SYSTEMS

1480 County Rd C, Roseville, MN
55113
Tel.: (763) 315-4771
Web Site: http://www.carbonair.com
Sales Range: $10-24.9 Million
Emp.: 20
Water Treatment Equipment, Indus-
trial
N.A.I.C.S.: 333310
Tom Fitzgerald (Pres)

CARBONE AUTO GROUP

5700 Horatio St, Utica, NY 13502
Tel.: (315) 724-4216
Web Site:
    http://www.carbonecars.com
Year Founded: 1929
Sales Range: $10-24.9 Million
Emp.: 43
Car Whslr
N.A.I.C.S.: 441110
David Palladino (Gen Mgr)
Betsy Rasmussen (Controller)

CARCARE COLLISION CEN-TERS, INC.

12319 S Route 59 Ste 102, Plainfield,
IL 60585
Tel.: (877) 362-7274
Web Site: http://www.carcarecollision
    centers.com
Automotive Collison Repair & Towing
Services
N.A.I.C.S.: 811198
James Missig (Co-Owner)
Bill Aeschliman (Co-Owner & CEO)

CARCHEX

118 Shawan Rd Ste 210, Hunt Valley,
MD 21030
Tel.: (410) 527-9280
Web Site: http://www.carchex.com
Year Founded: 2003
Sales Range: $10-24.9 Million
Emp.: 40
Direct Marketer of Vehicle Service
Contracts & Pre-Purchase Vehicle
Inspection Services

N.A.I.C.S.: 525990
Jason Goldsmith *(Co-Founder, Chm & CEO)*
Laurence Dorman *(Exec VP-Ops & Mktg)*
Scott Levy *(CFO)*
Joe Campanella *(Exec VP-Bus Dev)*
Hyun Lee *(CTO)*
Tom Stratchko *(VP-Ops)*

CARCO CAPITAL CORPORATION

2905 N 32nd St, Fort Smith, AR 72904
Tel.: (479) 441-3200
Web Site: http://www.carcotrans.com
Year Founded: 1930
Rev.: $36,023,825
Emp.: 25
Trucking Service
N.A.I.C.S.: 532120
Jim Cullen *(CFO)*
Rob Wiedenhoeft *(VP-Ops)*
Hulen Morton *(Mgr-Little Rock)*
Kenny Watts *(VP-Maintenance)*
Steve Hill *(Mgr-Oklahoma City)*
Carl D. Corley Sr. *(CEO)*

Subsidiaries:

Carco International, Inc. **(1)**
2721 Midland Blvd, Fort Smith, AR 72904
Tel.: (479) 441-3270
Web Site: http://www.carcoint.com
Truck Rental Services
N.A.I.C.S.: 532120

Carco Rentals, Inc. **(1)**
2905 N 32nd St, Fort Smith, AR 72904
Tel.: (479) 441-3200
Web Site: http://www.carcotrans.com
Sales Range: $10-24.9 Million
Industrial Truck Rental
N.A.I.C.S.: 532120

CARCO INTERNATIONAL, INC.

2721 Midland Blvd, Fort Smith, AR 72904-4208
Tel.: (479) 441-3270 **AR**
Web Site: http://www.carcoint.com
Year Founded: 1937
Sales Range: $10-24.9 Million
Emp.: 42
Retailer of Truck Tractors, Machinery & Equipment
N.A.I.C.S.: 423110
Patrick Jacobs *(Asst Gen Mgr)*

CARD SERVICES FOR CREDIT UNIONS, INC.

3031 N Rocky Point Dr W Ste 750, Tampa, FL 33607
Tel.: (813) 289-2728
Web Site: http://www.cscu.net
Year Founded: 1989
Sales Range: $1-9.9 Million
Emp.: 20
Financial Services
N.A.I.C.S.: 522299
Robert Hackney *(CEO)*
Bill Lehman *(Sr VP-Portfolio Consulting Svcs)*
Tom Davis *(Pres & COO)*
Patty Wisniewski *(VP-HR)*
Rod Staatz *(Vice Chm)*
Terry Leis *(Treas)*
Pat McPharlin *(Sec)*
Barry Shaner *(Chm)*

CARD-MONROE CORP.

4841 Adams Rd, Hixson, TN 37343
Tel.: (423) 842-3312
Web Site:
https://www.cardmonroe.com
Sales Range: $10-24.9 Million
Emp.: 190
Textile Machinery
N.A.I.C.S.: 333248

Charles Monroe *(Pres)*
Lewis Card *(Vice Chm)*
Brad Card *(VP-Sls)*

CARDATA, INC.

2745 E Atlantic Blvd Ste 302, Pompano Beach, FL 33062
Tel.: (754) 368-5845
Web Site: http://www.cardata.us
Year Founded: 2015
Sales Range: $1-9.9 Million
Emp.: 80
Advertising Agency Services
N.A.I.C.S.: 541810
John Finucane *(Mng Partner)*

CARDAX PHARMACEUTICALS, INC.

2800 Woodlawn Dr Ste 129, Honolulu, HI 96822
Tel.: (808) 457-1400 **DE**
Web Site:
https://www.cardaxpharma.com
Year Founded: 2006
Holding Company
N.A.I.C.S.: 551112
Nicholas Mitsakos *(Chm)*

Subsidiaries:

Cardax, Inc. **(1)**
2800 Woodlawn Dr Ste 129, Honolulu, HI 96822 **(52.9%)**
Tel.: (808) 457-1400
Web Site: https://www.cardaxpharma.com
Rev.: $538,946
Assets: $1,425,172
Liabilities: $11,623,168
Net Worth: ($10,197,996)
Earnings: ($5,055,507)
Emp.: 10
Fiscal Year-end: 12/31/2020
Holding Company; Pharmaceutical Developer
N.A.I.C.S.: 551112
David G. Watumull *(Founder, Pres & CEO)*
John B. Russell *(CFO & Treas)*
Gilbert M. Rishton *(Chief Science Officer)*
Timothy J. King *(VP-Res)*
Jon L. Ruckle *(Chief Medical Officer)*

Subsidiary (Domestic):

Cardax Pharma, Inc. **(2)**
2800 Woodlawn Dr Ste 129, Honolulu, HI 96822
Tel.: (808) 457-1400
Web Site: http://www.cardaxpharma.com
Pharmaceutical Developer
N.A.I.C.S.: 325412
Nicholas Mitsakos *(Chm)*

CARDCASH LLC

319 US Hwy 130 Ste 123, East Windsor, NJ 08520
Web Site: http://www.cardcash.com
Year Founded: 2008
Sales Range: $10-24.9 Million
Emp.: 28
Buys & Resells Consumers' Unwanted Gift Cards At A Discount
N.A.I.C.S.: 522210
Elliot Bohm *(Co-Founder & CEO)*
Marc Ackerman *(Co-Founder & COO)*
Alan Howitt *(VP-Fin)*
Raquel Abadi *(VP-Fin)*
Sara Erenthal *(VP-HR)*
Tom Ochoa *(Sr VP-Bus Dev)*

CARDEAN LEARNING GROUP, LLC

111 N Canal St Ste 455, Chicago, IL 60606-7204
Tel.: (312) 669-5222 **IL**
Year Founded: 1998
Sales Range: $1-9.9 Million
Emp.: 110
Online Business Courses
N.A.I.C.S.: 611699
Andrew M. Rosenfield *(Founder)*

CARDELL KITCHEN & BATH CABINETRY

3215 N Panam Expy, San Antonio, TX 78219
Tel.: (210) 225-0290
Web Site: http://www.vww1.com
Sales Range: $150-199.9 Million
Emp.: 2,000
Wood Kitchen Cabinets
N.A.I.C.S.: 337110
Bryan W. Tidwell *(CEO)*

CARDENAS MARKETING NETWORK INC.

1459 W Hubbard St, Chicago, IL 60642
Tel.: (312) 492-6424
Web Site: http://www.cmnevents.com
Year Founded: 2003
Sales Range: $25-49.9 Million
Emp.: 25
Theatrical Producers & Services
N.A.I.C.S.: 711320
Elena Sotomayor *(Exec VP-Mktg & Sls)*
Henry Cardenas *(Pres & CEO)*
Gus Trujillo *(Principal)*
Joshua Eagle Patron *(Exec Dir-Creative)*

CARDENAS MOTORS, INC.

1500 N Expy, Brownsville, TX 78521
Tel.: (956) 542-3541
Web Site:
https://www.cardenasautogroup.com
Sales Range: $25-49.9 Million
Emp.: 60
Car Whslr
N.A.I.C.S.: 441110
Renato Cardenas *(Founder)*
Andy Hagan *(Gen Mgr)*

CARDENAS PARTNERS, LLC

215 S Monroe Ste 602, Tallahassee, FL 32301
Tel.: (850) 222-8900
Web Site:
http://www.cardenaspartners.com
Sales Range: $1-9.9 Million
Emp.: 6
Governmental & Political Consulting Services
N.A.I.C.S.: 541618
Slater Bayliss *(Partner)*
Sarah Busk *(Dir-Government Affairs)*
Stephen Shiver Jr. *(Partner)*

CARDI CORPORATION

400 Lincoln Ave, Warwick, RI 02888-3049
Tel.: (401) 739-8300 **RI**
Web Site: https://www.cardi.com
Year Founded: 1967
Sales Range: $25-49.9 Million
Emp.: 250
Commercial Highway Construction Services
N.A.I.C.S.: 237310
Antonio B. Cardi *(Co-Founder & Pres)*
Stephen A. Cardi *(Co-Founder & Treas)*
Stephen A. Cardi II *(COO & Exec VP)*

Subsidiaries:

HOPKINS HILL SAND & STONE, LLC **(1)**
190 New London Tpke, West Greenwich, RI 02817
Tel.: (401) 392-0347
Web Site: http://www.cardi.com
Sand & Gravel Mining Services & Distr
N.A.I.C.S.: 212321

CARDIAC IMAGING SOLUTIONS, LLC

2403 Sidney St, Pittsburgh, PA 15203
Tel.: (610) 642-9500
Web Site:
http://www.tomaykogroup.com
Private Equity
N.A.I.C.S.: 523999
Susan Sullivan *(Exec Dir)*
Susan Sullivan *(Exec Dir)*

Subsidiaries:

Integrated Health 21 LLC **(1)**
2403 Sidney St, Ste 800, Pittsburgh, PA 15203
Tel.: (800) 451-6889
Web Site: https://integratedhealth21.com
Wellness & Fitness Services
N.A.I.C.S.: 713940

Subsidiary (Domestic):

Health Fitness Concepts RN, LLC **(2)**
45 Knollwood Rd Ste 200, Elmsford, NY 10523
Tel.: (914) 684-6064
Web Site: http://www.tryhfc.com
Sales Range: $1-9.9 Million
Emp.: 7
Ambulatory Health Care Services
N.A.I.C.S.: 621999
Kathy Freeman *(Founder & Pres)*

CARDIAC NETWORK, INC.

75180 Mediterranean Ste A-2, Palm Desert, CA 92211
Tel.: (760) 565-7336
Year Founded: 2004
Health Care Facility Services
N.A.I.C.S.: 621999
Malcolm Gulden *(Chm & CEO)*

CARDINAL ALUMINUM CO.

6910 Preston Hwy, Louisville, KY 40219-1810
Tel.: (502) 969-9302 **KY**
Web Site:
http://www.cardinalaluminum.com
Sales Range: $100-124.9 Million
Emp.: 290
Fabricated & Finished Aluminum Extrusion Mfr
N.A.I.C.S.: 331318

Subsidiaries:

Portland Willamette **(1)**
6800 NE 59th Pl, Portland, OR 97218-2714
Tel.: (503) 288-7511
Web Site: http://www.portwill.com
Sales Range: $10-24.9 Million
Emp.: 100
Mfr of Fireplace Appliances
N.A.I.C.S.: 332510

CARDINAL BANCORP INC.

7305 Manchester Rd, Saint Louis, MO 63143
Tel.: (314) 645-0666
Web Site: http://www.cnbstl.com
Rev.: $24,800,000
Emp.: 100
Bank Holding Company
N.A.I.C.S.: 551111
David Bentele *(Pres)*

Subsidiaries:

Citizens National Bank of Greater St Louis **(1)**
7305 Manchester Rd, Saint Louis, MO 63143
Tel.: (314) 645-0666
Web Site: http://www.cnbstl.com
Rev.: $22,030,000
Emp.: 76
National Commercial Banks
N.A.I.C.S.: 522110

Cardinal Bancorp Inc.—(Continued)

Timothy A. Rodden (Pres)
Eric Kappelmann (Sr VP-Comml Banking-St. Charles)
Colby Schmid (Sr VP)
Paul Van Stone (Sr VP-Comml Banking)

CARDINAL BUILDING MATERIALS, INC.

3634 Pennridge Dr, Bridgeton, MO 63044
Tel.: (314) 298-9090
Web Site: https://www.cardinal-building.com
Rev.: $19,400,000
Emp.: 30
Siding, Except Wood
N.A.I.C.S.: 423330
James Halpern (Pres)
Kevin Golden (Mgr-Pur)
Russ Eaton (Mgr-Roofing)

CARDINAL CARTRIDGE, INC.

2100 N 15th Ave, Elmhurst, IL 60126
Tel.: (630) 379-2525
Year Founded: 1995
Sales Range: $10-24.9 Million
Emp.: 85
Printer & Facsimile Cartridges Mfr
N.A.I.C.S.: 333310
John Carmine (Office Mgr)
Baltizar Marquez (Mgr-Production)
Mike Hatt (Mgr-Sls-Wholesale)

CARDINAL CHEMICALS INC.

1583 Hwy 258 S, Kinston, NC 28504
Tel.: (252) 523-1181
Web Site: http://cardinalchemicals.com
Sales Range: $10-24.9 Million
Emp.: 50
Chemicals, Agricultural
N.A.I.C.S.: 424910
Fred Worthington (VP)
Terry Kallam (Gen Mgr)

CARDINAL CHEVROLET CADILLAC

101 Cardinal Dr, Hazard, KY 41701
Tel.: (606) 436-2154
Web Site: http://www.cardinal-chevrolet-cadillac.com
Rev.: $30,000,000
Emp.: 39
Owner & Operator of Car Dealerships
N.A.I.C.S.: 441110
Larry Turner (Gen Mgr)
Frank Shoop (Pres)

CARDINAL COMMUNICATIONS, INC.

105 N 5th St #200, Canadian, TX 79014
Tel.: (806) 576-4882   NV
Sales Range: $25-49.9 Million
Emp.: 115
Wireless Internet Technology Services
N.A.I.C.S.: 517810
Ronald Bass (Principal Acctg Officer)
Edouard Garneau (Chm, Pres & CEO)

CARDINAL COMPONENTS INC.

145 Route 46 W, Wayne, NJ 07470
Tel.: (973) 785-1333
Web Site: http://www.cardinalxtal.com
Sales Range: $10-24.9 Million
Emp.: 18
Sales of Electronic Components
N.A.I.C.S.: 423690
Carl Fabend (Founder & Pres)

CARDINAL CONSTRUCTION INC.

531 Commercial St Ste 700, Waterloo, IA 50701-5443
Tel.: (319) 232-5400
Web Site: http://www.cardinalconst.com
Emp.: 135
Commercial & Office Building New Construction
N.A.I.C.S.: 236220
Angie Joerger (Mgr-Warehouse)
Dave Leonhart (VP)
Debbie Mattix (Asst Mgr-Bus)
Rachel Breuer (Project Mgr)
Brandon Schoborg (Project Mgr)

CARDINAL CUSHING CENTERS, INC.

405 Washington St, Hanover, MA 02339
Tel.: (781) 826-6371   MA
Web Site: http://www.cushingcenters.org
Year Founded: 1947
Sales Range: $10-24.9 Million
Emp.: 611
Community Welfare Services
N.A.I.C.S.: 525120
David Smith (Vice Chm)
Jansi Chandler (VP-Dev)
Jean Rogers (VP-Community & Adult Svcs)
Joanne Schatzlein (Dir-Corporate Ministry)
Michelle Markowitz (Pres & CEO)
Jeanine Mount (Co-Chm)
Jerry Vitti (Co-Chm)

CARDINAL ENERGY GROUP, INC.

14902 Preston Rd Ste 404-505, Dallas, TX 75254
Tel.: (325) 762-2112   NV
Web Site: http://www.cardinalenergy.com
Year Founded: 2007
CEGX—(OTCBB)
Oil & Gas Exploration & Production
N.A.I.C.S.: 211120
Stanley Robert Ford (CEO)
J. Richard Iler (CFO)

CARDINAL ENGINEERING CORPORATION

1 Moock Rd, Wilder, KY 41071
Tel.: (859) 581-9600
Web Site: https://www.cardinalengineering.net
Year Founded: 1968
Sales Range: $10-24.9 Million
Emp.: 20
Engineering Services
N.A.I.C.S.: 541330
Joseph G. Kramer (Pres-Engrg)
Kevin G. Hanson (VP)
Donald E. Stegman (VP)
Jeffrey S. Flaherty (VP-Engrg)

Subsidiaries:

Cardinal Engineering Corporation - Ohio   (1)
8072 Beechmont Ave, Cincinnati, OH 45255
Tel.: (513) 474-9950
Web Site: http://www.cardinalengineering.com
Emp.: 16
Engineering Services
N.A.I.C.S.: 541330
Joe Karmer (Pres)

CARDINAL EQUITY PARTNERS, LLC

280 E 96th St Ste 350, Indianapolis, IN 46240

Tel.: (317) 663-0205   IN
Web Site: http://www.cardinalep.com
Year Founded: 1993
Emp.: 6
Privater Equity Firm
N.A.I.C.S.: 523999
John F. Ackerman (Co-Founder & Mng Dir)
James L. Smeltzer (Co-Founder & Mng Dir)
Peter J. Munson (Co-Founder & Mng Dir)

CARDINAL ETHANOL, LLC

Tel.: (765) 964-3137   IN
Web Site: https://www.cardinalethanol.com
Year Founded: 2005
CRDE—(OTCIQ)
Rev.: $502,734,878
Assets: $232,768,247
Liabilities: $60,235,230
Net Worth: $172,533,017
Earnings: $69,818,591
Emp.: 72
Fiscal Year-end: 09/30/23
Methanol Mfr
N.A.I.C.S.: 325193
Robert John Davis (Chm)
Thomas E. Chalfant (Vice Chm)
Thomas C. Chronister (Sec)
Chad Lindow (Mgr-Process & Lab)
Bill Dartt (Pres, CFO, Chief Admin Officer, Chief HR Officer, Sec, Exec VP & Exec VP)
Jeremey Herlyn (Plant Mgr)
Casey Bruns (Mgr-Commodity)
Deanne McElhany (Mgr-EH&S)
Brian McEldowney (Mgr-Maintenance)
Chris Tucker (Mgr-Grain Ops)
Ashleigh Lawrence (Controller)
Jeff Painter (Pres & CEO)

CARDINAL GLASS COMPANY

1087 Research Pkwy, Rockford, IL 61105
Tel.: (815) 394-1400
Sales Range: $10-24.9 Million
Emp.: 25
Distribute & Install Glass Construction Materials
N.A.I.C.S.: 423390
Angelo Bruscato (Chm, Pres & CEO)

CARDINAL INDUSTRIAL FINISHES, INC.

1329 Potrero Ave, South El Monte, CA 91733
Tel.: (626) 444-9274   CA
Web Site: https://www.cardinalpaint.com
Year Founded: 1952
Sales Range: $25-49.9 Million
Emp.: 100
Paints & Allied Products
N.A.I.C.S.: 325510
Bob Daiker (Sls Mgr-Natl)
Mike Mitchinson (Exec Dir-Technical)
Pat Mathiesen (CFO)
Larry Felix (Pres & Exec Dir)

Subsidiaries:

Cardinal Industrial Finishes, Inc. - Powder Coating Manufacturing   (1)
15010 Don Julian Rd, City of Industry, CA 91746
Tel.: (626) 937-6767
Web Site: http://www.cardinalpaint.com
Sales Range: $10-24.9 Million
Emp.: 11
Paint & Coating Mfr
N.A.I.C.S.: 325510
Stan Ekstrom (Pres)
Keith Hocking (Mgr)

CARDINAL INDUSTRIES, INC.

19517 Riverside Dr, Grundy, VA 24614
Tel.: (276) 935-4545   VA
Web Site: https://www.cardinalcapjacket.com
Sales Range: $1-9.9 Million
Emp.: 4
Custom Screen Printed Apparel Mfr
N.A.I.C.S.: 323113

CARDINAL INDUSTRIES, INC.

724 Commerce St, Aberdeen, SD 57401-3312
Tel.: (605) 229-1015   MN
Web Site: https://www.cardinalmolding.com
Year Founded: 1972
Sales Range: $1-9.9 Million
Emp.: 82
Precision Plastic & Rubber Injected Molded Products Mfr
N.A.I.C.S.: 326199
Kary Harr (Mgr-Plant)

CARDINAL MACHINERY, INC.

7535 Appling Ctr Dr, Memphis, TN 38133
Tel.: (901) 377-3107
Web Site: http://www.cardinalmachinery.com
Sales Range: $10-24.9 Million
Emp.: 25
Supplier of Metalworking & Fabrication Equipment
N.A.I.C.S.: 423830
Steve M. Wherry (Pres)
Eddie Alexander (Mgr-Parts)

CARDINAL MANUFACTURING COMPANY, INC.

225 Eiler Ave, Louisville, KY 40214
Tel.: (502) 363-2661
Web Site: https://www.cardinalmfg.com
Year Founded: 1958
Sales Range: $10-24.9 Million
Emp.: 59
Rolled Steel Shape Mfr
N.A.I.C.S.: 331221
Eric Weisbach (Gen Mgr)

CARDINAL POINT MANAGEMENT, LLC

11300 4th St N Ste 250, Saint Petersburg, FL 33716
Tel.: (727) 577-4000
Web Site: http://www.cardinalpointmanage.com
Sales Range: $1-9.9 Million
Real Estate Investment & Property Management
N.A.I.C.S.: 523999
Gregory Williams (Co-Founder)
Rufus Williams IV (Co-Founder)

CARDINAL RESOURCES, INC.

201 Penn Center Blvd Ste 400, Pittsburgh, PA 15235
Tel.: (412) 374-0989   NV
Web Site: http://www.cardinalres.com
Year Founded: 2009
Environmental Services
N.A.I.C.S.: 541620
Kevin R. Jones (Pres & CEO)
Barbara H. Jones (Exec VP-Sustainable Sys)
Joyce M. O'Connor (Exec VP-Svcs)
Adam Kassab (CFO)

CARDINAL SCALE MANUFACTURING CO.

203 E Daugherty St, Webb City, MO 64870-1929
Tel.: (417) 673-4631   MO
Web Site: http://www.cardinalscale.com

Year Founded: 1956
Sales Range: $150-199.9 Million
Emp.: 420
Mfr of Scales & Weighing Devices
N.A.I.C.S.: 333998

Subsidiaries:

Detecto Scale Company   (1)
203 E Daugherty St, Webb City, MO
64870-1929   (100%)
Tel.: (417) 673-4631
Web Site: http://www.detectoscale.com
Sales Range: $50-74.9 Million
Emp.: 350
Beam & Digital Clinical Scales Mfr
N.A.I.C.S.: 333998
Fred Cox (VP-Sls)

CARDINAL SOLUTIONS GROUP, INC.

7755 Montgomery Rd Ste 510, Cincinnati, OH 45236
Tel.: (513) 984-6700
Web Site:
http://www.cardinalsolutions.com
Year Founded: 1996
Sales Range: $10-24.9 Million
Emp.: 300
Computer System Design Services
N.A.I.C.S.: 541512
Kelly D. Conway (Pres)
Jim Milam (VP-Sls-East Region)
Nick Peterson (VP-Sls-Central Region)
Chris Galligan (Dir-Sls)

CARDINAL TRANSPORT INC.

7180 East Reed Rd PO Box 6, Coal City, IL 60416
Tel.: (815) 634-4443
Web Site:
http://www.cardinaltransport.com
Sales Range: $50-74.9 Million
Emp.: 54
Contract Haulers
N.A.I.C.S.: 484121
Claudette Schmitt (Exec VP-Admin)
Tom Hicks (VP-Sls)
Kay Riley (Treas & Sec)
Greg Rouskey (Dir-Safety, Accidents, Claims & Insurance)
James Mikula (Exec VP-Ops)
Wendy Mikula (VP & Office Mgr)
Tom Nahas (Mgr-Info Sys)

CARDINALE AUTOMOTIVE GROUP

2 Heitzinger Plz, Seaside, CA 93955
Tel.: (831) 394-1233
Web Site:
http://www.cardinaleway.com
Sales Range: $25-49.9 Million
Emp.: 200
New & Used Car Dealers Service
N.A.I.C.S.: 441110
Joe Cardinale (Pres)

CARDIODX, INC.

2500 Faber Pl, Palo Alto, CA 94303
Tel.: (650) 475-2788   DE
Web Site: http://www.cardiodx.com
Year Founded: 2003
Sales Range: $1-9.9 Million
Emp.: 138
Cardiovascular Genomic Diagnostics
N.A.I.C.S.: 339112
David L. Levison (Founder & Chief Strategy Officer)
Mark Monane (Chief Medical Officer)
Susan Daniels (VP-Bus Dev)
Timothy Henn (CFO)
Khush Mehta (Pres & CEO)

CARDIOVASCULAR BIO-THERAPEUTICS, INC.

9500 Hillwood Dr Ste 200, Las Vegas, NV 89134

Tel.: (702) 839-7200   DE
Web Site: http://www.cvbt.com
Sales Range: Less than $1 Million
Emp.: 22
Biopharmaceutical Mfr
N.A.I.C.S.: 541713
Mickael A. Flaa (Pres & CFO)
Jon S. Ross (Sec)
Ori Ben-Yehuda (Chief Medical Officer)
Calvin A. Wallen III (Chm)

CARDIOVASCULAR CARE GROUP, INC.

3322 W End Ave Ste1100, Nashville, TN 37203
Tel.: (615) 515-9880
Web Site:
http://www.cardiovascularcare.com
Cardiovascular Inpatient & Ambulatory Services
N.A.I.C.S.: 621999
Harry R. Jacobson (Chm)
Steven T. Johnson (Pres)
Robert K. Stillwell (CFO)
Warren E. Beck (CEO)

Subsidiaries:

Bakersfield Heart Hospital   (1)
3001 Sillect Ave, Bakersfield, CA
93308   (53.31%)
Tel.: (661) 316-6000
Web Site:
http://www.bakersfieldhearthospital.com
Sales Range: $50-74.9 Million
Emp.: 400
Hospital Specializing in Cardiovascular Services
N.A.I.C.S.: 622310
Wafa El-Musselmani (VP-Clinical Svcs)
Brij Bhambi (Head-Central Cardiology)

Louisiana Heart Hospital, LLC   (1)
64030 Louisiana Hwy 434, Lacombe, LA
70445   (89.2%)
Tel.: (985) 690-7500
Web Site: http://www.louisianaheart.com
Sales Range: $50-74.9 Million
Cardiovascular Services
N.A.I.C.S.: 622310
Roy Wright (CEO)
Ginny Crow (Chief Nursing Officer)

CARDIOVASCULAR RESEARCH FOUNDATION

111 E 59th St 11th Fl, New York, NY 10022-1202
Tel.: (646) 434-4500   NY
Web Site: http://www.crf.org
Year Founded: 1991
Sales Range: $25-49.9 Million
Emp.: 176
Cardiovascular Disease Research Services
N.A.I.C.S.: 813212
Donald L. Abrams (Chief Legal Officer)
Gary S. Mintz (Chief Medical Officer)
Juan F. Granada (Pres & CEO)
Eric B. Woldenberg (Chm)
Martin B. Leon (Founder)
Gregg W. Stone (Co-Dir-Medical Res & Education)
David J. Cohen (Dir-Clinical & Outcomes Res)

CARDOLITE CORPORATION

500 Doremus Ave, Newark, NJ 07105
Tel.: (973) 344-5015
Web Site: http://www.cardolite.com
Year Founded: 1985
Sales Range: $10-24.9 Million
Emp.: 90
Mfr of Industrial Organic Chemicals
N.A.I.C.S.: 325199
Chris Ford (Mgr-QA)
Shailendra Bhatkhande (VP-Ops-Global)
Peter Morales (CFO)
Anbu Natesh (VP-R&D-Global)

CARDONE INDUSTRIES, INC.

5501 Whitaker Ave, Philadelphia, PA 19124
Tel.: (215) 912-3000   PA
Web Site: https://www.cardone.com
Year Founded: 1970
Sales Range: $350-399.9 Million
Emp.: 4,000
Remanufactured & New Motor Vehicle Parts & Accessories Supplier
N.A.I.C.S.: 336390
Michael Cardone III (CEO)

CARDOW JEWELERS

5195 Dronningens Gade Ste 1, Saint Thomas, VI 00802
Tel.: (340) 776-1140
Web Site: http://www.cardow.com
Jewelry Stores
N.A.I.C.S.: 458310
Odile Delyrot (VP & Dir-Merchandising)

CARDWORKS, INC.

101 Crossways Pk Dr W, Woodbury, NY 11797
Tel.: (516) 576-0404
Web Site: http://www.cardworks.com
Year Founded: 1987
Sales Range: $50-74.9 Million
Emp.: 600
Credit Card Processing, Origination & Collection Services
N.A.I.C.S.: 561440
Donald M. Berman (Chm & CEO)
John G. Strong (CIO & Exec VP-Info Sys & Tech)
Robert Perro (Vice Chm)

Subsidiaries:

CardWorks Servicing, LLC   (1)
101 Crossways Parkwest, Woodbury, NY
11797
Tel.: (516) 576-0404
Web Site: http://www.cms-lp.com
Rev.: $11,300,000
Emp.: 50
Adjustment & Collection Services
N.A.I.C.S.: 561440
Donald M. Berman (Chm & CEO)

Subsidiary (Domestic):

Dataline Systems, LLC   (2)
2709 Pemberton Dr, Apopka, FL 32703
Tel.: (407) 298-1234
Web Site: http://www.datalinesys.com
Rev.: $1,224,000
Emp.: 8
Data Processing, Hosting & Related Services
N.A.I.C.S.: 518210
Collin York (Founder)

Merrick Bank Corporation   (1)
10705 South Jordan Gateway, South Jordan, UT 84095
Tel.: (801) 545-6600
Web Site: http://www.merrickcd.com
Rev.: $7,700,000
Emp.: 240
Credit Card Services, Central Agency Collection
N.A.I.C.S.: 522320
Rick Lake (Pres)

CARE DIMENSIONS

75 Sylvan St Ste B102, Danvers, MA 01923
Tel.: (978) 774-7566   MA
Web Site:
https://www.caredimensions.org
Year Founded: 1979
Sales Range: $25-49.9 Million
Community Support Services
N.A.I.C.S.: 624190
Carmelina Procaccini (VP-HR & Community Programs)
Lyn Skarmeas (VP-Bus Dev)
Phil Cibelli (CFO & VP)
Judy Cranney (COO & VP)

Stephanie Patel (Chief Medical Officer & VP)
Nicole Foxe (Coord-Education)
Patricia Ahern (Pres & CEO)
Donna Deveau (VP-Philanthropy)

CARE INITIATIVES

1611 W Lakes Pkwy, West Des Moines, IA 50266
Tel.: (515) 224-4442   TX
Web Site:
https://www.careinitiatives.org
Year Founded: 1989
Sales Range: $150-199.9 Million
Emp.: 4,520
Nursing & Assisted Living Services
N.A.I.C.S.: 623312
William P. Havekost (VP-Care Initiatives Hospice)
Charleen A. Schlepp (VP & Dir-Ops)
Dave Dixon (CFO & VP)

CARE LINE INDUSTRIES INC.

2210 Lake Rd, Greenbrier, TN 37073-4626
Tel.: (615) 643-4797
Web Site:
https://www.carelineinc.com
Rev.: $24,100,000
Emp.: 60
Hospital Equipment & Supplies
N.A.I.C.S.: 423450
David Love (CEO)
Becky Hitchens (Mgr-Customer Svc)

CARE MEDICAL EQUIPMENT INCORPORATED

1877 NE 7th Ave, Portland, OR 97212
Tel.: (503) 288-8174
Web Site:
http://www.caremedical.com
Sales Range: $10-24.9 Million
Emp.: 300
Medical Apparatus & Supplies
N.A.I.C.S.: 456199
Donald H. Adler (Pres)

CARE NEW ENGLAND HEALTH SYSTEM, INC.

45 Willard Ave, Providence, RI 02905
Tel.: (401) 453-7900   RI
Web Site:
http://www.carenewengland.org
Year Founded: 1996
Emp.: 8,210
Hospital & Health System Association
N.A.I.C.S.: 813920
Joseph Iannoni (CFO, Exec VP & Asst Treas)
Alyssa V. Boss (Asst Sec)
James E. Fanale (Pres & CEO)
Kathleen Peirce (Chief Nursing Officer, Exec Dir & VP-Ops-VNA)
Charles R. Reppucci (Chm)
Gary E. Furtado (Co-Vice Chm)
Maribeth Q. Williamson (Co-Vice Chm)
Douglas Jacobs (Treas)
James A. Botvin (Sec)
Tish Devaney (Chief HR Officer & VP)
Ashley Taylor (Gen Counsel)
Mae Medeiros (VP-CNE Laboratory Svcs)
Gary Speciale (VP-CNE Risk Mgmt)
Matt Quin (Pres/COO-Women & Infants Hospital)
Raymond O. Powrie (Chief Clinical Officer)

CARE PLUS NJ, INC.

610 Valley Health Plz, Paramus, NJ 07652
Tel.: (201) 265-8200   NJ
Web Site: http://www.careplusnj.org

Care Plus NJ, Inc.—(Continued)

Year Founded: 1978
Sales Range: $25-49.9 Million
Emp.: 684
Mental Health Care Services
N.A.I.C.S.: 621420
Brigitte Johnson *(Sr VP-Corp Affairs)*
Tara Augustine *(Sr VP-Children & Family Svcs)*
Joe Masciandaro *(Pres & CEO)*
N. Jeremy Piccini *(Chm)*
Jerry Joseph *(VP-Addiction Medicine)*
Daniel Finch *(Chief Medical Officer)*
Tanya Lewis *(VP-Psychiatry)*
Katherine Coleman *(VP-Addiction Recovery Svcs)*
Ann Marie Zihal *(Sr VP-Clinical Svcs)*

CARE WISCONSIN FIRST, INC.
1617 Sherman Ave, Madison, WI 53704
Tel.: (608) 240-0020
Web Site: http://www.carewisc.org
Year Founded: 1976
Sales Range: $150-199.9 Million
Disability Assistance Services
N.A.I.C.S.: 624120
Myra Enloe *(Asst VP-Performance Excellence)*
Ken Eimers *(COO & CIO)*
Karen Musser *(Pres & CEO)*
Amy Ackermann *(VP-HR)*
Susan Crowley *(Sr VP-Govt Svcs)*

CARE-A-LOT PET SUPPLY
1617 Diamond Springs Rd, Virginia Beach, VA 23455
Tel.: (757) 460-9771
Web Site:
  https://www.carealotpets.com
Year Founded: 1988
Rev.: $10,300,000
Emp.: 90
Veterinary Products Whslr
N.A.I.C.S.: 459910
Robert Clarke *(Pres)*
Denise Clarke *(VP)*
Colleen Larkin *(Reg Mgr-Aquatics)*

CARE-USA
151 Ellis St NE, Atlanta, GA 30303
Web Site: https://www.care.org
Year Founded: 1945
Human Rights Organization Services
N.A.I.C.S.: 813311

CAREAGE INC.
4411 Point Fosdick Dr NW Ste 203, Gig Harbor, WA 98335
Tel.: (253) 432-8113
Web Site: https://www.careage.com
Sales Range: $10-24.9 Million
Emp.: 15
Operative Builders
N.A.I.C.S.: 236117
Gene E. Lynn *(Owner)*

CAREATC
4500 S 129th E Ave Ste 191, Tulsa, OK 74134-5891
Tel.: (800) 993-8244
Web Site: http://www.careatc.com
Year Founded: 2000
Sales Range: $10-24.9 Million
Emp.: 55
Health Insurance & Related Services to Public & Private Sector Employers
N.A.I.C.S.: 524298
Ron Woods *(Founder)*
Greg Bellomy *(CEO)*
Paul Keeling *(Chief Bus Dev Officer)*
Kim Hutton *(Chief Medical Officer)*
Jay Jackson *(CFO)*
Jackie Hope *(Dir-Quality)*
Wendy White *(Dir-Client & Clinical Svcs)*

Ann Stoeppelwerth *(Chief Engagement Solutions Officer)*
Jeremy Cavness *(Dir-Mktg)*
Keith Gucwa *(Dir-Facilities)*
Melissa Mata *(Dir-HR)*
Rusty Wyrick *(VP-IT)*
Vickie Rice *(Dir-Analytics)*
Scott Strickland *(Pres & COO)*
Lisa Ness *(Chief Revenue Officer)*

CARECALL INC.
200 14th Ave E, Sartell, MN 56377
Tel.: (320) 253-0800
Web Site: http://www.arraysg.com
Year Founded: 1991
Sales Range: $10-24.9 Million
Emp.: 250
Provides Customer Satisfaction Calls to Service-Based Companies
N.A.I.C.S.: 561421
Chuck Engebretson *(CFO)*
Matt Schmit *(Pres)*

CARECLIX HOLDINGS, INC.
1709 N Harbor City Blvd Ste 520, Melbourne, FL 32935
Tel.: (703) 832-4473
Year Founded: 2004
Rev.: $1,521,371
Assets: $2,081,076
Liabilities: $13,001,556
Net Worth: ($10,920,480)
Earnings: ($22,372,128)
Emp.: 20
Fiscal Year-end: 12/31/19
Holding Company
N.A.I.C.S.: 551112
Charles O. Scott *(Chm, CEO & CFO)*

CAREEN, INC.
15 Somsen St, New Ulm, MN 56073
Tel.: (507) 233-2034
Web Site: http://www.windings.com
Motor & Generator Mfr
N.A.I.C.S.: 335312
Nancy Patterson *(Mgr-Quality)*

Subsidiaries:

Pacific Magnetics Inc.   (1)
87 E Georgina St, Chula Vista, CA 91910-2208
Tel.: (619) 872-0343
Web Site: https://yoda.lexisai.aws.lexis.com
Relay & Industrial Control Mfr
N.A.I.C.S.: 335314
Marianne Hill *(CEO)*

CAREER CONCEPTS STAFFING SERVICES, INC.
4934 Peach St Ste 101, Erie, PA 16509
Tel.: (814) 868-2333
Web Site:
  https://www.careerconceptsinc.com
Sales Range: $10-24.9 Million
Emp.: 25
Employment Agencies
N.A.I.C.S.: 561311
Colleen Jennings *(Gen Mgr)*

CAREER GROUP INC.
10100 Santa Monica Blvd Ste 900, Los Angeles, CA 90067
Tel.: (310) 277-8188
Web Site:
  http://www.careergroupinc.com
Year Founded: 1981
Sales Range: $10-24.9 Million
Emp.: 2,000
Executive Placement
N.A.I.C.S.: 541612
Danie Dorinson *(Sr VP)*
Harry Levenson *(Controller)*
Kelly Alzer *(Acct Mgr)*

CAREER HORIZONS, INC.

5305 Lakeview Pkwy S Dr, Indianapolis, IN 46268-4113
Tel.: (317) 216-2240
Web Site:
  http://www.teleservicesdirect.com
Sales Range: $10-24.9 Million
Emp.: 1,000
Telemarketing Services
N.A.I.C.S.: 561422
Patricia Totton *(CEO)*
Dave Smith *(COO)*
Anthony Vesho *(COO)*

Subsidiaries:

TSD Global Inc.   (1)
4th floor 8/10 building Upper McKinley Hill, Fort Bonifacio, Taguig, Philippines
Tel.: (63) 28468226
Telemarketing Services
N.A.I.C.S.: 561422
Gina Valencia *(Mgr-Ops)*

TeleServices Direct   (1)
5305 Lakeview Pkwy S Dr, Indianapolis, IN 46268
Tel.: (317) 216-2240
Web Site: http://www.teleservicesdirect.com
Sales Range: $10-24.9 Million
Emp.: 25
Provider of Telemarketing Services
N.A.I.C.S.: 561422
Patricia Totton *(Co-CEO)*
Steve Lair *(Chief Admin Officer)*
Dean Weathers *(CIO)*
Adam Berkson *(Co-CEO)*
Steve Knight *(Sr VP-Client Svcs)*
Matt Miller *(VP-Fin)*
Mike Novak *(CTO)*
Anthony Vesho *(COO)*
Megan Wilson *(Sr VP-Client Svcs)*

CAREER MANAGEMENT PARTNERS
2435 N Central Expy Ste 830, Richardson, TX 75080
Tel.: (972) 680-9200
Web Site: http://careermp.com
Rev.: $1,020,000
Emp.: 6
Administrative Management & General Management Consulting Service
N.A.I.C.S.: 541611
Kathy Johnson *(Dir-Client Svcs)*
Keith O. Nave *(Founder)*
Susan Glen *(Sr VP-Client Rels)*
Bruce Weaver *(VP)*
Charlie Zinger *(VP)*
Claire Letard Heap *(Dir-Res)*
Dick Ulrich *(Sr VP)*
Joe Frodsham *(Pres)*
Robert Elam *(Mng Dir)*
Jackie Chabot *(Chief Client Officer)*
Maryanne Piña *(CEO)*

Subsidiaries:

Quest Management Consultants, Inc   (1)
6 Cardinal Wy Ste 900, Saint Louis, MO 63102-2807
Tel.: (314) 453-9999
Web Site: http://www.questmc.com
Administrative Management & General Management Consulting Services
N.A.I.C.S.: 541611
Gerald Wiley *(Pres)*

CAREER PATH TRAINING CORP.
11300 4th St N Ste 200, Saint Petersburg, FL 33716-2940
Tel.: (813) 831-4490
Web Site:
  http://www.careerpathtraining.com
Rev.: $15,000,000
Emp.: 15
Vocational Training Services
N.A.I.C.S.: 611430
Eric Brantley *(Supvr-Collections)*
Kenneth Whittington *(VP-School Ops)*
Rose Lynn Greene *(Dir-Compliance)*
Heidi McMahon *(Mgr-Trng)*

Subsidiaries:

Roadmaster Drivers School of Tampa, Inc.   (1)
5025 Orient Rd, Tampa, FL 33610
Tel.: (813) 626-2400
Web Site: http://www.roadmaster.com
Truck Driver Training
N.A.I.C.S.: 551112
Ken Whittington *(VP)*
Aura Hall *(Dir-School)*

CAREER TRAINING CONCEPTS, INC.
3640-A Hewatt Ct, Snellville, GA 30039
Tel.: (770) 326-9229
Web Site:
  http://www.careertrainingconcepts.com
Year Founded: 1973
Rev.: $11,200,000
Emp.: 14
Temporary Help Service
N.A.I.C.S.: 561320
Matthew D. Morgan *(VP)*
James C. Shafe *(Pres)*

CAREERLINK, INC.
12750 Merit Dr Bldg VII Ste 1015, Dallas, TX 75251
Tel.: (214) 987-1600
Year Founded: 2000
Sales Range: $1-9.9 Million
Emp.: 20
Staffing & Recruiting Services
N.A.I.C.S.: 561311
Charlie Quinn *(Mng Partner-Dallas)*
Suzanne Collins *(Founder & CEO)*
Denise Madrid *(Mng Partner-Houston)*

CAREERS IN TRANSITION, INC.
2181 Northlake Pkwy, Tucker, GA 30084
Tel.: (770) 414-1026
Web Site: http://www.career-transition.com
Year Founded: 1995
Sales Range: $1-9.9 Million
Emp.: 20
Human Resource Consulting Services
N.A.I.C.S.: 541612
Indigo Triplet *(CEO)*

CAREERSOURCE BREVARD
295 Barnes Blvd, Rockledge, FL 32955
Tel.: (321) 504-7600
Web Site:
  https://www.careersourcebrevard.com
Year Founded: 1990
Sales Range: $10-24.9 Million
Emp.: 35
Workforce Development Services
N.A.I.C.S.: 561311
Jeff Witt *(Mgr-IT)*
Carol Macrander *(Mgr-Aerospace Project)*
Judy Blanchard *(Dir-Indus Rels)*
Richard Meagher *(Dir-Fin Dept)*
Marci Brilley *(VP-Ops)*
Denise Biondi *(Dir-Comm)*
Lyn Sevin *(Mgr-Exec Office)*
Jenn Breitfeller *(First VP)*
Jennifer Lasser *(Mgr-Bus Svcs)*

CAREERSUSA, INC.
6501 Congress Ave Ste 200, Boca Raton, FL 33487-2840
Tel.: (561) 995-7000
Web Site:
  https://www.careersusa.com
Year Founded: 1981
Sales Range: $100-124.9 Million
Emp.: 15,000

Temporary Employment Services
N.A.I.C.S.: 561311
Marnie Bauman *(Sr VP-Admin)*
John Gommel *(CIO)*
Marilyn J. Ounjian *(Chm & CEO)*

CAREERXCHANGE, INC.
10689 N Kendall Dr Ste 209, Miami, FL 33176
Tel.: (305) 595-3800   FL
Web Site:
   https://www.careerxchange.com
Year Founded: 1988
Sales Range: $1-9.9 Million
Emp.: 50
Employment Placement Services
N.A.I.C.S.: 561311
Sue Romanos *(Pres)*

Subsidiaries:

Careerxchange, Inc.   (1)
9050 Pines Blvd Ste 150, Pembroke Pines, FL 33024
Tel.: (954) 437-0070
Web Site: http://www.careerxchange.com
Employment Placement Services
N.A.I.C.S.: 561311

CAREFIRST, INC.
10455 Mill Run Cir, Owings Mills, MD 21117
Tel.: (410) 581-3000
Web Site: http://www.carefirst.com
Sales Range: $1-4.9 Billion
Healtcare Services
N.A.I.C.S.: 923120
G. Mark Chaney *(Sr VP)*
Harry Fox *(Exec VP)*
Maria Tildon *(Sr VP)*
Meryl Burgin *(Sr VP)*
David S. Cohen *(Exec VP-Health Svcs)*
Fred Plumb *(Exec VP)*
Gwendolyn D. Skillern *(Exec VP)*
M. Bruce Edwards *(Exec VP)*
Steve Margolis *(Exec VP)*
Usha Nakhasi *(Exec VP)*
Wanda Oneferu-Bey *(Exec VP)*
Jennifer Baldwin *(Sr VP)*
Michelle Wright *(Sr VP)*
Peter Berry *(Sr VP)*
Destiny-Simone Ramjohn *(VP-Community Health & Social impact)*

Subsidiaries:

CareFirst of Maryland, Inc.   (1)
10455 and 10453 Mill Run Cir, Owings Mills, MD 21117-4208
Tel.: (410) 581-3000
Web Site: http://www.individual.carefirst.com
Sales Range: $100-124.9 Million
Emp.: 500
Not-For-Profit Managed Health Company
N.A.I.C.S.: 524114
Stephen L. Waechter *(Chm)*
Brian D. Pieninck *(Pres & CEO)*
Rahul Rajkumar *(Chief Medical Officer & Sr VP)*

Subsidiary (Domestic):

Capital Area Service Co. Inc.   (2)
200 Kanawha Blvd E, Charleston, WV 25301-2511
Tel.: (304) 346-3800
Web Site: http://www.cascicareers.com
Provides Claims Processing & Customer Service
N.A.I.C.S.: 524114

CareFirst Administrators   (2)
1501 S Clinton St Ste 700, Baltimore, MD 21224-5744
Tel.: (800) 853-9236
Web Site: http://www.carefirst.com
Sales Range: $100-124.9 Million
Self-Insured Group Accounts Services
N.A.I.C.S.: 525120

CareFirst BlueCross BlueShield   (2)
841 1st St NE, Washington, DC 20065-0001

Tel.: (202) 479-8000
Web Site: http://www.carefirst.com
Sales Range: $100-124.9 Million
Emp.: 280
Not-For-Profit Managed Health Company Which Along With Its Affiliates & Subsidiary Offer A Comprehensive Portfolio of Health Insurance Product Direct Health Care & Administrative Services
N.A.I.C.S.: 524128
Greg Mark Chaney *(CFO & Exec VP)*
Daniel J. Winn *(Chief Medical Officer & VP)*
David J. Corkum *(Exec VP-Comml Large/Mid & CFA)*
John David Kaercher *(CIO & Exec VP-Info Tech & Ops)*
Maria Harris Tildon *(Exec VP-Pub Policy & Govt Affairs)*
Meryl Burgin *(Gen Counsel, Sec & Exec VP-Legal Div)*
Rose Megian *(Exec VP-Comml Individual/Small & Specialty)*
Stacia A. Cohen *(Exec VP-Medical Affairs)*
David Schwartz *(VP-Pub Policy & Federal Affairs)*

CareFirst BlueCross BlueShield, Claims Center   (2)
7 Commerce Dr, Cumberland, MD 21502
Tel.: (724) 824-8001
Web Site: http://www.carefirst.com
Sales Range: $25-49.9 Million
Emp.: 120
Health Insurance Provider
N.A.I.C.S.: 621491

National Capital Administrative Services Inc.   (2)
3060 Williams Dr Ste 200, Fairfax, VA 22031
Tel.: (703) 934-6200
Web Site: http://www.ncas.com
Sales Range: $75-99.9 Million
Emp.: 80
Offers Third Party Administrative Services
N.A.I.C.S.: 524114

Potomac Physicians Practice Association   (2)
1829 Reisterstown Rd Ste 205, Pikesville, MD 21208
Tel.: (410) 602-9850
Web Site:
   http://www.potomacphysicians.com
Sales Range: $10-24.9 Million
Emp.: 25
Association of Medical Care Providers
N.A.I.C.S.: 622110

CAREFLITE
3110 S Great SW Pkwy, Grand Prairie, TX 75052
Tel.: (972) 339-4200
Web Site: http://www.careflite.org
Rev.: $15,000,000
Emp.: 15
Medical Transport Services
N.A.I.C.S.: 481219
Jan Cody *(VP-Clinical Svcs)*
Mark Kessler *(Sr Dir-Ground Ops & Comm)*
Larry Laforce *(Dir-Aircraft Maintenance)*
Kelly Wolfe *(Mgr-Education & Quality Mgmt)*
Jim Swartz *(Pres & CEO)*
Russell Kyler *(CFO & VP)*
Kevin Reynolds *(VP-Air Clinical Ops)*
Mark Davis *(CIO & Dir-IT)*
Amy Young *(Dir-Ground Ops-West)*
Robert Simonson *(Dir-Medical)*
Frank Wright *(Dir-Safety & Risk Mgmt)*
C. J. Trujillo *(Mgr-Comm & Ops)*
Doak Enabnit *(Sr Dir-Community & Govt Affairs)*
Doug Filbert *(VP-Ground Ops & Comm)*

CAREFREE INDUSTRIES, INC.
717 N Hammonds Ferry Rd Ste K, Linthicum Heights, MD 21090
Tel.: (410) 636-6383

Web Site:
   https://www.carefreeindustries.com
Sales Range: $10-24.9 Million
Emp.: 34
Custom Cabinet & Custom Kitchen Fixtures Mfr
N.A.I.C.S.: 423210
Jik Yousefi *(Pres)*

CAREFREE RV RESORTS
6991 Camelback Rd Ste B-310, Scottsdale, AZ 85251
Tel.: (480) 423-5700
Web Site:
   http://www.carefreervresorts.com
Year Founded: 2005
RV Resorts & Manufactured Home Properties
N.A.I.C.S.: 721211
Colleen Edwards *(Pres)*
Charles Ellis *(VP-Acq)*
Greg Barton *(VP)*

CAREGIVER, INC.
4800 Overton Plz Ste 440, Fort Worth, TX 76109
Tel.: (800) 299-5161
Web Site: http://www.cg-idd.com
Developmental Disabilities Long Term Care Services
N.A.I.C.S.: 621498
Mark Lashley *(CEO)*
Kathy Schaaf *(Chief People Officer)*

Subsidiaries:

Mosaic   (1)
4980 S 118th St, Omaha, NE 68137
Web Site: http://www.mosaicinfo.org
Sales Range: $200-249.9 Million
Intellectual Disabled People Assistance Services
N.A.I.C.S.: 561110
Keith Hohly *(Sec)*
Lisa Negstad *(Chm)*
Kathy Patrick *(Vice Chm)*
Linda Timmons *(Pres & CEO)*
Raul Saldivar *(COO)*
Keith Schmode *(Sr VP)*
Donna Werner *(Sr VP-Advocacy)*
Scott Hoffman *(CFO & Sr VP)*
Mike Lyons *(Gen Counsel & Sr VP)*
Renee Coughlin *(Sr VP-Mission Advancement)*
Sue Loerts *(Sr VP-HR)*
Wanda Winfree *(Chief Integrity Officer)*

CAREGROUP, INC.
109 Brookline Dr Ste 300, Boston, MA 02215
Tel.: (617) 667-1715   MA
Web Site: http://www.caregroup.org
Sales Range: $1-4.9 Billion
Emp.: 13,000
Hospital & Health Care Service Operator
N.A.I.C.S.: 622110
John Szum *(CFO & Exec VP)*
Robert Melzer *(Chm)*
Linda Sleeper *(Head-Ops)*

Subsidiaries:

Beth Israel Deaconess Medical Center   (1)
330 Brookline Ave, Boston, MA 02215-5400
Tel.: (617) 667-7000
Web Site: http://www.bidmc.harvard.edu
Sales Range: $1-4.9 Billion
Emp.: 7,600
Hospital Services
N.A.I.C.S.: 622110
John D. Halamka *(CIO & Sr VP-Info Sys)*
Steve Fischer *(CFO & Sr VP-Fin)*
Jerry Berger *(Dir-Media Rels)*
Kevin Tabb *(CEO)*
Daniel Jick *(Chm)*
Nancy Formella *(COO)*
Marsha Maurer *(Chief Nursing Officer & Sr VP-Patient Care Svcs)*

Carol Anderson *(Sec)*
Peter Healy *(Pres)*
Anthony Weiss *(Chief Medical Officer)*

CAREHERE, LLC
5141 Virginia Way Ste 350, Brentwood, TN 37027
Tel.: (615) 221-6152
Web Site: http://www.carehere.com
Year Founded: 2004
Emp.: 132
Health Care Srvices
N.A.I.C.S.: 621610
Lee Anglea *(VP-Pur & Facilities Mgmt)*
Michelle Anglea *(Chief Clinical Officer & Sr VP)*
Ben Baker *(COO)*
Ernie Clevenger *(Pres & CEO)*
Anthony V. Dallas Jr. *(Chief Medical Officer)*

CARELINK COMMUNITY SUPPORT SERVICES
1510 Chester Pike Ste 600, Eddystone, PA 19022
Tel.: (610) 874-1119   PA
Web Site:
   http://www.carelinkservices.org
Year Founded: 1981
Sales Range: $10-24.9 Million
Emp.: 408
Community Action Services
N.A.I.C.S.: 624190
Gary Woomer *(VP-Ops)*

CARENET
11845 Interstate 10 W, San Antonio, TX 78230
Tel.: (210) 595-2200   TX
Web Site: http://www.callcarenet.com
Year Founded: 1988
Sales Range: $10-24.9 Million
Emp.: 216
Patient Medical Care Coordination & Management
N.A.I.C.S.: 456199
John Erwin *(CEO)*
Vikie Spulak *(COO)*
Scott Schawe *(CFO)*
Jane Binzak *(VP-People Svcs)*
D. J. Toms *(VP-Tech Svcs)*
Kristin Blasko *(VP-Solution Strategy & Innovation)*
Jill Campbell *(VP-Workforce Plng & Analysis)*
Rick Hineline *(VP-Support Svcs)*
Frank I. Hoppe *(Gen Counsel)*
Kathy Lozano *(VP-Clinical Svcs)*
Mick Mazour *(Pres)*
Tom Nagle *(Exec VP-Sls & Mktg)*
Frank Schilling *(VP-Ops)*
Stacie Stoner *(VP-Customer Experience)*

CARENEX HEALTH SERVICES
15477 Ventura Blvd Ste LL, Sherman Oaks, CA 91403
Tel.: (818) 205-2500
Web Site: http://www.carenex.com
Sales Range: $10-24.9 Million
Emp.: 19
Healthcare Technology & Client Services
N.A.I.C.S.: 621399
Pejman Salimpour *(Founder, Pres & CEO)*
Pedram Salimpour *(Founder & Sr VP)*
Karen O'Sullivan *(Mgr-Neonatal ICU Case)*

Subsidiaries:

Plymouth Health   (1)
15477 Ventura Blvd Ste LL, Sherman Oaks, CA 91403

CareNex Health Services—(Continued)
Tel.: (818) 205-2500
Medical Investment Company
N.A.I.C.S.: 523999

CAREOREGON, INC.
315 SW 5th Ave Ste 900, Portland,
OR 97204
Tel.: (503) 416-1415   OR
Web Site: http://www.careoregon.org
Year Founded: 1994
Sales Range: $550-599.9 Million
Emp.: 475
Community Health Care Services
N.A.I.C.S.: 621498
Chantay Reid *(Exec Dir-HR)*
Amit Shah *(Chief Medical Officer)*
Teresa Learn *(CFO)*
Eric C. Hunter *(CEO)*
Greg Morgan *(Chief Network Officer)*
Amy Dowd *(COO)*

CAREPOINT PARTNERS
8280 Montgomery Rd Ste 101, Cin-
cinnati, OH 45236
Tel.: (513) 891-6666
Web Site:
   http://carepointpartners.com
Sales Range: $10-24.9 Million
Emp.: 250
Pharmaceutical Product Whslr
N.A.I.C.S.: 424210
Len Holman *(Owner)*

CARESOURCE
230 N Main St, Dayton, OH 45402
Tel.: (937) 224-3300   OH
Web Site:
   https://www.caresource.com
Year Founded: 1985
Sales Range: $1-4.9 Billion
Health Care Srvices
N.A.I.C.S.: 622110
Steve Ringel *(Pres-Ohio Market)*
Mark Chilson *(Gen Counsel & Exec VP)*
Paul Stoddard *(CIO)*
Dan McCabe *(Chief Admin Officer)*
Deirdra Yocum *(VP-Quality & Perfor-mance Outcomes)*
Steve Swart *(Exec Dir)*
Donald Wharton *(VP & Dir-Medical)*
Lisa Heckler *(VP-Info Security & Pri-vacy)*
Tony Tomazic *(Chief Consumer Offi-cer)*
Pamela Morris *(Founder)*
Fran Robinson *(Mgr-Media Rels)*
Molly Beyer *(VP-Ops)*
Christina Turner *(Chief Clinical Offi-cer)*
David Finkel *(Exec VP-Markets)*
Erhardt Preitauer *(CEO)*
Jeff Myers *(Exec VP-Strategic & Ex-ternal Rels)*
Tarlton Thomas III *(CFO)*

CARESYNTAX, INC.
800 Boylston St, Boston, MA 02199
Tel.: (617) 274-8787   MA
Web Site: http://www.caresyntax.com
Healthcare IT & Digital Health Ser-
vices
N.A.I.C.S.: 518210
Dennis Kogan *(Co-Founder, Chm & CEO)*
Bjorn von Siemens *(Co-Founder & Chief Bus Officer)*
Timothy Lantz *(Pres & COO)*
Matt Krueger *(Chief Comml Officer)*
Claire Masterson *(CFO)*

CARETECH SOLUTIONS INC.
901 Wilshirer Ste 100, Troy, MI
48084
Tel.: (248) 233-3000

Web Site:
   http://www.caretechsolutions.com
Rev.: $25,100,000
Emp.: 600
Data Processing & Preparation
N.A.I.C.S.: 518210
James J. Giordano *(Pres & CEO)*
Jim Hunter *(Dir-Monitoring & Secu-rity)*
Lisa Kennedy *(Dir-Mktg & Comm)*
Louis Caschera *(CIO)*

CARETTA PARTNERS, LLC
401 W Superior St Ste 200, Chicago,
IL 60654
Web Site: http://www.caretta.co
Year Founded: 2015
Emp.: 4
N.A.I.C.S.:
Eric D. Becker *(Founder & Mng Part-ner)*
Ryan Schultz *(VP-Investments)*

Subsidiaries:

HiTech Assets LLC   **(1)**
401 N Portland Ave, Oklahoma City, OK
73107
Tel.: (405) 604-4872
Web Site: http://www.hitech-assets.com
Emp.: 100
IT Asset Recovery Services
N.A.I.C.S.: 541512
Peter Roberts *(VP)*
Lane Epperson *(Founder & CEO)*
Rike Sandlin *(COO & Sr VP)*
Eric Harris *(VP-Sustainability & Govt Rels)*
David Ryan *(Sr VP-Bus Dev)*
Michael Schuler *(VP-Remarketing)*

CARETTI, INC.
4590 Industrial Park Rd PO Box 331,
Camp Hill, PA 17001-0331
Tel.: (717) 737-6759
Web Site:
   http://www.carettimasonry.com
Year Founded: 1953
Sales Range: $10-24.9 Million
Emp.: 20
Masonry Contracting Services
N.A.I.C.S.: 238140
Gregory R. Hess *(Pres & CEO)*
Tracy R. Wenrich *(Controller)*
Bill Lecher *(Mgr-Restoration)*
Ken Merencic *(Superintendent-Construction)*

CAREW CONCRETE & SUP-PLY CO. INC.
1811 W Edgewood Dr, Appleton, WI
54913-9708
Tel.: (920) 731-9771   WI
Web Site:
   https://www.carewconcrete.com
Year Founded: 1977
Sales Range: $10-24.9 Million
Emp.: 80
Provider of Concrete
N.A.I.C.S.: 327320
John Carew *(Pres)*
Chad Kaster *(Mgr-HR & Safety)*

CAREY COMPANY INC.
3204 Fruitvale Blvd, Yakima, WA
98902
Tel.: (509) 248-1500
Web Site:
   http://www.careymotors.com
Rev.: $25,000,000
Emp.: 45
New & Used Car Dealers
N.A.I.C.S.: 441120
Patrick J. Carey *(Pres)*

CAREY COUNSELING CEN-TER, INC.
408 Virginia St, Paris, TN 38242
Tel.: (731) 642-0521   TN

Web Site:
   https://www.careycounseling.org
Year Founded: 1970
Sales Range: $10-24.9 Million
Behavioral Healthcare Services
N.A.I.C.S.: 623220
Cindy H. West *(VP)*
Peggy Ball *(Sec)*
Robert D. Vaughn *(Exec Dir)*
Richard E. French *(Dir-Fiscal)*
Sherri Sedgebear *(Dir-Carroll County Site)*
Lori Hendon *(Dir-Obion & Weakley County Site)*
Sara Moody *(Dir-Gibson County Site)*
Joseph Williams *(Dir-Medical)*
Fran Howe *(Dir-Housing)*
Sean Jones *(Dir-Crisis & Benton County Site)*
Amanda Lifsey *(Dir-Residential Svcs)*
Andrea Chase *(Dir-Clinical)*
Brent Bullock *(Compliance Officer & Dir-Henry County Site)*
Dena Zipp *(Coord-Special Projects)*
Guy T. Wilkinson *(Chm)*
Dennis Richardson *(Treas)*

CAREY HILLIARDS DRIVE-IN RESTAURANT
11111 Abercorn St, Savannah, GA
31419
Tel.: (912) 925-2131
Web Site:
   https://www.careyhilliards.com
Rev.: $10,900,000
Emp.: 15
Barbecue Restaurant
N.A.I.C.S.: 722511
G. Timothy Hilliard *(Pres)*

CAREY JOHNSON OIL COM-PANY
701 SW F Ave, Lawton, OK 73501-
4542
Tel.: (580) 595-8305
Web Site:
   https://www.ezgostores.com
Sales Range: $50-74.9 Million
Emp.: 200
Petroleum Bulk Stations
N.A.I.C.S.: 424710
Paul Korhonen *(VP)*
Twyla McDonald *(Controller)*
Carey Johnson Jr. *(Chm & Pres)*

CARGAS SYSTEMS, INC
1310 Marshall Ave, Lancaster, PA
17601
Tel.: (717) 560-9928
Web Site: http://www.cargas.com
Year Founded: 1988
Rev.: $6,600,000
Emp.: 54
Business Software & Consulting Firm
N.A.I.C.S.: 541690
Chip Cargas *(Founder)*
Jon Clemens *(VP)*
Sandy Folts *(Sec)*
Nate Scott *(Pres & CEO)*
Keith Kuzio *(Chm)*
Dennis DiSabatino *(VP-Energy)*
Pamela Morrissey *(Dir-Energy Support-Energy)*
Kellee Morales *(VP-HR)*

CARGILL, INC.
PO Box 9300, Minneapolis, MN
55440-9300
Tel.: (952) 742-7575   DE
Web Site: https://www.cargill.com
Year Founded: 1865
Sales Range: $100-149.9 Billion
Emp.: 160,000
Grain & Field Bean Merchant Whole-
salers
N.A.I.C.S.: 424510

Marcel Smits *(Chm-Asia Pacific & Head-Corp Strategy)*
Jennifer Hartsock *(Chief Info & Digital Officer)*
Ruth S. Kimmelshue *(Sr VP-Animal Nutrition & Health Global Enterprise)*
Pilar Cruz *(Chief Sustainability Offi-cer)*
Anna Richo *(Gen Counsel)*
Julian Chase *(Chief Transformation Officer & Head-Bus Ops & Supply Chain)*
Stephanie A. Lundquist *(Chief HR Officer)*
Brian Sikes *(Pres & CEO)*
Coleen May *(Pres-Bioindustrial Grp)*
Ross Hamou-Jennings *(Chm-Asia Pacific)*
David Webster *(Chief Risk Officer)*

Subsidiaries:

Agribrands Purina (LangFang) Feed-
mill Co., Ltd.   **(1)**
No 52 Guangming Road East, Langfang,
065000, Hebei, China
Tel.: (86) 316 2026609
Animal Feed Mfr
N.A.I.C.S.: 311119

Agribrands Purina (Zhengzhou) Feed-
mill Co., Ltd.   **(1)**
No 4 Wutong West Road High-tech Devel-
opment Zone, Zhengzhou, 450001, Henan,
China
Tel.: (86) 371 67848377
Animal Feed Mfr
N.A.I.C.S.: 311119

Ardent Mills, LLC   **(1)**
1875 Lawrence St, Denver, CO
80202   **(44%)**
Tel.: (800) 851-9618
Web Site: http://www.ardentmills.com
Sales Range: $1-4.9 Billion
Flour & Other Grain Mill Products Milling
N.A.I.C.S.: 311211
Dan Dye *(CEO)*

Unit (Domestic):

Ardent Mills   **(2)**
905 W Marion St, Lake City, MN 55041-
2007
Tel.: (651) 345-3351
Sales Range: $10-24.9 Million
Emp.: 32
Self-Rising Prepared Blended Flour Pro-
ducer
N.A.I.C.S.: 311211
Deb Roschen *(Mgr-Admin)*

Subsidiary (Domestic):

Hinrichs Trading LLC   **(2)**
155 SE Kamiaken St, Pullman, WA 83501
Tel.: (509) 332-8888
Web Site: http://www.hinrichstrading.com
Commodity Contracts Dealing
N.A.I.C.S.: 523160
Phil Hinrichs *(CEO)*

Black River Asset Management
LLC   **(1)**
9320 Excelsior Blvd, Hopkins, MN 55343
Tel.: (952) 984-3863
Web Site: http://www.black-river.com
Asset Management Services
N.A.I.C.S.: 523940
Guilherme Schmidt *(Chief Investment Offi-cer)*

CLD Pacific Grain LLC   **(1)**
800 N River St, Portland, OR 97227-1715
Tel.: (503) 281-9177
Sales Range: $1-9.9 Million
Emp.: 30
Grain Whslr & Storage Services
N.A.I.C.S.: 424510

Cargill   **(1)**
935 S 4th W, Cheyenne Wells, CO 80810
Tel.: (719) 767-5625
Web Site: http://www.cargillag.com
Sales Range: $10-24.9 Million
Emp.: 7
Grain Elevators Mfr

N.A.I.C.S.: 424510

Cargill (Malaysia) Sdn Bhd (1)
Level 22 Menara TM Off Jalan Pantai Baru,
Kuala Lumpur, 59200, Malaysia
Tel.: (60) 3 2246 3111
Web Site: http://www.cargill.com.my
Sales Range: $50-74.9 Million
Emp.: 741
Farm Product Distr
N.A.I.C.S.: 423820
Kok Ee Pei *(Mgr-HR)*

Cargill AT & Enterprise Inc (1)
Mechnikova Str 3 4th floor, 01023, Kiev,
Ukraine
Tel.: (380) 44 230 1440
Web Site: http://www.cargill.com
Sales Range: $25-49.9 Million
Emp.: 160
Animal Feed & Oilseed Mfr
N.A.I.C.S.: 311119
Martin Schuldt *(Mgr)*

Cargill Ag Horizons (1)
1050 Kerper Blvd, Dubuque, IA 52001-2339
Tel.: (563) 556-4532
Web Site: http://www.cargillag.com
Sales Range: $10-24.9 Million
Emp.: 40
Grain Elevator Mfr & Service
N.A.I.C.S.: 333921

Cargill Ag Horizons (1)
71853 Rd A, Oxford, NE 68967 **(100%)**
Tel.: (308) 824-3225
Sales Range: $10-24.9 Million
Emp.: 25
Retail Farm Chemical & Fertilizer Producer
N.A.I.C.S.: 424910

Cargill Ag Horizons (1)
PO Box 187, Hamburg, IA
51640-0187 **(100%)**
Tel.: (712) 382-2422
Web Site: http://www.cargillag.com
Sales Range: $10-24.9 Million
Emp.: 8
Grain Elevator Mfr & Sales
N.A.I.C.S.: 424510
Jery Bery *(Mgr)*

Cargill AgHorizons (1)
2117 Hwy 6, Heartwell, NE 68945 **(100%)**
Tel.: (308) 563-2111
Web Site: http://www.cargillag.com
Sales Range: $10-24.9 Million
Emp.: 20
Grain & Fertilizer Distr
N.A.I.C.S.: 424510
Cody Richard *(Mgr-Montana)*

Cargill Agri Purina, Inc. (1)
5-8th Floor HanRimWom B/D 7-1 Gumi-
dong, Bundang-gu, Seongnam, 463 808,
Kyeonggi-do, Korea (South)
Tel.: (82) 31 710 6000
Sales Range: $50-74.9 Million
Emp.: 50
Animal Feed Nutrition Technology & Ser-
vices
N.A.I.C.S.: 311119

Plant (Domestic):

**Cargill Agri Purina, Inc. - Chunan
Plant** (2)
23-17 Dujeonggongdan 2-gil, Sebuk-gu,
Cheonan, 331-957, Chungcheongnam-do,
Korea (South)
Tel.: (82) 41 567 5751
Animal Feed Mfr & Whslr
N.A.I.C.S.: 311119

**Cargill Agri Purina, Inc. - Kunsan
Plant** (2)
45 Oehang 6-gil, Gunsan, 573-879,
Jeollabuk-do, Korea (South)
Tel.: (82) 63 469 8600
Web Site: http://www.cargill.kr
Animal Feed Mfr
N.A.I.C.S.: 311119

**Cargill Agri Purina, Inc. - Songtan
Plant** (2)
1029 Gyeonggi daero, Pyeongtaek, 459-
020, Gyeonggi-do, Korea (South)
Tel.: (82) 31 669 9000
Animal Feed & Oilseed Mfr
N.A.I.C.S.: 311224

Cargill Agricultura SRL (1)
11-15 Tipografilor St 2nd Floor A2 Building
District 1, Bucharest, 13714, Romania
Tel.: (40) 21 203 10 00
Web Site: http://www.cargill.ro
Wheat & Grain Whslr
N.A.I.C.S.: 111140

Plant (Domestic):

**Cargill Agricultura SRL - Cargill Nutri-
tie Animala Factroy** (2)
Str Garii No 56, Sura Mica, Sibiu, 557270,
Romania
Tel.: (40) 372 692 700
Animal Feed Mfr & Whslr
N.A.I.C.S.: 311119

Subsidiary (Domestic):

Cargill Oils S.A. (2)
Str Fabricii nr 1, 207465, Podari, Dolj, Ro-
mania
Tel.: (40) 251 339 807
Web Site: http://www.cargill.ro
Vegetable Oil Mfr
N.A.I.C.S.: 311225

Cargill Animal Nutrition (1)
PO Box 9300, Minneapolis, MN 55440-
9300
Tel.: (952) 742-7575
Web Site: http://www.cargill.com
Emp.: 20,000
Animal Feed & Poultry Feed Mfr
N.A.I.C.S.: 311119

Subsidiary (Non-US):

Agri Brand Purina Canada Inc. (2)
404 Main St, Woodstock, N4S 1T5, ON,
Canada **(100%)**
Tel.: (519) 539-8561
Web Site: http://www.agripurina.ca
Sales Range: $25-49.9 Million
Emp.: 80
Mfr of Agricultural Feeds
N.A.I.C.S.: 311111
Charles Lapointe *(Pres)*

Plant (Domestic):

Cargill Animal Nutrition (2)
14721 West Main Ave, Casa Grande, AZ
85193
Tel.: (520) 836-2131
Web Site:
http://www.cargillanimalnutrition.com
Rev.: $20,000,000
Emp.: 30
Prepared Feeds
N.A.I.C.S.: 311119

Cargill Animal Nutrition (2)
1800 E Elm Dr, Little Chute, WI 54140-
2512
Tel.: (920) 788-6233
Web Site: http://www.cargill.com
Sales Range: $25-49.9 Million
Emp.: 8
Prepared Feeds Producer
N.A.I.C.S.: 311119

Cargill Animal Nutrition (2)
1203 Timken Rd, Wooster, OH 44691-8345
Tel.: (330) 263-7771
Web Site: http://www.cargill.com
Rev.: $16,200,000
Emp.: 17
Grain & Field Beans Distr
N.A.I.C.S.: 424510
Brad Carter *(Plant Mgr)*
Susanna Wright *(Plant Mgr)*

Cargill Animal Nutrition (2)
104 S Progressive Rd, Hereford, TX 79045-
9500
Tel.: (806) 364-3891
Web Site: http://www.cargill.com
Sales Range: $25-49.9 Million
Emp.: 20
Prepared Feeds Mfr
N.A.I.C.S.: 311119

Cargill Animal Nutrition (2)
8 S Wood Blvd, Albany, NY 12211
Tel.: (518) 465-2481
Web Site:
http://www.cargillanimalnutrition.com

Sales Range: $25-49.9 Million
Emp.: 49
Animal Nutrition Services
N.A.I.C.S.: 424510

Cargill Animal Nutrition (2)
2100 S Robinson Ave, Oklahoma City, OK
73109-5943
Tel.: (405) 236-0525
Web Site:
http://www.cargillanimalnutrition.com
Sales Range: $25-49.9 Million
Emp.: 60
Prepared Feeds Mfr
N.A.I.C.S.: 311119

Cargill Animal Nutrition (2)
4344 S El Dorado St, Stockton, CA
95206-4904 **(100%)**
Tel.: (209) 982-4632
Web Site: http://www.cargill.com
Sales Range: $25-49.9 Million
Emp.: 100
Animal Nutrition Services
N.A.I.C.S.: 561110

Plant (Non-US):

Cargill Animal Nutrition (2)
1200 Pacific Ave, Brandon, R7A 0J3, MB,
Canada
Tel.: (204) 727-8401
Sales Range: $25-49.9 Million
Emp.: 8
Prepared Feeds for Animals Mfr
N.A.I.C.S.: 311119
Adel El-Mowafi *(Dir-Global Aqua Tech)*
Daniel Barziza *(Dir-Global Aqua R&D)*
Adriano Marcon *(CEO)*

Cargill Animal Nutrition (2)
627 Plinguet Street, Winnipeg, R2J 2W9,
MB, Canada **(100%)**
Tel.: (204) 954-3206
Web Site: http://www.cargill.com
Sales Range: $25-49.9 Million
Emp.: 5
Animal Feeds Production
N.A.I.C.S.: 311111

Cargill Animal Nutrition (2)
8502 Birnam Line, Arkona, N0M 1B0, ON,
Canada **(100%)**
Tel.: (519) 828-3385
Web Site: http://www.cargill.ca
Sales Range: $25-49.9 Million
Emp.: 19
Grain & Feed Distr
N.A.I.C.S.: 424510

Subsidiary (Domestic):

Pro-Pet, LLC (2)
1601 McKinley Rd, Saint Marys, OH 45885
Tel.: (419) 394-3374
Web Site: http://www.propet.com
Dog & Cat Food Mfr
N.A.I.C.S.: 311111
W. Michael Wright *(Chm)*
Jim Wiegmann *(Pres & CEO)*
Greg Wolking *(COO)*
Marcie J. Campion *(VP-Technical Svcs)*

Plant (Domestic):

Pro-Pet, LLC - Kansas City (3)
6833 Griffin Rd, Kansas City, KS 66111
Tel.: (913) 299-2326
Web Site: http://www.propet.com
Dog & Cat Food Mfr
N.A.I.C.S.: 311111

**Cargill Animal Nutrition (Nanjing) Co.,
Ltd** (1)
Tie Xin Qiao, Yu Hua Tai District, Nanjing,
210012, Jiangsu, China
Tel.: (86) 25 52891658
Animal Feed Mfr
N.A.I.C.S.: 311119

Subsidiary (Domestic):

**Agribrands Purina (Xinjiang) Feedmill
Co., Ltd.** (2)
Yushugou Developing Zone, Changji, Xinji-
ang, 831100, China
Tel.: (86) 994 2589868
Animal Feed Mfr
N.A.I.C.S.: 311119

**Cargill Asia Pacific Food Systems
(Beijing) Ltd.** (1)
Qiliqu Industrial Park, Changping District,
Beijing, 102206, China
Tel.: (86) 10 80704100
Animal Feed Mfr
N.A.I.C.S.: 311119

**Cargill Asia Pacific Holdings Pte
Limited** (1)
300 Beach Road 23-01 The Concourse,
Singapore, 199555, Singapore
Tel.: (65) 6295 1112
Sales Range: $50-74.9 Million
Emp.: 500
Food Product Mfr & Distr
N.A.I.C.S.: 423840

Cargill Australia Ltd (1)
Level 11 Twenty-8 Freshwater Place,
Southbank, 3006, VIC, Australia
Tel.: (61) 3 9268 7200
Web Site: http://www.cargill.com.au
Emp.: 400
Animal Feed Mfr
N.A.I.C.S.: 311119
Philippa Purser *(CEO)*

Subsidiary (Domestic):

AWB GrainFlow Pty. Ltd. (2)
380 Latrobe Street, Melbourne, 3000, VIC,
Australia
Tel.: (61) 392092000
Web Site: http://www.grainflow.com.au
Grain Storage Services
N.A.I.C.S.: 493130

Joe White Maltings Pty. Ltd. (2)
65 Magill Rd, Stepney, 5069, SA,
Australia **(100%)**
Tel.: (61) 8 8214 6701
Web Site: http://www.cargill.com.au
Emp.: 30
Malt Mfr
N.A.I.C.S.: 311213
Doug Stewart *(Gen Mgr-Technical)*
Trevor Turnbull *(Mgr-Engrg)*

**Cargill Austria Handelsgesellschaft
m.b.H.** (1)
Durisolstrasse 7, 4600, Wels, Austria
Tel.: (43) 7242 66316
Animal Feed Whslr
N.A.I.C.S.: 424910

Cargill Bulgaria EOOD (1)
Crystal Business Center Floor 4 office 4 1
38-40 Osogovo str, Sofia, 1303, Bulgaria
Tel.: (359) 2 402 9000
Sales Range: $10-24.9 Million
Emp.: 70
Animal Feed Mfr
N.A.I.C.S.: 111120

Cargill Caribe S.A. (1)
Torre Empresarial Suite 6-B Ens La Julia,
Santo Domingo, Dominican Republic
Tel.: (809) 732 5025
Animal Feed Mfr
N.A.I.C.S.: 311119

**Cargill Cocoa & Chocolate Co.,
Inc.** (1)
20 N Broad St, Lititz, PA 17543-1012
Tel.: (717) 626-1131
Web Site: http://www.wilburbuds.com
Sales Range: $25-49.9 Million
Emp.: 31
Chocolate
N.A.I.C.S.: 311351
Hugo Van der Goes *(VP-Sls)*
Inge Demeyere *(Mng Dir-EMEA & Asia)*
Jos de Loor *(Pres)*

Plant (Non-US):

**Cargill Cocoa & Choclate Co., Inc. -
Georgetown Plant** (2)
24 Ontario St, Georgetown, L7G 3K6, ON,
Canada
Tel.: (905) 874-3076
Emp.: 55
Chocolate Mfr
N.A.I.C.S.: 311351
Ryan Brown *(Plant Mgr)*

Plant (Domestic):

**Cargill Cocoa & Chocolate Co.
Inc.** (2)

Cargill, Inc.—(Continued)

200 Chocolate Ave, Mount Joy, PA 17552-2000
Tel.: (717) 653-1471
Web Site: http://www.wilburbuds.com
Sales Range: $25-49.9 Million
Emp.: 90
Chocolate Coating Mfr
N.A.I.C.S.: 311351
Florian Girthofer *(Mng Dir)*

Subsidiary (Domestic):

Wilbur Chocolate Co., Inc. **(2)**
20 N Broad St, Lititz, PA 17543-1005
Tel.: (717) 626-1131
Web Site: http://www.wilburchocolate.com
Sales Range: $50-74.9 Million
Emp.: 350
Chocolate, Chocolate Coatings, Bulk Cocoas, Chocolate Chips & Drops, Ice Cream Mixes, Confectionery Coatings Mfr
N.A.I.C.S.: 311351

Cargill Corn Milling **(1)**
3201 Needmore Rd, Dayton, OH 45414-4309
Tel.: (937) 236-1971
Web Site: http://www.cargill.com
Sales Range: $25-49.9 Million
Emp.: 300
Corn Starch
N.A.I.C.S.: 311221
Doug Myers *(Gen Mgr)*

Cargill Corn Milling **(1)**
2330 Buoy St, Memphis, TN 38113
Tel.: (901) 775-5800
Web Site: http://www.cargill.com
Sales Range: $25-49.9 Million
Emp.: 300
Wet Corn Milling Services
N.A.I.C.S.: 311221

Cargill Cotton
7101 Goodlett Farms Pkwy, Cordova, TN 38016-4909
Tel.: (901) 937-4500
Web Site: http://www.cargillcotton.com
Sales Range: $25-49.9 Million
Emp.: 320
Farm Products Services
N.A.I.C.S.: 493130

Subsidiary (Domestic):

Cargill Cotton **(2)**
1422 Burton Wood Dr, Gastonia, NC 28054-7124 **(100%)**
Tel.: (704) 867-6318
Web Site: http://www.cargillcotton.com
Sales Range: $25-49.9 Million
Emp.: 2
Cotton Merchants
N.A.I.C.S.: 424590
Anthony Wills *(Mgr-Gastonia)*

Cargill Cotton **(2)**
1212 13th St Ste 200, Lubbock, TX 79401-3942 **(100%)**
Tel.: (806) 762-5279
Web Site: http://www.cargillcotton.com
Sales Range: $25-49.9 Million
Emp.: 3
Raw Cotton Services
N.A.I.C.S.: 445292

Cargill Deicing Technologies **(1)**
2400 Ships Channel, Cleveland, OH 44113-2673 **(100%)**
Tel.: (216) 651-7200
Web Site: http://www.cargill.com
Sales Range: $25-49.9 Million
Emp.: 150
Miner of Salt
N.A.I.C.S.: 212390
Chris Gill *(Superintendent-Tech)*

Cargill Deicing Technologies **(1)**
191 Portland Point Rd, Lansing, NY 14882 **(100%)**
Tel.: (607) 533-4221
Web Site: http://www.cargill.com
Sales Range: $25-49.9 Million
Emp.: 225
Rock Salt Mining Services
N.A.I.C.S.: 212390
Stan Pamel *(Mgr-Ops Tech)*
Dave Plumeau *(Superintendent-Tech)*

Cargill Deicing Technologies **(1)**
Hwy 329 S, Avery Island, LA 70513 **(100%)**
Tel.: (337) 364-8164
Web Site: http://www.cargill.com
Sales Range: $25-49.9 Million
Emp.: 194
Salt Producer
N.A.I.C.S.: 212390
Marcia Etie *(Mgr-Accts)*

Cargill Dry Corn Ingredients Inc **(1)**
616 S Jefferson St, Paris, IL 61944
Tel.: (217) 465-5331
Web Site: http://www.cargill.com
Sales Range: $25-49.9 Million
Emp.: 150
Corn Meal Mfr
N.A.I.C.S.: 311211

Cargill Europe BVBA **(1)**
Bedregvenlaan 729, Mechelen, 2800, Belgium
Tel.: (32) 15400411
Web Site: http://www.cargill.com
Emp.: 350
Food Ingredient Mfr
N.A.I.C.S.: 311999
Goel Begrees *(Office Mgr)*

Subsidiary (Non-US):

Cargill B.V. **(2)**
Lelyweg 31, 4612 PS, Bergen-op-Zoom, Netherlands
Tel.: (31) 164 28 22 00
Web Site: http://www.cargill.nl
Sales Range: $25-49.9 Million
Emp.: 2,200
Sweeteners, Starch & Starch Derivatives Mfr
N.A.I.C.S.: 311999

Cargill Benelux B.V. **(2)**
Nijverheidsstraat 1, 4551 LA, Sas-van-Gent, Netherlands
Tel.: (31) 115459000
Web Site: http://www.cargill.com
Sales Range: $50-74.9 Million
Emp.: 450
Starch & Corn Derivative Mfr
N.A.I.C.S.: 311221

Subsidiary (Non-US):

Cerestar SAS **(3)**
18-20 rue de Gaudines, 78100, Saint Germain-en-Laye, France
Tel.: (33) 330613500
Starch Whslr
N.A.I.C.S.: 424510

Subsidiary (Domestic):

Cargill Chocolate Belgium SA **(2)**
Belgielei 37, Antwerp, 2018, Belgium
Tel.: (32) 3 239 79 50
Web Site: http://www.cargill.com
Emp.: 50
Cocoa & Chocolate Product Mfr
N.A.I.C.S.: 311351
Lode Oosterlynck *(Plant Mgr)*

Cargill NV **(2)**
Muisbroeklaan 43 Kaai 506, 2030, Antwerp, Belgium
Tel.: (32) 35401811
Web Site: http://www.cargill.be
Emp.: 1,000
Vegetable Oil Mfr
N.A.I.C.S.: 311225

Cargill Oil Packers BVBA **(2)**
Prins Albertlaan 12, 8870, Izegem, Belgium
Tel.: (32) 51 332 611
Web Site: http://www.cargill.be
Vegetable Oil Mfr
N.A.I.C.S.: 311225

Cargill Europe Limited **(1)**
Knowle Hill Park Fairmile Lane, Cobham, KT11 2PD, Surrey, United Kingdom
Tel.: (44) 1932 861000
Sales Range: $10-24.9 Million
Emp.: 120
Animal Feed Mfr
N.A.I.C.S.: 311119

Cargill Feed Sdn Bhd **(1)**
174 Air Keroh Industrial Area, Melaka, 75450, Malaysia

Tel.: (60) 6 232 0633
Web Site: http://www.cargill.com.my
Sales Range: $25-49.9 Million
Emp.: 200
Animal Feed Mfr & Whslr
N.A.I.C.S.: 311119
Joshua Su *(Mgr-Factory)*

Cargill Food Ingredients **(1)**
ZI du Plan, 6131, Grasse, France
Tel.: (33) 493097800
Web Site: http://www.cargill.com
Sales Range: $10-24.9 Million
Emp.: 100
Mfr of Food Flavor & Texture Enhancing Ingredients
N.A.I.C.S.: 325199
Maurice Dadoun *(Gen Mgr)*

Subsidiary (Non-US):

Cargill Food Ingredients Canada, Inc. **(2)**
5611 McAdam Rd, Mississauga, L4Z 1N4, ON, Canada
Tel.: (905) 633-8079
Sales Range: $1-9.9 Million
Emp.: 7
Supplier of Food Ingredients
N.A.I.C.S.: 311423

Cargill Foods France SAS **(1)**
ZI de la Saussaye Rue des fougeres, Saint Cyr-en-Val, 45075, Orleans, France
Tel.: (33) 2 38 69 58 00
Poultry Product Supplier
N.A.I.C.S.: 424470

Cargill Foods Inc. **(1)**
Ste 101 14645 NW 77th Ave, Hialeah, FL 33014-2569
Tel.: (305) 884-5112
Web Site: http://www.cargill.com
Sales Range: $10-24.9 Million
Emp.: 50
Food Distr
N.A.I.C.S.: 115114

Cargill Ghana Limited **(1)**
Tema Free Zones Enclave Tema PMB 251 Community 1, Tema, Ghana
Tel.: (233) 303 318 370
Sales Range: $25-49.9 Million
Emp.: 200
Cocoa Product Mfr
N.A.I.C.S.: 311351

Cargill GmbH **(1)**
Rudekenstrasse 51, 38239, Salzgitter, Germany
Tel.: (49) 5341 224 0
Animal Feed & Oilseed Mfr
N.A.I.C.S.: 311224

Cargill Grain & Oilseeds (Nantong) Co., Ltd. **(1)**
No 1 Tongxing Road Economic Technology Development Zone, Nantong, 226009, China
Tel.: (86) 513 85966067
Soybean Processing & Starch Mfr
N.A.I.C.S.: 311221

Cargill Hong Kong Ltd. **(1)**
37/F Dorest House Taikoo Place, Quarry Bay, China (Hong Kong)
Tel.: (852) 29689888
Sales Range: $10-24.9 Million
Emp.: 20
Food Product Mfr & Distr
N.A.I.C.S.: 423840

Cargill Inc. **(1)**
PO Box 240457, Charlotte, NC 28224
Tel.: (704) 523-0414
Web Site: http://www.cargill.com
Sales Range: $10-24.9 Million
Emp.: 120
Mfr of Cooking Oils
N.A.I.C.S.: 236115
Kristine Kangas *(Mgr-Facility)*

Cargill Inc. **(1)**
300 Levee Rd, New Madrid, MO 63869 **(100%)**
Tel.: (573) 748-5576
Web Site: http://www.cargillag.com
Sales Range: $10-24.9 Million
Emp.: 11
Grain Elevators Mfr

N.A.I.C.S.: 424510

Cargill Inc. **(1)**
2400 Industrial Dr, Sidney, OH 45365-8905 **(100%)**
Tel.: (937) 498-4555
Web Site: http://www.cargill.com
Sales Range: $10-24.9 Million
Emp.: 75
Soybean Oil Mills
N.A.I.C.S.: 311224

Cargill Inc. **(1)**
758 State Hwy N, Charleston, MO 63834-8251 **(100%)**
Tel.: (573) 683-3751
Web Site: http://www.cargill.com
Sales Range: $10-24.9 Million
Emp.: 12
Grain Elevator Services
N.A.I.C.S.: 424510

Cargill Inc. **(1)**
600 Cowan St, Nashville, TN 37207-5620 **(100%)**
Tel.: (615) 782-8500
Web Site: http://www.cargill.com
Sales Range: $10-24.9 Million
Emp.: 50
Steel Services
N.A.I.C.S.: 423510
Kevin Jost *(Mgr)*

Cargill Inc. **(1)**
250 7th Ave NE, West Fargo, ND 58078
Tel.: (701) 282-1600
Web Site: http://www.cargill.com
Sales Range: $10-24.9 Million
Emp.: 60
Soyabean Oil Mill Services
N.A.I.C.S.: 311224

Cargill Inc. **(1)**
PO Box 9300, Minneapolis, MN 55440-9300
Web Site: http://www.cargill.com
Sales Range: $10-24.9 Million
Emp.: 1,500
Corn Milling Services
N.A.I.C.S.: 541715

Cargill Inc. **(1)**
49387 Pioneer Rd, Oneill, NE 68763-9745 **(100%)**
Tel.: (402) 336-4010
Web Site: http://www.cargillag.com
Sales Range: $10-24.9 Million
Emp.: 8
Grain Services
N.A.I.C.S.: 424510

Cargill Inc. **(1)**
200 N 19th St, Tampa, FL 33605-6753
Tel.: (813) 247-3602
Web Site: http://www.cargill.com
Sales Range: $10-24.9 Million
Emp.: 13
Grain Elevator Services
N.A.I.C.S.: 424510

Cargill Inc. **(1)**
858 SW Vine St, Kingman, KS 67068-8646 **(100%)**
Tel.: (620) 532-2992
Sales Range: $10-24.9 Million
Emp.: 1
Grain Sales
N.A.I.C.S.: 424510

Cargill Inc. **(1)**
4201 HC 238, Bloomingburg, OH 43106
Tel.: (740) 437-7337
Web Site: http://www.cargillat.com
Sales Range: $10-24.9 Million
Emp.: 20
Grain Services
N.A.I.C.S.: 424510
Jill Adelsberger *(Mgr-Mktg)*

Cargill Inc. **(1)**
700 Hwy 194, Hart, TX 79043
Tel.: (806) 938-2178
Sales Range: $10-24.9 Million
Emp.: 2
Grain Elevators Mfr
N.A.I.C.S.: 424510

Cargill Inc. **(1)**
1060 Kerper Blvd, Dubuque, IA 52001-2339 **(100%)**
Tel.: (563) 556-1909

Web Site: http://www.cargill.com
Sales Range: $10-24.9 Million
Emp.: 6
Salt Production
N.A.I.C.S.: 424690

Cargill Inc. (1)
15100 Rowley Rd, Grantsville, UT
84029 **(100%)**
Tel.: (435) 884-0123
Web Site: http://www.cargill.com
Sales Range: $10-24.9 Million
Emp.: 80
Salt Sales
N.A.I.C.S.: 311942

Cargill Inc. (1)
100 Grain St, Albany, NY 12202
Tel.: (518) 465-2261
Web Site: http://www.cargill.com
Sales Range: $10-24.9 Million
Emp.: 10
Grain Mfr
N.A.I.C.S.: 424510

Cargill Inc. (1)
E Hwy 11, Ord, NE 68862 **(100%)**
Tel.: (308) 728-3653
Web Site: http://www.cargill.com
Sales Range: $10-24.9 Million
Emp.: 12
Grain Elevator Services
N.A.I.C.S.: 424910

Cargill Inc. (1)
PO Box 699, Russellville, AR
72811-0699 **(100%)**
Tel.: (479) 968-4560
Web Site: http://www.cargill.com
Sales Range: $10-24.9 Million
Emp.: 25
Prepared Feeds Mfr
N.A.I.C.S.: 311119

Cargill Inc. (1)
115 S Euclid Ave, Bloomington, IL 61701-
4785
Tel.: (309) 827-7100
Sales Range: $10-24.9 Million
Emp.: 55
Soybean Oil Mills
N.A.I.C.S.: 311224

Cargill Inc. (1)
PO Box 9300, Minneapolis, MN
55440-9300 **(100%)**
Tel.: (970) 522-6136
Sales Range: $10-24.9 Million
Emp.: 34
Agricultural Product Mfr & Distr
N.A.I.C.S.: 325320
Lorin DeBonte *(Dir-Tech, Oils & Fats-North America)*

Cargill Inc. (1)
2750 Jewel Ave, Los Angeles, CA 90058-
1224
Tel.: (323) 588-2274
Sales Range: $10-24.9 Million
Emp.: 35
Mfr of Edible Fats & Oils
N.A.I.C.S.: 311225

Cargill Inc. (1)
42136 Hwy 634, Arapahoe, NE 68922-5535
Tel.: (308) 962-7965
Sales Range: $10-24.9 Million
Emp.: 9
Fertilizer & Chemical Distr
N.A.I.C.S.: 424910
Chris Borland *(Branch Mgr)*

Cargill Inc. (1)
4340 18th Ave SW, Fargo, ND
58103 **(100%)**
Tel.: (701) 271-3500
Web Site: http://www.cargill.com
Sales Range: $25-49.9 Million
Emp.: 200
Financial Services
N.A.I.C.S.: 424510

Cargill Inc. (1)
400 East Diehl Rd Ste 330, Naperville, IL
60563-1361 **(100%)**
Tel.: (630) 505-7322
Web Site: http://www.cargill.com
Sales Range: $10-24.9 Million
Emp.: 25
Grain Milling Services
N.A.I.C.S.: 115114

Cargill Inc. (1)
650 Industrial Park Dr, Blair, NE
68008-2649 **(100%)**
Tel.: (402) 533-4100
Web Site: http://www.cargill.com
Sales Range: $25-49.9 Million
Emp.: 300
Grains Processing & Sales
N.A.I.C.S.: 424510

Cargill Inc. (1)
632 N Ctr St, Bremen, IN
46506-1170 **(100%)**
Tel.: (574) 546-2457
Web Site: http://www.cargill.com
Sales Range: $10-24.9 Million
Emp.: 8
Farm Supply Services
N.A.I.C.S.: 424510
Brandon Woodard *(Gen Mgr)*

Cargill Inc. (1)
County Rd 1100 N, Linden, IN 47955
Tel.: (765) 339-7251
Web Site: http://www.cargill.com
Sales Range: $10-24.9 Million
Emp.: 12
Grain Elevator Mfr & Service
N.A.I.C.S.: 424510
Jim Simpson *(Gen Mgr)*

Cargill Inc. (1)
980 Clark St, Sioux City, IA 51101
Tel.: (712) 279-1200
Web Site: http://www.cargill.com
Sales Range: $10-24.9 Million
Emp.: 86
Crop Preparation Services
N.A.I.C.S.: 115114

Cargill Inc. (1)
933 River Rd, Westwego, LA
70094-3028 **(100%)**
Tel.: (504) 436-5817
Web Site: http://www.cargill.com
Sales Range: $25-49.9 Million
Emp.: 135
Grain Elevators
N.A.I.C.S.: 424510
Cindy Favoie *(Sec)*
Lance Lamers *(Gen Mgr)*

Cargill Inc. (1)
1633 E Ave, Dakota City, NE
68731-3007 **(100%)**
Tel.: (402) 987-3854
Web Site: http://www.cargillag.com
Sales Range: $10-24.9 Million
Emp.: 7
Grain Products
N.A.I.C.S.: 424510

Cargill Inc. (1)
862 W Ridge Rd, Gainesville, GA 30501-
6911
Tel.: (770) 531-4700
Web Site: http://www.cargill.com
Sales Range: $10-24.9 Million
Emp.: 200
Refined Soybean Oil Sales
N.A.I.C.S.: 311225

Cargill Inc. (1)
340 SW Blvd, Kansas City, KS
66103-2150 **(100%)**
Tel.: (913) 831-3477
Web Site: http://www.cargill.com
Sales Range: $10-24.9 Million
Emp.: 8
Grain Distr
N.A.I.C.S.: 424510

Cargill Inc. (1)
816 Bainbridge St, La Crosse, WI 54603
Tel.: (608) 782-5126
Web Site: http://www.cargill.com
Sales Range: $10-24.9 Million
Emp.: 4
Grain Elevator Mfr & Service
N.A.I.C.S.: 424510
Tami Schroeder *(Mgr-Ops)*

Cargill Inc. (1)
107 S Hickory St, Langdon, KS
67583-9026 **(100%)**
Tel.: (620) 596-2202
Web Site: http://www.cargill.com
Sales Range: $10-24.9 Million
Emp.: 1
Grain Elevators

N.A.I.C.S.: 424510

Cargill Inc. (1)
8 Southwoods Blvd Ste 4, Albany, NY
12211-2554
Tel.: (860) 642-6259
Web Site: http://www.cargill.com
Sales Range: $10-24.9 Million
Emp.: 30
Animal Feed
N.A.I.C.S.: 424910

Cargill International S.A. (1)
14 chemin de Normandie, Geneva, 1206,
Switzerland
Tel.: (41) 22 703 2111
Web Site: http://www.cargill.com
Animal Feed & Oilseed Mfr
N.A.I.C.S.: 311224

Cargill Investments (China) Ltd. (1)
10F One ICC No 999 Huai Hai Road,
Shanghai International Commerce Center,
Shanghai, 200031, China
Tel.: (86) 21 33327888
Web Site: http://www.cargill.com.cn
Emp.: 500
Commodity Risk Management Services
N.A.I.C.S.: 551112
Robert Aspell *(Pres)*

Cargill Japan Limited (1)
Kokusai Bldg 3-1-1 Marunouchi Chiyoda-ku,
Tokyo, 100-0005, Japan
Tel.: (81) 3 3285 0800
Web Site: http://www.cargill.co.jp
Sales Range: $25-49.9 Million
Emp.: 300
Animal Feed & Oilseed Mfr
N.A.I.C.S.: 311224

Cargill Kitchen Solutions (1)
206 W 4th St, Monticello, MN 55362-8524
Tel.: (763) 271-5600
Web Site: http://www.usaeggs.com
Sales Range: $50-74.9 Million
Emp.: 400
Egg Products & Egg Based Entree Produc-
ers
N.A.I.C.S.: 311999
Chris Robert *(Pres)*

Plant (Domestic):

Cargill Kitchen Solutions (2)
3100 Bonanza Rd, Lake Odessa, MI
48849-9559
Tel.: (616) 374-4545
Web Site: http://www.sunnyfreshfoods.com
Sales Range: $50-74.9 Million
Emp.: 100
Egg Processing
N.A.I.C.S.: 311999
Carroll May *(Mgr-Ops)*

Cargill Limited (1)
240 Graham Ave Ste 300, PO Box 5900,
Winnipeg, R3C 0J7, MB, Canada
Tel.: (204) 947-0141
Web Site: http://www.cargill.ca
Sales Range: $1-4.9 Billion
Emp.: 6,000
Agriculture & Agra Food
N.A.I.C.S.: 111998
Jeff Vassart *(Pres)*

Unit (Domestic):

Cargill Ag Horizons (2)
6 Miles S of Regina On Hwy 6, PO Box
4200, Regina, S4P 3W5, SK,
Canada **(100%)**
Tel.: (306) 949-2088
Sales Range: $10-24.9 Million
Emp.: 8
Grain & Field Beans
N.A.I.C.S.: 424510
Ryan Ward *(Gen Mgr)*
Bryce Ingram *(Gen Mgr)*

Cargill Ag Horizons (2)
300-240 Graham Avenue, PO Box 5900,
Winnipeg, R3C 4C5, MB, Canada **(100%)**
Tel.: (204) 947-0141
Web Site: http://www.cargill.ca
Sales Range: $25-49.9 Million
Emp.: 12
Grain Distr
N.A.I.C.S.: 424510
Len Tenner *(Pres)*

Cargill Animal Nutrition (2)
235 36th St N, Lethbridge, T1H 5R8, AB,
Canada **(100%)**
Tel.: (403) 329-0787
Web Site: http://www.cargill.ca
Sales Range: $10-24.9 Million
Emp.: 40
Animal Feed Mfr
N.A.I.C.S.: 311111
Jennifer Henderson *(Gen Mgr)*

Subsidiary (Domestic):

Cargill Foods Limited (2)
71 Rexdale Blvd, Toronto, M9W 6Y2, ON,
Canada **(100%)**
Tel.: (416) 748-5001
Web Site: http://www.cargillfoods.com
Sales Range: $50-74.9 Million
Emp.: 800
Meat Packing Plants
N.A.I.C.S.: 311611
Jasao Turulaa *(Product Mgr)*

Unit (Domestic):

Cargill Limited (2)
940 Douglas Street, Brandon, R7A 7B2,
MB, Canada **(100%)**
Tel.: (204) 725-1242
Web Site: http://www.cargil.com
Sales Range: $25-49.9 Million
Emp.: 4
Farm Supply Services
N.A.I.C.S.: 444240

Cargill Limited (2)
312-837 W Hastings St, Vancouver, V6C
3N6, BC, Canada **(100%)**
Tel.: (604) 683-6531
Web Site: http://www.cargill.com
Sales Range: $10-24.9 Million
Emp.: 3
Grain & Field Beans Producer
N.A.I.C.S.: 424510

Cargill Limited (2)
39109 Talbot Line RR 7, Saint Thomas,
N5P 3T2, ON, Canada **(100%)**
Tel.: (519) 631-5750
Web Site: http://www.stage.cargillag.ca
Sales Range: $25-49.9 Million
Emp.: 10
Farm Supply & Grain Marketing Services
N.A.I.C.S.: 424510
Bill McClain *(Plant Mgr)*

Cargill Limited (2)
225 300 Du Saint Sacremen, Montreal, H2Y
1X4, QC, Canada **(100%)**
Tel.: (514) 844-1165
Web Site: http://www.cargill.com
Sales Range: $10-24.9 Million
Emp.: 10
Grain & Field Beans Producer
N.A.I.C.S.: 424510

Cargill Limited (2)
Railway Ave, PO Box 940, Unity, S0K 4L0,
SK, Canada **(100%)**
Tel.: (306) 228-4144
Web Site: http://www.cargillaghorizons.ca
Sales Range: $25-49.9 Million
Emp.: 5
Farm Supplies
N.A.I.C.S.: 444240

Cargill Limited (2)
1036 Green Valley Rd, London, N6N 1E3,
ON, Canada **(100%)**
Tel.: (519) 691-8100
Web Site: http://www.cargill.ca
Sales Range: $25-49.9 Million
Emp.: 2
Farm & Garden Services
N.A.I.C.S.: 444240

Cargill Limited (2)
10 Albert Drive, Mount Albert, L0G 1M0,
ON, Canada **(100%)**
Tel.: (905) 473-2449
Web Site: http://www.cargill.ca
Sales Range: $25-49.9 Million
Emp.: 15
Farm Supply Services
N.A.I.C.S.: 444240
Kyle Gallant *(Gen Mgr)*

Cargill Limited (2)
1 Cheviot Rd, PO Box 190, Clavet, S0K

Cargill, Inc.—(Continued)

0Y0, SK, Canada **(100%)**
Tel.: (306) 242-5400
Web Site: http://www.cargill.com
Sales Range: $25-49.9 Million
Emp.: 100
Canola Oil Crushing Services
N.A.I.C.S.: 311224

Cargill Limited **(2)**
Junction of Highway 72 and 806, Beiseker,
T0M 0G0, AB, Canada **(100%)**
Tel.: (403) 947-3844
Web Site: http://www.cargillaghorizons.com
Sales Range: $25-49.9 Million
Emp.: 4
Farm Supplies
N.A.I.C.S.: 444240
Elgon Hagil (Gen Mgr)

Cargill Limited **(2)**
Highway 32nd Ave, PO Box 2199, Moose
Jaw, S6H 7T2, SK, Canada **(100%)**
Tel.: (306) 692-0770
Web Site: http://www.cargill.ca
Sales Range: $25-49.9 Million
Emp.: 15
Farm Supply Services
N.A.I.C.S.: 444240
Tobi Nelson (Reg Mgr)

Cargill Limited **(2)**
13020 - 127 Avenue, Edmonton, T5L 4Z5,
AB, Canada **(100%)**
Tel.: (780) 454-0475
Web Site: http://www.cargill.ca
Sales Range: $10-24.9 Million
Emp.: 30
Grain Elevators
N.A.I.C.S.: 424510

Cargill Limited **(2)**
5035 County Rd 15, PO Box 730, Harrow,
N0R 1G0, ON, Canada **(100%)**
Tel.: (519) 738-2271
Web Site: http://www.cargill.ca
Sales Range: $25-49.9 Million
Emp.: 6
Farm Supply Sales
N.A.I.C.S.: 444240

Joint Venture (Domestic):

SynAgri LP **(2)**
5175 boulevard Laurier Est, Saint-
Hyacinthe, J2R 2B4, QC, Canada
Tel.: (450) 799-3226
Web Site: https://www.synagri.ca
Sales Range: $1-9.9 Million
Emp.: 100
Crop Harvesting Services
N.A.I.C.S.: 115113

Division (Domestic):

SynAgri **(3)**
5175 boulevard Laurier Est, Saint-
Hyacinthe, J2R 2B4, QC, Canada
Tel.: (450) 799-3226
Web Site: https://www.synagri.ca
Emp.: 20
Farm Supplies
N.A.I.C.S.: 444240
Sylvain Lavoie (Gen Mgr)

Cargill Meat Solutions Corp. **(1)**
151 N Main St, Wichita, KS 67202-1410
Tel.: (316) 291-2500
Web Site:
http://www.cargillmeatsolutions.com
Sales Range: $50-74.9 Million
Emp.: 645
Meat Product Sales
N.A.I.C.S.: 424440
Allison DiAlberto (Brand Mgr)
Ozlem Worpel (Brand Mgr-Sterling Silver)
John Keating (Pres)

Plant (Domestic):

Cargill **(2)**
3201 E Hwy 400, Dodge City, KS 67801
Tel.: (620) 225-2610
Meat Packing Services
N.A.I.C.S.: 713940
Brett Walters (Plant Mgr)

Unit (Domestic):

Cargill Food Distribution **(2)**

**5215 Wiley Post Way Ste 140, Salt Lake
City, UT 84116-3275**
Tel.: (801) 972-4545
Web Site:
http://www.cargillmeatsolutions.com
Sales Range: $10-24.9 Million
Emp.: 7
Meat Distribution Packer
N.A.I.C.S.: 311612

Cargill Food Distribution **(2)**
4475 E 50th Ave, Denver, CO 80216-4510
Tel.: (303) 283-3250
Web Site:
http://www.cargillmeatsolutions.com
Sales Range: $25-49.9 Million
Emp.: 12
Frozen Meat Distr
N.A.I.C.S.: 311612
Jeanne Schulz (Gen Mgr)

Cargill Logistics **(2)**
2901 N Mead St, Wichita, KS
67219-4242 **(100%)**
Tel.: (316) 832-7600
Sales Range: $10-24.9 Million
Emp.: 80
Contract Hauler Services
N.A.I.C.S.: 484121

Plant (Domestic):

Cargill Meat Solutions **(2)**
480 Coop Dr, Timberville, VA 22853
Tel.: (540) 896-7041
Web Site: http://www.cargillturkey.com
Sales Range: $50-74.9 Million
Emp.: 400
Turkey & Poultry Products Processing
N.A.I.C.S.: 561910

Cargill Meat Solutions **(2)**
8295 Arenzville Rd, Beardstown, IL 62618-
7859
Tel.: (217) 323-6200
Web Site:
http://www.cargillmeatsolutions.com
Sales Range: $125-149.9 Million
Pork Slaughterhouse Services
N.A.I.C.S.: 311611

Cargill Meat Solutions **(2)**
150 Onix Dr Ste 3, Kennett Square, PA
19348
Tel.: (610) 444-1025
Web Site:
http://www.cargillmeatsolutions.com
Sales Range: $10-24.9 Million
Emp.: 30
Meat Whslr
N.A.I.C.S.: 424470
Joe O'Malley (Mgr-Retail Sls-Eastern United
States)

Cargill Meat Solutions **(2)**
590 Rd 9, Schuyler, NE 68661 **(100%)**
Tel.: (402) 352-5411
Web Site: http://www.cargill.com
Sales Range: $125-149.9 Million
Meat Packing Plants
N.A.I.C.S.: 311611

Cargill Meat Solutions **(2)**
4 Miles W Hwy 60, Friona, TX
79035 **(100%)**
Tel.: (806) 295-3201
Web Site:
http://www.cargillmeatsolutions.com
Sales Range: $125-149.9 Million
Emp.: 2,000
Meat Packing Plants
N.A.I.C.S.: 311611
Jamin Phips (Gen Mgr)

Cargill Meat Solutions **(2)**
600 S Iowa Ave, Ottumwa, IA 52501-3657
Tel.: (641) 682-8532
Web Site:
http://www.cargillmeatsolution.com
Sales Range: $1-9.9 Million
Meat Packing Plants
N.A.I.C.S.: 311611
Doug McMullin (Mgr-Pur)

Cargill Meat Solutions **(2)**
Hwy 20 W, Marshall, MO 65340
Tel.: (660) 886-5522
Sales Range: $25-49.9 Million
Emp.: 300
Meat Packing Services

N.A.I.C.S.: 424520
Brian Taylor (Gen Mgr)

Cargill Meat Solutions **(2)**
33 Dart Rd, Newnan, GA 30265-1017
Tel.: (770) 252-5000
Sales Range: $50-74.9 Million
Emp.: 350
Meat Packing Plants
N.A.I.C.S.: 311611
Bradley Down (Gen Mgr)

Cargill Meat Solutions **(2)**
1505 E Burlington Ave, Fort Morgan, CO
80701-4611 **(100%)**
Tel.: (970) 867-8223
Web Site: http://www.cargill.com
Sales Range: $125-149.9 Million
Meat Packing Plants
N.A.I.C.S.: 311611
Mary Ginther (Dir-HR)
Allen Boelter (Gen Mgr)

Cargill Meat Solutions **(2)**
1400 N MacArthur Dr, Tracy, CA 95376-
2837
Tel.: (209) 832-0118
Web Site:
http://www.cargillmeatsolutions.com
Sales Range: $10-24.9 Million
Emp.: 19
Meat Products Producer
N.A.I.C.S.: 424470

Cargill Meat Solutions **(2)**
PO Box 760, Nebraska City, NE
68410-9701 **(100%)**
Tel.: (402) 873-8404
Sales Range: $25-49.9 Million
Emp.: 350
Meat Processing Machinery Mfr
N.A.I.C.S.: 112111

Unit (Domestic):

**Cargill Meat Solutions, Caprock
Cattle Feeders** **(2)**
2795 US Hwy 54 W, Dalhart, TX 79022
Tel.: (806) 384-2333
Sales Range: $10-24.9 Million
Emp.: 55
Grain Services
N.A.I.C.S.: 112112

Cargill Value Added Meats **(2)**
151 N Main St, Wichita, KS 67202
Tel.: (316) 291-2500
Web Site:
http://www.cargillmeatsolutions.com
Meat Product Sales
N.A.I.C.S.: 424440
Chris Seib (Mgr-Mktg)

Subsidiary (Domestic):

Excel Corporation **(2)**
124 Ludwig St, Bushnell, IL
61422-1716 **(100%)**
Tel.: (309) 772-3170
Sales Range: $25-49.9 Million
Emp.: 1
Cargo Loading & Unloading Services
N.A.I.C.S.: 541330

Cargill Middle East DMCC **(1)**
Jumeirah Lakes Towers Saba Tower 1 23rd
Floor Office 2303, PO Box 212453, Dubai,
United Arab Emirates
Tel.: (971) 4 427 8500
Sales Range: $25-49.9 Million
Emp.: 13
Commodity Trading Services
N.A.I.C.S.: 523160

Cargill Nordic A/S **(1)**
Ordrupvej 101 2nd, 2920, Charlottenlund,
Denmark
Tel.: (45) 45 46 9000
Starch & Oil Whslr
N.A.I.C.S.: 424990

Cargill Nordic Oy **(1)**
Toolonkatu 4A, Helsinki, 100, Finland
Tel.: (358) 20 7558 370
Sales Range: $10-24.9 Million
Emp.: 5
Starch Mfr
N.A.I.C.S.: 311221
Tom Karlsson (Mng Dir)

**Cargill Pakistan Holdings (Pvt)
Ltd.** **(1)**

5th Floor Tower B Technology Park
Shahra-e Faisal, Karachi, Pakistan
Tel.: (92) 21 32791227
Animal Feed & Oilseed Mfr
N.A.I.C.S.: 311119

Cargill S.A.C.I. **(1)**
Casilla de Correo 2494, 1000, Buenos Ai-
res, Argentina
Tel.: (54) 11 4317 7000
Web Site: http://www.cargill.com.ar
Sales Range: $250-299,9 Million
Emp.: 4,000
Grain & Oilseed Mfr & Whslr
N.A.I.C.S.: 111191

Cargill S.L.U. **(1)**
C/ Marie Curie n 6, Martorell, 08760, Barce-
lona, Spain
Tel.: (34) 93 773 38 00
Web Site: http://www.cargill.es
Animal Feed & Oilseed Mfr
N.A.I.C.S.: 311224

Cargill SACI Sucursal Uruguay **(1)**
El Gaucho Tower Constituyente 1467 21st
Floor Office 2101 B, 11200, Montevideo,
Uruguay
Tel.: (598) 2 408 7758
Animal Feed Mfr
N.A.I.C.S.: 311119

Cargill Salt **(1)**
9380 Excelsior Blvd MS 21-6, Hopkins, MN
55343 **(100%)**
Tel.: (952) 984-8280
Web Site: http://www.cargillsalt.com
Sales Range: $10-24.9 Million
Emp.: 85
Salt Product Mfr
N.A.I.C.S.: 311942
Sheila Ward (VP-Mktg)
Marcelo Montero (Pres-Bus Unit Leader
Cargill Salt)

Unit (Domestic):

Cargill Salt **(2)**
7220 Central Ave, Newark, CA 94560-4205
Tel.: (510) 797-1820
Web Site: http://www.cargillsalt.com
Salt Mfr
N.A.I.C.S.: 311942

Cargill Salt **(2)**
609 E Avenue G, Hutchinson, KS 67501
Tel.: (620) 663-2141
Web Site: http://www.cargill.com
Salt Mfr
N.A.I.C.S.: 311942

Cargill Salt **(2)**
518 E 4th St, Watkins Glen, NY 14891-
1219
Tel.: (607) 535-6300
Web Site: http://www.cargillsalt.com
Salt Production
N.A.I.C.S.: 311942

Cargill Salt Inc. **(2)**
1835 S Carferry Dr, Milwaukee, WI 53207-
1014
Tel.: (414) 482-2323
Web Site: http://www.cargill.com
Sales Range: $10-24.9 Million
Emp.: 9
Salt Distr
N.A.I.C.S.: 311942
Roy Telland (Gen Mgr)

Cargill South **(1)**
916 South Riverside Ave, Saint Clair, MI
48079-5335 **(100%)**
Tel.: (810) 326-2700
Sales Range: $25-49.9 Million
Emp.: 280
Salt Production
N.A.I.C.S.: 311942

Cargill Srl **(1)**
Via Repamonki 89, 20141, Milan, Italy
Tel.: (39) 02890441
Web Site: http://www.cargill.it
Sales Range: $10-24.9 Million
Emp.: 50
Animal Feed Mfr & Whslr
N.A.I.C.S.: 311119

Cargill Taiwan Corporation **(1)**
7th Fl 149 Hsin Yi Road Sec 3, Taipei,
10658, Taiwan

Tel.: (886) 2 2395 1211
Sales Range: $10-24.9 Million
Emp.: 80
Animal Feed Mfr
N.A.I.C.S.: 311119

Cargill Texturizing Solutions Deutschland GmbH & Co. KG (1)
Ausschlager Elbdeich 62, 20539, Hamburg, Germany
Tel.: (49) 40 78955 0
Web Site: http://www.cargilltexturizing.com
Sales Range: $25-49.9 Million
Emp.: 150
Emulsifier & Chemical Product Mfr
N.A.I.C.S.: 325613
Fabian Wilhelm (Mng Dir)

Cargill Turkey Products (1)
1 Kratzer Ave, Harrisonburg, VA 22802-4567
Tel.: (540) 568-1400
Web Site: http://www.cargillturkey.com
Sales Range: $550-599.9 Million
Emp.: 3,600
Poultry Processing; Feed Mill; Wholesale Building Supplies; Distribution Center
N.A.I.C.S.: 112330

Plant (Domestic):

Cargill Turkey Products (2)
2510 E Lk Shore Dr, Waco, TX 76705-1788
Tel.: (254) 412-3400
Web Site: http://www.cargill.com
Sales Range: $50-74.9 Million
Emp.: 680
Turkeys & Turkey Eggs Production
N.A.I.C.S.: 112330
Leonn Fletcher (Gen Mgr)

Subsidiary (Domestic):

Cargill Turkey Products Farms (2)
5688 S Valley Pke, Mount Crawford, VA 22841
Tel.: (540) 437-8000
Turkey Processing Services
N.A.I.C.S.: 311611

Cargill Turkey Products Feeds, Inc. (2)
1 Kratzer Ave, Harrisonburg, VA 22802-4567
Tel.: (540) 568-1400
Web Site: http://www.cargill.com
Sales Range: $25-49.9 Million
Emp.: 73
Turkey Feed Producers
N.A.I.C.S.: 311119

Plant (Domestic):

Cargill Turkey Products Inc. (2)
135 Huffman Dr, Dayton, VA 22821
Tel.: (540) 879-2521
Web Site: http://www.cargillturkey.com
Sales Range: $150-199.9 Million
Emp.: 1,500
Poultry Processing Services
N.A.I.C.S.: 311615

Cargill West Africa S.A (1)
Boulevard de Vridi Face Socopao, Freichville, Abidjan, Cote d'Ivoire
Tel.: (225) 21 75 2500
Sales Range: $50-74.9 Million
Emp.: 470
Cocoa Product Mfr
N.A.I.C.S.: 311351

Cargill Yug, LLC (1)
268 Kommunarov St, Krasnodar, 350020, Russia
Tel.: (7) 861 210 98 85
Web Site: http://www.cargill.ru
Grain & Oilseed Supplier
N.A.I.C.S.: 311224

Cargill Zimbabwe (Pvt) Limited (1)
Block B Virginia Office Park Virginia Close, Borrowdale, Harare, Zimbabwe
Tel.: (263) 4 851600
Sales Range: $100-124.9 Million
Emp.: 2,000
Cotton Ginning & Soybean Trading Services
N.A.I.C.S.: 115111

Cargill de Mexico, S.A. de C.V. (1)
Antonio Dovali Jaime No 70 Torres C y D Piso 11 Col Santa Fe, Alvaro Obregon Del-

egation, Mexico, 01210, Mexico
Tel.: (52) 5511057400
Web Site: http://www.cargill.com.mx
Emp.: 1,750
Agricultural Goods Distr
N.A.I.C.S.: 424910

Cargill, Inc. - Nutrena Feed (1)
4943 Stepherson Rd, Memphis, TN 38118-7509
Tel.: (901) 795-2660
Web Site: http://www.nutrenaworld.com
Sales Range: $10-24.9 Million
Emp.: 40
Prepared Feed Mfr
N.A.I.C.S.: 311119

Desa Cargill Sdn Bhd (1)
Lot 52 Lorong Sebor Jalan Kelombong off Jalan Tuaran, 88100, Kota Kinabalu, Sabah, Malaysia
Tel.: (60) 88 428996
Sales Range: $10-24.9 Million
Emp.: 60
Animal Feed Mfr & Whslr
N.A.I.C.S.: 311119

EWOS AS (1)
Tollbodallmenningen 1B, PO Box 4, Sentrum, 5803, Bergen, Norway
Tel.: (47) 55697000
Web Site: http://www.ewos.com
Sales Range: $1-9.9 Million
Emp.: 1,049
Fish Feed Mfr
N.A.I.C.S.: 311119
Ian Carr (Dir-Mktg-Westfield)
Brent Baumbusch (CFO)
Karl Tore Maeland (Dir-Sustainability & Quality Mgmt)
Terje Hjertnes (Mgr-IT Bus Relationship)

Subsidiary (Non-US):

EWOS Canada Ltd. (2)
7721 132nd Street, Surrey, V3W 4M8, BC, Canada
Tel.: (604) 591-6368
Web Site: http://www.ewos.com
Emp.: 81
Fish Feed Mfr
N.A.I.C.S.: 311119

EWOS Chile S.A. (2)
Freire 130 piso 6, Puerto Montt, Chile
Tel.: (56) 65 2321100
Web Site: http://www.ewos.com
Emp.: 368
Fish Feed Mfr
N.A.I.C.S.: 311119

Subsidiary (Domestic):

EWOS Chile Alimentos Ltda. (3)
Parque Industrial Escuadron Km 20 Camino, Coronel, Concepcion, Chile
Tel.: (56) 41 220 5700
Web Site: http://www.ewos.com
Fish Feed Mfr
N.A.I.C.S.: 311119
Liliana Barra (Sec)

Subsidiary (Domestic):

EWOS Innovation AS (2)
Dirdalsstranda 51, 4335, Dirdal, Norway
Tel.: (47) 5569 7800
Web Site: http://www.ewos.com
Emp.: 95
Fish Feed Research & Development
N.A.I.C.S.: 541715
Adel El-Mowafi (Mng Dir & Dir-CQN R&D-Sandnes)
Elisabeth S, Urdahl (Dir-HR & Admin Svcs)
Javier Gonzalez (Mgr-R&D)
Dag Torsvik (Mgr-Tech Center)
Elisabeth Eie (Mgr-Res Trial)
Karl Osterhus (Mgr-Lab)
Kjetil Fraejord (Mgr-Sea Sites)
Per Marton Holland (Mgr-Res Station)

Subsidiary (Non-US):

EWOS Limited (2)
Westfield, Bathgate, EH48 3BP, W Lothian, United Kingdom
Tel.: (44) 1506 633 966
Web Site: http://www.ewos.com
Emp.: 71
Fish Feed Mfr
N.A.I.C.S.: 311119

Douglas Low (COO-Other Markets & Mng Dir-UK)
David Morrice (Dir-Comml)
Karen McLeod (Mgr-Logistics)
Ewan Cameron (Acct Mgr)
Lindsay Pollock (Acct Mgr)

Five Star Custom Foods, Ltd. (1)
3709 E 1st St, Fort Worth, TX 76111
Tel.: (682) 647-2790
Web Site: http://www.fivestarcustomfoods.com
General Line Grocery Merchant Whslr
N.A.I.C.S.: 424410
Jeff Bledsoe (Pres)
Cyndi Anderson (Mgr-Office & Pur & Coord-Safety)

M. A. Cargill Trading Ltd. (1)
10-1Fl 149 Hsin Yi Rd Sec 3, Taipei, 10658, Taiwan
Tel.: (886) 2 2703 5308
Sales Range: $25-49.9 Million
Emp.: 15
Agricultural Commodity Trading & Processing Services
N.A.I.C.S.: 523160
Stephen Liu (Gen Mgr)

NatureWorks LLC (1)
15305 Minnetonka Blvd, Minnetonka, MN 55343 **(50%)**
Tel.: (952) 742-0400
Web Site: http://www.natureworksllc.com
Sales Range: $25-49.9 Million
Emp.: 25
Biopolymer Mfr
N.A.I.C.S.: 325414
Steve Davies, (Dir-Comml)
Erik Ripple (Pres & CEO)
Narongsak Jivakanun (Chm)

North American Grain Investments, Inc. (1)
15407 McGinty Rd W, Wayzata, MN 55391-2365
Tel.: (952) 742-7575
Sales Range: $800-899.9 Million
Emp.: 20,000
Grain & Field Bean Sales
N.A.I.C.S.: 424510

Nutrena Feeds (1)
2260 Industrial Park Rd, Giddings, TX 78942-6430
Tel.: (979) 542-3133
Web Site: http://www.nutrena.com
Sales Range: $10-24.9 Million
Emp.: 50
Poultry & Animal Feed Mfr
N.A.I.C.S.: 311119
John Dowell (Office Mgr)

OPX Biotechnologies Inc. (1)
2425 55th St Ste 100, Boulder, CO 80301-5700
Tel.: (303) 243-5190
Web Site: http://www.opxbio.com
Biotechnology Solutions for Development of Bio-Based Chemicals
N.A.I.C.S.: 541714
Michael J. Rosenberg (Pres & CEO)
Barbara E. Baring (VP-HR)
Doug A. Hogsett (CTO & VP-R&D)

Owensboro Grain Company, LLC (1)
822 E 2nd St, Owensboro, KY 42303-3302
Tel.: (270) 926-2032
Web Site: http://www.owensborograin.com
Sales Range: $100-124.9 Million
Emp.: 150
Agricultural Services
N.A.I.C.S.: 311224
John Wright (Exec VP)

Subsidiary (Domestic):

Owensboro Grain Biodiesel, LLC (2)
1145 Ewing Rd, Owensboro, KY 42301
Tel.: (270) 926-2032
Web Site: http://www.owensborograins.com
Chemical Products Mfr
N.A.I.C.S.: 325199
James Stahler (Mgr-Sls)

PT Cargill Indonesia (1)
Wisma 46 Kota BNI 28th FL Suite 2801 Jl Jend Sudirman Kav 1, Jakarta, 10220, Indonesia
Tel.: (62) 21 5746868

Web Site: http://www.cargill.co.id
Sales Range: $100-124.9 Million
Emp.: 1,000
Animal Feed Mfr
N.A.I.C.S.: 311119

Subsidiary (Domestic):

PT Cargill Indonesia Gunung Putri (2)
Jl Raya Tlajung Udik Gunung Putri Citeureup, Bogor, 16962, Jawa Barat, Indonesia
Tel.: (62) 21 8672263
Animal Feed Mfr
N.A.I.C.S.: 311119

PT Harapan Sawit Lestari (2)
Desa Manismata Kecamatan Manismata, Ketapang, West Kalimantan, Indonesia
Tel.: (62) 21 30022988
Palm Oil Mfr
N.A.I.C.S.: 311224

PT Hindoli (2)
Jl Raya Palembang-Jambi Desa Teluk Kemang, Kecamatan Sungai Lilin Muba, Palembang, South Sumatera, Indonesia
Tel.: (62) 714 321818
Oilseed Mfr & Whslr
N.A.I.C.S.: 424590

PT Sorini Agro Asia Corporindo Tbk. (1)
Jl Raya Surabaya - Malang Km 43, Kecamatan Gempol, Pasuruan, 67155, Jawa Timur, Indonesia **(85.01%)**
Tel.: (62) 343631776
Web Site: http://www.sorini.co.id
Sales Range: $150-199.9 Million
Emp.: 775
Starch & Starch Sweetener Supplier
N.A.I.C.S.: 311221

Pet Carousel Inc. (1)
2350 Academy Ave, Sanger, CA 93657
Tel.: (559) 875-2232
Web Site: http://www.petcarousel.com
Sales Range: $1-9.9 Million
Emp.: 25
Pet Treats & Chews Mfr
N.A.I.C.S.: 311111
Stephen Flores (Mgr)

Prairie Malt Limited (1)
602 4th Ave E, PO Box 1150, Biggar, S0K 0M0, SK, Canada
Tel.: (306) 948-3500
Web Site: http://www.prairiemalt.com
Sales Range: $25-49.9 Million
Emp.: 40
Barley Malt Mfr
N.A.I.C.S.: 311213
David Klinger (VP-Sls)

Provimi S.A. (1)
9-11 avenue Arago, F-78190, Trappes, France **(87.4%)**
Tel.: (33) 134827901
Web Site: http://www.provimi.com
Sales Range: $1-4.9 Billion
Emp.: 7,000
Holding Company; Pet & Farm Animal Feed & Nutritional Supplements Mfr
N.A.I.C.S.: 551112

Subsidiary (Non-US):

Provimi Holding B.V. (2)
Veilingweg 23, 5334 LD, Velddriel, Netherlands **(100%)**
Tel.: (31) 104239500
Web Site: http://www.provimi.nl
Sales Range: $125-149.9 Million
Emp.: 170
Holding Company
N.A.I.C.S.: 551112
Adriaan Smulders (Mgr-Tech & Strategic Mktg)
Jose Castillo (Mgr-Customer Svc)

Joint Venture (Non-US):

NuTec Southern Africa (Pty) Ltd. (3)
234 Royston Road, Willowton, 3201, Pietermaritzburg, South Africa **(75%)**
Tel.: (27) 333979405
Web Site: http://www.nutecsa.co.za
Sales Range: $25-49.9 Million
Emp.: 50
Animal Vitamin & Mineral Premix Mfr

Cargill, Inc.—(Continued)

N.A.I.C.S.: 311119

Subsidiary (Domestic):

Provimi B.V. **(3)**
Veerlaan 17-23, Rotterdam, 3072 AN, Netherlands **(100%)**
Tel.: (31) 104239500
Web Site: http://www.provimi.nl
Sales Range: $25-49.9 Million
Emp.: 150
Farm Animal Feed & Nutritional Supplements Mfr
N.A.I.C.S.: 311119
Mark Poes (CEO)

Subsidiary (Non-US):

Provimi France **(3)**
Parc d'activite de Ferchaud, BP 10, F-35320, Crevin, Ille-et-Vilaine, France **(100%)**
Tel.: (33) 299426262
Web Site: http://www.provimifrance.com
Animal Feed Nutritional Supplement Mfr
N.A.I.C.S.: 311119
Joel Jacquemard (Mgr-Export)

Subsidiary (US):

Provimi North America, Inc. **(3)**
10 Collective Way, Brookville, OH 45309
Tel.: (937) 770-2400
Web Site: http://www.provimi-na.com
Emp.: 400
Animal Feed & Nutritional Supplements Mfr
N.A.I.C.S.: 311119
Charles Shininger (Pres, CEO & Mng Dir)
Ken Bryant (VP & Mgr-Technical)
Dean Barker (Dir-Ops)
Brett Hartman (CFO & Treas)
Nicole Neal (Dir-HR)
Chad Meeks (Dir-Matls Mgmt)

Unit (Domestic):

Akey **(4)**
250 W Clay St, Lewisburg, OH 45338
Tel.: (937) 962-7038
Web Site: http://www.akey.com
Sales Range: $25-49.9 Million
Emp.: 50
Farm Animal Feed Nutritional Supplements Developer & Mfr
N.A.I.C.S.: 311119
Charles Shininger (Mng Dir)
Doug Cook (Dir-Innovation)
Jim Aldrich (Dir-Ruminant Nutrition)
Wayne Williams (Dir-Poultry Nutrition)
Kevin Cera (Dir-Tech Svcs-Swine)
Betsy Newton (Dir-Swine Tech Svcs)
Scott Andrews (Dir-Comml-Poultry)
Chris Steiner (Dir-Comml-Swine)
Clint Calk (Dir-Comml-Ruminant)

Subsidiary (Domestic):

Nutrius, LLC **(4)**
39494 Clarkson Dr, Kingsburg, CA 93631 **(100%)**
Tel.: (559) 897-5862
Web Site: http://www.nutrius.com
Animal Vitamins & Nutritional Supplements Mfr
N.A.I.C.S.: 311119
Bob Van Der Schaaf (Mgr-Sls-Texas)

Progressive Nutrition, LLC **(4)**
PO Box 429, Harlan, IA 51537 **(65%)**
Tel.: (712) 235-3185
Web Site: http://www.prognutrition.com
Sales Range: $50-74.9 Million
Emp.: 9
Equine Nutritional Supplements Mfr
N.A.I.C.S.: 311119
Tom Trotter (Gen Mgr)

Unit (Domestic):

Vigortone Ag Products **(4)**
10 Collective Way, Brookville, OH 45309
Tel.: (937) 770-2400
Web Site: http://www.vigortone.com
Sales Range: $50-74.9 Million
Emp.: 120
Farm Animal Feed Nutritional Supplements Mfr
N.A.I.C.S.: 311119

Randy Dew (Dir-Tech Svcs)
Tim Osborn (Reg Mgr-Sls)

Subsidiary (Domestic):

Virtus Nutrition, LLC **(4)**
520 Industrial Way, Corcoran, CA 93212 **(100%)**
Tel.: (559) 992-5033
Web Site: http://www.virtusnutrition.com
Dairy Cow Feed Nutritional Supplements Mfr
N.A.I.C.S.: 311119
Renee Smith (Mgr-Sls-West)
Daniel Andreasen (Mgr-Sls-East)
Jorge Matos (Mgr-Sls-Southern)
Kevin Murphy (Dir-Technical-Global)

Sanderson Farms, Inc. **(1)**
127 Flynt Rd, Laurel, MS 39443
Tel.: (601) 649-4030
Web Site: https://www.sandersonfarms.com
Rev.: $4,799,653,000
Assets: $2,345,033,000
Liabilities: $494,794,000
Net Worth: $1,850,239,000
Earnings: $455,089,000
Emp.: 17,662
Fiscal Year-end: 10/31/2021
Production of Fresh Ice Pack Poultry, Whole Birds & Parts, Frozen Frying Chicken Parts, Corn Dogs & Prepared Entrees
N.A.I.C.S.: 311615
Timothy F. Rigney (Chief Acctg Officer & Sec)

Division (Domestic):

Sanderson Farms, Inc. - Foods Division **(2)**
4418 Magum Dr Flodde, Jackson, MS 39232
Tel.: (601) 939-9790
Web Site: http://www.sandersonfarms.com
Production of Prepared Foods
N.A.I.C.S.: 311412

Sanderson Farms, Inc. - Processing Division **(2)**
PO Box 988, Laurel, MS 39441-0988
Tel.: (601) 649-4030
Web Site: http://www.sandersonfarms.com
Emp.: 3,000
Processing of Fresh & Frozen Poultry
N.A.I.C.S.: 311615
David Michael Cockrell (CFO & Treas)
Lampkin Butts (Pres & COO)
Joe Frank Sanderson Jr. (Chm & CEO)

Toshoku Ltd. **(1)**
Fuji Bldg 3 2 3 Marunouchi Chiyoda Ku, Tokyo, 100 0005, Japan
Tel.: (81) 352245600
Web Site: http://www.toshoku.co.jp
Sales Range: $1-4.9 Billion
Emp.: 200
Trader in Grain, Feedstuffs, Fertilizers, Agricultural & Marine Products
N.A.I.C.S.: 926140

Subsidiary (US):

Toshoku America, Inc. **(2)**
2 Executive Dr Ste 760, Fort Lee, NJ 07024-3310 **(100%)**
Tel.: (201) 363-0720
Sales Range: $50-74.9 Million
Emp.: 4
Trading
N.A.I.C.S.: 424490

CARGO LOGISTICS BY J. CIOFFI INC.
60 Minue St, Carteret, NJ 07008
Tel.: (732) 969-0035
Web Site:
http://www.j.cifficargomgmt.com
Rev.: $10,600,000
Emp.: 50
Truck Transportation Brokers
N.A.I.C.S.: 484121
Joseph Cioffi (Pres)

CARGO TRANSPORTATION SERVICES INC.
1300 Sawgrass Corporate Pkwy Ste

110, Sunrise, FL 33323-2823
Tel.: (954) 718-5555
Web Site: http://www.cargotsi.com
Year Founded: 1999
Sales Range: $75-99.9 Million
Emp.: 75
Logistics & Transportation Services
N.A.I.C.S.: 484121
Rawlee Genchi (Mgr-Bus Dev)

CARGO, LLC
914 Pendleton St Ste 300, Greenville, SC 29601
Tel.: (864) 704-1160 SC
Web Site:
http://www.thecargoagency.com
Advetising Agency
N.A.I.C.S.: 541810
Daniel L. Gliatta (CEO)
Rick Bryson (Assoc Creative Dir)
Miki Velemirovich (Pres-Canada)
Nicolas Rouleau (Mgr-Client Engagement)

CARHART LUMBER COMPANY
105 Main St, Wayne, NE 68787
Tel.: (402) 375-2110
Web Site:
https://www.carhartlumber.com
Sales Range: $10-24.9 Million
Emp.: 125
Lumber & Other Building Materials
N.A.I.C.S.: 423310
Scott Brian Carhart (Pres)
Judy Martindale (Controller)
Mike Herbolsheimer (VP & Mgr)
Tod Johnson (Mgr-Sls)
Mike Lech (VP & Mgr-North Platte)
Kelly Kerkman (Mgr-Neligh)
Mike Kaup (Mgr)
Dennis Ryan (VP & Mgr-O'Neill)
Kim McDaniel (Mgr-Norfolk)
John Kramer (Mgr-Hartington)
Kevin Mlady (Mgr-Bloomfield)
Kim Carhart (Mgr)
Brandi Lanman (Dir-Mktg)

CARHARTT, INC.
5750 Mercury Dr, Dearborn, MI 48126-4234
Tel.: (313) 271-8460 MI
Web Site: http://www.carhartt.com
Year Founded: 1889
Sales Range: $75-99.9 Million
Emp.: 40
Mfr of Utility & Work Clothes & Outer Wear
N.A.I.C.S.: 315250
William Hardy (Sr VP-Supply Chain)
Joe Monahan (Sr VP-Sls)
Linda Hubbard (Pres & COO)
Todd Corley (Sr VP-Inclusion & Sustainability)
Kerry Middlemas (VP-Bus Planning)
Katrina Agusti (CIO)
Susan Hennike (Chief Brand Officer)
Tara Roemke (VP-Global Mdsg)

CARI INVESTMENT COMPANY
1100 Poydras St Ste 2000, New Orleans, LA 70163-1121
Tel.: (504) 585-7730 LA
Year Founded: 1961
Sales Range: $50-74.9 Million
Emp.: 260
Security Brokers & Dealers
N.A.I.C.S.: 523150
Christian G. Vaccari (Chm, Pres & CEO)

Subsidiaries:

Cari Capital Company, LLC **(1)**
1100 Poydras St Ste 2000, New Orleans, LA 70163-1121 **(100%)**

Tel.: (504) 585-7730
Rev.: $240,000
Emp.: 3
Security Brokers & Dealers
N.A.I.C.S.: 523150

CARIBBEAN AUTO MART INC.
4025 Annas Retreat, Charlotte Amalie, VI 00802
Tel.: (340) 777-7600
Web Site:
http://www.caribbeanautomart.com
Sales Range: $10-24.9 Million
Emp.: 100
Sales of New & Used Cars
N.A.I.C.S.: 441110
Miguel Concepcion (Mgr-Svc)
Ira Mactavious (Mgr-Svc)

CARIBBEAN CINEMAS
1512 Fernandez Juncos Ave, San Juan, PR 00909
Tel.: (787) 727-7137
Web Site:
https://www.caribbeancinemas.com
Sales Range: $75-99.9 Million
Emp.: 800
Motion Picture Theater Operator
N.A.I.C.S.: 512131
Jose Feliciano (Controller)
Robert Carrady (Pres)

CARIBBEAN COFFEE COMPANY, INC.
495 Pine Ave Ste A, Goleta, CA 93117
Tel.: (805) 962-3201
Web Site:
http://www.caribbeancoffee.com
Year Founded: 1986
Sales Range: $10-24.9 Million
Emp.: 25
Roasted Coffee Mfr
N.A.I.C.S.: 311920
John Goerke (Owner)

CARIBBEAN FOOD DELIGHTS
117 Route 303 Ste B, Tappan, NY 10983
Tel.: (845) 398-3000
Web Site:
http://www.caribbeanfooddelights.com
Year Founded: 1978
Rev.: $18,300,000
Emp.: 70
Full-Service Restaurants
N.A.I.C.S.: 722511
Vincent HoSang (Pres & CEO)

CARIBBEAN INDUSTRIAL CONSTRUCTION SE
PO Box 29726, San Juan, PR 00929-0726
Tel.: (787) 287-3540
Sales Range: $50-74.9 Million
Emp.: 600
Civil Engineering Services
N.A.I.C.S.: 237310
Fred Gallo (Pres)
Gustavo Hermida (Pres)

CARIBBEAN MEDICAL BROKERS, INC.
3882 NW 124th Ave, Coral Springs, FL 33065
Tel.: (954) 752-5603 FL
Web Site:
http://www.specialtymedical.com
Year Founded: 1999
Sales Range: $10-24.9 Million
Emp.: 10
Medical, Dental & Hospital Equipment & Supplies Merchant Whslr
N.A.I.C.S.: 423450
Charles Starnes (Exec VP)

CARIBBEAN PACIFIC MARKETING, INC.
2295 Corporate Blvd NW Ste 131, Boca Raton, FL 33431
Tel.: (561) 208-6706   FL
Year Founded: 2012
Sun & Skin Care Products
N.A.I.C.S.: 325620
Thomas J. Hagan *(Pres)*
Kevin McDonnell *(Sec)*

CARIBBEAN TEMPORARY SERVICES INC.
1431 Ave Ponce De Leon, San Juan, PR 00909
Tel.: (787) 724-5643
Web Site: http://www.ctspr.com
Sales Range: $25-49.9 Million
Emp.: 70
Temporary Help Service
N.A.I.C.S.: 561320
Tere Durand Manzanal *(Founder & Pres)*
Xiomara Villamil *(VP)*
Rose Villimil *(VP)*

CARIBCOM, INC.
135 W 29th St Ste 404, New York, NY 10001
Tel.: (212) 242-4700
Web Site:
   http://www.caribcominc.com
Year Founded: 1988
Sales Range: $1-9.9 Million
Emp.: 4
Advetising Agency
N.A.I.C.S.: 541810
Scott Powers *(Pres)*

CARIBE FOOD CORPORATION
7350 NW 30th Ave, Miami, FL 33147
Tel.: (305) 835-7110
Web Site: http://www.caribefood.com
Rev.: $11,700,000
Emp.: 60
Fresh Fruit & Vegetable Merchant Whslr
N.A.I.C.S.: 424480
Magaly Machado *(Office Mgr)*
Hilda Rodriguez *(Treas)*
Guillermo P. Rodriguez *(Pres & CEO)*

CARIBE MEDIA, INC.
PO Box 192819, San Juan, PR 00919-2819
Tel.: (787) 771-6102
Web Site:
   http://www.caribemediainc.com
Holding Company
N.A.I.C.S.: 551112
Pedro Cabrera *(CEO)*
Rafael Rodriguez *(CFO)*
Rafael Santana *(Sr Dir-Ops)*
Amelia Paniagua *(Dir-CPO)*

Subsidiaries:

Axesa Servicios de Informacion, S. en C.   **(1)**
400 Ave Americo Miranda 5th Fl, San Juan, PR 00926
Tel.: (787) 758-2828
Web Site: http://www.axesa.com
Sales Range: $25-49.9 Million
Emp.: 250
Directory Publisher
N.A.I.C.S.: 513140
Rafael Rodriguez *(Dir-Fin)*

CARIBE BOAT SALES & MARINA INC.
81500 Overseas Hwy, Islamorada, FL 33036
Tel.: (786) 420-3834
Web Site:
   https://www.caribeeboats.com
Sales Range: $10-24.9 Million
Emp.: 20

Boat Dealers
N.A.I.C.S.: 441222
William Gilbert *(Pres)*
Dianne Harbaugh *(Mgr-Parts)*

CARIBEX WORLDWIDE INC.
4248 Piedmont Pkwy, Greensboro, NC 27410
Tel.: (336) 315-0443
Web Site: http://www.caribex.com
Sales Range: $25-49.9 Million
Emp.: 41
Freight Forwarding Services
N.A.I.C.S.: 488510
John Ford *(Pres)*

Subsidiaries:

CaribEx Worldwide Inc. - Cancun Facility   **(1)**
Calle Cholul Sm 502 M 6 Lt 27 Fraccionamiento Pehaltun, 77535, Cancun, Quintana Roo, Mexico
Tel.: (52) 998 267 80 65
Logistics Consulting Servies
N.A.I.C.S.: 541614

CaribEx Worldwide Inc. - Guatemala City Facility   **(1)**
4A Avenida A 13-72 Zona 9 Oficina 2-segundo nivel, Guatemala, Guatemala
Tel.: (502) 2502 8800
Web Site: http://www.caribexworldwide.com
Logistics Consulting Servies
N.A.I.C.S.: 541614
Jessica Lara *(Mgr)*

CaribEx Worldwide Inc. - Managua Facility   **(1)**
De Banpro Altamira 2 Cuadras Abajo No 75, Managua, Nicaragua
Tel.: (505) 270 3271
Logistics Consulting Servies
N.A.I.C.S.: 541614

CaribEx Worldwide Inc. - Olocuilta Facility   **(1)**
Zona Franca Miramar 7B Km 30 5 Carretera al Aeropuerto, Olocuilta, La Paz, El Salvador
Tel.: (503) 2325 7100
Logistics Consulting Servies
N.A.I.C.S.: 541614

CaribEx Worldwide Inc. - San Pedro Sula Facility   **(1)**
2do Anillo Periferico 20-27 Calle Edificio 22 Zip San Jose, San Pedro Sula, Honduras
Tel.: (504) 2544 1022
Logistics Consulting Servies
N.A.I.C.S.: 541614

CaribEx Worldwide Inc. - Santo Domingo Facility   **(1)**
Deposito 10 Zona de Carga Aeropuerto Las Americas, Santo Domingo, Dominican Republic
Tel.: (809) 549 0131
Logistics Consulting Servies
N.A.I.C.S.: 541614

CaribEx Worldwide, Inc.   **(1)**
Carr 110 Km 24.6 Bo Arenales, Aguadilla, PR 00604
Tel.: (787) 658-7000
Web Site: http://www.caribex.com
Global Logistics Services
N.A.I.C.S.: 481212
Peter A. Chatt *(VP)*
Joseph R. Chatt Jr. *(Pres)*

Division (Domestic):

CaribEx Worldwide   **(2)**
Carr 110 Km 24.6 Bo Arenales, Aguadilla, PR 00604
Tel.: (787) 658-7000
Web Site: http://www.caribex.com
Sales Range: $25-49.9 Million
Schedule Air Freight
N.A.I.C.S.: 488510
Yamil Gonzalez *(Gen Mgr)*
Joselin Ramos *(VP)*
John A. Ford *(Co-Pres)*
Pedro Vega *(Mgr-Sls)*
Joseph R. Chatt Jr. *(Co-Pres)*

Subsidiary (Non-US):

Caribe Freight   **(2)**
Ave George Washington 105, Santo Domingo, 5109, Dominican Republic
Tel.: (809) 687 0852
Web Site: http://www.caribex.com
Sales Range: $25-49.9 Million
Emp.: 35
Air & Ocean Freight Forwarding; Dominican Customs Broker
N.A.I.C.S.: 488510
Louredes Viloria *(Mng Dir)*

CARIBOU CORPORATION
5200 Ryder Rd, Eau Claire, WI 54701-9678
Tel.: (715) 834-9624   WI
Web Site: http://www.wrres.com
Year Founded: 1999
Sales Range: $25-49.9 Million
Emp.: 80
Holding Company
N.A.I.C.S.: 551112
James L. Hager *(Pres & CEO)*

Subsidiaries:

WRR Environmental Services Co., Inc.   **(1)**
5200 Ryder Rd, Eau Claire, WI 54701-9678   **(100%)**
Tel.: (715) 834-9624
Web Site: http://www.wrres.com
Sales Range: $10-24.9 Million
Mfr of Refuse Systems
N.A.I.C.S.: 562920
James L. Hager *(Pres & CEO)*
Eric Gunderson *(VP-Lab Ops)*
Bob Fuller *(Controller)*

Subsidiary (Domestic):

North West Enterprises   **(2)**
5100 State Rd 93, Eau Claire, WI 54701-9614
Tel.: (715) 834-8426
Web Site: http://www.nwe-co.com
Industrial Coatings & Metal Fabrication
N.A.I.C.S.: 423120
Dave Gram *(Gen Mgr)*

CARICO INTERNATIONAL INC.
2851 W Cypress Creek Rd, Fort Lauderdale, FL 33309
Tel.: (954) 973-3900
Web Site: https://www.carico.com
Year Founded: 1967
Sales Range: $50-74.9 Million
Emp.: 113
Provider of Home Furnishing Services
N.A.I.C.S.: 449129
Richard R. Cappadona *(Pres)*
David Hess *(Controller)*
Manju Torres *(VP)*
Ernie Spardy *(VP-Ops)*

CARILION HEALTH SYSTEM
1906 Belleview Ave, Roanoke, VA 24014
Tel.: (540) 981-7000
Web Site: http://www.carilionclinic.org
Sales Range: $750-799.9 Million
Emp.: 9,600
Hospital & Health Care Services
N.A.I.C.S.: 622110
Briggs W. Andrews *(Gen Counsel)*
Donald E. Lorton *(CFO)*
Brucie Boggs *(Sr VP-HR)*

CARING MATTERS HOME CARE
1333 Wayne St, Reading, PA 19601-1727
Tel.: (610) 374-6522
Web Site:
   http://www.caringmatterscare.com
Year Founded: 2002
Sales Range: $1-9.9 Million
Emp.: 220

Nursing Staff & Non-Medical Personal Care Services to In-Home Patients
N.A.I.C.S.: 561320
Russell Piper *(Founder & CEO)*

CARING PARTNERS INTERNATIONAL
601 Shotwell Dr, Franklin, OH 45005
Tel.: (937) 743-2744   IL
Web Site:
   https://www.caringpartners.org
Year Founded: 1992
Sales Range: $10-24.9 Million
Emp.: 6
Community Health Care Services
N.A.I.C.S.: 621498
Rhonda J. Reed *(Exec Dir)*
Andrew Wienhoff *(Mgr-Warehouse)*

CARING SENIOR SERVICE
201 E Park Ave Ste 200, San Antonio, TX 78212
Tel.: (210) 227-9494
Web Site:
   https://www.caringseniorservice.com
Year Founded: 1991
Sales Range: $1-9.9 Million
Emp.: 13
Senior Care Services
N.A.I.C.S.: 621610
Bob Hays *(CFO)*
Vanessa Wagster *(Dir)*

CARIS LIFE SCIENCES, LTD.
750 W John Carpenter Fwy Ste 800, Irving, TX 75039
Tel.: (866) 771-8946
Web Site:
   http://www.carislifesciences.com
Year Founded: 1996
Bio Technology Services
N.A.I.C.S.: 541714
David D. Halbert *(Chm & CEO)*
Matthew Oberley *(Exec Dir-Medical)*
David Spetzler *(Pres & Chief Scientific Officer)*
Brian J. Brille *(Vice Chm)*
Chadi Nabhan *(Chm-Precision Oncology Alliance)*
Rob Clark *(Chief Comm Officer & Sr VP)*
George W. Sledge Jr. *(Chief Medical Officer & Exec VP)*

Subsidiaries:

Pharmatech, Inc.   **(1)**
789 Sherman St Ste 310, Denver, CO 80203
Tel.: (720) 917-7477
Web Site: http://www.pharmatech.com
Commercial Physical Research Noncommercial Research Organization
N.A.I.C.S.: 541714
Matthew Wiener *(Pres)*

CARITAS CORPORATION
5520 Trabuco Rd, Irvine, CA 92620
Tel.: (949) 727-0568   CA
Web Site: http://www.caritascorp.org
Year Founded: 1996
Sales Range: $10-24.9 Million
Emp.: 3
Housing & Community Development Services
N.A.I.C.S.: 624229
Penny Serna *(CFO)*
John Woolley *(COO)*
Thomas A. Mauro *(Chief Mission Officer)*
Robert R. Redwitz *(CEO & Chm)*

CARITHERS WALLACE COURTENAY LLC
4343 NE Expwy, Atlanta, GA 30340
Tel.: (770) 493-8200

Carithers Wallace Courtenay
LLC—(Continued)

Web Site: https://www.c-w-c.com
Sales Range: $50-74.9 Million
Emp.: 155
Office Furniture
N.A.I.C.S.: 423210
Paul Conley *(Pres)*
Dave Randolph *(Principal)*
Hal Brandon *(Principal)*
Scott Marshall *(Principal)*
Kyle Ryan *(Principal)*

CARL BELT INC.
11521 Milnor Ave, Cumberland, MD
21502-5131
Tel.: (301) 729-8900   **MD**
Web Site:
   https://www.thebeltgroup.com
Year Founded: 1977
Sales Range: $25-49.9 Million
Emp.: 200
Nonresidential Construction Services
N.A.I.C.S.: 236220
Mark Ferris *(VP)*
Adam Sterne *(Project Mgr)*
Jared Burkett *(Project Mgr)*
Carl Belt Jr. *(Pres)*

CARL BLACK AUTOMOTIVE GROUP, LLC
1110 Roberts Blvd, Kennesaw, GA
30114
Tel.: (770) 424-2200   **GA**
Web Site:
   http://www.carlblackkennesaw.com
Emp.: 40
New & Used Automobile Dealer
N.A.I.C.S.: 441110
Mike Eowsher *(Pres)*
Rodney McDaniel *(Owner)*

Subsidiaries:

Carl Black of Orlando, LLC   (1)
11500 E Colonial Dr, Orlando, FL 32817
Tel.: (407) 849-0610
Web Site:
   http://www.carlblackchevybuickgmc.com
Sales Range: $50-74.9 Million
New & Used Car Dealer
N.A.I.C.S.: 441110
Omar Rodriguez *(Gen Mgr)*

CARL BLACK CHEVROLET CO., INC.
909 Elm Hill Pike, Nashville, TN
37210
Tel.: (615) 259-7510
Sales Range: $75-99.9 Million
Emp.: 250
Car Whslr
N.A.I.C.S.: 441110
RC Whiteaker *(Pres)*

CARL BLOOM ASSOCIATES, INC.
81 Main St Ste 126, White Plains, NY
10601-1711
Tel.: (914) 761-2800   **NY**
Web Site: http://www.carlbloom.com
Year Founded: 1976
Advetising Agency
N.A.I.C.S.: 541810
Carl Bloom *(Pres)*
Brooke Grossman Coneys *(Sr VP & Gen Mgr)*
Dave Johns *(VP-Mktg & Creative)*
Robert Bloom *(VP-Creative & Dir-Electronic Mktg)*
Carmen Oliveras *(Dir-Production)*
Yalexa Corchado *(Mgr-Traffic & Asst Mgr-Production)*
Norberto Malpica *(Mgr-Bus)*
Britt Rosenbaum *(Art Dir & Mgr-Studio)*
Deniz Isler *(Dir-Strategy & Plng)*

Carrie Bloom *(VP-Client Svcs)*
Mike Renna *(Office Mgr)*
Luke Vander Linden *(VP-Integrated Mktg Svcs)*
Theresa Jahn *(Designer)*
Maciej Przybylowski *(Dir-Database Mktg)*

CARL BOLANDER & SONS CO., INC.
251 Starkey St, Saint Paul, MN
55107-1821
Tel.: (651) 224-6299   **MN**
Web Site: https://www.bolander.com
Year Founded: 1924
Earthmoving, Excavating, Refuse
Systems Construction & Contractor
N.A.I.C.S.: 236210
Mark R. Ryan *(Co-Owner & Pres)*
Tim Gillen *(CFO)*
Rick O'Gara *(CEO)*

CARL BUDDIG & COMPANY
950 175th St, Homewood, IL 60430-
2027
Tel.: (708) 798-0900
Web Site: http://www.buddig.com
Year Founded: 1886
Processed & Smoked Meats & Other
Meat Products
N.A.I.C.S.: 311611
Robert Gay *(VP-Mktg)*

Subsidiaries:

Old Wisconsin Sausage   (1)
5030 Playbird Rd, Sheboygan, WI
53083-1878   (100%)
Tel.: (920) 458-4304
Web Site: http://www.oldwisconsin.com
Sales Range: $25-49.9 Million
Emp.: 200
Mfr of Specialty Sausage
N.A.I.C.S.: 311612
Charlie Reschke *(Coord-Label)*
Brian Jung *(Mgr-Warehouse)*
Diane Muscari *(Mgr-Bus Dev)*

CARL COLTERYAHN DAIRY INC.
1601 Brownsville Rd, Pittsburgh, PA
15210
Tel.: (412) 881-1408
Web Site:
   http://www.colteryahndairy.com
Rev.: $10,300,000
Emp.: 45
Dairy Products Producer.
N.A.I.C.S.: 424430
Dan Enis *(Controller)*
Carl Colteryahn Jr. *(VP & Gen Mgr)*
Carl Colteryahn III *(VP)*

CARL E. WOODWARD LLC
1019 South Dupre St, New Orleans,
LA 70125
Tel.: (504) 822-6443
Web Site:
   http://www.carlewoodward.com
Year Founded: 1924
Sales Range: $50-74.9 Million
Emp.: 200
Provider of Industrial Building Con-
struction Services
N.A.I.C.S.: 236210
Paul H. Flower *(Pres & CEO)*
Armand LaGardeur *(Chm)*
Terry McCubbin *(CFO)*
William R. LeCorgne Jr. *(COO)*

CARL ERIC JOHNSON INC.
1725 Macleod Dr, Lawrenceville, GA
30043-5718
Tel.: (678) 377-3100
Web Site: https://www.cejco.net
Emp.: 32
Pumps & Pumping Equipment Distr

N.A.I.C.S.: 423830
Roy Leffew *(Pres)*
Faye Madigan *(CFO)*
Ken Purl *(Mgr-Parts)*
Gordon Hamilton *(Engr)*

CARL F. STATZ & SONS INC.
6101 Hogan Rd, Waunakee, WI
53597
Tel.: (608) 849-4101
Web Site: https://www.carlfstatz.com
Sales Range: $10-24.9 Million
Emp.: 40
Farm Implements
N.A.I.C.S.: 423820
Ronald W. Statz *(Pres)*

CARL FISCHER, LLC
65 Bleecker St, New York, NY 10012-
2420
Tel.: (212) 777-0900
Web Site: http://www.carlfischer.com
Year Founded: 1872
Sales Range: $75-99.9 Million
Emp.: 25
Music Publisher Dealer Services
N.A.I.C.S.: 512230
Larry Clark *(VP & Editor-in-Chief)*
Hayden Connor *(Pres)*

Subsidiaries:

Carl Fischer Music Distributors,
Inc.   (1)
312 S. Wabash Ave., Chicago, IL 60604
Tel.: (312) 427-6652
Print Music Distributor & Retail Store
N.A.I.C.S.: 424990

CARL GREGORY CHRYSLER
3700 Bristol Hwy, Johnson City, TN
37604
Tel.: (423) 282-3011
Web Site:
   http://www.cgjohnsoncity.com
Sales Range: $25-49.9 Million
Emp.: 50
New & Used Car Dealers
N.A.I.C.S.: 441110
Robbie Clark *(Asst Mgr-Svc)*

CARL HOGAN AUTOMOTIVE, INC.
2333 Hwy 45 N, Columbus, MS
39705
Tel.: (662) 328-3514
Web Site: https://www.carlhogan.com
Year Founded: 1996
Sales Range: $10-24.9 Million
Emp.: 85
Car Whslr
N.A.I.C.S.: 441110
Carl Hogan *(Owner)*

CARL M. FREEMAN ASSOCI-ATES, INC.
111 Rockville Pike Ste 1100, Rock-
ville, MD 20850
Tel.: (240) 453-3000   **MD**
Web Site:
   http://www.freemancompanies.com
Year Founded: 1947
Sales Range: $150-199.9 Million
Emp.: 300
Real Estate Development & Manage-
ment
N.A.I.C.S.: 925120
Michelle DiFebo Freeman *(Owner, Pres & CEO)*
David E. Levitsky *(CFO & Sr VP)*
Valle Bonhag *(Mgr-Property)*
Louie Andrakakos *(Sr Mgr-Property)*

Subsidiaries:

Carl M. Freeman Communities,
LLC   (1)
18330 Village Ctr Dr Fl 2, Olney, MD 20832

Tel.: (240) 779-8000
Sales Range: $25-49.9 Million
Emp.: 50
Community Housing Development
N.A.I.C.S.: 925120

Carl M. Freeman Golf, LLC   (1)
18330 Village Ctr Dr, Olney, MD 20832
Tel.: (240) 779-8000
Golf Course Development
N.A.I.C.S.: 531390

Carl M. Freeman Retail LLC   (1)
111 Rockville Pike Ste 1100, Rockville, MD
20850
Tel.: (240) 453-3000
Web Site: http://www.cmfretail.com
Sales Range: $10-24.9 Million
Emp.: 50
Property Managers; Shopping Centers De-
velopers
N.A.I.C.S.: 531312
Michelle DiFebo Freeman *(Pres)*
Niel Burka *(VP-Retail Ops)*

CARL MARKS & CO., INC.
900 3rd Ave 33rd Fl, New York, NY
10022-4775
Tel.: (212) 909-8400
Web Site: http://www.carlmarks.com
Year Founded: 1925
Emp.: 100
Investment Bankers
N.A.I.C.S.: 523150
Mark L. Claster *(Pres)*
Robert Speer *(CFO)*
Katherine F. Boas *(Exec VP)*
Linda L. Caffin *(Chief Admin Officer)*
David F. Shnitkin *(Controller)*
Benjiman Godbout *(Mng Dir)*
David Endo *(Mng Dir)*
Jeffrey Pielusko *(VP)*
Joel R. Jacks *(Mng Partner)*
Marc L. Pfefferle *(Partner)*
Warren H. Feder *(Partner)*
Wesley H. R. Gaus *(Mng Partner)*
Evan Tomaskovic *(Mng Partner)*
Brian Williams *(Mng Partner)*

Subsidiaries:

CM Equity Partners, L.P.   (1)
900 3rd Ave 33rd Fl, New York, NY 10022-
2050
Tel.: (212) 909-8400
Web Site: http://www.cmequity.com
Sales Range: $25-49.9 Million
Emp.: 10
Equity Investment Services
N.A.I.C.S.: 523999
Joel R. Jacks *(Mng Partner)*
Peter M. Schulte *(Mng Partner)*
Wesley H. R. Gaus *(Mng Partner)*
David F. Shnitkin *(Controller)*
Robert A. Speer *(CFO)*
Martin J. Carmen *(Mng Partner)*
Steven D. Roth *(Dir-Bus Dev)*
Daniel Colon Jr. *(Partner)*

Holding (Non-US):

Evans Consoles, Inc.   (2)
1616 27th Ave NE, Calgary, T2E 8W4, AB,
Canada   (100%)
Tel.: (403) 291-4444
Web Site: http://www.evansonline.com
Sales Range: $50-74.9 Million
Emp.: 250
Distr of Consoles & Audio Visual Products
N.A.I.C.S.: 532490
Jeff Fairholm *(Reg Mgr-Sls)*

Holding (Domestic):

Graco Supply Company   (2)
1001 Miller Ave, Fort Worth, TX 76105
Tel.: (817) 535-3200
Web Site: http://www.gracosupply.com
Adhesive & Sealant Distr
N.A.I.C.S.: 424690
Clarlene Lenderman *(Dir-Quality)*
Chris Curtis *(Mgr-Programs Ops)*
Steve Novakovich *(CEO)*
Jeff Hazelrigg *(CFO)*
Jason Caldwell *(Pres & CEO)*
Mark Carmen *(Chm)*

Subsidiary (Domestic):

Pacific Coast Composites, Inc. (3)
11302 Steele St S Ste B, Lakewood, WA 98499-8734
Tel.: (253) 572-6262
Web Site: http://www.pccomposites.com
All Other Manufacturing
N.A.I.C.S.: 339999
Greg Fochtman (VP-Ops)

Styles Logistics, Inc. (3)
30 Airways Dr Ste 2, Lagrangeville, NY 12540
Tel.: (845) 677-8185
Web Site: http://www.skygeek.com
Sales Range: $10-24.9 Million
Emp.: 8
Aerospace & Defense Parts Mfr
N.A.I.C.S.: 336413
Steven T. Styles (Pres)
Jeffery Cross (Mgr)

Holding (Domestic):

Preferred Systems Solutions, Inc. (2)
7925 Jones Branch Dr Ste 6200, McLean, VA 22182-3983
Tel.: (703) 663-2777
Web Site: http://www.pssfed.com
Sales Range: $10-24.9 Million
Emp.: 300
Information Technology, Engineering, Management Support & Staff Augmentation Services
N.A.I.C.S.: 541519
Patty Williamson (Dir-HR)
Bill Rettig (Sr VP)
Pamela Romano (Dir-Project)
William Ryan (VP)
Bernadette Galloway (Dir-Proposal)
Jack Edelstein (Project Mgr-Network)
Kevin Krom (Program Dir)
Donald McKinley (VP-Natl Security)
Adam Wieder (Sr VP-Bus Dev)
Joe Fallone (Sr VP-Defense & Civilian Federal Grp)
Susan Day (VP-Acctg & Fin)
Rosemarie Floyd (VP-Contracts)
Dan Muse (CFO)
Craig Janus (Sr VP)
Cynthia Barreda (COO)
Babs Doherty (Pres & CEO)

Subsidiary (Domestic):

E.V. Roberts & Associates, Inc. (3)
18027 Bishop Ave, Carson, CA 90746
Tel.: (310) 204-6159
Web Site: http://www.evroberts.com
Sales Range: $75-99.9 Million
Adhesives, Sealants, Potting & Encapsulation Compounds Supplier & Mfr
N.A.I.C.S.: 424610
Ronald E. Cloud (CEO)

Subsidiary (Domestic):

Resin Formulators (4)
18027 Bishop Ave, Carson, CA 90746-4019 (100%)
Tel.: (310) 204-6159
Web Site: http://www.resinformulators.com
Sales Range: $10-24.9 Million
Emp.: 6
Mfr, Formulator & Distributor of Resins
N.A.I.C.S.: 424610

Subsidiary (Domestic):

Eagle Ray Technologies Group (3)
14425 Penrose Pl Ste 110, Chantilly, VA 20151
Tel.: (703) 961-9637
Web Site: http://www.eaglerayinc.com
Rev.: $3,000,000
Emp.: 20
Administrative Management & General Management Consulting Services
N.A.I.C.S.: 541611
Barberina Doherty (Sr VP)

GSM Consulting Inc. (3)
101 Wirt St Ste A, Leesburg, VA 20175-2919
Tel.: (703) 777-3538
Web Site: http://www.gsmconsulting.net
Computer System Design Services
N.A.I.C.S.: 541512

Donald McKinley (Pres)

Synaptic Solutions, Inc. (3)
1800 Alexander Bell Dr Ste 520, Reston, VA 20191-5473 (100%)
Web Site: http://www.gosynaptic.com
Information Technology & Software Services & Solutions
N.A.I.C.S.: 541511
Derrick Henley (Chm)
Josh Cury (CEO)

Tetra Concepts LLC (3)
604 Twilight Terrace Court, Mount Airy, MD 21771-5793
Tel.: (301) 543-4791
Web Site: http://www.tetraconcepts.com
Custom Computer Programming Services
N.A.I.C.S.: 541511
Brian Husted (VP)

Holding (Domestic):

RGS Associates, Inc. (2)
1800 S Bell St Ste 1000, Arlington, VA 22202
Tel.: (703) 769-5850
Web Site: http://www.rgsinc.com
General Management Consulting Services
N.A.I.C.S.: 541611
Tom McMahon (Pres & CEO)
Dyson Richards (Exec VP)
John Layne (Controller)
Monica Lee (Dir-DoD Sys Command Div)
Pete Dwyer (CFO)
Suzanne McDonald (Dir-DoD HQ Div)
Beth Jenkins Smith (Mgr)
Damian Gelband (Mgr)
Jay Pendarvis (Dir-DoD & Intelligence)
Jillian Fortin (Mgr)
Matt Beekman (VP-Civilian Agencies Div)
Robert Vogler (Sr Mgr)
Sylvia Kilpatrick (Mgr-HR)
Tina Filipczyk (Sr Mgr)
Olivia Horst (Project Engr-Trng-Lancaster)
Matthew J. Frye (First VP)
Darlene Michelson (First VP)

CARL OWNBY & CO. INC.
152 W Main St, Sevierville, TN 37862
Tel.: (865) 453-7141
Rev.: $11,697,532
Emp.: 44
Brick, Stone & Related Material
N.A.I.C.S.: 423320
Charles Ownby (Pres)

CARL ROSE & SONS INC
217 Elkin Wildlife Rd PO Box 786, Elkin, NC 28621
Tel.: (336) 835-7506
Rev.: $10,000,000
Emp.: 12
Surfacing & Paving
N.A.I.C.S.: 237310
Dale Rose (Sec & Treas)

CARL T. MADSEN INC.
3939 S Orchard St, Tacoma, WA 98466
Tel.: (253) 383-4546
Web Site: http://www.ctmgroup.com
Sales Range: $10-24.9 Million
Emp.: 130
Electrical Work
N.A.I.C.S.: 238210
Rocky Sharp (Pres & Mgr)
Greg Peterson (Controller)

CARL WARREN & COMPANY
770 S Placentia Ave, Placentia, CA 92780-6832
Web Site: http://www.carlwarren.com
Sales Range: $10-24.9 Million
Emp.: 112
Insurance Claims Management & Consulting
N.A.I.C.S.: 524291
Tom Boylan (Pres)
Allison Duncan (CFO)

CARL'S OIL COMPANY

9673 Somonauk Rd, Hinckley, IL 60520
Tel.: (815) 286-3281
Sales Range: $10-24.9 Million
Emp.: 2
Convenience Store
N.A.I.C.S.: 457210
Sharon Carls (Pres)

CARL'S SUPERMARKET INC.
999 Reed St, Nashville, MI 49073
Tel.: (517) 852-1991
Web Site: http://www.carlsmarkets.com
Sales Range: $10-24.9 Million
Emp.: 30
Supermarket
N.A.I.C.S.: 445110
Andy Joseph (Mgr-HR)
Dave Joseph (Pres)

CARLA & DAVID CRANE FOUNDATION
121 Steuart St, San Francisco, CA 94105
Tel.: (415) 777-0411   CA
Year Founded: 2007
Sales Range: $1-9.9 Million
Grantmaking Services
N.A.I.C.S.: 813219
Mark Reisbaum (Treas)
David Crane (Pres)
Warren S. Browner (VP)
Carla Crane (Sec)

CARLE FOUNDATION
611 W Park St, Urbana, IL 61801
Tel.: (217) 383-3311   IL
Web Site: http://www.carle.org
Year Founded: 1946
Sales Range: $200-249.9 Million
Emp.: 1,530
Health & Wellness Support Services
N.A.I.C.S.: 621498
Dan Baker (Dir-Major & Planned Gifts)
Lyn Jones (VP)
Pam Hulten (Dir-Annual Funds & Corporate Rels)
Linda Glazier (Dir-Philanthropy Comm)
Angie Lancaster (Mgr-Philanthropy Ops)
Phil Blankenburg (Chm)
Mary McGrath (Vice Chm)
V. B. Leister (Sec)

CARLEN ENTERPRISES INC.
1760 Apollo Ct, Seal Beach, CA 90740
Tel.: (562) 296-1055
Web Site: http://www.carlen.com
Year Founded: 1990
Sales Range: $10-24.9 Million
Emp.: 35
Supplier of Wholesale Nondurable Goods
N.A.I.C.S.: 424990
Michael Freede (Pres)
Sandra Carlson (Owner)

CARLETON CONSTRUCTION LTD.
5485 Belt Line Rd Ste 300, Dallas, TX 75254
Tel.: (972) 980-9810
Web Site: http://www.carletondevelopment.com
Sales Range: $25-49.9 Million
Emp.: 31
Residential Construction
N.A.I.C.S.: 236115
Jeff Fulenchek (CFO)
Ed Behnke (VP)
Neal Hildebrandt (Partner)

CARLETON EQUIPMENT COMPANY
4704 S 29th St, Kalamazoo, MI 49048
Tel.: (269) 343-2943   MI
Web Site: http://www.carletonequipment.com
Year Founded: 1938
Sales Range: $10-24.9 Million
Emp.: 50
Dealer of Industrial Machinery & Equipment
N.A.I.C.S.: 423830
Phillip Wurtzel (Pres)

CARLEY FOUNDRY, INC.
8301 Coral Sea St NE, Blaine, MN 55449
Tel.: (763) 780-5123
Web Site: https://www.carleyfoundry.com
Year Founded: 1955
Emp.: 201
Aluminum Casting Mfr
N.A.I.C.S.: 331524
Bob Carity (Engr-Sls)
Connie Schnerk (Engr-Sls)
Kevin Stensrud (Mgr-Sls)
Randy Oehrlein (VP-Engrg)

CARLEY LAMPS INC.
1502 W 228th St, Torrance, CA 90501
Tel.: (310) 325-8474
Web Site: https://www.carleylamps.com
Rev.: $20,100,000
Emp.: 300
Lamps & Glass
N.A.I.C.S.: 327212
Todd Cecil (Mgr-Engineering)

CARLIN CONTRACTING COMPANY, INC.
454 Boston Post Rd, Waterford, CT 06385-1510
Tel.: (860) 443-8337   MA
Web Site: https://www.carlincontracting.com
Year Founded: 1975
Sales Range: $25-49.9 Million
Emp.: 50
Nonresidential Construction
N.A.I.C.S.: 237110
Brian Carey (Pres)
Nelson Haeseler (VP)
Jamie York (VP-Fin)

CARLIN O'BRIEN INC.
1851 Howard St Ste M, Elk Grove Village, IL 60007
Tel.: (847) 228-0020
Web Site: http://www.carlinobrien.com
Emp.: 75
Private Investment Firm
N.A.I.C.S.: 523999
Bud Lowell (Sr VP-Sls & Mktg)
Jeffrey Mahler (Pres)
John Sabatino (Dir-Retail)
Louise Basgall (Mgr-Promotional Acctg)

Subsidiaries:

C A Fortune & Company (1)
1831 Howard St A, Elk Grove Village, IL 60007
Tel.: (630) 539-3100
Web Site: http://www.cafortune.com
Sales Range: $10-24.9 Million
Emp.: 50
Supermarkets & Other Grocery, except Convenience, Stores
N.A.I.C.S.: 445110
Tyler Lowell (CFO)

Carlin O'Brien Inc.—(Continued)

CARLIN SALES CORPORATION

8170 N Granville Woods Rd, Milwaukee, WI 53223
Tel.: (414) 355-2300
Web Site:
https://www.carlinsales.com
Rev.: $18,000,000
Emp.: 40
Distr of Greenhouse Equipment & Supplies
N.A.I.C.S.: 424910
Mark Maletzke (Owner)
Dan Groh (Pres)

CARLIN SYSTEMS INC.

31 Floyds Run, Bohemia, NY 11706
Tel.: (631) 471-2000
Web Site:
https://www.carlinsystems.com
Rev.: $10,902,907
Emp.: 19
Printed Circuit Boards
N.A.I.C.S.: 334412
John Giovan (Pres & Controller)

CARLING TECHNOLOGIES INC.

60 Johnson Ave, Plainville, CT 06062
Tel.: (860) 793-9266
Web Site: http://www.carlingtech.com
Year Founded: 1920
Sales Range: $75-99.9 Million
Emp.: 1,000
Electrical Components
N.A.I.C.S.: 335313
Richard W. Sorenson (Pres)
Paul Soucy (VP-Fin)
Micheal Fasno (VP)

CARLINVILLE AREA HOSPITAL

20733 N Broad St, Carlinville, IL 62626
Tel.: (217) 854-3141
Web Site: https://www.cahcare.com
Year Founded: 1947
Sales Range: $10-24.9 Million
Emp.: 223
Health Care Srvices
N.A.I.C.S.: 622110
Ken Reid (Pres & CEO)
Jamie Bray (Dir-Dev & Coord-Capital Campaign)
Ed Smith (Dir-Plant Ops)
Carmen Trump (Mgr-Bus)
Mike Brown (CFO)
Sara McPeak (Chief Nursing Officer)

CARLISLE CONTAINER CO.

750 Claremont Rd, Carlisle, PA 17013
Tel.: (717) 249-2444
Web Site: http://www.carl.net
Corrugated & Solid Fiber Box Mfr
N.A.I.C.S.: 322211
Chuck Wolf (Pres)

CARLISLE FOOD INC.

1605 Shearer Dr, Carlisle, PA 17013-9605
Tel.: (717) 218-9880
Web Site: http://www.carlislefsp.com
Sales Range: $25-49.9 Million
Emp.: 250
Bakery Products Mfr
N.A.I.C.S.: 311812
Steve Rinesmith (Mgr-Facilities)

CARLISLE PRODUCTIONS, INC.

1000 Bryn Mawr Rd, Carlisle, PA 17013
Tel.: (717) 243-7855

Web Site:
https://www.carlisleevents.com
Sales Range: $10-24.9 Million
Emp.: 25
Car Shows & Events
N.A.I.C.S.: 561920
Bill Miller (Co-Owner)
Lance Miller (Co-Owner)

CARLO LIZZA & SONS PAVING

200 Winding Rd, Old Bethpage, NY 11804
Tel.: (516) 938-2566
Sales Range: $100-124.9 Million
Emp.: 10
Surfacing & Paving
N.A.I.C.S.: 237310
Aly Lizza (Pres)
Jonathan Tomayo (Controller)

CARLO MANAGEMENT CORPORATION

45000 River Ridg Dr Ste 200, Clinton Township, MI 48038
Tel.: (586) 416-4500   MI
Holding Company; Construction & Development Services
N.A.I.C.S.: 551112

Subsidiaries:

John Carlo, Inc.   (1)
45000 River Rdg Dr Ste 200, Clinton Township, MI 48038
Tel.: (586) 416-4500
Sales Range: $25-49.9 Million
Emp.: 100
Highway & Street Construction Services
N.A.I.C.S.: 237990

CARLSEN VOLVO

4190 El Camino Real, Palo Alto, CA 94306
Tel.: (650) 493-1515
Web Site:
http://www.carlsenvolvo.com
Rev.: $24,100,000
Emp.: 48
Automobiles, New & Used
N.A.I.C.S.: 441110
Ramin Naimi (Gen Mgr)

CARLSON CAPITAL, L.P.

2100 McKinney Ave Ste 1800, Dallas, TX 75201
Tel.: (214) 932-9600   DE
Web Site:
https://www.carlsoncapital.com
Year Founded: 1993
Emp.: 100
Investment Management Service
N.A.I.C.S.: 523940
Troy Wuertz (Atty)
Clint D. Carlson (Pres & Chief Investment Officer)
Lynne Alpar (CFO)
Kristen Gregory (Dir-Ops)
Elizabeth Ewing (Partner-Connecticut Office & Head-IR)

Subsidiaries:

Carlson Capital, L.P. - New York Office   (1)
712 5th Ave, New York, NY 10019
Tel.: (212) 994-8400
Web Site: http://www.carlsoncapital.com
Emp.: 20
Investment Management Service
N.A.I.C.S.: 523940
Sean Shannon (Portfolio Mgr)

SWK Holdings Corporation   (1)
                                  (71%)
Tel.: (972) 687-7250
Web Site: https://www.swkhold.com
Rev.: $41,484,000
Assets: $299,621,000
Liabilities: $19,692,000
Net Worth: $279,929,000

Earnings: $13,491,000
Emp.: 21
Fiscal Year-end: 12/31/2022
Healthcare Industry Financing Services
N.A.I.C.S.: 523999
Jody Staggs (Pres & CEO)
Peter Blumberg (VP)
Kendall Papathanasiou (Dir-Human Resources)
John David Tamas (Dir-Underwriting)
Adam C. Rice (CFO)

Subsidiary (Domestic):

Enteris BioPharma, Inc.   (2)
83 Fulton St, Boonton, NJ 07005
Tel.: (973) 453-3518
Web Site: http://www.enterisbiopharma.com
Pharmaceuticals Product Mfr
N.A.I.C.S.: 325412
Rajiv Khosla (CEO)
Brian Zietsman (Pres & CFO)
Paul Shields (COO)
Gary A. Shangold (Chief Medical Officer)

CARLSON COMPANIES INC.

701 Carlson Pkwy, Minnetonka, MN 55305-8212
Tel.: (763) 212-5000   MN
Web Site: http://www.carlson.com
Year Founded: 1938
Sales Range: $25-49.9 Billion
Emp.: 100,000
Holding Company; Hotels, Inns, Resorts, Trading Stamps, Premium Promotions, Restaurants, Real Estate & Travel Agencies
N.A.I.C.S.: 551112
William A. Van Brunt (Gen Counsel & Exec VP)
Richard C. Gage (Chm)
Tammy Lee Stanoch (VP-Corp Comm)
Brad Hall (Chief Admin & Fin Officer & Exec VP)
Cindy Rodahl (Exec VP-HR & Comm)

Subsidiaries:

Carlson Hotels Management Corporation   (1)
701 Carlson Pkwy, Minnetonka, MN 55305   (100%)
Tel.: (763) 762-2222
Web Site: http://www.carlson.com
Sales Range: $900-999.9 Million
Emp.: 18,500
Hotel Operator
N.A.I.C.S.: 721110
Dinesh P. Chandiramani (VP-Dev-Americas)
Federico Gonzalez Tejera (CEO)
Eric de Neef (Chief Branding & Comml Officer-Global)
Ken Greene (Pres-Americas)
Charles McKee (Chief Comml Officer/Sr VP-Americas)
Terry Sanders (Chief Dev Officer-Americas)
Adrian Oyekanmi (Sr VP-Strategic Sourcing-Global)
Inigo Capell (Chief Resources Officer-Global & Exec VP)
Tim Cordon (Sr VP-Middle East, Turkey & Africa)
Chema Basterrechea (COO & Exec VP)
Mauro Vinci (Sr Dir-Bus Dev-Italy)
Adela Cristea (Sr Dir/Head-Dev-UK & Ireland)
Elie Younes (Chief Dev Officer/Exec VP-EMEA)
Gary Ye (VP-Ops-China)
Ross Hosking (VP-Sls & Distr-Americas)
Aly El-Bassuni (VP-Dev-Americas)
Mark William (VP-Dev-Americas)

Unit (Non-US):

Carlson Rezidor Hotel Group - Asia Pacific   (2)
3 Harbour Front Place 08-01/02 Harbour Front Tower 2, Singapore, 99254, Singapore
Tel.: (65) 65119266
Web Site: http://www.carlsonrezidor.com
Emp.: 50
Hospitality Operations, Including Hotels, Resorts & Restaurants

N.A.I.C.S.: 721110
K. B. Kachru (Exec VP-South Asia)
Andreas Flaig (Exec VP-Dev)
Sandy Russell (VP-Comml Ops)
Camilla Chiam (VP-PR & Comm)
Scott McConnell (Dir-Global Sls-Leisure)
Mark Sutton (Dir-Dev-Northeast USA)
Katerina Giannouka (Pres)
Saurabh Prakash (VP-Comml)

Subsidiary (Domestic):

Country Inns & Suites By Carlson Inc.   (2)
701 Carlson Pkwy, Minnetonka, MN 55305
Tel.: (763) 212-5000
Sales Range: $150-199.9 Million
Emp.: 2,000
Patent Owners & Lessors
N.A.I.C.S.: 533110
Marilyn Carlson Nelson (Chm & CEO)
Aurora Toth (VP-Mktg)

Park Inn Hotels   (2)
701 Carlson Pkwy, Minnetonka, MN 55305
Tel.: (763) 212-1342
Web Site: http://www.parkinn.com
Sales Range: $10-24.9 Million
Emp.: 30
Hotel
N.A.I.C.S.: 721110
Steve Mogck (COO & Exec VP-Franchise Ops)
Joan Cronson (Dir-PR & Comm)
David Berg (Pres)
Nuno Neves (Gen Mgr-Oman)

Park Plaza Bloomington   (2)
4460 W 78th St Cir, Bloomington, MN 55435
Tel.: (952) 831-3131
Web Site: http://www.parkplaza.com
Hotels & Resorts
N.A.I.C.S.: 721110
Michelle Wells (Gen Mgr-County Hall)

Provisions   (2)
701 Carlson Pkwy, Minnetonka, MN 55305   (100%)
Tel.: (763) 212-1606
Sales Range: $10-24.9 Million
Emp.: 10
Interior Design & Construction Services
N.A.I.C.S.: 721110
Scott Deibert (Sr Dir-Provisions)

Subsidiary (Non-US):

Radisson Hospitality AB   (2)
Avenue du Bourget 44, B-1130, Brussels, Belgium   (51.3%)
Tel.: (32) 2 702 9200
Web Site:
http://www.radissonhospitalityab.com
Rev.: $1,119,105,214
Assets: $1,337,438,719
Liabilities: $1,170,820,349
Net Worth: $166,618,370
Earnings: $24,621,242
Emp.: 4,248
Fiscal Year-end: 12/31/2019
Holding Company; Hotel & Resort Operator
N.A.I.C.S.: 551112
Eric de Neef (Chief Comml Officer-Global & Exec VP)
Elie Younes (Chief Dev Officer-Global & Exec VP)
Federico J. Gonzalez-Tejera (Pres & CEO)
Chema Basterrechea (COO & Exec VP)
Inigo Capell (Chief Resources Officer-Global & Exec VP)
Eva-Maria Erauw (Gen Counsel & Exec VP)
Sergio Amodeo (CFO)
Mingju Ma (Chm)
Lachlan Hoswell (Mng Dir-Australasia)
Ramzy Fenianos (Chief Dev Officer-Asia Pacific)

Subsidiary (Domestic):

Radisson Hotels & Resorts   (2)
701 Carlson Pkwy, Minnetonka, MN 55305
Tel.: (763) 212-1000
Web Site: http://www.radisson.com
Sales Range: $350-399.9 Million
Emp.: 5,000
Hotel Chain
N.A.I.C.S.: 721110
Kristen Richter (VP-Revenue Optimization-Americas)

Zubin Saxena *(CEO-South Asia)*
Eric De Neef *(Chief Comml Officer & Exec VP)*
Federico J. Gonzalez *(Chm)*
Inigo Capell *(Chief Resources Officer & Exec VP)*
Kevin Carl *(Chief IT Officer & Exec VP)*

Carlson Real Estate Company   (1)
301 Carlson Pkwy Ste 100, Minnetonka, MN 55305-5358   (100%)
Tel.: (952) 404-5000
Web Site: http://www.carlsonrealestate.biz
Sales Range: $10-24.9 Million
Emp.: 15
Commercial Industrial Real Estate & Investment Services
N.A.I.C.S.: 531210
Mark G. Herreid *(Pres)*

Carlson Restaurants Worldwide Inc.   (1)
4201 Marsh Ln, Carrollton, TX 75007
Tel.: (972) 662-5400
Web Site: http://www.carlson.com
Sales Range: $1-4.9 Billion
Emp.: 300
Holding Company; Restaurant Operator & Franchisor
N.A.I.C.S.: 551112
Diana L. Nelson *(Chm)*

Subsidiary (Domestic):

T.G.I. Friday's Inc.   (2)
4201 Marsh Ln, Carrollton, TX 75007
Tel.: (972) 662-5400
Web Site: http://www.tgifridays.com
Sales Range: $1-4.9 Billion
Emp.: 27,500
Holding Company; Restaurant Chain Operator & Franchisor
N.A.I.C.S.: 551112
Robert Palleschi *(Pres)*
Rebecca Epps *(Head-Corp Media)*
Brandon Coleman III *(CEO)*

Carlson Travel/Let's Talk Travel Inc.   (1)
301 N Main St Ste 114, Pueblo, CO 81003-4509
Tel.: (719) 544-8747
Sales Range: $10-24.9 Million
Emp.: 4
Travel Agencies
N.A.I.C.S.: 561510

Carlson Wagonlit Travel, Inc.   (1)
701 Carlson Pkwy, Minnetonka, MN 55305
Tel.: (763) 212-2197
Rev.: $25,500,000,000
Emp.: 22,000
Global Corporate Travel Services; Owned 55% by Carlson Companies, Inc. & 45% by JPMorgan Chase & Co.
N.A.I.C.S.: 561599
Bindu Bhatia *(Mng Dir-Asia Pacific)*
Patrick Andersen *(Pres & CEO)*
Chris Bowen *(Sr VP-UK & Ireland)*
Darren Toohey *(VP-Global Program Solutions-Americas)*
Cindy Fisher *(VP-Meetings & Events)*
Lauren Aste *(Gen Counsel & Exec VP)*
Matt Beatty *(Exec VP-Traveler Svcs)*
Scott J. Brennan *(Chief Growth Officer-RoomIt)*
Matt O'Keefe *(Chief Technology Officer-Hotel Distr)*
Matt Brennan *(VP-Hotel Ops)*
Kathy Orner *(Chief Risk Officer)*
Jared Anderson *(VP-Customer Experience)*
Alistair Hammond *(Dir-Media Rels-Global)*
Chris Reese *(Dir-Global Comm)*
Simon Nowroz *(CMO)*
Vishal Sinha *(CEO-India)*
Geeta Jain *(VP-Strategic Program)*
Ann Marie Stone *(Sr VP-Global Program Mgmt)*
Cathy Voss *(Exec VP-Global Program Solutions)*
Pam McTeer *(VP-Program Mgmt-Global)*
Sharon Burrell *(Head-Ops-Meeting & Events-UK, Ireland & Benelux)*
Paul Stoddart *(Mng Dir-Meetings & Events-UK, Ireland & Benelux)*
David Falter *(Pres-RoomIt-Chicago)*
Jack Staehler *(CTO-RoomIt-Chicago)*
Niklas Andreen *(Chief Traveler Experience Officer/Exec VP-London)*

Kelly Kuhn *(Chief Customer Officer)*
Courtney Mattson *(Treas)*
Julian Walker *(Chief Comm Officer)*
John Pelant *(Chief Experience & Tech Officer & Exec VP)*
Fernanda Petto *(VP-Fin Plng & Analysis)*
David Pitts *(VP-Revenue Mgmt-Global Supplier Mgmt)*
Brian Mogler *(Sr VP-Global Supplier Mgmt)*
Janet Wu Nuckles *(VP-Tax)*
Richard Thompson *(Head-ESG & Employee Experience-Global)*
Laura Watterson *(Chief HR Officer & Exec VP)*
Jim Shepherd *(CFO & Exec VP)*
Belinda Hindmarsh *(Chief Growth Officer & Exec VP)*

Subsidiary (Non-US):

CWT Asia Pacific   (2)
70 Anson Road 20-01 Hub Synergy Point level 18, Singapore, 79905, Singapore
Tel.: (65) 6220 2228
Web Site: http://www.carlsonwagonlit.sg
Sales Range: $50-74.9 Million
Emp.: 50
Travel Management
N.A.I.C.S.: 488999
Olivier Spaenle *(VP-Southeast Asia)*
Lim Joon Kiat *(Dir-Sls & Program Mgmt)*
Jessica Lim *(Dir-Fin)*
Frank Knauer *(Dir-Traveler & Transaction Svcs)*
Alice Loh *(Dir-HR & Admin)*
Geeta Jain *(VP-Strategic Program)*
Wai Mun Wong *(VP-Global Supplier Mgmt)*
Kai Chan *(Pres)*
Vishal Sinha *(CEO-India)*

CWT Canada   (2)
2425 Matheson Blvd E st 600, Mississauga, L4W 5K4, ON, Canada
Tel.: (905) 740-3500
Sales Range: $50-74.9 Million
Emp.: 800
Travel Agencies
N.A.I.C.S.: 561510
Sherry Saunders *(VP-Corp Ops)*
Patricia Quance *(Sr Dir-HR)*
Jack O'Neill *(COO)*

CWT France   (2)
40 Ave Pierre Lefaucheux, Paris, 92100, France
Tel.: (33) 141336500
Sales Range: $50-74.9 Million
Emp.: 400
Travel Management
N.A.I.C.S.: 561599
Catherine Maguire-Vielle *(Chief HR Officer & Exec VP)*

Subsidiary (Domestic):

Scheduled Airlines Traffic Offices, Inc.   (2)
4300 Wilson Blvd Ste 500, Arlington, VA 22203-4167
Tel.: (703) 682-7200
Web Site: http://www.cwtsatotravel.com
Rev.: $409,900,000
Emp.: 85
Military & Government Client Travel Arrangement Services
N.A.I.C.S.: 561510
Marc Stec *(VP-Bus Dev)*
Monnie Riggin *(VP-Leisure Ops)*

CARLSON HIGHLAND & CO., LLP
403 S Union Ave, Fergus Falls, MN 56537
Tel.: (218) 739-3267   MN
Web Site:
   http://www.carlsonhighland.com
Year Founded: 1986
Sales Range: $10-24.9 Million
Emp.: 60
Accounting, Tax Preparation & Business Consulting Services
N.A.I.C.S.: 541211

CARLSON HOLDINGS, INC.
10840 Harney St, Omaha, NE 68154-2638

Tel.: (402) 593-5300   NE
Web Site: http://www.csystems.com
Year Founded: 1947
Sales Range: $125-149.9 Million
Emp.: 300
Construction, Packaging Materials & Supplies Mfr
N.A.I.C.S.: 423840
Diana L. Nelson *(Co-Chm)*
Todd Carlson *(Exec VP-Sls)*
John Louis *(VP-Ops)*
Rob Puryear *(Reg VP)*

Subsidiaries:

Mid-Atlantic Fasteners Inc.   (1)
8220 Stayton Dr, Jessup, MD 20794-9618
Tel.: (410) 505-9200
Web Site:
   http://www.midatlanticfasteners.com
Rev.: $27,772,252
Emp.: 40
Fasteners, Nuts, Bolts & Screws Mfr
N.A.I.C.S.: 423840
Mike Walker *(Mgr-Sls)*

CARLSON TOOL & MANUFAC-TURING CORP.
W 57 N 14386 Doerr Way, Cedarburg, WI 53012
Tel.: (262) 377-2020
Web Site:
   https://www.carlsontool.com
Rev.: $21,900,000
Emp.: 140
Industrial Mold Mfr
N.A.I.C.S.: 333511
Jerome Edquist *(Pres)*

CARLTON FIELDS JORDEN BURT, P.A.
4221 W Boy Scout Blvd Ste 1000, Tampa, FL 33607
Tel.: (813) 223-7000   FL
Web Site: http://www.cafjblaw.com
Year Founded: 1901
Sales Range: $150-199.9 Million
Emp.: 650
Law firm
N.A.I.C.S.: 541110
Gary L. Sasso *(Pres & CEO)*
Anastasia C. Hiotis *(COO)*
Elizabeth Bergen Zabak *(CMO)*
Christina Calhoun *(Sr Mgr-Comm)*
Marcia Gaalswijk-Knetzke *(Asst Controller)*
Katie Heckert *(Atty)*
Beth Vecchioli *(Sr Dir-Govt Consulting)*
Steven J. Brodie *(Chm-Insurance Indus Grp)*
Chelsey Clements *(Atty-Orlando)*

Subsidiaries:

Carlton Fields Jorden Burt, P.A. - Simsbury   (1)
1 State St, Hartford, CT 06103
Tel.: (860) 392-5000
Web Site: http://www.cfjblaw.com
Emp.: 30
Law firm
N.A.I.C.S.: 541110
Anthony N. Cicchetti *(Partner & Head-Simsbury)*

CARLTON GROUP, INC.
120 Landmark Dr, Greensboro, NC 27409
Tel.: (336) 668-7677
Web Site:
   https://www.carltonscale.com
Sales Range: $10-24.9 Million
Emp.: 80
Scales Mfr
N.A.I.C.S.: 423440
Nelle Haywood *(VP-Ops)*
Ron Cutchins *(Engr-Sls Applications-Chesapeake)*

Ed Fudalik *(Gen Mgr & Engr-Sls Applications-Greenville)*
Eddie Goodwin *(Mgr-Ops-Greensboro)*
Boo Humphries *(Gen Mgr & Mgr-Svc)*
Dennis York *(Engr-Sls Application-Knoxville)*
Chris Trevey *(Pres & CEO)*

CARLTON MANUFACTURING, INC.
1101 SW 37th Ave, Ocala, FL 34474
Tel.: (352) 629-9113   IN
Web Site: http://www.carltonmfg.com
Year Founded: 1976
Sales Range: $75-99.9 Million
Emp.: 200
Mfr of Upholstered Wood Frames, Couches, Sofas, Chairs & Rockers
N.A.I.C.S.: 337121
Douglas Mercier *(Pres)*
Jean Rowe *(Controller)*
Forrest Hudspeth *(Sec & VP)*

CARLTON POOLS INC.
415 Constance Dr, Warminster, PA 18974
Tel.: (215) 674-8185
Web Site:
   https://www.carltonpools.com
Year Founded: 1973
Sales Range: $10-24.9 Million
Emp.: 80
Swimming Pool Construction
N.A.I.C.S.: 238990
Joseph Solana *(VP)*
Leon Psculkowski *(Project Mgr)*

CARLYLE CREDIT SOLU-TIONS, INC.
1 Vanderbilt Ave Ste 3400, New York, NY 10017
Tel.: (212) 813-4900   MD
Year Founded: 2017
Rev.: $197,695,000
Assets: $2,198,162,000
Liabilities: $1,046,661,000
Net Worth: $1,151,501,000
Earnings: $119,109,000
Emp.: 2,100
Fiscal Year-end: 12/31/22
Investment Management Service
N.A.I.C.S.: 523999
Desiree Annunziato *(Treas)*
Justin V. Plouffe *(Pres & CEO)*

CARLYLE CUSTOM CONVERT-IBLES, LTD.
6 Empire Blvd, Moonachie, NJ 07074
Tel.: (973) 546-4502
Web Site: http://www.carlylesofa.com
Sales Range: $10-24.9 Million
Emp.: 50
Furniture Mfr & Sales
N.A.I.C.S.: 449110
Albert Dematteo *(CEO)*
Susan Marino *(Controller)*

CARLYLE VAN LINES INC.
801 W Young St, Warrensburg, MO 64093
Tel.: (660) 747-8128
Web Site:
   http://www.carlylevanlines.com
Sales Range: $10-24.9 Million
Emp.: 90
Household Goods Transport
N.A.I.C.S.: 484210
Roy Carlyle *(Pres)*
Bill Carlyle Sr. *(Founder & VP)*

CARLYSLE ENGINEERING INC.
132 Brookside Ave, Boston, MA 02130

Carlysle Engineering Inc.—(Continued)

Tel.: (617) 522-6650   MA
Web Site: https://www.carlysle.net
Year Founded: 1946
Sales Range: $10-24.9 Million
Emp.: 75
Sprinkler Contracting Services
N.A.I.C.S.: 238220
John Duggan *(Pres)*

CARMACK CAR CAPITOL INC.
3724 N Vermilion St, Danville, IL
61832
Tel.: (217) 443-6803
Web Site:
   https://www.carmackcars.com
Sales Range: $10-24.9 Million
Emp.: 55
Automobiles, New & Used
N.A.I.C.S.: 441110
Gary Night *(Owner & Pres)*
Terri Cox *(Office Mgr)*

CARMEL CITY CENTER COM-MUNITY DEVELOPMENT COR-PORATION
3850 Priority Way S Ste 225, India-napolis, IN 46240
Tel.: (317) 844-4605   IN
Year Founded: 2009
Sales Range: Less than $1 Million
Community Care Services
N.A.I.C.S.: 624190
Jack Ragland *(Pres)*

CARMEL COUNTRY CLUB
4735 Carmel Rd, Charlotte, NC
28226
Tel.: (704) 945-9630   NC
Web Site:
   https://www.carmelcountryclub.org
Year Founded: 1947
Sales Range: $10-24.9 Million
Emp.: 271
Country Club Operator
N.A.I.C.S.: 713910
Richard Lancaster *(Controller)*
Diane Willi *(Dir-Comm)*
Philip Dodds *(Dir-Membership)*
John M. Schultz *(Gen Mgr)*
Ann Van Dyke *(Dir-HR)*

CARMELINA CAPITAL PART-NERS
1161 San Vicente Blvd Ste 195, Los
Angeles, CA 90049
Tel.: (310) 982-6100
Web Site: https://www.carmelina.com
Year Founded: 2010
Sales Range: $1-9.9 Million
Privater Equity Firm
N.A.I.C.S.: 523940
Kevin O'Malley *(Founder & Mng
Partner)*

CARMEN ANTHONY RESTAU-RANT GROUP, LLC
378 Chase Ave, Waterbury, CT
06704
Tel.: (203) 755-9514   CT
Web Site:
   http://www.carmenanthony.com
Sales Range: $25-49.9 Million
Restaurant Operators
N.A.I.C.S.: 551112
Carmen Anthony Vacalebre *(Pres)*

Subsidiaries:

Carmen Anthony Fishhouse LLC   (1)
757 Main St S, Woodbury, CT 06798
Tel.: (203) 755-9514
Web Site: http://www.carmenanthony.com
Rev.: $1,100,000
Emp.: 50
American Restaurant
N.A.I.C.S.: 722511

Carmen Anthony Vacalebre *(Pres & CEO)*

CARMENITA FORD TRUCK SALES INC.
13443 E Vly Dr, Santa Fe Springs,
CA 90670-5620
Tel.: (562) 921-1411
Web Site:
   http://www.carmenitatrucks.com
Rev.: $80,801,557
Emp.: 110
Trucks, Tractors & Trailers: New &
Used
N.A.I.C.S.: 441110
Gey Skeen *(Pres)*
Robert Zapotosky *(Treas & Sec)*

CARMICHAEL LEASING CO. INC.
2200 S Loomis St, Chicago, IL 60608
Tel.: (312) 666-8500
Web Site:
   https://www.carmichaelnl.com
Sales Range: $10-24.9 Million
Emp.: 40
Truck Leasing, Without Drivers
N.A.I.C.S.: 532120
Melvin Bechina *(Pres)*
Carri Bunch *(Sec)*
Juanita Thomas *(Mgr-Cash Mgmt)*

CARMODY TORRANCE SAN-DAK & HENNESSEY LLP
50 Leavenworth St, Waterbury, CT
06721-1110
Tel.: (203) 573-1200
Web Site:
   http://www.carmodylaw.com
Year Founded: 1905
Emp.: 100
Law firm
N.A.I.C.S.: 541110
James K. Robertson Jr. *(Partner)*

Subsidiaries:

Donahue Durham & Noonan PC   (1)
741 Boston Post Rd Ste 306, Guilford, CT
06437-2714
Tel.: (203) 458-9168
Web Site: http://www.ddnctlaw.com
Emp.: 100
Law firm
N.A.I.C.S.: 541110
Timothy W. Donahue *(Partner)*

CARNEGIE DARTLET LLC
210 Littleton Rd Ste 100, Westford,
MA 01886
Tel.: (978) 692-5092   DE
Web Site:
   https://www.carnegiehighered.com
Emp.: 100
Integrated Marketing Management
Services
N.A.I.C.S.: 541613
Joe Moore *(Chm)*

Subsidiaries:

Maguire Associates, Inc.   (1)
555 Virginia Rd, Concord, MA 01742
Tel.: (978) 371-1775
Web Site: http://www.maguireassoc.com
Rev.: $2,200,000
Emp.: 25
Marketing Research & Public Opinion Poll-ing
N.A.I.C.S.: 541910
Kristine Neil *(Dir-Fin)*
Linda Cox *(Exec VP)*
John Maguire *(Chm)*
Beth Pilgrim *(Dir-Client Dev)*
Dawn Provost *(Mgr-Ops)*
Jim Murtha *(Chm & CEO)*

CARNEGIE INSTITUTION OF WASHINGTON
1530 P St NW, Washington, DC
20005-1910

Tel.: (202) 387-6400   DC
Web Site:
   http://www.carnegieinstitution.org
Year Founded: 1902
Sales Range: $10-24.9 Million
Emp.: 30
Noncommercial Research Organiza-tion
N.A.I.C.S.: 541715
Susanne Garvey *(Dir-External Affairs)*
Gotthard Saghi-Szabo *(CIO)*

CARNEGIE INVESTMENT COUNSEL
30300 Chagrin Blvd, Pepper Pike,
OH 44124
Tel.: (216) 367-4114
Web Site:
   http://www.carnegieinvest.com
Year Founded: 1974
Investment Advisor
N.A.I.C.S.: 523940
Richard Alt *(CIO & Principal)*
Isabel Pedrosa *(Portfolio Mgr)*
Gary Wagner *(COO & Principal)*

Subsidiaries:

Crane Asset Management LLC   (1)
8383 Wilshire Blvd Ste 850, Beverly Hills,
CA 90211-2443
Tel.: (323) 852-9300
Web Site: http://www.craneasset.com
Investment Advice
N.A.I.C.S.: 523940
Sharon Blunk *(Co-Partner)*
John R. Frye *(Co-Partner)*

CARNES COMPANY INCOR-PORATED
448 S Main St, Verona, WI 53593
Tel.: (608) 845-6411
Web Site: https://www.carnes.com
Sales Range: $10-24.9 Million
Emp.: 275
Environmental Controls
N.A.I.C.S.: 334512
Dave Olson *(Mgr-Mktg)*

CARNETT'S MANAGEMENT COMPANY
631 B Indian Trail Rd NW, Lilburn,
GA 30047
Tel.: (770) 381-6900
Sales Range: $1-9.9 Million
Emp.: 200
Car Washing Services
N.A.I.C.S.: 811192
Bruce Arnett *(Sec)*
SrBruce P. Arnett *(CEO & CFO)*

CARNEY, INC.
100 N Pitt St Ste 401, Alexandria, VA
22314
Tel.: (703) 836-2400
Web Site:
   http://www.teamcarney.com
Year Founded: 1994
Sales Range: $25-49.9 Million
Emp.: 100
Distance Education, Training & Busi-ness Management Programs, IT Sup-port & Security to the Federal Gov-ernment
N.A.I.C.S.: 921190
John Carney *(Co-Founder & CEO)*
Bobby Hadley *(Engr-Software)*
Kerrie McCabe *(Program Dir)*
John Low *(Chief Creative Officer)*
Jiho Joung *(Mgr-Tech Ops)*
Allen Price *(Chief Culture & Talent
Officer)*
Sean Decker *(Dir-Technical Svcs)*
Janet McCoy *(Mgr-Performance Solu-tions Design)*
Carmina Carper *(Mgr-Program)*
Mary Matalas *(Mgr-Program)*
David Morris *(Mgr-Program)*

CARNIVORE MEAT COMPANY, LLC
2878 Ontario Rd, Bellevue, WI 54311
Web Site:
   http://www.vitalessentialsraw.com
Year Founded: 2012
Sales Range: $10-24.9 Million
Emp.: 94
Pet Food Mfr
N.A.I.C.S.: 311111
Lanny Viegut *(CEO)*
Cheryl Viegut *(CFO)*
Brett Simmons *(Plant Mgr)*
Melissa Olson *(VP-Sls & Mktg)*
Joey Weichmann *(Natl Mgr-Sls)*

CARO COMMUNITY HOSPITAL
401 N Hooper St, Caro, MI 48723-0435
Tel.: (989) 673-3141   MI
Web Site: http://www.cch-mi.org
Year Founded: 1999
Sales Range: $10-24.9 Million
Health Care Srvices
N.A.I.C.S.: 622110
Ron Srebinski *(VP-Fin)*
Kelly Whittaker *(VP-Nursing)*
Allyson Joyce *(VP-HR)*

CAROL ELECTRIC COMPANY INC.
3822 Cerritos Ave, Los Alamitos, CA
90720
Tel.: (562) 594-1174
Sales Range: $25-49.9 Million
Emp.: 43
Electrical Work
N.A.I.C.S.: 238210
John R. Fuqua *(Chm)*
Allen Moffitt *(Pres)*
Brian Moffitt *(Controller)*

CAROL H. WILLIAMS ADVER-TISING
1400 65th St Ste 200, Emeryville, CA
94608
Tel.: (510) 763-5200
Web Site:
   http://www.carolhwilliams.com
Year Founded: 1986
Emp.: 155
African-American Market, Communi-cations
N.A.I.C.S.: 541810
Carol H. Williams *(Pres, CEO & Chief
Creative Officer)*
Carlton Taylor *(Sr VP & Grp Creative
Dir)*
Sharon Kimbrough *(VP & Dir-Brdcst
Production)*
Robert Brown *(VP-Bus Dev)*
Carol Wyatt *(Dir-HR)*

Subsidiaries:

Carol H. Williams Advertising   (1)
875 N Michigan Ave Ste 2750, Chicago, IL
60611
Tel.: (312) 836-7900
Web Site: http://www.carolhwilliams.com
Emp.: 50
N.A.I.C.S.: 541810
Paa Kwesi Adams *(Mngmt Dir)*
Carol H. Williams *(Owner)*
Carlton Taylor *(Sr VP, Grp Creative Dir)*
Yvette Fischer *(Sr VP & Dir-Client Svcs)*

Carol H. Williams Advertising   (1)
1120 6th Ave 4th Fl, New York, NY 10017
Tel.: (646) 865-3888
Sales Range: $10-24.9 Million
Emp.: 10
N.A.I.C.S.: 541810
Austin Patrik *(Grp Acct Dir)*

CAROL MILGARD BREAST CENTER
4525 S 19th St, Tacoma, WA 98405
Tel.: (253) 759-2622   WA

Web Site:
https://www.carolmilgardbreast
center.org
Year Founded: 2009
Sales Range: $10-24.9 Million
Breast Health Care Services
N.A.I.C.S.: 622310
Khai A. Tran *(Dir-Medical)*
Jacquelyn B. Ostrom *(Exec Dir)*

CAROL'S LIGHTING AND FAN SHOP

1710 Humble Pl, Humble, TX 77338
Tel.: (281) 446-7613
Web Site:
https://www.carolslighting.com
Sales Range: $10-24.9 Million
Emp.: 20
Lighting Fixtures & Fans
N.A.I.C.S.: 423610
Don Gressett *(Pres)*

CAROLACE EMBROIDERY CO., INC.

65 Railroad Ave Unit 3, Ridgefield, NJ 07657
Tel.: (201) 945-2151
Web Site: http://www.carolace.com
Year Founded: 1951
Sales Range: $25-49.9 Million
Emp.: 280
Mfr of Schiffli Machine Embroideries
N.A.I.C.S.: 313220
David Mann *(Chm)*

Subsidiaries:

Carolace Industries Inc.   (1)
65 Railroad Ave Unit 3, Ridgefield, NJ 07657-2329
Tel.: (201) 945-2151
Web Site: http://www.carolace.com
Sales Range: $10-24.9 Million
Emp.: 6
Retailer of Piece Goods & Notions
N.A.I.C.S.: 424310

F.N.C. Textiles Inc.   (1)
3469 Black & Decker Rd, Hope Mills, NC 28348
Tel.: (910) 424-1997
Sales Range: $10-24.9 Million
Emp.: 40
Mfr of Pleating & Stitching
N.A.I.C.S.: 313310

CAROLE INC.

1607 S Grand Ave, Los Angeles, CA 90015
Tel.: (213) 749-7211
Web Site: https://www.caroleinc.com
Sales Range: $10-24.9 Million
Emp.: 122
Jewelry
N.A.I.C.S.: 423940
David Gordon *(CEO)*
Robert Koseff *(CFO)*
Mamie Yee *(Asst Controller)*
Debbie Laub *(Pres)*
Jennifer Paige *(VP)*

CAROLE WREN, INC.

3030 47th Ave, Long Island City, NY 11101-3492
Tel.: (718) 552-3800   NY
Web Site: http://www.carolewren.com
Year Founded: 1946
Sales Range: $25-49.9 Million
Emp.: 98
Mfr of Women's Sportswear
N.A.I.C.S.: 315250
Jocelyn Henriquez *(Coord-Textile)*

CAROLINA AIRCRAFT CORP.

3495 SW 9th Ave, Fort Lauderdale, FL 33315
Tel.: (954) 359-9900   FL
Web Site:
http://www.nationaljets.com

Year Founded: 1960
Sales Range: $10-24.9 Million
Emp.: 100
Flying Charter Service
N.A.I.C.S.: 481219
Samuel A. Robbin *(Pres & CEO)*
Mark Binko *(CFO)*

Subsidiaries:

National Jets, Inc.   (1)
3495 SW 9th Ave, Fort Lauderdale, FL 33315-3401
Tel.: (954) 359-9400
Web Site: http://www.nationaljets.com
Emp.: 90
Air Tranport & Airport Services
N.A.I.C.S.: 481211
Sam Robinson *(Pres)*

CAROLINA AIRCRAFT INC.

109 Kelvdon Dr, Kernersville, NC 27284
Tel.: (336) 996-4425
Web Site:
http://www.carolinaaircraft.com
Rev.: $37,000,000
Emp.: 5
Aircraft Instruments, Equipment Or Parts
N.A.I.C.S.: 441227
George W. Johnson III *(Pres)*

CAROLINA BANK AND TRUST CO.

72 Public Sq, Darlington, SC 29532
Tel.: (843) 398-8000
Web Site:
http://www.carolinabank.net
Year Founded: 1936
Sales Range: $10-24.9 Million
Emp.: 143
Provider of Banking Services
N.A.I.C.S.: 522110
Bryan Falcone *(Sr VP)*
R. W. De Maurice *(Sr VP)*

CAROLINA BEER & BEVERAGE, LLC

PO Box 1183, Mooresville, NC 28115
Tel.: (704) 799-2337
Web Site:
http://www.carolinabeverage.com
Year Founded: 1997
Sales Range: $25-49.9 Million
Emp.: 230
Brewery Mfr
N.A.I.C.S.: 312120
John Stritch *(Pres)*
Mike Smith *(VP)*
Michael J. Smith *(CEO)*
Mark R. Matteson *(Bd of Dirs, Executives)*

CAROLINA BIOLOGICAL SUPPLY COMPANY

2700 York Rd, Burlington, NC 27215-3398
Tel.: (336) 584-0381   NC
Web Site: https://www.carolina.com
Year Founded: 1927
Sales Range: $25-49.9 Million
Emp.: 530
Equipment & Supplies Merchant Whslr
N.A.I.C.S.: 423490
George Ross *(VP-Sls & Mktg)*

CAROLINA BUSINESS FURNITURE, LLC

535 Archdale Blvd, Archdale, NC 27263-8590
Tel.: (336) 431-9400   NC
Web Site:
http://www.carolinabusiness
furniture.com
Year Founded: 1946
Sales Range: $25-49.9 Million

Emp.: 125
Mfr of Wooden Furniture
N.A.I.C.S.: 337122
Omar Mohammed Yatim *(Sec)*
Hank Mienkie *(Pres)*
Mike Edwards *(Engr-Product)*

CAROLINA CANNERS INC.

300 Hwy 1 S, Cheraw, SC 29520-2835
Tel.: (843) 537-5281   SC
Web Site:
https://www.carolinacanners.com
Year Founded: 1968
Sales Range: $25-49.9 Million
Emp.: 350
Bottled & Canned Soft Drinks
N.A.I.C.S.: 312111
Jeff Stevens *(CEO)*
Mark Avent *(Pres)*
Tim Geddings *(CIO)*
Jeff Minges *(Treas)*
Maughan Hull *(Sec)*

Subsidiaries:

Carolina Canners Media   (1)
750-B S Bennett St, Southern Pines, NC 28387
Tel.: (910) 695-3001
Media Publishing Services
N.A.I.C.S.: 561990

Pepsi Cola Bottling Co. of Greenville, South Carolina   (1)
751 State Park Rd, Greenville, SC 29609-2903
Tel.: (864) 242-6041
Sales Range: $10-24.9 Million
Emp.: 110
Soft Drink Mfr & Bottler
N.A.I.C.S.: 312111
Wayne Holcombe *(Gen Mgr)*

CAROLINA CAPRI INC.

St A Corner Escorial Urban Industrial Mario Julia, San Juan, PR 00920
Tel.: (787) 793-7575
Sales Range: $10-24.9 Million
Emp.: 100
Departmental Store Operator
N.A.I.C.S.: 455110
Martin Pita *(VP)*
Jorge Pica Ruiz *(Pres)*

CAROLINA CERAMICS BRICK COMPANY

9931 Two Notch Rd, Columbia, SC 29223
Tel.: (803) 788-1916
Web Site:
http://www.carolinaceramics.com
Year Founded: 1939
Sales Range: $10-24.9 Million
Emp.: 83
Brick & Structural Clay Tile Mfr
N.A.I.C.S.: 327120
Michael Burden *(Pres)*
Frank K. Borden *(VP)*

CAROLINA CHICKEN INC.

986 Trinity Rd, Raleigh, NC 27607
Tel.: (919) 816-8491
Web Site:
http://www.carolinachicken.com
Rev.: $10,000,000
Emp.: 5
Fast Food Restaurant Operator
N.A.I.C.S.: 722513
John Alcott *(Pres)*
Justin Alcott *(Controller)*

CAROLINA COACH & MARINE

3300 Centennial Blvd, Claremont, NC 28610-9697
Tel.: (828) 459-9790
Web Site:
https://www.carolinacoach.com
Year Founded: 2001

Sales Range: $10-24.9 Million
Emp.: 92
New Car Whslr
N.A.I.C.S.: 441110
John Cathey *(Pres & CEO)*
Amelia Cathey *(Principal)*

CAROLINA COMPUTERS, INC.

1555 Whiskey Rd, Aiken, SC 29803-5311
Tel.: (803) 648-6107
Sales Range: $10-24.9 Million
Emp.: 25
Computer System Resale Services
N.A.I.C.S.: 541519
Elizabeth Campbell *(Owner)*

CAROLINA CONVENIENCE CORP.

557 Whiteford Way, Lexington, SC 29072
Tel.: (803) 356-2011
Rev.: $29,256,845
Emp.: 8
Floor Covering Stores
N.A.I.C.S.: 449121
Madhusudan Shrivastava *(Pres)*
Melissa Tilton *(Office Mgr)*

CAROLINA COUNTRY CLUB

2500 Glenwood Ave, Raleigh, NC 27608-1096
Tel.: (919) 787-3621   NC
Web Site: https://www.carolinacc.net
Year Founded: 1918
Sales Range: $10-24.9 Million
Emp.: 282
Golf Club Operator
N.A.I.C.S.: 713910
Robert G. Wright *(Pres)*
F. Timothy Nicholls *(VP)*
Steven C. Lilly *(Treas)*
Jack S. Slaughter *(Gen Mgr)*
William S. Cannon *(Dir-Tennis)*
Robert F. Andrews III *(Sec)*

CAROLINA DOOR CONTROLS, INC.

3424 Industrial Dr, Durham, NC 27704
Tel.: (919) 381-0094
Web Site:
http://www.carolinadoor.com
Sales Range: $50-74.9 Million
Emp.: 300
Distr of Automatic Doors
N.A.I.C.S.: 423710
Gerald Hendrick *(CEO)*

CAROLINA EASTERN INC.

PO Box 30008, Charleston, SC 29417
Tel.: (843) 571-0411   SC
Web Site: https://www.carolina-eastern.com
Year Founded: 1972
Rev.: $21,441,518
Emp.: 300
Farm Product Distr
N.A.I.C.S.: 424910
Alton C. Phillips *(Pres)*
Butch Rodgers *(Exec VP)*

Subsidiaries:

Carolina Eastern Aiken Inc.   (1)
1815 Park Ave SE, Aiken, SC 29801-6726
Tel.: (803) 648-9548
Sales Range: $10-24.9 Million
Emp.: 5
Farm Supplies
N.A.I.C.S.: 424910

Carolina Eastern-Molony Inc.   (1)
5701 Hwy 165, Ravenel, SC 29470-5713   (100%)
Tel.: (843) 889-2231
Web Site: http://www.carolinaeastern.com

Carolina Eastern Inc.—(Continued)

Sales Range: $10-24.9 Million
Emp.: 9
Farm Supplies
N.A.I.C.S.: 424910
Matt Bunch (Pres)

Port City Nitrogen Inc.　　　　(1)
214 Brampton Rd, Garden City, GA 31408-
2207
Tel.: (912) 964-5889
Sales Range: $10-24.9 Million
Emp.: 3
Farm Supplies
N.A.I.C.S.: 424910

CAROLINA EASTERN-VAIL INC.
4180 State Route 29, Salem, NY
12865
Tel.: (518) 854-9785
Web Site: https://www.carovail.com
Year Founded: 1979
Sales Range: $10-24.9 Million
Fertilizers & Agricultural Chemicals
Whslr & Distr
N.A.I.C.S.: 424910
Peter Vail Jr. (Pres)

CAROLINA EYE ASSOCIATES, P.A.
2170 Midland Rd, Southern Pines,
NC 28387
Tel.: (910) 295-2100
Web Site:
　　https://www.carolinaeye.com
Year Founded: 1977
Offices of Physicians (except Mental
Health Specialists)
N.A.I.C.S.: 621111
Judy Fleming (Mgr-Patient Care)

CAROLINA FARM CREDIT, ACA
146 Victory Ln, Statesville, NC 28625
Tel.: (704) 873-0276
Web Site:
　　https://www.carolinafarmcredit.com
Sales Range: $75-99.9 Million
Emp.: 200
Agricultural Credit Institutions
N.A.I.C.S.: 522299
Sarah J. Rachels (Chief HR Officer)
Maggie G. Hamm (CMO)
Chris H. Scott (CFO)
Vance C. Dalton Jr. (CEO)

CAROLINA FLUID COMPONENTS, LLC
9309 Stockport Pl, Charlotte, NC
28273
Tel.: (704) 588-6101
Web Site: http://www.cfcsite.com
Year Founded: 1978
Sales Range: $25-49.9 Million
Emp.: 50
Hydraulic Systems Equipment & Supplies
N.A.I.C.S.: 423830
Henry Campau (Controller)
Mark McDonald (VP)
Aaron Van Gilder (Engr-Electronic
Tech)

CAROLINA GLOVE COMPANY
116 S McLin Creek Rd, Conover, NC
28613
Tel.: (828) 464-1132　　　NC
Web Site:
　　https://www.carolinaglove.com
Year Founded: 1946
Sales Range: $100-124.9 Million
Emp.: 250
Glove Mfr
N.A.I.C.S.: 315990

Robert C. Abernethy (Pres, Treas &
Sec)
James S. Abernethy (VP)
Subsidiaries:

Carolina Glove Company - Carolina
Specialty Fabrics Division　　　(1)
28 N Caldwell Ave, Newton, NC 28658
Tel.: (828) 464-0367
Web Site:
　　http://www.carolinaspecialtyfabrics.com
Emp.: 50
Textile Fabric Mfr
N.A.I.C.S.: 313210
Dean Macintosh (Mgr)
Gary Bowers (Dir-Sls & Mktg)

CAROLINA HANDLING LLC
3101 Piper Ln, Charlotte, NC 28208
Tel.: (704) 357-6273
Web Site:
　　http://www.carolinahandling.com
Year Founded: 1966
Sales Range: $75-99.9 Million
Emp.: 375
Material Handling Equipment Distr
N.A.I.C.S.: 423830
Thomas Hilton (CEO)

CAROLINA HOSIERY MILLS INC.
710 Plantation Dr, Burlington, NC
27215
Tel.: (336) 226-5581
Rev.: $15,000,000
Emp.: 100
Socks
N.A.I.C.S.: 315120
Maurice J. Koury (Pres)
Miltom E. Petty (Exec VP)

CAROLINA IMAGING & COMPUTER PRODUCTS, INC.
4210 Beechwood Dr, Greensboro,
NC 27419
Tel.: (336) 299-8172
Web Site:
　　http://www.imagingproducts.net
Year Founded: 1996
Sales Range: $10-24.9 Million
Emp.: 16
Stationery & Office Supplies Whslr
N.A.I.C.S.: 424120
Mary Jo Painter (Pres)
Terry Presnell (VP)

CAROLINA INTERNATIONAL TRUCKS INC.
1619 Bluff Rd, Columbia, SC 29201
Tel.: (803) 799-4923
Web Site:
　　http://www.carolinainternational.com
Sales Range: $50-74.9 Million
Emp.: 200
New & Used Heavy, Medium & Service Trucks Dealer
N.A.I.C.S.: 441227
Richard D. Ryan (Pres-Dealer-
Columbia)
Sam Scarborough (Mgr-Svc)
Kate Hanson (Gen Mgr)
Dale Barksdale (Mgr-Parts Sls)
Jimmy Lariviere (Mgr-Parts)
Randy Downs (Mgr-New Truck Sls-
Columbia)
Eddie Altman (Mgr-Used Truck Sls-
Columbia)
Jason Hanson (Dir-Svc)
David Shinault (Gen Mgr-Florence)
J. B. Ryan (Gen Mgr-Charleston)
Jesse Cothran (Mgr-Leasing Svc-
Greenville)
Michael Evans (Gen Mgr-Columbia)
Mike Cox (Dir-Truck Leasing-
Columbia)

Subsidiaries:

Piedmont International Trucks,
LLC　　　　　　　　　　　(1)
2340 Hwy 70 SW, Hickory, NC 28602
Tel.: (828) 328-8156
Web Site:
　　http://www.piedmont.nationaltrucks.com
Sales Range: $25-49.9 Million
Emp.: 90
New & Used Heavy, Medium & Service
Trucks Dealer
N.A.I.C.S.: 441227

CAROLINA LEGAL STAFFING LLC
201 S College St Ste 1690, Charlotte,
NC 28202
Tel.: (704) 343-4822
Web Site:
　　http://www.carolinalegal.com
Year Founded: 1997
Rev.: $3,300,000
Emp.: 9
Legal Staffing, Placement & Temporary Help Services
N.A.I.C.S.: 561320
John Lassiter (Pres-Charlotte)
Ashley Howerton Smith (Dir-
Recruiting-Charlotte)
Barbara Fleming (Dir-Recruiting-
Charlotte)
Julie Clark (Dir-Recruiting-Raleigh)
Lisa King (Dir-Recruiting)

CAROLINA MACHINE & TOOL INC.
300 Industrial Dr, Greenville, SC
29607
Tel.: (864) 271-2871
Web Site:
　　https://www.cmtindustrial.com
Year Founded: 1983
All Other Miscellaneous Fabricated
Metal Product Mfr
N.A.I.C.S.: 332999
John Stevens (Pres)
Chris Blum (Dir-Sls)
Jason Dierks (Dir-Ops)
Trent Hackle (Controller)
Mike Shouse (Mgr-CSS Ops)

CAROLINA MEADOWS, INC.
100 Carolina Meadows, Chapel Hill,
NC 27517-8505
Tel.: (919) 942-4014　　　NC
Web Site:
　　http://www.carolinameadows.net
Year Founded: 1983
Sales Range: $25-49.9 Million
Emp.: 495
Lifecare Retirement Community Operator
N.A.I.C.S.: 623311
Diane Stimson (Chm)
John Modisett (Sec)
Joan C. Pharr (Treas)

CAROLINA MILLS INC.
618 N Carolina Ave, Maiden, NC
28650-1100
Tel.: (828) 428-9911　　　NC
Web Site:
　　https://www.carolinamills.com
Year Founded: 1928
Mfr of Yarn, Fabrics & Dying Services
to the Textile Industry
N.A.I.C.S.: 313110
Bryan E. Beal (Pres)

CAROLINA MOTOR CLUB, INC.
6600 Aaa Dr, Charlotte, NC 28212
Tel.: (704) 377-3600　　　NC
Web Site:
　　http://www.aaacarolinas.com
Year Founded: 1922

Sales Range: $50-74.9 Million
Emp.: 1,200
Membership Organization; Travel
Agency & Insurance Agent
N.A.I.C.S.: 813990
David E. Parsons (Pres & CEO)

Subsidiaries:

The Members Insurance
Company　　　　　　　　　(1)
6600 Aaa Dr, Charlotte, NC 28212-8259
Tel.: (704) 569-7854
Web Site: http://www.aaacarolinas.com
Emp.: 80
Property & Casualty Insurance
N.A.I.C.S.: 524126
Jim McCafferty (Pres & CEO)

Subsidiary (Domestic):

Universal Insurance Company　　(2)
770 Highland Oaks Dr, Winston Salem, NC
27103　　　　　　　　　　　(100%)
Tel.: (336) 771-0400
Web Site: http://www.uicnc.com
Sales Range: $75-99.9 Million
Property & Casualty Insurance
N.A.I.C.S.: 524126
Gregory L. Spray (Sr VP & Gen Mgr)
Kevin T. Roberson (Dir-Claims)
Kimberly L. Smith (Mgr-Mktg-North Carolina
Personal Automobile)
Joanna W. Collier (Mgr-Personal Auto Ops)
Xiaofeng Li (Mgr-Personal Auto Product &
Pricing)

CAROLINA OIL CO. OF CONCORD
754 Concord Pkwy N, Concord, NC
28027
Tel.: (704) 782-4101
Rev.: $11,000,000
Emp.: 19
Petroleum Products
N.A.I.C.S.: 424720
Robert C. Barbour (Pres)
Linda Fink (Controller)

CAROLINA QUALITY INC.
208 N Garnett St, Henderson, NC
27536
Tel.: (252) 492-2763
Sales Range: $10-24.9 Million
Emp.: 500
Fast Food Restaurant Operator
N.A.I.C.S.: 722513
Ray Meeks (Pres)
Lisa Simmons (Office Mgr)

CAROLINA RESTAURANT GROUP
8040 Arrowridge Blvd, Charlotte, NC
28273
Tel.: (704) 525-3434
Web Site:
　　https://www.classicburgers.com
Sales Range: $100-124.9 Million
Emp.: 40
Fast Food Restaurants
N.A.I.C.S.: 722513
Quint Graham (Pres)
Kathy Alvis (Dir-Mktg)

CAROLINA RIM & WHEEL COMPANY
1308 Uppr Asbury Ave, Charlotte, NC
28206
Tel.: (704) 334-7276
Web Site: http://www.carolinarim.com
Sales Range: $25-49.9 Million
Emp.: 24
Truck Parts & Accessories
N.A.I.C.S.: 423120
Cal Hallis (Controller)
Bill MacClements (Mgr-Pur)
Larry Duncan (Mgr-Sls)
Jerry Dunlap (Mgr-Parts)

CAROLINA TRACTOR &

EQUIPMENT CO.

9000 Statesville Rd, Charlotte, NC
28269-7680
Tel.: (704) 596-6700   NC
Web Site: http://www.carolinacat.com
Year Founded: 1926
Sales Range: $200-249.9 Million
Emp.: 500
Heavy Construction & Industrial
Equipment Sales & Service
N.A.I.C.S.: 423810
Mike Brown (*Sr VP & Gen Mgr-Power Sys Div*)
Matt Nazzaro (*CFO & VP*)
Kathy Taylor (*Chief People Officer & VP*)
Jason Williamson (*CMO & VP*)
Elvis Clemetson (*CIO, CTO & VP*)
Edward Innes Weisiger Jr. (*Pres & CEO*)

Subsidiaries:

Carolina Tractor & Equipment Co. - Pinnacle Cranes Division   (1)
9000 Statesville Rd, Charlotte, NC 28269
Tel.: (704) 731-7272
Web Site: http://www.pinnaclecranes.com
Crane Rental Services
N.A.I.C.S.: 532412

LiftOne LLC   (1)
440 E Westinghouse Blvd, Charlotte, NC 28273
Tel.: (704) 588-1300
Web Site: http://www.liftone.net
Lift Truck Equipment Rental Services
N.A.I.C.S.: 532490
Doug Tomlin (*Acct Mgr*)
Don Welch (*Branch Mgr*)
Dean Goss (*Mgr-Parts*)
Bill Cotreau (*Acct Mgr*)
Troy Garrison (*Mgr-Engred Sys Grp*)
Tom Dever (*Mgr-Rental & Central Product Support*)

CAROLINA TRAFFIC DEVICES INC.

11900 Goodrich Dr, Charlotte, NC 28278
Tel.: (704) 588-7899
Web Site:
http://www.carolinatrafficdevice.com
Year Founded: 2003
Sales Range: $10-24.9 Million
Emp.: 100
Highway, Street & Bridge Construction Services
N.A.I.C.S.: 237310
William Curtin (*Pres*)

CAROLINA TREE CARE

520 Webb Rd, Concord, NC 28025
Tel.: (704) 788-8733
Web Site:
https://www.carolinatree.com
Year Founded: 1987
Rev.: $12,800,000
Emp.: 225
Landscaping Services
N.A.I.C.S.: 561730
Bennie Wilson (*Area Mgr-Central SC*)
Gordon Spaugh (*VP*)
Marshall Crouse (*Area Mgr-Central NC*)
Andy Suggs (*Area Mgr-Western SC*)
Ray Snodgrass (*Area Mgr-Western SC*)
Matthew Rehlander (*Dir-Safety*)
Randy Austin (*Mgr-Fleet*)
Diane Burris (*Office Mgr*)
Jamie Johnson (*Reg Mgr*)

CAROLINA WHOLESALE OFFICE MACHINE COMPANY, INC.

425 E Arrowhead Dr, Charlotte, NC 28213-6378
Tel.: (704) 598-8101

Web Site: http://www.cwholesale.com
Year Founded: 1972
Office Machines Whslr & Distr
N.A.I.C.S.: 423420
Larry L. Huneycutt (*Pres & CEO*)
Rob Collins (*CFO & VP*)
Scott Lewis (*VP-Sls*)

Subsidiaries:

Monroe Systems For Business   (1)
511 William Leigh Dr St 15, Tullytown, PA 19007
Tel.: (267) 580-2600
Web Site: http://www.monroe-systems.com
Sales Range: $25-49.9 Million
Electronic Printing & Display Calculators Mfr & Distr
N.A.I.C.S.: 333310
William Ault (*COO*)

Smoltz Distributing, Inc.   (1)
6552 E Cave Creek Rd, Cave Creek, AZ 85331
Tel.: (480) 575-0534
Web Site: http://www.smoltz.com
Sales Range: $1-9.9 Million
Emp.: 6
Office Audio Equipment Whslr
N.A.I.C.S.: 423420
Boris Vasiljevic (*Gen Mgr*)

CAROLINA'S HOME MEDICAL EQUIPMENT, INC.

901 Sam Newell Rd Ste K, Matthews, NC 28105
Tel.: (704) 846-7503
Web Site: https://www.chmei.com
Year Founded: 2003
Sales Range: $1-9.9 Million
Emp.: 30
Healthcare Medical Equipment Distr
N.A.I.C.S.: 423450
Franklin H. Trammell (*Pres & CEO*)
Kaitlin Nacarato (*Dir-Regulatory & Revenue Enhancement*)
Martha Trammell (*VP*)
Andrew Trammell (*CFO & VP*)
Debby Gilbert (*Dir-Accts Receivable & Contracting*)
Terrell Harper (*Mgr-Warehouse*)
Cilia Dioguardo (*Mgr-Customer Svc*)
John Melton (*Mgr-Patient Svc*)
Joshua Hawkins (*Mgr-Pur*)

CAROLINAS CONSTRUCTIONS SOLUTIONS, INC.

6712 Old Pineville Rd, Charlotte, NC 28217
Tel.: (704) 578-1567
Web Site: http://www.staffccs.com
Year Founded: 2008
Sales Range: $1-9.9 Million
Emp.: 4
Construction Staffing Consulting Services
N.A.I.C.S.: 561320
Matt Telmanik (*Pres*)
Jason Perillo (*Sr Mgr-Recruiting*)
Jordan Elyasian (*Acct Mgr-NC*)
Levi Hayes (*Acct Mgr*)

CAROLINAS HEALTHCARE SYSTEM

1000 Blythe Blvd, Charlotte, NC 28203
Tel.: (704) 355-2000
Web Site:
http://www.carolinashealthcare.org
Sales Range: $5-14.9 Billion
Emp.: 48,702
Hospital Owner & Operator
N.A.I.C.S.: 622110
Paul S. Franz (*Exec VP*)
Greg A. Gombar (*CFO & Exec VP*)
Dennis J. Phillips (*Exec VP*)
Roger A. Ray (*Exec VP*)
Connie C. Bonebrake (*Sr VP*)

James T. McDeavitt (*Chief Academic Officer*)
Craig Richardville (*CIO & Sr VP*)
Keith A. Smith (*Gen Counsel & Sr VP*)
Robert H. Wiggins (*Sr VP-Fin*)
Mary Ann Wilcox (*Sr VP*)
Zachary J. Zapack (*Sr VP-Facilities Mgmt Grp*)
Eugene A. Woods (*Pres & CEO*)
Mary N. Hall (*Chief Academic Officer*)
Ken Haynes (*COO & Exec VP*)
Jerry Oliphant (*Exec VP-Reg Partnerships*)
Phyllis Wingate (*Pres-Northern Grp*)
George L. McLendon (*VP-Therapeutic R&D*)
Jim Dunn (*Chief HR Officer*)
Rasu Shrestha (*Chief Strategy Officer & Exec VP*)
Chandra Peterson (*Sr VP-Enterprise Strategy & Plng*)
John J. Knox III (*Chief Admin Officer & Exec VP*)
Edward J. Brown III (*Chm*)

CAROLLO ENGINEERS, INC.

4600 E Washington St Ste, 500, Phoenix, AZ 85034
Tel.: (602) 263-9500
Web Site: http://www.carollo.com
Year Founded: 1933
Rev.: $39,800,000
Emp.: 155
Environmental Engineering Services
N.A.I.C.S.: 541330
B. Narayanan (*CEO*)
Ron Joost (*Sr Mgr-Design*)
Stephen Horseman (*Assoc VP-Vancouver*)

CAROLRHODA BOOKS, INC.

241 1st Ave N Ste 1, Minneapolis, MN 55401
Tel.: (612) 332-3344
Year Founded: 1969
Sales Range: $1-9.9 Million
Emp.: 18
Book Publishers
N.A.I.C.S.: 513130
Adam Lerner (*CEO*)

Subsidiaries:

Sundance Publishing   (1)
33 Boston Post Rd W Ste 440, Marlborough, MA 01752
Tel.: (508) 571-6500
Web Site: http://www.sundancepub.com
Emp.: 150
Gradeschool Educational Materials Publisher & Distr
N.A.I.C.S.: 513130
Nancy Grant Mahoney (*Dir-Mktg & Product Mgmt*)
Paul Konowitch (*Pres & CEO*)

CAROLYN FABRICS INC.

1948 W Green Dr, High Point, NC 27261
Tel.: (336) 887-3101
Web Site:
https://www.carolynfabrics.com
Sales Range: $10-24.9 Million
Emp.: 9
Upholstery Fabrics, Woven
N.A.I.C.S.: 424310
Stephen A. Spillers (*Pres*)

CAROLYN GRISKO & ASSOCIATES INC.

400 W Erie St Ste 400, Chicago, IL 60654
Tel.: (312) 335-0100
Web Site: http://www.grisko.com
Year Founded: 1995
Sales Range: $10-24.9 Million
Emp.: 20

Public Relations
N.A.I.C.S.: 541820
Carolyn Grisko (*Pres & CEO*)
Holly Dotterer (*Acct Supvr*)
Ambar Mentor-Truppa (*VP*)
Terri Cornelius (*VP*)
Garlanda Freeze (*VP-Mktg Comm*)
Drita Durakovic (*CFO*)
Jody Spychalla (*Dir-Freelance Art*)
Jeff Steinhouse (*Exec Dir-Creative*)
Elisabeth Woodard (*Dir-Mktg*)

CAROMA CONSTRUCTION CO.

6168 Montridge Cv, Memphis, TN 38115-2739
Tel.: (901) 795-4580
Sales Range: $10-24.9 Million
Emp.: 20
Nonresidential Construction Services
N.A.I.C.S.: 236220
Dan Jones (*Pres*)

CAROUSEL CAPITAL PARTNERS

201 N Tryon St Ste 2450, Charlotte, NC 28202
Tel.: (704) 372-2040
Web Site: http://carouselcapital.com
Year Founded: 1996
Investment Management Service
N.A.I.C.S.: 523940
Charles S. Grigg (*Mng Partner*)
Adam Elmore (*Principal*)
Daniel J. Eassa (*CFO & Chief Compliance Officer*)
Peter L. Clark Jr. (*Partner*)
Alan C. Welch Jr. (*Partner*)

Subsidiaries:

Brasseler USA, Inc.   (1)
1 Brasseler Blvd, Savannah, GA 31419
Tel.: (912) 925-8525
Web Site: http://www.brasselerusa.com
Dental Equipment & Supplies
N.A.I.C.S.: 423450
Don Waters (*Pres & CEO*)

Subsidiary (Non-US):

Brasseler Canada, Inc.   (2)
4500 Henri Bourassa St Ste 230, Charlesbourg, G1H 3A5, QC, Canada
Tel.: (418) 622-1195
Web Site: http://www.brasseler.com
Rev.: $5,500,000
Emp.: 8
Dental Equipment & Supplies
N.A.I.C.S.: 339114
Dan McDuff (*Gen Mgr*)

Landscape Workshop, Inc.   (1)
3601 Parkwood Rd, Bessemer, AL 35022
Tel.: (205) 424-0244
Web Site:
http://www.landscapeworkshop.com
Sales Range: $1-9.9 Million
Emp.: 160
Lawn & Garden Services
N.A.I.C.S.: 561730
Amy Dobbs (*Treas & Sec*)
Matt Hottle (*VP-Sls & Mktg*)
Bill Cobb (*Gen Mgr-Central*)
Randy Owens (*Gen Mgr-Construction Div*)
Don DeMetz (*VP-Fin*)
Andy Dickerson (*Controller*)
Cynthia Hobson (*Mgr-Bus Dev*)

Subsidiary (Domestic):

Louisiana Landscape Specialty, Inc.   (2)
1701 Belle Chasse Hwy, Gretna, LA 70056
Tel.: (504) 391-1800
Web Site: https://landscapeworkshop.com
Rev.: $2,800,000
Emp.: 80
Landscaping Services
N.A.I.C.S.: 561730
Randy Loup (*Pres*)

Process Equipment Inc.   (1)
2770 Welborn St, Pelham, AL 35124

Carousel Capital Partners—(Continued)
Tel.: (205) 663-5330
Web Site: http://www.processbarron.com
Industrial & Commercial Fan Mfr & Material Handling Systems
N.A.I.C.S.: 333413
Ken Nolen (CEO)

Simpson Performance Products Inc.　　　　　　　(1)
328 FM 306, New Braunfels, TX 78130-2556　　　　　　(100%)
Tel.: (830) 625-1774
Web Site: http://www.teamsimpson.com
Sales Range: $50-74.9 Million
Emp.: 80
Mfr of Auto Safety Equipment for Racing
N.A.I.C.S.: 336390
Chuck Davies (CEO)
Debbie Bishop (VP-Mktg)

Subsidiary (Domestic):

Safety Solutions, Inc.　　　　　　(2)
185 Rolling Hills Rd, Mooresville, NC 28117
Tel.: (704) 799-6065
Web Site:
　　http://www.safetysolutionsracing.com
Mfr & Marketer of Auto Racing Safety Equipment
N.A.I.C.S.: 336390

Plant (Domestic):

Simpson Performance Products　　　(2)
1407 W 240th, Harbor City, CA 90710
Tel.: (310) 325-6035
Fire Suit Mfr
N.A.I.C.S.: 315990
Dave Nelson (VP-Ops-CA)

CAROUSEL CHECKS INC.
8906 S Harlem Ave, Bridgeview, IL 60455
Tel.: (708) 613-2452
Web Site:
　　http://www.carouselchecks.com
Year Founded: 2003
Sales Range: $1-9.9 Million
Emp.: 67
Customized Checks & Financial Documents & Accessories
N.A.I.C.S.: 525990
Andrew Crim (Pres)
Jason Ward (COO)

CARPARTS DISTRIBUTION CENTER
RR 125, Plaistow, NH 03865
Tel.: (603) 382-6253
Web Site: http://www.carpartsnh.com
Rev.: $13,000,000
Emp.: 52
Automotive Supplies & Parts
N.A.I.C.S.: 423120

CARPENTER & COMPANY, INC.
Charles Sq 20 University Rd, Cambridge, MA 02138
Tel.: (617) 864-2800　　　　MA
Web Site:
　　https://www.carpentercompany.com
Year Founded: 1898
Commercial & Multi-Family Residential Real Estate Acquisition, Development, Property Management & Brokerage Services
N.A.I.C.S.: 531210
Richard L. Friedman (Pres & CEO)
Phillip C. Vitali (CFO & VP)
Peter Diana (Gen Counsel & VP)
Darren D. Messina (VP-Design & Construction)

CARPENTER & PATERSON INC.
225 Merrimac St, Woburn, MA 01801
Tel.: (781) 935-2950
Web Site:
　　http://www.carpenterpaterson.com

Year Founded: 1913
Rev.: $19,137,679
Emp.: 32
Valves & Pipe Fittings
N.A.I.C.S.: 332919
Kathleen Tawa (Controller)
Chakib Nedjar (Dir-Matl Mgmt)
David Lynch (Pres)
Joe Burke (Branch Mgr)

CARPENTER BROTHERS INC.
7100 W Donges Bay Rd, Mequon, WI 53092
Tel.: (414) 354-6555
Web Site:
　　https://www.carpenterbrothers.com
Sales Range: $25-49.9 Million
Emp.: 100
Abrasives
N.A.I.C.S.: 423840
John E. Carpenter (CEO)
Julie Pierce (Controller)
Nick Gerrits (Pres)

CARPENTER CO.
5016 Monument Ave, Richmond, VA 23230
Tel.: (804) 359-0800　　　　VA
Web Site: http://www.carpenter.com
Year Founded: 1948
Sales Range: Less than $1 Million
Chemicals, Polyurethane & Carpet Cushions Mfr
N.A.I.C.S.: 326150
Stanley F. Pauley (Owner)
Michael Lowery (Pres)
Thomas P. Rohman (Chm)
Mark Willard (VP)

Subsidiaries:

Carpenter Belgium NV　　　　　　(1)
Wijnendalestraat 171, Roeselare, 8800, West Flanders, Belgium
Tel.: (32) 51 23 02 11
Web Site: http://www.carpenter.com
Sales Range: $10-24.9 Million
Emp.: 90
Mattress & Furniture Distr
N.A.I.C.S.: 423210
Kurt Derieuw (Gen Mgr)

Carpenter Co. - Morning Glory Products Div.　　　　　　(1)
302 Highland Dr, Taylor, TX 76574-1847
Tel.: (512) 365-5833
Web Site: http://www.carpenter.com
Rev.: $7,000,000
Emp.: 50
Mfr of Pillows, Mattress Pads, Quilt Batting & Craft Products For Home Quilting
N.A.I.C.S.: 314120
Kent Sasarik (Gen Mgr)

CARPENTER PAPER COMPANY
745 Overland St, North Salt Lake, UT 84054
Tel.: (801) 295-9475
Web Site:
　　http://www.carpenterpaperco.com
Sales Range: $10-24.9 Million
Emp.: 60
Whslr of Printing & Writing Paper
N.A.I.C.S.: 424110

CARPENTER REALTORS
8901 S Meridian St, Indianapolis, IN 46217
Tel.: (317) 888-3303
Web Site:
　　https://www.callcarpenter.com
Sales Range: $75-99.9 Million
Emp.: 620
Real Estate Broker
N.A.I.C.S.: 531210
Dave Cavenss (Pres)
John Asbury (Controller)

CARPENTER'S CAMPERS INC.

8450 Pensacola Blvd, Pensacola, FL 32534
Tel.: (850) 724-8968
Web Site:
　　https://www.carpenterscampers.com
Rev.: $13,000,000
Emp.: 45
Recreational Vehicle Sales & Service
N.A.I.C.S.: 441210
Marshall O. Carpenter III (Pres)
Jim Cook Jr. (VP)

CARPENTERS' HEALTH AND WELFARE FUND OF PHILADELPHIA AND VICINITY
1811 Spring Garden St, Philadelphia, PA 19130
Tel.: (215) 568-0430　　　PA
Year Founded: 1960
Sales Range: $150-199.9 Million
Emp.: 2,749
Employee Benefit Services
N.A.I.C.S.: 525120
James R. Davis (Co-Chm)
Edward Coryell Sr. (Co-Chm)

CARPET BARN INC.
2707 S Main St, Pine Bluff, AR 71601
Tel.: (870) 536-2123　　　AR
Web Site: https://www.carpetbarn.net
Year Founded: 1974
Rev.: $11,235,295
Emp.: 28
Carpets & Floor Covering
N.A.I.C.S.: 449121
Randy K. Drewry (Mgr-Store)
Bob Jones (Mgr)

CARPET CORNER INC.
900 Minnesota Ave, Kansas City, KS 66101
Tel.: (913) 342-4123
Web Site:
　　https://www.carpetcorneronline.com
Year Founded: 1968
Sales Range: $10-24.9 Million
Emp.: 60
Carpets
N.A.I.C.S.: 449121
James M. Mathews (Pres)

CARPET CUSHIONS & SUPPLIES, INC.
1520 Pratt Blvd, Elk Grove Village, IL 60007-5715
Tel.: (847) 364-6760
Web Site:
　　http://www.carpetcushions.com
Year Founded: 1979
Sales Range: $10-24.9 Million
Emp.: 100
Distr of Carpet Cushions & Accessories
N.A.I.C.S.: 423220
Aaron Karsen (Co-Owner & Pres)
Jeff Karsen (Co-Owner & VP)
Roger Tintner (Mgr-Sls)
Mel Cohen (Mgr-HR)

CARPET DECORATORS INC.
107 N 2nd St, Central City, KY 42330
Tel.: (270) 754-5041
Sales Range: $10-24.9 Million
Emp.: 26
Floor Laying & Floor Work
N.A.I.C.S.: 238330
Mark D. Young (Pres)
Vicki Hyde (Engr-Estimating)

CARPET FACTORY OUTLET INC.
3200 South 24th St, Kansas City, KS 66106
Tel.: (913) 261-6800
Web Site:
　　http://www.mcintyremann.com

Year Founded: 1976
Sales Range: $10-24.9 Million
Emp.: 57
Supplier of Carpets & Floor Coverings
N.A.I.C.S.: 449121
Gaylord Johnson (Pres)
Sherman Johnson (VP)

CARPET FAIR, INC.
7100 Rutherford Rd, Baltimore, MD 21244-2702
Tel.: (410) 298-5800
Web Site:
　　http://www.billscarpetfair.com
Sales Range: $100-124.9 Million
Emp.: 110
Carpet Retailer
N.A.I.C.S.: 449121
Butch Fields (General Mgr)

CARPET ONE BY VAN DRIE HOME FURNISHINGS
7591 S US 131, Cadillac, MI 49601
Tel.: (231) 775-8536
Web Site: https://www.vandrie.com
Sales Range: $10-24.9 Million
Emp.: 90
Furniture Stores
N.A.I.C.S.: 449121
Gerard Winkle (Owner)

CARPET WEAVERS INC.
616 Marketview Dr, Champaign, IL 61822
Tel.: (217) 398-1800
Web Site: https://www.carpetweavers flooring.com
Sales Range: $25-49.9 Million
Emp.: 250
Floor Covering Stores
N.A.I.C.S.: 449121
Scott Brown (CFO)
Mike Turner (Controller)
Stuart Hutchison (Mgr-Store)

CARPETS PLUS OF WISCONSIN INC.
4606 E Washington Ave, Madison, WI 53704
Tel.: (608) 249-0422
Web Site:
　　https://www.carpetspluswi.com
Sales Range: $10-24.9 Million
Emp.: 18
Carpets
N.A.I.C.S.: 449121
Michael Peters (Pres)
Shannon Howery (Mgr-Credit)

CARPIN MANUFACTURING INC.
411 Austin Rd, Waterbury, CT 06705
Tel.: (203) 574-2556
Web Site: https://www.carpin.com
Rev.: $10,200,000
Emp.: 107
Metal Stamping
N.A.I.C.S.: 332119
Ralph Carpinella (Owner & Chm)

CARPIONATO GROUP LLC
1414 Atwood Ave, Johnston, RI 02919
Tel.: (401) 273-6800　　　RI
Web Site:
　　https://www.carpionatogroup.com
Sales Range: $10-24.9 Million
Land Subdividers & Developers, Commercial
N.A.I.C.S.: 237210

Kelly MacArthur Coates *(Pres & CEO)*
Domenic Carpionato *(Sr VP)*
David Chamberland *(Sr VP-Construction)*

Subsidiaries:

Chateau Properties **(1)**
30 Oaklawn Ave, Cranston, RI 02920
Tel.: (401) 944-3000
Web Site:
 http://www.chateaupropertiesri.com
Rev.: $22,600,000
Emp.: 50
Operative Builders
N.A.I.C.S.: 236117
Alfred Carpionato *(Pres)*

CARR AND DUFF INC.
2100 Byberry Rd, Huntingdon Valley, PA 19006
Tel.: (215) 672-4200
Web Site: https://www.carrduff.com
Sales Range: $25-49.9 Million
Emp.: 70
General Electrical Contractor
N.A.I.C.S.: 238210
Robert W. Duff *(Pres)*
Edward J. Duff *(VP)*

CARR AUTO GROUP
15005 SW TV Hwy Ste 106, Beaverton, OR 97006
Tel.: (503) 644-2161
Web Site: http://www.carrauto.com
Sales Range: $125-149.9 Million
Emp.: 560
Automobile Sales
N.A.I.C.S.: 441110
Wally Preble *(Chm)*
Mary Blake *(Controller)*
Benjamin Bradshaw *(Gen Mgr)*
Brad Woods *(Mgr-Body Shop)*

CARR CHEVROLET, INC.
15005 SW Tualatin Valley Hwy, Beaverton, OR 97006-5137
Tel.: (503) 567-1218
Web Site:
 https://www.carrchevrolet.com
Sales Range: $10-24.9 Million
Emp.: 560
Car Whslr
N.A.I.C.S.: 441110
Wally Preble *(Chm)*

CARR CONSTRUCTION, INC.
2718 SW Water Ave, Portland, OR 97201
Tel.: (503) 235-3514
Sales Range: $10-24.9 Million
Emp.: 65
Structural Steel & Precast Concrete Contracting Services
N.A.I.C.S.: 238120
Kenneth Carr *(Pres & Sec)*
Linda Weatherssen *(Mgr-Ops)*

CARR ENTERPRISES INC.
5500 40th Ave Dr, Moline, IL 61265
Tel.: (309) 764-2481
Web Site:
 http://www.hilandtoyota.com
Sales Range: $10-24.9 Million
Emp.: 40
Automobiles, New & Used
N.A.I.C.S.: 441110
Derek Carr *(Pres)*
Tom Arnett *(Gen Mgr-Sls)*
Lonnie Tapscott *(Mgr-Internet Sls)*
Dale Wilson *(Mgr-New Cars)*
James Vanklavern *(Mgr-Used Cars)*

CARR LANE MANUFACTURING CO.
4200 Carr Lane Ct, Saint Louis, MO 63119

Tel.: (314) 647-6200
Web Site: https://www.carrlane.com
Sales Range: $10-24.9 Million
Emp.: 130
Special Dies, Tools, Jigs & Fixtures
N.A.I.C.S.: 333514
Alan K. Frost *(Pres)*
Colin Frost *(COO)*

CARR SUPPLY INC.
1415 Old Leonard Ave, Columbus, OH 43219
Tel.: (614) 252-7883
Web Site:
 https://www.carrsupply.com
Year Founded: 1917
Sales Range: $10-24.9 Million
Emp.: 106
Heating, Ventilation & Air Conditioning Equipment, Plumbing Parts & Supplies
N.A.I.C.S.: 423730
Ron Johnson *(CFO)*
Christopher Brandt *(Mgr-Comml Sls-HVAC Div)*
Matt Volk *(Mgr-HVAC)*

CARR TEXTILE CORPORATION
243 Wolfner Dr, Fenton, MO 63026
Tel.: (636) 343-6620
Web Site: http://www.carrtextile.com
Sales Range: $10-24.9 Million
Emp.: 55
Bindings, Textile
N.A.I.C.S.: 424310
Mike Carr *(Co-Owner)*

CARR VALLEY CHEESE COMPANY, INC.
S3797 County G, La Valle, WI 53941
Tel.: (608) 985-8200
Web Site:
 https://www.carrvalleycheese.com
Year Founded: 1902
Sales Range: $10-24.9 Million
Emp.: 75
Cheese Mfr
N.A.I.C.S.: 311513
Beth Wyttenbach *(Mgr-Sls)*
Sid Cook *(Owner)*

CARR'S TIRE SERVICE OF HARRISONBURG
4040 Early Rd, Harrisonburg, VA 22801
Tel.: (540) 434-1792
Web Site: http://www.bigltire.com
Sales Range: $10-24.9 Million
Emp.: 40
Automobile Tires & Tubes
N.A.I.C.S.: 423130
Randy Nesslerobt *(Pres)*
Donna Nesslerobt *(VP)*

CARR, RIGGS & INGRAM, LLC
901 Boll Weevil Cir Ste 200, Enterprise, AL 36330
Tel.: (334) 347-0088 FL
Web Site: http://www.cricpa.com
Year Founded: 1997
Accounting, Tax & Consulting Services
N.A.I.C.S.: 541211
William H. Carr *(Chm & Mng Partner)*
Sandi Guy *(Partner-Human Capital)*
LaDonna Lewis *(Pres, CEO & Partner)*
Emily Ackerman *(Head-Bus Dev)*
Brian Stone *(Dir-HR)*
Charles Graeub *(VP-Fin Analytics)*
Joel Sikes *(Partner & Mng Dir)*

Subsidiaries:

Auditwerx **(1)**
3000 Bayport Dr Ste 500, Tampa, FL 33607

Tel.: (813) 282-7297
Web Site: http://www.auditwerx.com
Sales Range: $1-9.9 Million
Auditing Services
N.A.I.C.S.: 541219
Annie Sergent *(Mgr-Mktg)*
Stacy Martin *(Mgr-Audit)*

Barraclough & Associates, PC **(1)**
807 Camino de Monte Reyt, Santa Fe, NM 87505
Tel.: (505) 983-3387
Web Site: http://www.barraclough.com
Accounting Firm
N.A.I.C.S.: 541219
John E. Barraclough *(Mng Principal)*
Annette Vigil Hayden *(Principal)*
Sandra M. Shell *(Principal)*

Carr, Riggs & Ingram, LLC - Atlanta, GA **(1)**
4360 Chamblee Dunwoody Rd Ste 420, Atlanta, GA 30341
Tel.: (770) 394-8000
Web Site: http://www.cricpa.com
Emp.: 30
Accounting, Tax & Consulting Services
N.A.I.C.S.: 541211
Kelly Bollinger *(Partner-Atlanta)*
Gary Boteler *(Partner)*
John Leslie *(Partner)*
Russ Frederick *(Partner)*
Richard Wilcox *(Partner)*
Scott Abrams *(Partner)*
Stafford Huff *(Partner)*
Shel Donner *(Partner)*
Robert Habif *(Partner)*
Pattie Weaver *(Partner)*
Oliver Holmes *(Partner)*
Max Gin *(Partner)*
Matthew Katzmark *(Partner)*
Matt Gunning *(Partner)*
Mac Smith *(Partner)*
Ken Breaux *(Partner)*
Kathie Gottlieb *(Partner)*
Jeff Silver *(Partner)*
Gill Fenerty *(Partner)*
Doug Mims *(Partner)*
Dick Babush *(Partner)*
Debra Carpenter *(Partner)*
Craig Thompson *(Partner)*
Chris Clayton *(Partner)*
Chad Sexton *(Partner)*
Bruce McFadden *(Partner)*
Barry Klein *(Partner)*
Andy Grant *(Partner)*
Adrian Grant *(Partner)*

Carr, Riggs & Ingram, LLC - Conroe **(1)**
414 W Phillips St Ste 102, Conroe, TX 77301-2880
Tel.: (936) 760-3369
Web Site: http://www.cricpa.com
Accounting, Tax & Consulting Services
N.A.I.C.S.: 541211
Virgina Miller *(Partner)*

Carr, Riggs & Ingram, LLC - The Woodlands, TX **(1)**
10200 Grogans Mill Rd Ste 420, The Woodlands, TX 77380-1166
Tel.: (713) 482-2960
Web Site: http://www.cricpa.com
Accounting, Tax & Consulting Services
N.A.I.C.S.: 541211
Paul Oman *(Partner)*

Sharrard, McGee & Co., P.A. **(1)**
1321 Long St, High Point, NC 27262
Tel.: (336) 884-0410
Web Site: http://www.sharrardmcgee.com
Other Accounting Services
N.A.I.C.S.: 541219

Shinn & Company, LLC **(1)**
1001 3rd Ave W Ste 500, Bradenton, FL 34205
Tel.: (941) 747-0500
Web Site: http://www.shinnandco.com
Certified Public Accountants
N.A.I.C.S.: 541211
Byron Shinn *(Mng Partner)*
Christine B. Yekel *(Partner)*
Millard J. Martin *(Partner)*
David Lanni *(Principal)*
Christy Cardillo *(Partner)*
Jamie M. Phillips *(Mgr-Client Rels)*
Garrett Shinn *(Partner)*

Logan Saltsman *(Dir-Mktg)*
Tim Gruters *(Partner)*
Kimberlie Buchanan *(Principal)*

CARRAFIELLO-DIEHL & ASSOCIATES, INC.
90 N Broadway, Irvington, NY 10533-1260
Tel.: (914) 674-3900 NY
Year Founded: 1973
Sales Range: $10-24.9 Million
Emp.: 25
Advertising Agencies
N.A.I.C.S.: 541810
Amy Stichman *(Assoc Dir-Creative)*

CARRARA MARBLE CO. OF AMERICA INC.
15939 Phoenix Dr, City of Industry, CA 91745
Tel.: (626) 961-6010 CA
Web Site: https://www.carrara.com
Year Founded: 1953
Sales Range: $50-74.9 Million
Emp.: 320
Providers of Terrazzo, Tile, Marble & Mosaic Work
N.A.I.C.S.: 238340
Bill Cordova *(Pres & CEO)*
Jose Ayala *(Sr Project Mgr)*
Jim Hogan *(Sr VP)*
Dirk Wietstock *(VP-Sls)*

CARRERA REVELL OF AMERICAS, INC.
Ste 307N 197 Rte 18, East Brunswick, NJ 08512
Tel.: (609) 409-8510
Web Site: http://www.carrera-toys.com
Year Founded: 2004
Sales Range: $1-9.9 Million
Emp.: 15
Toy & Hobby Goods & Supplies Merchant Whslr
N.A.I.C.S.: 423920
Frank Tiessen *(Co-Pres)*
Lou Aguilera *(Co-Pres)*

Subsidiaries:

Revell GmbH **(1)**
Henschelstrasse 20-30, Bunde, 32257, Germany
Tel.: (49) 5223 965 0
Web Site: http://www.revell.de
Model Kits & Die-Cast Collectibles Mfr & Distr
N.A.I.C.S.: 339930
Hans Remfert *(Pres)*

CARRFOUR SUPPORTIVE HOUSING, INC.
1398 SW 1st St Ste 1201, Miami, FL 33135
Tel.: (305) 371-8300 FL
Web Site: https://www.carrfour.org
Year Founded: 1993
Sales Range: $1-9.9 Million
Emp.: 100
Low Income Housing Construction
N.A.I.C.S.: 925110
Stephanie Berman-Eisenberg *(Pres & CEO)*
Paola Roman *(VP-Housing Dev)*
Irene Luzod *(Controller)*
Sandra Newson *(VP-Resident & Property Svcs)*

CARRIAGE CORPORATION
12631 State Rte 143, Highland, IL 62249-1145
Tel.: (618) 654-2181 IL
Web Site:
 http://www.steveschmitt.com
Year Founded: 1985
Sales Range: $25-49.9 Million
Emp.: 98

Carriage Corporation—(Continued)

New & Used Car Dealers
N.A.I.C.S.: 441110
Steven S. Schmitt (Pres)

Subsidiaries:

Security Leasing & Finance Inc. (1)
12631 State Route 143, Highland, IL 62249-1145
Tel.: (618) 654-2181
Web Site: http://www.stevesmithauto.com
Sales Range: $50-74.9 Million
Miscellaneous Business Credit Institution
N.A.I.C.S.: 522220
Steven S. Schmitt (Pres)
Bruce Turley (Controller)

Steve Schmitt Inc. (1)
12631 State Rte 143, Highland, IL 62249-1145
Tel.: (618) 654-2181
Web Site: http://www.steveschmittauto.com
Sales Range: $10-24.9 Million
Emp.: 30
New & Used Car Dealers
N.A.I.C.S.: 441110
Steven S. Schmitt (Pres)
Chris Martz (Gen Mgr)
Jeff Croak (Mgr-Inventory)
Paula Hormann (Supvr-Acctg)

CARRIAGE HOUSE INTERIORS SAN DIEGO

7341 Clairemont Mesa Blvd, San Diego, CA 92111
Tel.: (858) 277-0744
Rev.: $13,700,000
Emp.: 44
Furniture Retailer
N.A.I.C.S.: 449110

CARRICK CAPITAL PARTNERS, LLC

160 Spear St Ste 1620, San Francisco, CA 94105
Tel.: (949) 209-6202
Web Site:
    http://www.carrickcapital.com
Scientific & Technical Consulting Services
N.A.I.C.S.: 541690
James C. Madden (Co-Founder & Co-CEO)
Stephen M. Unterberger (Partner)
Alex Mason (Mng Dir)
Marc F. McMorris (Co-Founder & Co-CEO)
Mike Salvino (Operating Partner)
Paul Zolfaghari (Mng Dir-Ops)
Aaron Symanski (Sr VP-Tech Ops)
Kari L. Niblack (Pres-Blackwell Captive Solutions)
Arleigh Kennedy (VP-Sls-Natl)

CARRICK WILLIAMS HOLDINGS INC.

1450 Kinetic Rd, Lake Park, FL 33403
Tel.: (561) 844-5322
Web Site:
    https://www.carrickcontracting.com
Rev.: $17,100,000
Emp.: 55
Management Consulting Services
N.A.I.C.S.: 541618
Van C. Williams (VP)
Thomas J. Carrick (Pres)

CARRICO IMPLEMENT CO. INC.

3160 United States 24 Hwy, Beloit, KS 67420
Tel.: (785) 738-5744
Web Site:
    http://www.carricoimplement.com
Rev.: $25,946,756
Emp.: 94
Farm Implements

N.A.I.C.S.: 423820
Ronald Ellenz (Pres)
Karen Pespinger (CFO)
Jeremy Bedke (Mgr-Parts)

CARRIER COACH INC.

271 Buffalo St, Gowanda, NY 14070
Tel.: (716) 532-2600
Web Site:
    http://www.carriercoach.com
Rev.: $14,700,000
Emp.: 325
Transit & Ground Passenger Transportation
N.A.I.C.S.: 485999
Allen Miller (Pres)
Debbie Hultberg (Comptroller)

CARRIER TRUCK SALES, LLC

130 S Bemiston Ave # 604, Saint Louis, MO 63105
Tel.: (314) 727-7600
Web Site: http://www.big-ride.com
Rev.: $10,000,000
Emp.: 7
Truck Leasing, Without Drivers
N.A.I.C.S.: 532120

CARRIER VIBRATING EQUIPMENT, INC.

3400 Fern Valley Rd, Louisville, KY 40213
Tel.: (502) 969-3171 KY
Web Site:
    http://www.carriervibrating.com
Year Founded: 1950
Sales Range: $10-24.9 Million
Emp.: 150
Mfr of Vibrating Conveyors, Feeders, Process Equipment & Bin & Pile Dischargers
N.A.I.C.S.: 333922
John Nye (Mgr-Svc)
Jessica Zhu (Gen Mgr)
Charles E. Mitchell (VP-Sls)
Michael Deblaere (Mng Dir)
Douglas A. Schieber (Pres & CEO)

Subsidiaries:

Carrier Europe SCA (1)
Parc Industriel-Zone 1 Rue de l'Industrie 20, 1400, Nivelles, Belgium
Tel.: (32) 67 883753
Web Site: http://www.carriereurope.be
Emp.: 25
Industrial Machinery Mfr
N.A.I.C.S.: 423830
Micheal Deblaere (Mng Dir)

Carrier Vibrating Equipment (Canada) Ltd. (1)
PO Box 759, Aurora, L4G 4J9, ON, Canada
Tel.: (905) 727-3185
Emp.: 3
Industrial Equipment Distr
N.A.I.C.S.: 423830
Mike Doucette (Gen Mgr)

Carrier Vibrating Equipment (Shanghai) Co., Ltd. (1)
No 1 Building No 88 Shenzhou Road, Fengchen Town Fengxian District, Shanghai, 201411, China
Tel.: (86) 21 33925800
Web Site: http://www.carriervibrating.com
Emp.: 37
Industrial Machinery Mfr
N.A.I.C.S.: 333248
Jzhu Ting (Gen Mgr)

CARRIERE FAMILY FARMS, INC.

1640 State Hwy 45, Glenn, CA 95943
Tel.: (530) 934-8200
Web Site:
    https://www.carrierefarms.com
Year Founded: 1963
Sales Range: $10-24.9 Million
Emp.: 85

Walnut, Almond, Rice & Olive Farming Services
N.A.I.C.S.: 111335
Bill Carriere (Pres)
Jeni Carriere (Mgr-Grower Rels)
Gary Enos (Supvr-Ops-Farming)
Rick Enos (Mgr-Production-Walnut)
Ron Bryant (Plant Mgr)

CARRIEREQ, INC.

186 Lincoln St 3rd Fl, Boston, MA 02111
Tel.: (617) 841-7207 DE
Web Site: http://www.airfox.com
Year Founded: 2016
Rev.: $1,749
Assets: $9,711,295
Liabilities: $28,852,279
Net Worth: ($19,140,984)
Earnings: ($10,024,797)
Emp.: 68
Fiscal Year-end: 09/30/19
Software Development Services
N.A.I.C.S.: 541511
Victor Santos (Founder, Chm, Pres & CEO)
Emanuel Moecklin (CTO)
Douglas Lopes (CFO)
Justin Hoffmann (Exec VP)
Andrew Wang (VP-Ops)
Katie Sedat (VP-Mktg)
Jerry Harris (VP-Engrg)

CARRIKER FORD INC.

1201 S 17th St, Oskaloosa, IA 52577
Tel.: (641) 673-8373
Web Site:
    http://www.carrikerford.com
Sales Range: $50-74.9 Million
Emp.: 40
Automobiles, New & Used
N.A.I.C.S.: 441110

CARRILLO BUSINESS TECHNOLOGIES

750 The City Dr S Ste 225, Orange, CA 92868
Tel.: (714) 230-3720
Web Site: http://www.cbtechinc.com
Year Founded: 2001
Rev.: $81,900,000
Emp.: 50
Computer Software Services
N.A.I.C.S.: 449210
Andy Anderson (Sr Mgr-Client Svcs)
Teressa Catton (Mgr-IT)
Kelly Ireland (Founder & CEO)
Roger Cheng (Dir-Bus Dev)
Dwanna Jones Lynch (Dir-Corp Rels)
Rhondi Lenaker (Dir-Mktg & Comm)
Shelbey Guardalabene (Dir-Ops)
Tascha Muldrow (Mgr-Client Svcs)
Steve Christian (Sr VP-Federal Bus Ops)
Robin Kennedy (VP-Bus Dev)

CARRINGTON HOLDING CO.

599 W Putnam Ave, Greenwich, CT 06830-6005
Tel.: (949) 517-7100
Web Site:
    http://www.carringtonhc.com
Offices of Real Estate Agents & Brokers
N.A.I.C.S.: 531210
Greg Drakos (Exec VP-Carrington Retail Grp)

CARRIS FINANCIAL CORP.

49 Main St, Proctor, VT 05765-1178
Tel.: (802) 773-9111 VT
Web Site: http://www.carris.com
Year Founded: 1990
Sales Range: $300-349.9 Million
Emp.: 700
Holding Company

N.A.I.C.S.: 551112

Subsidiaries:

Carris Reels, Inc. (1)
49 Main St, Proctor, VT 05765-1178
Tel.: (802) 773-9111
Web Site: http://www.carris.com
Rev.: $100,000,000
Plywood Reels & Wood Spool Mfr
N.A.I.C.S.: 321999
Dave Ferraro (Pres)

Division (Domestic):

Carris Plastics (2)
64 W Wind Rd, Fincastle, VA 24090
Tel.: (540) 473-2210
Web Site: http://www.carris.com
Mfr of Plastic Reels
N.A.I.C.S.: 321999

Carris Reels, Inc.-North Carolina Wood Div (2)
1475 Winston Ave, Statesville, NC 28677-8406 (100%)
Tel.: (704) 872-0981
Web Site: http://www.carris.com
Sales Range: $25-49.9 Million
Emp.: 100
Wire & Cable Packaging Mfr
N.A.I.C.S.: 561910

Subsidiary (Domestic):

Carris of California, Inc. (2)
2100 W Almond Ave, Madera, CA 93637
Tel.: (559) 674-0804
Web Site: http://www.carrisreels.com
Sales Range: $25-49.9 Million
Emp.: 36
Mfr of Reels
N.A.I.C.S.: 321999
Lincoln Markwith (Gen Mgr)

Carris of Connecticut, Inc. (2)
11 Randolph St, Enfield, CT 06082 (100%)
Tel.: (860) 749-8308
Web Site: http://www.carris.com
Sales Range: $25-49.9 Million
Emp.: 75
Reels Mfr
N.A.I.C.S.: 332999
Steve Sabourin (Gen Mgr)

CARRIX, INC.

1131 SW Klickitat Way, Seattle, WA 98134
Tel.: (206) 382-4490 WA
Web Site: https://www.carrix.com
Year Founded: 1994
Holding Company; Marine & Rail Terminal Operator
N.A.I.C.S.: 551112
Jon F. Heminway (Chm)
Uffe Ostergaard (Pres & CEO)

Subsidiaries:

Ceres Terminals Incorporated (1)
606 Garfield Ave Ste 202, Duluth, MN 55802
Tel.: (218) 722-5858
Web Site: https://www.ceresglobal.com
Sales Range: $75-99.9 Million
Emp.: 1,500
Provider of Marine Cargo Handling Services
N.A.I.C.S.: 488320
Daniel Hall (Sr VP-Ops-East, Gulf Coasts & Great Lakes)
Brian S. Kern (VP-Mktg & Contract Mgmt)
Morten K. Nicolaisen (CFO & Sr VP)
W. Patrick Burgoyne (Pres & CEO)
Anthony Caputo (Dir-Cruise Svcs)
Alan McCorkle (Sr VP-West Coast Ops)

Subsidiary (Domestic):

Ceres Marine Terminals Inc. (2)
3100 Childs St 2nd Fl, Baltimore, MD 21226 (100%)
Tel.: (443) 874-7700
Web Site: http://www.ceresglobal.com
Sales Range: $10-24.9 Million
Emp.: 10
Loading & Unloading Vessels
N.A.I.C.S.: 493110
Douglas N. Wolfe (VP)

Ceres Terminals Inc. **(2)**
100 Westwood Pl Ste 300, Brentwood, TN 37027
Tel.: (615) 232-7800
Web Site: https://www.ceresglobal.com
Sales Range: $10-24.9 Million
Emp.: 10
Marine Cargo Handling
N.A.I.C.S.: 488320
Wilkin Mes (Sr VP-Dev & Cruise Strategy)
Craig Mygatt (CEO)

SSA Marine, Inc. **(1)**
1131 SW Klickitat Way, Seattle, WA 98134
Tel.: (206) 623-0304
Web Site: http://www.ssamarine.com
Rev.: $1,630,000,000
Emp.: 13,000
Ship Loading & Unloading Services
N.A.I.C.S.: 488320
Jon Hemingway (Chm)
Michael Schwank (Pres-Tideworks Tech)
Chris Hurley (Gen Mgr)
Joe Abram (Gen Mgr)
Mike Quinn (Gen Mgr-Ops-Seattle)
Paul Huculak (Gen Mgr)
Jaime Neal (Treas & Sr VP)
Knud Stubkjaer (CEO)
Rolf Hansen (Gen Mgr-Everett)
Bob Luxa (Gen Mgr-Tacoma)
Eli Bohm (Gen Mgr-Seattle)
Mike Patalano (Gen Mgr-Long Beach)
Bob Watters (Sr VP)
Carlos Urriola (Pres-Intl)
John Aldaya (CFO)
Manuel Fernandez (CEO-Mexico)
Mark Knudsen (Pres-Conventional)

Subsidiary (Non-US):

Greystones Cargo Systems **(2)**
No 34 Watford Rd, Coneella, Durban, 4001, Kwazulu Natal, South Africa **(100%)**
Tel.: (27) 312061845
Web Site: http://www.greystonescargo.co.za
Sales Range: Less than $1 Million
Emp.: 150
Load & Unload Ships
N.A.I.C.S.: 488320

Manzanillo International Terminal, Panama S.A. **(2)**
Avda Molten Coco Solo Sur, Zn Libre De Colon, Colon, Panama
Tel.: (507) 4309800
Web Site: http://www.mitpan.com
Sales Range: $100-124.9 Million
Emp.: 1,100
Provider of Ship Loading & Unloading Services
N.A.I.C.S.: 488320
Stacey Hatfield (Gen Mgr)

SSA Bangladesh Ltd. **(2)**
63 Dilkusha Com Area, Pepsi Tower 5th Floor, Dhaka, 1000, Bangladesh
Tel.: (880) 29557721
Provider of Ship Loading & Unloading Services
N.A.I.C.S.: 488320

SSA Mexico S.A. de C.V. **(2)**
Km 4 5 Carretera Delbet, Manzanillo, 2800, Mexico
Tel.: (52) 3143311000
Web Site: http://www.ssamexico.com
Sales Range: $25-49.9 Million
Emp.: 250
Provider of Ship Loading & Unloading Services
N.A.I.C.S.: 488320

STI-San Antonio Terminal Internacional **(2)**
Avda Ramon Barros Luco 1613 Piso 13, San Antonio, Chile
Tel.: (56) 352201600
Web Site: http://www.stiport.com
Sales Range: $25-49.9 Million
Emp.: 500
Provider of Ship Loading & Unloading Distr
N.A.I.C.S.: 488320
Cristobal Kulczewski (Mgr-Comml)

SVTI-San Vicente Terminal Internacional **(2)**
Puerto De San Vicente, PO Box 187, Avenida Latorre 1590, Talcahuano, Chile **(50%)**

Tel.: (56) 41503603
Web Site: http://www.svti.cl
Sales Range: $25-49.9 Million
Emp.: 500
Provider of Ship Loading & Unloading Services
N.A.I.C.S.: 488320

Sokhna Port Development Company **(2)**
29 Farid St, Heliopolis, Cairo, 11341, Egypt
Tel.: (20) 24184283
Provider of Ship Loading & Unloading Services
N.A.I.C.S.: 488320

Southern Cross Stevedoring **(2)**
60-64 upper Str Quay St, PO Box 292, Auckland, 1140, New Zealand **(100%)**
Tel.: (64) 93588050
Web Site: http://www.sxsint.co.nz
Sales Range: $50-74.9 Million
Emp.: 5
Provider of Ship Loading & Unloading Services
N.A.I.C.S.: 488320
Steve Bell (Mng Dir)

CARROLL & CARROLL INCORPORATED
Foundation Dr, Savannah, GA 31405
Tel.: (912) 964-7446
Web Site: http://www.cacasphalt.com
Year Founded: 1985
Sales Range: $10-24.9 Million
Emp.: 45
Contractor of Highway & Street Paving
N.A.I.C.S.: 561110
C. Arland Carroll (CEO)

CARROLL CAPITAL LLC
88 Field Point Rd, Greenwich, CT 06830
Tel.: (203) 742-9993
Web Site: https://www.carrollcapital.com
Rev.: $10,000,000
Emp.: 100
Privater Equity Firm
N.A.I.C.S.: 523999
Brian F. Carroll (Mng Partner)

Subsidiaries:

Elevator Service LLC **(1)**
823 Ottawa Ave NW, Grand Rapids, MI 49503
Tel.: (616) 235-4332
Web Site: https://www.esigr.com
Emp.: 100
Elevator Maintenance, Repair & Installation Services
N.A.I.C.S.: 333921
Brett McCay (Pres)

Subsidiary (Domestic):

Toledo Elevator & Machine, Co. **(2)**
221 N Detroit Ave, Toledo, OH 43607
Tel.: (419) 241-6422
Sales Range: $1-9.9 Million
Emp.: 14
Personal & Household Goods Repair & Maintenance
N.A.I.C.S.: 811490

CARROLL COMPANIES INC.
1640 Old 421 S, Boone, NC 28607
Tel.: (828) 264-2521
Web Site: https://www.clgco.com
Rev.: $60,795,451
Emp.: 125
Manufacture & Distribute Leather, Leather Goods & Furs
N.A.I.C.S.: 424990
Sterling C. Carroll (Pres)
Royce Carroll (VP)
Chad Fairchild (Mgr-Sls)
R. Craig Carlock (COO)

CARROLL COUNTY LIVESTOCK SALES BARN, INC.

PO Box 279, Carrollton, GA 30112-0005
Tel.: (770) 834-6608
Sales Range: $10-24.9 Million
Emp.: 30
Livestock Whslr
N.A.I.C.S.: 424520
Alan Banks (CEO)
Barry Robinson (CFO)
Sam Harman (Sec)

CARROLL COUNTY MEMORIAL HOSPITAL
1502 N Jefferson St, Carrollton, MO 64633
Tel.: (660) 542-1695   MO
Web Site: https://www.carrollcountyhospital.org
Year Founded: 1957
Sales Range: $10-24.9 Million
Emp.: 181
Health Care Srvices
N.A.I.C.S.: 622110
Rex Buhrmester (Pres)
Randall Barry (Sec)
Carolyn Lock (VP)
Jeff Buckley (Interim CEO)

CARROLL DANIEL CONSTRUCTION COMPANY
921 Athens St, Gainesville, GA 30501
Tel.: (770) 536-3241
Web Site: http://www.carrolldaniel.com
Year Founded: 1946
Sales Range: $25-49.9 Million
Emp.: 40
Commercial & Institutional Building Construction Services
N.A.I.C.S.: 236220
Brian Daniel (Pres)
Steve Hix (VP)
Scott Oberschlake (CFO)
Ashley Haynes (Project Mgr)
John Haynes (Project Mgr)
Henry Irvin (Project Mgr)
Tommy Wiley (Project Mgr)
Chris Erwin (Dir-Bus Dev)

CARROLL DISTRIBUTING & CONSTRUCTION SUPPLY
205 S Iowa Ave, Ottumwa, IA 52501
Tel.: (641) 683-1888
Web Site: http://www.carrolldistributing.com
Rev.: $20,000,000
Emp.: 15
Contractor's Materials
N.A.I.C.S.: 423810
Mike Hanshaw (Branch Mgr)

CARROLL ELECTRIC COOPERATIVE CORP.
920 Hwy 62 Spur, Berryville, AR 72616
Tel.: (870) 423-2161
Web Site: https://www.carrollecc.com
Rev.: $74,512,810
Emp.: 185
Distribution, Electric Power
N.A.I.C.S.: 221122
Carla Hathorn (Vice Chm)
Winfred Prier (Treas & Sec)

CARROLL ENGINEERING CORP.
949 Easton Rd, Warrington, PA 18976
Tel.: (215) 343-5700
Web Site: https://www.carrollengineering.com
Year Founded: 1973
Sales Range: $10-24.9 Million
Emp.: 88
Engineeering Services

N.A.I.C.S.: 541330
Alberto Vennettilli (VP)
Kenneth E. Heydt (Pres)

CARROLL FULMER LOGISTICS CORPORATION
8340 American Way, Groveland, FL 34736
Tel.: (352) 429-5000
Web Site: https://www.cfulmer.com
Year Founded: 1953
Sales Range: $75-99.9 Million
Emp.: 500
Freight Transportation Services
N.A.I.C.S.: 484121
Carroll Fulmer (Chm, Pres & CEO)

CARROLL INDEPENDENT FUEL COMPANY
2700 Loch Raven Rd, Baltimore, MD 21218
Tel.: (410) 235-1066
Web Site: http://www.carrollfuel.com
Sales Range: $200-249.9 Million
Emp.: 300
Fuel Oil Protein Service
N.A.I.C.S.: 424720
Richard B. Phelps III (Owner)

CARROLL ORGANIZATION, LLC
3340 Peachtree Rd NE, Atlanta, GA 30326
Tel.: (404) 812-8200   GA
Web Site: http://www.carrollorg.com
Year Founded: 2004
Sales Range: $50-74.9 Million
Emp.: 850
Real Estate Investment Services
N.A.I.C.S.: 531210
M. Patrick Carroll (Founder & CEO)
Jamie S. Lee (CFO)
David Perez (Pres & COO)
Andrew Zelman (Exec VP-Investments)
Brett Richards (Chief Investment Officer)

CARROLL PRODUCTS, INC.
44056 Phoenix Dr, Sterling Heights, MI 48314
Tel.: (586) 254-6300   MI
Web Site: http://www.carrollproducts.com
Year Founded: 1978
Sales Range: $10-24.9 Million
Emp.: 30
Fiscal Year-end: 12/31/11
Unsupported Plastics Bag Mfr
N.A.I.C.S.: 326111
Eugene Stys (Pres & Treas)
Joel Manardo (Owner & VP)

Subsidiaries:

Cello-Wrap Printing Company, Inc. **(1)**
110 N Main St, Farmersville, TX 75442
Tel.: (972) 782-7703
Web Site: http://www.cello-wrap.com
Sales Range: $1-9.9 Million
Emp.: 34
Commercial Printing
N.A.I.C.S.: 323111
Charles C. Whitaker (Pres & CEO)

CARROLL SEATING COMPANY INC.
2105 Lunt, Elk Grove Village, IL 60007
Tel.: (847) 434-0909
Web Site: https://www.carrollseating.com
Rev.: $16,653,377
Emp.: 35
Office & Public Building Furniture
N.A.I.C.S.: 423210

Carroll Seating Company Inc.—(Continued)

Michael Carroll *(VP)*
Ludwig Hoeft *(Project Mgr)*
Tom Madura *(Controller)*
Patrick J. Carroll Jr. *(Pres)*

CARROLL/WHITE
100 Ashford Ctr N Ste 440, Atlanta,
GA 30338-4863
Tel.: (770) 350-9800   **GA**
Year Founded: 1983
Sales Range: $10-24.9 Million
Emp.: 26
Advertising Agencies
N.A.I.C.S.: 541810
Brent Carroll *(Pres)*
Jim White *(VP)*
Jennifer Aaron *(Exec VP & Equity Partner)*
Manon Dutil *(Controller)*

CARROLLTON BANK
315 6th St, Carrollton, IL 62016-1247
Tel.: (217) 942-5408
Web Site:
   https://www.carrolltonbanking.com
Sales Range: $25-49.9 Million
Emp.: 80
State Commercial Banks
N.A.I.C.S.: 522110
Thomas S. Hough *(CEO)*
William O'Neil *(CFO & Sr VP)*
Larry Newberry *(Sr VP)*
James McGauley *(Exec VP)*
Suzanne Hough *(Officer-Community Dev)*
Nikki Woelfel *(VP-Community Dev)*

CARROLLTON ENTERPRISES LP
11785 Beltsville Dr Ste 1600, Calverton, MD 20705
Tel.: (301) 572-7800
Web Site:
   http://www.carrolltonenterprises.com
Rev.: $49,900,000
Emp.: 15
Shopping Center Operator
N.A.I.C.S.: 531312
Albert W. Turner *(Pres)*
William Steen *(Dir-PR & Mktg)*

CARRON NET COMPANY, INC.
1623-17th St, Two Rivers, WI 54241-0177
Tel.: (920) 793-2217
Web Site: https://www.carronnet.com
Year Founded: 1934
Sales Range: $25-49.9 Million
Emp.: 40
Sports & Tennis Nets, Volleyball Nets & Made to Order Nets Mfr
N.A.I.C.S.: 339920
Troy A. Christiansen *(CFO & Exec VP)*
William E. Kiel Jr. *(Pres & CEO)*

CARROT, LLC
950 SE Oak Ave, Roseburg, OR 97470
Web Site: http://www.carrot.com
Year Founded: 2013
Sales Range: $1-9.9 Million
Emp.: 19
Software Development Services
N.A.I.C.S.: 541511
Trevor Mauch *(CEO)*

CARRUTH CAPITAL LLC
116 Flanders Rd Ste 2000, Westborough, MA 01581
Tel.: (508) 898-3800   **MA**
Web Site:
   https://www.carruthcapital.com
Year Founded: 1991

Sales Range: $25-49.9 Million
Emp.: 21
Provider of Commercial Land & Building Leasing Services
N.A.I.C.S.: 525990
Christopher Egan *(Pres)*
Dave Rice *(Controller)*
Chris Shaw *(Mgr-Building)*

CARRUTHERS & ROTH, P.A.
235 N Edgeworth St, Greensboro,
NC 27402
Tel.: (336) 379-8651
Web Site: https://www.crlaw.com
Year Founded: 1947
Sales Range: $1-9.9 Million
Emp.: 59
Law firm
N.A.I.C.S.: 541110
John M. Flynn *(Mng Partner)*
Jeanna Childress *(Dir-Fin)*
Erin Molinaro *(Dir-Ops)*
Brandon Jones *(Atty)*
Trisha Barfield *(Assoc Atty-Comml Litigation Practice)*

CARSEY-WERNER LLC
16027 Ventura Blvd Ste 600, Encino,
CA 91436
Tel.: (818) 464-9600   **CA**
Web Site:
   https://www.carseywerner.com
Sales Range: $50-74.9 Million
Emp.: 35
Television Production Studio
N.A.I.C.S.: 512199
Marcy Carsey *(Founder)*

CARSON & ASSOCIATES, INC.
1310 W Daisy Bates Dr, Little Rock,
AR 72202-5432
Tel.: (501) 372-5816
Sales Range: $10-24.9 Million
Emp.: 15
Civil Engineering Services
N.A.I.C.S.: 236220
Janet Harris *(Treas, Sec & VP)*
Karen Gray *(Office Mgr)*

CARSON CITY TOYOTA
2590 S Carson St, Carson City, NV
89701-1203
Tel.: (775) 882-8211
Web Site:
   https://www.carsoncitytoyota.com
Year Founded: 1980
Sales Range: $10-24.9 Million
Emp.: 85
New Car Whslr
N.A.I.C.S.: 441110
Richard N. Campagni *(Owner & Pres)*

CARSON CONCRETE CORPORATION
5 Creek Pkwy, Boothwyn, PA 19061
Tel.: (610) 825-8600
Web Site:
   https://www.carsonconcrete.net
Sales Range: $10-24.9 Million
Emp.: 50
Concrete Work
N.A.I.C.S.: 238110
Bob Artz *(Controller)*
David Blatstein *(Project Coord)*
Anthony J. Samango Jr. *(Pres)*

CARSON DISTRIBUTING COMPANY
1905 A Jct Hwy, Kerrville, TX 78028
Tel.: (830) 895-3088
Sales Range: $10-24.9 Million
Emp.: 23
Beer & Other Fermented Malt Liquors
N.A.I.C.S.: 424810
George Carson *(Pres)*
Patrick Carson *(VP)*

CARSON DODGE CHRYSLER, INC.
3059 S Carson St, Carson City, NV
89701-4513
Tel.: (775) 883-2020
Web Site:
   http://www.carsondodge.com
Year Founded: 1987
Sales Range: $10-24.9 Million
Emp.: 60
New Car Retailer
N.A.I.C.S.: 441110
Stephen H. Christian *(Gen Mgr)*
James A. Cryer *(Sec & VP)*

CARSON FINANCIAL HOLDING COMPANY, INC.
24 W Division St, Stilwell, OK 74960
Tel.: (918) 696-7745   **OK**
Web Site:
   http://www.carsoncommunity.bank
Year Founded: 1997
Sales Range: $1-9.9 Million
Emp.: 42
Bank Holding Company
N.A.I.C.S.: 551111
Drew T. Carson *(Pres)*

Subsidiaries:

Carson Community Bank   (1)
24 W Division St, Stilwell, OK 74960
Tel.: (918) 696-7745
Web Site: http://www.bc-ok.bank
Sales Range: $1-9.9 Million
Commercial Banking
N.A.I.C.S.: 522110
Drew T. Carson *(Pres)*

CARSON HELICOPTERS INC.
952 Blooming Glen Rd, Perkasie, PA
18944-2965
Tel.: (215) 249-3535   **PA**
Web Site:
   http://www.carsonhelicopters.com
Year Founded: 1958
Sales Range: $25-49.9 Million
Emp.: 120
Helicopter Overhaul, Repair & Remanufacturing Services
N.A.I.C.S.: 488190
Franklin Carson *(Pres)*

Subsidiaries:

Carson Gravity Meter & Instrumentation Company Inc.   (1)
631 County Road 269, Bertram, TX 78605-3532
Tel.: (512) 515-6643
Rev.: $210,000
Emp.: 4
Repair Services
N.A.I.C.S.: 811210

CARSON OIL COMPANY
3125 NW 35th Ave, Portland, OR
97210
Tel.: (503) 224-8500   **OR**
Web Site:
   https://www.carsonteam.com
Year Founded: 1938
Dealer of Fuel Oil
N.A.I.C.S.: 424720
Lance Woodbury *(Pres)*
Will Papenfuss *(CFO)*
Jeff Rouse *(VP-Bus Dev)*
Marti Sharp *(Gen Counsel & Compliance Officer)*
Matt Benz *(Sr Dir-Sls & Sls Ops)*
Nate Woodbury *(Dir-Pricing & Analysis)*
James Haselhofer *(Dir-Marketing)*
Tim Love *(Sr Dir-Logistics Ops)*

CARSON PRIVATE CAPITAL INCORPORATED
500 Victory Plz E 3030 Olive St, Dallas, TX 75219

Tel.: (214) 999-1000   **TX**
Web Site:
   http://www.carsoncapital.com
Year Founded: 1990
Privater Equity Firm
N.A.I.C.S.: 523999
Michael T. Hearne *(Exec VP)*
Greg Giannini *(Chief Compliance Officer & Controller)*
Royal W. Carson III *(Pres & CEO)*

CARSON TAHOE REGIONAL HEALTHCARE
1600 Medical Pkwy, Carson City, NV
89703
Tel.: (775) 445-8000   **NV**
Year Founded: 2002
Sales Range: $200-249.9 Million
Emp.: 1,394
Community Health Care Services
N.A.I.C.S.: 621498
Annette C. Patellos *(Dir-Cardiac Svcs)*
Ann T. Beck *(CFO & VP-Fin)*
Kathleen Molina *(Dir-Nursing Svcs)*
Cynthia A. Kuperus *(Dir-Periperative Svcs)*

CARSON VALLEY CHILDREN'S AID
1419 Bethlehem Pike, Flourtown, PA
19031
Tel.: (215) 233-1960   **PA**
Web Site:
   http://www.carsonvalley.org
Year Founded: 1914
Sales Range: $25-49.9 Million
Emp.: 503
Child & Family Care Services
N.A.I.C.S.: 624190
Barry Astrowsky *(Treas)*
Rosemarie Romano *(Sec)*
Stephen A. Kelbick *(Asst Treas)*
Margaret P. Rux *(Pres)*
Richard Collier Jr. *(VP)*

CARSON'S NUT-BOLT & TOOL CO.
301 Hammett St Ext, Greenville, SC
29609
Tel.: (864) 242-4720
Web Site: http://www.carsons-nbt.com
Sales Range: $10-24.9 Million
Emp.: 65
Hardware & Tool Retailer
N.A.I.C.S.: 423710
Jane F. Carson *(Pres)*

CARSONS INCORPORATED
4200 Cheyenne Dr, Archdale, NC
27263
Tel.: (336) 431-1101
Web Site:
   http://www.carsonsofhp.com
Sales Range: $10-24.9 Million
Emp.: 150
Manufacture Upholstered Household Furniture
N.A.I.C.S.: 337121
Thomas C. Stout *(CEO)*
Barry Yates *(CFO)*
Janet Culler *(Treas)*

CARSTENS INC.
7310 W Wilson Ave, Chicago, IL
60706
Tel.: (708) 669-1500   **IL**
Web Site: https://www.carstens.com
Year Founded: 1936
Sales Range: $50-74.9 Million
Emp.: 100
Mfr of Hospital & Long Term Care Patient Charting Systems; Patient Chart Racks & Card-Indexers; Pressure Sensitive Labels

N.A.I.C.S.: 339112
Dave Waskin *(Mgr-Adv)*
Chris Chisom *(Asst Mgr-Customer Svcs)*
Michele Devers *(Mgr-Sls-Natl)*
Barbara Vanderkloot *(Pres & CEO)*

CARSWELL DISTRIBUTING COMPANY
3750 N Liberty St, Winston Salem, NC 27105
Tel.: (336) 767-7700
Web Site:
https://www.carswelldist.com
Sales Range: $25-49.9 Million
Emp.: 40
Lawn Machinery & Equipment
N.A.I.C.S.: 423820
Bill A. Parsley *(Pres & CEO)*
Tim Gupton *(VP)*

CART.COM, INC.
268 Pearl St, Beaumont, TX 77701
Web Site: http://www.cart.com
Year Founded: 2020
Ecommerce Software Services
N.A.I.C.S.: 423430
Jim Jacobsen *(Co-Founder & Exec Chm)*
Omair Tariq *(Co-Founder & CEO)*
Linda Xu *(Chief Growth Officer)*
Randy Ray *(Chief Revenue Officer)*
Kate Gunning *(Head-Mktg)*
Rachel Truair *(CMO)*
Gary Specter *(Pres)*

Subsidiaries:

AmeriCommerce, L.P. **(1)**
5390 Washington, Beaumont, TX 77707
Tel.: (409) 860-9006
Web Site: http://www.americommerce.com
Sales Range: $1-9.9 Million
Emp.: 20
E-Commerce Software
N.A.I.C.S.: 513210
Ed Sturrock *(Pres)*
Abel McBride *(Dir-Multimedia)*
Belinda Bourgeois *(Coord-Acctg & Office)*
Jack Cravy *(Dir-Internet Mktg)*
Jake Stack *(Dir-Bus Dev)*

CARTAGZ INC.
9701 Elk Grove Florin Rd Ste 101, Elk Grove, CA 95624
Web Site: http://www.cartagz.com
Year Founded: 2008
Sales Range: $10-24.9 Million
Emp.: 10
DMV Related Transactions
N.A.I.C.S.: 811198
Greg Sanders *(Co-Founder)*
Troy Greeson *(Co-Founder, Pres & CEO)*

CARTEL BLUE, INC.
214 Yacht Club Wy 11, Redondo Beach, CA 90277
Tel.: (575) 605-2375
Year Founded: 1992
Apparel & Accessory Mfr
N.A.I.C.S.: 315990
David Rhodes *(Pres)*

CARTER & ASSOCIATES, LLC
1440 Dutch Valley Pl Ste 1200, Atlanta, GA 30324
Tel.: (404) 888-3000   GA
Web Site: http://www.carterusa.com
Year Founded: 1958
Sales Range: $25-49.9 Million
Emp.: 350
Real Estate Development Services
N.A.I.C.S.: 531210
John E. Carter *(Vice Chm)*
Bob Peterson *(Chm)*
Scott Taylor *(Pres & CEO)*
Scott Stringer *(Exec VP)*

Jerome Hagley *(Exec VP)*
Frank Crittenden *(VP)*
John Jokerst *(Sr VP)*
Patti Neal *(Exec VP)*
David Nelson *(Exec VP)*
Gil Patterson *(CFO)*

Subsidiaries:

Carter Validus Advisors, LLC **(1)**
4890 W Kennedy Blvd Ste 650, Tampa, FL 33609
Tel.: (813) 387-1701
Web Site: http://www.cartervalidus.com
Real Estate Investment Advisory & Management Services
N.A.I.C.S.: 531390
Christopher Hammerli *(Chief Acq Officer)*
Stacy Sheedy *(Mgr-Mktg)*
Alex Stacy *(Sr VP-Healthcare)*
Reesha Smith *(Coord-Mktg)*
Sara Wayson *(Mgr-Asset)*
Jon Sajeski *(VP-Healthcare Acq)*

Affiliate (Non-US):

Sila Realty Trust, Inc. **(2)**
Tel.: (813) 287-0101
Web Site: https://www.silarealtytrust.com
Rev.: $179,986,000
Assets: $2,219,802,000
Liabilities: $664,707,000
Net Worth: $1,555,095,000
Earnings: ($7,978,000)
Emp.: 54
Fiscal Year-end: 12/31/2022
Real Estate Investment Trust
N.A.I.C.S.: 525990
Michael A. Seton *(Pres & CEO)*
Kay C. Neely *(CFO, Chief Acctg Officer & Exec VP)*
Jonathan Kuchin *(Chm)*
Christopher K. Flouhouse *(Chief Investment Officer & Exec VP)*
Samuel W. Brannan *(Chief Acctg Officer & Sr VP)*
Miles F. Callahan *(Sr VP-Capital Markets & Investor Relations)*
W. Todd Jensen *(Sr VP-Acquisitions)*
Jodi Poore *(Sr VP-Corp Acctg)*
Jon Beaudin *(VP-Res & Credit Underwriting)*
Kris Ellwanger *(VP-Information Technology & Corp Facilities)*
Michelle Leverone *(VP-Fin Reporting)*
Toni More *(VP-Property Mgmt)*
Corey Spellman *(VP-Fin Plng & Analysis)*
Tyler Sterns *(VP-Due Diligence & Closings)*
Laura Wagner *(VP-Human Capital)*
Randy Ziegler *(VP-Investment Mgmt)*

Subsidiary (Domestic):

Carter Validus Mission Critical REIT, Inc. **(3)**
4890 W Kennedy Blvd Ste 650, Tampa, FL 33609
Tel.: (813) 287-0101
Web Site:
http://www.cvmissioncriticalreit.com
Rev.: $91,226,000
Assets: $1,023,516,000
Liabilities: $260,796,000
Net Worth: $762,720,000
Earnings: ($3,959,000)
Fiscal Year-end: 12/31/2018
Real Estate Investment Trust
N.A.I.C.S.: 525990
John E. Carter *(Founder)*
Kay C. Neely *(CFO, Treas & Sec)*

CARTER & VERPLANCK, INC.
4910 W Cypress St, Tampa, FL 33607
Tel.: (813) 287-0709
Web Site:
https://www.carterverplanck.com
Sales Range: $25-49.9 Million
Emp.: 30
Water & Wastewater Equipment Supplier
N.A.I.C.S.: 423830
Saade M. Chibani *(CEO)*
Teresa Sullivan *(VP)*

CARTER BLOODCARE

2205 Hwy 121, Bedford, TX 76021
Tel.: (817) 412-5000   TX
Web Site:
http://www.carterbloodcare.org
Year Founded: 1959
Sales Range: $125-149.9 Million
Emp.: 1,288
Blood Transfusion Services
N.A.I.C.S.: 621991
Doug Heath *(Dir-Lab Ops)*
Linda Goelzer *(Dir-PR)*
Jennifer Maul *(Dir-Mktg)*
Nancy Arnett *(Dir-Quality Assurance)*

CARTER BROTHERS, LLC
100 Hartsfield Ctr Pkwy Ste 100, Atlanta, GA 30354
Tel.: (404) 767-2525
Web Site:
http://www.carterbrothers.com
Sales Range: $25-49.9 Million
Emp.: 59
Electronic Security Systems, IT, Business & Financial Services
N.A.I.C.S.: 561621
John Carter *(Pres & CEO)*
Cris Carter *(Chm)*
Gailyn Cherry *(Mgr-Project Controls)*

CARTER CHEVROLET CO.
1229 Main St, Manchester, CT 06040
Tel.: (860) 646-6464
Web Site:
http://www.carterchevrolet.com
Year Founded: 1946
Sales Range: $25-49.9 Million
Emp.: 50
New Car Retailer
N.A.I.C.S.: 441110
Paul Koldras *(Mgr-Sls)*
Rick Skovich *(Mgr-Svc)*
Casey Nadeau *(Coord-Product Support)*
John Nesbit *(Mgr-Collision Center)*

CARTER CHEVROLET, INC.
200 W Dixon Blvd, Shelby, NC 28152-6549
Tel.: (704) 482-4341
Sales Range: $10-24.9 Million
Emp.: 37
Car Whslr
N.A.I.C.S.: 441110
Conway Carter *(Owner)*

CARTER DAY INTERNATIONAL, INC.
500 73rd Ave NE, Minneapolis, MN 55432-3270
Tel.: (763) 571-1000   DE
Web Site: https://www.carterday.com
Year Founded: 1920
Sales Range: $10-24.9 Million
Emp.: 100
Processing Equipment Mfr
N.A.I.C.S.: 333241
Matthew Ernst *(Pres)*
Dale Anderson *(Controller)*
Todd Kipfer *(Dir-Jacobson Product)*
Ron Bornetun *(VP-Mfg)*

CARTER DISTRIBUTING COMPANY INC
1307 Broad St, Chattanooga, TN 37402
Tel.: (423) 266-0056
Web Site: http://www.carterdist.com
Sales Range: $10-24.9 Million
Emp.: 70
Beer & Ale
N.A.I.C.S.: 424810
Ben Baker *(Mgr-Ops)*

CARTER DUNCAN CORPORATION

5427 Hollister Ave, Santa Barbara, CA 93111-2345
Tel.: (805) 964-9610
Web Site:
https://www.seymourduncan.com
Rev.: $8,000,000
Emp.: 70
Musical Equipment & Electronic Components Mfr
N.A.I.C.S.: 334419
Seymour W. Duncan *(Chm)*
Cathy Carter Duncan *(CEO)*
Kevin Beller *(Chief Engr)*

CARTER LUMBER CO.
601 Tallmadge Rd, Kent, OH 44240
Tel.: (330) 673-6100   KY
Web Site:
http://www.carterlumber.com
Year Founded: 1932
Sales Range: $550-599.9 Million
Emp.: 3,500
Special Trade Contractors; Retail Building Materials & Garden Supplier
N.A.I.C.S.: 423310
Neil Sackett *(Pres & CEO)*
Judy Lee *(Sec)*
Jeff Seder *(Dir-Tech)*
Jeff Donley *(COO)*

Subsidiaries:

Carter Lumber Co. - Carter Components Plant **(1)**
601 Tallmadge Rd, Kent, OH 44240
Tel.: (877) 586-2374
Wood Building Material Installation Services
N.A.I.C.S.: 238130

Carter Lumber Co. - Carter Custom Millwork **(1)**
601 Tallmadge Rd, Kent, OH 44240
Tel.: (330) 673-6100
Web Site: http://www.carterlumber.com
Wood Building Material Installation Services
N.A.I.C.S.: 238130

Carter Lumber Co. - Griggs Lumber **(1)**
109 Impact Blvd, Elizabeth City, NC 27909
Tel.: (252) 264-2323
Web Site: http://www.griggslumber.com
Wood Building Material Installation Services
N.A.I.C.S.: 238130

Carter Lumber Co. - Kempsville Building Materials Division **(1)**
3300 Business Ctr Dr S, Chesapeake, VA 23323
Tel.: (757) 485-0782
Web Site:
http://www.kempsvillebuilding.com
Emp.: 250
Wood Building Material Installation Services
N.A.I.C.S.: 238130
Pat Nordon *(Mgr-Ops)*

Carter Lumber Co. - Kight Home Center **(1)**
5521 Oak Grove Rd, Evansville, IN 47715
Tel.: (812) 479-8281
Web Site: http://www.kighthomecenter.com
Emp.: 40
Wood Building Material Installation Services
N.A.I.C.S.: 238130

Carter Lumber Co. Inc. **(1)**
4292 N County Rd, Kokomo, IN 46901   **(100%)**
Tel.: (765) 457-5569
Rev.: $890,000
Emp.: 10
Lumber & Other Building Materials
N.A.I.C.S.: 423310

Carter Lumber of Virginia Inc. **(1)**
12144 Washington Hwy, Ashland, VA 23005
Tel.: (804) 798-1514
Web Site: http://www.carterlumber.com
Sales Range: $10-24.9 Million
Emp.: 12
Lumber & Other Building Materials
N.A.I.C.S.: 423310
Andy Hite *(Gen Mgr)*

Carter Lumber of the South Inc. **(1)**

Carter Lumber Co.—(Continued)

601 Tallmadge Rd, Kent, OH 44240-7331
Tel.: (330) 673-6100
Web Site: http://www.carterlumber.com
Sales Range: $25-49.9 Million
Emp.: 200
Lumber & Other Building Materials
N.A.I.C.S.: 423310

Carter Resources Inc. (1)
601 Tallmadge Rd, Kent, OH
44240-7331 (100%)
Tel.: (330) 673-6100
Web Site: http://www.carterlumber.com
Sales Range: $10-24.9 Million
Emp.: 2
Building Material Supplier
N.A.I.C.S.: 237210

Holmes Lumber & Building Center
Inc. (1)
6139 S R 39, Millersburg, OH 44654
Tel.: (330) 674-9060
Web Site: http://www.holmeslumber.com
Sales Range: $25-49.9 Million
Emp.: 160
Lumber, Plywood & Millwork Whslr
N.A.I.C.S.: 423310
Pam Skelly (Mgr-Admin)

The Carter-Jones Lumber Company
Inc. (1)
601 Tallmadge Rd, Kent, OH 44240-7331
Tel.: (330) 673-6100
Web Site: http://www.carterlumber.com
Sales Range: $25-49.9 Million
Emp.: 200
Lumber & Other Building Materials
N.A.I.C.S.: 423310

CARTER MACHINERY COM-PANY, INC.
1330 Lynchburg Tpke, Salem, VA
24153-5416
Tel.: (540) 387-1111 DE
Web Site:
http://www.cartermachinery.com
Year Founded: 1952
Construction Machinery Retailer
N.A.I.C.S.: 532412
Jim Parker (CEO)

Subsidiaries:

Alban Tractor Company Inc. (1)
8531 Pulaski Hwy, Baltimore, MD 21237-3005
Tel.: (410) 686-7777
Web Site: http://www.albancat.com
Tractor Sales & Service
N.A.I.C.S.: 423810
Cole Bacon (Mgr-Mktg)
Jim Sweeney (CFO)
John Rodal (VP-Svcs)
James C. Alban IV (Founder)

Subsidiary (Domestic):

Alban Rents, LLC (2)
8427 Pulaski Hwy, Baltimore, MD 21237-3022
Tel.: (410) 687-3689
Tractor Rental & Leasing Services
N.A.I.C.S.: 532120

Division (Domestic):

Alban Tractor Company Inc. - Alban
Machining & Hydraulics Division (2)
8864 Citation Rd, Baltimore, MD 21221
Tel.: (410) 780-4507
Industrial Engineering Services
N.A.I.C.S.: 541330

Alban Tractor Company Inc. - Alban
Rental Solutions Division (2)
6387 Old Washington Rd, Elkridge, MD
21075
Tel.: (410) 796-8000
Web Site: http://www.albancat.com
Emp.: 100
Industrial Engineering Services
N.A.I.C.S.: 541330

CARTER MOTOR COMPANY
400 S Railroad St, Warren, IL 61087

Tel.: (815) 745-2100
Web Site:
http://www.cartermotor.com
Year Founded: 1932
Sales Range: $25-49.9 Million
Emp.: 35
DC to AC Rotary Converters, Dyna-motors & Rotary Power Supplies, Mo-tors, Gearmotors & Tach Generators
N.A.I.C.S.: 335312
Keith Geisler (Owner)

CARTER MOTORS INC.
5202 Leary Ave NW, Seattle, WA
98107
Tel.: (206) 782-7474
Web Site: https://www.cartervw.com
Rev.: $55,000,000
Emp.: 150
Automobiles, New & Used
N.A.I.C.S.: 441110
Wade Carter III (Founder)

CARTER OF MANCHESTER
175 Hartford Tpke, Vernon, CT 06066
Tel.: (860) 646-6464
Web Site:
http://www.carterofmanchester.com
Sales Range: $25-49.9 Million
Emp.: 200
Sales of New & Used Automobiles
N.A.I.C.S.: 441110
Johnathan Larbee (Pres)

CARTER PAPER & PACKAG-ING, INC.
3400 SW Washington St, Peoria, IL
61602-1975
Tel.: (309) 637-7711
Web Site:
https://www.carterpaper.com
Sales Range: $10-24.9 Million
Emp.: 13
Paper & Packaging Materials Distr
N.A.I.C.S.: 424130
Greg Malek (Acct Exec)
Steve Bennett (Sr Acct Exec)
Ken Bachelor (Controller)
Mark Sutton (Mgr-Warehouse & Fa-cility)
Teri Phillips (Mgr-Pur)

CARTER THERMO KING INC.
4949 N Orange Blossom Trl, Orlando,
FL 32810
Tel.: (407) 293-7158
Web Site: http://www.thermoking.com
Sales Range: $10-24.9 Million
Emp.: 33
Refrigeration Units, Truck & Motor
Vehicles
N.A.I.C.S.: 811114
David Haroldson (Gen Mgr)

CARTER'S INC.
223 S Washington St, Charlotte, MI
48813-1546
Tel.: (517) 543-7833 MI
Web Site: http://www.carters.com
Year Founded: 1985
Sales Range: $25-49.9 Million
Emp.: 300
Grocery Stores
N.A.I.C.S.: 445110

CARTER'S SHOOTING CEN-TER INC.
6231 Treaschwig Rd, Spring, TX
77373
Tel.: (281) 443-8393
Sales Range: $10-24.9 Million
Emp.: 18
Retailer of Sporting Goods
N.A.I.C.S.: 459110
William O. Carter (Pres)

CARTERBALDWIN
200 Mansell Ct E Ste 450, Roswell,
GA 30076
Tel.: (678) 448-0000
Web Site:
http://www.carterbaldwin.com
Sales Range: $10-24.9 Million
Emp.: 25
Executive Search Service
N.A.I.C.S.: 541612
Jennifer Poole Sobocinski (Partner)
David M. Sobocinski (Partner)
Chris Guiney (Partner)
Price Harding III (Partner)

CARTERET-CRAVEN ELEC-TRIC COOPERATIVE
1300 Hwy 24, Newport, NC 28570
Tel.: (252) 247-3107
Sales Range: $25-49.9 Million
Emp.: 82
Distribution, Electric Power
N.A.I.C.S.: 221122
Craig Conrad (CEO & Gen Mgr)
Ben Ball (Pres)
Cheryl Slater (VP-Customer Svcs)
Sarah Grider (VP-Svcs)
Gary Zajac (VP-Mktg)
Jerry Eborn (VP-Acctg)
Peggy Horrell (VP-HR)

CARTESIAN CAPITAL GROUP, LLC
505 5th Ave 15th Fl, New York, NY
10017
Tel.: (212) 461-6363
Web Site:
https://www.cartesiangroup.com
Year Founded: 2006
Rev.: $2,000,000,000
Emp.: 22
Private Equity Investments
N.A.I.C.S.: 523999
Tom Armstrong (Partner)
Geoffrey Hamlin (Partner)
Bill Jarosz (Partner)
Paul Pizzani (Partner)
Peter Michael Yu (Mng Partner)
Beth S. Michelson (Sr Mng Dir)

CARTHAGE AREA HOSPITAL, INC.
1001 West St, Carthage, NY 13619
Tel.: (315) 493-1000 NY
Web Site:
https://www.carthagehospital.com
Year Founded: 1921
Sales Range: $25-49.9 Million
Emp.: 564
Community Health Care Services
N.A.I.C.S.: 622110
Rich Duvall (CEO)
Beth Barnes (COO)
Rob Bloom (CFO)
Steve Olsen (Dir-Nursing)
Natalie Burnham (Dir-Employee &
Community Engagement)
Michel Camidge (VP)
Victoria Hasseler Collins (VP)
Dale Klock (VP)
Gary Rowe (Pres)
Yolanda Skvorak (VP)
Mary Storms (VP)

CARTHAGE VETERINARY SERVICE, LTD.
PO Box 220, Carthage, IL 62321
Tel.: (217) 357-2173
Web Site: http://www.hogvet.com
Year Founded: 1948
Emp.: 337
Veterinary Services
N.A.I.C.S.: 541940
Sherri Biddenstadt (Mgr-Sow Re-cords)

CARTHAGE WATER & ELEC-TRIC PLANT
627 W Centennial Ave, Carthage, MO
64836
Tel.: (417) 237-7300
Web Site: http://www.cwepnet.com
Year Founded: 1898
Sales Range: $25-49.9 Million
Emp.: 80
Water Utility
N.A.I.C.S.: 221310
Chuck Bryant (Dir-Mktg-Tech Svcs)
Jane Hummel (Office Mgr)

CARTON SERVICE INC.
100 First Quality Dr, Shelby, OH
44875
Tel.: (419) 342-5010
Web Site:
http://www.cartonservice.com
Rev.: $33,039,394
Emp.: 200
Boxes Corrugated: Made From Pur-chased Materials
N.A.I.C.S.: 322211
Reid Lederer (Pres)
Scott Garverick (VP-Bus Dev)
Dave Higgins (Mgr-Production)
Diane Christie (Mgr-Pur)
Herbert Dibble (Co-Pres)

CARTWRIGHT AERIAL SUR-VEYS, INC.
5999 Freeport Blvd, Sacramento, CA
95822-3506
Tel.: (916) 421-3465 CA
Web Site: http://www.casmap.com
Year Founded: 1946
Sales Range: $10-24.9 Million
Emp.: 15
Surveying, Mapmaking Services &
Photogrammetry
N.A.I.C.S.: 541370
William Calmes (Pres)

CARUS CORPORATION
315 5th St, Peru, IL 61354-2859
Tel.: (815) 223-1500 DE
Web Site:
http://www.caruscorporation.com
Year Founded: 1915
Sales Range: $100-124.9 Million
Emp.: 250
Chemical Mfr; Potassium Perman-ganate & Industrial & Municipal Water
Treatment Chemicals
N.A.I.C.S.: 325180
Dave Kuzy (COO)

Subsidiaries:

CARUS CHEMICAL COMPANY (1)
1500 8th St, La Salle, IL 61301
Tel.: (815) 224-6868
Potassium Permanganate Mfr
N.A.I.C.S.: 325180

CARUS PHOSPHATES, INC. (1)
181 Woodlawn Ave, Belmont, NC 28012
Tel.: (815) 223-1500
Web Site: http://www.caruscorporation.com
Chemicals Mfr
N.A.I.C.S.: 325180

CARUSO AFFILIATED
101 The Grove Dr, Los Angeles, CA
90036
Tel.: (323) 900-8100
Web Site:
http://www.carusoaffiliated.com
Year Founded: 1987
Rev.: $23,800,000
Emp.: 90
Investment Holding Company
N.A.I.C.S.: 551112
Rick J. Caruso (Founder & CEO)
Bret M. Nielsen (Sr VP-Leasing &
Asset Mgmt)

Thomas A. Veje (*Exec VP-Construction*)
Jackie Levy (*Exec VP-Ops*)
Kelly Masuda (*Chief Investment Officer*)
Corinne Verdery (*Exec VP-Dev*)
Bryce Ross (*Sr VP-Acquisitions & Dev*)
Michael Gazzano (*VP-Dev*)
Doris Nesheiwat (*VP-Specialty Leasing*)
Peter Wilhelm (*CFO*)

Subsidiaries:

Century Investments Inc   (1)
101 The Grove Dr, Los Angeles, CA 90036
Tel.: (323) 900-8100
Web Site: http://www.carusoaffilated.com
Sales Range: $25-49.9 Million
Emp.: 120
Commercial & Industrial Building Operation
N.A.I.C.S.: 531120
Rick J. Caruso (*Pres & CEO*)

Crm Properties   (1)
101 The Grove Dr, Los Angeles, CA 90036
Tel.: (310) 458-0202
Rev.: $1,500,000
Emp.: 80
Subdividers & Developers, Nec
N.A.I.C.S.: 237210

CARUSO PRODUCE, INC.
2100 SE 4th Ave., Canby, OR 97013
Tel.: (503) 691-2626
Web Site:
    http://www.carusoproduce.com
Year Founded: 1944
Fresh Fruit & Vegetable Merchant Whslr
N.A.I.C.S.: 424480

Subsidiaries:

Washington Produce   (1)
1622 S Graham St, Seattle, WA 98108
Tel.: (206) 762-5262
Fresh Fruit & Vegetable Merchant Whslr
N.A.I.C.S.: 424480

CARVER CONSTRUCTION COMPANY
7080 Jackson Rd, Ann Arbor, MI 48103
Tel.: (734) 662-4350
Web Site:
    https://www.carverconstruction.com
Year Founded: 1978
Sales Range: Less than $1 Million
Emp.: 3
Commercial & Institutional Building Construction Services
N.A.I.C.S.: 236220
Earl Carver (*Pres*)

CARVIN CORP.
12340 World Trade Dr, San Diego, CA 92128
Tel.: (858) 487-1600
Web Site: http://www.carvin.com
Sales Range: $10-24.9 Million
Emp.: 105
Musical Instruments
N.A.I.C.S.: 339992
Carson Kiesel (*Pres*)

CARY RECONSTRUCTION INC.
2410 Reliance Ave, Apex, NC 27539
Tel.: (919) 467-5517
Web Site:
    http://www.responseteam1.com
Year Founded: 1991
Sales Range: $25-49.9 Million
Emp.: 175
Residential Remodeler
N.A.I.C.S.: 236118
Wayne Baker (*Owner*)

CARY STREET PARTNERS FINANCIAL LLC
901 E Byrd St Ste 1001, Richmond, VA 23219
Tel.: (804) 340-8100   VA
Web Site:
    http://carystreetpartners.com
Year Founded: 2002
Rev.: $1,100,000
Emp.: 18
All Other Business Support Services
N.A.I.C.S.: 561499
Mark M. Gambill (*Co-Founder & Mng Partner*)
Kip R. Caffey (*Mng Partner*)
Brett Bond (*Mng Dir-Investment Banking-Charlotte*)
Joseph R. Schmuckler (*CEO*)

Subsidiaries:

Waypoint Advisors LLC   (1)
2101 Parks Ave Ste 800, Virginia Beach, VA 23451
Tel.: (757) 623-1600
Web Site: http://www.waypointadvisors.net
Portfolio Management
N.A.I.C.S.: 523940
Elizabeth T. Patterson (*Pres*)
Jane Tower (*Exec VP*)
Lori Cochran (*Mgr-Ops*)
Susanna Adams (*VP & Chief Compliance Officer*)

CARYLON CORPORATION
2500 W Arthington St, Chicago, IL 60612-4108
Tel.: (312) 666-7700   IL
Web Site:
    http://www.caryloncorp.com
Year Founded: 1949
Sales Range: $450-499.9 Million
Emp.: 1,025
Sewer Cleaning Products & Services
N.A.I.C.S.: 562991
John Kofod (*Mgr-Risk*)

Subsidiaries:

Ace Pipe Cleaning, Inc.   (1)
6601 Universal Ave, Kansas City, MO 64120   (100%)
Tel.: (816) 241-2891
Web Site: http://www.acepipe.com
Rev.: $1,100,000
Emp.: 30
Sewer Cleaning Services
N.A.I.C.S.: 562991
Steve Hotz (*Pres*)

Bio-Nomic Services, Inc.   (1)
530 Woodlawn St, Belmont, NC 28012   (100%)
Tel.: (704) 529-0000
Web Site: http://www.bio-nomic.com
Rev.: $6,500,000
Emp.: 46
Liquid Waste Management Services
N.A.I.C.S.: 562998
Peter P. Fleetwood (*Pres*)

Deep South Industrial Services, Inc.   (1)
515 Industrial Dr, Rockmart, GA 30153
Tel.: (678) 757-1022
Web Site: http://www.deepsouthind.com
Emp.: 100
Environmental Engineering Services
N.A.I.C.S.: 541330
Angie Pickelsimer (*Mgr-Acctg*)

Metropolitan Environmental Services, Inc.   (1)
5055 Nike Dr, Hilliard, OH 43026-9140
Tel.: (614) 771-1881
Web Site: http://www.metenviro.com
Rev.: $7,000,000
Emp.: 58
Environmental Cleaning Services
N.A.I.C.S.: 541620
Rick Gaffey (*Pres*)

Mobile Dredging & Pumping Co.   (1)
3100 Bethel Rd, Chester, PA 19013-1488   (100%)
Tel.: (610) 497-9500

Web Site: http://www.caryloncorp.com
Rev.: $15,000,000
Emp.: 85
Industrial Environmental Services
N.A.I.C.S.: 562991
Dave Huggler (*VP*)
Fran Purcell (*Controller*)

National Industrial Maintenance, Inc.   (1)
4530 Baring Ave, East Chicago, IN 46312-3209   (100%)
Tel.: (219) 398-6660
Web Site: http://www.nimin.com
Sales Range: $10-24.9 Million
Emp.: 60
Environmental Maintenance Services
N.A.I.C.S.: 562999
Gale Gentry (*Project Coord-Safety*)

National Plant Services Inc.   (1)
1461 Harbor Ave, Long Beach, CA 90813-2741
Tel.: (562) 436-7600
Web Site:
    http://www.caryloncorporation.com
Rev.: $3,000,000
Emp.: 35
Sewer & Pipeline Cleaning Services
N.A.I.C.S.: 562991
Dennis Keene (*Gen Mgr*)

National Power Rodding Corporation   (1)
2500 W Arthington St, Chicago, IL 60612-4108
Tel.: (312) 666-7700
Web Site:
    http://www.nationalpowerrodding.com
Rev.: $7,400,000
Emp.: 100
Sewer Cleaning Services
N.A.I.C.S.: 562998

National Water Main Cleaning Co.   (1)
875 Summer Ave, Newark, NJ 07104-3684
Tel.: (973) 483-3200
Web Site: http://www.nwmcc.com
Sales Range: $1-9.9 Million
Emp.: 60
Repair Services
N.A.I.C.S.: 811310
Salvatore F. Perri (*Pres*)

Odesco Industrial Services, Inc.   (1)
100 Washington St, South Roxana, IL 62087-0862
Tel.: (618) 254-4874
Rev.: $68,000
Emp.: 20
Waste Management Services
N.A.I.C.S.: 562991
James Rhodes (*Mgr-Ops*)

Robinson Pipe Cleaning Co.   (1)
1 Rainey Rd, Eighty Four, PA 15330-0936
Tel.: (412) 921-2100
Web Site: http://www.robinsonpipe.com
Sales Range: $10-24.9 Million
Emp.: 40
Sewer Cleaning Services
N.A.I.C.S.: 562991

Robinson Pipe Services, Inc.   (1)
2309 E 28th St, Lorain, OH 44055-2003
Tel.: (440) 277-7473
Web Site:
    http://www.robinsonpipeservices.com
Sales Range: $10-24.9 Million
Emp.: 20
Repair Services
N.A.I.C.S.: 562991
Howard Harris (*Pres*)

Select Environmental Services, Inc.   (1)
12221 N US Hwy 301, Thonotosassa, FL 33592
Tel.: (813) 986-5400
Web Site:
    http://www.selectenvironmentalsvs.com
Emp.: 20
Environmental Consulting Services
N.A.I.C.S.: 541620
Ron Wilkes (*Gen Mgr*)

Sewer Systems Evaluations, Inc.   (1)
2500 W Arthington St, Chicago, IL 60612-4108

Tel.: (312) 666-7700
Web Site: http://www.caryloncorp.com
Rev.: $270,000
Emp.: 5
Surveying Services
N.A.I.C.S.: 541330
Al Burkner (*CEO*)

Specialized Maintenance and Services, Inc.   (1)
4533 Pasadena Blvd, Pasadena, TX 77503-3545
Tel.: (281) 476-1010
Web Site:
    http://www.specializedmaintenance.com
Emp.: 60
Building Maintenance Services
N.A.I.C.S.: 561720
Darrell Martin (*Pres*)

Video Industrial Service Inc.   (1)
113 Sheridan Rd, Birmingham, AL 35214-4671
Tel.: (205) 798-0300
Rev.: $6,267,548
Emp.: 40
Sewer Rehab
N.A.I.C.S.: 562991
Rodney Blckmon (*VP*)

Video Pipe Services Inc.   (1)
1566 Harding Hwy, Newfield, NJ 08344-5220   (100%)
Tel.: (856) 697-1900
Web Site: http://www.caryloncorp.com
Rev.: $5,500,000
Emp.: 40
Water Sewer & Utility Line Services
N.A.I.C.S.: 237110
John Terpak (*VP*)
Frank Constandino (*VP*)

CAS SEVERN INC
6201 Chevy Chase Dr, Laurel, MD 20707
Tel.: (301) 776-3400
Web Site:
    https://www.cassevern.com
Rev.: $14,600,000
Emp.: 148
Software Publisher
N.A.I.C.S.: 513210
Roy Jackson (*VP-Engrg Grp*)
Kate Benarick (*Controller*)
John Blanchette (*VP-Ops*)
Douglas Gerstmyer (*Co-Founder & CEO*)
Carson Soule (*CEO*)

CASA AUTO GROUP
5815 Montana Ave, El Paso, TX 79925
Tel.: (915) 221-1598
Web Site:
    https://www.casaautogroup.com
Car Dealership
N.A.I.C.S.: 441110
Justin Lowenfield (*CEO*)

Subsidiaries:

Casa Autoplex   (1)
470 W Boutz Rd, Las Cruces, NM 88005
Tel.: (575) 525-4560
Web Site: http://www.bormanautoplex.com
Automotive Body, Paint & Interior Repair & Maintenance
N.A.I.C.S.: 811121
Rob Karveller (*Mgr*)

CASA AUTOMOTIVE GROUP
14401 Ventura Blvd, Sherman Oaks, CA 91423
Tel.: (818) 981-2000
Web Site:
    http://www.casaautomotive.com
Sales Range: $25-49.9 Million
Emp.: 115
Automobiles; New & Used
N.A.I.C.S.: 441110
Howard Drake (*Owner*)
Bruce Tashjian (*Dir-Fixed Ops*)

Casa Automotive Group—(Continued)

CASA CENTRAL CORPORATION
1343 N California Ave, Chicago, IL 60622
Tel.: (773) 645-2300
Web Site: http://www.casacentral.org
Sales Range: $10-24.9 Million
Emp.: 550
Individual & Family Services
N.A.I.C.S.: 624190
Rosita Lopez (Chm)
John Filan (Treas)
Salvador F. Arana (Vice Chm)
Jose M. Munoz (CMO & VP-External Affairs)
Martin R. Castro (Interim Pres & Interim CEO)

CASA CHRYSLER JEEP MITSUBISHI
9733 Coors Blvd NW, Albuquerque, NM 87114
Tel.: (505) 897-8400
Web Site: http://www.casanet.com
Sales Range: $75-99.9 Million
Emp.: 270
Automobiles, New & Used
N.A.I.C.S.: 441110

CASA FORD INC.
5815 Montana Ave, El Paso, TX 79925
Tel.: (915) 779-2272
Web Site: http://www.casaford.com
Sales Range: $50-74.9 Million
Emp.: 200
New & Used Car Dealers
N.A.I.C.S.: 441110
Luke Lowenfield (VP-Ops)

CASA GRANDE REGIONAL MEDICAL CENTER
1800 E Florence Blvd, Casa Grande, AZ 85122
Tel.: (520) 381-6300
Web Site: http://www.bannerhealth.com
Year Founded: 1982
Sales Range: $125-149.9 Million
Emp.: 962
Healtcare Services
N.A.I.C.S.: 622110
Rona Curphy (CEO)
Cherie H. McGlynn (Chm)
John R. McEvoy (Sec)
Thomas Erickson (Treas)
David A. Fitzgibbons III (Vice Chm)

CASA HERRERA INC.
2655 N Pine St, Pomona, CA 91767
Tel.: (909) 392-3930
Web Site: https://www.casaherrera.com
Sales Range: $10-24.9 Million
Emp.: 133
Manufacture & Distribute Food Products Machinery
N.A.I.C.S.: 333241
Ron Meade (CEO)
Chris Herrera (Dir-Sls)
Brent Hodges (Mgr-Cust Svcs)

CASA LINDA FURNITURE INC.
4815 Whittier Blvd, Los Angeles, CA 90022
Tel.: (323) 263-3851
Web Site: https://www.furniturecasalinda.com
Rev.: $18,280,438
Emp.: 60
Furniture Retailer
N.A.I.C.S.: 449110

Ben Liberman (Pres)
Jorge Garro (Gen Mgr)
Carmen Macias (Mgr)

CASA PACIFICA CENTERS FOR CHILDREN & FAMILIES
1722 S Lewis Rd, Camarillo, CA 93012
Tel.: (805) 445-7800
Web Site: http://www.casapacifica.org
Year Founded: 1988
Sales Range: $25-49.9 Million
Emp.: 499
Individual & Family Support Services
N.A.I.C.S.: 624190
Myra Saltoun (Dir-Campus Svcs)
Vicki Murphy (Chief Advancement Officer & Dir-Alumni Svcs)
William Powell (Pres)
Shawna Morris (CEO)

CASA REDIMIX CONCRETE CORP.
886 Edgewooder Rd, Bronx, NY 10474
Tel.: (718) 589-1555
Web Site: https://www.casaredimix.com
Rev.: $11,000,000
Emp.: 10
Concrete & Cinder Block
N.A.I.C.S.: 444180
Mauro Perciballi (Pres)

CASA SYSTEMS, INC.
100 Old River Rd, Andover, MA 01810
Tel.: (978) 688-6706
Web Site: https://www.casa-systems.com
Year Founded: 2003
CASA—(NASDAQ)
Rev.: $286,537,000
Assets: $398,294,000
Liabilities: $348,893,000
Net Worth: $49,401,000
Earnings: ($79,205,000)
Emp.: 1,043
Fiscal Year-end: 12/31/22
Electronic Parts & Equipment Merchant Whslr
N.A.I.C.S.: 423690
Michael Glickman (Pres & CEO)
Jerry Guo (Chm)
Michael Picariello (Dir-IR)
Santanu Dasgupta (CTO)
Lucy Xie (Founder & Exec Officer)
Bill Styslinger (Dir)

Subsidiaries:

Casa Communications Limited **(1)**
National Technology Park, Plassey, Limerick, V94 RX49, Ireland
Tel.: (353) 61633000
Electronic Parts & Equipment Distr
N.A.I.C.S.: 423690

Casa Communications Technology S.L. **(1)**
Edificio Imper Carrer dels Traginers n 14, Office 12B Poligono Vara de Quart, 46014, Valencia, Spain
Tel.: (34) 960097220
Electronic Parts & Equipment Distr
N.A.I.C.S.: 423690

Guangzhou Casa Communication Technology Ltd. **(1)**
10th Floor Building F Gaotang Software Park No 15 Software Road, Tianhe District, Guangzhou, 510663, Guangdong, China
Tel.: (86) 2066346088
Electronic Parts & Equipment Distr
N.A.I.C.S.: 423690

NetComm Wireless Limited **(1)**
18-20 Orion Road, Lane Cove, Sydney, 2066, NSW, Australia
Tel.: (61) 294242070

Web Site: http://www.netcommwireless.com
Sales Range: $125-149.9 Million
Data Communications Equipment Mfr
N.A.I.C.S.: 334210

Subsidiary (Domestic):

C10 Communications Pty Ltd. **(2)**
Units R8 Regents Park Estate 391 Park Rd, Regents Park, 2143, NSW, Australia
Tel.: (61) 297223360
Web Site: http://www.c10.com.au
Sales Range: $25-49.9 Million
Emp.: 7
Telecommunication Products Designer & Mfr
N.A.I.C.S.: 334290

Subsidiary (Non-US):

Dynalink Modems Ltd. **(2)**
12c Te Kea Pl, Albany, Takapuna, 0752, Auckland, New Zealand
Tel.: (64) 94485548
Web Site: http://www.dynalink.co.nz
Modem & Router Marketing & Distr
N.A.I.C.S.: 423690

Subsidiary (Domestic):

NetComm Wireless **(2)**
Level 5 18-20 Orion Rd, Lane Cove, 2066, NSW, Australia
Tel.: (61) 294242070
Web Site: http://www.netcommwireless.com
Sales Range: $25-49.9 Million
Emp.: 100
Modems & Routers Mfr & Distr
N.A.I.C.S.: 334210

NetComm Wireless Limited **(1)**
Eastlands II London Road, Basingstoke, RG21 4AW, Hampshire, United Kingdom
Tel.: (44) 1256223155
Wireless Communication Network Services
N.A.I.C.S.: 517112

CASA VISCO
819 Kings Rd, Schenectady, NY 12303
Tel.: (518) 377-8814
Web Site: https://www.casavisco.com
Sales Range: $1-9.9 Million
Emp.: 16
Mayonnaise, Dressing & Other Prepared Sauce Mfr
N.A.I.C.S.: 311941
Joseph Viscusi Sr. (Owner)

CASABLANCA MINING LTD.
417 Orchid Ave, Corona Del Mar, CA 92625
Tel.: (619) 717-8047
Web Site: http://www.casablancamining.com
Year Founded: 2008
Sales Range: Less than $1 Million
Emp.: 14
Gold, Copper & Other Metal Mining Services
N.A.I.C.S.: 212220
Trisha Malone (Sec)
Juan Carlos Camus Villegas (Chm & CEO)
Thomas Ronk (Pres)

CASBY BROS, INC.
197 Gardner StÂ, West Roxbury, MA 02132
Tel.: (617) 327-2374
Sales Range: $1-9.9 Million
Emp.: 10
Commercial & Institutional Building Construction Services
N.A.I.C.S.: 236220
Mark William Casby (Pres)

CASCADE ASSET MANAGEMENT, LLC.
6701 Manufacturers Dr, Madison, WI 53704
Tel.: (608) 222-4800

Web Site: https://www.cascade-assets.com
Year Founded: 1999
Sales Range: $1-9.9 Million
Emp.: 73
Electronic & Precision Equipment Repair & Maintenance
N.A.I.C.S.: 811210
Neil Peters-Michaud (Co-Founder & CEO)
Jessica Peters-Michaud (Co-Founder)
Todd Barelmann (Dir-Ops)
Josh Kemp (Mgr-Ops-Indiana)
Michael Larson (Chief Investment Officer)
Alan C. Heuberger (Investment)

CASCADE AUTO GROUP, LTD.
4149 State Rd, Cuyahoga Falls, OH 44223
Tel.: (330) 929-1861
Web Site: https://www.cascadeautogroup.com
Year Founded: 1969
Sales Range: $10-24.9 Million
Emp.: 50
Car Whslr
N.A.I.C.S.: 441110
Michelle Primm (Partner)

CASCADE AUTOGLASS INCORPORATED
604 E 16th St, Vancouver, WA 98663
Tel.: (360) 750-4799
Web Site: https://www.cascadeautoglass.com
Sales Range: $10-24.9 Million
Emp.: 40
Automotive Glass Replacement Shops
N.A.I.C.S.: 811122
Brad Nelson (VP)
Paul Sharkey (Pres)
Lori Nickels (Mgr-Acct)

CASCADE BROADCASTING GROUP LLC
Ste 113 3055 N Campbell Ave, Tucson, AZ 85719-2875
Tel.: (520) 514-5722
Sales Range: $10-24.9 Million
Emp.: 3
Television Broadcasting Station
N.A.I.C.S.: 516120

Subsidiaries:

Tucson Communications LLC **(1)**
Ste 113 3055 N Campbell Ave, Tucson, AZ 85719-2875
Tel.: (520) 889-5800
Web Site: http://www.thecwtucson.com
Television Broadcasting Station
N.A.I.C.S.: 516120

CASCADE COFFEE, INC.
1525 75th St SW Ste 100, Everett, WA 98203
Tel.: (425) 347-3995
Web Site: http://www.cascadecoffeeinc.com
Rev.: $12,000,000
Emp.: 40
Roasted Coffee
N.A.I.C.S.: 311920
Philip L. Johnson (Owner & Chm)
Lou Johnson (Pres)
Nichole Hyde (Dir-Quality Assurance)

CASCADE COLUMBIA DISTRIBUTION COMPANY
6900 Fox Ave S, Seattle, WA 98108
Tel.: (206) 282-6334
Web Site: http://www.cascadecolumbia.com
Sales Range: $10-24.9 Million
Emp.: 18
Industrial Chemicals

N.A.I.C.S.: 424690
Robert Code *(Pres)*
Gary Miller *(Mgr-Admin Ops)*
Kim Beeler *(Asst Controller)*

CASCADE CONTROLS NORTHWEST
19785 NE San Raffael St, Portland, OR 97230
Tel.: (503) 252-3116
Web Site: http://www.cascade-nw.com
Year Founded: 1987
Sales Range: $25-49.9 Million
Emp.: 70
Mfr of Instruments & Control Equipment
N.A.I.C.S.: 423830
Chris White *(Pres)*
Cosmin Dragomir *(Engr-Electrical)*
Dave Burdett *(Acct Mgr)*
Michael Watterson *(Engr-Application)*

CASCADE DESIGNS, INC.
4000 1st Ave S, Seattle, WA 98134
Tel.: (206) 505-9500
Web Site:
https://www.cascadedesigns.com
Year Founded: 1972
Sales Range: $25-49.9 Million
Emp.: 400
Mfr of Outdoor Sporting Products & Equipment
N.A.I.C.S.: 326199
John Burroughs *(Founder)*
John Twomley *(Mgr-Distr Sls & European Mktg-Europe)*
James Cotter *(Mng Dir-Europe)*

Subsidiaries:

Cascade Designs, Inc. - MSR
Division   **(1)**
4000 1st Ave S, Seattle, WA
98134-2235   **(100%)**
Tel.: (206) 505-9500
Web Site: http://www.cascadedesign.com
Mfr of Mountaineering Equipment
N.A.I.C.S.: 326199
Joe Mcswiney *(CEO)*

CASCADE ENGINEERING SERVICES INC.
6640 185th Ave NE, Redmond, WA 98052
Tel.: (425) 895-8617
Web Site: https://www.cascade-eng.com
Year Founded: 1994
Sales Range: $10-24.9 Million
Emp.: 85
Engineeering Services
N.A.I.C.S.: 541330
Reza Yasseri *(Pres)*
Seyed Javad *(Dir-Ops)*

CASCADE ENGINEERING, INC.
3400 Innovation Ct SE, Grand Rapids, MI 49512-2085
Tel.: (616) 975-4800   MI
Web Site:
https://www.cascadeng.com
Year Founded: 1973
Sales Range: $100-124.9 Million
Emp.: 1,200
Plastic Injection Molded Systems
N.A.I.C.S.: 424610
Keith Maki *(Dir-Mktg & PR)*
Mark Miller *(Pres & CEO)*
Christina L. Keller *(Pres & CEO)*
Kenyatta Brame *(Exec VP)*
Steve Bushong *(VP-Ops)*

Subsidiaries:

CK Technologies, LLC   **(1)**
1701 Magda Dr, Montpelier, OH 43543
Tel.: (419) 485-1110

Web Site: http://www.cktech.biz
Plastic Injection Parts Mfr
N.A.I.C.S.: 326199
Tony Kramer *(Pres)*

Cascade Renewable Energy   **(1)**
3400 Innovation Ct SE, Grand Rapids, MI 49512
Tel.: (616) 975-4800
Web Site: http://www.cascadeng.com
Environmental Engineering Services
N.A.I.C.S.: 541330

Noble Polymers LLC   **(1)**
4855 37th St SE, Grand Rapids, MI 49512-4068
Tel.: (616) 975-4987
Web Site: http://www.noblepolymers.com
Sales Range: $1-9.9 Million
Thermoplastic Material Mfr
N.A.I.C.S.: 325211

Xtreme RFID   **(1)**
3400 Innovation Ct SE, Grand Rapids, MI 49512
Tel.: (616) 975-4846
Web Site: http://www.xtremerfid.com
Radio Frequency Identification Tag Mfr
N.A.I.C.S.: 334419
Mike Lewis *(Sr Mgr-Sls)*

CASCADE EVAPORATOR COMPANY
PO Box 1783, Lexington, SC 29071
Tel.: (803) 356-6699
Sales Range: $10-24.9 Million
Emp.: 9
Paper Mfr
N.A.I.C.S.: 322120
Jeff Sasko *(Owner)*

CASCADE HARDWOOD LLC
158 Ribelin Rd, Chehalis, WA 98532
Tel.: (360) 748-3317   WA
Web Site:
https://www.cascadehardwood.com
Sales Range: $10-24.9 Million
Emp.: 250
Sawmills
N.A.I.C.S.: 321113

CASCADE HEALTH SERVICES
510 W 5th St Fl 1, Kansas City, MO 64105
Tel.: (816) 229-5800
Web Site:
http://www.cascadestaff.com
Year Founded: 1988
Sales Range: $1-9.9 Million
Emp.: 21
Temporary & Permanent Healthcare Staffing Services
N.A.I.C.S.: 561311
Jonna Underhill *(Pres & Exec Dir)*
Kellen Weissenbach *(Owner)*
Tonja Reynolds *(Dir-Svcs)*

CASCADE INVESTMENT LLC
2365 Carillon Pt, Kirkland, WA 98033
Tel.: (425) 889-7900   WA
Sales Range: $50-74.9 Million
Emp.: 100
Institutional Investment Manager
N.A.I.C.S.: 523999
Michael Larson *(Chief Investment Officer & Bus Mgr)*
Dale Shrader *(Dir-Tax)*

Subsidiaries:

Four Seasons Hotels Inc.   **(1)**
1165 Leslie Street, Toronto, M3C 2K8, ON, Canada   **(71.25%)**
Tel.: (416) 449-1750
Web Site: http://www.fourseasons.com
Luxury Hotels & Resorts Operator
N.A.I.C.S.: 721110
Isadore Sharp *(Founder & Chm)*
Thomas Krooswijk *(Mgr-Hotel-Amman)*
Adrian Messerli *(Gen Mgr-Shanghai)*
Chloe Qian *(Dir-PR & Comm-Shanghai)*
Tom Roelens *(Gen Mgr-Kuala Lumpur)*
Vivian Koh *(Dir-PR & Content-Asia Pacific)*

Ashish Sharma *(Mgr-Beverage-Kuala Lumpur)*
Bart Carnahan *(Exec VP-Bus Dev-Global)*
Christian Clerc *(Pres-Hotel Ops-Worldwide)*
Edward A. Evans *(Chief Culture Officer & Chief People Officer)*
Peter Nowlan *(CMO & Exec VP)*
Vince Parrotta *(Pres-Hotel Ops-Americas)*
Sebastien Ganry *(Dir-Food & Beverage-Seoul)*
Alexandre Bernabe *(Gen Mgr-Seoul)*
Ranjith Premraj *(Dir-People & Culture-Bengaluru)*
Alejandro Reynal *(Pres & CEO)*
Sam Ioannidis *(Gen Mgr)*
Nate Ferguson *(Dir-Mktg)*

Unit (US):

Four Seasons Hotel Atlanta   **(2)**
75 14th St, Atlanta, GA 30309
Tel.: (404) 881-9898
Web Site: http://www.fourseasons.com
Hotel Services
N.A.I.C.S.: 721110
Richette Dean *(Mgr-Conference Svcs)*
Kate Pearce *(Mgr-Sls-Worldwide)*
Haytham Said *(Asst Dir-Food & Beverage)*
Yvette Thomas-Henry *(Gen Mgr)*
Shannon Fitzpatrick *(Mgr-Social Catering)*

Four Seasons Hotel Austin   **(2)**
98 San Jacinto Blvd, Austin, TX 78701-4039
Tel.: (512) 478-4500
Web Site: http://www.fourseasons.com
Hotel Operator
N.A.I.C.S.: 721110
Rebecca Patschke *(Dir-Fin)*
Rich McGonnigal *(Dir-Sls & Mktg)*

Four Seasons Hotel Boston   **(2)**
200 Boylston St, Boston, MA 02116
Tel.: (617) 338-4400
Web Site: http://www.fourseasons.com
Emp.: 300
Hotel Services
N.A.I.C.S.: 721110
Ryan Jimenez *(Dir-PR)*
Lindsay Otis *(Mgr-Catering Sls)*

Four Seasons Hotel Chicago   **(2)**
120 E Delaware Pl, Chicago, IL 60611-1428
Tel.: (312) 280-8800
Web Site: http://www.fourseasons.com
Hotel Services
N.A.I.C.S.: 721110
Bart Carnahan *(Exec VP-Global Bus Dev)*
Edward A. Evans *(Chief People & Culture Officer)*
Isadore Sharp *(Founder & Chm)*
Stephen Wancha *(Gen Mgr)*
Cory Cuff *(Mgr-Hotel)*

Four Seasons Hotel Houston   **(2)**
1300 Lamar St, Houston, TX 77010-3017
Tel.: (713) 650-1300
Web Site: http://www.fourseasons.com
Hotel Services
N.A.I.C.S.: 721110
Julie Barrow *(Mgr-Mktg)*
Mandi Rumski *(Dir-Sls)*
Cory Cuff *(Mgr-Ops)*
Karen Smith *(Mgr-Sls)*
Joanne Brosnan *(Mgr-Quattro Restaurant)*
William Panaretos *(Dir-Food & Beverage)*
Maria McGinity *(Dir-Catering)*

Unit (Non-US):

Four Seasons Hotel Istanbul   **(2)**
Tevkifhane Sokak 1, Sultanahmet Eminonu, Istanbul, 34122, Turkiye
Tel.: (90) 2124023000
Web Site: http://www.fourseasons.com
Sales Range: $100-124.9 Million
Hotel Services
N.A.I.C.S.: 721110

Unit (US):

Four Seasons Hotel Las Vegas   **(2)**
3960 Las Vegas Blvd S, Las Vegas, NV 89119
Tel.: (702) 632-5000
Web Site: http://www.fourseasons.com
Hotel Services
N.A.I.C.S.: 721110
Mark Hellrung *(Gen Mgr)*
Amanda Davis *(Mgr-Reservations)*

Matthew Romero *(Asst Dir-Rooms)*
Matthew Wiest *(Asst Mgr-Housekeeping)*
Radle Russell *(Asst Dir-Rooms)*
Shannon Mariani *(Dir-Spa)*

Unit (Non-US):

Four Seasons Hotel London   **(2)**
Hamilton Place Park Lane, London, W1J 7DR, United Kingdom
Tel.: (44) 2074990888
Web Site: http://www.fourseasons.com
Hotel Services
N.A.I.C.S.: 721110
Isadore Sharp *(Founder & Chm)*
Bart Carnahan *(Exec VP-Bus Dev & Portfolio Mgmt-Global)*

Unit (US):

Four Seasons Hotel Los Angeles at Beverly Hills   **(2)**
300 S Doheny Dr, Los Angeles, CA 90048
Tel.: (310) 273-2222
Web Site: http://www.fourseasons.com
Sales Range: $100-124.9 Million
Hotel Services
N.A.I.C.S.: 721110
Billy Cueto *(Dir-Rooms)*
Kim Kessler *(Dir-PR)*
Greg Velasquez *(Dir-Mktg)*
Mehdi Eftekari *(Gen Mgr)*
Deirdre Bradford *(Dir-Spa)*
Shannon Schwier *(Dir-Housekeeping)*
Sithong Kouangsavanh *(Coord-HR)*
Adrineh Mirzayan *(Mgr-HR)*
Amir Vahdani *(Dir-Food & Beverage)*
Linda Stigter *(Dir-HR)*

Unit (Non-US):

Four Seasons Hotel Mexico, D.F. **(2)**
Paseo de la Reforma 500, Colonia Juarez, Mexico, 6600, Mexico
Tel.: (52) 5552301818
Web Site: http://www.fourseasons.com
Hotel Services
N.A.I.C.S.: 721110

Four Seasons Hotel Milano   **(2)**
Via Gesu 6 8, Milan, 20121, Italy
Tel.: (39) 0000277088
Web Site: http://www.fourseasons.com
Sales Range: $100-124.9 Million
Hotel Services
N.A.I.C.S.: 721110

Unit (US):

Four Seasons Hotel New York   **(2)**
57 E 57th St, New York, NY 10022
Tel.: (212) 758-5700
Web Site: http://www.fourseasons.com
Emp.: 540
Hotel Services
N.A.I.C.S.: 721110
Thomas Carreras *(Gen Mgr-Iconic Downtown Hotel)*

Four Seasons Hotel Philadelphia **(2)**
1 N 19th St, Philadelphia, PA 19103-6933
Tel.: (215) 419-5000
Web Site: http://www.fourseasons.com
Hotel Services
N.A.I.C.S.: 721110
Ben Shank *(Gen Mgr)*
Isadore Sharp *(Founder & Chm)*
John Davison *(Pres & CEO)*
Bart Carnahan *(Exec VP-Global Bus Dev & Portfolio Mgmt)*
Edward A. Evans *(Chief People Officer, Chief Culture Officer & Exec VP)*
Sarah Cohen *(Gen Counsel, Sec & Exec VP)*

Unit (Non-US):

Four Seasons Hotel Ritz Lisbon **(2)**
Rua Rodrigo Da Fonseca 88, Lisbon, 1099-039, Portugal
Tel.: (351) 213811400
Web Site: http://www.fourseasons.com
Sales Range: $100-124.9 Million
Hotel Services
N.A.I.C.S.: 721110
Guelherme Costa *(Gen Mgr)*

Four Seasons Hotel Singapore   **(2)**
190 Orchard Boulevard, Singapore, 248646, Singapore
Tel.: (65) 67341110

Cascade Investment LLC—(Continued)

Web Site: http://www.fourseasons.com
Sales Range: $100-124.9 Million
Emp.: 300
Hotel Operator
N.A.I.C.S.: 721110
Chris Hart (Pres-Hotel Ops-Asia Pacific)
Michael A. Crawford (Pres-Asia Pacific)
William Mackay (Sr VP-Hotel Ops-Asia Pacific)
Isabelle Lim (Dir-PR)
Peter C. Draminsky (Reg VP & Gen Mgr)

Unit (Domestic):

Four Seasons Hotel Toronto (2)
60 Yorkville Avenue, Toronto, M4W 0A4,
ON, Canada
Tel.: (416) 964-0411
Web Site: http://www.fourseasons.com
Sales Range: $10-24.9 Million
Emp.: 50
Luxury Hotel Operator
N.A.I.C.S.: 721110
Vince Parrotta (Pres-Hotel Ops-West Americas)
Isadore Sharp (Founder & Chm)
Christian Clerc (Pres-Worldwide Hotel Ops)
Sarah Cohen (Exec VP)

Four Seasons Hotel Vancouver (2)
791 W Georgia St, Vancouver, V6C 2T4,
BC, Canada
Tel.: (604) 689-9333
Web Site: http://www.fourseasons.com
Sales Range: $25-49.9 Million
Emp.: 450
Hotel Services
N.A.I.C.S.: 721110
Paul Li (Dir-Sls)
Kate Colley (Mgr-PR)
Robert Cima (Gen Mgr)
Emily Edwards (Mgr-Event Sls)

Unit (US):

Four Seasons Hotel Washington,
DC (2)
2800 Pennsylvania Ave NW, Washington,
DC 20007
Tel.: (202) 342-0444
Web Site: http://www.fourseasons.com
Hotel Services
N.A.I.C.S.: 721110
David Bernand (Gen Mgr)

Unit (Non-US):

Four Seasons Hotels & Resorts (2)
Charlottenstrasse 49, Berlin, 10117, Germany
Tel.: (49) 3020388
Web Site: http://www.fourseasons.com
Sales Range: $100-124.9 Million
Hotel Services
N.A.I.C.S.: 721110
Rene Beauchamp (Gen Mgr)
Christopher W. Norton (Pres-Global Product & Ops)
Kristien Deleersnijder (VP-Sls-EMEA)
John H. Miller (Sr VP-Design & Construction)
Eileen Madigan (VP-Creative)
Vicki Richards (Sr Dir-Mktg-Collection-UK)
Bart Carnahan (Exec VP-Global Bus Dev-UK)
Christian Clerc (Pres-Worldwide Hotel Ops)
Vince Parrotta (Pres-Hotel Ops-Americas)
Simon Casson (Pres-Hotel Ops-EMEA)
Rainer Stampfer (Pres-Hotel Ops-Asia Pacific)
Kimberly S. Grant (Head-Restaurants & Bars-Global)
Sarah Tuite (Sr Dir-Corp PR)
Brian Dougherty (Sr Dir-Rose-Hulman Ventures)

Unit (US):

Four Seasons Resort & Club
Dallas (2)
4150 N MacArthur Blvd, Irving, TX 75038
Tel.: (972) 717-0700
Web Site: http://www.fourseasons.com
Resort Services
N.A.I.C.S.: 721110
Isadore Sharp (Founder, Chm & CEO)

Four Seasons Resort Aviara (2)

7210 Blue Heron Pl, Carlsbad, CA 92011
Tel.: (760) 603-3700
Web Site: http://www.fourseasons.com
Resort Services
N.A.I.C.S.: 721110
Jessica Roach (Mgr-Mktg)
Paul White (Reg VP)

Unit (Non-US):

Four Seasons Resort Bali (2)
Jimbaran, Denpasar, 80361, Bali, Indonesia
Tel.: (62) 361701010
Web Site: http://www.fourseasons.com
Resort Services
N.A.I.C.S.: 721110
Uday Rao (Gen Mgr)

Unit (US):

Four Seasons Resort Hualalai (2)
72-100 Ka'upulehu Dr, Kailua Kona, HI
96740
Tel.: (808) 325-8000
Web Site: http://www.fourseasons.com
Hotel & Resort Operator
N.A.I.C.S.: 721110
Colin Clark (Gen Mgr)

Four Seasons Resort Maui (2)
3900 Wailea Alanui Dr, Maui, HI 96753
Tel.: (808) 874-8000
Web Site: http://www.fourseasons.com
Resort Services
N.A.I.C.S.: 721110
Marc Bromley (Gen Mgr)

Unit (Non-US):

Four Seasons Resort Nevis (2)
PO Box 565, Pinneys Beach, Charlestown,
Saint Kitts & Nevis
Tel.: (869) 4656516
Web Site: http://www.fourseasons.com
Sales Range: $100-124.9 Million
Resort Services
N.A.I.C.S.: 721110
Billy Cueto (Gen Mgr)
Leon Patchett (Dir-Tennis)
Lawrence Tuck (Mgr-Resort)
Jamar K. Wilkins (Mgr-Travel Indus Sls)
Jim Bishop (Dir-Sls-Resort)
Gonzalo Guelman Ros (Gen Mgr)

Unit (US):

Four Seasons Resort Palm
Beach (2)
2800 S Ocean Blvd, Palm Beach, FL 33480
Tel.: (561) 582-2800
Web Site: http://www.fourseasons.com
Hotel Services
N.A.I.C.S.: 721110
Tony Rodriguez (Dir-Mktg)
Talal Adel (Asst Dir-HR)
Mohamed Elbanna (Reg VP & Gen Mgr)

Four Seasons Resort Santa
Barbara (2)
1260 Channel Dr, Santa Barbara, CA
93108
Tel.: (805) 969-2261
Web Site: http://www.fourseasons.com
Hotel Services
N.A.I.C.S.: 721110
Karen Earp (Gen Mgr)

The Ritz-Carlton Chicago (2)
160 E Pearson St at Water Tower Pl, Chicago, IL 60611-2308
Tel.: (312) 266-1000
Web Site: http://www.ritzcarlton.com
Hotel Services
N.A.I.C.S.: 721110
Peter Simoncelli (Gen Mgr)

Signature Aviation Limited (1)
Percival Way, Luton, London, LU2 9PA,
United Kingdom
Tel.: (44) 3300271281
Web Site: https://www.signatureaviation.com
Rev.: $1,413,900,000
Assets: $4,587,400,000
Liabilities: $2,997,300,000
Net Worth: $1,590,100,000
Earnings: $9,500,000
Emp.: 6,469
Fiscal Year-end: 12/31/2020
Holding Company; Aircraft Parts Mfr, Repair, Maintenance & Flight Support Services

---

N.A.I.C.S.: 551112
Tristan Dorian (Gen Mgr)

Group (US):

BBA Aviation Engine Repair & Overhaul Group (2)
900 Nolen Dr Ste 100, Grapevine, TX
76051-8641
Tel.: (214) 956-3000
Web Site: http://www.bbaviationero.com
Sales Range: $75-99.9 Million
Emp.: 220
Subsidiary Managing Office; Aircraft Engine Repair & Overhaul Services
N.A.I.C.S.: 551114
Hugh E. McElroy Jr. (Pres)
Nandakumar Madireddi (Sr VP-Bus Ops)
Dennis DiMarco (VP-Sls & Mktg-North America)
Doris Hastings (VP-HR)
Gerardo Gomez (Mgr-Sls-Mexico)

Subsidiary (Domestic):

Dallas Airmotive, Inc. (3)
900 Nolen Dr Ste 100, Grapevine, TX
76051-8641
Tel.: (214) 956-3001
Web Site: http://www.bbaviationero.com
Rev.: $42,750,769
Emp.: 80
Aircraft Engine Repair & Overhaul Services
N.A.I.C.S.: 336412

Unit (Domestic):

Dallas Airmotive, Inc. - Dallas
Facility (4)
2988 W Walnut Hill Ln DFW Airport, Dallas,
TX 75261
Tel.: (214) 956-3001
Web Site: http://www.dallasairmotive.com
Sales Range: $25-49.9 Million
Aircraft Engine Repair & Overhaul Services
N.A.I.C.S.: 336412
Thomas Kennedy (Mgr-Engine-Danvers Reg)

Subsidiary (Non-US):

H+S Aviation Limited (3)
Airport Service Road, Portsmouth, PO3
5PJ, Hampshire, United Kingdom
Tel.: (44) 2392304000
Web Site: https://www.hsaviation.co.uk
Emp.: 320
Aircraft Engine Repair & Overhaul Services
N.A.I.C.S.: 336412
Ann New (Dir-HR)

Group (US):

BBA Aviation Legacy Support
Group (2)
20400 Plummer St, Chatsworth, CA 91311
Tel.: (818) 678-6555
Web Site: http://www.bbaviation.com
Subsidiary Managing Office; Legacy Aircraft Parts Mfr & Whslr
N.A.I.C.S.: 551114

Subsidiary (Domestic):

International Governor Services,
LLC (3)
7290 W 118th Pl, Broomfield, CO 80020
Tel.: (303) 464-0043
Web Site:
    http://www.internationalgovernor.com
Emp.: 17
Small Aircraft Turbine Engine Controls Repair & Overhaul Services
N.A.I.C.S.: 335314

Subsidiary (Domestic):

Balderton Aviation Holdings
Limited (2)
20 Balderton Street, London, W1K 6TL,
United Kingdom
Tel.: (44) 20 7016 6800
Web Site: http://www.baldertoncapital.com
Emp.: 23
Investment Management Service
N.A.I.C.S.: 523999

Subsidiary (US):

Barrett Turbine Engine Company (2)
1626 Tobacco Rd, Augusta, GA 30906

Tel.: (706) 790-1977
Web Site:
    http://www.barrettturbineengine.com
Aircraft Engine Mfr
N.A.I.C.S.: 336412
Russell Cathey (VP & Gen Mgr)
Albert Poor (VP-Sls)

Subsidiary (Non-US):

Dallas Airmotive South Africa Pty
Limited (2)
Hanger 201 Lanseria International Airport
Airport Road, Lanseria, 1748, South Africa
Tel.: (27) 117012611
Aircraft Leasing & Rental Services
N.A.I.C.S.: 532411

Subsidiary (US):

EPIC Aviation, LLC (2)
222 W Las Colinas Blvd Ste 1425 N, Irving,
TX 75039
Tel.: (503) 362-3633
Web Site: https://www.epicfuels.com
Petroleum & Bulk Fuels
N.A.I.C.S.: 424720

General Aviation Flying Services,
Inc. (2)
485 Industrial Ave, Teterboro, NJ 07608
Tel.: (201) 288-5040
Sales Range: $1-9.9 Million
Emp.: 100
Air Courier Services
N.A.I.C.S.: 492110
Ken C. Forester (CEO)

Subsidiary (Non-US):

SFS Munich GmbH & Co. KG (2)
PO Box 241431, 85336, Munich, Germany
Tel.: (49) 8997597730
Aircraft Maintenance Services
N.A.I.C.S.: 488190
Oliver Trono (Gen Mgr)

Group (US):

Signature Flight Support Corp. (2)
13485 Veterans Way Ste 600, Orlando, FL
32827
Tel.: (407) 648-7200
Web Site: http://www.signatureflight.com
Sales Range: $550-599.9 Million
Emp.: 1,300
Private Aircraft Ground Support Services
N.A.I.C.S.: 488119
Tony Lefebvre (CEO)
Amy Alexy (Chief People Officer)
Derek DeCross (Sr VP)
Rick Elieson (Sr VP)
Mike Eshoo (CFO)
Maria Garton (Gen Counsel)
Anurag Gupta (CIO)
Marty Kretchman (Sr-VP)

Unit (Domestic):

Signature Flight Support - BED (3)
180 Hanscom Dr, Bedford, MA 01730
Tel.: (781) 274-0010
Web Site: https://www.signatureaviation.com
Emp.: 25
Air Transportation Support Services
N.A.I.C.S.: 488190

Signature Flight Support - MKE (3)
923 E Layton Ave, Milwaukee, WI 53207
Tel.: (414) 747-5100
Web Site: http://www.signatureflight.com
Sales Range: $25-49.9 Million
Emp.: 33
Private Aircraft Ground Support Services
N.A.I.C.S.: 488119

Signature Flight Support - MMU (3)
1 Airport Rd, Morristown, NJ 07960
Tel.: (973) 292-1300
Web Site: http://www.signatureflight.com
Emp.: 44
Private Aircraft Ground Support Services
N.A.I.C.S.: 488119
Pasquale Raguseo (Dir-Art-MQS & KMQS)

Signature Flight Support - PIE (3)
14525 Airport Pkwy, Clearwater, FL 33762
Tel.: (727) 531-1441
Web Site: http://www.signatureflight.com

Sales Range: $50-74.9 Million
Emp.: 120
Private Aircraft Ground Support Services
N.A.I.C.S.: 488119

Signature Flight Support - PWK (3)
1100 S Milwaukee Ave, Wheeling, IL 60090-6309
Tel.: (847) 537-1200
Web Site: http://www.signatureflight.com
Sales Range: $25-49.9 Million
Emp.: 13
Private Aircraft Ground Support Services
N.A.I.C.S.: 488119
Mark Costa (Gen Mgr)

Signature Flight Support - STL (3)
5995 James S McDonnell Blvd, Saint Louis, MO 63134
Tel.: (314) 731-7111
Web Site: http://www.signatureflight.com
Sales Range: $25-49.9 Million
Emp.: 30
Private Aircraft Ground Support Services
N.A.I.C.S.: 488119

Subsidiary (Non-US):

Signature Flight Support Paris SA (3)
45 Avenue de l'Europe Zone Aviation d'Affaires, 93350, Le Bourget, France
Tel.: (33) 149927581
Web Site: http://www.signatureflight.com
Sales Range: $25-49.9 Million
Emp.: 25
Oil Transportation Services
N.A.I.C.S.: 488190
Andriot Nathalie (Gen Mgr)

Subsidiary (US):

Signature Flight Support Washington National, Inc. (2)
1 General Aviation Terminal Hangar 7, Washington, DC 20001
Tel.: (703) 417-3500
Aircraft Maintenance Services
N.A.I.C.S.: 488190
Pablo Espitia (Gen Mgr)

CASCADE LUMBER COMPANY
1000 1st Ave E, Cascade, IA 52033
Tel.: (563) 852-3232
Web Site: https://www.caslbr.com
Year Founded: 1953
Sales Range: $25-49.9 Million
Emp.: 200
Lumber, Plywood & Millwork Whslr
N.A.I.C.S.: 423310

CASCADE MACHINERY & ELECTRIC
4600 E Marginal Way S, Seattle, WA 98134
Tel.: (206) 762-0500
Web Site: https://www.cascade-machinery.com
Rev.: $12,500,000
Emp.: 60
Industrial Machinery & Equipment
N.A.I.C.S.: 423830
John E. Spring (Pres)
Brian Hayward (VP)

CASCADE OHIO INC.
1209 Maple Ave, Conneaut, OH 44030-2120
Tel.: (440) 593-5800
Web Site: https://www.cwohio.com
Sales Range: $25-49.9 Million
Emp.: 225
Wood Windows & Window Parts & Trim
N.A.I.C.S.: 321911
Nicholas Noirot (Pres)

CASCADE ORTHOPEDIC SUPPLY INC.
2638 Aztec Dr, Chico, CA 95928
Tel.: (530) 879-1500

Web Site: https://www.cascade-usa.com
Sales Range: $10-24.9 Million
Emp.: 40
Orthopedic Equipment & Supplies
N.A.I.C.S.: 423450
Kirk Leavy (CEO)
Dave Campbell (VP)
Jeff Collins (Pres)

CASCADE SAWING & DRILLING, INC.
27500 16th Ave S, Federal Way, WA 98003
Tel.: (206) 385-1343   WA
Web Site: https://www.cascadeconcrete.com
Year Founded: 1980
Concrete & Asphalt Cutting Contractor
N.A.I.C.S.: 238990
G. E. Fourticq (Owner & Pres)

CASCADE SIERRA SOLUTIONS
4750 Village Plz Loop Ste 100, Eugene, OR 97401
Tel.: (541) 302-0900   OR
Web Site: http://www.cascadesierra.org
Year Founded: 2006
Sales Range: $10-24.9 Million
Emp.: 53
Natural Resource Preservation Services
N.A.I.C.S.: 813312
Bob Kennedy (Controller)
David Orton (Mgr-Comm)

CASCADE SOTHEBY'S INTERNATIONAL REALTY
650 SW Bond St, Bend, OR 97702
Tel.: (541) 383-7600
Web Site: http://www.cascadesothebys.com
Real Estate Offices
N.A.I.C.S.: 531210
Deb Tebbs (CEO)
Michael Kosmin (COO)

CASCADE TECHNOLOGIES, INC.
505 Huntmar Park Dr Herndon Plz Ste 225, Herndon, VA 20170
Tel.: (703) 793-7222
Web Site: http://www.cascadestech.com
Year Founded: 1998
Sales Range: $1-9.9 Million
Emp.: 60
Government IT Consulting Services
N.A.I.C.S.: 541690
Alfredo F. Casta (Founder, Pres & CEO)

CASCADE WOOD PRODUCTS, INC.
8399 14th St, White City, OR 97503
Tel.: (541) 826-2911
Web Site: https://www.cascadewood.com
Rev.: $73,000,000
Emp.: 490
Millwork
N.A.I.C.S.: 321918
Gary Trapp (CFO)
Jan Sesock (Mgr-HR)
Janet Clark (Mgr-Traffic)

CASCADES TECHNOLOGIES, INC.
505 Huntmar Park Dr Herndon Plz, Herndon, VA 20170
Tel.: (703) 793-7222
Web Site:
http://www.cascadestech.com

Sales Range: $1-9.9 Million
Emp.: 25
IT Consulting Services for United States Government
N.A.I.C.S.: 561499
Alfredo F. Casta (CEO)
Joseph Diprinzio (VP-Ops)
Jose A. Rivera (Dir-Corp Strategy)

CASCADIA HEALTHCARE LLC
408 S Eagle Rd Ste 205, Eagle, ID 83616
Tel.: (208) 401-9600   ID
Web Site: http://www.cascadiahc.com
Skilled Nursing & Health Care Services
N.A.I.C.S.: 623311
Owen Hammond (CEO & Principal)
Doug Bodily (COO & Principal)
Matt Smith (Principal)

Subsidiaries:

Libby Care Center of Cascadia   (1)
308 E 3rd St, Libby, MT 59923
Tel.: (406) 293-6285
Web Site: http://www.libbyofcascadia.com
Skilled Nursing & Health Care Services
N.A.I.C.S.: 623311

CASCO BAY VENDING ENTERPRISES, LLC
9 Saratoga St, Lewiston, ME 04240
Tel.: (207) 784-3828   ME
Web Site: http://www.cascobayvending.com
Year Founded: 2010
Holding Company; Vending Machine & Office Coffee Supplies Distr
N.A.I.C.S.: 551112
Ted Morton (Owner, Pres & CEO)

Subsidiaries:

Casco Bay Vending, LLC   (1)
9 Saratoga St, Lewiston, ME 04240   (100%)
Tel.: (207) 784-3828
Web Site: http://www.cascobayvending.com
Vending Machine & Office Coffee Supplies Distr
N.A.I.C.S.: 445132
Ted Morton (Pres & CEO)

CASCO INDUSTRIES INC.
607 W 62nd St, Shreveport, LA 71106
Tel.: (318) 865-5107
Web Site: https://www.cascoindustries.com
Sales Range: $10-24.9 Million
Emp.: 50
Firefighting Equipment
N.A.I.C.S.: 423850
Doug Schaumburg (Pres)

CASCO MANUFACTURING SOLUTIONS, INC.
3107 Spring Grove Ave, Cincinnati, OH 45225
Tel.: (513) 681-0003
Web Site: https://www.cascomfg.com
Sales Range: $10-24.9 Million
Emp.: 50
Sewn, Sealed & Upholstered Custom Design & Production Services
N.A.I.C.S.: 811420
Melissa Mangold (Pres)
Michelle Johnson (Mgr-Quality)
Jeff Hummeldorf (Asst Gen Mgr)
Nathan Bare (Mgr-Engrg)

CASDEN PROPERTIES INC.
9090 Wilshire Blvd Fl 3, Beverly Hills, CA 90211
Tel.: (310) 274-5553   CA
Web Site:
http://www.casdenproperties.com

Year Founded: 1984
Rev.: $42,500,000
Emp.: 70
Subdividers & Developers
N.A.I.C.S.: 237210
Jeannie Schinn (Office Mgr)

CASE CENTRAL
50 Calafornia St Ste 200, San Francisco, CA 94111
Tel.: (415) 989-2300
Web Site:
http://www.casecentral.com
Year Founded: 1994
Sales Range: $10-24.9 Million
Emp.: 103
On-Line Solutions for the Litigation & Regulatory Environments
N.A.I.C.S.: 541199
Christopher S. Kruse (Founder, Chm & Chief Strategy Officer)

CASE CONTRACTING COMPANY
2311 Turkey Creek Rd, Plant City, FL 33566
Tel.: (813) 754-3477
Web Site:
https://www.casecontracting.com
Year Founded: 1983
Sales Range: $25-49.9 Million
Emp.: 25
General Construction Contractor
N.A.I.C.S.: 236220
Kelly Benzrihem (Sec)
Stephen J. Spack (VP-Ops)
Timothy Walker (Pres & COO)
Charles Christiansen (Chm, CEO & Treas)

CASE DESIGN/REMODELING, INC.
4701 Sangamore Rd Ste P40, Bethesda, MD 20816
Tel.: (301) 229-4600
Web Site:
https://www.casedesign.com
Year Founded: 1961
Sales Range: $25-49.9 Million
Emp.: 250
Provider of Single-Family House Remodeling Services
N.A.I.C.S.: 236118
Frederick F. Case (Owner)
Bruce Case (Co-Chm & Pres)
Rick Matus (Sr VP)

CASE FOODS, INC.
1325 Mt Hermon Rd Ste 9B, Salisbury, MD 21804-5259
Tel.: (410) 749-3202   DE
Year Founded: 1987
Rev.: $200,000,000
Emp.: 1,050
Holding Company; Poultry Farms, Processor & Distr
N.A.I.C.S.: 551112
Thomas R. Shelton (Founder, Chm & CEO)
Michael Popowycz (Vice Chm & CFO)

Subsidiaries:

Case Farms, LLC   (1)
385 Pilch Rd, Troutman, NC 28166
Tel.: (704) 528-4501
Web Site: http://www.casefarms.com
Sales Range: $25-49.9 Million
Emp.: 30
Poultry Slaughtering & Processing
N.A.I.C.S.: 311615

Plant (Domestic):

Case Farms, LLC - Goldsboro Processing   (2)
330 Pecan Rd, Dudley, NC 28333
Tel.: (919) 735-5010

Case Foods, Inc.—(Continued)

Web Site: http://www.casefarms.com
Sales Range: $50-74.9 Million
Poultry Processing
N.A.I.C.S.: 311615
Sam Robinson *(Gen Mgr)*

Case Farms, LLC - Morganton Pro-
duction & Processing   **(2)**
121 Rand St, Morganton, NC 28655
Tel.: (828) 438-6900
Web Site: http://www.casefarms.com
Sales Range: $125-149.9 Million
Poultry Processing
N.A.I.C.S.: 311615
David McHugh *(Engr-Maintenance)*

Case Farms, LLC - Ohio
Processing   **(2)**
1818 County Rd 160, Winesburg, OH
44690-0185
Tel.: (330) 359-7141
Web Site: http://www.casefarms.com
Sales Range: $50-74.9 Million
Poultry Processing
N.A.I.C.S.: 311615

CASE FURNITURE & DESIGN, LLC.
1502 E Hadley St 100, Phoenix, AZ
85043
Tel.: (602) 253-6006
Web Site: http://www.casefd.com
Sales Range: $10-24.9 Million
Emp.: 100
Furniture Whslr
N.A.I.C.S.: 423210
Bruce H. Sanborn *(Mgr)*

CASE PAPER COMPANY INC.
500 Mamaroneck Ave Ste 203, Harri-
son, NY 10528-1633
Tel.: (914) 899-3500   NY
Web Site:
   https://www.casepaper.com
Year Founded: 1943
Sales Range: $200-249.9 Million
Emp.: 325
Coated & Uncoated Paper & Paper-
board Distr
N.A.I.C.S.: 424110
Peter Schaffer *(CEO)*
Keith Goldberg *(VP-Sls & Mktg)*
Alan Hochstadt *(CFO-New York)*
Glen Braziel *(Gen Mgr-Miami)*
Charles Argianas *(Exec VP & Gen
Mgr-Chicago)*
Louis Bernstein *(VP & Mgr-Sls-
Philadelphia)*
Todd Chesnut *(VP-Sls-Chicago)*
Ken Gettlin *(VP-Toronto)*
Robin Schaffer *(Pres & CEO)*
George Thornton *(Gen Mgr-Charlotte)*
Tim Resser *(Gen Mgr-California)*
Debbie Gwaltney *(Mgr-Credit)*
Jill McDonough *(Dir-Support Svcs)*

Subsidiaries:

Case Paper Co. of Illinois, Inc.   **(1)**
900 W 45th St, Chicago, IL 60609-3303
Tel.: (773) 927-4151
Web Site: http://www.casepaper.com
Sales Range: $25-49.9 Million
Emp.: 100
Tape Distr
N.A.I.C.S.: 424110
Peter Schaffer *(Chm)*
Charles Argianas *(Exec VP & Gen Mgr)*
Alan Hoechstra *(CFO)*
Barb Polletta *(Mgr-Credit)*
Robert Stec *(Mgr-Ops)*
Todd Chesnut *(VP-Sls)*

Case Paper Co., Inc.   **(1)**
499 E Tioga St, Philadelphia, PA 19134-
1118
Tel.: (215) 426-9500
Web Site: http://www.casepaper.com
Sales Range: $25-49.9 Million
Emp.: 200
Paper Convertor

N.A.I.C.S.: 424110
Peter Schaffer *(Pres)*
Robin Schaffer *(VP)*

CASE POMEROY & COMPANY INC.
521 5th Ave 36th Fl, New York, NY
10175
Tel.: (212) 867-2211   DE
Year Founded: 1916
Sales Range: $10-24.9 Million
Emp.: 13
Real Estate & Investments
N.A.I.C.S.: 531210
Robert H. Clark Jr. *(Chm, Pres &
CEO)*

CASE SUPPLY INC.
601 W Fayette St, Syracuse, NY
13204-2901
Tel.: (315) 425-6601
Web Site:
   http://www.casesupplyinc.com
Rev.: $20,000,000
Emp.: 50
Kitchen Cabinets
N.A.I.C.S.: 423310
Alfred J. Cicci *(Chm)*

CASECO TRUCK BODY
235 N Service Rd W, Saint Clair, MO
63077
Tel.: (636) 629-3704
Year Founded: 1932
Rev.: $16,218,671
Emp.: 90
Truck Bodies Mfr
N.A.I.C.S.: 336211
Emily Hilliard *(Pres)*

CASES BY SOURCE, INC.
215 Island Rd, Mahwah, NJ 07430
Tel.: (201) 831-0005
Web Site:
   http://www.casesbysource.com
Year Founded: 1985
Sales Range: $10-24.9 Million
Emp.: 15
Wood, Plastic & Metal Custom Pro-
tective Cases Designer & Mfr
N.A.I.C.S.: 321999
Alan Adler *(Pres)*
Renee Gordon *(Mgr-Customer Svc)*

CASEWISE SYSTEMS INC.
777 Summer St Ste 303, Stamford,
CT 06901-1022
Tel.: (856) 380-1400
Web Site: http://www.casewise.com
Sales Range: $75-99.9 Million
Emp.: 150
Computer Software
N.A.I.C.S.: 423430
Bernard Fisher *(CEO)*

CASEY & SAYRE
12517 Venice Blvd, Los Angeles, CA
90066
Tel.: (310) 636-1888
Web Site:
   http://www.caseysayre.com
Sales Range: $25-49.9 Million
Emp.: 15
Full-Service Public Relations Consult-
ing
N.A.I.C.S.: 541820
Barbara Sayre Casey *(Founder, Chm
& CEO)*
Meredith Red *(VP & Dir-Tech & Digi-
tal Media)*
Jo Ellen Ashton *(Controller)*
Elizabeth Valles *(Mgr-Tech & Digital
Media)*

CASEY AUTO GROUP, INC.

813 Diligence Dr Ste 117, Newport
News, VA 23606
Tel.: (757) 591-1000
Web Site:
   https://www.caseyauto.com
Year Founded: 1988
Sales Range: $10-24.9 Million
Emp.: 85
New Car Whslr
N.A.I.C.S.: 441110
Travis Wynn *(Mgr-Fin)*

CASEY CO.
180 E Ocean Blvd Ste 1010, Long
Beach, CA 90802-4711
Tel.: (562) 590-8835   CA
Petroleum Products Wholesaler
N.A.I.C.S.: 424720
Betti-Jane Reed *(Sec)*

Subsidiaries:

Kern Oil & Refining Company   **(1)**
7724 E Panama Ln, Bakersfield, CA 93307-
9210
Tel.: (661) 845-0761
Web Site: http://www.kernoil.com
Sales Range: $10-24.9 Million
Wholesale Distributor of Petroleum Prod-
ucts
N.A.I.C.S.: 324110
Bruce W. Cogswell *(VP-Mfg)*
Jacob C. Belin *(Pres)*
Robert W. Winchester *(CFO)*

CASEY INDUSTRIAL INC.
11845 Teller St, Broomfield, CO
80020
Tel.: (303) 460-1274
Web Site: http://www.caseyind.com
Year Founded: 1947
Sales Range: $150-199.9 Million
Emp.: 747
Industrial Contractor Specializing in
Concrete Foundations, Mechanical &
Electrical Installations, Structural
Steel Erection & Process Piping
N.A.I.C.S.: 236210
Tom Lepak *(VP-Bus Dev)*
Todd Lueck *(Mgr-Bus Dev)*

CASEY POTTERY COMPANY LLP.
1070 Pumpkin Ctr Rd, Marshall, TX
75672
Tel.: (903) 927-3500
Year Founded: 1992
Sales Range: $10-24.9 Million
Emp.: 200
Pottery Product Mfr
N.A.I.C.S.: 327110
David McMinn *(Pres)*

CASEY RESEARCH, LLC
PO Box 84900, Phoenix, AZ 85071
Tel.: (602) 445-2736
Web Site:
   http://www.caseyresearch.com
Year Founded: 2004
Sales Range: $10-24.9 Million
Emp.: 50
Financial Research & Publisher of
Financial Newsletter
N.A.I.C.S.: 525990
Doug Casey *(Founder & Chm)*
Olivier Garret *(CEO)*
David Galland *(Mng Dir)*

CASEY'S FOODS INC.
130 Holly Hills Mall, Hindman, KY
41822
Tel.: (606) 785-4600
Rev.: $11,000,000
Emp.: 32
Grocery Stores, Chain
N.A.I.C.S.: 445110
Jim Cox *(Pres)*

CASEY'S INC.
430 College St, Cedartown, GA
30125
Tel.: (770) 748-2205
Sales Range: $10-24.9 Million
Emp.: 80
Owner & Operator of Grocery Stores
N.A.I.C.S.: 445110

CASH & CARRY GROCER INC.
2577 W Armitage Ave, Chicago, IL
60647
Tel.: (773) 486-5403   IL
Web Site:
   http://www.mccwholesalechi
   cago.com
Year Founded: 1981
Sales Range: $25-49.9 Million
Emp.: 19
Sales of Groceries
N.A.I.C.S.: 424410
Arnulfo Vargas *(Pres, CEO & Dir-
Investor Rels)*

CASH FLOW SOLUTIONS INC.
5166 College Corner Pike, Oxford,
OH 45056
Tel.: (513) 524-2320
Web Site:
   http://www.followthefrog.com
Year Founded: 1994
Sales Range: $10-24.9 Million
Emp.: 51
Management Consulting Services
N.A.I.C.S.: 541618
Di Princell *(Pres)*

CASH REGISTER SALES INC.
4851 White Bear Pkwy, Saint Paul,
MN 55110-3325
Tel.: (612) 781-3474
Web Site: https://www.crs-usa.com
Sales Range: $25-49.9 Million
Emp.: 60
Cash Registers
N.A.I.C.S.: 423420
Jeff Dahlberg *(VP-Finance)*

CASH TECHNOLOGIES, INC.
1434 W 11th St, Los Angeles, CA
90015
Tel.: (213) 745-2000   DE
Web Site: http://www.cashtech.com
Year Founded: 1995
Sales Range: Less than $1 Million
Emp.: 33
Develops & Markets Data Processing
Products to the Healthcare Industries
N.A.I.C.S.: 518210
Bruce Korman *(Chm, Pres & CEO)*

Subsidiaries:

CPI Holdings, LLC   **(1)**
2005 W Ave B, Hope, AR 71801
Tel.: (870) 777-8821
Web Site: http://www.championparts.com
Automotive Truck & Tractor Parts Mfr
N.A.I.C.S.: 336390

CASH-WA DISTRIBUTING COMPANY
401 W 4th St, Kearney, NE 68845-
7825
Tel.: (308) 237-3151   NE
Web Site: https://www.cashwa.com
Year Founded: 1967
Sales Range: $200-249.9 Million
Emp.: 380
Food Service Distributor
N.A.I.C.S.: 424490
Thomas Henning *(Pres)*
Edward Bloomfield *(Controller)*
Gary Henning *(VP)*
James H. Kindig *(Sr VP-Sls)*

Subsidiaries:

Cash-Wa Food Service   (1)
810 3rd Ave SE, Aberdeen, SD 57401
Tel.: (605) 225-1275
Web Site: http://www.hrsfoodservice.com
Sales Range: $25-49.9 Million
Emp.: 75
Groceries & Related Products
N.A.I.C.S.: 424490

CASHCALL, INC.
1 City Blvd W Ste 1000, Orange, CA 92868
Tel.: (949) 225-4699   CA
Web Site: https://www.cashcall.com
Year Founded: 2003
Consumer & Small Business Lending
N.A.I.C.S.: 522291
Delbert Meeks (Treas)
John Paul Reddam (Founder, Pres & CEO)

CASHION'S FOOD MART INC.
19716 Oak St, Cornelius, NC 28031
Tel.: (704) 892-8801
Sales Range: $10-24.9 Million
Emp.: 30
Convenience Stores, Independent
N.A.I.C.S.: 445131
Robert T. Cashion (Pres)

CASHMAN & KATZ INTE-GRATED COMMUNICATIONS
76 Eastern Blvd, Glastonbury, CT 06033
Tel.: (860) 652-0300   CT
Web Site: http://www.cashman-katz.com
Year Founded: 1992
Rev.: $44,675,000
Emp.: 26
N.A.I.C.S.: 541810
Joni Krasusky (Dir-Facility Res)
Tony Cashman (Pres & CEO)
Amanda Mueller (Mgr-PR & Social Media)
Lorraine Dupont (Mgr-Bus)
Kendra Eckhart (VP & Acct Supvr)
Kerry Holland (Sr Dir-Art)
Christopher Senecal (Mgr-Pub Affairs)
April Pelletier (Coord-Media/Adminisrative Asst)
Tory Lawson (Mgr-Digital Svcs)
Shane Wirta (VP & Grp Dir-Media)
Tim Cyran (VP & Dir-Creative)
Dan Sullivan (Assoc Dir-Creative)
Heather Baker (Acct Supvr)
Liz Noli-Roberts (Dir-Art)
Bill Greer (VP-Account & Strategic Plng)
Michael Lecours (Sr Acct Exec)
Jeff Durham (Sr VP & Grp Dir-Creative)
Eric Schweighoffer (VP & Dir-Media)
Eric Cavoli (VP & Dir-Creative)

Subsidiaries:

Durham Group   (1)
11 Talcott Notch Rd, Farmington, CT 06032
Tel.: (860) 677-8885
Emp.: 10
Full Service
N.A.I.C.S.: 541810

CASHMAN EQUIPMENT COMPANY
3300 Saint Rose Pkwy, Henderson, NV 89052
Tel.: (702) 649-8777
Web Site:
    https://www.cashmanequipment.com
Rev.: $235,263,151
Emp.: 650
Alarm & Safety Equipment Stores
N.A.I.C.S.: 459999

Mary Kaye Cashman (CEO)
Brenda Harris (Mgr-DBS)
Mike Brenner (Mgr-Sls-Reno & Sparks)

CASHWELL APPLIANCE PARTS INC.
3485 Clinton Rd, Fayetteville, NC 28312
Tel.: (910) 323-1111
Web Site: https://www.cashwells.com
Sales Range: $10-24.9 Million
Emp.: 56
Appliance Parts, Household
N.A.I.C.S.: 423620
Susan Williams (Owner & Pres)
Darrell Staton (Controller)
Rhonda Faircloth (VP)

CASIANO COMMUNICATIONS INC.
1700 Fernandez Juncos Ave, San Juan, PR 00909
Tel.: (787) 728-3000
Web Site: http://www.casiano.com
Rev.: $31,562,470
Emp.: 250
Newspapers & Magazines
N.A.I.C.S.: 513110
Manuel A. Casiano (Chm & CEO)
Manoly Ponce (Sr VP-Sls)
Nora A. Casiano (VP)

CASINGS INC.
169 Maple Ave, Catskill, NY 12414
Tel.: (518) 943-9404
Web Site:
    https://www.casingsinc.com
Rev.: $23,400,000
Emp.: 70
Tires & Tubes
N.A.I.C.S.: 423130
Richard Evans (Pres)

CASINO JOURNAL PUBLISHING GROUP
8025 Black Horse Pike # 470, Pleasantville, NJ 08232
Tel.: (609) 484-8866
Web Site:
    http://www.casinocenter.com
Year Founded: 1984
Sales Range: $10-24.9 Million
Emp.: 35
Consumer Publishing
N.A.I.C.S.: 513120
Glenn Fine (Chm)

CASINO QUEEN, INC.
200 S Frnt St, East Saint Louis, IL 62201-1222
Tel.: (618) 874-5000   IL
Web Site:
    http://www.casinoqueen.com
Year Founded: 1993
Hotel & Casino Owner & Operator
N.A.I.C.S.: 721120
Jeffrey Watson (Pres)
Kim Cushshon (Dir-HR)
Terry Hanger (Asst Gen Mgr & CIO)
Michelle Hamlet (Mgr-Sls)
Ida Danley (Mgr-Benefits)

CASITA ENTERPRISES, INC.
5029 SE McKinney St, Rice, TX 75155-9780
Tel.: (903) 326-4717   TX
Web Site:
    http://www.casitatraveltrailers.com
Year Founded: 1983
Rev.: $6,200,000
Emp.: 75
Fiscal Year-end: 12/31/09
Travel Trailer & Camper Mfr
N.A.I.C.S.: 336214
Beth Bryan (Gen Mgr)

CASK, LLC
5151 Shoreham Pl Ste 140, San Diego, CA 92122
Web Site: http://www.caskllc.com
Year Founded: 2004
Sales Range: $1-9.9 Million
Emp.: 48
Management Consulting Services
N.A.I.C.S.: 541618
Elizabeth Guezzale (Pres)

CASKET SHELLS, INC.
432 1st St, Eynon, PA 18403-1466
Tel.: (570) 876-2642   PA
Web Site:
    http://www.casketshellsinc.com
Year Founded: 1953
Sales Range: $100-124.9 Million
Emp.: 250
Mfr of Metal Caskets
N.A.I.C.S.: 339995
Joseph R. Semon (Pres)

CASON NIGHTINGALE CREATIVE COMMUNICATIONS
708 3rd Ave 29th Fl, New York, NY 10017
Tel.: (212) 351-3360
Web Site:
    http://www.cncommunications.com
Year Founded: 1990
Sales Range: Less than $1 Million
Emp.: 20
N.A.I.C.S.: 541810
Angela Cason (Pres-Creative & CEO)
William N. Nightingale (Chm-Media & Strategy)
Thomas Marchini (Assoc Dir-Creative-Cason & Nightingale)

CASPER COLOSIMO & SON INC.
5170 Campbells Run Rd, Pittsburgh, PA 15205
Tel.: (412) 787-1266
Sales Range: $25-49.9 Million
Emp.: 85
Underground Utilities
N.A.I.C.S.: 237110
Francis J. Casilli (Pres & CEO)
John Herbert (Mgr-Fleet)
Jeff Casilli (Exec VP)

CASPERS COMPANY
4908 W Nassau St, Tampa, FL 33607
Tel.: (813) 287-2231
Web Site:
    https://www.casperscompany.com
Sales Range: $150-199.9 Million
Emp.: 1,200
McDonald's Restaurant Franchise Owner
N.A.I.C.S.: 722513
Blake J. Casper (Chm & CEO)

CASPIAN STAR CAVIAR INC.
538 Madison Ave, New York, NY 10022
Tel.: (212) 588-9335
Web Site:
    http://www.caspianstarcaviar.com
Sales Range: $10-24.9 Million
Emp.: 40
Fish & Seafood Distr
N.A.I.C.S.: 424460
David Magnotta (Gen Mgr)

CASPIO, INC.
2953 Bunker Hill Ln Ste 201, Santa Clara, CA 95054
Tel.: (650) 691-0900
Web Site: http://www.caspio.com
Sales Range: $1-9.9 Million
Emp.: 23
Online Application & Database Software Development Services

N.A.I.C.S.: 541511
Frank Zamani (Founder, Pres & CEO)
Ioannis Kritikopoulos (VP-Engrg & Ops)
Valaine Anderson (VP-Mktg)

CASS COUNTY ELECTRIC CO-OPERATIVE, INC.
3312 42nd St S Ste 200, Fargo, ND 58104
Tel.: (701) 277-4400   ND
Web Site: http://www.kwh.com
Year Founded: 1937
Sales Range: $100-124.9 Million
Electric Power Distr
N.A.I.C.S.: 221122
Chad Sapa (CFO & VP-Corp Svcs)
Brad Schmidt (VP-Engrg & Ops)
Tim Sanden (CIO & VP-IT)
Wendy Loucks (Chm)
Russell Berg (Vice Chm)
John Froelich (Sec)
Sid Berg (Treas)
Marshal Albright (Pres & CEO)
Paul Matthys (VP-Member & Energy Svcs)

CASS HOLDING LLC
12005 N Virginia Ave, Oklahoma City, OK 73120
Tel.: (405) 755-8448
Web Site:
    https://www.cassholdings.com
Sales Range: $10-24.9 Million
Emp.: 10
Lacquers, Varnishes, Enamels & Other Coatings
N.A.I.C.S.: 325510
W. Douglas Frans (Pres)

CASSADAY & COMPANY, INC.
8180 Greensboro Dr Ste 1180, McLean, VA 22102
Tel.: (703) 506-8200
Web Site: http://www.cassaday.com
Year Founded: 1993
Sales Range: $1-9.9 Million
Emp.: 25
Open-End Investment Funds
N.A.I.C.S.: 525910
Mike S. Carey (Sr VP)
Christopher A. Krell (Principal)
Christopher Young (Principal)
Stephan Quinn Cassaday (Founder, Chm & CEO)
Adam E. Huke (VP)
Alex Karkeek (Assoc VP)
Andrew Malay (Assoc VP)
Brandon Butler (Mgr-Res)
Justin P. Harris (Principal)
Kay N. Paradiso (Dir-Investment Ops)
Nicholas A. Harris (Sr VP)
Sean Gallahan (VP)
Allison Felix (Pres, COO & Principal)

CASSANO'S INC.
1700 E Stroop Rd, Kettering, OH 45429-5040
Tel.: (937) 294-5464   OH
Web Site: https://www.cassanos.com
Year Founded: 1953
Sales Range: $25-49.9 Million
Emp.: 775
Pizza Chain Operator
N.A.I.C.S.: 722513
Tim Sayer (Controller)
Laura Hammons (Coord-Mktg)
Chip Cassano (CEO)

CASSEL SALPETER & CO., LLC
801 Brickell Ave Ste 1900, Miami, FL 33131
Tel.: (305) 438-7700

Cassel Salpeter & Co., LLC—(Continued)

Web Site:
https://www.casselsalpeter.com
Sales Range: $25-49.9 Million
Emp.: 8
Investment Banking
N.A.I.C.S.: 523150
James Cassel (Co-Founder & Chm)
Scott Salpeter (Co-Founder & Pres)
Marcus Wai (VP)
Ira Leiderman (Mng Dir)
Margery B. Fischbein (Mng Dir-Healthcare)

CASSENA CARE LLC
225 Crossways Park Dr, Woodbury,
NY 11797
Tel.: (516) 422-7885
Web Site:
https://www.cassenacare.com
Emp.: 110
Rehabilitation & Nursing Care Facilities
N.A.I.C.S.: 623110
Anthony DeRosa (VP-Fin)
Arthur Cooperberg (VP-Fin)
Angela Bellizzi (Gen Counsel)

Subsidiaries:

Dewitt Rehabilitation & Nursing Center, Inc.   (1)
211 E 79th St, New York, NY 10075
Tel.: (212) 879-1600
Web Site: http://www.dewittnh.com
Rehabilitation & Nursing Care Facilities
N.A.I.C.S.: 623110
Irina Kvint (Dir-Activities)
Cassandra Barr (Dir-Admissions)
Robert DeMarco (CFO)
Edward Joskow (Mgr-Facility)

CASSENS TRANSPORT COMPANY
145 N Kansas St, Edwardsville, IL
62025-1770
Tel.: (618) 656-3006   IL
Web Site: https://www.cassens.com
Year Founded: 1936
Sales Range: $50-74.9 Million
Emp.: 40
Automobile Carrying Services
N.A.I.C.S.: 484230
Kay Cassens (Treas & Sec)
Lisa Shashek (VP-Sls & Mktg)

CASSITY JONES LP
302 Pine Tree Rd, Longview, TX
75604
Tel.: (903) 759-0736
Web Site:
https://www.cassityjones.com
Sales Range: $25-49.9 Million
Emp.: 150
Home Center Operator
N.A.I.C.S.: 444110
John Jones (CEO)
Dennis Casey (Mgr-Store)
Tim Moore (Gen Counsel)

CASSLING DIAGNOSTIC IMAGING INC.
13808 F St, Omaha, NE 68137
Tel.: (402) 334-5000
Web Site: https://www.cassling.com
Sales Range: $50-74.9 Million
Emp.: 140
X-Ray Machines & Tubes
N.A.I.C.S.: 423450
Bob R. Cassling (Chm)
Lindsay Cosimano (VP-Mktg)
Andy Beer (Exec VP)
Marty Huebner (Sr VP-Svc)
Steven Chambers (CFO & VP-Ops)

CASSON-MARK CORP.

10515 Markison Rd, Dallas, TX
75238
Tel.: (214) 340-0880
Web Site: http://www.cmarkcorp.com
Sales Range: $10-24.9 Million
Emp.: 40
Telephone & Telephone Equipment
Installation
N.A.I.C.S.: 238210
Paul Casson (Pres)
Kathy Schwizer (Controller)

CAST ALUMINUM SOLUTIONS, LLC
1310 Kingsland Dr, Batavia, IL 60510
Tel.: (630) 879-2696
Web Site:
https://www.castaluminum.com
Year Founded: 1978
Aluminum Cast Product Mfr
N.A.I.C.S.: 331523
Tony Meadors (VP-Sls & Mktg)

CAST TECHNOLOGIES INCORPORATED
1100 SW Washington St, Peoria, IL
61602
Tel.: (309) 676-2157
Web Site:
https://www.casttechnologies.net
Sales Range: $25-49.9 Million
Emp.: 150
Brass Foundry
N.A.I.C.S.: 331529
Bill Carman (CFO)

CAST-FAB TECHNOLOGIES, INC.
3040 Forrer St, Cincinnati, OH
45209-1016
Tel.: (513) 758-1000   OH
Web Site: http://www.cast-fab.com
Year Founded: 1988
Sales Range: $25-49.9 Million
Emp.: 200
Mfr of Gray & Ductile Iron Castings &
Steel Plate Fabrications
N.A.I.C.S.: 331511
Ross Bushman (Pres)
Dave Iles (Supvr-Pattern Shop)
Doug Dumond (Mgr-Mgmt Info Sys)
Ed Shelton (Mgr-Mold & Core)
James Gilbert (Mgr-Facilities)
Kim Bevington (Sr Acct Mgr)
John Brewer (Mgr-Mktg & Plng)
Monty Fullerton (Engr-Foundry)

CASTANEA PARTNERS, INC.
3 Executive Park Ste 304, Newton,
MA 02462
Tel.: (617) 630-2400   DE
Web Site:
http://www.castaneapartners.com
Year Founded: 2001
Sales Range: $25-49.9 Million
Emp.: 25
Privater Equity Firm
N.A.I.C.S.: 523999
Brian J. Knez (Mng Partner)
Robert A. Smith (Mng Partner)
Troy L. Stanfield (Partner)
Juan Marcos Hill (Partner)
Colleen Love (CFO)
Paul F. Gibbons (Partner)
Steven T. Berg (Partner)
Marion Schouten (Dir-Bus Dev & IR)
Adam Garcia Eveloff (Principal)
Julian Chu (Operating Partner)
Benjamin Tuttman (Principal)
Gerald T. Hughes (Partner-Ops)
Janet Gurwitch (Operating Partner)
Stephen C. Richards (Partner-Ops)
Tim Burke (Partner)
Michael H. Banu (VP)
Lindsay Z. Ting (VP)
Tom First (Operating Partner)

Subsidiaries:

Donald J Pliner of Florida, Inc.   (1)
1 N Lexington Ave 12th Fl, White Plains,
NY 10601
Tel.: (212) 688-6900
Web Site: http://www.donaldjpliner.com
Sales Range: $75-99.9 Million
Footwear & Accessories Mfr & Retailer
N.A.I.C.S.: 315990
Donald J. Pliner (Owner)
Lisa Pliner (Dir-Creative)

Urban Decay Cosmetics LLC   (1)
833 W 16th St, Newport Beach, CA 92663
Tel.: (949) 631-4504
Web Site: http://www.urbandecay.com
Sales Range: $1-9.9 Million
Cosmetics Mfr & Retailer
N.A.I.C.S.: 325620
Malena Higuera (Gen Mgr-US)

CASTELLA IMPORTS, INC.
60 Davids Dr, Hauppauge, NY 11788
Tel.: (631) 231-5500
Web Site: http://www.castella.com
Year Founded: 1992
Sales Range: $10-24.9 Million
Emp.: 110
Food Product Mfr & Whslr
N.A.I.C.S.: 311999
Gina Berezny (VP-Pur)
John Roumbos (CFO)

CASTELLINI COMPANY, INC.
2 Plum St, Newport, KY 41076
Tel.: (859) 442-4600   OH
Web Site:
http://www.castellinigroup.com
Year Founded: 1895
Sales Range: $50-74.9 Million
Emp.: 375
Fresh Fruits & Vegetables
N.A.I.C.S.: 424480
Ed Castellini (VP)
Richard Evans (Pres)

Subsidiaries:

Crosset Company LLC   (1)
10295 Toebben Dr, Independence, KY
41051
Tel.: (859) 283-5830
Web Site: http://www.crosset.com
Emp.: 200
Fruit & Vegetable Whslr
N.A.I.C.S.: 424480
Robert Norris (Dir-Ops)

Grant County Foods Inc.   (1)
1125 Dry Ridge Rd, Dry Ridge, KY 41035-
7417
Tel.: (859) 428-1903
Web Site: http://www.grantcountyfoods.com
Rev.: $14,600,000
Emp.: 100
Fresh Fruits & Vegetables
N.A.I.C.S.: 424480
Bill Piper (Gen Mgr)

R&O Transportation LLC   (1)
8 Plum St, Wilder, KY 41076-9120
Tel.: (859) 572-0920
Web Site: http://www.rwitrans.com
Sales Range: $10-24.9 Million
Emp.: 50
Trucking Service
N.A.I.C.S.: 484230
Cindy Coyne (Office Mgr)

RWI Transportation LLC   (1)
8 Plum St, Wilder, KY 41076-9120
Tel.: (859) 572-0920
Web Site: http://www.rwitrans.com
Sales Range: $50-74.9 Million
Emp.: 40
Trucking Service
N.A.I.C.S.: 484230
Richard Bauer (Exec VP)
John Adams (Mgr-Ops)
Mike Lense (Dir-Safety)
Matt Holbrook (Mgr-Customer Svc)
Daryl Harmon (Dir-Carrier Rels)
Chris Taylor (Dir-Sls & Mktg)

CASTILE VENTURES
890 Winter St, Waltham, MA 02451

Tel.: (781) 890-0060
Web Site:
http://www.castileventures.com
Rev.: $4,361,000
Emp.: 7
Commodity Contracts Dealing
N.A.I.C.S.: 523160
Nina Saberi (Mgr)

CASTLE (AM) & CO
3400 North Wolf Road, Franklin Park,
IL 60131
Web Site: http://www.amcastle.com
Rev.: $958,978,000
Assets: $423,735,000
Liabilities: $248,230,000
Net Worth: $175,505,000
Earnings: $38,909,000
Emp.: 1,604
Fiscal Year-end: 12/31/05
Metal Exploration Svcs
N.A.I.C.S.:

CASTLE ADVERTISING
2470 E St, San Diego, CA 92102
Tel.: (619) 515-9799   CA
Year Founded: 1966
Sales Range: $25-49.9 Million
Emp.: 22
Advertising Agencies
N.A.I.C.S.: 541810
David Castle (Pres & CEO)
Mike Marschesano (Bus Mgr)
Dru Kelly (Designer-Interactive)
Caroline Tall (Acct Exec)
Raquel Rodriguez (Coord-Acct/Media)

CASTLE BUICK PONTIAC GMC INC.
7400 W Cermak Rd, North Riverside,
IL 60546
Tel.: (866) 233-8519
Web Site: http://www.castlebpg.com
Rev.: $14,500,000
Emp.: 200
New Car Dealers
N.A.I.C.S.: 441110
Anthony Castelbuono (Pres)

CASTLE CHEVROLET, INC.
400 E Roosevelt Rd, Villa Park, IL
60181
Tel.: (630) 279-5200   IL
Web Site:
http://www.castlechevycars.com
Sales Range: $25-49.9 Million
Emp.: 200
Retail Auto Dealership
N.A.I.C.S.: 441110
Tony Castle (Pres)
Cody Meyer (Mgr-Car)
Joe Genna (Mgr-Sls)

CASTLE CO-PACKERS LLC.
204B Schreiber Industrial Park, New
Kensington, PA 15068
Tel.: (724) 339-4040
Web Site:
http://www.castlecopackers.com
Year Founded: 2004
Sales Range: $10-24.9 Million
Emp.: 122
Beverage Bottling & Logistics Services
N.A.I.C.S.: 312112
Greg Ewing (Plant Mgr)
Brian Dworkin (Pres & CEO)
Thomas Nagle (Controller)
Michelle Shorto Dugan (Mgr-Sls)
Jason White (Mgr-Logistics)
Kevin Morgan (VP)

CASTLE HARLAN, INC.
150 E 58th St, New York, NY 10155-
3799

Tel.: (212) 644-8600   DE
Web Site:
   http://www.castleharlan.com
Year Founded: 1987
Rev.: $3,500,000,000
Emp.: 30
Private Equity Investment Firm
N.A.I.C.S.: 523999
John K. Castle (Chm & CEO)
Leonard M. Harlan (Chm)
Marcel Fournier (Sr Mng Dir)
Sylvia F. Rosen (VP & Controller)
Beverly Fox (Office Mgr)
Joyce M. Demonteverde (VP)
Heidi Petroff (VP)
Eric Schwartz (VP)
David B. Pittaway (Vice Chm, Sr Mng Dir, Chief Compliance Officer, Sec & Sr VP)

Subsidiaries:

Sunless Inc.   (1)
8909 S Freeway Dr, Macedonia, OH 44056
Tel.: (877) 668-8826
Web Site: http://www.sunlessinc.com
Beauty Product Mfr & Distr
N.A.I.C.S.: 325620
Martin Kelly (Pres & CEO)

Subsidiary (Domestic):

Norvell Skin Solutions, LLC   (2)
115 Edgewood St, Alexandria, TN
37012   (100%)
Tel.: (615) 529-1250
Web Site: http://www.norvelltanning.com
Sales Range: $1-9.9 Million
Emp.: 50
Beauty Supplies & Equipment Distr & Spray Tanning Systems
N.A.I.C.S.: 456120
Rick Norvell (Pres)
Lynn Norvell (CFO)
Greg Norvell (VP)

CASTLE HONDA

8833 Waukegan Rd, Morton Grove, IL 60053
Tel.: (847) 965-8833
Web Site:
   http://www.castlehondacars.com
Rev.: $38,800,000
Emp.: 55
Automobiles, New & Used
N.A.I.C.S.: 441110
Thomas C. Sondag (Owner)
Marian Cierpiala (Mgr-Fin)
Shamoun Dahlan (Asst Mgr)

CASTLE ISLAND PARTNERS LLC

339 Auburn St Ste 12, Newton, MA 02466
Tel.: (617) 650-6236
Web Site:
   https://www.castleislandpartner.com
Privater Equity Firm
N.A.I.C.S.: 523999
Ryan Kim (Partner)
Jay Makadia (Partner)
Michael Barry (Partner)

Subsidiaries:

Boston Interiors Inc.   (1)
301 Page St, Stoughton, MA 02072
Tel.: (781) 847-4600
Web Site: http://www.bostoninteriors.com
Sales Range: $200-249.9 Million
Furniture Retailer
N.A.I.C.S.: 449110
Kenneth Loring (Pres & CEO)
Tom Kane (CFO)
Erica LeBlanc Guillette (Mgr-Visual Merchandising & Accessories)
Christina Preisser (Mgr)
Judith Molloy (Mgr)
Lynne McFadden (Gen Mgr)
Tina Rose Bellone (Mgr)

CASTLE JEWELRY

210 W New Circle Rd, Lexington, KY 40505-1426
Tel.: (859) 309-0041
Web Site:
   https://www.thecastlejewelry.com
Year Founded: 1988
Sales Range: $10-24.9 Million
Emp.: 93
Jewelry Whslr
N.A.I.C.S.: 458310
Philip Maurice Block (Pres)
Carol Taylor Harlin (CFO)
Donna Hoertz (Dir-Adv)

CASTLEHEAD, INC. ESCROWS

16911 Bellflower Blvd, Bellflower, CA 90706
Tel.: (562) 925-0411
Web Site:
   https://www.castleheadescrows.com
Sales Range: $10-24.9 Million
Emp.: 21
Escrow Agent Real Estate
N.A.I.C.S.: 531210
Ada Flores (Mgr-Svc Star Award)
Sandie Radaich (Mgr-Svc Star Award)
Pat Greer (Mgr-Svc Star Award)
Michelle Smith (Mgr)
Jennie Jennings (Mgr)
Irela Sanchez (Mgr)
Jennifer Fleischer (Mgr)
Jennifer Shrier (Mgr)
Kelli Johnson (Mgr)
Kerri Stimson (Mgr)
Lenee A. Dalton (Mgr)
Winnie Lam (Mgr)

CASTLELAKE, L.P.

90 S 7th St 4600 Wells Fargo Ctr, Minneapolis, MN 55402
Tel.: (612) 851-3000
Web Site: http://www.tpgcredit.com
Year Founded: 2005
Sales Range: $75-99.9 Million
Emp.: 36
Financial Vehicles
N.A.I.C.S.: 525990
Rory O'Neill (Exec Chm & Co-CEO)
Chris Buckley (Partner-Aviation)
Rich Barnett (Partner-Bus Dev & Capital Markets)
Brad Farrell (Partner & CFO)
Evan Carruthers (Co-CEO & Chief Investment Officer)
Yen-Wah Lam (Pres & Chief People Officer)

Subsidiaries:

Genesis Financial Solutions, Inc.   (1)
15220 NW Greenbrier Pkwy Ste 200, Beaverton, OR 97006
Tel.: (503) 350-4300
Web Site: http://www.genesis-fs.com
Sales Range: $10-24.9 Million
Emp.: 650
Consumer Financial Services
N.A.I.C.S.: 561440
Bruce Weinstein (Pres)
Lisa Nilsson (VP-Card Programs)
Vernon Fuller (Chief Risk Officer)
Evan Bryman (VP-Card Programs)
Gregg Atkinson (CFO)
Ellen Falbo (Sr VP-Risk)
Daryle Wilson (Sr VP-Ops)
Steven Carnegie (CIO & Sr VP-IT)
Kristen Martin (Sr VP-HR)
Steven Lee (Sr VP-Bus Dev)

Subsidiary (Non-US):

GFS Canada   (2)
325 Milner Avenue Suite 1111, Scarborough, M1B 5N1, ON, Canada
Tel.: (503) 350-4300
Web Site: http://www.genesis-fs.ca
Collection Agency
N.A.I.C.S.: 561440

CASTLETON COMMODITIES INTERNATIONAL LLC

2200 Atlantic St Ste 800, Stamford, CT 06902-6834
Tel.: (203) 564-8100   DE
Web Site: https://www.cci.com
Emp.: 500
Holding Company; Energy Properties Investment, Operation & Commodities Wholesale Trade Merchant
N.A.I.C.S.: 551112
Magesh Nair (COO & Exec VP)
Craig M. Jarchow (Pres & CEO-Castleton Resources LLC)
Dan Hines (CFO & Exec VP)
William C. Reed II (Pres & CEO)

Subsidiaries:

Castleton Commodities International LLC - Houston Office   (1)
811 Main St Ste 3500, Houston, TX 77002
Tel.: (281) 378-1100
Web Site: http://www.cci.com
Emp.: 150
Regional Managing Office; Oil & Natural Gas Extraction & Merchant Whslr
N.A.I.C.S.: 551114
Magesh Nair (COO & Exec VP)
Craig M. Jarchow (Pres-Upstream)
Jay Reynolds (VP-Enterprise Applications, Projects & Support)

Robinson's Bend Operating II, LLC   (1)
16030 Romulus Rd, Buhl, AL 35446
Tel.: (205) 333-9499
Oil & Natural Gas Extraction Services
N.A.I.C.S.: 211120
Carol McDaniel (Office Mgr)

CASTLEWOOD REALTY COMPANY

204 E Joppa Rd, Baltimore, MD 21286
Tel.: (410) 825-7737
Rev.: $12,000,000
Emp.: 10
Commercial & Industrial Building Operation
N.A.I.C.S.: 531120

CASTO

250 Civic Center Dr Ste 500, Columbus, OH 43215
Tel.: (614) 228-5331
Web Site: https://www.castoinfo.com
Sales Range: $75-99.9 Million
Emp.: 270
Real Estate Construction, Investment & Management
N.A.I.C.S.: 236220
Stephen E. Dutton (Partner)
Brett Hutchens (Partner)
Paul Lukeman (Partner)
Cheri Shirey (Sr VP & Controller)
Lindsey VanMeter (Dir-HR)
Deborah Zink (VP-Credit & Collections)
Shannon Dixon (Exec VP-Dev & Leasing-Raleigh Reg)
Aaron Bouldin (Sr VP-Property Ops)
Michelle Koehler (Accountant)
Elizabeth Krepp (Accountant)
Sheri Marinello (Accountant)
Tony Riffe (Accountant-Recovery)
Rachel Erskine (Asst Mgr-Property)
Amy Atkinson (Controller-Property)
Anita Aume (Controller-Property)
William Brown (Controller-Property)
Julia Cline (Controller-Property)
Sophia Jarvis (Controller-Property)
Jennifer Fleischer (Coord-Construction)
John Riat (Coord-Dev)
Dawn Green (Coord-Document Imaging)
Hilary Deason (Coord-Residential Mktg)

Molly Benadum (Coord-Sls & Reporting)
Christopher Bradley (Coord-Tenant)
Nicholas Sills (Coord-Tenant)
Rich Yaras (Coord-Tenant)
Kristine Coplin (Designer-Graphic)
Sheila Cowan (Dir-Admin)
Brent Sobczak (Dir-Asset Mgmt)
Jason Freeman (Dir-Dev)
Eric Leibowitz (Dir-Dev)
Sarah Benson Hatcher (Dir-Mktg & PR)
Matthew Kinkade (Dir-Property Acctg)
Mary Pat Baxter (Gen Counsel)
Neisha Vitello (Gen Mgr)
Skylar Dinkins (Mgr)
Josh Macklin (Mgr-Comml Property)
Craig Rhine (Mgr-Construction)
Justin Bird (Mgr-Dev)
David Bishop (Mgr-Property)
Bruce Engelhardt (Mgr-Property)
Kelly Fenimore (Mgr-Property)
Misha Jensen (Mgr-Property)
Stephanie Pisaris (Mgr-Property)
Nancy Reitz (Mgr-Property)
Angela Shaffner (Mgr-Property)
Beth VanderPol (Mgr-Property)
Kimberly Davis (Mgr-Property Acctg)
Brenda Kaufman (Mgr-Tax Compliance)
Michael Hanagan (Mgr-Tax Consulting)
Vadim Nikitine (Partner)
Billy Finn (Project Coord)
Susan Perkins (Project Coord)
Bob Cepuchowski (Project Mgr)
Scott Flading (Project Mgr)
Dana Butler (Sr Project Mgr)
Regina Keeton (Supvr-Accts Payable)
Abraham Faberlle (Supvr-Maintenance)
Doug Yaus (Supvr-Maintenance)
Martin Moehring (Treas & Mgr-Fin Ops)
C. H. Waterman (VP & Dir-Legal)
Lisa Boveine (VP-Capital Div)
James Conroy (VP-Dev)
Charlie Fraas (VP-Dev)
Lou Visco (VP-Dev)
Marsha Ruddle (VP-Tax)
Sydney Federer (Sr Dir-Leasing)
Chad Hamrick (Dir-Leasing)
Armand Mastropietro (Mng Dir-Comml Property Mgmt Ops)
Don M. Casto III (Partner)
Frank S. Benson III (Partner)

CASTONGIAS INC.

295 E Wood Rd, Rensselaer, IN 47978
Tel.: (219) 866-5117   IN
Web Site: http://www.castongias.com
Year Founded: 1939
Sales Range: $10-24.9 Million
Emp.: 20
Agricultural Machinery & Equipment
N.A.I.C.S.: 423820
Mark Voors (Mgr-Sls)

CASTOR & POLLUX PET WORKS

14340 SE Industrial Way, Clackamas, OR 97015
Tel.: (503) 802-4700
Web Site:
   http://www.castorpolluxpet.com
Year Founded: 2000
Rev.: $16,700,000
Emp.: 29
Miscellaneous Nondurable Goods Merchant Whslr
N.A.I.C.S.: 424990
Brian Connolly (Pres)
Karen M. Gunton (Sec)
Andrew Mitchell (VP-Sls & Mktg)

Castor & Pollux Pet Works—(Continued)

CASUAL ELEGANCE ENTER-PRISES, INC.
425 Roberts Rd, Oldsmar, FL 34677
Tel.: (813) 855-9789
Web Site:
　　http://www.connieduglinlinen.com
Sales Range: $10-24.9 Million
Emp.: 100
Linen & Chair Cover Mfr & Rental
Services
N.A.I.C.S.: 314120
Erik Fishkin (Mgr-Sls-Reg)
Evan Duglin (VP-Fin)
Connie Duglin (Pres)

CASUAL LAMPS OF CALIFOR-NIA, INC.
15000 S Broadway St, Gardena, CA 90248
Tel.: (310) 323-0105
Web Site:
　　http://www.casuallamps.com
Rev.: $10,000,000
Emp.: 63
Mfr of Lamps
N.A.I.C.S.: 335139

CATALINA CHANNEL EX-PRESS INC.
Berth 95, San Pedro, CA 90731
Tel.: (310) 519-7971
Web Site:
　　http://www.catalinaexpress.com
Rev.: $21,637,729
Emp.: 200
Excursion Boat Operators
N.A.I.C.S.: 487210
Greg Bombard (Pres)

CATALINA YACHTS, INC.
21200 Victory Blvd, Woodland Hills, CA 91367-2522
Tel.: (818) 884-7700　　　　　　**CA**
Web Site:
　　http://www.catalinayachts.com
Year Founded: 1970
Sales Range: $100-124.9 Million
Emp.: 260
Builder & Repairer of Yachts
N.A.I.C.S.: 336612
Sharon Day (Mgr-Natl Sls)
Gerry Douglas (VP-Engrg)

CATALOGS.COM
2800 Glades Cir Ste 135, Fort Lau-derdale, FL 33327
Tel.: (954) 659-9005
Web Site: http://www.catalogs.com
Year Founded: 1996
Sales Range: $1-9.9 Million
Emp.: 18
Online Catalogs
N.A.I.C.S.: 425120
Leslie Linevsky (Co-Founder)
Richard Linevsky (Co-Founder & Pres)

CATALYSIS GROUP, INC.
374 Santa Ynez Way, Sacramento, CA 95816-3420
Tel.: (916) 929-3629
Web Site:
　　http://www.catalysisgroup.com
Sales Range: $1-9.9 Million
Business Consulting Services
N.A.I.C.S.: 541611
Payson Hall (VP)

CATALYSIS HOLDING CORPO-RATION
1601 E John St, Seattle, WA 98112
Tel.: (206) 826-8000　　　　　　**WA**
Web Site: http://www.catalysis.com
Year Founded: 1992

Sales Range: $1-9.9 Million
Emp.: 46
Holding Company; Advertising Soft-ware Application Developer & Mar-keter
N.A.I.C.S.: 551112
Douglas Stanley-Hunt (Founder & CEO)
Doug Schurman (Dir-Fin)
Grant Good (Pres)
Katie Grimes (Mgr-Mktg)
Lisa Green (Mgr-Project)
Matt Gallagher (Dir-Strategic Accts)
Mitch Stuard (Mgr-Acctg)
Nancy Hadley (Mng Dir)
Rick Goral (Creative Dir)
Robyn Wilson (Sr Project Mgr)

Subsidiaries:

Catalysis LLC　　　　　　　　　　(1)
1601 E John St, Seattle, WA 98112
Tel.: (206) 826-8000
Web Site: http://www.catalysis.com
Sales Range: $1-9.9 Million
Advertising Software Application Developer
& Marketer
N.A.I.C.S.: 541511
Doug Stanley-Hunt (Founder & CEO)
Grant Good (Pres)
Nancy Hadley (Mng Dir)

CATALYST
475 Sansome St Ste 730, San Fran-cisco, CA 94111
Tel.: (415) 655-4200
Web Site: http://www.catalystsf.com
Sales Range: $25-49.9 Million
Emp.: 18
Advertising, Consulting, Corporate Identity, Interactive, Internet/Web De-sign, Market Research, Media Plan-ning, Strategic Planning/Research
N.A.I.C.S.: 541810
John Durham (CEO & Mng Gen Part-ner)
Cory Treffiletti (Mng Partner, Pres)
Jim Nichols (Sr Partner-Strategy)
Kevin Long (Dir-Acct Strategy)
Shannon Light (Sr Dir-Acct Strategy)
Christian Arens (Partner-Strategy)
Jon Branch (Mgr-Comm Insights)
Ali Khait (Dir-Bus Dev)
Daniel Gold (Sr Dir-Corp Accts)

CATALYST CONSTRUCTION
225 E Mason St Ste 600, Milwaukee, WI 53202
Tel.: (414) 727-6840
Web Site:
　　http://www.catalystbuilds.com
Year Founded: 2004
Sales Range: $10-24.9 Million
Emp.: 11
Nonresidential Construction Services
N.A.I.C.S.: 236220
Matthew M. Burow (Pres)

CATALYST DIRECT INC.
110 Marina Dr, Rochester, NY 14626
Tel.: (585) 453-8300
Web Site: http://www.catalystinc.com
Year Founded: 1990
Sales Range: $10-24.9 Million
Emp.: 80
Advetising Agency
N.A.I.C.S.: 541810
Mike Osborn (Mng Dir)
Jeff Cleary (Mng Dir)
Pauline Wilcox (Chief Talent Officer)
Ken Fitzgerald (Exec Dir-Creative)
William Cao (Chief Analytics Officer)
Jim Dellavilla (Chief Client Officer)
Damir Saracevic (Dir-Digital Mktg)

CATALYST EXPERIENTIAL, LLC

3400 W Chester Pike, Newtown Square, PA 19073
Tel.: (610) 975-9390
Web Site: http://www.catalystex.com
Year Founded: 2009
Sales Range: $10-24.9 Million
Emp.: 50
Advertising Agency Services
N.A.I.C.S.: 541810
Thaddeus Bartkowski (CEO)
Patrick T. Wolfington (Exec VP-Real Estate)
John Grabowski (CFO)
Timothy F. Earle (Exec VP-Investments)
Joe Weinlick (CMO)

CATALYST HANDLING SER-VICE CO., LLC.
12423 Jim Babin Rd, Saint Amant, LA 70774
Tel.: (225) 644-2302
Web Site:
　　https://www.catalysthandling.com
Year Founded: 1999
Sales Range: $10-24.9 Million
Emp.: 60
Chemical Cleaning Industrial Services
N.A.I.C.S.: 423830
Rodgers Thibodeaux (Owner)

CATALYST INVESTORS, LLC
711 5th Ave Ste 600, New York, NY 10022
Tel.: (212) 863-4848　　　　　　**DE**
Web Site:
　　http://www.catalystinvestors.com
Year Founded: 2000
Privater Equity Firm
N.A.I.C.S.: 523999
Tyler Newton (Partner)
Brian Rich (Co-Founder & Mng Part-ner)
Ryan McNally (Co-Founder & Part-ner)
Todd Clapp (Partner)
Tyler Newton (Partner)
Susan Bihler (Partner)

CATALYST MARKETING COM-MUNICATIONS INC.
2777 Summer St Ste 406, Stamford, CT 06905
Tel.: (203) 348-7541　　　　　　**CT**
Web Site: http://www.catalystmc.com
Year Founded: 1963
Sales Range: $1-9.9 Million
Emp.: 9
Advetising Agency
N.A.I.C.S.: 541810
Melissa A. LoParco (Pres)
Charles Wintrub (Pres)
Samantha Manz (Acct Exec)

CATALYST MARKETING DE-SIGN
930 S Calhoun St, Fort Wayne, IN 46802
Tel.: (260) 422-4888
Web Site: http://www.catalystsite.com
Year Founded: 1997
Sales Range: $10-24.9 Million
Emp.: 18
N.A.I.C.S.: 541810
Richard Gripp (Principal & Dir-Client Svcs)
Ted Kucinsky (Principal & Dir-Creative)
Connie Hunt (Controller)

CATALYST PARTNERS ACQUI-SITION CORP.
20 University Rd 4th Fl, Cambridge, MA 02138
Tel.: (617) 234-7000　　　　　　**Ky**
Year Founded: 2021

Investment Services
N.A.I.C.S.: 523999
James I. Cash (Chm & CEO)
Paul Sagan (Pres & Vice Chm)
Robin L. Washington (Chief Dev Offi-cer)
Kevin King (Partner-Investment)
Paul Fielding (COO)
Robin L. Washington (Chief Dev Officer)

CATALYST SOLUTIONS
2353 S Broadway, Denver, CO 80210
Tel.: (303) 393-8818
Web Site:
　　http://www.catalystsolutions.com
Year Founded: 1999
Sales Range: $1-9.9 Million
Emp.: 150
Technical Consulting Services
N.A.I.C.S.: 541690
Rachel Hennig (CEO)
Tara Watley (Mgr-Ops)

CATALYST STUDIOS
126 N 3rd St Ste 200, Minneapolis, MN 55401
Tel.: (612) 339-0735
Sales Range: $10-24.9 Million
Emp.: 10
N.A.I.C.S.: 541810
Jason Rysavy (Founder & Principal)
Jared Lukes (Dir-Interactive)

CATALYST TECHNOLOGY GROUP USA
215 Center Park Dr Ste 400, Knox-ville, TN 37922
Tel.: (865) 584-1333
Web Site: http://www.usacatalyst.com
Year Founded: 1978
Sales Range: $10-24.9 Million
Emp.: 25
Technology Services
N.A.I.C.S.: 541618
Patricia Beasley (Pres)
Matt Annalora (Mgr-Bus Dev)

CATALYST, INC.
120 Wall St 15th Fl, New York, NY 10005
Tel.: (212) 514-7600
Web Site: http://www.catalyst.org
Year Founded: 1962
Sales Range: $10-24.9 Million
Emp.: 85
Social Advocacy Organization
N.A.I.C.S.: 813319
Thomas J. Falk (Treas)
Michael J. Chamberlain (VP-Mktg-Global)
Jennifer Daniel-Davidson (CFO & Sr VP-Fin, HR & Admin)
Deborah Gillis (Pres & CEO)
Cynthia L. Hansen (Sr VP)
Maggie Wilderotter (Sec)
Brande Stellings (Sr VP-Advisory Svcs)
Margaret A. Kashmir (Sr VP-Comm)
Dnika J. Travis (VP)
Emma Sabin (VP)
Heather Foust-Cummings (VP)
Julie S. Nugent (VP)
Katherine Giscombe (VP)
Joy Ohm (VP & Editor-in-Chief)
Emily Zuckerman (VP-Admin-Global & Legal Affairs)
Tia T. Gordon (VP-Comm-Global)
Svetlana Mostovsky (VP-Dev)
Serena Fong (VP-Govt Affairs)
Jennifer Tarlow (VP-Human Capital)
Emily V. Troiano (VP-Information Center)
Laura Sabattini (VP-Res)
Lorraine Hariton (Pres & CEO)

Catherine Corley (Sr VP-Learning Products & Programs)
Iris Henries (Sr VP-Brand & Strategic Comm-Global)
Peter Robert Voser (Chm)

Subsidiaries:

Catalyst Canada Inc.   (1)
8 King Street East Suite 505, Toronto, M5C 1B5, ON, Canada
Tel.: (416) 815-7600
Social Advocacy Organization
N.A.I.C.S.: 813319

Catalyst Europe AG   (1)
c/o KPMG AG Landis-Gyr-Strasse 1, Zug, 6300, Switzerland
Tel.: (41) 44 208 3152
Web Site: http://www.catalyst.org
Social Advocacy Organization
N.A.I.C.S.: 813319
Allyson Zimmermann (Exec Dir)

Catalyst India WRC   (1)
B 601 Ivy Tower Vasant Valley, Goregaon (E), Mumbai, 400 097, India
Tel.: (91) 22 6700 0785
Social Advocacy Organization
N.A.I.C.S.: 813319
Shachi Irde (Exec Dir)

CATALYST, INC.
110 Marina Dr, Rochester, NY 14626
Tel.: (585) 453-8300   NY
Web Site: http://www.catalystinc.com
Year Founded: 1990
Sales Range: $10-24.9 Million
Emp.: 80
Advetising Agency
N.A.I.C.S.: 541810
Michael Osborn (Mng Dir)
Elizabeth Mertz (Dir-Client Svcs)
Pauline Wilcox (Chief Talent Officer)
Ken Fitzgerald (Exec Dir-Creative)
Dan Keating (CIO)
William Cao (Chief Analytics Officer)
Jim Dellavilla (Chief Client Officer)

CATALYST, INC.
275 Promenade St, Providence, RI 02908
Tel.: (401) 732-1886
Web Site:
   https://www.catalystb2b.com
Sales Range: $1-9.9 Million
Emp.: 15
B2B Brand Consulting & Marketing Communications
N.A.I.C.S.: 541810
Tom Hamlin (Chief Activation Officer)
Brian Odell (Pres & CEO)
Lindsey Hingorany (Dir-Ops)

CATALYTE, INC.
502 S Sharp St Ste 2200, Baltimore, MD 21201
Tel.: (410) 385-2500
Web Site: http://www.catalyte.io
Software Development Services
N.A.I.C.S.: 541511
Micheal Rosenbaum (Founder & CEO)
Scott Harris (Exec VP)

CATALYTIC SOFTWARE, INC.
550 Kirkland Way Ste 405, Kirkland, WA 98033
Tel.: (425) 739-2180
Web Site: http://www.catalytic.com
Year Founded: 2000
Rev.: $18,100,000
Emp.: 230
Software Development Solutions Provider
N.A.I.C.S.: 423430
Goutham Koka (Exec VP-Fin)

CATAMARAN SOLUTIONS, LLC
6 Silverstrand Pl, Woodlands, TX 77381
Web Site:
   http://www.catamaransolutions.com
Technology-enabled Construction & Maintenance Related Services
N.A.I.C.S.: 561499
E. Chip Ray (CEO)
Jim Bishop (Pres- Catamaran Indus Svcs)
Bret Swan (Pres-Catamaran Comml Svcs)
Scott Waguespack (Exec VP-Admin)
Chris Strickland (Exec VP-Ops)
Chip Staples (Chief Innovation Officer)
Charles Ray (Sr VP-IT)

Subsidiaries:

Reynolds Industrial Contractors, Inc.   (1)
142 Old Shreveport Rd, Minden, LA 71055
Tel.: (318) 377-2289
Web Site: http://www.reynoldsindustrialcontractors.com
Plate Work Mfr
N.A.I.C.S.: 332313
J. D. Greene (Mgr-OP)

CATAMOUNT CONSTRUCTORS, INC.
Ste 200 1250 Bergen Pkwy, Evergreen, CO 80439-9584
Tel.: (303) 679-0087
Web Site:
   http://www.catamountconstructors.com
Year Founded: 1997
Rev.: $67,000,000
Emp.: 100
General Contracting Services
N.A.I.C.S.: 236220
Geoffrey G. Wormer (CEO & Principal)
Sandi Wolff (Dir-Strategic Rels)
Jess Brovsky (Coord-Mktg & Proposal)

CATAMOUNT DAIRY HOLDINGS L.P.
6 Kimball Ln, Lynnfield, MA 01940
Tel.: (800) 343-6592
Web Site: http://hphood.com
Year Founded: 1995
Sales Range: $100-124.9 Million
Emp.: 1,800
Dairy Products Producer.
N.A.I.C.S.: 311511
John A. Kaneb (Chm, Pres & CEO)

Subsidiaries:

HP Hood LLC   (1)
6 Kimball Ln, Lynnfield, MA 01940
Tel.: (617) 887-3000
Web Site: https://www.hood.com
Sales Range: Less than $1 Million
Emp.: 3,400
Fluid Milk Manufacturing
N.A.I.C.S.: 311511
H. Scott Blake (Sr VP-Ops)
Lynne Bohan (VP-Comm & Govt Affairs)
Theresa M. Bresten (Treas & VP)
Gary R. Kaneb (CFO)
Jeffrey J. Kaneb (Exec VP)
James A. Marcinelli (VP & Controller)
Mike J. Suever (Sr VP-R&D & Engrg Procurement)
James F. Walsh (Exec VP-Sls)
Paul C. Nightingale (Gen Counsel & Sr VP)
Christopher S. Ross (VP-Mktg)
Jane Seitz (VP-HR)

Subsidiary (Domestic):

Crowley Foods, Inc.   (2)
93 Pennsylvania Ave, Binghamton, NY 13903
Tel.: (607) 779-3289
Web Site: http://www.crowleyfoods.com

Dairy, Frozen Desserts & Specialty Food Products Mfr
N.A.I.C.S.: 311511

Subsidiary (Domestic):

Axelrod Foods, Inc.   (3)
100 Thomas St, Paterson, NJ 07503-2315
Tel.: (973) 684-0600
Web Site: http://www.axelrod.com
Sales Range: $25-49.9 Million
Emp.: 35
Food Products Distr
N.A.I.C.S.: 424430

Crowley Foods, Inc.   (3)
330 N State St, Concord, NH 03301-3229
Tel.: (603) 225-3379
Web Site: http://www.crowleyfoods.com
Sales Range: $25-49.9 Million
Emp.: 150
Milk, Ice Cream & Ice Cream Mixes Processor
N.A.I.C.S.: 311514

Rosenbergers Dairies, LLC   (3)
847 Forty Foot Rd, Hatfield, PA 19440
Tel.: (215) 855-9074
Web Site: http://www.rosenbergers.com
Sales Range: $50-74.9 Million
Emp.: 280
Milk & Cream Producer & Retailer
N.A.I.C.S.: 311511

Subsidiary (Domestic):

Heluva Good, LLC   (2)
6551 Pratt Rd, Sodus, NY 14589
Tel.: (315) 483-6971
Web Site: http://www.heluvagood.com
Sales Range: $25-49.9 Million
Emp.: 150
Cheese, Dips, Salsa, Condiments & Dairy Products Mfr & Packager
N.A.I.C.S.: 424430

CATAPULT ACQUISITIONS CORP.
2808 Cowan Cir, Las Vegas, NV 89107
Tel.: (775) 781-4143   NV
Year Founded: 2013
Investment Services
N.A.I.C.S.: 523999
Richard A. Taulli (Pres, CEO, CFO, Chief Acctg Officer, Treas & Sec)

CATAPULT CONSULTANTS LLC
2300 Clarendon Blvd Ste 600, Arlington, VA 22201
Tel.: (703) 849-0960
Web Site:
   http://www.catapultconsultants.com
Year Founded: 2001
Sales Range: $1-9.9 Million
Emp.: 85
Financial Management
N.A.I.C.S.: 541618
Joshua Bogart (Owner)
John Kimmins (CTO)

CATAPULT DIRECT MARKETING LLC
300 Orchard City Dr Ste 131, Campbell, CA 95008
Tel.: (408) 369-8111
Web Site:
   http://www.catapultworks.com
Year Founded: 1992
Sales Range: $1-9.9 Million
Emp.: 80
Advetising Agency
N.A.I.C.S.: 541810
Tom Beck (Co-Founder & Pres-Demand Grp)
Dennis Totah (Co-Founder & Pres-Data Grp)
Bob Moore (COO & Sr VP)

CATAPULT EMPLOYERS ASSOCIATION, INC.

3020 W Arrowood Rd, Charlotte, NC 28273
Tel.: (704) 522-8011   NC
Web Site:
   http://www.employersassoc.com
Year Founded: 1958
Sales Range: $1-9.9 Million
Emp.: 28
Employer Association
N.A.I.C.S.: 561330
Byron Pruitt (Dir-Mgmt Trng & Dev)
Laura Hampton (VP-Mktg, Membership & Trng Svcs)
Dolores Gentry (Mgr-First Impressions)
Cathy Graham (Dir-Benefit Svcs)
Stephanie Oberg (Mgr-Compensation & Res)
Jennifer Solomonson (Dir-HR Svcs)
Kenny Colbert (Co-CEO)
Roy Brown (CFO)
Jen Henry (Project Mgr-HR)
Sara LeBaron (Mgr-Mktg & Memberships)
Bruce Clarke (Co-CEO)
Molly Hegeman (Chief Strategy Officer)

Subsidiaries:

Capital Associated Industries, Inc.   (1)
3150 Spring Forest Rd Ste 116, Raleigh, NC 27616
Tel.: (919) 878-9222
Web Site: http://www.capital.org
Rev.: $6,835,189
Assets: $12,635,511
Liabilities: $2,053,116
Net Worth: $10,582,395
Earnings: $533,636
Emp.: 67
Fiscal Year-end: 12/31/2013
Employer Association
N.A.I.C.S.: 813920
Molly Hegeman (VP-HR Svcs)
Doug Blizzard (VP-Membership)
Colleen Cunningham (VP-Learning Svcs)
Kaleigh Ferraro (Mgr-Affirmative Action Svcs)
John Gupton (Gen Counsel)

CATAPULT ENERGY SERVICES GROUP, LLC
3050 Post Oak Blvd Ste 650, Houston, TX 77056
Tel.: (832) 615-3660   DE
Web Site: https://catapultservices.net
Investment Services
N.A.I.C.S.: 523999
Gregory D. Laake (Mng Partner)

CATAPULT PR-IR, L.L.C.
6560 Gunpark Dr Ste C, Boulder, CO 80301
Tel.: (303) 581-7760
Web Site: https://www.catapultpr-ir.com
Sales Range: Less than $1 Million
Emp.: 7
Public & Investor Relations
N.A.I.C.S.: 541820
Terri Douglas (Co-Founder & Principal)
Guy Murrel (Co-Founder & Principal)

CATARACT STEEL INDUSTRIES, INC.
22nd Allen Ave, Niagara Falls, NY 14302
Tel.: (716) 282-0845
Web Site:
   http://www.cataractsteel.com
Year Founded: 1976
Heat Transfer Product Mfr
N.A.I.C.S.: 333414
Scott Costanzo (Pres)

Cataract Steel Industries, Inc.—(Continued)

Subsidiaries:

PVT Systems　　　　　　　　　(1)
1960 State Route 14, Montour Falls, NY
14865-9726
Web Site: http://www.pvtsystems.com
Commercial & Service Industry Machinery
Mfr
N.A.I.C.S.: 333310
Robert Prentice (Pres)

CATAUMET BOATS, INC.
1280 Route 28A, Cataumet, MA
02534-0147
Tel.: (508) 563-7102
Web Site:
　　https://www.cataumetboats.com
Year Founded: 1959
Sales Range: $10-24.9 Million
Emp.: 15
Boat Dealers
N.A.I.C.S.: 441222
Peter R. Way (Pres)
Sheila Way Giancola (Treas)

CATAWBA SOX LLC
1500 13th St SW, Hickory, NC 28603
Tel.: (828) 464-1690
Web Site: http://www.catawbasox.net
Year Founded: 1947
Sales Range: $10-24.9 Million
Emp.: 170
Socks Mfr
N.A.I.C.S.: 315120
Ken Wofford (Mgr-HR)
John Mills (Pres)
Lance Landin (Dir-Sls)

**CATAWISSA WOOD & COMPO-
NENTS INC.**
1015 W Valley Ave, Elysburg, PA
17824-7259
Tel.: (570) 644-1928　　　　　PA
Web Site: https://www.catlmbr.com
Year Founded: 2010
Hardwood Component Mfr
N.A.I.C.S.: 321999
Danny Vallee (VP)
Jean Philippe Gervais (Pres)

CATCH THE MOMENT
8850 Jameel Rd, Houston, TX 77040
Tel.: (713) 255-4500
Web Site: http://www.ctmevents.com
Year Founded: 1998
Sales Range: $1-9.9 Million
Emp.: 14
Automatic Vending Machines
N.A.I.C.S.: 333310
Dick Didow (Pres)
Robert Bryant (Dir-Tech)
Dolores Townley (Mgr-Sls-Natl)

**CATE EQUIPMENT COMPANY
INC.**
2055 S Pioneer Rd, Salt Lake City,
UT 84104
Tel.: (801) 515-7411　　　　　UT
Web Site:
　　http://www.cateequipment.com
Year Founded: 1975
Sales Range: $10-24.9 Million
Emp.: 100
Construction & Mining Machinery
N.A.I.C.S.: 532412
Perry Pardoe (Owner)
Dwight Goodwin (Controller)
Kaleb Ellis (Mgr-IT)

CATELLI BROS INC.
50 Ferry Ave, Collingswood, NJ
08103-3006
Tel.: (856) 869-9293
Web Site:
　　https://www.catellibrothers.com
Year Founded: 1980

Sales Range: $100-124.9 Million
Emp.: 230
Meat Whslr
N.A.I.C.S.: 424470
Monica D'Ancona (Mgr-Retail Accts)
Louis Licht (Dir-Food Svc)
Anthony Catelli Jr. (Pres & CEO)

CATHEDRAL ARMS INC.
PO Box 7070, Pasadena, CA 91109-
7070
Tel.: (323) 258-3512　　　　　CA
Year Founded: 2005
Sales Range: $1-9.9 Million
Emp.: 5
Elderly People Housing Assistance
Services
N.A.I.C.S.: 624229
Emili Wohl (Pres)
Robert L. Rentto (CFO & Sec)

CATHEDRAL CORPORATION
632 Ellsworth Rd, Rome, NY 13441
Tel.: (315) 338-0021
Web Site:
　　https://www.cathedralcorp.com
Sales Range: $10-24.9 Million
Emp.: 140
Commercial Printing
N.A.I.C.S.: 323111
Church Stewardship (VP-Sls & Mktg)
Marianne W. Gaige (Pres & CEO)
Mary Keating (VP-IT)
Aart Knyff (VP & Dir-Ops)

CATHEDRAL VILLAGE
600 E Cathedral Rd, Philadelphia, PA
19128
Tel.: (215) 487-1300　　　　　PA
Web Site:
　　http://www.cathedralvillage.com
Year Founded: 1980
Sales Range: $10-24.9 Million
Emp.: 296
Retirement Community Operator
N.A.I.C.S.: 623311
Catherine Chan-Ng (Exec Dir)
Richard Hartmann (Sec)
Dennis Koza (Pres & CEO)
William Scott (Chm)
Edwin Sheffield (Asst Sec)
William Cobb Jr. (Vice Chm)

**CATHOLIC CEMETERIES AS-
SOCIATION**
718 Hazelwood Ave, Pittsburgh, PA
15217-2807
Tel.: (412) 521-9133
Web Site: https://www.ccapgh.org
Sales Range: $10-24.9 Million
Emp.: 150
Cemetery Association
N.A.I.C.S.: 812220
Ron McHugh (Mgr-Cemetery)

**CATHOLIC CHARITIES COM-
MUNITY SERVICES**
4747 N 7th Ave, Phoenix, AZ 85013
Tel.: (602) 285-1999　　　　　AZ
Web Site:
　　https://www.catholiccharitiesaz.org
Year Founded: 1970
Sales Range: $25-49.9 Million
Emp.: 599
Community Care Services
N.A.I.C.S.: 624190
Steve Capobres (VP-Bus Dev)
Cathy Peterson (VP-Ops & Exec Dir-
Northern Arizona Reg)
Leslie Mar'Na (Sr Mgr-Program)
Erik Becker (CFO)

**CATHOLIC CHARITIES
HEALTH & HUMAN SERVICES**
7911 Detroit Ave, Cleveland, OH
44102

Tel.: (216) 334-2900　　　　　OH
Web Site:
　　http://www.clevelandcatholic
　　charities.org
Year Founded: 1999
Sales Range: $10-24.9 Million
Emp.: 179
Community Care Services
N.A.I.C.S.: 624229
Mark J. Griffiths (Dir-HR)
Lisa Gasbarre-Black (Gen Counsel)
Patricia M. Holian (COO)
Wayne C. Peel (CFO)

CATHOLIC CHARITIES MAINE
PO Box 10660, Portland, ME 04104-
6060
Tel.: (207) 781-8550　　　　　ME
Web Site: https://www.ccmaine.org
Year Founded: 1967
Sales Range: $25-49.9 Million
Emp.: 773
Social Service Organization
N.A.I.C.S.: 813410
Alyssa Pekins (Chief Admin Officer)
Jeff Tiner (COO)

**CATHOLIC CHARITIES OF
FAIRFIELD COUNTY INC.**
238 Jewett Ave Ste, Bridgeport, CT
06606
Tel.: (203) 416-1333　　　　　CT
Year Founded: 1995
Sales Range: $10-24.9 Million
Emp.: 198
Community Care Services
N.A.I.C.S.: 624190
Frank Caggiano (Chm)
Albert F. Barber (Pres)
Kevin T. Royal (VP)
Gustavo A. Falla (VP)
Jerald A. Doyle (Treas)

**CATHOLIC CHARITIES OF
SOUTHERN NEVADA**
1501 Las Vegas Blvd N, Las Vegas,
NV 89101
Tel.: (702) 385-2662　　　　　NV
Web Site:
　　https://www.catholiccharities.com
Year Founded: 1945
Sales Range: $25-49.9 Million
Emp.: 416
Community Welfare Services
N.A.I.C.S.: 624190
Thomas A. Roberts (Pres & CEO)
John B. Page (Treas)
Marilyn Spiegel (Sec)
Patricia Trent Morrissey (Co-Pres)
Joseph A. Pepe (Chm)
Marilyn Spiegel (Sec)

**CATHOLIC COMMUNITY
FOUNDATION**
Cathedral Square Plz 1404 E 9th St,
Cleveland, OH 44114-1722
Tel.: (216) 696-6525　　　　　OH
Web Site:
　　http://www.catholiccommunity.org
Year Founded: 1999
Sales Range: $10-24.9 Million
Emp.: 29
Christian Ministry Services
N.A.I.C.S.: 813110
Mark Counselman (Asst Dir-Database
Mgmt)
Mary Cosgrove (Dir-Grants Admin)
Fred M. DeGrandis (Vice Chm)
Timothy I. Panzica (Chm)

**CATHOLIC COMMUNITY
FOUNDATION OF MINNESOTA**
2610 University Ave W Ste 500, Saint
Paul, MN 55114
Tel.: (651) 389-0300　　　　　MN

Web Site: http://www.ccf-mn.org
Year Founded: 1992
Sales Range: $25-49.9 Million
Emp.: 12
Grantmaking Services
N.A.I.C.S.: 813211
Helen Twomey (Dir-Fin)
Bill Marsella (Dir-Partner Rels)
Jules Vierling (Mgr-Grants)
Anne Cullen Miller (Pres)
Meg Payne Nelson (Officer-Program)
Wayne A. Pelzel (Dir-Gift Plng -
Diocese-New Ulm)
Natalie Posteuca (First VP)
Angela Dimler (Dir-Strategic Comm)
Pam Buchanan (Mgr-Office)
Richard J. Olson (VP)
Christopher D. Nelson (VP-Dev &
Donor Engagement)
Casey Scott (VP-Fin & Admin)

**CATHOLIC COMMUNITY SER-
VICES OF SOUTHERN ARI-
ZONA, INC.**
140 W Speedway Blvd Ste 130, Tuc-
son, AZ 85705
Tel.: (520) 623-0344　　　　　AZ
Web Site: https://www.ccs-soaz.org
Year Founded: 1933
Sales Range: $10-24.9 Million
Emp.: 723
Community Action Services
N.A.I.C.S.: 624190
Teresa Cavendish (Dir-Operations)
Marguerite D. Harmon (CEO)
Patricia Torrington (VP)
Christopher Ahearn (VP)

**CATHOLIC EDUCATION ARI-
ZONA**
3550 N Central Ave Ste 1020, Phoe-
nix, AZ 85012
Tel.: (602) 218-6542　　　　　AZ
Web Site: http://www.ceaz.org
Year Founded: 2005
Sales Range: $50-74.9 Million
Emp.: 5
Educational Support Services
N.A.I.C.S.: 611710
Richard O. Cranmer (Treas)
Sally Bell-Sarlitto (Chm)
Maureen Adams (Pres)
Amy Brown (Sr VP-Ops & Fin)
Debby Castro (Sr VP-Ops & Fin)

CATHOLIC ELDERCARE
817 Main St NE, Minneapolis, MN
55413
Tel.: (612) 379-1370　　　　　MN
Web Site:
　　https://www.catholiceldercare.org
Year Founded: 1980
Sales Range: $10-24.9 Million
Emp.: 420
Elder Care Services
N.A.I.C.S.: 623312
Michael J. Shasky (CFO)
Thomas M. Beck (Vice Chm)
Dan Johnson (Pres & CEO)

CATHOLIC FINANCIAL LIFE
1100 W Wells St, Milwaukee, WI
53233
Tel.: (414) 273-6266　　　　　WI
Web Site:
　　https://www.catholicfinanciallife.org
Year Founded: 1885
Sales Range: $75-99.9 Million
Emp.: 125
Fire Insurance Services
N.A.I.C.S.: 524113
William R. O'Toole (Pres & CEO)
Kristen Mueller (Sec & VP-HR)

Subsidiaries:

Degree of Honor Protective Association (1)
1100 W Wells St, Milwaukee, WI 53201-3211
Tel.: (651) 228-7600
Web Site: http://www.degreeofhonor.com
Fraternal Life Insurance Organization
N.A.I.C.S.: 524113

CATHOLIC HEALTH INITIATIVES
198 Inverness Dr W, Englewood, CO 80112-5202
Tel.: (303) 298-9100   CO
Web Site:
    http://www.catholicinitiatives.org
Year Founded: 1996
Hospital & Health Care Services Organization
N.A.I.C.S.: 813910
Thomas R. Kopfensteiner *(Exec VP-Mission)*
A. Michelle Cooper *(Sr VP & Officer-Corp Responsibility)*
Philip L. Foster *(Sr VP-Enterprise Risk & Chief Risk Officer)*
Jeffrey S. Drop *(Exec Officer-Fargo Div & Sr VP)*
Anthony K. Jones *(Exec VP & COO)*
Mark C. Clement *(CEO-TriHealth)*
Paul Edgett III *(Exec VP & Chief Strategy Officer)*

Subsidiaries:

CHI Health Creighton University Medical Center - Bergan Mercy (1)
7500 Mercy Rd, Omaha, NE 68124
Tel.: (402) 398-6060
Web Site: http://www.chihealth.com
Health Care Srvices
N.A.I.C.S.: 622110

Consolidated Health Services Inc. (1)
1700 Edison Dr Ste 300, Milford, OH 45150
Tel.: (513) 576-0262
Web Site:
    http://www.consolidatedhealthservice.com
Sales Range: $50-74.9 Million
Emp.: 180
Women Healthcare Services
N.A.I.C.S.: 621610
Daniel S. Dietz *(Pres & CEO)*
Scott Herdtner *(CFO)*

Subsidiary (Domestic):

AmeriMed, Inc. (2)
9961 Cincinnati Dayton Rd, West Chester, OH 45069   (100%)
Tel.: (513) 942-3670
Web Site: http://www.chihealthathome.com
Sales Range: $25-49.9 Million
Emp.: 80
Women Healthcare Services
N.A.I.C.S.: 621610
Christa Miller *(Gen Mgr)*

American Nursing Care Inc. (2)
1700 Edison Dr, Milford, OH 45150-2786
Tel.: (513) 576-0262
Web Site:
    http://www.americannursingcare.com
Rev.: $44,800,000
Emp.: 200
Women Healthcare Services
N.A.I.C.S.: 621610
Daniel S. Dietz *(Pres & CEO)*
Jerry McKinney *(CFO & VP-Fin)*
Janice Connett *(VP-Prof Svcs)*
Tom Sayre *(VP-Bus Dev)*

Cornerstone Medical Services (2)
4460 Lake Forest Dr Ste 232, Blue Ash, OH 45242
Tel.: (513) 554-0222
Web Site:
    http://www.cornerstoneonecall.com
Sales Range: $1-9.9 Million
Emp.: 15
Home Medical Equipment & Respiratory Services
N.A.I.C.S.: 532283

Robert Nervo *(VP-Ops)*

Subsidiary (Domestic):

Cornerstone Medical Services - Akron (3)
453 S High St, Akron, OH 44311
Tel.: (330) 374-6802
Web Site:
    http://www.cornerstoneonecall.com
Sales Range: $1-9.9 Million
Home Medical Equipment & Respiratory Services
N.A.I.C.S.: 532283
Stephen M. Holian *(Dir-Ops)*

Legacy Medical Equipment (3)
1990 W Stanfield Rd, Troy, OH 45373
Tel.: (937) 335-9199
Web Site: http://legacymedical.net
Sales Range: $1-9.9 Million
Emp.: 11
Home Medical Equipment & Respiratory Services
N.A.I.C.S.: 532283

Dignity Health (1)
185 Berry St Ste 300, San Francisco, CA 94107-1739
Tel.: (415) 438-5500
Web Site: http://www.dignityhealth.org
Healthcare Facilities Management Services
N.A.I.C.S.: 622110
Tessie Guillermo *(Chm)*
Judy Carle *(Sec)*
Patrick S. Steele *(Vice Chm)*
Alan Shatzel *(CEO)*
Sacramentos Jahmal Miller *(Chief Admin Officer)*

Subsidiary (Domestic):

CDS of Nevada, Inc. (2)
2310 Paseo Delprado A12 Ste A 120, Las Vegas, NV 89102
Tel.: (702) 740-8020
Health Care Srvices
N.A.I.C.S.: 621999

Division (Domestic):

Dignity Health - Southern California (2)
251 S Lake Ave Fl 7, Pasadena, CA 91101-2186
Tel.: (626) 744-2310
Web Site: http://www.dignityhealth.org
Sales Range: $10-24.9 Million
Emp.: 125
Medical & Surgical Hospital
N.A.I.C.S.: 622110

Subsidiary (Domestic):

Bakersfield Memorial Hospital (3)
420 34th St, Bakersfield, CA 93301-2237
Tel.: (661) 327-4647
Web Site: http://www.dignityhealth.org
Emp.: 150
Providing Hospital Services
N.A.I.C.S.: 622110
Jon Van Boening *(Pres)*

CHW/Mercy Hospital Bakersfield (3)
2215 Truxtun Ave, Bakersfield, CA 93301-3602
Tel.: (661) 632-5000
Web Site: http://www.dignityhealth.org
Hospital
N.A.I.C.S.: 622110

California Hospital Medical Center (3)
1401 S Grand Ave, Los Angeles, CA 90015-3010
Tel.: (213) 748-2411
Web Site: http://www.dignityhealth.org
Hospital
N.A.I.C.S.: 622110
Jacob Rastegar *(Chm-OB & GYN)*
Margaret Lynn Yonekura *(Dir-Community Benefit)*
Phil Fairchild *(Dir-Diagnostic Imaging)*
Dorinda Perry *(Dir-Employee & Labor Rels)*
Sallie Weems *(Dir-GME & Trng Svcs)*
Susan L. Viker *(Dir-Infection Prevention & Epidemiology)*
Tina Lowe *(Dir-Rehab)*
Jamie Terrence *(Dir-Risk Mgmt Svcs)*
Laura Schneider *(Dir-Trauma Program)*

Ann Marie Ramon *(Mgr-Admin Svcs)*
Jane Lee *(Mgr-Physician Svcs)*
Tess Arellano *(Coord-Medical)*
Bryan Hubbard *(Assoc Dir-Trauma & Critical Care)*
Yuka Chen *(Assoc Dir-Grants & Contracts)*
Rebecca Cheng *(CFO & Sr VP-Fin)*
Theda S. Douglas *(Sec)*
Phillip C. Hill *(Chm)*
Carlos A. Vaquerano *(Vice Chm)*
Valarie Fleming *(Chief Nursing Officer)*
Margaret R. Peterson *(Pres)*
Bob Quarfoot *(VP-Bus Dev)*

Community Hospital of San Bernardino (3)
1805 Medical Ctr Dr, San Bernardino, CA 92411-1217
Tel.: (909) 887-6333
Web Site: http://www.chsb.org
Hospital
N.A.I.C.S.: 622110
June Collison *(Pres)*
Rhoda Harris *(Coord-Risk Mgmt & Patient Rels)*
Melissa Kolin *(Chief Nursing Officer & VP-Patient Care Svcs)*
Victoria Selby *(VP-Ancillary & Support Svcs)*

Glendale Memorial Hospital & Health Center (3)
1420 S Central Ave, Glendale, CA 91204
Tel.: (818) 502-1900
Web Site: http://www.dignityhealth.org
Buildings & Acoustic Barriers Mfr
N.A.I.C.S.: 333413

Mercy Westside Hospital (3)
110 E North St, Taft, CA 93268-3606
Tel.: (661) 763-4211
Hospital And Skilled Nursing
N.A.I.C.S.: 621111

Northridge Hospital Medical Center (3)
18300 Roscoe Blvd, Northridge, CA 91328-4105
Tel.: (818) 885-5321
Web Site: http://www.northridgehospital.org
Management of Healthcare Facilities
N.A.I.C.S.: 622110
Teddi Grant *(VP-Mktg)*
Ron Rozanski *(Sr VP-Ops)*
Ann Dechairo Marino *(Sr VP-Patient Care Svcs)*
Grace Leland *(VP-Hospital Rels)*
Michael Taylor *(CFO & VP-Fin)*
Paul Watkins *(Pres & CEO)*
Mark Dumais *(Chief Medical Officer)*

Sherman Way Campus (3)
14500 Sherman Cir, Van Nuys, CA 91405-3052
Tel.: (818) 997-0101
Sales Range: $10-24.9 Million
Emp.: 50
Retail Health Care Products
N.A.I.C.S.: 621112

St. Bernardine Medical Center (3)
2101 N Waterman Ave, San Bernardino, CA 92404-4836
Tel.: (909) 883-8711
Web Site: http://www.dignityhealth.org
Health Care Center
N.A.I.C.S.: 459420
Kathleen McDonnell *(Dir-Mission Integration)*
Douglas Kleam *(Pres)*
Kurt Weinmeister *(COO)*
Robert Carlson *(Chm)*
Adriana Velasco *(Chief Nursing Exec Officer)*

St. Elizabeth Community Hospital (3)
2550 Sister Mary Columba Dr, Red Bluff, CA 96080-4327
Tel.: (530) 229-8000
Health Care Srvices
N.A.I.C.S.: 622110

St. John's Pleasant Valley Hospital (3)
2309 Antonio Ave, Camarillo, CA 93010-1414
Tel.: (805) 389-5800
Web Site: http://www.stjohnshealth.org

Hospital
N.A.I.C.S.: 622110
Lydia Stevens *(Coord-Ops Room Scheduler & Surgical)*
Cynthia Pike *(Dir-Clinical Liaison & Mktg)*

St. John's Regional Medical Center (3)
1600 N Rose Ave, Oxnard, CA 93030-3722   (100%)
Tel.: (805) 988-2500
Web Site: http://www.dignityhealth.org
N.A.I.C.S.: 621410
John Rogers *(Dir-Laboratory Svcs)*
Gabriel Guillen *(Supvr-Faith Community Nurse Network)*
Brian Tuai *(Dir-Medical-Robotic Surgery)*
Darren Lee *(Pres & CEO)*

St. Mary Medical Center (3)
1050 Linden Ave, Long Beach, CA 90813-3321
Tel.: (562) 491-9000
Web Site:
    http://www.stmarymedicalcenter.com
Medical Devices
N.A.I.C.S.: 622110
Gail Daly *(COO)*
Jennifer Niles *(Supvr-Case Mgmt)*
Anthony Schiavoni *(Mgr-Svc Line & Bus Dev)*
Pat Meier *(Mgr-Trauma Program)*
Carolyn Caldwell *(Pres)*
Michael Neils *(Chief Philanthropy Officer)*

Trinitycare L.L.C. (3)
9221 Corbin Ave Ste 190, Northridge, CA 91324
Tel.: (818) 700-5670
Rev.: $28,915,778
Emp.: 20
Women Healthcare Services
N.A.I.C.S.: 621610

Subsidiary (Domestic):

Dignity Health Medical Group Nevada, LLC (2)
3001 Saint Rose Pkwy, Henderson, NV 89052
Tel.: (702) 616-5500
Web Site: http://www.dignityhealth.org
Health Care Srvices
N.A.I.C.S.: 621999
Mark Behl *(CEO)*
Tristan Kouk *(VP-Ops-Northern California)*

Dominican Hospital (2)
1555 Soquel Dr, Santa Cruz, CA 95065-1705   (100%)
Tel.: (831) 462-7716
Web Site: http://www.dignityhealth.org
Sales Range: $700-749.9 Million
Emp.: 16,000
Health Care Srvices
N.A.I.C.S.: 622110
Linda Plager *(Coord-Clinical)*
Felicity Simmons *(Coord-Comm)*
Laura Smith *(Coord-Nursing Student Unit)*
Sarah Edmundson *(Dir-Cardiovascular Svcs)*
Mike Lee *(Dir-Comm & Mktg)*
Lisa Akey *(Dir-Continuing Care Svcs)*
June Johnson *(Dir-Medical Staff Admin)*
Cindy Okuji *(Mgr-Nurse Case)*
Lee Vanderpool *(Sr Dir-IT)*
Susan MacMillan *(Sr Dir-Strategy & Bus Dev)*

Dominican Oaks Corporation (2)
3400 Paul Sweet Rd, Santa Cruz, CA 95065
Tel.: (831) 462-6257
Web Site: http://www.dominicanoaks.com
Sales Range: $1-9.9 Million
Continuing Care Retirement Community Services
N.A.I.C.S.: 623311
Brenda Baugh *(Dir-HR)*

Marian Medical Center (2)
1400 E Church St, Santa Maria, CA 93454-5906
Tel.: (805) 739-3000
Web Site:
    http://www.marianmedicalcenter.org
Sales Range: $75-99.9 Million
Emp.: 1,450
Hospital
N.A.I.C.S.: 813319

Catholic Health Initiatives—(Continued)

Chuck Cova *(Pres)*

Mark Twain Medical Center (2)
768 Mountain Ranch Rd, San Andreas, CA
95249-9707
Tel.: (209) 754-2603
Web Site: http://www.supportmarktwain.org
Sales Range: $25-49.9 Million
Emp.: 330
Acute Healthcare Services
N.A.I.C.S.: 622110
William Griffin *(Chm)*

Mercy General Hospital (2)
4001 J St, Sacramento, CA
95819-3626   **(100%)**
Tel.: (916) 453-4545
Web Site: http://www.mercygeneral.org
Sales Range: $25-49.9 Million
Emp.: 400
Hospital
N.A.I.C.S.: 621512
Denny Powell *(CEO)*
Ronald Kroll *(CFO)*
Edmundo Castaneda *(Pres)*

**Mercy Healthcare Sacramento
Inc.** (2)
3400 Data Dr, Rancho Cordova, CA 95670
Tel.: (916) 851-2000
Sales Range: $600-649.9 Million
Emp.: 600
General Medical & Surgical Hospitals
N.A.I.C.S.: 622110

**Mercy Hospital & Health
Services** (2)
2740 M St, Merced, CA 95340-2813
Tel.: (209) 384-6444
Medical Center
N.A.I.C.S.: 621410
Bruce Peters *(Pres & CEO)*

Mercy Hospital of Folsom (2)
1650 Creekside Dr, Folsom, CA 95630-
3400
Tel.: (916) 983-7512
Sales Range: $25-49.9 Million
Emp.: 450
Provides Hospital Services
N.A.I.C.S.: 622110
Michael Ricks *(CEO)*

**Mercy Medical Center Mt.
Shasta** (2)
914 Pine St, Mount Shasta, CA 96067
Tel.: (530) 926-6111
Web Site: http://www.dignityhealth.org
Sales Range: $25-49.9 Million
Emp.: 320
Hospital
N.A.I.C.S.: 622110
Kenneth Platau *(Pres)*
Sherie Ambrose *(VP-Patient Care)*

Mercy Medical Center Redding (2)
2175 Rosaline Ave, Redding, CA
96001-2509   **(100%)**
Tel.: (530) 225-6000
Web Site: http://www.mercyredding.org
Sales Range: $75-99.9 Million
Emp.: 1,600
Healtcare Services
N.A.I.C.S.: 622110
Doug Goodman *(Controller)*
Kate Grissom *(Dir-Mktg)*

Mercy San Juan Hospital (2)
6501 Coyle Ave, Carmichael, CA
95608-0306   **(100%)**
Tel.: (916) 537-5000
Web Site: http://www.mercysanjuan.org
Sales Range: $75-99.9 Million
Emp.: 2,000
Hospital
N.A.I.C.S.: 622110
Brian Ivie *(Pres & COO)*

Mercy Senior Housing, Inc. (2)
3400 Data Dr, Rancho Cordova, CA 95670
Tel.: (916) 851-2101
Community Housing Services
N.A.I.C.S.: 624229

Mercy Southwest Hospital (2)
400 Old River Rd, Bakersfield, CA 93311-
9781
Tel.: (661) 663-6000

Web Site: http://www.mercybakersfield.org
Sales Range: $150-199.9 Million
Emp.: 1,600
N.A.I.C.S.: 621410
Debbie Fowler *(Dir-HR)*

**Methodist Hospital of
Sacramento** (2)
7500 Hospital Dr, Sacramento, CA 95823-
5403
Tel.: (916) 423-3000
Web Site: http://www.mercysacramento.org
Sales Range: $75-99.9 Million
Emp.: 1,200
Hospital
N.A.I.C.S.: 622110
Bonnie Jenkins *(CFO)*
Mike Cox *(VP-Mission Integration)*

Oak Valley Hospital District (2)
350 S Oak Ave, Oakdale, CA 95361-3519
Tel.: (209) 847-3011
Web Site: http://www.oakvalleyhospital.com
Sales Range: $75-99.9 Million
Emp.: 500
N.A.I.C.S.: 622110
John McCormick *(Pres & CEO)*
Dan Cummins *(Chm)*
Louise Pooley-Sanders *(Vice Chm)*

**Saint Mary's Preferred Health Insur-
ance Company, Inc.** (2)
1510 Meadow Wood Ln, Reno, NV 89502-
8503
Tel.: (775) 770-6679
Health Insurance Services
N.A.I.C.S.: 524114

Sequoia Hospital (2)
170 Alameda Ave, Redwood City, CA
94062-2751
Tel.: (650) 369-5811
Web Site: http://www.sequoiahospital.org
Sales Range: $25-49.9 Million
Emp.: 150
Hospital
N.A.I.C.S.: 622110

Sierra Nevada Memorial Hospital (2)
155 Glasson Way, Grass Valley, CA 95945
Tel.: (530) 274-6000
Web Site: http://www.snmh.org
Sales Range: $125-149.9 Million
Emp.: 300
Health Care Srvices
N.A.I.C.S.: 622110

St. Francis Foundation (2)
900 Hyde St, San Francisco, CA 94109-
4806
Tel.: (415) 353-6650
Sales Range: $10-24.9 Million
Emp.: 10
Health Care Srvices
N.A.I.C.S.: 561990
Gay Morton *(Controller)*
Ann Lazarus *(Pres-Interim)*

**St. John's Regional Imaging Center,
LLC** (2)
1700 N Rose Ave, Oxnard, CA 93030
Tel.: (805) 983-0883
Emp.: 20
Laboratory Testing Services
N.A.I.C.S.: 541380
Angelique Vega *(Gen Mgr)*

**St. Joseph's Behavioral Health
Center** (2)
2510 N California St, Stockton, CA 95204-
5502
Tel.: (209) 461-2000
Web Site: http://www.stjosephscanhelp.org
Sales Range: $10-24.9 Million
Emp.: 175
Chemical Dependant Services
N.A.I.C.S.: 622110

**St. Joseph's Hospital & Medical
Center** (2)
350 W Thomas Rd, Phoenix, AZ 85013-
4409
Tel.: (602) 406-3000
Web Site: http://www.dignityhealth.org
Sales Range: $900-999.9 Million
Emp.: 6,000
Health Care Srvices
N.A.I.C.S.: 621491

St. Josephs Medical Center (2)

1800 N California St, Stockton, CA 95204-
6019
Tel.: (209) 943-2000
Web Site: http://www.stjosephscares.org
Sales Range: $250-299.9 Million
Emp.: 2,500
Acute Care Hospital
N.A.I.C.S.: 622110
Donald J. Wiley *(Pres & CEO)*
Arline DeLaCruz *(Supvr-Mobile Health Pro-
grams)*
Scott Neeley *(VP-Medical Affairs)*

**St. Mary Catholic Housing
Corporation** (2)
1120 Atlantic Ave, Long Beach, CA 90813
Tel.: (562) 435-0614
Community Housing Services
N.A.I.C.S.: 624229

St. Mary's Medical Center (2)
450 Stanyan St, San Francisco, CA 94117-
1079
Tel.: (415) 668-1000
Web Site:
http://www.stmarysmedicalcenter.org
Sales Range: $25-49.9 Million
Emp.: 150
N.A.I.C.S.: 622110
Alice Wong *(Dir-Health Info Mgmt)*
Barbara Brownell *(Dir-Case Mgmt & Utiliza-
tion Review)*
Mary Poppingo *(Mgr-Major Gifts & Planned
Giving)*

St. Rose Dominican Hospital (2)
102 E Lake Mead Pkwy, Henderson, NV
89015-5575
Tel.: (702) 564-2622
Web Site: http://www.dignity.com
Sales Range: $250-299.9 Million
Emp.: 3,000
Management of Healthcare Facilities
N.A.I.C.S.: 621112
Lawrence Barnard *(Pres/CEO-San Martin)*

**U.S. HealthWorks Medical Group,
Prof. Corp.** (2)
28035 Ave Stanford W, Valencia, CA 91355
Tel.: (661) 678-2300
Web Site: http://www.ushealthworks.com
Sales Range: $250-299.9 Million
Emp.: 2,700
Occupational Medicine & Urgent Care Cen-
ters Operator
N.A.I.C.S.: 621498
Joseph T. Mallas *(COO & Exec VP)*
Bernyce Peplowski *(Sr VP-Natl Medical
Policy & Innovation)*
Kevin Coyle *(Gen Counsel)*
Brian Arnds *(VP-HR)*
Diane Yu *(CMO & Chief Sls Officer)*
Mark Pucek *(Chief Medical Officer)*
Brooks F. Marshall *(VP-Bus Dev)*
Tom Hadley *(VP-Medical)*
Sherif Hanna *(Sr VP-Ops)*
Andy Parker *(Sr VP-Strategy)*

Woodland Healthcare (2)
1325 Cottonwood St, Woodland, CA 95695-
5131
Tel.: (530) 662-3961
Web Site:
http://www.woodlandhealthcare.org
Sales Range: $10-24.9 Million
Emp.: 100
Provider of General Surgical & Medical
Hospital Services
N.A.I.C.S.: 622110
Katy Trainer *(Coord-Recruitment & Com-
pensation)*
Justin Chatten-Brown *(Dir-Medical Emer-
gency Dept)*
Rajdeep Ranade *(Dir-Medical-Acute
Medical-Psychiatric Unit)*

Premier Health Partners (1)
110 N Main St, Dayton, OH 45402
Tel.: (937) 499-7364
Web Site:
http://www.premierhealthpartners.com
Emp.: 13,000
Hospital & Medical Facility Operator
N.A.I.C.S.: 622110
Thomas G. Breitenbach *(Pres & CEO)*
R. Daniel Sadlier *(Chm)*
Thomas M. Duncan *(CFO & VP)*

Subsidiary (Domestic):

Good Samaritan Hospital (2)

2222 Philadelphia Dr, Dayton, OH 45406
Tel.: (937) 278-2612
Web Site: http://www.goodsamdayton.com
Sales Range: $50-74.9 Million
Emp.: 350
Hospital
N.A.I.C.S.: 622110
Mark Shaker *(COO & Exec VP)*
Laura F. Sittler *(Chief Nursing Officer)*

Subsidiary (Domestic):

**Dayton Heart & Vascular
Hospital** (3)
2222 Philadelphia Dr, Dayton, OH 45406
Tel.: (937) 221-8000
Web Site:
http://www.daytonhearthospital.com
Sales Range: $50-74.9 Million
Emp.: 350
Provider of Cardiac Vascular Services
N.A.I.C.S.: 622110
Mary Garman *(COO)*

Subsidiary (Domestic):

**Lifestages, Samaritan Centers for
Women, Ltd.** (2)
2200 Philadelphia Dr Ste 101, Dayton, OH
45406-1891
Tel.: (937) 277-8988
Web Site: http://www.lifestagescenters.com
Women's Specialty Health Care Services
N.A.I.C.S.: 621111
Lloyd William Rettig III *(Pres)*

TriHealth Inc. (1)
619 Oak St, Cincinnati, OH 45206-1613
Tel.: (513) 569-5400
Web Site: http://www.trihealth.com
Sales Range: $150-199.9 Million
Emp.: 1,547
Operator of Hospitals & Healthcare Facili-
ties
N.A.I.C.S.: 622110
Ralph S. Michael III *(Vice Chm & Treas)*
Robert Collins *(Chief Medical Officer & Sr
VP-Quality)*
Mark Clement *(Pres & CEO)*
John Ward *(CIO & Sr VP)*
Michael R. Holbert *(Dir-Obstetrics & Gyne-
cology Residency Program)*
Gail Donovan *(COO)*
Andrew DeVoe *(CFO & Asst Treas)*
Kelley Ealy *(Chief Info Security Officer)*
Sally Duffy *(Sec)*
David Cook *(Chief HR Officer & Sr VP)*
Jennifer Skinner *(Sr VP)*
Kevin Joseph *(Chief Medical Officer & Sr
VP-Quality)*
Steve Gracey *(Officer-Compliance, Gen
Counsel & Sr VP)*

Subsidiary (Domestic):

Bethesda Healthcare Inc. (2)
619 Oak St, Cincinnati, OH 45206-1613
Tel.: (513) 569-6111
Web Site: http://www.trihealth.com
Offices & Clinics of Medical Doctors
N.A.I.C.S.: 622110
John Prout *(Pres & CEO)*

**Mccullough Hyde Memorial Hospital,
Inc.** (2)
110 N Poplar St, Oxford, OH
45056   **(100%)**
Tel.: (513) 523-2111
Web Site: http://www.mhmh.org
Sales Range: $50-74.9 Million
Emp.: 624
Health Care Srvices
N.A.I.C.S.: 622110
Richard Norman *(Chm)*
Alan D. Oak *(Treas)*
Dee Ellingwood *(Vice Chm)*
Brett Kirkpatrick *(Exec Dir-Hospital Ops)*
Michael Everett *(Pres & CEO)*

**CATHOLIC HEALTH SERVICES
OF LONG ISLAND**
992 N Village Ave, Rockville Centre,
NY 11570
Tel.: (516) 705-3700
Web Site: http://www.chsli.org
Year Founded: 1997
Emp.: 18,400
Heatcare Svcs

N.A.I.C.S.: 923120
Brian R. McGuire *(Vice Chm)*
Jerome M. Poller *(Sec)*
Christopher Pascucci *(Treas)*
Alan D. Guerci *(Pres & CEO)*
Dennis Verzi *(COO & Exec VP)*
Daniel DeBarba *(CFO & Exec VP)*
David DeCerbo *(Gen Counsel & Exec VP)*
Patrick M. O'Shaughnessy *(Chief Clinical Officer & Exec VP)*
Anthony Pellicano *(Chief HR Officer & Sr VP-HR)*
James Spencer *(Sr VP-Mission & Ministry)*
Salvatore F. Sodano *(Chm)*

Subsidiaries:

Catholic Home Care   **(1)**
110 Bi-County Blvd Ste 114, Farmingdale, NY 11735
Tel.: (631) 465-6830
Women Healthcare Services
N.A.I.C.S.: 621610
Thomas E. Christman *(Chm)*
Jennifer Hoffman *(Vice Chm)*
John O'Brien *(Treas)*
Michael Lambert *(Sec)*
Mary Ellen Polit *(Chief Admin Officer)*
Gail Silver *(COO & Sr VP)*
Kerrianne Page *(Chief Medical Officer)*
Danielle Desser *(VP-Fin)*
Mary Frawley *(Dir-Patient Svcs)*
Igor Nemov *(Dir-Performance Improvement & Clinical Education)*
Janice Remmers *(Dir-Patient Accts)*
Marguerite Whelan *(Dir-Clinical Infomatics & Education)*
Cathie Ciresi *(Dir-Bus Ops)*
Lisa Vecchione *(Dir-Bus Dev)*
Barbara Rowe *(Dir-Specialty Svcs)*

Good Samaritan Hospital Medical Center   **(1)**
1000 Montauk Hwy, West Islip, NY 11795
Tel.: (631) 376-3000
Web Site:
   http://www.goodsamaritan.chsli.org
Emp.: 3,774
Health Care Srvices
N.A.I.C.S.: 622110
Thomas Ockers *(Chief Admin Officer & Exec VP)*
Vincent Angeloro *(VP-Quality Mgmt & Accreditation)*
Richard Bie *(VP-Plant Engrg)*
Ralph Corbino *(VP-Imaging, Cancer & Cardiology Svcs)*
Gail Donheiser *(Officer-Patient & VP-Risk Mgmt)*
Gara Edelstein *(Chief Nursing Officer & VP-Patient Svcs)*
Gino Giorgini *(Dir-Medical-Care, Utilization Mgmt & Hospitalist Program)*
Jay Itzkowitz *(Assistant Chief Medical Officer)*
Joseph Loiacono *(Sr VP-Bus Dev & Plng)*
John McMurray *(COO)*
Lori Spina *(VP-HR)*
Christine Stehlik *(Asst VP-Fin)*
Donald Teplitz *(Chief Medical Officer & Sr VP-Medical Affairs)*
Stephen Trapani *(Sr VP-Fin)*

Good Samaritan Nursing Home, Inc.   **(1)**
101 Elm St, Sayville, NY 11782
Tel.: (631) 244-2400
Web Site:
   http://www.goodsamaritanhome.org
Nursing Care Facilities
N.A.I.C.S.: 623110
Alan D. Guerci *(Pres & CEO)*

Good Shepherd Hospice   **(1)**
110 Bi-County Blvd Ste 114, Farmingdale, NY 11735
Tel.: (631) 465-6300
Web Site:
   http://www.goodshepherdhospice.org
Health Care Srvices
N.A.I.C.S.: 622110
Mary Ellen Polit *(Chief Admin Officer)*
Gail Silver *(COO & Sr VP)*
Kerrianne Page *(Chief Medical Officer)*
Barbara Rowe *(Dir-Specialty Svcs)*

Mindy Poretsky *(Dir-Patient Svcs)*
Roger Sullivan *(Dir-Psychosocial & Supportive Care)*
Lisa Vecchione *(Dir-Bus Dev)*
Ellen Judson *(Dir-Performance Improvement)*
Maribeth McKeever *(Dir-Bereavement Svcs)*

Maryhaven Center of Hope   **(1)**
51 Terryville Rd, Port Jefferson Station, NY 11776
Tel.: (631) 474-4120
Web Site: http://www.maryhaven.chsli.org
Needy People Support Services
N.A.I.C.S.: 624190
Lewis Grossman *(CEO)*

Mercy Medical Center   **(1)**
1000 N Village Ave, Rockville Centre, NY 11570
Tel.: (516) 705-2525
Web Site:
   http://www.mercymedicalcenter.chsli.org
Emp.: 1,500
Health Care Srvices
N.A.I.C.S.: 622110
Peter Scaminaci *(Chief Admin Officer & Exec VP)*
Janine Rocco *(VP-Fin)*
Beth Vlahavas *(Chief Nursing Officer & VP-Patient Care Svcs)*
Shan Ahmed *(Chief Medical Officer & VP-Medical Affairs)*
Catherine Magone *(VP-Organization-Wide Performance Improvement)*
Joseph Libertelli *(VP-HR)*
Deborah Bitsoli *(Pres)*
Paul Mancinone *(Chm)*

Our Lady of Consolation Nursing & Rehabilitative Care Center   **(1)**
111 Beach Dr, West Islip, NY 11795
Tel.: (631) 587-1600
Web Site: http://www.olc.chsli.org
Nursing & Rehabilitation Services
N.A.I.C.S.: 624120
James Ryan *(Chief Admin Officer)*
John Haight *(VP-Fin)*
Robert Carlin *(Dir-Medical)*
Theresa Rosenthal *(VP-Clinical Svcs)*
Christine Smith *(Dir-HR)*
Cathy Argeroplos *(Dir-Admissions)*
John Dominici *(Dir-Culinary Svcs)*
Chris Cardinal *(Dir-Performance Improvement)*
Pegeen Kelly *(Dir-Patient & Community Rels)*
Christopher Lohan *(Dir-Rehabilitation Svcs)*
Eleanor Marien *(Dir-Staff Dev)*
Margaret Nixdorf *(Dir-Pastoral Care)*
Dorothy Scholz *(Dir-Health Information Mgmt)*
Yolanda Tricoche *(Dir-Environmental Svcs)*
Sal Sodano *(Chm)*
Brian McGuire *(Vice Chm)*
Joseph Tantillo *(Sec)*

St. Catherine of Siena Medical Center   **(1)**
50 NY-25A, Smithtown, NY 11787
Tel.: (631) 862-3000
Web Site: http://www.stcatherines.chsli.org
Health Care Srvices
N.A.I.C.S.: 622110
James O'Connor *(Chief Admin Officer & Exec VP)*
Mickel Khlat *(Chief Medical Officer)*
Mary Jane Finnegan *(Chief Nursing Officer)*
John Pohlman *(COO)*
Michelle Goldfarb *(Officer-Administrative & VP-Quality, Patient Safety & Regulatory)*
Giovanni V. Distefano *(Asst VP-Professional Svcs)*
Onorina Saporito *(Dir-HR)*
Heather Reynolds *(Dir-Public, External Affairs & Volunteer Svcs)*

St. Catherine of Siena Nursing & Rehabilitation Care Center   **(1)**
52 NY-25A, Smithtown, NY 11787
Tel.: (862) 862-3900
Web Site:
   http://www.stcatherinenursingrehab.org
Nursing & Rehabilitation Services
N.A.I.C.S.: 624120
Alan D. Guerci *(Pres & CEO)*

St. Charles Hospital   **(1)**
200 Belle Terre Rd, Port Jefferson, NY 11777

Tel.: (631) 474-6000
Web Site:
   http://www.stcharleshospital.chsli.org
Emp.: 1,772
Health Care Srvices
N.A.I.C.S.: 622110
James O'Connor *(Chief Admin Officer & Exec VP)*
Ronald Weingartner *(COO)*
Dante Latorre *(Chief Privacy Officer, Chief Security Officer & VP-Quality)*
Kathleen Vasi *(CFO)*
Sunil Dhuper *(Chief Medical Officer)*
Nicolette Fiore-Lopez *(Chief Nursing Officer)*
Laura Beck *(VP-Rehabilitation)*
Maureen Morris *(VP-HR)*
Karen Fielder *(Dir-Risk Mgmt)*
Marilyn Fabbricante *(Exec Dir-Pub & External Affairs)*

St. Francis Hospital   **(1)**
100 Port Washington Blvd, Roslyn, NY 11576
Tel.: (516) 562-6000
Web Site:
   http://www.stfrancisheartcenter.chsli.org
Health Care Srvices
N.A.I.C.S.: 622110
Paul K. Barry *(VP-Pub Affairs & Mktg)*
James Proce *(VP-Admin)*
Charles L. Lucore *(Pres)*
Richard A. Shlofmitz *(Chm-Cardiology)*
David J. Cohen *(Dir-Academic Affairs)*

St. Joseph Hospital   **(1)**
4295 Hempstead Tpke, Bethpage, NY 11714
Tel.: (516) 579-6000
Web Site:
   http://www.stjosephhospital.chsli.org
Emp.: 819
Health Care Srvices
N.A.I.C.S.: 622110
Peter Scaminaci *(Chief Admin Officer & Exec VP)*
Howard Sussman *Chief Medical Officer (Chief Medical Officer)*
Barbara Gibbons *(VP-Patient Care)*
Ihab Ibrahim *(VP-Patient Safety & Clinical Program Dev)*
John Morahan *(VP-Fin)*
Peter Chiacchiaro *(VP-HR)*
Barbara Smith *(Asst VP-Performance Improvement & Risk Mgmt)*
Christine Ophals *(Asst VP-Outpatient Svcs)*
Christine Codey *(Asst VP-Health Information & Reporting)*

CATHOLIC HEALTH SYSTEM, INC.

144 Genesee St, Buffalo, NY 14214
Tel.: (716) 862-2400   NY
Web Site: http://www.chsbuffalo.org
Year Founded: 1998
Sales Range: $800-899.9 Million
Emp.: 8,200
Non-Profit Healthcare Services Organization
N.A.I.C.S.: 813920
Michael F. Galang *(CIO)*
James Millard *(Pres/CEO-Kenmore Mercy Hospital)*
James Dunlop *(CFO & Exec VP)*
Mark A. Sullivan *(Pres & CEO)*
Maria Foti *(Chief Strategy Officer & Sr VP)*
Joyce Markiewicz *(Exec VP)*
Michael Moley *(Chief HR Officer)*
Bartholomew Rodrigues *(Chief Mission Officer & Sr VP)*
Nancy Sheehan *(Chief Legal Officer & Sr VP)*
Roger Walcott *(Specialist-Vascular Surgery)*
John Kane *(Sr VP-Quality & Patient Safety)*
Laura Cianflone *(VP-HR Svcs)*
James M. Garvey *(COO & Exec VP)*
William K. Buscaglia Jr. *(Chm)*

Subsidiaries:

Catholic Medical Partners - Accountable Care IPA, Inc.   **(1)**

1083 Delaware Ave, Buffalo, NY 14209
Tel.: (716) 862-2161
Web Site:
   http://www.catholicmedicalpartners.org
Healthcare Services Professional Organization
N.A.I.C.S.: 813920
Michael Edbauer *(Chief Medical Officer)*
Dennis Horrigan *(Pres & CEO)*
Kristin Cortese *(Coord-Clinical Transformation)*
Desiree Corrao *(Mgr-Care Mgmt)*
Dapeng Cao *(Mgr-Healthcare Analytics)*
Paula Conti *(Dir-Clinical Transformation)*
Sarah Cotter *(VP-Clinical Transformation)*
Barry Stelmach *(CFO)*
Lisa Hoffman *(Chm)*
David Martinke *(Chief Medical Officer)*
James Rycyna *(Chm)*
David Serra *(Assoc Dir-Medical)*
James Dunlop Jr. *(Treas)*

Kenmore Mercy Hospital   **(1)**
2950 Elmwood Ave, Kenmore, NY 14217
Tel.: (716) 447-6100
Web Site: http://www.chsbuffalo.org
General Hospital Operator
N.A.I.C.S.: 622110
Walter Ludwig *(Pres & CEO)*
James Fitzpatrick *(VP-Medical Affairs)*
Laura Verbanic *(Dir-Quality & Patient Safety)*
Dawn Cwierley *(Mgr-PR)*
Anne Hedges-Creighton *(Dir-Nursing-Perioperative Svcs)*
Jennifer Jacobs *(Dir-HR)*
Susan Jandzinski *(Exec Dir-Kenmore Mercy Hospital Foundation)*
Heather Telford *(Dir-Nursing Critical Care & Emergency Svcs)*
William Vaughan *(VP-Mission Integration)*

Mercy Hospital of Buffalo   **(1)**
565 Abbott Rd, Buffalo, NY 14220
Tel.: (716) 826-7000
Web Site: http://www.chsbuffalo.org
General Hospital Operator
N.A.I.C.S.: 622110
Charles J. Urlaub *(Pres & CEO)*
Timothy Gabryel *(VP-Medical Affairs)*
Kathleen Guarino *(Chief Nursing Officer & VP-Nursing)*
Eddie Bratko *(COO)*
John Kalinowski *(VP-Mission Integration)*
Kathy M. Swenson *(Exec Dir)*
Nancy Stoll *(Dir-Neuroscience Clinical Svcs)*
Joseph A. Scrivo Jr. *(Dir-HR)*

Sisters of Charity Hospital of Buffalo, New York   **(1)**
2157 Main St, Buffalo, NY 14214
Tel.: (716) 862-1000
Web Site: http://www.chsbuffalo.org
General Hospital Operator
N.A.I.C.S.: 622110
Nady Shehata *(VP-Medical Affairs)*
Mary Dillon *(VP-Patient Care Svcs)*
Paula Moscato *(VP-Mission Integration)*
David DeLorenzo *(Sr Dir-HR)*
John Sperrazza *(COO)*

Division (Domestic):

Sisters of Charity Hospital - St. Joseph Campus   **(2)**
2605 Harlem Rd, Cheektowaga, NY 14225
Tel.: (716) 891-2400
Web Site: http://www.chsbuffalo.org
General Hospital Operator
N.A.I.C.S.: 622110
Peter U. Bergmann *(Pres & CEO)*
Martin Boryszak *(COO)*
David DeLorenzo *(Sr Dir-HR)*
Mary Dillon *(VP-Patient Care Svcs)*
Paula Moscato *(VP-Mission Integration)*

CATHOLIC HEALTHCARE PARTNERS

1701 Mercy Health Pl, Cincinnati, OH 45237
Tel.: (513) 639-2800
Sales Range: $1-4.9 Billion
Emp.: 33,000
Acute Care Hospitals, Long-Term Care Facilities, Nursing Facilities, Home Healthcare, Hospices & Wellness Centers Operator

Catholic Healthcare Partners—(Continued)
N.A.I.C.S.: 622110
Michael A. Bezney *(Sr VP & Gen Counsel)*
R. Jeffrey Copeland *(Sr VP-Insurance & Physician Svcs)*
Jane Durney Crowley *(Exec VP-Clinical Integration & Bus Dev)*
Joseph Gage *(Sr VP-HR)*
Doris Gottemoeller *(Sr VP-Mission & Values Integration)*
Stephen R. Grossbart *(Sr VP & Chief Quality Officer)*
Brian Smith *(Exec VP-Networks)*
Rebecca Sykes *(Sr VP-Resource Mgmt & CIO)*
James R. Gravell Jr. *(Sr VP & CFO)*

Subsidiaries:

HealthSpan, Inc.　　　　　　　(1)
225 Pictoria Dr Ste 320, Cincinnati, OH 45246
Tel.: (513) 551-1400
Web Site: http://www.healthspan.org
Sales Range: $350-399.9 Million
Emp.: 1,600
HMO
N.A.I.C.S.: 524114
Kenneth C. Page *(Pres & CEO)*
Barb Eisenhard *(VP-Ops)*
Tim Pethick *(CEO-Guernsey)*

Humility House　　　　　　　　(1)
755 Ohltown Rd, Youngstown, OH 44515
Tel.: (330) 549-0740
Sales Range: $1-9.9 Million
Emp.: 100
Nursing & Personal Care Facilities
N.A.I.C.S.: 623110

Lifestar Ambulance, Inc.　　　(1)
1402 Lagrange St, Toledo, OH 43608
Tel.: (419) 245-6210
Sales Range: $1-9.9 Million
Emp.: 200
Ambulance Service
N.A.I.C.S.: 621910
William Sutton *(Pres)*

Mercy College of Ohio　　　　(1)
2221 Madison Ave, Toledo, OH 43604
Tel.: (419) 251-1313
Web Site: http://www.mercycollege.edu
Sales Range: $10-24.9 Million
Emp.: 40
Vocational School
N.A.I.C.S.: 611519
Lori Edgeworth *(VP-Strategic Plng & Enrollment Mgmt)*
Nancy Merkle *(Vice Chm)*
Steven Sondergaard *(Chm)*
Timothy Croak *(Treas)*
Kathryn Bubrig *(Officer-Comm)*
Jessica Coombs *(Officer-Admissions)*
Hannah Firsdon *(Officer-Admissions)*
Andrea Fleming *(CFO)*
Lisa Rockwell *(Officer-Financial Aid)*
Gina Schultz *(Officer-Admissions)*
Andrea Schuster *(Officer-Admissions)*

The Assumption Village　　　　(1)
9800 Market St, North Lima, OH 44452
Tel.: (330) 549-0740
Sales Range: $1-9.9 Million
Emp.: 200
Nursing Care Facilities
N.A.I.C.S.: 623110

West Central Ohio Group, Ltd.　(1)
801 Medical Dr Ste B, Lima, OH 45804
Tel.: (419) 224-7586
Sales Range: $10-24.9 Million
Emp.: 75
Medical Devices
N.A.I.C.S.: 621111

CATHOLIC HEALTHCARE SYSTEM
205 Lexington Ave 3rd Fl, New York, NY 10016
Tel.: (646) 633-4700　　　　NY
Web Site: http://www.ArchCare.org
Year Founded: 1955

CATHOLIC HOLY FAMILY SOCIETY
2021 Mascoutah Ave, Belleville, IL 62222
Tel.: (800) 240-2554　　　　IL
Web Site: http://www.chfsociety.org
Year Founded: 1914
Sales Range: $10-24.9 Million
Community Action Services
N.A.I.C.S.: 624190
Mary Lou Golf *(First VP)*
Jean Konrad *(Treas)*
Robert Kochevar *(Sec-Recording)*
Sandy Bouchard *(Sec)*
Jackie Sobania-Robison *(Chm & Pres)*
Daniel J. Wenzler Sr. *(CEO)*

CATHOLIC LIFE INSURANCE
1635 NE Loop 410, San Antonio, TX 78209-1616
Tel.: (210) 828-9921　　　　TX
Web Site: https://www.cliu.com
Year Founded: 1901
Sales Range: $50-74.9 Million
Emp.: 70
Life Insurance
N.A.I.C.S.: 524113
Jay Michael Belz *(Pres & CEO)*
Barbara Cheaney *(VP-Mktg Comm)*
Frank Gentile *(VP)*
Scott Brant *(VP-IT)*
Colleen Berger *(VP & Controller)*
Dawn Fanfelle *(Asst VP)*
Tommy Hoelscher *(Chm)*
Doris Short *(Sec)*
Kristy Winkler *(Asst VP-Acctg)*
Susan M. Skrzycki *(Asst VP-Ops)*
Patricia G. Gutierrez *(Co-Sec & VP-Ops)*

CATHOLIC MEDICAL CENTER
100 McGregor St, Manchester, NH 03102-3730
Tel.: (603) 668-3545　　　　NH
Web Site:
　https://www.catholicmedical
　center.org
Year Founded: 1993
Sales Range: $150-199.9 Million
Emp.: 1,300
General Medical & Surgical Hospitals
N.A.I.C.S.: 622110
Edward Dudley *(CFO)*
William Goodman *(Dir-Medical)*
Lauren Collins-Cline *(Dir-Comm & PR)*
Tina Legere *(Sr VP-Ops)*
Alex Walker *(Pres & CEO)*
Jason Cole *(VP)*
Jessica Arvanitis *(Exec Dir-Corp Compliance & Deputy Gen Counsel)*
Jennifer Higgins Pitre *(VP-Dev)*
John Cronin *(Chm)*

CATHOLIC MUTUAL GROUP
10843 Old Mill Rd, Omaha, NE 68154-2600
Tel.: (402) 551-8765
Web Site:
　https://www.catholicmutual.org
Sales Range: $25-49.9 Million
Emp.: 140
Liability Insurance
N.A.I.C.S.: 524126
Greg Standish *(Mgr-Mktg)*
Debbie Olsen *(Mgr-Fin)*

CATHOLIC ORDER OF FORESTERS
355 Shuman Blvd, Naperville, IL 60563-1270
Tel.: (630) 983-4900　　　　IL
Web Site:
　https://www.catholicforester.org
Year Founded: 1883
Sales Range: $150-199.9 Million
Emp.: 100
Life, Health & Accident Insurance
N.A.I.C.S.: 524113
David E. Huber *(Pres)*
Larry Mills *(Asst VP & Mgr-IT)*
Ann Baker *(VP-Acctg)*
Tom Adamson *(VP-Sls)*

CATHOLIC RESIDENTIAL SERVICES, INC.
3710 East Ave S, La Crosse, WI 54601
Tel.: (608) 784-5323　　　　WI
Web Site: http://www.crsinc.org
Sales Range: $10-24.9 Million
Emp.: 394
Elder Care Services
N.A.I.C.S.: 624120
Jim Gajewski *(Exec Dir)*

CATHOLIC SENIOR HOUSING & HEALTHCARE SERVICES, INC.
1200 Spring St, Bethlehem, PA 18018
Tel.: (610) 865-6245　　　　PA
Web Site: http://www.cshhcs.org
Year Founded: 1962
Sales Range: $10-24.9 Million
Emp.: 533
Elder Care Services
N.A.I.C.S.: 624120
Robin Nefak *(Dir-HR)*
Ann Ruggiero *(Dir-Dev)*
James Galle *(Dir-Mktg)*
James Fronheiser *(VP)*
Jared Markowitz *(Treas)*
John J. Martin *(Pres)*
Michael Melnic *(CFO & Treas)*
Pam Russo *(Sec)*

CATHOLIC SOCIAL SERVICES
222 N 17th St 3rd Fl, Philadelphia, PA 19103-1299
Tel.: (215) 587-3614　　　　PA
Web Site:
　http://www.catholicsocialservice.org
Year Founded: 1955
Sales Range: $10-24.9 Million
Emp.: 660
Individual & Family Support Services
N.A.I.C.S.: 624190
Gary Miller *(CFO)*

CATHOLIC UNITED FINANCIAL
3499 Lexington Ave N, Saint Paul, MN 55126
Tel.: (651) 490-0170　　　　MN
Web Site:
　https://www.catholicunited.org
Year Founded: 1878
Sales Range: $75-99.9 Million
Fraternal Life Insurance Services
N.A.I.C.S.: 524113
Harald Borrmann *(Chm & Pres)*
Michael Ahles *(Treas, Sec & Sr VP)*
Nate Lamusga *(Dir-Member Engagement)*

CATIE'S CLOSET
19 School St, Dracut, MA 01826
Tel.: (978) 957-2200　　　　MA
Web Site:
　https://www.catiescloset.org
Year Founded: 2010
Sales Range: Less than $1 Million
Emp.: 10
Anti-Poverty Advocacy Services
N.A.I.C.S.: 813319

Denise Trombly *(Co-Founder)*
Mickey Cockrell *(Exec Dir)*

CATO INSTITUTE
1000 Massachusetts Ave NW, Washington, DC 20001-5403
Tel.: (202) 842-0200　　　　KS
Web Site: https://www.cato.org
Year Founded: 1977
Sales Range: $25-49.9 Million
Emp.: 200
Community Action Services
N.A.I.C.S.: 813319
Claudia Ringel *(Mgr-Editorial Svcs)*
Virginia Anderson *(CIO)*
Gene Healy *(VP)*
John Samples *(VP)*

CATS CO.
2100 W Big Beaver Rd, Troy, MI 48084
Tel.: (248) 816-2287
Web Site:
　http://www.catscompany.com
Year Founded: 1980
Sales Range: $10-24.9 Million
Emp.: 30
Computers, Peripherals & Software
N.A.I.C.S.: 423430
Jacques K. Haddad *(Pres)*

CATSEYE PEST CONTROL, INC.
31 Commercial Dr, Castleton on Hudson, NY 12033
Tel.: (518) 869-5042
Web Site:
　http://www.catseyepest.com
Sales Range: $1-9.9 Million
Emp.: 62
Exterminating & Pest Control Services
N.A.I.C.S.: 561710
John Gagne *(Pres)*

CATSKILL REGIONAL MEDICAL CENTER
68 Harris Bushville Rd, Harris, NY 12742-0800
Tel.: (845) 794-3300　　　　NY
Web Site: http://www.crmcny.org
Year Founded: 1967
Sales Range: $100-124.9 Million
Medical Care Services
N.A.I.C.S.: 622110
Joanne Huber-Sturans *(Chief HR Officer)*
Scott Batulis *(Pres)*
Joe Anesi *(VP)*
Rosemary Baczewski *(VP-Quality & Health Info Mgmt)*
Rolland Bojo *(Chief Nursing Officer & VP-Patient Care Svcs)*
Jonathan Schiller *(CEO)*

CATTARAUGUS REHABILITATION CENTER, INC.
1439 Buffalo St, Olean, NY 14760
Tel.: (716) 375-4747　　　　NY
Web Site:
　https://www.rehabcenter.org
Year Founded: 1976
Sales Range: $10-24.9 Million
Emp.: 500
Disability Assistance Services
N.A.I.C.S.: 624120
Libby Smith *(Chm)*
Mary Howard *(CEO)*

CATTERTON MANAGEMENT COMPANY, LLC
599 W Putnam Ave, Greenwich, CT 06830
Tel.: (203) 629-4901　　　　DE
Web Site: http://www.lcatterton.com
Year Founded: 1989

Privater Equity Firm
N.A.I.C.S.: 523999
J. Michael Chu *(Co-CEO)*
David Heidecorn *(Partner)*
Jonathan H. Owsley *(Mng Partner-Growth Fund)*
Andrew C. Taub *(Mng Partner-Buyout Fund)*
Caroline Bartlett *(VP-Fin & Ops)*
Marc-David Bismuth *(Operating Partner)*
Howard Steyn *(Partner-Global Opportunities)*
Nikhil Thukral *(Mng Partner)*
David McPherson *(Chief Legal Officer)*
Ravinder Singh Thakran *(Mng Partner & Chm-Asia)*
Sebastien Katch *(Operating Partner)*
Andrea Ottaviano *(Mng Partner-Europe)*
Alain Hortion *(CFO-Real Estate & Partner)*
Jill Ramirez *(Chief Acctg Officer & Controller)*
Dan Reid *(Chief Compliance Officer & Gen Counsel)*
David Gester *(Chief Dev Officer-Real Estate & Partner)*
Alexandre Heriard-Dubreuil *(Chief Investment Officer-Real Estate & Partner)*
Tom Steinthal *(CIO)*
Mathieu Le Bozec *(Founder & Mng Partner)*
Karen Gordon *(Mng Partner-Portfolio Ops)*
Avik Pramanik *(Partner)*
Chris Roberts *(Partner)*
Matt Leeds *(Partner)*
Cara Hoy *(VP)*
Jason Levine *(VP & Head-Bus Dev)*
Matt Lischick *(Principal)*
Ravi Thakran *(Mng Partner & Chm-Asia)*
Robert S. Hull *(COO & CFO)*
Scott Arnold Dahnke *(Co-CEO)*
Michael J. Farello *(Mng Partner-Growth Fund)*
Marc Magliacano *(Mng Partner)*
Adam Hasiba *(VP)*

Subsidiaries:

Del Frisco's Restaurant Group, Inc.   (1)
2900 Ranch Trail, Irving, TX 75063
Tel.: (469) 913-1845
Web Site: http://www.dfrg.com
Sales Range: $350-399.9 Million
Restaurant Owner & Operator
N.A.I.C.S.: 722511
James W. Kirkpatrick *(VP-Real Estate)*
Lisa H. Kislak *(VP-Brand Mktg)*
Lisa H. Kislak *(VP-Brand Mktg)*
Thomas G. Dritsas *(VP-Culinary)*
Norman J. Abdallah *(CEO)*
Ray Risley *(Sr VP-Ops)*
Robert J. Stetson *(Founder)*
Richie Furino *(Reg VP)*
Lane DeYoung *(Gen Counsel)*
William S. Martens III *(VP-Dev & Construction)*
Ian R. Carter *(Chm)*
Ian R. Carter *(Chm)*

Subsidiary (Domestic):

California Sullivan's, Inc.   (2)
73-505 El Paseo Ste 2600, Palm Desert, CA 92260
Tel.: (760) 341-3560
Web Site:
  http://www.sullivanssteakhouse.com
Restaurant Operating Services
N.A.I.C.S.: 722511
Jacob Higgins *(Gen Mgr)*

Center Cut Hospitality, Inc.   (2)
920 S Kimball Ave Ste 100, Southlake, TX 76092-9021
Tel.: (817) 601-3421

Web Site: http://www.dfrg.com
Emp.: 60
Restaurant Operating Services
N.A.I.C.S.: 722511

Del Frisco's - Dallas, L.P.   (2)
2323 Olive St, Dallas, TX 75201
Tel.: (972) 490-9000
Web Site: http://www.delfriscos.com
Sales Range: $10-24.9 Million
Emp.: 100
Restaurant Operating Services
N.A.I.C.S.: 722511

Del Frisco's - Fort Worth, L.P.   (2)
812 Main St, Fort Worth, TX 76102
Tel.: (817) 877-3999
Web Site: http://www.delfriscos.com
Emp.: 100
Restaurant Operating Services
N.A.I.C.S.: 722511
Greg Kalina *(Gen Mgr)*
Misty Horner *(Coord-Private Party)*

Del Frisco's Grille of Atlanta, LLC   (2)
3376 Peachtree Rd NE, Atlanta, GA 30326
Tel.: (404) 537-2828
Web Site: http://www.delfriscosgrille.com
Restaurant Operating Services
N.A.I.C.S.: 722511
Kenny Perlman *(Reg Mgr)*
Sarah McAloon *(Pres-Brand)*

Del Frisco's Grille of New York, LLC   (2)
50 Rockefeller Plz, New York, NY 10020
Tel.: (212) 767-0371
Web Site: http://www.delfriscosgrille.com
Emp.: 100
Restaurant Operating Services
N.A.I.C.S.: 722511
Matt Triveri *(Gen Mgr)*

Del Frisco's Grille of Phoenix, LLC   (2)
2425 E Camelback Rd Ste 110, Phoenix, AZ 85016
Tel.: (602) 466-2890
Web Site: http://delfriscosgrille.com
Restaurant Operating Services
N.A.I.C.S.: 722511

Del Frisco's Grille of Washington DC, LLC   (2)
1201 Pennsylvania Ave NW, Washington, DC 20004
Tel.: (202) 450-4686
Web Site: http://www.delfriscosgrille.com
Emp.: 40
Restaurant Operating Services
N.A.I.C.S.: 722511

Del Frisco's of Boston, LLC   (2)
250 Northern Ave, Boston, MA 02210
Tel.: (617) 951-1368
Web Site: http://www.delfriscos.com
Restaurant Operating Services
N.A.I.C.S.: 722511
Courtney Kershaw *(Coord-Private Party)*

Del Frisco's of Chicago, LLC   (2)
58 E Oak St, Chicago, IL 60611
Tel.: (312) 888-2499
Web Site: http://delfriscos.com
Restaurant Operating Services
N.A.I.C.S.: 722511

Del Frisco's of Colorado, Inc.   (2)
8100 E Orchard Rd, Greenwood Village, CO 80111
Tel.: (303) 796-0100
Web Site: http://www.delfriscos.com
Emp.: 50
Restaurant Operating Services
N.A.I.C.S.: 722511
Amanda Springmeier *(Gen Mgr)*

Del Frisco's of Nevada, Inc.   (2)
3925 Paradise Rd, Las Vegas, NV 89169-4607
Tel.: (702) 796-0063
Web Site: http://www.delfriscos.com
Sales Range: $25-49.9 Million
Emp.: 200
Restaurant Operating Services
N.A.I.C.S.: 722511

Del Frisco's of New York, LLC   (2)
1221 Avenue of the Americas, New York, NY 10020

Tel.: (212) 575-5129
Web Site: http://www.delfriscos.com
Emp.: 65
Restaurant Operating Services
N.A.I.C.S.: 722511
Christina Migliorelli *(Coord-Private Party)*
Orlando Santana *(Gen Mgr)*

Del Frisco's of North Carolina, Inc.   (2)
4725 Piedmont Row Dr Ste 170, Charlotte, NC 28210
Tel.: (704) 552-5502
Web Site: http://delfriscos.com
Restaurant Operating Services
N.A.I.C.S.: 722511

Del Frisco's of Philadelphia, Inc.   (2)
1426-28 Chestnut St, Philadelphia, PA 19102
Tel.: (215) 246-0533
Web Site: http://www.delfriscos.com
Restaurant Operating Services
N.A.I.C.S.: 722511
Rich Furino *(Reg Mgr)*
Jessica Kiefer *(Coord-Private Party)*

Sullivan's - Austin, L.P.   (2)
300 Clolrado St Ste 200, Austin, TX 78701
Tel.: (512) 495-6504
Web Site:
  http://www.sullivanssteakhouse.com
Emp.: 100
Restaurant Operating Services
N.A.I.C.S.: 722511

Sullivan's Restaurants of Nebraska, Inc.   (2)
222 S 15th St Ste 100, Omaha, NE 68102
Tel.: (402) 342-0077
Web Site:
  http://www.sullivanssteakhouse.com
Restaurant Operating Services
N.A.I.C.S.: 722511

Sullivan's of Arizona, Inc.   (2)
1785 E River Rd, Tucson, AZ 85718
Tel.: (520) 299-4275
Web Site:
  http://www.sullivanssteakhouse.com
Sales Range: $10-24.9 Million
Emp.: 50
Restaurant Operating Services
N.A.I.C.S.: 722511

Sullivan's of Delaware, Inc.   (2)
5525 Concord Pike, Wilmington, DE 19803
Tel.: (302) 479-7970
Web Site:
  http://www.sullivanssteakhouse.com
Restaurant Operating Services
N.A.I.C.S.: 722511

Sullivan's of Illinois, Inc.   (2)
250 Marriott Dr, Lincolnshire, IL 60069
Tel.: (847) 883-0311
Web Site:
  http://www.sullivanssteakhouse.com
Restaurant Operating Services
N.A.I.C.S.: 722511

Sullivan's of Kansas, Inc.   (2)
4501 W 119th St, Leawood, KS 66209
Tel.: (913) 345-0800
Web Site:
  http://www.sullivanssteakhouse.com
Restaurant Operating Services
N.A.I.C.S.: 722511
Lisa Carl *(Gen Mgr)*

Sullivan's of North Carolina, Inc.   (2)
1928 S Blvd Ste 200, Charlotte, NC 28203
Tel.: (704) 335-8228
Web Site:
  http://www.sullivanssteakhouse.com
Restaurant Operating Services
N.A.I.C.S.: 722511

Sullivan's of Ohio, Inc.   (2)
141 N Fulton St, Wauseon, OH 43567
Tel.: (419) 335-0790
Web Site: http://www.sullivanswauseon.com
Restaurant Operating Services
N.A.I.C.S.: 722511

Sullivan's of Washington, LLC   (2)
621 Union St, Seattle, WA 98101
Tel.: (206) 494-4442
Web Site:
  http://www.sullivanssteakhouse.com
Restaurant Operating Services

N.A.I.C.S.: 722511

Hanna Andersson LLC   (1)
608 NE 19th Ave, Portland, OR 97232
Tel.: (503) 321-5277
Web Site: http://www.hannaandersson.com
Apparel & Accessories Mfr
N.A.I.C.S.: 458110
Louanne Wach *(Dir-Mktg)*
Joelle Maher *(Pres & CEO)*

Kodiak Cakes, LLC   (1)
8163 Gorgoza Pines Rd, Park City, UT 84098
Tel.: (801) 328-4067
Web Site: http://www.kodiakcakes.com
Sales Range: $100-124.9 Million
Emp.: 63
Food & Beverage Product Mfr
N.A.I.C.S.: 311412
Valerie Oswalt *(CEO)*
Joel Clark *(Co-Founder)*
Cameron Smith *(Pres)*

Len the Plumber, LLC   (1)
1552 Ridgely St, Baltimore, MD 21230
Tel.: (800) 950-4619
Web Site: https://lentheplumber.com
Plumbing & HVAC services
N.A.I.C.S.: 238220
Jeff Cooper *(CEO)*

Subsidiary (Domestic):

American Air & Heat, Inc.   (2)
502 S Econ Cir, Oviedo, FL 32765
Tel.: (407) 359-9501
Web Site:
  http://www.americanairandheat.net
Sales Range: $1-9.9 Million
Emp.: 35
Plumbing/Heating/Air Cond Contractor
N.A.I.C.S.: 238220
August L. Boni *(VP)*

Stan's Heating & Air Conditioning, Inc.   (2)
11700 Stnholw Dr Ste 100, Austin, TX 78758
Tel.: (512) 929-9393
Web Site: http://www.stansac.com
Sales Range: $1-9.9 Million
Emp.: 45
Plumbing, Heating & Air-Conditioning Contractors
N.A.I.C.S.: 238220
Stanley Johnson *(Pres)*
John Williams *(VP)*
Vienna Salazar *(Mgr-Pur)*

Noodles & Company   (1)
520 Zang St Ste D, Broomfield, CO 80021
Tel.: (720) 214-1900
Web Site: https://www.noodles.com
Rev.: $509,480,000
Assets: $343,843,000
Liabilities: $305,479,000
Net Worth: $38,364,000
Earnings: ($3,314,000)
Emp.: 600
Fiscal Year-end: 01/03/2023
Restaurant Operators
N.A.I.C.S.: 722511
Andrew H. Madsen *(CEO)*
Michael Hynes *(CFO)*
Brad West *(COO)*
Drew Madsen *(Interim CEO)*

PatientPoint Network solutions, LLC   (1)
5901 E Galbraith Rd Ste R1000, Cincinnati, OH 45236
Tel.: (888) 479-5600
Health Care Information Services
N.A.I.C.S.: 519290
Mike Collette *(CEO)*

Subsidiary (Domestic):

ContextMedia Health, LLC   (2)
330 N Wabash Ave Ste 2500, Chicago, IL 60611
Tel.: (800) 491-6972
Web Site: http://www.outcomehealth.com
Software Product Development Services
N.A.I.C.S.: 541511
Nandini Ramani *(COO)*
John Vaughan *(Gen Counsel & Chief Compliance Officer)*
Heidei Anderson *(Chief Growth Officer)*

Catterton Management Company, LLC—(Continued)

Daniel Dellacona (Chief HR Officer)
Rishi Shah (Co-Founder)
Shradha Agarwal (Co-Founder)

Subsidiary (Domestic):

ContextMedia, Inc. (3)
330 N Wabash Ave Ste 2500, Chicago, IL 60611
Tel.: (312) 239-6048
Software Product Development Services
N.A.I.C.S.: 541511
Matt McNally (CEO)

Subsidiary (Domestic):

Accenthealth LLC (4)
7844 Woodland Center Blvd, Tampa, FL 33614
Tel.: (813) 349-7100
Services Related to Advertising
N.A.I.C.S.: 541890

Steiner Leisure Limited (1)
770 S Dixie Hwy 2nd Fl, Coral Gables, FL 33146
Tel.: (305) 358-9002
Web Site: http://www.steinerleisure.com
Sales Range: $800-899.9 Million
Spa & Physical Fitness Facility Operator
N.A.I.C.S.: 713940
Sean C. Harrington (Pres-Elemis Limited)
Stephen B. Lazarus (CFO & COO)
Robert C. Boehm (Gen Counsel & Exec VP)
Glenn J. Fusfield (Pres/COO-The Onboard Spa)

Subsidiary (Domestic):

Ideal Image Development, Inc. (2)
1 N Dale Mabry Hwy Ste 1200, Tampa, FL 33609
Tel.: (813) 286-8100
Web Site: http://www.idealimage.com
Laser Hair Removal Services
N.A.I.C.S.: 812199
Scott Roan (CTO)
Christopher M. Barrett (COO)
Cheryl Hallinan (VP-Sls & Ops)
Scott LePage (Chief Consumer & Comml Officer)
Sharon Leite (CEO)

Subsidiary (Non-US):

Mandara Spa Asia Limited (2)
33-4 4th Floor Block H, Dataran Prima Jalan PJU 1/37, 47301, Petaling Jaya, Selangor Darul Ehsan, Malaysia
Tel.: (60) 378806588
Web Site: http://www.mandaraspa.com
Emp.: 100
Spa & Physical Fitness Center Operator
N.A.I.C.S.: 713940
Ranjit Kaur Gill (Dir-Fin)
Charlotte Tan (Sr Project Mgr)
Trent Munday (Sr VP-Intl)
Chaja Kersten (Mng Dir)

Subsidiary (Domestic):

Mandara Spa LLC (2)
c/o Steiner Management Services LLC 770 S Dixie Hwy 2nd Fl, Coral Gables, FL 33146
Tel.: (305) 358-9002
Web Site: http://www.mandaraspa.com
Spa & Physical Fitness Facility Operator
N.A.I.C.S.: 713940
Bruce Pine (Sr VP)
Jesus Padilla (VP-Fin-Land-Based Spas Div)
Darryll Leiman (VP-Ops-Pacific Reg)
Courtney Sullivan (Mgr-Sls & Revenue)
Paula Hodgson (VP-New Bus Dev)
Youlanda Deveaux (Reg VP-Bahamas, Caribbean & Latin America)

Steiner Education Group, Inc. (2)
2001 W Sample Rd Ste 100, Pompano Beach, FL 33064
Tel.: (954) 975-6400
Web Site: http://www.cortiva.edu
Natural Health Educational Services
N.A.I.C.S.: 611519
Jim Howard (COO)

Subsidiary (Domestic):

FCNH, Inc. (3)
2001 W Sample Rd Ste 100, Pompano Beach, FL 33064
Tel.: (954) 975-6400
Web Site: http://www.fcnh.com
Massage Therapy School Operator
N.A.I.C.S.: 611519
Debra Starr Cohen (Dir-Campus)
Paris LeLack Zupancic (Dir)

Virginia Massage Therapy, Inc. (3)
153 Zan Rd, Charlottesville, VA 22901
Tel.: (434) 293-4031
Web Site: http://www.vasom.com
Massage Therapy Training Center Operator
N.A.I.C.S.: 611519
Joe Carrick (Dir-Campus)

Thorne Healthtech, Inc. (1)
152 W 57th St, New York, NY 10019
Tel.: (929) 251-6321
Web Site: http://www.in.thorne.com
Rev.: $228,731,362
Assets: $229,804,021
Liabilities: $83,152,207
Net Worth: $146,651,814
Earnings: $15,674,040
Emp.: 544
Fiscal Year-end: 12/31/2022
Health Care Services
N.A.I.C.S.: 621610
Paul F. Jacobson (Founder, Chm & CEO)
Thomas P. McKenna (COO)
Will C. McCamy (Pres)
Scott R. Hurth (CTO)
Michelle L. Crow (CMO)
Stephen M. Phipps (Chief Innovation Officer)
Daniel McEvoy (CEO-Drawbridge Health)
Nathan D. Price (CEO-Onegevity)
Bodi Zhang (Chief Science Officer)
Kim R. Pearson (Gen Counsel)
Saloni S. Varma (CFO)
Rob Monteleone (Sr VP-Professional Sls)
Robert Rountree (Chief Medical Officer)
Wesley Barnett (VP-Athletic Bus Dev)
La Vonda Williams (CFO-Onegevity)

Subsidiary (Domestic):

WellnessFX, Inc. (2)
Hamm's Bldg 1550 Bryant St, San Francisco, CA 94103
Web Site: http://www.wellnessfx.com
Software Development Services
N.A.I.C.S.: 541511
Laura Luppens (VP-Fin)
Brent Vaughan (Founder)

Uncle Julio's Corporation (1)
1101 N Union Bower Rd 160, Irving, TX 75061
Tel.: (972) 554-6886
Web Site: http://www.unclejulios.com
Mexican Cuisine, Full-service, Restaurant Management
N.A.I.C.S.: 722511
Keith Strew (Dir-Learning & Dev)

CATTLE BARON RESTAURANTS INC.
901 S Main St, Roswell, NM 88203
Tel.: (575) 622-3311
Web Site: http://www.cattlebaron.com
Rev.: $15,200,000
Emp.: 15
Steak Restaurant
N.A.I.C.S.: 722511
Jeffrey W. Wilson (Founder & CEO)
LeeAnne Henson (Gen Mgr)

CATTLEMAN'S, INC.
1375 E 9th St Ste 2430, Cleveland, OH 44114-1786
Tel.: (313) 833-2700   DE
Year Founded: 1972
Sales Range: $125-149.9 Million
Emp.: 145
Operator of Meat Packing Plants
N.A.I.C.S.: 311612
Markus Rohtbart (Chm & Treas)
David S. Rohtbart (Pres & CEO)

CATTRELL COMPANIES, INC.
906 Franklin St, Toronto, OH 43964
Tel.: (740) 537-2481
Web Site: https://www.cattrell.com
Year Founded: 1939
Sales Range: $10-24.9 Million
Emp.: 25
Plumbing, Heating & Air-Conditioning Contracting Services
N.A.I.C.S.: 238220
George R. Cattrell (Pres & CEO)
Christine Cattrell Hargrave (Co-Owner, CFO, Treas & Sec)
Tom Wilson (Controller)
Brad Burkhead (Mgr-Toronto)

CATTY CORPORATION
6111 White Oaks Rd, Harvard, IL 60033
Tel.: (815) 943-2288
Web Site: https://www.cattycorp.com
Year Founded: 1907
Rev.: $10,000,000
Emp.: 65
Paper; Coated & Laminated Packaging
N.A.I.C.S.: 322220
Brian Smith (Mgr-Traffic)
Ken Zentner (Mgr-Maintenance)
Cindy Devries (Mgr-Acctg)
Ron Klint (VP-Engrg)

CAUDILL SEED & WAREHOUSE CO.
1402 W Main St, Louisville, KY 40203
Tel.: (502) 583-4402
Web Site: https://www.caudillseed.com
Sales Range: $25-49.9 Million
Emp.: 130
Seeds; Field, Garden & Flower
N.A.I.C.S.: 424910
S. Dan Caudill (CEO)

CAUDLE-HYATT, INC.
501 Westover Ave, Hopewell, VA 23860
Tel.: (804) 458-1555
Web Site: http://www.caudle-hyatt.com
Year Founded: 1965
Sales Range: $25-49.9 Million
Emp.: 225
Distr & Wholesaler of Commercial & Industrial Insulation & Abatement Supplies
N.A.I.C.S.: 238310
Onza E. Hyatt (Pres)
David B. Hyatt (COO)
Joseph Marshall (Controller)

CAUGHERTY HAHN COMMUNICATIONS, INC.
233 Rock Rd Ste 248, Glen Rock, NJ 07452
Tel.: (201) 251-7778
Web Site: http://www.chcomm.com
Year Founded: 1993
Sales Range: $1-9.9 Million
Emp.: 2
Public Relations Agency
N.A.I.C.S.: 541820
Lisa C. Hahn (Pres & CEO)
John N. Hahn (Partner & CFO)

CAUSAM ENERGY, INC.
9208 Falls of Neuse Rd Ste 215, Raleigh, NC 27615
Tel.: (919) 247-7439   DE
Web Site: http://www.causamenergy.com
Holding Company; Electric Power Grid Communication, Payment & Data Services Software Platform Developer

N.A.I.C.S.: 551112
Taylor Brockman (CTO)
Thomas Gordon (COO)
Ian DeCone (Sr VP-Bus Dev)
Joseph W. Forbes Jr. (CEO)

CAUSEWAY CAPITAL MANAGEMENT LLC
11111 Santa Monica Blvd, Los Angeles, CA 90025
Tel.: (310) 231-6100
Web Site: https://www.causewaycap.com
Year Founded: 2001
Rev.: $41,000,000,000
Emp.: 73
Investment Management Service
N.A.I.C.S.: 523940
Gracie V. Fermelia (COO)
Harry W. Hartford (Pres)
Sarah H. Ketterer (CEO)
Mark D. Osterkamp (Head-Institutional Sls & Mktg-Global)

CAUSEWAY LUMBER COMPANY
2601 S Andrews Ave, Fort Lauderdale, FL 33316
Tel.: (954) 763-1224
Year Founded: 2006
Rev.: $49,700,000
Emp.: 6
Lumber & Other Building Materials
N.A.I.C.S.: 423310
Angelyn Whiddon (Chm)
Scott M. Whiddon (Pres)
Scott Whiddon (Pres)
James Fitzgerald (Pres)

CAUTTRELL ENTERPRISES INC.
7618 N Broadway, Saint Louis, MO 63147
Tel.: (314) 385-4270
Web Site: https://www.cauttrellenterprises.com
Sales Range: $25-49.9 Million
Emp.: 80
Steel Supply Services
N.A.I.C.S.: 332312
Chris Cauttrell (Pres)

CAV INTERNATIONAL, INC.
125 The Parkway Ste 250, Greenville, SC 29615
Tel.: (864) 329-9000
Web Site: http://www.cavint.com
Year Founded: 1996
Sales Range: $10-24.9 Million
Emp.: 335
Air & Passenger Terminal Operations & Ground Handling Services
N.A.I.C.S.: 488190
Carroll A. Vaughn (Founder & Chm)

CAVALIER FORD INC.
1515 S Military Hwy, Chesapeake, VA 23320
Tel.: (757) 424-1111
Web Site: http://www.cavalierford.com
Rev.: $85,500,000
Emp.: 45
New & Used Automobiles
N.A.I.C.S.: 441110
Donald Klimkiewicz (Pres)
Marcey Catlin (Controller)

CAVALIER LOGISTICS INC
250 Sheffield St, Mountainside, NJ 07092-2303
Tel.: (908) 233-0600   NJ
Web Site: http://www.cavlog.com
Year Founded: 1984
Sales Range: $10-24.9 Million
Emp.: 60

Provider of Freight Transportation Services
N.A.I.C.S.: 488510
Tim Holdaway (Pres & CEO)

CAVALIER SERVICES, INC.
2722 Merrilee Dr Ste 300, Fairfax, VA 22031
Tel.: (703) 849-1100
Web Site:
    http://www.cavalierservices.com
Year Founded: 1977
Building Maintenance Services
N.A.I.C.S.: 561720
Kevin S. Rohan (Founder & CEO)
Paul Renick (CFO)
William T. Warnecki (Pres)
Carlos Ramirez (Mgr-Special Svcs)
Chris Decker (Dir-Sls & Mktg)

CAVALIERS OPERATING COMPANY, LLC
1 Center Ct, Cleveland, OH 44115-4001
Tel.: (216) 420-2000   OH
Web Site: http://www.theqarena.com
Year Founded: 2005
Sales Range: $25-49.9 Million
Emp.: 200
Professional Basketball Team & Sports Arena Manager
N.A.I.C.S.: 531312
Dan Gilbert (Chm & Mng Partner)
David Katzman (Vice Chm & Partner)

Subsidiaries:

Cleveland Cavaliers/Quicken Loans Arena   (1)
1 Center Ct, Cleveland, OH 44115-4001
Tel.: (216) 420-2000
Web Site: http://www.nba.com
Professional Basketball Services
N.A.I.C.S.: 711211
Dan Gilbert (Founder & Chm)
Tad Carper (VP)
Len Komoroski (CEO)
Koby Altman (Gen Mgr)
Trent Redden (Asst Gen Mgr)
Nic Barlage (Pres-Bus Ops)

CAVALRY CONSTRUCTION COMPANY INC.
6911 Breen Dr Ste C, Houston, TX 77086
Tel.: (281) 931-9900   TX
Web Site:
    https://www.cavalryconstruction.com
Year Founded: 1989
Rev.: $5,192,000
Emp.: 22
Residential Remodeler
N.A.I.C.S.: 236118
Debbie Frazier (Gen Mgr)
Frank Jones Sr. (CEO)

CAVANAUGH & CO., LLP
2381 Fruitville Rd, Sarasota, FL 34237
Tel.: (941) 366-2983   FL
Web Site: http://www.cavanaugh-co.com
Year Founded: 1994
Sales Range: $1-9.9 Million
Emp.: 20
Accounting, Auditing & Bookkeeping
N.A.I.C.S.: 541211
Gerald Cavanaugh (Founder)
Stephen D. Spangler (Partner)
Dave Hochsprung (Partner)
Michael R. Pender Jr. (Partner)

CAVANAUGH ELECTRICAL CONTRACTING, INC.
380 New Commerce Blvd, Wilkes Barre, PA 18706
Tel.: (570) 826-0389
Web Site: https://www.cavelect.com

Year Founded: 1984
Rev.: $21,500,000
Emp.: 100
Electrical Contractor
N.A.I.C.S.: 238210
Joseph Cavanaugh Jr. (VP)

CAVE CITY CHEVROLET/BUICK
302 Happy Vly St, Cave City, KY 42127
Tel.: (270) 773-3174
Sales Range: $10-24.9 Million
Emp.: 4
Automobile Dealership; Sales & Service of New & Used Vehicles
N.A.I.C.S.: 441110
Donald E. Massey (Pres)
Bobby Brown (Gen Mgr)
Lynn Brown (Controller)

CAVENDER AUTO GROUP
17811 San Pedro Ave, San Antonio, TX 78232
Web Site:
    http://www.cavenderauto.com
Car Dealer
N.A.I.C.S.: 441110

Subsidiaries:

Grande Ford Truck Sales, Inc.   (1)
4562 Interstate 10 E, San Antonio, TX 78219-4205
Tel.: (210) 666-7266
Web Site: http://www.grandetruck.com
Light Truck & Utility Vehicle Mfr
N.A.I.C.S.: 336110
Terri Kane (VP)

CAVENDER BROTHERS MANAGEMENT, LTD.
7625 N LP 1604 E, San Antonio, TX 78233
Tel.: (210) 226-7221
Sales Range: $50-74.9 Million
Emp.: 228
Car Whslr
N.A.I.C.S.: 441110
William B. Cavender (Pres)

CAVENDER BUICK COMPANY INC.
17811 San Pedro, San Antonio, TX 78232
Tel.: (210) 490-2000
Web Site:
    http://www.cavenderbuick.com
Year Founded: 1993
Sales Range: $10-24.9 Million
Emp.: 60
New & Used Automobiles
N.A.I.C.S.: 441110
Robert M. Cavender (Pres)
Kathy Schnieder (Controller)

CAVENDER CADILLAC
7625 N Loop 1604 E, San Antonio, TX 78233-2669
Tel.: (210) 944-1552
Web Site:
    https://www.cavendercadillac.com
Sales Range: $25-49.9 Million
Emp.: 100
Car Whslr
N.A.I.C.S.: 441110
William B. Cavender (Pres)
Bill Malloy (Dir-Fin)
Cavender Cadillac (Owner)

CAVENDER'S
7820 S Broadway Ave, Tyler, TX 75703-5241
Tel.: (903) 561-4992
Web Site: http://www.cavenders.com
Year Founded: 1965
Sales Range: $100-124.9 Million
Emp.: 600

Family Western Wear Boots, Apparel & Accessories Retailer
N.A.I.C.S.: 458210
James R. Cavender (CEO)
Cavender Clay (VP)

CAVERT WIRE COMPANY INCORPORATED
2282 University Dr, Lemont Furnace, PA 15456
Tel.: (724) 438-4545
Web Site: http://www.cavertwire.com
Rev.: $30,000,000
Emp.: 64
Wire Products, Ferrous/Iron: Made In Wiredrawing Plants
N.A.I.C.S.: 332618
William B. Spittler (Pres)
Michelle Spittler (Office Mgr)
Roger Caroway (CFO)

CAWOOD
1200 High St Ste 200, Eugene, OR 97401
Tel.: (541) 484-7052   OR
Web Site: https://www.cawood.com
Year Founded: 1979
Sales Range: $1-9.9 Million
Emp.: 11
Advertising & Public Relations Agency
N.A.I.C.S.: 541810
Liz Cawood (Pres)
Melinda Dille (Dir-Media)
Cari Ingrasia (Dir-Art)
Nathan Cawood (Dir-Ops)
Lindsey Ferguson (Dir-Bus Dev)

CAWOOD AUTO COMPANY
2516 Pine Grove Ave, Port Huron, MI 48060
Tel.: (810) 689-9204
Web Site:
    https://www.cawoodauto.com
Year Founded: 1919
Sales Range: $10-24.9 Million
Emp.: 45
Car Whslr
N.A.I.C.S.: 441110
Charles E. Barrett (Pres)

CAXTON ASSOCIATES LLC
731 Alexander Rd Bldg 2, Princeton, NJ 08540
Tel.: (609) 419-1800
Web Site: http://www.caxton.com
Rev.: $35,800,000
Emp.: 100
Commodity Traders, Contracts
N.A.I.C.S.: 523160
Bruce Stanley Kovner (Chm)

CAYCE COMPANY INC.
2710 S Irby St, Florence, SC 29505
Tel.: (843) 669-1816
Web Site:
    https://www.caycecompany.com
Year Founded: 1956
Sales Range: $10-24.9 Million
Emp.: 200
Heating, Ventilation, Air Conditioning & Plumbing Contractor
N.A.I.C.S.: 238220
M. Ernest Smith (Pres)
Lynn Brown (Treas)

CAYCE MILL SUPPLY COMPANY INC.
2225 Pembroke Rd, Hopkinsville, KY 42240
Tel.: (270) 886-3335
Web Site: https://www.caycemill.com
Year Founded: 1919
Sales Range: $10-24.9 Million
Emp.: 80

Electrical Apparatus & Equipment Distr
N.A.I.C.S.: 423730
Sue Dade (CFO)
Breck Cayce (Pres)
John Brown (Mgr-Ops)
Brooke Rives (Mgr-Bus Dev)
Andrew Pryor (Dir-IT)
Rhonda Boisseau (Mgr)
Cindy Powell (Mgr-Credit)

CAYMAN CHEMICAL COMPANY, INC.
1180 E Ellsworth Rd, Ann Arbor, MI 48108
Tel.: (734) 971-3335
Web Site:
    https://www.caymanchem.com
Year Founded: 1980
Sales Range: $1-9.9 Million
Emp.: 55
Pharmaceutical Preparations
N.A.I.C.S.: 325412
Jeffrey K. Johnson (VP-Academic Relations)
Kirk M. Maxey (Pres & CEO)

Subsidiaries:

Matreya LLC   (1)
2178 High Tech Rd, State College, PA 16803
Tel.: (814) 355-1030
Web Site: http://www.matreya.com
Research & Development in Biotechnology
N.A.I.C.S.: 541714

CAYMUS EQUITY PARTNERS LLC
1 Paces W 2727 Paces Ferry Rd SE Ste 1-1650, Atlanta, GA 30339
Tel.: (404) 995-8300
Web Site:
    https://www.caymusequity.com
Year Founded: 2001
Holding Company
N.A.I.C.S.: 551112
Geoff Faux (Mng Partner)
Blake Cummings (Partner)

Subsidiaries:

Quality Environmental Services, LLC   (1)
7124 W Grand River Rd, Fowlerville, MI 48836
Tel.: (517) 223-1100
Web Site: https://qualityenv.co
Sales Range: $1-9.9 Million
Emp.: 2
Environmental Consulting Services
N.A.I.C.S.: 541620

Seneca Resources, LLC   (1)
10701 Parkridge Blvd Ste 140, Reston, VA 20190
Tel.: (703) 390-9099
Web Site: http://www.senecahq.com
Sales Range: $1-9.9 Million
Information Technology Consulting Services
N.A.I.C.S.: 541512
Joseph Wire (Co-Founder & Mng Partner)
Robert Persiano (CEO)
Robert Hisel (Co-Founder)
Robert Hisel Jr. (Co-Founder & Partner)

CAYSET FASHIONS LTD.
1407 Broadway Ste 4103, New York, NY 10018
Tel.: (212) 789-7000
Web Site: http://www.cayre.com
Rev.: $65,000,000
Emp.: 70
Knit Outerwear
N.A.I.C.S.: 315120
Jack S. Cayre (CEO)

CAYUGA MEDICAL CENTER AT ITHACA
101 Dates Dr, Ithaca, NY 14850-1342
Tel.: (607) 274-4011   NY

Cayuga Medical Center At
Ithaca—(Continued)

Web Site:
https://www.cayugamed.org
Year Founded: 1980
Sales Range: $125-149.9 Million
Emp.: 1,000
General Medical & Surgical Hospitals
N.A.I.C.S.: 622110
John B. Rudd (CEO)
Noel Desch (Chm)

CAZENOVIA EQUIPMENT CO., INC.
2 Remington Park Dr, Cazenovia, NY
13035
Tel.: (315) 655-8620   NY
Web Site:
https://www.cazenoviaequip
ment.com
Year Founded: 1961
Emp.: 100
Farm & Garden Machinery & Equipment Merchant Whslr
N.A.I.C.S.: 423820
Jim Frazee (Pres)
Colleen Fox (Corp Mgr-Mktg)
Michael Frazee (VP)
Ben Frazee (VP)
Kristi Gerdon (Corp Mgr-HR)
Jennifer Kiehn (Dir-Acctg & Fin)
Jim Fitzgibbons (Mgr-Recruiting, Trng, and Dev)
Deb Podoliak (Mgr-Parts Inventory)
Adam DuBeau (Mgr-Wholegoods Inventory)
Brad Hathorn (Reg Sls Mgr)
Jay Smith (Reg Sls Mgr)

Subsidiaries:

LeBerge & Curtis, Inc.   (1)
6334 US Hwy 11, Canton, NY 13617
Tel.: (315) 386-2494
Web Site: http://www.lebergeandcurtis.com
Farm & Garden Machinery Whslr
N.A.I.C.S.: 423820
Ron Curtis (Co-Owner, Treas & Sec)

CAZENOVIA RECOVERY SYSTEMS, INC.
2671 Main St, Buffalo, NY 14214
Tel.: (716) 852-4331   NY
Web Site:
http://www.cazenoviarecovery.org
Year Founded: 1980
Sales Range: $1-9.9 Million
Emp.: 48
Psychiatric & Substance Abuse Hospitals
N.A.I.C.S.: 622210
Suzanne L. Bissonette (CEO)
John Anderson (Co-Treas)
Catherine M. Braniecki (VP)
Ed Cichon (Dir-Mktg & Comm)
Eileen Dietsch (Dir-Ops)
Kenneth Gholston (Dir-Grants & Contracts)
Sharon M. Hayes (Sec)
David H. Nelson (Pres)
Andrea Ocasio (Dir-Clinical Svcs)
Claudia Rejman (Comptroller)
Neldria Staton (Sec)

CAZLEY INC.
5899 Whitfield Ave Ste 200, Sarasota, FL 34243
Tel.: (941) 586-0441
Web Site: http://www.cazley.com
Sales Range: $1-9.9 Million
Emp.: 15
Small Business Financial Lender
N.A.I.C.S.: 522310
Brian Caswell (Pres & CEO)
Maurie West (CFO)
Elena Krapcheva (Partner & COO)

CB & K SUPPLY INC.
3939 Whitney St, Janesville, WI
53547
Tel.: (608) 755-5100
Web Site: http://www.cbkinc.com
Sales Range: $10-24.9 Million
Emp.: 50
Structural Shapes, Iron Or Steel & Plumbing
N.A.I.C.S.: 423720
Rodney Katz (Pres)
Al Vierthaler (Comptroller)
Robert Nuoffer (Dir-Pur)

CB CENTRAL BUILDERS INCORPORATED
11800 Nacogdoches Rd, San Antonio, TX 78217
Tel.: (210) 590-0235
Web Site:
https://www.centralbuilders.net
Rev.: $10,316,294
Emp.: 50
Commercial & Office Building Contractors
N.A.I.C.S.: 236220
Carl Ehrlich (Pres)
Bryan Ehrlich (Project Mgr)

CB DISTRIBUTORS, INC.
2500 Kennedy Dr, Beloit, WI 53511
Tel.: (608) 368-9909
Web Site:
http://www.cbdistributorsinc.com
General Line Grocery Merchant
Whslr
N.A.I.C.S.: 424410
Carlos Bengoa (Pres)
Loreen MacDonald (Mgr-Ops)
William Phillips (Mgr-Warehouse)

CB MANUFACTURING & SALES CO., INC.
4475 Infirmary Rd, Miamisburg, OH
45342
Tel.: (937) 866-5986
Web Site: http://www.cbmfg.com
Year Founded: 1965
Sales Range: $10-24.9 Million
Emp.: 110
Tool Mfr & Industrial Supplies Whslr
N.A.I.C.S.: 332216
Stephanie Stiffler (Coord-Import & Pur)
Brad Miller (Mgr-Sls)
Vernon Frazier (Dir-Info)
Austin Davidson (Acct Mgr)
Ron Shuk (Controller-Fin)

Subsidiaries:

American Cutting Edge, Inc.   (1)
480 Congress Park Dr, Centerville, OH
45459
Tel.: (888) 252-3372
Web Site:
http://www.americancuttingedge.com
Mfr of Machine Knives & Razor Blades
N.A.I.C.S.: 424210

CB MART INC.
142 W Rd, Belton, SC 29627
Tel.: (864) 338-8368
Rev.: $21,100,000
Emp.: 5
Independent Convenience Store
N.A.I.C.S.: 445131
Patrick B. O'Dell (Pres)

CB TRANSPORTATION
14 Phillips Ln, Chester Springs, PA
19425-3119
Tel.: (610) 590-0223
Web Site:
https://www.cbtransportation.com
Year Founded: 1995
Sales Range: $10-24.9 Million
Emp.: 13

Transportation Logistics
N.A.I.C.S.: 488999
Carole L. Borden (Founder & CEO)
Jenn Murray (Acct Mgr)
Michael Vallino (CFO & CIO)

CB TRAVEL CORP.
5588 S Green St Ste 300, Salt Lake City, UT 84123
Tel.: (801) 327-7700
Web Site:
http://www.christophersontravel.com
Year Founded: 1953
Rev.: $126,000,000
Emp.: 130
Travel Agency
N.A.I.C.S.: 561510
Michael Cameron (Pres & CEO)

CB&S BANK, INC.
200 Jackson Ave S, Russellville, AL
35653
Tel.: (256) 332-1710   AL
Web Site: http://www.cbsbank.com
Year Founded: 1989
Sales Range: $50-74.9 Million
Emp.: 407
Bank Holding Company
N.A.I.C.S.: 551111
Dennis Upchurch (Pres & CEO)
John Aldridge (CFO)

Subsidiaries:

CB&S Bank, Inc.   (1)
200 S Jackson Ave, Russellville, AL 35653
Tel.: (256) 332-1710
Web Site: http://www.cbsbank.com
Emp.: 200
Commericial Banking
N.A.I.C.S.: 522110
John Aldridge (CFO & Sr VP)
Donna Batchelor (Sr VP)
Kim Whitlock (VP & Personnel Officer)
Daryl Luna (VP & Mgr-Collections)
Mike Ross (Pres & CEO)
Greg Batchelor (Chm)

PrimeSouth BancShares, Inc.   (1)
301 Main St, Tallassee, AL 36078
Tel.: (334) 283-6594
Web Site: http://www.primesouthbank.com
Commericial Banking
N.A.I.C.S.: 522110
Jodi W. Turner (CFO & COO)
David W. Baggett Jr. (CEO)

CB&T HOLDING CORPORATION
1100 Poydras St Ste 100, New Orleans, LA 70163
Tel.: (504) 556-5950   LA
Web Site: http://www.cbtno.com
Sales Range: $25-49.9 Million
Bank Holding Company
N.A.I.C.S.: 551111
Fred B. Morgan III (Pres & Vice Chm)

Subsidiaries:

Crescent Bank & Trust   (1)
1100 Poydras St Ste 100, New Orleans, LA
70163   (100%)
Tel.: (504) 525-4381
Web Site: http://www.cbtno.com
Retail & Commercial Banking
N.A.I.C.S.: 522110
Fred B. Morgan III (Vice Chm & Pres)
Gary N. Solomon (Chm & CEO)

CBA INDUSTRIES INC.
669 Vivid Dr, Elmwood Park, NJ
07407
Tel.: (201) 587-1717
Sales Range: $10-24.9 Million
Emp.: 40
Newspapers
N.A.I.C.S.: 424920
Harold Matzner (Chm)
Barry Schiro (Pres)
Carl Casazza (CFO)

CBC BANCORP
19752 MacArthur Blvd Ste 100, Irvine, CA 92612
Tel.: (714) 431-7000   CA
Web Site: https://www.cbcal.com
Year Founded: 2000
Bank Holding Company
N.A.I.C.S.: 551111
Paul F. Folino (Chm)
Ash Patel (Pres & CEO)
Jonathan Matalon (Chief Acctg Officer & Exec VP)
Christopher Colella (Chief Credit Officer & Exec VP)
Jay Jannise (Chief IT Officer & Exec VP)
Thomas McCullough (Exec VP)
Houri Vartanian Simon (Exec VP-Payment Solutions)

Subsidiaries:

Commercial Bank of California   (1)
19752 MacArthur Blvd Ste 100, Irvine, CA
92612
Tel.: (714) 431-7000
Web Site: http://www.cbcal.com
Fiscal Year-end: 12/31/2015
Commericial Banking
N.A.I.C.S.: 522110
Ash Patel (Pres & CEO)
Jody Arata (Sr VP-Ops Admin)
Akash Patel (VP)
Christopher Colella (Chief Credit Officer & Exec VP)
Viktor Uehlinger (CFO & Exec VP)

CBC COMPANIES INC.
250 E Broad St, Columbus, OH
43215-4631
Tel.: (614) 222-4104   OH
Web Site: http://www.cbcinnovis.com
Year Founded: 1948
Sales Range: $75-99.9 Million
Emp.: 1,400
Credit Reporting Services
N.A.I.C.S.: 561450
Jeff Welch (Supvr-Telecom)
Tim Householder (Engr-Network)
Rick Pavliga (Dir-Application Dev)

Subsidiaries:

Amrent Inc.   (1)
PO Box 771176, Houston, TX 77215
Tel.: (713) 266-1870
Web Site: http://www.amrent.com
Sales Range: $10-24.9 Million
Emp.: 20
Credit Reporting Services
N.A.I.C.S.: 561450

CBC Companies Inc.   (1)
4605 West Homefield Dr, Sioux Falls, SD
57106-3511   (100%)
Tel.: (605) 336-7362
Web Site: http://www.cbc-companies.com
Sales Range: Less than $1 Million
Emp.: 20
Credit Reporting Services
N.A.I.C.S.: 561450

CBCS   (1)
2 Executive Park Dr, Bedford, NH 03110-
6915
Tel.: (603) 624-2600
Rev.: $3,200,000
Emp.: 40
Credit Reporting Services
N.A.I.C.S.: 561450

Credit Bureau of Greater Lansing
Inc.   (1)
520 S Washington Ave, Lansing, MI 48933-
2302
Tel.: (517) 487-6561
Rev.: $2,000,000
Emp.: 8
Credit Reporting Services
N.A.I.C.S.: 561450

The Credit Bureau Inc.   (1)
520 E Main St, Carnegie, PA 15106-2051
Tel.: (412) 429-2564
Rev.: $9,300,000
Emp.: 100

Credit Reporting Services
N.A.I.C.S.: 561450

CBC FRAMING INC.
21026 Osborne St, Canoga Park, CA 91304-1756
Tel.: (818) 718-2094
Year Founded: 1994
Sales Range: $25-49.9 Million
Emp.: 300
Provider of Carpentry Services
N.A.I.C.S.: 238130
John Vojtech (Pres)
Dennis Williams (Mgr)

CBC GROUP
5226 S 31st Pl, Phoenix, AZ 85040
Tel.: (800) 572-5780
Web Site:
http://www.cbcgroupco.com
Year Founded: 1948
Religious Gift Products Distr
N.A.I.C.S.: 459420
Lan Kang (Mng Dir & Head-Portfolio Mgmt)
Paul DiGiovanni (Pres)

Subsidiaries:

Christian Brands (1)
5226 S 31st Pl, Phoenix, AZ 85040
Tel.: (800) 572-5780
Web Site: http://catholic.christianbrands.com
Religious Gift Products Distr
N.A.I.C.S.: 459420

Subsidiary (Domestic):

Alfred Mainzer, Inc. (2)
39-33 29th St, Long Island City, NY 11101
Tel.: (718) 392-4200
Web Site: http://www.alfredmainzer.com
Publisher
N.A.I.C.S.: 513199
Barry Mainzer (Pres)

CBC SERVICES, INC.
1059 Hwy 501, Goldonna, LA 71031
Tel.: (318) 727-8920
Web Site:
http://www.cbcservicesinc.com
Year Founded: 1996
Sales Range: $10-24.9 Million
Emp.: 100
Water & Sewer Line Structures Construction Services
N.A.I.C.S.: 237110
Greg Caskey (Co-Founder)
Delton Caskey (Co-Founder)
Jeff Caskey (Co-Founder)
Keith Caskey (Sr Project Mgr & Engr)
Gavin Caskey (Project Mgr & Coord-HDD)

CBE GROUP
1309 Technology Pkwy, Cedar Falls, IA 50613-6976
Tel.: (319) 234-6686
Web Site: http://www.cbegroup.com
Rev.: $14,300,000
Emp.: 150
Provider of Collection Agency Services
N.A.I.C.S.: 561440
Thomas R. Penaluna (Pres & CEO)
Bob Kahler (CFO)
Greg Brandt (Dir-Strategy)
Harley Wilson (Dir-Ops)
Jen Weichers (Mgr-Tech Support)
Jeremy Nixon (Mgr-Strategy)
Jon Primus (Dir-Ops)
Sabrina Lowery (Mgr-Ops)

CBK GROUP
40 Eisenhower Dr Ste 200, Paramus, NJ 07652
Tel.: (201) 556-9404
Web Site: http://www.cbkgroup.com
Rev.: $30,000,000
Emp.: 10

N.A.I.C.S.: 541810
Carol Romeo (Owner)
Bill Troncone (Pres & Creative Dir)

CBM OF AMERICA, INC.
1455 W Newport Center Dr, Deerfield Beach, FL 33442
Tel.: (954) 698-9104
Web Site: https://www.cbmusa.com
Rev.: $11,050,531
Emp.: 300
System Integration Services
N.A.I.C.S.: 541512
Michael Stephens (Pres & CEO)
Eddie E. Sultan (CFO & VP-Fin)
Howard Mandel (Controller)
Valerie Malloy (Mgr-Customer Ops)
Charles Heineman (Mgr-Pur)
Christopher Scruggs (Mgr-Warehouse)

CBOL CORP.
19850 Plummer St, Chatsworth, CA 91311
Tel.: (818) 704-8200   KY
Web Site: http://www.cbol.com
Year Founded: 1979
Sales Range: $25-49.9 Million
Emp.: 110
Mfr of Semiconductors & Related Devices
N.A.I.C.S.: 334413
Kenneth Cheung (CFO)
Michael Lee (Project Mgr)
Steve Lee (Project Mgr)
Aaron Sung (Project Mgr)
Mike Han (Project Mgr)

CBP CARBON INDUSTRIES, INC.
10001 Woodloch Forest Dr Ste 325, Woodlands, TX 77380
Tel.: (832) 436-2710
Year Founded: 2005
Waste Management Services
N.A.I.C.S.: 562998
John Novak (Pres & CEO)

CBP ENGINEERING CORP.
185 Plumpton Ave, Washington, PA 15301
Tel.: (724) 229-1180
Web Site:
https://www.cbpengineering.com
Sales Range: $10-24.9 Million
Emp.: 65
Provider of Public Utility Holding Company Services
N.A.I.C.S.: 333519
Brian Gallagher (Chm)
Don Halulko (Dir-Sls & Mktg)
Paul Doman (Supvr-Engrg)

CBS BORING & MACHINE COMPANY, INC.
33750 Riviera Dr, Fraser, MI 48026
Tel.: (586) 294-7540
Web Site: https://www.cbsboring.com
Year Founded: 1967
Sales Range: $10-24.9 Million
Emp.: 110
Mfr of Industrial Machines
N.A.I.C.S.: 332710
Matt Mauchline (CEO)
Rick Frank (Supvr-Maintenance)

CBSET, INC.
500 Shire Way, Lexington, MA 02421
Tel.: (781) 541-5555   MA
Web Site: https://www.cbset.org
Year Founded: 2006
Sales Range: $10-24.9 Million
Emp.: 64
Biomedical Research Services
N.A.I.C.S.: 541715

James Stanley (Dir-Pathology)
Lynn Bailey (Dir-Interventional Svcs)
Brett G. Zani (Dir-Applied Sciences)
Elazer Edelman (Chm)
Peter M. Markham (Co-Founder, Pres & CEO)
Adam Groothuis (Co-Founder)
Rami Tzafriri (Dir-Res & Innovation)
Michael Naimark (Dir-Bus Dev)

CBSL TRANSPORTATION SERVICES, INC.
4750 S Merrimac Ave, Chicago, IL 60638
Tel.: (708) 496-1100
Web Site: https://www.cbsltrans.com
Sales Range: $10-24.9 Million
Emp.: 10
Railroad Maintenance & Repair Services
N.A.I.C.S.: 488210
Patrick Lynch (Controller)
Jeff Moore (Pres)

CBT CAMPUS, LLC
905 E Martin Luther King Jr Dr Ste 500, Tarpon Springs, FL 34689-4830
Tel.: (727) 724-8994
Web Site: http://www.cbtdirect.com
Year Founded: 1991
Sales Range: $10-24.9 Million
Emp.: 50
Interactive Education Software Mfr
N.A.I.C.S.: 513210
Tanya Whitmore (Supvr-Accts Receivable)

CBT NUGGETS, LLC
1550 Vly River Dr, Eugene, OR 97401
Tel.: (541) 284-5522
Web Site: http://www.cbtnuggets.com
Year Founded: 1999
Rev.: $5,400,000
Emp.: 150
Computer Training
N.A.I.C.S.: 611420
Dan Charbonneau (Founder & Owner)

CC 1 LIMITED PARTNERSHIP
Carr 174 Km 2 Luchetti Industrial Park, Bayamon, PR 00959
Tel.: (787) 288-6400   PR
Web Site: http://www.ccprb.com
Year Founded: 1995
Sales Range: $75-99.9 Million
Emp.: 900
Soft Drink Bottler, Coffee Mfr & Distr
N.A.I.C.S.: 312111
Alberto de la Cruz (Owner & Pres)

Subsidiaries:

Puerto Rico Coffee Roasters, LLC (1)
Urb Industrial Minillas Estate Rd 174 Lot 107, Bayamon, PR 00959
Tel.: (787) 721-3337
Web Site: http://www.yaucono.com
Coffee Mfr & Distr
N.A.I.C.S.: 311920
Alberto de la Cruz (Pres)

CC CAPITAL PARTNERS, LLC
200 Park Ave 58th Fl, New York, NY 10166
Tel.: (212) 355-5515
Web Site: http://www.cc.capital
Year Founded: 2016
Private Investment Firm
N.A.I.C.S.: 523940
Douglas B. Newton (Sr Mng Dir)
Chinh E. Chu (Founder & Sr Mng Dir)

Subsidiaries:

CC Neuberger Principal Holdings I (1)

200 Park Ave 58th Fl, New York, NY 10166
Tel.: (212) 355-5515
Web Site: https://www.ccnbprincipal.com
Holding Company
N.A.I.C.S.: 551112
Douglas B. Newton (Exec VP-Corp Dev)
Matthew Skurbe (CFO)

CC Neuberger Principal Holdings II (1)
200 Pk Ave 58th Fl, New York, NY 10166
Tel.: (212) 355-5515
Rev.: $1,805,787
Assets: $829,149,891
Liabilities: $947,121,938
Net Worth: ($117,972,047)
Earnings: ($2,703,894)
Emp.: 4
Fiscal Year-end: 12/31/2021
Investment Services
N.A.I.C.S.: 523999
Matthew Skurbe (CEO)

Subsidiary (Domestic):

Getty Images, Inc. (2)
605 5th Ave S Ste 400, Seattle, WA 98104
Tel.: (206) 925-5000
Web Site: http://www.gettyimages.com
Digital Media Publisher & Distr
N.A.I.C.S.: 541860
Andrew Saunders (Sr VP-Creative)
Nate Gandert (CTO & Chief Product Officer)
Gene Foca (CMO & Sr VP)
Ken Mainardis (Sr VP-Content)
Anne Boussarie (VP-Sls-France, Germany & Nordic Reg)
Kjelti Kellough (Gen Counsel & Sr VP)
Martin Lee (Sr VP-Global Strategic Dev)
Peter Orlowsky (Sr VP-Strategic Dev)
Rick Powell (CFO)
Lizanne Vaughan (Chief People Officer)
Pam Woehrle (Chief Comml Officer & Sr VP)
Mark H. Getty (Co-Chm)
Craig Peters (CEO)

Subsidiary (Non-US):

Getty Images (UK) Limited (3)
101 Bayham Street, London, NW1 0AG, United Kingdom
Tel.: (44) 2074286109
Web Site: http://www.gettyimages.co.uk
Digital Media Publisher & Distr
N.A.I.C.S.: 541890
Ken Leverenze (VP-Sls-UK & Ireland)

Getty Images France (3)
4 Boulevard Poissonniere, 75009, Paris, France
Tel.: (33) 1 5533 6600
Web Site: http://www.gettyimages.fr
Digital Media Publisher & Distr
N.A.I.C.S.: 541890
Jeff Guilbault (VP-Sls-Southern Europe & Benelux)
Anne Boussarie (Sr Dir-Sls)
Annsam Rocher (Dir-HR)
Mazer Simone (VP-Mktg-Intl)

Getty Images Pty. Ltd. (3)
Level 6 182 Blues Point Road, McMahons Point, 2060, NSW, Australia
Tel.: (61) 290042200
Web Site: http://www.GettyImages.com
Emp.: 85
Digital Media Publisher & Distr
N.A.I.C.S.: 541890
Stuart Hannagan (VP-Australasia & Dir-Photography-Asia)

PicScout Ltd. (3)
89 Medinat Hayehudim St, PO Box 12611, Herzliyya, 46766, Israel
Tel.: (972) 9 953 7100
Web Site: http://www.picscout.com
Image Recognition Fingerprinting & Indexing Services
N.A.I.C.S.: 518210

iStockphoto LP (3)
Suite 313 - 1240 20th Ave SE, Calgary, T2G 1M8, AB, Canada
Tel.: (403) 265-3062
Web Site: http://www.istockphoto.com
Sales Range: $25-49.9 Million
Emp.: 130
Stock Video, Still Photograph & Audio Database Publisher

CC Capital Partners, LLC—(Continued)

N.A.I.C.S.: 513140

The Dun & Bradstreet Corporation (1)
103 JFK Pkwy, Short Hills, NJ 07078
Tel.: (973) 921-5500
Web Site: http://www.dnb.com
Business Information, Publishing & Marketing Services
N.A.I.C.S.: 519290
Tim Solms (Gen Mgr-Govt Segment)
Gary Kotovets (Chief Data Officer)
Brian Hipsher (CFO & Treas)
Colleen Haley (Sec)
Virginia Green Gomez (Chief Product Officer)
Michael Manos (CTO)
Anthony M. Jabbour (CEO)
Anthony Pietrontone Jr. (Principal Acctg Officer & Controller)

Subsidiary (Domestic):

AllBusiness.com, Inc. (2)
650 Townsend St Ste 450, San Francisco, CA 94103
Tel.: (415) 694-5000
Web Site: http://www.allbusiness.com
Sales Range: $25-49.9 Million
Emp.: 40
Business Resource Website Operator
N.A.I.C.S.: 513199

Corinthian Leasing Corporation (2)
103 John F Kennedy Pkwy, Short Hills, NJ 07078-2708
Tel.: (973) 921-5500
Office Machinery Rental & Leasing Services
N.A.I.C.S.: 532420

D&B Acquisition Corp. (2)
12194 Monaco Dr, Brighton, CO 80602
Tel.: (303) 909-4502
Financial Investment Services
N.A.I.C.S.: 523999

Subsidiary (Non-US):

D&B Europe Limited (2)
The Point 37 North Wharf Road, London, W2 1AF, Buckinghamshire, United Kingdom
Tel.: (44) 1628492109
Web Site: http://www.db.com
Emp.: 400
Management Consulting Services
N.A.I.C.S.: 541618
Janets Storle (Mgr-IT & HR)

D&B Group Holdings (UK) (2)
The Point 37 North Wharf Road, London, W2 1AF, Buckinghamshire, United Kingdom
Tel.: (44) 1628492342
Investment Management Service
N.A.I.C.S.: 551112

D&B Holdings Australia Limited (2)
The Point 37 North Wharf Road, London, W2 1AF, United Kingdom
Tel.: (44) 1628492000
Web Site: http://www.dnb.co.uk
Emp.: 400
Investment Management Service
N.A.I.C.S.: 551112

Subsidiary (Domestic):

D&B Management Services Co. (2)
103 JFK Pkwy, Short Hills, NJ 07078-2708
Tel.: (973) 921-5500
Web Site: http://www.schooldata.com
Holding Company
N.A.I.C.S.: 551112

D&B Sales & Marketing Solutions (2)
460 Totten Pond Rd, Waltham, MA 02451
Tel.: (781) 672-9200
Sales Range: $10-24.9 Million
Emp.: 30
Computer Software Development
N.A.I.C.S.: 541511

Subsidiary (Non-US):

DBXB Netherlands B.V. (2)
Stationsplein 45 4th floor C, 3013 AK, Rotterdam, Netherlands
Tel.: (31) 107109400
Web Site: http://www.dnb-nederland.nl

Emp.: 25
Management Consulting Services
N.A.I.C.S.: 541618

DBXB S.r.l. (2)
48 Via Valtorta, 20127, Milan, Italy
Tel.: (39) 022814941
Management Consulting Services
N.A.I.C.S.: 541618

Dun & Bradstreet (HK) Ltd. (2)
13/F BEA Tower Millennium City 5, 418 Kwun Tong Rd, Kwun Tong, Kowloon, China (Hong Kong)
Tel.: (852) 25161111
Web Site: https://www.dnb.com.hk
Sales Range: $25-49.9 Million
Emp.: 100
Credit Services
N.A.I.C.S.: 561450
Thomas Tam (Controller)

Dun & Bradstreet (Israel) Ltd. (2)
53 Derech Hashalom St, Givatayim, 5345433, Israel
Tel.: (972) 37330330
Web Site: https://www.dbisrael.co.il
Sales Range: $25-49.9 Million
Emp.: 150
Credit Services
N.A.I.C.S.: 561450

Dun & Bradstreet (Singapore) Pte. Ltd. (2)
6 Shenton Way OUE Downtown 2 17-10, Singapore, 068809, Singapore
Tel.: (65) 65656161
Web Site: https://www.dnb.com.sg
Sales Range: $100-124.9 Million
Business Information Services
N.A.I.C.S.: 519290

Dun & Bradstreet (Vietnam) LLC (2)
Unit 2104 Floor 21 Saigon Trade Center, 37 Ton Duc Thang District 1, Ho Chi Minh City, Vietnam
Tel.: (84) 839117288
Web Site: http://www.dnb.com
Management Consulting Services
N.A.I.C.S.: 541611
Nhi Le Thi Phuong (Dir-Bus Dev)

Dun & Bradstreet B.V. (2)
Otto Reuchlinweg 1032, 3072 MD, Rotterdam, Netherlands
Tel.: (31) 107109400
Web Site: http://www.dnb-nederland.nl
Sales Range: $25-49.9 Million
Emp.: 100
Business Information Services
N.A.I.C.S.: 519290
D. Tebbitt (Mgr-Site)

Dun & Bradstreet Belgium N.V. (2)
Inter Access Park Pontbeekstraat 4, Dilbeek, 1702, Brussels, Belgium
Tel.: (32) 24818300
Web Site: http://www.dnb.com
Sales Range: $10-24.9 Million
Emp.: 40
Business Information Services
N.A.I.C.S.: 519290
Coraline van Hoeymissen (Dir-HR)

Dun & Bradstreet CIS (2)
3rd Khoroshevsky Proyezd 1 corpus 1, 123007, Moscow, Russia
Tel.: (7) 959401816
Web Site: http://www.dnb.ru
Sales Range: $10-24.9 Million
Emp.: 15
N.A.I.C.S.: 561450

Dun & Bradstreet Canada BV (2)
Otto Reuchlinweg 1032, Rotterdam, 3072 MD, Netherlands
Tel.: (31) 107109400
Web Site: http://www.dnb-netherlands.com
Emp.: 120
Management Consulting Services
N.A.I.C.S.: 541611
Darren Tebbitt (Gen Mgr)

Dun & Bradstreet Canada Ltd. (2)
B1-5770 Hurontario St, Mississauga, L5R 3G5, ON, Canada
Tel.: (800) 668-3033
Web Site: http://www.dnb.ca
Information Services
N.A.I.C.S.: 519290

Jenal Embry (VP-Supply Chain Solutions)
Brian Alster (Global Head-of Supply & Compliance Product)
Nipa Basu (Chief Analytics Officer)
Ilio Krumins-Beens (Global Head-PMO)
Daniel Sherman (Dir-Vulnerability Mgmt)

Subsidiary (Domestic):

Dun & Bradstreet Credibility Corp. (2)
22761 Pacific Coast Hwy Ste 226, Malibu, CA 90265
Tel.: (424) 644-0601
Web Site: http://www.dandb.com
Emp.: 575
Credit Monitoring Services
N.A.I.C.S.: 522390

Dun & Bradstreet Europe, Ltd. (2)
103 JFK Pkwy, Short Hills, NJ 07078
Tel.: (973) 921-5500
Web Site: http://www.dunandbradstreet.com
Management Consulting Services
N.A.I.C.S.: 541611

Subsidiary (Non-US):

Dun & Bradstreet Information Services India Pvt Ltd. (2)
iSprout Business Center 5th Floor Kochar Jade PLOT NO SP 22, T-S No 25 SIDCO Industrial Estate Guindy, Chennai, 600032, India
Tel.: (91) 2228574190
Web Site: http://www.dnb.com
Sales Range: $75-99.9 Million
Emp.: 350
Information Services
N.A.I.C.S.: 519290

Dun & Bradstreet International Consultant (Shanghai) Ltd. (2)
9th Floor Building 6 Hongqiao Vanke Center No 988 Shenchang Road, 318 Fu Zhou Road, Shanghai, 200001, China
Tel.: (86) 2123213636
Web Site: https://www.dnbchina.com
Sales Range: $50-74.9 Million
Emp.: 200
Credit Bureau Services
N.A.I.C.S.: 561450

Dun & Bradstreet Investments Limited (2)
The Point 37 North Wharf Road, London, W2 1AF, Buckinghamshire, United Kingdom
Tel.: (44) 1628492319
Web Site: http://www.dnb.co.uk
Investment Management Service
N.A.I.C.S.: 523999

Dun & Bradstreet Ltd. (2)
The Point 37 North Wharf Road, London, W2 1AF, Buckinghamshire, United Kingdom
Tel.: (44) 1628492000
Web Site: https://www.dnb.co.uk
Sales Range: $75-99.9 Million
Emp.: 400
Business Information Services
N.A.I.C.S.: 519290

Subsidiary (Domestic):

Dun & Bradstreet NetProspex (2)
300 3rd Ave, Waltham, MA 02451
Tel.: (888) 826-4877
Web Site: http://www.netprospex.com
B2B Business & Marketing Services
N.A.I.C.S.: 561499

Subsidiary (Non-US):

Dun & Bradstreet SpA (2)
Via Dei Valtorta 48, 20127, Milan, Italy
Tel.: (39) 02284551
Web Site: http://www.dnb.it
Sales Range: $75-99.9 Million
Emp.: 300
Credit Services
N.A.I.C.S.: 561450

Dun & Bradstreet Technologies & Data Services Private Limited (2)
Level 9 Prince Info City Phase 1 286/1, Kandanchavadi Rajiv Gandhi Salai OMR, Chennai, 600 096, India
Tel.: (91) 4466779999
Internet Service Provider
N.A.I.C.S.: 517121

Subsidiary (Domestic):

Dun & Bradstreet, Inc. - Credit Services (2)
400 Penn Ctr Blvd, Pittsburgh, PA 15235
Tel.: (412) 829-3731
Sales Range: $125-149.9 Million
Business Credit Management
N.A.I.C.S.: 522390

Duns Investing Corporation (2)
801 N West St Fl 2, Wilmington, DE 19801-1525
Tel.: (302) 656-8981
Investment Management Service
N.A.I.C.S.: 523940

Dunsnet, LLC (2)
189 S Orange Ave Ste 1500 S, Orlando, FL 32801
Tel.: (407) 476-9854
Web Site: https://www.dunsnet.com
Financial Transaction Services
N.A.I.C.S.: 522320

First Research, Inc. (2)
7700 W Parmer Ln Bldg A, Austin, TX 78729
Tel.: (512) 380-4808
Web Site: https://www.firstresearch.com
Sales Range: $1-9.9 Million
Emp.: 14
Industry Analysis & Marketing Products & Services
N.A.I.C.S.: 513199

Hoover's, Inc. (2)
5800 Airport Blvd, Austin, TX 78752-4204
Tel.: (512) 374-4500
Web Site: http://www.hoovers.com
Sales Range: $50-74.9 Million
Emp.: 231
Publisher of Business Information
N.A.I.C.S.: 541990

Subsidiary (Domestic):

Visible Path Corp. (3)
181 Metro Dr Ste 290, San Jose, CA 95110-1344
Tel.: (650) 356-2254
Sales Range: $10-24.9 Million
Emp.: 30
Online Business Networking Solutions
N.A.I.C.S.: 513210
Stephen Charles Pusey (CMO)

Subsidiary (Domestic):

Lattice Engines, Inc. (2)
1825 S Grant Ave Ste 510, San Mateo, CA 94402
Tel.: (877) 460-0010
Web Site: http://www.lattice-engines.com
Sales Range: $1-9.9 Million
Emp.: 40
Predictive Analytics to Sales & Marketing Consumers
N.A.I.C.S.: 513210
Shashi Upadhyay (CEO)
Kent McCormick (CTO)
Ian J. Scott (VP-Pro Svcs)
Scott Harralson (VP-Pro Svcs)
Jean-Paul Gomes (VP-Bus Dev)

Market Data Retrieval (2)
5335 Gate Pkwy, Jacksonville, FL 32256
Tel.: (973) 921-5500
Web Site: https://mdreducation.com
Sales Range: $25-49.9 Million
Emp.: 166
School Marketing Information & Services
N.A.I.C.S.: 541910

Purisma, Inc. (2)
2211 Bridgepointe Pkwy Ste 300, San Mateo, CA 94404
Tel.: (650) 350-3500
Web Site: http://www.purisma.com
Sales Range: $25-49.9 Million
Emp.: 15
Data Management Services
N.A.I.C.S.: 541511

Subsidiary (Non-US):

Shanghai Huaxia Dun & Bradstreet Business Information Consulting Co., Limited (2)
Unit 907-910 Cross Tower 318 Fu Zhou

Road, Shanghai, 200001, China
Tel.: (86) 2123213636
Web Site: http://www.huaxiadnb.com
Commercial Information Consulting Services
N.A.I.C.S.: 541611

The D&B Companies of Canada Ltd. (2)
6750 Century Ave Suite 305, Mississauga, L5N 0B7, ON, Canada
Tel.: (800) 668-3033
Web Site: http://www.dnb.com
Management Consulting Services
N.A.I.C.S.: 541611

Subsidiary (Domestic):

coAction.com LLC (2)
300 Carnegie Dr, Princeton, NJ 08540
Web Site: http://www.coaction.com
Sales Range: $1-9.9 Million
Business Collaboration Software
N.A.I.C.S.: 513210
Jagdish Talreja (CEO)

CC CARPET INC.
7600 Ambassador Row, Dallas, TX 75247
Tel.: (214) 631-0704
Web Site: http://www.cccarpet.com
Sales Range: $10-24.9 Million
Emp.: 30
Floor Covering Stores
N.A.I.C.S.: 449121
Morgan Fitzgerald (Dir-Mktg)

CC COMMUNICATIONS
50 W Williams, Fallon, NV 89406
Tel.: (775) 423-7171
Web Site: http://www.cccomm.net
Sales Range: $10-24.9 Million
Emp.: 103
Provider of Telephone Communication Services
N.A.I.C.S.: 517121
Lorrie Ford (Mgr-Acctg)
Jim Nugent (Supvr-Installation)
Gene Ponce (Engr-Network)
Mark Seest (Gen Mgr)

CC DILLON CO.
1342 Lonedell Rd, Arnold, MO 63010
Tel.: (636) 296-2700
Sales Range: $10-24.9 Million
Emp.: 50
Petroleum Bulk Stations
N.A.I.C.S.: 424710
Gary L. Litzsinger (Pres)

CC DISTRIBUTORS INC
210 McBride Ln, Corpus Christi, TX 78408
Tel.: (361) 289-0200
Web Site:
https://www.ccdistributors.com
Rev.: $25,600,000
Emp.: 300
Plumbing Fittings & Supplies
N.A.I.C.S.: 423720
Andrew Grey (VP-Base Ops & Contracts)
George A. Finley III (Pres)

CC FILSON CO.
1555 4th Ave S, Seattle, WA 98134
Tel.: (206) 624-4437
Web Site: http://www.filson.com
Year Founded: 1897
Sales Range: $10-24.9 Million
Emp.: 150
Men's & Boy's Work Clothing
N.A.I.C.S.: 315250
June Evans (Mgr-Tech Svcs)
Teresa Whittaker (Mgr-Production)
Danny Harmon (Dir-Art)

CC1 LIMITED PARTNERSHIP
220 Alhambra Cir Ste 304, Coral Gables, FL 33134

Tel.: (305) 446-1882
Sales Range: $50-74.9 Million
Emp.: 1,400
Bottled & Canned Soft Drinks
N.A.I.C.S.: 312111
Carlos de la Cruz (Pres)

CCA GLOBAL PARTNERS, INC.
4301 Earth City Expwy, Earth City, MO 63045-1334
Tel.: (314) 291-0000   DE
Web Site: http://www.ccaglobal.com
Rev.: $8,700,000,000
Emp.: 350
Business Support Services
N.A.I.C.S.: 561499
Howard Brodsky (Chm & Co-CEO)
Rick Bennet (Co-CEO)
Charlie Dilks (Chief Product Officer)
Jim Acker (CFO)
Bob Wilson (Chief Admin Officer)

Subsidiaries:

CCA For Social Good (1)
670 N Commercial St, Manchester, NH 03101
Tel.: (603) 626-0333
Information Technology Consulting Services
N.A.I.C.S.: 541512

CCA Global Partners, Inc. - BizUnite Division (1)
670 N Commercial St, Manchester, NH 03101
Tel.: (603) 628-2336
Web Site: http://www.bizunite.com
Information Technology Consulting Services
N.A.I.C.S.: 541512

CCA Global Partners, Inc. - Manchester (1)
670 N Commercial St, Manchester, NH 03101
Tel.: (800) 450-7595
Web Site: http://www.ccaglobal.com
Emp.: 110
Floor Covering Business Cooperative
N.A.I.C.S.: 813920
Keith Spano (Pres)
Nancy Trafford (VP-Member Svcs)
Frank Chiera (VP-Mktg & Advertising)
Andy Valeriani (VP-Digital Mktg)
Brian Dodson (Dir-Member Dev)

CCA Global Partners, Inc. - The Floor Trader Division (1)
4301 Earth City Expy, Saint Louis, MO 63045-1334
Tel.: (314) 506-0000
Web Site: http://www.floortrader.com
Carpet Whslr
N.A.I.C.S.: 423220

FEI Group (1)
811 Livingston Ct, Marietta, GA 30067
Tel.: (770) 528-4747
Web Site: http://www.feigroup.net
Floor Contracting Services
N.A.I.C.S.: 238330
Graham Howerton (VP)

Flooring America, Inc. (1)
670 N Commercial St, Manchester, NH 03101
Tel.: (800) 450-7595
Web Site: http://www.flooringamerica.com
Emp.: 20
Floor Covering Store Operator
N.A.I.C.S.: 449121
Keith Spano (Pres)
Frank Chiera (VP-Mktg & Adv)
Nancy Trafford (VP-Member Svcs)
Becky Propp (Mgr-Sls)
Cathy Gundlach (VP-Mdsg)

Innovia Community Management Cooperative (1)
4301 Earth City Expy, Saint Louis, MO 63045
Tel.: (800) 466-6984
Web Site: http://www.innoviacmc.com
General Management Consulting Services
N.A.I.C.S.: 541611

International Design Guild (1)

670 N Commercial St, Manchester, NH 03101
Web Site: http://www.ccaglobalpartners.com
Floor Coverings Whslr
N.A.I.C.S.: 423220
Frank Chiera (Sr VP-Mktg & Adv)
Keith Spano (Pres)

Lionsbridge Contractor Group (1)
4301 Earth City Expy, Earth City, MO 63045
Tel.: (800) 514-3472
Web Site:
http://www.lionsbridgecontractorgroup.net
Construction Engineering Services
N.A.I.C.S.: 541330

The Bike Cooperative (1)
670 N Commercial St, Manchester, NH 03101
Tel.: (800) 450-7595
Web Site:
http://www.thebikecooperative.com
Bicycle Retailer
N.A.I.C.S.: 459110
Bill Heins (Mgr-Supplier Rels)
Tim Leaver (VP-Mktg)
Carl Michelakos (VP-Ops)

CCB INC.
5 Star Industrial Park 65 Bradley Dr, Westbrook, ME 04092
Tel.: (207) 464-2626
Web Site: http://www.ccb-inc.com
Sales Range: $10-24.9 Million
Emp.: 100
Industrial Buildings, New Construction
N.A.I.C.S.: 236210
Beth L. Sturtevant (Co-Owner & Pres)
Al Brickett (Project Mgr)
Tom Donnelly (Dir-Bus Dev)
Kelly Flagg (Mgr-HR & Employee Dev)
Marc Belanger (Co-Owner & VP-Ops)
Sean Ferguson (Co-Owner & VP-Fin)
Newell E. Porter (Project Mgr)
Mike Goodwin (Project Mgr)
Larry Grenier (Project Mgr)
Jeff Verreault (Project Mgr)
Nate Roberts (Project Mgr)

CCC ASSOCIATES INC.
3601 Wetumpka Hwy, Montgomery, AL 36110
Tel.: (334) 272-2140
Web Site: https://www.caffco.com
Sales Range: $25-49.9 Million
Emp.: 175
Artificial Flowers
N.A.I.C.S.: 424930

CCC GROUP INC.
5797 Dietrich Rd, San Antonio, TX 78219-3507
Tel.: (281) 842-8343   TX
Web Site:
http://www.cccgroupinc.com
Year Founded: 1947
Sales Range: $450-499.9 Million
Emp.: 2,500
Industrial Buildings & Warehouses
N.A.I.C.S.: 236210
Nita McBride (CFO)
John Moran (VP)
Timothy J. Henning (Pres & CEO)

CCFW, INC.
2 Park Plz Ste 550, Irvine, CA 92614-2518
Tel.: (949) 261-8888   CA
Web Site:
http://www.carpentercompany.com
Year Founded: 1974
Holding Company; Banking Industry
Private Equity, Investment Advisory & Asset Management Services
N.A.I.C.S.: 551112
Edward J. Carpenter (Founder, Chm & CEO)

John David Flemming (Pres)
James B. Jones (Exec VP)
Maryam Hamzeh (Exec VP)
Arthur A. Hidalgo (Founder & Mng Partner-Carpenter Community Bancfund)
Curt A. Christianssen (CFO & Exec VP)
Michelle K. Kaull (CFO)
Joshua D. Ness (Sr VP)
Dennis Guida (Mng Dir)

Subsidiaries:

Carpenter Fund Management Company, LLC (1)
2 Park Plz Ste 550, Irvine, CA 92614-2518
Tel.: (949) 261-8888
Web Site:
http://www.carpentercompany.com
Emp.: 20
Investment Management & Private Equity Firm
N.A.I.C.S.: 523940
Edward J. Carpenter (Chm & CEO)
John David Flemming (Pres & COO)
James B. Jones (Exec VP)
Maryam Hamzeh (Exec VP)
Dennis Guida (Mng Dir)

Subsidiary (Domestic):

Carpenter Bank Partners, Inc. (2)
5 Park Plz Ste 950, Irvine, CA 92614-8527
Tel.: (949) 261-8888
Web Site:
http://www.carpentercompany.com
Bank Holding Company
N.A.I.C.S.: 551111
Edward J. Carpenter (Mng Partner)
John David Flemming (Mng Partner)
James B. Jones (Mng Partner)
Arthur A. Hidalgo (Mng Partner)

CCI MANUFACTURING INC.
2624 Joe Field Rd, Dallas, TX 75229
Tel.: (972) 488-8131
Web Site:
http://www.customstone.com
Sales Range: $25-49.9 Million
Emp.: 120
Ready Mixed Concrete
N.A.I.C.S.: 327320
Steve Bond (Pres)

CCI SYSTEMS INC.
105 Kent St, Iron Mountain, MI 49801-1507
Tel.: (906) 774-6621   MI
Web Site:
https://www.ccisystems.com
Year Founded: 1965
Sales Range: $450-499.9 Million
Emp.: 1,000
Construction Services
N.A.I.C.S.: 237130
Bill Peters (Dir-Cable Sls)

Subsidiaries:

Klungess Electronic Supply (1)
101 Merritt Ave, Iron Mountain, MI 49801
Tel.: (906) 774-1755
Web Site: http://www.cciinc.us
Sales Range: $25-49.9 Million
Emp.: 300
Consumer Electronics Distr
N.A.I.C.S.: 449210

CCM ACQUISITION CORP.
150 E 52nd St Ste 20001, New York, NY 10022
Tel.: (212) 858-9020   Ky
Year Founded: 2021
Emp.: 2
Investment Services
N.A.I.C.S.: 523999
Ming-Po Cai (Chm)
Andre Puong (CFO)
Kwok On Yeung (CEO)

CCM Acquisition Corp.—(Continued)

CCM MARKETING COMMUNI-CATIONS
11 E 47th St Fl 3, New York, NY 10017-7916
Tel.: (212) 689-8225 **NY**
Year Founded: 1978
Rev.: $7,000,000
Emp.: 18
Fiscal Year-end: 12/31/01
Advetising Agency
N.A.I.C.S.: 541810
Michael Chadwick *(Partner)*
Steve Polachi *(Partner)*

Subsidiaries:

CCM West **(1)**
4251 S Higuera St, San Luis Obispo, CA 93401
Tel.: (805) 788-0966
Sales Range: $10-24.9 Million
N.A.I.C.S.: 541810
Suzie DeSilva *(Partner)*

CCMP CAPITAL ADVISORS, LP
277 Park Ave 27th Fl, New York, NY 10172
Tel.: (212) 600-9600 **DE**
Web Site:
http://www.ccmpcapital.com
Year Founded: 2006
Privater Equity Firm
N.A.I.C.S.: 523999
Gregory D. Brenneman *(Exec Chm)*
Kevin G. O'Brien *(Mng Dir)*
Richard F. Zannino *(Mng Dir & Head-Consumer, Retail, and Media Prac-tice)*
Richard Jansen *(Mng Dir, Chief Com-pliance Officer & Gen Counsel)*
Jonathan R. Lynch *(Mng Dir)*
Esana Blank *(VP)*
Mark McFadden *(Co-Mng Partner & Mng Dir)*
Doug Cahill *(Mng Dir)*
Timothy Walsh *(Pres, CEO & Mng Dir)*
Kristin Steen *(Mng Dir)*
Christopher Behrens *(Mng Dir & Head-IR)*
Thomas Walker *(Mng Dir)*
Will Jaudes *(Mng Dir)*
Aaron Hurwitz *(Principal)*
Patrick McGrath *(Principal)*
Alan Wayne *(Principal)*
Mark McFadden *(Co-Mng Partner)*
Timothy Walsh *(Mng Dir)*

Subsidiaries:

CCMP Capital Advisors (UK), LLP **(1)**
Almack House 28 King St, 23 King Street, London, SW1Y 6XA, United Kingdom
Tel.: (44) 2073899100
Sales Range: $25-49.9 Million
Emp.: 7
Private Equity Investment Firm
N.A.I.C.S.: 523999
Thomas Walker *(Sr Partner)*

CCMP Capital Advisors, LLC - Hous-ton Office **(1)**
24 Waterway Ave Ste 750, The Woodlands, TX 77380
Tel.: (281) 363-2013
Web Site: http://www.ccmpcapital.com
Emp.: 5
Privater Equity Firm
N.A.I.C.S.: 523999
Gregory D. Brenneman *(Exec Chm)*
Will Jaudes *(Mng Dir)*

CCMP Growth Advisors, LP **(1)**
1 Rockefeller Plz 16th Fl, New York, NY 10020
Tel.: (212) 600-9600
Web Site: https://www.ccmpgrowth.com
Investment Services

N.A.I.C.S.: 523999
Joe Scharfenberger *(Mng Partner)*

Subsidiary (Domestic):

Decks & Docks Lumber Company Inc. **(2)**
1281 Court St, Clearwater, FL 33756
Tel.: (727) 466-9663
Web Site: https://www.decks-docks.com
Sales Range: $10-24.9 Million
Emp.: 100
Marine Construction Materials Distr
N.A.I.C.S.: 444110
Shawn Roberts *(CEO)*
Tyler Wallace *(Pres)*

Hayward Industries, Inc. **(1)**
620 Division St, Elizabeth, NJ 07201
Tel.: (908) 351-5400
Web Site: http://www.hayward-pool.com
Holding Company; Swimming Pool Equip-ment & Parts Mfr
N.A.I.C.S.: 551112
Kevin P. Holleran *(Pres & CEO)*
Dave MacNair *(VP-Mktg)*
Eifion Jones *(CFO & Sr VP)*

Subsidiary (Domestic):

Goldline Controls, Inc. **(2)**
61 Whitecap Dr, North Kingstown, RI 02852
Tel.: (401) 583-1100
Web Site: http://www.hayward.com
Sales Range: $10-24.9 Million
Emp.: 122
Electronic Pool Controls Mfr
N.A.I.C.S.: 334519
Laurie Roberto *(Dir-HR)*

Hayward Industrial Products, Inc. **(2)**
1 Hayward Industrial Dr, Clemmons, NC 27012
Tel.: (336) 712-9900
Web Site: http://www.haywardindustrial.com
Sales Range: $50-74.9 Million
Emp.: 600
Sales of Industrial Plastic Valves
N.A.I.C.S.: 333310

Hayward Pool Products, Inc. **(2)**
620 Division St, Elizabeth, NJ 07201-2012
Tel.: (908) 351-5400
Web Site: http://www.haywardnet.com
Sales Range: $25-49.9 Million
Emp.: 85
Mfr Of Service Machines
N.A.I.C.S.: 459999
Robert Davis *(Pres & CEO)*

Subsidiary (Non-US):

Hayward Pool Europe **(3)**
P.I. Plaine de l'ain, Allee des Chenes, 01150, Saint-Vulbas, France
Tel.: (33) 825000549
Web Site: http://www.haywardnet.com
Sales Range: $25-49.9 Million
Emp.: 50
N.A.I.C.S.: 459110

Hayward Pool Products Canada, Inc. **(3)**
2880 Plymouth Drive, Oakville, L6H 5R4, ON, Canada
Tel.: (905) 829-2880
Web Site: https://www.hayward-pool.ca
Sales Range: $10-24.9 Million
Emp.: 75
Pool Equipment Mfr
N.A.I.C.S.: 333414

Branch (Domestic):

Hayward Pool Products, Inc. **(3)**
1 Hayward Industrial Dr, Clemmons, NC 27102
Tel.: (908) 355-7995
Web Site: http://www.haywardpool.com
Sales Range: $50-74.9 Million
Pool Products Mfr
N.A.I.C.S.: 459999
Clarke Hale *(Pres)*

Unit (Domestic):

Hayward/IMG **(2)**
2875 Pomona Blvd, Pomona, CA 91768
Tel.: (909) 594-0082
Web Site: http://www.hayward-poolproducts.com

Sales Range: $10-24.9 Million
Emp.: 15
Pool Products
N.A.I.C.S.: 423910
Robert De Martini *(Gen Mgr)*
Gloria Ward *(Controller)*
Diego Gutierrez *(Mgr-Comml Technical Sls-Midwest)*
Paul Hammond *(Mgr-Comml Technical Sls-Northeast)*
Chad Norton *(Mgr-Comml Technical Sls-West & Southwest)*

Infogroup Inc. **(1)**
1020 E 1st St, Papillion, NE 68046
Tel.: (402) 593-4500
Web Site: http://www.infogroup.com
Sales Range: $500-549.9 Million
Holding Company; Business & Consumer Database Publisher
N.A.I.C.S.: 551112
Gretchen Littlefield *(Pres-Dir Mktg Svcs)*
Michael Fisher *(Pres-Yes Lifecycle Mktg)*
Amit Khanna *(Pres-Small & Medium Bus)*
Charles Teller *(Sr VP & Gen Mgr-Consumer-Media Solutions)*
Dean Brown *(VP-Channel Partnerships)*
Mary Ann Cardoso *(Sr VP-Bus Dev-Nonprofit Solutions)*
Melissa Cropsey *(Dir-Digital Svcs-Rain)*
Purandar Das *(CTO-Enterprise Tech)*
Matt Graves *(Chief Data Officer)*
Ed McCormick *(Chief Admin Officer)*
Jeffrey Tooley *(Asst Gen Counsel)*
Gayatri Bhalla *(VP/Gen Mgr-Audience Solu-tions)*
Tim Smith *(CMO-Local Mktg Solutions Div)*
Andy Goldstein *(CFO)*
Mark Cullinane *(Pres-Local Mktg Solutions Div)*
Michael L. Iaccarino *(Chm & CEO)*

Subsidiary (Domestic):

Direct Media Millard, Inc. **(2)**
10 Vose Farm Rd, Peterborough, NH 03458
Tel.: (402) 836-5100
Web Site: http://www.infogroup.com
Sales Range: $75-99.9 Million
Emp.: 2,000
List Management & Brokerage Services
N.A.I.C.S.: 541860
Linda Thompson *(VP-List Mgmt)*
Lisa Williams *(Dir)*
Lynn Wallis *(Acct Dir-List Mgmt Div)*
Mike Iaccarino *(CEO)*

Subsidiary (Domestic):

Infogroup Direct Marketing Solutions **(3)**
200 Pemberwick Rd, Greenwich, CT 06831
Tel.: (203) 532-1000
Web Site: http://www.infogroup.com
Sales Range: $50-74.9 Million
List Management & Brokerage Services
N.A.I.C.S.: 541860
Larry May *(Sr VP-Strategic Dev)*
Karen Mayhew *(Exec VP-List Mgmt Div)*
Thom Hansen *(VP-Mktg-Intl)*
John Briley *(VP-Fundraising Mgmt)*

Division (Domestic):

Infogroup Interactive **(2)**
309 SW 6th Ave Ste 700, Portland, OR 97204
Tel.: (503) 241-4185
Web Site: http://www.yesmail.com
Holding Company; Digital Marketing Solu-tions & Services
N.A.I.C.S.: 551112
John Ching *(VP-Applied Res)*
Bryan Finke *(VP-Comm Strategies)*
Kevin Gallant *(Mgr-Intelligence Products)*
John Hollands *(Sr VP-Sls)*
Bjorn Schulze *(Mgr-Database Admin)*
Erik Schulze *(VP-Customer Experience & Comm Strategy)*
Sue Zabran *(VP-Production)*

Subsidiary (Domestic):

YesMail, Inc. **(3)**
309 SW 6th Ave Ste 700, Portland, OR 97204
Tel.: (503) 241-4185
Web Site: http://www.yesmail.com
Sales Range: $10-24.9 Million
Email Marketing Solutions Services
N.A.I.C.S.: 513210

John Hollands *(Sr VP-Sls)*
Matt Hickman *(VP-Sls-Major Accts-West)*
Michael Fisher *(Pres)*
Kelly Kennedy *(Sr VP-Global Sls)*
David McRae *(COO)*
Keith Scheer *(Sr VP-Product Dev)*
Bryan Finke *(VP-Comm Strategies)*
Erik Schulze *(VP-Customer Experience & Comm Strategy)*
Jason Warnock *(VP-Intelligence Products)*
Sue Zabran *(VP-Production)*

Division (Domestic):

Infogroup Licensing **(2)**
1020 E 1st St NE 68046, Papillion, NE 68046
Tel.: (402) 593-4500
Web Site: http://www.license.infousa.com
Sales Range: $75-99.9 Million
Marketing Data Licensing
N.A.I.C.S.: 533110
Jim DeRouchey *(Pres)*

Infogroup Targeting Solutions **(2)**
1020 E 1st St, Papillion, NE 68046
Tel.: (866) 872-1313
Web Site: http://www.infogrouptargeting.com
List Management
N.A.I.C.S.: 513140
Kerry Alvarez *(Sr Mgr-Client Mktg & De-sign)*
Jeff Babcook *(VP-Program Mgmt)*
Sumit Bhalla *(VP-Client Svcs)*
Lynn Bolen *(VP-Mktg Strategy & Insights)*
Tom Defloria *(VP-Digital Solutions & Strate-gic Partnerships)*
Dana Hayman *(VP-Strategy & Insights)*
Mike Hrin *(VP-Digital Acq Solutions)*
Karen Mayhew *(VP-Consumer List Mgmt)*
Jeff Mungo *(VP-Sls)*
Sal Pecoraro *(VP-Mktg Tech & Support)*

Unit (Domestic):

Infogroup/Edith Roman Associates **(2)**
1 Blue Hill Plz 16th Fl PO Box 1556, Pearl River, NY 10965
Tel.: (845) 620-9000
Web Site: http://www.edithroman.com
Direct Mail Advertising Services
N.A.I.C.S.: 541860

Subsidiary (Domestic):

SalesGenie.com, Inc. **(2)**
1020 E 1st St, Papillion, NE 68046
Tel.: (402) 930-3500
Web Site: http://www.salesgenie.com
Business & Consumer Sales-Lead Data-base & Information Services
N.A.I.C.S.: 518210
Jeromy Schnell *(Dir-Ops)*
David Slobotski *(Mgr-Sls)*
Kari Hein *(Sr Acct Exec)*
Angela Huerta *(Acct Exec)*

Subsidiary (Non-US):

infoCanada Corp. **(2)**
1290 Central Parkway West Suite 500, Mis-sissauga, L5C 4R9, ON, Canada
Tel.: (905) 306-9800
Web Site: http://www.infocanada.ca
Sales Range: $25-49.9 Million
Emp.: 25
Business & Consumer Database Publisher
N.A.I.C.S.: 513140
Raj Padda *(Gen Mgr)*

Noble Environmental Power LLC **(1)**
8 Railroad Ave, Essex, CT 06426
Tel.: (860) 581-5010
Web Site: http://www.noblepower.com
Sales Range: $75-99.9 Million
Renewable Energy Services
N.A.I.C.S.: 221118
Jeffrey M. Nelson *(VP & Gen Mgr-Operating Projects)*
Harry Silton *(VP-Energy Markets)*
Pamela Sutton-Hall *(VP-Portfolio Mgmt & Treasury)*
C. Kay McCall *(Pres & CEO)*

Ollie's Bargain Outlet Holdings, Inc. **(1)**
6295 Allentown Blvd, Harrisburg, PA 17112
Tel.: (717) 657-8243

Web Site: https://www.ollies.us
Rev.: $2,102,662,000
Assets: $2,294,594,000
Liabilities: $786,362,000
Net Worth: $1,508,232,000
Earnings: $181,439,000
Emp.: 5,500
Fiscal Year-end: 02/03/2024
Holding Company; Discount Variety Stores
Operator
N.A.I.C.S.: 551112
Robert F. Helm *(CFO, Exec VP & Sr VP)*
Eric van der Valk *(Co-Pres, COO & Exec VP)*
Tom Kuypers *(Sr VP-Mktg & Adv)*
Scott Osborne *(Sr VP/VP-Store Ops)*
Chris Zender *(COO & Exec VP)*
Jim Comitale *(Gen Counsel & Sr VP)*
Larry Kraus *(CIO & Exec VP)*
Steven Horowitz *(Sr VP-Real Estate & Construction)*
Brian McNabb *(Sr VP-Supply Chain)*
Tirza Shreiber *(Sr VP-Human Resources)*
Shane Thornton *(VP-Merchandising)*
Timothy Maglowski *(VP-Divisional Merchandising & Mgr-Housewares & Clothing)*

Subsidiary (Domestic):

Ollie's Bargain Outlet, Inc.   (2)
6295 Allentown Blvd Ste 1, Harrisburg, PA
17112-2606
Tel.: (717) 657-2300
Web Site: http://www.ollies.us
Sales Range: $600-649.9 Million
Discount Variety Stores Operator
N.A.I.C.S.: 455219
John W. Swygert Jr. *(COO & Exec VP)*
Kevin McLain *(Sr VP & Gen Mgr-Mdse)*
Omar Segura *(Sr VP-Store Ops)*
Howard Freedman *(VP-Mdsg)*
Kelly Costanza *(Sr VP-HR)*
Robert Bertram *(Gen Counsel & VP)*
Andre Dickemann *(VP-Logistics & Distr)*
Dan Haines *(VP-Mktg & Adv)*
Jay Stasz *(CFO & Sr VP)*
Sean Trepiccione *(Mgr-Distr Safety & Risk)*
Bruce Pyke *(Dir-Loss Prevention)*
Daniel Turno *(Mgr-Loss Prevention-South Carolina)*

Shoes For Crews, LLC   (1)
250 S Australian Ave, West Palm Beach, FL
33401
Web Site: http://www.shoesforcrews.com
Footwear Mfr & Sales
N.A.I.C.S.: 316210
Matthew K. Smith *(Chm)*
Nathan Crary *(Exec VP-Product Creation & Innovation)*
Jim O'Connor *(VP/Gen Mgr-Indus Bus)*
Donald Watros *(Pres & CEO)*
Brian Bugara *(Exec VP-Sls & Bus Dev)*

Truck Hero, Inc.   (1)
5400 Data Ct, Ann Arbor, MI 48108
Tel.: (734) 677-0444
Web Site: http://www.truck-hero.com
Automotive Accessories Mfr
N.A.I.C.S.: 336390
William J. Reminder *(CEO)*
Marla Zwas *(Gen Counsel)*
Kelly Kneifl *(COO)*
Ryan Herman *(Exec VP-Sls)*
Mark Hickey *(Exec VP-Ops)*
Christina Baldwin *(Chief HR Officer)*

Subsidiary (Domestic):

Lund International Holding
Company   (2)
4325 Hamilton Mill Rd Ste 400, Buford, GA
30518
Tel.: (770) 339-5800
Web Site: http://www.lundinternational.com
Sales Range: $75-99.9 Million
Automotive Aftermarket Accessory Designer, Mfr & Distr
N.A.I.C.S.: 336390
Mitch Fogle *(Pres & CEO)*
Tammy Gracek *(COO & Gen Mgr-OE)*
Lee McGuire *(Sr Dir-Mktg-Jeep & Off Road)*

Subsidiary (Domestic):

Roadworks Manufacturing, Inc.   (3)
3565 E 300 N, Lafayette, IN 47905
Tel.: (765) 742-7200
Web Site: http://www.roadworksmfg.com
Motor Vehicle Body Mfr

N.A.I.C.S.: 336211

Roll-N-Lock Corp.   (3)
2033 W McNab Rd Ste 2, Pompano Beach,
FL 33069
Web Site: http://www.rollnlock.com
Sales Range: $1-9.9 Million
Emp.: 80
Manufactures Tonneau Covers & Other
Cargo Management Product Mfr
N.A.I.C.S.: 336120

Subsidiary (Domestic):

Omix-ADA, Inc.   (2)
460 Horizon Dr, Suwanee, GA 30024
Tel.: (770) 614-6101
Web Site: http://www.omix-ada.com
Automotive Accessories Mfr
N.A.I.C.S.: 336390

CCN INTERNATIONAL INC.
200 Lehigh St, Geneva, NY 14456
Tel.: (315) 789-4400
Web Site:
    http://www.ccninternational.com
Sales Range: $10-24.9 Million
Emp.: 100
Manufactures Wood Office Furniture
N.A.I.C.S.: 337211
Richard Conoyer *(Pres)*
Ann Nenneau *(Owner)*
Terri Fisher *(Controller)*
Tim Lesslie *(VP)*

CCNG REALTY, INC.
13453 Hwy 71 W, Bee Cave, TX
78738
Tel.: (512) 421-8520
Web Site: http://www.ccngrealty.com
Year Founded: 1998
Sales Range: $10-24.9 Million
Emp.: 12
Real Estate Development
N.A.I.C.S.: 531390
Kelley Cloud *(Exec VP)*

CCP FUND III MANAGEMENT LLC
6455 S Yosemite St 140, Greenwood
Village, CO 80111
Tel.: (720) 398-6500
Web Site:
    http://www.creocapitalpartners.com
Year Founded: 2005
Emp.: 5
Privater Equity Firm
N.A.I.C.S.: 523999
Rob W. Holland *(Co-Founder & Partner)*
Patrick Moulder *(Partner)*

Subsidiaries:

Brooks Group Insurance Agency,
LLC.   (1)
70 Bridge Plz Dr, Manalapan, NJ 07726
Tel.: (732) 972-0600
Web Site: http://www.brooks-ins.com
Insurance Agencies & Brokerages
N.A.I.C.S.: 524210

Mountain High Knitwear Ltd.   (1)
1791 W Dairy Pl, Tucson, AZ 85705
Tel.: (520) 690-2760
Sales Range: $25-49.9 Million
Mfr & Distr of Hosiery for Men & Women
N.A.I.C.S.: 315120

CCP GLOBAL INC.
PO Box 1645, Woodstock, IL 60098
Tel.: (913) 451-0400
Web Site: http://www.ccpglobal.com
Rev.: $13,435,845
Emp.: 10
Custom Computer Programming Services
N.A.I.C.S.: 541511
Christopher Wojcik *(Pres)*

CCRES, INC.

443 Boot Rd, Downingtown, PA
19335
Tel.: (484) 593-5040   PA
Web Site: http://www.ccres.org
Year Founded: 1999
Sales Range: $10-24.9 Million
Emp.: 881
Educational Support Services
N.A.I.C.S.: 611710
Joseph O'Brien *(Chm)*

CCS GLOBAL TECH
13475 Danielson St Ste 230, Poway,
CA 92064
Tel.: (858) 208-4131
Web Site:
    https://www.ccsglobaltech.com
Year Founded: 1997
Sales Range: $10-24.9 Million
Emp.: 300
It Consulting
N.A.I.C.S.: 541690
Raminder Singh *(CEO)*

CCS GROUP INC.
300 Connecticut Blvd, East Hartford,
CT 06108
Tel.: (860) 289-3461
Web Site:
    http://www.gengrasvolvohart
    ford.com
Sales Range: $25-49.9 Million
Emp.: 100
Dealer of New & Used Automobiles
N.A.I.C.S.: 441110
E. Clayton Gengras Jr. *(Pres)*

CCS MEDICAL HOLDINGS, INC.
1505 LBJ Freeway Ste 550, Farmers
Branch, TX 75234
Tel.: (972) 628-2100   DE
Web Site: http://www.ccsmed.com
Sales Range: $400-449.9 Million
Emp.: 1,500
Holding Company
N.A.I.C.S.: 551112
Barbara Escalante Hess *(Chief HR Officer)*
Tony Vahedian *(CEO)*

Subsidiaries:

CCS Medical, Inc.   (1)
14255 49th St N Ste 301, Clearwater, FL
33762
Tel.: (727) 531-9161
Web Site: http://www.ccsmed.com
Medical Supplies & Pharmaceutical Home
Delivery Services
N.A.I.C.S.: 423450

Branch (Domestic):

CCS Medical, Inc.   (2)
615 S Ware Blvd, Tampa, FL 33619-4444
Tel.: (813) 621-4800
Web Site: http://www.ccsmed.com
Sales Range: $50-74.9 Million
Emp.: 150
Medical Supplies & Pharmaceutical Home
Delivery Services
N.A.I.C.S.: 456110
Kristie Bibelhauser *(Mgr-Revenue Cycle)*
James Bailey *(Sr VP-Corp Dev)*
Rodney Carson *(Pres & CEO)*
Bob Hansen *(Sr VP-IT)*
Tom Hofmeister *(CFO)*
Linda Langiotti *(Sr VP-Sls Ops)*
Monica Raines *(Chief Compliance & Privacy Officer, Gen Counsel & Sr VP)*
David Tucker *(Sr VP-Bus Dev)*

CCS-INC.
105 Industrial Dr, Christiansburg, VA
24073
Tel.: (540) 382-4234
Web Site: http://www.ccs-inc.com
Year Founded: 1981
Sales Range: $10-24.9 Million
Emp.: 100

Mfr & Sales of Industrial Computing
Solutions
N.A.I.C.S.: 423430
William T. Fleshman *(Owner)*
Priscilla Fleshman *(VP)*
Tim Lawson *(CFO)*
Amy Ankrum *(Dir-Mktg)*
Marty Muscatello *(Pres & CEO)*

CCT RAIL SYSTEM CORPORATION
2095 Ave F, White City, OR 97503
Tel.: (509) 724-0101
Web Site:
    http://www.cctrailsystem.com
Year Founded: 2012
Sales Range: Less than $1 Million
Emp.: 3
Holding Company
N.A.I.C.S.: 551112
Scott B. DeVries *(Owner & Pres)*

Subsidiaries:

Rogue Valley Terminal Railroad
Corporation   (1)
2095 Avenue F, White City, OR
97503-3210   (100%)
Tel.: (541) 621-6736
Web Site: http://www.roguevalleyrr.com
Rev.: $250,000
Emp.: 6
Short-Line Railroad Distr
N.A.I.C.S.: 482112
Scott DeVries *(Pres & Gen Mgr)*

CCT TECHNOLOGIES INC.
482 W San Carlos St, San Jose, CA
95110-2627
Tel.: (408) 519-3200
Web Site: https://www.cland.com
Sales Range: $25-49.9 Million
Emp.: 60
Computers, Sale & Repair
N.A.I.C.S.: 423430
Connie Tang *(Pres)*
Mandy Yaghoubi *(Sr Dir-Sls)*
K. Pang *(Mgr-Ops)*
Kent Ho *(Engr-Sys)*
Kevin Nguyen *(Engr-Tech Support)*

CCTV CAMERA PROS, LLC
7142 N Seacrest Blvd, Lantana, FL
33462
Tel.: (561) 433-8488
Web Site:
    https://www.cctvcamerapros.com
Year Founded: 2006
Sales Range: $1-9.9 Million
Emp.: 7
Closed Circuit Television Product Mfr
& Whslr
N.A.I.C.S.: 517111
Mike Haldas *(Founder & Mng Partner)*

CCX CORPORATION
1399 Horizon Ave, Lafayette, CO
80026
Tel.: (303) 666-5206   CO
Web Site: http://www.ccxcorp.com
Year Founded: 1995
Sales Range: $10-24.9 Million
Emp.: 120
Cable Connector Mfr & Distr
N.A.I.C.S.: 335999
Cesar Martinez *(VP-Ops-Mexico)*
Jon Westerlind *(VP-Engrg & Quality)*
Nathan Montoya *(Mgr-NPI)*
Ray Sparkman *(CFO, CTO & VP-Fin & IT)*
Thomas Andrew Hanchin *(Co-Founder, Chm & CEO)*
David Videon *(Co-Founder & Pres)*
Eli Bustamante *(VP-Ops-USA)*

CD HARTNETT COMPANY

CD Hartnett Company—(Continued)

300 N Main St, Weatherford, TX
76086
Tel.: (817) 594-3813
Web Site: http://www.cd-hartnett.com
Sales Range: $10-24.9 Million
Emp.: 300
General Line Groceries
N.A.I.C.S.: 424410
Stephen E. Milliken (Pres)
Evelyn Bailey (VP)
Rick Maitlen (Mgr-Sls)
Jack Hodges (Dir-Pur)
Jody Ellis (Dir-Ops)

CD&M COMMUNICATIONS
22 York St, Portland, ME 04101
Tel.: (207) 774-7528
Web Site: https://cdmc.com
Year Founded: 1978
Advetising Agency
N.A.I.C.S.: 541810
Duncan Stout (Pres)
Linda Wagner Jones (Controller)
Theanna Twitchell (Mgr-Media)
Mike Yoder (Creative Dir)
Mike Yoder (Creative Dir)
Linda Spring (Art Dir)

Subsidiaries:

Briggs Advertising, Inc.   (1)
48 Free St, Portland, ME 04101
Tel.: (207) 443-2067
Web Site: http://www.briggsadv.com
Advertising Services
N.A.I.C.S.: 541810

CDA INCORPORATED
1 N 3rd St, Memphis, TN 38103-2610
Tel.: (901) 526-5313   TN
Web Site: http://www.cdaglobal.com
Year Founded: 1988
Sales Range: $10-24.9 Million
Emp.: 450
Security Guards & Patrol Services
N.A.I.C.S.: 561612
Clifton Dates (Pres)

Subsidiaries:

Maxsent Inc.   (1)
137 Mitchells Chance Rd, Edgewater, MD
21037
Tel.: (443) 221-2750
Commercial & Government Contract Security Program Management Services
N.A.I.C.S.: 561612
Todd A. Pattison (Pres & CEO)

CDA METALS
3900 E Broadway Ave, Spokane, WA
99202
Tel.: (509) 535-6363
Web Site: http://www.stocksteel.com
Year Founded: 1884
Rev.: $12,944,122
Emp.: 80
Metal Fabricating & Cutting Services
N.A.I.C.S.: 332312
Jimmie T. Coulson (Pres)
Larry Coulson (VP & Gen Mgr)

CDC DATA, LLC
9735 Lurline Ave, Chatsworth, CA
91311
Tel.: (818) 350-5072   CA
Web Site:
   https://www.chatsworthdata.com
Year Founded: 2010
Emp.: 20
Holding Company; Optical Mark Readers, Scanners, Impact Recording Devices & Cable Testers Designer, Mfr & Distr
N.A.I.C.S.: 551112
Ronald Ginther (Pres)
Armando Ponce (VP-Sls & Worldwide Bus Dev)

Subsidiaries:

Chatsworth Data Corporation   (1)
9735 Lurline Ave, Chatsworth, CA
91311   (100%)
Tel.: (818) 350-5072
Web Site: http://www.chatsworthdata.com
Sales Range: $1-9.9 Million
Emp.: 50
Optical Mark Readers, Scanners, Impact Recording Devices & Cable Testers Designer, Mfr & Distr
N.A.I.C.S.: 334118
Armando Ponce (VP)
Ronald Ginther (Pres)

CDC FOUNDATION
600 Peachtree St NE Ste 1000, Atlanta, GA 30308
Tel.: (404) 653-0790
Web Site:
   https://www.cdcfoundation.org
Year Founded: 1992
Health Organization Services
N.A.I.C.S.: 813212

CDC PUBLISHING LLC
2001 9th Ave, Vero Beach, FL 32960
Tel.: (772) 770-6003
Web Site: http://www.cdcnews.com
Year Founded: 1977
Sales Range: $25-49.9 Million
Emp.: 500
Publishers of Construction Leads
N.A.I.C.S.: 513120
Teresa Kessler (Acct Mgr)
Stephen Jarvis (Dir-Fin)
Chris Schroeder (Mgr-Sls)

CDEX INC.
4555 S Palo Verde Rd Ste 123, Tucson, AZ 85714
Tel.: (520) 745-5172   NV
Web Site: http://www.cdex-inc.com
Year Founded: 2001
Sales Range: Less than $1 Million
Emp.: 3
Chemical Products Mfr
N.A.I.C.S.: 325998
Jeffery K. Brumfield (Chm & CEO)

CDF CORPORATION
77 Industrial Park Rd, Plymouth, MA
02360-4868
Tel.: (508) 747-5858
Web Site: https://www.cdf1.com
Year Founded: 1971
Sales Range: $10-24.9 Million
Emp.: 100
Mfr of Plastic Liners & Lids for Pails & Drums
N.A.I.C.S.: 326199
David Newman (Controller)
Steve Gosling (Dir-Tech-New Product Dev)
Bill Harvey (VP-Mfg)
Joseph J. Sullivan Jr. (Pres)

CDHM ADVERTISING
1100 Summer St 1st Fl, Stamford, CT
06905
Tel.: (203) 967-7200   CT
Year Founded: 1964
Rev.: $10,000,000
Emp.: 15
Advetising Agency
N.A.I.C.S.: 541810
Gary W. Sumple (Mng Partner)
John E. Walker (Owner)
Don Vega (Sr Acct Exec)
Dana Markiewicz (Acct Exec)

CDI GROUP INC.
1330 Post Oak Blvd Ste 2390, Houston, TX 77056
Tel.: (713) 622-8201
Sales Range: $25-49.9 Million
Emp.: 17

Venture Capital Company
N.A.I.C.S.: 523910

CDI INTERNATIONAL INC.
525 S 4th St, Philadelphia, PA 19147
Tel.: (215) 829-4433
Web Site: https://www.cdimugs.com
Sales Range: $1-9.9 Million
Emp.: 7
Decorative Home Furnishings & Supplies
N.A.I.C.S.: 423220
Fredric Edelstein (Pres)

CDI MEDIA INC.
2323 S 3600 W, Salt Lake City, UT
84119
Tel.: (801) 977-0077
Web Site: http://www.cdimedia.com
Year Founded: 1982
Sales Range: $1-9.9 Million
Emp.: 100
Mfr & Duplicator of Electronic Media Products
N.A.I.C.S.: 512199
Gary G. Jackson (Founder, CEO & COO)
Allen Web (CFO)
Brian McMillan (Controller)

CDI SERVICES INC.
3610 Deahl Ct, South Bend, IN
46619
Tel.: (574) 271-2027
Web Site:
   http://www.911roadrepair.com
Year Founded: 1973
Sales Range: $10-24.9 Million
Emp.: 350
General Truck Repair
N.A.I.C.S.: 541614
Thomas Gast (Pres)

CDI, INC.
200 S 8th St, Terre Haute, IN 47807
Tel.: (812) 232-3327
Web Site: http://www.cdiinc.net
Year Founded: 1961
Sales Range: $25-49.9 Million
Emp.: 80
Building Construction Services
N.A.I.C.S.: 236210
Rita K. Wallace (CFO, Treas & Sec)

CDK BUILDERS INC.
44 Greenfield Ave, San Anselmo, CA
94960
Tel.: (415) 419-5643
Web Site:
   https://www.cdkbuilders.com
Year Founded: 1952
Sales Range: $1-9.9 Million
Emp.: 20
Single-Family Housing Construction
N.A.I.C.S.: 236115
Gary Suhrke (Owner & Pres)

CDL ELECTRIC COMPANY, INC.
1308 N Walnut St, Pittsburg, KS
66762
Tel.: (620) 231-6420
Web Site: http://www.cdl-electric.com
Rev.: $3,500,000
Emp.: 400
Electrical Contractor
N.A.I.C.S.: 238210
Larry Seward (Pres)
Tom Yoakam (CFO)

Subsidiaries:

Allpress & Moore Railroad Signal Contractors Inc.   (1)
9015 NE 136th St, Liberty, MO 64068-8213
Tel.: (816) 781-5734

Web Site: http://www... ...
Rev.: ... ...
Emp.: 7
Rail Transportation Services
N.A.I.C.S.: 488210

CDM INVESTMENT GROUP, INC.
4600 Martha Truman Rd, Grandview,
MO 64030
Tel.: (913) 317-8532   NE
Web Site:
   http://www.cdminvestmentgroup.com
Sales Range: $125-149.9 Million
Emp.: 1,300
Holding Company
N.A.I.C.S.: 551112
Kent Vipond (CEO)
Brian Baumert (CFO)
Bradley C. Sampson (CMO)

Subsidiaries:

Airtite Contractors Inc.   (1)
343 Carol Ln, Elmhurst, IL 60126
Tel.: (630) 530-9001
Sales Range: $25-49.9 Million
Emp.: 100
Interior Construction, Acoustical Ceilings, Acoustical Wall Panels, Access Flooring, Radiant Ceiling Systems & Drywall
N.A.I.C.S.: 238310

CDM Service Group, Inc.   (1)
13324 Chandler Rd, Omaha, NE 68138
Tel.: (402) 896-1614
Web Site:
   http://www.cdminvestmentgroup.com
Sales Range: $10-24.9 Million
Emp.: 29
Office Administrative Services
N.A.I.C.S.: 561110
Kent Vipond (CEO)
Brian Baumert (CFO)
Barry Sklenar (Project Mgr)
Bradley C. Sampson (CMO)

CDM SMITH INC.
75 State St Ste 701, Boston, MA
02109
Tel.: (617) 452-6000   MA
Web Site: http://www.cdmsmith.com
Year Founded: 1947
Sales Range: $650-699.9 Million
Emp.: 5,000
Civil & Environmental Engineering, Construction & Consulting Services
N.A.I.C.S.: 541330
Timothy B. Wall (Chm, Pres & CEO)
Thierry Desmaris (Exec VP-Fin, Mergers & Acquisitions)
David M. Neitz (CIO)
Stuart Richardson (Mng Dir-Australia)
Carlos Echalar (Chief HR Officer)
Russ Tamblyn (Dir-Virtual Design & Construction Grp)
Susan Glover (Mgr-Benefits & Wellness)
Jim Riley (Sr VP & Dir-Transportation-Natl)
Doug LaVoie (Sr VP & Grp Mgr-Transportation)
Anthony B. Bouchard (Pres-North America)
Beth Colling (Chief Compliance Officer)
Gwen Baker (Pres-Federal Svcs)
Julia B. Forgas (CMO)
Bill Schultz (VP-Bus Relationship Mgmt & PMO Functions-Business Tech)

Subsidiaries:

CDM Constructors Inc.   (1)
75 State St Ste701, Boston, MA
02109   (100%)
Tel.: (617) 452-6000
Web Site: http://www.cdm.com
Sales Range: $50-74.9 Million
Emp.: 700
Civil & Environmental Engineering & Construction Services

N.A.I.C.S.: 237990
Marc Goldman *(Dir-FP&A)*
Myles Johnson *(Mgr-Construction)*
John Weston *(VP & Area Mgr-Northeast)*

**CDM Federal Programs
Corporation** (1)
14420 Albemarle Point Pl Ste 210, Chantilly, VA 20151 **(100%)**
Tel.: (703) 968-0900
Web Site: http://www.cdm.com
Sales Range: $25-49.9 Million
Emp.: 65
Federal Engineering Program Management Services
N.A.I.C.S.: 541330

CDM Smith Consult GmbH (1)
Am Umweltpark 3-5, Bochum, 44793, Germany
Tel.: (49) 234687750
Web Site: http://www.cdmsmith.com
Sales Range: $100-124.9 Million
Emp.: 450
Civil & Environmental Engineering, Construction & Consulting Services
N.A.I.C.S.: 541690
Ralf Bufler *(Chm)*

CDM Smith Ireland Ltd. (1)
5th Floor O'Connell Bridge House D'Olier Street, Dublin, 2, Ireland
Tel.: (353) 1 672 2700
Engineeering Services
N.A.I.C.S.: 541330
Lorraine Gaston *(Project Mgr)*

CDM Smith Sp. z o.o. (1)
Al Jerozolimskie 123a, 02-017, Warsaw, Poland
Tel.: (48) 22 55193 00
Engineeering Services
N.A.I.C.S.: 541330

CDMM CORP.
1899 Wynkoop St Ste 550, Denver, CO 80202-1327
Tel.: (303) 571-5211   CO
Web Site: http://www.wrcolo.com
Year Founded: 1992
Sales Range: $25-49.9 Million
Emp.: 70
Office Furniture Whslr
N.A.I.C.S.: 423210
Carla Dore *(Pres & CEO)*
Martin Majka *(CFO)*
Catherine Hall *(VP-Svc Div)*
Steve Sharbo *(Dir-Distr)*
Rebecca Bahnsen *(Dir-IT)*
Tim Van Iddekinge *(Controller)*
Stephanie Jewell *(Mgr-Acct)*
Rick Golden *(VP-Sls)*

CDO TECHNOLOGIES INC.
3200 Springfield St Ste 320, Dayton, OH 45431
Tel.: (937) 258-0022
Web Site: http://www.cdotech.com
Sales Range: $10-24.9 Million
Emp.: 200
Computer Integrated Systems Design
N.A.I.C.S.: 541512
Alphonso Wofford *(Pres & CEO)*
Don Ertel *(VP-Sys Tech)*
Gary Volz *(VP-Fin)*
Dave Dunning *(Dir-Ops)*
Greg Greening *(Dir-Bus Dev)*

CDP SERVICES LLC
936 Lacon Dr, Newport News, VA 23608
Tel.: (757) 872-6417
Sales Range: $10-24.9 Million
Emp.: 4
Distributing Office Equipment
N.A.I.C.S.: 423420
Daniel Price *(Pres)*

CDR MAGUIRE INC.
8669 NW 36 St Ste 340, Doral, FL 33166
Tel.: (786) 235-8534   RI

Web Site:
  https://www.cdrmaguire.com
Year Founded: 1938
Emp.: 175
Engineeering Services
N.A.I.C.S.: 541330
Thomas Stockhausen *(Sr VP)*
Carlos A. Duart *(Pres)*
Andre A. Duart *(COO)*
Matthew Macey Sr. *(VP & Reg Dir-Mid-Atlantic)*

Subsidiaries:

**CDR Maguire Inc. - Connecticut
Office** (1)
2080 Silas Deane Hwy, Rocky Hill, CT 06067
Tel.: (860) 563-3158
Web Site: http://www.cdrmaguire.com
Engineeering Services
N.A.I.C.S.: 541330
Y. R. Anand *(Partner)*

**CDR Maguire Inc. - Pennsylvania
Office** (1)
503 Martindale St Ste 610, Pittsburgh, PA 15212
Tel.: (412) 322-8340
Web Site: http://www.cdrmaguire.com
Engineeering Services
N.A.I.C.S.: 541330
Louis Rocchini *(Sr VP & Mgr-Mid Atlantic Transportation)*
Michael S. Moorman *(Sr VP & Dir-Mid Atlantic Reg)*

**CDR Maguire Inc. - Rhode Island
Office** (1)
225 Chapman St 4th Fl, Providence, RI 02905
Tel.: (401) 272-6000
Web Site: http://www.cdrmaguire.com
Engineeering Services
N.A.I.C.S.: 541330

**CDR Maguire Inc. - Virgin Islands
Office** (1)
1142 King St, Saint Croix, VI 00820
Tel.: (340) 690-0308
Web Site: http://www.cdrmaguire.com
Engineeering Services
N.A.I.C.S.: 541330

McTish Kunkel & Associates Inc. (1)
3500 Winchester Road Ste 300, Allentown, PA 18104
Tel.: (610) 791-2700
Web Site: http://www.mctish.com
Engineeering Services
N.A.I.C.S.: 541330
John P. Ryan *(VP)*

CDS ENSEMBLES, INC.
300 Connecticut Ave, Greer, SC 29650
Tel.: (864) 848-3499   SC
Web Site:
  http://www.cdsensembles.com
Year Founded: 1981
Sales Range: $10-24.9 Million
Emp.: 100
Provider of Manmade or Silk Fabric Bedding
N.A.I.C.S.: 313210
David Krieger *(Chm)*

CDS GLOBAL LOGISTICS INC.
1001 Virgina Ave Ste 150, Atlanta, GA 30354
Tel.: (404) 762-0083
Year Founded: 1995
Sales Range: $10-24.9 Million
Emp.: 35
Customs Brokerage Services
N.A.I.C.S.: 488510
Henry Wiseman *(CEO)*
Rajiv Pant *(Chief Tech & Product Officer & Gen Mgr-Tech Platforms)*

CDS MONARCH, INC.
860 Hard Rd, Webster, NY 14580
Tel.: (585) 341-4600   NY

Web Site: http://www.cdsmonarch.org
Year Founded: 1977
Sales Range: $50-74.9 Million
Emp.: 1,109
Individual & Family Support Services
N.A.I.C.S.: 624190
Sylvester Zielinski *(COO)*
Jean Lowe *(Sec)*
Sankar Sewnauth *(Pres & CEO)*
Robert Mixon *(Exec VP-Strategic Plng & Staff Dev)*
Sharon Marble *(Exec VP-Program Ops & Org Dev)*

**CDS MOVING EQUIPMENT
INC.**
375 W Manville St, Rancho Dominguez, CA 90220
Tel.: (310) 631-1100
Web Site: https://www.cds-usa.com
Sales Range: $25-49.9 Million
Emp.: 75
Industrial Moving Equipment
N.A.I.C.S.: 423830
Allen J. Sidor *(Pres)*
Randy Williams *(VP-Sls)*
Eddie Scoseria *(Mgr-Customer Svc)*
Tom Roberts *(Acct Mgr)*

CDS, LLC
100 Church St S, New Haven, CT 06519
Tel.: (203) 776-2637
Web Site:
  https://www.cdsnewhaven.com
Year Founded: 1990
Sales Range: $10-24.9 Million
Emp.: 7
Commercial & Institutional Building Construction Services
N.A.I.C.S.: 236220
Clifford R. Winkel *(Pres)*

CDSNET, INC.
No 9 6053 W Century Blvd, Los Angeles, CA 90045-6430
Tel.: (213) 427-2000
Web Site: http://www.cds.net
Sales Range: $10-24.9 Million
Emp.: 85
Data Processing Services
N.A.I.C.S.: 518210

CDW MERCHANTS, INC.
8338 Austin Ave, Morton Grove, IL 60058
Tel.: (847) 733-1469
Web Site:
  http://www.cdwmerchants.com
Year Founded: 2005
Sales Range: $10-24.9 Million
Emp.: 20
3D Visual Retail Displays & E-Commerce Gift Packaging
N.A.I.C.S.: 459999

CDYNE CORPORATION
505 Independence Pkwy Ste 300, Chesapeake, VA 23320-5178
Tel.: (757) 544-9510
Web Site: https://www.cdyne.com
Year Founded: 2001
Sales Range: $1-9.9 Million
Emp.: 50
Web Services Solutions Encompassing Data Enhancement, Data Verification & Communication Tools
N.A.I.C.S.: 513210
Christopher M. Chenoweth *(CIO)*

CE COMPETITIVE EDGE LLC
5924 Red Arrow Hwy, Stevensville, MI 49127
Tel.: (269) 429-0404
Web Site: https://www.competitive-edge.net

Year Founded: 1993
Promotional Products & Business Gifts Whslr
N.A.I.C.S.: 424990
Terry Powers *(Sr Acct Mgr)*
Mary Jo Tomasini *(Founder & CEO)*
Lisa DeJong *(VP-Sls)*
Paula Wygonik *(Pres)*

Subsidiaries:

**Gaslight Promotional Consulting,
Inc.** (1)
535 Greenwood Ave SE Ste 300, Grand Rapids, MI 49506-2901
Tel.: (616) 451-4307
Web Site:
  http://www.gaslightpromotions.com
Telemarketing Bureaus & Other Contact Centers
N.A.I.C.S.: 561422

CE DE CANDY, INC.
1091 Lousons Rd, Union, NJ 07083
Tel.: (908) 964-0660   NJ
Web Site: http://www.smarties.com
Year Founded: 1949
Sales Range: $75-99.9 Million
Emp.: 115
Mfr of Candies
N.A.I.C.S.: 311340
Edward Dee *(Chm)*
Eric Ostrow *(VP-Sls & Mktg)*
Tina Moyer *(Controller)*

CE STAR HOLDINGS, LLC
c/o Commercial Metal Forming PO Box 599, Youngstown, OH 44501
Tel.: (330) 740-8300   DE
Web Site: http://www.ce-starllc.com
Year Founded: 2016
Holding Company; Engineered Specialty Metal Products Mfr
N.A.I.C.S.: 551112
Dennis Smith *(Chm)*

Subsidiaries:

Star Cases, LLC (1)
500 W 200 N, North Salt Lake, UT 84054
Tel.: (801) 298-5900
Web Site: http://www.zerocases.com
Metal Protective Cases & Enclosures Mfr
N.A.I.C.S.: 332431
Ryan Ramsey *(Pres)*

Star Forge, LLC (1)
8531 E Marginal Way S, Tukwila, WA 98108-4018
Tel.: (206) 762-1100
Web Site: http://www.jorgensenforge.com
Metal Forging Mfr
N.A.I.C.S.: 332112
Mike Jewell *(Pres & CEO)*

**Star Forming Manufacturing,
LLC** (1)
1775 Logan Ave, Youngstown, OH 44505
Tel.: (330) 740-8300
Web Site: http://www.cmforming.com
Metal Tank Mfr
N.A.I.C.S.: 332420
Bob Messaros *(Pres & CEO)*

Plant (Domestic):

**Star Forming Manufacturing, LLC -
Orange Plant** (2)
341 W Collins Ave, Orange, CA 92867
Tel.: (714) 532-6321
Web Site: http://www.cmforming.com
Forged Metal Products Mfr
N.A.I.C.S.: 332112
Mark Davidson *(Gen Mgr)*

CEACO INC.
70 Bridge St Ste 200, Newton, MA 02458
Tel.: (617) 926-8080
Web Site: https://www.ceaco.com
Year Founded: 1987
Rev.: $14,000,000
Emp.: 19
Puzzles Mfr

Ceaco Inc.—(Continued)
N.A.I.C.S.: 339930
Carol J. Glazer *(Pres)*
Alison Yada *(VP-Mktg)*

Subsidiaries:

Gamewright (1)
70 Ridge St Ste 200, Newton, MA 02458
Tel.: (617) 926-8080
Web Site: http://www.gamewright.com
Sales Range: $10-24.9 Million
Games & Puzzles Mfr & Sales
N.A.I.C.S.: 339930

CEAVCO AUDIO-VISUAL COMPANY
6240 W 54th Ave, Arvada, CO 80002
Tel.: (303) 539-3400
Web Site: http://www.ceavco.com
Sales Range: $1-9.9 Million
Emp.: 38
Electrical Appliances, Television &
Radio
N.A.I.C.S.: 423620
Brian Miller *(Branch Mgr)*

CECCHETTI WINE COMPANY
PO Box 637, Vineburg, CA 95487
Tel.: (707) 996-7221
Web Site:
http://www.cecchettiwineco.com
Year Founded: 2006
Sales Range: $10-24.9 Million
Emp.: 10
Winery
N.A.I.C.S.: 312130
Roy Cecchetti *(Co-Founder & CEO)*
Rachael Cecchetti *(Co-Founder)*
Bob Broman *(VP-Product Dev &
Winemaker)*

CECE FEINBERG PUBLIC RELATIONS
336 W 37th St Ste 840, New York,
NY 10018
Tel.: (212) 939-7265
Web Site: http://www.feinbergpr.com
Sales Range: Less than $1 Million
Emp.: 6
Entertainment, Fashion/Apparel, Local Marketing, Public Relations
N.A.I.C.S.: 541820
Cece Feinberg *(VP)*

CECE'S VEGGIE CO.
3714 Bluestein Dr Ste 650, Austin,
TX 78721
Tel.: (512) 200-3337
Web Site:
http://www.cecesveggieco.com
Year Founded: 2015
Sales Range: $10-24.9 Million
Emp.: 190
Organic Farming Services
N.A.I.C.S.: 111211
Mason Arnold *(Founder)*

CECIL I. WALKER MACHINERY CO.
1625 W Dupont Ave, Belle, WV
25015
Tel.: (304) 949-6400
Web Site: http://www.walker-cat.com
Sales Range: $125-149.9 Million
Emp.: 250
Front End Loaders
N.A.I.C.S.: 423810
Steve Walker *(Pres & COO)*
Jim Chrivia *(Branch Mgr)*
Bobbi Jo Thomas *(Controller-
Inventory)*
Josie Travis *(Coord-Employment)*
Andrew Newsom *(Coord-Inside Sls)*
Russ Bond *(Coord-Svc)*
Rodney Canterbury *(Gen Mgr-Power
Sys)*

Walter Clark *(Gen Mgr-Walker Express)*
Larry Holstine *(Mgr)*
Pam Booth *(Mgr-Credit)*
Trey Cooper *(Mgr-Ops)*
Tim McLean *(VP-Ops)*
Morris Pettus *(Acct Mgr-Mining)*
Ruth Brown *(Mgr-HR Ops)*
Steve Goff *(Mgr-Gen Parts Admin &
Inventory Control)*
Ed Pugh *(Mgr-2nd Shift Svc)*
Keith Shaffer *(Mgr-Product Support
Admin)*
Mike Taylor *(Office Mgr)*
Barney Goins *(Asst Mgr-Parts & Svc)*
Christopher Klingler *(Mgr-Charleston
Parts)*
Jody Green *(Mgr-Parts & Svc)*
Kevin Barnhouse *(Mgr-Sls)*
Easter Terry *(Mgr-Svc Dev)*
Andrew Southworth *(Sr VP)*
Tammy Argento *(Coord-Pur)*
Samples Brent *(Product Mgr-Support
Sls)*
Milam James *(Reg Mgr)*

CECO CONCRETE CONSTRUCTION LLC
10100 NW Ambassador Dr Ste 400,
Kansas City, MO 64153
Tel.: (816) 459-7000 DE
Web Site:
http://www.cecoconcrete.com
Year Founded: 1913
Sales Range: $100-124.9 Million
Emp.: 1,800
Framework Subcontractors
N.A.I.C.S.: 238990
Ron Schuster *(Pres)*

CEDAR BROOK FINANCIAL PARTNERS, LLC
5885 Landerbrook Dr Ste 200, Cleveland, OH 44124
Tel.: (440) 683-9200
Web Site:
https://www.cedarbrookfinancial.com
Sales Range: $25-49.9 Million
Emp.: 50
Wealth Management & Financial
Planning
N.A.I.C.S.: 523940
Azim Nakhooda *(Partner & Principal)*
David Robertson *(Partner)*
Eric Rubin *(Partner)*
Kenneth Rogat *(Partner)*
Mark Tichar *(Partner)*
Richard Anderson *(Partner & Dir-
Retirement Plans Div)*
Rebecca Bar-Shain *(Partner)*
Ryan C. Olds *(Partner)*
Shannon Barry *(Partner)*
William Hawke *(Partner)*
Anthony Podojil *(Partner)*
Tom Goodman *(Partner)*
William Glubiak *(CEO)*
Kevin Buzek *(Mgr-Ops)*

CEDAR COUNTRY COOPERATIVE
N6055 State Rd 40, Elk Mound, WI
54739
Tel.: (715) 879-5454
Web Site: http://www.cedarcountry-
coop.com
Year Founded: 1934
Sales Range: $10-24.9 Million
Emp.: 70
Feed
N.A.I.C.S.: 424910

CEDAR COUNTY COOPERATIVE
906 E 7th St Hwy 130 E, Tipton, IA
52772

Tel.: (563) 886-6177
Web Site:
https://www.cedarcountycoop.com
Sales Range: $10-24.9 Million
Emp.: 20
Farm Supplies
N.A.I.C.S.: 424910
Rich Northup *(Asst Mgr)*
David Summers *(Gen Mgr)*

CEDAR CREEK ENERGY CORPORATION
1285 114th Ave NW, Coon Rapids,
MN 55448
Tel.: (763) 432-5261 MN
Web Site:
http://www.cedarcreekenergy.com
Year Founded: 2007
Sales Range: $1-9.9 Million
Solar, Lighting & Building Automation
Installation Contractor
N.A.I.C.S.: 238210
Rob Appelhof *(Pres & CEO)*

CEDAR CREEK INN CORPORATION
27321 La Paz Rd, San Juan Capistrano, CA 92677-3608
Tel.: (949) 497-8696
Web Site:
http://www.cedarcreekinn.com
Rev.: $10,000,000
Emp.: 80
American Restaurant
N.A.I.C.S.: 722511

CEDAR CREEK PARTNERS LLC
10936 W Port Washington Rd, Milwaukee, WI 53202-6644
Tel.: (414) 272-5505 WI
Year Founded: 1997
Sales Range: $10-24.9 Million
Emp.: 4
Private Equity Firm
N.A.I.C.S.: 523999
Robert Cook *(Mng Dir)*
Daniel J. Jagla *(Mng Dir)*
Becky Diedrich *(VP)*

Subsidiaries:

Netcom, Inc. (1)
599 Wheeling Rd, Wheeling, IL 60090-4743
Tel.: (847) 537-6300
Web Site: http://www.netcominc.com
Emp.: 100
Electronic Components
N.A.I.C.S.: 334419
Evangelos Argoudelis *(Chm)*

CEDAR CREST SPECIALTIES INC.
7269 Hwy 60, Cedarburg, WI 53012
Tel.: (262) 377-7252
Web Site:
https://www.cedarcresticecream.com
Rev.: $16,723,049
Emp.: 40
Ice Cream Product Mfr
N.A.I.C.S.: 311520
Kenneth Kohlwey *(Pres)*

CEDAR ENTERPRISES INC.
1328 Dublin Rd Ste 300, Columbus,
OH 43215
Tel.: (614) 294-0631 OH
Web Site:
http://www.cedarenterprises.com
Year Founded: 1993
Sales Range: $200-249.9 Million
Emp.: 200
Holding Company; Restaurant Operations & Management Services
N.A.I.C.S.: 551112
James W. Evans *(Pres)*
Deborah Harmon *(Dir-HR Svcs)*

Subsidiaries:

Cedar of New England, Ltd. (1)
12 Northgate Dr, Windsor Locks, CT 06026
Tel.: (860) 627-7960
Web Site: http://www.cedarenterprises.com
Fast Food Restaurants
N.A.I.C.S.: 722513
Michael Paine *(VP-Div)*
Andy Boothby *(VP-Engrg & Dev)*
Shawn M. Hiller *(VP & Controller)*
Boyd Johanson *(Sr VP-Ops)*

SeaWend Ltd. (1)
19221 36th Ave W Ste 101, Lynnwood, WA
98036-5700
Tel.: (425) 774-3800
Web Site: http://www.cedarenterprises.com
Sales Range: $10-24.9 Million
Emp.: 10
Fast Food Restaurants
N.A.I.C.S.: 722513
Jay D. Karam *(Chm & CEO)*
David Antis *(Mgr)*

Trident Foods, Ltd. (1)
6409 Castleway Ct, Indianapolis, IN 46250
Tel.: (317) 594-3471
Web Site: http://www.cedarenterprises.com
Fast Food Restaurants
N.A.I.C.S.: 722513
Steve Socrates *(VP-Div)*
Lee Ann Cameron *(Office Mgr)*
Laurie Bergeson *(Dir-Trng)*
Andy Boothby *(VP-Engrg & Dev)*
Debbie Harmon *(Dir-HR Svc)*
Shawn M. Hiller *(VP & Controller)*
Boyd Johanson *(Sr VP-Ops)*
Mike Karam *(Dir-Legal Svc)*
Traci Kathleen Mills *(Dir-Mktg)*

Wendy's of Las Vegas, Inc. (1)
4336 Losee Rd Ste 5, North Las Vegas, NV
89030
Tel.: (702) 642-9011
Web Site: http://www.cedarenterprises.com
Fast Food Restaurants
N.A.I.C.S.: 722513

Wendy's of San Antonio, Inc. (1)
315 W Nakoma St, San Antonio, TX 78216-
2622
Tel.: (210) 349-1877
Web Site: http://www.cedarenterprises.com
Fast Food Restaurants
N.A.I.C.S.: 722513
Derrick Garcia *(VP-San Antonio)*
Sherrie Seidel *(Mgr-HR)*
Andy Boothby *(VP-Engrg & Dev)*
Shawn M. Hiller *(VP & Controller)*
Boyd Johanson *(Sr VP-Ops)*

CEDAR FALLS LUTHERAN HOME
7511 University Ave, Cedar Falls, IA
50613
Tel.: (319) 268-0401 IA
Web Site: https://www.newaldaya.org
Year Founded: 1958
Sales Range: $10-24.9 Million
Emp.: 498
Elder Care Services
N.A.I.C.S.: 624120
Millisa Tierney *(CEO & Exec Dir)*

CEDAR FARMS COMPANY, INC.
2100 Hornig Rd, Philadelphia, PA
19116
Tel.: (215) 934-7100 PA
Web Site:
https://www.cedarfarms.com
Year Founded: 1925
Sales Range: $125-149.9 Million
Emp.: 200
Wholesale Dairy Products, Poultry,
Frozen Foods, Meats & Meat Products
N.A.I.C.S.: 424430
Peter Pahides *(Pres & CEO)*
Michael Essaf *(Gen Mgr)*
Rose Cataldi *(Office Mgr)*

CEDAR LAKE FOODS - MGM FOODS

5333 Quarter Rd, Cedar Springs, MI
48812
Tel.: (989) 427-5143
Web Site:
http://www.cedarlakefoods.com
Year Founded: 1949
Sales Range: $10-24.9 Million
Emp.: 30
Frozen Food Product Mfr.
N.A.I.C.S.: 311412
Charles Smart (Gen Mgr)

CEDAR PETROCHEMICALS, INC.

110 Wall St 7th Fl, New York, NY
10005
Tel.: (212) 288-4320   NY
Web Site:
http://www.cedarpetrochemical.com
Year Founded: 2000
Sales Range: $200-249.9 Million
Emp.: 5
Commodity Brokerage Services
N.A.I.C.S.: 523160
Salim Harfouche (Founder & CEO)
Bill Sparke (CFO)
Charlene Silva (Mgr-Ops & Logistics)
Peter Koejris-Andersen (Mgr-Credit & Documentation)
Jennifer Marchi (Mgr-Intl Product)

CEDAR RIVER INTERNATIONAL TRUCKS INC.

2740 6th St Sw, Cedar Rapids, IA
52404
Tel.: (319) 364-2491   DE
Web Site:
http://www.hawkeyetrucks.com
Year Founded: 1998
Sales Range: $10-24.9 Million
Emp.: 200
Provider of Heavy & Medium Trucks
N.A.I.C.S.: 811111
Travis Thomson (Gen Mgr)

CEDAR RUSTIC FENCE CO.

99 Republic Ave, Joliet, IL 60435
Tel.: (847) 998-8180
Web Site:
https://www.cedarrustic.com
Year Founded: 1927
Rev.: $7,600,000
Emp.: 38
Construction Services
N.A.I.C.S.: 423390
Lynn Ward (Office Mgr)
Brian Yuccas (Mgr-Installation & Svc)
Michael O'Lena (Plant Mgr)
Greg Bergeron (Owner & Pres)

CEDAR SIDING & LUMBER INC.

147 East 2nd Ave, Rochelle, IL 61068
Tel.: (815) 562-6767
Web Site:
http://www.cedarsidinginc.com
Rev.: $14,330,166
Emp.: 92
Sales of Lumber & Similar Products
N.A.I.C.S.: 423310
Gerald Enoch (VP)
Monte Enoch (Founder & Gen Mgr)
Shawn Enoch (Dir-Mktg)
Ted King (CFO)

CEDAR SPRING CAPITAL LLC

Commonweatlh Hall Old Parkland
Campus 3899 Maple Ave Ste 150,
Dallas, TX 75219
Tel.: (469) 930-3000
Web Site:
http://www.cedarspringscapital.com
Year Founded: 2015
Investment Services
N.A.I.C.S.: 523999

Colin McGrady (Mng Partner)
Neset Pirkul (Principal)
David Landis (Principal)
Imran Hussain (VP)
Jamie Kaiser (Controller-Fund)

Subsidiaries:

CarePayment Technologies, Inc.   (1)
4015 Hillsboro Pike, Nashville, TN 37215
Tel.: (866) 625-8532
Web Site: http://www.carepayment.com
Hospital Software Development Services
N.A.I.C.S.: 541511
Craig S. Hodges (CEO)
Ed Caldwell (Chief Revenue Officer)
Wes Pass (Chief Strategy Officer)
Steve Kukulka (CTO)
james Oliff (CFO)

CEDAR VALLEY EXTERIORS, INC.

13501 Balsam Ln N Ste 120, Dayton,
MN 55327
Tel.: (763) 755-2221   MN
Web Site:
https://www.cedarvalleyexterior.com
Year Founded: 1997
Sales Range: $10-24.9 Million
Emp.: 50
Catastrophic Residential & Commercial Restorations
N.A.I.C.S.: 236118
Frank Mannella (Pres & CEO)

CEDAR VALLEY SERVICES, INC.

2111 4th St NW, Austin, MN 55912
Tel.: (507) 433-2303   MN
Web Site:
https://www.cedarvalleyservices.org
Year Founded: 1960
Sales Range: $10-24.9 Million
Emp.: 827
Disability Assistance Services
N.A.I.C.S.: 624120
Taggert Medgaarden (Dir-Mgmt Svcs)
Garry Hart (Dir-Albert Lea Div)
Karen Baier (Program Dir)
Kris Burkey (Dir-Finance)
Richard Pavek (Exec Dir)

CEDAR'S MEDITERRANEAN FOODS, INC.

50 Foundation Ave, Haverhill, MA
01835-6926
Tel.: (978) 372-8010
Web Site:
http://www.cedarsfoods.com
Rev.: $10,400,000
Emp.: 300
Specialty Food Items
N.A.I.C.S.: 424490
Charles Hanna (Pres)
Dominick Frocione (VP-Sls)
Joe Dunne (Mgr-Sls)
Mary Ann Donohoe (Mgr-Sls)

CEDARBROOK SAUNA & STEAM

5700 Vale Rd, Cashmere, WA 98815
Tel.: (425) 481-3333
Web Site:
https://www.cedarbrooksauna.com
Year Founded: 1974
Sales Range: $10-24.9 Million
Emp.: 20
Sauna Heaters, Rooms & Steam
Generators Mfr
N.A.I.C.S.: 459999
John Lysaker (Founder & Owner)

CEDARS-SINAI MEDICAL CENTER

8700 Beverly Blvd, Los Angeles, CA
90048
Tel.: (310) 423-3277

Web Site: http://www.cedars-sinai.org
Year Founded: 1902
Sales Range: $1-4.9 Billion
Emp.: 14,525
Hospitals & Other Medical Services
N.A.I.C.S.: 622110
James M. A. Lippman (Chm)
Thomas M. Priselac (Pres & CEO)
Peter E. Braveman (Sr VP-Legal Affairs)
Darren Dworkin (CIO & Sr VP)
Richard B. Jacobs (Chief Strategy Officer & Exec VP-Sys Dev)
Shlomo Melmed (Exec VP-Academic Affairs)
Arthur J. Ochoa (Chief Dev Officer & Sr VP-Community Rels & Dev)
Edward M. Prunchunas (CFO & Exec VP-Fin)
Leslie Vermut (Sec)
Richard Riggs (Chief Medical Officer & Sr VP-Medical Affairs)
John Jenrette (Exec VP-Medical Network)
Andrew Ortiz (Sr VP-HR & Org Dev)
Anne Wellington (Mng Dir-Accelerator)
Jeffrey A. Smith (COO & Exec VP-Hospital Ops)
James Laur (Executives)
Christina Harris (Chief Health Equity Officer & VP)
Pasy Wang (Chief Investment Officer)
David B. Kaplan (Vice Chm)

Subsidiaries:

Cedars-Sinai Medical Group   (1)
200 N Robertson Blvd Ste 101, Beverly
Hills, CA 90211-1769
Web Site: http://www.cedars-sinai.edu
Sales Range: $25-49.9 Million
Emp.: 500
Medical Devices
N.A.I.C.S.: 621111

CEDCO INC.

6720 W Serene Ave, Las Vegas, NV
89139-7340
Tel.: (702) 361-6550   NV
Web Site: http://www.cedcoinc.com
Year Founded: 1987
Sales Range: $10-24.9 Million
Emp.: 100
Provider of Masonry & Other Stonework Services
N.A.I.C.S.: 238140
William Davis (Pres)
Jenna Coppedge (Mgr-Pur)

CEE KAY SUPPLY INC.

5835 Manchester Ave, Saint Louis,
MO 63110
Tel.: (314) 644-3500
Web Site: http://www.ceekay.com
Sales Range: $25-49.9 Million
Emp.: 80
Welding Machinery & Equipment
N.A.I.C.S.: 423830
Thomas P. Dunn (CEO)
Steve Gianino (Dir-Ops)
Keith Hicks (Branch Mgr)
Ken Laboube (Branch Mgr)
Keith Meuser (Branch Mgr)
Earnie Simpson (Branch Mgr)
Tim Schaaf (Mgr-Technical Center)
Dave Healzer (Dir-Procurement & Repair)
Jacob Meeker (Mgr-Sls & Product-Indus Vending)
Brent Wingerter (Coord-Mktg)
Jean Lindsey (Dir-Fin)
Kevin Kimker (Dir-Gas Ops)
Brian Reutiman (Reg Mgr)
Timm Evans (VP-Sls)

CEECO, INC.

519 SW Park St, Okeechobee, FL
34972
Tel.: (863) 357-0798
Web Site: https://www.ceeco.net
Rev.: $1,300,000
Emp.: 15
Telephone Apparatus Mfr
N.A.I.C.S.: 334210
Penny C. McCreary (Pres)
Randy Rupp (Treas)

CEELOX, INC.

10801 Mastin Ste 920, Overland
Park, KS 66210
Tel.: (913) 884-3705   NV
Web Site: http://www.ceelox.com
Year Founded: 2003
Sales Range: Less than $1 Million
Fingerprint Biometric Technology & Encryption Software Solutions
N.A.I.C.S.: 513210

CEF ENTERPRISES INC.

773 Senter St, Tupelo, MS 38801
Tel.: (662) 844-0499
Sales Range: $10-24.9 Million
Emp.: 500
Fast-Food Restaurant, Chain
N.A.I.C.S.: 722513
C. E. Fletcher (Pres)

CEFCO CONVENIENCE STORES

6261 Central Pointe Pkwy, Temple,
TX 76504
Tel.: (254) 791-0009
Web Site:
https://www.cefcostores.com
Sales Range: $10-24.9 Million
Emp.: 1,000
Convenience Stores, Independent
N.A.I.C.S.: 445131
James Fikes (Owner)
Kim Fikes (Chief Admin Officer)
Raymond Smith (Exec VP)
Mark Lappierre (VP-Mdsg)
Mike Skidmore (VP-Mdsg)

CEI BOSTON LLC

15 Shire Dr, Norfolk, MA 02056-1579
Tel.: (508) 850-9420
Web Site: http://www.ceiboston.com
Sales Range: $1-9.9 Million
Emp.: 50
Contracting Services
N.A.I.C.S.: 236210
Andrew Clemons (CEO)
Brian Caffrey (Owner)
Peter Banks (Pres)

CEI ROOFING, INC.

2140 Industrial Dr, Howell, MI 48844
Tel.: (517) 548-0039
Web Site: http://www.ceigroupllc.com
Sales Range: $10-24.9 Million
Emp.: 75
Roofing Installation Services
N.A.I.C.S.: 238390
David Rosiek (Mgr-Svcs)

CEIBA TECHNOLOGIES

410 N Roosevelt Ave, Chandler, AZ
85226
Tel.: (480) 705-4541
Web Site: https://www.ceibatech.com
Year Founded: 1994
Sales Range: $10-24.9 Million
Emp.: 13
Silicon Wafers, Microchips & Optical
Drives Mfr & Distr
N.A.I.C.S.: 334118
John Vargas (Pres)
Yoshi Walker (Acct Mgr)

CEILINGS & PARTITIONS, INC.

Baltimore Washington Commerce

Ceilings & Partitions, Inc.—(Continued)

Park 7383 Washington Blvd Ste 101, Elkridge, MD 21075
Tel.: (301) 210-1300
Web Site:
http://www.ceilingsandpartition.com
Year Founded: 1977
Sales Range: $100-124.9 Million
Emp.: 210
Provider of Plastering, Drywall, Flooring & Insulation Services
N.A.I.C.S.: 238310
Mark Hallam *(Pres)*
Larry Gibson *(Sr Project Mgr)*

CEIPAL CORP.
687 Lee Rd Ste 208A, Rochester, NY 14606
Tel.: (585) 296-4563
Web Site: http://www.ceipal.com
Year Founded: 2015
Emp.: 100
Software Publisher for Recruitment & Staffing
N.A.I.C.S.: 513210
Dennis Farkos *(CFO)*
Amar Chadipirala *(Product Mgr)*
Scott Montminy *(Dir-Mktg & Comm)*
Sameer Penakalapati *(Founder & CEO)*
Peter Velikin *(CMO)*

Subsidiaries:

Zoniac Inc. (1)
9520 Hinton Dr, Santee, CA 92071
Tel.: (408) 329-4474
Web Site: http://www.zoniac.com
Data Processing, Hosting & Related Services
N.A.I.C.S.: 518210
Vittal Srimushnam *(Pres & CEO)*

CEJA CORPORATION
1437 S Boulder, Tulsa, OK 74119
Tel.: (918) 496-0770
Web Site: https://www.ceja.com
Rev.: $11,900,000
Emp.: 25
Crude Petroleum Production
N.A.I.C.S.: 533110
Ann C. Scogin *(Controller)*
Richard H. Carter *(Dir-Geophysics)*
Ron Snyder *(VP-Exploration)*
Weldon G. Spitzer *(VP-Production)*
Gregory W. Oliphant *(Chm)*
Donald P. Carpenter *(Pres)*
Sam Sheehan II *(Mgr-Production)*

CEL EDUCATION FUND
2150 Allston Way Ste 360, Berkeley, CA 94704
Tel.: (510) 875-2135
Web Site:
http://www.celeducationfund.org
Year Founded: 2011
Sales Range: $10-24.9 Million
Emp.: 5
Charitable Organization
N.A.I.C.S.: 813211
Julia Rhodes Davis *(Chief Dev Officer)*
Heidi Gatty *(Dir-Powerful Communities Program)*
Gaurav Vashist *(CFO)*
Ian Inaba *(Pres)*

CELEBIDDY, INC.
18 Narbonne, Newport Beach, CA 92660
Tel.: (626) 644-0070
Year Founded: 2016
Online-Dating Management Services
N.A.I.C.S.: 812990
Maria Malek *(Pres, CEO, CFO & Sec)*
John Malek *(VP)*

CELEBRATION WORLD RESORT LTD.
7503 Atlantis Way, Kissimmee, FL 34747
Tel.: (407) 396-4005
Web Site: http://festivaorlando.com
Rev.: $50,000,000
Emp.: 70
Sales, Leasing & Rental of Vacation Time-Shares
N.A.I.C.S.: 561990
Sherri Brady *(Dir-Mktg)*

CELEBRITY AUTO GROUP
6464 Parkland Dr, Sarasota, FL 34243
Tel.: (941) 371-6500
Web Site:
https://www.celebrityautogroup.com
Sales Range: $10-24.9 Million
Emp.: 5
Car Dealership
N.A.I.C.S.: 441110
Conor Delaney *(Founder)*

CELEBRITY INTERNATIONAL INC.
10 W 33rd St Ste 910, New York, NY 10001-2909
Tel.: (212) 279-1616
Web Site:
http://www.vitaminsbaby.com
Year Founded: 1965
Sales Range: $10-24.9 Million
Emp.: 65
Women's & Children's Clothing
N.A.I.C.S.: 424350
Morris D. Matalon *(Pres & CEO)*
Mona El Raheb *(Controller)*
Maria Nunez *(Coord-Import & Export)*

CELEBRITY MOTOR CAR COMPANY
130 State Rte 10, Whippany, NJ 07981
Tel.: (973) 319-7100
Web Site:
https://www.celebritymotorcar.com
New & Used Car Dealership
N.A.I.C.S.: 441110

Subsidiaries:

Celebrity Ford Of Toms River (1)
360 Rte 37 E, Toms River, NJ 18017-9401
Tel.: (732) 349-2240
Web Site: http://www.faulknersubaru.com
New Car Dealers
N.A.I.C.S.: 441110
Tom Arden *(Pres)*

CELEBROS, INC.
2 University Plz Ste 210, Hackensack, NJ 07601
Tel.: (888) 445-3266
Web Site: http://www.celebros.com
Year Founded: 2000
Sales Range: $1-9.9 Million
Software Publisher
N.A.I.C.S.: 513210
Roy Lauzon *(VP-R&D)*

Subsidiaries:

Celebros Ltd. (1)
Munchen Airport-Center Terminalstrasse Mitte 18, 85356, Munich, Germany
Tel.: (49) 89 97007 296
Web Site: http://www.celebros.com
Software Publisher
N.A.I.C.S.: 513210

Celebros Ltd. (1)
1 rue de la Haye, PO Box 12910, Roissy, 95731, Charles de Gaulle, France
Tel.: (33) 1 49192295
Web Site: http://www.celebros.fr
Software Publisher
N.A.I.C.S.: 513210

Celebros Ltd. (1)
8 Maskit St Building A, 46733, Herzliya Pituach, Israel
Tel.: (972) 9 9555257
Software Publisher
N.A.I.C.S.: 513210

Celebros Ltd. (1)
Medius House LG, 2 Sheraton Street, London, W1F 8BH, United Kingdom
Tel.: (44) 870 3664462
Software Publisher
N.A.I.C.S.: 513210

CELERANT TECHNOLOGY CORP.
4830 Arthur Kill Rd, Staten Island, NY 10309
Tel.: (718) 351-2000
Web Site: https://www.celerant.com
Year Founded: 1999
Rev.: $10,400,000
Emp.: 80
Developer of Retail Management Software
N.A.I.C.S.: 513210
Ian Goldman *(Pres & CEO)*
Robert Goldman *(CTO & VP)*
Gerard Toussaint *(Mgr-Software Support)*

Subsidiaries:

CAM Commerce Solutions, Inc. (1)
5555 Garden Grove Blvd Ste 100, Westminster, CA 92683
Tel.: (714) 338-0200
Web Site: http://www.camcommerce.com
Sales Range: $25-49.9 Million
Emp.: 100
Designs, Develops, Markets & Retails Payment Processing Solutions
N.A.I.C.S.: 513210
Ian Goldman *(CEO)*

CELERGO
750 Estate Dr Ste 110, Deerfield, IL 60015
Tel.: (847) 512-2600
Web Site: http://www.celergo.com
Year Founded: 2004
Sales Range: $10-24.9 Million
Emp.: 120
Outsourced Global Payroll Services with Expatriate Focus
N.A.I.C.S.: 541214
Michele Honomichl *(Founder)*
Kathy Hedley *(Exec VP-Sls & Mktg)*
Tim Callahan *(CEO)*
Cindy Ayling *(Dir-Mktg)*

CELERIT CORPORATION
216 Atkins Rd, Little Rock, AR 72211
Tel.: (501) 312-2900
Web Site: https://www.celerit.com
Year Founded: 1985
Sales Range: $10-24.9 Million
Emp.: 40
Information Technology Solutions & Staffing Services
N.A.I.C.S.: 541511
Terry Rothwell *(CEO)*

CELERITY SOLUTIONS, INC.
270 Bridge St, Dedham, MA 02026-1798
Tel.: (781) 329-1900
Web Site:
http://www.slingshotcity.com
Sales Range: $10-24.9 Million
Emp.: 71
Management Software Company
N.A.I.C.S.: 513210
Paul Carr *(CEO)*

CELERITY VENTURES LLC
107 S West St, Alexandria, VA 22314
Tel.: (800) 420-7004
Web Site: http://www.celerity-ventures.com
Year Founded: 2008

Sales Range: $10-24.9 Million
Emp.: 7
Purchases & Renovates Residential Properties
N.A.I.C.S.: 236118
Chris McCarrick *(Mng Partner)*

CELESTAR CORPORATION
9501 E US Hwy 92, Tampa, FL 33610
Tel.: (813) 627-9069
Web Site:
https://www.celestarcorp.com
Year Founded: 2001
Sales Range: $10-24.9 Million
Emp.: 145
Technology Consulting Services
N.A.I.C.S.: 541690
Gregory J. Celestan *(Chm & CEO)*
Lori Larsen *(Chief Strategy Officer)*
Lew Jolly *(COO)*
Mark A. Tocci-Gunny *(Mgr-Recruiting)*
Victor Handy *(Sr Mgr-COCOM Portfolio)*
Rich Spencer *(Dir-Ops-Natl Capital Reg)*
Alyssa Feliho *(Sr Mgr-Capture & Proposal)*
Jeannie Johnson *(Sr Mgr-HR)*
Tony Liberta *(Sr Portfolio Mgr)*

CELESTIX NETWORKS, INC.
3125 Skyway Ct, Fremont, CA 94539
Tel.: (510) 668-0700
Web Site: http://www.celestix.com
Year Founded: 2000
Sales Range: $10-24.9 Million
Emp.: 40
Computer Terminal Mfr
N.A.I.C.S.: 334118
Gabriele Sartori *(CTO)*
Thye Lin Yong *(CEO)*

Subsidiaries:

Celestix Networks Pte. Ltd. (1)
62 Ubi Road 1 #04-07, Singapore, 408734, Singapore
Tel.: (65) 6781 0700
Emp.: 4
Computer Terminal Mfr
N.A.I.C.S.: 334118

CELESTRON, LLC
2835 Columbia St, Torrance, CA 90503-3804
Tel.: (310) 328-9560
Web Site: https://www.celestron.com
Sales Range: $75-99.9 Million
Emp.: 100
Mfr of Telescopes, Telephoto Lenses, Binoculars & Spotting Scopes
N.A.I.C.S.: 333310
Ben Hauck *(Sr VP-Sls-North America)*
Corey Lee *(CEO)*
Eric Kopit *(VP-Product Dev)*

CELEXUS, INC.
8275 S Eastern Ave Ste 200, Las Vegas, NV 89123
Tel.: (702) 724-2636
Web Site: http://www.celexus.com
Year Founded: 2005
Assets: $44,862
Liabilities: $92,859
Net Worth: ($47,997)
Earnings: ($21,234)
Fiscal Year-end: 03/31/19
Holding Company
N.A.I.C.S.: 551112
Lisa Averbucho *(Pres)*
David Soto *(Chm, CEO, CFO, Treas & Sec)*

CELEY'S QUALITY PLUMBING, INC.

8991 NC Hwy 27 E, Benson, NC
27504-6450
Tel.: (919) 894-1813
Web Site: http://www.celeys.com
Year Founded: 1995
Sales Range: $10-24.9 Million
Emp.: 115
Plumbers & Backflow Prevention
Equipment Services
N.A.I.C.S.: 238220
Garry J. Celey *(Owner)*

CELIA CORPORATION
320 S Union St, Sparta, MI 49345-
1530
Tel.: (616) 887-7387   MI
Web Site:
   http://www.generalformulations.com
Year Founded: 1949
Sales Range: $25-49.9 Million
Emp.: 160
Coated & Laminated Paper
N.A.I.C.S.: 322220
Mike Clay *(Pres)*
Tim Leavenworth *(VP-Sls)*
Tammi Vajda *(Mgr-Sls-Texas)*
Pryor French *(Mgr-Sls-North Caro-
lina)*
Roger Jones *(Mgr-Sls-California)*
Peter Shore *(Mgr-Sls-Connecticut)*

CELINA INSURANCE GROUP
1 Insurance Sq, Celina, OH 45822
Tel.: (419) 586-5181
Web Site:
   http://www.celinainsurance.com
Sales Range: $75-99.9 Million
Emp.: 180
Fire, Marine & Casualty Insurance
N.A.I.C.S.: 524126
William W. Montgomery *(Pres &
CEO)*
Philip Fullenkamp *(CFO)*
Anne McMillan *(Sr Dir-Claims)*
Ted Wissman *(COO & Sr VP)*

CELL BUSINESS EQUIPMENT
4A Mason St, Irvine, CA 92618
Tel.: (949) 830-1400
Web Site:
   http://www.cbeofficesolutions.com
Year Founded: 1993
Rev.: $14,000,000
Emp.: 65
Business Products & Services
N.A.I.C.S.: 459999
Tarek Hafiz *(Pres)*
Mark Johnson *(Acct Mgr-Major)*
Ozzie Acosta *(Dir-Svc)*
Rick Nelson *(Supvr-Field Svc)*
Richard Ruedas *(Acct Mgr)*
Mike Salahi *(Mgr-Sls)*
Jeff Yirak *(Sr Acct Mgr)*
Birdie Kopp *(CFO)*

CELL MICROSYSTEMS, INC.
801 Capitola Dr, Ste 10, Durham, NC
27713
Tel.: (252) 285-9842
Web Site:
   https://cellmicrosystems.com
Year Founded: 2010
Biotechnology Research
N.A.I.C.S.: 541714

Subsidiaries:

Fluxion Biosciences Inc.   **(1)**
1901 Poplar St. Ste B, Oakland, CA 94607
Tel.: (650) 241-4777
Web Site: https://www.fluxionbio.com
Analytical Laboratory Instrument Mfr
N.A.I.C.S.: 334516
Niall Murphy *(VP-Fin)*

CELL TRADE NY INC.
575 Underhill Blvd Ste 211, Syosset,
NY 11791

Tel.: (212) 737-4300
Web Site: http://www.celltradeny.com
Year Founded: 2015
Sales Range: $10-24.9 Million
Emp.: 50
Wireless Device Distr
N.A.I.C.S.: 449210
Andy Panwar *(Founder & CEO)*

CELL-CRETE CORPORATION
135 E Railroad Ave, Monrovia, CA
91016
Tel.: (626) 357-3500   CA
Web Site: https://www.cell-crete.com
Year Founded: 1965
Sales Range: $10-24.9 Million
Emp.: 100
Installer of Floors
N.A.I.C.S.: 238990
Louis E. Fisher *(Pres)*
Joe Barclay *(VP-Ops)*
Patrick Barclay *(VP)*

CELL-NIQUE CORPORATION
65 East Ave 3rd Fl, Norwalk, CT
06851
Tel.: (203) 856-8550   DE
Web Site: http://www.cell-nique.com
Year Founded: 2005
Sales Range: $10-24.9 Million
Emp.: 4
Natural & Organic Fruit Beverages
Developer, Mfr & Marketer
N.A.I.C.S.: 311411
Dan Ratner *(Chm, CEO & CFO)*
Donna Ratner *(Vice Chm, CMO &
Sec)*

CELLCYTE GENETICS COR-
PORATION
14205 SE 36th St Ste 100, Bellevue,
WA 98006
Tel.: (425) 519-3755   NV
Year Founded: 2004
Stem Cell Research Medical Device
Mfr
N.A.I.C.S.: 339112
Douglas Pat Cerretti *(Pres)*

CELLECT LLC
12 New St, Saint Johnsville, NY
13452
Tel.: (518) 568-7036
Web Site: http://www.opflex.com
Year Founded: 2001
Sales Range: $10-24.9 Million
Emp.: 100
Packaging & Shipping Materials,
Foamed Plastics & Polyethylene
Foam Mfr
N.A.I.C.S.: 326199
Scott Smith *(Pres & CEO)*

CELLFISH MEDIA LLC
215 Lexington Ave 18th Fl, New York,
NY 10016-6023
Tel.: (212) 767-5200
Web Site:
   http://www.cellfishmedia.com
Sales Range: $100-124.9 Million
Emp.: 250
Mobile & Online Media & Entertain-
ment Services
N.A.I.C.S.: 513210
Fabrice Sergent *(Co-Founder & CEO)*
Julien Mitelberg *(Co-Founder & COO)*
David Weisz *(CMO)*
Dan Nemo *(CFO)*
Andre Tremblay *(Chm)*
Kevin O'Connor *(CEO)*

Subsidiaries:

Cellfish Media, Inc.   **(1)**
468 Saint-Jean Street Suite 200, Montreal,
H2Y 2S1, QC, Canada
Tel.: (514) 288-5858

Mobile & Online Media & Entertainment
Services
N.A.I.C.S.: 513210

CELLI ENTERPRISES INC.
2090 N Mannheim Rd, Melrose Park,
IL 60160
Tel.: (847) 678-0440
Sales Range: $10-24.9 Million
Emp.: 30
Truck Equipment & Parts
N.A.I.C.S.: 441330
Eugene M. Celli *(Pres)*

Subsidiaries:

Northwest Mack Parts & Service
Co.   **(1)**
2090 N Mannheim Rd, Melrose Park, IL
60160
Tel.: (847) 447-5500
Rev.: $8,104,652
Truck Parts & Accessories Distr
N.A.I.C.S.: 423120
Eugene M. Celli *(Pres)*
Eugene Panich *(Controller)*

CELLNET COMMUNICATIONS
INC.
31075 John R Rd, Madison Heights,
MI 48071-1907
Tel.: (248) 585-4520   MI
Web Site:
   http://www.cellnetonline.com
Year Founded: 1983
Sales Range: $25-49.9 Million
Emp.: 170
Radio & Telephone Communications
N.A.I.C.S.: 517112
Richard A. Goldsmith *(Pres)*

CELLNETIX PATHOLOGY &
LABORATORIES, LLC
1124 Columbia St Ste 200, Seattle,
WA 98104
Tel.: (206) 215-2062
Web Site: https://www.cellnetix.com
Year Founded: 2005
Emp.: 212
Medical Laboratory Services
N.A.I.C.S.: 621511
David J. Corwin *(Pres)*
Kathleen Fondren *(CEO)*

CELLO-PACK CORPORATION
55 Innsbruck Dr, Buffalo, NY 14227
Tel.: (716) 668-3111
Web Site: http://www.cellopack.com
Sales Range: $10-24.9 Million
Emp.: 125
Unsupported Plastics Film & Sheet
N.A.I.C.S.: 326113
Edmund Beckman *(Coord-Graphic)*

CELLOFOAM NORTH
AMERICA INC.
1917 Rockdale Industrial Blvd, Cony-
ers, GA 30012
Tel.: (770) 483-4491
Web Site: https://www.cellofoam.com
Year Founded: 1966
Sales Range: $75-99.9 Million
Emp.: 375
Expanded Polystyrene, Polyethylene,
Polyurethane & Copolymer Plastic
Foams Mfr
N.A.I.C.S.: 326140
Gregory R. Bontrager *(Pres)*

CELLTRUST CORPORATION
14822 N 73rd St Ste 113, Scottsdale,
AZ 85260
Tel.: (480) 515-5200
Web Site: http://www.celltrust.com
Year Founded: 2005
Sales Range: $1-9.9 Million
Emp.: 32
Mobile Marketing Services

N.A.I.C.S.: 541613
Sean Moshir *(Co-Founder, Chm &
CEO)*
Bob Lettieri *(CFO)*
Kevin Moshir *(Co-Founder, Pres &
COO)*
Brian Panicko *(Sr VP-Global Sls
Strategy)*
Rebecca R. Ruegg *(Gen Counsel)*
Bryan Glancey *(CTO)*
Nate Locke *(Mng Dir)*
Terence Caston *(Sr Dir-Sls Engrg)*
K. Royal *(VP & Asst Gen Counsel)*
Kathy Kim *(VP-Mktg Strategy &
Comm)*
Stuart Browne *(Chief Corp Dev Offi-
cer)*

CELLUCAP MANUFACTURING
CO.
4626 N 15th St, Philadelphia, PA
19140
Tel.: (215) 324-0213   PA
Web Site: https://www.cellucap.com
Year Founded: 1953
Sales Range: $10-24.9 Million
Emp.: 30
Disposable Protective Apparel &
Other Products Mfr
N.A.I.C.S.: 322291
Gilbert Wagenfeld *(Founder)*

Subsidiaries:

DISCO, Inc.   **(1)**
4626 N 15th St, Philadelphia, PA 19140
Web Site: http://www.discoinc.com
Sales Range: $1-9.9 Million
Cleaning & Specialty Disposable Product
Mfr
N.A.I.C.S.: 326299
Aaron P. Trull *(VP-HR)*

CELLUFUN INC.
48 Wall St 29th Fl, New York, NY
10005
Tel.: (212) 385-4954
Web Site: http://www.m.cellufun.com
Year Founded: 2005
Sales Range: $1-9.9 Million
Emp.: 19
Telecommunication Servicesb
N.A.I.C.S.: 517810
Arthur Goikhman *(Co-Founder)*
Stephen Dacek *(Co-Founder & Mng
Dir)*
Andy Bishop *(VP-Bus Dev)*

CELLULAR BIOMEDICINE
GROUP, INC.
9605 Medical Ctr Dri Ste 100, New
York, NY 10105
Tel.: (301) 825-5320   DE
Web Site:
   http://www.cellbiomedgroup.com
Year Founded: 2001
Biopharmaceutical & Medicinal Mfr
N.A.I.C.S.: 325412
Andrew K. Chan *(Chief Legal Officer-
Corp Dev & Sec)*
Tony Liu *(CEO & CFO)*
Chase Cheng Xiang Dai *(Gen Mgr-
Stem Cell Bus Unit)*
Helen Li Zhang *(Chief Production Of-
ficer)*
Yihong Yao *(Chief Scientific Officer)*
Hui Wan *(Sr VP-Clinical Dev)*

CELLULAR ONE OF EAST
CENTRAL ILLINOIS
28 Towne Ctr, Danville, IL 61832
Tel.: (217) 442-2355
Web Site: http://www.cellular1.net
Sales Range: $10-24.9 Million
Emp.: 42
Cellular Telephone Services
N.A.I.C.S.: 517112

Cellular One of East Central
Illinois—(Continued)

Arthur Abbey *(Owner & Pres)*
Lori Skoog *(Mgr-Carrier Rels)*
Todd Shaw *(Mgr-IT)*
Jake Kasper *(Mgr-Product Dev &
Data Svcs)*
Brenda Judy *(Coord-Store)*
Billy Hagley *(Mgr-Inventory Control)*

CELLULAR SALES OF KNOXVILLE, INC.
6513 Kingston Pike Ste 106, Knoxville, TN 37919
Tel.: (865) 584-7555
Web Site:
http://www.cellularsales.com
Year Founded: 1993
Sales Range: $450-499.9 Million
Emp.: 3,500
Cellular Telephone Services
N.A.I.C.S.: 517112
Margaret Scism *(Owner)*
James Thorne *(Dir-Ops)*
Dane Scism *(CEO)*
Eva Todd *(Dir-HR)*
Pam Kimball *(CFO)*
Reese K. Thomas *(Gen Counsel)*
Brett Patterson *(Exec VP)*

CELPAD, INC.
201 Santa Monica Blvd Ste 300,
Santa Monica, CA 90401-2224   DE
Web Site: http://www.celpad.com
Year Founded: 2010
Wireless Case & Receiver Mfr
N.A.I.C.S.: 334220
Gary L. Blum *(Chm, Pres, CEO, CFO
& Sec)*

CELS ENTERPRISES, INC.
3485 S La Cienega Blvd, Los Angeles, CA 90016-4409
Tel.: (310) 838-2103   NY
Web Site:
http://www.chineselaundry.com
Year Founded: 1971
Sales Range: $25-49.9 Million
Emp.: 100
Footwear
N.A.I.C.S.: 424340
Robert Goldman *(Pres)*

CELSTAR GROUP INC.
40 N Main Ste 2560, Dayton, OH
45423
Tel.: (937) 224-1730
Web Site: http://www.fiber-tech.com
Sales Range: $10-24.9 Million
Emp.: 150
Holding Company
N.A.I.C.S.: 326199
Robert H. Brethen *(Chm)*
David M. Brethen *(Pres & CEO)*

Subsidiaries:

Fiber Pro Inc.   **(1)**
1637 Marty Paul St, Cadillac, MI 49601
Tel.: (231) 775-0197
Web Site: http://www.fiber-tech.com
Rev.: $770,000
Emp.: 15
Panels, Hardwood Plywood
N.A.I.C.S.: 321211

Fiber-Tech Industries, Inc.   **(1)**
2000 Kenskill Ave, Washington Court
House, OH 43160-2290
Tel.: (740) 335-9400
Web Site: http://www.fiber-tech.net
Sales Range: $10-24.9 Million
Emp.: 93
Fiberglass Plastic Panel With Plywood Core
Mfr
N.A.I.C.S.: 326130
Terence M. Keegan *(Pres & CEO)*

Fiberglass Technology Industries **(1)**

3808 N Sullivan Rd Ste 31, Spokane, WA
99216
Tel.: (509) 928-8880
Web Site: http://www.fiber-tech.net
Rev.: $30,000,000
Emp.: 30
Fiberglass Reinforced Panels Mfr & Distr
N.A.I.C.S.: 326199

CELTIC MARINE CORPORATION
3888 S Sherwood Forest Blvd, Baton
Rouge, LA 70816-4359
Tel.: (225) 752-2490   LA
Web Site:
https://www.celticmarine.com
Year Founded: 1985
Sales Range: $10-24.9 Million
Emp.: 50
Deep Sea Freight Transportation
N.A.I.C.S.: 483111
Michael J. O'Connor *(Chm & CEO)*
Bob Bayham *(CFO & Sr VP)*

CEM CORPORATION
3100 Smith Farm Rd, Matthews, NC
28104
Tel.: (704) 821-7015   NC
Web Site: http://www.cem.com
Year Founded: 1972
Sales Range: $50-74.9 Million
Emp.: 180
Mfr of Analytical Instruments
N.A.I.C.S.: 334516
Richard Decker *(CFO, Treas, Sec &
VP-Fin)*

Subsidiaries:

CEM GmbH   **(1)**
Carl Friedrich Gauss Strasse 9, Kamp-
Lintfort, 47475, Germany   **(100%)**
Tel.: (49) 284296440
Web Site: http://www.cem.de
Sales Range: $10-24.9 Million
Emp.: 23
Provider of Microwave Laboratory Instrumentation for Microwave Chemistry & Process Control Applications
N.A.I.C.S.: 334515
Volka Schaible *(Mgr)*

CEM Japan K.K.   **(1)**
2-18-10 Takanawa Minato-ku, Tokyo, 108-
0074, Japan
Tel.: (81) 357938542
Web Site: http://ja.cem.com
Sales Range: $10-24.9 Million
Emp.: 10
Laboratory Instrument Mfr
N.A.I.C.S.: 334516
Paul Greenwood *(Mng Dir)*

CEM Microwave Technology (Ireland)
Ltd.   **(1)**
Sky Business Centre 9A, Plato Business
Park Damastown, Dublin, 15, Ireland
Tel.: (353) 1 885 1752
Web Site: http://www.cem.com
Emp.: 12
Laboratory Instrument Mfr
N.A.I.C.S.: 334516
Jane Currie *(Office Mgr)*

CEM Microwave Technology Ltd.   **(1)**
2 Middleslade, Buckingham Industrial Park,
Buckingham, MK18 1WA, United
Kingdom   **(100%)**
Tel.: (44) 1280822873
Web Site: http://www.cem.com
Sales Range: $10-24.9 Million
Emp.: 10
Provider of Microwave Laboratory Instrumentation for Microwave Chemistry & Process Control Applications
N.A.I.C.S.: 334515

CEM Mu Waves S.A.S.   **(1)**
Immeuble Ariane Dom tech de Saclay 4
Rue Rene Razel, 91400, Saclay, France
Tel.: (33) 169355780
Web Site: http://www.cemfrance.fr
Sales Range: $10-24.9 Million
Emp.: 8
Laboratory Instrument Mfr

N.A.I.C.S.: 334516
Mollare Christian *(Mng Dir)*

CEM S.r.l.   **(1)**
Via Dell Artigianato 6 8, Cologno Al Serio,
Bergamo, 24055, Lombardy, Italy **(100%)**
Tel.: (39) 035896224
Web Site: http://www.cem.com
Sales Range: $10-24.9 Million
Emp.: 9
Provider of Microwave Laboratory Instrumentation for Microwave Chemistry & Process Control Applications
N.A.I.C.S.: 334515

CEM ENTERPRISES INC.
1757 Benbow Ct, Apopka, FL 32703
Tel.: (407) 884-9148
Sales Range: $10-24.9 Million
Emp.: 80
General Contractors
N.A.I.C.S.: 236220
Norma E. Meeks *(Pres)*

CEMBELL INDUSTRIES INC.
740 CCC Rd Hwy 628, Montz, LA
70068
Tel.: (985) 652-1188
Web Site: https://www.cembell.com
Sales Range: $10-24.9 Million
Emp.: 120
Mfr of Metal Products
N.A.I.C.S.: 332313
Benjamin Brupbacher Jr. *(Pres)*

CEMENT INDUSTRIES, INC.
2925 Hanson St, Fort Myers, FL
33902-0823
Tel.: (239) 332-1440
Web Site:
https://www.cementindustries.com
Year Founded: 1953
Sales Range: $1-9.9 Million
Emp.: 38
Concrete Products Mfr
N.A.I.C.S.: 327390
Gay Rebel Thompson *(Pres)*
Vickie Dragich *(CFO)*

CEMSTONE PRODUCTS COMPANY INC.
2025 Centre Pointe Blvd Ste 300,
Mendota Heights, MN, 55120-1221
Tel.: (651) 688-9292   MN
Web Site: https://www.cemstone.com
Year Founded: 1927
Sales Range: $25-49.9 Million
Emp.: 850
Readymix Concrete Mfr
N.A.I.C.S.: 327320
Thor Becken *(Founder)*

Subsidiaries:

Cemstone Ready Mix, Inc.   **(1)**
W3770 State Hwy 10, Durand, WI 54736
Tel.: (715) 672-5008
Readymix Concrete Mfr
N.A.I.C.S.: 327320
David Cave *(Gen Mgr)*

CEN-MED ENTERPRISES, INC.
121 Jersey Ave, New Brunswick, NJ
08901
Tel.: (732) 447-1100
Web Site: https://www.cenmed.com
Year Founded: 1992
Sales Range: $1-9.9 Million
Emp.: 12
Medical, Dental & Hospital Equipment
& Supplies Merchant Whslr
N.A.I.C.S.: 423450
Shakila Chaudry *(Pres)*

CENDYN CORP.
980 N Federal Hwy Ste 200, Boca
Raton, FL 33432
Tel.: (800) 760-8152
Web Site: http://www.cendyn.com

Software Developer for Event & Leisure Hospitality Industries
N.A.I.C.S.: 513210
Charles Deyo *(Founder)*
Xudong Ding *(Sr VP-Software Dev)*
John Seaton *(Mng Dir-Intl)*
Jill Cully *(VP-Sls-Americas)*
Brad Noe *(CTO)*
Dave Morgan *(CFO)*
Tim Sullivan *(Pres & CEO)*

Subsidiaries:

Ovations Management Solutions,
LLC   **(1)**
1776 Peachtree St NW Ste 560, Atlanta,
GA 30308
Tel.: (404) 817-6684
Web Site:
http://www.ovationsmanagement.com
Sales Range: $1-9.9 Million
Emp.: 23
Custom Computer Programming Services
N.A.I.C.S.: 541511
Enoch Prow *(CEO)*

CENERGY COMMUNICATIONS,
LLC
728 Main St, East Aurora, NY 14052
Tel.: (716) 652-7400
Web Site:
http://www.activatingbrands.com
Year Founded: 2001
Sales Range: $1-9.9 Million
Emp.: 30
Advertising Related Services
N.A.I.C.S.: 541890
Ken Trabert *(Dir-Creative)*

CENERGY CORP.
1763 US Route 60 W, Milton, WV
25541
Tel.: (304) 743-4250
Web Site:
https://www.cenergyco.com
Year Founded: 2006
Sales Range: $10-24.9 Million
Emp.: 40
General Engineering Contractor
N.A.I.C.S.: 541330
Chuck King *(Owner)*

CENERGY CORPORATION
2650 Crossroads Park Dr, Houston,
TX 77065
Tel.: (713) 965-6150
Web Site:
http://www.cenergycorp.com
Year Founded: 1996
Sales Range: $10-24.9 Million
Emp.: 100
Staffing Services for Oil & Gas Companies
N.A.I.C.S.: 541612
June Ressler *(CEO)*

CENERGY PARTNERS LLC
12650 Crossroads Park Dr, Houston,
TX 77065
Tel.: (713) 965-6200   DE
Web Site: http://www.cenergyintl.com
Year Founded: 1996
Staffing & Consulting Services
N.A.I.C.S.: 561320
June Ressler *(CEO)*

Subsidiaries:

HKA Enterprises, LLC   **(1)**
337 Spartangreen Blvd, Duncan, SC 29334
Tel.: (800) 825-5452
Web Site: http://www.hkaa.com
Skilled Labor Staffing Services
N.A.I.C.S.: 561320
Bruce Clayman *(CEO)*

Midcom Workforce Solutions   **(1)**
1275 N Manassero St, Anaheim, CA 92807-
1714
Tel.: (714) 630-1999
Web Site: http://www.midcom.com

Employment Placement & Staffing Agency
N.A.I.C.S.: 561320

CENERGY, LLC.
1763 US Rte 60 W, Milton, WV 25541
Tel.: (304) 743-4250
Web Site:
   https://www.cenergyco.com
Year Founded: 2006
Sales Range: $10-24.9 Million
Emp.: 50
Commercial & Institutional Building Construction Services
N.A.I.C.S.: 236220
Chuck King *(Pres)*
Drew Pyles *(Exec VP)*
Todd Plumley *(Mgr-Mfg Div)*
Eric Pyles *(Dir-Engrg)*
Adam Curry *(Dir-Safety)*
Bob Dingess *(Project Mgr)*
Jamin Fagan *(Mgr-Bus Dev)*
Brad Yost *(Project Mgr)*

CENEXEL CLINICAL RE-SEARCH, INC.
650 E 4500 S Ste 350, Salt Lake City, UT 84107
Web Site: http://cenexelresearch.com
Clinical research Laboratory Services
N.A.I.C.S.: 621511
Tom Wardle *(Chm)*
Michele Baptista *(Sr Dir-Bus Dev)*
Casey Orvin *(Chief Comml Officer)*
Stuart Goldblatt *(CEO)*

Subsidiaries:

Citrials, Inc.   (1)
17800 Woodruff Ave Ste B, Bellflower, CA 90706
Tel.: (714) 979-4101
Web Site: http://www.citrials.com
Offices of Physicians (except Mental Health Specialists)
N.A.I.C.S.: 621111
Debra Hoffmeyer *(CEO)*

CENLAR CAPITAL CORPORA-TION
425 Phillips Blvd, Ewing, NJ 08618
Tel.: (609) 883-3900
Web Site: http://www.cenlar.com
Rev.: $26,460,000
Emp.: 750
Savings & Loans
N.A.I.C.S.: 522180
Greg S. Tornquist *(Chm)*
David J. Miller *(Exec VP & Dir-Bus Dev)*
Lori J. Pinto *(Sr VP-Bus Dev)*
Michael Conway *(Sr VP)*
James Daras *(CEO)*
Jim Scott *(VP)*
Bob Hora *(Sr VP-Default Ops)*
Adrienne R. Kowalski *(Dir-Corp Comm)*
Steven Taylor *(CIO & Sr VP)*
Rob Lux *(COO & Exec VP)*
Ang Shen *(VP-Model Risk Mgmt)*
Sara Avery *(Chief Risk Officer)*
Brad Cargile *(VP-IT Infrastructure)*
Marlon Groen *(Chief Compliance Officer)*
Jennifer Rowen *(Sr VP-Core Ops)*
Bill Moffett *(Sr VP-Loan Ops)*
Gabe Rinaldi *(VP-Enterprise Project Mgmt Office)*
David Schneider *(Pres)*
John Mezzasalma *(Acting CFO)*

CENNOX INC.
3010 Santa Fe Ct, Missoula, MT 59808
Tel.: (406) 251-5041
Web Site: https://www.cennox.com
Bus Supplies Mfr & Distr
N.A.I.C.S.: 424990

Clive Nation *(CEO)*

CENTARE GROUP, LTD.
125 N Executive Dr Ste 104, Brookfield, WI 53005
Tel.: (262) 827-1010   WI
Web Site: http://www.centare.com
Year Founded: 1999
Sales Range: $1-9.9 Million
Emp.: 50
Software Devolpement
N.A.I.C.S.: 541512
Chris Hayes *(Mgr-Dev Center)*
Jacob Scherrer *(VP)*
Chad Albrecht *(Pres)*

CENTAUR BUILDING SER-VICES, INC.
4401 Ridgewood Ave, Saint Louis, MO 63116
Tel.: (314) 752-7770
Web Site:
   http://www.centaurservices.com
Year Founded: 1984
Sales Range: $10-24.9 Million
Emp.: 850
Building Maintenance Services
N.A.I.C.S.: 561720
Janine Joubert-Dulay *(Pres)*
Frank P. Joubert *(CEO)*
John Q. Joubert *(COO)*
Ken Crowe *(VP-Ops)*
Russell Smith *(Chief Admin Officer)*
Tony Osborne *(Dir-Ops)*

CENTAUR CORPORATION
17802 Sky Pk Cir Ste 100, Irvine, CA 92614
Tel.: (949) 261-2123
Web Site:
   http://www.centaursales.com
Sales Range: $10-24.9 Million
Emp.: 15
Mfr of Electronic Parts & Components
N.A.I.C.S.: 423690
Bruce Cahill *(CEO)*
Leslie Wood *(Controller)*
Tony Guerra *(Gen Mgr)*

CENTAUR, INC.
640 La Voy Rd, Erie, MI 48133-9665
Tel.: (734) 848-2915   MI
Year Founded: 1983
Sales Range: $50-74.9 Million
Emp.: 780
Blast Furnaces, Steel Mills & Trucking Services
N.A.I.C.S.: 331110
John C. Bates Jr. *(Pres)*

Subsidiaries:

Mizar Motors, Inc.   (1)
6003 Benore Rd, Toledo, OH 43612-3905   (100%)
Tel.: (419) 729-2751
Sales Range: $25-49.9 Million
Emp.: 80
Full-Service Trucking Services
N.A.I.C.S.: 484121
Rudy Vogel *(Pres & CEO)*

CENTAURI SOLUTIONS, LLC.
675 N Washington St, Alexandria, VA 22314
Tel.: (703) 647-2753
Web Site: http://www.centauri-solutions.com
Year Founded: 2006
Sales Range: $10-24.9 Million
Emp.: 52
Other Scientific & Technical Consulting Services
N.A.I.C.S.: 541690
Robert W. Kelly *(Co-Founder & Mng Partner)*

Michael Yermakov *(Co-Founder & Mng Partner)*
Glenn R. Beach *(Co-Founder & Mng Partner)*

CENTECH GROUP INC.
6402 Arlington Blvd 10th Fl, Falls Church, VA 22042
Tel.: (703) 525-4444
Web Site:
   http://www.centechgroup.com
Year Founded: 1988
Sales Range: $150-199.9 Million
Emp.: 300
Computer Related Maintenance Services & Software Developement
N.A.I.C.S.: 811210
Jim Tindell *(Pres)*
Fernando V. Galaviz *(Chm, Pres & CEO)*
Margaret E. Lietzke *(Dir-Corp Comm)*
Ellen Hill *(VP)*
Kelly M. Davidson *(Sr VP-Admin & Contracts)*

CENTEGRA HEALTH SYSTEM
4201 W Medical Center Dr, McHenry, IL 60050-8409
Tel.: (815) 344-5000   IL
Web Site: http://www.centegra.org
Year Founded: 1982
Sales Range: $200-249.9 Million
Emp.: 3,695
Hospital & Health Facility Operator
N.A.I.C.S.: 622110
Steve Rankins *(Vice Chm)*
Terrence J. Bugno *(Chm)*
Irfan Hafiz *(Chief Medical Information Officer & Sr VP)*

Subsidiaries:

Horizons Behavioral Health LLC   (1)
500 Coventry Ln Ste 205, Crystal Lake, IL 60014-7555   (100%)
Tel.: (815) 455-7100
Web Site: http://www.horizonsbh.com
Rev.: $3,900,000
Emp.: 40
Medical Devices
N.A.I.C.S.: 621112

CENTENNIAL AMERICAN PROPERTIES, LLC
935 S Main St Ste 201, Greenville, SC 29601
Tel.: (864) 271-3894
Web Site: https://www.capllc.com
Year Founded: 1976
Sales Range: $10-24.9 Million
Emp.: 10
Commercial & Institutional Building Construction
N.A.I.C.S.: 236220
David Glenn *(CEO)*
Carrie Buchanan *(Controller)*
Rebecca Gault *(Dir-Leasing)*

CENTENNIAL HOMES, INC.
322 S Vivian St, Aberdeen, SD 57401
Tel.: (605) 225-8301
Web Site: http://www.centennial-homes.com
Year Founded: 1969
Rev.: $30,000,000
Emp.: 115
Retailer of Mobile Homes
N.A.I.C.S.: 459930
Michael Evans *(CEO)*
Chad Evans *(Pres)*
Kevin Foss *(VP)*
Kevin Fox *(VP-Sls)*

CENTENNIAL LEASING INC.
7150 S Joliet St, Englewood, CO 80112
Tel.: (303) 233-2277

Web Site:
   http://www.centleasing.com
Year Founded: 1984
Sales Range: $10-24.9 Million
Emp.: 50
Business Credit Services
N.A.I.C.S.: 423110
Gary Pranger *(Pres)*
Steve Perkins *(Owner & Gen Mgr)*

CENTENNIAL MEDICAL GROUP INC
2700 NW Stewart Pkwy, Roseburg, OR 97471
Tel.: (541) 677-3650   OR
Year Founded: 2009
Sales Range: $10-24.9 Million
Health Care Srvices
N.A.I.C.S.: 622110
Rahul Agarwal *(Treas & Sec)*
Jason Gray *(Pres)*
Kelly Morgan *(Chm)*

CENTER BROTHERS INCORPORATED
45 Ross Rd, Savannah, GA 31405
Tel.: (912) 232-6491   GA
Web Site:
   http://www.centerbrothers.com
Year Founded: 1946
Sales Range: $25-49.9 Million
Emp.: 50
Drywall
N.A.I.C.S.: 238310
Leo E. Center *(Co-Owner & Chm)*
Charles S. May *(Co-Owner & CEO)*
Henry W. Tuten Jr. *(Co-Owner, Pres & COO)*

CENTER FOR AIDS RE-SEARCH, EDUCATION AND SERVICES
1500 21st St, Sacramento, CA 95811
Tel.: (916) 443-3299   CA
Web Site:
   http://www.carecommunityhealth.org
Year Founded: 1989
Sales Range: $25-49.9 Million
Emp.: 104
Health Care Srvices
N.A.I.C.S.: 622110
Alexandra Stephens-Akaka *(Dir-HR)*
Bob Styron *(CFO)*
Janet Parker *(Dir-Strategy & Market Dev)*
Christy Ward *(CEO)*

CENTER FOR AMERICAN PROGRESS
1333 H St NW 10th Fl, Washington, DC 20005
Tel.: (202) 682-1611   DC
Web Site:
   https://www.americanprogress.org
Year Founded: 2002
Sales Range: $25-49.9 Million
Emp.: 372
Community Welfare Services
N.A.I.C.S.: 624190
Neera Tanden *(Pres)*
Carmel Martin *(Exec VP-Policy)*
Winnie Stachelberg *(Exec VP-External Affairs)*
Arkadi Gerney *(Sr VP)*
Daniella Gibbs Leger *(Sr VP-Comm & Strategy)*
Lindsay Hamilton *(VP)*
Madeleine Albright *(Sec)*
Brian DeMarco *(VP-Dev)*
Catherine Brown *(VP-Education Policy)*
Danielle Baussan *(Mng Dir)*
Melissa Boteach *(VP-Poverty to Prosperity Program)*
Maura Calsyn *(Mng Dir-Health Policy)*

Center for American Progress—(Continued)

Christy Goldfuss *(VP-Energy & Environment Policy)*
Andy Green *(Mng Dir)*
Katie Hamm *(VP-Early Childhood Policys)*
John Hanly *(VP-Tech)*
Deborah Holston *(VP-Fin)*
Marc Jarsulic *(VP-Economic Policy)*
Michele L. Jawando *(VP-Legal Process)*
Tom Jawetz *(VP-Immigration)*
Judd Legum *(Sr VP)*
Ashley Marvel *(VP-Admin)*
Ben Olinsky *(VP-Strategy & Policy)*
Allison Preiss *(Mng Dir-Comm)*
Will Ragland *(Mng Dir)*
Scott Sargrad *(Mng Dir)*
Vikram Singh *(VP-Natl Security & Intl Policy)*
Michael Sozan *(Sr VP-Govt Affairs)*
Rebecca Vallas *(Mng Dir)*
Marlene Cooper Vasilic *(VP-Outreach & Special Events)*
Lauren Vicary *(VP-Art & Editorial)*
Lashawn Y. Warren *(VP-Faith & Progressive Policy Initiative)*
Philip E. Wolgin *(Mng Dir-Immigration)*
Patrick Gaspard *(CEO)*

CENTER FOR COMMUNITY CHANGE

1536 U St NW, Washington, DC 20009
Tel.: (202) 339-9300   DC
Web Site:
  https://www.communitychange.org
Year Founded: 1968
Sales Range: $25-49.9 Million
Emp.: 100
Community Development Services
N.A.I.C.S.: 813319
Dorian T. Warren *(VP)*
Mary Lassen *(Mng Dir)*

CENTER FOR COMPUTER RESOURCES, LLC

36333 Mound Rd Ste C, Sterling Heights, MI 48310
Tel.: (248) 284-7100
Web Site: http://www.ccr1.com
Year Founded: 1981
Computer System Design Services
N.A.I.C.S.: 541512
Curtis Hicks *(CEO)*

Subsidiaries:

Business Communications Systems, Inc.   (1)
5670 18 Mile Rd, Sterling Heights, MI 48314
Tel.: (586) 276-3600
Web Site: http://bcs-nec.com
Sales Range: $1-9.9 Million
Emp.: 28
Telecommunications Resellers
N.A.I.C.S.: 517121
Jeffrey Newson *(CEO)*

CENTER FOR CREATIVE LEADERSHIP INC.

1 Leadership Pl, Greensboro, NC 27410-9427
Tel.: (336) 545-2810   NC
Web Site: https://www.ccl.org
Year Founded: 1970
Sales Range: $75-99.9 Million
Emp.: 500
Schools & Educational Services
N.A.I.C.S.: 611699
Bradley E. Shumaker *(Chief Fin & Admin Officer, Sec & Exec VP)*
David G. Altman *(COO)*
Karen Dyer *(Dir-Education & Non-Profit Sector)*

Jennifer Martineau *(VP-Res, Innovation & Product Dev)*
Portia Mount *(SR VP-Global Mktg)*
William Pasmore *(Sr VP-Organizational Dev)*
Peter L. Richardson *(Chm)*
Shera Clark *(Mgr-Nonprofit Sector)*
Thomas Goh *(Mng Dir/chief Client Officer-Asia Pacific)*
Jennifer Habig *(Mng Dir)*
Russ McCallian *(Mng Dir)*

Subsidiaries:

Center for Creative Leadership (CCL) Pte Ltd   (1)
89 Science Park Drive Singapore Science Park I The Rutherford Lobby B, Singapore, 118261, Singapore
Tel.: (65) 6854 6000
Professional Development Training Services
N.A.I.C.S.: 611430
Roland Smith *(Mng Dir)*

CENTER FOR DISABILITY SERVICES, INC.

314 S Manning Blvd, Albany, NY 12208
Tel.: (518) 437-5700   NY
Web Site: https://www.cfdsny.org
Year Founded: 1948
Sales Range: $75-99.9 Million
Emp.: 2,835
Disability Assistance Services
N.A.I.C.S.: 624120
Maria Kansas Devine *(Chief Medical Officer)*
D. Elliott Wilson *(Sr Dir-IT)*
Suzanne E. Beattie *(Sr Dir-Quality Improvement)*
Dennis Riley *(Sr Dir-Comml Svcs)*
Donna Lamkin *(Chief Program Officer)*
Gregory J. Sorrentino *(Pres & CEO)*
Mary H. Lisa *(Sr Dir-Upstate Rehabilitation Products)*
David Murray *(CIO)*

CENTER FOR EDUCATIONAL INNOVATION - PUBLIC EDUCATION ASSOCIATION

28 W 44th St Ste 300, New York, NY 10036
Tel.: (212) 302-8800   NY
Web Site: http://www.thecei-pea.org
Year Founded: 2000
Sales Range: $10-24.9 Million
Emp.: 129
Educational Support Services
N.A.I.C.S.: 611710
Clara Katz *(Dir-Leadership & Principal Trng)*
Eileen Witt *(Dir-HR)*
Jackie Pine *(Dir-Arts)*
John Falco *(VP)*
Michael Kohlhagen *(Dir-Education)*
Louis Benevento *(CFO)*
Ellen Padva *(Dir-Pro Svcs)*
Nancy Ramos *(Dir-Prof Svcs)*
Carlos Medina *(Dir-Special Projects)*
Deborah Wasser-Sachs *(Dir-Dev)*
Charles Amundsen *(Dir-Pro Svcs)*
Gerard Beirne *(Dir-Pro Svcs)*
Janice Brown *(Sec)*

CENTER FOR ELDERS' INDEPENDENCE

510 17th St, Oakland, CA 94612
Tel.: (510) 433-1150   CA
Web Site: http://www.cei.elders.org
Year Founded: 1989
Sales Range: $25-49.9 Million
Emp.: 306
Elder Care Services
N.A.I.C.S.: 623312

Linda Trowbridge *(CEO)*
Bing Isenberg *(CFO)*
Fiona Wilmot *(Chief Medical Officer)*
Aaron McPherson *(VP-Ops)*

CENTER FOR EMERGENCY MEDICINE OF WESTERN PA INC.

230 McKee Pl Ste 500, Pittsburgh, PA 15213
Tel.: (412) 647-5300
Web Site: http://www.centerem.com
Sales Range: $10-24.9 Million
Emp.: 12
Emergency Helicopter Carriers
N.A.I.C.S.: 621111
Don Goodman *(CFO)*

CENTER FOR EMPLOYMENT OPPORTUNITIES INC

50 Broadway 18th Fl, New York, NY 10004
Tel.: (212) 422-4430   NY
Web Site: https://www.ceoworks.org
Year Founded: 1996
Sales Range: $10-24.9 Million
Emp.: 230
Employment & Placement Services
N.A.I.C.S.: 561311
David I. Moskovitz *(Chm)*
Steven Fishner *(Treas)*
O. Peter Sherwood *(Sec)*

CENTER FOR EMPLOYMENT TRAINING INC.

701 Vine St, San Jose, CA 95110-2940
Tel.: (408) 287-7924   CA
Web Site: http://www.cetweb.org
Year Founded: 1967
Sales Range: $25-49.9 Million
Emp.: 350
Job Training & Related Services
N.A.I.C.S.: 624310
Hermelinda Sapien *(Pres & CEO)*
Luis Aguilar *(Dir-Education)*
Mohammad Aryanpour *(CFO)*
Asbjorn Osland *(Chm)*
Bob Martinez *(Vice Chm)*
Daniel Ezquerro *(Treas)*
Chris Longoria *(Sec)*

CENTER FOR GLOBAL DEVELOPMENT

2055 L St NW 5th Fl, Washington, DC 20036
Tel.: (202) 416-4000   DC
Web Site: https://www.cgdev.org
Year Founded: 2001
Sales Range: $10-24.9 Million
Environmental Research Services
N.A.I.C.S.: 541715
Lawrence H. Summers *(Chm)*

CENTER FOR HOSPICE CARE

111 Sunnybrook Ct, South Bend, IN 46637
Tel.: (574) 243-3100   IN
Web Site:
  http://www.centerforhospice.org
Year Founded: 1978
Sales Range: $10-24.9 Million
Emp.: 252
Hospice Care Services
N.A.I.C.S.: 621610
Mark M. Murray *(Pres & CEO)*
Mary Newbold *(Vice Chm)*
Wendell Walsh *(Chm)*
Craig Harrell *(Dir-Mktg & Access)*
Vanessa Johnson *(Dir-Medical-Hospice & Palliative Care Program)*

CENTER FOR INDEPENDENCE OF THE DISABLED, NEW YORK

841 Broadway Ste 301, New York, NY 10003
Tel.: (212) 674-2300   NY
Web Site: https://www.cidny.org
Year Founded: 1979
Sales Range: $10-24.9 Million
Emp.: 1,219
Disability Assistance Services
N.A.I.C.S.: 624120
Lourdes Rosa-Carrasquillo *(Dir-Advocacy)*
Heidi Siegfried *(Dir-Health Policy)*
Cyrus Kazi *(Dir-Admin)*
Van K. Ly *(Dir-Consumer Svcs)*
Susan Dooha *(Exec Dir)*

CENTER FOR INDEPENDENT LIVING

1142 Sanderson Ave, Scranton, PA 18509
Tel.: (570) 344-7211
Web Site: https://www.mycil.org
Sales Range: $75-99.9 Million
Emp.: 200
Disability Assistance Services
N.A.I.C.S.: 624120
Robert K. Treptow *(VP)*

CENTER FOR INNOVATIVE TECHNOLOGY

2214 Rock Hill Rd Ste 600, Herndon, VA 20170-4228
Tel.: (703) 689-3000   VA
Web Site: http://www.cit.org
Year Founded: 1984
Sales Range: $10-24.9 Million
Emp.: 44
Economic Development Services
N.A.I.C.S.: 541720
Robert Brooke *(Dir-Federal Funding Programs)*
Susan Aitcheson *(CFO)*
Alex Euler *(Dir-Investment)*
Michael Steed *(Chm)*
Walter Mazan *(Vice Chm)*
Bob Stolle *(Pres & CEO)*

CENTER FOR INTERNATIONAL PRIVATE ENTERPRISE

1211 Connecticut Ave NW Ste 700, Washington, DC 20036
Tel.: (202) 721-9200   DC
Web Site: https://www.cipe.org
Year Founded: 1985
Sales Range: $10-24.9 Million
Emp.: 80
Business Consulting Services
N.A.I.C.S.: 541611
Myron A. Brilliant *(VP)*
Steven B. Rogers *(Deputy Dir-Ops)*
Greg Lebedev *(Chm)*
Andrew Wilson *(Mng Dir)*
Denise L. Baer *(Chief Evaluation Officer)*
Thomas J. Donohue *(Pres)*
Sayed Muhibullah Hashmi *(Officer-Ops)*

CENTER FOR INVESTIGATIVE REPORTING, INC.

PO Box 584, San Francisco, CA 94104
Tel.: (415) 321-1700
Web Site: https://revealnews.org
Year Founded: 1977
Rev.: $1,500,000
Emp.: 10
Fiscal Year-end: 12/31/06
News Syndicates, Nsk
N.A.I.C.S.: 516210
Richard Hacker *(Vice Chm)*
Sara Frankel *(Treas)*
Susan Sachs *(Sec)*

CENTER FOR MAINE CON-

TEMPORARY ART
162 Russell Ave, Rockport, ME
04856
Tel.: (207) 236-2875   ME
Web Site: http://www.cmcanow.org
Year Founded: 1968
Rev.: $1,749,587
Assets: $2,010,711
Liabilities: $309,100
Net Worth: $1,701,611
Earnings: $1,420,200
Emp.: 3
Fiscal Year-end: 03/31/14
Museums
N.A.I.C.S.: 712110
Jonathan Laurence *(Dir-Creative)*
Charlotte Dixon *(Chm)*
Martin E. Lloyd *(Treas)*
Sandra Ruch *(Sec)*

CENTER FOR ORGAN RECOVERY & EDUCATION
204 Sigma Dr RIDC Park, Pittsburgh,
PA 15238   PA
Web Site: https://www.core.org
Year Founded: 1977
Sales Range: $25-49.9 Million
Emp.: 135
Organ Research & Education Services
N.A.I.C.S.: 541715
Cheri Rinehart *(Vice Chm)*

CENTER FOR PEOPLE IN NEED, INC.
3901 N 27th St, Lincoln, NE 68521
Tel.: (402) 476-4357   NE
Web Site:
   http://www.centerforpeople.org
Year Founded: 2003
Sales Range: $1-9.9 Million
Emp.: 66
Individual & Family Support Services
N.A.I.C.S.: 624190
Beatty Brasch *(Exec Dir)*

CENTER FOR RETINA AND MACULAR DISEASE
250 Ave K SW, Winter Haven, FL
33880
Tel.: (863) 297-5400
Web Site: https://www.crmd.net
Sales Range: $25-49.9 Million
Emp.: 100
Eye Specialists
N.A.I.C.S.: 621111
David M. Misch *(Founder)*

CENTER FOR SIGHT, P.L.
1360 E Venice Ave, Venice, FL 34285
Tel.: (941) 488-2020
Web Site:
   https://www.centerforsight.net
Sales Range: $25-49.9 Million
Emp.: 250
Eye Care Service
N.A.I.C.S.: 621111
David Shoemaker *(Founder & CEO)*

CENTER FOR SOCIAL CHANGE
6600 Amberton Dr, Elkridge, MD
21075
Tel.: (410) 579-6789   MD
Web Site:
   https://www.centerforchange.org
Year Founded: 1993
Sales Range: $10-24.9 Million
Emp.: 433
Disability Assistance Services
N.A.I.C.S.: 623210
Caitlin Coale *(Asst Dir-Programs & Clinic)*
Dana Dimas *(Dir-Programs)*
Nataliya Todorova *(Dir-Fin & HR)*

CENTER FOR SUSTAINABLE ENERGY
9325 Sky Park Ct Ste 100, San Diego, CA 92123
Tel.: (858) 244-1177   CA
Web Site:
   http://www.energycenter.org
Year Founded: 1996
Sales Range: $150-199.9 Million
Energy Conservation Services
N.A.I.C.S.: 541690
Lawrence P. Goldenhersh *(Pres)*

CENTER FOR THE ADVANCEMENT OF SCIENCE IN SPACE, INC.
6905 N Wickham Rd Ste 500, Melbourne, FL 32940
Tel.: (321) 253-5101   FL
Web Site: http://www.iss-casis.org
Year Founded: 2011
Sales Range: $10-24.9 Million
Emp.: 39
Space Research Support Services
N.A.I.C.S.: 541715
Ken Shields *(Dir-Flight Ops & Educational Opportunities)*
Diane Matthews *(Sr Project Mgr-STEM Education)*
Cynthia Bouthot *(Dir-Bus Dev)*
Warren Bates *(Dir-Portfolio Mgmt)*
Jorge Fernandez *(CFO & Dir-Admin)*
Duane Ratliff *(COO)*
Ed Harris *(Dir-Dev & Partnerships)*
Patrick O'Neill *(Mgr-Comm)*
Philip Schein *(Chm)*
Melody Kuehner *(Dir-HR)*
Brian Talbot *(Dir-Mktg)*
Joseph Vockley *(Pres & CEO)*

CENTER INDEPENDENT OIL COMPANY
407 Rowes Run Rd, Smock, PA
15480
Tel.: (724) 677-4408
Year Founded: 1923
Sales Range: $25-49.9 Million
Emp.: 60
Gasoline & Petroleum Products
N.A.I.C.S.: 424720
John R. Higgenbotham *(Pres)*
Kathryn Fullerton *(Mgr-Ops)*

CENTER LINE
310 S Harrington St, Raleigh, NC
27603
Tel.: (919) 821-2921
Web Site: http://www.centerline.net
Year Founded: 1996
Sales Range: $10-24.9 Million
Emp.: 30
Advertising, Brand Development & Integration, Communications, Computers & Software, Internet/Web Design, Local Marketing, Mobile Marketing, T.V., Technical Advertising
N.A.I.C.S.: 541810
Charles Long *(Founder & CEO)*
Jodi Schwartz *(Exec Project Mgr)*
Tami Gaythwaite *(VP-Acct Mgmt)*
John Lane *(Dir-Creative Svcs)*
Kristi Creamer *(Gen Mgr)*
David Schafermeyer *(Dir-Art & Team Mgr)*
Aimee Kuchta *(Sr Acct Mgr)*
Erin Craft *(Acct Exec)*
Shawn Lamons *(Acct Mgr)*

CENTER LINE ELECTRIC INC.
26554 Lawrence Ave, Center Line, MI
48015
Tel.: (586) 757-5505
Web Site: https://www.centerline-elec.com
Rev.: $60,883,461
Emp.: 250

General Electrical Contractor
N.A.I.C.S.: 238210
Mark Hodges *(Project Mgr)*
Retta Valko *(Mgr-Payroll)*
Thomas Miele *(Dir-Fin & Ops)*
Todd Bertolini *(Superintendent-Field)*

CENTER LINE WHEELS, INC.
15100 Radrus Pl, Santa Fe Springs,
CA 90670
Tel.: (562) 921-9637
Web Site:
   http://www.centerlinewheels.com
Sales Range: $10-24.9 Million
Emp.: 100
Motor Vehicle Wheels
N.A.I.C.S.: 336390
Ray Lipper *(Founder & Pres)*

CENTER ROCK CAPITAL PARTNERS, LP
8755 W Higgins Rd Ste 840, Chicago, IL 60631
Tel.: (312) 635-8075
Web Site:
   http://www.centerrockcapital.com
Privater Equity Firm
N.A.I.C.S.: 523999
Ian Kirson *(Partner)*
Terry Theodore *(Partner)*

Subsidiaries:

American Piping Products Inc.   (1)
825 Maryville Ctr Dr Ste 310, Chesterfield,
MO 63017
Tel.: (636) 536-1775
Web Site: http://www.amerpipe.com
Sales Range: $10-24.9 Million
Emp.: 25
Sells Pipes & Tubing Steel
N.A.I.C.S.: 423510
Kevin Koehler *(Mng Dir)*
Matt Danis *(Pres)*
Shep Hickey *(COO)*
Al Rheinnecker *(CEO)*

Wolverine Advanced Materials
LLC   (1)
3rd Floor 144/145 Kodambakkam High
Road Nungambakkam, Chennai, 600 034,
Tamil Nadu, India
Tel.: (91) 9791017143
Web Site: http://www.wamglobal.com
Automobile Parts Distr
N.A.I.C.S.: 423120
Ekambaram Maheswaran *(Acct Mgr)*
Laurent Crosnier *(VP & Gen Mgr)*
Kristine Frost *(Exec Dir)*
Marco Walter *(Exec Dir)*
Steve Sehmer *(Exec Dir)*
Ivan Martinez-Rivera *(Exec Dir)*
Abdul-Hafiz Afaneh *(VP)*
Scott Rauwald *(Exec Dir)*
Laurent Crosnier *(VP & Gen Mgr)*
Kristine Frost *(Exec Dir)*
Marco Walter *(Exec Dir)*
Steve Sehmer *(Exec Dir)*
Ivan Martinez-Rivera *(Exec Dir)*
Abdul-Hafiz Afaneh *(VP)*
Scott Rauwald *(Exec Dir)*

CENTER THEATRE GROUP OF LOS ANGELES, INC.
601 W Temple St, Los Angeles, CA
90012
Tel.: (213) 628-2772
Web Site:
   https://www.centertheatregroup.org
Year Founded: 1967
Sales Range: $25-49.9 Million
Emp.: 100
Theatrical Services
N.A.I.C.S.: 711110
Harold Applebaum *(Treas)*
Martin Massman *(Chm)*
Jim Royce *(Dir-Mktg & Comm)*
Michael Ritchie *(Dir-Art)*

CENTERBRIDGE PARTNERS, L.P.
375 Park Ave, New York, NY 10152
Tel.: (212) 672-5000   DE
Web Site: http://www.centerbridge.com
Privater Equity Firm
N.A.I.C.S.: 523999
Steven M. Silver *(Sr Mng Dir)*
Jeffrey H. Aronson *(Co-Founder & Mng Principal)*
Mark T. Gallogly *(Co-Founder & Mng Principal)*
Richard Grissinger *(Sr Mng Dir)*
Jared S. Hendricks *(Sr Mng Dir)*
William D. Rahm *(Sr Mng Dir)*
Bao Dinh Truong *(Sr Mng Dir)*
Gavin R. Baiera *(Partner, Sr Mng Dir & Portfolio Mgr)*
Jeremy W. Gelber *(Sr Mng Dir-New York)*
Barbara Cona Amone *(Sr Mng Dir)*
Carrie Braddock *(Sr Mng Dir)*
Adam M. Burinescu *(Sr Mng Dir)*
Brian W. Chu *(Sr Mng Dir)*
Susanne V. Clark *(Sr Mng Dir)*
Aaron S. Fink *(Sr Mng Dir)*
Jed A. Hart *(Sr Mng Dir)*
William Rahm *(Sr Mng Dir & Head-Real Estate)*
Conor Tochilin *(Mng Dir)*

Subsidiaries:

APCOA Parking AG   (1)
Flughafenstrasse 34, PO Box 23 04 63,
70624, Stuttgart, Germany
Tel.: (49) 711947910
Web Site: http://www.apcoa-europe.com
Sales Range: $650-699.9 Million
Emp.: 950
Parking Facility Management Services
N.A.I.C.S.: 561210

Subsidiary (Non-US):

APCOA Belgium N.V.   (2)
Terbekehofdreef 64, 2610, Wilrijk, Belgium
Tel.: (32) 32339423
Web Site: http://www.apcoa.be
Emp.: 100
Parking Facility Management Services
N.A.I.C.S.: 561210

APCOA Parking (UK) Ltd   (2)
Victoria Station Car Park Eccleston Bridge,
London, SW1W 9SJ, Middlesex, United
Kingdom
Tel.: (44) 3452224224
Web Site: http://www.apcoa.co.uk
Sales Range: $25-49.9 Million
Emp.: 80
Parking Facility Management Services
N.A.I.C.S.: 561210

APCOA Parking Austria GmbH   (2)
Landstrasser Hauptstr 146/13A, 1030, Vienna, Austria
Tel.: (43) 1 717 16 0
Web Site: http://www.apcoa.at
Sales Range: $25-49.9 Million
Emp.: 163
Parking Facility Management Services
N.A.I.C.S.: 561210
Stefan Sadleder *(Mng Dir)*

Subsidiary (Domestic):

APCOA Parking Deutschland
GmbH   (2)
Air Freight Centre 605/6 Level 6, 70629,
Stuttgart, Germany
Tel.: (49) 711947910
Web Site: https://www.apcoa.de
Sales Range: $25-49.9 Million
Emp.: 150
Automobile Parking Services
N.A.I.C.S.: 812930

Subsidiary (Non-US):

APCOA Parking Espana S.A.   (2)
C/Colombia n63 - 7A, 28016, Madrid, Spain
Tel.: (34) 917030447
Web Site: http://www.apcoa.es
Parking Facility Management Services
N.A.I.C.S.: 812930
Henk Bruin *(Gen Mgr)*

Centerbridge Partners, L.P.—(Continued)

APCOA Parking Ireland Ltd. (2)
Unit 11 Millbank Business Park Lower Lucan Road, Lucan Village, Dublin, Ireland
Tel.: (353) 18720432
Web Site: http://www.apcoa.ie
Parking Facility Management Services
N.A.I.C.S.: 561210
Aine Hanlon (Sec)

APCOA Parking Italia S.p.A. (2)
Via Renzo Zanellini 15, 46100, Mantua, Italy
Tel.: (39) 0376345000
Web Site: http://www.apcoa.it
Sales Range: $50-74.9 Million
Emp.: 25
Waste Treatment Services
N.A.I.C.S.: 221310
Arturo Benigna (Mng Dir & Gen Mgr)
Philippe Op de Beeck (Chm-Mgmt Bd)
Julia Hennig (Member-Mgmt Bd)

APCOA Parking Nederland B.V. (2)
Westblaak 88, 3012 KM, Rotterdam, Netherlands
Tel.: (31) 10850499899
Web Site: http://www.apcoa.nl
Parking Facility Management Services
N.A.I.C.S.: 561210

APCOA Parking Polska Sp.z o.o. (2)
Rondo Onz 1, 00-124, Warsaw, Poland
Tel.: (48) 22 354 83 80
Web Site: http://www.apcoa.pl
Sales Range: $25-49.9 Million
Emp.: 100
Parking Facility Management Services
N.A.I.C.S.: 561210
Philippe Op de Beeck (Member-Mgmt Bd)

APCOA Parking Switzerland AG (2)
Elisabethenanlage 7, 4051, Basel, Switzerland
Tel.: (41) 612716630
Web Site: http://www.apcoa.ch
Sales Range: $10-24.9 Million
Emp.: 50
Parking Facilities Management Services
N.A.I.C.S.: 561210
Stefan Sadleder (Mng Dir)

APCOA Parking Turkey (2)
ParkSistem Buyukdere Caddesi M Dervis Ibrahim, Gayrettepe, 34394, Istanbul, Turkiye
Tel.: (90) 2122752030
Web Site: http://www.apcoa.com.tr
Parking Facility Management Services
N.A.I.C.S.: 561210

Aareal Bank AG (1)
Paulinenstrasse 15, D-65189, Wiesbaden, Germany (37%)
Tel.: (49) 6113480
Web Site: https://www.aareal-bank.com
Rev.: $2,634,362,184
Assets: $50,542,844,809
Liabilities: $46,981,437,513
Net Worth: $3,561,407,295
Earnings: $76,624,218
Emp.: 3,463
Fiscal Year-end: 12/31/2023
Commercial Banking Services
N.A.I.C.S.: 522110
Jurgen Junginger (Head-IR)
Jean Pierre Mustier (Chm-Supervisory Bd)
Christof Winkelmann (Chief Market Officer & Member-Mgmt Bd)
Sebastian Gotzken (Dir-IR)
Hans-Hermann Lotter (Deputy Chm-Supervisory Bd)
Barbara Antonia Knoflach (Deputy Chm-Supervisory Bd)
Christian Klaus Ricken (CEO)
Karin Desczka (Mgr-IR)
Carsten Schafer (Dir-IR)
Marc Oliver Hess (CFO & Member-Mgmt Bd)
Klaus Novatius (Deputy Chm-Supervisory Bd)
Nina Babic (Chief Risk Officer & Member-Mgmt Bd)
Frank Finger (Head-Treasury)
Andy Halford (CFO)

Subsidiary (Non-US):

Aareal Bank AG (2)

29 bis rue d'Astorg, 75008, Paris, France (100%)
Tel.: (33) 14 451 6630
Web Site: http://www.aareal-bank.com
Sales Range: $50-74.9 Million
Emp.: 25
International Real Estate Financing
N.A.I.C.S.: 522292

Aareal Bank Asia Limited (2)
3 Church Street, Singapore, 49483, Singapore
Tel.: (65) 63729750
Web Site: http://www.aareal-bank.com
Emp.: 10
Real Estate Investment Services
N.A.I.C.S.: 522292

Subsidiary (US):

Aareal Bank Capital Funding Trust (2)
250 Park Ave Ste 820, New York, NY 10177
Tel.: (646) 465-8601
Web Site: http://www.aareal-capital-funding.com
Investment Banking Services
N.A.I.C.S.: 523150

Aareal Capital Corporation (2)
360 Madison Ave - 18th Fl, New York, NY 10017
Tel.: (212) 508-4080
Web Site: http://www.aareal-bank.com
Sales Range: $50-74.9 Million
Property Financing
N.A.I.C.S.: 522292

Subsidiary (Domestic):

Aareal Estate AG (2)
Paulinenstrasse 15, D 65189, Wiesbaden, Germany (100%)
Tel.: (49) 6113480
Web Site: http://www.aareal-bank.com
Emp.: 21
Development, Management & Marketing of Commercial Properties
N.A.I.C.S.: 531390

Aareal First Financial Solutions AG (2)
Isaac-Fulda-Allee 6, 55124, Mainz, Germany
Tel.: (49) 61314864500
Web Site: http://www.first-financial.biz
Software Development Services
N.A.I.C.S.: 541511

Aareal Gesellschaft fur Beteiligungen und Grundbesitz Dritte mbH & Co. KG (2)
Paulinenstr 15, 65189, Wiesbaden, Germany
Tel.: (49) 6113482950
Property Management Services
N.A.I.C.S.: 531312

Aareal Gesellschaft fur Beteiligungen und Grundbesitz Erste mbH & Co. KG (2)
Paulinenstr 15, 65189, Wiesbaden, Germany
Tel.: (49) 6113480
Web Site: http://www.aareal-bank.com
Emp.: 800
Real Estate Management Services
N.A.I.C.S.: 531390

Aareal IT Beteiligungen GmbH (2)
Paulinenstr 15, 65189, Wiesbaden, Germany
Tel.: (49) 6113480
Web Site: http://www.aareal-bank.com
Emp.: 2,200
Investment Management Consulting Services
N.A.I.C.S.: 523999

Aareal Valuation GmbH (2)
Paulinenstrasse 15, 65189, Wiesbaden, Germany (100%)
Tel.: (49) 6113480
Web Site: http://www.aareal-valuation.com
Sales Range: $25-49.9 Million
Property Valuation & Consulting Services
N.A.I.C.S.: 541618

Subsidiary (Non-US):

Aareal-Financial Service, spol. s r.o. (2)
Vaclavske Namesti 19, 11000, Prague, Czech Republic
Tel.: (420) 234656006
Web Site: http://www.aareal-bank.com
Financial Management Consulting Services
N.A.I.C.S.: 541611

Subsidiary (Domestic):

Aareon AG (2)
Isaac-Fulda-Allee 6, 55124, Mainz, Germany
Tel.: (49) 6 131 3010
Web Site: https://www.aareon.de
Sales Range: $400-449.9 Million
Emp.: 1,200
Software & IT Services for the Management of Residential & Commercial Properties
N.A.I.C.S.: 449210
Manfred Alflen (CEO & Member-Mgmt Bd)
Sabine Fischer (CMO & Member-Mgmt Bd)
Andre Rasquin (COO & Member-Mgmt Bd)
Christian M. Schmahl (CFO & Member-Mgmt Bd)
Imad Abdallah (Chief Digital & Ventures Officer & Member-Mgmt Bd)

Subsidiary (Non-US):

Aareon France S.A.S. (3)
Parc Tertiaire De Meudon Batiment Le Newton 9-11 Rue Jeanne Braconnier, Meudon La Foret, 92366, Meudon, Cedex, France
Tel.: (33) 145379230
Web Site: http://www.aareon.fr
Sales Range: $75-99.9 Million
Property Management Consulting Services
N.A.I.C.S.: 531312

Aareon UK Ltd. (3)
Building 500 Abbey Park, Stareton, Kenilworth, CV8 2LY, United Kingdom
Tel.: (44) 2476323723
Web Site: http://www.aareon.co.uk
Sales Range: $10-24.9 Million
Business Management Software Development Services
N.A.I.C.S.: 541511
Rob Griffiths (Mng Dir)

Subsidiary (Domestic):

Aareon Deutschland GmbH (2)
Im Muenchfeld 1-5, 55122, Mainz, Germany
Tel.: (49) 6131 301 295
Investment Banking Services
N.A.I.C.S.: 523150

Subsidiary (Non-US):

Aareon Finland Oy (2)
Pohjoisesplanadi 39, 00100, Helsinki, Finland
Tel.: (358) 317254380
Web Site: http://www.aareon.fi
Software Development Services
N.A.I.C.S.: 541511

Aareon Nederland B.V. (2)
Cornelis Houtmanstraat 36, 7825 VG, Emmen, Netherlands
Tel.: (31) 882420242
Web Site: http://www.aareon.nl
Software Development Services
N.A.I.C.S.: 541511

Aareon Norge AS (2)
Calmeyers Gate 5, 0183, Oslo, Norway
Tel.: (47) 90825054
Web Site: http://www.aareon.no
Software Development Services
N.A.I.C.S.: 541511

Subsidiary (Domestic):

Aareon Software Handelsgesellschaft mbH (2)
Isaac Fulda Allee 6, Mainz, 55124, Germany
Tel.: (49) 61313010
Web Site: http://www.aareon.com
Computer Peripheral Equipment Distr.
N.A.I.C.S.: 423430

Subsidiary (Non-US):

Aareon Sverige AB (2)

Flojelbergsgatan 10, 431 37, Molndal, Sweden
Tel.: (46) 317254300
Web Site: http://www.aareon.se
Software Development Services
N.A.I.C.S.: 541511

Subsidiary (Domestic):

Aareon Wodis GmbH (2)
Rheinlanddamm 199, Dortmund, 44139, Germany
Tel.: (49) 23177510
Web Site: http://www.aareon.com
Sales Range: $50-74.9 Million
Emp.: 100
Real Estate Manangement Services
N.A.I.C.S.: 531390

COREALCREDIT Bank AG (2)
Gruneburgweg 58-62, D-60322, Frankfurt am Main, Germany (99.9%)
Tel.: (49) 6971790
Web Site: http://www.corealcredit.de
Sales Range: $5-14.9 Billion
Emp.: 175
Mortgage Banking Services
N.A.I.C.S.: 522310

CalCon Deutschland GmbH (2)
Beethovenplatz 4, 80336, Munich, Germany
Tel.: (49) 895526980
Real Estate Services
N.A.I.C.S.: 531390

Capital Funding GmbH & Co. KG (2)
Steinweg 3-5, 60313, Frankfurt am Main, 60313, Germany
Tel.: (49) 6929925385
Web Site: http://www.capital-funding.de
Financial Management Consulting Services
N.A.I.C.S.: 523999
Florian Schluter (Gen Mgr)

Collect Artificial Intelligence GmbH (2)
Am Sandtorkai 50, 20457, Hamburg, Germany
Tel.: (49) 40609412950
Web Site: http://www.collect.ai
Emp.: 50
Ecommerce Services
N.A.I.C.S.: 541512
Thomas K. Sax (Mng Dir)
Frederik Werner (Co-Owner-Product)
Adeline Paasch (Head-People & Culture)
Wiebke Tschorn (Co-Owner-Product)
Nina Walz (Mgr-Corp Dev)

Deutsche Structured Finance GmbH (2)
Feuerbachstrasse 26-32, 60325, Frankfurt, Germany
Tel.: (49) 699714970
Web Site: http://www.dsf-fra.de
Financial Management Consulting Services
N.A.I.C.S.: 541611

Deutsche Structured Finance GmbH & Co. Alphard KG (2)
Feuerbachstrasse 26-32, Frankfurt am Main, Germany
Tel.: (49) 699714970
Web Site: http://www.dsf-fra.de
Sales Range: $25-49.9 Million
Emp.: 17
Financial Management Consulting Services
N.A.I.C.S.: 541611

Deutsche Structured Finance GmbH & Co. Deneb KG (2)
Feuerbachstr 26- 32, 60325, Frankfurt am Main, Germany
Tel.: (49) 699714970
Financial Management Consulting Services
N.A.I.C.S.: 541611

Deutsche Structured Finance GmbH & Co. Titan KG (2)
Westendstr 24, Frankfurt am Main, 60325, Germany
Tel.: (49) 699714970
Financial Management Consulting Services
N.A.I.C.S.: 541611

GEV GmbH (2)
Gadastr 4, Bergkirchen, 85232, Dachau, Germany
Tel.: (49) 8142652250

Web Site: http://www.gev-online.com
Catering Equipment Mfr & Whslr
N.A.I.C.S.: 333310

Subsidiary (Non-US):

IMMO Consulting S.p.A. (2)
Via Mercadante 12/14, 198, Rome, Italy
Tel.: (39) 0683004400
Financial Management Consulting Services
N.A.I.C.S.: 541611

Kalshoven Automation B.V. (2)
Kabelweg 37, 1014 BA, Amsterdam, Netherlands
Tel.: (31) 206068606
Web Site: http://www.kalshoven.nl
Software Development Services
N.A.I.C.S.: 541511

Subsidiary (Domestic):

Real Verwaltungsgesellschaft
mbH (2)
Elisabeth-Schwarzkopf-Weg, 65510, Idstein,
Germany
Tel.: (49) 6113480
Web Site: http://www.aareal-bank.com
Real Estate Management Services
N.A.I.C.S.: 531390

Rehabilitationsklinik Barby Besitzgesellschaft mbH (2)
Paulinenstr 15, 65189, Wiesbaden, Hessen,
Germany
Tel.: (49) 39298 61600
Health Insurance Services
N.A.I.C.S.: 524298

Subsidiary (Non-US):

SG Automatisering B.V. (2)
Cornelis Houtmanstraat 36, Postbus 2036,
7825 VG, Emmen, Netherlands
Tel.: (31) 591630111
Web Site: http://www.sg.nl
Software Development Services
N.A.I.C.S.: 541512

SG Detachering B.V. (2)
Cornelis Houtmanstraat 36, Emmen, 7825
VG, Drenthe, Netherlands
Tel.: (31) 591630111
General Management Consulting Services
N.A.I.C.S.: 541618

SG Facilitor B.V. (2)
Gronausestraat 710, 7534 AM, Enschede,
Netherlands
Tel.: (31) 534800710
Web Site: http://facilitor.nl
Sales Range: $25-49.9 Million
Software Development Services
N.A.I.C.S.: 541512

SG Professional Services B.V. (2)
Cornelis Houtmanstraat 36, Emmen, 7825
VG, Drenthe, Netherlands
Tel.: (31) 591666833
Software Development Services
N.A.I.C.S.: 541511

Tactile Limited (2)
International House 24 Holborn Viaduct,
London, EC1A 2BN, United Kingdom
Tel.: (44) 2071831222
Web Site: https://www.fixflo.com
Computer System Integration Services
N.A.I.C.S.: 541512

Subsidiary (Domestic):

Terrain-Aktiengesellschaft
Herzogpark (2)
Paulinenstr 15, 65189, Wiesbaden, Hessen,
Germany
Tel.: (49) 6113480
Web Site: http://www.aareal-bank.com
Real Estate Management Services
N.A.I.C.S.: 531390

Westdeutsche Immobilien Servicing
AG (2)
Kantstrasse 1, 55122, Mainz, Germany
Tel.: (49) 61313029890
Web Site: https://www.westimmo.com
Sales Range: $600-649.9 Million
Emp.: 274
Real Estate Financing & Investment Banking Services
N.A.I.C.S.: 522292

Westdeutsche Immobilien Servicing
AG (2)
Grosse Bleiche 54, 55116, Mainz, Germany
Tel.: (49) 61313029890
Web Site: http://www.westimmo.com
Software Development Services
N.A.I.C.S.: 541511

mse Augsburg GmbH (2)
Kurzes Geland 12, 86156, Augsburg, Germany
Tel.: (49) 821710040
Web Site: http://www.relion.business.site
Software Development Services
N.A.I.C.S.: 541511

mse Immobiliensoftware GmbH (2)
Jarrestrasse 2, 22303, Hamburg, Germany
Tel.: (49) 405343510
Web Site: http://www.mse-immo.com
Software Development Services
N.A.I.C.S.: 541511

plusForta GmbH (2)
Dusseldorf Talstr 24, 40217, Dusseldorf,
Germany
Tel.: (49) 2115426830
Web Site: http://kautionsfrei.de
Software Development Services
N.A.I.C.S.: 541511

Canopius Group Limted (1)
Gallery 9 One Lime Street, London, EC3M
7HA, United Kingdom
Tel.: (44) 2073373700
Web Site: http://www.canopius.com
Holding Company; Insurance & Reinsurance Products & Services
N.A.I.C.S.: 551112
Michael Watson (Grp Chm & Grp CEO)
Mike Duffy (Grp Chief Underwriting Officer)
Barbara Turner (Head-HR)
Laurie Davison (CEO-US & Bermuda)
Sheldon Lacy (Grp Head-Governance)
Neil Robertson (Grp Deputy CEO)
Gavin Phillips (Grp CFO)
Serena Lee (Chief Risk Officer & Gen
Counsel)
Ruchama Graff (Head-Actuarial-US)

Subsidiary (Non-US):

Canopius Bermuda Limited (2)
Ideation House Ground Floor The Waterfront 94 Pitts Bay Road, Pembroke, Hamilton, HM08, Bermuda
Tel.: (441) 292 9905
Web Site: http://www.canopius.com
Reinsurance Underwriting Services
N.A.I.C.S.: 524130
Charles Craigs (CEO)
Teresa Gallant (Head-Ops ILS)

Subsidiary (Domestic):

Canopius Managing Agents Ltd. (2)
Gallery 9 One Lime Street, London, EC3M
7HA, United Kingdom (100%)
Tel.: (44) 20 7337 3700
Web Site: http://www.canopius.com
Insurance & Reinsurance Underwriting Services
N.A.I.C.S.: 524298
Mike Duffy (Grp Chief Underwriting Officer)

Subsidiary (US):

Canopius Underwriting Agency
Inc. (2)
Ste 950 200 S Wacker Dr, Chicago, IL
60606
Tel.: (630) 994-5600
Web Site: http://www.canopius.com
Insurance Agency & Underwriting Services
N.A.I.C.S.: 524210

Civitas Solutions, Inc. (1)
313 Congress St 6th Fl, Boston, MA 02210
Tel.: (617) 790-4800
Web Site: http://www.thementornetwork.com
Health Care Management Services; Outpatient Health Care Facility Operator
N.A.I.C.S.: 621410
Denis M. Holler (CFO)
John J. Green (CFO/VP-Community Support Svcs)
Edwin J. Mikkelsen (Dir-Medical)
Dwight D. Robson (CMO & Chief Pub Strategy Officer)
Ed Traisman (Dir-Pediatric Medical)

Jeffrey M. Cohen (CIO)
Brett I. Cohen (COO)
William Duffy (Pres-Specialty Rehabilitation
Svcs)
Gina Martin (Chief Legal Officer)
Maria McGee (Chief HR Officer)
Gerry Morrissey (Chief Quality Officer)
Jen Bligh (VP-Financial Plng & Analysis)
Chris Kozakis (Treas & VP)
Pat Krippendorf (VP-Employee Svc & Human Capital Sys)
Joy Kruppa (VP-Organizational Dev & Talent Mgmt)
Joe Langenfeld (VP-Internal Audit)
Nate Lewis (VP-Mergers & Acquisitions)
Tom MacDonald (Controller)
Sarah Magazine (VP-External Affairs)
Kate Miller (VP-IT Bus Sys)
Mary Rodenberg-Roberts (Officer-Compliance & VP)
Susan Rodriguez (VP-Total Rewards)
John Sweeney (VP-Tax)
Bill Allen (Sr VP-Ops-Children & Family
Services Operating Group)
Sergio Cruz (CFO/VP-Specialty Rehabilitation Svcs)
Jon Fisher (VP-Ops-Community Support
Svcs Operating Grp)
Tori Harding (VP-Dev Specialty Rehabilitation Svcs)
Michael Hofmeister (Sr VP-Ops-Adult Day
Health Svcs)
Jane Imboden (VP-Ops-Specialty Rehabilitation Svcs)
Bruce Kuluris (VP-Ops-Specialty Rehabilitation Svcs)
Connie Menne (VP-Ops-Community Support Svcs Operating Grp)
James Para-Cremer (VP-Ops-Specialty Rehabilitation Svcs)
Dan Place (VP-Field HR & Community Support Svcs Operating Grp)
Stacey Risotti (VP-Ops-Community Support
Svcs Operating Grp)
Jane Wiemerslage (VP-Field Quality
Improvement-Community Support Svcs Operating Grp)

Subsidiary (Domestic):

Adult Day Health, Inc. (2)
764 N Main St, Brockton, MA 02301
Tel.: (508) 897-0600
Elder Care Services
N.A.I.C.S.: 624120

California Mentor Family Home
Agency, LLC (2)
9166 Anaheim Pl Ste 200, Rancho Cucamonga, CA 91730
Tel.: (909) 483-2505
Web Site: http://www.camentorfha.com
Elder Care Services
N.A.I.C.S.: 624120
Michelle Mainez (Reg Dir)
Tina Smith (Program Dir)

CareMeridian, LLC (2)
17724 Gridley Rd, Artesia, CA 90701
Tel.: (562) 865-0806
Web Site: http://www.caremeridian.com
Rehabilitation Services
N.A.I.C.S.: 622310
Jamison Ashby (Pres & CEO)
Dan Larson (Chief Dev Officer)
Mary Beth Formby (CFO)
Rita Pathmanaban (VP-Clinical Programs &
Quality Assurance)
Cindy Lubiarz (VP-Bus Dev)
Bruce W. Kuluris (VP-Ops)
Shawn Habibi (VP-Payer Rels)
Julie Barth (Natl Dir-Sls & Mktg)
Kirk Davis (Reg Dir-Ops)
Gretchen Adelmund (Dir-HR)
Deborah Doherty (Chief Medical Officer)

Cornerstone Living Skills, Inc. (2)
920 Baird Rd, Santa Rosa, CA 95409
Tel.: (707) 539-2174
Emp.: 35
Rehabilitation Services
N.A.I.C.S.: 623110

Creative Connections, Inc. (2)
6901 McDivitt Dr Ste B, Bakersfield, CA
93313
Tel.: (661) 831-7165
Web Site:
http://www.mycreativeconnectionsinc.org

Other Social Advocacy Organizations
N.A.I.C.S.: 813319
Andretta Stokes (Exec Dir)

E & J Health Care, LLC (2)
3202 N 4th St Ste 101, Longview, TX
75605
Tel.: (903) 753-6635
Web Site: http://www.core-rehab.com
Rehabilitation Services
N.A.I.C.S.: 622310
Tom Lorren (Mng Partner)

Family Advocacy Services, LLC (2)
7131 Rutherford Rd, Baltimore, MD 21244
Tel.: (410) 298-2691
Education Services
N.A.I.C.S.: 611110

First Step Independent Living Program, Inc. (2)
351 Wilkerson Ave, Perris, CA 92570
Tel.: (951) 943-2553
Elder Care Services
N.A.I.C.S.: 624120

Habilitative Services, Inc. (2)
220 Milwaukee St Ste 2, Lakefield, MN
56150-5000
Tel.: (507) 662-5236
Web Site: http://www.habsvinc.com
Residential Care
N.A.I.C.S.: 623220
Jessica Neitzel (Mgr-Housing)

Horrigan Cole Enterprises, Inc. (2)
9166 Anaheim Pl Ste 200, Rancho Cucamonga, CA 91730
Tel.: (909) 484-0852
Sales Range: $1-9.9 Million
Emp.: 75
Human Right Advocacy Services
N.A.I.C.S.: 813311
Gregory Torres (Pres)

Illinois Mentor, Inc. (2)
600 Holiday Plz Dr Ste 400, Matteson, IL
60443
Tel.: (708) 679-9137
Web Site: http://www.il-mentor.com
Elder Care Services
N.A.I.C.S.: 624120

Institute for Family Centered Services, Inc. (2)
11832 Rock Landing Dr Ste 203, Newport
News, VA 23606
Tel.: (757) 722-3466
Web Site: http://www.ifcsinc.com
Rehabilitation Services
N.A.I.C.S.: 623110

Loyds Liberty Homes, Inc. (2)
2540 W Shaw Ln Ste 111, Fresno, CA
93711
Tel.: (559) 226-5611
Nursing Care Services
N.A.I.C.S.: 623110

Massachusetts Mentor, LLC (2)
270 Bridge St Ste 201, Dedham, MA 02026
Tel.: (781) 407-0470
Web Site: http://www.ma-mentor.com
Rehabilitation Services
N.A.I.C.S.: 623110

Mentis Neuro El Paso, LLC (2)
4360 Doniphan Dr, El Paso, TX 79922
Tel.: (915) 351-4441
Health Care Srvices
N.A.I.C.S.: 622110

Mentis Neuro Houston, LLC (2)
9551 Fannin St, Houston, TX 77045
Tel.: (713) 331-0259
Health Care Srvices
N.A.I.C.S.: 622110

Mentis Neuro San Antonio, LLC (2)
6849 Crestway Dr Ste B, San Antonio, TX
78239
Tel.: (210) 599-4400
Health Care Services
N.A.I.C.S.: 622110

Mentor ABI Group (2)
313 Congress St 5th Fl, Boston, MA 02210
Tel.: (617) 790-4800
Sales Range: $25-49.9 Million
Emp.: 150
Health Care Srvices

Centerbridge Partners, L.P.—(Continued)
N.A.I.C.S.: 621410

Division (Domestic):

NeuroRestorative (3)
306 W Mill St, Carbondale, IL 62901-2727
Tel.: (618) 529-3060
Web Site: http://www.neurorestorative.com
Sales Range: $50-74.9 Million
Inpatient Rehabilitation Support Services for
Acquired or Sustained Brain Injuries
N.A.I.C.S.: 621112
Chris Williamson (Reg VP-Dev)

Subsidiary (Domestic):

Mentor ABI, LLC (2)
313 Congress St Fl 3, Boston, MA 02210
Tel.: (617) 790-4800
Web Site: http://www.thementornetwork.com
Rehabilitation Services
N.A.I.C.S.: 623110

Mentor Management, Inc. (2)
PO Box 836996, Dallas, TX 75083
Tel.: (214) 827-5325
Web Site:
    http://www.mentormanagement.com
Professional Training Services
N.A.I.C.S.: 611430
Lynda Butcher (Pres & CEO)
Lisa Gwaltney (VP-Assesment Center &
Programs)
Leslee Light (CFO)

Mentor Maryland, Inc. (2)
5720 Executive Dr, Catonsville, MD 21228
Tel.: (410) 455-4600
Web Site: http://www.md-mentor.com
Emp.: 40
Rehabilitation Services
N.A.I.C.S.: 623110

National Mentor Healthcare, LLC (2)
80 Cottontail Ln Ste 330, Somerset, NJ
08873
Tel.: (732) 627-9890
Rehabilitation Services
N.A.I.C.S.: 623220

National Mentor Holdings, Inc (2)
6 Oak Hill Dr, Bridgeton, NJ 08302-4124
Tel.: (856) 319-4177
Rehabilitation Services
N.A.I.C.S.: 623220

National Mentor Holdings, LLC (2)
422 S Minnesota Ave, Saint Peter, MN
56082
Tel.: (507) 934-4054
Holding Company
N.A.I.C.S.: 551112

Ohio Mentor, Inc. (2)
3085 W Market St, Fairlawn, OH 44333
Tel.: (330) 835-1468
Web Site: http://www.oh-mentor.com
Rehabilitation Services
N.A.I.C.S.: 623110

REM Arrowhead, Inc. (2)
5005-2 Matterhorn Dr, Duluth, MN 55811
Tel.: (218) 720-2995
Rehabilitation Services
N.A.I.C.S.: 623110
Mary Braun-Kapsner (Reg Dir)

REM Central Lakes, Inc. (2)
266 33rd Ave S Ste 10, Saint Cloud, MN
56301
Tel.: (320) 259-6022
Rehabilitation Services
N.A.I.C.S.: 623110
Lori Wirtzfeld (Reg Dir)

REM Community Options, LLC (2)
408 Jones Ave, Oak Hill, WV 25901
Tel.: (304) 294-8420
Rehabilitation Services
N.A.I.C.S.: 623110

REM Connecticut Community Ser-
vices, Inc. (2)
1275 Cromwell Ave Bldg B11, Rocky Hill,
CT 06067
Tel.: (860) 529-9156
Web Site: http://www.remct.com
Rehabilitation Services
N.A.I.C.S.: 623110
Efrain Lopez (Coord-Program)

REM Developmental Services,
Inc. (2)
2761 Oakdale Blvd Ste 4, Coralville, IA
52241
Tel.: (319) 665-2440
Rehabilitation Services
N.A.I.C.S.: 623110

REM East, LLC (2)
232 Market St Ste 200, Flowood, MS
39232-3339
Tel.: (863) 255-0892
Rehabilitation Services
N.A.I.C.S.: 623110

REM Heartland, Inc. (2)
210 Thomas Dr, Mankato, MN 56001
Tel.: (507) 387-3181
Rehabilitation Services
N.A.I.C.S.: 623110
Lori Larson (Reg Dir)

REM Hennepin, Inc. (2)
6040 Earle Brown Dr Ste 305, Brooklyn
Center, MN 55430
Tel.: (763) 852-5325
Rehabilitation Services
N.A.I.C.S.: 623110
Scott Rodwell (Reg Dir)

REM Indiana Community Services,
Inc. (2)
8925 N Meridian St Ste 200, Indianapolis,
IN 46260-2386
Tel.: (317) 581-2380
Rehabilitation Services
N.A.I.C.S.: 623110

REM Indiana, Inc. (2)
8337 N College Ave, Indianapolis, IN 46240
Tel.: (317) 254-1671
Rehabilitation Services
N.A.I.C.S.: 623110

REM Iowa Community Services,
Inc. (2)
4436 114th St, Urbandale, IA 50322
Tel.: (515) 278-4914
Emp.: 100
Rehabilitation Services
N.A.I.C.S.: 623110
Angela Reisdorf (Area Dir)

REM Iowa, Inc. (2)
1661 Boyson Sq Dr Ste 202, Hiawatha, IA
52233
Tel.: (319) 393-1944
Web Site: http://www.remiowa.com
Sales Range: $1-9.9 Million
Emp.: 380
Rehabilitation Services
N.A.I.C.S.: 623110

REM Maryland, Inc. (2)
5654 Sheerock Ct, Columbia, MD 21045
Tel.: (410) 992-9470
Residential Care Services
N.A.I.C.S.: 623990
Shannel Braxton (Asst Program Mgr)

REM Minnesota Community Services,
Inc. (2)
2586 7th Ave E Ste 201, North Saint Paul,
MN 55109
Tel.: (651) 644-7680
Rehabilitation Services
N.A.I.C.S.: 623110

REM Minnesota, Inc. (2)
6600 France Ave S Ste 500, Edina, MN
55435
Tel.: (952) 922-6776
Web Site: http://www.remminnesota.com
Sales Range: $1-9.9 Million
Emp.: 110
Rehabilitation Services
N.A.I.C.S.: 623110

REM Nevada, Inc. (2)
5693 S Jones Ste 118, Las Vegas, NV
89118
Tel.: (702) 889-9240
Rehabilitation Services
N.A.I.C.S.: 623110

REM North Dakota, Inc. (2)
1905 2nd St SE Ste 1A, Minot, ND 58701
Tel.: (701) 839-6630
Web Site: http://www.remnorthdakota.com
Rehabilitation Services

REM North Star, Inc. (2)
677 Anne St NW Ste B, Bemidji, MN 56601
Tel.: (218) 444-5876
Sales Range: $1-9.9 Million
Emp.: 64
Rehabilitation Services
N.A.I.C.S.: 623110
Bethany McKeon (Reg Dir)

REM Occazio, Inc. (2)
11 Gloria Dr, Trafalgar, IN 46181
Tel.: (317) 878-4267
Rehabilitation Services
N.A.I.C.S.: 623110

REM Ohio II, LLC (2)
214 Main St, Amherst, OH 44001
Tel.: (440) 986-3337
Health Care Srvices
N.A.I.C.S.: 621610

REM Ohio Waivered Services,
Inc. (2)
470 Portage Lake Dr, Akron, OH 44319
Tel.: (330) 644-9730
Rehabilitation Services
N.A.I.C.S.: 623110

REM Ohio, Inc. (2)
791 White Pond Dr Ste B, Akron, OH 44320
Tel.: (330) 864-5895
Web Site: http://www.rem-oh.com
Rehabilitation Services
N.A.I.C.S.: 623110
Jo Spargo (Dir-State)
Sandy Murray (Mgr-HR)

REM Ramsey, Inc. (2)
2266 N 2nd St, Saint Paul, MN 55109
Tel.: (651) 644-7680
Web Site: http://www.remminnesota.com
Health Care Srvices
N.A.I.C.S.: 621999

REM River Bluffs, Inc. (2)
1621 10th St SE, Rochester, MN 55904
Tel.: (507) 287-6824
Rehabilitation Services
N.A.I.C.S.: 623110

REM South Central Services,
Inc, (2)
307 12th Ave S Ste 102, Buffalo, MN 55313
Tel.: (763) 682-3142
Rehabilitation Services
N.A.I.C.S.: 623110
Lisa Thelen (Reg Dir)

REM Southwest Services, Inc. (2)
125 1st St E, Canby, MN 56220
Tel.: (507) 223-5633
Sales Range: $1-9.9 Million
Emp.: 173
Rehabilitation Services
N.A.I.C.S.: 623110
Peg Dallman (Reg Dir)

REM West Virginia, LLC (2)
748 McMechen St, Benwood, WV 26031
Tel.: (304) 233-3474
Web Site: http://www.remwestvirginia.com
Rehabilitation Services
N.A.I.C.S.: 623110
Jane Ketcham (Sr Exec Dir)

REM Wisconsin III, Inc. (2)
800 Wisconsin St Unit 12, Eau Claire, WI
54703
Tel.: (715) 833-3548
Sales Range: $1-9.9 Million
Emp.: 75
Rehabilitation Services
N.A.I.C.S.: 623110

REM Wisconsin, Inc. (2)
2005 W Beltline Hwy Ste 203, Madison, WI
53713
Tel.: (608) 276-1191
Web Site: http://www.remwisconsin.com
Emp.: 100
Rehabilitation Services
N.A.I.C.S.: 623110
Shelley Hansen-Blake (Exec Dir)
Angel Vang (State Dir-Dev)
Kimberly Mentink (Office Mgr-State)

REM Woodvale, Inc. (2)
301 N Main, Austin, MN 55912
Tel.: (507) 433-7301

Rehabilitation Services
N.A.I.C.S.: 623110
Stephanie Kalbach (Reg Dir)

South Carolina Mentor, Inc. (2)
3600 Forest Dr Ste 100, Columbia, SC
29204
Tel.: (803) 799-9025
Web Site: http://www.sc-mentor.com
Rehabilitation Services
N.A.I.C.S.: 623110

Tender Loving Care of Duluth (2)
1 E 1st St Ste 200, Duluth, MN 55802
Tel.: (218) 724-3640
Web Site:
    http://www.tenderlovingcareofduluth.com
Individual & Family Services
N.A.I.C.S.: 624190

Transitional Services, LLC (2)
5401 Vogel Rd 910, Evansville, IN 47715
Tel.: (812) 475-9960
Women Healthcare Services
N.A.I.C.S.: 621610

Unlimited Quest, Inc. (2)
250 S Date Ave, Rialto, CA 92376
Tel.: (909) 421-8753
Rehabilitation Services
N.A.I.C.S.: 623110

Duo Bank of Canada (1)
33 Yonge Street Suite 810, Toronto, M5E
1G4, ON, Canada
Tel.: (888) 331-6133
Web Site: https://www.fairstonebank.ca
Banking Services
N.A.I.C.S.: 522111
Stephen Smith (Chm)

Subsidiary (Domestic):

Fairstone Financial Inc.
630 Boulevard Rene-Levesque O, Montreal,
QC H3B 2M1, QC, Canada
Tel.: (800) 995-2274
Web Site: http://www.fairstone.ca
Loan & Mortgage Services
N.A.I.C.S.: 522310
Scott Wood (Pres & CEO)

Extended Stay Hotels LLC (1)
11525 N Community House Rd Ste 100,
Charlotte, NC 28277
Tel.: (980) 345-1600
Web Site:
    http://www.extendedstayamerica.com
Sales Range: $550-599.9 Million
Emp.: 7,600
Hotel Chain Developer, Owner & Operator;
Owned by Centerbridge Partners, L.P. &
The Blackstone Group L.P.
N.A.I.C.S.: 721110

Great Wolf Resorts, Inc. (1)
525 Junction Rd Ste 6000 S, Madison, WI
53717
Tel.: (608) 662-4700
Web Site: http://www.greatwolfresorts.com
Holding Company; Indoor Water Park Re-
sorts Operator
N.A.I.C.S.: 551112
Rodney S. Jones (VP-Design & Construc-
tion)
Craig J. Johnson (Gen Counsel)
Jay Markham (Sr VP-Fin)
Alan Genin (Chief Analytics Officer & Sr
VP-Revenue Mgmt)
Scott Wilson (Chief Comml Officer)
Edward Malinowski (CIO)
Murray Hennessy (CEO)
Brian Casebolt (Sr VP-Ancillary Revenue)
Bryan Robinson (Chief People Officer)
Erin Wallace (COO)
Greg Miller (Chief Dev Officer)
Mark Rucker (Sr VP-Ops)
Rubin McDougal (CFO)

Subsidiary (Domestic):

Blue Harbor Resort & Convention
Center (2)
725 Blue Harbor Dr, Sheboygan, WI 53081
Tel.: (920) 452-2900
Web Site: http://www.blueharborresort.com
Hotel Operating Services
N.A.I.C.S.: 721110
Susan Engler (Dir-Sls & Mktg)
David Sanderson (VP & Gen Mgr)

Great Lakes Services, LLC (2)
3517 Van Dyke Rd Ste B, Almont, MI 48003
Tel.: (586) 615-5744
Web Site:
 http://www.greatlakesservicesllc.com
Housekeeping Services
N.A.I.C.S.: 561720

Great Wolf Lodge Grand Mound (2)
20500 Old Hwy 99 SW, Centralia, WA 98531
Tel.: (360) 273-7718
Web Site: http://www.greatwolf.com
Hotel & Resort Operator
N.A.I.C.S.: 721110
Patrick Alvarez (Gen Mgr)

Great Wolf Lodge of Grapevine, LLC (2)
100 Great Wolf Dr, Grapevine, TX 76051
Tel.: (817) 488-6510
Web Site: http://www.greatwolf.com
Emp.: 200
Resort & Amusement Park Operator
N.A.I.C.S.: 721110
Phil Cunningham (Gen Mgr)

Great Wolf Lodge of Kansas City, LLC (2)
10401 Cabela Dr, Kansas City, KS 66111
Tel.: (913) 299-7001
Web Site: http://www.greatwolf.com
Emp.: 2,500
Hotel & Amusement Park Operator
N.A.I.C.S.: 721110
Keith Furness (Gen Mgr)

Great Wolf Lodge of Traverse City, LLC (2)
3575 N US Hwy 31 S, Traverse City, MI 49684
Tel.: (231) 941-3600
Web Site: http://www.greatwolf.com
Hotel & Amusement Park Operator
N.A.I.C.S.: 721110
Chris Ballou (Gen Mgr)

Great Wolf Lodge of the Carolinas, LLC (2)
10175 Weddington Rd, Concord, NC 28025
Tel.: (704) 549-8206
Web Site: http://www.greatwolf.com
Emp.: 500
Hotel & Resort Operator
N.A.I.C.S.: 721110
Angie Brown (Gen Mgr)

Greatwide Logistics Services, Inc. (1)
12404 Park Central Dr Ste 300S, Dallas, TX 75251
Tel.: (972) 228-7300
Web Site: http://www.greatwide.com
Sales Range: $1-4.9 Billion
Emp.: 3,200
Logistic Services
N.A.I.C.S.: 488510
Robert C. LaRose (CEO)
Robert C. Larose (CEO)

Subsidiary (Domestic):

Greatwide American Trans-Freight, LLC (2)
2150 Cabot Blvd W, Langhorne, PA 19047-1852
Tel.: (215) 736-2600
Web Site: http://www.greatwide.com
Rev.: $81,150,074
Emp.: 150
Freight Transportation Arrangement Services
N.A.I.C.S.: 488510
Robert Larosa (Pres)

Subsidiary (Domestic):

Greatwide Cheetah Transportation Inc. (3)
378 Williamson Rd, Mooresville, NC 28117-5935
Tel.: (704) 664-1171
Sales Range: $10-24.9 Million
Emp.: 30
Trucking Service
N.A.I.C.S.: 484230

Help at Home, LLC (1)
1 N State St Ste 800, Chicago, IL 60602
Tel.: (312) 663-4244

Web Site: http://www.helpathome.com
Emp.: 25,000
In-Home Health Care Services
N.A.I.C.S.: 621610
Tim O'Rourke (Pres)

Subsidiary (Domestic):

Excel Companion Care, Inc. (2)
1240 Old York Rd Ste 201, Warminster, PA 18974-2013
Tel.: (215) 675-4701
Web Site:
 http://www.excelcompanioncare.com
Emp.: 600
In-Home Non-Medical Care Services
N.A.I.C.S.: 624120
Joshua Drebes (Co-Founder)
John Gifford (Co-Founder)

Open Systems Healthcare, Inc. (2)
1818 Market St Ste 1105, Philadelphia, PA 19103
Tel.: (215) 399-1400
Web Site:
 http://www.opensystemshealthcare.com
Sales Range: $50-74.9 Million
Women Healthcare Services
N.A.I.C.S.: 621610
Charles Hill (Pres & CEO)
Ian Cooper (VP-Sls)
Kate Kolodey (VP-Ops & HR)
Erin Brown (Dir-HR)
Sara Stevens (Dir-Ops)

INDUS Realty Trust, Inc. (1)
641 Lexington Ave, New York, NY 10022
Tel.: (212) 218-7910
Web Site: https://www.indusrt.com
Rev.: $49,195,000
Assets: $596,807,000
Liabilities: $199,538,000
Net Worth: $397,269,000
Earnings: $6,110,000
Emp.: 32
Fiscal Year-end: 12/31/2022
Real Estate Investment Trust
N.A.I.C.S.: 525990
Michael S. Gamzon (CEO)
Matthew Homa (Dir-Internal Audit)
Thomas M. Daniells (Gen Counsel, Sec & Sr VP)
Ashley Pizzo (VP-Capital Markets & IR)
Jon W. Clark (CFO & Exec VP)
Dave Cocola (VP)
Andrew Ciani (Dir)
Andrew Albeck (Dir)
Randy Gudauskas (Controller)

Division (Domestic):

Griffin Land (2)
204 W Newberry Rd, Bloomfield, CT 06002-1308 (100%)
Tel.: (860) 286-7660
Web Site: http://www.griffinland.com
Sales Range: $1-9.9 Million
Emp.: 20
Real Estate Services
N.A.I.C.S.: 531390
Frederick Michael Danziger (Chm & CEO)
Randy Gudauskas (Controller)
Thomas M. Lescalleet (Sr VP)

KIK Custom Products Inc. (1)
101 MacIntosh Boulevard, Concord, L4K 4R5, ON, Canada
Tel.: (905) 660-0444
Web Site: http://www.kikcorp.com
Household Cleaning Product Mfr
N.A.I.C.S.: 325612
Stratis Katsiris (Pres-Classic Div)

Subsidiary (Non-US):

BLSA Industries (Pty) Ltd. (2)
22 Monte Carlo Crescent Kyalami Business Park, Atlantis Industria, Midrand, 1685, South Africa (100%)
Tel.: (27) 114661395
Web Site: http://blsa-industries.business.site
Pool & Spa Cleaning Chemical Products Mfr
N.A.I.C.S.: 325612

Subsidiary (US):

BioLab, Inc. (2)
1725 N Brown Rd Ste 300, Lawrenceville, GA 30043

Tel.: (678) 502-4000
Web Site: http://www.biolabinc.com
Cleaning Agents & Disinfectants Mfr
N.A.I.C.S.: 325612
Jon Viner (Pres)
Leon Bloom (Founder & CEO)

KIK (GEORGIA) LLC (2)
2030 Old Candler Rd, Gainesville, GA 30507-7262
Tel.: (770) 534-0300
Web Site: http://www.kikcorp.com
Polishes & Sanitation Products Mfr
N.A.I.C.S.: 325612

KIK (Virginia) LLC (2)
27 Mill Ln, Salem, VA 24153
Tel.: (540) 389-5401
Web Site: http://www.kikcorp.com
Bleach & Detergent Mfr
N.A.I.C.S.: 325611

Prestone Products Corp. (2)
1900 West Field Court, Lake Forest, IL 60045
Tel.: (847) 482-2000
Web Site: http://www.prestone.com
Automotive Products Mfr
N.A.I.C.S.: 424690
Jim Amerio (VP-Sls-North America)
Cathy Radlein (Dir-HR)

MacLean Power, LLC (1)
481 Munn Rd Ste 300, Fort Mill, SC 29715
Tel.: (803) 628-4321
Web Site: http://www.macleanpower.com
Electronic Components Mfr
N.A.I.C.S.: 334419
Megan Rowe (VP & Gen Mgr-Stockton Ops)
Steve Scharnhorst (CEO)

Subsidiary (Domestic):

Inertia Engineering & Machine Works, Inc. (2)
4690 E Waterloo Rd, Stockton, CA 95215
Tel.: (209) 931-1670
Sales Range: $1-9.9 Million
Emp.: 16
Switchgear & Switchboard Apparatus Mfr
N.A.I.C.S.: 335313

Subsidiary (Non-US):

MacLean Power Canada (2)
225 Boul Ford, Chateauguay, J6J 4Z2, QC, Canada
Tel.: (450) 698-0520
Electronic Components Mfr
N.A.I.C.S.: 334419

Subsidiary (Domestic):

Maclean Senior Industries LLC (2)
610 Pond Dr, Wood Dale, IL 60191
Tel.: (630) 350-1600
Web Site:
 http://www.macleanseniorindustries.com
Emp.: 20
Electronic Components Mfr
N.A.I.C.S.: 334419
Joe Francaviglia (Pres)

Norvax, Inc. (1)
214 W Huron St, Chicago, IL 60610
Tel.: (312) 226-0027
Web Site: http://www.norvax.com
Web-Based Sales Software for Insurance Industry Health Policies
N.A.I.C.S.: 334610
Brandon Cruz (Pres & CTO)

P.F. Chang's China Bistro, Inc. (1)
7676 E Pinnacle Peak Rd, Scottsdale, AZ 85255
Tel.: (480) 888-3000
Web Site: http://www.pfchangs.com
Sales Range: $1-4.9 Billion
Emp.: 26,000
Holding Company; Full-Service Asian Cuisine Restaurants Owner & Operator
N.A.I.C.S.: 551112

Subsidiary (Domestic):

PFC Hawaii LLC (2)
1288 Ala Moana Blvd Ste 216, Honolulu, HI 96814-4233
Tel.: (808) 457-1867
Restaurant Operating Services

N.A.I.C.S.: 722511

PFCCB Equipment LLC (2)
8377 E Hartford Dr, Scottsdale, AZ 85255
Tel.: (480) 888-3000
Web Site: http://www.pfcb.com
Emp.: 215
Restaurant Operating Services
N.A.I.C.S.: 722511
Richard Federico (CEO)

Reddy Ice Holdings, Inc. (1)
8750 N Central Expwy Ste 1800, Dallas, TX 75231
Tel.: (214) 526-6740
Web Site: http://www.reddyice.com
Emp.: 1,300
Holding Company; Packaged Ice Mfr & Distr
N.A.I.C.S.: 551112
Steven J. Janusek (CFO & Sec)
Deborah Conklin (CEO)

Subsidiary (Domestic):

City Ice Co. (2)
13600 Permilla Springs Dr, Chester, VA 23836
Tel.: (804) 796-9423
Web Site: http://www.roadtocool.com
Emp.: 18
Ice Mfr
N.A.I.C.S.: 312113
Mark Resnick (Pres & CEO)

Reddy Ice Corporation (2)
8750 N Central Expy Ste 1800, Dallas, TX 75231-6450
Tel.: (214) 526-6740
Web Site: http://www.reddyice.com
Sales Range: $75-99.9 Million
Emp.: 150
Packaged Ice Mfr & Distr
N.A.I.C.S.: 312113
Steven J. Janusek (CFO & Exec VP)

Plant (Domestic):

Reddy Ice (3)
624 Moreno St, Gainesville, GA 30501
Tel.: (770) 535-3705
Web Site: http://www.reddyice.com
Sales Range: $25-49.9 Million
Emp.: 10
Ice Mfr & Distr
N.A.I.C.S.: 312113

Suntex Marinas Investors LLC (1)
17330 Preston Rd Ste #220A, Dallas, TX 75252
Tel.: (972) 789-1400
Web Site: http://www.suntex.com
Marina Properties Management & Services
N.A.I.C.S.: 713930
Bryan Redmond (CEO)
Johnny Powers (Chm)

Subsidiary (Domestic):

Westrec Marinas Management, Inc. (2)
16633 Ventura Blvd Fl 6, Encino, CA 91436
Tel.: (818) 907-0400
Web Site: http://www.westrec.com
Marina Owner & Operator
N.A.I.C.S.: 531210
Michael M. Sachs (Chm & CEO)
Bill Anderson (Pres)

Subsidiary (Domestic):

Lake Las Vegas Marina LLC (3)
10 Costa Dilago, Henderson, NV 89001
Tel.: (702) 568-6024
Web Site:
 http://www.lakelasvegasyachts.com
Rev.: $4,689,916
Emp.: 50
Marina Facilities & Services
N.A.I.C.S.: 713930
Beady Printy (Mgr)

Marine Ventures Ltd. (3)
16633 Ventura Blvd Fl 6, Encino, CA 91436
Tel.: (818) 907-0400
Web Site: http://www.westrec.com
Sales Range: $10-24.9 Million
Emp.: 15
Marine Service Station
N.A.I.C.S.: 457120
Michael M. Sachs (CEO)

Centerbridge Partners, L.P.—(Continued)

Westrec Equities, Inc. (3)
16633 Ventura Blvd FL 6, Encino, CA
91436
Tel.: (818) 907-0400
Web Site: http://www.westrec.com
Rev.: $1,700,000
Emp.: 18
Real Property Lessor
N.A.I.C.S.: 531190
Michael M. Sachs (Chm & CEO)
Bill Anderson (Pres)
Scott Stevenson (Exec VP)

Westrec Marina Management, Inc. (3)
16633 Ventura Blvd FL 6, Encino, CA
91436
Tel.: (818) 907-0400
Web Site: http://www.westrec.com
Real Estate Managers
N.A.I.C.S.: 531210
Bill Anderson (Pres)

Westrec Properties, Inc. (3)
801 NE 3rd St, Dania Beach, FL 33004
Tel.: (954) 926-0300
Web Site:
　http://www.harbourtownemarina.net
Rev.: $67,000
Emp.: 25
Pleasure Boat Rental
N.A.I.C.S.: 541810

Westrec Properties, Inc. (3)
16633 Ventura Blvd Fl 6, Encino, CA 91436
Tel.: (818) 907-0400
Web Site: http://www.westrec.com
Rev.: $150,000
Emp.: 15
Administrative Management
N.A.I.C.S.: 561110
Michael M. Sachs (CEO)
Bill Anderson (Pres)

Superior Vision Services, Inc. (1)
939 Elkridge Landing Rd Ste 200, Linthicum, MD 21090
Tel.: (800) 243-1401
Web Site: http://www.superiorvision.com
Emp.: 500
Vision Care Insurance Services
N.A.I.C.S.: 524114

Title Resources Guaranty Company (1)
8111 LBJ Freeway Ste 1200, Dallas, TX
75251　　　　　　　　　　　　(70%)
Tel.: (972) 644-6500
Web Site: http://www.titleresources.com
Title Insurance Services
N.A.I.C.S.: 541191
Scott McCall (Pres & CEO)
Owen Girard (Sr VP)
Elizabeth C. Ray (Sr VP & Reg Mgr)
Morton Manassaram (Sr VP & Reg Mgr-Southeast)
Lynn Stillman (Sr VP & Reg Mgr)
Paul McNutt Jr. (Exec VP)

CENTERFIELD CAPITAL PARTNERS, LLC
10 W Market St 3000 Market Tower,
Indianapolis, IN 46204
Tel.: (317) 237-2323　　　　　　　　DE
Web Site:
　http://www.centerfieldcapital.com
Year Founded: 2000
Emp.: 11
Privater Equity Firm
N.A.I.C.S.: 523999
Scott Lutzke (Partner)
A. Faraz Abbasi (Mng Partner-Indianapolis)
Mark Hollis (Partner)
Michael Miller (Partner)
Jackie Byers (CFO)
Jill Margetts (Principal)

Subsidiaries:

Imaginetics LLC (1)
3410 A St SE, Auburn, WA 98002
Tel.: (253) 735-0156
Web Site: http://www.imagineticsinc.com

Sales Range: $1-9.9 Million
Emp.: 90
Sheet Metal Fabrication, CNC Machining &
Assembly Services
N.A.I.C.S.: 332322
Scott Strong (CEO)
Pat Prince (COO)

CENTERFIRE REAL ESTATE
2206 Sun Ranch Village Loop SW,
Los Lunas, NM 87031
Tel.: (505) 865-7800
Web Site:
　http://www.nmranchandland.com
Rev.: $20,000,000
Emp.: 10
Real Estate Services
N.A.I.C.S.: 237210
Cherie Kiehne (Founder & Owner)
Max Kiehne (Founder)

CENTERGATE CAPITAL, LP
900 S Capital of Texas Hwy Las Cimas IV Ste 478, Austin, TX 78746
Tel.: (512) 717-7100
Web Site:
　http://www.centergatecapital.com
Year Founded: 2014
Privater Equity Firm
N.A.I.C.S.: 523940
Tiffany Kosch (Mng Partner)
Tim Liu (Mng Dir)

Subsidiaries:

Cartridge Technologies, LLC (1)
15738 Crabbs Branch Way, Rockville, MD
20855
Tel.: (301) 417-7202
Web Site: http://www.ctimd.com
Rev.: $3,200,000
Emp.: 25
Computer & Office Machine Repair & Maintenance Services
N.A.I.C.S.: 811210
Ana M. Castro (Pres)
Bragi Valgeirsson (CFO)
Colin Murphy (CEO)

Mid-State Machine & Fabricating Inc (1)
2730 Mine Mill Rd, Lakeland, FL 33801
Tel.: (863) 665-6233
Web Site: http://midstatefl.com
Sales Range: $10-24.9 Million
Emp.: 150
Machine & Fabricating
N.A.I.C.S.: 332710
Harold E. Kersey (Pres)

Subsidiary (Domestic):

AZZ SMS LLC (2)
1615 118th Ave N, Saint Petersburg, FL
33716
Tel.: (727) 573-7828
Emp.: 30
Industrial Machinery Maintenance Services
N.A.I.C.S.: 811310

CENTERGISTIC SOLUTIONS, INC.
2112 Business Ctr Dr Ste 190, Irvine,
CA 92612
Tel.: (949) 222-4500
Software Development Services
N.A.I.C.S.: 541511
Ricardo G. Brutocao (Pres, CFO &
COO)

CENTERLIGHT HEALTH SYSTEM
1250 Waters Pl 6th Fl Ste 602,
Bronx, NY 10461
Tel.: (718) 519-4238　　　　　　　　NY
Web Site: http://www.centerlight.org
Year Founded: 1984
Sales Range: $10-24.9 Million
Emp.: 7
Health Care Srvices
N.A.I.C.S.: 622110
Nicole Tambini (Program Dir)

CENTERLINE HOMES, INC.
825 Coral Ridge Dr, Coral Springs,
FL 33071
Tel.: (954) 344-8040
Web Site:
　http://www.centerlinehomes.com
Sales Range: $75-99.9 Million
Emp.: 60
Home Builder; Real Estate Broker
N.A.I.C.S.: 236117
Craig Perry (Pres)
Deb Marton (VP-Sls)
Jim Coshun (Dir-Customer Care)
Rocco Tricarico (Mgr)
Sheryl Lewis (Mgr-HR)
Dawn Ferrari (Mgr-Starts)
Steve Margolis (Owner)
Jeff Auchter (VP-Mktg)

CENTERLINE MACHINING & GRINDING, INC.
760 Centerline Dr, Oneida, WI
54155-9249
Tel.: (920) 435-8668　　　　　　　　WI
Web Site:
　http://www.centerlinemg.com
Year Founded: 2000
Sales Range: $1-9.9 Million
Emp.: 33
Industrial Machinery Mfr
N.A.I.C.S.: 332710
Sara Dietzen (Co-Owner & CEO)
Greg Dietzen (Co-Owner)

CENTERLINE SOLUTIONS LLC
16035 Table Mountain Pkwy, Golden,
CO 80403
Tel.: (303) 993-3293
Web Site:
　http://www.centerlinesolutions.com
Year Founded: 2000
Sales Range: $10-24.9 Million
Emp.: 300
Wireless Telecommunication Infrastructure Design & Construction Services
N.A.I.C.S.: 237130
Charlie Kennamer (Sr VP-Corp Strategy)
Thomas A. Prestwood (CEO)
Pete Dyke (CFO)

Subsidiaries:

Cascadia PM, LLC (1)
3322 South Bay Rd NE, Olympia, WA
98506
Tel.: (360) 438-8002
Web Site: http://www.cascadiapm.com
Sales Range: $1-9.9 Million
Emp.: 50
Technical Consulting Services
N.A.I.C.S.: 541690
Jim Pribbenow (Sr Dir-Program Mgmt)
Rachelle Baranda-Crow (VP-HR)
Tom Durant (CFO)
Charlie Kennamer (VP-Engrg)

CENTEROAK PARTNERS LLC
100 Crescent Ct Ste 1700, Dallas, TX
75201-6917
Tel.: (214) 301-4201
Web Site:
　http://www.centeroakpartners.com
Privater Equity Firm
N.A.I.C.S.: 523999
Randall Fojtasek (Mng Partner)
Lucas Cutler (Mng Partner)
Jason Sutherland (Partner)
Chad York (CFO)
Jeremy Glass (Controller)
William Henry (Partner)

Subsidiaries:

Aakash Chemicals & Dyestuffs, Inc. (1)
561 Mitchell Rd, Glendale Heights, IL
60139

Tel.: (630) 469-3838
Web Site: http://www.aakashchemicals.com
Other Chemical & Allied Products Merchant
Whslr
N.A.I.C.S.: 424690
Frank Magdits (Mgr-Bus Dev-Pigment Dispersions)

Shamrock Environmental Corporation (1)
3500 Lake Herman Dr, Browns Summit, NC
27214
Tel.: (336) 375-1989
Web Site: http://www.shamrockenviro.com
Sales Range: $25-49.9 Million
Emp.: 150
Environmental Services
N.A.I.C.S.: 562998
Gail Buchanan (Owner & CEO)

Subsidiary (Domestic):

Virginia American Industries, LLC (2)
710 Hospital St, Richmond, VA 23219-1218
Tel.: (804) 644-2611
Web Site: http://www.recoconstructors.com
Fabricated Plate Work
N.A.I.C.S.: 332313
Mike Schleinkofer (Pres)

Subsidiary (Domestic):

American Investment LLC (3)
1839 Dunbar Rd, Cayce, SC 29033-2217
Tel.: (803) 794-3360
Sales Range: $1-9.9 Million
Fabricated Plate Work (Boiler Shop)
N.A.I.C.S.: 332313
Stuart Point (Pres)
Mike Maner (VP)

Temple Associates Inc. (1)
2930 Ramona Ave Ste 400, Sacramento,
CA 95826
Tel.: (916) 739-1992
Web Site: http://www.gritguy.com
Sales Range: $1-9.9 Million
Emp.: 11
Abrasives & Blast Equipments Mfr & Distr
N.A.I.C.S.: 423830

Turf Masters Brands, Inc. (1)
30 Mansell Ct Ste 200, Roswell, 30076, GA
Tel.: (888) 924-8873
Web Site: https://turfmastersbrands.com
Residential Lawn Care Services
N.A.I.C.S.: 561730
Andrew Kadrich (CEO)
Andy Kaldrich (CEO)

Subsidiary (Domestic):

Fairway Green Inc. (2)
3219 Northside Dr, Raleigh, NC 27615
Tel.: (919) 832-1774
Web Site: http://www.fairwaygreen.com
Rev.: $4,000,000
Emp.: 20
Landscaping Services
N.A.I.C.S.: 561730
Samuel Lang (Pres)

Turf Masters Lawn Care, Inc. (2)
St 439 Gunnin Rd, Woodstock, GA 30188
Tel.: (770) 924-7718
Rev.: $1,700,000
Emp.: 28
Landscaping Services
N.A.I.C.S.: 561730
Andrew Kadrich (Pres)

CENTERPLAN CONSTRUCTION COMPANY
10 Main St Ste B, Middletown, CT
06457
Tel.: (860) 398-5390
Web Site:
　http://www.centerplanconstruction.com
Year Founded: 2008
Sales Range: $50-74.9 Million
Emp.: 43
Construction Engineering Services
N.A.I.C.S.: 541330
Robert A. Landino (CEO)
Michael J. Lombardi (Pres)
Christopher D. Kohl (VP)

CENTERPOINT HEALTH INC
333 Conover Dr Ste B & D, Franklin, OH 45005-1900
Tel.: (513) 318-1188   OH
Web Site:
https://www.centerpointhealth.org
Year Founded: 1971
Sales Range: $10-24.9 Million
Emp.: 329
Behavioral Healthcare Services
N.A.I.C.S.: 621420
Neil Tilow (Chm)
Lorie Glenn (CEO)
Jennifer N. Feldman (Chief Medical Officer)

CENTERPOINT PROPERTIES TRUST
1808 Swift Dr, Oak Brook, IL 60523-1501
Tel.: (630) 586-8170   MD
Web Site: http://www.centerpoint-prop.com
Year Founded: 1984
Sales Range: $150-199.9 Million
Emp.: 109
Real Estate Investment Trust
N.A.I.C.S.: 525990
Scott Zimmerman (CMO & CIO)
James N. Clewlow (Chief Investment Officer)
Michael Murphy (Chief Dev Officer)
Robert M. Chapman (CEO)
Stacey Cizek (Dir-Insurance)
Sharon Purcell (Dir-Tax)
Nate Rexroth (Exec VP)
Ed Harrington (Sr VP)
Joe Nasca (Sr VP)
Paul Charlton (Sr VP)
Matt Mullarkey (Sr VP-Strategic Projects & Plng)
Mike Tortorici (Treas & Sr VP)
Kevin German (VP-IT)
Beverly Maestas (VP-Tech Ops)
Christopher J. Papa (CFO & Exec VP)

CENTERS FOR DIALYSIS CARE
18720 Chagrin Blvd, Shaker Heights, OH 44122
Tel.: (216) 295-7000   OH
Web Site: https://www.cdcare.org
Year Founded: 1973
Sales Range: $25-49.9 Million
Kidney Dialysis Services
N.A.I.C.S.: 621492
Diane Wish (CEO)
David Oppenlander (CFO)
Gary Robinson (Pres)

CENTERS FOR YOUTH & FAMILIES, INC.
PO Box 251970, Little Rock, AR 72225
Tel.: (501) 666-8686   AR
Web Site:
http://www.centersforyouth.org
Year Founded: 1970
Sales Range: $10-24.9 Million
Child & Family Support Services
N.A.I.C.S.: 624190
Heather Duran (Dir-Clinical Ops)
Zarina Shah (Dir-Medical)
Doug Stadter (Pres & CEO)
Melissa Dawson (COO)
Chad T. May (Vice Chm)
Mark Allison (Chm)

CENTERSTONE OF AMERICA, INC.
44 Vantage Way Ste 400, Nashville, TN 37228
Tel.: (615) 463-6610   IN
Web Site: http://www.centerstone.org

Year Founded: 1997
Sales Range: $1-9.9 Million
Mental Health Services
N.A.I.C.S.: 621420
Richard Fitzgerald (Co-Chm)
A. John Rose (Co-Chm)
Ramona Rhodes (Pres-Foundation)
Natalie Stone (VP-Creative Svcs)
Debbie Cagle Wells (CMO)
Wayne Easterwood (Chief Admin Officer)
Sherry Harrison (Chief Compliance Officer)
Lee Brackett (Vice Chm)
Kevin Norton (COO)
Peter Garrison (Sec)
Abbreial Drane (CEO-Kentucky)
Dan Smith (Chief HR Officer)
John Markley (CEO-Illinois)
Melissa Larkin-Skinner (CEO-Florida)
Prasad Kodali (CIO)
Richard C. Shelton (Mng Dir)
Robert N. Vero (CEO-Tennessee)
Suzanne Koesel (CEO-Indiana)
Carol Bean (CFO)
David C. Guth Jr. (CEO)

Subsidiaries:

Centerstone of Illinois, Inc.   (1)
200 N Emerald Ln, Carbondale, IL 62901
Tel.: (855) 608-3560
Mental Healthcare Treatment & Facility
N.A.I.C.S.: 623220
John Markley (CEO-Reg)

Subsidiary (Domestic):

The Fellowship House   (2)
800 N Main St, Anna, IL 62906
Tel.: (618) 833-4456
Web Site:
http://www.thefellowshiphouse.com
Rehabilitation Treatment Services
N.A.I.C.S.: 621498
Mickey Finch (CEO)
Kathryn Dread (Mgr-Case)

Centerstone of Indiana, Inc.   (1)
720 N Marr Rd, Columbus, IN 47201
Tel.: (812) 314-3400
Web Site: http://www.centerstone.org
Behavioral Healthcare Facilities & Services
N.A.I.C.S.: 622210
Suzanne Koesel (CEO)
Shirley Arney (Chief Admin Officer)
Robb Backmeyer (COO)
Thelma Chandler (Dir-Indiana Military Svcs)
Kathleen O'Brian Christoff (Dir-Adult & Family Svcs-LCSW)
Linda Grove-Paul (VP-Adult Svcs)
Jenny Harrison (VP-Access & Crisis Svcs)
Rona Krueger (VP-Quality Improvement-MSW)
Scott Lewellen (Dir-Mktg & Pub Rels)
Darcey Meridith (VP-Child Svcs)
Maria Nehrt (Dir-Facilities)
Amanda Pardue (Dir-Child Svcs)
Steven Reynolds (Dir-Fin)
Beth Rodriguez (Dir-Advancement)
Michelle Sears (Dir-Support Svcs)
Bob Siegmann (Sr VP-Integration Collaboration)
Meagan Terlep (Dir-Child & Family Svcs-LHMC)
Vinita Watts (Dir-Medical)
Terrye Davidson (Chm)
Linda Hobbs (Sec)
Douglas Leonard (Vice Chm)
Richard Prather (Officer-Compliance & Privacy)

Subsidiary (Domestic):

Centerstone of Florida, Inc.   (2)
391 6th Ave W, Bradenton, FL 34205
Tel.: (941) 782-4299
Web Site: http://www.manateeglens.org
Behavioral Health Services
N.A.I.C.S.: 622210
James T. Golden (Vice Chm)
Sean Gingras (CFO)
Ranjay Halder (Dir-Medical)
Jennifer Bencie (Co-Chm)
Timothy Knowles (Co-Chm)

Colleen Thayer (Sec)
Melissa Larkin-Skinner (CEO)
Mihaela Zdrali (VP-Outpatient Svcs)

Prairie Center Health Systems, Inc.   (2)
718 W Killarney St, Urbana, IL 61801
Tel.: (217) 328-4500
Web Site: http://www.prairie-center.com
Community Health Care Services
N.A.I.C.S.: 621498
Gail Raney (CEO)
Susan Perkins (Dir-Clinical)
Carl Harshbarger (Dir-Fin)
Pete Jones (VP)
Margaret Krol (Sec)
Jedd Swisher (VP)
Mike Tennant (Pres)
Marissa Harris (Dir-Clinical)
Andrew Timms (Treas)
Carol Bradford (Dir-Clinical-Urbana)
Laura Huth (Dir-Dev & Comm)
Sherri Rudicil (Dir-Prevention)
Jeffery Lehmann (Dir-HR)
Narain Mandhan (Dir-Medical)

CENTERVIEW PARTNERS LLC
31 W 52nd St 22nd fl, New York, NY 10019
Tel.: (212) 380-2650   DE
Web Site:
http://www.centerviewpartners.com
Year Founded: 2006
Sales Range: $75-99.9 Million
Emp.: 50
Corporate Financial Advisory & Private Equity Investment Services
N.A.I.C.S.: 523940
James Marshall Kilts (Partner)
Blair W. Effron (Co-Founder)
Robert A. Pruzan (Co-Founder)
Alexander Glantz (Partner)
Todd J. Davison (Partner)
Robin Budenberg (Chm-London)
Nick Reid (Partner)
Paul J. Collins (Partner)
Adam Beshara (Partner)
David M. Cohen (Partner)
John C. Bosacco (Partner)
John E. Cogan (Partner)
Joshua E. Boyd (Partner)
Kenneth T. Berliner (Partner)
Sean Carmody (Partner-Fin Svcs Practice)
John B. Rhea (Partner)
Todd Kaplan (Partner-San Francisco)
Amit Bajaj (Partner)
Karn S. Chopra (Partner)
William M. Edwards (Partner-Food & Consumer Products)
John Ferguson (Partner)
Tadhg J. Flood (Partner)
Richard Girling (Partner)
Samuel M. Greene (Partner)
Alan Hartman (Partner)
James Hartop (Partner)
David J. Hess (Partner)
Anthony Y. Kim (Partner)
Benjamin L. Kjome (Partner)
Jack Levy (Partner)
Michael Muntner (Partner)
David K. Neequaye (Partner)
Cathal J. O'Reilly (Partner)
Roland Phillips (Partner)
Marc D. Puntus (Partner)
Mark J. Robinson (Partner)
Andrew S. Rymer (Partner)
Stuart Smith (Partner)
Ercument Tokat (Partner)
Gayle Turk (Partner)
Andrew K. Woeber (Partner)

Subsidiaries:

Centerview Capital, L.P.   (1)
1 Greenwich Office Park, Greenwich, CT 06831
Tel.: (212) 429-2211
Web Site: http://www.centerviewcapital.com
Emp.: 10

Private Equity Firm
N.A.I.C.S.: 523999
Brian K. Ratzan (Partner)
David M. Hooper (Founder)
James Marshall Kilts (Founder, Chm & Partner)
David Wyatt Dorman (Partner)
Max Papkov (VP)
Melanie Harris (Head-IR)
Sandhya Venkatachalam (Partner-Founding-Tech)
Sangeen Zeb (Principal)
Yagyensh C. Pati (Partner)
Tony Zhang (Principal)
David J. West (Vice Chm & Partner)

Centerview Partners Management LLC   (1)
31 W 52nd St 22 Fl, New York, NY 10019
Tel.: (212) 380-2650
Web Site:
http://www.centerviewpartners.com
Sales Range: $50-74.9 Million
Privater Equity Firm
N.A.I.C.S.: 523999
David M. Hooper (Partner & Dir-Private Equity)
James Marshall Kilts (Partner)
Michelle K. Kaull (Controller)
Brett B. Lawrence (COO & Exec VP)
Joshua D. Ness (VP)

CENTEX HOUSE LEVELING
1120 E 52nd St, Austin, TX 78723
Tel.: (512) 444-5438
Web Site:
http://www.centexhouseleveling.com
Rev.: $45,800,000
Emp.: 200
Commercial & Office Buildings, Renovation & Repair
N.A.I.C.S.: 236220
Ben F. Cooper (Founder)
Jeff Griffith (Mgr-Mktg)

CENTIMARK CORPORATION
12 Grandview Cir, Canonsburg, PA 15317
Tel.: (724) 743-7777   PA
Web Site: http://www.centimark.com
Year Founded: 1968
Sales Range: $400-449.9 Million
Emp.: 2,500
Roofing Contracting Services
N.A.I.C.S.: 238160
Edward B. Dunlap (Chm & CEO)
Timothy M. Dunlap (Pres)
John Altvater (Grp Dir-QuestMark-East)
Kenneth W. Zmich (Exec VP-Svc)

Subsidiaries:

CentiMark Ltd.   (1)
7680 Winston Street, Burnaby, V5A 2H4, BC, Canada
Tel.: (604) 521-8911
Web Site: http://www.centimarkltd.com
Emp.: 50
Roofing Contractors
N.A.I.C.S.: 238160

Centimark Corporation - QuestMark Flooring Division   (1)
944 Marcon Blvd Ste 130, Allentown, PA 18109
Tel.: (484) 488-3040
Web Site: http://www.questmarkflooring.com
Flooring Contractors
N.A.I.C.S.: 238330
Brian Scanlon (VP-Ops)
Edward B. Dunlap (Chm & CEO)
Jim Gasper (VP-Sls)
John Scanlon (Exec VP)
Timothy M. Dunlap (Pres & COO)

CENTINEL BANK OF TAOS
512 Paseo del Pueblo Sur, Taos, NM 87571
Tel.: (575) 758-6700
Web Site:
http://www.centinelbank.com
Sales Range: $1-9.9 Million

Centinel Bank of Taos—(Continued)

Emp.: 50
Commericial Banking
N.A.I.C.S.: 522110
Rebeca Rainey (Chm & CEO)
Angel Reyes (Pres)
Isaiah Ortega (Asst Controller)

CENTON ELECTRONICS, INC.
27412 Aliso Viejo Pkwy, Aliso Viejo,
CA 92656
Tel.: (949) 855-9111
Web Site: http://www.centon.com
Year Founded: 1978
Rev.: $10,700,000
Emp.: 60
Computer Peripheral Equipment
N.A.I.C.S.: 334118
Gary Clack (Product Mgr)
Jay O'Neil (Mgr-Quality Sys)
Lauren Davies (Mgr-Channel Sls)
Stuart Atkins (Mgr-Dev Product)
David Hoang (Engr-Design)

CENTOR ENERGY, INC.
1801 Lee Rd Ste 265, Winter Park,
FL 32789   NV
Web Site: http://centorenergyinc.com
Year Founded: 2011
Metal Mining Services
N.A.I.C.S.: 212290
Frederick DaSilva (Pres, CEO, CFO,
Chief Accounting Officer, Treas &
Sec)

CENTORR VACUUM INDUS-
TRIES, INC.
55 Northeastern Blvd, Nashua, NH
03062-3126
Tel.: (603) 595-7233
Web Site: http://www.centorr.com
Year Founded: 1997
Sales Range: $25-49.9 Million
Emp.: 55
Industrial Furnaces Mfr
N.A.I.C.S.: 333994
William J. Nareski (CEO)
Vincent Massua (Mgr-Ops)
Kevin M. Janisse (COO)

CENTRA MARKETING & COM-
MUNICATIONS, LLC
1400 Old Country Rd Ste 420, West-
bury, NY 11590-5119
Tel.: (516) 997-3147   NY
Web Site: http://www.centra360.com
Year Founded: 1996
Sales Range: $1-9.9 Million
Emp.: 10
Fiscal Year-end: 03/31/16
Advetising Agency
N.A.I.C.S.: 541810
Robert A. Bell (COO)
Chariot Crespo (Vp-Partnerships)
Mark Biggin (Sr Vp-Experimental
Grp)
Howard Davidson (CMO)
David Schnitzer (Sr Dir-Activation)
Michelle Greenberg (Acct Exec)

CENTRA SOTA COOPERATIVE
805 Highway 55 E, Buffalo, MN
55313-4300
Tel.: (763) 682-1464   MN
Web Site:
    https://www.centrasota.com
Year Founded: 1922
Grain Whslr & Farm Supplies
N.A.I.C.S.: 424910
Jeff Johnson (CEO & Gen Mgr)
Steve Sievek (Chm)
Bill Holthaus (Sec & Treas)
Charles Krause (Vice Chm)

CENTRA, INC.

12225 Stephen Rd, Warren, MI
48089
Tel.: (586) 939-7000
Web Site:
    http://www.centraltransport.com
Sales Range: $25-49.9 Million
Emp.: 200
Holding Company
N.A.I.C.S.: 484121
Manuel J. Moroun (Owner, Pres &
CEO)
Patrick Moran (Exec VP & Gen
Counsel)

Subsidiaries:

Central Transport International
Inc.   (1)
12225 Stephens Rd, Warren, MI 48089-
2010
Tel.: (586) 467-1900
Web Site: http://www.centraltransport.com
Trucking Service
N.A.I.C.S.: 484121
Manuel Moroun (Chm & CEO)

Subsidiary (Domestic):

C.C. Southern Inc.   (2)
12225 Stephens Rd, Warren, MI 48089-
2010
Tel.: (586) 939-7000
Trucking Except Local
N.A.I.C.S.: 484121

Central Transport   (2)
12225 Stephens Rd, Warren, MI 48089-
2010
Tel.: (586) 467-1900
Local Trucking without Storage
N.A.I.C.S.: 484121

Central Transport International   (2)
34200 Mound Rd, Sterling Heights, MI
48310-6613
Tel.: (586) 467-1900
Web Site: http://www.centraltransportint.com
Rev.: $490,000
Emp.: 6
Telephone & Telegraph Apparatus
N.A.I.C.S.: 484121

Branch (Domestic):

Central Transport International -
Gibsonia   (2)
2850 Kramer Dr, Gibsonia, PA 15044
Tel.: (412) 453-4922
Freight Transportation Services
N.A.I.C.S.: 484122

Subsidiary (Domestic):

Central Transportation International
Inc   (2)
12225 Stephens Rd, Warren, MI 48089-
2010
Tel.: (586) 939-7000
Web Site: http://www.centraltransportint.com
Sales Range: $100-124.9 Million
Local Trucking without Storage
N.A.I.C.S.: 484121

Crown Enterprises Inc.   (2)
12225 Stephens Rd, Warren, MI 48089-
2010
Tel.: (586) 939-7000
Sales Range: $25-49.9 Million
Emp.: 15
Trucking Terminals
N.A.I.C.S.: 484121
Manuel J. Moroun (Pres)
Daniel Onifer (Dir-Third Party Projects)

Custom Services International
Ltd.   (2)
12225 Stephens Rd, Warren, MI 48089-
2010
Tel.: (586) 939-7000
Web Site: http://www.customservicesint.com
Rev.: $1,500,000
Emp.: 12
Freight Transportation Arrangement
N.A.I.C.S.: 488510

Mexican Town Real Estate Co.   (2)
12225 Stephens Rd, Warren, MI 48089-
2010

Tel.: (586) 755-0696
Rev.: $1,900,000
Emp.: 15
Providing Real Estate Services
N.A.I.C.S.: 237210

Michigan Jobber Broker Equipment &
Supplies Co. Inc.   (2)
12225 Stephens Rd, Warren, MI 48089
Tel.: (586) 939-7000
Rev.: $2,000,000
Emp.: 13
Motor Vehicle Supplies & New Parts
N.A.I.C.S.: 423120

Detroit International Bridge Co.
Inc.   (1)
12225 Stephens Rd, Warren, MI
48089   (100%)
Tel.: (586) 939-7000
Web Site:
    http://www.ambassadorbridge.com
Sales Range: $1-9.9 Million
Emp.: 40
Ambassador Bridge Toll Collector & Opera-
tor
N.A.I.C.S.: 488490
Dan Stamper (Pres)

CENTRABANC CORPORATION
8320 W Hwy 84, Waco, TX 76712
Tel.: (254) 776-3800   TX
Web Site: http://www.cnbwaco.com
Year Founded: 1981
Sales Range: $10-24.9 Million
Emp.: 100
Bank Holding Company
N.A.I.C.S.: 551111
William A. Nesbitt (Chm & CEO)
Joseph Nesbitt (VP-Real Estate &
Comml Lending)

Subsidiaries:

Central National Bank   (1)
8320 W Hwy 84, Waco, TX 76712
Tel.: (254) 776-3800
Web Site: http://www.cnbwaco.com
Rev.: $18,154,000
Emp.: 80
National Commercial Banks
N.A.I.C.S.: 522110
J. David Smith (Pres)
Mary R. Holley (CFO)
Heither Keeton (VP-HR)

CENTRACARE HEALTH FOUN-
DATION
1406 6th Ave N, Saint Cloud, MN
56303-1901
Tel.: (320) 240-2810
Web Site: http://www.centracare.com
Rev.: $8,000,000
Emp.: 9
Fiscal Year-end: 06/30/07
Healthcare Services
N.A.I.C.S.: 621491
Holly Gulden (VP)
Candyce Gregory (Mgr-Events)
Paula Eckerman (Mgr-Foundation
Data Sys)
Amy Hanfler (Dir-Sustaining Gifts)
Brenda Jacobson (Dir-Foundation
Ops)
Dan Super (Accountant)
Deb Paul (Mgr-Donor Relations)

CENTRACOMM COMMUNICA-
TIONS, LTD.
323 S Main St, Findlay, OH 45840
Tel.: (419) 423-2666   OH
Web Site: http://www.centracomm.net
Year Founded: 2001
Sales Range: $10-24.9 Million
Emp.: 12
Computer Security Solutions
N.A.I.C.S.: 541519
Mark Robinson (Pres)

CENTRAL ALABAMA ELEC-
TRIC COOPERATIVE

103 Jesse Samuel Hunt Blvd, Pratt-
ville, AL 36067
Tel.: (334) 365-6762
Web Site: http://www.caec.com
Rev.: $42,087,959
Emp.: 125
Distr of Electric Power
N.A.I.C.S.: 221122
Thomas Stackhouse (Pres & CEO)
David Loe (VP-Fin & Corp Svcs)
Jimmie Harrison (Vice Chm)
Jimmy Gray (VP-Engrg & Ops)
Julie Young (VP-Bus & Admin Svcs)
Chuck Billings (VP-Customer & En-
ergy Svcs)

CENTRAL ALLIED ENTER-
PRISES
1243 Raff Rd SW, Canton, OH
44710-1455
Tel.: (330) 477-6751   OH
Web Site: http://www.central-
allied.com
Year Founded: 1929
Sales Range: $150-199.9 Million
Emp.: 333
Asphalt & Asphatic Paving Mixtures;
Bituminous Concrete; Ready-Mixed
Concrete; Highway & Street Con-
struction; Sand & Gravel Construction
N.A.I.C.S.: 327320
David Bair (VP)

Subsidiaries:

Canton Aggregate Division   (1)
2905 Columbus Rd NE, Canton, OH
44705   (100%)
Tel.: (330) 580-4300
Web Site: http://www.central-allied.com
Sales Range: $10-24.9 Million
Emp.: 25
Mfr of Ready-Mixed Concrete
N.A.I.C.S.: 327320

Central Allied Enterprises - Massillon
Washed Gravel Division   (1)
6331 Blough Rd SW, Navarre, OH 44662
Tel.: (330) 879-2132
Gravel Whslr
N.A.I.C.S.: 423320

Ohio Tar Asphalt   (1)
1243 Raff Rd SW, Canton, OH 44710-1455
Tel.: (330) 477-6751
Sales Range: $25-49.9 Million
Emp.: 25
Bituminous Road Materials
N.A.I.C.S.: 238990

CENTRAL ARKANSAS PETRO-
LEUM INC.
2666 Oliver Lancaster Blvd, Malvern,
AR 72104-2336
Tel.: (501) 332-3683   AR
Year Founded: 1993
Sales Range: $25-49.9 Million
Emp.: 170
Provider of Petroleum Services
N.A.I.C.S.: 424710
Kimball Davis (Pres)

CENTRAL ARKANSAS RADIA-
TION THERAPY INSTITUTE
INC
PO Box 55050, Little Rock, AR 72215
Tel.: (501) 664-8573   AR
Web Site: http://www.carti.com
Year Founded: 1973
Sales Range: $250-299.9 Million
Emp.: 370
Oncology Treatment Services
N.A.I.C.S.: 622310
Jeff Burton (Treas & Treas)

CENTRAL AUTO BODY RE-
BUILDERS, INC.
3130 S Big Bend Blvd, Saint Louis,
MO 63143

Tel.: (314) 644-2151
Web Site:
https://www.centralautobody.net
Year Founded: 1955
Sales Range: $1-9.9 Million
Emp.: 25
Body, Paint & Interior Repair Services
N.A.I.C.S.: 811121
Chris Becker *(Pres)*
Skip Reynolds *(Mgr)*

CENTRAL BAG COMPANY
4901 S 4th St, Leavenworth, KS 66048
Tel.: (913) 250-0325
Web Site:
https://www.centralbagcompany.com
Sales Range: $10-24.9 Million
Emp.: 33
Mfr Bags, Paper & Disposable Plastic
N.A.I.C.S.: 424130
Jeff Chalabi *(Mgr-Sls)*

CENTRAL BANCSHARES, INC.
301 Iowa Ave, Muscatine, IA 52761
Tel.: (563) 263-3131
Web Site: http://www.cbibanks.com
Commericial Banking
N.A.I.C.S.: 522110
Daniel P. Stein *(Chm)*
Gregory J. Kistler *(Pres & CEO)*

CENTRAL BANK
11201 Clay Rd, Houston, TX 77041
Tel.: (713) 868-5577
Web Site:
http://www.centralbankhouston.com
Sales Range: $10-24.9 Million
Emp.: 27
State Trust Companies Accepting Deposits
N.A.I.C.S.: 522110
Jim MacIntyre *(Exec VP)*
Gary Noble *(Sr VP)*
Bonnie Selzer Purvis *(Sr VP & Mgr-Timbergrove Market)*
Kenny Beard *(Sr VP & Mgr-Market)*
Tracy Makransky *(Asst VP-Princeton)*

CENTRAL BANK
101 W Commercial St, Lebanon, MO 65536
Tel.: (417) 532-2151
Web Site: http://www.central-bank.net
Year Founded: 1917
Sales Range: $10-24.9 Million
Emp.: 80
Provider of Banking Services
N.A.I.C.S.: 522180
Mark Campbell *(Sr VP)*

CENTRAL BANK & TRUST CO.
300 W Vine St, Lexington, KY 40507-1621
Tel.: (859) 253-6222   KY
Web Site:
http://www.centralbank.com
Year Founded: 1938
Sales Range: $50-74.9 Million
Emp.: 275
State Commercial Banks
N.A.I.C.S.: 522110
Luther Deaton Jr. *(Pres, CEO & Chm)*

CENTRAL BANK CORPORA-TION
75 N University Ave, Provo, UT 84601
Tel.: (801) 375-1000
Web Site: https://www.cbutah.com
Sales Range: $10-24.9 Million
Emp.: 185
State Commercial Banks
N.A.I.C.S.: 522110

Rick Norman *(VP & Mgr-Lehi)*
Steve Patten *(VP & Mgr-Pleasant Grove)*
Gary Jensen *(VP & Mgr-Provo Riverside Plaza)*
Glen Roach *(VP & Mgr-Spanish Fork)*
Mark VanWagoner *(Sr VP & Mgr-American Fork)*
Brian Hulet *(VP & Mgr-Payson)*
Mark Packard *(Pres)*
Jeff Simonsen *(Sr VP-Provo)*
Tyler Hardy *(Officer-Provo)*
Hannah Packard *(Officer-Provo)*

Subsidiaries:

Central Bank   (1)
75 N University Ave, Provo, UT 84601
Tel.: (801) 375-1000
Web Site: http://www.cbutah.com
Sales Range: $25-49.9 Million
Emp.: 80
State Commercial Bank Services
N.A.I.C.S.: 522110
Mark Packard *(Pres)*
Deborah Lamb *(Officer-SBA & Mgr)*

CENTRAL BAPTIST VILLAGE
4747 N Canfield Ave, Norridge, IL 60706
Tel.: (708) 583-8500   IL
Web Site: http://www.cbvillage.org
Year Founded: 1896
Sales Range: $10-24.9 Million
Emp.: 279
Elder Care Services
N.A.I.C.S.: 623312
Karen Haedo *(Dir-Nursing)*
Lori Altman *(CFO)*
Pamela Yoelin *(Dir-Admin Svcs)*
Julie Stevens *(Dir-Sls & Mktg)*
James L. Renke *(Vice Chm)*
Judith Dunne Bernardi *(Sec)*
Julie Adams *(Treas)*
John M. Smith *(Pres)*
Anna-Liisa LaCroix *(CEO)*

CENTRAL BEEF IND., L.L.C.
PO Box 399, Center Hill, FL 33514
Tel.: (352) 793-3671
Sales Range: $10-24.9 Million
Emp.: 120
Veal Product Mfr
N.A.I.C.S.: 311611
Paul Beutler *(Controller)*
Javier De La Rosa *(Plant Mgr)*
Adam Chernin *(Partner)*
Jerry McLean *(Dir-Food Safety)*

CENTRAL BERING SEA FISH-ERMEN'S ASSOCIATION
140 Ellerman Heights, Saint Paul Island, AK 99660
Tel.: (907) 546-2597   AK
Web Site: https://www.cbsfa.com
Year Founded: 1992
Sales Range: $10-24.9 Million
Emp.: 29
Business Associations
N.A.I.C.S.: 813910
Phillip Lestenkof *(Pres)*
Jeffery P. Kauffman *(VP)*
Myron Melovidov *(Chm)*

CENTRAL BLACKTOP CO., INC.
6160 E Ave, Hodgkins, IL 60525
Tel.: (708) 482-9660
Web Site:
http://www.centralblacktop.com
Sales Range: $25-49.9 Million
Emp.: 25
Highway & Street Paving Contractor
N.A.I.C.S.: 237310
James Loukota *(Pres)*
John Goling *(VP)*

CENTRAL BUICK GMC OF NORWOOD
70 Boston Providence Hwy US Route 1, Norwood, MA 02062
Tel.: (617) 325-4200
Web Site:
https://www.centralgmcnorwood.com
Rev.: $30,000,000
Emp.: 25
New & Used Car Dealership
N.A.I.C.S.: 441110
Peter Catanese *(Owner)*

CENTRAL CADILLAC
2801 Carnegie Ave, Cleveland, OH 44115
Tel.: (216) 815-3671
Web Site:
https://www.centralcadillac.com
Sales Range: $100-124.9 Million
Emp.: 100
New & Used Automobiles
N.A.I.C.S.: 441110
Bill Miller *(Mgr-Bus)*
Curtice L. Johnson *(Gen Mgr)*
Paul Nathan *(Mgr-Sls)*

CENTRAL CALIFORNIA CHILD DEVELOPMENT SERVICES, INC.
2250 Rockefeller Dr Ste 1, Ceres, CA 95307
Tel.: (209) 581-9000   CA
Web Site: https://www.cccds.com
Year Founded: 1984
Sales Range: $10-24.9 Million
Emp.: 300
Child Day Care Services
N.A.I.C.S.: 624410
Conha Alvarez *(Exec Dir)*
Steve Pedrazzi *(Treas & Sec)*
Mike Perez *(Pres)*
Maria Quintero *(VP)*

CENTRAL CEILING PARTITION INC.
3900 Centennial Dr Ste A, Midland, MI 48642
Tel.: (989) 496-9195   MI
Year Founded: 1973
Sales Range: $10-24.9 Million
Emp.: 20
Provider of Home & Commercial Contracting Services
N.A.I.C.S.: 238310
Richard Scharich *(Pres)*
Dan Gay *(Pres)*

CENTRAL CHEVROLET COM-PANY INC.
3207 Stadium Blvd, Jonesboro, AR 72404-9359
Tel.: (870) 935-5575
Web Site:
https://www.centralchevrolet.com
Rev.: $23,500,000
Emp.: 48
New & Used Automobiles
N.A.I.C.S.: 441110
Doyle Yarbrough *(Pres)*

CENTRAL CHRYSLER JEEP DODGE
191 New State Hwy, Raynham, MA 02767
Tel.: (508) 823-0101
Web Site:
http://www.centralchryslerjeep.com
Sales Range: $10-24.9 Million
Emp.: 55
New Car Retailer
N.A.I.C.S.: 441110
Kim Albert *(Mgr-Svc)*
Adam Silver *(Gen Mgr-Sls)*

CENTRAL CITY COMMUNITY HEALTH CENTER
5230 E Beverly Blvd, Los Angeles, CA 90022
Tel.: (323) 728-7355   CA
Web Site:
http://www.centralcityhealth.org
Year Founded: 1994
Sales Range: $10-24.9 Million
Emp.: 152
Healtcare Services
N.A.I.C.S.: 622110
John Pazirandeh *(CFO)*

CENTRAL CITY CONCERN
232 NW 6th Ave, Portland, OR 97209
Tel.: (503) 294-1681   OR
Web Site:
https://www.centralcityconcern.org
Year Founded: 1979
Sales Range: $25-49.9 Million
Emp.: 783
Community Action Services
N.A.I.C.S.: 624190
Andy Mendenhall *(Sr Dir-Medical-Substance Use Disorder Svcs)*
Sean Hubert *(Chief Housing Officer & Chief Strategy Officer)*
Mercedes Elizalde *(Dir-Pub Policy)*

CENTRAL COAST WINES
712 Higuera St, San Luis Obispo, CA 93401
Tel.: (805) 784-9463
Web Site: http://www.ccwines.com
Sales Range: $25-49.9 Million
Emp.: 100
Wine Mfr
N.A.I.C.S.: 312130
Vaughn Taus *(Owner)*
Bob Ritchie *(Owner)*

CENTRAL COCA-COLA BOT-TLING COMPANY, INC.
1706 Roseneath Rd, Richmond, VA 23230
Tel.: (804) 359-3759   VA
Year Founded: 1980
Sales Range: $200-249.9 Million
Emp.: 550
Soft Drink Distr
N.A.I.C.S.: 424490

CENTRAL COMPUTER SYS-TEMS INC.
3777 Stevens Creek Blvd, Santa Clara, CA 95051-7364
Tel.: (408) 248-5888   CA
Web Site:
https://www.centralcomputer.com
Year Founded: 1986
Sales Range: $25-49.9 Million
Emp.: 100
Computer & Software Stores
N.A.I.C.S.: 449210
Saul Yeung *(Co-Founder & Pres)*
Ann Lai *(Mgr-HR)*
Sherry Yeung *(Co-Founder & CFO)*

CENTRAL CONCRETE COR-PORATION
166 Central St, Hudson, MA 01749
Tel.: (978) 567-8900
Rev.: $11,000,000
Emp.: 60
Flooring Contractors
N.A.I.C.S.: 238990

Subsidiaries:

Floorcon Corporation   (1)
135 Rinehardt Rd, Mooresville, NC 28115
Tel.: (704) 663-2303
Rev.: $1,500,000
Emp.: 40
Concrete Work
N.A.I.C.S.: 238110

Central Contra Costa Sanitary District—(Continued)

CENTRAL CONTRA COSTA SANITARY DISTRICT
5019 Imhoff Pl, Martinez, CA 94553-4316
Tel.: (925) 228-9500   CA
Web Site: https://www.centralsan.org
Year Founded: 1946
Sales Range: $50-74.9 Million
Emp.: 280
Waste Management Services
N.A.I.C.S.: 221320
Roger Bailey (Gen Mgr)
Emily Barnett (Mgr-Comm Svcs & Intergovernmental Rels)
Phil Leiber (Dir-Fin & Admin)

CENTRAL CONTRACTING COMPANY
3491 3rd St, Farmville, VA 23901
Tel.: (434) 392-4681
Sales Range: $10-24.9 Million
Emp.: 40
Bridge Construction
N.A.I.C.S.: 237310
V C Williamson (Pres)
M. S. Burnley (VP)

CENTRAL COOP
900 30th Pl NW, Owatonna, MN 55060-4063
Tel.: (507) 451-1230
Web Site:
  http://www.centralvalleycoop.com
Year Founded: 1922
Sales Range: $10-24.9 Million
Emp.: 97
Distr of Agricultural Chemicals Fertilizers & Other Agricultural Products
N.A.I.C.S.: 424910
Gary Mohr (Gen Mgr)
Kelly Gallagher (Office Mgr)
Steve Johnson (Mgr)
Dave Wager (Mgr)
Chuck Wagner (Mgr)
Albert McLean (CFO)
Patrick Hawkins (COO)
Dave Picha (Dir-Safety)
Kim Jones (Mgr-HR)
Al Macius (Mgr-Mktg)
Danny Dahlen (Mgr-Ops)
Dennis Jensen (Mgr-Petroleum Ops)
Kevin Kruize (Mgr-Precision Ag)
Ryan Larson (Mgr-Seed Dept)
Tim Donelan (VP-Grain)

CENTRAL CRUDE INC.
4187 Hwy 3059, Lake Charles, LA 70615
Tel.: (337) 436-1000
Web Site:
  https://www.centralcrude.com
Sales Range: $75-99.9 Million
Emp.: 31
Liquid Petroleum Transport, Non-Local
N.A.I.C.S.: 484230
Steven M. Jordan (Pres & CEO)
A. J. Vincent (Mgr-Ops)
Joe Milazzo (VP)
Donna Rutherford (Mgr-Compliance & HR)

CENTRAL DAIRY COMPANY
610 Madison St, Jefferson City, MO 65101-3199
Tel.: (573) 635-6148
Web Site: https://www.centraldairy.biz
Sales Range: $10-24.9 Million
Emp.: 84
Fluid Milk
N.A.I.C.S.: 311511
Ed Mullens (Pres)

CENTRAL DISTRIBUTING CO.
245 S Ave, Grand Junction, CO 81501
Tel.: (970) 243-0024
Web Site:
  http://www.centraldistributing.ws
Rev.: $26,663,265
Emp.: 85
Beer & Ale
N.A.I.C.S.: 424810
Jose Alvarez (Mgr-Sls)

CENTRAL ELECTRIC COOPERATIVE INC.
2098 N Hwy 97, Redmond, OR 97756-1209
Tel.: (541) 548-2144   OR
Web Site: http://www.cec.coop
Year Founded: 1940
Sales Range: $25-49.9 Million
Emp.: 81
Electronic Services
N.A.I.C.S.: 221122
Dave Markham (Pres & CEO)

CENTRAL ELECTRIC POWER ASSOCIATION
107 E Main St, Carthage, MS 39051
Tel.: (601) 267-5671
Web Site:
  https://www.centralepa.com
Year Founded: 1937
Sales Range: $10-24.9 Million
Emp.: 100
Distr of Electric Power
N.A.I.C.S.: 221121
Richard Wilson (Controller)
Brian Long (Dir-Engrg)

CENTRAL ELECTRIC POWER COOPERATIVE INC.
2106 Jefferson St, Jefferson City, MO 65109-2066
Tel.: (573) 634-2454   MO
Web Site: http://www.cepc.net
Year Founded: 1949
Sales Range: $25-49.9 Billion
Emp.: 98
Electronic Services
N.A.I.C.S.: 221122
Don Shaw (CEO & Gen Mgr)
Randy Carrender (Mgr-Fin)
Nancy Gibler (Dir-Bus Dev)
Mark Newbold (Mgr-HR)

CENTRAL ELECTRIC POWER COOPERATIVE, INC.
121 Greystone Blvd, Columbia, SC 29210
Tel.: (803) 779-4975   SC
Web Site: http://www.cepci.org
Year Founded: 1948
Sales Range: $1-4.9 Billion
Emp.: 44
Electric Power Distr
N.A.I.C.S.: 221122
James C. Lamb (Sr VP-Planning-Power Supply)

CENTRAL ENVIRONMENTAL INC.
311 N Sitka St, Anchorage, AK 99501-1841
Tel.: (907) 561-0125
Web Site: http://www.cei-alaska.com
Sales Range: $10-24.9 Million
Emp.: 100
Asbestos Removal & Encapsulation
N.A.I.C.S.: 562910
Stuart M. Jacques (Pres & CEO)
Lisa Bishop (Office Mgr)
Shane Durand (Mgr)

CENTRAL FEDERAL SAVINGS & LOAN ASSOCIATION
5953 W Cermak Rd, Cicero, IL 60804
Tel.: (708) 656-5000
Web Site:
  https://www.centralfederal.com
Year Founded: 1892
Sales Range: $25-49.9 Million
Emp.: 80
Federal Savings & Loan Associations
N.A.I.C.S.: 522180
Gary J. Nation (Pres)
Michelle Bednarz (Dir-Mktg)
Edward Oresar (VP)

CENTRAL FIBER LLC
4814 Fiber Ln, Wellsville, KS 66092
Tel.: (785) 883-4600   DE
Web Site: http://www.centralfiber.com
Sales Range: $10-24.9 Million
Cellulose Fiber Products Mfr
N.A.I.C.S.: 322299
Darren Traub (Pres & CEO)

CENTRAL FINANCIAL HOLDINGS, INC.
20701 Bruce B Downs Blvd, Tampa, FL 33647
Tel.: (813) 929-4477
Web Site:
  http://www.centralbankfl.com
Sales Range: $10-24.9 Million
Emp.: 46
Bank Holding Company
N.A.I.C.S.: 551111
John Thompson (Pres & CEO)

Subsidiaries:

Central Bank   (1)
20701 Bruce B Downs Blvd, Tampa, FL 33647
Tel.: (813) 929-4477
Web Site: http://www.centralbankfl.com
Sales Range: $10-24.9 Million
Commericial Banking
N.A.I.C.S.: 522110
Pat Duval (Chief Compliance Officer, Officer-BSA, Sr VP & Mgr-HR)
Scott Mathew Kohler (Chief Lending Officer & Exec VP)
John Thompson (Pres & CEO)
Nileshkumar C. Patel (Chief Risk Officer, Officer-Information Security & Exec VP)
W. Russell Andersen (CFO & Exec VP)
Rob Montgomery (Officer-Bank Security & Branch Admin & Sr VP)
Jason Hatcher (Chief Credit Officer & Sr VP)

CENTRAL FLORIDA BEHAVIORAL HEALTH NETWORK INC
719 S US Hwy 301, Tampa, FL 33619
Tel.: (813) 740-4811   FL
Web Site: https://www.cfbhn.org
Year Founded: 1998
Sales Range: $125-149.9 Million
Emp.: 63
Behavioral Healthcare Services
N.A.I.C.S.: 623220
Linda J. McKinnon (CEO)
Julie Patel (CFO)
P. Lawrence Allen (COO)

CENTRAL FLORIDA CARES HEALTH SYSTEM, INC.
707 Mendham Blvd Ste 104, Orlando, FL 32825
Tel.: (407) 985-3560   FL
Web Site:
  http://www.centralfloridacares.org
Year Founded: 2003
Sales Range: $50-74.9 Million
Emp.: 16
Behavioral Healthcare Services
N.A.I.C.S.: 623220
Mike Lupton (CIO)
Trinity Schwab (Mgr-Contract)
Maria Bledsoe (CEO)
Debbie Owens (VP)
Robert Wayne Holmes (Sec)

CENTRAL FLORIDA ELECTRIC COOPERATIVE INC.
11491 NW 50th Ave, Chiefland, FL 32626-1704
Tel.: (352) 493-2511   FL
Web Site: https://www.cfec.com
Year Founded: 1939
Sales Range: $25-49.9 Million
Emp.: 93
Provides Electric Services
N.A.I.C.S.: 221122

CENTRAL FLORIDA FAMILY HEALTH CENTER, INC.
4930 E Lake Mary Blvd, Sanford, FL 32771
Tel.: (407) 322-8645   FL
Web Site:
  https://www.mytruehealth.org
Year Founded: 1977
Health Care Srvices
N.A.I.C.S.: 622110
Jim Merrill (CFO)
Latrice Stewart (CEO)
Hylan Boxer (Dir-Pharmacy)
Tasha Casaccio (Dir-Mktg & Promotions)
Jannelle Dunn (COO)
L. Karenna Senors (Chief Medical Officer)
Travis Cox (CIO)
Deana Montella (Dir-Nursing)
Michelle Aliotti (Dir-Dental)
Tatra Thomas (Dir-Outreach & Enrollment)
Audrey D. Nazario (Dir-HR)
Sheilly Rodriguez (Mgr-Lake Underhill)
Lillian Liz (Mgr-Hoffner)
Selenita Delgado (Mgr-Sanford)
Sheyla Almedina (Dir-Ops)
Joseph Lebert (Mgr-Clinical-Sanford)
Sameeha Jessa (Mgr-Clinical-Hoffner)
Mikerlange Pierre (Mgr-Clinical-Lake Underhill & Cheney Wellness Cottage)
Lakia Saunders (Mgr-Casselberry & True Health Express)

CENTRAL FLORIDA INVESTMENTS INC.
5601 Windhover Dr, Orlando, FL 32819-7914
Tel.: (407) 351-3350   FL
Web Site:
  http://www.westgateresorts.com
Year Founded: 1970
Sales Range: $800-899.9 Million
Emp.: 3,800
Subdividers & Developers; Timeshare Services
N.A.I.C.S.: 237210
David A. Siegel (Founder, Pres & CEO)
Tom Dugan (CFO)
Mark Waltrip (COO)
Barry W. Siegel (Exec VP-Sls)
Jim Gissy (Exec VP)
Michael Marder (Gen Counsel)

Subsidiaries:

CFI Hospitality Group, Inc.   (1)
5601 Windhover Dr, Orlando, FL 32819-7914   (100%)
Tel.: (407) 352-6690
Web Site: http://www.westgateresorts.com
Rev.: $1,500,000
Emp.: 200
Management Consulting Services
N.A.I.C.S.: 541613
David A. Siegel (Pres & CEO)

CENTRAL FLORIDA PARTNERSHIP, INC.

75 S Ivanhoe Blvd, Orlando, FL 32804
Tel.: (407) 835-8005   FL
Web Site: http://www.centralflorida
   partnership.org
Year Founded: 2007
Sales Range: $1-9.9 Million
Emp.: 21
Economic Development & Marketing
N.A.I.C.S.: 926110
Jacob V. Stuart *(Pres & CEO)*
Scott P. Fagan *(CFO & Dir-Fin Svcs)*
Lisa Winkelbauer *(Dir-Admin Svcs & Dir-Events)*
Randy Woodall *(Dir-IT)*
Ruth Z. Mustian *(Dir-Comm)*
Chad Osburn *(Dir-Art)*
Ric Castro *(Mgr-Bus Dev)*
Lisa Booth *(Mgr-Bus Dev)*
Randy Woodall *(Dir-IT)*
Chad Osburn *(Dir-Art)*
Kathleen M. Cole *(Dir-Membership Investment)*
Kathy Panter *(VP-IR)*
Scott P. Fagan *(CFO)*
Liz Chiarello *(Coord-Acctg)*
Joe Horan *(Mgr-Bus Dev)*
Michael L. Ketchum *(VP-Pub Policy)*
Amanda Muley *(Dir-IT)*
Evelynn Perlman *(Dir-Mktg & Comm)*
Danielle Permenter *(Dir-Bus Dev)*
Dena Sandy *(Mgr-Bus Dev)*
Lisa Winkelbauer *(Dir-Events)*

CENTRAL FLORIDA RE-GIONAL TRANSPORT AU-THORITY
455 N Garland Ave, Orlando, FL 32801
Tel.: (407) 841-2279
Web Site: https://www.golynx.com
Year Founded: 1972
Sales Range: $25-49.9 Million
Emp.: 940
Bus Line Operations
N.A.I.C.S.: 485113
Noranne Downs *(Sec)*
Ismael Rivera *(Pres-Transit Union)*
Jim Harrison *(Interim CEO)*

CENTRAL FLYING SERVICE INC.
1501 Bond Ave, Little Rock, AR 72202
Tel.: (501) 580-1755
Web Site: https://www.central.aero
Sales Range: $25-49.9 Million
Emp.: 100
Self-Propelled Aircraft
N.A.I.C.S.: 441227
Cris Wilkins *(Dir-Propeller Maintenance)*
Susan Holbert *(Pres & COO)*
Richard Holbert *(Chm & CEO)*

CENTRAL FOREST PROD-UCTS INC.
PO Box 18130, Phoenix, AZ 85005-8130
Tel.: (602) 353-9300
Web Site:
   http://www.centralforest.com
Sales Range: $25-49.9 Million
Emp.: 30
Lumber Brokerage
N.A.I.C.S.: 423310
Ron Jones *(Controller)*

CENTRAL FREIGHT LINES, INC.
5601 W Waco Dr, Waco, TX 76710
Tel.: (800) 782-5036   TX
Web Site:
   http://www.centralfreight.com
Year Founded: 1925

Interstate Motor Carrier Services
N.A.I.C.S.: 484121
Subsidiaries:
Volunteer Express, Inc.   (1)
1116 Polk Ave, Nashville, TN 37210
Tel.: (865) 637-2869
Web Site: http://www.volunteerexpress.com
General Freight, LTL & Truckload Services
N.A.I.C.S.: 484121
Chuck Jenkins *(Mgr)*

CENTRAL FUND OF ISRAEL
980 Avenue of the Americas 3rd Fl, New York, NY 10018-7809
Tel.: (212) 646-8105   NY
Year Founded: 1979
Sales Range: $10-24.9 Million
Fundraising Services
N.A.I.C.S.: 813211
Arthur Marcus *(VP)*
Jeff Most *(Treas)*
Jay Marcus *(VP)*
Hadassah K. Marcus *(Pres)*

CENTRAL GEORGIA EMC FOUNDATION, INC.
923 S Mulberry St, Jackson, GA 30233
Tel.: (770) 775-7857   GA
Web Site: http://www.cgemc.com
Year Founded: 1937
Sales Range: $100-124.9 Million
Emp.: 97
Electric Power Distr
N.A.I.C.S.: 221122
Jeff Greeson *(VP-IT)*
Herschel Arant *(Sr VP-Engrg & Ops)*
George Weaver *(Pres & CEO)*
Marilyn Webb *(Dir-IR)*
Ben Thomason *(Dir-Field Svcs)*
D. T. Hamil *(Chm)*
Warren E. Holder *(Vice Chm)*
D. A. Robinson III *(Treas & Sec)*

CENTRAL GEORGIA HEALTH SYSTEM INC.
777 Hemlock St, Macon, GA 31201-2102
Tel.: (478) 633-1000   GA
Web Site: http://www.mccg.org
Year Founded: 1994
Sales Range: $350-399.9 Million
Emp.: 5,000
Health Care Srvices
N.A.I.C.S.: 622110
Ninfa M. Saunders *(Pres & CEO)*
Kenneth B. Banks *(Gen Counsel & Sec)*
Robert M. DiRenzo *(COO & Exec VP)*
Susan W. Harris *(COO-The Medical Center-Navicent Health)*
Elbert T. McQueen *(Sr VP-Post Acute Svcs)*
Rhonda Perry *(CFO & Exec VP)*
Starr H. Purdue *(Chm)*
Subsidiaries:
Central Georgia Health Ventures, Inc.   (1)
691 Cherry St Ste 700, Macon, GA 31201
Tel.: (478) 633-6942
Sales Range: $10-24.9 Million
Emp.: 2
Power Laundries, Family & Commercial
N.A.I.C.S.: 812310
Medcen Community Health Foundation Inc.   (1)
858 High St, Macon, GA 31201-2007   (100%)
Tel.: (478) 633-1555
Web Site: http://www.medcenfoundation.org
Rev.: $430,000
Emp.: 7
Business Services
N.A.I.C.S.: 561990

Physicians Billing & Support Services   (1)
2490 Riverside Dr, Macon, GA 31204
Tel.: (478) 633-6600
Sales Range: $10-24.9 Million
Emp.: 27
Billing & Other Administrative Services
N.A.I.C.S.: 541219
The Medical Center of Central Georgia, Inc.   (1)
724 Hemlock St Ste A, Macon, GA 31201
Tel.: (478) 633-1547
Health Care Srvices
N.A.I.C.S.: 621999

CENTRAL GROCERS CO-OP
2600 W Haven Ave, Joliet, IL 60433-1427
Tel.: (847) 451-0660   IL
Web Site: http://www.central-grocers.com
Sales Range: $200-249.9 Million
Emp.: 500
Groceries Distr
N.A.I.C.S.: 424410
James Denges *(Pres & CEO)*

CENTRAL HARDWOODS, INC.
1959 W Northwest Hwy, Dallas, TX 75220
Tel.: (972) 241-3571   TX
Web Site:
   https://www.centralhardwoods.com
Sales Range: $10-24.9 Million
Emp.: 45
Millwork Services
N.A.I.C.S.: 423310
Jean McDaniel *(Sr VP)*
Clay Walker *(Mgr-Pur)*

CENTRAL ILLIANA AG INC.
200 Sharon St, Atlanta, IL 61723
Tel.: (217) 648-2307
Web Site: http://www.centralilag.com
Sales Range: $10-24.9 Million
Emp.: 80
Agricultural Equipment Dealer
N.A.I.C.S.: 424910
Steve Schmidt *(Co-Owner)*
Michael Schmidt *(Co-Owner)*
Dave Evans *(Co-Owner)*
Bill Marcotte *(Co-Owner)*

CENTRAL ILLINOIS AG INC.
200 Sharon St, Atlanta, IL 61723
Tel.: (217) 648-2307
Web Site:
   https://www.centralilag.com
Rev.: $17,757,837
Emp.: 24
Farm Equipment & Supplies
N.A.I.C.S.: 459999
Steven P. Schmidt *(Owner & Pres)*
Todd Birky *(Mgr-Svc)*

CENTRAL ILLINOIS STEEL COMPANY
21050 Rte 4, Carlinville, IL 62626-0078
Tel.: (217) 854-3251   IL
Year Founded: 1967
Sales Range: $75-99.9 Million
Emp.: 100
Steel Slitting, Shearing & Decoiling Steel Manufacture, Mine Roof Plates
N.A.I.C.S.: 332312
Dan Millard *(Pres, CEO & COO)*
Tim Millard *(VP)*
C.J. Millard *(Dir-Traffic)*
Tom Drake *(Mgr-Saftey)*
Angie Formea *(Sec)*
Subsidiaries:
C.I.S. Co. of Alabama   (1)
2600 Railroad Ave, Guntersville, AL 35976-1547   (100%)
Tel.: (256) 582-2021

Sales Range: $10-24.9 Million
Emp.: 12
Steel Processor
N.A.I.C.S.: 332312

CENTRAL ILLINOIS TRUCKS, INC.
200 W Northtown Rd, Normal, IL 61761
Tel.: (309) 452-8392
Web Site: https://www.cittrucks.com
Rev.: $70,000,000
Emp.: 310
Truck Tractors; Sales Parts Service
N.A.I.C.S.: 423110
Erick Miner *(Owner, Pres & Principal)*
Jan Nussbaum *(VP & Gen Mgr)*

CENTRAL INDIANA COMMU-NITY FOUNDATION
615 N Alabama St Ste 119, Indianapolis, IN 46204-1498
Tel.: (317) 634-2423   IN
Web Site: http://www.cicf.org
Year Founded: 1997
Sales Range: $50-74.9 Million
Emp.: 49
Community Development Services
N.A.I.C.S.: 624190
Brian Payne *(Pres & CEO)*
Gregory F. Hahn *(Chm)*

CENTRAL INDIANA HARD-WARE CO.
9190 Corporation Dr, Indianapolis, IN 46256
Tel.: (317) 558-5700
Web Site: http://www.cih-indy.com
Year Founded: 1951
Sales Range: $25-49.9 Million
Emp.: 60
Provider of Builders' Materials
N.A.I.C.S.: 423710
Scott Erler *(Project Mgr-Sls)*
Bruce Volkel *(Mgr-Warehouse Sls)*
Howard Shook *(Mgr-Sls)*
Keith Allen *(Project Mgr)*
Ryan Schafhauser *(Project Mgr)*
Kelly Swangin *(Project Mgr)*

CENTRAL INK CORPORATION
1100 Harvester Rd, West Chicago, IL 60185-1608
Tel.: (630) 231-6500   IL
Web Site: https://www.cicink.com
Year Founded: 1968
Sales Range: $10-24.9 Million
Emp.: 97
Mfr of Printing Inks
N.A.I.C.S.: 325910
Greg Dahleen *(Pres)*
Scott Feigleson *(CFO)*

CENTRAL INVESTMENT LLC
4600 McAuley Pl Ste 320, Cincinnati, OH 45242
Tel.: (513) 563-4700
Web Site:
   http://www.centralinvestment.com
Sales Range: $150-199.9 Million
Emp.: 20
Soft Drinks Packaged In Cans & Bottles
N.A.I.C.S.: 312111
Steve Allison *(VP-Ops)*
Carl Myers *(Treas & VP)*
Fred Vickery *(Controller)*
Manny Zapata *(VP)*
Saran Soonthornsawad *(Dir-IT)*

CENTRAL IOWA POWER CO-OPERATIVE
1400 Hwy 13 SE, Cedar Rapids, IA 52403
Tel.: (319) 366-8011   IA
Web Site: https://www.cipco.net

Central Iowa Power Cooperative—(Continued)
Year Founded: 1946
Sales Range: $125-149.9 Million
Emp.: 120
Electronic Services
N.A.I.C.S.: 221122
Richard L. Anderson *(Sr VP-Utility Ops)*
Michelle Soyer *(Controller)*
Terry Sullivan *(CFO & VP)*
Dusky Terry *(VP-Growth Strategies)*
Janel Cerwick *(VP-Human Capital)*
Paul Hofman *(VP-IT)*
Bill Cherrier *(CEO & Exec VP)*
Gary Slaby *(VP-Utility Ops)*

Subsidiaries:

CMA Ventures, Inc.   (1)
2600 Grand Ave Ste 410, Des Moines, IA 50312
Tel.: (515) 309-3018
Web Site: http://www.cmaventures.net
Emp.: 2
Investment Management Service
N.A.I.C.S.: 523940
James B. Fogt *(Pres & CFO)*
Dustin L. Thomas *(VP)*

Subsidiary (Domestic):

Legosys Solutions, LLC   (2)
5435 NW 100th St Ste 201, Johnston, IA 50131
Tel.: (877) 933-5172
Web Site: http://www.legosyssolutions.com
Investment Management Service
N.A.I.C.S.: 523940
Paul Mumford *(VP-Client Mgmt)*

Central Iowa Energy Cooperative (1)
1400 Hwy 13 SE, Cedar Rapids, IA 52403
Tel.: (319) 366-8011
Web Site: http://www.cipco.net
Sales Range: $50-74.9 Million
Energy Cooperative Holding Company
N.A.I.C.S.: 551112
Andrew St. John *(CFO & VP)*

Subsidiary (Domestic):

Capital Management Associates Inc.   (2)
2600 Grand Ave Ste 410, Des Moines, IA 50312-5300
Tel.: (515) 288-3035
Web Site: http://www.cma-inc.net
Sales Range: $10-24.9 Million
Emp.: 3
Business Financial Services
N.A.I.C.S.: 561499
Howard R. Harris II *(Exec VP & Sr Principal)*

CENTRAL IQ, INC.
14527 Cotswolds Dr, Tampa, FL 33626-3369
Tel.: (813) 920-4001
Web Site: http://www.centraliq.com
Year Founded: 2006
Sales Range: $10-24.9 Million
Emp.: 204
Management Consulting Services
N.A.I.C.S.: 541611
Synthia Laura Molina *(Founder & Mng Partner)*

CENTRAL IRRIGATION SUPPLY INC.
8 Williams St, Elmsford, NY 10523-2515
Tel.: (914) 347-5656
Web Site:
   http://www.centralirrigation.com
Rev.: $14,797,468
Emp.: 24
Irrigation Equipment
N.A.I.C.S.: 423820
Bernardo Luciano *(Pres)*
Ralph Sepe *(Controller)*

CENTRAL LAKES COOPERATIVE
16319 Hwy 12 NE, Atwater, MN 56209
Tel.: (320) 974-8868
Web Site:
   http://www.centrallakescoop.com
Sales Range: $1-9.9 Million
Emp.: 45
Petroleum Bulk Stations
N.A.I.C.S.: 424710
Andy VanDerBill *(Treas & Sec)*
LeRoy Christensen *(Vice Chm)*
Frans Rosenquist *(Chm)*
Dave Hentges *(Mgr-Agronomy Ops)*
Dennis Just *(Mgr-Petroleum)*
Deb Knudsen *(Office Mgr)*
Mitch Altermatt *(CEO)*
Shane Steinbeisser *(Mgr-Midas Auto Svc)*

CENTRAL LINCOLN PEOPLE'S UTILITY DISTRICT
2129 N Coast HWY, Newport, OR 97365-0090
Tel.: (541) 265-3211   OR
Web Site: https://www.clpud.org
Year Founded: 1943
Sales Range: $75-99.9 Million
Emp.: 130
Electric Utility
N.A.I.C.S.: 221121
Judy Matheny *(VP)*

CENTRAL MAINE MOTORS AUTO GROUP
420 Kennedy Memorial Dr, Waterville, ME 04901-4519
Tel.: (207) 872-5591
Web Site:
   http://www.cmautogroup.com
Year Founded: 1935
Sales Range: $10-24.9 Million
Emp.: 80
New Car Dealers
N.A.I.C.S.: 441110
Eric Beckim *(Gen Mgr-Parts)*
Scott Pinnette *(Gen Mgr-Sls-Chrysler)*
Jeff Caron *(Mgr-Svc)*
Chris Wescott *(Mgr-Toyota Parts)*
Joe Brooks *(Mgr-Svc)*

CENTRAL MEDICAL EQUIPMENT RENTALS
2850 Douglas Rd Fl 3, Coral Gables, FL 33134
Tel.: (305) 441-0156
Web Site: http://www.empmed.com
Rev.: $47,000,000
Emp.: 87
Medical Equipment Rental
N.A.I.C.S.: 532283
Raul Cabrera *(CFO & VP-Fin)*
Osvaldo De la Pedraja Jr. *(Pres & CEO)*

CENTRAL MICHIGAN PAPER COMPANY
6194 Fulton St E, Ada, MI 49301
Tel.: (616) 676-9203
Web Site: http://www.cmpaper.com
Year Founded: 1885
Sales Range: $10-24.9 Million
Emp.: 50
Wholesale Distributor of Fine Paper
N.A.I.C.S.: 424110
James S. Barbour *(VP-Sls)*
Chuck Oleniczak *(Dir-Specification Sls)*
Richard A. Zemovich *(VP-Sls)*

CENTRAL MICHIGAN UNIVERSITY
1200 S Franklin St, Mount Pleasant, MI 48859
Tel.: (989) 774-4000
Web Site: https://www.cmich.edu
Year Founded: 1892

Colleges & Universities
N.A.I.C.S.: 611310
Sarah R. Opperman *(Vice Chm)*
Steven Johnson *(VP-Enrollment & Student Svcs)*
Kathleen Wilbur *(VP-Dev & External Rels)*
Mary Jane Flanagan *(Sec)*
Marcy Weston *(Interim Assoc VP & Dir-Athletics)*
Bob Davies *(Pres)*
Jonathan Webb *(Assoc VP-Facilities Mgmt)*
Lori Hella *(Assoc VP-HR)*
Mary Hill *(Interim VP-Fin & Admin Svcs, Controller & Assoc VP-Fin Svcs & Reporting)*

CENTRAL MILLING COMPANY
122 E Center St, Logan, UT 84321
Tel.: (435) 752-6625
Web Site:
   https://www.centralmilling.com
Year Founded: 1867
Sales Range: $25-49.9 Million
Emp.: 100
Flour & Grain Product Mfr
N.A.I.C.S.: 311212
Weston Fred *(Founder)*
Keith Giusto *(VP-Sls)*
Joni Harrison *(Mgr-Fin)*

CENTRAL MILLS INC.
1400 Broadway Ste 1605 Fl 16, New York, NY 10018-3405
Tel.: (212) 764-9011
Web Site: http://www.freeze-ny.com
Year Founded: 1986
Sales Range: $25-49.9 Million
Emp.: 200
Provider of Clothing
N.A.I.C.S.: 315250
Charles Gebele *(CFO)*

CENTRAL MINE EQUIPMENT COMPANY
4215 Rider Trl N, Saint Louis, MO 63045-1106
Tel.: (314) 291-7700
Web Site: https://www.cmeco.com
Rev.: $17,300,000
Emp.: 200
Mining Machinery
N.A.I.C.S.: 333131
Roberta Rassieur *(Owner)*
David Neibert *(Pres)*
Donald Siress *(CFO)*

CENTRAL MINNESOTA DIAGNOSTIC INC.
150 10th St NW, Milaca, MN 56353-1221
Tel.: (320) 983-6300   MN
Web Site: http://www.cmdi.org
Year Founded: 1986
Sales Range: $25-49.9 Million
Healtcare Services
N.A.I.C.S.: 622110

CENTRAL MINNESOTA FABRICATING INC.
2725 Gorton Ave W, Willmar, MN 56201-2381
Tel.: (320) 235-4181   MN
Web Site: https://www.cmf-inc.com
Year Founded: 1973
Sales Range: $10-24.9 Million
Emp.: 95
Provider of Fabricated Structural Metal
N.A.I.C.S.: 332312
Cathy Hedlof *(Gen Mgr)*

CENTRAL MISSOURI AGRI-SERVICE LLC
211 N Lyon, Marshall, MO 65340

Tel.: (660) 886-6976
Web Site: https://www.cm-as.com
Sales Range: $10-24.9 Million
Emp.: 66
Equipment Rental & Leasing
N.A.I.C.S.: 532490
John Fletcher *(Pres & Gen Mgr)*

CENTRAL MONTANA MEDICAL CENTER
408 Wendell Ave, Lewistown, MT 59457
Tel.: (406) 535-7711   MT
Web Site: http://www.cmmccares.net
Year Founded: 1971
Sales Range: $25-49.9 Million
Emp.: 441
Community Health Care Services
N.A.I.C.S.: 621498

CENTRAL MOTOR WHEEL OF AMERICA
125 Wheat Dr, Paris, KY 40361-2502
Tel.: (859) 987-0500
Web Site: https://www.cmwa.com
Year Founded: 1986
Sales Range: $25-49.9 Million
Emp.: 575
Motor Vehicle Wheels Mfr
N.A.I.C.S.: 336390
Mike Lewis *(VP & Gen Mgr-Steel Div)*
Tom Taylor *(Gen Mgr)*
Jay Jacoby *(Coord-Production)*
John Kirkpatrick *(Mgr-Engrg)*
Ken Holland *(Coord-Trng)*
Lynn Northcutt *(Mgr-Pur)*
Ryan Passage *(Coord-IT)*

CENTRAL MOVING & STORAGE CO.
256 W 36th St 3rd Fl, New York, NY 10018
Tel.: (212) 268-8989
Web Site:
   http://www.centralmoving.com
Sales Range: $10-24.9 Million
Emp.: 75
Commercial Moving & Storage Services
N.A.I.C.S.: 484110
Dennis Farrell *(Pres)*

CENTRAL MUTUAL INSURANCE COMPANY
800 S Washington St, Van Wert, OH 45891-2357
Tel.: (419) 238-1010   OH
Web Site: http://www.central-insurance.com
Year Founded: 1876
Rev.: $290,500,000
Emp.: 550
Property & Casualty Insurance Services
N.A.I.C.S.: 524126
Laura Ditto *(Mgr-Mktg Comm)*
P. W. Purmort *(Chm & Pres)*
Keith Goad *(CFO)*

Subsidiaries:

All America Insurance Company (1)
800 S Washington St, Van Wert, OH 45891-2357
Tel.: (419) 238-1010
Web Site: http://www.cmi.com
Sales Range: $100-124.9 Million
Emp.: 500
Property & Casualty Insurance
N.A.I.C.S.: 524210
Keith Goad *(CFO)*

CMI Lloyds   (1)
7301 N State Hwy 161 Ste 320, Irving, TX 75039-3005
                                  (100%)
Tel.: (419) 238-1010
Web Site: http://www.central-insurance.com

Sales Range: $50-74.9 Million
Emp.: 60
Insurance Agents
N.A.I.C.S.: 524126
Bill Purmort III *(Pres & CEO)*

Central Mutual Insurance Central Regional Office (1)
800 S Washington St, Van Wert, OH 45891-2357
Tel.: (419) 238-1010
Web Site: http://www.cmi.com
Sales Range: $25-49.9 Million
Emp.: 300
Property & Casualty Insurance
N.A.I.C.S.: 459210
Bill Permort *(Pres & CEO)*
Jeff Hanson *(CFO)*

CENTRAL NATIONAL BANK
800 SE Quincy St, Topeka, KS 66612
Tel.: (785) 238-4114
Web Site:
https://www.centralnational.com
Year Founded: 1884
Sales Range: $25-49.9 Million
Emp.: 20
Banking Services
N.A.I.C.S.: 522110
Robert Munson *(Pres)*
Jason Ray *(VP & Mgr-Farm)*

CENTRAL NATIONAL BANK
209 Clayton Ave, Poteau, OK 74953
Tel.: (918) 647-2233
Web Site: http://www.cnbpoteau.com
Rev.: $10,117,000
Emp.: 80
National Commercial Banks
N.A.I.C.S.: 522110
Chris Fenton *(Pres)*
Tracey Smith *(VP)*
Dusty Alexander *(VP)*
Mike Hall *(Exec VP)*
Sharron Whitlock *(VP)*
Stephen B. Holton *(Chm & CEO)*
Johnny Baker *(Exec VP)*
Steve Clay *(Sr VP)*
Ron Hall *(VP)*
Sherry Keisman *(Sr VP)*
Debbie Goines *(Asst VP)*
Pam Mullins *(Sr VP)*
Joe Allen *(VP)*
Carla Anglen *(Sr VP)*
Laura Taylor *(Sr VP)*
Stefanie Raines *(VP)*

CENTRAL NATIONAL BANK OF ENID
324 W Broadway Ave, Enid, OK 73701
Tel.: (580) 233-3535   OK
Web Site: http://www.cnb-ok.com
Year Founded: 1913
National Commercial Banks
N.A.I.C.S.: 522110
Todd Earl *(Pres-Market)*
Dennis Gerhard *(Exec VP & Ops Mgr)*
Justin Lee *(Sr VP)*

CENTRAL NATIONAL GOTTESMAN INC.
3 Manhattanville Rd, Purchase, NY 10577-2123
Tel.: (914) 696-9000   NY
Web Site: https://www.cng-inc.com
Year Founded: 1886
Emp.: 3,100
Printing & Writing Paper Merchant Wholesalers
N.A.I.C.S.: 424110
Jan Gottesman *(Pres-Kelly Spicer Inc.)*
Kenneth L. Wallach *(Exec Chm)*
Steven M. Eigen *(CFO)*
Michael T. M. Jones *(Co-Pres-Central National)*

J. Warren Pullen *(Co-Pres-Central National)*
Andrew Wallach *(Pres & CEO)*
William Meany *(Pres-Lindenmeyr Munroe)*
Cory Turner *(Pres-Spicers Canada)*
Peter Harding *(Pres-Lindenmeyr Central & Lindenmeyr Book Publishing Papers)*
Tom Clarkson *(VP-Sls)*

Subsidiaries:

**Central National Gottesman Inc. -
Central National Division** (1)
3 Manhattanville Rd, Purchase, NY 10577-2123
Tel.: (914) 696-9000
Web Site: http://www.cndivision.com
Packaging Paper Products Mfr
N.A.I.C.S.: 322220

Subsidiary (Non-US):

Central National Espanola S.A. (2)
Manuel Pombo Angulo 18-3 Puerta 9, Madrid, Spain
Tel.: (34) 917990979
Web Site: http://www.cndivision.com
Sales Range: $10-24.9 Million
Emp.: 3
Paper Whslr
N.A.I.C.S.: 424110
Hugo Carrillo *(Dir-Sls)*

Central National Gottesman Europe GmbH (2)
Altmannsdorfer Strasse 74, Vienna, 1120, Austria
Tel.: (43) 16006310
Web Site: http://www.cng-europe.com
Sales Range: $10-24.9 Million
Emp.: 30
Paper Goods Mfr
N.A.I.C.S.: 322299
Franz Buchtele *(Mng Dir)*
Josef Felsinger *(Dir-Fin)*

Italian American Corp. (1)
1515 Alvarado St, San Leandro, CA 94577-2640
Tel.: (510) 877-9000
Web Site: http://www.amerpkg.com
Industrial & Personal Service Paper Merchant Whslr
N.A.I.C.S.: 424130
Howard Edelman *(VP-Mktg)*
Kaye Leedham Herning *(Pres)*

Kelly Spicers Inc. (1)
12310 E Slauson Ave, Santa Fe Springs, CA 90670-2629   (100%)
Tel.: (562) 698-1199
Web Site: https://kellyspicers.com
Fine Paper Products Supplier
N.A.I.C.S.: 424110
Jan Gottesman *(Pres)*
Damien Bradley *(Sr VP-Print & Wide Format)*
Rick Anderson *(Sr VP)*
Rod Schaar *(Sr VP-Sls & Stores & Ops)*
John Luyben *(Sr VP-Pkg)*

Subsidiary (Domestic):

J.C. Paper (2)
47422 Kato Road, Fremont, CA 94538
Tel.: (510) 476-7770
Web Site: http://www.jcpaper.com
Printing & Service Paper Products Whslr
N.A.I.C.S.: 424110
Dennis Savage *(Sls Mgr)*

Kilmer Wagner And Wise Paper Co. Inc. (2)
12751 Monarch St, Garden Grove, CA 92841
Tel.: (714) 892-3380
Packaging, Shipping & Janitorial Supplies Mfr
N.A.I.C.S.: 322219

Premiere Packaging Industries, Inc. (2)
16401 Berwyn Rd, Cerritos, CA 90703
Tel.: (562) 799-9200
Web Site:
http://www.premierepackaging.com

Packaging & Labeling Services
N.A.I.C.S.: 561910

Subsidiary (Non-US):

Spicers Canada ULC (2)
200 Galcat Drive, Vaughan, L4L 0B9, ON, Canada
Tel.: (905) 265-5000
Web Site: http://www.spicers.ca
Emp.: 500
Fine Paper, Graphic Arts, Sign & Display & Industrial Packaging Equipment Distr
N.A.I.C.S.: 424110
Cory Turner *(Pres)*
Meherab Chothia *(VP-Fin & Admin)*
Jason Schneider *(VP-Western Canada)*
Christine Jacques *(VP-Eastern Canada)*
Tim Soro *(VP-Ops & IT)*
Carolyne Daly *(VP)*
Melanie Payne *(VP)*
James Tovell *(VP)*

Subsidiary (Domestic):

Shippers Supply Inc (3)
5219 47th St NW, Edmonton, T6B 3N4, AB, Canada
Tel.: (780) 444-7777
Web Site: http://www.shipperssupply.com
Packaging Supply & Warehouse Equipment Mfr
N.A.I.C.S.: 333993
Ron Brown *(Pres)*
Jerry Wertypora *(VP-Ops & Pur)*
Ruth Spetter *(VP-Mktg & Corp Dev)*
Jerry Pierce *(VP-Sls)*

Lewis Paper International Inc. (1)
1400 S Wolf Rd Ste 100, Wheeling, IL 60090-3225
Tel.: (847) 808-1343
Web Site: http://www.lewispaper.com
Sales Range: $25-49.9 Million
Emp.: 158
Provider of Printing & Writing Paper
N.A.I.C.S.: 424110
Richard Lewis *(Chm)*
Dennis Scholtens *(Asst Gen Mgr)*
Mike Gilbert *(Mgr-Sls)*

Lindenmeyr Book Publishing Papers (1)
521 5th Ave 6th Fl, New York, NY 10175
Tel.: (212) 551-3900
Web Site: http://www.lindenmeyrbook.com
Emp.: 20
Book Publishing Paper Distr
N.A.I.C.S.: 424130
Janet McCarthy Grimm *(VP)*

Lindenmeyr Central (1)
3 Manhattanville Rd, Purchase, NY 10577-2123   (100%)
Tel.: (914) 696-9300
Web Site: http://www.lindenmeyrcentral.com
Sales Range: $25-49.9 Million
Emp.: 200
Magazine & Commercial Marketing Paper Distr
N.A.I.C.S.: 424130
Robert G. McBride *(Exec VP)*
Timothy Christie *(VP-Sls-East)*
Robert Mckeown *(VP-Sls-West)*
Anne Kallaher *(Dir-Sls)*

Lindenmeyr Munroe (1)
3 Manhattanville Rd, Purchase, NY 10577
Tel.: (914) 696-9000
Web Site: http://www.lindenmeyr.com
Business & Commercial Printing Paper Distr
N.A.I.C.S.: 424110
Rich Cohen *(Mgr-Bus Dev)*
William Meany *(Pres)*
Christopher Johnston *(VP-Fin)*

Subsidiary (Domestic):

Ship-Pac Corp. (2)
460 Riverside St, Portland, ME 04103
Tel.: (207) 797-7444
Web Site: http://www.maineshipping.com
Rev.: $6,624,000
Emp.: 8
Industrial & Personal Service Paper Merchant Whslr
N.A.I.C.S.: 424130
Jeff Bryant *(Pres)*

Wilcox Paper LLC (2)

11100 Jefferson Hwy N, Champlin, MN 55316
Tel.: (763) 404-8400
Web Site: http://www.wilcoxpaper.com
Gasoline Engine & Engine Parts Mfr
N.A.I.C.S.: 336310
Terry Hudy *(Owner)*

CENTRAL NEBRASKA PUBLIC POWER & IRRIGATION DISTRICT, INC.
415 Lincoln St, Holdrege, NE 68949
Tel.: (308) 995-8601   NE
Web Site: https://www.cnppid.com
Year Founded: 1933
Sales Range: $10-24.9 Million
Emp.: 100
Electric & Other Services Combined
N.A.I.C.S.: 221118
David L. Rowe *(Pres)*
Robert Dahlgren *(Sec)*
Mike Drain *(Mgr-Natural Resources)*
Devin Brundage *(Gen Mgr)*
Ron Fowler *(VP)*
Marty Mueller *(Treas)*

CENTRAL NEW YORK AGENCY, LLC
7337 Oswego Rd, Liverpool, NY 13090
Tel.: (315) 802-4606
Web Site: http://www.cnyagency.com
Year Founded: 1986
Insurance Agencies & Brokerages
N.A.I.C.S.: 524210

CENTRAL NEW YORK REGIONAL TRANSPORTATION AUTHORITY
200 Cortland Ave, Syracuse, NY 13205-0820
Tel.: (315) 442-3333
Web Site: https://www.centro.org
Year Founded: 1970
Sales Range: $25-49.9 Million
Emp.: 675
Public Transportation Administration
N.A.I.C.S.: 926120
Darlene D. Lattimore *(Sec)*
Brian M. Shultz *(Chm)*
Christine Locurto *(CFO)*
Robert F. Cuculich *(Treas)*
Joseph DeGray *(Sr VP-Transit Ops)*
Robert LoCurto *(COO)*

Subsidiaries:

C.N.Y Centro Inc. (1)
200 Cortland Ave, Syracuse, NY 13205-3423
Tel.: (315) 442-3333
Web Site: http://www.central.org
Sales Range: $25-49.9 Million
Emp.: 500
Local & Suburban Transit
N.A.I.C.S.: 485113
Steve Koegel *(Dir-Mktg)*

Centro Auburn (1)
5 Frank Smith St, Auburn, NY 13021-1145
Tel.: (315) 253-5765
Web Site: http://www.centro.org
Sales Range: $10-24.9 Million
Emp.: 14
Regional Bus Charter Service
N.A.I.C.S.: 485510
Geoff Hoff *(Dir-Facilities Ops)*

Centro Call-A-Bus Inc. (1)
200 Cortland Ave, Syracuse, NY 13202-3423
Tel.: (315) 442-3300
Web Site: http://www.centro.org
Sales Range: $10-24.9 Million
Emp.: 25
Operators Of Local & Suburban Transit
N.A.I.C.S.: 485113
Frank Kobliski *(Exec Dir)*

Centro Parking, Inc. (1)
1 Centro Center 200 Cortland Ave, Syracuse, NY 13205

Central New York Regional Transportation Authority—(Continued)

Tel.: (315) 442-3333
Parking Garage Operator
N.A.I.C.S.: 812930

Centro of Oswego, Inc.   (1)
512 E Seneca St, Oswego, NY 13126
Tel.: (315) 342-4400
Rural Bus Transportation Services
N.A.I.C.S.: 485210

Intermodal Transportation Center, Inc.   (1)
1001 Jones St, Fort Worth, TX 76102
Tel.: (817) 215-8654
Bus Transportation Services
N.A.I.C.S.: 485210

CENTRAL OHIO DIABETES ASSOCIATION
1699 W Mound St, Columbus, OH 43201
Tel.: (614) 884-4400   OH
Web Site:
    http://www.diabetesohio.org
Year Founded: 1964
Non Profit Organization
N.A.I.C.S.: 813212
Tim Cotter (Pres)

Subsidiaries:

LifeCare Alliance   (1)
1699 W Mound St, Columbus, OH 43223
Tel.: (614) 278-3130
Web Site: http://www.lifecarealliance.org
Health Care Srvices
N.A.I.C.S.: 621610
Charles W. Gehring (Pres & CEO)
Mildred Gain (CFO & VP)
John Gregory (Sr VP-Ops)

CENTRAL OHIO FARMERS COOPERATIVE
730 Bellefontaine Ave, Marion, OH 43302-6104
Tel.: (740) 382-9610   OH
Web Site:
    http://www.centralohfarm.com
Year Founded: 1934
Sales Range: $50-74.9 Million
Emp.: 96
Grain & Field Beans
N.A.I.C.S.: 424510
Cheryl Crawford (Sec)

CENTRAL OHIO HEALTH CARE CONSORTIUM
200 S Hamilton Rd, Gahanna, OH 43230
Tel.: (614) 786-7353   OH
Year Founded: 1992
Sales Range: $10-24.9 Million
Health Insurance Services
N.A.I.C.S.: 524114
Lori Trego (Vice Chm)
Jennifer Teal (Treas)
Vikki Stoneking (Sec)

CENTRAL OIL & SUPPLY CORPORATION
2300 Booth St, Monroe, LA 71203-8314
Tel.: (318) 388-2602   LA
Web Site: http://www.central-oil.com
Year Founded: 1967
Sales Range: $25-49.9 Million
Emp.: 300
Petroleum Bulk Stations & Terminals
N.A.I.C.S.: 424710
Kathryn Reppond (Controller)
Conroy Hines (Mgr-Fuel)
John Hardeman Cordell Sr. (Pres)

Subsidiaries:

Central Oil & Supply Corp Shreveport   (1)

1111 North Market St, Shreveport, LA 71107   (100%)
Tel.: (318) 525-1244
Web Site: http://www.central-oil.com
Sales Range: Less than $1 Million
Emp.: 15
Petroleum & Fuel Distr
N.A.I.C.S.: 457210
J. Hardeman Cordell (Pres)

CENTRAL PAPER COMPANY INC.
140 W Oxmoor Rd, Birmingham, AL 35209
Tel.: (205) 942-6333
Web Site: https://www.centralpaper-al.com
Rev.: $17,900,000
Emp.: 85
Industrial & Personal Service Paper Merchant Whslr
N.A.I.C.S.: 424130
Paul Ross (Founder)

CENTRAL PARK MEDIA CORP.
250 W 57th St Ste 317, New York, NY 10107
Tel.: (212) 977-7456
Rev.: $12,000,000
Emp.: 20
Video Tape Production
N.A.I.C.S.: 512110

CENTRAL PARK WEST DENTISTRY PC
25 W 68th St Ste 1A, New York, NY 10023
Tel.: (212) 579-8885
Web Site:
    https://www.cpwdentistry.com
Year Founded: 2000
Sales Range: $1-9.9 Million
Emp.: 50
Dentist Center Operator
N.A.I.C.S.: 621210
John F. Lhota (Owner)
Holly Mitchell (Dir-Mktg)

CENTRAL PAYMENT
2350 Kerner Blvd Ste 300, San Rafael, CA 94901
Tel.: (415) 462-8335
Web Site: http://www.cpay.com
Year Founded: 2005
Sales Range: $25-49.9 Million
Emp.: 98
Processing of Credits, Debits & Gift Cards
N.A.I.C.S.: 522320
Matthew Hyman (Co-Founder & Mng Partner)
Zachary Hyman (Co-Founder & Mng Partner)
John Hinkle (Gen Counsel & CFO)

CENTRAL PENNSYLVANIA MEDICAL FOUNDATION
620 Howard Ave Altoona Hospital Campus, Altoona, PA 16601-4899
Tel.: (814) 889-4100   PA
Year Founded: 1982
Financial Support Services
N.A.I.C.S.: 525990
Benjamin Levine Jr. (Chm & Pres)

CENTRAL PLASTICS & RUBBER CO., INC.
3320 W Vernon Ave, Phoenix, AZ 85009
Tel.: (602) 268-6368   OK
Web Site:
    https://www.centralplastic.com
Year Founded: 1960
Sales Range: $10-24.9 Million
Emp.: 12
Plastic Fabrications
N.A.I.C.S.: 326199

Robert Weiss (Pres)

CENTRAL POWER DISTRIBUTORS
3801 Thurston Ave, Anoka, MN 55303
Tel.: (763) 576-0901
Web Site: http://www.cpdonline.com
Sales Range: $10-24.9 Million
Emp.: 50
Air-Cooled Engines & Parts
N.A.I.C.S.: 423830
John Schaller (Pres)
Tyler Nelson (Controller)
Paul Siemieniak (Mgr-Customer Svcs)
John Hedges (Dir-Sls & Mktg)

CENTRAL POWER SYSTEMS & SERVICES
9200 Liberty Dr, Liberty, MO 64068
Tel.: (816) 781-8070
Web Site: https://www.cpower.com
Sales Range: $50-74.9 Million
Emp.: 200
Diesel Engines & Parts
N.A.I.C.S.: 423830
Russell Redburn (Pres)
Bill Allen (CFO)

CENTRAL RESEARCH, INC.
122 N Bloomington Ste I, Lowell, AR 72745
Tel.: (479) 419-5456
Web Site: http://www.central-research.com
Year Founded: 2002
Sales Range: $1-9.9 Million
Emp.: 55
Administrative Management & Data Processing Services
N.A.I.C.S.: 541611
Scott Dillard (Founder & Chm)
Paul Nesbit (COO)
Bobby McKinnon (Pres & CEO)
Andra Grasis (COO & Sr VP-Ops-Mgmt Solutions)
Barry Wells Jr. (VP-Ops)

Subsidiaries:

Global Emergency Resources, LLC   (1)
2917 Professional Pkwy Ste A, Augusta, GA 30907-3204
Tel.: (706) 869-6911
Web Site: http://www.ger911.com
Computer Facilities Management Services
N.A.I.C.S.: 541513
Stan Kuzia (Founder, Chm & CEO)

Skyline Ultd, Inc.   (1)
16333 S Great Ste 121, Round Rock, TX 78681
Tel.: (703) 671-9200
Web Site: http://www.skyline-ultd.com
Sales Range: $1-9.9 Million
Emp.: 15
Computer System Design Services
N.A.I.C.S.: 541512
Joel Rhoades (CEO)
Keith Daniel (COO)
Tom Do (VP-Bus Dev)
Gary D. Boward (VP & Program Mgr-Medical Case Mgmt Program)
John Labash (VP & Program Mgr-Taa)
Mike Sumrall (CEO)
W. Mike Smith (VP & Mgr-Group-Multi Awards Schedules)

CENTRAL RURAL ELECTRIC COOPERATIVE
3304 S Boomer Rd, Stillwater, OK 74074
Tel.: (405) 372-2884   OK
Web Site: http://www.crec.coop
Year Founded: 1938
Sales Range: $50-74.9 Million
Emp.: 168
Electric Power Distribution Services

N.A.I.C.S.: 221122
David Swank (CEO)
Michelle Perzee (Chief Performance Officer)
Randy Jarvis (VP-Corp Dev)
Steve Henderson (VP-Safety & Facilities)
Candace Calloway (VP-Member Rels)
Jillianne Tebow (COO)
Stephanie Rossander (VP-Fin)
Hunter Robinson (VP-System Ops)
Karen Hendren (CFO)

CENTRAL SAVINGS BANK
511 Bingham Ave, Sault Sainte Marie, MI 49783
Tel.: (906) 635-6250   MI
Web Site:
    http://www.centralsavingsbank.com
Year Founded: 1904
Sales Range: $10-24.9 Million
Emp.: 75
State Commercial Bank
N.A.I.C.S.: 522110
W. W. La Joie (Chm)
Ron Meister (Pres & CEO)
Mark Ruotsala (CFO)

CENTRAL SEMICONDUCTOR CORP
145 Adams Ave, Hauppauge, NY 11788
Tel.: (631) 435-1040
Web Site:
    https://www.centralsemi.com
Year Founded: 1974
Sales Range: $10-24.9 Million
Emp.: 90
Electronic Circuits Mfr
N.A.I.C.S.: 334413

CENTRAL SERVICE ASSOCIATION
93 S Coley Rd, Tupelo, MS 38801
Tel.: (662) 842-5962
Web Site: https://www.csa1.com
Year Founded: 1938
Sales Range: $10-24.9 Million
Emp.: 120
Computer Integrated Systems Design
N.A.I.C.S.: 541512
Betty Landers (Dir-Mktg)
Scott Blassingame (Treas & Sec)
Tom Underwood (Gen Mgr)
Roger Smith (Dir-Bus Dev)

CENTRAL SHIPPEE, INC.
46 Star Lake Rd, Bloomingdale, NJ 07403
Tel.: (973) 838-1100   NJ
Web Site:
    http://www.centralshippee.com
Year Founded: 1926
Sales Range: $75-99.9 Million
Emp.: 25
Felt, Fabrics & Accessories Mfr
N.A.I.C.S.: 424990
Donald A. Hubner (Chm & CEO)
E. Brower (CFO)

Subsidiaries:

Allied Felt Group   (1)
46 Star Lake Rd, Bloomingdale, NJ 07403-1244
Tel.: (973) 838-1616
Web Site: http://www.thefeltpeople.com
Sales Range: $75-99.9 Million
Emp.: 12
Felt for Crafts & Hobbies
N.A.I.C.S.: 424990

CENTRAL SOUTH DISTRIBUTION, INC.
3730 Vulcan Dr, Nashville, TN 37211-3314

Tel.: (615) 833-5960 TN
Web Site:
http://www.centraldistribution.com
Year Founded: 1970
Sales Range: $10-24.9 Million
Emp.: 30
Provider of Recorded Music
N.A.I.C.S.: 423990
Randall L. Davidson *(CEO)*
Greg Davidson *(CFO)*
Chuck Adams *(Pres)*
John P. Bennett *(VP-Distr)*

CENTRAL STATE CONSTRUCTION, CORPORATION
15358 E Clarksville Rd, Marshall, IL 62441
Tel.: (217) 826-6152
Web Site:
http://www.centralstateco.com
Electrical & Plumbing Services
N.A.I.C.S.: 238220
Jack Acord *(Pres)*
Larry Yargus *(CEO)*

Subsidiaries:

Hannig Construction, Inc. (1)
815 Swan St, Terre Haute, IN 47807-4431
Tel.: (812) 235-6218
Web Site:
http://www.hannigconstruction.com
Commercial & Institutional Building Construction
N.A.I.C.S.: 236220
Jack Acord *(Pres)*

CENTRAL STATES BUS SALES INC.
2450 Cassens Dr, Fenton, MO 63026-2539
Tel.: (636) 343-6050 MO
Web Site:
http://www.centralstatesbus.com
Year Founded: 1975
Sales Range: $10-24.9 Million
Emp.: 48
New & Used Bus Dealer
N.A.I.C.S.: 441110
Jeff Reitz *(Pres & CEO)*
Joe Deeken *(Dir-Parts Sls)*
Kevin Fisher *(Mgr-Parts Sls)*
Tommie Keller *(Mgr-Parts Sls)*
Mike Wingerter *(Gen Mgr-Arkansas Ops)*
Randy Schumacher *(Mgr-Parts Sls)*
Derek Sears *(Reg Mgr-Sales)*
Louis Tagliaferre *(Mgr-Comml Bus Sls)*
Chuck Harvill *(Gen Mgr-Ops-Tennessee & Kentucky)*

Subsidiaries:

Central States Bus Sales Inc. - Arkansas Facility (1)
420 Lake Ln, North Little Rock, AR 72117
Tel.: (501) 955-2577
Web Site:
http://www.centralstatesbussales.com
Automobile Equipment Mfr
N.A.I.C.S.: 336390

Central States Bus Sales Inc. - Illinois Facility (1)
49 W 102 US Highway 30 Ste F, Big Rock, IL 60511
Tel.: (630) 556-3130
Web Site: http://www.centralstatesbus.com
Automobile Equipment Mfr
N.A.I.C.S.: 336390

Central States Bus Sales Inc. - Tennessee Facility (1)
303 Business Park Dr, Lebanon, TN 37090
Tel.: (615) 466-5040
Web Site: http://www.centralstatesbus.com
Emp.: 9
Automobile Equipment Mfr
N.A.I.C.S.: 336390
Chuck Harvill *(Gen Mgr)*

CENTRAL STATES ENTERPRISES, INC.
1275 Lake Heathrow Ln, Heathrow, FL 32746
Tel.: (407) 333-3503 IN
Web Site:
https://www.centralstatesent.com
Year Founded: 1980
Sales Range: $75-99.9 Million
Emp.: 90
Provider Of Agricultural Services
N.A.I.C.S.: 424510
Richard Shura *(Chm)*
Kenneth Cupples *(VP-Sls)*
Robert Nawrot *(CEO)*

CENTRAL STATES HEALTH & LIFE CO. OF OMAHA INC.
1212 N 96th St, Omaha, NE 68114-2274
Tel.: (402) 397-1111 NE
Web Site: https://www.cso.com
Year Founded: 1932
Sales Range: $50-74.9 Million
Emp.: 150
Provider of Accident & Health Insurance
N.A.I.C.S.: 525190
Richard T. Kizer *(Chm)*
T. Edward Kizer *(Pres)*
Jeffrey J. Wanning *(Sr VP-Credit Insurance Ops)*
Jaime M. Amodeo *(Chief Investment Officer & VP)*

CENTRAL STATES INC.
823 Commerce Dr Ste 200, Bensenville, IL 60523-8826
Tel.: (630) 595-9876 IL
Web Site: http://www.cstruck.com
Year Founded: 1980
Holding Company; Freight Trucking & Logistics Services
N.A.I.C.S.: 551112
Dan Elam *(Mgr-Terminal)*

CENTRAL STATES INDUSTRIAL SUPPLY, INC.
8720 S 137th Cir, Omaha, NE 68138-6198
Tel.: (402) 894-1003 NE
Web Site:
https://www.centralstatesgroup.com
Year Founded: 1971
Sales Range: $25-49.9 Billion
Emp.: 85
Metals Service Centers & Offices
N.A.I.C.S.: 423510
Joann Schacher *(CFO)*

Subsidiaries:

CPI Sales, Inc. (1)
520 50th Ave Dr SW, Cedar Rapids, IA 52404
Tel.: (319) 364-1581
Web Site: http://www.cpisales.com
Sales Range: $10-24.9 Million
Emp.: 30
Industrial Supplies
N.A.I.C.S.: 423840
Noel Koeppen *(Mgr-Ware House)*

Mueller Sales Corp. (1)
5104 Hillsboro Ave N, New Hope, MN 55428-4030
Tel.: (763) 531-2222
Web Site:
http://www.centralstatesgroup.com
Emp.: 4
Industrial Supplies Whslr
N.A.I.C.S.: 423840
Todd Ford *(CEO)*

CENTRAL STATES MANUFACTURING INC.
302 Jane Pl, Lowell, AR 72745
Tel.: (479) 770-0188

Web Site:
http://www.centralstatesmfg.com
Year Founded: 1988
Sales Range: $50-74.9 Million
Emp.: 182
Mfr of Panels for Prefabricated Metal Buildings
N.A.I.C.S.: 332311
Brett Griffin *(Area Mgr-Sls)*
Donna Leger *(Pres)*
Rob Kujawa *(Mgr-Bus Dev)*
Russ Sanders *(Mgr-Bus Dev)*
Brad Burke *(Mgr-Sls)*
Jim Sliker *(CEO)*

CENTRAL STATES, INC.
8471 Outer Rd, Mountain Grove, MO 65711
Tel.: (417) 926-9801 MO
Web Site:
https://www.centralstatesinc.com
Year Founded: 2002
Sales Range: $10-24.9 Million
Emp.: 20
Custom Fabricated & Machined Mill Equipment Mfr
N.A.I.C.S.: 332999
Bill Grisham *(Founder, Pres & CEO)*

CENTRAL STATION MONITORING
303 SW Zobrist, Estacada, OR 97023
Tel.: (503) 630-2896
Web Site: https://www.csmul.com
Year Founded: 1982
Security System Services
N.A.I.C.S.: 561621

CENTRAL SUPPLY CO., INC.
8900 E 30th St, Indianapolis, IN 46219-1502
Tel.: (317) 898-2411 IN
Web Site:
https://www.centralsupplyco.com
Year Founded: 1976
Sales Range: $75-99.9 Million
Emp.: 40
Provider of Wholesale Plumbing & Electrical Supplies
N.A.I.C.S.: 423720
Gene Burt *(Pres)*

CENTRAL SUPPLY COMPANY
515 Ferguson Dr, Orlando, FL 32805
Tel.: (407) 299-1841
Web Site:
http://www.centralcabinetry.com
Rev.: $12,000,000
Emp.: 10
Lumber, Plywood, Millwork & Wood Panel Merchant Whslr
N.A.I.C.S.: 423310
Judy Baldyga *(VP)*
Steve Ervin *(Pres)*

CENTRAL TEXAS COMMUNITY HEALTH CENTERS
15 Waller St 5th Fl, Austin, TX 78702
Tel.: (512) 978-9049 TX
Web Site:
http://www.communitycaretx.org
Year Founded: 2003
Sales Range: $50-74.9 Million
Emp.: 643
Health Care Srvices
N.A.I.C.S.: 622110
Carolyn Konecny *(CFO)*
Terri Sabella *(COO)*
Jaeson Fournier *(CEO)*
Alan Schalscha *(Chief Medical Officer)*
Lane Greer *(Chief Legal Officer)*
Susan Lara Willars *(Chief HR Officer)*

CENTRAL TEXAS TELEPHONE COOPERATIVE, INC.

1012 Reilly St, Goldthwaite, TX 76844
Tel.: (325) 648-2237
Web Site: https://www.centex.net
Year Founded: 1951
Sales Range: $25-49.9 Million
Emp.: 65
Local Telephone Communications
N.A.I.C.S.: 517121
Jamey Wigley *(Gen Mgr)*
Mike Higgins *(CEO)*
Lawana Drosche *(CFO)*
Maxine Geeslin *(Sec)*

CENTRAL TRANSPORTATION SYSTEMS, INC.
1600 W Loop 340, Waco, TX 76712
Tel.: (254) 662-2884
Web Site:
https://www.centralsystems.com
Sales Range: $10-24.9 Million
Emp.: 150
Personal & Commercial Moving & Storage Services
N.A.I.C.S.: 484210
Randy Berry *(VP-Sls & Mktg)*
Rita Rahn *(Coord-Re-Location)*
Pam Jeffrey *(Gen Mgr)*
Richard Pearson *(Gen Mgr)*
Doug Shifflett *(Gen Mgr)*
Karyn Jacobs *(Gen Mgr-Sls)*
Amanda Toothman *(Office Mgr)*

CENTRAL TRUCKING INC.
11930 N Hartman Dr Ste A, Edinburgh, IN 46124
Tel.: (812) 526-9737
Web Site: https://www.ctitruck.com
Sales Range: $50-74.9 Million
Emp.: 325
Long Distance Trucking
N.A.I.C.S.: 484121
Keith Robert *(Pres)*
Geneva Davis *(Controller)*
Mark Stahl *(Dir-Maintenance)*

CENTRAL UNION MISSION
65 Ma Ave Nw 2001, Washington, DC 20001
Tel.: (202) 745-7118 DC
Web Site: http://www.missiondc.org
Year Founded: 1887
Sales Range: $10-24.9 Million
Emp.: 95
Community Action Services
N.A.I.C.S.: 624190

CENTRAL VALLEY AG COOPERATIVE
2803 N Nebraska Ave, York, NE 68467
Tel.: (402) 362-0253
Web Site: https://www.cvacoop.com
Rev.: $18,000,000
Emp.: 250
Agricultural Services
N.A.I.C.S.: 424910
Carl Dickinson *(Pres & CEO)*
Don Swanson *(CFO)*
Bryan Reichmuth *(Sr VP-Ops)*
Peg Hopwood *(Sr VP-Member Svcs)*
Tom Palmertree *(Sr VP-Mktg)*
Robert Turek *(Sr VP-Feed)*
Jeff Ingalls *(Sr VP-Energy)*
Nic McCarthy *(Sr VP-Agronomy)*
Dave Beckman *(Chm)*
Mark Koss *(Vice Chm)*
Jacob Porter *(Sec)*

CENTRAL VALLEY BUILDERS SUPPLY
7030 Roseda Blvd, Reseda, CA 91335
Tel.: (818) 343-3838 CA
Web Site: https://www.cvbs.com
Year Founded: 1955

Central Valley Builders Supply—(Continued)
Sales Range: $25-49.9 Million
Emp.: 250
Lumber & Other Building Materials
N.A.I.C.S.: 423310
Audra Schorse (Mgr-HR)
Stephanie Phillips (Office Mgr)
Ed Berriard (Coord-Sls)

CENTRAL VALLEY CONCRETE INC.
3823 N Highway 59, Merced, CA 95348
Tel.: (209) 723-8846
Web Site:
https://www.centralvalleyconcrete.com
Sales Range: $50-74.9 Million
Emp.: 220
Concrete Mixtures
N.A.I.C.S.: 423320
Staci Neal (VP)

CENTRAL VALLEY MEAT HOLDING COMPANY
10431 8 3/4 Ave, Hanford, CA 93230
Tel.: (559) 583-9624   CA
Web Site:
http://www.centralvalleymeat.com
Holding Company
N.A.I.C.S.: 551112
Brian Coelho (Pres & CEO)

Subsidiaries:

Harris Ranch Beef Holding
Company   (1)
16277 S McCall Ave, Selma, CA 93662
Tel.: (559) 896-3081
Web Site: http://www.harrisranchbeef.com
Holding Company
N.A.I.C.S.: 551112

Subsidiary (Domestic):

Harris Feeding Co.   (2)
29475 Fresno Coalinga Rd, Coalinga, CA 93210
Tel.: (559) 884-2435
Web Site: http://www.harrisranch.com
Sales Range: $25-49.9 Million
Emp.: 175
Cattle Ranch & Feedlots Operator
N.A.I.C.S.: 112112
David E. Wood (CEO)

Harris Ranch Beef Company   (2)
PO Box 220, Selma, CA 93662-0269
Tel.: (559) 896-3081
Web Site: http://www.harrisranchbeef.com
Sales Range: $75-99.9 Million
Emp.: 700
Cattle Slaughtering, Beef Processing & Meat Whslr
N.A.I.C.S.: 311611

CENTRAL VAPORS, LLC
3733 E University Dr Ste 330, McKinney, TX 75069
Tel.: (469) 828-7307
Web Site:
http://www.centralvapors.com
Year Founded: 2013
Sales Range: $1-9.9 Million
Emp.: 18
Vapor Product Mfr & Distr
N.A.I.C.S.: 325998
Cameron Harris (Founder & CEO)

CENTRAL VERMONT HOME HEALTH AND HOSPICE
600 Granger Rd, Barre, VT 05641-5369
Tel.: (802) 223-1878
Web Site: https://www.cvhhh.org
Rev.: $11,759,139
Emp.: 220
Women Healthcare Services
N.A.I.C.S.: 621610

Sandy Rousse (Pres & CEO)
Connie Colman (Dir-Quality Improvement)
Daniel L. Pudvah (Dir-Dev)
Rebecca R. Bowen (Dir-HR)
Kim Farnum (Mgr-Community Rels & Dev)
Kelly Bishop (CFO)

CENTRAL VIRGINIA ELECTRIC COOPERATIVE INC.
800 Cooperative Way, Arrington, VA 22922-3300
Tel.: (434) 263-8336   VA
Web Site: http://www.forcvec.com
Year Founded: 1937
Sales Range: $25-49.9 Million
Emp.: 110
Provider of Electric Services
N.A.I.C.S.: 221118
David Trudel (Mgr)
Gregory Kelly (Mgr-Member Svcs)
Tina Mallia (CFO)

CENTRAL WASHINGTON CONCRETE
1351 S Wenatchee Ave, Wenatchee, WA 98801
Tel.: (509) 662-6375
Web Site:
http://www.centralwashingtonconcrete.com
Sales Range: $10-24.9 Million
Emp.: 100
Cement
N.A.I.C.S.: 423320
John Madden (Gen Mgr)

CENTRAL WASHINGTON GRAIN GROWERS, INC.
104 E Ash St, Waterville, WA 98858
Tel.: (509) 745-8551   WA
Web Site: http://www.cwgg.net
Year Founded: 1937
Sales Range: $50-74.9 Million
Emp.: 40
Grain & Field Beans
N.A.I.C.S.: 424510
Cindy Garrett (Asst Controller)
Paul Katovich (Gen Mgr)
Nikki Murison (Controller)

CENTRAL WELDING SUPPLY CO. INC.
PO Box 179 N, Lakewood, WA 98259
Tel.: (800) 697-0128
Web Site:
http://www.centralwelding.com
Sales Range: $10-24.9 Million
Emp.: 220
Welding Machinery & Equipment
N.A.I.C.S.: 423830
Mike Buell (VP)
Dale Wilton (Pres & CEO)
Michael Wilton (Founder & Chm)
Marshall Judy (Mgr-Sls)
Marnie Miller (Mgr-HR & Asset)
Misty Urban (Controller)
Nicole Sparrow (Office Mgr)
Debra Malmos (Mgr-Mktg)
Pete Hochstatter (Pres)

CENTRAL WHOLESALE ELECTRICAL DISTRIBUTORS INC.
6611 Preston Ave, Livermore, CA 94551
Tel.: (925) 245-9310   CA
Web Site: http://www.cwed.com
Year Founded: 1977
Sales Range: $25-49.9 Million
Emp.: 115
Distr of Electrical Apparatus
N.A.I.C.S.: 423610
Debra Givan (Mgr-Credit)
Lynn Wheeler (Branch Mgr)

Travis Delano (Branch Mgr)
Aimee Eala (Mgr-Ops)
Bill Edwards (Branch Mgr)
Klaus Hansen (Pres)
James Sullivan (Treas & Sec)
Lori Schall (Branch Mgr)

CENTRAL WHOLESALE SUPPLY CORPORATION
1532 Ingleside Rd, Norfolk, VA 23502
Tel.: (757) 855-3131
Web Site: http://www.central-wholesale.com
Sales Range: $10-24.9 Million
Emp.: 20
Lumber, Plywood & Millwork
N.A.I.C.S.: 423310
Steven W. Dominick (Pres)
E. L. Dominic (Chm)

CENTRAL WHOLESALERS, INC.
13401 Konterra Dr, Laurel, MD 20707
Tel.: (301) 419-2900
Web Site: http://www.cwip.com
Year Founded: 1981
Sales Range: $25-49.9 Million
Emp.: 150
Whslr of Plumbing Fittings & Supplies
N.A.I.C.S.: 423720
Douglas Sherman (Pres)
Richard Barron (VP)
David Baxley (VP-Ops)

CENTRAL WISCONSIN COOPERATIVE
2327 W Veterans Pkwy, Marshfield, WI 54449
Tel.: (715) 387-1291   WI
Web Site: http://www.cwco-op.com
Year Founded: 1996
Sales Range: $10-24.9 Million
Emp.: 120
Provider of Farm Supplies
N.A.I.C.S.: 424910
Joseph Fuchs (Pres)
Paul Dietsche (Mgr-Energy Div)
Thomas Hoffman (Mgr-Agronomy Div)
Robert Larson (Gen Mgr)

CENTRAL WOODWORK, INC.
870 Keough Rd, Collierville, TN 38017
Tel.: (901) 363-4141   TN
Web Site:
https://www.centralwoodwork.com
Year Founded: 1945
Sales Range: $25-49.9 Million
Emp.: 180
Windows, Doors, Lumber, Plywood & Millwork Distr
N.A.I.C.S.: 423310
Patrick Schaefer (Co-Pres & Sec)
Amy Gordon (VP)
Mark Schaefer (Chm & Co-Pres)

Subsidiaries:

Central Woodwork of Nashville, Inc.   (1)
717 Melrose Ave, Nashville, TN 37211-2166
Tel.: (615) 244-0086
Web Site: http://www.cenwood.com
Rev.: $13,000,000
Emp.: 100
Lumber, Plywood & Millwork
N.A.I.C.S.: 423310
Mark Schaefer (Pres)

Cenwood Kitchens   (1)
1217 Ridgeway Rd, Memphis, TN 38119
Tel.: (901) 737-4343
Web Site: http://www.cenwoodkitchens.com
Kitchen Appliance Whslr
N.A.I.C.S.: 423620
Mark Wakefield (Gen Mgr)

CENTRAL WV AGING SERVICES, INC.
8 N Spring St, Buckhannon, WV 26201
Tel.: (304) 472-0395   WV
Web Site:
https://www.centralwvaging.org
Year Founded: 1981
Sales Range: $10-24.9 Million
Emp.: 1,324
Elder Care Services
N.A.I.C.S.: 624120
Evelyn Post (Exec Dir)

CENTRAL WYOMING COUNSELING CENTER
1430 Wilkins Cir, Casper, WY 82601
Tel.: (307) 237-9583   WY
Web Site: https://www.cwcc.us
Year Founded: 1959
Counseling Services
N.A.I.C.S.: 624190
Brandon Wardell (CEO)
Joseph Forscher (Exec Dir-Clinical Ops)
Cherri Lester (Sr Dir-Residential Svcs)
Bill Howell (Dir-Outpatient Mental Health Program)
Carol King (Dir-Logistics)
Tabbi Madrigal (Dir-Recovery Svcs)
Erin Ford (Mgr-Outpatient Addictions)
Dee Ann Lippincott (Mgr-Client Svcs)

CENTRAL-MCGOWAN INC.
123 Roosevelt Rd, Saint Cloud, MN 56302
Tel.: (320) 252-5292
Web Site:
http://www.centralmcgowan.com
Sales Range: $10-24.9 Million
Emp.: 42
Welding Supplies
N.A.I.C.S.: 423840
Jeff Skumautz (Pres)

CENTRALREACH, LLC
371 S Federal Hwy, Pompano Beach, FL 33062
Tel.: (844)
Web Site:
http://www.centralreach.com
Year Founded: 2012
Sales Range: $10-24.9 Million
Emp.: 142
Software Development Services
N.A.I.C.S.: 541511
Chris Sullens (CEO)
Jonathan Gordon (CFO)
Cheryl Michael (Chief Product Officer)
Rich Barndt (CTO)
Rick Kubina (Dir-Research)

CENTRASTATE HEALTHCARE SYSTEM INC.
901 W Main St, Freehold, NJ 07728
Tel.: (732) 431-2000
Web Site:
https://www.centrastate.com
Sales Range: $75-99.9 Million
Emp.: 1,900
Healtcare Services
N.A.I.C.S.: 561110
John T. Gribbin (Pres & CEO)
John Dellocono (CFO & Sr VP)
Alice Guttler (Sr VP)
Linda Geisler (CFO & Chief Nursing Officer)
Frances Keane (VP-HR)
Cathleen Janzekovich (Asst VP-Nursing)
Kim A. Kelly (VP-Clinical Svcs)
Robert M. Nyman (Asst VP-Fin)
Debbie Connors (Asst VP-Budget Reimbursement)
Jan McAvenia (Asst VP-Patient Fin Svcs)

Jane Girling (Asst VP-Corp Matls Mgmt)
Thomas W. Scott (COO & Sr VP)

CENTRE 1 BANCORP, INC.
345 E Grand Ave, Beloit, WI 53511
Tel.: (608) 363-8000   WI
Web Site:
http://www.bankatfirstnational.com
Year Founded: 1983
Sales Range: $50-74.9 Million
Emp.: 281
Bank Holding Company
N.A.I.C.S.: 551111
Steven M. Eldred (Chm, Pres & CEO)
Donna K. Beilfuss (CFO & Treas)
Brian K. Bisbey (Chief Credit Officer)
Dennis A. Staaland (Sec & VP)

Subsidiaries:

The First National Bank & Trust Company   (1)
345 E Grand Ave, Beloit, WI 53511
Tel.: (608) 363-8000
Web Site:
http://www.bankatfirstnational.com
Commercial Banking
N.A.I.C.S.: 522110
Steven M. Eldred (Chm)
Donna K. Beilfuss (CFO & Treas)
Jessica Hernandez (Asst VP & Branch Mgr-Retail-Downtown Beloit/Main)
Dennis A. Staaland (Sec & VP)
Jose Moreno (Mgr-Clinton)
David N. McCoy (Pres & CEO)

CENTRE CARE INC.
502 E Howard St, Bellefonte, PA 16823-2128
Tel.: (814) 355-6777   PA
Web Site: http://www.centrecrest.org
Year Founded: 2013
Sales Range: $10-24.9 Million
Emp.: 251
Nursing Care Services
N.A.I.C.S.: 623110
Carl Raup (Treas)
Larry Bickford (VP)
Betsy Boyer (Pres)

CENTRE LANE PARTNERS, LLC
1 Grand Central Pl 60 E 42nd St Ste 1250, New York, NY 10165
Tel.: (646) 843-0710   DE
Web Site:
http://www.centrelanepartners.com
Year Founded: 2007
Private Investment Firm
N.A.I.C.S.: 523999
Mayank Singh (Mng Dir)
Quinn Morgan (Co-Founder & Mng Dir)
Kenneth Lau (Co-Founder & Mng Dir)
Rory Kirkpatrick (Mng Dir)
Kenneth Wong (Principal)
Luke Gosselin (Mng Dir & Portfolio Mgr)
William James (Principal)
Eric Drozdov (VP)
Greg Najarian (VP)
Olivia Zhao (VP)
Michael Hogan (Chief Compliance Officer)
Upacala Mapatuna (Mng Dir & Portfolio Mgr-Centre Lane Credit Partners Funds)
Chris Holdyk (VP)
Doug Schuster (Mng Dir)
Sherry Gao (CFO)

Subsidiaries:

Clickbooth.com LLC   (1)
5911 N Honore Ave #114, Sarasota, FL 34243
Tel.: (866) 867-6333
Web Site: http://www.clickbooth.com

Advertising Agencies
N.A.I.C.S.: 541830
Erin Cigich (CEO)
Lee Aho (Exec VP-Adv)
Brad Dobbins (Pres)
Julie Martin (VP-Product Dev)
Cara Redding (Exec VP-Ops)
Dzenis Softic (CTO)
Michael Hickman (CFO)
Craig McGlynn (Mng Dir & Exec VP-Agency)
Angie Stockman (VP-Client Svcs)
Mandi Pinar (Dir-Accts)
Quin Talaric (Dir-Acct)
Ami DeWille (VP-Mktg)

Easy Gardener Products, Inc.   (1)
3022 Franklin Ave, Waco, TX 76710
Tel.: (254) 753-5353
Web Site: http://www.easygardener.com
Lawn & Garden Supplies Mfr
N.A.I.C.S.: 333112
Richard Kurz (CFO)

Focus Products Group International, LLC   (1)
300 Knightsbridge Pkwy Ste 500, Lincolnshire, IL 60069-3638
Tel.: (224) 513-2007
Web Site: http://www.fpghospitality.com
Household Goods Mfr
N.A.I.C.S.: 335220
Sandra Kemp (Sr VP-Hospitality)
Scott Schwerman (VP-Chain Sls)
Sandy DiVito (VP-Field Sls)
Tim Walker (Mgr-Natl Acct)
Mike Latsis (Mgr-Natl Acct)
Tim Lavelle (Mgr-Natl Acct)
Mark Donovan (Mgr-Reg Acct)
Brenda James (Mgr-Reg Acct)

Hollander Sleep Products LLC   (1)
6501 Congress Ave Ste 300, Boca Raton, FL 33487-2746
Tel.: (561) 997-6900
Web Site: http://www.hollander.com
Sales Range: $300-349.9 Million
Emp.: 100
Household Furnishings Whslr
N.A.I.C.S.: 314120
Louis Smith (Dir-Brand Mgmt)
Beth Mack (Chief Mdsg Officer)
Amy Webster (VP-Mdsg)
Tim Landers (VP & Bus Mgr)
Jannice Cameron (VP-Mktg)

Subsidiary (Domestic):

Pacific Coast Feather Company   (2)
1736 4th Ave S Ste B, Seattle, WA 98134
Tel.: (206) 624-1057
Web Site: http://www.pacificcoast.com
Pillows, Cushions & Comforters Mfr
N.A.I.C.S.: 314120
Lisa Mark (Mgr-HR)

Subsidiary (Domestic):

Pacific Coast Feather Cushion Co.   (3)
7600 Industry Ave, Pico Rivera, CA 90660
Tel.: (562) 801-9995
Web Site: http://www.pcfcushion.com
Cushions Mfr
N.A.I.C.S.: 314120
Christina Kopecky (Pres)

Subsidiary (Domestic):

Sure Fit Inc.   (2)
8000 Quarry Rd, Alburtis, PA 18011
Tel.: (610) 264-7300
Web Site: http://www.surefit.net
Furniture Slipcovers Whslr & Online Retailer
N.A.I.C.S.: 423220
Terry Ackerman (Acct Mgr)
Nichole Koszi (Mgr-Brand & Mktg)

Infobase Holdings, LLC   (1)
132 W 31st St 16th Fl, New York, NY 10001
Tel.: (800) 322-8755
Web Site:
http://www.infobasepublishing.com
Educational Books & Other Media Publisher
N.A.I.C.S.: 513130
James Housley (CFO)
Laurie Likoff (Dir-Print & Editorial)
Paul Skordilis (Pres & CEO)
Kathy Tan (Dir-Video Acq)

Tara McCaffrey (Dir-Mktg & Online Products)
Chriss Plapp (Dir-Digital Strategy)
Doug Mingle (Dir-Sls)
Jenna Pavlak (Dir-HR)

Subsidiary (Domestic):

Omnigraphics, Inc.   (2)
615 Griswold St Ste 520, Detroit, MI 48226
Tel.: (313) 961-1340
Web Site: http://www.omnigraphics.com
Book Publishing, Nsk
N.A.I.C.S.: 513130
Angela Kilkenny (Dir)

World Almanac Education Group, Inc.   (2)
132 W 31st St 16th Fl, New York, NY 10001
Tel.: (800) 223-2336
Web Site: http://www.worldalmanac.com
Reference Book Publisher
N.A.I.C.S.: 513130
Sarah Janssen (Editor)

Inservco, Inc.   (1)
110 Commerce Dr, Lagrange, OH 44050
Tel.: (440) 284-2500
Web Site: https://www.vexos.com
Sales Range: $1-9.9 Million
Emp.: 119
Electronic Components Mfr
N.A.I.C.S.: 334419
Harry McCreedy (Mgr-HR)
Tim Benincasa (Dir-Sls & Mktg)

Subsidiary (Domestic):

Controltek Inc.   (2)
3905 NE 112th Ave, Vancouver, WA 98682
Tel.: (360) 896-9375
Web Site: http://www.controltek.com
Rev.: $3,086,000
Emp.: 100
Relay & Industrial Control Mfr
N.A.I.C.S.: 335314
Andy LaFrazia (Pres)
Dale Dillenberg (Production Mgr)
Jeff Skinner (VP-Engrg)
Joe Herz (Mgr-Engrg Mfg)
Sean Neill (VP-Ops)
Balbir Tulshi (VP-Fin)

Staci Corp.   (2)
110 Commerce Dr., LaGrange, OH 44050
Tel.: (440) 284-2501
Web Site: http://www.stacicorp.com
Durable Goods Merchant Whslr
N.A.I.C.S.: 423990
Greg Hebson (Sr VP-Sls & Mktg)

Lenox Corporation   (1)
1414 Radcliffe St, Bristol, PA 19007-0806
Tel.: (267) 525-7800
Web Site: http://www.lenox.com
Sales Range: $150-199.9 Million
Emp.: 295
Fine China, Crystal, Flatware, Tableware, Glassware & Giftware Mfr, Distr & Retailer
N.A.I.C.S.: 327110
Marc Utay (Chm)
Mads Ryder (CEO)
Brian Gowen (COO)

Subsidiary (Domestic):

Cambridge Silversmiths Ltd., Inc.   (2)
30 Hook Mountain Rd, Pine Brook, NJ 07058
Tel.: (973) 227-4400
Web Site:
http://www.cambridgesilversmiths.com
Emp.: 130
Flatware, Cutlery & Other Tabletop Accessories Designer & Distr
N.A.I.C.S.: 423220
Lisa Suter (Mgr-Product Dev)
Michael Honig (CFO)
Roger Freeman (Pres)
Harold Freeman (Exec VP)

Hampton Forge, Ltd.   (2)
442 State Route 35 S, Eatontown, NJ 07724
Tel.: (732) 389-5507
Web Site: http://www.hamptonforge.com
Sales Range: $1-9.9 Million
Emp.: 40
Home Furnishing Merchant Whslr

N.A.I.C.S.: 423220
Joni Amar (VP)

Plant (Domestic):

Lenox - Kinston Plant   (2)
1800 Dobbs Farm Rd, Kinston, NC 28504-8906
Tel.: (252) 523-5555
Web Site: http://www.lenox.com
Sales Range: $50-74.9 Million
Emp.: 300
China & Pottery Mfr
N.A.I.C.S.: 327110
Bob Lupica (Plant Mgr)

Monetate, Inc.   (1)
27 E 28th St, New York, NY 10016
Tel.: (484) 323-6313
Web Site: http://www.monetate.com
Emp.: 30
Software Development Services
N.A.I.C.S.: 541511
Bob Lawson (CFO)
Scott Rogers (Sr VP-Corp Dev)
Michelle Curless (VP-Svcs)
Michael Wasyluka (Exec VP-Sls & Mktg)
Mike Harris (VP)
Maribeth Ross (Sr VP)
George J. Kanuck III (Chief Sls Officer)
Shikhin Agarwal (VP-Products)
Scott Reynolds (Dir-Product Mgmt)
Kevin Luo (Product Mgr)
Tim Jeremicz (Dir-Program Mgmt)
Brandon Atkinson (COO)
Richard Rivera (Chief Revenue Officer)
Lisa Kalscheur (Chief Mktg Officer)
Jonathan Bartlett (Chief Product Officer)
Brian Wilson (CEO)

Saladworks, LLC   (1)
8 Tower Bridge 161 Washington St Ste 300, Conshohocken, PA 19428
Tel.: (610) 825-3080
Web Site: http://www.saladworks.com
Salads, Soups & Pasta Quick Service Restaurant
N.A.I.C.S.: 722513
Joe Giannetti (Dir-Distr & Procurement)
Patrick Sugrue (Pres)
Jena Henderson (VP-Brand Svcs)
Kelly Roddy (CEO)
Brian Farris (Chief Dev Officer)
Charles Bruton III (VP-Ops & Dev)

Synacor, Inc.   (1)
40 La Riviere Dr Ste 300, Buffalo, NY 14202
Tel.: (716) 853-1362
Web Site: http://www.synacor.com
Rev.: $81,362,000
Assets: $63,243,000
Liabilities: $29,767,000
Net Worth: $33,476,000
Earnings: ($11,561,000)
Emp.: 270
Fiscal Year-end: 12/31/2020
Internet Platform for Digital Content & Services
N.A.I.C.S.: 541512
Himesh Bhise (Pres & CEO)
Steve Davi (Exec VP-Tech)
Kenneth Lau (Mng Dir-Centre Lane)
Timothy J. Heasley (CFO)
Timothy J. Heasley (CFO)

Subsidiary (Non-US):

Zimbra Europe Limited   (2)
Office 408 Euston House 24 Eversholt St, London, EC1V 1NY, United Kingdom
Tel.: (44) 8000061225
Web Site: http://www.zimbra.com
Computer Peripheral Equipment Whslr
N.A.I.C.S.: 423430

Subsidiary (Domestic):

Zimbra Software, LLC   (2)
2591 Dallas Pkwy Ste 200, Frisco, TX 75034
Tel.: (972) 407-0688
Web Site: http://www.zimbra.com
Software Publisher
N.A.I.C.S.: 513210

The Merit Distribution Group, LLC   (1)
1310 Union St, Spartanburg, SC 29302
Tel.: (864) 583-3011

Centre Lane Partners, LLC—(Continued)

Web Site: http://www.lancasterco.com
Sales Range: $25-49.9 Million
Emp.: 200
Paint Sundry, Hardware & Drywall Related Products Distr
N.A.I.C.S.: 424950
Mitch Jolley (CEO)
John Hutchins (VP-Fin)
Robin Miller (Dir-IT)
Adrienne Melton (Mgr-Mktg Logistics)

Subsidiary (Non-US):

Dynamic Paint Products Inc. (2)
7040 Financial Dr, Mississauga, L5N 7H5, ON, Canada
Tel.: (905) 812-9319
Web Site: http://www.getpainting.com
Sales Range: $10-24.9 Million
Emp.: 100
Paint & Related Products Mfr
N.A.I.C.S.: 325510
Pooran Bishram (Mgr-Natl Sls)
James Mumby (Pres)
John Burke (VP-Mktg)
Derek Jang (Dir-Ops)

Turning Technologies, LLC (1)
255 W Federal St, Youngstown, OH 44503
Tel.: (330) 746-3015
Web Site:
http://www.turningtechnologies.com
Sales Range: $25-49.9 Million
Educational Technology & Solutions
N.A.I.C.S.: 513210
Mike Broderick (Founder)
Dave Kauer (Pres)
Sandra Mapus (Mgr-HR)
Tina Rooks (VP)
Sheila Hura (VP-Mktg)
Todd Craig (VP-Enterprise Sls)
Gary Morrison (VP-Intl)
Satish Shetty (VP-Mfg)
Mike Chiszar (VP-Enterprise Bus Dev)
Jeff Cunningham (Dir-Hardware R&D)
Fares Bouchedid (VP-Software R&D & Cloud Ops)
Stephanie Rose Nunzir (Mgr-Sls Trng)
Tara Metzger (Coord-Sls)
Ethan Cohen (CEO)

Subsidiary (Domestic):

Responsive Innovations, LLC (2)
255 W Federal St, Youngstown, OH 44503
Tel.: (330) 746-3015
Web Site:
http://www.turningtechnologies.com
Sales Range: $25-49.9 Million
Interactive Response Systems Developer
N.A.I.C.S.: 611710

eInstruction Corp. (2)
1330 Teasley Ln, Denton, TX 76205
Tel.: (480) 948-6540
Web Site: http://www.einstruction.com
Educational Technology
N.A.I.C.S.: 513210

Subsidiary (Domestic):

GTCO CalComp, Inc. (3)
14557 N 82nd St, Scottsdale, AZ 85260
Tel.: (480) 948-6540
Web Site: http://www.gtcocalcomp.com
Computer Equipment & Graphic Measurement Devices, Desktop Productivity Tools & Collaboration Solutions
N.A.I.C.S.: 334118
Kim Plasterer (Dir-Sls)

Vitamin World, Inc. (1)
3500 Sunrise Hwy Ste 210, Great River, NY 11739 (100%)
Tel.: (631) 650-0603
Web Site: http://www.vitaminworld.com
Nutritional Supplement Distr
N.A.I.C.S.: 456191

Zenfolio, Inc. (1)
3515A Edison Way, Menlo Park, CA 94025-1815
Tel.: (650) 412-1888
Web Site: http://www.zenfolio.com
Website Design, Client proofing & E-commerce Printing Services
N.A.I.C.S.: 323120

AmberAmber Minson (CMO)
John Loughlin (CEO)
Doug Massey (CFO)
Munib Siddiqi (VP-Product & Design)
Nadav Vansover (VP-Engrg)

CENTRE LIMITED INC.
11901 Cartwright Ave, Grandview, MO 64030-1151
Tel.: (816) 763-2700
Web Site:
http://www.cartwrighttrans.com
Year Founded: 1983
Sales Range: $10-24.9 Million
Emp.: 100
Freight Transportation Arrangement
N.A.I.C.S.: 488510
Ken Salvey (VP-Mktg)
Michael Cartwright (Officer)
Andy W. Cartwright (Pres)
Michael Hite (Controller)

Subsidiaries:

Cartwright International Van Lines Inc. (1)
11901 Cartwright Ave, Grandview, MO 64030-1151
Tel.: (816) 763-2700
Web Site: http://www.catwright.com
Rev.: $22,822,984
Emp.: 70
Freight Transportation Arrangement
N.A.I.C.S.: 488510
Michelle Owens (Office Mgr)

Cartwright Van Lines Inc. (1)
11901 Cartwright Ln, Grandview, MO 64030-1151
Tel.: (816) 763-2700
Trucking Except Local
N.A.I.C.S.: 488510
Mike Hite (CFO)

Transpo Service Ltd. Inc. (1)
4411 E 119th St, Grandview, MO 64030-1151
Tel.: (816) 763-3442
Web Site:
http://www.cartwrightcompanies.com
Sales Range: $10-24.9 Million
Emp.: 70
Data Processing & Preparation
N.A.I.C.S.: 518210
Michelle Owens (Office Mgr)

CENTRE PARTNERS MANAGEMENT LLC
601 Lexington Ave 55th Fl, New York, NY 10022
Tel.: (212) 332-5800   DE
Web Site:
http://www.centrepartners.com
Year Founded: 1986
Privater Equity Firm
N.A.I.C.S.: 523999
Bruce Glen Pollack (Mng Partner)
Jeffrey Bartoli (Mng Dir)
David Jaffe (Mng Partner)
William Tomai (CFO & COO)
Lester Pollack (Founder)
Guillaume Bebear (Sr Dir)
Andrew Vandekerckhove (Dir)
Daniel Brinkenhoff (Dir)
Jeremy Lipstein (Principal)
Vidur Mittal (VP)
Michael P. Schnabel (Sr Partner)

Subsidiaries:

Chesapeake Eye Care & Laser Center, LLC (1)
Sajak Pavilion 2002 Medical Pkwy Ste 320, Annapolis, MD 21401
Tel.: (410) 571-8733
Web Site:
http://www.chesapeakeeyecare.com
Eye Care Service
N.A.I.C.S.: 621320
Michael Dunn (CEO)
Maria Scott (Dir-Medical)

Subsidiary (Domestic):

Baltimore Eye Physicians, LLC (2)

6231 N Charles St, Baltimore, MD 21212
Tel.: (410) 377-2044
Web Site: http://www.bepeye.com
Eye Care Service
N.A.I.C.S.: 621399
Julee Holtman (Sec-Medical)
Marcos Doxanas (Founder)

The Arlington Eye Center, Inc. (2)
1635 N George Mason Dr Ste 100, Arlington, VA 22205
Tel.: (703) 524-5777
Web Site:
http://www.arlingtoneyecenter.com
Eye Care Physicians
N.A.I.C.S.: 621111

WhittenLaserEye, LLC (2)
37767 Market Dr Ste 103, Charlotte Hall, MD 20622
Tel.: (301) 825-5755
Web Site: http://www.whittenlasereye.com
Eye Care Physicians
N.A.I.C.S.: 621111

Covenant Care, LLC (1)
27071 Aliso Creek Rd Ste 100, Aliso Viejo, CA 92656
Tel.: (949) 349-1200
Web Site: http://www.covenantcare.com
Long-Term Care & Assisted Living Facilities Operator
N.A.I.C.S.: 623311
Robert A. Levin (Pres & CEO)
Mary A. Evans (COO)
Christine M. Sims (CFO)
Andrew F. Torok (Gen Counsel)
Judy Elmore (VP-Ancillary Svcs)
Debbie Nix (VP-HR)

Den-Mat Holdings, LLC (1)
1017 W Central Ave, Lompoc, CA 93436-2701
Tel.: (805) 346-3700
Web Site: http://www.denmat.com
Emp.: 300
Dental Product Mfr
N.A.I.C.S.: 339114
Robert Cartagena (COO)
Rich Hallworth (Chm)
David Casper (CEO)
Felix Silva (Dir-Laboratory Ops)

Subsidiary (Domestic):

PeriOptix, Inc. (2)
1017 W Central Ave, Lompoc, CA 93436
Tel.: (805) 922-8491
Web Site: http://www.perioptix.com
Sales Range: $10-24.9 Million
Medical & Dental Magnification & Illumination Equipment Developer & Mfr
N.A.I.C.S.: 339113
Keith Tholin (Co-Founder & Pres)

Gathr Outdoors (1)
155 Franklin Rd Ste 250, Brentwood, TN 37027
Tel.: (615) 620-8737
Web Site: http://www.gathroutdoors.com
Sports & Adventure Equipment Mfr
N.A.I.C.S.: 423850
Joe Henderson (Pres)
Keith Bornholtz (CEO)
Cory Tholl (Pres-Outdoors Camp)

Subsidiary (Domestic):

Argon Technologies, Inc. (2)
1265 West 1275 North Ste 1, Centerville, UT 84014
Tel.: (888) 559-6481
Web Site: http://www.klymit.com
Sales Range: $1-9.9 Million
Camping Goods Distr
N.A.I.C.S.: 423910
Cory Tholl (Pres & CEO)
Bart Miller (VP-Sls)
Matt Maxfield (VP-Dev & Ops)
Tanner Allen (Dir-Bus Dev & Mgr-Pivotal Sls)
Steve Smith (Reg Mgr-Sls)
Becky Stoker (Mgr-Customer Svc)
Kristen Curry (Mgr-Customer Svc)
Ken Rivas (Mgr-Consumer Special Events)
Micah Orvis (Mgr-E-commerce)

Cascadia Vehicle Tents, LLC (2)
1036 SE Paiute Way, Bend, OR 97702
Tel.: (541) 312-8368

Web Site: http://www.cascadiatents.com
Trailers & Car Camping Equipment Distr
N.A.I.C.S.: 423990
Robert Culpepper (Pres)

GCI Outdoor, Inc. (2)
457 Killingworth Rd, Higganum, CT 06441
Tel.: (860) 345-9595
Web Site: http://www.gcioutdoor.com
Rev.: $3,800,000
Emp.: 14
Inland Water Passenger Transportation
N.A.I.C.S.: 483212
Jeffrey Polke (Co-Owner)

Gray Energy Services, LLC (1)
1912 W Ave, Levelland, TX 79336
Tel.: (806) 894-6008
Web Site: http://www.graywireline.com
Sales Range: $50-74.9 Million
Emp.: 35
Holding Company; Oil & Gas Cased-Hole Wireline Services
N.A.I.C.S.: 551112

Guy & O'Neill, Inc. (1)
200 Indstrial Dr, Fredonia, WI 53021
Tel.: (262) 692-2469
Web Site: http://www.guyandoneill.com
Pharmaceuticals, Packaging & Multi-Pack Wet Wipes Mfr
N.A.I.C.S.: 325412
Tom Misgen (Pres & CEO)
Greg Fries (Sr VP-Retail Brands)
Tarry Zielinski (Sr VP-Contract Sls)
John Immen (VP-Retail Sls)
John Vavra (VP-Ops)

Subsidiary (Domestic):

Boomerang Laboratories, LLC (2)
4164 Shoreline, Spring Park, MN 55384
Tel.: (952) 471-9855
Web Site: http://www.boomeranglabs.com
Personal Care Product Mfr
N.A.I.C.S.: 325620

Pride Manufacturing Company, LLC (1)
10 N Main St, Burnham, ME 04922
Tel.: (207) 487-3322
Web Site: http://www.pridesports.com
Sales Range: $10-24.9 Million
Emp.: 120
Wood Golf Products & Golf Cleats Mfr
N.A.I.C.S.: 321999
Joe Zeller (Pres & CEO)

Subsidiary (Domestic):

MacNeill Engineering Co., Inc. (2)
140 Locke Dr, Marlborough, MA 01752
Tel.: (508) 481-8830
Rev.: $4,825,000
Emp.: 25
Sporting & Athletic Goods Mfr
N.A.I.C.S.: 339920

Sabrosura Foods, LLC (1)
7900 International Dr Ste 140, Bloomington, MN 55425
Web Site: http://sabrosurafoods.com
Hispanic Food Products Mfr Marketer & Distr
N.A.I.C.S.: 311991
Jeff Caswell (CEO)

Subsidiary (Domestic):

Panchos Mexican Foods, Inc. (2)
2715 US Hwy 411 S, Maryville, TN 37801
Tel.: (865) 982-2228
Web Site:
http://www.panchosmexicantn.com
Food Manufacturing
N.A.I.C.S.: 311999
Julia Eason (Controller)

Sun Orchard Incorporated (1)
1198 W Fairmont Dr, Tempe, AZ 85282
Tel.: (480) 966-1770
Web Site: http://www.sunorchard.com
Frozen Fruit Juices Producer
N.A.I.C.S.: 311411
Marc Isaacs (Pres & CEO)
Jean-Marc Rotsaert (Chm)
Steve Finn (Sr VP-Sls & Mktg)
JoAnne Martinez (VP-HR & Admin)
Carl Colletti (CFO)

Subsidiary (Domestic):

Sun Orchard of Florida Inc. (2)

1200 S 30th St, Haines City, FL 33844
Tel.: (877) 875-8423
Web Site: http://www.sunorchard.com
Emp.: 90
Frozen Fruit Juices Producer
N.A.I.C.S.: 311411

The Wireless Experience Group (1)
2360 Lakewood Rd Tri-City Plz, Toms
River, NJ 08755
Tel.: (732) 994-1387
Web Site:
    http://www.thewirelessexperience.com
Sales Range: $50-74.9 Million
Emp.: 300
Telecommunication Servicesb
N.A.I.C.S.: 517111
Brian Wainwright (Pres & CEO)
Michael Prendergast (Dir-Sls)
Robert Shaver (CFO)
Matt Mott (Dir-HR)
Chris Bulmer (Mgr-Supply Chain)
Bryan Quackenbush (Dir-Mktg)
Joseph Lepordo (Head-Staff)
Matt Langford Sr. (Dir-Sls Ops)

United Land Services, Inc. (1)
12276 San Jose Blvd Ste 747, Jacksonville,
FL 32223
Tel.: (904) 829-9255
Web Site:
    https://www.unitedlandservices.com
Landscape Installation & Design Services
N.A.I.C.S.: 561730
Bob Blandford (CEO)

Subsidiary (Domestic):

Georgia Scapes, Inc. (2)
1285 Turner Rd SW, Lilburn, GA 30047-
6728
Tel.: (770) 921-7938
Web Site: http://www.georgiascapes.com
Landscape Architectural Services
N.A.I.C.S.: 541320
Duane Carter (Pres)

**Landscape Service Professionals,
Inc.** (2)
11820 NW 37th St, Coral Springs, FL 33065
Tel.: (954) 721-6920
Web Site:
    http://www.landscapeservicepros.com
Landscape Design Services
N.A.I.C.S.: 541320
Sandra Benton (Pres)
Tom Benton (VP)
Karmen Burn (COO & VP)
Steve Burn (VP-Irrigation Div)
Mark Christofori (Gen Mgr)
Ed Barry (Mgr-Landscape Property Mainte-
nance)
Jennifer Benton (Coord-Bus Dev)

**Uno Restaurant Holdings
Corporation** (1)
100 Charles Park Rd, West Roxbury, MA
02132
Tel.: (617) 323-9200
Web Site: http://www.unos.com
Sales Range: $400-449.9 Million
Casual Theme Restaurant Operator
N.A.I.C.S.: 722511
Aaron D. Spencer (Chm)
William J. Golden (Co-COO)
Frederick W. Houston (VP-Franchising)
Alan D. LaBatte (CIO)
Richard K. Hendrie (Sr VP-Mktg)
Kimberly Boynton (Dir-Mktg)
Roger Zingle (Co-COO)
Andere Fuhrer (VP-Food & Beverage)
Dino Georgakopoulos (VP-Fin)
James Quackenbush (Chief Dev Officer)
Edward Soulier (Sr VP-HR)
Skip Weldon (CMO)
Brad Boston (Sr VP-Ops)
Derek Fournier (VP-Trng)
Brett Morgan (VP-Recruiting & Labor Rels)
Tom Williams (VP-Pur)
George W. Herz II (Gen Counsel & Sr VP)

**CENTRE STATE INTERNA-
TIONAL TRUCKS**
3313 SW Washington St, Peoria, IL
61602
Tel.: (309) 637-8483
Web Site: http://www.centrestate.com
Sales Range: $10-24.9 Million

Emp.: 60
Commercial Trucks
N.A.I.C.S.: 441110
Gary Prepejchal (Pres)
Ken McGuinness (Treas & Sec)

CENTREVILLE BANK
1218 Main St, West Warwick, RI
02893
Tel.: (401) 821-9100
Web Site:
    http://www.centrevillebank.com
Rev.: $36,255,000
Emp.: 170
Federal Savings Services
N.A.I.C.S.: 522180
Paula M. Fahlman (VP-Comml Svcs
& Govt Banking)
Sarah Gardner (Mgr-Coventry)
Jill DeShiro (CFO, Chief Admin Risk
Officer & Exec VP)
Julie M. Casey (Sr VP-Strategy &
Plng)
Christine Tetherly-Lewis (VP-IT)
Mary Murphy (Mgr-North Kingstown)
Harold M. Horvat (Chm, Pres & CEO)

Subsidiaries:

PB Bancorp, Inc. (1)
40 Main St, Putnam, CT 06260
Tel.: (860) 928-6501
Web Site: http://www.putnambank.com
Rev.: $18,651,000
Assets: $538,030,000
Liabilities: $452,958,000
Net Worth: $85,072,000
Earnings: $4,307,000
Emp.: 81
Fiscal Year-end: 06/30/2019
Bank Holding Company
N.A.I.C.S.: 551111
Thomas A. Borner (Pres & CEO)

Subsidiary (Domestic):

Putnam Bank (2)
40 Main St, Putnam, CT 06260
Tel.: (860) 928-6501
Web Site: http://www.putnambank.com
Sales Range: $10-24.9 Million
Emp.: 50
Commericial Banking
N.A.I.C.S.: 522110
Thomas A. Borner (Pres & CEO)
Jitendra K. Sinha (VP)
Robert J. Halloran Jr. (CFO, Treas & Exec
VP)
John F. LaFountain (Officer-Retail Loan &
Sr VP)
Lynn K. Bourque (Sr VP)
LeeAnn C. Kieltyka (Officer-Loan & VP)
Kim Brian Bushey (Chief Comml Lending
Officer & Sr VP)
Clara Angelos (VP & Mgr-Comml Credit)
Brenda Engel (Officer-Comml Loan & Asst
VP)
Robert Trivella (Chief Comml Bus Dev Offi-
cer)

**CENTREX TECHNICAL SALES,
LLC**
2558 Turkey Creek Rd Ste 1, Oilville,
VA 23129
Tel.: (804) 354-1511
Web Site: https://www.gocentrex.com
Year Founded: 2000
Sales Range: $10-24.9 Million
Emp.: 18
Heating & Cooling Products & Ser-
vices
N.A.I.C.S.: 333414
Will Pritchard (VP)
Ben Ottinger (Pres & Owner)

**CENTREXION THERAPEUTICS
CORPORATION**
200 State St 6th Fl, Boston, MA
02109
Tel.: (617) 837-6911   DE
Web Site: http://www.centrexion.com
Year Founded: 2013

Sales Range: Less than $1 Million
Emp.: 14
Pharmaceutical Product Mfr & Distr
N.A.I.C.S.: 325412
Isaac Blech (Vice Chm)
Sol J. Barer (Chm)
James N. Campbell (Pres & Chief
Scientific Officer)
Randall Stevens (Chief Medical Offi-
cer & Exec VP)
B. Nicholas Harvey (CFO, Treas &
Exec VP)
Peter Hanson (Chief Dev Ops Officer
& Exec VP)
Kerrie L. Brady (Chief Bus Officer &
Exec VP-Corp Strategy)
Jeffrey B. Kindler (CEO)

**CENTRI BUSINESS CONSULT-
ING, LLC**
8 Penn Ctr 1628 JFK Blvd Ste 500,
Philadelphia, PA 19103
Tel.: (215) 654-6850
Web Site:
    http://www.centriconsulting.com
Business Consulting Services
N.A.I.C.S.: 541611
Michael M. Aiello (Mng Partner)
Gerald R. Wik (Partner)
Stephan W. Parico (Partner)
Jaime Krug (Chief Quality Officer &
Partner)
Gerald Cullins (Partner)
Ryan Starkes (Partner)
Christopher Mora (Partner)
Kristen Wik (CFO & Chief People Of-
ficer)
Amanda Zeigler (Dir-Mktg)
Melissa Culbertson (Dir-HR)

CENTRIC BRANDS INC.
350 Fifth Ave 6th Fl, New York, NY
10118
Tel.: (646) 582-6000   DE
Web Site:
    http://www.centricbrands.com
Year Founded: 1987
Rev.: $596,602,000
Assets: $1,858,955,000
Liabilities: $1,775,578,000
Net Worth: $83,377,000
Earnings: ($129,910,000)
Emp.: 2,500
Fiscal Year-end: 12/31/18
Denim Products Mfr & Distr
N.A.I.C.S.: 315250
Marc Robert Compagnon (Pres-Asia)
Anurup Pruthi (CFO)
Jason Andrew Rabin (CEO)
Laura Ritchey (COO)
Cory Silverstein (Chief Revenue Offi-
cer)
Joe Favuzza (Chief Strategy Officer
& Pres-Bus Dev)
Steve Pinkow (Pres-Kids)
Jarrod Khan (Pres-Accessories)
Karen Coe (Chief HR Officer)
Roger Czuchra (CIO)
Marc Schneider (Chm)
Sid Keswani (Pres)
Tami Fersko (Chief Ops & Supply
Chain Officer)

Subsidiaries:

Joe's Jeans Subsidiary, Inc. (1)
2340 S Eastern Ave, Commerce, CA 90040-
1431
Tel.: (323) 837-3700
Web Site: http://www.joesjean.com
Emp.: 50
Broadwoven Fabric Mfr
N.A.I.C.S.: 313210
Hoss Hamidi (Gen Mgr)

RG Parent LLC (1)
264 W 40th St Fl 10, New York, NY 10018
Tel.: (855) 214-3350
Denim Product Mfr

N.A.I.C.S.: 315250

**CENTRIC BUSINESS SYS-
TEMS, INC.**
10702 Red Run Blvd, Owings Mills,
MD 21117
Web Site: http://www.centricbiz.com
Sales Range: Less than $1 Million
Computer Related Services
N.A.I.C.S.: 541519
Rick Bastinelli (Pres)
Loralea Sanderson (Sr VP-Fin & Ad-
min)
Felix Villanueva (VP-Technical Svc)
Diana Griffin (Sr Mgr-Customer Care)
Patty Penuell (Dir-HR & Talent Acqui-
sition)
Shawn Moran (VP-Sls)
Jeff Hart (VP-Sls)
Bob Mcmonagle (VP-Sls)

CENTRIC CONSULTING, LLC
1950 Composite Dr, Dayton, OH
45420-1475
Tel.: (614) 554-0113
Web Site:
    http://www.centricconsulting.com
Year Founded: 1999
Sales Range: $75-99.9 Million
Emp.: 500
Business & Technology Consulting
Services
N.A.I.C.S.: 541618
Larry English (Founder & CEO)
Eric Van Luven (COO)
Michael Brannan (VP-Tech)
Chad Caldwell (VP-Natl Ins)
Greg Klem (VP-Bus Consulting Svcs)
Jason Pohl (Natl Partner)
Andy Rahman (VP)
Andy Park (VP)
Chris Szaz (VP)
Ed Heberlein (VP-Energy & Utilities)
Errol Yudelman (VP)
Richard McGee (VP-Indianapolis)
Ted Goodman (VP)

Subsidiaries:

The Mako Group, LLC (1)
8555 River Rd - Ste 320, Indianapolis, IN
46240
Tel.: (877) 247-6256
Web Site: http://www.makopro.com
Sales Range: $1-9.9 Million
Emp.: 18
Security Consulting Services
N.A.I.C.S.: 541690
David Lefever (CEO)

CENTRIC DIGITAL LLC.
120 5th Ave 7th Fl, New York, NY
10011
Tel.: (347) 974-0980
Web Site:
    http://www.CentricDigital.com
Year Founded: 2009
Sales Range: $10-24.9 Million
Emp.: 140
Digital Transformation Consulting
Services
N.A.I.C.S.: 327910
Jason Albanese (Co-Founder & CEO)
Brian Manning (Co-Founder, Pres &
Chief Digital Officer)
Brendan Hammond (Pres-Australia)
Brian Dearth (Chief Strategy Officer)
Jean-Marcel Nicolai (Chief Product
Officer)
Stephen R. Morrissey (CTO)
David Palmieri (COO)

CENTRIC GROUP LLC
1260 Andes Blvd, Saint Louis, MO
63132
Tel.: (314) 214-2700
Web Site:
    http://www.centricgroup.com

Centric Group LLC—(Continued)

Year Founded: 1999
Rev.: $301,800,000
Emp.: 70
Drugs, Proprietaries & Sundries
N.A.I.C.S.: 424210
Jim Thiess (CEO)
Lawanda Boykin (Mgr-Accts Payable)
Russ Willey (CFO)
Cheryl Kawalec (Sr Acct Mgr)
Steve Ketterer (Engr-Sys)

Subsidiaries:

Access Catalog Company LLC (1)
10880 Linpage Pl, Saint Louis, MO 63132-1008
Tel.: (314) 301-3300
Web Site: http://www.courtesyproducts.com
Rev.: $24,000,000
Emp.: 60
Coffee, Green Or Roasted
N.A.I.C.S.: 423690

Betallic Llc (1)
2326 Grissom Dr, Saint Louis, MO 63146
Tel.: (314) 991-8800
Web Site: http://www.betallic.com
Rev.: $6,700,000
Emp.: 50
Balloons, Metal Foil Laminated With Rubber
N.A.I.C.S.: 326299
Craig Albrecht (Pres)

Courtesy Products Llc (1)
10840 Linpage Blvd, Saint Louis, MO 63132
Tel.: (314) 592-5100
Web Site: http://www.courtesyproducts.com
Coffee
N.A.I.C.S.: 445298

Keefe Group, Inc. (1)
13870 Corporate Woods Trl, Bridgeton, MO 63044
Tel.: (800) 831-6939
Web Site: http://www.keefegroup.com
Food & Electronic Product Distr
N.A.I.C.S.: 424450

Subsidiary (Domestic):

ICSolutions, LLC. (2)
2200 Danbury St, San Antonio, TX 78217
Tel.: (800) 661-3845
Web Site: http://www.icsolutions.com
Telecommunication Servicesb
N.A.I.C.S.: 517111

Keefe Supply Company (2)
1371 Tradeport Dr Ste 101, Jacksonville, FL 32218
Tel.: (904) 741-6776
Web Site: http://www.keefegroup.com
Food & Electronic Product Distr
N.A.I.C.S.: 424450
Tom Garris (Mgr)

CENTRIC SOFTWARE, INC.
655 Campbell Technology Pkwy Ste 200, Campbell, CA 95008
Tel.: (408) 574-7802
Web Site:
https://www.centricsoftware.com
Sales Range: $10-24.9 Million
Emp.: 42
Prepackaged Software
N.A.I.C.S.: 513210
Chris Groves (Pres & CEO)
Ronald S. Watson (VP-Product Dev)
Ravi Rangan (CTO)
Fabrice Canonge (Sr VP-Global Sls)
Humberto Roa (VP-Innovation)
Laurent Dubuisson (VP-Client Svcs)
Alice Gerbel (VP-Fin & Admin)
Anastasia Charbin (CMO)

CENTRIC TELECOM, INC.
1749 Old Meadow Rd Ste 120, McLean, VA 22102
Tel.: (703) 321-5070 VA
Web Site: http://www.centrictel.com
Year Founded: 2004
Telecommunication Servicesb

N.A.I.C.S.: 517121
Lawrence J. Dressel (Pres & CEO)

CENTRICS LLC
2275 Cassens Dr Ste 130, Fenton, MO 63026
Tel.: (636) 305-8500 DE
Web Site: http://www.centrics.com
Year Founded: 2003
Personalized Digital Products
N.A.I.C.S.: 541690
Tim Hufker (Pres & CEO)
Anthony Gianino (CTO)
Tim Kelly (Dir-Prod Dev)

CENTRICSIT, LLC.
3140 Northwoods Pkwy Ste 700, Norcross, GA 30071
Tel.: (678) 495-1301 GA
Web Site: https://www.centricsit.com
Year Founded: 2007
Sales Range: $50-74.9 Million
Emp.: 130
Information Technology & Services
N.A.I.C.S.: 519290
Derek Odegard (Founder & Pres)
Ryan Ritter (VP-Direct Sls)
Jon Hans (VP)
Patrick Keuller (VP-Global Svcs)
Cameron James (VP-Direct Sls)
Pete Bohman (VP-Ops)
Derik Reynecke (CFO)
Taylor Barnes (Dir-ITAD Svcs)

CENTRINET CORP
1720 Windward Concourse Ste 310, Alpharetta, GA 30005
Tel.: (678) 373-0440
Web Site:
http://www.centrinetcorp.com
Sales Range: $10-24.9 Million
Emp.: 19
Computer & Office Machine Repair & Maintenance
N.A.I.C.S.: 811210
Keith Paschall (Pres)
Sue Adamczyk (Acct Mgr-Fin)

CENTRIPETAL CAPITAL PARTNERS, LLC
6 Landmark Sq 3rd Fl, Stamford, CT 06901
Tel.: (203) 326-7600
Web Site: https://www.centricap.com
Emp.: 7
Privater Equity Firm
N.A.I.C.S.: 523999
Steven G. Chrust (Mng Dir & Sr Principal)
E. Bulkeley Griswold (Mng Dir & Sr Principal)
Jeffrey I. Brodlieb (Principal)
Stephen T. Rossetter (Principal)

Subsidiaries:

Pet Paradise Resort (1)
5130 University Blvd, Jacksonville, FL 32216
Tel.: (904) 363-3330
Web Site: http://www.petparadiseresort.com
Sales Range: $10-24.9 Million
Emp.: 250
Pet Boarding & Day Care Services
N.A.I.C.S.: 812910
Fred Goldsmith (Founder)
Fernando Acosta Rua (Pres & CEO)
Kevin English (COO & Sr VP-Fin)
Bill Joel (Gen Counsel & Sr VP)
Jaime Pickett (Chief Veterinary Officer)

CENTRIX FINANCIAL LLC
6782 S Potomac St, Centennial, CO 80112-3915
Tel.: (303) 223-7000
Web Site:
http://www.centrixfinancial.com
Year Founded: 1990

Sales Range: $10-24.9 Million
Emp.: 1,000
Adjustment & Collection Services
N.A.I.C.S.: 561440
Robert Sutton (Co-Chm)
H. Dane Hooks (Exec VP-Fin Ops)
Jerry Fitzgerald (Pres)
Daryl Bradley (Sr VP)
Pat Yokley (CEO)
Sue Brayman (Co-Chm)
Joe Ford (VP-Client Svcs)
Jeff Martin (Mgr-Natl Sls-Credit Union Markets)

CENTRO DE SALUD DE LARES, INC.
PO Box 379, Lares, PR 00669-0379
Tel.: (787) 897-2727 PR
Web Site: http://www.laressalud.com
Year Founded: 1986
Sales Range: $10-24.9 Million
Emp.: 168
Individual & Family Support Services
N.A.I.C.S.: 624190
Rigoberta Hernandez Nieves (Exec Dir)

CENTRO INC.
950 N Bend Dr, North Liberty, IA 52317-9300
Tel.: (319) 626-3200 IA
Web Site: http://www.centroinc.com
Year Founded: 1970
Sales Range: $1-9.9 Million
Emp.: 800
Specialty Distr & Sales of Control Product Solutions
N.A.I.C.S.: 334519
Brian Olesen (CEO)

CENTRO MART INC.
2150 W Alpine Ave, Stockton, CA 95204-2853
Tel.: (209) 948-4163
Year Founded: 1973
Sales Range: $25-49.9 Million
Emp.: 260
Provider of Grocery Services
N.A.I.C.S.: 445110
Mell Young (Pres)
Yi Zhang (Controller)

CENTRO MEDIA, INC.
22 W Hubbard Ste 400, Chicago, IL 60654
Tel.: (312) 423-1565
Web Site: http://www.centro.net
Sales Range: $75-99.9 Million
Emp.: 130
Media Services & Software
N.A.I.C.S.: 541830
Shawn Riegsecker (Founder & CEO)
Michael Radovancevich (CTO)
Katie Risch (Sr VP)
Kelly Wenzel (CMO)
Charlie Thomas (VP-Sls)
Kristin Haarlow (Reg VP-Media Ops)
Emily Barron (Exec VP-Talent & Dev)
Igor Fey (VP-Tech Ops)
Matt Miller (Exec VP-Fin)
Tyler Kelly (Pres)

Subsidiaries:

SiteScout Inc. (1)
579 Richmond Street West Suite 100, Toronto, M5V 1Y6, ON, Canada
Tel.: (647) 427-0330
Web Site: http://www.sitescout.com
Sales Range: $1-9.9 Million
Emp.: 65
Advertising Software
N.A.I.C.S.: 513210
Terry Taouss (Mng Dir)

CENTROCAMIONES INC.
Carr Ste 2 KM 28.5 BO Espinosa, Vega Alta, PR 00692

Tel.: (787) 784-8000
Web Site:
http://www.centrocamionespr.com
Sales Range: $75-99.9 Million
Emp.: 300
Trucks, Commercial
N.A.I.C.S.: 423110
Jorge M. Martinez (Pres)
Antonio Plasencia (Mgr-Fleet)

CENTRONIA
1420 Columbia Rd NW, Washington, DC 20009
Tel.: (202) 332-4200 DC
Web Site: https://www.centronia.org
Year Founded: 1991
Sales Range: $10-24.9 Million
Emp.: 352
Educational Support Services
N.A.I.C.S.: 611710
Cynthia Mercado (Sr Dir-Admin & Ops)
Rosalina Burgos (Sr Dir-Early Childhood Education)
Cesar Watts (Sr Dir-Community Engagement & Education)

CENTROS SOR ISOLINA FERRE INC
PO Box 7313, Ponce, PR 00732-7313
Tel.: (787) 842-0000 PR
Web Site: http://www.csifpr.org
Year Founded: 1957
Sales Range: $10-24.9 Million
Emp.: 562
Community Development Services
N.A.I.C.S.: 813319

CENTURA COLLEGE
4455 S Blvd, Virginia Beach, VA 23452
Tel.: (757) 456-5065
Web Site:
https://www.centuracollege.edu
Sales Range: $10-24.9 Million
Emp.: 200
Education Services
N.A.I.C.S.: 923110
Jerry Yagan (Pres)
Brian Stauss (Coord-Adv)
Mike Glover (Mgr-Internet Mktg)
Joel English (Reg Dir)
Pam Freund (Dir-Fin Aid)
Ellen Duckworth (Dir-Admissions)

Subsidiaries:

Aviation Institute of Maintenance (1)
4455 S Blvd, Virginia Beach, VA 23452
Tel.: (757) 233-6542
Web Site:
http://www.aviationmaintenance.edu
Emp.: 10
Flight Training & Maintenance Services
N.A.I.C.S.: 611512
Jerry Yagan (Pres)

Division (Domestic):

Aviation Institute of Maintenance Indianapolis (2)
7251 W McCarty St, Indianapolis, IN 46241-1445
Tel.: (317) 243-4519
Web Site:
http://www.aviationmaintenance.edu
Emp.: 25
Flight Training & Maintenance Services
N.A.I.C.S.: 611512
Rachel Gildon (Coord-Career & Student Svcs)
Andrew Duncan (Exec Dir-Campus)
Shannon Bigelow (Dir-Admissions)

CENTURIA CORPORATION
11955 Democracy Dr, Reston, VA 20190-5662
Tel.: (703) 435-4600
Web Site: http://www.centuria.com

Year Founded: 2002
Sales Range: $10-24.9 Million
Emp.: 106
Government Services
N.A.I.C.S.: 541611
Kevin M. Burke (Pres & CEO)
Marjan Hekmat (Exec VP-Fin)
Gary Arnett (VP)

CENTURION AUTO LOGISTICS
5912 New Kings Rd, Jacksonville, FL
32209
Tel.: (904) 766-8500
Web Site:
https://www.centurionauto
logistics.com
Year Founded: 1992
Sales Range: $25-49.9 Million
Emp.: 450
Automobile Transportation Services
N.A.I.C.S.: 488410
Vicki Shafer (Owner & Chm)
Charles McGarity (Vice Chm)
Venus Soto (Controller)
Jack McKinney (Sr VP)

Subsidiaries:

Centurion Auto Transport   (1)
5912 New Kings Rd, Jacksonville, FL
32209-2147
Tel.: (904) 766-8500
Sales Range: $10-24.9 Million
Emp.: 160
Trucking Service
N.A.I.C.S.: 484230
Sonia Daragjati (Dir-HR)

CENTURION COUNSEL, INC.
1282 Pacific Oaks Pl, Escondido, CA
92029
Tel.: (760) 471-8536
Web Site:
http://www.centurioncounsel.com
Sales Range: $10-24.9 Million
Emp.: 15
Brokers Security
N.A.I.C.S.: 523150
Jack Kendrick Heilbron (CEO & Chief
Investment Officer)
Steven Foss (Ops Mgr)
John D. Laurel (Chief Compliance
Officer)

Subsidiaries:

PIM Financial Services Inc.   (1)
1282 Pacific Oaks Pl, Escondido, CA 92029
Tel.: (760) 471-8536
Web Site: http://www.pimfinancial.com
Security Brokers
N.A.I.C.S.: 523940

CENTURION INDUSTRIES INC.
1107 N Taylor Rd, Garrett, IN 46738-
1880
Tel.: (260) 357-6665   IN
Web Site:
https://www.centurionind.com
Year Founded: 1989
Sales Range: $75-99.9 Million
Emp.: 1,000
Metal Fabrication & Industrial Con-
struction; Building Equipment Installa-
tion
N.A.I.C.S.: 238290
Brad Parrish (Pres)
Tim McCreg (Controller)
Barry Bender (Dir-HR)
Kenneth L. Tharp (Chm)

Subsidiaries:

A-Lert Construction Services Inc. (1)
401 N 6th St, Fredonia, KS 66736
Tel.: (620) 378-4131
Web Site:
http://www.alertconstructionservices.com
Construction Engineering Services
N.A.I.C.S.: 541330

Harry Oehlert (Founder)
Kenneth L. Tharp (Chm)
Bradley S. Parish (Pres)
Loren R. Troyer (Treas & Sec)

Plant (Domestic):

A-Lert Construction Services Inc. -
Fabrication Facility   (2)
4050 Bearsdale Rd, Decatur, IL 62526
Tel.: (217) 872-1100
Web Site:
http://www.alertconstructionservices.com
Fabricated Steel & Metal Mfr
N.A.I.C.S.: 332312
Bradley S. Parish (Pres)
Loren R. Troyer (Treas & Sec)

Centurion Industries Inc. - A-Lert
Building Systems Division   (1)
2065 FM 1102, New Braunfels, TX 78132
Tel.: (830) 626-7755
Web Site:
http://www.alertbuildingsystems.com
Building Component Mfr & Distr
N.A.I.C.S.: 332311

CENTURION INVESTMENTS
INC.
750 N Beechcraft, Chesterfield, MO
63005-3628
Tel.: (636) 532-2674   MO
Web Site: http://www.avmats.com
Year Founded: 1978
Sales Range: $25-49.9 Million
Emp.: 200
Holding Company; Transportation
Equipment & Services
N.A.I.C.S.: 423860
Arthur Giessman II (Pres)

CENTURION LAND TITLE, INC.
1008 Woodland Plz Run, Fort Wayne,
IN 46825
Tel.: (260) 755-4224
Web Site:
http://www.centurionlandtitle.com
Year Founded: 2013
Sales Range: $1-9.9 Million
Emp.: 22
Real Estate Services
N.A.I.C.S.: 531390
Angella Lee (VP & Mgr-Escrow)
Kurt Simpson (COO)
Andy Milentis (Chief Revenue Officer)
Samantha Simpson (Sls Mgr)
Jessica Rockwood (Branch Mgr-
Southwest Office)

CENTURION STRATEGIES LLC
301 W Platt St Ste 12, Tampa, FL
33606
Tel.: (813) 732-0180
Web Site: https://www.centurion-
strategies.com
Year Founded: 2008
Sales Range: $1-9.9 Million
Public Relations Agencies
N.A.I.C.S.: 541820
Michael Bilello (Founder, Pres &
CEO)

CENTURY 21 BEGGINS EN-
TERPRISES, INC.
6542 US Hwy 41 N Ste 101, Apollo
Beach, FL 33572
Tel.: (813) 645-8481
Web Site:
http://www.c21beggins.com
Year Founded: 1992
Sales Range: $25-49.9 Million
Emp.: 250
Real Estate Broker
N.A.I.C.S.: 531210
Ben DeBrocke (CFO & CIO)
Angelique Beggins (Dir-Interactive
Mktg-Agent Care)

CENTURY 21 HOMETOWN RE-
ALTY
1160 Price St, Pismo Beach, CA
93449
Tel.: (805) 773-2100
Emp.: 300
Real Estate Agency
N.A.I.C.S.: 531210
Jack Hardy (Pres & CEO)

Subsidiaries:

Peabody & Plum Realtors, Inc.   (1)
6755 El Camino Real, Atascadero, CA
93422-4240
Tel.: (805) 466-8000
Real Estate Agency
N.A.I.C.S.: 531210

CENTURY 21 INC.
22 Cortlandt St, New York, NY 10007
Tel.: (212) 227-9092
Web Site: http://www.c21stores.com
Year Founded: 1961
Rev.: $137,200,000
Emp.: 3,000
Discount Department Stores
N.A.I.C.S.: 455110
Abraham Gindi (Founder & Co-CEO)
Harry Roberts (CIO)
Eduardo Castro (Mgr-Grp Loss Pre-
vention)
Brad Milo (Mgr-Corp Loss Prevention
Trng & Compliance)
Raymond A. Gindi (Co-CEO)

CENTURY 21 NACHMAN RE-
ALTY, L.L.C.
720 Thimble Shoals Blvd Ste 116,
Newport News, VA 23606
Tel.: (757) 833-8400
Web Site:
https://www.century21nachman.com
Sales Range: $10-24.9 Million
Emp.: 40
Real Estate Services
N.A.I.C.S.: 237210
Vicki Andrews (Dir-Relocation)
Robert H. Burch (Gen Mgr)
Jennifer Elmore (Mgr-Property)
Craig Wool (Dir-Property Mgmt)

CENTURY 21 NORTH HOMES
REALTY, INC.
13322 Hwy 99 Ste 100, Everett, WA
98204
Tel.: (425) 743-3775
Web Site: http://www.century21north
homes.com
Rev.: $14,400,000
Emp.: 261
Real Estate Agents & Brokers
N.A.I.C.S.: 531210
Edward Heidel (Pres)

CENTURY 21 PINNACLE
3001 Emrick Blvd, Bethlehem, PA
18020
Tel.: (610) 252-6999
Web Site:
http://www.century21pinnacle.com
Rev.: $93,780,233
Emp.: 40
Real Estate Services
N.A.I.C.S.: 531390
Debbie Getz (Dir-Relocation)

CENTURY 21 PROMOTIONS,
INC.
2601 W Commodore Way, Seattle,
WA 98199-1231
Tel.: (206) 282-8200   WA
Web Site:
http://www.century21promotion.com
Year Founded: 1980
Sales Range: $1-9.9 Million
Emp.: 28

Importer of Hats, Caps & Jackets
N.A.I.C.S.: 424350
Jeffery H. Hoch (Pres)
Daniel Boule (Mgr-Custom Products)
Kraig Nagy (Mgr)
Irv Hoch (VP)

CENTURY 21 RONDEAU
729 Hope St, Bristol, RI 02809
Tel.: (401) 254-1900
Web Site:
http://www.c21rondeau.com
Sales Range: $25-49.9 Million
Emp.: 4
Real Estate Agency
N.A.I.C.S.: 531210

CENTURY AIR CONDITIONING
SUPPLY INC.
10510 W Sam Houston Pkwy S,
Houston, TX 77099
Tel.: (281) 530-2859   TX
Web Site: https://www.centuryac.com
Year Founded: 1973
Sales Range: $50-74.9 Million
Emp.: 125
Warm Air Heating & Air Conditioning
Whslr
N.A.I.C.S.: 423730
Dennis Bearden (CEO & Founder)

Subsidiaries:

Air Management Supply   (1)
12302 Cary Cir, La Vista, NE 68128
Tel.: (402) 339-5202
Web Site:
http://www.airmanagementsupply.com
Sales Range: $10-24.9 Million
Emp.: 14
Warm Air Heating & Air Conditioning
N.A.I.C.S.: 423730
John Simon (Mgr-Spotlight)

CENTURY AMERICA CORPO-
RATION
875 N Michigan Ave Ste 3707, Chi-
cago, IL 60611-1946
Tel.: (312) 266-1025   IL
Year Founded: 1938
Sales Range: $100-124.9 Million
Emp.: 200
Steel Processing Services
N.A.I.C.S.: 423510
Susan Pamzer (VP)

CENTURY BANCSHARES OF
FLORIDA, INC.
716 W Fletcher Ave, Tampa, FL
33612
Tel.: (813) 961-3300
Web Site: https://www.centurybk.com
Bank Holding Company
N.A.I.C.S.: 551111
Jose Vivero (Chm & CEO)
Gabriel Vivero (Pres)

Subsidiaries:

Century Bank of Florida   (1)
716 W Fletcher Ave, Tampa, FL 33612
Tel.: (813) 961-3300
Web Site: http://www.centurybk.com
Rev.: $2,829,000
Assets: $70,386,000
Liabilities: $64,833,000
Net Worth: $5,553,000
Earnings: $14,000
Emp.: 15
Fiscal Year-end: 12/31/2013
Commercial Banking
N.A.I.C.S.: 522110
Jose Vivero (Pres)
Susan Sutton (Sr VP-Credit Admin)

CENTURY BANCSHARES, INC.
201 W Woodford St, Lawrenceburg,
KY 40342
Tel.: (502) 859-5111   KY

Century Bancshares, Inc.—(Continued)

Web Site:
https://www.centurybankky.com
Year Founded: 2000
Sales Range: $1-9.9 Million
Emp.: 27
Bank Holding Company
N.A.I.C.S.: 551111
G. Anthony Busseni (Pres & CEO)
Darin L. Young (Pres/CEO-Century Bank of Kentucky)
Thomas H. Smith (Chm)

Subsidiaries:

Century Bank of Kentucky, Inc. (1)
201 W Woodford St, Lawrenceburg, KY 40342
Tel.: (502) 859-5111
Web Site: http://www.centurybankky.com
Sales Range: $1-9.9 Million
Commericial Banking
N.A.I.C.S.: 522110

CENTURY BANCSHARES, INC.
39 Ct Sq, Gainesville, MO 65655
Tel.: (417) 679-3321
Bank Holding Company
N.A.I.C.S.: 551111

Subsidiaries:

Legacy Bank & Trust Company (1)
10603 Highway 32, Plato, MO 65552
Tel.: (417) 458-4222
Web Site:
http://www.legacybankandtrust.com
Sales Range: $1-9.9 Million
Emp.: 25
Commericial Banking
N.A.I.C.S.: 522110
Ashley Watson (VP-Compliance)
Dee Barnes (VP)
Erma Forrest (VP)
Gary Crutchfield (VP)
Kerrie Zubrod (VP-Trng)
Kim Stigall (VP-Admin)
Missy Long (VP-Ops)
Rob Covey (VP)
Scott Harris (Pres & Chief Lending Officer)
Tim Austin (VP)
John Everet (Pres)

CENTURY BANK
400 Mystic Ave, Medford, MA 02155
Tel.: (866) 823-6887
Web Site:
http://www.centurybank.com
Rev.: $46,300,000
Emp.: 500
Commericial Banking
N.A.I.C.S.: 522110
Barry Sloane (Pres & CEO)
Linda Sloane Kay (Exec VP)
Frank Wagnon (Sr VP-Comml Lending Team)
Erica Saunders (Sr VP-Las Cruces)

CENTURY BANK & TRUST
100 W Chicago St, Coldwater, MI 49036
Tel.: (517) 278-1500
Web Site: http://www.centurybt.com
Rev.: $17,000,000
Emp.: 125
Regional Bank
N.A.I.C.S.: 522110
Rebecca Duke (Dir-Adv)

CENTURY BANK OF THE OZARKS
42 Court Sq, Gainesville, MO 65655
Tel.: (417) 679-3321
Web Site: https://www.cbozarks.com
Year Founded: 1894
Sales Range: $1-9.9 Million
Emp.: 75
Provider of Banking Services
N.A.I.C.S.: 522110
Chris Harlin (Pres & CEO)

CENTURY BATHWORKS, INC.
250 Lackawanna Ave, Woodland Park, NJ 07424
Tel.: (973) 785-4290
Web Site:
https://www.centurybathworks.com
Year Founded: 1946
Sales Range: $10-24.9 Million
Emp.: 100
Glass Door Mfr
N.A.I.C.S.: 327215
Michael MacMillan (Pres)
John Spazante (Mgr-Natl Sls & Mktg)
Mike McMillan (Acct Mgr & Mgr-Ops)

CENTURY BUSINESS SOLUTIONS, INC.
20 Pacifica Ste 1450, Irvine, CA 92618
Web Site:
http://www.centurybizsolutions.net
Year Founded: 2004
Sales Range: $10-24.9 Million
Emp.: 200
Financial Management Services
N.A.I.C.S.: 541611
Jessica Travis (VP-Mktg)

CENTURY BUSINESS TECHNOLOGIES, INC.
401 SW 30th St, Topeka, KS 66611
Tel.: (785) 267-4555
Web Site: https://www.centuryks.com
Year Founded: 1981
Sales Range: $10-24.9 Million
Emp.: 74
Copier Equipment Distr
N.A.I.C.S.: 423420
Dawna McCabe (Pres & COO)
Lawrence Reynoso (VP-Sls & Mktg)
Susie Weick (VP-Admin)
Mark McCabe (Pres & COO)

CENTURY CARPET, INC.
64 Southard Ave, Farmingdale, NJ 07727
Tel.: (732) 919-2050
Web Site:
https://www.centurycarpet.net
Year Founded: 1967
Sales Range: $10-24.9 Million
Emp.: 55
Carpet Installation, Sales & Maintenance
N.A.I.C.S.: 238330
David Croson (Pres)

CENTURY COMPANIES, INC.
39 Industrial Way, Lewistown, MT 59457
Tel.: (406) 538-2334
Web Site:
http://www.centurycompanies.com
Year Founded: 1976
Sales Range: $10-24.9 Million
Emp.: 150
Highway & Street Paving Contractor
N.A.I.C.S.: 237310
Jack Morgenstern (Chm)
Tom Evans (Sr VP)
Tracy Golik (CFO)

CENTURY CONSTRUCTION, INC.
34 Kenton Lands Rd, Erlanger, KY 41018
Tel.: (859) 331-6626
Web Site:
https://www.centuryconstruction.com
Year Founded: 1968
Rev.: $22,400,000
Emp.: 100
Nonresidential Construction Services
N.A.I.C.S.: 236220

Bill Frisch (VP-Plumbing)
David Hodge (VP)
John F. Hodge (Pres)

CENTURY CONTAINER, LLC
5331 State Rte 7, New Waterford, OH 44445
Tel.: (330) 457-2367
Web Site:
https://www.centurycontainerco.com
Year Founded: 1977
Sales Range: $10-24.9 Million
Plastic Containers Mfr; Adhesives & Sealants Mfr
N.A.I.C.S.: 326199

Subsidiaries:

Century Industries (1)
5331 State Rte 7, New Waterford, OH 44445
Tel.: (330) 457-2367
Web Site:
http://www.centuryindustriescorp.com
Adhesives & Sealants Mfr
N.A.I.C.S.: 325520

CENTURY CONTRACTORS, INC.
5100 Smith Farm Rd, Matthews, NC 28104-8132
Tel.: (704) 821-8050
Web Site:
https://www.centurycontractors.com
Year Founded: 1991
Sales Range: $50-74.9 Million
Emp.: 900
Industrial Buildings & Warehouses
N.A.I.C.S.: 236210
Howard Smith (VP)
Vicki Klutz (CFO)
J. D. Armstrong II (Chm)

CENTURY CONVEYOR, INC.
4 Gladys Ct, Edison, NJ 08817
Tel.: (732) 248-4900
Web Site:
http://www.centuryconveyor.com
Year Founded: 1981
Rev.: $17,481,354
Emp.: 59
Machinery Installation
N.A.I.C.S.: 238290
Ron Ferrara (Pres)
Jim Santore (Engr-Sls)

CENTURY DIRECT LLC
15 Enter Ln, Islandia, NY 11749
Tel.: (212) 763-0600
Web Site:
https://www.centurydirect.net
Year Founded: 1932
Sales Range: $1-9.9 Million
Emp.: 200
Direct Mail Advertising Services
N.A.I.C.S.: 541860
Michael Kellogg (CEO)
Jerome Nassau (Pres)
Eric Seid (COO)
Lawrence Korek (CMO)
Thomas McNeill (CFO)
Jeffrey Dorr (Pres-Madcar Div)

CENTURY DISTRIBUTORS, INC.
15710 Crabbs Branch Way, Rockville, MD 20855-2620
Tel.: (301) 212-9100
Web Site:
https://www.centurydist.com
Year Founded: 1976
Sales Range: $25-49.9 Million
Emp.: 180
Tobacco Product Distr
N.A.I.C.S.: 424940
Robert Kulacki (Mgr-Sls)
Debra Robins (Pres)
Lori Rodman (VP-Sls)

Jim Mullen (CFO)
Barry Ricketts (Mgr-Customer Svc)
Bob Essex (Mgr-Accts Payable)
Darren Pulvirenti (Mgr-Sls)
Lyn DeMambro (Mgr-Accts Receivable)
Mary Solla (Dir-HR)
Mike Wertz (Mgr-Warehouse)
Ron Winson (Mgr-Pur)

CENTURY EQUIPMENT INC.
5959 Angola Rd, Toledo, OH 43615-6332
Tel.: (419) 865-7400
Web Site:
https://www.centuryequip.com
Year Founded: 1950
Sales Range: $50-74.9 Million
Emp.: 100
Wholesales Industrial Equipment
N.A.I.C.S.: 423820
Ron Smolik (Gen Mgr)
John Mowat (Mgr-Sls)
Andy Platt (Mgr-Svc)
Jim Kuebler (Mgr-Credit)
Connie Spotts (Mgr-Distr)
Jason Moser (Mgr-Sls)
Al Vargo (Mgr-Svc)
Tom Handel (Pres & CFO)

Subsidiaries:

Century Equipment Inc. (1)
26565 Miles Rd Ste 100, Cleveland, OH 44128-5929 (100%)
Tel.: (216) 292-6911
Web Site: http://www.centuryequip.com
Sales Range: $25-49.9 Million
Emp.: 27
Outdoor Power Equipment Distr
N.A.I.C.S.: 423820
Ron Smolik (Mgr-Comml Bus)

Century Irrigation Station (1)
8650 Bilstein Blvd, Hamilton, OH 45015
Tel.: (866) 914-2609
Web Site:
http://www.centuryirrigationstation.com
Emp.: 30
Irrigation Equipment Mfr & Distr
N.A.I.C.S.: 332322
Mike Knepper (Mgr-Store)

CENTURY EQUITY PARTNERS LLC
100 Federal St 29th Fl, Boston, MA 02110
Tel.: (617) 863-2950
Web Site: https://www.cepfunds.com
Private Equity Investment Firm
N.A.I.C.S.: 523999
Davis Fulkerson (Mng Dir)
Charles Kline (Mng Dir)
Peter Laino (Mng Dir)
Chris Lalonde (Mng Dir)
Stephen Marquardt (Mng Dir)
Keith Roux (Principal)
Thomas Ryan (Principal)
Kevin McCarthy (Principal)
Kevin MacLaughlan (CFO)
Stephanie Viehl (Controller)

CENTURY FAST FOODS INC.
10350 Santa Monica Blvd, Los Angeles, CA 90025
Tel.: (310) 203-8404
Sales Range: $10-24.9 Million
Emp.: 400
Fast-Food Restaurant, Chain
N.A.I.C.S.: 722513
Robert Brunson (Pres)
Sheila Cook (Controller)

CENTURY FASTENERS CORP.
5020 Ireland St, Elmhurst, NY 11373-3734
Tel.: (718) 446-5000
Web Site:
http://www.centuryfasteners.com

Year Founded: 1955
Sales Range: $25-49.9 Million
Emp.: 215
Wholesale Distribution of Fasteners, Electronic Hardware & Electromechanical Components
N.A.I.C.S.: 423840
Jack Schlegel *(CEO)*
Evan Stieglitz *(Co-Pres)*
Tom Brodsky *(Co-Pres)*
Barbara Caraturo *(CFO)*
John Ringold *(Mktg Dir)*
Don Hershey *(Dir-Programs & Matls)*
Rich Monahan *(Dir-IT)*
David Clark *(Sls Dir)*
Adrienne Boyd *(Mgr-HR)*
Todd Sider *(Dir-Pur)*
Charles J. Salley *(Sls Mgr-West)*
Denise Murphy *(Branch Mgr-Syracuse)*
James D. Harding *(Dir-Ops)*
Nathan Howell *(Dir-Quality)*
Joseph P. Brock *(Sls Mgr-Northeast)*
Mark James *(Branch Mgr-Atlanta & Richmond)*
Gene Fedrick *(Dir-Pur)*
Michelle Olson *(Mgr-Strategic Sourcing)*
Robert D. Botticelli *(Dir-Bus Dev)*

CENTURY FENCE COMPANY
1300 Hickory St, Pewaukee, WI 53072-0727
Tel.: (262) 547-3331   WI
Web Site:
   https://www.centuryfence.com
Year Founded: 1917
Sales Range: $75-99.9 Million
Emp.: 100
Chain Link Fence & Gates; Steel Beam Guard Rail; Athletic Back Stops & Tennis Courts; Interstate Highway Fencing & Signing; Traffic Pavement Markings
N.A.I.C.S.: 238990
A. W. Bryant *(Chm)*
John Connell *(Pres)*

Subsidiaries:

Century Fence Co.   (1)
14839 Lake Dr, Forest Lake, MN 55025-0277
Tel.: (651) 464-7373
Web Site: http://www.centuryfence.com
Sales Range: $25-49.9 Million
Emp.: 10
Fencing Company
N.A.I.C.S.: 238990
John Bailey *(Branch Mgr)*

CENTURY FINANCIAL SERVICES CORP.
100 S Federal Pl, Santa Fe, NM 87501-1964
Tel.: (505) 982-1981
Sales Range: $10-24.9 Million
Emp.: 150
Bank Holding Company
N.A.I.C.S.: 522180
Don Padgett *(Pres)*

Subsidiaries:

Century Bank FSB   (1)
100 S Federal Pl, Santa Fe, NM 87501
Tel.: (505) 995-2500
Rev.: $17,825,086
Federal Savings & Loan Association
N.A.I.C.S.: 522180

CENTURY GAMING TECHNOLOGIES
600 Pilot Rd, Las Vegas, NV 89119
Tel.: (702) 270-7500
Web Site:
   http://www.centurygamingtech.com
Year Founded: 2000
Licensed Gaming Route Operator

N.A.I.C.S.: 713290
Steve Arntzen *(Pres & CEO)*

Subsidiaries:

Grand Vision Gaming LLC   (1)
1291 Weil St, Billings, MT 59101
Tel.: (406) 896-9900
Web Site:
   http://www.grandvisiongaming.com
Gambling & Casino
N.A.I.C.S.: 713290

CENTURY GROUP INC.
1106 W Napoleon St, Sulphur, LA 70663-3106
Tel.: (337) 527-5266
Web Site:
   https://www.centurygrp.com
Sales Range: $10-24.9 Million
Emp.: 100
Concrete Products, Precast
N.A.I.C.S.: 327390
George H. Vincent *(Pres)*
Hunter Vincent *(VP)*
Jerry McCombs *(VP-Sls & Mktg-Railroad Div)*
Johnny Bergeron *(VP-Sls & Mktg-Precast Products)*

CENTURY HOUSING
1000 Corporate Pointe, Culver City, CA 90230
Tel.: (310) 642-2000   CA
Web Site:
   http://www.centuryhousing.org
Year Founded: 1995
Sales Range: $25-49.9 Million
Emp.: 59
Low Income People Assistance Services
N.A.I.C.S.: 624229
Ronald M. Griffith *(Pres & CEO)*
Brian D'Andrea *(Sr VP-Housing)*
Alan R. Hoffman *(CFO & Sr VP)*
Fern Hendrickson *(VP-HR)*
Karen Bennett-Green *(VP-Loan Admin)*
Rosa Cardona Menart *(VP & Controller)*
William G. Brennan *(Chm)*
Josh Hamilton *(Sr VP-Lending)*

CENTURY III CHEVY
2430 Lebanon Church Rd, West Mifflin, PA 15122
Tel.: (412) 466-9210
Web Site:
   https://www.century3chevy.com
Sales Range: $50-74.9 Million
Emp.: 100
New Car Retailer
N.A.I.C.S.: 441110
John C. Auffenberg *(VP)*
Gary Lee *(Gen Mgr)*
Francis H. Auffenberg Jr. *(Pres)*

CENTURY INDUSTRIES INC.
1130 W Grove Ave, Orange, CA 92865-4131
Tel.: (714) 637-3691
Web Site:
   https://www.centuryindustries.com
Year Founded: 1979
Sales Range: $1-9.9 Million
Emp.: 10
All Other Miscellaneous Fabricated Metal Product Mfr
N.A.I.C.S.: 332999
Don Bibona *(Co-Founder)*

CENTURY INDUSTRIES, LLC
299 Prather Ln, Sellersburg, IN 47172
Tel.: (812) 246-3371
Web Site:
   https://www.centuryindustries.com
Year Founded: 1978

Sales Range: $1-9.9 Million
Emp.: 38
Mobile Staging, Spectator Seating & Concession Stand Mfr
N.A.I.C.S.: 332999
Robert Uhl *(Pres)*

CENTURY INTERNATIONAL ARMS CORPORATION
430 S Congress Ave Ste 1A, Delray Beach, FL 33445
Tel.: (561) 265-4500   FL
Web Site:
   http://www.centuryarms.com
Holding Company; Firearms & Ammunition Mfr & Whslr
N.A.I.C.S.: 551112
Michael Sucher *(Pres & CEO)*
Chip Hunnicutt *(Dir-Mktg)*
Jason Karvois *(Dir-Sls)*
William Sucher *(VP-Bus Dev)*
Jim Hester *(VP-Ops)*

Subsidiaries:

Century Arms, Inc.   (1)
430 S Congress Ave Ste 1A, Delray Beach, FL 33445
Web Site: http://www.centuryarms.com
Semi-Automatic Rifle Mfr & Whslr
N.A.I.C.S.: 332994
Michael Sucher *(Pres & CEO)*

CENTURY LLC
1000 Century Blvd, Oklahoma City, OK 73110
Tel.: (405) 732-2226   OK
Web Site:
   https://www.centurymartialarts.com
Year Founded: 1992
Sales Range: $25-49.9 Million
Emp.: 275
Sporting & Recreation Goods Distr
N.A.I.C.S.: 423910
Michael Dillard *(Founder)*

Subsidiaries:

Century Martial Art Supply LLC   (1)
1000 Century Blvd, Oklahoma City, OK 73110-7944
Tel.: (405) 732-2226
Web Site: http://www.centurymartialarts.com
Sales Range: $25-49.9 Million
Emp.: 250
Sporting & Athletic Goods
N.A.I.C.S.: 459110
Michael Dillard *(Owner)*

CENTURY MANUFACTURING, INC.
9750 E 50th St N, Wichita, KS 67226
Tel.: (316) 636-5423
Web Site: http://www.centurymfg.com
Year Founded: 1971
Sales Range: $10-24.9 Million
Emp.: 47
Mfr of Acrylic Awards, Promotional Products & Beer Tap Handles
N.A.I.C.S.: 332999
James V. Laubach *(CEO)*
Gary Kemnitz *(Pres)*

CENTURY MOLD CO., INC.
25 Vantage Pt Dr, Rochester, NY 14624-1142
Tel.: (248) 596-1817   NY
Web Site:
   http://www.centurymold.com
Year Founded: 1978
Sales Range: $25-49.9 Million
Emp.: 600
Plastics Products
N.A.I.C.S.: 326199
Ron Ricotta *(Pres & CEO)*
Terry Donovan *(CFO)*
Meg Collins *(VP-HR)*

CENTURY NOVELTY COMPANY, INC.
6271 Commerce Dr, Westland, MI 48185-5678
Tel.: (734) 464-0590   MI
Web Site:
   http://www.centurynovelty.com
Year Founded: 1963
Sales Range: $1-9.9 Million
Emp.: 26
Online Party Supplies & Decorations
N.A.I.C.S.: 459999
Kevin R. Madigan *(Pres & CEO)*

CENTURY PARK CAPITAL PARTNERS, LLC
2101 Rosecrans Ave Ste 4275, El Segundo, CA 90245
Tel.: (310) 867-2210   DE
Web Site:
   http://www.centuryparkcapital.com
Year Founded: 1999
Sales Range: $1-9.9 Million
Emp.: 10
Privater Equity Firm
N.A.I.C.S.: 523999
Martin A. Sarafa *(Mng Partner)*
Guy Zaczepinski *(Mng Partner)*
Chip Roellig *(Mng Partner)*
Gina Yang *(Controller)*
Tony Trevino *(VP)*

Subsidiaries:

Accelalpha Inc.   (1)
310 120th Ave NE Ste 201, Bellevue, WA 98005
Tel.: (888) 762-4695
Business & IT Consulting Firm
N.A.I.C.S.: 541519
Nat Ganesh *(CEO & Mng Dir)*

Subsidiary (Domestic):

Key Performance Ideas Inc.   (2)
268 Bush St 2800, San Francisco, CA 94104
Tel.: (530) 672-9145
Web Site:
   http://www.keyperformanceideas.com
Rev.: $1,700,000
Emp.: 20
Data Processing, Hosting & Related Services
N.A.I.C.S.: 518210
Nate Coate *(Co-Founder & CEO)*
Rob Redford *(Co-Founder)*

Better Life Technology, LLC   (1)
9736 Legler Rd, Lenexa, KS 66219-1282
Tel.: (913) 894-0403
Web Site: http://www.bltllc.com
Sales Range: $1-9.9 Million
Vinyl Flooring Mfr
N.A.I.C.S.: 449121
Brett Sneed *(Pres)*
Jerry Herbert *(COO)*

ICM Products, Inc.   (1)
805 Wolfe Ave, Cassopolis, MI 49031
Tel.: (269) 445-0847
Web Site: http://www.icmproducts.com
Sales Range: $1-9.9 Million
Silicone Polymers, Defoamers & Specialty Emulsion Chemicals Mfr
N.A.I.C.S.: 325998
Ken Charboneau *(Founder)*

Subsidiary (Non-US):

The Amber Chemical Company Ltd.   (2)
Amber House Showground Road, Bridgwater, TA6 6AJ, United Kingdom
Tel.: (44) 278 411400
Web Site: http://www.amberchemical.com
Organic Chemical Mfr
N.A.I.C.S.: 325199

Subsidiary (Domestic):

ACC Silicones Ltd.   (3)
Amber House Showground Road, Bridgwater, TA6 6AJ, United Kingdom
Tel.: (44) 1278411400
Web Site: http://www.acc-silicones.com

Century Park Capital Partners, LLC—(Continued)
Sales Range: $25-49.9 Million
Emp.: 45
Silicone Chemicals Mfr
N.A.I.C.S.: 325998
Frank Geerdsen (Mng Dir)

Subsidiary (Non-US):

Treco s.r.l.   (4)
Via Romagna N 8, Sesto Ulteriano, 20098,
Milan, Italy
Tel.: (39) 029880913
Web Site: http://www.acc-silicones.it
Silicone Mfr
N.A.I.C.S.: 325998

Subsidiary (Non-US):

Amber Silicones (Tianjin) Co.
Ltd.   (3)
F2 Hong Tai Industrial Park, Number 9
Road TEDA, 300457, Tianjin, China
Tel.: (86) 22 2532 3808 809
Silicone Mfr
N.A.I.C.S.: 325998
David Kong (Gen Mgr)

Subsidiary (US):

Quantum Silicones, Inc.   (3)
8021 Reycan Rd, Richmond, VA 23237
Tel.: (804) 271-9010
Web Site: http://www.quantumsilicones.com
Silicone Mfr
N.A.I.C.S.: 325998
Chris Martin (Mgr-Sls-East Coast)
Greg Wegener (Mgr-Sls-Midwest)
Matt Plimpton (Mgr-Sls-Great Lakes)
Sherry Anderson (Mgr-Sls-West Coast)

Siovation, LLC   (3)
1270 Progress Center Ave Ste 200, Law-
renceville, GA 30043
Tel.: (770) 339-4460
Web Site: http://www.siovation.com
Specialty Silicone-based Fluids Mfr
N.A.I.C.S.: 325998
Marcelo Zocchi (Mgr-Bus Dev)

MCCi, LLC   (1)
1958 A Commonwealth Ln, Tallahassee, FL
32303
Tel.: (850) 701-0725
Web Site: http://www.mccinnovations.com
Sales Range: $10-24.9 Million
Emp.: 40
Enterprise Content & Legislative Manage-
ment; Records Management Consulting
Services
N.A.I.C.S.: 541611
Donny Barstow (Founder, Pres & CEO)

Ryan's Express Transportation Ser-
vices, Inc.   (1)
412 E Gowan Rd N, Las Vegas, NV 89032
Tel.: (702) 795-7021
Web Site: http://www.ryansexpress.com
Sales Range: $1-9.9 Million
Charter Bus, Minin Bus, Limousine & Van
Transportation Services
N.A.I.C.S.: 485999
John Busskohl (Pres & CEO)

CENTURY PETROLEUM LTD.
147 Gazza Blvd, Farmingdale, NY
11735
Tel.: (631) 752-1688
Web Site: https://www.theoilnet.com
Rev.: $11,100,000
Emp.: 20
Petroleum Terminal
N.A.I.C.S.: 424710
Frank Rooney (Pres)
Cindy Tadler (CEO)
Tina Nardi (Office Mgr)

CENTURY PRECAST PROD-
UCTS, LLC
3222 Ne 24th St, Ocala, FL 34470-
3926
Tel.: (352) 335-0033
Year Founded: 2001
Sales Range: $1-9.9 Million
Emp.: 64

Concrete & Natural Stone Products
Mfr & Importer
N.A.I.C.S.: 327390
Thomas J. Rohs (Owner & Pres)

CENTURY READY MIX COR-
PORATION
3250 Armand St, Monroe, LA 71211
Tel.: (318) 322-4444
Web Site:
   https://www.centuryreadymix.com
Rev.: $11,700,000
Emp.: 85
Ready Mixed Concrete
N.A.I.C.S.: 327320
Robert Q. Humble (Pres)

CENTURY SAVINGS BANK
1376 W Sherman Ave, Vineland, NJ
08360
Tel.: (856) 451-3300
Web Site: http://www.centurysb.com
Year Founded: 1865
Sales Range: $10-24.9 Million
Emp.: 54
Federal Savings & Loan Association
N.A.I.C.S.: 522180
David Hemple (Pres & CEO)
Peter Bertram (Sr VP)
Carol Musso (VP-Bus Dev)
Harry H. Magazu (Vice Chm)
J. Alan Woodruff (Chm)
Martha Torres (Asst VP & Branch
Mgr)
Jillian L. Spena (VP/Dir-HR)

CENTURY SERVICE AFFILI-
ATES, INC.
22 Mercer St, Paterson, NJ 07524
Tel.: (973) 742-3516
Web Site:
   http://www.carrycasesplus.com
Year Founded: 1985
Sales Range: $1-9.9 Million
Emp.: 21
Carrying Cases with Foam Inserts &
Foam Packaging Products Mfr
N.A.I.C.S.: 326150
Lawrence Holand (VP)

CENTURY SOFTWARE LIM-
ITED
6465 S 3000 E Ste 104, Salt Lake
City, UT 84121
Tel.: (801) 268-3088
Web Site:
   https://www.centurysoftware.com
Sales Range: $10-24.9 Million
Emp.: 9
Computer & Computer Peripheral
Equipment & Software Merchant
Wholesalers
N.A.I.C.S.: 423430
Jason Kingan (Dir-R&D)
Gregory Haerr (Pres & CEO)

CENTURY SUPPLY CO. INC.
747 E Roosevelt Rd, Lombard, IL
60148-4742
Tel.: (630) 873-8200   IL
Web Site: http://www.century-tile.com
Year Founded: 1947
Sales Range: $25-49.9 Million
Emp.: 250
Floor Covering Stores
N.A.I.C.S.: 449121
Bob Kobliska (CFO)
Lorcan Dufrain (Mgr-Warehouse)

CENTURY TECHNOLOGY
GROUP
445 Pettis Ave SE, Ada, MI 49301
Tel.: (616) 554-7905
Web Site:
   https://www.centurytechgroup.com

Industrial Machinery & Equipment
Merchant Whslr
N.A.I.C.S.: 423830
Greg Dewitt (Owner)

Subsidiaries:

SpinDance, Inc.   (1)
238 S River Ave, Holland, MI 49423
Tel.: (616) 355-7000
Web Site: http://www.spindance.com
Software Development Services
N.A.I.C.S.: 541511
Karl Schripsema (CTO)
Mike Ellis (Pres)
Keith Pustover (VP-Ops)
Mike Stroud (Engr-Lead Software)

CENTURY TOOL & GAGE
200 S Alloy Dr, Fenton, MI 48430
Tel.: (810) 629-0784   MI
Web Site: http://www.centurytool.com
Year Founded: 1968
Sales Range: $25-49.9 Million
Emp.: 100
Compression Mold Builder
N.A.I.C.S.: 333511
Kevin Cummings (VP-Engrg & Sls)
Dennis Cummings (Controller)

Subsidiaries:

Century Tool & Gage   (1)
6835 Monroe Blvd, Taylor, MI 48180-1815
Tel.: (313) 292-5355
Web Site: http://www.centurytool.com
Machining Services
N.A.I.C.S.: 332710
Michael Swiecicki (Gen Mgr)

CENTURY TRAVEL SERVICE
INC.
27 E Augusta Ave, Spokane, WA
99207
Tel.: (509) 327-9585
Web Site:
   http://www.travelleaders.com
Sales Range: $25-49.9 Million
Emp.: 45
Travel Agencies
N.A.I.C.S.: 561510
Hugh Himmelreich (Exec VP)
David P. Holyoke (Pres)

CENTURY, INC.
2410 W Aero Park Ct, Traverse City,
MI 49686
Tel.: (231) 946-7500
Web Site: https://www.centinc.com
Sales Range: $25-49.9 Million
Emp.: 300
Special Dies, Tools, Jigs & Fixtures
N.A.I.C.S.: 333514
Todd MacKey (Dir-Sls & Mktg)

Subsidiaries:

Century Rollforming, Inc.   (1)
2410 W Aero Park Ct, Traverse City, MI
49686-9102
Tel.: (231) 798-3554
Web Site: http://www.centinc.com
Sales Range: $10-24.9 Million
Emp.: 10
Special Dies, Tools, Jigs & Fixtures
N.A.I.C.S.: 333519

Century Specialties   (1)
2410 W Aero Park Ct, Traverse City, MI
49686
Tel.: (231) 946-7500
Web Site: http://www.centinc.com
Rev.: $8,660,000
Emp.: 200
Special Dies, Tools, Jigs & Fixtures
N.A.I.C.S.: 333514
Joe Reid (Mgr-Inspection)
Todd Mackey (Dir-Sls)

CENVEO, INC.
200 1st Stamford Pl 2nd Fl, Stamford, CT 06902
Tel.: (203) 595-3000   CO

Web Site: http://www.cenveo.com
Year Founded: 1994
Sales Range: $1-4.9 Billion
Holding Company; Commercial Print-
ing & Printing-Related Products &
Services
N.A.I.C.S.: 551112
Ian Scheinmann (Gen Counsel &
Sec)
Michael Burton (Pres)
Ayman Zameli (Chief Strategy Officer
& Exec VP)
James Continenza (Chm)
Robert G. Burton Jr. (CEO)

Subsidiaries:

Cenveo Corporation   (1)
1 Canterbury Green 201 Broad St, Stam-
ford, CT 06901
Tel.: (203) 595-3000
Web Site: http://www.cenveo.com
Packaging Product Commercial Printing
Services
N.A.I.C.S.: 323111
Ian Scheinmann (Sr VP-Legal Affairs)
Robert G. Burton Sr. (Chm)
Michael G. Burton (Pres)
Robert G. Burton Jr. (CEO)

Unit (Domestic):

Cadmus Communications -
Hurlock   (2)
4810 Williamburg Rd, Hurlock, MD 21643
Tel.: (410) 822-2870
Offset Printing of Magazines & Catalogs;
Publishing
N.A.I.C.S.: 323111

Subsidiary (Domestic):

Cadmus Journal Services, Inc.   (2)
2901 Byrdhill Rd, Richmond, VA 23228-
5805
Tel.: (804) 261-3000
Emp.: 600
Offset Printing of Magazines & Catalogs;
Publishing
N.A.I.C.S.: 323111
Glenn Derosstt (Gen Mgr)

Unit (Domestic):

Cenveo Commercial Printing & Pack-
aging - St. Louis   (2)
101 Workman Ct, Eureka, MO 63025
Tel.: (314) 966-2000
Web Site: http://www.stlouis.cenveo.com
Sales Range: $50-74.9 Million
Emp.: 187
Offset Printing
N.A.I.C.S.: 323111

Group (Domestic):

Cenveo Corp. - Custom Resale
Group   (2)
4115 Profit Ct, New Albany, IN 47150
Tel.: (812) 945-2617
Web Site:
   http://www.customresalegroup.com
Holding Company; Labels, Envelopes &
Stationery Products Mfr & Distr
N.A.I.C.S.: 551112

Subsidiary (Domestic):

Discount Labels, Inc.   (3)
4115 Profit Ct, New Albany, IN
47150-7225   (100%)
Tel.: (812) 945-2617
Web Site: http://www.discountlabels.com
Sales Range: $450-499.9 Million
Emp.: 550
Mfr of Labels
N.A.I.C.S.: 322299

Unit (Domestic):

Cenveo Publisher Services   (2)
3575 Hempland Rd, Lancaster, PA 17601-
6912
Tel.: (717) 285-9095
Web Site: http://www.kwglobal.com
Offset Printing of Magazines & Catalogs;
Publishing
N.A.I.C.S.: 323111

Subsidiary (Domestic):

Cenveo Publisher Services (3)
5457 Twin Knolls Rd, Columbia, MD 21045
Tel.: (410) 850-0500
Web Site: http://www.kwglobal.com
Offset Printing of Magazines & Catalogs &
Packaging Solutions
N.A.I.C.S.: 323117
Debbie McClanahan (VP-Publ Svcs)

Subsidiary (Domestic):

Port City Press, Inc. (2)
1323 Greenwood Rd, Pikesville, MD 21208
Tel.: (410) 486-3000
Web Site: http://www.cenveo.com
Sales Range: $50-74.9 Million
Emp.: 157
Book & Catalog Printer
N.A.I.C.S.: 323117
Glenn Eddleman (Gen Mgr)
David Lepard (Mgr-Mfr)

**Cenveo McLaren Morris and Todd
Company** (1)
3270 American Drive, Mississauga, L4V
1B5, ON, Canada
Tel.: (905) 677-3592
Paper Products Mfr
N.A.I.C.S.: 322299
Carl Cox (Gen Mgr)

**Cenveo Publisher Services India
Limited** (1)
31 Kempapura Hebbal, Bengaluru, 560
024, India
Tel.: (91) 8040004888
Packaging & Labeling Services
N.A.I.C.S.: 561910

**Madison/Graham ColorGraphics,
Inc.** (1)
150 N Myers St, Los Angeles, CA 90033-
2109
Tel.: (323) 261-7171
Web Site: http://www.colorgraphics.com
Sales Range: $150-199.9 Million
Emp.: 400
Commercial Printing Services
N.A.I.C.S.: 323111

Branch (Domestic):

**ColorGraphics, Inc. - San
Francisco** (2)
665 3rdSt Ste 505, San Francisco, CA
94107
Tel.: (415) 821-7171
Web Site: http://www.colorgraphics.com
Commercial Lithographic Printing Mfr
N.A.I.C.S.: 323111

ColorGraphics, Inc. - Seattle (2)
6520 S 190th St, Kent, WA 98032
Tel.: (206) 720-6520
Web Site: http://www.colorgraphics.com
Emp.: 200
Commercial Lithographic Printing Services
N.A.I.C.S.: 323111
James Miller (Gen Mgr)

Subsidiary (Domestic):

**Madison/Graham ColorGraphics In-
terstate Services, Inc.** (2)
150 N Myers St, Los Angeles, CA 90033-
2109
Tel.: (323) 261-7171
Graphic Design Services
N.A.I.C.S.: 541430

Nashua Corporation (1)
11 Trafalgar Sq 2nd Fl, Nashua, NH 03063
Tel.: (603) 880-2323
Web Site: http://www.nashua.com
Sales Range: $250-299.9 Million
Emp.: 659
Specialty Imaging Products & Services for
Industrial & Commercial Customers; Prod-
ucts Include Thermal Papers, Pressure
Sensitive Labels & Specialty Papers, Toners
N.A.I.C.S.: 323111

Plant (Domestic):

**Nashua Merrimack Coated Paper
Products Plant** (2)
59 Daniel Webster Hwy, Merrimack, NH
03054

Tel.: (603) 880-1100
Web Site: http://www.nashua.com
Sales Range: $50-74.9 Million
Emp.: 100
Coated Paper Products Mfr
N.A.I.C.S.: 322220
Mike Valcourt (VP-Ops)

Rx Technology Corp. (1)
3301 Enterprise Ave, Joplin, MO 64801
Tel.: (417) 626-2999
Commercial Screen Printing Services
N.A.I.C.S.: 323113
Robert Burton (Pres)

Vaughn Printers Incorporated (1)
222 E Side Blvd, Hastings, NE 68901
Tel.: (402) 463-7721
Commercial Screen Printing Services
N.A.I.C.S.: 323113

CEPIA, LLC
121 Hunter Ave Ste 103, Saint Louis,
MO 63124
Tel.: (314) 725-4900   MO
Web Site: http://www.cepiallc.com
Year Founded: 2002
Sales Range: $1-9.9 Million
Emp.: 35
Boutique Designer, Mfr & Marketer of
Toys, Electronics & Children's Games
N.A.I.C.S.: 339930
Russell Hornsby (CEO)

CEPS, INC.
53 S Main St Ste 201, Hanover, NH
03755-2022
Tel.: (603) 298-7702
Year Founded: 1982
Sales Range: $1-9.9 Million
Emp.: 15
Plastic Injection Molded Components
& Sub-Assemblies Supplier
N.A.I.C.S.: 333511
James D. Umland (Pres)

CEQUEL III, LLC
12444 Powerscourt Dr Ste 450, Saint
Louis, MO 63131
Tel.: (314) 965-2020   DE
Web Site: http://www.cequel3.com
Year Founded: 2002
Sales Range: $25-49.9 Million
Emp.: 250
Investment Management Service
N.A.I.C.S.: 523940
Mary E. Meduski (Pres & CFO)
Howard L. Wood (Co-Founder)
Jerald L. Kent (Co-Founder, Chm &
CEO)
Wendy Knudsen (Chief Legal Officer,
Sec & Exec VP)
Mary Meduski (Pres & CFO)
Pete Abel (Sr VP-Mktg & Comm)
Gus Haug (Sr VP-Corp Dev)

Subsidiaries:

Cequel Data Centers, LLC (1)
520 Maryville Centre Dr Ste 300, Saint
Louis, MO 63141
Tel.: (314) 594-1300
Holding Company; Information Technology
Data Centers Operator
N.A.I.C.S.: 551112
Jerald L. Kent (Chm)

Subsidiary (Domestic):

TierPoint, LLC (2)
520 Maryville Centre Dr Ste 300, Saint
Louis, MO 63141
Tel.: (877) 859-8437
Web Site: http://www.tierpoint.com
Information Technology Data Centers Op-
erator
N.A.I.C.S.: 518210
Mary E. Meduski (Pres & CFO)
Jerald L. Kent (Chm)
Andy Stewart (Chief Strategy Officer)
Wendy Knudsen (Chief Legal Officer &
Exec VP)
Dennis Jesielowski (COO)

Jeff Bertocci (Sr VP-Svc Delivery)
Rob Carter (Sr VP-Solutions Engrg)
Rob Fewkes (VP-Cloud Tech)
Terry Morrison (Sr VP-Tech)
Keith Markley (Sr VP-Ops)
Robert Hicks (Sr VP-Ops)
David Foster (VP-Data Center Facilities)
Robert Lupo (Gen Mgr-Facility & Ops-
Jacksonville)
Keith Waldrup (VP-Sls-Missouri & Ken-
tucky)
Bret Dupuis (VP-Sls-Illinois, Indiana, Michi-
gan & Ohio)
John Holland (Sr VP-Sls)
Tyler Holley (VP-Sls-Jacksonville)
Paige Dirscherl (Sr Acct Exec)
Linda Bailey (VP-HR)
Bob Desantis (Chief Acctg Officer)
Shea Long (VP-Products)
Paul Mazzucco (Chief Security Officer)
Octavio Morales (Sr VP-Ops)
Miranda Smith (Acct Exec)
David Haggerty (VP-Sls-Wisconsin & Min-
nesota)
Dan Capra (Reg VP-Sls)
Dick Weisberg (VP-Sls-Pacific Northwest)
Jeff Waide (VP-Charlotte)
Tony Rossabi (Chief Revenue Officer &
Exec VP)
Kenny Ash (VP-Channel)

CERA-MET, LLC
2175 Ave C, Bethlehem, PA 18017-
2119
Tel.: (610) 266-0270   PA
Web Site: https://www.cera-met.com
Year Founded: 1974
Sales Range: $10-24.9 Million
Emp.: 130
Aluminum Investment Castings Mfr
N.A.I.C.S.: 331524
Henri Fine (Owner)
Dave Bertram (Mgr-Sls)
Maria Schwartz (Controller)
Jamie Raines (Mgr-HR)
Paul Krawiec (Engr-Dimensional)
Steve Huber (Mgr-Quality)
Marc Riquelme (COO & Gen Mgr)
Al Webb (Mgr-Front End Ops)

CERAM-TRAZ CORPORATION
325 Hwy 81, Osseo, MN 55369
Tel.: (763) 424-2044
Rev.: $10,000,000
Emp.: 52
Paint & Coating Mfr
N.A.I.C.S.: 325510
Lyle Sommers (CEO)

CERAMI SALES COMPANY,
INC.
524 Finney Ct, Gardena, CA 90248-
2037
Tel.: (310) 515-7560
Sales Range: $25-49.9 Million
Emp.: 13
Cheese Mfr
N.A.I.C.S.: 311513
John Cerami (Pres)
Cathy Cerami (VP)
Robert Cerami (VP)

CERAMIC COLOR & CHEMI-
CAL MFG. CO.
PO Box 297, New Brighton, PA
15066
Tel.: (724) 846-4000   PA
Web Site:
   https://www.ceramiccolor.com
Year Founded: 1929
Sales Range: $75-99.9 Million
Emp.: 25
Ceramic Colors & Chemicals, Oxides
& Industrial Chemicals Sales & Mfr
N.A.I.C.S.: 325130
Burges M. Hurd (Chm)
Bill Wenning (Pres)

CERAMICA AZULEJOS TER-
RAZZOS
Carr 167 Km 15 Hm 7 St CA, Baya-
mon, PR 00957
Tel.: (787) 730-3800
Sales Range: $10-24.9 Million
Emp.: 70
Ceramic Tile & Other Building Mate-
rial Dealer
N.A.I.C.S.: 444180
Ramon Fernandez (Pres)

CERBERUS CAPITAL MAN-
AGEMENT, L.P.
875 3rd Ave 10th Fl, New York, NY
10022
Tel.: (212) 891-2100   DE
Web Site: https://www.cerberus.com
Year Founded: 1992
Privater Equity Firm
N.A.I.C.S.: 523999
Stephen A. Feinberg (Co-Founder,
Co-CEO, CIO & Chief Investment
Officer)
Mark A. Neporent (Vice Chm, Sr Mng
Dir, COO & Sr Legal Officer)
W. Brett Ingersoll (Sr Mng Dir)
Seth P. Plattus (Chief Admin Officer,
Sr Mng Dir & Sr Legal Officer)
Robert C. Davenport (Sr Mng Dir &
Head-Corp Credit & Distressed Debt)
Andrew Kandel (Sr Mng Dir, Chief
Compliance Officer & Sr Legal Offi-
cer)
Joshua Weintraub (Sr Mng Dir &
CEO-Residential Opportunities)
Daniel E. Wolf (CEO-Bus Fin & Sr
Mng Dir-Cerberus Capital Mgmt)
John William Snow (Chm)
Gerald P. Strong (CEO-Cerberus Eu-
ropean Capital Advisors)
Paul Lusardi (Mng Dir)
Chris A. Schiermbock (Mng Dir)
Erik A. Wright (Mng Dir)
Joseph B. Spano (Mng Dir)
Ken J. Kohrs (Mng Dir)
Kevin S. McLeod (Sr Mng Dir)
Kyle R. Schneider (Mng Dir)
Marc J. Millman (Mng Dir)
Robert H. Milam (Mng Dir & Head-
Emerging Market Credit)
Robert J. Richter (Sr Mng Dir)
Scott A. Yedid (Sr Mng Dir)
Stephen Pozatek (Sr Mng Dir)
Xingbin Zhang (Sr Mng Dir)
Gregory S. Nixon (Head-Strategic
Investments & Sr Mng Dir)
Michael Sanford (Sr Mng Dir)
Patrick Moriarty (Mng Dir)
Frank W. Bruno (Co-CEO & Sr Mng
Dir)
John Raymond (Sr Mng Dir & Sr Mng
Dir-Supply Chain & Strategic Oppor-
tunities Platform)

Subsidiaries:

ABC Technologies Inc. (1)
2 Norelco Drive, Toronto, M9L 2X6, ON,
Canada
Tel.: (416) 246-1782
Web Site: https://abctechnologies.com
Automative & Industrial Thermoplastic Com-
ponents Mfr
N.A.I.C.S.: 326199

Ableco Finance, LLC (1)
875 3rd Ave L-2, New York, NY 10022
Tel.: (212) 891-1550
Web Site: http://www.cerberuscapital.com
Specialty Finance & Lending Services
N.A.I.C.S.: 523999
Stephen A. Feinberg (CEO)

AerCap Aviation Solutions (1)
Regus The Base B Evert van de Beekstraat
1-104, Stationsplein 965, 1118 CL, Schiphol, Netherlands
Tel.: (31) 207991675

Cerberus Capital Management, L.P.—(Continued)

Sales Range: $550-599.9 Million
Emp.: 182
Aircraft Leasing & Financing Services
N.A.I.C.S.: 532411

Branch (Non-US):

AerCap Ireland Ltd. (2)
Westpark Business Campus Bldg 4000
4450 Atlantic Avenue, Shannon, Ireland
Tel.: (353) 61723600
Sales Range: $25-49.9 Million
Emp.: 70
Aircraft Leasing
N.A.I.C.S.: 532411
Tom Kelly (CEO)

Albertsons Companies, Inc. (1)
250 Parkcenter Blvd, Boise, ID 83706
Tel.: (208) 395-6200
Web Site:
https://www.albertsonscompanies.com
Rev.: $79,237,700,000
Assets: $26,221,100,000
Liabilities: $23,473,600,000
Net Worth: $2,747,500,000
Earnings: $1,296,000,000
Emp.: 290,000
Fiscal Year-end: 02/24/2024
Grocery Stores & Pharmacies
N.A.I.C.S.: 445110
James L. Donald (Co-Chm)
Anuj Dhanda (CTO, Chief Transformation Officer & Exec VP)
Thomas M. Moriarty (Gen Counsel & Exec VP)
Chan W. Galbato (Co-Chm)
Susan D. Morris (COO & Exec VP)
Michael Theilmann (Chief HR Officer & Exec VP)
Evan Rainwater (Exec VP-Supply Chain-Manufacturing)
Rob Backus (Pres-Shaw's-Star Market Div)
Michelle Larson (Pres-Southwest Div)
Sharon L. McCollam (Pres & CFO)
B. Kevin Turner (Vice Chm)
Omer Gajial (Chief Merchandising Officer, Chief Digital Officer & Exec VP)
Jennifer Saenz (Exec VP-Pharmacy & Ecommerce)
Vivek Sankaran (CEO)

Subsidiary (Domestic):

New Albertson's, Inc. (2)
250 E Parkcenter Blvd, Boise, ID 83726
Tel.: (208) 395-6800
Holding Company; Supermarket Operator & Franchisor
N.A.I.C.S.: 551112
Robert Miller (Pres-Albertsons)

Subsidiary (Domestic):

Acme Markets, Inc. (3)
75 Vly Stream Pkwy, Malvern, PA 19355-1406
Tel.: (610) 889-4000
Web Site: http://www.acmemarkets.com
Retail Food Stores
N.A.I.C.S.: 445110
Dan Croce (Sr VP-Retail Ops)
Jim Perkins (Pres)

Albertson's LLC (3)
250 Parkcenter Blvd, Boise, ID 83726-0020
Tel.: (208) 395-6200
Web Site: http://www.albertsons.com
Sales Range: $15-24.9 Billion
Emp.: 52,400
Retail Food & Drug Chain
N.A.I.C.S.: 445110
Anuj Dhanda (CIO & Exec VP)
Andrew Scoggin (Exec VP-HR, Lab Rels, Pub Affairs & Govt Rels)
Bob Miller (Chm & CEO)
Shane Dorcheus (Pres-Southern California & Southwest Div & Exec VP-Retail Ops)
Wayne Denningham (Pres)
Mike Withers (Exec VP-Ops East)
Anuj Dhanda (CIO & Exec VP)
Bob Dimond (CFO & Exec VP)
Justin Ewing (Exec VP-Corp Dev & Real Estate)
Bob Gordon (Gen Counsel, Sec & Exec VP)
Jim Perkins (Exec VP-Retail Ops Special Projects)

Division (Domestic):

Albertson's, Inc.-Oregon Division (4)
17001 NE San Rafael St, Portland, OR 97230-6085
Tel.: (503) 251-9500
Sales Range: $25-49.9 Million
Emp.: 55
Retail Grocery Services
N.A.I.C.S.: 445110
Gineal Davidson (Pres)

Albertson's, Inc.-Southern California Division (4)
1421 Manhattan Ave, Fullerton, CA 92831-5221
Tel.: (714) 300-6000
Web Site: http://www.albertsons.com
Sales Range: $300-349.9 Million
Emp.: 160
Retail Grocery Services
N.A.I.C.S.: 445110

Division (Domestic):

Jewel-Osco (3)
150 Pierce Rd Ste 200, Itasca, IL 60143
Tel.: (630) 948-6000
Web Site: http://www.jewelosco.com
Food & Drug Stores
N.A.I.C.S.: 457110
Scott Nays (VP-Ops)
Anthony Suggs (VP-Mktg & Merchandising)
Paul Gossett (Pres)

Subsidiary (Domestic):

Jewel Food Stores, Inc. (4)
1955 W N Ave, Melrose Park, IL 60160-1131
Tel.: (708) 531-6000
Web Site: http://www.jewelosco.com
Sales Range: $75-99.9 Million
Emp.: 175
Retail Grocery Services
N.A.I.C.S.: 445110

Subsidiary (Domestic):

Safeway Inc. (3)
5918 Stoneridge Mall Rd, Pleasanton, CA 94588-3229
Tel.: (925) 467-3000
Web Site: http://www.safeway.com
Rev.: $36,330,200,000
Assets: $13,377,000,000
Net Worth: $5,450,400,000
Earnings: $112,500,000
Emp.: 137,000
Fiscal Year-end: 01/03/2015
Holding Company; Food & Drug Retailer
N.A.I.C.S.: 551112
David F. Bond (Chief Acctg Officer & Sr VP-Fin & Control)
Jerry Tidwell (Sr VP-Supply Ops)
Robert G. Miller Jr. (Chm & CEO)
Donald P. Wright (Sr VP-Real Estate & Engrg)
Robert A. Gordon (Gen Counsel, Sec & Sr VP)
Russell M. Jackson (Sr VP-HR)
Kelly Griffith (Exec VP-Retail Ops)
Barry J. Libenson (CIO & Sr VP)

Subsidiary (Domestic):

Lucerne Foods, Inc. (4)
250 E Parkcenter Blvd, Boise, ID 83706
Web Site: http://www.lucernefoods.com
Private Label Food Services, Distribution & National Brands
N.A.I.C.S.: 445110
Dorothy Kropf (Mgr-Customer Svc)
Peter Lancy (Mgr-Bus Dev)
Stephen Young (CFO)

Randalls Food & Drugs, LP (4)
2225 Louisiana St, Houston, TX 77002
Tel.: (713) 331-1042
Web Site: http://www.randalls.com
Sales Range: $125-149.9 Million
Emp.: 156
Regional Texas Supermarket Chain
N.A.I.C.S.: 445110

Subsidiary (Domestic):

Randalls Properties, Inc. (5)
9660 Westheimer Rd, Houston, TX 77063
Tel.: (713) 782-0982

Web Site: http://www.randalls.com
Supermarket Property & Real Estate Services
N.A.I.C.S.: 531210
Liz Lansord (Mgr)

Subsidiary (Non-US):

Safeway Global Sourcing Limited (4)
Unit 12-14 9/F The Gateway Tower 6, Tsim Sha Tsui Yau Tsim Mong, Kowloon, China (Hong Kong)
Tel.: (852) 35138888
Emp.: 50
Global Sourcing, Procurement & Logistics Services
N.A.I.C.S.: 541614
Julice Chen (Mng Dir)

Safeway Philtech Inc. (4)
21st Floor RCBC Plz Yuchengco Tower Ayala Ave Cor Sen G Puyat Ave, Makati, Philippines
Tel.: (63) 27576888
Web Site: http://www.safewaymanila.com
Emp.: 500
Information Technology & Services
N.A.I.C.S.: 519290
Sarah Mercado (Project Mgr-IT)

Subsidiary (Domestic):

Safeway Select Gift Source, Inc. (4)
4000 W Dimond Blvd, Anchorage, AK 99502
Tel.: (907) 339-1200
Web Site: http://www.safeway.com
Supermarket, Flowers & Prepaid Gift Card Services
N.A.I.C.S.: 445110

The Vons Companies, Inc. (4)
5918 Stoneridge Mall Rd, Pleasanton, CA 94588
Tel.: (626) 821-7000
Web Site: http://www.vons.com
Sales Range: $50-74.9 Million
Emp.: 234
Supermarket & Pharmacy Services
N.A.I.C.S.: 445110

Vons A Safeway Company (4)
745 E Naomi Ave, Arcadia, CA 91007-6300
Tel.: (626) 446-9483
Web Site: http://local.vons.com
Grocery Stores & Markets
N.A.I.C.S.: 445110

Unit (Domestic):

Pavilions (5)
130 W Foothill Blvd, Monrovia, CA 91016
Tel.: (626) 303-4547
Web Site: http://www.pavilions.com
Sales Range: $10-24.9 Million
Emp.: 500
Supermarket & Convenience Shopping
N.A.I.C.S.: 445110
Garrett McLaughlin (District Mgr)

Subsidiary (Domestic):

Shaw's Supermarkets, Inc. (3)
750 W Center St, West Bridgewater, MA 02379-1518
Tel.: (508) 313-4000
Web Site: http://www.shaws.com
Supermarket & Pharmacy Services
N.A.I.C.S.: 445110
Janet Lyons (Mgr-Customer Svc)
Steve Reimer (Mgr-Relief)
Cindy Garnett (VP-HR & Labor Rels)
Ken Rinaldi (VP-Retail Ops)
Paul Gossett (Pres)
Teresa Edington (Mgr-Media)

Star Markets Company, Inc. (3)
699 Mt Auburn St, Cambridge, MA 02138
Tel.: (617) 876-1450
Web Site: http://www.starmarket.com
Grocery & Pharmacy Services
N.A.I.C.S.: 445110
Jim Rice (Pres)
Joe Kelley (VP & Gen Mgr)
Russ Greenlaw (Dir-Ops)
John Scuccimarra (Dir-Sls & Mdsg)
Leeann Dias (Dir-Mktg)
Cindy Garnett (VP-HR & Labor Rels)

United Supermarkets, LLC (3)

7830 Orlando Ave, Lubbock, TX 79423-1942
Tel.: (806) 791-0220
Web Site: http://www.unitedtexas.com
Emp.: 13,000
Supermarket Operations in Texas
N.A.I.C.S.: 445110
Wes Jackson (Chief Mdsg Officer)
SuzAnn Kirby (CFO)
Paul Evans (VP-Ops & Intl Div)
Chad Wilkins (Asst Mgr-Produce)
Robert C. Taylor Jr. (CEO)

Subsidiary (Domestic):

Pak 'N Save, Inc. (2)
555 Floresta Blvd, San Leandro, CA 94578
Tel.: (510) 483-2681
Web Site: http://www.safeway.com
Sales Range: $1-4.9 Billion
Supermarket Services
N.A.I.C.S.: 445110
Robert Gordon (Exec VP & Gen Counsel)

Tom Thumb Food & Pharmacy (2)
7700 N West Hwy, Dallas, TX 75225
Tel.: (214) 346-1020
Web Site: http://www.tomthumb.com
Emp.: 600
Supermarket & Pharmacy Services
N.A.I.C.S.: 445110
Bill Davidson (Gen Mgr)

Aozora Bank, Ltd. (1)
6-1-1 Kojimachi, Chiyoda-ku, Tokyo, 102-8660, Japan (50.02%)
Tel.: (81) 367521111
Web Site: https://www.aozorabank.co.jp
Rev.: $1,628,036,390
Assets: $50,255,843,220
Liabilities: $47,670,817,640
Net Worth: $2,585,025,580
Earnings: ($329,865,440)
Emp.: 2,476
Fiscal Year-end: 03/31/2024
Corporate & Institutional Banking Services
N.A.I.C.S.: 522110
Koji Yamakoshi (Sr Mng Exec Officer)
Takashi Kato (Mng Exec Officer)
Jun Shinozaki (Exec Officer)
Masayoshi Ohara (Deputy Pres, Sr Mng Exec Officer & Exec Officer)
Masaki Onuma (Sr Mng Exec Officer & Exec Officer)
Akira Sakai (CFO, Sr Mng Exec Officer & Exec Officer)
Kazuhiro Yasuda (Mng Exec Officer & Exec Officer)
Akemi Hashimoto (Mng Exec Officer & Exec Officer)
Tetsuji Okuda (Mng Exec Officer & Exec Officer)
Hiroshi Suzuki (Exec Officer)
Shu Takahashi (Exec Officer)
Yukiko Morita (Exec Officer)
Naoko Tanaka (Exec Officer)
Hiroshi Kaneko (Exec Officer)
Mitsuhiro Segawa (Exec Officer)
Mayumi Takada (Exec Officer)
Kouji Igarashi (Exec Officer)
Kosuke Takai (Exec Officer)
Chiharu Hirota (Exec Officer)
Kimiaki Satou (Exec Officer)
Kei Tanikawa (Exec Officer)
Hideto Oomi (Pres & CEO)

Subsidiary (Domestic):

Aozora Investment Co., Ltd. (2)
3-1 Kudan-minami 1-chome, Chiyoda-ku, Tokyo, 102 8660, Japan
Tel.: (81) 332616061
Web Site: http://www.aozora-invest.co.jp
Sales Range: $50-74.9 Million
Emp.: 50
Venture Capital Investments
N.A.I.C.S.: 523999

Aozora Loan Services Co., Ltd. (2)
13-5 Kudan-kita 1-chome, Chiyoda-ku, Tokyo, 1020073, Japan
Tel.: (81) 332650456
Web Site: http://www.aozora-ls.co.jp
Sales Range: $75-99.9 Million
Emp.: 93
Distressed Loan Servicing
N.A.I.C.S.: 522310
Hiromi Watanabe (Pres & CEO)

Aozora Securities Co., Ltd. (2)

17 11 Kanda Nishikicho 3 chome, Chiyoda ku, Tokyo, Japan **(100%)**
Tel.: (81) 345206600
Securities Brokerage Services
N.A.I.C.S.: 523150

Aozora Trust Bank, Ltd. (2)
3 1 Kudan-minami 1 chome, Chiyoda ku, Tokyo, Japan
Tel.: (81) 3 3221 8011
Web Site: http://www.aozora-trust.co.jp
Trust & Banking Services
N.A.I.C.S.: 523991
Atsushi Sato *(Pres)*

Axsesstoday Limited (1)
Level 9 360 Collins Street, Melbourne, 3000, VIC, Australia
Tel.: (61) 1300586936
Web Site:
http://www.axsesstodaylimited.com.au
Sales Range: $10-24.9 Million
Finance Lending Services
N.A.I.C.S.: 522291
Fernando Tallarico *(Mng Dir)*
Patrick Volpe *(Sec)*

Subsidiary (Domestic):

A.C.N. 603 303 126 Pty Ltd (2)
Collins Street West, PO Box 213, Melbourne, 8007, VIC, Australia
Tel.: (61) 1300506720
Web Site: http://www.hssfinance.com.au
Loan Financing Services
N.A.I.C.S.: 522310

BlueLinx Holdings, Inc. (1)
1950 Spectrum Cir Ste 300, Marietta, GA 30067 **(55%)**
Tel.: (770) 953-7000
Web Site: https://www.bluelinxco.com
Rev.: $4,277,178,000
Assets: $1,317,454,000
Liabilities: $954,205,000
Net Worth: $363,249,000
Earnings: $296,133,000
Emp.: 2,055
Fiscal Year-end: 01/01/2022
Holding Company
N.A.I.C.S.: 551112
Shyam K. Reddy *(Pres & CEO)*
R. Andrew Wamser Jr. *(CFO & Sr VP)*
Kimberly A. DeBrock *(Chief Acctg Officer & VP)*
Dionne Vernon *(VP-Talent Mgmt)*
Gui Nebel *(VP-Fin & Treasury)*
Sean Dwyer *(Chief Strategy Officer)*
Joshua Teteak *(Chief Supply Chain Officer)*
Todd Skaggs *(VP-West)*
Todd Skaggs *(VP-West)*

Subsidiary (Domestic):

BLUELINX FLORIDA LP (2)
694 SE County Rd 245, Lake City, FL 32055
Tel.: (386) 752-7412
Building Product Distr
N.A.I.C.S.: 423310

Subsidiary (Non-US):

BlueLinx Building Products Canada Ltd. (2)
1024 Ridgeway Ave Suite 209, Coquitlam, V3J 1S5, BC, Canada **(100%)**
Tel.: (604) 931-6970
Sales Range: $25-49.9 Million
Emp.: 9
Construction Materials Whslr
N.A.I.C.S.: 423390

Subsidiary (Domestic):

BlueLinx Corporation (2)
1950 Spectrum Cir Ste 300, Marietta, GA 30067
Tel.: (770) 953-7000
Building Products Whslr
N.A.I.C.S.: 423310
Stephen T. Strohmeier *(VP-Structural Products)*
Eric A. Vaillancourt *(Executives)*

Subsidiary (Domestic):

Cedar Creek LLC (3)
450 N Macarthur Blvd, Oklahoma City, OK 73127-6619
Tel.: (405) 947-6900

Web Site: http://www.cedarcreek.com
Lumber & Building Materials Whslr
N.A.I.C.S.: 423310
D. Wayne Trousdale *(Chm)*

Subsidiary (Domestic):

Cedar Creek - Aitkin (4)
PO Box 310 995 Pacific St, Aitkin, MN 56431
Tel.: (218) 927-2125
Web Site:
http://www.northcentral.bluelinxco.com
Wood Products Mfr & Distr
N.A.I.C.S.: 423310

Subsidiary (Domestic):

Vandermeer Forest Products Inc. (2)
5110 196 St SW, Lynnwood, WA 98046-6155
Tel.: (425) 774-3544
Web Site: http://www.vandermeerfp.com
Sales Range: $10-24.9 Million
Emp.: 30
Lumber, Plywood & Millwork-Engineered Wood Products
N.A.I.C.S.: 423310
Dave Stadacher *(Pres)*

Brooklyn Bedding LLC (1)
5301 W Bethany Home Rd, Glendale, AZ
Tel.: (888) 210-8751
Web Site: https://brooklynbedding.com
Emp.: 100
Mattress Retail & Mfr
N.A.I.C.S.: 337910
John Merwin *(CEO)*

Subsidiary (Domestic):

Bear Mattress LLC (2)
720 Monroe St Ste C508, Hoboken, NJ 07030
Web Site: http://www.bearmattress.com
Sales Range: $10-24.9 Million
Emp.: 12
Mattress Product Distr
N.A.I.C.S.: 423210
Scott Paladini *(Founder)*

Burnes Group (1)
21 Cypress Blvd Ste 1010, Round Rock, TX 78665
Tel.: (512) 257-6500
Sales Range: $150-199.9 Million
Mfr of Picture Frames & Photo Albums
N.A.I.C.S.: 332999

CRE Bushkill Group, LLC (1)
1008 Sand Hill Creek Rd, East Stroudsburg, PA 18302
Tel.: (570) 588-6661
Resort Operator
N.A.I.C.S.: 721110

CTA Acoustics, Inc. (1)
25211 Dequindre Rd, Madison Heights, MI 48071
Tel.: (248) 544-2580
Web Site: http://www.ctaacoustics.com
Emp.: 3
Thermal Insulation Mfr
N.A.I.C.S.: 326140
Andrew Labady *(CEO, CFO & Chief Admin Officer)*

Plant (Domestic):

CTA Acoustics, Inc. - Corbin Manufacturing Facility (2)
100 CTA Blvd, Corbin, KY 40701
Tel.: (606) 528-8050
Thermal Insulation Mfr
N.A.I.C.S.: 326140
Don Hood *(Gen Mgr)*

Cerberus Beijing Advisors Ltd (1)
Room 1515 15th floor China World Tower III No 1 Jianguomenwai Avenue, Beijing, 100004, China
Tel.: (86) 10 57372677
Investment Management Service
N.A.I.C.S.: 523940

Cerberus California, LLC (1)
11812 San Vicente Blvd Ste 300, Los Angeles, CA 90049
Tel.: (310) 826-9200
Web Site: http://www.cerberuscapital.com
Investment Management Service

N.A.I.C.S.: 523940

Cerberus Capital Chicago, LLC (1)
155 N Wacker Dr Ste 4250, Chicago, IL 60606
Tel.: (312) 755-8100
Investment Management Service
N.A.I.C.S.: 523940

Cerberus European Capital Advisors, LLP (1)
84 Grosvenor Street, London, W1K 3JZ, United Kingdom
Tel.: (44) 20 7647 6000
Investment Advisory Services
N.A.I.C.S.: 523940
Liam Strom *(Mng Dir)*

Cerberus Global Investment Advisors, LLC (1)
875 3rd Ave, New York, NY 10022
Tel.: (212) 891-2100
Web Site: http://www.cerberuscapital.com
Equity Investment Firm
N.A.I.C.S.: 523999
James Danforth Quayle *(Chm)*
James Danforth Quayle *(Chm)*
Frank W. Bruno *(Pres)*

Cerberus Japan K.K. (1)
Marunouchi Mitsui Building 3rd Floor 2-2-2 Chiyoda, Marunouchi, Tokyo, 100-0005, Japan
Tel.: (81) 3 3287 1020
Web Site: http://www.cerberus.com
Investment Management Service
N.A.I.C.S.: 523940

Cerberus Mortgage Capital, Inc. (1)
875 3rd Ave 11th Fl, New York, NY 10022
Tel.: (212) 891-2100
Real Estate Investment Trust
N.A.I.C.S.: 525990

Cerberus Operations and Advisory Company, LLC (1)
875 3rd Ave 12th Fl, New York, NY 10022
Tel.: (212) 891-2100
Web Site: http://www.cerberuscapital.com
Investment Management Service
N.A.I.C.S.: 523940
Lisa A. Gray *(Vice Chm)*
Chan W. Galbato *(Executives)*
Olof Persson *(Mng Dir-UK)*
Gregory Nixon *(Mng Dir)*

Cerberus Telecom Acquisition Corp. (1)
875 3rd Ave, New York, NY 10022
Tel.: (212) 891-2100
Web Site:
http://www.cerberusacquisition.com
Investment Services
N.A.I.C.S.: 523999
Nicholas P. Robinson *(Co-Chief Investment Officer)*
Frank W. Bruno *(Chm)*
Timothy M. Donahue *(CEO)*
Shaygan Kheradpir *(CTO)*
Jeffrey L. Lomasky *(CFO)*
Nicholas P. Robinson *(Co-Chief Investment Officer)*
Michael K. Palmer *(Co-Chief Investment Officer)*

Closure Systems International, Inc. (1)
7820 Innovation Blvd Ste 100, Indianapolis, IN 46278-1683
Tel.: (317) 390-5000
Web Site: https://www.csiclosures.com
Plastic & Aluminum Closure Systems Developer & Mfr
N.A.I.C.S.: 322220

Subsidiary (Non-US):

CSI Japan Ltd. (2)
148 Nogimachi, Shimotsuga-gun, Shimotsuwa, 329-0114, Tochigi, Japan
Tel.: (81) 280562345
Web Site: http://www.csiij.jp
Sales Range: $300-349.9 Million
Emp.: 300
Aluminum & Plastic Cap Closures Mfr
N.A.I.C.S.: 326199
Douglas M. Cohen *(Pres & CEO)*

Plant (Domestic):

Closure Systems International-Kilgore (2)

1010 Energy Dr, Kilgore, TX 75662
Tel.: (903) 984-6229
Sales Range: $10-24.9 Million
Emp.: 300
Molded Plastic Closure Mfr
N.A.I.C.S.: 326199

CorePoint Lodging Inc. (1)
125 E John Carpenter Fwy Ste 1650, Irving, TX 75062
Tel.: (972) 893-3199
Web Site: http://www.corepoint.com
Rev.: $411,000,000
Assets: $1,766,000,000
Liabilities: $909,000,000
Net Worth: $857,000,000
Earnings: ($178,000,000)
Emp.: 32
Fiscal Year-end: 12/31/2020
Real Estate Investment Services
N.A.I.C.S.: 531210
Keith A. Cline *(Pres & CEO)*
Howard S. Garfield *(Chief Acctg Officer, Treas & Sr VP)*
Daniel E. Swanstrom II *(CFO & Exec VP)*

Cyanco Holding Corp. (1)
1920 Country Pl Pkwy 4th Fl, Pearland, TX 77584
Tel.: (832) 590-3641
Web Site: http://www.cyanco.com
Holding Company; Solid & Liquid Sodium Cyanide Mfr & Whslr
N.A.I.C.S.: 551112
Jeffrey Davis *(Pres & CEO)*
Justin Clark *(CFO)*

Subsidiary (Domestic):

Cyanco Corporation (2)
1920 Country Pl Pkwy 4th Fl, Pearland, TX 77584
Tel.: (832) 590-3641
Web Site: http://www.cyanco.com
Solid & Liquid Sodium Cyanide Mfr & Whslr
N.A.I.C.S.: 325180
Jeffrey Davis *(Pres & CEO)*
Justin Clark *(CFO)*
Paul C. Rostek *(Pres/Gen Mgr-Cyanco Intl)*
Greg Mitch *(VP-Ops & Plant Mgr-Winnemucca)*
Carlos Flores *(VP-Sls & Mktg-Latin America)*
Bob Warriner *(VP-Sls & Mktg)*
George Easterling *(Dir-Logistics & Transportation)*
Max Jones *(Dir-EHSS & ICMC)*
Roy Norcross *(Dir-Applied Tech & Quality Programs)*

Subsidiary (Domestic):

Cyanco Company, LLC (3)
5505 Cyanco Dr, Winnemucca, NV 89445
Tel.: (775) 623-1214
Web Site: http://www.cyanco.com
Liquid Sodium Cyanide Mfr & Whslr
N.A.I.C.S.: 325180
Greg Mitch *(VP-Ops & Plant Mgr)*

Cyanco International, LLC (3)
1920 Country Pl Pkwy 4th Fl, Pearland, TX 77584
Tel.: (832) 590-3641
Web Site: http://www.cyanco.com
Solid Sodium Cyanide Mfr & Whslr
N.A.I.C.S.: 325180
Paul C. Rostek *(Pres & Gen Mgr)*

Plant (Domestic):

Cyanco International, LLC - Houston Plant (4)
FM2917 1 Monsanto Rd, Alvin, TX 77511
Tel.: (281) 299-3185
Solid Sodium Cyanide Mfr
N.A.I.C.S.: 325180
Paul C. Rostek *(Pres & Gen Mgr)*

Delta Tucker Holdings, Inc. (1)
1700 Old Meadow Rd, McLean, VA 22102 **(100%)**
Tel.: (571) 722-0210
Web Site: http://www.dyn-intl.com
Rev.: $2,148,275,000
Assets: $718,299,000
Liabilities: $824,599,000
Net Worth: ($106,300,000)
Earnings: $84,497,000
Emp.: 13,200

Cerberus Capital Management, L.P.—(Continued)

Fiscal Year-end: 12/31/2018
Holding Company; Outsourced Professional
& Support Services
N.A.I.C.S.: 551112
George C. Krivo *(CEO)*
William T. Kansky *(CFO & Sr VP)*
John A. Gastright *(Sr VP-Govt Rels)*
Barbara D. Walker *(Sr VP-HR)*

Subsidiary (Domestic):

**Dyn Marine Services of Virginia
LLC** **(2)**
3190 Fairview Park Dr Ste 700, Falls
Church, VA 22042
Tel.: (571) 722-0206
Marine Transportation Services
N.A.I.C.S.: 488390

**DynCorp Aerospace Operations
Ltd.** **(2)**
13500 Heritage Pkwy Ste 400, Fort Worth,
TX 76177
Tel.: (817) 224-8200
Aircraft Parts Whslr
N.A.I.C.S.: 423860

DynCorp International LLC **(2)**
3190 Fairview Park Dr Ste 700, Falls
Church, VA 22042 **(100%)**
Tel.: (571) 722-0210
Web Site: http://www.dyn-intl.com
Sales Range: $1-4.9 Billion
Emp.: 120
Outsourced Professional & Support Ser-
vices
N.A.I.C.S.: 541990
James E. Geisler *(Chm)*
George C. Krivo *(CEO)*
William T. Kansky *(CFO & Sr VP)*
Mark Kelton *(Sr VP-Security Solutions-Natl)*

**Worldwide Recruiting and Staffing
Services LLC** **(2)**
8445 Freeport Pkwy Ste 400, Irving, TX
75063
Tel.: (972) 971-6790
Recruiting & Staffing Services
N.A.I.C.S.: 561499

**Electrical Components International,
Inc.** **(1)**
1 City Place Dr Ste 450, Saint Louis, MO
63141
Tel.: (314) 261-7700
Web Site: http://www.ecintl.com
Wire Harnesses, Subassemblies, Radiant
Glass Heaters & Power Cords Mfr
N.A.I.C.S.: 334419
Mike Balsei *(CEO)*

Subsidiary (Domestic):

Britech, Inc. **(2)**
775 Roble Rd, Allentown, PA 18109
Tel.: (610) 264-5400
Web Site: https://www.britech.com
Sales Range: $1-9.9 Million
Emp.: 50
Cable Harness Assemblies & Control Pan-
els
N.A.I.C.S.: 335314
Brian J. McCall *(CEO)*

Plant (Domestic):

**Electrical Components
International** **(2)**
11970 Pellicano Dr Ste 200, El Paso, TX
79936-7288
Tel.: (915) 860-8020
Web Site: http://www.eci.com
Sales Range: $25-49.9 Million
Emp.: 40
Wire Harnesses Mfr
N.A.I.C.S.: 334419
Victor Saenz *(Mgr-Pur Ops)*
Roberto Lopez *(Pres-Ops-North America)*
John Cahaly *(CEO)*
Bob Guilbert *(Mng Dir-Mktg & Products)*
Vinod Paul *(Mng Dir-Svc & Bus Dev)*
Steve Schoener *(CTO)*
William Tan *(Mng Dir-Tech & Corp Infra)*

Subsidiary (Domestic):

Fargo Assembly Company **(2)**
3300 7th Ave N, Fargo, ND 58102

Tel.: (701) 298-3803
Web Site: http://www.facnd.com
Current-Carrying Wiring Devices
N.A.I.C.S.: 335931

Subsidiary (Non-US):

Fargo Assembly of Europe Ltd **(3)**
Unit 12 Waterfield Way Sketchley Lane In-
dustrial Estate, Hinckley, LE10 3ER, Leics,
United Kingdom
Tel.: (44) 1455 639600
Web Site:
    http://www.fargoassemblyeurope.com
Wiring Harness Mfr
N.A.I.C.S.: 334419

Subsidiary (Domestic):

**Fargo Assembly of Mississippi,
LLC** **(3)**
PO Box 1285 Kosciusko-Attala Industrial
Park, Kosciusko, MS 39090
Tel.: (662) 289-3877
Electrical Component Mfr
N.A.I.C.S.: 335999

Fargo Assembly of PA, Inc. **(3)**
800 W Washington St, Norristown, PA
19404-0550
Tel.: (610) 272-6850
Web Site: http://www.fargopa.com
Electrical Wiring Mfr
N.A.I.C.S.: 335999
Bruce Hensley *(Mgr)*

Industrial Harness Co. **(3)**
100 Outlook Ln, Shippensburg, PA 17257
Tel.: (717) 477-0100
Wire & Harness Mfr
N.A.I.C.S.: 335999
Andy Lundeen *(Acct Mgr)*

OHE Industries LLC **(3)**
4480 8th Ave, Marion, IA 52302
Tel.: (319) 377-6844
Web Site: http://www.oheind.com
Electrical Component Mfr
N.A.I.C.S.: 335999
Maxwell Grant *(CEO)*
Lois McBurney *(Plant Mgr)*

Subsidiary (Domestic):

Flex-Tec Inc. **(2)**
1 Vance St, Byromville, GA 31007-0528
Tel.: (478) 433-6537
Web Site: https://www.flex-tec.com
Rev.: $11,081,556
Emp.: 80
Electronic Harness Assemblies Mfr
N.A.I.C.S.: 334419
Charles R. Fitch *(CEO)*

**Manufacturing Resource Group,
Inc.** **(2)**
930 Washington St, Norwood, MA 02062
Tel.: (781) 440-9700
Web Site: http://www.mrg-inc.com
Relay & Industrial Control Mfr
N.A.I.C.S.: 335314

**Omni Connection International,
Inc.** **(2)**
1611 Railroad St, Corona, CA 92880
Tel.: (951) 898-6232
Web Site: http://www.omni-conn.com
Rev.: $5,664,000
Emp.: 6
Other Miscellaneous Durable Goods Mer-
chant Whslr
N.A.I.C.S.: 423990
Henry Cheng *(Founder & CEO)*

Rochester Industrial Control, Inc. **(2)**
6400 Furnace Rd, Ontario, NY 14519
Tel.: (315) 524-4555
Web Site:
    http://www.rochesterindustrial.com
Sales Range: $1-9.9 Million
Emp.: 100
Electronics & Engineering Services
N.A.I.C.S.: 334417
Martin King *(Treas)*

Whitepath Fab Tech Inc. **(2)**
420 Industrial Blvd, Ellijay, GA 30540
Tel.: (706) 276-5510
Web Site: http://www.whitepath.com
Miscellaneous Fabricated Wire Products Mfr
N.A.I.C.S.: 332618

FGI Operating Company, LLC **(1)**
870 Remington Dr, Madison, NC 27025-
1776
Tel.: (336) 548-8700
Firearms Whslr
N.A.I.C.S.: 423990

Subsidiary (Domestic):

Outdoor Services, LLC **(2)**
2040 Cottage Ave Ste B, Columbus, IN
47201
Tel.: (812) 374-4572
Landscaping Services
N.A.I.C.S.: 561730

Garden Fresh Restaurant LLC **(1)**
15822 Bernardo Center Dr Ste A, San Di-
ego, CA 92127-2320
Tel.: (858) 675-1600
Web Site: http://www.soupplantation.com
Sales Range: $25-49.9 Million
Emp.: 80
Salad Buffet Restaurant Operator
N.A.I.C.S.: 722511
John Haywood *(CEO)*
Donald Breen *(CFO)*
Victor Phan *(VP-Supply Chain Ops & Dev)*

HHIC-Phil Inc. **(1)**
Green Beach 1 Redondo Peninsula Sitio
Agusuhin Brgy Cawag, Subic, Zambales,
Philippines
Tel.: (63) 473065100
Ship Building Services
N.A.I.C.S.: 336611

Hamburg Commercial Bank AG **(1)**
Gerhart-Hauptmann Platz 50, 20095, Ham-
burg, Germany **(42.45%)**
Tel.: (49) 4033330
Web Site: http://www.hcob-bank.de
Rev.: $2,462,572,140
Assets: $53,430,760,320
Liabilities: $47,048,678,180
Net Worth: $6,382,082,140
Earnings: $13,438,320
Emp.: 1,482
Fiscal Year-end: 12/31/2019
Commericial Banking
N.A.I.C.S.: 522110
Stefan Ermisch *(CEO & Member-Mgmt Bd)*
Uwe-Jens Werner *(Head-Savings Banks &
Institutional Clients)*
Judith Steinhoff *(Head-HR)*
Ralf Lowe *(Head-Treasury)*
Peter Axmann *(Head-Real Estate-Global)*
Barbara Himmel *(Head-Legal & Taxes)*
Oliver Waldeck *(Head-Bus Origination)*
Bernd Gabor *(Head-Shipping-Europe &
Americas)*
Loukas Lagaras *(Head-Shipping-Athens
Branch)*
Jutta Arlt *(Head-Cash & Trade Svcs)*
Ulrik Lackschewitz *(Deputy CEO, Chief Risk
Officer & Member-Mgmt Bd)*
Michael Rothehuser *(Head-Trade, Food,
Commodities, Industry & Svcs)*
Martin Jonas *(Head-IR)*
Franziska von Scholz *(Head-Strategic Proj-
ects)*
Stephan Otto *(Head-Risk Mgmt)*
Ian Banwell *(CFO & Member-Mgmt Bd)*
Nicolas Blanchard *(Chief Clients & Products
Officer & Member-Mgmt Bd)*
Christopher Brody *(Chief Investment Officer
& Member-Mgmt Bd)*
Thomas Jakob *(Head-Corp Banking & Advi-
sory)*
Stephen Scheuer *(Head-Corp Fin & Work-
ing Capital Solution)*
Inka Klinger *(Head-Infrastructure Project
Fin-Global)*
Jan-Philipp Rohr *(Head-Shipping-Global)*
Donald Banks *(Head-Capital Markets)*
Tilo Kraus *(Head-Sls & Syndicate-Global)*
Monika Feher *(Head-Middle Office & Bus
Dev)*
Markus Best *(Head-Transaction Banking)*
Nicole Neumann *(Head-Mktg & Digital Me-
dia)*
Katrin Steinbacher *(Head-Press)*
Eileen Maschmann *(Head-Corp & Securities
Compliance)*
Dirk von Thaden *(Head-Acctg)*
Jorg Reinicke *(Head-Regulatory Reporting)*
Henrik Stein *(Head-Internal Auditing)*
Svenja Neuhaus *(Head-Law)*
Juan Rodriguez Inciarte *(Chm-Supervisory
Bd)*

Subsidiary (Domestic):

**CAPCELLENCE Holding GmbH &
Co. KG** **(2)**
Gasstrasse 4, 22761, Hamburg, Germany
Tel.: (49) 40 30700700
Financial Management Services
N.A.I.C.S.: 551112

**HSH Facility Management
GmbH** **(2)**
Rosenstr 11, Hamburg, 20095, Germany
Tel.: (49) 40 33330
Financial Management Services
N.A.I.C.S.: 551112

HSH Move+More GmbH **(2)**
Martensdamm 6, 24103, Kiel, Schleswig-
Holstein, Germany
Tel.: (49) 43190001
Logistics Services & Consulting Services
N.A.I.C.S.: 541614

Subsidiary (US):

HSH N Financial Securities LLC **(2)**
230 Park Ave, New York, NY 10169
Tel.: (212) 407-6000
Financial Management Services
N.A.I.C.S.: 551112

Representative Office (Non-US):

**HSH Nordbank AG
(Luxembourg)** **(2)**
2 rue Jean Monnet, L-2180, Luxembourg,
Luxembourg
Tel.: (352) 424137
Web Site: http://www.hsh-nordbank.lu
Banking Services
N.A.I.C.S.: 522110

Subsidiary (Non-US):

HSH Nordbank Securities S.A. **(2)**
2 Rue Jean Monnet, Luxembourg, 2180,
Luxembourg
Tel.: (352) 42414111
Web Site: http://www.hshn-securities.com
Sales Range: $100-124.9 Million
Emp.: 145
Private Banking Services
N.A.I.C.S.: 522320
Carsten Backer *(Chm-Mgmt Bd, CFO &
Chief Risk Officer)*
Jan Luhrs-Behnke *(Mng Dir & Head-Bus
Unit)*
Franz-Josef Glauben *(Member-Mgmt Bd)*

Subsidiary (Domestic):

Kontora Family Office GmbH **(2)**
Ballindamm 39, 20095, Hamburg, Germany
Tel.: (49) 4032908880
Web Site: http://www.kontora-advisory.com
Financial Management Services
N.A.I.C.S.: 551112

Helix Sleep, Inc. **(1)**
1123 Broadway Suite 613, New York, NY
10010
Tel.: (831) 777-5976
Web Site: https://helixsleep.com
Emp.: 100
Home Bedroom Mattress & Mfr
N.A.I.C.S.: 337910

IWCO Direct Inc. **(1)**
7951 Powers Blvd, Chanhassen, MN
55317-9502
Tel.: (952) 474-0961
Web Site: http://www.iwco.com
Direct Marketing Services
N.A.I.C.S.: 541860
James S. Leone *(VP-Sls)*
Debora M. Haskel *(VP-Mktg & Corp Comm)*
James Gartrell *(VP-Content Dev)*
Mary Hyland *(VP-Bus Svcs)*
Wes Sparling *(CMO)*
Alan Sherman *(VP-Mktg Strategy)*
Michael Henry *(VP-IWCO Direct & Mail-
Gard)*
Jake Hertel *(CFO & Exec VP)*
Tom Hexamer *(Sr VP-Sls)*
Tedd Aurelius *(VP-Sls)*
Gary Masse *(CEO)*
Patrick Sondreal *(Chief Production Officer)*

Paul Overn (VP-Mfg Ops)
Mike Parker (Chief Mktg & Solutions Officer)
Rick Neumann (VP-Ops)
Ken McDonald (Chief Supply Chain Officer)
Reid Holmes (Exec Creative Dir)
Dave Ciocchi (Sr VP-Sls & Customer Solutions)
Melissa Smutny (Chief HR Officer)

Kellermeyer Bergensons Services, LLC (1)
3605 Ocean Ranch Blvd Ste 200, Oceanside, CA 92056
Tel.: (419) 867-4309
Web Site: http://www.kbs-services.com
Corporate Operations & Facilities Support Services
N.A.I.C.S.: 561210
Mark Minasian (Founder & CEO)
Zulfiqar Rashid (CIO & Pres-Ops)
Nathaniel Shaw (Chief Comml Officer)
Fergus O Connell (CFO)
Vicki Bernholz (Chief HR Officer)
Christian Cornelius-Knudsen (Pres)
Dan Oliver (Sr VP-Customer Experience)

Subsidiary (Domestic):

East Coast Lot & Pavement Maintenance Corp. (2)
20 Dunnell Ln, Pawtucket, RI 02860
Tel.: (401) 728-8419
Web Site: http://www.econsite.com
All Other Miscellaneous Waste Management Services
N.A.I.C.S.: 562998

Hospitality Staffing Solutions, LLC (2)
100 Glenridge Point Pkwy Ste 400, Atlanta, GA 30342
Tel.: (770) 612-0054
Web Site: http://www.hssstaffing.com
Emp.: 2,000
Janitorial Services
N.A.I.C.S.: 561720
Naveen Ahuja (VP-Sls)
Martin Mazy (Sr VP-West)
Randy Oloffson (Sr VP-Northeast)
Luke Lindahl (Sr VP-Southeast)
Vincent Lombardo (CFO)
Tim McPherson (CEO)
Gisela Gomez (VP-Managed Svcs-Outsourcing)
Kevin Murphy (Sr VP-Fin)

National Dentex Corporation (1)
11601 Kew Gardens Ave Ste 200, Palm Beach Gardens, FL 33410
Tel.: (508) 907-7800
Web Site: http://www.nationaldentex.com
Sales Range: $150-199.9 Million
Dental Laboratories Operator
N.A.I.C.S.: 621512

Subsidiary (Domestic):

Biotech Dental Prosthetics, Inc. (2)
3780 Burns Ste 8, Palm Beach Gardens, FL 33410
Tel.: (561) 721-9866
Web Site:
http://www.biotechdentalprosthetics.com
Dental Laboratories Operator
N.A.I.C.S.: 339116
Frank Lavonia III (Gen Mgr)

Keller Laboratories Inc. (2)
160 Lrkin Wllams Indus Ct, Fenton, MO 63026
Tel.: (636) 717-1755
Web Site: http://www.kellerlab.com
Dental Laboratories
N.A.I.C.S.: 339116
Ronald P. Keller (Chm)
Sheryl Dwyer (Acct Mgr)

NDX Albensi (2)
100 Colony Dr, Irwin, PA 15642
Tel.: (724) 864-8880
Web Site: http://nationaldentex.com
Full Service Dental Laboratories
N.A.I.C.S.: 339116
Donald R. Albensi (Founder & CEO)

Panavision Inc. (1)
6101 Variel Ave, Woodland Hills, CA 91367-2601
Tel.: (818) 316-1000

Web Site: http://www.panavision.com
Sales Range: $200-249.9 Million
Emp.: 1,200
Motion Picture Equipment Mfr & Distr
N.A.I.C.S.: 333310

Subsidiary (Non-US):

Panavision (Canada) Corp. (2)
900A Don Mills Rd, Toronto, M3C 1V6, ON, Canada
Tel.: (416) 444-7000
Web Site: http://www.panavision.com
Sales Range: $25-49.9 Million
Emp.: 25
Motion Picture Cameras & Equipment Rental Services
N.A.I.C.S.: 512199

Subsidiary (Domestic):

Panavision International, LP (2)
6219 De Soto Ave, Woodland Hills, CA 91367-2602 (100%)
Tel.: (818) 316-1000
Web Site: http://www.panavision.com
Sales Range: $25-49.9 Million
Cameras & Related Equipment
N.A.I.C.S.: 333310

Para USA, LLC (1)
10620 Southern Loop Blvd, Pineville, NC 28134-7381
Tel.: (704) 930-7600
Web Site: http://www.para-usa.com
Emp.: 85
Firearms Mfr
N.A.I.C.S.: 332994

Promontoria MMB SAS (1)
Tour Europlaza 20 avenue Andre Prothin, 92063, Paris, Cedex, France
Tel.: (33) 158132828
Web Site: http://www.mymoneybank.com
Holding Company
N.A.I.C.S.: 551112
Eric Shehadeh (CEO)
Thomas Schneegans (Deputy CEO & CFO)
Alain Demarolle (Chm)

Subsidiary (Domestic):

Banque Espirito Santo et de la Venetie S.A. (2)
45 avenue Georges Mandel, F-75116, Paris, France
Tel.: (33) 144344800
Web Site: http://www.besv.fr
Sales Range: $100-124.9 Million
Emp.: 150
Corporate & Private Banking
N.A.I.C.S.: 523150
Philippe Gilles Fernand Guiral (Pres)
Thomas Schneegans (CEO)
Alain Demarolle (Chm)

Subsidiary (Domestic):

Marignan Gestion S.A. (3)
45 Avenue Georges Mandel, 75116, Paris, France
Tel.: (33) 142663989
Web Site: http://www.marigest.com
Portfolio Management Services
N.A.I.C.S.: 523940

Subsidiary (Domestic):

My Money Bank S.A. (2)
Tour Europlaza 20 avenue Andre-Prothin, 92063, Paris, Cedex, France
Tel.: (33) 1 58 13 28 28
Banking Services
N.A.I.C.S.: 522110
Eric Shehadeh (CEO)
Alain Demarolle (Chm)

Red River Technology LLC (1)
21 Water St Ste 500, Claremont, NH 03743
Tel.: (603) 448-8880
Web Site: http://www.redriver.com
Information Technology Solutions Provider
N.A.I.C.S.: 518210
Dan McGee (COO)
Sera Gray (CIO)
Joe Hornyak (VP & Gen Counsel)
Ed Levens (VP-Mktg)
Jeff Sinclair (Sr VP-Customer Experience)
Jeff Snider (Chief Growth Officer)
Jennifer Hood (Sr VP-HR)

Warren Kohm (CFO)
Brian Roach (CEO)
Courtney Mitchell (Chief HR Officer)

Remington Outdoor Company Inc. (1)
870 Remington Dr, Madison, NC 27025-1776
Tel.: (336) 548-8700
Web Site:
http://www.remingtonoutdoorcompany.com
Rev.: $865,100,000
Assets: $920,800,000
Liabilities: $1,218,000,000
Net Worth: ($297,200,000)
Earnings: $19,100,000
Emp.: 3,400
Fiscal Year-end: 12/31/2016
Firearms, Ammunition & Related Products Mfr & Distr
N.A.I.C.S.: 332994
Melissa Cofield (Chief HR Officer & Exec VP)
Andrew J. Logan (Gen Counsel & Exec VP)
Matt Ohlson (VP-Pro Sls)
Anthony Acitelli (Chm & CEO)
John Flanagan (CFO)

Subsidiary (Domestic):

Remington Arms Company, Inc. (2)
870 Remington Dr, Madison, NC 27025-0700
Tel.: (336) 548-8700
Web Site: http://www.remington.com
Sales Range: $550-599.9 Million
Sporting Firearms, Ammunition, Traps, Targets & Powder Metal Products Mfr
N.A.I.C.S.: 332994
E. Scott Blackwell (Pres-Global Sls & Mktg)

Plant (Domestic):

Remington Arms Company, Inc. - Ammunition & Components Plant (3)
2592 Arkansas Hwy 15 N, Lonoke, AR 72086
Tel.: (501) 676-3161
Web Site: http://www.remington.com
Ammunition Mfr
N.A.I.C.S.: 332993
Chris White (Plant Mgr)

Remington Arms Company, Inc. - Mayfield Firearms Plant (3)
22 Rifle Trl, Hickory, KY 42051
Tel.: (270) 856-4200
Web Site: http://www.remington.com
Firearms Mfr
N.A.I.C.S.: 332994
Stacy Jackson (Controller)

Subsidiary (Domestic):

The Marlin Firearms Company, Inc. (3)
100 Kenna Dr, North Haven, CT 06473-2516
Tel.: (203) 239-5621
Web Site: http://www.marlinfirearms.com
Sales Range: $50-74.9 Million
Sporting Rifle & Shotgun & Mfr
N.A.I.C.S.: 332994
Frank Kenna III (Chm)

Reydel Automotive Holdings B.V. (1)
381 Avenue du General de Gaulle, 92140, Clamart, France
Tel.: (33) 1 7941 7200
Web Site: http://www.reydel.com
Holding Company; Automotive Interior Components Mfr
N.A.I.C.S.: 551112
Michel Serre (CEO)
Francois Godron (CFO)
Gladys Grinand (Mgr-Comm)
Sandrine Waechter (Gen Counsel & VP)
Benoit Rolland (VP-South Europe BU)
Ulrich Rottges (VP-North Europe BU)
Pierre d'Archemont (VP-South America BU)
Chin Weng Chow (VP-Asia BU)
Henri-Jerome Gradus (VP-Sls & Mktg)
Nicolas Larthois (VP-Product Dev)
Thierry Lafont (VP-HR)
Philippe Martin (VP-Industrial Ops)
Bernard Magnoux (VP-Pur)
Dominique Jacob (VP-Quality & Process Engrg)

Subsidiary (Non-US):

Reydel Automotive Spain, S.L.U. (2)

Pol Ind Les Comes Calle Francia 15, 08080, Igualada, Spain
Tel.: (34) 938048080
Web Site: http://www.reydel.com
Automotive Components Services
N.A.I.C.S.: 423120

Visteon Interior Systems Italia S.p.A. (2)
Corso Savona 45, 10029, Villastellone, Italy
Tel.: (39) 0119691611
Sales Range: $300-349.9 Million
Bumpers & Instrument Panels Mfr
N.A.I.C.S.: 336390
Liliana Sereno (Gen Mgr)

Source Code Corporation (1)
232 Vanderbilt Ave, Norwood, MA 02062
Tel.: (877) 722-3478
Web Site: http://www.sourcecode.com
Emp.: 150
Computer Peripheral Equipment
N.A.I.C.S.: 423430
Arthur N. Ataie (Founder & CEO)
Brian Corn (VP-Products & Integration)
Pamela Ochs-Piasecki (CFO)
Frank Vincentelli (CTO)
Nasser Khadjenoori (VP-Strategic Projects)
Eva Cherry (VP-HR)
Dave Lebov (Exec VP-Sls & Server)
Jay Patterson (Exec VP-Sls)
Parag Shah (COO & CTO-Edge)
Pamela Sufi (VP-Mktg)
Colin Broadberry (Pres-Europe)
Rob Canzanello (VP-Acq & Merger)
David Grieve (VP-Ops & Servers)

Subsidiary (Non-US):

Boston Limited (2)
Unit 5 Curo Park Frogmore, Saint Albans, AL2 2DD, Hertfordshire, United Kingdom
Tel.: (44) 1727876100
Web Site: http://www.boston.co.uk
General Marketing Services
N.A.I.C.S.: 541613

Subsidiary (Domestic):

Silicon Mechanics, Inc. (2)
16504 9th Ave SE STE 201, Mill Creek, WA 98012
Tel.: (866) 352-1173
Web Site: http://www.siliconmechanics.com
Rackmount Server Mfr
N.A.I.C.S.: 334111
Bob Heyer (Pres)

Spyglass Entertainment Group, LLC (1)
245 N Beverly Dr, Beverly Hills, CA 90210
Tel.: (310) 443-5800
Web Site:
http://www.spyglassentertainment.com
Sales Range: $1-9.9 Million
Motion Picture Production Services
N.A.I.C.S.: 512110
Roger Birnbaum (Co-Founder & Co-Chm)
Jose Gutierrez (CEO & CFO)
Gary Barber (Co-Founder & Co-Chm)

Staples Solutions B.V. (1)
Hoogoorddreef 62, 1101 BE, Amsterdam, Netherlands
Tel.: (31) 206511111
Web Site: http://www.staples.eu
Holding Company; Office Supplies & Equipment Retailer
N.A.I.C.S.: 551112
Olof Persson (Chm)
Dolph Westerbos (CEO)
Andy Bonney (Head-Comml)
Patrick Legro (Head-Retail)
Werner Kurt Domittner (Head-Corp Dev & Managed Svcs)
Sharon Tan (Head-Mdsg)
Bas Beurskens (Head-Supply Chain & Customer Svc)
Kenneth Murdoch (CFO)
Monica Mauri (Head-HR)
Keith Newman (CIO-Acting)
Yvonne van Eck (Head-Legal)

V.H.C Ltd., Inc. (1)
300 W Martin St, Winchester, IN 47394-1012
Tel.: (765) 584-2101
Web Site: http://www.maultech.com
Sales Range: $25-49.9 Million
Emp.: 25
Special Industry Machinery

Cerberus Capital Management, L.P.—(Continued)

N.A.I.C.S.: 333248

WFS Global SAS (1)
6 rue du Pave Zone de Fret 6, BP 11546,
Roissy CDG Airport, 95709, Paris, France
Tel.: (33) 1 70 76 00 00
Web Site: http://www.wfs.aero
Holding Company; Air Cargo Handling
N.A.I.C.S.: 551112
Francois Mirallie (Grp CFO)
Pedro Garcia (CIO)
Fabienne Bricaud (Head-People-Global)
Barry D. Nassberg (COO)
David Clark (Head-Global Safety & Security)
Pablo Garcia (Exec VP-Bus Dev)
Zahia Gandolfo (Exec Dir-WFS Foundations)

Subsidiary (Non-US):

WFS Asia Pacific, Africa & Middle East (2)
Worldwide House 1501A 19 Des Voeux
Road, Central, China (Hong Kong)
Tel.: (852) 2801 2980
Web Site: http://www.wfs.aero
Aircraft Support & Ground Handling Services
N.A.I.C.S.: 488190
Stewart Sinclair (Exec VP)

Subsidiary (Domestic):

WFS Europe (2)
6 Rue du Pave Zone De Fret 6, BP 11546,
95703, Roissy-en-France, France
Tel.: (33) 1 70 76 00 00
Web Site: http://www.wfs.com
Aircraft Support & Ground Handling Services
N.A.I.C.S.: 488190

Subsidiary (Non-US):

Fraport Cargo Services GmbH (3)
Gebaude 532, 60549, Frankfurt am Main,
Germany (51%)
Tel.: (49) 6969070155
Web Site: http://www.fraport-cargo.com
Cargo Handling Services
N.A.I.C.S.: 488190
Hans-Georg Emmert (Mng Dir)
Anne Smirr (Head-Sls & Mktg)
Elke Kleemann (Head-Controlling)
Klaus Klein (Head-Ops)
Steffen Kuhn (Head-Infrastructure, Quality & Project Mgmt)

Subsidiary (Domestic):

FraGround Fraport Ground Services GmbH (4)
CargoCity Nord Gebaude 458, 60549,
Frankfurt am Main, Germany
Tel.: (49) 6969070652
Web Site: http://www.fraground.de
Human Resource Management Services
N.A.I.C.S.: 923130
Mira Fisher (Mgr)

CERCO LLC
453 W McConkey St, Shreve, OH
44676-9769
Tel.: (330) 567-2145
Web Site: http://www.cercollc.com
Year Founded: 1940
Sales Range: $25-49.9 Million
Emp.: 200
Technical Ceramic Product Mfr
N.A.I.C.S.: 334419
Jim Jaskowiak (Gen Mgr)
Susan English (Product Mgr-Grinding Media & Mill Linings)
Jennifer Bee (Coord-Export-Customer Svc)
Joel Connor (Engr-Design)
Gary Troyer (Mgr-Engrg)
Karen Burns (Supvr-Shipping)
Sharen Brigham (Mgr-Quality Assurance)

Subsidiaries:

CerCo LLC - Cesco Plant (1)

416 Maple Ave, Crooksville, OH 43731
Tel.: (740) 982-2050
Web Site: http://www.cercocorp.com
Sales Range: $50-74.9 Million
Emp.: 45
Ceramic Armor Mfr
N.A.I.C.S.: 212323
Mick Pease (Plant Mgr)

CERCONE BROWN CURTIS
77 N Washington St Ste 304, Boston,
MA 02114-1913
Tel.: (617) 248-0680
Web Site:
http://www.cerconebrown.com
Year Founded: 2001
Rev.: $15,000,000
Emp.: 20
Brand Development, Communications
N.A.I.C.S.: 541810
Leonard Cercone (Partner)
Erika Brown (Partner)
Anne Houseman (Acct Supvr)
Emily McCavanagh (Acct Exec)
Caroline Budney (Acct Exec)
Tess Morton (Acct Exec)
Noelle Guerin (Acct Exec)
Robin Whalen (Sr Acct Exec)
Josh Caplan (Chief Creative Officer)

CERDANT, INC.
5747 Perimeter Dr Ste 110, Dublin,
OH 43017
Web Site: http://www.cerdant.com
Year Founded: 2002
Sales Range: $10-24.9 Million
Emp.: 49
Network Security Services
N.A.I.C.S.: 518210
Mike Johnson (Pres & CEO)

CEREAL BYPRODUCTS COMPANY INC.
55 E Euclid Ave Ste 410, Mount
Prospect, IL 60056-1285
Tel.: (847) 818-1550   IL
Web Site:
http://www.cerealbyproducts.com
Year Founded: 1917
Sales Range: $75-99.9 Million
Emp.: 28
Agricultural Services
N.A.I.C.S.: 424510
Del Danner (Pres)
Michael Kirwan (Controller)
Tim Thompson (VP)

CEREAL FOOD PROCESSORS INC.
2001 Shawnee Mission Pkwy, Mission Woods, KS 66205-2051
Tel.: (913) 890-6300   DE
Web Site: http://www.graincraft.com
Year Founded: 1972
Sales Range: $25-49.9 Million
Emp.: 380
Flour & Other Grain Mill Products
N.A.I.C.S.: 311211
Paul Myer (VP-Acctg)
J. Breck Barton (Pres)
Brent Wall (VP)
Bruce M. King (VP-Sls)
Fred L. Merrill (Chm)
Timothy S. Miller (Sr VP-Sls)
Mark L. Dobbins (Exec VP & Gen Mgr-Sls)
Steven J. Heeney (Exec VP-Fin & Admin)
Greg Edelblute (VP-Grain)
Joe Blanton (Plant Mgr)
Steve Hanauer (Plant Mgr)
Dave Hodges (Plant Mgr)

Subsidiaries:

Cereal Food Processors Inc. - Billings Facility (1)
3601 1st Ave S, Billings, MT 59101

Tel.: (406) 245-3131
Flour Product Mfr
N.A.I.C.S.: 311211
Dave Hodges (Plant Mgr)

Cereal Food Processors Inc. - Cleveland Facility (1)
1635 Merwin St, Cleveland, OH 44113
Tel.: (216) 621-3206
Flour Product Mfr
N.A.I.C.S.: 311211
Joe Blanton (Plant Mgr)

Cereal Food Processors Inc. - Great Falls Facility (1)
901 16th St N, Great Falls, MT 59401
Tel.: (406) 727-7366
Flour Product Mfr
N.A.I.C.S.: 311211
Dave Hodges (Plant Mgr)

Cereal Food Processors Inc. - Kansas City Facility (1)
56 Silver St, Kansas City, KS 66103
Tel.: (913) 262-1779
Flour Product Mfr
N.A.I.C.S.: 311211
Pat Eberle (Plant Mgr)

Cereal Food Processors Inc. - Los Angeles Facility (1)
1861 E 55th St, Los Angeles, CA 90058
Tel.: (323) 585-0131
Flour Product Mfr
N.A.I.C.S.: 311211
Steve Hanauer (Plant Mgr)

Cereal Food Processors Inc. - McPherson Facility (1)
416 N Main, McPherson, KS 67460
Tel.: (620) 241-2410
Emp.: 30
Flour Product Mfr
N.A.I.C.S.: 311211
Clint Church (Plant Mgr)

Cereal Food Processors Inc. - Ogden Facility (1)
220 W 30th St, Ogden, UT 84401
Tel.: (801) 394-4523
Flour Product Mfr
N.A.I.C.S.: 311211
Rick Thomas (Plant Mgr)

Cereal Food Processors Inc. - Portland Facility (1)
Municipal Terminal Ste 4, Portland, OR 97203
Tel.: (503) 286-1656
Flour Product Mfr
N.A.I.C.S.: 311211
Steve Hanauer (Plant Mgr)

Cereal Food Processors Inc. - Salt Lake City Facility (1)
425 W 500 S St, Salt Lake City, UT 84101
Tel.: (801) 355-2981
Flour Product Mfr
N.A.I.C.S.: 311211
Rick Thomas (Plant Mgr)

Cereal Food Processors Inc. - Wichita Facility (1)
701 E 17th St, Wichita, KS 67214
Tel.: (316) 267-7311
Flour Product Mfr
N.A.I.C.S.: 311211
Charlie Jackson (Plant Mgr)

CEREBAIN BIOTECH CORP.
600 Anton Blvd Ste 1100, Costa
Mesa, CA 92626
Tel.: (714) 371-4109   NV
Year Founded: 2007
Assets: $91,601
Liabilities: $5,675,428
Net Worth: ($5,583,827)
Earnings: ($4,918,792)
Emp.: 2
Fiscal Year-end: 06/30/18
Alzheimer's Disease Treatment Developer
N.A.I.C.S.: 325412
Eric Clemons (Pres & CEO)

CEREBRAL PALSY OF NORTH JERSEY

220 S Orange Ave Ste 300, Livingston, NJ 07039
Tel.: (973) 763-9900   NJ
Web Site: http://www.cpnj.org
Year Founded: 1964
Sales Range: $25-49.9 Million
Emp.: 721
Disabled People Assistance Services
N.A.I.C.S.: 624120
Joy England (Dir-Adult Svcs)
Angelica Diaz-Martinez (Sr VP-Ops)
David Bishop (VP-Dev & Comm)
Lori Hoffner (Dir-Community Svcs)
Rick Bornstein (CFO & VP-Fin)
Patti Murray (VP-HR)

CEREBRAL PALSY OF WESTCHESTER, INC.
1186 King St, Rye Brook, NY 10573
Tel.: (914) 937-3800   NY
Web Site:
http://www.cpwestchester.org
Year Founded: 1948
Sales Range: $10-24.9 Million
Emp.: 361
Disability Assistance Services
N.A.I.C.S.: 624120
Linda Kuck (Exec Dir)
Hortena Richmond (Dir-Day Treatment & Day Habilitation)
Kiyoko Brown (Sec)
Dennis Citarella (Treas)
Richard N. Osterer (Pres)
Lauren Bassin (Dir-Medicaid Svc Coordination)
Lindsay Buttenschon (Dir-Preschool & Daycare)
Odette Addison (Dir-Recruitment)
Sean Wade (Dir-Residential Svcs)
David Kelson (Exec VP)
Eileen Podlovits (CFO)
Randy Rifelli (Treas)
Lesmore Willis (Officer-Compliance)

CERES CLASSIC L.P.
522 5th Ave, New York, NY 10036   DE
Rev.: $205,700
Assets: $64,584,761
Liabilities: $3,135,203
Net Worth: $61,449,558
Earnings: ($5,405,610)
Fiscal Year-end: 12/31/20
Investment Services
N.A.I.C.S.: 523940
Patrick T. Egan (Pres)

CERES ENVIRONMENTAL SERVICES, INC.
6968 Professional Pkwy E, Sarasota,
FL 34240
Web Site:
https://www.ceresenvironmental.com
Year Founded: 1976
Emergency Management & Environmental Services
N.A.I.C.S.: 237990
David McIntyre (Founder)
Jeff Kulaszewicz (Controller)

CERES SOLUTIONS, LLP
2112 Indianapolis Rd, Crawfordsville,
IN 47933-3137
Tel.: (765) 362-6700   IN
Web Site: https://www.ceres.coop
Sales Range: $200-249.9 Million
Emp.: 125
Agricultural Cooperative
N.A.I.C.S.: 424910
Shan D. Unger (Vice Chm)
Jeffrey Troike (Pres & CEO)
Dan Weber (VP-Agronomy)
Howard Jones (VP-Energy & Special Projects)
Daryl Warren (VP-Ops)

Subsidiaries:

Ceres Solutions - Terre Haute   (1)
2500 S 13th St, Terre Haute, IN 47802-3204
Tel.: (812) 235-8123
Sales Range: $10-24.9 Million
Grain Marketing
N.A.I.C.S.: 424510
Dan Weber (VP-Agronomy)
Randy Fry (Mgr-Data Process & Info Sys)

CERES TRANSPORTATION GROUP, INC.
1911 Acc I ste A, Charlotte, NC 28217
Tel.: (704) 329-7113   NC
Web Site: http://www.ceresgroup.net
Sales Range: $10-24.9 Million
Emp.: 20
Freight Forwarding
N.A.I.C.S.: 488510
Charles Justice (CEO)
Jimmy Jackson (Pres)

CERIUM HOLDINGS, INC.
5204 E Ben White Blvd, Austin, TX 78741-7306
Tel.: (512) 691-7752   TX
Year Founded: 2011
Holding Company
N.A.I.C.S.: 551112
Clayton E. Fullwood (Pres)
Lynette Ballast (Dir-Ops)

Subsidiaries:

Cerium Laboratories, LLC   (1)
5204 E Ben White Blvd Bldg 1 Mailstop 512, Austin, TX 78741
Tel.: (512) 691-7752
Web Site: http://www.ceriumlabs.com
Sales Range: $75-99.9 Million
Semiconductor & Alternative Fuels Laboratory Services
N.A.I.C.S.: 541380
Clayton E. Fullwood (Pres & CEO)
Steve Popst (Dir-Bus Dev)
Tim Hossain (Chief Technical Officer)
Ted Neil (Mgr-Quality)
Lynette Ballast (Dir-Ops)

CERIUM TECHNOLOGY LLC
1717 McKinney Ave Ste 700, Dallas, TX 75202
Tel.: (214) 432-6323
Web Site: http://www.cerium-technology.com
Year Founded: 2013
Investment Services
N.A.I.C.S.: 523999
Eldon Klaassen (Mng Dir)

CERNI MOTOR SALES, INC.
5751 Cerni Pl, Youngstown, OH 44515
Tel.: (330) 652-9917   OH
Web Site:
  http://www.cernimotors.com
Year Founded: 1960
Sales Range: $10-24.9 Million
Emp.: 50
Commercial Truck Retailer
N.A.I.C.S.: 423110
John P. Cerni II (Pres)

CERRELL ASSOCIATES, INC.
320 N Larchmont Blvd, Los Angeles, CA 90004
Tel.: (323) 466-3445
Web Site: http://www.cerrell.com
Sales Range: $1-9.9 Million
Emp.: 30
Public Relations Agency
N.A.I.C.S.: 541820
Hal Dash (Chm & CEO)
Lee Cerrell (Partner)
Steve Bullock (CFO)
Lisa Gritzner (Pres)
Alisa Karlan (VP)

Brandon Stephenson (VP-Campaigns & Issues Mgmt)
Fernando Chavez (VP)
Marc Mitchell (VP)
Nicole Kuklok-Waldman (VP)
Alan Caldwell (VP-Media Rels & Crisis Comm)

CERRITOS INFINITI
11011 E South St, Cerritos, CA 90703
Tel.: (562) 345-1335
Web Site:
  http://www.cerritosinfiniti.com
Year Founded: 1857
Sales Range: $10-24.9 Million
Emp.: 43
New Car Retailer
N.A.I.C.S.: 441110
Bill Stephens (Gen Mgr)
Brian Walker (Gen Mgr-Sls)
Marcy Vargas (Mgr-Parts)
Paul Kim (Dir-Fin)
David Baker (Mgr-Internet Sls)
Grace Cercinca (Mgr-Internet Sls)
David Pelichowski (Mgr-Pre-Owned)
Joe Roell (Dir-Svc)

CERRITOS NISSAN
18707 Studebaker Rd, Cerritos, CA 90703-5331
Tel.: (714) 521-9200
Web Site:
  https://www.cerritosnissan.com
Year Founded: 1965
Sales Range: $25-49.9 Million
Emp.: 170
New Car Whslr
N.A.I.C.S.: 441110
Karen Tomasick (Mgr-Customer Rels)

CERSOSIMO LUMBER CO. INC.
1103 Vernon St, Brattleboro, VT 05301-5104
Tel.: (802) 254-4508   VT
Web Site:
  https://www.cersosimolumber.com
Year Founded: 1947
Sales Range: $25-49.9 Million
Emp.: 290
Mfr of Lumber & Kiln Drying
N.A.I.C.S.: 321113

CERTAIN, INC.
75 Hawthorne St Ste 550, San Francisco, CA 94105
Tel.: (415) 353-5330
Web Site: https://www.certain.com
Year Founded: 1994
Sales Range: $10-24.9 Million
Emp.: 51
Event Management Software Developer
N.A.I.C.S.: 513210
Douglas E. Goldman (Founder & Chm)
Peter Micciche (CEO)
Aleks Rabrenovich (CFO)
Mark Jauregui (VP-Svcs & Customer Success)
Gerard Larios (VP-Dev Ops & IT)
Jasvinder Matharu (VP-Engrg)
Glen Bentley (VP-Product Mgmt)
Kristen Alexander (VP-Mktg)
Todd Giuntini (VP-Sls)

CERTI-FRESH FOODS, INC.
7410 Scout Ave, Bell Gardens, CA 90201
Tel.: (562) 806-1100
Web Site: http://www.certi-fresh.com
Year Founded: 1979
Rev.: $6,666,666
Emp.: 160
Fresh & Breaded Seafood Products

N.A.I.C.S.: 424460
Nino Palma (Pres & CEO)
Pete Palma (Dir-Sls)
Ken Peterson (Mgr-Reg Sls)
Gaspare Guarrasi (Founder)

CERTIFIED AUTOMOTIVE PARTS ASSOCIATION
1000 Vermont Ave NW Ste 1010, Washington, DC 20005
Tel.: (202) 737-2212   DE
Web Site:
  http://www.capacertified.org
Year Founded: 1987
Sales Range: $10-24.9 Million
Automotive Parts Testing Services
N.A.I.C.S.: 811198
Jack Gillis (Exec Dir)

CERTIFIED AVIATION SERVICES, LLC
8659 Haven Ave Ste 100, Rancho Cucamonga, CA 91730
Tel.: (909) 605-0380   CA
Web Site:
  http://www.certifiedaviation.com
Year Founded: 1990
Sales Range: $25-49.9 Million
Emp.: 264
Aircraft Services
N.A.I.C.S.: 336413
Scott Diaz (Dir-Bus Rels)
Mike Scanlon (VP-Ops)
Jim Anderson (Dir-Bus Dev-Base Maintenance Grp)
Michael Turpin (Mng Dir-Recovery, Repairs & Modifications Bus)
Tom Hoffman (Controller)
Mike Jones (Dir-Customer Svc)
Paul Renn (Dir-Fin)
Johnnie Miller (Dir-HR)
Chris Solomon (Dir-Ops)
Rodney Garmany (Dir-Projects)
Travis Branch (Dir-Quality Assurance)
Brent Trotter (Gen Mgr)
Cesar Moya (Mgr-Quality Assurance)
Geoff Myrick (VP-Sls)
Michael Stafford (Pres-Line Svcs)
Brad Caban (Pres-Components)
Mark Lee (Chm)
April Singleton (Dir-Customer Svc-Components)

CERTIFIED COMPANIES, INC.
16951 Feather Craft Ln, Houston, TX 77058
Tel.: (281) 280-9500
Web Site: http://www.certified.com
Year Founded: 1974
Rev.: $13,598,000
Emp.: 50
Temporary Help Service
N.A.I.C.S.: 561320
Kelly Hill (Reg VP)
Nancy Warren (Owner)

CERTIFIED FREIGHT LINES INC.
1344 White Ct, Santa Maria, CA 93458
Tel.: (805) 925-9900
Web Site: https://www.certifiedfreight logistics.com
Year Founded: 1928
Sales Range: $10-24.9 Million
Emp.: 180
Refrigerated Products Transport
N.A.I.C.S.: 484230
Scott Cramer (Pres)

CERTIFIED LABORATORIES, INC.
65 Marcus Dr, Melville, NY 11747
Tel.: (516) 576-1400
Web Site: http://www.certified-laboratories.com

Year Founded: 1926
Full Service Quality Laboratory Testing Services
N.A.I.C.S.: 541380
Steve Mitchell (Vice Chm)
Todd Shea (Pres-Cosmetics & Personal Care)

Subsidiaries:

Microconsult Inc.   (1)
3218 Commander Dr Ste 100, Carrollton, TX 75006-2516
Tel.: (972) 250-2902
Web Site: http://www.microconsultinc.com
Microbiological, Chemical & Nutritional Testing Lab
N.A.I.C.S.: 541380
William L. Bryan (CEO)

CERTIFIED LANGUAGES INTERNATIONAL, INC.
4800 S Macadam Ave Ste 400, Portland, OR 97239
Tel.: (503) 525-9601
Web Site:
  https://www.certifiedlanguages.com
Year Founded: 1996
Sales Range: $10-24.9 Million
Emp.: 65
Translation & Interpretation Services
N.A.I.C.S.: 541930
Bill Graeper (Founder & Pres)

CERTIFIED LUMBER CORPORATION
470 Kent Ave, Brooklyn, NY 11211
Tel.: (718) 387-1233
Rev.: $15,000,000
Emp.: 15
Lumber, Plywood & Millwork
N.A.I.C.S.: 423310
Isack Rosenberg (Pres)

CERTIFIED MANUFACTURING, INC.
583 Armistead Blvd, Holt, FL 32564
Tel.: (850) 537-3777
Web Site:
  http://www.certifiedmanufac turing.com
Year Founded: 1998
Sales Range: $1-9.9 Million
Emp.: 35
Electronics Mfr
N.A.I.C.S.: 334419
Pamela B. Bechtold (Pres)
Judy Newton (Mgr-Sls)

CERTIFIED PARTS CORPORATION
405 E Fulton St, Edgerton, WI 53534
Tel.: (608) 884-0770   DE
Web Site:
  http://www.certifiedpartscorp.com
Year Founded: 1976
Transportation Equipment & Supplies Whslr
N.A.I.C.S.: 423860
James Grafft (Owner, Pres & CEO)

Subsidiaries:

Peerless Gear LLC   (1)
1555 S Jackson St, Salem, IN 47167
Tel.: (812) 883-3575
Web Site: http://www.peerlessgear.com
Transaxles & Transmissions
N.A.I.C.S.: 333613

CERTIFIED POWER SOLUTIONS
45 Northern Stacks Drive Suite 200, Fridley, MN 55421
Tel.: (763) 493-9380
Web Site:
  https://www.certifiedpowerso lutions.com
Year Founded: 1967

Certified Power Solutions—(Continued)

Emp.: 100
Fluid Power & Mfg
N.A.I.C.S.: 333995
Jeffrey Keating (Pres)

Subsidiaries:

Skarda Equipment Company,
Inc. (1)
2563 Farnam St, Omaha, NE 68131
Tel.: (402) 422-0430
Web Site: http://www.skarda.com
Durable Goods Merchant Whslr
N.A.I.C.S.: 423990
Lynn Nordquist (VP-Sls)

CERTIFIED RESTORATION DRYCLEANING NETWORK, LLC

2060 Coolidge Hwy, Berkley, MI
48072
Tel.: (248) 246-7878
Web Site: http://www.crdn.com
Year Founded: 2001
Sales Range: $1-9.9 Million
Emp.: 31
Textile Restoration Services
N.A.I.C.S.: 236118
Wayne Wudyka (CEO)
Jeff Schultz (VP-Comm)

CERTIFIED SLINGS, INC.

310 W Melody Ln, Casselberry, FL
32707
Tel.: (407) 260-9196
Web Site:
    https://www.certifiedslings.com
Year Founded: 1958
Sales Range: $10-24.9 Million
Emp.: 40
Mfr Materials Handling Machinery
N.A.I.C.S.: 423830
Connie Gahnz (CFO)
Douglas J. Worswick (CEO)
Dennis Worswick (Pres)
Robert Saxon (Chief Sls Officer)
Kim Vogt (Chief Process Officer)

CERTIFIED STAINLESS SERVICE INC.

2704 Railroad Ave, Ceres, CA 95307
Tel.: (209) 537-4747
Web Site: https://www.west-
    mark.com
Year Founded: 1967
Sales Range: $10-24.9 Million
Emp.: 90
Mfr of Metal Tanks & FireTruck Apparatus
N.A.I.C.S.: 332420
Todd Vincent (Mgr-Sls)
Darrel Watts (Mgr-Svc)
Scott Perkins (Mgr-Svc-Bakersfield)
Wayne Walker (Mgr-Svc-Fairbanks)
Eric Neufeld (Mgr-Parts)
Brian Andrews (Mgr-Parts-Bakersfield)
Brett Granger (Mgr-Parts-Fairbanks)
Josh Vincent (Dir-Fabrication)
Jeff Hurst (Mgr-Vacuum Div)

CERTIFIED TRANSMISSION REBUILDERS INC.

1801 S 54th St, Omaha, NE 68106
Tel.: (402) 558-2117
Web Site:
    http://www.certifiedtrans.com
Sales Range: $10-24.9 Million
Emp.: 250
Automotive Transmission Repair
N.A.I.C.S.: 811114
Peter Fink (Owner)

CERTIFIT, INC.

3160 S 925 W, Salt Lake City, UT
84119-3316

Tel.: (801) 973-6454
Web Site: https://www.certifit.com
Sales Range: $10-24.9 Million
Emp.: 300
Automotive Supplies & Parts
N.A.I.C.S.: 423120
Vyron Ostler (Pres)

CERTIGY INC.

1801 Hobbs Rd, Auburndale, FL
33823
Tel.: (863) 401-8686
Web Site: http://www.certigy.com
Year Founded: 1997
Sales Range: $150-199.9 Million
Emp.: 80
Human Resource, Payroll, Workers'
Compensation & Administrative Management Services
N.A.I.C.S.: 561330
James Knight (Owner & Partner)
Diana Bell (Mgr-Claims)
Eddie McGuire (VP-Sls)
Mark Ruggieri (Mng Partner)

CERTIPATH, INC.

1900 Reston Metro Plz Ste 303, Reston, VA 20190
Tel.: (703) 793-7870
Web Site: http://www.certipath.com
Professional, Scientific & Technical
Services
N.A.I.C.S.: 541990
Jeff Nigriny (Founder & CEO)

CERTIPORT, INC.

1276 S 820 E Ste 200, American
Fork, UT 84003
Tel.: (801) 847-3100
Web Site: http://www.certiport.com
Year Founded: 1998
Sales Range: $25-49.9 Million
Emp.: 165
Developer of Certification Exams &
Practice Tests for Academic Institutions, Staff Development & Corporate
IT Companies
N.A.I.C.S.: 611691
Robert Whelan (Pres & CEO)
Kevin Brice (Chief Strategy Officer)
Craig Bushman (VP-Mktg)
Neill Hopkins (VP-Global Ops)
Rob Moore (VP-Client Svcs)
Randy Richards (Dir-Certiport Field
Mktg)
Jeffrey Lewis (Dir-Channel Ops)
Kris Morris (Mgr-Bus Dev)
Sinead Hogan McSweeney (VP-
Content Dev)
Aaron Osmond (Gen Mgr-Certiport
Offering-Global)
Fiona Collins (VP-Market Dev)

CERTTECH, L.L.C.

14425 College Blvd Ste 140, Lenexa,
KS 66215
Tel.: (913) 814-9770
Web Site: http://www.certtech.com
Rev.: $4,290,000
Emp.: 21
Custom Computer Programming Services
N.A.I.C.S.: 541511
Paul Herrmann (VP-Bus Dev)
Jeff Gray (CEO)

Subsidiaries:

Wineman Technology, Inc. (1)
1668 Champagne Dr N, Saginaw, MI 48604
Tel.: (989) 771-3000
Web Site: http://www.winemantech.com
Sales Range: $10-24.9 Million
Emp.: 48
Design & Engineering of Test Equipment for
Manufacturing & Product Development
N.A.I.C.S.: 541330

James A. Wineman (Founder & CEO)
Matthew Eurich (Pres)

CERTUS PEST, INC.

268 Peddlers Rd, Guilford, CT
06437   DE
Web Site: http://www.certuspest.com
Pest Control Services
N.A.I.C.S.: 561710
Mike Givlin (Founder & CEO)
Ben Kaplan (CFO)
Ron Shakespeare (Pres-Florida Reg)
Rachel Lego (VP-Mktg)

Subsidiaries:

Hoskins Pest Control Inc. (1)
119 Corporation Way, Venice, FL 34285
Tel.: (941) 485-6313
Web Site:
    http://www.hoskinspestcontrol.com
Rev.: $1,092,000
Emp.: 14
Exterminating & Pest Control Services
N.A.I.C.S.: 561710

Patrick Exterminating, Inc. (1)
3226 SE Gran Park Way, Stuart, FL 34997
Tel.: (772) 286-6812
Web Site:
    http://www.patrickexterminating.com
Disinfecting And Pest Control Services
N.A.I.C.S.: 561710
Richard Patrick (Pres)

CERTUSHOLDINGS, INC.

1170 Peachtree St NW Ste 2300, Atlanta, GA 30309
Tel.: (678) 293-1045   DE
Web Site:
    http://www.certusholdingsinc.com
Year Founded: 2010
Sales Range: $25-49.9 Million
Emp.: 497
Bank Holding Company
N.A.I.C.S.: 551111
Bradford B. Kopp (Chm)
R. Hampton Painter III (CFO & Sr
Exec VP)

Subsidiaries:

CertusBank, N.A. (1)
6602 Calhoun Memorial Hwy, Easley, SC
29640
Tel.: (864) 306-2540
Web Site: http://www.certusbank.com
Federal Savings Bank
N.A.I.C.S.: 522180
Kelly Owens (Exec VP)
Emily Ledbetter (Comm Mgr)
Len Davenport (Interim CEO)

CERVERA REAL ESTATE, INC.

1492 S Miami Ave, Miami, FL 33130
Tel.: (305) 374-3434
Web Site: http://www.cervera.com
Sales Range: $1-9.9 Million
Emp.: 15
Real Estate Broker
N.A.I.C.S.: 531210
Veronica Cervera Goeseke (CEO)
Alicia Cervera Lamadrid (Mng Partner)
Javier Cervera (Principal)
Lizzie Giuffra (COO)
Nickel Goeske (Dir-Comml Div)
Anuca Valverde (Pres-Mktg)
Omar De Windt (VP-Corp Comm)
Monica Garcia (CFO)
James W. Hitchcock (Exec VP)
Julie Alvarez (Mgr-Ops)
Jesse D. Ottley (Pres-Dev Sls)
Alexandra Elfmont (VP-Mktg Dev Div)
Ana Lopez de Quintana (VP-Sls &
Ops)
Alexandra Goeseke (Dir-Gen Real
Estate Sls)
Harlan Goldberg (VP-Bus Dev-
Northeast)

CES POWER LLC

3500 Air Ctr Cove, Memphis, TN
38118
Tel.: (844) 237-7693
Web Site: https://www.cespower.com
Secure Power Solutions & Services
N.A.I.C.S.: 221122

Subsidiaries:

TOURtech Support, Inc. (1)
1723 Roundrock Dr, Raleigh, NC 27615
Tel.: (919) 261-1110
Web Site: https://roundrock.technology
Event Wi-Fi & Internet Services
N.A.I.C.S.: 517112
Allen W. Cook (CEO)

CES, INC.

465 S Main St, Brewer, ME 04412
Tel.: (207) 989-4824
Web Site: http://www.cesincusa.com
Year Founded: 1978
Rev.: $5,431,300
Emp.: 70
Engineeering Services
N.A.I.C.S.: 541330
James W. Parker (Co-Founder)
Denis St.Peter (Pres & CEO)
Jeff Teunisen (Exec VP & Dir-Survey
Div)
John Pond (Exec VP & Dir-
Environmental Div)
Travis Noyes (Exec VP & Dir-Engrg
Div)
Tracy Smith (CFO & Treas)
Josh Bragg (Sr VP & Mgr-Machias)
Jan Cannon (Chief HR Officer)
Kerrin Smith (COO)
Scott Miller (VP & Reg Mgr)

Subsidiaries:

Haley & Ward, Inc. (1)
63 Great Rd Ste 200, Maynard, MA 01754-
2097
Tel.: (978) 648-6025
Web Site: http://www.haleyward.com
Engineeering Services
N.A.I.C.S.: 541330
Gregory J. Eldridge (Sec)

CESAR CASTILLO, INC.

Rd 1 Km 21 1 Sector La Muda,
Guaynabo, PR 00971
Tel.: (787) 999-1616
Web Site:
    http://www.cesarcastillo.com
Year Founded: 1942
Sales Range: $50-74.9 Million
Emp.: 170
Drugs Proprietaries & Sundries;
Warehousing & Logistics
N.A.I.C.S.: 424210
Jose Luis Castillo (Pres & CEO)
Jose R. Castillo (Gen Mgr)

Subsidiaries:

UMECO, INC. (1)
361 Angel Buonomo Zona Industrial-Tres
Monjitas, Hato Rey, PR 00919-1536
Tel.: (787) 766-0011
Web Site: http://www.umedopr.com
Rev.: $12,084,721
Emp.: 100
Medical & Hospital Equipment
N.A.I.C.S.: 423450
Cesar Castillo (Pres)

CETAN CORPORATION

1001 Scenic Pkwy Ste 203, Chesapeake, VA 23323
Tel.: (757) 548-6420
Web Site: https://www.cetancorp.com
Sales Range: $10-24.9 Million
Emp.: 24
Computer Aided Services
N.A.I.C.S.: 541511
Brad Scott (Pres & CEO)
Tony Morelli (VP-Solutions Delivery)

CETERO RESEARCH
2000 Regency Pkwy Ste 255, Cary, NC 27518
Tel.: (919) 468-8582   NC
Web Site: http://www.cetero.com
Year Founded: 2006
Sales Range: $250-299.9 Million
Emp.: 4,000
Early-Stage Contract Research Solutions
N.A.I.C.S.: 541715
Murray Ducharme (*Chief Science Officer*)
Herb Smith (*VP-Quality Assurance*)
James Jay Dixon (*Sr VP-Quality & Compliance*)
Michael C. Fillios (*Chief Admin Officer*)
David Coggin (*VP-Biometrics*)
James Carlson (*CEO*)
Mark Ubert (*CFO*)
John Pottier (*Exec VP-Bus Dev*)

Subsidiaries:

Cetero Research   (1)
4801 Amber Valley Pkwy, Fargo, ND 58104
Tel.: (701) 239-4750
Web Site: http://www.cetero.com
Rev.: $15,000,000
Emp.: 180
Medical Research
N.A.I.C.S.: 541720

Cetero Research   (1)
5109 Medical Dr, San Antonio, TX 78229   (100%)
Tel.: (210) 615-5565
Web Site: http://www.cetero.com
Sales Range: $25-49.9 Million
Emp.: 275
On-Site Clinical Laboratory & Research Testing Facility
N.A.I.C.S.: 541380

Cetero Research   (1)
400 Fountain Lakes Blvd, Saint Charles, MO 63301   (100%)
Tel.: (636) 947-1200
Web Site: http://www.cetero.com
Clinical Pharmacology to Pharmaceutical, Biotechnology & Generic Industries
N.A.I.C.S.: 541714

CETRA, INC.
7804 Montgomery Ave Ste 7-10, Elkins Park, PA 19027
Tel.: (215) 635-7090
Web Site: https://www.cetra.com
Year Founded: 1997
Rev.: $2,700,000
Emp.: 14
Business Services
N.A.I.C.S.: 541930
Jiri Stejskal (*Pres & CEO*)
Angele Surault (*Gen Mgr*)
Tony Guerra (*Dir-Interpretation Svcs*)
Angela Wende (*CMO*)
Terry Adams (*Mgr-Vendor*)
Andrew Moszkowicz (*Mgr-Acct*)
Anukware Adzima (*Gen Mgr-Ghana*)
Adrian Wall (*Gen Mgr-Ireland*)
Kim Groff (*Sr Mgr-Translation Svcs Project*)
Molly Stejskal (*VP-Pennsylvania*)

CETROM INFORMATION TECHNOLOGY, INC.
8000 Towers Crescent Dr 13th Floor, Vienna, VA 22182
Tel.: (240) 631-8400
Web Site: http://www.cetrom.net
Year Founded: 2001
Sales Range: $10-24.9 Million
Emp.: 35
Administrative Management & General Management Consulting Service
N.A.I.C.S.: 541611
Christopher Stark (*Founder, Pres & CEO*)
Sherrill Hebert (*Mgr-Reg Sls*)
Jerry Shipley (*Dir-Bus Dev*)
Mark Wright (*CIO*)

CETRULO LLP
2 Seaport Ln, Boston, MA 02210
Tel.: (617) 217-5500
Web Site: http://www.cetllp.com
Year Founded: 1995
Sales Range: $10-24.9 Million
Emp.: 132
Law firm
N.A.I.C.S.: 541110
Lawrence G. Cetrulo (*Founder & Partner*)
Mark McCrystal (*Founder & Partner*)
Stephen T. Armato (*Sr Partner*)
Annette M. Boelhouwer (*Sr Partner*)
Rory FitzPatrick (*Sr Partner*)
Susan A. Jackson (*Sr Partner*)
Francis M. Lynch (*Sr Partner*)
Kyle E. Bjornlund (*Partner*)
Michael J. Cahalane (*Partner*)
A. Scott Marra (*Partner*)
Adam C. Martin (*Partner*)
Andrew R. McConville (*Partner*)
Matthew C. Oleyer (*Partner*)
Jason M. Saul (*Partner*)
Michael F. Sommerville (*Partner*)
Lawrence J. Sugarman (*Partner*)
Matthew J. Zamaloff (*Partner*)
Samuel P. Sears Jr. (*Partner*)

CEXEC, INC.
11440 Commerce Park Dr Ste 600, Reston, VA 20191
Tel.: (703) 435-0099
Web Site: http://www.cexec.com
Year Founded: 1976
Rev.: $27,000,000
Emp.: 40
Local Area Network Systems Integrator
N.A.I.C.S.: 541512
Douglas C. Rhodes (*Pres & CEO*)
Gail Parmentier (*CFO & Sr VP*)
Barry Murphy (*Sr VP-Dir-Ops*)
Weston Rhodes (*VP-Admin*)
Ron Ullrich (*VP-Network Solutions & Dir-Ops*)

CF FOODS LLC
1 Celebration Way, New Britain, CT 06053-1480
Tel.: (860) 827-8000
Sales Range: $25-49.9 Million
Emp.: 450
Ice Cream Mfr
N.A.I.C.S.: 311520
Stefania Paciello (*Mgr-Quality Assurance*)

CF GEAR HOLDINGS
3860 River Rd, Schiller Park, IL 60176
Tel.: (847) 671-1631   DE
Web Site:
    http://www.processgear.com
Sales Range: $10-24.9 Million
Emp.: 60
Custom Precision Manufactured Products
N.A.I.C.S.: 332710
Jonathan Hertl (*Gen Mgr*)

CF HOLDING COMPANY, INC.
2550 Hickory Blvd SW, Lenoir, NC 28645
Tel.: (336) 812-8207
Web Site:
    http://www.furnituretransport.com
Year Founded: 1956
Holding Company; Furniture Transportation services
N.A.I.C.S.: 551112

Subsidiaries:

Caldwell Freight Lines Inc.   (1)
2550 Hickory Blvd SW, Lenoir, NC 28645
Tel.: (828) 728-9231

Web Site: http://www.caldwellfreight.com
Sales Range: $25-49.9 Million
Emp.: 358
Freight Trucking Services
N.A.I.C.S.: 484121

CF MCDONALD ELECTRIC INC.
5044 Timber Creek Dr, Houston, TX 77017
Tel.: (713) 921-1368
Web Site:
    https://www.mcdonaldinc.com
Sales Range: $10-24.9 Million
Emp.: 153
Electrical Work
N.A.I.C.S.: 238210
Larry G. Stephenson (*Pres*)
Randy Berry (*Project Mgr*)
Aaron Pilcher (*Mgr-Svc Dept*)
Diane Dollar (*Office Mgr*)
Ike Osborn (*Dir-Safety*)
Harry Keller (*VP*)

CFC PRINT SOLUTIONS
2800 112th St Ste 300, Grand Prairie, TX 75050
Tel.: (972) 890-9248
Web Site: http://www.cfcprint.com
Year Founded: 2008
Sales Range: $1-9.9 Million
Emp.: 41
Document Printing
N.A.I.C.S.: 323120
Jodeen Lee (*Controller*)

CFC, INC.
30 E Oakton St, Des Plaines, IL 60018-1945
Tel.: (847) 257-8920
Web Site:
    http://www.columbusvegetables.com
Sales Range: $10-24.9 Million
Emp.: 100
Edible Fat & Oil Mfr
N.A.I.C.S.: 311225
Paulette Gagliardo (*CEO*)
Terence G. Matern (*Controller*)
John Healy (*Dir-Sls*)
Connie Gagliardo (*VP*)

CFD RESEARCH CORPORATION
215 Wynn Dr NW 5th Fl, Huntsville, AL 35805
Tel.: (256) 726-4800
Web Site: http://www.cfdrc.com
Year Founded: 1987
Sales Range: $10-24.9 Million
Emp.: 120
Provider of Computer Software Systems Analysis & Design Services
N.A.I.C.S.: 541511
Ashok Singhal (*Founder, Chm & Principal*)
Sameer Singhal (*Pres & CEO*)
Sami Habchi (*Exec VP*)
Deb Phipps (*Mgr-Contracts*)
Jing Qian (*Engr-Res*)
Richard Thoms (*Mgr-Tech Partnerships*)

CFE EQUIPMENT
818 Widgeon Rd, Norfolk, VA 23513
Tel.: (757) 858-2660
Web Site:
    https://www.cfeequipment.com
Materials Handling Machinery
N.A.I.C.S.: 423830
Tony Sessa (*Pres*)

CFH GROUP, LLC
1545 NW 15th St Rd, Miami, FL 33125
Tel.: (305) 545-0159   FL
Web Site: http://www.cfhgroup.com

Year Founded: 2003
Residential & Commercial Property Management Services
N.A.I.C.S.: 531311
Tom Cabrerizo (*CEO*)
Jim Kennedy (*CFO*)
Gliset Perez (*Reg VP*)
Ivan Fuentes (*Dir-Ops*)
Nathan Vedrani (*Dir-Acq*)

CFL PIZZA, LLC
1146 Celebration Blvd, Celebration, FL 34747
Tel.: (321) 939-3219
Web Site: http://www.cflpizzahut.com
Year Founded: 2009
Emp.: 291
Restaurant Operating Services
N.A.I.C.S.: 722511
Andy Rosen (*CEO*)
Carl Vannostrand (*COO*)
Vikki Hodgkins (*CFO*)
Janet Stewart (*Chief People Officer*)
Ruth Caraballo (*Mgr-HR*)
Meghan Strongrich (*Mgr-Mktg*)

CFM COMPANY
1440 S Lipan St, Denver, CO 80223-3411
Tel.: (303) 761-2291
Web Site:
    https://www.cfmcompany.com
Year Founded: 1971
Sales Range: $10-24.9 Million
Emp.: 50
Warm Air Heating & Air Conditioning
N.A.I.C.S.: 423730

CFM DISTRIBUTORS, INC.
1104 Union Ave, Kansas City, MO 64101
Tel.: (816) 842-5400
Web Site:
    https://www.cfmdistributors.com
Year Founded: 1971
Sales Range: $10-24.9 Million
Emp.: 50
Heating, Cooling & Refrigeration Products Mfr & Distr
N.A.I.C.S.: 423730

CFM EQUIPMENT DISTRIBUTORS INC.
1644 Main Ave Ste 1, Sacramento, CA 95838-2409
Tel.: (916) 447-7022
Web Site:
    https://www.cfmequipment.com
Year Founded: 1985
Emp.: 100
Air Conditioning Equipment Mfr
N.A.I.C.S.: 423730
Joe Souza (*VP-Ops*)
Andrew Barton (*CEO*)

CFM STRATEGIC COMMUNICATIONS, INC.
1050 SW 6th Ave Ste 1100, Portland, OR 97204
Tel.: (503) 294-9120
Web Site: http://www.cfm-online.com
Year Founded: 1990
Sales Range: $1-9.9 Million
Emp.: 14
Communications, Consulting, Consumer Marketing, Corporate Identity, Event Marketing, Government/Political/Public Affairs, Public Relations
N.A.I.C.S.: 541820
Gary Conkling (*Principal*)
Norm Eder (*Partner*)
Tom Eiland (*Partner*)
J. E. Isaac (*Principal*)
Joel Rubin (*Partner*)
Cindy Brown (*Office Mgr*)

CFM Strategic Communications, Inc.—(Continued)

Dana Tierney (Project Mgr)
Kirby Garrett (Mgr-Federal Affairs)
Dale Penn II (Partner)

Subsidiaries:

CFM Strategic Communications,
Inc. (1)
750 1st St NE Ste 1070, Washington, DC
20002
Tel.: (202) 347-9170
Web Site: http://www.cfm-online.com
Emp.: 2
Public Relations Agencies
N.A.I.C.S.: 541820
Julie Crockett (Mgr-Federal Affairs)

CFN SERVICES
13454 Sunrise Valley Dr 5 Fl, Herndon, VA 20171
Tel.: (703) 788-6633
Web Site: http://www.cfnservices.com
Year Founded: 2005
Sales Range: $10-24.9 Million
Emp.: 30
Managed Telecom Infrastructure Network Services
N.A.I.C.S.: 517112
Mark Casey (Pres & CEO)
Mike Weaver (VP-Client Solutions)

CFO SELECTIONS, LLC
14432SE Eastgate Way Ste 400,
Bellevue, WA 98007
Tel.: (206) 686-4480
Web Site:
http://www.cfoselections.com
Sales Range: $1-9.9 Million
Emp.: 30
Financial Recruiter
N.A.I.C.S.: 561311
Thomas L. Varga (Founder & Mng Partner)
Mark Tranter (Partner-Bus Dev)
Kevin Briscoe (Partner)

CFR, INC.
5314 S Yale Ave Ste 900, Tulsa, OK
74135-6257
Tel.: (918) 747-8631
Web Site: http://www.cfr-ins.com
Sales Range: $50-74.9 Million
Emp.: 85
Insurance Agents
N.A.I.C.S.: 524210
Glenn R. Day (Exec VP)
Kellie Jones (Acct Mgr)

CFS SERVICE CORPORATION
1010 Highams Ct, Woodbridge, VA
22191-1437
Tel.: (703) 497-0000
Web Site: https://www.cfsservice.net
Year Founded: 2003
Sales Range: $1-9.9 Million
Emp.: 65
Electrical Contractor
N.A.I.C.S.: 238210
Steve Perry (Pres)
Chris Malzahn (VP)
Fred Petrus (Treas)

CG AUTOMOTIVE GROUP, INC.
1900 SW 43rd Ter, Deerfield Beach,
FL 33442
Web Site:
http://www.cgautogroup.com
Year Founded: 2010
Aftermarket Automotive Accessories
Whslr
N.A.I.C.S.: 423120
Juan Cruz (Chm, Pres & CEO)
Vernon Grant (COO, CFO, VP, Sec & Treas)

CGF INDUSTRIES, INC.
2420 N Woodlawn St Bldg 500,
Wichita, KS 67220-3960
Tel.: (316) 691-4500
Web Site: http://www.cgfind.com
Year Founded: 1969
Sales Range: $100-124.9 Million
Emp.: 300
Holding Company; Manufactures
Steel Bifold Doors, Mirrored Doors,
Steel & Aluminum Door Frames
N.A.I.C.S.: 332321
Bruce G. Cochener (Owner)
Gary L. Armstrong (CFO)
Jessi Stang (CEO)

Subsidiaries:

Dunbarton Corporation (1)
1101 Technology Dr, Dothan, AL 36303
Tel.: (334) 794-0661
Web Site: http://www.dunbarton.com
Sales Range: $25-49.9 Million
Emp.: 150
Mfr of Steel Bifold Doors, Mirror & Closet
Doors & Steel & Aluminum Door Frames
N.A.I.C.S.: 332321
Artie Buckner (Reg Mgr-Sls)
Dave Goetzinger (Grp VP-Mktg)
John Klesath (Pres & COO)
Doug Schroeder (Dir-ESHS & Maintenance)
Douglas Webb (CFO & VP)

Keycentrix (1)
2420 N Woodlawn Blvd Bldg 500, Wichita,
KS 67220-3960 (100%)
Tel.: (316) 262-2231
Web Site: http://www.keycentrix.com
Sales Range: $10-24.9 Million
Emp.: 30
Developer of Pharmacy Software
N.A.I.C.S.: 541511
Elie M. Khalife (Pres & CEO)

CGH MEDICAL CENTER
100 E Le Fevre Rd, Sterling, IL
61081-1278
Tel.: (815) 625-0400
Web Site: https://www.cghmc.com
Year Founded: 1912
Sales Range: $75-99.9 Million
Emp.: 1,400
Hospital & Surgical Center
N.A.I.C.S.: 622110
Paul Steinke (CEO)

CGL CORPORATION
33601 Schoolcraft Rd, Livonia, MI
48150
Tel.: (734) 522-5000
Web Site: http://www.cglcorp.com
Year Founded: 1995
Sales Range: $10-24.9 Million
Emp.: 90
Heating & Air Conditioning Equipment
Distr
N.A.I.C.S.: 423730
R. Thomas Williams (Owner & CEO)
Gary Ehlers (Pres)

CGM ACOUSTICS
195 Island Brook Ave, Bridgeport, CT
06606
Tel.: (203) 579-7935
Web Site:
https://www.cgmacoustics.com
Year Founded: 1986
Sales Range: $10-24.9 Million
Emp.: 200
Plastering Services
N.A.I.C.S.: 238310
John Marus (Treas)

CGN & ASSOCIATES INC.
415 SW Washington St, Peoria, IL
61602
Tel.: (309) 672-6400
Web Site: http://www.cgn.net
Year Founded: 1995
Sales Range: $10-24.9 Million

Emp.: 100
Business Consulting Services
N.A.I.C.S.: 541611
Seshadri Guha (Founder & CEO)
Navneet Arora (Partner)
Rod Beeler (Mng Partner)

Subsidiaries:

Blackwell Global Consulting LLC (1)
30 N La Salle St Ste 4140, Chicago, IL
60602 (100%)
Tel.: (312) 553-0730
Web Site: http://www.bcsinc.com
Information Technology & Management
Consulting Services
N.A.I.C.S.: 541611
Rod Beeler (Pres & CEO)
Navneet Arora (COO)
Robert D. Blackwell Sr. (Founder & Partner)

CGR PRODUCTS INC.
4655 US Hwy 29 N, Greensboro, NC
27405-9446
Tel.: (336) 621-4568
Web Site:
http://www.cgrproducts.com
Year Founded: 1963
Sales Range: $10-24.9 Million
Emp.: 85
Gasket & Rubber Mfr
N.A.I.C.S.: 339991
Charles S. Keeley (Pres)

Subsidiaries:

Custom Tape Co Inc. (1)
6288 Claude Way, Inver Grove Heights, MN
55076
Tel.: (651) 228-7044
Web Site:
http://www.customtapecompany.com
Rev.: $1,200,000
Emp.: 8
Pressure Sensitive Tape Products Mfr
N.A.I.C.S.: 325520
Jeffrey Gilberg (Pres)

CGR VALLEY PRODUCTS INCORPORATED
4655 US Hwy 29 N, Greensboro, NC
27405
Tel.: (336) 621-4568
Web Site:
https://www.cgrproducts.com
Sales Range: $10-24.9 Million
Emp.: 66
Gaskets & Sealing Devices
N.A.I.C.S.: 339991
Charles S. Keeley Jr. (Chm & CEO)

CGS INDUSTRIES, INC.
3409 Queens Blvd, Long Island City,
NY 11101
Tel.: (718) 482-0700
Web Site:
http://www.cgsindustries.com
Sales Range: $75-99.9 Million
Emp.: 65
Sportswear for Men & Boys
N.A.I.C.S.: 424350
Lal Sani (Pres)
Sunil Sani (VP-Ops & Adv)
Leonard Braun (Treas)

CGS TECHNOLOGY ASSOCIATES, INC.
1001 Durham Ave Ste 300, South
Plainfield, NJ 07080
Tel.: (732) 750-4141
Web Site: http://www.cgsonline.com
Year Founded: 1983
Computer Related Consulting Services
N.A.I.C.S.: 541512
Augustus N. Guida (COO)
Vinay Kumar (CEO)
Catherine Dove (CTO)

CH HOLDINGS USA, INC.

2770 Blue Water Rd, Eagan, MN
55121
Tel.: (651) 796-6100
Web Site: http://www.enclos.com
Year Founded: 1947
Sales Range: $25-49.9 Million
Emp.: 750
Pre-Engineered Wall Systems for
Low & Mid Rise Buildings; Aluminum
Products
N.A.I.C.S.: 238150
Michel Michno (Head-Engrg)

CH MURPHY/CLARK-ULLMAN INC.
5565 N Dolphin St, Portland, OR
97217
Tel.: (503) 285-5030
Web Site: https://www.chmcu.com
Year Founded: 1935
Sales Range: $25-49.9 Million
Emp.: 50
Provider of Industrial Services
N.A.I.C.S.: 811310
Randy Lederbrand (Owner & Pres)
Mike Dolan (VP & Mgr-Tacoma)
Heather Mickler (Treas & Controller)

CH REAL ESTATE II, INC.
2851 B 1/2 Rd, Grand Junction, CO
81503
Tel.: (970) 924-6935
Year Founded: 2010
Sales Range: $1-9.9 Million
Emp.: 2
Real Estate Property Investment &
Development
N.A.I.C.S.: 531390
Curt Hansen (Founder, Chm, Pres,
CEO & CFO)
Mike Hansen (Treas)

CH REYNOLDS, INC.
1281 Wayne Ave, San Jose, CA
95131
Tel.: (408) 436-9280
Web Site:
https://www.chreynolds.com
Year Founded: 1983
Sales Range: $25-49.9 Million
Emp.: 71
Constructs Electrical Installations &
Data Communication Systems
N.A.I.C.S.: 238210
Robert Macias (Sr'VP)
Robert Oei (VP-Fin)
Rick White (COO & Exec VP)
Jason Bright (Sr Project Mgr)
Ron Zuccaro (Sr VP-Ops-Electrical &
Data)
Kathy Kathusha (VP-HR)
Derick Jackson (VP-Ops-IT Managed
Svcs Div)
John Anderson (Sr VP-Data Div)
Vijay Kammela (VP-Client Svcs-IT
Managed Svcs Div)

CH&D ENTERPRISES INC.
100 Brady Pl, New Stanton, PA
15672
Tel.: (724) 925-9832
Web Site: http://chtentinc.com
Sales Range: $10-24.9 Million
Emp.: 100
Excavation Drainage & Grading,
Building Construction
N.A.I.C.S.: 238910

CHA TECHNOLOGIES INC.
304 Arcadia Dr, Greenville, SC
29609-3858
Tel.: (864) 233-9733
Web Site:
http://www.chatechnologies.com
Year Founded: 1994
Sales Range: $25-49.9 Million

Emp.: 30
Automotive & Apparel Trimmings
N.A.I.C.S.: 314999
Mike Hollis *(Gen Mgr)*

Subsidiaries:

CHA Technologies Inc. **(1)**
304 Arcadia Dr, Greenville, SC 29609-3858
Tel.: (864) 233-0318
Web Site: http://www.castleindustries.com
Sales Range: $10-24.9 Million
Emp.: 25
Commercial Nonphysical Research
N.A.I.C.S.: 314999
Mike Hollis *(Gen Mgr)*

Fiber Innovation Technology Inc. **(1)**
398 Innovation Dr, Johnson City, TN 37604-7434
Tel.: (423) 232-0072
Web Site: http://www.fitfibers.com
Sales Range: $10-24.9 Million
Thread Mills Mfr
N.A.I.C.S.: 313110
Chris Parris *(Dir-Product Dev)*

CHACE BUILDING SUPPLY OF CT, INC.

90 Somers Tpke Rt 171, Woodstock, CT 06281
Tel.: (860) 928-2747
Web Site:
   https://www.chacebuildings.com
Rev.: $12,000,000
Emp.: 30
Lumber: Rough, Dressed & Finished
N.A.I.C.S.: 423310
Scott Chace *(Pres)*
Steve Williams *(Mgr-Shipping & Yard)*
Lisa Gaudreau *(Controller)*
Denise Maheu *(Mgr-Credit)*

CHACHA SEARCH, INC.

14550 Clay Ter Blvd Ste 130, Carmel, IN 46032
Tel.: (317) 660-6680
Web Site: http://www.chacha.com
Year Founded: 2005
Sales Range: $1-9.9 Million
Emp.: 70
Online & Mobile Answering Services
N.A.I.C.S.: 517810
Scott A. Jones *(CEO)*
Salim Tarazi *(Chief Revenue Officer)*
Thom Geraghty *(Dir-Integrated Mktg)*

CHAD T. WILSON LAW FIRM PLLC

455 E Medical Blvd Ste 555, Webster, TX 77598
Tel.: (832) 415-1432   TX
Web Site: http://www.cwilsonlaw.com
Year Founded: 2011
Sales Range: $1-9.9 Million
Emp.: 21
Law firm
N.A.I.C.S.: 541110
Chad T. Wilson *(Founder)*

CHADDSFORD WINERY LTD.

632 Baltimore Pike, Chadds Ford, PA 19317
Tel.: (610) 388-6221   PA
Web Site:
   https://www.chaddsford.com
Year Founded: 1982
Winery
N.A.I.C.S.: 312130
Eric B. Miller *(Co-Founder & Partner)*
Corey Krejcik *(VP & Gen Mgr)*
Lauren Pasquini *(Dir-Sls & Mktg)*
Victoria Mandich *(Mgr-Office)*
Kate Wilson *(Mgr-Retail)*
Amanda Massey *(Coord-Hospitality)*
Elaine Faso *(Mgr-Wholesale Acct)*
Danielle Welsh *(Mgr-Retail)*
Sandy Massey *(Asst Mgr-Retail)*

CHAI LIFELINE

151 W 30th St, New York, NY 10001
Tel.: (212) 465-1300   NY
Web Site: https://www.chailifeline.org
Year Founded: 1988
Sales Range: $10-24.9 Million
Child Care Services
N.A.I.C.S.: 624110
Simcha Scholar *(Exec VP)*
Abraham Cohen *(Exec Dir)*
Rabbi Heshy Augenbaum *(Chief Dev Officer)*
Nachman Maimon *(Program Dir)*
Esther Schwartz *(Dir-Hospital Svcs)*

CHAIONE

4900 Woodway Ste 880, Houston, TX 77056
Web Site: http://www.chaione.com
Year Founded: 2008
Sales Range: $1-9.9 Million
Emp.: 25
Custom Web & Mobile Applications & Provides Mobile Strategy Consulting & User Experience Design Services
N.A.I.C.S.: 541511
Chad Modad *(VP-Ops)*

CHAIR CITY MEATS INC.

766 W Broadway Rear, Gardner, MA 01440
Tel.: (978) 630-1050
Web Site:
   http://www.chaircitymeats.com
Sales Range: $1-9.9 Million
Emp.: 14
Meat Processing Services
N.A.I.C.S.: 311612
Bonnie Paddock *(Treas)*
Joshua Paddock *(Pres)*
Krystle Burdett *(Coord-Mktg)*

CHAIR CITY SUPPLY COMPANY, INC.

213 N Rd, Thomasville, NC 27360
Tel.: (336) 475-2191
Web Site:
   http://www.chaircitysupply.com
Sales Range: $10-24.9 Million
Emp.: 37
Abrasive, Adhesives & Fastener Distr
N.A.I.C.S.: 423840
Wayne Underwood *(Pres)*
Teresa Vanlandingham *(CFO)*

CHALET LIFESTYLES, INC.

124 41st Ave SE, Albany, OR 97322
Tel.: (541) 791-4610   NV
Web Site: http://www.chaletrv.com
Year Founded: 2014
Emp.: 20
Marketing & Consulting Services to Manufacturers & Distributors of Recreational Vehicles
N.A.I.C.S.: 541613
Don L. Rose *(Chm, CEO, CFO & Principal Acctg Officer)*
Patricia Rose *(VP & Sec)*
Mahamood Al Maya *(Owner)*

CHALK & VERMILLION FINE ARTS & MARTIN LAWRENCE GALLERIES

55 Old Post Rd No 2, Greenwich, CT 06830-6200
Tel.: (203) 869-9500   CT
Web Site:
   http://www.martinlawrence.com
Sales Range: $50-74.9 Million
Emp.: 40
Fine Arts Gallery
N.A.I.C.S.: 712110
Diane Goldman *(CFO)*

CHALKS TRUCK PARTS, INC.

838 McCarty Dr, Houston, TX 77029

Tel.: (713) 672-6344
Web Site: https://www.chalks.com
Sales Range: $10-24.9 Million
Emp.: 40
Truck Parts & Accessories Distributors
N.A.I.C.S.: 423120
Robert A. Chalk *(Chm)*
Larry Colley *(VP)*
John Lagrone *(Controller)*

CHALLENGE DAIRY PRODUCTS INC.

11875 Dublin Blvd B 230, Dublin, CA 94568-2843
Tel.: (925) 828-6160   CA
Web Site:
   http://www.challengedairy.com
Year Founded: 1911
Sales Range: $25-49.9 Million
Emp.: 175
Provider of Groceries & Related Products
N.A.I.C.S.: 424490
Michael Jenkins *(Coord-EDI)*
Daisrea Smith *(Office Mgr)*
Geoffrey Uy *(Controller)*
Lorraine Norton *(Mgr-HR)*

CHALLENGE MANUFACTURING COMPANY

3079 3 Mile Rd NW, Grand Rapids, MI 49534
Tel.: (616) 735-6500
Web Site: http://challenge-mfg.com
Sales Range: $25-49.9 Million
Emp.: 600
Mfr of Automotive Stampings
N.A.I.C.S.: 336370
Larry Bulson *(Engr-Mfg)*
Robert W. Abplanalp *(Engr-Quality)*

CHALLENGE UNLIMITED, INC.

4 Emmie L Kaus Ln, Alton, IL 62002
Tel.: (618) 465-0044   IL
Web Site: https://www.cuinc.org
Year Founded: 1960
Sales Range: $10-24.9 Million
Emp.: 1,058
Disability Assistance Services
N.A.I.C.S.: 624120
Stephanie Brown *(VP-Program Svcs)*
Deb Snyder *(VP-Ops)*
Mike Robinson *(VP-IT & Environmental Svc)*
Diane Tebbe *(VP-Residential Options)*
Floyd Raglin *(Sec)*
Jim Kasten *(Chm)*
John Gibbons *(Gen Counsel)*
Rosemary Gibson *(Vice Chm)*
Steve Brenegan *(Sr VP-Sls & Mktg)*
Darlene Ladd *(Coord-Svcs-Madison County)*
Tony Crawley *(Exec VP-Ops)*
Andy Esterer *(Exec VP-Fin & Support Svcs)*
Debbi McMahon *(Exec VP-Program Svcs)*
Becky Pelton *(VP-Admin & HR)*

CHALLENGER PALLET & SUPPLY INC.

24 N 3210 E, Idaho Falls, ID 83401
Tel.: (208) 523-1969
Web Site:
   https://www.challengerpallet.com
Year Founded: 1969
Rev.: $11,500,000
Emp.: 60
Pallet Mfr
N.A.I.C.S.: 332999
Bob Pierce *(Mgr-Logistics)*
Kelly Bennion *(Gen Mgr)*
Tad Hegsted *(Pres)*

CHALLENGER PIPE & STEEL, LLC

12309 E Mirabeau Pkwy Spokane Vly, Spokane, WA 99216
Tel.: (509) 534-7473
Web Site:
   http://www.challengerpipe.com
Year Founded: 2004
Rev.: $15,200,000
Emp.: 6
Metal Service Centers & Merchant Whslr
N.A.I.C.S.: 423510
Randy Hurst *(Pres)*
Barb Hormel *(Office Mgr)*

CHALLENGER, GRAY & CHRISTMAS, INC.

150 S Wacker Dr Ste 2800, Chicago, IL 60606
Tel.: (312) 332-5790
Web Site:
   https://www.challengergray.com
Year Founded: 1966
Emp.: 200
Outplacement Consulting Services
N.A.I.C.S.: 561311
John A. Challenger *(CEO)*
Lisa Turesky *(VP)*
Colleen Madden *(Dir-PR)*
Darren Veneri *(VP)*

CHALMERS & KUBECK, INC.

150 Commerce Dr, Aston, PA 19014
Tel.: (610) 494-4300
Web Site: https://www.candk.com
Year Founded: 1950
Sales Range: $25-49.9 Million
Emp.: 240
Industrial Machine Repair Shops Operator
N.A.I.C.S.: 332710
Jim Moore Sr. *(Pres-Nuclear Div)*

CHALMERS PROPERTY COMPANY

12150 Monument Dr Ste 865, Fairfax, VA 22033
Tel.: (703) 273-3010
Web Site:
   https://www.chalmersproperty.com
Year Founded: 1991
Sales Range: $1-9.9 Million
Property Development, Management & Investment
N.A.I.C.S.: 237210
David M. Chalmers *(Founder & Pres)*
Shannon Perkins *(Controller)*

CHAMBERLAIN AND ASSOCIATES

12103 Delta St, Taylor, MI 48180
Tel.: (734) 946-8005
Web Site: http://www.cmgestore.com
Rev.: $12,098,349
Emp.: 45
Men's & Boys' Hats
N.A.I.C.S.: 541890
Gerald A. Chamberlain *(CEO)*
Robert Ross *(VP-Ops)*

CHAMBERLAIN HOLDINGS LLC

2977 Hwy K Ste 228, O'Fallon, MO 63368
Tel.: (636) 249-1510
Web Site: http://www.joemccall.com
Year Founded: 2006
Sales Range: $1-9.9 Million
Emp.: 10
Real Estate Consulting Service
N.A.I.C.S.: 531390
Joe McCall *(Pres)*

CHAMBERLAIN OIL CO. INC.

112 Grace Ave, Clontarf, MN 56226

Chamberlain Oil Co. Inc.—(Continued)
Tel.: (320) 843-3434
Web Site:
https://www.chamberlainoil.com
Sales Range: $10-24.9 Million
Emp.: 26
Petroleum Bulk Stations
N.A.I.C.S.: 424710
Laura Rentz (Owner)

CHAMBERLAIN WHOLESALE GROCERY CO.
400 E Prospect, Chamberlain, SD 57325
Tel.: (605) 734-6513
Sales Range: $10-24.9 Million
Emp.: 30
Beer & Other Fermented Malt Liquors
N.A.I.C.S.: 424810
Tom Helland (Pres)

CHAMBERS & OWEN, INC.
1733 Morse St, Janesville, WI 53547-2348
Tel.: (608) 752-7865   WI
Web Site: https://www.chambers-owen.com
Year Founded: 1891
Sales Range: $50-74.9 Million
Emp.: 325
Grocery & Tobacco Products Whslr
N.A.I.C.S.: 424940
John K. Owen (Pres)

CHAMBERS BANCSHARES INC.
901 Main St, Danville, AR 72833
Tel.: (479) 495-2236   AR
Web Site: http://www.chambers-bank.com
Year Founded: 1986
Sales Range: $25-49.9 Million
Emp.: 150
Bank Holding Company
N.A.I.C.S.: 551111
Bill Donnell (Pres)
Philip Alexander (Chief Lending Officer-South Reg-Chambers Bank & Pres-South Reg)
Landi Mkhize (CFO & Controller)
Loren Shackleford (Chief Lending Officer-Northern Div)
Vickie Rounsaville (CIO)
Erica Preston (COO-Chambers Bank)
Mack Streety (Exec VP-Lending)
John Ed Chambers III (CEO)

Subsidiaries:
Chambers Bank   (1)
901 Main St, Danville, AR 72833
Tel.: (479) 495-2236
Web Site: http://www.chambers-bank.com
Sales Range: $50-74.9 Million
Emp.: 110
State Commercial Banks
N.A.I.C.S.: 522110
Bill Donnell (Vice Chm)
Philip Alexander (Pres & Chief Lending Officer)
Erica Preston (COO)
Vickie Rounsaville (CIO)
Loren Shackleford (Chief Lending Officer-Northern Div)
Mack Streety (Exec VP-Lending)
Beverly Elam (VP/Mgr-Comml Svcs-Fort Smith)
John Ed Chambers III (Chm & CEO)

CHAMBERS FABRICS INC.
1914 S Elm St, High Point, NC 27260
Tel.: (336) 887-4822
Sales Range: $10-24.9 Million
Emp.: 120
Sales of Upholstery Fabrics
N.A.I.C.S.: 424310
Ray Chambers (Pres)

CHAMBLISS LIMITED
6550 N Federal Hwy Ste 240, Fort Lauderdale, FL 33308
Tel.: (954) 938-7211
Sales Range: $10-24.9 Million
Emp.: 25
Petroleum Products
N.A.I.C.S.: 424720
Joe A. Chambliss (Partner)

CHAMELEON INTEGRATED SERVICES
1435 S 18th St Ste 150, Saint Louis, MO 63104
Tel.: (314) 773-7200
Web Site:
http://www.chameleonis.com
Sales Range: $1-9.9 Million
Emp.: 70
Information Technology Services
N.A.I.C.S.: 519290
Jeffery Kelley (Founder)
Drew Acree (Co-Owner & Pres)
Mary Burgess (COO)
Ryan Smith (VP-Solutions & Programs)

CHAMELEON TECHNOLOGIES, INC.
520 Kirkland Way Ste 101, Kirkland, WA 98033
Tel.: (425) 827-1173
Web Site:
http://www.chameleontechinc.com
Year Founded: 2000
Sales Range: $1-9.9 Million
Emp.: 90
Technical Staffing & Professional Services
N.A.I.C.S.: 561311
Melissa Acton-Buzard (Co-Founder & Principal)

CHAMPION ALUMINUM WINDOW CORPORATION
250 Kennedy Dr, Hauppauge, NY 11788
Tel.: (516) 921-6200   NY
Web Site:
http://www.championwindows.com
Year Founded: 1952
Sales Range: $50-74.9 Million
Emp.: 100
Mfr of Aluminum Replacement Windows
N.A.I.C.S.: 332321
Thomas Arcati (Chm)
John Arcati (Pres)
Teresa Trupiano (Sr VP)

CHAMPION AMERICA
20 Flax Mill Rd, Branford, CT 06405
Tel.: (203) 315-1181
Web Site: http://www.champion-america.com
Year Founded: 1989
Sales Range: $10-24.9 Million
Emp.: 150
All Types of Identification Products Including Signs, Tags, Labels & Pipemarkers Mfr
N.A.I.C.S.: 332812
Donna J. Canestri (Dir-Mktg Admin)
Janice Fowler (Mgr-Adv)
Frank Jarhnett (CEO)

CHAMPION BRANDS LLC
1001 Golden Dr, Clinton, MO 64735
Tel.: (660) 885-5145
Web Site:
https://www.championbrands.com
Sales Range: $10-24.9 Million
Emp.: 60
Oils & Greases, Blending & Compounding
N.A.I.C.S.: 324191

Rick Pereles (Gen Mgr)
Brian Scheetz (Mgr-Strategic Sls-Midwest Technical Sls & Svc)

CHAMPION CHEVROLET INC.
3127 W Tennessee St, Tallahassee, FL 32304
Tel.: (850) 576-4000
Web Site:
http://www.championchevy.com
Sales Range: $25-49.9 Million
Emp.: 120
Car Dealership Owner & Operator
N.A.I.C.S.: 441110
Tracy Thacker (Pres)

CHAMPION COMPUTER PRODUCTS INC.
2075 W Park Place Blvd Ste B, Stone Mountain, GA 30087-3542
Tel.: (770) 205-4000   GA
Web Site:
http://www.championcp.com
Year Founded: 1990
Sales Range: $10-24.9 Million
Emp.: 15
Computers, Peripherals & Software
N.A.I.C.S.: 449210
Scott Guenther (Pres)

CHAMPION CONSTRUCTION CORPORATION
941 Forest Ave, Staten Island, NY 10310
Tel.: (718) 818-8202
Web Site:
http://www.championcc.com
Sales Range: $10-24.9 Million
Emp.: 66
Commercial & Institutional Building Construction Services
N.A.I.C.S.: 236220

CHAMPION CONTAINER CORPORATION
180 Essex Ave E, Avenel, NJ 07001
Tel.: (732) 636-6700
Web Site:
https://www.championcontainer.com
Sales Range: $10-24.9 Million
Emp.: 40
Distr of Steel, Plastic, Tin, Fiber, Composite Containers, Glass Bottles & Jars
N.A.I.C.S.: 423840

CHAMPION CREDIT UNION
1 Academy St, Canton, NC 28716
Tel.: (828) 648-1515   NC
Web Site:
http://www.championcu.com
Year Founded: 1932
Sales Range: $10-24.9 Million
Emp.: 81
Credit Union Operator
N.A.I.C.S.: 522130
Ron Cole (Chief Credit Officer)
Jake Robinson (Pres & CEO)

Subsidiaries:

Ecusta Credit Union   (1)
2074 Asheville Hwy, Brevard, NC 28712
Tel.: (828) 884-7283
Web Site: http://www.ecustacu.com
Sales Range: $1-9.9 Million
Emp.: 13
Community Development Services
N.A.I.C.S.: 522390
Bill Bryson (VP)
Charles Shipman (Treas)
Helen Young (Sec)
Susan Holliday (Mgr)

CHAMPION ELEVATOR CORP.
1450 Broadway 5th fl, New York, NY 10017
Tel.: (212) 292-4430

Web Site: https://champion-elevator.com
Elevator Maintenance & Repair
N.A.I.C.S.: 333921

Subsidiaries:

PRO Elevator Services Inc   (1)
171 West St 311, Brooklyn, NY 11222
Tel.: (718) 389-2970
Sales Range: $1-9.9 Million
Emp.: 31
Personal & Household Goods Repair & Maintenance
N.A.I.C.S.: 811490
Richard Dorsey (Pres & CEO)

CHAMPION INDUSTRIAL CONTRACTORS INC.
1420 Coldwell Ave, Modesto, CA 95350-5704
Tel.: (209) 524-6601
Web Site:
http://www.championindustrial.com
Year Founded: 1933
Sales Range: $25-49.9 Million
Emp.: 140
Provider of Construction Services
N.A.I.C.S.: 238220
Darrell F. Champion (Owner & Pres)

CHAMPION LUMBER CO.
1313 Chicago Ave Ste 100, Riverside, CA 92507
Tel.: (951) 684-5670
Web Site:
https://www.championlumber.net
Year Founded: 1950
Sales Range: $50-74.9 Million
Emp.: 101
Building Materials Whslr
N.A.I.C.S.: 444180
Joe Audette (Owner)

CHAMPION MOTORSPORT
3101 Center Port Cir, Pompano Beach, FL 33064
Tel.: (954) 946-2136
Web Site:
https://www.championmotors.com
Year Founded: 1998
Sales Range: $150-199.9 Million
Emp.: 11
Aftermarket Automotive Parts & Accessories Designer & Mfr
N.A.I.C.S.: 441330
Naveen Maraj (Pres)
Dave Maraj (Owner)
Ramesh Narwani (CFO)

CHAMPION NUTRITION, INC.
1301 Sawgrass Corporate Pkwy, Sunrise, FL 33323-2813
Tel.: (954) 233-0320
Web Site:
http://www.championnutrition.com
Year Founded: 1983
Sales Range: $10-24.9 Million
Emp.: 50
Nutritional Products Distr
N.A.I.C.S.: 325412
Michael Zumpano (Founder)

CHAMPION PORSCHE
500 W Copans Rd, Pompano Beach, FL 33064-3266
Tel.: (954) 946-4020
Web Site: http://www.champion-motors.com
Year Founded: 1987
Sales Range: $25-49.9 Million
Emp.: 115
New Car Retailer
N.A.I.C.S.: 441110
Devindar A. Maraj (Pres)

CHAMPION SCREW MACHINE ENGINEERING, INC.

30419 Beck Rd, Wixom, MI 48393
Tel.: (248) 624-4545   MI
Web Site:
https://www.championscrew.com
Year Founded: 1945
Sales Range: $10-24.9 Million
Emp.: 20
Distr of Machine Tools & Accessories
N.A.I.C.S.: 423830
Katharine Coffman *(Pres)*
Mark Knedgen *(VP-Sls)*
Jim Merritt *(Mgr-Sls)*
Harvey Mascow *(Chm)*

CHAMPION SEED COMPANY
529 Mercury Ln, Brea, CA 92821
Tel.: (714) 529-0702
Web Site:
http://www.championseed.com
Sales Range: $10-24.9 Million
Emp.: 25
Vegetable Seeds Supplier
N.A.I.C.S.: 424910
Dan Marshburn *(Pres)*

CHAMPION TRANSPORTA-TION SERVICES, INC.
200 Champion Way, Northlake, IL
60164-1699
Tel.: (708) 562-4200   IL
Web Site: https://www.champlog.com
Year Founded: 1980
Sales Range: $10-24.9 Million
Emp.: 100
Freight Transportation Arrangement
N.A.I.C.S.: 488510
Kevin P. McConkey *(Pres)*

CHAMPION WINDOWS MANU-FACTURING INC.
12121 Champion Way, Cincinnati,
OH 45241
Tel.: (513) 346-4600
Web Site:
http://www.championwindow.com
Year Founded: 1953
Rev.: $28,490,000
Emp.: 200
Plastic Window Frames Mfr
N.A.I.C.S.: 326199
Donald R. Jones *(Pres & COO)*
Amberly Hudson *(Mgr-Payroll)*
Todd Dickson *(CEO)*

Subsidiaries:

Champion Window Company of Okla-
homa City, LLC   (1)
417 Hudiburg Cir Ste A, Oklahoma City, OK
73108
Tel.: (405) 345-4924
Web Site: http://www.championwindow.com
Lumber, Plywood, Millwork & Wood Panel
Merchant Whslr
N.A.I.C.S.: 423310

CHAMPION WIRE & CABLE LLC
695 Summa Ave, Westbury, NY
11590
Tel.: (516) 338-2000
Web Site:
https://www.champwire.com
Sales Range: $10-24.9 Million
Emp.: 25
Electrical Wire & Cable
N.A.I.C.S.: 423610
David Berger *(Pres)*
A. J. Perulla *(VP)*

CHAMPION, INC.
180 Traders Mine Rd, Iron Mountain,
MI 49801-3404
Tel.: (906) 779-2300   MI
Web Site:
https://www.championinc.com
Year Founded: 1921
Sales Range: $100-124.9 Million

Emp.: 150
Contracting Services
N.A.I.C.S.: 541618
Terry Alatalo *(Mgr-IT)*

Subsidiaries:

Gundlach Champion, Inc.   (1)
180 Traders Mine Rd, Iron Mountain, MI
49801
Tel.: (906) 779-2303
Web Site: http://www.gcfirst.com
Industrial Building Construction Services
N.A.I.C.S.: 236210
Jim Ebli *(Pres)*

CHAMPIONS FOR CHILDREN, INC.
3108 W Azeele St, Tampa, FL 33609
Tel.: (813) 673-4646
Web Site:
http://www.championsforchildren.org
Year Founded: 1977
Sales Range: $1-9.9 Million
Child Abuse Prevention & Family
Education Services
N.A.I.C.S.: 624190
Brian McEwen *(Exec Dir)*
Amy Haile *(Assoc Exec Dir)*
Maria Lewis *(Dir-Dev)*
Reynald Latortue *(CFO)*
Julia Miller *(Mgr-HR)*

CHAMPIONS MACHINE TOOL SALES, INC.
1151 E Cypresswood Dr, Spring, TX
77373
Tel.: (914) 965-5040   TX
Web Site:
https://www.championscnc.com
Year Founded: 1981
Rev.: $11,000,000
Emp.: 25
Machine Tools & Accessories
N.A.I.C.S.: 423830
Ronnie Dutton *(Co-Pres & Co-CEO)*
Rickey Martin *(Co-Pres & Co-CEO)*
Ricky Martin *(VP)*
Gene Haas *(Pres)*

CHAMPIONS PIPE & SUPPLY INC.
2 Northpoint Dr, Houston, TX 77060-
3235
Tel.: (713) 468-6544   TX
Web Site:
http://www.championspipe.com
Year Founded: 1985
Sales Range: $125-149.9 Million
Emp.: 22
Sales & Distribution of Metallic Pipes
N.A.I.C.S.: 423510
Clay Underwood *(Reg Mgr-Sls)*
Gerald Slayton *(Mgr)*
Bob Cipriani *(Controller)*

CHAMPLAIN BANK CORPO-RATION
3900 NYS Route 22, Willsboro, NY
12996
Tel.: (518) 963-4201
Web Site:
http://www.champlainbank.com
Year Founded: 1986
Rev.: $16,084,000
Assets: $357,286,000
Liabilities: $331,245,000
Net Worth: $26,041,000
Earnings: $2,907,000
Emp.: 70
Fiscal Year-end: 12/31/18
Bank Holding Company
N.A.I.C.S.: 551111
Roderic G. Giltz *(Vice Chm)*
Jennifer Pecore *(Asst VP & Mgr-Comml Portfolio & Collections)*
Lisa Roberts *(Sr VP)*

Carol Manley *(VP-Facilities & Secu-rity)*
Jacqueline Hallock *(VP & Dir-Mktg)*
Kevin Richard *(VP & Mgr-IT)*
Valarie Favaro *(VP-Audit & Compli-ance)*
Darlene Mirrer *(Sr VP-Retail Banking)*
Marilyn Strong *(VP & Mgr-Deposit & Loan Svcs)*
Steven G. Cacchio *(Pres & CEO)*
Sarah A. Schmidt *(CFO & Sr VP)*
Renee L. Darrah *(VP)*
Edward P. Finnerty *(VP)*
Judy L. Hoskins *(VP)*
Timothy J. Kononan *(VP)*
Lori Hebert *(Officer-Banking)*
Michelle Lafountain *(Officer-Banking)*
Melanie Porter *(Officer-Banking)*
Lena Robetoy *(VP)*
Medara Sherman *(Officer-Banking)*
Andrea Robare *(Mgr-Acctg)*
Peter S. Paine Jr. *(Chm)*
Peter S. Paine III *(Vice Chm)*

Subsidiaries:

Champlain National Bank   (1)
3900 NYS Route 22, Willsboro, NY 12996
Tel.: (518) 963-4201
Web Site: http://www.champlainbank.com
Sales Range: $50-74.9 Million
Banking Services
N.A.I.C.S.: 522110
Peter S. Paine *(Chm)*
Steven Cacchio *(Pres & CEO)*
Lori Verzillo *(Sr VP-Retail Banking & Ops)*
Gayle Bridge *(VP & Mgr-HR)*
Valarie Favaro *(VP-Audit & Compliance)*
Jacqueline Hallock *(VP & Dir-Mktg)*
Charles Hughes *(CFO & Sr VP)*
Kevin Richard *(VP & Mgr-IT)*
Lisa Roberts *(Sr VP)*

CHAMPLAIN CAPITAL MAN-AGEMENT LLC
1 Post St Ste 925, San Francisco,
CA 94104
Tel.: (415) 661-2500
Web Site:
https://www.champlaincapital.com
Year Founded: 2002
Privater Equity Firm
N.A.I.C.S.: 523999
Warren D. Feldberg *(Mng Partner)*
Dennis Leary *(Mng Partner)*
Pierre Simard *(Partner)*
Mark VanStekelenburg *(Partner)*
Katy C. Young *(CFO)*

Subsidiaries:

S.R. Smith, LLC   (1)
1017 SW Berg Pkwy, Canby, OR 97013-
3900
Tel.: (503) 266-2231
Web Site: http://www.srsmith.com
Swimming Pool Equipment & Accessory
Products Designer, Mfr & Distr
N.A.I.C.S.: 339920
Mike Dedona *(CFO & VP)*
Rich Lailta *(Pres & CEO)*

iPROMOTEu, Inc.   (1)
321 Commonwealth Rd Ste 101, Wayland,
MA 01778
Tel.: (508) 653-4410
Web Site: http://www.ipromoteu.com
Sales Range: $50-74.9 Million
Emp.: 35
Dry Goods Merchant Whslr
N.A.I.C.S.: 424310
Ross Silverstein *(Pres & CEO)*
David Blouin *(VP-Fin & Admin)*
Richard Badiner *(COO & Exec VP)*
Pat Caccamo *(Dir-Bus Dev)*

CHAMPLAIN OIL CO. INC.
45 San Remo Dr, South Burlington,
VT 05403
Tel.: (802) 864-5380
Web Site:
http://www.champlainoil.com

Sales Range: $25-49.9 Million
Emp.: 320
Petroleum Products
N.A.I.C.S.: 424720
Tony Cairns *(Pres)*
Keith White *(Mgr-Transportation)*
Steve Halibozek *(Mgr-Safety)*

CHAMPLAIN VALLEY OFFICE OF ECONOMIC OPPORTU-NITY, INC.
255 S Champlain St, Burlington, VT
05402
Tel.: (802) 862-2771   VT
Web Site: https://www.cvoeo.org
Year Founded: 1965
Sales Range: $10-24.9 Million
Emp.: 205
Economic Development Services
N.A.I.C.S.: 541720
Terri Terreri *(Dir-Human Resources)*
Rob Meehan *(Dir-Chittenden Emer-gency Food Shelf)*

CHANCELLOR & SON INC.
7474 Raleigh Lagrange Rd, Cordova,
TN 38018
Tel.: (901) 754-2063
Sales Range: $10-24.9 Million
Emp.: 65
General Contractor, Highway & Street
Construction
N.A.I.C.S.: 237310
Kimmy Chancellor *(Gen Mgr)*

CHANCELLOR, INC.
1228 W 5th St, Laurel, MS 39440
Tel.: (601) 518-6453
Web Site:
http://www.chancellorinc.com
Year Founded: 1966
Sales Range: $10-24.9 Million
Emp.: 38
Electrical Equipment Whslr
N.A.I.C.S.: 423610
Michael Chancellor *(Owner)*

CHANCEY DESIGN PARTNER-SHIP, INC.
1228 E 7th Ave, Tampa, FL 33605
Tel.: (813) 739-6101
Web Site:
https://www.chanceydesign.com
Year Founded: 1989
Sales Range: $1-9.9 Million
Emp.: 25
Architectural & Interior Design Ser-vices
N.A.I.C.S.: 541310
Walton H. Chancey *(Founder & Sr Mng Partner)*
Jose Calle *(Project Mgr)*
Larry Nuzum *(Mng Partner & Dir-Construction Admin & Quality)*
Sandra B. Chancey *(Partner)*

CHANDLER CHICCO AGENCY
450 W 15th St Ste 700, New York,
NY 10011
Tel.: (212) 229-8400
Web Site: http://www.ccapr.com
Year Founded: 1995
Sales Range: $25-49.9 Million
Emp.: 130
Advertising & Public Relations Ser-vices
N.A.I.C.S.: 541810

Subsidiaries:

Chandler Chicco Agency -
London   (1)
151 Shaftesbury Ave, Covent Garden, Lon-
don, WC2H 8AL, United Kingdom
Tel.: (44) 20 76321800
Web Site: http://www.ccapr.com

Chandler Chicco Agency—(Continued)

Sales Range: $50-74.9 Million
Emp.: 75
Advertising & Public Relations Services
N.A.I.C.S.: 541810
Neil McGregor-Paterson *(Head-Client Svcs)*

Chandler Chicco Agency - Los Angeles (1)
1315 Lincoln Blvd Ste 270, Santa Monica, CA 90401
Tel.: (310) 309-1000
Web Site: http://www.ccapr.com
Emp.: 27
Advertising & Public Relations Services
N.A.I.C.S.: 541810
Julie Adrian *(Dir)*

Chandler Chicco Agency - Paris (1)
17 Sq Edouard VII, 75009, Paris, France
Tel.: (33) 1 53 43 91 53
Advertising & Public Relations Services
N.A.I.C.S.: 541810

Chandler Chicco Agency - Washington (1)
25 Massachusetts Ave NWtfrs, Washington, DC 20001
Tel.: (202) 609-6000
Web Site: http://www.ccapr.com
Sales Range: $10-24.9 Million
Emp.: 17
Advertising & Public Relations Services
N.A.I.C.S.: 541810

CHANDLER CO-OP
151 5th St, Chandler, MN 56122
Tel.: (507) 677-2207
Sales Range: $10-24.9 Million
Emp.: 6
Farm Supplies
N.A.I.C.S.: 424910
Kevin Devereaux *(Gen Mgr)*

CHANDLER CONCRETE INC.
1006 S Church St, Burlington, NC 27215
Tel.: (336) 226-1181   NC
Web Site:
   https://www.chandlerconcrete.com
Year Founded: 1974
Sales Range: $25-49.9 Million
Emp.: 322
Central-mixed Concrete
N.A.I.C.S.: 327320
Robert Chandler *(Exec VP-Sls & Mktg)*
Kelly Leonard *(Controller)*
Ted Greene *(Gen Mgr)*

Subsidiaries:

Chandler Building Supply Company (1)
400 N Long St, Salisbury, NC 28145-0139
Tel.: (704) 636-4713
Web Site: http://www.chandlerconcrete.com
Emp.: 26
Building Materials Distr
N.A.I.C.S.: 423390

Chandler Concrete Company Inc. (1)
700 Block Ln, Christiansburg, VA 24073
Tel.: (540) 382-1734
Web Site: http://www.chandlerconcrete.com
Sales Range: $10-24.9 Million
Emp.: 75
Concrete Block Mfr
N.A.I.C.S.: 327320
Steven A. Marshall *(Pres)*
Johnny Underwood *(Plant Mgr)*

Chandler Concrete of Virginia, Inc. (1)
700 Block Ln, Christiansburg, VA 24073
Tel.: (540) 382-1734
Building Materials Distr
N.A.I.C.S.: 423390
George Kuhn *(Mgr-Tech Svcs-Virginia)*

CHANDLER ENTERPRISES INC.
810 W 1st Ave, Toppenish, WA 98948

Tel.: (509) 865-2550
Sales Range: $10-24.9 Million
Emp.: 30
Petroleum Bulk Stations
N.A.I.C.S.: 424710
Mike Chandler *(Pres)*

CHANDLER GROUP, INC.
747 Custer Ave Ste A, Evanston, IL 60201-4419
Tel.: (847) 475-7900
Year Founded: 1999
Sales Range: $10-24.9 Million
Emp.: 13
N.A.I.C.S.: 541613
Diane Chandler *(Pres)*

CHANDLER HALL HEALTH SERVICES, INC.
99 Barclay St, Newtown, PA 18940
Tel.: (215) 860-4000   PA
Web Site: http://www.chandlerhall.org
Year Founded: 1985
Sales Range: $10-24.9 Million
Emp.: 382
Housing & Health Care Services
N.A.I.C.S.: 623990

CHANDLER SIGNS, LP
3201 Manor Way, Dallas, TX 75235
Tel.: (214) 902-2000
Web Site:
   http://www.chandlersigns.com
Rev.: $37,000,000
Emp.: 350
Signs & Advertising Specialties
N.A.I.C.S.: 339950
Rockford V. Gray *(Pres)*
Chuck Riffe *(VP-West Coast)*
Gary Stevens *(VP & Mgr-Mfg)*
Mark Bergenz *(VP)*

CHANEN CORPORATION
3300 N 3rd Ave, Phoenix, AZ 85013
Tel.: (602) 266-3600
Web Site: https://www.chanen.com
Sales Range: $10-24.9 Million
Emp.: 25
Commercial & Office Building, New Construction
N.A.I.C.S.: 236220
Herman Chanen *(Founder)*

Subsidiaries:

Chanen Construction Co. Inc (1)
3300 N 3rd Ave, Phoenix, AZ 85013
Tel.: (602) 266-3600
Web Site: http://www.chanen.com
Farm Building Construction
N.A.I.C.S.: 236220
Herman Chanen *(Founder)*

Darling Development Inc. (1)
3300 N 3rd Ave, Phoenix, AZ 85013
Tel.: (602) 266-3600
Rev.: $630,000
Emp.: 4
Industrial Buildings Construction Services
N.A.I.C.S.: 236220
Herman Chanen *(Chm)*

CHANEY ENTERPRISES LP
12480 Mattawoman Dr, Waldorf, MD 20601
Tel.: (301) 932-5000
Web Site:
   http://www.chaneyenterprises.com
Year Founded: 1962
Sales Range: $10-24.9 Million
Emp.: 300
Sales of Ready-Mixed Concrete
N.A.I.C.S.: 327320
Francis Chaney *(Gen Partner)*
Donna Chaney Bunn *(Vice Chm)*
Kyle Murray *(Project Mgr-Land)*
Thomas W. Flynn *(CFO)*
Jan Holt *(Chief Customer Officer)*
Amie Long *(Dir-HR-Gambrills)*

Wyatt Wiggins *(Mgr-Sls & Bus Dev)*
Francis H. Chaney III *(CEO)*
Francis H. Chaney II *(Chm)*

CHANG INTERNATIONAL INC.
1611 Market St, Kirkland, WA 98033
Tel.: (206) 283-9098
Web Site:
   http://www.changinternational.com
Sales Range: $400-449.9 Million
Emp.: 800
Fish & Seafood Merchant Whslr
N.A.I.C.S.: 424460
Stone Wong *(Exec VP)*
Jianrong Chang *(Pres)*

CHANGE MANAGEMENT CONSULTING, INC.
82 Benson Dr, Wayne, NJ 07470
Tel.: (973) 696-7878
Web Site: https://www.cmc-changemanagement.com
Year Founded: 1993
Sales Range: $10-24.9 Million
Emp.: 36
Management Consulting & Training Services
N.A.I.C.S.: 541618
Stanley Cherkasky *(Founder, Mng Partner & CEO)*

CHANGE POINT, INC.
1700 NW 167th Pl Ste 240, Beaverton, OR 97006
Tel.: (503) 253-5954   OR
Web Site:
   http://www.changepointinc.com
Year Founded: 1983
Emp.: 50
Drug & Alcohol Addiction Treatment Services
N.A.I.C.S.: 621420
Richard Drandoff *(Owner)*
Linda Bradshaw *(Program Mgr)*
Cindy Ostlund *(Mgr-HR)*

Subsidiaries:

Change Point, Inc. - Main Office (1)
10621 NE Coxley Dr Ste 106, Vancouver, WA 98662-6122
Tel.: (360) 604-0068
Web Site: http://www.changepointinc.com
Emp.: 10
Drug & Alcohol Addiction Treatment Services
N.A.I.C.S.: 621420
Reggie Sherwood *(Mgr)*

CHANGE TO WIN
1900 L St NW Ste 900, Washington, DC 20036
Tel.: (202) 721-0660   DC
Web Site:
   https://www.changetowin.org
Year Founded: 2005
Sales Range: $10-24.9 Million
Emp.: 80
Labor Welfare Services
N.A.I.C.S.: 813930
Tom Woodruff *(Exec Dir)*
James P. Hoffa *(Chm)*
Mary Kay Henry *(Treas & Sec)*

CHANGSHENG INTERNATIONAL GROUP LIMITED
PO Box 1334, Franklin, TN 37174
Tel.: (615) 806-5988   DE
Year Founded: 2007
CSJT—(OTCIQ)
Liabilities: $188,458
Net Worth: ($188,458)
Earnings: ($750)
Fiscal Year-end: 06/30/19
Investment Holding Company
N.A.I.C.S.: 551112

CHANNEL ISLANDS DESIGN

2840 S Harbor Blvd C4 Channel Islands Harbor, Oxnard, CA 93035
Tel.: (805) 382-4243
Web Site: http://www.cid4design.com
Sales Range: Less than $1 Million
Emp.: 2
N.A.I.C.S.: 541810
Robert Gray *(Owner)*

CHANNEL KEY, LLC
5940 S Rainbow Blvd Ste 400 PMB 18703, Las Vegas, NV 89118
Tel.: (844) 700-1257
Web Site: http://www.channelkey.com
Advertising Services
N.A.I.C.S.: 541810

CHANNEL LUMBER COMPANY INC.
100 W Cutting Blvd, Richmond, CA 94804-4002
Tel.: (510) 234-0233   CA
Web Site:
   https://www.channellumber.com
Year Founded: 1956
Sales Range: $25-49.9 Million
Emp.: 75
Lumber, Plywood & Millwork
N.A.I.C.S.: 423310
Dan DeSimoni *(VP)*
Karen Rathe *(Pres)*
Octavio Ricart *(CFO)*
Michael DeSimoni Sr. *(Owner)*

CHANNEL PARTNERS LLC
6487 Sycamore Ct N, Maple Grove, MN 55369
Tel.: (763) 746-7760
Web Site:
   http://www.channelpartnersllc.com
Year Founded: 2009
Sales Range: $1-9.9 Million
Emp.: 12
Working Capital Loans
N.A.I.C.S.: 523999
Brad Peterson *(CEO)*
Carl Frasse *(VP-Bus Dev-East)*
Lee Ritter *(Sls Dir-West)*
Adam Peterson *(Sr. VP-Sls)*

CHANNELL CONSULTING COMPANY
501 Ridge Rd, Bellevue, NE 68005
Tel.: (402) 706-1646
Web Site:
   http://www.channellconsulting company.com
Year Founded: 1989
Sales Range: Less than $1 Million
Emp.: 2
Construction Services
N.A.I.C.S.: 236220
Michael Channell *(Founder, Owner & CEO)*

CHANNELLOCK, INC.
1306 S Main St, Meadville, PA 16335-3035
Tel.: (814) 724-8700   PA
Web Site:
   https://www.channellock.com
Year Founded: 1886
Sales Range: $150-199.9 Million
Emp.: 400
Mfr of Hand Tools
N.A.I.C.S.: 332216
William S. DeArment *(Chm & CEO)*
Mark Yoder *(Dir-Sls-North America)*
Stephen M. Sada *(Treas & Sec)*
Jonathan S. DeArment *(Pres & COO)*
Ryan DeArment *(VP-Sls & Mktg)*
Michael Smith *(VP-Mfg & Engrg)*
Ken C. Burchill *(Acct Mgr)*

Subsidiaries:

Hold-E-Zee, Ltd.   (1)

10745 Water St Extension, Meadville, PA
16335-6827
Tel.: (814) 337-9708
Sales Range: $10-24.9 Million
Emp.: 30
Mfr of Standard/Adjustable Screwdrivers &
Nut Drivers
N.A.I.C.S.: 332216

Tamarack Packaging Limited (1)
11124 Mercer Pike, Meadville, PA 16335-
0693
Tel.: (814) 724-2860
Web Site:
    http://www.tamarackpackaging.com
Sales Range: $10-24.9 Million
Emp.: 25
Mfr of Vinyl Binders & Pouches, Packaging
Material
N.A.I.C.S.: 323111
W. Dearment (Exec VP)

CHANNELNET
Three Harbor Dr Ste 206, Sausalito,
CA 94965
Tel.: (415) 332-4704
Web Site: http://www.channelnet.com
Rev.: $20,000,000
Emp.: 125
Multichannel Sales & Marketing Solu-
tions
N.A.I.C.S.: 541613
Paula George Tompkins (Founder &
CEO)
Molly Smith (VP-Ops)
Milad Elmir (Chief Experience Officer)
Jason Luke (Dir-Cyber Security-
Dearborn)
Samuel M. Inman III (Chm-Advisory
Bd)

CHANNING BETE CO., INC.
1 Community Pl, South Deerfield, MA
01373
Tel.: (413) 665-7611   MA
Web Site: http://www.channing-
    bete.com
Year Founded: 1946
Sales Range: $25-49.9 Million
Emp.: 300
Publisher & Printer of Scriptographic
Informational & Educational Booklets
& Related Materials
N.A.I.C.S.: 513130
Michael Bete (Pres & CEO)
Robert L. Underwood (Exec VP)
Carol W. Bete (Sr VP-Adv)
Daniel E. Carmody (Sr VP)
Kim Canuel (CFO)

CHANO INTERNATIONAL INC.
45 W 36th St 4th Fl, New York, NY
10018
Tel.: (212) 239-4222   NY
Year Founded: 1981
Sales Range: $10-24.9 Million
Emp.: 6
Men's & Boy's Underwear & Night-
wear Distr
N.A.I.C.S.: 315250
Elliot Jemal (CEO)

CHAPARRAL ENERGY, INC.
701 Cedar Lake Blvd, Oklahoma City,
OK 73114
Tel.: (405) 478-8770
Web Site:
    http://www.chaparralenergy.com
Rev.: $236,345,000
Assets: $988,432,000
Liabilities: $571,291,000
Net Worth: $417,141,000
Earnings: ($468,948,000)
Emp.: 121
Fiscal Year-end: 12/31/19
Oil & Natural Gas Production & Ex-
ploration
N.A.I.C.S.: 211120

Clint Calhoun (VP-Resource Dev)
Josh Walker (VP-Completions & Ops)
Stephanie Carnes (VP & Controller)
Justin Byrne (Gen Counsel, Sec &
VP)
Charles Duginski (Pres & CEO)

Subsidiaries:

Triumph Resources Inc (1)
701 Cedar Lake Blvd, Oklahoma City, OK
73114
Tel.: (405) 478-8770
Web Site: http://www.chaparralenergy.com
Rev.: $260,000
Emp.: 3
Crude Petroleum Production
N.A.I.C.S.: 211120

CHAPEL STEEL COMPANY
900 N Brook Dr, Trevose, PA 19053
Tel.: (215) 793-0899   PA
Web Site:
    http://www.chapelsteel.com
Year Founded: 1972
Sales Range: $10-24.9 Million
Emp.: 100
Metals Service Centers & Offices
N.A.I.C.S.: 423510
James Sutow (CEO)

CHAPEL VALLEY LANDSCAPE COMPANY
3275 Jennings Chapel Rd, Wood-
bine, MD 21797
Tel.: (410) 442-2310
Web Site:
    https://www.chapelvalley.com
Rev.: $20,032,066
Emp.: 450
Landscape Contractors
N.A.I.C.S.: 561730
Bonnie Szabo (CFO)
Jennifer Giunta (Mgr-Market Develop)
Jill Hartkopf (Mgr-Alexandria)
James Landon Reeve IV (Founder,
Pres & CEO)

CHAPIN HOME FOR THE AG-ING
165-01 Chapin Pkwy, Jamaica, NY
11432
Tel.: (718) 739-2523   NY
Web Site:
    https://www.chapinhome.org
Year Founded: 1869
Sales Range: $10-24.9 Million
Emp.: 342
Elder Care Services
N.A.I.C.S.: 624120
William B. O'Hara (CFO)
Andrew Lombardo (Dir-Environmental
Svcs)
Jennifer MacMan (Exec VP)

CHAPIN INTERNATIONAL, INC.
700 Ellicott St, Batavia, NY 14021-
0549
Tel.: (585) 343-3140
Web Site:
    https://www.chapinmfg.com
Year Founded: 1884
Rev.: $17,300,000
Emp.: 225
Metal Compressed Air Spray Mfr
N.A.I.C.S.: 561730
Debbie Mullen (Mgr-IS)
John White (Mgr-Natl Sls)
Eliot Schwartz (Mgr-Cost Acctg)
Jim Grant (VP-Fin)
Chuck Mattes (VP-S&M)
Chris Rumfola (Mgr-Sls-Natl)
Joseph Severino (Coord-Logistics)
Vince Vollo (Dir-Mktg)
Jim Campbell (Pres & CEO)

CHAPIN MEDICAL COMPANY INC.

PO Box 17729, Anaheim, CA 92817-
7729
Tel.: (909) 735-5300   CA
Year Founded: 1974
Sales Range: $10-24.9 Million
Emp.: 35
Drugs & Sundries Distr
N.A.I.C.S.: 424210

CHAPMAN & CUTLER LLP
111 W Monroe St, Chicago, IL 60603-
4080
Tel.: (312) 845-3000
Web Site: http://www.chapman.com
Year Founded: 1913
Sales Range: $150-199.9 Million
Emp.: 203
Law firm
N.A.I.C.S.: 541110
Timothy P. Mohan (CEO)
Thomas Zimmermann (Dir-Fin & Fin
Mgmt)
Anthony T. Freveletti (Dir-Legislative
Affairs)
Nancy Linder (Dir-Mktg)
Stacey Kielbasa (Dir-Pro Dev, Atty
Recruitment & Diversity)
Dan Reitz (Mgr-Govt Rels)
Wendy Reiner (Office Mgr)
Youlonda Wayne (Office Mgr)
Joseph Cottone (Office Mgr & Mgr-
Client Svcs-East Coast)
Kimberly L. Ahlgrim (Partner)
Scott R. Anderson (Partner)
David T. B. Audley (Partner)
Andrea G. Bacon (Partner)
Cynthia A. Baker (Partner)

CHAPMAN AUTOMOTIVE GROUP LLC
7455 W Orchid Ln, Chandler, AZ
85226
Tel.: (480) 344-4269   AZ
Web Site:
    http://www.chapmanchoice.com
Year Founded: 1978
Sales Range: $1-4.9 Billion
Emp.: 1,700
Holding Company; Automobile Deal-
ership Owner & Operator
N.A.I.C.S.: 551112
Jerry B. Chapman (Founder & Chm)

Subsidiaries:

Chapman Ford (1)
3950 N 89th St, Scottsdale, AZ 85251
Tel.: (480) 420-1460
Web Site: http://www.fivestarford.com
Sales Range: $150-199.9 Million
Emp.: 150
Automobiles, New & Used
N.A.I.C.S.: 441110
Kenneth Scholz (Chm)
Bill Veverka (Parts Mgr)
Mike Hanson (Mgr Body Shop)
Wayne Thibault (Fin Mgr)
Joe Sanchez (Mgr-Fin)
Bill Braatz (Dir-Fleet & Internet Sls)
Ken Denton (Acct Mgr)
Candace Gergen (Acct Mgr)
Vicki Orritt (Fin Mgr)
Bob Lechniak (Dir)
Richard Lewis (Mgr-Govt Vehicles)

CHAPMAN BMW ON CAMEL-BACK
830 E Camelback Rd, Phoenix, AZ
85014
Tel.: (602) 308-4269
Web Site:
    https://www.chapmanbmw.com
Year Founded: 1976
Sales Range: $10-24.9 Million
Emp.: 85
Car Whslr
N.A.I.C.S.: 441110

Mathew Dresp (Gen Mgr)
Doug Strobot (Dir-Svc)
B. J. Geisler (Mgr-CPO)
Ryan Brown (Mgr-Wholesale Parts)

CHAPMAN CHRYSLER JEEP
930 Auto Show Dr, Henderson, NV
89014
Tel.: (702) 558-3000
Web Site:
    https://www.chapmanchrysler.com
Sales Range: $10-24.9 Million
Emp.: 60
Car Whslr
N.A.I.C.S.: 441110
Nick Banker (Mgr-Internet Sls)

CHAPMAN DODGE CHRYS-LER JEEP RAM
3800 N 89th St, Scottsdale, AZ
85251
Tel.: (480) 424-3559
Web Site:
    https://www.chapmandodge.com
Year Founded: 1995
Sales Range: $50-74.9 Million
Emp.: 215
New Car Retailer
N.A.I.C.S.: 441110
Tina Escoto (Mgr-Svc)

CHAPMAN FORD SALES, INC.
9371 Roosevelt Blvd, Philadelphia,
PA 19114
Tel.: (215) 698-7000
Web Site:
    http://www.chapmancars.com
Sales Range: $10-24.9 Million
Emp.: 200
New & Used Automobiles
N.A.I.C.S.: 532111
Randy Chapman (Co-Owner & Chm)
Michael Chapman (Co-Owner &
CEO)
Mariann McNally (Controller)
Nick Iervolino (Co-Owner, VP & Gen
Mgr)
Kerry J. Petratos (Mgr-Sls-Comml &
Fleet)
Jim Casey (Gen Sls Mgr)

CHAPMAN FRUIT CO INC.
1075 US Hwy 17 S, Wauchula, FL
33873
Tel.: (863) 773-3161
Web Site:
    http://www.chapmanfruit.com
Sales Range: $25-49.9 Million
Emp.: 130
Fresh Fruit & Vegetable Merchant
Whslr
N.A.I.C.S.: 424480
Daniel L. Rosbough (Pres)
Adrian R. Chapman (CEO)
Carlene Schumann (Treas & Sec)

CHAPMAN INC.
622 E Lamar St, Sherman, TX
75090-6027
Tel.: (903) 893-8106
Web Site:
    http://www.chapmaninc.com
Year Founded: 1960
Sales Range: $10-24.9 Million
Emp.: 25
Petroleum Services
N.A.I.C.S.: 424710
Andrew Olmstead (Pres)

Subsidiaries:

West Ark Oil Company (1)
622 E Lamar St, Sherman, TX 75090
Tel.: (903) 893-8106
Rev.: $18,000,000
Emp.: 4
Petroleum Products Distr
N.A.I.C.S.: 424710

Chapman Innovations—(Continued)

CHAPMAN INNOVATIONS
343 W 400 S, Salt Lake City, UT
84123
Tel.: (801) 415-0025
Web Site: http://www.carbonx.com
Year Founded: 1998
Sales Range: $1-9.9 Million
Emp.: 6
Develops, Produces & Markets Thermal Fabric Solutions
N.A.I.C.S.: 313310
Carl Crosser (VP-Fin)

CHAPMAN PROPERTIES
100 Leetsdale Dr, Leetsdale, PA
15056
Tel.: (724) 266-2500   **PA**
Web Site:
    https://www.chapmanprop.com
Year Founded: 1987
Sales Range: $75-99.9 Million
Emp.: 25
Design & Construct Parking Structures
N.A.I.C.S.: 423850
Steven C. Thomas (Pres & CEO)
Kevin Withers (CFO)

CHAPMAN WATERPROOFING CO.
395 Columbia Rd, Boston, MA 02125
Tel.: (617) 288-3000
Web Site:
    http://www.chapmanwaterproof.com
Sales Range: $10-24.9 Million
Emp.: 230
Waterproofing & Construction
N.A.I.C.S.: 238990
Daniel Greene (Project Mgr)
Adam Packard (Pres)
John Pagnotta (Project Mgr)
John Thompson (Project Mgr)

CHAPMAN/LEONARD STUDIO EQUIPMENT, INC.
12950 Raymer St, North Hollywood,
CA 91605
Tel.: (818) 764-6726
Web Site: http://www.chapman-leonard.com
Year Founded: 1945
Sales Range: $10-24.9 Million
Emp.: 170
Motion Picture Rental Equipment
N.A.I.C.S.: 532490
Charles Huenergardt (Mgr-Outside Ops & Legal)

CHAPP & BUSHEY OIL COMPANY
37333 S Huron Rd, New Boston, MI
48164
Tel.: (734) 941-1610
Web Site: https://www.chappoil.com
Sales Range: $10-24.9 Million
Emp.: 19
Provider of Diesel Fuel
N.A.I.C.S.: 424720
Justine F. Russow (Pres)
J. R. Chapp (VP)

CHAPPELL AGENCY, INC.
6400 Rigsby Rd, Richmond, VA
23226-2917
Tel.: (804) 288-3621
Web Site:
    https://www.chapagency.com
Year Founded: 1981
Provider of Electrical Sales Consulting Services
N.A.I.C.S.: 423610
Richard B. Chappell (Pres)

CHAPPELL DOOR CO. INC.
MAIN OFFICE
1730 Washington Ave, Washington
Court House, OH 43160-2332
Tel.: (740) 335-2727
Web Site:
    https://www.chappelldoor.net
Year Founded: 1986
Sales Range: $10-24.9 Million
Emp.: 40
Doors & Window Frames Mfr
N.A.I.C.S.: 321911
Wayne Golley (Gen Mgr)

CHAPPELLROBERTS INC.
1600 E 8th Ave Ste A-133, Tampa,
FL 33605
Tel.: (813) 281-0088
Web Site:
    http://www.chappellroberts.com
Year Founded: 1978
Sales Range: $10-24.9 Million
Emp.: 30
Branding, Advertising, Marketing,
Public Relations & Digital Services
N.A.I.C.S.: 541810
Colleen F. Chappell (Pres & CEO)
Sarah Tildsley (Principal-Creative Svcs)
Scott Gattis (Principal-Acct Strategy)
Christine Turner (Principal & Exec VP)
Patrick Owings (Principal-Acct Svc)
Katy Berry (Bus Mgr)
Kaitlyn Loos (Asst Acct Exec)
Charlie Militello (Assoc Dir-Creative)
Hunter Taylor (Sr Dir-Acct Strategy)

CHAPTERS HEALTH SYSTEM, INC.
12470 Telecom Dr Ste 300 W,
Temple Terrace, FL 33637
Tel.: (813) 871-8111
Web Site:
    http://www.chaptershealth.org
Sales Range: $100-124.9 Million
Hospice & Senior Care Facilities &
Services
N.A.I.C.S.: 621498
Dave O'Neil (CFO)
H. Darrel White (Chief Legal Officer)
Sharon Jones (VP-Dev)
Gene Fogarty (Vice Chm)
Jack Kolosky (Chm)
Thomas Conger (Sec)
Andrew E. Esch (Dir-Medical-Population Health Mgmt & Palliative Care-Pasco, Herna)
Andrew Molosky (Pres & CEO)
Paola Bianchi Delp (Chief Bus Dev Officer)
Sheri Strobel (CIO)
Tara Friedman (Chief Medical Officer)
Nikki Romence (Chief People Officer)

CHARACTERS UNLIMITED INC.
709 Foothill Ct, Boulder City, NV
89005
Tel.: (702) 294-0563
Web Site:
    https://www.charactersunltd.com
Sales Range: $1-9.9 Million
Emp.: 5
Life-Sized Mechanically Animated
Character Mfr
N.A.I.C.S.: 339999
Olaf Stanton (Pres)

CHARAH, INC.
12601 Plantside Dr, Louisville, KY
40299-6386
Tel.: (502) 245-1353
Web Site: https://www.charah.com
Year Founded: 1987
Rev.: $39,500,000

Emp.: 265
Petroleum & Coal Products Mfr
N.A.I.C.S.: 324199
Charles Price (Pres & CEO)
Bruce Kramer (CFO & Exec VP)
Danny Gray (Exec VP-Govt & Environmental Affairs)
Nathan Boone (Sr VP-Bus Dev)
Randy Compton (VP-Sls)
Rob Reynolds (VP-Carolinas)
David Valentine (Dir-Safety)
Peter DeQuattro (Exec VP-Agricultural Products)
Josh Jones (VP-Process & Tech)
Norman Divers (Mgr-Engrg & Environmental)
Scott Ziegler (VP-Ash Sls & Mktg)
Scott Reschly (VP-Quality & Technical Services)

CHARAPP FORD NORTH
110 Route 908, Natrona Heights, PA
15065
Tel.: (724) 294-2000
Web Site:
    http://www.charappfordnorth.com
Year Founded: 1934
Sales Range: $10-24.9 Million
Emp.: 50
Car Whslr
N.A.I.C.S.: 441110
Ronald Charapp (Principal)

CHARFEN INSTITUTE
12400 W High Way71 Ste350330,
Austin, TX 78738
Web Site: http://www.charfen.com
Year Founded: 2008
Sales Range: $1-9.9 Million
Emp.: 40
Real Estate Manangement Services
N.A.I.C.S.: 525990
Chris Scott (VP-Mktg)
Adam Redowitz (Chief Comm Officer)

CHARGE & RIDE INC.
4701 Vernon Blvd, Long Island City,
NY 11101
Tel.: (718) 392-5200
Web Site:
    http://www.chargeandride.com
Rev.: $22,000,000
Emp.: 28
Limousine Rental
N.A.I.C.S.: 485320
Tariq Abbasi (Pres)

CHARGER INVESTMENT PARTNERS LP
2200 Pacific Coast Hwy Ste 316,
Hermosa Beach, CA 90254
Tel.: (310) 372-5525
Web Site: http://www.chargerinv.com
Privater Equity Firm
N.A.I.C.S.: 523940
Aaron Perlmutter (Co-Founder & Partner)
Chris Boyle (Co-Founder & Partner)
Kimberly Pollack (Co-Founder & Partner)

Subsidiaries:

Advanced Composite Products &
Technology, Inc.   **(1)**
15602 Chemical Ln, Huntington Beach, CA
92649
Tel.: (714) 895-5544
Web Site: http://www.acpt.com
Sales Range: $1-9.9 Million
Emp.: 45
Management Consulting Services
N.A.I.C.S.: 541618
James C. Leslie (Founder)

PerTronix, LLC   **(1)**
440 E Arrow Hwy, San Dimas, CA 91773
Tel.: (909) 599-5955
Web Site: http://www.pertronix.com

Sales Range: $10-24.9 Million
Emp.: 90
Motor Vehicle Electrical & Electronic Equipment Mfr
N.A.I.C.S.: 336320
Thomas Reh (CFO)
Russell Stephens (VP-Sls & Mktg-Performance Brands)
Robyn Hetland (CEO)

Wolf-Gordon Inc.   **(1)**
333 7th Ave 6th Fl, New York, NY 10001
Tel.: (212) 255-3300
Web Site: http://www.wolf-gordon.com
Whslr of Wall Coverings
N.A.I.C.S.: 424950
Rick Wolf (Pres)
David Gordon (VP)

CHARGIFY LLC
197 1st Ave Ste 200, Needham, MA
02494
Tel.: (617) 249-4603
Web Site: http://www.chargify.com
Sales Range: $1-9.9 Million
Automated Billing Software
N.A.I.C.S.: 513210
Lance Walley (Co-Founder & CEO)
Michael Klett (Co-Founder & CTO)
Siamak Taghaddos (Co-Founder)
David Hauser (Co-Founder)
Adam Feber (Dir-Mktg)
Drew Blas (Dir-Technical Ops)
Nathan Verni (Dir-Dev)
Suzanne Gedney (Dir-Customer Success)

CHARIOT VANS INC.
2994 Paul Dr, Elkhart, IN 46514
Tel.: (574) 264-7577
Web Site:
    http://www.chariotvans.com
Rev.: $12,000,000
Emp.: 50
Recreational Van Conversion
N.A.I.C.S.: 336213
John Wisolek (Pres)

CHARISMA BRANDS, LLC
23482 Peralta Dr Ste A, Laguna Hills,
CA 92653-1733
Tel.: (949) 587-9400   **CA**
Web Site:
    http://www.charismabrands.com
Year Founded: 1985
Sales Range: $25-49.9 Million
Emp.: 20
Designer, Developer & Marketer of
Jewelry Products
N.A.I.C.S.: 459120
Anthony P. Shutts (Pres & CEO)

Subsidiaries:

Charisma Manufacturing Company
Inc.   **(1)**
400 Broad St, Central Falls, RI
02863-3013   **(100%)**
Tel.: (401) 728-2040
Costume Jewelry
N.A.I.C.S.: 339910

TCJC Inc.   **(1)**
40 W 37th St, New York, NY
10018-7489   **(100%)**
Tel.: (212) 268-4100
Rev.: $8,271,637
Emp.: 10
Jewelry & Precious Stones
N.A.I.C.S.: 423940

CHARISMA MEDIA
600 Rinehart Rd, Lake Mary, FL
32746-4898
Tel.: (407) 333-0600
Web Site:
    https://www.charismamedia.com
Year Founded: 1975
Rev.: $6,000,000

Emp.: 150
Religious Materials Publisher
N.A.I.C.S.: 513120
Tessie Devore (Exec VP)
Cara Showers (VP-Production & Design-Magazines)

CHARISMA! COMMUNICA-TIONS

8358 SW Birch St, Portland, OR 97223
Tel.: (503) 245-3140
Web Site:
http://www.charismacommunications.com
Sales Range: Less than $1 Million
Emp.: 20
Collateral, Entertainment, Event Planning & Marketing, Graphic Design, Health Care, Logo & Package Design, Newspaper, Production, Public Relations, Real Estate, Retail, Web (Banner Ads, Pop-ups, etc.)
N.A.I.C.S.: 541820
Laurie Halter (Owner)

CHARITABLE ASSISTANCE TO COMMUNITY'S HOMELESS (CATCH), INC.

503 S Americana Blvd, Boise, ID 83702-6730
Tel.: (208) 246-8830   ID
Web Site:
http://www.catchprogram.org
Year Founded: 2010
Sales Range: $1-9.9 Million
Emp.: 12
Homeless Family Shelter & Food Services
N.A.I.C.S.: 623990
Jesse Fessenden (Mgr-Case)
Kylie Rainbolt (Mgr-Office & Resource)
Abby White (Mgr-Case)
Wyatt Schroeder (Exec Dir)
Andrew Kukla (Pres)

CHARITON VALLEY TELE-PHONE CORP.

1213 E Briggs Dr, Macon, MO 63552
Tel.: (660) 395-9000
Web Site: https://www.cvalley.net
Rev.: $11,700,000
Emp.: 40
Local Telephone Communications
N.A.I.C.S.: 517121
Rick Standley (Supvr-OSP)

CHARITY & WEISS INTERNA-TIONAL REALTY, LLC

1718 Main St Ste 200A, Sarasota, FL 34236
Tel.: (941) 365-0022
Web Site:
http://www.realtyinsarasota.com
Sales Range: $1-9.9 Million
Real Estate Broker
N.A.I.C.S.: 531210
Gabriele Charity (Co-Owner)
Ruediger Weiss (Co-Owner)

CHARITY DYNAMICS

3420 Executive Ctr Dr Livingston Bldg G100, Austin, TX 78731
Tel.: (512) 241-0561
Web Site:
http://www.charitydynamics.com
Year Founded: 2004
Sales Range: $1-9.9 Million
Emp.: 23
Online Fundraising Tool
N.A.I.C.S.: 517810
Donna Wilkins (Founder & CEO)
Dolores McDonagh (VP-Consulting-Washington)

CHARITY GLOBAL, INC.

40 Worth St Ste 330, New York, NY 10013
Tel.: (646) 688-2323   NY
Web Site: http://www.charitywater.org
Year Founded: 2006
Sales Range: $25-49.9 Million
Emp.: 57
Water Supply Services
N.A.I.C.S.: 221310
Michael Wilkerson (Chm)
Brook Hazelton (Sec)

CHARKIT CHEMICAL COM-PANY, LLC

32 Haviland St Unit 1, Norwalk, CT 06854-4906
Tel.: (203) 299-3220   CT
Web Site: http://www.charkit.com
Year Founded: 1982
Specialty Chemicals Mfr & Distr
N.A.I.C.S.: 325998
Charlie Marck (Mgr-Bus Dev)

Subsidiaries:

CA Specialties LLC   (1)
712 Wilson St, Chester, SC 29706-8567
Tel.: (803) 581-5800
Web Site: http://www.ca-specialities.com
Specialty Chemicals & Colorants Distr
N.A.I.C.S.: 424690
Cathy Clark (Pres & CEO)

ChayseChem Inc.   (1)
301 Oxford Vly Rd Ste 704B, Yardley, PA 19067
Tel.: (267) 573-4062
Web Site: http://www.chaysechem.com
Chemicals Mfr
N.A.I.C.S.: 325180
Dan Slick (Pres)

Optima Chemical Group, LLC   (1)
200 Willacoochee Hwy, Douglas, GA 31535
Tel.: (912) 384-5101
Web Site: http://www.optimachem.com
Sales Range: $10-24.9 Million
Emp.: 90
Specialty Chemical Product & Preparation Mfr
N.A.I.C.S.: 325998
Gene Williams (Pres)
Dina Mills (Mktg Dir)
Doug Cochran (VP-Bus Dev)
Jaqvir Singh (VP-R&D)
Kent Smith (Mgr-Tech)
Al Horner (Mgr-Environment, Health & Safety)

CHARLEROI FEDERAL SAV-INGS BANK

101 McKean Ave, Charleroi, PA 15022
Tel.: (724) 483-3566
Web Site:
http://www.charleroifederal.com
Year Founded: 1935
Rev.: $19,038,000
Emp.: 75
Federal Savings & Loan Associations
N.A.I.C.S.: 522180
Dave Galloni (VP-Ops)
James Safin (Asst VP-Specialty Lending & Mgr)
Holly L. Mosco (Treas & Asst Sec)
Robert Bury (Officer-Loan)
Keith A. Bassi (Gen Counsel, Treas & Asst Sec)
Lisa Bezusko (Supvr-Teller Ops)

CHARLES & VINZANT CON-STRUCTION CO. LLC

500 Southland Dr Ste 102, Birmingham, AL 35226
Tel.: (205) 823-6761
Web Site: http://www.charles-vinzant.com
Sales Range: $50-74.9 Million
Emp.: 39

Commercial & Office Building, New Construction
N.A.I.C.S.: 236220
Charles Ferlisi (Pres)

CHARLES A LUTHER, C.P.A.

1937 Oak Park Blvd Ste A, Pleasant Hill, CA 94523-4601
Tel.: (925) 945-6533
Sales Range: $10-24.9 Million
Emp.: 2
Accounting Services
N.A.I.C.S.: 541219
Charles A. Luther (Principal)

CHARLES A. KLEIN AND SONS, INC

5220 Klees Mill Rd, Sykesville, MD 21784
Tel.: (410) 549-6960
Web Site: https://www.caklein.com
Year Founded: 1978
Sales Range: $10-24.9 Million
Emp.: 135
Provider of Plumbing Contracts
N.A.I.C.S.: 238220
Cathy Batista (Mgr-HVAC Pur)
Tim Brown (Mgr-Svc)
Mike Klein (Owner & Pres)
Mike Karnes (Project Mgr)

CHARLES ATLAS, LTD.

PO Box D, New York, NY 10159-1049
Tel.: (201) 767-7704   NY
Web Site:
http://www.charlesatlas.com
Year Founded: 1929
Sales Range: $50-74.9 Million
Emp.: 12
Instructor of Health & Fitness; Mail Order Sales
N.A.I.C.S.: 611519
Jeffrey C. Hogue (Pres & CEO)
Cynthia Soroka (Exec VP)

CHARLES B. WANG COMMU-NITY HEALTH CENTER, INC.

268 Canal St, New York, NY 10013
Tel.: (212) 379-6998   NY
Web Site: https://www.cbwchc.org
Year Founded: 1972
Sales Range: $50-74.9 Million
Community Health Care Services
N.A.I.C.S.: 621498
Perry Pong (Chief Medical Officer)
Betty K. Cheng (COO)
Regina F. Lee (Chief Dev Officer)
Lynn D. Sherman (CFO)
Shao-Chee Sim (Chief Strategy Officer)

CHARLES BESELER CO.

PO Box 431, Stroudsburg, PA 18360
Tel.: (570) 517-0400
Web Site: http://www.beseler.com
Year Founded: 1869
Sales Range: $75-99.9 Million
Emp.: 100
Mfr of Packaging & Photographic Equipment
N.A.I.C.S.: 333310
Hank Gasikowski (Pres)

Subsidiaries:

Charles Beseler Co. - Shrink Packaging Division   (1)
2018 W Main St, Stroudsburg, PA 18360
Tel.: (570) 517-0400
Web Site:
http://www.beselershrinkpackaging.com
Packaging Machinery Mfr
N.A.I.C.S.: 333993

CHARLES BLALOCK & SONS INC.

1225 Pkwy, Sevierville, TN 37862
Tel.: (865) 453-2808
Web Site:
http://www.blalockconstruction.com
Rev.: $31,400,000
Emp.: 250
General Contractor, Highway & Street Construction
N.A.I.C.S.: 237310
Sid Blalock (CEO)
Kevin Blalock (VP)

CHARLES BLANCHARD CON-STRUCTION CORPORATION

2845 Rivers Ave, North Charleston, SC 29405
Tel.: (843) 747-5757
Web Site:
https://www.blanchardconst.com
Year Founded: 1958
Sales Range: $10-24.9 Million
Emp.: 60
Commercial & Institutional Building Construction Services
N.A.I.C.S.: 236220
Mike Blanchard (Pres)
Matt O'Donnell (VP)
John O'Donnell (Project Mgr)
Susan Vevon (Office Mgr-HR)

CHARLES BOWMAN & CO. INC.

3328 John F Donnelly Dr, Holland, MI 49424
Tel.: (616) 786-4000
Web Site:
https://www.charlesbowman.com
Rev.: $16,228,145
Emp.: 20
Pharmaceuticals
N.A.I.C.S.: 424210
Greg Christensen (CEO)

CHARLES C. LEWIS COM-PANY

209 Page Blvd, Springfield, MA 01101
Tel.: (413) 733-2121
Web Site:
https://www.charlesclewis.com
Sales Range: $10-24.9 Million
Emp.: 42
Metals Service Centers & Offices
N.A.I.C.S.: 423510
Bart Lewis (Pres)
Jack Corrigan (VP-Sls)
Ken Cizek (Treas)

CHARLES D. JONES & COM-PANY INC.

114 W Linwood Blvd, Kansas City, MO 64111-1312
Tel.: (816) 561-3761   MO
Web Site: http://www.cdjones.com
Year Founded: 1939
Sales Range: $10-24.9 Million
Emp.: 120
Wholesale Heating & Air Conditioning
N.A.I.C.S.: 423730
Royce Henderson (Pres)
Riley Davis (VP-Pur & Gen Mgr-Kansas City)
Ed Palmer (Branch Mgr)

CHARLES DAHER'S COM-MONWEALTH MOTORS

1 Commonwealth Dr, Lawrence, MA 01841
Tel.: (978) 683-5000
Web Site:
http://www.commonwealthmotor.com
Rev.: $37,800,000
Emp.: 125
New & Used Automobiles
N.A.I.C.S.: 441110
Charles Daher (Pres)

Charles David of California—(Continued)

CHARLES DAVID OF CALIFORNIA

5731 Buckingham Pkwy, Culver City, CA 90230
Tel.: (310) 348-5050
Web Site:
http://www.charlesdavid.com
Year Founded: 1987
Sales Range: $75-99.9 Million
Emp.: 62
Mfr & Design of Shoes
N.A.I.C.S.: 424340
Charles Malka *(Pres & CEO)*
Lyn Fleming *(Dir-Intl)*
Susan Davis *(Dir-Production)*
Jennifer Walcott *(Asst Dir-Retail)*
LeighAnne Santiago *(Coord-Sls-Intl)*
David Lann *(VP-Ops)*

CHARLES DEWEESE CONSTRUCTION, INC.

765 Industrial Bypass N, Franklin, KY 42134-5263
Tel.: (270) 586-9122
Web Site:
https://www.charlesdeweeseconstruction.com
Sales Range: $25-49.9 Million
Emp.: 200
Nonresidential Construction Services
N.A.I.C.S.: 236220
John Zaliquette *(Mgr)*

CHARLES DONALD PULPWOOD, INC.

1024 Noble Rd, Port Gibson, MS 39150
Tel.: (601) 437-4012
Web Site:
http://www.donaldtimber.com
Year Founded: 1946
Sales Range: $10-24.9 Million
Emp.: 23
Provider of Pulpwood Contracting Services
N.A.I.C.S.: 113310
David Donald *(VP)*
Charles Donald Jr. *(Pres)*

CHARLES DUNN COMPANY, INC.

800 W 6th St 6th Fl, Los Angeles, CA 90017
Tel.: (213) 481-1800
Web Site:
https://www.charlesdunn.com
Year Founded: 1921
Sales Range: $125-149.9 Million
Emp.: 210
Real Estate & Investment Services
N.A.I.C.S.: 531210
Walter J. Conn *(Mng Principal)*
Jerry Wang *(Exec VP-Intl Div)*
Florence Wang *(CFO)*
Eileen Conn *(Exec VP)*
Patrick Conn *(Pres & COO)*

Subsidiaries:

Charles Dunn Real Estate Services   **(1)**
800 W 6th St Fl 6, Los Angeles, CA 90017
Tel.: (213) 683-0500
Web Site: http://www.charlesdunn.com
Sales Range: $10-24.9 Million
Emp.: 80
Provider of Real Estate Broker Services
N.A.I.C.S.: 531210
Walter J. Conn *(Chm)*
Jerry Wang *(Exec VP-Mgmt Svcs)*
Florence Wang *(CFO)*
Bob Hitchcock *(Reg VP-Mgmt Svcs)*
Tom Arai *(VP)*
Susan Dunst *(Reg VP)*
Gregory R. Gill *(Sr Mng Dir)*
Bradley L. Colton *(Exec VP & Reg Mgr-Brokerage Svcs)*

Brian Jensen *(Dir-Brokerage Svcs)*
Barry Rothstein *(Mng Dir-Brokerage Svcs)*
Charles DeSantis *(Sr Mng Dir-Brokerage Svcs)*
Chris Runyen *(Sr Mng Dir-Brokerage Svcs)*
Chris Steck *(Sr Dir-Brokerage Svcs)*
Joseph Mackin *(Dir-Brokerage Svcs)*
Justin Mendelson *(Dir-Brokerage Svcs)*
Ramin Gheitanchi *(Dir-Brokerage Svcs)*
Tanel Harunzade *(Mng Dir-Brokerage Svcs)*
Tracy Taft *(Dir-Brokerage Svcs)*

CHARLES E. JARRELL CONTRACTING COMPANY, INC.

4208 Rider Trl N, Earth City, MO 63045
Tel.: (314) 291-0100
Web Site: http://www.cejarrell.com
Sales Range: $25-49.9 Million
Emp.: 150
Warm Air Heating & Air Conditioning Contractor
N.A.I.C.S.: 238220
Michael C. Jarrell *(CEO)*
Rick Clary *(Sr VP)*
Chris C. Jarrell *(CFO)*
Derek Kenkel *(Project Mgr)*
Dewayne Jefferson *(VP-Engrg)*
Gene O'Farrell *(Sr Mgr-Automation)*
Jim Stine *(Project Mgr)*

Subsidiaries:

Jarrell Contracting   **(1)**
4208 Rider Trl N, Earth City, MO 63045
Tel.: (314) 291-0100
Web Site: http://www.jarrellcontracting.com
Rev.: $1,336,976
Plumbing, Heating, Air-Conditioning
N.A.I.C.S.: 238220
Mike Jarrell *(Pres)*

CHARLES E. SINGLETON COMPANY INC

7015 E 14th Ave, Tampa, FL 33619
Tel.: (813) 623-5858
Web Site:
http://www.cesingleton.com
Year Founded: 1952
Sales Range: $10-24.9 Million
Emp.: 70
Manufacturers' Representative for Industrial Storage Batteries
N.A.I.C.S.: 423610
Fred L. Singleton *(Pres)*
Kevin Singleton *(VP)*
Paula Shields *(Controller)*
Brian Thompson *(Engrg Mgr)*
Dennis Gasky *(Svc Mgr)*
Steve Roberson *(Engrg Mgr-Georgia)*
Mark Parker *(Mgr-Ops)*

CHARLES EQUIPMENT ENERGY SYSTEMS LLC

530 Santa Rosa Dr, Des Plaines, IL 60018
Tel.: (630) 834-6000
Web Site:
https://www.charlesequipment.com
Sales Range: $10-24.9 Million
Emp.: 26
Industrial Engines Mfr & Distr
N.A.I.C.S.: 333618
Robert Conway *(Pres)*

CHARLES F. DAY & ASSOCIATES, INC.

700 North Carry St, Davenport, IA 52803
Tel.: (563) 324-1670
Web Site: http://www.cfday.net
Year Founded: 1999
Sales Range: $1-9.9 Million
Emp.: 85
Department of Defense Management Consulting Services
N.A.I.C.S.: 541611
Charles F. Day *(Pres & CEO)*
Theresa Day *(Co-Owner)*

CHARLES F. SHIELS & CO. INC.

1301 W 8th St, Cincinnati, OH 45203
Tel.: (513) 241-0239
Web Site:
https://www.shielslumber.com
Sales Range: $10-24.9 Million
Emp.: 50
Rough, Dressed & Finished Lumber
N.A.I.C.S.: 423310
Marc Shiels *(Pres)*

CHARLES F. VATTEROTT & CO.

10449 St Charles Rock Rd, Saint Ann, MO 63074
Tel.: (314) 427-4000
Web Site: http://www.vatterott.com
Sales Range: $50-74.9 Million
Emp.: 125
General Contractor of Single Family Houses; Provider of Real Estate & Property Management Services
N.A.I.C.S.: 423310
Gregory B. Vatterott *(Pres)*

CHARLES G. ALLEN CO.

25 Williamsville Rd, Barre, MA 01005-9502
Tel.: (978) 355-2911
Web Site:
https://www.chasgallen.com
Year Founded: 1874
Sales Range: $10-24.9 Million
Emp.: 30
Machine Tool Builder
N.A.I.C.S.: 333517
David Krupp *(Co-Owner)*

CHARLES G. LAWSON TRUCKING

7815 Mobile Hwy, Hope Hull, AL 36043
Tel.: (334) 284-3220
Sales Range: $10-24.9 Million
Emp.: 113
Refrigerated Products Transport
N.A.I.C.S.: 484230

CHARLES GABUS FORD, INC.

4545 Merle Hay Rd, Des Moines, IA 50310
Tel.: (515) 270-0707
Web Site: http://www.gabusford.com
Year Founded: 1968
Sales Range: $75-99.9 Million
Emp.: 180
New Car Retailer
N.A.I.C.S.: 441110
Dee Kading *(Pres & CEO)*
Nathan Bailey *(Mgr-Rental)*
Gary McKinney *(Mgr-Fin)*
Steve Sanders *(Mgr-Internet)*
Kenny Smith *(Mgr-Parts)*
Denny Anderson *(Mgr-Body Shop)*
Brenda Bracewell *(Mgr-Fin)*
Jamie Cleghorn *(Mgr-Inventory)*
Sean Sellers *(Gen Mgr)*

CHARLES GROUP HOTELS, INC.

4333 Collins Ave, Miami Beach, FL 33140
Tel.: (305) 532-3311
Web Site:
http://www.charlesgrouphotels.net
Sales Range: $25-49.9 Million
Emp.: 500
Managers of Resort Hotels
N.A.I.C.S.: 721110
Sharone Tzalik *(Dir-Ops)*
Fausto Vargas *(Mgr-Pur)*
Raul Gonzalez *(Controller)*
Concha Perdomo *(Mgr-Tour & Travel)*
Myra Roman *(Mgr-Tour & Travel)*

CHARLES H. WILSON CONSTRUCTION COMPANY

8221 Blaikie Ct, Sarasota, FL 34240
Tel.: (941) 957-1030
Web Site: http://www.chwcc.com
Year Founded: 1984
Sales Range: $1-9.9 Million
Emp.: 3
Construction Services
N.A.I.C.S.: 236220
Charles H. Wilson *(Owner & Pres)*

CHARLES KOMAR & SONS, INC.

16 E 34th St 10th Fl, New York, NY 10016-4328
Tel.: (212) 725-1500
Year Founded: 1908
Sales Range: $200-249.9 Million
Emp.: 900
Mfr of Women's Lingerie & Casual Wear
N.A.I.C.S.: 315250
Charles E. Komar *(Pres & CEO)*
David L. Komar *(Exec VP)*
Kathy Poe *(Dir-Sls & Mktg)*

Subsidiaries:

Renee Claire, Bedhead Pajamas, Inc.   **(1)**
8336 W 3rd St, Los Angeles, CA 90048-4311
Tel.: (323) 653-8336
Web Site: http://www.bedheadpjs.com
Family Clothing Stores
N.A.I.C.S.: 458110

CHARLES L. CRANE AGENCY

100 N Broadway Ste 900, Saint Louis, MO 63102
Tel.: (314) 241-8700
Web Site:
https://www.craneagency.com
Rev.: $11,600,000
Emp.: 200
Insurance Agents, Brokers & Service
N.A.I.C.S.: 524210
Michael T. Reedy *(Pres)*
Rick Werts *(COO)*

CHARLES LEONARD INC.

145 Kennedy Dr, Hauppauge, NY 11788
Tel.: (631) 273-6700
Web Site:
https://www.charlesleonard.com
Year Founded: 1946
Sales Range: $75-99.9 Million
Emp.: 25
School & Office Supplies Distr
N.A.I.C.S.: 424120
David J. Hirsch *(Pres & CEO)*
Martin Piller *(VP-Mktg)*

Subsidiaries:

Charles Leonard Inc., Inc.   **(1)**
145 Kennedy Dr, Hauppauge, NY 11788
Tel.: (631) 273-4600
Web Site: http://www.clnational.com
Sales Range: $10-24.9 Million
Loose Leaf Hardware & Other Bindery Components Mfr & Distr
N.A.I.C.S.: 332510
David J. Hirsch *(Owner)*

Subsidiary (Domestic):

Charles Leonard (Western), Inc.   **(2)**
235 W 140th St, Los Angeles, CA 90061-2128
Tel.: (310) 715-7464
Web Site: http://www.clnational.com
Sales Range: $1-9.9 Million
Loose Leaf Hardware & Other Bindery Components
N.A.I.C.S.: 332510
Ken Sherman *(Pres)*
Tip Morris *(Mgr-Sls)*

CHARLES MCMURRAY COMPANY

2520 N Argyle Ave, Fresno, CA
93727-1302
Tel.: (559) 292-5751   CA
Web Site:
https://www.charlesmcmurray.com
Year Founded: 1946
Sales Range: $10-24.9 Million
Emp.: 100
Wholesale Distributor of Household
Hardware Products
N.A.I.C.S.: 423710
Louis C. McMurray (Chm & Pres)

CHARLES N. WHITE CONSTRUCTION CO. INC.

613 Crescent Cir Ste 100, Ridgeland,
MS 39157
Tel.: (601) 898-5180   MS
Web Site:
https://www.whiteconst.com
Year Founded: 1968
Sales Range: $125-149.9 Million
Emp.: 200
Nonresidential Construction
N.A.I.C.S.: 236220
Guy White (Pres)
Bob Higgins (Sr VP)
John Brattlof (Dir-Corp Safety)
Tracy B. Bailey (Dir-Preconstruction
Svcs)
Dave Brunner (Superintendent)

CHARLES NAVASKY & COMPANY

300 Shadylane Dr, Philipsburg, PA
16866
Tel.: (814) 342-1160
Web Site:
http://www.falconesuits.com
Sales Range: $75-99.9 Million
Emp.: 100
Mfr of Men's & Boys' Suits
N.A.I.C.S.: 488510
Edward Navasky (Pres)

Subsidiaries:

Don Mart Clothes Inc.   (1)
300 Shady Ln, Philipsburg, PA
16866   (100%)
Tel.: (814) 342-1160
Rev.: $15,243,120
Emp.: 50
Men's & Boys Clothing
N.A.I.C.S.: 424350

CHARLES P. BLOUIN, INC.

203 New Zealand Rd, Seabrook, NH
03874
Tel.: (603) 474-3400
Web Site: https://cpblouin.com
Rev.: $18,200,000
Emp.: 70
Warm Air Heating & Air Conditioning
Contractor
N.A.I.C.S.: 238220
Joseph F. Cullin II (Pres)

CHARLES PANKOW BUILDERS, LTD.

3280 E Foothill Blvd Ste 100, Pasadena, CA 91107
Tel.: (626) 791-1125   CA
Web Site: http://www.pankow.com
Year Founded: 1963
Sales Range: $10-24.9 Million
Emp.: 130
New Construction of Commercial &
Office Buildings & Multi-Family Dwellings, Retail & Packaging Structures,
Hotel, Rentals & Condos, High Tech,
Health Care, Packing Structures &
Sports Facilities
N.A.I.C.S.: 236220
Dave Eichten (Reg Mgr)

CHARLES PENZONE INC.

1480 Manning Pkwy, Powell, OH
43065
Tel.: (614) 898-1160
Web Site:
http://www.charlespenzone.com
Sales Range: $10-24.9 Million
Emp.: 400
Hairdressers
N.A.I.C.S.: 812112
Beth Rupp (Dir-Hair)
Carol Beck (Sr Dir)
Colleen Petersen (Mgr-HR)
Irene McGarvey (Dir-Salon Support &
Tech Trng)
Joann Berry (Sr Dir)
Kyong Pilkington (Sr Dir)
Ryan Harsh (Mgr-Property)
Jessica Smith (Dir-Salon)

CHARLES PERRY PARTNERS, INC.

8200 NW 15th Pl, Gainesville, FL
32606
Tel.: (352) 333-9292
Web Site: http://www.cppi.com
Year Founded: 1968
Sales Range: $100-124.9 Million
Emp.: 140
General Contractor, Construction
Management & Design Building Services
N.A.I.C.S.: 236220
Kateara Stoner (Mgr-HR)
Breck A. Weingart (Pres & CEO)
Brian K. Leslie (Exec VP)
Jordan Aza (Superintendent)
Lovita Persaud (Project Coord-
Orlando)
Randy Fitkin (VP & Mgr-Tampa Bay)
Jody Fitzgerald (Superintendent)
William Cocca (Project Engr-Tampa)
Michael Hudgins (Superintendent)
Richard McSwain (Superintendent)
Mike Hatcher (Superintendent)
Frank Hughes (Superintendent)
Olivia Frick (Mgr-Bus Dev-North
Florida & Southeast Georgia)
Teri Tipton (Sr Project Mgr-
Healthcare)

CHARLES R. EVANS OIL CO. INC.

605 Live Oak St, Marlin, TX 76661
Tel.: (254) 883-3593
Sales Range: $10-24.9 Million
Emp.: 12
Petroleum Products
N.A.I.C.S.: 424720
Charles R. Evans (Pres)

CHARLES R. WOOD OIL CO. INC.

4701 Brewer Pl, Leavenworth, KS
66048-5073
Tel.: (913) 727-1163   KS
Year Founded: 1957
Sales Range: $1-9.9 Million
Emp.: 40
Gasoline Service Stations Owner &
Operator
N.A.I.C.S.: 457120
Charles M. Wood (Pres)

CHARLES RIVER ASSOCIATION FOR RETARDED CITIZENS INC.

59 E Militia Heights Rd, Needham,
MA 02492
Tel.: (781) 972-1000   MA
Web Site:
http://www.charlesrivercenter.org
Year Founded: 1964
Sales Range: $10-24.9 Million
Emp.: 704

Developmental Disability Assistance
Services
N.A.I.C.S.: 623210
Anne-Marie Bajwa (Pres & CEO)
William Day (Sec)
Alice Taylor (Vice Chm)
Kevin Kacavich (VP-Human Resources)
Hilary Ryan (VP-Development)
Gilbert W. Cox Jr. (Treas)

CHARLES RIVER VENTURES

568 Brannan St, San Francisco, CA
94107
Tel.: (415) 960-3000
Web Site: http://www.crv.com
Emp.: 20
Privater Equity Firm
N.A.I.C.S.: 523999
Bruce I. Sachs (Gen Partner)
Sachin Sood (CFO)

CHARLES ROSS & SON COMPANY

710 Old Willets Path, Hauppauge, NY
11788
Tel.: (631) 234-0500
Web Site: http://www.mixers.com
Rev.: $15,800,000
Emp.: 60
Industrial Mixers, Blenders, Dryers &
Dispersion Equipment Mfr
N.A.I.C.S.: 333248
Richard Ross (Owner)
Chris Ross (VP-Sls)
Bogard Lagman (Exec VP)
Tom O'Shaughnessy (Reg Mgr-Sls)
Desmond Allen (Engr-Mechanical)
Ed Urevich (Mgr-Engrg)
Rick OBoyle (Reg Mgr-Sls)
Joseph Martorana (Exec VP)

CHARLES RUTENBERG REALTY, INC.

1545 S Belcher Rd, Clearwater, FL
33764-7681
Tel.: (727) 538-9200
Web Site: https://www.gocrr.com
Year Founded: 2000
Real Estate Brokerage Services
N.A.I.C.S.: 531210
John Nestor (Founder)

CHARLES RUTENBERG REALTY, INC.

255 Executive Plz Ste 208, Plainview,
NY 11803
Tel.: (516) 575-7500
Web Site: https://www.crrli.com
Sales Range: $50-74.9 Million
Emp.: 900
Real Estate Broker
N.A.I.C.S.: 531210
Joe Moshe (Owner)
Fernando Branco (VP-Realtor NY &
CT)
Robert Bernstein (VP)

CHARLES RYAN ASSOCIATES INC.

300 Summers St Ste 1100, Charleston, WV 25301-1631
Tel.: (304) 342-0161   WV
Web Site:
http://www.charlesryan.com
Year Founded: 1974
Rev.: $30,000,000
Emp.: 40
Advetising Agency
N.A.I.C.S.: 541810
Rick Mogielski (Dir-Creative & VP)
Susan Lavenski (Mng Dir)
Thomas Winner (VP-Pub Affairs)
Michelle Merritt (Dir-Media)
Alicia Maddox (Sr Acct Exec)
Jennifer Vieweg (VP)

Linda Cook (Dir-Production)
Matt Isner (VP)
Kyra Richards (Acct Exec)
Matt McCloud (Acct Coord)

Subsidiaries:

Charles Ryan Associates   (1)
1813 E Broad St, Richmond, VA 23223
Tel.: (804) 643-3820
Web Site: http://www.charlesryan.com
Sales Range: Less than $1 Million
Emp.: 7
N.A.I.C.S.: 541810
Matt Fidler (VP & Dir-Creative)
Caryn Foster Durham (Mng Dir)

Charles Ryan Associates   (1)
150 Clay St Ste 410, Morgantown, WV
26501-5942
Tel.: (304) 549-5092
Web Site: http://www.charlesryan.com
N.A.I.C.S.: 541810

CHARLES SADEK IMPORT COMPANY INC.

125 Beechwood Ave, New Rochelle,
NY 10801
Tel.: (914) 633-8090
Web Site: http://www.sadek.com
Year Founded: 1936
Sales Range: $10-24.9 Million
Emp.: 75
Importer & Wholesaler of Gifts &
Novelties
N.A.I.C.S.: 424990
Norman W. Sadek (Chm)
Jim Sadek (Pres)
Andrea Sadek (VP)
Lauren Sadek (VP)

CHARLES SAMELSON, INC.

102 Madison Ave Fl 6, New York, NY
10016
Tel.: (212) 686-6829
Web Site: http://www.csamelson.com
Sales Range: $10-24.9 Million
Emp.: 25
Broadwoven Fabrics
N.A.I.C.S.: 424310
Mark Patel (Pres)
Winston Pottinger (Mgr-Custom Solutions)

CHARLES SARGENT IRRIGATION

South Hwy 21, Broken Bow, NE
68822
Tel.: (308) 872-2272
Web Site:
http://www.sargentirrigation.com
Sales Range: $10-24.9 Million
Emp.: 176
Water Well Drilling
N.A.I.C.S.: 237110
Michael L. Whitesel (Pres)

CHARLES SCATURRO & SONS INC.

25801 Hillside Ave, Floral Park, NY
11004
Tel.: (718) 347-1101
Sales Range: $10-24.9 Million
Emp.: 60
Grocery Stores
N.A.I.C.S.: 445110
Charles Scaturro (Pres)

CHARLES SELIGMAN DISTRIBUTING CO.

10885 Clydesdale Ct, Walton, KY
41094-8386
Tel.: (859) 344-1881
Web Site:
https://www.chasseligman.com
Sales Range: $25-49.9 Million
Emp.: 100

Charles Seligman Distributing Co.—(Continued)

Distr of Beer & Other Fermented Malt Liquors
N.A.I.C.S.: 424810
Ruth Doering (Owner, Pres & CEO)
Rick Ludeke (Controller)
Jennifer Doering (Exec VP & Gen Mgr)

CHARLES TOMBRAS ADVERTISING, INC.
620 S Gay St, Knoxville, TN 37902
Tel.: (865) 524-5376   **TN**
Web Site: http://www.tombras.com
Year Founded: 1946
Sales Range: $75-99.9 Million
Emp.: 79
Advertising Agency Services
N.A.I.C.S.: 541810
John Welsch (Sr VP-Bus Dev)
David Jacobs (Sr VP & Dir-Innovation & Strategy)
Laura Bower (VP & Dir-PR & Social Media)
Nicki Collett (Mgr-Production)
Keith Thomason (Dir-Art)
Jonathan Gardner (Dir-Technical)
Tommy Keeler (Acct Exec)
Cameron Gull (Dir-Technical)
Rad Davenport (Mgr-Pay Per Click)
Al Moffat (Sr VP-Special Projects)
Jeff Benjamin (Chief Creative Officer)
Charles P. Tombras Jr. (CEO)

Subsidiaries:

DS Tombras   (1)
4017 Hillsboro Pike Ste 408, Nashville, TN 37215
Tel.: (615) 321-0080
Sales Range: $10-24.9 Million
Emp.: 10
N.A.I.C.S.: 541810

CHARLESBANK CAPITAL PARTNERS, LLC
200 Clarendon St 54th Fl, Boston, MA 02116
Tel.: (617) 619-5400   **MA**
Web Site:
    http://www.charlesbank.com
Year Founded: 1998
Rev.: $5,000,000,000
Privater Equity Firm
N.A.I.C.S.: 523999
Michael Thonis (Founder)
Maura M. Turner (VP-Mktg & Comm)
Michael Richard Eisenson (Founding Partner & Mng Dir)
Michael W. Choe (CEO & Mng Dir)
Kim G. Davis (Mng Dir & Founding Partner)
Samuel P. Bartlett (Mng Dir)
Brandon C. White (Mng Dir)
Shira D. Goodman (Dir-Advisory)
Joshua A. Klevens (Mng Dir)
Josh Beer (Mng Dir)
J. Ryan Carroll (Mng Dir)
John Fiyod (CFO)
Stephanie Pare Sullivan (Mng Dir, COO & Chief Compliance Officer)
Hiren Mankodi (Mng Dir)
Camille DeLaite (Operating Partner-Talent)
Darren Battistoni (Mng Dir)
Maggie Littlefield Sahlman (Head-IR)
Hoon Cho (Mng Dir)
Jeff Sheu (Mng Dir)
Jerome McCluskey (Mng Dir & Gen Counsel)
Bert Duarte (Mng Dir)

Subsidiaries:

Aurora Organic Dairy
Corporation   (1)
1919 14th St Ste 300, Boulder, CO 80302
Tel.: (720) 564-6296

Web Site: http://www.auroraorganic.com
Sales Range: $50-74.9 Million
Producer & Processor of Organic Milk & Butter
N.A.I.C.S.: 311511
Marc Peperzak (Founder & Chm)
Scott McGinty (CEO)
John Beutler (VP-Plant Ops)
Cammie Muller (CFO)
Gary Sebek (COO)
Jason Lee (Chief Customer Officer)
Juan Velez (Chief Agricultural Officer)

Bridgepointe Technologies, Inc   (1)
999 Baker Wy ste 310, San Mateo, CA 94404
Tel.: (833) 240-2783
Web Site:
    https://bridgepointetechnologies.com
Emp.: 100
IT Services
N.A.I.C.S.: 519290
Scott Evars (Founder)
Charlie Bogart (Mng Dir)
Dan Fishman (Partner)
Dom Callandriello (Mng Partner-East)

Subsidiary (Domestic):

Cannon Group Enterprises, LLC   (2)
960 Harvest Dr, Blue Bell, PA 19422-1900
Tel.: (610) 930-1000
Web Site: http://www.cannongroupinc.com
Management Consulting Services
N.A.I.C.S.: 541618
Perry Cozzone (Pres)

Realcom Solutions   (2)
5 Cowboys Way Ste 300, Frisco, TX 75034
Tel.: (972) 220-0140
Web Site: http://www.realcomsolutions.com
Telecommunications
N.A.I.C.S.: 517810
Jeremy Kerth (Mgr)

CB Neptune Holdings, LLC   (1)
1185 Avenue of the Americas 27th Fl, New York, NY 10036
Tel.: (212) 782-8000
Web Site:
    https://www.neptuneretailsolutions.com
Marketing Services
N.A.I.C.S.: 541613
Heidi Gray (Chief HR Officer)
Nataraj Iyer (Sr VP & Gen Mgr-At-Home Bus)

Subsidiary (Domestic):

HarperCollins Publishers L.L.C.   (2)
195 Broadway, New York, NY 10007   **(100%)**
Tel.: (212) 207-7000
Web Site: https://www.harpercollins.com
Emp.: 900
General Trade & Children's Book Publisher
N.A.I.C.S.: 513130
Erin Crum (Sr VP-Corp Comm)
Janet Gervasio (CFO & Sr VP)
Brian Murray (Pres & CEO)
Chantal Restivo-Alessi (Chief Digital Officer & Exec VP-Intl)
Gisselda Nunez (VP-Diversity, Equity & Inclusion)

Subsidiary (Non-US):

Casa dos Livros Editora Ltda.   (3)
Rua Capitao Otavio Machado 259 Chacara Santo Antonio, Sao Paulo, 04718-000, Brazil
Tel.: (55) 1151854227
Web Site: http://www.casadelivros.com.br
Library Services
N.A.I.C.S.: 519210

Egmont UK Ltd.   (3)
First Floor The Yellow Building 1 Nicholas Road, London, W11 4AN, United Kingdom
Tel.: (44) 203 220 0400
Web Site: http://www.egmont.co.uk
Emp.: 200
Newspaper & Magazine Publisher
N.A.I.C.S.: 513120
Cally Poplak (Co-Mng Dir-Egmont Publ)
Alan Hurcombe (CFO)
Hilary Murray-Hill (Co-Mng Dir-Books)
Gillian Laskier (Co-Mng Dir-Magazines)
Alison David (Dir-Consumer Insight)
Claire Naddeo (Dir-HR)
Alison Kennedy (Dir-Prodution & Distr)

Harlequin Enterprises Limited   (3)
Bay Adelaide Centre East Tower 22 Adelaide Street West 41St Floor, Toronto, M5H 4E3, ON, Canada
Tel.: (416) 445-5860
Web Site: http://www.harlequin.com
Sales Range: $450-499.9 Million
Emp.: 350
Book Publishers
N.A.I.C.S.: 513130
Loriana Sacilotto (Exec VP-Global Publ & Strategy)
Craig Swinwood (CEO & Publr)
Christine Greco (VP-HR)
Brent Lewis (Exec VP-Mktg & Digital-North America)
John Reindl (VP-Ops)
Kirk Marshall (CFO)
Margaret Morrison (CIO & VP)
Shari Hosaki (Gen Counsel, Sec & VP)

Subsidiary (Non-US):

Cora Verlag GmbH & Co. KG   (4)
Valentinskamp 24, 20354, Hamburg, Germany
Tel.: (49) 40 63 66 420 0
Web Site: http://www.cora.de
Sales Range: $25-49.9 Million
Emp.: 30
Book Publishers
N.A.I.C.S.: 513130
Thomas Beckmann (Mng Dir)

Harlequin (UK) Limted   (4)
1 London Bridge Street, Bishopbriggs, London, SE1 9GF, United Kingdom   **(100%)**
Tel.: (44) 8448441351
Web Site: http://www.millsandboon.co.uk
Sales Range: $25-49.9 Million
Emp.: 100
Book Publishers
N.A.I.C.S.: 513130
Mandy Ferguson (Mng Dir)

Subsidiary (US):

Harlequin Magazines Inc   (4)
233 Bdwy Rm 1001 10th Fl, New York, NY 10279-0001
Tel.: (212) 553-4200
Sales Range: $25-49.9 Million
Emp.: 50
Book Publishers
N.A.I.C.S.: 513130
Lorianna Sacilotto (Exec VP-Global Publishing & Strategy)

Group (Domestic):

HarperCollins Children's Books Group - U.S.   (3)
195 Broadway, New York, NY 10007
Tel.: (212) 207-7000
Web Site: http://www.harpercollins.com
Sales Range: $300-349.9 Million
Emp.: 900
Children Book Publishing Services
N.A.I.C.S.: 513130
Karen Chaplin (Sr Editor)
Alison Klapthor (Art Dir)
Erin Fitzsimmons (Art Dir)
Claudia Gabel (Dir-Editorial)
Tamar Mays (Exec Editor)
Kim Silverton (Asst Mgr-Sls Forecasting & Analysis)
Mabel Hsu (Asst Editor)
Elizabeth Lynch (Asst Editor)
Suzanne Murphy (Pres & Publr)

HarperCollins General Books Group - U.S.   (3)
195 broadway, New York, NY 10007
Tel.: (212) 207-7000
Web Site: http://www.harpercollins.com
Sales Range: $450-499.9 Million
Publishing Books & Magazines
N.A.I.C.S.: 513130
Michael Morrison (Pres)

Unit (Domestic):

HarperOne   (4)
353 Sacramento St Ste 500, San Francisco, CA 94111-3653
Tel.: (415) 477-4400
Web Site: http://www.harpercollins.com
Sales Range: $100-124.9 Million
Book Publishers
N.A.I.C.S.: 513130

Judith Curr (Pres & Publr)
Anna Paustenbach (Assoc Editor)
Hilary Swanson (Editor)
Gideon Weil (VP, Gen Mgr & Dir-Editorial)
Kathryn Renz Hamilton (Sr Editor)
Laina Adler (Assoc Publr & VP)
Michael Maudlin (Sr VP & Exec Editor)
Miles Doyle (Sr Editor)
Shannon Welch (Exec Editor)
Sydney Rogers (Assoc Editor)

Subsidiary (Non-US):

HarperCollins Italia S.p.A   (3)
Viale Monte Nero 84, 20135, Milan, Italy
Tel.: (39) 0228038645
Web Site: https://www.harpercollins.it
Book Publishers
N.A.I.C.S.: 513130

Subsidiary (Domestic):

The Zondervan Corporation   (3)
5300 Patterson SE, Grand Rapids, MI 49530-0001   **(100%)**
Tel.: (616) 698-6900
Web Site: http://www.zondervan.com
Rev.: $106,000,000
Emp.: 500
Publisher & Distr of Religious Books & Music, Children & Adult Publications & Gifts
N.A.I.C.S.: 513130
Stanley N. Gundry (Editor-in-Chief)
Al Kerkstra (Sr VP-Support Ops & HR)
Casey Harrell (Sr Dir-Corp Comm)

Thomas Nelson, Inc.   (3)
501 Nelson Pl, Nashville, TN 37214
Tel.: (615) 889-9000
Web Site: http://www.thomasnelson.com
Sales Range: $200-249.9 Million
Emp.: 450
Bible & Religious Book Publisher
N.A.I.C.S.: 513130
Allison Carter (Mgr-Publicity)
Amanda Bostic (Publr)
Becky Monds (Dir-Editorial)
Kerri Potts (Mgr-Mktg)
Jocelyn Bailey (Editor-Acquisitions)
Jodi Hughes (Editor)
Kimberly Carlton (Assoc Editor-Acquisitions)
Laura Wheeler (Assoc Editor)
Paul Fisher (Sr Dir-Mktg)

Subsidiary (Domestic):

Grupo Nelson   (4)
501 Nelson Pl, Nashville, TN 37214
Tel.: (615) 889-9000
Web Site: http://www.gruponelson.com
Spanish Language Religious Books Publisher
N.A.I.C.S.: 513130
Mark Schoenwald (CEO)

Subsidiary (Domestic):

News America Marketing FSI L.L.C.   (2)
1 Ppg Pl Ste 3030, Pittsburgh, PA 15222-5419
Tel.: (412) 918-8000
Web Site:
    http://www.newsamericamarketing.com
Television Broadcasting Services
N.A.I.C.S.: 516120

News America Marketing In-Store Services L.L.C.   (2)
20 Westport Rd, Wilton, CT 06897-4550
Tel.: (203) 563-6600
Web Site: http://www.newsamerica.com
Advertising & Marketing Services
N.A.I.C.S.: 541890

News America Marketing Interactive L.L.C.   (2)
1211 6th Ave, New York, NY 10036-8701
Tel.: (212) 782-8000
Advertising Material Distr
N.A.I.C.S.: 541890
Hayley Cave (Acct Coord)
Nancy Perkins (Sr VP-Sls)
Gavin O'Day (VP & Mgr-Grp Sls)

News America Marketing Properties L.L.C.   (2)
303 E Wacker Dr, Chicago, IL 60601
Tel.: (203) 563-6757
Television Broadcasting Services

N.A.I.C.S.: 516120
Rob Augustinos *(Exec VP-Sls-Central)*

Quotient Technology Inc. (2)
1260 E Stringham Ave 6th Fl, Salt Lake City, UT 84106
Tel.: (650) 605-4600
Web Site: https://www.quotient.com
Rev.: $288,766,000
Assets: $363,159,000
Liabilities: $185,364,000
Net Worth: $177,795,000
Earnings: ($76,511,000)
Emp.: 880
Fiscal Year-end: 12/31/2022
Digital Promotions & Media Solutions
N.A.I.C.S.: 541890
Connie Chen *(Officer-Compliance, Gen Counsel & Sec)*
Renee Cutright *(Chief People Officer)*
Allison Metcalfe *(Chief Revenue Officer)*
Jeff Williams *(Chief Retail Officer)*

Subsidiary (Domestic):

Coupons, Inc. (3)
400 Logue Ave, Mountain View, CA 94043
Tel.: (650) 605-4600
Advertising Material Distribution Services
N.A.I.C.S.: 541870

Subsidiary (Non-US):

Coupons.com Limited (3)
2nd floor Landmark House Hammersmith Bridge Road, London, W6 9DP, United Kingdom
Tel.: (44) 2088651972
Advertising Material Distribution Services
N.A.I.C.S.: 541870

Subsidiary (Domestic):

Crisp Media Inc.
263 W 38th St 9th Fl, New York, NY 10018
Tel.: (212) 557-1850
Mobile Applications & Marketing
N.A.I.C.S.: 513210

Subsidiary (Non-US):

Elevaate Limited (3)
The Hub, Stamford, PE9 2BW, United Kingdom
Tel.: (44) 1780407521
Web Site: http://www.elevaate.com
Web Retailer Services
N.A.I.C.S.: 541611

Subsidiary (Domestic):

The New York Post (2)
1211 Ave of the Americas, New York, NY 10036-8701
Tel.: (212) 930-8000
Web Site: http://www.nypost.com
Sales Range: $300-349.9 Million
Emp.: 1,000
Newspaper Publishing
N.A.I.C.S.: 513110
Stephen Lynch *(Editor-in-Chief)*

CB-HDT Holdings Inc. (1)
30500 Aurora Rd Ste 100, Solon, OH 44139
Tel.: (216) 438-6111
Web Site: http://www.hdtglobal.com
Rugged & Transportable Mobile Enclosures Mfr
N.A.I.C.S.: 336992
David Yu *(Exec VP)*
Joshua A. Klevens *(Mng Dir)*

Subsidiary (Domestic):

DRS Environmental Systems, Inc. (2)
7375 Industrial Rd, Florence, KY 41042-2911
Tel.: (859) 525-2102
Web Site: http://www.hdtglobal.com
Military Equipment Mfr
N.A.I.C.S.: 333248

Federal Fabrics-Fibers Inc. (2)
45 W Adams St, Lowell, MA 01851
Tel.: (978) 441-3037
Web Site: http://www.federalfabrics.com
Rev.: $2,400,000
Emp.: 20
Research & Development in Biotechnology

N.A.I.C.S.: 541714
Bracha Horovitz *(Pres & CEO)*
David Retter *(Dir-Sls & Mktg)*
Fred Geurts *(Dir-Res)*
John Dolan *(CFO)*
Michael Hainsworth *(Gen Mgr)*

Charlesbank Capital Partners, LLC - New York Office (1)
70 E 55th St 20th Fl, New York, NY 10022
Tel.: (212) 903-1880
Web Site: http://www.charlesbank.com
Emp.: 10
Privater Equity Firm
N.A.I.C.S.: 523999
Kim G. Davis *(Co-Chm & Mng Dir)*
Karen S. Meister *(Office Mgr)*
Jason W. Pike *(Mng Dir)*
Scott Entwistle *(VP-IT)*
John K. Fiyod *(CFO)*
Dzovig Zoe Gharibian *(Dir-Treasury)*
David K. Kwan *(VP-Acctg)*
Maura M. Turner *(VP-Comm & IR)*

City Brewing Company, LLC (1)
925 S 3rd St, La Crosse, WI 54601
Tel.: (608) 785-4200
Web Site: http://www.citybrewery.com
Rev.: $34,000,000
Emp.: 1,000
Breweries
N.A.I.C.S.: 312120
Randy Hull *(VP-Sls & Bus Dev)*
Connie Michaels *(VP-HR)*
Ross Sannes *(CEO)*
Ryan Nelson *(Exec VP)*
Dave Poremba *(CFO)*
Hans Savonije *(Chm)*

DEI Holdings, Inc. (1)
1 Viper Way Ste C, Vista, CA 92081-7853
Tel.: (760) 598-6200
Web Site: http://www.deiholdings.com
Sales Range: $250-299.9 Million
Home Theater Speakers, Automobile Audio & Video Equipment, Vehicle Security Systems, Remote Starters & Satellite Radio Receivers Mfr & Distr
N.A.I.C.S.: 334310

Division (Domestic):

DEI Holdings, Inc. - Directed Division (2)
1 Viper Way, Vista, CA 92081
Tel.: (800) 876-0800
Web Site: http://www.directed.com
Vehicle Security Product Mfr
N.A.I.C.S.: 334290
Glenn R. Busse *(Sr VP-Global Sls)*
Michael Smith *(Sr VP-Global Ops)*
Robert J. Struble *(CEO)*

DEI Holdings, Inc. - Sound United Division (2)
1 Viper Way, Vista, CA 92081
Tel.: (760) 598-6200
Web Site: http://www.soundunited.com
Audio Device Distr
N.A.I.C.S.: 423990
James E. Minarik *(Chm & CEO)*
Kevin P. Duffy *(Pres)*
Blair Tripodi *(Pres-Intl)*
Joe Tristani *(COO)*
Michael Smith *(Sr VP-Global Ops)*
Scott Hagen *(Chief Sls Officer)*
Gary Fletcher *(VP-Global Sourcing)*
Michael Ditullo *(Chief Design Officer)*
Matthew Lyons *(Sr VP-New Product Dev)*
Arturas Rainys *(VP-Corp Dev)*

Subsidiary (Domestic):

Definitive Technology, Inc. (2)
11433 Cronridge Dr Ste K, Owings Mills, MD 21117-2294
Tel.: (410) 363-7148
Web Site: http://www.definitivetech.com
Loudspeaker Mfr
N.A.I.C.S.: 334310

Subsidiary (Non-US):

Directed Electronics Canada, Inc. (2)
2750 Alphonse Gariepy, Lachine, H8T 3M2, QC, Canada
Tel.: (450) 635-7777
Web Site: http://www.directed.ca

Sales Range: $25-49.9 Million
Home & Mobile Electronics Marketing & Distr
N.A.I.C.S.: 423620

Subsidiary (Domestic):

Polk Audio, Inc. (2)
5601 Metro Dr, Baltimore, MD 21215
Tel.: (410) 358-3600
Web Site: http://www.polkaudio.com
Sales Range: $25-49.9 Million
Designer of Home & Mobile Audio Equipment Mfr
N.A.I.C.S.: 334310
Al Baron *(Mgr-Audio Line)*
Joe Phelps *(Dir-Sls-Personal Audio)*

Empire Today, LLC (1)
333 NW Ave, Northlake, IL 60164
Tel.: (773) 588-2300
Web Site: http://www.empiretoday.com
Floor Covering & Window Treatment Provider
N.A.I.C.S.: 449121
Thomas Knapp *(CFO)*
Paul Connolly *(CIO)*
Hillary Victor *(Gen Counsel & Sr VP)*
Keith Weinberger *(CEO)*
Paul W. Carter *(Chief Procurement Officer)*

FULLBEAUTY Brands, Inc. (1)
1 New York Plz, New York, NY 10004
Tel.: (212) 613-9500
Web Site: http://www.fbbrands.com
Men & Women Plus-sized Clothing Mfr
N.A.I.C.S.: 458110
Flo Kamil Dessen *(Sr VP & Gen Mgr-Fullbeauty.com)*
David Reinke *(Sr VP & Gen Mgr)*
Emilie Arel *(CEO)*

Subsidiary (Domestic):

FULLBEAUTY Brands, L.P. (2)
2300 Southeastern Ave, Indianapolis, IN 46201
Tel.: (317) 266-3300
Web Site: http://www.fbbrands.com
Women's & Men's Special-Size Apparel Retailer
N.A.I.C.S.: 458110

OSP Group Management Services, L.P. (2)
2300 Southeastern Ave, Indianapolis, IN 46201
Tel.: (317) 266-3300
Mail Ordering Shopping Services
N.A.I.C.S.: 523940

Fullbeauty.com (1)
1 New York Plz, New York, NY 10004
Web Site: http://www.fullbeauty.com
Online Apparel Retailer
N.A.I.C.S.: 458110

Galls, LLC (1)
1340 Russell Cave Rd, Lexington, KY 40505
Tel.: (859) 266-7227
Web Site: http://www.galls.com
Safety Equipment & Apparel
N.A.I.C.S.: 313310
Douglas Means *(COO)*
Mike Fadden *(CEO)*

Subsidiary (Domestic):

Best Uniforms, LLC (2)
2716 Exchange Dr, Wilmington, NC 28405
Tel.: (910) 791-6050
Web Site: http://www.galls.com
Uniforms Dist & Safety Personnel Accessories
N.A.I.C.S.: 458110

QuarterMaster, LLC (2)
PO Box 4147, Cerritos, CA 90703
Tel.: (562) 304-7301
Web Site: http://www.qmuniforms.com
Mail-Order Sales
N.A.I.C.S.: 458110

Uniforms Unlimited, Inc. (2)
2220 Lyndale Ave S, Minneapolis, MN 55405
Tel.: (612) 377-0011
Web Site: http://www.galls.com
Clothing Stores
N.A.I.C.S.: 458110

Hearthside Food Solutions, LLC (1)
3333 Finley Rd Ste 800, Downers Grove, IL 60515
Tel.: (630) 967-3600
Web Site: https://www.hearthsidefoods.com
Sales Range: Less than $1 Million
Emp.: 13,000
All Other Miscellaneous Food Manufacturing
N.A.I.C.S.: 311999
Richard G. Scalise *(Founder & Chm)*
Steve England *(Sr VP-HR)*
Chuck Metzger *(CEO)*
Fred Jasser *(CFO & Sr VP-Fin)*
Darlene Nicosia *(CEO)*

Subsidiary (Domestic):

Greencore USA - CPG Partners, LLC (2)
1800 Averill Rd, Geneva, IL 60134
Tel.: (630) 845-9400
Web Site: http://www.hearthsidefoods.com
Integrated Food Packaging & Logistics Services
N.A.I.C.S.: 561910

Plant (Domestic):

Hearthside Food Solutions, LLC - Gibson City (2)
310 W 10th St, Gibson City, IL 60936-1327
Tel.: (217) 784-4238
Web Site: http://www.hearthsidefoods.com
Food & Consumer Product Contract Packaging Services
N.A.I.C.S.: 561910
Vicky Smitley *(VP-Sls & Mktg)*
Darryn Herrmann *(VP-Ops)*
Tracy Reinhart *(Dir-Customer Svcs)*

Hearthside Food Solutions, LLC - McComb (2)
312 Rader Rd, McComb, OH 45858-9751
Tel.: (419) 293-2911
Web Site: http://www.hearthsidefoods.com
Cookies & Crackers Mfr
N.A.I.C.S.: 311821
Rich Scalise *(Chm & CEO)*

Subsidiary (Domestic):

Quality Bakery Products, LLC (2)
888 E Las Olas Blvd Ste 700, Fort Lauderdale, FL 33301
Tel.: (856) 764-2006
Web Site: http://www.hearthsidefoods.com
Bakery Products Retailer
N.A.I.C.S.: 424420
Gerald J Mangano Jr. *(Head-Sls & Mktg)*

Ryt-way Industries, LLC (2)
21850 Grenada Ave, Lakeville, MN 55044-9076
Tel.: (952) 469-1417
Web Site: http://www.hearthsidefoods.com
Contract Food Packaging Services
N.A.I.C.S.: 424450

Horn Industrial Services (1)
2205 Ragu Dr, Owensboro, KY 42303
Tel.: (270) 683-6564
Engineering Consulting Services
N.A.I.C.S.: 541330
Mike Lampert *(CFO)*

MDVIP, LLC (1)
4950 Communication Ave Ste 100, Boca Raton, FL 33431-8561
Tel.: (561) 544-4000
Web Site: http://www.mdvip.com
Operational, Technological & Managerial Support (for Physicians)
N.A.I.C.S.: 561499
Matthew Hashem *(Pres & CFO)*
Bret Jorgensen *(Chm & CEO)*
Roy R. Harris *(Gen Counsel)*
Donald F. Hankus *(CIO)*
Chris Lillich *(CMO)*
Ben Behroozi *(Exec VP-Bus Dev & Ops)*
David Barrie *(Exec VP-Physician Dev)*

PF Concept International B.V. (1)
Kabelweg 1, 2371 DX, Roelofarendsveen, Netherlands
Tel.: (31) 71 33 28 911
Web Site: http://www.pfconcept.com
Holding Company; Promotional Products Mfr
N.A.I.C.S.: 551112

Charlesbank Capital Partners, LLC—(Continued)

Ralf Oster *(CEO)*
Alwin Hartog *(CFO)*
Frans Fels *(VP-IT Europe & Asia)*
Pieter Boonekamp *(Sr VP-Sls & Mktg)*
Joroen van der Heijden *(Sr VP-Ops & Logistic Europe)*

Subsidiary (Non-US):

PF Concept UK Operations Ltd   **(2)**
Neptune House Sycamore Trading Estate
Squires Gate Ln, Blackpool, FY4 3RL, Lancashire, United Kingdom
Tel.: (44) 1933673111
Web Site: http://www.pfconcept.com
Promotion Items Distr
N.A.I.C.S.: 424120
Philip Morgan *(Country Mgr)*

Trimark Sportswear Group Inc.   **(2)**
30 Staples Ave, Richmond Hill, L4B 4W3,
ON, Canada
Tel.: (905) 508-8882
Web Site: http://www.trimarksportswear.com
Sales Range: $25-49.9 Million
Emp.: 150
Logo Apparel Mfr & Distr
N.A.I.C.S.: 315250
Derrick Milne *(CEO)*
Bill Horst *(Dir-Mktg Comm-PCNA Apparel)*
Alan Meinstein *(Mng Dir-Production)*
Rocky Dundas *(Mgr-Natl Sls-Retail)*
Sharon Willochell *(Pres-PCNA Apparel)*

Park Place Technologies, LLC   **(1)**
5910 Landerbrook Dr, Cleveland, OH
44124   **(50%)**
Tel.: (877) 778-8707
Web Site:
  http://www.parkplacetechnologies.com
Hardware Maintenance Services
N.A.I.C.S.: 541513
Chris Adams *(Pres & CEO)*
Hal Malstrom *(Interim COO)*
Jennifer Deutsch *(CMO)*
Michael Vedda *(Chief Revenue Officer)*

Subsidiary (Domestic):

**Ardent Support Technologies,
LLC**   **(2)**
12 Crosby Rd, Dover, NH 03820
Web Site: http://www.ardentsupporttech.com
Computer Related Services
N.A.I.C.S.: 541519
Dave Daniels *(Mgr-Tech Support)*

**Custom Hardware Engineering &
Consulting, Inc.**   **(2)**
1576 Fencorp Dr, Fenton, MO 63026
Tel.: (636) 305-9669
Web Site: http://www.checonsulting.com
Sales Range: $1-9.9 Million
Emp.: 90
Computer Maintenance/Repair
N.A.I.C.S.: 811210
David York *(Pres & CEO)*

QC Supply LLC   **(1)**
574 Rd 11, Schuyler, NE 68661-0581
Tel.: (402) 352-3167
Web Site: http://www.qcsupply.com
Farm Products & Livestock Equipment Distr
N.A.I.C.S.: 424910
Carrie Horejsi *(Dir-HR)*

Subsidiary (Domestic):

QC Supply LLC   **(2)**
4105 Hwy US 12 E, Willmar, MN 56201
Tel.: (320) 235-0444
Web Site: http://www.qcsupply.com
Rev.: $14,000,000
Emp.: 25
Poultry Equipment Mfr
N.A.I.C.S.: 311615
Shea Carr *(Gen Mgr)*

Sagittarius Brands, Inc.   **(1)**
1717 Elm Hill Pike Ste A1, Nashville, TN
37210
Tel.: (615) 231-2328
Sales Range: $900-999.9 Million
Holding Company; Limited Service Restaurants Franchisor & Operator
N.A.I.C.S.: 551112

**Six Degrees Technology Group
Ltd.**   **(1)**

Commodity Quay St Katharine Docks, London, E1W 1AZ, United Kingdom
Tel.: (44) 8000128060
Web Site: http://www.6dg.co.uk
Managed Data & Communications Services
N.A.I.C.S.: 518210
Alastair R. Mills *(Founder & Chm)*
Campbell Williams *(Dir-Mktg & Strategy)*
Paul Mills *(Sls Dir-Group)*
David Howson *(CEO)*
Mike Ing *(COO)*
Gerry Grace *(CFO)*
Jonny Shanmuganathan *(Bus Dir-UC &
Data Line)*

Southcross Holdings LP   **(1)**
1717 Main St Ste 5200, Dallas, TX
75201   **(33.3%)**
Tel.: (214) 979-3700
Web Site:
  http://www.southcrossholdings.com
Holding Company
N.A.I.C.S.: 551112
John Bonn *(Pres)*

Holding (Domestic):

Southcross Energy Partners,LLC   **(2)**
1717 Main St Ste 5200, Dallas, TX 75201
Tel.: (214) 979-3720
Web Site: http://www.southcrossenergy.com
Sales Range: $400-449.9 Million
Oil & Gas Exploration
N.A.I.C.S.: 211120
Patrick Geroir *(CEO)*
James Lee *(CFO & Sr VP)*
William C. Boyer *(COO & Sr VP)*
John Happ *(Chief Comml Officer & Sr VP)*
Nicole Devore *(Dir-HR)*
William Waldheim *(Chm)*

Subsidiary (Domestic):

Southcross Energy GP LLC   **(3)**
1700 Pacific Ave Ste 2900, Dallas, TX
75201
Tel.: (214) 979-3700
Web Site: http://www.southxenergy.com
Gathering, Processing & Pipeline Transportation of Natural Gas
N.A.I.C.S.: 486210

**Southcross Mississippi Industrial Gas
Sales, L.P.**   **(3)**
1717 Main St Ste 5200, Dallas, TX 75201-
4617
Tel.: (214) 979-3700
Oil & Gas Operation Supporting Services
N.A.I.C.S.: 213112

**Southcross Mississippi Pipeline,
L.P.**   **(3)**
1700 Pacific Ave Ste 2900, Dallas, TX
75201-4666
Tel.: (214) 979-3760
Sales Range: $10-24.9 Million
Emp.: 12
Natural Gas Pipeline Transportation Services
N.A.I.C.S.: 486210

Southcross NGL Pipeline Ltd.   **(3)**
1717 Main St Ste 5200, Dallas, TX 75201
Tel.: (214) 979-3767
Web Site: http://www.southcrossenergy.com
Natural Gas Pipeline Transportation Services
N.A.I.C.S.: 486210

TLC Vision Corporation   **(1)**
50 Burnhamthorpe Road West Suite 101,
Mississauga, L5B 3C2, ON,
Canada   **(65%)**
Tel.: (905) 848-2297
Web Site: http://www.tlcvision.ca
Sales Range: $200-249.9 Million
Laser Vision Correction Facilities Operator
N.A.I.C.S.: 621399

Subsidiary (US):

TLC Vision Corporation   **(2)**
16305 Swingley Ridge Rd Ste 375, Chesterfield, MO 63017-1777
Tel.: (636) 534-2300
Web Site: http://www.tlcvision.com
Sales Range: $200-249.9 Million
Corrective Laser Eye Surgery Services
N.A.I.C.S.: 621111

Tecomet Inc.   **(1)**
115 Eames St, Wilmington, MA 01887-3379
Tel.: (978) 642-2400
Web Site: http://www.tecomet.com
Orthopedic Implant, Medical Device & Aerospace Component Mfr
N.A.I.C.S.: 339112
John Connolly *(CFO)*
Art Burghouwt *(Exec VP-Sls & Mktg)*
Robert Lynch *(VP-R&D)*
Dan Howell *(Exec VP-Global Ops)*
Vlad Miskovic *(Exec VP-Aerospace & Defense)*
Steve Hinora *(Exec VP-Quality & Regulatory)*
Pam Green *(VP-HR)*
Jim Bradley *(VP-IT)*

The Princeton Review, Inc.   **(1)**
24 Prime Pkwy, Natick, MA 01760   **(100%)**
Tel.: (570) 591-5910
Web Site: http://www.princetonreview.com
Sales Range: $75-99.9 Million
Test Preparation & Educational Support
Services
N.A.I.C.S.: 611710
Sharon Van Wyk *(Pres)*
John Katzman *(Founder)*

The Rockport Company, LLC   **(1)**
1220 Washington St, Newton, MA 02465
Tel.: (800) 762-5767
Web Site: http://www.rockport.com
Comfort Footwear Mfr & Distr
N.A.I.C.S.: 316210
John Daher *(Sr VP-Product Dev)*

Subsidiary (Domestic):

South Cone, Inc.   **(2)**
2701 Harbor Bay Pkwy, Alameda, CA
94502
Web Site: http://www.reef.com
Footwear & Apparel Designer, Mfr, Whslr &
Online Retailer
N.A.I.C.S.: 316210

**Titan Contracting & Leasing Co.
Inc.**   **(1)**
2205 Ragu Dr, Owensboro, KY 42303-1437
Tel.: (270) 683-6564
Web Site: http://www.titancontracting.com
Sales Range: $75-99.9 Million
Specialty Contracting Services, Including
Mechanical Construction, Maintenance &
Fabrication Services
N.A.I.C.S.: 238990
Josh Carmichael *(VP-HR)*
Kelly Duncan *(CFO)*
Tom Johnson *(VP-Quality Control)*
Mike Lampert *(COO)*
Jerry Maggard *(VP-Safety)*
Patrick Phister *(VP-Ops-Eastern)*
Zane Robinson *(Gen Mgr-Ops-Houston)*
Brent Smith *(CEO)*
Howard Wallin *(Gen Mgr-Florida Ops)*
Tony Zeigler *(Gen Mgr-Ops-Savannah)*

Vestcom International, Inc.   **(1)**
2800 Cantrell Rd Ste 500, Little Rock, AR
72204
Tel.: (501) 663-0100
Web Site: http://www.vestcom.com
Communication & Marketing Services
N.A.I.C.S.: 334290
Clifton Cook *(Sr VP-Innovation)*
John Lawlor *(Chm & CEO)*
Shannon Palmer *(CCOO, FO & Exec VP)*
Brett Holiman *(VP-Bus Dev)*
Kevin McGovern *(Sr VP-Sls)*
Michael Paley *(Gen Mgr & Sr VP)*
Ned Peverley *(Sr VP-Strategy, Innovation &
Mktg)*

**CHARLESGATE REALTY
GROUP, LLC**
867 Boylston St, Boston, MA 02116
Tel.: (617) 587-0100
Web Site:
  http://www.charlesgaterealty.com
Year Founded: 2003
Sales Range: $10-24.9 Million
Emp.: 45
Real Estate Services
N.A.I.C.S.: 531390
Michael Di Mella *(Mng Partner)*
P. T. Vineburgh *(Partner)*

Todd Mikelonis *(Gen Mgr)*
Lauren DiMella *(Ops Mgr)*
Kelly Robbins *(Dir-Project Mgmt)*

CHARLESTON AREA MEDICAL CENTER INC.
501 Morris St, Charleston, WV
25301-1326
Tel.: (304) 388-5432   **WV**
Web Site: http://www.camc.org
Year Founded: 1972
Sales Range: $1-4.9 Billion
Emp.: 5,000
General Medical & Surgical Hospitals
N.A.I.C.S.: 622110
Michael Williams *(VP)*
Eric A. Hicks *(Sec)*

Subsidiaries:

Charleston Area Medical Center
Foundation Inc.   **(1)**
3412 Staunton Ave, Charleston, WV 25304-
1227
Tel.: (304) 388-9860
Web Site: http://www.camc.org
Sales Range: $10-24.9 Million
Emp.: 6
Non Profit Fundraising
N.A.I.C.S.: 621111
Gail E. Pitchford *(Pres)*

CHARLESTON COMMISSIONERS OF PUBLIC WORKS
103 Saint Philip St, Charleston, SC
29403
Tel.: (843) 727-6800
Web Site:
  http://www.charlestoncpw.com
Year Founded: 1917
Sales Range: $75-99.9 Million
Emp.: 450
Water Supply
N.A.I.C.S.: 221310
Wesley Ropp *(CFO)*
Dorothy G. Harrison *(Chief Admin
Officer)*

CHARLESTON COUNTY AVIATION AUTHORITY
5500 International Blvd Ste 101,
North Charleston, SC 29418
Tel.: (843) 767-7000
Web Site: http://www.chs-airport.com
Sales Range: $10-24.9 Million
Emp.: 250
Airport
N.A.I.C.S.: 488119
Judith W. Olmstead *(Dir-Fin & Admin)*
Sherry E. Deese *(Mgr-Info Sys)*
Paul Campbell *(Dir-Airport)*

**CHARLESTON HEATING &
AIR, LLC**
2201 Mechanic St, North Charleston,
SC 29405
Tel.: (843) 216-9966
Web Site:
  http://www.charlestonheating.com
Year Founded: 2008
Sales Range: $1-9.9 Million
Emp.: 20
Heating & Air Conditioning Installation, Maintenance & Repairs
N.A.I.C.S.: 238220
Blake Miller *(Pres)*
Brent Doolittle *(VP-Fin)*
Doug Platt *(Supvr-Installation)*

CHARLESTON METAL PRODUCTS INC.
350 Grant St, Waterloo, IN 46793
Tel.: (260) 837-8211
Web Site:
  https://www.charlestonmetal.com
Sales Range: $10-24.9 Million
Emp.: 100

Screw Machine Products
N.A.I.C.S.: 332721
G. William Tucker *(Pres)*
Tera Heffley *(Sec)*

CHARLESTON SANITARY BOARD
208 26th St, Charleston, WV 25387
Tel.: (304) 348-8136
Web Site: https://www.csbwv.com
Sales Range: $10-24.9 Million
Emp.: 68
Sewage Treatment Services
N.A.I.C.S.: 221320
Crystal Sanders *(Mgr-Fin)*
Tim Haapala *(Mgr-Ops)*
Jeff West *(Asst Mgr-Ops-Treatment Plant)*
Donna Rigsby *(Mgr-Customer Svc)*
Steven Myers *(Mgr-Pur)*
Diana White *(Mgr-Payroll & HR)*
Danny Jones *(Chm)*
Renee Graley *(Mgr-Computer & Info Sys)*
Jim Downey *(Mgr-Engrg)*
Steve Cooper *(Gen Mgr)*

CHARLESTON STEEL & METAL CO.
2700 Spruill Ave, North Charleston, SC 29405
Tel.: (843) 722-7278
Web Site: https://www.charlestonsteel.com
Year Founded: 1893
Sales Range: $10-24.9 Million
Emp.: 104
Nonferrous Metal Alloying Services
N.A.I.C.S.: 331492
Bernard Steinberg *(Pres)*
Rose M. Baker *(Controller)*
Barry Wolff *(VP & Gen Mgr)*
Jonathan Steinberg *(VP & Mgr-Industrial Rels)*
Stephen Steinberg *(Mgr-Safety & En-vironmental)*
Michael Hardie *(Supvr-Ferrous-Mount Holly)*
Jimmy Maulding *(Supvr-Receiving)*

CHARLESTON TRANSITIONAL FACILITY
1902 Fox Dr Ste B, Champaign, IL 61820-7378
Tel.: (217) 352-1557
Web Site: http://www.ctfillinois.org
Year Founded: 2000
Sales Range: $10-24.9 Million
Emp.: 894
Developmental Disability Assistance Services
N.A.I.C.S.: 624120
Dennis Carpenter *(Pres & CEO)*

CHARLESTON/ORWIG, INC.
515 W North Shore Dr, Hartland, WI 53029-8312
Tel.: (262) 563-5100
Web Site: http://www.charlestonorwig.com
Year Founded: 1992
Rev.: $41,949,779
Emp.: 60
Advetising Agency
N.A.I.C.S.: 541810
Lyle E. Orwig *(CEO)*
Nancy Wegner *(Controller)*
Beth Andersen *(Mng Partner & Sr VP)*
Mike Opperman *(Sr Dir-Strategy & Plng)*
Sharon Schackel *(Dir-Production & Traffic)*
Betsy Andrews *(Dir-Admin Ops)*
Amy Richards *(Dir-Reputation Mgmt)*
Chuck Sanger *(Acct Mgr)*

Laura Henke *(Dir-Media Svcs)*
Laura Staton *(Acct Mgr)*
Kristi Eichman *(Dir-Bus Dev)*
Marcy Tessmann *(Pres)*
Bill Stadick *(Dir-Creative)*
Kevin Kasper *(Sr VP-Merger & Acq Comm)*
Jamie Schroeder *(Dir-Art)*
Brian Sterricker *(Sr Copywriter)*
Kimberly Keller *(Sr Dir-Reputation Mgmt)*

CHARLEVOIX AREA HOSPI-TAL
14700 Lake Shore Dr, Charlevoix, MI 49720
Tel.: (231) 547-4024
Web Site: http://www.cah.org
Year Founded: 1919
Sales Range: $25-49.9 Million
Emp.: 398
Health Care Srvices
N.A.I.C.S.: 622110
Bob Zimmerman *(CFO)*
Christine Wilhelm *(COO)*
Bernadette Cole *(Chief Nursing Offi-cer)*
N. Craig Boss *(Chief Medical Officer)*
Marc Lame *(Vice Chm)*
Michael Ortwine *(Treas & Sec)*
Ruth Hoppe *(Chm)*
Lyn Jenks *(CEO)*
Rob Wilcox *(CFO)*
Craig Wendt *(Chief Medical Officer)*

CHARLEYS CONCRETE CO.
700 Katy Rd, Keller, TX 76244
Tel.: (817) 431-2016
Web Site: http://www.charleysconcrete.com
Year Founded: 1991
Sales Range: $25-49.9 Million
Emp.: 60
Providers of Ready-Mixed Concrete
N.A.I.C.S.: 327320
Charles R. Pennington *(Pres)*
Susan Nunnery *(VP)*
Brent R. Pennington *(Pres)*

CHARLIE EARHART REALTY
2032 Bayshore Blvd, Dunedin, FL 34698
Tel.: (727) 733-7171
Web Site: http://www.earhartrealty.com
Sales Range: $1-9.9 Million
Emp.: 6
Real Estate Broker
N.A.I.C.S.: 531210
Karen Leonard *(Pres)*

CHARLIE'S CONTRACTING, INC.
75 Rosedale Rd, Watertown, MA 02472
Tel.: (617) 923-0112
Year Founded: 1980
Sales Range: $10-24.9 Million
Emp.: 70
Highway & Street Construction Ser-vices
N.A.I.C.S.: 237310
Charles Pentland Jr. *(Pres)*

CHARLIE'S DODGE, INC.
725 Illinois Ave, Maumee, OH 43537-1711
Tel.: (419) 893-0241
Web Site: http://www.charliesdodge.net
Sales Range: $10-24.9 Million
Emp.: 75
Car Whslr
N.A.I.C.S.: 441110

Michael Barchick *(Gen Mgr)*
Craig Dominic *(Mgr-Used Cars)*
Ken Millen *(Mgr-Sls-New Car)*

CHARLIE'S MOTOR MALL INC.
465 Western Ave, Augusta, ME 04330
Tel.: (207) 622-7327
Web Site: https://www.charliesmm.com
Rev.: $85,000,000
Emp.: 100
Car Dealership Owner & Operator
N.A.I.C.S.: 441110
Charles Shuman *(Pres)*
Andrew O'Hearn *(Dir-Internet Sls)*
Cory Lathrop *(Dir-Fixed Ops)*
Greg Eaton *(Mgr-Rental)*
Jay Wolfington *(Mgr-Fin)*
John Gallo *(Mgr-Sls)*
Mike Mahoney *(Mgr-Sls)*
Randy Roux *(Mgr-Fin)*
Sean Lilly *(Mgr-Sls)*
Tim DiBenedetti *(Gen Mgr-Sls)*
Roger Williams II *(Sr Mgr-Fin)*

CHARLIE'S TOBACCO OUT-LET
3720 Battleground Ave Ste H, Greensboro, NC 27410
Tel.: (336) 540-0555
Sales Range: $10-24.9 Million
Emp.: 20
Tobacco & Tobacco Products Distr & Sales
N.A.I.C.S.: 424940
Mike Patel *(Owner)*

CHARLOMA INC.
727 N Liberty St, Cherryvale, KS 67335
Tel.: (620) 336-2124
Web Site: http://www.charloma.com
Year Founded: 1969
Sales Range: $25-49.9 Million
Emp.: 250
Plastics Plumbing Fixture Mfr
N.A.I.C.S.: 326191
Scott Morris *(Controller)*

CHARLOTTE APPLIANCES INC.
3200 Lake Ave, Rochester, NY 14612
Tel.: (585) 663-5050
Web Site: https://www.charlotteappliance.com
Rev.: $14,507,156
Emp.: 45
Household Appliance Stores
N.A.I.C.S.: 449210
James A. Agostinelli *(Pres)*

CHARLOTTE CAPITAL CORP.
81 Dow Jones St Ste 8, Henderson, NV 89074
Tel.: (702) 466-3333
Year Founded: 2011
Investment Services
N.A.I.C.S.: 523999
Nicole Anderson *(Pres, Sec & Treas)*

CHARLOTTE COUNTRY CLUB
2465 Mecklenburg Ave, Charlotte, NC 28205
Tel.: (704) 334-0836
Web Site: https://www.charlottecountryclub.org
Year Founded: 1910
Sales Range: $10-24.9 Million
Emp.: 290
Country Club Operator
N.A.I.C.S.: 713910
Jon Cherry *(Mgr-Locker Room)*
Damon J. DiOrio *(CEO)*
Bill Francis *(Dir-Tennis)*
Dee Anna Clarke *(CFO)*

Gregg Leonard *(Asst Mgr)*
Laurie Montanus *(Dir-Comm)*
Andrew Shuck *(Head-Golf Pro)*
Karen Martin *(Dir-HR)*
Amanda Day *(Asst Mgr)*
Chelsie Hayes *(Dir-Club Events)*
Rachel Wykoff *(Dir-Youth Activities)*
Dan Porzio *(Mgr-Clubhouse)*

CHARLOTTE PAINT COMPANY INC.
1604 Lane Rd, Mount Holly, NC 28120
Tel.: (704) 827-1391
Web Site: https://www.charlottepaint.com
Year Founded: 1977
Sales Range: $10-24.9 Million
Emp.: 230
Commercial Painting
N.A.I.C.S.: 238320

CHARLOTTE PIPE & FOUNDRY COMPANY
2109 Randolph Rd, Charlotte, NC 28207
Tel.: (704) 372-5030
Web Site: http://www.charlottepipe.com
Year Founded: 1901
Rev.: $177,300,000
Emp.: 200
Iron & Plastics Pipe & Pipe Fittings Mfr
N.A.I.C.S.: 326122
Roddey Dowd *(Owner)*
William Hutaff *(CFO & Sr VP)*
Hooper Hardison *(Pres & CEO)*

Subsidiaries:

Neenah Enterprises, Inc.   (1)
2121 Brooks Ave, Neenah, WI 54956
Tel.: (920) 725-7000
Web Site: http://www.nfco.com
Holding Company: Foundry Operations
N.A.I.C.S.: 551112

Subsidiary (Domestic):

Neenah Foundry Company   (2)
2121 Brooks St, Neenah, WI 54956
Tel.: (920) 725-7000
Web Site: http://www.nfco.com
Sales Range: $150-199.9 Million
Emp.: 1,000
Construction & Industrial Iron Casting Mfr
N.A.I.C.S.: 331511
Jay Samolinski *(VP-Ops)*

Subsidiary (Domestic):

Gregg Industries, Inc.   (3)
10675 Hickson St, El Monte, CA 91731-1947
Tel.: (626) 575-7664
Sales Range: $75-99.9 Million
Emp.: 300
Iron Casting Mfr
N.A.I.C.S.: 331511

CHARLOTTE REGIONAL BUSI-NESS ALLIANCE
330 S Tryon St, Charlotte, NC 28202
Tel.: (704) 378-1300
Web Site: http://www.charlotteregion.com
Year Founded: 1915
Emp.: 100
Business Associations
N.A.I.C.S.: 813910
Janet Labar *(Pres & CEO)*
Joaquin Soria *(CFO)*
Joe Bost *(Chief Advocacy Officer)*
Danny Chavez *(Chief Business Re-cruitment Officer)*

Subsidiaries:

Charlotte Regional Partnership, Inc.   (1)
330 S Tryon St, Charlotte, NC 28202

Charlotte Regional Business Alliance—(Continued)
Tel.: (704) 378-1300
Web Site: http://www.charlotteusa.com
Economic Development Services
N.A.I.C.S.: 541720

CHARLOTTESVILLE AREA COMMUNITY FOUNDATION
114 4th St SE, Charlottesville, VA 22902
Tel.: (434) 296-1024   VA
Web Site: http://www.cacfonline.org
Year Founded: 1967
Sales Range: $10-24.9 Million
Emp.: 10
Community Welfare Services
N.A.I.C.S.: 624190
Brennan Gould (Dir-Grants & Strategic Initiatives)

CHARLOTTESVILLE OIL CO. INC.
RR 250, Charlottesville, VA 22901
Tel.: (434) 293-9107
Sales Range: $25-49.9 Million
Emp.: 15
Petroleum Products
N.A.I.C.S.: 424720
James F. Dulaney Jr. (Pres)

CHARM SCIENCES, INC.
659 Andover St, Lawrence, MA 01843-1032
Tel.: (978) 687-9200
Web Site: https://www.charm.com
Year Founded: 1978
Sales Range: $10-24.9 Million
Emp.: 64
Food Contamination Testing & Screening Kits Developer
N.A.I.C.S.: 325998
Andre Cevaer (Mgr-Sls & Bus-Brittany)
Steve Holmes (VP-Technical Support)

CHARMING CHARLIE USA CORP.
7700 San Felipe Ste 520, Houston, TX 77063
Tel.: (713) 579-1936   DE
Web Site:
http://www.charmingcharlie.com
Women's Fashion & Accessories Retailer
N.A.I.C.S.: 458110
Charlie Chanaratsopon (Founder)

CHARTER ATLANTIC CORPORATION
200 Park Ave Fl 11, New York, NY 10166
Tel.: (212) 681-3000
Web Site: http://fftw.com
Sales Range: $25-49.9 Million
Emp.: 100
Investment Advisory Services
N.A.I.C.S.: 523940

CHARTER BOARD PARTNERS
1638 R St NW Ste 300, Washington, DC 20009
Tel.: (202) 588-1137   DC
Web Site:
http://www.charterboards.org
Year Founded: 2010
Emp.: 150
Educational Support Services
N.A.I.C.S.: 611710
Emilie Sullivan (Mgr-IT)
Simmons Lettre (Co-Founder)
Kate Essex (Chief Program Officer)
Carrie Irvin (Pres & Co-Founder)
Shereen Williams (Dir-Governance & Partnerships)
Tom Vander Ark (Chm)
Sophie Klepper (Program Mgr)

Sarah Manes (Dir-Board Support & Evaluation)
Beth Moore (Fin Dir & Dir-Ops)

CHARTER DIRECT MARKETING
295 Maddison Ave Ste 1200, New York, NY 10017
Tel.: (212) 717-2770   NY
Web Site:
http://www.charterdirectmarketing.com
Year Founded: 1986
Emp.: 7
Advertising Agencies
N.A.I.C.S.: 541810
Terry Kollman (Pres & CEO)
John Golden (VP & Dir-Creative)
Stephen J. Brind (VP & Dir-Creative & Project Mgr)
Fred Calalang (Dir-Event Mktg)
Matt Soroka (Dir-Internet Svcs)

Subsidiaries:

Charter Digital Media Inc. (1)
295 Madison Ave ste 1200, New York, NY 10017
Tel.: (212) 717-2770
Web Site:
http://www.charterdigitalmedia.com
Rev.: $1,000,000
Emp.: 5
Digital Advertising
N.A.I.C.S.: 541810
Terence J. Kollman (Pres & CEO)
Jim Bilello (VP-Midwest Sls)
John Sutton (VP-West Coast Sls)

CHARTER FILMS, INC.
1901 Winter St, Superior, WI 54880
Tel.: (715) 395-8258
Web Site: http://www.charternex.com
Rev.: $12,200,000
Emp.: 140
Unlaminated Plastics Film & Sheet Mfr
N.A.I.C.S.: 326113
David Timm (VP)
Brian Beuning (VP-Sls & Mktg)

CHARTER FINANCIAL PUBLISHING NETWORK
499 Broad St Ste 120, Shrewsbury, NJ 07702
Tel.: (732) 450-8866
Web Site: http://www.fa-mag.com
Year Founded: 1999
Sales Range: Less than $1 Million
Emp.: 25
Financial Periodicals Publishing
N.A.I.C.S.: 513120
David Smith (Partner & Grp Publr)
Bob Paradise (Partner)
Keith Allaire (Partner)
Dawn Zarcaro (Office Mgr & Mgr-Adv Sls)
Dorothy Hinchcliff (Mng Editor)
Diane Rogala (Assoc Publr)
Laura Zavetz (Dir-Creative)
Jennifer Rhatigan (Dir-Mktg)
Steve Kimball (Mgr-Classified Ad Sls)
Susanna Marra (Mgr-Grp Circulation & Reprint)
Jodi Battaglia (Dir-Art)
Merri Chapin (Mgr-Digital Content)
Sherri Scordo (Editor-Survey)
Lori Chadwick (Controller)
Aimee Melli (Mgr-Production)
Gary Holland (Pres & CEO)

CHARTER MANUFACTURING COMPANY, INC.
1212 W Glen Oaks Ln, Mequon, WI 53092-3332
Tel.: (262) 243-4700   WI
Web Site:
https://www.chartermfg.com

Year Founded: 1932
Sales Range: $10-24.9 Million
Emp.: 1,100
Steel Billets, Bars, Wire & Wire Products Mfr
N.A.I.C.S.: 332618
Jack Lynch (Mgr-Mktg)
John W. Mellowes (CEO)

Subsidiaries:

Charter Automotive (1)
7850 N 81st S, Milwaukee, WI 53223
Tel.: (414) 365-5000
Web Site: http://www.charterautomotive.com
Emp.: 150
Automobile Parts Mfr
N.A.I.C.S.: 336390
Brian Norman (Mgr-Global Sls)
Craig Bierdemann (Mgr-Sls)
Jeff Hoey (Mgr-Customer Svc)
Jim Quick (Mgr-Global Ops)
Carolyn Flood (Mgr-HR)
Christopher LaBelle (Plant Mgr)
Shane Bonner (Dir-Global Ops)
Gary Brereton (Mgr-Bus Dev)
Scott Cline (Mgr-Global Quality Assurance)
Winnie Kong (Mgr-HR)
Desmond Lewis (Mgr-Quality)
Ian Reed (Plant Mgr)
George Tang (Plant Mgr)
Natalie Thiel (Mgr-Quality)
Jack Wu (Mgr-Quality)

Charter Dura-Bar (1)
2100 W Lk Shore Dr, Woodstock, IL 60098-7468
Tel.: (815) 338-3900
Web Site:
http://www.wellsmanufacturing.com
Iron & Metal Products Mfr
N.A.I.C.S.: 331511
Pete Murray (VP & Gen Mgr)

Charter Steel, Inc. (1)
1658 Cold Springs Rd, Saukville, WI 53080
Tel.: (262) 268-2403
Web Site: http://www.chartersteel.com
Steel Bar Mfr
N.A.I.C.S.: 331221

Charter Wire (1)
3700 W Milwaukee Rd, Milwaukee, WI 53208-4251
Tel.: (414) 390-3000
Web Site: http://www.charterwire.com
Steel Rod & Wire Mfr
N.A.I.C.S.: 331221
Mike Schueller (Mgr-Supply Chain)
Greg Windau (Plant Mgr-Engrg)

CHARTER OAK EQUITY, L.P.
10 Wright St Ste 230, Westport, CT 06880
Tel.: (203) 221-4752   DE
Web Site: http://www.charteroak-equity.com
Year Founded: 2006
Emp.: 4
Equity Investment Firm
N.A.I.C.S.: 523999
Paul E. Roughan (Mng Partner)
Zubin Avari (Mng Partner)
Mark Ullman (Mng Partner)

Subsidiaries:

Charter Oak International Partners, LLC (1)
10 Wright St Ste 210, Westport, CT 06880 (100%)
Tel.: (203) 221-4752
Web Site: http://www.charteroak-equity.com
Equity Investment Firm
N.A.I.C.S.: 523999

CHARTER OAK HEALTH CENTER, INC.
21 Grand St, Hartford, CT 06106
Tel.: (860) 550-7500   CT
Web Site:
http://www.thecharteroak.org
Year Founded: 1978
Sales Range: $10-24.9 Million
Emp.: 182

Health Care Srvices
N.A.I.C.S.: 622110
Nichelle A. Mullins (Pres & CEO)
Brimal Patel (Chief Medical Officer)

CHARTER ONE HOTELS & RESORTS, INC.
2032 Hillview St, Sarasota, FL 34239
Tel.: (941) 907-9017   FL
Web Site:
http://www.charteronehotels.com
Year Founded: 1981
Sales Range: $25-49.9 Million
Emp.: 875
Home Management Services
N.A.I.C.S.: 541611
John W. Balliett (Chm & CEO)
Scott Busby (Pres & COO)
Pamela Chaisson (VP-Team Svcs)
Melissa Masiello (Dir-Acctg Svcs)
Rachel Ward (Dir-HR-Northern Reg)
Sherry Bartley (Reg Dir-Ops)
Henry Piarrot (Reg Dir-Ops)
Patrick Shine (VP-Bus Dev)

CHARTER SCHOOL BUSINESS MANAGEMENT
237 W 35th St Ste 301, New York, NY 10001
Web Site: https://www.csbm.com
Year Founded: 2006
Sales Range: $1-9.9 Million
Emp.: 33
Business & Financial Training
N.A.I.C.S.: 561499
Raj Thakkar (Founder & CEO)
Karen Daniels (Pres & COO)
Sharon Denson (CFO & VP)

CHARTER SCHOOLS USA INC.
6245 N Federal Hwy 5th Fl, Fort Lauderdale, FL 33308
Tel.: (954) 202-3500
Web Site:
http://www.charterschoolsusa.com
Year Founded: 1997
Sales Range: $250-299.9 Million
Emp.: 4,500
Education Services
N.A.I.C.S.: 923110
Jonathan K. Hage (Founder, Chm, Pres & CEO)
Eric Paul (Reg Dir-Education-South Florida)
Amy Liebenson (Supvr-HR)
Carissa Carroll (Principal-BSCS)
David McKnight (Reg Dir)

CHARTER SOUTH INC.
215 Distribution Dr, Birmingham, AL 35209
Tel.: (205) 941-1173
Web Site:
http://www.chartersouth.com
Year Founded: 1985
Rev.: $23,887,374
Emp.: 17
Service Station Construction
N.A.I.C.S.: 236220
Ray McLeod (Pres)
Jeff McLeod (VP)
Wendell Duncan (Mgr-Ops)
Allie McLeod (Mgr-Acctg)

CHARTERED HOMES
5455 S Durango Dr #150, Las Vegas, NV 89113
Tel.: (805) 682-6064
Web Site:
http://www.charteredhomes.com
Year Founded: 1991
Sales Range: $10-24.9 Million
Emp.: 20
Residential Construction
N.A.I.C.S.: 236115
Ward Ritter (Pres)

Subsidiaries:

Chartered Development Corp.   (1)
6120 W Tropicana Ave, Las Vegas, NV
89103-4489
Tel.: (702) 873-3994
Web Site: http://www.charteredholdings.com
Sales Range: $10-24.9 Million
Emp.: 15
Residential Construction
N.A.I.C.S.: 236115

CHARTERHOUSE GROUP, INC.

92 River Rd, Summit, NJ 07901
Tel.: (212) 584-3200   DE
Web Site:
http://www.charterhousegroup.com
Year Founded: 1973
Privater Equity Firm
N.A.I.C.S.: 523999
Cheri E. Lieberman (CFO)
William M. Landuyt (Mng Dir)
C. Taylor Cole Jr. (Mng Dir)

Subsidiaries:

Cequel Data Centers, LLC   (1)
520 Maryville Centre Dr Ste 300, Saint
Louis, MO 63141
Tel.: (314) 594-1300
Holding Company; Information Technology
Data Centers Operator
N.A.I.C.S.: 551112
Jerald L. Kent (Chm)

Subsidiary (Domestic):

TierPoint, LLC   (2)
520 Maryville Centre Dr Ste 300, Saint
Louis, MO 63141
Tel.: (877) 859-8437
Web Site: http://www.tierpoint.com
Information Technology Data Centers Op-
erator
N.A.I.C.S.: 518210
Mary E. Meduski (Pres & CFO)
Jerald L. Kent (Chm)
Andy Stewart (Chief Strategy Officer)
Wendy Knudsen (Chief Legal Officer &
Exec VP)
Dennis Jesielowski (COO)
Jeff Bertocci (Sr VP-Svc Delivery)
Rob Carter (Sr VP-Solutions Engrg)
Rob Fewkes (VP-Cloud Tech)
Terry Morrison (Sr VP-Tech)
Keith Markley (Sr VP-Ops)
Robert Hicks (Sr VP-Ops)
David Foster (VP-Data Center Facilities)
Robert Lupo (Gen Mgr-Facility & Ops-
Jacksonville)
Keith Waldrup (VP-Sls-Missouri & Ken-
tucky)
Bret Dupuis (VP-Sls-Illinois, Indiana, Michi-
gan & Ohio)
John Holland (Sr VP-Sls)
Tyler Holley (VP-Sls-Jacksonville)
Paige Dirscherl (Sr Acct Exec)
Linda Bailey (VP-HR)
Bob Desantis (Chief Acctg Officer)
Shea Long (Sr VP-Products)
Paul Mazzucco (Chief Security Officer)
Octavio Morales (Sr VP-Ops)
Miranda Smith (Acct Exec)
David Haggerty (VP-Sls-Wisconsin & Min-
nesota)
Dan Capra (Reg VP-Sls)
Dick Weisberg (VP-Sls-Pacific Northwest)
Jeff Waide (VP-Charlotte)
Tony Rossabi (Chief Revenue Officer &
Exec VP)
Kenny Ash (VP-Channel)

FrontStreet Management Group
LLC   (1)
106 Apple St Ste 225, Tinton Falls, NJ
07724
Tel.: (855) 444-3734
Web Site: http://www.frontstgroup.com
Commercial Infrastructure Management
Services
N.A.I.C.S.: 561210
Kristen Bunnell (CEO)
Jay Gates (Chm)
Vince Scheerer (Chief Bus Dev Officer)

Subsidiary (Domestic):

FrontStreet Facility Solutions,
Inc.   (2)

4170 Veterans Memorial Hwy, Bohemia, NY
11716
Tel.: (631) 244-8474
Web Site: http://www.frontstreetfs.com
Sales Range: $10-24.9 Million
Emp.: 150
Commercial Facilities Maintenance & Man-
agement Support Services
N.A.I.C.S.: 561210
Thomas J. Hutzel (CEO)
Skip Warner (COO)

CHARTIO INC.

445 Bryant St, San Francisco, CA
94107
Tel.: (855) 232-0320
Web Site: http://www.chartio.com
Sales Range: $1-9.9 Million
Data Analytics Software
N.A.I.C.S.: 513210
Dave Fowler (Founder & CEO)
Justin Davis (CTO)

CHARTWELL AGENCY

120 W State St Ste 305, Rockford, IL
61101
Tel.: (815) 282-9976
Web Site: https://www.chartwell-
agency.com
Year Founded: 2002
Emp.: 9
Public Relations & Brand Identity
N.A.I.C.S.: 541820
Rebecca Epperson (Pres)
Emily Hartzog (VP)

Subsidiaries:

Chartwell Agency   (1)
4230 E Towne Blvd Ste 292, Madison, WI
53704
Tel.: (608) 239-0745
Public Relations
N.A.I.C.S.: 541820

Chartwell Agency   (1)
677 Ave of the Cities, East Moline, IL 62144
Tel.: (309) 738-1662
Public Relations Agency
N.A.I.C.S.: 541820
Rebecca Epperson (Pres)

CHARTWELL INVESTMENTS

570 Lexington Ave 44th Fl, New York,
NY 10022
Tel.: (212) 521-5500
Web Site:
http://www.chartwellinvestment.com
Year Founded: 1992
Sales Range: $750-799.9 Million
Privater Equity Firm
N.A.I.C.S.: 523999
Michael S. Shein (Founder)
C. Larry Davis (Partner)

Subsidiaries:

Advance Ross Electronics
Corporation   (1)
3000 E Marshall Ave, Longview, TX 75601-
6118
Tel.: (903) 758-3395
Web Site: http://www.ppcair.com
Electrostatic Precipitator Designer Mfr
N.A.I.C.S.: 333413

Carey International, Inc.   (1)
4530 Wisconsin Ave NW, Washington, DC
20016
Tel.: (202) 895-1200
Web Site: http://www.carey.com
Sales Range: $250-299.9 Million
Chauffeur Services & Ground Transporta-
tion Logistics Management Services
N.A.I.C.S.: 485320
Mitchell J. Lahr (CFO)
Sandy Miller (CEO)
Dan Miller (COO)

CHAS F. WILLIAMS CO. INC.

328 Lipscomb St, Fort Worth, TX
76104
Tel.: (817) 332-6363

Web Site:
https://www.chasfwilliams.com
Rev.: $10,000,000
Emp.: 45
Metal Doors, Sash & Trim
N.A.I.C.S.: 423310
Jerry E. Williams (Pres)
Harley Daugherty (Mgr-Ops)
Kevin Hutchins (Project Mgr)
Scott Ryan (Project Mgr)

CHAS H. BILZ INSURANCE AGENCY, INC.

412 Madison Ave, Covington, KY
41011
Tel.: (859) 431-1235
Web Site:
https://www.bilzinsurance.com
Rev.: $20,000,000
Emp.: 25
Insurance Agents
N.A.I.C.S.: 524210
Charles M. Berger (Pres)
Dick Berger (VP)
Ashley Winburn (Acct Mgr-Personal
Lines)
Bridget Kubera (Acct Mgr-Comml)

CHAS P. SMITH & ASSOCI-ATES, PA, CPA'S

1509 S Florida Ave, Lakeland, FL
33803
Tel.: (863) 688-1725
Web Site: http://www.cpalliance.com
Year Founded: 1975
Sales Range: $1-9.9 Million
Emp.: 22
Accounting & Financial Advisory Ser-
vices
N.A.I.C.S.: 541211
Michael A. Riskin (Dir-Taxation)
Bob Herring (Dir-Technical & Support
Svcs)
James M. Luffman (Partner)
Peter C. Golotko (Pres, Partner &
Principal)
Nolen Bailey (Dir-Retirement Plan
Svcs)
Esther Barnette (Supvr-Portfolio
Mgmt)
Holly Kelley (Supvr-Tax)

CHAS ROBERTS AIR CONDI-TIONING, INC.

9828 N 19th Ave, Phoenix, AZ
85021-1906
Tel.: (602) 386-2732   AZ
Web Site:
https://www.chasroberts.com
Year Founded: 1942
Sales Range: $100-124.9 Million
Emp.: 1,000
Heating & Air Conditioning Contract-
ing Services
N.A.I.C.S.: 238220
Michelle Hushman (Mgr-Acctg)
Nicole Barnett (Office Mgr)
Ty Eshelman (Engr-Mechanical-
HVAC)
Laurie Barnes (CFO)
Karla Smith (Dir-HR)
Jeff Zimmerman (Gen Mgr-Svc)
Ken Anderson (Mgr-Plumbing Svc)
Brad Hall (Pres)
Rod Tomita (VP-Sls)
Roberta M. Roberts Shank (Pres &
CEO)

CHASCO CONSTRUCTORS, LTD., LLP.

2801 E Old Settlers Blvd, Round
Rock, TX 78665
Tel.: (512) 244-0600
Web Site: https://www.chasco.com
Year Founded: 1979
Sales Range: $50-74.9 Million

Emp.: 340
Commercial & Institutional Building
Construction Services
N.A.I.C.S.: 236220
Chaz Glace (Founder)

CHASE BREXTON HEALTH SERVICES, INC.

1111 N Charles St, Baltimore, MD
21201
Tel.: (410) 837-2050   MD
Web Site:
https://www.chasebrexton.org
Year Founded: 1989
Sales Range: $50-74.9 Million
Emp.: 271
Health Care Srvices
N.A.I.C.S.: 622110
Robin Brooks (CFO)
Carolyn Kennedy (Pres)
Jack K. Boyson (VP)
Kristine Holmes (Sec)
Michelle Barrera (COO)
Becky Frank (VP-Dev & Mktg)
Shanae Murray (VP-HR)
Patrick Mutch (Pres & CEO)
Juan Negrin (Treas)
Jermaine Wyatt (VP-Psychosocial
Svcs)
Robert Stern (Dir-Medical-Glen Bur-
nie Center)

CHASE CHEVROLET CO., INC.

6441 Holman Rd, Stockton, CA
95212-2703
Tel.: (209) 475-6600   CA
Web Site:
http://www.chasechevrolet.com
Year Founded: 1944
Sales Range: $75-99.9 Million
Emp.: 125
Automobile Sales & Service
N.A.I.C.S.: 441330
John W. Chase (Pres)
John Ferraiolo (Gen Mgr)
Amy Clark (Controller)

CHASE ENTERPRISES, INC.

225 Asylum St 29th Fl, Hartford, CT
06103
Tel.: (860) 549-1674   CT
Web Site:
http://www.chaseenterprises.com
Year Founded: 1973
Sales Range: $25-49.9 Million
Emp.: 350
Professional Organization Manage-
ment Services
N.A.I.C.S.: 541611
Arnold L. Chase (Exec VP)

Subsidiaries:

Chase G.P. Corporation   (1)
225 Asylum St 29th Fl, Hartford, CT 06103-
3509
Tel.: (860) 549-1674
Web Site: http://www.chaseenterprises.com
Sales Range: $25-49.9 Million
Emp.: 65
Operators Of Nonresidential Buildings
N.A.I.C.S.: 531120
David T. Chase (Pres & CEO)

Communication Site Management
Corp.   (1)
225 329 Fl, Hartford, CT 06103-3509
Tel.: (860) 525-6507
Sales Range: $10-24.9 Million
Emp.: 2
Operators Of Nonresidential Buildings
N.A.I.C.S.: 531120

David T. Chase Enterprises Inc. (1)
225 Asylum St, Hartford, CT 06103
Tel.: (860) 549-1674
Sales Range: $10-24.9 Million
Emp.: 50
Provider of General Contracting Services

Chase Enterprises, Inc.—(Continued)
N.A.I.C.S.: 541219

CHASE GENERAL CORPORATION
1307 S 59th St, Saint Joseph, MO 64507
Tel.: (816) 279-1625 **MO**
Web Site:
http://www.cherrymash.com
Year Founded: 1876
Rev.: $3,395,505
Assets: $1,584,038
Liabilities: $779,687
Net Worth: $804,351
Earnings: ($92,077)
Emp.: 17
Fiscal Year-end: 06/30/24
Candy Mfr
N.A.I.C.S.: 311340
Barry M. Yantis (Chm, Pres, CEO, CFO & Treas)
Brian A. Yantis (Sec)

CHASE OIL COMPANY INC.
403 W Lucas St, Florence, SC 29501
Tel.: (843) 662-1594
Rev.: $10,000,000
Emp.: 11
Convenience Stores, Independent
N.A.I.C.S.: 445131
Charles G. Howard Sr. (Pres)

CHASE PLASTIC SERVICES, INC.
6467 Waldon Center Dr Ste 200, Clarkston, MI 48346-4830
Tel.: (248) 620-2120 **MI**
Web Site:
http://www.chaseplastics.com
Year Founded: 1992
Sales Range: $10-24.9 Million
Emp.: 90
Mfr of Plastics Materials & Basic Shapes
N.A.I.C.S.: 424610
Kevin J. Chase (Pres)
Carole Chase (VP)
Alan Arduini (Reg Mgr-Acct)
Mike Nielsen (Mgr-Acct)

CHASE TECHNOLOGY CONSULTANTS, LLC
15 Broad St 1st Fl, Boston, MA 02109
Tel.: (617) 227-5000
Web Site:
http://www.chasetechconsultants.com
Year Founded: 2007
Sales Range: $1-9.9 Million
Emp.: 25
Technology Staffing Services
N.A.I.C.S.: 561320
Jared Franklin (Pres & Founder)
Tristan Marchette (VP-Bus Dev)

CHASE, CLARKE, STEWART & FONTANA, INC.
101 State St 8th Fl, Springfield, MA 01102
Tel.: (413) 788-4531 **MA**
Web Site: https://www.chaseins.com
Year Founded: 1827
Sales Range: $1-9.9 Million
Insurance Agents
N.A.I.C.S.: 524210
Dan Fontana (VP)
Raymond Lukas (VP)
Jim Stewart (VP)
Lisa M. Clewes (Mgr-Ops)
Robert A. Stewart Jr. (Pres)

CHASE-DURER LTD.

9601 Wilshire Dr Ste 1118, Beverly Hills, CA 90210
Tel.: (310) 550-7280
Web Site: http://www.chase-durer.com
Rev.: $3,500,000
Emp.: 15
Watch Designer & Mfr
N.A.I.C.S.: 423940
Brandon Chase (Founder)

CHASE-WALTON ELASTOMERS INC.
29 Apsley St, Hudson, MA 01749-1543
Tel.: (978) 562-0085
Web Site: http://www.chase-walton.com
Year Founded: 1955
Rev.: $11,200,000
Emp.: 120
Silicone Rubbers
N.A.I.C.S.: 325212

CHASTAIN CONSTRUCTION INC.
623 Meeting St, Charleston, SC 29403
Tel.: (843) 722-4555
Web Site:
https://www.chastainconstruction.com
Year Founded: 1995
Rev.: $3,068,000
Emp.: 15
Residential Remodeling Services
N.A.I.C.S.: 236118
Kevin Townsend (Pres & Project Mgr)
Liston Guerry (VP & Project Mgr)

Subsidiaries:

Trade Mark Construction, Inc. **(1)**
903 Industry Way Ste B, El Centro, CA 92243
Tel.: (760) 337-9488
Sales Range: $1-9.9 Million
Residential Construction
N.A.I.C.S.: 236115

CHASTANG ENTERPRISES, INC.
6200 N Loop E, Houston, TX 77026-1936
Tel.: (713) 671-0101
Web Site:
https://www.chastangford.com
Sales Range: $10-24.9 Million
Emp.: 80
Sales of Trucks & Tractors
N.A.I.C.S.: 423110
Joseph Chastang (Pres)
Steve Bobo (Controller)
Patrick Chastang (Gen Mgr)
Dan Miller (VP-Sls)

CHAT INC.
299 Stallings Bridge Rd, Tylertown, MS 39667
Tel.: (601) 876-3374
Sales Range: $10-24.9 Million
Emp.: 2
Eating Place
N.A.I.C.S.: 722513
Vicki Baskins (Office Mgr)

CHATAM INTERNATIONAL INCORPORATED
2633 Trenton Ave, Philadelphia, PA 19125-1837
Tel.: (215) 425-9300 **DE**
Year Founded: 1979
Sales Range: $10-24.9 Million
Emp.: 165
Distilled & Blended Liquors
N.A.I.C.S.: 312140
Norton J. Cooper (Pres)

Subsidiaries:

Charles Jacquin Et Cie Inc. **(1)**
2633 Trenton Ave, Philadelphia, PA 19125-1837 **(100%)**
Tel.: (215) 425-9300
Distilled & Blended Liquors
N.A.I.C.S.: 312140
Norton J. Cooper (Pres)
Patty Sutton (Art Dir)
Carrie Russo (Mgr-Quality Assurance)

Whitehall Advertising Inc. **(1)**
2633 Trenton Ave, Philadelphia, PA 19125-1837
Tel.: (215) 425-9350
Sales Range: $1-9.9 Million
Emp.: 3
House Agencies
N.A.I.C.S.: 541810

CHATCHING, INC.
1061 E Indiantown Rd #400, Jupiter, FL 33477
Tel.: (561) 316-3867
Year Founded: 2011
Social Networking Website
N.A.I.C.S.: 516210
Steven L. Pfirman (Pres & Sec)

CHATEAU INTERNATIONAL INC.
330 5th Ave Rm 605, New York, NY 10001
Tel.: (212) 967-6705
Web Site:
http://www.chateauinternational.com
Sales Range: $10-24.9 Million
Emp.: 35
Handbags
N.A.I.C.S.: 424350
Robert Chang (Pres)

CHATEAU RESTAURANT OF WALTHAM INC.
195 School St, Waltham, MA 02451
Tel.: (781) 894-3339
Web Site:
http://www.chateaurestaurant.com
Rev.: $17,971,172
Emp.: 180
Italian Restaurant
N.A.I.C.S.: 722511
Joseph Nocera (Pres)

CHATHAM ASSET MANAGEMENT, LLC
40 Main St Ste 204, Chatham, NJ 07928-2432
Tel.: (973) 701-2431
Investment Management Service
N.A.I.C.S.: 523940
Gene Gaeta (Dir-Bus Dev)

Subsidiaries:

American Media, Inc. **(1)**
4 New York Plz, New York, NY 10004
Tel.: (212) 545-4800
Web Site:
http://www.americanmediainc.com
Holding Company; Periodical Publisher
N.A.I.C.S.: 551112
David J. Pecker (Chm, Pres & CEO)
Kevin Hyson (CMO & Exec VP)
Chris Scardino (Exec VP & Grp Publr)
Robert M. O'Neill (Sr VP-Ops)
Dave Thompson (CIO & Exec VP)
Eric S. Klee (Gen Counsel, Sec & Sr VP)
Neil Goldstein (Publr & Sr VP)
Dylan Howard (Chief Content Officer-AMI Celebrity Grp)
James Robertson (Editor-OK!)

Subsidiary (Domestic):

Distribution Services, Inc. **(2)**
1665 Palmbeach Blvd Ste 401, West Palm Beach, FL 33401
Tel.: (561) 688-0097
Web Site: http://www.dsi-force.com

Sales Range: $10-24.9 Million
Emp.: 52
Marketing & Merchandising Services
N.A.I.C.S.: 513110

Odyssey Magazine Publishing Group Inc. **(2)**
4 New York Plz, New York, NY 10004
Tel.: (212) 545-4800
Entertainment Industry Periodical Publisher
N.A.I.C.S.: 513120
Neil Goldstein (Sr VP & Publr)

Unit (Domestic):

OK! Magazine **(3)**
4 New York Plz, New York, NY 10004
Tel.: (212) 545-4800
Web Site: http://www.okmagazine.com
Celebrity News Periodical Publisher
N.A.I.C.S.: 513120
Dylan Howard (Chief Content Officer)

Soap Opera Digest **(3)**
261 Madison Ave, New York, NY 10016
Tel.: (212) 915-4249
Web Site: http://www.soapdigest.com
Sales Range: $10-24.9 Million
Emp.: 60
Periodical Publishers
N.A.I.C.S.: 513120

Star Magazine **(3)**
1 Park Ave, New York, NY 10016
Tel.: (212) 545-4800
Web Site: http://www.starmagazine.com
Magazine Publishing
N.A.I.C.S.: 513120
Kelly Allen (Asst Editor)

US Weekly Magazine **(3)**
One State St Plz 27th Fl, New York, NY 10004
Tel.: (212) 484-1616
Web Site: http://www.usmagazine.com
Magazine; Owned 50% by Wenner Media LLC & 50% by The Walt Disney Company
N.A.I.C.S.: 513120
John M. Lagana (CFO & VP)
Terry McDonell (Editor)
Brian Beaudry (Circulation Dir)
Michael Steel (Editor-in-Chief)
Jennifer Peros (Editor)

Unit (Domestic):

The National Enquirer **(2)**
1000 American Media Way, Boca Raton, FL 33464-1000
Tel.: (561) 989-1221
Web Site: http://www.nationalenquirer.com
Tabloid Publisher
N.A.I.C.S.: 513120
David Jackson (Publr)

Subsidiary (Domestic):

Weider Publications, LLC **(2)**
21100 Erwin St4 New York Plz, New York, NY 10004
Tel.: (212) 545-4800
Health & Fitness Magazines Publisher
N.A.I.C.S.: 513120

Postmedia Network Canada Corp. **(1)**
365 Bloor Street East, Toronto, M4W 3L4, ON, Canada **(66%)**
Tel.: (416) 383-2300
Web Site: https://www.postmedia.com
Rev.: $358,459,471
Assets: $165,354,435
Liabilities: $322,774,204
Net Worth: ($157,419,769)
Earnings: ($58,445,703)
Emp.: 2,098
Fiscal Year-end: 08/31/2022
Holding Company; Newspaper Publishing Services
N.A.I.C.S.: 551112
John Bode (CFO, Chief Transformation Officer & Exec VP)
Andrew MacLeod (Pres & CEO)

Subsidiary (Domestic):

Brunswick News, Inc. **(2)**
939 Main St Moncton, Dieppe, E1C 8P, NB, Canada
Tel.: (506) 859-4900
Web Site: http://www.telegraphjournal.com
Sales Range: $100-124.9 Million
Emp.: 500
Newspaper Publishers
N.A.I.C.S.: 513110

J. K. Irving *(CEO)*
Tim O'Briant *(Exec Editor)*

Subsidiary (Domestic):

Northern Light (3)
275 Main St, Bathurst, E2A 1A9, NB,
Canada
Tel.: (506) 546-4491
Web Site: http://www.canadaeast.com
Sales Range: $25-49.9 Million
Emp.: 12
Newspapers
N.A.I.C.S.: 513110
Jean-Claude D'Amours *(Gen Mgr)*

Subsidiary (Domestic):

Postmedia Network Inc. (2)
365 Bloor St E 12th Fl, Toronto, M4W 3L4,
ON, Canada
Tel.: (416) 383-2300
Web Site: http://www.canada.com
Sales Range: $100-124.9 Million
Emp.: 400
Newspaper Publishers
N.A.I.C.S.: 513110
Andrew MacLeod *(Pres & CEO)*
Duncan Clark *(Chief Content Officer)*
Phyllise Gelfand *(VP-Comm)*

Unit (Domestic):

Belleville Intelligencer (3)
199 Front St Ste 535, Belleville, K8N 5H5,
ON, Canada
Tel.: (613) 962-9171
Web Site: http://www.intelligencer.ca
Sales Range: $10-24.9 Million
Emp.: 50
Daily Newspaper
N.A.I.C.S.: 513110

Calgary Herald (3)
215 - 16 Street S E, PO Box 2400, Calgary,
T2E 7P5, AB, Canada
Tel.: (403) 235-7100
Web Site: http://www.calgaryherald.com
Sales Range: $100-124.9 Million
Emp.: 200
Newspaper Publishing
N.A.I.C.S.: 513110
Lorne Motley *(Exec VP-Editorial-West Reg)*

Cobourg Daily Star (3)
884 Division Street Unit 212 Building 2, Co-
bourg, K9A 5V6, ON, Canada
Tel.: (905) 373-7355
Web Site:
http://www.northumberlandtoday.com
Sales Range: $10-24.9 Million
Emp.: 13
Daily Newspaper
N.A.I.C.S.: 513110

Cornwall Standard-Freeholder (3)
1150 Montreal Road, Cornwall, K6H 1E2,
ON, Canada
Tel.: (613) 933-3160
Web Site: http://www.standard-
freeholder.com
Sales Range: $10-24.9 Million
Emp.: 15
Daily Newspaper
N.A.I.C.S.: 513110

Subsidiary (Domestic):

Edmonton Journal Group Inc. (3)
10006-101st St, Edmonton, T5J 0S1, AB,
Canada **(100%)**
Tel.: (780) 498-5500
Web Site: http://www.edmontonjournal.com
Sales Range: $75-99.9 Million
Emp.: 367
Cybergraphics Services
N.A.I.C.S.: 541430

Unit (Domestic):

Edmonton Journal (4)
10006 - 101 Street, Edmonton, T5J 0S1,
AB, Canada
Tel.: (780) 429-5100
Web Site: http://www.edmontonjournal.com
Sales Range: $50-74.9 Million
Emp.: 20
Newspaper Publishing Services
N.A.I.C.S.: 513110

Unit (Domestic):

Kingston Whig-Standard (3)
6 Cataraqui St, Kingston, K7L 4Z7, ON,
Canada
Tel.: (613) 544-5000
Web Site: http://www.thewhig.com
Sales Range: $25-49.9 Million
Emp.: 130
Newspaper Publishers
N.A.I.C.S.: 513110

Leader Post (3)
300 - 1964 Park Street, Regina, S4N 7M5,
SK, Canada
Tel.: (306) 781-5211
Web Site: http://www.leaderpost.com
Emp.: 50
Newspaper Publishers
N.A.I.C.S.: 513110

Mackenzie Times Newspaper (3)
403 MacKenzie Blvd Suite 125, Mackenzie,
V0J 2C0, BC, Canada
Tel.: (250) 997-6675
Sales Range: $25-49.9 Million
Emp.: 2
Newspaper Publishers
N.A.I.C.S.: 513110
Jackie Benton *(Office Mgr)*

Montreal Gazette (3)
2055 Peel St Suite 700, Montreal, H3A
1V4, QC, Canada **(100%)**
Tel.: (514) 987-2222
Web Site: http://www.montrealgazette.com
Sales Range: $100-124.9 Million
Emp.: 350
Newspaper Publishers
N.A.I.C.S.: 513110
Lucinda Chodan *(Editor)*

Subsidiary (Domestic):

National Post, Inc. (3)
365 Bloor St East 3rd Floor, Toronto, M4W
3L4, ON, Canada
Tel.: (416) 383-2300
Web Site: http://www.nationalpost.com
Financial Information Services & Newspa-
per Publisher
N.A.I.C.S.: 513110

Pacific Newspaper Group Inc. (3)
200 Granville Street Suite 1, Vancouver,
V6C 3N3, BC, Canada **(100%)**
Tel.: (604) 605-2000
Web Site: http://www.sunprovince.com
Sales Range: $100-124.9 Million
Emp.: 400
Newspaper Publishers
N.A.I.C.S.: 513110

Unit (Domestic):

The Province (4)
400 - 2985 Virtual Way, Vancouver, V5M
4X7, BC, Canada
Tel.: (604) 605-7381
Web Site: http://www.theprovince.com
Newspaper Publishers
N.A.I.C.S.: 513110

The Vancouver Sun (4)
400 - 2985 Virtual Way, Vancouver, V5M
4X7, BC, Canada **(100%)**
Tel.: (604) 605-7381
Web Site: http://www.vancouversun.com
Sales Range: $100-124.9 Million
Newspaper Publishing
N.A.I.C.S.: 513110
Harold Munro *(Editor-in-Chief)*

Unit (Domestic):

Port Hope Evening Guide (3)
99 King St, Cobourg, K9A 2M2, ON,
Canada
Tel.: (905) 885-2471
Web Site:
http://www.northumberlandtoday.com
Sales Range: $25-49.9 Million
Emp.: 20
Daily Newspaper
N.A.I.C.S.: 513110

Rannie Publications Inc. (3)
4991 King St, PO Box 400, Beamsville, L0R
1B0, ON, Canada **(100%)**
Tel.: (905) 957-3315

Web Site:
http://www.niagaranewspapers.com
Sales Range: $25-49.9 Million
Emp.: 15
Newspapers
N.A.I.C.S.: 513110

The Brantford Expositor (3)
195 Henry St Building 4 Unit 1, Brantford,
N3S 5C9, ON, Canada
Tel.: (519) 756-2020
Web Site: http://www.brantfordexpositor.ca
Sales Range: $25-49.9 Million
Emp.: 75
Daily Newspaper
N.A.I.C.S.: 513110

The Calgary Sun (3)
215 -16 St S E, Calgary, T2E 7P5, AB,
Canada
Tel.: (403) 235-7100
Web Site: http://www.calgarysun.com
Emp.: 250
Daily Newspaper Publisher
N.A.I.C.S.: 513110
Martin Hudson *(Mng Editor)*

The Chatham Daily News (3)
138 King St W, PO Box 2007, Chatham,
N7M 1E3, ON, Canada
Tel.: (519) 354-2000
Web Site: http://www.chathamdailynews.ca
Sales Range: $10-24.9 Million
Emp.: 30
Daily Newspaper
N.A.I.C.S.: 513110

The Edmonton Sun (3)
10006 101 Street, Edmonton, T5J 0S1, AB,
Canada **(100%)**
Tel.: (780) 468-0100
Web Site: http://edmontonsun.com
Sales Range: $50-74.9 Million
Emp.: 250
Daily Newspaper
N.A.I.C.S.: 513110

The London Free Press (3)
210 Dundas Street Suite 201, PO Box
2280, London, N6A 5J3, ON,
Canada **(100%)**
Tel.: (519) 679-1111
Web Site: http://www.lfpress.com
Sales Range: $25-49.9 Million
Emp.: 85
Publisher
N.A.I.C.S.: 513110
Sherri Walker *(Reg Dir-Distr-Ontario West &
London)*

The North Bay Nugget (3)
259 Worthington St W, North Bay, P1B
3B5, ON, Canada
Tel.: (705) 472-3200
Web Site: http://www.nugget.ca
Sales Range: $25-49.9 Million
Emp.: 89
Daily Newspaper
N.A.I.C.S.: 513110

The Northern News (3)
8 Duncan Avenue, Kirkland Lake, P2N 3L4,
ON, Canada
Tel.: (705) 567-5321
Web Site: http://www.northernnews.ca
Sales Range: $25-49.9 Million
Emp.: 6
Daily Newspaper
N.A.I.C.S.: 513110

The Observer (Sarnia) (3)
140 Front St S, Sarnia, N7T 7M8, ON,
Canada
Tel.: (519) 344-3641
Web Site: http://www.theobserver.ca
Sales Range: $10-24.9 Million
Emp.: 37
Daily Newspaper
N.A.I.C.S.: 513110

The Ottawa Citizen (3)
1101 Baxter Road, PO Box 5020, Ottawa,
K2C 3M4, ON, Canada
Tel.: (613) 829-9100
Web Site: http://www.ottawacitizen.com
Sales Range: $100-124.9 Million
Emp.: 300
Newspaper Publishers
N.A.I.C.S.: 513110

The Ottawa Sun (3)

1101 Baxter Rd, PO Box 9729, Station T,
Ottawa, K2C 3M4, ON, Canada **(100%)**
Tel.: (613) 829-9100
Web Site: http://www.ottawasun.com
Sales Range: $25-49.9 Million
Emp.: 100
Daily Newspaper
N.A.I.C.S.: 513110

The Post (3)
413 18th Ave, Hanover, N4N 3S5, ON,
Canada
Tel.: (519) 364-2001
Web Site: http://www.thepost.on.ca
Sales Range: $25-49.9 Million
Emp.: 10
Daily Newspaper
N.A.I.C.S.: 513110

The Sault Star (3)
145 Old Garden River Rd, Sault Sainte Ma-
rie, P6A 5M5, ON, Canada
Tel.: (705) 759-3030
Web Site: http://www.saultstar.com
Emp.: 25
Daily Newspaper
N.A.I.C.S.: 513110

The StarPhoenix (3)
204 Fifth Ave N, Saskatoon, S7K 2P1, SK,
Canada **(100%)**
Tel.: (306) 657-6320
Web Site: http://www.thestarphoenix.com
Sales Range: $50-74.9 Million
Emp.: 250
Newspaper Publishers
N.A.I.C.S.: 513110
Andrea Hill *(Editor)*

The Sudbury Star (3)
128 Pine St Ste 201, Sudbury, P3C 1X3,
ON, Canada
Tel.: (705) 674-5271
Web Site: http://www.thesudburystar.com
Sales Range: $10-24.9 Million
Emp.: 20
Daily Newspaper
N.A.I.C.S.: 513110
Mariette Valade *(Gen Mgr)*

The Sun Times (3)
290 9th St E, Owen Sound, N4K 5P2, ON,
Canada
Tel.: (519) 376-2250
Web Site:
http://www.owensoundtimes.com
Sales Range: $25-49.9 Million
Emp.: 65
Daily Newspaper
N.A.I.C.S.: 513110
Doug Edgar *(Mng Editor)*

Subsidiary (Domestic):

**The Toronto Sun Publishing
Corporation** (3)
365 Bloor St E 6th Floor, Toronto, M4W
3L4, ON, Canada **(100%)**
Tel.: (416) 383-2300
Web Site: http://torontosun.com
Sales Range: $50-74.9 Million
Emp.: 200
Daily Newspaper
N.A.I.C.S.: 513110
Adrienne Batra *(Editor-in-Chief)*

Unit (Domestic):

The Wiarton Echo (3)
573 Berford St, PO Box 220, Wiarton, N0H
2T0, ON, Canada
Tel.: (519) 534-1560
Web Site: http://www.wiartonecho.com
Sales Range: $25-49.9 Million
Emp.: 3
Newspaper Publishers
N.A.I.C.S.: 513110

The Windsor Star (3)
300 Ouellette Ave, Windsor, N9A 7B4, ON,
Canada
Tel.: (519) 255-5711
Web Site: http://www.windsorstar.com
Sales Range: $100-124.9 Million
Emp.: 300
Newspaper Publishers
N.A.I.C.S.: 513110

Timmins Daily Press (3)

Chatham Asset Management, LLC—(Continued)

187 Cedar St S, Timmins, P4N 7G1, ON, Canada
Tel.: (705) 268-5050
Web Site: http://www.timminspress.com
Sales Range: $10-24.9 Million
Emp.: 45
Daily Newspaper
N.A.I.C.S.: 513110

R.R. Donnelley & Sons Company (1)
35 W Wacker Dr, Chicago, IL 60601
Tel.: (630) 322-6000
Web Site: https://www.rrd.com
Rev.: $4,766,300,000
Assets: $3,130,900,000
Liabilities: $3,374,700,000
Net Worth: $(243,800,000)
Earnings: $98,500,000
Emp.: 33,000
Fiscal Year-end: 12/31/2020
Commercial Printing (except Screen & Books)
N.A.I.C.S.: 323111
John Pecaric (Pres-Bus Svcs)
Deborah L. Steiner (Chief Admin Officer, Chief Compliance Officer, Gen Counsel & Sec)
Elif Sagsen-Ercel (Chief Strategy & Transformation Officer & Exec VP)
Johan Nystedt (Sr VP-Fin)
Thomas J. Quinlan III (CEO)
Drew Coxhead (CFO)
Al DuPont (Chief Comml Officer)
Dave Houck (CIO & Exec VP)
Pat Pericht (Grp CFO)

Subsidiary (Domestic):

Banta Global Turnkey LLC (2)
6315 W By Northwest Blvd, Houston, TX 77040
Tel.: (713) 354-1300
Computer Peripheral Equipment Mfr
N.A.I.C.S.: 334118

Subsidiary (Non-US):

Banta Global Turnkey Ltd. (2)
Hollyhill Industrial Estate, Cork, Ireland
Tel.: (353) 214397515
Web Site: http://www.rrd.com
Sales Range: $25-49.9 Million
Emp.: 100
Supply Chain Management Services
N.A.I.C.S.: 541611
E. Padraic Allen (Pres)

Subsidiary (Non-US):

Banta Global Turnkey (Singapore) PTE LTD (3)
30 Toh Guan Rd TT International Tradepark, Jurong, 608838, Singapore
Tel.: (65) 67901800
Business Services
N.A.I.C.S.: 561499
Hwang Yang Chng (Gen Mgr)

Subsidiary (Domestic):

Banta Global Turnkey Ltd. - Limerick (3)
Block 1 International Science Center National Technology Park, Limerick, Ireland
Tel.: (353) 61303888
Web Site: http://www.rrd.com
Sales Range: $125-149.9 Million
Emp.: 30
Supply Chain Management Services
N.A.I.C.S.: 541611

Subsidiary (Non-US):

Banta Global Turnkey, Ltd. (3)
2 Fraser Rd Kirkton Campus, Livingston, EH54 7BU, W Lothian, United Kingdom
Tel.: (44) 1506404400
Sales Range: $50-74.9 Million
Supply Chain Management Services
N.A.I.C.S.: 541614

Banta Global Turnkey, s.r.o. (3)
Turanka 102, Slatina, Brno, 62700, Czech Republic
Tel.: (420) 532189138
Web Site: http://www.rrdonnelley.com
Lithographic Printing Services

N.A.I.C.S.: 323111

Bowne International Ltd. (3)
25 Copthall Ave, London, EC2R 7BP, United Kingdom
Tel.: (44) 2075515000
Sales Range: $25-49.9 Million
Emp.: 100
Lithographic Printing Services
N.A.I.C.S.: 323111

Subsidiary (Domestic):

Consolidated Graphics, Inc. (2)
5858 Westheimer Ste 200, Houston, TX 77057
Tel.: (713) 787-0977
Rev.: $1,048,237,000
Assets: $644,643,000
Liabilities: $366,269,000
Net Worth: $278,374,000
Earnings: $22,225,000
Emp.: 5,288
Fiscal Year-end: 03/31/2013
Sheetfed, Web & Digital Commercial Printing Services
N.A.I.C.S.: 323111

Subsidiary (Domestic):

AGS Custom Graphics, Inc. (3)
8107 Bavaria Rd, Macedonia, OH 44056
Tel.: (330) 963-7770
Web Site: http://www.agscustomgraphics.com
Commercial Printing Services
N.A.I.C.S.: 323111

Anderson LA, Inc. (3)
3550 Tyburn St, Los Angeles, CA 90065-1427
Tel.: (323) 460-4115
Commercial Printing Services
N.A.I.C.S.: 323111
Luke Westlake (Pres)

Subsidiary (Non-US):

Annan & Bird Lithographers, Inc. (3)
1060 Tristar Dr, Mississauga, L5T 1H9, ON, Canada
Tel.: (905) 670-0604
Commercial Printing Services
N.A.I.C.S.: 323111
Harry Nash (Plant Mgr)

Subsidiary (Domestic):

Apple Graphics, Inc. (3)
1858 Evergreen St, Duarte, CA 91010
Tel.: (626) 301-4277
Sales Range: $25-49.9 Million
Emp.: 50
Commercial Printing Services
N.A.I.C.S.: 323111
Kevin Polley (CEO)
Nancy Bremer (VP-Mfg)
Matt Baki (Pres)

Automated Graphic Systems, Inc. (3)
4590 Graphics Dr, White Plains, MD 20695
Tel.: (301) 274-4441
Web Site: http://www.ags.com
Sales Range: $100-124.9 Million
Emp.: 285
Commercial Printing Services
N.A.I.C.S.: 323111

Bridgetown Printing Co. (3)
5300 N Channel Ave, Portland, OR 97217-7626
Tel.: (503) 863-5300
Web Site: http://www.bridgetown.com
Sales Range: $25-49.9 Million
Emp.: 75
Commercial Printing Services
N.A.I.C.S.: 323111
Margo L. Yohner (Pres)

CDS Publications (3)
2661 S Pacific Hwy, Medford, OR 97501
Tel.: (541) 773-7575
Web Site: http://www.cdspublications.com
Sales Range: $25-49.9 Million
Emp.: 300
Bound Publications Printing
N.A.I.C.S.: 323111
Steven A. Brown (Pres)

Subsidiary (Non-US):

CGX Yamagata Japan GK (3)
495-35 Hane Hagiwara-cho, Gero, 509-2506, Gifu, Japan
Tel.: (81) 576532064
Web Site: http://www.cgxyamagata.com
Sales Range: $25-49.9 Million
Emp.: 5
Commercial Printing Services
N.A.I.C.S.: 323111

Subsidiary (Domestic):

Clear Visions, Inc. (3)
121 Interpark Blvd Ste 801, San Antonio, TX 78216-1842
Tel.: (210) 580-8082
Web Site: http://www.clearvisionsinc.com
Sales Range: $25-49.9 Million
Emp.: 50
Commercial Printing Services
N.A.I.C.S.: 323111
Eric Koenigs (Pres)

Consolidated Carqueville Printing Company (3)
1536 Bourbon Pkwy, Streamwood, IL 60107
Tel.: (630) 837-4500
Web Site: http://www.carqueville.com
Commercial Printing Services
N.A.I.C.S.: 323111

Copy-Mor, Inc. (3)
767 N Industrial Dr, Elmhurst, IL 60126-1500
Tel.: (312) 666-4000
Web Site: http://www.cmiart.com
Commercial Printing Services
N.A.I.C.S.: 323111

EGT Printing Solutions, LLC (3)
32031 Townley, Madison Heights, MI 48071
Tel.: (248) 583-2500
Web Site: http://www.egtgo.com
Commercial Printing Services
N.A.I.C.S.: 323111

Electric City Printing Company (3)
730 Hampton Rd, Williamston, SC 29697
Tel.: (864) 224-6331
Web Site: http://www.ecprint.com
Sales Range: $25-49.9 Million
Emp.: 50
Commercial Printing Services
N.A.I.C.S.: 323111
Jim Gunter Jr. (Controller)

Emerald City Graphics, Inc. (3)
23328 66th Ave S, Kent, WA 98032
Tel.: (253) 520-2600
Web Site: http://www.emeraldcg.com
Emp.: 100
Commercial Printing Services
N.A.I.C.S.: 323111

Frederic Printing Company (3)
14701 E 38th Ave, Aurora, CO 80011-1215 (100%)
Tel.: (303) 371-7990
Web Site: http://www.fredericprinting.com
Sales Range: $25-49.9 Million
Emp.: 200
Commercial Sheetfed Offset Printing
N.A.I.C.S.: 323111
Kurt Hamlin (Pres)

GSL Fine Lithographers (3)
8386 Rovana Cir, Sacramento, CA 95828-2527
Tel.: (916) 231-1410
Web Site: http://www.gslitho.com
Sales Range: $25-49.9 Million
Emp.: 40
Commercial Printing Services
N.A.I.C.S.: 323111

Garner Printing Company (3)
1697 NE 53rd Ave, Des Moines, IA 50313
Tel.: (515) 266-2171
Web Site: http://www.rrd.com
Commercial Printing Services
N.A.I.C.S.: 323111

Geyer Printing Company, Inc. (3)
55 38th St, Pittsburgh, PA 15201
Tel.: (412) 682-3633
Web Site: http://www.geyerprinting.com
Sales Range: $10-24.9 Million
Emp.: 50
Book Printing Services

N.A.I.C.S.: 323117

Graphcom, LLC (3)
1375 Highlands Ridge Rd SE, Smyrna, GA 30082-4858
Tel.: (404) 355-3415
Web Site: http://www.graphcomprints.com
Sales Range: $25-49.9 Million
Emp.: 45
Commercial Printing Services
N.A.I.C.S.: 323111

Graphic Technology of Maryland, Inc. (3)
8620 Old Dorsey Run Rd, Jessup, MD 20794
Tel.: (301) 317-0100
Emp.: 40
Commercial Printing Services
N.A.I.C.S.: 323111
Russ Hewitt (Pres)

Graphtec (3)
8620 Old Dorsey Run Rd, Jessup, MD 20794
Tel.: (301) 317-0100
Web Site: http://www.graphtec.com
Sales Range: $10-24.9 Million
Emp.: 40
Commercial Printing Services
N.A.I.C.S.: 323111

H&N Printing & Graphics, Inc. (3)
1913 Greenspring Dr, Timonium, MD 21093
Tel.: (410) 252-5300
Web Site: http://www.rrd.com
Commercial Printing Services
N.A.I.C.S.: 323111

Hickory Printing Solutions (3)
725 Reese Dr SW, Conover, NC 28613-2935
Tel.: (828) 465-3431
Web Site: http://www.hickoryprinting.com
Sales Range: $50-74.9 Million
Emp.: 250
Commercial Web, Sheetfed & Package Printing Services
N.A.I.C.S.: 323111

Branch (Domestic):

Hickory Printing (4)
308 Friendship Dr, Greensboro, NC 27409
Tel.: (336) 855-8070
Web Site: http://www.hickoryprinting.com
Commercial Printing Services
N.A.I.C.S.: 323111

Subsidiary (Domestic):

Ironwood Lithographers, Inc. (3)
455 S 52nd St, Tempe, AZ 85281
Tel.: (480) 829-7700
Web Site: http://www.ironwoodlitho.com
Sales Range: $25-49.9 Million
Emp.: 75
Commercial Printing Services
N.A.I.C.S.: 323111
Don Benner (Pres)

John C. Otto Company, Inc. (3)
341 Shaker Rd, East Longmeadow, MA 01028-0367
Tel.: (413) 525-4131
Sales Range: $10-24.9 Million
Emp.: 35
Book Binding Services
N.A.I.C.S.: 323120
Andy Timmons (Mgr-Sls)

Keys Printing Company (3)
1004 Keys Dr, Greenville, SC 29615
Tel.: (864) 288-6560
Web Site: http://www.keysprinting.com
Sales Range: $50-74.9 Million
Emp.: 50
Commercial Printing Services
N.A.I.C.S.: 323111

Maryland Composition (3)
14880 Sweitzer Ln, Laurel, MD 20707-2913
Tel.: (410) 760-7900
Web Site: http://www.ags.com
Sales Range: $10-24.9 Million
Emp.: 9
Commercial Printing Services
N.A.I.C.S.: 323111

Maximum Graphics (3)

1245 Lakeview Dr, Chaska, MN 55318-9506
Tel.: (952) 448-5100
Web Site: http://www.maxgraphics.com
Sales Range: $50-74.9 Million
Emp.: 150
Commercial Sheetfed Printing Services
N.A.I.C.S.: 323111

Mercury Printing, Inc. (3)
4650 Shelby Air Dr, Memphis, TN 38118-7405 **(100%)**
Tel.: (901) 345-8480
Web Site: http://www.mercuryprintingco.com
Sales Range: $25-49.9 Million
Emp.: 100
Commercial Printing, Typesetting & Bookbinding Services
N.A.I.C.S.: 323111

Metropolitan Printing Services, LLC (3)
720 S Morton St, Bloomington, IN 47403
Tel.: (812) 332-7279
Commercial Printing Services
N.A.I.C.S.: 323111

Mobility, Inc. (3)
14880 Sweitzer Ln, Laurel, MD 20707-2913
Tel.: (804) 264-9031
Sales Range: $50-74.9 Million
Commercial Printing Services
N.A.I.C.S.: 323111

Mount Vernon Printing Company (3)
13201 Mid Atlantic Blvd Ste 100, Laurel, MD 20708
Tel.: (301) 341-5600
Web Site: http://www.mvprint.com
Sales Range: $25-49.9 Million
Emp.: 40
Commercial Printing Services
N.A.I.C.S.: 323111
Scott Kravitz (Pres)

Nies/Artcraft Companies, Inc. (3)
5900 Berthold Ave, Saint Louis, MO 63110
Tel.: (314) 951-0400
Web Site: http://www.nies.com
Sales Range: $25-49.9 Million
Emp.: 110
Commercial Printing Services
N.A.I.C.S.: 323111

Orange County Printing (3)
2485 Da Vinci, Irvine, CA 92614-5844
Tel.: (949) 475-1900
Web Site: http://www.ocpc.com
Sales Range: $25-49.9 Million
Emp.: 150
Commercial Sheetfed Printing Services
N.A.I.C.S.: 323111

PBM Graphics Inc. (3)
3700 S Miami Blvd, Durham, NC 27703-9130
Tel.: (919) 544-6222
Web Site: http://www.pbmgraphics.com
Sales Range: $125-149.9 Million
Emp.: 600
Commercial Printing Services
N.A.I.C.S.: 323111
Adam Geerts (Pres)

Division (Domestic):

PBM Graphics, Inc - Packaging Division (4)
604 W Hwy 34, Howard, SD 57349
Tel.: (605) 772-4436
Web Site: http://www.pbmgraphics.com
Sales Range: $25-49.9 Million
Emp.: 120
Commercial Packaging Services
N.A.I.C.S.: 322220

PBM Graphics, Inc - Triad Division (4)
415 Westcliff Rd, Greensboro, NC 27409
Tel.: (336) 664-5800
Web Site: http://www.pbmgraphics.com
Sales Range: $25-49.9 Million
Emp.: 40
Sheetfed & Digital Commercial Printing Services
N.A.I.C.S.: 323111

Subsidiary (Domestic):

PCA, LLC (3)

15 W Aylesbury Rd Ste 2, Lutherville Timonium, MD 21093-4146
Tel.: (410) 561-5533
Commercial Printing Services
N.A.I.C.S.: 323111

Precision Litho, Inc. (3)
1185 Joshua Way, Vista, CA 92081
Tel.: (760) 727-9400
Web Site: http://www.plitho.com
Emp.: 40
Commercial Lithographic Printing
N.A.I.C.S.: 323111

Printing Control Graphics (3)
1011 Andover Park E, Tukwila, WA 98188
Tel.: (206) 575-4114
Web Site: http://www.printingcontrol.com
Sales Range: $1-9.9 Million
Emp.: 40
Offset Printing Services
N.A.I.C.S.: 323111

Rush Press (3)
3553 California St, San Diego, CA 92101-1115
Tel.: (619) 296-7874
Web Site: http://www.rushpress.com
Sales Range: $100-124.9 Million
Printing & Bindery Services
N.A.I.C.S.: 513199
Gene Valles (Pres)

Spangler Graphics, LLC (3)
2930 S 44th St, Kansas City, KS 66106-3700
Tel.: (913) 722-4500
Web Site: http://www.spanglergraphics.com
Emp.: 100
Commercial Printing Services
N.A.I.C.S.: 323111
Brian Yokley (Pres)

Storter Childs Printing Company, Inc. (3)
1540 NE Waldo Rd, Gainesville, FL 32641
Tel.: (352) 376-2658
Web Site: http://www.storterchilds.com
Sales Range: $25-49.9 Million
Emp.: 25
Commercial Printing Services
N.A.I.C.S.: 323111

Tewell Warren Printing Company (3)
4710 Lipan St, Denver, CO 80211-2333
Tel.: (303) 458-8505
Web Site: http://www.tewellwarren.com
Sales Range: $25-49.9 Million
Emp.: 50
Commercial Printing Services
N.A.I.C.S.: 323111
Sean Bermingham (Pres)

The Cyril-Scott Company (3)
3950 State Rte 37 E, Lancaster, OH 43130-7899
Tel.: (740) 654-2112
Web Site: http://www.rrdonnelley.com
Commercial Printing Services
N.A.I.C.S.: 323111

The Hennegan Company (3)
7455 Empire Dr, Florence, KY 41042-2923
Tel.: (859) 282-3600
Web Site: http://www.hennegan.com
Sales Range: $100-124.9 Million
Emp.: 275
Lithographic Printing Services
N.A.I.C.S.: 323111
Clinton Humphrey (Pres)

The Jackson Group Corporation (3)
5804 Churchman Bypass, Indianapolis, IN 46203
Tel.: (317) 791-9000
Web Site: http://www.rrd.com
Commercial Lithographic Printing
N.A.I.C.S.: 323111
Mark Leggio (Pres)

The Jarvis Press, Inc. (3)
9112 Viscount Row, Dallas, TX 75247
Tel.: (214) 637-2340
Web Site: http://www.jarvispress.com
Emp.: 50
Commercial Printing Services
N.A.I.C.S.: 323111
Dave Carpenter (Pres)

The McKay Press, Inc. (3)
7600 W Wackerly Rd, Midland, MI 48642

Tel.: (989) 631-2360
Web Site: http://www.mckaypress.com
Commercial Printing Services
N.A.I.C.S.: 323111

Theo Davis Sons, Incorporated (3)
1415 W Gannon Ave, Zebulon, NC 27597
Tel.: (919) 269-7401
Sales Range: $25-49.9 Million
Emp.: 50
Commercial Printing Services
N.A.I.C.S.: 323111
Michelle Hernandez (Pres)
Michael Davis (CEO)

Thousand Oaks Printing & Specialties, Inc. (3)
5334 Sterling Center Dr, Westlake Village, CA 91361-4612
Tel.: (818) 706-8330
Web Site: http://www.toprinting.com
Sales Range: $25-49.9 Million
Emp.: 100
Commercial Printing Services
N.A.I.C.S.: 323111

Tucker Printers, Inc. (3)
270 Middle Rd, Henrietta, NY 14467
Tel.: (585) 359-3030
Web Site: http://www.tuckerprinters.com
Sales Range: $25-49.9 Million
Emp.: 50
Commercial Printing Services
N.A.I.C.S.: 323111
Anthony Antinetto (Plant Mgr)
Glenn Marino (VP-Pkg)
Peter Ashe (VP-Pkg)
Al Owens (Mgr-Acct)
Rick Tatanus (Acct Mgr)
Jody Sherman (Acct Mgr)
Mike Steppe (Pres)
Brian Gerstner (Mgr-QA & EHS)
Betty Kiessel (Controller)
Stacey Vossler (Mgr-Pre-Press & Digital)
Larry Wedgwood (Mgr-Bindery)

Tursack Incorporated (3)
701 Hemlock Rd Morgantown Business Pk, Morgantown, PA 19543
Tel.: (610) 286-6866
Web Site: http://www.tursack.com
Sales Range: $50-74.9 Million
Emp.: 150
Printing Services
N.A.I.C.S.: 323111

Valcour Printing, Inc. (3)
400 Valley School Dr, Valley Park, MO 63088
Tel.: (866) 446-6328
Sales Range: $25-49.9 Million
Emp.: 50
Commercial Printing Services
N.A.I.C.S.: 323111

Veritas Document Solutions, LLC (3)
913 Commerce Ct, Buffalo Grove, IL 60089-2375
Tel.: (847) 278-8469
Web Site: http://www.meetveritas.com
Commercial Printing Services
N.A.I.C.S.: 323111
Michelle Steinberg (Pres)

Wentworth Corporation (3)
101 N 12th St, West Columbia, SC 29169-6452
Tel.: (803) 739-4506
Web Site: http://www.wentworthprinting.com
Emp.: 50
Commercial Printing Services
N.A.I.C.S.: 323111

Wentworth Printing Corporation (3)
101 N 12th St, West Columbia, SC 29169
Tel.: (803) 796-9990
Web Site: http://www.wentworthprinting.com
Sales Range: $25-49.9 Million
Emp.: 75
Commercial Printing Services
N.A.I.C.S.: 323111

Wetzel Brothers, LLC (3)
2401 E Edgerton, Cudahy, WI 53110
Tel.: (414) 271-5444
Web Site: http://www.wetzelbrothers.com
Sales Range: $25-49.9 Million
Emp.: 75
Commercial Printing Services
N.A.I.C.S.: 323111

Gregg Weber (Pres)
Randy Hoffman (VP-Sls & Mktg)
Lisa Redlin (Controller)
John Starich (Mgr-Pur & Scheduling)

Subsidiary (Non-US):

Courier Technologia em Servicos Graficos Ltda (2)
Pc Antonio Prado 33 Conj Cj 1708 Parte, Sao Paulo, 01010-010, Brazil
Tel.: (55) 1131015055
Software Development Services
N.A.I.C.S.: 541512

Subsidiary (Domestic):

DDM-Digital Imaging, Data Processing and Mailing Services, L.C. (2)
1223 William St, Buffalo, NY 14206
Tel.: (716) 893-8671
Web Site: http://www.ddmdirect.com
Direct Mail Advertising Services
N.A.I.C.S.: 541860

Subsidiary (Non-US):

Devonshire GmbH (2)
Bockenheimer Landstr 17-19, 60325, Frankfurt am Main, Germany
Tel.: (49) 69710455150
Web Site: http://www.devonshire.de
Sales Range: $25-49.9 Million
Emp.: 6
Human Resource Consulting Services
N.A.I.C.S.: 541612
Michal Mlynarczyk (Mng Dir)
Michal Golgowski (Country Mgr)
Ilona Piatkowska-Kotkowiak (Office Mgr)

Devonshire Sp. z o.o (2)
Aleje Jerozolimskie 56C, 00-803, Warsaw, Poland
Tel.: (48) 228209360
Web Site: http://www.devonshire.pl
Sales Range: $25-49.9 Million
Emp.: 26
Human Resource Consulting Services
N.A.I.C.S.: 541612

Subsidiary (Domestic):

Express Postal Options International LLC (2)
3541 Lomita Blvd, Torrance, CA 90505
Tel.: (310) 784-8485
Web Site: http://www.xpomail.com
Sales Range: $25-49.9 Million
Emp.: 50
Direct Mail & Bulk Mail
N.A.I.C.S.: 561431

Hoechstetter Printing (2)
218 N Braddock Ave, Pittsburgh, PA 15208
Tel.: (412) 241-8200
Web Site: http://www.rrdonnelley.com
Sales Range: $75-99.9 Million
Emp.: 240
Commercial Offset Printing
N.A.I.C.S.: 323111

IPD Printing (2)
5800 Peachtree Rd, Atlanta, GA 30341
Tel.: (770) 458-6351
Web Site: http://www.rrdonnelley.com
Sales Range: $100-124.9 Million
Emp.: 300
Commercial Offset Printing
N.A.I.C.S.: 323111

Iridio Color Service Inc. (2)
5050 1st Ave S, Seattle, WA 98134-5507
Tel.: (206) 587-0278
Web Site: http://www.iridio.com
Sales Range: $25-49.9 Million
Emp.: 100
Visual Communications Production
N.A.I.C.S.: 323120

Mercury Printing Company, LLC (2)
4650 Shelby Air Dr, Memphis, TN 38118
Tel.: (901) 345-8480
Web Site: http://www.mercuryprintingco.com
Emp.: 100
Commercial Printing Services
N.A.I.C.S.: 323111

Subsidiary (Non-US):

Moore IMS BV (2)
Industrieterrein Kapelbeemd, Hooge Zijde

Chatham Asset Management, LLC—(Continued)

28, Eindhoven, 5626, Netherlands
Tel.: (31) 402663430
Web Site: http://www.rrdonnelley.com
Sales Range: $25-49.9 Million
Emp.: 24
Lithographic Printing Services
N.A.I.C.S.: 323111

Moore Paragon (Caribbean) Ltd. (2)
Bimap Drive Wildey St Michael, Saint Michael, 14007, Barbados
Tel.: (246) 4296762
Business Receipts Printing Services
N.A.I.C.S.: 323111
Steven Lewis (Gen Mgr)

Moore Response Marketing B.V. (2)
Hooge Zijde 28, 5626 DC, Eindhoven, Netherlands
Tel.: (31) 402663430
Web Site: http://www.rrdonnelley.com
Sales Range: $10-24.9 Million
Emp.: 25
Commercial Printing Services
N.A.I.C.S.: 323111

Subsidiary (Domestic):

Nies/Artcraft, Inc. (2)
3049 Chouteau Ave, Saint Louis, MO 63103
Tel.: (314) 951-0400
Web Site: http://www.niesartcraft.com
Commercial Printing Services
N.A.I.C.S.: 323111

Omega Studios-Southwest Inc. (2)
168 E Highland Ave, Elgin, IL
60120-5564 (100%)
Tel.: (972) 869-4840
Web Site: http://www.omega-studios.com
Sales Range: $10-24.9 Million
Emp.: 10
Commericial Photography
N.A.I.C.S.: 541922

Precision Dialogue Direct, Inc. (2)
5501 W Grand Ave, Chicago, IL 60639
Tel.: (773) 237-2264
Web Site: http://www.precisiondialogue.com
Emp.: 500
Marketing Materials Commercial Printing & Mailing Services
N.A.I.C.S.: 541860

Subsidiary (Domestic):

Precision Dialogue Marketing,
LLC (3)
905 Corporate Way, Westlake, OH 44145
Tel.: (440) 471-6001
Web Site: http://www.precisiondialogue.com
Interactive Marketing & Consulting Services
N.A.I.C.S.: 541890
Cathleen Zapata (Chief Experience Officer)

Subsidiary (Non-US):

R. R. Donnelley (U.K.) Limited (2)
88 Wood Street, London, EC2V 7QT, United Kingdom
Tel.: (44) 2030474500
Sales Range: $25-49.9 Million
Emp.: 50
Commercial Printing Services
N.A.I.C.S.: 323111

R. R. Donnelley Deutschland
GmbH
An der Welle 5, Frankfurt am Main, Germany
Tel.: (49) 6917088300
Sales Range: $25-49.9 Million
Emp.: 12
Lithographic Printing Services
N.A.I.C.S.: 323111

R. R. Donnelley Document Solutions
(Switzerland) GmbH (2)
In the 17 Luberzen, Urdorf, 8902, Zurich, Switzerland
Tel.: (41) 447353311
Sales Range: $25-49.9 Million
Emp.: 60
Scanning Services
N.A.I.C.S.: 323111

R. R. Donnelley Europe Sp. z
o.o (2)

ul Obroncow Modlina 11, 30-733, Krakow, Poland
Tel.: (48) 128887100
Web Site: http://www.rrdonnelley.com
Lithographic Printing Services
N.A.I.C.S.: 323111

R. R. Donnelley Limited (2)
Flaxby Moor Division, Knaresborough, HG5 0XJ, United Kingdom
Tel.: (44) 1423796500
Lithographic Printing Services
N.A.I.C.S.: 323111

Subsidiary (Domestic):

R. R. Donnelley Printing
Company (2)
77 W Wacker Dr Lobby, Chicago, IL 60601-1604
Tel.: (312) 326-8000
Commercial Lithographic Printing Services
N.A.I.C.S.: 323111

Subsidiary (Non-US):

R. R. Donnelley Starachowice Sp. z
o.o (2)
Bema 2 c, 27-200, Starachowice, Poland
Tel.: (48) 418887600
Lithographic Printing Services
N.A.I.C.S.: 323111

R. R. Donnelley de El Salvador, S.A.
de C.V. (2)
Boulevard del Ejercito Nacional Km 7 1/2, Soyapango, El Salvador
Tel.: (503) 25079400
Commercial Printing Services
N.A.I.C.S.: 323111

R. R. Donnelley de Guatemala,
S.A. (2)
Empresarial El Cortijo 2 Ofibodega 303 Calz Atanasio Tzul 22-00, Guatemala, 01012, Guatemala
Tel.: (502) 24219999
Web Site: http://www.rrd.com
Emp.: 16
Commercial Printing Services
N.A.I.C.S.: 323111

Subsidiary (Domestic):

R. R. Donnelley-Atlanta West
Plant (2)
3900 N Commerce Dr Ste 100, East Point, GA 30344
Tel.: (404) 494-4500
Web Site: http://www.rrdonnelley.com
Sales Range: $75-99.9 Million
Emp.: 235
Commercial Printing
N.A.I.C.S.: 323111

Branch (Domestic):

R.R. Donnelley (2)
1 Prindle Ln, Danbury, CT 06811
Tel.: (203) 792-5500
Web Site: http://www.rrd.com
Sales Range: $125-149.9 Million
Emp.: 250
Direct Marketing Materials Printing
N.A.I.C.S.: 323111

R.R. Donnelley (2)
150 Cambridge Park Dr, Cambridge, MA 02140-1188
Tel.: (312) 326-8000
Sales Range: $10-24.9 Million
Emp.: 30
Software Development Services
N.A.I.C.S.: 513210

R.R. Donnelley (2)
1077 Prospect Ln, Kaukauna, WI 54130-1104
Tel.: (920) 766-6666
Sales Range: $10-24.9 Million
Emp.: 50
Packaging & Forwarding Services
N.A.I.C.S.: 561910

R.R. Donnelley (2)
5 Henderson Dr, West Caldwell, NJ 07006-6607
Tel.: (973) 882-7000
Sales Range: $25-49.9 Million
Emp.: 200

Producer & Distr of Time-Sensitive Documents for Other Companies
N.A.I.C.S.: 541613
Stacie Frost (Mgr-Intl Sls & Ops)

R.R. Donnelley (2)
W 6545 Quality Dr, Greenville, WI 54942
Tel.: (920) 997-3600
Sales Range: $25-49.9 Million
Emp.: 100
Print-Related Outsourcing Services
N.A.I.C.S.: 561499

R.R. Donnelley (2)
1025 N Washington St, Greenfield, OH 45123
Tel.: (937) 981-2161
Sales Range: $25-49.9 Million
Emp.: 100
Magazine Sorting, Mailing & Re-Print Services
N.A.I.C.S.: 561431

R.R. Donnelley (2)
3201 Kimberly Ct, Johnson City, TN 37604
Tel.: (423) 282-9111
Sales Range: $75-99.9 Million
Emp.: 140
Book Printing Services
N.A.I.C.S.: 323117
Jim Foster (VP)

R.R. Donnelley (2)
1025 Willow Springs Rd, Harrisonburg, VA 22801-9729
Tel.: (540) 564-3900
Web Site: http://www.rrd.com
Sales Range: $50-74.9 Million
Emp.: 200
Book Printing Services
N.A.I.C.S.: 323117

R.R. Donnelley (2)
3401 Heartland Dr, Liberty, MO 64068-3376
Tel.: (816) 792-5300
Web Site: http://www.rrd.com
Sales Range: $125-149.9 Million
Emp.: 500
Magazine Sorting, Mailing & Re-Print Services
N.A.I.C.S.: 561431

R.R. Donnelley (2)
100 Banta Rd, Long Prairie, MN 56347-1900
Tel.: (320) 732-2121
Web Site: http://www.rrd.com
Sales Range: $200-249.9 Million
Emp.: 600
Magazine Sorting, Mailing & Re-Print Services
N.A.I.C.S.: 561499

R.R. Donnelley (2)
5111 S 9th St, Milwaukee, WI 53221-8013
Tel.: (414) 744-5111
Web Site: http://www.rrd.com
Sales Range: $50-74.9 Million
Emp.: 100
Product Label Printing Services
N.A.I.C.S.: 323111

R.R. Donnelley (2)
1457 Earl St, Menasha, WI 54952-1416
Tel.: (920) 751-7800
Web Site: http://www.rrd.com
Sales Range: $25-49.9 Million
Emp.: 50
Trade Color Separation, Photo Engraving & Color Proofing
N.A.I.C.S.: 323111

R.R. Donnelley (2)
7401 Kilmer Ln N, Maple Grove, MN 55369-5677
Tel.: (763) 315-8100
Sales Range: $75-99.9 Million
Emp.: 500
Catalog Printing
N.A.I.C.S.: 323111
Fred Phipgen (Gen Mgr)

R.R. Donnelley (2)
2600 N Main St, Spanish Fork, UT 84660-9596
Tel.: (801) 798-0800
Sales Range: $50-74.9 Million
Emp.: 150
Book Printing Services
N.A.I.C.S.: 323117

R.R. Donnelley (2)
99 High St, Boston, MA 02110
Tel.: (617) 542-1926
Sales Range: $25-49.9 Million
Emp.: 60
Corporate & Commercial Printers
N.A.I.C.S.: 323111

R.R. Donnelley (2)
3500 Maple Ave Ste 810, Dallas, TX 75219
Tel.: (214) 651-1001
Web Site: http://www.rrdonnelley.com
Sales Range: $75-99.9 Million
Emp.: 200
Corporate, Financial & Commercial Printers
N.A.I.C.S.: 323111

R.R. Donnelley (2)
500 W Madison Ste 3200, Chicago, IL
60661 (100%)
Tel.: (312) 707-9790
Sales Range: $25-49.9 Million
Emp.: 100
Corporate, Financial & Commercial Printers
N.A.I.C.S.: 323111
Shandra Miskell (Controller)
Sushil Gupta (Mgr-Strategic Svcs)

R.R. Donnelley & Sons Co. (2)
259 30th St, Greeley, CO
80631-7425 (100%)
Tel.: (970) 350-0700
Web Site: http://www.rrdonnelley.com
Sales Range: $75-99.9 Million
Emp.: 275
Publishing & Printing of Telephone Directories
N.A.I.C.S.: 323111

Branch (Non-US):

R.R. Donnelley & Sons Co. (2)
6100 Vipond Dr, Mississauga, L5T 2X1, ON, Canada
Tel.: (905) 362-3100
Web Site: http://www.rrd.com
Sales Range: $50-74.9 Million
Emp.: 300
Print Management & Outsourced Communications Services
N.A.I.C.S.: 323111

Branch (Domestic):

R.R. Donnelley & Sons Co. (2)
90 Spencer Dr, Wells, ME 04090-5548
Tel.: (207) 646-9926
Sales Range: $10-24.9 Million
Emp.: 3
Commercial Offset Printing
N.A.I.C.S.: 323111

R.R. Donnelley & Sons Co. (2)
9410 D Ducks Ln, Charlotte, NC 28273-4552
Tel.: (704) 588-9900
Sales Range: $75-99.9 Million
Emp.: 200
Offset Printing of Magazines & Catalogs
N.A.I.C.S.: 323117

R.R. Donnelley & Sons Co. (2)
19681 Pacific Gateway Dr, Torrance, CA
90502-1116 (100%)
Tel.: (310) 516-3100
Web Site: http://www.rrdonnelley.com
Sales Range: $100-124.9 Million
Emp.: 300
Printing, Binding, Composition, Separation, Distribution, Creative
N.A.I.C.S.: 323111

R.R. Donnelley & Sons Co. (2)
1501 Washington St, Mendota, IL 61342-1476
Tel.: (815) 539-7402
Web Site: http://www.rrd.com
Sales Range: $50-74.9 Million
Emp.: 200
Printing, Binding, Composition, Separation & Distr Services
N.A.I.C.S.: 323111

R.R. Donnelley & Sons Co. (2)
801 N Union St, Dwight, IL 60420 (100%)
Tel.: (815) 584-2770
Sales Range: $100-124.9 Million
Printing Telephone Book
N.A.I.C.S.: 323117

R.R. Donnelley & Sons Co. (2)

3201 Lebanon Rd, Danville, KY 40422
Tel.: (859) 238-7910
Web Site: http://www.rrd.com
Printing Services
N.A.I.C.S.: 323111

R.R. Donnelley & Sons Co. (2)
1714 Deer Tracks Trl Ste 130, Saint Louis,
MO 63126-1017
Tel.: (314) 966-0909
Web Site: http://www.rrd.com
Sales Range: $350-399.9 Million
Emp.: 15
Publishing & Printing Services
N.A.I.C.S.: 513130

Branch (Non-US):

R.R. Donnelley & Sons Co. (2)
Planta Av Guayamure, Zona Industrial La
Hamaca, Maracay, Aragua, Venezuela
Tel.: (58) 02432722711
Web Site: http://www.moore.com.ve
Commercial Printing Services
N.A.I.C.S.: 323111

Branch (Domestic):

R.R. Donnelley & Sons Co. (2)
2347 Kratzer Rd, Harrisonburg, VA 22802
Tel.: (540) 434-8833
Sales Range: $75-99.9 Million
Emp.: 600
Book Printing Services
N.A.I.C.S.: 323117
Barbara Miller *(Mgr-HR)*
Devon Phillips *(Mgr-Customer Svc)*

**R.R. Donnelley & Sons Co. - Chicago
(111 Wacker) Office** (2)
111 Wacker Dr Ste 3600, Chicago, IL
60606-4300
Tel.: (920) 478-3551
Commercial Printing
N.A.I.C.S.: 513120
Timothy M. Smith *(VP)*
Bill Orndorff *(VP-Materials)*

**R.R. Donnelley & Sons Co. -
Nashville** (2)
1530 Antioch Pike, Antioch, TN 37013
Tel.: (615) 833-3251
Web Site: http://www.check-printers.com
Rev.: $19,200,000
Emp.: 400
Check Printing Services
N.A.I.C.S.: 323111

**R.R. Donnelley & Sons Co. -
Pineville** (2)
10519 Industrial Dr, Pineville, NC 28134
Tel.: (312) 326-8000
Sales Range: $50-74.9 Million
Emp.: 150
Advertising Literature Printing
N.A.I.C.S.: 323111
Brian Lyons *(Gen Mgr)*
Leslie Dover *(VP)*

Plant (Domestic):

R.R. Donnelley - Litho Plant (2)
Page Pointe Ctr 1 Litho Way, Durham, NC
27703
Tel.: (919) 596-7000
Web Site: http://www.rrd.com
Sales Range: $75-99.9 Million
Emp.: 76
Printing Services
N.A.I.C.S.: 323111
Mark Worra *(Pres)*

Subsidiary (Domestic):

**R.R. Donnelley Commercial
Press** (2)
955 Gateway Ctr Way, San Diego, CA
92102
Tel.: (619) 527-4600
Web Site: http://www.rrdonnelley.com
Sales Range: $50-74.9 Million
Emp.: 150
Offset Printing Services
N.A.I.C.S.: 323111

**R.R. Donnelley Global Turnkey
Solutions** (2)
1600 Disk Dr, Plover, WI 54467-0220
Tel.: (715) 341-0544
Web Site: http://www.rrdonnelley.com

Sales Range: $25-49.9 Million
Emp.: 200
Supply Chain Management Services
N.A.I.C.S.: 541614

R.R. Donnelley Logistics (2)
8200 Slauson Ave, Pico Rivera, CA 90660
Tel.: (562) 949-3067
Web Site: http://www.rrd.com
Sales Range: $25-49.9 Million
Emp.: 72
Contract Haulers
N.A.I.C.S.: 484121

Plant (Domestic):

R.R. Donnelley Manufacturing (2)
1009 Sloan St, Crawfordsville, IN 47933-
2741
Tel.: (765) 362-1300
Web Site: http://www.rrd.com
Sales Range: $350-399.9 Million
Emp.: 1,000
Books Printing
N.A.I.C.S.: 323117

Subsidiary (Domestic):

R.R. Donnelley Norwest Inc. (2)
17401 NE Halsey St, Portland, OR
97230-6027 **(100%)**
Tel.: (503) 251-3513
Sales Range: $75-99.9 Million
Emp.: 250
Printing & Publishing of Telephone Directo-
ries
N.A.I.C.S.: 323111

R.R. Donnelley Receivables, Inc. (2)
14100 Lear Blvd Ste 130, Reno, NV 89506
Tel.: (775) 829-4403
Web Site: http://www.rrdonnelley.com
Sales Range: $75-99.9 Million
Emp.: 16
Printing Services
N.A.I.C.S.: 323111

**R.R. Donnelley Response Marketing
Services** (2)
18780 W 78th St, Chanhassen, MN 55317-
9310
Tel.: (952) 937-9764
Web Site: http://www.rrdonnelley.com
Sales Range: $50-74.9 Million
Emp.: 331
Direct Marketing Materials Printing
N.A.I.C.S.: 323111

R.R. Donnelley Seymour Inc. (2)
709 A Ave E, Seymour, IN
47274-3234 **(100%)**
Tel.: (812) 523-1800
Web Site: http://www.rrd.com
Sales Range: $50-74.9 Million
Emp.: 150
Book Printing, Binding, Composition &
Separation
N.A.I.C.S.: 323111

Subsidiary (Non-US):

**R.R. Donnelley de Costa Rica
S.A.** (2)
La Uruca 250 Sur y 50 oeste de la Rotonda
Juan Pablo II, Sobre calle paralela al
puente detras de Incomex, San Jose,
11801, Costa Rica
Tel.: (506) 22442633
Web Site: http://www.rrdca.com
Sales Range: $25-49.9 Million
Emp.: 90
Business Forms & Related Products
N.A.I.C.S.: 323111

Subsidiary (Domestic):

R.R. Donnelley of Puerto Rico (2)
Royal Ind Park Rd 869 Km 1.5, Catano, PR
00962
Tel.: (787) 788-8500
Web Site: http://www.rrdonelley.com
Sales Range: $10-24.9 Million
Emp.: 25
Commercial Printing Services
N.A.I.C.S.: 323111

Subsidiary (Non-US):

**RR Donnelley (Australia) Pty
Limited** (2)
Suite 34 26-32 Pirrama Road, Pyrmont,

2009, NSW, Australia
Tel.: (61) 291998711
Commercial Printing Services
N.A.I.C.S.: 323111

**RR Donnelley (Chengdu) Printing
Co., Ltd.** (2)
No 888 Ganghua Road the Northe Region
of Chengdu Modern Industrial, Port Pixian,
Chengdu, China
Tel.: (86) 2867581618
Emp.: 1,000
Commercial Printing Services
N.A.I.C.S.: 323111
Robin Xu *(Supvr-Pre-press & Press)*

**RR Donnelley (China) Holding Co.,
Ltd.** (2)
32F Lansheng Building No 2-8 Huaihai
Road, Huangpu District, Shanghai, 200021,
China
Tel.: (86) 2131011588
Holding Company
N.A.I.C.S.: 551112

**RR Donnelley (Shanghai) Information
Technology Co., Ltd.** (2)
1F Block 2 No 857 Tiangong Road, Jinshan
industrial Zone, Shanghai, China
Tel.: (86) 2131197254
Information Technology Services
N.A.I.C.S.: 541512

**RR Donnelley Asia Printing Solutions
Limited** (2)
Unit 2010 11 20 F C Bons International
Center, 108 Wai Yip Street Kwun Tong,
Kowloon, China (Hong Kong)
Tel.: (852) 26373611
Web Site: http://www.rrdonnelley.com
Commercial Printing Services
N.A.I.C.S.: 323111

**RR Donnelley Editora e Grafica
Ltda.** (2)
Av Tucunare 299, Barueri, 06460-020, Bra-
zil
Tel.: (55) 1121483500
Web Site: http://www.rrdonnelley.com
Commercial Printing Services
N.A.I.C.S.: 323111

**RR Donnelley Electronics (Suzhou)
Co., Ltd.** (2)
No 12 Baiyu Road, Suzhou Industrial Park,
Suzhou, China
Tel.: (86) 51285557666
Commercial Printing Services
N.A.I.C.S.: 323111

**RR Donnelley Financial Comunicacao
Corporativa Ltda.** (2)
Rua Dom Jerrado 46 4th Floor, Rio de Ja-
neiro, 22250-908, Brazil
Tel.: (55) 2121030525
Web Site: http://www.dfsco.com
Emp.: 50
Commercial Printing Services
N.A.I.C.S.: 323111

RR Donnelley Finland Oy (2)
Myllyojankatu 18-20, 24100, Salo, Finland
Tel.: (358) 27271690
Lithographic Printing Services
N.A.I.C.S.: 323111

**RR Donnelley Global Turnkey Solu-
tions Mexico, S. de R.L. de C.V.** (2)
Via Gustavo Baz No 182 Col San Jeronimo
Tepetlacalco, Tlalnepantla, 54090, Mexico,
Mexico
Tel.: (52) 5550916200
Commercial Printing Services
N.A.I.C.S.: 323111

**RR Donnelley India Outsource Pri-
vate Limited** (2)
Pamba 1st Flr Technopark, Thiruvanan-
thapuram, 695581, Kerala, India
Tel.: (91) 4716602015
Web Site: http://www.rrv.com
Emp.: 1,500
Lithographic Printing Services
N.A.I.C.S.: 323111

**RR Donnelley International de
Mexico, S.A. de C.V.** (2)
Cll Buffon 12 Anzures, Mexico, 11590, DF,
Mexico

Tel.: (52) 5552550052
Commercial Printing Services
N.A.I.C.S.: 323111

RR Donnelley Italy S.r.l. (2)
Via Nisrone, 2001, Milan, Italy
Tel.: (39) 0289015596
Web Site: http://www.rrdonnelley.com
Emp.: 15
Computer Programming Services
N.A.I.C.S.: 541511

RR Donnelley Japan, Inc. (2)
PMO Kanda Tsukasamachi 9F 2-8-1
Kanda-Tsukasamachi, Chiyoda-ku, Tokyo,
101-0048, Japan
Tel.: (81) 362069920
Financial Management Services
N.A.I.C.S.: 541611

**RR Donnelley Korea Electronic Solu-
tion LLC** (2)
Suite No 904 13 Heungdeok-1-ro, Giheung-
gu, Yongin, Gyeonggi, Korea (South)
Tel.: (82) 316607330
Commercial Printing Services
N.A.I.C.S.: 323111

Subsidiary (Domestic):

**RR Donnelley Logistics Services
Worldwide, Inc.** (2)
1000 Windham Pkwy, Bolingbrook, IL
60490-3507
Tel.: (630) 226-6354
Lithographic Printing Services
N.A.I.C.S.: 323111

Subsidiary (Non-US):

**RR Donnelley Singapore Pte
Ltd.** (2)
2 Battery Road 24-01 Maybank Tower, Sin-
gapore, 49907, Singapore
Tel.: (65) 65366288
Web Site: http://www.dfsco.com
Financial Management Services
N.A.I.C.S.: 541611

Subsidiary (Domestic):

RRD Dutch Holdco, Inc. (2)
111 S Wacker Dr, Chicago, IL 60606-4302
Tel.: (312) 326-8000
Lithographic Printing Services
N.A.I.C.S.: 323111

Subsidiary (Non-US):

**RRD Pendaflex de Mexico, S. de
R.L. de C.V.** (2)
16 De Septiembre San Jeronimo Tepetla-
calco, Tlalnepantla, 54090, Mexico, Mexico
Tel.: (52) 5553935022
Commercial Printing Services
N.A.I.C.S.: 323111

Subsidiary (Domestic):

RRD Secaucus Financial, Inc. (2)
215 County Ave, Secaucus, NJ
07094-2006 **(100%)**
Tel.: (201) 271-1000
Computer-Based Document Preparation
Services
N.A.I.C.S.: 323111

Subsidiary (Non-US):

RRD Starachowice sp. z o.o. (2)
ul Bema 2 c, 27-200, Starachowice, Poland
Tel.: (48) 418887600
Commercial Printing Services
N.A.I.C.S.: 323111

**Shanghai Donnelley PreMedia Tech-
nology Co., Ltd.** (2)
Room A202 206 No 9 Building 125 Jiangsu
Bei Rd, Shanghai, 200042, China
Tel.: (86) 2123211888
Magazines Books Publisher
N.A.I.C.S.: 513130

Subsidiary (Domestic):

StorterChilds Printing Co., Inc. (2)
1540 NE Waldo Rd, Gainesville, FL 32641
Tel.: (352) 376-2658
Web Site: http://www.storterchilds.com
Emp.: 35
Commercial Printing Services

Chatham Asset Management, LLC—(Continued)
N.A.I.C.S.: 323111

W.E. Andrews (2)
140 S Rd, Bedford, MA 01730
Tel.: (781) 275-0720
Sales Range: $75-99.9 Million
Emp.: 120
Commercial Offset Printing & Color Separation Services
N.A.I.C.S.: 323111

Subsidiary (Domestic):

Andrews Connecticut (3)
151 Redstone Rd, Manchester, CT 06042-8754
Tel.: (860) 649-5570
Web Site: http://www.r.r.donelly.com
Sales Range: $75-99.9 Million
Offset Printing & Prepress Services
N.A.I.C.S.: 323111

Subsidiary (Domestic):

Walnut Circle Press, Inc. (2)
308 Friendship Dr, Greensboro, NC 27409
Tel.: (336) 855-8070
Web Site: http://www.walnutcirclepress.com
Commercial Printing Services
N.A.I.C.S.: 323111

Watermark Press, Ltd. (2)
950 Tennessee St, San Francisco, CA 94107
Tel.: (415) 282-5100
Web Site: http://www.watermarkpress.com
Commercial Printing Services
N.A.I.C.S.: 323111

Westland Printers (2)
14880 Sweitzer Ln, Laurel, MD 20707-2913
Tel.: (410) 792-2922
Web Site: http://www.westlandprinters.com
Commercial Printing Services
N.A.I.C.S.: 323111

Westland Printers, Inc. (2)
14880 Sweitzer Ln, Laurel, MD 20707-2913
Tel.: (301) 384-7700
Web Site: http://www.rrd.com
Commercial Printing Services
N.A.I.C.S.: 323111
Rene Szynal (Pres)

The McClatchy Company (1)
1601 Alhambra Blvd Ste 100, Sacramento, CA 95816
Tel.: (916) 321-1855
Web Site: http://www.mcclatchy.com
Newspaper Publishers
N.A.I.C.S.: 513110
Robyn Tomlin (Chief News Officer)
Tony Berg (Sr VP-Advertising)
Tony W. Hunter (Chm & CEO)
Jeffrey Dorsey (COO)
Don MacGregor (VP-Customer & Product)

Subsidiary (Domestic):

Aboard Publishing, Inc. (2)
1 Herald Plz 4th Fl, Miami, FL 33132
Tel.: (305) 376-4954
Web Site: http://www.eaglelatitudes.com
Magazine Publisher
N.A.I.C.S.: 513120

Bellingham Herald Publishing, LLC (2)
2100 Q St, Sacramento, CA 95816
Tel.: (916) 321-1828
Magazine Publisher
N.A.I.C.S.: 513120

Big Valley, Inc. (2)
1308 5th St NE, Washington, DC 20002-7004
Tel.: (202) 544-7500
Advertising Agencies
N.A.I.C.S.: 541810

Cypress Media, Inc. (2)
2100 Q St, Sacramento, CA 95816
Tel.: (916) 321-1848
Web Site: http://www.kansascity.com
Newspaper Publishers
N.A.I.C.S.: 513110

Cypress Media, LLC (2)
1601 McGee St, Kansas City, MO 64108-1413

Tel.: (816) 234-4636
Web Site: http://www.kansascity.com
Newspaper Publishers
N.A.I.C.S.: 513110

El Dorado Newspapers (2)
2100 Q St, Sacramento, CA 95816-6816
Tel.: (916) 321-1826
Web Site: http://www.mcclatchy.com
Emp.: 150
Newspaper Publishers
N.A.I.C.S.: 513110

Gulf Publishing Company, Inc. (2)
205 Debuys Rd, Gulfport, MS 39507
Tel.: (228) 896-2100
Web Site: http://www.sunherald.com
Emp.: 100
Newspaper Publishers
N.A.I.C.S.: 513110

Lexington H-L Services, Inc. (2)
100 Midland Ave, Lexington, KY 40508
Tel.: (859) 231-3100
Web Site: http://www.kentucky.com
Newspaper Publishers
N.A.I.C.S.: 513110

McClatchy Interactive (2)
111 W Hargett St, Raleigh, NC 27601
Tel.: (919) 861-1200
Web Site:
    http://www.mcclatchyinteractive.com
Sales Range: $50-74.9 Million
Emp.: 200
Multimedia News Delivery
N.A.I.C.S.: 513110
Christian A. Hendricks (VP-Interactive Media)
Fraser Van Asch (Exec VP & Gen Mgr)
Brian Kirlik (Sr VP-Market Svcs)
Christian A. Hendricks (VP-Interactive Media)

McClatchy Management Services, Inc. (2)
2100 Q ST, Sacramento, CA 95816
Tel.: (916) 321-1831
Web Site: http://www.mcclatchy.com
Management Consulting Services
N.A.I.C.S.: 541618

Division (Domestic):

McClatchy Newspapers (2)
2100 Q St, Sacramento, CA 95816-6899
Tel.: (916) 321-1855
Web Site: http://www.mcclatchy.com
Sales Range: $1-4.9 Billion
Printing, Newspaper Publishing; Operation of On-line Database Services
N.A.I.C.S.: 513110

Subsidiary (Domestic):

Belleville News-Democrat (3)
120 S Illinois St, Belleville, IL 62220-2130
Tel.: (618) 234-1000
Web Site: http://www.bnd.com
Sales Range: $100-124.9 Million
Emp.: 100
Newspaper Publishers
N.A.I.C.S.: 513110
Jeffry Couch (Gen Mgr & Editor)
Dawn Peil (Dir-HR)

Subsidiary (Domestic):

Highland News-Leader (4)
1 Woodcrest Professional Park, Highland, IL 62249
Tel.: (618) 654-2366
Web Site: http://www.highlandnl.com
Sales Range: $10-24.9 Million
Emp.: 8
Newspaper Publishers
N.A.I.C.S.: 513110

O'Fallon Progress (4)
120 S Illinois St, Belleville, IL 62269
Tel.: (618) 632-3643
Web Site: http://www.ofprogress.com
Sales Range: $10-24.9 Million
Emp.: 8
Weekly Newspaper Publisher
N.A.I.C.S.: 513110

Subsidiary (Domestic):

Belton Publishing Company (3)
419 Main St, Belton, MO 64012

Tel.: (816) 331-5353
Web Site: http://www.demo-mo.com
Sales Range: $10-24.9 Million
Emp.: 5
Newspaper Publishers
N.A.I.C.S.: 513110

Cass County Publishing Company, Inc. (3)
301 S Lexington St, Harrisonville, MO 64701
Tel.: (816) 380-3228
Web Site: http://www.demo-mo.com
Sales Range: $10-24.9 Million
Emp.: 6
Newspaper Publishers
N.A.I.C.S.: 513110
John Beaudoin (Publr)

Chapel Hill Publishing Co. (3)
505 W Franklin St, Chapel Hill, NC 27516-2315 (100%)
Tel.: (919) 932-2000
Web Site: http://www.chapelhillnews.com
Sales Range: $25-49.9 Million
Emp.: 50
Publishing & Printing Newspapers
N.A.I.C.S.: 513110

Fort Worth Star-Telegram (3)
808 Throckmorton St, Fort Worth, TX 76102
Tel.: (817) 390-7400
Web Site: http://www.star-telegram.com
Sales Range: $500-549.9 Million
Emp.: 2,000
Newspaper Publishers
N.A.I.C.S.: 513110
Lee Williams (Mng Editor-News)
David Humphrey (Editor-Sports)
Steve Coffman (Exec Editor)
Michael Currie (Mng Editor-Audience)
Amy McDaniel (Editor-Breaking News)
Juan Antonio Ramos (Editor-The Star)
Michael Ryan (Editor-Opinion)
Ryan Mote (Publr)
Phil Schroder (VP-Audience Dev)
Stephanie Boggins (VP-Adv)

Subsidiary (Domestic):

Nor-Tex Publishing, Inc. (4)
PO Box 337, Mansfield, TX 76063-0337
Tel.: (817) 473-4451
Web Site:
    http://www.mansfieldnewsmirror.com
Sales Range: $10-24.9 Million
Emp.: 8
Newspaper Publishers
N.A.I.C.S.: 513110

Subsidiary (Domestic):

Idaho Statesman (3)
1200 N Curtis Rd, Boise, ID 83707 (100%)
Tel.: (208) 377-6200
Web Site: http://www.idahostatesman.com
Newspaper Publishers
N.A.I.C.S.: 513110
Michelle Philippi (Mgr-Retail Sls)
Logan Osterman (Mgr-Sls)
Rhonda Prast (Exec Editor)
Rebecca Poynter (Publr)

Keynoter Publishing Company, Inc. (3)
3015 Overseas Hwy, Marathon, FL 33050-0158
Tel.: (305) 743-5551
Web Site: http://www.flkeysnews.com
Sales Range: $10-24.9 Million
Emp.: 20
Newspaper Publishers
N.A.I.C.S.: 513110
Kathie Bryan (Dir-Fin)
Todd Swift (Dir-Production)

Lee's Summit Journal (3)
415 SE Douglas St, Lees Summit, MO 64063
Tel.: (816) 524-2345
Web Site: http://www.lsjournal.com
Sales Range: $10-24.9 Million
Emp.: 10
Newspaper Publishers
N.A.I.C.S.: 513110

Lexington Herald-Leader (3)
100 Midland Ave, Lexington, KY 40508-1999
Tel.: (859) 231-3100

Web Site: http://www.kentucky.com
Sales Range: $75-99.9 Million
Emp.: 270
Newspaper Publishers
N.A.I.C.S.: 513110
Michael Wells (Dir-HR)
Kim Young Woods (VP-Adv)
Peter Baniak (Gen Mgr & Editor)

News Tribune (3)
1950 S State St, Tacoma, WA 98405
Tel.: (253) 597-8742
Web Site: http://www.thenewstribune.com
Sales Range: $75-99.9 Million
Emp.: 620
Newspaper Publishers
N.A.I.C.S.: 513110

Subsidiary (Domestic):

The News Tribune (4)
1950 S State St, Tacoma, WA 98405
Tel.: (253) 597-8742
Web Site: http://www.thenewstribune.com
Sales Range: $50-74.9 Million
Emp.: 200
Publisher of Newspapers
N.A.I.C.S.: 513110
Dale Phelps (VP-News & Editor)
Rebecca Poynter (Pres & Publr)
Dawn Leibold (Dir-Sls-NW)

Subsidiary (Domestic):

Nittany Printing & Publishing Co. (3)
3400 E College Ave, State College, PA 16801
Tel.: (814) 238-5000
Web Site: http://www.centredaily.com
Sales Range: $50-74.9 Million
Emp.: 90
Newspaper Publishers
N.A.I.C.S.: 513110
Debra Leithauser (Pres & Publr)

Sun Publishing Company, Inc. (3)
914 Frontage Rd E, Myrtle Beach, SC 29577-6700
Tel.: (843) 626-8555
Web Site:
    http://www.myrtlebeachonline.com
Sales Range: $25-49.9 Million
Emp.: 100
Newspaper Publishers
N.A.I.C.S.: 513110

Subsidiary (Domestic):

The Sun News (4)
PO Box 406, Myrtle Beach, SC 29578
Tel.: (843) 626-8555
Web Site:
    http://www.myrtlebeachonline.com
Sales Range: $75-99.9 Million
Newspaper Publishers
N.A.I.C.S.: 513110
Stephanie Pedersen (Exec Editor)

Subsidiary (Domestic):

The Beaufort Gazette (3)
10 Buck Island Rd, Bluffton, SC 29910
Tel.: (843) 524-3183
Web Site: http://www.beaufortgazette.com
Sales Range: $25-49.9 Million
Emp.: 80
Newspaper Publishing
N.A.I.C.S.: 513110

The Bellingham Herald (3)
1155 N State St, Bellingham, WA 98225-5037
Tel.: (360) 676-2600
Web Site: http://www.bellinghamherald.com
Sales Range: $50-74.9 Million
Emp.: 50
Newspaper Publishers
N.A.I.C.S.: 513110
Julie Shirley (Exec Editor)
Gary Wortel (Publr-West)
Rusty Dodge (VP-Adv & Gen Mgr)
Rebecca Poynter (Pres & Publr)
Dave Gallagher (Editor-Bus)
Travis Kane (Dir-Adv Sls)
Anthony Martin (District Mgr-Delivery)
Ross Meyer (District Mgr-Delivery)
Andrea Neil (Asst Dir-Fin)

The Bradenton Herald (3)
1111 3rd Ave W, Bradenton, FL 34205
Tel.: (941) 748-0411

Web Site: http://www.bradenton.com
Sales Range: $25-49.9 Million
Emp.: 75
Newspaper Publishers
N.A.I.C.S.: 513110
Darren Haimer *(VP-Adv & Gen Mgr)*
Tim Whitley *(CFO)*
Marc R. Masferrer *(Sr Editor)*
Craig Skinner *(Coord-Audience Logistics)*
Jacqueline Middlemus *(Mgr-HR)*
Mike Garbett *(Editor-News)*
Henry Howard *(Editor-Design & Copy)*
Kelly Lipp *(Editor-Design & Copy)*
Vincent Safuto *(Editor-Design Copy)*
Tiffany Tompkins *(Editor-Visuals)*
Josie Hatley *(Mgr-Community Rels & Project)*

The Charlotte Observer Publishing Co. (3)
550 S Caldwell St, Charlotte, NC 28202-1880
Tel.: (704) 358-5000
Web Site: http://www.charlotteobserver.com
Sales Range: $350-399.9 Million
Emp.: 800
Newspaper Publishers
N.A.I.C.S.: 513110
Bernie Heller *(Chief Revenue Officer & VP-Adv)*
Letitia Smith *(Partner-HR Bus)*
Sherry Chisenhall *(Pres & Editor)*

The Columbus Ledger-Enquirer (3)
945 Broadway Ste 102, Columbus, GA 31901-2413
Tel.: (706) 324-5526
Web Site: http://www.ledger-enquirer.com
Sales Range: $50-74.9 Million
Emp.: 90
Newspaper Publishers
N.A.I.C.S.: 513110
Dimon Kendrick-Holmes *(Exec Editor)*

The Fresno Bee (3)
1626 E St, Fresno, CA 93786-0001
Tel.: (559) 441-6111
Web Site: http://www.fresnobee.com
Sales Range: $300-349.9 Million
Emp.: 500
Daily Newspaper
N.A.I.C.S.: 513110
John Coakley *(Sr VP-Sls & Strategic Mktg)*
Jim Boren *(Sr VP & Exec Editor)*
Stephen Dana *(VP-Digital)*
Mari Wylie *(VP-Fin)*
Tim Ritchey *(Publr)*

The Herald (3)
132 W Main St, Rock Hill, SC 29730
Tel.: (803) 329-4000
Web Site: http://www.heraldonline.com
Sales Range: $50-74.9 Million
Emp.: 175
Daily Newspaper
N.A.I.C.S.: 513110
Justin Rumbach *(Publr & Editor)*
Lynn Adams *(Mng Editor)*

The Island Packet (3)
10 Buck Island Rd, Bluffton, SC 29910
Tel.: (843) 706-8100
Web Site: http://www.islandpacket.com
Sales Range: $25-49.9 Million
Emp.: 100
Newspapers
N.A.I.C.S.: 513110
Jolie Bagonzi *(VP-HR)*

The Kansas City Star Company (3)
1729 Grand Blvd, Kansas City, MO 64108-1413
Tel.: (816) 234-4636
Web Site: http://www.kansascity.com
Sales Range: $450-499.9 Million
Emp.: 1,910
Newspaper Publishers
N.A.I.C.S.: 513110
Mike Fannin *(Pres & Editor)*
Michael Lindenberger *(VP & Editor-Editorial Page)*

The Macon Telegraph Publishing Co. (3)
1675 Montpelier Ave, Macon, GA 31201-3444
Tel.: (478) 744-4200
Web Site: http://www.macon.com
Sales Range: $50-74.9 Million
Emp.: 215
Newspaper Publishers

N.A.I.C.S.: 513110
Caleb Slinkard *(Sr Editor)*

The Miami Herald Media Company (3)
3511 NW 91 Ave, Miami, FL 33172
Tel.: (305) 350-2111
Web Site: http://www.miamiherald.com
Sales Range: $100-124.9 Million
Newspaper Publishing
N.A.I.C.S.: 513110
Aminda Marques Gonzalez *(Pres, Publr & Exec Editor)*
Lourdes M. Alvarez *(Dir-Mktg & Community Partnerships)*
Greg Curling *(CFO & VP-Fin)*
Jeff Sauls *(Dir-Ops)*
Bernie Kosanke *(Reg Dir-Audience Dev)*
Lesley DeCanio *(VP-Adv)*

Subsidiary (Domestic):

El Nuevo Herald (4)
1 Herald Plz, Miami, FL 33132
Tel.: (305) 350-2111
Web Site: http://www.miami.com
Sales Range: $25-49.9 Million
Emp.: 55
Newspaper Publishers
N.A.I.C.S.: 513110
Alexandra Villoch *(Publr & VP)*

The Miami Herald (4)
1 Herald Plz, Miami, FL 33132
Tel.: (305) 350-2111
Web Site: http://www.miami.com
Newspaper Publishers
N.A.I.C.S.: 513110

Subsidiary (Domestic):

The Modesto Bee (3)
1325 H St, Modesto, CA 95354-2427
Tel.: (209) 578-2000
Web Site: http://www.modbee.com
Sales Range: $100-124.9 Million
Emp.: 100
Local Newspaper
N.A.I.C.S.: 513110
Tim Ritchey *(VP-Adv & Gen Mgr)*
Leigh Bisaro *(Dir-Employee Rels & Trng)*
Laurie Dugo *(Controller)*
Juanita Toth *(Mgr-Local Sls)*
Daniel Arreguín *(Mgr-Automotive Sls)*
Javi Cuiriz *(Mgr-Client Success)*
Jose Ibarra *(Coord-Adv Traffic & VIDA)*
Cindy McNamara *(Coord-Legals)*
Maria Ravera *(VP-Audience Dev)*
Brian Clark *(Editor)*
Patty Guerra *(Mng Editor)*
Garth Stapley *(Editor-Opinions Page)*
Joan Barnett Lee *(Editor-Visuals)*
Pat Clark *(Editor-Scene)*

The News & Observer (3)
215 S McDowell St, Raleigh, NC 27602-9150
Tel.: (919) 829-4500
Web Site: http://www.newsobserver.com
Sales Range: $100-124.9 Million
Emp.: 600
Daily Newspaper
N.A.I.C.S.: 513110
John Drescher *(Sr VP & Exec Editor)*
Sara Glines *(Publr)*
Jim Puryear *(VP-Audience Dev)*
Caroline Willingham *(VP-Fin)*

The Olathe News (3)
514 S Kansas Ave, Olathe, KS 66061-4548
Tel.: (913) 764-2211
Web Site: http://www.olathedailynews.com
Sales Range: $10-24.9 Million
Emp.: 40
Newspaper Publishers
N.A.I.C.S.: 513110

The Olympian (3)
111 Bethel St NE, Olympia, WA 98506-4212 (100%)
Tel.: (360) 754-5400
Web Site: http://www.theolympian.com
Sales Range: $75-99.9 Million
Emp.: 25
Newspaper Publishers
N.A.I.C.S.: 513110

The Puyallup Herald (3)
103 W Stewart, Puyallup, WA 98371-0170
Tel.: (253) 841-2481

Web Site: http://www.puyallupherald.com
Sales Range: $10-24.9 Million
Emp.: 7
Weekly Newspaper
N.A.I.C.S.: 513110

The Sacramento Bee (3)
2100 Q St, Sacramento, CA 95814
Tel.: (916) 321-1000
Web Site: http://www.sacbee.com
Sales Range: $500-549.9 Million
Emp.: 2,000
Daily Newspaper
N.A.I.C.S.: 513110
Scott Lebar *(Mng Editor)*

The State-Record Company (3)
1401 Shop Rd, Columbia, SC 29201
Tel.: (803) 771-6161
Web Site: http://www.thestate.com
Sales Range: $100-124.9 Million
Newspaper Publishers
N.A.I.C.S.: 513110
Andrae Houghlan *(Gen Mgr-Acctg)*
Gary Young *(Dir-Production)*
Lauren Libet *(VP-Adv)*
Richard Curtis *(Coord-Logistics)*
Jim Bourn *(Coord-Local Retail)*
Debbie Henderson *(Partner-HR Bus-Reg)*
Brian Tolley *(Exec Editor)*
Gina Smith *(Editor-Reg Projects)*
Dwayne McLemore *(Editor-Breaking News & Sports)*
Lewis Bezjak *(Coord-Prep Sports)*
Kelly Cobb *(Editor-Print Plng-Reg)*
Kevin McLendon *(Editor-Sports Plng-Reg)*

The Sun Herald (3)
205 DeBuys Rd, Gulfport, MS 39507-2837
Tel.: (228) 896-2390
Web Site: http://www.sunherald.com
Sales Range: $75-99.9 Million
Emp.: 180
Newspaper Publishers
N.A.I.C.S.: 513110
Blake Kaplan *(Gen Mgr & Editor)*

The Tribune (3)
3825 S Higuera St, San Luis Obispo, CA 93401
Tel.: (805) 781-7800
Web Site: http://www.sanluisobispo.com
Sales Range: $50-74.9 Million
Emp.: 150
Newspaper Publishers
N.A.I.C.S.: 513110

The Wichita Eagle (3)
825 E Douglas Ave, Wichita, KS 67202
Tel.: (316) 268-6000
Web Site: http://www.kansas.com
Sales Range: $25-49.9 Million
Emp.: 400
Newspaper Publishers
N.A.I.C.S.: 513110
Sherry Chisenhall *(Editor)*
Marcia Werts *(Editor)*
Dale Seiwert *(Gen Mgr)*
Michael Roehrman *(Editor)*
Jean Hays *(Editor-Investigations)*
Jeff Rosen *(Editor-Sports)*
Jaime Green *(Editor-Video)*
Julie Mah *(Editor-Social Media)*

Tri-City Herald (3)
333 W Canal Dr, Kennewick, WA 99336
Tel.: (509) 582-1500
Web Site: http://www.tri-cityherald.com
Sales Range: $75-99.9 Million
Emp.: 200
Daily Newspapers
N.A.I.C.S.: 323111
Todd Frantz *(VP-Adv & Gen Mgr)*

Subsidiary (Domestic):

McClatchy Newsprint Company (2)
6855 S Red Rd Ste 200, South Miami, FL 33143
Tel.: (305) 740-8800
Newspaper Publishers
N.A.I.C.S.: 513110

McClatchy Shared Services, Inc. (2)
3511 NW 91st Ave, Doral, FL 33172
Tel.: (305) 740-8800
Web Site: http://www.mcclatchy.com
Sales Range: $10-24.9 Million
Emp.: 50
Financial Processing & Purchasing Services

N.A.I.C.S.: 541219

Joint Venture (Domestic):

McClatchy-Tribune Information Services (2)
435 N Michigan Ave St 1500, Chicago, IL 60611 (50%)
Tel.: (202) 383-6095
Web Site: http://www.mctinfoservices.com
Sales Range: $25-49.9 Million
Emp.: 100
News Wire Services
N.A.I.C.S.: 516210
Rapier Copeland *(Dir-IT)*

Subsidiary (Domestic):

Olympic-Cascade Publishing, Inc. (2)
2100 Q St, Sacramento, CA 95816
Tel.: (916) 321-1000
Newspaper Publishers
N.A.I.C.S.: 513110

San Luis Obispo Tribune, LLC (2)
3825 S Higuera St, San Luis Obispo, CA 93406
Tel.: (805) 781-7800
Web Site: http://www.sanluisobispo.com
Newspaper Publishers
N.A.I.C.S.: 513110

Joint Venture (Domestic):

Seattle Times Company (2)
1000 Denny Way, Seattle, WA 98109 (49.5%)
Tel.: (206) 464-2111
Web Site: http://company.seattletimes.com
Sales Range: $500-549.9 Million
Emp.: 3,020
Newspaper Publishers
N.A.I.C.S.: 513110
Frank A. Blethen *(CEO & Publr)*
Alan Fisco *(Pres)*
Sharon Pian Chan *(VP-Innovation, Product & Dev)*
Levi Pulkkinen *(Editor-Bus)*

Subsidiary (Domestic):

Rotary Offset Press (3)
6600 S 231st St, Kent, WA 98032-1847
Tel.: (253) 813-9900
Web Site: http://www.rotaryoffsetpress.com
Sales Range: $75-99.9 Million
Emp.: 215
Lithographic Commercial Printing
N.A.I.C.S.: 323111
Ken Hatch *(Gen Mgr)*

Subsidiary (Domestic):

Star-Telegram, Inc. (2)
808 Throckmorton St, Fort Worth, TX 76102
Tel.: (817) 332-3333
Web Site: http://www.star-telegram.com
Newspaper Publishers
N.A.I.C.S.: 513110
Roger Provost *(CFO & VP)*
Stephanie Boggins *(VP-Adv)*
Ryan Mote *(Publr)*
Phil Schroder *(VP-Audience Dev)*
Steve Coffman *(Exec Editor)*
Tom Johanningmeier *(Mng Editor-News & Projects)*
Michael Currie *(Mng Editor-Audience)*
Amy McDaniel *(Editor-Breaking News)*
Juan Antonio Ramos *(Editor-La Estrella)*
Michael Ryan *(Editor-Opinion)*
William Wilkerson *(Editor-Sports)*

Tacoma News, Inc. (2)
1950 S State St, Tacoma, WA 98405
Tel.: (253) 597-8742
Web Site: http://www.thenewstribune.com
Sales Range: $150-199.9 Million
Emp.: 700
Newspaper Publishers
N.A.I.C.S.: 513110

The Gables Publishing Company (2)
2100 Q St, Sacramento, CA 95816-6816
Tel.: (916) 321-1810
Book Publishers
N.A.I.C.S.: 513130

The News and Observer Publishing Company (2)

Chatham Asset Management, LLC—(Continued)

421 Fayetteville St Ste 104, Raleigh, NC 27601
Tel.: (919) 829-4500
Web Site: http://www.newsobserver.com
Newspaper Publishers
N.A.I.C.S.: 513110

The State Media Company   (2)
1401 Shop Rd, Columbia, SC 29201-4843
Tel.: (803) 771-7653
Web Site:
    http://www.thestatemediacompany.com
Newspaper Publishers
N.A.I.C.S.: 513110

CHATHAM CORPORATION
1 N Lasalle St Ste 300, Chicago, IL 60602
Tel.: (847) 634-5506
Rev.: $42,600,000
Emp.: 3
Printing Trades Machinery
N.A.I.C.S.: 333248
Garry Brainin (Pres)

CHATHAM CREATED GEMS INC.
360 Post St Ste 701, San Francisco, CA 94108
Tel.: (415) 397-8450
Web Site:
    http://www.chathamgems.com
Sales Range: $10-24.9 Million
Emp.: 12
Precious Stones (Gems)
N.A.I.C.S.: 423940
Thomas Chatham (Pres)
Diana Chatham (VP)

CHATHAM MOTOR SALES, INC.
7 Park of Commerce Way, Savannah, GA 31405
Tel.: (912) 231-2020
Web Site:
    http://www.chathammotorsales.com
Year Founded: 1997
Sales Range: $75-99.9 Million
Emp.: 135
Car Whslr
N.A.I.C.S.: 441110
James Mollica (Gen Mgr)

CHATMETER
225 Broadway Ste 1700, San Diego, CA 92101
Tel.: (619) 795-6262
Web Site: http://www.chatmeter.com
Year Founded: 2009
Sales Range: $1-9.9 Million
Emp.: 59
Real Estate Services
N.A.I.C.S.: 531390
Collin Holmes (Founder)
Cynthia Sener (Chief Revenue Officer)
Jared Norris (VP-Ops)
John Fitzgerald (CFO)
Tehsin Daya (Head-Strategic Partnerships)
Giselle Bardwell (Head-Healthcare)
John Mazur (CEO)

CHATSWORTH PRODUCTS INC.
4175 Guardian St, Simi Valley, CA 93063
Tel.: (818) 735-6100   DE
Web Site: http://www.chatsworth.com
Year Founded: 1991
Rev.: $38,300,000
Emp.: 100
Data Processing Hosting & Related Services
N.A.I.C.S.: 518210

Michael Custer (Pres & CEO)
Ted Behrens (Exec VP-Engrg, Product Mgmt & Mktg-Global)
Melissa Aleman (Chief HR Officer)
Larry Varblow (CFO)
Jeff Steen (Exec VP-Global Sls)
Ron Orris (Sr VP-Electronics, Software & Global Engrg)

Subsidiaries:

Chatsworth Products - Chatsworth   (1)
9353 Winnetka Ave, Chatsworth, CA 91311-6033
Tel.: (818) 882-8595
Web Site: http://www.chatsworth.com
Sales Range: $25-49.9 Million
Emp.: 70
Mfr of Fabricated Metal Products
N.A.I.C.S.: 332999
Mike Custer (Pres)

Chatsworth Products - Georgetown   (1)
3004 S Austin Ave, Georgetown, TX 78626
Tel.: (512) 863-7800
Web Site: http://www.chatsworth.com
Sales Range: $25-49.9 Million
Emp.: 175
Mfr of Fabricated Metal Products
N.A.I.C.S.: 332996
Michael Custer (Pres & CEO)

Chatsworth Products International, Ltd.   (1)
Cavendish House Bourne End Business Park, Cores End Road, Bourne End, SL8 5AS, Bucks, United Kingdom
Tel.: (44) 1628 524 834
Web Site:
    http://www.chatsworthproducts.co.uk
Emp.: 12
Electronic Components Mfr
N.A.I.C.S.: 334419
Larry Renaud (Pres & CEO)
Michael Custer (Exec VP-Global Sls, Mktg, Intl Ops, Supply Chain & Quality)
Alex Lopez (Chief HR Officer)

Oberon, Inc.   (1)
1315 S Allen St Ste 410, State College, PA 16801
Tel.: (814) 867-2312
Web Site: http://www.oberonwireless.com
Mounting Solutions (for Wifi Access Points)
N.A.I.C.S.: 334118
Scott D. Thompson (Pres)

CHATTANOOGA AREA FOOD BANK
2009 Curtain Pole Rd, Chattanooga, TN 37406
Tel.: (423) 622-1800   TN
Web Site:
    https://www.chattfoodbank.org
Year Founded: 1972
Sales Range: $25-49.9 Million
Emp.: 38
Community Food Services
N.A.I.C.S.: 624210
Eddie Lundien (Mgr-Warehouse)
Marisa Ogles (Dir-Dev & Comm)
Buck Gentry (CFO)
Carla Johnson (Treas)
Mike Andrews (Sec)
Gina Crumbliss (Pres & CEO)
Mark Hilling (Dir-Ops)

CHATTANOOGA BAKERY INC.
900 Manufacturers Rd, Chattanooga, TN 37405-3763
Tel.: (423) 267-3351   TN
Web Site: https://www.moonpie.com
Year Founded: 1902
Sales Range: $10-24.9 Million
Emp.: 150
Commercial Bakeries
N.A.I.C.S.: 311812
Tory Johnston (VP-Mktg)
Keith Holt (CFO & Controller)
John Campbell (VP-Sls)
Samuel H. Campbell III (Chm)

Subsidiaries:

Brownie Special Products Co. Inc.   (1)
900 Manufacturers Rd, Chattanooga, TN 37405-4418
Tel.: (423) 267-3351
Web Site: http://www.moonpie.com
Sales Range: $25-49.9 Million
Emp.: 130
Groceries & Related Products
N.A.I.C.S.: 424490
Tory Johnston (VP-Mktg-New Bus Dev)
Samuel H. Campbell IV (Pres)

CHATTANOOGA CHRISTIAN COMMUNITY FOUNDATION
345 Frazier Ave Unit 205, Chattanooga, TN 37405
Tel.: (423) 266-5257   TN
Web Site:
    https://www.thegenerositytrust.org
Year Founded: 1993
Sales Range: $25-49.9 Million
Emp.: 6
Christian Ministry Services
N.A.I.C.S.: 813110
James R. Barber (Pres)
J. Tom Glenn (Treas)
Bruce C. Zeiser (Sec)
Jennifer M. Sheffield (Dir-Finance-Accounting-Administration)

CHATUGE REGIONAL HOSPITAL
110 S Main St, Hiawassee, GA 30546
Tel.: (706) 896-2222   GA
Web Site:
    https://www.chatugehospital.org
Year Founded: 1955
Sales Range: $10-24.9 Million
Emp.: 334
Health Care Srvices
N.A.I.C.S.: 622110
Penny Lloyd (Mgr-Lab)

CHAVES BAKERY II, INC.
1365 State St, Bridgeport, CT 06605
Tel.: (203) 333-6254   CT
Web Site:
    http://www.chavesbakery2.com
Year Founded: 1992
Rev.: $22,100,000
Emp.: 100
Bakery Products
N.A.I.C.S.: 424490
John Chaves (Pres)

CHAYAH CONSULTING GROUP LLC
4055 St Cloud Dr Ste 250, Loveland, CO 80538
Tel.: (970) 578-0184   CO
Web Site: https://www.chayah-cg.com
Civil Engineering Services
N.A.I.C.S.: 237990
Cody Geisendorfer (Founder & Engr)

Subsidiaries:

Shear Engineering Corp.   (1)
4055 St Cloud Dr Ste 250, Loveland, CO 80538
Tel.: (970) 226-5334
Web Site: http://www.shearengineering.com
Engineeering Services
N.A.I.C.S.: 541330

CHAZAK VALUE CORP.
10 Rockefeller Plz Ste 601, New York, NY 10020
Tel.: (212) 265-7013   DE
Web Site:
    http://www.debtacquisitiongroup.com
Year Founded: 1913
Investments in Distressed Assets
N.A.I.C.S.: 523940

Marc B. Ross (CFO, Treas & Sec)
Joseph E. Sarachek (Pres & CEO)

Subsidiaries:

Infineer, Ltd.   (1)
Balloo Ave, Bangor, BT19 7QT, Northern Ireland, United Kingdom   (100%)
Tel.: (44) 2891476000
Web Site: http://www.infineer.com
Sales Range: $10-24.9 Million
Developer of SmartCard Products & Solutions
N.A.I.C.S.: 323111

CHC MECHANICAL CONTRACTORS
347 E Stevens St, Cookeville, TN 38501-3541
Tel.: (931) 528-5514
Web Site: https://www.chccompanies.com
Sales Range: $10-24.9 Million
Emp.: 80
Air Conditioning System Installation Services
N.A.I.C.S.: 238220
Garry Floeter (Pres)

CHE INTERNATIONAL GROUP, LLC
9435 Waterstone Blvd Ste 140, Cincinnati, OH 45249
Tel.: (513) 229-7595
Web Site:
    https://www.cheinternational.com
Year Founded: 2005
Sales Range: $25-49.9 Million
Emp.: 150
Investment Management Service
N.A.I.C.S.: 523940
Christopher Che (Pres & CEO)

CHEBANSE CROP SERVICE INC.
7089 S Chestnut St, Chebanse, IL 60922
Tel.: (815) 697-2392   IL
Year Founded: 1970
Sales Range: $10-24.9 Million
Emp.: 22
Grain & Field Beans
N.A.I.C.S.: 424510
Donald Schafer (VP)
Dean Schafer (Pres)

CHEBELLE CORPORATION
601 13th St, Belle Plaine, IA 52208
Tel.: (319) 444-3144   IA
Web Site:
    http://www.chelseasavingsbank.com
Bank Holding Company
N.A.I.C.S.: 551111
Curtis Dean Brown (Pres & CEO)

Subsidiaries:

Chelsea Savings Bank   (1)
609 13th St, Belle Plaine, IA 52208
Tel.: (319) 444-3144
Web Site:
    http://www.chelseasavingsbank.com
Rev.: $4,869,000
Emp.: 12
Commericial Banking
N.A.I.C.S.: 522110
Curtis D. Brown (Pres & CEO)

CHEBOYGAN LUMBER COMPANY
829 N Huron St, Cheboygan, MI 49721
Tel.: (231) 627-5661   MI
Web Site: http://www.clclumber.com
Year Founded: 1889
Sales Range: $10-24.9 Million
Emp.: 58
Residential & Commercial Construction
N.A.I.C.S.: 423310

Roy A. Schryer *(Pres)*

CHECK INTO CASH INC.
201 Keith St SW Ste 80, Cleveland, TN 37311-5867
Tel.: (423) 479-2400   DE
Web Site:
http://www.checkintocash.com
Year Founded: 1993
Sales Range: $50-74.9 Million
Emp.: 200
Holding Company
N.A.I.C.S.: 522390
W. Allan Jones *(CEO)*
Steve Scoggins *(Pres)*
Bill Lane *(CFO)*

Subsidiaries:

Check Into Cash of Indiana LLC   (1)
5670 Grape Rd, Mishawaka, IN
46545-1246   (100%)
Tel.: (574) 254-1222
Rev.: $360,000
Emp.: 2
Financial Services
N.A.I.C.S.: 522390

Check Into Cash of Kentucky
LLC   (1)
1555 E New Cir Rd Ste M, Lexington, KY 40509
Tel.: (423) 479-2400
Rev.: $2,900,000
Emp.: 1
Financial Services
N.A.I.C.S.: 522390
Eric Johnson *(VP-Ops)*

Check Into Cash of Wisconsin
LLC   (1)
3046 Fish Hatchery Rd, Madison, WI 53713-3125
Tel.: (608) 278-1700
Web Site: http://www.checkintocash.com
Rev.: $99,000
Emp.: 2
Financial Services
N.A.I.C.S.: 522390

Creditcorp of Tennessee Inc.   (1)
201 Keith St SW Ste 80, Cleveland, TN 37311-5867
Tel.: (423) 479-2400
Web Site: http://www.checkintocash.com
Rev.: $2,500,000
Emp.: 20
Financial Services
N.A.I.C.S.: 522110

Jones Management Services,
LLC   (1)
201 Keith St Ste 80, Cleveland, TN 37311   (100%)
Tel.: (423) 472-1000
Web Site:
http://www.jonesmanagement.com
Rev.: $1,500,000
Emp.: 100
Business Management Services
N.A.I.C.S.: 541611
W. Allan Jones *(Chm & CEO)*
D. Lynn DeVault *(Pres)*
Rachel Ingram *(Controller)*
Will Jones *(VP)*
Joe Mason *(CFO)*
Tom Wilhoit *(Dir-Maintenance)*

Jones Properties, LLC   (1)
201 Keith St Ste 80, Cleveland, TN 37311
Tel.: (423) 472-4000
Web Site: http://www.jonesproperties.biz
Property Management
N.A.I.C.S.: 531312
W. Allan Jones *(Chm & CEO)*

CHECK-6, INC.
9224 S Elwood Ave Ste C, Jenks, OK 74037
Tel.: (918) 528-6439
Web Site: http://www.checksix.us
Sales Range: $10-24.9 Million
Emp.: 65
Safety Consulting Services
N.A.I.C.S.: 541690

Brian Brurud *(Founder)*
Dan Gilkey *(Dir-Technical Sls)*
Jason McAlister *(VP-Ops, Trng Sys)*
Joe Krasinski *(Gen Mgr-Trng Sys)*
Josh Lewis *(CTO-Trng Sys)*
Laura Owen *(CEO)*
James Weynand *(Chief Revenue Officer)*
Dana Frawley *(Mgr-Mktg)*
Dan Baxter *(Sr VP)*
David Hazell *(VP-Eastern Hemisphere)*
Vincent Saporito *(VP-Western Hemisphere)*

CHECK-N-GO FINANCIAL CORP.
7755 Montgomery Rd Ste 400, Cincinnati, OH 45236
Tel.: (513) 336-7735   OH
Web Site: http://www.checkngo.com
Year Founded: 1994
Sales Range: $250-299.9 Million
Emp.: 2,200
Check-Cashing Services & Payday Loans
N.A.I.C.S.: 522320
John Rabenold *(VP-Govt Affairs)*
A. David Davis *(Pres & CEO)*
Miriam Giachetto *(VP-Strategic Mktg)*

CHECKALT, LLC
5979 W 3rd St Ste 200, Los Angeles, CA 90036
Tel.: (917) 579-3107
Web Site: http://www.checkalt.com
Year Founded: 2004
Payment Processing Services
N.A.I.C.S.: 522320
George Karfunkel *(Co-Chm)*
Allison Murray *(Exec VP-Bus Dev)*
Shai Stern *(Co-Chm & CEO)*
Jeryl Lederman *(CTO)*
Tiffany Rider *(Mng Dir-Comm)*
Ram Bajaj *(CIO)*
Leilani Doyle *(Sr VP-Product Mgmt)*
Rachel Book *(Chief People Officer)*
Laurence Dunne *(Dir-Product Mgmt)*
Adam Halliday *(Sr Product Mgr)*
Chuck Ross *(Sr VP-Improvement)*

Subsidiaries:

ERAS   (1)
13851 SW 119th Ave, Miami, FL 33186
Tel.: (305) 255-1452
Sales Range: $1-9.9 Million
Emp.: 120
Payment Processing Solutions
N.A.I.C.S.: 541511
Kelly Patenaude *(Mgr-Product & Customer Svc)*
Anthony Alonzo *(Dir-IT & R&D)*
Deborah Mount *(Mgr-Ops)*
Tamir Shafer *(Mng Dir-Client Rels)*

Klik Technologies Corp.   (1)
711 Executive Blvd #H, Valley Cottage, NY 10989
Tel.: (845) 573-0900
Web Site: http://www.klik.com
Sales Range: $1-9.9 Million
Emp.: 80
Data Processing, Hosting & Related Services
N.A.I.C.S.: 518210
David Jonas *(COO)*
Richard Sirota *(Chm)*

US Dataworks, Inc.   (1)
14100 SW Fwy Ste 550, Sugar Land, TX 77478
Tel.: (281) 504-8000
Web Site: http://www.usdataworks.com
Application Software for Financial Services
N.A.I.C.S.: 334610
Leilani Doyle *(Sr VP-Product Mgmt)*
Daye Depinet *(CTO)*
David Peterson *(Pres)*

CHECKER LEASING INCORPORATED

1306 Municipal Rd, Roanoke, VA 24012
Tel.: (540) 366-2436
Web Site: http://www.avis.com
Rev.: $11,000,000
Emp.: 15
Truck Rental, Without Drivers
N.A.I.C.S.: 532120
Geoffrey M. Ottaway *(Chm)*
Mike McGuire *(Pres)*

CHECKER NOTIONS COMPANY INC.
400 W Dussel Dr Ste B, Maumee, OH 43537
Tel.: (419) 893-3636
Web Site:
https://www.checkerdist.com
Year Founded: 1948
Sales Range: $10-24.9 Million
Emp.: 60
Quilting & Sewing Products Supplier
N.A.I.C.S.: 459130
J. R. Krieger *(Pres)*

CHECKERED FLAG MOTOR CAR CO.
5225 Virginia Beach Blvd, Virginia Beach, VA 23462
Tel.: (757) 490-1111
Web Site:
http://www.checkeredflag.com
Sales Range: $25-49.9 Million
Emp.: 600
New & Used Car Dealers
N.A.I.C.S.: 441110
Fred Kirschbaum *(CFO)*

CHECKMATE ADVISORS, LLC
3 Loucroft St, Haddonfield, NJ 08033
Tel.: (856) 546-5245
Web Site:
http://checkmateadvisors.com
Year Founded: 2016
Sales Range: Less than $1 Million
Emp.: 2
Investment Advisory Services
N.A.I.C.S.: 523940
Stephen G. Ayscue *(Pres)*

CHECKOUTSTORE INC.
319 37th St, Brooklyn, NY 11232
Tel.: (800) 676-0134
Web Site:
http://www.checkoutstore.com
Year Founded: 2002
Sales Range: $1-9.9 Million
Emp.: 7
Media Storage Products
N.A.I.C.S.: 334112
Kevin Feng *(Chm)*

CHECKPOINT TECHNOLOGIES INC.
6153 Native Woods Dr, Tampa, FL 33625
Tel.: (813) 818-8324
Web Site:
http://www.checkpointech.com
Year Founded: 2003
Sales Range: $1-9.9 Million
Emp.: 25
IT Consulting & Services
N.A.I.C.S.: 541519
Robert Crews *(Pres)*

CHEESE MERCHANTS OF AMERICA
1301 Schiferl Rd, Bartlett, IL 60103
Tel.: (630) 221-0580
Web Site:
https://www.cheesemerchants.com
Year Founded: 1998
Sales Range: $10-24.9 Million
Emp.: 75
Cheese Mfr

N.A.I.C.S.: 311513
Robert Greco *(Mng Partner & Exec VP)*
Paul DelleGrazie *(Dir-Pur & Quality Assurance)*
Jim Smart *(Exec VP-Sls)*
John Perazzo *(Mgr-Sls Div)*
Mark Lewis *(Mgr-Sls Div)*
Frank Leto *(Mgr-Sls-Southeast)*
Tom Niccoli *(Mgr-Sls-Northeast)*
Jeff Wright *(Mgr-Sls-Northwest)*
Michael Maiello *(Mgr-Sls-Central)*
Jim Wittig *(Dir-Retail Sls)*
Chris Craig *(Mgr-Central Div)*
Eric Bach *(Reg Mgr)*
Alexandro Caruso *(Reg Mgr)*
Mike Costa *(Reg Mgr)*

CHEESMAN LLC
2200 State Rte 119, Fort Recovery, OH 45846
Tel.: (419) 375-4132
Web Site:
https://www.cheeseman.com
Year Founded: 1948
Sales Range: $25-49.9 Million
Emp.: 300
Transportation & Supply Chain Solutions; Specialized Less-Than-Truckload Transportation & Truckload Services
N.A.I.C.S.: 484122
Craig Watcke *(COO)*
Doug Wall *(CFO)*
Ed Zumstein *(CEO)*
Sam Hoops *(VP-Safety & HR)*

CHEETAH HOLDING CORPORATION
4412 8th St SW, Vero Beach, FL 32968
Tel.: (772) 584-3308   DE
Year Founded: 2010
Investment Services
N.A.I.C.S.: 523999
Ronald A. Davis *(Pres)*
Ronald G. Brigham *(Treas & Sec)*

CHEF'S INTERNATIONAL, INC.
62 Broadway, Point Pleasant Beach, NJ 08742-2606
Tel.: (732) 295-0350   DE
Web Site:
https://www.chefsinternationalnj.com
Year Founded: 1975
Sales Range: $10-24.9 Million
Emp.: 500
Restaurant
N.A.I.C.S.: 722511
Martin W. Fletcher *(CFO)*
Robert J. Lombardi *(Chm)*
Robert Cooper *(Pres)*

CHELCO GROUP OF COMPANIES INC.
Chelco Bldg 1432 1440 Randolph Ave, Avenel, NJ 07001-2402
Tel.: (732) 381-0080
Web Site:
https://www.chelcogroup.com
Year Founded: 1976
Sales Range: $75-99.9 Million
Emp.: 950
Holding Company; Electronic Parts & Equipment Whslr & Real Estate Services
N.A.I.C.S.: 551112
Samuel Hassine *(Owner)*

Subsidiaries:

Chelco Realty Corp.   (1)
1432 Randolph Ave, Avenel, NJ 07001-2402
Tel.: (732) 381-0080
Rev.: $2,600,000
Emp.: 40

Chelco Group of Companies Inc.—(Continued)

Nonresidential Building Operators
N.A.I.C.S.: 531120

CHELDA, INC.
3017 High Pt Rd 2nd Fl, Greensboro,
NC 27403
Tel.: (336) 851-4800　　　　NC
Web Site:
　http://www.hamsrestaurants.com
Sales Range: $25-49.9 Million
Emp.: 750
Restaurants Owner & Operator
N.A.I.C.S.: 722511
Lindsey Schumacher (Dir-
Franchising)

CHELSEA & SCOTT, LTD.
75 Albrecht Dr, Lake Bluff, IL 60044
Tel.: (847) 615-2110
Web Site:
　http://www.onestepahead.com
Rev.: $65,000,000
Emp.: 140
Direct Sales of Children's & Baby
Products
N.A.I.C.S.: 458110
Karen B. Scott (Pres)
Susan O'Malley (Controller)

CHELSEA CLOCK CO., INC.
101 2nd St, Chelsea, MA 02150-1598
Tel.: (617) 884-0250
Web Site:
　https://www.chelseaclock.com
Year Founded: 1897
Sales Range: $10-24.9 Million
Emp.: 30
Clock Mfr
N.A.I.C.S.: 334519
Douglas B. Mauch (VP-Supply Chain
& Mgr-Matls)
J. K. Nicholas (CEO)

CHELSEA GREEN PUBLISH-ING COMPANY
85 N Main St, White River Junction,
VT 05001
Tel.: (802) 295-6300
Web Site:
　http://www.chelseagreen.com
Rev.: $2,200,000
Emp.: 20
Fiber Optic Cable Mfr
N.A.I.C.S.: 335921
Brianne Goodspeed (Sr Editor & Mgr-
Subrights)
Michael Weaver (Mgr-Trade Sls)
Margaret Baldwin (Pres)
Darrell Koerner (Mgr-Special & Corp
Sls)
Alex Bullett (Coord-Production)
Jenna Stewart (Mgr-Author Events)
Patricia Stone (Dir-Production)
Sandi Eaton (Dir-Bus & Distr)
Shay Totten (Dir-Comm)

CHELSEA GROTON SAVINGS BANK INC.
1 Franklin Sq, Norwich, CT 06360-
5825
Tel.: (860) 823-4912　　　CT
Web Site:
　https://www.chelseagroton.com
Year Founded: 1854
Sales Range: $50-74.9 Million
Emp.: 225
Provider of Banking Services
N.A.I.C.S.: 522180
Rich Morelli (CFO, Treas & Sr VP)
Michael Rauh (Pres)
Carolyn Welch (Sr VP & Mgr-Comml
Lending)
Tony Joyce (Exec VP)

CHELSEA INVESTMENTS

CORPORATION
6339 Paseo Del Lago, Carlsbad, CA
92011
Tel.: (760) 456-6000
Web Site:
　https://www.chelseainvestco.com
Year Founded: 1986
Sales Range: $25-49.9 Million
Emp.: 150
Real Estate Investment Company
N.A.I.C.S.: 525990
James J. Schmid (Founder & CEO)
Cheri Hoffman (Pres)
Charles Schmid (COO)
Buddy Bohrer (Dir-Acq)
Mariana Crawford (Sr Project Mgr-
Fin)
Tim M. Gray (CFO)

Subsidiaries:

CIC Management　　　　　　　(1)
5993 Avenida Encinas Ste 101, Carlsbad,
CA 92008
Tel.: (760) 456-6000
Sales Range: $50-74.9 Million
Emp.: 50
Investment Services
N.A.I.C.S.: 523999
Robin Pelton (Sr Mgr-Assets)

CHELSEA LUMBER COMPANY
1 Old Barn Cir, Chelsea, MI 48118
Tel.: (734) 475-9126
Web Site:
　https://www.chelsealumber.com
Year Founded: 1908
Sales Range: $10-24.9 Million
Emp.: 120
Lumber & Hardware Supply
N.A.I.C.S.: 423310
Dick McCalla (VP & Gen Mgr)

Subsidiaries:

Bridgewater Lumber Co　　　　(1)
8370 Boettner Rd, Bridgewater, MI 48115
Tel.: (734) 429-7062
Sales Range: $10-24.9 Million
Emp.: 6
Lumber & Other Building Materials
N.A.I.C.S.: 423310
John Daniel (Office Mgr)

CHELSEA MILLING COMPANY
201 W North St, Chelsea, MI 48118-
0460
Tel.: (734) 475-1361　　　　MI
Web Site: https://www.jiffymix.com
Year Founded: 1901
Sales Range: $100-124.9 Million
Emp.: 300
Mfr of Prepared Baking Mixes
N.A.I.C.S.: 311211
William F. McCreadie (Dir-Sls)
Howard S. Holmes (Pres & CEO)
John Powers (CFO & VP)
Ed Hostetter (Dir-Purchase)

CHELSEA PIERS LP
62 Chelsea Piers Ste 300, New York,
NY 10011
Tel.: (212) 336-6800
Web Site:
　https://www.chelseapiers.com
Sales Range: $25-49.9 Million
Emp.: 1,000
Roller Skating Rink Operation
N.A.I.C.S.: 713940
Roland W. Betts (Chm)
David A. Tewksbury (Exec VP)
Tom A. Bernstein (Pres)
Chelsea Piers (Sr Dir-Racquets-
Connecticut)
David Beltre (VP & Gen Mgr-The Golf
Club)
Mike Braito (Sr VP & Gen Mgr)
Jim Bugenhagen (Dir-Rinks-
Connecticut)

Dana B. Thayer (Sr VP & Dir-Mktg &
Sponsorship)
Suzanne McGoldrick (CFO & Sr VP)
Stuart Sheinbaum (VP & Dir-Comm)
Greta Wagner (Exec Dir-Connecticut)
Keith C. Champagne (Sr VP-HR &
IT)
Leigh Dean (Dir-Rink-Connecticut)
Natalie Grainger (Dir-Squash-
Connecticut)

CHELSEA PLACE CARE CEN-TER, LLC.
25 Lorraine St, Hartford, CT 06105
Tel.: (860) 233-8241
Web Site:
　https://www.chelseaplacecenter.com
Sales Range: $10-24.9 Million
Emp.: 600
Nursing Care Facilities
N.A.I.C.S.: 623110
Denise Mackinnon (VP-Fin Svcs)
Chris S. Wright (Pres-icare)
Michael Plausse (CFO)

CHELSEA SENIOR LIVING LLC
316 S Ave, Fanwood, NJ 07023
Tel.: (908) 889-4200
Web Site:
　https://www.chelseaseniorliving.com
Year Founded: 1990
Sales Range: $75-99.9 Million
Emp.: 200
Skilled Nursing Care Facility
N.A.I.C.S.: 623110
Herbert Heflich (CEO)
Roger Bernier (Pres & COO)
Deena Schaffer (CFO & VP)
Edie Empirio (Sr VP-Ops)
Kathleen Merkel (Dir-HR)
Patricia Banta (Reg Dir-Health Svcs)

Subsidiaries:

CA Tinton Falls, LLC　　　　　(1)
One Hartford Dr, Tinton Falls, NJ 07701
Tel.: (732) 784-8924
Sales Range: $10-24.9 Million
Emp.: 15
Continuing Care Retirement Community
Operator
N.A.I.C.S.: 623311

CHELSEA STATE BANK
1010 S Main St, Chelsea, MI 48118-
1435
Tel.: (734) 426-6000　　　　MI
Web Site:
　http://www.chelseastate.bank
Year Founded: 1897
Sales Range: $200-249.9 Million
Emp.: 60
Provider of Banking Services
N.A.I.C.S.: 522110
John Mann (CEO)
Scott Tanner (Exec VP)
Michael Willis (VP)
Jessica M. Stubbs (CFO & Sr VP)
Joanne Rau (Pres)
Matthew Noggle (Asst VP)

CHELSEY DIRECT, LLC
1500 Harbor Blvd, Weehawken, NJ
07086
Tel.: (201) 863-7300
Web Site:
　http://www.hanoverdirect.com
Sales Range: $400-449.9 Million
Holding Company
N.A.I.C.S.: 551112
William B. Wachtel (Chm)

Subsidiaries:

Hanover Direct, Inc.　　　　　(1)
1200 Harbor Blvd, Weehawken, NJ
07086　　　　　　　　　　(100%)
Tel.: (201) 863-7300
Web Site: http://www.hanoverdirect.com

Sales Range: $400-449.9 Million
Emp.: 1,840
Catalog Publisher & Direct Marketer
N.A.I.C.S.: 459420

Subsidiary (Domestic):

Brawn of California, Inc.　　　(2)
1500 Harbor Blvd Ste A, Weehawken, NJ
07086-6732
Tel.: (201) 863-7300
Web Site: http://www.undergear.com
Sales Range: $25-49.9 Million
Emp.: 42
Men's Clothing Designer
N.A.I.C.S.: 458110

Hanover Company Store, LLC　(2)
455 Park Plz, La Crosse, WI 54601-4445
Tel.: (608) 791-6000
Web Site: http://www.thecompanystore.com
Sales Range: $25-49.9 Million
Emp.: 200
Company Store Catalog Mfr
N.A.I.C.S.: 513199

Scandia Down　　　　　　　(2)
2929 Airport Rd, La Crosse, WI 54602
Tel.: (608) 791-6000
Web Site: http://www.scandiadown.com
Down Comforter & Pillow Designer, Mfr &
Retailer
N.A.I.C.S.: 314999

CHEM CAN SERVICES, INC.
2605 N 11th St, Enid, OK 73701
Tel.: (580) 237-1267　　　　OK
Web Site: http://www.chemcan.com
Year Founded: 1972
Sales Range: $1-9.9 Million
Emp.: 35
Repair Shops & Related Services
N.A.I.C.S.: 562991
Diana Siegmann (Sec)

CHEM GRO OF HOUGHTON INC.
504 Main St, Houghton, IA 52631
Tel.: (319) 469-2611
Sales Range: $10-24.9 Million
Emp.: 22
Fertilizer & Fertilizer Materials Distr
N.A.I.C.S.: 115112
Harold Dyer (Pres)
Tami Arbogast (Controller)
Paula Spiekermeier (Coord-Hr)

CHEM NUT, INC.
Hwy 82 W 800 Business Park Dr,
Leesburg, GA 31763
Tel.: (229) 883-2298
Web Site: http://www.chemnut.com
Year Founded: 1974
Emp.: 105
Health Care Srvices
N.A.I.C.S.: 621999
Chris Payne (Pres & CEO)
Gregory Stephen Fowler (Sr VP)
Keith Thomas (CFO)
Brinson Lanier (Chm)
Mark Bishop (VP-Sls & Bus Dev)

CHEM QUIP INC.
2551 Land Ave, Sacramento, CA
95815
Tel.: (916) 923-5091
Web Site: http://www.chemquip.com
Sales Range: $10-24.9 Million
Emp.: 24
Swimming Pool & Spa Chemicals
N.A.I.C.S.: 424690
Carlos Cheng (Mgr-Fresno)
Carl Davis (Mgr-Sacramento)
Chris Sanders (Branch Mgr)
Mark Frese (Mgr-Bridgeport)
Christian Prieto (Mgr-Bridgeport)

CHEM-IMPEX INTERNA-TIONAL, INC.
935 Dillon Dr, Wood Dale, IL 60191

Tel.: (630) 766-2112
Web Site:
   https://www.chemimpex.com
Year Founded: 1981
Sales Range: $10-24.9 Million
Emp.: 15
Whslr of Amino Acids & Peptides
N.A.I.C.S.: 424210
Nitin Shah *(Pres)*
Meena Shah *(CEO)*
Julio Hernandez *(Supvr-Warehouse)*

CHEM-PLATE INDUSTRIES INC.
1800 Touhy Ave, Elk Grove Village, IL 60007
Tel.: (847) 640-1600
Web Site:
   https://www.chemplateindustry.com
Sales Range: $25-49.9 Million
Emp.: 300
Metal Heat Treating
N.A.I.C.S.: 332813
Martin Straus *(Pres)*
Brian Isola *(Dir-Sls)*
Joe Pacilio *(Dir-Customer Svc)*
Linette Neal *(Dir-Quality)*
Porfirio Martinez *(Dir-Heat Treat & Sorting)*
Aaron Straus *(Gen Mgr)*

CHEM-TAINER INDUSTRIES, INC.
361 Neptune Ave, West Babylon, NY 11704-5818
Tel.: (631) 661-8300   NY
Web Site:
   https://www.chemtainer.com
Year Founded: 1958
Sales Range: $100-124.9 Million
Emp.: 275
Rotationally Molded Plastic Containers Mfr
N.A.I.C.S.: 326199
James Glen *(Pres)*
Anthony Lamb *(VP)*
Joe Destefano *(CFO)*

Subsidiaries:

Aquaworld Products   **(1)**
361 Neptune Ave, West Babylon, NY 11704
Tel.: (800) 275-2436
Web Site: http://www.aquaworld-products.com
Emp.: 35
Bait Tank Mfr
N.A.I.C.S.: 339999
Jim Goenn *(Pres)*

Chem-Tainer of Hawaii   **(1)**
16118 Li'l Li'l St, Keaau, HI 96749
Tel.: (800) 870-5494
Web Site:
   http://www.chemtainerofhawaii.com
Sales Range: $10-24.9 Million
Emp.: 5
Molded Plastic Tank Mfr
N.A.I.C.S.: 326199
Dave Cerny *(Mgr)*

Todd Enterprises   **(1)**
530 Wellington Ave, Cranston, RI 02910-2950   **(100%)**
Tel.: (401) 467-2750
Web Site: http://www.toddusa.com
Sales Range: $25-49.9 Million
Emp.: 85
Mfr of Boating Equipment
N.A.I.C.S.: 326199

Tracy International   **(1)**
361 Neptune Ave, West Babylon, NY 11704
Tel.: (631) 661-8300
Web Site: http://www.tracy-intl.com
Boat Seat & Accessory Mfr
N.A.I.C.S.: 336612

CHEM-TECH FINISHERS INC.
1904 S Hamilton St, Dalton, GA 30720-5345
Tel.: (706) 278-8312

Web Site: http://www.chemtech-finishers.net
Sales Range: $10-24.9 Million
Emp.: 90
Carpet & Rug Cleaning Services
N.A.I.C.S.: 561740
David Arnold *(Plant Mgr)*
Ray Evans *(Mgr-Acctg)*
Brad Price *(Mgr-Pur)*

CHEMALLOY COMPANY INC.
996 E Railroad Ave, Bryn Mawr, PA 19010
Tel.: (610) 527-3700
Web Site: http://www.chemalloy.com
Rev.: $20,000,000
Emp.: 120
Alloys, Metals, Minerals & Chemicals
N.A.I.C.S.: 325180
Anthony C. Demos *(Pres)*
Madge Malone *(Treas & Sec)*
Jamie Sampson *(Mgr-Quality)*

CHEMART COMPANY
15 New England Way, Lincoln, RI 02865
Tel.: (401) 333-9200
Web Site: https://www.chemart.com
Year Founded: 1976
Sales Range: $10-24.9 Million
Emp.: 90
Petrochemical Etching
N.A.I.C.S.: 332812
Richard Beaupre *(CEO)*
Michael Ryfa *(CFO)*
Ana Lopes *(VP-Sls & Mktg)*

CHEMBRIDGE CORPORATION
11199 Sorrento Valley Rd Ste 206, San Diego, CA 92121
Tel.: (858) 451-7400
Web Site:
   https://www.chembridge.com
Year Founded: 1993
Sales Range: $10-24.9 Million
Emp.: 200
Chemical Product & Preparation Mfr
N.A.I.C.S.: 325998
Eugene Vaisberg *(Co-Founder, Chm & CEO)*
Sergey Altshteyn *(Co-Founder & Pres)*
Gala Vaisberg *(Co-Founder & Partner)*
Dmitriy Lvovskiy *(VP)*
Duncan Beniston *(Exec Dir-Sls & Mktg)*

CHEMCO MANUFACTURING COMPANY INC.
515 Huehl Rd, Northbrook, IL 60062
Tel.: (847) 480-7700
Web Site:
   http://www.chemcomfg.com
Sales Range: $10-24.9 Million
Emp.: 42
Industrial Filters Mfr
N.A.I.C.S.: 333998
Tom Sammis *(Acct Exec)*

CHEMCO PRODUCTS COMPANY
6401 E Alondra Blvd, Paramount, CA 90723-3758   MI
Web Site:
   https://www.chemcoprod.com
Year Founded: 1962
Sales Range: $25-49.9 Million
Emp.: 75
Specialty Cleaning & Sanitation Preparation Services
N.A.I.C.S.: 238990
Elaine S. Cooper *(Co-Owner & CEO)*
Lyman M. Cole *(Founder)*
Janis C. Utz *(Co-Owner & Pres)*

CHEMCOTE, INC.
7599 Fishel Dr N, Dublin, OH 43016
Tel.: (614) 792-2683   OH
Web Site: https://www.chemcote.com
Year Founded: 1985
Sales Range: $10-24.9 Million
Emp.: 50
Fiscal Year-end: 12/31/13
Highway, Street & Bridge Construction
N.A.I.C.S.: 237310
Lynn Bucci *(Controller)*

CHEMEX CORPORATION
Banco Popular Ctr Ste 1831, San Juan, PR 00918
Tel.: (787) 763-7205
Sales Range: $10-24.9 Million
Emp.: 5
Chemicals & Allied Products
N.A.I.C.S.: 424690
Eduardo Perez Jr. *(Gen Mgr)*

CHEMICAL EXCHANGE INDUSTRIES, INC.
900 Clinton Dr, Galena Park, TX 77547-3461
Tel.: (713) 455-1206   TX
Year Founded: 1968
Sales Range: $200-249.9 Million
Emp.: 45
Holding Company; Specialty Chemical Mfr
N.A.I.C.S.: 551112
David Smith *(Pres)*

Subsidiaries:

Texmark Chemicals, Inc.   **(1)**
900 Clinton Dr, Galena Park, TX 77547-3461
Tel.: (713) 455-1206
Web Site: http://www.texmark.com
Sales Range: $10-24.9 Million
Chemical Production Plant
N.A.I.C.S.: 325211
Mike Curry *(Mgr-Safety)*
Advani Prem *(VP)*
Vickie Harrison *(Controller)*

CHEMICAL INTERCHANGE CO.
2932 S Brentwood Blvd, Saint Louis, MO 63144
Tel.: (314) 962-9002
Rev.: $12,000,000
Emp.: 10
Distr of Chemicals & Allied Products
N.A.I.C.S.: 424690
Thomas A. Moore *(Treas & VP)*
Randall S. Moore *(Pres)*
Elizabeth Moore Phelan *(Sec)*

CHEMICAL PACKAGING CORP.
3566 Olivett Church Rd, Paducah, KY 42001-7146
Tel.: (270) 443-4578
Rev.: $28,500,000
Emp.: 1
Chemical Preparations
N.A.I.C.S.: 325998
C. Wayne Golightly *(Pres)*

CHEMICAL PACKAGING CORPORATION
2700 SW 14th St, Pompano Beach, FL 33069
Tel.: (954) 974-5440
Web Site:
   http://www.cpcaeroscience.com
Rev.: $12,100,000
Emp.: 75
Polishes & Sanitation Goods Mfr
N.A.I.C.S.: 325612
Terry Colker *(Pres)*

CHEMICAL SOLVENTS INC.

3751 Jennings Rd, Cleveland, OH 44109-2858
Tel.: (216) 741-9310   OH
Web Site:
   https://www.chemicalsolvents.com
Year Founded: 1970
Sales Range: $10-24.9 Million
Emp.: 110
Chemical Solvents Distr
N.A.I.C.S.: 424690
Blaine Davidson *(VP-Sls)*
Terri Shimenski *(Mgr-Mktg)*
Tim McNeilly *(Dir-Technical)*
Jerry Schill *(VP-Ops)*
Dave Weber *(Mgr-Facility-Recycling Dept)*

CHEMICAL TRANSFER COMPANY
3105 S El Dorado St, Stockton, CA 95206
Tel.: (209) 466-3554
Rev.: $14,447,951
Emp.: 22
Contract Haulers
N.A.I.C.S.: 484121
Michael J. Ellis *(Pres)*
Allen Genetti *(CFO)*

Subsidiaries:

California Tank Lines Inc.   **(1)**
3105 S El Dorado St, Stockton, CA 95206   **(100%)**
Tel.: (209) 466-3554
Trucking Service
N.A.I.C.S.: 484121
Michael Ellis *(Pres & CEO)*

CHEMIMAGE CORP.
7301 Penn Ave, Pittsburgh, PA 15208-2528
Tel.: (412) 241-7335
Web Site:
   http://www.chemimage.com
Year Founded: 1994
Sales Range: $1-9.9 Million
Emp.: 47
Hyperspectral Imaging Instrumentation & Software Mfr
N.A.I.C.S.: 334516
Patrick Treado *(Founder & CTO)*
Jim McGlone *(Pres)*
Tricia Wood *(VP)*
John Belechak *(COO)*
Carl Denys *(VP-Medical Devices)*

CHEMISPHERE CORPORATION
2101 Clifton Ave, Saint Louis, MO 63139
Tel.: (314) 644-1300   MO
Web Site:
   https://www.chemispherecorp.com
Year Founded: 1974
Sales Range: $10-24.9 Million
Emp.: 34
Industrial Chemical Whslr
N.A.I.C.S.: 424690
Michael Clote *(VP & Gen Mgr)*
Robert Schwent *(Pres & Sec)*
John Block *(Mgr-Pur)*
Daniel Kuchler *(Mgr-Production)*

CHEMISTRY COMMUNICATIONS, INC.
3030 Penn Ave 2nd Fl, Pittsburgh, PA 15201-1521
Tel.: (412) 642-0642   PA
Web Site: http://visitthelab.com
Year Founded: 1977
Sales Range: $10-24.9 Million
Advetising Agency
N.A.I.C.S.: 541810
Mark Zelkovic *(Jr Acct Exec)*
Christina Deasy *(Mgr-HR)*
Emily Watson *(Acct Exec)*
Laura Forester *(Assoc Dir-Social Media & Strategy)*

Chemithon Enterprises, Inc.—(Continued)

CHEMITHON ENTERPRISES, INC.

5430 W Marginal Way SW, Seattle, WA 98106-1517
Tel.: (206) 937-9954   WA
Web Site:
  https://www.chemithon.com
Year Founded: 1993
Sales Range: $10-24.9 Million
Emp.: 50
Holding Company; Special Industry Machinery Mfr
N.A.I.C.S.: 551112
Harriett Lettich (Mgr-Admin-Chemithon Corp)
Brian W. MacArthur (VP-Ops)
Berton Brooks (Founder & Chm-Chemithon Corp)
Hal Busick (Mgr-Sls)

Subsidiaries:

Chemithon Constructors LLC   (1)
20611 Bothell Everett Hwy, Bothell, WA 98012-7146   (80%)
Tel.: (425) 423-9594
Web Site: http://www.chemithon.com
Sales Range: $10-24.9 Million
Emp.: 7
Industrial Buildings & Warehouses
N.A.I.C.S.: 333248

Chemithon Engineers Pvt. Ltd.   (1)
Shiv Anand-A 1st Fl 372/374 SV Rd, Gore-gaon W, Mumbai, 400 104, Maharashtra, India
Tel.: (91) 2228720331
Web Site: http://www.chemithon.co.in
Sales Range: $10-24.9 Million
Special Industry Machinery
N.A.I.C.S.: 333310
Sanjay N. Trivedi (Reg Dir)

Chemithon Surface Finishing Inc.   (1)
5430 W Marginal Way SW, Seattle, WA 98106-1598
Tel.: (206) 937-9954
Web Site: http://www.chemithon.com
Rev.: $9,247,000
Emp.: 5
Equipment, Processes & Supplies for the Surface Finishing & Printed Circuit Board Industries
N.A.I.C.S.: 423830
Jerald Toussaint (Pres)

Branch (Domestic):

Chemithon Surface Finishing, Inc.   (2)
12502 NE Marx St, Portland, OR 97230-1056
Tel.: (503) 256-2777
Web Site: http://www.chemithon.com
Equipment Processe & Supply for the Surface Finishing & Printed Circuit Board Distr
N.A.I.C.S.: 423840
Keith Thompson (Dist Mgr)

The Chemithon Corp.   (1)
5430 W Marginal Way SW, Seattle, WA 98106-1598
Tel.: (206) 937-9954
Web Site: http://www.chemithon.com
Sales Range: $10-24.9 Million
Emp.: 49
Special Industry Machinery
N.A.I.C.S.: 333248
Brooks Burton (Pres)

CHEMONICS INTERNATIONAL, INC.

1717 H St NW, Washington, DC 20006
Tel.: (202) 955-3300   DC
Web Site: http://www.chemonics.com
Year Founded: 1975
Sales Range: $150-199.9 Million
Emp.: 600
Provider of Technical & Management Services
N.A.I.C.S.: 541611

Susanna Mudge (Pres & CEO)
Grace Adeya (Dir-Supply Chain Solutions)

CHEMPACE CORPORATION

339 Arco Dr, Toledo, OH 43607
Tel.: (419) 535-0101   OH
Web Site: http://www.chempace.com
Year Founded: 1968
Sales Range: $1-9.9 Million
Emp.: 17
Deodorant, Cleaning, Sanitation & Other Specialized Chemical Products Mfr & Whslr
N.A.I.C.S.: 325612
Richard Shall (Pres & CEO)
Terry O'Neill (VP)
Sue Klotz (Controller)
Tom Gordon (Mgr-Ops)

CHEMPETITIVE GROUP, LLC

730 W Randolph St 5th Fl, Chicago, IL 60661
Tel.: (312) 997-2436
Web Site:
  http://www.chempetitive.com
Year Founded: 2002
Sales Range: $1-9.9 Million
Emp.: 35
Advetising Agency
N.A.I.C.S.: 541810
Murad Sabzali (Co-Founder & Mng Partner-Chicago)
Jeff Bergau (Co-Founder & Mng Partner-Chicago)
Steve Johnson (Mng Partner & Exec VP-Strategy & Insight-Chicago)
Erik Clausen (Mng Partner & Exec VP-PR-San Diego)
Ken Li (Dir-Acct & PR-Chicago)
Jeremiah Worth (Exec Dir-Creative-Chicago)

CHEMSOLV INC.

1140 Industrial Ave SE, Roanoke, VA 24013
Tel.: (540) 427-4000
Web Site: https://www.chemsolv.com
Rev.: $13,800,000
Emp.: 75
Industrial Chemicals
N.A.I.C.S.: 424690
L. Glenn Austin (Pres)
Shane Duff (Mgr-Dispatcher & Logistics)

CHEMSTAR PRODUCTS COMPANY

3915 Hiawatha Ave, Minneapolis, MN 55406-3203
Tel.: (612) 722-0079
Web Site: http://www.chemstar.com
Year Founded: 1965
Rev.: $18,000,000
Emp.: 70
Industrial Starch
N.A.I.C.S.: 311221
Paul F. Werler (Founder & CEO)
James F. Werler (Pres)
Greg Swensson (Plant Mgr)

CHEMTRAK, INC.

1555 Oakbrook Dr Ste 100, Norcross, GA 30093
Tel.: (770) 449-6233
Web Site: http://www.chemtrac.com
Year Founded: 1985
Monitoring & Control Instrument Mfr
N.A.I.C.S.: 334513
Carl Byron (Reg Mgr-Sls-Northeast)

CHEMTRUSION, INC.

7115 Clinton Dr, Houston, TX 77020-8135
Tel.: (713) 675-1616

Web Site:
  https://www.chemtrusion.com
Sales Range: $25-49.9 Million
Emp.: 160
Plastics Compounding Services
N.A.I.C.S.: 325211
Scott Owens (Pres)
Edward Bourbonais (VP-Mktg & Tech)
John Sutjak (CFO)

CHEMUNG SUPPLY CORPORATION

2420 Corning Rd, Elmira, NY 14903
Tel.: (607) 733-5506
Web Site:
  https://www.chemungsupply.com
Sales Range: $75-99.9 Million
Emp.: 40
Metals Service Centers & Offices
N.A.I.C.S.: 423510
Carl Perine (Mgr-Sls)
Susanne Carrier (Sec)
Marc Stemerman (Pres)
Stephen Knowles (Mgr-Matl & Production)

CHEN & ASSOCIATES CIVIL & ENVIRONMENTAL ENGINEERS, INC.

500 W Cypress Creek Rd Ste 630, Fort Lauderdale, FL 33309
Tel.: (954) 730-0707   FL
Web Site:
  https://www.chenandassociates.com
Year Founded: 1986
Sales Range: $1-9.9 Million
Emp.: 60
Engineeering Services
N.A.I.C.S.: 541330
Ben Chen (Founder & Chm)
Peter Moore (Pres & CEO)

CHEN PR

71 Summer St Penthouse, Boston, MA 02110
Tel.: (781) 466-8282
Web Site: http://www.chenpr.com
Sales Range: $1-9.9 Million
Emp.: 20
Public Relations
N.A.I.C.S.: 541820
Chris Carleton (Partner)
Barbara Ewen (Partner)
Kevin Kosh (Partner)

CHENEGA CORPORATION

3000 C St Ste 301, Anchorage, AK 99503-3975
Tel.: (907) 277-5706
Web Site: https://www.chenega.com
Sales Range: $25-49.9 Million
Emp.: 6,500
Real Property Lessor Services
N.A.I.C.S.: 531190
Jeff Hueners (COO & Exec VP)

Subsidiaries:

Access Quality Care Services   (1)
2929 Mossrock Dr, San Antonio, TX 78230
Tel.: (210) 349-0096
Web Site: http://www.accessqualitycare.com
Sales Range: $1-9.9 Million
Emp.: 50
Women Healthcare Services
N.A.I.C.S.: 621610
Robert Rodriguez (Principal)

Chenega Integrated Systems, LLC   (1)
5911 Kingstowne Village Pkwy Ste 300, Alexandria, VA 22315
Tel.: (703) 822-2872
Web Site: http://www.cis-llc.net
Rev.: $340,000
Emp.: 4
Armed Guard Services for Military Locations
N.A.I.C.S.: 561612

E&M International, Inc.   (1)
2840 Vassar Dr NE, Albuquerque, NM 87107
Tel.: (505) 883-8955
Sales Range: $1-9.9 Million
Emp.: 10
Miscellaneous Durable Goods Merchant Whslr
N.A.I.C.S.: 423990
Edward Vaillancourt (Pres)

SecuriGence LLC   (1)
101 1st St, Los Altos, CA 94022
Tel.: (650) 888-5725
Web Site: http://www.securigence.com
Sales Range: $1-9.9 Million
Emp.: 10
Software Publisher
N.A.I.C.S.: 513210
Rich Larsen (Principal)
Michael J. Barnhart (Pres)
Philip W. Chambers (Dir-Bus Dev)
Tai K. Truong (VP)

CHENEY BROTHERS, INC.

1 Cheney Way, Riviera Beach, FL 33404
Tel.: (561) 845-4700
Web Site:
  https://www.cheneybrothers.com
Year Founded: 1925
Sales Range: $1-4.9 Billion
Emp.: 3,000
Other Grocery & Related Products Merchant Whslr
N.A.I.C.S.: 424490
Byron Russell (CEO)
Gene Allison (VP-Sls-Intl)
John Haber (CIO)

CHENEY LIME & CEMENT CO. INC.

478 Graystone Rd, Allgood, AL 35013
Tel.: (205) 625-3031
Web Site:
  https://www.cheneylime.com
Sales Range: $10-24.9 Million
Emp.: 51
Mfr Of Lime
N.A.I.C.S.: 327410
Rick Townson (Gen Mgr)
Alan B. Cheney Jr. (Pres)

CHENIERE CORPUS CHRISTI HOLDINGS, LLC

700 Milam St Ste 1900, Houston, TX 77002
Tel.: (713) 375-5000   DE
Web Site: https://www.cheniere.com
Year Founded: 2014
Rev.: $5,465,000,000
Assets: $16,976,000,000
Liabilities: $8,444,000,000
Net Worth: $8,532,000,000
Earnings: $7,150,000,000
Emp.: 1,605
Fiscal Year-end: 12/31/23
Holding Company
N.A.I.C.S.: 551112
Leonard E. Travis (Chief Acctg Officer)
Aaron Stephenson (Mgr)
Zach Davis (Pres, CFO & Mgr)

Subsidiaries:

Cheniere Corpus Christi Pipeline, L.P.   (1)
700 Milam St Ste 1900, Houston, TX 77002
Tel.: (713) 375-5000
Web Site: https://www.cheniere.com
Rev.: $66,116,000
Assets: $407,504,000
Liabilities: $12,791,000
Net Worth: $394,713,000
Earnings: $34,038,000
Fiscal Year-end: 12/31/2019
Natural Gas Pipeline Transportation Services
N.A.I.C.S.: 486210
Michael J. Wortley (Pres & CFO)

Corpus Christi Liquefaction, LLC **(1)**
700 Milam St Ste 1900, Houston, TX 77002
Tel.: (713) 375-5000
Web Site: https://www.cheniere.com
Assets: $11,304,581,000
Liabilities: $499,278,000
Net Worth: $10,805,303,000
Earnings: $77,686,000
Fiscal Year-end: 12/31/2019
Natural Gas Pipeline Transportation Services
N.A.I.C.S.: 486210
Michael J. Wortley *(Pres & CFO)*

Corpus Christi Pipeline GP, LLC **(1)**
700 Milam St Ste 1900, Houston, TX
77002-2835
Tel.: (713) 375-5000
Assets: $1,000
Liabilities: $10,000
Net Worth: ($9,000)
Earnings: ($10,350)
Fiscal Year-end: 12/31/2019
Natural Gas Pipeline Transportation Services
N.A.I.C.S.: 486210
Michael J. Wortley *(Pres & CFO)*

**CHERBONNIER, MAYER & AS-
SOCIATES INC.**
8180 YMCA Plaza Dr, Baton Rouge,
LA 70810
Tel.: (225) 927-9200
Web Site:
https://www.cmaontheweb.com
Sales Range: $100-124.9 Million
Emp.: 45
Custom Computer Programing
N.A.I.C.S.: 541511
Ben Cherbonnier *(Pres)*
B. Chad Lemaire *(Treas & Sec)*
David Renaud *(VP)*

**CHERNE CONTRACTING COR-
PORATION**
9855 W 78th St Ste 400, Eden Prai-
rie, MN 55344-8016
Tel.: (952) 944-4399   DE
Web Site: http://www.cherne.com
Year Founded: 1916
Industrial, Union General Contractor;
Heavy Construction
N.A.I.C.S.: 236210
Troy Sensabaugh *(Project Quality
Coordinator)*

**CHERNER AUTOMOTIVE
GROUP**
8550 Leesburg Pike, Vienna, VA
22182
Tel.: (703) 893-0800
Web Site: http://www.cherner.com
Year Founded: 1999
Sales Range: $10-24.9 Million
Emp.: 45
New Car Retailer
N.A.I.C.S.: 441110
Bob Hubbard *(CFO)*

CHERNOFF NEWMAN, LLC
1411 Gervais St 5th Fl, Columbia, SC
29201-3125
Tel.: (803) 254-8158   SC
Web Site:
https://www.chernoffnewman.com
Year Founded: 1971
Sales Range: $50-74.9 Million
Emp.: 45
Advertising & Public Relations
Agency
N.A.I.C.S.: 541810
A. Richard Silver *(Vice Chm)*
David Campbell *(Pres & COO)*
W. Lee Bussell *(Chm & CEO)*
David Anderson *(Vice Chm)*
Nickie Dickson *(CFO & Sr VP)*
Tye Price *(Sr VP)*
Heather Price *(Sr VP & Creative Dir)*
Sara Anders *(VP & Dir-Media)*

Peter Wertimer *(Pres-Adv Div)*
Bruce Jacobs *(Sr VP)*
Louise Dixon *(Pres-PR)*
Adam Bernstein *(Sr VP)*
Fenton Overdyke *(VP & Dir-Mktg
Svcs)*
Amanda DeWeese *(Dir-PR)*
Peter H. LaMotte *(Sr VP)*
Prussia George *(Controller)*
Elizabeth Bonner *(Acct Mgr-PR)*

Subsidiaries:

Carolina Public Relations/Marketing
Associates, Inc.   **(1)**
1017 E Morehead St Ste 150, Charlotte,
NC 28204
Tel.: (704) 374-9300
Web Site: http://www.carolinapr.com
Public Relations Agency
N.A.I.C.S.: 541820
Adam Bernstein *(Sr VP)*
Louise Dixon *(Sr VP)*
Amanda Kirkpatrick Deweese *(Acct Supvr)*

CHERNOFF SALES INC.
6280 NW 27th Way, Fort Lauderdale,
FL 33309
Tel.: (954) 972-1414
Web Site:
https://www.chernoffsales.com
Sales Range: $10-24.9 Million
Emp.: 25
Food Industry Equipment; Refrigera-
tion
N.A.I.C.S.: 423830
Joe Andisman *(Pres)*
Timothy Walker *(Controller)*
Michael Turetzky *(VP-Sls & Mktg)*

**CHEROKEE BRICK & TILE
COMPANY**
3250 Waterville Rd, Macon, GA
31206-1246
Tel.: (478) 781-6800   GA
Web Site:
https://www.cherokeebrick.com
Year Founded: 1908
Sales Range: $100-124.9 Million
Emp.: 250
Bricks Mfr
N.A.I.C.S.: 327120
Kenneth D. Sams *(CEO)*
Carl Capps *(CFO)*
Mike Peavy *(Pres)*
John Thigpen *(VP)*

**CHEROKEE CHEMICAL CO.
INC.**
3540 E 26th St, Vernon, CA 90058
Tel.: (323) 265-1112   CA
Web Site:
https://www.ccichemical.com
Year Founded: 1964
Sales Range: $10-24.9 Million
Emp.: 20
Distr of Specialty Cleaning & Sanita-
tion Preparations
N.A.I.C.S.: 424690
Denny A. Criswell *(Pres)*
Barbara Dunlop *(Controller)*

**CHEROKEE COMMUNICA-
TIONS INC.**
11 River Rise Rd, New City, NY
10956-5602
Tel.: (845) 638-6700   NJ
Web Site:
https://www.millercherokee.com
Year Founded: 1986
Sales Range: Less than $1 Million
Emp.: 2
Advetising Agency
N.A.I.C.S.: 541810
Kent Murphy *(Pres)*

CHEROKEE COUNTY ELEC-

**TRIC COOPERATIVE ASSO-
CIATION**
29880 Hwy 69 N, Rusk, TX 75785
Tel.: (903) 683-2248   TX
Web Site: https://www.cceca.net
Year Founded: 1939
Sales Range: $25-49.9 Million
Emp.: 74
Electric Power Distribution Services
N.A.I.C.S.: 221122
Kyle Griffith *(Pres)*
Steven R. Guy *(Atty)*
B. R. Darby *(Treas & Sec)*
Greg Jones *(Gen Mgr)*
Jim Tarrant Jr. *(VP)*

**CHEROKEE COUNTY WATER
SEWAGE AUTHORITY**
140 W Main St, Canton, GA 30114
Tel.: (770) 479-1813
Web Site: https://www.ccwsa.com
Year Founded: 1955
Sales Range: $25-49.9 Million
Emp.: 150
Water Supply
N.A.I.C.S.: 221310
Steven Woodruff *(Sec)*

CHEROKEE DATA SOLUTIONS
PO Box 1121, Claremore, OK 74018
Tel.: (918) 343-3577
Web Site: http://www.okcds.com
Year Founded: 2001
Sales Range: $1-9.9 Million
Emp.: 10
Supplier IT Equipment & Office Prod-
ucts to Healthcare Organizations,
Educational Institutions, Federal
Agencies & State & Tribal Govern-
ment
N.A.I.C.S.: 541519
P. C. Johnston *(Mgr-Sls)*

**CHEROKEE DISTRIBUTING
COMPANY, INC.**
200 Miller Main Cir, Knoxville, TN
37919-6017
Tel.: (865) 588-7641   TN
Web Site:
https://www.cherokeedistributer.com
Year Founded: 1958
Sales Range: $25-49.9 Million
Beer & Non-Alcoholic Beverage Distr
N.A.I.C.S.: 424810
George Burton Sampson *(Pres)*

Subsidiaries:

Family Brands International LLC   **(1)**
1001 Elm Hill Rd, Lenoir City, TN
37771-4339   **(100%)**
Tel.: (865) 986-8005
Web Site: http://www.fbico.com
Sales Range: $10-24.9 Million
Emp.: 115
Provider of Meat Packing Services
N.A.I.C.S.: 311611

**CHEROKEE ENTERPRISES,
INC.**
14474 Commerce Way, Miami Lakes,
FL 33016
Tel.: (305) 828-3353   FL
Web Site:
http://www.cherokeecorp.com
Year Founded: 1999
Sales Range: $1-9.9 Million
Emp.: 43
Environmental & Civil Engineering
N.A.I.C.S.: 541620
Alex Sanchez *(VP)*
Melissa Muirhead *(Asst Mgr-Acctg)*
Ronnie Rodriguez *(Mgr-Acctg)*

**CHEROKEE INFORMATION
SERVICES, INC.**

2850 Eisenhower Ave Ste 210, Alex-
andria, VA 22314
Tel.: (703) 416-0720
Web Site: http://www.cherokee-
inc.com
Year Founded: 1990
Sales Range: $25-49.9 Million
Emp.: 500
Provider of Information Technology,
Management, Logistics & Acquisition
Services
N.A.I.C.S.: 541512
Scott R. Johnson *(Dir-Bus Dev)*

**CHEROKEE MANUFACTURING
INC.**
501 Richmond St E, South Saint
Paul, MN 55075
Tel.: (651) 451-6568
Web Site:
http://www.cherokeemfg.com
Year Founded: 1940
Sales Range: $10-24.9 Million
Emp.: 100
Mfr of Baskets, Steel Wire
N.A.I.C.S.: 331222
John Gunderman *(Pres)*

**CHEROKEE NATION BUSI-
NESSES**
777 W Cherokee St, Catoosa, OK
74015
Tel.: (918) 384-7474
Web Site:
https://cherokeenationbusiness.com
Year Founded: 2004
Holding Company
N.A.I.C.S.: 551112
Chris Moody *(VP-Bus Dev-Federal)*

Subsidiaries:

Cherokee Nation Entertainment   **(1)**
State Hwy 62 4 Miles S, Tahlequah, OK
74465
Tel.: (918) 207-3600
Web Site: http://www.cherokeecasino.com
Sales Range: $200-249.9 Million
Emp.: 1,000
Hotel & Casino Services
N.A.I.C.S.: 721121
Chad Smith *(Principal)*
David Stewart *(Pres & CEO)*
Callie Catcher *(Treas & Sec)*
Molly Jarvis *(VP-Cultural & PR)*
Jay Hannah *(Chm)*

Subsidiary (Domestic):

MGM Resorts Mississippi, Inc.   **(2)**
1010 Casino Center Dr, Robinsonville, MS
38664
Tel.: (662) 357-1111
Web Site: https://goldstrike.mgmresorts.com
Hotel & Casino
N.A.I.C.S.: 721120

**CHEROKEE REGIONAL MEDI-
CAL CENTER**
333 Sioux Valley Dr, Cherokee, IA
51012
Tel.: (712) 225-1185   IA
Web Site:
http://www.cherokeermc.org
Year Founded: 1916
Sales Range: $25-49.9 Million
Emp.: 296
Health Care Srvices
N.A.I.C.S.: 622110

CHERRY BEKAERT LLP
3800 Glenwood Avenue Suite 200,
Raleigh, NC 27612
Tel.: (804) 673-5700
Web Site: http://www.cbh.com
Year Founded: 1947
Emp.: 1,250
Accounting, Tax, Auditing & Consult-
ing Services
N.A.I.C.S.: 541211

Cherry Bekaert LLP—(Continued)

August P. Keller *(Chief Mktg & Sls Officer)*
William F. Becker *(Partner-Tax)*
William Poad *(Dir-Tax Svc)*
John D. Richardson *(Dir-Risk Advisory Svcs Grp)*
Paul D. Fedorkowicz *(Chief Admin Officer)*
Mark Giallonardo *(Member-Exec Bd)*
Lourdes De Los Santos *(Partner)*
Michael B. East *(Mgr-Fraud & Forensic Svcs)*
Cristian Nieto *(Partner)*
Nick Stone *(Dir-Risk Advisory Svcs)*
Edward T. Burke *(Member-Exec Bd)*
Kip Plowman *(Mng Partner-Strategic Markets)*
Kurt W. Taves *(Mng Partner-Tax Svcs)*
Michelle Loyd Thompson *(Mng Partner/CEO-Raleigh Practice)*
Scott M. Moss *(Mng Partner-Advisory Svcs)*
Steven A. Wolf *(Partner-Forensic & Litigation Advisory Svcs)*
Matthew Brady *(Partner-Tax)*
Christopher Rux *(Mng Partner-Tampa Bay)*
Amanda M. Adams *(Mng Dir-Nonprofit Tax Svcs-Atlanta)*
Christopher C Neal *(Partner-Tax)*
Dawn G. Patrick *(Mng Partner-Nashville)*
Brooks E. Nelson *(Partner-Tax Svcs)*
Anne Oliver *(Dir-Specialty Tax Svcs-Washington)*
Chad Blackburn *(Dir-Bus Dev)*
Collin G. Hill *(Mng Partner)*
Christine W. Pierce *(Mng Partner & Member-Exec Bd)*
David T. Bettler *(Partner & Member-Exec Bd)*
Cathie Stanton *(Partner & Member-Exec Bd)*
Luis Reyes *(Partner-Assurance-Atlanta)*
Ross Burden *(Partner-Assurance-Nashville)*
Srikant Sastry *(Mng Principal-Advisory Svcs-Tysons)*
Scott Anderson *(Dir-Assurance)*
Jeff Horsley *(Partner)*
Ron Farmer *(Partner)*
Kim Roddy *(Partner)*
Kathryn Dillon *(Partner)*
David Mobley *(Partner)*
Robert E. Martin III *(Mng Partner)*

Subsidiaries:

Archerpoint, L.L.C.   **(1)**
1 Meca Way, Norcross, GA 30093
Tel.: (678) 389-4283
Web Site: http://www.archerpoint.com
Rev.: $4,800,000
Emp.: 45
Computer System Design Services
N.A.I.C.S.: 541512
Greg Kaupp *(CEO)*
Scott Peetz *(CFO)*

CoNexus CPA Group LLC   **(1)**
900 Cir 75 Pkwy SE Ste 1100, Atlanta, GA 30339
Tel.: (770) 980-1080
Web Site: http://www.conexuscpa.com
Financial Consulting Services
N.A.I.C.S.: 541611

Legier & Company   **(1)**
1100 Poydras St 34th Fl, New Orleans, LA 70163-1101
Tel.: (504) 561-0020
Web Site: http://www.legier.com
Offices of Certified Public Accountants
N.A.I.C.S.: 541211
Bill Legler *(Mng Dir)*

Taxgroup Partners Inc.   **(1)**

777 S Figueroa St Ste 2870, Los Angeles, CA 90017-5862
Tel.: (213) 873-1200
Web Site: http://www.taxgrouppartners.com
Other Accounting Services
N.A.I.C.S.: 541219
Al Sanifar *(Partner)*

Treacy & Company, Inc.   **(1)**
1220 S St, Needham, MA 02492
Tel.: (773) 453-5970
Web Site: http://www.treacyandco.com
General Management Consulting Services
N.A.I.C.S.: 541611
Michael E. Treacy *(Pres, CEO, CFO & Treas)*
Jill Deborah Smith *(Co-Founder)*

CHERRY CAPITAL CADILLAC SUBARU, LLC.
1747 S Garfield Ave, Traverse City, MI 49686-4337
Tel.: (231) 947-9000
Web Site: http://www.cherrycapital.com
Sales Range: $10-24.9 Million
Emp.: 50
Car Whslr
N.A.I.C.S.: 441110
Joseph Serra *(Owner)*

CHERRY CENTRAL COOPERATIVE, INC.
1771 N US 31 S, Traverse City, MI 49684
Tel.: (231) 946-1860   MI
Web Site: https://www.cherrycentral.com
Year Founded: 1973
Sales Range: $75-99.9 Million
Emp.: 35
Processor & Marketer of Fresh Fruits & Vegetables
N.A.I.C.S.: 424420
Brent Tackett *(Mgr-Natl Sls)*

Subsidiaries:

Dunkley International   **(1)**
1910 Lake St, Kalamazoo, MI 49001-3274   **(100%)**
Tel.: (269) 343-5583
Web Site: http://www.dunkleyintl.com
Sales Range: $10-24.9 Million
Emp.: 20
Food Product Machinery Mfr
N.A.I.C.S.: 333241
Nick Hatzinikolis *(Gen Mgr)*

Oceana Foods   **(1)**
168 Lincoln St, Shelby, MI 49455-0156
Tel.: (231) 861-2141
Sales Range: $25-49.9 Million
Emp.: 115
Fruit Processor
N.A.I.C.S.: 311421
Richard Bogard *(Pres)*
Jeff Tucker *(Gen Mgr)*

CHERRY CREEK MORTGAGE CO. INC.
7600 E Orchard Rd Ste 250-N, Greenwood Village, CO 80111
Tel.: (303) 320-4040
Web Site: http://www.cherrycreekmortgage.com
Sales Range: $50-74.9 Million
Emp.: 200
Mortgage Lending Services
N.A.I.C.S.: 522310
Jeffrey S. May *(Pres & CEO)*
Stacey Harding *(Sr VP)*
Tom Ninness *(VP & Reg Mgr-Production)*
Philip J. Teigen *(Gen Counsel, Sec & VP)*
Tara Healy *(Chief Compliance Officer)*
Rick Seehausen *(Pres & COO)*
Ty Kern *(Exec Mng Dir)*

CHERRY ENERGY
2947 Hull Rd, Kinston, NC 28504
Tel.: (252) 624-3277
Web Site: https://www.cherryenergy.com
Year Founded: 1928
Petroleum Bulk Stations
N.A.I.C.S.: 424710
Armistead Mauck *(VP)*

CHERRY GROWERS INC.
6331 US Hwy 31 PO Box 90, Grawn, MI 49637
Tel.: (231) 276-9241
Web Site: http://www.cherrygrowers.net
Sales Range: $25-49.9 Million
Emp.: 125
Cherry Products Producer
N.A.I.C.S.: 311411
Dan Winwicke *(CFO)*
Charles Roderick *(Plant Mgr)*

CHERRY HOUSE INC.
2419 S Highway 53, La Grange, KY 40031
Tel.: (502) 222-0343
Web Site: https://www.cherryhouse.com
Year Founded: 1969
Sales Range: $10-24.9 Million
Emp.: 50
Owner of Furniture Stores
N.A.I.C.S.: 449110
Lesley Whitehouse *(Pres)*
Steve Whitehouse *(CFO)*
Deboraa Reese *(Mgr)*

CHERRY STIX LTD.
1407 Broadway Rm 1503, New York, NY 10018
Tel.: (212) 221-5100
Rev.: $92,528,825
Emp.: 65
Women's & Children's Sportswear
N.A.I.C.S.: 424350
Charles Gammal *(Pres)*
David Apperman *(Controller)*
Christine Longsworth *(Mgr-Import Traffic Logistics)*

CHERRY-AIR
4584 Claire Chennault St, Addison, TX 75001
Tel.: (972) 248-1707
Web Site: http://www.cherryair.com
Rev.: $22,478,979
Emp.: 100
Provider of Air Cargo Carrier Services
N.A.I.C.S.: 481219
Jerry Monter *(Dir-Mktg)*

Subsidiaries:

Cherry-Air Inc, Chartered Air Cargo   **(1)**
4584 Claire Chennault St, Addison, TX 75001
Tel.: (972) 248-1707
Web Site: http://www.cherryair.com
Sales Range: $10-24.9 Million
Emp.: 75
Flying Charter Service
N.A.I.C.S.: 481219

CHERRYBROOK PREMIUM PET SUPPLIES
181 Bronico Way, Phillipsburg, NJ 08865-2778
Tel.: (908) 689-7979
Web Site: http://www.cherrybrook.com
Sales Range: $10-24.9 Million
Emp.: 45
Pet Food Supplies
N.A.I.C.S.: 424990
Roy Loomis *(Pres & CEO)*

CHERRYLAND ELECTRIC CO-OPERATIVE
US 31 S, Grawn, MI 49637
Tel.: (231) 486-9200
Web Site: http://www.cherrylandelectric.com
Year Founded: 1938
Rev.: $23,644,614
Emp.: 50
Distribution, Electric Power
N.A.I.C.S.: 221122
Terry Lautner *(Chm)*
Tony Anderson *(Gen Mgr)*
Melinda Lautner *(Sec)*

CHERRYROAD TECHNOLOGIES INC.
301 Gibraltar Dr Ste 2C, Morris Plains, NJ 07950
Tel.: (973) 402-7802   NJ
Web Site: http://www.cherryroad.com
Year Founded: 1983
Sales Range: $50-74.9 Million
Emp.: 400
Technical & Management Consulting Services
N.A.I.C.S.: 541512
Jeremy Gulban *(CEO)*
Glenn Zaleski *(Mng Dir)*
Nicholas Visco *(CFO)*

Subsidiaries:

Superb Internet Corp   **(1)**
711 Kapiolani Blvd Ste 975, Honolulu, HI 96813-5294
Tel.: (808) 544-0387
Web Site: http://www.superb.net
Rev.: $10,146,002
Emp.: 46
Fiscal Year-end: 03/31/2015
Internet Web & Cloud Hosting
N.A.I.C.S.: 517810
Haralds Jass *(Founder & Pres)*
Ken Nunes *(COO)*
Curtis R. Curtis *(Sr VP-Sls & Mktg)*

CHESAPEAKE BANK OF MARYLAND
2001 E Joppa Rd, Baltimore, MD 21234
Tel.: (410) 665-7600
Web Site: https://www.chesapeakebank.com
Rev.: $10,455,000
Emp.: 70
Federal Savings & Loan Associations
N.A.I.C.S.: 522180
Dan Dunbar *(Asst VP-Consumer Lending)*
Sarah J. Collier *(Asst VP & Mgr-Bel Air)*
Dody C. Sharp *(Mgr-Loan)*
Cynthia A. Spragg *(Asst VP-Residential Lending)*
Matt Mullen *(Chief Lending Officer & Sr VP)*
Jodi Beal *(CFO & Exec VP)*

CHESAPEAKE BAY FOUNDATION
6 Herndon Ave, Annapolis, MD 21403
Tel.: (410) 268-8816   MD
Web Site: http://www.cbf.org
Year Founded: 1966
Sales Range: $25-49.9 Million
Emp.: 236
Bay Restoration & Protection Services
N.A.I.C.S.: 541620
Elizabeth Buckman *(VP-Comm)*
Jon A. Mueller *(VP-Litigation)*
Rebecca LePrell *(Exec Dir-Virginia)*
Lisa Feldt *(VP-Environmental Protection & Restoration)*
Hilary Harp Falk *(Pres & CEO)*

CHESAPEAKE BAY SEAFOOD

HOUSE ASSOCIATES, LLC
1960 Gallows Rd, Vienna, VA 22182
Tel.: (703) 827-0320
Web Site:
http://www.chesapeakerestau
rants.com
Year Founded: 1974
Sales Range: $10-24.9 Million
Emp.: 1,700
Fish & Seafoods
N.A.I.C.S.: 424460
Paul Truskey (Dir-Fin)

CHESAPEAKE EMPLOYERS' INSURANCE COMPANY
8722 Loch Raven Blvd, Towson, MD
21286-2235
Tel.: (410) 494-2000   MD
Year Founded: 2012
Emp.: 108
Insurance Services
N.A.I.C.S.: 524298
Thomas Phelan (Pres)
Timothy Michels (COO)
Paige Beck (Chief Admin Officer)
Francis Linardi (CFO)
Kallie Shrader (Dir-Bus Advisory
Svcs)
Tammy Wescott (Dir-Claims)
Brian Furr (Asst VP-Legal Svcs-SIU
& Premium Audit)
Joan Adelman (VP-Legal Svcs)

CHESAPEAKE SPRINKLER COMPANY
1913 Betson Ct, Odenton, MD 21113
Tel.: (410) 674-7041
Web Site:
http://www.chesapeakesprink
lermd.com
Sales Range: $10-24.9 Million
Emp.: 150
Fire Sprinkler System Installation
N.A.I.C.S.: 238220
Marsha Milliken (Office Mgr)

CHESHIRE OIL COMPANY INC.
678 Marlboro St, Keene, NH 03431
Tel.: (603) 352-0001   NH
Web Site: http://www.cheshireoil.com
Year Founded: 1921
Sales Range: $25-49.9 Million
Emp.: 300
Providers of Energy Products & Ser-
vices to Commercial & Residential
Customers
N.A.I.C.S.: 457210
James C. Robertson (Pres)
Jean Wright (Office Mgr)

CHESKIN ADDED VALUE
3400 Cahuenga Blvd W, Los Ange-
les, CA 90068
Tel.: (650) 802-2100
Web Site: http://www.cheskin.com
Rev.: $14,000,000
Emp.: 60
Business Consulting Services
N.A.I.C.S.: 541611
Stephen Palacios (Exec Dir)
Brian Kushnir (Mng Dir & Exec VP)
Edward Farias (CFO)
Helen Firth (Sr VP-Brand Dev)
Jennifer Fox (Sr VP)
Wai Leng Loh (Sr VP)

CHESS COMMUNICATIONS GROUP
901 E Fayette St, Baltimore, MD
21202-4731
Tel.: (410) 732-7400   MD
Web Site: http://www.chesscg.com
Year Founded: 1960
Sales Range: $10-24.9 Million
Emp.: 11
Media Buying Services

N.A.I.C.S.: 541810
Bruce Lannatuono (Chm & Pres)
Ken Wahler (Sr VP-Interactive Mktg)

CHESSCO INDUSTRIES, INC.
1300 Post Rd E, Westport, CT
06880-5537
Tel.: (203) 255-2804   DE
Year Founded: 1968
Sales Range: $75-99.9 Million
Emp.: 100
Mfr of Specialty Chemicals Used in
the Medical, Auto & Electronic Indus-
tries, Surgical & Hospital Industry &
Inks for the Packaging Industry
N.A.I.C.S.: 327910
Jeffrey Radler (Pres & CEO)

Subsidiaries:

Chemionics Corporation   (1)
390 Munroe Falls Rd, Tallmadge, OH 44278
Tel.: (330) 733-8834
Web Site: http://www.chemionics.com
Sales Range: $25-49.9 Million
Emp.: 35
Mfr of Latexes, Water-Based Adhesives,
Plastisols & Epoxy Polymer Systems; Sup-
pliers of Quality Compounds, Coating &
Adhesives
N.A.I.C.S.: 326299
John Blackfan (VP)

Chessco Process Research
Products   (1)
1013 Whitehead Rd Ext, Trenton, NJ
08638-2418
Tel.: (609) 882-0400
Web Site: http://www.processresearch.com
Sales Range: $10-24.9 Million
Emp.: 20
Electronic Device Ball Bearing & Automotive
Part Sapping Compound for the Semi-
Conductor Industry Mfr
N.A.I.C.S.: 325180
Phylis Joan (VP-Admin)

CHESTER COUNTY COMMUNITY FOUNDATION
28 W Market St The Lincoln Bldg,
West Chester, PA 19382
Tel.: (610) 696-8211   PA
Web Site: https://www.chescocf.org
Year Founded: 1994
Sales Range: $10-24.9 Million
Emp.: 15
Grantmaking Services
N.A.I.C.S.: 813211
Beth Harper Briglia (VP-Donor Svcs
& Grantmaking)
Robert Ferguson (Controller)

CHESTER COUNTY NATURAL GAS AUTHORITY
2605 Dawson Dr, Chester, SC 29706
Tel.: (803) 385-3157
Web Site: http://www.chestergas.com
Year Founded: 1954
Sales Range: $25-49.9 Million
Emp.: 25
Natural Gas Distribution
N.A.I.C.S.: 221210
Mike Enoch (Gen Mgr & Mgr-Gas
Sys)
Joey Neal (Mgr-Customer Rels &
Ops)
David White (Dir-IT)
Mike Austin (Mgr-Svcs)

CHESTER DAIRY COMPANY
1915 State St, Chester, IL 62233
Tel.: (618) 826-2394
Sales Range: $10-24.9 Million
Emp.: 50
Bottlers Of Milk
N.A.I.C.S.: 311511
Brenda Potler (Sec)
Jason Ohlau (Pres)

CHESTER INC.

555 Eastport Centre Dr, Valparaiso,
IN 46383
Tel.: (219) 462-1131   IN
Web Site:
https://www.chesterinc.com
Year Founded: 1955
Sales Range: $10-24.9 Million
Emp.: 75
Provider of Commercial & Office
Building Contracts
N.A.I.C.S.: 236220
Lynn Goetz (Project Mgr)

CHESTER TELEPHONE COMPANY
112 York St, Chester, SC 29706
Tel.: (803) 385-2191
Web Site: http://www.chestertel.com
Rev.: $20,646,039
Emp.: 100
Local Telephone Communications
N.A.I.C.S.: 517121
Bob Wilkinson (Mgr-Mktg)
Cheryl Wylie (Controller)
Brian Singleton (CEO & VP)
Pracy Starnes (Plant Mgr)

CHESTER WATER AUTHORITY
415 Welsh St, Chester, PA 19013
Tel.: (610) 876-8185
Web Site:
https://www.chesterwater.com
Rev.: $25,737,172
Emp.: 150
Water Supply
N.A.I.C.S.: 221310
Brian P. MacEwen (Dir-Engrg)
Thomas Moore (Dir-Bus Dev)
Cynthia Felzer Leitzell (Chm)
Paul Andriole (Vice Chm)
Agnes Woebkenberg (CFO)
Robert A. Judge Sr. (Mgr)
Wendell N. Butler Jr. (Treas)

CHESTERMAN CO.
4700 S Lewis Blvd, Sioux City, IA
51106
Tel.: (712) 255-8814
Web Site:
https://www.chesterman.com
Sales Range: $75-99.9 Million
Emp.: 200
Soft Drinks: Packaged In Cans,
Bottles, Etc.
N.A.I.C.S.: 312111
Cy W. Chesterman (Pres)
Jay Chesterman (VP)
Gina Colvert (Mgr-Consumer Affairs)
Carl Stolze (Supvr-Production)
Jordan Lester (Asst Controller)
Rean Anderson (Supvr-Production)

CHESTNUT COMMUNICATIONS, INC.
15 E Putnam Ave, Greenwich, CT
06830-7242
Tel.: (203) 629-9098   CT
Year Founded: 1980
Sales Range: $10-24.9 Million
Advertising Agencies
N.A.I.C.S.: 541810
Albert S. Kestnbaum (Pres)

CHESTNUT HEALTH SYSTEMS, INC.
1003 Martin Luther King Jr Dr,
Bloomington, IL 61701
Tel.: (309) 827-6026   IL
Web Site: https://www.chestnut.org
Year Founded: 1970
Sales Range: $50-74.9 Million
Emp.: 880
Health Care Srvices
N.A.I.C.S.: 622110
Karen S. Rettick (CFO)
Alan Sender (COO)

James G. Fraser (Dir-Bus Dev)
Christy Scott (Dir-Lighthouse Insti-
tute)
David A. Sharar (Chief Clinical Offi-
cer)
Joan A. Hartman (Reg Mgr-Central)
Mark W. Campbell (Dir-HR)
Orville D. Mercer (Mgr-Southern)
Puneet Leekha (Gen Counsel)
Judith J. Smithson (Chm)
Laura Haas (Sec)
Mary Ann Webb (Vice Chm)
Parker Kemp (Treas)
Jim Wallis (Dir-Bus Dev)
Matt Mollenhauer (Mng Dir)

CHESTNUT RIDGE COUNSELING SERVICES, INC.
100 New Salem Rd, Uniontown, PA
15401
Tel.: (724) 437-0729   PA
Web Site: https://www.crcsi.org
Year Founded: 1969
Sales Range: $10-24.9 Million
Emp.: 238
Behavioral Healthcare Services
N.A.I.C.S.: 623220
William Blaney (Treas & Sec)

CHESTNUT RIDGE FOAM INC.
Rte 981 N, Latrobe, PA 15650
Tel.: (724) 537-9000
Web Site:
http://www.chestnutridgefoam.com
Year Founded: 1986
Sales Range: $10-24.9 Million
Emp.: 130
Mfr of Foam Rubber Products
N.A.I.C.S.: 326299
Carl Ogburn (Pres)
John McManamy (Mgr-Sls)
Mark Brown (Dir-Tech)
Tonia McCallen (Mgr-Ops)
Brandon Hohman (Mgr-Production)
Greg Bittner (Mgr-Transportation)
Rob Bologna (CFO)
Joe Jamison (Supvr)

CHESTON & GIBBENS INC.
475 W 57th St Ste 17A, New York,
NY 10019
Tel.: (212) 977-5097   NY
Year Founded: 1978
Sales Range: $10-24.9 Million
Emp.: 4
N.A.I.C.S.: 541810
Paul Cheston (Pres)

CHET MORRISON CONTRACTORS INC.
9 Bayou Dularge Rd, Houma, LA
70363
Tel.: (985) 868-1950
Web Site:
http://www.chetmorrison.com
Sales Range: $25-49.9 Million
Emp.: 330
Industrial Plant Construction
N.A.I.C.S.: 237990
Jerome Shaw (VP-Marine Construc-
tion)
Leroy Guidry (Pres & CFO)
Kelly Reeves (VP-Mktg)
Kirt Templet (Dir-HR)
John DeBlieux (VP-Deepwater Riser
Svcs)
Steve Becnel (VP-Fabrication, Off-
shore & Land Construction)
Chester F. Morrison Jr. (CEO)

CHETTA B INC.
1410 Broadway 16th Fl, New York,
NY 10018
Tel.: (212) 947-2006
Web Site: http://www.chettab.com
Sales Range: $10-24.9 Million

Chetta B Inc.—(Continued)
Emp.: 40
Mfr & Sales of Women's, Junior's & Misses' Dresses & Apparel
N.A.I.C.S.: 315250
Jerry Retto (CFO)
Alan Schwinger (Mgr-Sls)

CHETU, INC.
3350 SW 148th Ave Ste 204, Plantation, FL 33027
Tel.: (954) 342-5676
Web Site: http://www.chetu.com
Year Founded: 2000
Sales Range: $10-24.9 Million
Emp.: 1,500
IT Products & Services
N.A.I.C.S.: 519290
Atal Bansal (Founder & CEO)
Dave Wood (Dir-Sls, Supply Chain & Mktg)
Atit Shah (Mgr-Technical Project)
Ashish Bhadouria (Project Mgr-Technical)
Raj Kumar (Project Mgr-Technical)
Joshua Newman Rossie (Acct Mgr-Natl)
Adam Melrose (Acct Mgr-Natl)
James Diamond (Acct Mgr-Natl)
Francisco Jose Garcia (Acct Mgr-Natl)
Thomas Lynn Beck (Acct Mgr-Natl)
Antwan Lapree Burks (Acct Mgr-Natl)
Galvin Chance (Acct Mgr-Natl)
Todd Kennedy (Acct Mgr-Natl)
Francis Wallace (Acct Mgr-Natl)
Scott Forgy (Acct Mgr-Natl)
Jerrold Galloway (Acct Mgr-Natl)
Nathaniel Stewart (Acct Mgr-Natl)
Kris Sibley (Acct Mgr-Natl)
John Ryerson (Acct Mgr-Natl)
Christopher Ulrich (Acct Mgr-Natl)
Peter Kwon (Acct Mgr-Natl)
Deepak Borole (Project Mgr-Technical)
Michael Stilwill (Acct Mgr-Natl)
Sunil Singh (Project Mgr-Technical)
Devendra Verma (Project Mgr-Technical)
Ashutosh Karnatak (Project Mgr-Technical)
Michael Dunbar (Dir-Sls Enablement)

CHEVALIER ADVERTISING, INC.
1 Centerpointe Dr Ste 550, Lake Oswego, OR 97035
Tel.: (503) 639-9190
Web Site: http://www.chevalier-adv.com
Year Founded: 1953
Sales Range: Less than $1 Million
Emp.: 13
N.A.I.C.S.: 541810
Gregory Chevalier (Pres)
Chris George (Art Dir)
Robin Kizzar (Creative Dir)
Connie Gray (Production Mgr)

CHEVROLET 21, INC.
1100 Hellertown Rd Ste 1124, Bethlehem, PA 18015
Tel.: (610) 838-2200
Web Site: http://www.chevy21.com
Sales Range: $10-24.9 Million
Emp.: 75
Car Whslr
N.A.I.C.S.: 441110
Mary Hannah (Controller)
Jerold Horst (Pres)

CHEVROLET CENTER INC.
101 Cypress Gardens Blvd SW, Winter Haven, FL 33880
Tel.: (863) 294-7371

Web Site: http://www.chevroletcenter.com
Rev.: $24,900,000
Emp.: 90
New Car Dealers
N.A.I.C.S.: 441110
Sam W. Portlock (Pres)
Bill Parker (Mgr-Svcs)

CHEVROLET OF MONTE-BELLO
310 W Whittier Blvd, Montebello, CA 90640
Tel.: (323) 728-9181
Web Site: http://www.chevroletmontebello.com
Sales Range: $25-49.9 Million
Emp.: 110
New & Used Automobiles
N.A.I.C.S.: 441110
Ed Loera (Mgr-Sls)
Oscar Uzeta (Mgr-Fin)
Ted Eck (Gen Mgr)

CHEVROLET OF WOOSTER
1119 W Old Lincoln Way, Wooster, OH 44691
Tel.: (330) 264-2300
Web Site: https://www.chevroletofwooster.com
Emp.: 25
Car Whslr
N.A.I.C.S.: 441110
Jan Bunting (Mgr-Customer Svc)
Brett Tomassetti (Gen Sls Mgr)
Linda Mullet (Controller)
T. J. Herrington (Dir-Svc)
Mike Martz (Mgr-Svc)
Robin Shields (Mgr-Parts)
Noal Danial (Bus Mgr)
Dale B. Wolf (Gen Mgr)

CHEVROLET-BUICK OF QUINCY
2039 W Jefferson St, Quincy, FL 32351
Tel.: (850) 875-4200
Web Site: http://www.plattnerautomotive.com
Sales Range: $10-24.9 Million
Emp.: 20
New & Used Car Dealers Service & Parts
N.A.I.C.S.: 441110
Doug Plattner (Owner)

CHEVY CHASE CARS
7725 Wisconsin Ave, Bethesda, MD 20814-3521
Tel.: (301) 657-4000
Web Site: http://www.chevychasecars.com
Year Founded: 1939
Sales Range: $125-149.9 Million
Emp.: 150
Retail New & Used Automobiles
N.A.I.C.S.: 441110
John Bowis (Pres)
Aziz Elhallou (Dir-Used Car)
Kaveh Jahed (Dir-Sls)
Ralph Kolius (Mgr-Sls)
Robert Coley (Mgr-Fin)
Robert Cumberland (Mgr-Sls)
Aaron Zimmerman (Dir-Svcs)
Sam Weaver Jr. (VP-Sls)

CHEWNING & WILMER IN-CORPORATED
2508 Mechanicsville Tpke, Richmond, VA 23223
Tel.: (804) 231-7373
Web Site: http://www.chewningandwilmer.com
Year Founded: 1924
Sales Range: $50-74.9 Million
Emp.: 300

General Electrical Contractor
N.A.I.C.S.: 238210
Evan Rogers (Project Mgr)
Jay Atkinson (VP)
Lisa Morris (Asst Mgr-Svc)
Stephen McEntyre (Supvr-Electrical Project)
Michael Stone (Controller)
Robert Zahn (Pres)

CHEWSE, INC.
1161 Mission St, San Francisco, CA 94103
Web Site: http://www.chewse.com
Year Founded: 2011
Sales Range: $10-24.9 Million
Emp.: 250
Food Catering Services
N.A.I.C.S.: 722320
Tracy Lawrence (Founder & CEO)

CHEX FINER FOODS
71 Hampden Rd Ste 100, Mansfield, MA 02048
Tel.: (508) 226-0660
Web Site: https://www.chexfoods.com
Year Founded: 1965
Sales Range: $25-49.9 Million
Emp.: 50
Whslr & Distr of Specialty & Natural Foods to New England Retailers
N.A.I.C.S.: 424410
Jeremy Isenberg (Owner & Pres)
Michael Isenberg (VP)
John Speyer (CFO)

CHEYENNE CAMPING CENTER CO.
2960 N Plainview Rd, Walcott, IA 52773-8522
Tel.: (563) 284-6868
Web Site: https://www.cheyennecenter.com
Sales Range: $10-24.9 Million
Emp.: 39
Recreational Vehicle Whslr
N.A.I.C.S.: 441210
Kevin Frazer (Pres)

CHEYENNE INDUSTRIES, LLC
1008 Beau Terre Dr, Bentonville, AR 72712
Tel.: (501) 374-2822
Web Site: http://www.cheyenneproducts.com
Year Founded: 1980
Portable Lighting & Home Furnishings Whslr
N.A.I.C.S.: 423610
David Jeffers (VP)

CHF HOME FURNISHINGS
104 S Orchard St, Boise, ID 83705
Tel.: (208) 343-7769
Web Site: https://www.shopchf.com
Sales Range: $10-24.9 Million
Emp.: 50
Furniture & Appliances Stores
N.A.I.C.S.: 449110
Lyndon Johns (Pres)
Evan Weeks (Mgr-Appliance)

CHF INDUSTRIES, INC.
1 Park Ave, New York, NY 10016
Tel.: (212) 951-7800
Web Site: https://www.chfindustries.com
Year Founded: 1927
Sales Range: $100-124.9 Million
Emp.: 250
Curtains, Draperies, Bedding & Bath Products
N.A.I.C.S.: 423220

Frank M. Foley (CEO)
Joan Karron (Partner)
Spencer Foley (Pres & Chief Mdsg Officer)

Subsidiaries:

Aberdeen Manufacturing Corporation   (1)
1 Pk Ave, New York, NY 10016-5802
Tel.: (704) 522-5000
Sales Range: $25-49.9 Million
Emp.: 15
Handle Invoices, Sales for Manufacturing Division
N.A.I.C.S.: 238130

CHHJ FRANCHISING LLC
1513 E 9th Ave, Tampa, FL 33605
Tel.: (813) 701-2020
Web Site: http://www.collegehunkshauling.com
Year Founded: 2005
Sales Range: $10-24.9 Million
Emp.: 500
Junk Removal & Moving Service
N.A.I.C.S.: 484210
Nick Freidman (Co-Founder & Pres)
Omar Soliman (Co-Founder & CEO)

CHI CENTERS, INC.
10501 New Hampshire Ave, Silver Spring, MD 20903-1197
Tel.: (301) 445-3350
Web Site: http://www.chicenters.org
Year Founded: 1948
Sales Range: $10-24.9 Million
Emp.: 735
Disability Assistance Services
N.A.I.C.S.: 624120
Lawrence Skok (Pres)

CHI ENTERPRISES, INC.
1435 N Brasher Ave, Anaheim, CA 92807
Tel.: (714) 777-1542
Web Site: https://www.chi-health.com
Year Founded: 1986
Sales Range: $25-49.9 Million
Emp.: 10
Sale & Development of Health Food Products
N.A.I.C.S.: 423450
Cheryl Chi (Gen Mgr)

CHIANTI CHEESE COMPANY
207 Hanover St, Pemberton, NJ 08068
Tel.: (609) 894-0900
Sales Range: $10-24.9 Million
Emp.: 50
Natural & Processed Cheese Mfr & Distr
N.A.I.C.S.: 311513
Doug Kantner (Owner)

CHIAPPETTI WHOLESALE MEAT CORPORATION
100 E Wisconsin Ave Ste 1400, Milwaukee, WI 53202-4107
Tel.: (773) 847-1556
Web Site: http://www.chiappettilamb.com
Year Founded: 1983
Sales Range: $25-49.9 Million
Emp.: 140
Meat Packing Plants
N.A.I.C.S.: 311611
Brian Chiappetti (Co-Founder)
Dennis Chiappetti (Co-Founder)

CHIASSO LLC
1440 N Dyton St Ste 203, Chicago, IL 60622
Tel.: (312) 932-2000
Web Site: http://www.chiasso.com
Sales Range: $10-24.9 Million
Emp.: 25

Lighting, Lamps & Accessories
N.A.I.C.S.: 541511
Chris Segal (Pres)

CHICAGO AEROSOL, LLC
1300 N St, Coal City, IL 60416
Tel.: (708) 598-7100
Web Site:
   http://www.chicagoaerosol.com
Emp.: 215
Aerosol Products Mfr
N.A.I.C.S.: 325998
Wally Bransen (Pres & CEO)
Sarah Trumbull (VP-Fin)
Mike Cohen (Gen Counsel & Dir-
Compliance)
Jim Gleichman (Sr VP-Sls)
Bob Peter (VP-Sls)
Bobbie Jemilo (Mgr-Customer Svc)
Michelle Martin (Dir-Pur)
Carol Schmatz (VP-Technical Svcs)
Michelle Martin Valerio (Dir-Pur)
Ed Piszynski (VP-Laboratory Svcs)
Wayne Arndt (VP-Ops)
Bryan Smith (VP-Sls-Bridgeview)

Subsidiaries:

Re-Grip Inc.   (1)
32295 Mission Trl Ste #8-269, Lake
Elsinore, CA 92530-2306
Tel.: (800) 607-8931
Web Site: http://www.re-grip.com
Cylindrical & Semi-Cylindrical Tool & Handle
Replacement Grips Mfr
N.A.I.C.S.: 339999
John Vernieu (Co-Founder)
Pat Roscopf (Co-Founder)
Howard Paul (Mgr-Sls & Bus Dev-Western
Reg)

CHICAGO APARTMENT FIND-
ERS INC.
906 W Belmont Ave, Chicago, IL
60657
Tel.: (773) 883-8800
Web Site:
   http://www.chicagoapartments.com
Year Founded: 2002
Rev.: $5,300,000
Emp.: 100
Consumer Services
N.A.I.C.S.: 812990
Justin Elliott (Branch Mgr)
Maria Diaz (Mgr-Property)
Craig Hundley (Asst Mgr-Leasing)
Natalia Zieba (Project Coord)
Andrew Gruesser (Gen Mgr-Condo
Rental Mgmt)
Angela Fucigna (Acct Mgr-Closing
Dept)
Linda Corman (Office Mgr)
Robert Richmond (Reg Mgr-Sls)
Manny Capozzi (Dir-Ops)
Andy Ahitow (Founder)
Andrew Croegaert (Sr Mgr-Leasing)

CHICAGO ARCHITECTURE
FOUNDATION
224 S Michigan Ave, Chicago, IL
60604
Tel.: (312) 922-3432   IL
Web Site: http://www.architecture.org
Year Founded: 1966
Sales Range: $10-24.9 Million
Emp.: 91
Architectural Services
N.A.I.C.S.: 541310
John C. Pintozzi (Chm)
Alvin Katz (Sec)
Sandra L. Helton (Treas)

CHICAGO BEARS FOOTBALL
CLUB, INC.
Halas Hall 1920 Football Dr, Lake
Forest, IL 60045
Tel.: (847) 295-6600   IL

Web Site:
   http://www.chicagobears.com
Year Founded: 1920
Sales Range: $75-99.9 Million
Emp.: 150
Professional Football Franchise
N.A.I.C.S.: 711211
Scott Hagel (Sr VP-Mktg & Comm)
Karen Murphy (CFO & Sr VP-Bus
Strategy)
Cliff Stein (Gen Counsel & Sr VP)
Kevin F. Warren (Pres & CEO)
Tanesha Wade (Sr VP-Diversity, Eq-
uity & Inclusion)
Joseph Laine (Dir-Football Admin)
Lee Twarling (Sr VP-Sls & Customer
Rels)
George H. McCaskey (Chm)
Virginia McCaskey (Sec)
Brian J. McCaskey (VP)
Patrick McCaskey (VP)
Kevin Warren (Pres & CEO)

CHICAGO BLOWER CORPO-
RATION
1675 Glen Ellyn Rd, Glendale
Heights, IL 60139-2503
Tel.: (630) 858-2600
Web Site:
   https://www.chicagoblower.com
Year Founded: 1947
Sales Range: $10-24.9 Million
Emp.: 225
Mfr of Blowers & Fans
N.A.I.C.S.: 333413
Joe Dubeck (Pres)
Rick Hambel (VP-Mfg)
Bob Cowan (Mgr-Quality Sys)
Kathleen Redington (Mgr-HR)
Daniel Klomparens (Mgr-IT)
Scott Kossman (VP-Sls)
James Gratzke (Engr-Design)
Lauren Andrewski (Mgr-Mktg)
Jim Deloughery (Mgr-Sls-Natl)

CHICAGO CITY CAPITOL
GROUP
980 N Michigan Ave Ste 1675, Chi-
cago, IL 60611
Tel.: (312) 397-1675
Sales Range: $25-49.9 Million
Emp.: 2
Private Investment Company
N.A.I.C.S.: 523999
John F. Manley (Pres)

Subsidiaries:

Medcom Inc   (1)
6060 Phyllis Dr, Cypress, CA 90630
Tel.: (714) 891-1443
Web Site: http://www.medcomrn.com
Audio-Visual Program Production
N.A.I.C.S.: 512110
Larry Gorum (CEO)
Patricia Muecke (VP-Fin)

CHICAGO COATING SYSTEMS
394 38th Ave, Saint Charles, IL
60174-5424
Tel.: (630) 443-9602
Sales Range: $10-24.9 Million
Emp.: 15
Converted Paper Product Mfr
N.A.I.C.S.: 322299
Denis E. Wienhoff (Pres)

CHICAGO COMMONS ASSO-
CIATION
515 E 50th St Ste 200, Chicago, IL
60615
Tel.: (773) 373-5055
Web Site:
   https://www.chicagocommons.org
Sales Range: $25-49.9 Million
Emp.: 800
Education Services
N.A.I.C.S.: 611699

Willard S. Evans (Chm)
Michael D. Pratt (Treas)
Dhiren Shah (CFO)
Edgar R. Ramirez (Pres & CEO)
Steven Sparks (Vice Chm)
Cary Crawford (VP-Senior Care)
Sarah Frick (Sr VP-External Affairs &
Strategy)
Mary E. Timmons (Sec)
Andrew Krugly (VP-Education & Pro-
gram Ops)
Carman Weathington (VP-HR)
Julio Paz (Chief Dev Officer)

CHICAGO DENTAL SOCIETY
401 N Michigan Ave Ste 200, Chi-
cago, IL 60611
Tel.: (312) 836-7300   IL
Web Site: https://www.cds.org
Year Founded: 1864
Sales Range: $10-24.9 Million
Emp.: 15
Dental Care Services
N.A.I.C.S.: 621210
Randall Grove (Exec Dir)
Will Conkis (Dir-Publ)
Mohammed Adil (Mgr-Fin & Info Sys)
Lisa Girardi (Dir-Exhibit Svcs)
Rachel Azark Schafer (Mgr-Comm)
Phillip Fijal (Pres)
Louis Imburgia (VP)
Lennoree Cleary (Office Mgr)
Joanne Girardi (Dir-Member Svcs)
Dean Nicholas (Treas)
Cheryl Watson-Lowry (Sec)
Barry Ranallo (Assoc Exec Dir)
Helen Rabitoy (Mgr-Mediation & Peer
Review)
Ted Borris (Dir-Scientific Programs)

CHICAGO DIVERSIFIED
FOODS INC.
400 E 22nd St Ste E, Lombard, IL
60148-6104
Tel.: (630) 889-1818   IL
Year Founded: 1986
Sales Range: $25-49.9 Million
Emp.: 750
Provider of Food Services
N.A.I.C.S.: 722511
Anthony Basile (Pres)

CHICAGO EXHIBIT PRODUC-
TIONS, INC.
755 Remington Blvd, Bolingbrook, IL
60440
Tel.: (630) 378-4848
Web Site: http://www.cepexhibits.com
Rev.: $13,000,000
Emp.: 55
Trade Show Arrangement
N.A.I.C.S.: 561920
Werner Koos (CEO)
Mark Rogers (VP-Client Svcs)
Mike Ebert (Pres)

Subsidiaries:

Chicago Exhibit Productions Inc.   (1)
1600 Central Florida Pky Ste 100, Orlando,
FL 32837
Tel.: (407) 857-7607
Web Site: http://www.cepexhibits.com
Sales Range: $10-24.9 Million
Emp.: 10
Trade Show Arrangement Services
N.A.I.C.S.: 561920
Werner Koos (Owner & CEO)
Dennis Mahoney (Exec VP-Laborsource)

CHICAGO FLAG & DECORAT-
ING CO.
65 Shields Rd, Huntsville, AL 35811
Tel.: (256) 851-2225
Web Site: http://www.cflag.com
Rev.: $12,000,000
Emp.: 150
Flags, Fabric

N.A.I.C.S.: 314999

CHICAGO FOOD CORPORA-
TION
5825 N Tripp Ave, Chicago, IL 60646
Tel.: (773) 478-0007
Web Site:
   http://www.chicagofood.com
Year Founded: 1980
Rev.: $19,071,514
Emp.: 20
Groceries & Related Products Re-
tailer
N.A.I.C.S.: 424490
Ki Pyo Hong (Pres)

CHICAGO GROWTH PART-
NERS, LLC
159 N sangamon ste 400, Chicago,
IL 60607
Tel.: (312) 698-6300   DE
Web Site: http://www.cgp.com
Sales Range: $25-49.9 Million
Emp.: 5
Privater Equity Firm
N.A.I.C.S.: 523999
Robert D. Blank (Partner)
David G. Chandler (Mng Partner)
Robert P. Healy (Mng Partner)
Arda M. Minocherhomjee (Mng Part-
ner)
Timothy M. Murray (Partner)
Jeffery M. Farrero (Principal)
Corey Dossett (CFO)
Devin Matthews (Mng Partner)
Kristina Heinze (Principal)
Arda M. Minocherhomjee (Founder &
Mng Partner)

Subsidiaries:

Marathon Data Systems, Inc.   (1)
4810 Belmar Blvd, Wall Township, NJ
07753
Tel.: (732) 938-7950
Web Site: http://www.marathondata.com
Sales Range: $10-24.9 Million
Software-as-a-Service Solutions
N.A.I.C.S.: 541511
Chris Sullens (Pres & CEO)
Jason Kochel (CTO)
Joe Bonelli (Sr Dir-Corp Mktg)

CHICAGO HARDWARE & FIX-
TURE COMPANY
9100 Parklane Ave, Franklin Park, IL
60131
Tel.: (847) 455-6609
Web Site:
   https://www.chicagohardware.com
Rev.: $20,400,000
Emp.: 140
Hardware
N.A.I.C.S.: 332510
Greg Carlevato (Controller)
Jay Richmond (Mgr-Sls)
Thomas A. Herbstritt Jr. (Pres)

CHICAGO HARLEY-DAVIDSON
INC.
2929 Patriot Blvd, Glenview, IL 60026
Tel.: (773) 338-6868
Web Site:
   http://www.chicagoharley.com
Sales Range: $10-24.9 Million
Emp.: 73
Motorcycles
N.A.I.C.S.: 441227
Barry Brown (Pres)

CHICAGO HEIGHTS CON-
STRUCTION CO.
1535 Otto Blvd, Chicago Heights, IL
60411
Tel.: (708) 754-0252
Web Site:
   https://www.chicagoheightscon
   struction.com
Sales Range: $10-24.9 Million

Chicago Heights Construction Co.—(Continued)
Emp.: 8
Industrial Buildings
N.A.I.C.S.: 236210
Timothy Bergin *(VP)*
Daniel Bergin Jr. *(Pres)*

CHICAGO HEIGHTS STEEL
211 E Main St, Chicago Heights, IL 60411-4270
Tel.: (708) 756-5619
Web Site: http://www.chs.com
Year Founded: 1985
Sales Range: $75-99.9 Million
Emp.: 260
Mfr of Shapes, Bars & Posts for Fabricated Metal Products
N.A.I.C.S.: 331110
Jim Stolte *(Supvr-Gen Electrical)*
Tony Keilman *(Supvr-Electrical)*

CHICAGO HISTORY MUSEUM
1601 N Clark St, Chicago, IL 60614
Tel.: (312) 642-4600
Web Site: http://www.chicagohs.org
Year Founded: 1857
Sales Range: $10-24.9 Million
Emp.: 126
Historical Museum
N.A.I.C.S.: 712110
Walter C. Carlson *(Sec)*
Russell L. Lewis *(Exec VP)*
Patrick W. Dolan *(Treas)*
T. Bondurant French *(Chm)*
Donald E. Lassere *(Pres & CEO)*

CHICAGO HORTICULTURAL SOCIETY
1000 Lake Cook Rd, Glencoe, IL 60022
Tel.: (847) 835-5440
Year Founded: 1890
Sales Range: $50-74.9 Million
Emp.: 745
Botanical Garden
N.A.I.C.S.: 712130
James F. Boudreau *(VP-Mktg & Dev)*
Aida Giglio *(VP-HR)*

CHICAGO LUMBER COMPANY OF OMAHA
1324 Pierce St, Omaha, NE 68103
Tel.: (402) 342-0840
Web Site:
http://www.chicagolumberco.com
Sales Range: $10-24.9 Million
Emp.: 64
Home Centers Lumber
N.A.I.C.S.: 423710
Rick Hullinger *(Pres)*
Brenda Huebner *(Controller)*

CHICAGO MACK SALES & SERVICES INC.
7900 Bulldog Dr, Summit Argo, IL 60501
Tel.: (708) 594-5151
Web Site:
http://www.chicagomack.com
Rev.: $34,000,000
Emp.: 95
Automobile Dealers
N.A.I.C.S.: 423110
Gary Dobbs *(VP-Ops)*

CHICAGO MEAT AUTHORITY, INC.
1120 W 47th Pl, Chicago, IL 60609
Tel.: (773) 254-3811
Web Site:
https://www.chicagomeat.com
Year Founded: 1990
Sales Range: $75-99.9 Million
Emp.: 325
Meat Processor & Whslr

N.A.I.C.S.: 311612
Alicia Lopez *(Supvr-Production)*

CHICAGO METAL FABRICATORS, INC.
3724 S Rockwell St, Chicago, IL 60632-1051
Tel.: (773) 523-5755
Web Site:
https://www.chicagometal.com
Year Founded: 1908
Sales Range: $1-9.9 Million
Metal Fabricating Services
N.A.I.C.S.: 332119
Randy Hauser *(Pres)*

CHICAGO METAL ROLLED PRODUCTS CO.
3715 S Rockwell St, Chicago, IL 60632
Tel.: (773) 523-5757
Web Site: https://www.cmrp.com
Sales Range: $10-24.9 Million
Emp.: 68
Fabricated Structural Metal
N.A.I.C.S.: 332312
George F. Wendt *(Pres)*
Joseph R. Wendt *(VP)*

CHICAGO NATIONAL LEAGUE BALL CLUB, LLC
1060 W Addison St, Chicago, IL 60613-4397
Tel.: (773) 404-2827
Web Site:
http://chicago.cubs.mlb.com
Sales Range: $75-99.9 Million
Emp.: 300
Professional Baseball Club
N.A.I.C.S.: 711211
Carl Rice *(VP-Wrigley Field Restoration & Expansion)*
Crane H. Kenney *(Pres)*
Randy Bush *(Asst Gen Mgr)*
Peter Chase *(Dir-Media Rels)*
Jason Carr *(Asst Dir-Media Rels)*
Michael Lufrano *(Chief Legal Officer & Exec VP-Community & Govt Affairs)*
Joseph Rios *(Mgr-Brdcst Rels)*
Brian Garza *(Dir-Ticket Svc)*
Thomas S. Ricketts *(Chm)*
Alex Sugarman *(VP-Strategy & Dev)*
John Greifenkamp *(CFO & Sr VP-Acctg & Fin)*
Lydia Wahlke *(Gen Counsel & VP)*
Julian Green *(VP-Comm & Community Affairs)*
Jed Hoyer *(Exec VP & Gen Mgr)*
Jason McLeod *(Sr VP-Player Dev & Amateur Scouting)*
Shiraz Rehman *(Asst Gen Mgr)*
Jaron Madison *(Dir-Player Dev)*
Lukas McKnight *(Asst Dir-Amateur Scouting)*
Dana Noeltner *(Mgr-Equipment)*
Jason Sondag *(Dir-Strategy & Dev)*
Patrick Meenan *(Sr Dir-Facilities & Procurement)*
Theresa Bacholzky *(Mgr-Disbursements & Collections)*
Matt Kenny *(Sr Dir-Wrigley Field Event Ops)*
Julius Farrell *(Mgr-Protective Svcs)*
Andrew McIntyre *(Dir-IT)*
Steve Inman *(Asst Dir-Application Dev)*
John Morrison *(Asst Dir-Brand Dev & Activation)*
Colin Faulkner *(Sr VP-Sls & Mktg)*
Cale Vennum *(Sr Dir-Ticketing)*
Miguel DeJesus *(Mgr-Wrigley Field Ticket Office)*
Kevin Enerson *(Mgr-Season Ticket Svc)*

Karry Kerness *(Mgr-Season Ticket Svc)*
Andy Blackburn *(Dir-Ticket Sls)*
Andrew Bassett *(Coord-Pro Scouting)*
Chris Moore *(Dir-R&D)*
Joshua Lifrak *(Dir-Mental Health Program)*
Mike Burkhart *(Mgr-Visiting Clubhouse)*
Michele Dietz *(Pres-Bus Ops)*
Ann Weiser *(VP-HR)*
David Ross *(Mgr)*
David Clark *(Ops Mgr-Spreckley)*
Theo N. Epstein *(Pres-Baseball Ops)*

CHICAGO OAKBROOK FINANCIAL GROUP
903 Commerce Dr Ste 300, Oak Brook, IL 60523
Tel.: (630) 954-5572
Web Site: http://www.cofgroup.com
Year Founded: 1997
Sales Range: $1-9.9 Million
Emp.: 17
Financial Planning Services for Businesses & Individuals
N.A.I.C.S.: 525990
David N. Navarro *(Pres)*

CHICAGO PACIFIC FOUNDERS
980 N Michigan Ave Ste 1998, Chicago, IL 60611
Tel.: (312) 273-4750
Web Site:
https://www.cpfounders.com
Emp.: 15
Health Care Private Equity Investment Firm
N.A.I.C.S.: 523999
Mary Tolan *(Co-Founder & Co-Mng Partner)*
Larry Leisure *(Mng Partner)*
Vance Vanier *(Co-Founder & Co-Mng Partner)*
John Rijos *(Operating Partner)*
Etienne Deffarges *(Operating Partner)*
Greg Kazarian *(Operating Partner)*
Krista Hatcher *(Partner)*
Michael Wilson *(CFO & Chief Compliance Officer)*
Matthew Doyle *(VP-IR & Ops)*
Sameer Mathur *(Principal)*
Aaron Joseph *(Mng Dir-Fund Strategy & Dev)*
Mary A. Tolan *(Co-Founder & Co-Mng Partner)*
Gregory N. Kazarian *(Operating Partner)*
Lawrence B. Leisure *(Co-Founder & Mng Partner)*

Subsidiaries:

CPF Senior Living Acquisitions LLC **(1)**
400 N Michigan Ave Ste 560, Chicago, IL 60611
Tel.: (312) 273-4750
Senior Living Communities Operations
N.A.I.C.S.: 623312
John Rijos *(CEO)*

Subsidiary (Domestic):

Dirigo Pines Retirement Community LLC **(2)**
9 Alumni Dr, Orono, ME 04473
Tel.: (207) 866-3400
Web Site: http://www.dirigopines.com
Sales Range: $1-9.9 Million
Emp.: 100
Retirement Community
N.A.I.C.S.: 623311
Steve Bowler *(Dir-Mktg)*
Karyn Woolley *(Dir-HR)*

Town Village Sterling Heights, LLC **(2)**

4500 Dobry Dr, Sterling Heights, MI 48314
Tel.: (586) 803-0900
Web Site:
http://www.townvillagesterlingheights.com
Sales Range: $1-9.9 Million
Emp.: 90
Senior Living Community
N.A.I.C.S.: 623311
Grace Dezern *(Exec Dir)*

Town Village Vestavia Hills, LLC **(2)**
2385 Dolly Ridge Rd, Birmingham, AL 35243
Tel.: (205) 979-2702
Web Site:
http://www.townvillagevestaviahills.com
Sales Range: $1-9.9 Million
Emp.: 40
Senior Living Community
N.A.I.C.S.: 623311
Desiree Soriano *(Dir-Sls & Mktg)*

Vintage Park at Lenexa, LLC **(2)**
8710 Caenen Lake Rd, Shawnee Mission, KS 66215
Tel.: (913) 894-6979
Web Site:
http://www.vintageparkassistedliving.com
Sales Range: $1-9.9 Million
Emp.: 16
Assisted Living Retirement Community
N.A.I.C.S.: 623311
Jayne MacDonald *(Exec Dir)*

Sight Medical Doctors, PLLC **(1)**
125 Kennedy Dr Ste 400A, Hauppauge, NY 11788
Tel.: (855) 295-4144
Web Site: http://www.sightmd.com
General Eye Care & Ophthalmic Plastic Surgery
N.A.I.C.S.: 621320
John Passarelli *(Co-Founder & Chm)*

Subsidiary (Domestic):

Athwal Eye Associates PC **(2)**
14 Mule Rd Ste 1, Toms River, NJ 08755
Tel.: (732) 286-0900
Web Site: http://www.athwaleye.com
Offices of Physicians (except Mental Health Specialists)
N.A.I.C.S.: 621111
Robyn Piwowarski *(Mgr)*

CHICAGO PACKAGING CORPORATION
1100 Kirk St Elk Grove Village, Chicago, IL 60007
Tel.: (773) 523-6000
Web Site:
http://www.chicagopackaging.com
Sales Range: $10-24.9 Million
Emp.: 94
Food Containers Mfr
N.A.I.C.S.: 322212
John Pack *(Pres)*

CHICAGO PETROMARTS INC.
9739 Irving Park Rd, Schiller Park, IL 60176
Tel.: (847) 928-9999
Rev.: $30,200,000
Emp.: 200
Gasoline Stations
N.A.I.C.S.: 457120
Begi Mani *(VP)*
Geevanghese Cherian *(Pres)*
Irsan Dhagat *(VP)*
Mohamned Ahmed *(Pres)*

CHICAGO PROFESSIONAL SPORTS LIMITED PARTNERSHIP
1901 W Madison St, Chicago, IL 60612-2459
Tel.: (312) 455-4000
Web Site: http://www.nba.com
Year Founded: 1966
Sales Range: $50-74.9 Million
Emp.: 100

Professional Basketball Team
N.A.I.C.S.: 711211
Jerry Reinsdorf *(Chm)*
John Paxson *(Exec VP-Basketball Ops)*
Keith Brown *(VP-Ticket & Premium Seating)*
Karen Stack-Umlauf *(Sr Dir-Basketball Admin)*
John Ligmanowski *(Mgr-Equipment)*
Joe O'Neil *(Sr Dir-Ticket Ops)*
Greg Hanrahan *(Sr Dir-Premium Seating)*
David Dowd *(Sr Dir-Ticket Sls)*
Jon Shoemaker *(Dir-Creative Svcs)*
Curtis Baddeley *(Dir-Rental Suites)*
Tony Rokita *(Dir-Community Rels & Player Programs)*
Pam Sher *(Dir-Ticket Ops)*
Tony Hyde *(Sr Mgr-Corp Comm)*
Jeff Pitcock *(Mgr-Creative Svcs)*
Nancy DeFauw *(Sr Mgr-Ticket Tech)*
Michael Reinsdorf *(Pres & COO)*
Lisa Nucci *(Dir-Mktg)*
Susan Goodenow *(VP-Mktg & Comm)*
Ram Padmanabhan *(Gen Counsel & VP-Fin)*
Matt Kobe *(VP-Bus Strategy & Analytics)*
Arturas Karnisovas *(VP-Basketball Ops)*
Marc Eversley *(Gen Mgr)*
J. J. Polk *(Asst Gen Mgr)*
Pat Connelly *(VP-Player Personnel)*

CHICAGO PUBLIC MEDIA, INC.
848 E Grand Ave 3rd Fl, Chicago, IL 60611
Tel.: (312) 948-4600   IL
Web Site:
   http://www.chicagopublicmedia.org
Year Founded: 1989
Sales Range: $10-24.9 Million
Emp.: 164
Multimedia Holding Company; Radio Broadcasting & Newspaper Publisher
N.A.I.C.S.: 551112
James W. Mabie *(Chm)*
Scott P. Marks *(Treas)*
Cynthia Photos Abbott *(Gen Counsel & VP)*
Jennifer Bell *(VP-Dev)*
Silvia Rivera *(Mng Dir)*
Merrill Smith *(Sec)*
Rivera Stephenson *(VP-Mktg & Membership)*
Jen Surma *(VP-HR)*
Bryan Traubert *(Chm)*
Angela Rozas O'Toole *(Sr Editior-Govt & Politics)*
Andi McDaniel *(CEO)*
James N. Perry Jr. *(Treas)*

Subsidiaries:

Chicago Sun-Times Media, Inc.   (1)
Navy Pier 848 E Grand Ave, Chicago, IL 60611
Tel.: (312) 321-3000
Web Site: https://chicago.suntimes.com
Newspaper Publishers
N.A.I.C.S.: 513110

Subsidiary (Domestic):

ST Media Holdings, LLC   (2)
350 N Orleans St 10 S, Chicago, IL 60654
Sales Range: $300-349.9 Million
Emp.: 2,200
Holding Company; Newspaper Publisher & Distr
N.A.I.C.S.: 551112
Pam Henson *(Sr VP-Sls & Mktg)*

Unit (Domestic):

Chicago Reader   (3)

2930 S Michigan Ave Ste 102, Chicago, IL 60616
Tel.: (312) 392-2970
Web Site: http://www.chicagoreader.com
Sales Range: $10-24.9 Million
Emp.: 50
Newspaper Publishers
N.A.I.C.S.: 513110
Philip Montoro *(Editor-Music)*
Guadalupe Carranza *(VP-New Media)*
Luca Cimarusti *(Coord-Music Listings)*
John Dunlevy *(Dir-Digital)*
Paul John Higgins *(Dir-Creative)*
Danielle A. Scruggs *(Dir-Photography)*
Salem Collo-Julin *(Mng Editor)*
Tracy Baim *(Publr)*
Enrique Limon *(Editor-in-Chief)*

Chicago Sun-Times   (3)
350 N Orleans Ste 9 10, Chicago, IL 60654
Tel.: (312) 321-3000
Web Site: http://www.suntimes.com
Sales Range: $300-349.9 Million
Daily Newspaper
N.A.I.C.S.: 513110
Edwin Eisendrath *(CEO)*

Midwest Suburban Publishing   (3)
18312 W Creek Dr, Tinley Park, IL 60477-1789
Tel.: (708) 633-6700
Web Site: http://www.southtownstar.com
Sales Range: $50-74.9 Million
Emp.: 600
Commercial Printing & Newspaper Publishing Combined
N.A.I.C.S.: 513110

Branch (Domestic):

Midwest Suburban Publishing   (4)
5959 S Harlem Ave, Chicago, IL 60638-3131
Tel.: (773) 586-8801
Web Site: http://www.dailysouthcown.com
Sales Range: $50-74.9 Million
Emp.: 300
Newspapers
N.A.I.C.S.: 513110

Unit (Domestic):

Pioneer Newspapers   (3)
3701 W Lake Ave, Glenview, IL 60026-1216
Tel.: (847) 486-9200
Web Site: http://www.pioneerlocal.com
Sales Range: $25-49.9 Million
Emp.: 200
Publisher of Weekly Community Newspapers Distributed Throughout Chicago Suburbs
N.A.I.C.S.: 513110
John Barron *(Pres)*

Branch (Domestic):

Pioneer Press - West Group   (4)
1010 W Lk St, Oak Park, IL 60301-1049
Tel.: (708) 383-3200
Web Site: http://www.pioneerlocal.com
Sales Range: $25-49.9 Million
Emp.: 35
Newspapers Publishing & Printing
N.A.I.C.S.: 513110

Unit (Domestic):

The Beacon News   (3)
350 N Orleans 10th Fl, Chicago, IL 60504
Tel.: (630) 978-8880
Web Site: http://www.suntimes.com
Newspapers
N.A.I.C.S.: 541840
Barbara Ercoli *(Sr Mgr-HR)*

The Courier News   (3)
495 N Commons Dr Ste 200, Aurora, IL 60504-8295
Tel.: (847) 888-7800
Web Site:
   http://www.suburbanchicagonews.com
Sales Range: $10-24.9 Million
Emp.: 70
Newspapers
N.A.I.C.S.: 513110

The Herald News   (3)
3109 W Jefferson St, Joliet, IL 60435
Tel.: (815) 439-5304
Web Site: http://www.heraldnewsonline.com

Sales Range: $10-24.9 Million
Emp.: 92
Newspapers
N.A.I.C.S.: 541820

The News Sun   (3)
1225 Tri State Pkwy Ste 520, Gurnee, IL 60031-9163
Tel.: (847) 336-7000
Web Site: http://newssunonline.com
Sales Range: $10-24.9 Million
Emp.: 75
Newspapers
N.A.I.C.S.: 513110
Barry Rochford *(Mng Editor)*

The Post-Tribune   (3)
350 N Orleans St 10 S, Chicago, IL 60654
Tel.: (219) 648-3000
Web Site: http://www.post-trib.com
Sales Range: $10-24.9 Million
Emp.: 70
N.A.I.C.S.: 513110
Lisa Tatina *(Publr)*

CHICAGO SCHOOL SUPPLY
PO Box 932, Westmont, IL 60559
Web Site:
   http://www.chicagoschoolsupply.com
Year Founded: 2006
Sales Range: $1-9.9 Million
Emp.: 10
School Supply Sales
N.A.I.C.S.: 459410
Michael Ockrim *(Founder & Pres)*

CHICAGO STEEL LIMITED PARTNERSHIP
700 Chase St, Gary, IN 46404-1211
Tel.: (219) 949-1111
Web Site: http://www.chisteel.com
Year Founded: 1991
Sales Range: $10-24.9 Million
Emp.: 56
Provider of Business Services
N.A.I.C.S.: 561990
Bruce Mannakee *(Owner)*
Kathy Paxton *(CFO)*
Bill Boak *(VP-Sls & Mktg)*
Dan Phillips *(Pres)*
Mike Espinosa *(Mgr-Ops)*

CHICAGO WHITE METAL CASTING, INC.
Rte 83 & Fairway Dr, Bensenville, IL 60106
Tel.: (630) 595-4424   IL
Web Site:
   http://www.cwmdiecast.com
Year Founded: 1937
Sales Range: $75-99.9 Million
Emp.: 140
Custom Die Castings & Subassemblies Mfr
N.A.I.C.S.: 331523
William Baraglia *(VP-Mfg)*
Mike Dimitroff *(VP-Sls & Mktg)*
Eric Treiber *(Pres & COO)*
Roy Finch *(Dir-Quality Assurance)*
Walter G. Treiber Jr. *(Chm)*

CHICAGO WHITE SOX LTD.
333 W 35th St, Chicago, IL 60616-3651
Tel.: (312) 674-1000   IL
Web Site: http://www.whitesox.com
Year Founded: 1900
Sales Range: $900-999.9 Million
Emp.: 4,000
Professional Baseball Club
N.A.I.C.S.: 711211
Jerry M. Reinsdorf *(Owner & Chm)*
Rick Hahn *(Sr VP & Gen Mgr)*
Grace Guerrero Zwit *(Sr Dir-Minor League Ops)*
Chris Taylor *(Mgr-Acctg)*
Bob Beghtol *(Dir-Media Rels)*
Mike Mazza *(Dir-Ticket Ops)*
Brooks Boyer *(Sr VP-Sls & Mktg)*

Sam Lawson *(Mgr-Corp Dev & Ticket Sls)*
John Corvino *(Gen Counsel)*

CHICAGO ZOOLOGICAL SOCIETY, INC.
3300 Golf Rd, Brookfield, IL 60513-1060
Tel.: (708) 485-0263
Web Site:
   http://www.brookfieldzoo.org
Year Founded: 1934
Rev.: $50,000,000
Emp.: 450
Zoological Park
N.A.I.C.S.: 712130
Sondra Katzen *(Mgr-Media Rels)*
Stuart Strahl *(Pres & CEO)*
Richard G. Gamble *(COO & Exec VP-Ops)*
Cindy Zeigler *(Chief Advancement Officer)*

CHICAGO-SOFT, LTD.
4757 N Hermitage, Chicago, IL 60640
Tel.: (773) 506-1900
Web Site: http://www.chicago-soft.com
Sales Range: $10-24.9 Million
Emp.: 15
Computer Software
N.A.I.C.S.: 423430

CHICAGO-WILCOX MFG. COMPANY, INC.
16928 State St, South Holland, IL 60473
Tel.: (708) 339-5000   IL
Web Site:
   https://www.chicagowilcox.com
Year Founded: 1906
Sales Range: $10-24.9 Million
Emp.: 40
Gaskets, Metal Stampings Mfr
N.A.I.C.S.: 339991
Mike Sullivan *(VP-Ops)*
Hank Schneider *(Mgr-Sls)*
Ed Gardiner *(VP-Admin)*

CHICAGOLAND ENTREPRENEURIAL CENTER
222 Merchandise Mart Plz Ste 1212, Chicago, IL 60654
Tel.: (312) 494-6777   IL
Web Site:
   http://www.chicagolandec.org
Year Founded: 2006
Sales Range: $1-9.9 Million
Emp.: 12
Community Development Services
N.A.I.C.S.: 624190
Melissa Lederer *(CMO)*
Abbie Torgeson *(Office Mgr)*
Kristin Barrett *(VP)*
Mike Huffstetler *(VP-Dev)*
Bryant L. Keil *(Co-Chm)*
Jim O'Connor *(Co-Chm & Interim CEO)*

Subsidiaries:

1871   (1)
222 W Merchandise Mart Pl Ste 212, Chicago, IL 60654
Tel.: (312) 239-0310
Web Site: http://www.1871.com
Digital Technology Hub
N.A.I.C.S.: 541511
Betsy Ziegler *(CEO)*
Jenna Blaszczykiewicz *(Dir-Mktg)*

Subsidiary (Domestic):

Illinois Technology Association   (2)
20 N Wacker Dr Ste 1200, Chicago, IL 60606
Tel.: (312) 435-2805
Web Site: http://www.illinoistech.org

Chicagoland Entrepreneurial
Center—(Continued)

Technology Association
N.A.I.C.S.: 813910
Julia Kanouse *(Sr VP-Membership & Mktg)*
Nola Lazin *(Mgr-Member Engagement)*
Trisha Degg *(Dir-Talent Programs)*
Michelle Cox *(Mgr-Mktg & Comm)*
Fred Hoch *(CEO)*

CHICANOS POR LA CAUSA, INC.

1112 E Buckeye Rd, Phoenix, AZ 85034
Tel.: (602) 257-0700   AZ
Web Site: http://www.cplc.org
Year Founded: 1967
Sales Range: $50-74.9 Million
Emp.: 947
Community Development Services
N.A.I.C.S.: 624190
Martin Quintana *(Chm)*
Rudy Perez *(Sec)*
Andres L. Contreras *(Exec VP)*
John Ramirez *(Exec VP)*
Maria Spelleri *(Gen Counsel & Exec VP)*
Max Gonzales *(Exec VP)*
Jimmy Vigil *(Treas)*
Thelma Lopez *(Sec)*
Nancy M. Alamo *(Vice Chm)*
Daniel Fernandez *(Vice Chm)*
Yadira Garcia *(Sec)*
Luz Garnica *(Treas)*
Nikkie Martinez *(VP)*
Alicia Nunez *(Exec VP)*
German Reyes *(Exec VP)*
Jose Martinez *(Exec VP-Economic Dev)*
David M. Adame *(Pres & CEO)*

CHICK-FIL-A, INC.

5200 Buffington Rd, Atlanta, GA 30349-2998
Tel.: (404) 305-7700   GA
Web Site: https://www.chick-fil-a.com
Year Founded: 1967
Sales Range: $5-14.9 Billion
Emp.: 140,000
Limited-Service Restaurants
N.A.I.C.S.: 722513
Donald M. Cathy *(Pres-Dwarf House & Exec VP)*
James B. McCabe *(Exec VP)*
Philip A. Barrett *(VP-Corp Fin Svcs)*
Timothy P. Tassopoulos *(Pres & COO)*
S. Truett Cathy *(Founder)*
William F. Faulk *(VP-Innovation & Design)*
Dan T. Cathy *(Chm)*
William T. Boggs *(Sr Dir-Admin)*
Mark L. Brackett *(Sr Dir-Enterprise Applications)*
Janet Bridges *(VP-Treasury)*
Jonathan B. Bridges *(CMO & Sr VP)*
Mary Kathy Buckley *(Dir-Payroll Svcs)*
Saleitha L. Champion *(Sr Dir-Restaurant Fin Reporting)*
B. Lynn Chastain *(Gen Counsel & VP)*
Michael F. Erbrick *(CIO & VP-IT)*
Kevin R. Fannin *(Dir-Bus Solutions)*
Michael S. Garrison *(Sr Dir-Environmental Stewardship & Pkg)*
Glenn H. Hewitt *(Sr Dir-Tax Acctg)*
Donna W. Kirbow *(VP-Risk Mgmt & Benefits)*
Kelly D. Ludwick *(Sr Dir-Corp Legal)*
Kimberly M. McMillian *(Sr Dir-Fin Plng & Reporting)*
Sandra T. Moody *(VP-Bus Insights)*
S. Tammy Pearson *(Asst Gen Counsel-Corp Legal & VP)*
Brent Ragsdale *(CFO & Sr VP)*

Daniel J. Strain *(Sr Dir-IT & Shared Svcs)*
Christopher W. Taylor *(Dir-IT Architecture)*
Donald B. Crocker *(Sr Dir-Real Estate)*
Alejandro Dominguez *(Sr Dir-Real Estate)*
Brian T. Grady *(Sr Dir-Kitchen Sys & Facility Design)*
Gregory E. Lollis *(Sr Dir-Restaurant Dev)*
Thomas A. Nolan *(Sr Dir-Restaurant Dev)*
Erwin C. Reid *(VP-Real Estate)*
David B. Farmer *(VP-Product Strategy & Dev)*
Clifford T. Robinson *(Sr VP-Field Ops)*
Barry V. White *(VP-Mktg Svcs)*
J. Mark Ashworth *(Dir-Strategic Events)*
Cheryl B. Dick *(Sr Dir-Field Ops & Licensing)*
Robert P. Dugas *(VP-Supply Chain)*
Todd A. Grubbs *(Sr Dir-Company Owned Restaurants)*
C. Steve Hester *(Sr Dir-Strategic Initiatives)*
T. Mark Miller *(VP-Org Effectiveness & Dev)*
Gregory B. Thompson *(Sr Dir-Corp Comm)*
Dee Ann Turner *(VP-Corp Talent)*
R. David Turner *(Sr Dir-Svcs & Dev)*
W. Timothy Yancey *(Sr Dir-Supply Chain)*
Amy G. Rooks *(Sr Dir-Real Estate Legal)*
Jodee W. Morgan *(Sr Dir-Talent Acq)*
Roger H. Shealy *(Dir-Production Design)*
Colin M. Gromley *(Dir-Real Estate)*
Jay C. Kimsey *(Sr Dir-Atlantic)*
Richard C. Matherne *(VP-Southeast Reg)*
Mark G. Moraitakis *(Dir-Hospitality & Svc Design)*
Robert L. McLaughlin *(Dir-Mktg Svcs)*
Alex B. Doverspike *(Dir-Fin Project Mgmt & Staff Dev)*
Paul D. Wiley *(Sr Dir-Restaurant Fin Svcs)*
Lynette E. Smith *(Sr Dir-Corp Legal)*
Onome Okuma *(Sr Dir-Bus Growth & Supply Chain Solutions)*
Carrie J. Kurlander *(VP-Corp PR)*
Courtney D. LaVallee *(Dir-Mktg Comm)*
Barron K. Vaughan *(Dir-Menu Dev)*
Mary Clancy Peak *(Dir-Adv & Campaigns)*
L. J. Yankosky *(Dir-Sponsorships & Event Mktg)*
Andrew Truett Cathy *(CEO)*
Jonathan Villacampa *(Dir-HR)*
Anita E. Costello *(Dir-Midwest)*
Bedford Cox *(Dir-Innovation & Design)*
Bruce B. Cameron *(Dir-Northeast)*
Cynthia T. Cornog *(Dir-Trng Res)*
Harold King *(Dir-Food & Product Safety)*
Jason B. Fischer *(Dir-Distr & Logistics)*
Lindsey D. Barron *(Dir-Bus Insights)*
Shane A. Benson *(Dir-Atlantic)*
Shannon J. Gardner *(Dir-Risk Mgmt)*
Stephen A. Dull *(Dir-Field Ops)*
Liz Stephens *(Dir-Events & Mktg)*
Rodney D. Bullard *(VP-Community Affairs)*
Roger E. Blythe Jr. *(VP-Fin Plng & Dev)*

John H. McCleskey Jr. *(VP-Restaurant Dev)*
Howard M. Baker Jr. *(Sr Dir-Grand Openings)*
William J. Dunphy Jr. *(VP-Field Talent)*
Philip Orazi III *(Sr Dir-Field Staff Dev)*
Tom A. Morder Jr. *(Dir-Strategic Insights)*

CHICKASAW HOLDING COMPANY

124 W Vinita Ave, Sulphur, OK 73086-3821
Tel.: (580) 622-2111   OK
Web Site:
  https://www.chickasawholding.com
Year Founded: 1990
Rev.: $44,020,171
Emp.: 450
Holding Company; Telephone Communication Services
N.A.I.C.S.: 551112
J. B. Bright *(Pres)*

Subsidiaries:

BrightNet Oklahoma   (1)
124 W Vinita Ave, Sulphur, OK 73086
Tel.: (580) 622-4046
Web Site: http://www.brightok.net
Internet Service Provider
N.A.I.C.S.: 517810

Chickasaw Finance Company   (1)
124 W Vinita Ave, Sulphur, OK 73086-3821
Tel.: (580) 622-2111
Web Site: http://www.chickasawphone.com
Rev.: $30,221
Emp.: 4
Short-Term Business Credit
N.A.I.C.S.: 517121

Chickasaw Long Distance
Company   (1)
124 W Vinita Ave, Sulphur, OK 73086-3821
Tel.: (580) 622-4400
Web Site: http://www.chickasawphone.com
Rev.: $1,849,824
Emp.: 25
Telephone Communication, Except Radio
N.A.I.C.S.: 517121

Chickasaw Personal Communications, Inc.   (1)
51 Tiffany Plz Ste 51A, Ardmore, OK 73401-2534
Tel.: (580) 622-2111
Web Site: http://www.chickasawphone.com
Rev.: $845,418
Emp.: 5
Radiotelephone Communication
N.A.I.C.S.: 517112

Chickasaw Telecom, Inc.   (1)
5 N McCormick St, Oklahoma City, OK 73127-6620   (100%)
Tel.: (405) 946-1200
Web Site: http://www.chickasawtel.com
Sales Range: $1-9.9 Million
Emp.: 40
Electronic Parts & Equipment
N.A.I.C.S.: 238210
Brent Nelson *(Acct Mgr)*
Heather Thomas *(Project Mgr)*
Jana Reagan *(Sr Acct Mgr)*
Jeffrey Downey *(Gen Mgr)*
Jesse Jorgensen *(Sr Engr-Sys)*
Kyle Rogers *(Engr-Network)*
Jamie McGranahan *(Sr Engr-Sys)*
Darin Dout *(Acct Mgr)*

Chickasaw Telecommunications Services, Inc.   (1)
504 S Main St, Stillwater, OK 74074
Tel.: (405) 372-1069
Web Site: http://www.ctsiok.com
Telecommunication Services
N.A.I.C.S.: 517810

Chickasaw Telephone Company   (1)
124 W Vinita Ave, Sulphur, OK 73086-3821   (100%)
Tel.: (580) 622-2111
Web Site: http://www.chickasawphone.com
Rev.: $12,720,049
Emp.: 85

Telephone Communication, Except Radio
N.A.I.C.S.: 517121

Indian Nations Fiber Optics, Inc.   (1)
124 W Vinita Ave, Sulphur, OK 73086-3821   (100%)
Tel.: (580) 622-2111
Web Site: http://www.infofiber.net
Rev.: $2,828,850
Emp.: 6
Equipment Rental & Leasing
N.A.I.C.S.: 532490

Telco Data Systems, Inc.   (1)
124 W Vinita Ave, Sulphur, OK 73086 3821
Tel.: (580) 622-2118
Rev.: $300,000
Emp.: 4
Custom Computer Programming Services
N.A.I.C.S.: 541511

Telco Supply Company   (1)
124 W Vinita Ave, Sulphur, OK 73086-3821   (100%)
Tel.: (800) 344-3430
Web Site: http://www.telcosupply.com
Rev.: $5,500,002
Emp.: 30
Water, Sewer & Utility Lines
N.A.I.C.S.: 237130
Lori Bright *(Exec VP)*

CHICKASHA OF GEORGIA, LLC

109 Jordan Rd, Tifton, GA 31793
Tel.: (229) 388-8008
Web Site:
  http://www.chickashaofgeorgia.com
Rev.: $26,700,000
Emp.: 50
Cotton
N.A.I.C.S.: 424590
Andy Borem *(Pres & CEO)*
Brad Moretz *(Mgr-Mktg & Logistics)*
John Walker *(Superintendent-Mill)*
Sammy Wright *(VP-Mktg)*

CHICO ENTERPRISES, INC.

281 Don Knotts Blvd, Morgantown, WV 26501-6737
Tel.: (304) 292-9433
Web Site:
  http://www.chicoenterprises.com
Year Founded: 1925
Sales Range: $50-74.9 Million
Emp.: 325
Grocery Stores
N.A.I.C.S.: 445131
Samuel A. Chico Jr. *(Chm)*
Samuel A. Chico III *(Pres & CEO)*

CHICO NISSAN, INC.

575 Manzanita Ave, Chico, CA 95926-1322
Tel.: (530) 891-1777
Web Site:
  https://www.chiconissan.com
Year Founded: 1960
Sales Range: $10-24.9 Million
Emp.: 50
New Car Retailer
N.A.I.C.S.: 441110
Brian Bowen *(Owner & CEO)*

CHIEF CORPORATION

8604 Cliff Cameron Dr Ste 105, Charlotte, NC 28269
Tel.: (541) 342-7011
Web Site: http://www.cheifsupply.com
Sales Range: $10-24.9 Million
Emp.: 170
Police Supply Stores
N.A.I.C.S.: 459999
John Noone *(Pres)*

CHIEF ENERGY, INC.

918 McDonald Ave, Brooklyn, NY 11218
Tel.: (718) 438-6676

Web Site:
http://www.chiefenergy.com
Rev.: $18,672,077
Emp.: 20
Fuel Oil Dealers
N.A.I.C.S.: 457210
Vincent A. Rizzuto (Pres)

CHIEF EXECUTIVES ORGANI-ZATION

1825 K St NW Ste 1450, Washington, DC 20006
Tel.: (202) 813-1880　　　　DE
Web Site: https://www.ceo.org
Year Founded: 1958
Sales Range: $10-24.9 Million
Emp.: 33
Professional Organizations
N.A.I.C.S.: 813920
Stephen Knight Pond (VP-Education)
James A. Dick (Sr VP, Sr VP, VP-Events-Marketing-Communications & VP-Events-Marketing-Communications)
James L. Bildner (VP-Membership)
Norman Ross Adler (Pres)

CHIEF INDUSTRIES, INC.

3942 W Old Hwy 30, Grand Island, NE 68802
Tel.: (308) 389-7200　　　　DE
Web Site: http://www.chiefind.com
Year Founded: 1954
Sales Range: $100-124.9 Million
Emp.: 1,800
Prefabricated Metal Building Component Mfr
N.A.I.C.S.: 332311
Lori Schuppen (Mgr-HR)
Mike Lewis (Pres/Gen Mgr-Agri Div)
Christa Britton (Coord-Mktg)
Chris Riggleman (Engr-Sls-Grain Drying, Aeration & Customer Svc)

Subsidiaries:

Arrowhead Steel Fabricators　　(1)
1821 S N Rd, Grand Island, NE 68802-2078
Tel.: (308) 389-7455
Web Site:
http://www.arrowheadsteelfab.com
Fabricated Steel Mfr
N.A.I.C.S.: 332312
Josh Hawley (Supvr-Detailing)

BonnaVilla　　(1)
111 Grant St PO Box 127, Aurora, NE 68818
Tel.: (402) 694-5250
Web Site: http://www.bonnavilla.com
Emp.: 75
Housing Construction Services
N.A.I.C.S.: 236115

Chief Carriers, Inc.　　(1)
2405 S North Rd, Grand Island, NE 68803
Tel.: (308) 389-7250
Web Site: http://www.chiefcarriers.com
Sales Range: $10-24.9 Million
Emp.: 120
Logistics Consulting Servies
N.A.I.C.S.: 541614
Bob Clark (Gen Mgr)

Chief Construction Company　　(1)
3935 Westgate Rd, Grand Island, NE 68803
Tel.: (308) 389-7222
Web Site: http://www.chiefconstruction.us
Sales Range: $10-24.9 Million
Emp.: 40
Building Construction Services
N.A.I.C.S.: 236210
Roger Bullington (VP-Construction & Dev)
Jaye Monter (Controller)

Chief Environmental Products　　(1)
611 Willow St, Grand Island, NE 68801
Tel.: (308) 381-0585
Web Site:
http://www.environmentalproducts.com
Emp.: 15
Wastewater Treatment System Mfr

N.A.I.C.S.: 334513
Shawn Jaeger (Mgr-Sls)

Chief Ethanol Fuels, Inc.　　(1)
4225 ESSt, Hastings, NE 68901
Tel.: (402) 463-6885
Web Site: http://www.chiefethanol.com
Sales Range: $10-24.9 Million
Emp.: 62
Ethanol Fuel Mfr
N.A.I.C.S.: 325193
Duane Kristensen (Gen Mgr)
Mark Spencer (Mgr-Quality Control)

Chief Industries UK Ltd　　(1)
Beckingham Business Park Tolleshunt Major, Maldon, CM9 8LZ, Essex, United Kingdom
Tel.: (44) 1621 868944
Web Site: http://www.chief.co.uk
Sales Range: $10-24.9 Million
Emp.: 20
Grain Storage & Handling Services
N.A.I.C.S.: 493130
Rod Watso (Mng Dir)

Chief Industries, Inc. - Chief Agri/Industrial Division　　(1)
4400 E 39th St, Kearney, NE 68848-0848
Tel.: (308) 237-3186
Web Site: http://www.agri.chiefind.com
Sales Range: $10-24.9 Million
Emp.: 100
Grain Equipment Mfr
N.A.I.C.S.: 333111
Ed Benson (Gen Mgr-Sls)
Steve Ginter (Mgr-Mktg)
Allen Mitchel (Mgr-Intl Sls)
Don Lien (Mgr-Bus Dev)

Chief Industries, Inc. - Chief Buildings Division　　(1)
3942 W Old Hwy 30, Grand Island, NE 68802-2078
Tel.: (308) 389-7200
Web Site: http://www.chiefbuildings.com
Metal Building System Mfr
N.A.I.C.S.: 332999

Chief Industries, Inc. - Chief Custom Products Division　　(1)
1721 Raymond Dr, Grand Island, NE 68803
Tel.: (308) 389-7213
Web Site:
http://www.customproducts.chiefind.com
Metal Door & Window Mfr
N.A.I.C.S.: 332321

Chief Industries, Inc. - Fabrication Division　　(1)
1119 S Adams St, Grand Island, NE 68801
Tel.: (308) 389-2100
Web Site: http://www.chieffabrication.com
Emp.: 160
Metal Fabricating Services
N.A.I.C.S.: 332312
Mark Kjar (Gen Mgr)

Chief Transportation Products, Inc.　　(1)
13840 L St, Omaha, NE 68137
Tel.: (402) 861-4213
Web Site: http://www.ctp.chiefind.com
Sales Range: $10-24.9 Million
Emp.: 40
Fabricated Steel Mfr
N.A.I.C.S.: 332312
Roger Hike (Mgr-Quality Assurance)
Doug Samson (Mgr-Ops)

Eagle Crest Homes, Inc.　　(1)
2318 Kent Ave W Hwy 30, Grand Island, NE 68803
Tel.: (308) 382-3866
Web Site: http://www.bonnavilla.com
Recreational Vehicle Dealers
N.A.I.C.S.: 441210

Phenix-Rousies Industries, S.A.　　(1)
Impasse Willame, 59131, Rousies, France
Tel.: (33) 3 27 69 42 42
Web Site: http://www.silos-phenix.com
Sales Range: $10-24.9 Million
Emp.: 40
Grain Storage System Mfr
N.A.I.C.S.: 332439

CHIHULY INC.

1111 NW 50th St, Seattle, WA 98107

Tel.: (206) 781-8707
Web Site: https://www.chihuly.com
Rev.: $10,800,000
Glassware, Art Or Decorative
N.A.I.C.S.: 327212
Britt Cornett (Mgr-Exhibitions)

Subsidiaries:

Chihuly Workshop　　(1)
PO Box 70856, Seattle, WA 98127
Tel.: (206) 297-1304
Web Site: http://www.chihulyworkshop.com
Emp.: 50
Original Prints, Books, Films & Other Artist-Related Merchandise Publisher & Mail Order
N.A.I.C.S.: 513199
Dale Chihuly (Pres)

CHILCO RIVER HOLDINGS, INC.

20717 Marilla St Chatsworth, Los Angeles, CA 91311
Tel.: (307) 217-6522
Amusement & Recreation Services
N.A.I.C.S.: 713990
Tom Liu (CEO)

CHILCOTE COMPANY

2160 Superior Ave E, Cleveland, OH 44114
Tel.: (216) 781-6000
Web Site: http://www.tap-usa.com
Year Founded: 1906
Sales Range: $10-24.9 Million
Emp.: 115
Photographic Mats, Mounts & Folders Mfr
N.A.I.C.S.: 322299
J. Anthony Hyland (Pres & CEO)
David B. Chilcote (Chm)

CHILD & FAMILY

31 John Clarke Rd, Middletown, RI 02842
Tel.: (401) 849-2300　　　　RI
Web Site:
https://www.childandfamilyri.com
Year Founded: 1970
Sales Range: $10-24.9 Million
Emp.: 300
Child & Family Care Services
N.A.I.C.S.: 624190
Susan Cross (VP-Fin)

CHILD & FAMILY SERVICES

3057 Acushnet Ave, New Bedford, MA 02745
Tel.: (508) 742-1040　　　　MA
Web Site: https://www.child-familyservices.org
Year Founded: 1938
Sales Range: $25-49.9 Million
Emp.: 575
Child & Family Services
N.A.I.C.S.: 624110
Anne Sampaio (Exec Dir)

CHILD AND FAMILY CENTER

21545 Centre Pointe Pkwy, Santa Clarita, CA 91350
Tel.: (661) 259-9439　　　　CA
Web Site:
https://www.childfamilycenter.org
Year Founded: 1984
Sales Range: $10-24.9 Million
Emp.: 234
Children & Family Services
N.A.I.C.S.: 624110
Bert Paras (VP-Ops)
Steven Zimmer (Chm)
Michael Berger (Sr VP)
William Cooper (Chm)
Alan Sandler (Dir-Medical)
Cody Evjen (Dir-Ops)
Glesteree Blades (Dir-HR)
Joan Aschoff (Pres & CEO)

Kelly Morehouse-Smith (Dir-Community Based Svcs)
Cheri Fleming (Vice Chm)
Ginger LeVang (Sec)

CHILD AND FAMILY GUIDANCE CENTER

9650 Zelzah Ave, Northridge, CA 91325
Tel.: (818) 993-9311　　　　CA
Web Site:
https://www.childguidance.org
Year Founded: 1962
Sales Range: $10-24.9 Million
Emp.: 301
Individual & Family Support Services
N.A.I.C.S.: 624190
Roy Marshall (Pres & CEO)
Jeff Adler (Dir-Ops)
Duc Tu (Dir-Fin)
Kathleen Welch-Torres (Dir-Programs)
Susan Hall-Marley (Dir-Trng)
Ken Teasdale (Vice Chm)
Deborah M. Neal (Sec)
Joyce L. Barkin (Treas)
Melissa Broadwell (Chm)

CHILD AND FAMILY SERVICES

330 Delaware Avenue, Buffalo, NY 14202
Tel.: (716) 842-2750　　　　NY
Web Site: http://www.cfsbny.org
Year Founded: 1973
Sales Range: $10-24.9 Million
Emp.: 442
Child & Family Support Services
N.A.I.C.S.: 624190
Mary Cornwell (Dir-PR & Dev)
Ian Long (CFO)
Francisco M. Vasquez (Pres & CEO)
David R. Barrett (Chm)
Christine Garvelli (Sec)
William Loecher (Treas)
Elizabeth B. Constantine (Vice Chm)
Michael K. Walsh (Chm)
Laura Yager (Dir-Corp Compliance & Quality Assurance)
Lauren Gousy (Coord-Community Rels)
William J. Dimmig (Chief Risk Officer)
Elizabeth McPartland (COO)
Richard A. Wall (Treas)

CHILD CARE ASSOCIATES

3000 E Belknap St, Fort Worth, TX 76111
Tel.: (817) 838-0055　　　　TX
Web Site:
https://www.childcareassociates.org
Year Founded: 1968
Sales Range: $50-74.9 Million
Emp.: 787
Child Care Services
N.A.I.C.S.: 624110
Arva Peters (VP)
Kara Waddell (Pres & CEO)
Karanae Spradlin (CFO)
Teresa Williamson (Dir-Fin)
Rhonda Nelson (Chief HR Officer)

CHILD CARE LINKS

6601 Owens Dr Ste 100, Pleasanton, CA 94588
Tel.: (925) 417-8733　　　　CA
Web Site:
http://www.childcarelinks.org
Year Founded: 1976
Sales Range: $10-24.9 Million
Emp.: 44
Child & Family Support Services
N.A.I.C.S.: 624190
Helen Fulgado (Mgr-Fin)
Julie Camberg (Dir-HR)

Child Care Links—(Continued)

CHILD CARE RESOURCE CENTER

20001 Prairie St, Chatsworth, CA 91311
Tel.: (818) 717-1000   CA
Web Site: http://www.ccrcla.org
Year Founded: 1976
Sales Range: $200-249.9 Million
Emp.: 527
Child Care & Development Services
N.A.I.C.S.: 624110
Ellen Cervantes (COO & VP)
Denise Trinh (CFO)
Shirley Cameron (VP-HR)
Jeriel Smith (Sec)
Susan Montalvo (Dir-Comm & Bus Center)
Donna Sneeringer (Dir-Govt Rels)
Susan Savage (Dir-Res)
Michael Olenick (Pres & CEO)
Michelle Torres (Chm)
Adrian Stern (Vice Chm)
Shelia Jones (Treas)

CHILD CRAFT INDUSTRIES, INC.

1010 Keller Dr, New Salisbury, IN 47161
Tel.: (812) 206-2200   IN
Web Site:
http://www.childcraftIndustries.com
Year Founded: 1911
Sales Range: $25-49.9 Million
Emp.: 80
Mfr of Wooden Infant Furniture
N.A.I.C.S.: 337122
Rhonda Geralde (Reg Mgr-Sls)

Subsidiaries:

ETC, Environmental Teen
Concepts   (1)
501 E Market St, Salem, IN
47167-2141   (100%)
Tel.: (812) 883-3111
Sales Range: $50-74.9 Million
Mfr of Infant & Juvenile Furniture
N.A.I.C.S.: 337122

CHILD DEVELOPMENT INC.

20 Creek Oaks Blvd Ste 200, San Jose, CA 95119
Tel.: (408) 556-7300   CA
Web Site: http://www.cdicdc.org
Year Founded: 1975
Sales Range: $25-49.9 Million
Emp.: 994
Child Development Services
N.A.I.C.S.: 624110
Araceli De Angelo Lopez (Co-Sec)

CHILD DIMENSIONS INSURANCE COMPANY

1 Perkins Sq, Akron, OH 44308
Tel.: (330) 543-8171   VT
Year Founded: 1988
Sales Range: $10-24.9 Million
Health Insurance Association
N.A.I.C.S.: 813920
Alicia Lamancusa (VP-Fin)
Grace Wakulchik (COO)
Michael Bird (VP-Loss Prey & Quality)
Michelle Lafleur (VP-CDIC)
Mary Link (Gen Counsel & VP-Claims)

CHILD FOCUS, INC.

551 Cincinnati-Batavia Pike, Cincinnati, OH 45244
Tel.: (513) 752-1555
Web Site: http://www.child-focus.org
Year Founded: 1977
Rev.: $11,354,571
Emp.: 260
Child Day Care Services

N.A.I.C.S.: 624410
Tim Beechuk (VP)
Keith Kral (Treas)
Susan Graham (Chief Admin Officer & VP)
Pamela Lindeman (CEO)

CHILD GUIDANCE & FAMILY SOLUTIONS

18 N Forge St, Akron, OH 44304-1317
Tel.: (330) 762-0591   OH
Web Site: https://www.cgfs.org
Year Founded: 1944
Sales Range: $10-24.9 Million
Emp.: 206
Behavioral Health Services
N.A.I.C.S.: 623210
Dawn Carter (Dir-Clinical Svcs)
Steven W. Jewell (VP & Dir-Medical)
Patrick Bravo (Sec)
Pamela Wright (Treas)
Steven J. Hopp (Chm)
Karen Talbott (VP-IT)
Elizabeth Harwood (VP-HR)

CHILD GUIDANCE RESOURCE CENTERS

2000 Old West Chester Pike, Havertown, PA 19083
Tel.: (484) 454-8700   PA
Web Site: https://www.cgrc.org
Year Founded: 1956
Sales Range: $10-24.9 Million
Emp.: 645
Behavioral Healthcare Services
N.A.I.C.S.: 621420
Colleen McNichol (COO)
Terry Clark (CFO)
Brad Barry (Pres & CEO)
Andrew Kind-Rubin (Chief Clinical Officer)
Aimee Salas (Chief Innovations Officer)
Carol Hanson (Vice Chm)
Ronald Eyler (Chm)

CHILD START INC.

1069 S Glendale St, Wichita, KS 67218-3203
Tel.: (316) 682-1853
Web Site: http://www.childstart.org
Rev.: $13,000,000
Emp.: 252
Child Day Care Services
N.A.I.C.S.: 624410
Teresa I. Rupp (Exec Dir)
Cheryl Dunn (Dir-CCR & R Program)
JoAnn Henry (Mgr-Early Childhood)
Sue Shinn (Mgr-Early Childhood)
Anne Sixkiller (Dir-Dev)
Glenda Wilcox (Dir-Early Childhood Program)
Tina Viramontez (Dir-Fin)
Anna Meyerhoff (Treas)
Mark Meier (Chm)
Patrick Lowrance (Vice Chm)

CHILD TRENDS, INC.

7315 Wisconsin Ave, Ste 1200W, Bethesda, MD 20814
Tel.: (240) 223-9200   NY
Web Site: https://www.childtrends.org
Year Founded: 1979
Sales Range: $10-24.9 Million
Emp.: 212
Child Care Services
N.A.I.C.S.: 624110
Angele Akitani (Mgr-Acctg)
Kathleen Ryan Skinner (Sr Dir-Contracts, Compliance & Admin-Bethesda)
August Aldebot-Green (Dir-Comm)
Natalia E. Pane (Sr VP-Res & Ops)
Gregory R. Niblett (Chm)
Fred Bollerer (Treas)

Carol Emig (Pres)
Judy Nee (Vice Chm)
Brenda Lilienthal Welburn (Sec)
Karen Calloo (CFO)
Michael Admassu (Supvr-Acctg)
Alicia Torres (Sr Dir-Comm)
Alana Ward (Sr Mgr-Health Comm & Policy)
Kate Maloney Williams (Mgr-Proposal & Compliance-Bethesda)
Charity Lewis Powell (Office Mgr)
Karin Malm (Sr Dir-Program Area & Child Welfare)
Kristin Anderson Moore (Dir-Youth Dev)
Kathryn Tout (Dir-Program Area & Early Childhood Dev)
Kelly Maxwell (Dir- Early Childhood Dev)
Carlise King (Exec Dir-Early Childhood Data Collaborative)
Jennifer Cleveland (Mgr-Research Ops)
Deborah Temkin (Dir-Education)
Lina Guzman (Dir-Child Trends Hispanic Institute & Reproductive Health)
Zakia Redd (Dir-Program Area, Youth Dev, Poverty & Inequality)
Jennifer Manlove (Dir-Reproductive Health & Family Formation)
Brigitte Gavin Vaughn (Sr Mgr-Comm)
Kristine Andrews (Dir-Program Area)
Mindy E. Scott (Dir-Reproductive Health & Family Formation)
Elizabeth Wildsmith (Deputy Dir-Program Area, Reproductive Health & Family Formation)
Lauren Supplee (Dir-Early Childhood Dev)

CHILD-ADULT RESOURCE SERVICES, INC.

201 N Dormeyer Ave, Rockville, IN 47872
Tel.: (765) 569-2076   IN
Web Site: https://www.cars-services.org
Year Founded: 1968
Sales Range: $10-24.9 Million
Emp.: 353
Disability Assistance Services
N.A.I.C.S.: 624120
Basil Weinman (CEO)

CHILD-PARENT CENTERS, INC.

602 E 22nd St, Tucson, AZ 85713
Tel.: (520) 882-0100   AZ
Web Site:
https://www.childparentcenters.org
Year Founded: 1967
Sales Range: $25-49.9 Million
Emp.: 618
Child & Youth Care Services
N.A.I.C.S.: 624110
Dora Montez (Dir-Program Svcs)
Erin Lyons (CEO)
Kathy Sutherland (Dir-Admin Svcs)
Nidiam Conesa (Dir-HR)
Peg Heslinga (Dir-Fiscal Unit)
Robin Bundy (Dir-IT)
Rosie Kennedy (Dir-Health & Nutrition Svcs)
Teresa Acevedo (Dir-Admin Svcs Unit)
Altair Helber (VP)

CHILDCARE LEARNING CENTERS, INC.

64 Palmer's Hill Rd, Stamford, CT 06902
Tel.: (203) 323-5944   CT
Web Site: http://www.clcstamford.org
Year Founded: 1902

Sales Range: $10-24.9 Million
Emp.: 241
Child Care & Development Services
N.A.I.C.S.: 624110
Anna Witkowski (Dir-Child Dev Program)
Penny Lehman (Dir-Program Svcs)
Sonya Kelepecz (Dir-Dev)
Barbara Garvin-Kester (CEO)
Darrell T. Ingram (CFO)
Jennifer Hallissey (Dir-Strategic Partnerships)
Carol Sargent (Dir-School Readiness Program)
Marc E. Jaffe (CFO)
Marc Teichman (Dir-HR)
Ellen Mellis (VP)
Heather Alexander (Sec)
Robert Mattis (Chm)
Robert Rahilly (Exec VP)
Christopher J. Lafond (Treas)

CHILDCAREGROUP

1420 W Mockingbird Ln Ste 300, Dallas, TX 75247
Tel.: (214) 630-7911   TX
Web Site:
https://www.childcaregroup.org
Year Founded: 1901
Sales Range: $10-24.9 Million
Emp.: 284
Child Care Services
N.A.I.C.S.: 624110
Mark Browder (CFO & COO)
Wendy Ogren (VP-Early Childhood Programs)
Theresa Irwin (Dir-HR)
Tori Mannes (Pres & CEO)
Shari Anderson (VP-Child Care Assistance)
Regina Montoya (Chm)
Linda Turner (VP-Community Outreach & Admin)
Amanda Finney (VP-Dev & Mktg)

CHILDERS OIL CO.

51 Highway 2034, Whitesburg, KY 41858
Tel.: (606) 633-2525
Web Site:
https://www.doublekwik.com
Sales Range: $75-99.9 Million
Emp.: 800
Petroleum Bulk Stations
N.A.I.C.S.: 424710
William Don Childers (Pres)
Donna Childers (VP)
Charles Matthews (CFO)
Ina Michelle Matthews (Founder & Pres)

CHILDNET

1100 W McNab Rd, Fort Lauderdale, FL 33309
Tel.: (954) 414-6000   FL
Web Site: https://www.childnet.us
Year Founded: 2001
Sales Range: $50-74.9 Million
Emp.: 389
Child Care Services
N.A.I.C.S.: 624110
Donna Skees (Officer-Program & Admin)
Dawn Liberta (Asst VP-Case Mgmt)
Mark Shults (Asst VP-Ops)
Armando Fana (Sec)
Joseph Rogers (Treas)
Melida Akiti (Vice Chm)
Sigrid McCawley (Chm)
Theresa Kennedy (Officer-Case Mgmt Program)
Lourdes Pons (COO)
Deena Ponto (Officer-Case Mgmt Program)
Sheryl Williams (Officer-Case Mgmt Program)

Larry Rein *(Pres & CEO)*
Donna Eprifania *(CFO)*

CHILDRE NISSAN, INC.
126 Roberson Mill Rd NE, Milledge-
ville, GA 31061-4901
Tel.: (478) 452-5535
Web Site:
   https://www.childrenissan.com
Year Founded: 1992
Sales Range: $10-24.9 Million
Emp.: 28
New Car Whslr
N.A.I.C.S.: 441110
Jason Childre *(Mgr-Website & Mktg)*

CHILDREN & FAMILIES OF IOWA
1111 University Ave, Des Moines, IA
50314
Tel.: (515) 288-1981   IA
Web Site: https://www.cfiowa.org
Year Founded: 1888
Sales Range: $10-24.9 Million
Emp.: 417
Child Care Services
N.A.I.C.S.: 624110
Jennifer Pavlovec *(VP-Fin)*
Amy Stapp-Arpy *(Chief Dev Officer &
VP-Dev & Comm)*
Amy Yeager *(CFO)*

CHILDREN AND ADULT DIS-ABILITY AND EDUCATIONAL SERVICES
401 Rutgers Ave, Swarthmore, PA
19081-2434
Tel.: (610) 328-5955   PA
Web Site: https://www.cades.org
Year Founded: 1951
Sales Range: $10-24.9 Million
Emp.: 625
Disability Assistance Services
N.A.I.C.S.: 624120
William Benson *(Exec Dir)*

CHILDREN AND FAMILIES FIRST DELAWARE INC
2005 Baynard Blvd, Wilmington, DE
19802
Tel.: (302) 658-5177   DE
Web Site: http://www.cffde.org
Year Founded: 1919
Sales Range: $10-24.9 Million
Emp.: 305
Individual & Family Support Services
N.A.I.C.S.: 624190
Paul L. McCommons *(Asst Treas)*
Kirsten Olson *(Chief Strategy Officer)*
Zakiya Bakari-Griffin *(Chief Program
Officer)*

CHILDREN INTERNATIONAL
2000 E Red Bridge Rd, Kansas City,
MO 64121
Tel.: (816) 942-2000   MO
Web Site: http://www.children.org
Year Founded: 1936
Sales Range: $100-124.9 Million
Emp.: 177
Child Assistance Services
N.A.I.C.S.: 813319
Lisa Thome-Ha *(VP-Sponsorship
Svcs)*
Danielle Mitchell *(VP-Fin)*
Susana Eshleman *(Pres & CEO)*
David Cacioppo *(Chm)*
Jack McCanna *(VP-Program Svcs)*
Eric McCullough *(VP-HR)*
Vickie Wiedenmann *(Sec & Asst VP)*
Claire Bishop *(VP-Mktg & Engage-
ment)*
Matt Gerard *(VP-Dev)*
Bill Brewster *(VP-Ops)*
Shelly Spritzer *(Dir-Outreach Mktg)*
Jamie Deaner *(Engr-IT Infrastructure)*

Kim Carter *(Dir-Global Brand & Con-
tent)*
Teresa Gaffney *(Dir-Loyalty & Advo-
cacy Mktg)*
John D. Clause *(VP-Philanthropy-
Global)*
Cynthia Currence *(Dir-Philanthropy-
Natl)*

CHILDREN'S AID & FAMILY SERVICES, INC.
200 Robin Rd, Paramus, NJ 07652
Tel.: (201) 261-2800   NJ
Web Site: https://www.cafsnj.org
Year Founded: 1899
Sales Range: $10-24.9 Million
Emp.: 383
Child & Family Support Services
N.A.I.C.S.: 624190
Ellen Elias *(Sr VP-Prevention-
Community Svcs)*

CHILDREN'S CANCER RE-COVERY FOUNDATION
249 Lincoln Way E, New Oxford, PA
17350
Tel.: (717) 688-7940   CA
Web Site:
   https://www.childrenscancerre
   covery.org
Year Founded: 1990
Sales Range: $10-24.9 Million
Cancer Treatment Support Services
N.A.I.C.S.: 813212
Amy O'Leary *(Exec Dir)*
Tara Bryan *(Mgr-Grants & Dev)*
Felicia Ellis *(Dir-Mktg & Program
Svcs)*
Victoria Ohm *(Treas & Sec)*
Martin Dumic *(Pres-Interim)*

CHILDREN'S CARE HOSPITAL & SCHOOL
2501 W 26th St, Sioux Falls, SD
57105
Tel.: (605) 444-9500   SD
Web Site: http://www.cchs.org
Year Founded: 1952
Sales Range: $10-24.9 Million
Emp.: 628
Health Care Srvices
N.A.I.C.S.: 622110
Kimberly Marso *(COO)*
Angie Brown *(VP-Mktg)*
Lon Clemensen *(VP-Program Sup-
port)*

CHILDREN'S CENTER FOR DEVELOPMENTAL ENRICH-MENT
900 Club Dr, Westerville, OH 43081
Tel.: (614) 899-2838   OH
Web Site: http://www.ccde.org
Year Founded: 1999
Sales Range: $10-24.9 Million
Emp.: 236
Behavioral Healthcare Services
N.A.I.C.S.: 623220
Lisa Lawless *(Sec)*
Doug Brown *(VP)*
Ed Snodgrass *(Treas)*
Galen Stover *(Pres)*

CHILDREN'S CENTER FOR TREATMENT AND EDUCATION
800 E Main St, Bradford, PA 16701
Tel.: (814) 817-1400   PA
Web Site: https://www.beacon-
light.org
Year Founded: 1994
Sales Range: $10-24.9 Million
Emp.: 577
Behavioral Healthcare Services
N.A.I.C.S.: 623220
Richard Seager *(Pres & CEO)*

CHILDREN'S CHOICE, INC.
211 Benigno Blvd, Bellmawr, NJ
08031
Tel.: (610) 521-6270   PA
Web Site:
   https://www.childrenschoice.org
Year Founded: 1982
Sales Range: $10-24.9 Million
Emp.: 157
Specialized Community-Based Ser-
vices for Individuals & Families
N.A.I.C.S.: 624110
Carolyn Eberwein *(Pres & CEO)*
Bernard Keels *(Chm)*
Richard J. Devine *(Treas)*
Sheila D. Thompson *(Sec)*
Terence P. Egan *(CFO)*
William J. Eberwein II *(Pres & CEO)*

CHILDREN'S COUNCIL SAN FRANCISCO
445 Church St, San Francisco, CA
94114
Tel.: (415) 276-2900   CA
Web Site:
   https://www.childrenscouncil.org
Year Founded: 1973
Sales Range: $50-74.9 Million
Emp.: 131
Child Care Services
N.A.I.C.S.: 624110
Sandee Blechman *(Exec Dir)*
Janet Zamudio *(Dir-Parent Svcs)*
Phillip Warner *(Dir-Family Subsidy
Svcs)*
Debra Ballinger Bernstein *(Dir-
Advancement)*
Elena Schmid *(Pres)*
Renita Sinn *(Sec)*
Wendy Bear *(Deputy Dir-Fin & Ops)*

CHILDREN'S CRISIS TREAT-MENT CENTER
1080 N Delaware Ave, Philadelphia,
PA 19125
Tel.: (215) 496-0707   PA
Web Site: http://www.cctckids.org
Year Founded: 1978
Sales Range: $10-24.9 Million
Emp.: 376
Child Behavioral Health Care Ser-
vices
N.A.I.C.S.: 622210
Antonio Valdes *(CEO)*
Ileana Helwig *(COO)*
Gordon E. Shopp *(CFO)*
Gabe Canuso *(Chm)*
Jaqueline P. Link *(Sec)*
Richard M. Horowitz *(Treas)*
Sharon Tobin-Kestenbaum *(Vice
Chm)*
Ismael Alvarez *(Dir-Center-Based
Svcs Div)*
Leslie Becton *(Dir-School-Based
Svcs Div)*
Andrea S. Ettingoff *(Dir-Clinical &
Quality Affairs)*
Rose Galan *(Mgr-Billing)*
Ellyn Hill *(Dir-Outpatient Svcs)*
Jaime Pearlstine *(Dir-Mktg & Comm)*
Sean Halloran *(Dir-Montgomery
County Svcs Div)*
Edith Lopez *(Dir-Community-Based
Svcs Div)*
Nicole Rich *(Dir-Care Coordination
Svcs)*
John Moeller *(Dir-Dev)*

CHILDREN'S DEFENSE FUND
25 East St NW, Washington, DC
20001
Tel.: (202) 628-8787   DC
Web Site:
   http://www.childrensdefense.org
Year Founded: 1969
Sales Range: $10-24.9 Million

Emp.: 328
Child Care Services
N.A.I.C.S.: 624110
Marian Wright Edelman *(Pres)*

CHILDREN'S FRIEND
153 Summer St, Providence, RI
02903
Tel.: (401) 276-4300   RI
Web Site: https://www.cfsri.org
Year Founded: 1834
Sales Range: $10-24.9 Million
Emp.: 376
Child & Youth Care Services
N.A.I.C.S.: 624110
Stacy Couto *(VP-External Affairs)*
Aimee Mitchell *(Sr VP-Programs &
Ops & Dir-Head Start)*
Kelly Wishart *(VP-Professional Dev &
Quality)*
Mark E. Lima *(VP-HR)*
Carmen A. Mirabal *(Sec)*
Eva C. Hulse-Avila *(Vice Chm)*
Mark Griffin *(Treas)*
William J. Allen *(Chm)*
Gregory Barishian *(VP-Fin)*
David Caprio *(Pres & CEO)*

CHILDREN'S HEALTH COUN-CIL
650 Clark Way, Palo Alto, CA 94304
Tel.: (650) 326-5530   CA
Web Site: https://www.chconline.org
Year Founded: 1953
Sales Range: $10-24.9 Million
Emp.: 114
Individual & Family Healthcare Ser-
vices
N.A.I.C.S.: 621498
Rosalie Whitlock *(Exec Dir)*
Joan Baran *(Dir-Community Clinic)*
Glen R. Elliott *(Dir-Medical)*
Elaine Hahn *(Chm)*
Julie Terrell Hooper *(Sec)*
Manuel A. Henriquez *(Treas)*
Rebecca B. Robertson *(Vice Chm)*
Bill Gray *(Dir-Advancement)*
Terry Boyle *(CFO & COO)*

CHILDREN'S HEALTHCARE OF ATLANTA
1405 Clifton Road NE, Atlanta, GA
30322-1062
Web Site: http://www.choa.org
Sales Range: $1-4.9 Billion
Emp.: 6,758
Hospital Operator
N.A.I.C.S.: 622110
Donna W. Hyland *(Pres & CEO)*
Ruth Fowler *(CFO)*
Ron Frieson *(COO)*
Linda Matzigkeit *(Chief Admin Officer)*
Daniel Salinas *(Chief Medical Officer)*
Jamila Pope *(Dir-Govt Affairs)*
Thomas M. Holder *(Chm)*

CHILDREN'S HOME + AID
125 S Wacker Dr 14th Fl, Chicago, IL
60606
Tel.: (312) 424-0200   IL
Web Site:
   http://www.childrenshomeaid.org
Year Founded: 1883
Sales Range: $50-74.9 Million
Emp.: 1,301
Child Care Services
N.A.I.C.S.: 624110
Paula Corrigan-Halpern *(VP-Pub
Policy & Strategic Initiatives)*
Beverley A. Sibblies *(Chm)*
Alan Conkle *(Treas)*

Children's Home + Aid—(Continued)

Sara Irmen *(VP-Resource Dev & Comm)*
Jan Stepto-Millett *(VP-Education Svcs)*
Renae Storey *(Reg VP)*

CHILDREN'S HOME OF BRAD-FORD, PA.
800 E Main St, Bradford, PA 16701 PA
Web Site:
    https://www.journeyhealth.org
Sales Range: $50-74.9 Million
Emp.: 1,150
Behavioral Health Services Organization
N.A.I.C.S.: 621112
Craig Moffatt *(CFO)*

Subsidiaries:

Beacon Light Behavioral Health
Systems   (1)
800 E Main St, Bradford, PA 16701
Tel.: (800) 345-1780
Web Site: http://www.beacon-light.org
Sales Range: $25-49.9 Million
Emp.: 650
Behavioral Health Services
N.A.I.C.S.: 622210
Richard B. Seager III *(Pres & CEO)*
Kasandra Cyphert *(Mgr-Blended Case)*
Denise Bean *(VP-Clinical Svcs)*
Peg Shirey *(Dir-Nursing)*

Stairways Behavioral Health   (1)
2185 W 8th St, Erie, PA 16505
Tel.: (814) 453-5806
Web Site: http://www.stairwaysbh.org
Sales Range: $25-49.9 Million
Emp.: 500
Behavioral Healthcare Services
N.A.I.C.S.: 623220
Robin Dowling *(Exec Dir)*
Gregory Larocca *(Treas)*
Penny Chapman *(Dir-Medical)*
Melanie Hake *(Dir-Residential Svcs)*
Steve Heitzenrater *(Dir-Risk Mgmt)*
Chris Knoll *(Dir-Health Care Info)*
Brenda Sanford *(Dir-HR)*
Kim Stucke *(Chief Dev Officer)*
Jennifer Valerio *(Controller)*
Thomas Tredway *(Vice Chm)*

CHILDREN'S HOME OF WYO-MING CONFERENCE
1182 Chenango St, Binghamton, NY
13901
Tel.: (607) 772-6904   NY
Year Founded: 1919
Sales Range: $10-24.9 Million
Emp.: 369
Child & Family Welfare Services
N.A.I.C.S.: 624190
Ann MacLaren *(CFO)*
Robert Houser *(CEO)*
Janet Williams *(Treas)*
Joseph Silvanic *(Vice Chm)*
Robert Ford *(Sec)*
David Chambers *(Chm)*

CHILDREN'S HOME SOCIETY OF CALIFORNIA
1300 W 4th St, Los Angeles, CA
90017
Tel.: (213) 240-5900   CA
Web Site: https://www.chs-ca.org
Year Founded: 1891
Sales Range: $50-74.9 Million
Emp.: 184
Child Care Services
N.A.I.C.S.: 624110
Beverly Tidwell *(CEO)*

CHILDREN'S HOME SOCIETY OF FLORIDA
1485 S Semoran Blvd Ste 1448, Winter Park, FL 32792
Tel.: (321) 397-3000   FL

Web Site: http://www.chsfl.org
Year Founded: 1964
Sales Range: $100-124.9 Million
Emp.: 2,619
Child Care Services
N.A.I.C.S.: 624110
Andry E. Sweet *(COO)*
Frank Gonzalez *(Chief Compliance Officer & Gen Counsel)*
Heather Vogel *(Chief Talent Officer)*
Heather Morgan *(VP-Comm & Brand)*
Summer Pfeiffer *(VP-Government Relations)*
Tara Hormell *(Sr VP-Operations)*

CHILDREN'S HOME SOCIETY OF NORTH CAROLINA, INC.
604 Meadow St, Greensboro, NC
27405
Tel.: (336) 274-1538   NC
Web Site: https://www.chsnc.org
Year Founded: 1904
Sales Range: $10-24.9 Million
Emp.: 270
Child Care Services
N.A.I.C.S.: 624110
Vicki Barringer *(VP-Fin & IT)*
Hector McEachern *(VP-Ops)*
Brian Maness *(Pres & CEO)*
Rebecca Starnes *(VP-Programs & Quality Improvement)*
Sandra Yarborough *(VP-Permanency)*
Burns Jones *(Chm)*
Matt Anderson *(VP-Programs & Bus Dev)*
Kristen Brown Smalley *(VP-Philanthropy)*

CHILDREN'S HOME SOCIETY OF SOUTH DAKOTA
801 N Sycamore Ave, Sioux Falls,
SD 57110
Tel.: (605) 334-6004   SD
Web Site: https://www.chssd.org
Year Founded: 1895
Rev.: $26,729,229
Assets: $102,325,954
Liabilities: $3,123,456
Net Worth: $99,202,498
Emp.: 466
Fiscal Year-end: 06/30/18
Individual & Family Support Services
N.A.I.C.S.: 624190
Nathan Headley *(Mgr-Info Sys)*
Muriel Nelson *(COO)*
Tami Gronseth *(CFO)*
Bobby Sundby *(Pres)*
Bill Colson *(Exec Dir)*
Gina Hopkins *(VP)*
Greg Schweiss *(Treas)*
Lisa Richmond-Kirby *(Sec)*
Scott Barbour *(VP)*
Linda Daugaard *(Sec)*
Jeff Skinner *(Treas)*

CHILDREN'S HOME SOCIETY OF WASHINGTON
3300 NE 65th St, Seattle, WA 98115
Tel.: (206) 695-3200
Web Site:
    http://www.childrenshomesociety.org
Year Founded: 1896
Rev.: $9,500,000
Emp.: 400
Fiscal Year-end: 12/31/06
Individual/Family Services Residential Care Services
N.A.I.C.S.: 624110

Subsidiaries:

Childhaven   (1)
316 Broadway, Seattle, WA 98122-5325
Tel.: (206) 624-6477
Web Site: http://www.childhaven.org

Sales Range: $10-24.9 Million
Emp.: 216
Child Abuse Prevention Services
N.A.I.C.S.: 624110
Melissa Williams *(VP-Bus Ops & Dir-Fin)*
Curt Anderson *(Vice Chm & Treas)*
Jake Domer *(Chm)*

CHILDREN'S HOPE ALLIANCE
156 Frazier Loop, Statesville, NC
28677
Tel.: (704) 872-4157   NC
Web Site:
    http://www.childrenshopealliance.org
Year Founded: 1891
Child & Youth Services
N.A.I.C.S.: 624110
Celeste Dominguez *(Chief Bus Rels Officer)*
John Koppelmeyer *(Pres & CEO)*
Kimberly Lawrence *(Treas)*
Jason Ainsley *(CFO)*
Bill Wasulko *(Chm)*
Ron Turner Jr. *(Vice Chm)*

Subsidiaries:

Children's Hope Alliance
Foundation   (1)
Tel.: (704) 872-4157
Web Site:
    https://www.childrenshopealliance.org
Child Care Services
N.A.I.C.S.: 624110
Spurgeon Mackie *(Chm)*
Ben Klein *(Treas)*
Carolyn Leith *(Sec)*

CHILDREN'S HOSPITAL
200 Henry Clay Ave, New Orleans,
LA 70118
Tel.: (504) 899-9511   LA
Web Site: https://www.chnola.org
Year Founded: 1949
Sales Range: $400-449.9 Million
Emp.: 1,807
Child Health Care Services
N.A.I.C.S.: 622110
John Heaton *(Chief Medical Officer)*
Mary Perrin *(Co-Pres & Co-CEO)*

CHILDREN'S HOSPITAL & MEDICAL CENTER
8200 Dodge St, Omaha, NE 68114
Tel.: (402) 955-5400
Web Site:
    https://www.childrensomaha.org
Sales Range: $75-99.9 Million
Emp.: 1,700
Pediatric Hospital
N.A.I.C.S.: 622110
Casey Burg *(Dir-Medical)*
Russell J. Hopp *(Dir-Medical)*
Rodrigo Lopez *(Pres-Interim & CEO)*
Amy Bones *(Gen Counsel & Sr VP)*
Mike Brown *(Chief Strategy & Transformation Officer & Exec VP)*
Steven Burnham *(Sr VP-Physician Networks)*
Amy Hatcher *(CFO & Sr VP)*
Christopher Maloney *(Chief Medical Officer & Sr VP-Medical Affairs)*
Suzanne Nocita *(Chief HR Officer & Sr VP)*
Donny Suh *(Sr VP-Interim)*
Jerry Vuchak *(CIO & Sr VP)*
Pam Johnson-Carlson *(Chief Nursing Officer & Sr VP)*
Chanda Chacon *(Pres & CEO)*
Kathy English *(COO & Exec VP)*

Subsidiaries:

Children's Home Healthcare   (1)
4156 S 52nd St, Omaha, NE 68117-1324
Tel.: (402) 734-6741
Web Site: http://www.childrensomaha.org
Sales Range: $1-9.9 Million
Emp.: 80
Medical Equipment Rental

N.A.I.C.S.: 532283
Brian Allison *(Exec Dir)*
Roger Lewis *(Exec Dir)*
Casey Burg *(Dir-Medical)*

CHILDREN'S HOSPITAL COLORADO HEALTH SYSTEM
13123 E 16th Ave, Aurora, CO 80045
Tel.: (720) 777-1234   CO
Web Site:
    https://www.childrenscolorado.org
Year Founded: 2011
Sales Range: $10-24.9 Million
Investment Management Service
N.A.I.C.S.: 523940
Jeffrey Harrington *(CFO & Sr VP)*
Jena Hausmann *(CEO)*
Duncan Wilcox *(Dir-Center for Children's Surgery)*

CHILDREN'S HOSPITAL LOS ANGELES
4650 W Sunset Blvd, Los Angeles,
CA 90027
Tel.: (323) 660-2450   CA
Web Site: http://www.chla.org
Year Founded: 1901
Sales Range: $800-899.9 Million
Emp.: 5,204
Child Care & Development Services
N.A.I.C.S.: 622110
DeAnn S. Marshall *(CMO, Chief Dev Officer & Sr VP)*
Paul S. Viviano *(Pres & CEO)*
Jaclyn Biegel *(Dir-Personalized Medicine)*
Philippe Friedlich *(Dir-Center for Fetal and Neonatal Medicine)*
Roberta Williams *(Interim Chm-Department of Pediatrics)*
James Stein *(Chief Medical Officer & Sr VP)*
Omkar P. Kulkarni *(Chief Innovation Officer)*
Jeffrey Worthe *(Chm)*
Matthew S. Keefer *(Chief Medical Informatics Officer & Pres-Medical Grp)*
Lara Khouri *(COO & Exec VP)*
Kelly M. Johnson *(Chief Nursing Officer & Sr VP)*

CHILDREN'S HOSPITAL MEDICAL CENTER OF AKRON
1 Perkins Sq, Akron, OH 44308-1062
Tel.: (330) 543-1000   OH
Web Site:
    https://www.akronchildrens.org
Year Founded: 1897
Sales Range: $600-649.9 Million
Emp.: 5,046
Child Health Care Services
N.A.I.C.S.: 622110
Alicia LaMancusa *(VP-Fin)*
Shawn Lyden *(Exec VP)*

CHILDREN'S HOSPITAL MEDICAL PRACTICE CORPORATION
298 Henry Clay Ave, New Orleans,
LA 70118
Tel.: (504) 896-9827   LA
Web Site: http://www.chmpc.org
Year Founded: 1996
Sales Range: $10-24.9 Million
Emp.: 213
Child Health Care Services
N.A.I.C.S.: 622110
Steve Worley *(Pres & CEO)*
Doug Mittelstaedt *(Dir-HR)*
Alan Robson Sr. *(Dir-Medical)*

CHILDREN'S HOSPITAL PEDIATRIC ASSOCIATES, INC.
300 Longwood Ave, Boston, MA
02115

Tel.: (617) 355-6000   MA
Web Site:
https://www.childrenshospital.org
Year Founded: 2002
Sales Range: $200-249.9 Million
Emp.: 418
Healtcare Services
N.A.I.C.S.: 622110
Sandra L. Fenwick *(Pres & CEO)*

CHILDREN'S HOSPITALS AND CLINICS OF MINNESOTA

2525 Chicago Ave, Minneapolis, MN 55404
Tel.: (612) 813-6000   MN
Web Site: http://www.childrensmn.org
Year Founded: 2011
Sales Range: $25-49.9 Million
Emp.: 195
Child & Family Health Services
N.A.I.C.S.: 624190
Phillip Kibort *(Chief Medical Officer & VP-Medical Affairs)*
Samantha Hanson *(Chief HR Officer)*
Bjorn Gunnerud *(VP-Mktg & Comm)*
Maria C. Christu *(Chief Legal Officer & VP-Advocacy & Health Policy)*
Todd Ostendorf *(CFO)*
Jennifer Olson *(COO & Sr VP)*
Michael Morrey *(VP-Ops)*
Jeffrey Young *(CIO)*
Marc Gorelick *(Pres & CEO)*
Anne Boisclair-Fahey *(Interim Chief Nursing Officer)*
James C. Burroughs II *(Chief Equity & Inclusion Officer & VP)*

CHILDREN'S HUNGER FUND

13931 Balboa Blvd, Sylmar, CA 91342
Tel.: (818) 979-7100   CA
Web Site:
https://www.childrenshungerfund.org
Year Founded: 1991
Sales Range: $25-49.9 Million
Emp.: 64
Hunger Relief Services
N.A.I.C.S.: 624210
Christopher Sue *(Exec Dir-Fin & Ops)*
Jeff Holder *(Exec Dir-Comm)*

CHILDREN'S LAW CENTER OF CALIFORNIA

201 Centre Plz Dr Ste 10, Monterey Park, CA 91754-2178
Tel.: (323) 980-1700   CA
Web Site: http://www.clcla.org
Year Founded: 1989
Sales Range: $10-24.9 Million
Emp.: 296
Social Advocacy Organization
N.A.I.C.S.: 813319
John Moll *(Dir-Ops)*
Jody Leibman Green *(Dir-Policy)*
Leslie Starr Heimov *(Exec Dir)*
Richard E. Drooyan *(Chm)*

CHILDREN'S LEUKEMIA RESEARCH ASSOCIATION, INC.

585 Stewart Ave Ste 18, Garden City, NY 11530
Tel.: (516) 222-1944   NY
Web Site:
http://www.childrensleukemia.org
Year Founded: 1966
Sales Range: $1-9.9 Million
Emp.: 2
Fundraising Services
N.A.I.C.S.: 813211

CHILDREN'S LITERACY INITIATIVE

2314 Market St, Philadelphia, PA 19103
Tel.: (215) 561-4676   PA

Web Site: http://www.cli.org
Year Founded: 1988
Sales Range: $1-9.9 Million
Emp.: 57
Teaching Professional Development Services
N.A.I.C.S.: 611430
Pat Federman *(Co-Founder)*
Victoria Raivitch *(Treas)*
Caryn Henning *(Dir-Program Design & Dev)*
John Bonow *(CEO & Mng Dir)*
Adam Spector *(Mng Partner)*

CHILDREN'S MEDICAL CENTER DALLAS

1935 Medical District Dr, Dallas, TX 75235
Tel.: (214) 456-7000
Web Site: https://www.childrens.com
Sales Range: $900-999.9 Million
Emp.: 1,000
Children's Hospital Owner & Operator
N.A.I.C.S.: 622310
Christopher J. Durovich *(Pres & CEO)*
Mary Stowe *(Chief Nursing Officer)*
David Eager *(CFO & Exec VP)*
Kern Wildenthal *(Pres & Exec VP)*
Lawrence L. Foust *(Chief Legal Officer, Gen Counsel & Exec VP-Legal Svcs)*
Peter W. Roberts *(Pres)*
W. Robert Morrow *(Pres & Chief Clinical Officer)*
Kim Besse *(Chief HR Officer & Exec VP)*
Matt Davis *(Exec VP)*
Jeremiah Radandt *(Exec VP-North)*
Pete Perialas Jr. *(Chief Strategy Officer & Exec VP)*

CHILDREN'S MUSEUM OF HOUSTON

1500 Binz St, Houston, TX 77004
Tel.: (713) 522-1138   TX
Web Site: https://www.cmhouston.org
Year Founded: 1981
Sales Range: $10-24.9 Million
Emp.: 292
Child Museum
N.A.I.C.S.: 712110

CHILDREN'S POPULATION HEALTH

1935 Medical District Dr, Dallas, TX 75235
Tel.: (214) 456-7000   TX
Year Founded: 2013
Sales Range: $10-24.9 Million
Child Health Care Services
N.A.I.C.S.: 622110
Lister Robertson *(VP-Clinc Integrated Population Health)*
Stephanie K. Smith *(Sec)*
Patricia Sumler *(VP-Resource Dev Population Health)*
Kimberly Altman *(VP-Population Health Care Mgmt Sys)*
Ray Dziesinski *(Chief Treasury Officer & Sr VP)*
Jodi Landon *(VP-Managed Care)*
Summer Collins *(VP-Population Health Data Strategies)*
Paul Hain *(VP-Population Health & Dir-Medical)*
Patricia U. Winning *(Sr VP-Strategy Phys Orgs)*
Denise Levis-Hewson *(VP-Clinc Integrated Network)*
Peter W. Roberts *(Pres & Exec VP-CMC)*

CHILDREN'S PROGRESS, INC.

108 W 39 St Ste 1300, New York, NY 10018
Tel.: (212) 730-0905   DE
Web Site:
http://www.childrensprogress.com
Year Founded: 1999
Sales Range: $1-9.9 Million
Emp.: 19
Prepackaged Software
N.A.I.C.S.: 513210
Kevin Greaney *(Pres, CEO, Treas & Sec)*
Eugene Galanter *(Founder, Chm & Chief Scientific Officer)*

CHILDREN'S SERVICES OF ROXBURY, INC.

520 Dudley St, Roxbury, MA 02119
Tel.: (617) 445-6655   MA
Web Site: https://www.csrox.org
Year Founded: 1990
Sales Range: $10-24.9 Million
Emp.: 414
Welfare & Economic Development Program Services
N.A.I.C.S.: 926110
Ed D'Amato *(CFO)*
Susan Villeda *(Dir-HR)*
Anita Burke-Johnson *(VP-Housing & Stabilization)*
Ed Malone *(VP-Family Svcs)*
Salesia Hughes *(VP-Behavioral Health)*

CHILDRENS BUREAU, INC.

1575 Dr Martin Luther King Jr St, Indianapolis, IN 46202
Tel.: (317) 634-5050   IN
Web Site:
https://www.childrensbureau.org
Year Founded: 1851
Sales Range: $10-24.9 Million
Emp.: 321
Child & Youth Care Services
N.A.I.C.S.: 624110
Tina Cloer *(Pres & CEO)*
Mark Kern *(CFO)*
Annie Martinez *(VP-Dev)*

CHILDRENS HOSPITAL OF WISCONSIN

8915 W Connell Ct, Milwaukee, WI 53226
Tel.: (414) 266-2000
Web Site: https://www.childrenswi.org
Year Founded: 1894
Health Care Srvices
N.A.I.C.S.: 621610

CHILDRENS SERVICE CENTER OF WYOMING VALLEY, INC.

335 S Franklin St, Wilkes Barre, PA 18702-3897
Tel.: (570) 825-6425   PA
Web Site: https://www.cscwv.org
Year Founded: 1938
Sales Range: $10-24.9 Million
Emp.: 525
Behavioral Healthcare Services
N.A.I.C.S.: 623220
Summer Krochta *(Dir-Residential Svcs)*
Michael P. Hopkins *(Pres & CEO)*
Joel Smith *(Dir-IT)*
Denise Namowicz *(VP-Clinical Svcs)*
Carolanne Jones-Leco *(Sr Dir-Clinical Ops)*

CHILDRESS-KLEIN PROPERTIES, INC.

301 S College St Ste 2800, Charlotte, NC 28202-6014
Tel.: (704) 342-9000

Web Site:
https://www.childressklein.com
Year Founded: 1988
Sales Range: $450-499.9 Million
Emp.: 358
Commercial Real Estate Services
N.A.I.C.S.: 237210
Frederick W. Klein *(Sr Mng Partner)*
J. Donald Childress *(Sr Mng Partner)*
Gordon Buchmiller *(Mng Partner)*
David Pitser *(Dir-Property Mgmt)*
Chris Case *(Dir-Property Mgmt)*
Debbie Duniec *(CFO & Partner)*
Jeff Crane *(Reg Mgr-Property)*
Paul DeVine *(Partner-Office)*
Connie L. Engel *(Partner-Atlanta Office Div)*

CHILDS MANAGEMENT INC.

2716 E Lancaster Ave, Fort Worth, TX 76103
Tel.: (817) 531-3913
Sales Range: $10-24.9 Million
Emp.: 16
Industrial Buildings, New Construction
N.A.I.C.S.: 236210
Steve Luebbehusen *(VP)*

CHILLER TECHNOLOGY, INC.

22 6th Rd Ste 4, Woburn, MA 01801
Tel.: (781) 491-0910
Web Site:
https://www.chillertechnology.com
Year Founded: 2001
Sales Range: $10-24.9 Million
Emp.: 30
Refrigeration Services
N.A.I.C.S.: 811412
Johnathan White *(Mgr-Svc)*

CHIME INC.

239 E 5th St 4B, New York, NY 10003   DE
Web Site: http://www.wave.com
Mobile Money Transfer Application Developer & Services
N.A.I.C.S.: 541511
Will Fogel *(CEO)*

CHINA BULL MANAGEMENT INC.

665 Ellsworth Ave, New Haven, CT 06511
Tel.: (203) 562-8899   NV
Web Site:
http://www.uschinachannel.net
Year Founded: 2010
Financial Consulting Services
N.A.I.C.S.: 541611
Andrew Chien *(Chm, Pres, CEO & CFO)*

CHINA CONCENTRIC CAPITAL GROUP, INC.

800 3rd Ave 9th Fl, New York, NY 10022
Tel.: (646) 688-4028   VG
Investment Holding Company
N.A.I.C.S.: 551112
Ethan Chuang *(VP)*

CHINA CRESCENT ENTERPRISES, INC.

14860 Montfort Dr Ste 210, Dallas, TX 75254
Tel.: (214) 722-3040   NV
Sales Range: $75-99.9 Million
Emp.: 315
Systems Integrator & Hardware Value Added Reseller (VAR) for Telecommunications Industry
N.A.I.C.S.: 541512
Philip J. Rauch *(CFO)*
James Jiang *(Pres & CEO)*

China Crescent Enterprises, Inc.—(Continued)

CHINA HOLDINGS GROUP, INC.
73726 Alessandro Ste 103, Palm Desert, CA 92260
Tel.: (760) 219-2776   NV
Year Founded: 1994
Aircraft Parts Sales
N.A.I.C.S.: 423860
Dempsey K. Mork (Chm, Pres, CFO, Treas & Sec)

CHINA INC.
12808 W Airport Ste 303L, Sugar Land, TX 77478
Tel.: (281) 776-9100   NV
Year Founded: 2008
Solar Panels, Inverters & Solar Hot Water Heaters Sales & Distr
N.A.I.C.S.: 423610
Tian Jia (CEO, CFO, Treas & Sec)

CHINA KING SPIRIT GROUP LTD.
1900 Ave of the Stars, Los Angeles, CA 90067
Tel.: (310) 843-9300   NV
Year Founded: 2014
Assets: $13,985
Liabilities: $26,825
Net Worth: ($12,840)
Earnings: ($18,746)
Fiscal Year-end: 06/30/18
Cork Products Mfr & Distr
N.A.I.C.S.: 321999
Zanfang Wang (Pres, CFO & Principal Acctg Officer)

CHINA RESOURCES & CONSULTING, INC.
1237 E Shadow Gate Cir, Sandy, UT 84094
Tel.: (801) 523-6275   NV
Year Founded: 2008
Sales Range: $25-49.9 Million
Emp.: 1
Investment Services
N.A.I.C.S.: 523999
Ronald T. Jones (Chm, Pres, CEO & CFO)
Patricia Jones (Sec)

CHINA WI-MAX COMMUNICATIONS, INC.
1009 Washington St, Grafton, WI 53024-1913
Tel.: (920) 912-7444   NV
Web Site: http://www.chinawi-max.com
Year Founded: 2006
Emp.: 5
Broadband Communications
N.A.I.C.S.: 517112
Eric Hager (Acting Pres & VP)

CHINA WU YI MOUNTAIN LTD.
1900 Ave of the Stars, Los Angeles, CA 90067
Tel.: (310) 843-9300   NV
Year Founded: 2016
Assets: $593
Liabilities: $118,840
Net Worth: ($118,247)
Earnings: ($32,655)
Fiscal Year-end: 08/31/22
Organic Coconut Water Mfr & Distr
N.A.I.C.S.: 312111
Lei Wang (Pres, Chm, CEO, Treas & CFO)
Ying Zhang (Sec)

CHINESE COMMUNITY HEALTH CARE ASSOCIATION

445 Grant Ave Ste 300, San Francisco, CA 94108
Tel.: (415) 216-0088   CA
Web Site: https://www.cchca.com
Year Founded: 1982
Sales Range: $75-99.9 Million
Emp.: 20
Health & Welfare Services
N.A.I.C.S.: 525120
William Chung (Treas)
Eric L. Leung (VP)

CHINESEINVESTORS.COM, INC.
227 W Vly Blvd Ste 208A, San Gabriel, CA 91776   IN
Web Site: http://www.chinesefn.com
Year Founded: 1999
CIIX—(OTCBB)
Rev.: $6,476,442
Assets: $4,423,808
Liabilities: $7,639,946
Net Worth: ($3,216,138)
Earnings: ($10,191,162)
Emp.: 31
Fiscal Year-end: 05/31/19
Online Financial Advisory Services
N.A.I.C.S.: 519290

CHINOOK LUMBER INC.
17606 Hwy 9 Route SE, Snohomish, WA 98296
Tel.: (360) 668-8800
Web Site: http://www.chinooklumber.com
Sales Range: $10-24.9 Million
Emp.: 30
Sales of Lumber & Other Building Materials
N.A.I.C.S.: 423310
Eric Fritch (Pres)
Joost Douwes (VP & Gen Mgr)
Rob Starrett (Treas)

CHIP GANASSI RACING TEAMS, INC.
400 Beta Dr, Pittsburgh, PA 15238
Tel.: (412) 391-3660   MI
Web Site: http://www.chipganassiracing.com
Sales Range: $100-124.9 Million
Emp.: 300
Holding Company; Professional Motorsports Organization
N.A.I.C.S.: 551112
Doug Duchardt (COO)
Floyd R. Ganassi Jr. (Owner & Chm)

Subsidiaries:

Chip Ganassi Racing Teams, Inc. - IndyCar   (1)
7777 Woodland Dr, Indianapolis, IN 46278   (100%)
Tel.: (317) 802-0000
Web Site: http://www.chipganassiracing.com
Sales Range: $10-24.9 Million
Emp.: 100
Professional Open-Wheel Motorsports Team
N.A.I.C.S.: 711211

Chip Ganassi Racing with Felix Sabates, LLC   (1)
8500 Westmoreland Dr NW, Concord, NC 28027
Tel.: (704) 662-9642
Web Site: http://www.chipganassiracing.com
Sales Range: $25-49.9 Million
Emp.: 175
Professional Stock Car Motorsports Team
N.A.I.C.S.: 711211
Max Jones (Mng Dir-NASCAR)
Chip Ganassi (Owner & CEO)
Mike Hull (Mng Dir-INDYCAR)
Rob Kauffman (Owner)

CHIP-TECH, LTD.
175 Central Ave, Farmingdale, NY 11735
Tel.: (631) 227-3000

Web Site: http://www.chiptech.com
Year Founded: 1989
Rev.: $14,508,316
Emp.: 25
Electronic Parts
N.A.I.C.S.: 423690
Robert Silverman (CEO)
Neal Stevens (Pres)
Barry Reed (COO)
Rob Meakin (VP-Sls & Mktg)
Alan Scott (VP-Sls)
Lorrine Lindner (Mgr-Shipping)
Ivy Raffe (VP-Accts)

CHIPMAN & TAYLOR CHEVROLET
SE 250 Bishop Blvd, Pullman, WA 99163-4914
Tel.: (509) 334-3555
Web Site: https://www.chipmantaylor.com
Year Founded: 1976
Sales Range: $25-49.9 Million
Emp.: 40
New Car Retailer
N.A.I.C.S.: 441110
Fran Amend (Owner & Gen Mgr)
Tom Taylor (Mgr)
Mark Yrazabal (Mgr-New Car)
Dick Zimmer (Mgr-Used Car)
Jerry Broemmeling (Mgr-Parts)
Dale Pool (Mgr-Svc)
Geoff Parrish (Controller)
Vance Freer (Mgr-Detail Department)

CHIPMAN CORPORATION
Ste 100 1040 Marina Village Pkwy, Alameda, CA 94501-6478
Tel.: (510) 748-8700
Web Site: http://www.chipmancorp.com
Year Founded: 1939
Sales Range: $25-49.9 Million
Emp.: 300
Household Goods Moving & Storage, Local
N.A.I.C.S.: 484210
Justin Chipman (Chm & Pres)

Subsidiaries:

National Transfer & Storage, Inc.   (1)
6350 Sky Creek Dr Ste 600, Sacramento, CA 95828
Tel.: (916) 383-8800
General Freight Trucking Services
N.A.I.C.S.: 484110

CHIPPEWA ENTERPRISES INCORPORATED
13245 Riverside Dr Fl 6, Sherman Oaks, CA 91423
Tel.: (818) 905-1200
Sales Range: $10-24.9 Million
Emp.: 5
Patrol Services, Insurance
N.A.I.C.S.: 531120
Donald C. Parker (Owner & Pres)
Lilly Hanson (Controller)

CHIPPEWA VALLEY AGRAFUELS COOPERATIVE
270 20th St NW, Benson, MN 56215
Tel.: (320) 843-4813
Web Site: https://www.cvec.com
Year Founded: 1996
Sales Range: $25-49.9 Million
Emp.: 50
Dried or Unmixed Corn Syrup Mfr
N.A.I.C.S.: 311221
David Thompson (Chm)
Chuck DeGrote (Vice Chm)
Dan Benson (Treas)
Jan Lundebrek (Sec)

Subsidiaries:

Chippewa Valley Ethanol Company, LLC   (1)

270 20th St NW, Benson, MN 56215
Tel.: (320) 843-4813
Web Site: http://www.cvec.com
Sales Range: $25-49.9 Million
Emp.: 32
Automotive News Publisher
N.A.I.C.S.: 513110
Debra Mennis (CFO)

CHIPPEWA VALLEY BANK
5150N Main St, Winter, WI 54896
Tel.: (715) 266-3501
Web Site: http://www.chippewavalleybank.com
Year Founded: 1917
Sales Range: $1-9.9 Million
Emp.: 60
Commericial Banking
N.A.I.C.S.: 522110
Randy Somerville (Pres)

CHIPPEWA VALLEY BEAN COMPANY INC.
N2960 730th St, Menomonie, WI 54751
Tel.: (715) 664-8342
Web Site: http://www.cvbeans.com
Sales Range: $50-74.9 Million
Emp.: 15
Fruit & Vegetable Canning Pickling & Drying
N.A.I.C.S.: 311421
Cynthia A. Brown (Pres)

CHIRAL QUEST CORP.
7 Deer Park Dr Ste C1, Monmouth Junction, NJ 08852
Tel.: (732) 274-0399   DE
Web Site: https://www.chiralquest.com
Year Founded: 2000
Emp.: 220
Holding Company
N.A.I.C.S.: 551112
James Wu (CEO)
Ian Lennon (Sr VP-Bus Dev-Global)

Subsidiaries:

Chiral Quest, Inc.   (1)
7 Deer Park Dr Ste E, Monmouth Junction, NJ 08852
Tel.: (732) 274-0498
Sales Range: $10-24.9 Million
Emp.: 25
Chiral Pharmaceutical Products Development, Research & Mfr
N.A.I.C.S.: 325412
Xumu Zhang (Founder)
James Wu (CEO)
Jingyang Zhu (Sr VP-Technical Ops)
Ian C. Lennon (Sr VP-Global Bus Dev)

Plant (Non-US):

Chiral Quest (Jiashan) Co., Ltd.   (2)
9th Floor B1 Biobay Suzhou Industrial Park, Suzhou, 215123, Jiangsu, China
Tel.: (86) 51262956066
Chiral Products Mfr
N.A.I.C.S.: 325412
Joseph Marasco (CEO)
Tian Qian (Mgr)

CHIRO ONE WELLNESS CENTERS
2625 Butterfield Rd Ste 301N, Oak Brook, IL 60523
Tel.: (630) 468-1824
Web Site: http://www.chiroone.net
Sales Range: $25-49.9 Million
Emp.: 500
Chiropractic Care Services
N.A.I.C.S.: 621310
Sam Wang (COO)
Brett Penager (CMO)
Mark Lagerkvist (Exec Dir-Clinical Ops)

CHIRONET LLC

3149 Lackland Ste 104, Fort Worth, TX 76116
Tel.: (817) 886-8890
Web Site:
http://www.chironetservices.com
Year Founded: 2002
Sales Range: $1-9.9 Million
Emp.: 4
Network for Chiropractors
N.A.I.C.S.: 561990
Christy Smith (Dir-Ops)

CHIROTOUCH
9265 Sky Park Ct Ste 200, San Diego, CA 92123
Tel.: (619) 528-0040
Web Site:
https://www.chirotouch.com
Sales Range: $10-24.9 Million
Emp.: 100
Software Development Services
N.A.I.C.S.: 541511
Robert Moberg (Pres)
Jennifer Hay (Coord-Acct)
Michelle Butler (Acct Mgr)
Diana Simeonova (Controller)
Hannah Natarajan (Engr-Software)
Stephanie Cadirci (Mgr-Client Events)
Carrie Kimsey (Mgr-Funding)
David Johnson (Mgr-IT Dept)
Elizabeth Marrone (Office Mgr)
George Ahn (Vice Chm & CEO)

CHIRPIFY, INC.
317 SW Alder St Ste 1100, Portland, OR 97204
Tel.: (503) 208-3068
Web Site: http://www.chirpify.com
Multi-Channel Marketing Services
N.A.I.C.S.: 541613
Chris Teso (Founder & CEO)
Chris Mike (VP-Accts)

Subsidiaries:

Measureful Inc. (1)
1104 NW 15th Ave Ste 500, Portland, OR 97209
Tel.: (541) 510-1393
Web Site: http://www.measureful.com
Visual Analytics Software
N.A.I.C.S.: 513210
John Koenig (CEO)

CHISANO MARKETING GROUP, INC.
2170 W State Rd 434 Ste 280, Longwood, FL 32779-4993
Tel.: (407) 788-7070
Year Founded: 1980
Rev.: $22,000,000
Emp.: 23
Fiscal Year-end: 12/31/03
N.A.I.C.S.: 541810
Skip Masland (Dir-Creative)
Karen Lamonica (Dir-Pub Rels)
Joe Bouch (Pres)
Scott Feltman (Sr Acct Exec)
David Hemelgarn (Sr VP)

CHISESI BROTHERS MEAT PACKING CO.
5221 Jefferson Hwy, New Orleans, LA 70123
Tel.: (504) 822-3550
Web Site:
https://www.chisesibros.com
Sales Range: $25-49.9 Million
Emp.: 30
Hams & Picnics, From Meat Slaughtered On Site
N.A.I.C.S.: 311611
Philip N. Chisesi (Treas & Sec)

CHISOLM TRAIL RV
12020 Central Ave SE, Albuquerque, NM 87123
Tel.: (505) 296-1800

Web Site:
https://www.chisolmtrailrv.com
Year Founded: 2002
Sales Range: $10-24.9 Million
Emp.: 19
Recreational Vehicle Retailer
N.A.I.C.S.: 441210
Joe Spacagna (Mgr-Sls & Fin)
Jeff Dixon (Mgr-Svc & Parts)

CHITIKA, INC.
1800 W Park Dr Ste 300, Westborough, MA 01581
Tel.: (508) 449-3870
Web Site: http://www.chitika.com
Year Founded: 2003
Sales Range: $1-9.9 Million
Emp.: 40
Advertising Services
N.A.I.C.S.: 541810
Venkat Kolluri (CEO)
Alden DoRosario (CTO)
Matt Kojalo (Gen Mgr-Mobile Adv)
Harlan Lieberman-Berg (Dir-Engrg & Ops)

Subsidiaries:

Chitika, Inc. (1)
2nd Floor Capella The V IT Park Plot 17, Software Units Layout, Madhapur, Hyderabad, 500081, Andhra Pradesh, India
Tel.: (91) 40 646 26227
Advertising Services
N.A.I.C.S.: 541810

CHITTENDEN & EASTMAN CO.
100 New Rand Rd, Sweet Springs, MO 65351-9399
Tel.: (319) 753-2811   IA
Year Founded: 1866
Sales Range: $25-49.9 Million
Emp.: 80
Mfr of Mattresses
N.A.I.C.S.: 337910

CHIULISTA SERVICES, INC.
6613 Brayton Dr, Anchorage, AK 99507-2127
Tel.: (907) 278-2208
Web Site: http://www.calistacorp.com
Snack & Nonalcoholic Beverage Bars
N.A.I.C.S.: 722515
Matthew Nicolai (Pres)

Subsidiaries:

Yulista Holding, LLC (1)
8600 Advanced Gateway SW, Huntsville, AL 35808
Tel.: (256) 713-1360
Web Site: https://yulista.com
Aviation & Aerospace Component Mfg.
N.A.I.C.S.: 334511

Subsidiary (Domestic):

Dsoft Technology Company (2)
7222 Commerce Center Dr, Colorado Springs, CO 80919
Tel.: (719) 598-7107
Web Site: http://www.dsoft-tech.com
Sales Range: $1-9.9 Million
Emp.: 23
Custom Computer Programming Services
N.A.I.C.S.: 541511

Yulista Management Services, Inc. (1)
7272 Governors Dr NW, Huntsville, AL 35806
Tel.: (256) 713-0483
Web Site: http://www.yulista.com
Sales Range: $1-9.9 Million
Emp.: 22
Facilities Support Services
N.A.I.C.S.: 561210
Darrell Harrison (Pres & CEO)
Joseph M. Parsley (Dir-Bus Dev)
Joshua Herren (CEO & Pres)
Paul May (COO & VP)
Richard Harville (Dir-Fin)

CHL BUSINESS INTERIORS, LLC
1627 I St Ste 825, Washington, DC 20006-4044
Tel.: (202) 835-1444
Web Site: http://www.chlbi.com
Sales Range: $10-24.9 Million
Emp.: 25
Mfr of Office Furniture
N.A.I.C.S.: 423210
Jim Weitz (Controller)
Frank Licari (Exec VP)
Mary Hoover (Pres)
Mary Hoover (Pres)

CHL MEDICAL PARTNERS
1055 Washington Blvd 6th Fl, Stamford, CT 06901-2219
Tel.: (203) 324-7700
Web Site: http://www.chlmedical.com
Medical Industry Private Equity Investment Firm
N.A.I.C.S.: 523999
Jeffrey J. Collinson (Partner)
Myles D. Greenberg (Partner)
Timothy F. Howe (Partner)
Gregory M. Weinhoff (Partner)

CHMC ANESTHESIA FOUNDATION, INC.
20 Overland St Ste 203, Boston, MA 02215
Tel.: (617) 919-1340   MA
Web Site:
http://www.childrenshospital.org
Year Founded: 1980
Sales Range: $100-124.9 Million
Emp.: 129
Medical Research & Educational Services
N.A.I.C.S.: 541715
Sandra L. Fenwick (Pres & CEO)

CHOATE CONSTRUCTION COMPANY
8200 Roberts Dr Ste 600, Atlanta, GA 30350
Tel.: (678) 892-1200
Web Site: https://www.choateco.com
Sales Range: $350-399.9 Million
Emp.: 350
Commercial & Office Building Construction
N.A.I.C.S.: 236220
David A. Page (CFO)
Bill Bland (VP-Sls & Dev)
Adam Simpson (Sr Mgr-Virtual Construction)
Dave Priester (Pres & COO)
Tom Key (Dir-Preconstruction-Raleigh)
William Millard Choate (Pres & CEO)

CHOATE HALL & STEWART LLP
Two International Pl, Boston, MA 02110
Tel.: (617) 248-5000
Web Site: http://www.choate.com
Year Founded: 1899
Sales Range: $150-199.9 Million
Emp.: 201
Legal Advisory Services
N.A.I.C.S.: 541110
Christian A. Atwood (Partner)
Kristin T. Abati (Partner)
Charles A. Cheever (Co-Mng Partner)
Sarah Hunt Broughel (Partner)
David J. Brown (Partner)
Mark D. Cahill (Partner)
Fangli Chen (Partner)
John M. Cornish (Partner)
David B. Currie (Partner)
Howard S. Rosenblum (Partner)
Bob Licht (Partner)
Sarah Camougis (Partner)

Stephen Meredith (Partner)
Christopher Nelson (Partner)
Paul Pysher (Partner)
William P. Gelnaw Jr. (Co-Mng Partner)
Robert M. Buchanan Jr. (Partner)
Lyman G. Bullard Jr. (Partner)

CHOBANI INC.
669 County Rd 25, New Berlin, NY 13411
Tel.: (607) 847-7413   DE
Year Founded: 2021
Holding Company
N.A.I.C.S.: 551112
Hamdi Ulukaya (CEO, Founder & Chm)
Kathleen Leo (Chief Legal Officer, Sec & Gen Counsel)
Jason Blaisure (Chief Supply Chain Officer)
Tarkan Gurkan (CFO)
Tom Cullen (CIO)
Kevin Burns (Pres & COO)

CHOBANI, LLC
147 State Hwy 320, Norwich, NY 13815
Tel.: (212) 364-6490   NY
Web Site: http://www.chobani.com
Year Founded: 2005
Sales Range: $900-999.9 Million
Emp.: 3,000
Dairy Products Mfr & Whslr
N.A.I.C.S.: 424430
Hamdi Ulukaya (Founder & CEO)
Federico Muyshondt (Chief Customer Officer)
Jason Blaisure (Sr VP-Supply Chain)
Parag Agrawal (CIO)
Michelle Brooks (Chief Bus Dev Officer & Treas)
Cristina Alesci (Chief Corp Affairs Officer)
Nishant Roy (Chief Comm & Impact Officer)
Kevin Burns (Pres & COO)
Shari Eaton (Chief People Officer)
Marjorie De La Cruz (Chief Legal Officer)
Tarkan Gurkan (CFO)
Kenneth Bishop (Sr VP-Intl Market Dev)

Subsidiaries:

Chobani Australia Pty Ltd (1)
453-455 Hammond Road, Dandenong South, 3164, VIC, Australia
Tel.: (61) 3 9706 4707
Web Site: http://www.chobani.com.au
Yogurt Mfr & Marketer
N.A.I.C.S.: 424430
Damian Young (Gen Mgr-Mktg)
Peter Morgan (Gen Mgr-Ops)
Peter Meek (Mng Dir)
Lyn Radford (Gen Mgr-Sls & Category Mgmt)
Jonathan P. Payne (Gen Mgr-Fin)

CHOCOLATE CANDY CREATIONS INC.
130 Shore Rd Ste 238, Port Washington, NY 11050
Tel.: (516) 238-5535   DE
Web Site:
http://www.smilesonchocolate.com
Year Founded: 2006
Sales Range: Less than $1 Million
Promotional Chocolate, Candy, Cookie & Cake Products Mfr & Sales
N.A.I.C.S.: 311351
Alyssa Cohen (Pres, CEO, CFO, Chief Acctg Officer & Sec)

CHOCOLATE SOUP INC.
5855 Raytown Rd, Raytown, MO 64133-3319

Chocolate Soup Inc.—(Continued)
Tel.: (816) 525-2222
Rev.: $10,593,861
Emp.: 118
Mfr & Retailer of Girls', Children's & Infants' Clothing
N.A.I.C.S.: 315250
James Levitt *(Pres)*
Bob Bazan *(CFO)*

CHOCOLATES A LA CARTE, INC.
24836 Ave Rockeseller, City of Industry, CA 91355
Tel.: (661) 257-3700
Web Site: http://www.chocolates-ala-carte.com
Sales Range: $10-24.9 Million
Emp.: 170
Custom-Designed Chocolates for the Foodservice Industry Mfr & Sales
N.A.I.C.S.: 311352
Steve Arnold *(VP-Sls)*

CHOCTAW ELECTRIC COOP-ERATIVE, INC.
PO Box 758 Hwy 93 N, Hugo, OK 74743-0758
Tel.: (580) 326-6486   OK
Web Site: http://www.choctawelectric.com
Year Founded: 1940
Sales Range: $25-49.9 Million
Emp.: 65
Provider of Electricity Services
N.A.I.C.S.: 221122
Jimmie K. Ainsworth *(Dir-Acctg & Fin)*
Guy Dale *(Dir-Safety & Loss Control)*

CHOCTAWHATCHEE ELEC-TRIC COOPERATIVE INC.
1350 W Baldwin Ave, Defuniak Springs, FL 32435
Tel.: (850) 892-2111
Web Site: http://www.chelco.com
Year Founded: 1941
Sales Range: $25-49.9 Million
Emp.: 120
Electronic Services
N.A.I.C.S.: 221122
Ronald C. Jones *(Co-Pres)*
Wayne Thompson *(CFO)*
Donny Fugate *(VP-Ops)*
Gerald Edmondson *(Co-Pres)*
Kathy Morrow *(Dir-Comm)*
Bert Prutzman *(Treas & Sec)*
Brady Bearden *(Treas & Asst Sec)*
Steve Rhodes *(CEO)*

Subsidiaries:

CHELCO Services, Inc.   (1)
1350 W Baldwin Ave, Defuniak Springs, FL 32435
Tel.: (850) 951-0070
Web Site: http://www.chelco.com
Sales Range: $1-9.9 Million
Emp.: 18
Cable Laying Contractor & Software Developer
N.A.I.C.S.: 237110
J. E. Smith *(Pres)*

CHOICE CANNING CO., INC.
15 Exchange Place Ste 520, Jersey City, NJ 07302
Tel.: (732) 661-6400
Web Site: http://www.choicegroup.com
Sales Range: $25-49.9 Million
Emp.: 45
Distr of Frozen, Ready-to-Cook & Eat Shrimp
N.A.I.C.S.: 424460
Jose Thomas *(Pres)*
Alok Modani *(VP-Acctg & Fin)*

CHOICE FOOD GROUP, INC.
618 Church St Ste 220, Nashville, TN 37219
Tel.: (615) 248-9255   TN
Web Site: https://www.choicefood.com
Year Founded: 2004
Holding Company; Food Mfr & Distr; Food & Party Supplies Retailer
N.A.I.C.S.: 551112
Michael D. Shmerling *(Chm)*

Subsidiaries:

Choice Food of America, LLC   (1)
6167 Cockrill Bend Cir, Nashville, TN 37209
Tel.: (615) 620-2149
Web Site: http://www.choicefoodofamerica.com
Prepared Sauces Mfr
N.A.I.C.S.: 311941
Mark Johnson *(CFO)*

CHOICE FOODSERVICES, INC.
2000 Crow Canyon Pl Ste 130, San Ramon, CA 94583
Tel.: (925) 837-0104
Web Site: http://www.choicelunch.com
Year Founded: 2003
Rev.: $3,900,000
Emp.: 100
General Line Grocery Merchant Whslr
N.A.I.C.S.: 424410
Justin Gagnon *(CEO)*

CHOICE FOUNDATION
1010 Common St Ste 2950, New Orleans, LA 70112
Tel.: (504) 861-8370   LA
Web Site: http://www.choicefoundation.org
Year Founded: 2004
Sales Range: $10-24.9 Million
Emp.: 185
Educational Support Services
N.A.I.C.S.: 611710
Hans Jonassen *(Treas)*
James Swanson *(Pres)*

CHOICE HOME WARRANTY
1090 King Georges Post Rd, Edison, NJ 08837
Tel.: (732) 486-3188
Web Site: http://www.choicehomewarranty.com
Year Founded: 2005
Sales Range: $25-49.9 Million
Emp.: 60
Home Warranty Services
N.A.I.C.S.: 524126
Troy McDermott *(Supvr)*
Charlie Dillon *(VP)*

CHOICE LOGISTICS INC.
1 Whitehall City, New York, NY 10001
Tel.: (212) 370-1999
Web Site: http://www.choicelogistics.com
Sales Range: $125-149.9 Million
Emp.: 200
Courier Or Messenger Service
N.A.I.C.S.: 561499
Ed Katz *(Founder)*
Michael Katz *(Exec Chm)*
Gary Weiss *(Exec VP-Global Ops)*
Anne Yarmark *(Exec VP-HR & Admin)*
James Adams *(COO)*
Matthew McKeever *(CEO)*
Jordan Kaufman *(CIO)*
Robb Porter *(Chief Customer Officer & Exec VP)*
Patrick White *(Sr VP-Client Svcs-Americas)*

CHOICE MINISTRIES INC.
515 Garson Dr NE, Atlanta, GA 30324
Tel.: (404) 816-0483   GA
Year Founded: 1985
Sales Range: $10-24.9 Million
Emp.: 40
Christian Ministry Services
N.A.I.C.S.: 813110
Lori Mallard *(CFO)*

CHOICE SOLUTIONS LLC
7015 College Blvd Ste 300, Overland Park, KS 66211
Tel.: (913) 338-4950
Web Site: http://www.choicesolutions.com
Year Founded: 1998
Emp.: 40
Computer Applications/Data Integrated Systems Design
N.A.I.C.S.: 541512
Jim Steinlage *(Pres & CEO)*
Robin Rottinghaus *(Dir-Mktg)*

CHOICE USA BEVERAGE INC.
603 Groves St, Lowell, NC 28098
Tel.: (704) 823-1651
Web Site: http://www.choiceusavending.com
Rev.: $16,800,000
Emp.: 75
Carbonated Beverages, Nonalcoholic; Packaged in Cans, Bottles
N.A.I.C.S.: 312111
Benny Franklin *(Acct Mgr-Key)*
Evelyn Moore *(Mgr-HR)*
Jeannie Gilliam *(Mgr-Acctg)*
Ty Withers *(Gen Mgr)*

CHOICELUNCH
2000 Crow Canyon Place #130, San Ramon, CA 94583
Tel.: (925) 837-0104
Web Site: http://www.choicelunch.com
Year Founded: 1992
Sales Range: $1-9.9 Million
Emp.: 100
Distr of Healthy, Sustainable School Lunches
N.A.I.C.S.: 624210
Justin Gagnon *(CEO & Co-Founder)*
Keith Cosbey *(VP-Sls & Co-Founder)*
Ryan Mariotti *(COO & Co-Founder)*

CHONG HING GOLDSMITH CORP.
956 N Hill St, Los Angeles, CA 90012
Tel.: (213) 680-4799
Web Site: http://www.chonghing.com
Rev.: $15,000,000
Emp.: 12
Jewelry Stores
N.A.I.C.S.: 458310
Ronald Lee *(Pres)*

CHOO CHOO PARTNERS L.P.
1400 Market St, Chattanooga, TN 37402
Tel.: (423) 266-5000
Web Site: http://www.choochoo.com
Year Founded: 1989
Sales Range: $125-149.9 Million
Emp.: 350
Holding Company; Hotel & Resort Owner & Operator
N.A.I.C.S.: 551112
Jim Bambrey *(Gen Mgr)*
Adam Kinsey *(Gen Mgr)*

Subsidiaries:

Chattanooga Choo-Choo Holiday Inn   (1)
1400 Market St, Chattanooga, TN 37408
Tel.: (423) 266-5000

Web Site: http://www.choochoo.com
Sales Range: $25-49.9 Million
Hotel Operator
N.A.I.C.S.: 721110

CHOPTANK COMMUNITY HEALTH SYSTEM, INC.
301 Randolph St, Denton, MD 21629
Tel.: (410) 479-4306   MD
Web Site: https://www.choptankhealth.org
Year Founded: 1978
Sales Range: $10-24.9 Million
Emp.: 180
Community Health Care Services
N.A.I.C.S.: 621498
Kimberly Love *(Fin Dir)*
Anthony Pucci *(Dir-IT)*

CHOPTANK ELECTRIC COOP-ERATIVE, INC.
24820 Meeting House Rd, Denton, MD 21629
Tel.: (410) 479-0380
Web Site: http://www.choptankelectric.com
Rev.: $146,083,381
Assets: $412,716,529
Liabilities: $256,790,211
Net Worth: $155,926,318
Earnings: $13,988,012
Emp.: 158
Fiscal Year-end: 12/31/18
Distribution, Electric Power
N.A.I.C.S.: 221122
Jeffrey D. Rathell *(Chm)*
Douglas D. Scott *(Treas & Sec)*
John J. Burke Jr. *(Vice Chm)*

CHOR YOUTH AND FAMILY SERVICES, INC.
1010 Centre Ave, Reading, PA 19601
Tel.: (610) 478-8266   PA
Web Site: http://www.childrenshomeofrdg.org
Year Founded: 1997
Sales Range: $10-24.9 Million
Emp.: 250
Child & Family Care Services
N.A.I.C.S.: 624190
Vincent J. LaSorsa *(Pres & CEO)*
Jonathan H. Kurland *(Asst Sec)*
Douglas F. Smith *(Vice Chm)*

CHORDOMA FOUNDATION
PO Box 2127, Durham, NC 27702
Tel.: (919) 809-6779   NC
Year Founded: 2007
Sales Range: $1-9.9 Million
Emp.: 7
Disease Research Services
N.A.I.C.S.: 813212
Josh Sommer *(Pres)*
Heather Lee *(Chm)*
John Therien *(Sec)*

CHORUS CALL, INC.
2420 Mosside Blvd, Monroeville, PA 15146
Tel.: (412) 373-6964
Web Site: https://www.choruscall.com
Audio Conferencing, Video Conferencing, Audio & Video Media Streaming & Collaboration Tool Solutions
N.A.I.C.S.: 517810
Giorgio Coraluppi *(Pres & CEO)*

Subsidiaries:

Chorus Call (Pty) Ltd.   (1)
Daisy Street Office Park 135 Daisy Street, Sandton, 2146, South Africa
Tel.: (27) 11 305 2000
Web Site: http://www.choruscall.com
Emp.: 11
Audio Conferencing, Video Conferencing, Audio & Video Media Streaming & Collaboration Tool Solutions

N.A.I.C.S.: 517810
Ari Meyerthal *(Mng Dir)*

Chorus Call Australia Pty Ltd. **(1)**
Level 2 346 Turbot Street, Brisbane, 4000, QLD, Australia
Tel.: (61) 7 3036 8188
Audio Conferencing, Video Conferencing, Audio & Video Media Streaming & Collaboration Tool Solutions
N.A.I.C.S.: 517810

Chorus Call Canada Corp. **(1)**
Royal Centre Suite 2020, 1055 W Georgia Street, Vancouver, V6E 3R5, BC, Canada
Tel.: (604) 638-5300
Web Site: http://www.choruscallcanada.ca
Audio Conferencing, Video Conferencing, Audio & Video Media Streaming & Collaboration Tool Solutions
N.A.I.C.S.: 517810

Chorus Call Conferencing Services India Private Ltd. **(1)**
302/303 Trade Centre opp MTNL Telephone Exchange Bandra Kurla Complex, Bandra East, Mumbai, 400 051, Maharashtra, India
Tel.: (91) 22 33065 1111
Web Site: http://www.choruscall.com
Audio Conferencing, Video Conferencing, Audio & Video Media Streaming & Collaboration Tool Solutions
N.A.I.C.S.: 517810

Branch (Domestic):

Chorus Call Conferencing Services India Private Ltd. **(2)**
405 4th Floor Time Tower MG Road, Gurgaon, 122 002, Haryana, India
Tel.: (91) 124 4994545
Web Site: http://www.choruscall.com
Audio & Video Conferencing, Audio & Video Media Streaming & Collaboration Tool Solutions
N.A.I.C.S.: 517810

Chorus Call Germany GmbH **(1)**
Bockenheimer Landstrasse 20, Frankfurt am Main, 60323, Germany
Tel.: (49) 69 710 488 800
Web Site: http://www.choruscall.com
Emp.: 5
Audio Conferencing, Video Conferencing, Audio & Video Media Streaming & Collaboration Tool Solutions
N.A.I.C.S.: 517810
Michael Merz *(Gen Mgr)*

Chorus Call Hellas A.E. **(1)**
Imittou 7 & Pentelis Streets, P Faliro, Athens, 17564, Greece
Tel.: (30) 2109427300
Web Site: http://www.choruscall.com
Emp.: 12
Audio Conferencing, Video Conferencing, Audio & Video Media Streaming & Collaboration Tool Solutions
N.A.I.C.S.: 517810
Themistocles Kardambikes *(Gen Mgr)*

Chorus Call Italia s.r.l. **(1)**
Via San Clemente 1, Milan, 20122, Italy
Tel.: (39) 02 806 1371
Web Site: http://www.choruscallitalia.it
Emp.: 10
Audio Conferencing, Video Conferencing, Audio & Video Media Streaming & Collaboration Tool Solutions
N.A.I.C.S.: 517810

Chorus Call SA **(1)**
via al Mulino 22a, Cadempino, 6814, Switzerland
Tel.: (41) 91 612 4300
Web Site: http://www.choruscall.com
Emp.: 15
Audio Conferencing, Video Conferencing, Audio & Video Media Streaming & Collaboration Tool Solutions
N.A.I.C.S.: 517810
Carmen Vece Sanchez *(Gen Mgr)*

Conference Call do Brasil **(1)**
Sala 3201 Alameda Tocantins 125, Alphaville Barueri, Sao Paulo, 06455-020, Brazil
Tel.: (55) 11 4688 6200
Web Site: http://www.choruscall.com.br
Emp.: 22

Audio Conferencing, Video Conferencing, Audio & Video Media Streaming & Collaboration Tool Solutions
N.A.I.C.S.: 517810
Mauricio Tashiro *(Controller)*
Marco Casini *(Dir-Ops & Sls)*

Incomm Solutions, Inc. **(1)**
208 Harristown Rd Ste 101, Glen Rock, NJ 07452
Tel.: (201) 612-9696
Web Site:
http://www.incommconferencing.com
Sales Range: $1-9.9 Million
Emp.: 50
Conferencing Solutions
N.A.I.C.S.: 517810

CHORUS COMMUNICATIONS, INC.
210 Church St Unit D, Philadelphia, PA 19106
Tel.: (215) 922-1862
Web Site:
http://www.choruscommunications.com
Year Founded: 1995
Sales Range: $1-9.9 Million
Emp.: 10
Telecommunication Consulting & Networking Solutions
N.A.I.C.S.: 541690
Dan Cronin *(Pres)*
Robert Molinaro *(VP)*
Buffy Harakidas *(Dir-Mktg)*
Amy Servis *(Mgr-Channel)*

CHORUS GIRL INC.
1407 Broadway 1611, New York, NY 11101
Tel.: (212) 764-0576
Sales Range: $10-24.9 Million
Emp.: 8
Womens Clothing
N.A.I.C.S.: 424350
Roger Batra *(Pres)*
Nina Batra *(VP)*
Lance Joseph *(CFO)*

CHR CORP.
2295 Susquehanna Trl Ste C, York, PA 17404
Tel.: (717) 848-9827 **PA**
Web Site: http://www.rutters.com
Year Founded: 1921
Sales Range: $75-99.9 Million
Emp.: 750
Operator of Convenience Stores
N.A.I.C.S.: 445131
Scott Hartman *(Pres & CEO)*
Gabe Olives *(Dir-Fuels)*
Jerry Weiner *(VP-Food Svc)*
Suzanne Cramer *(VP-HR)*

CHR GROUP LLC
333 7th Ave 6th Fl, New York, NY 10001
Tel.: (212) 863-4196 **DE**
Web Site:
http://www.thechrgroup.com
Year Founded: 2012
Holding Company; Marketing Services
N.A.I.C.S.: 551112
Peter Clark *(CEO)*
Jonathan Zaback *(Partner & Chief Strategy Officer)*
Edmond Huot *(Partner & Exec Creative Dir)*

Subsidiaries:

Clark Huot LLC **(1)**
333 7th Ave 6th Fl, New York, NY 10001
Tel.: (212) 564-8716
Web Site: http://www.clarkhuot.com
Advetising Agency
N.A.I.C.S.: 541810
Peter Clark *(CEO)*

JVST, Inc. **(1)**
25 Stillman St Ste 200, San Francisco, CA 94107
Tel.: (415) 358-1900
Web Site: http://www.jvst.us
Sales Range: $1-9.9 Million
Emp.: 15
Digital Advertising & Design Agency
N.A.I.C.S.: 541810
James Song *(Co-Founder & Executive Dir-Creative)*
Roderick van Gelder *(Co-Founder & Exec Producer)*

Raker Goldstein & Co., Inc. **(1)**
333 Seventh Ave 6th Fl, New York, NY 10001
Tel.: (212) 863-4198
Web Site: http://www.rakergoldstein.com
Sales Range: Less than $1 Million
Emp.: 6
Public Relations Agency
N.A.I.C.S.: 541820
Heidi Raker Goldstein *(Founder & Principal)*
Stuart Goldstein *(Principal & Dir-Fin Svcs & Sports Mktg)*

Stan Adler Associates, Inc. **(1)**
333 7th Ave Fl 6, New York, NY 10001
Tel.: (212) 863-4100
Web Site: http://www.stanadler.com
Emp.: 45
Graphic Design Services
N.A.I.C.S.: 541430
Stan Adler *(Chm & Dir-Creative)*
Diego Casco *(Mng Dir-Toronto)*
Adrienne Metzinger *(Dir-Design)*
Joella Autorino *(Dir-Acct & New Media)*
Maura Ryan *(Dir-Bus Dev)*
Jim Barattolo *(Mgr-Production Design)*
Claudia L. Meyers *(Mgr-Pre-Press Dept)*
Laura Samet *(Mgr-Print Production)*

Studio One Networks Inc. **(1)**
333 Seventh Ave 6th Fl, New York, NY 10001
Tel.: (212) 863-4194
Web Site: http://www.studioone.com
Digital Advertising Content Syndication Services
N.A.I.C.S.: 541830

Zlokower Company LLC **(1)**
575 8th Ave Fl 11, New York, NY 10018
Tel.: (212) 863-4120
Web Site: http://www.zlokower.com
Advetising Agency
N.A.I.C.S.: 541810
Harry Zlokower *(Pres)*
Gail Horowitz *(Sr VP)*
Dave Closs *(VP)*

CHR SOLUTIONS, INC.
1515 N Sanborn Blvd, Mitchell, SD 57301-1021
Tel.: (605) 996-9646 **SD**
Web Site:
http://www.chrsolutions.com
Year Founded: 1971
Sales Range: $25-49.9 Million
Emp.: 250
Computer Integrated Systems Design
N.A.I.C.S.: 541512
Arun Pasrija *(Pres & CEO)*
Don Benson *(Chm)*

Subsidiaries:

CHR Solutions Inc. - Dallas **(1)**
2711 Lbj Fwy, Dallas, TX 75234
Tel.: (972) 484-2323
Sales Range: $1-9.9 Million
Emp.: 50
Computer Integrated Systems Design
N.A.I.C.S.: 541512
Moss Adams *(Mgr-Fin Svc)*

CHR Solutions, Inc. - Houston **(1)**
4424 W Sam Houston Pkwy N Ste 420, Houston, TX 77041
Tel.: (713) 995-4778
Web Site: http://www.chrsolutions.com
Sales Range: $25-49.9 Million
Emp.: 25
Computer Integrated Systems Design
N.A.I.C.S.: 541512
Gary Knee *(Head-Software Solutions Bus Unit)*

Don Benson *(Chm)*
Bill Gerski *(VP-Bus Dev & Engrg Svcs)*
Mike Beecher *(Exec VP-Engrg Svcs)*

CHR Solutions, Inc. - Lubbock **(1)**
4747 S Loop 289, Lubbock, TX 79424
Tel.: (806) 722-7700
Emp.: 50
Computer Integrated Systems Design
N.A.I.C.S.: 541512
Arun Pasrija *(CEO)*

CHRIS ALBRITTON CONSTRUCTION COMPANY, INC.
2100 Bush Dairy Rd, Laurel, MS 39443
Tel.: (601) 425-9100
Year Founded: 1982
Sales Range: $25-49.9 Million
Emp.: 50
Nonresidential Construction Services
N.A.I.C.S.: 236220
Chris Albritton *(Pres)*
Debbie English *(Office Mgr)*

CHRIS AUFFENBERG FORD INC.
5840 Hwy 100, Washington, MO 63090-4950
Tel.: (636) 239-4500
Web Site:
http://www.auffenbergwashington.net
Sales Range: $10-24.9 Million
Emp.: 60
Retailer of New & Used Cars
N.A.I.C.S.: 441110
Maurice Brinker *(Mgr-Parts)*
Dennis Norton *(Bus Mgr)*
Gus Beffa *(Gen Mgr)*
Ted Stahl *(Gen Mgr-Sls)*
Darrell Brinker *(Mgr-Svc)*
Walter Conner *(Mgr-Body Shop)*

Subsidiaries:

Auffenberg of Carbondale **(1)**
1015 E Walnut, Carbondale, IL 62901
Tel.: (618) 457-3391
Web Site:
http://www.auffenbergcarbondale.net
Automobiles, New & Used
N.A.I.C.S.: 441110

CHRIS CAM CORPORATION
808 W Cherokee St, Sioux Falls, SD 57104-0341
Tel.: (605) 336-1190 **SD**
Web Site: http://www.heartland-paper.com
Year Founded: 1950
Sales Range: $25-49.9 Million
Emp.: 90
Provider of Industrial & Personal Service Paper
N.A.I.C.S.: 424130
Dempster Christenson *(VP)*
Sandra Christenson *(Pres)*

CHRIS LEITH CHEVROLET, INC.
10956 Star Rd, Wake Forest, NC 27587-7772
Tel.: (919) 556-3137
Sales Range: $25-49.9 Million
Emp.: 110
Car Whslr
N.A.I.C.S.: 441110
Linda J. Leith *(Sec)*
Johnny Dudley *(Mgr-Ops)*

CHRIS NIKEL'S AUTOHAUS INC.
2920 N Aspen Ave, Broken Arrow, OK 74012-1187
Tel.: (918) 355-5000
Web Site: http://www.chrisnikel.com
Sales Range: $50-74.9 Million
Emp.: 165
Automobiles, New & Used

Chris Nikel's Autohaus Inc.—(Continued)
N.A.I.C.S.: 441110
Chris Nikel *(Pres)*

CHRIS POSEY, INC.
2516 Hwy 15 N, Laurel, MS 39362
Tel.: (601) 649-4800
Web Site: http://www.chrisposey.com
Sales Range: $10-24.9 Million
Emp.: 46
Car Whslr
N.A.I.C.S.: 441110
Chris Posey Jr. *(Mgr)*

CHRIS-CRAFT CORPORATION
8161 15th St E, Sarasota, FL 34243
Tel.: (941) 351-4900
Web Site: http://www.chriscraft.com
Year Founded: 1861
Runabouts, Fish Boats, Cruisers &
Fiberglass Sportboats Mfr
N.A.I.C.S.: 336612
Stephen Heese *(Pres & CEO)*
Mark Poncin *(CFO)*
Steve Callahan *(VP-Materials)*
Chris Collier *(VP-Engrg)*
Matt McGinnis *(VP-Mfg)*
Gavan Hunt *(VP-Sls)*
Ron Berman *(VP-Engrg)*
Allison Scharnow *(Dir-Mktg)*
Kathy Alder *(Dir-HR)*

CHRIS-MORE INCORPORATED
1324 Springbrook Ave, Memphis, TN
38116
Tel.: (901) 332-8120
Web Site: http://www.chris-
moreincorporated.com
Sales Range: $10-24.9 Million
Emp.: 55
Plumbing Fittings & Supplies
N.A.I.C.S.: 423720
Bobby Christensen *(Gen Mgr)*

CHRIST COMMUNITY HEALTH SERVICES
2595 Central Ave, Memphis, TN
38104
Tel.: (901) 842-3160   TN
Web Site:
https://www.christcommunity.org
Year Founded: 1994
Sales Range: $25-49.9 Million
Emp.: 403
Community Health Care Services
N.A.I.C.S.: 621498
Lance Luttrell *(COO)*
Shantelle Leatherwood *(CEO)*
Bonnie Hollabaugh *(Dir-Dev)*
David Pepperman *(Co-Founder)*
Marcus Lewis *(Treas)*
Joseph Aldridge *(Sec)*
Rick Donlon *(Co-Founder)*
Ross Dyer *(Chm)*
Paul Makris *(CFO)*
Laura A. Schwent Shultz *(Chief Be-
havioral Health Officer)*
Jim Shultz *(Chief Spiritual Health
Officer)*

CHRIST'S HOUSEHOLD OF FAITH
355 Marshall Ave, Saint Paul, MN
55102
Tel.: (651) 265-3400
Year Founded: 1972
Sales Range: $10-24.9 Million
Emp.: 30
Religious Organizations
N.A.I.C.S.: 813110
Donald Alsbury *(Pres)*
James Sarbacker *(Dir-Athletic)*

Subsidiaries:

North Star Surfaces, LLC   **(1)**

23 Empire Dr, Saint Paul, MN 55103
Tel.: (651) 602-3200
Web Site: http://www.nssurfaces.com
Sales Range: $1-9.9 Million
Emp.: 25
Interior-Surfacing Materials Distr
N.A.I.C.S.: 423390
Charles Geerdes *(Pres)*

CHRISTA CONSTRUCTION LLC
119 Victor Heights Pkwy, Victor, NY
14607
Tel.: (585) 924-3050   NY
Web Site: http://www.christa.com
Year Founded: 1976
Sales Range: $10-24.9 Million
Emp.: 60
Nonresidential Construction
N.A.I.C.S.: 236220
David F. Christa *(CEO)*

CHRISTENSEN BROTHERS INC.
39 N Main St, Richfield, UT 84701
Tel.: (435) 896-6466
Sales Range: $10-24.9 Million
Emp.: 90
Department Stores, Non-Discount
N.A.I.C.S.: 455110
H. Clark Christensen *(Pres)*
David Christensen *(VP)*
Allen Christensen *(Controller)*

CHRISTENSEN FARMS MID-WEST, LLC
23971 County Rd 10, Sleepy Eye,
MN 56085
Tel.: (507) 794-5310
Web Site:
https://www.christensenfarms.com
Year Founded: 1980
Sales Range: $10-24.9 Million
Emp.: 1,000
Hog Production
N.A.I.C.S.: 112210
Dave Rosenhamer *(VP-Supply Chain
& Environmental Compliance)*
Glenn Stolt *(CEO)*

Subsidiaries:

Exetare Partnership, L.L.P.   **(1)**
1013 10th St, Clarkfield, MN 56223
Tel.: (320) 669-3300
Sales Range: $1-9.9 Million
Emp.: 30
Animal Production
N.A.I.C.S.: 112990
Ken Berg *(Principal)*

CHRISTENSEN INC.
501 E Wine Country Rd, Grandview,
WA 98930-1091
Tel.: (509) 882-2115   WA
Web Site: http://www.repowell.net
Year Founded: 1980
Sales Range: $10-24.9 Million
Emp.: 100
Provider of Petroleum & Trucking
Services
N.A.I.C.S.: 424710
Gary B. Christensen *(Chm, Pres &
CEO)*
Todd Hurlburt *(Controller)*
Tony Christensen *(Pres & CEO)*

Subsidiaries:

Yorkston Oil Co.   **(1)**
2801 Roeder Ave, Bellingham, WA 98225-
2053
Tel.: (360) 734-2201
Web Site: http://www.yorkstonoil.com
Provider of Petroleum Services
N.A.I.C.S.: 424720
David Yorkston *(CFO)*
Bernard Yorkston Jr. *(Pres)*

CHRISTENSEN SHIPYARDS LTD.
4400 SE Columbia Way, Vancouver,
WA 98661
Tel.: (360) 831-9800
Web Site:
https://www.christensenyachts.com
Rev.: $35,200,000
Emp.: 380
Boat Building
N.A.I.C.S.: 336612
Chris Farley *(Dir-Pur)*
Dean C. Anderson *(Treas)*
Brian Harris *(Dir-Personnel)*
Mike Magee *(Dir-Quality Control)*
Khiem Nguyen *(Dir-Engrg Staff)*
Patricia Withee *(Sec)*
David Christensen *(Chm)*
Joe Foggia *(Pres)*

CHRISTENSON ELECTRIC, INC.
17201 NE Sacramento St, Portland,
OR 97230
Tel.: (503) 419-3300   OR
Web Site:
https://www.christenson.com
Year Founded: 1945
Sales Range: $200-249.9 Million
Emp.: 400
Electrical Contracting Services
N.A.I.C.S.: 238210
Chris Kosmas *(Acct Mgr)*
Michele Bocchetti *(Mgr-Project Sup-
port)*
Joanne Gaspari *(Mgr-HR)*

Subsidiaries:

Entrance Controls Integrated
Security   **(1)**
1923 E 5th St Ste D, Vancouver, WA 98661
Tel.: (360) 256-4416
Web Site: http://www.ec-is.com
Security System Services
N.A.I.C.S.: 561621
Kurt Braun *(Mgr-Div)*

CHRISTENSON, BARCLAY & SHAW, INC.
10500 Barkley St Ste 101, Overland
Park, KS 66212-1838
Tel.: (913) 327-0030   KS
Year Founded: 1954
Rev.: $22,000,000
Emp.: 25
Fiscal Year-end: 12/31/00
N.A.I.C.S.: 541810
Jan Christenson *(Pres)*
Sherry Branan *(VP-Ops & Acct
Supvr)*
Lori Hanson *(VP & Mgr-Mktg)*

CHRISTIAN AID MINISTRIES
PO Box 360, Berlin, OH 44610
Tel.: (330) 893-2428   OH
Web Site:
http://www.christianaidministries.org
Year Founded: 1981
Rev.: $144,111,107
Assets: $78,302,759
Liabilities: $1,802,029
Net Worth: $76,500,730
Earnings: $9,089,972
Emp.: 139
Fiscal Year-end: 12/31/18
Christian Ministry Services
N.A.I.C.S.: 813110
Nolan W. Byler *(Vice Chm)*
Thomas Wagler *(Chm)*
Scott Hoover *(Officer-Fin)*

CHRISTIAN AND MISSIONARY ALLIANCE FOUNDATION, INC.
8595 Explorer Dr, Colorado Springs,
CO 80920
Tel.: (719) 599-9999

Web Site: https://www.cmalliance.org
Religious Organizations
N.A.I.C.S.: 813110
Gary Benedict *(Pres)*

Subsidiaries:

Shell Point Retirement
Community   **(1)**
15000 Shell Point Blvd Ste 100, Fort Myers,
FL 33908
Tel.: (239) 466-1131
Web Site: http://www.shellpoint.org
Sales Range: $25-49.9 Million
Emp.: 960
Continuing Care Retirement Community
N.A.I.C.S.: 623311
Tim Lochridge *(CFO)*
Laura Slack *(Dir-Resident Life)*

CHRISTIAN BROTHERS AUTO-MOTIVE CORPORATION
15995 N Barkers Landing Rd Ste
145, Houston, TX 77079-2400
Tel.: (281) 870-8900   TX
Web Site: http://www.cbac.com
Year Founded: 1982
Sales Range: $10-24.9 Million
Emp.: 41
Automotive Repair Services
N.A.I.C.S.: 811111
Mark Carr *(Founder)*
Donnie Carr *(Pres)*
John Foster *(Interim CFO)*
Janis Jarosz *(VP-Mktg)*
David Domine *(VP-Tech Solutions)*
Brad Fink *(VP-Leadership Dev)*
Zack Bynum *(VP-Neighborly)*
Michael Allnutt *(VP-Ops)*
James Stuard *(Controller)*
Sheila Powell *(Controller-Franchise
Acctg)*

CHRISTIAN CARE COMMUNI-TIES
12710 Townepark Way Ste 1000,
Louisville, KY 40243
Tel.: (502) 254-4200   KY
Web Site:
http://www.christiancares.org
Year Founded: 1884
Sales Range: $25-49.9 Million
Emp.: 724
Community Care Services
N.A.I.C.S.: 813910
Keith Knapp *(Pres & CEO)*
Sue Napper *(Sec)*
Phil Steenbergen *(Treas)*
Marie Smart *(Chm)*

CHRISTIAN CARE COMPA-NIES, INC.
2002 W Sunnyside Dr, Phoenix, AZ
85029
Tel.: (602) 943-1800
Web Site:
http://www.christiancare.org
Sales Range: $10-24.9 Million
Emp.: 250
Senior Living & Health Care Ministry
N.A.I.C.S.: 531110
Kathleen Condon *(CFO)*
Alan Hieb *(CEO)*

CHRISTIAN COMMUNITY CREDIT UNION
255 N Lone Hill Ave, San Dimas, CA
91773
Tel.: (800) 347-2228   CA
Web Site: http://www.myccu.com
Year Founded: 1957
Sales Range: $25-49.9 Million
Emp.: 136
Credit Union
N.A.I.C.S.: 522130
Stan Wahl *(CFO & Sr VP)*
David South *(Sr VP-HR)*
Marji Hughes *(COO & Exec VP)*

Dennis E. Endert *(Sec)*
Blair Korschun *(CEO)*
Dale Torry *(Chm)*
Aaron Caid *(CMO)*
Mike Poirier *(Sr VP-Ministry Lending)*

CHRISTIAN COMMUNITY DEVELOPMENT CORPORATION
4515 Poplar Ave Ste 324, Memphis, TN 38117
Tel.: (901) 682-6201   TN
Year Founded: 1999
Sales Range: $10-24.9 Million
Religious Organizations
N.A.I.C.S.: 813110
Mike Harris *(Pres)*
Shana South *(CFO)*

CHRISTIAN COMMUNITY HEALTH CENTER
2320 Thornton-Lansing Rd, Lansing, IL 60438
Tel.: (773) 233-4100   IL
Web Site: http://www.cchc-online.org
Year Founded: 1991
Sales Range: $10-24.9 Million
Emp.: 264
Health Care Srvices
N.A.I.C.S.: 622110
Deborah H. Johnson *(Dir-Quality Assurance & Corp Compliance)*
Kenneth Burnett *(CEO)*

CHRISTIAN EMERGENCY RELIEF TEAMS INTERNATIONAL
3211 Tabor Loop, Crossville, TN 38557
Tel.: (931) 707-9328   TN
Web Site: http://www.certinternational.org
Year Founded: 2001
Sales Range: $10-24.9 Million
Emp.: 6
Emergency Relief Services
N.A.I.C.S.: 624230
Jim Mersereau *(VP-Operations)*

CHRISTIAN FOUNDATION FOR CHILDREN AND AGING
1 Elmwood Ave, Kansas City, KS 66103
Tel.: (913) 384-6500   MO
Web Site: http://www.cfcausa.org
Year Founded: 1981
Sales Range: $100-124.9 Million
Emp.: 4,500
Grantmaking Services
N.A.I.C.S.: 813219
Paul Pearce *(Dir-Global Strategy)*
Dan Pearson *(Dir-Intl Programs)*
Martin Kraus *(Dir-Fin)*

CHRISTIAN HEALTH CARE CENTER
301 Sicomac Ave, Wyckoff, NJ 07481
Tel.: (201) 848-5200   NJ
Web Site: http://www.christianhealthcare.org
Year Founded: 1911
Sales Range: $50-74.9 Million
Emp.: 1,000
Community Health Care Services
N.A.I.C.S.: 621498
Gordon Stanley *(Chm-Foundation)*
R. Scott Sheldon *(Dir-Dev-Foundation)*
Stephen Dumke *(COO & Exec VP)*
David Visbeen *(Sec)*
Mark Reitsma *(Treas)*
Matthew D. Kuiken *(Asst Treas)*
Rick De Bel *(Vice Chm)*

CHRISTIAN HEALTHCARE MINISTRIES, INC.
127 Hazelwood Ave, Barberton, OH 44203-1316   OH
Web Site: https://www.chministries.org
Year Founded: 1981
Sales Range: $75-99.9 Million
Emp.: 82
Health Care Srvices
N.A.I.C.S.: 622110
Carity Beall *(CFO)*
James Detwiler *(Chm)*
Joseph C. Emert *(Sec)*

CHRISTIAN HORIZONS
200 N Postville Dr, Lincoln, IL 62656-1978
Tel.: (217) 732-9651   IL
Web Site: http://www.christianhomes.org
Year Founded: 1962
Elder Care Services
N.A.I.C.S.: 624120
Billy D. Carter *(Treas)*
Scott Williams *(Sec)*
Don Fitzgerald *(Vice Chm)*
Nicholas Filing *(Chm)*
Jake Bell *(CEO)*
Chuck Schmitz *(CFO)*
Ray Dickison *(COO)*
Jenelle Bertolino-Ishmael *(Chief Strategy Officer)*
Illa David *(CIO)*
Gordon D. Venturella *(Sr VP-Mktg & Dev)*
Keith H. Ray *(VP-Mission Integration)*
Connie Rhoads *(VP-Corporate Compliance)*

CHRISTIAN HOSPITAL FOUNDATION
Christian Hospital 11133 Dunn Rd, Saint Louis, MI 63136
Tel.: (314) 653-5000
Web Site: https://www.christianhospital.org
Year Founded: 1903
Health Care Srvices
N.A.I.C.S.: 621610

CHRISTIAN MEDICAL & DENTAL ASSOCIATIONS
2604 US Hwy 421, Bristol, TN 37620
Tel.: (423) 844-1000   IL
Web Site: http://www.cmda.org
Year Founded: 1946
Sales Range: $1-9.9 Million
Emp.: 80
Medical & Dental Care Services
N.A.I.C.S.: 621210
Gene Rudd *(Sr VP)*
Nathan Dale Willis *(Treas & Sec)*
Richard E. Johnson *(Pres)*
David L. Stevens *(CEO)*

CHRISTIAN OPPORTUNITY CENTER
1553 Broadway St, Pella, IA 50219
Tel.: (641) 628-1162   IA
Web Site: http://www.christianopportunity.org
Year Founded: 1969
Sales Range: $10-24.9 Million
Emp.: 559
Disability Assistance Services
N.A.I.C.S.: 623210
Bob Kroese *(VP)*
Mike Maakestad *(Sec)*
Ron Groenenboom *(Pres)*
Amy Zuck *(Dir-Pub Info)*
John Eilers *(Exec Dir)*

CHRISTIAN WHOLESALE DISTRIBUTORS, INC.
11048 Grissom Ln, Dallas, TX 75229
Tel.: (972) 241-0633
Web Site: https://www.ccwhole.com

Year Founded: 1975
Sales Range: $10-24.9 Million
Emp.: 66
Hardware Distr
N.A.I.C.S.: 423710
Jim Christian *(Pres)*
Bobby Ekes *(VP-Ops)*
Robin George *(VP-IT)*
Reese Little *(Mgr-Sls)*

CHRISTIANA CARE CORPORATION
501 W 14th St, Wilmington, DE 19801
Tel.: (302) 733-1000   DE
Web Site: http://www.christianacare.org
Sales Range: $1-9.9 Million
Emp.: 1,000
Operates Hospital & Health Care Services
N.A.I.C.S.: 622110
Michele A. Schiavoni *(Sr VP-External Affairs)*
Dana Hall *(Sr VP-HR)*

CHRISTIANA CARE HEALTH SYSTEM, INC.
501 W 14th St, Wilmington, DE 19801
Tel.: (302) 733-1000   DE
Web Site: https://www.christianacare.org
Year Founded: 1985
Health Care Srvices
N.A.I.C.S.: 622110
Janice E. Nevin *(Pres & CEO)*
Thomas L. Corrigan *(CFO & Sr VP-Fin)*
Randall Gaboriault *(CIO)*
Rosa M. Colon-Kolacko *(Sr VP & Exec Dir)*
Gary Ferguson *(COO & Exec VP)*
Sharon Anderson *(Sr VP-Quality, Patient Safety & Population Health Mgmt)*
Eric T. Johnson *(Vice Chm)*
Audrey C. Van Luven *(Chief HR Officer & Sr VP)*
Rich Szumel *(Pres)*

Subsidiaries:

Affinity Health Alliance, Inc.   (1)
106 Bow St, Elkton, MD 21921
Tel.: (410) 398-4000
Web Site: http://www.uhcc.com
Health Care Srvices
N.A.I.C.S.: 622110
Jose Ma *(VP-Medical Affairs)*
David Gipson *(COO & Sr VP)*
Caren Lewis *(Sr VP-Patient Care Svc)*
Laurie Beyer *(CFO & Sr VP)*
Jack Goldstein *(Chm)*
Kenneth S. Lewis *(Pres & CEO)*
Martin J. Healy *(Vice Chm)*
Richard Guttendorf *(Treas)*
Ronald Graybeal *(Sec)*

CHRISTIANITY TODAY INTERNATIONAL
465 Gundersen Dr, Carol Stream, IL 60188-2415
Tel.: (630) 260-6200   IL
Web Site: http://www.christianitytoday.org
Year Founded: 1955
Sales Range: $75-99.9 Million
Emp.: 110
Christian Magazines Publisher
N.A.I.C.S.: 513120
Eugene B. Habecker *(Chm)*
Billy Graham *(Founder)*
Theresa Hossner *(Sr VP)*
Timothy Dalrymple *(Pres & CEO)*
Edward Gilbreath *(VP-Strategic Partnerships)*

CHRISTIANSEN IMPLEMENT COMPANY, INC.
2986 S Frontage Rd, American Falls, ID 83211
Tel.: (208) 226-5001
Web Site: http://www.christiansenimpl.com
Rev.: $32,000,000
Emp.: 30
Farm Equipment & Supplies
N.A.I.C.S.: 459999
John Hoybjerg *(Owner)*

CHRISTMAS BY KREBS CORPORATION
3911 S Main St, Roswell, NM 88203
Tel.: (575) 624-2882
Web Site: http://www.christmasbykrebs.com
Rev.: $23,000,000
Emp.: 100
Christmas Ornaments Mfr
N.A.I.C.S.: 327215
Eberhard Krebs *(Pres)*

CHRISTMAS LIGHTS, ETC.
205 Curie Dr, Alpharetta, GA 30005
Tel.: (678) 341-1225
Web Site: https://www.christmaslightsetc.com
Year Founded: 2000
Sales Range: $1-9.9 Million
Emp.: 20
Holiday Lighting & Decorations for Homes, Commercial Decorators & Businesses
N.A.I.C.S.: 449129
Mike Streb *(Dir-Sls & Mktg)*
Bill Moch *(Mgr-Warehouse)*
Dustin Lambert *(Dir-Tech)*
Jeanette DiCamillo *(Mgr-Web Content)*
Jill Ekhlas *(Coord-Pur)*
Karen Ramminger *(Mgr-Ops)*

CHRISTMAS LUMBER COMPANY INC.
101 Roane St, Harriman, TN 37748
Tel.: (865) 882-2362
Web Site: https://www.christmaslumber.com
Sales Range: $10-24.9 Million
Emp.: 26
Lumber & Other Building Materials
N.A.I.C.S.: 423310
Tee Cleveland *(VP)*

CHRISTMAS TREE HILL INC.
2801 S George St, York, PA 17403
Tel.: (717) 741-2669
Web Site: https://www.christmastreehill.com
Rev.: $10,923,351
Emp.: 100
Gift Shop
N.A.I.C.S.: 459420
Carrie Mathiot *(Mgr)*

CHRISTOFFERSON COMMERCIAL BUILDERS
3235 Fillmore Ridge Hts, Colorado Springs, CO 80907
Tel.: (719) 548-0999
Web Site: https://ccbuildersinc.com
Sales Range: $10-24.9 Million
Emp.: 25
Provider of Commercial & Office Buildings, Renovation & Repair Services
N.A.I.C.S.: 236220
Curtis Christofferson *(Pres)*
Tim Pool *(VP)*
Dave Walton *(CFO)*

CHRISTOPHER B. BURKE ENGINEERING LTD.

Christopher B. Burke Engineering Ltd.—(Continued)

9575 W Higgins Rd Ste 600, Rosemont, IL 60018
Tel.: (847) 823-0500
Web Site: http://www.cbbel.com
Year Founded: 1986
Emp.: 230
Consulting, Engineering & Surveying Services
N.A.I.C.S.: 541330
Christopher B. Burke (Founder & Pres)
Jeff Ehrhart (Asst Head-Structural Engrg)

Subsidiaries:

Christopher B. Burke Engineering, LLC   (1)
115 W Washington St Ste 1368 South Tower, Indianapolis, IN 46204
Tel.: (317) 266-8000
Web Site: http://www.cbbel-in.com
Emp.: 35
Engineeering Services
N.A.I.C.S.: 541330
Jon Stolz (Mgr)
Zach Bishton (Mgr-Bus Ops)

CHRISTOPHER REEVE FOUNDATION

636 Morris Tpke Ste 3A, Short Hills, NJ 07078
Tel.: (973) 379-2690   NJ
Web Site:
  https://www.christopherreeve.org
Year Founded: 1988
Sales Range: $10-24.9 Million
Emp.: 47
Disease Research Fundraising Services
N.A.I.C.S.: 813212
Susan Howley (Exec VP-Res)
John M. Hughes (Chm)
Peter T. Wilderotter (Pres & CEO)
Jeffrey P. Cunard (Sec)
John E. McConnell (Vice Chm)
Matthew Reeve (Vice Chm-Intl Dev)
Maggie Goldberg (VP-Policy & Programs)
Rebecca Laming (VP-Mktg & Comm)
Michele Loiacono (VP-Ops)
Henry G. Stifel III (Vice Chm)
Frank P. Mascia III (VP-Dev)

CHRISTOPHER TOOL & MFG CO.

30500 Carter St, Solon, OH 44139
Tel.: (440) 248-8080
Web Site:
  https://www.christophertool.com
Year Founded: 1951
Sales Range: $10-24.9 Million
Emp.: 89
Metal Stamping Services
N.A.I.C.S.: 332119
Partrick Christopher (Pres)
Tom Sikler (Mgr-Quality)

CHRISTOPHER'S DODGE WORLD

16655 W Colfax Ave, Golden, CO 80401-3866
Tel.: (720) 923-8853
Web Site: https://www.cdodge.com
Year Founded: 1990
Sales Range: $50-74.9 Million
Emp.: 200
Car Whslr
N.A.I.C.S.: 441110
Christopher Hall (Co-Owner)

CHRISTOPHER, SMITH, LEONARD, BRISTOW & STANELL, P.A.

1001 3rd Ave W Ste 700, Bradenton, FL 34205

Tel.: (941) 748-1040   FL
Web Site: http://www.cslcpa.com
Year Founded: 1954
Sales Range: $1-9.9 Million
Emp.: 46
Accounting, Auditing & Bookkeeping
N.A.I.C.S.: 541211
Rick Smith (Principal)
Lisa Bristow (Principal)
Bob Stanell (Mng Principal)
Jay Clarkson (Principal)
Randy Dillingham (Principal)
Lisa Johnson (Principal)
Susan Thompson (Principal)
Aubrey Lynch (Principal)
Bob Christopher (Principal)
Jennifer Messal (Sr Mgr-Tax)
Jeff Gerhard (Principal)
Kenneth M. Johns III (Chm)

CHRISTOPHERSON HOMES INC.

1400 North Dulton Ste 14, Santa Rosa, CA 95403
Tel.: (707) 524-8222
Web Site:
  http://www.christophersonhome.com
Rev.: $93,106,327
Emp.: 20
Speculative Builder, Single-Family Houses
N.A.I.C.S.: 236115
Amy Bolten (Dir-Community Rels)

CHRISTOVICH & ASSOCIATES, LLC

112 Seagate Ave, Neptune Beach, FL 32266
Tel.: (407) 319-4653
Web Site:
  http://www.christovichandassociates.com
Sales Range: $1-9.9 Million
Golf Course Receivership & Foreclosure Management
N.A.I.C.S.: 561499
Greg Christovich (Pres & COO)
Tony Johnson (VP-Ops)
Lisa McDermott (Controller)

CHRISTUS HEALTH

Tel.: (469) 282-2000   TX
Web Site:
  http://www.christushealth.org
Year Founded: 1999
Hospital & Health Care Services
N.A.I.C.S.: 622110
Arthur M. Southam (Chm)
Dennis Box (Chm)

Subsidiaries:

CHRISTUS Lake Area Hospital   (1)
4200 Nelson Rd, Lake Charles, LA 70605
Tel.: (337) 474-6370
Web Site: http://www.christushealth.org
General Medical & Surgical Hospitals
N.A.I.C.S.: 622110
Bryan Bateman (CEO)

CHRISTWOOD

100 Christwood Blvd, Covington, LA 70433
Tel.: (985) 898-0515   LA
Year Founded: 1999
Sales Range: $10-24.9 Million
Emp.: 220
Continuing Care Retirement Community Operator
N.A.I.C.S.: 623311
Nancy Lee (VP)
Diane G. Winston (Sec)
James Dombrowski (Pres)
Leon S. Holzhalb III (Exec Dir)
William Mason III (Treas)

CHRISTY ENTERPRISES, INC.

655 E Ball Rd, Anaheim, CA 92805-3310
Tel.: (714) 507-3300
Web Site: https://www.tchristy.com
Year Founded: 1972
Sales Range: $10-24.9 Million
Emp.: 57
Farm Equipment Whslr
N.A.I.C.S.: 423820
Michael Snouse (VP-Sls)
Jon Christy (Pres)

CHRISTY REFRACTORIES COMPANY LLC

4641 McRee Ave, Saint Louis, MO 63110
Tel.: (314) 773-7500
Web Site: https://www.christyco.com
Sales Range: $10-24.9 Million
Emp.: 100
Refractory Material
N.A.I.C.S.: 423840
Frank R. O'Brien (Owner)
Brian Osborne (VP)
Victor Wendt (Controller)

CHRISTY SPORTS LLC

875 Parfet St, Lakewood, CO 80215-5780
Tel.: (303) 237-6321   CO
Web Site:
  https://www.christysports.com
Year Founded: 1958
Sales Range: $25-49.9 Million
Emp.: 400
Retailer of Ski, Snowboard Equipment & Leisure Furniture
N.A.I.C.S.: 459110
Cathy Schwartz (Mgr)

Subsidiaries:

AOSKGL, Inc.   (1)
11 Lone Peak Dr, Big Sky, MT 59716
Tel.: (406) 995-2939
Web Site: http://www.grizzlyoutfitters.com
Recreational Goods Rental
N.A.I.C.S.: 532284

CHRISTY WEBBER LANDSCAPES

2900 W Ferdinand St, Chicago, IL 60612
Tel.: (773) 533-0477
Web Site:
  https://www.christywebber.com
Year Founded: 2007
Sales Range: $10-24.9 Million
Emp.: 200
Landscape Architectural Services
N.A.I.C.S.: 541320
Christy Webber (Pres)
Roger Post (Gen Mgr)
Larissa Mariano (Mgr-Mktg)

CHRISTY-FOLTZ INCORPORATED

740 S Main St, Decatur, IL 62521
Tel.: (217) 428-8601
Web Site: https://www.christy-foltz.com
Sales Range: $10-24.9 Million
Emp.: 120
Construction of Industrial Buildings
N.A.I.C.S.: 236210
Thomas R. Dickes (Chm)
Donna Thorpe (Controller)
Larry Bafford (VP-Field Ops)
Brian Blade (Project Mgr)
Ron Grigg (Gen Mgr)
Mitch Schiinzler (Project Mgr)

CHROMA TECHNOLOGY CORPORATION

10 Imtec Ln, Bellows Falls, VT 05101
Tel.: (802) 428-2500
Web Site: http://www.chroma.com

Year Founded: 1991
Rev.: $12,000,000
Emp.: 110
Interference Filters Mfr
N.A.I.C.S.: 334516
Chip Siler (Mgr-Facilities & HS&E)
Janette Bombardier (Chief Engrg Officer)
Dan Johnson (CFO)
Newell Lessell (CEO)

CHROMASCAPE, LLC

2055 Enterprise Pkwy, Twinsburg, OH 44087
Tel.: (330) 998-7574
Web Site:
  http://www.chromascape.com
Year Founded: 1998
Sales Range: $1-9.9 Million
Emp.: 90
Wood Products Mfr
N.A.I.C.S.: 321999
George M. Chase (Chm)
Joe Majewski (CEO)

Subsidiaries:

Greenville Colorants LLC   (1)
90 Paterson St, New Brunswick, NJ 07305-4727
Tel.: (201) 595-0200
Web Site:
  http://www.greenvillecolorants.com
Sales Range: $10-24.9 Million
Emp.: 10
Dyes & Colorants Distr
N.A.I.C.S.: 424690
Ronald Weiss (Chm)
Robert Weiss (Treas & VP)
Joseph Lynch (Pres & CEO)
Peter Rumore (VP)
Raymond O'Connor (Acct Mgr)
Howard Printz (Pres-Global Textile Div)
Mike Junkins (COO-Global Textile Div)

Plant (Domestic):

Greenville Colorants, LLC   (2)
105 Wood St, Greenville, SC 29611-4056
Tel.: (864) 295-1170
Web Site:
  http://www.greenvillecolorants.com
Colorant Mfr & Supplier
N.A.I.C.S.: 325130
Ed Tessener (VP-Sls)

CHROMATIC TECHNOLOGIES, INC.

1096 Elkton Dr Ste 600, Colorado Springs, CO 80907
Tel.: (719) 592-1557
Web Site: https://www.ctiinks.com
Year Founded: 1993
Sales Range: $1-9.9 Million
Emp.: 58
Mfr of Inks & Coatings Used for Commercial Packaging & Products
N.A.I.C.S.: 325910
Lyle Small (Founder & Pres)

CHROME CAPITAL, LLC

3073 Horseshoe Dr S Ste 206, Naples, FL 34104
Tel.: (239) 213-9922
Web Site:
  http://www.chromecapital.com
Sales Range: $1-9.9 Million
Emp.: 34
Harley-Davidson Motorcycle Leasing & Loan Services
N.A.I.C.S.: 532120
Peter Wasmer (CEO)

CHROMOLOGIC LLC

180 N Vinedo Ave, Pasadena, CA 91107
Tel.: (626) 381-9974
Web Site:
  http://www.chromologic.com
Year Founded: 2007
Sales Range: $1-9.9 Million

Emp.: 15
Developer of Next Generation Diagnostic & Optic Technology to Physical Systems for Various Applications
N.A.I.C.S.: 325413
Naresh Menon (CEO)
Theresa Nguyen (Dir-Fin & Administration)

CHRONIC DISEASE FUND, INC.

6900 N Dallas Pkwy Ste 200, Plano, TX 75024
Tel.: (877) 968-7233   TX
Web Site: http://www.cdfund.org
Year Founded: 2003
Sales Range: $200-249.9 Million
Emp.: 55
Financial Support Services
N.A.I.C.S.: 523999
Clorinda Walley (Exec Dir)
Peggy Foley (Dir-Mktg)

CHRONICLE OF HIGHER EDUCATION

1255 23rd St NW Ste 700, Washington, DC 20037
Tel.: (202) 466-1000
Web Site: http://www.chronicle.com
Year Founded: 1966
Sales Range: $10-24.9 Million
Emp.: 200
Newspapers, Publishing & Printing
N.A.I.C.S.: 513110
William J. Peyser (CFO)
Michael G. Riley (Pres & Editor-in-Chief)
Don Sargent (CTO)
Samuel Eziemefe (Dir-Acctg)
Valerie Owens (Dir-Bus Solutions)
Tim Froemling (Dir-Digital Products)
Cindy Kennedy (Dir-Info Sys)
Greg Channel (Dir-Product Engrg)
Steve Smith (Dir-Publ Platforms)
Michael Maloon (Dir-Sls & Ops)
Michael Sisk (Chief Revenue Officer & Publr)
Brock Read (Editor)
Angela DeLeon (Chief HR Officer)

CHRONISTER OIL COMPANY INC.

2026 N Republic St, Springfield, IL 62702-1850
Tel.: (217) 523-5050
Web Site: https://www.qiknez.com
Year Founded: 1967
Sales Range: $25-49.9 Million
Emp.: 160
Owner & Operator of Grocery Stores
N.A.I.C.S.: 445131
Grady Chronister (Pres)
Amy Chronister (VP)

CHRYSALIS VENTURES

101 S 5th St Ste 1650, Louisville, KY 40202-3122
Tel.: (502) 583-7644
Web Site: http://www.chrysalisventures.com
Year Founded: 1993
Rev.: $400,000,000
Emp.: 35
Equity Investment Firm
N.A.I.C.S.: 523999
Wright Steenrod (Partner)
John Willmoth (Venture Partner)
Doug Cobb (Partner)
Irv Bailey (Partner)
David A. Jones Jr. (Chm)

Subsidiaries:

Nextimage Medical, Inc.   (1)
3390 Carmel Mountain Rd Ste 150, San Diego, CA 92121
Tel.: (888) 318-5111
Web Site: http://www.nextimagemedical.com
Worker Compensation Services
N.A.I.C.S.: 541214
Liz Griggs (Chm & CEO)
Bob Giargiari (COO & CFO)
Shri Shrivas (CTO)
Christine Douheret (Dir-Client Svcs & Acct Mgmt)

Subsidiary (Domestic):

Workwell Systems, Inc.   (2)
11 E. Superior St Ste 410, Duluth, MN 55802
Tel.: (218) 728-6454
Web Site: http://www.workwell.com
Sales Range: $1-9.9 Million
Emp.: 30
Soft Tissue Illness Treatment & Prevention Services
N.A.I.C.S.: 541611

CHRYSLER JEEP 24

1020 Belmont St, Brockton, MA 02301-5515
Tel.: (781) 512-7904
Web Site: https://www.chryslerjeep24.com
Year Founded: 1977
Sales Range: $10-24.9 Million
Emp.: 40
Car Whslr
N.A.I.C.S.: 441110
Al Vieira (Gen Mgr-Sls)

CHRYSLER MUSEUM OF ART

1 Memorial Pl, Norfolk, VA 23510
Tel.: (757) 664-6200   VA
Web Site: http://www.chrysler.org
Year Founded: 1939
Sales Range: $1-9.9 Million
Emp.: 112
Museum Operator
N.A.I.C.S.: 712110
Mary Collins (Mgr-Special Events)
Colleen Higginbotham (Dir-Visitor Svcs)
Anne Corso (Dir-Education & Pub Programs)
Lelia Graham Webb (Vice Chm)
Michael Berlucchi (Mgr-Community Engagement)
Jane Cleary (Mgr-Graphics)
Ramon Betancourt (Mgr-Security)
Megan Frost (Mgr-Digital Engagement)
Charlotte Potter (Dir-Programming & Mgr-Glass Studio)
Dana Fuqua (CFO & Dir-Ops)
Allison M. Taylor (Dir-Education)
Heather Sherwin (Dir-Dev)
Lewis W. Webb III (Sec)
Thomas L. Stokes Jr. (Chm)

CHS CAPITAL LLC

10 S Wacker Dr Ste 3175, Chicago, IL 60606-7407
Tel.: (312) 876-1840   DE
Web Site: http://www.chsonline.com
Year Founded: 1988
Emp.: 35
Investment Company
N.A.I.C.S.: 551112
Brian P. Simmons (Mng Partner)
David O. Hawkins (Partner)
Ronelle DeShazer (VP-IT & Office Ops)
Robert G. Hogan (Principal)
Douglas J. Knoch (Principal)
Thomas J. Formolo (Partner)
Shawn R. Domanic (Principal)

CHS OF WALTHAM INC.

66 Newton St, Waltham, MA 02453-6063
Tel.: (781) 893-0240   MA
Web Site: https://www.maristhill.org
Year Founded: 1996
Sales Range: $10-24.9 Million
Emp.: 154
Nursing & Rehabilitation Services
N.A.I.C.S.: 624120
Suzanne McCluskey (Dir-Admissions)

CHUCK ANDERSON FORD INC.

1910 W Jesse James Rd, Excelsior Springs, MO 64024
Tel.: (816) 630-3673
Web Site: https://www.chuckandersonford.com
Rev.: $11,900,000
Emp.: 46
New Car Dealers
N.A.I.C.S.: 441110
Mike Anderson (Owner)
Kim Wales (Treas)

CHUCK FAIRBANKS CHEVROLET, INC.

629 N Beckley Ave, Desoto, TX 75115
Tel.: (972) 223-7611
Web Site: http://www.chuckfairbankschevy.com
Sales Range: $25-49.9 Million
Emp.: 84
Car Whslr
N.A.I.C.S.: 441110
Chuck Fairbanks Jr. (Owner)

CHUCK HUTTON CHEVROLET COMPANY

2471 Mt Moriah Rd, Memphis, TN 38115-1507
Tel.: (901) 365-9700   TN
Web Site: http://www.chuckhutton.com
Year Founded: 1919
Sales Range: $50-74.9 Million
Emp.: 320
Provider of Automobile Sales
N.A.I.C.S.: 441110
Brent Ragsdale (Mgr-Used Car)
Darryl Smith (Asst Mgr-Used Car)
Freeman Peterman (Mgr-Internet & Bus Dev)
Greg Echols (Mgr-Fin)
John Taylor (Gen Mgr-Sls)
Kerry Melson (Sr VP)
Loran Laughlin (Mgr-New Car Sls)
Ricky Parrish (Mgr-Fin)
Wilbert Jones (Mgr-Fin)

CHUCK LATHAM ASSOCIATES, INC.

18403 Longs Way Unit 102, Parker, CO 80134
Tel.: (303) 699-2905
Web Site: http://www.clareps.com
Year Founded: 1984
Rev.: $34,100,000
Emp.: 1,500
Pet Specialty Retailer
N.A.I.C.S.: 424990
Chuck Latham (Founder & CEO)
Daniel Gartner (Sr VP-Ops)
Jeff Kahler (CFO)

CHUCK PATTERSON AUTO WORLD

200 E Ave, Chico, CA 95926
Tel.: (530) 895-1771
Web Site: http://www.chuckpattersonauto.com
Rev.: $37,229,649
Emp.: 100
Automobiles, New & Used
N.A.I.C.S.: 441110
Chuck H. Patterson (Pres)
Mike Patterson (VP)
Pat Patterson (CFO)
Sharon Patterson (Sec)

CHUCK STEVENS AUTOMOTIVE, INC.

1304 Hwy 31 S, Bay Minette, AL 36507
Tel.: (251) 937-2961
Web Site: http://www.chuckstevensauto.com
Year Founded: 1946
Sales Range: $10-24.9 Million
Emp.: 50
Car Whslr
N.A.I.C.S.: 441110
Charles S. Stevens (Pres)

CHUCK VAN HORN DODGE, INC.

3000 Eastern Ave, Plymouth, WI 53073
Tel.: (920) 893-6591
Web Site: http://www.vanhorndodge.com
Year Founded: 1987
Sales Range: $10-24.9 Million
Emp.: 50
Car Whslr
N.A.I.C.S.: 441110
Dick Strong (Pres)
Charles Van Horn (Owner)

CHUDY PAPER CO. INC.

2615 Walden Ave, Cheektowaga, NY 14225
Tel.: (716) 825-1935
Web Site: http://www.chudypaper.com
Year Founded: 1913
Sales Range: $10-24.9 Million
Emp.: 50
Napkins, Paper
N.A.I.C.S.: 424130
Frank Michalski (CEO)
Michelle Bauer (Mgr-Bus Dev)
Max Chudy Jr. (Owner)

CHUGACH ALASKA CORPORATION

3800 Centerpoint Dr Ste 1200, Anchorage, AK 99503
Tel.: (907) 563-8866   AK
Web Site: https://www.chugach.com
Year Founded: 1972
Sales Range: $75-99.9 Million
Emp.: 5,400
Educational Construction Information Technology Environmental & Employment Services
N.A.I.C.S.: 561210
Sheri D. Buretta (Chm)
David J. Totemoff (Sec)
Violet F. Yeaton (Treas)
Matthew P. McDaniel (Vice Chm)
Gabriel Kompkoff (CEO)
Angela Astle (Exec VP-Fin)
Melanie Osborne (Chief Compliance Officer, Gen Counsel & Exec VP)
Scott Davis (Sr VP-Ops)

Subsidiaries:

Chugach Government Solutions, LLC   (1)
3800 Ctr point Dr, Ste 800, Anchorage, AK 99503
Tel.: (907) 868-2875
Web Site: https://www.chugachgov.com
Technical IT & Cyber Services
N.A.I.C.S.: 513210
Scott Davis (Pres)

Subsidiary (Domestic):

Vector Planning & Services, Inc.   (2)
591 Camino De La Reina, Ste 1200, San Diego, CA 92108
Tel.: (619) 297-5656
Web Site: https://www.myvpsi.com
Engineeering Services
N.A.I.C.S.: 541330
Greg Hammond (Pres)

Chugach Alaska Corporation—(Continued)

Chugach Industries, Inc. (1)
103 Research Dr, Hampton, VA 23666
Tel.: (757) 848-5244
Construction Engineering Services
N.A.I.C.S.: 541330

Chugach Management Services Inc. (1)
3800 Centerpoint Dr Ste1200, Anchorage, AK 99503-4161
Tel.: (907) 563-8866
Web Site: http://www.chugach.com
Rev.: $3,547,771
Emp.: 15
Management Consulting Services
N.A.I.C.S.: 541611
Mel Lynch (Pres)

CHUGACH ELECTRIC ASSO-CIATION, INC.
5601 Electron Dr, Anchorage, AK 99518
Tel.: (907) 563-7494
Web Site:
    http://www.chugachelectric.com
Year Founded: 1948
Rev.: $212,516,561
Assets: $834,585,271
Liabilities: $640,118,358
Net Worth: $194,466,913
Earnings: $5,119,627
Emp.: 295
Fiscal Year-end: 12/31/19
Other Electric Power Generation
N.A.I.C.S.: 221118
Sherri L. McKay-Highers (CFO)
Lee D. Thibert (CEO)
Susan Reeves (Vice Chm)
Tyler E. Andrews (Exec VP-Employee Svcs & Comm)
Bettina Chastain (Chm)
Stuart Parks (Sec)
Rachel Morse (Treas)
Brian J. Hickey (COO)
Arthur W. Miller (Exec VP-Regulatory & External Affairs)
Matthew C. Clarkson (Gen Counsel & VP)
Mark B. Fouts (Exec VP-Fuel & Corp Plng)

CHULA VISTA ELECTRIC CO.
127 Press Ln, Santee, CA 92071
Tel.: (619) 420-4500
Web Site: http://www.c-v-e.com
Year Founded: 1925
Sales Range: $10-24.9 Million
Emp.: 60
General Electrical Contractor
N.A.I.C.S.: 238210
Robert A. Friar (Pres)

CHUMA HOLDINGS INC.
20945 Devonshire St Ste 208, Chatsworth, CA 91311
Tel.: (702) 751-8455   NV
Web Site: http://chuma.us
Year Founded: 2006
Sales Range: Less than $1 Million
Emp.: 12
Cannabis Services
N.A.I.C.S.: 325411
Paul Shively (Interim Pres & Interim CEO)
Vinisha Agnihotri (VP-Fin)

CHUMNEY & ASSOCIATES
660 US Hwy 1 Fl 2, North Palm Beach, FL 33408
Tel.: (864) 297-7022
Web Site:
    https://www.chumneyads.com
Year Founded: 1996
Rev.: $50,000,000
Emp.: 50

Advertising, Automotive, Direct Response Marketing, Internet/Web Design, Print, Radio, Sales Promotion, T.V.
N.A.I.C.S.: 541810
Mike Chumney (Gen Mgr)

CHUNG'S FOODS INC.
Apt 11 6631 Fairway Dr, Houston, TX 77087-2278
Tel.: (713) 741-2118
Web Site:
    http://www.chungsfoods.com
Year Founded: 1986
Sales Range: $25-49.9 Million
Emp.: 230
Gourmet Egg Rolls
N.A.I.C.S.: 311991
Vreij Kolandjian (CEO)

CHURCH & CASUALTY INSURANCE AGENCY INC.
3440 Irvine Ave Ste 150, Newport Beach, CA 92660
Tel.: (949) 852-8558
Web Site: http://www.church-casualty.com
Year Founded: 1983
Rev.: $12,300,000
Emp.: 28
Provider of Fire, Marine & Casualty Insurance Services
N.A.I.C.S.: 524126
Richard Riddle (Pres)
Travis Tjepkema (Pres)

CHURCH & CHURCH INC.
107 S Squirrel Rd, Auburn Hills, MI 48326-3224
Tel.: (248) 852-3600   MI
Web Site:
    https://www.churchslumber.com
Year Founded: 1890
Sales Range: $10-24.9 Million
Emp.: 100
Retailer of Lumber & Building Materials
N.A.I.C.S.: 423310
William R. Church (Owner)
David C. Kohl (Pres)
Jeaneane Henry (Mgr-HR)

CHURCH & CHURCH LUMBER CO.
863 New Browns Ford Rd, Wilkesboro, NC 28697
Tel.: (336) 973-5700
Web Site:
    http://www.churchlumber.com
Rev.: $10,000,000
Emp.: 88
Lumber
N.A.I.C.S.: 321912
Bruce Church (Pres)

CHURCH & MAIN ADVERTISING
9 Church St, Keene, NH 03431
Tel.: (603) 357-5898
Web Site:
    http://www.churchandmain.com
Year Founded: 1980
Sales Range: $10-24.9 Million
Emp.: 4
N.A.I.C.S.: 541810
Elizabeth V. Brown (Owner & Pres)
Joey Morgan (Dir-Art)
Diana Rokes (Controller)

CHURCH & MURDOCK ELECTRIC, INC.
5709 Wattsburg Rd, Erie, PA 16514
Tel.: (814) 825-3456   PA
Web Site:
    http://www.churchandmurdock.com
Year Founded: 1912

Sales Range: $10-24.9 Million
Emp.: 85
Provider of General Electrical Contracts
N.A.I.C.S.: 238210
Jess M. Murdock (CEO)
Gordon N. Murdock (VP)
Michael Murdock (Treas & Sec)

CHURCH & STAGG OFFICE SUPPLY INC
3421 6th Ave S, Birmingham, AL 35222
Tel.: (205) 251-2951
Web Site:
    http://www.churchandstagg.com
Rev.: $11,759,737
Emp.: 70
Office Forms & Supplies
N.A.I.C.S.: 459410
Dennis Williams (CEO)

CHURCH CHAIR INDUSTRIES, INC.
7007 New Calhoun Hwy NE, Rome, GA 30161
Tel.: (706) 235-0115
Web Site:
    https://www.churchchair.com
Year Founded: 1985
Sales Range: $10-24.9 Million
Emp.: 240
Church Furniture Mfr
N.A.I.C.S.: 337127
Dell Scott (Plant Mgr)

CHURCH HILL CLASSICS
594 Pepper St, Monroe, CT 06468
Tel.: (203) 268-1535
Web Site:
    https://www.diplomaframe.com
Year Founded: 1991
Sales Range: $1-9.9 Million
Emp.: 60
Frames for Diplomas & Awards
N.A.I.C.S.: 322220
Lucie Voves (Founder)
Jessica Joram (Mgr-Mktg)
Caroline Corbett (Mgr-HR)

CHURCH MUTUAL INSURANCE COMPANY
3000 Schuster Ln, Merrill, WI 54452-3863
Tel.: (715) 536-5577   WI
Web Site:
    http://www.churchmutual.com
Year Founded: 1897
Sales Range: $250-299.9 Million
Emp.: 735
Fire, Marine & Casualty Insurance
N.A.I.C.S.: 524210
Cheryl A. Kryshak (VP-Risk Control)
J. P. Jordan (VP-Sls & Mktg)
Herman W. Vandenberg (Treas, VP & Controller)
Randy J. Brandner (VP-Product Mgmt)
Robert M. Buckley (Chief Strategy Officer & VP-Res)
Scott M. Names (VP)
Breigh Voigt (VP-Comml Ops)
Angela K. Bailey (VP-HR)
Rod Flanders (Dir-Agency Div)
Robert White (COO-CM Regent & Chief Underwriting Officer/VP-Pennsylvania)
Roy Jacobs (Pres-CM Regent)
Michael M. Smith (Gen Counsel, Sec & VP)
Kevin Root (Exec VP-Ops)
John Tribble (Chief Admin Officer/VP-CM Regent Insurance Co.)
Peter Mahler (Asst VP-Direct Underwriting)

Todd Griffith (Asst VP-Broker Underwriting)
Craig Huss (CIO & Asst VP-IT)
Alan S. Ogilvie (Pres & CEO)
Jeffrey D. Steffen (CFO & Sr VP)
Jeffrey R. Szalacinski (VP-Claims)
Sandra Woller (Chief Compliance Officer & Asst VP)
Scott Steele (CMO & VP)
Janet Selnes (Asst VP-Broker Distr)
Guy Russ (Asst VP-Risk Control)
Laura Huggins (Asst VP-Mktg)
Gregory Smith (Vice Chm)
Dawn Bernatz (Dir-Corp Comm)
Dwayne Gantz (Sr VP-Fin)
Brett Eater (Chief Underwriting Officer/VP-CM Regent Insurance Co)

CHURCH OF GOD HOME
801 N Hanover St, Carlisle, PA 17013
Tel.: (717) 249-5322   PA
Web Site:
    http://www.churchofgodhome.org
Year Founded: 1948
Sales Range: $10-24.9 Million
Emp.: 231
Lifecare Retirement Community Operator
N.A.I.C.S.: 623311
Robert Fodor (VP-Clinical Svcs)

CHURCH STREET ENTERTAINMENT
33 W Church St, Orlando, FL 32801
Tel.: (407) 649-4270
Web Site:
    http://www.churchstreetbars.com
Sales Range: $25-49.9 Million
Bars & Night Clubs
N.A.I.C.S.: 722410
Doug Taylor (Owner)
Adam Sewell (Mgr)

CHURCHILL CORPORATE SERVICES
56 Utter Ave, Hawthorne, NJ 07506
Tel.: (973) 636-9400
Web Site:
    http://www.churchillcorp.com
Year Founded: 1972
Sales Range: $25-49.9 Million
Emp.: 75
Complimentary Relocation, Real Estate & Temporary Housing Services
N.A.I.C.S.: 624229
Yudel Kahan (CEO)
Julio Morales (Exec VP-Sls Dev)

CHURCHILL EQUITY, INC.
333 S 7th St Ste 3100, Minneapolis, MN 55402
Tel.: (612) 673-6680   MN
Web Site:
    http://www.churchillequity.com
Privater Equity Firm
N.A.I.C.S.: 523999
John Fauth (Chm)
Lori Johnson (Office Mgr)

Subsidiaries:

Churchill Capital, LLC (1)
333 S 7th St Ste 2400, Minneapolis, MN 55402
Tel.: (612) 673-6636
Sales Range: $25-49.9 Million
Emp.: 35
Equity Investment Firm
N.A.I.C.S.: 523999
Charlene Wu (VP)

Holding (Domestic):

Arvan Inc. (2)
14083 S Normandie Ave, Gardena, CA 90249-2614
Tel.: (310) 327-1818
Web Site: http://www.arvaninc.com

Sales Range: $25-49.9 Million
Aircraft Parts & Equipment
N.A.I.C.S.: 336413
Marc Farris *(Mgr-Quality)*

Churchill Industries, Inc. (1)
333 S 7th St Ste 3100, Minneapolis, MN
55402-2442
Tel.: (612) 673-6700
Sales Range: $50-74.9 Million
Emp.: 13
Industrial Investment Holding Company
N.A.I.C.S.: 551112
John Fauth *(Pres & Mng Partner-Equity)*

Holding (Domestic):

DICKEY-john Corporation (2)
5200 Dickey John Rd, Auburn, IL 62615
Tel.: (217) 438-3371
Web Site: http://www.dickey-john.com
Sales Range: $25-49.9 Million
Measuring & Controlling Devices
N.A.I.C.S.: 334519
Jeff Schertz *(VP-Ops)*
John Wood *(Product Mgr-OEM)*

Subsidiary (Domestic):

DICKEY-john International Ltd. (3)
5200 Dickey John Rd, Auburn, IL 62615
Tel.: (217) 438-3371
Web Site: http://www.dickey-john.com
Sales Range: $10-24.9 Million
Emp.: 1
Public Relations Services
N.A.I.C.S.: 541820
Jeff Schertz *(Gen Mgr)*

Holding (Domestic):

Worthington Aviation Parts, Inc. (2)
2995 Lone Oak Cir St, Eagan, MN 55121-
2277
Tel.: (651) 994-1600
Web Site: http://www.worthingtonav.com
Sales Range: $25-49.9 Million
Aircraft Parts & Equipment
N.A.I.C.S.: 336413
Vernice Dabu *(Controller)*
Martin Coleman *(CFO)*
Mark Harris *(Pres & CEO)*
Ike Knudson *(Dir-Reg Sls)*
Mike Mager *(Sr VP-Sls)*
Dale Printy *(Dir-Technical Svcs)*
Tracy Schleicher *(Dir-Repair Admin)*
Paul Stewart *(CTO)*
Mary Wanke *(VP-Sls)*
Dave Weiss *(Mgr-Matls)*

**CHURCHILL LEADERSHIP
GROUP, INC.**
9817 Bay Island Ste 100, Tampa, FL
33615
Tel.: (813) 956-3445
Web Site:
    http://www.churchillleadership.com
Sales Range: $10-24.9 Million
Emp.: 30
Leadership Development Consulting
& Coaching
N.A.I.C.S.: 541612
Jayne Jenkins *(Founder & CEO)*
Dave Chubb *(Dir-Sls Trng)*

**CHURCHILL TRANSPORTA-
TION INC.**
2455 24th St, Detroit, MI 48216-1030
Tel.: (313) 896-1500   MI
Web Site:
    https://www.churchilltrans.com
Year Founded: 1977
Sales Range: $25-49.9 Million
Emp.: 200
Provider of Trucking Services
N.A.I.C.S.: 484121
Barb Nevins *(Dir-Administrative Ser-
vices)*

Subsidiaries:

Churchill Freight Services Inc. (1)
2455 24th St, Detroit, MI 48216-1030
Tel.: (313) 896-1500
Rev.: $470,000
Emp.: 5

Freight Transportation Arrangement
N.A.I.C.S.: 488510

CHUTES INTERNATIONAL
33 Industrial Park Dr, Waldorf, MD
20602
Tel.: (240) 448-5000
Web Site: https://www.chutes.com
Year Founded: 1989
Rev.: $7,700,000
Emp.: 145
Debris Removal Systems
N.A.I.C.S.: 562998
Heidi Wood *(Mgr-Administration &
Sec)*
Hadi Boustani *(Owner, Pres & CEO)*

CI CAPITAL PARTNERS LLC
500 Park Ave 8th Fl, New York, NY
10022-8029
Tel.: (212) 752-1850   DE
Web Site: http://www.cicapllc.com
Year Founded: 1993
Privater Equity Firm
N.A.I.C.S.: 523999
Timothy T. Hall *(Mng Dir)*
Joost F. Thesseling *(Mng Dir)*
Jordan S. Bernstein *(Gen Counsel)*
William M. Swayne *(Mng Dir)*
Patrick Farrell *(CFO)*
Frederick J. Iseman *(Chm & CEO)*

Subsidiaries:

Dempsey Group, Inc. (1)
50 Mill Plain Rd, Danbury, CT 06811
Tel.: (203) 792-1834
Web Site: http://www.techair.com
Holding Company; Industrial Equipment &
Supplies Whslr
N.A.I.C.S.: 551112
James J. Weis *(CFO)*
Jerry Girodo *(COO)*
Eric Nordin *(Mgr)*
Myles P. Dempsey Jr. *(Pres & CEO)*

Subsidiary (Domestic):

County Welding Products, Inc. (2)
465 Knollwood Rd, White Plains, NY 10603
Tel.: (914) 949-5151
Web Site: http://www.techair.com
Holding Company
N.A.I.C.S.: 551112

Subsidiary (Domestic):

Tech Air of New York, Inc. (3)
465 Knollwood Rd, White Plains, NY 10603
Tel.: (914) 949-5151
Web Site: http://www.techair.com
Sales Range: $1-9.9 Million
Industrial Gas Distr
N.A.I.C.S.: 423840
Jane Dempsey *(Treas)*
Craig Dahlman *(VP)*
Kevin Haley *(Mgr)*
Paul Viani *(Mgr)*

Subsidiary (Domestic):

**Gas & Alloy Supply Company,
Inc.** (4)
3116 Quebec St, Dallas, TX 75247
Tel.: (214) 905-2001
Web Site: http://www.gascotx.com
Sales Range: $1-9.9 Million
Emp.: 12
Natural Gas Distribution Services
N.A.I.C.S.: 221210

Gasco Affiliates, LLC (4)
320 Scarlet Blvd, Oldsmar, FL 34677-3018
Tel.: (813) 343-5631
Web Site: http://www.gascogas.com
Hermetic Compressors Mfr
N.A.I.C.S.: 333415
David Glaser *(CFO)*
Brad Hanway *(COO)*

Gases & Arc Supply, Inc. (4)
5691 N Franklin St, Denver, CO 80216
Tel.: (303) 477-8037
Web Site: http://www.gasesandarc.com

Sales Range: $1-9.9 Million
Emp.: 12
Industrial Gas Distr
N.A.I.C.S.: 424690
Bob Backowies *(Pres)*

L&M Welding Supply, Inc. (4)
2789 Macmae Dr, Mobile, AL 36606
Tel.: (251) 470-9997
Web Site: http://www.weld-supply.com
Sales Range: $1-9.9 Million
Emp.: 10
Welding Equipment & Accessory Distr
N.A.I.C.S.: 423830

Liquid Technology Corporation (4)
340 Scarlet Blvd, Oldsmar, FL 34677
Tel.: (407) 292-2990
Web Site: http://www.liquidtechcorp.com
Sales Range: $1-9.9 Million
Emp.: 4
Special Gas Distr
N.A.I.C.S.: 424690
Jeremy Brown *(Mgr-Ops)*
Justin Moody *(Mgr-Houston Acct)*

Impact Group, LLC (1)
950 W Bannock Ste 850, Boise, ID 83702
Tel.: (208) 343-5800
Web Site: http://www.impactgrp.com
Sales & Marketing Services; Food & Gro-
cery Broker
N.A.I.C.S.: 541613
Carl Pennington *(Pres & CEO)*
Tim Clare *(VP-Natl Clients)*
Tom Hicks *(COO)*
Pat Hobby *(CFO)*
Matt Buskirk *(Pres)*
Todd Wieble *(CIO)*
Sandy Gonzales *(VP-Mktg)*
Jarrod Davis *(VP-Corp Dev)*
Jeff Russell *(VP-Client Dev)*
Glen Scott *(VP-HR)*
Jeff Nelson *(Chief Sls Officer)*
Shane Wright *(Chief People Officer)*
Steve Shoemaker *(CFO)*

Subsidiary (Domestic):

Harlow-HRK, LLC (2)
300 Dave Cowens Dr Ste 900, Newport, KY
41071
Tel.: (513) 671-0800
Web Site: http://hhrk.net
Sales & Marketing Services for Grocery
Industry
N.A.I.C.S.: 541613
Matt Buskirk *(Exec VP)*
Pat Hobby *(CFO)*
Dave Slusher *(VP-Natural Foods)*
Rob James *(VP-Bus Solutions)*
Randy York *(VP-Multicultural)*
Linda Hodnett *(VP-Grocery)*
Jim Uryga *(VP-Arlowe & Intl Bazaar)*

Wildfire Sales Inc. (2)
65 Sea Cliff Ave, Glen Cove, NY 11542-
2771
Tel.: (516) 609-9166
Public Relations Agencies
N.A.I.C.S.: 541820

Interactive Health, Inc. (1)
1700 E Golf Rd Ste 900, Schaumburg, IL
60173
Tel.: (847) 590-0200
Web Site:
    http://www.interactivehealthinc.com
Wellness & Health Management Solutions
N.A.I.C.S.: 621999
Cathy Kenworthy *(CEO)*
Tricia Johnson *(Dir-Mktg)*
Charlie Estey *(Exec VP-Bus Dev)*
Tim Hardy *(CIO)*
Lidia Nelkovski *(Dir-Medical)*
Stacey Nevara *(VP-Client Rels)*
Jane Ruppert *(VP-Health Svcs)*

Subsidiary (Domestic):

Relax the Back Corporation (2)
4600 E Conant St, Long Beach, CA 90808-
1874
Tel.: (714) 523-2870
Web Site: http://www.relaxtheback.com
Ergonomic Chairs, Work Stations, Mat-
tresses, Pillows & Other Sleep Accessories
Mfr & Sales
N.A.I.C.S.: 449110
Richard Palfreyman *(Pres & CEO)*

Intrapac Group (1)
2475 Northwinds Pwy Ste 200, Alpharetta,
GA 30009-4808
Tel.: (770) 753-6300
Packaging Services
N.A.I.C.S.: 561910
Randy Churchill *(Plant Mgr-Harrisonburg)*
Ray Grupinski *(CEO)*
Gregg Lambert *(Plant Mgr-Plattsburg)*
Harry Logan *(Plant Mgr-Calgary)*
Marlon Moreno *(Plant Mgr-Envasa)*
Robert Thiessen *(Plant Mgr-Mississauga)*
Peter Gamoff *(Dir-Sls)*
John W. Struble *(CFO)*

PT Network, LLC (1)
501 Fairmount Ave Ste 302, Towson, MD
21286
Web Site:
    http://www.pivotphysicaltherapy.com
Physical Therapy Services
N.A.I.C.S.: 621340
Harris Thompson *(Pres & CEO)*
Gary Katz *(Co-Founder & Chief Dev Offi-
cer)*
Thomas Yoviene *(Co-Founder & Reg Pres-
Eastern Shore & Delaware)*
Greg Smith *(Co-Founder & Sr VP-Strategic
Initiatives)*
Steve Berger *(CFO)*
Christopher Horowicz *(Reg Pres-
Western/Central Maryland, DC, West Vir-
ginia & Virginia)*
Kevin Dintino *(Reg Pres-Southern Virginia)*
Brad Hancock *(Reg Pres-Delaware & East-
ern Maryland)*
Stephen Reed *(Reg Pres-North Carolina)*
Brian Hoy *(VP-Clinical Svcs)*
Katie Bond *(Dir-Sls)*
Scott Ellis *(Dir-Sports Medicine Outreach &
Dev)*
Todd Herring *(Dir-Market)*

The Cadmus Group, LLC (1)
100 5th Ave Ste 100, Waltham, MA 02451
Tel.: (617) 673-7000
Web Site: http://www.cadmusgroup.com
Sales Range: $25-49.9 Million
Emp.: 200
Environmental & Energy Consulting Ser-
vices
N.A.I.C.S.: 541620
Ian Kline *(Pres & CEO)*
Gene Fax *(Co-Founder & Chm)*
Ralph T. Jones *(Co-Founder)*
Paul S. Hovsepian *(VP-Contracts & Pro-
curement)*
Nathan Smith *(Sr VP)*
Cindy Shephard *(COO)*
Neil Pickard *(VP)*
Jeff Newell *(Sr VP-Safety, Security & Resil-
ience Svcs)*
Kevin O'Prey *(Sr VP)*
Alan V. Seferian *(CFO)*
Alan B. Snyder *(Principal)*
Amy Ellsworth *(Principal)*
Anne West *(Principal)*
Brad Jones *(Principal)*
David Waldman *(Principal)*
Dennis Lauer *(CIO)*
Ed Miller *(Sr VP)*
Helle Huxley *(CMO)*
Henning Banthein *(Sr VP)*
Hossein Haeri *(Sr VP)*
James Hanlon *(Principal)*
Jane Colby *(Principal)*
Jeff Cropp *(Principal)*
Jim Steward *(Principal)*
Jon Crowe *(Principal)*
Nitin Natarajan *(Principal)*
Peter Jardine *(Sr VP-Corp & Bus Dev)*
Sarah Scafidi *(Principal)*
Shawn Shaw *(Principal)*
Steve Cofer *(Principal)*
Susan Chodakewitz *(Chief Growth Strategy
Officer)*

Subsidiary (Domestic):

**Constructive Technologies Group,
Inc.** (2)
8105 Irvine Ctr Dr Ste 150, Irvine, CA
92618
Tel.: (949) 790-0010
Sales Range: $10-24.9 Million
Emp.: 24
Multi-Disciplinary Technical Consulting Ser-
vices
N.A.I.C.S.: 541690

CI CAPITAL PARTNERS LLC

U.S. PRIVATE

CI Capital Partners LLC—(Continued)

Branch (Domestic):

The Cadmus Group, Inc. - Portland (2)
720 SW Washington St Ste 400, Portland, OR 97205
Tel.: (503) 228-2992
Sales Range: $1-9.9 Million
Emp.: 75
Energy Services
N.A.I.C.S.: 541620
M. Sami Khawaja (VP-Energy Svcs Grp)

Subsidiary (Domestic):

The Wheelhouse Group, Inc. (2)
2200 Wilson Blvd Ste 102-455, Arlington, VA 22201-3397
Tel.: (202) 430-6944
Web Site: http://www.wheelhousegroup.com
Management Consulting Services
N.A.I.C.S.: 541618
Beth McDonald (Founder & Pres)

Ventera Corporation (2)
1881 Campus Commons Dr Ste 350, Reston, VA 20191
Tel.: (703) 760-4600
Web Site: http://www.ventera.com
Sales Range: $25-49.9 Million
Emp.: 100
Information Technology Services & Management Consulting
N.A.I.C.S.: 541511
Robert Acosta (CEO)
Chris Ford (Exec VP-Comml Svcs)
Jeff Smith (Exec VP-Govt Svcs)
Joe McMahon (Exec VP-Bus Dev)
Christina Pritchett (VP-Human Capital Mgmt)
Hugh J. Shaw (CFO)
Doug Bullard (Sr VP-Comml Svcs & Bus Dev)
Praveen Nedungottil (VP-Solutions Delivery)

WTS International, Inc. (1)
3200 Tower Oaks Blvd Ste 400, Rockville, MD 20852
Tel.: (301) 622-7800
Web Site: http://www.wtsinternational.com
Amusement & Recreation Industries
N.A.I.C.S.: 713990
Gary Henkin (Founder & Chm)
Scott Krosnowski (CFO)
Ralph Newman (Sr VP)
Kim Matheson Shedrick (Sr VP)
Jackie Henkin (Sr VP-Bus Dev)
Chris Griebe (Sr VP-Lifestyle & Fitness)
Susan Hammer (VP-Spa Division)
Catherine Warren (VP-Training)
Abhishek Jain (VP-Intl Ops)
John Casterline (Gen Counsel)
Steven A. Rudnitsky (Vice Chm)
Barry Goldstein (CEO)

CI2I SERVICES, INC.
410 Bellevue Way SE Ste 205, Bellevue, WA 98004
Tel.: (425) 818-0560   WA
Web Site:
http://www.ci2iservices.com
Year Founded: 2003
Sales Range: $1-9.9 Million
Emp.: 12
Information Technology Consulting & Staffing Services
N.A.I.C.S.: 541690
Ajay Sikka (Pres & CEO)
Raul Ramos (VP-Sls & Ops)
Dan Clem (Mktg Mgr)

CIANBRO CORPORATION
101 Cianbro Sq, Pittsfield, ME 04967
Tel.: (207) 487-3311   ME
Web Site: https://www.cianbro.com
Year Founded: 1949
Heavy Construction Services
N.A.I.C.S.: 236210
Andi Vigue (Pres & CEO)

Subsidiaries:

A/Z Corporation (1)

46 Norwich Westerly Rd, North Stonington, CT 06359
Tel.: (800) 400-2420
Web Site: http://www.a-zcorp.com
Commercial & Institutional Building Construction
N.A.I.C.S.: 236220
Greg Cox (Pres)
Donald Swanson (VP)
Robert Rose (VP)
Kevin Chronley (VP)
Janos Angeli (Reg Mgr-Ops)
Steve Johnson (Dir-Specialty Svcs)
Steve Williams (Ops Mgr-Mid-Atlantic)
Steven Lusi (Ops Mgr-Electrical)
John Novak (Dir-Field Svcs)
Stephen Pryor (Ops Mgr-Telecom)

Cianbro Corporation - Eastern Manufacturing Facility (1)
1 Cianbro Sq, Brewer, ME 04412
Tel.: (207) 992-9001
Construction Machinery Mfr
N.A.I.C.S.: 333120

Cianbro Corporation - Georgetown Fabrication Facility (1)
3 Farm Ln, Georgetown, MA 01833
Tel.: (978) 352-2591
Web Site: http://www.cianbro.com
Emp.: 50
Fabricated Structural Metal Mfr
N.A.I.C.S.: 332312
Jack Klipm (Gen Mgr)

Cianbro Corporation - Rickers Wharf Marine Facility (1)
60 Cassidy Point Dr, Portland, ME 04102
Tel.: (207) 773-5852
Web Site: http://www.cianbro.com
Marine Equipment Mfr
N.A.I.C.S.: 334290

Cianbro Equipment, LLC (1)
198 Hunnewell Ave, Pittsfield, ME 04967
Tel.: (207) 679-2281
Construction Machinery Mfr
N.A.I.C.S.: 333120
Tom Ruksznis (Mgr-Ops)

Cianbro Fabrication & Coating Corporation (1)
605 Pittman Rd, Baltimore, MD 21226
Tel.: (410) 636-3000
Web Site: http://www.cianbro.com
Fabricated Structural Metal & Coating Mfr
N.A.I.C.S.: 325510

RC Stevens Construction Company (1)
28 S Main St, Winter Garden, FL 34787
Tel.: (407) 299-3800
Web Site: http://www.rcstevens.com
Industrial Building Construction
N.A.I.C.S.: 236210
Timothy M. Keating (Pres)
Kyle Donnelly (Project Mgr)

CIAO GROUP, INC.
8390 LBJ Fwy 10th Fl, Dallas, TX 75243
Tel.: (347) 560-5040   NV
Year Founded: 2009
Emp.: 1
Outside Construction Including Outdoor Kitchens, Grills, Retaining Walls & Garden Structures
N.A.I.C.S.: 238990
Aubrey Brown (Pres, CEO, CFO, Treas & Sec)

CIATTO CONSTRUCTION CO.
1325 Allegheny Ave, Reading, PA 19601
Tel.: (610) 375-4919
Web Site:
https://www.ciattoconstruction.com
Year Founded: 1998
Sales Range: $1-9.9 Million
Emp.: 18
General & Commercial Construction & Project Management
N.A.I.C.S.: 236220
Greg Ciatto (Pres)

CIB CORPORATION
692 B Saint Mario Julia Industrial Park, San Juan, PR 00920
Tel.: (787) 793-2000
Web Site: http://www.cibcorp.com
Sales Range: $10-24.9 Million
Emp.: 72
Valves & Fittings
N.A.I.C.S.: 423830
Fernado Quijano (Pres & Treas)
Jose Adolfo (Exec VP)

CIBOLAN GOLD CORPORATION
1155 W 4th St Ste 210, Reno, NV 89503
Tel.: (775) 583-4636   DE
Year Founded: 1994
Emp.: 1
Gold & Silver Exploration Services
N.A.I.C.S.: 212220
Daniel J. Forbush (Pres, CEO & CFO)

CIBRO MANAGEMENT INC.
1331 S International Pkwy Ste 1291, Lake Mary, FL 32746-1405
Tel.: (407) 333-3278
Web Site:
http://www.gatorsdockside.com
Sales Range: $10-24.9 Million
Emp.: 7
Management Investment, Open-End
N.A.I.C.S.: 525910
Paul Cipparone (Pres)

CIC GROUP, INC.
555 Maryville University Dr Ste 250, Saint Louis, MO 63141
Tel.: (314) 682-2900
Web Site: http://www.cicgroup.com
Sales Range: $450-499.9 Million
Emp.: 1,062
Business Services
N.A.I.C.S.: 541618
Ross Osiek (Chm, Pres & CEO)
Terry Jansing (CFO)
Marty Jones (Supvr-Enterprise Datacenter)

Subsidiaries:

Nooter Corporation (1)
1500 S 2nd St, Saint Louis, MO 63104
Tel.: (314) 421-7200
Web Site: http://www.nooter.com
Sales Range: $350-399.9 Million
Emp.: 75
Holding Company; Engineering Services
N.A.I.C.S.: 332420
Keith Strohkirch (Coord-Matl)
Katherine Ross (Coord-Payroll Field)
Bob Grundmann (Engr-Contracting)
Brian Hickman (Engr-QA & QC)
Johnie Rollins (Project Mgr)
Price Steve (Project Mgr-DBA)
Denise Votrain (Project Mgr-ERP)

Subsidiary (Domestic):

Nooter Construction Co. (2)
1500 S 2nd St, Saint Louis, MO 63104-4513
Tel.: (314) 421-7600
Web Site:
http://www.nooterconstruction.com
Sales Range: $25-49.9 Million
Emp.: 50
Fabricate Erects & Repairs Processing Vessel & Related Equipment for Oil Chemical Pulp & Paper Services
N.A.I.C.S.: 236220
Jimmy Nelson (Pres)

St. Louis Metallizing Co. (2)
4123 Sarpy Ave, Saint Louis, MO 63110-1745
Tel.: (314) 531-5253
Web Site: http://www.stlmetallizing.com
Sales Range: $25-49.9 Million
Full Service Thermal Spray & Finishing Shop

N.A.I.C.S.: 332812
Joseph Stricker (Pres)
John Naes (Engr-Sls)
John Passmore (Mgr-Quality)
Mark Mierkowski (Engr-Sls)

Wyatt Field Service Co. (2)
PO Box 3052, Houston, TX 77253-3052
Tel.: (713) 570-2000
Web Site: http://www.wyattfieldservice.com
Sales Range: $25-49.9 Million
Field Fabrication, Maintenance & Emergency Field Services for Refineries, Chemical Plants, Power, Pulp & Paper Plants
N.A.I.C.S.: 238290

Holding (Domestic):

Nooter/Eriksen, Inc. (1)
1509 Ocello Dr, Fenton, MO 63026
Tel.: (636) 651-1000
Web Site: http://www.ne.com
Sales Range: $25-49.9 Million
Emp.: 200
Heat Recovery Equipment Mfr
N.A.I.C.S.: 332410
Tim Peterson (Pres)
Dan Sullivan (Mgr-Projects)
Darla Gavin (Dir-Sls)

Subsidiary (Non-US):

Nooter/Eriksen Srl (2)
Via A Volta 50, Cardano al Campo, 21010, Varese, Italy
Tel.: (39) 0331232500
Heat Recovery Systems Mfr
N.A.I.C.S.: 332410

CIC INTERNATIONAL LTD.
20 Waterside Plz #33A, New York, NY 10010
Tel.: (212) 213-0089
Web Site: http://www.cic-international.com
Year Founded: 1930
Sales Range: $700-749.9 Million
Emp.: 718
Producer of Military Equipment
N.A.I.C.S.: 333248
S. G. Fassoulis (CEO)
Xavier G. Emery (Mgr-Bus Dev-Intl)

CIC PARTNERS, L.P.
3879 Maple Ave Ste 400, Dallas, TX 75219
Tel.: (214) 871-6812
Web Site:
https://www.cicpartners.com
Equity Investment Firm
N.A.I.C.S.: 523999
Marshall Payne (Partner)
Fouad Z. Bashour (Co-CFO)
Amir Yoffe (Partner)
Sandy Nelson (Chief Admin Officer)
Diane Gross (Controller)
Alan Buehler (Co-CFO)

Subsidiaries:

Activa Resources, LLC (1)
403 E Commerce Str, San Antonio, TX 78205   (70%)
Tel.: (210) 271-9875
Oil & Gas Exploration Services
N.A.I.C.S.: 213112
John W. Hayes (Pres & Member-Mgmt Bd)

CICOA AGING & IN-HOME SOLUTIONS
4755 Kingsway Dr Ste 200, Indianapolis, IN 46205
Tel.: (317) 254-5465   IN
Web Site: http://www.cicoa.org
Year Founded: 1974
Sales Range: $10-24.9 Million
Emp.: 253
Disability Assistance Services
N.A.I.C.S.: 624120

CID CAPITAL II, INC.
10201 N Illinois St Ste 200, Carmel, IN 46290
Tel.: (317) 818-5030
Web Site: https://www.cidcap.com

Privater Equity Firm
N.A.I.C.S.: 523999
Steve A. Cobb *(Mng Dir)*
John C. Aplin *(Mng Dir)*
Eric Bruun *(Mng Dir)*
Scot Swenberg *(Mng Dir)*
Deborah Morgan *(Chief Compliance Officer & Dir-Fin)*
Cory Heck *(VP)*
Eric Derheimer *(VP)*
Adam Bolerjack *(Mgr-Bus Dev)*

CIGI DIRECT INSURANCE SERVICES, INC.
232 F St, Salida, CO 81201
Tel.: (719) 539-3000
Web Site: https://www.eterm.com
Year Founded: 1986
Sales Range: $25-49.9 Million
Emp.: 120
Insurance Brokerage
N.A.I.C.S.: 524110
John Robert Hightower *(Pres)*
Jim Webster *(Sr VP)*
Melissa Hightower *(Treas)*

CIGNYS-SAGINAW
68 Williamson St, Saginaw, MI 48601
Tel.: (989) 753-1411
Web Site: https://www.cignys.com
Sales Range: $10-24.9 Million
Emp.: 150
Conveyors & Conveying Equipment
N.A.I.C.S.: 333922
Nicolaos A. Rapanos *(Owner)*
Charles Lange *(Pres)*
John Hutchinson *(CFO & Controller)*

CIK POWER DISTRIBUTORS, LLC.
240 W Grove Ave, Orange, CA 92865
Tel.: (714) 938-0297
Web Site: https://www.cikpower.com
Year Founded: 2005
Sales Range: $10-24.9 Million
Emp.: 65
Telecommunication Servicesb
N.A.I.C.S.: 517810
Steve Carter *(Owner)*

CIM GROUP, LLC
4700 Wilshire Blvd, Los Angeles, CA 90010
Tel.: (323) 860-4900   CA
Web Site: http://www.cimgroup.com
Year Founded: 1994
Real Estate Investment Trusts, Nsk
N.A.I.C.S.: 525990
Avraham Shemesh *(Co-Founder & Principal)*
Shaul Kuba *(Co-Founder)*
Charles Garner *(Principal-Investment)*
David Thompson *(CFO & Principal)*
Bradley Aaronson *(Mng Dir-Bus Dev)*
Mukya Porter *(Chief Compliance Officer & Mng Dir)*
Monica Yamada *(Principal-Media)*

Subsidiaries:

CCO Capital, LLC   (1)
2398 E Camelback Rd 4th Fl, Phoenix, AZ 85016
Tel.: (602) 224-4237
Real Estate Investment Advisor & Management Services
N.A.I.C.S.: 523940

Affiliate (Domestic):

CIM Real Estate Finance Trust, Inc.   (2)
2398 E Camelback Rd 4th Fl, Phoenix, AZ 85016
Tel.: (602) 778-8700
Web Site: https://www.cimgroup.com
Rev.: $568,859,000
Assets: $6,446,476,000
Liabilities: $4,180,399,000

Net Worth: $2,266,077,000
Earnings: $28,078,000
Fiscal Year-end: 12/31/2023
Real Estate Investment Trust
N.A.I.C.S.: 525990
Richard S. Ressler *(Chm, Pres & CEO)*

CIMARRON EXPRESS INC.
21611 State Rte 51 W, Genoa, OH 43430-1245
Tel.: (419) 855-7713
Web Site: http://www.cimarronexpress.com
Year Founded: 1984
Sales Range: $10-24.9 Million
Emp.: 55
Provider of Trucking Services
N.A.I.C.S.: 484121
Glenn Grady *(Pres & CEO)*

CIMARRON HEALTHCARE CAPITAL LLC
6440 S. Wasatch Blvd., Ste 380, Salt Lake, UT 84121
Tel.: (801) 849-9293
Web Site: https://www.cimarronhc.com
Year Founded: 2015
Investment Management
N.A.I.C.S.: 523940
James Nadauld *(Founder & Mng Partner)*

CIMARRON INC.
180050 Saturn Ln Ste 280, Houston, TX 77058
Tel.: (281) 226-5100
Web Site: http://www.cimarroninc.com
Year Founded: 1981
Emp.: 350
Control Center Systems Engineering & Software Development
N.A.I.C.S.: 541511
Darren Crowell *(Pres)*
Walter Medsger *(CFO)*
Jeannie L. Crowell *(CEO)*

Subsidiaries:

Cimarron Inc. - Executive Office   (1)
4526 Research Forest Dr Ste 300, The Woodlands, TX 77381-4079
Tel.: (281) 480-4266
Web Site: http://www.cimarroninc.com
Executive Office; Control Center Systems Engineering & Software Development
N.A.I.C.S.: 921110
Darren Crowell *(Pres)*
Jeannie L. Crowell *(CEO)*
Harry Miller *(VP-Comml Svcs)*
Walter Medsger *(CFO)*

CIMARRON UNDERGROUND SERVICES, LLC
7822 Chef Menteur Hwy, New Orleans, LA 70126
Tel.: (504) 241-6831   KS
Web Site: http://cimarronus.com
Year Founded: 1977
Water, Sewer & Utility Lines
N.A.I.C.S.: 237110

CIMBAR PERFORMANCE MINERALS, INC.
49 Jackson Lk Rd, Chatsworth, GA 30705
Emp.: 100
Mining
N.A.I.C.S.: 212311
John Hinton Waters *(CEO)*

Subsidiaries:

Excalibar Minerals LLC   (1)
21920 Merchants Way, Katy, TX 77449
Tel.: (281) 872-4539
Web Site: http://www.newpark.com
Processor & Supplier of Industrial Minerals
N.A.I.C.S.: 212390

Carlos Cisneros *(Mgr-Customer Svc)*
Mark Brooks *(Gen Mgr)*
Jay Esty *(Acct Mgr)*

CIMINELLI DEVELOPMENT COMPANY, INC.
Centerpointe Corp Park 350 Essjay Rd Ste 101, Williamsville, NY 14221-8200
Tel.: (716) 631-8000
Web Site: http://www.ciminelli.com
Year Founded: 1981
Sales Range: $75-99.9 Million
Emp.: 70
Provider of Real Estate Services
N.A.I.C.S.: 531210
Jim Cottsting *(Asst Treas)*
Robert G. McDonnell *(Sr VP-Brokerage Svc)*
Paul Ciminelli *(Pres & CEO)*
James M. Gottstine *(COO)*

CINCINNATI ART MUSEUM
953 Eden Park Dr, Cincinnati, OH 45202
Tel.: (513) 721-2787
Web Site: https://www.cincinnatiartmuseum.org
Sales Range: $10-24.9 Million
Emp.: 150
Museum of Twentieth Century & Contemporary Art & Design
N.A.I.C.S.: 712110
Carol Edmondson *(CFO)*
Dave Linnenberg *(Chief Admin Officer)*

CINCINNATI ARTS ASSOCIATION
650 Walnut St, Cincinnati, OH 45202-2517
Tel.: (513) 621-2787   OH
Web Site: https://www.cincinnatiarts.org
Year Founded: 1990
Sales Range: $10-24.9 Million
Emp.: 427
Art Development Services
N.A.I.C.S.: 711310
Van Ackerman *(Dir-Mktg & PR)*
Brenda A. Carter *(Dir-HR)*
Joyce Bonomini *(Dir-Education & Community Rels)*
Deborah A. Morgan *(Dir-Dev)*
Stephen A. Loftin *(Pres & Exec Dir)*
Tina Loeb Carroll *(VP-Fin)*
Otto M. Budig Jr. *(Treas)*

CINCINNATI BENGALS, INC.
1 Paul Brown Stadium, Cincinnati, OH 45202-3418
Tel.: (513) 621-3550   OH
Web Site: http://www.bengals.com
Year Founded: 1968
Sales Range: $50-74.9 Million
Emp.: 130
Professional Football Franchise
N.A.I.C.S.: 711211
Mike Brown *(Pres)*
Katie Blackburn *(Exec VP)*
Troy Blackburn *(VP)*
Johanna Kappner *(Controller)*
Eric Ball *(Dir-Player Rels)*
Tim Kelly *(Dir-Ticket Ops)*
Monty Montague *(Mgr-Merchandising)*
Brian Sells *(CMO & VP)*
Paul Brown *(VP-Player Personnel)*
Duke Tobin *(Dir-Player Personnel)*
Jeff Brickner *(Mgr-Equipment)*
Travis Brammer *(Dir-Video)*
Alex Simons *(Mgr-Suite Svcs)*
Katherine B. Blackburn *(Exec VP)*
Andrew Brown *(Dir-Sls Analytics)*

Duane Haring *(Dir-Ticket Sls-Svc)*
Ron Runk *(Mgr-Warehouse)*
Ryan Holmes *(Dir-Corp Sls)*

CINCINNATI CENTER CITY DEVELOPMENT CORPORATION
1410 Race St, Cincinnati, OH 45202
Tel.: (513) 621-4400   OH
Web Site: http://www.3cdc.org
Year Founded: 2003
Sales Range: $10-24.9 Million
Emp.: 49
Real Estate Development Services
N.A.I.C.S.: 531390
Adam Gelter *(Exec VP-Development)*

CINCINNATI COMMERCIAL CONTRACTING, LLC.
4760 Red Bank Rd Ste 226, Cincinnati, OH 45227
Tel.: (513) 561-6633
Web Site: http://www.cccontracting.com
Year Founded: 1999
Sales Range: $10-24.9 Million
Emp.: 25
Real Estate Services
N.A.I.C.S.: 531210
John Westheimer *(Pres)*
Tom Shumaker *(Dir-Bus Dev)*
Larry Knasel *(VP-Construction)*
Heather Moore *(VP & Coord-Project)*
Jason Manni *(CFO)*
Amy Westheimer *(Dir-Sls)*
Jenna Martini *(Dir-BIM)*
Jake Busch *(Dir-Bus Dev)*
Justin Platt *(Pres)*

CINCINNATI CONTAINER COMPANY INCORPORATED
5060 Duff Dr, Cincinnati, OH 45246
Tel.: (513) 874-6874
Web Site: https://www.cincinnaticontainer.com
Year Founded: 1932
Sales Range: $10-24.9 Million
Emp.: 40
Glass Bottles
N.A.I.C.S.: 423840
Paul Johnson *(Pres)*
Bill Fox *(VP-Sls & Mktg)*

CINCINNATI FEDERAL SAVINGS & LOAN ASSOCIATION
6581 Harrison Ave, Cincinnati, OH 45247
Tel.: (513) 574-3025
Web Site: https://www.cincinnatifederal.com
Year Founded: 1922
Federal Savings Bank
N.A.I.C.S.: 522180
Joseph V. Bunke *(Pres)*
Gregory W. Meyers *(CFO)*
Rob Overbeck *(VP-Sls)*

CINCINNATI FLOOR COMPANY INC.
5162 Broerman Ave, Cincinnati, OH 45217
Tel.: (513) 641-4500
Web Site: http://www.cincifloor.com
Sales Range: $10-24.9 Million
Emp.: 50
Floor Laying & Floor Work
N.A.I.C.S.: 238330
Jill Drenik *(CFO)*

CINCINNATI GEARING SYSTEMS INC.
5757 Mariemont Ave, Cincinnati, OH 45227
Tel.: (513) 527-8600
Web Site: https://www.cincinnatigearings.com

Cincinnati Gearing Systems Inc.—(Continued)

Sales Range: $10-24.9 Million
Emp.: 125
Metal Heat Treating Services
N.A.I.C.S.: 332811
Kenneth Kiehl (VP-Sls & Engrg)
Bill Tibbe (Mgr-Sls-Component Gearing)
Jim Barnhorst (Mgr-Sls-Enclosed Drives)
Kenneth Lawrence (Mgr-Sls-Spare Parts & Svc)
Maeve McGoff (Coord-Sls & Mktg)

CINCINNATI HEALTH NETWORK

2825 Burnet Ave, Cincinnati, OH 45219
Tel.: (513) 961-0600   OH
Web Site:
    http://www.cintihealthnetwork.org
Year Founded: 1986
Sales Range: $1-9.9 Million
Emp.: 16
Community Health Care Services
N.A.I.C.S.: 621498
Nancy Elder (Chief Medical Officer)
Kate Bennett (CEO)
Mat Jackson (Chm)
Mike Angeline (Vice Chm)
Regina Woods (Treas)
Jerry Bedford (Sec)
Amy Harpenau (Mgr-Case)
Austin Maddox (CFO)
Brain Vanderhorst (COO)

CINCINNATI INCORPORATED

7420 Kilby Rd, Harrison, OH 45030-8915
Tel.: (513) 367-7100   OH
Web Site: https://www.e-ci.com
Year Founded: 1898
Sales Range: $150-199.9 Million
Emp.: 400
Metal Working Equipment Mfr
N.A.I.C.S.: 333517
John Prevish (Mgr-Sls)
Matt Garbarino (Mgr-Mktg)
Todd Kirchoff (Mgr-Machine Tool Products)
Rakesh Kumar (VP-Sls, Mktg & Svc)

CINCINNATI METROPOLITAN HOUSING AUTHORITY

1627 Western Ave, Cincinnati, OH 45214-2001
Tel.: (513) 721-4580
Web Site: https://www.cintimha.com
Year Founded: 1933
Sales Range: $100-124.9 Million
Emp.: 330
Real Estate Manangement Services
N.A.I.C.S.: 531110
Angela Stearns (Asst Gen Counsel)
Jason Best (Engr-Network)
Gregory Johnson (Exec Dir)

CINCINNATI PARKS FOUNDATION

421 Oak St, Cincinnati, OH 45219
Tel.: (513) 861-0023   OH
Web Site:
    https://www.cincinnatiparksfoun
    dation.org
Year Founded: 1995
Sales Range: $10-24.9 Million
Emp.: 5
Park Conservation Services
N.A.I.C.S.: 712190
Jennifer Spieser (Exec Dir)

CINCINNATI SYMPHONY ORCHESTRA

1241 Elm St, Cincinnati, OH 45202
Tel.: (513) 621-1919

Web Site:
    https://www.cincinnatisymphony.org
Year Founded: 1895
Emp.: 150
Symphony Orchestra
N.A.I.C.S.: 711130
Heather L. Stengle (Dir-Ops)
M. Todd Bezold (Dir-Mktg & Subscriptions)
Amy Catanzarl (Dir-Sls)
Sharon D. Grayton (Mgr-Data Svcs)
Emily Selzer (Mgr-Leadership Giving)
Richard Freshwater (CFO & VP)
Eric Smith (Controller)
Meghan Berneking (Dir-Comm)
Melissa Scott (Dir-Data Sys)
Hannah Johnson (Dir-Events)
Walter Zeschin (Dir-Orchestra Personnel)
Ron Cropper (Dir-Special Campaigns)
Christopher Pinelo (VP-Comm)
Sherri Prentiss (VP-Mktg)
Pamela Taylor (Mgr-Individual Giving)
Louis Langre (Dir-Music)

CINCINNATI THERMAL SPRAY, INC.

5901 Creek Rd, Cincinnati, OH 45242-4011
Tel.: (513) 793-0670   OH
Web Site: https://www.cts-inc.net
Sales Range: $75-99.9 Million
Emp.: 100
Plasma Coating of Aircraft Engine Parts
N.A.I.C.S.: 332812
Dale Harmon (Dir-Quality & Trng)

CINCINNATI TOOL STEEL CO., INC.

5190 28th Ave, Rockford, IL 61109
Tel.: (815) 226-8800
Web Site: https://www.cintool.com
Year Founded: 1976
Sales Range: $25-49.9 Million
Emp.: 140
Steel
N.A.I.C.S.: 423510
Brian Cincinnati (Pres & CEO)
Julie Hansberry (CFO)
Karl Ptak (Mgr-MIS)
Ronald J. Cincinnati (VP-Sls)
Kevin Schoonover (Mgr-Machining & Maintenance)

CINCINNATI UNITED CONTRACTORS, INC.

7143 E Kemper Rd, Cincinnati, OH 45249-1028
Tel.: (513) 677-0060   OH
Web Site: https://www.cintiunited.com
Year Founded: 1978
Sales Range: $75-99.9 Million
Emp.: 30
Provider of Contracting & Construction Services
N.A.I.C.S.: 238990
Charles Kubicki (Pres & CEO)
Chance Truemper (VP)
Marc Chiaramonte (VP-Construction)
Pati Velten (Office Mgr)
Scott Kessler (Project Mgr)

CINCO MEDIA COMMUNICATIONS

1801 N Lamar Ste 400, Dallas, TX 75202
Tel.: (214) 574-5551
Sales Range: Less than $1 Million
Emp.: 15
N.A.I.C.S.: 541810
Amber Gracia (Owner & Chief Strategist)
Shannon Rubio (Dir-Client Svcs)
Rene Gracia (Exec Dir-Creative)

CINDERELLA INC.

1215 S Jefferson Ave, Saginaw, MI 48601
Tel.: (989) 755-7741
Web Site:
    https://www.cinderellainc.com
Sales Range: $10-24.9 Million
Emp.: 40
Swimming Pools, Equipment & Supplies
N.A.I.C.S.: 423910
David M. Jaffe (Chm & CEO)
Shawn Finney (Mgr-Tech)

CINDISUE MINING CORP.

11255 Tierrasanta Blvd Unit 78, San Diego, CA 92124
Tel.: (858) 278-1166   DE
Year Founded: 2010
Metal Ore Exploration Services
N.A.I.C.S.: 213114

CINE MAGNETICS, INC.

100 Bus Pk Dr, Armonk, NY 10504-1721
Tel.: (914) 273-7500   NY
Web Site:
    http://www.cinemagnetics.com
Year Founded: 1972
Sales Range: $100-124.9 Million
Emp.: 75
Provider of Film Processing, Editing & Titling; Motion Picture Photographing, Still or Video; Photofinishing Laboratory; Laser Printing
N.A.I.C.S.: 334610
Kenneth Wynne (Owner)
Elias T. Kabous (Controller)

Subsidiaries:

Cine Magnetics Video & Digital
Laboratories   (1)
3765 Cahuenga Blvd W, Studio City, CA 91604-3504   (100%)
Tel.: (818) 623-2560
Web Site: http://www.cminyla.com
Sales Range: $10-24.9 Million
Emp.: 12
Post Production Video Duplication Services
N.A.I.C.S.: 334610
Yelena Makarczyk (Dir-Localization Svcs)
John O'Connor (CTO)
Haitham Wahab (Co-Owner & CEO)

Cine Magnetics Video & Digital
Laboratories   (1)
100 Business Park Dr, Armonk, NY 10504   (100%)
Tel.: (914) 273-7500
Web Site: http://www.cinemagnetics.com
Emp.: 47
DVD, CD & Video Services
N.A.I.C.S.: 512199
Elias Kabous (Controller)

Cine Magnetics Video & Digital
Laboratories   (1)
957 Wheely Rd, Charlotte, VT 05445
Tel.: (802) 425-3131
Sales Range: $25-49.9 Million
N.A.I.C.S.: 561311

CINEMA ENTERTAINMENT CORP.

1621 Division St, Waite Park, MN 56387
Tel.: (320) 251-9131
Web Site:
    http://www.cectheaters.com
Sales Range: $10-24.9 Million
Emp.: 500
Motion Picture Theater, Except Drive-In
N.A.I.C.S.: 512131
Robert Ross (Pres)

CINEQUIPT INC.

2601 49th Ave N Ste 500, Minneapolis, MN 55430

Tel.: (612) 627-9080
Web Site: https://www.cinequipt.com
Sales Range: $25-49.9 Million
Emp.: 18
Rental & Leasing of Video Equipment
N.A.I.C.S.: 532289
Bryan Heiber (Mgr-Sls)
Kellie Kreller (Owner & CFO)
Dawn Mans (Pres)

CINERGY ENTERTAINMENT GROUP, INC.

8250 E Hwy 191, Odessa, TX 79765
Tel.: (432) 400-2444
Web Site: http://www.cinergy.com
Year Founded: 2008
Sales Range: $25-49.9 Million
Cinema Entertainment Services
N.A.I.C.S.: 512131
Jeff Benson (CEO)

CINETRANSFORMER INTERNATIONAL

134 South Dixie Hwy Ste 219, Miami, FL 33009
Tel.: (305) 576-5970
Web Site:
    http://www.cinetransformer.com
Sales Range: $10-24.9 Million
Emp.: 500
Entertainment, Event Marketing, Hispanic Marketing, Local Marketing, Sales Promotion
N.A.I.C.S.: 541810
Raul Fernandez (COO)
Michael Pine (VP-Bus Dev-North America)

CINFAB INC.

5240 Lester Rd, Cincinnati, OH 45213
Tel.: (513) 396-6100
Web Site: https://www.cinfab.com
Sales Range: $10-24.9 Million
Emp.: 40
Sheet Metalwork
N.A.I.C.S.: 238390
Doug Agricola (CEO)
Dave Davis (Treas)

CINIUM FINANCIAL SERVICES CORPORATION

195 Lake Louise Marie Rd, Rock Hill, NY 12775
Tel.: (845) 791-6700
Web Site: http://www.cinium.com
Year Founded: 2006
Sales Range: $1-9.9 Million
Emp.: 25
Holding Company: Specialty Insurance & Financial Programs
N.A.I.C.S.: 551112
Jeffrey Camp (Pres & CEO)
Robert Alan Berman (Co-Founder)

CINPAK, INC.

9200 Broadway St Ste 120, San Antonio, TX 78217
Tel.: (210) 967-9600
Web Site: http://www.cinpak.com
Year Founded: 1994
Non-Durable Goods Whslr
N.A.I.C.S.: 424990
Anthony Lasita (Pres)

Subsidiaries:

Henson Sales Group Ltd.   (1)
487 Devon Park Dr Ste 200, Wayne, PA 19087-1808
Tel.: (610) 971-9005
Web Site: http://www.hensonsales.com
Durable Goods Merchant Whslr
N.A.I.C.S.: 423990
Peter Henson (Owner)

CIO PARTNERS, INC.

2840 Johnson Ferry Rd Ste 250, Marietta, GA 30062
Tel.: (770) 971-0324
Web Site:
https://www.ciopartners.com
Year Founded: 2001
Sales Range: Less than $1 Million
Emp.: 8
Human Resouce Services
N.A.I.C.S.: 541612
H. Michael Burgett *(Pres, Mng Partner & VP)*

CIO SOLUTIONS

150 Castilian Dr #100, Goleta, CA 93117
Tel.: (805) 692-6700   CA
Web Site:
http://www.ciosolutions.com
Year Founded: 1986
Sales Range: $1-9.9 Million
Emp.: 35
Managed IT Networks & Technology Consulting Services
N.A.I.C.S.: 541512
John Petote *(Founder & Chm)*
Eric Egofl *(Pres)*
Hannah Rich *(Mgr-Media)*
Craig Prater *(CTO)*

CIOCIOLA COMMUNICATIONS, INC.

PO Box 276, Martins Creek, PA 18063
Tel.: (215) 429-5444   PA
Web Site: http://www.ciociola.com
Year Founded: 1983
Marketing Consulting Services
N.A.I.C.S.: 541613
Melvin Ciociola *(Founder & Pres)*

CIP CAPITAL FUND, L.P.

400 Madison Ave Ste 3A, New York, NY 10017
Tel.: (212) 257-5000
Web Site: http://www.cip-capital.com
Year Founded: 2010
Private Equity Investment Fund
N.A.I.C.S.: 525990
Scott Marden *(Mng Partner)*
Melissa Vlak *(COO & Mng Dlr)*
Yan Levinski *(VP)*
Kevin Formica *(Principal)*

Subsidiaries:

Carnegie Learning, Inc.   (1)
501 Grant St Union Trust Bldg Ste 1075, Pittsburgh, PA 15219
Web Site: http://www.carnegielearning.com
Math Education Material Publisher
N.A.I.C.S.: 513130
Barry Malkin *(CEO)*
Dennis Grinberg *(CTO)*
Chris Hedrick *(Chief Revenue Officer)*

Subsidiary (Domestic):

EMC School, LLC   (2)
875 Montreal Way, Saint Paul, MN 55102
Tel.: (800) 328-1452
Digital & Blended Language Learning Solutions Dist
N.A.I.C.S.: 611630
Eric Cantor *(Chm & CEO)*

Mondo Publishing, Inc.   (2)
980 Ave Of The Americas 2, New York, NY 10018
Tel.: (212) 268-3560
Web Site: http://www.mondopub.com
Book Publishers
N.A.I.C.S.: 513130
Mark Vineis *(Pres)*
Sallye Scott-Drinkard *(Mgr-Production)*
Yatin Bavishi *(CFO)*

Scientific Learning Corporation   (2)
1956 Webster St Ste 200, Oakland, CA 94612-2040
Tel.: (510) 444-3500

Web Site: http://www.scilearn.com
Rev.: $16,744,000
Assets: $8,897,000
Liabilities: $21,042,000
Net Worth: ($12,145,000)
Earnings: ($873,000)
Emp.: 100
Fiscal Year-end: 12/31/2018
Programs Developer & Services for Education
N.A.I.C.S.: 611710
Sherrelle Jiggitts Walker *(Chief Education Officer)*
Jeffrey Thomas *(CEO)*
Christopher J. Brookhart *(Gen Counsel, Sec & Sr VP)*
Steve Nathan *(CFO & Treas)*

CIPHER TECH SOLUTIONS, INC.

407 N Highland Ave, Nyack, NY 10960
Tel.: (845) 636-9606
Web Site:
http://www.ciphertechsolutions.com
Year Founded: 2006
Sales Range: $1-9.9 Million
Emp.: 20
Software Engineering
N.A.I.C.S.: 513210
Keith D. Bertolino *(CEO & Co-Founder)*
Matthew B. Kowalski *(Co-Founder & CTO)*

CIPHERMAX, INC.

3Results Way, Cupertino, CA 95014
Tel.: (408) 861-3697
Year Founded: 2000
Sales Range: $1-9.9 Million
Emp.: 94
Storage Security Solutions Software Mfr
N.A.I.C.S.: 334112
Keriyun J. Liu *(Co-Founder & VP-Asia Pacific Sls)*
John W. Jeng *(VP-Opers & Support)*
Jack LeWinter *(VP-Sls)*
Steven Tan *(VP-Engrg)*
Eugene Lee *(VP-Fin)*
Eugene Lee *(VP-Fin)*

CIPLEX

1621 Santa Monica Blvd, Los Angeles, CA 90038
Tel.: (310) 461-0330
Web Site: http://www.ciplex.com
Year Founded: 2000
Sales Range: $1-9.9 Million
Emp.: 45
Advertising & Marketing
N.A.I.C.S.: 541810
Ilya Pozin *(Founder & Pres)*
Nikola Mickic *(CEO)*
Adam Lilly *(Dir-Acct)*
Naiha Ali *(Office Mgr)*

CIRALIGHT GLOBAL, INC.

670 E Parkridge Ave Ste 112, Corona, CA 92879   NV
Web Site:
http://www.ciralightglobal.com
Year Founded: 2009
Sales Range: $1-9.9 Million
Emp.: 4
Advanced Skylight Mfr & Whslr
N.A.I.C.S.: 335132
Jeffrey S. Brain *(Pres, CEO, COO & Treas)*
Terry Scot Adams *(Chm)*

CIRCA CAPITAL CORPORATION

3100 McKinnon Ste 905, Dallas, TX 75201-7053
Tel.: (214) 954-4100
Web Site: http://www.circacapital.com
Sales Range: $10-24.9 Million

Emp.: 5
Operators of Hotels & Real Estate Managers
N.A.I.C.S.: 531210
Frank M. Aldridge *(Pres & CEO)*
Lamont L. Meek *(COO)*

Subsidiaries:

Hotel Venture LP   (1)
3100 McKinnon St Ste 905, Dallas, TX 75201-7016
Tel.: (214) 954-4100
Operators Of Nonresidential Buildings
N.A.I.C.S.: 531120

CIRCA CORPORATION

1330 Fitzgerald Ave, San Francisco, CA 94124
Tel.: (415) 822-1600
Web Site: http://www.circacorp.com
Year Founded: 1967
Sales Range: $25-49.9 Million
Emp.: 200
Mfr of Leather Belts
N.A.I.C.S.: 316990

CIRCA INC.

415 Madison Ave 19th Fl, New York, NY 10017
Tel.: (212) 486-6013
Web Site: http://www.circajewels.com
Year Founded: 1998
Sales Range: $75-99.9 Million
Support Services
N.A.I.C.S.: 561499
Jeffrey Singer *(Co-Founder & VP)*
Richard Tilles *(Co-Founder & Pres)*

CIRCADENCE CORPORATION

4888 Pearl E Cir Ste 101, Boulder, CO 80301
Tel.: (303) 413-8800
Web Site: http://www.circadence.com
Year Founded: 1995
Sales Range: $25-49.9 Million
Emp.: 120
Enterprise Technology Security Services
N.A.I.C.S.: 928110
Michael J. Moniz *(Founder & CEO)*
Christopher T. Blisard *(COO)*
Peter-Christian Olivo *(Gen Counsel & Exec VP)*
Todd L. Kannegieter *(VP-Fin)*
R. Bradley Prewitt *(VP-Govt Rels & Mississippi Sls)*
Alf L. Andreassen *(Chm)*
George Wright *(Exec VP-R&D)*
Kristy Butler *(Mgr-Mktg & Comm)*
Gary Morton *(VP-Product Delivery & Quality Assurance)*
John Nipp *(Sr VP-Cyber Ops)*
Keenan Skelly *(VP-Partnerships & Security Evangelist-Global)*
Laura Lee *(Exec VP-Cyber Trng & Assessments)*
Bradley Hayes *(CTO)*
John M. Harlan Jr. *(Owner & Pres)*

CIRCLE A CONSTRUCTION INC.

212 Highland Ave, Twin Falls, ID 83301
Tel.: (208) 734-5533
Sales Range: $10-24.9 Million
Emp.: 40
Local Trucking
N.A.I.C.S.: 484110
Marvin Aslett *(Pres)*
Steve Aslett *(CEO)*

CIRCLE AUTO GROUP

641 Shrewsbury Ave, Shrewsbury, NJ 07702
Tel.: (732) 741-3130

Web Site: https://www.circleauto.com
Rev.: $38,852,498
Emp.: 50
Automobiles, New & Used
N.A.I.C.S.: 441110
Dolores DeFelice *(Pres)*
Robert Kearns *(Mgr-Fin)*

CIRCLE BOLT & NUT COMPANY INC.

158 Pringle St, Kingston, PA 18704-2763
Tel.: (570) 718-6001
Web Site: http://www.circlebolts.com
Sales Range: $10-24.9 Million
Emp.: 75
Nuts (Hardware)
N.A.I.C.S.: 423710
Mary Kay Sperling *(Treas)*
Jim Castellino *(Pres)*

CIRCLE CITY BROADCASTING INC.

1950 N Meridian St, Indianapolis, IN 46202
Tel.: (317) 956-8863
Web Site:
http://www.circlecitybroadcasting.com
Broadcast & Digital News Media Network
N.A.I.C.S.: 516210
DuJuan A. McCoy *(Owner, Pres & CEO)*

CIRCLE COMPUTER RESOURCES, INC.

845 Capital Dr, Cedar Rapids, IA 52404-4426
Tel.: (319) 362-2384   IA
Web Site: https://www.ccr.net
Year Founded: 1986
Sales Range: $1-9.9 Million
Emp.: 85
Specialized IT Services
N.A.I.C.S.: 541511
Marie Tessau *(Mgr-HR)*

Subsidiaries:

Orbit Business Technologies   (1)
845 Capital Dr SW, Cedar Rapids, IA 52404
Tel.: (800) 492-3913
Web Site: https://orbittechnology.com
IT Consulting Services
N.A.I.C.S.: 518210

Sandwire Corp.   (1)
990 Stewart Ave Ste 450, Garden City, NY 11530
Tel.: (516) 334-8880
Web Site: http://www.sandwire.com
Rev.: $1,570,000
Emp.: 10
Custom Computer Programming Services
N.A.I.C.S.: 541511
Adam Schwam *(Pres)*

CIRCLE FURNITURE INC.

19 Craig Rd, Acton, MA 01720
Tel.: (978) 263-4509
Web Site:
http://www.circlefurniture.com
Sales Range: $10-24.9 Million
Emp.: 50
Furniture Retailer
N.A.I.C.S.: 449110
Harold Tubman *(Pres)*
Richard Tubman *(Treas)*
Peggy Burns *(Owner)*

CIRCLE HOME, INC.

847 Rogers St Ste 201, Lowell, MA 01852
Tel.: (978) 459-9343   MA
Web Site:
http://www.circlehomehealth.org
Year Founded: 1909
Sales Range: $10-24.9 Million
Emp.: 147

Circle Home, Inc.—(Continued)
Healthcare Services
N.A.I.C.S.: 622110
Rachel Chaddock (Exec Dir)
Jonathan Mitchell (Dir-IT Svcs)

CIRCLE IMPORTS
1850 Outer Traffic Cir Dr, Long
Beach, CA 90815
Tel.: (562) 597-3663
Year Founded: 1977
Sales Range: $10-24.9 Million
Emp.: 62
New Car Whslr
N.A.I.C.S.: 441110
Rudolph Erm (Pres & Treas)
Michael Harrison (Mgr-Fin)

CIRCLE INFINITI
300 Hwy 36, West Long Branch, NJ
07764
Tel.: (732) 389-1200
Web Site: http://www.circleinfiniti.com
Sales Range: $10-24.9 Million
Emp.: 34
Car Whslr
N.A.I.C.S.: 441110
Daniella Albano (Principal)
David DeFilippo (Gen Mgr)
Ed Lennon (Pres)

CIRCLE INTERNET FINAN-CIAL, LLC
99 High St, Ste. 1701, Boston, MA
02110
Tel.: (888) 762-4966
Web Site: https://www.circle.com
Year Founded: 2013
Emp.: 100
Financial Services
N.A.I.C.S.: 523999
Jeremy Allaire (Founder & CEO)

CIRCLE OF LIFE HOSPICE
901 Jones Rd, Springdale, AR 72762
Tel.: (479) 750-6632   **AR**
Web Site:
https://www.nwacircleoflife.com
Year Founded: 2000
Sales Range: Less than $1 Million
Emp.: 200
Hospice Care Services
N.A.I.C.S.: 623110
Catherine Grubbs (CEO)
Diya LeDuc (Chief Clinical Officer)
Ryan Langston (CFO)
Jett Cato (Treas & Sec)
Dee Bowers (Chief Dev Officer)

CIRCLE PEAK CAPITAL LLC
270 Lafayette St Ste 1400, New York,
NY 10012
Tel.: (646) 230-8812
Web Site:
http://www.circlepeakcapital.com
Year Founded: 2002
Sales Range: $300-349.9 Million
Emp.: 3
Private Investment Firm
N.A.I.C.S.: 523940
R. Adam Smith (Founder, Pres &
CEO)

Subsidiaries:

Rocket Dog Brands, LLC   **(1)**
11854 S Alameda St, Lynwood, CA 90262
Web Site: http://www.rocketdog.com
Footwear Designer, Developer & Distr
N.A.I.C.S.: 316210

CIRCLE PRESSROOM, INC.
121 Varick St 1 St Fl, New York, NY
10013
Tel.: (212) 924-4277

Web Site:
http://www.circlepressroom.com
Rev.: $13,000,000
Emp.: 80
Provider of Commercial Printing Ser-
vices
N.A.I.C.S.: 323111

CIRCLE STAR ENERGY CORP.
7065 Confederate Park Rd Ste 102,
Fort Worth, TX 76108
Tel.: (817) 744-8502   **NV**
Web Site:
http://www.circlestarenergy.com
Year Founded: 2007
Sales Range: Less than $1 Million
Emp.: 3
Gas & Oil Investment Services
N.A.I.C.S.: 211120
Jayme Wollison (VP-Ops)
S. Jeffrey Johnson (Founder, Chm,
CEO, Interim CFO & Interim Sec)

CIRCLE T WESTERN WEAR INC.
5349 Drane Dr, Dallas, TX 75209-
5501
Tel.: (214) 351-5553
Sales Range: $10-24.9 Million
Emp.: 42
Mfr of Women's & Juniors' Shirts
N.A.I.C.S.: 315250
William W. Lenox (Pres)

CIRCUIT VISION INC.
12411 Telecom Dr, Tampa, FL 33637
Tel.: (813) 972-2441
Web Site:
http://www.circuitvision.com
Sales Range: $10-24.9 Million
Emp.: 24
Software Developer
N.A.I.C.S.: 513210
E. Beegle (Pres)
Félix Hernández (CTO & VP)

CIRCUITRONICS, INC
1920 Hurd Dr, Irving, TX 75038
Tel.: (972) 573-1140   **TX**
Web Site:
http://www.circuitronics.com
Year Founded: 1971
Sales Range: $1-9.9 Million
Emp.: 40
Electronic Products Mfr
N.A.I.C.S.: 334419
Renee Rumpf (CFO)
Tim Harmon (VP-Ops)
Ken Mount (Mgr-Quality)

CIRCULAR CONNECTORS INC.
3250 Corte Malpaso, Camarillo, CA
93012
Tel.: (805) 987-8145
Web Site: https://www.circularinc.com
Rev.: $10,000,000
Emp.: 24
Connectors, Electronic
N.A.I.C.S.: 423690
Dan Van Gelderen (Gen Mgr)

CIRCUSTRIX LLC
PO Box 302, Provo, UT 84603
Tel.: (385) 482-1020
Web Site: http://www.circustrix.com
Year Founded: 2011
Recreational Park Operator
N.A.I.C.S.: 713990
Case Lawrence (Founder & Chm)
Rich Cook (COO)
Steve Chesnut (CFO)
Zane Hansen (VP)
Brendan Burke (CMO)

Subsidiaries:

Rockin' Jump Holdings LLC   **(1)**
5000 Hopyard Rd Ste 301, Pleasanton, CA
94588
Tel.: (925) 828-7676
Web Site: http://www.rockinjump.com
Amusement & Recreation Industries
N.A.I.C.S.: 713990
Mike Gray (VP-Mktg)

CIRQUE ENERGY, INC.
414 W Wackerly St, Midland, MI
48640-4701
Tel.: (989) 266-9100
Year Founded: 1998
Emp.: 4
Energy Renewable Services
N.A.I.C.S.: 221118
Roger Silverthorn (Chm, Pres &
CEO)

CIRSCO, INC.
311 S Falkenburg Rd, Tampa, FL
33619
Tel.: (813) 655-8080
Web Site: https://www.cirsco.com
Year Founded: 2002
Sales Range: $1-9.9 Million
Emp.: 28
Roof Consulting & Project Manage-
ment to Multiple-Facility Building
Owners
N.A.I.C.S.: 238160
Hig M. Rodriguez Dillinger (Pres)

CIS INC.
18 Chatham Ctr S, Savannah, GA
31405
Tel.: (912) 236-5440
Rev.: $20,615,413
Emp.: 23
Life Insurance Agency
N.A.I.C.S.: 524210

CISCO BROS. CORP.
5955 S Western Ave, Los Angeles,
CA 90047-1124
Tel.: (323) 778-8612
Web Site:
http://www.ciscobrothers.com
Year Founded: 1990
Nonupholstered & Upholstered Wood
Household Furniture Mfr, Distr & Re-
tailer
N.A.I.C.S.: 337122
Francisco Pinedo (CEO)

Subsidiaries:

Cisco Home, Inc.   **(1)**
5955 S Western Ave, Los Angeles, CA
90047-1124
Tel.: (323) 778-8612
Web Site: http://www.ciscobrothers.com
Household Furniture Retailer
N.A.I.C.S.: 449110
Francisco Pinedo (CEO)

Environment Furniture, Inc.   **(1)**
8126 Beverly Blvd Ste 108, Los Angeles,
CA 90048
Tel.: (323) 935-1330
Web Site:
http://www.environmentfurniture.com
Sales Range: $10-24.9 Million
Emp.: 13
Manufactures & Wholesales Furniture Prod-
ucts
N.A.I.C.S.: 337122
Camilla Trigano (Dir-Mktg)
Davide Berruto (Creative Dir)

CISCO FORD EQUIPMENT, INC.
520 SE Loop 338, Odessa, TX 79762
Tel.: (432) 367-9181
Web Site: https://www.cisco-
equipment.com
Year Founded: 1978

Industrial Machinery & Equipment
Rental & Sales
N.A.I.C.S.: 423830
CJ Sibert (COO)

Subsidiaries:

Cisco Equipment - Artesia   **(1)**
1706 S 1st St, Artesia, NM 88210
Tel.: (575) 748-1314
Web Site: http://www.cisco-equipment.com
Farm & Construction Equipment Rental &
Sales
N.A.I.C.S.: 532412

Cisco Equipment - Lubbock   **(1)**
2707 Slaton Hwy, Lubbock, TX 79404
Tel.: (806) 745-9595
Web Site: http://www.cisco-equipment.com
Farm & Construction Equipment Rental &
Sales
N.A.I.C.S.: 423820
Brad Sibert (Gen Mgr)
Woody Wilson (Mgr-Ops & Sls)
Rockey Hernandez (Mgr-Parts)
Tim Allison (Mgr-Svc)

Cisco Equipment - San Angelo   **(1)**
620 N Bell St, San Angelo, TX 76903
Tel.: (325) 653-2121
Web Site: http://www.cisco-equipment.com
Farm & Construction Equipment Rental &
Sales
N.A.I.C.S.: 423820
Bob Crenshaw (Gen Mgr)
Joel Senior (Mgr-Rental)
John Maier (Mgr-Rental)
Marty Behrens (Sls Mgr)
Billy Goetz (Mgr-Svc)

CISCO-EAGLE INC.
2120 Vly View Ln, Dallas, TX 75234-
8911
Tel.: (972) 406-9330
Web Site: http://www.cisco-
eagle.com
Sales Range: $10-24.9 Million
Emp.: 80
Provider of Storage & Handling Ser-
vices
N.A.I.C.S.: 423830
Warren W. Gandall (Chm & CEO)
Chris Doyle (Dir-Mktg)

Subsidiaries:

Cisco-Eagle Inc.   **(1)**
5208 S 100th E Ave, Tulsa, OK 74146-5729
Tel.: (918) 622-9010
Provider of Materials Movement, Storage &
Handling Services
N.A.I.C.S.: 423830
Scott Stone (Mgr-Adv)
Tammy Barnes (Controller)

Cisco-Eagle Inc. - Little Rock   **(1)**
1419 WestPark Ste F, Little Rock, AR
72204
Tel.: (501) 562-1985
Web Site: http://www.cisco-eagle.com
Material Handling Services
N.A.I.C.S.: 561499
Warren W. Gandall (Chm & CEO)
Chris Doyle (Dir-Sls-Texas)
Robert S. Hauck (CIO & VP)
James Murphy (Dir-Sls-Arkansas)
Scott Stone (Dir-Mktg)
Larry Trowbridge (Dir-Ops)

Cisco-Eagle Incorporated   **(1)**
6000 NW 2nd St Ste 400, Oklahoma City,
OK 73127
Tel.: (405) 947-7706
Web Site: http://www.ciscoeagle.com
Design And Sales Of Industrial Equipments
N.A.I.C.S.: 423830
Mark Wertz (VP-Sls)
Susan Poole (Gen Mgr)

CISIVE INC.
5000 Corporate Ct Ste 203, Holts-
ville, NY 11742
Tel.: (631) 862-9300
Web Site: https://www.cisive.com
Year Founded: 1977

Human Capital & Risk Management Solution Services
N.A.I.C.S.: 541612
James C. Owens (Pres)
Peter L. O'Neill (Chm)
Bruce E. Berger (Chief Compliance Officer, Sec & VP)
Fred G. Giles (Sr VP-Strategic Initiatives)
John Davidson (Sr VP-Res)
Robert Pichler (VP-Ops-Inspection Div)
Dave Bennett (COO)
William Pagan (Sr VP-Inspection)
Paul Jackson (Sr VP-Bus Dev)
Pauline Smith (VP)
Alan Gordon (Pres-Fin & Bus Svcs)
Larry Neal (CEO)

Subsidiaries:

PreCheck, Inc.   (1)
2500 East TC Jester Blvd Ste 600, Houston, TX 77008
Tel.: (713) 861-5959
Web Site: http://www.precheck.com
Health Care Srvices
N.A.I.C.S.: 813212
Robert Sartain (Chm)
Vinh Nguyen (Exec Dir-IT)
Glenn Woolsey (CEO)
Dana Sangerhausen (VP-Ops)
Bruce Butler (Treas)
Vu Do (VP-Compliance)
Zach Daigle (Pres)
Tom Combs (VP-Govt Affairs)
Rene Hatfield (Dir-HR)
Rick Dittamore (Controller-Acctg & Fin)
Debbie Klarfeld (VP-Product Strategy)
Darrin Fagan (Exec VP-Sls, Mktg & Strategic Partnerships)

CITADEL COMMUNICATIONS LLC

117 Pondfield Rd Ste 12, Bronxville, NY 10708-4103
Tel.: (914) 793-3400   VT
Web Site: http://www.citadelltd.com
Sales Range: $25-49.9 Million
Emp.: 200
Holding Company; Television Broadcasting Stations Owner & Operator
N.A.I.C.S.: 551112
Philip Lombardo (CEO)
Ray Cole (Pres & COO)
Colleen Gally (CFO)

CITADEL ENTERPRISE AMERICAS LLC

131 S Dearborn St, Chicago, IL 60603
Tel.: (312) 395-2100   DE
Web Site: http://www.citadel.com
Year Founded: 1990
Sales Range: $25-49.9 Million
Emp.: 325
Investment Services
N.A.I.C.S.: 523999
Kenneth Cordele Griffin (Founder, CEO & Co-Chief Investment Officer)
Gerald A. Beeson (COO)
Edwin Lin (Head-Global Fixed Income)
James Yeh (Pres & Co-Chief Investment Officer)
Navneet Arora (Head-Global Quantitative Strategies)
Sebastian Barrack (Head-Commodities)
Phillip Lee (Head-Surveyor Capital)
Justin Lubell (Head-Citadel Global Equities)
Sean Salji (Head-Intl Equities)
Pablo Salame (Head-Global Credit)
Matt Simon (Head-Ashler Capital)
Joanna Welsh (Chief Risk Officer)
Shawn Fagan (Chief Legal Officer)
Tripp Kyle (Chief Corp Affairs & Comm Officer)

Ed O'Reilly (Sr Mng Dir & Head-Client & Partner Grp-Global)
Andrew Philipp (CFO)
Umesh Subramanian (CTO)

CITADEL FEDERAL SOLUTIONS LLC

2201 Cooperative Way Ste 600, Herndon, VA 20171
Web Site: http://www.falcontek.com
Year Founded: 2008
Sales Range: $1-9.9 Million
Emp.: 50
Staffing & Recruiting Services
N.A.I.C.S.: 561311
David Courtney (Exec VP-Defense & Intel)
Shane Prosser (Pres)
Brandon Nelson (Pres)
Brandon Nelson (Pres)

Subsidiaries:

Core Mission Solutions, LLC   (1)
3135 Green Vly Rd, Clover, VA 24534-3183
Tel.: (434) 454-6237
Web Site:
   http://www.coremissionsolutions.com
Translation & Interpretation Services
N.A.I.C.S.: 541930
David Courtney (CEO)
Daryll Toomer (CEO)

CITADEL INSURANCE SERVICES, LC

826 E State Rd Ste 100, American Fork, UT 84003
Tel.: (801) 610-2700
Web Site: https://www.citadelus.com
Year Founded: 2007
Sales Range: $1-9.9 Million
Emp.: 20
Specialty Insurance Program Broker
N.A.I.C.S.: 524210
Anthony Eardley (Mng Partner)
Heather Ricks (Acct Mgr-Insurance)
Bret Christopherson (Program Dir)

CITARELLA

2135 Broadway, New York, NY 10023
Tel.: (212) 874-0383   NY
Web Site: http://www.citarella.com
Year Founded: 1912
Sales Range: $10-24.9 Million
Emp.: 700
Gourmet & Specialty Grocer
N.A.I.C.S.: 445110
Anthony Castagnazzi (Supvr-Store)

CITATION GLOBAL, INC.

5111 N Scottsdale Rd Ste 200, Scottsdale, AZ 85250
Tel.: (480) 994-4560   AZ
Web Site:
   http://www.citationtechnologies.com
Environmental, Health & Safety Compliance Management Software Publisher
N.A.I.C.S.: 513210
David Carlson (Pres & CEO)
Sam Buffington (CFO)
Tom Bonetto (Sr VP-Sls & Mktg)

CITATION OIL & GAS CORP.

14077 Cutten Rd, Houston, TX 77069-2212
Tel.: (281) 891-1000
Web Site: https://www.cogc.com
Year Founded: 1985
Sales Range: $25-49.9 Million
Emp.: 300
Crude Petroleum & Natural Gas
N.A.I.C.S.: 211120
Wayne Wiesen (Gen Counsel, Sec & Sr VP)
Mark Bing (Mgr-Central Reg)
Thomas Patrick (VP-Taxation)

Eddie Harrell (Chm)
Craig K. Townsend (VP & Controller)
Curtis F. Harrell (Pres & CEO)

Subsidiaries:

Citation Crude Marketing, Inc.   (1)
14077 Cutten Rd, Houston, TX 77069
Tel.: (281) 891-1000
Web Site: http://cogc.com
Sales Range: $25-49.9 Million
Emp.: 170
Wholesalers of Petroleum Products
N.A.I.C.S.: 424720
Curtis Harrel (CEO)
Doris C. Anderson (Mgr-Acctg)
Mark A. Anchondo (VP-Info Sys)
Nancy A. Anglin (VP-HR)
Steve K. Anna (COO & Sr VP)
Scott A. Loosley (VP-Comml Activities & Bus Dev)
Thomas E. Patrick (VP-Taxation)
Christopher A. Phelps (CFO, Chief Admin Officer & Sr VP)
Craig K. Townsend (VP & Controller)
Wayne Wiesen (Gen Counsel, Sec & Sr VP)

CITCO COMMUNITY BANCSHARES, INC.

300 Broad St, Elizabethton, TN 37643
Tel.: (423) 543-2265   TN
Web Site:
   http://www.citizensbank24.com
Year Founded: 1994
Bank Holding Company
N.A.I.C.S.: 551111
Larry Estepp (Pres)
C. Scott Greer (CFO, COO & Exec VP)
Joe LaPorte III (Chm & CEO)

Subsidiaries:

Citizens Bank   (1)
300 Broad St, Elizabethton, TN 37643
Tel.: (423) 543-2265
Web Site: http://www.citizensbank24.com
Sales Range: $50-74.9 Million
Emp.: 193
Commericial Banking
N.A.I.C.S.: 522110
Sam LaPorte (Vice Chm)
Richard C. Tetrick (Sec)
Larry Estepp (Pres)
C. Scott Greer (CFO, COO & Exec VP)
Joe LaPorte III (Chm & CEO)

CITG CAPITAL PARTNERS, LLC

354 Indusco Ct, Troy, MI 48083
Web Site: http://www.citgcapital.com
Privater Equity Firm
N.A.I.C.S.: 523999
Naimish Patel (Mng Dir)

CITI PERFORMING ARTS CENTER, INC.

270 Tremont St, Boston, MA 02116
Tel.: (617) 482-9393
Web Site: http://www.citicenter.org
Rev.: $34,000,000
Emp.: 40
Performing Arts Center
N.A.I.C.S.: 711310
Eric Neill (Dir-Theatre Ops)
Michael Szczepkowski (VP & Gen Mgr)
Josiah A. Spaulding Jr. (Pres & CEO)
Joanne Stanway (Sr Dir-Mktg & Comm)
Corey Evans (Sr Dir-Education)
Vivian Baguer Holland (Assoc Dir-Special Projects)
Christine Callahan (Asst Treas-Box Office)
Wendell Webb (Asst Treas-Box Office)
John Perkins (CFO)

Sue Dahling Sullivan (Chief Strategic Officer)
Lisa Muise (Controller)
Ashley McGlone (Dir-Annual Giving & Database Mgmt)
Joe Donlavey (Dir-Sls & Corp Dev)
Francis X. Moynihan (Mgr-Budgeting & Fin Reporting)
Marie Coste (Mgr-Grants)
Chris Bullock (Mgr-Production)
Sean Gilbertson (Mgr-Special Events)
Paul Guzzi (Chm)

CITIBANK CREDIT CARD ISSUANCE TRUST

388 Greenwich St, New York, NY 10013
Tel.: (212) 559-1000   DE
Year Founded: 2000
Credit Financial Support Services
N.A.I.C.S.: 522210
Bennett L. Kyte (VP)

CITICORP TRUST SOUTH DAKOTA

5800 S Corporate Pl Mc482, Sioux Falls, SD 57108
Tel.: (605) 370-6261
Asset Management Services
N.A.I.C.S.: 523999

CITIES WEST PUBLISHING

6310 E Thomas Rd Ste 200, Scottsdale, AZ 85251
Tel.: (480) 664-3960
Web Site:
   http://www.phoenixmag.com
Rev.: $5,000,000
Emp.: 50
Publisher of Guide to Local Entertainment Social Events
N.A.I.C.S.: 513120
Mike Shoemaker (CFO)
Bill Phalen (CEO)
Rie Walsh (Controller)
Ron Matejko (Dir-Mktg)

CITIHOPE INTERNATIONAL, INC.

629 Main St Ste 2, Margaretville, NY 12455
Tel.: (845) 586-6202   NY
Web Site: http://www.citihope.org
Year Founded: 1979
Sales Range: $75-99.9 Million
Emp.: 10
Social Welfare & Public Relation Services
N.A.I.C.S.: 813410
Letty Johnson (Dir-Donor Rels)
Hannah Estifanos (Dir-Food & Nutrition Programs)
Jessica Moore (CFO)
Thomas Smock (Treas)
Austin Landes (COO)
Andre Muelenaer (Chief Medical Officer & VP)
Paul Moore Sr. (Chm)
Paul S. Moore II (Pres & CEO)

CITIROOF CORPORATION

9510 Berger Rd, Columbia, MD 21046-1577
Tel.: (410) 381-3100
Web Site: https://www.citiroof.com
Year Founded: 1990
Sales Range: $10-24.9 Million
Emp.: 50
Roofing Installation Services
N.A.I.C.S.: 238390
Sally Bond (Controller)

CITIUSTECH INC.

2 Research Way, 2nd Fl, Princeton, NJ 08540
Tel.: (877) 248-4871

CitiusTech Inc—(Continued)

Web Site: http://www.citiustech.com
Year Founded: 2005
Healthcare Technology Services
N.A.I.C.S.: 621999
William Winkenwerder *(Chm)*
Eric Schultz *(Exec VP)*
Bhaskar Sambasivan *(Pres)*
Rizwan Koita *(Co-Founder)*
Jagdish Moorjani *(Co-Founder & COO)*
Sudhir Kesavan *(COO)*
Rajan Kohli *(CEO)*

Subsidiaries:

FluidEdge Consulting, Inc.   (1)
565 E Swedesford Rd Ste 214, Wayne, PA 19087
Tel.: (610) 293-1830
Web Site:
    http://www.fluidedgeconsulting.com
Sales Range: $1-9.9 Million
Emp.: 38
Healthcare & Management Consulting Services
N.A.I.C.S.: 541611
Mike Green *(Mng Partner)*
Sean White *(VP)*
Mary Ellen Moakes *(VP)*
Scott Shohen *(Partner-Life Sciences Practice)*
Carolyn Luther *(Partner)*
Marty Brennan *(Partner)*
Sharon Wolf *(VP-Bus Intelligence & Informatics)*
Eric Schultz *(Pres)*

SDLC Partners, L.P.   (1)
1 PPG Place Ste 3200, Pittsburgh, PA 15222
Tel.: (412) 251-0848
Web Site: http://www.sdlcpartners.com
Management Consulting Services
N.A.I.C.S.: 541618
Christy Maruca *(Founder)*
Alan Lawson *(CTO)*
Chris Simchick *(CEO)*

CITIZANT INC.

15000 Conference Center Dr Ste 500, Chantilly, VA 20151
Tel.: (703) 667-9420
Web Site: http://www.citizant.com
Year Founded: 1999
Sales Range: $10-24.9 Million
Emp.: 200
Custom Computer Programming Services
N.A.I.C.S.: 541511
Alba M. Aleman *(CEO)*
Bruce Milligan *(VP-Mktg)*
Greg Gorgone *(CFO)*
Sheila Murphy *(VP-Recruiting)*
Tammi Carnes *(VP-HR)*
David Romola *(Pres & COO)*

CITIZEN ENERGY OPERATING LLC

320 S Boston Ave Ste 900, Tulsa, OK 74103
Tel.: (918) 949-4680
Web Site:
    http://www.citizenenergyok.com
Year Founded: 2012
Oil & Energy Exploration Services
N.A.I.C.S.: 333132
Rick Gideon *(CEO)*

Subsidiaries:

Blue Mountain Midstream LLC   (1)
320 S Boston Ave Ste 900, Tulsa, OK 74103
Tel.: (918) 949-4680
Web Site:
    http://www.bluemountainmidstream.com
Oil & Gas Services
N.A.I.C.S.: 213112
Greg Harper *(Pres & CEO)*
Brad Reese *(Chief Dev Officer & Exec VP)*

David Weathers *(Chief Comml Officer & Exec VP)*
Chris Ditzel *(COO & Exec VP)*
Noor Kaissi *(CFO)*

Pressburg, LLC   (1)
14701 Hertz Quail Springs Pkwy, Oklahoma City, OK 73134
Tel.: (405) 896-8050
Natural Gas Distribution Services
N.A.I.C.S.: 221210

Subsidiary (Domestic):

Linn Energy, Inc.   (2)
600 Travis, Houston, TX 77002
Tel.: (281) 840-4000
Web Site: http://www.linnenergy.com
Holding Company; Petroleum & Natural Gas Extraction
N.A.I.C.S.: 551112

Subsidiary (Domestic):

Linn Energy Holdings, LLC   (3)
600 Travis Ste 1400, Houston, TX 77002
Tel.: (281) 840-4000
Holding Company
N.A.I.C.S.: 551112

CITIZEN ENGAGEMENT LABORATORY

2150 Allston Way Ste 360, Berkeley, CA 94704
Tel.: (510) 875-2135   CA
Web Site:
    http://www.engagementlab.org
Year Founded: 2008
Sales Range: $10-24.9 Million
Emp.: 68
Social Welfare Services
N.A.I.C.S.: 813410
Catherine Huang *(Dir-Tech)*
Jackie Mahendra *(Dir-Strategic Collaboration)*
Rae Thomas *(Mgr-HR & Ops)*
Heidi Gatty *(Dir-Accleration Svcs Program)*
Julia Rhodes Davis *(Chief Dev Officer)*
Gaurav Vashist *(CFO)*
Hannah Pham *(Mgr-HR)*
Jane Barker *(Mgr-Fin)*
Jennifer Cheyne *(Mgr-Acceleration Svcs Program)*
Jessi Burger *(Accountant)*
Robin Beck *(Dir-Innovation)*
Tracy Van-Slyke *(Dir-Culture Lab)*
Vanessa Rose Pierce *(Dir-Ops & HR)*
Vanessa Fajans-Turner *(Chm)*
Fenny Choo *(Co-CFO)*

CITIZEN, INC.

2001 NW 19th Ave Ste 105, Portland, OR 97209
Tel.: (800) 928-6890
Web Site: http://www.pluscitizen.com
Year Founded: 2005
Sales Range: $10-24.9 Million
Emp.: 32
Mobile Strategy & Design, Conceptualization, Technical Strategy & Implementation of Media Content & Consumer Apps
N.A.I.C.S.: 541613
Drew Klonsky *(Founder)*
Piper Carr *(Chief Strategy Officer)*
Kate Sommers *(Dir-Ops)*
Jenny Moede *(CEO)*

CITIZENS 1ST BANK

125 N Main St, Rusk, TX 75785
Tel.: (903) 683-2277
Web Site:
    https://www.citizens1stbank.com
Year Founded: 1920
Sales Range: $25-49.9 Million
Emp.: 58
Provider of Banking Services
N.A.I.C.S.: 522110

James I. Perkins *(Chm & Pres)*
Amanda Gray *(Asst VP)*

CITIZENS B & T HOLDINGS, INC.

717 Gunter Ave, Guntersville, AL 35976
Tel.: (256) 505-4600
Web Site:
    http://www.citizensbanktrust.com
Year Founded: 2006
CBTH—(OTCBB)
Bank Holding Company
N.A.I.C.S.: 551111
Charlie Williams *(Pres & CEO)*

Subsidiaries:

Citizens Bank & Trust   (1)
404 Gunter Ave, Guntersville, AL 35976
Tel.: (256) 505-4600
Web Site: http://www.citizensbanktrust.com
Sales Range: $1-9.9 Million
Emp.: 22
Banking
N.A.I.C.S.: 522110
Stanley Patterson *(Exec VP)*
Michael Alred *(VP)*

CITIZENS BANCORPORATION OF NEW ULM, INC.

105 N Minnesota St, New Ulm, MN 56073
Tel.: (507) 354-3165   MN
Web Site: http://www.citizensmn.com
Year Founded: 1982
Sales Range: $10-24.9 Million
Emp.: 74
Bank Holding Company
N.A.I.C.S.: 551111
Lou Geistfeld *(Pres)*
Bill Brennan *(Sr VP)*
Mark Furth *(Chm)*
Mark Furth *(Chm)*

Subsidiaries:

Citizens Bank Minnesota   (1)
105 N Minnesota St, New Ulm, MN 56073
Tel.: (507) 354-3165
Web Site: http://www.citizensmn.com
Retail & Commercial Banking
N.A.I.C.S.: 522110
Lou Geistfeld *(Pres)*
Bill Brennan *(Sr VP)*
Mark Furth *(Chm)*

CITIZENS BANCSHARES CORPORATION

124 E Main St, Olanta, SC 29114
Tel.: (843) 657-2001   SC
Web Site:
    http://www.thecitizensbank.cc
Sales Range: $10-24.9 Million
Emp.: 118
Bank Holding Company
N.A.I.C.S.: 551111
C. Dorn Smith III *(Chm & CEO)*
H. Blake Gibbons Jr. *(Pres & COO)*

Subsidiaries:

The Citizens Bank   (1)
124 E Main St, Olanta, SC 29114
Tel.: (843) 396-4314
Web Site: http://www.thecitizensbank.cc
Sales Range: $10-24.9 Million
Commercial Banking
N.A.I.C.S.: 522110
Ashley Wheeler *(Sr VP)*
H. Blake Gibbons Jr. *(Pres & COO)*
C. Dorn Smith III *(Chm & CEO)*

CITIZENS BANCSHARES OF BATESVILLE, INC.

655 St Louis St, Batesville, AR 72501
Tel.: (870) 793-4441   AR
Web Site:
    https://www.thecitizensbank.net
Year Founded: 1984
Sales Range: $50-74.9 Million

Emp.: 150
Bank Holding Company
N.A.I.C.S.: 551111

Subsidiaries:

The Citizens Bank   (1)
200 S 3rd St, Batesville, AR 72501
Tel.: (870) 793-4441
Web Site: http://www.citizensbank.net
Sales Range: $50-74.9 Million
Personal & Commercial Banking & Lending Services
N.A.I.C.S.: 522110
Karen Shaw *(Sr VP-Retail Banking)*
Greg Shaver *(Exec VP)*
Ron Lewallen *(Officer-Credit Admin & VP)*
Robin Brock *(Sr VP)*
Pam Jones *(Sr VP-Loan Ops)*
Don Hale *(Sr VP-Mktg)*
Tim Byers *(VP-Mktg)*
Phil Baldwin *(CEO)*
Janet Moore *(COO & Exec VP)*
Scott Hammerbacher *(Sr VP)*
Michael Dolan *(Sr VP)*
Katherine Harris *(Asst VP & Branch Mgr-Retail)*
Adam Mitchell *(Pres)*
Melissa Wood *(Mgr-Retail-Eagle Mountain)*
Scott Shelby *(Mgr-Retail-Imboden)*

CITIZENS BANCSHARES OF HUTCHISON, INC.

102 Main St S, Hutchinson, MN 55350
Tel.: (320) 587-2233   MN
Web Site: http://www.cbhutch.com
Year Founded: 1967
Sales Range: $1-9.9 Million
Emp.: 40
Bank Holding Company
N.A.I.C.S.: 551111
Thomas A. Burich *(Chm & CEO)*
Timothy B. Ulrich *(Vice Chm, Sec, Pres/COO-Comml & AG Lending)*
Michael P. Cannon *(Exec VP-Personal Banking & Comm Lending)*
Anthony Hanson *(Exec VP-Comml Lending)*

Subsidiaries:

Citizens Bank & Trust Co.   (1)
102 Main St S, Hutchinson, MN 55350
Tel.: (320) 587-2233
Web Site: http://www.cbhutch.com
Sales Range: $1-9.9 Million
Emp.: 42
Retail & Commercial Banking
N.A.I.C.S.: 522110
Thomas A. Burich *(Chm & CEO)*
Timothy B. Ulrich *(Vice Chm, Pres, COO-Comml & Ag Lending & Sec)*
Michael P. Cannon *(Exec VP-Personal Banking & Comml Lending)*
Anthony Hanson *(Exec VP-Comml Lending)*

CITIZENS BANCSHARES, INC.

102 S Main St, Bluffton, OH 45817
Tel.: (419) 224-0400   OH
Web Site: https://www.cnbohio.com
Year Founded: 2003
Sales Range: $100-124.9 Million
Emp.: 150
Bank Holding Company
N.A.I.C.S.: 551111
J. Michael Romey *(Pres & CEO)*

Subsidiaries:

The Citizens National Bank of Bluffton   (1)
102 S Main St, Bluffton, OH 45817
Tel.: (419) 358-8040
Web Site: http://www.cnbohio.com
Sales Range: $100-124.9 Million
Emp.: 28
Retail & Commercial Banking
N.A.I.C.S.: 522110
J. Michael Romey *(CEO)*
Bob Everett *(Controller)*
Tom Moorhead *(VP)*

Wally Buroker (VP)
Pat Ryan (Sr VP)
Eric Faulkner (Pres & CEO)

CITIZENS BANCSHARES, INC.
1 E 1st St, Edmond, OK 73034
Tel.: (405) 359-2697 OK
Web Site:
http://www.citizensedmond.com
Year Founded: 1998
Sales Range: $10-24.9 Million
Emp.: 65
Bank Holding Company
N.A.I.C.S.: 551111
Jill Castilla (Pres & CEO)
Mike Thompson (Chm)
Lisa Trent (CFO & Officer-Info Security)
W. Roger Webb (Vice Chm)
Bill Nelson (Chief Credit Officer & Exec VP)
Chelsea Bradshaw (Chief Risk Officer)
Cynthia Hendershot (COO)

Subsidiaries:

The Citizens Bank of Edmond (1)
1 East 1 St, Edmond, OK 73034
Tel.: (405) 341-6650
Web Site: http://www.citizensedmond.com
Sales Range: $10-24.9 Million
Commericial Banking
N.A.I.C.S.: 522110
Jill Castilla (Pres & CEO)
Ray Hibbard (Chm)

CITIZENS BANK
411 Dysart Way, Mount Vernon, KY 40456
Tel.: (606) 256-2500
Web Site:
https://www.citizensbankrb.com
Sales Range: $100-124.9 Million
Emp.: 47
Provider of Banking Services
N.A.I.C.S.: 522110
Corey C. Craig (Pres)
John Hopkins (COO & Mgr-HR)

CITIZENS BANK
100 Circle Dr, New Haven, MO 63068
Tel.: (573) 237-3051
Web Site:
https://www.citizensbankmo.com
Year Founded: 1934
Sales Range: $1-9.9 Million
Emp.: 75
Provider of Banking Services
N.A.I.C.S.: 522110
Gary P. Kuhn (Pres & COO)
Sandy Anderson (Sr VP)
Sara Brundick (Asst VP)
Donald E. Brandt (Chm & CEO)

CITIZENS BANK
407 Main St N, Carthage, TN 37030
Tel.: (615) 735-1490
Web Site: http://www.citizensbank
carthagetn.com
Year Founded: 1929
Sales Range: $25-49.9 Million
Emp.: 94
Provider of Banking Services
N.A.I.C.S.: 522110
Paul Hackett (Pres)
Dewayne Wilmore (CFO)
Walter G. Birdwell Jr. (Chm)

CITIZENS BANK
275 SW 3rd St, Corvallis, OR 97333
Tel.: (541) 752-5161
Web Site:
http://www.citizensebank.com
Sales Range: $10-24.9 Million
Emp.: 142
State Commercial Banks

N.A.I.C.S.: 522110
Bill Hubel (COO & Exec VP)
Bobbie Carter (VP & Mgr-HR)
Steve Terjeson (Chief Lending Officer & Exec VP)
Gordon Zimmerman (Pres & CEO)
Cameron R. Howell (CFO & Exec VP)
Brad Webster (Chief Bus Dev Officer & Exec VP)

CITIZENS BANK & TRUST COMPANY
57910 Main St, Plaquemine, LA 70764
Tel.: (225) 687-1916
Web Site:
https://www.citizensbanktrust.com
Year Founded: 1916
Sales Range: $1-9.9 Million
Emp.: 68
Provider of Banking Services
N.A.I.C.S.: 522110
Jocelyn F. Lamothe (VP & Controller)
William C. Blackwood Jr. (Sr VP)

CITIZENS BANK AND TRUST CO.
126 S Main St, Blackstone, VA 23824
Tel.: (434) 292-8100
Web Site:
http://www.greatbanksva.com
Sales Range: $10-24.9 Million
Emp.: 100
State Commercial Banks
N.A.I.C.S.: 522110
Joseph D. Borgerding (Pres & CEO)

CITIZENS BANKSHARES INC.
500 W Broadway, Farmington, NM 87401
Tel.: (505) 599-0100
Web Site: http://www.cbnm.com
Sales Range: $10-24.9 Million
Emp.: 100
Bank Holding Company
N.A.I.C.S.: 551111
Jeff Howle (Pres)

Subsidiaries:

Citizens Bank (1)
500 W Broadway, Farmington, NM 87401
Tel.: (505) 599-0100
Web Site: http://www.cbnm.com
Rev.: $22,334,000
Emp.: 70
Commercial Banks, Nec
N.A.I.C.S.: 522110
Jeff Howell (Pres)

CITIZENS CORPORATION
814 Main St, Columbia, MS 39429
Tel.: (601) 736-2601 MS
Web Site: http://www.citizensbk.com
Year Founded: 1987
Sales Range: $10-24.9 Million
Emp.: 129
Bank Holding Company
N.A.I.C.S.: 551111
Henry M. Williamson (Pres & Chief Lending Officer)
Richard H. Davis (Chm)

Subsidiaries:

Citizens Bank (1)
814 Main St, Columbia, MS 39429
Tel.: (601) 736-2601
Web Site: http://www.citizensbk.com
Sales Range: $10-24.9 Million
Emp.: 52
Retail & Commercial Banking
N.A.I.C.S.: 522110
Henry M. Williamson (Pres & Chief Lending Officer)
Lee H. Fedric (CEO)

CITIZENS ELECTRIC CORPO-RATION

150 Merchant St, Perryville, MO 63775
Tel.: (573) 883-3511 MO
Web Site: http://www.cecmo.com
Year Founded: 1947
Sales Range: $100-124.9 Million
Emp.: 86
Electric Services
N.A.I.C.S.: 221122
Van Robinson (CEO)
Richard DeWilde (Treas)
William Odneal (VP)
Doyle Oehl (Treas)

CITIZENS ENERGY GROUP
2020 N Meridian St, Indianapolis, IN 46202
Tel.: (317) 924-3311
Web Site:
https://www.citizensenergy.com
Year Founded: 1935
Sales Range: $750-799.9 Million
Emp.: 1,150
Gas Distribution Company; Foundry Coke & Blast Furnace Coke Mfr
N.A.I.C.S.: 221210
Carey B. Lykins (Pres & CEO)
Jeff S. Brown (Dir-Sls & Mktg)
Aaron Johnson (VP-Strategy & Corp Dev)

Subsidiaries:

Citizens Energy Group - Citizens Gas Division (1)
2150 Dr Martin Luther King Jr St, Indianapolis, IN 46202
Tel.: (317) 927-6000
Sales Range: $200-249.9 Million
Emp.: 1,000
Natural Gas Distr
N.A.I.C.S.: 221210
Carey Lykins (Gen Mgr)

Citizens Energy Group - Citizens Resources Division (1)
2020 N Meridian St, Indianapolis, IN 46202
Tel.: (317) 924-3311
Natural Gas Distr
N.A.I.C.S.: 221210

Citizens Energy Group - Citizens Thermal Division (1)
366 Kentucky Ave, Indianapolis, IN 46225
Tel.: (317) 261-8794
Steam & Hot Water Distr
N.A.I.C.S.: 221310

Citizens Energy Group - Citizens Water Division (1)
4300 Allisonville Rd, Indianapolis, IN 46202
Tel.: (317) 924-3311
Water & Wastewater Services
N.A.I.C.S.: 221310

Citizens Mechanical Services, LLC (1)
2020 N Meridian St, Indianapolis, IN 46202-1306
Tel.: (317) 334-5656
Sales Range: $10-24.9 Million
Emp.: 20
Provide Residential & Commercial Customers with Cost-Effective Solutions to Their Hot Water, Heating & Plumbing Needs
N.A.I.C.S.: 532490

Citizens Resource Development Corporation, Inc. (1)
2020 N Meridian St, Indianapolis, IN 46202-1306
Tel.: (317) 927-6001
Sales Range: $25-49.9 Million
Emp.: 300
Buy, Sell, Invest in & Explore for Oil & Gas for the Benefit of Citizens Gas & Coke Utility Customers & Trust Beneficiaries
N.A.I.C.S.: 541613

CITIZENS EQUITY FIRST CREDIT UNION
PO Box 1715, Peoria, IL 61656-1715
Tel.: (309) 633-7048 IL
Web Site: https://www.cefcu.com

Year Founded: 1937
Sales Range: $150-199.9 Million
Emp.: 937
Credit Union
N.A.I.C.S.: 522130
Mark A. Hoffmire (VP)
Matthew J. Mamer (COO)
Keith M. Reynolds (Sr VP)
Theresa A. Lake (VP)
Erec D. Montgomery (Vice Chm)
Joseph R. Needham (Sec)
Mark A. Spenny (Pres & Treas)
Robert M. Metzinger (Vice Chm)
Todd C. Gwillim (Vice Chm)
Jeffrey D. Thomas (VP)
Joseph E. Varda (VP)
Mary E. Conrady (VP)
Todd R. Haller (VP)

CITIZENS FOR CITIZENS, INC.
264 Griffin St, Fall River, MA 02724
Tel.: (508) 679-0041 MA
Web Site: https://www.cfcinc.org
Year Founded: 1965
Sales Range: $25-49.9 Million
Emp.: 517
Community Action Services
N.A.I.C.S.: 624190
David Biltcliffe (Exec Dir)

CITIZENS GAS UTILITY DISTRICT
12519 Scott Hwy, Helenwood, TN 37755
Tel.: (423) 627-4122
Web Site: http://www.citizensgas.org
Sales Range: $10-24.9 Million
Emp.: 44
Gas Transmission & Distribution
N.A.I.C.S.: 221210
Greg Bell (CEO)

CITIZENS LLC
870 S Main St, Vermontville, MI 49096
Tel.: (517) 726-0514
Web Site:
http://www.citizenselevator.com
Sales Range: $10-24.9 Million
Emp.: 25
Farm Supplies
N.A.I.C.S.: 424910
Robert C. Mansfield (Pres)
Bruce Wymer (VP-Foodgrade Soybeans)
Angie Maguire (VP-Grain)

CITIZENS NATIONAL BANK
200 N Elm St, Waxahachie, TX 75165
Tel.: (972) 938-4300
Web Site: http://www.cnboftexax.com
Sales Range: $25-49.9 Million
Emp.: 120
National Commercial Banks
N.A.I.C.S.: 522310
Lou Ella Carmack (VP-Trng & Dev)
Lindsay Bruton (Asst VP)
Stephanie Starrett (VP)
Clint Almand (Sr VP)
Judd McCutchen (VP)
Mark E. Singleton III (Pres)

CITIZENS NATIONAL BANK INC.
200 Forks of the River Pkwy, Sevierville, TN 37862
Tel.: (865) 453-9031
Web Site: http://www.cnbtn.com
Year Founded: 1973
Sales Range: $10-24.9 Million
Emp.: 180
Banking Services

Citizens National Bank Inc.—(Continued)
N.A.I.C.S.: 522110
David C. Verble (Pres & CEO)
Bill Kilpatrick (Chm)
Jason Holliman (CFO & Sr VP)
Terri McKelvaine (Chief HR Officer)

CITIZENS NATIONAL BANK OF MERIDIAN
512 22nd Ave, Meridian, MS 39301
Tel.: (601) 484-5237
Web Site:
   http://www.ecitizensnational.com
Year Founded: 1888
Sales Range: $10-24.9 Million
Emp.: 305
National Commercial Banks
N.A.I.C.S.: 522110
Chip Hines (Chief Credit Officer)
Teresa Thornhill (Chief Wealth Mgmt Officer)
Kyle McCoy (Pres-Market-DeSoto County)
Lee Meyer (Exec VP)
Archie R. McDonnell Jr. (Pres & CEO)

CITIZENS PROPERTY INSURANCE CORPORATION
2312 Killearn Ctr Blvd, Tallahassee, FL 32309-3524
Tel.: (500) 575-3727
Web Site: http://www.citizensfla.com
Year Founded: 2002
Sales Range: $750-799.9 Million
Property & Casualty Insurance Carrier
N.A.I.C.S.: 524126
Barry Gilway (Pres, CEO & Exec Dir)
John Rollins (Chief Risk Officer)
Violet Bloom (VP-HR)
Dan Sumner (Chief Legal Officer & Gen Counsel)
Christopher B. Gardner (Chm)
Donald F. Glisson Jr. (Vice Chm)

CITIZENS SAVINGS BANK
500 S State St, Clarks Summit, PA 18411
Tel.: (570) 587-0655
Web Site: https://www.citizens-savings.com
Sales Range: $10-24.9 Million
Emp.: 110
Federal Savings & Loan Associations
N.A.I.C.S.: 522180
John W. Reuther (Pres & CEO)
Noreen N. Joyce (Sec)
Lisa M. Bonacci (Sr VP-Human Resources-Marketing)
JoAnn P. Jones (VP)
Mark A. Mecca (Sr VP-Information Technology)
Eileen Applegate-Huegel (Asst VP-IT)
Vincent W. Martone (Asst VP & Branch Mgr)

CITIZENS STATE BANK
114 W Main St, Wyoming, IA 52362
Tel.: (563) 488-2211
Web Site:
   https://www.csbwyoming.com
Sales Range: $1-9.9 Million
Emp.: 21
Provider of Banking Services
N.A.I.C.S.: 522110
Matthew McCallum (VP)

CITIZENS TELEPHONE COOPERATIVE
220 Webbs Mill Rd, Floyd, VA 24091
Tel.: (540) 745-2111   VA
Web Site: https://www.citizens.coop
Year Founded: 1953
Sales Range: $10-24.9 Million

Emp.: 65
Telecommunication Servicesb
N.A.I.C.S.: 517810
Chris J. Bond (Controller)
J. Gregory Sapp (CEO & Gen Mgr)

CITIZENS UNITED
1006 Pennsylvania Ave SE, Washington, DC 20003
Tel.: (202) 547-5420   VA
Web Site:
   https://www.citizensunited.org
Year Founded: 1988
Sales Range: $10-24.9 Million
Emp.: 18
Civic & Social Organization
N.A.I.C.S.: 813410
David N. Bossie (Chm & Pres)
Michael Boos (Gen Counsel, VP & Sec)
Kirby Wilbur (Treas)

CITOC INC.
21175 Tomball Pkwy Ste 407, Houston, TX 77070
Tel.: (713) 490-5000   TX
Web Site: http://www.citoc.com
Year Founded: 1995
Sales Range: $1-9.9 Million
Emp.: 25
Business Technology Consulting Service
N.A.I.C.S.: 541990
B. J. Farmer (Owner)
Joyce Tate (Dir-HR)

CITRIN COOPERMAN & COMPANY, LLP
529 5th Ave, New York, NY 10017
Tel.: (212) 697-1000   NY
Web Site:
   http://www.citrincooperman.com
Sales Range: $150-199.9 Million
Emp.: 700
Accounting, Tax Preparation & Consulting Services
N.A.I.C.S.: 541211
Joel A. Cooperman (CEO)
John J. Bonelli (Gen Counsel & Principal)
David E. Kells (COO & Principal)
Laura F. Kucera (CMO)
Kenny Li (CTO & Principal)
Joseph Turkewitz (Partner-Audit)
Michael A. Bartels (Dir-New Bus)
Joe Persells (Assoc Dir-IT)

Subsidiaries:

Citrin Cooperman & Company, LLP - Maryland   (1)
2 Bethesda Metro Ctr, Bethesda, MD 20814-4876
Tel.: (301) 654-9000
Web Site: http://www.citrincooperman.com
Emp.: 25
Accounting, Tax & Consulting Services
N.A.I.C.S.: 541211
Aaron D. Cohen (Principal)
Seth C. Allen (Partner)
Philip R. Baker (Partner)
Douglas A. Dowling (Partner)
Brian J. Giganti (Partner)
Paul J. Gnatt (Partner)
Nick Thompson (Partner)
Celso T. Mataac Jr. (Partner)

Citrin Cooperman & Company, LLP - Massachusetts   (1)
10 Forbes Rd W, Braintree, MA 02184
Tel.: (781) 356-2000
Web Site: http://www.citrincooperman.com
Emp.: 50
Accounting, Tax Preparation & Consulting Services
N.A.I.C.S.: 541211
Sean Killgoar (Partner)
Bonnie Simmons (Partner)
Kenneth Kirkland (Mng Partner)

Citrin Cooperman & Company, LLP - Rhode Island   (1)
10 Weybosset St Ste 700, Providence, RI 02903
Tel.: (401) 421-4800
Web Site: http://www.citrincooperman.com
Emp.: 60
Accounting, Tax Preparation & Consulting Services
N.A.I.C.S.: 541211
Martha C. Hultzman (Dir-Audit)
Renee C. Aloisio (Principal)
Pamela L. Sawin (Dir-Audit)
Michael T. Crawley (Dir-Audit)
Richard J. DeRienzo (Mng Partner)
Michael Camacho (Partner)
Michael E. Criscione (Partner)
Stephen Geremia (Partner)
Gerald Iadeluca Jr. (Dir-Tax)

Gettry Marcus CPA, P.C.   (1)
88 Froehlich Farm Blvd 3rd Fl, Woodbury, NY 11797
Tel.: (516) 364-3390
Web Site: https://www.gettrymarcus.com
Sales Range: $10-24.9 Million
Accounting, Tax & Consulting Services
N.A.I.C.S.: 541211
Andrew J. Rubin (Partner-Construction Grp)
Steven L. Marcus (Mng Partner)
Mark S. Warshavsky (Partner-Bus Valuation & Litigation Svcs Grp)
Stuart Kertzner (Partner-Health Care Grp)
Paul D. Bella (Partner-Small Bus Grp)
Robert Bjelke (Partner-Acctg & Auditing Grp)
Jed P. Dallek (Partner-Real Estate Practice)
Joel C. Dressner (Partner-Real Estate Grp)
Lee Ferber (Partner-Bus Advisory Grp)
Howard H. Fine (Partner-Acctg & Auditing Grp)
Russell T. Glazer (Partner-Bus Valuation & Litigation Svcs Grp)
Marc Heppen (Partner)
Steven Oppenheim (Partner-Real Estate Grp)
Robin Rokuson (Partner & Head-Tax Dept)
Andrew P. Ross (Partner-Bus Valuation & Litigation Svcs Grp)
Scott Sanders (Partner)
Steve Bibas (Partner-Acctg & Auditing Grp)
Michael Bloom (Partner)
Pam Burman (Principal-Acctg & Auditing Grp)
Steven J. Eller (Partner)
Benjamin S. Greenbaum (Partner)
Bruce T. Lange (Principal-Acctg & Auditing)
Peter S. Marx (Partner-Acctg & Tax Svcs)
Gabe H. Shurek (Partner-Bus Valuation & Litigation Svcs Grp)
Lester Weingarten (Partner-Tax Dept)
Alan M. Willinger (Partner-Tax Dept)

Branch (Domestic):

Gettry Marcus CPA, P.C. - New York City (East Side) Office   (2)
1407 Broadway, New York, NY 10018
Tel.: (212) 684-3399
Web Site: http://www.gettrymarcus.com
Accounting, Tax & Consulting Services
N.A.I.C.S.: 541211
Michael Bloom (Partner)
Pam Burman (Principal-Acctg & Auditing Grp)
Benjamin S. Greenbaum (Partner)
Steve Bibas (Partner)
Steven J. Eller (Partner)
Bruce T. Lange (Partner-Acctg & Auditing)
Peter S. Marx (Partner-Acctg & Tax Svcs)
Gabe H. Shurek (Partner)
Lester Weingarten (Partner-Tax Dept)
Alan M. Willinger (Partner)

Gettry Marcus CPA, P.C. - New York City (West Side) Office   (2)
1407 Broadway 10018, New York, NY 10018
Tel.: (212) 302-6000
Web Site: http://www.gettrymarcus.com
Emp.: 65
Accounting, Tax & Consulting Services
N.A.I.C.S.: 541211
Peter S. Marx (Partner)
Bruce T. Lange (Partner)
Lester Weingarten (Partner)

CITRUS AND ALLIED ESSENCES LTD.
65 S Tyson Ave, Floral Park, NY 11001
Tel.: (516) 354-1200
Web Site:
   https://www.citrusandallied.com
Rev.: $14,000,000
Emp.: 29
Essential Oils
N.A.I.C.S.: 325998
Richard C. Pisano Sr. (Pres)

CITRUS HEALTH NETWORK, INC.
4175 W 20th Ave, Hialeah, FL 33012
Tel.: (305) 825-0300   FL
Web Site:
   https://www.citrushealth.org
Year Founded: 1978
Sales Range: $50-74.9 Million
Emp.: 1,041
Health Care Srvices
N.A.I.C.S.: 622110
Norma Campos (Dir-Medical)
Maria Alonso (COO)
Noel Fernandez (Dir-Medical)
Renan Llanes (CIO)
Ana Rivas-Vazquez (Dir-Clinical)
Tyrone L. Coverson (Treas)
Gil Lopez (Sec)
Mario Jardon (Pres & CEO)
Maria T. Sanjuan (Chm)

CITRUS HILL INVESTMENT PROPERTIES
2400 N Terra Vista Blvd, Hernando, FL 34442
Tel.: (352) 746-6121
Web Site: http://www.citrushill.com
Sales Range: $10-24.9 Million
Emp.: 25
Provider of Golf Range Services
N.A.I.C.S.: 237210
George Sleeman (Gen Mgr-Mktg)

CITRUS HILLS CONSTRUCTION COMPANY LLC
2476 N Essex Ave, Hernando, FL 34442
Tel.: (352) 746-3994
Web Site: http://www.citrushills.com
Rev.: $12,500,000
Emp.: 15
Single-Family Housing Construction
N.A.I.C.S.: 236115
John Pastor (Treas)
Eric Abel (Sec)

CITRUS MOTORS ONTARIO, INC.
1375 S Woodruff Way, Ontario, CA 91761
Tel.: (909) 390-0930
Web Site:
   http://www.citrusmotors.com
Sales Range: $75-99.9 Million
Emp.: 250
Car Whslr
N.A.I.C.S.: 441110

CITRUS PLUS, INC.
7209 Jurupa Ave, Riverside, CA 92504
Tel.: (951) 352-6595
Web Site:
   https://www.citrusplusinc.com
Year Founded: 2000
Sales Range: $10-24.9 Million
Emp.: 25
Fresh Fruit & Vegetable Whslr
N.A.I.C.S.: 424480
Pablo Mercado (Founder & CEO)

CITRUS PRODUCTS INC.
154 Marsh St, Newark, NJ 07114
Tel.: (973) 589-4044   NY
Year Founded: 1985

Sales Range: $10-24.9 Million
Fresh Citrus Fruit Whslr
N.A.I.C.S.: 424480
Celso V. Barison (CEO)

CITRUS VALLEY HEALTH PARTNERS

210 W San Bernardino Rd, Covina, CA 91723
Tel.: (626) 331-7331   CA
Web Site: http://www.cvhp.org
Year Founded: 1983
Sales Range: $50-74.9 Million
Emp.: 335
Health Care Srvices
N.A.I.C.S.: 621610
Tracy Dallarda (Chief Comm Officer)
Roger Sharma (CFO & Exec VP)
William T. Choctaw (Chief Transformation Officer)
Humberto Galleno (Partner)
Gurjeet Kalkat (Chief Medical Officer)
Robert H. Curry (Pres & CEO)
Michelle Stoddard (CEO)
Mary Zimmer (Chief Clinical Svcs Officer)
Martin Kleinbart (Chief Strategy Officer)
Ryan Burke (VP-HR)

CITRUS WORLD, INC.

20205 US Hwy 27 N, Lake Wales, FL 33853-1111
Tel.: (863) 676-1411   FL
Web Site:
   http://www.floridasnatural.com
Year Founded: 1934
Sales Range: $600-649.9 Million
Emp.: 975
Citrus Processor & Packager Agricultural Co-op Services
N.A.I.C.S.: 311421
Stephen M. Caruso (CEO)
Dan McSpadden (Dir-Mktg)
Gene Eugene Everett (Sr Mgr-Process Improvement)
Leslie Powell (Sr Mgr-Sls-Indus Product)
Terry Klein (Mgr-Cost Acctg)
Chris Groom (VP-Sls & Mktg)
Leila Richards (Sr Mgr-Indus Procurement & Food Safety)

Subsidiaries:

Florida's Natural Growers   (1)
20205 US Hwy 27, Lake Wales, FL 33853
Tel.: (863) 676-1411
Web Site: http://www.floridasnatural.com
Sales Range: $600-649.9 Million
Emp.: 700
Citrus Processors & Packager Agricultural Co-op Mfr
N.A.I.C.S.: 311421
Robert Behr (COO)
Chip Hendry (CFO)
David Crumbley (VP-Fruit Procurement)
Christopher Groom (CEO)

CITY ADVERTISING LLC

3333 S Congress Ave Ste 303, Delray Beach, FL 33445   FL
Web Site:
   http://www.cityadvertising.com
Sales Range: $1-9.9 Million
Emp.: 16
Niche Industry & Small Business Directory Providers
N.A.I.C.S.: 561499
Darren Cleveland (Co-Founder, Pres & CEO)
Jeff Bhavnanie (Co-Founder)
Ilene A. Mercier (Office Mgr)

CITY ANIMATION CO

57 Pk St, Troy, MI 48083
Tel.: (248) 589-0600

Web Site:
   http://www.cityanimation.com
Sales Range: $10-24.9 Million
Emp.: 8
Video & Audio Equipment
N.A.I.C.S.: 334310
Eric Schultz (CEO & Gen Mgr)

CITY AUTO SALES, LLC.

4932 Elmore Rd, Memphis, TN 38128
Tel.: (901) 377-9502
Web Site: https://www.cityauto.com
Year Founded: 1987
Sales Range: $10-24.9 Million
Emp.: 100
Motor Vehicle Whslr
N.A.I.C.S.: 423110
David Andrews (Owner)
Gary Mccarter (COO)
Lynsey Freeman (Mgr-Mktg)
Priscilla Guy (Mgr-Customer Svc)
Stan Norton (Area Mgr)
Tim Coggins (Treas & Sec)
William Brigance (Gen Mgr)

CITY BEVERAGE COMPANY, INC.

1471 Weeksville Rd, Elizabeth City, NC 27909
Tel.: (252) 330-5539
Web Site:
   http://www.citybeverageco.com
Year Founded: 1939
Sales Range: $10-24.9 Million
Emp.: 52
Alcoholic Beverages Distr
N.A.I.C.S.: 424810
James T. Dixon (VP & Mgr-Sls)
Jeffrey L. Dixon (Pres)
Michael T. Dixon (VP-Fin & Tech)
Annette Dixon (Sec)
Jimmie Dixon Jr. (Chm & CEO)

CITY BLUE INC.

2050 Byberry Rd, Philadelphia, PA 19116
Tel.: (215) 677-4040   PA
Web Site:
   https://www.cityblueshop.com
Year Founded: 1981
Sales Range: $25-49.9 Million
Men's Clothing Stores
N.A.I.C.S.: 458110
Joseph Nadav (Pres)

CITY CADILLAC BUICK GMC

43-60 Northern Blvd, Long Island City, NY 11101
Tel.: (718) 786-3535   DE
Web Site:
   http://www.citycaddyhummer.com
Sales Range: $25-49.9 Million
Emp.: 16
New & Used Car Dealers
N.A.I.C.S.: 441110
Samuel Fox (Owner, Pres & CEO)
Kathy Fodor (Controller)

CITY CAPITAL ADVISORS, LLC

444 N Michigan Ave Ste 3200, Chicago, IL 60611
Tel.: (312) 494-9800
Web Site: https://www.city-cap.com
Year Founded: 2006
Financial Advisory Services
N.A.I.C.S.: 523999
Richard M. King (Co-Founder & Mng Dir)
Mark A. Timmerman (Co-Founder & Mng Dir)
Daniel P. Dicaro (Dir-Ops)
P. Nicholas Hurtgen (Mng Dir)
Barry A. Craig (Mng Dir)
Matthew A. Phillips (Mng Dir)

Rachel Corn Kluge (Mng Dir)
Scott H. Lang (Mng Dir)
Sharon Stewart (Dir-Admin)
Timothy C. Coleman (Mng Dir)
Carter E. Smith (Mng Dir)
Daniel J. Kipp (Mng Dir)

Subsidiaries:

City Capital Ventures, LLC   (1)
444 N Michigan Ave Ste 3250, Chicago, IL 60611
Tel.: (312) 546-7999
Web Site:
   http://www.citycapitalventures.com
Privaer Equity Firm
N.A.I.C.S.: 523999
Dan Kipp (Founder & Mng Partner)
Allen Tibshrany (Mng Dir)

Holding (Domestic):

Diedrich Manufacturing, Inc.   (2)
24 Emerald Industrial Park Rd, Ponderay, ID 83852
Tel.: (208) 263-1276
Web Site: http://www.diedrichroasters.com
Sales Range: $1-9.9 Million
Emp.: 60
Coffee Roasting Equipment Mfr
N.A.I.C.S.: 333310
Michael Paquin (CEO)

CITY CARTON INC.

3 E Benton St, Iowa City, IA 52240-1509
Tel.: (319) 351-2848   IA
Web Site: http://www.citycarton.com
Year Founded: 1972
Sales Range: $25-49.9 Million
Emp.: 150
Provider of Recycling Services
N.A.I.C.S.: 423930
Bill Lundberg (Pres)

CITY CENTER OF MUSIC AND DRAMA INC.

70 Lincoln Center Plz, New York, NY 10023-6580
Tel.: (212) 870-5656   NY
Year Founded: 1943
Sales Range: $10-24.9 Million
Emp.: 556
Theater Operator
N.A.I.C.S.: 711310
Timothy Odell (Asst Mgr-Property)
Alair Townsend (Chm)
Gillian Attfield (Treas & Sec)

CITY COUNTY CREDIT UNION

1982 N State Rd 7, Margate, FL 33063
Tel.: (954) 745-2400   FL
Web Site:
   http://www.citycountycu.org
Year Founded: 1952
Sales Range: $10-24.9 Million
Emp.: 126
Credit Union
N.A.I.C.S.: 522130
Lloyd Gill (Pres & CEO)
Nancy Bourdon-Meyer (CIO & VP)
Jennifer Burns (CMO & VP)
Sandra Spence (VP-Adv & Pub)
Touch Reath (CFO & VP)

CITY ELECTRIC COMPANY INC.

514 W Genesee St, Syracuse, NY 13204
Tel.: (315) 474-7841
Web Site:
   http://www.cityelectricweb.com
Sales Range: $25-49.9 Million
Emp.: 70
Electrical Construction Materials
N.A.I.C.S.: 423610
Sandra J. Rosecrans (Pres & CEO)
Andrew Esce (Exec VP)

CITY ELECTRIC SUPPLY COMPANY

400 S Record St Ste 900, Dallas, TX 75202
Tel.: (214) 123-1234
Web Site:
   https://www.cityelectricsupply.com
Year Founded: 1951
Emp.: 2,700
Electrical Supplies, Nec
N.A.I.C.S.: 423610
Burt Rice (Branch Mgr)
Robert Nommenson (CFO & Treas)
Dallin Wayment (Gen Counsel, Treas & Sec)
Shawn Warner (Sr VP & Mgr-Wyoming Div)

Subsidiaries:

Coventry Electrical Supplies Ltd.   (1)
2589 Oscar Johnson Dr, North Charleston, SC 29405
Tel.: (843) 744-3001
Web Site: http://www.cityelectricsupply.com
Emp.: 20
Electrical Apparatus & Equipment
N.A.I.C.S.: 423610
Jason Hyman (Branch Mgr)

CITY EMPLOYEES CLUB OF LOS ANGELES

311 S Spring St Ste 1300, Los Angeles, CA 90013
Tel.: (213) 620-0388   CA
Web Site:
   http://www.cityemployeesclub.com
Year Founded: 1928
Sales Range: $10-24.9 Million
Employer Association
N.A.I.C.S.: 813920
Brian G. Trent (CFO)
Cecilia Talbot-Mulkerrin (Dir-Claims)
Robert Larios (Founder)
Arlene Herrero (Dir-Product Dev)
Noelle Kauffman (Mgr-Sls)
Angel Gomez (Dir-Sls)

CITY FEED & LUMBER COMPANY INC.

44 Lower Newton St, Saint Albans, VT 05478
Tel.: (802) 370-3149
Web Site:
   https://www.sticksandstuff.com
Year Founded: 1914
Sales Range: $10-24.9 Million
Emp.: 70
Retailer of Lumber & Other Building Materials
N.A.I.C.S.: 423310
Aaron Bachelder (Mgr-Credit)

CITY FIBERS INC.

2500 S Santa Fe Ave, Los Angeles, CA 90058
Tel.: (323) 583-1013
Web Site: https://www.cityfibers.com
Sales Range: $25-49.9 Million
Emp.: 100
Supplier of Waste Paper
N.A.I.C.S.: 423930
David Jones (Pres)
Kipp Jones (Gen Mgr)

CITY FINANCE

1330 N McDonald St, McKinney, TX 75071
Tel.: (972) 548-0092
Year Founded: 1989
Sales Range: $1-9.9 Million
Emp.: 21
Personal Credit Services
N.A.I.C.S.: 522291
Kurt Grojean (Owner)

CITY FORD, LLC

City Ford, LLC—(Continued)

3040 E Business Hwy 30, Columbia City, IN 46725
Tel.: (260) 244-5171   IN
Web Site: http://www.gocityford.com
Sales Range: $10-24.9 Million
Emp.: 40
New & Used Car Dealer
N.A.I.C.S.: 441110
Jim Scarbeary (Co-Owner)
Douglas G. McKibben (Co-Owner)

CITY FURNITURE INC.
6701 Hiatus Rd, Tamarac, FL 33321-6406
Tel.: (954) 597-2200
Web Site: http://www.city-furniture.com
Year Founded: 1971
Sales Range: $200-249.9 Million
Emp.: 930
Furniture Retailer
N.A.I.C.S.: 449110
Steve Wilder (CFO)
Keith Koenig (Pres)
Kristin Goff (Mgr-Interior Design)
Pam Hill (Product Mgr)
Juan Lamonaca (Mgr-Quality)
Brenda Pagliaro (Gen Counsel)
Kevin Riggott (VP-Fin & Controller)
Garry Ikola (Sr VP-Sls)
Susan LoBianco (Mgr-Comml Sls)
Linda May (Mgr-Facilities)
Leah Hicks (Dir-Adv)
Sandra Beckett (Chief HR Officer)

CITY GLATT, INC.
1600 Naud St, Los Angeles, CA 90012
Tel.: (323) 276-8070
Web Site: http://www.tzalis.com
Year Founded: 1992
Sales Range: $10-24.9 Million
Emp.: 25
Kosher Whslr & Distr
N.A.I.C.S.: 424420
Levi Sasran (Mgr)

CITY HALL PROPERTIES LLC
427 Franklin St, Fayetteville, NC 28301
Tel.: (910) 483-2525
Year Founded: 1956
Sales Range: $10-24.9 Million
Emp.: 40
Real Estate Investment Properties
N.A.I.C.S.: 531390
Ron Pleasant (CEO)

CITY ISUZU
10575 Atlantic Blvd, Jacksonville, FL 32225
Tel.: (904) 565-2489
Web Site:
https://www.citymitsubishi.com
Year Founded: 1988
Sales Range: $10-24.9 Million
Emp.: 55
Car Whslr
N.A.I.C.S.: 441110
John Galeani (Pres)

CITY LIFT PARKING, LLC
1901 Poplar St Ste B, Oakland, CA 94607
Tel.: (510) 243-8086
Web Site:
http://www.cityliftparking.com
Year Founded: 2015
Sales Range: $10-24.9 Million
Emp.: 40
Elevator Equipment Mfr
N.A.I.C.S.: 333921
Scott Gable (CEO)
Brandon Richardson (Chief Product Officer)

Clifford Schuch (CFO)
Kelly Smith (VP-Installation)
Dave Taylor (Sr VP-Sls)

CITY LINK EXPRESS, INC.
100 Piedmont Ct Ste G, Doraville, GA 30340
Tel.: (770) 409-8994
Web Site:
https://www.citylinkexp.com
Year Founded: 2000
Sales Range: $10-24.9 Million
Emp.: 30
Logistics & Transportation
N.A.I.C.S.: 484121
Tim Cross (Pres)
Dave Thompson (VP)
Tom Fields (VP)

CITY LIQUIDATORS INC.
823 SE 3rd Ave, Portland, OR 97214
Tel.: (503) 238-1367
Web Site:
http://www.cityliquidators.com
Sales Range: $75-99.9 Million
Emp.: 42
Furniture Stores
N.A.I.C.S.: 455219
Walter D. Pelett (Founder & Owner)

CITY LUMBER & TRUSS COMPANY
3312 Bob Wallace Ave, Huntsville, AL 35805
Tel.: (256) 533-0110
Web Site:
http://www.citylumberco.com
Year Founded: 1970
Rev.: $12,000,000
Emp.: 75
Millwork & Lumber
N.A.I.C.S.: 444110
Lisa Ambrose (VP-Ops-Pur)
Jason Terry (VP-Fin & Sls)

CITY LUMBER INC.
4947 31st St, Long Island City, NY 11101
Tel.: (212) 695-3393
Web Site:
http://www.citylumberusa.com
Rev.: $13,100,000
Emp.: 50
Lumber & Other Building Materials
N.A.I.C.S.: 722513
Bruce Miller (VP-Pur)

CITY MAINTENANCE SUPPLY
3020 SW 10th St, Pompano Beach, FL 33069
Tel.: (954) 968-4554
Web Site: https://neeldpaper.com
Emp.: 100
Industrial Supplies Whslr & Electrical Contractors
N.A.I.C.S.: 423840
Chuck Need (CEO)

Subsidiaries:
West Florida Supply, Co.   (1)
1184 N Washington Blvd, Sarasota, FL 34236
Tel.: (941) 365-2838
Sales Range: $1-9.9 Million
Emp.: 20
Service Establishment Equipment & Supplies Merchant Whslr
N.A.I.C.S.: 423850

CITY MASONRY INC.
2443 S Cherry St, Tomball, TX 77375
Tel.: (713) 691-1000
Web Site:
https://www.citymasonry.com
Sales Range: $10-24.9 Million
Emp.: 150
Masonry Contracting Services

N.A.I.C.S.: 238140
Paul McCurdy (Exec VP)
Billy Cox (VP)
Rachel Diaz (Sec & Treas)
Glenn Whitehead (Dir-Safety)

CITY MATTRESS INC.
101 Benbro Dr, Cheektowaga, NY 14225
Tel.: (716) 681-8080
Web Site:
http://www.citymattress.com
Sales Range: $25-49.9 Million
Emp.: 140
Retailer of Mattresses
N.A.I.C.S.: 449110

CITY MILL COMPANY LTD.
660 N Nimitz Hwy, Honolulu, HI 96817
Tel.: (808) 533-3811
Web Site: https://www.citymill.com
Rev.: $49,381,460
Emp.: 450
Lumber & Other Building Materials
N.A.I.C.S.: 423310
Steven Ai (Pres & CEO)

CITY MOTOR COMPANY
3900 10th Ave S, Great Falls, MT 59405-3648
Tel.: (406) 564-1464
Web Site:
https://www.citymotorgm.com
Rev.: $22,100,000
Emp.: 85
New & Used Car Dealers
N.A.I.C.S.: 441110
Leslie Oakland (Pres)
John Kennard (Mgr-Svc)

CITY OF GLENDALE MUNICIPAL PROPERTY CORP.
5850 W Glendale Ave, Glendale, AZ 85301-2599
Tel.: (623) 930-2480   AZ
Web Site: http://www.glendaleaz.com
Year Founded: 1982
Sales Range: $25-49.9 Million
Property Management Services
N.A.I.C.S.: 921190

CITY OF HOPE NATIONAL MEDICAL CENTER
1500 E Duarte Rd, Duarte, CA 91010
Tel.: (626) 256-4673
Web Site: https://www.cityofhope.org
Year Founded: 1913
Sales Range: $300-349.9 Million
Emp.: 200
Cancer Research Hospital
N.A.I.C.S.: 622110
Robert W. Stone (Pres & CEO)
Kristin Bertell (Chief Philanthropy Officer)
John D. Carpten (Chief Scientific Officer)
Ken Chaplin (CMO-System)
Jo Ann Escasa-Haigh (Chief Bus Officer-System)
Pete Govorchin (Pres)
Harlan Levine (Pres-Health Innovation & Policy)
Kevin Manemann (Chief Integration Officer & Exec VP)
Nisha Morris (Chief Comm Officer & Sr VP)
Simon Nazarian (CTO, Chief Digital Officer & Exec VP)
Cristin O'Callahan (Gen Counsel & Sec)
Angelique L. Richard (COO)
Joline Treanor (Chief HR Officer-System)
Glenn D. Steele Jr. (Chm)

Subsidiaries:
Cancer Treatment Centers of America   (1)
5901 Broken Sound Pkwy NW Ste 200, Boca Raton, FL 33487
Tel.: (847) 342-7400
Web Site: http://www.cancercenter.com
Management of In-Patient Cancer Care Programs
N.A.I.C.S.: 622310
Anne Meisner (Chief Hospital Ops Officer)
Scott Jones (Pres & CEO-Midwestern Reg Medical Center)
Nancy Hesse (Pres & CEO-Eastern Reg Medical Center)
Maurie Markman (Pres-Medicine & Science)
Kevin Tulipana (Dir-Medical-Hospital Medicine)
Timothy Flanigan (Chief Legal Officer)
Robert Gould (Pres/CEO-Hospital-Arizona)
Zane Zumbahlen (Chief HR Officer & Chief Talent Officer)
Pat Basu (Pres)
Thomas Biby Jr. (VP-Fin)

CITY OF SCOTTSDALE MUNICIPAL PROPERTY CORPORATION
3939 N Drinkwater Blvd, Scottsdale, AZ 85251
Tel.: (480) 312-3111   AZ
Web Site:
https://www.scottsdaleaz.gov
Year Founded: 1951
Sales Range: $50-74.9 Million
Emp.: 2,400
Financial Support Services
N.A.I.C.S.: 921190
Sharron Walker (Auditor-City)

CITY PAPER COMPANY
3700 1st Ave N, Birmingham, AL 35222
Tel.: (205) 328-2626
Web Site:
http://www.citypapercompany.com
Rev.: $11,888,696
Emp.: 50
Bags, Paper & Disposable Plastic
N.A.I.C.S.: 424130
Mark Friedman (COO & Exec VP)
Paul Friedman Jr. (Pres)

CITY PLUMBING & ELECTRIC SUPPLY COMPANY
730 EE Butler Pkwy, Gainesville, GA 30501
Tel.: (770) 532-4123
Web Site: https://www.cpesupply.com
Sales Range: $10-24.9 Million
Emp.: 45
Plumbing Fittings & Supplies
N.A.I.C.S.: 423720
Stewart Teaver (Pres)
Roger Moore (Mgr-Ops)
Chris McGee (Mgr)

CITY POSTAL, INC.
421 7th Ave 5 N 11th St, New York, NY 10001-2002
Tel.: (212) 279-4300   DE
Web Site: http://www.citystores.com
Year Founded: 1977
Sales Range: $100-124.9 Million
Emp.: 150
Provider of Air Courier & Freight Services
N.A.I.C.S.: 488510
Louis Weiner (Pres & CEO)

CITY SEA FOODS, INC.
531 Towne Ave, Los Angeles, CA 90013-2126
Tel.: (213) 626-5586
Web Site:
http://www.cityseafoods.com
Year Founded: 1961
Sales Range: $10-24.9 Million

Emp.: 75
Distr of Fish & Seafoods
N.A.I.C.S.: 424460
Joe Heidelmaier *(VP)*
Don Kanner *(Pres)*

CITY SERVICE, INC.
640 W Montana, Kalispell, MT 59901-5777
Tel.: (406) 755-4321   MT
Web Site:
    http://www.cityservicevalcon.com
Year Founded: 1932
Sales Range: $50-74.9 Million
Emp.: 140
Provider of Petroleum Services
N.A.I.C.S.: 424210
Dallas I. Herron *(CEO)*
Kary Konjem *(Pres)*
Ed Croymans *(Head-Aviation)*

CITY SITES SPORTSWEAR INC.
2421 McDonald Ave, Brooklyn, NY 11223
Tel.: (718) 375-2990
Sales Range: $10-24.9 Million
Emp.: 23
Sales of Women's Clothing
N.A.I.C.S.: 315250
Sylvia Goldbetter *(Pres)*

CITY STATIONERY INC.
Rd 1 Kilo 53 5, Cayey, PR 00736
Tel.: (787) 263-7002
Sales Range: $10-24.9 Million
Emp.: 26
Furniture Retailer
N.A.I.C.S.: 449110
Pedro Rodriguez *(Owner)*

CITY SUNSTONE PROPERTIES LLC
9555 Hillwood Dr Ste 103, Las Vegas, NV 89134
Tel.: (702) 405-0333
Web Site:
    http://www.citysunstone.com
Year Founded: 2012
Real Estate Investment Services
N.A.I.C.S.: 531210
Rodney S. Atamian *(Co-Founder & Mng Partner)*
Daniel Khoshaba *(Co-Founder & Principal)*
Lisa Brady *(VP)*

CITY TIRE CO. INC.
25 Avocado St, Springfield, MA 01104
Tel.: (413) 737-1419   MA
Web Site: https://www.city-tire.com
Year Founded: 1927
Sales Range: $10-24.9 Million
Emp.: 90
Sales of Automotive Tires
N.A.I.C.S.: 441340
Peter Greenberg *(Pres)*
Jeff Martin *(VP-Ops & Controller)*
Daniel Greenberg *(VP & VP-Sls)*
Peter Greenberg *(Pres)*
Daniel Greenberg *(VP-Sls)*

CITY TOURS INC.
299 Murray Hill Pkwy, East Rutherford, NJ 07073
Tel.: (201) 939-4154
Web Site: https://www.citytours.com
Year Founded: 1978
Rev.: $10,400,000
Emp.: 60
Tour Operators & Promoters
N.A.I.C.S.: 561520
Raymond Thomas *(Pres)*

CITY TRANSFER CO. INC.
15001 Fogg St, Plymouth, MI 48170

Tel.: (734) 354-9400
Web Site:
    http://www.citytransfercourier.com
Sales Range: $10-24.9 Million
Emp.: 850
Provider of Package Delivery Services
N.A.I.C.S.: 492210

CITY VENTURES, INC.
3121 Michelson Dr Ste 150, Irvine, CA 92612
Tel.: (949) 258-7555   DE
Web Site:
    https://www.cityventures.com
Sales Range: $75-99.9 Million
Emp.: 81
New Single-Family Housing Construction
N.A.I.C.S.: 236115
Scott Homan *(CFO)*
Mark Buckland *(CEO)*
Craig Atkins *(Chm)*
Phil Kerr *(CEO-Homebuilding)*
Kim Prijatel *(VP-Dev)*
Ryan Aeh *(VP-Land Acq)*
Patrick W. Hendry *(VP-Land Acq-Northern California)*
Michelle Thrakulchavee *(VP-Land Acq)*

CITY WATER & LIGHT
400 E Monroe Ave, Jonesboro, AR 72401
Tel.: (870) 935-5581
Web Site:
    https://www.jonesborocwl.org
Year Founded: 1906
Sales Range: $50-74.9 Million
Emp.: 200
Electric & Other Services Combined
N.A.I.C.S.: 221118
Jake Rice *(Gen Mgr)*

CITY WIDE GOURMET FOODS INC.
801 Service St, Houston, TX 77009
Tel.: (713) 862-2530
Rev.: $16,100,000
Emp.: 80
Groceries & Related Products
N.A.I.C.S.: 424410
Jerry W. Court *(Pres)*

CITY WIDE INSULATION OF MADISON INC.
4405 Triangle St, McFarland, WI 53558
Tel.: (608) 222-2182
Sales Range: $25-49.9 Million
Emp.: 250
Provider of Insulation Services
N.A.I.C.S.: 238310
Jean Murphy *(VP)*

CITY WIDE MAINTENANCE OF COLORADO
3131 S Vaughn Way Ste 600, Denver, CO 80014-1851
Tel.: (720) 833-0300
Web Site: http://www.gocitywide.com
Year Founded: 2002
Sales Range: $1-9.9 Million
Emp.: 20
Janitor Service
N.A.I.C.S.: 561720
Doug Brown *(Pres)*

CITY WINDOW & CONSTRUCTION COMPANY
311 Ohio Ave, Clarksburg, WV 26301
Tel.: (304) 623-2573
Web Site:
    http://www.citywindowconstruction.com
Rev.: $21,900,000

Emp.: 34
Commercial & Institutional Building Construction
N.A.I.C.S.: 236220
George Pollock *(Controller-Acctg)*
Nancy Pollock *(Office Mgr)*
Bud Henderson *(Pres)*
Mark Henderson *(VP)*
Jason McQuain *(Project Mgr)*
Beau Henderson *(VP)*

CITYMEALS-ON-WHEELS
355 Lexington Ave, New York, NY 10017
Tel.: (212) 687-1234   NY
Web Site: https://www.citymeals.org
Year Founded: 1991
Rev.: $21,547,714
Assets: $33,491,203
Liabilities: $579,967
Net Worth: $32,911,236
Earnings: $1,906,033
Emp.: 29
Fiscal Year-end: 06/30/14
Hunger Relief Services
N.A.I.C.S.: 624210
Gael Greene *(Co-Founder & Chm)*
Joseph M. Cohen *(Vice Chm)*
Joan H. Tisch *(Vice Chm)*
Daniel Boulud *(Co-Pres)*
Anne E. Cohen *(Co-Pres)*
Robert S. Grimes *(VP)*
Jeffrey Mayer *(VP)*
Richard E. Piluso *(Treas & Sec)*
Beth Shapiro *(Exec Dir)*
Rachel Sherrow *(Assoc Exec Dir)*
Jose Luis Sanchez *(Coord-Program)*
Vivienne Brown-O'Neill *(Dir-Volunteer Programs)*
Sheila Clay *(Coord-Volunteer)*
Jennifer Joyce *(Dir-Major Gifts)*
Malcolm Murray *(Dir-Direct Mktg)*
Robyn Stein *(Dir-Partnerships & Events)*
Emily Cleveland Smith *(Sr Mgr-Special Events)*
Robert Chapman *(COO & Assoc Exec Dir)*
Patrick Bernard *(Controller)*
Kathryn Baron *(Mgr-Mktg & Comm)*
Gail Nickerson *(Mgr-Database)*

CITYPARKING INC.
801 E Main St Ste 1002, Richmond, VA 23219
Tel.: (804) 344-3353
Web Site:
    http://www.cityparkingonline.com
Sales Range: $1-9.9 Million
Emp.: 10
Parking Lot Services
N.A.I.C.S.: 812930
David L. Sharrar *(CFO & Principal)*
Katie Mattes *(VP-Accts)*
David J. Sharrar *(CEO)*

CITYSIDE SUBARU, INC.
790 Pleasant St, Belmont, MA 02478
Tel.: (781) 641-1900
Web Site:
    https://www.citysidesubaru.com
Sales Range: $10-24.9 Million
Emp.: 29
New Car Dealers
N.A.I.C.S.: 441110
Richard White *(Gen Mgr)*

CITYTWIST
1200 N Federal Hwy Ste 417, Boca Raton, FL 33432
Web Site: https://www.citytwist.com
Year Founded: 2003
Sales Range: $1-9.9 Million
Emp.: 50
Direct Mail Conversion Services to Email Marketing

N.A.I.C.S.: 541860
Lou Nobile *(Founder & Chm)*
Marc Lefevre *(VP-Sls)*
Jason Elston *(VP-Ops)*

CITYWIDE INSULATION
1725 3rd Ave W, Shakopee, MN 55379
Tel.: (952) 445-1387
Web Site:
    https://www.citywideinsul.com
Rev.: $13,000,000
Emp.: 55
Insulation, Buildings
N.A.I.C.S.: 238310
Linda Carnahan *(Pres & CEO)*
Duane Kriese Sr. *(Mgr)*

CIVC PARTNERS LLC
191 N Wacker Dr Ste 1100, Chicago, IL 60606
Tel.: (312) 873-7300   DE
Web Site: https://www.civc.com
Year Founded: 1970
Sales Range: $75-99.9 Million
Emp.: 17
Equity Investment Firm
N.A.I.C.S.: 523999
Chris McLaughlin *(Principal)*
Daniel Helle *(Partner)*
Marcus Wedner *(Partner)*
Keith Yamada *(Partner)*
Marc McManus *(VP)*
John Compall *(Principal)*
Scott Schwartz *(Principal)*
Christopher J. Perry *(Partner)*
Doug Potters *(VP)*
J. D. Wright *(Partner)*
Nicholas Canderan *(Dir-Bus Dev)*

Subsidiaries:

Datavail Corporation   (1)
11800 Ridge Pkwy Ste 125, Broomfield, CO 80021
Tel.: (303) 926-4888
Web Site: https://www.datavail.com
Sales Range: $10-24.9 Million
Emp.: 218
Database Administration Services
N.A.I.C.S.: 541519
Mark Perlstein *(Pres & CEO)*
David Boyle *(Sr VP-Sls)*
Robin Caputo *(CMO)*
Eric Russo *(Sr VP-Database Svcs)*
John Kaufling *(Sr VP-Oracle Applications & Data Mgmt)*
Patrick Gates *(Sr VP-Global Delivery Center Ops)*
Scott Frock *(COO & Exec VP)*
Rick Gaisser *(CFO)*
Dan Russell *(Sr VP-Strategic Accounts & Alliances)*
Brook Shuford *(Chief Info Security Officer)*

Subsidiary (Non-US):

Navantis Inc.   (2)
21 Randolph Ave 2nd Floor, Toronto, M6P 4G4, ON, Canada
Tel.: (647) 258-9031
Web Site: http://www.navantis.com
Computer Related Services
N.A.I.C.S.: 541519
Jason Martin *(Co-Founder)*
Andy Papadopoulos *(CEO)*

Fitness International, LLC   (1)
2600 Michelson Dr Ste 600, Irvine, CA 92612-4406
Tel.: (949) 255-7330
Web Site: http://www.lafitness.com
Sales Range: $1-4.9 Billion
Health & Fitness Club Operator
N.A.I.C.S.: 713940
Louis Welch *(CEO)*

Honor Finance LLC   (1)
909 Davis St Ste 260, Evanston, IL 60201
Tel.: (847) 440-2555
Web Site: http://www.honorfinance.com
Sales Range: $1-9.9 Million
Financial Management Services
N.A.I.C.S.: 523999

CIVC Partners LLC—(Continued)

Robert DiMeo (COO)
Patrick Geraty (VP)
James R. Collins (Pres & CEO)
Martin Collins (Sr VP)
Lionel Lenz (CFO)

Pipeline Industries, Inc. (1)
2150 E 58th Ave, Denver, CO 80216
Tel.: (303) 696-9599
Web Site: http://www.pipelineindustries.com
Sewer Line Repair Services
N.A.I.C.S.: 237110
Steve Wakeham (Gen Mgr)

CIVES CORPORATION
1825 Old Alabama Rd Ste 200, Roswell, GA 30076-2201
Tel.: (770) 993-4424 DE
Web Site: http://www.cives.com
Year Founded: 1952
Sales Range: $350-399.9 Million
Emp.: 1,021
Structural Steel Fabrication; Snow Plow Manufacturer
N.A.I.C.S.: 332312
Ronald W. Shaw (Vice Chm)
Raymond A. Phillips (Chm)
John S. Donovan (Sec & Exec VP)
John M. Connor (Treas)
Richard Connelly (Pres & CEO)

Subsidiaries:

Cives Corporation - MID-ATLANTIC DIVISION (1)
210 Cives Ln, Winchester, VA 22603
Tel.: (540) 667-3480
Web Site: http://www.cives.com
Emp.: 150
Fabricated Metal Mfr
N.A.I.C.S.: 332312
Craig Alderman (Gen Mgr)

Cives Corporation - MID-SOUTH DIVISION (1)
219 Port Terminal Rd, Rosedale, MS 38769
Tel.: (662) 759-6265
Web Site: http://www.cives.com
Sales Range: $10-24.9 Million
Emp.: 130
Steel Products Mfr
N.A.I.C.S.: 331110
Chipper Hutchinson (Gen Mgr)

Cives Corporation - MID-WEST DIVISION (1)
337 N 700 W, Wolcott, IN 47995
Tel.: (219) 279-4000
Web Site: http://www.cives.com
Emp.: 125
Steel Products Mfr
N.A.I.C.S.: 331110
Brian Wessel (Gen Mgr)

Cives Corporation - NEW ENGLAND DIVISION (1)
103 Lipman Rd, Augusta, ME 04330
Tel.: (207) 622-6141
Web Site: http://www.cives.com
Steel Products Mfr
N.A.I.C.S.: 331110

Cives Corporation - NORTHERN DIVISION (1)
8 Church St, Gouverneur, NY 13642
Tel.: (315) 287-2200
Web Site: http://www.cives.com
Emp.: 200
Steel Product Distr
N.A.I.C.S.: 423510
Ted Totton (Gen Mgr)

Cives Corporation - SOUTHERN DIVISION (1)
102 Airport Rd, Thomasville, GA 31757
Tel.: (229) 228-9780
Web Site: http://www.cives.com
Sales Range: $25-49.9 Million
Emp.: 140
Fabricated Structural Steel Mfr & Distr
N.A.I.C.S.: 332312
Gregory Orff (Pres & Gen Mgr)

Cives Engineering Corporation (1)

1825 Old Alabama Rd Ste 200, Roswell, GA 30076
Tel.: (770) 993-4424
Web Site: http://www.cives.com
Sales Range: $10-24.9 Million
Emp.: 20
Engineering Services
N.A.I.C.S.: 541330
Patrick J. Fortney (Mgr & Chief Engr)

Viking-Cives, Ltd. (1)
42626 Gray Road 109, Mount Forest, N0G2L0, ON, Canada (100%)
Tel.: (519) 323-4433
Web Site: http://www.viking-cives.com
Sales Range: $10-24.9 Million
Emp.: 150
Mfr & Sale of Highway & Heavy Airport Snow Plows
N.A.I.C.S.: 333120
William J. Reeves (Pres)

CIVIC AUTOMOTIVE GROUP INC.
5802 University Blvd, Coraopolis, PA 15108
Tel.: (412) 269-4100 PA
Web Site: http://www.moonhonda.com
Year Founded: 1939
Sales Range: $125-149.9 Million
Emp.: 2,000
New & Used Cars Dealers
N.A.I.C.S.: 441110
Angelo Falconi (Pres)

CIVIC LIGHT OPERA ASSOCIATION OF PITTSBURGH
719 Liberty Ave, Pittsburgh, PA 15222
Tel.: (412) 281-3973 PA
Web Site: https://www.pittsburghclo.org
Year Founded: 1946
Sales Range: $10-24.9 Million
Emp.: 369
Musical Theater
N.A.I.C.S.: 711110
Timothy K. Zimmerman (VP)
Alvaro Garcia-Tunon (VP-Long Range Plng)
Tony Bucci (VP-Dev)
Ronald L. Violi (VP-Dev)
Robin S. Randall (VP)
Kristen Lane (VP)
Charlene Petrelli (VP-HR)
Christine M. Kobus (VP-Education & Outreach)
Daniel I. Booker (VP-Cabaret Theater)
Edward T. Karlovich (Treas)
Frederick C. Leech (VP-Construction Center & Facilities)
G. Reynolds Clark (VP)
Gary R. Truitt (VP-Education & Outreach)
Helen Hanna Casey (VP-Production)
James R. Kane (VP)
Johanna G. O'Loughlin (Sec)
John E. Kosar (VP-Construction Center & Facilities)
Laurie M. Mushinsky (VP-Special Events)
Mark J. Minnaugh (VP-Dev)
Michael E. Bleier (VP-Long Range Plng)
Michael F. Walsh (VP-Mktg)
Peter J. Germain (VP-Production)
Richard S. Hamilton (VP-Mktg)
Scott F. Neill (VP-Nominating)
Todd C. Moules (VP-HR)
William M. Lambert (Pres)
John C. Williams Jr. (VP-Budget & Fin)

CIVICSCIENCE, INC.
6101 Penn Ave Ste 501, Pittsburgh, PA 15206

Tel.: (412) 281-1954
Web Site: http://www.civicscienceinc.com
Sales Range: $10-24.9 Million
Emp.: 25
Market Research Services
N.A.I.C.S.: 541910
John Dick (Founder & CEO)
Annette Brady (VP-Pub Dev)
Aparna Nigam (Mgr-PR)
Bill Conaway (VP-Client Dev)
Kerry Oslund (Sr VP-Pub & Emerging Media)
Laura Albert (Mgr-Mktg)
Mark Cuban (Owner)
Pedro Barelli (COO)
Tod Johnson (Chm & CEO)
Lee Ann Stern (VP-Bus Dev)
D. J. Cavanaugh Sr. (VP-Bus Dev)

CIVIL & ENVIRONMENTAL CONSULTANTS, INC.
333 Baldwin Rd, Pittsburgh, PA 15205
Tel.: (412) 429-2324
Web Site: http://www.cecinc.com
Year Founded: 1989
Rev.: $50,824,875
Emp.: 600
Environmental Consulting Services
N.A.I.C.S.: 541620
Bill Carroll (VP-Civil Engrg)
Carrie Cote (VP-Water Resources & Public Sector)
Ryan Stucki (VP-Civil Engrg-Tucson)
Dan Cleland (Principal-Landscape Architecture)
Chris Forsha (VP)
Stephen B. Dixon (VP)
Keith Robinson (Dir-Corp Safety)
Matt Hanson (Asst Project Mgr-Environmental Practice)
Jeff DePaolis (Principal & Head-Transportation Engrg Svcs)
Fadi Maroun (Sr Project Mgr)
Tony Amicon (VP)
Jim Zentmeyer (VP)
Karlis Skulte (Principal-Civil Engrg Practice-Boston)
Ron Hager (Principal-Environmental Practice)
Adam Flege (Project Mgr-Environmental)
Dennis Dinkelacker (Project Mgr-Survey)
Mark Burgess (Project Mgr-Civil Engrg)
Craig Straub (Principal)
Dustin Doherty (Sr Project Mgr-Civil Engrg)
Pete Brothers (Principal-Survey & Geospatial Practice)
Christina E. Kelly (Project Mgr-Cultural Resources)
Deborah J. Blankenship (Sr Project Mgr-Environmental)
John Frydrych (Principal-Civil Engrg)

Subsidiaries:

Engineering & Environmental Consultants, Inc. (1)
4625 E Fort Lowell Rd, Tucson, AZ 85712-1110
Tel.: (520) 321-4625
Web Site: http://www.eec-info.com
Engineering Services
N.A.I.C.S.: 541330
Ray P. Montoya (Sr VP & Dir-Water & Wastewater Svcs)

CIVIL CONSTRUCTION CONTRACTORS INC.
112 Leo St, Hahnville, LA 70057
Tel.: (985) 783-6893
Web Site: http://www.civil-construction.com
Rev.: $16,300,000

Emp.: 81
Heavy Construction Local Trucking Operator; Whole Brick & Stone Materials
N.A.I.C.S.: 237990
Garrett Zeringue (VP)
Pete Harmon (Pres)
Mark Harmon (Treas & Sec)

CIW ENTERPRISES, INC.
24 Elmwood Ave, Mountain Top, PA 18707
Tel.: (570) 474-6773 DE
Web Site: https://www.cornelliron.com
Sales Range: $75-99.9 Million
Emp.: 250
Holding Company
N.A.I.C.S.: 332321
Lauretta O'Hara (Dir-Human Resources)

CIXTA ENTERPRISES INC.
10147 San Fernando Rd, Pacoima, CA 91331
Tel.: (818) 485-0596
Web Site: http://www.vallartasupermarkets.com
Rev.: $13,500,000
Emp.: 60
Meat & Fish Markets
N.A.I.C.S.: 445240
Luis Gonzalez (Pres)

CJ HORNER COMPANY INC.
105 W Grand Ave, Hot Springs, AR 71901
Tel.: (501) 321-9600
Web Site: https://www.cjhornerinc.com
Sales Range: $10-24.9 Million
Emp.: 90
Ready Mixed Concrete
N.A.I.C.S.: 327320
Jim Horner (Pres)

CJ LOGGING EQUIPMENT LLC
PO Box 661, Boonville, NY 13309
Tel.: (315) 942-5431 NY
Web Site: http://www.cjlogequip.com
Year Founded: 1981
Sales Range: $1-9.9 Million
Emp.: 40
Logging Equipment Sales
N.A.I.C.S.: 532490
Mark Bourgeois (Pres)
Linda Bourgeois (Treas & Sec)

Subsidiaries:

Lyons Equipment Company, Inc. (1)
5445 State Rte 353, Little Valley, NY 14755-0107
Tel.: (716) 938-9175
Construction & Mining Machinery Sales
N.A.I.C.S.: 423810

CJ MABARDY INC.
51 Mooney St, Cambridge, MA 02138
Tel.: (617) 354-7580
Web Site: http://www.cjmabardy.com
Rev.: $17,000,000
Emp.: 29
Construction Sand Mining
N.A.I.C.S.: 212321
Kenneth Racicot (Gen Mgr)

CJ PONY PARTS, INC.
7461 Allentown Blvd, Harrisburg, PA 17112
Tel.: (717) 657-9252
Web Site: http://www.cjponyparts.com
Year Founded: 1985
Sales Range: $10-24.9 Million
Emp.: 65

Automotive Parts & Accessories
Stores
N.A.I.C.S.: 441330
Jay Zeigler *(Pres)*
Andrew King *(Coord-Mktg)*
Mike Large *(Gen Mgr)*
Rich Boone *(VP-Sls & Mktg)*

CJA & ASSOCIATES, INC.
791 10th St S Ste 202, Naples, FL
34102
Tel.: (239) 298-8210
Web Site: http://www.rmcgp.com
Year Founded: 1991
Sales Range: $1-9.9 Million
Emp.: 20
Benefits & Retirement Planning
N.A.I.C.S.: 524292
Raymond Anker *(Pres & CEO)*
Douglas Tashma *(VP-Admin)*
George Evenson *(VP-Pensions)*
Stephanie Strauss *(VP-Mktg)*
Jeff Bleiweis *(Gen Counsel & VP)*
Shane Biltz *(Mgr-New Bus)*
Joseph Badway *(CFO)*
Ray Ankner *(Pres & CEO)*
John Hansen *(Pres-First Actuarial
Corp)*
Colin Hurley *(Reg Dir-Mktg)*
Tom Bacharach *(VP-Northeast)*
Ken Akiva Shapero *(VP-Southeast)*

CJB LEASING CO.
32 Produce Row 42, Saint Louis, MO
63102
Tel.: (314) 231-3787
Rev.: $22,100,000
Emp.: 41
Fresh Fruit & Vegetable Merchant
Whslr
N.A.I.C.S.: 424480
James Heimos *(Pres)*

CJBS, LLC
2100 Sanders Rd Ste 200, North-
brook, IL 60062-6141
Tel.: (847) 945-2888   IL
Web Site: https://www.cjbs.com
Sales Range: $10-24.9 Million
Emp.: 50
Accounting & Consulting Services
N.A.I.C.S.: 541211
Andrew R. Lotts *(Mng Partner)*
Larry G. Goldsmith *(Partner)*
Jeffrey T. Stuart *(Mng Partner)*
Matthew S. Bergman *(Partner)*
Michael W. Blitstein *(Partner)*
Lorena C. Johnson *(Partner)*
Donald J. Schaffer *(Partner)*
Kurt Vietinghoff *(Partner)*
Jeffrey L. Krupp *(Partner)*
Julian Levy *(Partner)*

CJK GROUP, INC.
3323 Oak St, Brainerd, MN 56401
Tel.: (218) 829-2877
Web Site: http://www.cjkgroup.com
Portfolio Company
N.A.I.C.S.: 523999
Chris Kurtzman *(CEO)*

Subsidiaries:

Quad/Graphics, Inc. - Versailles   (1)
100 Us 60 Bypass, Versailles, KY 40383
Tel.: (859) 879-4100
Commercial Printing Services
N.A.I.C.S.: 323111
Lelia Brannen *(Mgr-Pur)*
Bill Jalbert *(Plant Mgr)*

The Sheridan Group, Inc.   (1)
11311 McCormick Rd Ste 260, Hunt Valley,
MD 21031-1437
Tel.: (410) 785-7277
Web Site: http://www.sheridan.com
Sales Range: $250-299.9 Million
Emp.: 1,460
Sheet Fed Offset & Web Printing

N.A.I.C.S.: 323111
Robert M. Jakobe *(CFO)*

Subsidiary (Domestic):

Sheridan Books, Inc.   (2)
100 N Staebler Rd, Ann Arbor, MI 48103-
9755
Tel.: (734) 662-3291
Web Site: http://www.sheridan.com
Sales Range: $10-24.9 Million
Emp.: 100
Mfr of Books & Litho Printing
N.A.I.C.S.: 323111
Joe Thomson *(VP-Sls & Mktg)*
James Rodriguez *(Mgr-Sls-Direct & West
Reg)*
Kim Kerrigan *(Dir-HR)*
Pat Stricker *(Pres & COO)*
Ed Blissick *(Mgr-Customer Svc)*
Paul Loy *(VP-Ops)*

Sheridan Dexter Inc.   (2)
613 E Industrial Dr, Chelsea, MI 48118
Tel.: (734) 475-9145
Web Site: http://www.sheridan.com
Bindary Services; Collecting, Folding, Bind-
ing of Printed Photocopied & Typewritten
Materials, Photographic Printing, Printing of
Books & Typesetting
N.A.I.C.S.: 323120

Subsidiary (Domestic):

Thomson-Shore, Inc.   (3)
7300 W Joy Rd, Dexter, MI 48130
Tel.: (734) 426-3939
Book Publishers
N.A.I.C.S.: 513130

Division (Domestic):

Sheridan Magazine Services   (2)
11311 McCormick Rd Ste 260, Hunt Valley,
MD 21031
Tel.: (410) 785-7277
Web Site: http://www.sheridan.com
Magazine Printing
N.A.I.C.S.: 323111
John Saxton *(Pres & CEO)*

Subsidiary (Domestic):

Dartmouth Printing Co. Inc.   (3)
69 Lyme Rd, Hanover, NH
03755-1293   (100%)
Tel.: (603) 643-2220
Web Site: http://www.dpc-nh.com
Rev.: $25,100,000
Emp.: 250
Lithographic Commercial Printing
N.A.I.C.S.: 323111
John Gilliatt *(Mgr-Press)*
Gary Kittredge *(Mng Dir)*
Mike Hepp *(Dir-Tech Strategy)*
Barbara Biemeck *(Mgr-Publ Svcs)*
Laurene Booth *(Mgr-Publ Tech)*
Nancy Devaux *(Mgr-Process Improvement)*
Rachel Digiammarino *(Mgr-Client Svcs)*
Cynthia Roux *(Coord-Billing)*
Lisa Ryan *(Mgr-IT)*

The Sheridan Press   (3)
450 Fame Ave, Hanover, PA 17331-1585
Tel.: (717) 632-3535
Web Site: http://www.sheridan.com
Emp.: 350
Offset Print & Digital Journal Publications
N.A.I.C.S.: 323111
Cindy Eyler *(Acct Mgr)*
Deb Rausch *(Acct Mgr)*
Sandy Deamer *(Acct Mgr)*
Michael Klauer *(VP-Sls)*
Kim Salois *(Acct Mgr)*
Lisa Darrow *(Acct Mgr)*
Kari Ellis *(Acct Mgr)*
Gail Hallman *(Acct Mgr)*
Lisa Harrold *(Acct Mgr)*
Angie Myers *(Acct Mgr)*
Kathi Ortman *(Acct Mgr)*
Amy Schriver *(Acct Mgr)*
Sue Moul *(Acct Mgr)*
Neil Myers *(Acct Mgr)*
Lin Pearson *(Supvr-Acct Mgmt Grp)*
Pat Stricker *(Pres & COO)*
Tim Hurd *(Dir-Tech)*
Chris Jones *(Acct Mgr)*

Subsidiary (Domestic):

United Litho, Inc.   (2)

21800 Beaumeade Cir, Ashburn, VA 20147-
6201
Tel.: (703) 858-1000
Web Site: http://www.unitedlitho.com
Sales Range: $25-49.9 Million
Emp.: 200
Commercial Printing & Lithographic Ser-
vices
N.A.I.C.S.: 323111

Worzalla, Inc.   (2)
3535 Jefferson St, Stevens Point, WI
54481-4374
Tel.: (715) 344-9600
Web Site: http://www.worzalla.com
Sales Range: $50-74.9 Million
Emp.: 274
Provider of Publishing & Printing Services
N.A.I.C.S.: 323117
Kim Deuel *(Mgr-Customer Svc)*
Richard Letchinger *(VP-Sls & Mktg)*
Bernie Patterson *(Sec)*
Jim Fetherston *(Vice Chm, Pres & CEO)*

CK COMMUNICATIONS, INC.
457 Montreal Ave, Melbourne, FL
32935
Tel.: (321) 752-5802
Web Site: http://www.CKC411.com
Year Founded: 1999
Sales Range: $1-9.9 Million
Emp.: 9
Advetising Agency
N.A.I.C.S.: 541810
R. Craig Kempf *(CEO & Dir-Art)*
Caroline Kempf *(Pres)*
Monique Seaman *(Mgr-Accts)*
Deb Hill *(Office Mgr)*

CK ENVIRONMENTAL, INC.
1020 Turnpike St Ste 8, Canton, MA
02021
Tel.: (781) 828-5200
Web Site:
http://www.ckenvironmental.com
Year Founded: 1994
Sales Range: $1-9.9 Million
Emp.: 11
Scientific & Technical Consulting Ser-
vices
N.A.I.C.S.: 541690
Michael F. Kelley *(Pres)*
Karen Ciriello *(Office Mgr)*
Steve Phillips *(Project Mgr)*

CK HOBBIE INC.
3429 Hamilton Blvd, Allentown, PA
18103
Tel.: (610) 433-3677
Web Site:
http://www.theckhobbiegroup.com
Year Founded: 1970
Sales Range: $1-9.9 Million
Emp.: 25
Help Supply Services
N.A.I.C.S.: 561320
C. Andrew Hobbie *(Pres)*
Amanda Marcks *(Mgr-Acct)*

CKA SALES L.L.C.
PO Box 30540, Columbus, OH
43230-0540
Tel.: (614) 619-6148
Web Site: http://www.ckasales.com
Sales Range: $10-24.9 Million
Emp.: 4
Plumbing & Heating Equipment Sup-
ply Whslr
N.A.I.C.S.: 423720
Steve Graves *(Pres)*

CKS PACKAGING, INC.
350 Great Southwest Pkwy, Atlanta,
GA 30336
Tel.: (404) 691-8900
Web Site:
https://www.ckspackaging.com
Year Founded: 1985
Sales Range: $350-399.9 Million

Emp.: 3,000
Plastic Containers, Except Foam Mfr
N.A.I.C.S.: 326199
Charles K. Sewell *(Chm)*
Dewayne Phillips *(Exec VP)*
Lloyd Martin *(VP-Ops)*
Jim Meyman *(VP-Ops)*
Drew W. Sewell *(COO)*
Scott K. Sewell *(COO-Ops)*
Dan Fischer *(CFO)*

Subsidiaries:

CKS Packaging, Inc. -
Naugatuck   (1)
10 Great Hill Rd, Naugatuck, CT 06770
Tel.: (203) 723-6300
Web Site: http://www.ckspackaging.com
Emp.: 75
Plastic Bottle & Container Mfr
N.A.I.C.S.: 326160
William D. Padgett *(Plant Mgr)*

CL RIECKHOFF COMPANY
26265 Northline Rd, Taylor, MI 48180
Tel.: (734) 946-8220
Web Site: https://www.rieckhoff.com
Year Founded: 1963
Sales Range: $10-24.9 Million
Emp.: 125
Sheet Metal Work Mfg
N.A.I.C.S.: 332322
John Rieckhoff *(Pres)*
Tim Smith *(Controller)*
Mark Smolinske *(Mgr-HR)*
Al Shriver *(Project Mgr)*

CL&D GRAPHICS, INC.
1101 W 2nd St, Oconomowoc, WI
53066
Tel.: (262) 569-4060
Web Site:
http://www.cldgraphics.com
Sales Range: $25-49.9 Million
Emp.: 200
Flexographic Printing
N.A.I.C.S.: 323111
Mike Dowling *(Pres)*

CLACK CORPORATION
4462 Duraform Ln, Windsor, WI
53598
Tel.: (608) 846-3010
Web Site: https://www.clackcorp.com
Rev.: $52,241,150
Emp.: 210
Sewage & Water Treatment Equip-
ment
N.A.I.C.S.: 333310
Bob Bishop *(Mgr-Natl Sls)*
Pete Chermak *(Pres)*
Steve Ballweg *(Reg Mgr-Sls)*
John Piasecki *(Reg Mgr-Sls)*

CLAFFEY POOLS
1625 Brumlow Ave, Southlake, TX
76092
Tel.: (817) 918-8258
Web Site:
https://www.claffeypools.com
Year Founded: 2001
Rev.: $22,944,599
Emp.: 61
Swimming Pool Products Supplier
N.A.I.C.S.: 327110
Ted Bilsky *(Mgr-Sls)*

CLAGGETT & SONS, INC.
3396 Sharon Valley Rd NE, Newark,
OH 43055
Tel.: (740) 366-5241
Web Site: https://www.claggett.net
Year Founded: 1958
Sales Range: $10-24.9 Million
Emp.: 25
Nonresidential Construction Services
N.A.I.C.S.: 236220
Thad Claggett *(Pres)*

Claiborne Electric Co-Op Inc.—(Continued)

CLAIBORNE ELECTRIC CO-OP INC.
12525 Hwy 9, Homer, LA 71040
Tel.: (318) 927-3504
Web Site:
   http://www.claiborneelectric.org
Year Founded: 1938
Sales Range: $100-124.9 Million
Emp.: 75
Provider of Electric Services
N.A.I.C.S.: 221122
Joey White (Dir-Comm & Mktg)
Mark Brown (CEO)
Jamie Dixon (Mgr-Warehouse)

CLAIMIFY, LLC
181 Ballardvale St, Wilmington, MA
01887   MA
Web Site: http://www.claimify.com
Year Founded: 2013
Sales Range: $1-9.9 Million
Emp.: 10
Insurance Consulting Services
N.A.I.C.S.: 524210
Brett Albren (Founder & CEO)
Cliff Jefferson (Pres & COO)
Michael Megna (Chief Strategy Officer)
Seth Bostock (CTO)
Amanda Correia (Ops Mgr)

CLAIN AUTOMOTIVE TEAM
11701 Colonel Glenn Rd, Little Rock,
AR 72210
Tel.: (501) 604-1500
Web Site: https://www.crainteam.com
Sales Range: $75-99.9 Million
Emp.: 50
Car Dealership Owner & Operator
N.A.I.C.S.: 441110

CLAIRON METALS CORPORATION
11194 Alcovy Rd, Covington, GA
30014
Tel.: (770) 786-9681
Web Site:
   https://www.claironmetals.com
Rev.: $11,000,000
Emp.: 180
Metal Stamping
N.A.I.C.S.: 332119
Ted Rushworth (Pres)
Chuck Berry (Mgr-Safety & Facilities)
Scott Hopes (Mgr-Production Control)
Jason Armstrong (Dir-Engrg)

CLAIRSON PLASTICS LLC
2811 NE 14th St, Ocala, FL 34470
Tel.: (352) 732-3244
Web Site: http://www.clairson.com
Sales Range: $10-24.9 Million
Emp.: 137
Injection Molding Of Plastics
N.A.I.C.S.: 326199
Robert David (VP)

CLAIRVOYANT TECHNOSOLUTIONS INC
5700 Kirkwood Hwy Ste 107, Wilmington, DE 19808
Tel.: (302) 999-7172
Web Site: http://www.ctsit.com
Year Founded: 2003
Rev.: $4,100,000
Emp.: 85
Software Services
N.A.I.C.S.: 513210
Sundar Sethuraman (Founder & CEO)

CLALLAM COUNTY PUBLIC UTILITY DISTRICT
104 Hooker Rd, Sequim, WA 98382

Tel.: (360) 452-9771
Web Site: https://www.clallampud.net
Sales Range: $10-24.9 Million
Emp.: 115
Distr of Electric Power, Water & Sewage; Wholesaler of Fiber Optics
N.A.I.C.S.: 221122
Fred Mitchell (Mgr-Power Supply & Utility Svcs)
Dennis Shaw (Mgr-Procurement)

CLAMPITT PAPER COMPANY
9207 Ambassador Row, Dallas, TX
75247-4506
Tel.: (210) 599-9600
Web Site: https://www.clampitt.com
Year Founded: 1941
Sales Range: $125-149.9 Million
Emp.: 155
Supplier of Printing & Writing Paper
N.A.I.C.S.: 424110

CLANCY & THEYS CONSTRUCTION COMPANY
516 W Cabarrus St, Raleigh, NC
27603
Tel.: (919) 834-3601
Web Site:
   http://www.clancytheys.com
Year Founded: 1949
Rev.: $63,900,000
Emp.: 275
Industrial Building Construction
N.A.I.C.S.: 236210
Tim Clancy (Pres)
Joel Clancy (Exec VP)
John Andras (VP-Preconstruction)
Cara Greening (Dir-Mktg)
C. Andrew Holland (Mgr-Mktg)
Rob Bridgers (Dir-Bus Dev)
Zach Cromer Estimator (Mgr-Pre-Construction Svcs)
Bill Goggins (CEO & VP)
Jeff Mock (VP)
Stephen Fuller (Dir-Environmental Health & Safety)
Kelsey Doulis (Controller)
Angela Gillon (Coord-Diversity, Equity, Inclusion & Safety)

Subsidiaries:

Clancy & Theys Construction
Company   (1)
7730 England St, Charlotte, NC 28273-2449
Tel.: (704) 357-6602
Web Site: http://www.clancytheys.com
Emp.: 25
Industrial Building Construction
N.A.I.C.S.: 236210
Ben Pruitt (Dir-Preconstruction Svcs)

Clancy & Theys Construction Company - Newport News   (1)
11830 Fishing Point Dr Ste 201, Newport News, VA 23606
Tel.: (757) 873-6869
Web Site: http://www.clancytheys.com
Industrial Building Construction
N.A.I.C.S.: 236210
Holly McGuire (Office Mgr)

Clancy & Theys Construction Company - Orlando   (1)
7308 Greenbriar Pkwy, Orlando, FL 32819
Tel.: (407) 578-1449
Web Site: http://www.clancytheys.com
Industrial Building Construction
N.A.I.C.S.: 236210

CLANCY SYSTEMS INTERNATIONAL, INC.
2149 S Grape St, Denver, CO 80222
Tel.: (303) 759-4276   CO
Web Site:
   http://www.clancysystems.com
Year Founded: 1986
Software Publisher
N.A.I.C.S.: 513210

Naveen Doki (Chm & CEO)

CLANCY'S INC.
120 Carey Dr, Noblesville, IN 46060
Tel.: (317) 773-3284   IN
Web Site:
   http://www.grindstonecharleys.com
Year Founded: 1964
Sales Range: $10-24.9 Million
Emp.: 250
Holding Company; Casual Themed
Restaurant Owner & Operator
N.A.I.C.S.: 551112
Perry Fogelsong (Pres & CEO)
Jerry Graham (CFO)

CLARA BARTON HOSPITAL
250 W 9th St, Hoisington, KS 67544
Tel.: (620) 653-2114   KS
Web Site:
   http://www.clarabartonhospital.org
Year Founded: 1946
Sales Range: $10-24.9 Million
Emp.: 223
Health Care Srvices
N.A.I.C.S.: 622110
Marla Mooney (Vice Chm)
Kathy Kaiser (Sec)
Jim Carney (Treas)
Jim Blackwell (Pres & CEO)
Lisa Beran (Chm)

CLARE BEDDING MFG. CO.
433 Stephenson Ave, Escanaba, MI
49829-2733
Tel.: (906) 789-9902
Web Site:
   http://www.clarebedding.com
Year Founded: 1936
Sales Range: $10-24.9 Million
Emp.: 30
Mattress Mfr
N.A.I.C.S.: 337910
David Peck (Supvr-Plant)

CLARE CONTROLS LLC
7519 Pennsylvania Ave Ste 104,
Sarasota, FL 34243
Tel.: (941) 328-3991
Web Site:
   http://www.clarecontrols.com
Year Founded: 2009
Sales Range: $1-9.9 Million
Emp.: 60
Home Automation Systems
N.A.I.C.S.: 541511
Brett Price (Founder & CEO)
Brian Dietsch (VP-Bus Dev)
Joel Rieger (Product Mgr)
Hank Alexander (Dir-Sls)
Jeff Zemanek (VP-Sls)
Charles Parrelli (Dir-Sls-East)
Delia Hansen (Dir-Distr Sls)

CLARE ROSE INC.
100 Rose Executive Blvd, Shirley, NY
11967
Tel.: (631) 475-1840   NY
Web Site:
   http://www.clareroseinc.com
Year Founded: 1936
Sales Range: $75-99.9 Million
Emp.: 99
Budweiser Beer Distributors
N.A.I.C.S.: 531120
F. Rose (CEO)
Sean Rose (Chm & CEO)

CLAREITY CONSULTING LTD.
3939 River Oaks Dr, Des Moines, IA
50312
Tel.: (515) 528-9100
Web Site: http://www.clareityltd.com
Sales Range: $10-24.9 Million
Emp.: 11

Real Estate Industry Management &
IT Consulting
N.A.I.C.S.: 541618
W. B. Freeman II (Sr Partner)

CLAREMONT COUNTRY CLUB
5295 Broadway Ter, Oakland, CA
94618
Tel.: (510) 653-6789   CA
Web Site:
   https://www.claremontcountry
   club.com
Year Founded: 1903
Sales Range: $10-24.9 Million
Emp.: 238
Country Club
N.A.I.C.S.: 713910
Eric Gregory (Gen Mgr)
Randal Gai (Dir-Grounds)
Steve Shaw (Gen Mgr)

CLAREMONT FLOCK CORPORATION
107 Scott Dr, Leominster, MA 01453-3320
Tel.: (978) 534-6191   NH
Web Site:
   http://www.claremontflock.com
Year Founded: 1915
Sales Range: $75-99.9 Million
Emp.: 45
Cotton, Rayon & Synthetic Flock for
Compounding & Surface Coating Applications Mfr
N.A.I.C.S.: 314999
Rajesh Shah (Pres)

CLAREMONT SAVINGS BANK
145 Broad St, Claremont, NH 03743
Tel.: (603) 542-7711   NH
Web Site:
   http://www.claremontsavings.com
Year Founded: 1907
Sales Range: $25-49.9 Million
Emp.: 90
Banking Services
N.A.I.C.S.: 522180
Lorraine C. Brasseur (VP & Auditor)
Jolene D. Tenney (Sr VP-Ops)
Tausha L. Shute (VP & Mgr-Retail
Relationship)
Terri A. Decker (VP & Mgr-Retail Relationship)
Lynn H. Smith (CFO)
Timothy D. Bates (VP-IT)
Vicki L. Corliss (VP & Mgr-Ops)
Chrissy Fratzel (VP & Head-HR)
Wendy M. Hodgdon (VP-Comm)
James A. Lynch (Sr VP-Comml Banking)
Brandy Blackinton (Sr VP)
Reggie Greene Jr. (Pres & CEO)

CLARENCE DAVIDS & COMPANY
22901 Ridgeland Ave, Matteson, IL
60443
Tel.: (708) 720-4100
Web Site:
   https://www.clarencedavids.com
Rev.: $15,500,000
Emp.: 50
Landscape Contractors
N.A.I.C.S.: 561730
William J. Davids (Chm)
Todd Meyer (VP-Ops)

CLARENCE L. BOYD COMPANY
4220 W Reno Ave, Oklahoma City,
OK 73107-6532
Tel.: (405) 942-8000   OK
Web Site: https://www.clboyd.com
Year Founded: 1980
Rev.: $38,000,000
Emp.: 70

Sell & Rent Construction & Mining Equipment
N.A.I.C.S.: 423810
Robert H. Crews *(Pres)*
Jim Meisner *(VP)*
Ericia Wenthold *(VP-Admin)*
Phillip Ruth *(Mgr-Parts)*
Steve Decker *(Sr VP-Ops)*
Mark Fulk *(Mgr-Customer Solutions)*
Ross Phillips *(VP-Customer Support)*
Boyd Blackaby *(Mgr-Sls Admin)*

Subsidiaries:

Undercarriage Specialists Inc.   (1)
1600 W Reno Ave, Oklahoma City, OK 73106-3214
Tel.: (405) 232-0290
Web Site: http://www.usiparts.com
Sales Range: $10-24.9 Million
Emp.: 3
Construction & Mining Equipment Whslr
N.A.I.C.S.: 423810
Paul Freeman *(Mgr-Store)*

CLARENCE W GOSNELL INC

8130 Boone Blvd, Vienna, VA 22182
Tel.: (703) 893-1221
Web Site: http://www.gosnell.com
Rev.: $10,000,000
Emp.: 15
New Construction, Single-Family Houses
N.A.I.C.S.: 236115
J. R. Altavena *(Mgr-Property)*

CLARI, INC.

444 Castro St, Mountain View, CA 94041-2017
Tel.: (650) 265-2111
Web Site: http://www.clari.com
Electronics Stores
N.A.I.C.S.: 449210
Andy Byrne *(CEO)*

Subsidiaries:

Groove Labs, Inc.   (1)
660 4th St Ste 684, San Francisco, CA 94107
Tel.: (650) 999-0200
Web Site: http://www.groove.co
Sales Range: $1-9.9 Million
Emp.: 32
Software Development Services
N.A.I.C.S.: 541511
Chris Rothstein *(Founder & CEO)*
Craig Thomas *(Sr VP-Ops)*
Mike Guerchon *(Sr VP-People)*
Patrick Neise *(Chief Info Security Officer)*

CLARINDA CO-OP

520 S Schenck Rd, Clarinda, IA 51632
Tel.: (712) 542-2146
Web Site:
   http://www.clarindacoop.com
Year Founded: 1959
Sales Range: $10-24.9 Million
Emp.: 45
Provider of Grains.
N.A.I.C.S.: 522130
Jason Sunderman *(Pres)*
Mark Mazankowski *(Gen Mgr)*

CLARION BATHWARE INC.

44 Amsler Ave, Shippenville, PA 16254
Tel.: (814) 226-5374
Web Site:
   http://www.clarionbathware.com
Year Founded: 1973
Sales Range: $25-49.9 Million
Emp.: 150
Provider of Bathroom Related Services
N.A.I.C.S.: 326191
David Groner *(Pres & CEO)*
Marcus Bingham *(VP-Ops)*
Lee Wentling *(Sr VP-Sls & Mktg)*
Susan Geyer *(VP-Fin)*

CLARION CAPITAL PART-NERS, LLC

527 Maddison Ave 10th Fl, New York, NY 10022
Tel.: (212) 821-0111   DE
Web Site: https://www.clarion-capital.com
Year Founded: 1999
Privater Equity Firm
N.A.I.C.S.: 523999
Douglas K. Mellinger *(Mng Dir & Head-Mktg)*
Mark A. Utay *(Mng Partner)*
Eric D. Kogan *(Partner)*
David B. Ragins *(Mng Dir)*
Jonathan M. Haas *(Mng Dir)*
Matthew S. Feldman *(Principal)*
Janice W. Chan *(CFO)*
Doug K. Mellinger *(Mng Dir & Head-Mktg)*
Lily Kwag *(Asst Controller)*
Edward W. Martin *(VP)*
Brandon M. Katz *(VP)*
Andrew Horowitz *(Controller-Fin Team)*

Subsidiaries:

Cara Communications LLC   (1)
12233 W Olympic Blvd, Los Angeles, CA 90064
Tel.: (310) 442-5600
Web Site: http://www.vdbp.com
Sales Range: $1-9.9 Million
Emp.: 50
Independent Artists, Writers & Performers
N.A.I.C.S.: 711510

Madison Logic, Inc.   (1)
257 Park Ave S 5th Fl, New York, NY 10010
Tel.: (646) 937-5800
Web Site: http://www.madisonlogic.com
Advertising & Marketing Services
N.A.I.C.S.: 541613
Vin Turk *(Founder & COO)*
Thomas O'Regan *(CEO)*
Sonjoy Ganguly *(Chief Product Officer)*
Jenn Steele *(CMO)*
Gary Starr *(CFO)*
Ajay Sathyanath *(CTO)*
Teresa Martins *(Chief People Officer)*
Glenn Brien *(Sr VP-EMEA Sls)*

Subsidiary (Domestic):

HG Data Co,   (2)
1 N Calle Cesar Chavez Ste 100, Santa Barbara, CA 93103   (100%)
Tel.: (805) 880-1100
Web Site: http://www.hgdata.com
Emp.: 100
Prepackaged Software
N.A.I.C.S.: 513210
Craig Harris *(Founder & Chm)*
Nick Cronin *(CFO)*
Tracy York *(VP-Client Success)*
Rob Fox *(CTO)*
John Connell *(VP-Digital)*
Elizabeth Cholawsky *(CEO)*

US Nursing Corporation   (1)
6399 S Fiddlers Green Cir Ste 100, Greenwood Village, CO 80111
Tel.: (303) 792-8550
Web Site: http://www.usnursing.com
Sales Range: $75-99.9 Million
Emp.: 150
Nursing Staffing Services
N.A.I.C.S.: 561311
Ellen Kuhnert *(VP-Bus Dev)*
Avi Khilnani *(Exec VP)*
Allison Beer *(CEO)*

Subsidiary (Domestic):

FASTAFF   (2)
6501 S Fiddlers Green Cir Ste 200, Greenwood Village, CO 80111
Tel.: (303) 692-1818
Web Site: http://www.fastaff.com
Sales Range: $25-49.9 Million
Nursing & Medical Staffing Services
N.A.I.C.S.: 561311
Jeff Files *(VP-Recruiting)*
Avi Khilnani *(Exec VP)*
Allison Beer *(CEO)*

CLARION CONSTRUCTION INC.

58 Eisenhower Ln, Lombard, IL 60148
Tel.: (630) 925-0880
Rev.: $13,700,000
Emp.: 55
Commercial & Institutional Building Construction
N.A.I.C.S.: 236220
Ken Johnson *(Dir-Project Mgmt Grp)*
Phil Martorano *(Dir-Acctg)*
Vincent A. Martorano *(Pres & Treas)*

CLARION HIGHLANDER HO-TEL AND CONFERENCE CEN-TER

2525 N Dodge St, Iowa City, IA 52245
Tel.: (319) 354-2000
Web Site:
   http://www.clarionhighlander.com
Sales Range: $10-24.9 Million
Emp.: 75
Hotel & Restaurant Operator
N.A.I.C.S.: 722511
Gautam Sharma *(Pres)*
Jeffery Hickman *(Gen Mgr)*

CLARION HOSPITAL

1 Hospital Dr, Clarion, PA 16214
Tel.: (814) 226-9500   PA
Web Site:
   http://www.clarionhospital.org
Year Founded: 1951
Sales Range: $50-74.9 Million
Emp.: 525
Health Care Srvices
N.A.I.C.S.: 622110
Al Taylor *(Interim CEO)*

CLARION SAFETY SYSTEMS, LLC

190 Old Milford Rd, Milford, PA 18337
Tel.: (570) 296-5686   PA
Web Site:
   http://www.clarionsafety.com
Year Founded: 1990
Safety Label Designer & Mfr
N.A.I.C.S.: 323111
Geoffrey Peckham *(Founder)*
Angela Lambert *(Dir-Standards Compliance)*
Todd Wilson *(Dir-Bus Dev)*
Ron Crawford *(CEO)*

CLARION TECHNOLOGIES, INC.

170 College Ave Ste 300, Holland, MI 49423-2982
Tel.: (616) 698-7277   DE
Web Site:
   https://www.clariontechnologies.com
Year Founded: 1998
Sales Range: $125-149.9 Million
Emp.: 800
Injection Molding Services for Automotive, Consumer Goods & Office Environment Industries
N.A.I.C.S.: 336211
John Brownlow *(CEO)*

Subsidiaries:

Clarion Technologies, Inc. - Ames   (1)
3100 S Riverside Dr, Ames, IA 50010-8659
Tel.: (641) 621-0149
Injection Molder Services for the Automotive, Consumer Goods & Office Environment Industries
N.A.I.C.S.: 336211

Clarion Technologies, Inc. - Anderson   (1)
3410 Hwy 24, Anderson, SC 29626
Tel.: (864) 225-2539

Web Site:
   http://www.clariontechnologies.com
Injection Molder Services for the Automotive, Consumer Goods & Office Environment Industries
N.A.I.C.S.: 336211
Jack Smith *(Mgr-HR)*

Clarion Technologies, Inc. - Caledonia   (1)
5041 68th St SE, Caledonia, MI 49316
Tel.: (616) 698-6630
Injection Molder Services for the Automotive, Consumer Goods & Office Environment Industries
N.A.I.C.S.: 336211

Clarion Technologies, Inc. - Greenville   (1)
501 S Cedar St, Greenville, MI 48838
Tel.: (616) 754-1199
Web Site:
   http://www.clariontechnologies.com
Sales Range: $25-49.9 Million
Emp.: 50
Injection Molder Services for the Automotive, Consumer Goods & Office Environment Industries
N.A.I.C.S.: 336211

CLARITY CHILD GUIDANCE CENTER

8535 Tom Slick, San Antonio, TX 78229
Tel.: (210) 616-0300   TX
Web Site: https://www.claritycgc.org
Year Founded: 1886
Sales Range: $10-24.9 Million
Emp.: 301
Child & Youth Care Services
N.A.I.C.S.: 622210
Michael Bernick *(CFO & Exec VP)*
Gina Massey *(VP-HR)*
Frederick H. Hines *(Pres & CEO)*
Geoff Gentry *(Sr VP-Clinical Svcs)*
Chris Bryan *(VP-IT & Pub Policy)*
Joe L. Nerios *(Asst Dir-Nursing)*
Christina Attebery *(Dir-Admissions, Intake, Referral & Social Svcs)*
Soad Michelsen *(Sr Dir-Medical)*
Carol Carver *(VP-Patient Svcs)*

CLARITY COVERDALE FURY ADVERTISING, INC.

120 S 6th St Ste 1300, Minneapolis, MN 55402-1810
Tel.: (612) 339-3902   MN
Web Site:
   http://www.claritycoverdalefury.com
Year Founded: 1979
Rev.: $68,700,000
Emp.: 35
Advertising Agency
N.A.I.C.S.: 541810
Rob Rankin *(Pres)*
Jim Landry *(Exec Dir-Creative)*
Abbey Jensen *(Mgr-Production & Project Mgmt)*
Beth Morgan *(CFO)*
Robin Pfeifer *(Supvr-Brand Dev)*
Karen Schultz *(Dir-Bus Dev)*
Robin Rooney *(Dir-Acct)*
Andy Brunn *(Media Dir)*

Subsidiaries:

Parachute Design, Inc.   (1)
120 S 6th St Ste 1300, Minneapolis, MN 55402-1815
Tel.: (612) 340-0333
Rev.: $50,000,000
Emp.: 30
Brand Development, Strategic Planning
N.A.I.C.S.: 541810
Tim B. Clarity *(Pres & CEO)*

CLARITY PARTNERS, L.P.

100 N Crescent Dr, Beverly Hills, CA 90210
Tel.: (310) 432-0100

Clarity Partners, L.P.—(Continued)

Web Site:
http://www.claritypartners.net
Sales Range: $10-24.9 Million
Emp.: 15
Private Equity Services
N.A.I.C.S.: 523999
Stephen P. Rader (Co-Founder & Mng Gen Partner)
Joshua L. Gutfreund (Gen Partner)
Clinton W. Walker (Partner)
David L. Lee (Mng Gen Partner)
Barry A. Porter (Mng Gen Partner)
W. Jack Kessler Jr. (CFO & Partner)

Subsidiaries:

Modern Luxury Media, LLC (1)
192 Lexington Ave 4th Fl, New York, NY 10016
Tel.: (212) 582-4440
Web Site: http://www.modernluxury.com
Magazine Publr
N.A.I.C.S.: 513120
Patricia Alfonso Tortolani (Editor-in-Chief-Ocean Drive Magazine)

Naylor Publications Incorporated (1)
5950 NW 1st Pl, Gainesville, FL 32607
Tel.: (352) 332-1252
Web Site: http://www.naylor.com
Publication Printing; Owned by ZelnickMedia Corp. & by Clarity Partners, L.P.
N.A.I.C.S.: 323111
Michael Moss (Vice Chm)

CLARITY RESOURCE GROUP
8601 FM 2222 Blvd III Ste 400, Austin, TX 78730
Tel.: (512) 491-8004
Web Site: http://www.clarity-us.com
Year Founded: 2004
Rev.: $9,100,000
Emp.: 8
Employment Placement Agencies
N.A.I.C.S.: 561311
James N. Urhausen III (Founder & Partner-Application Dev Practice Lead)

CLARITY SOFTWARE SOLUTIONS, INC.
2351 Boston Post Rd Ste 210, Guilford, CT 06437
Tel.: (203) 453-3999
Web Site: http://www.clarityssi.com
Year Founded: 2007
Sales Range: $10-24.9 Million
Emp.: 31
Software Development Services
N.A.I.C.S.: 541511
Sean Rotermund (Founder, Pres & CEO)
Stephen Mongelli (Chief Growth Officer)
Brian Higgins (Chief Architect)
Dan Schlaff (COO)
Kathy Dolan (Dir-Project Mgmt)
Rose Levy (Dir-Client Svcs)
Patricia Pensa (Dir-Fin)
Amy Dickman (Dir-HR)

CLARITYSOFT LLC
5874 Moray Ct, Dublin, OH 43017
Tel.: (614) 766-4112
Web Site: http://www.claritysoft.com
Sales Range: $1-9.9 Million
Emp.: 15
CRM Software
N.A.I.C.S.: 513210
Steve Schade (Pres)

CLARK & ASSOCIATES
11180 Sun Center Dr Ste 100, Rancho Cordova, CA 95670
Tel.: (916) 635-2424 CA
Web Site:
http://www.clarkadvertising.com

Year Founded: 1980
Rev.: $18,000,000
Emp.: 6
N.A.I.C.S.: 541810
Edward J. Clark (Pres & CEO)
Debbie Kovich (VP-Strategic Plng)
Marc Rausch (Creative Dir)

CLARK & CLARK INC.
13221 W Watson Rd, Saint Louis, MO 63127
Tel.: (314) 994-9155
Web Site: https://www.clark-clark.net
Rev.: $10,000,000
Emp.: 5
Electric Household Appliances
N.A.I.C.S.: 423620
James E. Clark (Pres)

CLARK & SULLIVAN CONSTRUCTION, INC.
4180 W Dewey Dr, Las Vegas, NV 89118
Tel.: (702) 798-5400
Web Site:
http://www.clarksullivan.com
Year Founded: 1980
Sales Range: $25-49.9 Million
Emp.: 35
Industrial Building Construction Services
N.A.I.C.S.: 236210
B. J. Sullivan (Founder)
Dave Clark (Founder)

CLARK ASSOCIATES, INC.
2205 Old Philadelphia Pike, Lancaster, PA 17602
Tel.: (717) 392-7550
Web Site:
https://www.clarkassociatesinc.biz
Year Founded: 1971
Emp.: 1,000
Holding Company; Food Equipment & Supplies Distr; Business Support Services; Mechanical Contracting Services
N.A.I.C.S.: 551112
Fred E. Clark (CEO)
Rachael Weaver (Dir-Pur)

Subsidiaries:

11400, Inc. (1)
2207 Old Philadelphia Pike, Lancaster, PA 17602
Tel.: (717) 392-7429
Web Site: http://www.11400inc.com
Food Service Equipment Contractor
N.A.I.C.S.: 238290
James M. Stephens (Pres)
Taylor Adams (VP-Project Dev)

Clark Mechanical Services, Inc. (1)
2445A Old Philadelphia Pike, Lancaster, PA 17602
Tel.: (717) 396-0545
Web Site: http://www.cms-lanc.com
Electrical, Heating, Ventilation & Air Conditioning Contractor
N.A.I.C.S.: 238990
Barry Martin (Pres)

CLARK CAPITAL MANAGEMENT GROUP, INC.
1 Liberty Place 53rd Fl 1650 Market St, Philadelphia, PA 19103
Tel.: (215) 569-2224 PA
Web Site: https://www.ccmg.com
Year Founded: 1986
Investment Advisory & Portfolio Management Services
N.A.I.C.S.: 523940
Harry J. Clark (Founder & Chm)
Paul Binnion (Exec VP & Dir-Strategic Dev)
Joseph Bell (Exec VP-Key Accts)
Colene Bittone (COO)
Brendan Clark (CEO)

K. Sean Clark (Chief Investment Officer)
Denise Clark Williams (COO & Chief Compliance Officer)
Glenn Dorsey (Sr Mgr-Client Portfolio)
Christopher Cullen (Mgr-Sls-Natl)
Jonathan Fiebach (Exec VP-Fixed Income)
Peter J. Eisenrich (VP & Portfolio Mgr-Client)
Eric Kazatsky (Portfolio Mgr-Tax Free Fixed Income Strategy & Duration Neutral)

CLARK CONTAINER INCORPORATED
6895 Bates Crossing Industrial Park, Lyles, TN 37098
Tel.: (931) 670-4400
Web Site:
https://www.clarkcontainer.com
Sales Range: $10-24.9 Million
Emp.: 100
Bags: Plastic, Laminated & Coated
N.A.I.C.S.: 322220
Wayne Erwin (Plant Mgr)
Ann Hooten (Mgr-Customer Svc)

CLARK COUNTY PUBLIC TRANSPORTATION BENEFIT AREA
2425 NE 65th Ave, Vancouver, WA 98661
Tel.: (360) 696-4494
Web Site: http://www.c-tran.com
Sales Range: $1-9.9 Million
Emp.: 400
Bus Line Operations
N.A.I.C.S.: 485113
Scott Patterson (Dir-Dev & Pub Affairs)
Jeff Hamm (CEO)
Melissa York (Mgr-Market)

CLARK COUNTY WATER RECLAMATION DISTRICT
5857 E Flamingo Rd, Las Vegas, NV 89122
Tel.: (702) 668-8888
Web Site:
https://www.cleanwaterteam.com
Year Founded: 1956
Sales Range: $75-99.9 Million
Emp.: 214
Sewerage Systems
N.A.I.C.S.: 221320
Thomas Minwegen (Gen Mgr)
Larry Brown (Chm)
Daniel C. Fischer (Deputy Gen Mgr-Plant Ops & Laboratory)
Mark Binney (Asst Gen Mgr-Fin & Tech Solutions)
Steve Sisolak (Vice Chm)
Laura Fitzpatrick (Treas)

CLARK DESIGN
1316 W Alameda Ave, Burbank, CA 91506-2810
Tel.: (818) 566-1133
Year Founded: 2001
Rev.: $1,255,000
Emp.: 2
Fiscal Year-end: 12/31/03
N.A.I.C.S.: 541810

CLARK ELECTRIC COOPERATIVE
1209 W Dall Berg Rd, Greenwood, WI 54437
Tel.: (715) 267-6188
Web Site: https://www.cecoop.com
Sales Range: $10-24.9 Million
Emp.: 40
Electric Power Distr
N.A.I.C.S.: 221122

Timothy E. Stewart (Gen Mgr)
Donna Abel (Office Mgr)
Mike Ruff (Dir-Ops)

CLARK ENTERPRISES, INC.
4445 Willard Ave Ste 740, Chevy Chase, MD 20815
Tel.: (301) 657-7100 MD
Web Site:
https://www.clarkenterprises.com
Year Founded: 1972
Sales Range: $350-399.9 Million
Emp.: 4,500
Other Activities Related to Real Estate
N.A.I.C.S.: 531390
Lawrence C. Nussdorf (Chm & CEO)
Terri Klatzkin (VP)
Robert J. Flanagan (CEO)
Joe Del Guercio (Pres)

Subsidiaries:

Clark Construction Group, LLC (1)
7500 Old Georgetown Rd, Bethesda, MD 20814-6133
Tel.: (301) 272-8100
Web Site: http://www.clarkconstruction.com
Sales Range: $50-74.9 Million
General Building Construction Services
N.A.I.C.S.: 236220
Brian A. Abt (Pres & CEO-Mid-Atlantic Reg)
Frank J. Baltz (Chief Legal Officer & Sr VP)
Richard M. Heim (Pres & CEO-Western Reg)
Sidney J. Jordan (Pres & CEO-Southern Reg)
Susan Williamson Ross (Pres, CEO & Exec VP)
Brian Flegel (Sr VP-Talent)
Carlos Gonzalez (Exec Officer & Sr VP-Western-South)
Chip Hastie (Sr VP-Ops)
David P. Trolian (Sr VP-Northern)
Jim M. McLamb (Officer-Ops & Sr VP-Western)
Mike W. Ricker (Exec Officer & Sr VP-Western-North)
Sameer Bhargava (CFO & Exec VP)
Steve J. Dell'Orto (Officer-Acquisition & Sr VP-Western)
Robert D. Moser Jr. (Pres & CEO)
William R. Calhoun Jr. (Vice Chm & Exec VP)
Harold K. Roach Jr. (COO & Exec VP)

Subsidiary (Domestic):

Clark Construction Group - California, LP (2)
575 Anton Blvd Ste 100, Costa Mesa, CA 92626
Tel.: (714) 429-9779
Building Construction Services
N.A.I.C.S.: 236220
James M. McLamb (Officer-Reg Ops & Sr VP-Western)
Roger Fricke (VP-Irvine)

Clark Construction Group - Chicago, LLC (2)
216 S Jefferson St Ste 502, Chicago, IL 60661
Tel.: (312) 474-5500
Web Site: http://www.clarkconstruction.com
Building Construction Services
N.A.I.C.S.: 236220

Guy F. Atkinson Construction, LLC (2)
11001 W 120th Ave Ste 310, Broomfield, CO 80021
Tel.: (303) 410-2542
Web Site: http://www.atkn.com
Heavy, Civil Construction & Manufacturing Operations
N.A.I.C.S.: 237990
Ryan Ostoyich (Mgr-Bus Dev)

Division (Domestic):

Atkinson Construction (3)
600 Naches Ave SW, Renton, WA 98057
Tel.: (425) 255-7551
Web Site: http://www.atkn.com

Sales Range: $25-49.9 Million
Emp.: 20
Construction of Major Civil Works: Power-plants, Highways, Tunnels, Bridges, Marine Work
N.A.I.C.S.: 236210
Bob Adams *(VP)*
Pamela Jerpe *(Mgr-Proposal)*
Jeff Roth *(CFO & VP)*

Subsidiary (Domestic):

Atkinson Underground Group   **(4)**
350 Indiana St Ste 600, Golden, CO 80401
Tel.: (303) 985-1660
Web Site: http://www.clarkconstruction.com
Sales Range: $50-74.9 Million
Emp.: 7
N.A.I.C.S.: 237210
Kim Ricks *(Bus Mgr)*

Division (Domestic):

Guy F. Atkinson Construction, LLC - NORTHWEST DIVISION   **(3)**
707 S Grady Way Ste 500, Renton, WA 98057
Tel.: (425) 255-7551
Building Construction Services
N.A.I.C.S.: 236210

Guy F. Atkinson Construction, LLC - SOUTHERN CALIFORNIA DIVISION   **(3)**
27422 Portola Pkwy Ste 250, Foothill Ranch, CA 92610
Tel.: (949) 855-9755
Construction Engineering Services
N.A.I.C.S.: 541330

Subsidiary (Domestic):

Shirley Contracting Company LLC   **(2)**
8435 Backlick Rd, Lorton, VA 22079-1498
Tel.: (703) 550-8100
Web Site: http://www.shirleycontracting.com
Civil Engineering Services
N.A.I.C.S.: 541330

Clark Realty Capital, L.L.C.   **(1)**
4401 Wilson Blvd Ste 600, Arlington, VA 22203
Tel.: (703) 294-4500
Web Site: http://www.clarkrealtycapital.com
Sales Range: $10-24.9 Million
Emp.: 75
Real Estate Management Services
N.A.I.C.S.: 531390
Cleve Johnson *(Mng Dir)*

Subsidiary (Domestic):

Clark Energy Group LLC   **(2)**
1005 N Glebe Rd Ste 620, Arlington, VA 22201
Tel.: (703) 294-5600
Web Site: http://www.cegsolutions.com
Emp.: 25
Energy Consulting Services
N.A.I.C.S.: 541690

CLARK FOUNDATION COMPANY
7707 Rickle St, Lansing, MI 48917
Tel.: (517) 322-0370   MI
Web Site:
    http://www.ldclarkcompanies.com
Year Founded: 1955
Excavation Services
N.A.I.C.S.: 238910
Lawrence D. Clark *(Founder & Pres)*

CLARK FREIGHT LINES INC.
5129 Pine Ave, Pasadena, TX 77503
Tel.: (281) 487-3160
Web Site:
    https://www.clarkfreight.com
Sales Range: $10-24.9 Million
Emp.: 50
Long Haul & Local Trucking
N.A.I.C.S.: 484121
David Schnautz *(Gen Mgr)*
John Steelman *(Dir-Acctg & Mgmt Info Sys)*

CLARK GAS & OIL COMPANY INC.
685 Commerce St, Stuart, VA 24171
Tel.: (276) 694-3772
Web Site:
    https://www.clarkgasandoil.com
Year Founded: 1928
Sales Range: $25-49.9 Million
Emp.: 130
Distr of Home Heating Oil; Owner & Operator of Convenience Stores
N.A.I.C.S.: 445131

CLARK GRAVE VAULT COMPANY
375 E 5th Ave, Columbus, OH 43201-2819
Tel.: (614) 294-3761   OH
Web Site: http://www.clarkvault.com
Year Founded: 1898
Sales Range: $75-99.9 Million
Emp.: 150
Carbon/Galvanized Steel, Copper, Grave & Urn Vaults Mfr
N.A.I.C.S.: 339995
Mark A. Beck *(Plant Mgr)*

Subsidiaries:

CTL Steel Co.   **(1)**
375 E 5th Ave, Columbus, OH
43201-2819   **(100%)**
Tel.: (614) 291-8800
Web Site: http://www.ctlsteel.com
Sales Range: $10-24.9 Million
Emp.: 10
Cut to Length Steel Mfr
N.A.I.C.S.: 331221
Mark A. Beck *(Plant Mgr)*
David A. Beck II *(Pres)*

CLARK HILL PLC
500 Woodward Ave Ste 3500, Detroit, MI 48226
Tel.: (313) 965-8300
Web Site: http://www.clarkhill.com
Year Founded: 1895
Emp.: 223
Law firm
N.A.I.C.S.: 541110
John E. Berg *(Atty)*
Anthony A. Agosta *(Atty)*
Jordan S. Bolton *(Partner)*
Jay M. Berger *(Atty)*
Reginald M. Turner Jr. *(Executives)*
Shannon L. Deeby *(Atty)*
Robert D. Gordon *(Atty)*
Jonathan W. Hugg *(Atty)*
Sherry Lowe Johnson *(Atty)*
Scott N. Schreiber *(Atty)*
Kimberly L. Wakim *(Atty)*
Amy C. Lachowicz *(Sr Atty)*
Jonathan D. Klein *(Atty)*
Robert Davis *(Dir-Real Estate Growth & Expansion-Mid-Atlantic Reg)*
Joshua Ciccone *(Sr Atty-Corp Law Practice)*
William G. Asimakis Jr. *(Atty)*

Subsidiaries:

Conrad O'Brien, P.C.   **(1)**
1500 Market St Ste 3900, Philadelphia, PA 19102
Tel.: (215) 864-9600
Web Site: http://www.conradobrien.com
Law firm
N.A.I.C.S.: 541110
Louis C. Bechtle *(Atty)*
John Jack A. Guernsey *(Atty)*
Nancy J. Gellman *(Atty)*
James J. Rohn *(Atty)*
William J. O'Brien *(Atty)*
Patricia A. Hennessy *(Partner)*
Patricia Gallagher *(Dir-HR)*
Robyn Henry *(Dir-Admin)*
Alexis R. Madden *(Mgr-Mktg & Bus Dev)*

CLARK HUNT CONSTRUCTION, INC.
2165 Logan St, Clearwater, FL 33765
Tel.: (727) 441-1559   FL
Web Site: https://www.clarkhunt.com
Year Founded: 1981
Sales Range: $1-9.9 Million
Emp.: 40
Water, Sewer Line & Related Underground Construction; Site Preparation Contractor
N.A.I.C.S.: 237110
Warren C. Hunt *(Owner)*

CLARK KNAPP MOTOR COMPANY, LLC
900 N Sugar Rd, Pharr, TX 78577
Tel.: (956) 467-4182
Web Site:
    https://www.clarkknapphonda.com
Sales Range: $25-49.9 Million
Emp.: 1,000
Car Whslr
N.A.I.C.S.: 441110
Kirk A. Clark *(Owner)*
Ruben Reyna *(Mgr-Customer Svc)*

CLARK MACHINERY COMPANY
11525 Mabelvale W Rd, Mabelvale, AR 72103
Tel.: (501) 455-4200
Web Site:
    https://www.clarkmachineryco.com
Sales Range: $10-24.9 Million
Emp.: 31
General Construction Machinery & Equipment
N.A.I.C.S.: 423810
Cliff Furcron *(Pres)*

CLARK MOBILE COUNTIES GAS DISTRICT
2003 College Ave, Jackson, AL 36545
Tel.: (251) 246-2428
Web Site: https://www.cmcgas.com
Sales Range: $25-49.9 Million
Emp.: 37
Gas Transmission & Distr
N.A.I.C.S.: 221210
Sheldon Day *(VP)*

CLARK NEXSEN, INC.
4525 Main St Ste 1400, Virginia Beach, VA 23462
Tel.: (757) 455-5800
Web Site:
    http://www.clarknexsen.com
Year Founded: 1920
Emp.: 400
Architecture & Engineering Design Solutions
N.A.I.C.S.: 541330
Paul Battaglia *(Principal)*

Subsidiaries:

Ken Ross Architects Inc.   **(1)**
210 E Watauga Ave, Johnson City, TN 37601-4630
Tel.: (423) 929-2191
Web Site: http://www.kenross.com
Architectural Services
N.A.I.C.S.: 541310
David Arnold *(Project Mgr)*

CLARK OIL CO. INC.
720 Sta St, Waynesboro, MS 39367
Tel.: (601) 735-4847
Web Site: http://www.clark-oil.com
Sales Range: $10-24.9 Million
Emp.: 200
Petroleum Products Distr
N.A.I.C.S.: 713940
Penny James *(Assoc Field Mgr)*

CLARK PACIFIC
1980 S River Rd, West Sacramento, CA 95691-2817

Tel.: (916) 371-0305   CA
Web Site: http://www.clarkpacific.com
Year Founded: 1963
Sales Range: $100-124.9 Million
Emp.: 15
Architectural Pre-Cast Concrete Products Mfr
N.A.I.C.S.: 327390
Donald G. Clark *(Co-Owner & Pres-Bus Dev)*
Robert Clark *(Co-Owner & Pres-Ops)*
Carlo de Eisenhof Eisner *(Gen Mgr-Integrated Glass Ops)*
Jim Lewis *(Dir-Sls-Architectural Facade Sys)*
Kristofer Kumfert *(Chief HR Officer)*
Aaron Alhady *(Gen Mgr-Design-Build Parking Div)*

Subsidiaries:

Clark Metal Works   **(1)**
1781 S River Rd, West Sacramento, CA 95691
Tel.: (916) 374-9600
Fabricated Structural Metal Mfr
N.A.I.C.S.: 332312

Clark Pacific - FONTANA PLANT   **(1)**
13592 Slover Ave, Fontana, CA 92337-6978
Tel.: (909) 823-1433
Emp.: 50
Precast Concrete Block Mfr
N.A.I.C.S.: 327331

Clark Pacific - IRWINDALE PLANT   **(1)**
13131 Los Angeles St, Irwindale, CA 91706
Tel.: (626) 962-8751
Emp.: 60
Precast Concrete Block Mfr
N.A.I.C.S.: 327331

Clark Pacific - WOODLAND PLANT   **(1)**
40600 County Rd 18C, Woodland, CA 95776
Tel.: (916) 371-0305
Web Site: http://www.clarkpacific.com
Precast Concrete Block Mfr
N.A.I.C.S.: 327331

Pacific Embedded Products   **(1)**
15135 Boyle Ave, Fontana, CA 92337
Tel.: (909) 350-0466
Fabricated Structural Metal Mfr
N.A.I.C.S.: 332312

CLARK PUBLIC UTILITIES
1200 Fort Vancouver Way, Vancouver, WA 98663
Tel.: (360) 992-3000
Web Site: http://www.clarkpud.com
Year Founded: 1938
Sales Range: $400-449.9 Million
Emp.: 314
Electric Power & Water Distr
N.A.I.C.S.: 221122
Wayne Nelson *(CEO & Gen Mgr)*
Doug Quinn *(Dir-Water Svcs)*
Melissa Ankeny *(Interim Dir-Fin)*

CLARK REALTY BUILDERS LLC
4401 Wilson Blvd Ste 600, Arlington, VA 22203
Tel.: (703) 294-4500
Web Site: http://www.clarkrealty.com
Sales Range: $10-24.9 Million
Emp.: 100
Apartment Building Construction
N.A.I.C.S.: 236116
Glenn Ferguson *(Pres & CEO)*
Stephanie Anderson *(Dir-Corp Comm)*

CLARK RETIREMENT COMMUNITY
1551 Franklin St SE, Grand Rapids, MI 49506

Clark Retirement Community—(Continued)

Tel.: (616) 452-1568 MI
Web Site:
https://www.clarkretirement.org
Year Founded: 1906
Sales Range: $25-49.9 Million
Emp.: 645
Community Retirement Services
N.A.I.C.S.: 623311
Brian Pangle *(Pres & CEO)*
Craig Courts *(CFO & VP-Fin)*

CLARK STEEL FABRICATORS, INC.
12610 Vigilante Rd, Lakeside, CA 92040
Tel.: (619) 390-1502
Web Site:
https://www.clarksteelfab.com
Year Founded: 1977
Sales Range: $10-24.9 Million
Emp.: 35
Steel Framing Services
N.A.I.C.S.: 238120
Kimberley Clark *(Pres & CFO)*
Kim Clark *(CEO)*
Kevin Clark *(VP, Mgr-Ops & Coord-Bid)*
Mark Mendoza *(Gen Mgr)*
Walt Pietila *(Coord-Field Ops)*
Rick Bosco *(Project Mgr)*

Subsidiaries:

Clark Steel Framing Systems (1)
1001 Northwest 58th Ct, Fort Lauderdale, FL 33309-1944
Tel.: (954) 772-6500
Metal Framing Mfr
N.A.I.C.S.: 332322

CLARK TIRE & AUTO INCORPORATED
220 S Center St, Hickory, NC 28602
Tel.: (828) 322-2303
Web Site: http://www.clarktire.com
Sales Range: $10-24.9 Million
Emp.: 140
Automotive Tires
N.A.I.C.S.: 441340
John D. Clark *(Owner)*
Matthew Miller *(Mgr-Distr)*
Scott Stilwell *(Coord-Trng)*
Kenneth Amon *(Mgr-Rettread Plant)*
Dwyan Rhymer *(Mgr-Store)*

CLARK TRANSFER INC.
800A Paxton St, Harrisburg, PA 17104
Tel.: (717) 238-6581
Web Site:
https://www.clarktransfer.com
Sales Range: $10-24.9 Million
Emp.: 20
Trucking Except Local
N.A.I.C.S.: 484121
Norma Molitch Deull *(Pres)*
Barbara Bohn *(CFO)*
Cindy Seigle *(VP-Ops)*
Jeff Hess *(Mgr-Ops)*
Denise Weber *(Dir-Admin)*
Jonathan Deull *(Exec VP)*
Gail Fishel *(Dir-Customer Svc)*
Mary Reiprich *(Dir-Safety & Licensing)*
Tawna Woolstenhulme *(Dir-Bus Dev)*
Angelo Talenti *(Co-Owner)*
Joann Tomko *(Co-Owner)*
Melodie Vobrak *(Co-Owner)*
Sheldon Whitman *(Co-Owner)*
Billy Connelly *(Dir-Mktg-NativeEnergy)*

CLARK WAYLAND BUILDERS L.C.
15170 North Hayden Rd Ste 2, Scottsdale, AZ 85260
Tel.: (602) 840-1010
Web Site: http://www.clark-wayland.com
Year Founded: 1974
Sales Range: $25-49.9 Million
Emp.: 25
Residential Construction Services
N.A.I.C.S.: 236118

CLARK, INC.
300 Freehill Rd, Hendersonville, TN 37075
Tel.: (615) 826-7631 TN
Web Site:
http://www.clarkdistributing.com
Year Founded: 1976
Sales Range: $1-9.9 Million
Emp.: 10
Vegetarian Food Whslr & Distr
N.A.I.C.S.: 424480
Don Erickson *(Co-Owner)*

CLARK, SCHAEFER, HACKETT & CO.
10100 Innovation Dr Ste 400, Dayton, OH 45342
Tel.: (513) 424-5000
Web Site: http://www.cshco.com
Rev.: $20,769,858
Emp.: 75
Certified Public Accountants
N.A.I.C.S.: 541211
Patty Conrad *(Controller)*
John R. Masheck *(Principal)*
Dan Labin *(Controller)*
Stephanie R. Pyles *(Mgr-Store-Retail)*
Brian Mosier *(Principal)*
Lance E. Drummond *(Principal)*
Jon Plunkett *(Principal)*
David M. Klopfer *(Principal)*
Kristen A. Hildebrand *(Mgr)*
Patrick J. Hinker *(Mgr)*
Calandra M. James *(Mgr)*
Kevin E. Allmandinger *(Principal)*
Michael L. Schoonover *(Principal)*
Jonathon D. Horn *(Chief HR Officer)*
Ann E. Knerr-Smith *(Principal)*
Chad Person *(CMO)*
Bradley R. Self *(Chief Talent Officer)*

CLARK-CUTLER-MCDERMOTT CO.
5 Fisher St, Franklin, MA 02038
Tel.: (508) 528-1200
Web Site: http://www.airloc.com
Sales Range: $25-49.9 Million
Emp.: 250
Nonwoven Fabrics
N.A.I.C.S.: 313230
Thomas R. McDermott *(Pres)*
James P. McDermott *(CEO)*

CLARK-POWELL ASSOCIATES INC.
110 Regent Dr, Winston Salem, NC 27103
Tel.: (336) 760-4932
Web Site: http://www.clark-powell.com
Sales Range: $10-24.9 Million
Emp.: 60
Radio & Television Equipment & Parts
N.A.I.C.S.: 423690
Kathi Cline *(Mgr-HR)*
Susan Pinch *(Pres)*

CLARK-RELIANCE CORPORATION
16633 Foltz Pkwy, Strongsville, OH 44149
Tel.: (440) 572-1500
Web Site: http://www.clark-reliance.com
Rev.: $46,286,728
Emp.: 300

Steam Fittings & Specialties
N.A.I.C.S.: 332919
Doyle Gould *(VP-Sls & Mktg-Filtration)*
Kowalsky John *(Mgr-Mfg Filtration Equipment)*
Matthew Figgie *(Vice Chm)*
Hedayatnia Amir *(Mgr-Intl Sls)*
Chris Fadden *(Dir-Mktg)*
Greg Davison *(Product Mgr)*
Nat Dickinson *(Product Mgr)*
Rob M. Wilber Jr. *(Engr-R&D)*

CLARK/NIKDEL/POWELL INC.
62 4th St NW, Winter Haven, FL 33881
Tel.: (863) 299-9980
Web Site:
http://www.clarknikdelpowell.com
Year Founded: 1991
Sales Range: $1-9.9 Million
Emp.: 15
Advertising Agencies
N.A.I.C.S.: 541810
Christine E. Nikdel *(CEO & Dir-Art)*
Anne Powell *(VP & Art Dir)*
Melea Gernert *(Bus Mgr)*
Alex Nikdel *(Pres)*
Mark Adkins *(Dir-Creative)*
Katie Worthington *(Dir-PR & Media)*
Seth Wilson *(Mgr-Online Mktg)*
Bobbi Zagrocki *(Project Coord)*
Jarrett Smith *(Dir-Digital)*
Martin Corbin *(Designer-Graphic)*

CLARKCOUNTY CREDIT UNION
2625 N Tenaya Way, Las Vegas, NV 89128
Tel.: (702) 228-2228 NV
Web Site: https://www.ccculv.org
Year Founded: 1951
Sales Range: $25-49.9 Million
Credit Union
N.A.I.C.S.: 522130
Christie Jordan *(CFO)*
Mark Andrews *(CMO)*
Chad Heese *(COO)*
Matthew Kershaw *(Pres & CEO)*
Lynn Reiter *(VP-HR)*

CLARKE ADVERTISING & PUBLIC RELATIONS, INC.
401 N Cattlemen Rd Ste 200, Sarasota, FL 34232
Tel.: (941) 365-2710 FL
Web Site:
http://www.clarkeadvertising.com
Year Founded: 1987
Sales Range: $10-24.9 Million
Emp.: 22
Advertising & Public Relations Agency
N.A.I.C.S.: 541810
Patricia Courtois *(Pres, Principal & COO)*
Bill Pierson *(CEO & Principal)*
Heather McLain *(Dir-PR)*
Rue Ann Porter *(Dir-Media)*
Joan Burnell *(Mgr-Creative Svcs)*
Richard Skiermont *(Dir-Creative)*
Harriet Hritz *(Dir-Art)*
Deborah Obeid *(Office Mgr)*

CLARKE DISTRIBUTORS INC.
472 Winchester St, Keene, NH 03431
Tel.: (603) 352-0344
Web Site:
http://www.abwholesaler.com
Sales Range: $25-49.9 Million
Emp.: 400
Retailer of Beer & Other Fermented Malt Liquors
N.A.I.C.S.: 424810
Jeffrey A. Clarke *(CEO)*
Jennifer Nolan *(Mgr-Mgmt Info Sys)*

Gary Denio *(Dir-Brand)*
Todd Watters *(Dir-Art)*
Kevin Brassil *(Mgr-Category Space)*
Don Glaser *(Mgr-Key Acct)*
Allan Lagasse *(Mgr-Mdsg)*
William Lenahan III *(Mgr-Brand Dev)*

CLARKE ELECTRIC COOPERATIVE, INC.
1103 N Main St, Osceola, IA 50213
Tel.: (641) 342-2173 IA
Web Site: https://www.cecnet.net
Year Founded: 1939
Sales Range: $10-24.9 Million
Emp.: 32
Electric Power Distr
N.A.I.C.S.: 221122
Don Lange *(Mgr-Ops)*
Jodee Eckels *(Mgr-HR & Comm)*
Brad Wilson *(Mgr-Engrg)*
Bill Freeman *(Gen Mgr)*
Randy Gaumer *(Co-Treas)*
Randy Rouse *(Sec)*
Frank Riley *(Pres)*
Kyle Keiso *(Sec)*
Tom Carson *(VP)*

CLARKE HEALTH CARE PRODUCTS
1003 International Dr, Oakdale, PA 15071
Tel.: (724) 695-2122
Web Site:
http://www.clarkehealthcare.com
Year Founded: 1995
Rev.: $11,700,000
Emp.: 22
Hospital Equipment & Supplies Merchant Whslr
N.A.I.C.S.: 423450
Gerard C. Clarke *(Pres)*
Bridget Clarke *(Treas & Sec)*

CLARKE POWER SERVICES, INC.
3133 E Kemper Rd, Cincinnati, OH 45241-1516
Tel.: (513) 771-2200 OH
Web Site:
https://www.clarkepowerservice.com
Year Founded: 1964
Diesel Drivetrain Sales & Services
N.A.I.C.S.: 423630
Randy Keach *(VP-Materials)*
Mike McGathy *(VP-Ops)*
Riley Asher *(VP-Bus Dev)*
Don Bixler *(VP-New Product Sls)*
Robert Jameson *(Dir-Product Dev Gliders & Refurbs)*
Mike Brinker *(Mgr-Regional Customer Support/West)*
Mike Ledford *(Mgr-Regional Customer Support/East)*
Mike Dowling *(Dir-Training-West)*
Billy Sharpe *(Dir-Training-East)*
Kelly Pohlman *(Asst Mgr-Credit)*

CLARKE-MOBILE COUNTIES GAS DISTRICT
2003 College Ave, Jackson, AL 36545
Tel.: (251) 246-2428
Web Site: http://www.cmcgas.com
Rev.: $49,300,000
Emp.: 37
Natural Gas Distr
N.A.I.C.S.: 221210
Richard Long *(Pres)*
Sheldon Day *(Sec)*

CLARKS QUALITY ROOFING INC.
334 Anderson Ave, Salt Lake City, UT 84107
Tel.: (801) 266-3575

Web Site: http://www.cqrinc.com
Sales Range: $10-24.9 Million
Emp.: 140
Provider of Roofing Services
N.A.I.C.S.: 238160
Carl Clark (Pres)
Matt Rife (Mgr-Ops)

CLARKSON CONSTRUCTION COMPANY
4133 Gardner Ave, Kansas City, MO 64120-1833
Tel.: (816) 483-8800   MO
Web Site:
   http://www.clarksonconstruction.com
Year Founded: 1880
Sales Range: $200-249.9 Million
Emp.: 500
Provider of Contracting & Construction Services
N.A.I.C.S.: 237310
Robert Ohl (Supvr-Traffic Control)
Colin Douthit (Project Mgr)

Subsidiaries:

Micro-Lite, LLC   (1)
3731 S Santa Fe Ave, Chanute, KS 66720-3247
Tel.: (620) 431-0530
Web Site: http://www.micro-litellc.com
Vermiculite Mining Services
N.A.I.C.S.: 212390

Superior Bowen Asphalt
Company   (1)
2501 Manchester Trafficway, Kansas City, MO 64129
Tel.: (816) 921-8200
Web Site: http://www.superiorbowen.com
Highway, Street & Bridge Construction
N.A.I.C.S.: 237310

Subsidiary (Domestic):

O'Donnell & Sons Construction
Co.   (2)
15301 Broadmoor St, Overland Park, KS 66283
Tel.: (913) 681-2155
Web Site: http://www.odonnell-sons.com
Resurfacing Contractor
N.A.I.C.S.: 237310
Larry O'Donnell (VP)

CLARKSTOWN INTERNATIONAL COLLISION, INC.
95 Route 304, Nanuet, NY 10954
Tel.: (845) 353-3900   NY
Web Site:
   http://www.cicautobody.com
Year Founded: 1992
Sales Range: $1-9.9 Million
Emp.: 26
Automotive Body, Paint & Interior Repair & Maintenance
N.A.I.C.S.: 811121
Anna Cortes (VP)
Christina Mellozzo (Gen Mgr)

CLARKSVILLE OIL & GAS COMPANY INC.
100 Hwy 37 N Star St, Clarksville, TX 75426
Tel.: (903) 427-5696
Web Site:
   http://www.clarksvilleoil.com
Year Founded: 1977
Sales Range: $25-49.9 Million
Emp.: 15
Petroleum Bulk Stations & Terminals
N.A.I.C.S.: 447110
Wendell Reeder (Pres)

CLARMIL MANUFACTURING CORPORATION
30865 San Clemente St, Hayward, CA 94544-7136
Tel.: (510) 476-0700
Sales Range: $10-24.9 Million

Emp.: 98
Food Products Mfr
N.A.I.C.S.: 311999
Lito Paulite (Controller)
Myrna Bandian (Mgr-Food Processing)
Ann Mabana (Mgr-Production)

CLARO'S ITALIAN MARKET, INC.
1003 E Valley Blvd, San Gabriel, CA 91776
Tel.: (626) 288-2026
Web Site: https://www.claros.com
Sales Range: $25-49.9 Million
Emp.: 92
Supermarkets & Other Grocery
N.A.I.C.S.: 445110
Frank Claro (Pres)
George Daddona (VP)
Marylinda Daddona (Treas & Sec)
Robert Lippman (VP)

CLARVIEW REST HOME INC.
14663 Route 68, Sligo, PA 16255
Tel.: (814) 745-2031   PA
Year Founded: 1978
Sales Range: $10-24.9 Million
Emp.: 206
Nursing Care Services
N.A.I.C.S.: 621610
John Stroup (VP)
Barbara Barger (Pres)
Ron Botz (Treas & Sec)
Ronald Scott Jordan (Dir-Nursing)

CLARY BUSINESS MACHINES COMPANY
6224 Ferris Sq Ste C, San Diego, CA 92121
Tel.: (858) 552-0290   CA
Web Site:
   http://www.clarybusinessmachines.com
Year Founded: 1974
Sales Range: $10-24.9 Million
Emp.: 22
Sales of Medical Equipment, Security Systems & Office Technology Supplies
N.A.I.C.S.: 423420
Sufian Munir (Pres & CEO)

CLARY CORPORATION
150 E Huntington Dr, Monrovia, CA 91016-4847
Tel.: (626) 359-4486   CA
Web Site: https://www.clary.com
Year Founded: 1939
Sales Range: $1-9.9 Million
Emp.: 40
Uninterruptible Power System Mfr
N.A.I.C.S.: 334220
John G. Clary (Pres & CEO)

CLARY HOOD, INC.
150 Conway Black Rd, Spartanburg, SC 29307-0000
Tel.: (864) 579-8881
Web Site: https://www.claryhood.com
Year Founded: 1980
Sales Range: $10-24.9 Million
Emp.: 100
Civil Engineering Services
N.A.I.C.S.: 237310
Clary Hood (CEO)

CLARY SOLAR
10360 Sorrento Valley Rd Ste C, San Diego, CA 92121
Web Site: http://www.clarysolar.com
Year Founded: 2008
Sales Range: $1-9.9 Million
Emp.: 20
Commercial & Residential Solar Installer

N.A.I.C.S.: 333414
Junaid Qazi (CEO)

CLASON PONTIAC BUICK-GMC INC.
2915 E Ave S, La Crosse, WI 54601
Tel.: (608) 788-7246
Sales Range: $10-24.9 Million
Emp.: 40
Car Whslr
N.A.I.C.S.: 441110
Timothy J. Clason (Principal)

CLASS TECHNOLOGIES INC.
1717 N St NW Ste 1, Washington, DC
Web Site: http://www.class.com
Year Founded: 2020
Emp.: 237
Educational Software Publisher
N.A.I.C.S.: 513210
Michael Chase (Founder & CEO)

Subsidiaries:

Blackboard Inc.   (1)
1111 19th St NW, Washington, DC 20036
Tel.: (202) 463-4860
Web Site: http://www.blackboard.com
Sales Range: $400-449.9 Million
Emp.: 1,780
Online Educational Software Mfr
N.A.I.C.S.: 513210
David Marr (Chief Dev Officer-Enterprise Ops)
William L. Ballhaus (Chm, Pres & CEO)
Lee Blakemore (Pres-Client Ops & Success-Global)
Mark Gruzin (Pres-Markets-Global)
Timothy Atkin (Chief Client Officer)
Denise Haselhorst (Chief People Officer)
Stuart Kupinsky (Chief Legal Officer & Gen Counsel)
Lily Ladd (Chief Strategy Officer)
Phill Miller (Chief Learning & Innovation Officer)
Tim Tomlinson (Chief Product Officer)
Kathleen Vieira (Chief Portfolio Officer)
Brian A. Napack (Vice Chm)

Subsidiary (Non-US):

Blackboard (Australia) Pty Ltd.   (2)
Level 11 Ste 2 3 Spring St, Sydney, 2000, NSW, Australia
Tel.: (61) 292514499
Sales Range: $10-24.9 Million
Emp.: 50
Online Education & Communication Services
N.A.I.C.S.: 611710

Blackboard Collaborate   (2)
403 33rd St NE Suite 200, Calgary, T2A 1X5, AB, Canada
Tel.: (403) 204-7896
Web Site: http://www.blackboard.com
Sales Range: $25-49.9 Million
Emp.: 140
Learning & Collaboration Software Developer
N.A.I.C.S.: 513210

Blackboard Czech s.r.o.   (2)
Kotlarska 51a, 60200, Brno, Czech Republic
Tel.: (420) 515534855
Sales Range: $10-24.9 Million
Emp.: 50
Educational Support Services
N.A.I.C.S.: 611710

Blackboard Educational (Canada)
Corporation   (2)
#101-2389 Health Sciences Mall, University of British Columbia, Vancouver, V6T IZ4, BC, Canada
Tel.: (604) 225-2225
Sales Range: $10-24.9 Million
Emp.: 19
Online Education & Communication Services
N.A.I.C.S.: 611710

Blackboard Germany GmbH   (2)
Herriotstrasse 1, Frankfurt, 60528, Germany
Tel.: (49) 69 6 77 33 552

Web Site: http://www.blackboard.com
Educational Support Services
N.A.I.C.S.: 611710

Branch (Domestic):

Blackboard Inc.   (2)
22601 N 19th Ave Ste 130, Phoenix, AZ 85027-1321
Tel.: (623) 476-1400
Web Site: http://www.blackboard.com
Sales Range: $50-74.9 Million
Emp.: 135
Computer Hardware And Software Services
N.A.I.C.S.: 334111
Timothy R. Chi (Co-Founder)
Stuart Kupinsky (CFO-Interim, Chief Legal Officer & Gen Counsel)
Lee Blakemore (Chief Client Officer & Pres-Global Markets)
Emily Crespin (Sr VP-Operational Excellence)
Tim Atkin (Chief Admin Officer)
Kathy Vieira (CMO, Chief Strategy Officer & Chief Portfolio Officer)
Tim Tomlinson (Chief Product Officer)
Phill Miller (Chief Learning Officer & Chief Innovation Officer)
Denise Haselhorst (Chief People Officer)

Subsidiary (Non-US):

Blackboard International B.V.   (2)
Paleis Straat 1-5, 1012 RB, Amsterdam, Netherlands
Tel.: (31) 207882450
Sales Range: $10-24.9 Million
Emp.: 50
Online Education & Communication Services
N.A.I.C.S.: 611710
Sabina Russells (Dir-Ops)

Blackboard Japan K.K.   (2)
2-9-10 Shibuya Aoyama King Bldg 2F, Shibuya-Ku, Tokyo, 150-0002, Japan
Tel.: (81) 3 5468 6151
Web Site: http://www.blackboard.jp
Sales Range: $75-99.9 Million
Online Education & Communication Services
N.A.I.C.S.: 611710

Division (Domestic):

Blackboard Student Services   (2)
12012 Sunset Hills Rd Ste 800, Reston, VA 20190
Tel.: (703) 464-0800
Web Site: http://www.presidiuminc.com
Rev.: $15,000,000
Emp.: 250
Administrative & Academic Support Services
N.A.I.C.S.: 561499

Subsidiary (Non-US):

CERNET-Blackboard Information
Technology (Beijing) Co. Ltd   (2)
Tsinhua Science Park 8-B 10th Fl 1 E, Zhongguancun Rd Haidian Dist, Beijing, 100084, China
Tel.: (86) 1062603842
Web Site: http://www.cernet.com
Sales Range: $10-24.9 Million
Emp.: 60
Online Education & Communication Services
N.A.I.C.S.: 611710

Subsidiary (Domestic):

Sequoia Retail Systems, Inc.   (2)
660 W Dana St, Mountain View, CA 94041   (100%)
Tel.: (650) 237-9000
Web Site: http://www.sequoiars.com
Sales Range: $1-9.9 Million
Emp.: 59
Independent & Comprehensive Solutions for Campus Services, Including Stores, Dining, Convenience, Stadium & Auxiliary Services
N.A.I.C.S.: 541512
Jim Zaorski (CEO)
John Diaz (COO)
Rick Hill (Dir-Client Svcs)
Shane Cassedy (Sls Dir-Campus Stores)
John Grantz (Dir-Ops)
Mike Strom (Dir-Acctg)

ClassBook.com—(Continued)

CLASSBOOK.COM
34 Commercial Dr, Albany, NY 12033
Tel.: (518) 370-5606
Web Site: http://www.classbook.com
Sales Range: $1-9.9 Million
Emp.: 47
Online Book Retailer
N.A.I.C.S.: 513130
Carrie Graziano (Mgr-Acctg)

CLASSIC AIR'S ONE HOUR HEATING & AIR CONDITION-ING
2680 Production Rd, Virginia Beach, VA 23454
Tel.: (757) 868-7600
Web Site:
https://www.onehourcomfort.com
Year Founded: 1979
Sales Range: $1-9.9 Million
Emp.: 40
Heating & Air Conditioning System Services
N.A.I.C.S.: 333415
Todd D. Kletz (Pres)
Eric Bridgeman (Mgr-Ops)

CLASSIC AMERICAN HARD-WOODS INC.
1245 N 7th St, Memphis, TN 38107
Tel.: (901) 522-9663
Web Site:
https://www.cahmemphis.com
Rev.: $34,500,000
Emp.: 40
Lumber, Plywood, Millwork & Wood Panel Merchant Whslr
N.A.I.C.S.: 423310
Douglas Johnson (Reg Mgr-Sls)

CLASSIC AVIATION INC.
4990 Wing Way 2nd Floor, Paso Robles, CA 93446
Tel.: (801) 295-5700
Web Site:
http://www.classicaviation.net
Year Founded: 1985
Sales Range: $10-24.9 Million
Emp.: 130
Private Jet Charter Services
N.A.I.C.S.: 532411
Tony Henderson (CEO)
Alicia Bradbeer (Mgr-Mktg)
Richard Willard (Dir-Flight Ops)

CLASSIC BANK
102 N Houston Ave, Cameron, TX 76520
Tel.: (254) 697-6461
Web Site:
http://www.classicbank.com
Sales Range: $10-24.9 Million
Emp.: 50
National Commercial Banks
N.A.I.C.S.: 522110
Robert Davis (Exec VP)
Richard Earl Williams Jr. (Pres)

CLASSIC CADILLAC GMC
420 Quintard Ave, Anniston, AL 36201
Tel.: (256) 236-4444
Web Site:
http://www.classiccadillacgmc.com
Sales Range: $25-49.9 Million
Emp.: 25
New & Used Car Dealers
N.A.I.C.S.: 441110
Jerry Jacobs (Gen Mgr-Store)

CLASSIC CARRIERS, INC.
151 Industrial Pkwy, Versailles, OH 45380
Tel.: (937) 526-5100

Web Site:
https://www.classiccarriers.com
Year Founded: 1985
Sales Range: $10-24.9 Million
Emp.: 150
Trucking Service
N.A.I.C.S.: 484121
Jim Subler (Pres)
Ed Ruhe (VP-Ops)
Kurt Rhoades (VP-IT)
Jerold Richards (CFO)

CLASSIC CHEVROLET INC.
6190 W Blue Rd, Lake City, MI 49651-8604
Tel.: (231) 839-7231   MI
Web Site:
http://www.classicchevymi.com
Year Founded: 1984
Sales Range: $75-99.9 Million
Emp.: 150
Sales of New & Used Automobiles
N.A.I.C.S.: 441110
Terry Corrigan (Pres)

CLASSIC CHEVROLET, INC.
1101 W State Hwy 114, Grapevine, TX 76051
Tel.: (817) 421-1200
Web Site:
http://www.classicchevrolet.com
Year Founded: 1960
Sales Range: $50-74.9 Million
Emp.: 350
Motor Vehicle Dealership Operator
N.A.I.C.S.: 441110

CLASSIC COLLISION, INC.
375 Northridge Rd. Ste 450, Atlanta, GA 30350
Tel.: (833) 425-2771
Web Site: https://classiccollision.com
Year Founded: 1983
Paint Mfr & Upholstery Repair Services
N.A.I.C.S.: 423620
Toan Nguyen (CEO)

CLASSIC COMPONENTS CORP.
23605 Telo Ave, Torrance, CA 90505-4028
Tel.: (310) 539-5500   CA
Web Site: https://www.class-ic.com
Year Founded: 1985
Sales Range: $25-49.9 Million
Emp.: 350
Provider of Electric Parts & Equipment
N.A.I.C.S.: 423690
Mike Thomas (VP & Gen Mgr-Global)
Daniel Lee (Dir-Tech & Ops)
Perry Klein (VP-Sls)

Subsidiaries:

Classic Components France   (1)
Parcdes Nations Paris 383, Rue de la Belle,
50261, Paris, CDG, France
Tel.: (33) 148177777
Sales Range: $10-24.9 Million
Emp.: 9
Provider of Electric Parts & Equipment
N.A.I.C.S.: 335999

CLASSIC COSMETICS, INC.
9530 De Soto Ave, Chatsworth, CA 91311
Tel.: (818) 773-9042
Web Site:
https://www.classiccosmetics.com
Rev.: $10,000,000
Emp.: 125
Cosmetic Preparations
N.A.I.C.S.: 325620
Wesley Dixon (Plant Mgr & Engr-Production)

Maria Perez (Mgr-Production)
Paul Mellott (Engr-Mfg)
Michelle Wright-Jurgaitis (Gen Mgr)

CLASSIC DISTRIBUTING & BEVERAGE GROUP, INC.
120 N Punente Ave, City of Industry, CA 91746
Tel.: (626) 934-3700   CA
Web Site: http://www.cdbginc.com
Rev.: $86,647,712
Emp.: 300
Beer & Other Fermented Malt Liquors
N.A.I.C.S.: 312111
Victor Fiss (Pres)
Joseph Sanchez III (Owner)

CLASSIC FOODS LTD.
304 E Rosser Ave Ste 200, Bismarck, ND 58501
Tel.: (701) 223-8499
Rev.: $17,400,000
Emp.: 6
Family Restaurants
N.A.I.C.S.: 722511
Bill Daniel (Owner)

CLASSIC FOODS, L.P.
PO Box 549, Temple, TX 76503
Tel.: (817) 332-1071
Web Site: http://classicfoods.biz
Sales Range: $10-24.9 Million
Emp.: 16
Canned Food Mfr
N.A.I.C.S.: 311423
Claudia Johnson (Mgr-HR)
Beth Lozoya (Reg Mgr-Area District)

CLASSIC FORWARDING INC.
1901 Camino Vida Roble, Carlsbad, CA 92008
Tel.: (760) 931-1447
Rev.: $20,400,000
Emp.: 16
Freight Transportation Arrangement
N.A.I.C.S.: 488510
Mark McNamara (Mgr-Ops)
Ella Helders (Owner)
Debbie Payne (Office Mgr)

CLASSIC INDUSTRIES CORP
18460 Gothard St, Huntington Beach, CA 92648-1229
Tel.: (714) 847-6887   CA
Web Site:
http://www.classicindustries.com
Year Founded: 1976
Automotive Part & Accessory Distr
N.A.I.C.S.: 441330
Jeff Leonard (CEO)

Subsidiaries:

California Mustang Sales & Parts, Inc.   (1)
19400 San Jose, City of Industry, CA 91748
Tel.: (909) 598-3383
Automotive Parts & Accessories Stores
N.A.I.C.S.: 441330

CLASSIC INSTRUMENTS
826 Moll Dr, Boyne City, MI 49712
Tel.: (231) 582-0461
Web Site:
https://www.classicinstruments.com
Rev.: $2,600,000
Emp.: 21
Electrical Measuring Instrument Mfr
N.A.I.C.S.: 334515
John McLeod III (Owner)
Bill Mullins (Mgr-Sls-Natl)

CLASSIC INTERNATIONAL, INC.
2551 Som Ctr Rd, Willoughby Hills, OH 44094
Tel.: (440) 255-2501   OH

Web Site:
http://www.driveclassic.com
Rev.: $21,900,000
Emp.: 80
New & Used Car Dealer
N.A.I.C.S.: 441110
James Brown (Pres)
Bob Phillips (Mgr-HR)
Larry Dallines (CFO)
Cliff Murphy (Mgr-IT)

CLASSIC LEATHER, INC.
203 Simpson St, Conover, NC 28613-8207
Tel.: (828) 328-2046   NC
Web Site: https://www.classic-leather.com
Year Founded: 1966
Sales of Upholstered Household Furniture
N.A.I.C.S.: 337121
Thomas H. Shores Jr. (Pres & CEO)

CLASSIC LIMOUSINE INC.
18315 Mount Baldy Cir, Fountain Valley, CA 92708
Tel.: (714) 963-9522   CA
Web Site: http://www.classiclimo.com
Year Founded: 1988
Sales Range: $10-24.9 Million
Emp.: 75
Limousines Mfr
N.A.I.C.S.: 336110

Subsidiaries:

Classic International Armoring   (1)
18315 Mt Baldy Circle, Fountain Valley, CA 92708
Web Site: http://www.classiclimo.com
Rev.: $12,000,000
Automobile Assembly, Including Specialty Automobiles
N.A.I.C.S.: 336110

CLASSIC PRODUCTS CORP.
4617 Industrial Rd, Fort Wayne, IN 46825
Tel.: (260) 484-2695
Web Site:
https://www.classicproducts.com
Year Founded: 1987
Sales Range: $10-24.9 Million
Emp.: 70
Mfr of Bowling Equipment
N.A.I.C.S.: 423910
Mike Eid (Pres)

CLASSIC SOFT TRIM INC.
15301 N IH 35 Ste A, Pflugerville, TX 78660
Tel.: (512) 873-7770
Web Site:
http://www.classicsofttrim.com
Year Founded: 1969
Sales Range: $10-24.9 Million
Emp.: 50
Automotive Interior Accessories Mfr
N.A.I.C.S.: 424990
Dwight Forrester (Pres & CEO)
Amy Huber (Asst Controller)
Duane Schuch (Controller)
Patti Walker (Mgr-Sls)
Cynthia Cantu (Mgr-Payroll)
Darrin Woods (Project Mgr-Creative)
Andrei Duta (VP-Strategy)

CLASSIC TILE INC.
325 Pine St, Elizabeth, NJ 07206
Tel.: (908) 289-8400
Web Site: http://www.classictile.com
Sales Range: $10-24.9 Million
Emp.: 20
Floor Coverings
N.A.I.C.S.: 423220
Jack Teitel (Treas)
Leaha Teitel (Pres)

CLASSIC TRANSPORT, INC.
58050 County Rd 3, Elkhart, IN 46517
Tel.: (574) 294-5361
Web Site: http://www.classic-transportinc.com
Sales Range: $25-49.9 Million
Emp.: 25
Transportation Agents & Brokers
N.A.I.C.S.: 488510
Dan Groulx *(CEO)*
Jodi Schieber *(Pres)*
Dennis Pontius *(VP)*
Adam Warner *(CFO)*

CLASSIC TURNING, INC.
3000 E S St, Jackson, MI 49201
Tel.: (517) 764-1335
Web Site: https://www.classicturning.com
Year Founded: 1985
Sales Range: $10-24.9 Million
Emp.: 152
Mfr of Precision Metal Parts for Aerospace & Medical Equipment
N.A.I.C.S.: 332710
Dan Wagoner *(Mgr-McDevitt Street Plant)*
Alan Symonds *(Pres & CEO)*
Rick Meyer *(VP-Mfg)*
Bill Keirns *(Dir-Ops)*

CLASSICAL KING FM 98.1
10 Harrison St Ste 100, Seattle, WA 98109-4509
Tel.: (206) 691-2981   WA
Web Site: http://www.king.org
Year Founded: 2010
Sales Range: $1-9.9 Million
Emp.: 28
Classical Music Promotion Services
N.A.I.C.S.: 711310
Steven A. Clifford *(Treas)*
Christopher T. Bayley *(Pres)*
Jim Duncan *(VP)*
Steven A. Clifford *(Treas)*
Jim Duncan *(VP)*
Patricia Tall-Takacs *(Sec)*
Christopher T. Bayley *(Pres)*

CLASSICAL NUMISMATIC GROUP, INC.
101 Centerville Rd, Lancaster, PA 17603-4006
Tel.: (717) 390-9194
Web Site: http://www.cngcoins.com
Year Founded: 1975
Sales Range: $10-24.9 Million
Emp.: 8
Antique Coin Dealers
N.A.I.C.S.: 459999
Victor England *(Owner)*
Kathy England *(Controller)*

CLASSIFIED ADVERTISING PLUS, LLC
5020 W Linebaugh F Ste 210, Tampa, FL 33624
Tel.: (813) 920-0197
Web Site: http://www.myclassifiedads.net
Year Founded: 2004
Sales Range: $1-9.9 Million
Emp.: 12
Advetising Agency
N.A.I.C.S.: 541810
Steve Juanette *(Dir-Fin Ops)*
Blaire Fanning *(CEO)*
Cathi Helm *(Dir-Labor Certification Media)*
Raenelle Turnbull *(Coord-Press Release & Newspaper Support)*
Rusty Rich *(Controller)*
Melissa Springstead *(Coord-Media)*

Tamara Huber *(Coord-Natl Broadcast Media)*
RaeAnne Meyer *(Dir-Media Strategy)*

CLASSIFIED SOLUTIONS GROUP, INC.
200 W 57th St Ste 507, New York, NY 10019
Tel.: (646) 416-6665   DE
Web Site: http://www.classifiedsolutions.com
Sales Range: $25-49.9 Million
Emp.: 19
Internet Recruiting Network
N.A.I.C.S.: 334220
Rudolph Karundeng *(Chm)*

Subsidiaries:

Career Engine Solutions   (1)
200 W 57th St Ste 507, New York, NY 10019
Tel.: (212) 977-2200
Sales Range: $10-24.9 Million
Emp.: 2
Application Service Provider; Builds, Hosts & Maintains Turnkey Career Sites
N.A.I.C.S.: 517810

CareerEngine Network   (1)
200 W 57th St Ste 1103, New York, NY 10019   (100%)
Tel.: (212) 775-0400
Web Site: http://www.careerengine.com
Sales Range: $10-24.9 Million
Emp.: 5
Career Services
N.A.I.C.S.: 541611

CLASSIQUE FOOTWEAR INC.
160 Greg St, Lodi, NJ 07644
Tel.: (201) 587-1779
Rev.: $21,122,004
Emp.: 15
Shoes
N.A.I.C.S.: 424340
Morris Abboudi *(Pres)*

CLASSROOM ESSENTIALS ONLINE
186 Hickory Springs Industrial Dr Ste B, Canton, GA 30115
Tel.: (770) 479-7671
Web Site: https://www.classroomonline.com
Year Founded: 2009
Sales Range: $1-9.9 Million
Emp.: 5
Commercial Furniture Retailer
N.A.I.C.S.: 423490
Deborah Washabaugh *(Co-Owner)*
Matthew Washabaugh *(Co-Owner)*
Meghan Washabaugh *(Gen Mgr)*

CLASSY CLOSETS ETC INC.
4320 W Chandler Blvd, Chandler, AZ 85226
Tel.: (480) 757-5895
Web Site: https://www.classyclosets.com
Rev.: $13,708,574
Emp.: 130
Closet Organizers, Installation & Design
N.A.I.C.S.: 238990
Jeffrey Curtis *(Founder)*

CLASSYAUTO.COM
4819 S 107th Ave, Omaha, NE 68127
Tel.: (402) 342-1570
Web Site: https://www.classyauto.com
Year Founded: 1999
Rev.: $3,700,000
Emp.: 52
Marketing Consulting Services
N.A.I.C.S.: 541613
John Richard Glock *(Principal)*

CLAUDE GABLE CO. INC.
322 Fraley Rd, High Point, NC 27263
Tel.: (336) 883-1351
Sales Range: $10-24.9 Million
Emp.: 200
Upholstered & Wooden Chairs
N.A.I.C.S.: 337121

CLAUDE NOLAN CADILLAC INC.
4700 Southside Blvd, Jacksonville, FL 32216
Tel.: (904) 677-8806
Web Site: http://www.claudenolan.com
Year Founded: 1905
Sales Range: $25-49.9 Million
Emp.: 80
New Car Retailer
N.A.I.C.S.: 441110
John Helmick *(Pres)*

CLAUS ETTENSBERGER CORPORATION
10349 Santa Monica Blvd, West Los Angeles, CA 90025
Tel.: (310) 767-1111
Web Site: http://www.cecwills.com
Year Founded: 1990
Sales Range: $10-24.9 Million
Emp.: 45
Luxury Automotive Accessories, Customizing & Tuning
N.A.I.C.S.: 423120
Sherif Yassa *(VP)*

CLAVERACK RURAL ELECTRIC COOPERATIVE
32750 Rte 6, Wysox, PA 18854
Tel.: (570) 265-2167
Web Site: http://www.claverack.com
Rev.: $31,324,226
Assets: $94,143,044
Liabilities: $40,332,508
Net Worth: $53,810,536
Earnings: $3,459,530
Emp.: 43
Fiscal Year-end: 12/31/18
Distribution, Electric Power
N.A.I.C.S.: 221122
Douglas Nichols *(Dir-Ops)*
Shelley Young *(Dir-Fin Svcs)*
Brian Zeidner *(Dir-Member Svcs)*
Stacey Ammerman *(Coord-Information Sys)*
Steven Allabaugh *(Dir-Engrg)*
Nicole Newton *(Supvr-Billing Process)*

CLAWSON COMMUNICATIONS INC.
474 Park 800 Dr, Greenwood, IN 46143
Tel.: (317) 887-9250
Web Site: http://www.clawsons.com
Sales Range: $10-24.9 Million
Emp.: 90
Telephone & Telephone Equipment Installation
N.A.I.C.S.: 238210
Brian Ballard *(Engr-Design)*
Karl Clawson *(Sr VP)*
Garry Pottenger *(Dir-Integrated Comm Sys)*
Kimberly Thompson *(Project Coord)*
Richard Miller *(Mgr-IT)*

CLAXTON-HEPBURN MEDICAL CENTER
214 King St, Ogdensburg, NY 13669
Tel.: (315) 393-3600   NY
Web Site: https://www.claxtonhepburn.org
Year Founded: 1917
Sales Range: $75-99.9 Million
Emp.: 900

Health Care Srvices
N.A.I.C.S.: 622110
David Ferris *(Chief Nursing Officer)*
Kelley Tiernan *(CFO)*
Vickie Perrine *(COO & VP)*
Bryan Felitto *(Sec)*
Russell Strait *(Treas)*
Chet Truskowski *(Chm)*
Nate Howell *(Pres & CEO)*
M. Sandra Lyons *(Vice Chm)*

CLAY COUNTY ELECTRIC CO-OPERATIVE CORPORATION
300 Missouri Ave, Corning, AR 72422
Tel.: (870) 857-3521
Web Site: http://www.claycountyelectric.com
Sales Range: $25-49.9 Million
Emp.: 65
Electric Power Distr
N.A.I.C.S.: 221122
David Smith *(Gen Mgr)*
Gala Blanchard *(Mgr-Fin & Admin)*

CLAY COUNTY RURAL TELE-PHONE COOPERATIVE, INC.
2 S West St, Cloverdale, IN 46120
Tel.: (765) 795-4261   IN
Web Site: https://www.weendeavor.com
Sales Range: $10-24.9 Million
Emp.: 145
Telecommunication Utilities Administration Organization
N.A.I.C.S.: 926130
Ralph Cunha *(Pres & CEO)*

CLAY ELECTRIC COOPERATIVE INC.
225 W Walker Dr, Keystone Heights, FL 32656
Tel.: (352) 473-8000
Web Site: http://www.clayelectric.com
Sales Range: $350-399.9 Million
Emp.: 184
Electric Power Distr
N.A.I.C.S.: 221122
Mark Maxwell *(CFO)*
John Henry Whitehead *(VP)*
Susan Reeves *(Treas)*
Cheryl Rogers *(Dir-Internal Audit)*
Derick Thomas *(Dir-Member & PR)*
Dale Furlong *(Mgr-Keystone Heights)*
Andy Chaff *(Mgr-Orange Park)*
Jim Beeler *(Mgr-Palatka & Salt Springs)*
Wayne T. Mattox *(Mgr-Comm)*
Richard K. Davis *(CEO & Gen Mgr)*
Kathy Richardson *(Editor)*
Troy Adams *(Mgr-Gainesville & Lake City)*
Carl Hagglund *(Sec)*

CLAY INGELS COMPANY, LLC
914 Delaware Ave, Lexington, KY 40505
Tel.: (859) 252-0836
Web Site: https://www.clayingels.com
Sales Range: $25-49.9 Million
Emp.: 150
Windows Mfr
N.A.I.C.S.: 444110
Teresa Steele *(Mgr-Accts)*
William S. Chapman Jr. *(Pres)*

CLAY LACY AVIATION INC.
7435 Valjean Ave, Van Nuys, CA 91406
Tel.: (818) 989-2900
Web Site: https://www.claylacy.com
Year Founded: 1972
Sales Range: $10-24.9 Million
Emp.: 100
Airport Terminal Services
N.A.I.C.S.: 488119

Clay Lacy Aviation Inc.—(Continued)

Clay H. Lacy (*CEO*)
Bill Staunton (*CFO*)
Scott Cutshall (*VP-Mktg*)
Joseph Barber (*Dir-Bus Dev*)

CLAY NISSAN
431 Washington St, Newton, MA
02458
Tel.: (617) 964-3000
Web Site: http://www.claynissan.com
Sales Range: $10-24.9 Million
Emp.: 100
Sales of Automobiles
N.A.I.C.S.: 441110
David Clay (*Pres*)
Guy Bognanno (*Mgr-Inventory-Sls*)
Jason Piva (*Mgr-Comml Truck*)

CLAY OIL CORP.
6353 Argyle Forest Blvd Ste 1, Jacksonville, FL 32244-6602
Tel.: (904) 272-9548
Web Site: http://www.clayoil.com
Sales Range: $75-99.9 Million
Emp.: 16
Petroleum Bulk Stations
N.A.I.C.S.: 424710

CLAYCO CONSTRUCTION COMPANY INC.
2199 Innerbelt Business Center Dr,
Saint Louis, MO 63114-5721
Tel.: (314) 429-5100
Web Site: https://www.claycorp.com
Year Founded: 1984
Sales Range: $25-49.9 Million
Emp.: 3,000
Industrial Building Construction
N.A.I.C.S.: 236210
Robert G. Clark (*Founder & Chm*)
Steve R. Sieckhaus (*COO & Sr VP*)
Dave Moses (*Exec VP*)
Russ Burns (*Pres*)
Anthony Johnson (*Exec VP*)
Kevin McKenna (*Exec VP*)
Tony Schofield (*CFO*)
Kirk Warden (*Exec VP*)
Caroline Saunders (*Co-Gen Counsel*)
Carmen Hernandez (*Co-Gen Counsel*)
Sandra Marks (*Sr VP*)
Ryan Mcguire (*VP*)
Rick Moeckel (*VP*)
Steve Street (*VP*)
Kay Maschek (*Dir-Design Strategy*)
Michelle Swims (*VP-Talent Dev*)
James Clancy (*VP-Preconstruction-Pacific Region*)
Edward Piscopo (*Dir-Economic Dev*)
Kim Poole (*VP-Economic Dev*)
John Vander Lans (*Sr VP-Ops-Pacific Reg*)
Sai Kesanapalli (*VP-Data Analytics & Engrg*)
Eric Jaegers (*Sr VP*)
Trevor Brown (*Dir-Preconstruction*)

CLAYMAN ADVERTISING
809 White Pond Dr Ste C, Akron, OH
44320
Tel.: (330) 865-5559
Web Site: http://www.clayad.com
Year Founded: 1986
Sales Range: Less than $1 Million
Emp.: 7
Business-To-Business
N.A.I.C.S.: 541810
Larry Clayman (*Pres*)

CLAYTON BLOCK CO. INC.
PO Box 3015, Lakewood, NJ 08701
Tel.: (732) 363-1995
Web Site: http://www.claytonco.com
Sales Range: $25-49.9 Million

Emp.: 700
Concrete Or Cinder Blocks
N.A.I.C.S.: 423320
Lois Kapp (*Mgr*)

CLAYTON CORPORATION
866 Horan Dr, Fenton, MO 63026-2416
Tel.: (636) 349-5333 DE
Web Site:
https://www.claytoncorp.com
Year Founded: 1945
Sales Range: $500-549.9 Million
Emp.: 150
Mfr of Aerosol Valves & Accessories;
Consumer Energy Saving Sealant
Products Sold to Retail Trade; Tamper Evident Closures & Covers
N.A.I.C.S.: 332911
Byron R. Lapin (*Pres*)

Subsidiaries:

Clayton Plastics Corp. (1)
866 Horan Dr, Fenton, MO
63026-2416 (100%)
Tel.: (636) 349-5333
Sales Range: $10-24.9 Million
Emp.: 75
Mfr of Aerosol Valves And Plastic Moulding
N.A.I.C.S.: 332911

Convenience Products, Inc. (1)
866 Horan Dr, Fenton, MO
63026-2416 (100%)
Tel.: (636) 349-5855
Web Site:
http://www.convenienceproducts.com
Sales Range: $10-24.9 Million
Emp.: 100
Foam Sealants & Adhesives Mfr
N.A.I.C.S.: 325998

CLAYTON COUNTY WATER AUTHORITY
1600 Battle Creek Rd, Morrow, GA
30260-4302
Tel.: (770) 961-2130
Web Site: https://www.ccwa.us
Year Founded: 1955
Sales Range: $50-74.9 Million
Emp.: 350
Water Supply & Wastewater Services
Administration Organization
N.A.I.C.S.: 924110
Pete McQueen (*Chm*)
Rodney Givens (*Vice Chm*)
Mike Thomas (*Mgr*)

CLAYTON ENGINEERING COMPANY
57-18th St, Wheeling, WV 26003
Tel.: (304) 233-0960
Web Site:
https://www.claytonengineering.com
Sales Range: $10-24.9 Million
Emp.: 20
Electrical Apparatus & Equipment
N.A.I.C.S.: 423610
Bill Snodgrass (*Pres*)

CLAYTON HC, INC.
102 E Main St, Camden, TN 38320
Tel.: (731) 584-8236 TN
Web Site: http://www.apexbank.com
Year Founded: 2002
Sales Range: $50-74.9 Million
Bank Holding Company
N.A.I.C.S.: 551111
Matthew Daniels (*Pres & CEO*)

Subsidiaries:

Apex Bank (1)
102 E Main St, Camden, TN 38320
Tel.: (731) 584-8236
Web Site: http://www.apexbank.com
Sales Range: $50-74.9 Million
Emp.: 164
Commercial Banking
N.A.I.C.S.: 522110

Matthew Daniels (*Pres & CEO*)

CLAYTON INDUSTRIES CO.
17477 Hurley St, City of Industry, CA
91744-5106
Tel.: (626) 435-1200
Web Site:
http://www.claytonindustries.com
Year Founded: 1930
Sales Range: $150-199.9 Million
Emp.: 600
Steam Generators Mfr
N.A.I.C.S.: 333998
Allen Cluer (*Exec VP-Mfg & Engrg*)
Alexander Smirnoff (*CFO*)
Mark Yun (*Engr*)
Rob Ripley (*Engr-Mechanical Design*)

Subsidiaries:

Clayton Sales & Service Ltd. (1)
910 Rowntree Dairy Rd Unit 32, Vaughan,
L4L 5W6, ON, Canada (100%)
Tel.: (905) 791-3322
Web Site: http://www.claytonindustries.com
Sales Range: $10-24.9 Million
Emp.: 15
Steam Generators & Boilers Sales & Servicer
N.A.I.C.S.: 333611
Glenn Adgey (*Gen Mgr*)

Clayton Scandinavia A/S (1)
Enggaten 34, PO Box 393, N 2303, Hamar,
Norway (100%)
Tel.: (47) 62533877
Web Site: http://www.clayton.no
Sales Range: $10-24.9 Million
Emp.: 6
Steam Generators & Boilers Sales & Distr
N.A.I.C.S.: 335210

Clayton Sistemas de Vapor, S. L. (1)
C/ Vallespir 19, 08173, Sant Cugat del
Valles, Spain
Tel.: (34) 935 763 579
Web Site: http://www.clayton.es
Boiler Mfr & Whslr
N.A.I.C.S.: 423720

Clayton Thermal Products, Ltd. (1)
5 Boleyn Court Manor Park Industrial Estate, Runcorn, WA7 1SR, Cheshire, United
Kingdom (100%)
Tel.: (44) 1928579009
Web Site: http://www.claytonindustries.co.uk
Sales Range: $10-24.9 Million
Emp.: 7
Steam Generator Mfr
N.A.I.C.S.: 335210
Gerry Rooney (*Gen Mgr*)

Clayton de Mexico, S.A de C.V (1)
Manuel Luis Stampa 54, Nueva Indus
Vallejo, Mexico, 7700, Mexico
Tel.: (52) 5555865100
Web Site: http://www.claytonmexico.com.mx
Sales Range: $10-24.9 Million
Emp.: 100
Steam Generator Sales & Servicer
N.A.I.C.S.: 335210

Clayton of Belgium N.V. (1)
Rijksweg 30, 2880, Bornem, Belgium
Tel.: (32) 38905700
Web Site: http://www.clayton.be
Sales Range: $10-24.9 Million
Emp.: 100
Steam Generators Sales & Distr
N.A.I.C.S.: 335210
Derik Van Dijck (*Gen Mgr*)

Subsidiary (Non-US):

Clayton Deutschland GmbH (2)
Mevissenstrasse 64a, D 47803, Krefeld,
Germany (100%)
Tel.: (49) 215187750
Web Site: http://www.claytonindustries.com
Sales Range: $10-24.9 Million
Emp.: 4
Steam Generators Sales
N.A.I.C.S.: 335210

Clayton Nederland B.V. (1)
PO Box 254, 1130 AG, Amsterdam, Volendam, Netherlands (100%)
Tel.: (31) 786139811

Web Site: http://www.clayton.nl
Sales Range: $10-24.9 Million
Emp.: 3
Steam Generators Sales
N.A.I.C.S.: 335310
Roel Leminckx (*Mgr-Sls*)

Clayton de France, S.A.R.L. (2)
160 rue du Tuboeuf Brie Comte Robert,
F-77170, Paris, France
Tel.: (33) 1 64 05 3824
Web Site: http://www.clayton.fr
Sales Range: $10-24.9 Million
Emp.: 9
Steam Generators Distr
N.A.I.C.S.: 335210
Marc Garoscio (*Gen Mgr*)

CLAYTON WATKINS CONSTRUCTION COMPANY, INC.
100 Wabuck Dr, Leitchfield, KY
42754
Tel.: (270) 259-9361
Year Founded: 1983
Sales Range: $10-24.9 Million
Emp.: 32
Residential Construction Services
N.A.I.C.S.: 236118
Clayton Watkins (*Pres*)

CLAYTON, DUBILIER & RICE, LLC
375 Park Ave 18th Fl, New York, NY
10152-1899
Tel.: (212) 407-5200 DE
Web Site: https://www.cdr.com
Year Founded: 1978
Private Equity Investment Firm
N.A.I.C.S.: 523999
Donald J. Gogel (*Co-Chm*)
Ravi Sachdev (*Partner*)
Michael G. Babiarz (*Partner*)
David A. Novak (*Co-Pres*)
Christian Rochat (*Partner*)
Marco Herbst (*Partner*)
J. L. Zrebiec (*Partner*)
Eric Rouzier (*Partner*)
John C. Compton (*Partner*)
Jillian Griffiths (*CFO*)
Gregory Lai (*Partner*)
Vindi Banga (*Partner*)
Orla Beggs (*Partner*)
David Winokur (*Partner*)
Richard J. Schnall (*Co-Pres*)
Harsh Agarwal (*Partner*)
Marta Benedek (*Dir-Europe Portfolio Company Sourcing Program-Europe*)
Lori Butler (*Dir-Environmental Stewardship*)
Andrew Campelli (*Partner*)
Romain Dutartre (*Partner*)
Ravi Evany (*CTO*)
Lisa Gawronski (*Head-Office & Administrative Svcs & Dir-U.S*)
Dan Glaser (*Partner*)
Jeff Hawn (*Partner*)
Ben Knappmiller (*Head-Tax*)
Joao Margarido (*Head-Luxembourg & Dir*)
Randy Moore (*Pres-Foundation*)
Nic Ng (*Mng Dir*)
Matthias Osthoff (*Mng Dir*)
Terrianne Patnode (*Chief Compliance Officer & Gen Counsel*)
Roberto Quarta (*Co-Chm-Europe*)
Emily Robinson (*Dir-Admin-Europe*)
Nathan Schray (*Dir-Talent & Organizational Dev*)
Kevin A. Smith (*Partner*)
Diego Straziota (*Mng Dir*)
Ulrika Werdelin (*Mng Dir & Head-Europe-Europe*)
Hannah-Polly Williams (*Head-Sustainability-Europe & Dir*)
Kevin J. Conway (*Vice Chm*)
Kenneth A. Giuriceo (*Partner*)
Sarah Kim (*Partner*)
Stephen W. Shapiro (*Partner*)

Philip W. Knisely *(Operating Partner & Partner)*
Sandra E. Peterson *(Partner)*
Russell P. Fradin *(Operating Partner & Partner)*
Sid Jhaver *(Partner & Mng Dir)*
Jon Selib *(Partner & Mng Dir)*
Mittu Sridhara *(Mng Dir & Principal-Operating)*
Joseph L. Rice III *(Founder)*
John Krenicki, Jr. *(Vice Chm & Partner)*
James G. Berges *(Partner)*

Subsidiaries:

American Greetings Corporation   **(1)**
1 American Rd, Cleveland, OH 44144
Tel.: (216) 252-7300
Web Site:
   http://www.americangreetings.com
Rev.: $1,900,790,000
Assets: $1,603,449,000
Liabilities: $1,174,155,000
Net Worth: $429,294,000
Earnings: $129,842,000
Emp.: 7,000
Fiscal Year-end: 02/29/2016
Greeting Card, Gift Wrap, Stationery & Giftware Mfr & Distr
N.A.I.C.S.: 513191
Erwin Weiss *(Sr VP)*
Morry J. Weiss *(Chm)*
Brian T. McGrath *(Sr VP-HR)*
Douglas W. Rommel *(CIO & Sr VP)*
Gregory M. Steinberg *(CFO)*
Robert D. Tyler *(Chief Acctg Officer & Controller)*
Christopher W. Haffke *(Gen Counsel, Sec & VP)*
Gary Weiss *(VP-Papyrus SAM)*
Joe Arcuri *(CEO)*

Group (Domestic):

AG Interactive   **(2)**
1 American Rd, Cleveland, OH 44144
Tel.: (216) 889-5000
Web Site: http://www.aginteractive.com
Sales Range: $1-4.9 Billion
Developer of Online & Mobile Telecommunication Entertainment Products
N.A.I.C.S.: 513199
Josef Mandelbaum *(Pres & CEO-AG Intellectual Property Grp)*
Joseph Yanoska *(VP-Tech)*
Tom Page *(Dir-Art)*
Linda Marshall *(Dir-Creative & Brand Mgr)*

Subsidiary (Domestic):

PhotoWorks, Inc.   **(3)**
71 Columbia St, Seattle, WA 98104-1444
Tel.: (206) 281-1390
Web Site: http://www.photoworks.com
Sales Range: $10-24.9 Million
Emp.: 55
Online Photography Services
N.A.I.C.S.: 812921

Group (Domestic):

American Greetings Corp. - North American Social Expression Products   **(2)**
1 American Rd, Cleveland, OH 44144-2301
Tel.: (216) 252-7300
Web Site: http://www.amgreetings.com
Emp.: 2,000
Greeting Cards
N.A.I.C.S.: 513191

Plant (Domestic):

American Greetings Corp. - Ripley Facility   **(3)**
1236 American Way, Ripley, TN 38063-7362
Tel.: (731) 635-3000
Web Site:
   http://www.americangreetings.com
Sales Range: $25-49.9 Million
Emp.: 120
Lithography Plant
N.A.I.C.S.: 513191

Subsidiary (Domestic):

Carlton Cards Retail, Inc.   **(3)**

1 American Rd, Cleveland, OH 44144-2301
Tel.: (216) 252-7300
Web Site:
   http://www.americangreetings.com
Retail Card & Gift Stores
N.A.I.C.S.: 459420
Zev Weiss *(Co-CEO)*
Jeff Weiss *(Co-CEO)*

Subsidiary (Non-US):

Carlton Cards Limited   **(4)**
1460 The Queensway, Toronto, M8Z 1S7, ON, Canada   **(100%)**
Tel.: (416) 255-9131
Web Site: http://www.carltoncards.ca
Sales Range: $25-49.9 Million
Emp.: 130
Greeting Card Services
N.A.I.C.S.: 513191

Subsidiary (Domestic):

Papyrus-Recycled Greetings, Inc.   **(3)**
111 N Canal St Ste 700, Chicago, IL 44145
Tel.: (773) 348-6410
Web Site: http://www.prgreetings.com
Sales Range: $25-49.9 Million
Emp.: 72
Recycled Paper Greeting Cards Publisher & Distr
N.A.I.C.S.: 513191
Christy Kaprosy *(Pres)*

Subsidiary (Domestic):

Plus Mark LLC   **(2)**
1 American Rd, Cleveland, OH 44144-2301   **(100%)**
Tel.: (216) 252-6770
Web Site:
   http://www.americangreetings.com
Sales Range: $450-499.9 Million
Emp.: 3,000
Greeting Cards
N.A.I.C.S.: 513191
Michael Goulder *(Sr VP-Ops)*
John S. Charlton *(Sr VP-Ops)*

Subsidiary (Non-US):

UK Greetings Limited   **(2)**
Mill Street East, Dewsbury, WF12 9AW, United Kingdom
Tel.: (44) 1924465200
Web Site: http://www.ukgreetings.co.uk
Greeting Card Publishers
N.A.I.C.S.: 513191
Gary Rowley *(CEO)*

Artera Services, LLC   **(1)**
3100 Interstate N Cir SE Ste 300, Atlanta, GA 30339
Tel.: (678) 208-6420
Web Site: http://www.artera.com
Holding Company; Electric & Gas Utility Services
N.A.I.C.S.: 551112
John Krenicki, Jr. *(Chm)*
Mickey Hanner *(VP-HR)*
W. Thomas Newell *(Chief Legal Officer)*
Rick Dunn *(CFO)*
Lyle Hildebrand *(VP-Bus Dev & Strategy)*
Ron Ridout *(VP-Fin)*
Joe Branco *(VP-Safety)*
Brian C. Palmer *(CEO)*

Subsidiary (Domestic):

Distribution Construction, LLC   **(2)**
2609 Greengate Dr, Greensboro, NC 27416
Tel.: (336) 272-0775
Web Site:
   http://www.distributionconstruction.com
Sales Range: $10-24.9 Million
Natural Gas Pipeline Engineering & Construction Services
N.A.I.C.S.: 237120
Danny Gonzalez *(Mgr-Trng)*
Todd Day *(Pres)*
Jeremy Howard *(VP-Ops)*
Tim Hunt *(Controller)*
Richard Lopez *(Mgr-Fleet & Facilities)*
Donnie Pittsinger *(Dir-Environmental, Health, Safety & Fleet)*
Kimberly Rogosky *(Mgr-HR)*

KS Energy Services, LLC   **(2)**

19705 W Lincoln Ave, New Berlin, WI 53146
Tel.: (262) 574-5100
Web Site: http://www.ksenergyservices.com
Construction Engineering Services
N.A.I.C.S.: 541330
Dennis Klumb Jr. *(Pres & CEO)*

Otis Eastern Service, Inc.   **(2)**
1 S Brooklyn Ave, Wellsville, NY 14895
Tel.: (585) 593-4760
Web Site: http://www.otiseastern.com
Sales Range: $1-9.9 Million
Emp.: 15
Oil & Gas Pipeline & Related Structures Construction
N.A.I.C.S.: 237120
Charles H. Joyce *(Pres & CEO)*
Charlie Howland *(Project Mgr)*
Ron Gill *(Office Mgr-Field)*
Dickey Joyce *(VP)*
Melissa Shutt *(Office Mgr)*

Atkore Inc.   **(1)**
16100 S Lathrop Ave, Harvey, IL 60426   **(77.2%)**
Tel.: (708) 339-1610
Web Site: https://www.atkore.com
Rev.: $3,202,053,000
Assets: $3,021,403,000
Liabilities: $1,481,503,000
Net Worth: $1,539,900,000
Earnings: $472,872,000
Emp.: 5,600
Fiscal Year-end: 09/30/2024
Holding Company; Electrical Conduit, Cable Products, Steel Tube & Pipe Products Mfr & Distr
N.A.I.C.S.: 551112
Daniel S. Kelly *(Gen Counsel, Sec & VP)*
William E. Waltz Jr. *(Pres & CEO)*
Lisa Winter *(VP-Corp Comm)*
Steve Robins *(VP-Strategic Sourcing)*
Angel Lowe *(VP-HR-Global)*
Melissa Kidd *(Sr VP-Electrical Raceway Sls)*
Michael V. Schrock *(Chm)*
Mark F. Lamps *(Pres-Safety & Infrastructure)*
John W. Pregenzer *(Pres-Electrical)*
John P. Stampfel *(VP-Bus Dev & Strategy)*
John M. Deitzer *(CFO & VP)*

Subsidiary (Domestic):

Atkore International Holdings Inc. **(2)**
16100 S Lathrop Ave, Harvey, IL 60426   **(100%)**
Tel.: (708) 339-1610
Web Site: http://www.atkore.com
Holding Company; Electrical Conduit, Cable Products, Steel Tube & Pipe Products Mfr & Distr
N.A.I.C.S.: 551112
John P. Williamson *(Pres & CEO)*
Kevin P. Fitzpatrick *(VP-Global HR)*

Subsidiary (Domestic):

Atkore International, Inc.   **(3)**
16100 S Lathrop Ave, Harvey, IL 60426   **(100%)**
Tel.: (708) 339-1610
Web Site: http://www.atkore.com
Electrical Conduit, Cable Products, Steel Tube & Pipe Products Mfr & Distr
N.A.I.C.S.: 331210
James A. Mallak *(CFO, Chief Acctg Officer & VP)*
James A. Mallak *(CFO, Chief Acctg Officer & VP)*
Kevin P. Fitzpatrick *(VP-HR-Global)*
Daniel Kelly *(Gen Counsel, Sec & VP)*
Lee Paree *(VP-IT)*
Steve Robins *(VP-Strategic Sourcing)*
Melissa Kidd *(Sr VP-Electrical Raceway Sls)*
William E. Waltz *(CEO)*
David P. Johnson *(VP)*
Mark F. Lamps *(Pres)*
John W. Pregenzer *(Pres)*
John M. Deitzer *(VP)*

Subsidiary (Domestic):

AFC Cable Systems, Inc.   **(4)**
960 Flaherty Dr, New Bedford, MA 02745-1222
Tel.: (508) 998-1131
Web Site: http://www.afcweb.com

Sales Range: $10-24.9 Million
Electrical Distribution Product Designer Mfr
N.A.I.C.S.: 332618
Robert Pereira *(VP-Ops)*

Subsidiary (Domestic):

Georgia Pipe Company   **(5)**
1206 Sunset Dr, Thomasville, GA 31792-6355
Tel.: (229) 226-7337
Plastic & Metal Pipe Mfr
N.A.I.C.S.: 326122

Kaf-Tech   **(5)**
2000 Tall Pines Dr, Largo, FL 33771
Tel.: (727) 539-0588
Web Site: http://www.kaf-tech.com
Electric Conduits & Fittings
N.A.I.C.S.: 335932

Subsidiary (Domestic):

Allied Tube & Conduit Corporation   **(4)**
16100 Lathrop Ave, Harvey, IL 60426-6021
Tel.: (708) 339-1610
Web Site: http://www.alliedtube.com
Sales Range: $50-74.9 Million
Steel Tubular Product Mfr
N.A.I.C.S.: 335932
William Taylor *(Pres)*

Branch (Domestic):

Allied Tube & Conduit   **(5)**
600 Dean Sievers Pl, Morrisville, PA 19067
Tel.: (215) 295-8813
Sales Range: $25-49.9 Million
Iron & Steel Mills
N.A.I.C.S.: 331110

Subsidiary (Domestic):

TJ Cope Inc.   **(5)**
11500 Norcom Rd, Philadelphia, PA 19154-2303
Tel.: (215) 961-2570
Web Site: http://www.tjcope.com
Sales Range: $50-74.9 Million
Metal Products
N.A.I.C.S.: 332999

Subsidiary (Domestic):

American Pipe & Plastics, Inc.   **(4)**
958 Rte 11, Kirkwood, NY 13795
Tel.: (607) 775-4340
Web Site: http://www.ampipe.com
Plastic Mfr
N.A.I.C.S.: 326122
Cecile Cranmer *(VP-Sls)*
Bill McGowan *(Mgr-Site)*
Mick Nickerson *(Mgr-Inside Sls)*
Eric Telfer *(Mgr-Traffic)*

Subsidiary (Non-US):

Columbia-MBF, Inc.   **(4)**
6560 Northwest Drive, Mississauga, L4V 1P2, ON, Canada
Tel.: (905) 362-0180
Web Site: http://www.columbiambf.ca
Sales Range: $25-49.9 Million
Emp.: 15
Noncurrent-Carrying Wiring Devices & Mechanical Tubing Distr
N.A.I.C.S.: 423610
Chris Roode *(Controller)*

Subsidiary (Domestic):

Heritage Plastics, Inc.   **(4)**
861 North Lisbon St, Carrollton, OH 44615
Tel.: (330) 627-8002
Web Site: http://www.heritageplastics.com
Sales Range: $10-24.9 Million
Plastic Pipe & Pipe Fitting Mfr
N.A.I.C.S.: 326122
Sylvia Nall *(Mgr-HR)*
Norma Ryan *(Dir-HR)*

Unit (Domestic):

Heritage Plastics, Inc. - Tampa   **(5)**
5128 W Hanna Ave, Tampa, FL 33634
Tel.: (813) 884-2525

Clayton, Dubilier & Rice, LLC—(Continued)

Sales Range: $1-9.9 Million
Plastic Pipe & Pipe Fitting Mfr
N.A.I.C.S.: 326122

Subsidiary (Domestic):

Unistrut Corporation (4)
4045 2nd St, Wayne, MI 48184
Tel.: (734) 722-1400
Web Site: http://www.unistrut.com
Sales Range: $25-49.9 Million
Metal Framing Products Mfr
N.A.I.C.S.: 332311
Keith Murray (Mgr-Eastern Reg)

Branch (Domestic):

Unistrut Corporation (5)
323 E 151st St, Harvey, IL 60426
Tel.: (708) 225-2974
Web Site: http://www.unistrut.com
Sales Range: $50-74.9 Million
Emp.: 10
Metal Products
N.A.I.C.S.: 332311
John Williamson (Pres)

Subsidiary (Non-US):

FRE Composites Inc. (2)
75 Wales St, St-Andre-d'Argenteuil, J0V
1X0, QC, Canada
Tel.: (450) 537-3311
Web Site: http://www.frecomposites.com
Nonmetallic Mineral Product Mfr
N.A.I.C.S.: 327999
Benoit Arsenault (Pres)
Hal Milleman (Mgr-Sls-Northern Sls)

Subsidiary (Domestic):

Northwest Polymers LLC (2)
291 Commercial Pkwy, Molalla, OR 97038
Tel.: (503) 829-3550
Web Site: http://www.nwpoly.com
Unsupported Plastics Profile Shape Mfr
N.A.I.C.S.: 326121
Mark Shuholm (Founder)
Fred Gorski (Gen Mgr)
Angie Mitchell (Office Mgr)
Jeff Walter (Mgr-Pur & Sls)

Queen City Plastics, Inc. (2)
2650 Bennett Rd, Fort Mill, SC 29715
Tel.: (803) 548-0685
Web Site: http://www.queencityplastics.com
Noncurrent-Carrying Wiring Device Mfr
N.A.I.C.S.: 335932
Claude H. Marston (Sec)

B&M Retail Limited (1)
The Vault Dakota Drive, Estuary Commerce
Park Speke, Liverpool, L24 8RJ, United
Kingdom (60%)
Tel.: (44) 151 728 5400
Web Site: http://www.bmstores.co.uk
Sales Range: $1-4.9 Billion
Emp.: 12,000
Variety Stores
N.A.I.C.S.: 455219
Simon Arora (Mng Dir)
Bobby Arora (Mng Dir)
Terry Leahy (Chm)
Paul McDonald (Fin Dir)
Stephanie Tonge (Head-HR)
John Ward (Head-Security)

BUT SAS (1)
1 Avenue Spinoza, 77184, Emerainville-
Malnoue, France (50%)
Tel.: (33) 164612626
Web Site: http://www.but.fr
Sales Range: $1-4.9 Billion
Emp.: 4,989
Home Appliances, Furniture & Decor Re-
tailer
N.A.I.C.S.: 449210
Thierry Lernon (Dir-Internet)

CD&R LLP (1)
Cleveland House 33 King Street, London,
SW1Y 6RJ, United Kingdom
Tel.: (44) 207 747 3800
Investment Advisory Services
N.A.I.C.S.: 523940

Carestream Dental, LLC (1)
3625 Cumberland Blvd Ste 700, Atlanta,
GA 30339-2037 (75%)

Tel.: (800) 944-6365
Web Site: http://www.carestreamdental.com
Digital Imaging, Software & Management
Services to the Dental Sector
N.A.I.C.S.: 621512
Edward Shellard (Chief Dental Officer)
Lisa Ashby (CEO)
Jane Guinn (VP-Global Customer Care)
Nicola Gizzi (Gen Mgr-EMEA)
Pinkesh Garg (Reg Mng Dir-Asia Pacific)
Philippe Maillet (Gen Mgr-Imaging Equip-
ment)
Satish Hemachandran (Gen Mgr-Dental
Practice Mgmt Software)
Brian Baggett (CIO)
Nonni Ellison (Gen Counsel, Chief Compli-
ance Officer & Sec)
Tim Donovan (CFO)
John M. Dineen (Chm)

Cloudera, Inc. (1)
5470 Great America Pkwy, Santa Clara, CA
95054
Tel.: (650) 362-0488
Web Site: http://www.cloudera.com
Rev.: $869,258,000
Assets: $2,508,601,000
Liabilities: $1,380,671,000
Net Worth: $1,127,930,000
Earnings: ($162,734,000)
Emp.: 2,728
Fiscal Year-end: 01/31/2021
Business & Financial Data Management
Software Development Services
N.A.I.C.S.: 541511
Amr Awadallah (Founder)
Mick Hollison (Pres)
Kevin Cook (VP-Corp Dev & IR)
Scott Aronson (COO)
Scott Reasoner (Chief Acctg Officer)
Arun C. Murthy (Chief Product Officer)
Bob Mahan (Chief HR Officer)

Subsidiary (Non-US):

**Cloudera (Shanghai) Software Co.
Ltd.** (2)
Shanghai Mart Office Tower Floor 26 Suite
2612 No 2299, Yan'an Road, Shanghai,
200336, China
Tel.: (86) 2162369001
Software Development Services
N.A.I.C.S.: 541511

Cloudera (UK) Limited (2)
30 Old Broad Street 5th Floor, London,
EC2N 1HT, United Kingdom
Tel.: (44) 2038261405
Software Development Services
N.A.I.C.S.: 541511

Cloudera GmbH (2)
Birketweg 31, 80639, Munich, Germany
Tel.: (49) 22165078699
Software Development Services
N.A.I.C.S.: 541511

Cloudera Hungary Kft. (2)
Roosevelt Building Szechenyi Istvan ter 7-8
level 7, 1051, Budapest, Hungary
Tel.: (36) 17011201
Software Development Services
N.A.I.C.S.: 541511

Cloudera Inc. (2)
81 Rivington Street, London, EC2A 3AY,
United Kingdom
Tel.: (44) 203 178 4857
Software Publisher
N.A.I.C.S.: 513210

Cloudera K.K. (2)
26th Floor Kyobashi Edogrand Kyobashi
2-2-1, Chuo-ku, Tokyo, 104-0031, Japan
Tel.: (81) 367481506
Web Site: http://www.cloudera.com
Software Publisher
N.A.I.C.S.: 513210

Cloudera Korea, Inc. (2)
41/F Gangnam Finance Center 152
Teheran-ro, Gangnam-gu, Seoul, 06236,
Korea (South)
Tel.: (82) 220084595
Software Development Services
N.A.I.C.S.: 541511

Subsidiary (Domestic):

Hortonworks Inc. (2)

5470 Great America Pkwy, Santa Clara, CA
95054
Tel.: (408) 916-4121
Web Site: http://www.hortonworks.com
Rev.: $261,810,000
Assets: $250,733,000
Liabilities: $315,769,000
Net Worth: ($65,036,000)
Earnings: ($204,507,000)
Emp.: 1,175
Fiscal Year-end: 12/31/2017
Software Developer
N.A.I.C.S.: 513210
Paul A. Krieger (Mgr-Revenue)

Subsidiary (Domestic):

Agniv, Inc. (3)
7100 Stevenson Blvd, Fremont, CA 94538-
2485
Tel.: (510) 585-3289
Business Support Services
N.A.I.C.S.: 561499

**Cornerstone Building Brands,
Inc.** (1)
5020 Weston Pkwy Ste 400, Cary, NC
27513
Web Site:
    https://www.cornerstonebuildings.com
Rev.: $5,402,434,000
Assets: $6,933,341,000
Liabilities: $5,288,471,000
Net Worth: $1,644,870,000
Earnings: ($75,525,000)
Emp.: 17,600
Fiscal Year-end: 12/31/2023
Holding Company; Metal Building Compo-
nents & Engineered Building Systems Mfr &
Metal Coil Coating Services
N.A.I.C.S.: 551112
Rose Lee (Pres & CEO)
Colleen Pritchett (Pres-Windows-US)
Jeffrey S. Lee (CFO & Exec VP)
John L. Buckley (Pres-Siding Bus Unit)
Susan S. Selle (CMO)
Alan Strassner (Sr VP-Strategy & Bus Dev)
Alena Brenner (Gen Counsel, Sec & Exec
VP)
Matthew Ackley (Pres-Engineered Building
Sys)
Pete Andrich (Chief HR Officer & Exec VP)
Wayne F. Irmiter (Chief Acctg Officer & Sr
VP)
Lisa Domnisch (Pres-Canadian Bus Unit)

Subsidiary (Domestic):

A&S Building Systems, Inc. (2)
1880 Hwy 116, Caryville, TN 37714
Tel.: (865) 426-2141
Web Site: http://www.a-s.com
Designs, Manufactures & Markets Metal
Building Systems & Components for Non-
Residential Use
N.A.I.C.S.: 332311

American Building Components (2)
515 13th Ave E, Oskaloosa, IA 52577
Tel.: (641) 673-7099
Web Site: http://www.abcmetalroofing.com
Metal Roofing & Building Panel Mfr
N.A.I.C.S.: 332311

CENTRIA, Inc. (2)
1005 Beaver Grade Rd, Moon Township,
PA 15108-2964
Tel.: (800) 759-7474
Web Site: http://www.centria.com
Metal Clad Building Materials, Wall & Roof
Panels, Industrial Ventilation Equipment Mfr
N.A.I.C.S.: 332322
Greg Lusty (Dir-Product Mgmt & R&D)
Preston Bowen (Pres)

Division (Domestic):

CENTRIA Architectural Systems (3)
1005 Beaver Grade Rd, Moon Township,
PA 15108
Tel.: (800) 759-7474
Web Site: http://www.centria.com
Emp.: 100
Architectural Metal Enclosure Systems Mfr
N.A.I.C.S.: 332322

Subsidiary (Domestic):

HH Robertson Floor Systems (3)
12620 Wilmot Rd, Kenosha, WI 53142

Web Site: http://www.hhrobertson.com
Cellular Steel Deck & Frame Mfr
N.A.I.C.S.: 332312

Subsidiary (Domestic):

Ceco Building Systems (2)
2400 Hwy 45 N, Columbus, MS 39705-
1398
Tel.: (662) 328-6722
Web Site: http://www.cecobuildings.com
Sales Range: $25-49.9 Million
Pre-Engineered Steel Buildings Mfr
N.A.I.C.S.: 332311
Lynn Chesnut (VP-Sls)
Tim Schrock (Pres)

Branch (Domestic):

**Ceco Building Systems-Eastern
Region** (3)
100 Red Iron Rd, Rocky Mount, NC 27804
Tel.: (252) 977-2131
Web Site: http://www.cecobuildings.com
Sales Range: $25-49.9 Million
Emp.: 40
Prefabricated Metal Building Mfr
N.A.I.C.S.: 332311
Tim Schrock (Pres)

Subsidiary (Domestic):

**Eastern Metal Supply Inc. - Eastern
Architectural Systems Division** (3)
10030 Bavaria Rd, Fort Myers, FL 33913
Tel.: (239) 369-9696
Web Site:
    http://www.easternarchitectural.com
Window & Door Mfr
N.A.I.C.S.: 332321

Environmental Materials LLC (2)
6300 E Stapleton Dr S, Denver, CO 80216
Tel.: (303) 309-3040
Web Site: http://www.estoneworks.com
Designer, Mfr & Installer of Stone Veneer
Products
N.A.I.C.S.: 327991
Charles Stein (Pres & CEO)
Steve Bohn (CFO)

Garco Building Systems, Inc. (2)
2714 S Garfield Rd, Airway Heights, WA
99001
Tel.: (509) 244-5611
Web Site: http://www.garcobuildings.com
Steel Building Systems Design Mfr & Distr
N.A.I.C.S.: 332311
Mike Berry (Mgr-Bus Dev)

Harvey Industries, LLC (2)
1400 Main St, Waltham, MA 02451-1689
Tel.: (781) 899-3500
Web Site: http://www.harveybp.com
Roofing, Siding & Insulation, Metal Doors,
Sash, Trim & Millwork
N.A.I.C.S.: 423330
Scott Lassonde (CFO)

Plant (Domestic):

**Harvey Industries, Inc. - Dartmouth
Manufacturing Facility** (3)
7 Ledgewood Blvd N, Dartmouth, MA
02747
Tel.: (508) 998-9779
Door & Window Mfr
N.A.I.C.S.: 321911

Subsidiary (Domestic):

**Northeast Building Products
Corp.** (3)
4280 Aramingo Ave, Philadelphia, PA 19124
Tel.: (215) 535-7110
Web Site: http://www.nbpwindows.com
Sales Range: $10-24.9 Million
Metal Doors & Windows Mfr
N.A.I.C.S.: 332321
Alan Levin (Owner & Pres)
Fran Levin (Chief Administrative Officer)

Soft-Lite LLC (3)
10250 Philipp Pkwy, Streetsboro, OH 44241
Tel.: (330) 528-3400
Web Site: http://www.soft-lite.com
Vinyl Windows & Patio Doors Mfr
N.A.I.C.S.: 321999
Bruno Brunatti (Controller)
John Bartlebaugh (Dir-Credit & Collections)

Subsidiary (Domestic):

Mesco Buildings Solutions (2)
5244 Bear Creek Ct, Irving, TX
75061 **(100%)**
Tel.: (214) 687-9999
Web Site: http://www.mescobuildings.com
Sales Range: $25-49.9 Million
Metal Buildings Mfr
N.A.I.C.S.: 423390
Steve Heil (VP-Engrg)

Metal Building Components Inc. (2)
14031 W Hardy, Houston, TX 77060
Tel.: (281) 897-7788
Web Site: http://www.mbci.com
Sales Range: $125-149.9 Million
Mfr of Prefabricated Metal Buildings
N.A.I.C.S.: 332311
Phillip Wilkerson (VP-Mfr)

Metal Coaters LP (2)
10943 N Sam Houston Pkwy W, Houston,
TX 77064
Tel.: (281) 897-7788
Web Site: http://www.metalcoaters.com
Metal Coil Coating Services
N.A.I.C.S.: 332812
Gary D. Nesbit (Mgr-Bus Dev)
Dan Happel (Mgr-Sls-Western Reg-
California)
Dan Losin (Mgr-Sls-Eastern Reg-Georgia)
Donnie Snow (Mgr-Acct-Georgia)
Joe Turjanica (Mgr-Acct-Ohio)

Plant (Domestic):

Metal Coaters - Houston Plant (3)
501 N Greenwood St, Houston, TX 77011-
5304
Tel.: (713) 921-7997
Web Site: http://www.metalcoaters.com
Metal Coil Coating Services
N.A.I.C.S.: 332812

Metal Coaters of Georgia (3)
1150 Marietta Industrial Dr, Marietta, GA
30062-2446
Tel.: (770) 427-9471
Web Site: http://www.metalcoaters.com
Sales Range: $25-49.9 Million
Metal Sheetwork
N.A.I.C.S.: 332812
Dan Losin (Mgr-Sls-Eastern)

Metal Coaters of Mississippi (3)
951 Prisock Rd, Jackson, MS 39272
Tel.: (601) 373-0374
Web Site: http://www.metalcoaters.com
Sales Range: $50-74.9 Million
Metal Coil Coating Services
N.A.I.C.S.: 332812
Dirren Valentina (Mgr-Sls)
Michael Thorenburg (Mgr-Quality)

Subsidiary (Domestic):

Metallic Building Company (2)
7301 Fairview, Houston, TX 77041
Tel.: (713) 466-7788
Web Site: http://www.metallic.com
Sales Range: $50-74.9 Million
Pre-Fabricated Buildings; Steel Buildings
N.A.I.C.S.: 332311

Metl-Span LLC (2)
1720 Lakepointe Dr Ste 101, Lewisville, TX
75057
Tel.: (972) 221-6656
Web Site: http://www.metlspan.com
Sales Range: $150-199.9 Million
Building Panel Products Mfr
N.A.I.C.S.: 332311
Karl Hielscher (Gen Mgr)

Ply Gem Holdings, Inc. (2)
5020 Weston Pkwy Ste 400, Cary, NC
27513
Tel.: (866) 419-0042
Web Site: http://www.plygem.com
Holding Company; Residential Exterior
Building Products Mfr
N.A.I.C.S.: 551112

Subsidiary (Domestic):

AWC Holding Company (3)
5020 Weston Pkwy Ste 400, Cary, NC
27513-2322
Tel.: (919) 677-3900
Plastics Product Mfr

N.A.I.C.S.: 326199

Aluminum Scrap Recycle, L.L.C. (3)
5020 Weston Pkwy Ste 400, Cary, NC
27513
Tel.: (919) 677-3900
Aluminum Recycling Services
N.A.I.C.S.: 562920

New Glazing Industries, Ltd. (3)
3706 La Reunion Pkwy, Dallas, TX 75212
Tel.: (214) 239-0585
Building Material Mfr & Distr
N.A.I.C.S.: 326199

Ply Gem Industries, Inc. (3)
5020 Weston Pky Ste 400, Cary, NC
27513 **(100%)**
Tel.: (919) 677-3900
Web Site: http://www.plygem.com
Sales Range: $1-4.9 Billion
Exterior Vinyl & Aluminum Siding, Compos-
ite Railing & Fence Products, Wood & Metal
Windows Mfr & Distr
N.A.I.C.S.: 326199

Subsidiary (Domestic):

Great Lakes Window, Inc. (4)
30499 Tracy Rd, Walbridge, OH 43465-
9777
Tel.: (419) 666-5555
Web Site: http://www.greatlakeswindow.com
Sales Range: $50-74.9 Million
Vinyl Replacement Windows & Patio Doors
N.A.I.C.S.: 326199

MW Manufacturers Inc. (4)
433 N Main St PO Box 559, Rocky Mount,
VA 24151
Tel.: (540) 483-0211
Web Site: http://www.mwwindows.com
Sales Range: $125-149.9 Million
Windows, Doors & Building Materials Mfr
N.A.I.C.S.: 321911

**Ply Gem Pacific Windows
Corporation** (4)
5001 D St NW, Auburn, WA 98001
Tel.: (253) 850-9000
Window & Door Whslr
N.A.I.C.S.: 423220
Jeff Kufowski (Plant Mgr)

Subsidiary (Domestic):

Simonton Windows, Inc. (4)
3948 Townsfair Way Ste 200, Columbus,
OH 43219
Tel.: (614) 532-3500
Web Site: http://www.simonton.com
Vinyl Window Frames & Sashes Mfr
N.A.I.C.S.: 326199

Subsidiary (Domestic):

Simex, Inc. (4)
181 Pleasants Industrial Ctr, Saint Marys,
WV 26170-8011
Tel.: (304) 665-1104
Construction Materials Whslr
N.A.I.C.S.: 423390

Subsidiary (Non-US):

**Robertson Building Systems
Limited** (2)
1343 Sandhill Drive, Ancaster, L9G 4V5,
ON, Canada
Tel.: (905) 304-1111
Web Site:
http://www.robertsonbuildings.com
Sales Range: $10-24.9 Million
Steel Building Systems Designer
N.A.I.C.S.: 331513

Subsidiary (Domestic):

Star Building Systems (2)
8600 S Interstate 35 Service Rd, Oklahoma
City, OK 73149
Tel.: (405) 636-2010
Web Site: http://www.starbuildings.com
Sales Range: $25-49.9 Million
Metal Building Systems & Metal Component
Products Mfr
N.A.I.C.S.: 332311
David Alexander (Pres)
Dan DeKalb (Dir-Drafting)
Dave Rutherford (Dir-Bus Affairs)
Gene Bell (VP-Ops)

Ron Welch (Controller)
Bryan Arlington (Dir-Estimating & Customer
Svc)
Doug Clark (VP-Sls)
Allen Hurtz (Dir-Engrg)
Gabe Savely (Dir-Components)

Plant (Domestic):

**Star Building Systems -
Monticello** (3)
101 W S St, Monticello, IA 52310-1938
Tel.: (319) 465-3595
Web Site: http://www.starbuildings.com
Sales Range: $25-49.9 Million
Emp.: 140
Pre-Engineered Metal Buildings Mfr
N.A.I.C.S.: 236220
Paul Steven (Gen Mgr)

Subsidiary (Domestic):

Steel Systems Inc. (2)
7301 Fairview, Houston, TX 77041 **(100%)**
Tel.: (713) 466-6393
Web Site: http://www.steelsys.com
Sales Range: $25-49.9 Million
Emp.: 15
Metal Buildings
N.A.I.C.S.: 236220

Steelbuilding.com, Inc. (2)
2612 Gribble N, Little Rock, AR 72114
Tel.: (501) 945-6500
Web Site: http://www.steelbuilding.com
Sales Range: $25-49.9 Million
Emp.: 15
Commercial & Residential Garage Door
Supplier
N.A.I.C.S.: 423440
Barry Clifton (Mgr-Sls)

Union Corrugating Company (2)
701 S King St, Fayetteville, NC 28301
Web Site: http://www.unioncorrugating.com
Brick, Stone & Related Construction Mate-
rial Merchant Whslr
N.A.I.C.S.: 423320
Jason Thornton (VP-Mktg & Accts-Natl)

Subsidiary (Domestic):

Reed's Metals, Inc. (3)
19 E Lincoln Rd NE, Brookhaven, MS
39601
Tel.: (601) 823-6516
Web Site: http://www.reedsmetals.com
Home Center Operator
N.A.I.C.S.: 444110
Bernard T. Reed (Founder, Pres & CEO)

Subsidiary (Domestic):

Oakland Metal Buildings, Inc. (4)
24350 County Road 14, Florence, AL 35633
Tel.: (256) 764-7943
Prefabricated Metal Buildings, Nsk
N.A.I.C.S.: 332311

Subsidiary (Domestic):

Window Products, Inc. (2)
10507 E Montgomery Dr, Spokane Valley,
WA 99206
Tel.: (800) 442-8544
Web Site: http://www.cascadewindows.com
Emp.: 200
Custom Windows & Doors Mfr
N.A.I.C.S.: 332321
Randy Emerson (Pres & CEO)
Randy Bell (CFO & VP)
Ralph Goldman (Dir-Mktg)

Covetrus, Inc. (1)
12 Mountfort St, Portland, ME 04101-4307
Web Site: https://www.covetrus.com
Rev.: $4,575,000,000
Assets: $3,410,000,000
Liabilities: $1,899,000,000
Net Worth: $1,511,000,000
Earnings: ($54,000,000)
Emp.: 5,275
Fiscal Year-end: 12/31/2021
Veterinary Services
N.A.I.C.S.: 541940
Philip W. Knisely (Chm)
Ajoy H. Karna (CFO & Exec VP)
Michelle Bonfiglio (Chief People Officer)
Michael Ellis (Pres-Europe & Exec VP)
David Hinton (Pres-APAC & Emerging Mar-
kets & Exec VP)

Timothy Ludlow (Chief Transformation Offi-
cer & Exec VP)
Anthony Providenti (Exec VP-Corp Dev)
Georgina Wraight (Pres-Tech Solution-
Global & Exec VP)
Dustin Finer (Chief Admin Officer)
Ditte Marstrand Wulf (Chief HR Officer)
Matthew Malenfant (Pres-Customer Ops-
North America)
Steve Palmucci (CIO-Global)
Jamey Seely (Sec)
Stacey M. M. Shirra (VP-Talent Mgmt-
Global)
Link Welborn (Chief Veterinary Officer-North
America)
Rens van Dobbenburgh (Chief Veterinary
Officer-Europe)
Pete Perron (Pres-Strategic Partnerships)
Andrew B. Coxhead (Chief Acctg Officer,
VP & Controller)
Bekki Kidd (Head-North America Ops &
Global Operational Excellence)
Andras Bolcskei (Pres-Intl)
Margie B. Pritchard (Gen Counsel)

Subsidiary (Domestic):

Direct Vet Marketing, Inc. (2)
110 Exchange St, Portland, ME 04101
Web Site: http://www.vetsfirstchoice.com
Pharmacy Service for Pets
N.A.I.C.S.: 459910

Henry Schein Animal Health (2)
400 Metro Pl N Ste 100, Dublin, OH 43017-
7545
Tel.: (614) 761-9095
Web Site: http://www.henryscheinvet.com
Sales Range: $450-499.9 Million
Emp.: 900
Animal Health Products Distr
N.A.I.C.S.: 424210

Subsidiary (Domestic):

**Butler Animal Health Holding Com-
pany, LLC** (3)
4274 Shackleford Rd, Norcross, GA 30093-
2952
Tel.: (770) 925-7100
Veterinarian Equipment Distr
N.A.I.C.S.: 423450

Butler Animal Health Supply (3)
445 SW 52nd Ave Ste 100, Ocala, FL
34474-8508
Tel.: (352) 237-1246
Veterinary Healthcare Supplies
N.A.I.C.S.: 423450

ImproMed, LLC (3)
304 Ohio St, Oshkosh, WI 54902-5888
Tel.: (920) 236-7070
Web Site: http://www.impromed.com
Sales Range: $25-49.9 Million
Emp.: 100
Veterinary Software Developer
N.A.I.C.S.: 513210
Ronald Detjen (Pres)

Merritt Veterinary Supplies Inc. (3)
102 Distribution Dr, Birmingham, AL 35209-
6309
Tel.: (205) 942-4744
Animal Health Products Supplier
N.A.I.C.S.: 423450
Robert Mims (Mgr)

SmartPak Equine, LLC (3)
40 Grissom Rd Ste 500, Plymouth, MA
02360 **(60%)**
Tel.: (774) 773-1100
Web Site: http://www.smartpakequine.com
Sales Range: $100-124.9 Million
Emp.: 325
Equine & Canine Supplies & Supplements
N.A.I.C.S.: 311119

Subsidiary (Non-US):

**Henry Schein Animal Health Holdings
Limited** (2)
Medcare House Centurion Close Gillingham
Business Park, Gillingham, ME8 OSB,
United Kingdom
Tel.: (44) 8708490872
Holding Company
N.A.I.C.S.: 551112

Provet Holdings Limited (2)

Clayton, Dubilier & Rice, LLC—(Continued)

48 Bel-Are Ave, Northgate, 4013, QLD, Australia
Tel.: (61) 736216000
Web Site: http://www.provet.com.au
Sales Range: $250-299.9 Million
Emp.: 150
Veterinary Products & Services
N.A.I.C.S.: 459910
Stanley M. Bergman *(CEO)*

Subsidiary (Domestic):

Provet QLD Pty Ltd. (3)
48 Bell-Are Ave, Northgate, Brisbane, 4013, QLD, Australia
Tel.: (61) 736216000
Web Site: http://www.provet.com.au
Sales Range: $25-49.9 Million
Emp.: 60
Veterinary Medicines Distr
N.A.I.C.S.: 424210
Nigel Nichols *(CEO)*

Subsidiary (Domestic):

Provet (NSW) Pty Ltd. (4)
21-25 Interchange Drive, Eastern Creek, 2766, NSW, Australia
Tel.: (61) 288675177
Web Site: http://www.provet.com.au
Sales Range: $25-49.9 Million
Emp.: 15
Veterinary Products Distr
N.A.I.C.S.: 423490
Jim Aspinall *(Mng Dir)*

Subsidiary (Non-US):

Provet NZ Pty Limited (4)
8 Kordel Pl, East Tamaki, 2013, Auckland, New Zealand
Tel.: (64) 99204440
Web Site: http://www.provet.co.nz
Sales Range: $25-49.9 Million
Emp.: 55
Veterinary Products Distr
N.A.I.C.S.: 423490

Subsidiary (Domestic):

Provet SA Pty Ltd. (4)
Unit 5 Butler Blvd Burbridge Bus Park, Adelaide Airport, Adelaide, 5950, SA, Australia
Tel.: (61) 881545455
Web Site: http://www.provet.com.au
Veterinary Products Distr
N.A.I.C.S.: 423490

Provet VMS Pty Ltd. (4)
Lot 39 Stenhouse Dr, Newcastle, 2286, NSW, Australia
Tel.: (61) 249554488
Web Site: http://www.provet.com.au
Emp.: 60
Veterinary Products Distr
N.A.I.C.S.: 423490

Provet Victoria Pty Ltd. (4)
27 Sunmore Close, Heatherton, 3202, VIC, Australia
Tel.: (61) 395405700
Web Site: http://www.provet.net.au
Sales Range: $25-49.9 Million
Emp.: 30
Veterinary Products Distr
N.A.I.C.S.: 423490

Provet WA Pty Ltd. (4)
1936 Beach Rd, Malaga, 6090, WA, Australia
Tel.: (61) 8 9241 8400
Web Site: http://www.provet.com.au
Emp.: 18
Veterinary Products Whslr
N.A.I.C.S.: 423490

Cynosure, LLC (1)
5 Carlisle Rd, Westford, MA 01886
Tel.: (978) 256-4200
Web Site: http://www.cynosure.com
Light-Based Aesthetic & Medical Treatment Systems Developer & Mfr
N.A.I.C.S.: 334517
Sandra E. Peterson *(Chm)*
Richard Bankowski *(VP-Global Clinical Affairs)*
James Boll *(VP-R&D)*
Eric Brown *(Sr VP-Engrg)*
Bill Fruhan *(VP-Mktg)*

Jim Palastra *(VP-Global Svcs & Ops)*
Jorge Pinedo *(Exec VP-Intl)*
Andrea Schwab *(VP-Sls)*
Maureen Tarca *(VP-HR)*
Sujat Sukthankar *(Exec VP-Res & Product Dev)*
Katie Cheng *(CMO)*
Nadav Tomer *(CEO)*

Subsidiary (Non-US):

Cynosure France S.A.R.L. (2)
Energy Park-Batiment 6, 132-134 Boulevard de Verdun, 92400, Courbevoie, France
Tel.: (33) 146672250
Web Site: http://www.cynosure.fr
Electromedical & Electrotherapeutic Apparatus Mfr
N.A.I.C.S.: 334510

Cynosure GmbH (2)
Dammtorwall 7a, D-20354, Hamburg, Germany
Tel.: (49) 40 36 00 66 56 0
Web Site: http://www.cynosure.de
Medical Equipment Mfr
N.A.I.C.S.: 339113
Emanuel Fischer *(Mgr-Sls & Mktg)*
Nadia Ben Messaoud *(Mgr-Area & Sls)*

Cynosure Pty Ltd. (2)
Ground Floor 14-16 Suakin Street, Pymble, Sydney, 2073, NSW, Australia
Tel.: (61) 2 9484 4546
Web Site: http://cynosureaustralia.com
Light-Based Aesthetic & Medical Systems Mfr & Developer
N.A.I.C.S.: 334510
Dennis Cronje *(Mng Dir)*
Andrew Poulos *(Mgr-Natl Svc & Logistics)*
Harry Izmirlian *(Fin Mgr)*
Paul Vujevic *(Mgr-Natl Sls)*
Tracey Cannon *(Mgr-Natl Mktg)*
Sandra Sostres *(Mgr-Natl Clinical)*

Subsidiary (Domestic):

Ellman International, LLC (2)
400 Karin Ln, Hicksville, NY 11801
Tel.: (516) 569-1482
Web Site: http://www.ellman.com
Surgical & Medical Instruments Mfr
N.A.I.C.S.: 339112

Palomar Medical Technologies, LLC (2)
5 Carlisle Rd, Westford, MA 01886
Tel.: (781) 993-2300
Cosmetic Lasers & Intense Pulsed Light (IPL) Systems Mfr
N.A.I.C.S.: 334510

Subsidiary (Domestic):

Palomar Medical Products, LLC (3)
5 Carlisle Rd, Westford, MA 01886
Tel.: (781) 993-2300
Surgical, Laser & Electromedical Equipment & Supplies Mfr
N.A.I.C.S.: 339112

Epicor Software Corporation (1)
804 Las Cimas Pkwy, Austin, TX 78746
Tel.: (512) 328-2300
Web Site: http://www.epicor.com
Integrated Enterprise & E-Business Software Solutions Designer, Developer & Marketer
N.A.I.C.S.: 334610
Bill Wilson *(CTO)*
Samuel Monti *(CFO)*
Lisa Pope *(Pres)*
Jeff Hawn *(Chm)*
Steve Murphy *(CEO)*
Clarke Pich *(Head-Professional Svcs-Global)*
Jason Taylor *(Head-Support-Global)*
Vaibhav Vohra *(Chief Product Officer)*
Rich Murr *(CIO)*
Juliet Patterson *(Chief HR Officer)*
James Taylor *(Chief Legal Officer)*
Joe Ayers *(CFO & Exec VP)*
Aaron Masterson *(Head-Corp Comm-Global)*

Subsidiary (Domestic):

Epicor EDI Source, Inc. (2)
31875 Solon Rd, Solon, OH 44139
Tel.: (440) 542-9107

Web Site: http://www.1edisource.com
Electronic Data Interchange Software & Services
N.A.I.C.S.: 513210

Subsidiary (Non-US):

Epicor Software (Asia) Pte Ltd. (2)
238A Thomson Road 23-06, Novena Square Tower A, 307684, Singapore, Singapore
Tel.: (65) 6333 8121
Web Site: http://www.epicor.com
Integrated Enterprise & E-Business Software Solutions Designer, Developer & Marketer
N.A.I.C.S.: 334610

Epicor Software (Beijing) Company, Ltd. (2)
Room 1501 15/F Building A Parkview Green, 9 Dongdaqiao Road Chaoyang District, Beijing, 100020, China
Tel.: (86) 10657306188
Web Site: http://www.epicor.com
Integrated Enterprise & E-Business Software Solutions Designer, Developer & Marketer
N.A.I.C.S.: 334610

Epicor Software (M) Sdn Bhd (2)
Unit 1101C Level 11 Tower C Uptown 5 No 5 Jalan SS21/39, Damansara Uptown, Petaling Jaya, 47400, Selangor, Malaysia
Tel.: (60) 3 7962 8800
Web Site: http://www.epicor.com
Integrated Enterprise & E-Business Software Solutions Designer, Developer & Marketer
N.A.I.C.S.: 334610

Epicor Software (North Asia) Ltd. (2)
Rm 1806 Tower 2, 33 Canton Road Tsimshatsui, Hong Kong, China (Hong Kong)
Tel.: (852) 25639930
Web Site: http://www.epicor.com
Emp.: 1
Integrated Enterprise & E-Business Software Solutions Designer, Developer & Marketer
N.A.I.C.S.: 334610
Luice Lai *(Office Mgr)*

Epicor Software (SEA) Pte Ltd. (2)
238A thomson Road 23-06, Novena Square Office Tower, Singapore, 307684, Singapore
Tel.: (65) 63338121
Web Site: http://www.epicor.com
Integrated Enterprise & E-Business Software Solutions Designer, Developer & Marketer
N.A.I.C.S.: 334610

Epicor Software (Shanghai) Co., Ltd. (2)
Suite 2008 Ascendas Cross Tower, 318 Fuzhou Road, Shanghai, 200001, China
Tel.: (86) 2123067777
Web Site: http://www.epicor.com
Integrated Enterprise & E-Business Software Solutions Designer, Developer & Marketer
N.A.I.C.S.: 334610

Branch (Domestic):

Epicor Software Corporation-Minneapolis (2)
Ste 2000 600 S Hwy 169, Minneapolis, MN 55426
Tel.: (952) 417-5000
Web Site: http://www.epicor.com
Integrated Enterprise & E-Business Software Solutions Designer, Developer & Marketer
N.A.I.C.S.: 513210

Subsidiary (Non-US):

Epicor Software Cprus Ltd. (2)
jacivides Tower 1st Floor Office 129 81-83, Grivas Digenis Avenue, Nicosia, 2404, Engomi, Cyprus
Tel.: (357) 22503053
Web Site: http://www.epicor.com
Integrated Enterprise & E-Business Software Solutions Designer, Developer & Marketer
N.A.I.C.S.: 334610

Glenn Lambert *(Gen Mgr)*

Epicor Software Czech s.r.o (2)
Na Pankraci 1724/129 Praha Gemini Budova B, Na Pankraci 1724-129, Prague, 140 00, Czech Republic
Web Site: http://www.epicor.com
Integrated Enterprise & E-Business Software Solutions Designer, Developer & Marketer
N.A.I.C.S.: 334610

Epicor Software Deutschland GmbH (2)
WeWork Taunusanlage, Taunusanlage 8, 60325, Frankfurt, Germany
Tel.: (49) 8000007802
Web Site: http://www.epicor.com
Integrated Enterprise & E-Business Software Solutions Designer, Developer & Marketer
N.A.I.C.S.: 334610

Epicor Software Estonia OU (2)
Sopruse pst 151, 13417, Tallinn, Estonia
Tel.: (372) 6997640
Web Site: http://www.epicor.com
Integrated Enterprise & E-Business Software Solutions Designer, Developer & Marketer
N.A.I.C.S.: 334610

Epicor Software Finland Oy (2)
Teknobulevardi 3.5, Vantaa, 01510, Finland
Tel.: (358) 207 410 850
Web Site: http://www.epicor.com
Integrated Enterprise & E-Business Software Solutions Designer, Developer & Marketer
N.A.I.C.S.: 334610

Epicor Software Hungary Kft (2)
Vaci U 76 VI Torony 2 EM, Budapest, H-1133, Hungary
Tel.: (36) 1 452 7500
Web Site: http://www.epicor.com
Integrated Enterprise & E-Business Software Solutions Designer, Developer & Marketer
N.A.I.C.S.: 334610

Epicor Software Italia s.r.l. (2)
Regus Business Centres Italia Srl Unico Socio Viale Luca Gaurico, 00143, Rome, Italy
Tel.: (39) 0654832093
Web Site: http://www.epicor.com
Integrated Enterprise & E-Business Software Solutions Designer, Developer & Marketer
N.A.I.C.S.: 334610

Epicor Software Japan K.K. (2)
5-13-1 Toranomon 40th Building 7th Floor, Minato-ku, 105-0001, Tokyo, Japan
Tel.: (81) 345309738
Web Site: http://www.epicor.com
Integrated Enterprise & E-Business Software Solutions Designer, Developer & Marketer
N.A.I.C.S.: 334610

Epicor Software Latvija SIA (2)
Regus 4th & 5th floors Terbatas Street, Riga, Lv-1011, Latvia
Tel.: (371) 67118383
Web Site: http://www.epicor.com
Emp.: 1
Integrated Enterprise & E-Business Software Solutions Designer, Developer & Marketer
N.A.I.C.S.: 334610

Epicor Software Poland Sp. z O.O. (2)
Aleje Jerozolimskie 96 XII pietro, 00-807, Poznan, Poland
Tel.: (48) 222755767
Web Site: http://www.epicor.com
Integrated Enterprise & E-Business Software Solutions Designer, Developer & Marketer
N.A.I.C.S.: 334610

Epicor Software SRL (2)
Regus Rosetti City Centre str CA Rosetti nr 17 Etaj 2 biroul, Campus 01 Bucuresti, 020011, Bucharest, Romania
Tel.: (40) 21 212 1024
Web Site: http://www.epicor.com

Integrated Enterprise & E-Business Software Solutions Designer, Developer & Marketer
N.A.I.C.S.: 334610

Epicor Software Slovakia, s.r.o. (2)
Dvorakovo Nabrezie 4, 81109, Bratislava, Slovakia
Tel.: (421) 2 3500 2300
Web Site: http://www.epicor.com
Integrated Enterprise & E-Business Software Solutions Designer, Developer & Marketer
N.A.I.C.S.: 334610

Epicor Software UK, Ltd. (2)
Regional Headquarters 1 Bracknell 6 Arlington Square West, Bracknell, RG12 1PU, Berkshire, United Kingdom
Tel.: (44) 1344 468468
Web Site: http://www.epicor.com
Integrated Enterprise & E-Business Software Solutions Designer, Developer & Marketer
N.A.I.C.S.: 334610
Andy Coussins (Sr VP & Head-Sls-Intl)

Subsidiary (Domestic):

Internet Autoparts, Inc. (2)
7600 N Capital Of Texas H, Austin, TX 78731
Tel.: (512) 527-8966
Web Site: http://www.iapshop.com
Internet Services
N.A.I.C.S.: 517810

Mechanicnet Group, Inc. (2)
6700 Koll Center Pkwy Suite 109, Pleasanton, CA 94566
Tel.: (877) 632-4638
Web Site: http://www.mechanicnet.com
Computer Related Services
N.A.I.C.S.: 541519
Dave Peterson (VP & COO)

Smart Software, Inc. (2)
4 Hill Rd, Belmont, MA 02478-4303
Tel.: (617) 489-2743
Web Site: http://www.smartcorp.com
Sales Range: $1-9.9 Million
Emp.: 10
Business Planning & Forecasting Software Developer
N.A.I.C.S.: 513210
Charles Smart (Pres)
Thomas Willemain (VP)
Greg Hartunian (Pres)
Jeffrey Scott (VP-Mktg & Bus Dev)
Katherine Afonso (VP-Software Dev & Customer Support)

Focus Financial Partners Inc. (1)
875 3rd Ave 28th Fl, New York, NY 10022
Tel.: (646) 519-2456
Web Site: https://focusfinancialpartners.com
Rev.: $2,143,321,000
Assets: $4,866,754,000
Liabilities: $3,563,459,000
Net Worth: $1,303,295,000
Earnings: $91,784,000
Emp.: 5,000
Fiscal Year-end: 12/31/2022
Holding Company; Investment Advisory & Wealth Management Services
N.A.I.C.S.: 551112
Ruediger Adolf (Co-Founder, Chm & CEO)
James Shanahan (CFO)
Rajini Sundar Kodialam (Co-Founder & COO)
Leonard R. Chang (Co-Founder, Sr Mng Dir & Head-M&A)

Subsidiary (Domestic):

Focus Financial Partners, LLC (2)
875 3rd Ave 28 Fl, New York, NY 10022
Tel.: (646) 519-2456
Web Site: https://www.focusfinancialpartners.com
Sales Range: $1-4.9 Billion
Investment Advisory & Wealth Management Services
N.A.I.C.S.: 523940
Ruediger Adolf (Co-Founder, Chm & CEO)
James Shanahan (CFO)
Leonard R. Chang (Co-Founder & Sr Mng Dir)
Faizan Tukdi (VP & Asoc Gen Counsel)
Rajini Kodialam (COO)

Eric Amar (Mng Dir)
Travis Danysh (Mng Dir)
Pradeep Jayaraman (Mng Dir)
Sukanya Kuruganti (Mng Dir)
Timothy Connor (VP)
Alexander Gleeson (VP)
Brian Gracia (VP)
Tony Khalilov (VP)
Peter Lydon (VP)
Alec Pickering (VP)
Jack Spitsin (VP)

Subsidiary (Domestic):

BFSG, LLC (3)
2040 Main St Ste 720, Irvine, CA 92614
Tel.: (949) 955-2552
Web Site: https://www.bfsg.com
Investment Consulting & Wealth Management Services
N.A.I.C.S.: 523940
Christopher Rowey (Principal)
Michael Allbee (Chief Compliance Officer)

Subsidiary (Domestic):

Pacwest Financial Management, Inc. (4)
1643 E Bethany Home Rd, Phoenix, AZ 85016
Tel.: (888) 997-8882
Web Site: http://www.pacwestfn.com
Investment Consulting Services
N.A.I.C.S.: 523940

Subsidiary (Domestic):

Bridgewater Wealth & Financial Management LLC (3)
7475 Wisconsin Ave Ste 600, Bethesda, MD 20814
Tel.: (301) 656-1200
Web Site: http://www.bridgewaterwealth.com
Wealth Management Services
N.A.I.C.S.: 523940
Ron Rubin (CEO & Mng Partner)
Jessica Brede (CFO & Partner)
Steve Schuler (Chief Investment Officer & Partner)
Nina Mitchell (Partner & Sr Wealth Advisor)
Wayne Zussman (Partner & Sr Wealth Advisor)
Kim Allred (Chief Compliance Officer & Dir-Client Svcs)
Jane DiNardo (Dir-Human Capital)

Buckingham Asset Management, LLC (3)
8182 Maryland Ave Ste 500, Saint Louis, MO 63105
Tel.: (314) 725-0455
Web Site: http://www.buckinghamassets.com
Emp.: 400
Investment Advisory & Management Services
N.A.I.C.S.: 523940

Subsidiary (Domestic):

Buckingham Strategic Partners, LLC (4)
8182 Maryland Ave Ste 500, Saint Louis, MO 63105
Tel.: (314) 725-0455
Web Site: https://www.buckinghampartners.com
Investment Advisory Services
N.A.I.C.S.: 523940
Jared Kizer (Chief Investment Officer)
Alex Potts (Pres)
Adam Birenbaum (CEO)
Kristen Donovan (Dir-Retirement Solutions)
Mike Clinton (Chief Bus Officer)
Steven Atkinson (Mng Dir)
Howard Lee (Mng Dir-Svc, Trading & Ops)
Cynthia Chu (VP-Advisor Svcs)
Amy Michaelson (Dir-Trading)

Subsidiary (Domestic):

Connectus Group LLC (3)
875 3rd Ave 28th Fl, New York, NY 10022
Tel.: (646) 560-4000
Financial Services
N.A.I.C.S.: 523999

Crestwood Advisors Group, LLC (3)

1 Liberty Square, Suite 500, Boston, MA 02109
Tel.: (617) 523-8880
Web Site: https://www.crestwoodadvisors.com
Emp.: 100
Investment Advice
J. Michael Costello (Mng Partner)
Michael Eckton (CEO & Mng Partner)

Subsidiary (Domestic):

Crestwood Advisors LLC (4)
50 Federal St, Boston, MA 02110
Tel.: (617) 523-8880
Web Site: http://www.crestwoodadvisors.com
Rev.: $1,000,000
Emp.: 9
Portfolio Management
N.A.I.C.S.: 523940
Michael Eckton (CEO, Mng Partner & Portfolio Mgr)
John W. Morris (Mng Partner & Mgr-Wealth)
Michelle Herd (Mgr-Relationship)
Roy Treible (Chief Compliance Officer, Partner & Mng Dir-Client Svc & Ops)
Alyson L. Nickse (Mgr-Rels)
Leah R. Sciabarrasi (Pres)

Endurance Wealth Management, Inc. (4)
121 N Main St, Providence, RI 02903-1309
Tel.: (401) 854-0993
Web Site: http://www.endurancewealth.com
Offices of Real Estate Agents & Brokers
N.A.I.C.S.: 531210
J. Michael Costello (Founder)
John J. Webber (Dir-Res)

Subsidiary (Domestic):

Douglas C Lane & Associates, Inc. (3)
885 2nd Ave 42nd Fl, New York, NY 10017
Tel.: (212) 262-7670
Web Site: https://www.dclainc.com
Emp.: 33
Investment Advice
N.A.I.C.S.: 523940
Douglas C. Lane (Co-Founder, Partner & Portfolio Mgr)

Fort Pitt Capital Group, Inc. (3)
680 Anderson Dr, Pittsburgh, PA 15220
Tel.: (412) 921-1822
Web Site: http://www.fortpittcapital.com
Portfolio Management
N.A.I.C.S.: 523940
Charlie Smith (Partner & Chief Investment Officer)

Jones Barclay Boston (3)
1718 Gaylord St, Denver, CO 80206
Web Site: http://www.jb2.net
Investment Advice
N.A.I.C.S.: 523940
Lynda Hanshaw (Gen Mgr)

Kovitz Investment Group, LLC (3)
71 S Wacker Dr Ste 1860, Chicago, IL 60606
Tel.: (312) 334-7300
Web Site: https://www.kovitz.com
Rev.: $3,600,000
Emp.: 30
Portfolio Management
N.A.I.C.S.: 523940
Jonathan A. Shapiro (Co-Founder, Principal & Portfolio Mgr)
Joel D. Hirsh (Principal & Portfolio Mgr)
Marc S. Brenner (Co-Founder, Pres & Principal)
Mitch A. Kovitz (Co-Founder, Principal & Portfolio Mgr)
Mark C. Rosland (Principal)
Bruce A. Weininger (Principal)
Edward W. Edens (Principal)
Leonard S. Gryn (Principal)
Theodore J. Rupp (Principal)
Robert A. Contreras (Principal & Gen Counsel)
Patrick B. Wiese (CIO & Principal)
Harold Gianopulos Jr. (Principal)

Subsidiary (Domestic):

Northern Capital Management, LLC (4)

8000 Excelsior Dr Ste 201, Madison, WI 53717-1914
Tel.: (608) 831-8018
Web Site: http://www.norcap.com
Sales Range: $150-199.9 Million
Emp.: 10
Investment & Asset Management Services
N.A.I.C.S.: 523940
Stephen L. Hawk (Chm & CEO)
Daniel T. Murphy (Pres & Chief Investment Officer)
Paul A. Perry (Dir-Acct Mgmt)

Subsidiary (Domestic):

Patton Albertson & Miller Group, LLC (3)
3340 Peachtree Rd NE Ste 2320, Atlanta, GA 30326
Tel.: (404) 917-2727
Web Site: http://www.pattonalbertsonmiller.com
Financial Investment Activities
N.A.I.C.S.: 523999
James B. Patton (Co-Founder & CEO)
J. Marc Albertson (Co-Founder & Dir-Client Svcs)
Jennifer McCarthy (Partner)
Julia A. Davis (Partner)
R. David Maloy Jr. (Partner)

Telemus Capital Partners, LLC (3)
2 Towne Sq Ste 800, Southfield, MI 48076
Tel.: (248) 827-1800
Web Site: http://www.telemus.com
Sales Range: $1-4.9 Billion
Emp.: 25
Investment Advisory Services
N.A.I.C.S.: 523940
Gary Ran (Chm, CEO & Partner)
Robert J. Schlagheck (CFO)
Andrew Bass (Mng Dir & Chief Wealth Officer)
Eric C. Oppenheim (COO, Gen Counsel & Mng Dir)
Joshua S. Levine (Partner)
Mary Bakhaus (Partner & Sr Portfolio Mgr)
Thomas E. Uber (Portfolio Mgr-Municipal Bonds)
James M. Housler (Partner)
Matthew Espinosa (Mgr-Portfolio Acctg)
Lloyd A. Perlmutter (COO)
David Post (Chief Investment Officer)
Lyle Mathew Wolberg (Partner)

The Colony Group, LLC (3)
2 Atlantic Ave, Boston, MA 02110
Tel.: (617) 723-8200
Web Site: http://www.thecolonygroup.com
Sales Range: $25-49.9 Million
Emp.: 140
Wealth Management Services
N.A.I.C.S.: 523940
Michael J. Nathanson (Chm, Pres & CEO)
Stephen T. Sadler (Mng Dir)
Elisabeth L. Talbot (Mng Dir)
Brian W. Katz (Chief Investment Officer & Pres-Colony Investment Mgmt)
Seth P. Hieken (Exec VP & Dir-Proprietary Strategies)
Stephen R. Stelljes (Pres-Client Svcs)
Cheryl L. Wilkinson (COO)
Gina K. Bradley (COO & Gen Counsel)
Vincent J. Gratch (Chief Compliance Officer)
Robert J. Glovsky (Vice Chm)
Cary P. Geller (Mng Dir)
Amy C. McMaster (Dir-Investment Svcs)
Denise M. Duffy (VP)
Erin N. Manganello (VP)
Jay A. Lupica (Sr VP)
Jeffrey T. Craig (VP)
Nan Vlad (Sr VP)
Ted Schiela (Sr VP)
Terri A. Feeney (CFO)
Faith A. Hill (Deputy Chief Compliance Officer)
Robert H. Schundler (VP & Dir-Res)
Jonathan Thrun (VP & Dir-Fixed Income)
John C. White (Chief Admin Officer)
Andrew J. Wig (VP & Dir-Equity Portfolios)
Robert Kohl (Principal & VP)
Alexander I. Hock (Principal & VP)
Ian Barclay (Mng Dir-Rocky Mountain)
Tim Delay (Officer-Bus Dev)
Jennifer Geoghegan (Chief Strategy Officer)
Max Haspel (Mng Dir & Principal)
Matthew C. Ilteris (Principal & VP)
Craig S. Jones (Mng Dir-Rocky Mountain)
Jeremy K. Kuhlen (Principal & VP)

Clayton, Dubilier & Rice, LLC—(Continued)

Vestor Capital, LLC (3)
10 S Riverside Plz Ste 1400, Chicago, IL 60606
Tel.: (312) 641-2400
Web Site: https://www.vestorcapital.com
Investment Advisory Services
N.A.I.C.S.: 523999
Martin Buehler (Partner)

Healogics, Inc. (3)
5220 Belfort Rd Ste 130, Jacksonville, FL 32256
Tel.: (904) 446-3400
Web Site: http://www.healogics.com
Sales Range: $300-349.9 Million
Wound Care Management Solutions
N.A.I.C.S.: 622110
Jeff Nelson (Pres)
Gregory G. Martin (COO)
Craig Albright (Exec VP-Mktg)
Scott Covington (Chief Medical Officer)
Michael Licata (Exec VP-Dev)
Christopher A. Morrison (Exec Dir-Healogics Specialty Physicians)
Linda Ellis (Pres-Physician Practice)
David Bassin (CEO)
Deborah Leblanc (Chief Nursing Officer)
William Ennis (Chief Scientific Officer)
Carol Murdock (Exec VP-Mktg)
Kelly Priegnitz (Chief Compliance Officer)
John Dineen (Chm)
Banks Willis (VP-Corp Comm)
Allan Woodward (CFO)
David Jollow (Chief Info Security Officer)
Ty Smith (CIO)
Rob Doll (CMO)
Leslie Niblock (Dir-Mktg & Comm)

High Ridge Brands Co. (1)
333 Ludlow St S Tower 2nd Fl, Stamford, CT 06902
Tel.: (203) 674-8080
Web Site: http://www.highridgebrands.com
Emp.: 130
Personal Care Product Mfr
N.A.I.C.S.: 325611
John Compton (Chm)
Amanda D. H. Allen (CFO)
Jasmin Manner (CMO & Gen Mgr-Hair Care & Skin Cleansing)
Mark Walsh (Pres-Oral Care & Intl)
Richard S. Kirk Jr. (COO)

Hussmann International, Inc. (1)
12999 Saint Charles Rock Rd, Bridgeton, MO 63044-2419
Tel.: (314) 291-2000
Web Site: http://www.hussmann.com
Sales Range: $1-4.9 Billion
Emp.: 9,100
Holding Company; Commercial Refrigeration Equipment Mfr
N.A.I.C.S.: 551112

Indicor of NC, LLC (1)
11605 N Community House Rd Ste 250, Charlotte, NC 28277
Tel.: (336) 854-3353
Web Site: https://indicor.com
Industrial Machinery Mfr
N.A.I.C.S.: 333248
Doug Wright (CEO)
Tiffany Fuller (VP-HR)

Subsidiary (Domestic):

AGR International, Inc. (2)
615 Whitestown Rd, Butler, PA 16001
Tel.: (724) 482-2163
Web Site: https://www.agrintl.com
Sales Range: $100-124.9 Million
Emp.: 185
Container Testing Equipment Mfr
N.A.I.C.S.: 334519
Robert S. Cowden (COO)
Christian Kapsamer (Dir-Northwestern Europe)
Sudha Jebadurai (Pres)

Subsidiary (Non-US):

Agr Asia Limited (3)
1705 Tianjin International Bldg 75 Nanjing Road, Tianjin, 300050, China
Tel.: (86) 15261519029
Measuring & Controlling Device Whslr
N.A.I.C.S.: 423830

Agr Bangkok Ltd (3)
38/1 Latprao 101 Road Yaek 38 Klong Chan Bang Kapi, Bangkok, 10240, Thailand
Tel.: (66) 27315144
Web Site: http://www.agrintl.com
Measuring & Controlling Device Mfr
N.A.I.C.S.: 334519
Martin Kuestner (Gen Mgr)

Agr Europe GmbH (3)
Oehmer Feld 1 Gebaude 4, Leese, 31633, Germany
Tel.: (49) 5761907192
Web Site: http://www.agrintl.com
Emp.: 5
Measuring & Controlling Device Whslr
N.A.I.C.S.: 423830
Martin Kastner (Gen Mgr)

Agr Europe S.r.l. (3)
Via Torricelli n 14, Montecchio Emilia, 42027, Italy
Tel.: (39) 0522861190
Web Site: http://www.agrintl.com
Emp.: 8
Bottling Machinery Distr
N.A.I.C.S.: 423830
Marco Palma (Mgr)

Subsidiary (Domestic):

American Glass Research (3)
603 Evans City Rd, Butler, PA 16001
Tel.: (724) 482-2163
Web Site: http://www.americanglassresearch.com
Emp.: 15
Testing Laboratory Services
N.A.I.C.S.: 541380
David Machak (Mgr-Pharmaceutical Svcs)
William G. Slusser (Mgr-Res Svcs)
Brian Collins (Engr-Res)
Steve Spence (Engr-Res)
Brad Salitrik (Engr-Res)
Linda Pilosi (Coord-Seminar)
Christian Kostner (Coord-Seminar)

Inizio Group Limited (1)
8th Floor Holborn Gate 26 Southampton Buildings, London, WC2A 1AN, United Kingdom - England
Tel.: (44) 2038613999
Web Site: https://inizio.health
Holding Company
N.A.I.C.S.: 551112
Paul Taaffe (CEO)

Subsidiary (US):

Evolution Road, LLC (2)
15 John St, Chatham, NJ 07928-2208
Tel.: (201) 739-2031
Web Site: http://www.evolutionroad.com
Marketing Consulting Services
N.A.I.C.S.: 541613
Paul Ivans (CEO & Founder)

Holding (Non-US):

Huntsworth Limited (2)
8th Floor Holborn Gate 26 Southampton Buildings, London Wall, London, WC2A 1AN, United Kingdom
Tel.: (44) 2038613999
Web Site: http://www.huntsworth.com
Sales Range: Less than $1 Million
Marketing Communication Services
N.A.I.C.S.: 541613
Paul Taaffe (CEO)
Neil Jones (COO)
Martin Morrow (Sec & Grp Dir-Tax)
Helen Apostolidis (Chief Talent Officer)
Ben Jackson (CFO)
Liam FitzGerald (Chm)
Annabelle Sandeman (Head-Comml Strategy-Global)

Subsidiary (Domestic):

Citigate Dewe Rogerson (3)
3 London Wall Bldg, London Wall, London, EC2M 5SY, United Kingdom
Tel.: (44) 2076389571
Web Site: http://www.citigatedr.co.uk
Sales Range: $25-49.9 Million
Emp.: 100
Public Relations
N.A.I.C.S.: 541820
Ian Morris (Dir-Manchester)

Branch (US):

Citigate Cunningham (4)
101 2nd St Fl 22 Ste 2250, San Francisco, CA 94105
Tel.: (415) 618-8700
Sales Range: $25-49.9 Million
Emp.: 56
Public Relations
N.A.I.C.S.: 541820

Citigate Cunningham (4)
1 Memorial Dr 17th Fl, Cambridge, MA 02142
Tel.: (617) 494-8202
Public Relations
N.A.I.C.S.: 541820

Subsidiary (Non-US):

Citigate First Financial B.V. (4)
James Wattstraat 100, 1081 GC, Amsterdam, Netherlands
Tel.: (31) 205754010
Web Site: http://www.citigateff.nl
Sales Range: $10-24.9 Million
Emp.: 27
Business Consulting Services
N.A.I.C.S.: 561499
Uneke Dekkers (Mng Dir)

Citigate Gunpowder S.r.l. (4)
Viale Bianca Maria 31, 20122, Milan, Italy
Tel.: (39) 0276001633
Sales Range: $10-24.9 Million
Emp.: 50
Marketing Communication Services
N.A.I.C.S.: 541613

Branch (Domestic):

Citigate MARCHCom (4)
Eldon House 1 Dorset St, London, W1U 4EG, United Kingdom (100%)
Tel.: (44) 2075359803
Web Site: http://www.citigatemc.com
Public Relations
N.A.I.C.S.: 561499

Citigate Public Affairs (4)
26 Grosvenor Gardens, London, SW1W 0GT, United Kingdom (100%)
Tel.: (44) 2078384800
Public Relations
N.A.I.C.S.: 561499

Subsidiary (Non-US):

Citigate SA (4)
PO Box 6767, Roggebaai, Cape Town, 8012, South Africa (100%)
Tel.: (27) 214434200
Sales Range: $10-24.9 Million
Emp.: 21
Communication Consulting Services
N.A.I.C.S.: 561499

Citigate Sanchis (4)
Paseo de la Castellana 8-5 IZQ, 28046, Madrid, Spain (100%)
Tel.: (34) 915221008
Web Site: http://www.citigatesanchis.com
Sales Range: $10-24.9 Million
Emp.: 30
Communication Consulting Services
N.A.I.C.S.: 561499
Eduardo Fuentes (CEO)

Subsidiary (US):

Connecting Point Communications (3)
665 3rd St Ste 100, San Francisco, CA 94107
Tel.: (415) 442-2400
Public Relations
N.A.I.C.S.: 541820

Giant Creative Strategy LLC (3)
1700 Montgomery Ste 485, San Francisco, CA 94111 (90.2%)
Tel.: (415) 655-5200
Web Site: http://www.evokegiant.com
Advetising Agency
N.A.I.C.S.: 541810
Steven Gold (CEO)
Adam Gelling (Pres)
Tonya Joseph-Helwig (Dir-Content Strategy)
Josh Yoburn (VP & Dir-Scientific)
Jeffrey Nemy (CFO)
Purr Drummey (VP & Dir-Creative Svcs)

V. A. Lopes (Sr VP)
Dana Nakagawa (Sr Dir-Art)
Lawrence Caringi (Dir-New Bus Dev)
Ben Mallory (Gen Mgr & Exec Dir-Creative-Philadelphia)
Susan Osterloh (VP & Grp Dir-Creative)
Kristina Ellis (Exec VP & Exec Dir-Creative)
Andrew Wint (Sr VP-Tech)
Aaron Sklar (VP-Brand Experience)

Subsidiary (Domestic):

Grayling Global (3)
8th Floor Holborn Gate 26 Southampton Buildings, London, WC2A 1AN, United Kingdom
Tel.: (44) 2079321850
Web Site: http://www.grayling.com
Sales Range: $125-149.9 Million
Emp.: 60
Public Relations
N.A.I.C.S.: 541820
Richard Jukes (Chm)

Subsidiary (Non-US):

Grayling Austria (4)
Siebensterngasse 31, 1070, Vienna, Austria
Tel.: (43) 152443000
Web Site: http://www.grayling.com
Sales Range: $10-24.9 Million
Emp.: 35
Public Relations
N.A.I.C.S.: 541820

Grayling Barcelona (4)
Aribau 171 2 Fl 1 Door, 08006, Barcelona, Spain
Tel.: (34) 932922264
Web Site: http://www.grayling.com
Emp.: 3
Advertising Services
N.A.I.C.S.: 541810

Grayling Belgium (4)
Avenue Des Arts 46 4th Fl, Brussels, 1000, Belgium
Tel.: (32) 27327040
Web Site: http://www.grayling.com
Sales Range: $10-24.9 Million
Emp.: 35
Public Relations
N.A.I.C.S.: 541820
Russell McCleave Patten (CEO)

Grayling Bulgaria (4)
35 Hristo Botev Boulevard Floor 3 Ap 9, 1606, Sofia, Bulgaria
Tel.: (359) 29523727
Sales Range: $25-49.9 Million
Emp.: 6
Public Relations
N.A.I.C.S.: 541820

Grayling China (4)
19 Floor #1901 Chinachem Hollywood Centre 1 Hollywood Road, Central, China (Hong Kong)
Tel.: (852) 21648880
Web Site: http://www.grayling.com
Sales Range: $25-49.9 Million
Emp.: 6
Public Relations
N.A.I.C.S.: 541820
Nancy Wu (Mng Dir)
Stephanie Stamatakou (CEO)

Grayling Croatia (4)
Eugena Kumicica 8, Zagreb, Croatia
Tel.: (385) 14882868
Web Site: http://www.grayling.com
Sales Range: $25-49.9 Million
Emp.: 10
Public Relations
N.A.I.C.S.: 541820
Natasa Trslic Stambak (Mng Dir-South East Europe)

Grayling Czech Republic (4)
Nitranska 6, 101 00, Prague, Czech Republic
Tel.: (420) 224251555
Web Site: http://www.grayling.com
Sales Range: $25-49.9 Million
Emp.: 20
Public Relations
N.A.I.C.S.: 541820
Peter Fecko (Mng Dir)

Grayling Deutschland GmbH (4)

Ratherstr 49 3rd Floor, Dusseldorf, 40476, Germany
Tel.: (49) 211964850
Web Site: http://www.grayling.com
Sales Range: $10-24.9 Million
Emp.: 30
Public Relations
N.A.I.C.S.: 541820
Frank Schonrock (CEO)

Grayling Deutschland GmbH (4)
Bleichstrasse 52-56, 60313, Frankfurt am Main, Germany
Tel.: (49) 699622190
Web Site: http://www.grayling.com
Sales Range: $25-49.9 Million
Public Relations
N.A.I.C.S.: 541820

Grayling Deutschland GmbH (4)
Neuer Wall 50, D-20354, Hamburg, Germany
Tel.: (49) 40822186145
Web Site: http://www.grayling.com
Sales Range: $25-49.9 Million
Emp.: 4
Public Relations
N.A.I.C.S.: 541820
Frank Schonrock (CEO)

Grayling France (4)
43 rue du Rendez-vous, Paris, 75012, France
Tel.: (33) 155307070
Web Site: http://www.grayling.fr
Sales Range: $25-49.9 Million
Emp.: 25
Public Relations
N.A.I.C.S.: 541820
Clarisse Boidot (Mgr-Mktg-Bus Dev)
Remy Debrant (Mng Dir)

Branch (US):

Grayling Global (4)
101 6th Ave, New York, NY 10013
Tel.: (646) 284-9400
Web Site: http://www.grayling.com
Sales Range: $10-24.9 Million
Emp.: 35
Public Relations
N.A.I.C.S.: 541820

Subsidiary (Non-US):

Grayling Global (4)
55 Market Street Unit No 02-02, Singapore, 48941, Singapore
Tel.: (65) 63254606
Web Site: http://www.grayling.com
Sales Range: $25-49.9 Million
Emp.: 16
Public Relations
N.A.I.C.S.: 541820

Grayling Global (4)
1-11 Palmerstown Ave, Dublin, 20, Ireland
Tel.: (353) 15482378
Web Site: http://www.grayling.com
Sales Range: $25-49.9 Million
Emp.: 4
Public Relations
N.A.I.C.S.: 541820

Grayling Global (4)
No 15/2 Bebek, Istanbul, 34342, Turkiye
Tel.: (90) 5334776183
Public Relations
N.A.I.C.S.: 541810
Ana Dodea (Country Mgr)
Loretta Ahmed (CEO-Middle East, Turkey & Africa)
Julio Romo (Head-Digital-Middle East & Turkey)

Grayling Hungary (4)
Terez korut 46, 1066, Budapest, Hungary
Tel.: (36) 12667833
Web Site: http://www.grayling.com
Sales Range: $25-49.9 Million
Emp.: 11
Public Relations
N.A.I.C.S.: 541820
Peter Fecko (Mng Dir)

Grayling Madrid (4)
Castellana 8 5th Fl, 28046, Madrid, Spain
Tel.: (34) 915221008
Web Site: http://www.grayling.com
Sales Range: $25-49.9 Million
Emp.: 20
Advertising Agencies

N.A.I.C.S.: 541810
Eduardo Fuentes (CEO)

Grayling Netherlands (4)
James Wattstraat 100, 1097 DM, Amsterdam, Netherlands
Tel.: (31) 205754000
Web Site: http://www.grayling.com.nl
Public Relations
N.A.I.C.S.: 541820

Grayling Poland (4)
Al Jana Pawla II 80 C lok 10A, 00-175, Warsaw, Poland
Tel.: (48) 225360440
Web Site: http://www.grayling.com
Sales Range: $10-24.9 Million
Emp.: 37
Public Relations
N.A.I.C.S.: 541820

Grayling Portugal (4)
Edificio Empresarial Alameda Antonio Sergio 7 2A, 2795-023, Lisbon, Portugal
Tel.: (351) 213513720
Web Site: http://www.grayling.com
Sales Range: $10-24.9 Million
Emp.: 5
Advertising Agencies
N.A.I.C.S.: 541810

Grayling Romania (4)
Calea Serban Voda nr 56 District 4, Bucharest, Romania
Tel.: (40) 747118537
Sales Range: $25-49.9 Million
Emp.: 15
Public Relations
N.A.I.C.S.: 541820

Grayling Russia (4)
Krasnoproletarskaya Ulitsa 16 Building 3 Entrance 8, 127473, Moscow, Russia
Tel.: (7) 4957886784
Web Site: http://www.grayling.com
Rev.: $2,600,000
Emp.: 30
N.A.I.C.S.: 541820
Vladimir Melnikov (Pres)
Eugenia Skobeleva (Country Mgr)

Grayling Schweiz AG (4)
Niederdorfstrasse, 8034, Zurich, Switzerland
Tel.: (41) 0443889111
Web Site: http://ch.grayling.com
Sales Range: $25-49.9 Million
Public Relations
N.A.I.C.S.: 541820

Grayling Seville (4)
Avenida San Francisco Javier 22 Edificio Catalana Occidente, Modulo 307 planta 3, 41018, Seville, Spain
Tel.: (34) 954933100
Web Site: http://www.grayling.com
Sales Range: $25-49.9 Million
Emp.: 3
Advertising Agencies
N.A.I.C.S.: 541810
Antonio Ravero (Dir-Andalucia Office)

Grayling Slovakia (4)
Palisady 36, 81106, Bratislava, Slovakia
Tel.: (421) 259201444
Web Site: http://www.grayling.com
Sales Range: $25-49.9 Million
Emp.: 12
Public Relations
N.A.I.C.S.: 541820
Peter Fecko (Mng Dir)
Monika Revayova (Deputy Mng Dir)

Grayling Slovenia (4)
Mala Ulica 8, 1000, Ljubljana, Slovenia
Tel.: (386) 14364682
Public Relations
N.A.I.C.S.: 541820
Spela Bizjak (Deputy Dir)

Grayling Stockholm (4)
Birger Jarlsgatan 58, 114 29, Stockholm, Sweden
Tel.: (46) 52780800
Web Site: http://www.grayling.com
N.A.I.C.S.: 541810

Grayling Suisse SA (4)
20 quai Gustave-Ador Case Postale 6254, CH-1211, Geneva, Switzerland

Tel.: (41) 227870740
Web Site: http://www.grayling.com
Sales Range: $25-49.9 Million
Emp.: 8
Public Relations
N.A.I.C.S.: 541820

Grayling Ukraine (4)
23A Pushkinska Str, 01004, Kiev, Ukraine
Tel.: (380) 442882908
Web Site: http://www.grayling.com
Public Relations
N.A.I.C.S.: 541820

Noesis Communicazione (4)
Via Savona 19/A, 20144, Milan, Italy
Tel.: (39) 028310511
Sales Range: $25-49.9 Million
Emp.: 23
Public Relations
N.A.I.C.S.: 541820

Branch (US):

Rose & Kindel (4)
1414 K St Ste 220, Sacramento, CA 95814
Tel.: (916) 441-1034
Web Site: http://www.rosekindel.com
Sales Range: Less than $1 Million
Emp.: 6
Advetising Agency
N.A.I.C.S.: 541810
Michael Murphy (CEO)
Dan Yardley (CFO)
Carl London (CFO)
Beverly Johnson (Office Mgr)

Rose & Kindel (4)
626 Wilshire Blvd Ste 1000, Los Angeles, CA 90017
Tel.: (213) 624-1030
Web Site: http://www.rosekindel.com
Sales Range: $25-49.9 Million
Emp.: 12
Advetising Agency
N.A.I.C.S.: 541810

Subsidiary (Domestic):

Haslimann Taylor Public Relations (3)
2nd Floor Lancaster House 67 Newhall Street, Sutton Coldfield, Birmingham, B72 1RT, United Kingdom
Tel.: (44) 1213553446
Web Site: http://www.haslimanntaylor.com
Sales Range: $25-49.9 Million
Emp.: 15
Public Relations Services
N.A.I.C.S.: 541820

Huntsworth Health (3)
Morris Pl Liston Rd, Marlow, SL7 1DF, Bucks, United Kingdom
Tel.: (44) 1628483196
Web Site: http://www.hhealth.com
Sales Range: $25-49.9 Million
Emp.: 50
Advertising Services
N.A.I.C.S.: 541810
Annabelle Sandeman (Chief Comml Officer)

Subsidiary (Domestic):

Tonic Life Communications Ltd. (4)
22 Chapter St, London, SW1P 4NP, United Kingdom
Tel.: (44) 2077989900
Web Site: http://www.toniclc.com
Sales Range: $1-9.9 Million
Emp.: 40
Public Relations
N.A.I.C.S.: 541820
Theresa Dolge (Chief Media Rels Officer)
Maryellen Royle (CEO-Global)
Stephanie DeViteri (Mng Dir-Philadelphia)
Dana Lynch (Exec VP-Global Strategy & Bus Dev)
Kelly Kutchinsky (Exec VP-Global Insights & Innovation)
Robyn Ungar (Sr VP-Philadelphia)
Ann Bartling (Mng Dir-Europe)

Subsidiary (US):

nitrogen (4)
One S Broad St Fl 11, Philadelphia, PA 19107
Tel.: (215) 625-0111
Rev.: $156,582,500
Advertising Services

N.A.I.C.S.: 541810
Jon Clark (CEO-Global)

Branch (Domestic):

nitrogen - San Francisco (5)
343 Sansome Ste 900, San Francisco, CA 94104
Tel.: (415) 362-8018
Emp.: 20
Advertising Services
N.A.I.C.S.: 541810

Subsidiary (Domestic):

Stephanie Churchill PR (3)
15-17 Huntsworth Mews, London, NW1 6DD, United Kingdom
Tel.: (44) 2072986530
Web Site:
          http://www.stephaniechurchillpr.com
Sales Range: $1-9.9 Million
Emp.: 15
Public Relations Services
N.A.I.C.S.: 541820

The Red Consultancy (3)
41 44 Gr Windmill St, London, W1D 7NF, United Kingdom (100%)
Tel.: (44) 2070256500
Web Site: http://www.redconsultancy.com
Sales Range: $25-49.9 Million
Emp.: 120
Public Relations Services
N.A.I.C.S.: 541820
Mike Morgan (CEO)
Amanda Duncan (Deputy CEO)
Avril Lee (Mng Dir-Health Div)

Branch (US):

The Red Consultancy (4)
405 Lexington Ave Fl 7, New York, NY 10174-0700
Tel.: (212) 508-3495
Web Site: http://www.redconsultancy.com
Public Relations Services
N.A.I.C.S.: 541820

The Red Consultancy (4)
171 2nd St Ste 500, San Francisco, CA 94105
Tel.: (415) 618-8810
Web Site: http://www.redconsultancy.com
Sales Range: $25-49.9 Million
Emp.: 20
Public Relations
N.A.I.C.S.: 541820

Subsidiary (US):

Vitiello Communications Group, LLC (3)
825 Georges Rd Ste 6, North Brunswick, NJ 08902-3357
Tel.: (732) 238-6622
Web Site: http://www.vtlo.com
General Management Consulting Services
N.A.I.C.S.: 541611
Jill Vitiello (Partner & Exec VP)

Italtel S.p.A. (1)
Via Reiss Romoli, Localita Castelletto, 20019, Settimo Milanese, Italy (50%)
Tel.: (39) 0243881
Web Site: http://www.italtel.com
Mfr of Telecommunications Systems
N.A.I.C.S.: 517111
Stefano Pileri (CEO)
Domenico Favuzzi (Chm)

Kalle GmbH (1)
Rheingaustrasse 190-196, Wiesbaden, 65203, Germany
Tel.: (49) 61196207
Web Site: http://www.kalle.de
Sales Range: $250-299.9 Million
Emp.: 1,800
Sausage Casing & Sponge Cloth Mfr
N.A.I.C.S.: 311999
Oswald Schmid (Pres & CEO)
Johannes Burgheim (Mng Dir)
Michael Pies (Mng Dir & CFO)
John Lample (Pres-Kalle USA, Inc.)
Timke Precht (VP-Ops)
Hans Fusser (Dir-R&D-Global)
Pierre Ferracci (Dir-Sls Dev-Global)
Olaf De Wit (Dir-Sls Dev-Global)
Michael Schmalholz (Head-Corp Affairs Kalle Group & Gen Counsel)
Holger Thies (Dir-HR-Global)
Jorg Weidenfeld (Mng Dir)

Clayton, Dubilier & Rice, LLC—(Continued)

Subsidiary (Non-US):

Foodpack B.V. (2)
Marie Curiestraat 19, PO Box 16, 3840 AA, Harderwijk, Netherlands **(100%)**
Tel.: (31) 341462100
Web Site: http://www.foodpack.nl
Meat Product Distr
N.A.I.C.S.: 424470
John Clements (Acct Mgr-Natl)

Subsidiary (US):

Jif-Pak Manufacturing Inc. (2)
1451 Engineer St, Vista, CA 92081
Tel.: (760) 597-2665
Web Site: http://www.jifpak.com
Meat Processing
N.A.I.C.S.: 311613

Subsidiary (Non-US):

Kalle Austria GmbH (2)
Industriestr 9/3, 2353, Guntramsdorf, Austria
Tel.: (43) 22362051510
Web Site: http://www.kalle.at
Meat Product Distr
N.A.I.C.S.: 424470
Josef Strablegg (Mng Dir)

Kalle CZ, s.r.o. (2)
Skandinavska 995, 26753, Zebrak, Czech Republic
Tel.: (420) 3115338947
Web Site: http://www.kalle.cz
Meat Product Distr
N.A.I.C.S.: 424470

Kalle Chile S.A. (2)
Cordillera No 321 - Modulo A-9, Quilicura, Santiago, Chile
Tel.: (56) 29159700
Meat Product Distr
N.A.I.C.S.: 424470

Kalle Nalo Polska Sp. z o.o. (2)
ul Pojezierska 90D, 91-341, Lodz, Poland
Tel.: (48) 426407150
Web Site: http://www.kalle.pl
Meat Product Distr
N.A.I.C.S.: 424470

Kalle Nordic ApS (2)
Halkjaervej 14, 9200, Aalborg, Denmark **(100%)**
Tel.: (45) 70238060
Web Site: http://www.kalle-nordic.dk
Meat Product Distr
N.A.I.C.S.: 424470
Claus Jensen (Mng Dir)
Klaus Bruun (Mgr-Sls)

Subsidiary (US):

Kalle USA Inc. (2)
5750 Centerpoint Ct Ste B, Gurnee, IL 60031
Tel.: (847) 775-0781
Web Site: http://www.kalle.de
Meat Product Distr
N.A.I.C.S.: 424470
John Lample (Pres)

Subsidiary (Domestic):

OSKUtex GmbH (2)
Osterheide 3, 49124, Georgsmarienhutte, Germany
Tel.: (49) 540186790
Web Site: http://www.oskuda.com
Meat Product Distr
N.A.I.C.S.: 424470

Motor Fuel Group Ltd. (1)
Building 2 Abbey View Everard Close, Saint Albans, AL1 2QU, Herts, United Kingdom
Tel.: (44) 1727 898 890
Web Site: http://www.motorfuelgroup.com
Holding Company; Gas Station Owner & Operator
N.A.I.C.S.: 551112
William Bannister (CEO)
Tom Biggart (Chief Investment Officer)
Jeremy Clarke (COO)
Jackie Ledwich (Mgr-Food Svcs Dev)
Paul Deary (Head-Food Svcs)
Michael O'Loughlin (Mng Dir-Acq & Bus Dev)

Paresh Patel (Dir-IT)
Paul Dennis (Dir-Retail)
Graham Wilson (Dir-Property)

Subsidiary (Domestic):

Motor Fuel Limited (2)
Building 2 Abbey View Everard Close, Saint Albans, AL1 2QU, Herts, United Kingdom
Tel.: (44) 1727 898 890
Web Site: http://www.motorfuelgroup.com
Gas Station Operator Distr
N.A.I.C.S.: 457110

Primary Provider Management Company (1)
2115 Compton Ave Ste 301, Corona, CA 92881 **(100%)**
Tel.: (951) 280-7700
Web Site: http://www.ppmcinc.com
Emp.: 112
Develops & Implements Technology & Analytics Infrastructure & the Documentation of Clinical & Operational Best Practices
N.A.I.C.S.: 513210
Carl Lewis (CTO)

S&S Activewear LLC (1)
220 Remington Blvd, Bolingbrook, IL 60440
Tel.: (800) 523-2155
Web Site: http://www.ssactivewear.com
Activewear & Uniform Whslr
N.A.I.C.S.: 339920
Alaina K. Brooks (Chief Legal Officer)
Jim Shannon (Pres)

Subsidiary (Domestic):

TSC Apparel, LLC (2)
10856 Reed Hartman Hwy, Cincinnati, OH 45242
Tel.: (800) 289-5400
Web Site: http://www.tscapparel.com
Clothing & Apparel Distr
N.A.I.C.S.: 424350
Robert Winget (Co-Pres)
Marty Ostendorf (VP-Sls)
Pete Tuff (Dir-Pur, Inventory & Supply Chain Mgmt)
Andy Reeder (Gen Mgr)
Dave Klotter (CEO)

SPIE SA (1)
SPIE Operations 10 avenue de l'Entreprise, 95863, Cergy, Cedex, France
Tel.: (33) 134418181
Web Site: https://www.spie.com
Rev.: $8,756,502,266
Assets: $9,634,777,682
Liabilities: $7,588,878,696
Net Worth: $2,045,898,986
Earnings: $166,075,977
Emp.: 48,073
Fiscal Year-end: 12/31/2022
Holding Company; Engineering Services
N.A.I.C.S.: 551112
Gauthier Louette (Chm & CEO)
Pablo Ibanez (Dir-Operational Support)
Markus Holzke (Mng Dir-Deutschland & Zentraleuropa)
Jerome Vanhove (Dir-Strategy, Dev & M&A)
Lieve Declercq (Mng Dir-Nederland)
Christophe Bernhart (Mng Dir)
Pascal Lekeu (Mng Dir-Belgium)
Pawel Skowronski (Mng Dir-Central Europe)
Arnaud Tirmarche (Mng Dir-France)
Severine Walser (Dir-Human Resources)

Subsidiary (Non-US):

Christof Electrics GmbH & Co KG (2)
Lastenstrasse 19, 1230, Vienna, Austria
Tel.: (43) 1863860
Web Site: http://www.christof-electrics.at
Electrical Engineering Services
N.A.I.C.S.: 541330
Hans Joachim Rinner (Gen Mgr)

ROBUR Industry Service Group GmbH (2)
Akademiestrasse 7, 80799, Munich, Germany
Tel.: (49) 89 5484 3970
Web Site: http://www.robur-industry-service.com
Sales Range: $150-199.9 Million
Holding Company; Industrial Support Services
N.A.I.C.S.: 551112

Daniel Beringer (Member-Mgmt Bd)
Florian Kopp (Member-Mgmt Bd)
Jan-Jorg Muller-Seiler (Member-Mgmt Bd)

Subsidiary (Domestic):

ROBUR Prototyping & Materials GmbH (3)
Aue 23-27, 09112, Chemnitz, Germany
Tel.: (49) 371503480
Web Site: http://www.robur-prototyping.com
Road & Rail Transportation Vehicle Prototype Engineering & Testing Services
N.A.I.C.S.: 541330
Steffen Schaarschmidt (Mng Dir)

emnos GmbH (3)
Theresienhohe 12, 80339, Munich, Germany
Tel.: (49) 892050736
Web Site: http://www.emnos.com
Customer Management Consulting Services
N.A.I.C.S.: 541613
Jesus Garcia (COO)

Subsidiary (Non-US):

SPIE Belgium SA-ICS Division (2)
Chaussee de Louvain 431C, 1380, Lasne, Belgium
Tel.: (32) 23528311
Web Site: http://www.spie-ics.be
Business Services
N.A.I.C.S.: 561439

Subsidiary (Domestic):

SPIE Communications (2)
ZA Pre Catelan 1 rue Delesalle, F 59110, La Madeleine, France
Tel.: (33) 320125900
Web Site: http://www.spie.com
Sales Range: $150-199.9 Million
Emp.: 2,000
Telephone Equipment Distr
N.A.I.C.S.: 423690

SPIE Communications SA (2)
10 avenue de l'Enterprise, Pole Vinci, 95800, Cergy-Pontoise, France
Tel.: (33) 141464146
Sales Range: $150-199.9 Million
Emp.: 2,200
Telecommunications Mfr
N.A.I.C.S.: 517112
Joelle Tavano (Mgr-Comm)
Gilles Brazey (Mng Dir)
Mike Svetozar Zafirovski (Mgr-Fin)

Subsidiary (Non-US):

SPIE Energy Solutions GmbH (2)
Speditionstrasse 15, 40221, Dusseldorf, Germany
Tel.: (49) 211 60 170 550
Web Site: http://www.spie-energysolutions.de
Sales Range: $75-99.9 Million
Energy Consulting Services
N.A.I.C.S.: 541690
Thomas Raach (Mgr-Northeast Reg)
Hans Loest (Member-Mgmt Bd)
Peter Antic (Chm-Mgmt Bd)

SPIE ICS AG (2)
Sonnenplatz 6, 6020, Emmenbrucke, Switzerland
Tel.: (41) 58 301 11 11
Web Site: http://www.spie.ch
Emp.: 600
Information & Communications Technology Services
N.A.I.C.S.: 541512
Pierre Savoy (CEO)
Michael Suderow (CFO)
Juraj Kis (Mng Dir-East)
Stefan Schlafli (Mng Dir-Central)
Luis Becerra (Mng Dir-West)

SPIE WHS Limited (2)
The Mill South Hall Street Off Ordsall Lane, Salford, M5 4TP, Mancs, United Kingdom
Tel.: (44) 161 836 7260
Web Site: http://www.spiewhs.com
Electrical, Plumbing, Heating & Air Conditioning Contractor
N.A.I.C.S.: 238990
Steven Nanda (Mng Dir)
Shaun McGillycuddy (Comml Dir)

---

car.e Facility Management GmbH (2)
Oststrasse 2 C, 38122, Braunschweig, Germany
Tel.: (49) 1 505 8791
Web Site: http://www.care.de
Facility Management Services
N.A.I.C.S.: 561210

STS Operating Inc. (1)
2301 Windsor Ct, Addison, IL 60101
Tel.: (800) 345-0316
Web Site: http://www.sun-source.com
Hydraulic Systems Equipment & Supplies Distr
N.A.I.C.S.: 423830
Charles Freeman (CFO & Exec VP-Admin)

Subsidiary (Domestic):

Ryan Herco Products Corp. (2)
3010 N San Fernando Blvd, Burbank, CA 91504
Tel.: (818) 841-1141
Web Site: http://www.rhfs.com
Corrosion-Resistant Fluid Handling, Filtration & Flow Control Products Distr
N.A.I.C.S.: 423720
Rod Grin (VP & Dir-Strategic Bus Dev)

Subsidiary (Domestic):

Engineered Machinery, Inc. (3)
12451 SW Leveton Dr, Tualatin, OR 97062
Tel.: (503) 210-0100
Pump Assembly, Testing & Repair Services; Other Pumping Equipment Mfr
N.A.I.C.S.: 333914

Subsidiary (Domestic):

The United Distribution Group, Inc. (2)
1241 Volunteer Pkwy Ste 1000, Bristol, TN 37620
Tel.: (423) 573-7300
Web Site: http://www.udginc.com
Holding Company; Industrial Equipment & Supplies Distr
N.A.I.C.S.: 551112
Darrell H. Cole (Pres & CEO)
Daniel D. Ahuero (VP-Mergers & Acq)

Subsidiary (Domestic):

United Central Industrial Supply Company (3)
914 Ploof Dr, Hueytown, AL 35023
Tel.: (205) 491-9969
Web Site: http://www.unitedcentral.net
Mining Machinery & Equipment, Except Petroleum
N.A.I.C.S.: 423810
Henry E. Looney (Pres)
D. Scott Kesner (VP-Matls Mgmt)
Christopher P. McClendon (VP-Matls Mgmt)

Subsidiary (Domestic):

GHX Holdings, LLC (4)
13311 Lockwood Rd, Houston, TX 77044
Tel.: (713) 341-3407
Web Site: http://www.ghxinc.com
Holding Company
N.A.I.C.S.: 551112
Richard Harrison (Pres & CEO)
Roy Torres (VP-Sourcing & Supply Chain)

Subsidiary (Domestic):

GHX Industrial, LLC (5)
13311 Lockwood Rd, Houston, TX 77044
Tel.: (713) 222-2231
Web Site: http://www.ghxinc.com
Industrial Equipment & Supplies Distr
N.A.I.C.S.: 423840
Richard Harrison (Pres & CEO)
Roy Torres (VP-Sourcing & Supply Chain)

Subsidiary (Domestic):

McCarty Equipment Co., Ltd. (6)
1103 Industrial Blvd, Abilene, TX 79602
Tel.: (325) 691-5558
Web Site: http://www.mccartyequipment.com
Oil & Gas Drilling Machinery & Related Accessory Whslr
N.A.I.C.S.: 423830
Kelly McCarty (Pres)
Brad D. Stephenson (VP & Gen Mgr)

Shearer's Foods, LLC (1)
100 Lincoln Way E, Massillon, OH 44646
Tel.: (330) 834-4030
Web Site: http://www.shearers.com
Snack Food Mfr
N.A.I.C.S.: 311919
Fritz Kohmann (CFO)
Lisa George (Chief HR Officer)
Rick Thielen (Chief Procurement Officer)
David Kaissling (Chief Supply Chain Officer)

The Capital Markets Company (1)
77 Water St 10th Fl, New York, NY
10005 (60%)
Tel.: (212) 284-8600
Web Site: http://www.capco.com
Management Consulting Services
N.A.I.C.S.: 541618
Lance Levy (CEO)
Michael Pugliese (Mng Partner-US)
Garrett Hrncir (Partner)
Trevor Williams (Partner)

Subsidiary (Domestic):

NEOS LLC (2)
20 Church St, Hartford, CT 06103
Tel.: (860) 519-5601
Web Site: http://www.neosllc.com
Sales Range: $1-9.9 Million
Emp.: 30
Management Consulting & Technology Services
N.A.I.C.S.: 541618
Ernst Renner (Mng Partner & CEO)
Robert Nocera (Partner)
Randall J. Love (Partner)
Carla Gregory (Sr Principal)
Eric Truntz (Principal)

Subsidiary (Non-US):

The Capital Markets Company (UK) Limited (2)
77-79 Great Eastern St, London, EC2A
3HU, United Kingdom
Tel.: (44) 2074261500
Web Site: http://www.capco.com
Software Services
N.A.I.C.S.: 513210

The Capital Markets Company GmbH (2)
Neue Mainzer Strasse 28, 60311, Frankfurt,
Germany
Tel.: (49) 69 976 090 000
Software Services
N.A.I.C.S.: 541511

Truist Insurance Holdings, Inc. (1)
301 College St Ste 208, Asheville, NC
28801
Tel.: (828) 225-2044
Web Site: http://www.truistinsurance.com
Holding Company
N.A.I.C.S.: 551112
Wes Dasher (Pres)
Kenya Odoms (Chief Talent Officer)
Kedar Bryan (Chief Mktg & Comm Officer)
Mike Clark (Chief Risk Officer)
Amanda Martin (Chief Admin Officer)
Andrea Holder (CFO)
Matt Spriggs (CIO)
Tammy Stringer (Gen Counsel)
Todd Wartchow (Exec VP-Business
Development-Strategy)
Henry Wright (Officer)
Kedar Bryan (Chief Mktg & Comm Officer)
Mike Clark (Chief Risk Officer)
Amanda Martin (Chief Admin Officer)
Andrea Holder (CFO)
Matt Spriggs (CIO)
Tammy Stringer (Gen Counsel)
Todd Wartchow (Exec VP-Business
Development-Strategy)
Henry Wright (Officer)
John Howard (Chm & CEO)

Subsidiary (Domestic):

8121 Insurance Management, Inc. (2)
2201 Cantu Ct Ste 102, Sarasota, FL
34232
Tel.: (941) 377-4842
Sales Range: $1-9.9 Million
Emp.: 10

Direct Property & Casualty Insurance Carriers
N.A.I.C.S.: 524126
Alex Hahn (CEO)

BB&T Insurance Services, Inc. (2)
4309 Emperor Blvd Ste 300, Durham, NC
27703
Tel.: (919) 281-4500
Sales Range: $75-99.9 Million
Insurance Services
N.A.I.C.S.: 524210
Wes Dasher (Pres-Insurance-Mid,Atlantic
Reg)
Mike Arnaud (Sr VP)
Randy McGann (Sr VP-Employee Benefits)
Read Davis (CEO)
Renee Keen (CFO)
Robert Drew (Pres-Insurance-South Reg)
Patrick Dessauer (Pres-Insurance-West
Reg)
Steve Aldrich (Mng Dir)
Southgate Jones III (Chief Sls Exec Officer)

Subsidiary (Domestic):

AmRisc, LP (3)
20405 State Hwy Ste 430, Houston, TX
77070
Tel.: (281) 257-6700
Web Site: http://www.amrisc.com
Underwriting Services
N.A.I.C.S.: 561499

Unit (Domestic):

BB&T - J. Rolfe Davis Insurance (3)
850 Concourse Pkwy S Ste 200, Maitland,
FL 32751-6145
Tel.: (407) 691-9600
Web Site: http://insurance.bbt.com
Sales Range: $1-9.9 Million
Emp.: 45
Insurance Agents
N.A.I.C.S.: 524210

BB&T - J.V. Arthur (3)
112 N Loudoun St, Winchester, VA 22601-
3310
Tel.: (540) 662-3865
Web Site: http://www.insurance.bbt.com
Sales Range: $1-9.9 Million
Emp.: 40
Insurance Agents
N.A.I.C.S.: 524210

BB&T - John Burnham Insurance Services (3)
750 B St Ste 2400, San Diego, CA 92101-
2476
Tel.: (619) 525-2807
Web Site: http://www.insurance.bbt.com
Sales Range: $10-24.9 Million
Emp.: 75
Insurance Agents
N.A.I.C.S.: 524210

BB&T Insurance Services, Inc. - Burkey Risk Services (3)
1661 Sandspur Rd, Maitland, FL 32751
Tel.: (407) 682-1122
Web Site: http://insurance.bbt.com
Sales Range: $1-9.9 Million
Emp.: 9
Insurance Agents
N.A.I.C.S.: 524210

BB&T Insurance Services, Inc. - Frederick Underwriters (3)
5280 Corporate Dr Ste 250A, Frederick, MD
21703-2852
Tel.: (301) 662-1147
Sales Range: $1-9.9 Million
Emp.: 60
Insurance Underwriting Services
N.A.I.C.S.: 524298

BB&T Insurance Services, Inc. - TCFC (3)
47 Airpark Ct, Greenville, SC 29607
Tel.: (864) 297-4444
Sales Range: $1-9.9 Million
Emp.: 105
Insurance Agencies & Brokerages
N.A.I.C.S.: 524210
Thomas Parrish (VP)
Donald M. Harris (Sr VP)

Subsidiary (Domestic):

Liberty Benefit Insurance Services, Inc. (3)

5446 Thornwood Dr Ste 200, San Jose, CA
95123
Tel.: (408) 360-0300
Sales Range: $25-49.9 Million
Emp.: 48
Insurance Services
N.A.I.C.S.: 524210

Subsidiary (Domestic):

Constellation Affiliated Partners LLC (2)
667 Madison Ave 16th Fl, New York, NY
10065
Tel.: (212) 235-1000
Insurance Services
N.A.I.C.S.: 524298
Bill Goldstein (CEO)

Holding (Domestic):

Coastal Insurance Underwriters, Inc. (3)
816 Hwy A1A Ste 206, Ponte Vedra Beach,
FL 32082
Tel.: (904) 285-7683
Web Site: http://www.ciuins.com
Insurance Services
N.A.I.C.S.: 524298
Charles Bushong (Pres & CEO)
Faye Leto (COO & VP)
Sim Bridges (VP-Underwriting)
Kimberly Bushong Petrillo (VP)
Michele T. Ortiz (Dir-Underwriting)
Faye Leto (COO & VP)
Sim Bridges (VP-Underwriting)
Kimberly Bushong Petrillo (VP)
Michele T. Ortiz (Dir-Underwriting)

Subsidiary (Domestic):

Cybercom International Corp. (4)
232 Canal Blvd, Ponte Vedra Beach, FL
32082-3744
Tel.: (904) 517-5610
Web Site: http://www.cybercom-intl.com
Business to Business Electronic Markets
N.A.I.C.S.: 425120
Erez Wolf (Owner)

Subsidiary (Domestic):

Kensington Vanguard National Land Services, LLC (2)
39 W 37th St 3rd Fl, New York, NY 10018
Tel.: (212) 532-8686
Web Site: http://www.kvnational.com
Insurance Agencies
N.A.I.C.S.: 524210
Brian M. Cooper (Co-CEO)
Jarett Fein (Co-CEO)

Subsidiary (Domestic):

GRS Title Services, LLC (3)
901 E Byrd St Suite 1100, Richmond, VA
23219
Tel.: (804) 486-9465
Web Site: http://www.grs-global.com
Insurance Services
N.A.I.C.S.: 524127
Stephen W. Francis (Dir)

Subsidiary (Domestic):

Wellington Insurance Group, Inc. (2)
6801 Calmont Ave, Fort Worth, TX 76116
Tel.: (817) 732-2111
Web Site:
http://www.wellingtoninsgroup.com
Holding Company
N.A.I.C.S.: 551112
Paul R. Poston (Pres & CEO)

UDG Healthcare plc (1)
20 Riverwalk, Citywest Business Campus
Citywest, Dublin, 24, Ireland
Tel.: (353) 1 468 9000
Web Site: http://www.udghealthcare.com
Rev.: $1,279,194,000
Assets: $1,763,988,000
Liabilities: $780,447,000
Net Worth: $983,541,000
Earnings: $92,841,000
Emp.: 7,834
Fiscal Year-end: 09/30/2020
Outsourced Healthcare Services Including,
Supply Chain, Packaging, Regulatory &
Sales & Marketing
N.A.I.C.S.: 561499

Keith Byrne (Head-IR & Comm)
Damien Moynagh (Gen Counsel & Sec)
Ryan Quigley (COO)
Eimear Kenny (Exec VP-HR)
Liam Logue (Exec VP-Corp Dev)
Colin Stanley (Pres-Ashfield Advisory)
Greg Flynn (Pres-Ashfield Clinical &
Comml)
Amar Urhekar (Pres-Ashfield Comm)

Subsidiary (Non-US):

Ashfield Healthcare GmbH (2)
Harrlachweg 11, 68163, Mannheim, Germany
Tel.: (49) 621750200
Web Site:
http://www.ashfieldhealthcare.com
Sales Range: $800-899.9 Million
Emp.: 500
Marketing & Sales Solutions
N.A.I.C.S.: 541613
Dominique Dieterle (Head-HR)
Fabienne Wild (Bus Dir)

Subsidiary (Domestic):

Ashfield Healthcare Ireland Limited (2)
United Drug House Magna Dr Magna Bus
Park, Citywest Rd, Dublin, 24, Ireland
Tel.: (353) 14632444
Web Site: http://www.ashfieldhealthcare.ie
Sales Range: $50-74.9 Million
Emp.: 90
Contract Sales Provider
N.A.I.C.S.: 424210
Mike Hodgkiss (Head-Quality &
Compliance-UK)
Carey Galvin (Head-Quality & Compliance-
Global)
Eoin McAtamney (Mng Dir)

Subsidiary (US):

Cambridge Biomarketing Group, LLC (2)
53 State St 24th Fl, Boston, MA 02109
Tel.: (617) 225-0001
Web Site: http://www.cambridgebmg.com
Advetising Agency
N.A.I.C.S.: 541810
Maureen Nugent Franco (CEO)
Shauna Horvath (Head-Ops)
Alisa Shakarian (Head-Experience & Art-
istry)
Alyse Sukalski (Mng Dir-CB West)
Prescott Taylor (Head-Fin)
Annemarie Crivelli (Head-Experience & In-
novation)
Marissa McNally-Costello (Head-Strategy)
Carina Whitridge (Dir-Client Svcs)
Julianne Dunphy (Dir-Medical)
Ben Beckley (Pres)

Canale Communications Inc. (2)
4010 Goldfinch St, San Diego, CA 92103
Tel.: (619) 849-6000
Web Site: https://www.evokegroup.com
Strategic Communications Agency Services
N.A.I.C.S.: 541820
Jason Ian Spark (Mng Dir)
Carin Canale-Theakston (CEO)
Heidi Chokeir (Mng Dir)
Ian Stone (Mng Dir)

Create Group NYC, LLC (2)
285 Madison Avenue 22nd Fl, New York,
NY 10014
Tel.: (646) 682-7791
Web Site: http://www.createnyc.com
Marketing & Advertising Services
N.A.I.C.S.: 541613
Susan Cohen (CFO)
Natalie McDonald (Founder, Pres & CEO)
Lauren Wetmore (Dir-Acct Svcs)
Katie Vecchiano Sutherland (Dir-New Bus
Strategy)
Maria Perez (Dir-Ops)
Christen Jones (Dir-Creative Svcs)

Drug Safety Alliance, Inc. (2)
5003 S Miami Blvd Ste 500, Durham, NC
27703
Tel.: (919) 401-8003
Web Site: http://www.drugsafetyalliance.com
Sales Range: $10-24.9 Million
Emp.: 94
Safety & Risk Management Services
N.A.I.C.S.: 541618

Clayton, Dubilier & Rice, LLC—(Continued)

Catherine Crumpton *(Pres & CEO)*
Brendon Ball *(CIO)*
Susan Gordon *(CEO)*
Michael E. Pierce *(Chief Compliance Officer)*

KnowledgePoint360 Group LLC (2)
125 Chubb Ave, Lyndhurst, NJ 07071
Tel.: (201) 271-6000
Web Site:
http://www.knowledgepoint360.com
Sales Range: $100-124.9 Million
Emp.: 650
Healthcare Information & Medical Communication Services
N.A.I.C.S.: 561499

Unit (Non-US):

Medex-Media (3)
Peakside House Alder Court Tytherington
Business Park, Tytherington, Macclesfield,
SK10 2XG, Cheshire, United Kingdom
Tel.: (44) 1625 668 000
Web Site: http://www.medex-media.com
Emp.: 30
Healthcare Industry Exhibition Design &
Management Services
N.A.I.C.S.: 541490

Subsidiary (US):

MicroMass Communications, Inc. (2)
100 Regency Forest Dr Ste 400, Cary, NC
27518
Tel.: (919) 851-3182
Web Site: http://www.micromass.com
Sales Range: $1-9.9 Million
Emp.: 100
Healthcare Communication & Marketing
Services
N.A.I.C.S.: 541613
Phil Stein *(CEO)*
Mark Rinehart *(CTO)*
Alyson Connor *(Pres)*
Bonnie Overton *(Grp Assoc Dir-Creative)*
Eric Connor *(Assoc Dir-Creative)*
John Hamilton *(Exec VP & Dir-Client Svc)*
Diane Rahn *(Coord-Agency)*
Ethan Messier *(Controller)*
Jessica Brueggeman *(Exec VP-Health Behavior Grp)*
Amber Eaton *(VP & Acct Dir)*
Philip Mann *(VP & Acct Dir)*
Greg Dosmann *(Grp Assoc Dir-Creative)*
Chris Libey *(Assoc Dir-Creative)*
Chenoah Mickalites *(Assoc Dir-Creative)*
Paul Boehling *(Dir-IT)*
Jude Kelly *(Mgr-Bus Dev)*
Emily Poole *(Dir-Project Mgmt)*
Rob Peters *(Exec VP-Strategy)*
Patty Zipfel *(VP-Scientific Strategy)*
Will Stewart *(Acct Dir)*
Taylor Preston *(Project Mgr)*
Sharron Umstead *(Project Mgr)*
Samantha Konkus *(Dir-Resourcing)*
Renny Buddin *(Project Mgr)*
Phil Winn *(Dir-Art)*
Mike Gold *(Project Mgr)*
Mike Franke *(Assoc Dir-Creative)*
Megan Myers *(Supvr-Editorial Svcs)*
Matthew Weyer *(Project Mgr)*
Maria Denisco *(Dir-Art)*
Leiana Henson *(Sr Dir-Art)*
Lindsay Huey *(Dir-Art)*
Laureen Redlund *(Dir-Art)*
Laura Slipsky *(Sr Dir-Art)*
Kyle Peck *(Dir-Art)*
Kyle Davis *(Acct Dir)*
Kristen Maynard *(Acct Dir)*
Kim Zdanowicz *(Assoc Dir-Creative)*
Kate Schabot *(Assoc Dir-Creative)*
Julie Jeleniewski *(Acct Dir)*
Joshua Burke *(Acct Supvr)*
John Pettaris *(Mgr-Production Svcs)*
Angie Clark *(Project Mgr)*

Subsidiary (Domestic):

**Pemberton Marketing International
Limited** (2)
Magna Dr Magna Business Park, Citywest
Rd, Dublin, 24, Ireland
Tel.: (353) 14598877
Web Site: http://www.pemberto.ie
Sales Range: $50-74.9 Million
Emp.: 80
Consumer Products Distr

N.A.I.C.S.: 522291
Flan Hassett *(Gen Mgr)*

Subsidiary (US):

Putnam Associates, LLC (2)
501 Boylston St, Boston, MA 02116
Tel.: (781) 273-5480
Web Site: http://www.putassoc.com
Emp.: 120
Business Strategy Consulting Services
N.A.I.C.S.: 561499
John Gordon *(Partner)*
Eric Auger *(Partner)*
Scott Gilbert *(Partner)*
Remco Op Den Kelder *(CEO)*
Matthew Riordan *(Partner)*
Shauna Collins *(CFO)*
Domenick Bertelli *(Partner)*
Paul Bogorod *(Partner)*
Joseph Feingold *(Partner)*
Ben Diop *(Partner)*
Ryan Wyrtzen *(Partner)*
Kirsten Moffat *(Principal)*
Alexander Busch *(Principal)*

Subsidiary (Non-US):

**Sharp Clinical Services (UK)
Limited** (2)
Unit 28 Heol Klockner Heads Of The Valleys Ind Est, Rhymney, NP22 5RL, Powys,
United Kingdom
Tel.: (44) 1873 812182
Web Site: http://www.sharpservices.com
Sales Range: $10-24.9 Million
Emp.: 75
Packaging & Labeling Services for Pharmaceuticals
N.A.I.C.S.: 561910
Ian Morgan *(Gen Mgr)*
Robert O'Beirn *(Mng Dir)*
Robert Feltz *(Dir-Analytical & Formulation
Svcs)*
Michael MacNeir *(VP-Bus Dev-Global)*

Subsidiary (US):

Sharp Clinical Services, Inc. (2)
300 Kimberton Rd, Phoenixville, PA 19460
Tel.: (610) 935-4300
Web Site: http://www.sharpclinical.com
Sales Range: $50-74.9 Million
Emp.: 190
Pharmaceutical & Healthcare Product Research & Development
N.A.I.C.S.: 621511
Sascha Sonnenberg *(Head-Bus DevGlobal)*
Frank Lis *(Pres)*

SmartAnalyst Inc. (2)
285 Madison Ave Fl 22, New York, NY
10017
Tel.: (212) 331-0010
Web Site: http://www.smartanalyst.com
Management Consulting Services
N.A.I.C.S.: 541618
Manu Bammi *(Co-Founder & CEO)*
Donald Boland *(Dir-Fin)*
Robin Gasloli *(Mng Dir & VP)*
Ritu Kishwar *(VP-Res & Mgr-India)*

Subsidiary (Domestic):

Unitech Limited (2)
Magna Dr Magna Bus Pk, Citywest, Dublin,
24, Ireland
Tel.: (353) 14048300
Web Site: http://www.unitech.ie
Sales Range: $25-49.9 Million
Emp.: 40
Medical & Scientific Sector Services
N.A.I.C.S.: 423450

Subsidiary (US):

Vynamic LLC (2)
1600 Arch St Ste 200, Philadelphia, PA
19103-2031
Tel.: (267) 498-5268
Web Site: http://www.vynamic.com
Emp.: 110
Healthcare Management Consulting Services
N.A.I.C.S.: 541618
Alison Calpas *(Dir)*
Brian Babcock *(Dir-Consulting)*
Michael Hudson *(Dir)*
Laura Brechter *(Dir)*

Stephen O'Kane *(Dir-Bus Dev)*
Vincent Annerhed-Harris *(Dir)*
Saurabh Raman *(Dir)*
Jennifer Dee-Yuzuk *(Mgr-Talent Acquisition)*
Jeff Dill *(CEO)*
Stefanie Christmas *(Dir)*
Christopher Wuenschel *(Dir)*
Eric Wood *(Dir)*
Dan Calista *(Founder)*

Subsidiary (Non-US):

pharmexx UK Ltd. (2)
Ashfield House Resolution Road, Ashby de
la Zouch, LE65 1HW, Leicestershire, United
Kingdom
Tel.: (44) 1530562487
Web Site: http://www.pharmexx.co.uk
Emp.: 160
Marketing & Sales Solutions
N.A.I.C.S.: 541613

Vera Whole Health, Inc. (1)
1201 2nd Ave Ste 1400, Seattle, WA 98101
Tel.: (206) 395-7870
Web Site: http://www.verawholehealth.com
Healthcare Related Software Development
Services
N.A.I.C.S.: 513210
Ryan Schmid *(Pres & CEO)*
Ronald Williams *(Chm)*

Veritiv Corporation (1)
1000 Abernathy Rd NE Bldg 400 Ste 1700,
Atlanta, GA 30328
Tel.: (770) 391-8200
Web Site: https://www.veritiv.com
Rev: $7,146,300,000
Assets: $2,089,600,000
Liabilities: $1,333,500,000
Net Worth: $756,100,000
Earnings: $337,900,000
Emp.: 5,000
Fiscal Year-end: 12/31/2022
Holding Company; Printing, Packaging &
Facility Maintenance Supplies Distr
N.A.I.C.S.: 551112
Salvatore A. Abbate *(CEO)*
Dean A. Adelman *(Chief HR Officer & Sr
VP)*
Eric J. Guerin *(CFO)*
Karen K. Renner *(CIO & Sr VP)*
Stephanie E. Mayerle *(Sr VP-Sls)*
Susan B. Salyer *(Gen Counsel, Sec & Sr
VP)*
David W. Backus *(Sr VP-Print Solutions)*
Christopher S. Martin *(Sr VP-Operations)*
Tony Ventry *(Chief HR Officer & Sr VP)*
Stuart L. Crockford *(Sr VP-Business Development)*

Subsidiary (Domestic):

Alco Realty, Inc. (2)
182 S Main St, Cleveland, GA 30528
Tel.: (706) 219-3700
Web Site: https://www.alcorealty.com
Emp.: 8
Real Estate Brokerage Services
N.A.I.C.S.: 531210

**All American Containers of Georgia,
LLC** (2)
4400 N Commerce Dr, East Point, GA
30344
Tel.: (770) 997-1992
Paper Product Whslr
N.A.I.C.S.: 424130

**All American Containers of Puerto
Rico, LLC** (2)
Rd 869 km 1 5 Royal Industrial Park Bldg
J5 Bo Palma, Catano, PR 00962
Tel.: (787) 275-2670
Paper Product Whslr
N.A.I.C.S.: 424130

**All American Containers of Southern
California Inc.** (2)
2390-B Ward Ave, Simi Valley, CA 93065
Tel.: (805) 416-5971
Paper Product Whslr
N.A.I.C.S.: 424130

**All American Containers of Tampa,
LLC** (2)
4507 Eagle Falls Pl, Tampa, FL 33619
Tel.: (813) 248-2023
Paper Product Whslr
N.A.I.C.S.: 424130

Leif Wahlquist *(VP-Sls)*

**All American Containers of Texas
Inc.** (2)
1180 W Loop N Fwy Ste C, Houston, TX
77055
Tel.: (713) 353-7342
Paper Product Whslr
N.A.I.C.S.: 424130

All American Containers of the Midwest Inc. (2)
899 E Park Ave, Libertyville, IL 60048
Tel.: (847) 367-5126
Paper Product Whslr
N.A.I.C.S.: 424130

All American Containers of the Northeast, LLC (2)
635 Pierce St Ste B, Somerset, NJ 08873
Tel.: (732) 537-0430
Paper Product Whslr
N.A.I.C.S.: 424130
Eric Hammesfahr Sr. *(Sls Mgr)*

**All American Containers of the Pacific
Coast Inc.** (2)
2013 Farallon Dr, San Leandro, CA 94577
Tel.: (510) 357-1033
Paper Product Whslr
N.A.I.C.S.: 424130

All-American Containers, LLC (2)
4507 Eagle Falls Plc, Tampa, FL 33619
Tel.: (813) 248-2023
Plastic, Glass & Metal Container Mfr
N.A.I.C.S.: 327213

Bulkley Dunton, Inc. (2)
1 Penn Plz Ste 2814 250 W 34th St, New
York, NY 10119
Tel.: (212) 863-1800
Web Site: https://www.bulkleydunton.com
Paper Brokerage Business & Distribution
Services
N.A.I.C.S.: 322299
John Biscanti *(Sr VP-Publ & Print Mgmt)*
Terence Sheehy *(Dir-Sls)*

Subsidiary (Non-US):

MC xpedx, S. de R.L. de C.V. (2)
11367 Alejandro Dumas Int 5 Complejo Industrial Chihuahua, 31136, Chihuahua,
Chih, México
Tel.: (52) 6144162685
Printing Paper Distr
N.A.I.C.S.: 322299

Veritiv Europe GmbH (2)
Hochstrasse 15, 86399, Bobingen,
Germany (100%)
Tel.: (49) 82348021389
Web Site: http://www.veritivppm.com
Emp.: 13
Print & Paper Management
N.A.I.C.S.: 541618
Chris van Zijl *(Mng Dir & Head-Europe)*

Unit (Non-US):

Graphic Communications UK (3)
The Atrium Business Center, Curtis Road,
Dorking, RH4 1XA, Surrey, United Kingdom
Tel.: (44) 1306644060
Web Site: http://www.veritivppm.com
Emp.: 115
End-to-End Paper & Print Management
Communications
N.A.I.C.S.: 323120

Subsidiary (Non-US):

Unisource Belgium BVBA (3)
Winninglaan 3, 9140, Temse, Belgium
Tel.: (32) 37105750
Web Site: http://www.veritivppm.com
Emp.: 1,000
Printing Paper Operational Service Center
N.A.I.C.S.: 322299

Subsidiary (Domestic):

Veritiv Operating Company (2)
6600 Governors Lake Pkwy, Norcross, GA
30071
Tel.: (770) 447-9000
Web Site: http://www.veritiv.com
Emp.: 13,400
Paper Products Distr & Print Management
Solutions

N.A.I.C.S.: 323111
Dave Hudson *(CIO)*

Subsidiary (Domestic):

Graphic Communications Holdings, Inc. (3)
5700 Darrow Rd Ste 111, Hudson, OH 44236
Tel.: (330) 650-5522
Web Site: http://www.graphiccommunications.com
Sales Range: $25-49.9 Million
Emp.: 160
Holding Company; Paper Products Distr
N.A.I.C.S.: 551112
Matt Dawley *(Pres)*
Bill King *(Sr VP-Ops-North American)*
John Patneau *(Sr VP-Print Solutions)*

Branch (Domestic):

PaperPlus (3)
12065 34th St N, Saint Petersburg, FL 33716
Tel.: (727) 556-9020
Web Site: http://www.veritivcorp.com
Printing Papers & Packaging Products
N.A.I.C.S.: 424110

PaperPlus (3)
201 Ritchie Rd Bldg B, Capitol Heights, MD 20743
Tel.: (301) 499-3599
Web Site: http://www.veritivcorp.com
Printing Paper, Packaging Products, Facilities Supplies
N.A.I.C.S.: 561210

PaperPlus (3)
125 S Arthur St Ste 2, Spokane, WA 99202
Tel.: (509) 535-0229
Web Site: http://www.veritivcorp.com
Printing Papers & Packaging Products
N.A.I.C.S.: 561910

PaperPlus (3)
8623 & 8625 S 212 th St, Kent, WA 98031
Tel.: (253) 395-6080
Web Site: http://www.veritivcorp.com
Printing Papers & Packaging Products
N.A.I.C.S.: 323120

PaperPlus (3)
605 Glendale Ave Ste 105A, Sparks, NV 89431
Tel.: (775) 352-9228
Web Site: http://www.veritivcorp.com
Printing Papers & Packaging Products
N.A.I.C.S.: 561910

PaperPlus (3)
8847 Complex Dr, San Diego, CA 92123
Tel.: (858) 292-5608
Web Site: http://www.veritivcorp.com
Emp.: 4
Printing Paper, Packaging Products & Facilities Supplies
N.A.I.C.S.: 424110

PaperPlus (3)
290 Quadrum Ste C290, Oklahoma City, OK 73108
Tel.: (405) 948-1120
Web Site: http://www.veritivcorp.com
Packaging, Facility & Printing Supplies
N.A.I.C.S.: 561910

Subsidiary (Non-US):

Unisource Canada Inc. (3)
4300 Hickmore Street, Saint Laurent, H4T 1K2, QC, Canada
Tel.: (418) 683-2256
Web Site: http://www.unisource.ca
Emp.: 1,000
Paper & Printing Products Distr
N.A.I.C.S.: 323120

Subsidiary (Domestic):

Veritiv (3)
5786 Collett Rd, Farmington, NY 14425
Tel.: (585) 742-1110
Web Site: http://www.veritivcorp.com
Sales Range: $75-99.9 Million
Emp.: 100
Distr Printing & Writing Paper, Industrial Packaging & Warehousing Solutions
N.A.I.C.S.: 424110

Veritiv (3)
1200 Highlands Dr Ste 1B, Westampton, NJ 08060
Tel.: (609) 518-9700
Web Site: http://www.veritivcorp.com
Sales Range: $100-124.9 Million
Emp.: 175
Fine & Printing Paper Distr
N.A.I.C.S.: 424110

Veritiv (3)
6285 Tri-Ridge Blvd, Loveland, OH 45140-8318 (100%)
Tel.: (513) 965-2900
Web Site: http://www.xpedx.com
Sales Range: $100-124.9 Million
Emp.: 500
Warehousing & Paper Distribution Services
N.A.I.C.S.: 493190

Veritiv (3)
3344 Walden Ave, Depew, NY 14043
Tel.: (716) 206-2424
Web Site: http://www.veritivcorp.com
Sales Range: $75-99.9 Million
Emp.: 100
Paper & Packaging Warehousing
N.A.I.C.S.: 424110

Veritiv (3)
2920 New Beaver Ave, Pittsburgh, PA 15233
Tel.: (412) 732-7500
Web Site: http://www.veritivcorp.com
Sales Range: $50-74.9 Million
Emp.: 60
Paper Supplies & Packaging Products
N.A.I.C.S.: 424110

Veritiv (3)
1900 E 17th St, Des Moines, IA 50316
Tel.: (515) 262-9555
Web Site: http://www.veritivcorp.com
Sales Range: $75-99.9 Million
Emp.: 50
Printing Paper & Supplies Distr
N.A.I.C.S.: 424130

Veritiv (3)
2614 E Henry Ave, Tampa, FL 33610
Tel.: (813) 466-6230
Web Site: http://www.veritivcorp.com
Sales Range: $100-124.9 Million
Emp.: 130
Paper & Packaging Distribution Services
N.A.I.C.S.: 424130

Veritiv (3)
222 W 63rd St, Shreveport, LA 71106
Tel.: (318) 869-0791
Web Site: http://www.veritivcorp.com
Sales Range: $50-74.9 Million
Emp.: 13
Printing Papers Warehousing
N.A.I.C.S.: 424130

Veritiv (3)
500 Kalanianaole Ave, Hilo, HI 96720 (100%)
Tel.: (808) 935-6446
Web Site: http://www.veritivcorp.com
Sales Range: $50-74.9 Million
Emp.: 3
Distr of Printing & Writing Papers
N.A.I.C.S.: 424110

Veritiv (3)
330 Stevens St, Jacksonville, FL 32254 (100%)
Tel.: (904) 783-0550
Web Site: http://www.veritivcorp.com
Sales Range: $50-74.9 Million
Emp.: 200
Printing Paper & Packaging Mfr
N.A.I.C.S.: 551114

Veritiv (3)
844 N 47Th Ave, Phoenix, AZ 85043
Tel.: (602) 233-6600
Web Site: http://www.veritivcorp.com
Sales Range: $50-74.9 Million
Emp.: 90
Janitorial & Sanitary Products & Printing Papers
N.A.I.C.S.: 424110

Veritiv (3)
9001 Wyoming Ave N, Brooklyn Park, MN 55445-1835
Tel.: (763) 488-7347

Veritiv (3)
Web Site: http://www.veritivcorp.com
Sales Range: $75-99.9 Million
Emp.: 95
Warehousing & Distr of Professional & Personal Papers
N.A.I.C.S.: 424110

Veritiv (3)
5900 Middlebrook Pike NW, Knoxville, TN 37909 (100%)
Tel.: (865) 584-0753
Web Site: http://www.veritivcorp.com
Sales Range: $50-74.9 Million
Emp.: 42
Distr of Printing & Writing Paper Products
N.A.I.C.S.: 424110

Veritiv (3)
541 Republic Cir, Birmingham, AL 35214 (100%)
Tel.: (205) 798-8380
Web Site: http://www.veritivcorp.com
Sales Range: $75-99.9 Million
Emp.: 50
Printing & Writing Paper Distr
N.A.I.C.S.: 424110

Veritiv (3)
11800 N Lakeridge Pkwy, Ashland, VA 23005
Tel.: (804) 496-2200
Web Site: http://www.veritivcorp.com
Sales Range: $75-99.9 Million
Emp.: 55
Printing & Writing Paper Distr
N.A.I.C.S.: 424110

Veritiv (3)
1700 Fortune Ct, Lexington, KY 40509
Tel.: (859) 293-7522
Web Site: http://www.veritivcorp.com
Sales Range: $50-74.9 Million
Emp.: 4
Printing, Packaging Paper Warehousing, Sales & Distribution
N.A.I.C.S.: 493110

Veritiv (3)
4395 S Minnewawa Ave Ste 101, Fresno, CA 93725-2110
Tel.: (559) 486-6440
Web Site: http://www.veritivcorp.com
Sales Range: $50-74.9 Million
Emp.: 20
Packaging & Printing Paper Solutions
N.A.I.C.S.: 424130

Veritiv (3)
7445 New Ridge Rd, Hanover, MD 21076-3105 (100%)
Tel.: (410) 694-8500
Web Site: http://www.veritivcorp.com
Sales Range: $125-149.9 Million
Emp.: 185
Printing, Writing Paper & Packaging Supplies Warehousing
N.A.I.C.S.: 424110

Veritiv (3)
1340 N Illinois St, Indianapolis, IN 46202
Tel.: (317) 686-2993
Web Site: http://www.veritivcorp.com
Sales Range: $75-99.9 Million
Emp.: 10
Industrial & Warehousing Paper Services & Packaging
N.A.I.C.S.: 459410

Veritiv (3)
6839 Market Ave, El Paso, TX 79915 (100%)
Tel.: (915) 779-2240
Web Site: http://www.veritivcorp.com
Sales Range: $50-74.9 Million
Emp.: 45
Distr of Printing & Writing Papers
N.A.I.C.S.: 424110

Veritiv (3)
3 Charles Blvd, Albany, NY 12205-5705
Tel.: (518) 489-1788
Web Site: http://www.veritivcorp.com
Sales Range: $25-49.9 Million
Emp.: 3
Industrial & Personal Service Paper
N.A.I.C.S.: 424110

Veritiv (3)
9 Crystal Pond Rd, Southborough, MA 01772
Tel.: (508) 480-6000

Web Site: http://www.veritivcorp.com
Sales Range: $25-49.9 Million
Emp.: 2
Distr & Storage of Printing & Writing Paper
N.A.I.C.S.: 424110

Unit (Domestic):

Veritiv (3)
5355 S Westridge Dr, New Berlin, WI 53151
Tel.: (262) 782-2100
Web Site: http://www.veritivcorp.com
Sales Range: $10-24.9 Million
Emp.: 4
Distr of End-to-End Packaging, Printing, Facility & Logistic Solutions
N.A.I.C.S.: 541614

Veritiv (3)
1060 Hawn Ave, Shreveport, LA 71107
Tel.: (318) 221-5294
Web Site: http://www.veritivcorp.com
Paper Warehousing & Storage Facilities
N.A.I.C.S.: 493110

Subsidiary (Domestic):

Veritiv - Denver (3)
3900 Lima St, Denver, CO 80239
Tel.: (303) 375-2377
Web Site: http://www.veritivcorp.com
Sales Range: $100-124.9 Million
Emp.: 150
Warehousing & Distribution of Printing, Writing & All Types Of Papers
N.A.I.C.S.: 424110

Veritiv - Indianapolis (3)
5021 W 81st Street, Indianapolis, IN 46268
Tel.: (317) 334-0898
Web Site: http://www.veritivcorp.com
Sales Range: $50-74.9 Million
Emp.: 45
Printing & Writing Paper Warehousing & Distribution
N.A.I.C.S.: 424110

Group (Domestic):

Veritiv Distribution Group (3)
6285 Tri-Ridge Blvd, Loveland, OH 45140
Tel.: (513) 965-2900
Web Site: http://www.veritivcorp.com
Sales Range: $450-499.9 Million
Emp.: 1,000
Distribution of Printing, Packaging, Industrial & Graphic Arts Supplies & Equipment
N.A.I.C.S.: 322120

Branch (Domestic):

Veritiv Express (3)
1090 Bailey Hill Rd, Eugene, OR 97402
Tel.: (541) 345-3223
Web Site: http://www.veritivcorp.com
Printing Paper, Packaging & Facilities Supplies
N.A.I.C.S.: 424110
David Wied *(Mgr-Store)*

Veritiv Express (3)
4901 Gibbon Rd, Charlotte, NC 28269
Tel.: (704) 372-4224
Web Site: http://www.veritivcorp.com
Printing Paper, Packaging Products & Facilities Supplies
N.A.I.C.S.: 333993
Tim Kingery *(Branch Mgr)*

Veritiv Express (3)
1140 Booth St, Kansas City, KS 66103
Tel.: (913) 573-2042
Web Site: http://www.veritivcorp.com
Emp.: 2
Printing Papers & Packaging Products Mfr
N.A.I.C.S.: 322299
Gary Jennings *(Mgr)*

Veritiv Express (3)
7862 12th Ave S, Bloomington, MN 55425
Tel.: (952) 854-5899
Web Site: http://www.veritivcorp.com
Paper Packaging & Printing Papers
N.A.I.C.S.: 561910

Subsidiary (Domestic):

Veritiv Operating Company - New Berlin (3)

Clayton, Dubilier & Rice, LLC—(Continued)

5355 S Westridge Dr, New Berlin, WI
53151
Tel.: (262) 782-2100
Web Site: http://www.veritivcorp.com
Industrial & Personal Service Paper Distri-
bution
N.A.I.C.S.: 424130

Subsidiary (Non-US):

Veritiv, S.A. de C.V. **(2)**
6857 Calle Aeronautica 1 Puente Alto Ciu-
dad Juarez, 32695, Chihuahua, Mexico
Tel.: (52) 6561705444
Packaging & Facility Maintenance Services
N.A.I.C.S.: 561910

Subsidiary (Domestic):

Vivabox Solutions, LLC **(2)**
9211 Corporate Blvd Ste 110, Rockville, MD
20850
Tel.: (212) 652-2024
Web Site: https://www.vivaboxsolutions.com
Packaging Design & Mfr
N.A.I.C.S.: 322211
Desiree Paquette (CEO)

Subsidiary (Domestic):

Design Packaging, Inc. **(3)**
7880 E McClain Dr, Scottsdale, AZ 85260
Tel.: (480) 483-1988
Packaging Design & Mfr
N.A.I.C.S.: 322219

Subsidiary (Non-US):

xpedx, S.A. de C.V. **(2)**
Calle Aeronautica 6857-1 Puente Alto,
32695, Chihuahua, Juarez, Mexico
Tel.: (52) 6561705444
Web Site: http://www.xpedx.mx
Paper Distribution
N.A.I.C.S.: 322299

White Cap Supply Holdings LLC **(1)**
6250 Brook Hollow Pwy Ste 100, Norcross,
GA 30071 **(65%)**
Tel.: (800) 944-8322
Web Site: https://about.whitecap.com
Construction Materials Distr
N.A.I.C.S.: 423320
Philip W. Knisely (Chm)
Alan Sollenberger (CEO)

Subsidiary (Domestic):

Blue Bug Inc. **(2)**
280 SE Bridgeford Blvd, Bend, OR 97702
Tel.: (541) 382-9200
Rev.: $1,290,000
Emp.: 5
Home Center Operator
N.A.I.C.S.: 444110
Dave Baker (Mgr)

Crimson Steel Supply LLC **(2)**
10336 E 58th St, Tulsa, OK 74146
Tel.: (918) 994-5330
Web Site:
http://www.crimsonsteelsupply.com
Site Preparation Contractor
N.A.I.C.S.: 238910
Dustin Wright (CEO)

Form Tech Concrete Forms Inc. **(2)**
48575 Downing St, Wixom, MI 48393
Tel.: (248) 344-8260
Web Site: http://www.formtechinc.com
Sales Range: $10-24.9 Million
Emp.: 350
Rent & Sell Concrete Equipment
N.A.I.C.S.: 423810
Michael A. Fidelholtz (Pres)
Craig Wisbiski (Mgr-Pur)

**Tri-Boro Construction Supplies
Inc.** **(2)**
465 Locust St, Dallastown, PA 17313
Tel.: (717) 246-3095
Web Site: http://www.tri-borosupplies.com
Sales Range: $10-24.9 Million
Emp.: 100
Masonry Equipment & Supplies
N.A.I.C.S.: 423810
Douglas White (Plant Mgr)

Tri-Supply and Equipment Inc. **(2)**
831 S Dupont Pkwy, New Castle, DE 19720

Tel.: (302) 838-6333
Web Site:
http://www.trisupplyandequipment.com
Rev.: $5,600,000
Emp.: 38
Home Center Operator
N.A.I.C.S.: 444110
Amy Phillips (Mgr-Credit & Tri-Properties)
Marybeth Schreiber (Controller)

Triumph Geo-Synthetics, Inc. **(2)**
1235 N Grove St, Anaheim, CA 92806-2114
Tel.: (714) 237-1549
Web Site: http://www.triumphgeo.com
Construction Material Merchant Whslr
N.A.I.C.S.: 423390
Cissy McCaa (Pres)

Valley Supply, Inc. **(2)**
700 Independence Ave, Mechanicsburg, PA
17055
Tel.: (717) 697-8259
Web Site: http://www.valleysupply.cc
Rev.: $2,400,000
Emp.: 13
Brick, Stone & Related Construction Mate-
rial Merchant Whslr
N.A.I.C.S.: 423320
Harvey Sipe (VP & Gen Mgr)
Lisa Essig (Mgr-Acctg)

White Cap, L.P. **(2)**
6250 Brook Hollow Pkwy, Norcross, GA
30071
Tel.: (404) 879-7740
Hardware, Tools & Concrete Accesories
Distr
N.A.I.C.S.: 423710

Subsidiary (Non-US):

HD Supply Canada Inc. **(3)**
70 Carson Street, Toronto, M8W 4Z6, ON,
Canada
Tel.: (416) 521-4500
Web Site: https://www.hdsupplysolutions.ca
Provider of Home Improvement Services
N.A.I.C.S.: 236118

Subsidiary (Domestic):

**HD Supply Repair & Remodel,
LLC** **(3)**
1695 Eureka Rd, Roseville, CA 95661
Tel.: (916) 751-2300
Web Site: http://www.hdsupplyhis.com
Building Materials & Home Improvement
Supplies
N.A.I.C.S.: 423710

Reno Hardware & Supply Inc. **(3)**
2901 Thornton Ave, Burbank, CA 91504
Tel.: (818) 842-3667
Web Site: http://www.renohardware.com
Sales Range: $10-24.9 Million
Emp.: 48
Distr of Hardware
N.A.I.C.S.: 444140
Dan Gainey (CFO)
Kurt Nicolai (Treas)

**White Cap Construction Supply,
Inc.** **(3)**
6250 Brook Hollow Pkway, Norcross, GA
30071
Tel.: (404) 879-7740
Hardware, Tools & Construction Materials
Mfr
N.A.I.C.S.: 423710

**Wilsonart International Holdings
LLC** **(1)**
2501 Wilsonart Dr, Temple, TX 76504
Tel.: (254) 207-7000
Web Site: http://www.wilsonartfuture.com
Holding Company; Industrial Machinery Mfr
N.A.I.C.S.: 551112

Subsidiary (Domestic):

Flagg Inc. **(2)**
9195 Seward Rd, Fairfield, OH 45014
Tel.: (513) 874-5900
Web Site: http://www.flagginc.com
Sales Range: $10-24.9 Million
Emp.: 29
Lumber, Plywood & Millwork
N.A.I.C.S.: 423310
Eric Leonard (Controller)
Don Graessle (Mgr)
Kimberly Locey (VP)

Group (Domestic):

Wilsonart Engineered Surfaces **(2)**
2501 Wilsonart Dr, Temple, TX 76504
Tel.: (254) 207-7000
Web Site:
http://www.wilsonartengineers.com
High Pressure Decorative Laminate, Acrylic
& Specialty Adhesives Mfr
N.A.I.C.S.: 423390
Timothy J. O'Brien (Pres & CEO)

Subsidiary (Domestic):

Wilsonart International, Inc. **(3)**
2400 Wilson Pl, Temple, TX 76504-5131
Tel.: (254) 207-7000
Web Site: http://www.wilsonart.com
Sales Range: $700-749.9 Million
Emp.: 3,400
Decorative Laminate Products & Adhesives
Mfr & Distr
N.A.I.C.S.: 337110
Timothy J. O'Brien (Pres & CEO)
Jay Krishnamurthy (CIO)
Randy Patterson (VP-HR-Global)
Joe Thesing (Gen Counsel)
Ron Timperio (VP-Ops-Global)
Rajesh Ramamurthy (VP-Innovation &
Tech-Global)
Tim Atkinson (VP-Sls)
Ron Ubertini (VP-Product Mgmt & Pricing-
Global)
Andrew Korzen (VP-Product Mgmt & Engi-
neered Solid Surfaces)
Jeff Petru (VP-Bus Dev & Strategy)
Tim Pearson (Pres-Western Europe)
Peter Chan (Pres-APAC)

Subsidiary (Domestic):

Durcon, LLC **(4)**
206 Allison Dr, Taylor, TX 76574
Tel.: (512) 595-8000
Web Site: http://www.durcon.com
Sales Range: $10-24.9 Million
Emp.: 130
Laboratory Epoxy-Resin Work Surfaces &
Sinks Mfr
N.A.I.C.S.: 326199

Subsidiary (Non-US):

**Durcon Company of Poland Sp. z
o.o.** **(5)**
ul Ceglana 10, 87-100, Torun, Poland
Tel.: (48) 56 659 9805
Web Site: http://www.durcon.com.pl
Emp.: 18
Laboratory Epoxy-Resin Work Surfaces &
Sinks Mfr; Engineered Quartz, Granite &
Marble Stone Surface Products Mfr
N.A.I.C.S.: 326199
Adam Kalisz (Mgr-Sls & Mktg)

Subsidiary (Non-US):

Resopal GmbH **(4)**
Hans-Bockler Strasse 4, PO Box 1120,
64823, Gross-Umstadt, Germany **(100%)**
Tel.: (49) 6078800
Web Site: http://www.resopal.de
Sales Range: $250-299.9 Million
Emp.: 530
Surface Materials Mfr
N.A.I.C.S.: 325613
Tim Pearson (CEO)

Subsidiary (Domestic):

Wilsonart LLC **(4)**
2501 Wilson Dr, Temple, TX 76503-6110
Tel.: (254) 207-7000
Web Site: http://www.wilsonart.com
Decorative Laminate Products & Adhesives
Mfr & Distr
N.A.I.C.S.: 337110
Timothy J. O'Brien (Pres & CEO)

Plant (Domestic):

Wilsonart LLC - Boston **(5)**
29 Concord St, North Reading, MA 01864-
2601
Tel.: (978) 664-5230
Web Site: http://www.wilsonart.com
Sales Range: $300-349.9 Million
Laminates & Related Products Distr
N.A.I.C.S.: 337110
Timothy J. O'Brien (Grp Pres & CEO)

Wilsonart LLC - Tampa **(5)**
1210 N US Hwy 301 Ste C, Tampa, FL
33619-5332
Tel.: (813) 247-2502
Web Site: http://www.wilsonart.com
Sales Range: $10-24.9 Million
Emp.: 50
Laminates & Related Products Distr
N.A.I.C.S.: 449121

Wm Morrison Supermarkets PLC **(1)**
Hilmore House Gain Lane, Bradford, BD3
7DL, United Kingdom
Tel.: (44) 8456115000
Web Site:
http://www.morrisons-corporate.com
Rev.: $23,173,441,050
Assets: $13,139,358,748
Liabilities: $8,490,280,232
Net Worth: $4,649,078,516
Earnings: $65,639,990
Emp.: 104,813
Fiscal Year-end: 10/29/2023
Household Product Distr
N.A.I.C.S.: 445110
Andrew Thomas Higginson (Chm)
Michael Gleeson (CFO)

Subsidiary (Non-US):

**Bos Brothers Fruit And Vegetables
Bv** **(2)**
Amersgat 17, Hoek van Holland, 3151ZJ,
Netherlands
Tel.: (31) 174531444
Sales Range: $25-49.9 Million
Emp.: 50
Friuts & Vegetables Whslr
N.A.I.C.S.: 424480
Liz Taylor (Gen Mgr)

Subsidiary (Domestic):

Farmers Boy Limited **(2)**
Greenside Park Cemetary Rd, Bradford,
BD89RU, United Kingdom
Tel.: (44) 1274549222
General Grocery Products Mfr
N.A.I.C.S.: 424410

Wm Morrison Produce Limited **(2)**
Cutler Heights Lane, Bradford, BD4 9LR,
United Kingdom
Tel.: (44) 1274687202
Sales Range: $250-299.9 Million
Emp.: 600
Fruits & Vegetables Whslr
N.A.I.C.S.: 424480
Angela Lee Haigh (Coord-Shift)

CLAYTON-DAVIS & ASSOCI-
ATES, INCORPORATED

230 S Bemiston Ave Ste 1400, Clay-
ton, MO 63105-3643
Tel.: (314) 862-7800 **MO**
Year Founded: 1953
Rev.: $24,750,000
Emp.: 35
Advetising Agency
N.A.I.C.S.: 541810
Irvin Davis (Chm)
Adele K. Solit (Dir-Media & Space
Buyer)
Jennifer Davis (Pres)

CLBL, INC.

101 N Plains Indus Rd, Wallingford,
CT 06492-2360
Tel.: (203) 294-1648 **CT**
Web Site: http://www.cduniverse.com
Year Founded: 1996
Sales Range: $10-24.9 Million
Emp.: 20
Online CD Music Store
N.A.I.C.S.: 449210
Charles Beilman (Pres)

CLC CONSTRUCTION GROUP
INC.

5940 E Shields Ave Ste 101, Fresno,
CA 93727-8066
Tel.: (559) 277-8555
Web Site: http://www.clcinc.us
Year Founded: 1996

Sales Range: $1-9.9 Million
Emp.: 35
Construction, Engineering, Management & Design Firm
N.A.I.C.S.: 236210
Daniel Payne *(Founder & CEO)*
Sandy Slumberger *(CFO)*

CLEAN AIR ENGINEERING INC.
500 W Wood St, Palatine, IL 60067-4929
Tel.: (847) 991-3300
Web Site: https://www.cleanair.com
Sales Range: $10-24.9 Million
Emp.: 120
Air Pollution Measuring Service
N.A.I.C.S.: 541990
William I. Walker *(Pres & CEO)*
Allen Kephart *(Sr VP-Corp Sls & Mktg)*

CLEAN AIR GARDENING
2266 Monitor St, Dallas, TX 75207
Tel.: (214) 819-9500
Web Site:
    http://www.cleanairgardening.com
Year Founded: 1997
Rev.: $3,500,000
Emp.: 10
Retail Nurseries & Garden Supplies
N.A.I.C.S.: 444240
Steve Vesper *(Mgr)*
Lars Hundley *(Owner & Pres)*

CLEAN CONTROL CORPORATION
1040 Booth Rd, Warner Robins, GA 31088
Tel.: (478) 922-5340
Web Site:
    https://www.cleancontrol.com
Sales Range: $10-24.9 Million
Emp.: 100
Cleaning Product Mfr
N.A.I.C.S.: 325612
Stephen Davison *(Founder & Pres)*

CLEAN DESIGN, INC.
10 Laboratory Dr Bldg 2 Ste 200, Research Triangle Park, NC 27709
Tel.: (919) 544-2193
Web Site:
    http://www.cleandesign.com
Rev.: $15,000,000
Emp.: 18
Advertising, Brand Development & Integration, Digital/Interactive, Environmental, Graphic Design, Identity Marketing, Media Planning, Public Relations
N.A.I.C.S.: 541810
Natalie Perkins *(CEO)*
Bill Campbell *(VP & Brand Strategy Dir)*
Scott Scaggs *(VP & Dir-Creative)*
Jennifer Hazelett *(VP & Dir-Acct Mgmt)*
Dickens Sanchez *(Mgr-Client Relationship)*
Carrie Stewart *(Dir-Content Mktg & PR)*
Taylor Raasch *(Mgr-PR)*
Glen Fellman *(Dir-Experience Creative)*
Kate Benson *(Acct Mgr)*
Eleanor Talley *(Sr Acct Mgr)*
Lindsay Beavers *(Acct Dir)*
Jenna Bolognini *(Acct Coord)*
Ashley Casson *(Acct Coord)*
Diane Manoukian *(Acct Coord)*
Jenny Storey *(Coord-Social Media)*
Julianne Smith *(Assoc Dir-Creative)*
Travis Conte *(Assoc Dir-Strategy)*

CLEAN FUEL CONNECTION INC.
11800 Clark St, Arcadia, CA 91006
Tel.: (626) 445-1445
Web Site:
    http://www.cleanfuelconnection.com
Year Founded: 1999
Sales Range: $1-9.9 Million
Emp.: 5
Energy Consulting Services
N.A.I.C.S.: 541690
Enid Joffe *(Owner)*

CLEAN POWER FINANCE INC.
201 Mission St 11th Fl, San Francisco, CA 94105
Tel.: (866) 525-2123
Web Site:
    http://www.cleanpowerfinance.com
Sales Range: $50-74.9 Million
Emp.: 90
Solar Power System Software & Financing Services
N.A.I.C.S.: 522220
Alison Mickey *(Mgr-PR & Corp Comm)*
Nat Kreamer *(Pres & CEO)*
Rajiv Ghatalia *(Chm)*
Robert Prigge *(Chief Comml Officer)*
Adam Marsh *(Co-Founder)*
Nicholas Mack *(Gen Counsel, Sec & Sr VP)*
Micah Myers *(Sr VP-Corp Dev)*
Steve Olszewski *(Sr VP-Ops)*
Tom Harvey *(Sr VP-Sls)*
David Peterson *(Mng Dir-Renewable Capital Markets)*

CLEAN TEXTILE SYSTEMS INC.
51st & Avrr St, Pittsburgh, PA 15201
Tel.: (412) 681-7600
Web Site: http://www.clncare.com
Year Founded: 1933
Sales Range: $10-24.9 Million
Emp.: 210
Provider of Linen Supply Services
N.A.I.C.S.: 812331
Linda Burgman *(Gen Mgr-Distr)*
Woody Ostrow *(Pres)*
Ann Bate *(Controller)*

CLEAN THE WORLD FOUNDATION, INC.
400A Pittman St, Orlando, FL 32801
Tel.: (407) 574-8353
Web Site:
    http://www.cleantheworld.org
Year Founded: 2009
Sales Range: $1-9.9 Million
Emp.: 35
Respiratory Infection & Diarrheal Disease Illness & Death Prevention Services
N.A.I.C.S.: 624190
Shawn Seipler *(Pres & CEO)*
Oscar Gonzalez *(Dir-Partner Rels)*
Noel Alamo *(Mgr-Ops & Logistics)*

CLEAN VENTURE INC.
201 S 1st St, Elizabeth, NJ 07206
Tel.: (908) 355-5800
Web Site: http://www.cyclechem.com
Year Founded: 1977
Toxic Or Hazardous Waste Cleanup
N.A.I.C.S.: 562910
Debbie Scerbo *(Mgr-Sls & Mktg)*
Jesse Rivera *(Project Coord)*
Joseph Angelone *(Dir-Transportation Div)*
Jose Class *(Project Coord)*
Jarrod Hamilton *(Project Coord)*
Jeff Loeffler *(Project Coord)*
Allen Chodkiewicz *(Mgr-Corp Pur)*

Patrick McGovern *(Mgr-Ops)*
Jaime Fisher *(Office Mgr)*
Marvin Gallardo *(Supvr)*

CLEAN WATER SERVICES
2550 SW Hillsboro Hwy, Hillsboro, OR 97123
Tel.: (503) 681-3600   OR
Web Site:
    https://www.cleanwaterservices.org
Year Founded: 1970
Sales Range: $10-24.9 Million
Emp.: 311
Sewerage Systems; Public Utilities
N.A.I.C.S.: 921110
Bill Gaffi *(Gen Mgr)*
Mark Jockers *(Mgr-Govt & Pub Affairs)*
Mark Poling *(Dir-Bus Svcs Dept)*
Diane Taniguchi-Dennis *(Deputy Gen Mgr)*
Nate Cullen *(Dir-Wastewater Treatment Dept)*
Bruce Roll *(Dir-Watershed Mgmt Dept)*
Jerry Linder *(Gen Counsel)*
Kathy Leader *(Mgr-Fin)*

CLEANAIR SOLUTIONS, INC.
826 Bayridge Pl, Fairfield, CA 94534
Tel.: (707) 864-9499   CA
Web Site:
    https://www.cleanairspecialists.com
Year Founded: 1998
Sales Range: $1-9.9 Million
Cleanroom Systems Designer & Construction Services
N.A.I.C.S.: 236210
Kathie Kalafatis *(Pres & CEO)*

CLEANERS CLOSET INC.
4282 S 590 W, Salt Lake City, UT 84123
Tel.: (800) 660-5803
Web Site:
    http://www.interlinksupply.com
Carpet Cleaning Products & Restoration Equipment Distr
N.A.I.C.S.: 423440

Subsidiaries:

Allen Equipment, Inc.   (1)
600 S 56th St Ste 3, Chandler, AZ 85226-4207
Tel.: (480) 961-5307
Equipment Electrical Repair & Supplies Merchant Whslr
N.A.I.C.S.: 423850

CLEANGOAL ENERGY, CORP.
1717 N Bayshore Dr Ste 2831, Miami, FL 33132
Tel.: (786) 631-4174   DE
Web Site: http://www.cleangoal.com
Year Founded: 2015
Renewable Energy Consulting Services
N.A.I.C.S.: 541690
Bill MacGillivary *(Pres, CEO & COO)*
Kenneth Lelek *(CFO & Sec)*

CLEANHILL PARTNERS
430 Park Ave 19th Fl, New York, NY 10022
Tel.: (917) 631-7200
Web Site:
    https://cleanhillpartners.com
Year Founded: 2021
Holding Company
N.A.I.C.S.: 551112
Rakesh Wilson *(Mng Partner)*

Subsidiaries:

EPC Power Corp.   (1)
13100 Kirkham Way Ste 209, Poway, CA 92064-7128
Web Site: http://www.epcpower.com

Electronic Components Mfr
N.A.I.C.S.: 334419
Allan Abela *(Pres)*
Devin Dilley *(Co-Founder & CEO)*

CLEANING BUTLERS INTERNATIONAL, INC.
7341 Professional Pkwy E, Sarasota, FL 34240
Tel.: (941) 907-3200
Web Site:
    http://www.cleaningbutlers.com
Year Founded: 2009
Sales Range: $1-9.9 Million
Emp.: 7
Cleaning Service
N.A.I.C.S.: 561720
Lynne Dowd *(Founder & Pres)*

CLEANING SOLUTIONS, INC.
4080 Roger B Chaffee, Wyoming, MI 49548
Tel.: (616) 243-0555
Web Site:
    http://www.cleaningsolutionsinc.com
Year Founded: 1990
Sales Range: $10-24.9 Million
Emp.: 20
Chemicals Mfr
N.A.I.C.S.: 325320
Ronald Balk *(Pres)*
Vanessa Birman *(Controller)*
Sarah Gillette *(Dir-Sls & Mktg)*

CLEANSCAPES, INC.
117 S Main St Ste 300, Seattle, WA 98104
Tel.: (206) 859-6700   WA
Web Site:
    http://www.cleanscapes.com
Year Founded: 1997
Sales Range: $25-49.9 Million
Emp.: 260
Recycling, Garbage & Compost Collection Services
N.A.I.C.S.: 562998
Violet McDowell *(Controller)*
Kevin Kelly *(Mgr-Govt & Community Affairs)*
Erika Melroy *(Mgr-Govt & Community Affairs Grp)*
Quinn Apuzzo *(Mgr-Waste Zero)*
Todd Burnstein *(Mgr-Acct)*

CLEANTECH BIOFUELS, INC.
7386 Pershing Ave, Saint Louis, MO 63130
Tel.: (314) 862-8670   DE
Web Site:
    http://www.cleantechbiofuels.net
Year Founded: 2007
CLTH—(OTCIQ)
Sales Range: Less than $1 Million
Emp.: 4
Industrial Organic Chemicals
N.A.I.C.S.: 512250
Edward P. Hennessey Jr. *(CEO)*

CLEANTECH GROUP, INC.
33 New Montgomery St Ste 220, San Francisco, CA 94105
Tel.: (415) 233-9700   DE
Web Site: http://www.cleantech.com
Sales Range: $10-24.9 Million
Industry Research, Information & Environmental Consulting Services
N.A.I.C.S.: 519290
Sheeraz D. Haji *(CEO)*
Dave Couch *(VP-Fin)*

Subsidiaries:

GreenOrder, LLC   (1)
175 Varick St, New York, NY 10014
Tel.: (212) 725-4848
Web Site: http://www.greenorder.com
Sales Range: $1-9.9 Million
Emp.: 20

Cleantech Group, Inc.—(Continued)

Corporate Environmental Consulting Services
N.A.I.C.S.: 541620
Andrew L. Shapiro (Pres)

CLEANTECH OPEN
425 Broadway St, Redwood City, CA 94063
Tel.: (888) 989-6736   CA
Web Site:
http://www.cleantechopen.org
Year Founded: 2010
Sales Range: $1-9.9 Million
Emp.: 11
Energy & Environment Conservation Services
N.A.I.C.S.: 813312

CLEAR BLUE FINANCIAL HOLDINGS LLC
200 S College St Ste 2250, Charlotte, NC 28202
Tel.: (980) 299-9520   PR
Web Site:
http://www.clearblueinsurance.com
Holding Company; Specialty Property & Casualty Insurance Products & Services
N.A.I.C.S.: 551112
Jerome Breslin (Founder, Pres & CEO)
Jeffrey Downey (CFO)
Peter Klope (COO)
Jim Mann (Chief Risk Officer & Chief Underwriter)

Subsidiaries:

Clear Blue Insurance Services,
Inc.   (1)
200 S College St Ste 2250, Charlotte, NC 28202
Tel.: (980) 299-9520
Web Site:
http://www.clearblueinsurancegroup.com
Property & Casualty Insurance Services
N.A.I.C.S.: 524298
Jerome Breslin (Pres & CEO)
Jeffrey Downey (CFO)
Peter Klope (COO)
Jim Mann (Chief Risk Officer & Chief Underwriter)

Clear Blue Specialty Insurance
Company   (1)
200 S College St Ste 2250, Charlotte, NC 28202
Tel.: (980) 299-9520
Specialty Property & Casualty Insurance Products & Services
N.A.I.C.S.: 524126
Jerome Breslin (Pres & CEO)

CLEAR C2, INC.
724 Canyon Dr, Coppell, TX 75019
Tel.: (972) 304-7100
Web Site: https://www.clearc2.com
Year Founded: 1993
Sales Range: $25-49.9 Million
Emp.: 70
CRM, Sales Force Automation, Customer Support, Marketing & Campaign Management
N.A.I.C.S.: 513210
Darrell Dontje (Mgr-Outreach)

CLEAR HARBOR, LLC
3050 Royal Blvd S, Alpharetta, GA 30022
Tel.: (678) 566-3212
Web Site: http://www.clearharbor.biz
Year Founded: 2004
Sales Range: $1-9.9 Million
Emp.: 556
Business & Technical Support Solutions
N.A.I.C.S.: 561499

Lee Waters (Founder)
Tut Smith (Co-Founder & Pres-Bus Dev)
Grey Wood (CEO)
Brian Lambert (COO)
Stacey Kissel (Dir-Client Mgmt)
Mary Quinones (Gen Mgr-Dominica)
Jeff Malchow (Gen Mgr-Grenada)

CLEAR INVESTIGATIVE ADVANTAGE, LLC.
2801 Internet Blvd Ste 101, Frisco, TX 75034
Tel.: (214) 382-2727
Web Site:
http://www.ciaresearch.com
Sales Range: $1-9.9 Million
Emp.: 11
Private Investigation Services
N.A.I.C.S.: 561611
Jason Johnston (Co-Founder & CEO)
Chris Wilson (Co-Founder & Pres)

CLEAR TECHNOLOGIES, INC.
1199 S Belt Line Rd, Coppell, TX 75019
Tel.: (972) 906-7500
Web Site:
http://www.cleartechnologies.net
Year Founded: 1993
Sales Range: $25-49.9 Million
Emp.: 50
Installer of Hardware & Software; Computer Maintenance
N.A.I.C.S.: 449210
James W. Hargis (CEO)
Mickey Patton (Pres/COO-C2 Div)
William Van Symons (COO)
Greg Colley (Founder)
Jim Ballard (VP-Pro Svcs)

CLEAR TOUCH INTERACTIVE, INC.
1100 Thousand Oaks Blvd, Greenville, SC 29607
Tel.: (864) 973-7973
Web Site:
http://www.getcleartouch.com
Year Founded: 2012
Sales Range: $25-49.9 Million
Emp.: 34
Software Development Services
N.A.I.C.S.: 541511
Keone Trask (Pres & CEO)

CLEAR VIEW BAG CO. INC.
5 Burdick Dr, Albany, NY 12205
Tel.: (518) 458-7153
Web Site:
http://www.clearviewbag.com
Rev.: $12,000,000
Emp.: 80
Polyethylene Film
N.A.I.C.S.: 326113
Lloyd Taylor (Supvr-Maintenance)

CLEARABILITY, INC.
5630 Weatherby Dr, Columbia, MD 21046
Tel.: (410) 635-8519
Web Site: http://www.clearability.com
Year Founded: 2007
Sales Range: $1-9.9 Million
Emp.: 14
Network, Systems & Software Engineering & Administration
N.A.I.C.S.: 541715
David Hall (CEO)
Brian Middleton (Engr-Systems)
Tom Whartenby (COO)

CLEARAVENUE, LLC
939 Elkridge Landing Rd Ste 195, Linthicum, MD 21090
Tel.: (410) 999-6403

Web Site:
http://www.clearavenue.com
Year Founded: 2002
Sales Range: $1-9.9 Million
Emp.: 22
Systems Integration, Software Development & Infrastructure Services
N.A.I.C.S.: 519290
Harini S. Kankanahalli (Pres)
Srinivas Kankanahalli (CTO & Exec VP-Engrg)

CLEARBRIDGE TECHNOLOGY GROUP
6 Fortune Dr, Billerica, MA 01821
Tel.: (781) 916-2284
Web Site:
https://www.clearbridgetech.com
Year Founded: 2005
Sales Range: $10-24.9 Million
Emp.: 100
Specialists in Technology & Staffing Services
N.A.I.C.S.: 561311
Joseph Wetmore (Co-Founder & Pres-Sls & Ops)
Tim Powell (Co-Founder & Pres-Ops)
Jennifer Wetmore (Dir-Fin)
Amber Giove (Mgr-HR)

CLEARCAPITAL.COM, INC.
10875 Pioneer Trl, Truckee, CA 96161
Tel.: (530) 550-2500
Web Site:
http://www.clearcapital.com
Year Founded: 2001
Sales Range: $50-74.9 Million
Emp.: 315
Online Real Estate Services
N.A.I.C.S.: 531390
Duane Andrews (Co-Founder & CEO)
Kevin Marshall (Co-Founder & Pres)
Kenon Chen (Exec VP-Product & Data)
Luke Frederick (Exec VP-Ops)
Sarah Lambert (VP-HR)
Helge Richard Hukari (Gen Counsel)
Dave Newell (Mgr-Customer Dev)
Jim Smith (Sr VP-Customer Dev-Natl)
Jeff Allen (Exec VP-Valuation Strategy)
Larry Robinson (CTO)
Tim O'Brien (Gen Mgr-Appraisal Ops)
Sarah Hartshorn (Dir-Mktg)
Ron Rowan (CFO)
Sheila Ryan (Chief People Officer)

CLEARCORRECT, INC.
15151 Sommermeyer St, Houston, TX 77041-5332
Tel.: (713) 850-0136
Web Site:
http://www.clearcorrect.com
Year Founded: 2006
Sales Range: $1-9.9 Million
Emp.: 130
Mfr of Custom, Removable Dental Braces
N.A.I.C.S.: 339114
Jarrett Pumphrey (CEO)
Edward W. Hlousek (CFO)

CLEARCUBE TECHNOLOGY, INC.
8834 Capital of Texas Hwy N, Austin, TX 78759
Tel.: (512) 652-3500
Web Site: http://www.clearcube.com
Year Founded: 1997
Sales Range: $25-49.9 Million
Emp.: 160
Computer Mfr
N.A.I.C.S.: 334118

Kirk Powell (Pres & CEO)
Matt Straiter (Dir-Federal Sls)
Ray DuPont (Dir-Engrg)
Scott Laughland (Dir-Matls)

CLEAREDGE IT SOLUTIONS, LLC.
10620 Guilford Rd Ste 200, Annapolis Junction, MD 20794
Tel.: (443) 212-4700
Web Site:
https://www.clearedgeit.com
Year Founded: 2002
Sales Range: $10-24.9 Million
Emp.: 66
Information Technology Services
N.A.I.C.S.: 541512
Christine Puglisi (Founder & Principal)
Martin O'Neill (COO)
Philip Marshall (Dir-Programs)

CLEARENT LLC
11330 Olive Blvd Ste 200, Creve Coeur, MO 63141
Tel.: (314) 732-0515
Web Site: http://www.clearent.com
Year Founded: 2005
Payment Processing Services
N.A.I.C.S.: 522320
Dan Geraty (Founder & Chm)
Mark Sundt (CTO)
Melinda Vedder (Sr VP-HR)
Matthew Morrow (Chief Revenue Officer)
Brent Coles (CFO)

Subsidiaries:

SPOT Business Systems, LLC.   (1)
12345 S 300 E, Draper, UT 84020-8790
Tel.: (801) 495-1200
Web Site: http://www.spotpos.com
Software Publisher
N.A.I.C.S.: 513210
Mark Jones (VP-Ops)
Thomas Beidle (Gen Mgr)
Toran Brown (Mgr-Product)
Jeff Bunker (Mgr-Tech Ops)
Tina Vuu (Dir-Fin)
Craig Johnson (VP-Tech)

CLEARFIELD BANK & TRUST CO.
11 N 2nd St, Clearfield, PA 16830
Tel.: (814) 765-7551
Web Site: http://www.cbtfinancial.com
Year Founded: 1902
Sales Range: $10-24.9 Million
Emp.: 100
Retail & Commercial Banking
N.A.I.C.S.: 522110
William A. Shiner (Chief Risk Officer, Sec, Sr VP & Mgr-HR)
Richard W. Ogden (CFO & Exec VP)
Debra Bowser (Asst VP & Mgr-Community)
Kristi J. Johnson (Asst VP & Mgr-Mortgage)
William E. Wood (Chm, Pres & CEO)

CLEARFLY COMMUNICATIONS
450 Townsend St Fl 1 Rm 100, San Francisco, CA 94107-1510
Tel.: (866) 652-7520
Web Site: http://www.clearfly.net
Year Founded: 2007
Telecommunication Servicesb
N.A.I.C.S.: 517810
Vivek Khuller (Pres & CEO)

CLEARFORK MIDSTREAM LLC
5049 Edwards Ranch Rd Fl 4, Fort Worth, TX 76109
Tel.: (817) 752-5305   TX
Web Site:
http://www.clearforkmidstream.com

Year Founded: 2020
Midstream Solutions Services for Oil & Gas Industry
N.A.I.C.S.: 213112
Kipper Overstreet *(CEO)*
Corey Lothamer *(Chief Comml Officer)*
Kevin Venturini *(Exec VP)*
George Grau Jr. *(COO)*

Subsidiaries:

Azure Midstream Energy LLC   (1)
12377 Merit Dr Ste 300, Dallas, TX 75251
Tel.: (972) 674-5200
Web Site: http://www.azuremidstream.com
Natural Gas Gathering, Processing & Pipeline Transportation Services
N.A.I.C.S.: 486210
Victor B. Davis *(VP-Ops)*
Dennie W. Dixon *(VP-Engrg)*
David F. Garrett *(VP-Comml)*
I. J. Berthelot II *(Pres)*

CLEARHAVEN PARTNERS LP

46F 200 Claredon St, Boston, MA 02116
Tel.: (617) 221-7721
Web Site:
http://www.clearhavenpartners.com
Privater Equity Firm
N.A.I.C.S.: 523999
Bill Hannon *(CFO & Chief Compliance Officer)*
Kevin Wood *(Co-Founder & Operating Partner)*
Michelle Noon *(Co-Founder & Mng Partner)*

Subsidiaries:

SundaySky Inc.   (1)
229 W 36th St 2nd Fl, New York, NY 10018
Tel.: (212) 929-8111
Web Site: http://www.sundaysky.com
Sales Range: $1-9.9 Million
Emp.: 90
Webcasting Software
N.A.I.C.S.: 513210
Shmulik Weller *(Co-Founder & Pres)*
Yaniv Axen *(Co-Founder & CTO)*
Guy Atzmon *(Sr VP-Creative & Industry Solutions)*
Dror Harel *(Sr VP-Ops)*
Ben Reich *(VP-R&D)*
Mark Flaharty *(COO-Adv)*
Ayal Shiran *(Chm)*
Eric Porres *(CMO)*
Jim Dicso *(CEO)*
Glen Sussman *(CFO)*
Seth Marlowe *(Sr VP-NA Sls & Customer Success)*

Subsidiary (Non-US):

SundaySky Israel   (2)
24 Raoul Wallenberg St Bldg B, 69719, Tel Aviv, Israel
Tel.: (972) 73 7912777
Web Site: http://www.sundaysky.com
Webcasting Software
N.A.I.C.S.: 513210
Moran Avisar *(Gen Mgr)*

TimeTrade Systems, Inc.   (1)
100 Crosby Dr, Bedford, MA 01730
Tel.: (781) 541-5800
Web Site: http://www.timetrade.com
Wired Telecommunications Carriers
N.A.I.C.S.: 517111
John Loring *(Co-Founder)*
Gary Ambrosino *(Pres)*
Rip Haak *(CFO & Sr VP)*
William Clark *(CEO)*

CLEARINGHOUSE COMMUNITY DEVELOPMENT FINANCIAL INSTITUTION

23861 El Toro Rd Ste 401, Lake Forest, CA 92630
Tel.: (949) 859-3600   CA
Web Site:
http://www.clearinghousecdfi.com
Year Founded: 1996

Sales Range: $25-49.9 Million
Emp.: 42
Financial Services
N.A.I.C.S.: 523999
Douglas J. Bystry *(Pres & CEO)*
Andrew W. Gordon *(Pres-Arizona Market)*
Jay Harrison *(CIO)*
Kristy Ollendorff *(Chief Credit Officer)*
Terrin Enssle *(CFO)*

CLEARLAKE CAPITAL GROUP, L.P.

233 Wilshire Blvd Ste 800, Santa Monica, CA 90401
Tel.: (310) 400-8800   DE
Web Site: https://clearlake.com
Year Founded: 2006
Privater Equity Firm
N.A.I.C.S.: 523999
Prashant Mehrotra *(Partner)*
Behdad Eghbali *(Co-Founder & Mng Partner)*
James Pade *(Partner & Mng Dir)*
Jose E. Feliciano *(Co-Founder & Mng Partner)*
Paul Huber *(Mng Dir)*
Colin M. Leonard *(Partner)*

Subsidiaries:

Alteryx, Inc.   (1)
3347 Michelson Dr Ste 400, Irvine, CA 92612
Web Site: https://www.alteryx.com
Rev.: $970,000,000
Assets: $1,912,000,000
Liabilities: $1,722,000,000
Net Worth: $190,000,000
Earnings: ($179,000,000)
Emp.: 2,300
Fiscal Year-end: 12/31/2023
Data Analytics Software Developer
N.A.I.C.S.: 513210
Christopher Natali *(Interim CFO)*
Deven Parekh *(Partner-Insight)*
Boris Treskunov *(Partner-Insight)*
Amir Ravandoust *(Partner-Insight)*
Mark Anderson *(CEO)*
Edward P. Harding Jr. *(Founder)*

Subsidiary (Non-US):

Alteryx Czech Republic s.r.o.   (2)
Havlickova 1029/3, 110 00, Prague, Czech Republic
Tel.: (420) 777571433
Data Analytics & Software Publisher
N.A.I.C.S.: 513210

Alteryx GmbH   (2)
Tel.: (49) 8992561966
Web Site: http://www.alteryx.com
Data Analytics & Software Publisher
N.A.I.C.S.: 513210

Subsidiary (Domestic):

Lore IO, Inc.   (2)
100 S Murphy Ave Ste 200, Sunnyvale, CA 94086
Tel.: (408) 256-1521
Web Site: https://www.getlore.io
Computer Programming Services
N.A.I.C.S.: 541511
Digvijay Lamba *(CEO & Founder)*
Bill Chickering *(CTO)*
Steven Dozen *(Head-Marketing)*
Praveen Dua *(Head)*
Maurin Lenglart *(Head)*

Subsidiary (Non-US):

Trifacta GmbH   (2)
Neue Grunstrasse 17-18, 10179, Berlin, Germany
Tel.: (49) 22168943009
Software Services
N.A.I.C.S.: 541511

Subsidiary (Domestic):

Trifacta, Inc.   (2)
575 Market St 11th Fl, San Francisco, CA 94105
Tel.: (415) 226-4252

Web Site: https://www.trifacta.com
Data Processing Services
N.A.I.C.S.: 518210

BBB Industries LLC   (1)
29627 Renaissance Blvd, Daphne, AL 36526
Tel.: (251) 438-2737
Web Site: http://www.bbbind.com
Sales Range: $10-24.9 Million
Emp.: 50
Motor Vehicle Replacement Parts Mfr & Distr
N.A.I.C.S.: 336390
Jeff Bigler *(Exec VP)*
Tom Rae *(Product Mgr)*
John Boyer *(VP-Product & Category Mgmt)*
Joshua McCabe *(Dir-Category Mgmt-Dallas)*
Timothy Roth *(Exec VP-Bus Dev & Strategy)*
Don Garrett *(VP-Pur & Supplier Dev)*
Christopher Garner *(Exec VP-Sls)*
Joe Bergsieker *(VP-Sls-Chicago)*
Mark Nugent *(Sr Dir-Bus Dev)*
Michael Hansen *(CFO & Exec VP)*
Ross Bratlee *(Chief Transformation Officer & Exec VP)*
Duncan Gillis *(CEO)*
Russ Schinzing *(VP-Electronics)*
John Amyot *(Exec VP-CV, OES & New Product Dev)*
Gonzalo Cajade *(Chief People Officer & Exec VP)*
John B. Smart III *(Pres & Chief Comml Officer)*

Subsidiary (Domestic):

Hydraulex International Holdings Ltd.   (2)
48175 Gratiot Ave, Chesterfield, MI 48051
Tel.: (586) 949-4240
Web Site: http://www.hydraulex.com
Holding Company
N.A.I.C.S.: 551112
Shirish Pareek *(CEO)*

Subsidiary (Domestic):

Attica Hydraulic Exchange, Inc.   (3)
48175 Gratiot Ave, Chesterfield, MI 48051
Tel.: (586) 949-4240
Web Site: http://www.ahx1.com
Hydraulic Equipment Mfr
N.A.I.C.S.: 423830
Sam Caruso *(VP-Supply Chain)*

Flint Hydrostatics, Inc.   (3)
4084 E Shelby Dr, Memphis, TN 38118
Tel.: (901) 794-2462
Web Site: http://www.flinthydrostatics.com
Pump & Pumping Equipment Mfr
N.A.I.C.S.: 333914
Mike Lambard *(Mgr-Sls)*

Hydraulic Repair and Design, Inc.   (3)
701 N Levee Rd, Puyallup, WA 98371
Tel.: (253) 604-0400
Web Site: http://www.h-r-d.com
Hydraulic Pump Repair Services
N.A.I.C.S.: 811310

Metaris Corp.   (3)
1519 Hwy 35 N, Forest, MS 39074
Tel.: (601) 469-1987
Hydraulic Pump Distr
N.A.I.C.S.: 423830

Subsidiary (Non-US):

Metaris, Inc.   (4)
101 Canarctic Dr, Toronto, M3J 2N7, ON, Canada
Tel.: (416) 638-6000
Web Site: http://www.metaris.com
Emp.: 40
Hydraulic Pump Distr
N.A.I.C.S.: 423830
Steve Smith *(Mgr-Product Dev)*

Bluefly, Inc.   (1)
42 W 39th St 9th Fl, New York, NY 10018-3809
Tel.: (212) 944-8000
Web Site: http://www.bluefly.com
Rev.: $93,444,000
Assets: $36,543,000
Liabilities: $31,606,000

Net Worth: $4,937,000
Earnings: ($24,911,000)
Emp.: 80
Fiscal Year-end: 12/31/2012
Online Apparel & Home Accessories Retailer
N.A.I.C.S.: 458110
Melissa Payner *(Chief Mdsg Officer)*
Neel Grover *(Co-Chm & CEO)*
Sharon French *(COO)*
Tony Barnes *(CTO)*

Chelsea FC plc   (1)
Stamford Bridge Fulham Road, London, SW6 1HS, United Kingdom
Tel.: (44) 3718111955
Web Site: http://www.chelseafc.com
Holding Company; Professional Soccer Club & Sports Arena Operator
N.A.I.C.S.: 551112
Bruce Buck *(Chm)*
Todd Boehly *(Chm)*
David Barnard *(Dir-Football Ops)*

Subsidiary (Domestic):

Chelsea Football Club Limited   (2)
Stamford Bridge Fulham Road, London, SW6 1HS, United Kingdom
Tel.: (44) 2073869373
Web Site: http://www.chelseafc.com
Professional Soccer Club
N.A.I.C.S.: 711211
Bruce Buck *(Chm)*
Chris Alexander *(Dir-Fin & Ops)*
David Barnard *(Sec & Dir-Admin-Football Dept)*
Gary Twelvetree *(Dir-Mktg)*
Guy Laurence *(CEO)*
Paul Winstanley *(Dir-Global Talent & Transfers)*
Todd Boehly *(Chm & Owner)*

Constant Contact, Inc.   (1)
Reservoir Pl 1601 Trapelo Rd, Waltham, MA 02451
Tel.: (781) 472-8100
Web Site: http://www.constantcontact.com
Web-Based Services for E-Mail Marketing Campaigns
N.A.I.C.S.: 561499
Jonathan Kateman *(Gen Mgr)*

Cornerstone OnDemand, Inc.   (1)
1601 Cloverfield Blvd Ste 620 S, Santa Monica, CA 90404
Tel.: (310) 752-0200
Web Site:
http://www.cornerstoneondemand.com
Rev.: $740,916,000
Assets: $2,134,569,000
Liabilities: $1,865,695,000
Net Worth: $268,874,000
Earnings: ($39,982,000)
Emp.: 2,900
Fiscal Year-end: 12/31/2020
Learning & Talent Management Software & Services
N.A.I.C.S.: 513210
Himanshu Palsule *(CEO)*
Mark Goldin *(CTO)*
Mark Goldin *(CTO)*
Vincent Belliveau *(Chief International Officer)*
Adam Weiss *(Chief Admin Officer & Gen Counsel)*
Jeffrey Lautenbach *(Pres-Field Ops-Global)*
Kimberly Cassady *(Chief Talent Officer)*
Patricia Coughlin *(Chief Acctg Officer)*
Heidi Spirgi *(Chief Strategy & Growth Officer)*
Ajay Awatramani *(Chief Product Officer)*
Duane La Bom *(Chief Diversity Officer)*
Karen Williams *(Sr VP-Customer Support & Svcs)*
Theresa Damato *(CMO)*
Jeff Miller *(Chief Learning Officer)*
Bernd Leger *(CMO)*
Himanshu Palsule *(CEO)*
Ryan Courson *(CFO)*

Subsidiary (Non-US):

Cornerstone OnDemand Limited   (2)
4 Coleman Street, London, EC2R 5AR, United Kingdom
Tel.: (44) 2037002900
Web Site:
http://www.cornerstoneondemand.co.uk

Clearlake Capital Group, L.P.—(Continued)

Sales Range: $10-24.9 Million
Emp.: 2
Prepackaged Software Services
N.A.I.C.S.: 513210
Vincent Belliveau (CEO-EMEA)

Subsidiary (Domestic):

Grovo Learning Inc. (2)
50 W 23rd St, New York, NY 10010
Tel.: (212) 924-2579
Web Site: http://www.grovo.com
Education Services
N.A.I.C.S.: 611710

Subsidiary (Non-US):

Saba Software Sp. z o.o. (2)
High5ive Building 5 Pawia 23, 31-154, Krakow, Poland
Tel.: (48) 223070606
Software Development Services
N.A.I.C.S.: 541511

Subsidiary (Domestic):

Saba Software, Inc. (2)
4120 Dublin Blvd Ste 200, Dublin, CA 94568
Tel.: (650) 581-2500
Web Site: http://www.saba.com
People Management Software Products & Services
N.A.I.C.S.: 334610

Subsidiary (Non-US):

Lumesse Limited (3)
475 The Boulevard, Capability Green, Luton, LU1 3LU, United Kingdom
Tel.: (44) 1582 816555
Web Site: http://www.lumesse.com
Sales Range: $125-149.9 Million
Human Resources Software Publishers
N.A.I.C.S.: 513210

Subsidiary (US):

Lumesse, Inc. (4)
2705 Bee Cave Rd Ste 160, Austin, TX 78746
Tel.: (512) 600-9300
Web Site: http://www.lumesse.us
Sales Range: $25-49.9 Million
Emp.: 16
Human Resources Software Publishers
N.A.I.C.S.: 513210

Subsidiary (Non-US):

Saba Software (UK) Ltd. (3)
Circa Building The Ring, Bracknell, RG12 1AA, Berks, United Kingdom
Tel.: (44) 1344382950
Web Site: http://www.saba.com
Emp.: 60
Assessment Consulting Services
N.A.I.C.S.: 541612

Saba Software GmbH (3)
Nymphenburger Strasse 4, 80335, Munich, Germany
Tel.: (49) 89208027380
Web Site: http://www.saba.com
Emp.: 15
Organization Development Consulting Services
N.A.I.C.S.: 541612

Subsidiary (Domestic):

SumTotal Systems LLC (2)
2850 NW 43rd St Ste 150, Gainesville, FL 32606
Tel.: (352) 264-2800
Web Site: http://www.sumtotalsystems.com
Infrastructure Software Products & Services
N.A.I.C.S.: 513210
John Ambross (Gen Mgr)

Branch (Domestic):

SumTotal Systems - Parsippany (3)
600 Parsippany Rd, Parsippany, NJ 07054-4274
Tel.: (973) 364-0480
Sales Range: $25-49.9 Million
Workforce & Expense Management Software Developer
N.A.I.C.S.: 513210

Morne P. Swart (VP-Product Mgmt)

SumTotal Systems - West Des Moines (3)
5550 Wild Rose Ln Ste 200, West Des Moines, IA 50266
Tel.: (515) 222-9903
Sales Range: $50-74.9 Million
Learning Management Software
N.A.I.C.S.: 513210
Todd Premo (Dir-Product Mgmt)

DigiCert, Inc. (1)
2801 N Thanksgiving Way Ste 500, Lehi, UT 84043
Tel.: (801) 701-9600
Web Site: http://www.digicert.com
Software Publisher
N.A.I.C.S.: 513210
Flavio Martins (COO)
Chris Call (Engr-Support)
Jeremy Rowley (Exec VP-Emerging Markets)
John Merrill (CEO)
Sue Allen (Office Mgr)
Eric Porter (VP-Fin & Admin)
Mike Nelson (VP-Healthcare Solutions)
Michael Olson (CFO)
Jeff Chandler (Dir-PR)
Alan Raymond (VP-Sls)
Jason Sabin (CTO)
Benjamin T. Wilson (VP-Compliance & Indus Rels)
Mark Packham (VP-Mktg)
Mike Johnson (Gen Counsel)
Amit Sinha (Pres & CEO)

Subsidiary (Domestic):

Mocana Corporation (2)
1735 N 1st St Ste 306, San Jose, CA 94104
Tel.: (415) 617-0055
Web Site: http://www.mocana.com
Software Publisher
N.A.I.C.S.: 513210
Brian Nugent (Chm)
Dave Smith (Chief Revenue Officer)
Hope Frank (CMO & Chief Digital Officer)
Jeanne Pardo (CFO)
W. William Diotte (CEO)
Srinivas Kumar (CTO)

Subsidiary (Non-US):

Mocana Solutions Private Limited (3)
10 Shreeniwas Classic 273/1/1+2/1 Baner, Pune, 411 045, Maharashtra, India
Tel.: (91) 20 27291608
Software Publisher
N.A.I.C.S.: 513210

Discovery Education, Inc. (1)
1560 Sherman Ave Ste 100, Evanston, IL 60201
Tel.: (800) 323-9084
Web Site:
  http://www.discoveryeducation.com
Standards-based Digital Content
N.A.I.C.S.: 516120
Marty Creel (Chief Academic Officer & VP-Curriculum & Instruction)
Erick Lang (Sr Dir-Digital Learning)
Mark J. Stout (Dir-Global Curriculum)
Robin Porter (Sr Dir-Digital Content)
Jamie Jenkins (Mgr-Instructional Design)
Lisa Katz (Sr Dir-Res & Analysis)
Camsie McAdams (Dir-STEM Curriculum)
Amy Gensemer (Dir-Science Instruction)
Patrick Vennebush (Dir-Mathematics)
Jeremy Cowdrey (CEO)

Subsidiary (Non-US):

Discovery Education Europe Ltd. (2)
Hythe House 200 Shepherds Bush Road, London, W6 7NL, United Kingdom
Tel.: (44) 2078704500
Web Site:
  http://www.discoveryeducation.co.uk
Broadcasting Services
N.A.I.C.S.: 516210

Subsidiary (Domestic):

Dream Box Learning Inc. (2)
305 108th Ave Ne Ste 200, Bellevue, WA 98004-5706
Tel.: (425) 637-8900

Web Site: http://www.dreambox.com
Educational Software Publisher
N.A.I.C.S.: 513210
Jessie Woolley-Wilson (CEO)
Jessie Woolley-Wilson (CEO)

Subsidiary (Domestic):

Taylor Associates/Communications, Inc. (3)
200 E 2nd St Ste 2, Huntington Station, NY 11746
Tel.: (631) 549-3000
Web Site: http://www.ta-comm.com
Sales Range: $1-9.9 Million
Emp.: 20
Computer System Design Services
N.A.I.C.S.: 541512
Alexandra Spichtig (Dir-Product Dev)
Karen Feller (Chief Academic Officer)
Karl Hummel (Dir-Sls)
Kelly Scannell (COO)
Mark Taylor (CEO)
Rick Cusick (CIO)

Edwards Building Center, Inc. (1)
33636 Highway 6, Edwards, CO 81632
Tel.: (970) 926-3381
Web Site:
  http://edwardsbuildingcenterinc.net
Hardware Stores; Batteries, Chainsaw & Trimmers
N.A.I.C.S.: 444140

Endurance International Group Holdings, Inc. (1)
10 Corporate Dr Ste 3000, Burlington, MA 01803
Tel.: (781) 852-3200
Web Site: http://www.endurance.com
Rev.: $1,113,278,000
Assets: $2,584,086,000
Liabilities: $2,387,132,000
Net Worth: $196,954,000
Earnings: ($12,347,000)
Emp.: 3,762
Fiscal Year-end: 12/31/2019
Holding Company; Internet Hosting & Back-End Technologies Support Services
N.A.I.C.S.: 551112
David C. Bryson (Chief Legal Officer-Endurance International Group)
James C. Neary (Chm)
Tom Aurelio (Chief HR Officer-Endurance International Group)
Christine Timmins Barry (COO-Web Presence Brands)
Timothy R. Oakes (Chief Acctg Officer)
Jeffrey H. Fox (Pres & CEO)
Allen M. Chaves Jr. (CTO-Endurance International Group)

Subsidiary (Domestic):

Bluehost Inc. (2)
1958 S 950 E, Provo, UT 84606
Tel.: (801) 765-9400
Web Site: http://www.bluehost.com
Internet Hosting Services
N.A.I.C.S.: 518210

FastDomain Inc. (2)
1958 S 950 E, Provo, UT 84606
Tel.: (801) 765-9400
Web Site: http://www.fastdomain.com
Internet Hosting Services
N.A.I.C.S.: 518210
Marc Montagner (CFO)
James Grierson (VP-Bus Dev)
David Bryson (Chief Legal Officer)
Hari Ravichandran (CEO)
Katie Forsgren (Mgr-Affiliate)

HostGator.com LLC (2)
11251 NW Fwy Ste 400, Houston, TX 77092
Tel.: (713) 574-5287
Web Site: http://www.hostgator.com
Internet Hosting Services
N.A.I.C.S.: 518210

Newfold Digital Inc. (2)
5335 Gate Pkwy, Jacksonville, FL 32256
Web Site: https://newfold.com
Data Processing, Hosting & Related Services
N.A.I.C.S.: 518210
Sharon T. Rowlands (Pres & CEO)

Subsidiary (Domestic):

MarkMonitor Inc. (3)

50 California St Ste 200, San Francisco, CA 94111
Tel.: (415) 278-8400
Web Site: http://www.markmonitor.com
Domain Management Services
N.A.I.C.S.: 541511

Subsidiary (Domestic):

The Endurance International Group, Inc. (2)
10 Corporate Dr, Burlington, MA 01803
Tel.: (781) 852-3200
Web Site: http://www.endurance.com
Sales Range: $400-449.9 Million
Internet Hosting & Back-End Technologies Support Services
N.A.I.C.S.: 541519
Hari K. Ravichandran (Founder & CEO)
Katherine J. Andreasen (Chief Admin Officer)
Jean McCarthy (Sr VP-Mktg)
David C. Bryson (Chief Legal Officer)
James C. Neary (CFO)
Mitchell Haber (Sr VP-Partnerships-Global)

Entelos, Inc. (1)
2 Waters Park Dr Ste 200, San Mateo, CA 94403
Tel.: (650) 572-5400
Web Site: http://www.entelos.com
Sales Range: $10-24.9 Million
Pharmaceutical Development Services
N.A.I.C.S.: 541715
Alex L. Bangs (Co-Founder & CTO)
Thomas Paterson (Co-Founder)

Futuris Pty. Ltd. (1)
80 Turner Street, Port Melbourne, Melbourne, 3207, VIC, Australia
Tel.: (61) 396444222
Web Site: http://www.futurisgroup.com
Emp.: 5,000
Holding Company; Automotive Interior Components Designer, Mfr & Whslr
N.A.I.C.S.: 551112
Mark G. De Wit (Mng Dir)

Subsidiary (US):

CNI Enterprises, Inc. (2)
1451 E Lincoln Ave, Madison Heights, MI 48071
Tel.: (248) 586-3300
Web Site: http://www.cniinc.cc
Sales Range: $25-49.9 Million
Emp.: 300
Automotive Interior Trim Components Mfr & Whslr
N.A.I.C.S.: 336360
Jorge J. Morales (Pres & CEO)
Paul Olinzock (VP-Sls)

Subsidiary (Domestic):

Futuris Automotive Interiors (Australia) Pty. Ltd. (2)
80 Turner Street, Port Melbourne, 3207, VIC, Australia
Tel.: (61) 396444222
Web Site: http://www.futurisautomotive.com
Sales Range: $50-74.9 Million
Automotive Interior Design & Mfr
N.A.I.C.S.: 336360
Mark G. De Wit (Mng Dir)
David Chutter (CMO)

Subsidiary (Non-US):

Futuris Automotive Interiors Trading (Shanghai) Co. Ltd. (2)
No 228 Room 305-308 Meiyuan Road, Shanghai, 200070, China
Tel.: (86) 2161670838
Web Site:
  http://www.futurisautomotive.com.cn
Sales Range: $25-49.9 Million
Emp.: 35
Automotive Interior Distr
N.A.I.C.S.: 423120
Ross Mahon (COO-China & India)

GlobeLTR Energy, Inc. (1)
306 W Wall St Ste 900, Midland, TX 79701
Tel.: (432) 218-7888
Web Site: http://www.globetrenergy.com
Emp.: 1,250

Holding Company; Oilfield Services
N.A.I.C.S.: 551112
Keith Muncy (CFO)
Troy Burton (COO-Globe Enerrgy Svcs)
Patrick Bond (Co-CEO)
Philip Wright (Sec & Exec VP)
Troy Botts Jr. (Co-CEO)

Subsidiary (Domestic):

Globe Energy Services, LLC (2)
3204 W Hwy 180, Snyder, TX 79549
Tel.: (325) 573-1310
Web Site:
http://www.globeenergyservices.com
Oil & Gas Field Support Services
N.A.I.C.S.: 213112
Philip Wright (Exec VP)
Troy Burton (COO)
Mike Hughes (Pres-Tech Mgmt)
Zeb Alexander (VP-HR)
Ricky Harper (VP-Fishing & Rental)
Kenneth Porter (VP-Well Servicing)
Jason Taylor (VP-Completion Sys)
Mark Zimmerman (VP-Bus Dev)
Danny Sanders (Dir-Fluid Svcs)
Troy Botts Jr. (Founder, Pres & CEO)

Light Tower Rentals, LLC (2)
2330 E I-20 S Service Rd, Odessa, TX
79766-8842
Tel.: (432) 530-3330
Web Site: http://www.lighttowerrentals.com
Commercial & Industrial Machinery &
Equipment Rental & Leasing
N.A.I.C.S.: 532490
Justin Builta (Branch Mgr)

Intertape Polymer Group Inc. (1)
9999 Cavendish Blvd Suite 200, Ville Saint
Laurent, H4M 2X5, QC, Canada
Tel.: (941) 739-7574
Rev.: $1,531,469,000
Assets: $1,333,752,000
Liabilities: $981,504,000
Net Worth: $352,248,000
Earnings: $70,005,000
Emp.: 4,100
Fiscal Year-end: 12/31/2021
Specialized Polyolefin Plastic & Paper
Packaging Products Developer & Mfr
N.A.I.C.S.: 322220
Jeffrey Crystal (CFO)
Joseph Tocci (Sr VP-Sourcing-Global &
Supply Chain)
Douglas Nalette (Sr VP-Ops)
Shawn Nelson (Sr VP-Sls)
Peter C. Durette (CEO)
Randi Booth (Gen Counsel & Sr VP)
Mary Beth Thompson (Sr VP-HR)
Silvano Iaboni (VP-Engineered Coated
Products)

Subsidiary (US):

Better Packages, Inc. (2)
4 Hershey Dr, Ansonia, CT 06484
Tel.: (203) 926-3100
Web Site: http://www.betterpackages.com
Packaging Machinery Mfr
N.A.I.C.S.: 333993
Philip L. White (Pres & CEO)

Subsidiary (Non-US):

**Capstone Polyweave Private
Limited** (2)
C-3/5 Prashant Vihar Sector-14 Rohini,
Delhi, 11085, India
Tel.: (91) 9811450884
Web Site: http://www.cappl.in
Plastic Tarpaulin Mfr & Distr
N.A.I.C.S.: 314910

**FIBOPE Portuguesa-Filmes Biorienta-
dos, S.A.** (2)
Estrada da Praia n 1087, Barqueiros, 4740-
696, Barcelos, Portugal
Tel.: (351) 253 859 270
Web Site: http://www.fibope.pt
Emp.: 70
Packaging Film Mfr
N.A.I.C.S.: 326112
Loek J. K. Verhoef (Mgr-Sls & Mktg)
Martin Krips (Mgr-Area Sls)
Nicola Martello (Mgr-Area Sls)

Holding (US):

IPG (US) Holdings Inc. (2)

100 Paramount Dr Ste 300, Sarasota, FL
34232
Tel.: (941) 727-5788
Web Site: http://www.ipg.com
Emp.: 120
Plastic Packaging Products Mfr
N.A.I.C.S.: 326199

Subsidiary (US):

Intertape Polymer Corp. (2)
3647 Cortez Rd W Ste 102, Bradenton, FL
34219
Tel.: (208) 340-3077
Packaging Products Mfr
N.A.I.C.S.: 326112

Subsidiary (Non-US):

Intertape Polymer Europe GmbH (2)
Gronfahrtweg 3, Harrislee, 24955, Germany
Tel.: (49) 461 15065201
Web Site: http://www.itape.com
Emp.: 9
Packaging Products Mfr
N.A.I.C.S.: 326112

Subsidiary (Domestic):

Intertape Polymer Inc. (2)
11171 Okanagan Centre Road West, Win-
field, V4V 1H3, BC, Canada
Tel.: (250) 766-9193
Emp.: 1
Plastic Packaging Products Mfr
N.A.I.C.S.: 326199
Danny Leboe (Gen Mgr)

Subsidiary (US):

Maiweave LLC (2)
1800 E Pleasant St, Springfield, OH 45505
Tel.: (800) 521-3898
Web Site: http://www.maiweave.com
Synthetic Plastic Products Mfr
N.A.I.C.S.: 326113

Subsidiary (Domestic):

Polyair Inter Pack Inc. (2)
330 Humberline Drive, Toronto, M9W 1R5,
ON, Canada
Tel.: (416) 679-6600
Web Site: http://www.polyair.com
Protective Packaging Mfr
N.A.I.C.S.: 326140
Robert Carr (Exec VP-Ops)

Division (US):

**Polyair Inter Pack Inc. - Sacramento
Division** (3)
1802 Enterprise Blvd Ste 1802, Sacra-
mento, CA 95691
Tel.: (951) 737-7125
Web Site: http://www.polyair.com
Protective Packaging Products Mfr
N.A.I.C.S.: 322220

Polyair Inter Pack, Atlanta (3)
6035-B Lagrange Blvd SW, Atlanta, GA
30336-2817
Tel.: (404) 344-4413
Web Site: http://www.polyair.com
Sales Range: $25-49.9 Million
Emp.: 50
Protective Packaging Mfr & Developer
N.A.I.C.S.: 326140

Polyair Inter Pack, Bardstown (3)
300 Spencer Mattingly Ln, Bardstown, KY
40004-9103
Tel.: (502) 348-7020
Web Site: http://www.polyair.com
Sales Range: $25-49.9 Million
Emp.: 48
Protective Packaging Mfr & Developer
N.A.I.C.S.: 326140

Polyair Inter Pack, Chicago (3)
808 E 113th St, Chicago, IL 60628-5150
Tel.: (773) 995-1818
Web Site: http://www.polyair.com
Sales Range: $50-74.9 Million
Emp.: 100
Protective Packaging Mfr & Developer
N.A.I.C.S.: 326140

Polyair Inter Pack, Corona (3)
1692 Jenks Dr, Corona, CA 92880
Tel.: (951) 737-7125

Web Site: http://www.polyair.com
Sales Range: $50-74.9 Million
Emp.: 50
Protective Packaging Mfr & Developer
N.A.I.C.S.: 326140

Polyair Inter Pack, Dallas (3)
1600 Kelly Blvd Ste 140, Carrollton, TX
75006-4702 **(100%)**
Tel.: (972) 820-6484
Sales Range: $25-49.9 Million
Emp.: 45
Bubble Wrap Mfr
N.A.I.C.S.: 326112
Steve Labus (Plant Mgr)

Polyair Inter Pack, New Jersey (3)
495 Meadow Ln, Carlstadt, NJ 07072-3006
Tel.: (201) 804-1700
Web Site: http://www.polyair.com
Sales Range: $25-49.9 Million
Emp.: 40
Protective Packaging Mfr & Developer
N.A.I.C.S.: 326140

Subsidiary (Non-US):

**Powerband Industries Private
Limited** (2)
354/3 4 5 Vapi-Kachigam Road Near
Kachigam Char Rasta, Daman, 396210,
India
Tel.: (91) 2603053000
Web Site: http://www.powerband.in
Adhesive Tape Mfr
N.A.I.C.S.: 325520

IronGate Energy Services, LLC (1)
19500 State Hwy 249 Ste 600, Houston, TX
77070
Tel.: (832) 678-8585
Web Site: http://www.irongatees.com
Sales Range: $100-124.9 Million
Emp.: 250
Rental Equipment & Tubular Services for
Oil & Gas Exploration & Production
N.A.I.C.S.: 532490
Twight Gross (Pres)

Ivanti Software, Inc. (1)
698 W 10000 S Ste 500, South Jordan, UT
84095
Tel.: (888) 253-6201
Web Site: http://www.ivanti.com
Emp.: 2,000
Systems Lifecycle Management, Endpoint
Security & Information Technology Manage-
ment Software Publisher & Support Ser-
vices
N.A.I.C.S.: 513210
Steve Workman (VP-Corp Strategy & Plng)
Mark McBride (Exec VP)
Mitch Rowe (Exec VP-Global Software Sls)
Sue Urses (VP-HR)
Scott Sorensen (COO)
Peter De Bock (CFO)
Jim Schaper (Chm)
Jeff Abbott (CEO)
Mary Trick (Chief Customer Officer & Exec
VP)
John Flavin (Sr VP & Gen Mgr- Independ-
ent, Supply Chain & License Mgmt)
Mark Chamberlain (Sr VP-Global Ops)
Amberly Asay Janke (Sr Mgr-Corp Comm)
Melissa Puls (CMO & Sr VP)
Carrie Laudie (Assoc Dir-PR)
Thomas Charles Davis Jr. (CTO & Exec
VP)

Subsidiary (Domestic):

HEAT Software USA Inc. (2)
490 N McCarthy Blvd Ste 100, Milpitas, CA
95035
Tel.: (408) 601-2800
Web Site: http://www.heatsoftware.com
Business Management Software Developer,
Publisher, Whslr & Support Services
N.A.I.C.S.: 513210
Tony La Rosa (CIO)

Subsidiary (Non-US):

HEAT Software France SAS (3)
65 Rue des 3 Fontanot, 92000, Nanterre,
France
Tel.: (33) 1 5551 3090
Business Management Software Whslr &
Support Services
N.A.I.C.S.: 423430

Ivanti Germany GmbH (3)
Carl-von-Linde-Strasse 38, 85716, Unter-
schleissheim, Germany
Tel.: (49) 89 5599970
Web Site: http://www.ivanti.com
Business Management Software Whslr &
Support Services
N.A.I.C.S.: 423430

Janus International Group, Inc. (1)
135 Janus International Blvd, Temple, GA
30179
Tel.: (770) 562-2850
Web Site: https://www.janusintl.com
Rev.: $750,150,000
Assets: $1,122,002,000
Liabilities: $853,715,000
Net Worth: $268,287,000
Earnings: $43,801,000
Emp.: 1,577
Fiscal Year-end: 01/01/2022
Commercial Roll-Up Sheet Doors & Storage
Facility Components Mfr
N.A.I.C.S.: 332331
Roger B. Fradin (Chm)
David B. Curtis (Founder & Chm)
Ramey Jackson (CEO)
Vic Nettie (VP-Ops)
Terry Bagley (Pres-Door Entry & Facility
Automation Div)
Jeff Higashi (Pres-Western Div-Self Stor-
age)
Morgan Hodges (VP-Technical Sls)
Roc Hughes (VP-Bus Dev)
Colin Jeromson (Mng Dir-European Market)
Troy Bix (Pres-R3 Div)
Anselm Wong (CFO & Exec VP)
David Vanevenhoven (Chief Acctg Officer)

Subsidiary (Domestic):

**Access Control Technologies,
Inc.** (2)
1028 W Washington St, Orlando, FL 32805
Tel.: (407) 422-8850
Web Site: http://www.actflorida.com
Sales Range: $1-9.9 Million
Emp.: 45
Whol Electronic Parts/Equipment Electrical
Contractor
N.A.I.C.S.: 423690
Dan Lowery (VP)

Juniper Industrial Holdings, Inc. (2)
14 Fairmount Ave, Chatham, NJ 07928
Tel.: (973) 507-0359
Web Site: http://www.juniperindustrial.com
Rev.: $1,390
Assets: $349,398,602
Liabilities: $344,398,595
Net Worth: $5,000,007
Earnings: ($2,786,637)
Emp.: 2
Fiscal Year-end: 12/31/2020
Holding Company
N.A.I.C.S.: 551112
Brian Cook (CEO)

Kofax Inc. (1)
15211 Laguna Canyon Rd, Irvine, CA
92618-3146
Tel.: (949) 783-1000
Web Site: http://www.kofax.com
Emp.: 1,900
Software Development Services
N.A.I.C.S.: 513210
Reynolds C. Bish (CEO)
Jim Nicol (Exec VP-Products)
Lynne Scheid (Sr VP-HR)
Karl Doyle (Sr VP-Corp Dev)
Peter Hantman (Pres & COO)
Cort Townsend (CFO)
Greg Mermis (Gen Counsel & Sr VP-Legal
Affairs)
Kevin McKay (Exec VP-Customer Success)
Tim Battis (Exec VP-Global Sls)
Kathleen Delaney (CMO)
Chris Huff (Chief Strategy Officer)
Nicolas Rochard (Sr VP-Growth Mktg)

Subsidiary (Domestic):

Atalasoft, Inc. (2)
15211 Laguna Canyon Rd, Irvine, CA
92618
Tel.: (781) 743-2119
Web Site: http://www.atalasoft.com
Software Developer
N.A.I.C.S.: 513210

Clearlake Capital Group, L.P.—(Continued)

Mark Goldblatt *(Acct Exec)*

Ephesoft Inc. (2)
8707 Research Dr, Irvine, CA 92618
Tel.: (949) 331-7500
Web Site: http://www.ephesoft.com
Electronics Stores
N.A.I.C.S.: 449210
Ike Kavas *(Founder & CEO)*
Naren Goel *(CFO)*
Stephen Boals *(Sr VP-Strategy & Evangelism)*
Lynn Tanatannawin *(Head-Strategy)*
Heather Dilley *(Sr VP-Culture & People)*

Subsidiary (Non-US):

Kofax Australia Pty. Ltd. (2)
6-10 O'Connell Street Suite 701, Sydney,
2000, NSW, Australia
Tel.: (61) 289160200
Software Publisher
N.A.I.C.S.: 513210

Kofax Austria GmbH (2)
Talpagasse 1, 1230, Vienna, Austria
Tel.: (43) 18664555000
Electronic Mass Data Capture & Retrieval
Product Mfr
N.A.I.C.S.: 334112

Kofax Benelux NV (2)
Schalienhoevedreef 20 E, 2800, Mechelen,
Belgium
Tel.: (32) 15444900
Software Development Services
N.A.I.C.S.: 513210

Kofax Danmark A/S (2)
Lottenborgvej 26 Blok B 2 sal, Lyngby, Copenhagen, Denmark
Tel.: (45) 4324 1650
Applications Software Developer
N.A.I.C.S.: 513210

Kofax Deutschland AG (2)
Wentzinger Strasse 19, 79106, Freiburg,
Germany
Tel.: (49) 761 452 690
Applications Software Developer
N.A.I.C.S.: 513210
Frank Carl *(Dir-Technical Support Svcs)*
Christian Hefner *(Gen Counsel & VP)*

Kofax Holding AG (2)
Grundstrasse 14, 6343, Rotkreuz, Switzerland
Tel.: (41) 41 799 82 82
Holding Company
N.A.I.C.S.: 551112

Subsidiary (Domestic):

Kofax Schweiz AG (3)
Grundstrasse 14, 6343, Rotkreuz, Switzerland
Tel.: (41) 41 799 82 82
Applications Software Developer
N.A.I.C.S.: 513210

Subsidiary (Non-US):

Kofax Italia S.r.l. (2)
Viale Monza 270, 20128, Milan, Italy
Tel.: (39) 02 252051
Applications Software Developer
N.A.I.C.S.: 513210

Kofax Japan Co. Ltd. (2)
9F SOC Takanawa Building 3-19-26 Takanawa, Minato-ku, Tokyo, 108-0074, Japan
Tel.: (81) 3 6853 0001
Applications Software Developer
N.A.I.C.S.: 513210

Kofax Malaysia Sdn. Bhd. (2)
Suite 13 06 Level 13 The Gardens South
Tower Mid Valley City, Lingkaran Syed Putra, Kuala Lumpur, 59200, Malaysia
Tel.: (60) 3 2092 0202
Applications Software Developer
N.A.I.C.S.: 513210

Kofax Netherlands BV (2)
Papendorpseweg 99 5th Floor, 3528 BJ,
Utrecht, Netherlands
Tel.: (31) 30 264 3030
Applications Software Developer
N.A.I.C.S.: 513210
Martin van Ginkel *(VP-Sls-Benelux)*

Kofax Portugal, S.A. (2)
Av Clotilde Edificio Centro Congressos do
Estoril 4A, 2765-211, Estoril, Portugal
Tel.: (351) 21 464 6190
Applications Software Developer
N.A.I.C.S.: 513210

**Kofax Produtos de Imagem Do Brasil
Ltda** (2)
R Gomes de Carvalho 1069 CJ 102, Itaim
Bibi, 04547-004, Sao Paulo, Brazil
Tel.: (55) 11 3047 4000
Applications Software Developer
N.A.I.C.S.: 513210

Kofax Singapore Pte. Ltd. (2)
9 Raffles Place Suite 53-01 Republic Plaza,
Singapore, 048619, Singapore
Tel.: (65) 62787662
Applications Software Developer
N.A.I.C.S.: 513210
Jesslyn Lee *(Dir-HR-Asia Pacific)*

Kofax Software Iberica S.A.U. (2)
Torre Mapfre C/ de la Marina 16-18 11-B,
08005, Barcelona, Spain
Tel.: (34) 934 090 459
Applications Software Developer
N.A.I.C.S.: 513210

Kofax Sverige AB (2)
Energigaten 11 Rm 308, 434 37, Kungsbacka, Sweden
Tel.: (46) 8 566 110 00
Applications Software Developer
N.A.I.C.S.: 513210

Kofax UK Ltd. (2)
7 Elmwood Chineham Business Park,
Chineham, Basingstoke, RG24 8WG,
United Kingdom
Tel.: (44) 1256 89 1000
Applications Software Developer
N.A.I.C.S.: 513210
Darryl Heffernan *(VP-Global Sls Ops)*

Kofax Vietnam Co., Ltd. (2)
521 Kim Ma Street 11 Fl A Tower RESCO
Building, Ba Dinh District, Hanoi, 100000,
Vietnam
Tel.: (84) 4 3771 2546 7
Applications Software Developer
N.A.I.C.S.: 513210

Subsidiary (Domestic):

PSIGEN Software, Inc. (2)
7027 Old Madison Pike NW Ste 108,
Huntsville, AL 35806
Tel.: (949) 916-7700
Web Site: http://www.psigen.com
Sales Range: $1-9.9 Million
Emp.: 16
Custom Computer Programming Services
N.A.I.C.S.: 541511
Bruce Hensley *(CEO)*
Victoria Hensley *(COO)*
Joe Do *(Dir-Global Products & Svcs)*
Glenn Johnson *(Pres)*
Robert Esquivel *(Dir-Channel Enablement-West)*

Subsidiary (Non-US):

Tungsten Corporation PLC (2)
Leaf A Level 1 Tower 42 25 Old Broad
Street, London, EC2N 1HQ, United Kingdom
Tel.: (44) 2072807807
Web Site: http://www.tungsten-network.com
Rev.: $49,035,416
Assets: $109,042,566
Liabilities: $32,684,394
Net Worth: $76,358,173
Earnings: ($47,093,876)
Emp.: 260
Fiscal Year-end: 04/30/2021
Invoicing Software
N.A.I.C.S.: 513210
Cort Steven Townsend *(Sec)*

Subsidiary (US):

Tungsten Network Inc (3)
1040 Crown Pointe Pkwy Ste 350, Atlanta,
GA 30338
Tel.: (770) 698-1420
Electronic Invoicing Services
N.A.I.C.S.: 561499
Prabhat Vira *(Pres-Fin)*
Rick Hurwitz Rick Hurwitz *(CEO-Americas)*

Subsidiary (Domestic):

Image Intergration Systems, Inc. (4)
885 Commerce Dr, Perrysburg, OH 43551
Tel.: (419) 872-1930
Web Site: http://www.docusphere.com
Emp.: 25
Data Processing, Hosting & Related Services
N.A.I.C.S.: 518210
Bradley White *(Pres & CEO)*
Tina Dominique *(VP-Professional Svcs)*
Dave Litzenberg *(VP-Sls & Mktg)*
Kathleen Faltys *(Controller)*

Mediant Communications LLC (1)
17 State St, New York, NY 10004
Tel.: (212) 514-5202
Web Site: http://www.mediantonline.com
Custom Computer Programming Services
N.A.I.C.S.: 541511
Antal Foldi *(CFO)*
Jennifer Delevante-Moulen *(Dir-Mktg)*
Gussie V. Tate *(Head-Ops)*
Sherry Moreland *(Pres)*

Meek's Lumber Company (1)
1311 E Woodhurst Dr, Springfield, MO
65804-4282
Tel.: (417) 521-2801
Web Site: http://www.meeklumber.com
Sales Range: $300-349.9 Million
Emp.: 700
Home Improvement Centers Operator
N.A.I.C.S.: 444110
Terry O. Meek *(Pres)*
Charlie Meek *(Gen Mgr)*
Kent May *(CFO)*

Subsidiary (Domestic):

Meek's, Inc. (2)
1651 Response Rd Ste 200, Sacramento,
CA 95815
Tel.: (916) 576-3042
Web Site: http://www.meeks.com
Home Improvement Centers Operator
N.A.I.C.S.: 444110

Perforce Software, Inc. (1)
400 N 1st Ave Ste 200, Minneapolis, MN
55401
Tel.: (615) 517-2100
Web Site: http://www.perforce.com
Computer Software Publisher
N.A.I.C.S.: 513210
Tim Russell *(Chief Product Officer)*
Mark Ties *(Pres & CEO)*
Mike Goergen *(CFO)*
Wes Fredenburg *(Chief Legal Officer)*

Subsidiary (Domestic):

Delphix Corp. (2)
275 Middlefield Rd Ste 50, Menlo Park, CA
94025-4008
Tel.: (703) 629-8989
Web Site: http://www.delphix.com
Software Solutions
N.A.I.C.S.: 541519
Rick Hopfer *(CIO)*
Marc Aronson *(Sr VP-Engrg)*
Tony Orlando *(Sr VP-Field Ops-Global)*
Monika Saha *(CMO)*
Eric Schrock *(CTO)*
Orlando de Bruce *(VP-Corp Mktg & Brand)*
Tammi Warfield *(Sr VP-Customer Success)*
Alex Hesterberg *(Chief Customer Officer)*
Steve Barrett *(Sr VP-Intl Ops)*

Subsidiary (Domestic):

Axis Technology, LLC (3)
70 Federal St, Boston, MA 02110
Tel.: (857) 445-0110
Web Site: http://www.axistechnologyllc.com
IT Consulting Services
N.A.I.C.S.: 541519
Ron Sherwood *(VP-Sls)*
John E. David *(Co-Founder & Pres)*
Michael Logan *(Co-Founder & Pres)*
Randy Barron *(VP-Ops & HR)*
George Barroso *(Mng Dir-Data Svcs)*
Michael Stiglianese *(Sr Mng Dir)*

Subsidiary (Non-US):

Perforce Software Pty. Ltd. (2)
Level 13 Suite 5 56 Berry Street, North
Sydney, 2060, NSW, Australia

Tel.: (61) 290543712
Web Site: http://www.perforce.com
Computer Software Publisher
N.A.I.C.S.: 513210

Perforce Software UK Ltd. (2)
West Forest Gate Wellington Road, Wokingham, RG40 2AT, Berks, United Kingdom
Tel.: (44) 1189 771020
Web Site: http://www.perforce.com
Computer Software Publisher
N.A.I.C.S.: 513210

Subsidiary (Domestic):

Perforce Software, Inc.-Ohio (2)
6960 Cintas Blvd, Mason, OH 45040
Tel.: (513) 754-1655
Web Site: http://www.perforce.com
Application Lifecycle Management Software
Developer & Publisher
N.A.I.C.S.: 513210

Rogue Wave Software, Inc. (2)
1315 W Century Dr Ste 150, Louisville, CO
80027
Tel.: (303) 473-9118
Web Site: http://www.roguewave.com
Sales Range: $25-49.9 Million
Cross-Platform Application Software Developer & Publisher
N.A.I.C.S.: 541511
Brian Pierce *(CEO)*
Ted Smith *(CIO & VP-Engrg)*
Christine Bottagaro *(CMO)*
Rod Cope *(CTO)*
Ian McLeod *(Chief Product Officer)*

Subsidiary (Non-US):

**Rogue Wave Software Japan
K.K.** (3)
Bancho Fifth Building 5-5 Nibancho,
Chiyoda-ku, Tokyo, 102-0084, Japan
Tel.: (81) 3 5211 7760
Web Site: http://www.roguewave.jp
Sales Range: $50-74.9 Million
Cross-Platform Application Software Developer & Publisher
N.A.I.C.S.: 513210
Toshitomo Kobayashi *(Pres)*

Subsidiary (Domestic):

Zend Technologies, Inc. (3)
10080 N Wolfe Rd Ste SW3 301, Cupertino, CA 95014
Tel.: (408) 253-8800
Web Site: http://www.zend.com
Custom Computer Programming & Consulting Services
N.A.I.C.S.: 541511
Zeev Suraski *(Founder & CTO)*

Precisely, Inc. (1)
1700 District Ave #300, Burlington, MA
01803
Tel.: (877) 700-0970
Web Site: http://www.precisely.com
Data Integration Software Developer & Publisher
N.A.I.C.S.: 513210
Josh Rogers *(CEO)*
Tendu Yogurtcu *(CTO)*
Jay Johnson *(Sr VP-Sls-Americas)*
Jason Smith *(CFO)*
Bryan Ashley *(Sr VP-Sls-APAC)*
Mads Toubro *(VP-Sls-EMEA)*
Kevin Ruane *(CMO)*
Lisa Crawford *(Chief HR Officer)*
Amy O'Connor *(CIO & Chief Data Officer)*

Subsidiary (Domestic):

Infogix, Inc. (2)
1240 E Diehl Rd Ste 400, Naperville, IL
60563
Tel.: (630) 505-1800
Data Controls & Analytics Software Services
N.A.I.C.S.: 513210

PlaceIQ, Inc. (2)
1732 1st Ave Ste 20951, New York, NY
10128
Tel.: (646) 963-5062
Web Site: http://www.placeiq.com
Media Representatives
N.A.I.C.S.: 541840

Anna Nguyen *(COO)*
Nadya Kohl *(Sr VP-Bus Dev)*
John Sedlak *(Chief Revenue Officer)*
Mandeep Mason *(Gen Mgr-EMEA)*
Duncan McCall *(Founder & CEO)*

Vision Solutions, Inc.   (2)
15300 Barranca Pkwy Ste 250, Irvine, CA 92618
Tel.: (949) 253-6500
Web Site: http://www.visionsolutions.com
Information Technology Solutions
N.A.I.C.S.: 513210
Edward Vesely *(CMO & Exec VP)*
Mike Khattab *(VP-Sls-Growth Markets)*
Robert Johnson *(Exec VP-Sls)*
Rob Humbach *(VP-Sls-Americas)*
Chuck Davis *(VP-Fin)*
Kristin Brooks *(Gen Counsel)*

Pretium Packaging Corporation   (1)
1555 Page Industrial Blvd, 63132, St. Louis, MO
Tel.: (314) 727-8200
Web Site: http://www.pretiumpkg.com
Plastic Packaging Mfr
N.A.I.C.S.: 326160
George Abd *(Pres & CEO)*
Kelly Daleen *(Dir-Mktg & Customer Svc)*

Subsidiary (Domestic):

Olcott Plastics, Inc.   (2)
95 N 17th St, Saint Charles, IL 60174
Tel.: (630) 584-0555
Web Site: http://www.olcottplastics.com
All Other Plastics Product Mfr
N.A.I.C.S.: 326199

Patrick Products, Inc.   (2)
150 S Werner St, Leipsic, OH 45856
Tel.: (419) 943-3733
Web Site: http://www.patrickproducts.com
Sales Range: $1-9.9 Million
Plastics Materials & Basic Forms & Shapes Merchant Whslr
N.A.I.C.S.: 424610
Robert S. Patrick *(Pres)*

Plant (Domestic):

Pretium Packaging - Manchester   (2)
1 Devco Dr, Manchester, PA 17345-1337
Tel.: (717) 266-6687
Web Site: http://www.pretiumpkg.com
Sales Range: $1-9.9 Million
Plastic Packaging Mfr
N.A.I.C.S.: 326160
Myles Detterman *(Plant Mgr)*

Pretium Packaging - Philmont   (2)
370 Stevers Crossing Rd, Philmont, NY 12565-0784
Tel.: (518) 672-7721
Web Site: http://www.pretiumpkg.com
Sales Range: $50-74.9 Million
Plastic Packaging Mfr
N.A.I.C.S.: 326160

Subsidiary (Domestic):

Tri-Pack Enterprises Inc.   (2)
946 S Andreasen Dr, Escondido, CA 92029
Tel.: (760) 737-7995
Web Site:
   http://www.customblowmoulding.com
Rev.: $10,000,000
Emp.: 88
All Other Plastics Product Mfr
N.A.I.C.S.: 326199
William W. McNeal *(Pres)*

PrimeSource Building Products, Inc.   (1)
1321 Greenway Dr, Irving, TX 75038-2504
Tel.: (972) 999-8500
Web Site: http://www.primesourcebp.com
Emp.: 1,200
Building Products Whslr
N.A.I.C.S.: 423310
Tom Koos *(Pres & CEO)*

Sunbelt Supply Co.   (1)
3750 TX-225, 77503, Pasadena, TX
Tel.: (713) 672-2222
Web Site: http://www.sunbeltsupply.com
Oil, Gas & Industrial Manual & Automated Valve Products
N.A.I.C.S.: 423830

Subsidiary (Domestic):

Severe Service Specialists Inc.   (2)
4251 Praytor Way Ste 121, Trussville, AL 35173-2426
Tel.: (205) 655-1163
Web Site: http://www.sssvalve.com
Specialty Flow Control Solutions
N.A.I.C.S.: 334513
Toby Hollier *(Founder & Pres)*
John Hollier *(Sls Mgr)*
John Fey *(Branch Mgr-Ops)*
Jeff Ellis *(Mgr)*

Team Technologies, Inc.   (1)
5949 Commerce Blvd, Morristown, TN 37814
Tel.: (423) 587-2199
Web Site: http://www.teamtech.com
Sales Range: $10-24.9 Million
Emp.: 250
Healthcare & Oral Care Products Mfr
N.A.I.C.S.: 423840
Clark Bow *(Mgr-Engrg)*
Ted Miller *(Mgr-Engrg)*
Bob Walton *(VP & Plant Mgr)*
Marshall White *(Pres & CEO)*
Steve Lents *(Chief Revenue Officer)*

Subsidiary (Domestic):

Baril Corporation   (2)
50 Ward Hill Ave, Haverhill, MA 01835
Tel.: (978) 373-7910
Web Site: http://www.barilcorp.com
Sales Range: $1-9.9 Million
Emp.: 19
Integrated Device Mfr
N.A.I.C.S.: 322299
Dana Greenlay *(Mgr-Production)*
Daniel Baril *(CEO)*
Michael Curtis *(Pres)*
Neil Muchin *(VP-Sls & Mktg)*

Unifrax I LLC   (1)
600 Riverwalk Pkwy, 14150, Buffalo, NY
Tel.: (716) 768-6500
Web Site: https://alkegen.com
Specialty Materials Mfr; Battery Technologies, Electric Vehicles, Filtration Media & Specialty Insulation Materials
N.A.I.C.S.: 327999
John Dandolph *(Pres & CEO)*
Brian Walker *(Sr VP-HR)*
Joseph Kuchera *(VP-Product Stewardship & Compliance)*
James Olchawski *(Sr VP-GM Thermal Mgmt & VP-Thermal Mgmt-Sls & Mktg)*

Subsidiary (Non-US):

Luyang Energy-Saving Materials Co., Ltd.   (2)
No 11 Yihe Road, Yiyuan County, Zibo, Shandong, China
Tel.: (86) 5333288764
Web Site: https://www.luyangwool.com
Rev.: $473,145,515
Assets: $549,703,038
Liabilities: $145,282,326
Net Worth: $404,420,712
Earnings: $81,761,729
Fiscal Year-end: 12/31/2022
Ceramic Fiber Product Mfr
N.A.I.C.S.: 313110
John Charles Dandolph IV *(Chm)*

Saffil Ltd.   (2)
Pilkington Sullivan Rd Tanhouse Ln, Widnes, WA8 0US, Cheshire, United Kingdom
Tel.: (44) 1514226700
Web Site: http://www.saffil.com
Sales Range: $25-49.9 Million
Emp.: 75
Sales & Development of High Temperature Solutions & Performance Materials for Automotive, Ceramic, Iron & Steel & Petrochemical Industries
N.A.I.C.S.: 332999
Peter Weaver *(Mgr-Site)*

Subsidiary (Domestic):

Saffil Automotive Limited   (3)
Unit 34 Greenfield Business Park, Greenfield, Holywell, CH87HJ, Flintshire, United Kingdom
Tel.: (44) 1352712331
Web Site: http://www.unifrax.com

Sales Range: $10-24.9 Million
Nonmetallic Mineral Product Mfr
N.A.I.C.S.: 327999
Alan Blythe *(Gen Mgr)*

Subsidiary (Non-US):

Saffil Automotive South Africa (Pty) Limited   (3)
31 Kohler Road Perseverance Industrial Park, PO Box 27279, Greenacres, 6057, Port Elizabeth, South Africa   (100%)
Tel.: (27) 414631240
Web Site: http://www.saffil.com
Sales Range: $10-24.9 Million
Emp.: 6
Nonmetallic Mineral Product Mfr
N.A.I.C.S.: 327999
Gary Duffin *(Gen Mgr)*

Vendor Credentialing Service LLC   (1)
315 Capitol St Ste 100, Houston, TX 77002
Tel.: (281) 863-9500
Web Site: http://www.symplr.com
Healthcare Credentialing & Compliance Services
N.A.I.C.S.: 561499
Tres Thompson *(CFO & COO)*
Jason Rupert *(Chief Sls Officer)*
B. J. Schaknowski *(CEO)*
Brian Fugere *(Chief Product Officer)*
Kristin Russel *(CMO)*

Subsidiary (Domestic):

API Healthcare Corporation   (2)
1550 Innovation Way, Hartford, WI 53027
Tel.: (262) 673-6815
Web Site: http://www.apihealthcare.com
Sales Range: $75-99.9 Million
Emp.: 350
Healthcare Business Management Software & Services
N.A.I.C.S.: 513210

Subsidiary (Domestic):

API Healthcare Corporation - San Diego   (3)
9276 Scranton Rd Ste 400, San Diego, CA 92121
Tel.: (262) 673-6815
Web Site: http://www.apihealthcare.com
Sales Range: $10-24.9 Million
Emp.: 50
Healthcare Staffing Solutions
N.A.I.C.S.: 561311

Subsidiary (Domestic):

Res-Q Healthcare Systems, Inc.   (4)
9276 Scranton Rd Ste 400, San Diego, CA 92121
Tel.: (858) 882-8500
Sales Range: $1-9.9 Million
Management Consulting Services
N.A.I.C.S.: 541618
Michael Meisel *(Pres & CEO)*

Subsidiary (Domestic):

CBR Associates Inc.   (2)
1415 Broad St, Durham, NC 27705-3534
Tel.: (919) 286-1326
Web Site: http://www.cbrassociates.com
Healthcare Credentialing Solutions
N.A.I.C.S.: 513210
Brenda Sorrell *(CEO)*

HealthcareSource HR, Inc.   (2)
100 Sylvan Rd Ste 100, Woburn, MA 01801
Tel.: (781) 368-1033
Web Site: http://www.healthcaresource.com
Healtcare Services
N.A.I.C.S.: 621999
J. P. Fingado *(Pres)*
Kerry Unflat *(VP-Talent Mgmt)*
David Wilkins *(CMO)*
Gabe Camera *(CFO)*
Bob Zurek *(CTO & Sr VP)*
Chris Martins *(Mgr-Product Mktg)*
Lisa Frank *(Sr Mgr-Product Mktg)*
Norma Gaffin *(Sr Mgr-Content Mktg)*
Kelli Rice *(Dir-Mktg Insight)*
Sarah Joyce *(VP-Client Ops)*
Katherine Shuman *(Chief Sls Officer)*
Patrick McDonough *(CTO)*
Michael Grossi *(CEO)*

ISG Group LLC   (2)
61 Split Brook Rd, Nashua, NH 03060
Tel.: (603) 888-0542
Web Site: http://www.intellisoftgroup.com
Medical Credentialing, Provider Enrollment & Contract Management Software Publisher & Whslr
N.A.I.C.S.: 513210
Mike Melville *(Grp CEO)*
Mitch Martin *(Pres)*
Mike Aha *(Dir-Dev)*
Karen Roy *(Dir-Ops)*
Marcia Wessell *(Dir-Mktg Comm)*

Medkinetics, LLC   (2)
124 1st Ave S Ste 200, Franklin, TN 37064-6326
Tel.: (615) 599-1627
Healthcare Credentialing & Compliance Services
N.A.I.C.S.: 561499
Jim Cox *(Pres)*

TractManager, Inc.   (2)
2711 N Haskell #1450, Dallas, TX 75204
Tel.: (423) 267-9300
Web Site: http://www.tractmanager.com
Contract Management Services
N.A.I.C.S.: 561499
Donald Deieso *(Chm)*
Trace Devanny *(CEO)*
Sandra L. Taylor *(CMO)*
Patrick Flynn *(Chief Product Officer)*
Kimberly Hartsfield *(Chief Date Officer)*

Subsidiary (Domestic):

MD Buyline, Inc.   (3)
5910 N Cntrl Expy, Dallas, TX 75206
Tel.: (214) 891-6700
Web Site: http://www.mdbuyline.com
Sales Range: $1-9.9 Million
Information Network Service For High-Tech Medical Electronic Products & Provides Information On Information Systems Industry
N.A.I.C.S.: 513199
Lyle Ellerbach *(VP)*
Kevin Hodges *(Dir-Ops)*
Eric Slimp *(Mgr-Purchased Svcs)*
Katie Regan *(Mgr-Clinical Publ)*
Nicole Hodges *(VP-Ops)*
Peter Stelling *(Gen Mgr-Purchased Svcs)*

WellPet LLC   (1)
200 Ames Pond Dr, Tewksbury, MA 01876
Tel.: (978) 289-5500
Web Site: http://www.wellpet.com
Dog & Cat Food
N.A.I.C.S.: 311111
Camelle Kent-Rizkalla *(CEO)*
Roger Parsons *(VP-Sls)*
Bill McDonald *(CFO)*
Clark Reinhard *(CMO)*
Tricia DiPersio *(VP-Food Safety, Quality Assurance & Regulatory Affairs)*

Subsidiary (Domestic):

Sojourner Farms LLC   (2)
2300 Kennedy St NE Ste 110, Minneapolis, MN 55413
Tel.: (612) 343-7262
Web Site: http://www.sojos.com
Sales Range: $1-9.9 Million
Emp.: 6
Manufactures & Sells Dog & Cat Food Products
N.A.I.C.S.: 311119
Ward Johnson *(Owner & Pres)*
Maggie Johnson *(VP)*

Wheel Pros, LLC   (1)
17880 Fitch Ave, Irvine, CA 92614
Web Site: http://www.wheelpros.com
Wheels, Tires & Related Accessories Distr
N.A.I.C.S.: 423130
Jody Groce *(Co-Founder)*
Randy White *(Co-Founder)*

Subsidiary (Domestic):

Amcor Industries, Inc.   (2)
6131 Knott Ave, Buena Park, CA 90620
Tel.: (323) 585-2852
Web Site: http://www.gorilla-auto.com
Motor Vehicle Parts Mfr
N.A.I.C.S.: 336390

Just Wheels & Tires Co.   (2)
3172 Nasa St, Brea, CA 92821

Clearlake Capital Group, L.P.—(Continued)

Web Site: http://www.tsw.com
Automotive Parts & Accessories Stores
N.A.I.C.S.: 441330
Terence Scheckter (CEO)

ReadyLIFT Suspension, Inc. (2)
7490 Commercial Way, Henderson, NV
89011
Tel.: (702) 410-2300
Web Site: http://www.readylift.com
Motor Vehicle Parts Mfr
N.A.I.C.S.: 336390
Byrce Castleton (Pres)

Teraflex, Inc. (2)
5247 S 300 W, Salt Lake City, UT 84107
Tel.: (801) 288-2585
Rev.: $2,900,000
Emp.: 22
Industrial Truck, Tractor, Trailer & Stacker
Machinery Mfr
N.A.I.C.S.: 333924
Mark Falkner (Pres)
Brian Smith (Treas)

Zywave, Inc. (1)
10100 W Innovation Dr Ste 300, Milwaukee,
WI 53226
Tel.: (414) 454-6100
Web Site: http://www.zywave.com
Sales Range: $10-24.9 Million
Insurance Management Software Publisher
N.A.I.C.S.: 513210
Joe Gibson (CFO & Exec VP)
Adam Karl (VP-Product Dev)
Katie Conley (Sr VP-Customer Success)
Marlon Davis (VP-Product Mgmt)
Jason Liu (CEO)
Jim Lindner (Chm)
Eric Bluhm (Sr VP-Sls)
Doug Marquis (CTO)
Eric Rentsch (Sr VP-Product Mgmt)
Jon Maury (VP-Intl Ops)

Subsidiary (Domestic):

Advisen Ltd. (2)
1430 Broadway 8th Fl, New York, NY
10018
Tel.: (212) 897-4800
Web Site: http://www.advisen.com
Sales Range: $10-24.9 Million
Emp.: 48
Offerer of Strategic Information Services for
the Global, Commercial Insurance Industry
N.A.I.C.S.: 517810
Jeff Cohen (Pres)
David Dahlquist (CFO)
John Pagliaccio (Chief Analytics Officer)
Kate Schaub (Dir-Client Mgmt)
Rebecca Bole (Exec VP & Editor-in-Chief)
Liz Novielli (Dir-Events)
Knut Danielsen (Dir-Fin)
Glenn Trutner (Dir-Loss Insight)
Jim Blinn (Exec VP-Client Solutions & Mgr-
Global Product)
Dennis Sauer (Exec VP & Program Mgr)
Lucy Buggy (Sec)
Charlene Farside (Chief Mktg Officer &
Exec VP)
Ricardo Hernandez (Exec VP-Product
Mgmt)
Scott Worland (Dir-Subscriptions & Circula-
tion)
Brian Reinert (CTO & Exec VP)
Lucy Blinn (Exec VP & Mgr-Product-Global)
Ron Adiel (CEO)

IBQ Systems LLC (2)
1010 N Normandie St, Spokane, WA
99201-2270
Tel.: (509) 984-1110
Web Site: http://www.ibqsystems.com
Software Publisher
N.A.I.C.S.: 513210
Brian Hopkins (CEO)

**Insurance Technologies
Corporation** (2)
1415 Halsey Way Ste 314, Carrollton, TX
75007
Tel.: (972) 245-3660
Insurance Industry Marketing, Rating &
Management Software Publisher
N.A.I.C.S.: 513210

Subsidiary (Domestic):

Agency Matrix LLC (3)

2425 Commerce Ave Ste 300, Duluth, GA
30096
Tel.: (800) 456-2874
Web Site: http://www.agencymatrix.com
Agency Management Software Services
N.A.I.C.S.: 541511
Laird Rixford (CEO)

Branch (Domestic):

**Insurance Technologies Corp. -
TurboRater** (3)
1415 Halsey Wy Ste 314, Carrollton, TX
75007
Tel.: (972) 245-3660
Web Site: http://www.multico.com
Insurance Industry Rating Software Pub-
lisher
N.A.I.C.S.: 513210
Laird Rixford (CEO)
Scott Upfield (Founder & COO)
Dale Meredith (CFO)
Becky Schroeder (CMO)
Justin Costa (Sr VP-Carrier Ops)
Stuart Ganis (Sr VP-Sls & Bus Dev)

CLEARLOGIC FINANCIAL, INC.
11107 Sunset Hills Rd Ste 220, Res-
ton, VA 20190
Tel.: (703) 476-3521
Web Site:
http://clearlogicfinancial.com
Sales Range: $10-24.9 Million
Emp.: 6
Investment Advisory & Financial Plan-
ning Services
N.A.I.C.S.: 523940
Joel D. Ticknor (Founder)
Mark Atherton (Partner & CEO)
Kevin Loser (Partner & COO)
Helen Burnett (Mgr-Client Svcs)
Delinda Ramberg (Office Mgr)

CLEARONE ADVANTAGE, LLC
1501 S Clinton St Ste 320, Baltimore,
MD 21224
Tel.: (800) 657-3328
Web Site:
https://www.clearoneadvantage.com
Year Founded: 2007
Sales Range: $1-9.9 Million
Emp.: 100
Full-Service Debt Resolution
N.A.I.C.S.: 522390
Tomas Gordon (CEO)
Nicholas E. Kosmas (Gen Counsel)

CLEARPATH SOLUTIONS GROUP
13800 Coppermine Rd Ste 400,
Herndon, VA 20171
Tel.: (866) 892-3154
Web Site:
http://www.clearpathsg.com
Year Founded: 2006
Sales Range: $10-24.9 Million
Emp.: 25
Data Storage & Management
N.A.I.C.S.: 518210
Niko Alexiou (Acct Mgr)
Heather Coleman (Acct Mgr)
Greer Lindholm (Project Mgr)
Dave Westervelt (Reg Dir-Sls)
Josh Terry (Acct Mgr)
Imran Ahmed (CTO)
Julie Wetzel (VP-Client Rels)
Helen Lao (Founder & Pres)

CLEARPOINT ENTERPRISES, INC.
215 Commercial St Ste 4, Portland,
ME 04101-4674   MA
Web Site: http://www.clearpoint.com
Year Founded: 1994
Sales Range: Less than $1 Million
Emp.: 15
Mfr of Computer Memory Equipment
N.A.I.C.S.: 334112

Peter S. Carpenter (CEO & Mng Dir)
Pierre T. Gallant (CFO & COO)
Stephen J. Dipietro (Mng Dir)
Kevin T. Overbey (Mng Dir)
Peter Radynski (Acct Mgr)

CLEARRIVER COMMUNICA-
TIONS GROUP
2401 Eastlawn Dr, Midland, MI 48640
Tel.: (989) 631-9560
Web Site: http://www.clear-river.com
Year Founded: 1955
Sales Range: $50-74.9 Million
Emp.: 20
N.A.I.C.S.: 541810

CLEARSENSE, LLC
13901 Sutton Park Dr S, Jackson-
ville, FL 32224
Tel.: (904) 364-5629
Web Site: http://clearsense.com
Healthcare Data Analytics Software
Publisher
N.A.I.C.S.: 513210
Charles Boicey (Co-Founder & Chief
Innovation Officer)
Gene Scheurer (CEO)
Jason Mabry (Co-Founder & Princi-
pal)
Kevin Field (Pres)
Kay Dickason (COO)
Pamela Fowler (CMO)
Rick Shepardson (Chief Strategy
Officer)

Subsidiaries:

Compellon, Inc. (1)
23161 Lake Ctr #215, Lake Forest, CA
92630
Tel.: (949) 713-9555
Web Site: http://www.compellon.com
Healthcare Data Analytics Software Pro-
vider
N.A.I.C.S.: 513210
Ken Charhut (Co-Founder, Chm & Chief
Strategy Officer)
Mark Pollard (Co-Founder & Chief Revenue
Officer)
Nikolai Liachenko (Co-Founder)
Marc Bir (CTO)
Jesse Treger (Sr Dir-Product Mgmt & Strat-
egy)
Carv Moore (CEO)
E. Casey Roche III (VP-Bus Dev)

CLEARSOURCE, INC.
5 Commonwealth Rd Ste 3A, Natick,
MA 01760
Tel.: (508) 647-1090
Year Founded: 1997
Sales Range: $25-49.9 Million
Emp.: 120
Bottled Water Mfr & Distr
N.A.I.C.S.: 312112
James M. Morgan (Pres & CEO)
David Reed (VP-Sls)

CLEARSTAR, INC.
6250 Shiloh Rd Ste 300, Alpharetta,
GA 30005
Tel.: (770) 416-1900
Web Site: http://www.clearstar.net
Year Founded: 1995
Rev.: $20,113,000
Assets: $7,818,000
Liabilities: $2,674,000
Net Worth: $5,144,000
Earnings: ($1,337,000)
Emp.: 78
Fiscal Year-end: 12/31/18
Background Screening Software &
Services for Employment, Back-
ground & Tenant Screening Compa-
nies
N.A.I.C.S.: 513210
Todd Shoulberg (Pres-Medical Infor-
mation Svcs)

Nicolas Dufour (Gen Counsel, Sec &
Exec VP)
Matt Peace (CFO)
Jennifer Balleza (VP-Fin)
Traci Ivester (COO)
Brad Carlson (Chief Revenue Officer)
Angela Kimbell (VP-Mktg)
Bill White (Co-Founder)
Mike Pritts (CEO)
Tom Skelton (Chm)
Robert James Vale Jr. (Co-Founder)
Kenneth W. Dawson Jr. (Co-Founder,
CIO & Chief Information Security
Officer)

Subsidiaries:

ClearStar Logistics, Inc. (1)
418 Pirkle Ferry Rd Ste 109, Cumming, GA
30040   (100%)
Tel.: (678) 455-0384
Web Site: http://www.clearstar.net
Security Screening Reporting Agency
N.A.I.C.S.: 928110

CLEARSTONE VENTURE
PARTNERS
725 Arizona Ave Ste 304, Santa
Monica, CA 90401
Tel.: (310) 460-7900
Web Site: http://www.clearstone.com
Year Founded: 1998
Sales Range: $10-24.9 Million
Emp.: 20
Investment Services
N.A.I.C.S.: 523999
Bill Elkus (Founder & Mng Dir)
Jim Armstrong (Mng Dir)
Dana Moraly (CFO)
Sumant Mandal (Mng Dir)
Vish Mishra (Dir-Venture)
Craig Reston (Controller)
Rajan Mehra (Partner-Venture)
Rita Cardenas (Accountant)
William Quigley (Mng Dir)

CLEARVIEW BUSINESS IN-
TELLIGENCE, LLC
4022 S 1900 W, Roy, UT 84067
Tel.: (801) 900-6875
Web Site:
http://www.clearviewlive.com
Year Founded: 2012
Sales Range: $1-9.9 Million
Emp.: 50
Software Development Services
N.A.I.C.S.: 541511
Paul Liljenquist (Pres)
Ben Johnson (VP-Tech)
Randy Pulsipher (Project Mgr-IT)
Karen Hanson (Dir-Channel Mgmt)
Landon Rich (Dir-Domestic Sls)

CLEARVIEW CAPITAL, LLC
1010 Washington Blvd 11th Fl, Stam-
ford, CT 06901
Tel.: (203) 698-2777   DE
Web Site:
https://www.clearviewcap.com
Year Founded: 1999
Rev.: $15,000,000
Private Equity Firm
N.A.I.C.S.: 523999
James G. Andersen (Co-Founder &
Mng Partner)
Matthew W. Blevins (Principal)
John Cerra (CFO)
Calvin Neider (Co-Founder & Mng
Partner)
Paul M. Caliento (Partner)
Anthony J. Veith (Partner)
Matt Rumilly (Principal)
Nicholas M. Berry (VP-Bus Dev)
Gerald Cummins (Chief Compliance
Officer)
Melissa A. Frederick (Dir-Mktg)
Lawrence R. Simon (Principal)

Geoffrey L. Faux *(VP)*
Jon Van Tuin *(Principal)*
Brent A. Simon *(VP)*
William F. Case Jr. *(Partner)*

Subsidiaries:

Novik Inc. **(1)**
160 rue des Grands Lacs, Saint-Augustin-de-Desmaures, G3A 2K1, QC, Canada
Tel.: (418) 878-6161
Web Site: http://www.novik.com
Sales Range: $25-49.9 Million
Polymer Exterior Products Mfr
N.A.I.C.S.: 326199
Ralph Bruno *(CEO)*

Subsidiary (US):

Novik Sales Corp. **(2)**
487 Atlantic Hwy, Brooklyn, NY 11563
Tel.: (516) 599-8678
Exterior Covering & Roofing Products Distr
N.A.I.C.S.: 423330
Mark Eliasson *(Dir-Sls-Key Accts)*

Tando Building Products **(2)**
1111 NW 165th St, Miami, FL 33169-5819
Tel.: (954) 556-1800
Web Site: http://www.tandobp.com
Architectural Building Product Mfr & Distr
N.A.I.C.S.: 327991
Frank McCormack *(VP-Sls)*

Quest Information Systems Inc. **(1)**
8720 Castle Creek Pkwy E Dr Ste 231, Indianapolis, IN 46250
Tel.: (317) 806-8800
Web Site: http://www.questis.com
Emp.: 25
Software Publisher
N.A.I.C.S.: 513210

Wilson Irrigation & Orchard Supply, Inc. **(1)**
1104 East Mead, Yakima, WA 98903
Tel.: (509) 453-9983
Web Site: http://www.wilsonirr.com
Water Supply & Irrigation Systems
N.A.I.C.S.: 221310
Steven Kuhn *(Mgr-Sls & Mktg)*

CLEARVIEW ELECTRIC, INC.
PO Box 130659, Dallas, TX 75313
Tel.: (214) 884-1740
Web Site:
 http://www.clearviewenergy.com
Year Founded: 2006
Sales Range: $25-49.9 Million
Emp.: 20
Electricity Supplier
N.A.I.C.S.: 221122
Frank McGovern *(Pres)*
Rebecca Herrera *(CIO)*

CLEARWATER ENVIRO TECHNOLOGIES, INC.
8767 115th Ave, Largo, FL 33773
Tel.: (727) 562-5186
Web Site: http://www.clearwater-enviro.com
Year Founded: 1989
Sales Range: $1-9.9 Million
Emp.: 20
Water Purification Systems Mfr
N.A.I.C.S.: 221310
Jeff Conway *(CEO)*
Bill Glass *(VP-Sls & Ops)*

CLEARWATER MARINE AQUARIUM, INC.
249 Windward Passage, Clearwater, FL 33767
Tel.: (727) 441-1790 FL
Web Site: http://www.seewinter.com
Year Founded: 2005
Sales Range: $10-24.9 Million
Emp.: 189
Aquarium & Animal Rescue Services
N.A.I.C.S.: 712130
John L. Draheim *(Chm)*
Brent Howie *(Treas)*

CLEARWATER MARINE INC.
1045 33rd St, Saint Cloud, MN 56301
Tel.: (320) 251-3551
Web Site: http://www.weeres.com
Sales Range: $25-49.9 Million
Emp.: 10
Marine Craft
N.A.I.C.S.: 336612
Gordon Brown Jr. *(Pres)*

CLEARWATER MATTRESS, INC.
11025 Spring St, Largo, FL 33774-4336
Tel.: (727) 479-1600
Year Founded: 1931
Sales Range: $25-49.9 Million
Emp.: 109
Retailer of Mattresses
N.A.I.C.S.: 449110
Mel Jones *(Pres & CEO)*

CLEARWATER POWER COMPANY
4230 Hatwai Rd, Lewiston, ID 83501
Tel.: (208) 743-1501
Web Site:
 https://www.clearwaterpower.com
Sales Range: $100-124.9 Million
Emp.: 48
Electric Power Distr
N.A.I.C.S.: 221122
Pamela Anderson *(Pres)*

CLEARWATER SYSTEMS INC.
1411 Vernon Odom Blvd, Akron, OH 44320
Tel.: (330) 836-4946
Web Site:
 https://www.clearwatersystems.com
Sales Range: $10-24.9 Million
Emp.: 80
Provider of Water Purification Equipment
N.A.I.C.S.: 449210

CLEARY BUILDING CORP.
190 Paoli St, Verona, WI 53593
Tel.: (608) 845-9700
Web Site:
 https://www.clearybuilding.com
Rev.: $111,000,000
Emp.: 900
Commercial & Institutional Building Construction
N.A.I.C.S.: 236220
Roger Solberg *(VP-Engrg)*
Tim Johnson *(VP)*
Cory DeSmet *(Asst Mgr-Production Engrg)*
Dan Oconnell *(Reg Mgr-Production)*
Lynn Duerst *(Accountant)*

CLEARY DEVELOPMENTS INC.
32055 Edward Ave, Madison Heights, MI 48071
Tel.: (248) 588-7010
Web Site: http://www.belmont4.com
Rev.: $30,000,000
Emp.: 75
Industrial Machinery & Equipment
N.A.I.C.S.: 423830

CLEARY GOTTLIEB STEEN & HAMILTON LLP
1 Liberty Plz, New York, NY 10006
Tel.: (212) 225-2000
Web Site:
 https://www.clearygottlieb.com
Year Founded: 1946
Sales Range: $1-4.9 Billion
Emp.: 3,000
Legal Advisory Services
N.A.I.C.S.: 541110

Michael Albano *(Partner)*
Christopher E. Austin *(Partner)*
Luke A. Barefoot *(Partner)*
Kimberly Brown Blacklow *(Partner)*
Jonathan I. Blackman *(Partner)*
Craig B. Brod *(Partner)*
David E. Brodsky *(Partner)*
James L. Bromley *(Partner)*
Lee C. Buchheit *(Partner)*
Richard J. Cooper *(Partner)*
Roger A. Cooper *(Partner)*
Lev L. Dassin *(Partner)*
Robert P. Davis *(Partner)*
Michael D. Dayan *(Partner)*
Claudia Annacker *(Partner-Paris)*
Gamal M. Abouali *(Partner-Abu Dhabi)*
Gabriele Antonazzo *(Partner-Hong Kong)*
Gabriele Apfelbacher *(Partner-Frankfurt)*
Murat N. Akuyev *(Partner-Moscow)*
Sam Bagot *(Partner-London)*
Michael A. Gerstenzang *(Mng Partner)*
Nallini Puri *(Partner)*
Carmine D. Boccuzzi Jr. *(Partner)*

CLECO CORPORATE HOLDINGS LLC
2030 Donahue Ferry Rd, Pineville, LA 71360-5226
Tel.: (318) 484-7400 LA
Web Site: https://www.cleco.com
Year Founded: 1934
Rev.: $2,239,132,000
Assets: $8,253,749,000
Liabilities: $5,306,682,000
Net Worth: $2,947,067,000
Earnings: $188,811,000
Emp.: 2,109
Fiscal Year-end: 12/31/22
Electric Power & Energy Services
N.A.I.C.S.: 221122
William G. Fontenot *(Pres & CEO)*
F. Tonita Laprarie *(Chief Acctg Officer & Controller)*
Peggy B. Scott *(Chm)*
Justin S. Hilton *(Pres-Cleco Power LLC)*
Kristin L. Guillory *(CFO)*
Normanique G. Preston *(Chief HR & Diversity Officer)*
Mark Madsen *(Chief Information & Supply Chain Officer)*
Richard Sharp *(Interim Pres)*

CLEGG INSURANCE GROUP, INC.
1314 S Fort Harrison Ave, Clearwater, FL 33756
Tel.: (727) 216-6555
Web Site:
 https://www.clegginsurance.com
Sales Range: $1-9.9 Million
Emp.: 5
Insurance Agents
N.A.I.C.S.: 524210
Ryan J. Clegg *(Pres & CEO)*
Alexandra Faust *(VP)*
Andrew Hughes *(COO)*

CLEGG'S TERMITE AND PEST CONTROL, INC.
2401 Reichard St, Durham, NC 27705
Tel.: (919) 477-2134
Web Site: https://www.cleggs.com
Sales Range: $10-24.9 Million
Emp.: 275
Termite & Pest Control
N.A.I.C.S.: 561710
Phillip G. Clegg Sr. *(Pres)*

CLEMCO INDUSTRIES CORP.

1 Cablecar Dr, Washington, MO 63090-1119
Tel.: (636) 239-0300
Web Site:
 https://www.clemcoindustries.com
Sales Range: $50-74.9 Million
Emp.: 120
Mfr of a Full Range of Blast Machines & Specialized Equipment
N.A.I.C.S.: 333310
Patti Roman *(VP-Mktg)*
Arnie Sallaberry *(Pres)*
Mike Moshman *(Controller)*

Subsidiaries:

Clemco Danmark ApS **(1)**
Niels Bohrs Vej 40, 8660, Skanderborg, Denmark
Tel.: (45) 7013 1030
Web Site: http://www.clemco.dk
Industrial Machinery Mfr
N.A.I.C.S.: 333248

Clemco International GmbH **(1)**
Carl-Zeiss-Str 21, Bruckmuhl, 83052, Germany
Tel.: (49) 80 62 90 08 0
Web Site: http://www.clemco-international.com
Industrial Machinery Mfr
N.A.I.C.S.: 333248
J. Douglas R. Bottrich *(Mng Dir)*

Clemco International, S.A. **(1)**
Pol Ugaldeguren I Parcela 1-III-B, 48170, Zamudio, Bizkaia, Spain
Tel.: (34) 94 453 5712
Web Site: http://www.clemco.es
Industrial Machinery Mfr
N.A.I.C.S.: 333248

Clemco KFT **(1)**
Agfalvi U 12, 9400, Sopron, Hungary
Tel.: (36) 99336770
Industrial Machinery Mfr
N.A.I.C.S.: 333248

Munkebo Clemco A/S **(1)**
Smedeloekken 5-7, 5330, Munkebo, Denmark
Tel.: (45) 65 97 4 380
Web Site: http://www.munkebo.com
Industrial Machinery Mfr
N.A.I.C.S.: 333248

CLEMENS & ASSOCIATES INSURANCE AGENCY INC.
2806 E Empire St, Bloomington, IL 61702
Tel.: (309) 662-2100
Web Site: http://www.clemensins.com
Year Founded: 1948
Emp.: 200
Insurance Property & Casualty Services
N.A.I.C.S.: 524210
Richard J. Percy *(Pres)*
Jeff Niepagen *(Pres-Property & Casualty Div)*

CLEMENS AVIATION LLC
3628 N Jabara Rd, Wichita, KS 67226
Tel.: (316) 260-8840
Web Site:
 https://www.clemensaviation.com
Emp.: 100
Aircraft Maintenance Services
N.A.I.C.S.: 488190
Dwayne Clemens *(Owner)*

Subsidiaries:

Midwest Corporate Aviation, Inc. **(1)**
3512 N Webb Rd, Wichita, KS 67226
Tel.: (316) 636-9700
Web Site: http://www.midwestaviation.com
Rev.: $6,565,000
Emp.: 100
Other Airport Operations
N.A.I.C.S.: 488119
Brian Strunk *(CFO)*
Kerry Lehman *(Mgr-Customer Svc)*

Clemens Construction Co. Inc.—(Continued)

CLEMENS CONSTRUCTION CO. INC.
1435 Walnut St, Philadelphia, PA, 19102-3219
Tel.: (215) 567-5757   PA
Web Site:
https://www.clemensconstruction.com
Year Founded: 1979
Sales Range: $50-74.9 Million
Emp.: 175
Contracting Construction Company
N.A.I.C.S.: 236220
Stephen Pouppirt (Pres)
Ruben Martinez (Mgr-Safety)
Betty Roselle (Controller)
David Russell (CFO)
Graham Stewart (VP)
Ron Meyers (VP-Ops)
Paul Horning (VP-Preconstruction)

Subsidiaries:

Clemens Construction Co. Inc   (1)
1435 Walnut St 2nd Fl, Philadelphia, PA 19102
Tel.: (215) 567-5757
Web Site:
http://www.clemensconstruction.com
Sales Range: $10-24.9 Million
Emp.: 100
Contracting Construction Company
N.A.I.C.S.: 236220

CLEMENS FAMILY CORPORATION
2700 Clemens St, Hatfield, PA 19440
Tel.: (215) 368-2500
Web Site:
http://www.clemensfamilycorp.com
Sales Range: $200-249.9 Million
Emp.: 1,200
Holding Company
N.A.I.C.S.: 112210
Douglas C. Clemens (Pres)
Philip A. Clemens (Chm & CEO)

Subsidiaries:

Hatfield Quality Meats, Inc.   (1)
2700 Clemens Rd, Hatfield, PA 19440-0902
Tel.: (215) 368-2500
Web Site:
http://www.hatfieldqualitymeats.com
Sales Range: $400-449.9 Million
Meat Packing
N.A.I.C.S.: 311611
Douglas C. Clemens (Pres)

CLEMENT CONTRACTING GROUP INC.
1325 Kershaw St, Montgomery, AL 36108
Tel.: (334) 265-0200
Web Site: http://www.clement-inc.com
Year Founded: 1978
Sales Range: $10-24.9 Million
Emp.: 60
Provider of General Contracting Services
N.A.I.C.S.: 236220
Diana Lee Gaines (Sec)
John Story (Controller)
Todd Hicks (VP & Project Mgr)

CLEMENTINA-CLEMCO HOLDING INC.
445 Bush St Fl 9, San Francisco, CA 94108
Tel.: (415) 296-8400
Web Site:
http://www.clemcoindustries.com
Sales Range: $25-49.9 Million
Emp.: 350
Holding Company; Sandblasting Equipment
N.A.I.C.S.: 333310

Mark Cleary (Pres)
Dan Ryan (CFO)

CLEMENTS FOODS COMPANY
6601 N Harvey Pl, Oklahoma City, OK 73116-7911
Tel.: (405) 842-3308   OK
Web Site:
http://www.clementsfoods.com
Year Founded: 1954
Sales Range: $100-124.9 Million
Emp.: 250
Jellies, Preserves, Mayonnaise, Salad Dressing, Syrups, Mustard, Vinegar & Peanut Butter Mfr
N.A.I.C.S.: 311421
Edward B. Clements (Pres)
Richard H. Clements (Chm & CFO)
Robert H. Clements (Exec VP)

Subsidiaries:

Clements Nut Co.   (1)
614 E Main St, Lewisville, TX 75057
Tel.: (972) 436-4596
Emp.: 45
Mfr of Peanut Butter
N.A.I.C.S.: 311911
Edward B. Clements (Pres)
Jack Pattengale (Plant Mgr)

CLENDENIN BROTHERS INC.
4309 Erdman Ave, Baltimore, MD 21213
Tel.: (410) 327-4500
Web Site:
https://www.clendeninbrothers.com
Year Founded: 1969
Sales Range: $10-24.9 Million
Emp.: 100
Nails: Aluminum, Brass, Or Other Nonferrous Metal Or Wire
N.A.I.C.S.: 332722
Jay Corckran (Owner)
Kent Smith (Mgr-Sys)
John C. Cochran Jr. (Pres)

CLEO BAY USED CARS
2125 E Stan Schlueter Loop, Killeen, TX 76542
Tel.: (254) 634-3175
Web Site:
https://www.cleobaysubaru.com
Sales Range: $10-24.9 Million
Emp.: 47
Car Whslr
N.A.I.C.S.: 441110
Brett Dehm (Mgr-Svc)

CLEO COMMUNICATIONS, INC.
4949 Harrison Ave Ste 200, Rockford, IL 61108
Tel.: (815) 282-7695   IL
Web Site: https://www.cleo.com
Year Founded: 1976
Sales Range: $10-24.9 Million
Business-to-Business Software Publisher
N.A.I.C.S.: 513210
Mahesh Rajasekharan (Pres & CEO)
Jorge Rodriguez (Sr VP-Product Dev)
Dave Brunswick (VP-Solutions)
Ken Lyons (Sr VP-Worldwide Sls)
Kerrie Carroll (Dir-HR)
John Thielens (CTO)
Stanley Stec (VP-Fin)
Tushar Patel (CMO)
Vidya Chadaga (VP-Products)

Subsidiaries:

Extol International Inc.   (1)
529 Terry Reiley Way 3rd Fl, Pottsville, PA 17901
Tel.: (815) 282-7695
Web Site: http://www.extol.com
Emp.: 80

Data Transformation & Software Integration Solutions
N.A.I.C.S.: 541519

CLEOPATRA'S BARGE FINE JEWELRY
1197 3rd St S, Naples, FL 34102
Tel.: (239) 261-7952
Web Site:
https://www.cleopatrasbarge.com
Year Founded: 1966
Sales Range: Less than $1 Million
Emp.: 5
Jewelry Designer & Retailer
N.A.I.C.S.: 458310
Marilyn Janss (Owner)

CLERIO VISION INC.
150 Lucios Gordon Dr, West Henrietta, NY 14586
Tel.: (941) 739-1382
Web Site: http://www.cleriovision.com
Year Founded: 2014
Laser-Based Vision Correction Solutions
N.A.I.C.S.: 333310
Alex Zapesochny (Chm & Co-CEO)
Mikael Totterman (Co-CEO)
Trevor McCaw (Pres & COO)
Jay Baker (CFO)

Subsidiaries:

Hydrogel Vision Corp.   (1)
7575 Commerce Court, 34243, Sarasota, FL
Tel.: (941) 739-1382
Web Site: http://www.hydrogelvision.com
Sales Range: $1-9.9 Million
Emp.: 28
Ophthalmic Goods Merchant Whslr
N.A.I.C.S.: 423460

CLEVE BATTE CONSTRUCTION INC.
3837 E St, Texarkana, AR 71854
Tel.: (870) 773-0300
Rev.: $11,600,000
Emp.: 25
Site Preparation Contractor
N.A.I.C.S.: 238910
Nelda Batte (Sec & VP)
Cleve Batte (Pres)
Juanita Buckley (Office Mgr)

CLEVELAND BROTHERS EQUIPMENT CO., INC.
5300 Paxton St, Harrisburg, PA 17111
Tel.: (717) 564-2121   DE
Web Site:
https://www.clevelandbrothers.com
Year Founded: 1948
Sales Range: $400-449.9 Million
Emp.: 1,300
Construction Machinery Rental, Sale & Parts Whslr
N.A.I.C.S.: 423810
J. W. Cleveland Jr. (Pres & CEO)

Subsidiaries:

Cleveland Brothers Equipment   (1)
4565 William Penn Hwy, Murrysville, PA 15668-2003
Tel.: (724) 327-1300
Web Site: http://beckwith.cat.com
Sales Range: $25-49.9 Million
Emp.: 200
Whslr of Non-Electrical Machinery
N.A.I.C.S.: 423810
David Hough (Sr Mgr-Credit)
Jay W. Cleveland Jr. (Pres & CEO)

CLEVELAND BROWNS FOOTBALL COMPANY LLC
76 Lou Groza Blvd, Berea, OH 44017-1238
Tel.: (440) 824-6284   DE
Web Site:
http://www.clevelandbrowns.com

Sales Range: $150-199.9 Million
Emp.: 200
Professional Football Franchise
N.A.I.C.S.: 711211
David Lee (Sr Mgr-Ticket Ops)
Laurie Rice (Controller)
David A. Jenkins (CFO & Exec VP)
Michael Nikolaus (Chief HR Officer)
Gregory Rush (Dir-Fin)
Brandon Covert (Dir-IT)
Matthew Srodek (Mgr-Berea Facilities)
Jimmy Haslam (Owner)
Rob Pavlas (Asst Dir-Video)

CLEVELAND CAPITAL HOLDINGS, INC.
681 NC 120 Hwy, Mooresboro, NC 28114-6713
Tel.: (828) 453-2200   NC
Sales Range: $75-99.9 Million
Emp.: 50
Holding Company
N.A.I.C.S.: 424720
Mike Frost (CEO)
Hampton C. Hager (Pres)
Margie Malarchik (Controller)

Subsidiaries:

Petroleum World, Inc.   (1)
681 NC 120 Hwy, Mooresboro, NC 28114-6713   (100%)
Tel.: (828) 453-7351
Sales Range: $125-149.9 Million
Crude Oil & Petroleum Field Services
N.A.I.C.S.: 424720
Deborah Sailors Potter (Pres)

CLEVELAND CEMENT CONTRACTORS INC.
4823 Van Epps Rd, Cleveland, OH 44131-1015
Tel.: (804) 524-2280
Web Site:
https://www.clevelandcement.com
Year Founded: 1968
Sales Range: $50-74.9 Million
Emp.: 400
Concrete Work Services
N.A.I.C.S.: 238110
Michael H. Simonetti (Pres)
Tedric Wilkinson (VP)

CLEVELAND CITY FORGE
46950 State Rte 18 W, Wellington, OH 44090
Tel.: (440) 647-5400
Web Site:
https://www.clevelandcityforge.com
Year Founded: 1864
Forged Steel Fasteners Mfr
N.A.I.C.S.: 332722
Jim Evans (Gen Mgr-IT & Pur)
Shelly Fairchild (Mgr-Mktg Div)

CLEVELAND COIN MACHINE EXCHANGE, INC.
#2 3860 Ben Hur Ave, Willoughby, OH 44094-6370
Tel.: (216) 692-0960   OH
Web Site: http://www.ccme.net
Year Founded: 1937
Sales Range: $10-24.9 Million
Emp.: 60
Supplier of Vending Machines
N.A.I.C.S.: 423850
Ronald Gold (CEO)
Ron Nickleson (Controller)
Sheldon Gisser (VP)
Barbara Bardin (VP)

CLEVELAND COMMUNICATIONS
Wardsworth Vlg 130 Center St, Danvers, MA 01923
Tel.: (978) 777-9151

Media Buying Services
N.A.I.C.S.: 541830
Melissa Noyes (VP & Dir-Media)

CLEVELAND CONSTRUCTION INC.

8620 Tyler Blvd, Mentor, OH 44060-4348
Tel.: (513) 398-8900
Web Site:
http://www.clevelandconstruction.com
Year Founded: 1980
Sales Range: $150-199.9 Million
Emp.: 800
Construction Contracting Services
N.A.I.C.S.: 236220
Richard G. Small (Founder, Chm & CEO)
Jon Small (Pres)
Mark T. Small (CFO, Treas & Sr VP-Project Mgmt)
Jeff Campbell (Dir-Client Dev)

CLEVELAND DIE & MANUFACTURING, CO.

20303 1st Ave, Middleburg Heights, OH 44130
Tel.: (440) 243-3404
Web Site:
https://www.clevelanddie.com
Year Founded: 1973
Sales Range: $10-24.9 Million
Emp.: 125
Metal Stamping Services
N.A.I.C.S.: 332119
Juan Chahda (Owner & Pres)
Liliana Chahda (VP & CFO)
Vladimir Haoui (Plant Mgr)

CLEVELAND FOUNDATION

6601 Euclid Ave, Cleveland, OH 44103
Tel.: (216) 861-3810
Web Site:
https://www.clevelandfoundation.org
Year Founded: 1914
Social Organization Services
N.A.I.C.S.: 813920

CLEVELAND GROUP, INC.

1281 Fulton Industrial Blvd NW, Atlanta, GA 30336-1527
Tel.: (404) 696-4550   GA
Web Site: http://www.clevelectric.com
Sales Range: $10-24.9 Million
Emp.: 500
Holding Company; Electrical, Mechanical & Instrumentation Construction & Construction Management Services
N.A.I.C.S.: 551112
J. R. Cleveland (Owner & Pres)
A. Eddy Zai (CEO)

Subsidiaries:

Aviation Constructors, Inc.   (1)
601 N Ashley Dr Ste 1100, Tampa, FL 33602   (100%)
Tel.: (813) 490-4300
Sales Range: $10-24.9 Million
Emp.: 50
General Construction & Construction Management Services
N.A.I.C.S.: 238210

Cleveland Electric Co.   (1)
1281 Fulton Industrial Blvd NW, Atlanta, GA 30336-1527   (100%)
Tel.: (404) 696-4550
Web Site: http://www.clevelectric.com
Sales Range: $10-24.9 Million
Emp.: 50
Plumbing, Heating & Air Conditioning Installation
N.A.I.C.S.: 238210
James R. Cleveland Jr. (Pres)

CLEVELAND HARDWARE & FORGING CO.

3270 E 79th St, Cleveland, OH 44104
Tel.: (216) 641-5200
Web Site:
https://www.clevelandhardware.com
Year Founded: 1878
Sales Range: $25-49.9 Million
Emp.: 180
Hardware Mfr & Distr
N.A.I.C.S.: 423710
Kathy Carpenter (Mgr-Inside Sls)
William E. Hoban (CEO)
Jim Socha (CFO)

CLEVELAND HOUSING NETWORK

2999 Payne Ave, Cleveland, OH 44114
Tel.: (216) 574-7100   OH
Web Site: http://www.chnnet.com
Year Founded: 1981
Sales Range: $25-49.9 Million
Emp.: 210
Community Housing Services
N.A.I.C.S.: 624229
Mary Smigelski (CFO)
Mark Whipkey (Dir-Asset Mgmt)
Rob Curry (Exec Dir)
Jeanne Morton (Dir-Community Resources)
Pat Kenney (COO)

CLEVELAND INDIANS BASEBALL COMPANY, INC.

2401 Ontario St, Cleveland, OH 44115
Tel.: (216) 420-4200   OH
Web Site: http://www.indians.com
Year Founded: 1901
Sales Range: $50-74.9 Million
Emp.: 150
Professional Baseball Club
N.A.I.C.S.: 711211
Bob DiBiasio (Sr VP-Publ Affairs)
Sara Lehrke (Chief Diversity Officer & VP-HR)
Ross Atkins (VP-Player Dev)
Curtis Danburg (Sr Dir-Comm)
Sarah Taylor (Controller)
Jerry Crabb (Sr Dir-Ballpark Ops)
Paul Joseph Dolan (Chm & CEO)
John Mirabelli (Sr Dir-Scouting)
Whitney Kuszmaul (Dir-IT)
Neil Weiss (CIO & Sr VP-Tech)

CLEVELAND INSTITUTE OF ELECTRONICS

1776 E 17th St, Cleveland, OH 44114
Tel.: (216) 781-9400   OH
Web Site: https://www.cie-wc.edu
Year Founded: 1934
Independent Study Electronics Training School
N.A.I.C.S.: 611519
John Randall Drinko (Pres)

Subsidiaries:

World College   (1)
593 Shore Dr Ste 105, Virginia Beach, VA 23455   (100%)
Tel.: (757) 464-4600
Web Site: http://www.worldcollege.edu
Sales Range: $10-24.9 Million
Emp.: 10
Electronic Engineering Educational Services
N.A.I.C.S.: 611519

CLEVELAND MACK SALES INC.

1287 US Hwy 59 N, Cleveland, TX 77328
Tel.: (281) 593-8888

Web Site:
https://www.performancetruck.com
Rev.: $93,600,000
Emp.: 225
Commercial Truck Sales Part & Service
N.A.I.C.S.: 423110
Robert C. Sweeten (Pres)
Lee Bailey (CEO)

CLEVELAND MARBLE MOSAIC COMPANY

4595 Hinckley Industrial, Cleveland, OH 44109
Tel.: (216) 749-2840
Web Site:
https://www.clevelandmarble.com
Rev.: $17,761,280
Emp.: 246
Marble Installation, Interior
N.A.I.C.S.: 238340
Robert J. Zavagno (Pres)

CLEVELAND MEDICAL DEVICES, INC.

4415 Euclid Ave Ste 400, Cleveland, OH 44103
Tel.: (216) 791-6720   OH
Web Site: http://www.clevemed.com
Year Founded: 1991
Sales Range: $1-9.9 Million
Emp.: 43
Electromedical Equipment Mfr
N.A.I.C.S.: 334510
Robert N. Schmidt (Founder, Chm & CEO)
Hani Kayyali (Pres)

CLEVELAND MUSEUM OF ART

11150 E Blvd, Cleveland, OH 44106
Tel.: (216) 421-7350   OH
Web Site:
https://www.clevelandart.org
Year Founded: 1913
Sales Range: $75-99.9 Million
Emp.: 465
Art Gallery Services
N.A.I.C.S.: 712110
James A. Ratner (Vice Chm)
Edward Bauer (Treas)
Scott C. Mueller (Vice Chm)
Sarah S. Cutler (Vice Chm & Sec)
William Griswold (Pres & CEO)
Heather Saunders (Dir-Ingalls Library)

CLEVELAND MUSEUM OF NATURAL HISTORY

1 Wade Oval Dr, Cleveland, OH 44106
Tel.: (216) 231-4600   OH
Web Site: https://www.cmnh.org
Year Founded: 1920
Sales Range: $10-24.9 Million
Museum Operator
N.A.I.C.S.: 712110
Jonathon L. Grimm (Chm)
James L. Hambrick (Vice Chm)
R. Douglas McCreery (Sec)
Sonia Winner (Pres & CEO)
Melissa Santee (Chief Philanthropy Officer)
Meenakshi Sharma (Chief Strategy Officer)
Jeannie Sureck (Chief HR & Ops Officer)
Kenneth Outcalt (Treas)

CLEVELAND PLANT AND FLOWER COMPANY

12920 Corporate Dr, Parma, OH 44130
Tel.: (216) 898-3500
Web Site: http://www.cpfco.com
Rev.: $29,871,722

Emp.: 28
Flowers, Fresh
Walter James Priest (Gen Mgr)

CLEVELAND PLUMBING SUPPLY CO., INC.

143 E Washington St, Chagrin Falls, OH 44022
Tel.: (440) 247-2555   OH
Web Site:
https://www.clevelandplumbing.com
Year Founded: 1932
Sales Range: $10-24.9 Million
Emp.: 12
Distr of Plumbing Supplies
N.A.I.C.S.: 423720
Bob Talenda (Dir-Fin)
Bob Pleban (Mgr-Medina)
Curtis Mullet (Mgr-Middlefield)
Fred Cruz (Mgr-Mentor)
Jeff Gilson (Mgr-Wooster)
Tom Barnard (Mgr-Cleveland)
Gene Groff (Mgr-Chagrin Falls)
Bart Morvilius (VP)
Thom Brabenec (VP-Ops)
Rick Bacher (Coord-Product-North Ridgeville)

CLEVELAND STEEL CONTAINER CORPORATION

30310 Emerald Vly Pkwy Ste 400, Glenwillow, OH 44139
Tel.: (440) 349-8000
Web Site: http://www.cscpails.com
Year Founded: 1963
Metal Tank Mfr
N.A.I.C.S.: 332431
Chris Page (Owner)

Subsidiaries:

Pipeline Packaging Corporation   (1)
30310 Emerald Vly Pkwy Ste 500, Glenwillow, OH 44139
Tel.: (800) 446-0351
Web Site: http://www.pipelinepackaging.com
Services Related to Advertising
N.A.I.C.S.: 541890
Susan Washburn (Mgr)
Chris Nelson (Pres)

Subsidiary (Domestic):

HAZMATPAC, Inc.   (2)
7905 Blankenship Dr, Houston, TX 77055-1005
Tel.: (713) 923-2222
Web Site: http://www.hazmatpac.com
Corrugated & Solid Fiber Box Mfr
N.A.I.C.S.: 322211
Donald H. Hausmann (Pres)

Midstates Container Company   (2)
4170 Geraldine Ave, Saint Louis, MO 63115
Tel.: (314) 696-2312
Web Site:
http://www.midstatescontainer.com
Rev.: $3,700,000
Emp.: 4
Industrial Containers Distr
N.A.I.C.S.: 423990
Gregg Tureen (Principal)

CLEVELAND UTILITIES

2450 Guthrie Ave NW, Cleveland, TN 37311
Tel.: (423) 472-4521
Web Site:
https://www.clevelandutilities.com
Sales Range: $25-49.9 Million
Emp.: 180
Other Electric Power Generation
N.A.I.C.S.: 221118
Philip Luce (Mgr-Water Div Engrg)
Walt Vineyard (Exec VP)
Dean Watson (Mgr-Ops)

CLEVELAND VICON CO. INC.

4550 Willow Pkwy, Cleveland, OH 44125

Cleveland Vicon Co. Inc.—(Continued)

Tel.: (216) 341-3300
Web Site:
   http://www.clevelandvicon.com
Sales Range: $10-24.9 Million
Emp.: 50
Provider of Building Supplies & Services
N.A.I.C.S.: 423710
Greg Poe (Pres)

CLEVER DEVICES LTD.
300 Crossways Park Dr, Woodbury, NY 11797
Tel.: (516) 433-6100
Web Site:
   https://www.cleverdevices.com
Rev.: $12,000,000
Emp.: 150
Intelligent Transportation Systems
N.A.I.C.S.: 334419
Andrew Stanton (COO)
Buddy Coleman (Exec VP)
Frank Ingrassia (CEO)
Monica Malhotra (Sr VP-Bus Ops)
Mike Elgarten (Chief Strategy Officer)
Mauricio Consulo (Mng Dir-Latin America)
Amy Miller (Mng Dir-Mktg & Sls Ops)
Robert Manaseri (Mng Dir-Svc)
Joe Saporita (Sr VP-Bus Dev)
Diane Mincarelli (VP-Rail Tech)
Saundra Graman (VP-Strategic Accts)
Darryl Curtis (VP-Tech)
Linda Amper (Chief People Officer)
Christos Karanicolas (VP-Engrg)

CLEVERMETHOD, INC.
1200 Maple Rd, Elma, NY 14059
Tel.: (716) 805-1065
Web Site:
   http://www.clevermethod.com
Year Founded: 2000
Sales Range: $10-24.9 Million
Emp.: 15
Customized Software & Web Development
N.A.I.C.S.: 541512
Bob Henry (Mgr-Web Dev)
Matt Hasselback (Partner)
Doug Kasperek (Partner)

CLEVERTECH
535 Forest Ave, Woodmere, NY 11598
Web Site: http://www.clevertech.biz
Year Founded: 2000
Sales Range: $1-9.9 Million
Emp.: 45
Custom Software Designers & Mfr
N.A.I.C.S.: 513210
Kuty Shalev (CEO)

CLEVERWORKS
150 River Rd Unit G2A, Montville, NJ 07045
Tel.: (973) 794-4941
Web Site: http://www.cleverworks.us
Year Founded: 2005
Rev.: $32,000,000
Emp.: 4
N.A.I.C.S.: 541810
Mike McHale (Founder)

CLEWS & STRAWBRIDGE
310 Lancaster Ave, Frazer, PA 19355
Tel.: (610) 644-3529
Web Site: http://www.clewsboats.com
Year Founded: 1954
Sales Range: $10-24.9 Million
Emp.: 48
Boat & Ship Retailer
N.A.I.C.S.: 441222
Tom McCabe (Mgr-Svc)

CLH INC.
638-640 Summer St, Lynn, MA 01905
Tel.: (781) 592-6444
Sales Range: $10-24.9 Million
Emp.: 50
Adhesives Production
N.A.I.C.S.: 325520
Leopoldo A. Johnson (Pres)

CLH INTERNATIONAL INC.
1337 E University Dr, Tempe, AZ 85281
Tel.: (480) 829-1350
Web Site: http://www.clh.com
Sales Range: $1-9.9 Million
Emp.: 9
Computer & Computer Peripheral Equipment & Software Merchant Wholesalers
N.A.I.C.S.: 423430
Will Aussenhofer (Sr Acct Exec)

CLI CORPORATION
Ste 201 6108 Brownsville Rd Ext, Finleyville, PA 15332-4132
Tel.: (724) 348-4800
Web Site: http://www.clicorp.com
Year Founded: 1987
Sales Range: $10-24.9 Million
Emp.: 23
Engineering Consulting & Design Services
N.A.I.C.S.: 541330
David Hartley (Gen Mgr-Ops)
William C. Stein Jr. (Pres & Principal)

Subsidiaries:

Homer City Coal Processing Co.   (1)
Ste 201 6108 Brownsville Rd Ext, Finleyville, PA 15332-4132
Tel.: (724) 348-4800
Web Site: http://www.clicorp.com
Dual Circuit, Multi-Gravity, Heavy Media Cyclone Plant
N.A.I.C.S.: 212114

CLIC TECHNOLOGY, INC.
20200 W Dixie Hwy Ste 1202, Miami, FL 33180
Tel.: (305) 918-1202   NV
Web Site:
   http://www.clictechnology.com
Year Founded: 2015
Rev.: $7,500
Assets: $594,686
Liabilities: $911,369
Net Worth: ($316,683)
Earnings: $696,940
Emp.: 14
Fiscal Year-end: 09/30/18
Investment Services
N.A.I.C.S.: 523999
Richard Keller (CEO)

CLICK CAMERA SHOP INCORPORATED
7602 N Main St, Clayton, OH 45415
Tel.: (937) 890-4687   OH
Web Site:
   http://www.clickcamera.com
Year Founded: 1945
Sales Range: $10-24.9 Million
Emp.: 35
Retailer of Cameras
N.A.I.C.S.: 449210
Mack Leonard (Pres & CEO)

CLICK HERE, INC.
2801 N Central Expy Ste 100, Dallas, TX 75204
Tel.: (214) 891-5325
Web Site: http://www.clickhere.com
Year Founded: 1995
Rev.: $151,000,000
Emp.: 140
Advertising Agencies
N.A.I.C.S.: 541810

Pete Lerma (Principal)
Kyle Sawai (Principal & Dir-Acct Mgmt)
Brian Nadurak (Principal & Dir-Digital Creative)
Randy Bradshaw (Dir-Technical Production)
Cheryl Huckabay (Principal)
Cort Gorman (Principal-Digital Media)
James Hering (Acct Dir-Digital)

Subsidiaries:

Click Here   (1)
7777 Center Ave Ste 150, Huntington Beach, CA 92647
Tel.: (214) 891-7625
N.A.I.C.S.: 541810

CLICKAWAY CORPORATION
457 E McGlincy Ln Ste 1, Campbell, CA 95008
Tel.: (408) 626-9050
Web Site: http://www.clickaway.com
Year Founded: 2002
Sales Range: $1-9.9 Million
Emp.: 35
Data & Networking Services & Computer Maintenance & Repair
N.A.I.C.S.: 811210
Rick Sutherland (Pres & CEO)
Nick Vellios (Mgr)
Susanna Simonyan (Mgr-Acctg)
Oliver Rowen (VP-Ops)

CLICKCULTURE
3739 National Dr Ste 210, Raleigh, NC 27612
Tel.: (919) 420-7736
Web Site: http://www.clickculture.com
Sales Range: $10-24.9 Million
Emp.: 10
Advertising Agencies
N.A.I.C.S.: 541810
Lloyd Jacobs (Pres & CEO)
Carol Lewis (Exec Dir-Media)

CLICKER INC.
1111 Kane Concourse Ste 304, Bay Harbor Islands, FL 33154
Tel.: (786) 309-5190   NV
Web Site: http://www.clickerinc.com
Year Founded: 1984
Sales Range: Less than $1 Million
Internet Publisher & Broadcaster
N.A.I.C.S.: 516210
Willis Arndt Jr. (Interim CEO)

CLICKIT VENTURES, LLC
1698 Hwy 160 W Ste 240, Fort Mill, SC 29708
Tel.: (803) 802-3513
Web Site:
   http://www.clickitventures.com
Year Founded: 2001
Rev.: $2,100,000
Emp.: 5
Office Administrative Services
N.A.I.C.S.: 561110
Chris Quinn (Founder, Pres & Mng Partner)
Robert Browning (Mng Partner & VP)

CLICKMAIL MARKETING, INC.
155 Bovet Rd Ste 310, San Mateo, CA 94402
Tel.: (650) 653-8055
Web Site: http://clickmail.com
Year Founded: 2001
Sales Range: $10-24.9 Million
Emp.: 16
Business-To-Business, Consumer Marketing, Corporate Identity, Crisis Communications, Email, High Technology, Integrated Marketing
N.A.I.C.S.: 541810

Russ Cerminaro (CFO)
Cameron Kane (CTO)
Marco Marini (CEO)
Jessa Halford (Dir-Customer Success)

CLICKSHOPS INC.
509 N 5th Ave Ste H, Sandpoint, ID 83864
Tel.: (208) 946-4737
Web Site: http://www.clickshops.com
Year Founded: 2005
Sales Range: $1-9.9 Million
Emp.: 11
Owns & Operates 25 Niche Market Websites, Assisting Customers Locate Unique Products
N.A.I.C.S.: 459999
Michelle Tufford (COO)

CLICKSPRING DESIGN
200 Lexington Ave, New York, NY 10016
Tel.: (212) 220-0962
Web Site:
   http://www.clickspringdesign.com
Sales Range: $10-24.9 Million
Emp.: 13
N.A.I.C.S.: 541810
Erik Ulfers (Principal)
Steven Dvorak (Designer)
Karen Engelmann (Copywriter)
Tom Schwinn (Dir-Ops)
Nicholas Pecsok (Designer)
Shweta Votra (Designer)
Raeford Dwyer (Partner-Strategic)
Peter Provost (Partner-Strategic)
Lori Nadler (Sr VP-Fin & Ops)
Tarrant Smith (Designer)
Robin Jacobs (Dir-Sls & Mktg)

CLICKSTOP INC.
202 Blue Creek Dr, Urbana, IA 52345
Web Site: https://www.clickstop.com
Year Founded: 2005
Sales Range: $1-9.9 Million
Emp.: 55
Online Retail Stores Operator
N.A.I.C.S.: 541613
Todd Kuennen (Chief Intelligence Officer & Exec VP)
Jim Mayhew (Chief Culture Officer)
Adam Shouse (Dir-Sls & Svc)
Tammy Karr (Gen Mgr-Bling)
Tom Altman (VP-Tech)
Monica Steffeck (VP-Talent Enrichment)
Jeremy Meyer (Dir-Mfg)
Joe Rauch (Dir-Freight & Shipping)
Travis Matuska (Supvr-Receiving & Inventory Control)
Jim Waite (Mgr-Quality)
Alex Ledger (VP-Sls & Mktg)
Sara Alden (Dir-Agile Mktg)
Matt Mitchell (Dir-Analytical Mktg)
Kerry Trenkamp (Dir-Creative Mktg)
Patrick Weber (Dir-Internet Mktg)
Krystal Talbert (Dir-Bus Intelligence)
Kala Liebe (Dir-Talent)
Summer Smith (Dir-Community & Engagement)
Chad Brandmeyer (CFO)
Phil Akin (CMO)
Zach Schmit (Chief Sls Officer)

CLICKTOSHOP, LLC
2001 County Rd C2 W, Roseville, MN 55113
Web Site: http://www.clicktoshop.com
Year Founded: 2007
Sales Range: $1-9.9 Million
Emp.: 14
Niche Online Retailer of Home, Garden & Seasonal Merchandise
N.A.I.C.S.: 459999
Brendan McCarthy (Founder & Pres)

CLIENT 1ST ADVISORS, INC.
611 Druid Rd E Ste 707, Clearwater, FL 33756
Tel.: (727) 450-2301
Web Site:
http://www.client1stadvisors.com
Sales Range: $1-9.9 Million
Emp.: 5
Portfolio Management
N.A.I.C.S.: 523940
Craig Phillips (CEO & Mng Partner)
Dave Stieh (COO & Mng Partner)
Andrea Mears (Mng Partner)
Herbert Pontzer (Chief Compliance Officer)
Irene Kijak (Office Mgr)
Michelle Mabry (Pres & Mng Dir)

CLIENT ATTRACTION LLC
PO Box 62, Stamford, CT 06904
Web Site:
http://www.clientattraction.com
Year Founded: 2006
Sales Range: $1-9.9 Million
Emp.: 10
Marketing Consulting
N.A.I.C.S.: 541613
Fabienne Fredrickson (Pres)

CLIENT RESOURCES, INC
Omaha Tower Ste 1300 2120 S 72nd St, Omaha, NE 68124
Tel.: (402) 926-2000
Web Site:
https://www.clientresourcesinc.com
Year Founded: 1999
Sales Range: $10-24.9 Million
Emp.: 135
Information Technology Consulting Services
N.A.I.C.S.: 541512
Susan Thaden (Pres & CEO)
Jackie Austin (VP)
Todd Bittner (CFO)

CLIENT SERVICES INC.
3451 Harry S Truman Blvd, Saint Charles, MO 63301
Tel.: (636) 947-2321
Web Site:
https://www.clientservices.com
Rev.: $12,442,658
Emp.: 1,000
Collection Agency, Except Real Estate
N.A.I.C.S.: 561440
Brian Sommer (Mgr)
Dan Phlipot (VP)
Erik Stunkel (Mgr-Recovery)
Jeff Marshall (Mgr-Recovery)

CLIENT SOLUTION ARCHITECTS
52 Gettysburg Pike, Mechanicsburg, PA 17055
Tel.: (717) 795-9104
Web Site:
https://www.csaassociates.com
Year Founded: 2003
Sales Range: $10-24.9 Million
Emp.: 121
Business Support Services
N.A.I.C.S.: 561439
Neftali Arroyo (Chm & Pres)
Steven C. Quagliani (CFO)
David Hickey (Chief Branding Officer)
Dan Gomrick (VP-Acct Mgmt)
Brenda Johnson (Dir-HR)
Brian Keller (Dir-Ops Support)
John Landry (Dir-Infrastructure Mgmt)
Jason Cox (Dir-IT)
Jeff Smithers (Dir-Acctg)
Paul Doyle (Dir-Ops-Southwest)
Scott Crawford (Dir-Proposal Dev)
Suzanne Franklin (Dir-Svc Line Mgmt)

Todd Yanik (Dir-Ops-Northeast)
Jay Heroux (Chief Sls & Mktg Officer)
Tim Spadafore (COO)
Ronald Hahn (Chief Growth Officer)
Amy Bleken (CEO)
Robert Johnson (VP-Bus Dev Ops)
Marshall Denney (VP-Navy Bus Unit)
Koren Odermann (VP-Bus Dev-Army & Other Agencies)
Mary Shambora (VP-Bus Dev-Navy)

CLIFF AVE ACCEPTANCE INC.
4733 N Cliff Ave, Sioux Falls, SD 57104
Tel.: (605) 336-3270
Sales Range: $10-24.9 Million
Emp.: 20
Mobile Home Dealers
N.A.I.C.S.: 459930
Dave Driver (CFO)
William Krum (Pres)

CLIFF DEVELOPMENT SALES & APPRAISALS, INC.
705 Pleasant Grove Rd Ste 106, Pleasant Grove, AL 35127
Tel.: (205) 744-0500
Year Founded: 1973
Sales Range: $10-24.9 Million
Emp.: 2
Real Estate Services
N.A.I.C.S.: 531210
Mickey Hankins (Pres)

CLIFF ROSS
The National Bldg 400 Northampton St Ste 509, Easton, PA 18042
Tel.: (610) 829-1333
Web Site: http://www.cliffross.com
Year Founded: 2010
Sales Range: $1-9.9 Million
Emp.: 3
Ad Design, Media Buying & Marketing Services
N.A.I.C.S.: 541820
Cliff Ross (Owner)

CLIFF VIESSMAN INC.
215 Main St, Gary, SD 57237
Tel.: (605) 272-5241
Web Site:
https://www.viessmantrucking.com
Year Founded: 1949
Sales Range: $10-24.9 Million
Emp.: 30
Trucking Company
N.A.I.C.S.: 484121
Clifford Viessman (Pres)
Wayne Viessman (Gen Mgr)

CLIFFORD PAPER INC.
Sherbrooke Office Ctr 600 E Crescent Ave, Upper Saddle River, NJ 07458
Tel.: (201) 934-5115
Web Site:
https://www.cliffordpaper.com
Year Founded: 1985
Sales Range: $450-499.9 Million
Emp.: 40
Tape Distr
N.A.I.C.S.: 424110
Paul Clifford (Sr VP-Sales-Marketing)

CLIFFORD POWER SYSTEMS INC.
9310 E 46th St N, Tulsa, OK 74117
Tel.: (918) 836-0066
Web Site:
https://www.cliffordpower.com
Year Founded: 1985
Sales Range: $10-24.9 Million
Emp.: 75
Provider of Power Generation & Automatic Transfer Switch Products
N.A.I.C.S.: 423610

Kenneth P. Clifford (Co-Pres)
Stephanie Benson (Dir-Ops)
Rocky Kitchingham (Mgr-Sls-OK & TX)
Rusty Mills (Mgr-Estimating)
Dana Birkes (CMO)
Rhonda Mills (Mgr-Inventory Control & Parts)
Frauke Quiroga (CFO)
Tom Clifford (Co-Pres)

CLIFT BUICK GMC
1115 S Main St, Adrian, MI 49221
Tel.: (517) 265-6107
Web Site: http://www.clickoncliff.com
Sales Range: $10-24.9 Million
Emp.: 55
New Car Retailer
N.A.I.C.S.: 441110
Garry Clift (Pres)
Dara O'Regan (Coord-Internet)

CLIFTON STEEL COMPANY
16500 Rockside Rd, Maple Heights, OH 44137
Tel.: (216) 662-6111
Web Site: http://www.cliftonsteel.com
Sales Range: $10-24.9 Million
Emp.: 40
Metal Parts
N.A.I.C.S.: 332312
Herb Neides (Owner)

CLIFTONLARSONALLEN LLP
220 S 6th St Ste 300, Minneapolis, MN 55402-1436
Tel.: (612) 376-4500
Web Site:
https://www.claconnect.com
Year Founded: 2012
Accounting & Consulting Services
N.A.I.C.S.: 541211
Dennis Schleper (CEO)
Jen Leary (Chief Strategy Officer)
Yassir Karam (Chief Outsourcing Officer-Indianapolis)
Wendi Boddy (Mng Partner-Charlotte)
Brandon Martin (Principal)
Nathan DiNatale (Dir-Valuation Svcs Practice)
Sheila Eichelberger (Principal-Charlotte)
Michael Smith (Principal-Tax Svcs Grp-Global)
Steve DeBruyn (Chief Practice Officer-Eastern Midwest Reg)
Charity Holst (Dir-Signing)
Subsidiaries:

Frost & Co. PLLC (1)
2412 N 30th St Ste 201, Tacoma, WA 98407-6372
Tel.: (253) 272-1555
Web Site: http://www.frostco-cpa.com
Offices of Certified Public Accountants
N.A.I.C.S.: 541211
Timothy S. Golob (Owner)

Schenck SC (1)
200 E Washington St, Appleton, WI 54912-1739
Tel.: (920) 731-8111
Web Site: http://www.schencksc.com
Sales Range: $25-49.9 Million
Emp.: 500
Accounting Services
N.A.I.C.S.: 541219
Amy Biersteker (Mgr-Bus Optimization)
Diane Roundy (Dir-Bus Dev)
Sarah Evans (Sr Mgr-State & Local Tax)
Kristine Hackbarth-Horn (Dir-People & Culture)
Steve Hyde (CIO & Dir-Tech Svcs)
Doug Bengson (Mgr-Ops Consulting)
Edita Rimalovsky (Mgr-Milwaukee)
Daniel Young (Pres)
Mark Fenlon (Pres & CEO-Schenck Investment Solutions)

CLIMATE CONTROL MECHANICAL SERVICES, INC.
PO Box 3038, Ocala, FL 34478
Tel.: (352) 291-0185
Web Site:
http://www.climatecontrolflorida.com
Year Founded: 2001
Sales Range: $1-9.9 Million
Emp.: 125
Internal Sheet Metal Fabrication, Insulation, Installation & Pipe-Fitting Faucets
N.A.I.C.S.: 332322
Sam Simms (Mgr-Warehouse)
Louie Wise III (Pres)

CLIMATE ENGINEERS INC.
883 Shaver Rd NE, Cedar Rapids, IA 52402
Tel.: (319) 364-1569
Web Site: http://www.climate-engr.com
Year Founded: 1947
Sales Range: $10-24.9 Million
Emp.: 80
Provider of Sheet Metalwork
N.A.I.C.S.: 332322
Heath Allard (Project Mgr)
John Watson Jr. (Pres)

CLIMBTECH
7303 Burleson Rd Ste 901, Austin, TX 78744
Tel.: (512) 308-6440
Web Site: https://www.climbtech.com
Year Founded: 2001
Sales Range: $1-9.9 Million
Emp.: 11
Anchorage Systems For Fall Protection
N.A.I.C.S.: 314994
Karl Guthrie (Founder)

CLIMCO COILS COMPANY
701 Klimstra Ct, Morrison, IL 61270
Tel.: (815) 772-3717
Web Site: https://www.climco.com
Sales Range: $10-24.9 Million
Emp.: 130
Aluminum Sheet & Foil Mfr
N.A.I.C.S.: 331315
Ted Volckmann (Head-Engrg)

CLINE ENERGY INC.
1890 S Main St, Harrisonburg, VA 22801
Tel.: (540) 434-7344
Rev.: $23,637,606
Emp.: 50
Petroleum Products Mfr
N.A.I.C.S.: 424720
Mike Davis (Pres)

CLINE RESOURCE & DEVELOPMENT CO.
430 Harper Park Dr, Beckley, WV 25801
Tel.: (304) 255-7458
Year Founded: 1959
Rev.: $29,500,000
Emp.: 37
Bituminous Coal-Underground Mining Services
N.A.I.C.S.: 541611
John Dickerson (Dir)

CLINGAN STEEL INC.
2525 Arthur Ave, Elk Grove Village, IL 60007
Tel.: (847) 228-6200
Web Site:
https://www.clingansteel.com
Rev.: $15,177,026
Emp.: 50
Cold Finishing of Steel Shapes Services

Clingan Steel Inc.—(Continued)
N.A.I.C.S.: 423510
R. Steve Clingan (Pres)
Paula Fisher (Controller)

CLINICAL RADIOLOGY FOUN-DATION

3901 Rainbow Blvd, Kansas City, KS 66160-1234
Tel.: (913) 588-6830   KS
Year Founded: 1970
Sales Range: $10-24.9 Million
Emp.: 26
Health Care Srvices
N.A.I.C.S.: 622110
Clifford R. Gray (Treas & Sec)
Alan Reeves (VP)
Philip L. Johnson (Pres)

CLINICAL REFERENCE LABO-RATORY, INC.

8433 Quivira Rd, Lenexa, KS 66215-2802
Tel.: (913) 492-3652
Web Site: http://www.crlcorp.com
Medical Laboratories
N.A.I.C.S.: 621511
David Porter (Chief Compliance Offi-cer & Sec)
Robert Thompson (Pres & CEO)

Subsidiaries:

Confirm Biosciences, Inc.   (1)
10123 Carroll Canyon Rd, San Diego, CA 92131
Web Site:
http://www.confirmbiosciences.com
Drug Abuse Testing Products
N.A.I.C.S.: 339112
Zeynep Ilgaz (Co-Founder & Chm)
Serhat Ilgaz (Co-Founder)
Albert Berger (CEO)
Nikhil Nayak (COO)

CLINICAL RESOURCE NET-WORK, LLC.

One Pky N Blvd Ste 250-S, Deerfield, IL 60015
Tel.: (847) 215-1224
Web Site:
http://www.clinicalresource.net
Year Founded: 2003
Rev.: $3,100,000
Emp.: 18
Women Healthcare Services
N.A.I.C.S.: 621610
Laurie Streling (CFO)
Nicki M. Norris (CEO)
Ellen Weiss (Dir-Bus Dev)

CLINICAL RESOURCES LLC

3338 Peachtree Rd NE Ste 102, At-lanta, GA 30326
Tel.: (404) 343-7227
Web Site:
https://www.clinicalresources.com
Year Founded: 2006
Sales Range: $1-9.9 Million
Emp.: 8
Health Care Staffing
N.A.I.C.S.: 561320
Jennifer L. Scully (Pres & CEO)
Sadie B. Kulla (VP-Fin)

CLINICAL SERVICES, INC.

1005 Boulder Dr, Gray, GA 31032
Tel.: (478) 741-1117   GA
Web Site: http://www.ethicahealth.org
Sales Range: $75-99.9 Million
Healthcare & Consulting Services
N.A.I.C.S.: 623110
Diana Wilks (Pres)

CLINICAL SPECIALTIES, INC.

6955 Treeline Dr, Brecksville, OH 44141

Tel.: (440) 717-1700
Web Site: http://www.csi-infusion.com
Year Founded: 1987
Sales Range: $10-24.9 Million
Emp.: 200
Provider of Home-Based Health Care Services
N.A.I.C.S.: 325412
Edward Rivalsky (Pres & CEO)
Rob Leonhardt (Mgr-Payor Rels)
Ryan Garst (Mgr-Pharmacy)

CLINICAL TRIAL NETWORK

7080 SW Fwy, Houston, TX 77074
Tel.: (713) 484-6947
Web Site: https://www.ctntexas.com
Year Founded: 2004
Sales Range: $1-9.9 Million
Emp.: 30
Clinical Research Facility
N.A.I.C.S.: 541715
Mahmood Mehkri (Coord-Res)

CLINICALMIND LLC

640 W 28th St 5th Fl, New York, NY 10001
Tel.: (646) 979-5444
Web Site:
http://www.clinicalmind.com
Year Founded: 2012
Sales Range: $10-24.9 Million
Emp.: 40
Online Marketing Services
N.A.I.C.S.: 541870
Jeanne Martel (CEO)
Maddy Zamel (VP-Ops)
Ashley Kamil (VP-Digital)
Thomas Sproat (Sr Vp-Scientific Svcs)
Michael Linde (Sr Dir-Medical-Antivirals & Liver Disease)
Jeff Goldberg (Dir-Editorial)
Kevin McHale (Chief Creative Officer)

CLINICAS DE SALUD DEL PUEBLO, INC.

1166 K St, Brawley, CA 92227
Tel.: (760) 344-9951   CA
Web Site: http://www.cdsdp.org
Year Founded: 1970
Sales Range: $25-49.9 Million
Emp.: 424
Health Care Srvices
N.A.I.C.S.: 621111
Lisa Gaxiola-Davis (CIO)
Gloria Santillan (CFO)
Jean Fisher (COO)
Claudia Galvez (Dir-Pub Affairs)

CLINICAS DEL CAMINO REAL, INC.

200 S Wells Rd 200, Ventura, CA 93004
Tel.: (805) 659-1740   CA
Web Site: http://www.clinicas.org
Year Founded: 1971
Sales Range: $25-49.9 Million
Emp.: 598
Health Care Srvices
N.A.I.C.S.: 622110
Gagan Pawa (Chief Medical Officer)

CLINILABS, INC.

423 W 55th St Fl 4, New York, NY 10019
Tel.: (646) 215-6400   DE
Web Site: http://www.clinilabs.com
Year Founded: 2001
Sales Range: $10-24.9 Million
Emp.: 120
Clinical Drug Development Services
N.A.I.C.S.: 325412
Gary K. Zammit (Pres & CEO)
Yu Ding (Sr VP-Ops)
Xiang Zhou (Sr Mgr-Data)
Amy McCoy (Sr Dir-Data Svcs)

Magdy Shenouda (Dir-Medical)
Berrin Onbas-Uzun (Dir-Quality As-surance & Regulatory Affairs)
Jeanine Estrada (Sr Dir-Sls & Mktg)
James Meringolo (VP-Fin)
Michael Sciortino (VP-Fin)

CLINIX MEDICAL INFORMA-TION SERVICES LLC

278 Franklin Rd Ste300, Brentwood, TN 37027
Tel.: (615) 309-5953
Web Site: http://www.clinixmis.com
Year Founded: 1985
Sales Range: $1-9.9 Million
Emp.: 40
Software Developer Incorporating Cloud Computing Services for Health Practice Management Billing & Elec-tronic Health Records
N.A.I.C.S.: 334610
Jerry Killough (Pres & CEO)
Leonard McGugin (VP-PR)

CLINOVATIONS, LLC.

1701 Pennsylvania Ave NW Ste 450, Washington, DC 20006
Tel.: (202) 448-1200
Web Site:
http://www.clinovations.com
Year Founded: 2008
Sales Range: $10-24.9 Million
Emp.: 41
Healthcare Management Consulting Services
N.A.I.C.S.: 541611
Trenor Williams (CEO)
Anita Samarth (Co-Founder)
Kevin Coloton (Pres)
John Kontor (CMO)
Michele Behme (Sr VP)
Daniel Clark (Sr VP)
Steven Merahn (Sr VP)
Steve Strode (Sr VP)
Jon D. Morrow (Sr VP-Life Sciences)
Rick Francis (Dir-Medical)
Anoop Sangha (Dir-Medical)
Rodrigo Martinez (VP)

CLINT NEWELL MOTORS INC.

1481 NE Stephens St, Roseburg, OR 97470
Tel.: (541) 673-7000
Web Site: http://www.clintnewell.com
Sales Range: $25-49.9 Million
Emp.: 80
Sales of New & Used Automobiles
N.A.I.C.S.: 441110
Clint Newell (Pres & Principal)
Kevin Gowey (Comptroller)

CLINTON BANCSHARES, INC.

12225 Saint Helena St, Clinton, LA 70722
Tel.: (225) 683-3371   LA
Web Site:
http://www.landmarkbankla.com
Year Founded: 1983
Sales Range: $1-9.9 Million
Emp.: 38
Bank Holding Company
N.A.I.C.S.: 551111
Thomas B. Legleu (Pres & CEO)

Subsidiaries:

Landmark Bank   (1)
12225 Saint Helena St, Clinton, LA 70722
Tel.: (225) 683-3371
Web Site: http://www.landmarkbankla.com
Sales Range: $1-9.9 Million
Commericial Banking
N.A.I.C.S.: 522110
Thomas B. Legleu (Pres & CEO)
Leslie Ligon Jr. (Chm)

CLINTON COUNTY ELECTRIC

COOPERATIVE, INC.
475 N Main St, Breese, IL 62230
Tel.: (618) 526-7282   IL
Web Site: https://www.cceci.com
Year Founded: 1939
Sales Range: $10-24.9 Million
Emp.: 36
Electric Power Distr
N.A.I.C.S.: 221122
Harry Buller (Mgr-Ops)
Ralph Kuhl (Mgr-Admin Svcs)
Mike Johnson (COO & Mgr)
Tim Hanke (Treas & Sec)
Vernon Mohesky (Chm)
Ron Becker (Vice Chm)
Randy Renth (Vice Chm)

CLINTON COUNTY HOSPITAL, INC.

723 Burkesville Rd, Albany, KY 42602
Tel.: (606) 387-6421   KY
Web Site:
http://www.clintoncountyhospital.com
Year Founded: 1965
Sales Range: $10-24.9 Million
Emp.: 197
Health Care Srvices
N.A.I.C.S.: 622110
J. D. Mullins Jr. (CEO)

CLINTON ELECTRONICS COR-PORATION

6701 Clinton Rd, Loves Park, IL 61111-3863
Tel.: (815) 633-1444
Web Site:
https://www.clintonelectronics.com
Year Founded: 1963
Rev.: $25,000,000
Emp.: 98
Electron Tubes Mfr
N.A.I.C.S.: 334419
David Bachand (Engr-Accts & Sls-Natl)
Mary Van Over (Coord-Acctg)

CLINTON FAMILY FORD LIN-COLN MERCURY OF ROCK HILL, INC.

1884 Canterbury Glen Ln, Rock Hill, SC 29730-7081
Tel.: (803) 366-3181
Web Site:
http://www.clintonfamilyford.com
Sales Range: $10-24.9 Million
Emp.: 51
Car Whslr
N.A.I.C.S.: 441110
Tom Clinton (Owner)
Angie Harkey (Office Mgr)
Sharon Martof (Pres & CEO)
Rhett McJunkin (Dir-Svc)

CLINTON FORD LINCOLN

2850 Valley W Dr, Clinton, IA 52732
Tel.: (563) 242-7011
Web Site:
https://www.clintonautogroup.com
Sales Range: $10-24.9 Million
Emp.: 40
New & Used Car Dealer
N.A.I.C.S.: 441110
Steven Lindquist (VP)
Craig Miller (Pres)
Glenn Seemayer (Gen Mgr)

CLINTON HEALTH ACCESS INITIATIVE, INC.

383 Dorchester Ave Ste 400, Boston, MA 02127
Tel.: (617) 774-0110   AR
Web Site:
http://www.clintonhealthaccess.org
Year Founded: 2009

Sales Range: $75-99.9 Million
Emp.: 260
HIV Prevention Services
N.A.I.C.S.: 813212
Joan Muasa (Sr Dir-Institutional Rels-Program Review)
Alice Kang'ethe (COO)
David Ripin (Chief Scientific Officer & Exec VP-Access-Malaria)
Ira C. Magaziner (Co-Founder & CEO)
Mphu Ramatlapeng (Exec VP-HIV-AIDS-TB-Health Spending)
William J. Clinton (Co-Founder & Pres)

CLINTON INDUSTRIES, INC.
207 Redneck Ave, Little Ferry, NJ 07643-1320
Tel.: (201) 440-0400
Web Site: http://www.clintonind.com
Year Founded: 1954
Sales Range: $1-9.9 Million
Emp.: 14
Mfr of Peripherals for Industrial Sewing Machines
N.A.I.C.S.: 333248
Harry Klein (Pres)
Larry Paricio (COO)
Dara Silver (VP-HR)
Bob Pulliam (Mgr-Sls & Mktg)
Joe Hoxholli (Dir-Sls)
Steve Capuano (Mgr-Pur & Production)

CLINTON NURSERY PRODUCTS INC.
114 W Main St, Clinton, CT 06413
Tel.: (860) 669-8611
Rev.: $11,700,000
Emp.: 57
Fertilizers, Mixing Only
N.A.I.C.S.: 325314

CLINTON SAVINGS BANK
200 Church St, Clinton, MA 01510
Tel.: (978) 365-4591
Web Site: http://www.clintonsavings.com
Sales Range: $10-24.9 Million
Emp.: 112
Federal Savings Bank
N.A.I.C.S.: 522110
Ellen J. McGovern (CMO & Sr VP)
Majlinda Haxhiaj (VP & Mgr-Branch Admin-Clinton)
Robert M. Farragher (Vice Chm)
Leonard Anctil (Officer-Comml Lending & Sr VP)
Sheila A. Azorandia (VP & Comptroller)
Danielle M. McCarter (Asst VP & Mgr-HR)
Mary T. Dean (CIO & Sr VP-Ops)
Linda M. Midura (Sr VP & Dir-HR)
Michele Hazelhurst (Mgr-Boylston)
David A. Harmon (Sr VP & Mgr-Comml Rels)
Debra M. Minor (VP & Mgr-Credit)
Edward M. Powers (Chief Lending Officer & Sr VP)
Holly A. Connors (VP & Mgr-Ops)
Lynne McCormack (Asst VP & Portfolio Mgr)
Daniel J. Kelser (Sr VP & Mgr-Comml Rels)
Paula E. Paldino (Officer-Compliance & Security & VP)
Larry R. Palmer (Officer-IT & VP)
Robert G. Rivard (Sr VP & Mgr-Comml Relationship)
Debra A. Colonna (VP & Mgr-Mortgage Ops)
Nicole L. Martin (VP & Mgr-Retail Sls)
Bernard Gagnon (Sr VP & Mgr-Comml Relationship)

Robert J. Paulhus Jr. (Pres & CEO)
William E. O'Neil Jr. (Chm)
Richard R. Hayward Jr. (CFO, Treas & Sr VP)

CLINTONVILLE LUMBER INC.
10 5th St, Clintonville, WI 54929
Tel.: (715) 823-3114
Web Site: http://www.clintonvillewi.org
Rev.: $36,392,640
Emp.: 158
Retail Lumber & Other Building Materials & Construction
N.A.I.C.S.: 423310
John A. Torborg (Pres)

CLIPPARD INSTRUMENT LABORATORY INC.
7390 Colerain Ave, Cincinnati, OH 45239-5306
Tel.: (513) 521-4261
Web Site: https://www.clippard.com
Year Founded: 1941
Sales Range: $10-24.9 Million
Emp.: 255
Mfr of Pneumatic Components
N.A.I.C.S.: 332912
Jennifer Clippard-Caunin (VP-HR)
Robin Rutschilling (Mgr-Mfg Ops)

Subsidiaries:

Clippard Europe, S.A. (1)
Parc Scientifique Einstein Rue du Bosquet 6, 1348, Louvain-la-Neuve, Belgium
Tel.: (32) 1045 2134
Web Site: http://www.clippard.eu
Emp.: 5
Industrial Valve Distr
N.A.I.C.S.: 423830
Francis Deruette (Gen Mgr)

CLIPPER MAGAZINE, LLC
3708 Hempland Rd, Mountville, PA 17554
Tel.: (717) 569-5100
Web Site: http://www.clippermagazine.com
Year Founded: 1983
Sales Range: $75-99.9 Million
Emp.: 4,500
Direct Mail Advertising Services
N.A.I.C.S.: 541860
Barbara Valinski (VP-HR)
Christine Gimber (Dir-Recruiting)

CLIPPER PETROLEUM INC.
5317 T L Bower Way, Flowery Branch, GA 30542-4059
Tel.: (770) 965-7240
Web Site: https://www.clipperpetroleum.com
Year Founded: 1974
Sales Range: $25-49.9 Million
Emp.: 200
Petroleum Product Mfr
N.A.I.C.S.: 445131
Steve Hall (Sr VP & Gen Mgr)
Andy Williams (Dir-Wholesale)
Mark Linkesh (Dir-Real Estate)
Ed Hong (VP-Retail Ops)
Lynn Cleveland (Mgr-Retail Support)
Rhonda Palmer (Mgr-Wholesale Ops)
Mark R. Cole (CFO)
Caroline Filchak (Dir-HR)
Paul Sherman (Mgr-Wholesale Bus Dev-Georgia)
Thomas L. Bower III (Pres & CEO)

CLISE PROPERTIES, INC.
1700 7th Ave Ste 1800, Seattle, WA 98101
Tel.: (206) 623-7500
Web Site: https://www.cliseproperties.com
Year Founded: 1889
Sales Range: $50-74.9 Million

Emp.: 65
Owner & Manager of Real Estate
N.A.I.C.S.: 531390
Howard Cohen (VP & Gen Mgr-Hotel Div)
Bryan Joyner (CFO)
Richard Stevenson (Pres & COO)
Ben Barron (VP-Dev)
Kyle Peters (VP-Westin Building)
Doug Smart (Gen Counsel & VP)
Ed Luera (VP)
Jeremy McPherson (Mgr-Property)
Lyn Krizanich (Mgr-Property)

CLIVE DANIEL HOME - NAPLES, LLC
2777 Tamiami Trl N, Naples, FL 34103
Tel.: (239) 261-4663
Web Site: http://www.clivedaniel.com
Sales Range: $10-24.9 Million
Emp.: 100
Furniture Retailer; Interior Design Services
N.A.I.C.S.: 449110
Dan Lubner (Pres)
Bonnie Kern (Gen Mgr)
Fern Schmidt (Dir-Real Estate Rels)
Madeline Tracy (Dir-Bus Dev)

CLIX MARKETING, LLC
217 La Grange Rd, Pewee Valley, KY 40056
Tel.: (502) 777-7591
Web Site: http://www.clixmarketing.com
Year Founded: 2003
N.A.I.C.S.: 541810
Mae Flint Polczynski (Mng Partner)
John Lee (Mng Partner)

CLJM LLC
8235 Forsyth Blvd Ste 1200, Clayton, MO 63105-1643
Tel.: (314) 746-4700 MO
Web Site: http://www.hmrisk.com
Year Founded: 1991
Sales Range: $50-74.9 Million
Emp.: 105
Insurance Brokerage & Risk Management Services
N.A.I.C.S.: 524210
Michael F. Shanahan Jr. (Chm, Pres & CEO)

Subsidiaries:

CLJM LLC - Springfield Office (1)
2925 E Battlefield Ste 120, Springfield, MO 65806-2131
Tel.: (417) 895-4600
Web Site: http://www.hmrisk.com
Sales Range: Less than $1 Million
Emp.: 20
Insurance Brokerage & Risk Management Services
N.A.I.C.S.: 524210

CLK, INC.
72295 Manufacturing Rd, Thousand Palms, CA 92276
Tel.: (760) 341-2992 CA
Year Founded: 1985
Sales Range: $25-49.9 Million
Emp.: 1,000
Franchise Fast-Food Restaurants Owner & Operator
N.A.I.C.S.: 722513
Salwa Schmidt (Office Mgr)
Kelly Carter (VP)

CLM ASSOCIATES LLC
299 Kisco Ave, Mount Kisco, NY 10549
Tel.: (914) 241-4444
Web Site: http://www.mtkiscovolvo.com
Rev.: $70,000,000

Emp.: 92
New & Used Automobile Dealer
N.A.I.C.S.: 441110
Tom Coughlin (CEO)

CLM EQUIPMENT COMPANY, INC.
3135 Hwy 90 E, Broussard, LA 70518-3222
Tel.: (337) 837-6693 LA
Web Site: https://www.clmequipment.com
Year Founded: 1973
Construction & Mining Machinery
N.A.I.C.S.: 423810
Floyd Degueyter (Pres)
Syd Crawford (CFO)

CLOCK RESTAURANT INC.
902 Clint Moore Rd Ste 126, Boca Raton, FL 33487-2846
Tel.: (561) 994-3440
Year Founded: 1968
Sales Range: $25-49.9 Million
Emp.: 400
Provider of Management Services
N.A.I.C.S.: 561110
James Tringali (Pres)
John Tringali (VP)

CLOCKSHARK, LLC
900 Fortress St Ste 100, Chico, CA 95973
Tel.: (530) 433-0981
Web Site: http://www.clockshark.com
Year Founded: 2014
Sales Range: $1-9.9 Million
Emp.: 25
Software Development Services
N.A.I.C.S.: 541511
Cliff Mitchell (Co-Founder & CEO)
Joe Mitchell (Co-Founder & CTO)

CLOCKWORK MARKETING SERVICES, INC.
10245 Centurion Pkwy N Ste 315, Jacksonville, FL 32256
Tel.: (904) 280-7960
Web Site: http://www.clockworkmarketing.com
Sales Range: $1-9.9 Million
Emp.: 9
Public Relations, Marketing Consulting, Marketing Research, Web Design & Media Buying Services
N.A.I.C.S.: 541820
Maxine McBride (Pres)
Sarah Rachfal (Acct Exec)
Penny Martin (Mgr-Ops)
Lauren Conn (Acct Exec)

CLOFINE DAIRY & FOOD PRODUCTS INC.
1407 New Rd, Linwood, NJ 08221-1114
Tel.: (609) 653-1000 NJ
Web Site: https://www.clofinedairy.com
Year Founded: 1930
Sales Range: $200-249.9 Million
Emp.: 18
Provider of Groceries & Related Products
N.A.I.C.S.: 424490
Fred Smith (Pres & CEO)
H. Lawrence Clofine (Chm)
Butch Harmon (VP-Fin)
Andri Kuswendra (Acct Mgr)
Jennifer Ingram (Mgr-Manufactured Products)

Subsidiaries:

Clofine Food Products International Inc. (1)
1407 New Rd, Linwood, NJ 08221-1114
Tel.: (609) 653-1000

CLOFINE DAIRY & FOOD PRODUCTS INC.

Clofine Dairy & Food Products Inc.—(Continued)

Web Site: http://www.clofinedairy.com
Sales Range: $10-24.9 Million
Emp.: 15
Provider Of Groceries & Related Products
N.A.I.C.S.: 424490
Fred Smith (Pres & CEO)
Larry Clofine (Chm)
Butch Harmon (VP-Fin)

CLORACKS CORPORATION
3311 S Rainbow Blvd Ste 108, Las Vegas, NV 89146
Tel.: (702) 581-4063 NV
Year Founded: 2012
Emp.: 5
Various Products Mfr
N.A.I.C.S.: 339999
Raul Mansueto (Pres, CEO & Principal Acctg Officer)
Dhan D. Kausal (Exec VP)
Josefa Gerona (CFO & Treas)

CLORE AUTOMOTIVE LLC
8735 Rosehill Rd Ste 220, Lenexa, KS 66215
Tel.: (913) 310-1050
Web Site: http://www.cloreautomotive.com
Sales Range: $10-24.9 Million.
Emp.: 100
Electric Arc Welders, Battery Chargers, Antifreeze, Recycling Machines & Industrial Truck Equipment
N.A.I.C.S.: 335311
Jim Chasim (Pres & CEO)
Brian Chasm (Mgr-Mktg)
Paul Zainea (VP-Ops)
Kirk Clore (VP-Sls)
Molly Coffman (Mgr-Supply Chain)

Subsidiaries:

Clore Automotive - Solar Div. (1)
8735 Rosehill Rd 220, Lenexa, KS 66215
Tel.: (913) 310-1050
Web Site: http://www.cloreautomotive.com
Automotive Aftermarket Electric Welder Plasma Cutter & Battery Charger Mfr.
N.A.I.C.S.: 335311
Mike Canipe (CFO)

CLOS LACHANCE WINERY
1 Hummingbird Ln, San Martin, CA 95046
Tel.: (408) 686-1050
Web Site: https://www.clos.com
Sales Range: $10-24.9 Million
Emp.: 25
Wine Mfr
N.A.I.C.S.: 312130
Bill Murphy (Founder & CEO)
Gina Sanders (Mgr-Wine Club)
Roy Froom (Mgr-Tasting Room)
Jennifer Hildebrand (Mgr-Sls & Mktg)
Ben Scorsur (Mgr-Vineyard)

CLOSE LUMBER
1600 Acacia Ave, Sutter, CA 95982
Tel.: (530) 755-0055
Web Site: https://www.closelumber.com
Rev.: $10,100,000
Emp.: 48
Lumber Plywood Millwork & Wood Panel Merchant Whslr
N.A.I.C.S.: 423310
William Norman (VP)
Darrell R. Close (Pres)

CLOSE OUT STORE
1628 S Central, Los Angeles, CA 90221
Tel.: (213) 748-5279
Web Site: http://www.closeoutstore.net
Year Founded: 2004

Sales Range: $1-9.9 Million
Emp.: 12
Owner of Liquidated, Returned & Salvaged Merchandise
N.A.I.C.S.: 424990
Cedar Augusto Leon (Pres)

CLOSED LOOP PARTNERS LLC
888 7th Ave 10th Fl, New York, NY 10106
Tel.: (646) 475-0201 DE
Web Site: https://www.closedlooppartners.com
Financial Services
N.A.I.C.S.: 523999
Martin Aares (Mng Dir)
Ron Gonen (CEO)

Subsidiaries:

Sage Sustainable Electronics LLC (1)
2801 Charter St, Columbus, OH 43228
Tel.: (844) 472-4373
Web Site: http://www.sagese.com
Recycling Services
N.A.I.C.S.: 562998
Chris Knopp (VP-Compliance)

Subsidiary (Domestic):

Hugo Neu Recycling, LLC (2)
249 E Sandford Blvd, Mount Vernon, NY 10550
Tel.: (914) 530-2350
Material Recycling Services
N.A.I.C.S.: 562920
Jason Bermudez (Mgr-Logistics)

CLOSET & STORAGE CONCEPTS
991 Senate Dr, Dayton, OH 45459
Tel.: (937) 428-0990
Web Site: http://www.closetandstorage.com
Sales Range: $1-9.9 Million
Emp.: 11
Ret Lumber/Building Materials
N.A.I.C.S.: 444180

Subsidiaries:

More Space Place, Inc. (1)
5040 140th Ave N, Clearwater, FL 33760
Tel.: (727) 539-1611
Web Site: http://www.morespaceplace.com
Furniture Store
N.A.I.C.S.: 449110

CLOSET WORLD, INC.
3860 Capitol Ave, Whittier, CA 90601
Tel.: (562) 699-9945 DE
Web Site: http://www.closetworld.com
Rev.: $38,200,000
Emp.: 40
Cabinet Building & Installation
N.A.I.C.S.: 238130
Frank Melkonian (Chm & CEO)
Alex Jivalagian (VP-Ops)
Sherry Lynn Sarmiento (Coord-HR Benefits)
Willie Arias (VP-Pur)

CLOSETS UNLIMITED, INC.
Glendale Executive Campus 1000 White Horse Rd Ste 404, Voorhees, NJ 08043
Tel.: (856) 627-5700 NJ
Year Founded: 1987
Sales Range: $1-9.9 Million
Emp.: 21
Interior Design Services
N.A.I.C.S.: 541410
Robert Lewis (Pres)

CLOUD 8 SIXTEEN, INC.
115 Wild Basin Ste 200, Austin, TX 78746 DE

Web Site: http://www.cloud8sixteen.com
Rev.: $4,000,000
Emp.: 60
Website Design Provider
N.A.I.C.S.: 518210
Kim Curtis (COO)
Joel Davis (Dir-Bus Dev)
Joe Devine (CEO)
Rodney Organ (CTO)

CLOUD COUNTY HEALTH CENTER
1100 Highland Dr, Concordia, KS 66901
Tel.: (785) 243-1234 KS
Web Site: http://www.cchc.com
Year Founded: 1970
Sales Range: $10-24.9 Million
Emp.: 213
Health Care Srvices
N.A.I.C.S.: 622110
Eric Andersen (Vice Chm)
Monte Wentz (Chm)
S. Christy Hasch (Sec)
Charles Zimmerman (Treas)

CLOUD CREEK SYSTEMS, INC.
31255 Cedar Vly Dr Ste 319, Westlake Village, CA 91362
Tel.: (818) 865-2800
Web Site: http://www.cloudcreek.com
Sales Range: $1-9.9 Million
Emp.: 18
Information Technology Consulting Services
N.A.I.C.S.: 541512
Bryan F. Coville (Founder)

CLOUD EQUITY GROUP, LLC
14 Wall St 20th fl, New York, NY 10005
Tel.: (212) 618-1298
Web Site: http://cloudequitygroup.com
Privater Equity Firm
N.A.I.C.S.: 523999
Sean Frank (Mng Partner)

Subsidiaries:

ComfortHost.NET (1)
350 Main St, Buffalo, NY 14202
Tel.: (772) 828-2116
Web Site: http://www.comforthost.net
Web Hosting Services
N.A.I.C.S.: 518210

Subsidiary (Domestic):

Advantagecom Networks, Inc. (2)
6 SW 13th Ste 2, College Place, WA 99324
Tel.: (509) 522-3696
Web Site: http://www.advantagecom.net
Data Processing, Hosting & Related Services
N.A.I.C.S.: 518210
Andrew Kinney (Pres & CTO)
Amy Kinney (COO)

Data Network Services Inc. (1)
2121 N Hamilton St Ste A, Richmond, VA 23230-4124
Tel.: (804) 359-1633
Web Site: http://www.dns-net.com
Computer & Office Machine Repair & Maintenance
N.A.I.C.S.: 811210
David Campbell (Pres)

Integrated Enterprise Solutions, Inc. (1)
3 Nancy Ct, Wappingers Falls, NY 12590
Tel.: (845) 226-9983
Web Site: http://www.ies-ny.com
Rev.: $1,100,000
Emp.: 12
Custom Computer Programming Services
N.A.I.C.S.: 541511
Alexandra Laubacker (Pres)

CLOUD MELLOW CONSULTING LTD. CO.
5899 Preston Rd Ste 1103, Frisco, TX 75034
Tel.: (904) 644-1817
Web Site: https://cloudmellow.com
Year Founded: 2015
Digital Marketing Agency
N.A.I.C.S.: 541613
Shreyans Jain (Co-Founder)
Vijay Konda (Co-Founder)

Subsidiaries:

Primary Design Inc. (1)
85 Emaex St, Haverhill, MA 01832
Tel.: (978) 373-1565
Web Site: https://primary360.com
Graphic Design Services
N.A.I.C.S.: 541430
John Schroeder (Pres & CEO)
Aashruti Patel (Coord-Office)
Alison Szetela (Designer-Graphic)
Annmarie Guerriero-Lamy (Acct Exec)
David Vadala (Dir-Art)
Gina Lane (Mgr-Media)
Jamie Randazzo (Dir-Creative)
Kristin Morgovnik (Supvr-Acct)
Lynne Rempelakis (Mgr-Production)
Niko Matses (Designer-Web)
Liz Fedorzyn Sr. (Dir-Art)

CLOUD PEAK ENERGY INC.
748 T-7 Rd, Gillette, WY 82718
Tel.: (307) 687-6000 DE
Web Site: http://www.cloudpeakenergy.com
Year Founded: 2008
Rev.: $832,405,000
Assets: $928,656,000
Liabilities: $634,982,000
Net Worth: $293,674,000
Earnings: ($717,963,000)
Emp.: 1,300
Fiscal Year-end: 12/31/18
Holding Company; Coal Mining
N.A.I.C.S.: 551112
Todd A. Myers (Pres & CEO)

Subsidiaries:

Antelope Coal LLC (1)
505 S Gillette Ave, Gillette, WY 82717-3009
Tel.: (307) 687-6000
Web Site: http://www.cloudpeakenergy.com
Emp.: 130
Coal Production & Exploration Services
N.A.I.C.S.: 212114

Cloud Peak Energy Services Company (1)
505 S Gillette Ave, Gillette, WY 82716
Tel.: (307) 687-6000
Web Site: http://www.cloudpeakenergy.com
Emp.: 130
Coal Mining Support Services
N.A.I.C.S.: 213113
Colin Marshall (Pres & CEO)

Sequatchie Valley Coal Corporation (1)
443 Svc Rd, Dunlap, TN 37327
Tel.: (423) 949-4698
Coal Production & Exploration Services
N.A.I.C.S.: 212114

Spring Creek Coal LLC (1)
505 S Gillette Ave, Gillette, WY 82716
Tel.: (307) 687-6000
Coal Production & Exploration Services
N.A.I.C.S.: 212114

CLOUD SERVICE PARTNERS, INC.
650 California St fl 25, San Francisco, CA 94108
Tel.: (833) 427-7762
Web Site: http://www.appsmart.com
Year Founded: 2009
Information Technology & Services
N.A.I.C.S.: 513210
Nicolas Desmarais (Chm & Co-CEO)
Daniel Saks (Pres & Co-CEO)

Subsidiaries:

MicroCorp, LLC (1)
4901 Olde Towne Pkwy Ste 200, Marietta, GA 30068
Tel.: (770) 649-1919
Web Site: http://www.microcorp.com
Rev.: $3,996,000
Emp.: 12
Wired Telecommunications Carriers
N.A.I.C.S.: 517111
Scott MacIntire *(Dir-Partner Enablement-Dallas)*
Phil Keenan *(Pres)*
Karin Fields *(CEO)*

CLOUDBEES, INC.

400 Tradecenter Ste 4950, Woburn, MA 01801
Tel.: (408) 805-3552
Web Site: http://www.cloudbees.com
Year Founded: 2010
Sales Range: $1-9.9 Million
Software Publisher
N.A.I.C.S.: 513210
Sacha Labourey *(Founder & Chief Strategy Officer)*
Francois Dechery *(VP-Support & Pro Svcs)*
Mike Lambert *(VP-Worldwide Sls)*
Andre Pino *(VP-Mktg)*
Spike Washburn *(VP-Engrg)*
Kohsuke Kawaguchi *(CTO)*
Laurence Poussot *(VP-Fin)*
Harpeet Singh *(VP-Product Mgmt)*
Brad Johnson *(VP-Product Mktg)*
Mathew Pitre *(Dir-Sls-Americas)*
Daniel McLaughlin *(COO)*
Marc Gemassmer *(Chief Revenue Officer)*
Christina Noren *(Chief Product Officer)*
Shawn Ahmed *(CMO)*
Prakash Sethuraman *(Chief Info Security Officer)*
Audrey Zhao *(CFO)*
Anuj Kapur *(Pres & CEO)*
Brianna Taylor *(Mgr-PR)*

Subsidiaries:

CloudBees Europe (1)
Rue des Colonies 11, 1000, Brussels, Belgium
Tel.: (32) 2 517 6168
Software Publisher
N.A.I.C.S.: 513210

CLOUDBURST CONSULTING GROUP, INC.

8400 Corporate Dr Ste 550, Landover, MD 20785-2231
Tel.: (301) 918-4400
Web Site:
https://www.cloudburstgroup.com
Year Founded: 2005
Sales Range: $1-9.9 Million
Emp.: 57
Administrative Management Consulting Services
N.A.I.C.S.: 541611
Patrick Moynahan *(Founder)*
Denise Lomuntad *(Sr Mgr-Contracts)*
J. P. Morgan *(CFO)*
Meggan Medina *(COO)*
Michelle Hayes *(Pres, CEO & Principal)*

CLOUDIT, LLC

920 E Madison St Ste 120, Phoenix, AZ 85034
Tel.: (602) 875-5400
Web Site: http://www.cloudit.co
Year Founded: 2015
Sales Range: $1-9.9 Million
Emp.: 45
Information Technology Management Services
N.A.I.C.S.: 541512

Vince Kent *(Pres & CEO)*

CLOUDSCALE365, INC.

4633 Trousdale Ste A, Nashville, TN 37204
Web Site:
http://www.cloudscale365.com
Year Founded: 1996
Cloud & Web Hosting Services
N.A.I.C.S.: 518210
Jose Maldonado *(VP-Ops)*
Alvin Sanchez *(VP-Engrg)*
Steve Daneshgar *(Grp Mng Dir)*

Subsidiaries:

Firefly It Services Inc. (1)
1731 Howe Ave, Sacramento, CA 95825-2209
Tel.: (916) 457-8324
Web Site: http://www.fireflytechs.com
Professional, Scientific & Technical Services
N.A.I.C.S.: 541990

Moore Communications Systems, Inc. (1)
127 Red Lion Rd, Southampton, NJ 08088
Tel.: (609) 859-1000
Web Site: http://www.mcstel.com
Electrical Contractor
N.A.I.C.S.: 238210

CLOUDTICITY, LLC

1301 Spring St Ste 25i, Seattle, WA 98104
Web Site: http://www.cloudticity.com
Year Founded: 2011
Sales Range: $1-9.9 Million
Software Development Services
N.A.I.C.S.: 541511
Gerry Miller *(CEO)*
Nicole Chaika *(CFO)*
Robert Williams *(Dir-Tech & Product Mgmt)*
Thomas Zinn *(Dir-Project Mgmt & Customer Delivery)*
Christopher Whaley *(Sr VP-Bus Dev)*
Karl Reeves *(Dir-Client Delivery)*
Pete Fox *(Sr VP-Sls)*

CLOVELLY CORPORATION

1420 Commerce Rd, Richmond, VA 23224
Tel.: (804) 232-2373
Rev.: $43,100,000
Convenience Stores, Independent
N.A.I.C.S.: 531190
Thomas N. Allen *(Chm & CEO)*

CLOVER CORPORATION

345 7th Ave 3rd Fl, New York, NY 10001
Tel.: (212) 633-4900   NY
Year Founded: 1992
Sales Range: $10-24.9 Million
Emp.: 40
Jewelry & Precious Stones
N.A.I.C.S.: 423940
Clover Friedlander *(Pres)*

CLOVER CREEK PARTNERS, LLC

4554 W Woolworth Ave, Milwaukee, WI 53218
Tel.: (414) 559-2166
Web Site:
http://www.ccreekpartners.com
Privater Equity Firm
N.A.I.C.S.: 523999
Randall M. Perry *(Founding Partner)*

Subsidiaries:

Airsan Corporation (1)
4554 W Woolworth Ave, Milwaukee, WI 53218
Tel.: (414) 353-5800
Web Site: http://www.airsan.com

Sales Range: $1-9.9 Million
Emp.: 10
Air Filters Designer & Mfr
N.A.I.C.S.: 333413
Randal Perry *(Pres)*

CLOVER FARMS DAIRY COMPANY

3300 Pottsville Pike, Reading, PA 19612
Tel.: (610) 921-9111
Web Site:
https://www.cloverfarms.com
Year Founded: 1937
Sales Range: $100-124.9 Million
Emp.: 285
Fluid Milk
N.A.I.C.S.: 311511

CLOVER FINANCIAL CORPORATION

4300 Haddonfield Rd Ste 314, Pennsauken, NJ 08109-3376
Tel.: (856) 662-1116   NJ
Web Site:
http://www.resourceinv.com
Sales Range: $200-249.9 Million
Emp.: 950
Real Estate Investment Services
N.A.I.C.S.: 531120
Steve Zalkind *(VP)*

CLOVER LEAF ENVIRONMENTAL SOLUTIONS, INC.

11005 Spain Rd NE Ste 5, Albuquerque, NM 87111
Tel.: (505) 314-0682   NM
Web Site:
http://www.cloversolutions.us
Year Founded: 2005
Sales Range: $1-9.9 Million
Emp.: 23
Environmental Consulting Services
N.A.I.C.S.: 541620
John Killoran *(Pres & CEO)*

CLOVER STORNETTA FARMS INC.

1800 S McBowell Ste 100, Petaluma, CA 94954-1168
Tel.: (707) 778-8448   CA
Web Site:
http://www.cloverstornetta.com
Year Founded: 1977
Sales Range: $25-49.9 Million
Emp.: 210
Dairy Products Mfr & Distr
N.A.I.C.S.: 311511
Marcus Benedetti *(Pres & CEO)*

Subsidiaries:

Clover Lake County Inc. (1)
21131 Washington St, Middletown, CA 95461
Tel.: (707) 987-3373
Sales Range: $10-24.9 Million
Emp.: 9
Supplier of Dairy Products
N.A.I.C.S.: 424430

CLOVER SYSTEMS INC.

1910 NW 97th Ave, Miami, FL 33172
Tel.: (305) 592-4300
Web Site:
http://www.clovergroup.com
Year Founded: 1947
Sales Range: $10-24.9 Million
Emp.: 75
Freight Forwarders; Custom Brokers & Non Vessel Operating Common Carriers
N.A.I.C.S.: 488510
Luis Alonso *(Pres)*
Yamira Gonzalez *(Controller)*

Subsidiaries:

Clover Internacional LLC (1)

14134 Vickery Dr, Houston, TX 77032
Tel.: (281) 449-9700
Web Site: http://www.clovergroup.com
Freight Forwarding Services
N.A.I.C.S.: 488510
Danielle Grandini *(Mgr-Bus Dev)*

Clover Internacional, C.A. (1)
Urb Industrial La Fe, Macarao, Caracas, Venezuela
Tel.: (58) 212 903 1374
Freight Forwarding Services
N.A.I.C.S.: 488510

Teknik Trading Inc. (1)
1910 NW 97th Ave, Miami, FL 33172
Tel.: (305) 592-4300
Web Site: http://www.clovergroup.com
Rev.: $500,000
Emp.: 6
Industrial Machinery & Equipment
N.A.I.C.S.: 423830
Luis Angel Rincon *(Pres)*

CLOVER TECHNOLOGIES GROUP LLC

4200 Columbus St, Ottawa, IL 61350
Tel.: (815) 431-8100
Web Site: http://www.clovertech.com
Year Founded: 1995
Sales Range: $75-99.9 Million
Emp.: 255
Provider of Remanufacturered Laser Cartridges & Ink Jet Cartridges
N.A.I.C.S.: 333310
James Cerkleski *(Chm)*
Dan Ruhl *(Pres)*
George Milton *(CEO-Clover Imaging)*
Bashar Nejdawi *(CEO-Global Wireless Bus)*
Brian Regan *(Exec VP)*
Mark Perry *(Mng Dir)*
Richard X. Fischer *(Gen Counsel & Exec VP)*
Dan Perez *(CEO-Clover Wireless)*

CLOVER WIRELESS

2700 W Higgins Rd Ste 100, Hoffman Estates, IL 60169
Tel.: (949) 783-7979
Web Site:
http://www.cloverwireless.com
Year Founded: 2003
Reseller of Wireless Devices
N.A.I.C.S.: 517112
Juanita Ramirez *(Mgr-Pur)*

Subsidiaries:

Teleplan International N.V. (1)
Schiphol Boulevard 201, 1118, Schiphol, Netherlands
Tel.: (31) 85 273 36 76
Web Site: http://www.teleplan.com
Sales Range: $400-449.9 Million
After-Sales Repair Services to Information Technology Industry
N.A.I.C.S.: 811210
Patrick Ring *(CMO, Chief Sls Officer & Member-Mgmt Bd)*
Gotthard Haug *(CEO)*
Jan Piet Valk *(CFO)*
Monika Collee *(Dir-Comm & IR)*
Jack Rockwood *(Pres-North America)*
Charles Stewardson *(Pres-Europe,Middle East & Africa)*
Jo-Ann Garbutt *(Dir-Global HR)*
Sven Boddington *(VP-Mktg & Client Solutions)*
Alan Wong *(Dir-IT)*
Anthony Abraham *(Dir-Program)*
Dolph Westerbos *(Chm)*

Subsidiary (Domestic):

Teleplan & White Electronics B.V. (2)
Werner Von Siemensstraat 17, 2712PN, Zoetermeer, Netherlands
Tel.: (31) 852733676
Web Site: http://www.teleplan.com
Sales Range: $10-24.9 Million
Emp.: 30
Computer & Office Machine Repair & Maintenance

Clover Wireless.—(Continued)

N.A.I.C.S.: 811210

**Teleplan Central Europe Holding
B.V.** (2)
Schiphol Blvd 201, 1118BG, Schiphol,
Netherlands (100%)
Tel.: (31) 852733676
Web Site: http://www.teleplan.com
Sales Range: $10-24.9 Million
Emp.: 30
Computer & Office Machine Repair & Main-
tenance
N.A.I.C.S.: 811210
Nathalie Van Donzel (Office Mgr)

Subsidiary (Non-US):

Teleplan Colchester Ltd. (2)
Mason Road Cowdray Centre, Colchester,
CO11 BX, United Kingdom (100%)
Tel.: (44) 1206785000
Web Site: http://www.teleplan.com
Computer & Office Machine Repair & Main-
tenance
N.A.I.C.S.: 811210

Subsidiary (Domestic):

Teleplan Communications B.V. (2)
Werner Von Siemensstraat 15-17, 2712PN,
Zoetermeer, Netherlands (100%)
Tel.: (31) 793304300
Sales Range: $150-199.9 Million
Computer & Office Machine Repair & Main-
tenance
N.A.I.C.S.: 811210

**Teleplan Communications Holding
B.V.** (2)
De Run 1120, 5503LA, Veldhoven,
Netherlands (100%)
Tel.: (31) 402558670
Web Site: http://www.teleplan.com
Management Consulting Services
N.A.I.C.S.: 541618

Subsidiary (Non-US):

**Teleplan Electronic Technology
(Shanghai) Co. Ltd.** (2)
3/F North Bldg No 239 Gang!ao Road, Wai
Gao Qiao Free Trade Zone, 200131,
Shanghai, China (100%)
Tel.: (86) 2150484255
Computer & Office Machine Repair & Main-
tenance
N.A.I.C.S.: 811210

Teleplan Germany GmbH (2)
Feldstr 16, 64331, Weiterstadt,
Germany (100%)
Tel.: (49) 61519571306
Consumer Electronics Repair & Mainte-
nance
N.A.I.C.S.: 811210

Subsidiary (Domestic):

Teleplan Rhein-Main GmbH (3)
Feldstr 16, 64331, Weiterstadt,
Germany (100%)
Tel.: (49) 61519571306
Web Site: http://www.teleplan.com
Consumer Electronics Repair & Mainte-
nance
N.A.I.C.S.: 811210

Subsidiary (Non-US):

Teleplan Polska Sp. z o.o. (2)
Ul Przemyslowa 8, 85 758, Bydgoszcz,
Poland (100%)
Tel.: (48) 523646200
Web Site: http://www.teleplan.com
Sales Range: $25-49.9 Million
Emp.: 25
Computer Facilities Management Services
N.A.I.C.S.: 541513
Pierre Gingras (Mng Dir)

**Teleplan Technology Services Sdn
Bhd** (2)
2580 Tingkat Perusahaan 4 B, Zon Perda-
gangan Bebas Dua, Perai, 13600, Penang,
Malaysia (100%)
Tel.: (60) 43890700
Web Site: http://www.teleplan-my.com
Sales Range: $150-199.9 Million
Emp.: 600

Computer & Office Machine Repair & Main-
tenance
N.A.I.C.S.: 811210
Jk Ong (Gen Mgr)

Subsidiary (US):

**Teleplan Videocom Solutions,
Inc.** (2)
101 W Commons Blvd, New Castle, DE
19720
Tel.: (302) 323-8503
Web Site: http://www.teleplan.com
Sales Range: $10-24.9 Million
Emp.: 35
Computer & Office Machine Repair & Main-
tenance
N.A.I.C.S.: 811210
Lindsay Smith (Office Mgr)
Joe Neff (Gen Mgr)

CLOVER YARNS INC.
715 S Washington St, Milford, DE
19963-2305
Tel.: (302) 422-4518
Year Founded: 1972
Sales Range: $100-124.9 Million
Emp.: 60
Commission Yarn Processing
N.A.I.C.S.: 313110
Edward J. Steiner (Pres)

Subsidiaries:

Clover Yarns (1)
1030 10 Yard Branch Trl, Clover, VA 24534-
0008
Tel.: (434) 454-7151
Sales Range: $25-49.9 Million
Emp.: 61
Reprocesses Textile Waste Fibers
N.A.I.C.S.: 313110
Keith Garrett (Plant Mgr)

CLOVERDALE EQUIPMENT
CO.
13133 Cloverdale St, Oak Park, MI
48237-3205
Tel.: (248) 399-6600
Web Site: https://www.cloverdale-
equip.com
Year Founded: 1963
Sales Range: $75-99.9 Million
Emp.: 50
Construction & Industrial Equipment
Rental, Sales & Service
N.A.I.C.S.: 532412
Todd A. Moilanen (Pres)
William E. Hake (Treas & Sec)
Brian M. Omerod (VP-Product Sup-
port)
John F. Price Jr. (VP-Sls)

Subsidiaries:

**Cloverdale Equipment Co. of West
Michigan** (1)
7175 Enterprise Dr, Norton Shores, MI
49456
Tel.: (231) 739-9525
Web Site: http://www.cloverdale-equip.com
Sales Range: $10-24.9 Million
Emp.: 16
Construction Equipment Distr
N.A.I.C.S.: 423810
Ed Van Sweden (VP & Gen Mgr)

Hasper Equipment Co. (1)
3662 Airline Rd, Muskegon, MI
49444-3863 (100%)
Tel.: (231) 739-9525
Web Site: http://www.cloverdale-equip.com
Sales Range: $10-24.9 Million
Emp.: 19
Construction & Industrial Equipment Rental,
Sales & Service
N.A.I.C.S.: 532412

CLOVERDALE FOODS COM-
PANY INC.
3015 34th St NW, Mandan, ND
58554-1312
Tel.: (701) 663-9511

Web Site:
http://www.cloverdalefoods.com
Year Founded: 1915
Sales Range: $25-49.9 Million
Emp.: 240
Sausages & Other Prepared Meats
N.A.I.C.S.: 311612

CLOVERLEAF TRANSPORTA-
TION, INC.
PO Box 812309, Wellesley, MA
02482
Tel.: (617) 797-4553
Web Site:
http://www.cloverleaftransport.com
Year Founded: 1976
Sales Range: $1-9.9 Million
Emp.: 100
Trucking Service
N.A.I.C.S.: 484121
Bruce E. Rogoff (Pres)

CLOVIS MEDIA, INC.
521 Pile St, Clovis, NM 88102
Tel.: (575) 763-3431
Web Site:
https://www.newmexiconews.com
Year Founded: 1929
Sales Range: $10-24.9 Million
Emp.: 80
Newspaper Publishing Services
N.A.I.C.S.: 513110
David Stevens (Editor)
Joyce Cruce (Dir-HR)
Teresa McKennon (Bus Mgr)
Paul Tiedemann (Mgr-Info Sys)
Gary W. Stevenson (Pres & CEO)
Cindy Cole (Dir-Circulation)
Rob Langrell (Publr)
Leslie Nagy (Dir-Adv & Mktg)
Jeff Haworth (Dir-Production)
Annie Stout (Mgr-Bus)

Subsidiaries:

Quay County Sun (1)
902 S 1st St, Tucumcari, NM 88401
Tel.: (575) 461-1952
Web Site: http://www.qcsunonline.com
Sales Range: $10-24.9 Million
Emp.: 4
Newspaper Services
N.A.I.C.S.: 513110
Cindy Cole (Dir-Circulation)
Joyce Cruce (Dir-HR)
Rob Langrell (Publr)
Leslie Nagy (Dir-Adv & Mktg)
Annie Stout (Mgr-Bus)
Paul Tiedemann (Mgr-Info Sys)

CLOW STAMPING COMPANY
23103 County Rd 3, Merrifield, MN
56465
Tel.: (218) 765-3111
Web Site:
https://www.clowstamping.com
Sales Range: $10-24.9 Million
Emp.: 300
Metal Stamping Services
N.A.I.C.S.: 332119
Everett Clow (CEO)
Reginal Clow (Pres & CEO)
Larry Rono (VP-Sls & Mktg)

CLP CORPORATION
121 Summit Pkwy, Homewood, AL
35209-4707
Tel.: (205) 942-0451
Web Site: http://www.clp.com
Year Founded: 1970
Sales Range: $10-24.9 Million
Emp.: 40
Eating Places
N.A.I.C.S.: 722513
Max Cooper (CEO)
Richard Wood (Comptroller)
Jim Black (Pres)

CLUB 24 CONCEPT GYMS,
LTD.
920 S Colony Rd Route, Wallingford,
CT 06492
Tel.: (203) 303-7281
Web Site:
https://www.club24gyms.com
Year Founded: 2004
Sales Range: $1-9.9 Million
Emp.: 90
Fitness Programs
N.A.I.C.S.: 713940
Edward Fogarty (Owner)

CLUB AT SEABROOK ISLAND
INC.
3772 Seabrook Island Rd, Seabrook,
SC 29455
Tel.: (843) 768-2500
Web Site:
http://www.discoverseabrook.com
Sales Range: $10-24.9 Million
Emp.: 60
Distr of Club Memberships
N.A.I.C.S.: 713910
Patti Baumil (Controller)
Laurie Benjamin (Dir-HR)
Sean Hardwick (Dir-Golf Course
Maintenance)
Brian Thelan (Head-Golf Pro)
Caleb Elledge (COO & Gen Mgr)

Subsidiaries:

Seabrook Island Realty (1)
1002 Landfall Way, Johns Island, SC 29455
Tel.: (843) 768-2560
Web Site:
http://www.seabrookislandrealestate.com
Rev.: $60,000,000
Emp.: 32
Real Estate Brokers & Agents
N.A.I.C.S.: 531210
John Wilcox (Dir-Engrg)

CLUB DEMONSTRATION SER-
VICES, INC.
9520 Towne Ctr Dr Ste 120, San Di-
ego, CA 92121
Tel.: (858) 581-8700
Web Site: http://www.clubdemo.com
Year Founded: 1988
Provider of Business Services
N.A.I.C.S.: 561990
Mark Egan (VP-US Sls-Operations)
Kathleen Owen (VP-Sales)

CLUB ONE INC.
555 Market Fl 13, San Francisco, CA
94105
Tel.: (415) 477-3000
Year Founded: 1991
Sales Range: $10-24.9 Million
Emp.: 35
Nonresidential Building Operators
N.A.I.C.S.: 713940
Bonnie Weedbeet (Controller)

CLUB PILATES LLC
4901 Morena Blvd Ste 210, San Di-
ego, CA 92117-7353
Tel.: (858) 531-2348
Web Site:
http://www.clubpilatesstudio.com
Year Founded: 2007
Sales Range: $1-9.9 Million
Fitness & Recreational Sports Cen-
ters
N.A.I.C.S.: 713940
Allison Beardsley (Founder)
Anthony Geisler (CEO)

CLUBESSENTIAL HOLDINGS,
LLC
4600 McAuley Pl Ste 350, Cincinnati,
OH 45242
Tel.: (513) 321-2780

Web Site:
http://www.clubessential.com
Year Founded: 1998
Web Design & Development
N.A.I.C.S.: 541511
Brian T. Carley *(CFO & Sr VP)*
Carl Gable *(Owner)*
Scott Strong *(Pres)*
Randy Eckels *(CEO)*

Subsidiaries:

BlueGolf, LLC **(1)**
724 W Lancaster Ave, Wayne, PA 19087
Tel.: (610) 293-0998
Web Site: http://www.bluegolf.com
Computer Related Services
N.A.I.C.S.: 541519
Ed Hughes *(CEO)*

PrestoSports, Inc. **(1)**
451 Hungerford Dr Ste 325, Rockville, MD 20850
Tel.: (301) 789-1807
Sports Technology Solutions & Support
N.A.I.C.S.: 541511
Keith Womac *(Pres)*

Subsidiary (Domestic):

Immersion Media, Inc. **(2)**
3520 Prestwick Dr, Fayetteville, NC 28303-4629
Tel.: (910) 868-8441
Web Site: http://www.imsports.com
Custom Computer Programming Services
N.A.I.C.S.: 541511
Rick Perko *(Pres)*

Vermont Systems, Inc. **(1)**
12 Market Pl, Essex Junction, VT 05452
Tel.: (802) 879-6993
Web Site: http://www.vermontsystems.com
Computer Software Product Mfr
N.A.I.C.S.: 541511
Dave Wirtz *(Mgr-Sls)*
Kate Mitchell *(Treas & VP)*
Laura Valley *(VP)*
John Wiley *(VP-Mktg & Sls)*
Giles Willey *(Pres)*

CLUBSYSTEMS GROUP INC.
330 South Warminster Rd Ste 360, Hatboro, PA 19040
Tel.: (215) 887-2515
Web Site: https://www.clubsys.com
Year Founded: 1972
Rev.: $20,145,848
Emp.: 90
Computers, Peripherals & Software
N.A.I.C.S.: 423430
John Tyrrell *(Acct Mgr)*
Jeannie Vanover *(Acct Mgr)*
George Heath *(Dir-R&D)*
Susan Lyle *(Pres)*
Dennis Linberger *(VP-Customer Mgmt)*
Michael McCleary *(VP-Sls & Svcs)*
Thomas J. Serino *(COO & Gen Mgr)*

CLUETT AMERICAN INVESTMENT CORP.
48 W 38th St 8th Fl, New York, NY 10018-6248
Tel.: (212) 984-8900   DE
Web Site:
http://www.goldtoemoretz.com
Sales Range: $75-99.9 Million
Emp.: 15
Holding Company
N.A.I.C.S.: 424350
James A. Williams *(Pres)*
Chuck Ward *(CFO)*

Subsidiaries:

Cluett International Group **(1)**
48 West 38th St, New York, NY 10018-6248
Tel.: (646) 735-2249
Sales Range: $10-24.9 Million
Emp.: 6
Technical Licencing Services For Sanforized Trademarks
N.A.I.C.S.: 424350

CLUNE CONSTRUCTION CO.
10 S La Salle St Ste 300, Chicago, IL 60603-1095
Tel.: (312) 726-6103   IL
Web Site: http://www.clunegc.com
Year Founded: 1956
Sales Range: $150-199.9 Million
Emp.: 100
Provider of Construction Management & Consulting Services
N.A.I.C.S.: 541330
Michael T. Clune *(Chm)*
Tom Nickele *(Mng Dir & CFO)*
Ben Walker *(Pres-New York & Exec Mng Dir-New York)*
Dave Hall *(Exec Mng Dir & Pres-Midwest)*
Vince Gutekanst *(Exec Mng Dir-Midwest)*

CLUSIAU SALES & RENTAL, INC.
815 NW 4th St, Grand Rapids, MN 55744-2304
Tel.: (218) 326-9421
Web Site:
http://www.clusiausalesrental.com
Sales Range: $10-24.9 Million
Emp.: 36
Car Whslr
N.A.I.C.S.: 441110

CLW INC.
10001 Fm 2025 Rd, Cleveland, TX 77328-8334
Tel.: (281) 592-4691
Web Site: http://www.clwlumber.com
Year Founded: 1978
Sales Range: $10-24.9 Million
Emp.: 265
Lumber Product Mfr & Whslr
N.A.I.C.S.: 321999
Zachary Lowe *(Owner)*
Hugh Lowe *(VP)*
Rosemary C. Weinheimer *(Co-Treas & Asst Sec)*
Claudette C. Lowe *(Co-Treas & Asst Sec)*

CLYDE COMPANIES INC.
730 N 1500 W, Orem, UT 84057
Tel.: (801) 802-6900   UT
Web Site: https://www.clydeinc.com
Year Founded: 1997
Emp.: 100
Highway & Street Construction
N.A.I.C.S.: 237310
Jeremy Hafen *(Pres)*
Scott Okelberry *(COO & Exec VP)*
Wilford C. Clyde *(Chm & CEO)*
Ray Gammell *(VP-Equipment & Facilities)*
Daniel C. Walker *(Chief HR Officer & VP)*
Bill Holman *(CIO & VP-Admin)*
Ryan Meyer *(CFO & Exec VP)*
Brandon Hale *(Gen Counsel)*
Ally Isom *(CMO, Chief Strategy Officer & VP)*

Subsidiaries:

Beehive Insurance Agency, Inc. **(1)**
302 W 5400 S Ste 101, Murray, UT 84107
Tel.: (801) 685-6860
Web Site: http://www.beehiveinsurance.com
General Insurance Services
N.A.I.C.S.: 524210
Doug Snow *(Pres & CEO)*
Dennis Dunbar *(Acct Mgr)*
Gretchen Lafave *(Acct Mgr)*
Kim Beal *(Acct Mgr)*
Lisa Bonacci *(Acct Mgr)*
Teresa Hughes *(Mgr-Acct)*
Aaron Griffith *(Sr Acct Exec)*
Adam Snow *(Acct Exec)*
Brady Thorn *(VP)*
Corey Ford *(Acct Exec)*
Dave Comer *(Acct Exec)*

Jace Pearson *(Sr Acct Exec)*
Jim Dickson *(VP)*
Kay Howland *(Sr Acct Exec)*

Clements Concrete Co **(1)**
501 E 41st St, Garden City, ID 83714
Tel.: (208) 343-6965
Web Site: http://www.clementsconcrete.com
Readymix Concrete Mfr
N.A.I.C.S.: 327320

Subsidiary (Domestic):

C & A Paving Co. **(2)**
4015 Banner St, Boise, ID 83709
Tel.: (208) 362-4244
Web Site: http://www.capaving.com
Sales Range: $1-9.9 Million
Emp.: 60
Excavation Services
N.A.I.C.S.: 238910
Shannon Reed *(Office Mgr)*

Geneva Rock Products Inc. **(1)**
1565 W 400 N, Orem, UT 84057
Tel.: (801) 765-7800
Web Site: http://www.genevarock.com
Rev.: $110,000,000
Emp.: 100
Concrete Mixtures
N.A.I.C.S.: 423320
Jim Golding *(Pres)*
Shane Albrecht *(VP-Area Construction Ops)*
Nathan Schellenberg *(VP-Specialty Construction Ops)*
Jay Ritchie *(Exec VP)*

Gorge Rock Products, Inc. **(1)**
507 Smith St, Rock Springs, WY 82901
Tel.: (307) 362-2362
Web Site: http://www.gorgerock.com
Emp.: 40
Concrete Products Mfr
N.A.I.C.S.: 327390
Curg Murray *(Gen Mgr)*

Sunpro Corporation **(1)**
482 W 800 W, Orem, UT 84057
Tel.: (801) 222-3300
Web Site: http://www.sunpro.build
Building Materials Distr
N.A.I.C.S.: 423390
Greg Templeman *(Pres)*
Matthew S. McDonald *(VP-Building Materials)*
Steve Broadbent *(VP-Specialty Products)*
Jason Butterfield *(Div Mgr)*

Subsidiary (Domestic):

Depatco, Inc. **(2)**
497 N Capital Ave, Idaho Falls, ID 83402
Tel.: (208) 458-4000
Web Site: http://www.depatco.com
Emp.: 200
Site Preparation Contractor
N.A.I.C.S.: 238910
Chris J. Stoddard *(VP & Mgr-Equipment)*
Greg L. Stoddard *(Pres & CEO)*
Jed O. Stoddard *(VP & Dir-Field Ops)*
Daniel D. Stoddard *(CFO & Treas)*
Jonathan L. Stoddard *(VP-Mktg & Sls & Project Mgr)*

Sierra Truss, LLC **(2)**
4100 E Monsanto Dr, Sierra Vista, AZ 85650
Tel.: (520) 378-2374
Truss Mfr
N.A.I.C.S.: 321215

Stone's, Inc. **(2)**
412 2nd St S, Nampa, ID 83651
Tel.: (208) 466-2463
Web Site: http://www.stonelumber.com
Sales Range: $1-9.9 Million
Emp.: 16
Lumber & Building Material Whslr
N.A.I.C.S.: 423310

Sunroc Corporation **(1)**
3657 S River Rd, Saint George, UT 84790
Tel.: (435) 673-7829
Web Site: http://www.sunroc.com
Readymix Concrete Mfr
N.A.I.C.S.: 327320
Jeremy Hafen *(Pres)*
Mark Wimmer *(VP-Construction)*
Russell Leslie *(VP-Construction Materials)*

W.W. Clyde and Company **(1)**

1375 N Main St, Springville, UT 84663
Tel.: (801) 802-6800
Web Site: http://www.wwclyde.net
Emp.: 10
Construction Engineering Services
N.A.I.C.S.: 541330
Scott Okelberry *(VP-Construction)*
Jeff Clyde *(Pres)*
Dustin Olson *(VP-Field Ops)*
Bryan Flake *(Dir-HR)*
Bruce Dallin *(Dir-Safety)*
Brad Christofferson *(Dir-Bus Dev)*

CLYDE DUNEIER INC.
415 Madison Ave 6th, New York, NY 10017
Tel.: (212) 398-1122
Web Site:
http://www.clydeduneier.com
Sales Range: $10-24.9 Million
Emp.: 100
Mfr & Distributor of Fine Jewelry
N.A.I.C.S.: 339910
Dana Duneier *(CEO)*

CLYDE REVORD MOTORS
7900 Evergreen Way, Everett, WA 98203
Tel.: (425) 353-1170
Web Site: https://www.revord.com
Sales Range: $10-24.9 Million
Emp.: 40
New Car Retailer
N.A.I.C.S.: 441110
Patty Johnson *(Controller)*

CLYDE, INC.
3236 M St NW, Washington, DC 20007-3615
Tel.: (202) 333-9180   DC
Web Site: https://www.clydes.com
Year Founded: 1963
Sales Range: $100-124.9 Million
Emp.: 1,500
Restaurant Operators
N.A.I.C.S.: 722511
Jeff Owens *(CFO)*

Subsidiaries:

Walrus Corporation **(1)**
675 15th St NW, Washington, DC 20005-5702
Tel.: (202) 347-4800
Web Site: http://www.ebbitt.com
Rev.: $17,000,000
Emp.: 200
Restaurant Operators
N.A.I.C.S.: 722511
David Moran *(Gen Mgr)*
Dan Harding *(Gen Mgr)*
Megan Kilby *(Mgr-Event)*
Lucy Pear *(Mgr-Event)*
Jillian Dressed *(Creative Dir)*
Kemi Adewumi *(Acct Dir)*
Evan Vosburgh *(Assoc Dir-Creative)*

CM COMPANY INC.
431 W McGregor Ct, Boise, ID 83705
Tel.: (208) 384-0800
Web Site:
https://www.cmcompany.com
Year Founded: 1987
Sales Range: $10-24.9 Million
Emp.: 20
Nonresidential Construction Services
N.A.I.C.S.: 236220
Trey Crookston *(Pres)*

CMA CONSULTING SERVICES
700 Troy-Schenectady Rd, Latham, NY 12110
Tel.: (518) 783-9003
Web Site: https://www.cma.com
Sales Range: $1-9.9 Million
Emp.: 400
Information Technology Consulting Services
N.A.I.C.S.: 541512

CMA Consulting Services—(Continued)

Kay Stafford *(Pres & CEO)*
Ken Romanski *(Exec VP-Bus Dev)*
Gary Davis *(Exec VP-Ops)*
Rachel Harpootlian *(CFO)*
Tom Mullen *(VP)*
Peter Chynoweth *(VP)*
George McCabe *(VP)*
Stephen J. Zizzi *(CTO)*
Dan Wall *(Gen Counsel)*

CMC CONSULTING BOSTON, INC.
1 Grant St Ste 400, Framingham, MA 01702
Tel.: (774) 777-5255
Web Site: http://www.alirahealth.com
Year Founded: 1999
Healthcare & Life Sciences Advisory Services Firm
N.A.I.C.S.: 541690
Paolo Morelli *(Exec VP-Biometrics)*
Gabriele Brambilla *(CEO)*

Subsidiaries:

CROS NT SRL **(1)**
Via Germania 2, 37136, Verona, Italy
Tel.: (39) 0458202666
Web Site: http://www.crosnt.com
Statistical Consultancy, Programming & Analysis, Clinical Data Management; Medical Writing, Pharmacovigilance & Technology Services
N.A.I.C.S.: 541618
Paolo Morelli *(CEO)*
Andrew MacGarvey *(CEO)*
Paul Fardy *(COO)*
Gianni Saccomani *(CFO & Head-Fin, Admin & HR)*
Mark Paul *(Pres-North America)*
Fabio Gambini *(Chief Medical Officer)*

Subsidiary (US):

Stat Tech Services, LLC. **(2)**
501 Eastowne Dr Ste 230, Chapel Hill, NC 27514
Tel.: (919) 929-5015
Web Site: http://www.stattechservices.com
Sales Range: $10-24.9 Million
Emp.: 15
General Management Consulting Services
N.A.I.C.S.: 541611
Jeff Welch *(VP-Bus Dev)*
Tracy L. Hofmann *(Dir-Project Ops)*
Andrew MacGarvey *(Pres & CEO)*
Chelsea Bradshaw *(Mgr-Biostatistics)*

CMC ENERGY SERVICES, INC.
550 Pinetown Rd Ste 340, Fort Washington, PA 19034
Tel.: (215) 540-5800   MD
Web Site: http://www.cmcenergy.com
Year Founded: 1977
Clean Energy Technologies & Energy Conservation Marketing Consulting Services
N.A.I.C.S.: 541613
Mimi Ikle-Khalsa *(Chm)*
Lisa Stotts *(CFO)*
Leila Banihani *(VP-Ops)*
Blaine Fox *(VP-Bus Dev)*
Tom Desimpel *(Dir-Ops)*
John McQuiggan *(Sr Program Mgr)*
Tina Bennett *(Pres & CEO)*
Paul Mackay *(CIO)*

CMC GROUP INC.
12836 S Dixie Hwy, Bowling Green, OH 43402
Tel.: (419) 354-2591
Web Site: https://www.cmcgp.com
Sales Range: $25-49.9 Million
Emp.: 200
Investment Holding Companies, Except Banks
N.A.I.C.S.: 551112

Albert J. Caperna *(Co-Owner & Chm)*
Craig Dixon *(CEO)*
Jeff Palmer *(Pres)*

CMC INC.
1151 Jessamine Sta Rd, Nicholasville, KY 40356
Tel.: (859) 885-4955
Web Site: http://www.cmclimo.com
Sales Range: $10-24.9 Million
Emp.: 80
Decontamination Services
N.A.I.C.S.: 238990
Clay M. Corman *(Pres)*
Lorie Fairchild *(Dir-HR)*

CMC REALTY INC.
6151 W Century Blvd Ste 307, Los Angeles, CA 90045-5330
Tel.: (310) 258-9000   CA
Web Site:
http://www.carlsbergmgt.com
Year Founded: 1990
Sales Range: $25-49.9 Million
Emp.: 60
Real Estate Agents & Managers
N.A.I.C.S.: 531210
Esther Cordero *(Controller)*

Subsidiaries:

Carlsberg Management Company Inc. **(1)**
6171 W Century Blvd Ste 100, Los Angeles, CA 90045-5300
Tel.: (310) 258-9000
Web Site: http://www.carlsbergmgt.com
Sales Range: $10-24.9 Million
Emp.: 24
Real Estate Agents & Managers
N.A.I.C.S.: 531210

Sunrise Golf Development Corp. **(1)**
1178 Grant St, Hollywood, FL 33019-3126
Tel.: (954) 792-5111
Rev.: $500,000
Emp.: 4
Nonresidential Building Operators
N.A.I.C.S.: 531120

CMC SUPPLY INC.
2510 Johnson Ave, Roanoke, VA 24017
Tel.: (540) 982-1095
Web Site:
https://www.cmcsupply.com
Year Founded: 1975
Sales Range: $10-24.9 Million
Emp.: 52
Plumbing & Hydronic Heating Supplies
N.A.I.C.S.: 423720
Steven Chisholm *(Pres)*
Conrad Massey *(Treas & Sec)*
Suzann Bowman *(VP-Ops)*
Leon Arthur *(Mgr-Inside Sls)*

CMD CORPORATION
2901 E Pershing St, Appleton, WI 54912
Tel.: (920) 730-6888
Web Site: https://www.cmd-corp.com
Sales Range: $10-24.9 Million
Emp.: 150
Plastics Working Machinery
N.A.I.C.S.: 333248
Shaughn Hanley *(Dir-Intl Sls)*
Stephen Sakai *(Pres)*
Scott Fuller *(Mgr-Intermittent Motion Product Line)*
Ricardo Abud *(VP-Mktg & Bus Dev)*

CMD INC.
1631 NW Thurman St, Portland, OR 97209-2558
Tel.: (503) 223-6794
Web Site:
https://www.cmdagency.com
Year Founded: 1978

Sales Range: $25-49.9 Million
Emp.: 170
Advetising Agency
N.A.I.C.S.: 541810
Phil Reilly *(Pres)*
Jeff Zabel *(Mng Dir-Promotion Mktg)*
Darcie Meihoff *(VP & Exec Dir-Earn Media)*
Patti Cody *(Mng Dir-Paid Media)*
Brad Wignall *(VP-Creative Svcs)*
Jon McAnnis *(CTO & VP)*
Mark Adams *(Acct Dir)*
Arden Owens *(Mng Dir-HR)*
Steven Burdorf *(Pres-Roseville)*
Darren Rankin *(Co-Pres)*

CMDS
13 Cherry Tree Farm Rd, Middletown, NJ 07748
Tel.: (732) 706-5555
Web Site:
http://www.cmdsonline.com
Sales Range: Less than $1 Million
Emp.: 5
Advetising Agency
N.A.I.C.S.: 541810
Christopher J. Mulvaney *(Pres)*

CME CORPORATION
7235 Vicksburg Pike, Fort Wayne, IN 46804-5546
Tel.: (260) 745-0251   IN
Web Site: http://www.cmebuildright.com
Year Founded: 1972
Rev.: $5,600,000
Emp.: 40
Commercial & Institutional Building Construction
N.A.I.C.S.: 236220
Mark Hellinger *(Pres)*

Subsidiaries:

Storage Systems Unlimited, Inc. **(1)**
318 Seaboard Ln, Franklin, TN 37067
Tel.: (615) 261-0414
Web Site: http://www.storagesystemsul.com
Rev.: $1,900,000
Emp.: 11
Medical, Dental & Hospital Equipment & Supplies Merchant Whslr
N.A.I.C.S.: 423450
Linley White *(CFO)*
Karen Kreager *(Pres)*
Charles Spann *(Project Mgr)*
Catherine Adkins *(Project Mgr)*

CMES, INC.
6555 McDonough Dr NW, Norcross, GA 30093
Tel.: (770) 982-1905
Web Site: https://www.cmesinc.net
Sales Range: $10-24.9 Million
Emp.: 50
Highway, Street & Bridge Construction Services
N.A.I.C.S.: 237310
Chatur B. Chhabhaya *(CEO & Sec)*
Ramesh S. Suhagia *(CFO)*

CMFG LIFE INSURANCE COMPANY
5910 Mineral Point Rd, Madison, WI 53705
Tel.: (608) 238-5851   IA
Web Site:
http://www.cunamutual.com
Year Founded: 1935
Sales Range: $1-4.9 Billion
Emp.: 4,000
Holding Company; Insurance, Asset Management & Financial Services
N.A.I.C.S.: 551112
Robert J. Marzec *(Chm)*
Robert N. Trunzo *(Pres & CEO)*
Janet V. Whitehouse *(Vice Chm)*
Martin Powell *(VP-Strategic Acct Dev & Mgmt)*

Subsidiaries:

CPI Qualified Plan Consultants Inc. **(1)**
1809 24th St, Great Bend, KS 67530
Tel.: (620) 793-8473
Web Site: http://www.cpiqpc.com
Sales Range: $125-149.9 Million
Emp.: 500
Pension & Retirement Plan Consultants
N.A.I.C.S.: 523930
Al Seymour *(Reg Mgr)*

CUNA Brokerage Services, Inc. **(1)**
2000 Heritage Way, Waverly, IA 50677-9208 **(100%)**
Web Site: http://www.cunabrokerage.com
Sales Range: $100-124.9 Million
Emp.: 120
Security Broker & Dealer Services
N.A.I.C.S.: 523150
Jo Henn *(Mgr-Ops)*
Rob Comfort *(Pres)*

CUNA Caribbean Insurance Society Limited **(1)**
37 Wrightson Road, Port of Spain, Trinidad, Trinidad & Tobago
Tel.: (868) 623 7963
Web Site: http://www.cunacaribbean.com
Group & Individual Insurance for Credit Unions & Credit Union Members
N.A.I.C.S.: 524128
Anthony Hall *(Gen Mgr)*
Andre Goindoo *(Mgr-Fin)*

CUNA Mutual Insurance Agency, Inc. **(1)**
5910 Mineral Point Rd, Madison, WI 53701-0391 **(100%)**
Tel.: (608) 238-5851
Web Site: http://www.cunamutual.com
Sales Range: $750-799.9 Million
Emp.: 2,500
Leasing & Brokerage Company
N.A.I.C.S.: 524210

CUNA Mutual Insurance Group **(1)**
5910 Mineral Point Rd, Madison, WI 53701-0391 **(100%)**
Tel.: (608) 238-5851
Web Site: http://www.cunamortgage.com
Holding Company
N.A.I.C.S.: 524126
Julie Winslow *(Head-Internal Sls-Annuity Natl Sls)*
Martin Powell *(VP & Head-Annuity Distr)*

MEMBERS Life Insurance Company **(1)**
2000 Heritage Way, Waverly, IA 50677 **(100%)**
Tel.: (319) 352-4090
Web Site:
http://www.eservice.cunamutual.com
Rev.: $429,000
Assets: $399,381,000
Liabilities: $380,166,000
Net Worth: $19,215,000
Earnings: $161,000
Fiscal Year-end: 12/31/2014
Life Insurance & Annuity Services
N.A.I.C.S.: 524113
Robert N. Trunzo *(Pres)*
Steven R. Suleski *(Sec)*
Brian J. Borakove *(Treas)*

CMG FINANCIAL SERVICES INC.
3160 Crow Canyon Rd Ste 400, San Ramon, CA 94583
Tel.: (925) 983-3000   CA
Web Site: http://www.cmgfi.com
Year Founded: 2003
Sales Range: $75-99.9 Million
Emp.: 400
Holding Company; Mortgage Brokerage & Financial Services
N.A.I.C.S.: 551112
Christopher M. George *(Pres & CEO)*
Kristen Shevlin *(Mgr-ISA)*
Renee Bareilles *(Coord-HVCC Appraisal)*
Drew Dyet *(Sr VP-Wholesale Lending Channel)*

Dan Humes *(Sls Mgr-North & East Texas, Arkansas, Oklahoma & Missouri)*
Chris Blevins *(Sls Mgr-Central Div)*
Jas Sohal *(VP-Northern California & Northern Nevada)*
Chip Larson *(VP-Retail Lending-West)*

Subsidiaries:

CMG Mortgage, Inc.   (1)
3160 Crow Canyon Rd Ste 400, San Ramon, CA 94583   **(100%)**
Tel.: (925) 983-3000
Web Site: http://www.cmgfi.com
Rev.: $14,500,000
Emp.: 150
Mortgage Brokerage & Lending Services
N.A.I.C.S.: 522310
Christopher M. George *(Founder, Chm & CEO)*
Doug Nesbit *(CMO)*
Todd L. Hempstead *(Sr VP-IR)*
A. J. George *(Chief Admin Officer)*
Adam Millstein *(Sr VP-Wholesale Lending)*
Brett Sinnott *(VP-Fin & Capital Markets)*
Charlie Rogers *(Sr VP-Retail Lending)*
Joe Cabrall *(VP-Correspondent Lending Ops)*
Kimberly Callas *(Exec VP)*
Liz Crowley *(Sr VP-HR)*
Melissa Richards *(Chief Legal & Risk Officer)*
Paul Akinmade *(Sr VP-Mktg)*
Peter Gilbert *(Chief Credit & Operating Officer)*

CMG WORLDWIDE, INC.

10500 Crosspoint Blvd, Indianapolis, IN 46256-3331
Tel.: (317) 570-5000   IN
Web Site:
   http://www.cmgworldwide.com
Year Founded: 1972
Sales Range: $10-24.9 Million
Emp.: 45
Advertising Services
N.A.I.C.S.: 541810
Mark Roesler *(Founder & Chm)*
Maria Gejdosova *(CFO)*

CMH INC.

2816 Dorr Ave, Fairfax, VA 22031
Tel.: (703) 698-8855
Web Site:
   http://www.croppmetcalfe.com
Sales Range: $25-49.9 Million
Emp.: 210
Warm Air Heating & Air Conditioning Contractor
N.A.I.C.S.: 238220
Mitchell Cropp *(CEO)*
Ben Kelley *(Mgr-Ops)*
Tim Cropp *(Pres)*

CMI ARCHITECTURAL PRODUCTS, INC.

20621 Southeast Hwy 25, De Smet, SD 57231
Tel.: (605) 854-3326
Web Site: http://www.cmiarch.com
Sales Range: $10-24.9 Million
Emp.: 50
Aluminum Extruded Products
N.A.I.C.S.: 331318
Edward Hiller *(Project Mgr-Engrg)*
Randy Provart *(Mgr-Sls)*
Rex Geyer *(Mgr-Materials-Production)*
Shelly DeJong *(Project Mgr-Engrg)*

CMI ENTERPRISES INC.

13145 NW 45th Ave, Miami, FL 33054-4305
Tel.: (305) 685-9651
Web Site: https://www.cmi-enterprises.com
Rev.: $30,001,248
Emp.: 40

Distr of Knit Fabrics
N.A.I.C.S.: 424310
Michael Novick *(Pres)*
Rick Porras *(CFO)*

CMI STONE GROUP INC.

2010 NW 33rd Ct, Pompano Beach, FL 33064
Tel.: (954) 975-8442
Web Site: http://www.cmistone.com
Sales Range: $10-24.9 Million
Emp.: 7
Marble Building Stone
N.A.I.C.S.: 423320
Meozzi Valcavi *(Pres)*

CMI, INC.

2262 Groom Rd, Baker, LA 70714
Tel.: (225) 778-6400   DE
Web Site:
   https://www.corrosionmaterials.com
Sales Range: $10-24.9 Million
Emp.: 150
Whslr of Corrosion-Resistant Alloys
N.A.I.C.S.: 331492

CMI-MANAGEMENT SERVICES INC.

Ste 100 29580 NW Hwy, Southfield, MI 48034-1031
Tel.: (248) 415-3950
Year Founded: 1999
Sales Range: $25-49.9 Million
Emp.: 223
Provider of Steel Investment Foundries
N.A.I.C.S.: 513210

CMJ ENTERPRISES INC.

14271 Sw 120th St Ste 104, Miami, FL 33186-7282
Tel.: (305) 253-8631   FL
Web Site:
   http://www.anoseforclothes.com
Year Founded: 1986
Sales Range: $10-24.9 Million
Emp.: 35
Retailer of Ready-To-Wear Women's Apparel
N.A.I.C.S.: 458110
Syed Gilani *(Pres)*

CMMS DATA GROUP, INC.

123 W Madison St Ste 1100, Chicago, IL 60602
Tel.: (312) 957-8580
Web Site: http://www.cdg.com
Year Founded: 2000
Sales Range: $1-9.9 Million
Emp.: 41
Software Development Services
N.A.I.C.S.: 541511
Ruth Hughes *(Founder & CEO)*
Jonathan Clark *(COO)*
Nick Kissel *(Sls Dir)*
Kevin Taylor *(Mgr-Technical Support)*
Willie Mena *(Mgr-Consulting)*

CMR CONSTRUCTION & ROOFING LLC

3006 N Lindbergh Blvd Ste 703, Saint Ann, MO 63074-3242
Tel.: (314) 962-3600
Web Site:
   https://www.cmrconstruction.com
Year Founded: 2002
Sales Range: $25-49.9 Million
Emp.: 200
Roofing, Siding & Other Constuction Services
N.A.I.C.S.: 238160
Steve Soule *(CEO)*
Joe Fouquet *(Supvr-Comml Inspection)*

Subsidiaries:

CMR Construction & Roofing of Texas   (1)
4308 Garland Dr, Haltom City, TX 76117
Tel.: (817) 656-7663
Web Site: http://www.cmrconstruction.com
Emp.: 8
Roofing, Siding & Other Constuction Services
N.A.I.C.S.: 238160
Bryan Jones *(Gen Mgr)*

CMR Construction Columbus   (1)
1799 W 5th Ave Ste 201, Columbus, OH 43212
Tel.: (855) 766-3267
Web Site: http://cmrconstruction.com
Roofing, Siding & Other Constuction Services
N.A.I.C.S.: 238160

CMR Construction Kansas   (1)
128 Oak St Ste B, Bonner Springs, KS 66012
Tel.: (913) 441-3803
Web Site: http://www.cmrconstruction.info
Roofing, Siding & Other Constuction Services
N.A.I.C.S.: 238160

CMR Construction Louisiana   (1)
1409 B Kuebel, Harahan, LA 70123
Tel.: (504) 569-9549
Roofing, Siding & Other Constuction Services
N.A.I.C.S.: 238160

CMR Construction Minnesota   (1)
1601 109th Ave NE, Blaine, MN 55434
Tel.: (763) 398-7663
Web Site: http://www.cmrconstruction.info
Roofing, Siding & Other Constuction Services
N.A.I.C.S.: 238160

CMR Construction Missouri - St Louis   (1)
10734 Trenton Ave, Saint Louis, MO 63132
Tel.: (314) 733-1317
Web Site: http://www.cmrconstruction.com
Roofing, Siding & Other Constuction Services
N.A.I.C.S.: 238160

CMR Construction North Dakota   (1)
1617 1st Ave N Unit B, Fargo, ND 58102
Tel.: (701) 281-3475
Web Site: http://www.cmrconstruction.com
Roofing, Siding & Other Constuction Services
N.A.I.C.S.: 238160
James McLaughlin *(Gen Mgr)*

CMR PARTNERS LLP

9715 Kincaid Dr ste 1280, Fishers, IN 46037
Tel.: (317) 845-1250
Web Site: http://www.cmr-restaurants.com
Sales Range: $10-24.9 Million
Emp.: 8
Real Estate Managers
N.A.I.C.S.: 531210
Toby Cox *(Gen Mgr)*
Mike Rees *(Chm)*

CMS COMMUNICATIONS INC.

722 Goddard Ave, Chesterfield, MO 63005-1132
Tel.: (636) 530-1320   MO
Web Site: https://www.cmsc.com
Year Founded: 1985
Sales Range: $10-24.9 Million
Emp.: 115
Provider of Electronic Parts, Equipment & Service
N.A.I.C.S.: 423690
Tray Luina *(CFO)*
Christy Daniels *(VP-Ops)*
Bob Axley *(Mgr-Pur & Inventory)*
Jeanne Pfadenhauer *(Acct Mgr)*

CMS EAST, INC.

400 Agnew Rd, Jeannette, PA 15644

Tel.: (724) 527-6700
Web Site: http://www.cmseast.com
Year Founded: 1975
Rev.: $10,286,800
Emp.: 14
Memorial Park Developer & Manager
N.A.I.C.S.: 812220
Judith Nesbitt *(Bus Dir)*

CMS OPERATIONS

701 Emerson Rd Ste 400, Saint Louis, MO 63141
Tel.: (314) 432-6688
Year Founded: 1987
Sales Range: $10-24.9 Million
Emp.: 150
Other Management Consulting Services
N.A.I.C.S.: 541618
Seelin Naidoo *(CEO)*
David Buergler *(VP-Ops)*
Vergel J. Dytuco *(VP-Tech)*
Robert Stolph *(VP-Ops)*
Catarino Soto *(VP)*

CMSA ADVERTISING & PUBLIC RELATIONS

2142 Palm Harbor Blvd Ste A, Palm Harbor, FL 34683
Tel.: (727) 447-3396
Web Site: https://www.cmsa.com
Sales Range: $1-9.9 Million
Emp.: 3
Advertising & Public Relations
N.A.I.C.S.: 541810

CMT HOLDINGS INC.

590 Laurelwood Rd, Santa Clara, CA 95054
Tel.: (408) 734-3339
Web Site: http://www.gocmt.com
Sales Range: $25-49.9 Million
Emp.: 15
Computers, Peripherals & Software
N.A.I.C.S.: 423430
Kurt Klein *(CEO)*

CMTA INC.

10411 Meeting St, Prospect, KY 40059
Tel.: (502) 326-3085
Web Site: http://www.cmtaegrs.com
Rev.: $3,950,000
Emp.: 25
Engineeering Services
N.A.I.C.S.: 541330
Thom Anderson *(Engr-Mechanical-Cincinnati)*
Andy Metzger *(Engr-Cincinnati)*
Cindy Jackson *(Mgr-Mktg-Cincinnati)*
James Benson *(Pres)*

Subsidiaries:

Acts 29 Consulting, LLC   (1)
800 E Campbell Rd Ste 341, Richardson, TX 75040
Tel.: (469) 222-8489
Web Site: http://www.acts29consulting.com
Engineering Consulting Services
N.A.I.C.S.: 541611
Matt Short *(Pres & CEO)*

CMTI, INC.

819 N Atlantic Ave, Cocoa Beach, FL 32931
Tel.: (321) 799-4022
Web Site: http://www.cmtfl.com
Sales Range: $10-24.9 Million
Emp.: 100
Administrative Management & General Management Consulting Services
N.A.I.C.S.: 541611
Trox Austell *(CEO)*
Susan Black *(VP)*

CMX TECHNOLOGIES

CMX Technologies—(Continued)

11710 Plz America Dr Ste 2000, Reston, VA 20190
Tel.: (703) 464-5533
Web Site: http://www.cmx-tech.com
Year Founded: 2005
Sales Range: $1-9.9 Million
Emp.: 25
Technical, Consulting & Engineering Services to Government Organizations & Commercial Businesses
N.A.I.C.S.: 541690
Charles Bobbish (Pres & CEO)
Tony Campanella (VP-Intelligence Programs)
Christopher Hamilton (COO & VP-Bus Dev)
Matt Pundzak (VP)

CMXL INC.
1300 National Dr Ste 150, Sacramento, CA 95834
Tel.: (916) 285-8888
Commercial Real Estate Funding Services
N.A.I.C.S.: 523999
David Syme (Co-Founder & Partner)

CN WOOD CO. INC.
200 Merrimac St, Woburn, MA 01801
Tel.: (781) 935-1919
Web Site: https://www.cn-wood.com
Rev.: $14,000,000
Emp.: 78
General Construction Machinery & Equipment
N.A.I.C.S.: 423810
Bill Linane (Coord-Sls & Inventory)
Dick Thomas (Mgr-Credit)

CNC ASSOCIATES NY INC.
101 Kentile Rd, Plainfield, NJ 07080
Tel.: (718) 416-3853
Web Site:
    http://www.cncassociates.com
Sales Range: $10-24.9 Million
Emp.: 100
Kitchen Cabinets
N.A.I.C.S.: 423310
Nathan Indig (Pres)

Subsidiaries:

Infinity Design LLC　　　　　　　(1)
101 Kentile Rd, South Plainfield, NJ 07080
Tel.: (718) 416-3853
Web Site: http://www.cncassociates.com
Sales Range: $10-24.9 Million
Emp.: 10
Wood Kitchen Cabinets
N.A.I.C.S.: 337110

CNC METAL PRODUCTS
2061 Sylvan Rd, Wooster, OH 44691
Tel.: (330) 264-6640
Web Site:
    https://www.cncmetalproducts.com
Year Founded: 2002
Sales Range: $10-24.9 Million
Emp.: 84
Metal & Plastic Product Mfr
N.A.I.C.S.: 212290
Bob Lapsley (Pres)

CNC SYSTEMS INC.
40 Water St, Kennebunk, ME 04043
Tel.: (207) 985-6503
Web Site:
    https://www.cncsystems.com
Rev.: $26,631,973
Emp.: 12
Machine Tools & Metalworking Machinery
N.A.I.C.S.: 423830
Steve Arcari (Pres)
Anne Smith (Coord-Sls)
Guy Williams (Mgr-Matls)
Shawn Smith (Mgr-Engrg)

CNE DIRECT, INC.
100 Cummings Ctr Ste 162F, Beverly, MA 01915
Tel.: (978) 741-8686
Web Site: http://www.cnedirect.com
Year Founded: 2002
Sales Range: $25-49.9 Million
Emp.: 64
Computer & Computer Peripheral Equipment & Software Merchant Whslr
N.A.I.C.S.: 423430
Paul Knight (Founder & Chm)
Joe Nye (VP-Ops)
Jon-David Allen (Dir-Ops-Asia)
Jerry Quill (CFO)
Omur Bagci (CEO)
Ed Penniman (VP-Platform)

CNFA, INC.
1828 L St NW Ste 710, Washington, DC 20036
Tel.: (202) 296-3920　　　　　　DC
Web Site: https://www.cnfa.org
Year Founded: 1985
Sales Range: $10-24.9 Million
Emp.: 57
Economic Development Services
N.A.I.C.S.: 541720
Alan Pieper (COO)
Russ Webster (VP-Program Dev)
Sylvain Roy (Pres & CEO)

CNJ DISTRIBUTING CORPORATION
PO Box 20878, Billings, MT 59104-0878
Tel.: (406) 248-8728　　　　　　MT
Year Founded: 1973
Sales Range: $250-299.9 Million
Emp.: 300
Entertainment Services
N.A.I.C.S.: 423990
Judy Frank (Sec)

CNL FINANCIAL GROUP, INC.
450 S Orange Ave, Orlando, FL 32801-3336
Tel.: (407) 650-1000　　　　　　FL
Web Site: https://www.cnl.com
Year Founded: 1973
Sales Range: $800-899.9 Million
Emp.: 300
Financial Holding Company Investment Banking Brokerage Private Equity & Portfolio Management Services
N.A.I.C.S.: 551111
James M. Seneff Jr. (Exec Chm)
Stephen H. Mauldin (Co-CEO)
Tammy J. Tipton (CFO & Sr VP)
John McRae (Chief Investment Officer-Real Estate Investments)
Lisa A. Schultz (Chief Svcs Officer)
Paul W. Drury (Sr Mng Dir)
Brett Schlemovitz (Mng Dir-Bus Dev)
Chirag J. Bhavsar (Co-CEO)
John F. Starr (COO)
Tracey B. Bracco (Gen Counsel)
Erin M. Gray (Chief Compliance Officer & Gen Counsel)
Safak Subasi (Sr VP-Fin & Fund Ops)

Subsidiaries:

CNL Growth Properties, Inc.　　　(1)
CNL Ctr at City Commons 450 S Orange Ave, Orlando, FL 32801
Tel.: (407) 650-1000
Web Site:
    http://www.cnlgrowthproperties.com
Sales Range: $25-49.9 Million
Real Estate Investment Trust
N.A.I.C.S.: 525990
Thomas Kent Sittema (Chm)
Holly J. Greer (Gen Counsel, Sec & Sr VP)
Scott C. Hall (Sr VP-Ops)

CNL Healthcare Properties II, Inc.　　　　　　　　　　　　　　　(1)
CNL Center at City Commons 450 S Orange Ave, Orlando, FL 32801
Tel.: (407) 650-1000
Web Site:
    http://www.cnlhealthcarepropertiesii.com
Rev.: $7,437,316
Assets: $67,289,375
Liabilities: $25,624,140
Net Worth: $41,665,235
Earnings: ($1,805,183)
Fiscal Year-end: 12/31/2018
Real Estate Investment Trust
N.A.I.C.S.: 525990
John F. Starr (COO)
Tammy J. Tipton (CFO/Treas/Sr VP-CHP II Advisors, LLC)
Ixchell C. Duarte (CFO, Principal Acctg Officer, Treas & Sr VP)
John McRae (Sr VP)
Tracey B. Bracco (Gen Counsel, Sec & VP)
Brett Bryant (VP)
Lisa L. Smith (VP-Asset Mgmt)
Sarah W. Nixon (VP & Mng Dir-Seniors Housing)
Cetin Aygen (VP)
John McRae (Sr VP)

CNL Healthcare Properties, Inc.　(1)
450 S Orange Ave Ste 1400, Orlando, FL 32801
Tel.: (407) 650-1000
Web Site:
    https://www.cnlhealthcareproperties.com
Rev.: $322,661,000
Assets: $1,437,303,000
Liabilities: $647,009,000
Net Worth: $790,294,000
Earnings: ($1,453,000)
Fiscal Year-end: 12/31/2022
Real Estate Investment Trust
N.A.I.C.S.: 525990
James M. Seneff Jr. (Chm)
Stephen H. Mauldin (Vice Chm, Pres & CEO)
Michael Tetrick (Sr VP)
Ixchell C. Duarte (CFO, Treas & Sr VP)
John McRae (Chief Investment Officer & Sr VP)
Sarah J. Pettit (Sr Mng Dir)
Lisa L. Smith (Sr VP)

CNL Lifestyle Properties, Inc.　　(1)
450 S Orange Ave, Orlando, FL 32801
Tel.: (407) 650-1000
Web Site: http://www.cnllifestylereit.com
Rev.: $241,115,000
Assets: $842,422,000
Liabilities: $192,093,000
Net Worth: $650,329,000
Earnings: $65,948,000
Fiscal Year-end: 12/31/2016
Real Estate Investment Trust
N.A.I.C.S.: 525990
Thomas Kent Sittema (Vice Chm)

CNL Private Equity Corp.　　　　(1)
450 S Orange Ave, Orlando, FL 32801-3383　　　　　　　　　　(100%)
Tel.: (407) 650-1000
Web Site: http://www.cnlonline.com
Sales Range: $50-74.9 Million
Emp.: 100
Privater Equity Firm
N.A.I.C.S.: 523999
Michael Tetrick (Sr VP)

CNL Securities Corp.　　　　　　(1)
450 S Orange Ave, Orlando, FL 32801-3336　　　　　　　　　　(100%)
Tel.: (407) 650-1000
Web Site: http://www.cnlsecurities.com
Sales Range: $125-149.9 Million
Emp.: 350
Security Brokerage & Dealing Services
N.A.I.C.S.: 523150

CNL STRATEGIC CAPITAL MANAGEMENT LLC
450 South Orange Ave, Orlando, FL 32801
Tel.: (407) 650-1000
Web Site:
    https://www.cnlstrategiccapital.com
Emp.: 100
Financial Investment Services

N.A.I.C.S.: 523999

Subsidiaries:

CNL Strategic Capital, LLC　　　(1)
450 S Orange Ave, Orlando, FL 32801
Tel.: (407) 650-1000
Web Site:
    https://www.cnlstrategiccapital.com
Rev.: $46,956,000
Assets: $732,543,000
Liabilities: $23,444,000
Net Worth: $709,099,000
Earnings: $16,716,000
Fiscal Year-end: 12/31/2022
Financial Investment Services
N.A.I.C.S.: 523940
Tammy J. Tipton (CFO & Interim COO)
Paul W. Drury (Sr Mng Dir)
Safak Subasi (Sr VP)
Chirag J. Bhavsar (Pres & CEO)
Tammy J. Tipton (CFO)

Subsidiary (Domestic):

Alex N Sill Company　　　　　　(2)
6000 Lombardo Ctr Ste 600, Cleveland, OH 44131
Tel.: (216) 524-9999
Web Site: http://www.sill.com
Sales Range: $1-9.9 Million
Emp.: 40
Claims Adjusting
N.A.I.C.S.: 524291
Donald J. Dragony (CFO, Sr VP & Dir-Forensic Acctg)

Douglas Machines Corporation　(2)
2101 Calumet St, Clearwater, FL 33765　　　　　　　　　　　(90%)
Tel.: (727) 461-3477
Web Site: http://www.dougmac.com
Sales Range: $25-49.9 Million
Automated Washing & Sanitizing Equipment Mfr
N.A.I.C.S.: 333310
Susan Mader (VP-Fin & Acctg)
Kevin Lemen (VP-Sls & Mktg)
Dale Breedlove (Mgr-Svc)
Rosie Rachel (Coord-Sls & Mktg)
Paul Claro (Pres & CEO)

Polyform Products Company, Inc.　　　　　　　　　　　　　(2)
1901 Estes Ave, Elk Grove Village, IL 60007-5415
Web Site: https://www.sculpey.com
Polyform Product Distr
N.A.I.C.S.: 424490
Cori Hubbard (Dir-R&D)

Subsidiary (Non-US):

Shina Corporation　　　　　　　(2)
1005 28 Hwangsaeul-Ro 200Beon-Gil, Bundang-Gu, Seongnam, 13595, Gyeonggi-do, Korea (South)
Tel.: (82) 317118180
Web Site: https://www.shinacor.co.kr
Medical Device Mfr
N.A.I.C.S.: 339112

Subsidiary (Domestic):

Tactical Medical Solutions, Inc.　(2)
1250 Harris Bridge Rd, Anderson, SC 29621
Tel.: (864) 224-0081
Web Site: https://www.tacmedsolutions.com
Medical, Dental & Hospital Equipment & Supplies Merchant Whslr
N.A.I.C.S.: 423450
R. Alan Hester (VP)

Subsidiary (Domestic):

TraumaFX Solutions, Inc.　　　　(3)
506 Sandau Rd #250, San Antonio, TX 78216
Tel.: (800) 200-7465
Web Site: http://www.traumafx.net
Medical Simulation & Training Technologies
N.A.I.C.S.: 339112
Graham Palmer (Sr VP)

Subsidiary (Domestic):

Ultimed, Inc.　　　　　　　　　(2)
350 Hwy 7, Excelsior, MN 55331
Tel.: (833) 835-9051
Web Site: https://www.ultimedinc.com
Medical Device Mfr

N.A.I.C.S.: 339112
Jim Erickson (Pres & CEO)
Dennis Wagner (CFO)
Sarah Hanssen (VP-Sls & Mktg)
Pete Vaillant (VP-Ops)
Tom Sauro (Dir-Ops)

CNS CORPORATION

500 E 9th St, Kansas City, MO
64106-2627
Tel.: (816) 842-6300
Web Site: http://www.ozark-
national.com
Year Founded: 1982
Sales Range: $50-74.9 Million
Emp.: 70
Holding Company; Life Insurance &
Mutual Fund Investment Services
N.A.I.C.S.: 551112

CO-ADVANTAGE RESOURCES INC.

3350 Buschwood Park Dr Ste 200,
Tampa, FL 33618
Tel.: (813) 935-2000
Web Site:
https\://www.coadvantage.com
Year Founded: 1990
Sales Range: $200-249.9 Million
Emp.: 5,000
Professional Employer Organizations
N.A.I.C.S.: 561330
Wade Latham (Sr VP-Risk & Corp
Strategy)
Mark Zimmerman (CIO)
Chris Kephart (VP-Sls & Ops-Texas)
Carl H. Kleimann (VP-Industry Rels)
Clinton Burgess (COO)
Peter Grabowski (Co-CFO)
Philip Devine (Chief Integration Offi-
cer)
Kimberley A. Robbins (Chief Legal
Officer)
Julie Seiner (Sr VP-Client Svcs &
Implementation)
Scott Gordon (Sr VP-Sls)
Kat Bush (Sr VP-Payroll & Benefits
Ops)
John Hale (CTO)
John McAllister (Sr VP-Benefits Prod-
ucts)

CO-ALLIANCE LLP

5250 E US Hwy 36, Avon, IN 46123
Tel.: (317) 745-4491   IN
Web Site: https\://www.co-
alliance.com
Year Founded: 1927
Sales Range: $25-49.9 Million
Emp.: 500
Petroleum Bulk Stations & Terminals-
Farm Supplies
N.A.I.C.S.: 424710
Kevin Still (CEO)
Vince Seward (Mgr-Agronomy)
John Stebbins (Reg Mgr-Agronomy)
Danny Hutson (Mgr)
Russ Hammer (Mgr)

CO-COMMUNICATIONS, INC.

4 W Red Oak Ln Ste 109, White
Plains, NY 10604
Tel.: (914) 666-0066   NY
Web Site:
https\://www.cocommunications.com
Year Founded: 1997
Sales Range: $1-9.9 Million
Emp.: 15
Advertising & Public Relations
Agency
N.A.I.C.S.: 541820
Stacey Cohen (Pres)
Jessica Lyon (COO & Exec VP)
Kelly Lee (Acct Mgr)
Danielle Cyr (VP-Integrated Mktg)
Kayleigh Lentz (Acct Supvr)
Andrew Saginor (Mgr-Creative Svcs)

CO-FREE INCORPORATED

1149 NE 35th St, Ocala, FL 34479
Tel.: (352) 732-8589
Rev.: $13,000,000
Emp.: 6
Convenience Store
N.A.I.C.S.: 445131
Larry Freeman (Pres)

CO-MO ELECTRIC COOPERA-TIVE

29868 Hwy 5 PO Box 220, Tipton,
MO 65081
Tel.: (660) 433-5521
Web Site: http://www.co-mo.coop
Year Founded: 1939
Sales Range: $25-49.9 Million
Emp.: 78
Provider of Electric Services
N.A.I.C.S.: 221118
Michael Nelson (Mgr-Fin)
Jon Schulte (Mgr-Engrg)
Ryan Cornelius (Mgr-Comm)
Gene Eulinger (Chm)
Aaron Bradshaw (CEO & Gen Mgr)

CO-OP COUNTRY FARMERS ELEVATOR

340 Dupont Ave NE, Renville, MN
56284
Tel.: (320) 329-8377   MN
Web Site:
http://www.coopcountry.com
Year Founded: 1986
Sales Range: $75-99.9 Million
Emp.: 40
Sales & Marketing of Grain & Field
Crops
N.A.I.C.S.: 424510
Craig Hebrink (Pres & CEO)
Lynn Payne (VP & Controller)
Gerry Kodet (Mgr-Agronomy)

CO-OP PROMOTIONS

2301 S Ocean Dr Ste 2504, Holly-
wood, FL 33019
Tel.: (954) 922-2323   FL
Web Site: http://www.co-
oppromotions.com
Year Founded: 1987
Sales Range: $1-9.9 Million
Emp.: 10
Sales Promotion
N.A.I.C.S.: 541810
Arthur S. Averbook (Founder & Pres)

Subsidiaries:

CO-OP PROMOTIONS   (1)
658 Timpson St, Pelham, NY 10803-2632
Tel.: (914) 738-6025
Web Site: http://www.co-oppromotions.com
Emp.: 1
Advertising Services
N.A.I.C.S.: 541810

CO-OP SERVICE CENTER INC.

506 E Washington St, Jackson, MO
63755
Tel.: (573) 243-3563
Web Site:
http://www.coopservicecenter.com
Rev.: $18,000,000
Emp.: 21
Farm Supplies Merchant Whslr
N.A.I.C.S.: 424910
Tom McDowel (Gen Mgr)

CO-OPERATIVE ELEVATOR CO. INC.

7211 E Michigan Ave, Pigeon, MI
48755
Tel.: (989) 453-4500   MI
Web Site: https\://www.coopelev.com
Year Founded: 1915
Sales Range: $25-49.9 Million
Emp.: 135
Retailer of Grain & Field Beans

CO-OPERATIVE FEED DEAL-ERS, INC.

380 Broome Corp Pkwy, Conklin, NY
13748
Tel.: (607) 651-9078   NY
Web Site: http://www.co-opfeed.com
Year Founded: 1935
Sales Range: $10-24.9 Million
Emp.: 100
Grain & Animal Feed Distr
N.A.I.C.S.: 424510
Lon Stephens (Gen Mgr)
Glenn Wolfe (Dir-Sls & Mktg)
Ed Kozloski (Mgr-Traffic)
Fred Darrow (Mgr-Warehouse)
Bob VanKleeck (Treas)

COACH HOUSE, INC.

3480 Technology Dr, Nokomis, FL
34275
Tel.: (941) 485-0984
Web Site:
https\://www.coachhouserv.com
Year Founded: 1985
Sales Range: $1-9.9 Million
Emp.: 45
Motor Home Mfr
N.A.I.C.S.: 336213
David Gerzeny (Pres)
Steve Gerzeny (VP)
Armando Gaona (Mgr-Svc)

COACHELLA VALLEY HOUS-ING COALITION

45-701 Monroe St Ste G, Indio, CA
92201
Tel.: (760) 347-3157   CA
Web Site: https\://www.cvhc.org
Year Founded: 1982
Sales Range: $10-24.9 Million
Emp.: 44
Community Housing Services
N.A.I.C.S.: 624229
Pedro Rodriguez (CFO)
Michael Walsh (Project Mgr)
Marvin Contreras (Mgr-Acctg)
Richard Levine (Treas)
Bob Wright (Pres)
Emilia Mojica (Dir-Single Family)
Martha Juarez (Mgr-Contracts)
Josseth Mota (Coord-Community
Svcs)

COACHELLA VALLEY WATER DISTRICT

PO Box 1058, Coachella, CA 92236
Tel.: (760) 398-2651
Web Site: https\://www.cvwd.org
Year Founded: 1918
Sales Range: $250-299.9 Million
Emp.: 506
Water Processing & Control Services
N.A.I.C.S.: 221310
Luis Maciel (Dir-Info Sys)
John P. Powell Jr. (Pres)

COADY DIEMAR PARTNERS, LLC

270 Lafayette St Ste 204, New York,
NY 10012
Tel.: (212) 901-2600   DE
Web Site:
https\://www.coadydiemar.com
Year Founded: 2003
Sales Range: $10-24.9 Million
Corporate Consulting Services
N.A.I.C.S.: 541611
Bob Diemar (Mng Partner)
Colin Knudsen (Mng Dir)
Brian Mullen (Mng Dir)
Clifford Adams (Mng Dir)
Robert Diemar (Mng Dir)
Clifford G. Adams (Mng Dir)
Michael R. Pagano (VP)

N.A.I.C.S.: 424510

John Scott Magrane Jr. (Vice Chm &
Mng Dir)
J. Scott Magrane Jr. (Mng Dir)

COAKLEY & WILLIAMS CON-STRUCTION INC.

16 S Summit Ave Ste 300, Gaithers-
burg, MD 20877
Tel.: (301) 963-5000
Web Site:
http://www.coakleywilliams.com
Year Founded: 1961
Sales Range: $25-49.9 Million
Emp.: 210
Nonresidential Construction Services
N.A.I.C.S.: 236220
Sean Coakley (VP-Interiors)
Mark Williams (Pres)

COAKLEY BROS. COMPANY INC.

400 S 5th St, Milwaukee, WI 53204
Tel.: (414) 278-7060   WI
Web Site:
https\://www.coakleybrothers.com
Year Founded: 1888
Sales Range: $75-99.9 Million
Emp.: 100
Provider of General Warehousing &
Commercial Moving
N.A.I.C.S.: 493110
Peggy Coakley (Pres & CEO)
Joe Lindahl (CFO)
Kevin Kaufmann (VP-Residential Re-
location)
Tom Sullivan (VP-Installations &
Warehousing)
Beth Kuzbek (Dir-Sls)

COAL ENERGY RESOURCES INC.

966 W Main St Ste C, Abingdon, VA
24210
Tel.: (276) 676-3101
Sales Range: $75-99.9 Million
Emp.: 10
Coal
N.A.I.C.S.: 423520
Jim Gott (Pres)
Martin Gott (VP-Real Estate)
Greg Jordan (VP-Sls)

COAL NETWORK, INC.

7697 Innovation Way Ste 100, Ma-
son, OH 45040
Tel.: (513) 398-2625
Web Site:
http://www.coalnetwork.com
Sales Range: $50-74.9 Million
Emp.: 6
Coal Marketing Services
N.A.I.C.S.: 423520
Gerald Quitter (Pres)
Amy Larkin (Controller)

COALITION FOR HISPANIC FAMILY SERVICES

315 Wyckott Ave 4th Fl, Brooklyn, NY
11237
Tel.: (718) 497-6090   NY
Web Site:
https\://www.hispanicfamilyny.org
Year Founded: 1989
Sales Range: $10-24.9 Million
Emp.: 231
Child & Youth Care Services
N.A.I.C.S.: 624110
Franc Villalobos (Dir-Family Dev
Svcs)
Abigail Feliciano (Dir-Community
Based Svcs)
Laura Paris (Dir-Arts, Literacy After
School & Summer Program)
Denise Rosario (Exec Dir)
Sal Morales Jr. (Mgr-Ops & Con-
tracts)

Coalition of Cancer Cooperative Groups—(Continued)

COALITION OF CANCER CO-OPERATIVE GROUPS

1818 Market St Ste 1100, Philadelphia, PA 19103
Tel.: (215) 789-3600   IL
Web Site:
http://www.cancertrialshelp.org
Year Founded: 1997
Sales Range: $25-49.9 Million
Emp.: 70
Healtcare Services
N.A.I.C.S.: 622110
Robert B. Catalano *(VP-Regulatory Affairs)*
Donna Marinucci *(VP-Ops)*

COALITION TO SALUTE AMERICA'S HEROES

552 Fort Evans Rd Ste 300, Leesburg, VA 20176
Tel.: (703) 291-4605   DC
Web Site:
https://www.saluteheroes.org
Year Founded: 1984
Sales Range: $10-24.9 Million
Emp.: 74
Disabled Veteran Assistance Services
N.A.I.C.S.: 623210
Mary Price *(Mgr-Donor Rels)*
Neida Sotomayor *(Sr Dir-Emergency Fin Aid & Veteran Svcs & Mgr-Case)*
Sara Miller *(Dir-Events & Donor Rels)*
Elizabeth Bashara *(Dir-Bus Dev)*
David W. Walker *(Pres & CEO)*

COALMARCH PRODUCTIONS LLC

208 S Wilmington St Ste 204, Raleigh, NC 27601
Tel.: (919) 481-2895
Web Site: http://www.coalmarch.com
Sales Range: $1-9.9 Million
Emp.: 12
Internet Advertising & Marketing Services
N.A.I.C.S.: 541890
Jason Stanley *(Mng Dir & Creative Dir)*
Maria Mayorga *(Coord-Mktg)*
Todd Robert *(Dir-Art)*

COAST 2 COAST FINANCIAL GROUP, LLC

2207 Concord Pike, Wilmington, DE 19803   FL
Web Site:
http://coast2coastlenders.com
Year Founded: 2019
Holding Company; Consumer Lending Services
N.A.I.C.S.: 551112
Kevin J. Gordon *(CEO)*

Subsidiaries:

Coast 2 Coast Lenders, LLC   (1)
2207 Concord Pike, Wilmington, DE 19803
Web Site: http://coast2coastlenders.com
Consumer Lending Services
N.A.I.C.S.: 522291
Kevin J. Gordon *(CEO)*

COAST ALUMINUM & ARCHI-TECTURAL INC.

30551 Huntwood Ave, Hayward, CA 94544-7019
Tel.: (510) 441-6600   CA
Web Site:
https://www.coastaluminum.com
Year Founded: 1991
Sales Range: $50-74.9 Million
Emp.: 250
Metal Service Centers & Offices
N.A.I.C.S.: 423510
Thomas C. Clark *(Pres)*

COAST AUTO CENTER INC.

530 Chetco Ave, Brookings, OR 97415
Tel.: (541) 469-5321
Web Site:
http://www.coastautocenter.com
Sales Range: $10-24.9 Million
Emp.: 50
New & Used Car Dealers
N.A.I.C.S.: 441110
Ronald Walker *(Pres)*

COAST BMW NISSAN

12100 Los Osos Vly Rd, San Luis Obispo, CA 93405
Tel.: (805) 543-4423
Web Site: http://www.coastbmw.com
Year Founded: 2000
Sales Range: $10-24.9 Million
Emp.: 44
Car Whslr
N.A.I.C.S.: 441110
Eric Idleman *(Gen Mgr)*

COAST CENTRAL CREDIT UNION

2650 Harrison Ave, Eureka, CA 95501
Tel.: (707) 445-8801   CA
Web Site: https://www.coastccu.org
Year Founded: 1950
Sales Range: $25-49.9 Million
Emp.: 221
Credit Union
N.A.I.C.S.: 522130
Ron Rudebock *(Chm)*
Pat Brown *(Vice Chm)*
Joyce Jury *(Sec)*
Robert Gearheart *(Treas)*
James T. Sessa *(Pres & CEO)*

COAST CITRUS DISTRIBU-TORS INC.

7597 Bristow Ct, San Diego, CA 92154-7419
Tel.: (619) 661-7950   CA
Web Site:
http://www.coasttropical.com
Year Founded: 1950
Sales Range: $25-49.9 Million
Emp.: 350
Distr of Fresh Fruits & Vegetables
N.A.I.C.S.: 424480
Margarita Alvarez *(CEO)*

COAST COUNTIES GLASS INC.

4 Upper Ragsdale Dr, Monterey, CA 93940
Tel.: (831) 649-4444
Web Site:
http://www.coastcountiesglass.com
Sales Range: $10-24.9 Million
Emp.: 30
Supplier of Metal Doors, Sash & Trim Glass
N.A.I.C.S.: 423310
Ted Golding *(Pres)*
Linda Beard *(Project Mgr)*

COAST COUNTIES TRUCK & EQUIPMENT CO.

1740 N 4th St, San Jose, CA 95112
Tel.: (408) 453-5510
Web Site:
https://www.coastcounties.com
Rev.: $38,000,000
Emp.: 46
Trucks, Tractors & Trailers: New & Used
N.A.I.C.S.: 441110
Mike Sorensen *(Gen Mgr)*

COAST CUTLERY COMPANY

8033 NE Holman St, Portland, OR 97218-4019

Tel.: (503) 234-4545   OR
Web Site: https://www.coastportland.com
Year Founded: 1919
Sales Range: $75-99.9 Million
Emp.: 40
Sporting Knives & LED Lighting Products Mfr
N.A.I.C.S.: 339920
David C. Brands *(Pres)*
Donna Chung *(Controller)*

COAST DENTAL SERVICES, INC.

4010 W Boy Scout Blvd Ste 1100, Tampa, FL 33607-5796
Tel.: (813) 288-1999   DE
Web Site:
http://www.coastdental.com
Year Founded: 1992
Sales Range: $50-74.9 Million
Emp.: 750
Dental Practices Management Services
N.A.I.C.S.: 621210
Adam Diasti *(Founder & Pres)*
Thomas J. Marler *(CEO)*
Michael Smith *(CIO)*
Patricia A. Huie *(Gen Counsel)*
Cindy V. Roark *(Dir-Clinical)*
Leslie Spencer *(Dir-Mktg, Comm & PR)*

COAST LINE SUPPLY & EQUIPMENT COMPANY

7949 Ramona Ave, Sacramento, CA 95826-3888
Tel.: (916) 452-4849
Web Site:
https://www.coastlinesupplyco.com
Commercial Winery & Beverage Supplies & Equipment Whslr
N.A.I.C.S.: 423440
David J. Inderkum *(Owner)*

COAST PACKAGING COM-PANY

3401 Etiwanda Ave 711A, Mira Loma, CA 91752
Tel.: (951) 681-0666
Web Site:
http://www.coastpackaging.com
Sales Range: $25-49.9 Million
Emp.: 10
Packaging Materials
N.A.I.C.S.: 424990
Kirk Allen *(VP)*

COAST PACKING COMPANY

3275 E Vernon Ave, Vernon, CA 90058-1820
Tel.: (323) 277-7700
Web Site:
https://www.coastpacking.com
Year Founded: 1922
Sales Range: $75-99.9 Million
Emp.: 50
Mfr of Vegetable Oils, Animal Fats & Baking, Frying & Shortening Products
N.A.I.C.S.: 311225
Ronald R. Gustafson *(Pres & COO)*
Alan Green *(Controller)*

COAST PAD & TRIM CORP.

12658 Cisneros Ln, Santa Fe Springs, CA 90670
Tel.: (562) 298-1298
Web Site: https://www.coastpad.com
Rev.: $20,000,000
Emp.: 20
Distribute Sewing Accessories
N.A.I.C.S.: 424310
Jindas B. Shah *(Chm)*
Eric Shah *(Pres)*

COAST PLATING, INC.

128 W 154th St, Gardena, CA 90248
Tel.: (323) 770-0240
Web Site:
http://www.coastplating.com
Year Founded: 1965
Emp.: 55
Metal Finishing Services
N.A.I.C.S.: 332813
Roy Murdock *(Owner)*
K. Means *(CFO)*

Subsidiaries:

Blue Streak Finishers, Ltd.   (1)
1520 80th St SW Ste A, Everett, WA 98203
Tel.: (425) 347-1944
Web Site: http://www.bluestreak-finishers.com
Plating & Polishing Services
N.A.I.C.S.: 332813

COAST PLAZA DOCTORS HOSPITAL INC.

13100 Studebaker Rd, Norwalk, CA 90650-2531
Tel.: (562) 868-3751   CA
Web Site:
https://www.coastplazahospital.com
Year Founded: 1991
Sales Range: $10-24.9 Million
Emp.: 250
General Medical & Surgical Hospitals
N.A.I.C.S.: 622110
Thelma Tucker *(Coord-Quality)*

COAST PRODUCE COMPANY INC.

1791 Bay St, Los Angeles, CA 90021-1936
Tel.: (213) 689-0919
Web Site:
http://www.coastproduce.com
Year Founded: 1955
Sales Range: $25-49.9 Million
Emp.: 150
Fresh Fruits & Vegetables
N.A.I.C.S.: 424480
John K. Dunn *(Pres)*

COAST PROFESSIONAL, INC.

214 Expo Cir Ste 7, West Monroe, LA 71292
Tel.: (318) 807-4500   LA
Web Site:
http://www.coastprofessional.net
Year Founded: 1976
Sales Range: $10-24.9 Million
Emp.: 148
Collection Agency Services
N.A.I.C.S.: 561440
Everett Stagg *(Pres)*
Michele Malczewski *(Chief HR Officer)*

COAST PUMP & SUPPLY CO. INC.

610 Groveland Ave, Venice, FL 34285
Tel.: (941) 484-3738
Web Site:
http://www.coastpumpwatertech.com
Sales Range: $10-24.9 Million
Emp.: 100
Irrigation Equipment
N.A.I.C.S.: 423820
Gordon W. Phillips *(Pres)*
Mathew Phillips *(VP)*
David Jacobson *(Controller)*

COAST TO COAST CAR-PORTS, INC.

22525 I-40, Knoxville, AR 72845
Tel.: (479) 885-1258
Web Site: https://www.coast-to-coastcarports.com
Rev.: $2,200,000
Emp.: 25

Prefabricated Metal Building & Component Mfr
N.A.I.C.S.: 332311
Venancio Torres *(Pres)*
Jorge Zavala *(Treas & Sec)*
Terri Franklin *(Mgr-AR)*

COAST TO COAST TICKETS LLC
2002 A Guadalupe St #275, Austin, TX 78705
Tel.: (512) 419-9888
Web Site:
    http://www.coasttocoasttickets.com
Sales Range: $10-24.9 Million
Emp.: 20
Event Ticket Brokerage & Consulting Services
N.A.I.C.S.: 561499
Michael D. Randall *(Co-Founder & Pres)*
Jason Randall *(Co-Founder & CEO)*

COASTAL AGROBUSINESS INC.
3702 S Evans St, Greenville, NC 27834-5408
Tel.: (252) 756-1126   NC
Web Site:
    http://www.coastalagro.com
Year Founded: 1953
Sales Range: $50-74.9 Million
Emp.: 90
Agricultural Chemical & Fertilizer Mfr
N.A.I.C.S.: 325314
Tandy Oliver Dunn *(Dir-Health, Safety & Environmental Affairs)*
Jim Pearce *(Dir-Mktg & Product Dev)*
Donna Stearns *(Office Mgr)*
Tom McKemie *(Mgr-Technical Svcs)*
Scott Griffin *(CFO)*
James Clarence Whitehurst Jr. *(Founder, Pres & CEO)*

Subsidiaries:

Coastal AgroBusiness Inc. - Colerain Plant   **(1)**
542 Morris Ford Rd, Colerain, NC 27924
Tel.: (252) 356-4500
Web Site: http://www.agrobusiness.com
Emp.: 16
Agricultural Chemical Product Whslr
N.A.I.C.S.: 424910
Walter Byrum *(Mgr-Sls)*

Coastal AgroBusiness Inc. - Dillon Plant   **(1)**
2015 Hwy 301 S, Dillon, SC 29536-0589
Tel.: (843) 774-8204
Web Site: http://www.coastalagro.com
Emp.: 8
Agricultural Chemical Product Whslr
N.A.I.C.S.: 424910
Robert Tallon *(Mgr-Sls)*

Coastal AgroBusiness Inc. - Hamilton Plant   **(1)**
12011 NC Hwy 125, Hamilton, NC 27840
Tel.: (252) 798-3481
Web Site:
    http://www.coastalagrobusiness.com
Emp.: 12
Agricultural Chemical Product Whslr
N.A.I.C.S.: 424910
Sam Whitehead *(Mgr-Sls)*

Coastal AgroBusiness Inc. - Henderson Plant   **(1)**
205 Vicksboro Rd, Henderson, NC 27536-0787
Tel.: (252) 492-3713
Web Site: http://www.coastalagro.com
Agricultural Chemical Product Whslr
N.A.I.C.S.: 424910
Phil Walters *(Mgr-Sls)*

Coastal AgroBusiness Inc. - Hendersonville Plant   **(1)**
814 McMurray Rd, Flat Rock, NC 28731
Tel.: (828) 697-2220
Web Site: http://www.businessagro.com
Emp.: 10

Agricultural Chemical Product Whslr
N.A.I.C.S.: 424910
Chuck Francis *(Mgr-Sls)*

Coastal AgroBusiness Inc. - Kinston Plant   **(1)**
3102 Hwy NC 11 N, Kinston, NC 28501
Tel.: (252) 523-1363
Web Site: http://www.coastalagro.com
Emp.: 15
Agricultural Chemical Product Whslr
N.A.I.C.S.: 424910
Joe Warren *(Mgr-Sls)*

Coastal AgroBusiness Inc. - Murfreesboro Plant   **(1)**
130 Underwood Rd, Murfreesboro, NC 27855-1404
Tel.: (252) 398-5675
Agricultural Chemical Product Whslr
N.A.I.C.S.: 424910
Travis Badgett *(Mgr-Sls)*

Coastal AgroBusiness Inc. - Pantego Plant   **(1)**
510 Swindell Rd, Pantego, NC 27860
Tel.: (252) 943-2388
Web Site:
    http://www.coastalagrobusiness.com
Agricultural Chemical Product Whslr
N.A.I.C.S.: 424910
James Allen *(Mgr-Sls)*

COASTAL BEHAVIORAL HEALTHCARE, INC.
1565 State St, Sarasota, FL 34236
Tel.: (941) 927-8900   FL
Web Site: http://www.coastalbh.org
Year Founded: 1971
Sales Range: $10-24.9 Million
Emp.: 319
Behavioral Healthcare Services
N.A.I.C.S.: 623220
Joanne Radcliffe *(CFO)*
Marlene Hauck *(Dir-Dev)*

COASTAL BEND COMMUNITY FOUNDATION
615 N Upper Broadway Ste 1950, Corpus Christi, TX 78401
Tel.: (361) 882-9745   TX
Web Site:
    http://www.cbcfoundation.org
Year Founded: 1980
Sales Range: $10-24.9 Million
Emp.: 5
Fundraising Services
N.A.I.C.S.: 813211
Karen W. Selim *(Pres & CEO)*
Tracy M. Ramirez *(Dir-Comm)*

COASTAL BRIDGE COMPANY, LLC
4825 Jamestown Ave, Baton Rouge, LA 70808-3225
Tel.: (225) 766-0244   LA
Web Site:
    http://www.coastalbridge.com
Year Founded: 1955
Sales Range: $25-49.9 Million
Emp.: 170
Bridges, Tunnels & Elevated Highway Construction
N.A.I.C.S.: 237310
Kelly Sills *(Pres)*

Subsidiaries:

Coastal Bridge Company, LLC - Convent Asphalt Plant   **(1)**
91490 Winnie Rd, Convent, LA 70723
Tel.: (225) 562-7026
Highway Construction Services
N.A.I.C.S.: 237310
John Jackson *(Plant Mgr)*

Coastal Bridge Company, LLC - Port Allen Asphalt Plant   **(1)**
3371 Highway 1 N, Port Allen, LA 70767
Tel.: (225) 214-9254
Highway Construction Services
N.A.I.C.S.: 237310

John Cook *(Plant Mgr)*

COASTAL CAPITAL ACQUISITION CORP.
725 1st Ave, Columbus, GA 31901
Tel.: (706) 987-8100
Holding Company Services
N.A.I.C.S.: 551112
Anthony Dinorcia *(Chm & CEO)*

COASTAL CLOUD LLC
1 Hammock Beach Pkwy Ste 200, Palm Coast, FL 32137
Tel.: (386) 693-1595
Web Site:
    http://www.coastalcloud.com
Year Founded: 2012
Sales Range: $1-9.9 Million
Emp.: 15
IT Consulting & Other Computer Related Services
N.A.I.C.S.: 541690
Sara Hale *(Mng Partner)*
Tim Hale *(Mng Partner)*
Jennifer Flake *(Mng Dir-Svc Cloud)*
Lori Lenehan *(Mng Dir-Sls Cloud)*
Gene Nix *(Mng Dir-Cloud Solutions)*

COASTAL COCKTAILS INC.
151 Kalmus Dr Ste H6, Costa Mesa, CA 92626
Tel.: (949) 250-8951
Web Site:
    http://www.moderngourmetfood.com
Sales Range: $10-24.9 Million
Emp.: 16
Gourmet Gift Product Distr
N.A.I.C.S.: 445290
Boaz Shonfeld *(Exec VP)*
Mark Greenhall *(Pres)*
Yaron Bart *(Coord-Trade Show)*
Jason Hoffman *(VP-Sls & Natl Accounts)*

COASTAL COMMUNITY AND TEACHERS CREDIT UNION
6810 Saratoga Blvd, Corpus Christi, TX 78414
Tel.: (361) 985-6810   TX
Web Site: http://www.myccatcu.com
Year Founded: 1935
Sales Range: $10-24.9 Million
Emp.: 121
Credit Union Operator
N.A.I.C.S.: 522130
Javier Leal *(Treas)*
Ken Combs *(Chm)*

COASTAL COMMUNITY BANK
2817 Colby Ave, Everett, WA 98201
Tel.: (425) 257-9000
Web Site:
    https://www.coastalbank.com
Rev.: $11,500,000
Emp.: 80
Commericial Banking
N.A.I.C.S.: 522110
Eric M. Sprink *(CEO)*
Brett Schuelke *(Mgr-Relationship)*
Elizabeth Johnson *(Mgr-Relationship)*
Jim Croasdill *(Mgr-Relationship)*
Julie Lienhard *(Mgr-Relationship)*
Larry Young *(Mgr-Relationship)*
Lindsey Purdy *(Mgr-Relationship)*
Mike Spencer *(Mgr-Relationship)*
Seth Jones *(Mgr-Relationship)*
Melissa Hemrich *(VP-Snohomish)*
Jennifer Shelton *(Dir-The Washington Small Bus Dev Center)*
Rhonda Matthes *(VP)*
David Cope *(VP & Branch Mgr)*
Bill Morrow *(VP/Mgr-Customer Rels-Woodinville)*

Keith Dingfield *(VP/Mgr-Customer Rels-Woodinville)*
Eric M. Sprink *(CEO)*
Curt Queyrouze *(Pres)*

COASTAL COMMUNITY FOUNDATION
635 Rutledge Ave Ste 201, Charleston, SC 29403
Tel.: (843) 723-3635   SC
Web Site:
    http://www.coastalcommunity.org
Year Founded: 1974
Sales Range: $10-24.9 Million
Emp.: 24
Community Care Services
N.A.I.C.S.: 624190
Paul Kohlheim *(Treas & Sec)*
Darrin Goss Sr. *(Pres & CEO)*

COASTAL CONCRETE INC.
118 Pipemakers Cir Ste 100, Pooler, GA 31322-4164
Tel.: (843) 757-5035   SC
Web Site:
    http://www.coastalconcrete.com
Year Founded: 1985
Sales Range: $10-24.9 Million
Emp.: 12
Ready Mixed Concrete
N.A.I.C.S.: 333120
Hans Karlander *(Chm)*
Alan Wessel *(CEO)*
Fredrik Hoeglund *(Dir-Fin & Bus Dev)*
Joe Click *(Dir-Fleet Svcs)*
John Cook *(Dir-Technical Svcs)*

COASTAL CONSERVATION ASSOCIATION
6919 Portwest Ste 100, Houston, TX 77024
Tel.: (713) 626-4234   TX
Web Site: https://www.joincca.org
Year Founded: 1978
Sales Range: $10-24.9 Million
Emp.: 73
Environmental Conservation Services
N.A.I.C.S.: 813312
Ted Venker *(Dir-Conservation)*
Patrick D. Murray *(Pres)*
Teresa Donaldson *(Dir-Comm)*

COASTAL CONSTRUCTION GROUP OF SOUTH FLORIDA INC.
5959 Blue Lagoon Dr Ste 200, Miami, FL 33126-2052
Tel.: (305) 559-4900   FL
Web Site:
    https://www.coastalconstruction.com
Year Founded: 1997
Sales Range: $200-249.9 Million
Emp.: 210
Residential Construction
N.A.I.C.S.: 236115
Dan Whiteman *(Vice Chm)*
John Murphy *(VP-Field Ops)*
Sean Murphy *(Co-Pres)*
Mike Murphy *(VP-Quality Assurance)*
Thomas P. Murphy Jr. *(Founder, Chm & CEO)*
Jason Anderson *(VP-Coastal Homes)*
Sean DeMartino *(Pres-Central & North Florida Div)*
Tom C. Murphy V *(VP-Pre-Construction Svcs)*

COASTAL DENTAL, INC.
Smoketree Plz 601 Daily Dr Ste 215, Camarillo, CA 93010
Web Site:
    http://www.thecdigroup.com
Year Founded: 2007
Sales Range: $1-9.9 Million
Emp.: 15

Coastal Dental, Inc.—(Continued)
Partners with Dental Practice Management Companies Offering Discounted Dental Plans
N.A.I.C.S.: 524298
Neil Schroeder *(Pres)*

COASTAL DEVELOPMENT LLC
745 5th Ave 18th Fl, New York, NY 10151
Tel.: (212) 355-6161
Web Site:
    http://www.coastaldevelopment.com
Year Founded: 1998
Sales Range: $10-24.9 Million
Emp.: 20
Real Estate Development Services
N.A.I.C.S.: 531390
Richard T. Fields *(Chm & CEO)*

COASTAL DEVELOPMENTAL SERVICES FOUNDATION
5901 Green Valley Cir Ste 320, Culver City, CA 90230
Tel.: (310) 258-4000   CA
Web Site: https://www.westsiderc.org
Year Founded: 1983
Sales Range: $125-149.9 Million
Emp.: 198
Developmental Disability Assistance Services
N.A.I.C.S.: 624120
Debra Ray *(Supvr-Res)*
Mary-Lou Stusser *(Dir-Community Svcs)*
Carmine Manicone *(Exec Dir)*

COASTAL DOOR & WINDOW INC.
5360 Commerce Blvd E, Mobile, AL 36619
Tel.: (251) 666-7306
Web Site: http://www.coastaldw.com
Sales Range: $25-49.9 Million
Emp.: 62
Mfr & Sales of Doors & Windows
N.A.I.C.S.: 423310
David W. Miller *(Pres)*

COASTAL ECONOMIC DEVELOPMENT CORPORATION
4 Merrill Industrial Dr Ste 201, Hampton, NH 03842
Tel.: (603) 929-9244   NH
Web Site: http://www.coastaledc.com
Year Founded: 1998
Rev.: $1,082,240
Assets: $7,394,508
Liabilities: $5,343,634
Net Worth: $2,050,874
Earnings: ($10,361)
Emp.: 2
Fiscal Year-end: 06/30/14
Economic Development Services
N.A.I.C.S.: 541720
Daniel Gray *(Mng Dir)*
Anne Russell *(Chm)*
Doc Noel *(Vice Chm)*
Ellen Lavin *(Treas)*

COASTAL ENTERPRISES, INC.
36 Water St, Wiscasset, ME 04578
Tel.: (207) 882-7552   ME
Web Site: http://www.ceimaine.org
Year Founded: 1977
Sales Range: $10-24.9 Million
Emp.: 91
Community Action Services
N.A.I.C.S.: 624190
Keith Bisson *(Sr VP-Program Dev)*

COASTAL EYE ASSOCIATES PLLC
100 E Nasa Pkwy, Webster, TX 77598
Tel.: (281) 488-7213
Web Site:
    http://www.coastaleyeassocs.com
Offices of Optometrists
N.A.I.C.S.: 621320
Pat Sherer *(Mgr)*

COASTAL FAMILY HEALTH CENTER
1046 Division St, Biloxi, MS 39530
Tel.: (228) 374-2494   MS
Web Site:
    https://www.coastalfamilyhealth.org
Year Founded: 1976
Sales Range: $10-24.9 Million
Emp.: 255
Health Care Srvices
N.A.I.C.S.: 622110
Larry Knight *(COO)*
Angel Greer *(CEO)*
Kwantrell Green *(Pres)*
Roy A. Tolbert *(Treas)*

COASTAL FINANCIAL CORP.
1100 Laskin Rd Ste 201, Virginia Beach, VA 23451
Tel.: (757) 491-6600   VA
Web Site:
    http://www.wefinancefun.com
Year Founded: 1989
Sales Range: $10-24.9 Million
Emp.: 10
Boat Loans & Financing
N.A.I.C.S.: 522291
Rebecca Osborn *(Coord-Mktg)*

Subsidiaries:

Coastal Federal Bank   (1)
2619 Oak St, Myrtle Beach, SC 29577-3129
Tel.: (843) 205-2000
Web Site: http://www.coastalfederal.com
Banking Services
N.A.I.C.S.: 522180

COASTAL FOREST RESOURCES COMPANY
8007 FL-GA Hwy, Havana, FL 32333
Tel.: (850) 539-6432
Web Site:
    http://www.coastalplywood.com
Hardwood Lumber, Pine Lumber, Plywood, Treated Wood Products & Hardwood Dimension Products Mfr
N.A.I.C.S.: 321113
Joshua Travis Bryant *(Pres & CEO)*

COASTAL GROUP
1201 Industrial Ave, Holland, MI 49423
Tel.: (615) 355-9800
Web Site: http://www.coastal-container.com
Sales Range: $1-9.9 Million
Emp.: 75
Solid Fiber Box Mfr
N.A.I.C.S.: 322211
Brent Patterson *(Pres & CEO)*
Bill Baumgartner *(VP & Gen Mgr)*
Mike Dozeman *(Corp Controller)*
Greg Groh *(Mgr-Design)*
Curt Shosten *(Mgr-Logistics)*
Jeff Greenwood *(Mgr-IT)*
Paul Doyle *(CEO)*

Subsidiaries:

Veecor Co., Inc   (1)
108 Industrial Pkwy Dr, Bogalusa, LA 70427
Tel.: (985) 732-5919
Web Site: http://www.veecor.com
Paper Bag & Coated & Treated Paper Mfr
N.A.I.C.S.: 322220
Robert Pounds *(Pres)*

COASTAL GUNITE CON-
STRUCTION CO
16 Washington St, Cambridge, MD 21613
Tel.: (410) 228-8100
Web Site:
    https://www.coastalgunite.com
Rev.: $12,700,000
Emp.: 150
Concrete Work
N.A.I.C.S.: 238110
Shelly Blake *(VP)*

COASTAL INTEGRATED SERVICES, INC.
5348 Vegas Dr Ste 552, Las Vegas, NV 89108
Tel.: (702) 720-6757
Web Site:
    http://www.coastalservices.com
Plastic Disposable Lids
N.A.I.C.S.: 326199

COASTAL INTERNATIONAL INC.
3 Harper Dr Ste 211, Sausalito, CA 94965-1917
Tel.: (415) 339-1700   NV
Web Site:
    http://www.coastalinternational.com
Year Founded: 1984
Sales Range: $75-99.9 Million
Emp.: 1,300
Provider of Trade Show Services
N.A.I.C.S.: 561920
Bruce Green *(Pres)*
Kathy Spangler *(Mgr-HR)*

COASTAL LOGISTICS GROUP, INC.
50 Sonny Perdue Dr, Garden City, GA 31408
Tel.: (912) 964-0707
Web Site: http://www.clg-inc.com
Year Founded: 2004
Sales Range: $1-9.9 Million
Emp.: 65
Logistic Services
N.A.I.C.S.: 541614
Chad Barrow *(Co-Owner & CEO)*
Richard Barrow *(Co-Owner & CEO)*

COASTAL LUXURY MANAGEMENT
95 Prescott Ave, Monterey, CA 93940
Tel.: (831) 324-0771
Web Site:
    http://www.coastalluxurymanagement.com
Year Founded: 2007
Sales Range: $10-24.9 Million
Emp.: 350
Event & Hospitality Management Firm Specializing in Luxury & Lifestyle Sectors
N.A.I.C.S.: 711310
James Velarde *(VP-Brand Rels)*
Anand Menon *(COO)*
Dorothy Maras *(Coord-Event)*
David Alan Bernahl III *(Partner & Co-Founder)*

COASTAL MACHINERY COMPANY, INC.
6701 Mobile Hwy, Pensacola, FL 32526
Tel.: (850) 944-2002   FL
Web Site:
    https://www.coastalmachinery.com
Year Founded: 1984
Sales Range: $1-9.9 Million
Emp.: 25
Construction, Mining & Forestry Machinery & Equipment Rental & Leasing
N.A.I.C.S.: 532412
Joe Meeks *(Pres)*

COASTAL MARINA MANAGEMENT LLC
2100 Thomas Dr, Panama City, FL 32408
Tel.: (850) 233-1633
Web Site:
    http://www.coastalmarinamanagement.com
Marinas
N.A.I.C.S.: 713930
Scott Burt *(Owner)*

Subsidiaries:

Maker 1 Marina   (1)
343 Causeway Blvd, Dunedin, FL 34698
Tel.: (727) 733-9324
Web Site: http://www.marker1marina.com
Marinas
N.A.I.C.S.: 713930
Steve Arndt *(Dir-Marina)*

COASTAL MEDICAL ASSOCIATES INC
55 Fogg Rd, South Weymouth, MA 02190
Tel.: (781) 624-8431   MA
Year Founded: 1992
Sales Range: $10-24.9 Million
Emp.: 87
Health Care Srvices
N.A.I.C.S.: 622110
John Stevenson *(Pres)*
Michael Cullen *(Treas)*

COASTAL PACIFIC FOOD DISTRIBUTORS, INC.
1015 Performance Dr, Stockton, CA 95206
Tel.: (209) 983-2454   CA
Web Site: https://www.cpfd.com
Year Founded: 1986
Sales Range: $25-49.9 Million
Emp.: 600
Distr of Groceries, General Line For Military
N.A.I.C.S.: 424410
Debbie May *(Bus Mgr)*
Frank Costa *(Dir-Bus Dev-Resale)*
Jeffrey P. King *(COO & Exec VP)*
Julie Terrel *(Dir-Prime Vendor Ops)*
Katie Hoyt *(Bus Mgr)*
Keith Gleason *(Bus Mgr)*
Marc Knadler *(Bus Mgr)*
Matthew W. Payne *(CFO & Exec VP)*
Tamara Andrews *(Dir-Mdsg)*

COASTAL PROPERTIES GROUP INTERNATIONAL, LLC
423 Mandalay Ave Ste 102, Clearwater Beach, FL 33767
Tel.: (727) 493-1555
Web Site: https://www.coastalpgi.com
Sales Range: $1-9.9 Million
Emp.: 160
Real Estate Broker
N.A.I.C.S.: 531210
Alex Jansen *(Co-Founder)*
Laren Jansen *(Co-Founder & COO)*
Myra Sload *(Pres)*
Robert Barber *(VP-Comml)*
Sharon Simms *(VP-Intl Markets)*
Corinna Evans *(Dir-Mktg)*
Michelle Dailey *(Dir-Advisor Svcs, Closing & Compliance)*
Patti Bowie *(Coord-Listing)*

COASTAL SHEET METAL, CORP.
1125 Close Ave, Bronx, NY 10472
Tel.: (845) 365-3556   NY
Year Founded: 1977
Sales Range: $1-9.9 Million
Emp.: 59
Roofing/Siding Contractor
N.A.I.C.S.: 238390
Larry Kay *(CEO)*

COASTAL STRATEGIES, INC.
PO Box 26172, Tampa, FL 33623
Tel.: (813) 391-0302
Web Site:
http://www.coastalstrategies.com
Year Founded: 1987
Sales Range: $1-9.9 Million
Business Development Consulting
Services
N.A.I.C.S.: 541611
Steve Toner (Principal)

COASTAL TRANSPORT CO. INC.
1603 Ackerman Rd, San Antonio, TX
78219-3511
Tel.: (210) 661-4287   TX
Year Founded: 1958
Sales Range: $25-49.9 Million
Emp.: 510
Provider of Local Trucking Services
N.A.I.C.S.: 484220
Barry Detlefsen (VP-Safety)
Joel Redman (Dir-Mgmt Info Sys)

COASTAL WELDING SUPPLY INC.
25 N 4th St, Beaumont, TX 77701
Tel.: (409) 838-3757
Web Site: https://www.coastalws.com
Sales Range: $10-24.9 Million
Emp.: 85
Welding Machinery & Equipment
N.A.I.C.S.: 423830
Tom Johnson (CFO)
Emilo Flores (Mgr-Safety & Compliance)
Gilbert Martin (Supvr-Repair Shop)
John Roland (Mgr-Credit)
Jerry Neeb (Mgr-Ops)

COASTER OF AMERICA INC.
12928 Sandoval St, Santa Fe
Springs, CA 90670-4061
Tel.: (562) 944-7899   CA
Web Site:
http://www.coastercompany.com
Year Founded: 1979
Emp.: 800
Furniture Distr
N.A.I.C.S.: 423210
Michael Yeh (Pres)
John Rodriguez (VP-Ops)
Matthew Chen (VP-HR)

COASTLINE ELDERLY SERVICE, INC.
1646 Purchase St, New Bedford, MA
02740
Tel.: (508) 999-6400   MA
Web Site:
http://www.coastlineelderly.org
Year Founded: 1977
Sales Range: $10-24.9 Million
Emp.: 213
Senior Citizen Center
N.A.I.C.S.: 624120
Jean Breault (Dir-HR)
Justin Lees (Dir-Fiscal)
Ana Hayes (Dir-Home Care)
Paula Shiner (CEO)
Charles McCullough (VP)
Rita L'Etoile (Pres)
Michelle Beneski (VP)
Lisa Mills (VP)

COATES FIELD SERVICE, INC.
4800 N Santa Fe, Oklahoma City, OK
73118
Tel.: (405) 528-5676
Web Site:
http://www.coatesfieldservice.com
Year Founded: 1950
Rev.: $15,000,000
Emp.: 200
Land Acquisition Services

N.A.I.C.S.: 237210
Elaine Lipon (VP-Western Div)
Sue Evans (VP-Western Div)
Mark R. Roby (VP-Houston Div)
John J. Coates III (Pres)
Andrew Sachs (VP-Personnel)
Barbara DeCastro (Treas & Sec)
Bill Dow (VP-Northeastern Div)
Karen J. Mundee (VP-Transportation)
Mark Handley (VP-Southeastern Div)
Mark Self (CFO)

COATESVILLE SAVINGS BANK
185 E Lincoln Hwy, Coatesville, PA
19320
Tel.: (610) 384-8282
Web Site:
http://www.coatesvillesavings.com
Year Founded: 1919
Sales Range: $10-24.9 Million
Emp.: 32
Provider of Banking Services
N.A.I.C.S.: 522180
Claudy Geraldino (Officer-Bus Dev-
Oxford)
Kenneth R. Kramer (Officer-Lending
& Sr VP-Bus Dev-Coatesville)
Shannon L. Croll (CFO & VP)
Steven C. Cunningham (VP-Bus Dev-
Coatesville)
Teresa L. Greider (Officer-Bank Ops
& VP)

COATING & ADHESIVES CORPORATION
1901 Popular St NE, Leland, NC
28451
Tel.: (910) 371-3184
Web Site:
https://www.cacoatings.com
Year Founded: 1987
Sales Range: $25-49.9 Million
Emp.: 150
Mfr & Distributors of Adhesives &
Coatings
N.A.I.C.S.: 325510
Richard Pasin (Pres)

COATINGS APPLICATION WATERPROOFING CO., INC.
5125 N 2nd St, Saint Louis, MO
63147
Tel.: (314) 241-6370
Web Site: https://www.cawco.com
Rev.: $18,000,000
Emp.: 16
Roofing Contractors
N.A.I.C.S.: 238160
Kerry Garner (Mgr)

COATS ROSE, P.C.
9 Greenway Plz Ste 1000, Houston,
TX 77046
Tel.: (713) 651-0111   TX
Web Site: https://www.coatsrose.com
Year Founded: 1989
Emp.: 200
Law firm
N.A.I.C.S.: 541110
Richard L. Rose (Pres & Mng Dir)

COAXIAL COMPONENTS CORP.
1501 SE Decker Ave Ste 201, Stuart,
FL 34994
Tel.: (772) 287-5000
Web Site: https://www.coaxicom.com
Year Founded: 1984
Sales Range: $10-24.9 Million
Emp.: 18
Connectors, Adapters & Cable Assemblies Mfr
N.A.I.C.S.: 335921
David A. Leiman (Founder & Pres)

COBALT ASTRA LLC
5913 Woodson Rd, Mission, KS
66202
Tel.: (913) 378-1900
Web Site: http://www.cobaltastra.com
Year Founded: 1999
Sales Range: $10-24.9 Million
Emp.: 12
Human Resource Support Services
N.A.I.C.S.: 541612
Shane Jones (CEO)

COBALT INTERNATIONAL ENERGY, INC.
Cobalt Ctr 920 Memorial City Way
Ste 100, Houston, TX 77024
Tel.: (713) 579-9100   DE
Web Site: http://www.cobaltintl.com
Year Founded: 2005
Rev.: $53,891,000
Assets: $1,596,754,000
Liabilities: $3,390,702,000
Net Worth: ($1,793,948,000)
Earnings: ($968,258,000)
Emp.: 85
Fiscal Year-end: 12/31/17
Oil & Gas Exploration & Production
Services
N.A.I.C.S.: 211120
William P. Utt (Chm)
Jeffrey A. Starzec (Gen Counsel &
Exec VP)
David D. Powell (CFO)
Rod Skaufel (Pres-Ops)
Tim Nicholson (Sr VP-Exploration &
Appraisal)

Subsidiaries:

Cobalt International Energy, L.P.   (1)
920 Memorial City Way Ste 100, Houston,
TX 77024
Tel.: (713) 452-2322
Web Site: http://www.cobaltintl.com
Emp.: 61
Oil & Gas Exploration Services
N.A.I.C.S.: 213112

COBB MECHANICAL CONTRACTORS
2906 Morrison St, Colorado Springs,
CO 80904-3128
Tel.: (719) 471-8958
Web Site:
https://www.cobbmechanical.com
Sales Range: $50-74.9 Million
Emp.: 150
Plumbing Services
N.A.I.C.S.: 238220
Bobby Robbins (Dir-Safety)

COBB PEDIATRIC THERAPY SERVICES
3104 Creekside Vlg Dr Ste 404, Kennesaw, GA 30144
Tel.: (888) 288-1048
Web Site:
http://www.cobbpediatric.com
Year Founded: 1989
Sales Range: $1-9.9 Million
Emp.: 140
Speech Language Pathologists, Occupational Therapists & Physical
Therapists
N.A.I.C.S.: 621340
Mark Norris (COO)
Pam Wetmore (Mgr-HR)
June Whitehead (Pres & CEO)
Jay Owensby (Controller)

COBB, FENDLEY & ASSOCIATES, INC.
13430 NW Fwy Ste 1100, Houston,
TX 77040
Tel.: (713) 462-3242
Web Site:
https://www.cobbfendley.com

Year Founded: 1980
Sales Range: $25-49.9 Million
Emp.: 200
Civil Engineering & Land Surveying
Services
N.A.I.C.S.: 541330
William F. Fendley (Co-Founder)
Royal Harrison (Sr Project Mgr-
Telecom Dept-Mountain Reg)

COBB-HALL INSURANCE AGENCIES, INC.
223 W Grand River Ave Ste 1, Howell, MI 48843-2270
Tel.: (517) 546-1600
Web Site: https://www.cobbhall.com
Sales Range: $10-24.9 Million
Emp.: 15
Provider of Insurance Services
N.A.I.C.S.: 524210
Michael Hall (Pres & CEO)
Terry Moran (Dir-Customer Svc)

COBBS, ALLEN & HALL INC.
115 Ofc Park Dr No 200, Birmingham, AL 35223
Tel.: (205) 414-8100
Web Site: http://www.cahins.com
Sales Range: $10-24.9 Million
Emp.: 120
Insurance Agents, Nec
N.A.I.C.S.: 524210
Bruce S. Denson (CEO)
Randy Mayfield (CFO)
Mary Breckenridge (Asst Mgr-
Collections)
Richard Kohn (VP)
Fran Holt (Sr Acct Mgr)
Grantland Rice III (Pres)

COBE CAPITAL LLC
708 3rd Ave 31st Fl, New York, NY
10017
Tel.: (212) 338-0235
Web Site:
http://www.cobecapital.com
Sales Range: $25-49.9 Million
Emp.: 10
Privater Equity Firm
N.A.I.C.S.: 523999
Neal Cohen (Founder & Mng Dir)
Shuja Haque (Dir-Ops-North America)
Knuth Schmidt (Dir-Ops-Germany,
Austria & Switzerland)

Subsidiaries:

Plantin BVBA   (1)
Kareelovenlaan 5, B-1140, Brussels, Belgium
Tel.: (32) 27273111
Emp.: 150
Office Supplies & Services
N.A.I.C.S.: 459410
Hans Huyghe (Gen Mgr)

Volker GmbH   (1)
Alter Flugplatz 34 Industriegebiet West,
49377, Vechta, Germany
Tel.: (49) 444191760
Web Site: http://www.voelker-gmbh.com
Egg Packaging Machinery Mfr
N.A.I.C.S.: 333248

Warendorfer Kuchen GmbH   (1)
Mielestrasse 1, 48231, Warendorf,
Nordrhein-Westfalen, Germany
Tel.: (49) 2581590
Web Site: http://www.warendorf.eu
Sales Range: $50-74.9 Million
Modular Kitchen Design & Installation Services
N.A.I.C.S.: 238390

COBIAN CORP.
1739 Melrose Dr Ste 101, San Marcos, CA 92078-2100
Tel.: (760) 734-1915
Web Site:
https://www.cobianusa.com

Cobian Corp.—(Continued)

Sales Range: $10-24.9 Million
Emp.: 25
Sandals Whslr
N.A.I.C.S.: 424340
John Cobian (Pres)
Claudia De Soto (CFO)

COBLENTZ DISTRIBUTING INC.

26141 State Rte 39, Walnut Creek, OH 44687
Tel.: (330) 852-2888
Web Site:
   https://www.walnutcreekcheese.com
Sales Range: $10-24.9 Million
Emp.: 38
Mfr Cheese
N.A.I.C.S.: 424430
Mark Coblentz (Pres)
Jerry Shoup (CFO & Controller)
Julian L. Coblentz (CEO)

COBLESKILL STONE PRODUCTS INC.

112 Rock Rd, Cobleskill, NY 12043
Tel.: (518) 234-0221   NY
Web Site:
   http://www.cobleskillstone.com
Year Founded: 1936
Sales Range: $10-24.9 Million
Emp.: 15
Distr of Crushed & Broken Limestone
N.A.I.C.S.: 212312
Emil Galasso (Owner)

COBORN'S INCORPORATED

1921 Coborn Blvd, Saint Cloud, MN 56301
Tel.: (320) 252-4222   MN
Web Site: http://www.cobornsinc.com
Year Founded: 1921
Sales Range: $400-449.9 Million
Emp.: 6,700
Owner & Operator of Grocery Stores
N.A.I.C.S.: 445110
Chris Coborn (Chm & CEO)
Becky Estby (Sr VP-HR & Org Dev)
Rebecca Kurowski (Mgr-Comm)
Emily Coborn (VP-Retail Svcs)
Dave Meyer (Pres & COO)
Dennis Host (VP-Mktg)
Dale Monson (VP-IT)
David Pack (Dir-IT)
Scott Morris (Sr VP-Center Store)
Cheryl Graham (Dir-Private Label & Topco Rels)
Marti Sunderlin (VP-Center Store & Fresh Mdsg)
Sarah Putnam (Sr Dir-Fresh Mdsg)
Troy Vosburgh (VP-Ops-East)
Jenn Weisgram (Sr Dir-Fresh Mdsg)

Subsidiaries:

Cash Wise Flower Shoppe Inc.   (1)
113 Waite Ave S, Waite Park, MN 56387-1348
Tel.: (320) 259-1140
Web Site: http://www.cashwise.com
Rev: $160,000
Emp.: 10
Florists & Grocery Store
N.A.I.C.S.: 456110

Coborns Delivers LLC   (1)
3440 Winpark Dr, New Hope, MN 55427
Tel.: (763) 656-5600
Web Site: http://www.cobornsdelivers.com
Online Grocery Shopping Solutions
N.A.I.C.S.: 492210
Dave Hartmann (Gen Mgr)

Marketplace Foods, Inc.   (1)
330 S Main St, Rice Lake, WI 54868
Tel.: (715) 234-6991
Web Site:
   http://www.marketplacefoodsonline.com
Grocery Stores
N.A.I.C.S.: 445110

Todd Brunner (Mgr-Store)

COBRA BEC, INC.

7211 W Flightline Blvd Ste 108, Spokane, WA 99224
Tel.: (509) 455-4043
Web Site:
   http://www.cobraresults.com
Year Founded: 1983
Sales Range: $25-49.9 Million
Emp.: 165
Roofing Installation Services
N.A.I.C.S.: 238390
Travis Dix (Owner)
Kim Orr (Asst VP)

COBRE VALLEY REGIONAL MEDICAL CENTER

5880 S Hospital Dr, Globe, AZ 85501
Tel.: (928) 425-3261   AZ
Web Site: https://www.cvrmc.org
Year Founded: 1988
Sales Range: $25-49.9 Million
Emp.: 332
Community Health Care Services
N.A.I.C.S.: 621498
Byron G. Belew (Vice Chm)
Edward C. Carpenter (Chm)
Janice L. Cook (Sec)
James B. Rasmussen (Treas)

COBURN SUPPLY COMPANY INC

350 Pine St Ste 850, Beaumont, TX 77701
Tel.: (409) 838-6363
Web Site: http://www.coburns.com
Sales Range: $10-24.9 Million
Emp.: 35
Warm Air Heating & Air Conditioning
N.A.I.C.S.: 423730
Donald J. Maloney (Pres)
Wade Perkins (Branch Mgr)
Bill Geyser (Sr VP & Gen Mgr)
Merlin Frederick (Reg Mgr)
Jody LaPoint (Mgr-HVAC Tech Svc)
Stephanie Tritico (Mgr-Show Room)
Jessica Stelly (Mgr-Web Ops)
Paul Lee (CFO)

COBURN TECHNOLOGIES, INC.

55 Gerber Rd E, South Windsor, CT 06074
Tel.: (860) 648-6600   CT
Web Site:
   http://www.coburntechnologies.com
Sales Range: $25-49.9 Million
Emp.: 200
Designs, Develops, Manufactures & Services Computer-Controlled Systems, Software & Aftermarket Supplies for Processing Ophthalmic Lenses
N.A.I.C.S.: 339115
Edward G. Jepsen (Chm & CEO)
Ram Narayanan (Exec Dir-Sls-Intl)
Mike Dolen (VP-HR)
Wayne Labrecque (VP-Sls-Americas)
Alex Incera (Pres)
Nick Coppola (Exec Dir-Svc Ops)

Subsidiaries:

Coburn Technologies (U.K.), Ltd.   (1)
1600 Park Ave Aztec West, Almondsbury, Bristol, BS32 4UA, United Kingdom
Tel.: (44) 1454200780
Web Site:
   http://www.coburntechnologies.com
Sales Range: $1-9.9 Million
Emp.: 4
Optical Product Mfr
N.A.I.C.S.: 333310
Ian Hendy (Mgr-Ops)

COC PROPERTIES, INC.

110 MacKenan Dr Ste 300, Cary, NC 27511
Tel.: (919) 462-1100   NC
Web Site: http://www.caryoil.com
Year Founded: 1959
Sales Range: $75-99.9 Million
Emp.: 225
Home Heating Oil Suppliers
N.A.I.C.S.: 457210
Craig Stephenson (Pres & CEO)
R. Mark Maddox (COO)

Subsidiaries:

Cary Oil Company, Inc.   (1)
110 MacKenan Dr, Cary, NC 27511
Tel.: (919) 462-1100
Web Site: http://www.caryoil.com
Sales Range: $10-24.9 Million
Emp.: 38
Petroleum Bulk Station & Terminal Services
N.A.I.C.S.: 424710
Don Stephenson (Pres)
Jim Bosworth (VP-Real Estate & Strategic Growth)
Mark Maddox (VP-Branded Mktg)
Paul Stephenson (Dir-Brand Mgmt)
Avery Wagoner (Dir-Wholesale & Comml Sls)

COCA-COLA BOTTLING CO. UNITED, INC.

4600 E Lake Blvd, Birmingham, AL 35217-4032
Tel.: (205) 841-2653   AL
Web Site:
   https://www.cocacolaunited.com
Year Founded: 1902
Sales Range: $1-4.9 Billion
Emp.: 2,900
Bottler & Distributor of Soft Drinks
N.A.I.C.S.: 312111
Claude B. Nielsen (Chm)
Clyde C. Tuggle (Sr VP)
John H. Sherman (Pres & CEO)
Gianetta Jones (VP-HR)
Hafiz Chandiwala (CFO, Chief Admin Officer & Exec VP)
Lucas B. Gambino (Gen Counsel & VP)
Williams Goodwyn (Vice Chm & Sec)
Eric Steadman (CIO, VP & Controller)
Craig Neely (Treas)

Subsidiaries:

Augusta Coca-Cola Bottling Company   (1)
1901 N Leg Rd, Augusta, GA 30909
Tel.: (706) 736-2211
Sales Range: $25-49.9 Million
Emp.: 200
Soft Drinks Mfr
N.A.I.C.S.: 312111

Baton Rouge Coca-Cola Bottling Company   (1)
9696 Plank Rd, Baton Rouge, LA 70811
Tel.: (225) 293-2570
Sales Range: $50-74.9 Million
Emp.: 520
Soft Drinks Mfr
N.A.I.C.S.: 312111
Jennifer Gullo (Dir-HR)

Birmingham Coca-Cola Bottling Company   (1)
4600 E Lake Blvd, Birmingham, AL 35217
Tel.: (205) 841-2653
Web Site: http://www.cocacolaunited.com
Sales Range: $50-74.9 Million
Emp.: 525
Soft Drinks Mfr
N.A.I.C.S.: 312111
Bo Taylor (VP)
David Gulledge (Dir-North Alabama)

Brunswick Coca-Cola Bottling Company   (1)
508 Mansfield St, Brunswick, GA 31520
Tel.: (912) 267-0044
Sales Range: $10-24.9 Million
Emp.: 45
Soft Drinks Mfr

N.A.I.C.S.: 312111
Lance McLain (Mgr)
Joey Peacock (Mgr-Warehouse)
Todd Bullard (Area Mgr)
Lance Middleton (Mgr-Bulk)
Bulk Wolff (Mgr-On Premise)

Chattanooga Coca-Cola Bottling Company   (1)
2111 W Shepherd Rd, Chattanooga, TN 37421
Tel.: (423) 624-4681
Sales Range: $50-74.9 Million
Emp.: 476
Soft Drinks Mfr
N.A.I.C.S.: 312111
Darren Hodges (Dir-Tennessee Valley Div)
Wayne Taylor (Mgr-Svc-TVD)

Cullman Coca-Cola Bottling Company   (1)
1145 County Rd 437, Cullman, AL 35057
Tel.: (256) 734-0613
Sales Range: $10-24.9 Million
Emp.: 19
Soft Drinks Mfr
N.A.I.C.S.: 312111
Jeff Williams (Mgr-Sls Center)

Lafayette Coca-Cola Bottling Company   (1)
1314 Eraste Landry Rd, Lafayette, LA 70506
Tel.: (337) 232-8413
Sales Range: $25-49.9 Million
Emp.: 200
Soft Drinks Mfr
N.A.I.C.S.: 312111

Lake Charles Coca-Cola Bottling Company   (1)
2401 Hwy 14, Lake Charles, LA 70601
Tel.: (337) 433-1721
Web Site: http://www.cocacolaunited.com
Sales Range: $25-49.9 Million
Emp.: 137
Soft Drinks Mfr
N.A.I.C.S.: 312111
Ken Francis (Mgr)
Del Calloway (Office Mgr)
Karl Corbello (Mgr-Home Market)
Blaine Royer (Mgr-On Premise)
Clyde Fulmer (Mgr-Distr)

McComb Coca-Cola Bottling Company   (1)
310 W Presley Blvd, McComb, MS 39648
Tel.: (601) 684-8223
Sales Range: $10-24.9 Million
Emp.: 62
Soft Drinks Mfr
N.A.I.C.S.: 312111
Barney Albritton (Mgr-Sls)

McRae Coca-Cola Bottling Company   (1)
20 N 3rd Ave, McRae, GA 31055
Tel.: (229) 868-5607
Sales Range: $10-24.9 Million
Emp.: 40
Soft Drinks Mfr
N.A.I.C.S.: 312111
Charlie Yawn (Mgr-Sls Center)
Luke Spires (Mgr-Warehouse)
Michael Brown (Sls Mgr-Ops)

Savannah Coca-Cola Bottling Company   (1)
102 Coleman Blvd, Savannah, GA 31408
Tel.: (912) 748-0033
Web Site: http://www.cocacolaunited.com
Sales Range: $25-49.9 Million
Emp.: 200
Soft Drinks Mfr
N.A.I.C.S.: 312111
Rick Terrell (VP-Coastal Div)
Bill Maness (Mgr-On Premise)
Joel Clark (Mgr-Distr)
Randy Johnson (Mgr-Sls Center)
Tim Ellis (Mgr-Div Svc)
Robert Crawford (Mgr-Loading & Shipping)
Benny Wilkinson (Mgr-Fleet-Coastal Div)
Lindsey Bollinger (Mgr-Acctg-Coastal Div)
Jeff Crow (Key Acct Dir)
Bill Barton (Mgr-HR-Coastal Div)

Spartanburg Coca-Cola Bottling Co.   (1)
500 W Main St, Spartanburg, SC 29301

Tel.: (864) 582-3467
Web Site: http://www.cocacolaunited.com
Sales Range: $10-24.9 Million
Emp.: 105
Soft Drinks Mfr
N.A.I.C.S.: 312111
Tony Price (Mgr-Sls Center)
Stephen Hardin (Mgr-Home Market)

Statesboro Coca-Cola Bottling Company (1)
104 Raybon Anderson Blvd, Statesboro, GA 30458
Tel.: (912) 681-2653
Sales Range: $10-24.9 Million
Emp.: 30
Soft Drinks Mfr
N.A.I.C.S.: 312111
Dennis Key (Mgr-Sls Center)
Chad Henry (Mgr-On Premise)
Phillip Story (Mgr-On Premise Bus Dev)
Deron Kicklighter (Mgr-Warehouse)
Hank Durden (Area Mgr)
Alan Wilson (Area Mgr)

Waycross Coca-Cola Bottling Company (1)
101 N Nichols St, Waycross, GA 31503
Tel.: (912) 283-3525
Sales Range: $10-24.9 Million
Emp.: 25
Soft Drinks Mfr
N.A.I.C.S.: 312111
Terry Murray (Mgr-Sls Center)
Danny Howard (Mgr-Warehouse)

West Alabama Coca-Cola Bottling Company (1)
4959 Prospect Rd, Carbon Hill, AL 35549
Tel.: (205) 924-9922
Sales Range: $10-24.9 Million
Emp.: 49
Soft Drinks Mfr
N.A.I.C.S.: 312111
Claude Nielsen (CEO)
Jeff Center (Mgr-Sls Center)
Jim Carlo (Mgr-Sls)

COCA-COLA BOTTLING COMPANY HIGH COUNTRY
2150 Coca Cola Ln, Rapid City, SD 57702-9358
Tel.: (605) 342-8222
Web Site: http://www.coca-colahighcountry.com
Year Founded: 1956
Sales Range: $25-49.9 Million
Emp.: 200
Soft Drinks Mfr
N.A.I.C.S.: 312111
Trevor Messinger (Pres)
Trask Messinger (VP-Sls)
Bev Morris (Dir-HR)
Al Rodriguez (Mgr-IT)

Subsidiaries:

Glendive Coca Cola Bottling Co Inc. (1)
220 S Douglas St, Glendive, MT 59330
Tel.: (406) 377-2653
Web Site: http://www.glendivechamber.com
Rev.: $1,400,000
Emp.: 9
Soft Drinks Mfr
N.A.I.C.S.: 312111
Daryl Clingingsmith (Gen Mgr)

COCA-COLA BOTTLING COMPANY OF KOKOMO INDIANA
2305 N Davis Rd, Kokomo, IN 46901
Tel.: (765) 457-4421
Web Site: https://www.cckokomo.com
Sales Range: $10-24.9 Million
Emp.: 80
Bottled & Canned Soft Drinks
N.A.I.C.S.: 312111
Craig Severns (VP)
Edmond P. Severns Jr. (Pres)

COCA-COLA BOTTLING WORKS OF TULLAHOMA, INC.

1502 E Carrol St, Tullahoma, TN 37388
Tel.: (931) 455-3466   TN
Year Founded: 1920
Sales Range: $10-24.9 Million
Emp.: 50
Soft Drink Bottler
N.A.I.C.S.: 312111
Charlotte Ennis (Chm)
Tony Grantham (Controller)
Vincent Guilliams (Mgr-IT)

Subsidiaries:

Coca-Cola Bottling Company of Elizabethtown (1)
321 Peterson Dr, Elizabethtown, KY 42701-9375   (100%)
Tel.: (270) 737-4000
Soft Drink Bottler
N.A.I.C.S.: 312111

COCC, INC.
100 Exec Blvd, Southington, CT 06489
Tel.: (860) 678-0444   CT
Year Founded: 1967
Sales Range: $25-49.9 Million
Emp.: 287
Real Banking Technology Solutions
N.A.I.C.S.: 518210
Richard A. Leone (CEO)
David K. Christie (CFO & Sr VP)
Jotham F. Trafton (Chief Strategic Officer & Sr VP)
John P. Huber (Sr VP-Sys & Programming)
Joseph D. Lockwood (COO & Exec VP)
Deborah Lynch (First VP-Sys & Programming)
Brent Biernat (Sr VP-Bus Dev)
Jamie L. Perry (Mgr-Corp Risk Mgmt)
Marco F. Bernasconi Jr. (Chief Svcs Officer & Sr VP)

COCCA DEVELOPMENT, LTD.
100 DeBartolo Pl Ste 400, Boardman, OH 44512
Tel.: (330) 729-1010
Web Site: https://www.coccadevelopment.com
Sales Range: $10-24.9 Million
Emp.: 70
Real Estate Development & Management
N.A.I.C.S.: 237210
Anthony L. Cocca (Pres & CEO)
Lynn E. Davenport (CFO)
Kelly A. Cocca (Dir-Ops)
Jim Shipley (VP-Comml Leasing)
Marc Barca (VP-Comml Leasing)
Brice A. Jackson (Mgr-Design)
William Myers (Gen Counsel)

COCCIA LINCOLN-MERCURY INCORPORATED
577 E Main St, Wilkes Barre, PA 18702
Tel.: (570) 823-8888
Sales Range: $50-74.9 Million
Emp.: 70
Sales of New & Used Automobiles
N.A.I.C.S.: 441110
Joseph Coccia (Pres)
Lynda Coccia (Controller)
Greg Martin (Gen Mgr)
Barry Williams (Mgr-Fin)
Terry Joyce (Mgr-Sls)
Joe Nocera (Mgr-Pre-Owned Sls)
Rudy Podest (Mgr-Svc)

COCHRAN BROS COMPANY INCORPORATED
320 S Jefferson St, Dublin, GA 31021
Tel.: (478) 272-2143

Sales Range: $25-49.9 Million
Emp.: 200
Tobacco & Tobacco Products
N.A.I.C.S.: 424940

COCHRAN EXTERIORS, LLC
8461 Castlewood Dr, Indianapolis, IN 46250
Tel.: (317) 593-8866
Web Site: https://www.cochranexteriors.com
Year Founded: 2010
Sales Range: $10-24.9 Million
Emp.: 42
Roofing & Gutters Mfr
N.A.I.C.S.: 332322
John Cochran (Co-Owner)
Ross Cochran (Co-Owner)

COCHRAN INC.
12500 Aurora Ave N, Seattle, WA 98133
Tel.: (206) 367-1900
Web Site: https://www.cochraninc.com
Emp.: 75
General Electrical Contractor
N.A.I.C.S.: 238210
Bill Doran (Pres)
Steve Burnett (Dir-Preconstruction & Estimating)
Matt Flatt (Dir-Large Electrical Construction)
Mike Thomas (COO)
Tom Griffin (CFO)
Stephanie Swenson (Coord-Svc)
Alan Klockman (Mgr-AV Sls)
Jay Fodrea (Mgr-Preconstruction)
Jim Murray (Mgr-Svc)
Gerald Pence Jr. (Dir-Tech)

COCKBURN ENTERPRISES INC.
334 Washington St, Muscle Shoals, AL 35661
Tel.: (256) 381-3620
Web Site: http://www.ckbent.com
Year Founded: 1969
Sales Range: $10-24.9 Million
Emp.: 140
Mfr of Extrusion Dies
N.A.I.C.S.: 333514
Gary Cockburn (CEO)
Terry Cockburn (Pres)

Subsidiaries:

Central Extrusion Die Co (1)
336 E Washington Dr, Muscle Shoals, AL 35661
Tel.: (256) 381-8262
Web Site: http://www.ckbent.com
Sales Range: $10-24.9 Million
Emp.: 48
Extrusion Dies
N.A.I.C.S.: 333514
Gary Cockburn (Pres)

COCO MART INC.
102 A Elm St, Claremont, NH 03743-2023
Tel.: (603) 542-8444   NH
Year Founded: 1990
Sales Range: $25-49.9 Million
Emp.: 300
Owner & Operator of Grocery Stores
N.A.I.C.S.: 445131
Charles A. Cairns (Pres)
Dwight LaFoungain (Gen Mgr)
George Beato (CFO)

COCO PAZZO OF ILLINOIS LLC
300 W Hubbard St, Chicago, IL 60654
Tel.: (312) 836-0900

Web Site: https://www.cocopazzochicago.com
Year Founded: 1992
Sales Range: $400-449.9 Million
Emp.: 60
Italian Restaurant Franchiser
N.A.I.C.S.: 722511
Jack Weiss (Pres)

COCONUT GROVE BANK
2701 S Bayshore Dr, Miami, FL 33133
Tel.: (305) 858-6666
Web Site: http://www.coconutgrovebank.com
Year Founded: 1926
Sales Range: $10-24.9 Million
Emp.: 125
Banking Services
N.A.I.C.S.: 522110
Cesar Arguelles (VP & Mgr-Aventura)
Daniel Chavez (CFO & Sr VP)
Richard A. Kuci Jr. (Chm, Pres & CEO)

COCREATIV TAMPA BAY LLC
3902 Henderson Blvd 2nd Fl Ste 208, Tampa, FL 33629   FL
Web Site: http://www.coreativ.com
Commercial Office Space Leasing & Support Services
N.A.I.C.S.: 531190
Tony M. Wong (Owner)

COD CO. INC.
12475 Knoll Rd, Elm Grove, WI 53122
Tel.: (262) 786-3165
Web Site: http://www.codcompany.com
Sales Range: $10-24.9 Million
Emp.: 5
Tobacco & Tobacco Products
N.A.I.C.S.: 424940
Daryl E. Pilgreen (Pres)

CODA HOLDINGS, INC.
10250 Santa Monica Blvd 133, Los Angeles, CA 90067
Tel.: (424) 249-1616
Web Site: http://www.codaautomotive.com
Electric Vehicle & Lithium-Ion Battery System Mfr
N.A.I.C.S.: 335910
Philip F. Murtaugh (CEO)

Subsidiaries:

Energy Control Systems Engineering Inc. (1)
135 E Maple Ave Unit C, Monrovia, CA 91016
Tel.: (626) 303-2882
Web Site: http://www.energycs.com
Sales Range: $10-24.9 Million
Emp.: 20
Engineeering Services
N.A.I.C.S.: 541330

CODA RESOURCES, LTD.
960 Alabama Ave, Brooklyn, NY 11207
Tel.: (718) 649-1666   NY
Web Site: http://www.codaresources.com
Year Founded: 1947
Sales Range: $1-9.9 Million
Emp.: 40
Management Consulting Services
N.A.I.C.S.: 541611
Henry Galarza (Coord-Pur & Logistics)
Joe Li (Mgr-Quality & Engrg)

Subsidiaries:

Design Plastics, Inc. (1)
4000 Lubbock Ave, Fort Worth, TX 76110

Coda Resources, Ltd.—(Continued)

Tel.: (817) 921-3131
Web Site: http://www.designplasticsinc.net
Sales Range: $1-9.9 Million
Emp.: 20
Mfg Plastic Products
N.A.I.C.S.: 326199
William Hart (Pres)

CODA, INC.

30 Industrial Ave, Mahwah, NJ 07430
Tel.: (201) 825-7400
Web Site:
    https://www.codamount.com
Photographic Equipment & Supplies
Mfr
N.A.I.C.S.: 333310

CODAC BEHAVIORAL HEALTH SERVICES, INC.

1650 E Fort Lowell Rd Ste 202, Tucson, AZ 85719
Tel.: (520) 327-4505
Web Site: https://www.codac.org
Year Founded: 1970
Sales Range: $25-49.9 Million
Emp.: 404
Behavioral Healthcare Services
N.A.I.C.S.: 623220
Dennis Regnier (Pres & CEO)
Laura J. Kolb (Sr VP-Admin Svcs)
Steve Bupp (Dir-Medical)
Nora Navarro-Hernandez (Sr VP-Compliance & Outcomes)
Paul Hooker (Sec)
Robert Barrasso (Vice Chm)
Kristine Welter Hall (Sr VP-Mktg, Fundraising & Plng)

CODDING ENTERPRISES

1400 Valley House Dr Ste 100, Rohnert Park, CA 94928-4923
Tel.: (707) 795-3550
Web Site: http://www.codding.com
Sales Range: $10-24.9 Million
Emp.: 35
Shopping Center, Property Operation
Only
N.A.I.C.S.: 531120
Bradley E. Baker (Pres & CEO)
Lisa Chodrick (COO)
Kirstie Moore (Mgr-Dev)

Subsidiaries:

Codding Construction Co   (1)
1400 Valley House Dr Ste 100, Rohnert Park, CA 94928
Tel.: (707) 795-3550
Web Site: http://www.codding.com
Rev.: $5,584,923
Emp.: 10
Commercial & Office Building Contractors
N.A.I.C.S.: 236220
Rick Freeman (Gen Mgr)

Codding Maintenance Inc   (1)
3510 Unocal Place Ste 300, Santa Rosa, CA 95403
Tel.: (707) 795-3550
Web Site: http://www.codding.com
Rev.: $2,071,810
Emp.: 5
Building Maintenance, Except Repairs
N.A.I.C.S.: 561720

CODE 42 SOFTWARE, INC.

1 Main St SE Ste 400, Minneapolis, MN 55414-1035
Tel.: (612) 333-4242
Web Site: http://www.code42.com
Year Founded: 2001
Sales Range: $10-24.9 Million
Emp.: 600
Computer Software Publisher & Whslr
N.A.I.C.S.: 513210
Matthew Dornquast (Co-Founder)
Brian Bispala (Co-Founder)
Liz Fortier (Gen Counsel)

Kristin Dean (Dir-HR)
Joseph P. Payne (Pres & CEO)
Rick Orloff (Chief Security Officer)
Timothy H. Connor (CFO)
Steve Buege (Sr VP & Gen Mgr-Consumer & Small Bus)
Nic Scott (Mng Dir-UK & Ireland)
Leslie Pendergrast (Sr VP-People)
Richard Agnew (VP-UK, Ireland & Northern Europe)
Jeremy Bauer (CIO)
Carsten Graf (Mng Dir-DACH)
Jadee Hanson (Chief Info Security Officer & VP-Info Sys)
Alexandra Gobbi (CMO)
Kristin McKenzie (Principal-PR)
Gerri Dyrek (VP-Corp Mktg)
Lisa Woodson (Chief People Officer)

CODE ONE ENTERPRISES NJ CORP

3906 2nd Ave, Brooklyn, NY 11232
Tel.: (848) 203-3608
Rev.: $12,801,533
Emp.: 30
Variety Stores
N.A.I.C.S.: 455219
David Cohen (Pres)

CODE.ORG

1301 5th Ave Ste 1225, Seattle, WA 98101
Tel.: (206) 420-1376
Web Site: http://www.code.org
Year Founded: 2012
Sales Range: $10-24.9 Million
Emp.: 16
Educational Support Services
N.A.I.C.S.: 611710
Hadi Partovi (Co-Founder & Pres)
Michelle Page (VP-Fin & Admin)
Ali Partovi (Co-Founder)
Alice Steinglass (VP-Product & Mktg)
Pat Yongpradit (VP-Education)
David Bernier (Mgr-District)
Cameron Wilson (COO & VP-Govt Affairs)
Jake Baskin (Dir-District Mgmt)
Carina Box (Mgr-Ops)
Josh Caldwell (Program Mgr-Education)

CODESMART HOLDINGS, INC.

275 7th Ave 7th Fl, New York, NY 10001
Tel.: (646) 248-8550
Year Founded: 2012
Sales Range: Less than $1 Million
Emp.: 15
Training & Consulting Services for
ICD-10 Preparation, Education & Implementation
N.A.I.C.S.: 541618

CODESMITH TOOLS, LLC

5250 Hwy 78 Ste 750-324, Sachse, TX 75048
Tel.: (800) 719-3309
Web Site:
    http://www.codesmithtools.com
Year Founded: 2004
Sales Range: $1-9.9 Million
Software Publisher
N.A.I.C.S.: 513210
Eric J. Smith (CEO)

CODEWORKS, INC.

17800 W Capitol Dr, Brookfield, WI 53045
Tel.: (262) 432-8333
Web Site: https://www.codeworks-inc.com
Year Founded: 1995
Sales Range: $10-24.9 Million
Emp.: 115

Software Developer & IT Infrastructure Services
N.A.I.C.S.: 541512
Keith Kraft (Co-Founder & VP)
Matt Goebel (Owner & Sr Acct Mgr)
Pete Neja (Mgr-Resource)
Jen Anderson (Acct Mgr)
Stephanie Stuesser Rick (Acct Mgr)

CODY CHEVROLET, INC.

Barre-Montpelier Rd, Montpelier, VT 05602
Tel.: (802) 223-6337
Web Site:
    http://www.codychevrolet.com
Year Founded: 1956
Sales Range: $10-24.9 Million
Emp.: 43
Car Whslr
N.A.I.C.S.: 441110

CODY COMPANY INC.

4200 N Interstate 45, Ennis, TX 75119
Tel.: (972) 875-5884
Web Site:
    https://www.codycompany.com
Year Founded: 1963
Sales Range: $10-24.9 Million
Emp.: 140
Mfr of Prefab Duct Heating & Air Conditioning
N.A.I.C.S.: 332322
Steve Stephen (Chm, Pres & CEO)

CODY CONSULTING SERVICES, INC.

PO Box 151634, Tampa, FL 33684
Tel.: (855) 990-2639
Web Site: http://www.codyent.com
Year Founded: 2006
Sales Range: $10-24.9 Million
Emp.: 25
Healthcare Consulting Services & Software
N.A.I.C.S.: 541618
Deb Mabari (Founder & CEO)
Brian Yavorsky (VP-Tech)
Douglas Pray (Dir-CodyPrint)

COE DISTRIBUTING INC.

1020 Franklin Dr Ste 5, Smock, PA 15480
Tel.: (724) 437-8202
Web Site:
    https://www.coedistributing.com
Year Founded: 1987
Sales Range: $10-24.9 Million
Emp.: 30
Office Furniture Distr
N.A.I.C.S.: 423210
J. D. Ewing (Pres & CEO)
Stan Idzi (Sr VP-Sls & Mdsg)
Melanie Ewing (Dir-Mktg)
Julie Idzi (Mgr-Dealer Dev & Territory)
Angela Strope (Mgr-Sys Support)
John Townsend (Mgr-Warehouse-Pennsylvania)
Donna Jeffries (Mgr-Customer Svc)
Brian Vance (Mgr-Facilities-North Carolina)
Joe Mathieu (Natl Sls Mgr)

COE PRESS EQUIPMENT CORP.

40549 Brentwood Dr, Sterling Heights, MI 48310
Tel.: (586) 979-4400
Web Site: https://www.cpec.com
Year Founded: 1977
Sales Range: $10-24.9 Million
Emp.: 80
Machine Tool Attachments & Accessories
N.A.I.C.S.: 333519

John C. Coe (Chm)
Bruce Grant (Mgr-R&D)
Jim Ward (Dir-Engrg)
Brian Robichaud (Mgr-Sls-Svcs)
Dave Boissonneault (CFO)
Steve Donnay (Dir-Sls)
Rob Elliot (Mgr-Controls Engrg)
Don Stephens (Mgr-Machining Plant)
Kevin Dombrowski (Mgr-Mechanical Engrg)
Paul Keary (Mgr-MIS IT)
Brian Levinski (Mgr-Parts-Columbus)
Timothy Nowland (Mgr-Pur)
Mike Pulice (Mgr-Warehouse)
Hunter Coe (CEO)

COEN OIL COMPANY

1000 Philadelphia St, Canonsburg, PA 15317
Tel.: (724) 223-5500
Web Site: http://www.coenoil.com
Year Founded: 1923
Sales Range: $10-24.9 Million
Emp.: 60
Petroleum Whslr
N.A.I.C.S.: 424720
Andrew M. McIlvanie (Pres & CEO)
Terry L. Kalna Jr. (COO & VP)

Subsidiaries:

Cogo's Co.   (1)
2589 Boyce Plz Rd, Pittsburgh, PA 15241
Tel.: (412) 257-4122
Web Site: http://www.cogos.com
Convenience Store Franchises
N.A.I.C.S.: 445131
Carl A. Colteryahn Jr. (Founder)
John Eby III (Pres & CEO)

COESTER VMS

7529 Standish Pl Ste 200, Rockville, MD 20855
Tel.: (301) 231-7669
Web Site:
    http://www.coestervms.com
Year Founded: 2005
Sales Range: $10-24.9 Million
Emp.: 56
Management Consulting Services
N.A.I.C.S.: 541618
Brian C. Coester (CEO)
Jacob Guertin (Dir-Ops)
Kim Jackson (Mgr-Quality Assurance)

COEUR D'ALENE BUILDERS SUPPLY

655 W Clayton Ave, Coeur D'Alene, ID 83815
Tel.: (208) 667-6481
Web Site: http://www.cdabldrs.com
Rev.: $11,300,000
Emp.: 140
Building Materials, Interior
N.A.I.C.S.: 423310
Mike Uemoto (Mgr-Ops)

COEUR MINING, INC.

104 S Michigan Ave Ste 900, Chicago, IL 60603
Tel.: (312) 489-5800
Web Site: http://www.coeur.com
Metal Mining Services
N.A.I.C.S.: 213114
Paul DePartout (Dir-IR)

COFC LOGISTICS, LLC

7015 Spring Meadows W Dr Ste 202, Holland, OH 43528
Tel.: (419) 725-0700
Web Site:
    http://www.cofclogistics.com
Year Founded: 2012
Sales Range: $50-74.9 Million
Emp.: 9
Intermodal Equipment Distr
N.A.I.C.S.: 423120

Garry Old *(Founder & Pres)*
Robin Harter *(VP)*
Chris Jablonski *(Mgr-Pricing & Yield Mgmt)*
Geoff Smock *(Asst VP-Sls & Mktg)*
Pete Sarullo *(Asst VP-Ops)*

COFFEE AMERICA (USA) CORPORATION
30 Wall St Fl 9, New York, NY 10005-3805
Tel.: (212) 422-7750
Sales Range: $200-249.9 Million
Emp.: 32
Distr Of Cocoa
N.A.I.C.S.: 424490
Richard Emanuele *(Pres & CEO)*
R. Noel Smith *(Exec VP)*
Kieran J. Keaveney *(CFO & VP)*
Stephen A. Junpinka *(Controller)*
Ricardo Schwartz *(VP)*
Tom Hogan *(Exec VP)*
William Fritsch *(VP)*
Richard Maksimowich *(Treas)*
Megan Clay *(Office Mgr)*

Subsidiaries:

Genco Futures Inc. (1)
110 Wall St Fl 25, New York, NY 10005
Tel.: (212) 422-7520
Web Site: http://www.coffeeamericausa.com
Rev.: $4,500,000
Emp.: 30
Commodity Brokers, Contracts
N.A.I.C.S.: 523160

COFFEE CUP FUEL STOPS & CONVENIENCE STORES, INC.
706 Smain St, Aberdeen, SD 57401
Tel.: (605) 229-4793 **SD**
Web Site:
http://www.coffeecupfuelstops.com
Year Founded: 1985
Rev.: $15,200,000
Emp.: 7
Convenience Store
N.A.I.C.S.: 457120
Duane D Harms *(Pres)*
Lisa Van Beek *(Controller)*

Subsidiaries:

Coffee Cup Fuel Stop, Inc. (1)
706 S Main, Aberdeen, SD 57401
Tel.: (605) 229-4793
Sales Range: $10-24.9 Million
Truck Stops
N.A.I.C.S.: 445131
Lisa VanDeek *(Controller)*

COFFEE DISTRIBUTING CORP.
200 Broadway, Garden City Park, NY 11040
Tel.: (516) 746-7010
Web Site: https://www.cdccoffee.com
Year Founded: 1963
Sales Range: $25-49.9 Million
Emp.: 300
Provider of Office Refreshment Products & Services
N.A.I.C.S.: 424130
Robert A. Friedman *(Pres)*
Debbie Sansolo *(VP-Admin)*
Bob Friedman *(Controller)*

COFFEE FOR LESS
250 S 18th St Ste 802, Philadelphia, PA 19103
Tel.: (215) 844-1126
Web Site:
https://www.coffeeforless.com
Year Founded: 1976
Sales Range: $10-24.9 Million
Emp.: 20
Office Coffee Services
N.A.I.C.S.: 561499

Dave Gellman *(Pres)*
Jack Kirshner *(Owner)*
Lynn Kirshner *(CEO)*

COFFEE REGIONAL MEDICAL CENTER, INC.
1101 Ocilla Rd, Douglas, GA 31533
Tel.: (912) 384-1900 **GA**
Web Site:
https://www.coffeeregional.org
Year Founded: 1995
Sales Range: $75-99.9 Million
Emp.: 750
Health Care Srvices
N.A.I.C.S.: 622110
Charles Andrew Bagwell *(Dir-Medical)*
Barry Bloom *(VP & Controller)*
Vicki Lewis *(Pres & CEO)*
Shelly McLean *(VP-Ops)*
Sherry Thomas *(VP-Patient Care Svcs)*
Lavonda Cravey *(CFO)*

COFFEECUP SOFTWARE INC.
165 Courtland St Ste A, Atlanta, GA 30303
Tel.: (678) 495-3480
Web Site: http://www.coffeecup.com
Year Founded: 1996
Sales Range: $1-9.9 Million
Emp.: 30
Software Development & Search Engine Submission
N.A.I.C.S.: 513210
Scott Swedorski *(VP-Software Dev)*
Hans Top *(CEO)*
Bob Visser *(CFO)*

COFFEYVILLE REGIONAL MEDICAL CENTER
1400 W 4th St, Coffeyville, KS 67337
Tel.: (620) 251-1200 **KS**
Web Site: http://www.crmcinc.com
Year Founded: 1996
Sales Range: $25-49.9 Million
Emp.: 475
Health Care Srvices
N.A.I.C.S.: 622110

COFFIN TURBO PUMP INC.
326 S Dean St, Englewood, NJ 07631
Tel.: (201) 568-4700
Web Site:
https://www.coffinpump.com
Sales Range: $10-24.9 Million
Emp.: 34
Pumps & Pumping Equipment
N.A.I.C.S.: 333914
Jim Kinneary *(Pres)*

COFFMAN ENGINEERS, INC.
1601 5th Ave Ste 900, Seattle, WA 98101-1620
Tel.: (206) 623-0717 **WA**
Web Site: http://www.coffman.com
Year Founded: 1979
Sales Range: $10-24.9 Million
Emp.: 440
Engineering Consultancy Services
N.A.I.C.S.: 541330
Arvind K. Nerurkar *(Gen Mgr)*
Jim Ivers *(CFO)*
Chris Barker *(Principal & Engr-Electrical)*
Don Iverson *(Principal & Engr-Mechanical)*
Emery S. Ojala *(Principal & Engr-Structural)*
Michel Sotura *(Principal & Engr-Mechanical)*
Patrick J. Piermattei *(Sr VP)*
Timber Chinn *(VP-HR)*
Bryan Derr *(Engr-Fire Protection)*
Renato Molina *(Sr Engr-Fire Protection)*

Jamisen Hirota *(Sr Engr-Civil Engrg)*
Jonathan Wirthlin *(Gen Mgr-LA-OC)*
Christopher Haight *(Ops Mgr-Orange County)*
Steven Dannaway *(Ops Mgr-Downtown LA)*
Dave Ruff *(Pres & CEO)*
Jodie Buchholz *(Engr-Structural-Portland)*
Justin Freeman *(VP-Carbon Capture Utilization & Storage & Hydrogen)*
Paul W. Jones III *(Principal & Engr-Electrical)*

Subsidiaries:

BRC Acoustics & Audiovisual Design (1)
1741 1st Ave S Ste 401, Seattle, WA 98134-1403
Tel.: (206) 270-8910
Web Site: http://www.brcacoustics.com
Tobacco Mfr
N.A.I.C.S.: 312230

Coffman Engineers, Inc. - Anchorage Office (1)
800 F St, Anchorage, AK 99501
Tel.: (907) 276-6664
Web Site: http://www.coffman.com
Emp.: 100
Engineering Consultancy Services
N.A.I.C.S.: 541330
Logan R. Haines *(Principal & Engr-Electrical)*
Will Veelman *(Chm & Principal-Civil & Structural-Anchorage)*
Jim Ivers *(CFO & Principal-Seattle)*
Jeff L. Gries *(Principal & Engr-Mechanical)*
David Gardner *(Sr VP-Federal Programs-Anchorage)*
C. Dan Stears *(Principal-Corrosion Control Engrg)*
Michael A. Frison *(Principal-Civil Engrg-Anchorage Alaska)*
Tom E. Looney *(Mng Principal-Electrical Engrg-Anchorage Alaska)*
David L. Peden *(Principal & Engr-Structural-Spokane Washington)*
G. Craig Lee *(Principal & Engr-Structural-Spokane Washington)*
Kurt J. Niven *(Principal & Engr-Electrical-Spokane Washington)*
Philip Pintor *(Principal & Engr-Mechanical-Spokane)*
Thomas L. Arnold *(Principal & Engr-Civil-Spokane Washington)*
Traci Hanegan *(Principal & Engr-Mechanical-Spokane Washington)*
Canaan Bontadelli *(Mng Principal & Engrg-Structural-Bozeman)*

Coffman Engineers, Inc. - Honolulu Office (1)
851 Fort St Ste 300, Honolulu, HI 96813
Tel.: (808) 687-8884
Web Site: http://www.coffman.com
Engineering Consultancy Services
N.A.I.C.S.: 541330
John W. Thielst *(Mng Principal & VP-Honolulu)*
Ben Momblow *(Principal & Sr Mgr-Project-Honolulu)*
Helen Gauh *(Coord-Mktg)*
Beth Ito *(Mgr-Corp Comm)*

Coffman Engineers, Inc. - Spokane Office (1)
10 N Post St Ste 500, Spokane, WA 99201
Tel.: (509) 328-2994
Web Site: http://www.coffman.com
Emp.: 90
Engineering Consultancy Services
N.A.I.C.S.: 541330
David T. Ruff *(Pres, CEO & Engr-Mechanical)*
Thomas L. Arnold *(Principal & Engr-Civil)*
Luke J. Bergeron *(Principal & Engr-Mechanical)*
Traci Hanegan *(Principal & Engr-Mechanical)*
Chad Heilbigner *(Principal & Engr-Civil)*
Kurt J. Niven *(Principal & Engr-Electrical)*
David L. Peden *(Principal & Engr-Structural)*
Philip Pintor *(Principal & Engr-Mechanical)*

Donald F Dickerson Associates (1)

18425 Burbank Blvd Ste 404, Tarzana, CA 91356
Tel.: (818) 385-3600
Web Site: http://www.dfda1.com
Sales Range: $1-9.9 Million
Emp.: 40
Consulting Engineer
N.A.I.C.S.: 541330
April K. Trafton *(Pres)*
David Gushyan *(Mgr-Electrical Projects)*

Ecs, Inc. (1)
615 Piikoi St Ste 207, Honolulu, HI 96814
Tel.: (808) 591-8181
Sales Range: $1-9.9 Million
Emp.: 17
Engineeering Services
N.A.I.C.S.: 541330
Lennox Nishimura *(Pres & CEO)*
Glenn Karamatsu *(VP)*

COFFMAN EXCAVATION INC.
13014 Clackamas River Dr, Oregon City, OR 97045-1171
Tel.: (503) 656-7000 **OR**
Web Site:
https://www.coffmanexcavation.com
Year Founded: 1979
Sales Range: $25-49.9 Million
Emp.: 175
Excavation Services
N.A.I.C.S.: 238910
Ruth Chaffin *(Controller)*
Jim Shannon *(Pres)*

COFFMAN INTERNATIONAL INC.
4185 Ross Clark Cir, Dothan, AL 36303-4480
Tel.: (334) 794-4111
Web Site:
http://www.coffmaninternational.com
Year Founded: 1976
Sales Range: $10-24.9 Million
Emp.: 33
Trucks, Tractors & Trailers: New & Used
N.A.I.C.S.: 441110
Robert George Coffman *(Pres)*

COFFMAN TRUCK SALES, INC.
1149 S Lake St, Aurora, IL 60507
Tel.: (630) 892-7093
Web Site:
https://www.coffmantrucks.com
Year Founded: 1946
Sales Range: $75-99.9 Million
Emp.: 96
New Car Dealers
N.A.I.C.S.: 441110
Zimmerman Diane *(Bus Mgr)*

COG MARKETERS LTD.
3055 W M 21, Saint Johns, MI 48879
Tel.: (989) 224-4117
Web Site: https://www.agroliquid.com
Sales Range: $25-49.9 Million
Emp.: 150
Fertilizer Mfr & Distr
N.A.I.C.S.: 325312
Douglas Cook *(Founder)*
Aarron Stahl *(Mgr-Sls Acct)*

COGDALL CONSTRUCTION CO.
915 SE Sandy Blvd, Portland, OR 97214
Tel.: (503) 230-1250
Web Site: https://www.cfmfloors.com
Year Founded: 1981
Sales Range: $25-49.9 Million
Emp.: 80
Floor Coverings Whslr & Distr
N.A.I.C.S.: 423220
Tim Bechtold *(Co-Pres)*
J. William Cogdall Jr. *(Co-Pres)*

Cogdill Farm Supply Inc.—(Continued)

COGDILL FARM SUPPLY INC.
108 N 6th St, Dunlap, IA 51529
Tel.: (712) 643-5360
Web Site:
  https://www.cogdillfarmsupply.com
Sales Range: $10-24.9 Million
Emp.: 13
Grains
N.A.I.C.S.: 424510
Sam Cogdill *(Pres)*
Pat Cogdill *(VP)*

COGENIC, LLC
405 Lyell Ave, Rochester, NY 14606
Tel.: (585) 458-7000
Web Site: https://cogenicmech.com
Year Founded: 1949
Sales Range: $10-24.9 Million
Emp.: 30
General & Mechanical Commercial
Contracting
N.A.I.C.S.: 238290
Joseph Lancaster *(Pres)*

COGENT DATA SOLUTIONS, LLC
2500 W Higgins Rd Ste 1165, Hoffman Estates, IL 60169
Web Site:
  http://www.cogentdatasolutions.com
Year Founded: 2007
Sales Range: $1-9.9 Million
Emp.: 50
IT Services in ERP, Database, Data Warehousing, Business Intelligence, Master Data Management & Content Management
N.A.I.C.S.: 519290
Anitha Sakamuri *(Pres & CEO)*

COGENT HMG, INC.
5410 Maryland Way Ste 300, Brentwood, TN 37027
Tel.: (615) 377-5600
Web Site: http://www.cogenthmg.com
Sales Range: $75-99.9 Million
Emp.: 1,200
Hospital Management Services
N.A.I.C.S.: 622110
Billy Watson *(VP-Market Dev & Strategy)*
Ralph H. Thurman *(Chm)*

COGENT, INC.
318 Broadway, Kansas City, MO 64105
Tel.: (816) 795-8511
Web Site:
  http://www.cogentcompanies.com
Year Founded: 1954
Sales Range: $50-74.9 Million
Emp.: 167
Pumping & Process Equipment Distr
N.A.I.C.S.: 423830
Tim Howard *(CEO)*
Ming Hsieh *(Co-Founder)*

COGGIN & FAIRCHILD ENVIRONMENTAL CONSULTANTS, INC.
1144 Siesta Key Ln, Elgin, IL 60120
Tel.: (630) 497-9700
Year Founded: 1993
Sales Range: $10-24.9 Million
Emp.: 2
Brownfield Clean-Up, Groundwater Remediation & Other Environmental Services
N.A.I.C.S.: 541620
Jim Fairchild *(Principal-Engrg)*

COGHLIN CONSTRUCTION SERVICE
100 Prescott St, Worcester, MA 01605
Tel.: (508) 793-0300
Web Site: http://www.coghlin.com
Year Founded: 1885
Rev.: $29,800,000
Emp.: 375
Electrical Work
N.A.I.C.S.: 238210
Dick Sabatalo *(Dir-Safety)*

COGNETIX, INC.
1866 Wallenberg Blvd Ste B, Charleston, SC 29407
Tel.: (843) 225-5558
Sales Range: Less than $1 Million
Emp.: 10
N.A.I.C.S.: 541810
Jeff Taylor *(Co-Founder & Partner)*
Dale Lanford *(Co-Founder-Cognetix Mktg, Graphic Design & Partner)*

COGNITO THERAPEUTICS, INC.
1218 Massachusetts Ave Ste 200, Cambridge, MA 02138
Tel.: (857) 201-5088
Web Site: http://www.cognitotx.com
Biotechnology Research & Development Services
N.A.I.C.S.: 541714
Gregory L. Weaver *(CFO)*
Ed Boyden *(Co-Founder)*
Zach Malchano *(Pres)*
Mihaly Hajos *(Chief Scientific Officer)*
Fred Tobia *(VP-RA, CA & QA)*
Martin Williams *(VP-Bus Dev & Mktg)*
Kim Kwan *(VP-R&D)*
Alyssa Boasso *(Dir-Translational Res)*
Colleen Cotter *(Dir-Product User Experience Design)*
Evan Hempel *(Dir-Clinical Affairs)*
Karen Martin *(Mgr-Clinical Trial)*
Taylor Travers *(Office Mgr)*
Brent Vaughan *(CEO)*
Gerald Lokchung Chan *(Chm)*
Jennifer Newberger *(VP & Head-Regulatory Affairs & Compliance)*
Christian Howell *(Chief Comml Officer)*

COGNIUS, INC.
One Kendall Sq Ste B2106, Cambridge, MA 02139
Web Site: http://www.hopjump.com
Travel Arrangement Services
N.A.I.C.S.: 561599
Anne Beckett *(CEO)*
Jordan Staab *(Co-Founder & Pres)*

Subsidiaries:

Smarter Travel Media LLC   **(1)**
226 Causeway St 3rd Fl, Boston, MA 02114
Tel.: (617) 886-5555
Web Site: http://www.smartertravel.com
Sales Range: $10-24.9 Million
Emp.: 42
Publisher of Travel Information Website
N.A.I.C.S.: 561599

Unit (Domestic):

SmarterTravel.com   **(2)**
226 Causeway St 3rd Fl, Boston, MA 02114
Tel.: (617) 886-5555
Web Site: http://www.smartertravel.com
Website for Travel Information
N.A.I.C.S.: 513199
Josh Roberts *(Editor-Contributing)*
Ashley Rossi *(Sr Editor-Content & Social Media)*
Christine Sarkis *(Exec Editor)*
Carol McPherson *(Editor-Video)*
Shannon McMahon *(Editor-News & Features)*
Ed Perkins *(Editor-Contributing)*
Carl Unger *(Editor-Contributing)*

COGSDILL TOOL PRODUCTS, INC.
1001 Guion Dr, Lugoff, SC 29078-8715
Tel.: (803) 438-4000   **MI**
Web Site: https://www.cogsdill.com
Year Founded: 1914
Sales Range: $25-49.9 Million
Emp.: 300
Precision Metalworking Tool Mfr
N.A.I.C.S.: 333515
Kay Fife *(Vice Chm)*
Mike Burr *(VP)*
John Schwab *(Pres & CEO)*
Gordon White *(Sr VP-Sls)*
David Lopes *(VP-Sls & Mktg)*
Ron Buckingham *(Mgr-Midwest)*
Randy Baytes *(Mgr-South Carolina)*

Subsidiaries:

Cogsdill-Nuneaton, Ltd.   **(1)**
St George S Way Bermuda Industrial Estate, Nuneaton, CV10 7JS, United Kingdom   **(100%)**
Tel.: (44) 2476383792
Web Site: http://www.cogsdill.co.uk
Sales Range: $25-49.9 Million
Emp.: 50
Precision Metalworking Tool Mfr
N.A.I.C.S.: 332216
Lee Donaldson *(Mng Dir)*
Bob Fife *(Chm)*

COGSWELL MOTORS INC.
1900 E Main St, Russellville, AR 72801
Tel.: (479) 968-2665
Web Site:
  https://www.cogswellmotors.com
Sales Range: $25-49.9 Million
Emp.: 71
New & Used Car Dealers
N.A.I.C.S.: 441110
Jay Henley *(Dir-Fin)*
Amber McDonald *(Coord-Bus Dev)*
Keith B. Cogswell III *(Pres)*

COGUN INC.
11369 Market St, North Lima, OH 44452-9782
Tel.: (330) 549-5321   **OH**
Web Site: http://www.cogun.com
Year Founded: 1970
Sales Range: $10-24.9 Million
Emp.: 50
Construction of Churches
N.A.I.C.S.: 236220
Daryl Conklin *(Dir-Construction)*
Tim Bell *(Dir-Estimating)*

COHEN & COMPANY
1350 Euclid Ave Ste 800, Cleveland, OH 44115
Tel.: (216) 579-1040   **OH**
Web Site: https://www.cohencpa.com
Year Founded: 1977
Accounting, Tax & Advisory Services
N.A.I.C.S.: 541211
Randall S. Myeroff *(Pres & CEO)*
Ronald B. Cohen *(Founder)*
Michael Meckstroth *(Sr Mgr-Audit)*
Mark Danczak *(CIO)*
Jami S. Blake *(Partner)*
Jim Boland *(Partner)*
Chris Bellamy *(Co-Pres-Investment Indus Svcs)*
Rob MacKinlay *(Pres-Private Company Svcs)*
Corey McLaughlin *(Co-Pres-Investment Indus Svcs)*
Anthony Bakale *(Partner-Tax)*
Tom Bechtel *(Partner-Svcs)*
Thomas Beard *(Partner)*

Subsidiaries:

Arthur F. Bell, Jr. & Associates, LLC   **(1)**

201 International Cir Ste 400, Hunt Valley, MD 21030
Tel.: (410) 771-0001
Web Site: http://www.cohencpa.com
Consulting & Business Advisory Services
N.A.I.C.S.: 541611

Cohen & Company - St. Clair Shores   **(1)**
21420 Greater Mack Ave, Saint Clair Shores, MI 48080
Tel.: (586) 772-8100
Web Site: http://www.cohencpa.com
Accounting, Tax & Advisory Services
N.A.I.C.S.: 541211
Ronald P. Tank *(Partner-Tax)*

Cohen & Company - Youngstown Office   **(1)**
201 E Commerce St Ste 400, Youngstown, OH 44503
Tel.: (330) 743-1040
Web Site: http://www.cohencpa.com
Emp.: 20
Accounting Tax & Advisory Services
N.A.I.C.S.: 541211
Neil J. Kaback *(VP)*
Kevin Carney *(Sr Mgr-Tax)*
Adam M. Fink *(Sr Mgr-Tax)*
Clifford A. Holmyard *(Partner-Assurance)*
Keith D. Klodnick *(Partner-Assurance)*
Cathleen Lorenz *(Partner-Tax)*
Kimberly Palmer *(Partner-Tax)*
Adam Schultz *(Dir-Assurance)*
Kathy Walsh *(Partner-Tax)*
Lisa Loychik *(Partner-Tax)*
Lisa Metzinger *(Partner-Assurance)*

COHEN BROTHERS, INC.
1520 14th Ave, Middletown, OH 45044-4348
Tel.: (513) 422-3696
Web Site: http://www.cohenusa.com
Year Founded: 1924
Sales Range: $75-99.9 Million
Emp.: 100
Scrap Recycling Services
N.A.I.C.S.: 423930
Adam Dumes *(Sr VP)*

Subsidiaries:

Baker Iron & Metal Co. Inc.   **(1)**
740 Rockcastle St, Lexington, KY 40505-3713
Tel.: (859) 255-5676
Web Site: http://www.bakeriron.com
Sales Range: $25-49.9 Million
Emp.: 90
Ferrous Metal Scrap & Waste
N.A.I.C.S.: 423930
Don Mynear *(Mgr-Safety & HR)*
Elena Moore *(Controller)*

I.H. Schlezinger, Inc.   **(1)**
1041 Joyce Ave, Columbus, OH 43219-2448   **(100%)**
Tel.: (614) 252-1188
Web Site: http://www.ihschlezinger.com
Sales Range: $10-24.9 Million
Emp.: 40
Collection & Processing of Recyclable Scrap Materials
N.A.I.C.S.: 423930
John Miller *(VP)*

Moskowitz Bros Inc.   **(1)**
5300 Vine St, Cincinnati, OH 45217
Tel.: (513) 242-2100
Web Site: http://moskowitzbros.com
Recyclable Material Merchant Whslr
N.A.I.C.S.: 423930
Bob Moskowitz *(Mgr)*

COHEN FOODS, INC.
2301 Illinois Ave, Granite City, IL 62040-3299
Tel.: (618) 452-3156
Web Site: https://www.cohenfoods.com
Year Founded: 1930
Sales Range: $10-24.9 Million
Emp.: 33
General Line Grocery Whslr
N.A.I.C.S.: 424410
Scott Cohen *(Pres)*

COHEN FURNITURE COMPANY
1203 E Marietta Ave, Peoria Heights, IL 61616-6323
Tel.: (309) 687-3100   IL
Web Site: http://www.gocohens.com
Year Founded: 1879
Sales Range: $125-149.9 Million
Emp.: 150
Owner & Operator of Furniture Stores
N.A.I.C.S.: 449110
Harry M. Goldstein *(Chm)*
Richard J. Graf *(Pres & CEO)*
Raymond Burns *(VP & Controller)*

COHEN MEDIA GROUP, LLC
750 Lexington Ave 5th Fl, New York, NY 10022
Tel.: (646) 380-7929   NY
Web Site:
   https://www.cohenmedia.net
Year Founded: 2008
Motion Picture Theater Operator
N.A.I.C.S.: 512131
Charles S. Cohen *(Chm & CEO)*

Subsidiaries:

Silver Cinemas Acquisition Co.   **(1)**
2222 S Barrington Ave, Los Angeles, CA 90064
Tel.: (310) 473-6701
Web Site: http://www.landmarktheatres.com
Motion Picture Theater Owner & Operator
N.A.I.C.S.: 512131
Ted Mundorff *(CEO)*
Michael Fant *(Sr VP-Real Estate & Dev)*
Paul Serwitz *(Pres & COO)*
Charles S. Cohen *(Owner & Chm)*

Unit (Domestic):

Spectrum 8 Theatres   **(2)**
290 Delaware Ave, Albany, NY 12209
Tel.: (518) 449-8995
Web Site: http://www.spectrum8.com
Sales Range: $1-9.9 Million
Emp.: 30
Motion Picture Theater Operator
N.A.I.C.S.: 512131
Joe Crowe *(Mgr)*

COHEN PRIVATE VENTURES, LLC
72 Cummings Point Rd, Stamford, CT 06902
Tel.: (203) 890-2000
Investment Services
N.A.I.C.S.: 523999
Andrew Booke Cohen *(Founder & Chief Investment Officer)*

Subsidiaries:

Collectors Universe Inc.   **(1)**
1610 E Saint Andrew Pl, Santa Ana, CA 92705
Tel.: (949) 567-1234
Web Site: http://www.collectorsuniverse.com
Rev.: $78,891,000
Assets: $55,482,000
Liabilities: $30,470,000
Net Worth: $25,012,000
Earnings: $10,786,000
Emp.: 446
Fiscal Year-end: 06/30/2020
Authentication, Grading, Appraisal, Information & Exchange Services
N.A.I.C.S.: 561990
Joseph J. Wallace *(CFO & Sr VP)*
Nataniel S. Turner *(Chm)*

COHERENT SOLUTIONS, INC.
1600 Utiva Ave S Ste 120, Minneapolis, MN 55416
Tel.: (612) 279-6262   MN
Web Site:
   https://www.coherentsolutions.com
Year Founded: 1995
Sales Range: $10-24.9 Million
Emp.: 600
Software Development Services
N.A.I.C.S.: 541511

Igor Epshteyn *(Pres & CEO)*
Maksim Belov *(CTO)*
Robert Duff *(COO)*
Alexandre Schneerson *(Gen Mgr-Minsk Dev Center)*
Gennadiy Cherkes *(Dir-Technical-Minsk Dev Center)*
Igor Kotlovskiy *(Pres & CEO)*
Michael Kittock *(Mgr-Jingit Deliver)*
Renee Pellinger *(Mgr-Delivery)*
Dmitry Petruchenya *(Head-Innovation Center, Project Mgr & Mgr-Delivery)*

COHESANT, INC.
23400 Commerce Park, Beachwood, OH 44122
Tel.: (216) 910-1700   DE
Web Site: http://www.cohesant.com
Year Founded: 1931
Sales Range: $10-24.9 Million
Specialized Spray Finishing & Coating Application Equipment & Specialty Coating Products Designer, Developer & Mfr
N.A.I.C.S.: 333248
Brian LeMaire *(Chm-CuraFlo & Sr VP)*
Steve Goden *(Sr VP-Admin)*
Bruce Glick *(VP-Online Svcs)*
David Dunn *(VP-R&D)*
Jack Prause *(Pres-CuraFlo & VP)*

Subsidiaries:

Raven Lining Systems, Inc.   **(1)**
13105 E 61st St Ste A, Broken Arrow, OK 74012
Tel.: (918) 584-2810
Web Site: http://www.ravenlining.com
Sales Range: $10-24.9 Million
Emp.: 12
Epoxy Mfr
N.A.I.C.S.: 325510

COHESIVE CAPITAL PARTNERS
650 5th Ave 16th Fl, New York, NY 10019
Tel.: (212) 616-9678
Web Site:
   https://www.cohesivecapital.com
Privater Equity Firm
N.A.I.C.S.: 523999
John Barber *(Mng Partner)*
Tony Bienstock *(Partner)*
Gregory Angrist *(Partner)*

Subsidiaries:

Forman Mills, Inc.   **(1)**
1070 Thomas Busch Memorial Hwy, Pennsauken, NJ 08110-2313
Tel.: (856) 486-1447
Web Site: http://www.formanmills.com
Miscellaneous Apparel & Accessory Sales
N.A.I.C.S.: 458110
Scott Sanford *(Dir-Loss Prevention)*

COHESIVE INFORMATION SOLUTIONS, INC.
125 Townpark Dr Ste 240, Kennesaw, GA 30144
Tel.: (678) 233-1280
Web Site:
   https://www.cohesivesolutions.com
Sales Range: $10-24.9 Million
Emp.: 37
Asset Management Software Consulting Services
N.A.I.C.S.: 541512
George J. Lowry *(Pres)*
Alex Szaro *(Founder)*
C. Scott MacMillan *(Founder)*
Lance Morris *(Co-Founder, CFO & Principal)*

COHN & GREGORY, INC.
5450 Midway Rd, Haltom City, TX 76117

Tel.: (817) 831-9998   TX
Web Site: https://www.cgsupply.com
Year Founded: 1977
Sales Range: $10-24.9 Million
Emp.: 40
Industrial Pipes, Valves & Fittings Distr
N.A.I.C.S.: 423840
Scott Mahaffey *(Owner, Pres & CEO)*
Clyde Gregory *(VP & Gen Mgr)*

COHN WHOLESALE FRUIT & GROCERY
3511 Camino Del Rio S, San Diego, CA 92108
Tel.: (619) 528-1113
Sales Range: $10-24.9 Million
Emp.: 10
Fruits & Grocery Products Whslr
N.A.I.C.S.: 424990
Aaron Cohn *(VP)*

COHNREZNICK LLP
1212 Ave of the Americas, New York, NY 10036
Tel.: (212) 297-0400
Web Site:
   http://www.cohnreznick.com
Year Founded: 1919
Sales Range: $550-599.9 Million
Emp.: 2,500
Accounting, Tax & Consulting Services
N.A.I.C.S.: 541211
Steven J. Mayer *(Mng Partner-Strategic Growth-New York & New Jersey)*
Charles G. Ludmer *(Chief Mktg & Practice Dev Officer & Principal)*
Robert DeMeola *(COO & Partner)*
Ted Gunther *(Partner)*
Dean Nelson *(Principal-Advisory & Dir-Tech & Digital Advisory Practice-Natl)*
Lynne H. Gummo *(Partner)*
Kent Burgess *(Principal)*
Christina Lee *(Partner)*
Jeff Moskowitz *(Partner)*
Blaise Moreland *(Partner)*
Pushpita Kotikalapudi *(Partner)*
Cheryl Joseph *(Partner)*
Asael Meir *(Partner)*
Christopher Mahon *(Mng Partner-Tysons)*
A. George Sparacio *(Partner)*
Alan Bordogna *(Partner)*
Alan M. Wohl *(Partner)*
Amy Benbrook *(Partner)*
Dana S. Fried *(Mng Dir-Natl Tax Svcs)*
Shellie M. Gifford *(Partner)*
Ryan J. Holbert *(Partner-Tax Practice)*
Leonard E. Korn *(CFO)*
Carolyn J. Danna *(Chief HR Officer & Partner)*
Matthew J. Stille *(Mng Partner-Austin)*
Rose Ann Slawson *(Mng Partner-Eatontown)*
Michael Monahan *(Mng Partner-Long Island)*
Jeffrey W. Rossi *(Mng Partner-Stamford)*
Andrew Lines *(Principal)*
Anthony Nazzaro *(Principal)*
Claudine Cohen *(Principal)*
Corey L. Rosenthal *(Principal)*
Eddie Delgado *(Principal)*
Gary Purpura *(Principal)*
Margaret Shanley *(Principal)*
Nicholas Ratti *(Principal)*
Richard Shevak *(Principal)*
Risa Lavine *(Principal)*
Tama Huang *(Principal)*

Michelle Fleishman *(Principal & Gen Counsel)*
Robert L. Golden *(Partner)*

Subsidiaries:

CohnReznick LLP - Atlanta   **(1)**
3560 Lenox Rd NE Ste 2800, Atlanta, GA 30326-4276
Tel.: (404) 847-9447
Web Site: http://www.cohnreznick.com
Accounting, Tax & Consulting Services
N.A.I.C.S.: 541211
Kenneth E. Baggett *(Co-CEO)*
Katy Breazeale *(Partner)*
Wendy R. Langlais-Tillery *(Mng Partner-Georgia)*
Julie E. McNulty *(Partner)*
Bernadette Daniel *(Partner-Tax Practice)*
Frank Longobardi *(CEO)*
Amy Benbrook *(Partner)*
Alan Bordogna *(Partner)*
Alan M. Wohl *(Partner)*

CohnReznick LLP - Baltimore   **(1)**
500 E Pratt St Ste 200, Baltimore, MD 21202
Tel.: (410) 783-4900
Web Site: http://www.cohnreznick.com
Accounting, Tax & Consulting Services
N.A.I.C.S.: 541211
Joel D. Cohn *(Principal)*
Jonette Hahn *(Principal)*
George Murchie *(Principal)*
Jill Paskoff *(Principal)*
Gary C. Perlow *(Principal)*
Joyce S. Price *(Principal)*
Ira Weinstein *(Co-Mng Partner-Baltimore)*
Mary Beth Norwood *(Co-Mng Partner-Baltimore)*
William Huber *(Mng Dir)*
Kayla Gross *(Principal)*
Frank Longobardi *(CEO)*
Amy Benbrook *(Partner)*
Alan Bordogna *(Partner)*
Alan M. Wohl *(Partner)*

CohnReznick LLP - Bethesda   **(1)**
7501 Wisconsin Ave Ste 400 E, Bethesda, MD 20814-6583
Tel.: (301) 652-9100
Web Site: http://www.cohnreznick.com
Accounting, Tax & Consulting Services
N.A.I.C.S.: 541211
David Reznick *(Partner)*
Ivan B. Silverman *(Principal)*
Lee E. Isaacson *(Partner)*
Winell H. C. Belfonte *(Partner-Audit)*
Anton Cohen *(Partner & Dir-Renewable Energy Indus Practice-Natl)*
Peter M. Hodgson *(Partner-Audit)*
David A. Kessler *(CEO)*
Terence W. Kimm *(Partner)*
Richard Mahan *(Partner-Audit)*
James P. Martinko *(Mng Partner-Bethesda)*
Thomas C. Nice *(Partner)*
Russell Phillips *(Partner-Audit)*
Marc W. Podnos *(Partner-Audit)*
Paul S. Raffensperger *(Principal-Advisory Grp & Dir-Govt Svcs-Natl)*
Lorraine Reale *(Partner-Tax)*
Edward S. Ryan *(Partner-Tax)*
Anne E. Schrantz *(Partner)*
Renee G. Scruggs *(Partner-Audit)*
Cherrie Harrison *(Partner-Tax)*
Ken Slater *(Partner)*
Jeremy Colville *(Partner)*
Richard Davies *(Partner)*
Gary Franklin *(Partner)*
Cheryl V. Joseph *(Partner)*
Pushpita Kotikalapudi *(Partner)*
Blaise Moreland *(Partner)*
Amy Benbrook *(Partner)*
Alan Bordogna *(Partner)*
A. George Sparacio *(Partner)*
Alan M. Wohl *(Partner)*
Kimberly Kilkenney *(Chief People Officer & Principal)*
Mark D. Ein *(Partner)*

CohnReznick LLP - Charlotte   **(1)**
525 N Tryon St Ste 100, Charlotte, NC 28202
Tel.: (704) 332-9100
Web Site: http://www.cohnreznick.com
Emp.: 50
Accounting, Tax & Consulting Services
N.A.I.C.S.: 541211
Melissa W. Boone *(Mng Partner-Charlotte)*
Jonathan M. Gross *(Partner)*

CohnReznick LLP—(Continued)

Allan C. Kitchen *(Partner-Audit)*
Cristi Lewis *(Partner)*
Anthony V. Portal *(Partner)*
Joseph A. Wallace *(Partner)*
Marshall Phillips *(Principal)*
Nicholas S. Mathias *(Partner-South & Central)*
Frank Longobardi *(CEO)*
Amy Benbrook *(Partner)*
Alan Bordogna *(Partner)*
Alan M. Wohl *(Partner)*

CohnReznick LLP - Edison (1)
333 Thornall St, Edison, NJ 08837
Tel.: (732) 549-0700
Web Site: http://www.cohnreznick.com
Accounting, Tax & Consulting Services
N.A.I.C.S.: 541211
Kevin P. Clancy *(Mng Partner-Office)*
Frank Longobardi *(CEO)*
Amy Benbrook *(Partner)*
Alan Bordogna *(Partner)*
Alan M. Wohl *(Partner)*

CohnReznick LLP - Glastonbury (1)
180 Glastonbury Blvd 350 Church St, Hartford, CT 06103
Tel.: (860) 633-3000
Web Site: http://www.cohnreznick.com
Emp.: 200
Accounting, Tax & Advisory Services
N.A.I.C.S.: 541211
Frank P. Longobardi *(CEO)*
Christopher G. Aroh *(Partner)*
Paul R. Ballasy *(Partner)*
Lisa Cantone *(Partner)*
Jonathan R. Collett *(Partner)*
Patrick J. Duffany *(Mng Partner-Tax)*
Stephen H. Jackson *(Partner)*
Mathew S. Krukoski *(Partner)*
Donald B. Stevens *(Mng Partner-Private Client Svcs)*
John Toscano *(Partner)*
Amy Benbrook *(Partner)*
Alan Bordogna *(Partner)*
Alan M. Wohl *(Partner)*

CohnReznick LLP - Roseland (1)
4 Becker Farm Rd, Roseland, NJ 07068
Tel.: (973) 228-3500
Web Site: http://www.cohnreznick.com
Emp.: 400
Accounting, Tax & Consulting Services
N.A.I.C.S.: 541211
Michael Cohen *(Mng Partner)*
John Yin *(Principal)*

CohnReznick LLP - Sacramento (1)
400 Capitol Mall Ste 1200, Sacramento, CA 95814
Tel.: (916) 442-9100
Web Site: http://www.cohnreznick.com
Accounting, Tax & Consulting Services
N.A.I.C.S.: 541211
Eric Jones *(Mng Partner-Sacramento)*
Ahamadou Alainchar Bocar *(Partner-Audit)*
Brian Brewer *(Partner)*
Laura Wilder *(Partner)*
Frank Longobardi *(CEO)*
Amy Benbrook *(Partner)*
Alan Bordogna *(Partner)*
Alan M. Wohl *(Partner)*

Daszkal Bolton LLP (1)
2401 NW Boca Raton Blvd, Boca Raton, FL 33431-6632
Tel.: (561) 367-1040
Web Site: https://www.dbllp.com
Sales Range: $10-24.9 Million
Emp.: 119
Accounting & Auditing
N.A.I.C.S.: 541211
Michael I. Daszkal *(Mng Partner)*
Andrea Perrillo *(Sr Mgr)*
Colleen DeWoody Bracci *(Principal)*
Katherine Hughes *(Mgr)*
Mary Gelinas *(Principal)*
Brett Burgan *(Dir-Litigation Support)*
Timothy R. Devlin *(Partner)*
Kevin E. Reynolds *(Partner)*
Michelle Shulman *(Sr Mgr)*
Debra Onkenhout *(Sr Mgr)*
Sonja VanLangevelde *(CFO)*
Kathryn Migliore Salvia *(Principal)*
Stephen H. Barnett *(Mng Partner)*

COHO DISTRIBUTING LLC

6840 N Cutter Cir, Portland, OR 97217
Tel.: (503) 289-9600   OR
Web Site: http://www.coldist.com
Year Founded: 2008
Emp.: 500
Beer & Non-Alcoholic Beverage Distr
N.A.I.C.S.: 424810
Gregg R. Christiansen *(CEO)*

Subsidiaries:

Marine View Beverage, Inc.   (1)
22200 Dauntless Dr NW, Poulsbo, WA 98370
Tel.: (360) 394-9631
Beverage Whslr
N.A.I.C.S.: 424810

Unit (Domestic):

Marine View Beverage, Inc. - Sumner   (2)
1402 Puyallup St, Sumner, WA 98390
Tel.: (253) 891-9829
Beer & Ale Merchant Whslr
N.A.I.C.S.: 424810

Marine View Beverage, Inc. - Tumwater   (2)
3166 Cougar Ln SW, Tumwater, WA 98512
Tel.: (360) 357-5579
Beer & Ale Merchant Whslr
N.A.I.C.S.: 424810

COIL CONSTRUCTION INC.
209 E Broadway, Columbia, MO 65203
Tel.: (573) 874-1444
Year Founded: 1976
Sales Range: $10-24.9 Million
Emp.: 20
Commercial & Office Building, New Construction
N.A.I.C.S.: 236220
Kevin Buckler *(VP-Ops)*
Randy Coil *(Pres)*
Karin Martin *(VP-Bus Dev & Project Mgmt & Office Mgr)*
Terry Bruns *(Sr Project Mgr)*
David Coil *(Sr Project Mgr)*
Michael Hemme *(VP-Bus Dev & Project Mgmt)*
Jim Holman *(Sr Mgr-Engrg)*
Karin Martin *(VP-Bus Dev & Project Mgmt)*

COIL COUNTS FORD & CHENEY, INC.
150 E Huron St Ste 1250, Chicago, IL 60611
Tel.: (312) 649-6300   IL
Year Founded: 1987
Rev.: $15,000,000
Emp.: 25
N.A.I.C.S.: 541810
Kirk Borland *(Dir-Strategic Plng)*
Ben Counts *(Dir-Creative)*
George Kase *(Pres)*
Mike Cheney *(Dir-Creative)*
Ron Coil *(Exec Producer)*
Paul Ouankeo *(Dir-IT)*
Marc Solbe *(CFO)*

COIL TUBING TECHNOLOGY, INC.
22305 Gosling Rd, Spring, TX 77389
Tel.: (281) 651-0200   NV
Web Site:
    http://www.coiltubingtechnology.com
Sales Range: $1-9.9 Million
Emp.: 26
Coil Tubing Tools Mfr
N.A.I.C.S.: 333517

COILCRAFT, INC.
1102 Silver Lake Rd, Cary, IL 60013-1658
Tel.: (847) 639-6400   IL

Web Site: https://www.coilcraft.com
Year Founded: 1946
Sales Range: $100-124.9 Million
Emp.: 250
Intermediate Frequency Coils, Power Transformers, Industrial Coils, Transformers & Chip Inductors Mfr
N.A.I.C.S.: 334416
Tom Liebman *(Pres)*
Richard J. Roberts *(Treas)*
John Stellberg *(Dir-Mktg Comm)*

Subsidiaries:

Coilcraft CPS   (1)
1102 Silver Lake Rd, Cary, IL 60013
Tel.: (847) 639-6400
Web Site: http://www.coilcraft-cps.com
Magnetic Product Mfr
N.A.I.C.S.: 334513

Subsidiary (Non-US):

Coilcraft CPS Taiwan   (2)
No 91-2 Section 2 Chung-Yang Road Tu-Cheng, Taipei, Taiwan
Tel.: (886) 2 2264 3646
Magnetic Product Mfr
N.A.I.C.S.: 334513

Coilcraft Hong Kong Ltd.   (2)
Unit 207 2/F HK Spinners Industrial Building VI, No 481 Castle Peak Road Lai Chi Kok, Kowloon, China (Hong Kong)
Tel.: (852) 2770 9428
Magnetic Product Mfr
N.A.I.C.S.: 334513

Coilcraft Japan, Inc.   (2)
505 MS Center Bldg 1 -2-2 Minami Naruse, Machida, 194-0045, Tokyo, Japan
Tel.: (81) 427 20 5404
Magnetic Product Mfr
N.A.I.C.S.: 334513

Coilcraft Singapore Pte. Ltd.   (2)
No 2 Ang Mo Kio Street 64 02-02 Ang Mo Kio Industrial Park 3, Singapore, 569084, Singapore
Tel.: (65) 6484 8448
Web Site: http://www.coilcraft.com
Magnetic Product Mfr
N.A.I.C.S.: 334513
Anson Tang *(Sr Engr-Sls)*
Josephine Chua *(Controller-Fin)*

Coilcraft Europe Ltd   (1)
21 Napier Place Wardpark North, Cumbernauld, G68 0LL, United Kingdom
Tel.: (44) 1236 730595
Web Site: http://www.coilcraft.com
Magnetic Product Mfr
N.A.I.C.S.: 334513
Carol Holden *(Mgr)*

COILHOSE PNEUMATICS INC.
19 Kimberly Rd, East Brunswick, NJ 08816
Tel.: (732) 390-8480
Web Site: https://www.coilhose.com
Year Founded: 1969
Sales Range: $10-24.9 Million
Emp.: 250
Mfr of Pneumatic Hose & Air Filters
N.A.I.C.S.: 333998
Cris Glen *(Gen Mgr)*
Joan DeSantis *(Mgr-HR)*

Subsidiaries:

Acme Automotive   (1)
19 Kimberly Rd, East Brunswick, NJ 08816
Tel.: (732) 432-7177
Web Site: http://www.acmeautomotive.com
Sales Range: $10-24.9 Million
Emp.: 109
Mfr of Tire Guages, Tire Repair Products, Wheel Hardware & Compressor Accessories
N.A.I.C.S.: 326211

Freelin-Wade   (1)
1730 NE Miller St, McMinnville, OR 97128
Tel.: (503) 434-5561
Web Site: http://www.freelin-wade.com
Plastic Tubing, Hose, Coils & Tether Mfr
N.A.I.C.S.: 423820

Scott Schwarm *(Gen Mgr)*

COILS INC.
11716 Algonquin Rd, Huntley, IL 60142-7176
Tel.: (847) 669-5115   IL
Web Site: http://www.coilinc.com
Year Founded: 1961
Sales Range: $10-24.9 Million
Emp.: 60
Mfr of Electronic Coils & Transformers
N.A.I.C.S.: 334416
James P. Plunkett *(VP)*
Greg Plunkett *(Pres)*

COIN ACCEPTORS, INC.
300 Hunter Ave, Saint Louis, MO 63124-2013
Tel.: (314) 725-0100   MO
Web Site: http://www.coinco.com
Year Founded: 1958
Sales Range: $350-399.9 Million
Emp.: 1,100
Coin Handling Devices for Vending Machines
N.A.I.C.S.: 333310
Parker B. Condie *(Pres)*
Mark Giroux *(Dir-Sls-Natl)*
Charlie Holland *(Mgr-Quality)*
Steve Costello *(Mgr-Engrg)*

Subsidiaries:

Coin Acceptors Europe Limited   (1)
4 The Felbridge Centre Imberhorne Lane, East Grinstead, RH19 1XP, West Sussex, United Kingdom
Tel.: (44) 1342 315724
Web Site: http://www.coinco-europe.com
Sales Range: $10-24.9 Million
Emp.: 10
Payment System Mfr
N.A.I.C.S.: 335999

Coin Acceptors GmbH   (1)
Siemensring 44D, 47877, Willich, Germany
Tel.: (49) 2154 205000
Web Site: http://www.coinco-gmbh.de
Payment System Mfr
N.A.I.C.S.: 335999

Coin Acceptors Pty Ltd   (1)
Unit 1 2 Morton ST, Parramatta, 2150, NSW, Australia
Tel.: (61) 2 9890 5433
Web Site: http://www.coincoaustralia.com.au
Payment Device Mfr
N.A.I.C.S.: 335999

Coin Acceptors, Inc.   (1)
3-435 Four Valley Dr, Concord, L4K 5X5, ON, Canada
Tel.: (905) 738-5777
Web Site: http://www.coinco.com
Sales Range: $10-24.9 Million
Emp.: 8
Payment System Design & Mfr
N.A.I.C.S.: 335999
Paul Holmes *(Gen Mgr)*

COIN WRAP INC.
PO Box 62067, Harrisburg, PA 17106
Tel.: (717) 986-0448
Web Site: https://www.coinwrap.com
Year Founded: 1979
Sales Range: $10-24.9 Million
Emp.: 25
Provider of Packaging & Labeling Services
N.A.I.C.S.: 561910

COINCO INC.
23727 US Hwy 322, Cochranton, PA 16314
Tel.: (814) 425-7407
Web Site: http://www.coinco.org
Sales Range: $10-24.9 Million
Emp.: 50
Metal Stamping Plant
N.A.I.C.S.: 339999

James A. Cokley (Pres & CEO)
James E. Morell (Gen Mgr)

COINEX INC.
2512 Artesia Lactony, Redondo Beach, CA 90278-6119
Tel.: (213) 629-4460 CA
Web Site: http://www.coinexinc.com
Year Founded: 1989
Sales Range: $10-24.9 Million
Emp.: 6
Whslr of Jewelry & Precious Stones & Metals
N.A.I.C.S.: 423940
Kevin Chakaran (Pres)
Nancy Klanjian (Office Mgr)

COINS FOR ANYTHING, INC.
10430 Courthouse Rd, Spotsylvania, VA 22553
Tel.: (540) 376-7000
Web Site:
https://www.coinsforanything.com
Year Founded: 2004
Rev.: $2,800,000
Emp.: 7
Miscellaneous Store Retailers
N.A.I.C.S.: 459999
Jeffery Morin (Owner)

COIT SERVICES, INC.
897 Hinckley Rd, Burlingame, CA 94010-1502
Tel.: (650) 727-1549 CA
Web Site: https://www.coit.com
Year Founded: 1948
Rev.: $35,578,446
Emp.: 495
Provider of Carpet & Upholstery Cleaning Services
N.A.I.C.S.: 561740
Timmie Smith (Gen Mgr)
Donna Bunt (Mgr-Pur & Safety)
Doug Kitzmiller (CFO)
Ellison Penos (Mgr-Bus Dev)
Brad Humble (Mgr-Mktg)
Sally Wassink (VP-Mktg)

Subsidiaries:

Coit Services (1)
9001 Spring Branch Dr, Houston, TX 77080-7407 (100%)
Tel.: (281) 358-4424
Web Site: http://www.coit.com
Rev.: $71,000
Emp.: 30
Carpet & Upholstery Cleaning
N.A.I.C.S.: 561740
Gus Velasco (Gen Mgr)

Coit Services Pennsylvania Inc (1)
609 Grace St, Somerdale, NJ 08083
Tel.: (856) 566-0700
Rev.: $320,000
Emp.: 13
Provider of Carpet & Upholstery Cleaning Services
N.A.I.C.S.: 561740

COKEM INTERNATIONAL LTD.
3880 4th Ave E, Shakopee, MN 55379
Tel.: (763) 545-4500
Web Site: http://www.cokem.com
Year Founded: 2000
Sales Range: $75-99.9 Million
Emp.: 100
Computer Software
N.A.I.C.S.: 423430
Charles F. Bond (Founder, Pres & CEO)
Joe Rehak (VP-Ops, Fulfillment, Warehousing & Logistics)
Paul Eibeler (Chm)
Julianne Turk (VP-Fin)

COKER TIRE COMPANY
1317 Chestnut St, Chattanooga, TN 37402-4418

Tel.: (423) 265-6368 TN
Web Site: http://www.coker.com
Year Founded: 1958
Sales Range: $25-49.9 Million
Emp.: 50
Supplier of Vintage & Antique Tires
N.A.I.C.S.: 423130
Mike Crutchfield (VP-Performance Brands)

COKINOS ENERGY CORPORATION
5718 Westheimer Ste 900, Houston, TX 77057-5745
Tel.: (713) 974-0101 TX
Web Site:
https://www.cokinosenergy.com
Year Founded: 1982
Sales Range: Less than $1 Million
Emp.: 11
Distr of Natural Gas
N.A.I.C.S.: 221210
Michael Evan Cokinos (Pres & CEO)
Natalie McGinley (Mgr-Ops)

Subsidiaries:

Cokinos Natural Gas Company (1)
5718 Westheimer Rd, Houston, TX 77057-5745 (100%)
Tel.: (512) 288-2988
Web Site: http://www.cokinosenergy.com
Gas Trading Services
N.A.I.C.S.: 221210

COL-MET SPRAY BOOTHS, INC.
1635 Innovation Dr, Rockwall, TX 75032
Tel.: (972) 772-1919
Web Site: http://www.colmetsb.com
Year Founded: 1997
Sales Range: $10-24.9 Million
Emp.: 140
Industrial Spray Paint Booth Mfr
N.A.I.C.S.: 333248
Charles Cecil (Pres)
Chris Schoch (Mgr-Sls-Western)
Aaron Kriegel (Mgr-Northeast)
Chet Sweatman (Mgr-Southeast Territory)

COLA, INC.
9881 Broken Land Pkwy Ste 200, Columbia, MD 21046-3016
Tel.: (410) 381-6581 MD
Web Site: https://www.cola.org
Year Founded: 1988
Sales Range: $10-24.9 Million
Emp.: 91
Medical Care Services
N.A.I.C.S.: 621511
John Daly (Chief Medical Officer)

COLAMCO INC.
224 W Central Pkwy Ste 1006, Altamonte Springs, FL 32714
Tel.: (407) 331-3737
Web Site: https://www.colamco.com
Sales Range: $10-24.9 Million
Emp.: 23
Computer Supplies & Accessories
N.A.I.C.S.: 424120
Juan G. Saldarriaga (Pres)
Dawn Tola (Mgr-Credit & Collections)

COLASANTI SPECIALTY SERVICES
24500 Wood Ct, Macomb, MI 48042-5398
Tel.: (586) 598-9700 MI
Web Site:
https://www.colasantigroup.com
Year Founded: 1954
Sales Range: $10-24.9 Million
Emp.: 35
Provider of Concrete Services
N.A.I.C.S.: 238110

Angelo Colasanti (Founder)
Patrick Wysocki (Co-Pres)
Scott Meredith (VP-Ops-CCSI)
Keith Colasanti (Exec VP)
John Clappison (CFO)

COLASKA INC.
500 108th Ave NE Ste 960, Bellevue, WA 98004
Tel.: (425) 827-3193
Web Site: http://www.colaska.com
Sales Range: $25-49.9 Million
Emp.: 4
Highway & Street Construction
N.A.I.C.S.: 237310
Debbie Langermann (Office Mgr)
Cindi Davis (Office Mgr)

COLAVITA USA, LLC
1 Runyons Ln, Edison, NJ 08817
Tel.: (732) 404-8300
Web Site: https://www.colavita.com
Year Founded: 1978
Importer & Distr Olive Oil, Pasta & Other Food Products
N.A.I.C.S.: 424490
John J. Profaci (VP-Mktg)
Giovanni Colavita (CEO)

COLAW RV SALES
10389 Cimarron Rd, Carthage, MO 64836-3458
Tel.: (417) 548-2125
Web Site: http://www.colawrv.com
Rev.: $14,455,613
Emp.: 35
Recreational Vehicle Dealers
N.A.I.C.S.: 441210
Bill Colaw (Pres)

COLBERT PACKAGING CORPORATION
28355 N Bradley Rd, Lake Forest, IL 60045
Tel.: (847) 367-5990
Web Site: http://www.colbertpkg.com
Year Founded: 1959
Sales Range: $10-24.9 Million
Emp.: 200
Mfr of Folding Paperboard Boxes
N.A.I.C.S.: 322212
Kraig Lang (CFO)
Jim Hamilton (Chm)
Bill Snyder (VP-Admin)
Ruben Palos (Mgr-Finishing)
Sarah McCarthy (Dir-First Impressions)
John Lackner (Pres & COO)
Kevin Kenjarski (VP-Sls & Mktg)

COLBY EQUIPMENT COMPANY INC.
3048 Ridgeview Dr, Indianapolis, IN 46226
Tel.: (317) 545-4221 IN
Web Site:
https://www.colbyequipment.com
Year Founded: 1928
Emp.: 24
Industrial & Commercial HVAC Equipment
N.A.I.C.S.: 333415
Kim Colby (Pres)
Deb Jeter (Controller)
Nick Colby (VP)

COLD HEADING CO.
21777 Hoover Rd, Warren, MI 48089-2544
Tel.: (586) 497-7000 MI
Web Site:
https://www.coldheading.com
Year Founded: 1951
Sales Range: $75-99.9 Million
Emp.: 300
Mfr of Automotive Fasteners

N.A.I.C.S.: 332722
Greg Stevens (VP)
Jessica Callon (Mgr-Pur)
Walt Phlypo (Engr-Quality)

Subsidiaries:

Ajax Metal Processing (1)
4651 Bellevue St, Detroit, MI 48207-1713
Tel.: (313) 267-2100
Web Site: http://www.ajaxmetal.com
Sales Range: $25-49.9 Million
Emp.: 150
Provides Heat Treating & Plating Of Metal Formed & Stamped Parts
N.A.I.C.S.: 332811
Frank Buono (Co-CEO)

COLD JET LLC
455 Wards Corner Rd, Loveland, OH 45140
Tel.: (513) 831-3211 OH
Web Site: https://www.coldjet.com
Year Founded: 1986
Sales Range: $25-49.9 Million
Emp.: 118
Dry Ice Blasting Products Mfr
N.A.I.C.S.: 333248
Eugene L. Cooke (Pres & CEO)
Ned Portune (VP-Info Sys & Tech)

COLD SPRING BREWING CO.
219 Red River Ave N, Cold Spring, MN 56320
Tel.: (320) 685-8686
Web Site:
http://www.coldspringbrewery.com
Year Founded: 1857
Sales Range: $25-49.9 Million
Emp.: 225
Beer Mfr
N.A.I.C.S.: 312120
John P. Lenore (Owner)
Horace Cunningham (Dir-Brewing)

COLD SPRING CAPITAL INC.
115 Lone Tree Farm Rd, New Canaan, CT 06840-4229
Tel.: (203) 966-9457 DE
Web Site:
http://www.coldspringcapital.com
Sales Range: Less than $1 Million
Emp.: 2
Investment Services
N.A.I.C.S.: 523999
Joseph S. Weingarten (Pres)

COLD SPRING GRANITE COMPANY
17482 Granite W Rd, Cold Spring, MN 56320-2508
Tel.: (320) 685-3621 MN
Year Founded: 1898
Sales Range: $500-549.9 Million
Emp.: 1,420
Dimensional Stone Mfr for the Construction Industry, Stone Products for the Memorial Industry, Stone Tile & Interior Products
N.A.I.C.S.: 327991
Patrick Alexander (Chm & CEO)
Greg Flint (VP-Ops & Strategy)

Subsidiaries:

Cold Spring Granite (Canada) Ltd. (1)
17482 Granite W Rd, Cold Spring, MN 56320-2508
Tel.: (320) 685-3621
Sales Range: $75-99.9 Million
Emp.: 800
Mfr of Granite Furniture, Landscape Materials, Pavers & Retaining Wall Blocks
N.A.I.C.S.: 212311
Ed Charles (Mng Dir)

Cold Spring Granite Co. (1)
Rte 9N S, Au Sable Forks, NY 12912
Tel.: (518) 647-8192

Cold Spring Granite Company—(Continued)

Sales Range: $25-49.9 Million
Emp.: 35
Natural Stone Products & Memorials Mfr
N.A.I.C.S.: 212313

Granit-Bronz, Inc.   (1)
17482 Granite W Rd, Cold Spring, MN
56320   **(100%)**
Tel.: (320) 685-3621
Web Site: http://www.coldspringusa.com
Sales Range: $50-74.9 Million
Emp.: 150
Natural Stone Products & Memorials Mfr
N.A.I.C.S.: 212311

Granite Mountain Stone Design   (1)
2400 Hwy 1431 W, Marble Falls, TX 78654
Tel.: (830) 693-4316
Web Site:
   http://www.granitemountaindesign.com
Sales Range: $25-49.9 Million
Emp.: 150
Quarrier & Mfr of Granite
N.A.I.C.S.: 212311

Raymond Granite Co.   (1)
36772 Rd 606, Raymond, CA 93653-9703
Tel.: (559) 689-3257
Web Site: http://www.coldspringgranite.com
Sales Range: $10-24.9 Million
Emp.: 80
Supplier of Granite Materials
N.A.I.C.S.: 327991

Royal Melrose Granites   (1)
17482 Granite W Rd, Cold Spring, MN
56320-4578
Tel.: (320) 685-3621
Web Site:
   http://www.coldspringusa.com
Sales Range: $75-99.9 Million
Emp.: 400
Natural Stone Products & Memorials Mfr
N.A.I.C.S.: 212313
John Mackie (Pres & CEO)

COLD SPRING HARBOR LABORATORY

1 Bungtown Rd, Cold Spring Harbor,
NY 11724-2209
Tel.: (516) 367-8397   DE
Web Site: http://www.cshl.org
Year Founded: 1890
Sales Range: $75-99.9 Million
Emp.: 1,000
Provider of Scientific Research
N.A.I.C.S.: 541720
Bruce W. Stillman (Pres & CEO)
Lari Russo (CFO & VP-Fin)
David Stewart (Exec Dir-Meetings &
Courses Program)
Jan Witkowski (Exec Dir)
Walter Goldschmidts (VP-Sponsored
Programs)
Jamie C. Nicholls (Chm)
Marilyn H. Simons (Vice Chm)
Sydney Gary (Dir-Res Ops)
Katherine Raftery (VP)
Philip Lembo (VP)
Paul J. Taubman (Sec)
Robert D. Lindsay (Co-Vice Chm)
Leo A. Guthart (Treas)
Charles Vincent Prizzi (Chief Dev Of-
ficer & VP-Dev)
Arthur Brings (Chief Facilities Officer
& VP)
Michael Marchesiello (VP)
Dagnia Zeidlickis (VP-Comm)
W. Dillaway Ayres Jr. (COO)

COLDER'S INC.

333 S Hwy 100, West Allis, WI
53214-1132
Tel.: (414) 476-1574   WI
Web Site: http://www.colders.com
Year Founded: 1942
Sales Range: $25-49.9 Million
Emp.: 280
Furniture, Consumer Electronics &
Appliance Stores
N.A.I.C.S.: 449110
Robert Felker (Pres)

COLDIRON COMPANIES, INC.

200 N Sooner Rd, Edmond, OK
73034
Tel.: (405) 562-2910
Web Site:
   https://coldironcompanies.com
Year Founded: 1959
Sales Range: $10-24.9 Million
Emp.: 30
Freight Transportation Arrangement
Services
N.A.I.C.S.: 488510
Kelly Coldiron (VP-Sls & Mktg)
Phil Coldiron (Pres & CEO)

COLDQUANTA, INC.

1600 Range St Ste 103, Boulder, CO
80301-2739
Tel.: (303) 440-1284
Web Site: http://www.coldquanta.com
Research & Development in the
Physical, Engineering & Life Sciences
N.A.I.C.S.: 541715
Paul A. Morton (VP & Gen Mgr-Santa
Barbara)
Dan Caruso (Chm & Interim CEO)
Rushton McGarr (CFO)
Chester Kennedy (Pres-Res Security
Solutions)
Barry Behnken (Exec VP-Engrg)
Laura Hale (VP-Govt Programs)
Chris Wood (CTO)
Dana Anderson (Chief Strategy Offi-
cer)
M. Scott Faris (CEO)

Subsidiaries:

Morton Photonics, Inc.   (1)
3301 Velvet Vly Dr, West Friendship, MD
21794-9430
Tel.: (443) 745-4779
Web Site: http://www.mortonphotonics.com
Communication Equipment Mfr
N.A.I.C.S.: 334290

COLDSTREAM HOLDINGS, INC.

1 100th Ave NE Ste 102, Bellevue,
WA 98004
Tel.: (425) 283-1600
Web Site:
   https://www.coldstream.com
Holding Company
N.A.I.C.S.: 551112

COLDWELL BANKER BURNET

3033 Excelsior Blvd, Minneapolis, MN
55416-4688
Tel.: (612) 920-5605
Web Site: http://www.cbburnet.com
Sales Range: $1-9.9 Million
Emp.: 100
Real Estate Services
N.A.I.C.S.: 531210
Matt Baker (Pres)
Brian Bolier (Sr VP)

COLDWELL BANKER SCHMIDT REALTORS

402 E Front St, Traverse City, MI
49686
Tel.: (231) 922-2350
Web Site:
   https://www.cbgreatlakes.com
Year Founded: 1927
Sales Range: $10-24.9 Million
Emp.: 30
Other Activities Related to Real Es-
tate
N.A.I.C.S.: 531390
Pat Vredevoogd Combs (VP)
Thomas Gray (COO & Pres-Northern
Reg)

Subsidiaries:

Coldwell Banker Sunstar-Morris Realty, Inc.   (1)

1980 Kings Hwy, Port Charlotte, FL 33980
Tel.: (941) 629-1243
Web Site:
   http://www.coldwellbankerflorida.com
Sales Range: $10-24.9 Million
Offices of Real Estate Agents & Brokers
N.A.I.C.S.: 531210
Donald Randolp (Pres)

COLE CHEMICAL & DISTRIB-UTING, INC.

1500 S Dairy Ashford Ste 450, Hous-
ton, TX 77077
Tel.: (713) 465-2653   TX
Web Site: https://www.colechem.com
Year Founded: 1980
Sales Range: $75-99.9 Million
Emp.: 6
Mfr of Chemicals & Allied Products
N.A.I.C.S.: 424690
Donna Fujimoto Cole (Pres & CEO)

COLE CHEVROLET-GEO INC.

1325 Yellowstone, Pocatello, ID
83201
Tel.: (208) 242-3405   DE
Web Site:
   http://www.colechevrolet.com
Year Founded: 1995
New & Used Car Dealers
N.A.I.C.S.: 441110
Kevin Jordan (Sls Mgr)
John Mahood (CFO)
Art Beery (Gen Mgr)
Mario Ciciliot (Gen Mgr-Sls)
Ray Fillmore (Mgr-Sls Ops)
Joe Osterman (Mgr-Svc)
Jim Sutton (Bus Mgr)

COLE INDUSTRIAL, INC.

5924 203rd St SW, Lynnwood, WA
98036
Tel.: (425) 774-6602   WA
Web Site: https://www.coleindust.com
Year Founded: 1964
Rev: $11,400,000
Emp.: 35
Boilers Sales & Services
N.A.I.C.S.: 423720

COLE LUMBER COMPANY INC.

1035 Division St, Paducah, KY 42003
Tel.: (270) 442-7171
Web Site: http://www.colelumber.com
Sales Range: $10-24.9 Million
Emp.: 79
Lumber: Rough, Dressed & Finished
N.A.I.C.S.: 423310
Ronnie Goode (Pres)
Bobby Lindsey (VP)

COLE PAPERS INC.

1300 38th St N, Fargo, ND 58102
Tel.: (701) 282-5311   ND
Web Site:
   https://www.colepapers.com
Year Founded: 1918
Sales Range: $50-74.9 Million
Emp.: 160
Industrial Papers, Printing Papers &
Wholesale Floor & Counter Coverings
Distr
N.A.I.C.S.: 424130
Gregory Hanson (VP-Mktg)
Kenneth D. Dahl (VP-Credit)
Brian Haugen (CFO)

COLE SPORT, INC.

1615 Park Ave, Park City, UT 84060-
5146
Tel.: (435) 649-4800
Web Site: https://www.colesport.com
Year Founded: 1982
Sales Range: $10-24.9 Million
Emp.: 25
Sporting Goods Retailer

N.A.I.C.S.: 459110
Jana Cole (Co-Owner)

COLE VALLEY MOTOR COM-PANY, LTD.

4111 Elm Rd NE, Warren, OH 44483
Tel.: (330) 372-1665   OH
Web Site: http://www.colecars.com
Sales Range: $10-24.9 Million
Emp.: 62
New & Used Car Dealerships
N.A.I.C.S.: 441110
David C. Cole (Pres & Partner)
Tom Cole (Partner)

Subsidiaries:

Cole Valley Cadillac   (1)
4111 Elm Rd NE, Warren, OH 44483
Tel.: (330) 984-4668
Web Site: http://www.colevalleycadillac.com
New & Used Car Dealer
N.A.I.C.S.: 441110
David C. Cole (Pres & Partner)
Joe Sember (Mgr-Sls)
Chris Cole (Mgr-Internet Sls)
Shannon Montgomery (Mgr-Fin)
Lenny Niederhiser (Mgr-Svc)

COLE WIRE & CABLE CO. INC.

620 Margate Dr, Lincolnshire, IL
60069-4247
Tel.: (847) 634-4300
Web Site: https://www.colewire.com
Year Founded: 1979
Sales Range: $1-9.9 Million
Emp.: 15
Electronic Wire & Cable
N.A.I.C.S.: 423690
Michelle Miller (Mktg Mgr)
Shel Cole (Founder)

COLE'S QUALITY FOODS, INC.

1188 Lakeshore Dr, Muskegon, MI
49441-1676
Tel.: (231) 722-1651   MI
Web Site: https://www.coles.com
Year Founded: 1943
Sales Range: $25-49.9 Million
Emp.: 150
Frozen Garlic Bread Mfr
N.A.I.C.S.: 311812
John Sommavilla (Pres)
Cinthia Havard (CFO)
Wesley F. Devon Jr. (Chm)

COLE'S SALON INC

15050 Cedar Ave S, Apple Valley,
MN 55124
Tel.: (952) 891-4112   MN
Web Site:
   https://www.colessalon.com
Year Founded: 1979
Unisex Hair Salons
N.A.I.C.S.: 812112
Alli J. (Designer)

COLEMAN & ASSOCIATES ENTERPRISES, INC.

9256 Bendix Rd Ste 102, Columbia,
MD 21045-1843
Tel.: (410) 730-7592
Year Founded: 1990
Sales Range: $10-24.9 Million
Emp.: 6
Computer System Design Services
N.A.I.C.S.: 541512
Steven Burnette (Co-Owner)
Ronald K. Coleman (Co-Owner &
Pres)

COLEMAN AMERICAN COM-PANIES, INC.

1 Covan Dr, Midland City, AL 36350
Tel.: (334) 983-6500   KS

Web Site:
http://www.colemanamerican.com
Year Founded: 1914
Rev.: $73,836,029
Emp.: 900
Provider of Local Trucking Services
With Storage
N.A.I.C.S.: 484210
Tony Bridges *(Dir-Mktg)*
James Coleman *(CEO)*
Jeff Coleman *(Pres)*

Subsidiaries:

Coleman American Allied **(1)**
12905 Shawnee Mission Pkwy, Shawnee
Mission, KS 66216-1850
Tel.: (913) 631-1440
Web Site: http://www.covan.com
Sales Range: $10-24.9 Million
Emp.: 35
Local Trucking Service With Storage
N.A.I.C.S.: 484210

Coleman American Moving Services
Inc. **(1)**
1 Covan Dr, Midland City, AL 36350
Tel.: (334) 983-6500
Web Site: http://www.covan.com
Sales Range: $25-49.9 Million
Emp.: 150
Local Trucking with Storage
N.A.I.C.S.: 484210
Jeff Coleman *(Pres & CEO)*

Covan International Inc. **(1)**
1 Covan Dr, Midland City, AL 36350
Tel.: (334) 983-6505
Web Site: http://www.covan.com
Rev.: $20,000,000
Emp.: 300
Trucking Except Local
N.A.I.C.S.: 484210
Joyce Farish *(CFO)*
William Brakefeild *(Pres)*

Covan Worldwide Moving Inc. **(1)**
1 Covan Dr, Midland City, AL
36350 **(100%)**
Tel.: (334) 983-6500
Web Site: http://www.covan.com
Rev.: $3,500,000
Emp.: 300
Trucking Except Local
N.A.I.C.S.: 484210
Tony Bridges *(Dir-Mktg)*
Jeff Coleman *(CEO)*
Lacy Brakefeild *(Pres)*

Eagle Van Lines Inc. **(1)**
1 Covan Dr, Midland City, AL
36350 **(100%)**
Tel.: (334) 983-6505
Web Site: http://www.covan.com
Rev.: $120,000
Emp.: 5
Local Trucking without Storage
N.A.I.C.S.: 484210
Tony Bridges *(Dir-Mktg)*

COLEMAN AUTO GROUP
1710 N Olden Ave, Ewing, NJ 08638
Tel.: (609) 883-2800
Web Site:
http://www.colemancars.com
Year Founded: 1967
Sales Range: $25-49.9 Million
Emp.: 65
Owner & Operator of Car Dealerships
N.A.I.C.S.: 441110
Bruce Coleman *(Pres)*
Mike Colavito *(Mgr-Sls)*

COLEMAN COMPANY
5125 South Hwy 16, Rapid City, SD
57701
Tel.: (605) 721-3700
Web Site:
http://www.blackhillsgold.com
Rev.: $34,000,000
Emp.: 125
Jewelry, Precious Metal
N.A.I.C.S.: 339910
Dwight Sobczak Sr. *(Chm & Pres)*

COLEMAN DISTRIBUTING COMPANY
800 S Greenleaf St, Brownwood, TX
76801
Tel.: (325) 643-2546
Rev.: $10,698,079
Emp.: 17
Beer & Other Fermented Malt Liquors
N.A.I.C.S.: 424810

COLEMAN INSIGHTS
909 Aviation Pkwy Ste 400, Morris-
ville, NC 27560
Tel.: (919) 571-0000
Web Site:
https://www.colemaninsights.com
Year Founded: 1978
Sales Range: $10-24.9 Million
Emp.: 25
Media & Marketing Research Ser-
vices
N.A.I.C.S.: 541910
Jon A. Coleman *(Founder & CEO)*
Warren Kurtzman *(Pres)*
John Monninghoff *(Pres-Coleman
European Radio Div)*
John Boyne *(VP)*
Sam Milkman *(VP)*
David Baird *(VP-Res Ops)*
Eileen Genna *(VP-Bus Ops)*
Jay Nachlis *(Dir-Mktg)*

COLEMAN INSTRUMENT COMPANY
11575 Goldcoast Dr, Cincinnati, OH
45249
Tel.: (513) 489-5745
Web Site:
http://www.colemaninstrument.com
Year Founded: 1985
Sales Range: $10-24.9 Million
Emp.: 35
Process Control Instrumentation
Whslr
N.A.I.C.S.: 423830
Dan Corbett *(Mgr-Svcs)*

COLEMAN OIL COMPANY
335 Mill Rd, Lewiston, ID 83501
Tel.: (208) 799-2000
Web Site:
https://www.colemanoil.com
Year Founded: 1953
Sales Range: $25-49.9 Million
Emp.: 50
Petroleum Product Mfr
N.A.I.C.S.: 424710
Kristi Hogan *(Dir-Bus Sys)*
Ian Coleman *(Chief Revenue Officer)*
Bob Ward *(CFO)*
Robert S. Coleman Jr. *(Owner &
Pres)*

COLEMAN RESEARCH GROUP, INC. (CRG)
575 5th Ave 21st Fl, New York, NY
10017
Tel.: (212) 223-0185
Web Site: http://www.colemanrg.com
Year Founded: 2003
Sales Range: $25-49.9 Million
Emp.: 200
Intermediary Investment & Business
Services for Clients & Institutions
N.A.I.C.S.: 523910
Kevin Coleman *(Founder & CEO)*
Craig Farrell *(VP-Product Mgmt)*
Eva Zaeschmar *(CMO)*
Peter Dolezal *(Chief Compliance Offi-
cer & Gen Counsel)*
Venkat Krishnamoorthy *(CTO)*
Alan Banner *(Co-CFO & COO)*

Subsidiaries:

Coleman Research Group, Inc. **(1)**

3 St Helen's Place, London, EC3A 6AB,
United Kingdom **(100%)**
Tel.: (44) 20 7065 7000
Web Site: http://www.colemanrg.com
Intermediary Management & Investment
Services
N.A.I.C.S.: 523910

COLEMAN-ADAMS CON-STRUCTION, INC.
1031 Performance Rd, Forest, VA
24551
Tel.: (434) 525-4700
Web Site: https://www.coleman-
adams.com
Year Founded: 1971
Sales Range: $10-24.9 Million
Emp.: 100
Commercial & Institutional Building
Construction Services
N.A.I.C.S.: 236220
A. C. Coleman *(CEO)*

COLEMAN-TAYLOR AUTO-MATIC TRANSMISSION COM-PANY, INC.
1210 Midas Cove, Cordova, TN
38108
Tel.: (901) 526-1477
Rev.: $12,000,000
Emp.: 130
Automotive Parts & Accessories Mfr
N.A.I.C.S.: 811114
Larry Coleman *(Pres)*

COLES ENERGY INC.
3619 E State Rd 113, Milan, OH
44846
Tel.: (419) 499-1120
Web Site:
https://www.colesenergyinc.com
Sales Range: $50-74.9 Million
Emp.: 250
Petroleum Products
N.A.I.C.S.: 424720
Edwin M. Coles *(Pres)*
Danny Coles *(VP & Gen Mgr)*
Kimberly Hiemstra *(Asst Controller)*

COLES HARDWARE INC.
101 Bloom St, Danville, PA 17821
Tel.: (570) 275-4878 **PA**
Web Site:
http://www.coleshardware.com
Year Founded: 1945
Sales Range: $10-24.9 Million
Emp.: 150
Owner & Operator of Hardware
Stores & Services
N.A.I.C.S.: 444140
Bo Cole *(VP)*
Jason Budman *(Dir-HR & Store Ops)*
Samuel Miller *(Asst Mgr)*
William H. Cole Jr. *(Pres)*

COLES MARKETING COMMU-NICATIONS, INC.
3950 Priority Way Ste 106, India-
napolis, IN 46240
Tel.: (317) 571-0051 **IN**
Web Site:
http://www.colesmarketing.com
Year Founded: 1985
Public Relations Agency
N.A.I.C.S.: 541820
Barbara L. Coles *(Pres)*
Tim Coulon *(VP-Creative)*
Teresa Tanner *(Mgr-Fin & Coord-
Events)*
Brian Coles *(Co-Owner & Chief Mktg
Technologist)*
Shawn Sorrells *(Mgr-Bus & Client
Devel)*
Chris Ryan *(Sr Copywriter, Acct Mgr
& Creative Strategist)*
Tiffany Stochel *(Acct Mgr & New Me-
dia Specialist)*

Kevin Moore *(Web Developer)*
Duane Brodt *(Acct Mgr)*
Tiffany Whisner *(VP-PR)*
Caroline Voelz *(Mgr-Social Media)*
Anna Wetzel *(Mktg Mgr-Email)*

COLES OF LA JOLLA INCOR-PORATED
1170 W Morena Blvd, San Diego, CA
92110
Tel.: (619) 276-5140
Web Site:
http://www.colescarpets.com
Sales Range: $10-24.9 Million
Emp.: 70
Floor Covering Stores
N.A.I.C.S.: 449121
Steve Coles *(Pres)*

COLES PETROLEUM PROD-UCTS INC.
1200 S Egan Ave, Madison, SD
57042
Tel.: (605) 256-3082
Sales Range: $10-24.9 Million
Emp.: 3
Diesel Fuel
N.A.I.C.S.: 424720

COLES-MOULTRIE ELECTRIC COOPERATIVE
104 Dewitt Ave E, Mattoon, IL 61938
Tel.: (217) 235-0141
Web Site: https://www.cmec.coop
Year Founded: 1938
Sales Range: $10-24.9 Million
Emp.: 35
Electric Power Distribution Services
N.A.I.C.S.: 221122
Darla M. Rankins *(Mgr)*
Kim Leftwich *(Pres & CEO)*

COLETTE MALOUF INC.
594 Brdwy, New York, NY 10012
Tel.: (212) 941-9588
Web Site:
http://www.colettemalouf.com
Sales Range: $1-9.9 Million
Emp.: 12
Jewelry Designer & Retailer
N.A.I.C.S.: 339910
Colette Malouf *(Pres)*

COLISEUM CAPITAL MAN-AGEMENT LLC
105 Rowayton Ave, Rowayton, CT
06853
Tel.: (203) 883-0100 **DE**
Investment Services
N.A.I.C.S.: 523999

COLISEUM LEXUS OF OAK-LAND
7273 Oakport St, Oakland, CA 94621
Tel.: (510) 895-3987
Web Site:
http://www.coliseumlexus.com
Year Founded: 2001
Sales Range: $10-24.9 Million
Emp.: 50
New Car Retailer
N.A.I.C.S.: 441110
Ron Fortt *(Gen Mgr)*
Ed Shakalia *(Gen Mgr-Sls)*
Isabel Fuentes *(Coord-Appointment)*
Jory Picazo *(Mgr-Parts Dept)*
Carol Wong *(Mgr-Fin)*
Sayed Massoud *(Mgr-Fin)*
Rick Santos *(Mgr-Sls)*

COLISEUM MOTOR COMPANY
6351 E 2nd St, Casper, WY 82609-
4264

Coliseum Motor Company—(Continued)

Tel.: (307) 577-9999
Web Site:
https://www.coliseummotors.com
Year Founded: 1914
Sales Range: $25-49.9 Million
Used Car & Trucks Dealer
N.A.I.C.S.: 441120
Mike Holland (Gen Mgr)
Bill Nolen (Pres)

COLLABERA INC.
110 Allen Rd, Basking Ridge, NJ
07920
Tel.: (973) 889-5200
Web Site: http://www.collabera.com
Sales Range: $250-299.9 Million
Emp.: 4,000
IT Services For Financial, Manufacturing & Technology Industries
N.A.I.C.S.: 519290
Hiten Patel (Co-Founder & Chm)
Ashwin Rao (Exec VP)
Bala Variyam (Head-R&D)
Debasish Pattanayak (Head-Enterprise Software Solutions)
Sham Patel (Co-Founder, CFO & Head-Prof Svcs)
Dhar Patadia (Co-Founder & CIO/CTO)
Karthik Krishnamurthy (CEO)

COLLABORATEMD
225 E Robinson St Ste 145, Orlando, FL 32801
Tel.: (407) 902-2960
Web Site:
http://www.collaboratemd.com
Year Founded: 1999
Rev.: $3,900,000
Emp.: 25
Software Publisher
N.A.I.C.S.: 513210
Douglas A. Kegler (Founder & CEO)
Eric Rosselot (Dir-Sls)
Jennifer Wilson (Mgr-Sls)
Robert J. Woodrow (Vice Chm)

COLLABRALINK TECHNOLOGIES
211 W Chicago Ave Ste 213, Hinsdale, IL 60521
Tel.: (630) 323-3100
Web Site:
http://www.CollabraLink.com
Year Founded: 2003
Sales Range: $1-9.9 Million
Emp.: 27
Computer Management Services
N.A.I.C.S.: 518210
Rahul Pandhi (Pres)
Mohit Manocha (Dir-Ops & Fin)
Haresh Bhungalia (Chief Strategy Officer)
Phil Crowe (VP-Bus Dev)
Launa Lewis (COO)
Mike Deutsch (VP-Digital Svcs)
George Batsakis (CEO)
Megan Hanik (Chief People Officer)

COLLAGES.NET INC.
444 Oxford Valley Rd Ste 230, Langhorne, PA 19047
Tel.: (267) 572-5000
Web Site: http://www.collages.net
Year Founded: 2001
Rev.: $4,600,000
Emp.: 42
Data Processing & Hosting Services
N.A.I.C.S.: 518210
Kevin Casey (Pres & CEO)

COLLEGE CITY HOMES INC.
7920 Lakeville Blvd, Lakeville, MN 55044
Tel.: (952) 469-6900

Sales Range: $25-49.9 Million
Emp.: 30
New Construction, Single-Family
Houses
N.A.I.C.S.: 236115
Don Pavek (CEO)

COLLEGE NETWORK INC.
3815 River Crossing Pkwy Ste 260, Indianapolis, IN 46240
Tel.: (317) 334-7337
Web Site:
http://www.collegenetwork.com
Sales Range: $10-24.9 Million
Emp.: 240
Publisher of College Guides
N.A.I.C.S.: 513199

COLLEGE OF AMERICAN PATHOLOGISTS
325 Waukegan Rd, Northfield, IL 60093-2750
Tel.: (847) 832-7000
Web Site: http://www.cap.org
Year Founded: 1947
Sales Range: $150-199.9 Million
Emp.: 705
Medical Professional Association
N.A.I.C.S.: 813920
Stephen Myers (CEO)
Elizabeth Usher (CMO)
Mary Katherine Krause (VP-Comm)
Branden Marty (Dir-Exec Ops)
Greg Gleason (CIO & VP-IT Svcs)
George Fiedler (Sr VP)
Shanawaz Khan (VP-Sls)
Patrick Godbey (Pres)
Alain C. Borczuk (Editor-in-Chief)
Catherine Dolf (Sr Mgr-Media Rels)

COLLEGE POSSIBLE NATIONAL
755 Prior Ave N Ste 210, Saint Paul, MN 55104
Tel.: (651) 288-9455 MN
Web Site:
http://www.collegepossible.org
Year Founded: 2000
Rev.: $21,411,591
Assets: $14,311,022
Liabilities: $1,275,936
Net Worth: $13,035,086
Earnings: $915,488
Fiscal Year-end: 06/30/18
Educational Support Services
N.A.I.C.S.: 611710
Al Fan (Interim CEO)
Austin Buchan (Sr VP-Program & Tech Innovation)
Scott Del Rossi (VP-College & Career Success)
Catherine Marciano (VP-Partnerships)
Lavada Williams (Sr VP-People & Culture)

COLLEGE PROWLER, INC.
5830 Ellsworth Ave Ste 101, Pittsburgh, PA 15232
Tel.: (412) 361-5084
Web Site:
http://www.collegeprowler.com
Year Founded: 2002
Sales Range: $1-9.9 Million
Emp.: 13
Online Educational Support Services
N.A.I.C.S.: 513199
David Rush (Product Mgr)

COLLEGE TRACK
111 Broadway St Ste 101, Oakland, CA 94607
Tel.: (510) 834-3295 CA
Web Site: http://www.collegetrack.org
Year Founded: 1997
Sales Range: $10-24.9 Million

Emp.: 321
Student Support & Development Services
N.A.I.C.S.: 611710
Elissa Salas (CEO)
Tina Kim (Dir-Learning & Dev)

COLLEGIATE ASSOCIATION RESOURCE OF THE SOUTHWEST
TCU Box 297005, Fort Worth, TX 76129
Tel.: (817) 257-5975 TX
Web Site:
http://www.caresbenefits.org
Year Founded: 2004
Sales Range: $25-49.9 Million
Medical Benefit Services
N.A.I.C.S.: 524292
Scott Kiedaisch (Exec Dir)
Keith Larey (Treas)
Karen Baker (Sec)
Brian Murray (Pres)

COLLEGIATE ENTREPRENEURS
150 Wood Rd Ste 401, Braintree, MA 02184
Web Site: http://www.cepaint.com
Year Founded: 1999
Sales Range: $1-9.9 Million
Emp.: 750
House Painting
N.A.I.C.S.: 238320
Eric C. Crews (Founder & Pres)

COLLEGIATE HOUSING SERVICES, INC.
5175 E 65th St, Indianapolis, IN 46220
Tel.: (317) 920-2600
Web Site:
https://www.housingservices.com
Year Founded: 1988
Sales Range: $10-24.9 Million
Emp.: 50
Real Estate Management Services
N.A.I.C.S.: 531390
David Neal (Pres)

COLLEGIATE RETAIL ALLIANCE
610 W Germantown Pike Ste 305, Plymouth Meeting, PA 19462-1047
Tel.: (610) 828-8630
Web Site:
http://www.collegiatealliance.com
Collegiate Bookstores Operator & Support Products Developer
N.A.I.C.S.: 459210
Melanie Sparks (Chm)
Sherry Pollard (Vice Chm)
Ross Rosati (Treas)

Subsidiaries:

PrismRBS, LLC (1)
610 W Germantown Pike Ste 305, Plymouth Meeting, PA 19462
Tel.: (610) 828-8630
Web Site: http://www.prismrbs.com
Collegiate Retail Software & Related Technologies Developer & Whslr
N.A.I.C.S.: 513210

Ratex Business Solutions, Inc. (1)
610 W Germantown Pike Ste 305, Plymouth Meeting, PA 19462
Tel.: (610) 828-8630
Collegiate Retail Software & Related Technologies Developer & Whslr
N.A.I.C.S.: 513210
Jere B. Warner (Pres & CEO)
Tom Whitmore (Product Mgr-Dev)

COLLEGIATE RISK MANAGEMENT, LLC

110 Athens St Ste 200, Tarpon Springs, FL 34689
Tel.: (727) 939-1333
Web Site:
https://www.collegiaterisk.com
Year Founded: 1996
Sales Range: $1-9.9 Million
Emp.: 10
Direct Health Insurance Carriers
N.A.I.C.S.: 524114
Vonda White (Pres)

COLLEGIS LLC
1415 W 22nd St Ste 220, Oak Brook, IL 60523
Tel.: (630) 210-3400
Web Site:
http://collegiseducation.com
Schools & Educational Services
N.A.I.C.S.: 611710
James Cowie (Pres & CEO)

Subsidiaries:

Education Management Solutions, Inc (1)
436 Creamery Way Ste 300, Exton, PA 19341
Tel.: (610) 701-7002
Web Site: http://www.simulationiq.com
Sales Range: $10-24.9 Million
Emp.: 86
Software Development Services
N.A.I.C.S.: 611710
Laurie L. Kerns (VP-Education Svcs)
Mike Brookhouser (VP-Sls)
Susan Truskey (VP-Mktg)
Mark Owens (Dir-Govt Sls)

COLLEGIUM HOLDINGS, INC.
5 Penn Plz 23rd Fl PMB# 23043, New York, NY 10001
Tel.: (212) 849-6834
Web Site:
http://www.collegiumholdings.com
Holding Company
N.A.I.C.S.: 551112
Craig Leach (CEO)

Subsidiaries:

Ruotolo Associates, Inc. (1)
580 Sylvan Ave Ste MB, Englewood Cliffs, NJ 07632
Tel.: (201) 568-3898
Web Site: http://www.ruotoloassociates.com
Sales Range: $1-9.9 Million
Emp.: 12
Management Consulting & Professional Advisory Services
N.A.I.C.S.: 541618
Theresa A. Shubeck (Exec VP)
George C. Ruotolo (Chm & CEO)
Steve Michalek (Dir-Church Div)

COLLETTE TRAVEL SERVICES
162 Middle St, Pawtucket, RI 02860-1013
Tel.: (401) 728-3805 RI
Web Site:
http://www.collettevacations.com
Year Founded: 1960
Sales Range: $25-49.9 Million
Emp.: 400
Tour Operator
N.A.I.C.S.: 561520
Daniel Sullivan Jr. (Owner & Exec Chm)
Paula Twidale (Exec VP)
Melissa Snape (VP-Product)
Jaclyn Leibl-Cote (CEO)

COLLIER BUILDING SPECIALTIES
1485 Bayshore Blvd Ste 153, San Francisco, CA 94124
Tel.: (415) 467-9235
Web Site: https://www.colliersf.com
Rev.: $10,000,000
Emp.: 13

Skylights, All Materials
N.A.I.C.S.: 423310
Carmen Pisani *(Mgr-Accounting)*

COLLIER DEVELOPMENT CO. INC.
204 Sharon Dr, Pigeon Forge, TN 37863
Tel.: (865) 453-2526
Web Site:
https://www.smokymountains.com
Sales Range: $10-24.9 Million
Emp.: 65
Hotel
N.A.I.C.S.: 721110
James Steve Collier *(Pres)*
Don Collier *(Chm)*
Elizabeth K. Collier *(Exec VP)*

COLLIER DRUG STORES
PO Box 1085, Fayetteville, AR 72701
Tel.: (479) 442-6262
Web Site: http://www.collierdrug.com
Sales Range: $10-24.9 Million
Emp.: 65
Pharmacy & Drug Product Distr
N.A.I.C.S.: 456110
Mel Collier *(Pres & Treas)*
Marci Gies *(Sec)*

COLLIER ENTERPRISES, INC.
2550 Goodlette Rd N Ste 100, Naples, FL 34103
Tel.: (239) 261-4455   FL
Web Site:
http://www.collierenterprises.com
Year Founded: 1976
Holding Company; Real Estate Management, Development & Brokerage Services
N.A.I.C.S.: 551112
Robert D. Corina *(CFO & Sr VP)*
Eleanor Taft *(Gen Counsel & VP)*
Pat Utter *(VP-Real Estate & Club Ops)*
Don Huffner *(CEO)*
J. Andrew Hogshead *(Pres)*

Subsidiaries:

Collier Enterprises Management, Inc.   (1)
2550 Goodlette Rd N Ste 100, Naples, FL 34103
Tel.: (239) 261-4455
Web Site: http://www.collierenterprises.com
Sales Range: $10-24.9 Million
Real Estate Management, Development & Brokerage Services
N.A.I.C.S.: 237210
Patrick L. Utter *(VP-Real Estate & Club Ops)*
Robert D. Corina *(CFO & Sr VP)*
Christian Spilker *(VP-Land Mgmt)*

Subsidiary (Domestic):

Collier Land Development, Inc.   (2)
2550 Goodlette Rd N Ste 100, Naples, FL 34103
Tel.: (239) 261-4455
Web Site: http://www.collierenterprises.com
Real Estate Developers
N.A.I.C.S.: 237210
Thomas J. Flood *(Co-Chm)*
Patrick L. Utter *(VP)*

COLLIN STREET BAKERY
401 W 7th Ave, Corsicana, TX 75110-6362
Tel.: (903) 872-8111   TX
Web Site:
http://www.collinstreetbakery.com
Year Founded: 1896
Sales Range: $75-99.9 Million
Emp.: 72
Deluxe Fruit Cakes & Gifts via Direct Mail
N.A.I.C.S.: 311812

Robert P. McNutt *(Pres)*
Jerry Grimmett *(VP)*

COLLINS & DUPONT INTERIORS, INC.
8911 Brighton Ln, Bonita Springs, FL 34135
Tel.: (239) 948-2400
Web Site: http://www.collins-dupont.com
Year Founded: 1987
Sales Range: $1-9.9 Million
Emp.: 42
Interior Designer
N.A.I.C.S.: 541410
Sherron DuPont *(Co-Founder & Pres)*
Kim Collins *(Co-Founder & VP)*
Michael Pineau *(Interior Designer)*

COLLINS AUTO GROUP, LLC
4220 Bardstown Rd, Louisville, KY 40218-3295
Tel.: (502) 459-9550   DE
Web Site:
http://www.billcollinsford.com
Year Founded: 1969
Sales Range: $125-149.9 Million
Emp.: 200
Provider of Sales & Leasing of Automobiles
N.A.I.C.S.: 441110
Kevin Collins *(Owner & Pres)*

COLLINS BROTHERS CORPORATION
16 Forest Pkwy Bldg J, Forest Park, GA 30297-2015
Tel.: (404) 363-4710   GA
Web Site:
http://www.collinsbrosproduce.com
Year Founded: 1982
Sales Range: $10-24.9 Million
Emp.: 75
Producer of Fresh Fruits & Vegetables
N.A.I.C.S.: 424480
Mike Collins *(Pres)*

Subsidiaries:

Delta Star Corporation   (1)
16 Forest Pkwy Bldg J, Forest Park, GA 30297-2015   (100%)
Tel.: (404) 363-4710
Sales Range: $10-24.9 Million
Emp.: 2
Provider of Trucking Services
N.A.I.C.S.: 484121

COLLINS BROTHERS MOVING CORP.
620 5th Ave, Larchmont, NY 10538
Tel.: (914) 834-0048
Web Site:
https://www.collinsbros.com
Year Founded: 1910
Sales Range: $25-49.9 Million
Emp.: 300
Furniture Moving & Storage
N.A.I.C.S.: 484220

COLLINS DISTRIBUTING COMPANY
3326 Commercial Pkwy, Memphis, TN 38116
Tel.: (901) 396-4484
Web Site:
http://www.collinsdistributing.com
Sales Range: $25-49.9 Million
Emp.: 15
Office Equipment Distr
N.A.I.C.S.: 423420
Bruce Collins *(Pres)*
Susan Howell *(Controller)*

COLLINS ELECTRIC COMPANY, INC.

53 2nd Ave, Chicopee, MA 01020-4624
Tel.: (413) 592-9221   MA
Web Site:
https://www.collinselectricco.com
Year Founded: 1906
Sales Range: $75-99.9 Million
Emp.: 100
General Electrical Contracting Services
N.A.I.C.S.: 238210
Lawrence F. Eagan *(Co-Pres)*

Subsidiaries:

Collins Electric Company, Inc. - Berkshire Division   (1)
163 4th St Ste 3, Pittsfield, MA 01201
Tel.: (413) 442-0824
Electrical Contracting Services
N.A.I.C.S.: 238210

COLLINS ELECTRICAL COMPANY
3412 Metro Dr, Stockton, CA 95215
Tel.: (209) 466-3691   CA
Web Site:
https://www.collinselectric.com
Year Founded: 1928
Sales Range: $75-99.9 Million
Emp.: 700
Provider of Electrical & Engineering Contracts
N.A.I.C.S.: 238210
Eugene C. Gini *(Pres & CEO)*
Gail M. Wardell *(CFO)*
Jeff Withers *(Mgr-Bus Dev)*
Kevin Gini *(VP & Branch Mgr-Sacramento)*
Brian Gini *(VP & Branch Mgr)*
Craig J. Gini *(VP & Gen Mgr-Renewables)*

COLLINS ENTERTAINMENT INC.
1341 Rutherford Rd, Greenville, SC 29609
Tel.: (864) 268-1111
Rev.: $10,600,000
Emp.: 75
Coin-Operated Amusement Devices
N.A.I.C.S.: 713120
Joe Macockey *(Treas)*

COLLINS PIPE & SUPPLY CO., INC.
11 Thompson Rd, East Windsor, CT 06088-9697
Tel.: (860) 292-5341
Web Site:
https://www.collinspipe.com
Sales Range: $25-49.9 Million
Emp.: 40
Pipe, Valve & Fittings Distr
N.A.I.C.S.: 423720
Brian P. Tuohey *(Pres)*
Jack Jorgensen *(Engr-Sls)*
Michael O'Neill *(Dir-Power & Energy)*
Paul Andruszkiewicz *(VP-Sls)*
Joe Clemente *(Mng Partner)*
Jay Fahy *(Territory Mgr)*
Kyle Gerner *(Engr-Sls)*
Robert Brogle *(Dir-Tech Svcs)*
Tom Strauss *(Mgr-Warehouse)*

Subsidiaries:

Washburn Garfield Corporation   (1)
100 Prescott St, Worcester, MA 01605
Tel.: (508) 753-7225
Web Site: http://www.washgar.com
Sales Range: $1-9.9 Million
Emp.: 20
Plumbing & Heating Equipment Whslr
N.A.I.C.S.: 423720
Richard O'Hearn Jr. *(Pres)*

COLLINSWORTH, ALTER, FOWLER DOWLING &

FRENCH GROUP INC
8000 Governors Sq Blvd Ste 301, Hialeah, FL 33016
Tel.: (305) 822-7800   FL
Web Site:
http://www.collinsworthalter.com
Year Founded: 1981
Sales Range: $75-99.9 Million
Emp.: 49
Provider of Insurance Services Specializing in Insurance & Bonds for Architectural, Engineering & Environmental Contractors
N.A.I.C.S.: 524210
David I. Alter *(Treas)*

COLLIS FOODS INC.
1021 Cambridge Sq, Alpharetta, GA 30009-1860
Tel.: (770) 664-4339   GA
Year Founded: 1969
Sales Range: $50-74.9 Million
Emp.: 2,500
Owner & Operator of Fast Food Restaurants
N.A.I.C.S.: 722511
Gene Petway *(Treas & Sec)*
Glenn Collis *(Chm)*
Steve Hutches *(Pres)*

COLLIS ROOFING, INC.
485 Commerce Way, Longwood, FL 32750-7570
Tel.: (321) 441-2300
Web Site:
https://www.collisroofing.com
Sales Range: $25-49.9 Million
Emp.: 655
Roofing Installation Services
N.A.I.C.S.: 238390
Michael Chmura *(CFO)*
Joyce Lanier *(Owner & VP)*
Matt Mason *(Coord-Residential Sls & Estimating)*
Nino Ramirez *(Dir-Safety)*
Justin Shelton *(Mgr)*
Wendy Staats *(Mgr-Invoicing)*
Doug Lanier *(Owner & CEO)*
Wallace Fulton III *(Pres)*

COLLISION REVISION, INC.
1225 E Washington St, Joliet, IL 60433
Tel.: (815) 723-3996   DE
Web Site:
http://www.collisionrevision.com
Year Founded: 1976
Rev.: $29,047,411
Emp.: 350
Automotive Body Repair Shops
Owner & Operator
N.A.I.C.S.: 811121
Roger A. D'Orazio *(CEO)*
Bryan Perino *(VP-Ops)*

Subsidiaries:

Collision Revision 13081 Inc.   (1)
13081 Metro Pkwy, Fort Myers, FL 33912
Tel.: (239) 768-3900
Web Site: http://www.collisionrevision.com
Rev.: $600,000
Emp.: 40
Automotive Body Repair Shop Operator
N.A.I.C.S.: 811121
Roger A. D'Orazio *(CEO)*

COLLISION WORKS, INC.
3224 SE 29th St, Del City, OK 73115
Tel.: (405) 670-2500
Web Site: http://www.collisionworks.com
Year Founded: 1996
Collision Repair Services
N.A.I.C.S.: 811121
Jake Nossaman *(Owner)*
Barry Hadlock *(Pres)*
Byron Johnson *(COO)*

Collision Works, Inc.—(Continued)

COLLMAN & KARSKY ARCHITECTS, INC.
4301 Anchor Plz Pkwy Ste 100, Tampa, FL 33634-7525
Tel.: (813) 884-2000　　　FL
Web Site: http://www.collman-karsky.com
Year Founded: 1961
Sales Range: $1-9.9 Million
Emp.: 14
Architectural Services
N.A.I.C.S.: 541310
Bryan L. Karsky (Exec VP & Principal)
Rodney L. Collman (Pres & Principal)

COLLUM'S LUMBER MILL, INC.
1723 Barnwell Hwy, Allendale, SC 29810-1711
Tel.: (803) 584-3451　　　SC
Web Site:
　　https://www.collumlumber.com
Year Founded: 1936
Sales Range: $50-74.9 Million
Emp.: 300
Mfr of Wood Products
N.A.I.C.S.: 321114
Henry C. Scott (Pres & CEO)
William C. Scott (VP)
Billy Berry (Mgr-Sls & Pur)

COLMAN, BROHAN & DAVIS, INC.
54 W Hubbard St Concourse Level E, Chicago, IL 60654
Tel.: (312) 661-1050
Web Site:
　　https://www.cbdmarketing.com
Year Founded: 1988
Sales Range: $1-9.9 Million
Emp.: 27
Advetising Agency
N.A.I.C.S.: 541810
Liz Brohan (Pres & Co-CEO)
Doug Davila (Sr VP-Agency Strategy & Dev)
Jean Ban (Exec VP-Acct Svc)
Lori Colman (Founder & Co-CEO)
Mark Shevitz (Exec VP & Dir-Brand Strategy & Plng)
Kari Brua (VP & Dir-Acct)
Mary Olivieri (Exec VP & Creative Dir)

COLO4
3000 Irving Blvd, Dallas, TX 75247
Tel.: (214) 630-3100　　　TX
Web Site: http://www.colo4.com
Year Founded: 2000
Sales Range: $1-9.9 Million
Emp.: 20
Secure Data Colocation Services
N.A.I.C.S.: 518210
Dave Ellis (Dir-Tech Ops)

COLOMA FROZEN FOODS INC.
4145 Coloma Rd, Coloma, MI 49038
Tel.: (269) 849-0500
Web Site:
　　https://www.colomafrozen.com
Sales Range: $10-24.9 Million
Emp.: 150
Frozen Fruits & Vegetables
N.A.I.C.S.: 311411
Brad Wendzel (Pres & Mgr-Sls)
Ed Sill (Mgr-Sls)
Denny Ostyn (Mgr)

COLOMEX INC.
717 N Tejon St, Colorado Springs, CO 80903-1011
Tel.: (719) 633-2500　　　CO

Year Founded: 1983
Sales Range: $25-49.9 Million
Emp.: 900
Eating Place
N.A.I.C.S.: 722513
Jerry Grage (Owner)
Kelly Roldan (Controller)

COLON BROTHERS INC.
Carle 3 Edef Toin B Zona Portuerie, San Juan, PR 00936
Tel.: (787) 792-4330
Web Site:
　　http://www.colosofoods.com
Sales Range: $10-24.9 Million
Emp.: 34
Groceries, General Line
N.A.I.C.S.: 424410
Jose R. Colon (Pres)

COLONIAL AUTO SUPPLY CO.
135 Commerce Dr, Fort Washington, PA 19034
Tel.: (215) 643-3699
Web Site:
　　http://www.bandiautosupply.com
Rev.: $29,500,000
Emp.: 80
Automotive Supplies
N.A.I.C.S.: 423120
Joseph Pluck (Pres)
Chris Bell (CFO)

COLONIAL AUTOMOTIVE GROUP, INC.
171 Great Rd, Acton, MA 01720
Tel.: (978) 263-1000　　　MA
Web Site:
　　https://www.buycolonial.com
Year Founded: 1996
Sales Range: $150-199.9 Million
Emp.: 450
Holding Company; New & Used Car Dealerships Owner & Operator
N.A.I.C.S.: 551112
Lawrence M. Gordon (Chm, Pres & CEO)
Daniel Fontaine (Dir-e-Commerce)

Subsidiaries:

Colonial Chevrolet of Acton　　(1)
171 Great Rd, Acton, MA 01720
Tel.: (978) 631-1211
Web Site:
　　http://www.buycolonialchevrolet.com
Sales Range: $25-49.9 Million
Emp.: 38
New & Used Car Dealer
N.A.I.C.S.: 441110
Lawrence M. Gordon (Pres & CEO)

Colonial West Chevrolet of Fitchburg　　(1)
314 John Fitch Hwy, Fitchburg, MA 01420
Tel.: (978) 342-8713
Web Site: http://www.buycolonialwest.com
New & Used Car Dealer
N.A.I.C.S.: 441110
Jeff Chandler (Gen Mgr)

North End Mazda of Lunenburg　　(1)
747 Chase Rd, Lunenburg, MA 01462
Tel.: (978) 582-7767
Web Site:
　　http://www.buynorthendmazda.com
New & Used Car Dealer
N.A.I.C.S.: 441110

North End Subaru of Lunenburg　　(1)
757 Chase Rd, Lunenburg, MA 01462
Tel.: (978) 582-4911
Web Site: http://www.northendsubaru.com
Sales Range: $25-49.9 Million
Emp.: 39
New & Used Car Distr
N.A.I.C.S.: 441110
Martin Babineau (Gen Mgr)

COLONIAL BAG COMPANY
PO Box 929, Lake Park, GA 31636
Tel.: (229) 559-8484

Web Site: http://www.colonial-bag.com
Sales Range: $10-24.9 Million
Emp.: 150
Bags: Uncoated Paper & Multiwall
N.A.I.C.S.: 322220
Mike Drumheller Jr. (Pres)

COLONIAL COMPANY
2000 Interstate Park Dr, Montgomery, AL 36109
Tel.: (334) 270-6565
Year Founded: 1956
Sales Range: $10-24.9 Million
Emp.: 90
Single-Family Housing Construction
N.A.I.C.S.: 236115
Purser L. McLeod (Pres & CEO)
James K. Lowder (Chm & Pres)

Subsidiaries:

Colonial Commercial Development　　(1)
5251 Hampstead High St Unit 205, Montgomery, AL 36116
Tel.: (334) 270-6700
Web Site: http://www.colonialcommercial.net
Developer of Multifamily Communities Focusing on Garden Apartments, Assisted & Independent Living & Condominiums
N.A.I.C.S.: 541618

Colonial Commercial Realty　　(1)
2000 Interstate Park Dr Ste 300, Montgomery, AL 36109
Tel.: (334) 270-6700
Web Site:
　　http://www.colonialcommercialrealty.com
Provider of Full Service Commercial Real Estate Sales, Investment, Leasing, Development & Tenant Representation
N.A.I.C.S.: 541618

Colonial Insurance　　(1)
5251 Hampstead High St Ste 200, Montgomery, AL 36116
Tel.: (334) 270-6824
Web Site: http://www.colonial-insurance.com
Provider of Insurance Policies & Financial Services
N.A.I.C.S.: 524210
Chris Setzer (Mgr-Acct-Personal)
David Peel (Acct Exec-Comml Lines)
Lindsey Cook (Mgr-Acct-Comml)

Lowder Construction Company, Inc.　　(1)
2000 Interstate Park Dr Ste 401, Montgomery, AL 36109
Tel.: (334) 270-6524
Web Site: http://www.lowder-construction.com
Sales Range: $10-24.9 Million
Emp.: 5
General Contractors
N.A.I.C.S.: 236220

Lowder New Homes　　(1)
5272 Hamstead Hagh St Unit 204, Montgomery, AL 36116
Tel.: (334) 270-6789
Web Site: http://www.lowdernewhomes.com
Sales Range: $10-24.9 Million
Emp.: 15
Single Family Home Builder
N.A.I.C.S.: 236115
Ed Lowder (Founder)
James W. Rutland IV (Pres)

COLONIAL COUNTRY CLUB
3735 Country Club Cir, Fort Worth, TX 76109
Tel.: (817) 927-4200
Web Site: https://www.colonialfw.com
Year Founded: 1936
Sales Range: $10-24.9 Million
Emp.: 200
Golf Course & Country Club Operating Services
N.A.I.C.S.: 713910
Alexis Groesch (Dir-Member Svcs & Comm)
Mike Rushing (Gen Mgr)

Robert M. Doby (Pres)
Jonathan D. Mock (VP)
Charles G. Scherer (VP)

COLONIAL DEALERSHIP GROUP
200 W St Rd, Feasterville Trevose, PA 19053
Tel.: (215) 355-8800
Web Site:
　　http://www.colonialdirect.net
Sales Range: $25-49.9 Million
Emp.: 150
Dealer Sales Of New & Used Cars,
N.A.I.C.S.: 441227
James Boyle (Pres)

COLONIAL DIVERSIFIED POLYMER PRODUCTS LLC
2055 Forrest St, Dyersburg, TN 38024
Tel.: (731) 287-3636
Web Site:
　　http://www.colonialdpp.com
Sales Range: $10-24.9 Million
Emp.: 130
Custom Compound Purchased Resins
N.A.I.C.S.: 325991
Ladon Byars (CFO)

COLONIAL ENGINEERING INC.
6400 Corporate Ave, Portage, MI 49002
Tel.: (269) 323-2495
Web Site:
　　https://www.colonialengineering.com
Sales Range: $10-24.9 Million
Emp.: 10
Thermal Plastic Valves & Custom Injection Molding
N.A.I.C.S.: 326122
Mark Bainbridge (VP-Sls)

COLONIAL EQUIPMENT COMPANY
5171 Intercoastal Ct, Monrovia, MD 21770
Tel.: (301) 698-5100
Web Site:
　　https://www.colonialbus.com
Sales Range: $10-24.9 Million
Emp.: 21
Transportation Solution Provider
N.A.I.C.S.: 488210
Donald Combs (Pres & CEO)
Craig Combs (Gen Mgr & Mgr-Svc)
Diana Putman (Office Mgr)
Rick Schrider (Mgr-Parts)

COLONIAL FARM CREDIT A.C.A.
7104 Mechanicsville Tpke, Mechanicsville, VA 23111-3661
Tel.: (804) 746-1252　　　VA
Web Site:
　　http://www.colonialfarmcredit.com
Year Founded: 1989
Sales Range: $50-74.9 Million
Emp.: 80
Miscellaneous Business Credit Institution
N.A.I.C.S.: 522299
James Belfield (CIO)
Paul B. Franklin (Pres & CEO)
Michael Lacks (Chief Lending Officer-Comml Loans)
Sue Nicely (Sec & Dir-HR)
Diane Fowlkes (CFO)
Patrick Tewell (Chief Credit Officer)
Ronnie Gill (Chief Lending Officer-Branch Ops)

COLONIAL FORD TRUCK SALES, INC.

1833 Commerce Rd, Richmond, VA 23224
Tel.: (804) 232-3492
Web Site:
https://www.colonialtruck.net
Year Founded: 1963
Sales Range: $75-99.9 Million
Emp.: 150
Whslr of Trucks, Automobiles & Automobile Parts
N.A.I.C.S.: 423110
Steve Usry (VP & Gen Mgr)

Subsidiaries:

Colonial Tire Distributor Inc   (1)
1833 Commerce Rd, Richmond, VA 23224
Tel.: (804) 232-6700
Web Site: http://www.colonialtruck.com
Rev.: $3,200,000
Emp.: 35
Automotive, Truck & Off Road Tire Distr
N.A.I.C.S.: 441340
Bob Barkley (Pres)

Colonial Truck Sales Inc.   (1)
11430 Air Park Rd, Ashland, VA 23005
Tel.: (804) 798-7242
Web Site: http://www.colonivolvtruck.com
Rev.: $10,000,000
Emp.: 50
Automobiles & Other Motor Vehicles
N.A.I.C.S.: 423110
Allen Martin (Gen Mgr)
Dave Fenner (Mgr-Parts)
George R. Barkley Jr. (Pres)

COLONIAL FREIGHT SYSTEMS INC.
10924 McBride Ln, Knoxville, TN 37932
Tel.: (865) 966-9711
Web Site: https://www.cfsi.com
Rev.: $38,868,019
Emp.: 80
Trucking Service
N.A.I.C.S.: 484121
Scott Simmons (Dir-Safety)
Lorraine Thompson (Office Mgr-Maintenance)
Michael Barnes (VP-Ops)
Ruby Mcbride (Pres)

COLONIAL GROUP, INC.
101 N Lathrop Ave, Savannah, GA 31415   GA
Web Site:
https://www.colonialgroupinc.com
Year Founded: 1921
Sales Range: $1-4.9 Billion
Emp.: 2,200
Petroleum Bulk Stations & Terminals
N.A.I.C.S.: 424710
Robert H. Demere Jr. (Chm)
Francis A. Brown (Exec VP-Fin)
Brett H. Giesick (COO & Exec VP)
J. Ryan Chandler (VP)
Christian B. Demere (Pres)
Clayton D. Cheshire (Exec VP-Fin)
Alexandra McCants (VP-HR)
William A. Baker Jr. (Exec VP-Ops)
R. Houstoun Demere III (Sec)

Subsidiaries:

Chatham Towing Company, Inc.   (1)
101 Lathrop Ave, Savannah, GA 31415
Tel.: (912) 236-1331
Web Site: http://www.ctc.com
Rev.: $2,000,000
Emp.: 15
Water Transportation of Freight
N.A.I.C.S.: 483211

Colonial Caribbean, Inc.   (1)
3 Riverway Ste 2000, Houston, TX 77056
Tel.: (713) 629-7563
Petroleum Product Whslr
N.A.I.C.S.: 424720

Colonial Chemical Solutions, Inc.   (1)
916 W Lathrop Ave, Savannah, GA 31415
Tel.: (912) 236-7891
Web Site: http://www.colonialchemicals.com

Emp.: 85
Chemical Product Whslr
N.A.I.C.S.: 424690
Jeremy Detwiler (Asst VP)
Rob Roberts (VP & Gen Mgr)

Colonial Energy, Inc.   (1)
101 North Lathrop Ave, Savannah, GA 31415-1054
Tel.: (912) 236-1331
Web Site: http://www.colonialgroupinc.com
Sales Range: $50-74.9 Million
Emp.: 300
Natural Gas Distribution
N.A.I.C.S.: 221210
David Deason (Gen Mgr)

Colonial Oil Industries, Inc.   (1)
101 N Lathrop Ave, Savannah, GA 31415-1054
Tel.: (912) 236-1331
Web Site: http://www.colonialgroupinc.com
Sales Range: $25-49.9 Million
Emp.: 300
Special Trade Contractors; Service Stations; Miscellaneous Retail Stores; Real Estate Developer; Wholesale & Retail Distributor of Petroleum & Petroleum Products
N.A.I.C.S.: 441110
Robert H. Demere Jr. (Pres & CEO)
William A. Baker (VP-Ops)
Francis A. Brown (VP-Fin)

Colonial Terminals, Inc.   (1)
101 N Lathrop Ave, Savannah, GA 31415-1054
Tel.: (912) 236-1331
Web Site: http://www.colonialterminals.com
Rev.: $7,600,000
Emp.: 139
General Warehousing & Storage Services
N.A.I.C.S.: 493110
Michael Mashburn (Asst Mgr-Liquid Ops)

Compliance Systems, Inc.   (1)
26 E Bryan St, Savannah, GA 31401-2602
Tel.: (912) 233-8181
Web Site: http://www.colonialmarine.com
Sales Range: Less than $1 Million
Emp.: 5
Management Consulting Services
N.A.I.C.S.: 541614

Enmark Stations, Inc.   (1)
2112 Rankin St, Savannah, GA 31415
Tel.: (912) 443-6908
Web Site: http://www.enmarketenroll.com
Sales Range: $50-74.9 Million
Emp.: 500
Gasoline Service Stations
N.A.I.C.S.: 457120
Matt Clements (Dir-Mktg-Savannah)

Georgia Kaolin Terminals, Inc.   (1)
509 Foundation Dr, Garden City, GA 31408-2215   (100%)
Tel.: (912) 236-1331
Web Site: http://www.colonialgroup.com
Sales Range: $10-24.9 Million
Emp.: 25
General Warehousing & Storage
N.A.I.C.S.: 493110
William A. Baker (VP-Ops)

COLONIAL HARDWARE CORP.
33 Commerce St, Springfield, NJ 07081
Tel.: (212) 741-8989
Web Site:
https://www.blackbookoftools.com
Sales Range: $10-24.9 Million
Emp.: 30
Hand Tools
N.A.I.C.S.: 423710
Michael J. O'Connell (Pres)
Franny Flanigan-Hargey (Mgr-Ops)

COLONIAL HOMES INC.
4328 Flagstaff Cove, Fort Wayne, IN 46815
Tel.: (260) 486-2500
Web Site:
http://www.visitcolonialhomes.com
Year Founded: 1976
Sales Range: $1-9.9 Million
Emp.: 10

Home Builder & Remodeler
N.A.I.C.S.: 236115
Larry Delagrange (Pres)

COLONIAL HYUNDAI OF DOWNINGTOWN
4423 W Lincoln Hwy, Downingtown, PA 19335
Tel.: (610) 981-1012
Web Site:
https://www.colonialhyundai.com
Sales Range: $10-24.9 Million
Emp.: 75
Car Whslr
N.A.I.C.S.: 441110
Jeffrey Feldman (Pres)

COLONIAL ICE CREAM INC.
333 N Randall Rd Ste 1, Saint Charles, IL 60174
Tel.: (630) 584-0088
Web Site:
http://www.colonialcafe.com
Sales Range: $10-24.9 Million
Emp.: 425
Restaurant, Family: Chain
N.A.I.C.S.: 722511
Thomas S. Anderson (Pres)
Clinton Anderson (Dir-Ops)

COLONIAL IMPORTS CORP.
10 Marmon Dr, Nashua, NH 03060-5204
Tel.: (603) 888-3555   NH
Web Site:
http://www.toyotaofnashua.com
Year Founded: 1962
Sales Range: $25-49.9 Million
Emp.: 200
New & Used Car Dealers
N.A.I.C.S.: 441110
Chris Piekarski (Pres, Owner & Treas)

COLONIAL INC.
520 Eaton Ave, Hamilton, OH 45013
Tel.: (513) 785-4750   OH
Web Site:
http://www.colonialseniors.com
Sales Range: $25-49.9 Million
Emp.: 493
Senior Living Services
N.A.I.C.S.: 623311

COLONIAL INDUSTRIAL PRODUCTS
400 Victoria Rd, Youngstown, OH 44515
Tel.: (330) 792-4700
Sales Range: $10-24.9 Million
Emp.: 23
Provider of Men's & Boy's Apparel
N.A.I.C.S.: 424350

COLONIAL LLC.
536 Townsend Ave, High Point, NC 27263
Tel.: (336) 434-5600
Web Site: http://www.colonialllc.com
Year Founded: 1982
Sales Range: $1-9.9 Million
Emp.: 40
Textile Product Mills
N.A.I.C.S.: 314999
Mark Hobson (Pres)
Wes Keever (Exec VP-Sls)
Jimmy Keever (COO)
Jim Dunlap (Sr VP-Ops)
Larry Ausley (Sr VP-Fin)
Monica Craig (Office Mgr-Customer Svc)
Megan Williams (Dir-Art-Printing)
Amy Pierce (Dir-Art-Embroidery)
Marsha Presnell (Mgr-Logistics)
Robert Blackwelder (Supvr-Shipping)
Jim Keever Sr. (Chm & CEO)

COLONIAL METALS CO.
217 Linden St, Columbia, PA 17512-1179
Tel.: (717) 684-2311   PA
Web Site:
http://www.colonialmetalsco.com
Year Founded: 1979
Sales Range: $75-99.9 Million
Emp.: 154
Metal Smelters
N.A.I.C.S.: 331492
David Serls (CEO)
Kathryn Markley (VP-Sls)

COLONIAL MOTOR MART
349 N 4th St, Indiana, PA 15701
Tel.: (724) 349-5600
Web Site:
http://www.colonialcars.com
Year Founded: 1946
Rev.: $16,000,000
Emp.: 40
Automobiles, New & Used
N.A.I.C.S.: 441110
Charles A. Spadafora (Pres)

COLONIAL NISSAN, INC.
117 Bustleton Pike, Langhorne, PA 19053
Tel.: (215) 322-2297
Web Site:
https://www.colonialnissan.com
Year Founded: 1985
Sales Range: $25-49.9 Million
Emp.: 75
New Car Dealers
N.A.I.C.S.: 441110
Jeff Garfinkel (Gen Mgr-Sls)

COLONIAL PANTRY LTD.
811 Springfield Ave Ste 206, Champaign, IL 61820-8401
Tel.: (217) 352-6789
Web Site:
http://www.colonialpantry.com
Rev.: $18,938,997
Emp.: 100
Convenience Store
N.A.I.C.S.: 445131
John P. Miller (Pres)

COLONIAL PARTNERS, INC.
1505 The Boardwalk, Huntsville, AL 35816
Tel.: (256) 539-2279   AL
Web Site:
http://www.colonialpmp.com
Year Founded: 1990
Commercial Printing, Lithographic
N.A.I.C.S.: 323111

COLONIAL PIPELINE COMPANY
1185 Sanctuary Pkwy Ste 100, Alpharetta, GA 30004-4765
Tel.: (678) 762-2200   DE
Web Site: http://www.colpipe.com
Year Founded: 1962
Sales Range: $150-199.9 Million
Emp.: 670
Provider of Pipeline Distribution of Petroleum Products
N.A.I.C.S.: 486910
Rodney L. Gray (VP)

COLONIAL SAVINGS, F.A.
2600 West Fwy, Fort Worth, TX 76102
Tel.: (817) 390-2380
Web Site:
http://www.colonialsavings.com
Year Founded: 1962
Sales Range: $100-124.9 Million
Emp.: 600
Federal Savings Bank
N.A.I.C.S.: 522180

Colonial Savings, F.A.—(Continued)

James S. Du Bose (Chm)
Ben Dempsey (CFO & Sr VP)
Kara Sagedal (Mgr-Ops)
Tony Neal (Mgr-Reg Sls)
Leticia Mijes (Mgr-Multicultural Market)
Joe Chapman (VP-Retail Production)
David Motley (Pres)

Subsidiaries:

Colonial National Mortgage   (1)
2626 W Fwy, Fort Worth, TX 76102-7109
Tel.: (817) 390-2200
Web Site: http://www.cnmcs.com
Mortgage Lending Services
N.A.I.C.S.: 522310

DuBose & Associates Insurance Company   (1)
2501 Parkview Dr Ste 610, Fort Worth, TX 76102
Tel.: (817) 390-2300
Web Site: http://www.duboseandassociates.com
Emp.: 7
Insurance Management Services
N.A.I.C.S.: 524298
James Dubose (Pres)

First Western Title Company   (1)
3211 W 4th St, Fort Worth, TX 76107
Tel.: (817) 877-9500
Web Site: http://www.firstwesterntitle.com
Sales Range: $1-9.9 Million
Emp.: 4
Title Insurance Services
N.A.I.C.S.: 524127
Pamela Barrett (VP & Branch Mgr)
Evan Clark (VP, Branch Mgr & Atty)
Sandra Cole (VP & Branch Mgr)
Christopher Drumm (Sr VP)
Steve Harriman (VP & Dir-Comml Mktg)
Sandy Houghton (VP & Branch Mgr)
Jim Moran (CEO)
Diana Pyndus (VP & Branch Mgr)
Lisa Walt (VP-Corp Ops)

COLONIAL SQUARE REALTY, INC.
1250 Tamiami Trl N Ste 101, Naples, FL 34102
Tel.: (239) 261-2627
Web Site: http://www.colonialsquare.net
Year Founded: 1990
Emp.: 20
Real Estate Broker
N.A.I.C.S.: 531210
Clifford Olson (Mng Member)
Anthony Emma (CEO)
Shelly Mandell (Mgr-Property)
Shaun Gillis (Mgr-Property)
Kim Gaglia (Sr Mgr-Property)

COLONIAL SUBARU, INC.
89 Newtown Rd, Danbury, CT 06810
Tel.: (203) 744-8383
Web Site: https://www.colonialsubaruct.com
Year Founded: 1993
Sales Range: $10-24.9 Million
Emp.: 45
New Car Dealers
N.A.I.C.S.: 441110
George Samaha (Gen Mgr)
Gary Helbing (Mgr-Pre-Owned Sls)
Jim Meehan (Bus Mgr)
Nick Forese (Mgr-Fin)
Art Azzarito (Mgr-Svc)

COLONIAL TOYOTA
550 George Washington Hwy, Smithfield, RI 02917
Tel.: (401) 831-6000
Web Site: http://www.colonialtoyota.com
Year Founded: 1926
Sales Range: $10-24.9 Million
Emp.: 40

Sales & Service Of New & Used Automobiles
N.A.I.C.S.: 441110
Jim Botvin (Pres)
Henry Rheaume (Bus Mgr)
Jimmy Maiers (Mgr-Sls)
Noah Kim (Mgr-Sls)
Rick Reid (Mgr-Sls)

COLONIAL VOLKSWAGEN
89 Turnpike Rd, Westborough, MA 01581
Tel.: (508) 366-8383
Web Site: https://www.buycolonialvw.com
Sales Range: $10-24.9 Million
Emp.: 35
New Car Dealers
N.A.I.C.S.: 441110
Mark Schelfhaudt (Gen Mgr)
Tony Strozina (Mgr-Sls)

COLONNA BROS., INC.
4102 Bergen Tpke, North Bergen, NJ 07047-2510
Tel.: (201) 864-1115
Web Site: https://www.colonnabrothers.com
Year Founded: 1918
Sales Range: $10-24.9 Million
Emp.: 50
Distr of Cheese, Flavored Bread Crumbs, Plain Bread Crumbs, Private Label Packaging, Spices, Croutons & Stuffing Mix
N.A.I.C.S.: 311513
Peter Colonna (Pres)
Mark Colonna (VP)
Diane Maniscalco (Treas & Sec)

COLONNAS SHIPYARD INCORPORATED
400 E Indian River Rd, Norfolk, VA 23523
Tel.: (757) 545-2414
Web Site: https://www.colonnaship.com
Rev.: $24,800,000
Emp.: 300
Commercial Cargo Ships; Building & Repairing
N.A.I.C.S.: 336611
Tom Godfrey (Pres & CEO)
Kenny Mebane (VP)
Richard Sobocinski (VP-Contracts)
Steve Walker (VP-Ops)
Rebecca Wieters (CFO & VP)
Jordan Webb (VP-Ops)
Randall Crutchfield (VP-Industrial Ops & Facilities)
Willoughby W. Colonna Jr. (Chm)

COLONY BRANDS, INC.
1112 7th Ave, Monroe, WI 53566-1364
Tel.: (608) 328-8400
Web Site: http://www.swisscolony.com
Year Founded: 1926
Sales Range: $400-449.9 Million
Emp.: 1,300
Cheese, Meats, Pastries, Candies, Fruits, Nuts & Gift Packs Mfr; Retail Operations; Dining Facilities
N.A.I.C.S.: 424430
John Baumann (Pres & CEO)

COLONY HARDWARE SUPPLY CO. INC.
15 Stiles St 269 S, New Haven, CT 06512
Tel.: (203) 466-5252
Web Site: http://www.colonyhardware.com
Sales Range: $50-74.9 Million
Emp.: 110

Distr of Hardware
N.A.I.C.S.: 423710
Michael Weiner (Pres)
Mark Patton (CFO & COO)
Sara Lane (Coord-Mktg)
Kevin Lamoureux (Dir-Mktg)

COLONY HEATING & AIR CONDITIONING INC.
2224 16th Ave SW, Cedar Rapids, IA 52404
Tel.: (319) 364-4328
Web Site: https://www.colonyheating.com
Year Founded: 1972
Rev.: $11,400,000
Emp.: 65
Plumbing, Heating & Air-Conditioning Contractors
N.A.I.C.S.: 238220
Tim Stecklein (Mgr)
Doug Kohoutek (Mgr-Svc)
P. J. Kalb (Mgr-Fireplace Sls)
Steve Thatcher (Mgr)
Brian Klinefelter (Mgr)
Mary Flansburg (Mgr-Acctg)
Brian Miller (Mgr-Plumbing)
Casey Gatewood (Mgr-Shop)

COLONY TIRE CORPORATION
1415 N Broad St, Edenton, NC 27932-9613
Tel.: (252) 482-8080
Web Site: http://www.colonytire.com
Year Founded: 1976
Sales Range: $50-74.9 Million
Emp.: 365
Tire Whslr
N.A.I.C.S.: 441340
Charles A. Creighton (CEO)
Jimmy Reese (Mgr)
Ashley Aydlett (Mgr-Mktg)
Barry Hollowell (Mgr-Logistic)
David Coltrain (Mgr)

COLOR ART OFFICE INTERIORS INC.
1325 N Warson Rd, Saint Louis, MO 63132-1807
Tel.: (314) 432-3000
Web Site: http://www.color-art.com
Year Founded: 1995
Sales Range: $50-74.9 Million
Emp.: 150
Wholesale of Furniture
N.A.I.C.S.: 423210
Gary Mindel (CEO)
Christine Hoffmann (Pres-Furniture)
Mark Richert (Pres-Construction)
Jennifer Graham (Exec VP-Workplace Strategies & Design)
Todd Nixon (Exec VP-Furniture)

Subsidiaries:

Commercial Installation & Construction Company   (1)
1325 N Warson Rd, Saint Louis, MO 63132   (100%)
Tel.: (314) 567-7292
Web Site: http://www.cic-ca.com
Sales Range: $10-24.9 Million
Emp.: 100
Nonresidential Construction
N.A.I.C.S.: 236220
Mark Richard (Pres)

COLOR CAULK INC.
1105 S Frontenac St, Aurora, IL 60504
Tel.: (630) 978-7766
Rev.: $15,407,527
Emp.: 115
Caulking Compounds
N.A.I.C.S.: 444120

COLOR COMMUNICATIONS, INC.

4000 W Fillmore St, Chicago, IL 60624
Tel.: (773) 638-1400
Web Site: https://www.ccicolor.com
Year Founded: 1972
Sales Range: $25-49.9 Million
Emp.: 400
Lithographic Commercial Printing
N.A.I.C.S.: 323111
Stanley Lerner (Pres)
Harald Karlsson (VP-Sls)
Steve Winter (Pres)
Russ Zavacki (Dir-Sls)

COLOR IMAGE APPAREL INC.
6670 Flotilla St, Los Angeles, CA 90040
Tel.: (323) 727-2005
Web Site: http://www.bellacanvas.com
Year Founded: 1992
T-Shirts & Tops Mfr & Dist
N.A.I.C.S.: 315120
Marco Degeorge (Owner)
Audrey Young (Office Mgr)

COLOR IMAGING INC.
4350 Peachtree Industrial Blvd Ste 100, Norcross, GA 30071
Tel.: (770) 840-1090
Web Site: http://www.colorimaging.com
Year Founded: 1989
Sales Range: $10-24.9 Million
Emp.: 100
Develops, Manufactures & Markets Products Used in Electronic Printing
N.A.I.C.S.: 333248
Sueling Wang (Pres)
Morris E. Van Asperen (Exec VP)
Frank Shaw (Mgr-IT)

COLOR INC.
47 October Hill Rd, Holliston, MA 01746
Tel.: (508) 474-2900
Web Site: https://www.thecolorstores.com
Year Founded: 1976
Sales Range: $10-24.9 Million
Emp.: 25
Sports Apparel
N.A.I.C.S.: 458110
Tom Emmons (VP)
Al Shameklis (Pres & COO)
Doreen Shameklis (Dir-Buying)

COLOR INK, INC.
W250 N 6681 Highway 164, Sussex, WI 53089
Tel.: (262) 246-5000
Web Site: http://www.colorink.com
Year Founded: 1985
Sales Range: $1-9.9 Million
Emp.: 95
Commercial Printing, Lithographic
N.A.I.C.S.: 323111
Jason Wick (Supvr-Warehouse)
Rick Tweed (VP-Production)

Subsidiaries:

HM Graphics Inc.   (1)
7840 W Hicks St, West Allis, WI 53219
Tel.: (414) 321-6600
Web Site: http://www.hmgraphics.com
Rev.: $21,100,000
Emp.: 220
Commercial Lithographic Printing
N.A.I.C.S.: 323111
Greg Dooley (CFO)

COLOR MASTER, INC.
810 S Broadway, Butler, IN 46721
Tel.: (260) 868-2320

Web Site: https://www.color-master.com
Year Founded: 1991
Sales Range: $10-24.9 Million
Emp.: 55
Synthetic Organic Dye & Pigment Mfr
N.A.I.C.S.: 325130
Jodie Evans (Mgr-Sls)
Jeff Von Sprecken (Mgr-Pur & Mfg)

COLOR ME BEAUTIFUL, INC.
7000 Infantry Ridge Rd Ste 200, Manassas, VA 20109
Tel.: (703) 471-6400   MD
Web Site:
    https://www.colormebeautiful.com
Year Founded: 1974
Sales Range: $350-399.9 Million
Emp.: 60
Cosmetics Mfr & Distr
N.A.I.C.S.: 424210
Steve DiAntonio (Owner)

Subsidiaries:

Flori Roberts   (1)
7000 Eastern Infantry Ridge Rd Ste 200,
Manassas, VA 20109-3225
Tel.: (703) 471-6400
Web Site: http://www.floriroberts.com
Sales Range: $10-24.9 Million
Emp.: 50
Retailer of Cosmetics
N.A.I.C.S.: 424210

COLOR ME MINE ENTER-PRISES, INC.
3722 San Fernando Rd, Glendale, CA 91204
Tel.: (818) 291-5900   CA
Web Site:
    http://www.colormemine.com
Sales Range: $50-74.9 Million
Emp.: 300
Holding Company; Ceramic Painting Store Operator & Franchisor
N.A.I.C.S.: 551112
Michael Mooslin (Pres & COO)
Ned Mooslin (Dir-Pur & Product Dev)
Shannon Adler (Mgr-Accts Receivable)
Tara Thomman (Dir-Mktg)
Mark Hegstrom (Dir-IT)
David Hoff (Dir-Technical Support)
Bruce Westenfelder (VP-Franchise Dev & Ops)
Larry Duncan (Chm & CEO)
Lindsay Craine (Dir-Franchise Coordination)
Sean Goodwin (Dir-Franchise Ops & Support)
Maria Baker (Exec Dir-Franchise Dev)

Subsidiaries:

Color Me Mine Franchising, Inc.   (1)
3722 San Fernando Rd, Glendale, CA 91204
Tel.: (818) 291-5900
Web Site: http://www.colormemine.com
Sales Range: $10-24.9 Million
Emp.: 8
Ceramic Painting Store Franchisor
N.A.I.C.S.: 533110
Michael Mooslin (Pres & COO)
Bruce Westenfelder (VP-Franchise Support & Dev)
Maria Baker (Sr Dir-Franchise Admin)
Lindsay Craine (Dir-Franchise Coordination)
Larry Duncan (CEO)

COLOR SPOT NURSERY, INC.
2575 Olive Hill Rd, Fallbrook, CA 92028
Tel.: (760) 695-1430   DE
Web Site: http://www.colorspot.com
Year Founded: 1995
Sales Range: $200-249.9 Million
Emp.: 2,800

Wholesale Nursery; Distributor of Plants, Vegetables, Herbs, Shrubs & Christmas Trees
N.A.I.C.S.: 111422
Rodney Omps (CFO)
Michael F. Vukelich Jr. (Co-Founder, Chm & CEO)

Subsidiaries:

Color Spot Nursery, Inc. - Carson Facility   (1)
321 W Sepulveda Blvd, Carson, CA 90745
Tel.: (310) 549-7470
Plant Cultivation Services
N.A.I.C.S.: 111421

Color Spot Nursery, Inc. - Chino Valley Facility   (1)
1670 E Perkinsville Rd, Chino Valley, AZ 86323
Tel.: (928) 227-1086
Plant Cultivation Services
N.A.I.C.S.: 111421

Color Spot Nursery, Inc. - Huntsville Facility   (1)
16 Wire Rd, Huntsville, TX 77320
Tel.: (936) 291-8411
Plant Cultivation Services
N.A.I.C.S.: 111421

Color Spot Nursery, Inc. - Katy Facility   (1)
11015 FM 359, Richmond, TX 77320
Tel.: (832) 757-1300
Plant Cultivation Services
N.A.I.C.S.: 111421

Color Spot Nursery, Inc. - Lodi Facility   (1)
5400 E Harney Ln, Lodi, CA 95240
Tel.: (209) 333-0235
Plant Cultivation Services
N.A.I.C.S.: 111421

Color Spot Nursery, Inc. - Salinas Facility   (1)
420 Espinosa Rd, Salinas, CA 93907
Tel.: (831) 449-2416
Web Site: http://www.colorspot.com
Emp.: 200
Plant Cultivation Services
N.A.I.C.S.: 111421

Color Spot Nursery, Inc. - San Antonio Facility   (1)
7960 Cagnon Rd, San Antonio, TX 78252-2202
Tel.: (210) 258-3600
Plant Cultivation Services
N.A.I.C.S.: 111421

Color Spot Nursery, Inc. - San Juan Capistrano Facility   (1)
31101 Ortega Hwy, San Juan Capistrano, CA 92675
Tel.: (949) 625-1400
Web Site: http://www.colorspot.com
Emp.: 140
Plant Cultivation Services
N.A.I.C.S.: 111421
David Hernandez (Gen Mgr)

Color Spot Nursery, Inc. - Troup Facility   (1)
15255 State Hwy 110N, Troup, TX 75789
Tel.: (903) 266-1106
Plant Cultivation Services
N.A.I.C.S.: 111421

Color Spot Nursery, Inc. - Waco Facility   (1)
2901 S 12th St, Waco, TX 76703
Tel.: (254) 752-2241
Plant Cultivation Services
N.A.I.C.S.: 111421

Color Spot Nursery, Inc. - Walnut Springs Facility   (1)
260 County Rd 2710, Walnut Springs, TX 76690
Tel.: (254) 523-0165
Plant Cultivation Services
N.A.I.C.S.: 111421

COLOR WHEEL PAINT MANU-FACTURING CO. INC.

2814 Silver Star Rd, Orlando, FL 32808
Tel.: (407) 293-6810   FL
Web Site: http://www.colorwheel.com
Year Founded: 1960
Sales Range: $25-49.9 Million
Emp.: 230
Paints & Allied Products Mfr & Distr
N.A.I.C.S.: 325510

COLOR-AD, INC.
7200 Gary Rd, Manassas, VA 20109
Tel.: (703) 369-3330
Web Site: https://www.color-ad.com
Sales Range: $1-9.9 Million
Emp.: 62
Sign Mfr
N.A.I.C.S.: 339950
Dave Velke (Founder)
Dawn Bures (Pres)

COLORADANS FOR RESPON-SIBLE ENERGY DEVELOP-MENT
1099 18th St Ste 1800, Denver, CO 80202
Tel.: (720) 929-6018   CO
Web Site: http://www.cred.org
Year Founded: 2013
Sales Range: $10-24.9 Million
Emp.: 1
Energy Development Association
N.A.I.C.S.: 813910
Ted Brown (Chm)

COLORADO BAG N' BAG-GAGE
299 Milwaukee St Ste 400, Denver, CO 80206
Tel.: (303) 292-0060
Web Site:
    http://www.coloradobaggage.com
Rev.: $10,900,003
Emp.: 10
Luggage & Leather Goods Stores
N.A.I.C.S.: 458320
Rachael Stiedemann (Dir-Mktg)

COLORADO CATTLEMEN'S ASSOCIATION
8833 Ralston Rd, Arvada, CO 80002
Tel.: (303) 431-6422
Web Site:
    https://www.coloradocattle.org
Year Founded: 1867
Beef Production
N.A.I.C.S.: 112111
Philip Anderson (Co-Pres)
Robert Farnam (Co-Pres)
Tom Harrington (First VP)
Curt Russell (Second VP)
Brett Datteri (Treas)

Subsidiaries:

Colorado Cattlemen's Agricultural Land Trust   (1)
8833 Ralston Rd, Arvada, CO 80002
Tel.: (303) 225-8677
Web Site: https://ccalt.org
Agricultural Land Conservation Services
N.A.I.C.S.: 813910
Erik Glenn (Exec Dir)
Megan Knott (Dir-Stewardship)
Anne Rogers (Controller)
Tawny Halandras (Treas & Sec)
Tom Stoever (VP)
Rye Austin (VP)
Orlando Gonzalez (VP)

COLORADO CLEANUP SER-VICES, INC.
642 W 43rd Ave, Denver, CO 80216
Tel.: (303) 237-4406
Web Site: http://www.ccsmold.com
Year Founded: 2004
Emp.: 25
Cleaning Service

N.A.I.C.S.: 561740
Jim Minter (Mgr-Mktg)
Scherry Bumpus (Office Mgr)
Ben Davis (Project Mgr)

COLORADO COMMODITY TRADERS
1826 1st Ave, Greeley, CO 80631
Tel.: (970) 352-0593
Sales Range: $25-49.9 Million
Emp.: 6
Grain Merchandising
N.A.I.C.S.: 424510
Mike Seyler (Pres)

COLORADO DENTAL SER-VICE, INC.
4582 S Ulster St Ste 800, Denver, CO 80237
Tel.: (303) 741-9300   CO
Web Site:
    http://www.deltadentalco.com
Year Founded: 1958
Sales Range: $250-299.9 Million
Emp.: 126
Oral Health Services
N.A.I.C.S.: 623990
Linda Arneson (COO & VP)

COLORADO DRYWALL SUP-PLY LLC
4760 N Holly St, Denver, CO 80216
Tel.: (303) 297-0401
Web Site:
    http://www.coloradodrywall.com
Sales Range: $10-24.9 Million
Emp.: 30
Workers Compensation Insurance
N.A.I.C.S.: 423320
Ed Sleeman (Owner & Pres)
Dennis Trujillo (Mgr-Sls-Specialties & Fasteners)
Tom Hejl (Controller)

COLORADO FARM BUREAU MUTUAL INSURANCE CO.
9177 E Mineral Cir, Englewood, CO 80112
Tel.: (303) 749-7500   CO
Web Site: http://www.cfbmic.com
Year Founded: 1950
Sales Range: $125-149.9 Million
Emp.: 230
Property & Casualty Insurance Products & Services
N.A.I.C.S.: 524126
Art Wallace (Mgr-Claims)
Keating Jerry (VP-Claims)

Subsidiaries:

Farm Bureau Insurance Agency of Colorado, Inc.   (1)
9177 E Mineral Cir, Englewood, CO 80112-3494
Tel.: (303) 749-7500
Web Site: http://www.cfbmic.com
Sales Range: $25-49.9 Million
Emp.: 50
Insurance Agents
N.A.I.C.S.: 524210
Jack Anderson (Pres)

COLORADO FEDERAL SAV-INGS BANK
8400 E Prentice Ave Ste 545, Greenwood Village, CO 80111
Tel.: (303) 793-3555
Web Site:
    http://www.coloradofederalbank.com
Rev.: $170,000,000
Emp.: 10
Federal Savings Bank
N.A.I.C.S.: 522180
Pat Fogerty (Exec VP)
Brad Dietz (CFO)
Sam Adams (Mgr)

Colorado Financial Management, Inc.—(Continued)

COLORADO FINANCIAL MANAGEMENT, INC.
4848 Thompson Pkwy Ste 320, Johnstown, CO 80534
Tel.: (970) 613-1392
Web Site:
https://www.colofinancial.com
Year Founded: 1991
Sales Range: $1-9.9 Million
Emp.: 30
Financial Investments Advisory Services
N.A.I.C.S.: 523999
Gary D. Premer *(Founder)*
Richard Lawrence *(Pres & CEO)*
Luke Daniel *(Partner)*
Meagan D'Angelo *(Partner)*
Brad Bickham *(Mng Partner & Chief Investment Officer)*

Subsidiaries:

Sargent Bickham Lagudis LLC **(1)**
4840 Pearl East Circle Ste 300E, Boulder, CO 80301
Tel.: (303) 443-2433
Web Site: http://colofinancial.com
Emp.: 50
Fee-Only Customized Investment Management Strategies & Financial Planning
N.A.I.C.S.: 523940
Brad Bickham *(Mng Partner)*
Richard Lawrence *(Pres & CEO)*

COLORADO FIRST CONSTRUCTION CO.
14062 Denver W Pkwy Ste 110, Lakewood, CO 80401-3121
Tel.: (303) 277-8600
Web Site: http://www.cfcc.com
Sales Range: $10-24.9 Million
Emp.: 60
Commercial & Office Building, New Construction
N.A.I.C.S.: 237210
E. J. Olbright *(CEO)*
Robert Wiese *(CFO)*
Orville Hinerman *(Exec VP)*

COLORADO FOOD PRODUCTS INC.
3600 S Yosemite St Ste 800, Denver, CO 80237
Tel.: (303) 409-8400
Web Site:
https://www.coloradofoods.com
Sales Range: $100-124.9 Million
Emp.: 15
Meat, Frozen: Packaged
N.A.I.C.S.: 424420
Kenneth Gurrentz *(Pres)*
Jim Windholtz *(Controller)*

COLORADO GOLDFIELDS INC.
10920 W Alameda Ave Ste 201, Lakewood, CO 80226
Tel.: (303) 984-5324
Web Site: http://www.cologold.com
Year Founded: 2004
Sales Range: Less than $1 Million
Emp.: 3
Gold Mining Services
N.A.I.C.S.: 212220
C. Stephen Guyer *(CFO)*
John Ferguson *(Dir-Ops)*

COLORADO HEALTH & REHAB, LLC
5980 Stetson Hills Blvd Ste 100, Colorado Springs, CO 80923
Tel.: (719) 574-3111
Web Site: http://www.strivept.net
Year Founded: 2014
Sales Range: $1-9.9 Million
Emp.: 37

Health Care Srvices
N.A.I.C.S.: 621610
Diane Baggs *(CEO)*
Mark Archambault *(VP-Ops)*

COLORADO INCOME HOLDINGS INC.
7899 S Lincoln Ct Ste 205, Littleton, CO 80122
Tel.: (303) 539-3000
Sales Range: Less than $1 Million
Real Estate Financial Lending
N.A.I.C.S.: 522310
Michael Bonn *(CEO & CFO)*

COLORADO LEGAL SERVICES
1905 Sherman St Ste 400, Denver, CO 80203
Tel.: (303) 837-1313
Web Site:
https://www.coloradolegalservices.org
Year Founded: 1942
Sales Range: $10-24.9 Million
Emp.: 120
Law firm
N.A.I.C.S.: 541110
Tina Smith *(Vice Chm)*
MacKenzie O'Shea *(Sec)*
Larry Gaddis *(Treas)*
Alan C. Stine *(Chm)*

COLORADO MECHANICAL SERVICES, LLC
7094 S Revere Pkwy, Centennial, CO 80112
Tel.: (720) 535-9789
Web Site:
http://www.coloradomech.com
Construction & Maintenance Services
N.A.I.C.S.: 423390
Joshuah F. Skinner *(Pres)*

Subsidiaries:

Ami Mechanical, Inc. **(1)**
12141 Pennsylvania St, Thornton, CO 80241
Tel.: (303) 280-1401
Web Site: http://www.amimechanical.com
Rev.: $7,500,000
Emp.: 69
Site Preparation Contractor
N.A.I.C.S.: 238910
Manuel Gonzales *(CEO)*

COLORADO MUSEUM OF NATURAL HISTORY
2001 Colorado Blvd, Denver, CO 80205
Tel.: (303) 370-6000
Web Site: https://www.dmns.org
Year Founded: 1900
Sales Range: $25-49.9 Million
Emp.: 587
Museums
N.A.I.C.S.: 712110
Mary Hacking *(VP-Visitor Experience)*
George Sparks *(Pres & CEO)*
Montgomery C. Cleworth *(Chm)*
Serena Bruzgo *(VP-Dev)*
Nancy Walsh *(VP-Partnerships & Programs)*

COLORADO NONPROFIT DEVELOPMENT CENTER
789 Sherman St Ste 250, Denver, CO 80203
Tel.: (720) 855-0501
Web Site: https://www.cndc.org
Year Founded: 1998
Sales Range: $10-24.9 Million
Emp.: 280
Community Development Services
N.A.I.C.S.: 624190

Kevin Van Vleet *(CFO)*
Monica Frimml *(Mgr-AP, AR & Payroll)*
Laurie Anderson *(Chm)*
Carol Bush *(Treas)*
Karen Tomb *(Sec)*
Rich Martinez *(Pres & CEO)*

COLORADO OUTDOOR RETAIL GROUP
1545 Pearl St, Boulder, CO 80302
Tel.: (303) 442-7616
Web Site:
http://www.boulderarmystore.com
Rev.: $10,424,118
Emp.: 14
Army-Navy Goods Stores
N.A.I.C.S.: 455219
Shannon Long *(Owner)*

COLORADO PETROLEUM PRODUCTS CO.
5590 High St, Denver, CO 80216
Tel.: (303) 294-0302
Web Site: https://www.colopetro.com
Rev.: $27,375,262
Emp.: 33
Diesel Fuel
N.A.I.C.S.: 424720
Clark Thompson *(Pres)*

COLORADO PRIME FOODS LLC
500 Bi County Blvd Ste 400, Farmingdale, NY 11735-3996
Tel.: (631) 694-1111
Web Site:
http://www.reordermenu.com
Year Founded: 1959
Sales Range: Less than $1 Million
Emp.: 15
Home Food Service Company
N.A.I.C.S.: 445298
Paul Roman *(CEO)*

COLORADO RIVER FORD LINCOLN-MERCURY
3601 Stockton Hill Rd, Kingman, AZ 86409
Tel.: (928) 757-3131
Web Site:
http://www.coloradoriverford.com
Year Founded: 1995
Sales Range: $50-74.9 Million
Emp.: 55
Car Whslr
N.A.I.C.S.: 441110
Buford B. Wiley *(Owner)*

COLORADO ROCKIES BASEBALL CLUB, LTD.
Coors Field 2001 Blake St, Denver, CO 80205-2000
Tel.: (303) 292-0200
Web Site: http://www.rockies.com
Year Founded: 1993
Sales Range: $25-49.9 Million
Emp.: 120
Professional Baseball Club
N.A.I.C.S.: 711211
Gregory D. Feasel *(COO & Exec VP)*
Kevin H. Kahn *(Chief Customer Officer & VP-Ballpark Ops)*
Michael J. Kent *(VP-Fin)*
William E. Schmidt *(VP-Scouting)*
Elizabeth E. Stecklein *(VP-HR)*
Gary Lawrence *(Sr Dir-Pur)*
James P. Kellogg *(VP-Community & Retail Ops)*
Aaron Heinrich *(Dir-Retail Ops)*
Steven Burke *(Sr Dir-Guest Svcs)*
Randy Carlill *(Dir-Engrg)*
Dan Olsen *(Dir-Facilities)*
Phil Emerson *(Sr Dir-Acctg)*
Kevin Flood *(Asst Dir-Ticket Ops)*

Albert Valdes *(Sr Dir-Food Svc Ops & Dev)*
Greg Sexton *(Dir-Security)*
Scott Magennis *(Mgr-Audio & Video)*
Dallas Davis *(Asst Dir-Community Affairs)*
Antigone Vigil *(Mgr-Community Affairs)*
Richard L. Monfort *(Co-Owner, Chm & CEO)*
Dick Mon *(Owner, Chm & CEO)*

COLORADO SERUM CO.
4950 York St, Denver, CO 80216-2246
Tel.: (303) 295-7527
Web Site: http://www.colorado-serum.com
Year Founded: 1923
Sales Range: $75-99.9 Million
Emp.: 100
Mfr of Anti Serums, Vaccines, Laboratory Reagents, Animal Blood Products & Serums, Veterinary Serums, Biologicals; Producer of Veterinary, Dental & Surgical Instruments
N.A.I.C.S.: 325414
Ed Lehigh *(VP-Mktg)*

Subsidiaries:

Professional Biological Company **(1)**
4950 York St, Denver, CO 80216
Tel.: (303) 295-7527
Biological Product Mfr
N.A.I.C.S.: 325414

COLORADO SPRINGS COCA COLA BOTTLING
1075 Vapor Trl, Colorado Springs, CO 80916-2751
Tel.: (719) 633-2653
Sales Range: $10-24.9 Million
Emp.: 100
Soft Drinks Mfr
N.A.I.C.S.: 312111
Kristina Woods *(Mgr-IT)*
Joe Paladino *(Supvr-Fin)*

COLORADO SPRINGS UTILITIES, INC.
111 S Cascade Ave, Colorado Springs, CO 80903
Tel.: (719) 448-4800
Web Site: https://www.csu.org
Year Founded: 1925
Sales Range: $800-899.9 Million
Emp.: 2,000
Utility Services
N.A.I.C.S.: 221118

Subsidiaries:

Young Gas Storage Company **(1)**
2 N Nevada Ave, Colorado Springs, CO 80903-1715
Tel.: (719) 473-2300
Web Site: http://www.kindermorgan.com
Sales Range: $10-24.9 Million
Emp.: 20
Natural Gas Storage & Pipeline Transporation
N.A.I.C.S.: 486210
Kimberly Allen Dang *(Pres)*
Richard D. Kinder *(Chm)*
Steven L. Kean *(CEO)*
Adam Forman *(Sec & VP)*
Anthony B. Ashley *(Treas & VP-IR)*
David P. Michels *(CFO & VP)*
Dax A. Sanders *(Chief Strategy Officer & Exec VP)*
James Holland *(Pres-Products Pipelines)*
Jesse Arenivas *(Officer-Ops)*
John W. Schlosser *(Pres-Terminals)*
Jordan H. Mintz *(Chief Tax Officer & VP)*
Mark Huse *(CIO & VP)*
Tom Martin *(Pres-Natural Gas Pipelines)*

COLORADO STRUCTURES INC.

540 Elkton Dr Ste 202, Colorado Springs, CO 80907-8503
Tel.: (719) 522-0500   CO
Web Site: https://www.csigc.com
Year Founded: 1989
Sales Range: $10-24.9 Million
Emp.: 75
Nonresidential Construction
N.A.I.C.S.: 236220
Timothy J. Phelan *(Co-Owner & CEO)*
Rob Oldach *(Co-Owner)*

COLORADO SWEET GOLD LLC
8714 State Hwy 60, Johnstown, CO 80534
Tel.: (970) 587-6535
Year Founded: 1926
Sales Range: $10-24.9 Million
Emp.: 55
Producer of Corn Starch for the Brewing, Food & Paper Industries
N.A.I.C.S.: 311221

COLORADO SYMPHONY ASSOCIATION INC.
1000 14th St No 15, Denver, CO 80202-2333
Tel.: (303) 623-7876
Web Site:
    https://www.coloradosymphony.org
Rev.: $9,000,000
Emp.: 110
Symphony Orchestra
N.A.I.C.S.: 711130
Larry Brezicka *(Mgr-Orchestra Personnel)*
Doug Yost *(Dir-Info Svcs)*

COLORADO-WEST EQUIPMENT INC.
7920 E 88th Ave, Henderson, CO 80640
Tel.: (303) 288-1300
Web Site: https://www.cowest.net
Sales Range: $10-24.9 Million
Emp.: 9
Bus Mfr
N.A.I.C.S.: 423110
O. B. Begley *(Pres)*
Pat Carroll *(Controller)*
Jeff Koza *(Owner)*

COLOREP, INC.
9119 Milliken Ave, Rancho Cucamonga, CA 91730
Tel.: (909) 484-2855
Web Site: http://www.colorep.com
Digital Color Printing Products & Services
N.A.I.C.S.: 323111
Larry Levy *(CEO)*

Subsidiaries:

Transprint USA, Inc.   (1)
1000 Pleasant Vly Rd, Harrisonburg, VA 22801-9790
Tel.: (540) 433-9101
Web Site: http://www.airdyesolutions.com
Sales Range: $10-24.9 Million
Emp.: 105
Commercial Printing & Gravure Services
N.A.I.C.S.: 323111
Evan R. Smith *(CEO)*

COLORESCIENCE, INC.
2141 Palomar Airport Rd Ste 200, Carlsbad, CA 92011-4226   DE
Web Site:
    https://www.colorescience.com
Year Founded: 2002
Cosmetics Developer, Mfr & Distr
N.A.I.C.S.: 325620
Mary M. Fisher *(CEO)*
Theodore Ebel *(Chief Bus Officer)*
Steve P. Loomis *(CFO & COO)*

COLORPLAY STUDIO
PO Box 5855, Eugene, OR 97405
Tel.: (541) 687-8262   OR
Web Site:
    http://www.garyschubert.com
Year Founded: 1976
Sales Range: Less than $1 Million
Emp.: 1
Advetising Agency
N.A.I.C.S.: 541810
Gary J. Schubert *(Pres)*
Gwendoline M. Schubert *(Exec VP & Acct Supvr)*

COLORS FOR PLASTICS INC.
2245 Pratt Blvd, Elk Grove Village, IL 60007
Tel.: (847) 437-0033
Web Site:
    https://www.colorsforplastics.com
Year Founded: 1972
Sales Range: $10-24.9 Million
Emp.: 75
Inorganic Pigments
N.A.I.C.S.: 325130
John Dalleska *(Pres)*
Mary Stankowitz *(Mgr-HR)*
Cindy Verity *(VP-Sls)*

COLORSPEC COATINGS INTERNATIONAL
1716 Church St, Holbrook, NY 11741
Tel.: (631) 472-8251
Web Site:
    http://www.colorspeccoatings.com
Year Founded: 2001
Rev.: $2,900,000
Emp.: 10
Wood Preservation
N.A.I.C.S.: 321114
Lisa Bancalari *(Pres)*

COLORTONE AUDIO VISUAL STAGING & RENTALS, INC.
5401 Naiman Pkwy, Cleveland, OH 44139
Tel.: (440) 914-9500
Web Site: http://www.colortone.com
Sales Range: $1-9.9 Million
Emp.: 23
Audio-Visual Equipment & Supply Rental
N.A.I.C.S.: 532289
Robert E. Leon *(Owner & Pres)*
Karen Leon *(VP)*
Andrew Kramer *(Dir-Production)*
Rob Mier *(Dir-Sls)*

COLORVISION INTERNATIONAL, INC.
2400 Lake Orange Dr Ste 200, Orlando, FL 32837
Tel.: (407) 851-0103
Web Site:
    https://www.amazingpictures.com
Year Founded: 1977
Sales Range: $10-24.9 Million
Emp.: 350
Photographic Services
N.A.I.C.S.: 541922
Bryan Wilkins *(VP-Software Dev)*
Mark Simmons *(Pres & CEO)*
Henry Tyson *(Exec VP)*

COLORWARE INC.
2050 W 4th St, Winona, MN 55987
Tel.: (507) 474-6567
Web Site:
    http://www.colorwarepc.com
Year Founded: 2000
Sales Range: $1-9.9 Million
Emp.: 50
Custom Colored & Engraved Versions of Computers, Portable Electronics & Home Entertainment Systems

Justin Cisewski *(CEO)*

COLOURS INC.
50 Dana St, Wilkes Barre, PA 18702
Tel.: (570) 208-5655
Web Site: http://www.gocolours.com
Rev.: $10,900,000
Emp.: 14
Automotive Paints, Coatings & Accessories Distr
N.A.I.C.S.: 424950
Marty Hill *(Mgr)*
Brian Marcks *(VP)*
Jeff Kahler *(Acct Mgr-Automotive, Fleet & Indus Coatings)*

COLOVOS COMPANY
4444 W Ohio St, Chicago, IL 60624-1036
Tel.: (773) 533-4444
Sales Range: $10-24.9 Million
Emp.: 50
Work Tools Importer & Whslr
N.A.I.C.S.: 333517
Marc Levitt *(Pres)*
Mirna Figueroa *(Supvr-Ops)*

Subsidiaries:

Palmgren Steel Products, Inc.   (1)
4444 Ohio St, Chicago, IL 60624
Tel.: (773) 265-5700
Web Site: http://www.palmgren.com
Sales Range: $10-24.9 Million
Emp.: 26
Machine Vises, Milling Attachments & Tables, Rotary Tables, Cable Connectors & Weld Stands Mfr
N.A.I.C.S.: 333515

COLQUITT ELECTRIC MEMBERSHIP CORPORATION
15 Rowland Dr, Moultrie, GA 31768-4169
Tel.: (229) 985-3620   GA
Web Site:
    http://www.colquittmc.com
Year Founded: 1936
Sales Range: $25-49.9 Million
Emp.: 165
Electric Services
N.A.I.C.S.: 221151
James H. Griner *(Pres)*
Wanda Moore *(Supvr-District Office)*
Lawrence Lott *(Engr-Plng)*

COLSA CORPORATION
6728 Odyssey Dr, Huntsville, AL 35806-3302
Tel.: (256) 964-5555   DE
Web Site: https://www.colsa.com
Year Founded: 1980
Sales Range: $25-49.9 Million
Emp.: 900
Information Technology; Software Integration & Software & Hardware Engineering Services
N.A.I.C.S.: 541512
Joe Anderson *(VP-North Florida Ops)*
Frank J. Collazo *(Chm & CEO)*
Barry Gosnell *(COO & Exec VP)*
Cathy Dickens *(VP-Bus Mgmt)*
Jamie Combs *(VP-Advanced Res Center)*
Jim Hunter *(VP-Federal Svcs & Solutions)*
Mike Ledbetter *(VP-Cyber Programs)*
Richard Amos *(Pres)*
Robert Kincade *(Chief Growth Officer & Exec VP)*

COLSKY MEDIA
2740 Van Ness Ave Ste 220, San Francisco, CA 94109-0216
Tel.: (415) 673-5400   CA
Web Site:
    http://www.colskymedia.com

Year Founded: 1973
Sales Range: $25-49.9 Million
Emp.: 9
Media Buying Services
N.A.I.C.S.: 541810
Richard A. Colsky *(Pres & CEO)*

COLSON & COLSON GENERAL CONTRACTORS
2260 McGilchrist St SE, Salem, OR 97302
Tel.: (503) 586-7401
Web Site: http://www.colson-colson.com
Sales Range: $125-149.9 Million
Emp.: 30
Residential Construction
N.A.I.C.S.: 236115
William E. Colson *(Founder)*

COLSON ASSOCIATES, INC.
1 N Franklin St Ste 2400, Chicago, IL 60606
Tel.: (312) 980-1100
Web Site:
    https://www.colsonassociates.com
Sales Range: $700-749.9 Million
Emp.: 2,000
Casters & Medical Devices
N.A.I.C.S.: 332510
Louhon Tucker *(Pres & CEO)*

COLT ATLANTIC SERVICES, INC.
4135 Industry Way, Flowery Branch, GA 30542
Tel.: (770) 965-1000
Web Site: http://www.colt.us.com
Sales Range: $10-24.9 Million
Emp.: 52
Commercial & Industrial Machinery & Equipment Distr
N.A.I.C.S.: 811310
Terence H. M. Barford *(CEO)*
John W. Clark *(CFO & Sec)*

COLT DEFENSE LLC
547 New Park Ave, West Hartford, CT 06110
Tel.: (860) 232-4489   DE
Web Site: http://www.colt.com
Year Founded: 2002
Small Arms & Weapon System Services
N.A.I.C.S.: 332992
Kenneth Juergens *(Sr VP-Govt & Military Programs)*
Ronald Belcourt *(Sr VP-Ops)*

Subsidiaries:

Colt's Manufacturing Company, Inc.   (1)
PO Box 1868, Hartford, CT 06144-1868
Tel.: (860) 236-6311
Web Site: http://www.coltsmfg.com
Sales Range: $100-124.9 Million
Emp.: 125
Firearms Mfr
N.A.I.C.S.: 332994
William M. Keys *(Pres & CEO)*
Mark Redl *(Mgr-Product)*
Paul Spitale *(Sr VP-Comml Bus)*
Richard Harris *(Interim CFO)*

COLT PRINT SERVICES, INC.
2525 Frontier Ave, Boulder, CO 80301
Tel.: (303) 449-2760   CO
Web Site: http://www.coltprint.com
Year Founded: 1995
Commercial Printing Services
N.A.I.C.S.: 323111

Colt Print Services, Inc.—(Continued)

John Albertson (Pres)
Jean-Michel Bertrand (Pres)

COLT REFINING INC.
12A Star Dr, Merrimack, NH 03054
Tel.: (603) 429-9966
Web Site:
https://www.coltrefining.com
Sales Range: $10-24.9 Million
Emp.: 40
Precious Metals
N.A.I.C.S.: 331410
Harvey Gottlieb (Pres)
Mitch Coughlin (VP-Refining)
Jim Maher (VP)
Joe Meuse (Controller)
Ron Coste (Dir-Refining Svcs)
Bill Dorazio (Dir-Metals Processing)
Steve Snyder (Mgr-Security)
John Cianciarulo (Gen Mgr)

COLTALA HOLDINGS, LLC
640 Taylor St Ste 2550, Fort Worth, TX 76102
Tel.: (817) 546-4600
Web Site: http://www.coltala.com
Year Founded: 2017
Holding Company
N.A.I.C.S.: 551112
Melanie Barton (Exec VP)

Subsidiaries:

Choice Health at Home, LLC   (1)
6760 Old Jacksonville Hwy Ste 106, Tyler, TX 75703
Tel.: (855) 485-8273
Web Site: https://choicehealthathome.com
Women Healthcare Services
N.A.I.C.S.: 621610
David Jackson (Founder & CEO)
Oliver Fultz (Reg VP-Ops)

Subsidiary (Domestic):

Instant Care of Arizona LLC   (2)
2310 W Bell Rd 1, Phoenix, AZ 85023
Tel.: (602) 993-0297
Rev.: $3,240,000
Emp.: 60
Women Healthcare Services
N.A.I.C.S.: 621610

Trudela Partners LLC   (1)
8900 John Carpenter Fwy, Dallas, TX 75247
Tel.: (561) 213-2061
Web Site: http://www.trudela.com
Home Repairs & Maintenance Services
N.A.I.C.S.: 811411
Paul S.A Adams (CEO)

Subsidiary (Domestic):

Big Bear A/C & Heating, LLC   (2)
228 E 700 N, Centerville, UT 84014-1913
Tel.: (972) 998-9990
Web Site: http://www.bigbearair.com
Plumbing, Heating & Air-Conditioning Contractors
N.A.I.C.S.: 238220
Hubert Hendriks (Owner)

COLTEC ENGINEERING, INC.
12169 SW 131st Ave, Miami, FL 33186
Tel.: (305) 256-0046
Web Site:
http://www.coltecengineering.com
Rev.: $25,800,000
Emp.: 25
Plumbing Heating & Air-Conditioning Contractors
N.A.I.C.S.: 238220
Lorenzo Fernandez (Pres)

COLTER & PETERSON INC.
418 E 16th St, Paterson, NJ 07514
Tel.: (973) 684-0901
Web Site: http://www.colter-peterson.com

Sales Range: $10-24.9 Million
Emp.: 45
Provider of Paper Industries Machinery Services
N.A.I.C.S.: 531210
Bruce Peterson (Pres & CEO)
Eric Peterson (Exec VP-Svcs)
Don Shields (Exec VP-Tech Support)
Vince Payne (VP-West Central)

Subsidiaries:

C&P Microsystems, LLC   (1)
1260 Holm Rd Ste C, Petaluma, CA 94954
Tel.: (707) 776-4500
Web Site: http://www.microcutsystems.com
Paper Cutter Mfr & Distr
N.A.I.C.S.: 339940

Tri-State Grinding   (1)
3 S Gold Dr, Robbinsville, NJ 08691
Tel.: (609) 890-4989
Web Site: http://www.tristateknife.com
Sales Range: $10-24.9 Million
Emp.: 15
Commercial & Industrial Grinding & Precision Services
N.A.I.C.S.: 811310
Scott Peterson (Pres)

COLTON REAL ESTATE GROUP INC.
515 N Cabrillo Park Dr, Santa Ana, CA 92701
Tel.: (949) 475-4200   CA
Web Site:
http://www.coltoncompany.com
Year Founded: 1959
Sales Range: $50-74.9 Million
Emp.: 65
Property Management Services
N.A.I.C.S.: 531190
John Mcclintock (CFO)
David Colton (Pres)

COLTON'S RESTAURANT GROUP, INC.
5 Shackleford Plz Ste 200, Little Rock, AR 72211
Tel.: (501) 978-7490   AR
Rev.: $10,900,000
Emp.: 260
Eating Place
N.A.I.C.S.: 722511
Joe Marqui (Adv Dir)

COLUMBIA ARTISTS MANAGEMENT LLC
5 Columbus Cir 1790 Broadway, New York, NY 10019-1412
Tel.: (212) 841-9500
Web Site: http://www.cami.com
Year Founded: 1930
Rev.: $20,000,000
Emp.: 100
Entertainer Management Agency
N.A.I.C.S.: 711410
Tim Fox (CN)
R. Douglas Sheldon (Sr VP)
Andrew S. Grossman (Sr VP)

COLUMBIA BASIN PIZZA HUT INC.
1101 Summitview Ave, Yakima, WA 98902
Tel.: (509) 452-6329
Sales Range: $10-24.9 Million
Emp.: 600
Pizza Hut Chain
N.A.I.C.S.: 722513
Jerry Miller (CEO)

COLUMBIA CAPITAL MANAGEMENT
6700 Antioch Rd. Ste 250, Merriam, KS 66204
Tel.: (913) 248-8500

Web Site:
http://www.columbiacapital.com
Rev.: $2,490,000
Emp.: 6
Financial Advice
N.A.I.C.S.: 522320
Dennis Lloyd (Pres)

COLUMBIA CAPITAL, LLC
204 S Union St, Alexandria, VA 22314
Tel.: (703) 519-2000
Web Site: http://www.colcap.com
Year Founded: 1989
Sales Range: $25-49.9 Million
Emp.: 28
Venture Capital Firm
N.A.I.C.S.: 523999
Ross W. Manire (Operating Partner)
Mark J. Kington (Founder)
Jim Fleming (Partner)
Arun Gupta (Partner)
Jeff Patterson (Partner)
Jason Booma (Partner)
Monish Kundra (Partner)
Rodney Rogers (Venture Partner)
Don Doering (Partner)
Patrick Hendy (Partner)
John Siegel (Partner)
Cheryl Ghadban (Mgr-Tax)
Evan DeCorte (Principal)
Ben Lewis (CFO)

COLUMBIA CARE SERVICE, INC
3587 Heathrow Way, Medford, OR 97504
Tel.: (541) 858-8170   OR
Web Site:
https://www.columbiacare.org
Year Founded: 2004
Sales Range: $10-24.9 Million
Emp.: 313
Residential Health Care Services
N.A.I.C.S.: 623990
Ginger Swan (Vice Chm)
Jean Work (Chm)

COLUMBIA CASCADE COMPANY
1300 SW 6th Ave Ste 310, Portland, OR 97201
Tel.: (503) 223-1157
Web Site: http://www.timberform.com
Rev.: $10,200,000
Emp.: 35
Mfr of Playground Equipment
N.A.I.C.S.: 339920
S. Kenneth Kirn (Pres)

COLUMBIA CORRUGATED BOX CO.
12777 SW Tualatin Sherwood Rd, Tualatin, OR 97062
Tel.: (503) 692-3344
Web Site: https://www.ccbox.com
Year Founded: 1967
Rev.: $25,000,000
Emp.: 300
Mfr of Corrugated Boxes
N.A.I.C.S.: 322211
Marvin L. Lince (Pres)
Jerry Anderson (Controller)
James G. Tanner (Sec & VP)

COLUMBIA CURB & GUTTER CO.
4105 I-70 Dr SE, Columbia, MO 65201-6701
Tel.: (573) 474-6186
Web Site:
https://www.ccgmissouri.com
Year Founded: 1968
Sales Range: $10-24.9 Million
Emp.: 75

Provider of Heavy Highway Contracting Services
N.A.I.C.S.: 237310
Terry Duncan (Mgr)

COLUMBIA DEVELOPMENT COMPANIES
302 Washington Avenue Ext, Albany, NY 12203
Tel.: (518) 862-9133
Web Site:
https://www.columbiadev.com
Year Founded: 1988
Commercial Real Estate Development & Construction Services
N.A.I.C.S.: 236220
Joseph R. Nicolla (Pres)
Richard A. Rosen (Partner & VP)

COLUMBIA DISTRIBUTING INC.
255 Appleyard Dr, Wenatchee, WA 98801
Tel.: (509) 662-1673
Web Site:
https://www.columbiadistr.com
Rev.: $11,500,000
Emp.: 50
Beer & Other Fermented Malt Liquors
N.A.I.C.S.: 424810
Brad Selland (Chm, Pres & CEO)
Tommie Thompson (Owner & Gen Mgr)

COLUMBIA FOREST PRODUCTS INC.
7900 McCloud Dr Ste 200, Greensboro, NC 27409
Tel.: (503) 224-5300   OR
Web Site:
http://www.columbiaforestprod.com
Year Founded: 1976
Sales Range: $1-4.9 Billion
Emp.: 4,000
Hardwood Veneer & Plywood Products Mfr
N.A.I.C.S.: 321211
Steve Pung (VP-Tech)
Greg Pray (Exec VP)

Subsidiaries:

Columbia Forest Products   (1)
225 Prince Street, Hearst, P0L 1N0, ON, Canada   (100%)
Tel.: (705) 362-4242
Sales Range: $25-49.9 Million
Emp.: 200
Hardwood Veneer & Plywood
N.A.I.C.S.: 321211
Chantal Chabot (Controller)

Columbia Forest Products Corporation   (1)
222 SW Columbia St, Portland, OR 97201-6600   (100%)
Tel.: (503) 224-5300
Web Site:
http://www.columbiaforestproducts.com
Sales Range: $10-24.9 Million
Emp.: 50
Hardwood Veneer & Plywood
N.A.I.C.S.: 321211

Columbia Plywood Corporation   (1)
4949 South Hwy 97, Klamath Falls, OR 97603
Tel.: (503) 224-5300
Sales Range: $10-24.9 Million
Emp.: 50
Hardwood Veneer & Plywood
N.A.I.C.S.: 321211

Columbia West Virginia Corporation   (1)
222 SW Columbia St, Portland, OR 97201-6600
Tel.: (503) 224-5300
Sales Range: $10-24.9 Million
Emp.: 70
Burls, Wood
N.A.I.C.S.: 113310

COLUMBIA INSURANCE GROUP, INC.
2102 White Gate Dr, Columbia, MO 65202
Tel.: (573) 474-6193　　　　　MO
Web Site: http://www.colinsgrp.com
Year Founded: 1941
Rev.: $65,369,329
Emp.: 270
Commercial Property & Casualty Insurance
N.A.I.C.S.: 524126
Gary Thompson *(Pres & CEO)*
Michael LeBlanc *(Mgr-Georgia Branch Claims)*
Claire Owen *(Gen Counsel & VP)*

Subsidiaries:

Association Casualty Insurance Company　　　　　(1)
3420 Executive Center Dr Ste 200, Austin, TX 78731-9728　　(100%)
Tel.: (512) 345-7500
Web Site:
　http://www.insuranceproviders.com
Sales Range: $1-9.9 Million
Emp.: 25
Life & Casualty Insurance
N.A.I.C.S.: 524210

Columbia Insurance Group Inc.　(1)
4370 Peachtree Rd NE, Atlanta, GA 30319-3054
Tel.: (404) 442-1100
Sales Range: $75-99.9 Million
Emp.: 200
Property, Casualty & Specialty Insurance Services
N.A.I.C.S.: 524126

Columbia Insurance Group Inc.　(1)
2102 Whitegate Dr, Columbia, MO 65202-2335
Tel.: (573) 474-6193
Sales Range: $25-49.9 Million
Emp.: 175
Insurance Agents, Brokers & Services
N.A.I.C.S.: 561499
Gary Thompson *(Pres)*

Columbia National Insurance Co. Inc.　　　　　(1)
10820 Harney St, Omaha, NE 68154-2638　　　(100%)
Tel.: (402) 330-5600
Web Site: http://www.colinsgrp.com
Sales Range: $50-74.9 Million
Emp.: 160
Fire, Marine & Casualty Insurance Services
N.A.I.C.S.: 524126
Gary Thompson *(Pres & CEO)*

COLUMBIA MACHINE INC.
107 Grand Blvd, Vancouver, WA 98661-7728
Tel.: (360) 694-1501　　　　　WV
Web Site:
　https://www.columbiamachine.com
Year Founded: 1937
Sales Range: $50-74.9 Million
Emp.: 525
Special Industry Machinery Mfr
N.A.I.C.S.: 333248
Rick Goode *(Pres)*

COLUMBIA MANAGEMENT INVESTMENT ADVISORS, LLC
225 Franklin St, Boston, MA 02110
Tel.: (612) 671-3452　　　　　MN
Web Site: http://www.columbiathread needleus.com
Year Founded: 1972
Sales Range: $75-99.9 Million
Emp.: 2,000
Investment Services
N.A.I.C.S.: 523999
Colin Moore *(Chief Investment Officer-Global)*
William Frederick Truscott *(Chm & Pres)*

COLUMBIA MEMORIAL HOSPITAL
71 Prospect Ave, Hudson, NY 12534
Tel.: (518) 828-7601　　　　　NY
Web Site:
　https://www.columbiamemorial
　health.org
Year Founded: 1889
Emp.: 1,682
Health Care Srvices
N.A.I.C.S.: 622110
Donald E. Gibson *(Treas)*
Lawrence Perl *(Chief Medical Officer)*
Hila Richardson *(Sec)*
Nicole Williams *(COO)*

COLUMBIA NATIONAL GROUP INC
6600 Grant Ave, Cleveland, OH 44105
Tel.: (216) 883-4972　　　　　OH
Web Site: http://www.univsteel.com
Year Founded: 1984
Sales Range: $75-99.9 Million
Emp.: 50
Holding Company for Steel Related Business Centers
N.A.I.C.S.: 423510
David P. Miller *(Chm, Pres & CEO)*
Steve Ruscher *(CFO)*

Subsidiaries:

CR Construction Company　　(1)
6600 Grant Ave, Cleveland, OH 44105　　　　　　　(100%)
Tel.: (216) 641-0030
Web Site: http://www.crconstructionco.com
Railroad Construction
N.A.I.C.S.: 236210
Steven Estok *(Asst Gen Mgr)*

Matt Construction Services Inc.　(1)
6600 Grant Ave, Cleveland, OH 44105-5624　　　　(100%)
Tel.: (216) 883-4972
Web Site: http://www.cnggroup.com
Emp.: 10
Construction Services
N.A.I.C.S.: 236220
George Giallourakis *(Gen Mgr)*

Mercer Company　　　　　(1)
3 Logan Square 1717 Arch St Ste 1100, Philadelphia, PA 19103-2713　(51%)
Tel.: (215) 982-4600
Scrap Metal Dealers
N.A.I.C.S.: 331110

The Universal Steel Co.　　(1)
6600 Grant Ave, Cleveland, OH 44105-5624　　　　(100%)
Tel.: (216) 883-4972
Web Site: http://www.univsteel.com
Sales Range: $10-24.9 Million
Emp.: 20
Steel Mfr & Distr
N.A.I.C.S.: 332322
David P. Miller *(Chm)*

COLUMBIA NUTRITIONAL, LLC
6317 NE 131st Ave, Vancouver, WA 98682
Tel.: (360) 737-9966　　　　　WA
Web Site:
　https://www.columbianutritional.com
Year Founded: 2002
Nutritional Supplements Mfr
N.A.I.C.S.: 311999
Darla Udy *(Controller)*
Jack Rasmusson *(Mgr-Acctg)*

COLUMBIA PIPE & SUPPLY COMPANY
1120 W Pershing Rd, Chicago, IL 60609-1445
Tel.: (773) 927-6600　　　　　IL
Web Site:
　https://www.columbiapipe.com
Year Founded: 1976

Sales Range: $125-149.9 Million
Emp.: 300
Distr of Plumbing & Hydronic Heating Supplies & Industrial Fittings
N.A.I.C.S.: 423510
William D. Arenberg *(CEO)*
Tim P. Arenberg *(Pres)*
Mike Moore *(CFO & Treas)*
Donna Troy *(Sec)*

COLUMBIA POWER & WATER SYSTEMS
201 Pickens Ln, Columbia, TN 38401
Tel.: (931) 388-4833
Web Site: https://www.cpws.com
Rev.: $59,693,381
Emp.: 86
Water Supply & Irrigation Systems
N.A.I.C.S.: 221310
James R. Clark *(Mgr-Pur)*
Glenn Jernigan *(Dir-Broadband Ops)*
Modean Dale *(Sec-Engrg)*
Daryl Williamson *(Dir-Customer Svc)*
Kelley McCall *(Dir-Fin & Admin)*
Doug Burgess *(Dir-Power Ops)*
Wes Kelley *(Exec Dir)*
Holly Alsup *(Mgr-Acctg)*
Ashley Maddux *(Mgr-Acctg)*
Kathy Walker *(Sec-Engrg)*
Steve Farris *(Supvr-Warehouse)*

COLUMBIA RESIDENTIAL
1718 Peachtree St NW Ste 684, Atlanta, GA 30309
Tel.: (404) 874-5000
Web Site:
　https://www.columbiares.com
Year Founded: 1991
Sales Range: $1-9.9 Million
Emp.: 235
Multi-Family Housing Development, Construction & Management
N.A.I.C.S.: 237210
Noel Khalil *(Founder, Chm, CEO, Partner & Principal)*
James S. Grauley *(Pres & COO)*
Bill Kopec *(VP-Fin)*
Brad Barnes *(VP-Asset Mgmt)*
Clara Trejos *(VP-Tax Credit Ops)*
Ray Kuniansky *(VP-Dev Ops)*
Carolyn Carr *(VP-HR)*
Nan Maddux *(VP-Compliance)*
Robert Barfield *(VP-Construction Svcs)*
Jennifer Owens *(VP-Resident Svcs)*
Ashley Monroe *(Pres-Property Mgmt & Principal)*
Ka'Ren Sarvis *(VP-Assoc Dev)*
Malaika Taylor *(VP-Property Mgmt)*
Aaron Swain *(Pres-Property Mgmt & Ops)*

COLUMBIA RESTAURANT GROUP
2025 E 7th Ave, Tampa, FL 33605
Tel.: (813) 248-3000
Web Site:
　http://www.columbiarestaurant.com
Year Founded: 1905
Sales Range: $25-49.9 Million
Emp.: 800
Restaurant Owner & Operator
N.A.I.C.S.: 722511
Richard Gonzmart *(Pres)*
Angela Geml *(Mgr-Mktg & PR)*
John Monetti *(Gen Mgr-Sarasota)*
John Pedaggi *(Gen Mgr-Saint Augustine)*
Lee Michaud *(Gen Mgr-Clearwater Beach)*
Joseph T. Doyle *(Dir-Ops-Italian Concepts)*
Hung Pham *(Mgr-Facilities Construction & Maintenance)*
Mark Rodrigue *(Mgr-Wine & Beverage)*

Subsidiaries:

Gonzmart Family Foundation　　(1)
2025 E 7th Ave, Tampa, FL 33605
Tel.: (813) 248-3000
Web Site:
　http://www.columbiarestaurant.com
Sales Range: $10-24.9 Million
Emp.: 100
Grantmaking Foundations
N.A.I.C.S.: 813211
Richard Gonzmart *(Pres)*

COLUMBIA RIVER CARBONATES
300 N Pekin Rd, Woodland, WA 98674
Tel.: (360) 225-6505
Web Site:
　http://www.columbiarivercar
　bonates.com
Sales Range: $10-24.9 Million
Emp.: 63
Mfr of Calcium Compounds, Salts & Inorganic Chemicals
N.A.I.C.S.: 325180
Joerg A. Bleeck *(Gen Partner)*
Eric Wishart *(Mgr-Technical Sls)*
Heather Reznick *(Mgr-Transportation-Warehouse)*
Jim Renton *(Mgr-Matls)*
Nigel Cundy *(Dir-Mktg)*
Peter Mahrt *(Mgr-Maintenance)*
Michael Hammond *(Mgr-Transportation-Warehouse)*
Patrick Sypher *(Mgr-Production)*

COLUMBIA RIVER MENTAL HEALTH SERVICES
6926 NE 4th Plain Blvd, Vancouver, WA 98661
Tel.: (360) 993-3000　　　　　WA
Web Site: http://www.crmhs.org
Year Founded: 1953
Sales Range: $10-24.9 Million
Emp.: 254
Behavioral Healthcare Services
N.A.I.C.S.: 623220
Craig Pridemore *(Exec Dir)*

COLUMBIA SERVICES GROUP INC.
11306 Lilting Ln, Fairfax Station, VA 22039-1718
Tel.: (703) 207-1000
Web Site:
　http://www.columbiaservices.com
Rev.: $15,776,551
Emp.: 30
Computer Maintenance Services
N.A.I.C.S.: 541519

COLUMBIA SPECIALTY COMPANY, INC.
5875 N Obispo Ave, Long Beach, CA 90805-3715
Tel.: (562) 634-6425
Web Site:
　http://www.columbiaspecialty.com
Sales Range: $10-24.9 Million
Emp.: 62
Industrial Machinery & Equipment Merchant Whslr
N.A.I.C.S.: 423830
Mike Taylor *(Pres)*
John Fitzgerald *(CEO)*
Sandy Bujanowski *(Controller)*
Ryan Del Real *(Mgr-San Diego)*
Eddie Long *(VP-Northern California)*

COLUMBIA STEEL CASTING CO., INC.
10425 N Bloss Ave, Portland, OR 97203-0095
Tel.: (503) 286-0685　　　　　OR
Web Site:
　https://www.columbiasteel.com

Columbia Steel Casting Co., Inc.—(Continued)

Year Founded: 1901
Sales Range: $25-49.9 Million
Emp.: 400
Impact & Wear Resistant Repacement Parts for Machinery Mfr
N.A.I.C.S.: 331513
Martha Cox (CEO)

COLUMBIA SUSSEX CORPORATION

740 Centre View Blvd, Crestview Hills, KY 41017
Tel.: (859) 578-1100   **KY**
Web Site:
https://www.columbiasussex.com
Year Founded: 1972
Sales Range: $550-599.9 Million
Emp.: 28,000
Hotels Owner & Operator
N.A.I.C.S.: 721110
Ted Mitchell (Treas)
Chris Ballad (CFO)

COLUMBIA SWEEPING SERVICES INC.

2424 W Lewis St, Pasco, WA 99301-4558
Tel.: (509) 542-8100
Web Site: http://www.cpm-css.com
Building Equipment Contractors
N.A.I.C.S.: 238290
John Stephens (Pres)

Subsidiaries:

Columbia Property Maintenance   (1)
2424 West Lewis St, Pasco, WA 99301
Tel.: (509) 542-8100
Web Site: http://www.cpm-css.com
New Single-Family Housing Construction, except Operative Builders
N.A.I.C.S.: 236115

COLUMBIA UNIVERSITY PRESS

61 W 62nd St, New York, NY 10023
Tel.: (212) 459-0600
Web Site:
http://www.columbiauniversity
press.com
Year Founded: 1893
Sales Range: $10-24.9 Million
Emp.: 50
Publishing
N.A.I.C.S.: 513130
Meredith Howard (Dir-Publicity)
Julia Kushnirsky (Dir-Art)
James Pakiela (Dir-HR)
Jessica Schwarz (Mgr-Production)
Michael Haskell (Mgr-Pur Sys)
Jonathan Ori (Coord-Instructional & Ops Support)
Sheri Whitley (Dir-Multimedia Dev)
Patricia Seifert (Dir-Strategic Donor Rels & Stewardship)
Flores Forbes (Assoc VP)
Deidre Fuchs (Asst Dir)
Cathleen Clark (Asst Dir-Dev & Alumni Rels)
Edith Miller (Asst Dir-Fin & Admin)
James Wang (Asst VP-Fin Svcs)
Genevieve Reilly (Coord-Transplant)
Donna See (Dir-Coulter Translational Res Partnership-Columbia)
Edmund Petro (Dir-Faculty Practice)
Diana Catz (Mgr-Clinical Res-Vascular Surgery Div)
David Greenberg (VP-Facilities Fin & Admin)
Joe Mannino (VP-Plng & Capital Project Mgmt)
Sara-Ann Gusik (Assoc Dir)
Mary Pickett (Assoc Dir-Intensive)
Marcelo Velez (Assoc VP)
Louisa Gilbert (Co-Dir-Social Intervention Grp)

Victoria Hamilton (Coord-Res Initiatives)
Nancy Wong (Deputy Dir)
Marilyn Hernandez (Dir-Billing Compliance Office)
Teresa Spada (Dir-Doctors Eastside-Columbia)
Peter Vaughan (Dir-Film & Video Tech)
Jim McMenamin (Dir-Gifts)
John Evanko (Dir-Gynecology Div)
Kristin Lynch (Dir-Leadership Gifts)
Jorge Sepulveda (Dir-Medical-Laboratory Informatics)
Courtney Roosa (Dir-Parents Fund)
Terry Park (Dir-Procurement IT)
Jose Rosado (Dir-Pub Safety)
Wayne Tang (Dir-Res Admin & Special Projects)
Jeannine Jennette (Exec Dir-Pub Safety Dept)
Maxine Griffith (Exec VP)
Ricardo Morales (Mgr)
Renee Douglas (Mgr-Bus Svcs)
Marissa Lafontant (Mgr-Earl Hall Center Building)
Rahima Hoque (Mgr-Lab)
Paul Wayne (Mgr-Scheduling)
Remi Moss (Mgr-Student Svcs)
Tahira Alleyne (Office Mgr-Billing)
Keith George (Project Mgr-Capital Mgmt)
Richard Hall (Sr Dir-Enterprise Budget & Bus Intelligence Applications)

COLUMBIA VENDING SERVICE INC.

6424 Frankford Ave, Baltimore, MD 21206
Tel.: (410) 485-3700   **MD**
Web Site: http://www.columbiaamuse
ments.com
Year Founded: 1950
Sales Range: $10-24.9 Million
Emp.: 50
Vending Machine Rental Services
N.A.I.C.S.: 532289
Norbort T. Paszkiewicz (Pres)
Marlene Freburger (Office Mgr)

COLUMBIA VENTURES CORPORATION

14301 SE 1st Ste110, Vancouver, WA 98684
Tel.: (360) 816-1840   **WA**
Web Site:
http://www.colventures.com
Year Founded: 1996
Sales Range: $100-124.9 Million
Emp.: 7
Privater Equity Firm
N.A.I.C.S.: 523999
Kenneth D. Peterson Jr. (Founder & CEO)
David M. Brewer (Vice Chm)
Susan D. Cruz (CFO)

Subsidiaries:

Columbia Ventures Broadband, LLC   (1)
203 SE Park Plz Dr Ste 270, Vancouver, WA 98684-5890   **(100%)**
Tel.: (360) 882-1052
Sales Range: $25-49.9 Million
Holding Company
N.A.I.C.S.: 517121
Kenneth D. Peterson Jr. (CEO)
Kenneth D. Peterson Jr. (CEO)

Grab On Grips LLC   (1)
350 E Beech Ave, Walla Walla, WA 99362
Tel.: (509) 529-9800
Web Site: http://www.grabongrips.com
Rubber Products Mfr
N.A.I.C.S.: 326299

PocketiNet Communications Inc.   (1)

45 Terminal Loop Rd Ste 210, Walla Walla, WA 99362   **(93%)**
Tel.: (509) 526-5026
Web Site: http://www.pocketinet.com
Broadband Internet Services
N.A.I.C.S.: 517810
Todd Brandenburg (Founder & Pres)
Steve Hoffmann (CTO)
Marshall Keymer (VP-Ops)

Rockwall Property Corporation   (1)
1200 E Washington St, Rockwall, TX 75087
Tel.: (972) 771-5362
Sales Range: $25-49.9 Million
Security Brokers & Dealers
N.A.I.C.S.: 237110

SlideStorm LLC   (1)
12503 SE Mill Plain Blvd Ste 120, Vancouver, WA 98684
Tel.: (360) 450-0045
Web Site: http://www.slidestorm.net
Web Conferencing Services
N.A.I.C.S.: 561499

COLUMBIAN FOODS INCORPORATED

4700 Belmont Ave, Youngstown, OH 44505
Tel.: (330) 759-2377
Sales Range: $25-49.9 Million
Emp.: 215
Operator of Supermarket Chain
N.A.I.C.S.: 445110
Cheryl Salguca (VP-HR)
Kim Cross (Office Mgr)
Bob Graff (VP-Store Ops)
Ronald C. Graff Sr. (Pres)

COLUMBIAN HOME PRODUCTS

1600 Beech St, Terre Haute, IN 47804
Tel.: (812) 232-0500
Web Site:
http://www.columbianhp.com
Sales Range: $10-24.9 Million
Emp.: 45
Cookware Mfr
N.A.I.C.S.: 335220
Dick Ryan (Owner)

Subsidiaries:

Joyce Chen Division   (1)
1600 Beech St, Terre Haute, IN 47804
Tel.: (812) 238-5000
Web Site: http://www.joycechen.com
Sales Range: $10-24.9 Million
Emp.: 19
Developers & Sales of Kitchen Accessories
N.A.I.C.S.: 332215

COLUMBIAN MUTUAL LIFE INSURANCE COMPANY

Vestal Pkwy E, Binghamton, NY 13902
Tel.: (607) 724-2472   **NY**
Web Site: https://www.cfglife.com
Year Founded: 1882
Sales Range: $250-299.9 Million
Emp.: 250
Life & Health Insurance
N.A.I.C.S.: 524210
Thomas Rattmann (Chm & CEO)
Alice Cobb (Reg Dir-Sls)
Jack Greenberg (VP-Pricing & Product Dev)
Karen W. Amitrano (Second VP-Underwriting)
Michael C. S. Fosbury (Pres)
Gerald J. Hennenhoefer (VP-Sls)
Patrick A. Mannion (Vice Chm)
Amy Purdy Godleski (CFO & Sr VP)
Frank L. Lettera (Chief Compliance Officer, Gen Counsel, Sec & Sr VP)
Lesley Frey (Sr VP-HR)
Steve Szubert (Treas, VP & Controller)
Jordan G. Baug (CIO & VP)
Dale A. Spencer (Chief Investment Officer & VP)

Subsidiaries:

Columbian Family Life Insurance Company   (1)
4704 Vestal Pkwy E, Binghamton, NY 13902
Tel.: (607) 724-2472
Web Site: http://www.cfglife.com
Rev.: $48,000,000
Emp.: 200
Life Insurance & Annuities
N.A.I.C.S.: 524210
Thomas Rattmann (Chm, Pres & CEO)

Columbian Financial Group   (1)
4704 Vestal Pkwy E, Binghamton, NY 13902-1381   **(100%)**
Tel.: (607) 724-2472
Web Site: http://www.cfglife.com
Emp.: 200
Life & Health Insurance
N.A.I.C.S.: 524210

Columbian Life Insurance Company   (1)
Homer Glen, Chicago, IL 60491
Tel.: (708) 301-6900
Web Site: http://www.cfglife.com
Fire Insurance Services
N.A.I.C.S.: 524113
Tomas Rettman (Pres)

Columbian Mutual Life Insurance Company   (1)
507 Plum St, Syracuse, NY 13204
Tel.: (607) 724-2472
Web Site: http://www.cfglife.com
Sales Range: $50-74.9 Million
Emp.: 180
Life Insurance & Annuities Services
N.A.I.C.S.: 524113
Thomas E. Rattmann (Chm)
Jeanne M. Clarke (Chief Admin Officer)
Richard S. Relf (CMO & Sr VP)

Columbian Mutual Life Insurance Company - Syracuse   (1)
507 Plumb St, Syracuse, NY 13250
Tel.: (315) 448-7000
Sales Range: $50-74.9 Million
Emp.: 75
Fire Insurance Services
N.A.I.C.S.: 524113

COLUMBINE SPECIALTY PRODUCTS, INC.

4880 E 41st Ave, Denver, CO 80216-4402
Tel.: (303) 294-0315
Web Site:
http://www.columbinesp.com
Sales Range: $10-24.9 Million
Emp.: 7
N.A.I.C.S.: 322220
Robert W. McNamara (Pres & Gen Mgr)
Tom McNamara (VP)

COLUMBUS AIRPORT AUTHORITY

4600 International Gateway, Columbus, OH 43219-1779
Tel.: (614) 239-4000
Web Site:
http://www.columbusairports.com
Year Founded: 1991
Sales Range: $25-49.9 Million
Emp.: 360
Airports & Flying Fields & Services
N.A.I.C.S.: 488119
Elaine Roberts (Pres & CEO)

COLUMBUS ASSOCIATION FOR THE PERFORMING ARTS CORPORATION

55 E State St, Columbus, OH 43215
Tel.: (614) 469-1045
Web Site: http://www.capa.com
Sales Range: $10-24.9 Million

Emp.: 705
Theater Building, Ownership & Operation
N.A.I.C.S.: 531120
Chad Whittington (Pres & CEO)
Todd Bemis (VP-Ops)
Richard Helmreich (Chm)

COLUMBUS BLUE JACKETS
Nationwide Arena 200 W Nationwide Blvd 3rd Fl, Columbus, OH 43215
Tel.: (614) 246-4625
Web Site: http://www.bluejackets.com
Year Founded: 1997
Sales Range: $10-24.9 Million
Emp.: 150
Professional Hockey Team
N.A.I.C.S.: 713940
Greg Kirstein (Gen Counsel & Sr VP)
Larry Hoepfner (Exec VP-Bus Ops)
Jarmo Kekalainen (Gen Mgr)
Kathryn Dobbs (VP-Community Rels & Exec Dir-Foundation)
Jessica Smith (Dir-Corp Dev)
Justin Baldinger (Acct Exec-Corp Dev)
Sam Morgan (Acct Exec-Corp Dev)
Basil McRae (Dir-Player Personnel)
Ryan Shirk (VP-Corp Partnerships)
Becky Coffey (VP-Partner Activation & Premium Svcs)

COLUMBUS BUILDERS SUPPLY INC.
900 W 3rd Ave, Columbus, OH 43212-3198
Tel.: (614) 294-4991
Web Site: http://www.columbusbuilders.net
Rev.: $11,000,000
Emp.: 30
Lumber & Other Building Materials
N.A.I.C.S.: 423310
Chris Herold (Pres)
Timothy McNichols (Controller)

COLUMBUS CITIZENS FOUNDATION
8 E 69th St, New York, NY 10021
Tel.: (212) 249-9923   NY
Web Site: http://www.columbuscitizensfd.org
Year Founded: 1994
Sales Range: $1-9.9 Million
Emp.: 24
Educational Support Services
N.A.I.C.S.: 611710
David J. Iommarini (Exec Dir)
Romeo Nesi (Mgr-Dining Room)
Maria Wilson (Mgr-Banquet)
John L. Boden (Gen Mgr)
Angelo Vivolo (Pres)
Ralph V. Balzano (Vice Chm)
Michael F. Pedone (Sec)
Lawrence E. Auriana (Treas)
Frank G. Fusaro (Chm)

COLUMBUS DOWNTOWN DEVELOPMENT CORPORATION
150 S Front St Ste 210, Columbus, OH 43215-3416
Tel.: (614) 545-5042   OH
Year Founded: 2002
Sales Range: $25-49.9 Million
Emp.: 30
Community Development Services
N.A.I.C.S.: 624190
Bruce A. Soll (Vice Chm)
Nicole Werner (CFO)
Guy V. Worley (Pres & CEO)
Amy E. Taylor (COO)
Matthew Lutz (Gen Counsel & Sec)
Stephen D. Steinour (Vice Chm)
Bruce A. Soll (Vice Chm)

COLUMBUS FOODS COMPANY
30 E Oakton St, Des Plaines, IL 60018-1945
Tel.: (847) 257-8920
Web Site: http://www.columbusfoods.com
Year Founded: 1930
Sales Range: $75-99.9 Million
Emp.: 100
Oils; Animal Or Vegetable
N.A.I.C.S.: 424990
Joe Loveshe (Dir-Sls)
Timothy Fallon (Pres & CEO)
John Piccetti (Chm)

COLUMBUS HOSPICE
7020 Moon Rd, Columbus, GA 31909
Tel.: (706) 569-7992   GA
Web Site: https://www.columbushospice.com
Year Founded: 1979
Sales Range: $10-24.9 Million
Emp.: 281
Hospice Care Services
N.A.I.C.S.: 621610
Diane Taylor (VP-Mktg)
Terri Roberts (Dir-Volunteer Svcs)
Wanda Johnson (VP-Clinical Support)
Bob Tompkins (CFO & VP-Fin)
David Edwards (Chm)
Donna Morgan (Pres & CEO)
Shari Evans (Sec)

COLUMBUS INDUSTRIES, INC.
2938 State Hwy 752, Ashville, OH 43103
Tel.: (740) 983-2552   OH
Web Site: http://www.colind.com
Year Founded: 1965
Sales Range: $25-49.9 Million
Emp.: 405
Supplier of Blowers & Fans
N.A.I.C.S.: 333413
Harold T. Pontius (Chm & CEO)

COLUMBUS LIFE AND WATER
420 4th Ave S, Columbus, MS 39701
Tel.: (662) 328-7192
Web Site: http://www.columbus-lw.com
Rev.: $13,400,000
Emp.: 80
Electric & Other Services Combined
N.A.I.C.S.: 221118
David Shelton (Chm)

COLUMBUS NISSAN INC.
100 Hwy 12 E, Columbus, MS 39702
Tel.: (662) 328-6691
Web Site: https://www.columbusnissan.com
Sales Range: $10-24.9 Million
Emp.: 50
Automobiles, New & Used
N.A.I.C.S.: 441110
Charles W. Rigdon (Pres)
Russel P. Street (Gen Mgr)

COLUMBUS PIPE & EQUIPMENT COMPANY
773 E Markison Ave, Columbus, OH 43207
Tel.: (614) 444-7871   OH
Year Founded: 1934
Sales Range: $1-9.9 Million
Emp.: 10
Mfr of Steel Plumbing Fittings & Supplies
N.A.I.C.S.: 423510
Bruce Jay Silberstein (Pres)
Jonathan A. Silberstein (VP)
Jeff Saco (CFO)

COLUMBUS PROPERTIES LP

909 Poydras St Ste 1700, New Orleans, LA 70112
Tel.: (504) 584-5000
Web Site: http://www.columbusdev.com
Sales Range: $25-49.9 Million
Emp.: 40
Commercial & Industrial Building Services
N.A.I.C.S.: 531120
Joseph C. Canizaro (Chm, Pres & CEO)

COLUMBUS TRUCK AND EQUIPMENT CO. INC.
1688 E 5th Ave, Columbus, OH 43219
Tel.: (614) 252-3111
Web Site: http://www.columbusmac.com
Sales Range: $10-24.9 Million
Emp.: 70
Truck Parts & Accessories
N.A.I.C.S.: 423120
Vicky Wolfinger (Office Mgr)

COLUMBUS WATER WORKS
1421 Veterans Pkwy, Columbus, GA 31902
Tel.: (706) 649-3400
Web Site: http://www.cwwga.org
Rev.: $33,406,762
Emp.: 210
Water Supply
N.A.I.C.S.: 221310
Bob Tant (Pres)
Emory Blount (CFO & Sr VP)

COLUMBUS ZOOLOGICAL PARK ASSOCIATION
PO Box 400, Powell, OH 43065-0400
Tel.: (614) 645-3457   OH
Year Founded: 1930
Sales Range: $50-74.9 Million
Emp.: 1,849
Zoo Association
N.A.I.C.S.: 712130
Carman J. Wirtz (Sr VP-HR)
Thomas Hof (VP-Philanthropy)
Lewis Greene (Sr VP-Animal Care)
Thomas Stalf (CEO)
Gregory Bell (Sr VP-Fin)

COLUMN TECHNOLOGIES, INC.
10 E 22nd St Ste 300, Lombard, IL 60148
Tel.: (630) 515-6660
Web Site: http://www.columnit.com
Year Founded: 1998
Sales Range: $25-49.9 Million
Emp.: 200
Corporate Infrastructure Management Solutions
N.A.I.C.S.: 541618
Mark Nelson (Mgr-IT)

COLUMN5 CONSULTING
4800 N Scottsdale Rd Ste 2300, Scottsdale, AZ 85251
Tel.: (480) 779-6990
Web Site: http://www.column5.com
Year Founded: 2005
Sales Range: $10-24.9 Million
Emp.: 100
Enterprise Performance Management Solutions & Software Developer
N.A.I.C.S.: 513210
David Den Boer (Founder & CEO)
Michael Sullivan (VP-Reg Ops)
Steve Sussman (VP-Global Sls, Mktg & Bus Dev)
David J. H. Jones (Mng Dir-UK & EMEA)

COLUSSY CHEVROLET INC.

3073 Washington Pike, Bridgeville, PA 15017
Tel.: (412) 221-1600
Web Site: http://www.colussy.com
Year Founded: 1918
Sales Range: $10-24.9 Million
Emp.: 80
New Car Dealers
N.A.I.C.S.: 441110
Timothy L. Colussy (Pres)

COLVILLE CAPITAL LLC
201 S College St Ste 2770, Charlotte, NC 28244
Tel.: (704) 323-4400   NC
Web Site: https://www.colvillecapital.com
Year Founded: 2006
Privater Equity Firm
N.A.I.C.S.: 523999
Mark W. Mealy (Founder & Mng Partner)
Michael A. Steinback (Operating Partner)
Daniel Sanderson (Partner)

Subsidiaries:

Motion & Flow Control Products, Inc.   (1)
7941 Shaffer Pkwy, Littleton, CO 80127
Tel.: (303) 762-8012
Web Site: http://www.mccoysales.com
Sales Range: $10-24.9 Million
Hydronic Heating Equipment, Fluid Connectors, Hoses, Seals, Pneumatics, Hydraulics & Other Related Products Distr
N.A.I.C.S.: 423840
Chad Caskey (VP-Heating Div)

Subsidiary (Domestic):

Jackovich Industrial & Construction Supply, Inc.   (2)
1607 Wells St, Fairbanks, AK 99701
Tel.: (907) 456-4414
Web Site: http://www.jackovich.com
Sales Range: $1-9.9 Million
Emp.: 40
Industrial Supplies Whslr
N.A.I.C.S.: 423840
Dennis Thies (Mgr-Ops)
Rick Thompson (Mgr-Sls)
Troy Jackovich (Mgr-Store)

Northeast Battery & Alternator Inc.   (1)
240 Washington St, Auburn, MA 01501
Tel.: (508) 832-2700
Web Site: http://www.northeastbattery.com
Emp.: 25
Battery Distr
N.A.I.C.S.: 444230
Thomas J. Scarduzio (Pres & CEO)

COLVILLE INC.
Spine Rd, Prudhoe Bay, AK 99734
Tel.: (907) 659-3198
Web Site: https://www.colvilleinc.com
Sales Range: $25-49.9 Million
Emp.: 70
Distr of Crude Oil
N.A.I.C.S.: 424720
Mark Helmericks (Owner)
Kelly Droop (COO)
Dave Pfeifer (CEO)

COLWELL INDUSTRIES, INC.
123 N 3rd St, Minneapolis, MN 55401-1657
Tel.: (612) 340-0365   MN
Web Site: http://www.colwellind.com
Year Founded: 1951
Sales Range: $50-74.9 Million
Emp.: 500
Mfr of Merchandising Aids for Other Manufacturers or Distributors
N.A.I.C.S.: 323111
Donovan J. Freeland (Pres & CEO)
Felton Colwell (Vice Chm)
Dan Nicklay (CFO, Treas & Exec VP)
Tony Hoeben (Dir-IT)

Colwell Industries, Inc.—(Continued)

Subsidiaries:

Colwell North America   **(1)**
2605 Marian Dr, Kendallville, IN
46755   **(100%)**
Tel.: (260) 347-1981
Web Site: http://www.colwellcolour.com
Sales Range: $25-49.9 Million
Emp.: 250
Mfr of Merchandising Aids
N.A.I.C.S.: 323111
Jim Skinner (Plant Mgr)

COLWEN MANAGEMENT INC.
230 Commerce Way Ste 200, Portsmouth, NH 03801
Tel.: (603) 897-6100
Web Site:
    https://www.colwenhotels.com
Year Founded: 1996
Emp.: 376
Management Services
N.A.I.C.S.: 541611
Leo Xarras (Chm)
Michael Colavecchio (Dir-Loss Prevention)
Terry Bickhardt (Sr VP)
Jim Riker (VP-Ops)
John R. Mitchell (VP-Ops)

COLWILL ENGINEERING, INC.
4750 E Adamo Dr, Tampa, FL 33605
Tel.: (813) 241-2525   **FL**
Web Site:
    https://www.colwillengineering.com
Year Founded: 1989
Sales Range: $1-9.9 Million
Emp.: 50
Electrical Contractor
N.A.I.C.S.: 238210
Charles Colwill (Pres)
Joseph Stolz (VP)
Phillip Cochran (VP)
Michael Cessna (VP)

COM-ESCO, LLC
2929 E Comml Blvd Ste 608, Fort Lauderdale, FL 33308
Web Site: http://www.com-esco.com
All Other Specialty Trade Contractors
N.A.I.C.S.: 238990

COM2000, INC.
1575 W Horizon Ridge Pkwy Ste 531401, Henderson, NV 89012
Tel.: (650) 430-6380   **NV**
Web Site: https://www.com2000.com
Year Founded: 2020
Software Development Services
N.A.I.C.S.: 541511
Michael Gaard (Chm)
Jacob Lakhany (Pres & CMO)
David Wong (CFO)
Victor Tong (Sec)

COMANCHE CONSTRUCTION INC.
16510 W 119th St, Olathe, KS 66061
Tel.: (913) 782-2980
Sales Range: $10-24.9 Million
Emp.: 6
Provider of Bridge Construction
N.A.I.C.S.: 237310
George Hornung (Pres)

COMANCHE COUNTY ELECTRIC COOPERATIVE ASSOCIATION
201 W Wrights Ave, Comanche, TX 76442
Tel.: (325) 356-2533   **TX**
Web Site: http://www.ceca.coop
Year Founded: 1938
Sales Range: $25-49.9 Million
Emp.: 58
Electric Power Distr

N.A.I.C.S.: 221122

COMANCHE COUNTY MEDICAL CENTER
10201 Highway 16, Comanche, TX 76442
Tel.: (254) 879-4900   **TX**
Web Site:
    https://www.comanchecmc.org
Year Founded: 2010
Sales Range: $10-24.9 Million
Emp.: 158
Health Care Srvices
N.A.I.C.S.: 622110
Jerry Morgan (Chm)
Robert Pratt (Sec)
Mike Hare (Vice Chm)

COMANCHE ELECTRIC COOP ASSOCIATION
201 W Wrights Ave, Comanche, TX 76442
Tel.: (325) 356-2533
Rev.: $16,442,309
Emp.: 37
Transmission, Electric Power
N.A.I.C.S.: 221121
Alan Lesley (Gen Mgr)
Eddie Strube (Dir-Ops)

COMAR, LLC
220 Laurel Rd, Voorhees, NJ 08043
Tel.: (856) 692-6100
Web Site: http://www.comar.com
Year Founded: 1949
Plastic Packaging Mfr; Custom Packaging,Bottles, Dispensing, Closures, Injection & Blow Molding
N.A.I.C.S.: 326199
Ben Pagano (Engr-Automation Process)
John Viola (Mgr-Quality)
John Daly (Dir-Tech Ops)
Benjamin Singer (Regl Sls Mgr)
Tom Sine (Mgr-Bus Sys)
Jason Ecclestone (Mgr-Logistics)
Mike Ruggieri (Chm)
Brian M. Larkin (Pres & CEO)

Subsidiaries:

iMARK Molding, Inc.   **(1)**
104 Park Ave, Woodville, WI 54028
Tel.: (715) 698-3144
Web Site: http://www.imarkmolding.com
Sales Range: $1-9.9 Million
Emp.: 20
Plastic Injection Moldings Mfr & Distr
N.A.I.C.S.: 326199
Linda Sturtevant (VP-Fin)
Greg Fischer (VP-Sls)
Steve Schmidt (Mgr-Engrg)
John Porter (VP-Ops)
Dejon Schroeder (Mgr-Quality)
Mark Sturtevant (Pres)

COMARCO, INC.
28202 Cabot Rd Ste 300, Laguna Niguel, CA 92677
Tel.: (949) 599-7400   **CA**
Web Site: http://www.comarco.com
Year Founded: 1971
Rev.: $1,709,000
Assets: $632,000
Liabilities: $395,000
Net Worth: $237,000
Earnings: $845,000
Emp.: 1
Fiscal Year-end: 01/31/17
Computer Systems & Engineering Services; Software Documentation; Decision Aiding Services; Computer Technology; Engineering Services
N.A.I.C.S.: 541519

Subsidiaries:

Comarco Wireless Technologies, Inc.   **(1)**

25541 Commercentre Dr, Lake Forest, CA 92630   **(100%)**
Tel.: (949) 599-7400
Web Site: http://www.comarco.com
Sales Range: $25-49.9 Million
Telephone Apparatus Manufacturing
N.A.I.C.S.: 334210

Select Staffing   **(1)**
15371 Bonanza Rd, Victorville, CA 92392-2479   **(100%)**
Tel.: (760) 245-1460
Web Site: http://www.selectstaffing.com
Sales Range: $10-24.9 Million
Commercial Staffing Service
N.A.I.C.S.: 561320
Tom Bickes (CEO)

COMARK COMMUNICATIONS, LLC
104 Feeding Hills Rd, Southwick, MA 01077
Tel.: (413) 998-1100   **DE**
Web Site: https://www.comarktv.com
Year Founded: 1972
Sales Range: $25-49.9 Million
Emp.: 65
Mfr of Television Broadcasting & Transmission Equipment
N.A.I.C.S.: 334220
Richard E. Fiore Jr. (Pres)

COMARK, LLC
440 Fortune Blvd, Milford, MA 01757
Tel.: (508) 359-8161   **DE**
Web Site:
    https://www.comarkcorp.com
Year Founded: 1974
Commercial Computing Equipment & Components Whslr & Customized Engineering Services
N.A.I.C.S.: 423430
J. Robin Palermo (Dir-Mktg & Comm)
Jeff Roberts (CEO)

Subsidiaries:

Nematron Corporation   **(1)**
5840 Interface Dr, Ann Arbor, MI 48103
Tel.: (734) 214-2000
Web Site: http://www.nematron.com
Sales Range: $10-24.9 Million
Emp.: 16
Commercial Computing Equipment & Components Whslr & Customized Engineering Services
N.A.I.C.S.: 423430
Greg Chandler (Gen Mgr)

COMBAT BRANDS, LLC
15850 W 108th St, Lenexa, KS 66219-1340   **KS**
Web Site:
    http://www.combatbrands.com
Year Founded: 2012
Emp.: 30
Sporting & Recreational Goods Distr & Retailer
N.A.I.C.S.: 423910
Greg Orman (Owner)

COMBE INCORPORATED
1101 Westchester Ave, White Plains, NY 10604-3503
Tel.: (914) 694-5454   **DE**
Web Site: http://www.combe.com
Year Founded: 1949
Sales Range: $150-199.9 Million
Emp.: 600
Pharmaceuticals Product Mfr
N.A.I.C.S.: 325620
John P. Alberto (Sr VP-HR)
Keech Combe Shetty (Chm)
Jane Wildman (Pres)

Subsidiaries:

BioFilm, Inc.   **(1)**
3225 Executive Rdg, Vista, CA 92081
Tel.: (760) 727-9030

Sales Range: $1-9.9 Million
Emp.: 54
Personal Health Products Distr
N.A.I.C.S.: 456191
Doris Untalan-Kent (Mgr-Pur & Plng)
Damien DeCrausaz (Sr Mgr-Ops)
Mike Sund (Supvr-QC)

Combe International Limited   **(1)**
AMP House 4th Fl Dingwall Rd, Croydon, CR9 2AU, Surrey, United Kingdom **(100%)**
Tel.: (44) 2086802711
Web Site: http://www.combe.com
Sales Range: $10-24.9 Million
Emp.: 30
Supplier of Consumer Healthcare Products
N.A.I.C.S.: 325412

COMBINE INTERNATIONAL INC.
354 Indusco Ct, Troy, MI 48083-4643
Tel.: (248) 585-9900
Web Site: https://www.combine.com
Rev.: $17,300,000
Emp.: 225
Jewelry Mfr
N.A.I.C.S.: 339910
Roger D. Parsons (CFO)

COMBINED EXPRESS INC.
3685 Marshall Ln, Bensalem, PA 19020
Tel.: (215) 633-1535
Web Site:
    https://www.combinedexpress.com
Rev.: $30,000,000
Emp.: 80
Freight Consolidation Services
N.A.I.C.S.: 488510
Mark Kraeuter (Pres)
Linda Mayes (VP)
Daniel Crosby (Controller)

COMBINED JEWISH PHILANTHROPIES OF GREATER BOSTON, INC.
126 High St, Boston, MA 02110-2700
Tel.: (617) 457-8500   **MA**
Web Site: https://www.cjp.org
Year Founded: 1895
Rev.: $389,826,000
Assets: $2,055,086,000
Liabilities: $518,444,000
Net Worth: $1,536,642,000
Emp.: 191
Fiscal Year-end: 06/30/18
Jewish Community Services
N.A.I.C.S.: 624190
Christopher J. Policinski (CEO)
Andi Pollinger (VP-Plng)
Dena Boronkay Rashes (Chm)
Geraldine Acuna-Sunshine (Chm)
Gil Preuss (Exec VP)

COMBINED TRANSPORT INC.
5656 Crater Lk Ave, Central Point, OR 97502
Tel.: (541) 826-7486
Web Site:
    http://www.combinedtransport.com
Rev.: $62,608,061
Emp.: 600
Truck Transportation Brokers
N.A.I.C.S.: 488510
Stephan Abrams (Mgr-Sls-West Coast)
Scott Waggoner (Mgr-Heavy Haul)
Tony Keller (Gen Mgr)
Michael Paradis (Mgr-Commodity Sls)

COMBS & COMPANY
3426 Old Cantrell Rd, Little Rock, AR 72202-1860
Tel.: (501) 664-3000   **AR**
Web Site: https://www.combsco.com
Year Founded: 1972
Sales Range: $25-49.9 Million

Emp.: 30
Advertising Agencies
N.A.I.C.S.: 541810
Cheri Holt *(Mgr-Bus)*
Jud Chapin *(Dir-Creative)*

COMBS OIL CO. INC.
1500 Airport Rd S, Naples, FL 34104
Tel.: (239) 774-2666
Rev.: $10,500,000
Emp.: 12
Petroleum Bulk Stations
N.A.I.C.S.: 424710
Dennis R. Combs *(Pres)*

COMCAM INTERNATIONAL, INC.
1140 McDermott Dr Ste 200, West Chester, PA 19380
Tel.: (610) 436-8089   DE
Web Site: http://www.comcam.net
Sales Range: $1-9.9 Million
Emp.: 14
Network Video Command & Control Products Mfr
N.A.I.C.S.: 334310
Don Gilbreath *(Chm & CEO)*

COMCAR INDUSTRIES, INC.
502 E Bridgers Ave, Auburndale, FL 33823
Tel.: (863) 967-1100   FL
Web Site: http://www.comcar.com
Year Founded: 1953
Sales Range: $350-399.9 Million
Emp.: 3,000
Provider of Commercial Transportation Services
N.A.I.C.S.: 484121
Daniel McNamee *(VP-HR)*
Bill Braman *(COO)*
Michele Baum *(CFO & Exec VP)*
Christopher Shepherd *(VP-Pur & Fleet Mgmt)*
Randall T. Clark *(Pres & CEO)*

Subsidiaries:

CT Transportation LLC   (1)
322 Grange Rd, Port Wentworth, GA 31407
Tel.: (912) 264-8467
Web Site: http://www.cttransportation.com
Transit & Ground Passenger Transportation
N.A.I.C.S.: 485999
Jeff Lee *(Mgr)*

CTL Transportation LLC   (1)
548 E Bridgers Ave, Auburndale, FL 33823
Tel.: (863) 965-6898
Liquid Bulk Chemical Transport & Logistic Services
N.A.I.C.S.: 484230
John Brown *(Mgr)*

COMCAST CABLEVISION MD LP
8031 Corporate Dr, Baltimore, MD 21236
Tel.: (410) 931-4600
Web Site: http://www.comcast.com
Rev.: $46,500,000
Emp.: 200
Cable Television Services
N.A.I.C.S.: 516210
Mary McLaughlin *(Sr VP-Beltway-Northeast-Comcast Cable)*

COMCO PLASTICS INC.
9834 Jamaica Ave, Jamaica, NY 11421-2212
Tel.: (718) 849-9000   NY
Web Site:
http://www.comcoplastics.com
Year Founded: 1956
Sales Range: $25-49.9 Million
Emp.: 210
Mfr & Developer of Unsupported Plastics Film & Sheet
N.A.I.C.S.: 326113

COMCOUNT INC.
4111 N Wheeling Ave, Muncie, IN 47304
Tel.: (765) 289-3321
Web Site: https://www.pizzaking.com
Sales Range: $25-49.9 Million
Emp.: 30
Billing & Bookkeeping Service
N.A.I.C.S.: 541219
Jerry Riley *(Gen Mgr)*

COMDESIGN INC.
9850 16th St N, Saint Petersburg, FL 33716
Tel.: (727) 579-1600
Web Site:
http://www.comdesigninc.com
Emp.: 150
IT Infrastructure & Network Cabling Installation
N.A.I.C.S.: 238210
Robert Wilkin *(Pres)*

COME ON STRONG INC.
PO Box 66181, Auburndale, MA 02466
Tel.: (781) 209-2663
Web Site:
http://www.comeonstrong.com
Sales Range: $10-24.9 Million
Emp.: 4
Men's & Boy's Clothing
N.A.I.C.S.: 424350
B. Levy *(Pres)*

COMEAUX FURNITURE & AP-PLIANCES INC.
415 Veterans Blvd, Metairie, LA 70005
Tel.: (504) 831-1365
Web Site:
http://www.comeauxfurniture.com
Year Founded: 1953
Sales Range: $10-24.9 Million
Emp.: 80
Furniture Retailer
N.A.I.C.S.: 449110
Rene Fontaine *(CFO)*

COMEGYS INSURANCE AGENCY, INC.
1 Beach Dr SE 2nd Fl, Saint Petersburg, FL 33701
Tel.: (727) 521-2100   FL
Web Site: https://www.comegys.com
Year Founded: 1939
Emp.: 50
Insurance Brokers
N.A.I.C.S.: 524210
Linda Berset *(Pres)*
Derek Berset *(VP)*
Lori Ballis *(Comptroller)*
Jason Berset *(VP-SAN-Florida)*
Mark Steven Berset *(CEO)*

COMET INDUSTRIES INC.
2405 Nicholson Ave, Kansas City, MO 64120-1104
Tel.: (816) 245-5400   DE
Web Site: https://www.cometind.com
Year Founded: 1963
Sales Range: $10-24.9 Million
Emp.: 110
Servicing of Transportation Equipment & Supplies
N.A.I.C.S.: 423860
Steve Woodson *(Pres)*

Subsidiaries:

Comet Electronics, LLC   (1)
2301 Burlington St North, Kansas City, MO 64116
Tel.: (816) 245-5400
Web Site: http://www.cometind.com
Emp.: 10
Rail Communication & Signal Equipment Mfr

N.A.I.C.S.: 334290
Steve Woodson *(Pres)*

COMFORT BILT LLC
213 22nd Ave, Brookings, SD 57006
Tel.: (605) 692-5345
Rev.: $23,000,000
Emp.: 50
Screen & Storm Doors Mfr
N.A.I.C.S.: 332321
Brian Johnson *(Mgr)*

COMFORT ENGINEERS, INC.
4008 Comfort Ln, Durham, NC 27715-2955
Tel.: (919) 383-2502
Web Site:
http://www.comfortengineers.com
Sales Range: $10-24.9 Million
Emp.: 150
Plumbing, Heating & Air-Conditioning Services
N.A.I.C.S.: 238220
Alan Williams *(Pres)*
Barry Grinstead *(Mgr-Construction)*
David Duchene *(Project Mgr)*
Mike Garrard *(Mgr-Svc)*

COMFORT MEDICAL SUPPLY LLC
615 S Yonge St, Ormond Beach, FL 32174
Tel.: (386) 673-6902
Web Site:
http://www.comfortmedicalllc.com
Year Founded: 2005
Sales Range: $1-9.9 Million
Emp.: 27
In Home Delivery of Medical Equipment
N.A.I.C.S.: 423450
Lee Wheatley *(Mgr-Field)*

COMFORT ONE SHOES L-1 CORPORATION
201 King St., Alexandria, VA 22314
Tel.: (571) 257-7510
Web Site:
https://comfortoneshoes.com
Year Founded: 1997
Footwear Whslr
N.A.I.C.S.: 424340

Subsidiaries:

Saxon Shoes, Inc.   (1)
11800 W Broad St Ste 2750, Richmond, VA 23233
Tel.: (804) 285-3473
Web Site: http://www.saxonshoes.com
Sales Range: $10-24.9 Million
Emp.: 80
Shoe Whslr
N.A.I.C.S.: 458210

COMFORT SERVICES INC.
2215 S West St, Wichita, KS 67213-1113
Tel.: (316) 945-8268
Rev.: $13,400,000
Emp.: 3
Warm Air Heating & Air Conditioning
N.A.I.C.S.: 423730

Subsidiaries:

Airpro Inc.   (1)
8849 Brookside Ave Ste 201, West Chester, OH 45069
Tel.: (513) 469-2000
Web Site: http://www.airpro.com
Emp.: 9
Warm Air Heating & Air Conditioning Contractor
N.A.I.C.S.: 238220
Doug Anderson *(Gen Mgr)*

Condition-Aire Inc.   (1)
3458 S Hoover Rd, Wichita, KS 67215
Tel.: (316) 945-8208
Heating & Air Conditioning Contractors

N.A.I.C.S.: 238220

COMFORT SUPPLY
305 Arlington Ave, Nashville, TN 37210
Tel.: (615) 244-0920
Web Site:
http://www.comfortsupplyhvac.com
Year Founded: 1971
Sales Range: $10-24.9 Million
Emp.: 40
Air Conditioning Equipment Whslr
N.A.I.C.S.: 423730

COMFORT SUPPLY, INC.
150 Kisow Dr, Pittsburgh, PA 15205
Tel.: (412) 921-6600
Web Site:
http://www.comfortsupplypgh.com
Year Founded: 1985
Sales Range: $10-24.9 Million
Emp.: 22
Heating & Air Conditioning Equipment Distr
N.A.I.C.S.: 423730
Frank W. Heckler *(Founder)*
David H. Heckler *(Pres)*
Jeff Wappler *(Territory Mgr)*
Don Moore *(Territory Mgr)*
Mark Devich *(Territory Mgr)*

COMFORT WINDOW CO. INC.
3624 John Glenn Blvd, Syracuse, NY 13209
Tel.: (315) 888-4845
Web Site:
https://www.comfortwindows.com
Year Founded: 1979
Sales Range: $10-24.9 Million
Emp.: 200
Window Mfr
N.A.I.C.S.: 444110
Jerry More *(Mgr-Sls)*
Adam Whitbeck *(Project Mgr)*
Bill Johnston *(Mgr-Ops)*

COMFORT-AIR ENGINEERING, INC.
11403 Jones Maltsberger Rd, San Antonio, TX 78216
Tel.: (210) 987-5073
Web Site: https://www.comfort-air.com
Year Founded: 1964
Sales Range: $10-24.9 Million
Emp.: 100
Plumbing, Heating & Air-Conditioning Services
N.A.I.C.S.: 238220
Matthew Allen Freund *(Pres)*
Victor F. Jendrzey *(Mgr-Svcs)*
Clint T. Wurzbach *(Project Mgr)*
Keith Brunner *(Mgr-Plumbing Svc)*
Robert DeBehenke *(Project Mgr)*
Daniel Simpson *(Mgr-Replacement)*
Brad Sobotik *(Mgr-Customer Svc)*
Mike Stahl *(Gen Mgr-Construction Ops)*
Eric Randall *(Mgr-Residential Svc)*
David Kollman *(Mgr-Sls-Residential & Light Comml)*

COMHEAR, INC.
3020 Callan Rd, San Diego, CA 92121
Tel.: (619) 722-0639   DE
Web Site: http://www.comhear.com
Year Founded: 2013
Audio Product Mfr
N.A.I.C.S.: 334310
Andrew H. Sassine *(Chm)*
Perry Teevens *(Pres)*
Tom Craft *(CTO)*
Peter Otto *(Chief Science Officer)*
Gerry Chastelet *(CEO)*

Comhear, Inc.—(Continued)

Eric Haskell (CFO)
Paul O'Callaghan (Sr VP-Sls)
Greg Thener (Reg VP-Sls)

COMLINK CONTRACTORS INC.
7308 Aspen Ln N #160, Brooklyn Park, MN 55428-1027
Tel.: (763) 391-7483
Web Site: http://www.comlink-usa.com
Sales Range: $10-24.9 Million
Emp.: 30
Communications Cabling Installation & Service
N.A.I.C.S.: 237130
Jim Galloway (Pres)

Subsidiaries:

Comlink Midwest Inc.   (1)
7308 Aspen Ln N #160, Brooklyn Park, MN 55428
Tel.: (763) 391-7483
Web Site: http://www.comlink-usa.com
Sales Range: $1-9.9 Million
Emp.: 12
Communications Cabling Installation & Service
N.A.I.C.S.: 237130

Subsidiary (Domestic):

Underground Piercing, Inc.   (2)
14320 James Rd, Rogers, MN 55374-9406
Tel.: (763) 428-7930
Web Site:
   http://www.undergroundpiercing.com
Sales Range: $1-9.9 Million
Emp.: 9
Specialty Trade Contractors
N.A.I.C.S.: 238990
Stacy Fouquette (Office Mgr)
Rob Halland (Gen Mgr)

Comlink Southwest, LLC   (1)
2443 W 12th St Ste 6, Tempe, AZ 85281
Tel.: (480) 303-0150
Communications Cabling Installation & Service
N.A.I.C.S.: 517810
Jim Galloway (Pres)

COMM NET INTERNATIONAL INC.
1 Dutchtown Rd, Voorhees, NJ 08043
Tel.: (856) 719-1000
Web Site: http://www.commnetinternational.com
Rev.: $23,327,184
Emp.: 35
System Integration Services
N.A.I.C.S.: 541512
Bob Puphal (Dir-Technical Svcs)
Ron Connors (Mgr-Sls)
Art Leiby (VP-Tech)

COMM-WORKS, LLC
1405 Xenium Ln N Ste 120, Minneapolis, MN 55441
Tel.: (763) 225-2276   DE
Web Site: http://www.comm-works.com
Year Founded: 1995
Voice & Data Solutions
N.A.I.C.S.: 517810
Alan Lampe (CEO)
Jim Stewart (CFO)

Subsidiaries:

Comm-Works, LLC - Indianapolis   (1)
1007 3rd Ave SW, Carmel, IN 46032
Tel.: (317) 816-6900
Web Site: http://www.commworks.com
Cabling Equipment & Installation
N.A.I.C.S.: 238210

COMM3
3939 Beltline Rd Ste 760, Addison, TX 75001

Tel.: (214) 389-2600
Web Site: http://www.comm3.net
Year Founded: 1987
Rev.: $23,000,000
Emp.: 12
Scientific & Technical Consulting Services
N.A.I.C.S.: 541690
David L. Blum (Pres, Mng Partner & Gen Mgr)
Troy L. Cryer (CEO & Partner)

COMMAND DECISIONS SYSTEMS & SOLUTIONS, INCORPORATED
14101 Parke Long Ct Ste T, Chantilly, VA 20151
Tel.: (703) 988-9206
Web Site: http://www.cds2.com
Year Founded: 1994
Rev.: $8,100,000
Emp.: 40
Security Guards & Patrol Services
N.A.I.C.S.: 561612
Barbara A. Hennessy (Pres)

COMMAND LANGUAGES, INC.
3902 N Marguerite St, Tampa, FL 33603
Tel.: (813) 872-0600
Web Site: http://www.clisolutions.com
Sales Range: $1-9.9 Million
Emp.: 50
Military-Based Translation, Intelligence Operations, Engineering, IT Management & Consulting Services
N.A.I.C.S.: 541930
A.H. Atari (CEO)

COMMAND MANAGEMENT SERVICES, INC.
921 SW Washington St Ste 333, Portland, OR 97205
Tel.: (503) 224-5600
Web Site: http://www.cms-corp.com
Year Founded: 1983
Sales Range: $10-24.9 Million
Emp.: 150
Relocation & Contracting Services
N.A.I.C.S.: 561990
Monica Anderson (Pres & CEO)
Brian Anderson (CMO)
Jeffery K. Downes (Exec VP)
Joseph P. Marx (VP-Mktg)

COMMAND PLASTIC CORPORATION
124 West Ave, Tallmadge, OH 44278-2206
Tel.: (330) 434-3497   OH
Web Site:
   https://www.commandplastic.com
Year Founded: 1971
Sales Range: $75-99.9 Million
Emp.: 80
Heat Sealed Vinyl Packaging for Banking, Music, Collectibles & Tool Pouch Industries Mfr
N.A.I.C.S.: 326112
Richard S. Ames (Pres & CEO)
Ed Krise (VP-Sls)
Graham F. Klintworth (VP-Fin)
Ann Ames (Principal)

COMMANDER TERMINALS
1 Comander Sq, Oyster Bay, NY 11771-1503
Tel.: (516) 922-7600   NY
Sales Range: $50-74.9 Million
Emp.: 15
Fuel Oil Mfr & Distr
N.A.I.C.S.: 493110

COMMDEX CONSULTING, LLC
655 Engrg Dr Ste 100, Norcross, GA 30092

Tel.: (770) 349-0400
Web Site: http://www.commdex.com
Year Founded: 2001
Sales Range: $1-9.9 Million
Emp.: 70
Telecommunication Networks
N.A.I.C.S.: 517112
Brenda Mendes (Office Mgr)

COMMENCE CORPORATION
2 Industrial Way W 2nd Fl, Eatontown, NJ 07724
Tel.: (732) 380-9100
Web Site:
   https://www.commence.com
Year Founded: 1988
Customer Relationship Management Applications & e-Business Solutions
N.A.I.C.S.: 513210
Larry Caretsky (CEO)

COMMENCEMENT BANK
1102 Commerce St, Tacoma, WA 98402
PO Box 98115
Tel.: (253) 284-1800
Web Site: http://www.commencementbank.com
Year Founded: 2006
Rev.: $16,883,000
Assets: $357,471,000
Liabilities: $315,010,000
Net Worth: $42,461,000
Earnings: $5,036,000
Emp.: 55
Fiscal Year-end: 12/31/18
Commericial Banking
N.A.I.C.S.: 522110
H. R. Russell (Chm)
Patrick Lewis (Sr VP-Comml Loan)
Tricia Ott (Sr VP-Ops & Mgmt)
Thomas Nixon (Vice Chm)
John Manolides (Pres & CEO)
Rick Larson (Chief Credit Officer & Sr VP)
Tom Dhamers (CFO & Exec VP)
Jerald Kennedy (Officer-IT & Sr VP)
Rebecca Williamson (VP & Mgr-HR)
Greg Hansch (Sr VP & Mgr-Retail Banking)
Juliet Hart (Asst VP & Branch Mgr)
Joy Johnson (Officer-Comml Loan & Sr VP)
Tyler Gore (Officer-Comml Loan & Asst VP)
Andrey Dombrowski (Officer-Comml Loan & Asst VP)
Jami Block (Officer-Cash Mgmt & VP)
Christina Haworth (Officer-Cash Mgmt)
Dan Howard (Officer-Comml Loan & VP)

COMMERCE AUTO GROUP
105 State Hwy 224, Commerce, TX 75428
Tel.: (903) 886-4014
Web Site:
   http://www.commerceautos.com
Sales Range: $10-24.9 Million
Emp.: 500
Automobile Dealership
N.A.I.C.S.: 423110
Charlie Grey (Pres)

COMMERCE BANCSHARES, INC.
322 W 6th St, Chelsea, OK 74016
Tel.: (918) 789-2567   OK
Web Site: https://www.bankboc.com
Year Founded: 1996
Sales Range: $1-9.9 Million
Emp.: 56
Bank Holding Company
N.A.I.C.S.: 551111
George H. Ramey (Chm)

Subsidiaries:

Bank of Commerce   (1)
322 W 6th St, Chelsea, OK 74016
Tel.: (918) 789-2567
Web Site: http://www.bankboc.com
Sales Range: $1-9.9 Million
Federal Savings Bank
N.A.I.C.S.: 522180
George H. Ramey (Chm)

COMMERCE CONTROLS INC.
41069 Vincenti Ct, Novi, MI 48375
Tel.: (248) 476-1442
Web Site:
   https://www.commercecontrols.com
Year Founded: 1978
Sales Range: $10-24.9 Million
Emp.: 105
Mfr Of Control Panels, Electric
N.A.I.C.S.: 335313
Harold J. Gardynik (Pres)
Nick Stoffins (Dir-Ops)
Bob Gendron (Project Mgr)
Dan Jordan (Engr-Sls)
Gareth Ross (Project Mgr)

COMMERCE MORTGAGE
3130 Crow Canyon Pl Ste 300, San Ramon, CA 94583
Tel.: (925) 275-6844   CA
Web Site:
   http://www.commercehomemortgage.com
Year Founded: 1994
Emp.: 200
Mortgage Financing Services
N.A.I.C.S.: 522292
Scott Simonich (Pres & CEO)
Mario De Tomasi (CEO)
Jeff Simonich (VP-Secondary Mktg)
Dione Thompson (VP-Ops)
Faramarz Moeen-Ziai (VP-Natl Sls)
Jeremy Trimm (VP-IT)
Kristie Berg (VP-Mktg)
Ravi R. Correa (CFO)
Shain Brooks (VP-Capital Markets)

COMMERCE QUALITY FOODS LLC
3185 Maysville Rd, Commerce, GA 30529
Tel.: (706) 335-5050
Web Site:
   https://www.shopqualityfoods.com
Sales Range: $10-24.9 Million
Emp.: 85
Grocery Stores
N.A.I.C.S.: 445110
Betty Miller (Office Mgr)
Verlin Reece (Pres)

COMMERCEBYUS, INC.
5535 Bull Creek Rd, Tarentum, PA 15084
Tel.: (609) 450-8929   PA
Year Founded: 2020
Emp.: 4
Investment Services
N.A.I.C.S.: 523999
Tom BontempoPres (Pres)

COMMERCIAL & HOME FURNISHINGS, INC.
620 NE 19th Ave, Portland, OR 97232-3315
Tel.: (503) 226-4151   OR
Web Site: http://www.smithcfi.com
Year Founded: 1941
Sales Range: $1-9.9 Million
Emp.: 68
Office Furniture Whslr & Repair Refinishing
N.A.I.C.S.: 423210
Graham Hook (Controller)
Jeff Iwasaki (Pres)
Shannon Ferrigno (Dir-Workplace Design Studio)

COMMERCIAL & INDUSTRIAL DESIGN COMPANY INC.
20 Odyssey, Irvine, CA 92618-1886
Tel.: (949) 872-2555   CA
Web Site: http://www.cidesign.com
Year Founded: 1984
Sales Range: $10-24.9 Million
Emp.: 50
Mfr of Computers, Peripherals & Software
N.A.I.C.S.: 423430
Jeff Wu (Pres)

COMMERCIAL AIRCRAFT INTERIORS, LLC
19405 68th Dr NE Ste A, Arlington, WA 98223
Tel.: (360) 757-3117   WA
Web Site: http://www.cai.aero
Year Founded: 2002
Sales Range: $1-9.9 Million
Emp.: 55
Airports, Flying Fields, And Services
N.A.I.C.S.: 488190
Kristin Manley (Mgr)

Subsidiaries:

TTF Aerospace, Inc.   (1)
601 Union St Ste 2600, Seattle, WA 98101-2302
Tel.: (253) 520-6920
Web Site: http://www.ttfaero.com
Search, Detection, Navigation, Guidance, Aeronautical & Nautical System & Instrument Mfr
N.A.I.C.S.: 334511
Brad Wilson (Co-Founder)
Tim Morgan (Co-Founder)

COMMERCIAL ARMATURE WORKS
10029 Marker St Rd, Houston, TX 77029
Tel.: (713) 672-7873
Web Site:
https://www.commercialarmature.com
Year Founded: 1963
Rev.: $1,500,000
Emp.: 10
Fiscal Year-end: 01/31/10
Commercial & Industrial Machinery & Equipment (except Automotive & Electronic) Repair & Maintenance
N.A.I.C.S.: 811310

COMMERCIAL ASSET PARTNERS REALTY
2511 Seven Springs Blvd, Trinity, FL 34655
Tel.: (727) 376-4900
Web Site:
http://www.caprealtypartners.com
Sales Range: $1-9.9 Million
Emp.: 8
Commercial Real Estate Broker
N.A.I.C.S.: 531210
Heidi Ann Tuttle-Beisner (Owner)

COMMERCIAL BANCGROUP, INC.
6710 Cumberland Gap Pkwy, Harrogate, TN 37752
Tel.: (423) 869-5151   TN
Web Site: http://www.cbtn.com
Year Founded: 1975
Sales Range: $10-24.9 Million
Emp.: 150
Bank Holding Company
N.A.I.C.S.: 551111

Subsidiaries:

Commercial Bank   (1)
6710 Cumberland Gap Pkwy, Harrogate, TN 37752
Tel.: (423) 869-5151
Web Site: http://www.cbtn.com

Sales Range: $10-24.9 Million
Emp.: 38
Provider of Banking Services
N.A.I.C.S.: 522110
Terry L. Lee (CEO)
Michelle Huddleston (COO, Chief Compliance Officer & Exec VP)
Craig E. Robertson (Chm)
Alan Gilbert (Officer-Lending, Mortgage & Consumer & Exec VP)
Bernard Kwas (Officer-Western Reg & Exec VP)
Charles E. Lewis (Exec VP-Non-Traditional Banking)
Billy Mayes (Exec VP-HR)
Adam Robertson (Pres)
Rick Sprinkle (Chief Credit Officer & Exec VP)
Dean LaRue (Officer-Southern Reg & Exec VP)
Eddie Jones (Officer-Central Reg & Exec VP)
Phil Metheny (CFO, Chief Risk Officer & Exec VP)
Steve Rhodes (Officer-Northern Reg & Exec VP)
Kenneth N. Raff (Officer-Eastern Reg & Exec VP)

COMMERCIAL BARGAINS INC.
2005 S 54th St, West Allis, WI 53219
Tel.: (414) 581-8015
Web Site:
http://www.commercialbargains.com
Year Founded: 2005
Sales Range: $1-9.9 Million
Emp.: 10
Retail Product Whslr & Distr
N.A.I.C.S.: 423710
John Kenenakhone (Owner)

COMMERCIAL CONSTRUCTION SERVICES, INC.
3621 St Augustine Rd, Jacksonville, FL 32207
Tel.: (904) 551-3003
Web Site:
http://www.ccsjacksonville.com
Year Founded: 2014
Sales Range: $1-9.9 Million
Construction Services
N.A.I.C.S.: 236116
Dan Davis (Owner)

COMMERCIAL CONTRACTORS GROUP INC.
38541 Rhonswood Dr, Northville, MI 48167
Tel.: (248) 477-2503
Web Site: http://www.cccnetwork.com
Sales Range: $1-9.9 Million
Emp.: 25
New Single-Family Housing Construction
N.A.I.C.S.: 236115
Eric A. Adams (Pres)

COMMERCIAL CONTRACTORS INC.
4920 Fairbanks St, Anchorage, AK 99503
Tel.: (907) 563-1911
Web Site: https://www.alaskacci.com
Sales Range: $10-24.9 Million
Emp.: 65
Installer & Furnisher of Floor Coverings
N.A.I.C.S.: 449121
Chris Petersen (Owner)

COMMERCIAL CONTRACTORS, INC.
1205 York Rd, Lutherville Timonium, MD 21093
Tel.: (410) 825-8400
Sales Range: $50-74.9 Million
Emp.: 23
Country Club Membership
N.A.I.C.S.: 236220

Louis Mangione (Pres)
Ed Watt (Controller)

COMMERCIAL CREAMERY CO.
159 S Cedar St, Spokane, WA 99201
Tel.: (509) 747-4131
Web Site:
https://www.cheesepowder.com
Year Founded: 1908
Sales Range: $150-199.9 Million
Emp.: 80
Dairy Products Mfr
N.A.I.C.S.: 311514
Michael Gilmartin (Pres)
Peter Gilmartin (VP)
Megan Gilmartin (Head-Sls)
William Gilmartin (Mgr-Ops)

COMMERCIAL DATA SYSTEMS INC.
50 S Bertania St Ste C 208 B, Honolulu, HI 96813
Tel.: (808) 527-2000
Sales Range: $10-24.9 Million
Emp.: 50
Provider of Computer Part Information Services
N.A.I.C.S.: 449210
Mark Wong (Co-Founder & CEO)
Guy Merola (Co-Founder & CFO)
James Altamirano (Pres)
Tammy Byrd (VP-Svcs)

COMMERCIAL DESIGN ENGINEERING
2710 Delta Pl, Colorado Springs, CO 80910
Tel.: (719) 390-0555
Rev.: $15,887,199
Emp.: 90
Mechanical Contractor
N.A.I.C.S.: 238220
John F. Garvelink (Exec VP)
Mary Garvelink (Pres)
Steve Richardson (Co-Project Mgr)
Dennis Robbins (Mgr-Sls)

COMMERCIAL DESIGN SERVICES, INC.
5805 Barry Rd, Tampa, FL 33634
Tel.: (813) 886-0580
Web Site: http://www.cdstampa.com
Year Founded: 1988
Sales Range: $25-49.9 Million
Emp.: 90
Furniture Retailer
N.A.I.C.S.: 449110
Greg Larsen (Mgr-Ops)
Monica Miller (Dir-Ops)
Stephanie Olenoski (Dir-Design)
Stewart Davis (Owner & Pres)
Mike Bruton (Mgr-Ops-Orlando)
Christopher Ellis (VP)
Michael Head (VP)

COMMERCIAL ENERGY LLC
118 E Main St, Cut Bank, MT 59427
Tel.: (406) 873-3300
Web Site:
https://www.commercialenergy.net
Year Founded: 1997
Rev.: $17,000,000
Emp.: 25
Distr of Natural Gas & Electricity
N.A.I.C.S.: 211120
Ron Perry (Owner, Pres & CEO)
Barbara Perry (Owner)

COMMERCIAL ENTERPRISES LIMITED
625 Middle St, Honolulu, HI 96819
Tel.: (808) 843-8550
Rev.: $14,000,000
Emp.: 18

Packaged Frozen Food Merchant Whslr
N.A.I.C.S.: 424420
Dennis Chun (VP)
Randall Chun (Pres)
Steven Chun (VP)

COMMERCIAL FINANCIAL CORP.
600 Lake Ave, Storm Lake, IA 50588
Tel.: (712) 732-2190
Web Site:
http://www.centralbankonline.com
Sales Range: $1-9.9 Million
Emp.: 200
Bank Holding Company
N.A.I.C.S.: 551111

Subsidiaries:

Central Bank   (1)
600 Lake Ave, Storm Lake, IA 50588
Tel.: (712) 732-2190
Web Site: http://www.centralbankonline.com
Banking Services
N.A.I.C.S.: 522110
Timothy J. Brown (Chm & CEO)
Randy Johnson (COO, Pres-Market & Sr VP)
Michael H. Todd (Sr VP-Comml Lending)
Gary Nagle (Loan Officer & Asst VP)
Judy Ploeger (VP-Branch Ops)
Charlie Larson (Officer-Mortgage Loan & VP)
Larry Anderson (Officer-Bus Dev)
Karen Benecke-Renken (Officer-Mortgage Loan)
Steve Boden (VP & Mgr-Retail Banking & Cash Mgmt)
William Boord (Asst VP & Branch Mgr)
Kevin Brown (Officer-Comml Loan & VP)
John Brown (Pres, CFO & Sec)
Matt Campbell (Officer-Comml Loan & VP)
Stephen Comes (Asst VP & Mgr-Bankcard Svcs)
Vicki Davis (Officer-Mng Mortgage Loan & VP)
Jeff Eaton (Officer-Comml Loan & VP)

COMMERCIAL FIRE & COMMUNICATIONS, INC.
6510-B 125th Ave N, Largo, FL 33773
Tel.: (727) 530-4521   FL
Web Site: http://www.cfcsystems.com
Year Founded: 1980
Sales Range: $1-9.9 Million
Emp.: 70
Fire Alarms, Sprinklers & Security Systems
N.A.I.C.S.: 561621
Richard Haigley (Mgr-Sls)
Mike Brown (Mgr-Svc)
Mark Lediet (Mgr-Installation)
Sean Guthrie (Mgr-Sprinkler)
Chris Mendel (Mgr-Engrg)
Tom Novak (Project Mgr)
Joe Lundin (Project Mgr)
Kimberly Whitt (Office Mgr)
Michael Mariani (Pres)

COMMERCIAL INSURANCE SERVICE CORP
3744 Willow Rdg Rd, Lexington, KY 40514
Tel.: (859) 278-0349
Sales Range: Less than $1 Million
Emp.: 4
Insurance Agents
N.A.I.C.S.: 524210
David Hudson (Pres)

COMMERCIAL INTERIORS INC.
7464 New Ridge Rd Ste 5, Hanover, MD 21076
Tel.: (410) 859-4141
Web Site: http://www.commercial-interiors.com
Rev.: $11,300,000

Commercial Interiors Inc.—(Continued)

Emp.: 186
Drywall & Insulation Contractors
N.A.I.C.S.: 238310
Kevin M. Johnson *(Pres & CEO)*
Bruce D. Tabler *(CFO)*
Ana Garcia *(Controller)*

COMMERCIAL INVESTIGA-TION INCORPORATED

3301C Rte 66, Neptune, NJ 07753
Tel.: (732) 643-0100
Web Site:
   http://www.commercialinvesti
   gation.com
Year Founded: 1975
Rev.: $11,000,000
Emp.: 80
Provider of Insurance Inspection &
Investigation Services
N.A.I.C.S.: 524298
Linda O'Neill *(Pres)*

COMMERCIAL KITCHEN PARTS & SERVICE

1377 N Brazos St, San Antonio, TX
78207
Tel.: (210) 735-2811
Web Site:
   https://www.commercialkitchen.com
Year Founded: 1946
Rev.: $11,200,000
Emp.: 85
Business Products & Services
N.A.I.C.S.: 541910
Vidal Munoz *(Mgr-Svcs)*
Leo Guerra *(Mgr-Svcs)*

COMMERCIAL LAWN CARE SERVICES INC.

4807 110th Ter N, Clearwater, FL
33762
Tel.: (727) 573-5284
Web Site:
   https://www.clcslawncare.com
Sales Range: $1-9.9 Million
Emp.: 30
Landscaping Services
N.A.I.C.S.: 561730
Raylena Kaye Cather *(Pres)*
Linda Osborne *(VP)*

COMMERCIAL LUMBER & PALLET CO.

135 Long Ln, City of Industry, CA
91746
Tel.: (626) 968-0631
Web Site: https://www.clcpallets.com
Rev.: $15,400,000
Emp.: 145
Pallets, Wood
N.A.I.C.S.: 321920
Raymond Gutierrez Sr. *(Pres & CEO)*

COMMERCIAL OFFICE FURNI-TURE CO.

2200 N American St, Philadelphia, PA
19133
Tel.: (215) 291-4648
Web Site: http://www.cofcogroup.com
Sales Range: $10-24.9 Million
Emp.: 70
Furniture Retailer
N.A.I.C.S.: 449110
Joan Waters *(CEO)*

COMMERCIAL PIPE & SUPPLY CORP

1920 Elmwood Ave, Buffalo, NY
14207
Tel.: (716) 875-1300
Web Site:
   https://www.commpipe.com
Rev.: $10,500,000
Emp.: 32

Plumbing & Hydronic Heating Sup-
plies
N.A.I.C.S.: 423720
John L. Hurley Sr. *(Pres)*

COMMERCIAL PLASTERING INC.

212 7th St E, Bradenton, FL 34208
Tel.: (941) 748-0772
Web Site:
   https://commercialplasteringfl.com
Sales Range: $10-24.9 Million
Emp.: 100
Drywall & Insulation Contractors
N.A.I.C.S.: 238310
Christopher Van Hoose *(VP)*
William R. Rice *(Pres)*
Thomas Tyson *(Treas)*

COMMERCIAL POOL SPE-CIALIST, INC.

6400 Topaz Ct Unit 2, Fort Myers, FL
33966
Tel.: (239) 633-5230
Web Site:
   http://www.commercialpoolspe
   cialist.com
Sales Range: $1-9.9 Million
Pool Contractors
N.A.I.C.S.: 238990
Scott Chambers *(Pres)*

COMMERCIAL PROPERTY SOUTHWEST FLORIDA, LLC

5220 Summerlin Commons Blvd Ste
500, Fort Myers, FL 33907
Tel.: (239) 489-3600
Web Site: https://www.cpswfl.com
Sales Range: $10-24.9 Million
Emp.: 10
Commercial Real Estate Broker
N.A.I.C.S.: 531210
Gary Tasman *(CEO)*

COMMERCIAL READY MIX PRODUCTS INC.

115 US 158 W, Winton, NC 27986
Tel.: (252) 358-5461
Web Site: https://www.crmpinc.com
Year Founded: 1975
Sales Range: $10-24.9 Million
Emp.: 130
Concrete & Cinder Block
N.A.I.C.S.: 423320
Bill Ballance *(Mgr-Ahoskie)*
Steve Duncan *(Area Mgr)*
Charles Harrell *(Gen Mgr)*

COMMERCIAL REAL ESTATE CONSULTANTS, LLC

12140 Carissa Commerce Ct Ste
102, Fort Myers, FL 33966
Tel.: (239) 481-3800
Web Site:
   https://www.creconsultants.com
Sales Range: $10-24.9 Million
Emp.: 40
Commercial Real Estate Broker
N.A.I.C.S.: 531210
Scott Dunnuck *(Partner)*
Fred Kermani *(Partner)*
Erin Luthringer *(Partner)*
Randal Mercer *(Partner)*
Raymond F. Sandelli *(Mng Partner)*
Stan Stouder *(Partner)*
Jodie Wilkerson *(Sr Mgr-Real Estate)*
Jim Clement *(Dir-Asset Svcs)*

COMMERCIAL RESINS COM-PANY

8100 East 96th Ave, Henderson, CO
80640
Tel.: (918) 438-6522
Web Site:
   http://www.commercialresins.com

Year Founded: 1968
Sales Range: $10-24.9 Million
Emp.: 20
Corrosion Control Installation Ser-
vices
N.A.I.C.S.: 238990
Patti Savolt *(Office Mgr)*
Martin Gandarilla *(Gen Mgr)*

Subsidiaries:

Commercial Resins Company, Corro-
sion Coating and Technology &
Services   (1)
8100 E 96 Ave, Henderson, CO 80640
Tel.: (303) 288-3914
Web Site: http://www.commercialresins.com
Providers of Pipeline Field Services & Pipe-
line Project Supplies
N.A.I.C.S.: 238990

COMMERCIAL ROOFERS, INC.

3865 W Naples Dr, Las Vegas, NV
89103-5526
Tel.: (702) 876-1777   **NV**
Web Site: https://www.commroof.com
Year Founded: 1945
Sales Range: $25-49.9 Million
Emp.: 250
Installation & Repair of Industrial &
Commercial Roofing Systems
N.A.I.C.S.: 238160
Dennis Conway *(Principal & VP)*
Penny Padilla *(Controller & Office
Mgr)*
Bruce Martin *(Gen Mgr-Sls & Sr Proj-
ect Mgr)*
Dennis Perry *(Sr Project Mgr & Mgr-
Ops)*
Ray Snow *(Mgr-Svcs)*
David Ramos *(Dir-Safety)*

COMMERCIAL ROOFING SPE-CIALTIES INC.

2703 Peachtree Sq, Atlanta, GA
30360-2634
Tel.: (678) 547-1084   **GA**
Web Site: http://www.crssupply.com
Year Founded: 1981
Sales Range: $10-24.9 Million
Emp.: 43
Roofing Supplies
N.A.I.C.S.: 423330
Larry Burns *(Founder & Pres)*
Jeanette Akins *(Mgr-Credit)*
Adam Yelton *(VP)*

COMMERCIAL SERVICES GROUP INCORPORATED

11603 Shelbyville Rd Ste 3, Louis-
ville, KY 40243
Tel.: (502) 244-6900
Web Site: http://www.collectcsg.com
Sales Range: $100-124.9 Million
Emp.: 20
Adjustment & Collection Services
N.A.I.C.S.: 561440
Charles Neumann *(Pres)*
Larry Cundiff *(VP-Sls)*
Steve Gray *(Dir-Legal)*
Robert Davis *(CTO)*

COMMERCIAL SERVICES INC.

1201 NW 65th Pl, Fort Lauderdale,
FL 33309
Tel.: (954) 971-9393
Year Founded: 1979
Sales Range: $100-124.9 Million
Emp.: 1,050
Jewelry Stores Owner & Operator
N.A.I.C.S.: 458310
Tom Hoy *(CEO)*

COMMERCIAL SIDING AND MAINTENANCE CO

8860 Lambright Rd, Houston, TX
77075

Tel.: (440) 352-7800
Web Site:
   http://www.commercialsiding.com
Year Founded: 1960
Sales Range: $10-24.9 Million
Emp.: 30
Roofing Contractors
N.A.I.C.S.: 238160
Tim Lane *(Pres)*

COMMERCIAL STEEL PROD-UCTS LLC

3626 N Hall St Ste 910, Dallas, TX
75219
Tel.: (469) 405-2220
Web Site: https://www.cspmetals.com
Emp.: 100
Steel Product Distr
N.A.I.C.S.: 331110
Thomas Sfikas *(Pres)*

Subsidiaries:

ACE Steel Supply, Inc.   (1)
203 Blue Bell Rd, Houston, TX 77037-1307
Tel.: (832) 300-1030
Web Site: http://www.acesteelsupply.com
Metal Service Centers & Other Metal Mer-
chant Whslr
N.A.I.C.S.: 423510
Adam Osborn *(Pres)*

COMMERCIAL STEEL TREAT-ING CORP.

31440 Stephenson Hwy, Madison
Heights, MI 48071-1621
Tel.: (248) 588-3300   **MI**
Web Site:
   http://www.commercialsteel.com
Year Founded: 1927
Sales Range: $50-74.9 Million
Emp.: 240
Metal Coating Services
N.A.I.C.S.: 332812
Scott Hoensheid *(Pres)*
Randy Morrison *(Controller)*
Joe Bonfoey *(Engr-Sls)*
Curt Holmes *(VP-Quality & Metal-
lurgy)*

Subsidiaries:

Curtis Metal Finishing Co., Inc.   (1)
6645 Sims Dr, Sterling Heights, MI 48313-
3726
Tel.: (586) 939-2851
Web Site: http://www.curtismetal.com
Sales Range: $25-49.9 Million
Emp.: 150
Metal Coating Services
N.A.I.C.S.: 332812

COMMERCIAL STOREFRONT SERVICES, INC.

1265 John Fitch Blvd, South Windsor,
CT 06074
Tel.: (860) 282-7122
Sales Range: $1-9.9 Million
Emp.: 11
Commercial & Institutional Building
Construction Services
N.A.I.C.S.: 236220
Kenneth R. Jeski *(Pres)*

COMMERCIAL TIRE INC.

2095 E Commercial St, Meridian, ID
83642
Tel.: (208) 888-8800
Web Site:
   https://www.commercialtire.com
Year Founded: 1968
Sales Range: $10-24.9 Million
Emp.: 300
Tires & Automotive Products
N.A.I.C.S.: 811114
Mike Hampton *(VP-Administration)*

COMMERCIAL TRAVELERS MUTUAL INSURANCE COM-PANY

70 Genesee St, Utica, NY 13502
Tel.: (315) 797-5200 NY
Web Site:
http://www.commercialtravelers.com
Year Founded: 1883
Sales Range: $25-49.9 Million
Emp.: 100
Mutual Insurance Company; School &
College Health & Accident Insurance,
Sports Coverage, Small Employer
Group Life & Disablity Income
N.A.I.C.S.: 524113
Vincent Pugliese (Mgr-Sys & Pro-
gramming)

Subsidiaries:

Monitor Life Insurance Company of
New York (1)
70 Genesee St, Utica, NY
13502-3502 (100%)
Tel.: (315) 797-5200
Web Site:
http://www.commercialtravelers.com
Sales Range: $25-49.9 Million
Emp.: 45
Life Insurance
N.A.I.C.S.: 524113
Phil Grece (VP)

COMMERCIAL WAREHOUSE & CARTAGE, INC.
3402 Meyer Rd, Fort Wayne, IN
46803
Tel.: (260) 426-7825
Web Site: https://www.cwclogon.com
Sales Range: $10-24.9 Million
Emp.: 575
General Warehousing
N.A.I.C.S.: 493110
Gregg Parrish (Owner & Pres)

COMMERCIAL WARRANTY SOLUTIONS, LLC
4343 Will Rogers Pkwy, Oklahoma
City, OK 73108-1817
Tel.: (405) 947-2827
Web Site: http://www.assetintel.com
Holding Company
N.A.I.C.S.: 551112
Fernando Hernandez (Owner)

Subsidiaries:

Kemper Cost Management, Inc. (1)
4343 Will Rogers Pkwy, Oklahoma City, OK
73108-1817
Tel.: (405) 947-2827
Web Site: http://www.assetintel.com
Sales Range: $10-24.9 Million
Emp.: 30
Insurance Information & Consulting Ser-
vices
N.A.I.C.S.: 524298

COMMERCIAL WORKS INC.
1299 Boltonfield St, Columbus, OH
43228
Tel.: (614) 870-2342
Web Site: https://www.commercial-
works.com
Sales Range: $10-24.9 Million
Emp.: 220
Trucking Except Local
N.A.I.C.S.: 484121
Kevin McCreary (VP-Sls & Mktg)
Michael Robinson (Dir-HR & Safety)
Greg Clark (CEO & COO)
Todd Hartman (VP-Furniture)
Randy Weinstein (Dir-Ops)
Cheri Cobb (Reg VP)
Michael Keeney (Reg VP)
Tim Cooper (Mgr-Sls)

COMMISSION ON ACCREDITA-TION OF REHABILITATION FA-CILITIES
6951 E Southpoint Rd, Tucson, AZ
85756-9407

Tel.: (520) 325-1044 AZ
Web Site: https://www.carf.org
Year Founded: 1994
Sales Range: $25-49.9 Million
Emp.: 1,260
Accreditation Services
N.A.I.C.S.: 561990
Brian J. Boon (Pres & CEO)
Cindy L. Johnson (Chief Resource &
Strategic Dev Officer)
Bettye Harrison (Acct Mgr)
Mary Jo Fitzgerald (Mgr-Acct)
Di Shen (Chief Res Officer)

COMMISSION ON ECONOMIC OPPORTUNITY
165 Amber Ln, Wilkes Barre, PA
18702
Tel.: (570) 826-0510 PA
Web Site:
https://www.ceopeoplehelping
people.org
Year Founded: 1966
Sales Range: $10-24.9 Million
Emp.: 212
Anti-Poverty Advocacy Services
N.A.I.C.S.: 813319
David Aikens (VP)
Dan McGowan (CEO & VP)
Gary Lamont (Treas)
Hugh Mundy (Pres)

COMMISSIONERS OF PUBLIC WORKS
121 W Ct Ave, Greenwood, SC
29646-2748
Tel.: (864) 942-8100
Web Site:
https://www.greenwoodcpw.com
Sales Range: $50-74.9 Million
Natural Gas, Electricity & Water
Transmission
N.A.I.C.S.: 486210
Arthur C. Bush (Chm)
Michael G. Monaghan (Sec)
Steve D. Reeves Jr. (Mgr)

COMMITTED CAPITAL ACQUI-SITION CORPORATION II
712 5th Ave 22nd Fl, New York, NY
10019
Tel.: (212) 759-2020 DE
Year Founded: 2011
CCAQ—(OTCBB)
Sales Range: Less than $1 Million
Emp.: 2
Investment Services
N.A.I.C.S.: 523999
Michael Rapoport (Chm & CEO)

COMMITTEE FOR A RESPON-SIBLE FEDERAL BUDGET
1899 L St NW Ste 400, Washington,
DC 20036
Tel.: (202) 596-3597 DC
Web Site: http://www.crfb.org
Year Founded: 1981
Sales Range: $10-24.9 Million
Emp.: 21
Financial Advisory Services
N.A.I.C.S.: 813410
Mike Murphy (Dir-Strategic Initiatives)
Marc Goldwein (Sr VP & Sr Dir-
Policy)
Leon Panetta (Co-Chm)
Timothy Penny (Co-Chm)
Maya MacGuineas (Pres)

COMMODITY BLENDERS INC.
10510 Myers Rd, West Salem, OH
44287
Tel.: (419) 846-3155
Web Site:
https://www.commodityblender.com
Year Founded: 1978
Sales Range: $25-49.9 Million

Emp.: 9
Animal Feed Mfr
N.A.I.C.S.: 311119
Bruce A. Keener (Pres)
Deanna Keener (VP)
Paul Keener (Mgr-Ops)

COMMODITY COMPONENTS INTERNATIONAL
100 Summit St, Peabody, MA 01960
Tel.: (978) 538-0020
Web Site: http://www.cci-inc.com
Rev.: $35,154,282
Emp.: 40
Semiconductor Devices
N.A.I.C.S.: 423690
Marc S. Levin (Founder & Chm)
Jeff MacBurnie (Mgr-OEM Sls)
Doug Sutherland (Gen Mgr)
Tammy Wile (Dir-Ops)

COMMODITY MARKETING COMPANY
8480 Holcomb Bridge Rd Ste D200,
Alpharetta, GA 30022
Tel.: (678) 566-7820
Web Site:
http://www.commoditymktg.com
Year Founded: 1935
Sales Range: $50-74.9 Million
Emp.: 7
Animal Feed
N.A.I.C.S.: 424910
Vince Connolly (Pres)

COMMODITY RESOURCE & ENVIRONMENTAL INC
116 E Prospect Ave, Burbank, CA
91502-9946
Tel.: (818) 843-2811
Web Site: https://www.creweb.com
Sales Range: $10-24.9 Million
Emp.: 10
Provider of Precious Metals
N.A.I.C.S.: 331410
Larry J. Dewitt (Pres)
Aleksandra Jaric (Mgr-Corp Acctg &
Mktg)
Charles Yohn (VP-Sls)
Natasa Zeljkovic-Karabuva (Mgr-HR)
Stacy Aesoph (Pres)

COMMODITY SERVICES INC.
6 Krahmer Dr, Fairmont, MN 56031
Tel.: (507) 238-9411
Web Site:
http://www.commodityservice.com
Year Founded: 1980
Sales Range: $10-24.9 Million
Emp.: 13
Brokers of Truck Transportation
N.A.I.C.S.: 488510
Terry Maakestad (Pres)

COMMODITY SPECIALISTS COMPANY INC.
920 2nd Ave S Ste 850, Minneapolis,
MN 55402
Tel.: (612) 330-9100 DE
Web Site: http://www.csc-world.com
Year Founded: 1993
Sales Range: $10-24.9 Million
Emp.: 105
Provider of Agricultural Products
Trading & Marketing Services
N.A.I.C.S.: 424910
Bill Mikkelson (Chm)
Gordon Stengel (Mgr)
Phil Lindau Jr. (Pres)

Subsidiaries:

CSC Transportation LLC (1)
4929 1 Mile Rd, Fremont, MI 49412
Tel.: (231) 924-5578
Trucking & Transport Services
N.A.I.C.S.: 484121

Steve Tanner (District Mgr-Albany)
Heidi Cook (Coord-Albany)
Rhonda Mott (Mgr-Trucking-Baldwinville &
Merrimack)
Debra Vines (Coord-Carterville)
Tom Grube (Mgr-Trucking-Columbus)
Bonnie Carney (Mgr-Trucking-Jacksonville)
Doreen Dintelman (Mgr-Transportation Dev
& Safety)
Bill Cromie (Mgr-Natl Trucking-Tampa)
Mike Krusenklaus (Mgr-Terminal-
Williamsberg)
Janet Brownley (Coord-Williamsberg)

COMMODORE BUILDERS
404 Wyman St Ste 400, Waltham,
MA 02451
Tel.: (617) 614-3500
Web Site:
http://www.commodorebuilders.com
Year Founded: 2002
Sales Range: $25-49.9 Million
Emp.: 110
General Contractor & Construction
Management Services
N.A.I.C.S.: 236220
Joe Albanese (Founder & CEO)
John Grady (Mgr-MEP)
Jim Hennelly (Mgr-Safety)
Tom Winterhalter (Mng Dir-Ops)
Dave Jolin (CFO)
Sean Curtin (Dir-Bus Dev-Comml
Market)
Michael Roche (Gen Counsel & VP)
Paul Martini (Principal, Sr VP & Dir-
Bus Dev)
Kelli Mcleod (Dir-Mktg)
Carol Roby (Dir-Learning & Dev)
Michael Orbank (Mgr-Sustainability)
Mike Clark (Dir-Preconstruction)
Marcia Carlson (Sr Project Mgr-
Institutional Grp)

COMMODORE INSURANCE SERVICES
140 Mayhew Way Ste 300, Pleasant
Hill, CA 94523
Tel.: (510) 899-6500
Web Site:
http://www.commodoreins.com
Rev.: $24,000,000
Emp.: 40
Insurance Brokers
N.A.I.C.S.: 524210
Dan Murphy (CEO)
Lupe Velasquez (Sr VP & Dir-
Contractors Svcs)
Tony Tollman (Sr VP)

COMMODORE MANUFACTUR-ING CORPORATION
3913 2nd Ave, Brooklyn, NY 11232
Tel.: (718) 788-2600
Rev.: $14,100,000
Emp.: 60
Christmas Novelties
N.A.I.C.S.: 333517
Abraham Damast (Pres)

COMMON ANGLE, INC.
616 Petoskey St Ste 300, Petoskey,
MI 49770
Web Site:
http://www.commonangle.com
Year Founded: 2012
Sales Range: $1-9.9 Million
Emp.: 50
Information Technology Consulting
Services
N.A.I.C.S.: 541512
Des Moore (Pres)

COMMON APPLICATION
3033 Wilson Blvd 500, Arlington, VA
22201
Tel.: (703) 378-9788 VA

Common Application—(Continued)

Web Site:
http://www.commonapp.org
Year Founded: 2000
Sales Range: $10-24.9 Million
Emp.: 7
Educational Support Services
N.A.I.C.S.: 611710
Jenny Rickard (Exec Dir)

COMMON INTEREST MANAGEMENT SERVICES INC.
315 Diablo Rd Ste 221, Danville, CA 94526-3409
Tel.: (925) 743-3080
Web Site:
https://www.commoninterest.com
Year Founded: 1990
Real Estate Management Services
N.A.I.C.S.: 531311
Jean Salvia (Mgr)

Subsidiaries:

Jones & Forrest, Inc. (1)
3851 Charter Park Dr, San Jose, CA 95136
Tel.: (408) 269-9040
Web Site: http://www.jonesandforrest.com
Sales Range: $1-9.9 Million
Emp.: 12
Real Estate Management Services
N.A.I.C.S.: 531311

COMMON SENSE OFFICE FURNITURE
820 W Washington St, Orlando, FL 32805
Tel.: (407) 206-5040
Web Site:
https://www.commonsenseof.com
Year Founded: 1997
Sales Range: $1-9.9 Million
Emp.: 12
Office Furniture Sales, Leasing & Rental Services
N.A.I.C.S.: 449110
Craig Caswell (Pres)

COMMONBOND COMMUNITIES
1080 Montreal Ave, Saint Paul, MN 55116
Tel.: (651) 291-1750
Web Site:
http://www.commonbond.org
Sales Range: $10-24.9 Million
Emp.: 230
Land Subdividing Services
N.A.I.C.S.: 237210
Paul Fate (Pres)
Andrew Michaelson (Sr Project Mgr)
Allyssa Woodford Hughes (Sr Project Mgr)
Ann Ruff (VP-Resource Dev)
Deirdre Lal Schmidt (Pres & CEO)
Anne Elise Tschida (Treas)
Richard Wicka (Vice Chm)
Bob Mueller (Dir-Construction Mgmt)
Lisa Wilcox-Erhardt (Exec VP-Housing & Svcs)
Tammie Fallon (Mgr-Construction Project)
Kelly Matter (VP-Advantage Svcs)
Ellen Higgins (VP-Bus Dev)
Andrew Babula (Dir-Acq & Dev)
Debora M. Frodl (Chief Strategy Officer)

COMMONSPIRIT HEALTH
444 W Lk St Ste 2500, Chicago, IL 60606-0097
Tel.: (312) 741-7000
Web Site:
https://www.commonspirit.org
Hospital & Health Care Services
N.A.I.C.S.: 622110
Marvin O'Quinn (Pres & COO)

COMMONWEALTH ARCHITECTS, P.C.
101 Shockoe Slip 3rd Fl, Richmond, VA 23219
Tel.: (804) 648-5040   VA
Web Site: http://www.comarchs.com
Year Founded: 1999
Architectural Services
N.A.I.C.S.: 541310
Dominic Venuto (Co-Founder & Principal)
Robert C. Burns (Principal)
Lee A. Shadbolt (Principal)
Kenneth W. Pope (Principal)
Thomas B. Heatwole (Principal)
Walter Redfearn (Pres)
Shannon MacKenzie (Coord-Mktg)
Bryan Green (Dir-Historic Reservation)
David Abbott (Coord-Mktg)

COMMONWEALTH BANCORP
2812 Santa Monica Blvd Ste 204, Santa Monica, CA 90404
Tel.: (310) 450-3100
Web Site:
http://www.commonwealthbank.com
Rev.: $11,000,000
Emp.: 5
Mortgage Brokers Arranging for Loans
N.A.I.C.S.: 522310
Juan D. Guiga (Pres)
Brian Maynard (Acct Exec)
Elena McClelland (Acct Exec)
Heather Kuhn (Acct Exec)
Ambrose Price (Acct Exec)
Martha Johnston (Acct Exec)
Carole Jones (Acct Exec)

COMMONWEALTH CAPITAL CORP.
17755 US Hwy 19 N Ste 400, Clearwater, FL 33764-6500
Tel.: (727) 450-0750
Web Site: http://www.ccclease.com
Year Founded: 1978
Sales Range: $10-24.9 Million
Emp.: 85
Equipment Leasing & Investment Banking Services
N.A.I.C.S.: 532420
Kimberly A. Springsteen-Abbott (Owner, Chm & CEO)
Henry J. Abbott (Pres & CEO)
Jay Dugan (CTO, Chief Security Officer & Exec VP)
Mark Hershenson (Sr VP & Mgr-Relationship)
James Pruett (Chief Compliance Officer & Sr VP)
David Riggleman (Sr VP & Portfolio Mgr)

Subsidiaries:

Commonwealth Capital Securities Corp. (1)
17755 US Hwy 19 N Ste 400, Clearwater, FL 33764-6500
Tel.: (727) 938-5933
Web Site: http://www.ccclease.com
Investment Banking
N.A.I.C.S.: 523150
Henry J. Abbott (Chm, Pres & CEO)
Jay Dugan (CTO & Exec VP)
Lynn A. Franceschina (COO & Exec VP)
Mark Hershenson (Sr VP & Mgr-Rels)
James Pruett (Chief Compliance Officer & Sr VP)
David Riggleman (Sr VP)

COMMONWEALTH CARE ALLIANCE, INC.
30 Winter St, Boston, MA 02108
Tel.: (617) 426-0600   MA
Web Site:
http://www.commonwealthcare.org

Year Founded: 2003
Sales Range: $250-299.9 Million
Emp.: 622
Community Health Care Services
N.A.I.C.S.: 621498
John Loughnane (Sr VP-Medical Svcs)
Jan Levinson (Sr VP-Clinical Program Dev)
Toyin Ajayi (Chief Medical Officer)
Courtney Sullivan Murphy (Pres-Markets)
Mihir Shah (CFO)
Chris Palmieri (Pres & CEO)
Don Stiffler (Chief Corp Dev Officer)
Elizabeth Cahn Goodman (Chief Legal & Pub Affairs Officer)

COMMONWEALTH CENTRAL CREDIT UNION
5890 Silver Creek Valley Rd, San Jose, CA 95138
Tel.: (408) 531-3100   CA
Web Site: https://www.wealthcu.org
Year Founded: 1958
Sales Range: $10-24.9 Million
Emp.: 110
Credit Union
N.A.I.C.S.: 522130
Lisa Brown (VP-HR & Admin)
Sylvia Granger (VP-Retail Svcs)
Craig Weber (Pres & CEO)
Viktoria Earle (CFO & VP-Fin)
James Crawford (Chm)
Lyle Chambers (Treas)
Robert Bryant (Sec)
Jerry Weltzin (Vice Chm)

COMMONWEALTH CREATIVE ASSOCIATES
345 Union Ave, Framingham, MA 01702
Tel.: (508) 620-6664
Web Site:
http://www.commcreative.com
Sales Range: $50-74.9 Million
Emp.: 20
Advertising, Brand Development & Integration, Digital/Interactive, Education, Financial, Health Care, Local Marketing, New Technologies, Nonprofit/Social Marketing, Public Relations
N.A.I.C.S.: 541810
Bob Fields (Pres)
Steve Close (VP & Dir-Creative)
Myles Bristowe (CMO)
Alex Nosevich (Dir-Creative)
Donna Phelps (Sr Acct Exec)
Joanna Bittle (Dir-Interactive Svcs)

COMMONWEALTH CREDIT UNION
PO Box 978, Frankfort, KY 40602-0978
Tel.: (502) 564-4775   KY
Web Site: https://www.ccuky.org
Year Founded: 1951
Sales Range: $25-49.9 Million
Emp.: 324
Financial Support Services
N.A.I.C.S.: 813219
Gloria Thomas (Chief Branch Svcs Officer)
David Young (Exec VP)
Karen Maxfield (Chief HR Officer)
Jim Chadwell (Treas & Sec)
Karen Harbin (Pres & CEO)
Regina Grubbs (Vice Chm)
Bethany Patton (Mgr-Louisville Road)
Danielle Luigart (Mgr-Meijer)
Kim Durrum (VP-Branch Svcs)
Stephen Bellas (CFO)
Patty Smith (CMO)

COMMONWEALTH CRYSTAL HOLDING II, INC.
11777 San Vicente Blvd Ste 900, Los Angeles, CA 90049
Tel.: (310) 820-6661   DE
Year Founded: 2004
Sales Range: $10-24.9 Million
Real Estate Services
N.A.I.C.S.: 531390
Michael S. Balaban (VP)
Salve A. Pennya (VP & Asst Sec)
Peter R. O'Keeffe (VP)
Katya J. Naman (VP)
Kerri A. O'Neill (VP)
Bleecker P. Seaman III (Pres)

COMMONWEALTH DESIGNS, INC.
161 N Eagle Creek Dr Ste 200, Lexington, KY 40509
Tel.: (859) 277-1600
Web Site: https://www.cwdky.com
Residential Construction
N.A.I.C.S.: 236115
John D. Barlow (Pres)

COMMONWEALTH DODGE
6408 Preston Hwy, Louisville, KY 40219-1818
Tel.: (502) 785-9648
Web Site:
https://www.commonwealth
dodge.com
Sales Range: $25-49.9 Million
Emp.: 92
New Car Retailer
N.A.I.C.S.: 441110
Chris Coffman (Controller)
William E. Hays Sr. (Pres)

COMMONWEALTH ELECTRIC COMPANY OF THE MIDWEST INC.
1901 Y St Ste 100, Lincoln, NE 68503-2446
Tel.: (402) 474-1341   NE
Web Site:
http://www.commonwealthelec
tric.com
Year Founded: 1987
Sales Range: $25-49.9 Million
Emp.: 463
Electrical Services
N.A.I.C.S.: 238210
Mike King (Branch Mgr)

COMMONWEALTH EQUITY SERVICES LLP
29 Sawyer Rd, Waltham, MA 02453
Tel.: (781) 736-0700
Web Site:
http://www.commonwealth.com
Year Founded: 1979
Sales Range: $600-649.9 Million
Emp.: 500
Securities Brokerage & Investment Banking
N.A.I.C.S.: 523150
Joseph S. Deitch (Founder & Chm)
Richard Hunter (Mng Partner)
David Kelly (Mng Principal-Ops-Trading & Brokerage)
Kate Creagh (Mng Principal-HR)
Wayne Bloom (CEO)
Peter Wheeler (Vice Chm)
Andrew Daniels (Mng Principal-Bus Dev)
Darren Tedesco (Mng Principal-Innovation & Strategy)
Joni Youngwirth (Mng Principal-Practice Mgmt)
John Rooney (Mng Principal-San Diego)
Trap Kloman (Pres & COO)
Karen McColl (Sr VP-Wealth Mgmt)

Greg Gohr *(Mng Principal-Wealth Mgmt)*
Kristin Albano *(Mgr-Mktg Comm)*
Peggy Ho *(Gen Counsel & Sr VP)*

COMMONWEALTH HOSIERY MILLS
4964 Is Ford Rd, Randleman, NC 27317
Tel.: (336) 498-2621
Web Site: http://www.commonwealth-hosiery.com
Sales Range: $10-24.9 Million
Emp.: 200
Socks
N.A.I.C.S.: 315120
John Freeze *(CEO)*

COMMONWEALTH INCOME & GROWTH FUND 8, LP
Brandywine Office Park 2 Christy Dr Ste 200, Chadds Ford, PA 19317 PA
Investment Services
N.A.I.C.S.: 523999
Kimberly A. Springsteen-Abbott *(Chm & CEO)*
Henry J. Abbott *(Pres)*

COMMONWEALTH PACKAGING COMPANY
5490 Linglestown Rd, Harrisburg, PA 17112
Tel.: (717) 657-3113
Web Site: https://www.commonwealthpackaging.com
Year Founded: 1958
Sales Range: $10-24.9 Million
Emp.: 50
Distr of Custom Packaging
N.A.I.C.S.: 424130
Mark Maisel *(CEO)*
Steve Maisel *(Pres)*

Subsidiaries:

Commonwealth Packaging Company, Packaging Service **(1)**
7652 Trade St Ste B, San Diego, CA 92121
Tel.: (858) 695-2779
Web Site: http://www.commonwealthpackaging.com
Sales Range: $10-24.9 Million
Emp.: 10
Distr of Custom Packaging
N.A.I.C.S.: 424130
Mark Maisel *(CEO)*

COMMONWEALTH PUBLIC BROADCASTING CORP.
23 Sesame St, Richmond, VA 23235
Tel.: (804) 320-1301
Web Site: http://www.ideastations.org
Year Founded: 1964
Sales Range: $10-24.9 Million
Emp.: 90
Operator of Public Television & Radio Broadcasting Stations
N.A.I.C.S.: 516120
A. Curtis Monk *(Pres & CEO)*
Lisa Tait *(VP-Dev)*
John H. Felton *(VP & Gen Mgr-Television)*

COMMONWEALTH REALTY PARTNERS, INC.
PO Box 1083, Newburyport, MA 01950
Tel.: (978) 255-2949 NV
Year Founded: 2009
Real Estate Investment Services
N.A.I.C.S.: 525990
Chris Cronin *(Pres, CEO, Treas & Sec)*

COMMONWEALTH TOY & NOVELTY COMPANY
45 W 25th St, New York, NY 10010-2003
Tel.: (212) 242-4070 NY
Web Site: http://www.commonwealthtoy.com
Year Founded: 1934
Sales Range: $50-74.9 Million
Emp.: 25
Mfr & Wholesale Distributor of Stuffed Toys; Sales Promotion
N.A.I.C.S.: 339930
Harvey Greenfield *(Chm)*
Lee Schneider *(Pres)*
Lindya Lauro *(VP-Admin)*
Matt Giadanno *(Controller)*

COMMONWEALTH VENTURE FUNDING GROUP
PO Box 3009, Wakefield, MA 01880
Tel.: (781) 684-0095
Web Site: https://www.cvfg.com
Year Founded: 1998
Rev.: $60,000,000
Equity Investment Management Company
N.A.I.C.S.: 551112
Thomas H. Conway *(Founder & Pres)*
William J. Booth *(Partner & VP)*
Richard G. Phipps *(Partner & VP)*

COMMONWEALTH WINE & SPIRITS LLC
2300 Stanley Gault Pkwy, Louisville, KY 40223
Tel.: (502) 254-8600
Web Site: https://www.rndc-usa.com
Sales Range: $50-74.9 Million
Emp.: 100
Wholesalers Of Wine
N.A.I.C.S.: 424820
Bertner Smith *(CEO)*
Bob Ware *(Pres)*
Greg Johnson *(CFO)*
Tom Cole *(Co-Pres)*

COMMONWEALTH WOOD PRESERVERS
5604 City Line Rd, Hampton, VA 23661
Tel.: (757) 247-3621
Web Site: http://www.commonwealthwood.com
Year Founded: 1976
Sales Range: $50-74.9 Million
Emp.: 80
Lumber: Rough, Dressed & Finished
N.A.I.C.S.: 423310
Glenn Matheny *(Mgr-Transportation)*

COMMONWEALTH WORLD-WIDE CHAUFFEURED TRANSPORTATION
250 Everett St, Allston, MA 02134
Tel.: (617) 787-5575
Web Site: http://www.commonwealthlimo.com
Year Founded: 2004
Sales Range: $25-49.9 Million
Emp.: 360
Chauffeured Transportation Services
N.A.I.C.S.: 485320
Dawson Rutter *(Founder & Pres)*
Keith Jones *(Coord-Travel)*
Colleen Bowdren *(Supvr-Billing)*
Rebecca S. Sahlin *(VP-Sls)*
Stephen McLane *(CFO)*
Diane Pessolano *(Controller)*
Joseph Rucker *(Dir-Chauffeur Svcs)*
Min Zhang *(Dir-IT)*

COMMONWEALTH ZOOLOGICAL CORPORATION
1 Franklin Park Rd, Boston, MA 02121
Tel.: (617) 989-2000
Web Site: https://www.zoonewengland.org
Sales Range: $10-24.9 Million
Emp.: 175
Zoo Operator
N.A.I.C.S.: 712130
John Linehan *(Pres & CEO)*
Brooke Waldrop *(Dir-Comm)*

COMMOTION PROMOTIONS, LTD.
2999 N 44th St Ste 340, Phoenix, AZ 85018-7246
Tel.: (602) 996-0006 AZ
Web Site: http://www.commotionpromotions.com
Year Founded: 1984
Sales Range: $1-9.9 Million
Emp.: 30
Advertising Services
N.A.I.C.S.: 541613
Kenneth Kravitz *(Co-Owner, CEO, Sec & VP)*
Aliza Kravitz *(Mgr-PR)*
Karen Kravitz *(Pres & Co-Owner)*

COMMUNE HOTELS & RESORTS, LLC
530 Bush St Ste 501, San Francisco, CA 94108
Tel.: (415) 835-0300 DE
Web Site: http://www.communehotels.com
Holding Company; Hotel & Resort Investment & Management Services
N.A.I.C.S.: 551112
John Pritzker *(Chm)*
Niki Leondakis *(CEO)*
Stephen Miano *(CFO)*
Rick Colangelo *(Exec VP-Ops)*
Greg Smith *(Exec VP-People Svcs)*
Jorge Trevino *(Exec VP-Brand Ops)*
Todd Wynne-Parry *(Exec VP-Acq & Dev)*
Karolina Kielbowicz *(Sr Dir-PR)*

Subsidiaries:

Commune Hotels & Resorts Asia Pte. Ltd. **(1)**
15 Scotts Road #04-10 Thong Teck Building, Singapore, 228218, Singapore
Tel.: (65) 6735 8300
Web Site: http://www.communehotels.com
Hotel & Resort Investment & Management Services
N.A.I.C.S.: 721110
Mark Edleson *(Pres)*
Frederic Flageat-Simon *(CEO)*

Destination Hotels and Resorts, Inc. **(1)**
10333 E Dry Creek Rd Ste 450, Englewood, CO 80112 **(100%)**
Tel.: (303) 799-3830
Hotels & Motels
N.A.I.C.S.: 721110
James Sabatier *(CEO)*
Mark Hays *(CFO & Sr VP)*
Marie Torres *(VP-Mktg & Branding)*
Dani Stern *(Sr VP-Ops-Western Reg)*
Maureen Callahan *(VP-Mktg, Comm & PR)*
Max Roth *(Dir-Sls & Mktg)*
Thomas P. Luersen *(COO)*
Lou Trope *(Sr VP-Food & Beverage Experiences)*
Mark Jennings *(Sr VP-Ops-East)*
Andre Fournier *(Exec VP-Sls & Mktg)*
Mark Hickey *(Exec VP-Mgmt Contracts)*
Candace Johnson *(VP-Market Analysis)*
Robert Mellwig *(Sr VP-Really Cool People)*
Kevin Regan *(Sr VP-Ops-Western)*
Shirli J. Sensenbrenner *(Sr VP-Design & Devt Svcs)*
Freddy Hernandez *(Dir-Mktg & PR-Quirk Hotel)*
Jorge E. Trevino *(Exec VP-Brand Ops)*
Rick Colangelo *(Exec VP-Ops)*
Landy Labadie *(Sr VP-Restaurants, Bars & Nightlife)*
Becky Lumly *(Sr VP-Fin)*

Kathleen A. Cullen *(Sr VP-Revenue & Distr)*
Steve Santomo *(Sr VP-Destination & Retail Mgmt)*
Paolo Torchio *(VP-E-Commerce & Digital)*
Frederic Flageat-Simon *(CEO-Asia (Alila))*
Mark Edleson *(Pres-Asia (Alila))*

Unit (Domestic):

Hilton Denver Inverness **(2)**
200 Inverness Dr W, Englewood, CO 80112-5200
Tel.: (303) 799-5800
Web Site: http://www.hiltondenverinverness.com
Hotels & Motels
N.A.I.C.S.: 721110
David Larson *(Dir-Ops)*

Subsidiary (Domestic):

New Suncadia, LLC **(2)**
3600 Suncadia Trail, Cle Elum, WA 98922
Tel.: (509) 649-3000
Resort Operations
N.A.I.C.S.: 721110
Roger Beck *(Mng Dir)*

Joie de Vivre Hospitality, LLC **(1)**
530 Bush St Ste 501, San Francisco, CA 94108
Tel.: (415) 835-0300
Web Site: http://www.jdvhotels.com
Hotel & Resort Investment & Management Services
N.A.I.C.S.: 721110

Thompson Hotels LLC **(1)**
60 Thompson St, New York, NY 10012
Tel.: (212) 431-0400
Web Site: http://www.thompsonhotels.com
Hotel & Resort Investment & Management Services
N.A.I.C.S.: 721110
Niki Leondakis *(CEO)*

COMMUNICA, INC.
31 N Erie St, Toledo, OH 43604
Tel.: (419) 244-7766
Web Site: http://www.communica.world
Year Founded: 1989
Sales Range: $10-24.9 Million
Emp.: 40
Advetising Agency
N.A.I.C.S.: 541810
Jeff Kimble *(Founder, Co-Owner & CEO)*
Debbie Monogan *(Co-Owner & Pres)*
Jim Rush *(Sr VP-New Bus)*
David Kanarowski *(Sr VP-Bus Dev)*
Christina Redrup *(VP-Mktg & Media Svcs)*

COMMUNICAR CORP.
7310 88th St, Glendale, NY 11385-7950
Tel.: (718) 418-1100
Web Site: https://www.communicar.com
Year Founded: 1976
Sales Range: $10-24.9 Million
Emp.: 80
Ground Transportation Services
N.A.I.C.S.: 485999
Vidim Pitchkin *(Pres)*

Subsidiaries:

Corporate Car Ltd. Inc. **(1)**
7310 88th St, Glendale, NY 11385-7950
Tel.: (718) 418-1200
Sales Range: $10-24.9 Million
Local Passenger Transportation Services
N.A.I.C.S.: 485320

COMMUNICARE, INC.
4700 Ashwood Dr Ste 200, Cincinnati, OH 45241
Tel.: (513) 489-7100 OH
Web Site: http://www.communicarehealth.com
Year Founded: 1984
Emp.: 115
Nursing Care Facilities Operator

Communicare, Inc.—(Continued)

N.A.I.C.S.: 623110
Stephen L. Rosedale *(Founder & CEO)*

Subsidiaries:

Aristocrat Berea Skilled Nursing and Rehabilitation Center   (1)
255 Front St, Berea, OH 44017
Tel.: (440) 243-4000
Web Site:
   http://www.communicarehealth.com
Sales Range: $1-9.9 Million
Office Equipment Distr
N.A.I.C.S.: 623110
Karen Ketterer *(Mgr-HR)*
Denver Fawcett *(Reg Mgr-Property)*

Baldwin Health Center Inc   (1)
1717 Skyline Dr, Pittsburgh, PA 15227
Tel.: (412) 885-8400
Web Site:
   http://www.communicarehealth.com
Sales Range: $300-349.9 Million
Lessor of Real Estate Property
N.A.I.C.S.: 531190

Copley Health Center Inc   (1)
115 Heritage Woods Dr, Copley, OH 44321
Tel.: (330) 666-0980
Sales Range: $10-24.9 Million
Emp.: 40
Lessor of Real Estate Property
N.A.I.C.S.: 531190

Hanover House   (1)
435 Avis Ave NW, Massillon, OH 44646
Tel.: (330) 837-1741
Web Site:
   http://www.communicarehealth.com
Sales Range: $75-99.9 Million
Lessors of Other Real Estate Property
N.A.I.C.S.: 327910
Gerri Mcgonagle *(Mgr)*

COMMUNICATION ASSOCIATES
244 Madison Ave, New York, NY 10016
Tel.: (718) 351-2557
Web Site: http://www.comm-associates.com
Year Founded: 1987
Sales Range: Less than $1 Million
Emp.: 10
Advetising Agency
N.A.I.C.S.: 541810
David J. Rampulla *(Pres)*
Teresa Rampulla *(Mgr-Adv Sls)*
Warren Lowe *(Sr Dir-Art)*

Subsidiaries:

FerryAds.com   (1)
83 Cromwell Ave, Staten Island, NY 10304
Tel.: (718) 351-2557
Web Site: http://www.ferryads.com
Rev.: $4,000,000
Out-of-Home Media, Transit
N.A.I.C.S.: 541810
Teresa Rampulla *(Pres)*

COMMUNICATION COMPANY OF SOUTH BEND, INC.
5320 S Main St, South Bend, IN 46614
Tel.: (574) 299-0020
Web Site:
   https://www.communication-co.com
Sales Range: $1-9.9 Million
Emp.: 31
Communication System Installation & Maintenance Services
N.A.I.C.S.: 238210
Daniel Schmidtendorff *(Pres & CEO)*
Barry Schleiger *(VP-Ops)*
Tadd Tomoske *(Mgr-Svcs)*

COMMUNICATION CONCEPTS INC.
2339 Destiny Way, Odessa, FL 33556

Tel.: (727) 807-6902
Web Site:
   http://www.communicationcon cepts.com
Year Founded: 1993
Sales Range: $1-9.9 Million
Emp.: 20
Communication Products & Services
N.A.I.C.S.: 811210
Mark Mills *(Pres)*

COMMUNICATION INFRA-STRUCTURE CORPORATION
1000 Town Ctr Dr Ste 300, Oxnard, CA 93036
Tel.: (805) 961-9101
Web Site: http://www.cicusa.com
Year Founded: 2002
Sales Range: $25-49.9 Million
Emp.: 104
Management Consulting Services
N.A.I.C.S.: 541618
Deborah Hatchell *(VP-Admin)*
Stephan Clancy *(Mgr-Field Svcs)*
Michael Steingrebe *(CFO)*
James Snyder *(Pres & CEO)*
Glen Olson *(VP-Bus Dev)*
Mark Gonzalez *(Dir-Microwave Engrg)*
Brooke Holmes *(Mgr-Site Dev)*

COMMUNICATION POWER CORP. (CPC)
80 Davids Dr Ste 3, Hauppauge, NY 11788
Tel.: (631) 434-7306   NY
Web Site: https://www.cpcamps.com
Year Founded: 1994
Sales Range: $1-9.9 Million
Emp.: 36
Designs & Manufactures Radio Frequency Power Amplifiers for Pharmaceutical, Medical Imaging & Industrial Scientific Research
N.A.I.C.S.: 334220
Daniel Myer *(Pres)*

COMMUNICATION SERVICE FOR THE DEAF, INC.
102 N Krohn Pl, Sioux Falls, SD 57103
Tel.: (605) 367-5760   SD
Web Site: http://www.c-s-d.org
Year Founded: 1924
Sales Range: $25-49.9 Million
Emp.: 1,306
Deaf Technology Development Services
N.A.I.C.S.: 541715
Brad Hermes *(Treas)*
Faye Kuo *(Sec)*
Christopher Soukup *(CEO)*
Willie King *(CTO)*
Ryan Hutchison *(VP-CSD Neighborhood)*
Juli Robinson *(VP-CSD Global Contact Centers)*
Brandi Rarus *(VP-PR, Engagement & Policy)*
Jonathan Pecora *(VP-Talent & Culture)*
Dominic Lacy *(Chief Innovation Officer)*
Rogelio Fernandez Mota *(Chm)*

COMMUNICATION SERVICES
50 Colvin Ave, Albany, NY 12206
Tel.: (518) 438-2826
Web Site:
   http://www.commservices.net
Year Founded: 1984
Sales Range: Less than $1 Million
Emp.: 4
Direct Marketing, Electronic Media, Government/Political/Public Affairs, Graphic Design, Internet/Web Design, Print

N.A.I.C.S.: 541810
Libby Post *(Pres)*
Terry Tyson *(Exec VP)*
Lilly Ruby *(Graphic Designer)*
Wendy Williams MacRoberts *(Dir-Art)*

COMMUNICATION SERVICES INC.
2151 E Broadway Rd Ste 217, Tempe, AZ 85282
Tel.: (480) 905-8689
Web Site: http://www.com-serv.com
Rev.: $25,100,000
Emp.: 30
Telephone Communication, Except Radio
N.A.I.C.S.: 517121
Doug Walsh *(Pres)*

COMMUNICATION TECHNOLOGIES, INC.
3684 Centerview Dr Ste 100, Chantilly, VA 20151-4301
Tel.: (703) 961-9080
Web Site:
   http://www.comtechnologies.com
Year Founded: 1990
Sales Range: $25-49.9 Million
Emp.: 500
Telecommunications, Managed Services & Information Security Services
N.A.I.C.S.: 517810
Joseph E. Fergus *(Founder, Pres & CEO)*

COMMUNICATION TECHNOLOGY SERVICES
33 Locke Dr, Marlborough, MA 01752-1146
Web Site: http://www.cts1.com
Rev.: $25,221,927
Emp.: 80
Voice, Data & Video Wiring Contractor
N.A.I.C.S.: 811210

COMMUNICATIONS DATA GROUP, INC.
102 S Duncan Rd, Champaign, IL 61824-4036
Tel.: (217) 355-8400
Web Site: http://www.cdg.ws
Year Founded: 1970
Telecommunications Billing Support Services
N.A.I.C.S.: 561499
Bob LaBonte *(Pres & CEO)*
Phil Goble *(CIO)*
Stan Redden *(VP-Product Dev)*
Mike Chalk *(VP-Product Dev)*
Mike Runyon *(VP-Product Support)*
Andrew Sabatuk *(VP-Sls)*
Dewaine Wilson *(VP-Fin)*
Kim Belanger *(VP-Fin & HR)*

COMMUNICATIONS ENGINEERING CO.
405 Boyson Rd, Hiawatha, IA 52233
Tel.: (319) 294-9000
Web Site: https://www.cecinfo.com
Year Founded: 1946
Audio/Video, IT, Safety & Security, Structured Cabling & Two-Way Communications
N.A.I.C.S.: 541512
Randy Montelius *(VP)*
Kelley Cole *(VP-Fin)*
Shereen Bender *(VP-HR)*
Kim Lehrman *(CEO)*

Subsidiaries:

Select Sound Service, Inc.   (1)
107 E National Ave, Milwaukee, WI 53204
Tel.: (414) 645-1600
Web Site: http://selectsoundservice.com
Speakers & Microphones Seller

N.A.I.C.S.: 334310

COMMUNICATIONS INFRA-STRUCTURE INVESTMENTS, LLC
2010 8th St, Boulder, CO 80302
Tel.: (303) 414-5027   DE
Investment Holding Company
N.A.I.C.S.: 551112
Scott E. Beer *(Gen Counsel & Sec)*

COMMUNICATIONS INTERNATIONAL (NY)
630 5th Ave Ste 2109, New York, NY 10111-0100
Tel.: (212) 218-7525   DE
Web Site:
   http://www.bannerdirect.com
Year Founded: 1975
Sales Range: $50-74.9 Million
Emp.: 5
Publishing & Advertising Services
N.A.I.C.S.: 541930
Trudy Maus *(Creative Dir)*
Michael Walsch *(VP-Strategy)*

COMMUNICATIONS INTERNATIONAL INC.
4450 US Highway 1, Vero Beach, FL 32967
Tel.: (772) 569-5355   FL
Web Site: http://www.ask4cii.com
Year Founded: 1975
Sales Range: $10-24.9 Million
Emp.: 160
Wireless Telecommunication Systems Services
N.A.I.C.S.: 517112
Barry Keim *(CFO)*

COMMUNICATIONS PRODUCTS & SERVICES
1740 W Warren Ave, Englewood, CO 80110
Tel.: (303) 922-4519
Web Site: https://www.oncps.com
Sales Range: $1-9.9 Million
Emp.: 15
Cable Conduit
N.A.I.C.S.: 423610
Fred Briggs *(Owner)*

COMMUNICATIONS PRODUCTS INC.
7301 E 90th St, Indianapolis, IN 46256
Tel.: (317) 576-0332
Web Site: http://www.commprod.com
Sales Range: $10-24.9 Million
Emp.: 72
Electronic Parts & Equipment, Merchant Whslr
N.A.I.C.S.: 423690
Cliff Arellano *(Pres)*
Deb Corson *(Controller)*
Chris Dellen *(Dir-Mktg Staff)*
Steve McKinney *(Dir-Consulting-North America)*

COMMUNICATIONS RESOURCE, INC.
8280 Greensboro Dr Ste 400, McLean, VA 22102
Tel.: (703) 245-4120
Web Site: http://www.cri-solutions.com
Sales Range: $10-24.9 Million
Emp.: 130
Technology Management Consulting
N.A.I.C.S.: 541690
Victoria Johnson *(CEO)*
Michael Lybarger *(Project Mgr)*

COMMUNICATIONS STRATEGIES, INC.

135 Main St, Madison, NJ 07940
Tel.: (973) 635-6669
Web Site: http://www.cstratinc.com
Year Founded: 1992
Sales Range: $1-9.9 Million
Emp.: 15
Public Relations & Marketing Consulting Services
N.A.I.C.S.: 541613
Donna Pepe *(Pres)*

COMMUNICATIONS TELEVIDEO LTD

9301 Georgia Ave, Silver Spring, MD 20910-1713
Tel.: (301) 585-6311
Web Site:
http://www.ctlcommunications.com
Sales Range: $10-24.9 Million
Emp.: 22
Provider of Electronic Parts & Equipment
N.A.I.C.S.: 423690
Brandon Waddell *(Mgr-Comm)*

COMMUNICATIONS TEST DESIGN INC.

1373 Enterprise Dr, West Chester, PA 19380-5959
Tel.: (610) 436-5203   PA
Web Site: https://www.ctdi.com
Year Founded: 1975
Sales Range: $200-249.9 Million
Emp.: 3,800
Telecommunications Repair & Logistics Solutions
N.A.I.C.S.: 811210
Jerry Parsons *(Chm & CEO)*
Barry Young *(VP-Network Svcs Div)*
Eric Miller *(VP-Products Supply Div)*
Duane D. Knecht *(VP-Network Svcs Div)*
Leo D. Parsons *(Pres & COO)*
Jonathan Friedman *(Co-CFO & VP-Corp Affairs)*
Ron Hartz *(VP-Corp Ops)*
Dieter Hollenbach *(CEO-Europe)*
James O'Hara *(VP-Mktg)*
Kevin Parsons *(VP-Network Program Svcs)*
Michael Parsons *(VP-Set-Top Box Div)*
Monika Ruth *(CFO-Europe)*

Subsidiaries:

CTDI - Australia Pty Limited   **(1)**
Unit 4 20-22 St Albans Road, Kingsgrove, 2208, NSW, Australia
Tel.: (61) 291 504 243
Web Site: http://www.ctdi.com
Telecommunication Servicesb
N.A.I.C.S.: 517810
David Cauz *(Mgr-Ops)*

CTDI Europe Gmbh.   **(1)**
Stephanstr 4-8, 76316, Malsch, Germany
Tel.: (49) 7246 80 1700
Telecommunication Servicesb
N.A.I.C.S.: 517810

CTDI Hong Kong Limited   **(1)**
14/F South China Bldg 1-3 Wyndham Street, Central, Hong Kong, China (Hong Kong)
Tel.: (852) 29423842
Telecommunication Servicesb
N.A.I.C.S.: 517810

CTDI Nethouse Services Kft.   **(1)**
Toth Arpad Utca 1/B, 1183, Budapest, Hungary
Tel.: (36) 1 4141030
Telecommunication Servicesb
N.A.I.C.S.: 517810

CTDI Nethouse Services Ltd   **(1)**
Featherstone Road, Wolverton, Milton Keynes, MK12 6LA, United Kingdom
Tel.: (44) 1908 682310
Telecommunication Servicesb
N.A.I.C.S.: 517810

CTDI S.r.l.   **(1)**
Via M Idiomi 8b, 20090, Assago, Milan, Italy
Tel.: (39) 02 45716093
Telecommunication Servicesb
N.A.I.C.S.: 517810

CTDI do Brazil Ltda   **(1)**
Rua Domingos Cazotti 262, Santa Genebra, Campinas, 13080-000, Sao Paulo, Brazil
Tel.: (55) 19 3381 2202
Telecommunication Services517919
N.A.I.C.S.: 517810

COMMUNICATIONS WORKERS OF AMERICA

501 3rd St NW, Washington, DC 20001
Tel.: (202) 434-1100
Web Site: https://www.cwa-union.org
Year Founded: 1940
Emp.: 300
Labor Union
N.A.I.C.S.: 813930
Christopher Shelton *(Pres)*
Sara Steffens *(Treas & Sec)*
Ameenah Salaam *(Treas & Sec)*
Claude Cummings Jr. *(Pres)*

COMMUNICREATIONS

1135 3rd Ave Apt 203, Vero Beach, FL 32960-7057
Tel.: (360) 990-6500   WA
Web Site:
http://www.communicreations.com
Year Founded: 1993
Sales Range: $100-124.9 Million
Emp.: 8
N.A.I.C.S.: 541810
Sharon Zerr *(Owner, Pres & CEO)*
Jasper Mookel *(Dir-HR)*
Isabel LeVeaux *(Special Project Dir)*
Bart Treate *(Bus-to-Bus Mgr)*
Darcy Pearce *(Dir-Mktg)*
Colleen Kelly *(Graphic Designer)*
Andrea Sittig *(New Client Svcs Dir)*

COMMUNITECH

80 Emerson Ln Ste 1303, Bridgeville, PA 15017-3472
Tel.: (412) 221-4550
Web Site: http://ctechrocks.com
Sales Range: $10-24.9 Million
Emp.: 10
Advetising Agency
N.A.I.C.S.: 541810
Pam Selker Rak *(Founder & Pres)*

COMMUNITIES FOR PEOPLE, INC.

418 Commonwealth Ave, Boston, MA 02215
Tel.: (617) 267-1031   MA
Web Site: https://www.communities-for-people.org
Year Founded: 1976
Sales Range: $10-24.9 Million
Emp.: 359
Community Care Services
N.A.I.C.S.: 624190
Craig Gordon *(COO)*
Joan Valcourt *(Dir-Ops)*
Joan McGregor *(Dir-Family Networks)*
Elizabeth B. Ison *(Dir-Counseling & Wellness)*
Joseph M. Leavey *(Pres)*

COMMUNITY ACCESS UNLIMITED, INC.

80 W Grand St, Elizabeth, NJ 07202
Tel.: (908) 354-3040
Web Site: https://www.caunj.org
Year Founded: 1979
Rev.: $15,806,956
Emp.: 1,000
Residential Care Services
N.A.I.C.S.: 623990
Sidney W. Blanchard *(Exec Dir)*

COMMUNITY ANCILLARY SERVICES, INC.

213 3rd St, Macon, GA 31201
Tel.: (478) 621-2040   GA
Web Site:
http://www.eldercarepharmacy.org
Year Founded: 1989
Sales Range: $50-74.9 Million
Women Healthcare Services
N.A.I.C.S.: 621610
Lorraine T. Taylor *(CFO)*
Joseph A. Wall *(Chm)*
Ronnie D. Rollins *(CEO)*
Mark A. Waldrop *(COO)*

COMMUNITY AND ECONOMIC DEVELOPMENT ASSOCIATION OF COOK COUNTY, INCORPORATED

208 S Lasalle Ste 1900, Chicago, IL 60604
Tel.: (312) 795-8844   IL
Web Site: http://www.cedaorg.net
Year Founded: 1966
Sales Range: $150-199.9 Million
Emp.: 772
Individual & Family Support Services
N.A.I.C.S.: 624190
Glen Ofenloch *(CFO)*
Harold T. Rice *(Pres & CEO)*
John Pady *(Program Dir)*

COMMUNITY ANTI-DRUG COALITIONS OF AMERICA

625 Slaters Ln Ste 300, Alexandria, VA 22314
Tel.: (703) 706-0560   VA
Web Site: http://www.cadca.org
Year Founded: 1992
Sales Range: $10-24.9 Million
Emp.: 54
Alcohol & Drug Abuse Rehabilitation Services
N.A.I.C.S.: 623220
Andrea de la Flor *(Sr Mgr-Evaluation-Res)*

COMMUNITY ASPHALT CORP.

9725 NW 117 Ave Ste 110, Miami, FL 33178
Tel.: (305) 829-0700   FL
Web Site: http://www.cacorp.net
Year Founded: 1980
Sales Range: $25-49.9 Million
Emp.: 280
Provider of Asphalt Paving Mixtures & Blocks
N.A.I.C.S.: 237310
John Morris *(VP & Gen Mgr)*
Norman A. Caldera *(Mgr-Pur)*

COMMUNITY ASSOCIATION MANAGEMENT SPECIALIST, INC.

1612 Military Cutoff Rd Ste 108, Wilmington, NC 28403
Tel.: (910) 256-2021   NC
Web Site: https://www.camsmgt.com
Year Founded: 1991
Emp.: 125
Community & Condominium Association Management Services
N.A.I.C.S.: 561499
Michael B. Stonestreet *(Co-Owner & Pres)*

Subsidiaries:

Benchmark Management Group, Inc.   **(1)**
2423 Hwy 17 S, North Myrtle Beach, SC 29582
Tel.: (843) 249-1779
Web Site:
http://www.benchmarkmgmtgroup.com
Residential Property Managers
N.A.I.C.S.: 531311

Jane Whieldon *(Pres)*
Jane Harris *(VP)*

COMMUNITY ASSOCIATION UNDERWRITERS OF AMERICA

2 Caufield Pl, Newtown, PA 18940
Tel.: (267) 757-7100
Web Site: http://www.cauinsure.com
Rev.: $10,700,000
Emp.: 50
Fire, Marine & Casualty Insurance
N.A.I.C.S.: 524126
Chris Hutchinson *(Office Mgr)*
Denise Hume *(Supvr-Claims)*
Jane Hutchinson *(Mgr-Acctg)*
Jean Collins *(Asst Sec-Fin & Acctg)*
Richard Crooks *(Supvr-Litigation)*

COMMUNITY ASSOCIATIONS INSTITUTE

6402 Arlington Blvd Ste 500, Falls Church, VA 22042
Tel.: (703) 750-3644   DC
Web Site: http://www.caidc.org
Year Founded: 1973
Sales Range: $10-24.9 Million
Emp.: 52
Community Action Services
N.A.I.C.S.: 624190

COMMUNITY BANCORP OF LOUISIANA, INC.

4626 Hwy 1, Raceland, LA 70394
Tel.: (985) 537-5283   LA
Web Site: http://www.ucbanking.com
Year Founded: 1983
Sales Range: $25-49.9 Million
Emp.: 122
Bank Holding Company
N.A.I.C.S.: 551111
Michael B. Riche *(Pres & CEO)*
William J. Barbera *(CFO, Treas & Sr VP)*

Subsidiaries:

United Community Bank   **(1)**
4626 Hwy 1, Raceland, LA 70394
Tel.: (985) 537-5283
Web Site: http://www.ucbanking.com
Sales Range: $25-49.9 Million
Commericial Banking
N.A.I.C.S.: 522110
David Dunmar *(Sr VP & Head-Loan Dept)*
Kevin McCartney *(VP)*

COMMUNITY BANCSHARES OF MISSISSIPPI, INC.

1255 W Government St, Brandon, MS 39042
Tel.: (601) 825-4323
Web Site:
https://www.communitybank.net
Sales Range: $75-99.9 Million
Emp.: 500
Bank Holding Company
N.A.I.C.S.: 551111
Timothy P. Gray *(Vice Chm & CFO)*
Wyman Jones *(Vice Chm & Chief Credit Officer)*
Freddie J. Bagley *(Chm)*
Darrell Brown *(Vice Chm-Admin)*
David M. Hughes *(COO)*
Beth McGaugh *(CFO)*
David Russell *(Chief Investment Officer)*
Patrick D. Franklin *(COO & Exec VP)*
Stacey Wall *(CEO)*

Subsidiaries:

Community Bank North Mississippi   **(1)**
147 Hwy 82 E, Indianola, MS 38751
Tel.: (662) 887-4513
Web Site: http://www.communitybank.net
Sales Range: $25-49.9 Million
Emp.: 20
State Commercial Banks

Community Bancshares of Mississippi,
Inc.—(Continued)

N.A.I.C.S.: 522110
Simon F. Weir II (Pres & CEO)

Community Bank of Mississippi (1)
323 E 3rd St, Forest, MS 39074
Tel.: (601) 825-4323
Web Site: http://www.communitybank.net
Sales Range: $1-9.9 Million
Emp.: 45
State Commercial Banks
N.A.I.C.S.: 551111
Charlie Dellenger (Sr VP)
Brad Stevens (Pres-Amory Div)
Eric Chambless (Pres-Mississippi Div)
Darney Derouen (Sr VP)
Marshall Eleuterius (Pres-Harrison County)
Tim Leitaker (Exec VP)
Ray Riley (Sr VP)
Darnell McCormick (Sr VP)
Ken Sims (Exec VP)
Cory Rawson (Sr VP)
Chris Strebeck (Pres-Forest & Raleigh Div)
Mitchell Hill (Pres-Indianola Div)
Alan McCaskill (Sr VP)
Anthony Webb (Sr VP)
Bobby Knox (Vice Chm)
Bo Bounds (Exec VP)
Bebe Williams (Sr VP)
Kyle Covington (Pres-Meridian Div)
Lance Waltman (Officer-Loan)
Sherri Johnson (Officer-Bus Dev)
Tiffany Moses (Officer-Branch Ops)
Whitt Conner (Officer-Loan)
Jeff King (Exec VP)
Ben Beavers (Sr VP)
Valerie Boykin (Sr VP)
Mike Webb (CEO-North Reg)
Tim Pickett (VP)
Amanda Krebs (Asst VP)

COMMUNITY BANK & TRUST INC.
1800 Washington Ave, Waco, TX 76701
Tel.: (254) 753-1521
Web Site: http://www.cbtwaco.com
Year Founded: 1952
Sales Range: $10-24.9 Million
Emp.: 110
Provider of Banking Services
N.A.I.C.S.: 522110
David Lacy (Pres)
Lisa Hull (VP)
Beverly Fallon (Dir-Mktg & Asst VP)

COMMUNITY BANK HOLDINGS OF TEXAS, INC.
321 N 15th St, Corsicana, TX 75110
Tel.: (903) 654-4500
Web Site: https://www.mybanktx.com
Year Founded: 1979
Sales Range: $25-49.9 Million
Emp.: 145
Bank Holding Company
N.A.I.C.S.: 551111
K. C. Wyatt (Pres & CEO)

Subsidiaries:

Community National Bank & Trust of
Texas (1)
321 N 15th St, Corsicana, TX 75110
Tel.: (903) 654-4500
Web Site: http://www.mybanktx.com
Commericial Banking
N.A.I.C.S.: 522110
K. C. Wyatt (Chm)
Tommy Neyland (VP & Branch Mgr-Buffalo)
Rusty Hitt (CEO)
Tim Stites (Pres)

COMMUNITY BANK OF THE BAY
180 Grand Ave Ste 120, Oakland, CA 94612
Tel.: (510) 433-5400
Web Site: http://www.bankcbb.com
Year Founded: 1996
Rev.: $17,595,168
Assets: $390,771,488

Liabilities: $343,095,839
Net Worth: $47,675,649
Earnings: $2,826,921
Emp.: 17
Fiscal Year-end: 12/31/18
State Commercial Banks
N.A.I.C.S.: 522110
William S. Keller (Pres & CEO)
Chaula M. Pandya (CTO & Sr VP)
William E. Purcell (Chm)
Raymond J. Figone (Vice Chm)
Margie Perry (Chief Customer Experience Officer & Sr VP)
Mark Roach (Chief Banking Officer & Sr VP)
Mukhtar Ali (Chief Credit Officer & Exec VP)
Daniel A. Northway (CFO & Sr VP)
Kay F. Adler (COO & Sr VP)
John Norawong (Sr VP & Sr Mgr-Relationship)
Tom Rodriguez (Officer-Construction Loan & Sr VP)
Karen Chen (VP & Mgr-Relationship)
Wilbur Hobbs (Sr VP & Dir-Community Impact)
Helen Wyman (Officer-Community Banking & Asst VP)
Samuel M. Hedgpeth III (Vice Chm)

COMMUNITY BANKSHARES, INC.
201 Broad St, Lagrange, GA 30240
Tel.: (706) 884-7999
Web Site:
http://www.redapplebank.com
Year Founded: 1980
Sales Range: $1-9.9 Million
Emp.: 60
Bank Holding Company
N.A.I.C.S.: 551111
William R. Stump (Pres & CEO)

Subsidiaries:

Community Bank & Trust
Alabama (1)
202 N Powell St, Union Springs, AL 36089
Tel.: (334) 738-5322
Web Site: http://www.redapplebank.com
Rev.: $2,986,000
Emp.: 23
Fiscal Year-end: 12/31/2012
Retail & Commercial Banking
N.A.I.C.S.: 522110
Jannette Tompkins (VP)

Community Bank & Trust - West
Georgia (1)
201 Broad St, Lagrange, GA 30240
Tel.: (706) 884-7999
Web Site: http://www.redapplebank.com
Sales Range: $1-9.9 Million
Emp.: 37
Retail & Commercial Banking
N.A.I.C.S.: 522110
William R. Stump (Pres & CEO)

COMMUNITY BASED CARE OF CENTRAL FLORIDA, INC.
4001 Pelee St Ste 200, Orlando, FL 32817
Tel.: (321) 441-2060
Web Site: http://www.cbccfl.org
Year Founded: 2001
Sales Range: $50-74.9 Million
Emp.: 115
Child Care & Development Services
N.A.I.C.S.: 624110
Debbie Leon (Dir-Dev)
Denise Bower (Dir-Fin)
Glen Casel (Pres & CEO)

COMMUNITY BASED SERVICES INC.
3 Fields Ln, North Salem, NY 10560
Tel.: (914) 277-4771
Web Site:
https://www.commbasedservices.org

Year Founded: 1981
Sales Range: $10-24.9 Million
Emp.: 200
Community Action Services
N.A.I.C.S.: 624190
Christopher Laubis (Dir-Clinical Svcs)
Janice Davis (Dir-HR)
Cathy Mathes (Dir-Staff Dev)

COMMUNITY BEHAVIORAL HEALTH
801 Market St 7th Fl, Philadelphia, PA 19107-3126
Tel.: (215) 413-3100
Web Site: http://www.dbhmrs.org
Year Founded: 1994
Sales Range: $750-799.9 Million
Emp.: 396
Mental Health Care Services
N.A.I.C.S.: 623220
Glenn Taylor (COO)
Larry Finkel (CIO)
Peter Bezrucik (Chief Admin Officer)
Catherine Torhan (CFO)
Nancy Lucas (CEO)
Arthur C. Evans (Pres)
Michael J. Covone (Treas & Sec)
Roland Lamb (VP)

COMMUNITY BLOOD CENTER
4040 Main St, Kansas City, MO 64111-2390
Tel.: (816) 753-4040
Web Site:
https://www.savealifenow.org
Year Founded: 1953
Sales Range: $25-49.9 Million
Emp.: 417
Community Blood Donation Services
N.A.I.C.S.: 621991
Elizabeth J. McQuail (COO & Sr VP)
Kim Peck (Sr Dir-Technical Svcs)
David Graham (Exec Dir)
Patsy Shipley (Sr Dir-Recruitment & Collections)
Kim Mielenz (Dir-Quality Sys)
Christopher D. Hillyer (Pres & CEO)

COMMUNITY BLOOD CENTER OF THE OZARKS
220 W Plainview Rd, Springfield, MO 65810
Tel.: (417) 227-5000
Web Site: https://www.cbco.org
Year Founded: 1995
Sales Range: $10-24.9 Million
Emp.: 249
Blood Bank
N.A.I.C.S.: 621991
Chance Wistrom (Treas)
Gerald R. Lee (Sec)
Michele Stewart (Vice Chm)
Dave Puckett (Chm)

COMMUNITY BLOOD COUNCIL OF NEW JERSEY, INC.
1410 Parkside Ave, Ewing, NJ 08638
Tel.: (609) 883-9750
Web Site: http://www.givebloodnj.org
Year Founded: 1966
Sales Range: $10-24.9 Million
Emp.: 81
Blood Distribution Services
N.A.I.C.S.: 621991
William K. Hogan (Pres)

COMMUNITY BUILDERS INC.
95 Berkeley St Ste 500, Boston, MA 02116
Tel.: (617) 695-9595
Web Site: http://www.tcbinc.org
Year Founded: 1964
Sales Range: $25-49.9 Million
Emp.: 80
Real Estate Developers Managers
N.A.I.C.S.: 531210

Beverly J. Bates (Sr VP-Dev)
Susan McCann (VP-Dev)
Bart Mitchell (Pres & CEO)
Elizabeth Gonzalez Suarez (VP-Community Life)
Jullie Patterson (Dir-Fund Dev)
Thomas Buonopane (VP-Fin & Asset Mgmt)
Jeff Heisler (VP-Design & Construction Svcs)
Brian L. P. Fallon (Chm)
Edward H. Marchant (Treas)
Lisa Wilcox-Erhardt (Sr VP-Property Mgmt)

COMMUNITY CARE COMPANIONS INC.
180 Keyland Ct, Bohemia, NY 11716
Tel.: (631) 689-6131
Web Site:
http://www.communitycarehhs.com
Year Founded: 1986
Sales Range: $1-9.9 Million
Emp.: 125
Women Healthcare Services
N.A.I.C.S.: 621610
Mark Gatien (Pres)

COMMUNITY CENTER OF NORTHERN WESTCHESTER
84 Bedford Rd, Katonah, NY 10536
Tel.: (914) 232-6572
Web Site:
http://www.communitycenternw.org
Year Founded: 1992
Rev.: $1,706,318
Assets: $1,096,101
Liabilities: $32,502
Net Worth: $1,063,599
Earnings: $11,513
Emp.: 8
Fiscal Year-end: 06/30/14
Community Food Services
N.A.I.C.S.: 624210
Sherry Wolf (Exec Dir)
Noya Guerrero (Asst Dir-Client Svcs)
Manuel Mendez (Program Mgr)
Clare Murray (Asst Dir-Ops)
Christine Meyer (Pres)
Maureen Thompson (VP)
Steve Peeples (Sec)
Tracie Cronin (Treas)

COMMUNITY CHARITY ADVANCEMENT, INC.
4699 N Federal Hwy, Pompano Beach, FL 33064
Tel.: (877) 239-5756
Year Founded: 2008
Sales Range: $10-24.9 Million
Emp.: 2
Health Care Srvices
N.A.I.C.S.: 621991
John Robert Thomas (Treas)
Kerry Sharon (Pres)

COMMUNITY CHILD CARE COUNCIL OF SANTA CLARA COUNTY, INC.
150 River Oaks Pkwy Ste F-1, San Jose, CA 95134
Tel.: (408) 487-0747
Web Site: http://www.4c.org
Year Founded: 1972
Sales Range: $25-49.9 Million
Emp.: 176
Child Care & Development Services
N.A.I.C.S.: 624110
Alfredo Villasenor (Exec Dir)

COMMUNITY CHOICE FINANCIAL INC.
6785 Bobcat Way Ste 200, Dublin, OH 43016
Tel.: (614) 798-5900

Web Site: http://www.ccfi.com
Sales Range: $350-399.9 Million
Emp.: 2,829
Consumer Financial Services
N.A.I.C.S.: 525990
Kyle F. Hanson *(Pres & COO)*
Michael J. Durbin *(CFO, Chief Admin Officer, Treas & Exec VP)*
Bridgette Roman *(Gen Counsel, Sec & Exec VP)*
William E. Saunders Jr. *(Chm)*

Subsidiaries:

Checksmart Financial Company **(1)**
6785 Bobcat Way Ste 200, Dublin, OH 43016
Tel.: (614) 798-5900
Emp.: 33
Consumer Financial Services
N.A.I.C.S.: 525990

COMMUNITY CO-OPS OF LAKE PARK
14583 Hwy 10 W, Lake Park, MN 56554
Tel.: (218) 238-5911
Web Site:
  https://www.communitycoops.com
Rev.: $10,030,643
Emp.: 50
Petroleum Products
N.A.I.C.S.: 424720
David Blomseth *(Gen Mgr)*

COMMUNITY COFFEE COMPANY LLC
3332 Partridge Ln, Baton Rouge, LA 70809
Tel.: (225) 368-3900   LA
Web Site:
  https://www.communitycoffee.com
Year Founded: 1919
Sales Range: $10-24.9 Million
Emp.: 1,500
Mfr of Roasted Coffee
N.A.I.C.S.: 311920
David Belanger *(Pres & CEO)*
Annette Vaccaro *(CFO, Treas & Sr VP)*

COMMUNITY COMPUTER SERVICE
15 Hulbert St, Auburn, NY 13021
Tel.: (315) 255-1751   NY
Web Site: http://www.medent.com
Year Founded: 1968
Sales Range: $10-24.9 Million
Emp.: 108
Provider of Computer Software Systems
N.A.I.C.S.: 541512
Edward L. Cuthbert *(Owner & Chm)*
Cynthia Grillo *(Mgr)*

COMMUNITY COUNCIL OF IDAHO, INC.
317 Happy Day Blvd Ste 250, Caldwell, ID 83607
Tel.: (208) 454-1652   ID
Web Site:
  http://www.communitycouncil
  ofidaho.org
Year Founded: 1971
Sales Range: $10-24.9 Million
Emp.: 491
Community Care Services
N.A.I.C.S.: 624190
Elisha Suldan *(Dir-Fin)*
Arnold Cantu *(Dir-Clinic)*
Korene Gonzalez *(Dir-Employment & Trng)*
Irma Morin *(Exec Dir)*
Kathy Parker *(Dir-Dev)*
Rebecca De Leon *(Dir-Comm)*

COMMUNITY COUNSELING CENTERS, INC.
2500 Show Low Lake Rd Bldg B, Show Low, AZ 85901
Tel.: (928) 368-4110   AZ
Web Site: http://www.ccc-az.org
Year Founded: 1966
Sales Range: $10-24.9 Million
Emp.: 223
Behavioral Health Care & Developmental Disability Assistance Services
N.A.I.C.S.: 623220
Paula Kaye Martin *(Dir-Quality Mgmt)*
Chris Rohrer *(Mgr-Ops)*
Darwin West *(Dir-Program-Snowflake)*
Jeffrey Oakes *(CEO)*
Brad Head *(Dir-Special Ops)*
Shelly Ehmann *(COO)*
Diane Clark *(Chm)*
Debra West *(Treas & Sec)*

COMMUNITY COUNSELING OF BRISTOL COUNTY, INC.
1 Washington St, Taunton, MA 02780
Tel.: (508) 828-9116   MA
Web Site:
  https://www.comcounseling.org
Year Founded: 1988
Sales Range: $10-24.9 Million
Emp.: 522
Mental Health Counseling & Substance Abuse Rehabilitation Services
N.A.I.C.S.: 623220
Philip Shea *(Pres & CEO)*
Andrea Klein-Yancho *(CFO)*
Andrew Dawley *(COO)*
Paul Weiss *(Dir-Medical)*

COMMUNITY COUNSELING SERVICES, INC.
2458 Stetzer Rd, Bucyrus, OH 44820
Tel.: (419) 562-2000   OH
Year Founded: 1978
Sales Range: $1-9.9 Million
Mental Health & Substance Abuse Rehabilitation Services
N.A.I.C.S.: 623220

COMMUNITY DENTAL CARE
1670 Beam Ave Ste 204, Maplewood, MN 55109
Tel.: (651) 925-8400   MN
Web Site: https://www.cdentc.org
Year Founded: 2004
Sales Range: $10-24.9 Million
Emp.: 204
Dental Care Services
N.A.I.C.S.: 622310
Phil Lacher *(CFO)*
Andrew F. Peterson *(Co-Founder)*
Kori Schultz *(Dir-HR)*
Bonnie Seymour *(Gen Mgr)*
Vacharee S. Peterson *(Co-Founder & CEO)*
Carolyn Bass *(Gen Mgr-Saint Paul Clinic)*
Tiffany Young *(Gen Mgr-Rochester Clinic)*
Sean Yang *(Gen Mgr-Robbinsdale Clinic)*

COMMUNITY ENTERPRISES, INC.
441 Pleasant St, Northampton, MA 01060
Tel.: (413) 584-1460
Web Site: http://www.communityenter
  prises.com
Year Founded: 1972
Rev.: $10,887,899
Emp.: 200
Vocational Rehabilitation Services
N.A.I.C.S.: 624310
William D. Donohue *(Chm)*
Joanne Carlisle *(Sec)*

Dick Venne *(Pres & CEO)*
Gary Daniele *(Dir-Greenfield Community Employment & Trng Programs)*
Paula Tessier *(Dir-Employment & Trng Programs-Greenfield)*

COMMUNITY FINANCIAL CORP
101 E Union St, Edgewood, IA 52042
Tel.: (563) 928-6425   IA
Web Site: https://www.csbiowa.com
Year Founded: 1985
Sales Range: $25-49.9 Million
Emp.: 84
Bank Holding Company
N.A.I.C.S.: 551111
Steven A. Brady *(Pres)*
Brian Brown *(Pres-Market)*
Marcia Correll *(VP-Comml Lending)*
Jackie Johnson *(Exec VP)*

Subsidiaries:

Community Savings Bank **(1)**
101 E Union St, Edgewood, IA 52042
Tel.: (563) 928-6428
Web Site: https://www.csbiowa.com
Rev.: $27,828,000
Emp.: 84
Fiscal Year-end: 12/31/2023
Commericial Banking
N.A.I.C.S.: 522110
Steven A. Brady *(Pres)*
Lisa Maiers *(Branch Mgr)*
Jackie Johnson *(Exec VP)*
Kent Stock *(VP-Bus Dev)*
Patrick Dinan *(VP-Lending)*
Marcia Correll *(VP-Comml Lending)*
Elaine Funke *(VP)*
Marshall Johnson *(VP-Investments)*
Tim Larson *(VP-Mortage)*
Brett Nagel *(Sr VP)*
Dodd Scroggin *(VP-Lending)*
Sandra Wegmann *(Supvr-CSA)*

COMMUNITY FINANCIAL SERVICES
PO Box 467, Benton, KY 42025
Tel.: (270) 527-4600
Web Site: http://www.cfsbky.com
Year Founded: 1890
Sales Range: $10-24.9 Million
Emp.: 160
State Commercial Banks
N.A.I.C.S.: 522110
Betsy Flynn *(Chm & CEO)*
Jennifer Apple *(Chief Client Officer)*
Jason Jones *(Pres-Marshall County Market)*
Nathan Rowton *(Asst VP)*

COMMUNITY FIRST BANCSHARES, INC.
915 W Ft Scott St, Butler, MO 64730
Tel.: (660) 679-3135   MO
Web Site:
  http://www.communityfirstbank.net
Year Founded: 1997
Bank Holding Company
N.A.I.C.S.: 551111
Bruce D. Jessup *(Pres-Bank & VP)*
Glenn R. Hamilton *(Pres & CEO)*

Subsidiaries:

Community First Bank **(1)**
915 W Ft Scott St, Butler, MO 64730
Tel.: (660) 679-3135
Web Site:
  http://www.communityfirstbank.net
Sales Range: $1-9.9 Million
Commericial Banking
N.A.I.C.S.: 522110
Bruce D. Jessup *(Pres)*

COMMUNITY FIRST BANK OF INDIANA
201 W Sycamore St, Kokomo, IN 46901
Tel.: (765) 236-0600   IN

Web Site:
  https://www.cfbindiana.com
Sales Range: $10-24.9 Million
Emp.: 42
Banking Services
N.A.I.C.S.: 522110
Robb Blume *(Pres & CEO)*
Craig Huffman *(CFO & Exec VP)*

COMMUNITY FIRST FOUNDATION
5855 Wadsworth Byp Unit A, Arvada, CO 80003
Tel.: (720) 898-5900   CO
Web Site:
  https://www.communityfirstfoun
  dation.org
Year Founded: 1975
Sales Range: $25-49.9 Million
Emp.: 18
Philanthropic Services
N.A.I.C.S.: 813211
Kenneth R. Kirwin *(CFO)*
Noah M. Atencio *(VP-Community Impact)*

COMMUNITY FIRST SOLUTIONS
230 Ludlow St, Hamilton, OH 45011
Tel.: (513) 785-4060   OH
Web Site: http://www.community-first.org
Sales Range: $1-9.9 Million
Emp.: 45
Individual Care Services
N.A.I.C.S.: 624190
Juan Cortes *(COO)*
Melissa Park *(Exec VP-HR)*
Dick Bower *(Exec VP-Construction & Facilities)*
Mark Zoellner *(CFO)*
Jeffrey P. Thurman *(Pres & CEO)*
Rhonda Huber *(Exec VP-Corp Strategy)*
Stephan C. Sullivan *(Chm)*

Subsidiaries:

Lifespan, Inc. **(1)**
1900 Fairgrove Ave, Hamilton, OH 45011
Tel.: (513) 868-3210
Web Site: http://www.lifespanohio.org
Health & Social Services
N.A.I.C.S.: 624190
Peter K. Markell *(CFO & Exec VP)*

COMMUNITY FOOD BANK OF EASTERN OKLAHOMA, INC.
1304 N Kenosha Ave, Tulsa, OK 74106
Tel.: (918) 585-2800   OK
Web Site:
  https://www.okfoodbank.org
Year Founded: 1982
Sales Range: $25-49.9 Million
Emp.: 73
Community Food Services
N.A.I.C.S.: 624210
Eileen Bradshaw *(Exec Dir)*
Frances Bevel *(Mgr-Grants)*
Ron Moton *(Mgr-Warehouse)*
Eric M. Kunkel *(Pres)*
Joanne Burdick *(Dir-Agency Rels)*
Steve Lehto *(Mgr-Rural Hunger & Veterans Outreach)*
Mike McAndrews *(VP)*
Ryan Walker *(COO)*
David Parrack *(Dir-Fin & Acctg)*
Susan Schulte *(Dir-HR)*
Rochelle Dowdell *(Dir-Philanthropy & Comm)*
Ken Bacon *(Mgr-Donor Rels)*
Cindy Cummins *(Mng Dir-Customer Rels & Capacity)*
Jason Smith *(Treas)*
John McCarthy *(Dir-Community Initiatives)*
Johnny Mahaffey *(Dir-Ops)*
Lori Lewis Dryer *(Sec)*

Community Foundation for Greater Atlanta
Inc—(Continued)

COMMUNITY FOUNDATION FOR GREATER ATLANTA INC
191 Peachtree St NE Ste 1000 10th
Fl, Atlanta, GA 30303
Tel.: (404) 688-5525
Web Site:
    https://www.cfgreateratlanta.org
Year Founded: 1951
Social Organization Services
N.A.I.C.S.: 813920

COMMUNITY FOUNDATION FOR GREATER BUFFALO
726 Exchange St Ste 525, Buffalo,
NY 14210
Tel.: (716) 852-2857   NY
Web Site: https://www.cfgb.org
Year Founded: 1919
Sales Range: $10-24.9 Million
Community Action Services
N.A.I.C.S.: 624190
Clotilde Perez-Bode Dedecker (Pres
& CEO)
Cara Matteliano (VP-Community)
Betsy Constantine (Exec VP)
William Joyce (Chm)
Francisco Vasquez (Vice Chm)
Gary L. Mucci (Sec)
Ross Eckert (Treas)
Melissa Baumgart (Vice Chm)
Felicia Beard (Dir-Racial Equity Initia-
tives)
Andrew Gaerte (Dir-Client Rels)
Gerald Reger (CFO & Chief Admin
Officer)
Myra S. Lawrence (VP-Fin)
Bridget Niland (Dir-Youth Sports Ini-
tiatives)
Cindy Odom (Chief Community Im-
pact Officer)

COMMUNITY FOUNDATION FOR MONTEREY COUNTY
2354 Garden Rd, Monterey, CA
93940
Tel.: (831) 375-9712   CA
Web Site: http://www.cfmco.org
Year Founded: 1945
Sales Range: $10-24.9 Million
Philanthropic Services
N.A.I.C.S.: 813211
Laurel Lee-Alexander (VP-Grants &
Programs)
Diane Nonella (Dir-Fin & HR)
Julie Conrad (Mgr-Admin Svcs)
Christine Dawson (VP-Philanthropic
Svcs)
Ken Petersen (Vice Chm)

COMMUNITY FOUNDATION FOR MUSKEGON COUNTY
425 W Western Ave Ste 200, Mus-
kegon, MI 49444
Tel.: (231) 722-4538   MI
Web Site: http://www.cffmc.org
Year Founded: 1961
Sales Range: $10-24.9 Million
Emp.: 15
Grantmaking Services
N.A.I.C.S.: 813211
Chris McGuigan (Pres & CEO)
Heidi Sytsema (Dir-Donor Svcs)
Ann Van Tassell (VP-Fin)

COMMUNITY FOUNDATION FOR PALM BEACH AND MARTIN COUNTIES
700 S Dixie Hwy Ste 200, West Palm
Beach, FL 33401
Tel.: (561) 659-6800   FL
Web Site:
    https://www.yourcommunityfoun
    dation.org

Year Founded: 1972
Sales Range: $10-24.9 Million
Emp.: 14
Community Action Services
N.A.I.C.S.: 624190
Gloria Ortega (CFO & VP-Fin & Ad-
min)
Bradley Hurlburt (Pres & CEO)
Kati Erickson (Officer-Donor Rels)
Renee Constantino (VP-Community
Investment)
Andrew Kushner (Sec)
Jane M. Mitchell (Vice Chm)
Roy J. Zuckerberg (Chm)
January Romero Reissman (VP-
Community Impact)
Vicki Pugh (VP-Philanthropic Giving)

COMMUNITY FOUNDATION FOR SOUTHEAST MICHIGAN
333 W Fort St Ste 2010, Detroit, MI
48226-3134
Tel.: (313) 961-6675   MI
Web Site: https://www.cfsem.org
Year Founded: 1984
Sales Range: $50-74.9 Million
Emp.: 30
Philanthropic Services
N.A.I.C.S.: 813211
Karen L. Leppanen (VP-Fin & Admin)
Robin D. Ferriby (VP-Philanthropic
Svcs)
Katie G. Brisson (VP-Program)
James B. Nicholson (Chm)
Joseph L. Hudson (Founder & Chm)
Mary H. Weiser (Sec)
Michael T. Monahan (Treas)
Penny B. Blumenstein (Vice Chm)
David M. Hempstead (Vice Chm)
Reginald M. Turner Jr. (Vice Chm)
Mariam C. Noland (Pres)
Matthew Lewis (Officer-Comm)

COMMUNITY FOUNDATION FOR SOUTHWEST WASHINGTON
610 Esther St Ste 201, Vancouver,
WA 98660
Tel.: (360) 694-2550   WA
Web Site: https://www.cfsww.org
Year Founded: 1984
Sales Range: $10-24.9 Million
Emp.: 10
Grantmaking Services
N.A.I.C.S.: 813211
Jennifer Rhoads (Pres)
Mary Pringle (CFO & VP)
Pam Cabanatuan (Controller)

COMMUNITY FOUNDATION OF ACADIANA
1035 Camellia Blvd Ste 100, Lafay-
ette, LA 70508
Tel.: (337) 769-4840   LA
Web Site: https://www.cfacadiana.org
Year Founded: 2000
Sales Range: $10-24.9 Million
Emp.: 6
Grantmaking Services
N.A.I.C.S.: 813211
Eric Guidry (COO)
Erin Winder (Dir-Comm & Dev)

COMMUNITY FOUNDATION OF GREATER BIRMINGHAM
2100 1st Ave N Ste 700, Birmingham,
AL 35203-4223
Tel.: (205) 327-3800   AL
Web Site: https://www.cfbham.org
Year Founded: 1997
Sales Range: $25-49.9 Million
Emp.: 21
Grantmaking Services
N.A.I.C.S.: 813211

Ginger Jefferson (Dir-Marketing-
Communications)
Christopher Nanni (Pres & CEO)
Gus Heard-Hughes (VP-Programs)
Lora Terry (VP-Philanthropic Svcs)

COMMUNITY FOUNDATION OF GREATER DES MOINES
1915 Grand Ave, Des Moines, IA
50309
Tel.: (515) 883-2626   IA
Web Site:
    https://www.desmoinesfounda
    tion.org
Year Founded: 1969
Sales Range: $75-99.9 Million
Emp.: 21
Fundraising Services
N.A.I.C.S.: 813211
Lynne Yontz (Dir-Advancement)
Wade A. Den Hartog (Dir-Affiliates &
Charitable Partners)
Joe Sorenson (Dir-Affiliate Rels)
Sheila Kinman (Chief Advancement
Officer)
Anna Nalean (Dir-Nonprofit Rels)
Sara Bonney (VP-Mktg & Comm)
Kris Pete-Swanson (VP-Fin & Con-
troller)
Angie Dethlefs-Trettin (Chief Commu-
nity Impact Officer)
Addie Olson (Coord-Mktg & Events)
Jordan Richardson (Dir-Charitable
Partners)
David Adelman (Pres)
Kyle J. Krause (Pres & CEO)

COMMUNITY FOUNDATION OF GREATER GREENSBORO
330 S Greene St Ste 100, Greens-
boro, NC 27401
Tel.: (336) 379-9100   NC
Web Site: http://www.cfgg.org
Year Founded: 1983
Sales Range: $10-24.9 Million
Emp.: 18
Grantmaking Services
N.A.I.C.S.: 813211
Walker Sanders (Pres)
Emily G. Thompson (Dir-Donor Svcs)

COMMUNITY FOUNDATION OF GREATER MEMPHIS
1900 Union Ave, Memphis, TN 38104
Tel.: (901) 728-4600   TN
Web Site: https://www.cfgm.org
Year Founded: 1969
Sales Range: $25-49.9 Million
Emp.: 18
Community Action Services
N.A.I.C.S.: 624190
Angela Lexner (Accountant)
Stephen Webster (Dir-Fin)
Sutton Mora Hayes (COO & Exec
VP)
Mack E. McCaul Jr. (Treas & VP-Fin)

COMMUNITY FOUNDATION OF KANKAKEE RIVER VALLEY
701 S Harrison Ave, Kankakee, IL
60901
Tel.: (815) 939-1611   IL
Web Site: https://www.cfkrv.org
Year Founded: 1982
Sales Range: $10-24.9 Million
Emp.: 3
Community Development Support
Services
N.A.I.C.S.: 624190
Nicole Smolkovich (Exec Dir)

COMMUNITY FOUNDATION OF LORAIN COUNTY
9080 Leavitt Rd, Elyria, OH 44035
Tel.: (440) 984-7390   OH

Web Site:
    https://www.peoplewhocare.org
Year Founded: 1980
Sales Range: $10-24.9 Million
Emp.: 12
Grantmaking Services
N.A.I.C.S.: 813211
Brian R. Frederick (Pres & CEO)
Theresa Eged (Mgr-IT)
Nancy Huller (Mgr-Fin)
Rachel Ocasio (Mgr-Relationship)

COMMUNITY FOUNDATION OF MIDDLE TENNESSESE
3833 Cleghorn Ave Ste 400, Nash-
ville, TN 37215-2519
Tel.: (615) 321-4939   TN
Web Site: https://www.cfmt.org
Year Founded: 1991
Sales Range: $25-49.9 Million
Grantmaking Services
N.A.I.C.S.: 813211
Melisa Currey (CFO)
Belinda Dinwiddie (Dir-Donor En-
gagement)
Amy Fair (VP-Donor Svcs)
Cynthia Copeland (Mgr-Acctg)
Ellen E. Lehman (Pres)
Kerry Graham (Chm)

COMMUNITY FOUNDATION OF NEW JERSEY
35 Knox Hill Rd, Morristown, NJ
07960
Tel.: (973) 267-5533   NJ
Web Site: https://www.cfnj.org
Year Founded: 1979
Sales Range: $25-49.9 Million
Emp.: 13
Philanthropic Services
N.A.I.C.S.: 813211
Hans Dekker (Pres)

COMMUNITY FOUNDATION OF NORTH LOUISIANA
401 Edwards St Ste 105, Shreveport,
LA 71101
Tel.: (318) 221-0582   LA
Web Site: http://www.nlacf.org
Year Founded: 1961
Sales Range: $10-24.9 Million
Emp.: 11
Grantmaking Services
N.A.I.C.S.: 813211
Paula Hickman (Exec Dir)
Eugenie Bryant (Mgr-Ops)
Paige Carlisle (Dir-Fin)
Jennifer Steadman (Dir-External
Rels)
Elizabeth M. LaBorde (Dir-Community
Investment)
Thomas H. Murphy (Chm)
Margaret Thompson (Sec)
Glenn Kinsey (Treas)
Rand Falbaum (Vice Chm)
Carla q D. Burgos (Dir-Special Initia-
tives)

COMMUNITY FOUNDATION OF NORTH TEXAS
306 W 7th Ste 1045, Fort Worth, TX
76102
Tel.: (817) 877-0702   TX
Web Site: http://www.northtexas.org
Year Founded: 1989
Sales Range: $25-49.9 Million
Emp.: 13
Asset Adminstration & Charity Ser-
vices
N.A.I.C.S.: 813219
Nancy E. Jones (Pres & CEO)
Rob Miller (Dir-Fin)
Vicki Andrews (Dir-Ops & Donor
Svcs)
James DeMoss (Treas)
Alfred Saenz (Sec)
Bill Dismuke (Vice Chm)

Larry G. Autrey *(Treas)*
Christopher M. Huckabee *(Chm)*
Elaine Petrus *(VP-Grants)*

COMMUNITY FOUNDATION OF NORTHERN COLORADO
4745 Wheaton Dr, Fort Collins, CO 80525
Tel.: (970) 224-3462   CO
Web Site:
  https://www.nocofoundation.org
Year Founded: 1975
Sales Range: $10-24.9 Million
Emp.: 15
Community Care Services
N.A.I.C.S.: 624190

COMMUNITY FOUNDATION OF NORTHWEST CONNECTICUT, INC.
32 City Hall Ave, Torrington, CT 06790
Tel.: (860) 626-1245   CT
Web Site: http://www.cfnwct.org
Year Founded: 1999
Sales Range: $1-9.9 Million
Community Action Services
N.A.I.C.S.: 624190
Victoria Patrick *(Treas)*
Douglas K. O'Connell *(Chm)*
Gayle Moraski *(Vice Chm)*
Christopher G. Wall *(Sec)*
Guy Rovezzi *(Pres & CEO)*
Brad Hoar *(VP-Philanthropic Svcs)*
Nicole Carlson Easley *(Dir-Comm)*

COMMUNITY FOUNDATION OF SOUTH GEORGIA
135 N Broad St Ste 201, Thomasville, GA 31792
Tel.: (229) 228-5088   GA
Web Site: http://www.cfsga.net
Year Founded: 1995
Sales Range: $10-24.9 Million
Emp.: 3
Grantmaking Services
N.A.I.C.S.: 813211
David Carlton *(Pres)*
Lisa Hitt *(Controller)*

COMMUNITY FOUNDATION OF THE GREAT RIVER BEND
852 Middle Rd Ste 100, Bettendorf, IA 52722
Tel.: (563) 326-2840   IA
Web Site: http://www.cfgrb.org
Year Founded: 1964
Sales Range: $10-24.9 Million
Emp.: 50
Grantmaking Services
N.A.I.C.S.: 813211
Marie Zelnio Ziegler *(Treas)*
Susan Skora *(Pres)*
Jill McLaughlin *(Sec)*
Anne Calder *(VP-Dev)*
Sherry Ristau *(Pres & CEO)*

COMMUNITY FOUNDATION OF WEST GEORGIA, INC.
807 S Park St, Carrollton, GA 30117
Tel.: (770) 832-1462   GA
Web Site: https://www.cfwg.net
Year Founded: 2003
Sales Range: $10-24.9 Million
Emp.: 3
Community Action Services
N.A.I.C.S.: 624190
Kim Jones *(Pres)*
Crystal Burford *(Dir-Ops)*

COMMUNITY FOUNDATION OF WESTERN NEVADA
50 Washington St Ste 300-A, Reno, NV 89503
Tel.: (775) 333-5499   NV
Web Site: http://www.nevadafund.org
Year Founded: 1998
Rev.: $11,806,540
Assets: $106,681,192
Liabilities: $20,417,288
Net Worth: $86,263,904
Earnings: ($1,679,577)
Emp.: 7
Fiscal Year-end: 12/31/18
Grantmaking Services
N.A.I.C.S.: 813211
Margaret Stewart *(Dir-Comm)*
Kevin Melcher *(Vice Chm)*
Steve Carrick *(Chm)*
Leslie Daane *(Treas)*

COMMUNITY FOUNDATION OF WESTERN PA & EASTERN OH
7 W State St Ste 301, Sharon, PA 16146
Tel.: (724) 981-5882   PA
Web Site: https://www.comm-foundation.org
Year Founded: 1981
Sales Range: $10-24.9 Million
Emp.: 19
Philanthropic Services
N.A.I.C.S.: 813211

COMMUNITY FOUNDATION SANTA CRUZ COUNTY
7807 Soquel Dr, Aptos, CA 95003
Tel.: (831) 662-2000   CA
Web Site: https://www.cfscc.org
Year Founded: 1982
Sales Range: $25-49.9 Million
Emp.: 26
Charitable Organization
N.A.I.C.S.: 813211
Lance Linares *(CEO)*
Jim Brown *(Mgr-Grants)*
Christina Cuevas *(Program Dir)*
Sam Leask *(Dir-Philanthropic Svcs)*
Michael K. O'Farrell *(Pres)*
Linda Fawcett *(Sec)*
Jennifer Boyle *(Office Mgr)*

COMMUNITY FOUNDATION SONOMA COUNTY
250 D St Ste 205, Santa Rosa, CA 95404
Tel.: (707) 579-4073   CA
Web Site: http://www.sonomacf.org
Year Founded: 1983
Sales Range: $10-24.9 Million
Emp.: 11
Grantmaking Services
N.A.I.C.S.: 813211

COMMUNITY HARVEST FOOD BANK OF NORTHEAST INDIANA, INC.
999 E Tillman Rd, Fort Wayne, IN 46816
Tel.: (260) 447-3696   IN
Web Site: http://www.chfb.org
Year Founded: 1984
Rev.: $22,455,367
Assets: $9,283,862
Liabilities: $69,762
Net Worth: $9,214,100
Emp.: 45
Fiscal Year-end: 06/30/18
Hunger Relief Services
N.A.I.C.S.: 624210
Mary Carpenter *(Dir-Ops)*
Hicham Mannir *(Mgr-Community Cupboard)*
Deb Treesh *(Sec)*
Ben Williams *(Pres)*
John R. Wolf *(CEO)*
Jeff Beights *(VP)*
Sue Ladig *(Mgr-Inventory Control)*
Bruce Whittaker *(Supvr-Maintenance)*
Burt Brunner *(Treas)*

COMMUNITY HEALTH ACCREDITATION PARTNER, INC.
1275 K St NW Ste 800, Washington, DC 20005
Tel.: (202) 862-3413   NY
Web Site: http://www.chapinc.org
Year Founded: 1988
Sales Range: $10-24.9 Million
Emp.: 105
Health Care Accreditation Services
N.A.I.C.S.: 561990
Maureen Spivack *(Chm)*

COMMUNITY HEALTH CARE
1019 Pacific Ave Ste 300, Tacoma, WA 98402
Tel.: (253) 597-4550   WA
Web Site: http://www.commhealth.org
Year Founded: 1987
Sales Range: $25-49.9 Million
Emp.: 369
Healtcare Services
N.A.I.C.S.: 622110
Jeff Reynolds *(Dir-Dental)*
David Flentge *(Pres & CEO)*
Jeffrey Smith *(Dir-Medical)*
Godwin Asemota *(Dir-Pharmacy)*

COMMUNITY HEALTH CENTER
725 E Market St, Akron, OH 44305
Tel.: (330) 434-4141   OH
Web Site:
  http://www.commhealthcenter.org
Year Founded: 1974
Sales Range: $10-24.9 Million
Community Health Care Services
N.A.I.C.S.: 621498
Barbara Van Dike *(Dir-HR)*
Robert Terry *(Chief Compliance Officer)*
Nancy Jones Keogh *(Dir-Clinical)*
Greg Johnson *(Dir-Medical)*
Janet L. Wagner *(COO)*

COMMUNITY HEALTH CENTER OF SOUTHEAST KANSAS
3011 N Michigan St, Pittsburg, KS 66762
Tel.: (620) 231-9873   KS
Web Site: https://www.chcsek.org
Year Founded: 2002
Sales Range: $10-24.9 Million
Emp.: 174
Health Care Srvices
N.A.I.C.S.: 622110

COMMUNITY HEALTH CENTER, INC.
675 Main St, Middletown, CT 06457
Tel.: (860) 347-6971   CT
Web Site: https://www.chc1.com
Year Founded: 1972
Sales Range: $50-74.9 Million
Emp.: 662
Health Care Srvices
N.A.I.C.S.: 622110
Daren Anderson *(Chief Quality Officer)*
Allen Schweitzer *(CFO & VP)*
Agi Erickson *(Dir-Project Echo)*

COMMUNITY HEALTH CENTERS OF THE CENTRAL COAST, INC.
150 Tejas Pl, Nipomo, CA 93444-0430
Tel.: (805) 929-3211   CA
Web Site:
  http://www.communityhealth.org
Year Founded: 1978
Sales Range: $50-74.9 Million
Emp.: 577
Community Health Care Services
N.A.I.C.S.: 621498

Ron Castle *(CEO)*

COMMUNITY HEALTH CENTERS OF THE RUTLAND REGION
215 Stratton Rd, Rutland, VT 05701
Tel.: (802) 773-3386   VT
Web Site: https://www.chcrr.org
Year Founded: 2004
Sales Range: $10-24.9 Million
Emp.: 265
Health Care Srvices
N.A.I.C.S.: 621610
Bradley Berryhill *(Dir-Medical)*
Grant Whitmer *(Exec Dir)*
Mike Gardner *(Treas & Fin Dir)*
Bob Hedden *(Vice Chm)*
Roland Gibson *(Vice Chm)*
Larry Jensen *(Chm)*

COMMUNITY HEALTH CONNECTIONS, INC.
326 Nichols Rd, Fitchburg, MA 01420
Tel.: (978) 878-8100   MA
Web Site: https://www.chcfhc.org
Year Founded: 1997
Sales Range: $25-49.9 Million
Emp.: 300
Individual & Family Healthcare Services
N.A.I.C.S.: 621498
Sarah Johnson *(VP-HR)*
Jacqueline Buckley *(COO)*
Lucille Songer *(Chief Quality & Compliance Officer)*
Mark Sullivan *(CIO)*

COMMUNITY HEALTH GROUP
2420 Fenton St Ste 100, Chula Vista, CA 91914
Tel.: (619) 422-0422   CA
Web Site: http://www.chgsd.com
Year Founded: 1982
Sales Range: $25-49.9 Million
Emp.: 224
Community Health Care Services
N.A.I.C.S.: 621498
Norma Diaz *(CEO)*

COMMUNITY HEALTH NETWORK FOUNDATION
7240 Shadeland Station Ste 125, Indianapolis, IN 46256
Tel.: (317) 355-4483
Web Site:
  http://www.ecommunity.com
Year Founded: 1976
Emp.: 350
Fund Raising Hospital Organization
N.A.I.C.S.: 561990
Joyce Irwin *(Pres-Community Health Network Foundation & Exec VP)*
Joe Kessler *(CFO)*
Ron Thieme *(Chief Experience Officer & Exec VP)*
Karen Ann Lloyd *(Gen Counsel & Exec VP)*
Ryan Chelli *(CMO & VP-Donor-Rels)*
Dave Baldwin *(Vice Chm)*
Bob Shortle *(Chm)*
Ramarao Yeleti *(Sec)*
Jean Putnam *(Chief Nursing Officer)*
Tim Wright *(Treas)*
Karen Lightbourne *(Dir-Community Collaborations-East)*
Jason Fahrlander *(COO)*
David Kiley *(Pres-South)*
Nichole Goddard *(COO-South)*
Donetta Gee-Weiler *(COO-North)*
Tom Malasto *(Chief Patient Experience Officer & Sr VP)*
Bryan A. Mills *(Pres & CEO)*
Virginia Davidson *(Chief Compliance Officer & Exec VP)*
Kyle Fisher *(CFO & Exec VP)*

Community Health Network
Foundation—(Continued)

Tim Hobbs *(Exec VP)*
John Kunzer *(Pres-Community Physician Network & Exec VP)*
Joseph Hooper *(Pres-Howard & Sr VP)*
Dee Moonesinghe *(Pres-North & Sr VP)*
Beth Tharp *(Pres-Anderson & Sr VP)*
Al Larsen *(VP-Mktg & Comm)*
Rob Baker *(VP-Ops)*
Diane McDaniel *(Chief Diversity Officer)*

COMMUNITY HEALTH NETWORK OF CONNECTICUT, INC.
11 Fairfield Blvd, Wallingford, CT 06492
Tel.: (203) 949-4000   CT
Web Site: https://www.chnct.org
Year Founded: 1995
Sales Range: $50-74.9 Million
Emp.: 525
Health Care Srvices
N.A.I.C.S.: 622110
Waldemar Rosario *(Chief Medical Officer)*

COMMUNITY HEALTH OF SOUTH FLORIDA, INC.
10300 SW 216th St, Miami, FL 33190
Tel.: (305) 253-5100   FL
Web Site: https://www.chisouthfl.org
Year Founded: 1971
Sales Range: $50-74.9 Million
Community Health Care Services
N.A.I.C.S.: 621498
St. Anthony Amofah *(Chief Medical Officer)*
Tiffani Helberg *(VP-Comm & Dev)*
Monica Mizell *(Chief Nursing Officer & VP)*
Jean Pierre *(VP-Behavioral Health Svcs)*
Allison Madden *(Asst VP-Care Mgmt)*
Sean St. Louis *(CFO)*
Brodes H. Hartley Jr. *(Pres & CEO)*

COMMUNITY HEALTH PLAN OF WASHINGTON
720 Olive Way Ste 300, Seattle, WA 98101-1830
Tel.: (206) 521-8830
Web Site: http://www.chpw.org
Sales Range: $10-24.9 Million
Emp.: 250
Direct Health & Medical Insurance Services
N.A.I.C.S.: 524114
Lance Hunsinger *(CEO)*
Patty Jones *(Sr VP-Health Svcs)*
Ethan Norris *(Sr VP-Bus & Product Dev)*

COMMUNITY HEALTH PROGRAMS, INC.
444 Stockbridge Rd, Great Barrington, MA 01230
Tel.: (413) 528-9311   MA
Web Site:
http://www.communityhealth.org
Year Founded: 1976
Sales Range: $10-24.9 Million
Emp.: 168
Community Health Services
N.A.I.C.S.: 621498
Lia Spiliotes *(CEO)*
Jodi Rathbun-Briggs *(Pres)*
Thomas Walbridge *(CFO)*
Elizabeth Strickler *(Chief Comm Officer)*

COMMUNITY HEALTH RESOURCES
995 Day Hill Rd, Windsor, CT 06095
Tel.: (860) 731-5522   CT
Web Site: http://www.chrhealth.org
Year Founded: 1965
Sales Range: $25-49.9 Million
Emp.: 699
Behavioral Healthcare Services
N.A.I.C.S.: 623220
Kathy Schiessl *(Sr VP-Child-Family Svcs)*

COMMUNITY HEALTH SERVICES OF GEORGIA
213 3rd St, Macon, GA 31201
Tel.: (478) 621-2040   GA
Web Site: http://www.chs-ga.org
Year Founded: 2003
Sales Range: $10-24.9 Million
Emp.: 43
Healtcare Services
N.A.I.C.S.: 622110
Lorraine T. Taylor *(CFO)*
Mark A. Waldrop *(COO)*
Ronnie D. Rollins *(Pres & CEO)*
Diana Wilks *(Sr VP-Inpatient Svcs)*
Freddie Walter *(Sr VP-Application Support)*
Michelle Moore Andrews *(Sr VP-Clinical Support Svcs)*

COMMUNITY HEALTH SERVICES, INC.
500 Albany Ave, Hartford, CT 06120
Tel.: (860) 249-9625   CT
Web Site:
https://www.chshartford.org
Year Founded: 1967
Sales Range: $10-24.9 Million
Emp.: 177
Community Health Care Services
N.A.I.C.S.: 621498
Gregory Stanton *(CEO)*
Scott Brabant *(CFO)*
Katherine Golar *(Chief Medical Officer)*

COMMUNITY HEALTH SOLUTIONS OF AMERICA, INC.
1000 118th Ave N, Saint Petersburg, FL 33716
Web Site:
http://www.chsamerica.com
Sales Range: $1-9.9 Million
Medical Care Management Services
N.A.I.C.S.: 541611
Barbara Freeman *(Chief Medical Officer)*
Dale F. Schmidt *(CEO)*

COMMUNITY HEALTHLINK INC.
72 Jaques Ave, Worcester, MA 01610-2476
Tel.: (508) 860-1121   MA
Web Site:
http://www.communityhealthlink.org
Year Founded: 1978
Sales Range: $25-49.9 Million
Emp.: 1,000
Specialty Outpatient Clinics, Outpatient for Mental Health
N.A.I.C.S.: 621420
Deborah Ekstrom *(Pres & CEO)*
Debra Grollman *(Dir-Children's Outpatient-Victim Svcs)*

COMMUNITY HOME HEALTH & HOSPICE
1035 11th Ave, Longview, WA 98632
Tel.: (360) 425-8510   WA
Web Site: https://www.chhh.org
Year Founded: 1988
Sales Range: $10-24.9 Million

Emp.: 318
Hospice Care Services
N.A.I.C.S.: 621610
Greg Pang *(CEO)*
Corey Balkan *(VP)*
Daniel Spjut *(Pres)*
Jaime Boaglio *(Treas & Sec)*
Stephen Sande *(Dir-Info Safety)*
Angelica Thomas *(Mgr-QI & Medical Records)*
Melissa Young *(Mgr-HR)*

COMMUNITY HOME HEALTH SERVICES, INC.
9894 E 121st St, Fishers, IN 46037
Tel.: (317) 621-4800   IN
Year Founded: 1975
Sales Range: $25-49.9 Million
Emp.: 377
Women Healthcare Services
N.A.I.C.S.: 621610
Jessie Westlund *(CEO)*
David J. Schulte *(CFO)*
Lisa Collins *(COO)*

COMMUNITY HOME SUPPLY CO. INC.
3924 N Lincoln Ave, Chicago, IL 60613
Tel.: (773) 281-2181   IL
Web Site: http://www.comhs.com
Rev.: $16,197,128
Emp.: 30
Plumbing & Heating Supplies
N.A.I.C.S.: 459999
Robert Lando *(Pres)*
Ralph Richardson *(VP)*

COMMUNITY HOSPICE & PALLIATIVE CARE
4266 Sunbeam Rd, Jacksonville, FL 32257
Tel.: (904) 268-5200   FL
Web Site:
https://www.communityhospice.com
Year Founded: 1979
Health Care Srvices
N.A.I.C.S.: 622110
Carlos Bosque *(Exec VP)*
Susan Ponder-Stansel *(Pres & CEO)*
Char Miller *(Dir-Mktg & Comm)*

COMMUNITY HOSPICE OF TEXAS
6100 Western Pl Ste 105, Fort Worth, TX 76107
Tel.: (817) 870-2795   TX
Web Site: https://www.chot.org
Year Founded: 1996
Sales Range: $25-49.9 Million
Emp.: 278
Hospice Care Services
N.A.I.C.S.: 621610
Patricia Jackson *(COO)*

COMMUNITY HOSPICE, INC.
1480 Carter Ave, Ashland, KY 41101
Tel.: (606) 329-1890   KY
Web Site: https://www.chospice.org
Year Founded: 1979
Sales Range: $10-24.9 Million
Emp.: 160
Community Health Care Services
N.A.I.C.S.: 621498
Susan Hunt *(Exec Dir)*
Lisa Barker *(Dir-Medical)*
Pat Steen *(Pres)*
Michael Hobbs *(Pres)*
Jennifer Sparks *(VP)*
Fennell Jansen *(Treas)*
Brandon Webb *(Assoc Dir-Medical)*

COMMUNITY HOSPITAL, INC.
2959 US Hwy 275, Hamburg, IA 51640
Tel.: (712) 382-1515   IA

Web Site:
http://www.grapehospital.com
Year Founded: 1955
Sales Range: $10-24.9 Million
Emp.: 127
Community Health Care Services
N.A.I.C.S.: 621498
Hilary Christiansen *(CFO)*
Nancy Tiemeyer *(Dir-Health Info Mgmt)*
Gloria Mattice *(Dir-Nursing)*
Chris Thomas *(Pres & CEO)*
Amy Jordan *(Dir-HR)*
Joe Gerardi *(Chief Ops & Nursing Officer)*
Matt Lewis *(Dir-Safety & Security-Grand Junction)*

COMMUNITY HOSPITALS AND WELLNESS CENTERS
433 W High St, Bryan, OH 43506
Tel.: (419) 636-1131   OH
Web Site:
http://www.chwchospital.com
Year Founded: 1969
Sales Range: $75-99.9 Million
Emp.: 700
Health Care Srvices
N.A.I.C.S.: 622110
Janice A. David *(VP-Patient Care)*
Craig Buell *(Dir-Pharmacy)*
Marilyn Nussbaumer *(Dir-Cath Lab)*
Michael Culler *(COO & VP)*
James A. Rupp *(Chm)*
Philip L. Ennen *(Pres, CEO & Sec)*

COMMUNITY HOUSING CONCEPTS, INC.
6875 E Evans Ave, Denver, CO 80224
Tel.: (303) 226-9121   CO
Web Site:
https://www.communityhousing.org
Year Founded: 2005
Sales Range: $10-24.9 Million
Community Housing Assistance Services
N.A.I.C.S.: 624229
Neal Bhamre *(Treas)*

COMMUNITY HOUSING DEVELOPMENT CORPORATION
614 N 1st St Ste 100, Minneapolis, MN 55401-3101
Tel.: (612) 332-6264   MN
Web Site: http://www.chdcmn.org
Year Founded: 1991
Sales Range: $10-24.9 Million
Emp.: 7
Housing Assistance Services
N.A.I.C.S.: 624229
Elizabeth Flannery *(Pres)*
Heidi Rathmann *(VP-Housing Dev)*
Peg Dorale *(Dir-Fin & Admin)*
Dan Walsh *(VP-Housing Dev)*
George Sherman *(Chm)*
Carolyn Olson *(Treas & Sec)*

COMMUNITY HOUSING INNOVATIONS, INC.
75 S Broadway Ste 340, White Plains, NY 10601
Tel.: (914) 683-1010   NY
Web Site: http://www.chigrants.org
Year Founded: 1991
Sales Range: $10-24.9 Million
Housing Assistance Services
N.A.I.C.S.: 624229
Rosemary Dehlow *(Chief Program Officer)*
Jerome J. August *(CFO, Chief Fiscal Officer & Comptroller)*
Julie Stern *(Sr Mgr-Homeownership Counseling & Grants)*
Libby Hightower *(Mgr-Office Admin)*
Deborah Post *(Sr Fin Dir & Sr Dir-Housing Dev)*

COMMUNITY HOUSING PARTNERS CORPORATION

448 Depot St Ne, Christiansburg, VA 24073-2050
Tel.: (540) 382-2002
Web Site:
https://www.communityhousing
partners.org
Sales Range: $10-24.9 Million
Emp.: 300
New Construction, Single-Family Houses
N.A.I.C.S.: 236115
Janaka Casper (CEO)
Todd Peacock (Dir-Construction)
Melissa Hammond (Mgr-Comm)
Lance Sutherland (VP-Fin & Acctg)
Ben Brewer (Dir-Procurement)
John Randolph (Chm)
Chrystal Strickler (Dir-Compliance)
Kimberly Strahm (Dir-Corp Dev)
Laura Croft (Dir-Human Capital)
Walter Engelken (Dir-Single-Family Realty & Dev)
Phil Hull (Dir-Trng)
Caleb Simon (Project Mgr)
Kirsten Anderson (VP-Asset Mgmt)
David Schultz (VP-Dev)
Mark Jackson (VP-Energy Solutions)
Angie Dobbins (VP-Resident Svcs)
Karen Turner (Chief Admin Officer & Exec VP)
Andy Hall (COO & Exec VP)
Scott Reithel (VP-Property Mgmt)

COMMUNITY INITIATIVES

354 Pine St Ste 700, San Francisco, CA 94104
Tel.: (415) 230-7700   CA
Web Site:
http://www.communityin.org
Year Founded: 1997
Sales Range: $10-24.9 Million
Emp.: 154
Grantmaking Services
N.A.I.C.S.: 813211
Alison Fong (Treas)
Ruth Williams (Chm)

COMMUNITY INITIATIVES DE-VELOPMENT CORPORATION

12105 Beeflower Dr, Lakewood Ranch, FL 34202
Tel.: (941) 756-5700   PA
Web Site: http://www.cidconline.com
Year Founded: 1992
Sales Range: $10-24.9 Million
Emp.: 3
Residential Support Services
N.A.I.C.S.: 623990
Mary Ann Loewenstein (Admin Officer & Asst Sec)
William S. Loewenstein (Pres & CEO)

COMMUNITY INTERACTIONS, INC.

740 S Chester Rd, Swarthmore, PA 19081
Tel.: (610) 328-9008   PA
Web Site: https://www.ciinc.org
Year Founded: 1973
Sales Range: $10-24.9 Million
Emp.: 713
Disability Assistance Services
N.A.I.C.S.: 624120
Donald T. Szegda (Pres & CEO)
Gary Clift (CFO & Sr VP)
Diane Hannah-Wilson (VP-HR)

COMMUNITY INVESTMENT GROUP, LTD.

112 S Orange St, Havana, IL 62644
Tel.: (309) 543-3361   IL
Web Site:
http://www.havanabank.com

Year Founded: 2000
Bank Holding Company
N.A.I.C.S.: 551111
Jeffery A. Bonnett (Pres & CFO)
Bradley S. Armbrust (CEO)

Subsidiaries:

The Havana National Bank   (1)
112 S Orange St, Havana, IL 62644
Tel.: (309) 543-3361
Web Site: http://www.havanabank.com
Sales Range: $1-9.9 Million
Emp.: 49
Commericial Banking
N.A.I.C.S.: 522110
Jeffery A. Bonnett (Pres & CFO)
Bradley S. Armbrust (CEO)
William H. Knuppel (Chm)
Donald J. Roch (COO)

COMMUNITY INVESTORS, INC.

1290 Broadway Ste 1400, Denver, CO 80203
Tel.: (800) 992-4384
Web Site: http://www.frontsteps.com
Community & HOA Websites & Plat-form
N.A.I.C.S.: 541511
John Roberts (Ops Mgr-Sls)
Robin Pederson (Chm)

Subsidiaries:

IHomefinder, Inc.   (1)
1900 Addison St Ste 300, Berkeley, CA 94704
Tel.: (510) 644-0230
Web Site: http://www.ihomefinder.com
Real Estate Search Technology & Websites
N.A.I.C.S.: 541511
Flynn Waters (VP-Prod Mgmt)

COMMUNITY INVOLVEMENT PROGRAMS

1600 Broadway St NE, Minneapolis, MN 55413
Tel.: (612) 362-4400   MN
Web Site: http://www.cipmn.org
Year Founded: 1971
Sales Range: $25-49.9 Million
Mental Health Care Services
N.A.I.C.S.: 623220
Ernest Johnson (Dir-Ops)
John Everett (Exec Dir)
Marsha Claiborne (Dir-Mental Health Svcs)
Jolene Thibedeau Boyd (Dir-Employment & Community Supports)
Tom Ruff (Dir-Residential Svcs)
Twila Jensen (Dir-Fin)
Gay Gonnerman (Sec)
Jane Lawrence (Dir-Family Svcs & Admin Resources)
Jesse Mason (Treas)
John Ottman (Vice Chm)

COMMUNITY JUSTICE PROJ-ECT

118 Locust St, Harrisburg, PA 17101
Tel.: (717) 236-9486   PA
Web Site:
https://www.communityjustice
project.org
Year Founded: 1996
Sales Range: $1-9.9 Million
Emp.: 30
Legal Aid Services
N.A.I.C.S.: 541199
James P. Deangelo (Pres)
Deborah Freedman (Sec)
Peter Zurflieh (Exec Dir)

COMMUNITY LEGAL SER-VICES OF MID-FLORIDA, INC.

128 Orange Ave Ste 300, Daytona Beach, FL 32114
Tel.: (386) 506-5396
Web Site: http://www.clsmf.org
Sales Range: $10-24.9 Million

Emp.: 100
Law firm
N.A.I.C.S.: 541199
Sue Edmunds (Mgr-Resource Dev & Grants)
Michelle Lilavois (Comptroller)
Christine Parrish (Sec)
Jeffrey Harvey (Dir-Ops)
Joseph Colombo (Pres)
Josh Lazar (Dir-IT)
Kimberly Sanchez (Exec Dir)
Melissa Miller (VP)
Myron Sears (Treas)

COMMUNITY LIVING ALLI-ANCE, INC.

1414 MacArthur Rd, Madison, WI 53714
Tel.: (608) 242-8335   WI
Web Site: http://www.clanet.org
Year Founded: 1999
Sales Range: $10-24.9 Million
Emp.: 815
Elderly People Assistance Services
N.A.I.C.S.: 624120
Alice Holbrow (Dir-Info Sys)
Todd Costello (Exec Dir)

COMMUNITY LIVING AND SUPPORT SERVICES

1400 S Braddock Ave, Pittsburgh, PA 15213
Tel.: (412) 683-7100   PA
Web Site:
http://www.classcommunity.org
Year Founded: 1951
Sales Range: $25-49.9 Million
Emp.: 2,058
Disability Assistance Services
N.A.I.C.S.: 624120
Melva Gooden-Ledbetter (Chief Pro Officer)
Lucy Spruill (Dir-Pub Policy & Com-munity Rels)
Joyce A. Redmerski (CFO)
Jack Snook (Dir-Centre Svcs)
Darla J. Lynn (Chief Residential Offi-cer)
Jonathan Hobaugh (Dir-Tech)
Rebecca Miklos (Dir-Home Svcs)
Ron Ruppen (Dir-Facilities)
Shannon McCarty (Dir-Dev)

COMMUNITY LIVING OPPOR-TUNITIES

11627 W 79th St, Lenexa, KS 66214
Tel.: (913) 341-9316   KS
Web Site: http://www.clokan.org
Year Founded: 1977
Sales Range: $25-49.9 Million
Community Support Services
N.A.I.C.S.: 624190
Michael Strouse (CEO)

COMMUNITY MEDIA GROUP

805 S Logan St, West Frankfort, IL 62896-2637
Tel.: (618) 937-6412
Web Site:
https://www.communitymedia.com
Year Founded: 1996
Sales Range: $10-24.9 Million
Emp.: 12
Daily & Weekly Newspapers Pub-lisher
N.A.I.C.S.: 516210
Larry J. Perrotto (Chm & Pres)
Mark J. Perrotto (CEO)
John H. Satterwhite (Vice Chm)
John D. Perrotto (Exec VP & Dir-Mfg)
Joan R. Williams (CFO)
Paul Barrett (VP)

Subsidiaries:

Finger Lakes Times   (1)
218 Genesee St, Geneva, NY 14456-2323

Tel.: (315) 789-3333
Web Site: http://www.fltimes.com
Sales Range: $10-24.9 Million
Newspaper Publishing
N.A.I.C.S.: 513110
Mark Lukas (Gen Mgr)

Fountain County Neighbor Inc.   (1)
113 S Perry St, Attica, IN 47918-1349
Tel.: (765) 762-2411
Web Site:
http://www.fountaincountyneighbor.com
Sales Range: $10-24.9 Million
Newspaper Publishers
N.A.I.C.S.: 513110
Greg Willhite (Gen Mgr)

Hartford City News Times Inc.   (1)
123 S Jefferson St, Hartford City, IN 47348
Tel.: (765) 348-0110
Web Site:
http://www.hartfordcitynewstimes.com
Rev.: $480,000
Newspaper Publishers
N.A.I.C.S.: 513110
Tami Robbins Roach (Editor-Education)
Eric Daugherty (Mgr-Production)
Robyn Rogers (Mng Editor)
Cynthia Eschbach Payne (Publr)

Newton County Enterprises Inc.   (1)
305 E Graham St, Kentland, IN
47951-1235   (100%)
Tel.: (219) 474-5532
Web Site:
http://www.newtoncountyenterprise.com
Sales Range: Less than $1 Million
Emp.: 2
Newspaper Publishers
N.A.I.C.S.: 513110
Larry Perrotto (Pres)

The Chronicle   (1)
308 E Main St, Hoopeston, IL
60942-1505   (100%)
Tel.: (217) 283-5111
Web Site:
http://www.thehoopestonchronicle.com
Sales Range: $10-24.9 Million
Emp.: 3
Newspaper Publishers
N.A.I.C.S.: 513110
Misty Courtney (Gen Mgr)

Twin States Publishing Co. Inc.   (1)
1492 E Walnut St, Watseka, IL
60970-1806   (100%)
Tel.: (815) 432-5227
Web Site: http://www.timesrepublic.info
Sales Range: $10-24.9 Million
Newspaper Publishers
N.A.I.C.S.: 513110
Carla Waters (Mng Dir)
Kevin Arnold (Mng Dir)
Cyndi Grace (Reg Dir-Circulation)

COMMUNITY MEDICAL CEN-TERS, INC.

7210 Murray Dr, Stockton, CA 95210
Tel.: (209) 373-2800   CA
Web Site:
https://www.communitymedical.org
Year Founded: 1978
Sales Range: $25-49.9 Million
Emp.: 441
Community Health Care Services
N.A.I.C.S.: 621498
Christine Noguera (CEO)

COMMUNITY MEMORIAL HEALTH SYSTEM

147 N Brent St, Ventura, CA 93003
Tel.: (805) 652-5011   CA
Web Site:
https://www.cmhshealth.org
Year Founded: 1933
Sales Range: $300-349.9 Million
Health Care Srvices
N.A.I.C.S.: 622110
Gary L. Wolfe (Treas)
Gregory H. Smith (Vice Chm)
Richard R. Rush (Chm)
F. Ted Muegenburg Jr. (Sec)

COMMUNITY MEMORIAL

COMMUNITY MEMORIAL —(CONTINUED)

HEALTHCARE, INC.
708 N 18th St, Marysville, KS 66508
Tel.: (785) 562-2311   **KS**
Web Site: https://www.cmhcare.org
Year Founded: 1955
Sales Range: $10-24.9 Million
Community Health Care Services
N.A.I.C.S.: 621498
Donna Craig (Dir-Patient Accts)
Beverly Fiferlick (CFO)
Curtis Hawkinson (Pres & CEO)

COMMUNITY MEMORIAL HEALTHCENTER
125 Buena Vista Cir, South Hill, VA 23970
Tel.: (434) 447-3151   **VA**
Web Site: http://www.cmh-sh.org
Year Founded: 1954
Sales Range: $75-99.9 Million
Emp.: 1,017
Health Care Srvices
N.A.I.C.S.: 622110
Ursula Butts (VP-Patient Care Svcs)
Brenda T. Palmore (Asst VP-Practice Mgmt & Physician Rels)
Nancy Prince (Asst VP-Extended Care & Clinical Svcs)
Kenneth W. Libby Jr. (VP-Fin)

COMMUNITY MORTGAGE CORPORATION
142 Timber Creek Dr, Cordova, TN 38018
Tel.: (901) 759-4400
Web Site: https://www.communitymtg.com
Year Founded: 1988
Rev.: $29,951,726
Emp.: 45
Mortgage Services
N.A.I.C.S.: 522310
L. Patrick Sandlin (Founder & CEO)
Kevin Ruby (Exec VP)
Mike Wells (CFO & Exec VP)

COMMUNITY MOTOR CO. INC.
4521 University Ave, Cedar Falls, IA 50613
Tel.: (319) 277-5010
Web Site: http://www.communitymotors.com
Rev.: $28,700,000
Emp.: 75
Automobiles, New & Used
N.A.I.C.S.: 441110
James T. Skarlis (Owner)
Steve Miller (Mgr-Parts)

COMMUNITY NATIONAL BANK & TRUST
14 North Lincoln, Chanute, KS 66720
Tel.: (620) 431-2265
Web Site: https://www.mybankcnb.com
Year Founded: 1987
Emp.: 444
Bank Holding Company
N.A.I.C.S.: 551111

Subsidiaries:

Quarry City Savings and Loan Association Inc.   (1)
713 PCA Rd, Warrensburg, MO 64093
Tel.: (660) 747-5513
Web Site: http://www.quarrycity.com
Savings & Loan Institution
N.A.I.C.S.: 522180
Steve Andrew (Pres & CEO)
David Andrew (CFO & Exec VP)

COMMUNITY NEWSPAPERS INC.
2365 Prince Ave Ste A, Athens, GA 30606

Tel.: (706) 548-0010
Web Site: https://www.cninewspapers.com
Year Founded: 1989
Sales Range: $25-49.9 Million
Emp.: 10
Newspapers, Publishing & Printing
N.A.I.C.S.: 513110
Mark Major (CFO & VP)
Tom Wood (Chm)
Joel Jenkins (Dir-Mktg)
Tracy McCormick Dishman (Editor-News-Leader)
W. H. NeSmith Jr. (Pres)

Subsidiaries:

Lake City Reporter   (1)
180 E Duval St, Lake City, FL 32055-4083
Tel.: (386) 752-1293
Web Site: http://www.lakecityreporter.com
Sales Range: $10-24.9 Million
Newspapers
N.A.I.C.S.: 513110
Todd Wilson (Publr)
Jamie Wachter (Publr)
Monja Slater (Mgr-Bus Dev)

News-Leader   (1)
511 Ash St, Fernandina Beach, FL 32034-3930
Tel.: (904) 261-3696
Web Site: http://www.fbnewsleader.com
Sales Range: $10-24.9 Million
Newspaper Publishing
N.A.I.C.S.: 513110
Foy Maloy (Publr)
Robert Fiege (Dir-Production)
Mike Hankins (Dir-Adv)
Beth Jones (Editor-Sports)
Angeline Mudd (Bus Mgr)
Bob Timpe (Dir-Circulation)
Scott J. Bryan (Editor)

Palatka Daily News   (1)
1825 St Johns Ave, Palatka, FL 32177-4442
Tel.: (386) 312-5200
Web Site: http://www.palatkadailynews.com
Sales Range: $10-24.9 Million
Daily Newspaper
N.A.I.C.S.: 513110
Mary Kaye Wells (Dir-Adv)
Michael Leonard (Publr)

COMMUNITY NURSING SERVICE OF DU PAGE COUNTY
690 E North Ave, Carol Stream, IL 60188
Tel.: (630) 665-7000   **IL**
Web Site: http://www.cadencehealth.org
Sales Range: $10-24.9 Million
Home Health & Hospice Services
N.A.I.C.S.: 621610
Terry Jacobson (CEO)
Robin White (Mgr-Mktg)

COMMUNITY OF CARING
245 E 8th St, Erie, PA 16503
Tel.: (814) 456-6661   **PA**
Web Site: http://www.cocerie.com
Year Founded: 1980
Sales Range: $1-9.9 Million
Emp.: 27
International Organization Providing Food, Clothing, Shelter & Other Necessities to Local Erie Communities & Throughout the World.
N.A.I.C.S.: 624190
John Magenau (Pres)
Michael Hale (Sec)
Edward Myers (Treas)

COMMUNITY OF HOPE
1717 Massachusetts Ave NW Ste 805, Washington, DC 20036
Tel.: (202) 407-7747   **DC**
Web Site: http://www.communityofhopedc.org
Year Founded: 1980
Sales Range: $10-24.9 Million

Emp.: 157
Community Care Services
N.A.I.C.S.: 624190
Kelly Sweeney McShane (Exec Dir)

COMMUNITY PARTNERS
113 Crosby Rd Ste 1, Dover, NH 03820
Tel.: (603) 516-9300   **NH**
Web Site: http://www.communitypartners.org
Year Founded: 1982
Sales Range: $25-49.9 Million
Emp.: 554
Behavioral Healthcare Services
N.A.I.C.S.: 623220
Mark Guptill (Dir-IT)
R. J. Allister (Dir-Medical)
Brian Collins (Exec Dir)
Christopher Kozak (COO-Behavioral Health)
Kathleen Boisclair (Pres)
Ann Landry (Sec)
Kathleen Stocker (CFO)
Wayne Goss (VP)
Janet Salsbury (Dir-Behavioral Health Svcs QI)
Lucy Putnam (Dir-Behavioral Health Youth & Family Svcs)
Pamela Dushan (Dir-Developmental Svcs Case Mgmt)
Deirdre Watson (Dir-Developmental Svcs Family Support)
Suzanne Iverson (Dir-Developmental Svcs Family Centered Early Supports & Svcs)
Karen Vanwormer (Dir-Behavioral Health Adult Svcs)
Anthony Demers (Treas)

COMMUNITY PARTNERSHIP FOR CHILDREN
135 Executive Cir 2nd Fl, Daytona Beach, FL 32114
Tel.: (386) 238-4900   **FL**
Web Site: https://www.communitypartners.org
Year Founded: 1999
Sales Range: $25-49.9 Million
Emp.: 216
Child Care Services
N.A.I.C.S.: 624110
Karin Flositz (COO)

COMMUNITY PARTNERSHIP OF SOUTHERN ARIZONA
4575 E Broadway Blvd, Tucson, AZ 85711
Tel.: (520) 325-4268   **AZ**
Web Site: http://www.cpsaarizona.org
Year Founded: 1995
Sales Range: $250-299.9 Million
Emp.: 281
Behavioral Healthcare Services
N.A.I.C.S.: 623220

COMMUNITY PHARMACY OF RANDOLPH
268 Water St, Randolph, ME 04346
Tel.: (207) 588-2482
Teleproduction & Other Postproduction Services
N.A.I.C.S.: 512191

COMMUNITY PHYSICIANS NETWORK
1040 Division St, Mauston, WI 53948-1931
Tel.: (608) 643-5888   **WI**
Web Site: http://www.cpnetwork.org
Year Founded: 1983
Sales Range: $10-24.9 Million
Emp.: 31
Medical Management Services
N.A.I.C.S.: 813920
D. Keith Ness (Chm)

COMMUNITY PROPERTIES OF OHIO
910 E Broad St, Columbus, OH 43205-1101
Tel.: (614) 253-0984
Web Site: https://www.cpoms.org
Year Founded: 1997
Sales Range: $10-24.9 Million
Emp.: 60
Provider of Real Estate Services
N.A.I.C.S.: 531210
Ted Pearson (Mgr-Project)
Barry Stayer (CFO)
Chad Ketler (Pres & CEO)
Rod Suman (Mgr-IT)
Shawn Steen (COO)
Halle Pelger (COO)
Sharon Pheifer (Chief Analytics Officer)
Regina Clemons (Chief Program Officer)

COMMUNITY REHABILITATION SERVICES, INC.
1013 Riverburch Pkwy Ste 2, Dalton, GA 30721
Tel.: (478) 621-2060   **GA**
Web Site: http://www.integrarehab.org
Year Founded: 2005
Sales Range: $25-49.9 Million
Emp.: 621
Health Care Srvices
N.A.I.C.S.: 622110
Vicki Hill-Hoffman (Sr VP-Clinical Svcs)
Bernice Cash (VP-Bus Ops)
Yolanda Pence (VP-Compliance & Quality Mgmt)

COMMUNITY RENEWAL TEAM, INC.
555 Windsor St, Hartford, CT 06120
Tel.: (860) 560-5600   **CT**
Web Site: https://www.crtct.org
Year Founded: 1964
Sales Range: $50-74.9 Million
Emp.: 1,127
Community Development Services
N.A.I.C.S.: 624190
Sudhakar Vamathevan (CFO)
Gustave Keach-Longo (VP-Senior Svcs)
Chris McCluskey (VP-Housing & Community Svcs)
Lena Rodriguez (Pres & CEO)

COMMUNITY RESOURCE CREDIT UNION
2900 Decker Dr, Baytown, TX 77520
Tel.: (281) 422-3611   **TX**
Web Site: http://www.crcu.org
Year Founded: 1935
Sales Range: $10-24.9 Million
Emp.: 138
Credit Union Operator
N.A.I.C.S.: 522130
Randall Sanders (Chm)
Russell Ballard (Pres & CEO)

COMMUNITY RESOURCES FOR INDEPENDENCE
3410 W 12th St, Erie, PA 16505
Tel.: (814) 838-7222   **PA**
Web Site: https://www.crinet.org
Year Founded: 1991
Sales Range: $50-74.9 Million
Emp.: 1,697
Disability Assistance Services
N.A.I.C.S.: 624120
Carl Berry (Dir-HR)
Tom Pushchak (Dir-Mgmt Info Sys)
Timothy J. Finegan (Exec Dir)

COMMUNITY SENIOR LIFE INC
25819 Canal Rd, Orange Beach, AL 36561
Tel.: (251) 981-0200   AL
Web Site:
  https://www.communityseniorlife.org
Year Founded: 1989
Sales Range: $10-24.9 Million
Senior Living Services
N.A.I.C.S.: 623311
J. Douglas Warren *(Pres & CEO)*
Daniel Scarbrough *(Exec VP & Dir-Medical)*
Steven Globetti *(Corp Compliance Officer & Exec VP)*
Robin Johnson *(VP-Fin)*
Patrick Willingham *(Co-Founder)*

COMMUNITY SERVICE BUILDING CORPORATION
100 W 10th St Ste 201, Wilmington, DE 19801-1680
Tel.: (302) 777-0922   DE
Web Site: https://www.csbcorp.org
Year Founded: 1995
Sales Range: $10-24.9 Million
Emp.: 3
Nonprofit Association
N.A.I.C.S.: 813920
Tim Meyer *(Mgr-Garage)*
Jerry A. Bilton *(Exec Dir)*
Jaime Bohn *(Dir-Facility)*
Edward B. Du Pont *(VP)*
Peter C. Morrow *(Pres)*

COMMUNITY SERVICE COUNCIL
16 E 16th St Ste 202, Tulsa, OK 74119-4402
Tel.: (918) 585-5551   OK
Web Site: http://www.csctulsa.org
Year Founded: 1941
Sales Range: $10-24.9 Million
Emp.: 128
Community Development Services
N.A.I.C.S.: 813319

COMMUNITY SERVICE NETWORK INC
52 Broadway, Stoneham, MA 02180
Tel.: (781) 438-1977   MA
Web Site: http://www.csninc.org
Year Founded: 1985
Sales Range: $25-49.9 Million
Emp.: 7
Community Service
N.A.I.C.S.: 624190
Sheila Herbeck *(Pres)*
Bryna Davis *(Exec Dir)*

COMMUNITY SERVICES AND EMPLOYMENT TRAINING, INC.
312 NW 3rd Ave, Visalia, CA 93291-3626
Tel.: (559) 732-4194   CA
Web Site: https://www.cset.org
Year Founded: 1976
Sales Range: $10-24.9 Million
Emp.: 1,027
Community Action Services
N.A.I.C.S.: 624190
Maria Rodriguez *(Dir-HR)*

COMMUNITY SERVICES FOR THE DEVELOPMENTALLY DISABLED, INC.
180 Oak St, Buffalo, NY 14203
Tel.: (716) 883-8888   NY
Web Site: http://www.csdd.net
Year Founded: 1989
Sales Range: $25-49.9 Million
Emp.: 1,079
Developmental Disability Assistance Services
N.A.I.C.S.: 623210

Daniel Weintraub *(Chm)*
Shari Cook *(Treas)*
Rebecca Boyle *(Sec)*
Kevin P. Wicka *(Vice Chm)*
Kelly Kinderman *(VP-Program Support & Dev)*
Caroline Hurley *(Coord-Comm & Fundraising)*

COMMUNITY SPECIALISTS CORPORATION
900 Agnew Rd, Pittsburgh, PA 15227
Tel.: (412) 885-5200   PA
Year Founded: 1981
Sales Range: $10-24.9 Million
Emp.: 215
Community Support Services
N.A.I.C.S.: 624190
Ken Curcio *(Dir-Fin Ops)*
Frank Wentzel *(Exec Dir)*
Scott Bartos *(COO)*
Daniel McCann *(VP)*
William Nunn *(Pres)*

COMMUNITY STATE BANK
1500 Main St, Union Grove, WI 53182
Tel.: (262) 878-3763
Web Site:
  http://www.communitystatebank.net
Sales Range: $25-49.9 Million
Emp.: 110
Banking Services
N.A.I.C.S.: 522110
David D. Albrecht *(Officer-Loan & Exec VP)*
Heidi Conde *(Officer-Compliance & Asst VP)*
Dianne Funk *(VP)*
Sue Young *(Officer-Security & Asst VP)*
Peter Huck *(Chm)*
Richard Swantz *(Vice Chm)*
Dave Moyer *(Sr VP & Mgr-Agriculture)*
Scott Huedepohl *(Pres & CEO)*
Michael Ploch *(Pres-Market & Sr VP-Lake Geneva)*
Gregory Wall *(Asst VP & Dir-Mktg)*
James Muraski *(Officer-IT & Asst VP)*
Katie Stolp *(Dir-Retail Ops)*
Kim Terpstra *(Officer-Mortgage Loan)*
Steve Donovan *(Pres-Market & Sr VP)*
Carol Klimke *(Officer-Special Ops)*
Colin Hennessey *(VP & Dir-Retail Sls)*
Karen Jorgensen *(Officer-Loan Ops & Asst VP)*
Kelly Huston *(Pres-Market-Paddock Lake)*
Kim Ligocki *(Officer-HR & Asst VP)*
Peter Schumacher *(CFO & Sr VP)*
Shakil Haider *(VP & Mgr-Mortgage)*
Neil Buchanan *(Pres-Market)*

COMMUNITY SUFFOLK INC.
304 Second St, Everett, MA 02149-4739
Tel.: (617) 389-5200   MA
Web Site:
  http://www.communitysuffolk.com
Year Founded: 1968
Sales Range: $50-74.9 Million
Emp.: 40
Fresh Fruits & Vegetables
N.A.I.C.S.: 424480
Joseph Piazza *(Pres)*

COMMUNITY SUPPORT SERVICES, INC.
150 Cross St, Akron, OH 44311
Tel.: (330) 996-9141   OH
Web Site: https://www.cssbh.org
Year Founded: 1969

Sales Range: $10-24.9 Million
Emp.: 565
Community Support Services
N.A.I.C.S.: 624190
Terrence B. Dalton *(Pres & CEO)*
Frank Sepetauc *(COO & VP-Rehabilitation)*
Douglas A. Wagner *(Dir-Admin)*
Manzoor Elahi *(Dir-Medical)*
Michael Davis *(Sec)*
Karl Henley *(Treas)*

COMMUNITY SYSTEMS, INC.
7926 Jones Branch Dr Ste 105, McLean, VA 22102
Tel.: (703) 448-0606   DE
Web Site:
  http://www.communitysystems.org
Year Founded: 1984
Sales Range: $10-24.9 Million
Emp.: 459
Disability Assistance Services
N.A.I.C.S.: 624120
Janet Butler *(COO & Sr VP)*
Amy Yento *(Chm)*
James Campbell *(Exec Dir)*
Guri L. Davis *(Exec Dir)*
David Paige *(Exec Dir)*

COMMUNITY TELEVISION OF SOUTHERN CALIFORNIA
4401 W Sunset Blvd, Los Angeles, CA 90027
Tel.: (323) 666-6500
Web Site: http://www.kcet.org
Sales Range: $25-49.9 Million
Emp.: 175
Television Broadcasting Station
N.A.I.C.S.: 516120
Al Jerome *(Pres & CEO)*
Nancy Rishagen *(Exec VP-Dev)*
Renee Williams *(VP-Membership)*

COMMUNITY TIES OF AMERICA, INC.
2969 Armory Dr Ste 200, Nashville, TN 37204
Tel.: (615) 661-4544
Web Site: http://www.comties.com
Year Founded: 1998
Rev.: $4,500,000
Emp.: 70
Management Consulting Services
N.A.I.C.S.: 541611
Ronald Lee *(Pres)*

COMMUNITY TIRE COMPANY INC.
9124 Pershall Rd, Hazelwood, MO 63042
Tel.: (314) 241-7135
Web Site:
  http://www.communitytire.com
Sales Range: $25-49.9 Million
Emp.: 100
Automobile Tires & Tubes
N.A.I.C.S.: 423130
Philip Berra *(Pres)*
Andrew Berra *(VP)*

COMMUNITY, WORK & INDEPENDENCE, INC.
88 Broad St, Glens Falls, NY 12801
Tel.: (518) 793-4700   NY
Web Site: http://www.cwinc.org
Year Founded: 1963
Sales Range: $10-24.9 Million
Emp.: 847
Disability Assistance Services
N.A.I.C.S.: 624120
Karl Smoczynski *(Officer-Corp Compliance)*
Andrew J. Collins *(Sec)*
Kurt Moser *(Treas)*

COMMUNITYAMERICA CREDIT UNION
9777 Ridge Dr, Lenexa, KS 66219
Tel.: (913) 905-7000   MO
Web Site: http://www.cacu.com
Year Founded: 1940
Sales Range: $100-124.9 Million
Emp.: 895
Credit Union
N.A.I.C.S.: 522130
Lisa Ginter *(CEO)*
Tim Saracini *(CFO)*
Rich Miller *(Chm)*
Brad Douglas *(Vice Chm)*
Kerry Domke *(Treas & Sec)*
Staci Parker *(Dir-Treasury Mgmt Sls)*
Ashley Toma *(Dir-Concierge Banking)*

COMMUNITYCARE, INC.
218 W 6th St, Tulsa, OK 74119-1004
Tel.: (918) 594-5200   OK
Web Site: https://www.ccok.com
Year Founded: 1994
Sales Range: $100-124.9 Million
Emp.: 480
Hospital & Medical Service Plans
N.A.I.C.S.: 524114

COMMUNITYHEALTH
2611 W Chicago Ave, Chicago, IL 60622
Tel.: (773) 395-9900   IL
Web Site:
  https://www.communityhealth.org
Year Founded: 1992
Sales Range: $10-24.9 Million
Emp.: 52
Community Health Care Services
N.A.I.C.S.: 621498
Megan Doerr *(Dir-Clinic Ops)*
Judith Haasis *(Exec Dir)*
Heather Jacobsen *(Fin Dir & Dir-Admin)*

COMMUTER AIR TECHNOLOGY
7200 NW 63rd St, Oklahoma City, OK 73008
Tel.: (405) 694-4755
Web Site:
  http://www.commuterair.com
Year Founded: 1987
Sales Range: $25-49.9 Million
Emp.: 67
Airborne Navigational System Mfr
N.A.I.C.S.: 334511
Darryl Wilkerson *(Pres)*
Jennifer Johnson *(VP-Fin & Admin)*
Ken Haley *(VP-Technical Svcs)*
James Crawford *(Dir-Signals Intelligence Trng)*
Stan Green *(Dir-Special Programs)*
Greg Meacham *(CFO)*

COMNET COMMUNICATIONS LLC
9 Park Ridge Dr, Bethel, CT 06883
Tel.: (203) 794-8040
Web Site:
  https://www.comnetcomm.com
Sales Range: $25-49.9 Million
Emp.: 35
Telephone & Telephone Equipment Installation
N.A.I.C.S.: 238210
Alex Merrifield *(Pres)*
Jody Ticer *(Dir-Ops)*
Norma Vaughn *(Sr VP)*
James Nicholson *(Project Mgr-Natl Accts)*
Rick Damo *(Project Mgr)*
Glenn Wagner *(VP-Northeast Div)*
Ray Larnerd *(CFO)*
Norma Nelson *(Sr VP-HR)*
William Bielmyer *(VP-Southeast Reg)*
Jim Phillips *(VP-Southwest Reg)*

Comnet Communications LLC—(Continued)

Subsidiaries:

Comnet Communications LLC (1)
4343 W Royia Land Ste 118, Irving, TX
75063
Tel.: (972) 245-5022
Web Site: http://www.comnetcomm.com
Sales Range: $1-9.9 Million
Fiber Optic Cable Installation
N.A.I.C.S.: 517111
Alex Merrifield (Pres & CEO)
William Bielmyer (VP-Southeast)
Ray Larnerd (CFO)
Norma Nelson (Sr VP-HR)
Glenn Wagner (VP-Northeast)

COMNET TELECOM SUPPLY, INC.

1 Kimberly Rd Bldg 101, East Bruns-
wick, NJ 08816
Tel.: (732) 967-1501   NJ
Web Site:
http://www.comnetsupply.com
Year Founded: 1993
Sales Range: $1-9.9 Million
Emp.: 17
Telecommunications & Data Products
Mfr & Distr
N.A.I.C.S.: 334290
Robert Portera (Founder & Pres)

COMO LUBE & SUPPLIES, INC.

1108 Port Terminal Rd, Duluth, MN
55802
Tel.: (218) 722-2920   MN
Web Site: https://www.comolube.com
Year Founded: 1980
Sales Range: $10-24.9 Million
Emp.: 42
Petroleum Product Whslr
N.A.I.C.S.: 424720
Zane Swanson (CEO)
Ron Swanson (Pres)

COMODO GROUP, INC.

1255 Broad St, Clifton, NJ 07310
Tel.: (201) 963-0004
Web Site: http://www.comodo.com
Year Founded: 1998
Sales Range: $25-49.9 Million
Emp.: 600
Security & Other Computer Software
N.A.I.C.S.: 513210
Melih Abdulhayoglu (Chm)
Michael Whittam (CFO)
Robin Alden (CTO)
Beverley Daynes (Exec VP-Fin)
Patricia Forsyth (Gen Counsel)
Egemen Tas (CTO-Innovation Lab)
James Langman (VP-Bus Dev)
Michael Fowler (Sr Mgr-Bus Dev)
Christopher Morcella (Dir-Mktg Ana-
lytics & Insights)
Stanley P. Jaworski Jr. (VP-Global
Mktg)
Charles Zinkowski (Dir-Comm)
Edward Giaquinto (Dir-IT)
Fatih Orhan (Dir-Tech)
Ugur Gulaydin (Dir-Web Ops)
Steve Subar (Pres & CEO)

COMP VIEW INC.

10035 SW Arctic Dr, Beaverton, OR
97005
Tel.: (503) 641-8439
Web Site: http://www.compview.com
Sales Range: $25-49.9 Million
Emp.: 50
Projection Apparatus Services
N.A.I.C.S.: 423410
Scott Birdsall (Pres)

COMPACT INFORMATION SYSTEMS, INC.

7120 185th Ave NE Ste 150, Red-
mond, WA 98052
Tel.: (425) 869-1379   WA
Web Site:
https://www.compactlists.com
Year Founded: 1988
Sales Range: $10-24.9 Million
Emp.: 30
Data Processing/Preparation
N.A.I.C.S.: 518210
Joseph P. Wiley (Founder)

Subsidiaries:

AccuData Holdings, Inc. (1)
5220 Summerlin Commons Blvd Ste 200,
Fort Myers, FL 33907
Tel.: (239) 425-4400
Web Site: http://www.accudata.com
Database Marketing Services
N.A.I.C.S.: 519290
Bree Verrengia (COO)
Ted Dietrich (VP-Client Svcs)
Denise Abbattista (Controller)
Connie Wagner (Mgr-HR)
Karen Blanchard (VP-Mktg)
Marylou Bushman (VP-Bus Tech)
Nate Petel (Sr VP-Sls & Svc)
Dustin Williams (VP-Tech Solutions & Client
Svcs)

COMPANIA CERVECERA DE PUERTO RICO

100 Alfonso Valdes Blvd, Mayaguez,
PR 00680
Tel.: (787) 834-1000
Web Site:
https://www.cerveceradepr.com
Rev.: $60,000,000
Emp.: 200
Beer Mfr
N.A.I.C.S.: 312120
Grace G. Valdes (Chm)
Camalia Valdes (Pres)
Craig Hylwa (Mgr-Ops)
Jorge Bracero (Dir-Promos)

COMPANIES (TC) LLC.

1070 E 800 N, Orem, UT 84097
Tel.: (801) 841-3314
Year Founded: 2008
Sales Range: $10-24.9 Million
Real Estate Development Services
N.A.I.C.S.: 531190
Mike Krohn (CFO)

COMPANION PROFESSIONAL SERVICES LLC

1301 Gervais St Ste 1700, Columbia,
SC 29201
Tel.: (803) 765-1310
Web Site: https://www.tmfloyd.com
Rev.: $20,885,576
Emp.: 20
Computer Related Consulting Ser-
vices
N.A.I.C.S.: 561320
Terry M. Floyd (Founder, Mng Partner
& VP)

COMPANIONS & HOMEMAK-ERS INC.

613 New Britain Ave, Farmington, CT
06032
Tel.: (860) 677-4948
Web Site:
https://www.companionsand
homemakers.com
Sales Range: $10-24.9 Million
Emp.: 80
Personal Shopping Service
N.A.I.C.S.: 812990
Linda Grigerek (Pres)

COMPANY C, INC.

102 Old Tpke Rd, Concord, NH
03301
Tel.: (603) 226-4460   NH
Web Site: http://www.companyc.com

Year Founded: 1994
Sales Range: $10-24.9 Million
Emp.: 57
Home Furnishings Designer & Mfr
N.A.I.C.S.: 423220
Chris Chapin (Co-Founder)
Walter Chapin (Co-Founder)
Michael Ackelbein (VP-Sls & Distr-
Global)

COMPARENETWORKS, INC.

395 Oyster Point Blvd Ste 321, South
San Francisco, CA 94080
Tel.: (650) 243-5212
Web Site:
http://www.comparenetworks.com
Year Founded: 2000
Sales Range: $10-24.9 Million
Emp.: 81
Online Marketing Services
N.A.I.C.S.: 459999
Brian Cowley (CEO)
Bo Purtic (Chief Revenue Officer)
Paul Gatti (Founder)
Andy Miller (CTO)
Mike Okimoto (Chief Content Officer)
Ken Coffee (VP-Ops)

COMPAS, INC.

4300 Haddonfield Rd Ste 200, Penn-
sauken, NJ 08109
Tel.: (856) 667-8577
Web Site:
http://www.compasonline.com
Year Founded: 1990
Sales Range: $200-249.9 Million
Emp.: 80
Media Buying Services
N.A.I.C.S.: 541830
Stan Woodland (Founder & Chm)
James Woodland (CEO)
Nicole Woodland-DeVan (Sr VP-
Buying Svcs & Deliverables)
Nancy Logue (VP-HR)
Marjolein Bruurs (CFO)

COMPASS ADJUSTERS & IN-VESTIGATORS, INC.

96 Haarlem Ave, White Plains, NY
10603
Tel.: (914) 428-9224
Web Site:
https://www.compassadj.com
Sales Range: $25-49.9 Million
Emp.: 56
Inspection & Investigation Services,
Insurance
N.A.I.C.S.: 524210
Louis J. Margam (Owner)

COMPASS ADVISERS GROUP LLC

825 3rd Ave 32nd Fl, New York, NY
10022
Tel.: (212) 702-9800   DE
Year Founded: 2009
Holding Company; Financial Advisory
& Investment Services
N.A.I.C.S.: 551112
Stephen M. Waters (Mng Partner)
Philip Keevil (Partner)
Lorraine Costelloe (CFO & Sr Mng
Dir)
Ze'ev Goldberg (Partner)
Allan Melville Chapin (Partner)
Allan Melville Chapin (Partner)
Betty Li (CFO)
Antoine Pupin (Partner)
Thomas Tullo (Mng Dir)
Angela Leung (Office Mgr & Mgr-HR)
Frank Rudd (Partner-Secondary Di-
rect Investment)
Alister Wormsley (Partner-Secondary
Direct Investment)
Tim Wright (Partner-Secondary Direct
Investment)

Subsidiaries:

Compass Advisers Limited (1)
1 Grosvenor Place, London, SW1X 7JH,
United Kingdom
Tel.: (44) 2075209435
Web Site: http://www.ca-llp.com
Sales Range: $25-49.9 Million
Emp.: 6
Financial Advisory & Investment Services
N.A.I.C.S.: 523940
Philip Keevil (Partner)
Jai Singh (Mng Dir)
Gal Nadir (Mng Dir)

Compass Partners Advisors, LLP (1)
825 3rd Ave 32nd Fl, New York, NY 10022
Tel.: (212) 702-9800
Emp.: 15
Financial Advisory & Investment Services
N.A.I.C.S.: 523940
Stephen M. Waters (Mng Partner)
Philip Keevil (Partner)
Ze'ev Goldberg (Partner)
Allan Melville Chapin (Partner)
Allan Melville Chapin (Partner)
Eugene Co (Mng Dir)
Neil Ghosh (VP)
Thomas Tullo (Mng Dir)
Rishi Das (VP)
James Waters (VP)
Eugeneco Ancoineputine (Mng Dir)

Compass Partners Asset Manage-
ment LLC (1)
825 3rd Ave 32nd Fl, New York, NY 10022
Tel.: (212) 702-9800
Private Equity Firm
N.A.I.C.S.: 523999
Stephen M. Waters (Founder & Partner)
Melissa Vlak (COO & Mng Dir)
Thomas Tullo (Mng Dir)
Allan Chapin (Partner)
Philip Keevil (Partner)
Antoine Pupin (Partner)

Compass Partners Capital LLC (1)
1 Harbor Point Sq 2200 Atlantic St Ste 520,
Stamford, CT 06902
Tel.: (212) 702-8650
Web Site: https://compasspartners.com
Privater Equity Firm
N.A.I.C.S.: 523999
Stephen M. Waters (Mng Partner)

Joint Venture (Domestic):

Precinmac, LP (2)
79 Prospect Ave, South Paris, ME 04281
Tel.: (207) 743-6344
Web Site: https://www.precinmac.com
High Tolerance Precision Machined Compo-
nents & Assemblies Mfr
N.A.I.C.S.: 332721
Eric C. Wisnefsky (CEO)

Subsidiary (Domestic):

Petersen Inc. (3)
1527 N 2000 W, Ogden, UT 84404
Tel.: (801) 732-2000
Web Site: http://www.PetersenInc.com
Sales Range: $50-74.9 Million
Emp.: 445
Machinery Equipment Distr
N.A.I.C.S.: 423810
Jon Ballantyne (CEO)
Mark Jenkins (CEO)
Rob Despain (VP-Bus Dev)
Stephen Grange (VP-Ops)
Kirk Douglass (Dir-Quality)
Tom Burkland (Mgr-Engrg)
Dave Dixon (Mgr-HR)
Frank Shaw (Dir-Program Office)

Compass Partners International
LLP (1)
26 Mount Row, London, W1K 8SQ, United
Kingdom
Tel.: (44) 2077612000
Web Site: http://www.cpil.co.uk
Privater Equity Firm
N.A.I.C.S.: 523999
Stephen M. Waters (Mng Partner)
Frank Rudd (Partner)
Tim Wright (Partner)
Anthony Marraccino (CFO)

Holding (Non-US):

CTL Logistics S.A. (2)

ul Dluga 90, 41-208, Sosnowiec, Poland
Tel.: (48) 322990275
Web Site: http://www.ctl.pl
Logistics & Freight Transportation Services
N.A.I.C.S.: 541614
Jaroslaw Krol *(Chm)*

Rodenstock GmbH (2)
Elsenheimer St 33 Munich, 0687, Munich,
Germany
Tel.: (49) 8972020
Web Site: http://www.rodenstock.com
Sales Range: $400-449.9 Million
Mfr & Marketer of Ophthalmic Frames &
Lenses
N.A.I.C.S.: 339115
Dieter Henning *(Head-Adv)*
Giancarlo Galli *(CEO)*
Christian Kluenper *(Mgr-HR)*
Oliver Kastalio *(CEO)*
Anders Hedegaard *(CEO)*

Holding (Non-US):

Rodenstock Australia Pty. Ltd. (3)
100 108 Asquith Street, Silverwater, 2128,
NSW, Australia
Tel.: (61) 297480988
Sales Range: $25-49.9 Million
Emp.: 25
Ophthalmic Product Mfr
N.A.I.C.S.: 327215
Tim McCann *(Gen Mgr)*

Rodenstock Canada Inc. (3)
172 Towers Road Unit 30, Vaughan, L4L
8A7, ON, Canada
Tel.: (905) 851-7183
Web Site: http://www.rodenstock.ca
Sales Range: $25-49.9 Million
Emp.: 25
Spectacle Frames & Ophthalmic Lenses
N.A.I.C.S.: 333310
Jeremy Carvalho *(Gen Mgr-Ops)*

Rodenstock Osterreich GmbH (3)
Mariahilfer Str 116, PO Box 82, 1072, Vi-
enna, Austria
Tel.: (43) 159900200
Sales Range: $25-49.9 Million
Emp.: 70
Provider of Ophthalmic Products
N.A.I.C.S.: 327215
Moritzer Clemens *(Gen Mgr)*

Rondelli Advisers S.r.l. (1)
Via S Radegonda 11, 20121, Milan, Italy
Tel.: (39) 02 30309 5800
Financial Advisory & Investment Services
N.A.I.C.S.: 523940

COMPASS ENERGY HOLD-INGS, INC.
3170 Holmestown Rd, Myrtle Beach,
SC 29588
Tel.: (843) 274-5974   NV
Year Founded: 2009
Sales Range: $10-24.9 Million
Emp.: 25
Convenience Store & Gasoline Sta-
tion Owner
N.A.I.C.S.: 457110
Peter Iodice *(Pres, CEO, CFO & Sec)*

COMPASS EQUITY PART-NERS, LLC
222 W Las Colinas Blvd Ste 1320N,
Irving, TX 75039
Tel.: (866) 628-2374
Web Site:
    http://www.compassequity.com
Privater Equity Firm
N.A.I.C.S.: 523999
Michael Stanley *(CEO & Mng Gen
Partner)*
Tom Bartlett *(Partner & Mng Dir)*
J. Keith Jennette *(Partner & Mng Dir)*
Ransom Horne *(Partner & Mng Dir)*

Subsidiaries:

Cornerstone Appraisal Services,
Inc.   (1)
951 Transport Dr, Valparaiso, IN 46384
Tel.: (219) 531-8832

Web Site: http://www.cornerstone-
appraisals.com
Sales Range: $1-9.9 Million
Emp.: 25
Residential Appraisal Services
N.A.I.C.S.: 531320

COMPASS FORWARDING CO., INC.
159-15 Rockaway Blvd, Jamaica, NY
11434-4837
Tel.: (718) 528-3589   NY
Web Site:
    https://www.compassfwd.com
Sales Range: $10-24.9 Million
Emp.: 41
Freight Transportation & Logistics
Services
N.A.I.C.S.: 488510
Richard A. Shelala *(Pres)*
John Skrabut *(Mgr-Boston)*
Robert M. Shelala *(CFO & VP)*

COMPASS GROUP MANAGE-MENT LLC
301 Riverside Ave 2nd Fl, Westport,
CT 06880
Tel.: (203) 221-1703
Web Site:
    http://www.compassequity.com
Year Founded: 1998
Investment & Portfolio Management
Services
N.A.I.C.S.: 523940
Patrick A. Maciariello *(Partner &
COO)*
Ryan J. Faulkingham *(CFO & Exec
VP)*
Elias Joseph Sabo *(CEO & Partner)*

COMPASS GROUP, LLC
7701 Forsyth Blvd, Saint Louis, MO
63105
Tel.: (314) 721-2800   MO
Web Site: http://www.cgep.com
Year Founded: 2001
Equity Investment Firm
N.A.I.C.S.: 523999
John D. Huhn *(Mng Partner)*
Chris Gibson *(Mng Dir)*
Marc Lee *(Operating Partner)*
Patrick Murray *(VP)*
Stuart Noel *(Dir-Bus Dev)*
Ed Place *(VP)*
Jeff Roberts *(Operating Partner)*
Greg Siwak *(Operating Partner)*
David Weiss *(Operating Partner)*

Subsidiaries:

Compass Electronics Group (1)
7701 Forsyth Blvd, Saint Louis, MO 63105
Tel.: (314) 721-2800
Holding Company
N.A.I.C.S.: 551112
Jeff Roberts *(Pres & COO)*

Subsidiary (Domestic):

Logic PD, Inc. (2)
6201 Bury Dr, Eden Prairie, MN 55346
Tel.: (952) 941-8071
Web Site: http://www.compasses.com
Printed Circuit Boards
N.A.I.C.S.: 334412

COMPASS HEALTH
4526 Federal Ave Bldg 1-9, Everett,
WA 98203
Tel.: (425) 349-6200   WA
Web Site:
    https://www.compasshealth.org
Year Founded: 1984
Sales Range: $25-49.9 Million
Emp.: 650
Mental Health Services
N.A.I.C.S.: 621420
Alex deSoto *(Treas)*
Dave Finstad *(Vice Chm)*

Eric Carlsen *(Chm)*
Laura Carlsen *(Sec)*
Tom Sebastian *(Pres & CEO)*
Barbara McFadden *(Assoc Dir-
Medical)*
Becky Olson-Hernandez *(Dir-
Emergency Svcs & Healthcare Inte-
gration)*
Heather Fennell *(Chief Quality, Info &
Privacy Officer)*
Jill Henson *(Chief Admin Officer)*
Kay Tillema *(Dir-Reg Svcs)*
Stacey Alles *(COO)*
Dave Schneider *(Sec)*

Subsidiaries:

Whatcom Counseling & Psychiatric
Clinic   (1)
3645 E Mcleod Rd, Bellingham, WA 98226
Tel.: (360) 676-2220
Web Site: http://www.compasshealth.org
Sales Range: $1-9.9 Million
Emp.: 120
Health Counseling & Psychiatric Clinic
N.A.I.C.S.: 621112
Tom Sebastian *(Pres & CEO)*
David Schneider *(Sec)*
Stacey Alles *(COO)*

COMPASS HOUSING ALLI-ANCE
77 S Washington St 5th Fl, Seattle,
WA 98104
Tel.: (206) 474-1000   WA
Web Site:
    https://www.compasshousing
    alliance.org
Year Founded: 1928
Sales Range: $10-24.9 Million
Emp.: 292
Homeless People Housing Assistance
Services
N.A.I.C.S.: 624229
Janet Pope *(Exec Dir)*
Bill Reddy *(COO)*
Joshua Cooper *(Treas)*

COMPASS POINT MEDIA
510 Marquette Ave, Minneapolis, MN
55402-3362
Tel.: (612) 347-6900   MN
Web Site: http://www.compasspoint-
media.com
Year Founded: 1976
Sales Range: $400-449.9 Million
Emp.: 40
Direct Marketing, Media Buying Ser-
vices & Strategic Planning/Research
N.A.I.C.S.: 541830
Pete Engebretson *(Dir-Client Svcs)*
Clinton Lugert *(Assoc Dir-Creative)*
Randy Gerda *(Dir-Art)*
Wendy Hansen *(Dir-Art)*
Heath Rudduck *(Dir-Art)*

COMPASS PRECISION LLC
4600 Westinghouse Blvd, Charlotte,
NC 28273
Tel.: (704) 210-8600
Web Site:
    https://compassprecision.com
Emp.: 100
Automation Machinery Mfr
N.A.I.C.S.: 333248
Gary Holcomb *(Pres & CEO)*

Subsidiaries:

Strom Manufacturing Inc. (1)
PO Box 1669, Hillsboro, OR 97124-6495
Tel.: (503) 447-1021
Web Site: http://www.strom-mfg.com
Machine Shops
N.A.I.C.S.: 332710
Bill Strom *(Pres)*

COMPASS SOLUTIONS, LLC.

1627 K St NW Ste 400, Washington,
DC 20005
Tel.: (202) 393-5454
Web Site:
    https://www.compasscentral.com
Year Founded: 1998
Sales Range: $1-9.9 Million
Emp.: 43
Data Security & Data Management
Services
N.A.I.C.S.: 518210
Anthony Onyewuchi *(CEO & CTO)*
Valerie Cooper *(Mgr-HR)*

COMPASS WORKING CAPITAL
89 South St Ste 203, Boston, MA
02111
Tel.: (617) 790-0810   MA
Web Site:
    http://www.compassworkingcap
    ital.org
Year Founded: 2005
Rev.: $1,471,852
Assets: $1,115,932
Liabilities: $75,858
Net Worth: $1,040,074
Earnings: $674,714
Emp.: 10
Fiscal Year-end: 08/31/14
Financial Services
N.A.I.C.S.: 523940
Sandra Suarez *(Mgr-Ops)*
Viviana Ramos *(Program Mgr)*
Caileen Foley *(Sr Mgr-Housing
Policy)*
Luke Brown *(Program Mgr)*
Brian Vallimont *(Fin Dir & Dir-Admin)*
Sherry Riva *(Founder)*
Ann Lentell *(Dir-Programs)*

COMPASSION COALITION, INC.
509 Lafayette St, Utica, NY 13502
Tel.: (315) 266-0039   NY
Web Site: http://www.compassion-
coalition.com
Year Founded: 1999
Sales Range: $10-24.9 Million
Emergency Relief Services
N.A.I.C.S.: 624230
David Nicolette *(Dir-Ops)*
Charlie Sweet *(Exec Dir)*

COMPASSMSP LLC
100 N Laura St Ste 601, Jacksonville,
FL 32202
Tel.: (904) 777-0087
Web Site:
    http://www.compassmsp.com
Year Founded: 2016
Software Development & Managed IT
Services
N.A.I.C.S.: 513210
Josh Kotler *(Chief Strategy Officer &
Head-Acq)*
Ari Santiago *(CEO)*
Gael Tannenbaum *(Dir-Mktg)*

Subsidiaries:

IT Direct, LLC (1)
67 Prospect Ave Ste 202, West Hartford,
CT 06106
Tel.: (860) 656-9110
Web Site:
    http://www.gettingyouconnected.com
IT Consulting Services
N.A.I.C.S.: 519290
Ari Santiago *(Founder & Pres)*

COMPATICO, INC.
4710 44th St SE, Grand Rapids, MI
49512
Tel.: (616) 940-1772   MI
Web Site: http://www.compatico.com
Year Founded: 1990
Rev.: $14,000,000
Emp.: 35
Furniture Hardware Sales
N.A.I.C.S.: 423710

Compatico, Inc.—(Continued)
Cheryl Daniels (VP-Fin)
John Rea (Pres)
Steve Tuzzolino (Dir-Sls-Midwest USA)

COMPDENT OF GEORGIA, INC.
100 Mansell Ct E Ste 400, Roswell, GA 30076-8228
Tel.: (770) 998-8936
Sales Range: $25-49.9 Million
Emp.: 1,000
Direct Health & Medical Insurance Services
N.A.I.C.S.: 524114
David R. Klock (CEO)
Bruce A. Mitchell (Sec)
Sharon S. Graham (CFO)

COMPEER FINANCIAL, ACA
1921 Premier Dr, Mankato, MN 56001
Tel.: (507) 387-4174
Web Site: https://www.compeer.com
Year Founded: 1916
Rev.: $871,137,000
Assets: $20,754,237,000
Liabilities: $17,152,258,000
Net Worth: $3,601,979,000
Earnings: $403,846,000
Fiscal Year-end: 12/31/18
Federal & Federally Sponsored Credit Agencies
N.A.I.C.S.: 522299
Rodney W. Hebrink (Pres & CEO)
Terry Hinds (Chief Risk Officer)
Jase Wagner (CFO)
Jerry Wiese (CIO)

COMPENDIUM, INC.
2100 N Pacific St, Seattle, WA 98103
Tel.: (206) 812-1640   WA
Web Site: http://www.live-inspired.com
Year Founded: 1985
Sales Range: $1-9.9 Million
Emp.: 25
Mfr of Stationery
N.A.I.C.S.: 322230
Dan Zadra (Founder)
Andrea Summers (Supvr-Warehouse)
Jessica Springer (Acct Mgr-Wholesale)
Jim Darragh (CFO & COO)
Tote Yamada (Dir-Ops)

COMPETITION ACCESSORIES
343 W Leffel Ln, Springfield, OH 45506
Tel.: (937) 323-0513
Web Site: http://www.ridemotorcycleinc.com
Rev.: $10,200,000
Emp.: 55
Catalog & Mail Order Houses
N.A.I.C.S.: 441227
Dean Kruse (Pres)
Shawn Bowshier (CFO)

COMPETITION CAMS INC.
3406 Democrat Rd, Memphis, TN 38118
Tel.: (901) 795-2400   TN
Web Site: https://www.compcams.com
Year Founded: 1976
Sales Range: $50-74.9 Million
Emp.: 230
Motor Vehicle Parts & Accessories
N.A.I.C.S.: 336310
Ronnie Hopper (Controller)
Tommy McIntyre (Mgr-Production)
Rick Sporks (Mgr-Adv & Mktg)

Chris Brown (Mgr-Ops)
Ethel Pigram (Pres)
Rick Vanelli (Mgr-Quality Control)

COMPETITION PRODUCTS, INC.
280 W 35th Ave, Oshkosh, WI 54902
Tel.: (920) 233-2023
Web Site: https://www.competitionproduct.com
Rev.: $14,000,000
Emp.: 35
Motor Vehicle Supplies & New Parts Merchant Whslr
N.A.I.C.S.: 423120
Robert Lou (VP)
Steven Mugerauer (Pres)

COMPETITION SPECIALTIES INC.
2402 W Valley Hwy N, Auburn, WA 98001
Tel.: (253) 833-6211
Web Site: https://www.compspecialties.com
Year Founded: 1966
Rev.: $18,000,000
Emp.: 130
High Performance Automotive Parts & Off-Road Accessories Distr & Whslr
N.A.I.C.S.: 423120
Ken Woomer (Owner & Pres)
Jim Lucero (Mgr-Ops)
Tom Cline (Mgr-Natl Sls)
Gordy Geise (Mgr-Sls)
David Green (VP)

COMPETITION TIRE LLC
12666 US Hwy 12, Brooklyn, MI 49230
Tel.: (517) 592-6681
Web Site: http://www.competitiontire.com
Sales Range: $10-24.9 Million
Emp.: 80
Automobile Tires & Tubes
N.A.I.C.S.: 423130
Randy Lawrence (Pres)

COMPETITIVE ENGINEERING INC.
3371 E Hemisphere Loop, Tucson, AZ 85706
Tel.: (520) 746-0270
Web Site: http://www.ceiglobal.com
Sales Range: $10-24.9 Million
Emp.: 65
Machine Shop, Jobbing & Repair
N.A.I.C.S.: 332710
Don Martin (Pres)

COMPETITIVE INNOVATIONS, LLC
200 N Glebe Rd Ste 314, Arlington, VA 22203
Tel.: (703) 698-5000
Web Site: http://www.cillc.com
Year Founded: 1999
Sales Range: $1-9.9 Million
Emp.: 30
Web & Information Technology Solutions, Including Hardware, Software, Implementation, Installation & Lifecycle Maintenance Services
N.A.I.C.S.: 541512
Michael Kennedy (Founder, Pres & CEO)

COMPETITIVE RANGE SOLUTIONS, LLC
20 W Kinzie St 17th Fl, Chicago, IL 60654
Web Site: http://www.getcrs.com
Year Founded: 2011
Sales Range: $10-24.9 Million
Emp.: 94

Information Technology Management Services
N.A.I.C.S.: 541512
Noah Vasquez (CEO)

COMPEX CORPORATION
7918 Jones Branch Dr Ste 540, McLean, VA 22102
Tel.: (703) 642-5910
Web Site: http://www.compexhq.com
Year Founded: 1980
Rev.: $12,000,000
Emp.: 3
Information Technology Management Solutions Services
N.A.I.C.S.: 541611
Harry G. Garcia (Pres & CEO)

COMPLEMAR PARTNERS
500 Lee Rd, Rochester, NY 14606
Tel.: (585) 647-5800
Web Site: https://www.complemar.com
Sales Range: $10-24.9 Million
Emp.: 60
Packaging & Labeling Services
N.A.I.C.S.: 459999
Bill Bosy (Controller)
Jeff Cagwin (Dir-IT)
Robert Ramos (Dir-Ops-Complemar West)
Roy LaRue (Dir-Ops-Complemar Print)
Stephanie Bieg (Dir-Client Solutions)
Tim Leverett (Dir-Mktg & Brand Strategy)

COMPLERE ENGINEERING GROUP, INC.
4230 Kiernan Ave Ste 210, Modesto, CA 95356-9323
Tel.: (209) 545-8165
Web Site: https://www.complere.com
Year Founded: 1991
Administrative Services for Workers Compensation
N.A.I.C.S.: 541330

COMPLETE BOWLING SERVICE, INC.
808 Washington Ave N, Kent, WA 98032
Tel.: (253) 854-6000   WA
Web Site: http://www.cbsbowling.com
Year Founded: 1975
Sales Range: $10-24.9 Million
Emp.: 15
Bowling Equipment
N.A.I.C.S.: 423910

COMPLETE COLLEGE AMERICA INC.
429 E Vermont St Ste 300, Indianapolis, IN 46202
Tel.: (317) 829-0483   IN
Web Site: http://www.completecollege.org
Year Founded: 2009
Sales Range: $1-9.9 Million
Emp.: 11
Educational Support Services
N.A.I.C.S.: 611710
Dhanfu E. Elston (VP-Strategy)
Jim Geringer (Chm)
Yolanda Watson Spiva (Pres)

COMPLETE DISCOVERY SOURCE, INC.
345 Park Ave, New York, NY 10154
Tel.: (212) 813-7000
Web Site: http://www.cdslegal.com
Year Founded: 2003
Sales Range: $25-49.9 Million
Emp.: 121
Information Technology Services
N.A.I.C.S.: 541512

Paul Kelley (VP-Sls)
Matthew Hirsch (Dir-Sls)
Dino E. Medina (Gen Counsel)
Jeff Salling (Dir-Bus Dev)
Pete Smith (Sr VP-Sls)
Vinnie Budhram (Chief Admin Officer)
Joseph Wheeler Jr. (VP-Bus Dev)

COMPLETE ENVIRONMENTAL PRODUCTS, INC.
3500 Pasadena Fwy, Pasadena, TX 77503
Tel.: (713) 921-7900   TX
Web Site: https://www.cepsorbents.com
Sales Range: $10-24.9 Million
Emp.: 30
Sells Petroleum Industry Products
N.A.I.C.S.: 423830
Chad Clay (Owner & Pres)

COMPLETE GENERAL CONSTRUCTION CO. INC.
1221 E 5th Ave, Columbus, OH 43219-2456
Tel.: (614) 258-9515   OH
Web Site: https://www.completegeneral.com
Year Founded: 1929
Sales Range: $50-74.9 Million
Emp.: 600
Provider of Bridge, Tunnel & Elevated & Underground Highway Work
N.A.I.C.S.: 237310
Lee Guzzo (CEO)
Peter Guzzo (VP-Admin)
Bill Cooper (CFO & Treas)
Jim George (VP-Ops)
Subsidiaries:

Complete Resources Company   (1)
1275 E 5th Ave, Columbus, OH 43219
Tel.: (614) 253-6415
Web Site: http://www.complete-resources.com
Sales Range: $1-9.9 Million
Emp.: 29
Aggregate Crushing & Recycling Services
N.A.I.C.S.: 423930
Butch Cherrington (Pres)
Nick Guzzo (Controller)

State Tire & Service   (1)
705 Harrison Dr, Columbus, OH 43204
Tel.: (614) 276-1711
Web Site: http://www.statetireandservice.com
Automotive Repair & Maintenance Services
N.A.I.C.S.: 811198

Underground Locating & Excavating   (1)
1311 E 5th Ave, Columbus, OH 43219
Tel.: (614) 384-2824
Web Site: http://www.ulesco.net
Underground Excavation & Drill Mud Removal Services
N.A.I.C.S.: 238910

COMPLETE HEALTHCARE RESOURCES INC
200 Dryden Rd Ste 3100, Dresher, PA 19025-1049
Tel.: (215) 441-7700   PA
Web Site: http://www.completehealthcare.com
Year Founded: 1989
Sales Range: $1-9.9 Million
Emp.: 200
Health Care Management Services
N.A.I.C.S.: 561110
Cathy Otto (COO)

COMPLETE HOME CONCEPTS INC.
4380 Belgium Blvd, Riverside, MO 64150
Tel.: (816) 471-4663

Web Site:
https://www.completehomes.com
Sales Range: $10-24.9 Million
Emp.: 130
Provider of Concrete Products
N.A.I.C.S.: 327390

COMPLETE INDUSTRIAL ENTERPRISES
1220 Wenzel Rd, Peru, IL 61354
Tel.: (815) 224-1510
Web Site:
http://www.completeindustrial.com
Rev.: $16,000,000
Emp.: 33
Electric Motor Repair & Distributors
N.A.I.C.S.: 811310
Dave Mattioda *(Gen Mgr)*

COMPLETE MECHANICAL SERVICES, LLC.
11415 Grooms Rd, Cincinnati, OH 45242
Tel.: (513) 489-3080
Web Site:
http://www.completemech.com
Year Founded: 1999
Sales Range: $10-24.9 Million
Emp.: 86
Plumbing, Heating & Air-Conditioning Services
N.A.I.C.S.: 238220
Tom Blaha *(Pres)*

COMPLETE MERCHANT SOLUTIONS (CMS)
815 W University Pkwy, Orem, UT 84058
Tel.: (801) 623-4000
Web Site:
http://secure.cmsonline.com
Year Founded: 2008
Sales Range: $10-24.9 Million
Emp.: 40
Full-Service Electronic Payments Solutions
N.A.I.C.S.: 525990
Jack Wilson *(CEO)*
Dave Decker *(Co-Founder & Pres)*
Trever Hansen *(Co-Founder & COO)*
Kyle Hall *(Co-Founder & CIO)*
Scott Davis *(Sr VP-Sls)*
Chris Henneman *(Sr VP-Bus Dev)*
Doug Hansen *(VP-Ops & Client Svcs)*
Greg Sorenson *(Dir-Product Dev)*
Jayci Allan *(Dir-Fin & Controller)*

COMPLETE MILLWORK SERVICES, INC.
4909 Goni Rd, Carson City, NV 89706-0351
Tel.: (775) 246-0485
Web Site: https://www.cmsrno.com
Year Founded: 1998
Sales Range: $10-24.9 Million
Emp.: 130
Millwork Whslr
N.A.I.C.S.: 423310
Miguel Perez *(Project Mgr)*

COMPLETE NUTRITION HOLDINGS INC.
17220 Wright St Ste 200, Omaha, NE 68130
Tel.: (402) 333-5155
Web Site:
http://www.completenutrition.com
Year Founded: 2004
Sales Range: $50-74.9 Million
Emp.: 100
Nutritional Supplement Retail Stores
N.A.I.C.S.: 456191
Cory Wiedel *(Founder)*
Ryan Zink *(Pres)*
Jason Moore *(VP-Ops)*

COMPLETE PETMART INC.
1239 Lyons Rd Bldg G, Dayton, OH 45458
Tel.: (937) 433-0355
Sales Range: $10-24.9 Million
Emp.: 300
Pet Supplies
N.A.I.C.S.: 459910
Tim Rogers *(VP)*

COMPLETE PROFESSIONAL SERVICES, LLC
11325 Random Hills Rd Ste 300, Fairfax, VA 22030
Tel.: (703) 791-1919
Web Site: http://www.cps-corp.com
Year Founded: 2002
Rev.: $11,300,000
Emp.: 45
Government Services
N.A.I.C.S.: 921190
Joseph R. Webb *(Pres & CEO)*
Adam J. Attard *(Co-Founder)*
Charles Perry *(Sr VP & Dir-Corp Dev)*

COMPLETE PROPERTY SERVICES, INC.
13505 Prestige Pl, Tampa, FL 33635
Tel.: (727) 793-9777
Web Site:
https://www.completeproperty.com
Year Founded: 1984
Rev.: $44,000,000
Emp.: 148
Commercial & Institutional Building Construction
N.A.I.C.S.: 236220
Hank Gatti *(Pres)*
Angela Krueger *(Sec)*
Guy Lindsey *(Exec VP)*
Richard K. Krueger *(CEO)*

COMPLETE RECOVERY CORPORATION
5184 W Wiley Post Way, Salt Lake City, UT 84116-2833
Tel.: (801) 269-8888
Web Site:
http://www.completerecovery.com
Year Founded: 2003
Sales Range: $1-9.9 Million
Emp.: 112
Collection Services
N.A.I.C.S.: 561440
Aaron Meier *(VP-Ops)*

Subsidiaries:

Prince-Parker & Associates Inc   (1)
8625 Crown Crescent Ct, Charlotte, NC 28227
Tel.: (704) 841-2424
Web Site: http://www.princeparker.com
Rev.: $3,400,000
Emp.: 41
Collection Agencies
N.A.I.C.S.: 561440
Jeff Parker *(Pres)*

COMPLETE SALES & SERVICE
215 Prarie Lake Rd, East Dundee, IL 60118
Tel.: (630) 594-2468
Sales Range: $10-24.9 Million
Emp.: 45
Game Machines, Coin-Operated
N.A.I.C.S.: 423990
Frank Gumma *(Pres)*

COMPLETELY BARE SPA, INC.
103 5th Ave 4th Fl, New York, NY 10003
Tel.: (212) 366-6060   NY
Web Site:
http://www.completelybare.com
Year Founded: 2002
Sales Range: $1-9.9 Million

Emp.: 20
Personal Care Services
N.A.I.C.S.: 812199
Howard Barshop *(Pres)*
Gary Liotta *(Dir-Mktg)*
Sam Shuster *(Dir-Customer Svc)*
Christine Sediva *(Dir-HR)*
Laura Greco *(Dir-Sls)*

COMPLETERX, LTD.
3100 S Gessner Ste 640, Houston, TX 77063
Tel.: (713) 355-1196
Web Site: http://www.completerx.com
Year Founded: 1998
Sales Range: $100-124.9 Million
Emp.: 381
Specialty Hospitals & Pharmacy Management Services
N.A.I.C.S.: 622310
Terry E. Andrus *(Pres)*
Mark Stubbs *(CFO)*
Rick Burnett *(COO)*
Dana Fox *(Mgr-Program Dev)*
Justin Sotomayor *(Dir-Pharmacy Informatics)*

COMPLEX CHEMICAL COMPANY, INC.
177 Complex Rd, Tallulah, LA 71282
Tel.: (318) 574-0382   MS
Web Site:
https://www.complexchemical.com
Year Founded: 1974
Sales Range: $10-24.9 Million
Emp.: 100
Lubricating Oil Mfr
N.A.I.C.S.: 324191
Jerry Melton *(Owner & Pres)*

COMPLEX MEDIA, INC.
229 W 43rd Str 10th Fl, New York, NY 10036
Tel.: (917) 793-5831   DE
Web Site:
http://www.complexmediainc.com
Year Founded: 2002
Music, Style & Lifestyle Media Network & Magazine Publisher
Rich Antoniello *(Co-Founder & CEO)*
Marc Ecko *(Co-Founder)*

Subsidiaries:

Complex Magazine   (1)
40 W 23rd St 2nd Fl, New York, NY 10010
Tel.: (917) 262-4000
Web Site: http://www.complex.com
Sales Range: $10-24.9 Million
Emp.: 50
Young Men's Style & Lifestyle Magazine Publisher
N.A.I.C.S.: 513120
Rich Antoniello *(CEO & Publr)*
Brian Kelley *(Gen Mgr)*
Noah Callahan-Bever *(Editor-in-Chief)*
Kencle Satchell-McKoy *(Dir-Newsstand)*

COMPLEXA INC.
1055 Westlakes Dr Ste 200, Berwyn, PA 19312
Tel.: (484) 329-8436
Web Site:
http://www.complexarx.com
Biotechnology Research & Development Services
N.A.I.C.S.: 541714
Francisco D. Salva *(Pres & CEO)*
Theodore Danoff *(Chief Medical Officer)*
David Mott *(Chm)*

COMPLIANCE CORPORATION
21617 S Essex Dr Ste 34, Lexington Park, MD 20653
Tel.: (301) 863-8070

Web Site:
https://www.compliancecorp.com
Rev.: $12,300,000
Emp.: 94
Management Consulting & Engineering Services
N.A.I.C.S.: 541330
Harold Herndon Sr. *(Pres & CEO)*

COMPLIANCE SCIENCE, INC.
136 Madison Ave, New York, NY 10016
Tel.: (212) 327-1533
Web Site: http://www.complysci.com
Year Founded: 2003
Compliance Technology Solutions
N.A.I.C.S.: 541512
Amy Kadomatsu *(CEO)*

Subsidiaries:

National Regulatory Services   (1)
29 Brook St, Lakeville, CT 06039
Tel.: (860) 435-0200
Web Site: http://www.nrs-inc.com
Financial Compliance Consulting Services
N.A.I.C.S.: 541611
John Gebauer *(Pres)*
Marilyn Miles *(VP-Consulting)*
Mederic Daigneault *(Sr Dir-Consulting Ops)*
Jessica Laine *(Dir-Sls)*
Desire Karp *(Dir-Events)*

Subsidiary (Domestic):

Fire Solutions, Inc.   (2)
29 Brook St, Lakeville, CT 06039
Tel.: (860) 435-0200
Compliance & Training Solutions Publisher
N.A.I.C.S.: 513199

COMPLIANCEQUEST INC.
10006 Cross Creek Blvd Ste 71, Tampa, FL 33647
Tel.: (408) 458-8343
Web Site:
http://www.compliancequest.com
Year Founded: 2013
Sales Range: $1-9.9 Million
Emp.: 60
Software Development Services
N.A.I.C.S.: 541511
Prashanth Rajendran *(CEO)*
Atulya Risal *(COO)*
Govardhan Muralidhar *(Sr VP-Customer Success)*
Shalini Chowdhary *(VP-Mktg & Strategic Alliances)*
Kim Engler *(VP-Quality Assurance & Knowledge Mgmt)*

COMPLIANCESIGNS.COM
56 S Main St, Chadwick, IL 61014
Tel.: (815) 684-5764
Web Site:
http://www.compliancesigns.com
Year Founded: 2004
Sales Range: $1-9.9 Million
Emp.: 60
OSHA-Compliant & Other Signage Mfr
N.A.I.C.S.: 339950
Paul Sandefer *(Pres)*
Deb Miller *(Coord-e-Commerce)*

COMPONENT ASSEMBLY SYSTEMS, INC.
620 5th Ave, Pelham, NY 10803-1208
Tel.: (914) 738-5400   NY
Web Site: https://www.componentassembly.com
Year Founded: 1964
Sales Range: $25-49.9 Million
Emp.: 300
Provider of Carpentry Services
N.A.I.C.S.: 238130
Art Doerner *(Pres)*

Component Assembly Systems, Inc.—(Continued)

Subsidiaries:

Component West, Inc.   (1)
353 Pilot Rd Ste A, Las Vegas, NV 89118
Tel.: (702) 260-6596
Web Site: http://www.componentwest.com
Emp.: 12
Drywall Contracting Services
N.A.I.C.S.: 238310
Dave Scognamiglio (VP)
Robert Perricone (VP)

COMPONENT HARDWARE GROUP, INC.

1890 Swarthmore Ave, Lakewood, NJ 08701
Tel.: (732) 363-4700
Web Site:
   https://www.componenthardware.com
Year Founded: 1981
Sales Range: $10-24.9 Million
Emp.: 30
Hardware Mfr
N.A.I.C.S.: 332510
Ed Whartnaby (VP-Sls & Mktg)
Kevin Tumpey (Mgr-Inside Sls)
Doug Reasoner (Mgr-Sls-Natl)
Frank Probst (CFO)
Partha Biswas (Pres & CEO)
John Frank (Head-Sls)
Mark Beattie (Gen Mgr-Canada)
Steve King (VP-Sls & Mktg-North America)

COMPONENT INTERTECH-NOLOGIES, INC.

2426 Perry Hwy, Hadley, PA 16130
Tel.: (724) 253-3161
Web Site: https://www.cit-hadley.com
Sales Range: $10-24.9 Million
Emp.: 7
Mfr of Electronic Circuits
N.A.I.C.S.: 334419
John Haggerty (Gen Mgr)

COMPONENTONE LLC

201 S Highland Ave Fl 3, Pittsburgh, PA 15206
Tel.: (412) 681-4343
Web Site:
   http://www.componentone.com
Rev.: $10,000,000
Emp.: 40
Computer Software Development
N.A.I.C.S.: 541511
Sunny Wong (Mng Dir)
Eve Turzillo (Mgr-Comm)
Justin Mack (Engr-Tech Engagement)

COMPONENTS CENTER INC.

1 Oldfield, Irvine, CA 92618
Tel.: (714) 979-0433
Web Site:
   http://www.componentscenter.com
Year Founded: 1971
Rev.: $26,100,000
Emp.: 20
Electronic Parts
N.A.I.C.S.: 423690
Edward J. Bush (Owner)
Bob Miele (Pres)

Subsidiaries:

Dalis Electronics   (1)
3645 E Atlanta Ave, Phoenix, AZ 85040
Tel.: (602) 275-2626
Web Site: http://www.daliselectronics.com
Sales Range: $10-24.9 Million
Emp.: 4
Retailer of Electronic Parts to Professional Contractors, Engineers & Buyers
N.A.I.C.S.: 423690
Bill Watson (Gen Mgr)

COMPONENTS CORPORATION OF AMERICA, INC.

5950 Berkshire Ln Ste 1550, Dallas, TX 75225-5843
Tel.: (214) 969-0166   NY
Web Site: http://www.components-corp-amer.com
Year Founded: 1916
Sales Range: $50-74.9 Million
Emp.: 170
Mfr of Electronic Inductors & Electrical Components & Uninterruptible Power Supplies, Push Button Switches & Power Conditioning Equipment
N.A.I.C.S.: 334416
Cary M. Maguire (Chm)
Jeffrey Nick (CFO)
B. Hess (Exec VP)

Subsidiaries:

Para Systems Inc.   (1)
1455 Lemay Dr, Carrollton, TX 75007-4931   (100%)
Tel.: (972) 446-7363
Web Site: http://www.minutemanups.com
Sales Range: $10-24.9 Million
Emp.: 25
Power Supply Mfr
N.A.I.C.S.: 334419
Rod Pullen (Pres)
Bob Hoover (CFO)

StacoEnergy Products Co.   (1)
301 Gaddis Blvd, Dayton, OH 45403-1314
Tel.: (937) 253-1191
Web Site: http://www.stacoenergy.com
Sales Range: $10-24.9 Million
Emp.: 70
Electronic & Electromechanical Mfr
N.A.I.C.S.: 334416
Jim Clark (VP-Engrg)
Miguel Rivera (Dir-Intl Sls)
Paul Heiligenberg (Mgr-Sls Ops)
Jim Clark (VP-Engrg)

Stacoswitch, Inc.   (1)
7 Morgan, Irvine, CA 92618-2005
Tel.: (714) 549-3041
Web Site: http://www.stacoswitch.com
Sales Range: $10-24.9 Million
Emp.: 59
Mfr of Electronic & Electromechanical Switches
N.A.I.C.S.: 335313

COMPONENTS DISTRIBUTORS INC.

2601 Blake St Ste 450, Denver, CO 80205
Tel.: (303) 531-1800
Web Site: http://www.cdiweb.com
Sales Range: $10-24.9 Million
Emp.: 48
Electronic Parts
N.A.I.C.S.: 423690
John Williammee (Pres)

COMPONENTSOURCE HOLDING CORPORATION

650 Claremore Professional Way Ste 100, Woodstock, GA 30188-5188
Tel.: (770) 250-6100
Web Site:
   https://www.componentsource.com
Year Founded: 1995
Rev.: $8,000,000
Emp.: 70
Software Sales
N.A.I.C.S.: 513210
Sam Patterson (CEO)

COMPORIUM GROUP

330 E Black St, Rock Hill, SC 29730-5377
Tel.: (803) 326-6450
Web Site: http://www.comporium.com
Year Founded: 1912
Sales Range: $25-49.9 Million
Emp.: 1,177
Provider of Telephone Communication Services

N.A.I.C.S.: 517121
Bryant Barnes (Pres & CEO)

Subsidiaries:

Citizens Telephone Company   (1)
190 E Main St, Brevard, NC 28712
Tel.: (828) 884-3950
Web Site: http://www.comporium.com
Telecommunication Servicesb
N.A.I.C.S.: 517111
Frank Porter (Gen Mgr)

Community Long Distance, Inc.   (1)
1869 Great Falls Hwy, Lancaster, SC 29720
Tel.: (803) 285-4253
Telecommunication Servicesb
N.A.I.C.S.: 517810

Comporium   (1)
1660 Juniper Springs Rd, Gilbert, SC 29054
Tel.: (803) 685-3121
Sales Range: $10-24.9 Million
Emp.: 100
Local Telephone Communications
N.A.I.C.S.: 517121
Glenn Martin (Sr VP-Ops)

Comporium Data Services   (1)
471 Lakeshore Pkwy, Rock Hill, SC 29730-3392
Tel.: (803) 326-4100
Sales Range: $10-24.9 Million
Emp.: 50
Provider of Data Processing & Preparation Services
N.A.I.C.S.: 518210

Comporium Publishing   (1)
471 Lksor Pkwy, Rock Hill, SC 29730-5339
Tel.: (803) 324-5233
Web Site: http://www.comporium.com
Sales Range: $10-24.9 Million
Emp.: 35
Telephone Directory Publishing Services
N.A.I.C.S.: 513140

Comporium Telecom Inc.   (1)
332 Main St, Rock Hill, SC 29730-9075
Tel.: (803) 326-6011
Web Site: http://www.comporium.com
Sales Range: $125-149.9 Million
Telecommunication Servicesb
N.A.I.C.S.: 237110

Fort Mill Telephone Company   (1)
200 Tom Hall St, Fort Mill, SC 29715
Tel.: (803) 548-9011
Sales Range: $1-9.9 Million
Telecommunication Servicesb
N.A.I.C.S.: 517810

Lancaster Telephone Company   (1)
318 Stewman St, Lancaster, SC 29720
Tel.: (803) 286-7117
Telecommunication Servicesb
N.A.I.C.S.: 517810

Springbeach Telecom, LLC   (1)
2215 Ayrsley Town Blvd Ste 1, Charlotte, NC 28273
Tel.: (704) 365-8890
Emp.: 22
Telecommunications Consulting Services
N.A.I.C.S.: 541690
Greg Austin (Gen Mgr)

COMPOSIDIE INC.

1295 Route 380, Apollo, PA 15613-9658
Tel.: (724) 727-3466
Web Site:
   https://www.composidie.com
Year Founded: 1971
Sales Range: $10-24.9 Million
Emp.: 125
Die Sets for Metal Stamping
N.A.I.C.S.: 333514
Kevin Schreiber (Engr-Design)
Matt Honkala (Mgr-Process)
Dave Abel (VP-Engrg & Stamping)
Andy Flock (Plant Mgr)
Bob Burkley (Dir-Bus Dev)
Tom Graff (VP-Sls & Mktg)
Shari Slagle (Mgr-Acctg)
Gary Felentzer (Mgr-Quality)

COMPOSITE RESOURCES, INC.

485 Lakeshare Pkwy, Rock Hill, SC 29730
Tel.: (803) 366-9700
Web Site: https://www.composite-resources.com
Year Founded: 1992
Sales Range: $10-24.9 Million
Emp.: 30
Composite Carbon Fiber Component Designer & Mfr
N.A.I.C.S.: 335991
Jonathan Bennett (Founder)
Michael Griffin (Mgr-Machine Shop)
Kent Downs (Mgr-IT & Sys)
Carolina Martinez (Supvr-Mfg)

COMPOSITES ONE

3000 Wesley Way, Fort Worth, TX 76118
Tel.: (817) 595-4991
Web Site:
   http://www.compositesone.com
Sales Range: $10-24.9 Million
Emp.: 35
Fiberglass & Composite Materials
N.A.I.C.S.: 424610
Steve Dehmlow (CEO)
Leon Daroufalin (Pres)
Karen Drennen (Controller)
Marcy Offner (Mgr-Mktg Comm)

COMPQSOFT, INC.

505N Sam Houston Pkwy E Ste 682, Houston, TX 77060
Tel.: (281) 914-4428   TX
Web Site: http://www.compqsoft.com
Year Founded: 1997
Sales Range: $10-24.9 Million
Emp.: 42
Custom Computer Programing
N.A.I.C.S.: 541511
Madina Shaik (Founder & CEO)
Syed Shahabuddin (Mgr-Resources)

COMPREHENSIVE BEHAVIORAL HEALTH

801 N Quincy St Ste 601, Arlington, VA 22203
Tel.: (703) 812-4642
Web Site: https://www.cbhmh.com
Mental Health Treatment Center
N.A.I.C.S.: 621330
Neel Nene (Founder)

Subsidiaries:

Psych Associates of Maryland, LLC   (1)
9520 Berger Rd Ste 203, Columbia, MD 21046-1543
Tel.: (410) 290-6940
Web Site: https://www.pamllc.us
Psychiatric & Substance Abuse Hospitals
N.A.I.C.S.: 622210
Karen Fultz (Mgr)

COMPREHENSIVE BEHAVIORAL HEALTHCARE, INC.

516 Valley Brook Ave, Lyndhurst, NJ 07071
Tel.: (201) 935-3322   NJ
Web Site: https://www.cbhcare.com
Year Founded: 1969
Sales Range: $10-24.9 Million
Emp.: 354
Behavioral Healthcare Services
N.A.I.C.S.: 623220

COMPREHENSIVE COMMUNITY ACTION PROGRAM

311 Doric Ave, Cranston, RI 02910
Tel.: (401) 467-9610   RI
Web Site: https://www.comcap.org
Year Founded: 1965
Sales Range: $10-24.9 Million

Emp.: 633
Community Action Services
N.A.I.C.S.: 624190
Ed Zawot *(Dir-IT)*
Joanne McGunagle *(Pres & CEO)*
Elena Kwetkowski *(Dir-Medical)*
Peter McGrath *(Dir-Special Projects)*
Joanne Gregory *(Dir-Social Svcs)*
Jason Bouchard *(Chm)*
Jeanine Marrocco *(Sec)*
Kevin Cote *(CFO)*
Mary Beth Corrente *(Treas)*
Javier Ramirez *(Chief Dental Officer)*
William Hochstrasser-Walsh *(COO & Sr VP)*
Toni Enright *(VP-Child Svcs)*
Lee Beliveau *(VP-Dev & Corp Affairs)*
Christopher Mansfield *(VP-Family Dev)*
Marie Costa *(VP-HR)*

COMPREHENSIVE COMPUTER CONSULTING, INC.
990 Hammond Dr, Atlanta, GA 30328-4592
Tel.: (770) 512-0100   GA
Web Site: http://www.ccciatlanta.com
Year Founded: 1978
Sales Range: $25-49.9 Million
Emp.: 375
Computer Staffing & Consulting Services
N.A.I.C.S.: 541512
Rob MacLane *(Pres)*

COMPREHENSIVE ENERGY SERVICES, INC.
777 Bennett Dr, Longwood, FL 32750
Tel.: (407) 682-1313
Web Site:
   https://www.cesmechanical.com
Year Founded: 1992
Sales Range: $10-24.9 Million
Emp.: 135
Security Products & Services
N.A.I.C.S.: 238220
Michael Ohare *(Mgr)*

COMPREHENSIVE ENVIRONMENTAL ASSESSMENTS, INC.
127 Hartwell St, West Boylston, MA 01583
Tel.: (508) 835-8822
Web Site: http://www.cea-inc.com
Year Founded: 1985
Rev.: $11,400,000
Emp.: 11
Business Consulting Services
N.A.I.C.S.: 541690
Scott Vandersea *(Reg Mgr)*

Subsidiaries:

Stonehill Environmental, Inc.   (1)
600 State St Ste 2, Portsmouth, NH 03801-3801
Tel.: (603) 433-1935
Web Site:
   http://www.stonehillenvironmental.com
Research & Development in the Physical, Engineering & Life Sciences
N.A.I.C.S.: 541715
Elissa H. Stone *(Project Mgr)*

COMPREHENSIVE FINANCE, INC.
801 Hanover Dr Ste 750, Grapevine, TX 76051
Web Site: http://www.cfico.com
Year Founded: 2011
Sales Range: $1-9.9 Million
Emp.: 21
Business Management Services
N.A.I.C.S.: 561499
Michael D. Brown *(Pres & CEO)*
Charles Brown *(COO)*

Ryan Mullin *(Controller)*
Steven Incontrera *(Dir-Digital Mktg)*
Amanda Brown *(Mgr-Brand)*

COMPREHENSIVE HEALTH SERVICES, INC.
10701 Parkridge Blvd Ste 200, Reston, VA 20191
Tel.: (703) 760-0700
Web Site: http://www.chsonsite.com
Sales Range: $150-199.9 Million
Health Care Srvices
N.A.I.C.S.: 621999
Mel Hall *(Owner & Chm)*
Ned Cooper *(CFO)*
Gary G. Palmer *(Pres & CEO)*
Joseph J. Mignogna *(Chief Medical Officer)*
Shannon Farrington *(Owner & CFO)*
Stuart Clark *(Owner)*
Tiphanie Forst *(VP-Bus Dev)*
Patrick Hogenbirk *(Chief Compliance Officer & Sr VP)*
Ryan Elliott *(VP-Federal Domestic Programs)*
Doug Magee *(Sr VP-Bus Dev)*
Kelley DeConciliis *(VP-Intl Dev)*
Celeste Gushee *(Sr VP-Bus Mgmt-Cape Canaveral)*

Subsidiaries:

W Squared Dynamics, Inc.   (1)
5500 Maryland Way Ste 200, Brentwood, TN 37027
Tel.: (615) 577-4927
Web Site: http://www.wsquared.com
Sales Range: $1-9.9 Million
Emp.: 93
Business Process Outsourcing Services
N.A.I.C.S.: 561499
Casey Correnti *(Sr VP-Bus Dev)*
Deborah Long *(VP-Procurement Svcs)*
Moreen Logsdon *(VP-Enterprise Bus Solutions)*
Lyn Cotton *(VP-HR & Payroll)*
Joe Cron *(CTO)*
Chris Morgan *(VP-Acctg & Implementation)*
Ashley Patterson *(VP-Acctg & Client Svcs)*
Dave Roberts *(CIO)*
Donna Schilling *(VP-HR & Payroll)*
Michael Smith *(VP-Acctg & Sys)*
Walker Willse *(VP-Bus Dev)*
Tammy Wolcott *(CEO)*

COMPREHENSIVE MEDICAL PRACTICE MANAGEMENT, INC.
9976 Brewster Ln Ste 100, Powell, OH 43065
Tel.: (614) 717-9840
Web Site: http://www.cmpminc.com
Year Founded: 1995
Rev.: $10,394,222
Emp.: 200
Medical Billing Services
N.A.I.C.S.: 541219
Daniel R. Crocker *(Pres)*
Jimmy Dado *(Mgr-Practice Dev)*

COMPREHENSIVE OPTIONS FOR DRUG ABUSERS
1027 E Burnside St, Portland, OR 97214
Tel.: (503) 239-8400   OR
Web Site: https://www.codainc.org
Year Founded: 1969
Sales Range: $10-24.9 Million
Emp.: 266
Behavioral Healthcare Services
N.A.I.C.S.: 623220

COMPREHENSIVE SOFTWARE SYSTEMS
25178 Genesee Trl Rd, Golden, CO 80401
Tel.: (303) 876-1500

Web Site:
   http://www.csssoftware.com
Rev.: $13,500,000
Emp.: 70
Computer Software Development
N.A.I.C.S.: 541511
Nelson M. Graham *(Sr VP)*
Dennis M. Kortman *(CFO & Sr VP)*
Mike Landy *(Pres)*

COMPRESSOR ENGINEERING CORPORATION
5440 Alder Dr, Houston, TX 77081
Tel.: (713) 664-7333
Web Site: https://www.tryceco.com
Year Founded: 1964
Sales Range: $50-74.9 Million
Emp.: 110
Gas Transmission & Petrochemical Industry Compressors & Other Equipment Mfr, Distr & Support Services
N.A.I.C.S.: 333912
E. Mark Hotze *(Pres & CEO-CECO Pipeline Svcs)*
Richard K. Hotze *(Pres & COO)*
Joe Miniot *(VP-Sls)*
Heath W. Cleaver *(Pres & CFO)*

Subsidiaries:

CECO Pipeline Services Company, Inc.   (1)
5402 Alder Dr, Houston, TX 77081
Tel.: (713) 663-1671
Web Site: http://www.tryceco.com
Gas & Petrochemical Pipeline Support Services
N.A.I.C.S.: 541990
E. Mark Hotze *(Pres & CEO)*
Bart Delatte *(Mgr-Emissions Testing)*
Luke Hotze *(Gen Mgr)*

COMPRESSOR WORLD, LLC
6 Norfolk Ave, South Easton, MA 02375
Tel.: (508) 230-7118
Web Site:
   http://www.compressorworld.com
Year Founded: 2001
Sales Range: $10-24.9 Million
Emp.: 2
Industrial Air Compressors, Dryers, Filters, Tanks & Accessories
N.A.I.C.S.: 333912
Matthew Murphy *(Mgr-Sls)*

COMPROBASE, INC.
21351 Gentry Dr, Sterling, VA 20166
Tel.: (703) 444-2525
Web Site:
   https://www.comprobase.com
Year Founded: 2004
Rev.: $3,500,000
Emp.: 40
Computer Related Services
N.A.I.C.S.: 541512
Juned Khan *(CEO)*
Maria Khan *(Pres)*

COMPRODUCTS INC.
1740 Ste F Harmon Ave, Columbus, OH 43223
Tel.: (614) 276-5552
Web Site:
   http://www.bnccommunications.com
Year Founded: 1963
Sales Range: $25-49.9 Million
Emp.: 73
Radio Parts & Accessories Mfr
N.A.I.C.S.: 423690
Tom Harb *(CEO)*
Leland Haydon *(Pres)*

COMPSOURCE, INC.
3241 Superior Ave E, Cleveland, OH 44114
Tel.: (216) 566-7767   OH

Web Site:
   http://www.compsource.com
Year Founded: 1991
Sales Range: $1-9.9 Million
Emp.: 10
Retail Computers/Software Computer Rental/Leasing
N.A.I.C.S.: 449210
Cathy Bellone *(CFO & VP)*
Dean Bellone *(Pres & CEO)*

COMPTECH CORPORATION
15946 Derwood Rd, Rockville, MD 20855
Tel.: (301) 519-3402
Sales Range: $10-24.9 Million
Emp.: 23
Military Parts Whslr
N.A.I.C.S.: 423830
Kavita Dawson *(Pres)*

COMPTROL INCORPORATED
4700 Lakeland Blvd, Eastlake, OH 44095
Tel.: (216) 587-5200
Web Site:
   http://www.comptrolinc.com
Sales Range: $10-24.9 Million
Emp.: 50
Industrial Supplies
N.A.I.C.S.: 335999
Wayne Foley *(Pres)*

COMPU-LINK CORPORATION
1205 Gandy Blvd N, Saint Petersburg, FL 33702-2428
Tel.: (727) 579-1500   FL
Web Site: http://www.compulink-usa.com
Year Founded: 1984
Sales Range: $25-49.9 Million
Emp.: 475
Computer Services
N.A.I.C.S.: 334118
Steve Shevlin *(Pres)*

COMPUDATA INC.
47913 Fremont Blvd, Fremont, CA 94538
Tel.: (510) 438-0185
Sales Range: $25-49.9 Million
Emp.: 12
Electronic Parts Whslr
N.A.I.C.S.: 423690
Roger Koo *(Pres)*

COMPUGAIN, INC.
13241 Woodland Park Rd Ste 610, Herndon, VA 20171
Tel.: (703) 956-7500
Web Site: http://www.compugain.com
Year Founded: 2000
Sales Range: $25-49.9 Million
Emp.: 139
Computer Programming Services
N.A.I.C.S.: 541511
Nick Patel *(COO)*
Sai Alluru *(CTO)*
Joseph Casper *(Pres)*
Justin R. Schuback *(Mgr-Mktg)*

COMPULINK BUSINESS SYSTEMS, INC.
1100 Business Ctr Cir, Newbury Park, CA 91320
Tel.: (800) 456-4522   CA
Web Site:
   https://www.compulinkadvantage.com
Year Founded: 1985
Software Publisher
N.A.I.C.S.: 513210
Cole Galbraith *(Dir-IT)*
Link Wilson *(Founder & CEO)*

Compulink Business Systems, Inc.—(Continued)

Subsidiaries:

My Eye Store **(1)**
4801 W 81st St Ste 111, Minneapolis, MN 55437
Tel.: (952) 463-1200
Web Site: http://www.myeyestore.com
All Other General Merchandise Stores
N.A.I.C.S.: 455219
Stephannie Keller *(Pres & CEO)*

COMPULINK CABLE ASSEMBLIES, INC.
1205 Gandy Blvd N, Saint Petersburg, FL 33702-2428
Tel.: (727) 579-1500
Web Site: https://www.compulink.com
Year Founded: 1984
Sales Range: $75-99.9 Million
Emp.: 600
Fiber Optic Cables & Wire Harnesses Mfr
N.A.I.C.S.: 335921
Stephen Shevlin *(Pres)*
Phil Raymond *(Mgr-Quality)*

COMPUNET CLINICAL LABORATORIES, INC.
2308 Sandridge Dr, Dayton, OH 45439-1847
Tel.: (937) 296-0844
Web Site:
https://www.compunetlab.com
Year Founded: 1986
Sales Range: $25-49.9 Million
Emp.: 600
Medical Laboratories
N.A.I.C.S.: 621511
John Manier *(CFO & VP-Finance)*

COMPUNET CONSULTING GROUP, INC.
6535 Shiloh Rd Ste 300, Alpharetta, GA 30005
Tel.: (678) 965-6500
Web Site: https://www.ccgi.net
Year Founded: 1996
Computer System Design Services
N.A.I.C.S.: 518210
Graham McGehee *(Founder)*
Scott McMillan *(VP)*

COMPUNNEL SOFTWARE GROUP
103 Morgan Ln Ste 102, Plainsboro, NJ 08536
Tel.: (609) 606-9010
Web Site:
https://www.compunnel.com
Rev.: $19,768,319
Emp.: 500
Custom Computer Programming Services
N.A.I.C.S.: 541511
Amit Gaur *(Owner)*
Rakesh Shah *(Pres & CEO)*
Milind Naik *(VP-Sls & Recruiting)*
Sriraj Mallick *(Pres-Learning & Tech Svcs)*
Mike Russo *(Dir-Sls)*
Nick Neumann *(Dir-Sls & Staffing)*

COMPUPROS LTD
16479 Dallas Pkwy Ste 800, Addison, TX 75001-6805
Tel.: (972) 250-4504 TX
Web Site: http://www.compupros.com
Year Founded: 1987
Sales Range: $10-24.9 Million
Emp.: 50
Custom Computer Programming Services
N.A.I.C.S.: 541511
Ken Rossi *(CFO & Controller)*
Tom Dodd *(Chm)*

COMPUSOFT INTEGRATED SOLUTIONS INC.
31500 W 13 Mile Rd Ste 200, Farmington Hills, MI 48334
Tel.: (248) 538-9494 MI
Web Site: https://www.compusoft-is.com
Year Founded: 1997
Sales Range: $10-24.9 Million
Emp.: 87
Computer Software Development & Consulting
N.A.I.C.S.: 513210
Pratap Koganti *(Principal)*

COMPUTECH CORPORATION
100 W Kirby St Ste 101, Detroit, MI 48202-4044
Tel.: (248) 594-6500
Web Site:
https://www.computechcorp.com
Year Founded: 1995
Sales Range: $10-24.9 Million
Emp.: 130
Developer of Software & IT Systems; Custom Computer Programming Services
N.A.I.C.S.: 541511
Sruthi Reddy Boyapati *(Acct Mgr-Staffing)*
Al Fields *(Exec VP)*
Michele Nunn *(Mgr-HR)*

COMPUTECH INTERNATIONAL INC.
525 Northern Blvd Ste 102, Great Neck, NY 11021
Tel.: (516) 487-0101
Web Site: http://www.cti-intl.com
Year Founded: 1995
Rev.: $93,609,922
Emp.: 40
Digital Content Creation & Management Solutions
N.A.I.C.S.: 423430
Eyal Seachi *(Owner & CEO)*
Judith Seachi *(Controller)*

COMPUTER ADD-ONS INC.
86 Denton Ave, New Hyde Park, NY 11040-2231
Tel.: (718) 939-7976 NJ
Web Site:
https://www.compuaddons.com
Year Founded: 1991
Sales Range: $10-24.9 Million
Emp.: 10
Computers, Peripherals & Software
N.A.I.C.S.: 423430
Asad Ali *(Pres)*

COMPUTER ADVANTAGE INC.
7810 N Tamiami Trl, Sarasota, FL 34243
Tel.: (941) 351-2415
Web Site:
https://www.computeradvantage.us
Year Founded: 1991
Sales Range: $1-9.9 Million
Emp.: 15
Computer & Software Sales & Service
N.A.I.C.S.: 449210
Ronald K. Blunden *(Owner & Pres)*

COMPUTER AGE ELECTRONICS, INC.
3302 W Cypress St Ste 101, Tampa, FL 33607
Tel.: (813) 877-5522 FL
Web Site:
https://www.2computerage.com
Year Founded: 1987
Sales Range: $1-9.9 Million
Emp.: 10

Computer Equipment Maintenance & Distr
N.A.I.C.S.: 811210
Luann Hoffmann *(Pres)*
Todd Moran *(Founder & CEO)*

COMPUTER AID, INC.
1390 Ridgeview Dr, Allentown, PA 18104-9065
Tel.: (610) 530-5000 PA
Web Site: http://www.compaid.com
Year Founded: 1981
Sales Range: $100-124.9 Million
Emp.: 1,500
Custom Computer Programming Services & Consulting
N.A.I.C.S.: 541511
Anthony J. Salvaggio *(Founder, Pres & CEO)*
Gene Clater *(CIO)*

Subsidiaries:

CAI Canada Inc **(1)**
161 Bay Street Suite 2700, Toronto, M5J 2S1, ON, Canada
Tel.: (416) 572-2079
Information Technology Consulting Services
N.A.I.C.S.: 541512

COMPUTER AIDED PRODUCTS, INC.
2 Centennial Dr, Peabody, MA 01960
Tel.: (978) 977-9889 MA
Web Site: http://www.capinc.com
Year Founded: 1989
Rev.: $7,800,000
Emp.: 25
Computer Aided Products
N.A.I.C.S.: 811210
Jason Pancoast *(Mgr-Engrg)*
Dana J. Seero *(Pres)*
Eric Doberstein *(VP-Sls)*
Matt Sheidow *(Mgr-Solid Works Sls)*
Alan Zullo *(Mgr-Technical Support)*
Andy Jaskey *(Engr-Applications)*
Art Woodbury *(Engr-Applications)*
Crystal Yazvac *(Engr-Applications)*
Jay Thompson *(Engr-Applications)*
Jennifer Pouliot *(Engr-Applications)*
Lynn Miano *(Project Mgr)*
Paul Hagenow *(Engr-Applications)*
Shuvom Ghose *(Project Mgr & Engr-Mktg)*

COMPUTER AUTOMATION SYSTEMS, INC.
971 Coley Dr, Mountain Home, AR 72653
Tel.: (870) 425-6933
Web Site:
http://www.computerautomation.com
Education Plan Management Software Mfr
N.A.I.C.S.: 513210
Harvey Hughes *(Founder)*

Subsidiaries:

Technical Perspectives, Inc. **(1)**
1475 Richardson Dr Ste 230, Richardson, TX 75080
Tel.: (972) 705-9182
Web Site: http://www.classplus.com
Educational Assessment & Curriculum Software
N.A.I.C.S.: 513210
Jean M. Walling *(Founder)*
Hilary Myers *(Pres)*

COMPUTER CABLE CONNECTION INC.
2810 Harlan Dr, Bellevue, NE 68005-3506
Tel.: (402) 291-9500 NE
Web Site: http://www.cccne.com
Year Founded: 1987
Sales Range: $25-49.9 Million
Emp.: 240

Electrical Apparatus & Equipment
N.A.I.C.S.: 238210
Eric M. Parks *(Pres & Treas)*

COMPUTER CONCEPTS INC.
11652 Dorsett Rd, Maryland Heights, MO 63043
Tel.: (314) 291-0733
Web Site: http://www.cci-stl.com
Year Founded: 1989
Sales Range: $10-24.9 Million
Emp.: 100
Retailer of Compact Discs
N.A.I.C.S.: 449210

COMPUTER CONFIGURATION SERVICES
3002 Dow Ave Ste 402, Tustin, CA 92780
Tel.: (949) 476-0874
Web Site:
http://www.ccseservers.com
Rev.: $30,096,466
Emp.: 16
Custom Computer Programming Services
N.A.I.C.S.: 541511
Mike Grasso *(Pres)*

COMPUTER CONSULTANTS OF AMERICA
24901 NW Hwy, Southfield, MI 48075
Tel.: (248) 353-0830
Web Site: http://www.computer-consultants.com
Sales Range: $10-24.9 Million
Emp.: 100
Data Processing & Information Technology Services
N.A.I.C.S.: 518210
Nicole Meathe *(CEO)*

COMPUTER ENTERPRISES INC.
1000 Omega Dr Ste 1150, Pittsburgh, PA 15205
Tel.: (412) 341-3541 PA
Web Site:
https://www.ceiamerica.com
Year Founded: 1992
Sales Range: $50-74.9 Million
Emp.: 400
Computer Consultancy Services
N.A.I.C.S.: 541512
D. Raja *(CEO & Partner)*
J. William A. Kenawell *(COO & Gen Counsel)*
Dilip Balsaraf *(Dir-Mgmt Info Svcs)*
Ed Funaro *(Pres)*
Martin Vuono *(CFO)*

Subsidiaries:

Computer Enterprises, Inc. **(1)**
Bldg Oven No 10 12 Venketnarayana Rd, T Nagar, Chennai, 600017, India **(100%)**
Tel.: (91) 4452147393
Web Site: http://www.ceiamerica.com
Sales Range: $50-74.9 Million
Emp.: 80
Capital Management
N.A.I.C.S.: 523910

COMPUTER EXPRESS INC.
301 North Ave, Wakefield, MA 01880
Tel.: (781) 246-4477
Web Site:
http://www.computerexpress.com
Rev.: $13,400,000
Emp.: 11
Computer Related Consulting Services
N.A.I.C.S.: 541511
Michael Harris *(Pres)*
Toni Marie Cremone *(Mgr-Acctg)*

COMPUTER GENERATED SOLUTIONS INC.

3 World Financial Ctr 200 Vesey St 27th Fl, New York, NY 10281-1017
Tel.: (212) 408-3800   DE
Web Site: http://www.cgsinc.com
Year Founded: 1984
Sales Range: $250-299.9 Million
Emp.: 5,000
Computer Integrated System Services
N.A.I.C.S.: 541512
Philip Friedman *(Pres & CEO)*
Paul Magel *(Pres-Bus Applications & Tech Outsourcing Div)*
Carl S. Heringer *(Gen Counsel & Sr VP)*
Tali Rabin *(Sr VP)*
Alex Esclamado *(Sr VP-Contact Center Ops-North America)*
Doug Stephen *(Sr VP-Learning Div & Mgr-Canada)*
Edward P. Galati *(CFO & Sr VP)*
Elena Filimonova *(Sr VP-Mktg & Strategy-Global)*
Jeffrey Friedman *(VP-Strategic Initiatives)*
John Samuel *(CIO-Global & Sr VP)*
Liviu Pandrea *(Mng Dir-CGS Europe)*
Michael Mills *(Sr VP-Sls-Global-Contact Center Div)*
Pablo Rossel Estay *(Sr VP & Mgr-Chile)*

Subsidiaries:

Computer Generated Solutions Canada Ltd.   (1)
30 Broadway Avenue, Saint John, E2L 5E8, NB, Canada
Tel.: (506) 642-4247
Web Site: http://www.computergeneratedsolutions.com
Emp.: 100
Computer Integrated System Services
N.A.I.C.S.: 541512
Lorri Perry *(Office Mgr)*

Computer Generated Solutions India Pvt Ltd   (1)
4th Floor Plot No 5 6 Image Gardens Road Silicon Valley, Madhapur, Hyderabad, 500 081, India
Tel.: (91) 40 67433333
Web Site: http://www.cgsinc.com
Emp.: 150
Computer Integrated System Services
N.A.I.C.S.: 541512
Jithu Battu *(Country Mgr)*
Phil Friedman *(Pres & CEO)*
Peter Kalotschke *(CFO)*
Steven Petruk *(Pres-Global Outsourcing Div)*

Computer Generated Solutions Romania   (1)
319 Splaiul Independentei Sector 6, Bucharest, Romania
Tel.: (40) 21 2099935
Web Site: http://www.cgseurope.com
Computer Integrated System Services
N.A.I.C.S.: 541512

Prego S.A.   (1)
Estado 337 Piso 10, Santiago, Chile
Tel.: (56) 2 782 14 00
Web Site: http://www.cgswym.com
Information Technology Consulting Services
N.A.I.C.S.: 541512
Nicolas Kokaly *(Mgr)*

COMPUTER GUIDANCE CORPORATION
15035 N 75th St, Scottsdale, AZ 85260
Tel.: (480) 444-7000
Web Site: http://www.computer-guidance.com
Sales Range: $10-24.9 Million
Emp.: 110
Computer Software Development
N.A.I.C.S.: 541511
Steve Gross *(VP-Client Solutions)*
Mike Bihlmeier *(Pres)*
Stephanie Meyer *(Controller)*

COMPUTER NETWORK SOLUTIONS LLC
131 Hoffman Ln, Islandia, NY 11749
Tel.: (516) 937-0300
Web Site: http://www.computerns.com
Sales Range: $10-24.9 Million
Emp.: 90
Sales of Computers, Peripherals & Software
N.A.I.C.S.: 423430
Alan Cook *(Pres)*
Michael Koprowski *(Dir-NOC & Helpdesk Svcs)*
Mark Scott *(Owner)*
Joe Cuervo *(VP-Managed Svcs)*
Bernadette D'Alessandro *(Dir-HR)*
Robert Swanson *(Sr Acct Exec)*
Debbie Lovis *(Sr Acct Mgr)*
Patty Collins *(Mgr-Pur)*
Josmar Ramirez *(Dir-Engrg)*
Dennis Morea *(Dir-Sls)*

COMPUTER OPTIONS INC.
399 Grand Ave, Oakland, CA 94610
Tel.: (510) 444-5700
Web Site: http://www.cco.com
Year Founded: 1986
Sales Range: $10-24.9 Million
Emp.: 65
Provider of Systems Integration Services
N.A.I.C.S.: 541512
Rand Morimoto *(CEO & Partner)*
Chris Amaris *(CTO & Partner)*
Rich Dorfman *(VP-Client & Prof Svcs)*
Colin Spence *(Partner)*
Valerie Hallstrom *(VP-Fin-Ops)*

COMPUTER PACKAGES INCORPORATED
414 Hungerford Dr Ste 300, Rockville, MD 20850
Tel.: (301) 424-8890
Web Site: http://www.computerpackages.com
Year Founded: 1968
Sales Range: $10-24.9 Million
Emp.: 145
Computer Software Development
N.A.I.C.S.: 541511
Jerrold Van Winter *(Founder & Pres)*
Linda Wright *(Mgr)*

COMPUTER PARADISE INC.
Consolidated Mall C-17, Caguas, PR 00725
Tel.: (787) 746-9195
Web Site: http://www.computer-paradise.net
Sales Range: $10-24.9 Million
Emp.: 80
Sales of Personal Computers
N.A.I.C.S.: 449210
Virginia Scandroglio *(Mgr-Sls)*
Miguel Garcia *(Comptroller)*
Juan H. Vazquez *(Pres)*
Henry Rodriguez *(Mgr-Sls)*

COMPUTER PERFORMANCE INC.
2695 Walsh Ave, Santa Clara, CA 95051-0920
Tel.: (408) 588-1110
Web Site: http://www.digital-loggers.com
Sales Range: $10-24.9 Million
Emp.: 35
Sales of Computer Peripheral Equipment
N.A.I.C.S.: 423430
Martin Bodo *(Chm)*

COMPUTER PRODUCTS CORPORATION

2106 Florence Ave, Cincinnati, OH 45206-2427
Tel.: (513) 221-0600
Web Site: https://www.cpc-i.com
Year Founded: 1962
Sales Range: $10-24.9 Million
Emp.: 48
Sale of Used Merchandise
N.A.I.C.S.: 459510

COMPUTER PROFESSIONALS, INC.
205 Powell Pl, Brentwood, TN 37027
Tel.: (615) 369-0888
Sales Range: $10-24.9 Million
Emp.: 65
Information Technology Staffing Services
N.A.I.C.S.: 561320
Marsha Harrington *(Pres)*

COMPUTER SITES INC.
1225 S Huron St, Denver, CO 80223
Tel.: (303) 871-0550
Web Site: https://www.computersites.net
Sales Range: $10-24.9 Million
Emp.: 40
Nonresidential Construction
N.A.I.C.S.: 236220
Gary Springstead *(Chm & Pres)*
Tom Hare *(Mgr-Design)*
Rodney Manely Jr. *(Principal & Mgr-Mechanical Installation)*

Subsidiaries:

Access Systems Inc.   (1)
1215 S Huron St, Denver, CO 80223
Tel.: (303) 777-6676
Web Site: http://www.computersites.net
Rev.: $1,125,062
Emp.: 6
Nonresidential Construction, Nec
N.A.I.C.S.: 236220

COMPUTER SOLUTIONS & SOFTWARE INTERNATIONAL, INC.
4800 Lyons Tech Pkwy, Coconut Creek, FL 33073
Tel.: (954) 419-1008   FL
Web Site: http://www.solutionsoftware.com
Year Founded: 1993
Sales Range: $1-9.9 Million
Emp.: 200
Custom Computer Programming Services
N.A.I.C.S.: 541511
Stephen A. Bruno *(Pres & CEO)*
Melvin N. Lechner *(Chm)*
Abhinav Dave *(Exec VP)*
Sekhar Babu Madala *(Dir-Tech Ops)*
Roger LaVine *(VP-Product Dev)*

COMPUTER SOLUTIONS INTERNATIONAL
3511 Thomas Rd Ste 5, Santa Clara, CA 95054
Tel.: (408) 727-2900
Web Site: https://www.cybercsi.com
Rev.: $11,400,000
Emp.: 70
Computers, Peripherals & Software
N.A.I.C.S.: 493110
David W. Sanders *(CEO)*

COMPUTER STORES NORTHWEST INC.
9730 S W Hillman Ct Ste 600, Wilsonville, OR 97070
Tel.: (503) 783-7460   OR
Web Site: http://www.csnw.com
Year Founded: 1987
Sales Range: $10-24.9 Million
Emp.: 30
Sale of Computers & Software

N.A.I.C.S.: 449210
Peter Wong *(CFO)*

COMPUTER TECHNOLOGY LINK CORP
9700 SW Harvest Ct Bldg 100, Beaverton, OR 97005
Tel.: (503) 646-3733
Web Site: http://www.ctl.net
Sales Range: $25-49.9 Million
Emp.: 60
Computer Peripheral Equipment
N.A.I.C.S.: 334118
Mike Mahanay *(VP-Bus Dev & Govt Affairs)*
Erik Stromquist *(CEO)*
Stephen Moll *(VP-Pur & Ops)*
Mark Jorgensen *(Mktg Mgr)*
Michelle Manson *(VP-Mktg)*

COMPUTER TRAINING SOURCE INC.
4900 Hopyard Rd Ste 100, Pleasanton, CA 94588
Tel.: (925) 847-2656
Web Site: https://www.computertrainingsource.com
Year Founded: 1996
Emp.: 10
Computer & Softwear Training
N.A.I.C.S.: 611420
Jim Rose *(Pres)*

COMPUTER WORLD
PO Box 6134-16, Douglas, AZ 85655
Tel.: (563) 259-0100
Web Site: http://www.computerworld.com
Year Founded: 2007
Sales Range: $10-24.9 Million
Emp.: 140
Public Relations Services
N.A.I.C.S.: 541820
Marlene Vanbuskirk *(Gen Counsel)*

COMPUTER WORLD SERVICES CORP.
100 Indiana Ave NW Ste 400, Washington, DC 20001
Tel.: (202) 637-9699
Web Site: http://www.cwsc.com
Sales Range: $10-24.9 Million
Emp.: 25
Computer Maintenance & Repair
N.A.I.C.S.: 811210
Farrukh Hameed *(Pres & CEO)*
Monique Milas *(Dir-HR)*

COMPUTERS UNLIMITED
2407 Montana Ave, Billings, MT 59101
Tel.: (406) 255-9500
Web Site: https://www.cu.net
Sales Range: $10-24.9 Million
Emp.: 160
Computer & Software Stores
N.A.I.C.S.: 449210
Michael Schaer *(Founder & Chm)*
Becky Madison *(Dir-Admin & Acctg)*
Davis Almanza *(Mgr)*
Kevin Fichtner *(Mgr-Indus Dev)*
Penny Mayer *(Mgr-ACM, Propane & ECommerce)*
Jim McKenney *(Dir-Sys Dev)*
Karen Morgan *(Mgr-Escalation & Upgrade)*
Chris Little *(Mgr-Technical Svcs)*
Blaine Salveson *(Mgr-Emerging Tech)*
Megan Devenny *(Mgr-Application Support)*
Annabelle Blake *(Mgr-Audiology Support Svcs)*
Jason Kaatz *(Mgr-Project Mgmt)*

Computing Research Association—(Continued)

COMPUTING RESEARCH AS-SOCIATION
1828 L St NW Ste 800, Washington, DC 20036-4632
Tel.: (202) 234-2111　　DC
Web Site: https://www.cra.org
Year Founded: 1990
Sales Range: $10-24.9 Million
Emp.: 13
Computing Research & Development Services
N.A.I.C.S.: 541715
Ann Drobnis (Dir-Computing Community Consortium)
Peter Harsha (Dir-Govt Affairs)
Erik Russell (Dir-Programs)
Betsy Bizot (Dir-Statistics & Evaluation)
Andrew Bernat (Exec Dir)
Susan B. Davidson (Chm)

COMPUTING SYSTEM INNOVATIONS
791 Piedmont-Wekiwa Rd, Apopka, FL 32703
Tel.: (407) 598-1800
Web Site: https://www.csisoft.com
Sales Range: $10-24.9 Million
Emp.: 77
Inventory Computing Services
N.A.I.C.S.: 561990

COMPUTING TECHNOLOGIES INC.
3028 Javier Rd Ste 400, Fairfax, VA 22031
Tel.: (703) 280-8800
Web Site: http://www.cots.com
Sales Range: $25-49.9 Million
Emp.: 50
Computer Systems Analysis & Design
N.A.I.C.S.: 541512
Mary Polston Sosa (Chief HR Officer & VP-HR & Security)
Ann Marie Gillikin (CFO & VP-Fin & Acctg)
Jim Gill (Chief Quality Officer, VP & Gen Mgr)
Bob Ward (Mgr-Program)
David Neault (VP-Software Engrg & Sys Integration)
Manuel Sosa, Jr. (Pres & CEO)

COMPUTING TECHNOLOGY INDUSTRY ASSOCIATION
3500 Lacey Rd Ste 100, Downers Grove, IL 60515
Tel.: (630) 678-8300　　CT
Web Site: http://www.comptia.org
Year Founded: 1982
Sales Range: $50-74.9 Million
Emp.: 164
Business Associations
N.A.I.C.S.: 813910
Nancy Hammervik (Sr VP-Indus Rels)
Randy Gross (CIO)
Tim Herbert (VP-Res-Market Intelligence)
Mj Shoer (Chm)
Todd Thibodeaux (Pres & CEO)

Subsidiaries:

TestOut Corp.　　(1)
50 South Main St, Pleasant Grove, UT 84062
Tel.: (801) 785-7900
Web Site: http://www.testout.com
Rev.: $3,000,000
Emp.: 25
Other Management Consulting Services
N.A.I.C.S.: 541618
Don Whitnah (VP-Res-Dev)
Douglas Edwards (VP-HR)
Noel Vallejo (CEO)

John J. Harris (VP-Sls)
Ladd Timpson (VP-Mktg)
Sean Trewartha (CFO)

COMPUTIZE, INC.
1008 Wirt Rd, Houston, TX 77055-6865
Tel.: (713) 957-0057
Web Site: http://www.computizeinc.com
Year Founded: 1983
Sales Range: $10-24.9 Million
Emp.: 65
Computer Peripheral Services
N.A.I.C.S.: 423430
Sam Ryu (Pres)

COMPUTYPE INC.
2285 County Rd C W, Saint Paul, MN 55113
Tel.: (651) 633-0633　　MN
Web Site: https://www.computype.com
Year Founded: 1975
Sales Range: $25-49.9 Million
Emp.: 150
Commercial Printing
N.A.I.C.S.: 323111
Bruce R. Wray (Mgr-Mktg)
Cindy Roberts (Dir-Employee Svcs)
Peter Baker (VP)
Kelly Hansen (Project Mgr-Mktg)
Scott Hietpas (CEO)
Todd Roach (Co-Owner)
Eric Roach (Co-Owner)

COMPUWAVE INC.
1839 Knoll Dr, Ventura, CA 93003
Tel.: (805) 650-8808
Web Site: http://www.compuwave.com
Sales Range: $10-24.9 Million
Emp.: 30
System Integration Services
N.A.I.C.S.: 541512
Mohan Asnani (CEO)

COMPWEST INSURANCE COMPANY
3 Hutton Centre Dr Ste 550, Santa Ana, CA 92707
Tel.: (517) 708-5625
Web Site: https://www.compwestinsurance.com
Year Founded: 2004
Sales Range: $10-24.9 Million
Emp.: 140
Property & Casualty Insurance Services
N.A.I.C.S.: 524126
Bryan Bogardus (Pres)
Gene Simpson (VP-Underwriting & Mktg)
Robert A. Shatsnider (VP & Officer-Claims)

COMRISE TECHNOLOGY, INC.
1301 State Route 36 Concord Ctr Bldg 2 Ste 9, Hazlet, NJ 07730
Tel.: (732) 739-2330
Web Site: http://www.comrise.com
Year Founded: 1984
Sales Range: $75-99.9 Million
Emp.: 340
IT & Scientific Consulting Services
N.A.I.C.S.: 541519
Gwo Ching Liou (Chm)
Sincia Liu (Pres)

COMROD INC.
12820-30 Triskett Rd, Cleveland, OH 44111-0000
Tel.: (216) 252-6610
Web Site: http://www.comrod.com

Radio, Television Broadcasting & Wireless Communications Equipment Mfr
N.A.I.C.S.: 334220
Niklas Hermansson (Pres & CEO)

Subsidiaries:

Triad RF Systems Inc.　　(1)
6 Lisa Ct, Millstone Township, NJ 08510-8526
Web Site: http://www.triadrf.com
Radio, Television Broadcasting & Wireless Communications Equipment Mfr
N.A.I.C.S.: 334220
David Campbell (Partner)
Adam Krumbein (VP-Mktg)

COMS INTERACTIVE, LLC
60 W Streetsboro St Ste 5, Hudson, OH 44236-2868
Tel.: (330) 650-9900
Web Site: http://www.comsllc.com
Sales Range: Less than $1 Million
Emp.: 55
Healthcare Software Developer
N.A.I.C.S.: 513210
Edward J. Tromczynski (CEO)
James J. Riemenschneider (Vice Chm)
Anthony J. Stanfar (Exec VP-Products & Svcs)
Alison R. Martin (VP-Corp Comm)
Terry Sullivan (Chief Medical Officer)
Simon Mittal (Dir-Medical Affairs)

COMSOFT CORPORATION
100 N Constitution Dr Ste 2, Yorktown, VA 23692
Tel.: (757) 890-2801　　VA
Year Founded: 1996
Sales Range: $10-24.9 Million
Emp.: 35
Computer Programming Services
N.A.I.C.S.: 513210
Richard Gdovic (Chm)

COMSONICS, INC.
1350 Port Republic Rd, Harrisonburg, VA 22801-3514
Tel.: (540) 434-5965　　VA
Web Site: https://www.comsonics.com
Year Founded: 1972
Sales Range: $75-99.9 Million
Emp.: 170
Test & Measurement Equipment Mfr & Provider of Repair Services for Cable TV & Communications Industry
N.A.I.C.S.: 334220
Don Meyerhoffer (COO)
Bret Harrison (Dir-Repair Svcs)
Jack Brian (Pres & CEO)

Subsidiaries:

ComSonics, Inc. - California Repair Facility　　(1)
9779 Business Park Dr Ste G, Sacramento, CA 95827
Tel.: (916) 366-0261
Community Antenna Television Equipment Repair Services
N.A.I.C.S.: 811210

COMSTOCK PARTNERS LC
11465 Sunset Hills Rd 4 Fl, Reston, VA 20190
Tel.: (703) 230-1230
Web Site: http://www.comstockcompanies.com
Year Founded: 1985
Sales Range: $25-49.9 Million
Emp.: 12
Private Equity Firm
N.A.I.C.S.: 523999
Christopher Clemente (Principal)

COMTEC SOLUTIONS

65 Elmgrove Park, Rochester, NY 14624
Tel.: (585) 621-9303
Web Site: http://www.comtecsolutions.com
Sales Range: $10-24.9 Million
IT Consulting Services
N.A.I.C.S.: 541990
Rob Moyer (Pres)

Subsidiaries:

RAM Software Systems Inc.　　(1)
1701 N Collins Blvd Ste 200, Richardson, TX 75080-3554
Tel.: (972) 669-0763
Web Site: http://www.ramsys.com
Sales Range: $10-24.9 Million
Custom Computer Programming Services
N.A.I.C.S.: 541511

COMTEC SYSTEMS, INC.
2658 N West Blvd, Vineland, NJ 08360
Tel.: (856) 691-5111　　NJ
Web Site: http://www.comtecusa.net
Year Founded: 1988
Sales Range: $1-9.9 Million
Emp.: 37
Security Services
N.A.I.C.S.: 561621
Michael W. Vertolli (Pres & CEO)

COMTEL CORPORATION
39810 Grand River Ave Ste 180, Novi, MI 48375-2143
Tel.: (248) 888-4730
Web Site: http://www.comtel.com
Sales Range: $10-24.9 Million
Emp.: 18
Computer Peripheral Equipment
N.A.I.C.S.: 423430
William Boroughf (Pres)
Jenny Boroughf (Controller)

COMTEL HOLDINGS INC.
14101 Myford Rd, Tustin, CA 92780
Tel.: (714) 505-3136
Rev.: $50,400,398
Emp.: 250
Electrical Equipment & Supplies
N.A.I.C.S.: 334419

COMUS INTERNATIONAL INC.
454 Allwood Rd, Clifton, NJ 07012
Tel.: (973) 777-6900
Web Site: http://www.comus-intl.com
Sales Range: $10-24.9 Million
Emp.: 75
Switches & Electric Power
N.A.I.C.S.: 335313
Robert P. Romano (Pres)
Patricia Galasso (Office Mgr)
Joseph Perez (COO)
Joseph Romano (Sr VP)

COMVEST GROUP HOLDINGS LLC
525 Okeechobee Blvd Ste 1050, West Palm Beach, FL 33401
Tel.: (561) 727-2000　　DE
Web Site: http://www.comvest.com
Year Founded: 2000
Private Equity Firm
N.A.I.C.S.: 523999
Robert Anthony O'Sullivan (Mng Partner)
W. Marshall Griffin (Principal)
Cecilio Rodriguez (CFO & Partner)
Roger Marrero (Mng Partner)
Lee Bryan (Partner)
Daniel Lee (Partner)
Greg Reynolds (Partner)
Bryce Peterson (Mng Dir)
Colleen Gurda (Sr VP)
Carlos Soto (Principal)
Matt Gullen (Partner)

Tom Goila *(Mng Dir)*
Joe Higginbotham *(VP)*
Kevin Lahatte *(Partner)*
Brad Nii *(Mng Dir)*
Palmer Rosemond *(VP)*
Michael Altschuler *(Chief Administrative Officer & Gen Counsel)*
Deborah Nordell *(Controller)*
Lisa Lutton *(VP-HR)*
Emilie Schaffer *(VP-Fin Planning & Analysis)*
Michael S. Falk *(Founder, Chm & Mng Partner)*
Michael S. Falk *(Founder, Chm & Mng Partner)*

Subsidiaries:

Adayana Inc. **(1)**
3500 DePauw Blvd Ste 3080, Indianapolis, IN 46268
Tel.: (317) 415-0500
Web Site: http://www.adayana.com
Sales Range: $10-24.9 Million
Emp.: 300
Training & Workforce Development Services
N.A.I.C.S.: 611430
Steve Kerschenbaum *(CTO & Gen Counsel)*
Steve Shamblott *(Exec VP-Bus Dev)*
Charley Grady *(VP-Strategic Fin)*
Sandra L. Mathes *(VP-HR)*
Dave Buell *(VP-Indus Sls)*
Raymond R. Richie *(Pres-Indus Grp)*
John Burwell *(Sr VP-Sls & Mktg)*
David Hollinrake *(VP-Bus Dev-Indus Grp)*
Jeffrey H. Moon *(CFO)*
Jeff Kidwell *(Pres-Govt Grp)*

Subsidiary (Domestic):

Adayana Government Group **(2)**
3141 Fairview Park Dr Ste 800, Falls Church, VA 22042
Tel.: (703) 564-7100
Web Site: http://www.adayana.com
Sales Range: $10-24.9 Million
Emp.: 35
Technical Consulting Services
N.A.I.C.S.: 541690
Gail Azaroff *(VP-Bus Dev)*
George F. Close Jr. *(Pres)*

Subsidiary (Non-US):

Adayana Learning Solutions Pvt Ltd **(2)**
E2 Mariner Block Plot no-17 Hi-Tech City, Madhapur, Hyderabad, 500081, India
Tel.: (91) 4066564101
Web Site: http://www.adayana.com
Management & Technical Consulting Services
N.A.I.C.S.: 611430
Srinivas Rao *(CEO)*

Subsidiary (Domestic):

Adayana, Inc. **(2)**
3905 Vincennes Rd Ste 402, Indianapolis, IN 46268
Tel.: (317) 415-0500
Web Site: http://www.adayana.com
Training & Workforce Development for Food, Agriculture & Life Science Industries
N.A.I.C.S.: 611430
Ryan Elliott *(Mgr-Bus Dev)*

AutoInfo, Inc. **(1)**
6413 Congress Ave Ste 260, Boca Raton, FL 33487
Tel.: (561) 988-9456
Rev.: $278,171,000
Assets: $64,404,000
Liabilities: $35,059,000
Net Worth: $29,345,000
Earnings: $4,356,000
Emp.: 100
Fiscal Year-end: 12/31/2012
Holding Company; Commercial Freight Logistics & Transportation Arrangement Services
N.A.I.C.S.: 551112

Subsidiary (Domestic):

Sunteck Transport Group, Inc. **(2)**

6413 Congress Ave Ste 260, Boca Raton, FL 33487 **(100%)**
Tel.: (561) 988-9456
Web Site: http://www.suntecktransportgroup.com
Sales Range: $25-49.9 Million
Emp.: 45
Commercial Freight Logistics & Transportation Arrangement Services
N.A.I.C.S.: 488510
Warren Cohen *(VP-Distr & Logistics)*
Ken Forster *(CEO)*
Sean Clancy *(CIO)*

Comvest Group Holdings LLC - New York Office **(1)**
295 Madison Ave 17th Fl, New York, NY 10017
Tel.: (212) 829-5880
Web Site: http://www.comvest.com
Privater Equity Firm
N.A.I.C.S.: 523999
Joseph J. Pallotta Jr. *(VP-Sls & Mktg)*

Critical Information Network, LLC **(1)**
4101 International Pkwy, Carrollton, TX 75007
Tel.: (972) 309-4000
Web Site: http://www.criticalinfonet.com
Sales Range: $50-74.9 Million
Emp.: 60
Internet-based Police, Firefighter, First-Responder & Public Safety Training Solutions
N.A.I.C.S.: 611430

D&S Residential Services, LP **(1)**
8911 N Capital of Texas Hwy Bldg 1 Ste 1300, Austin, TX 78759-8759
Tel.: (512) 327-2325
Web Site: http://www.dscommunity.com
Intellectual & Developmental Disability Care Facilities Operator
N.A.I.C.S.: 623210
Mickey Atkins *(Pres & CEO)*
Michael Clark *(CFO)*
Robert Ham *(Chief Compliance Officer & VP-Ops-Texas)*
Mike Burke *(Reg Dir-Field Ops)*
Jon Moore *(Reg Dir-Field Ops)*
Jamie Cook *(Dir-Implementation)*
April Wappes *(Dir-Quality Assurance)*
Robn Traugott *(Dir-Trng & Dev)*
Donna Jackson *(Dir-Health Svcs)*

GAI Consultants, Inc. **(1)**
385 E Waterfront Dr, Homestead, PA 15120
Tel.: (412) 476-2000
Web Site: http://www.gaiconsultants.com
Sales Range: $150-199.9 Million
Emp.: 900
Engineering Consulting Services
N.A.I.C.S.: 541330
Gary M. Dejidas *(Chm & CEO)*
Anthony F. Morrocco *(COO & Exec VP)*
Pamela Walaski *(Dir-Health & Safety)*
Larry Gendzier *(Asst VP)*
Teresa C. Browne *(Dir-Bus Support Svcs)*
Karl Palvisak *(CFO & VP)*
Gregory T. Nettuno *(Sr VP-Infrastructure Bus Unit)*
Stephen E. Gould *(Sr VP-Energy Bus Unit)*
Jeffrey Hill *(Chief Admin Officer & VP)*
Enrique Bazan-Arias *(Mgr-Engrg)*
Donald Spaeder *(VP)*
Harry Trout *(VP)*
Richard Cima *(VP)*
Robert Schanck *(VP)*
Bob Hurley *(Dir-Bus Dev)*

Subsidiary (Domestic):

Creighton Manning Engineering, Llp. **(2)**
17 Computer Dr W, Albany, NY 12205
Tel.: (518) 446-0396
Web Site: http://www.cmellp.com
Sales Range: $1-9.9 Million
Emp.: 30
Engineering Services, Nsk
N.A.I.C.S.: 541330
Gregory Gibbons *(Engr-Civil)*
Teresa York *(Coord-Mktg)*
Douglas Teator *(Project Mgr)*
Dawna Morrill *(Mgr-HR)*
Lucas Short *(Asst Project Engr)*
Mark Nadolny *(Project Mgr)*
Susan Torelli *(Project Mgr)*

Crispell-Snyder, Inc. **(2)**

700 Geneva Pkwy N, Lake Geneva, WI 53147
Tel.: (262) 348-5600
Web Site: http://www.gaiconsultants.com
Professional Consulting Services
N.A.I.C.S.: 541618
Daniel F. Snyder *(CEO)*

Division (Domestic):

Eland Engineering, Inc. **(2)**
5100 NW 33rd Ave, Fort Lauderdale, FL 33309
Tel.: (954) 678-3999
Web Site: http://www.elandeng.com
General Management Consulting Services
N.A.I.C.S.: 541611
Bo Qian *(Pres)*

Subsidiary (Domestic):

GAI Construction Monitoring Services, Inc. **(2)**
470 Drew Ct, King of Prussia, PA 19406 **(100%)**
Tel.: (610) 731-0430
Web Site: http://www.gaiconsultants.com
Sales Range: $10-24.9 Million
Emp.: 3
Construction Monitoring Expertise In Highway & Bridge Construction Projects
N.A.I.C.S.: 541618
Gary DeJidas *(CEO)*

GAI Consultants Inc. **(2)**
618 E South St Ste 700, Orlando, FL 32801-2842 **(100%)**
Tel.: (407) 423-8398
Sales Range: $10-24.9 Million
Emp.: 100
Engineering Consulting Services
N.A.I.C.S.: 541330
Gary M. Dejidas *(Chm & CEO)*
Stephen Boylan *(Asst VP)*
Peg Brenner *(Mgr-HR)*
John Saunders *(Dir-Engrg & Transportation)*
Jack Thompson *(Dir-Aviation-Florida)*
Jeffrey Hill *(Chief Admin Officer & VP)*
Kathy Leo *(VP & Dir-Private Dev)*

GAI Consultants Inc. **(2)**
1301 River Pl Blvd Ste 900, Jacksonville, FL 32207 **(100%)**
Tel.: (904) 363-1110
Web Site: http://www.gaiconsultants.com
Rev.: $200,000,000
Emp.: 28
Engineeering Services
N.A.I.C.S.: 541330
Gregory T. Nettuno *(Sr VP & Dir-Infrastructure Bus Unit)*
Kevin R. Leadbetter *(VP)*
Anthony Morrocco *(COO & Exec VP)*
Larry Gendzier *(Asst VP)*
Karl Palvisak *(CFO & VP)*

Lee-Simpson Associates, Inc. **(2)**
203 W Weber Ave, Du Bois, PA 15801
Tel.: (814) 371-7750
Web Site: http://www.gai.com
Emp.: 30
Environmental Engineering Services
N.A.I.C.S.: 541330
Edward Nasuti *(Pres)*

Lotspeich and Associates, Inc. **(2)**
618 E South St Ste 700, Orlando, FL 32801
Tel.: (407) 740-8482
Web Site: http://www.lotspeichandassociates.com
Ecological Consulting Services
N.A.I.C.S.: 541620
Karl G. Lotspeich *(VP)*
Renee L. Thomas *(VP)*
D. J. Silverberg *(Dir-Ecological Svcs)*

Metz and Associates, LLC **(2)**
618 E South St Ste 630, Orlando, FL 32801
Tel.: (407) 366-3800
Web Site: http://www.metzbridges.com
Structural Engineering Services
N.A.I.C.S.: 541330
Daniel Metz *(Founder)*

Real Estate Research Consultants, Inc. **(2)**
618 E South St Ste 600, Orlando, FL 32801
Tel.: (407) 843-5635
Web Site: http://www.rercinc.com
Real Estate Consulting Service

N.A.I.C.S.: 531390
Owen M. Beitsch *(Sr Principal)*
Thomas R. Kohler *(Sr Principal)*
David R. Darsey *(Sr Principal)*

Gen3 Marketing LLC **(1)**
960B Harvest Dr Ste 210, Blue Bell, PA 19422
Tel.: (215) 525-2851
Web Site: http://www.gen3marketing.com
Digital Marketing Services
N.A.I.C.S.: 541613
Alison Pozielli *(Sr Mgr-Mktg)*

Groundlink, Inc. **(1)**
134 W 37th St, New York, NY 10018
Tel.: (212) 527-7498
Web Site: http://www.groundlink.com
Sales Range: $25-49.9 Million
Emp.: 126
Passenger Transportation Software Developer Services
N.A.I.C.S.: 513210
Michael Mooradian *(Chief Sls Officer)*
Jelena Picuric *(VP-Global Ops)*
George Tadros *(Dir-DA Net & Supply Network)*

Haggen, Inc. **(1)**
2211 Rimland Dr Ste 300, Bellingham, WA 98226
Tel.: (360) 733-8720
Web Site: http://www.haggen.com
Sales Range: $700-749.9 Million
Emp.: 3,200
Supermarket Operator
N.A.I.C.S.: 445110
Scott Smith *(VP-Mktg)*
Michael Rose *(Dir-Ops)*
John Clougher *(CEO)*

Inoveris, LLC **(1)**
7001 Discovery Blvd, Dublin, OH 43017
Tel.: (614) 761-2000
Web Site: http://www.inoveris.com
Rev.: $49,694,924
Emp.: 250
CD-ROM & DVD Production & Digital Distribution Services
N.A.I.C.S.: 334610

Spinrite LP **(1)**
320 Livingstone Ave N, Listowel, N4W 1P7, ON, Canada
Tel.: (519) 291-3780
Web Site: http://www.spinriteyarns.com
Craft Yarn Mfr
N.A.I.C.S.: 313110
Brenda Pfeffer *(Coord-Employee Rels)*

Subsidiary (US):

Coats & Clark Inc. **(2)**
3430 Toringdon Way Ste 301, Charlotte, NC 28277
Tel.: (704) 329-5800
Sewing Thread, Dual Duty Plus Threads, Crochet Cotton, Embroidery Threads, Zippers, Narrow Fabrics, Red Heart Yarns, Needlework Kits & Instruction Books
N.A.I.C.S.: 313110

Subsidiary (Non-US):

Coats Canada **(3)**
10 Roybridge Gate Suite 200, Vaughan, L5T 2T5, ON, Canada
Tel.: (905) 850-9200
Coats Mfr & Distr
N.A.I.C.S.: 313110

Zomax, Incorporated **(1)**
5353 Nathan Ln N, Plymouth, MN 55442-1952
Tel.: (763) 553-9300
Sales Range: $150-199.9 Million
Emp.: 1,000
Digital Visual Disks & Compact Disks Mfr
N.A.I.C.S.: 334610

Subsidiary (Non-US):

Zomax Canada Company **(2)**
10 Didak Dr, Arnprior, K7S 3H2, ON, Canada
Tel.: (613) 623-7901
Sales Range: $25-49.9 Million
Emp.: 196
Digital Visual Disks & Compact Disks Mfr
N.A.I.C.S.: 334610

Comvest Group Holdings LLC—(Continued)

Zomax Limited   (2)
Unit 1A Cloverhill Industrial Estate, Clondalkin, Dublin, 22, Ireland
Tel.: (353) 14056222
Web Site: http://www.dunsel.com
Sales Range: $25-49.9 Million
Emp.: 200
Mfr of Digital Visual Disks & Compact Disks
N.A.I.C.S.: 334610

CON AM MANAGEMENT CORPORATION
3990 Ruffin Rd Ste100, San Diego, CA 92123
Tel.: (858) 614-7200
Web Site: https://www.conam.com
Rev.: $13,927,888
Emp.: 140
Real Estate Managers
N.A.I.C.S.: 531210
Daniel J. Epstein (Founder & Chm)
Brad Forrester (Pres & CEO)
Donna Leonard (Controller)

CON-DEA SUPPLY CORP.
2121 44th Rd, Long Island City, NY 11101
Tel.: (718) 392-3232
Web Site:
    http://www.condeasupply.com
Sales Range: $10-24.9 Million
Emp.: 25
Sheets, Metal
N.A.I.C.S.: 423510
Mark Chalpin (Pres)

CON-TECH COMPANIES
366 West 4th, Eureka, MO 63025-1803
Tel.: (636) 938-4748
Sales Range: $10-24.9 Million
Emp.: 100
Carpentry Services
N.A.I.C.S.: 238350
Dan Covert (Principal)
Craig McPartlin (Pres)

CONAM CONSTRUCTION
301 W Northern Lights Blvd Ste 300, Anchorage, AK 99503
Tel.: (907) 278-6600
Web Site: https://www.conamco.com
Sales Range: $10-24.9 Million
Emp.: 30
Oil & Gas Pipeline Construction
N.A.I.C.S.: 237120
Robert W. Stinson (Pres)
Dale Kissee (Mgr-Ops)
Bill Binford (Mgr-North Slope)

CONATSER SITE SERVICES TX, L.P.
5327 Wichita St, Fort Worth, TX 76119
Tel.: (817) 546-5148
Web Site:
    https://www.conatsersiteser
    vicestx.com
Emp.: 130
Commercial & Municipal Construction
N.A.I.C.S.: 236220
Jerry Conatser (Pres & Owner)
Ryan Pollard (Partner)
Jay Arnell (Coord-Final Projects)

CONAX TECHNOLOGIES LLC
2300 Walden Ave, Buffalo, NY 14225-4740
Tel.: (716) 684-4500   NY
Web Site:
    https://www.conaxtechnologies.com
Year Founded: 1955
Sales Range: $50-74.9 Million
Emp.: 100

Mfr of Thermocouples & Temperature Sensors
N.A.I.C.S.: 334513
Robert Fox (CEO)
Tom Mech (Sr Engr-Sls Application)
Ronald Miller (Engr-Sls Application)
Gary Talboys (Engr-Sls Application)
Rick Lyon (Mgr-Strategic Acct)
Ken Hugh (Mgr-Sls-Northeast US)
Chris Jank (Engr-Sls Applications)

CONCANNON CORPORATION
2950 SE Stark St Ste 230, Portland, OR 97214-3082
Tel.: (503) 231-8881   OR
Web Site:
    https://www.concannonlumber.com
Year Founded: 1980
Sales Range: $10-24.9 Million
Emp.: 33
Lumber Product Distr
N.A.I.C.S.: 423310
Patrick R. Concannon (Pres)
Bryan J. Concannon (VP)
Randal Eckerdt (Mgr-Utility Div)

Subsidiaries:

Concannon Lumber Company   (1)
14888 Hwy 105 W Ste 101, Montgomery, TX 77356   (100%)
Tel.: (936) 588-4287
Web Site: http://www.concannonlbr.com
Emp.: 1
Lumber Moldings Panels & Flooring Whslr
N.A.I.C.S.: 444110

CONCANNON MILLER & CO., P.C.
1525 Valley Center Pkwy Ste 300, Bethlehem, PA 18017-2285
Tel.: (610) 433-5501
Web Site:
    https://www.concannonmiller.com
Sales Range: $10-24.9 Million
Emp.: 100
Certified Public Accountants
N.A.I.C.S.: 541211
Bob Oster (CEO)
Melissa A. Daley (Mgr-Acctg-Audit & Tax Grp)
Gail Boyle (Mgr-Tampa Bay)

CONCAST METAL PRODUCTS CO.
131 Myoma Rd, Mars, PA 16046
Tel.: (724) 538-4000   PA
Web Site: https://www.concast.com
Year Founded: 1891
Sales Range: $50-74.9 Million
Emp.: 50
Mfr of Brass & Bronze Ingots
N.A.I.C.S.: 331529
Rick Hartman (Mgr)
Russell Hinchberger (Plant Mgr)
Kathy Mylott (Mgr)

Subsidiaries:

Concast Metal Products Co. - Ohio Production Facility   (1)
14315 State Route 113, Wakeman, OH 44889
Tel.: (800) 288-7856
Metal Products Mfr
N.A.I.C.S.: 331529

Concast Metal Products Co. - Pennsylvania Production Facility   (1)
131 Myoma Rd, Mars, PA 16046
Web Site: http://www.concast.com
Copper Alloy Mfr
N.A.I.C.S.: 331529
Alal Parbour (CEO)

CONCENTRA BIOSCIENCES, LLC
4747 Executive Dr Ste 210, San Diego, CA 92121
Tel.: (858) 281-5372

Web Site:
    https://www.concentrabiosci
    ences.com
Bio Technology Services
N.A.I.C.S.: 541714
Kevin Tang (CEO)

Subsidiaries:

Jounce Therapeutics, Inc.   (1)
780 Memorial Dr, Cambridge, MA 02139
Tel.: (857) 259-3840
Web Site: https://www.jouncetx.com
Rev.: $82,000,000
Assets: $212,550,000
Liabilities: $29,438,000
Net Worth: $183,112,000
Earnings: ($50,919,000)
Emp.: 141
Fiscal Year-end: 12/31/2022
Biotechnology Research & Development Services
N.A.I.C.S.: 541714
Michael Hearne (CFO)

Theseus Pharmaceuticals, Inc.   (1)
314 Main St, Cambridge, MA 02142
Tel.: (857) 400-9491
Web Site: https://www.theseusrx.com
Rev.: $3,478,000
Assets: $222,447,000
Liabilities: $14,832,000
Net Worth: $207,615,000
Earnings: ($50,608,000)
Emp.: 38
Fiscal Year-end: 12/31/2022
Biotechnology Research & Development Services
N.A.I.C.S.: 541714
Kevin Tang (CEO)
Kristine Callahan (VP & Controller)
Katie Dahlstrom (VP-Clinical Ops)
Alicja Januszewicz (Sr VP-People & Culture)
David P. Kerstein (Chief Medical Officer)
Nachu Narasimhan (Sr VP-Drug Metabolism & Preclinical Safety)
Len Rozamus (Sr VP-Technical Ops)
Michael Hearne (CFO)
Stew Kroll (Chief Dev Officer)
Thomas Wei (Chief Bus Officer)

CONCENTRIC HEALTHCARE STAFFING
4250 N Drinkwater Blvd Ste 100, Scottsdale, AZ 85251
Tel.: (480) 444-7777   AZ
Web Site:
    https://www.concentrichealth
    care.com
Year Founded: 2002
Sales Range: $10-24.9 Million
Emp.: 325
Staff Recruiting Services
N.A.I.C.S.: 541612
Chris Bollinger (CEO)
Kyle Silk (Pres & COO)
David Walker (Acct Mgr-Nursing Div)

CONCENTRIC MARKETING
101 W Worthington Ave Ste 108, Charlotte, NC 28203
Tel.: (704) 731-5100
Web Site:
    http://www.getconcentric.com
Year Founded: 2000
Rev.: $12,500,000
Emp.: 19
Marketing Agency
N.A.I.C.S.: 541810
Robert Shaw (Pres)
Lisa George (CFO)

CONCENTRIC PHARMA ADVERTISING
175 Varick St 9th Fl, New York, NY 10014
Tel.: (212) 633-9700
Web Site: http://www.concentric-rx.com
Year Founded: 2002
Sales Range: $10-24.9 Million

Emp.: 10
Advertising Agencies
N.A.I.C.S.: 541810
Michael Sanzen (Co-Founder & Chief Creative Officer)
Adam Cohen (Mng Partner & Dir-Creative)
Ken Begasse Jr. (Co-Founder & CEO)

CONCEPT CHASER CO., INC.
16500 S Western Ave Ste 102, Gardena, CA 90247-4659
Tel.: (310) 615-0700   CA
Web Site:
    http://www.conceptchaser.net
Year Founded: 1987
Rev.: $11,000,000
Emp.: 24
Advetising Agency
N.A.I.C.S.: 541810
Yoshihisa Hayakawa (Pres)
Lynette Goh (CFO)
Yuko Kimoto (Dir-Creative)
Stacy Herkert (Sr Copywriter)
Takeshi Shimada (Graphic Designer)
Dana Scoby (Mng Partner & Head-Pub Rel)
Mike Smith (Partner & Dir-Creative)
Art Silver (Dir-Art)
Keith Park (Copywriter)
Claudio Martinez-Valle (Dir-Creative & Assoc Partner)

CONCEPT INDUSTRIES INC
4950 Kraft Ave SE, Grand Rapids, MI 49512
Tel.: (616) 554-9000
Web Site: http://www.conceptind.com
Rev.: $10,600,000
Emp.: 200
Plastics Foam Products & Fibers
N.A.I.C.S.: 326150
Dave Foote (CFO)

CONCEPT MACHINE TOOL SALES, LLC
15625 Medina Rd, Minneapolis, MN 55447
Tel.: (763) 559-1975   MN
Web Site:
    http://www.conceptmachine.com
Year Founded: 1974
Sales Range: $1-9.9 Million
Emp.: 40
Industrial Equipment Whsr
N.A.I.C.S.: 423830
Dan Murphy (Gen Mgr)
Andrew Hecker (CEO)

Subsidiaries:

American Calibration, Inc.   (1)
4410 Il Rte 176 Ste 11, Crystal Lake, IL 60014-3710
Tel.: (815) 356-5839
Web Site:
    http://www.americancalibration.com
Calibration & Equipment Parts & Rental Services
N.A.I.C.S.: 423830
Todd Gibson (Pres)

CONCEPT ONE ACCESSORIES
1411 Bdwy 7th Fl, New York, NY 10018
Tel.: (212) 868-2590
Web Site: http://www.concept1.com
Year Founded: 1999
Licensed Fashion, Sports & Entertainment Accessories Mfr
N.A.I.C.S.: 315990
Sam Hafif (CEO)
Bernie Hafif (VP)

CONCEPT PLASTICS INC.
1210 Hickory Chapel Rd, High Point, NC 27260
Tel.: (336) 889-2001
Web Site: https://www.cpico.com

Year Founded: 1970
Rev.: $22,200,000
Emp.: 112
Casting Of Plastics
N.A.I.C.S.: 326199

CONCEPT RESTAURANTS INC.

1227 Spruce St Ste 201, Boulder, CO 80302
Tel.: (303) 443-8424
Rev.: $30,500,000
Emp.: 12
Restaurant Operators
N.A.I.C.S.: 541219
Frank B. Day *(Pres)*
Jacob Kesler *(Gen Mgr)*

CONCEPT TECHNOLOGY INC.

1009 3rd Ave N Ste 200, Nashville, TN 37201
Tel.: (615) 321-6428
Web Site:
https://www.concepttechnology.com
Sales Range: $1-9.9 Million
Emp.: 25
Information Technology Consulting Services
N.A.I.C.S.: 541512
Jason McMahan *(Dir-Tech)*
Sarah Murphy *(Dir-Client Svcs)*
Megan Long *(Controller)*
Whitney Wachter *(Coord-Fin & Benefits)*
Madison Thetford *(Coord-Sls & Mktg)*
Ted Wheeler *(Mgr-IT Sourcing)*
Ryan Link *(Engr-Support)*

CONCEPT THREE INC.

424 S Main St, Davison, MI 48423-1608
Tel.: (810) 653-1002
Web Site:
http://www.conceptthree.com
Year Founded: 1980
Sales Range: Less than $1 Million
Emp.: 5
Advertising Specialties, Audio/Visual, Cable T.V., Collateral, Consulting, Graphic Design, Industrial, Logo & Package Design, Media Buying Services, Retail
N.A.I.C.S.: 541810
James R. Slater *(Pres)*
Susan R. Slater *(VP-Brdcst Production)*
Tony Hill *(Art Dir)*
Olivia Taylor *(Office Mgr-Media)*
Briony Skerjance *(Designer)*

CONCEPTBAIT, INC.

4123 8th Ave S, Saint Petersburg, FL 33711
Tel.: (727) 321-5350
Web Site:
http://www.conceptbait.com
Sales Range: $1-9.9 Million
Emp.: 8
Event Design, Decor & Floral Services
N.A.I.C.S.: 541490
Lynn McGhee *(Co-Owner & Chief Creative Officer)*
Frank Clemente *(Co-Owner & VP-Creative Visual Arts)*

CONCEPTS & STRATEGIES INC

1432 K St Nw Ste 300, Washington, DC 20005
Tel.: (202) 216-9880
Web Site: http://www.constrat.net
Year Founded: 2005
Sales Range: $10-24.9 Million
Emp.: 115
Communication Consulting Services

N.A.I.C.S.: 541618
Jason J. Hinton *(Pres)*

CONCEPTS NREC, INC.

217 Billings Farm Rd, White River Junction, VT 05001-9486
Tel.: (802) 296-2321   VT
Web Site:
https://www.conceptsnrec.com
Year Founded: 1980
Sales Range: $10-24.9 Million
Emp.: 110
Turbomachinery Consulting Firm
N.A.I.C.S.: 513210
Alexander L. Monteforte *(Assoc Dir-Dynamometer Products & Mgr-Dynamometer Ops)*
Scott Hanratty *(Mgr-Sls-Latin America)*

CONCEPTSOLUTIONS, LLC

11600 Sunrise Valley Dr Ste 300, Reston, VA 20191
Tel.: (703) 889-8444
Web Site: https://www.concept-solutions.com
Year Founded: 1999
Sales Range: $10-24.9 Million
Emp.: 50
Information Management & Technology Consulting Services
N.A.I.C.S.: 541690
Phong Mai *(Pres & CEO)*
John Krahulec *(COO & Exec VP)*
Todd Schaberg *(CIO & Exec VP)*

CONCERT GOLF PARTNERS, LLC

1 Coastal Oak, Newport Beach, CA 92657
Tel.: (949) 715-0602
Web Site:
http://www.concertgolfpartners.com
Golf Course Management
N.A.I.C.S.: 713910
Peter Nanula *(CEO)*

Subsidiaries:

Crestview Country Club   **(1)**
1000 N 127th St E, Wichita, KS 67206
Tel.: (316) 733-1344
Web Site:
http://www.crestviewcountryclub.com
Rev.: $6,467,746
Assets: $8,406,255
Liabilities: $5,332,704
Net Worth: $3,073,551
Earnings: ($346,018)
Emp.: 291
Fiscal Year-end: 12/31/2013
Country Club
N.A.I.C.S.: 713910
Sharon Grate *(Controller)*

Heathrow Country Club   **(1)**
1200 Bridgewater Dr, Heathrow, FL 32746
Tel.: (407) 333-1450
Web Site: http://www.heathrowcc.com
Sales Range: $1-9.9 Million
Emp.: 20
Country Club
N.A.I.C.S.: 713910
Toni Curlin *(Dir-Catering Sls)*
Barry Myers *(Dir-Tennis)*
Brendan Kennedy *(Dir-Golf Instruction)*
Edwin Rolland *(Dir-Culinary Ops)*
Jeff Jones *(Dir-Grp Instruction)*
John Kopack *(Dir-Agronomy)*
Ryan Fahler *(Gen Mgr)*
Rebecca Lang *(Mgr-Catering Sls)*
Noor Sohail *(Controller)*

The Country Club at Woodmore   **(1)**
12320 Pleasant Prospect, Mitchellville, MD 20721
Tel.: (301) 249-6100
Web Site: http://www.ccwoodmore.com
Sales Range: $1-9.9 Million
Emp.: 60
Country Club
N.A.I.C.S.: 713910

The Golf Club of Amelia Island   **(1)**
4700 Amelia Island Pkwy, Amelia Island, FL 32084
Tel.: (904) 277-8015
Web Site: http://www.golfclubofamelia.com
Sales Range: $1-9.9 Million
Emp.: 50
Golf Club
N.A.I.C.S.: 713910
Pam McDonald *(Controller)*
David DeMay *(Dir-Golf)*
Kellie Douzuk *(Dir-Catering Sls & Food & Beverage)*
Brian Friederichs *(Dir-Membership)*

CONCERTED SERVICES, INC.

2100 Riverside Ave, Waycross, GA 31502
Tel.: (912) 285-6083   GA
Web Site:
http://www.concertedservices.org
Year Founded: 1968
Sales Range: $10-24.9 Million
Emp.: 450
Social & Economic Services
N.A.I.C.S.: 813410
Carlos Nelson *(Chm)*
Bryan Singleton *(Exec Dir)*
Jack Parker *(Dir-Fiscal)*
Sonja Eason *(Dir-HR)*
Joey Wilkes *(Dir-IT)*

CONCESSIONS INTERNATIONAL INC.

566 Wells St SW, Atlanta, GA 30312
Tel.: (470) 788-8508
Web Site: https://www.cintl.com
Sales Range: $50-74.9 Million
Emp.: 1,000
Concessionaire
N.A.I.C.S.: 722513
Donata Russell Major *(CEO)*
Anthony Joseph *(Pres)*
LeMonica Hakeem *(VP-Bus Dev)*

CONCHO SUPPLY INC.

4102 Sherwood Way, San Angelo, TX 76901
Tel.: (325) 949-4649
Rev.: $20,980,000
Emp.: 26
Automotive Supplies & Parts
N.A.I.C.S.: 423120
Jack Hinson *(Pres)*
Mark Powell *(Mgr-Ops)*
Steve Gonzales *(Office Mgr)*

CONCIERGE BUILDING SERVICES, LLC

7100 Broadway Ste 6 L, Denver, CO 80221
Tel.: (216) 256-3786   DE
Year Founded: 2019
Investment Services
N.A.I.C.S.: 523999
James Vaughan *(Pres & CEO)*

Subsidiaries:

Kleen-Tech Services, LLC   **(1)**
7100 Broadway Ste 6-L, Denver, CO 80221
Tel.: (866) 385-0672
Web Site: https://www.kleen-tech.com
Janitorial Services
N.A.I.C.S.: 561720

Subsidiary (Domestic):

KTSC Janitorial Inc.   **(2)**
7100 Broadway Ste 6L, Denver, CO 80221
Tel.: (866) 385-0672
Web Site: https://www.kleen-tech.com
Janitorial Services
N.A.I.C.S.: 561720

CONCILIO DE SALUD INTEGRAL DE LOIZA, INC.

PO Box 509, Loiza, PR 00772
Tel.: (787) 876-2042
Sales Range: $10-24.9 Million

Community Health Care Services
N.A.I.C.S.: 621498
Ramon L. Rivera Allende *(Accountant)*
Carmen Camacho *(Sec)*
Vilmayra Santiago *(Dir-HR)*
Jannette Diaz *(Fin Dir)*
Maria De Los Rodriguez *(Dir-Medical)*

CONCISE CAPITAL MANAGEMENT LP

1111 Brickell Ave Ste 1525, Miami, FL 33131
Tel.: (305) 371-4578   DE
Web Site:
http://www.concisecapital.com
Year Founded: 2004
N.A.I.C.S.:
Tom Krasner *(Co-Founder & Portfolio Mgr)*
Glenn Koach *(Co-Founder)*
Andrew Relph *(Mng Dir & Head-Bus Ops-Europe)*

Subsidiaries:

Nebraska Book Holdings, Inc.   **(1)**
4700 S 19th St, Lincoln, NE 68501-0529
Web Site: http://www.neebo.com
Holding Company; College Book Stores Owner & Operator
N.A.I.C.S.: 551112
David Collard *(Sr VP-Sls Strategy & Ops)*
Ed Dillon *(VP-Sls, Strategy & Ops)*
Kara Bunde-Dunn *(Sr VP-Sls & Mktg)*
Gary Shapiro *(Pres & CEO)*
Joe Miller *(CFO)*
Jennifer Goetsch *(VP-Customer Success & Mktg)*

Subsidiary (Domestic):

Nebraska Book Company, Inc.   **(2)**
4700 S 19th St, Lincoln, NE
68512-1216   **(100%)**
Tel.: (402) 421-7300
Web Site: http://www.nebook.com
Sales Range: $300-349.9 Million
Emp.: 3,000
College Book Store Operator
N.A.I.C.S.: 459210
Ruth Marino *(Mgr-HR)*
Kara Bunde-Dunn *(Sr VP-Mktg & Sls Support)*
Jay Amond *(Pres & CEO)*

Joint Venture (Domestic):

PrismRBS, LLC   **(3)**
610 W Germantown Pike Ste 305, Plymouth Meeting, PA 19462
Tel.: (610) 828-8630
Web Site: http://www.prismrbs.com
Collegiate Retail Software & Related Technologies Developer & Whslr
N.A.I.C.S.: 513210

CONCORD COMPANIES INCORPORATED

4215 E McDowell Rd Ste 201, Mesa, AZ 85215
Tel.: (480) 962-8080
Web Site: http://www.concordinc.com
Sales Range: $10-24.9 Million
Emp.: 30
Commercial & Office Building Contractors
N.A.I.C.S.: 236220

CONCORD DISPOSAL SERVICE

4080 Mallard Dr, Concord, CA 94520
Tel.: (925) 682-9113
Web Site:
http://www.concorddisposal.com
Rev.: $10,500,000
Emp.: 95
Rubbish Collection & Disposal
N.A.I.C.S.: 562111
Mary C. Garaventa *(Pres)*

CONCORD GENERAL MU-

CONCORD GENERAL MU—(CONTINUED)

TUAL INSURANCE CO., INC.
4 Bouton St, Concord, NH 03301-5006
Tel.: (603) 224-4086   NH
Web Site:
https://www.concordgroupin
surance.com
Year Founded: 1928
Sales Range: $50-74.9 Million
Emp.: 240
Provider of Fire, Marine & Casualty
Insurance Services
N.A.I.C.S.: 524126
Daniel L. McCabe (VP-Ops)
Michael P. Nolin Jr. (VP-Underwriting-
Personal Lines)

Subsidiaries:

Green Mountain Insurance Company,
Inc.   (1)
Pier Barre, Berlin, VT 05641
Tel.: (800) 660-3838
Emp.: 8
General Insurance Services
N.A.I.C.S.: 524210
Richard Kemp (Gen Mgr)

State Mutual Insurance Co., Inc. (1)
572 Kitty Hawk Ave, Auburn, ME 04211
Tel.: (207) 784-7337
Web Site:
http://www.concordgroupinsurance.com
Sales Range: $50-74.9 Million
Emp.: 36
Provider of Fire, Marine & Casualty Insur-
ance Services
N.A.I.C.S.: 524210
John Johnson (Mgr-Claims)

Sunapee Mutual Fire Insurance Co.,
Inc.   (1)
4 Bouton St, Concord, NH
03301-5006   (100%)
Tel.: (603) 224-4086
Web Site:
http://www.concordgroupinsurance.com
Sales Range: $50-74.9 Million
Emp.: 100
Provider of Fire, Marine & Casualty Insur-
ance Services
N.A.I.C.S.: 524210
Linda Day (Pres & CEO)

Vermont Accident Insurance Co.,
Inc.   (1)
27 Piper Rd, Barre, VT 05641
Tel.: (802) 229-0355
Web Site: http://www.concordgroupins.com
Sales Range: $25-49.9 Million
Emp.: 9
Provider of Fire, Marine & Casualty Insur-
ance Services
N.A.I.C.S.: 524114
John Lyons (Mgr-Claims)

CONCORD HOSPITALITY INC.
1701 Windhoek Dr, Lincoln, NE
68512-1273
Tel.: (402) 421-2551   NE
Web Site: https://www.concordei.com
Year Founded: 1986
Sales Range: $1-9.9 Million
Emp.: 80
Eating Place Services
N.A.I.C.S.: 722511
Larry Bird (Pres)
Nancy Bird (VP)
Stacie Hooks (VP-Corp Ops)
Bill Hooks (VP-Ops)
Hai Nguyen (VP-Sls & Mktg)

Subsidiaries:

Concord Neighborhood Corp.   (1)
1701 Windhoek Dr, Lincoln, NE 68512-1273
Tel.: (402) 421-2551
Provider of Eating Place Services
N.A.I.C.S.: 722511

CONCORD LIMOUSINE, INC.

712 3rd Ave, Brooklyn, NY 11232-1113
Tel.: (718) 965-6100   NY
Web Site:
https://www.concordlimo.com
Year Founded: 1984
Rev: $10,000,000
Emp.: 175
Local Passenger Transportation
N.A.I.C.S.: 485320
Alex Gavrilov (Pres)

CONCORD LITHO GROUP
92 Old Turnpike Rd, Concord, NH
03301-7309
Tel.: (603) 225-3328   NH
Web Site:
http://www.concordlitho.com
Year Founded: 1958
Sales Range: $100-124.9 Million
Emp.: 200
Provider of Full Color Printing &
Bronzing Services & Greeting Cards
N.A.I.C.S.: 323111
Tom Cook (Pres)
Walter Herrick (VP-Greeting Cards)

CONCORD LUMBER CORP.
55 White St, Littleton, MA 01460-1718
Tel.: (978) 486-9877   MA
Web Site:
http://www.concordlumbercorp.com
Year Founded: 1946
Sales Range: $10-24.9 Million
Emp.: 120
Sales of Lumber & Other Building
Materials
N.A.I.C.S.: 423310
Dave Perry (CFO)
David Robblee (Mgr-IT)
Dennis Lassell (Project Mgr)
Kristen Koehler (Mgr-Mktg)
Lori Oliveira (Mgr-HR)
Rick Ursch (VP)
Al Foss (Branch Mgr)

CONCORD MANAGEMENT LTD.
1551 Sandspur Rd, Maitland, FL
32751-6138
Tel.: (407) 741-8600
Web Site:
http://www.concordrents.com
Rev: $19,600,000
Emp.: 800
Lessors of Residential Buildings &
Dwellings
N.A.I.C.S.: 531110
Liliana Tardio (Mgr-Payroll)
Olivia Khan (Coord-Staffing)
Sue Popejoy (Coord-Tech Support)
Jaimie Pereira (Asst Dir-Community)
Doug Selin (CFO)
Robin Robuck (CIO)
Dayami Reyes (Dir-Community)
Melissa Lovett (Dir-HR)
Karla Coble (Exec VP)
Khalil Kabbourim (Dir-Maintenance)
Justin Turner (Reg Mgr)
Wayne McDaniel (VP-Ops-Florida)

CONCORD PAPER CORP.
538 Larkfield Rd, East Northport, NY
11731
Tel.: (631) 368-5200
Rev: $16,900,000
Emp.: 40
Party Favors & Paper Products Mfr
N.A.I.C.S.: 424990
David Rosenberg (Pres)

CONCORD SERVICING CORP.
4725 N Scottsdale Rd, Scottsdale, AZ
85251
Tel.: (480) 998-7585   AZ

Web Site:
http://www.concordservicing.com
Year Founded: 1988
Sales Range: $1-9.9 Million
Emp.: 150
Business Support Services
N.A.I.C.S.: 561499
Robert N. Bertrand (Founder & Chm)
Aida Witt (Dir-Bus Dev-Mexico)
Alicia Vander Kooi (VP-Ops-US)
Randy L. Babcock (Sr VP-IT)
Shaun W. O'Neill (Pres & COO)
Evan Green (VP-Intl Ops)
Kyle Derry (Dir-Bus Dev, Collection &
Contact Center)
Sonja M. Yurkiw (Gen Counsel & VP)
Jon Catlin (Controller)
Stephen Bertrand (CFO)
Jason Alexander (CEO)

Subsidiaries:

Equiant Financial Services, Inc. (1)
5401 N Pima Rd, Scottsdale, AZ 85250
Tel.: (480) 423-2300
Web Site: http://www.equiant.com
Collection Agencies
N.A.I.C.S.: 561440
Eric St. Smith (Sr VP)
Frank Morrisroe (Pres)

CONCORDANCE HEALTH-CARE SOLUTIONS, LLC
3901 W 34th North, Sioux Falls, SD
57107
Tel.: (800) 843-7948   SD
Web Site:
http://www.concordancehealth.com
Year Founded: 2016
Holding Company; Medical Supplies
Distr
N.A.I.C.S.: 551112
Lisa Hohman (CEO)
Jaysen Stevenson (Pres-Govt Div)
Jim Wheeler (VP-Acute Care Sls)
Kaylin Waltrip (Mktg Mgr)
Doreen Nersesian (Exec VP-HR)
Cody Fisher (VP-Fin)
Jennifer Rolls (Mgr-Acct)
Eric Hepinstall (Acct Mgr-Acute Care
at Concordance Healthcare Solu-
tions)

CONCORDE APPAREL CO. LLC
300 Brook St, Scranton, PA 18505
Tel.: (570) 343-6587
Sales Range: $10-24.9 Million
Emp.: 8
Mfr of Clothing
N.A.I.C.S.: 315250
Jim Alperin (Pres)

CONCORDE BATTERY CORP
2009 W San Bernardino Rd, West
Covina, CA 91790
Tel.: (626) 962-4006   CA
Web Site:
http://www.concordbattery.com
Year Founded: 1970
Sales Range: $10-24.9 Million
Emp.: 100
Dry Cell Batteries Mfr
N.A.I.C.S.: 335910
Don Godber (CEO)
Dave Vutetakis (Dir-Advanced Battery
Tech)
Shelley Johnson (Dir-Customer Svs)
Anthony Mistretta (Dir-Drafting)
Ed Frey (VP-Mfg)
Skip Koss (VP-Mktg)
Lynda Gardiner-Bergman (VP-Sls)

CONCORDIA ELECTRIC CO-OPERATIVE, INC.
1865 Hwy 84, Jonesville, LA 71343-0098

Tel.: (318) 339-7969   LA
Web Site:
http://www.concordiaelectric.com
Year Founded: 1940
Sales Range: $10-24.9 Million
Emp.: 76
Electric Power Transmission Services
N.A.I.C.S.: 221122
Dewayne Bailey (CEO & Gen Mgr)
Betty Hardie (Mgr-Office Svcs)

CONCORDIA INTERNATIONAL FORWARDING INC.
70 E Sunrise Hwy, Valley Stream, NY
11581-1233
Tel.: (516) 561-1100
Web Site:
http://www.concordiafreight.com
Year Founded: 1978
Sales Range: $10-24.9 Million
Emp.: 230
Freight Transportation Arrangement
Services
N.A.I.C.S.: 488510
Paul Emposimato (VP)
Wayne Bolton (VP-Europe)
Keith Wright (Mng Dir-UK)
Brian Durham (Mgr)
Phyllis Maraventano (VP-Sls)

Subsidiaries:

Concordia International Forwarding
GmbH   (1)
Flughafen-Cargo City Sud / Gebaeude 638
/ Eingang F, 60549, Frankfurt, Germany
Tel.: (49) 69 6980180
Web Site: http://www.concordiafreight.com
Air Freight Transportation Services
N.A.I.C.S.: 481212
Freddy Meier (Mgr)
Detlef Markmann (Mgr-Sls)

Concordia International Forwarding
Ltd.   (1)
Shackeleton House Challange Rd, Ashford,
TW1 51AX, Mddx, United
Kingdom   (100%)
Tel.: (44) 1784262200
Sales Range: $10-24.9 Million
Emp.: 45
Freight Transportation Arrangement Ser-
vices
N.A.I.C.S.: 488510
Mark Gazzard (Gen Mgr)

Concordia International Forwarding
Pte Ltd   (1)
02-05 Cargo Agents Building E Changi
Airport/No 7 Airline Rd, Singapore, 819834,
Singapore
Tel.: (65) 6542 1249
Air Freight Transportation Services
N.A.I.C.S.: 481212
Mohd Nasir (Mng Dir)
Peow Soon Quek (Dir-Fin)

Concordia International Forwarding
Pty. Ltd.   (1)
8 Green Street, Botany, 2019, NSW, Aus-
tralia
Tel.: (61) 2 9666 3444
Web Site: http://www.concordiafreight.com
Air Freight Transportation Services
N.A.I.C.S.: 481212
Bruce Allan (Mng Dir)

CONCORDIA PUBLISHING HOUSE
3558 S Jefferson Ave, Saint Louis,
MO 63118-3968
Tel.: (314) 268-1000   MO
Web Site: https://www.cph.org
Year Founded: 1869
Sales Range: $25-49.9 Million
Emp.: 250
Religious Books, Magazines & Music
Publishers
N.A.I.C.S.: 513130
Steve Harris (Exec Dir-Innovation
Technologies)
Bruce G. Kintz (Pres & CEO)
Peggy Anderson (Exec Dir-Fin)

Jonathan D. Schultz *(VP)*
Bob Rothmeyer *(Dir-Ops)*
Karen Capps *(Exec Dir-Production Control & Quality Sys)*
Paul Brunette *(Dir-Sls)*
Tim Agnew *(Dir-Graphic Design)*
Tony Shimkus *(Dir-Facilities)*
Loren Pawlitz *(Exec Dir-Mktg & ECommerce)*
Erin MacKenzie *(Mgr-Mktg-Multilingual Resources)*
Collin Bivens *(Dir-Fin)*
Dana Neuhaus *(Dir-HR)*
Paul T. McCain *(Exec Dir-Editorial)*

CONCOTE CORPORATION
600 Freeport Pkwy Ste 150, Coppell, TX 75019
Tel.: (214) 956-0055
Web Site: https://www.concote.com
Year Founded: 1967
Rev.: $10,170,248
Emp.: 100
Adhesives, Tape & Plasters
N.A.I.C.S.: 423840
Robert E. Hanton *(CEO & CFO)*
Barry Taylor *(Plant Mgr)*
Heidi Roberts *(Gen Mgr)*
Dan Cook *(Mgr-Logistics)*

CONCOURS MOTORS INC.
1400 W Silver Spring Dr, Milwaukee, WI 53209
Tel.: (414) 290-1400
Web Site:
http://www.concoursmotors.com
Sales Range: $75-99.9 Million
Emp.: 180
Automobiles, New & Used
N.A.I.C.S.: 441110
Karl Wuesthoff *(Pres)*
Bob Murphy *(Dir-Fixed Ops)*
Tony Sanfilippo *(Mgr-Sls)*
Lee Wuesthoff *(Owner)*
Andrew Horwich *(Mgr-Sls)*
Ashley Murray *(Mgr-Svc)*
Brittany Froze *(Coord-Mktg)*
Laura Backe *(Dir-HR)*
Jerry Dreckmann *(Mgr-Mazda Parts)*

CONCOURSE FEDERAL GROUP, LLC
1001 Connecticut Ave NW Ste 704, Washington, DC 20036
Web Site:
http://www.concoursefederal.com
Year Founded: 2009
Sales Range: $10-24.9 Million
Emp.: 43
Technical Consulting Services
N.A.I.C.S.: 541690
Geoff Perkins *(Co-Founder & Pres)*
Thomas Shea *(Co-Founder)*
Fariha Qureshi *(Mgr-HR)*
Marshall Contino *(VP-Architecture & Engrg)*
Ian Musa *(VP-Mgmt Consulting)*

CONCRETE ACCESSORIES COMPANY, INC.
1040 S West St, Wichita, KS 67213
Tel.: (316) 263-7251
Web Site: https://www.conacc.com
Concrete & Masonry Products, Supplies & Equipment Whslr
N.A.I.C.S.: 423810

CONCRETE COMPANY SPRINGFIELD
431 S Jefferson Ste 250, Springfield, MO 65806
Tel.: (417) 831-7622
Web Site:
http://www.concocompanies.com
Sales Range: $25-49.9 Million
Emp.: 1,500

Ready Mixed Concrete
N.A.I.C.S.: 327320
David Karr *(Controller)*
Andrew Baird *(Pres)*

CONCRETE CUTTING & BREAKING INC.
4501 Airwest SE, Grand Rapids, MI 49512
Tel.: (616) 554-4876 MI
Web Site: http://www.concut.com
Year Founded: 1974
Sales Range: $25-49.9 Million
Emp.: 170
Provider of Wrecking & Demolition Services
N.A.I.C.S.: 238910
Louie Bosma *(Mgr-Highway Svcs)*
Russ Hamm *(Mgr-Northern Florida)*
Rick Olson *(Mgr-Eastern Michigan)*
Jeff Miller *(Mgr-Northern & Mid Ohio)*
Mark Navel *(Mgr-Western New York)*
Art Szczepanski *(Mgr-Southern Florida)*

CONCRETE EXPRESS INC.
46 Skyline Dr, Salem, CT 06420
Tel.: (860) 859-2312
Web Site: https://www.concrete-express.com
Year Founded: 1991
Sales Range: $10-24.9 Million
Emp.: 117
Construction Materials Whslr
N.A.I.C.S.: 423320
Donald B. Mullin *(Pres)*
Bronwyn Mullin *(Sec)*

CONCRETE GENERAL, INC.
8000 Beechcraft Ave, Gaithersburg, MD 20879
Tel.: (301) 948-4450
Web Site:
https://www.concretegeneral.com
Sales Range: $25-49.9 Million
Emp.: 150
Highway, Street & Bridge Construction Services
N.A.I.C.S.: 237310
Michael Miller *(VP)*

CONCRETE MEDIA
43 E Moonachie Rd, Hackensack, NJ 07601
Tel.: (201) 440-2626
Year Founded: 1997
Rev.: $15,000,000
Emp.: 5
Advetising Agency
N.A.I.C.S.: 541810
Rachel Wolfe *(Dir-Creative)*
Tim Billings *(Sr Graphic Designer)*
Andy Sansone *(Pres)*
Anne Ferro *(Acct Dir)*
Eleanor Glavin *(Acctg Mgr)*
John Spitaletta *(CEO)*
Mark Bristow *(Sr Acct Mgr)*
Steve Stoltz *(Sr Sls Assoc)*

CONCRETE SUPPLY CO.
3823 Raleigh St, Charlotte, NC 28206-2042
Tel.: (704) 372-2930 NC
Web Site:
https://www.concretesupplyco.com
Year Founded: 1958
Sales Range: $25-49.9 Million
Emp.: 300
Central-Mixed Concrete
N.A.I.C.S.: 327320
Henry Batten *(Pres)*
Brian Webb *(Dir-Customer Svc)*

CONCRETE TECHNOLOGY CORP.

1123 Port of Tacoma Rd, Tacoma, WA 98421
Tel.: (253) 383-3545 WA
Web Site:
https://www.concretetech.com
Year Founded: 1951
Sales Range: $100-124.9 Million
Emp.: 170
Mfr of Prestressed & Precast Concrete
N.A.I.C.S.: 327390
Carl Anderson *(Chm)*
James R. Anderson *(Pres)*
Lawrence M. Christiansen *(Controller)*
Millard Barney *(Dir-Mktg)*

CONCRETE TECHNOLOGY INCORPORATED
8770 133rd Ave, Largo, FL 33773
Tel.: (727) 535-4651 FL
Web Site: https://www.flycti.com
Year Founded: 1992
Sales Range: $1-9.9 Million
Emp.: 15
Concrete Products
N.A.I.C.S.: 327390
Kevin Rosenberger *(Founder & Pres)*
Bradley Hieneman *(Exec VP-Sls-Mktg Staff)*

CONCRETE TIE INDUSTRIES INCORPORATED
130 E Oris St, Compton, CA 90222
Tel.: (310) 886-1000
Web Site: http://www.concretetie.net
Sales Range: $10-24.9 Million
Emp.: 80
Concrete & Cinder Building Products
N.A.I.C.S.: 423320
Paul Schoendienst *(Pres)*
Steve Sims *(Controller)*
Kirt Schoendienst *(VP)*

CONCURRENT TECHNOLOGIES CORPORATION
100 CTC Dr, Johnstown, PA 15904-1935
Tel.: (800) 282-4392 PA
Web Site: http://www.ctc.com
Year Founded: 1987
Sales Range: $150-199.9 Million
Emp.: 1,100
Research & Development Services
N.A.I.C.S.: 541715
George W. Appley *(Sr VP-Tech Grp)*
Vicki Barbur *(CTO & Sr VP)*
Dale M. Mosier *(Vice Chm)*
David A. Schario *(Sr VP-Svcs Grp)*
David Artman *(Sr VP-Engrg Grp)*
Jeffrey K. Harris *(Chm)*
John E. Klein *(CFO, Treas & VP)*
Peter Bruno *(Sr Dir-Bus Dev)*
Bob Kubler *(VP)*
Tim Tibbits *(VP)*
Edward J. Sheehan Jr. *(Pres & CEO)*

Subsidiaries:

CTC (1)
5780 W Werner Rd, Bremerton, WA 98312
Tel.: (888) 282-6163
Management & Technology Based Solutions
N.A.I.C.S.: 522299

CTC Public Benefit Corporation (1)
1233 Washington St, Columbia, SC 29201
Tel.: (803) 929-6062
Web Site: http://ctcpbc.org
Community Development Services
N.A.I.C.S.: 925120

Concurrent Technologies Corporation (1)
7995 114th Ave, Largo, FL 33773
Tel.: (727) 549-7000
Web Site: http://www.ctc.com
Sales Range: $10-24.9 Million
Emp.: 45
Provider or Management & Technology Based Solutions

N.A.I.C.S.: 611519

Enterprise Ventures Corporation (1)
100 CTC Dr, Johnstown, PA 15904
Tel.: (814) 248-7804
Web Site: http://www.evc.ctc.com
Trailer Hitch Mfr
N.A.I.C.S.: 336390
David R. Davis *(Mng Dir-Software Sls & Consulting)*
Edward D. Peretin *(Interim Pres)*
Michele K. Adams *(Mng Dir-Bus Ops)*
Timothy P. Brown *(VP)*
Jeffrey A. Anderson *(Mng Dir-Pro Svcs)*
George E. McAllister *(Mng Dir-Bus Dev)*

CONCUSSION, LLP
707 W Vickery Blvd #103, Fort Worth, TX 76104
Tel.: (817) 336-6824
Web Site:
http://www.pavlovagency.com
Year Founded: 2001
Sales Range: $10-24.9 Million
Emp.: 50
Advertising Agencies
N.A.I.C.S.: 541810
Allen Wallach *(Owner)*
Khris Kesling *(Dir-Creative)*

CONDAL DISTRIBUTORS INC.
531 Dupont St, Bronx, NY 10474-6616
Tel.: (718) 589-1100 NY
Web Site: http://www.condalfood.com
Year Founded: 1960
Sales Range: $75-99.9 Million
Emp.: 60
Distr of Ethnic Food Products
N.A.I.C.S.: 424410
Victor Medina *(Exec VP)*
Carmen Fernandez *(Pres & CEO)*

CONDE GROUP, INC.
1666 Garnet Ave No 415, San Diego, CA 92019
Web Site:
http://www.condegroup.com
Year Founded: 2003
Sales Range: $1-9.9 Million
Emp.: 85
Recruitment Services
N.A.I.C.S.: 541612
Karen R. Conde *(Founder, Pres & CEO)*
Claudia Plazola *(Office Mgr)*
Donna Harris *(Mgr-Client Solutions)*

CONDIRE MANAGEMENT LP
2000 McKinney Ave Ste 2125, Dallas, TX 75201
Tel.: (214) 572-8921
Investment Services
N.A.I.C.S.: 523999

CONDITIONED AIR CORP. OF NAPLES INC.
3786 Mercantile Ave, Naples, FL 34104
Tel.: (239) 643-2445
Web Site:
https://www.conditionedair.com
Year Founded: 1962
Sales Range: $25-49.9 Million
Emp.: 200
HVAC Contractors
N.A.I.C.S.: 238220
Carol Papesh *(CFO & Sr VP)*
Vito DiPalma *(Mgr-New Construction)*
Tim Dupre *(Pres & COO)*
Jeffrey L. Zanella *(Gen Mgr-Fort Myers)*
Kurt Englund *(Mgr-HR)*
Mark Black *(Mgr-Estimating)*
Adiel Soler *(Mgr-Pur)*
Erik Greenman *(Mgr-IT)*
Joe Forester *(Mgr-Comml Replacements)*

Conditioned Air Corp. of Naples Inc.—(Continued)

Frankie Sanchez *(Mgr-Warehouse)*
Micah Yeater *(Mgr-Production Housing)*
Andrew Freitas *(Mgr)*
Jon Kunz *(Dir-Construction Svcs)*
W. Theodore Etzel III *(Owner & CEO)*

CONDOMINIUM MANAGMENT GROUP, INC.
7800 66th St N Ste 205, Pinellas Park, FL 33781
Tel.: (727) 381-1717
Web Site: https://www.condogrp.com
Year Founded: 1988
Sales Range: $1-9.9 Million
Emp.: 15
Condominium & Homeowner Associations Management & Accounting Services
N.A.I.C.S.: 541611
Tonie Jackson *(Pres)*

CONDON & ROOT
200 N Northwest Hwy, Barrington, IL 60010
Tel.: (847) 381-6575
Year Founded: 1998
Sales Range: Less than $1 Million
Emp.: 2
N.A.I.C.S.: 541810
Keith Condon *(Partner)*
Jim Root *(Partner)*

CONDON LEASING CO. INC.
4625 Singing Hills Blvd, Sioux City, IA 51106
Tel.: (712) 274-6622
Web Site:
   http://www.condonauto.com
Sales Range: $10-24.9 Million
Emp.: 70
New & Used Automobile Sales
N.A.I.C.S.: 441110
Mark Condon *(VP)*
Bob Barto *(Mgr-New Vehicle Sls)*
Don Jorgenson *(Mgr-Parts)*

CONDON OIL COMPANY, INC.
126 E Jackson St, Ripon, WI 54971-1378
Tel.: (920) 748-3186
Web Site:
   https://condoncompanies.com
Year Founded: 1928
Sales Range: $200-249.9 Million
Emp.: 500
Wholesale Distributor of Oil
N.A.I.C.S.: 424710
Karla Block *(Sec & Controller)*
Kraig Bauman *(Pres)*
Tom Reinsch *(VP-Petroleum Distr)*
Bob Reiser *(VP-Ops)*

Subsidiaries:

Payless Tire & Exhaust   (1)
126 E Jackson St, Ripon, WI 54971
Tel.: (800) 452-1212
Web Site:
   http://www.payless.ultimartstores.com
Tire & Exhaust Car Care Parts Distr
N.A.I.C.S.: 423120
Mike Buelow *(Mgr-Field Sls Dept)*
Jeff Seidl *(Coord-Sls)*
Sheila Swansby *(Mgr-Credit)*

CONDON-JOHNSON & ASSOCIATES INC.
480 Roland Way Ste 200, Oakland, CA 94621-2053
Tel.: (510) 636-2100   CA
Web Site: https://www.condon-johnson.com
Year Founded: 1974
Sales Range: $25-49.9 Million
Emp.: 150

Contractors & Engineering Services
N.A.I.C.S.: 238190
Jerry Condon *(VP-Ops)*
James Johnson *(VP)*
Dominic Parmantier *(VP-Northwest)*
Mansoureh Mohebali *(Controller)*
Mark Morrison *(VP & Mgr-Corp Estimating)*
George Burrough *(VP-Southern California)*

CONDOR CORP.
124 W Airport Rd, Lititz, PA 17543-7624
Tel.: (717) 560-1882
Sales Range: $10-24.9 Million
Emp.: 110
Cookie & Cracker Mfr
N.A.I.C.S.: 311821
Mark Hasson *(Mgr-Production)*
Mac Bryce *(Plant Mgr)*
George M. Phillips *(Pres)*
Bob Wenger *(Mgr-Maintenance)*
Bill Noye *(Reg Mgr-Sls)*

CONDOR SNACK COMPANY
4300 Oneida St, Denver, CO 80216-6616
Tel.: (303) 333-6075
Year Founded: 1983
Sales Range: $10-24.9 Million
Emp.: 110
Snack Food & Chocolate Mfr
N.A.I.C.S.: 311919
Don Dixon *(Pres)*
Kevin Kobza *(Mgr-Maintanance)*
Kevin Gawel *(Mgr-Ops)*

CONDUANT CORPORATION
1501 S Sunset St Ste D, Longmont, CO 80501-6757
Tel.: (303) 485-2721
Web Site: https://www.conduant.com
Year Founded: 1996
Sales Range: $10-24.9 Million
Emp.: 20
High Speed Digital Recording Devices Mfr for Scientific Researchers & Defense Firms
N.A.I.C.S.: 334610
Ken Owens *(CEO)*
Bill Buccholz *(CFO)*
Jane Christian *(Mgr-Inventory)*
Phil Brunelle *(CTO)*

CONDUCTOR, INC.
2 Park Ave 15th Fl, New York, NY 10016
Tel.: (212) 213-6251
Web Site: http://www.conductor.com
Year Founded: 2005
SEO Measurement & Optimization Services
N.A.I.C.S.: 541519
Seth Besmertnik *(Co-Founder & CEO)*
Josh Rosenblum *(Co-Founder & Dir-Tech)*
Seth Dotterer *(VP-Mktg)*
Jim Caci *(CFO)*
Kerry Ancheta *(VP-Global Sls)*
Sheridan Orr *(Sr Dir-Product Mktg)*
Shamoun Murtza *(CTO)*
Neetu Rajpal *(VP-Product Dev)*
Baruch Toledano *(Chief Product Officer)*
Marc Chabot *(VP-Sls)*

CONDUSIV TECHNOLOGIES CORPORATION
7590 N Glenoaks Blvd, Burbank, CA 91504-1052
Tel.: (818) 771-1600   CA
Web Site: http://www.condusiv.com
Year Founded: 1981
Sales Range: $100-124.9 Million

Emp.: 160
Systems Software Mfr
N.A.I.C.S.: 513210
Craig Jensen *(Founder, Chm & CEO)*
Gary Quan *(Sr VP-Tech Strategy)*

Subsidiaries:

Condusiv Technologies
Corporation   (1)
Garland Court Garland Road, East Grinstead, RH19 1DN, West Sussex, United Kingdom
Tel.: (44) 1342 821 300
Systems Software Mfr
N.A.I.C.S.: 513210

CONE & GRAHAM, INC.
5101 Cone Rd, Tampa, FL 33610
Tel.: (813) 623-2856
Web Site:
   https://www.conegraham.com
Year Founded: 1979
Sales Range: $10-24.9 Million
Emp.: 150
Road & Bridge Construction
N.A.I.C.S.: 237310
Robert Graham *(Pres & Treas)*
Dave Tozlosky *(VP & Sec)*
Rusty Birchall *(Project Mgr)*
Heath Noss *(Project Mgr)*

CONE DISTRIBUTING INC.
500 NW 27th Ave, Ocala, FL 34475
Tel.: (352) 732-4111
Web Site:
   http://www.conedistributing.com
Rev.: $50,000,000
Emp.: 120
Beer & Ale
N.A.I.C.S.: 424810
Steve Conner *(Brand Mgr-Craft & Specialty)*
Bill Omalley *(Mgr-On-Premise)*
Clarence Thomas *(Mgr-Ops)*
Charlie Ingrilli *(VP-Sls)*
Jeff Floyd *(Mgr-Sls)*
Ty Belanger *(Mgr-Inventory Control)*
Walter Marsh *(Mgr-Zone Delivery)*
Douglas P. Cone Jr. *(Pres)*

CONE ENGINEERING CONTRACTORS
4 Crow Canyon Ct Ste 100, San Ramon, CA 94583
Tel.: (925) 838-5685   CA
Web Site:
   http://www.conecompany.com
Year Founded: 1990
Sales Range: $10-24.9 Million
Emp.: 15
Highway & Street Construction
N.A.I.C.S.: 237310
Roger Cone *(Pres)*
Roger Cone *(Pres)*

CONE FINANCIAL GROUP INC.
406 S Broad St, Thomasville, GA 31792
Tel.: (229) 226-2909
Web Site:
   http://www.teamambassador.com
Rev.: $42,394,628
Emp.: 11
Employment Agencies
N.A.I.C.S.: 561311
Doug Wilson *(Co-Pres)*

CONEMAUGH STATION
682 Philadelphia St, Indiana, PA 15701
Tel.: (724) 349-1205
Rev.: $65,300,000
Emp.: 8
Generation, Electric Power & Utilities
N.A.I.C.S.: 221118
Fred Humphrey *(Adv Mgr)*

CONESTOGA CERAMIC TILE DISTRIBUTORS
4335 Lewis Rd, Harrisburg, PA 17111
Tel.: (717) 564-6860
Web Site:
   https://www.conestogatile.com
Year Founded: 1958
Sales Range: $10-24.9 Million
Emp.: 49
Distr of Ceramic Wall & Floor Tile
N.A.I.C.S.: 423320
Stephen R. Vogel *(VP)*

CONESTOGA SUPPLY CORP.
11011 Sheldon Rd, Houston, TX 77044
Tel.: (832) 391-9400
Web Site:
   http://www.conestogasupply.com
Year Founded: 1986
Sales Range: $10-24.9 Million
Emp.: 10
Pipe & Tubing & Plate, Steel
N.A.I.C.S.: 423510
Wayne Caldwell *(Pres & CEO)*
Patrick Persons *(CFO & Exec VP)*

CONESTOGA WOOD SPECIALTIES CORP.
245 Reading Rd, East Earl, PA 17519-9549
Tel.: (717) 445-6701   PA
Web Site:
   https://www.conestogawood.com
Year Founded: 1964
Sales Range: $125-149.9 Million
Emp.: 2,000
Decorative Wood Doors, Drawers & Components for the Kitchen & Bath Industry Mfr
N.A.I.C.S.: 321911
Norman Hahn *(Chm)*
Elizabeth Hahn *(Treas & Sec)*
Anthony Hahn *(Pres & CEO)*
Jeff Eichenseer *(Dir-Mktg)*

CONEXA LLC
147 US Hwy 87, Comfort, TX 78013
Tel.: (210) 796-4000
Web Site: http://www.connexa.com
Year Founded: 2008
Sales Range: $1-9.9 Million
Emp.: 200
Industrial Equipment Mfr & Distr
N.A.I.C.S.: 333248
Mike Postel *(Pres)*

CONEXUS CATTLE CORP.
242 W Main St, Hendersonville, TN 37075
Tel.: (212) 508-2175   NV
Year Founded: 2004
Rev.: $1,932,111
Assets: $141,552
Liabilities: $1,807,309
Net Worth: $(1,665,757)
Earnings: $1,013,426
Emp.: 2
Fiscal Year-end: 06/30/15
Investment Services
N.A.I.C.S.: 523999
Stephen Price *(CEO)*
Gerard Daignault *(CFO & Sec)*

CONFEDERATED BUILDERS INC.
503 N Buckner St, Derby, KS 67037
Tel.: (316) 788-3913
Sales Range: $1-9.9 Million
Emp.: 9
General Contractors
N.A.I.C.S.: 423310
Charles E. Powell *(Pres)*
Joe Waugh *(Project Mgr)*

CONFEDERATED TRIBES OF

WARM SPRINGS
1233 Veterans St, Warm Springs, OR 97761
Tel.: (541) 553-1161
Web Site: https://www.warmsprings-nsn.gov
Sales Range: $75-99.9 Million
Emp.: 1,200
Economic Development Services
N.A.I.C.S.: 926110
Dan Martinez *(Mgr-Tribal Emergency)*
Lori Switzler *(Supvr-Cash Mgmt)*
Loui Pitt Sr. *(Dir-Plant Ops)*

Subsidiaries:

Warm Springs Economic Develop-
ment Corporation   (1)
3240 Walsey Ln, Warm Springs, OR 97761
Tel.: (541) 553-3565
Web Site: http://www.warmsprings.com
Sales Range: $25-49.9 Million
Emp.: 7
Private Investment Capital
N.A.I.C.S.: 523999

CONFERENCE ASSOCIATES, INC.
180 E Main St Ste 205, Patchogue, NY 11772
Tel.: (631) 654-0600   NY
Web Site:
    https://www.conferenceny.com
Sales Range: $100-124.9 Million
Emp.: 60
Third Party Insurance Administration Services
N.A.I.C.S.: 524292
Dawn Gorman *(VP & Dir-Svcs)*
Neil Weingarten *(VP-Brokerage Ops)*

CONFERENCE ON JEWISH MATERIAL CLAIMS AGAINST GERMANY, INC.
1359 Broadway Rm 2020, New York, NY 10018
Tel.: (646) 536-9100   NY
Web Site: https://www.claimscon.org
Year Founded: 1952
Sales Range: $800-899.9 Million
Victim Assistance Services
N.A.I.C.S.: 624190

CONFERENCE TECHNOLO-GIES, INC.
11653 Adie Rd, Maryland Heights, MO 63043-3509
Tel.: (314) 993-1400
Web Site: https://www.cti.com
Year Founded: 1988
Audio & Video Equipment Mfr
N.A.I.C.S.: 334310
Jimmy Lomonaco *(Chief HR Officer)*

Subsidiaries:

Vistacom, Inc.   (1)
1902 Vultee St, Allentown, PA 18103
Tel.: (610) 791-9081
Web Site: http://www.vistacominc.com
Sales Range: $10-24.9 Million
Emp.: 73
Design & Installation of Audio Video Com-
munication Systems
N.A.I.C.S.: 334310
David Martini *(Mgr-Ops)*
Angela Nolan *(Gen Mgr)*
Mark Ripley *(Mgr-Software Dev)*
Tom Iasiello *(Mgr-Svc-AV)*

CONFERO, INC.
535 Keisler Dr Ste 204, Cary, NC 27518-9308
Tel.: (919) 469-5200
Web Site:
    https://www.conferoinc.com
Year Founded: 1986
Rev.: $2,600,000
Emp.: 23
Business Products & Services

N.A.I.C.S.: 541910
Elaine Buxton *(Pres)*
Paul Jacobi *(Dir-Data Svcs)*
Laura Leary *(Mgr-Client Svc)*
Janet Morrison *(Mgr-Bus Dev)*
Kara Gammon *(Mgr-Client Svcs)*
Lana Meade *(Mgr-Client Svcs)*
Rob Barry *(Dir-Quality Assurance)*

CONFIANCE GROUP
11950 Democracy Dr Ste 300, Res-
ton, VA 20190
Tel.: (703) 260-6877
Web Site:
    http://www.confiancegroup.com
Year Founded: 2007
Sales Range: $1-9.9 Million
Emp.: 20
Business Transformation & Environ-
mental Assessment
N.A.I.C.S.: 541620
David S. Wolcott *(CEO)*

Subsidiaries:

Confiance Group   (1)
3 Badminton House Chepstow Place Foley
Road East, Sutton Coldfield, B74 3AG,
West Midlands, United Kingdom
Tel.: (44) 1926 882674
Web Site: http://www.confiancegroup.com
Business Transformation & Environmental
Assessments to Companies
N.A.I.C.S.: 561499
Ralph Thompson *(VP-European Ops)*

CONFIDENCE PLUS INSUR-ANCE SERVICES
6852 Pacific Ave Ste B, Stockton, CA 95207
Tel.: (209) 473-4403
Web Site: https://www.allstate.com
Rev.: $13,000,000
Emp.: 20
Insurance Agents, Brokers & Service
N.A.I.C.S.: 524210

CONFIGERO
3885 Crestwood Pkwy Ste 150, Du-
luth, GA 30096
Web Site: http://www.configero.com
Year Founded: 2009
Sales Range: $1-9.9 Million
Emp.: 21
Cloud Applications & Consulting Ser-
vices
N.A.I.C.S.: 513210
Marty Apple *(Dir-Bus Dev)*
Alex Sartogo *(VP-Tech)*
Jody Hamlett *(Founder & Mng Dir)*
Kimya Coker *(Dir-Mktg)*

CONFIGURATION MANAGE-MENT INC.
766 Shrewsbury Ave Ste E303, Tin-
ton Falls, NJ 07724
Tel.: (732) 450-1100
Web Site: http://www.cmi.com
Year Founded: 1992
Computer Related Consulting Ser-
vices
N.A.I.C.S.: 541690
William P. Anderson *(Pres)*

CONFLUENCE
525 17th St, Des Moines, IA 50309
Tel.: (515) 288-4875
Web Site:
    http://www.thinkconfluence.com
Landscape Design Services
N.A.I.C.S.: 541320
Christopher Cline *(Sr VP)*

Subsidiaries:

studioINSITE LLC   (1)
3457 Ringsby Ct Unit 223, Denver, CO 80216
Tel.: (303) 433-7100

Web Site: http://www.studio-insite.com
Sales Range: $1-9.9 Million
Emp.: 11
Landscape Architectural Services
N.A.I.C.S.: 541320
Scottie Mercy *(Mgr)*

CONFLUENCE WATER-SPORTS CO. INC.
575 Mauldin Rd Ste 200, Greenville, SC 29607
Tel.: (888) 525-2925
Web Site:
    http://www.confluencesports.com
Sales Range: $50-74.9 Million
Emp.: 200
Boat Mfr
N.A.I.C.S.: 336612
Sue Rechner *(CEO)*

CONFLUENT DEVELOPMENT, LLC
2240 Blake St Ste 200, Denver, CO 80205
Tel.: (303) 573-6500   CO
Web Site:
    http://www.confluentdev.com
Year Founded: 2015
Emp.: 25
Commercial & Real Estate Invest-
ment & Leasing Services
N.A.I.C.S.: 531390
Marshall M. Burton *(Pres & CEO)*
Celeste Tanner *(Chief Dev Officer)*
Jon Rankin *(CFO & Sr VP)*
Christine Hayes *(Gen Counsel)*
Dean Barber *(Exec VP-Dev Mgmt)*
John Reinsma *(Mng Dir)*

CONFLUENT HEALTH, LLC
1650 Lyndon Farm Ct, Louisville, KY 40223
Tel.: (866) 922-0012
Web Site: https://goconfluent.com
Year Founded: 2014
Emp.: 307
Physical, Occupational & Speech Therapists
N.A.I.C.S.: 621340

Subsidiaries:

MOTION PT Group, Inc.   (1)
160 E 56th St., New York, NY 10022
Tel.: (212) 355-7827
Web Site: https://motionptg.com
Health Care Srvices
N.A.I.C.S.: 621610
Edward R. Miersch *(Pres & CEO)*

Subsidiary (Domestic):

PTPC Physical Therapy & Perfor-
mance Center   (2)
28 Indian Rock Ste B, Suffern, NY 10901-4907
Tel.: (845) 368-2180
Web Site:
    http://www.ptpcphysicaltherapy.com
Offices of Mental Health Practitioners (ex-
cept Physicians)
N.A.I.C.S.: 621330

CONGAREE CONSTRUCTION CO., INC.
1634 Pineview Dr, Columbia, SC 29209
Tel.: (803) 783-7812   SC
Year Founded: 1964
Sales Range: Less than $1 Million
Emp.: 3
Provider of Contracting & Construc-
tion Services
N.A.I.C.S.: 236220

CONGOLEUM CORPORATION
3500 Quaker Bridge Rd, Mercerville, NJ 08619
Tel.: (609) 584-3000   DE
Web Site: http://www.congoleum.com

Year Founded: 1886
Sales Range: $125-149.9 Million
Emp.: 523
Resilient Sheet & Tile Vinyl Flooring Mfr
N.A.I.C.S.: 326199
Christopher O'Connor *(Pres & CEO)*
Jonathan Fisher *(CFO)*

Subsidiaries:

Congoleum Corporation   (1)
861 Sloan Ave, Trenton, NJ 08619-2102   (100%)
Tel.: (609) 584-3000
Rev.: $250,000,000
Emp.: 80
Vinyl Floor Covering Products Mfr
N.A.I.C.S.: 326113

CONGREGATIONAL HOMES INC
900 E Harrison Ave, Pomona, CA 91767
Tel.: (909) 624-5061   CA
Web Site:
    https://www.msagardens.org
Year Founded: 1957
Sales Range: $10-24.9 Million
Emp.: 339
Senior Living Services
N.A.I.C.S.: 623311
Lisa Atilano *(VP-Health Care Svcs)*
Patricia Williams *(CFO)*

CONGRESS ASSET MANAGE-MENT CO.
2 Seaport Ln 5th Fl, Boston, MA 02210
Tel.: (617) 428-4300
Web Site:
    https://www.congressasset.com
Intermediation Services
N.A.I.C.S.: 523910
Christopher M. Lagan *(COO)*
Larry Thorndike *(Exec VP & Mng Dir)*

Subsidiaries:

Century Capital Management
LLC   (1)
1 Liberty Sq Ste 12, Boston, MA 02109-4825
Tel.: (617) 482-3060
Web Site: http://www.centurycap.com
Investment Advice & Associated Services
N.A.I.C.S.: 523940
Allan W. Fulkerson *(Mgr)*

CONGRESSIONAL BANCSHARES, INC.
6701 Democracy Blvd Ste 400, Bethesda, MD 20817
Tel.: (301) 299-8810   MD
Web Site:
    http://www.congressionalbank.com
Year Founded: 2005
Sales Range: $50-74.9 Million
Emp.: 280
Bank Holding Company
N.A.I.C.S.: 551111
James H. Peterson *(COO, Chief Credit Officer & Exec VP)*
Amy Y. Heller *(Exec VP-Healthcare Lending)*
Anne M. Balcer *(Gen Counsel & Exec VP)*
Don Cole *(CEO)*
James Robertson *(Sr VP-HR)*
Kenneth F. Elias *(Chief Lending Offi-cer & Exec VP)*
Mark Wendel *(CFO & Exec VP)*
Patience C. Gaskill *(Exec VP-Deposits)*
Tony Delucca *(Sr VP-Comml Lend-ing)*

Congressional Bancshares, Inc.—(Continued)

Subsidiaries:

Congressional Bank (1)
6701 Democracy Blvd Ste 400, Bethesda, MD 20817
Tel.: (301) 299-8810
Web Site:
http://www.congressionalbank.com
Emp.: 45
Commercial Banking
N.A.I.C.S.: 522110
John R. Lane (Vice Chm & Exec VP-Corp Dev)
Dale G. Phelps (CFO & Exec VP)
James H. Peterson (COO & Exec VP)
Kenneth F. Elias (Exec VP-Corp Lending)
Anne M. Balcer (Gen Counsel & Exec VP)
Tony DeLucca (Sr VP-Comml Lending)
Patience C. Gaskill (Sr VP-Deposit Sls)
Amy Y. Heller (Exec VP-Healthcare Lending)
Cesar Cabrejas (Exec VP-Comml Deposits)
Don Cole (CEO)
James Robertson (Sr VP-HR)
Mark Wendel (CFO & Exec VP)

CONGRESSIONAL COUNTRY CLUB

8500 River Rd, Bethesda, MD 20817
Tel.: (301) 469-2000 MD
Web Site: https://www.ccclub.org
Year Founded: 1941
Sales Range: $25-49.9 Million
Emp.: 547
Country Club Operator
N.A.I.C.S.: 713910

CONGRUENT INVESTMENT PARTNERS, LLC

3400 Carlisle St Ste 430, Dallas, TX 75204
Tel.: (214) 760-7411 DE
Web Site:
http://www.congruentinv.com
Year Founded: 2009
Privater Equity Firm
N.A.I.C.S.: 523999
Jim Barsness (VP)
Travis Baldwin (Co-Founder & Principal)
Matthew Killebrew (CFO & Chief Compliance Officer)
Barrett Lidji (VP)
Preston Massey (Co-Founder & Principal)
Kyle Okita (Assoc VP)
John Zimmermann (VP)

Subsidiaries:

Independent Rough Terrain Center LLC (1)
103 Guadalupe Dr Rd No 303, Cibolo, TX 78108
Tel.: (210) 599-6541
Web Site: http://www.irtc-tx.com
Container Handling Equipment Mfr.
N.A.I.C.S.: 333923
Stephen Speakes (Pres & CEO)

CONGRUITY HR, LLC

508 Arbor Hill Rd, Kernersville, NC 27184
Web Site: http://www.congruityhr.com
Year Founded: 2011
Sales Range: $200-249.9 Million
Emp.: 6,195
Human Resource Consulting Services
N.A.I.C.S.: 541612
Darrin Hunter (Founder & Pres)
Michael Bowman (COO)
Keith W. Reeves (CFO)
Matt Lewis (VP)

CONIGENT

134 Kings Hwy E Ste B, Cherry Hill, NJ 08002
Web Site: http://www.conigent.com

Year Founded: 2007
Sales Range: $1-9.9 Million
Emp.: 25
Information Technology Design & Implementation
N.A.I.C.S.: 519290
Ameet Shah (Founder & CEO)
Roger Sybrowsky (COO)

CONKLIN COMPANY INC.

551 Vly Pk Dr S, Shakopee, MN 55379-1802
Tel.: (952) 445-6010 MN
Web Site: http://www.conklin.com
Year Founded: 1954
Sales Range: $25-49.9 Million
Emp.: 125
Mfr of Specialty Chemicals
N.A.I.C.S.: 324122
Charles Herbster (Co-Owner, Chm, Pres & CEO)
Judith A. Herbster (Co-Owner & Exec VP)

CONKLIN FANGMAN INVESTMENT CO.

1400 E 11th Ave, Hutchinson, KS 67501
Tel.: (620) 662-4467
Web Site: http://www.conklincars.com
Rev.: $16,500,000
Emp.: 68
Passenger Car Leasing
N.A.I.C.S.: 532112
Kent Hilst (Controller)

Subsidiaries:

Stuart Conklin Buick Inc (1)
1400 E 11th Ave, Hutchinson, KS 67501
Tel.: (620) 662-4467
Web Site: http://www.conklin.com
New Car Dealers
N.A.I.C.S.: 441110
Stuart Conklin Jr. (Mgr-Sls)

CONKLIN METAL INDUSTRIES

236 Moore St SE, Atlanta, GA 30312
Tel.: (404) 688-4510
Web Site:
http://www.conklinmetal.com
Sales Range: $10-24.9 Million
Emp.: 120
Metals Service Centers & Offices
N.A.I.C.S.: 423510
Robert A. Thompson (Pres & Co-Owner)
Melissa James (Mgr-Credit)

CONKLIN OFFICE SERVICES, INC.

56 Canal St, Holyoke, MA 01040
Tel.: (413) 315-6777
Web Site:
http://www.conklinoffice.com
Year Founded: 1981
Sales Range: $10-24.9 Million
Emp.: 75
Furniture Retailer
N.A.I.C.S.: 449110
Jeffrey Hart (Mgr-Sls)
Tyler Arnold (Principal)

CONLEASCO INC.

13150 1st St, Becker, MN 55308
Tel.: (763) 262-9000
Web Site:
https://www.beckerfurniture.com
Sales Range: $25-49.9 Million
Emp.: 175
Furniture Retailer
N.A.I.C.S.: 449110
Douglas V. Huseby (Owner)

CONLEE OIL COMPANY

12076 N Linden Rd, Clio, MI 48240
Tel.: (810) 686-5600 MI
Web Site: https://www.conleeoil.com

Year Founded: 1936
Sales Range: $10-24.9 Million
Emp.: 70
Gasoline Stations With Convenience Stores Owner & Operator
N.A.I.C.S.: 457110
Jeff Conlee (Owner)

CONLEY BUICK GMC SUBARU

800 Cortez Rd W, Bradenton, FL 34207
Tel.: (941) 757-8661
Web Site:
https://www.conleybuickgmc.com
Rev.: $42,900,000
Emp.: 70
New & Used Automobile Dealership
N.A.I.C.S.: 441110
Jeff Conley (Owner)
Herb Hoelle (Gen Mgr)

CONLEY FROG/SWITCH & FORGE COMPANY

387 E Bodley Ave, Memphis, TN 38109-2507
Tel.: (901) 948-4591 TN
Year Founded: 1907
Sales Range: $10-24.9 Million
Emp.: 57
Mfr of Commercial Forgings & Railroad Accessories
N.A.I.C.S.: 332111

CONLEY PUBLISHING GROUP LTD.

115 Monroe St, Beaver Dam, WI 53916
Tel.: (920) 885-7800 WI
Web Site: http://www.gmtoday.com
Year Founded: 1969
Sales Range: $25-49.9 Million
Emp.: 400
Provider of Commercial Printing Services
N.A.I.C.S.: 323111
Sarah Diels (Dir-HR)

Subsidiaries:

Freeman Newspapers LLC (1)
801 N Barstow St, Waukesha, WI 53186
Tel.: (920) 885-7800
Sales Range: $10-24.9 Million
Emp.: 2
Provider of Newspaper Services
N.A.I.C.S.: 513110

CONLEY SUBARU

816 Cortez Rd W, Bradenton, FL 34207
Tel.: (941) 755-8531
Web Site:
https://www.conleysubaru.com
Year Founded: 1966
Sales Range: $10-24.9 Million
Emp.: 53
New Car Dealers
N.A.I.C.S.: 441110
Herb Hoelle (Gen Mgr)
Jeff Conley (Pres)
Robert Mulroy (Bus Mgr)

CONLIN'S FURNITURE INC.

739 S 20th St, Billings, MT 59102
Tel.: (406) 656-4900
Web Site: https://www.conlins.com
Year Founded: 1937
Rev.: $15,000,000
Emp.: 350
Furniture Stores Owner & Operator
N.A.I.C.S.: 449110
Lollie Ray (CEO)

CONLON CONSTRUCTION CO. INC.

1100 Rockdale Rd, Dubuque, IA 52003-7875
Tel.: (563) 583-1724 IA
Web Site: http://www.conlonco.com
Year Founded: 1935
Sales Range: $25-49.9 Million
Emp.: 151
Provider of Nonresidential Construction Services
N.A.I.C.S.: 236220
Stephen Conlon (Pres)
Michael Conlon (VP)
Steve McCarron (CFO & Controller)
Timothy Conlon (Sec & VP)

CONNAUGHTON CONSTRUCTION CORP

564 Main St Ste 202, Waltham, MA 02452
Tel.: (781) 899-1438
Web Site:
http://www.connaughtonconstruction.com
Year Founded: 1981
Rev.: $11,454,871
Emp.: 13
General Constructor: Brownstone Renovations & New Construction
N.A.I.C.S.: 236115

CONNECT

4110 CAmpus Point CT, San Diego, CA 92121
Tel.: (858) 964-1300
Web Site: http://www.connect.org
Year Founded: 1985
Membership Organization
N.A.I.C.S.: 813990
Mike Krenn (CEO)
Matt Alamo (Program Mgr)
Christie Marcella (COO)
Taryn Goode (Head-Life Sciences)
Tre Braquet (Sr Mgr-Mktg)

Subsidiaries:

San Diego Venture Group (1)
4110 Campus Point CT, San Diego, CA 92121
Tel.: (858) 558-8750
Non Profit Organization
N.A.I.C.S.: 813319
Mike Krenn (Pres)

CONNECT DIRECT, INC.

805 Veterans Blvd Ste 316, Redwood City, CA 94063
Tel.: (650) 306-9060 CA
Year Founded: 1990
Rev.: $6,000,000
Emp.: 16
Fiscal Year-end: 12/31/01
N.A.I.C.S.: 541810
Ann Corbin (Bus Mgr)
Mary Pat Davey (Sr Acct Exec)
Dave Dumanis (Dir-Creative)
Andi Clot (Office Mgr)

Subsidiaries:

Connect Direct, Inc. (1)
175 Parfitt Way SW, Bainbridge Island, WA 98110
Tel.: (206) 780-0836
N.A.I.C.S.: 541810

CONNECT INTERACTIVE, INC.

3365 Las Vegas Blvd S Ste 378, Las Vegas, NV 89109
Tel.: (631) 932-1226 NV
Year Founded: 2014
Online & Mobile Application Dating Service
N.A.I.C.S.: 516210
Jeremy Draper (Chm, CEO, CFO, Principal Acctg Officer & Sec)

CONNECT MARKETING, INC.

One Market St 36th Fl, San Francisco, CA 94105

Tel.: (415) 222-9691
Web Site:
http://www.connectmarketing.com
Year Founded: 1989
Sales Range: $1-9.9 Million
Emp.: 50
High Tech Marketing Services
N.A.I.C.S.: 541613
Janeen Bullock *(Mng Partner)*
Holly Hagerman *(Sr Partner)*
Sherri Walkenhorst *(Sr Partner)*

CONNECT PUBLIC RELATIONS
881 W State Rd Ste 140-102, Pleasant Grove, UT 84062
Tel.: (801) 373-7888
Web Site:
http://www.connectmarketing.com
Year Founded: 1989
Sales Range: $10-24.9 Million
Emp.: 31
High Technology, Information Technology, Public Relations
N.A.I.C.S.: 541820
Janeen Bullock *(Mng Partner)*
Neil Myers *(Founder & Pres)*
Sherri Walkenhorst *(Sr Partner)*
Holly Hagerman *(Sr Partner)*
Mike Bradshaw *(Partner)*
Chris Walker *(Partner)*

Subsidiaries:

Connect Public Relations   (1)
One Market St 36th Floor, San Francisco, CA 94105
Tel.: (415) 222-9691
Web Site: http://www.connectmarketing.com
Emp.: 5
Public Relations
N.A.I.C.S.: 541820
Holly Hagerman *(Sr Partner)*

CONNECT2 COMMUNICATIONS
3211 Rogers Rd Ste 200, Wake Forest, NC 27587
Tel.: (919) 554-3532
Web Site:
http://www.connect2comm.com
Year Founded: 2003
Sales Range: Less than $1 Million
Emp.: 10
Business-To-Business, Collateral, Communications, Crisis Communications, Internet/Web Design, Investor Relations, Local Marketing, Media Relations, Product Placement, Strategic Planning/Research
N.A.I.C.S.: 541810
Richard M. Williams *(Pres)*
Joyce Wady *(VP-Client Svcs)*
Elizabeth Starrmiller *(Sr Acct Mgr)*
Carmen A. Harris *(Sr Acct Mgr)*
Sue O'Keefe *(Mng Dir-Boston)*

CONNECTAMERICA.COM, LLC
816 Pk Wy, Broomall, PA 19008
Tel.: (800) 906-0872
Web Site:
http://www.connectamerica.com
Mobile Medical Alert Systems Provider
N.A.I.C.S.: 334516

Subsidiaries:

Tunstall Americas   (1)
36-36 33rd St Ste 104, Long Island City, NY 11106
Tel.: (800) 286-2622
Web Site: http://www.tunstall.com
Safety Equipment Distr
N.A.I.C.S.: 561621
Casey Pittock *(Pres & CEO)*

CONNECTED APPAREL COMPANY LLC
6015 Bandini Blvd, Commerce, CA 90040
Tel.: (323) 890-8000
Sales Range: $25-49.9 Million
Emp.: 30
Women Dresses
N.A.I.C.S.: 315250
J. Balaban *(CEO)*
Ira Fogelman *(CFO)*

CONNECTED DEVELOPMENT
5020 Weston Pkwy Ste 215, Cary, NC 27513
Tel.: (919) 678-1488
Web Site:
http://www.connecteddev.com
Year Founded: 2010
Sales Range: $10-24.9 Million
Emp.: 17
Wireless & M2M Network Services
N.A.I.C.S.: 517112
Stefan Lindvall *(Co-Founder)*
Dave Hoover *(Co-Founder & CTO)*
Gregor Bleimann *(Pres)*

CONNECTED LOGISTICS, INC.
6767 Old Madison Pike Bldg 2 Ste 270, Huntsville, AL 35806
Tel.: (703) 220-2410
Web Site: https://www.logc2.com
Year Founded: 2007
Sales Range: $10-24.9 Million
Emp.: 60
Logistics Consulting Servies
N.A.I.C.S.: 541614
Forrest Burke *(CEO)*
Billy Pratt *(Dir-Ops)*
Bill Boyett *(Dir-HR)*
Jeannie Terrell *(Dir-Fin)*
Eric Strauss *(Dir-Bus Dev)*

CONNECTED NATION, INC.
360 E 8th Ave Ste 411, Bowling Green, KY 42101
Tel.: (270) 781-4320   KY
Web Site:
http://www.connectednation.org
Year Founded: 2001
Sales Range: $10-24.9 Million
Emp.: 102
Broadband Service Provider
N.A.I.C.S.: 237110
Ryan Johnson *(Mgr-IT Ops)*
Jessica Ditto *(Dir-Comm)*
Eric Mills *(Gen Counsel)*
Tom Ferree *(Chm & CEO)*
Lindsay Shanahan *(Exec Dir-Connect Ohio)*
Jiten Shah *(Exec Dir)*
Heather Gate *(VP-Digital Inclusion)*

CONNECTED SOLUTIONS GROUP, LLC
8529 Meadowbridge Rd Ste 300, Mechanicsville, VA 23116
Tel.: (804) 396-5985
Web Site:
http://www.connectedsolutions.net
Year Founded: 2015
Sales Range: $10-24.9 Million
Emp.: 72
Hardware Mfr
N.A.I.C.S.: 332510
Michael C. Pittman *(Founder & Pres)*

CONNECTICUT ATTORNEYS TITLE INSURANCE CO.
101 Corporate Pl, Rocky Hill, CT 06067
Tel.: (860) 257-0606
Rev.: $41,600,306
Emp.: 70
Title Insurance
N.A.I.C.S.: 524127
Jim Czapiga *(Pres)*

CONNECTICUT BAR FOUNDATION, INC
31 Pratt St Ste 420, Hartford, CT 06103
Tel.: (860) 722-2494   CT
Web Site: https://www.ctbarfdn.org
Year Founded: 1952
Sales Range: $10-24.9 Million
Emp.: 8
Law firm
N.A.I.C.S.: 541199
Anne Goico *(Dir-Fin)*

CONNECTICUT CARPENTERS BENEFIT FUNDS
10 Broadway, Hamden, CT 06518-2699
Tel.: (203) 281-5511   CT
Web Site:
http://www.ctcarpentersfunds.org
Year Founded: 1969
Sales Range: $25-49.9 Million
Employee Benefit Services
N.A.I.C.S.: 525120
John Leahy *(Co-Chm)*

Subsidiaries:

The Connecticut Carpenters Pension Fund   (1)
10 Broadway, Hamden, CT 06518
Tel.: (203) 281-5511
Web Site: http://ctcarpentersfunds.org
Other Financial Vehicles
N.A.I.C.S.: 525990

CONNECTICUT CENTER FOR ADVANCED TECHNOLOGY, INC.
222 Pitkin St Ste 101, East Hartford, CT 06108
Tel.: (860) 291-8832   CT
Web Site: https://www.ccat.us
Year Founded: 2004
Sales Range: $10-24.9 Million
Economic Development Services
N.A.I.C.S.: 541720
Elliot Ginsberg *(Pres & CEO)*
Tom Maloney *(CTO)*
John Glidden *(CFO)*
Natalie Real *(Chief Admin Officer)*

CONNECTICUT CHILDREN'S MEDICAL CENTER CORPORATION, INC.
282 Washington St, Hartford, CT 06106-3322
Tel.: (860) 545-9000
Web Site:
https://www.connecticutchildrens.org
Year Founded: 1985
Emp.: 2,200
Hospital Association
N.A.I.C.S.: 813910
William C. Popik *(Vice Chm)*
Patrick Garvey *(CFO & Sr VP)*
Craig Bonanni *(Pres & Dir-Anesthesiology)*
Ann Taylor *(Chief Admin Officer & Exec VP)*
Kelly R. Styles *(CIO & Sr VP-Ops)*
Andrea L. Benin *(Sr VP-Quality & Patient Safety)*
Paul Dworkin *(Exec VP-Office for Community Child Health)*
Lawrence Milan *(Chief HR Officer & Sr VP)*
Nicholas Bennett *(Head-Infectious Disease & Immunology)*
Audrey Wise *(CMO & VP)*
James E. Shmerling *(Pres & CEO)*
E. Clayton Gengras III *(Chm)*

Subsidiaries:

CCMC Affiliates, Inc.   (1)
282 Washington St, Hartford, CT 06106-3322

Tel.: (860) 545-8550
Holding Company; Pediatric Hospitals
N.A.I.C.S.: 551112
Martin J. Gavin *(Pres & CEO)*

CCMC Ventures, Inc.   (1)
282 Washington St, Hartford, CT 06106-3322
Tel.: (860) 545-8550
Hospital Investment & Development Services
N.A.I.C.S.: 523999
Martin J. Gavin *(Pres & CEO)*

Connecticut Children's Medical Center   (1)
282 Washington St, Hartford, CT 06106-3322
Tel.: (860) 545-9000
Web Site:
http://www.connecticutchildrens.org
Emp.: 1,500
Pediatric Hospital Operator
N.A.I.C.S.: 622110
Craig Bonanni *(Pres-Medical Staff & Dir-Anesthesiology)*
Cheryl Hoey *(Chief Nursing Officer & Sr VP-Clinical Svcs)*
David Kinahan *(Pres-Foundation)*
Kelly R. Styles *(CIO & Sr VP)*
Tina Brown-Stevenson *(Sec)*
Gil Peri *(Co-Pres & COO)*
Seth Van Essendelft *(CFO & Treas)*
Moses Vargas *(Gen Counsel & VP)*

Connecticut Children's Medical Center Foundation, Inc.   (1)
282 Washington St, Hartford, CT 06106-1914   (100%)
Tel.: (860) 545-9000
Web Site:
http://www.connecticutchildrens.org
Sales Range: Less than $1 Million
Emp.: 27
Charitable Foundation
N.A.I.C.S.: 813219
Alison Auciello *(Sr VP-Foundation)*
Rob Keane *(Assoc VP-Planned Giving)*
Greg Latz *(Asst VP-Dev)*
Amanda Humphrey *(Officer-Annual Giving-Foundation Ops)*
David Kinahan *(Pres)*
Seth Van Essendelft *(CFO & Treas)*
Shari G. Cantor *(Sec)*
Daryl L. Jackson *(Vice Chm)*
Jeffrey P. Klenk *(Chm)*

CONNECTICUT COMMUNITY CARE, INC.
43 Enterprise Dr, Bristol, CT 06010-7472
Tel.: (860) 589-6226   CT
Web Site:
https://www.ctcommunitycare.org
Year Founded: 1980
Sales Range: $10-24.9 Million
Emp.: 324
Community Care Services
N.A.I.C.S.: 624190
Anne Burns *(Vice Chm)*
Maureen Mohyde *(Sec)*
Teresa Torrey *(Treas)*
Marilyn Toland *(Chm)*

CONNECTICUT CONTAINER CORPORATION
455 Sackett Point Rd, North Haven, CT 06473-3116
Tel.: (203) 248-2161   CT
Web Site: https://www.unicorr.com
Year Founded: 1946
Sales Range: $100-124.9 Million
Emp.: 240
Corrugated Shipping Container Mfr
N.A.I.C.S.: 322211
Stephen Sundholm *(VP-Sls)*

Subsidiaries:

K&H Corrugated Case Corp.   (1)
330 Lake Osisris Rd, Walden, NY 12586-2605
Tel.: (845) 778-3555
Web Site: http://www.unicorr.com

Connecticut Container Corporation—(Continued)
Sales Range: $10-24.9 Million
Emp.: 35
N.A.I.C.S.: 322211
Bob Schaedel (Gen Mgr)

Massachusetts Container Corporation (1)
300 Cedar Hill St, Marlborough, MA 01752-3069 (100%)
Tel.: (508) 481-1100
Web Site: http://www.unicorr.com
Sales Range: $10-24.9 Million
Emp.: 90
Corrugated Boxes
N.A.I.C.S.: 322211

Nutmeg Container Corp. (1)
100 Canal St, Putnam, CT 06260-1912 (51%)
Tel.: (860) 963-6727
Sales Range: $10-24.9 Million
Emp.: 75
Mfr of Corrugated Shipping Containers
N.A.I.C.S.: 322211
Charles Pious (VP-Sls & Contract Pkg)
James Pious (VP & Gen Mgr)
Sandy Dupre (Office Mgr)

Technology Container Corp. (1)
207 Greenwood St, Worcester, MA 01607
Tel.: (508) 845-6333
Web Site: http://www.techcontainer.com
Sales Range: $25-49.9 Million
Emp.: 45
N.A.I.C.S.: 322211

Tristate Container Corp. (1)
1440 Bridgewater Rd, Bensalem, PA 19020
Tel.: (215) 638-1311
Web Site: http://www.tristatecontainer.com
Corrugated & Solid Fiber Box Mfr
N.A.I.C.S.: 322211
Allen Friedman (Pres)

Unicorr Packaging Group (1)
Back River Rd, Sharon, VT 05065 (100%)
Tel.: (802) 763-8363
Web Site: http://www.unicorr.com
Sales Range: $10-24.9 Million
Emp.: 30
Corrugated Shipping Containers
N.A.I.C.S.: 322211
Mike Duebeo (Gen Mgr)

CONNECTICUT FOOD BANK INC.
2 Research Pkwy, Wallingford, CT 06492
Tel.: (203) 469-5000
Web Site: https://www.ctfoodbank.org
Rev.: $19,514,433
Emp.: 43
Food Distribution Services
N.A.I.C.S.: 624190
Edward Sagnella (Mgr-East Haven Warehouse)
James Stuhlman (Mgr-Fairfield Branch Warehouse)
Rob Levine (Pres)
Bernard J. Beaudreau (CEO)
Alex Hutchinson (Chm)
Paul O'Leary (COO)
Wesley Higgins (Vice Chm)
Jaime S. Foster (Sr Dir-Community Partnerships & Programs)

CONNECTICUT HOSPICE INC.
100 Double Beach Rd, Branford, CT 06405-4909
Tel.: (203) 315-7301
Web Site: https://www.hospice.com
Rev.: $5,900,000
Emp.: 350
Home Health Care Srvcs
N.A.I.C.S.: 621610
F. J. Mancheski (Chm)
Louis Gonzales (Dir-Admin)

CONNECTICUT MEDICAL IN-SURANCE COMPANY INC.
80 Glastonbury Blvd, Glastonbury, CT 06033

Tel.: (860) 633-7788 CT
Web Site: http://www.cmic.biz
Year Founded: 1984
Sales Range: $25-49.9 Million
Emp.: 30
Professional Insurance
N.A.I.C.S.: 524126
Denise A. Funk (CEO)
John Hornby (VP)
Stewart Bober (Sec)
Kevin M. Bresnahan (Dir-Claims)
Jeffery B. Hopkins (VP)
Stephen Gallant (COO)
Edmund Schiavoni (Pres)
James Pellegrini (Treas)
Mark Tramontozzi (Co-Sec)
Michael Conneely (CFO & Sec)

CONNECTICUT MUNICIPAL ELECTRICAL ENERGY COOP-ERATIVE
30 Stott Ave, Norwich, CT 06360-1526
Tel.: (860) 889-4088
Web Site: https://www.cmeec.com
Year Founded: 1976
Sales Range: $150-199.9 Million
Emp.: 50
Electric Utilities
N.A.I.C.S.: 926130
Brian Forshaw (Chief Risk & Regula-tory Officer)
Edward Pryor (CFO)
Gabriel Stern (Dir-Strategic Plng)
Philip Sussler (Gen Counsel)
Drew Rankin (CEO)
Justin Connell (Dir-Portfolio Mgmt)
Ellen Kachmar (Office Mgr & Mgr-Facility)
James Smith (Treas)
Jake Pagragan (Dir-Customer & Community Prosperity)

CONNECTICUT PEER REVIEW ORGANIZATION, INC.
936 Silas Deane Hwy Ste 1A, Wethersfield, CT 06109-4337
Tel.: (860) 632-2008 CT
Web Site: http://www.qualidigm.org
Year Founded: 1983
Health Care Srvices
N.A.I.C.S.: 622110
Timothy Elwell (Pres & CEO)
Eric Boone (VP-Fin & Ops)
Nancy Kelly (VP-Mktg & Comms)
Joan Orr (VP-Consulting Svcs)

CONNECTICUT PLYWOOD CORP
9 Andover Dr, West Hartford, CT 06110
Tel.: (860) 953-0060
Web Site: http://www.connply.com
Sales Range: $75-99.9 Million
Emp.: 25
Cabinet Maker Supplier
N.A.I.C.S.: 423310
Charles J. Dionisio (Pres)
Ken Lazy (Mgr-Sls)

CONNECTICUT PUBLIC BROADCASTING CORP.
1049 Asylum Ave, Hartford, CT 06105
Tel.: (860) 278-5310
Web Site: http://www.cpbi.org
Year Founded: 1962
Sales Range: $25-49.9 Million
Emp.: 75
Television & Radio Broadcasting Sta-tions Owner & Operator
N.A.I.C.S.: 516120
Meg Sakellarides (Treas)
Nancy Bauer (VP-Sls & Corp Spon-sorships)

John Dankosky (Dir-News)
Mark G. Contreras (Pres & CEO)
Tom Barnes (Chm)

CONNECTICUT RESOURCES RECOVERY AUTHORITY
211 Murphy Rd, Hartford, CT 06114-2100
Tel.: (860) 757-7700
Web Site: http://www.crra.org
Year Founded: 1973
Sales Range: $150-199.9 Million
Emp.: 60
Sanitary Landfill Operator
N.A.I.C.S.: 562212
Thomas D. Kirk (Pres)
Peter W. Egan (Dir-Ops & Environ-mental Svcs)

CONNECTICUT SPRING & STAMPING CORPORATION
48 Spring Ln, Farmington, CT 06032
Tel.: (860) 677-1341 CT
Web Site: https://www.ctspring.com
Year Founded: 1939
Sales Range: $25-49.9 Million
Emp.: 325
Mfr of Springs & Stampings
N.A.I.C.S.: 332119
William Stevenson (Pres)
Steven Dicke (Exec VP)
Peter Youmans (Owner & CEO)
Robert Allen (VP-Ops)
David Fischler (VP-Finance)
Lynn Bousquet (Dir-HR)
Scott Tassinari (Dir-Quality Assur-ance)
Tony Luis (Mgr-Spring Mfg)
Richard Poinatale (VP-Fin)

CONNECTICUT STATE EM-PLOYEES CREDIT UNION, INC.
84 Wadsworth St, Hartford, CT 06106
Tel.: (860) 522-5388 CT
Web Site: https://www.csecreditunion.com
Year Founded: 1946
Sales Range: $10-24.9 Million
Credit Union Operator
N.A.I.C.S.: 522130
John Frenett (Treas)
Dean Skevas (Sec)
Arthur Gamache (VP)
Patricia Wilson (Pres)

CONNECTIONS COMMUNITY SUPPORT PROGRAMS, INC.
3821 Lancasper, Wilmington, DE 19805
Tel.: (302) 268-6194 DE
Web Site: http://www.connectionscsp.org
Year Founded: 1985
Sales Range: $25-49.9 Million
Emp.: 633
Community Action Services
N.A.I.C.S.: 813319
Bob Byrd (Sec)

CONNECTIVA SYSTEMS, INC.
19 W 44th St Ste 611 612, New York, NY 10036
Tel.: (646) 722-8741
Web Site: http://www.connectivasystems.com
Year Founded: 2001
Sales Range: $25-49.9 Million
Emp.: 400
Revenue Management Software
N.A.I.C.S.: 513210
Avi Basu (Founder, Pres & CEO)
Jack Kundamal (COO)
Amitava Maulik (Chief Scientist)

Anandan Jayaraman (Chief Product & Mktg Officer)
Kaustav Ghosh (Sr VP-Bus Dev & Alliances-India)
Krishnendu Sen Gupta (Sr VP & Gen Mgr-India)
Adam Maghrouri (VP-Sls-North America)
Ram Ramamoorthy (VP-Sls-Asia Pacific)

CONNECTIVITY MARKETING & MEDIA AGENCY, LLC
475 Central Ave Ste 205, Saint Pe-tersburg, FL 33701
Tel.: (727) 538-7774
Web Site: http://www.connectivityagency.com
Year Founded: 2009
Sales Range: $10-24.9 Million
Emp.: 10
Advertising Agencies
N.A.I.C.S.: 541810
Sean Halter (CEO)
Cheryl MyCoy (Dir-Media)
D. J. Hamilton (Sr Acct Mgr)
Chris Tomasso (Pres-First Watch Restaurants)

CONNECTOR CAPITAL COR-PORATION
970 Wt Broadway PMB 402 PO Box 30000, Jackson, WY 83002
Tel.: (307) 633-2831
Year Founded: 2012
Investment Services
N.A.I.C.S.: 523999
Jonathan J. Ledecky (Chm, Pres & CEO)

CONNECTOR CASTINGS INC.
1600 N 22nd St, Saint Louis, MO 63106
Tel.: (314) 421-5895
Web Site: https://www.connectorcastings.com
Year Founded: 1987
Sales Range: $10-24.9 Million
Emp.: 60
Mfr of Electronic Generation Equip-ment
N.A.I.C.S.: 335999
Peter E. Fuerst (Owner)
Robert A. Fuerst (Pres & CFO)
Edward S. Youngblood (VP-Sls & Mktg)

CONNECTOR MANUFACTUR-ING COMPANY
3501 Symmes Rd, Hamilton, OH 45015-1369
Tel.: (513) 860-4455 OH
Web Site: http://www.cmclugs.com
Year Founded: 1976
Sales Range: $25-49.9 Million
Emp.: 250
Mfr of Electrical Connectors
N.A.I.C.S.: 335931
Bridgette Pooler (Mgr-HR)

CONNECTOR SPECIALIST INC.
175 James Dr E, Saint Rose, LA 70087
Tel.: (504) 469-1659
Web Site: https://www.connectorspecialists.com
Year Founded: 1977
Sales Range: $10-24.9 Million
Emp.: 27
Pipe & Tubing, Steel
N.A.I.C.S.: 423510
Joanne Stubb (Pres)
Aubrey Achord (Mgr)

CONNECTSOLUTIONS, INC.
731 Market St Ste 600, San Francisco, CA 94103
Tel.: (415) 343-7600   DE
Web Site:
http://www.connectsolutions.com
Year Founded: 2010
Managed Cloud Data Services
N.A.I.C.S.: 518210
Glen D. Vondrick (CEO)
Andrew Peterson (COO)
Stephanie Nevin (VP-Adobe Connect Bus)
Barbara Velline (CFO)
Chris Tennant (CTO)

CONNELL CHEVROLET
2828 Harbor Blvd, Costa Mesa, CA 92626
Tel.: (714) 546-1200
Web Site:
https://www.connellchevrolet.com
Year Founded: 1950
Sales Range: $100-124.9 Million
Emp.: 152
New Car Dealers
N.A.I.C.S.: 441110
Wayne Doddridge (Gen Mgr)
Eddie Cuadra (Mgr-Fleet)
Dan Winters (Mgr-Fleet)

CONNELL GRAIN GROWERS INC.
433 N Columbia St, Connell, WA 99326
Tel.: (509) 234-2641
Web Site: http://www.connellgg.com
Year Founded: 1930
Sales Range: $10-24.9 Million
Emp.: 30
Producer of Grain & Field Beans
N.A.I.C.S.: 424510
Sheri Phillips (Mgr-Office & Credit)
Roland Wynhoff (Mgr-Seed Dept)
Austin Davis (Mgr-Seed Sls)
Tyson Chick (Gen Mgr)

CONNELL LIMITED PARTNERSHIP
1 International Pl Fl 31, Boston, MA 02110-2635
Tel.: (617) 737-2700   DE
Web Site: http://www.connell-lp.com
Year Founded: 1987
Sales Range: $650-699.9 Million
Emp.: 3,000
Holding Company; Industrial Equipment Mfr
N.A.I.C.S.: 331313
Kurt J. Keady (Pres & COO)
Catherine R. Gallagher (VP)

Subsidiaries:

SencorpWhite, Inc.   (1)
400 Kidds Hill Rd, Hyannis, MA 02601
Tel.: (508) 771-9400
Web Site: http://www.sencorpwhite.com
Thermoforming, Blister Packaging & Sealing Equipment Mfr
N.A.I.C.S.: 333248
Brian Urban (Pres & CEO)
Corey Calla (Pres & CEO)

Subsidiary (Domestic):

Minerva Associates, Inc.   (2)
5910 Pacific Ctr Blvd Ste 330, San Diego, CA 92121
Tel.: (858) 792-8626
Web Site: http://www.minerva-associates.com
Inventory Management Software Services
N.A.I.C.S.: 541511
Lisa Minerd (Founder)

The Anchor Danly Company   (1)
2590 Ouellette Avenue, Windsor, N8X 1L7, ON, Canada
Tel.: (519) 966-4031

Web Site: http://www.anchordanly.com
Emp.: 100
Metal Die Set & Plate Mfr
N.A.I.C.S.: 333514
Roy Verstraete (Pres & CEO)

Subsidiary (US):

Danly IEM Set Division   (2)
6779 Engle Rd, Cleveland, OH 44130-7926
Tel.: (440) 239-7600
Web Site: http://www.connell-lp.com
Rev.: $50,000,000
Emp.: 40
Mfr of Die Making Supplies & Components
N.A.I.C.S.: 333514

CONNELL NISSAN
2850 Harbor Blvd, Costa Mesa, CA 92626
Tel.: (714) 444-4220
Web Site:
http://www.connellnissan.com
Rev.: $90,000,000
Emp.: 250
New Car Dealers
N.A.I.C.S.: 441110
Luis Santillan (Gen Mgr-Stores)
Ken Garff (Owner)

CONNELL OIL INCORPORATED
1015 N Oregon Ave, Pasco, WA 99301
Tel.: (509) 547-3326
Web Site: https://www.connelloil.com
Sales Range: $50-74.9 Million
Emp.: 25
Gasoline & Lubricants Supplier
N.A.I.C.S.: 424710
Brad Bell (Owner & Pres)
Jeff Garoutte (Mgr-Fuel Sls)
Danny Gastineau (Mgr-Connell)

CONNELL RESOURCES INC.
7785 Highland Meadows Pkwy Ste 100, Fort Collins, CO 80528-8989
Tel.: (970) 223-3151
Web Site:
https://www.connellresources.com
Rev.: $16,200,000
Emp.: 275
Sewer Line Construction & Asphalt Paving
N.A.I.C.S.: 237110
Richard Connell (Pres)
Bill Anderson (VP-Estimating)
Jeff Laugel (Mgr-Site)
John Warren (VP-Ops)

CONNELLY BILLIARD MANUFACTURING
7115 Belton St, Richland Hills, TX 76118
Tel.: (520) 624-6000
Web Site:
http://www.connellybilliards.com
Sales Range: $10-24.9 Million
Emp.: 15
Billiard & Pool Equipment & Supplies, General
N.A.I.C.S.: 339920
Angie Fox Hoden (Controller)

CONNELLY PARTNERS, LLC
46 Waltham St 4th Fl, Boston, MA 02118
Tel.: (617) 521-5400   MA
Web Site:
http://www.connellypartners.com
Year Founded: 1999
Emp.: 125
Advetising Agency
N.A.I.C.S.: 541810
Steve Connelly (Pres)
Scott Madden (Sr Partner & Dir-Empathy & Evolution)
Dana Wantman (Sr Partner & Dir-Brand Leadership)

Alyssa Toro (Chief Creative Officer & Sr Partner)
Scott Savitt (Dir-Digital & Sr Partner)
Salvatore A. Deluca (CFO)

CONNELLY PAVING
917 N Tulsa Ave, Oklahoma City, OK 73147
Tel.: (405) 943-8388
Web Site:
https://www.connellypaving.com
Sales Range: $10-24.9 Million
Emp.: 100
Civil Engineering Services
N.A.I.C.S.: 237310
James A. Connelly (Pres)

CONNELLY SKIS, INC.
20621 52nd Ave W, Lynnwood, WA 98036-7611
Tel.: (425) 775-5416   WA
Web Site:
https://www.connellyskis.com
Sales Range: $75-99.9 Million
Emp.: 100
Mfr & Distributor of Water Skis & Related Accessories
N.A.I.C.S.: 339920

CONNER INDUSTRIES, INC.
3800 Sandshell Ste 235, Fort Worth, TX 76137-2429
Tel.: (817) 847-0361   DE
Web Site:
https://www.connerindustries.com
Year Founded: 1981
Sales Range: $25-49.9 Million
Emp.: 230
Industrial Wood Products & Services
N.A.I.C.S.: 321912
Chris Kester (VP-Ops)
David A. Dixon (CEO)

Subsidiaries:

Conner Industries, Inc. - Alamo Facility   (1)
700 N Tower Rd, Alamo, TX 78516
Tel.: (800) 641-0215
Wood Container & Pallet Mfr
N.A.I.C.S.: 321920

Conner Industries, Inc. - Conroe Facility   (1)
104 FM 3083, Conroe, TX 77301
Tel.: (888) 686-2892
Wood Container & Pallet Mfr
N.A.I.C.S.: 321920

Conner Industries, Inc. - Fayetteville Facility   (1)
171 Industrial Blvd, Fayetteville, TN 37334
Tel.: (931) 433-1163
Wood Container & Pallet Mfr
N.A.I.C.S.: 321920

Conner Industries, Inc. - Haslet Facility   (1)
1951 Keller Hick Rd, Fort Worth, TX 76177
Tel.: (817) 439-3555
Wood Container & Pallet Mfr
N.A.I.C.S.: 321920

Conner Industries, Inc. - Hogansville Facility   (1)
395 Industrial Dr, Hogansville, GA 30230
Tel.: (706) 637-5620
Web Site: http://www.connerindustries.com
Emp.: 42
Wood Container & Pallet Mfr
N.A.I.C.S.: 321920

Conner Industries, Inc. - Houston Facility   (1)
5707 Mitchelldale St, Houston, TX 77092
Tel.: (713) 944-6766
Wood Container & Pallet Mfr
N.A.I.C.S.: 321920

Conner Industries, Inc. - Stilwell Facility   (1)
Route 3 Hwy 59, Stilwell, OK 74960
Tel.: (918) 696-5885

Wood Container & Pallet Mfr
N.A.I.C.S.: 321920

Conner Transport, Inc.   (1)
3800 Sandshell Dr, Fort Worth, TX 76137
Tel.: (817) 847-0361
Web Site: http://www.connerindustries.com
Sales Range: $10-24.9 Million
Emp.: 45
Trucking Service
N.A.I.C.S.: 484121

Continental Timber Co. Inc.   (1)
202 S Cedar Ave, Valley Center, KS 67147-2211
Tel.: (316) 755-2361
Web Site: http://www.continentaltimber.com
Lumber, Plywood & Millwork Supplier
N.A.I.C.S.: 423310
Dwayne Rea (CFO, Treas & Sec)
Michael Davison (Gen Mgr-Sls)
Al Stahlheber (Sls Mgr)
Casey Watkins (Production Mgr)
Wesley Chapple (Production Mgr)
Jerry Weimer (Sls Mgr-Western)
Vicki Weimer (Office Mgr)

Denver Reel & Pallet Co.   (1)
4600 Monaco St, Denver, CO 80216
Tel.: (303) 321-1920
Web Site:
http://www.denverreelandpallet.com
Rev.: $3,744,000
Emp.: 32
All Other Miscellaneous Wood Product Mfr
N.A.I.C.S.: 321999
Kurt Heimbrock (Pres)
Dareld Herrera (VP-Sls)

Guardian Packaging Industries, LP   (1)
3615 Security St, Garland, TX 75042
Tel.: (214) 349-1500
Web Site:
http://www.guardianpackaging.com
Sales Range: $1-9.9 Million
Emp.: 35
Whol Industrial Supplies
N.A.I.C.S.: 423840
Norman Stuart (Principal)

CONNER INSURANCE AGENCY INC.
8445 Keystone Crossing Ste 200, Indianapolis, IN 46240-2496
Tel.: (317) 808-7711
Web Site:
http://www.conneragency.com
Year Founded: 1973
Sales Range: $25-49.9 Million
Emp.: 20
Insurance Services
N.A.I.C.S.: 524210
Todd Hufford (COO)
Megan Talpas (Coord-Wellness)

CONNER PRAIRIE MUSEUM, INC.
13400 Allisonville Rd, Fishers, IN 46038
Tel.: (317) 776-6000   IN
Web Site:
https://www.connerprairie.org
Year Founded: 2005
Sales Range: $10-24.9 Million
Emp.: 384
Historical Museum
N.A.I.C.S.: 712110
Ellen M. Rosenthal (Pres & CEO)
Richard Cooper (Chief Programs Officer & VP)
Susana Suarez (CMO & VP)

CONNER STRONG & BUCKELEW
40 Lake Center Executive Park 401 Route 73 N Ste 300, Marlton, NJ 08053
Tel.: (856) 552-8565
Web Site:
http://www.connerstrong.com
Year Founded: 1959
Emp.: 290

Conner Strong & Buckelew—(Continued)

Insurance Brokerage Services
N.A.I.C.S.: 524210
Michael Tiagwad *(Pres & CEO)*
John F. Muscella *(Mng Dir, CFO & Exec VP)*
Susan D. Hudson *(Mng Dir, Chief Admin Officer & Sr VP)*
Carole A. Mack *(Sr VP)*
Jack Tarditi *(Mng Dir)*
Tammy L. Brown *(Mng Dir & Sr VP)*
Colleen Kelly *(VP)*
William Kimmel *(VP)*
Kristine Klepper *(Mng Dir & Sr VP)*
Roger Ladda *(VP-Alternative Risk)*
Paul Laracy *(Sr VP)*
William Laughlin *(VP-Data Analytics)*
Joseph V. Porch *(VP)*
Frank C. Proctor *(Mng Dir & Exec VP-Bus Dev)*
Phyllis M. Saraceni *(Mng Dir & Sr VP)*
Heather A. Steinmiller *(Gen Counsel & Sr VP)*
Terrence J. Tracy *(Mng Dir & Exec VP)*
Franz Wagner *(Mng Dir & Sr VP-Major Accounts)*
Karen R. Wallace *(VP & Dir-Mktg)*
Thomas Trullinger *(Sr VP-Mergers & Acq-Camden)*
Patrick Keating *(Chief Security Officer/VP-Camden)*
Anil Jampana *(CIO & Sr VP)*

CONNEX CREDIT UNION
412 Washington Ave, North Haven, CT 06473
Tel.: (203) 603-5700   CT
Web Site: http://www.connexcu.org
Year Founded: 1940
Sales Range: $10-24.9 Million
Emp.: 149
Credit Union
N.A.I.C.S.: 522130
Carl Casper *(COO & Exec VP)*
Frank Mancini *(Pres & CEO)*
Frank Pomarico *(Mgr-Branch)*
Gezim Stroka *(Mgr-Branch)*
Michael Nowicky *(Mgr-Branch)*
Kerry Perrotta Jr. *(Mgr-Branch)*

CONNEX INTERNATIONAL INC.
46 Federal Rd Ste F, Danbury, CT 06810
Tel.: (203) 731-5400
Web Site: https://www.connexintl.com
Sales Range: $10-24.9 Million
Emp.: 70
Telephone Communication, Except Radio
N.A.I.C.S.: 517121
Deborah Volansky *(Pres)*

CONNEXION SYSTEMS & ENGINEERING, INC.
490 Boston Post Rd, Sudbury, MA 01776
Tel.: (978) 579-0030
Web Site: https://www.csetalent.com
Year Founded: 1999
Employment Agency
N.A.I.C.S.: 561311
Daniel Cushing *(Co-Founder & Mng Partner)*
Ken Dimaggio *(Co-Founder & Mng Partner)*

CONNEXION TECHNOLOGIES
111 Corning Rd Ste 250, Cary, NC 27518
Tel.: (919) 674-0036
Year Founded: 2002
Sales Range: $10-24.9 Million

Emp.: 474
Management & Customization of Telecommunication Networks
N.A.I.C.S.: 517112
Walter Daniels *(Chief Legal Officer)*
Eric Fichtner *(Exec VP-Ops)*
Carter Teague *(Exec VP-Sls & Mktg)*

CONNEXUS CREDIT UNION
2600 Pine Ridge Blvd, Wausau, WI 54401
Tel.: (715) 847-4700   WI
Web Site: https://www.connexuscu.org
Year Founded: 1935
Sales Range: $10-24.9 Million
Emp.: 150
Credit Union Operator
N.A.I.C.S.: 522130
J. David Christenson *(Pres & CEO)*
Boyd Gustke *(COO)*
Mary Burgoyne *(CIO)*
Mark Steinberg *(Vice Chm)*
Jane Kittel *(Sec)*
Todd McDonald *(Treas)*
Ron Dins *(Chm)*

CONNEXUS ENERGY
14601 Ramsey Blvd NW, Ramsey, MN 55303-6024
Tel.: (763) 323-2600   MN
Web Site: https://www.connexusenergy.com
Year Founded: 1936
Sales Range: $200-249.9 Million
Emp.: 250
Provider of Electric Cooperative Services
N.A.I.C.S.: 221122
Peter Wojciechowski *(Chm)*
Fran Bator *(Treas & Sec)*
Mark Ethen *(Vice Chm)*
Gordon Westerlind *(Treas & Asst Sec)*
Brian Burandt *(VP-Power Supply & Bus Dev)*
Don Haller *(VP-Member Svcs, Products & Sls)*
Greg Ridderbusch *(Pres & CFO)*
Matt Yseth *(VP-Electric Ops)*
Pete Miller *(VP-HR)*

CONNOILS LLC
W230S7115 Guthrie School Rd, Big Bend, WI 53103
Tel.: (262) 662-5533
Web Site: http://www.connoils.com
Year Founded: 2007
Sales Range: $10-24.9 Million
Emp.: 25
Organic Oil Mfr & Distr
N.A.I.C.S.: 325311
Stacy Peterson *(Founder)*

CONNOISSEURS PRODUCTS CORPORATION
17 Presidential Dr, Woburn, MA 01801
Tel.: (781) 932-3949
Web Site: http://www.connoisseurs.com
Year Founded: 1997
Rev.: $19,600,000
Emp.: 90
Jewelry & Silver Care Products Mfr
N.A.I.C.S.: 325612
Douglas Dorfman *(Owner)*
John Archambault *(Exec VP-Fin & Admin)*
Angel Caso *(Mgr-Sls Ops & Admin)*

CONNOR & GASKINS UNLIMITED LLC
1998 Trade Center Way Ste 2, Naples, FL 34109
Tel.: (239) 260-5068

Web Site: https://www.cgunlimited.com
Year Founded: 2010
Sales Range: $10-24.9 Million
Emp.: 7
Residential Construction & Remodeling
N.A.I.C.S.: 236117
Barry Connor *(Co-Founder & CEO)*
Craig Gaskins *(Co-Founder & COO)*
Mike Ludington *(Dir-Ops)*
Tom Carrico *(Project Mgr)*
Andrew Twetan *(Sr Mgr-Construction)*
Jason McCabe *(Superintendent)*
Rowland Hand *(Sr Mgr-Construction)*
Jonathan Lawrence *(Project Mgr)*

CONNOR CO. INC.
2800 NE Adams, Peoria, IL 61603-2806
Tel.: (309) 688-1068   IL
Web Site: https://www.connorco.com
Year Founded: 1936
Sales Range: $10-24.9 Million
Emp.: 250
Plumbing Fixtures, Equipment & Supplies Mfr
N.A.I.C.S.: 423720
Stan Collins *(Pres)*

CONNOR CONCEPTS INCORPORATED
10911 Turkey Dr, Knoxville, TN 37934
Tel.: (865) 777-2677
Web Site: https://www.thechophouse.com
Year Founded: 1992
Steak Restaurant
N.A.I.C.S.: 722511
Mike Connor *(Pres & CEO)*
Brian Keyes *(VP-Ops)*
Nicki Dawson *(CFO)*
Angela Hawkins *(Controller)*

CONNOR CORPORATION
10633 Cold Water Rd Ste 200, Fort Wayne, IN 46845-1417
Tel.: (260) 424-1601   IN
Web Site: http://www.connorcorp.com
Year Founded: 1994
Sales Range: $75-99.9 Million
Emp.: 12
Rubber & Plastic Products Mfr
N.A.I.C.S.: 326199
William S. Esther *(Chm & CEO)*
Yvan Carriere *(Pres & COO)*

CONNOR-WINFIELD CORP.
2111 Comprehensive Dr, Aurora, IL 60505
Tel.: (630) 851-4722
Web Site: https://www.conwin.com
Year Founded: 1963
Rev.: $29,000,000
Emp.: 300
Mfr of Electronic Frequency Timing Devices
N.A.I.C.S.: 335314
Daniel Olp *(Gen Mgr)*

CONNORS, DAMESHEK, FONG & MANCUSO, INC.
20 Whitcher St, Lisbon, NH 03585
Tel.: (603) 838-6694   NH
Web Site: http://www.whitemt.com
Sales Range: $25-49.9 Million
Emp.: 20
Footwear
N.A.I.C.S.: 424340
Gregory Connors *(Pres)*
Roger Gingue *(Controller)*

CONO ITALIANO, INC.
10 Main St, Keyport, NJ 07735   NV

Web Site: http://www.conoitaliano.com
Sales Range: Less than $1 Million
Emp.: 3
Pizza Products Distr
N.A.I.C.S.: 424490
Mitchell Brown *(Founder, Pres & COO)*
Alex J. Kaminski *(CFO & Treas)*
Steve Savage *(Sec)*

CONOLOG CORPORATION
5 Columbia Rd, Somerville, NJ 08876
Tel.: (908) 722-8081
Year Founded: 1969
Sales Range: Less than $1 Million
Electronics Engineering, Design & Manufacturing
N.A.I.C.S.: 334419
Michael Horn *(Chm, Pres & CEO)*
Albert S. Lenhardt *(VP-Production)*

Subsidiaries:

INIVEN   (1)
5 Columbia Rd, Somerville, NJ 08876
Tel.: (908) 722-3770
Web Site: http://www.iniven.com
Audio Communications Electronic Equipment Mfr
N.A.I.C.S.: 334419
Mark Benou *(Pres)*

CONOVER TUTTLE PACE
77 N Washington St, Boston, MA 02114
Tel.: (617) 412-4000
Web Site: http://www.ctpboston.com
Year Founded: 1996
Rev.: $12,000,000
Emp.: 45
N.A.I.C.S.: 541810
Chip Tuttle *(Partner)*
Brian Heffron *(Partner & Exec VP)*
Todd Graff *(Dir-Project Mgmt)*
Mark Bappe *(VP & Dir-Creative)*
Steve Angel *(VP & Dir-Strategic Dev)*
Mark Fredrickson *(Dir-Creative & VP)*
Allison Spitaels *(Dir-Account Management & Sr VP)*
Lee Allen *(Dir-Digital & VP)*

CONQUEST MANUFACTURING, LLC
28408 Lorna Ave, Warren, MI 48092-4533
Tel.: (586) 576-7600
Web Site: http://www.conquest-firespray.com
Year Founded: 1998
Duct Fabricator
N.A.I.C.S.: 332313
James Miller *(CEO)*

CONQUEST SYSTEMS, INC.
7617 Harlington Rd, Bethesda, MD 20814
Tel.: (202) 289-4240
Sales Range: Less than $1 Million
Emp.: 7
Provider of IT Services
N.A.I.C.S.: 541512
Richard Landry *(Pres & CEO)*

CONRAC, INC.
5124 Commerce Dr, Baldwin Park, CA 91706
Tel.: (626) 480-0095   DE
Web Site: http://conrac.us
Year Founded: 1939
Sales Range: $50-74.9 Million
Emp.: 9
Mfr of CRT & Flat Panel Displays
N.A.I.C.S.: 334310
Ray Allen *(CFO)*
William Moeller *(Pres)*

CONRAD COMPANY INCOR-PORATED

8200 Pax Dr 230, Austin, TX 78736
Tel.: (512) 342-1636
Rev.: $25,140,952
Emp.: 18
Brick, Stone & Related Material
N.A.I.C.S.: 423320

CONRAD IMPORTS INC.

540 Barneveld Ave, San Francisco, CA 94124-1805
Tel.: (415) 626-3303
Web Site:
https://www.conradshades.com
Rev.: $14,313,216
Emp.: 43
Window Furnishings
N.A.I.C.S.: 423220
Ruth M. Holland (Pres)
Helen Cereghino (Dir-Customer Rels)
Yolonda Greenwell-Reese (Mgr-HR)

CONRAD INDUSTRIES, INC.

22 A B Emblem Dr, Weaverville, NC 28787-9252
Tel.: (828) 645-3015   NC
Web Site:
https://www.abemblem.com
Year Founded: 1962
Sales Range: $10-24.9 Million
Emp.: 120
Swiss Embroidered Emblems Mfr
N.A.I.C.S.: 314999
Andrew Nagle (Exec VP)
Bernhard Conrad (Pres & CEO)
Ruth Plemmons (Mgr-Pur)

Subsidiaries:

A-B Emblems and Caps   (1)
291 Merrimon Ave, Weaverville, NC 28787-0695
Tel.: (828) 645-3015
Web Site: http://www.abemblems.com
N.A.I.C.S.: 314999
Andrew Nagle (Gen Mgr)

CONRAD J. FREEMAN INC.

958 San Leandro Ave Ste 900, Mountain View, CA 94043
Tel.: (650) 940-4200
Rev.: $10,900,000
Emp.: 500
Fast-Food Restaurant Owner
N.A.I.C.S.: 722511
Conrad J. Freeman Jr. (Pres)

CONRAD SCHMITT STUDIOS, INC.

2405 S 162nd St, New Berlin, WI 53151
Tel.: (262) 786-3030
Web Site:
https://www.conradschmitt.com
Sales Range: $10-24.9 Million
Emp.: 80
Nonresidential Construction Services
N.A.I.C.S.: 236220
Bernard Gruenke (Pres)

CONRAD'S TIRE SERVICE INC.

14577 Lorain Ave, Cleveland, OH 44111
Tel.: (216) 941-3333
Web Site: http://www.econrads.com
Year Founded: 1969
Sales Range: $10-24.9 Million
Emp.: 150
General Automotive Repair Shops; Wholesaler of Tires
N.A.I.C.S.: 811111
John Turk (Pres & CEO)

CONROY & CONROY CON-TRACTORS, INC.

48 Spellman Rd, Plattsburgh, NY 12901
Tel.: (518) 562-2460
Sales Range: $10-24.9 Million
Emp.: 24
Nonresidential Construction Services
N.A.I.C.S.: 236220
William Conroy (Pres)

CONSCIOUS CONTENT ME-DIA, INC.

460 Park Ave S 4th Fl, New York, NY 10016
Tel.: (646) 580-4534   DE
Web Site:
http://www.speakaboos.com
Children's Interactive Reading Application Developer & Services
N.A.I.C.S.: 541511
Neal Shenoy (Co-Founder & CEO)
Stephanie Dua (Pres & COO)

CONSEJO DE SALUD DE PUERTO RICO, INC.

PO Box 220, Mercedita, PR 00715-0220
Tel.: (787) 843-9393   PR
Web Site: http://www.medcentro.org
Year Founded: 1971
Sales Range: $25-49.9 Million
Emp.: 318
Health Care Srvices
N.A.I.C.S.: 622110
Francisco Bayanilla (Dir-Fin)
Awilda Garcia (Dir-Medical)
Liznette Rodriguez (Dir-Pharmacy)
Allan Cintron Salichs (CEO & Exec Dir)

CONSEL, INC.

7935 Drew Cir, Fort Myers, FL 33967
Tel.: (239) 313-5567   FL
Web Site: https://www.conselinc.com
Year Founded: 1983
Concrete Repair And New Construction Single-Family Homes
N.A.I.C.S.: 238110

CONSELLO MANAGEMENT LP

590 Madison Ave., New York, NY 10022
Tel.: (212) 884-9304
Web Site: https://consello.com
Financial Services
N.A.I.C.S.: 523999
Mindy F. Grossman (Partner)

Subsidiaries:

Consello Capital LLC   (1)
590 Madison Ave., New York, NY 10022
Tel.: (212) 884-9304
Web Site: https://consello.com
Financial Services
N.A.I.C.S.: 523999

Subsidiary (Domestic):

Prosearch Strategies, Inc.   (2)
3250 Wilshire Blvd Ste 301, Los Angeles, CA 90010
Tel.: (213) 355-1271
Web Site:
http://www.prosearchstrategies.com
Law firm
N.A.I.C.S.: 541199
Dan Kinney (VP-Bus Dev)

CONSENSYS, INC.

49 Bogart St, Brooklyn, NY 11206
Tel.: (646) 389-4240
Web Site: http://www.consensys.net
Blockchain Company & Services
N.A.I.C.S.: 525990
Richard Anthony Brewster (Chief Compliance Officer)
Joseph Lubin (Founder)

Subsidiaries:

ConsenSys Digital Securities, LLC   (1)
100 Bogart St 3rd Fl, Brooklyn, NY 11206
Tel.: (646) 389-4240
Financial Services
N.A.I.C.S.: 522320
Richard Anthony Brewster (Chief Compliance Officer)

Subsidiary (Domestic):

Heritage Financial Systems   (2)
1 E Uwchlan Ave, Exton, PA 19341
Tel.: (610) 524-3135
Web Site: http://www.hfsadvisory.com
Portfolio Management
N.A.I.C.S.: 523940

CONSERO GLOBAL SOLU-TIONS LLC

106 E 6th St Ste 912, Austin, TX 78701
Tel.: (214) 306-6472
Web Site:
http://www.conseroglobal.com
Year Founded: 2006
Sales Range: $1-9.9 Million
Emp.: 125
Outsourced Financial Services
N.A.I.C.S.: 541618
Scott Tynes (CEO)
Bill Klein (Pres)
Kiran Jagannath (CFO)
Chris Hartenstein (Exec Partner & Head-Client Mgmt)
Mike Dansby (VP-CFO Svcs)
Jeanine Nosker (VP-Svcs)
Ed Taylor (CEO-Collective Grp)
Natalie Townsend (VP-Sls)

CONSERV FS INC.

1110 McConnell Rd, Woodstock, IL 60098
Tel.: (815) 334-5950   IL
Web Site: https://www.conservfs.com
Year Founded: 1928
Sales Range: $100-124.9 Million
Emp.: 150
Agricultural Cooperative
N.A.I.C.S.: 926140
Michael Glennding (Mgr-Petroleum)
Dave Mottet (Gen Mgr)

Subsidiaries:

Blake Oil Company   (1)
401 W Main St, Kirkland, IL 60146
Tel.: (815) 522-3521
Web Site: http://www.blakeoil.com
Sales Range: $25-49.9 Million
Emp.: 10
Whslr of Petroleum Products
N.A.I.C.S.: 424710
John D. Blake (Pres)

CONSERVATION SERVICES GROUP, INC.

50 Washington St Ste 3000, Westborough, MA 01581
Tel.: (508) 836-9500   MA
Web Site: http://www.csgrp.com
Year Founded: 1984
Sales Range: $100-124.9 Million
Emp.: 938
Energy Conservation Services
N.A.I.C.S.: 541690
Paul Cimino (Gen Counsel & VP)
King Tang (Mgr-Engrg)

CONSERVATIVE REFORM NETWORK

219 Pennsylvania Ave SE 3rd Fl, Washington, DC 20003
Tel.: (703) 232-1464   DE
Web Site:
http://www.conservativereform.com
Year Founded: 2011
Sales Range: $10-24.9 Million

Emp.: 8
Social, Education & Legal Services
N.A.I.C.S.: 813410
Stacey Johnson (Exec Dir)
Travis Hall (Dir-Comm)
Neil Bradley (Chief Strategy Officer)

CONSERVE

200 Cross Keys Office Pk, Fairport, NY 14450
Tel.: (585) 421-1011
Web Site: http://www.conserve-arm.com
Year Founded: 1985
Rev.: $20,500,000
Emp.: 262
Business Products & Services
N.A.I.C.S.: 561440
Mark E. Davitt (Pres)
Richard Klein (CFO)
Steve DiPaola (CIO)
Pamela D. Baird (Gen Counsel)
Kevin J. Gelabert (CMO)
George Huyler (VP-HR)
Richard Russell (Dir-Ops)
Felicia Ferrari (Mgr-Frontline)
Pamela A. Murphy (Officer-Compliance & VP-Privacy)
J. Christopher Lang (VP-Contract Admin)

CONSERVICE

595 Riverwoods Pkwy Ste 300, Logan, UT 84321
Tel.: (435) 792-3300
Web Site: http://www.conservice.com
Year Founded: 2001
Rev.: $15,000,000
Emp.: 162
Business Services
N.A.I.C.S.: 561499
Rich Seeley (Dir-IT)

CONSEW

400 Veterans Blvd, Carlstadt, NJ 07072-7201
Tel.: (212) 741-7788
Web Site: https://www.consew.com
Year Founded: 1898
Sales Range: $75-99.9 Million
Emp.: 15
Mfr of Industrial Sewing Machines, Clutch Motors, Parts & Related Accessories
N.A.I.C.S.: 423830
Murray Feit (Pres)
Doug Glenn (Dir-Sls)
Michael Feit (Owner)

Subsidiaries:

Consew Consolidated Sewing Machine Corp.   (1)
4077 NW 79th Ave, Miami, FL 33166
Tel.: (305) 513-9220
Web Site: http://www.consew.com
Sales Range: $25-49.9 Million
Emp.: 11
Consew Industrial Sewing Machines, Cutting Machines, Clutch Motors & Accessories, Sewing Machine Parts & Needles
N.A.I.C.S.: 423830
Murray Feit (Pres)

CONSIGLI CONSTRUCTION CO., INC.

72 Sumner St, Milford, MA 01757
Tel.: (508) 473-2580
Web Site: http://www.consigli.com
Year Founded: 1905
Emp.: 318
General Contracting Services
N.A.I.C.S.: 236210
Matthew Consigli (VP)
Anthony Consigli (Pres)
Robert Lizza (Gen Counsel & VP)
Robert Score (Dir-Historic Preservation)

Consist Software Solutions, Inc.—(Continued)

CONSIST SOFTWARE SOLUTIONS, INC.
535 5th Ave Rm 201, New York, NY 10017-8026
Tel.: (212) 759-2100
Web Site: http://www.consist.com
Year Founded: 1989
Sales Range: $50-74.9 Million
Emp.: 1,000
Information Technology Applications
N.A.I.C.S.: 541511
Natalio Fridman (Founder & CEO)
Anthony Berkowitz (VP-Admin)
Paul Marx (VP-Bus Dev)

CONSISTENT COMPUTER BARGAINS, INC.
2823 Carolisoe Ave, Racine, WI 53404
Tel.: (262) 886-4222
Web Site:
    http://www.ccbnonprofits.com
Year Founded: 1991
Sales Range: $1-9.9 Million
Emp.: 40
Licensing, Software & Hardware Retailer
N.A.I.C.S.: 449210
Chris Booth (CEO)
Tom Haven (Mgr-Acct-Natl)
Barb Wren (Dir-HR)
Nancy Ribeiro (Mgr-Acct-Natl)
Stacey Neideffer (VP-Acctg & Fin)
Patrick Booth (Pres)
Logan McCoy (VP-Svcs)
Melody Bernhardt (VP-Mktg)
Scott McElroy (Acct Mgr-Nonprofit)
Paula Rorek (Acct Mgr-Natl)
Patti Lojeski (Acct Mgr-Natl)
Rachel Bowker (Dir-Mktg)
Rich LoCascio (Acct Mgr)
Nick Selimos (Acct Mgr)
Molly Cacciotti (Dir-Pur)
Michael F. Hoefler (Acct Mgr)
Jake Jones (Acct Mgr)
Jacob Ward (Acct Mgr)
Anna Gierowski (Dir-Relationship Mgmt)
Adam Heusdens (Dir-IT)
Cameron Gaither (Dir-Sls)
Jon Hermanson (Engr-Sls)
Kyle Jolly (Dir-Sls)
Nik Lipor (Engr-Sls)

CONSO INTERNATIONAL CORPORATION
6050 Dana Way, Antioch, TN 37013
Tel.: (864) 427-9004   SC
Web Site: http://www.conso.com
Year Founded: 1867
Sales Range: $150-199.9 Million
Emp.: 370
Mfr of Drapery & Upholstery Trimmings, Decorative Trimmings, Workroom Supplies & Notions & Patterns
N.A.I.C.S.: 313220
Judy Raymond (Sr VP-Pattern Prods)
J. Cary Findlay (Chm, Pres & CEO)

Subsidiaries:

British Trimmings Ltd.   (1)
Coronation Street, PO Box 46, Stockport, SK5 7PJ, Cheshire, United Kingdom   (100%)
Tel.: (44) 614806122
Sales Range: $10-24.9 Million
Emp.: 40
Mfr of Textile Decorative Trimmings
N.A.I.C.S.: 313210

Simplicity Pattern Co. Inc.   (1)
261 Madison Ave Fl 4, New York, NY 10016-5701
Tel.: (212) 372-0500
Web Site: http://www.simplicity.com

Sales Range: $25-49.9 Million
Emp.: 150
Mfr of Drapery & Upholstery Trimmings, Decorative Trimmings, Workroom Supplies & Notions & Patterns
N.A.I.C.S.: 513199

Simplicity Patterns International Ltd. Inc.   (1)
261 Madison Ave Fl 4, New York, NY 10016-3906
Tel.: (212) 372-0500
Web Site: http://www.simplicity.com
Rev.: $360,000
Emp.: 150
Industrial & Personal Service Paper
N.A.I.C.S.: 424130

CONSOLIDATED ANALYTICS, INC.
1 MacArthur Pl Ste 100, Santa Ana, CA 92707
Tel.: (800) 320-9490
Web Site:
    http://www.consolidatedanalytics.com
Year Founded: 1996
Offices of Real Estate Agents & Brokers
N.A.I.C.S.: 531210
Brian Gehl (Pres)
Arvin Wijay (CEO)

CONSOLIDATED BRICK & BUILDING SUPPLIES INC.
650 Bodwell St, Avon, MA 02322
Tel.: (508) 587-6600   MA
Web Site:
    https://www.consolidatedbrick.com
Year Founded: 1968
Sales Range: $10-24.9 Million
Emp.: 55
Mfr of Brick, Stone & Related Materials
N.A.I.C.S.: 423320
Paul Carey (Pres)
Patricia Meade (Controller)
Lynn Donohue (Mgr)

CONSOLIDATED CARPET-TRADE WORKROOM
45 W 25th St 8th Fl, New York, NY 10010
Tel.: (212) 226-4600
Web Site:
    http://www.consolidatedcarpet.com
Sales Range: $10-24.9 Million
Emp.: 150
Carpet Laying
N.A.I.C.S.: 238330
David T. Meberg (Pres & CEO)
Tom Ruchalski (CFO)

CONSOLIDATED CATFISH COMPANIES, LLC
299 S St, Isola, MS 38754
Tel.: (662) 962-3101   MS
Web Site:
    http://www.countryselect.com
Year Founded: 1991
Sales Range: $125-149.9 Million
Emp.: 550
Holding Company; Catfish Processor & Whslr
N.A.I.C.S.: 551112
Richard D. Stevens (Pres & CEO)
David Gray (CFO)

Subsidiaries:

Country Select Catfish Company II, LLC   (1)
S City Limits Rd, Isola, MS 38754   (100%)
Tel.: (662) 962-3101
Web Site: http://www.countryselect.com
Emp.: 500
Catfish Processor & Whslr
N.A.I.C.S.: 311710
Richard D. Stevens (Pres & CEO)
Jack Perkins (VP-Sls & Mktg)
Kim Cox (VP-Customer Svc)

Barbie King (Bus Mgr)
Brad Stevens (VP)
David Allen (VP)
David Gray (CFO)
John Rutledge (Dir-Quality Assurance)

CONSOLIDATED CHEMICAL CORPORATION
431 Stephenson Hwy, Troy, MI 48083
Tel.: (248) 583-0184.
Web Site: https://www.tri-chem.com
Year Founded: 1968
Rev.: $15,400,000
Emp.: 100
Industrial Tools
N.A.I.C.S.: 423840
Ira Berkowitz (VP-Sls)
Jessica Zeer (Acct Mgr-Sls)
Lindsey Barylski (Acct Mgr-Sls)
Christy Winters (Mgr-Sls)

CONSOLIDATED CONTRACTING SERVICE
181 Avenida La Pata Ste 200, San Clemente, CA 92673
Tel.: (949) 498-7500
Web Site:
    https://www.consolidatedcontracting.com
Rev.: $25,000,000
Emp.: 39
Commercial & Office Building, New Construction
N.A.I.C.S.: 236220
Joseph Troya (Principal)
Kari McFall (Dir-Dev)

CONSOLIDATED COTTON CO. INC.
1515 Texas Ave Ste 205, Lubbock, TX 79401
Tel.: (806) 765-8914
Sales Range: $10-24.9 Million
Emp.: 5
Cotton Merchants
N.A.I.C.S.: 424590
Louise Hicks (Pres)

CONSOLIDATED ELECTRIC COOPERATIVE
3940 E Liberty St, Mexico, MO 65265-0540
Tel.: (573) 581-3630   MO
Web Site:
    https://www.consolidatedelectric.com
Year Founded: 1938
Sales Range: $10-24.9 Million
Emp.: 35
Electric Power Distr
N.A.I.C.S.: 221122
Linda Forster (Accountant)
Melanie Oetting (Mgr-Admin Svcs)
Carol Willingham (Interim Gen Mgr)
Felicity Goodpasture-Culwell (Sec)
Joan Woods (VP)
Mike Van Maanen (Treas)
Carl Aulbur (Superintendent-Ops)
Dale Hopke (Chm)
Dave Null (Mgr-Technical Svcs)

CONSOLIDATED ENGINEERING CO
1971 McCollum Pkwy NW, Kennesaw, GA 30144
Tel.: (770) 422-5100
Web Site: http://www.cec-intl.com
Sales Range: $25-49.9 Million
Emp.: 60
Industrial Furnaces & Ovens
N.A.I.C.S.: 333994
Cott Crafton (Pres)

CONSOLIDATED ENGINEERING LABS

2001 Crow Canyon Rd Ste 100, San Ramon, CA 94583-5387
Tel.: (925) 314-7100
Rev.: $18,200,000
Emp.: 225
Testing Laboratories
N.A.I.C.S.: 541715

CONSOLIDATED FABRICATORS CORP
14620 Arminta St, Van Nuys, CA 91402
Tel.: (323) 586-4500
Web Site: http://www.con-fab.com
Year Founded: 1975
Sales Range: $10-24.9 Million
Emp.: 110
Dumpsters; Garbage
N.A.I.C.S.: 332431
Michael Melideo (Pres)
Barbara Ross (Mgr-Mktg)

Subsidiaries:

Centennial Steel   (1)
4848 S Santa Fe Ave, Los Angeles, CA 90058
Tel.: (323) 586-4545
Web Site: http://www.centennialsteel.com
Wholesalers of Excess & Non-prime Flat Rolled Steel Products
N.A.I.C.S.: 332431

Consolidated Fabricators Corp., Building Products Division   (1)
8584 Mulberry Ave, Fontana, CA 92335   (100%)
Tel.: (909) 770-8920
Web Site: http://www.confabbpd.com
Sales Range: $10-24.9 Million
Emp.: 75
Steel Framing Products Mfr
N.A.I.C.S.: 332618
Evelyn Davila (Office Mgr)

CONSOLIDATED FIBERGLASS PRODUCTS CO.
3801 Standard St, Bakersfield, CA 93308
Tel.: (661) 323-6026
Web Site: http://www.conglas.com
Year Founded: 1972
Fiberglass Insulation
N.A.I.C.S.: 327993
Maria Lewis (Mgr-Bus Devel)

CONSOLIDATED FIBERS, INC.
8100 S Blvd, Charlotte, NC 28273-5950
Tel.: (704) 554-8621   NC
Web Site:
    http://www.consolidatedfibers.com
Year Founded: 1946
Consolidated & Specialty Fibers Mfr
N.A.I.C.S.: 325220
Robert Kunik (Pres & Treas)

CONSOLIDATED FUEL OIL COMPANY
12310 159th St, Olathe, KS 66062
Tel.: (913) 451-3764
Sales Range: $10-24.9 Million
Emp.: 2
Petroleum Products Mfr
N.A.I.C.S.: 424720
Walter Grether (VP)
Norman L. Leblond III (Pres)

CONSOLIDATED GRAPHICS GROUP, INC.
1614 E 40th St, Cleveland, OH 44103
Tel.: (216) 881-9191
Web Site: https://www.csinc.com
Year Founded: 1996
Sales Range: $10-24.9 Million
Emp.: 140
Offset Printing, Prepress, Digital Printing & Other Marketing Communications Services
N.A.I.C.S.: 323111

Kenneth A. Lanci *(Chm)*
Neil Gallagher *(VP-Ops)*
Terry Hartman *(CEO)*
Wally Lanci *(Gen Counsel)*
Oliver Moeritz *(CFO)*
Matt Reville *(COO)*
Michelle Hilston *(Dir-Postal Solutions & Client Rels)*
Rick Spector *(Pres-Consolidated Technologies)*

CONSOLIDATED HEALTH SYSTEMS INC

5000 KY Rt 321, Prestonsburg, KY 41653
Tel.: (606) 886-8511   KY
Web Site: http://www.hrmc.org
Year Founded: 1984
Sales Range: $10-24.9 Million
Emp.: 61
Health Care Srvices
N.A.I.C.S.: 622110
Edward R. Nairn *(Sec)*
Burl W. Spurlock *(Vice Chm)*
Paul D. Nunn *(Treas)*
Harold C. Warman Jr. *(Pres & CEO)*

CONSOLIDATED INDUSTRIES, INC.

677 Mixville Rd, Cheshire, CT 06410-3836
Tel.: (203) 272-5371   CT
Web Site:
   https://www.consolindustries.com
Year Founded: 1940
Sales Range: $10-24.9 Million
Emp.: 101
Ferrous & Non-Ferrous Die Forging Mfr
N.A.I.C.S.: 331523
John D. Wilbur *(Pres)*
Tim McHenry *(Dir-Quality)*

Subsidiaries:

Arnprior Aerospace Inc.   (1)
107 Baskin Drive East, Arnprior, K7S 3M1, ON, Canada
Tel.: (613) 623-4267
Web Site:
   http://www.arnprioraerospace.com
Emp.: 300
Commercial Aircraft Components Mfr
N.A.I.C.S.: 336413
Tom Melvin *(Pres)*

CONSOLIDATED INVESTMENT CORPORATION

8 N State St Ste 420, Painesville, OH 44077
Tel.: (440) 946-9320   OH
Web Site:
   http://www.consolidatedinvest
   ment.com
Year Founded: 1969
Sales Range: $10-24.9 Million
Emp.: 20
Real Estate Management
N.A.I.C.S.: 722513

CONSOLIDATED INVESTMENT GROUP, LLC

6400 S Fiddlers Green Cir, Englewood, CO 80111
Tel.: (303) 789-2664
Web Site: http://www.ciginvest.com
Year Founded: 1999
Sales Range: $1-9.9 Million
Emp.: 10
Miscellaneous Financial Investment Activities
N.A.I.C.S.: 523999
Heidi Brendemihl *(Portfolio Mgr)*

Subsidiaries:

Sicilian Chefs, Inc.   (1)
1001 Lower Landing Rd, Blackwood, NJ 08012

Tel.: (856) 227-2585
Sales Range: $1-9.9 Million
Frozen Specialty Food Mfr
N.A.I.C.S.: 311412

CONSOLIDATED LUMBER CO.

808 N 4th St, Stillwater, MN 55082-4004
Tel.: (651) 439-3138   MN
Web Site: http://www.abc-clc.com
Year Founded: 1903
Sales Range: $100-124.9 Million
Emp.: 200
Retailer of Lumber & Building Materials; Provider of Architectural Services
N.A.I.C.S.: 423310
Ron Schumacher *(Pres & CEO)*
Brad Spaulding *(Gen Mgr-Window Svcs)*
Brent Meissner *(Gen Mgr-River Falls)*
Denis Carteron *(Gen Mgr-Amery)*
Henry Studtmann *(Gen Mgr-Milltown)*
Jesse Barr *(Gen Mgr-Cabinet Gallery)*

Subsidiaries:

Arrow Building Centers   (1)
2000 Tower Dr W, Stillwater, MN 55082-7517
Tel.: (651) 439-3518
Web Site: http://www.abc-clc.com
Sales Range: $25-49.9 Million
Emp.: 120
Retailer of Lumber & Building Materials
N.A.I.C.S.: 423310
David L. Majeski *(Pres)*

Division (Domestic):

Arrow Building Center - Post Frame Division   (2)
876 County Rd U, Hudson, WI 54016
Tel.: (715) 556-7656
Post Frame Construction Services
N.A.I.C.S.: 236210

CONSOLIDATED MARKETING SERVICES, INC. OF MA

28 Cobble Hill Rd, Somerville, MA 02143
Tel.: (978) 658-5756
Web Site:
   http://www.cmsassociates.com
Rev.: $1,800,000
Emp.: 15
Administrative Management & General Management Consulting Service
N.A.I.C.S.: 541611
Stephen L. Crampe *(CFO)*

Subsidiaries:

Progressive Promotions, Inc.   (1)
145 Cedar Ln, Englewood, NJ 07631
Tel.: (201) 945-0500
Web Site:
   http://www.progressivepromotions.com
Sales Range: $1-9.9 Million
Emp.: 18
Services Related to Advertising
N.A.I.C.S.: 541890
Julie Levi *(Pres)*
Donna Anastasio *(Exec VP-Sls)*
Pam Abramowitz *(VP-Ops & Fin)*

CONSOLIDATED METAL PRODUCTS, INC.

1028 Depot St, Cincinnati, OH 45204-2012
Tel.: (513) 251-2626   OH
Web Site: https://www.cmpubolt.com
Year Founded: 1942
Sales Range: $75-99.9 Million
Emp.: 130
Threaded Steel Bar Products & U-bolt Mfr
N.A.I.C.S.: 332722
Fred Madden *(VP-Admin)*
Ronald Eldridge *(Mgr-HR)*
John Bernloehr *(Pres)*

Subsidiaries:

Consolidated Metal Products, Inc.-Europe   (1)
4th Fl Imperial House, 15-19 Kingsway, London, WC2B 6UN, United Kingdom
Tel.: (44) 2076321650
Web Site: http://www.cmpubolt.com
Metal Products Sales
N.A.I.C.S.: 423510

Consolidated Metal Products, Inc.-Germany   (1)
Riesling Weg 1, PO Box 110124, D 76487, Baden-Baden, Germany   (100%)
Tel.: (49) 7221504840
Web Site: http://www.doerr-iv.de
Sales Range: $10-24.9 Million
Emp.: 10
N.A.I.C.S.: 331221

Consolidated Metal Products, Inc.-Japan   (1)
3-15-8 Hayamiya, Nerima-ku, Tokyo, 179-0085, Japan
Tel.: (81) 3 5912 3567
Web Site: http://www.cmpubolt.com
Sales Range: $10-24.9 Million
Emp.: 1
Metal Product Distr
N.A.I.C.S.: 423510

Consolidated Metal Products, Inc.-South America   (1)
Camino a la Toma s/n Villa de Soto, CP 5284, Cordoba, Argentina
Tel.: (54) 3549 480020
U-Bolts Mfr
N.A.I.C.S.: 331221

CONSOLIDATED MIDWEST, INC.

3600 Hwy 157, La Crosse, WI 54601-1834
Tel.: (608) 781-1010   WI
Year Founded: 1947
Sales Range: $75-99.9 Million
Emp.: 50
Gases; Liquefied Petroleum; Gasoline; Propane Gas; Natural Gas Distr
N.A.I.C.S.: 424720
Richard A. Linton *(Treas & Controller)*

Subsidiaries:

Midwest Bottle Gas Company   (1)
3600 State Rd 157, La Crosse, WI 54601-1834   (100%)
Tel.: (608) 781-1010
Sales Range: $25-49.9 Million
Retail Liquefied Petroleum Gas & Appliances, Refined Gasoline & Fuel Oils
N.A.I.C.S.: 424720

CONSOLIDATED NEURO SUPPLY, INC.

1038 Techne Center Dr, Milford, OH 45150
Web Site:
   https://www.neurosupply.com
Year Founded: 2003
Sales Range: $1-9.9 Million
Emp.: 6
Neurodiagnostic Medical Supplies
N.A.I.C.S.: 423450
Jason Mayer *(Pres)*

CONSOLIDATED PIPE & SUPPLY COMPANY

1205 Hilltop Pkwy, Birmingham, AL 35204-5002
Tel.: (205) 323-7261   AL
Web Site:
   https://www.consolidatedpipe.com
Year Founded: 1960
Sales Range: $250-299.9 Million
Emp.: 530
Wholesale & Retail Distributor of Steel Pipe, Valves & Fittings; Manufacturer of PVC Pipe, Coat & Wrap Pipe & Fusion Bond Coat Steel Pipe
N.A.I.C.S.: 423510

Howard J. Kerr *(Pres & CEO)*

Subsidiaries:

Vulcan Plastics Inc   (1)
207 Durham Dr S W Breeding Industrial Park, Athens, AL 35611
Tel.: (256) 233-3520
Web Site: http://www.consolidatedpipe.com
Plastic Tank Mfr
N.A.I.C.S.: 326199

CONSOLIDATED PLANNING INC.

4201 Congress St Ste 215, Charlotte, NC 28209
Tel.: (704) 552-8507
Web Site: http://www.cplanning.com
Sales Range: $10-24.9 Million
Emp.: 50
Investment Advisory Services
N.A.I.C.S.: 523940
Andy Brincefield *(Pres & CEO)*
Sarah Hampton *(Mgr-Brokerage)*
Becky Thompson *(Dir-Talent Acq)*
Neal Brincefield *(Mng Partner)*
Todd Achberger *(Sr VP)*
James B. Mathis III *(Dir-Mktg & Community Affairs)*

CONSOLIDATED PLASTICS CO. INC.

4700 Prosper Dr, Stow, OH 44224
Tel.: (330) 425-3900
Web Site:
   https://www.consolidatedplastics.com
Year Founded: 1981
Sales Range: $10-24.9 Million
Emp.: 14
Plastics Materials & Basic Shapes Distr
N.A.I.C.S.: 424610
Brenton Taussig *(Pres)*

CONSOLIDATED PLASTICS CORP.

14954 La Palma Dr, Chino, CA 91710
Tel.: (909) 393-8222
Web Site:
   https://www.planetplastics.com
Rev.: $12,100,000
Emp.: 15
Plastics Sheets & Rods
N.A.I.C.S.: 424610
Gloria Bouris *(Pres)*

CONSOLIDATED PRESS, INC.

6511 Oakton St, Morton Grove, IL 60053
Tel.: (847) 967-3600
Web Site: http://www.cpipress.com
Year Founded: 1965
Sales Range: $10-24.9 Million
Emp.: 100
Printing & Data Archive Solutions
N.A.I.C.S.: 323111

Subsidiaries:

NCL Communications   (1)
1880 Busse St, Elk Grove Village, IL 60007
Tel.: (847) 593-2610
Web Site: http://www.nclgraphics.com
Rev.: $336,000
Emp.: 60
Lithographic Printing Services
N.A.I.C.S.: 323111

CONSOLIDATED PRODUCTS SYSTEMS

118 Wendel Rd, Irwin, PA 15642
Tel.: (724) 864-9200
Rev.: $13,100,000
Emp.: 50
Candy Distr
N.A.I.C.S.: 424450
James Williamson Jr. *(Pres & CEO)*

Consolidated Reinforcements—(Continued)

CONSOLIDATED REINFORCE-MENTS
13801 Ave K, Austin, TX 78728
Tel.: (512) 251-1044
Web Site: https://www.critexas.com
Sales Range: $10-24.9 Million
Emp.: 20
Cable, Wire
N.A.I.C.S.: 423510
Travis Gilpin (CFO)
Dennard Gilpin (Pres)

CONSOLIDATED RESTAU-RANTS OF CALIFORNIA
15375 Barranca Pkwy Ste G105, Ir-
vine, CA 92618
Tel.: (949) 453-9181
Sales Range: $10-24.9 Million
Emp.: 8
Fast Food Restaurant Operator
N.A.I.C.S.: 722513
Michael J. Kourie (Pres)

CONSOLIDATED SAFETY SERVICES, INC.
10301 Democracy Ln Ste 300, Fair-
fax, VA 22030
Tel.: (703) 691-4612
Web Site: http://www.css-
dynamac.com
Year Founded: 1987
Sales Range: $25-49.9 Million
Emp.: 375
Environmental, Health & Safety Con-
sulting Services
N.A.I.C.S.: 541620
Jolanda Janczewski (Chm)
Dianne N. Janczewski (Sr VP-
Scientific Applications)
Georgeann N. Morekas (Sr VP-
Emergency Response & Disaster Re-
covery)
W. Mark Pierce (Sr VP-Health &
Safety)
W. Dennis Lauchner (CEO)
Jill Meyer (Dir-Coastal Programs &
Natural Resources)
Jennifer Hodges (Dir-IT)
Duane Ratliff (Sr VP-Space Pro-
grams)
Michael Wray (VP-Comm & Bus Dev)
Dixie Harvey (VP-Contracts)
James J. Wano (VP-Fin)
Joseph W. Craver III (Pres & COO)

CONSOLIDATED SCRAP RE-SOURCES
120 Hokes Mill Rd, York, PA 17404
Tel.: (717) 843-0931
Web Site:
https://www.consolidatedscrap.com
Sales Range: $10-24.9 Million
Emp.: 100
Junk & Scrap Metal Processing
N.A.I.C.S.: 423930
Richard E. Abrams (Chm & CEO)
Martin Fogle (Sr VP)
Steve Marcus (VP)

CONSOLIDATED SERVICES GROUP
Brookview Corp Ctr 1240 S Broad St
Ste 200, Lansdale, PA 19446
Tel.: (215) 661-0500
Web Site: http://www.csg-inc.net
Year Founded: 1980
Sales Range: $10-24.9 Million
Emp.: 500
Medical Claims Management
N.A.I.C.S.: 524298
Michael A. Morrone (Founder & Chm)
Craig Goldstein (Pres)
Maria Longworth (Sr VP-Medical
Case Mgmt Svcs)

Stan Tomasevich (CIO & Sr VP)
Mark Hepperlen (Sr VP & Dir-Ops)
Mike Schrauben (VP-Bus Dev-
Midwest)
Nicole Bianchi (Sr VP-Medical Bill
Review Svcs)

Subsidiaries:

CHN Solutions (1)
300 American Metro Blvd Ste 170, Hamil-
ton, NJ 08619
Tel.: (609) 631-0474
Web Site: http://www.chn.com
Preferred Provider & Managed Healthcare
Services
N.A.I.C.S.: 561499

CONSOLIDATED SHOE COM-PANY INC.
22290 Timberlake Rd, Lynchburg, VA
24502-7305
Tel.: (434) 239-0391
Web Site:
https://www.musthaveshoes.com
Year Founded: 1907
Sales Range: $10-24.9 Million
Emp.: 50
Mfr of Footwear
N.A.I.C.S.: 424340
William Carrington (CEO)

CONSOLIDATED SMART SYS-TEMS GROUP
620 W 135th St, Gardena, CA 90248
Tel.: (310) 515-0533
Web Site:
http://www.consolidatedsmart.com
Rev: $36,431,961
Emp.: 170
Laundry, Coin-Operated
N.A.I.C.S.: 812310
Bob Benton (Owner)

CONSOLIDATED SNACKS INC.
6647 Molly Pitcher Hwy, Chambers-
burg, PA 17201
Tel.: (717) 375-2243
Sales Range: $10-24.9 Million
Emp.: 220
Snack Food Mfr
N.A.I.C.S.: 311919
Jim Appold (CEO)
Robert Feulner (Pres)

CONSOLIDATED STEEL SER-VICES, INC.
632 Glendale Valley Blvd, Fallentim-
ber, PA 16639
Tel.: (814) 944-5890
Web Site: https://www.csteel.com
Emp.: 50
Steel Products Whslr
N.A.I.C.S.: 423510
Cynthia Cack (Pres)

CONSOLIDATED STORAGE COMPANIES, INC.
225 Main St, Tatamy, PA 18085
Tel.: (610) 253-2775
Web Site:
http://www.consolidatedstorage.com
Holding Company; Storage Products
Mfr & Distr
N.A.I.C.S.: 551112

Subsidiaries:

Equipto, Inc. (1)
4550 Beltway Dr, Addison, TX 75001
Tel.: (610) 253-2775
Sales Range: $10-24.9 Million
Storage Products Mfr & Distr
N.A.I.C.S.: 337215

CONSOLIDATED SUPPLY CO.
7337 SW Kable Ln, Tigard, OR
97224-7942
Tel.: (503) 620-7050

Web Site:
https://www.consolidatedsupply.com
Year Founded: 1928
Sales Range: $200-249.9 Million
Emp.: 230
Plumbing Services
N.A.I.C.S.: 423720
Kevin R. Neupert (Treas & Sec)
Robert Bruce (CFO & Sr VP)
Judy Miller (Controller)
Rod Sanders (Dir-IT)
Randy Vos (Dir-Pur)
Karla Neupert Hockley (Pres)
Pat Jones (Dir-Credit)
Pauline Mueller (Dir-HR)
Karolyn Neupert Gordon (Chm)
Todd Coleman (Dir-Ops-Bus)
Patrick Tulloch (Gen Mgr-Western
Washington)
Greg Jackson (Mgr-Boise)
Jurgen Ruttke (Mgr-Nampa)
Judie Eaton (Mgr-Corp Showroom)
Mark Smith (Mgr-Eastern)
Brad Press (Mgr-Mktg & Adv)
Rob Luttrell (Mgr-Ops-East)
Chuck Panella (Mgr-Sls-Fusion Prod-
ucts)
Mike Smith (Mgr-Sls-Heating)
Scott Narum (Mgr-Sls-Water Works)

Subsidiaries:

Consolidated Supply Co. (1)
805 NW 42nd St, Seattle, WA 98107-4552
Tel.: (206) 784-0047
Web Site:
http://www.consolidatedsupply.com
Sales Range: $10-24.9 Million
Emp.: 21
Plumbing Services
N.A.I.C.S.: 423720
Gary Johnson (Sls Mgr-Western Washing-
ton)
Karolyn Neupert Gordon (Chm)
Kevin R. Neupert (Treas & Sec)
Tom J. Bedell (VP-Sls & Branches)
Pat Jones (Dir-Credit)
Judy Miller (Controller)
Pauline Mueller (Dir-HR)
Randy Vos (Dir-Pur)

Consolidated Supply Co. (1)
777 N 5 Mile, Boise, ID
83713-8922 (100%)
Tel.: (208) 322-5511
Web Site:
http://www.consolidatedsupply.com
Sales Range: $10-24.9 Million
Emp.: 16
Wholesale Provider Of Plumbing Services
N.A.I.C.S.: 423720
Greg Jackson (Gen Mgr)

Consolidated Supply Co. - Water
Works Divison (1)
2203 Inter Ave Ste A, Puyallup, WA 98372
Tel.: (253) 848-9337
Plumbing Contracting Services
N.A.I.C.S.: 238220

Fluid Systems Hawaii Inc. (1)
96-1407 Waihona Pl, Pearl City, HI
96782-1953 (100%)
Tel.: (808) 456-5966
Web Site:
http://www.consolidatedsupply.com
Sales Range: $10-24.9 Million
Emp.: 10
Provider of Industrial Machinery & Equip-
ment Services
N.A.I.C.S.: 423830
Calvin Okinaka (Branch Mgr)

CONSOLIDATED SUPPLY COMPANY INC
10325 J St, Omaha, NE 68127
Tel.: (402) 331-0500
Web Site:
http://www.consolidatedkitchen.com
Rev: $20,249,068
Emp.: 125
Kitchen Cabinets
N.A.I.C.S.: 423310

Julie Lukken (Controller)

CONSOLIDATED TELECOM-MUNICATIONS COMPANY
1102 Madison St, Brainerd, MN
56401
Tel.: (218) 454-1234
Web Site: http://www.connectctc.com
Year Founded: 1950
Sales Range: $10-24.9 Million
Emp.: 76
Telephone & Other Communication
Services
N.A.I.C.S.: 517810
Kathy Kobliska (Treas)
Morris Nelson (VP)
John Luce (Pres)
Paul Nieman Jr. (Sec)

CONSOLIDATED TOURS INC.
505 8th Ave Ste 801, New York, NY
10018-6598
Tel.: (212) 586-5230
Web Site: https://www.amta.com
Year Founded: 1976
Sales Range: $10-24.9 Million
Emp.: 25
Travel Services
N.A.I.C.S.: 561520
Zbigniew Wegiel (Pres)
Alex Wegiel (VP)

CONSOLIDATED UTILITY DIS-TRICT
709 New Salem Hwy, Murfreesboro,
TN 37129
Tel.: (615) 893-7225
Web Site: https://www.cudrc.com
Year Founded: 1970
Sales Range: $10-24.9 Million
Emp.: 61
Water Supply
N.A.I.C.S.: 221310
Judy Bowling (Office Mgr)
Mark Elgin (Asst Mgr-Maintenance)
Paul Long (Comptroller)
Bill Dunnill (Gen Mgr)

CONSOLIDATED VENDORS CORP.
953 West Seminole Rd, Norton
Shores, MI 49441
Web Site:
http://www.cvcvendors.com
Rev: $13,900,000
Emp.: 25
Food Vending Machines
N.A.I.C.S.: 445132

CONSOLIDATED WATER WORKS DISTRICT 1
8814 Main St, Houma, LA 70363
Tel.: (985) 879-2495
Web Site:
http://www.consolidatedwater.org
Year Founded: 1955
Sales Range: $10-24.9 Million
Emp.: 82
Water Supply Services
N.A.I.C.S.: 221310
Michael Sobert (Gen Mgr)

CONSONANCE CAPITAL PARTNERS LLC
1370 6th Ave 33rd Fl, New York, NY
10019
Tel.: (212) 660-8060
Web Site:
https://www.consonancecapital.com
Year Founded: 2005
Privater Equity Firm
N.A.I.C.S.: 523999
Nancy-Ann M. DeParle (Co-Founder
& Mng Partner)
Stephen McKenna (Co-Founder &
Mng Partner)

Mitchell Blutt *(Co-Founder & Mng Partner)*
Benjamin Edmands *(Co-Founder & Mng Partner)*
Sean Breen *(Principal)*
Sapna Tejwani Jethwa *(VP)*
Javier Starkand *(Principal)*
Edward J. Cook *(COO & VP-Legal Affairs)*

Subsidiaries:

Enclara Health, LLC   (1)
1480 Imperial Way, West Deptford, NJ 08066
Tel.: (856) 384-5887
Web Site: http://www.enclarahealth.com
Hospice-Specialty Pharmacy Services
N.A.I.C.S.: 424210
Andrew Horowitz *(Founder & CEO)*
Eric Hersh *(CFO)*
Rushi Patel *(Exec VP-Ops)*
Scott Baach *(Chief Admin Officer, Gen Counsel & Exec VP)*
Betsy Rothley *(Chief Dev Officer)*
Walter Valentine *(VP-Ops)*
Matthew Sudduth *(CFO & Exec VP)*
Loren Brook *(Exec Vp-Client Svcs)*

Subsidiary (Domestic):

PBM-Plus, Inc.   (2)
300 TechneCentre Dr Ste B, Milford, OH 45150
Tel.: (513) 248-3071
Web Site: http://www.pbmplus.com
Pharmacy Benefit Management Services & Pharmaceutical Mail-Order Services
N.A.I.C.S.: 524292
Tony Diana *(Dir-Client Svcs)*

excelleRx, Inc.   (2)
1601 Cherry St Ste 1700, Philadelphia, PA 19102
Tel.: (215) 282-1600
Web Site:
    http://www.hospicepharmacia.com
Hospice-Specialty Pharmaceutical Distr
N.A.I.C.S.: 424210
Michael Cinque *(VP-Ops)*
Tom Stieritz *(Sr VP & Gen Mgr)*
Steve Lemak *(VP-IT)*
Michael Giardetti *(Sr Mgr-Network Sys)*
Paul Williams *(Mgr-HR)*
Scott Baach *(Chief Admin Officer, Gen Counsel & Exec VP)*
Loren Brook *(Exec VP-Client Svcs)*
Andrew Horowitz *(Founder & CEO)*
Rushi Patel *(Exec VP-Ops)*
Matthew Sudduth *(CFO & Exec VP)*

CONSORTA , INC.
Schaumburg Corp Ctr 1475 E Woodfield Rd Ste 400, Schaumburg, IL 60173
Tel.: (847) 592-7800
Sales Range: $75-99.9 Million
Emp.: 50
Cooperative Healthcare Management Services
N.A.I.C.S.: 541618
Linda Hicks *(Dir-HR)*
W. Darrel Weatherford *(Pres & COO)*

CONSORTIUM FOR OCEAN LEADERSHIP, INC.
1201 New York Ave NW 4th Fl, Washington, DC 20005
Tel.: (202) 232-3900   DE
Web Site:
    http://www.oceanleadership.org
Year Founded: 1994
Sales Range: $100-124.9 Million
Ocean Research & Education Support Services
N.A.I.C.S.: 541715
Yan Xing *(CFO)*

CONSORTIUM FOR OLDER ADULT WELLNESS
2575 S Wadsworth Blvd, Lakewood, CO 80227-3218
Tel.: (303) 984-1845   CO

Web Site: http://www.coaw.org
Year Founded: 2001
Sales Range: $1-9.9 Million
Emp.: 9
Community Health Care Support Services
N.A.I.C.S.: 813920
Lynnzy McIntosh *(Exec Dir)*
Christine Katzenmeyer *(Founder & Dir-Community Health)*
Maripat Gallas *(Dir-Implementation)*
Joni Saunders *(Coord-Program)*
Tim Cusick *(Mgr-Acctg)*
Lynnzy McIntosh *(Exec Dir)*
Christine Katzenmeyer *(Founder & Dir-Community Health)*
Paul Dietel *(Pres)*
George Mitchell *(VP)*
Julya Bridgewater *(Treas & Sec)*
Paul Dietel *(Pres)*
George Mitchell *(VP)*
Julya Bridgewater *(Treas & Sec)*

CONSORTIUM FOR WORKER EDUCATION INC.
275 7th Ave 18th Fl, New York, NY 10001-6708
Tel.: (212) 647-1900
Web Site: http://www.cwe.org
Year Founded: 1985
Sales Range: $10-24.9 Million
Emp.: 150
Provider of Job Training & Related Services
N.A.I.C.S.: 624310
Joseph McDermott *(Exec Dir)*
Debbie Buxton *(Dir-Workforce Education)*
Tarmo Kirsimae *(Dir-Child & Healthcare Initiatives)*
Vincent Alvarez *(VP)*

CONSTANTINE'S WOOD CENTER OF FLORIDA, INC.
1040 E Oakland Park Blvd, Fort Lauderdale, FL 33334
Tel.: (954) 561-1716
Web Site:
    https://www.constantines.com
Catalog Mail Order House
N.A.I.C.S.: 459420

CONSTELLATION HEALTHCARE TECHNOLOGIES, INC.
3200 Wilcrest Dr Ste 600, Houston, TX 77042
Tel.: (713) 432-1100   DE
Web Site:
    http://www.constellationhealth.com
Sales Range: $75-99.9 Million
Healtcare Services
N.A.I.C.S.: 621999
Sotirios Zaharis *(CFO)*

Subsidiaries:

Phoenix Health Care Inc.   (1)
560 Sylvan Ave, Englewood Cliffs, NJ 07632-3119
Tel.: (201) 567-4364
Web Site:
    http://www.phoenixhealthcarenj.com
Emp.: 138
Offices of Mental Health Practitioners (except Physicians)
N.A.I.C.S.: 621330
Kathy Carroll *(Pres)*

CONSTELLATION REAL ESTATE GROUP, INC.
750 E Pratt St, Baltimore, MD 21202
Web Site:
    http://www.constellationreg.com
Year Founded: 2015
Privater Equity Firm
N.A.I.C.S.: 523999
Scott Smith *(Pres)*

Subsidiaries:

SmartZip Analytics, Inc.   (1)
227 Central Ave, Sarasota, FL 34236
Tel.: (855) 661-1064
Web Site: http://www.smartzip.com
Activities Related to Real Estate
N.A.I.C.S.: 531390

Top Producer Systems Company ULC   (1)
Suite 300 10271 Shellbridge Way, Richmond, V6X 2W8, BC, Canada
Tel.: (604) 270-8819
Web Site: http://www.topproducer.com
Computer Software Developer
N.A.I.C.S.: 513210

CONSTELLATION SOFTWARE ENGINEERING, CORP.
180 Admiral Cochrane Dr Ste 230, Annapolis, MD 21401
Tel.: (301) 805-8880
Web Site: https://www.cse-corp.com
Year Founded: 2002
Rev.: $5,300,000
Emp.: 32
Computer System Design Services
N.A.I.C.S.: 541512
Rodger Blevins *(CEO)*
Vijay Mishra *(Pres)*
Scott Blackburn *(CFO)*
Carolynn Popp *(Dir-Human Resources)*
Renee Campbell *(Sr Mgr-Proposal)*
Tiss Araya-Pajotee *(Mgr-Contracts)*
Margarita Smith *(Mgr-Accounting)*

CONSTRUCT SOLUTIONS, INC.
9378 Castlegate Dr, Indianapolis, IN 46256
Tel.: (317) 288-5331
Web Site:
    http://www.constructsolutions.com
Year Founded: 2007
Sales Range: $1-9.9 Million
Emp.: 22
Roofing Installation & Repair Services
N.A.I.C.S.: 238160
Joshua Mike Glassburn *(Pres)*

CONSTRUCT TWO GROUP
30 S Ivey Ln, Orlando, FL 32811
Tel.: (407) 295-9812
Web Site:
    http://www.constructtwo.com
Rev.: $4,900,000
Emp.: 3
Commercial & Institutional Building Construction
N.A.I.C.S.: 236220
Derrick Wallace *(Chm)*
Keith Williams *(Pres & CEO)*

CONSTRUCTION AND SERVICE SOLUTIONS CORP.
700 Howard St, Buffalo, NY 14206-2211
Tel.: (716) 852-1219
Web Site: http://www.csscbuilds.com
Year Founded: 2002
Sales Range: $1-9.9 Million
Emp.: 47
Commercial Construction Services
N.A.I.C.S.: 236220
Suzanne Witnauer *(Pres)*

CONSTRUCTION EQUIPMENT COMPANY
18650 SW Pacific Hwy, Tualatin, OR 97062
Tel.: (503) 692-9000
Web Site:
    http://www.ceccrushers.com
Sales Range: $10-24.9 Million
Emp.: 60

Crushing, Pulverizing & Screening Machinery
N.A.I.C.S.: 423810
Gary D. Smith *(Pres)*
Pat Andrew *(VP-Natl Sls)*

CONSTRUCTION FORMS, INC.
777 Maritime Dr, Port Washington, WI 53074-0308
Tel.: (262) 284-7800   NJ
Web Site: https://www.conforms.com
Year Founded: 1969
Sales Range: $10-24.9 Million
Emp.: 100
Concrete Pumping System Mfr
N.A.I.C.S.: 332996
Terry Skebba *(CFO)*
Thomas Edward Hamilton *(Bd of Dirs, Executives)*
Tom Hamilton *(Pres)*
Pat Bartling *(COO)*
Stephan Achs *(CMO & Chief Sls Officer)*

Subsidiaries:

CF Ultra Tech   (1)
777 Maritime Dr, Port Washington, WI 53074-0308   (100%)
Tel.: (262) 284-7800
Web Site: http://www.conforms.com
Concrete Pumping Systems & Accessories
N.A.I.C.S.: 332996
Greg Gescheidle *(Mgr)*

Con Forms   (1)
777 Maritime Dr, Port Washington, WI 53074
Tel.: (262) 284-7800
Web Site: http://www.conforms.com
Sales Range: $10-24.9 Million
Concrete Pumps & Related Equipment
N.A.I.C.S.: 333914

Con Forms Asia Sdn Bhd   (1)
No 6 Jalan Belati 1 Taman Perindustrian Maju Jaya, 81300, Johor Bahru, Malaysia
Tel.: (60) 7 5591 868
Construction Equipment Whslr
N.A.I.C.S.: 423810

ESSER-WERKE GmbH & Co. KG   (1)
Zum Puddelhammer 25, 59581, Warstein, Germany
Tel.: (49) 2902 896 0
Web Site: http://www.esser-werke.de
Fabricated Pipe Mfr
N.A.I.C.S.: 332996
Stefan Harbig *(Co-CEO)*
Tom Hamilton *(Co-CEO)*

CONSTRUCTION MANAGEMENT SERVICE
3600 Silverside Rd, Wilmington, DE 19810
Tel.: (302) 478-4200   DE
Web Site:
    https://www.hatzelandbuehler.com
Year Founded: 1984
Rev.: $57,000,000
Emp.: 600
Construction Management; General Electric Contractors
N.A.I.C.S.: 238210
William Goeller *(Co-Pres)*
Gerard Herr *(Pres)*

Subsidiaries:

Hatzel & Buehler, Inc.   (1)
3600 Silverside Rd, Wilmington, DE 19810   (100%)
Tel.: (302) 478-4200
Web Site: http://www.hatzelandbuehler.com
Sales Range: $10-24.9 Million
Emp.: 20
General Electrical Contractor
N.A.I.C.S.: 238210
William A. Goeller *(Pres)*
Scott Eyester *(VP & Branch Mgr-New Jersey)*

Construction Management Service—(Continued)

James C. Ivey *(VP & Branch Mgr-Ohio)*
Gerald Herr *(Treas & VP)*
Kevin Martin *(Branch Mgr)*

Pinnacle Electronic Systems (1)
1157 Phoenixville Pike Ste 107, West Chester, PA 19380-1203
Tel.: (610) 430-0212
Web Site: http://www.pinnaclesys.com
Rev.: $1,815,401
Emp.: 25
Security Integrator
N.A.I.C.S.: 561621

CONSTRUCTION MARKETING ADVISORS
1220 Iroquois Ave Ste 210, Naperville, IL 60563
Tel.: (630) 868-5061
Web Site:
https://www.constructionmarketing association.org
Year Founded: 1996
Sales Range: $1-9.9 Million
Emp.: 7
Advetising Agency
N.A.I.C.S.: 541810
Neil M. Brown *(Principal)*

CONSTRUCTION MATERIALS INC.
6725 Oxford St, Minneapolis, MN 55426
Tel.: (952) 929-0431
Web Site:
https://www.constructionma terialsinc.com
Sales Range: $10-24.9 Million
Emp.: 20
Brick, Stone & Related Material
N.A.I.C.S.: 332312
Dick Galligan *(Pres)*

CONSTRUCTION MATERIALS INC.
12400 Olive St, Kansas City, MO 64146
Tel.: (816) 942-9783
Year Founded: 1970
Sales Range: $10-24.9 Million
Emp.: 15
Lumber, Plywood & Millwork
N.A.I.C.S.: 423310
Ray Goffinet *(Pres)*
Butch Bazil *(VP)*

CONSTRUCTION METALS INC.
13169 Unit B Sover Ave, Fontana, CA 92337
Tel.: (909) 390-9880
Web Site:
http://www.constructionmetals.com
Sales Range: $25-49.9 Million
Emp.: 37
Mfr of Sheet Metalwork
N.A.I.C.S.: 423330
Aurea Ramos *(Mgr-Shared Svcs)*

CONSTRUCTION SEALANTS SUPPLY
4450 W Diablo Dr, Las Vegas, NV 89118
Tel.: (702) 873-0203
Web Site:
https://www.theleakstopshere.com
Rev.: $12,000,000
Emp.: 16
Chemical Product Whslr
N.A.I.C.S.: 424690
Vern Phillips *(Pres)*
Tyler Phillips *(VP)*

CONSTRUCTION SERVICES 2000, INC.
604 S Mulberry St, Millstadt, IL 62260
Tel.: (618) 476-9119

Year Founded: 1996
Rev.: $4,600,000
Emp.: 69
Drywall & Insulation Contractors
N.A.I.C.S.: 238310

CONSTRUCTION SERVICES BRANFORD LLC
63 3 N Branford Rd Ste 3, Branford, CT 06405
Tel.: (203) 488-0712
Web Site: https://www.csofb.com
Sales Range: $10-24.9 Million
Emp.: 20
General Construction & Construction Management Firm Specializing in Wireless Telecommunications Facility Development
N.A.I.C.S.: 236220
John Centore *(Office Mgr)*

CONSTRUCTION SPECIAL-TIES, INC.
3 Werner Way, Lebanon, NJ 08833-2223
Tel.: (908) 236-0800   **NJ**
Web Site: http://www.c-sgroup.com
Year Founded: 1948
Sales Range: $150-199.9 Million
Emp.: 800
Mfr of Aluminum Architectural Building Products
N.A.I.C.S.: 332323
Subsidiaries:

C/S Construction Specialties (Malaysia) Sdn Bhd
Lot 7920 Bukit Cerakah Jalan Pekan Subang, 40150, Shah Alam, Selangor, Malaysia
Tel.: (60) 3 7859 1711
Sales Range: $10-24.9 Million
Emp.: 6
Architectural Product Distr & Whslr
N.A.I.C.S.: 337212

C/S Construction Specialties Company (1)
895 Lakefront Promenade, Mississauga, L5E 2C2, ON, Canada   **(100%)**
Tel.: (905) 274-3611
Web Site: http://www.c-sgroup.com
Sales Range: $10-24.9 Million
Emp.: 90
Producer of Architectural Products
N.A.I.C.S.: 327390

C/S Construction Specialties Middle East LLC (1)
1705 Dubai World Trade Centre Sheikh Zayed Road, PO Box 9260, Dubai, United Arab Emirates
Tel.: (971) 4 3312167
Web Site: http://www.c-sgroup.ae
Architectural & Building Product Mfr
N.A.I.C.S.: 332323

C/S Deutschland GmbH (1)
Heerstrasse 74, Herne, 45772, Germany
Tel.: (49) 2325 640392 0
Web Site: http://www.c-sgroup.de
Emp.: 20
Building Materials Mfr
N.A.I.C.S.: 326199
Anga Becker *(Mgr)*

C/S France (1)
135 rue Edouard Isambard, BP 66, Pacy-sur-Eure, Cedex, France
Tel.: (33) 2 32 67 00 00
Web Site: http://www.cs-france.fr
Building Product Mfr
N.A.I.C.S.: 332311

C/S Polska Sp. ZO.O (1)
ul Szczecinska 34, Kobylanka, 73108, Szczecin, Poland
Tel.: (48) 91 391 35 10
Web Site: http://www.cspolska.pl
Emp.: 30
Building Product Mfr
N.A.I.C.S.: 332311

Conspec International (Hong Kong) Ltd. (1)

Room A B & C 20th Floor West Gate Power 7 Wing Hong Street, Cheung Sha Wan, Kowloon, China (Hong Kong)
Tel.: (852) 2892 0917
Emp.: 10
Architectural Product Distr & Whslr
N.A.I.C.S.: 332323
Tom Lo *(Gen Mgr)*

Construction Specialites (UK) Ltd. (1)
1010 Westcott Venture Park, Westcott, HP18 0XB, Bucks, United Kingdom
Tel.: (44) 1296 652828
Web Site: http://www.c-sgroup.co.uk
Sales Range: $25-49.9 Million
Emp.: 50
Building Product Mfr
N.A.I.C.S.: 332311
Wendy Duckham *(Mng Dir)*

Construction Specialties, Inc. - Dec-c cLink Products Division (1)
225 Regency Ct Ste 103, Brookfield, WI 53045-6166
Tel.: (262) 789-1750
Web Site: http://www.csgroup.com
Sales Range: $10-24.9 Million
Emp.: 13
Architectural Building Products Mfr
N.A.I.C.S.: 332323

Construction Specialties (Gulf) LLC (1)
705 Floor Dubai World Trade Centre, Dubai, United Arab Emirates
Tel.: (971) 4 3312167
Web Site: http://www.c-sgroup.me
Sales Range: $10-24.9 Million
Emp.: 75
Building Product Mfr
N.A.I.C.S.: 332311
Franz Silhanek *(Mng Dir)*

Construction Specialties (Singapore) Pte. Ltd. (1)
298 Tiong Bahru Road 08-06 Central Plaza, Singapore, 168730, Singapore
Tel.: (65) 6276 4276
Web Site: http://www.c-sgroup.com
Sales Range: $10-24.9 Million
Emp.: 16
Specialty Coating Mfr
N.A.I.C.S.: 325110
John Lim *(Dir-Sls)*

Construction Specialties Australia Pty. Ltd. (1)
6/26 Cosgrove Road, Enfield, Sydney, 2136, NSW, Australia
Tel.: (61) 1300 272 602
Web Site: http://www.c-sgroup.com.au
Sales Range: $10-24.9 Million
Emp.: 20
Architectural Product Mfr
N.A.I.C.S.: 337212
Bill Maloukis *(Mng Dir)*

Construction Specialties Ltd. (1)
Shanghai Xuhui Office China Lingling Road, Xuhui District, Shanghai, 200030, China
Tel.: (86) 21 6443 9787
Web Site: http://www.c-sgroup.asia
Sales Range: $10-24.9 Million
Emp.: 30
Architectural Product Mfr
N.A.I.C.S.: 332323
Pingping Grant *(Gen Mgr)*

Construction Specialties, Inc. (1)
6696 st Rte 405 Hwy, Muncy, PA 17756
Tel.: (570) 546-5941
Web Site: http://www.c-sgroup.com
Sales Range: $25-49.9 Million
Emp.: 350
Mfr of Wall Protection Expansion Joint Covers, Entrance Floors
N.A.I.C.S.: 331318

Construction Specialties, Inc. (1)
49 Meeker Ave, Cranford, NJ 07016-3163   **(100%)**
Tel.: (908) 272-5200
Web Site: http://www.c-sgroup.com
Rev.: $7,000,000
Emp.: 60
Architectural Designers
N.A.I.C.S.: 423310
Arthur LaPointe *(VP & Gen Mgr)*
Debi O'Grady *(Acct Exec)*

Data Aire, Inc. (1)
230 W Blueridge Ave, Orange, CA 92865-4225   **(100%)**
Tel.: (714) 921-6000
Web Site: http://www.dataaire.com
Sales Range: $25-49.9 Million
Emp.: 150
Mfr of Environmental Process Cooling Systems
N.A.I.C.S.: 333415
Duncan Mossat *(Pres)*
Edward Kaye *(Reg Mgr)*
Jeff Trower *(Gen Mgr-Sls)*
John Gutierrez *(Reg Mgr)*

General Cubicle (1)
49 Meeker Ave, Cranford, NJ 07016
Tel.: (800) 526-6930
Building Protection Services
N.A.I.C.S.: 238390
Stacy Gaskill *(Dir-HR)*

Impact Specialties, Inc. (1)
4005 Royal Dr Ste 300, Kennesaw, GA 30144
Tel.: (888) 424-6287
Web Site: http://www.impactspecialties.com
Entrance Flooring & Wall Protection Services
N.A.I.C.S.: 238330
R. J. Dadd *(VP & Gen Mgr)*
Mike Hanlin *(Mgr-Ops & Sls)*
Ashley Moore *(Mgr-Sls Support)*
Kevin Fitzpatrick *(Dir-Mktg)*
Mike Danylyshyn *(Mgr-Global Sourcing)*
Leslie Fulton *(Mgr-HR)*
Cari Dadd *(Mgr-Accts Receivable)*

CONSTRUCTION TECHNOL-OGY GROUP
2605 N Airport Rd, Plant City, FL 33563
Tel.: (813) 752-2959
Web Site: https://www.ctg-inc.com
Rev.: $15,274,463
Emp.: 10
Commercial & Office Building Contractors
N.A.I.C.S.: 236220
Karen Riddle *(Office Mgr)*

CONSTRUCTION TOOL SER-VICE INC.
3500 Liberty Ave, Pittsburgh, PA 15201
Tel.: (412) 681-6673
Web Site:
https://www.constructiontools.com
Sales Range: $10-24.9 Million
Emp.: 27
Provider of Hardware Services
N.A.I.C.S.: 423710
Ed Huss *(Office Mgr)*

CONSTRUCTION-CAD SOLU-TIONS, INC.
701 Executive Dr, Willowbrook, IL 60527
Tel.: (708) 216-9972
Web Site: https://www.concadinc.com
Rev.: $16,700,000
Emp.: 191
New Single-Family Housing Construction
N.A.I.C.S.: 236115
Pervis O. Conway *(Pres & CEO)*
Will Watkins *(VP-New Bus)*
Marcus Mars *(VP-Ops & Mfg)*

CONSTRUCTORS INC.
1815 Y St, Lincoln, NE 68508-1233
Tel.: (402) 434-1764   **NE**
Web Site:
https://www.constructorslincoln.com
Year Founded: 1948
Sales Range: $10-24.9 Million
Emp.: 60
Highway & Street Construction Services
N.A.I.C.S.: 237310
Ted Butler *(Pres)*

Subsidiaries:

Kerford Limestone Co. Inc.   **(1)**
1815 Y St, Lincoln, NE
68508-1233   **(100%)**
Tel.: (402) 434-1212
Web Site: http://www.kerfordlimestone.com
Supplier of Crushed & Broken Limestone
N.A.I.C.S.: 212312

Trafcon Inc.   **(1)**
1815 Y St, Lincoln, NE 68508-1233
Tel.: (402) 434-1212
Web Site: http://www.trafconinc.com
Sales Range: $10-24.9 Million
Emp.: 30
Provider of Equipment Rental & Leasing
Services
N.A.I.C.S.: 532490
Randy Morse *(Pres)*

CONSULATE HEALTH CARE, LLC

800 Concourse Pkwy S Ste 200, Maitland, FL 32751
Tel.: (407) 571-1550
Web Site:
http://www.consulatemgt.com
Sales Range: $1-9.9 Million
Emp.: 100
Senior Living Facility Management
N.A.I.C.S.: 623312
Debra Mason *(VP-HR)*
Joseph D. Conte *(Vice Chm)*
Daniel E. Dias *(Chief Corp Counsel)*
Bill Mathies *(Chm)*
Chris R. Bryson *(CEO)*
Todd Mehaffey *(COO)*
Steve Van Camp *(CFO)*
Andrea Clark *(Chief Nursing Officer)*
Mark Crandall *(CIO)*
Russell D. Ragland *(CFO)*
Veronique Keller *(Chief Strategy Officer)*
Cindy Chrispell *(Chief HR Officer)*

CONSULTANTS & BUILDERS, INC.

3100 Medlock Bridge Rd Ste 420, Norcross, GA 30071
Tel.: (770) 729-8183
Web Site:
http://www.consultantsbuilders.com
Sales Range: $10-24.9 Million
Emp.: 20
Financial Institution Designer &
Builder
N.A.I.C.S.: 236220
Todd Williams *(CEO)*
Tyler Williams *(Pres)*
Scott Carter *(Sr VP)*
Norman Cox *(VP-Consulting)*
Scott Foerst *(Sr VP-Design)*

CONSULTANTS2GO

University Science Park 105 Lock St
Ste 309, Newark, NJ 07103
Tel.: (973) 645-0098
Web Site:
http://www.consultants2go.com
Year Founded: 2002
Sales Range: $1-9.9 Million
Emp.: 70
Marketing & Analytic Consulting Services
N.A.I.C.S.: 541613
Sandi Webster *(Co-Founder & Principal)*
Peggy McHale *(Co-Founder & Principal)*
Doug Wilder *(CFO)*
Annette Giordano *(VP-Bus Dev)*

CONSULTEDGE, INC.

300 Littleton Rd Ste 200, Parsippany,
NJ 07054-4841
Tel.: (973) 884-1400
Year Founded: 2000

Sales Range: $25-49.9 Million
Emp.: 70
Voice & Data Communication Systems
N.A.I.C.S.: 517810
Diane Pabst *(Acct Mgr-Natl)*
John Ruiz *(Acct Mgr-Natl)*

CONSULTING ENGINEERS GROUP, INC.

21875 Grenada Ave, Lakeville, MN
55044
Tel.: (651) 463-6263   **MN**
Web Site: http://www.ceg-
engineers.com
Year Founded: 1998
Sales Range: $50-74.9 Million
Emp.: 15
Power Transmission & Distribution
Infrastructure Engineering Services
N.A.I.C.S.: 541330
Pete Malamen *(VP)*
Vince Granquist *(Pres)*

CONSULTING FOR ARCHITECTS INC.

236 5th Ave Fl 9, New York, NY
10001
Tel.: (212) 532-4360
Web Site: http://www.cons4arch.com
Year Founded: 1998
Sales Range: Less than $1 Million
Emp.: 3
Employment Agencies
N.A.I.C.S.: 561311
David McFadden *(Founder & CEO)*

CONSULTING SERVICES, INC.

4420 E Interstate 240 Service Rd,
Oklahoma City, OK 73135
Tel.: (405) 526-1030
Web Site:
http://www.csioklahoma.com
Year Founded: 2002
Sales Range: $10-24.9 Million
Emp.: 190
Information Technology Consulting
Services
N.A.I.C.S.: 541690
Ken Novotny *(Pres & CEO)*
Daniel Guilbault *(Dir-Bus Dev)*

CONSUMABLE, INC.

680 S Cache St Ste 100, Jackson,
WY 83001
Web Site:
http://www.consumable.com
Year Founded: 2011
Sales Range: $1-9.9 Million
Emp.: 10
Digital Advertising Services
N.A.I.C.S.: 541810
Mark Levin *(CEO)*

CONSUMER ACQUISITIONS, INC.

2509 N Rdg Rd E, Lorain, OH 44055
Tel.: (440) 926-2911
Rev.: $22,000,000
Emp.: 150
Ready Mixed Concrete
N.A.I.C.S.: 327320
Jeffrey F. Riddell *(Pres & CEO)*

Subsidiaries:

Grafton Ready Mix Concrete   **(1)**
1155 Elm St, Grafton, OH 44044
Tel.: (440) 926-2911
Web Site: http://www.graftonreadymix.com
Rev.: $1,400,000
Emp.: 22
Ready Mixed Concrete
N.A.I.C.S.: 327320

CONSUMER CAPITAL GROUP INC.

136-82 39 Ave 4th Fl Flushing, New
York, NY 11354
Tel.: (646) 346-3735   **DE**
Web Site: http://www.ccgusa.com
Year Founded: 2008
CCGN—(OTCBB)
Sales Range: $1-9.9 Million
Emp.: 23
Online Marketing & E-Commerce
Services
N.A.I.C.S.: 541613
Jianmin Gao *(Chm & CEO)*
Fei Gao *(COO)*

CONSUMER CREDIT COUNSELING SERVICE OF GREATER DALLAS INC.

8737 King George Dr No 200, Dallas,
TX 75235
Tel.: (214) 638-2227
Web Site: http://www.cccs.net
Rev.: $11,502,407
Emp.: 60
Debt Counseling or Adjustment Service Individuals
N.A.I.C.S.: 812990
Ken Goodgames *(Pres & CEO)*
Gloria Swanzy *(Asst Sec)*

CONSUMER CREDIT COUNSELING SERVICE OF SAN FRANCISCO

595 Market St 15th Fl, San Francisco, CA 94105   **CA**
Web Site: https://www.cccssf.org
Year Founded: 1969
Sales Range: $10-24.9 Million
Emp.: 203
Credit Counseling Services
N.A.I.C.S.: 541990
Rico Delgadillo *(VP-Counseling Programs)*
Kathryn J. Davis *(Pres & CEO)*
Marco Chavarin *(VP-Development)*
Darrell Christoff *(CIO)*

CONSUMER DEPOT LLC

3332 Powell Ave, Nashville, TN
37204
Tel.: (615) 851-2125
Web Site:
http://www.consumerdepot.com
Sales Range: $10-24.9 Million
Emp.: 40
Computer Peripheral Equipment
N.A.I.C.S.: 423430
Martin Fike *(Pres)*
Pratik Shah *(Controller)*

CONSUMER ENERGY SOLUTIONS, INC.

1255 Cleveland St Ste 400, Clearwater, FL 33755
Tel.: (727) 724-5811
Web Site:
https://www.consumerenergy.com
Year Founded: 1999
Sales Range: $10-24.9 Million
Emp.: 140
Energy Consulting Services
N.A.I.C.S.: 541620
George Clouden *(Pres)*
Clayton W. Francis *(Sr Mgr-Sls)*
Bev Hepner *(CFO)*
Diana Sipple *(Dir-Sls Support)*
Marta Long *(Dir-Quality Control)*
Christian Jacobson *(Dir-IT)*

CONSUMER GROWTH PARTNERS LLC

445 Hamilton Ave Ste 1102, White
Plains, NY 10601
Tel.: (914) 220-8337
Web Site: http://consumergrowth.com
Privater Equity Firm
N.A.I.C.S.: 523999

Richard Baum *(Mng Partner)*

CONSUMER GUILD FOODS, INC.

5035 Enterprise Blvd, Toledo, OH
43612-3839
Tel.: (419) 726-3406
Year Founded: 1966
Sales Range: $10-24.9 Million
Emp.: 15
Dried & Dehydrated Food Mfr
N.A.I.C.S.: 311423
Robert J. Petrick *(VP)*
Wilbur R. Ascham *(Pres & Treas)*
Ann Ascham *(Mgr)*

CONSUMER POWER INC.

6990 SW Hills Rd, Philomath, OR
97370
Tel.: (541) 929-3124
Web Site: http://www.cpi.com
Sales Range: $10-24.9 Million
Emp.: 60
Transmission, Electric Power
N.A.I.C.S.: 221121
Roman E. Gillen *(Pres & CEO)*

CONSUMER PRODUCT DISTRIBUTORS, INC.

705 Meadow St, Chicopee, MA
01013-4820
Tel.: (413) 592-4141   **MA**
Web Site: http://www.jpolep.com
Year Founded: 1986
Sales Range: $50-74.9 Million
Emp.: 400
Convenience Store Products Distr
N.A.I.C.S.: 722310
Jeffrey Polep *(Chm)*
Kenny Moore *(Exec VP)*
Eric Polep *(Pres & CEO)*
Brian Neeld *(CFO & VP)*

CONSUMER RECOVERY ASSOCIATES, LLC

2697 International Pkwy Ste 4-270,
Virginia Beach, VA 23452
Tel.: (757) 214-9186
Web Site:
http://www.consumerrecovery.com
Sales Range: $1-9.9 Million
Emp.: 101
Debt Collection Agency Services
N.A.I.C.S.: 561440
Kalin Scott *(Pres)*

CONSUMER SERVICES, INC.

585 Jewett Rd, Mason, MI 48854
Tel.: (517) 833-8100   **MI**
Web Site:
http://www.consumerservicesinc.org
Year Founded: 2003
Sales Range: $10-24.9 Million
Emp.: 444
Behavioral Healthcare Services
N.A.I.C.S.: 621420
Chelsea Gleason *(Dir-HR)*
Leslie Wireman *(Dir-Clinical)*
Jack Calhoun *(Dir-Quality Mgmt)*
Sean Duffey *(Dir-Info Svcs)*
Kim Rogers *(CFO)*

CONSUMER UNITED

31 St James Pl, Boston, MA 02116
Tel.: (617) 482-4700
Web Site:
https://www.consumerunited.com
Year Founded: 2006
Sales Range: $1-9.9 Million
Emp.: 88
Insurance Agency Services
N.A.I.C.S.: 524210
Daniel A. Weaver *(VP-Carrier Rels)*
Amit Basak *(Pres)*
Steve Kezirian *(CEO)*
Paul Williams *(CIO)*

Consumer United—(Continued)

Brian Hiener *(Sr VP-Sls)*
Jason Kibilko *(Sr VP-Software & Tech)*
Shantanu Dhaka *(VP-Mktg & Analytics)*
Michael Schwed *(VP-Ops)*

CONSUMERMETRICS, INC.
2299 Perimeter Park Dr, Atlanta, GA 30341
Tel.: (678) 805-4000 **GA**
Web Site:
http://www.cmiresearch.com
Year Founded: 1989
Sales Range: $10-24.9 Million
Emp.: 42
Research & Analytical Services
N.A.I.C.S.: 326121
Michael Mabey *(Acct Mgr)*
Bronwen Clark *(Mgr-Qualitative)*
Laura Johnson *(Mgr-Qualitative)*
Ellen Cabacungan *(Mgr-Qualitative)*
Nan Norton *(Mgr-Res)*
Sherri Kindlmann *(Mgr-Res)*
Ellen Mowbray *(Sr VP-Bus Strategy)*
Laura Caraway *(Sr VP-Ops)*
Bill Salokar *(VP-Bus Dev)*
Janet Ziffer *(VP-Client Svcs)*
Hannah Baker Hitzhusen *(VP-Qualitative Res)*
Angela Wells *(VP-Sls & Mktg)*
Scott Layne *(Pres & COO)*
Marie Rice *(VP)*
Paul Prewett *(Dir-Tech Svcs)*
Serap Alvarez Bilis *(Dir-Advanced Analytics)*
Pete Kuz *(Sr VP-Health & Pharmaceuticals Div)*
Brooke Shafer *(CEO)*

CONSUMERS BEVERAGES INC.
2230 S Park Ave, Buffalo, NY 14220
Tel.: (716) 826-9200 **NY**
Web Site:
http://www.consumerbeverage.com
Year Founded: 1948
Sales Range: $10-24.9 Million
Emp.: 150
Distr of Beer
N.A.I.C.S.: 445320
Neil Kavanaugh *(Pres)*
Donna Kihl *(Controller)*

CONSUMERS CHOICE COFFEE, INC.
1118 Quality Choice Pl, Louisville, KY 40210
Tel.: (502) 588-1000
Web Site:
http://www.consumerschoice.com
Year Founded: 1971
Sales Range: $10-24.9 Million
Emp.: 32
Coffee, Tea & Hot Beverage Distr
N.A.I.C.S.: 424490
Robert Patterson *(Owner)*
Karen Bryant *(Controller)*

CONSUMERS CONCRETE CORPORATION
3508 S Sprinkle Rd, Kalamazoo, MI 49001-0813
Tel.: (269) 342-0136
Web Site:
http://www.consumersconcrete.com
Year Founded: 1933
Sales Range: $25-49.9 Million
Emp.: 15
Mfr, Supplier & Recycler of Ready Mix Concrete
N.A.I.C.S.: 327320

Melissa Kline *(Mgr-Credit)*
Gary Schripsema *(Mgr-Bus Dev & Mktg)*
Brett Minges *(Mgr-Concrete Products)*
Jeff Brueck *(Coord-Sls)*
Ike Warner *(Mgr-HR)*
Randy Parsons *(Mgr-Pur)*
Steve Cronkite *(Mgr-Ready Mix)*
Fred Statler *(Mgr-Sls-Concrete Products)*
Bill Dyke *(Mgr-Sls-Ready Mix)*
Bruce Blair *(Pres & CEO)*
Thomas Richeal *(Mgr-Mktg)*

CONSUMERS COOP ASSOCIATION EAU CLAIRE
1201 S Hastings Way, Eau Claire, WI 54701
Tel.: (715) 836-8700
Web Site: http://www.megafoods.com
Rev.: $88,900,000
Emp.: 515
Grocery Stores
N.A.I.C.S.: 445110
Mike Buck *(Gen Mgr)*

CONSUMERS COOP ASSOCIATION LITCHFIELD
1025 E Frontage Rd, Litchfield, MN 55355
Tel.: (320) 693-2821
Sales Range: $10-24.9 Million
Emp.: 50
Mixing Fertilizers Only
N.A.I.C.S.: 325314
Terry McNamara *(Gen Mgr)*

CONSUMERS COOP RICHLAND COUNTY
300 S Main St, Richland Center, WI 53581
Tel.: (608) 647-6171
Web Site:
http://www.consumerscoop.com
Sales Range: $10-24.9 Million
Emp.: 45
Feed
N.A.I.C.S.: 424910

CONSUMERS CREDIT UNION
1075 Tri-State Pkwy Ste 850, Gurnee, IL 60031
Tel.: (877) 275-2228 **IL**
Web Site:
http://www.myconsumers.org
Year Founded: 1930
Rev.: $55,080,306
Assets: $1,231,505,462
Liabilities: $1,131,366,375
Net Worth: $100,139,087
Earnings: $7,860,400
Emp.: 236
Fiscal Year-end: 12/31/18
Credit Union Operator
N.A.I.C.S.: 522130
Sean M. Rathjen *(CEO)*
John R. Janezic *(Chm)*
Ann Campanella *(Vice Chm)*
Frank C. Soyka *(Treas)*

CONSUMERS INTERSTATE CORPORATION
2 Consumers Ave, Norwich, CT 06360
Tel.: (800) 223-7475
Web Site: http://www.cicgo.com
Year Founded: 1947
Janitorial, Office & Industrial Supply Distr
N.A.I.C.S.: 423840
Kenn Fischburg *(Owner & CEO)*
John Twomey *(Pres)*
Jim Stringfellow *(Gen Sls Mgr)*
Dave Beaulieu *(CIO)*
Shawn Ahearn *(VP-Ops)*

Chris Platt *(Sec)*
Lori Shaker *(Controller)*
Donna Coombs *(Mgr-Inventory)*
Sharon Alger *(Mgr-Sls Support)*
Karla Toth *(Credit Mgr)*

CONSUMERS KITCHENS & BATHS
717 Broadway Ave, Holbrook, NY 11741-4905
Tel.: (631) 563-3200 **NY**
Web Site:
http://www.consumerskitchens.com
Year Founded: 1976
Sales Range: $125-149.9 Million
Emp.: 220
Retail & Wholesale Kitchen & Bath Equipment; Ready-To-Assemble Furniture
N.A.I.C.S.: 449210
James Baloga *(CEO)*

Subsidiaries:

Consumers Warehouse Center Inc. **(1)**
717 Broadway Ave, Holbrook, NY 11741
Tel.: (631) 563-3200
Web Site:
http://www.consumerskitchens.com
Household Appliance Whslr
N.A.I.C.S.: 423620
Ryan Davis *(Mgr-HR)*
Phil Peluso *(Exec Mgr-Education)*

CONSUMERS OIL AND SUPPLY CO
100 Railroad St, Braymer, MO 64624
Tel.: (660) 645-2215
Sales Range: $10-24.9 Million
Emp.: 17
Grain Elevator, Storage Only
N.A.I.C.S.: 493130
Wayne Leamer *(Gen Mgr)*

CONSUMERS PIPE & SUPPLY CO
13424 Arrow Blvd, Fontana, CA 92335
Tel.: (323) 685-6870
Web Site:
https://www.consumerspipe.com
Sales Range: $10-24.9 Million
Emp.: 50
Distr of Pipe Valves & Fittings
N.A.I.C.S.: 423510
Ray Gonzales *(Mgr-Sls)*

CONSUMERSOFT
210 W 29th St 7th Floor, New York, NY 10001
Web Site:
http://www.consumersoft.com
Year Founded: 2006
Sales Range: $1-9.9 Million
Emp.: 10
Mfr & Distr of Utility Software
N.A.I.C.S.: 513210
Trisha Burns *(Head-Mktg)*
Joseph Bursky *(CEO)*

CONSUN FOOD INDUSTRIES INCORPORATED
123 N Gateway Blvd, Elyria, OH 44035
Tel.: (440) 322-6301
Web Site:
http://www.myconvenient.com
Rev.: $30,425,584
Emp.: 65
Convenience Store
N.A.I.C.S.: 445131
Dennis J. Walter *(Pres)*

CONTACT INDUSTRIES
9200 SE Sunnybrook Blvd Ste 200, Clackamas, OR 97015-5195

Tel.: (503) 228-7361
Web Site: http://www.contactind.com
Year Founded: 1946
Sales Range: $25-49.9 Million
Emp.: 400
Moulding & Millwork Mfr
N.A.I.C.S.: 321918
Frank Pearson *(Pres)*
Pete Himes *(Mgr-Indus Sls)*

CONTAINER COMPONENTS INC.
355 Parkside Dr, San Fernando, CA 91340
Tel.: (818) 882-4300
Web Site:
https://www.containercomponents.com
Year Founded: 1985
Sales Range: $10-24.9 Million
Emp.: 30
Plastic Container Mfr
N.A.I.C.S.: 326199
Craig Taylor *(Pres)*
Tom Holder *(CFO)*
Karl Taylor *(VP-Sls)*

CONTAINER GRAPHICS CORPORATION
114 Edinburgh S Dr Ste 104, Cary, NC 27511-7932
Tel.: (919) 481-4200 **NC**
Web Site:
https://www.containergraphics.com
Sales Range: $150-199.9 Million
Emp.: 535
Flexographic Printing Plates & Cutting Dies Mfr
N.A.I.C.S.: 333514
Neil Saunders *(CEO)*
Graham Philip Saunders *(VP-Bus Dev)*
Bob Troy *(Mgr-IT Dev)*
Michael Clark *(Engr-Software)*

Subsidiaries:

Container Graphics Corporation **(1)**
1137 Graphics Dr, Modesto, CA 95351-1501
Tel.: (209) 577-0181
Web Site: http://www.containergraphics.com
Sales Range: $10-24.9 Million
Emp.: 80
Printing Equipment & Material Mfr & Distr
N.A.I.C.S.: 333248
James McGinnis *(Mgr-Production)*

CONTAINER MARKETING INC.
110 Matthews Dr, Americus, GA 31709
Tel.: (229) 924-5622
Web Site: http://www.iwantcmi.com
Sales Range: $10-24.9 Million
Emp.: 172
Dining Room Furniture Mfr
N.A.I.C.S.: 423210
Holli Bruck *(Pres)*
Norman Burnatine *(VP-Sls)*
Tammye Hewett *(Mgr-Traffic)*

CONTAINER PRODUCTS CORPORATION
112 N College Rd, Wilmington, NC 28406
Tel.: (910) 392-6100
Web Site: https://www.c-p-c.net
Sales Range: $10-24.9 Million
Emp.: 75
Metal Storage & Shipping Containers for the Nuclear Industry
N.A.I.C.S.: 493190
Dwight Campbell *(Pres)*
Mike Lewis *(Mgr-QA)*
Kelley Jones *(Dir-HR)*
Barbara Ellison *(Mgr-Pur)*

CONTAINER RESEARCH COR-PORATION
2 New Rd, Aston, PA 19014
Tel.: (610) 459-2160
Web Site: https://www.crc-flex.com
Year Founded: 1956
Sales Range: $10-24.9 Million
Emp.: 100
Metal Barrels, Drums & Pails
N.A.I.C.S.: 332439
William Swan *(Exec VP)*
Chris Leiser *(Dir-Engrg)*

CONTAINER ROYALTY SUPPLEMENTAL CASH BEN-EFIT PLAN
899 Morrison Dr, Charleston, SC 29413
Tel.: (843) 723-5561   **SC**
Year Founded: 2014
Sales Range: $10-24.9 Million
Emp.: 794
Employee Welfare Fund Services
N.A.I.C.S.: 525120
G. W. Adams *(Co-Chm)*
Neal Edgertown *(Co-Chm)*

CONTAINER SERVICES LLC
Linda Bloom 1 E Wacker Dr Shore
Capital Ste 2900, Chicago, IL 60601
Tel.: (620) 947-2664
Web Site: https://www.csibottles.com
Year Founded: 1991
Plastic Container Mfr
N.A.I.C.S.: 326199

Subsidiaries:

Apex Plastics Inc.   (1)
570 S Main St, Brookfield, MO 64628
Web Site: http://www.apexplastics.com
Sales Range: $10-24.9 Million
Plastics Bottle Mfr
N.A.I.C.S.: 326160
Damon Neff *(Pres)*

CONTAINER SYSTEMS INC.
205 E Burlington Ave, Westmont, IL 60559
Tel.: (630) 960-3000
Web Site:
 www.containersystems.com
Year Founded: 1969
Sales Range: $10-24.9 Million
Emp.: 20
Materials Handling Machinery
N.A.I.C.S.: 423830

CONTAINER TECHNOLOGY AND SUPPLY INTERNATIONAL INCORPORATED
1046 Annunciation St, New Orleans, LA 70130
Tel.: (504) 523-4785
Web Site: https://www.con-techinternational.com
Sales Range: $10-24.9 Million
Emp.: 15
Iron & Steel (Ferrous) Products
N.A.I.C.S.: 423510
Robbie Evans *(Pres)*
Joyce Blanson *(Controller)*
Isis Espinosa *(Asst Product Mgr-Steel)*
Delmy Orellana *(VP-Sls, Drum & Pail Dept)*
Terry Mitchell *(Asst Mgr-Product-IBC Components & Custom Mfg)*
Rodney Berry *(Mgr-Shipping & Distr)*
William J. Oberhelman III *(VP/Product Mgr-IBC Components & Custom Mfg)*

CONTAINERFREIGHT/EIT LLC
6150 Paramount Blvd, Long Beach, CA 90805
Tel.: (562) 220-2433

Web Site: http://www.cfreighteit.com
Rev.: $28,000,000
Emp.: 42
Local Trucking without Storage
N.A.I.C.S.: 484110
Jane Sato *(Dir-Sls)*

CONTAMINANT CONTROL INC.
PO Box 64399, Hope Mills, NC 28306
Tel.: (910) 484-7000
Web Site: http://www.cci-env.com
Sales Range: $10-24.9 Million
Emp.: 100
Asbestos Removal & Encapsulation
N.A.I.C.S.: 561210
Mark Vestal *(Pres)*
Al Bustin *(VP-Asbestos, Lead & Mold Div)*

CONTEC INC.
525 Locust Grove, Spartanburg, SC 29303-4832
Tel.: (864) 503-8333   **SC**
Web Site: https://www.contecinc.com
Year Founded: 1988
Sales Range: $25-49.9 Million
Emp.: 150
Produces Presaturated Wipers Non-woven Wipers Swabs & Other Indus-try Critical Products
N.A.I.C.S.: 423850
Avi Lawrence *(Pres & CFO)*

CONTECH RESEARCH, INC.
750 Narragansett Park Dr, Rumford, RI 02916-1035
Tel.: (401) 865-6440
Web Site:
 https://www.contechresearch.com
Year Founded: 1981
Chemical Laboratory, Except Testing
N.A.I.C.S.: 541715
Tom Peel *(Pres & Dir-Test Program Dev)*
Thomas Lamoureux *(Mgr-Quality)*

CONTEGIX, LLC
11951 Freedom Dr 13th Fl, Reston, VA 20190
Tel.: (314) 622-6200
Web Site: http://www.contegix.com
Year Founded: 2004
Computer Related Services
N.A.I.C.S.: 541519
John Emard *(Chief Revenue Officer)*
Brad Hokam *(CEO)*
Elizabeth Clor *(CMO)*
Joe Deney *(COO)*

CONTEGRA CONSTRUCTION COMPANY, L.L.C.
22 Gateway Commerce Center Dr W Ste 110, Edwardsville, IL 62025-2894
Tel.: (618) 931-3500
Web Site:
 https://www.contegracc.com
Year Founded: 2003
Sales Range: $25-49.9 Million
Emp.: 55
Civil Engineering Services
N.A.I.C.S.: 237310
Eric Gowin *(Pres)*

CONTEMPO ADVERTISING + DESIGN
1006 Ash Ave Ste 3E, McAllen, TX 78501
Tel.: (956) 627-2660
Web Site:
 http://www.contempodesign.com
Sales Range: $1-9.9 Million
Emp.: 10
Advetising Agency
N.A.I.C.S.: 541810

Andres De La Rosa *(Owner)*

CONTEMPO CARD CO., INC.
69 Tingley St Ste 1A, Providence, RI 02903-1085
Tel.: (401) 272-4210
Web Site:
 https://www.contempocard.com
Year Founded: 1978
Sales Range: $10-24.9 Million
Emp.: 75
Corrugated & Solid Fiber Box Mfr
N.A.I.C.S.: 322211
Kyle Gray *(Mgr-Pur)*
Vark Markarian *(Pres)*

CONTEMPO CERAMIC TILE CORP.
3732 S 300 W, Salt Lake City, UT 84115
Tel.: (801) 262-1717
Web Site:
 http://www.contempotile.com
Sales Range: $10-24.9 Million
Emp.: 95
Ceramic Wall & Floor Tile
N.A.I.C.S.: 423320
Mike Becker *(Pres)*

CONTEMPORARY COMPUTER SERVICES, INC.
200 Knickerbocker Ave, Bohemia, NY 11716
Tel.: (631) 563-8880   **NY**
Web Site: http://www.ccsinet.com
Year Founded: 1974
Sales Range: $10-24.9 Million
Emp.: 75
Information Technology Security & Data Services
N.A.I.C.S.: 541519
John R. Riconda *(Pres & CEO)*

CONTEMPORARY MOTOR CARS, INC.
100 Oceanport Ave, Little Silver, NJ 07739-1294
Tel.: (732) 842-5353   **NJ**
Web Site:
 http://www.mercedeslittlesilver.com
Sales Range: $10-24.9 Million
Emp.: 45
New & Used Automobiles
N.A.I.C.S.: 441110
Scott Coleman *(Treas & Sec)*
Mike Green *(Controller)*
John Kellner *(Dir)*

CONTEMPORARY SERVICES CORP.
17101 Superior St, Northridge, CA 91325
Tel.: (818) 885-5150
Web Site:
 http://www.contemporaryser
 vices.com
Sales Range: $25-49.9 Million
Emp.: 100
Protective Services, Guard
N.A.I.C.S.: 561612
Damon Zumwalt *(Pres & CEO)*
Paul McDermott *(Branch Mgr-Svcs)*
Roy Sukimoto *(Branch Mgr-Svcs)*
Lonnie Sutton *(Branch Mgr-Svcs)*
Lenny Lambert *(Reg Mgr)*

CONTEMPORARY SIGNED BOOKS, INC.
600 Lexington Ave 10th Fl, New York, NY 10022
Tel.: (212) 319-0503   **DE**
Year Founded: 2010
Sales Range: Less than $1 Million
Autographed Book Internet Retailer
N.A.I.C.S.: 424920

Mary McClean *(Pres & CEO)*
Jeffrey Hillock *(VP)*
Jacqui Samuels *(Treas & Sec)*

CONTEMPORARY STAFFING SOLUTIONS INC.
161 Gaither Dr Ste 100, Mount Laurel, NJ 08054
Tel.: (856) 222-0020
Web Site:
 http://www.contemporarystaffing.com
Sales Range: $10-24.9 Million
Emp.: 20
Help Supply Services
N.A.I.C.S.: 561320
Steve Pearson *(COO)*
Mike Pearson *(Pres)*
Sharon M. Tsao *(CMO)*
Rasheda Smith *(Acct Mgr)*
Tom Verratti *(CFO)*
Josline Jose *(Mgr-Philadelphia)*
Parisa Dionisi *(Mgr-Jacksonville)*
Evan Violette *(Mng Dir)*
Alyssa Mastrangelo *(Dir-Recruiting)*

CONTENT PARTNERS LLC
10877 Wilshire Blvd Ste 1404, Los Angeles, CA 90024
Tel.: (310) 208-7300
Web Site: https://www.contentllc.com
Emp.: 8
Investment Services
N.A.I.C.S.: 523999
Steven H. Kram *(Co-Founder & CEO)*
Steven E. Blume *(Co-Founder, COO & CFO)*
John M. Mass *(Exec VP)*
David A. Davis *(Sr VP-Fin)*
Brendan Haley *(VP)*
Todd R. Wagner *(Co-Founder & Part-ner)*
Paul D. Wachter *(Co-Founder & Part-ner)*
Lawrence N. Goldstein *(Co-Founder & Partner)*
Rob Amir *(Sr Exec VP)*

Subsidiaries:

Revolution Studios   (1)
225 Santa Monica Blvd 9th Fl, Santa Monica, CA 90401
Tel.: (310) 255-7000
Web Site: http://www.revolutionstudios.com
Sales Range: $25-49.9 Million
Emp.: 10
Motion Picture & Video Production
N.A.I.C.S.: 512110
Marla Levine *(Gen Counsel & Head-Bus Affairs)*
Vince Totino *(CEO)*
Scott Hemming *(Pres & COO)*

CONTENT RULES INC.
1484 Pollard Rd Ste 255, Los Gatos, CA 95032
Tel.: (408) 395-8178
Web Site:
 https://www.contentrules.com
Year Founded: 1994
Sales Range: $1-9.9 Million
Emp.: 10
Business Products & Services
N.A.I.C.S.: 519290
Val Swisher *(Founder & CEO)*
Tim Steele *(Pres)*
Greg Swisher *(CTO)*

CONTENTCHECKED HOLD-INGS INC.
8730 Sunset Blvd Ste 240, West Hollywood, CA 90069
Tel.: (424) 205-1777   **NV**
Web Site:
 http://www.contentchecked.com
Year Founded: 2011
VSTT—(OTCBB)
Food Allergy App Designer

ContentChecked Inc.—(Continued)
N.A.I.C.S.: 325412
David R. Wells (Treas)
Kalle Bergman (Chief Creative Officer)
Olav Madland (CTO)
Victoria Nunez (Dir-Bus Dev)
Tory Tedrow (Dir-Nutrition)
John W. Martin (Pres, CEO, Gen Counsel & Sec)

CONTEXT TRAVEL
2216 S St, Philadelphia, PA 19146
Tel.: (215) 392-0303
Web Site:
http://www.contexttravel.com
Sales Range: $1-9.9 Million
Emp.: 11
Tour Arrangement Services
N.A.I.C.S.: 561520
Paul Bennett (Co-Founder)
Lani Bevacqua (Co-Founder)

CONTEXTURE, INC
45 Dan Rd Ste 350, Canton, MA 02021
Tel.: (781) 821-0858
Web Site: https://contextureusa.com
Year Founded: 1985
Emp.: 100
Building Construction
N.A.I.C.S.: 236210
Brianna Goodwin (CEO)

Subsidiaries:

Commonwealth Blinds & Shades, Inc. (1)
8529 Meadowbridge Rd Ste 500, Mechanicsville, VA 23116-1509
Tel.: (804) 746-9112
Web Site:
http://www.commonwealthblinds.com
Building Finishing Contractors
N.A.I.C.S.: 238390
Chris Witte (Pres)

CONTI CAUSEWAY FORD INC.
375 Route 72, Manahawkin, NJ 08050
Tel.: (609) 597-8083
Web Site:
http://www.causewayford.net
Sales Range: $25-49.9 Million
Emp.: 99
Car Whslr
N.A.I.C.S.: 441110
David Wintrode (Owner)

CONTI ELECTRIC INC.
6417 Center Dr Ste 120, Sterling Heights, MI 48312
Tel.: (586) 274-4800
Web Site: http://www.conticorp.com
Rev.: $92,000,000
Emp.: 300
Provider of General Electrical Contracting Services
N.A.I.C.S.: 238210
Allen Oblak (Dir-Safety)
Bill Stephenson (Project Mgr)
David Kalish (Controller)
Randy Harris (Project Dir)
David Post (Project Mgr)

CONTINENTAL ALLOY WHEEL CORPORATION
c/o Befumo & Schaeffer PLLC 1629 K St NW Ste 300, Washington, DC 20006
Tel.: (202) 973-0186
Year Founded: 2010
Investment Services
N.A.I.C.S.: 523999
Andrew J. Befumo (Pres, CEO, CFO, Treas & Sec)

CONTINENTAL AMERICAN CORPORATION
5000 E 29th St N, Wichita, KS 67220-2111
Tel.: (316) 685-2266
Web Site:
https://www.pioneerworldwide.com
Year Founded: 1974
Sales Range: $400-449.9 Million
Emp.: 1,000
Mfr & Printer of Latex & Metallic Balloons
N.A.I.C.S.: 326299
Daniel Flynn (COO)

Subsidiaries:

Globos Qualatex de Pioneer, S.A. de C.V. (1)
San Bernardo 301 Letra A y B Corredor Industrial Sanctorum, Cuautlancin, Mexico
Tel.: (52) 222 273 3700
Web Site: http://www.qualatex.com.mx
Balloon Mfr
N.A.I.C.S.: 326299
Itamar Silva (Dir-Sls)

Pioneer National Latex Company (1)
246 E 4th St, Ashland, OH 44805-2412
Tel.: (419) 289-3300
Sales Range: $25-49.9 Million
Emp.: 100
Balloons, Play Balls, Punch Balls & Exercise & Therapy Balls Mfr
N.A.I.C.S.: 326299
Lisa Bennett (Dir-Mktg)

Qualatex Balloon Pty. Ltd. (1)
Unit F 140 Old Pittwater Road, PO Box 7148, Warringah Mall, Brookvale, NSW, Australia
Tel.: (61) 2 9905 9333
Web Site: http://www.qualatex.com.au
Balloon Mfr
N.A.I.C.S.: 326299
Rachelle Fraser (Mgr-Mktg)

CONTINENTAL CARS, INC.
6757 Airport Blvd, Austin, TX 78752
Tel.: (512) 454-6821
Web Site: http://www.mbofaustin.com
Sales Range: $50-74.9 Million
Emp.: 111
Automobiles, New & Used
N.A.I.C.S.: 441110
Bryan Hardeman (Pres)
Chris Hirsh (Mgr-Svcs)
Jim McGuane (Gen Mgr)

CONTINENTAL CASTING, LLC
801 2nd St, Monroe City, MO 63456
Tel.: (573) 735-4577
Web Site:
http://www.continentalcasting.com
Year Founded: 1999
Sales Range: $25-49.9 Million
Emp.: 150
Metal Services
N.A.I.C.S.: 423510
Don Hays (Sr VP-Bus Dev)
Ray McCurdy (Controller)

CONTINENTAL CONCESSION SUPPLIES, INC.
575 Jericho Tpke, Jericho, NY 11753
Tel.: (516) 739-8777
Web Site: http://www.ccsicandy.com
Sales Range: $10-24.9 Million
Emp.: 40
Popcorn & Supplies
N.A.I.C.S.: 424450
Aaron Slonim (Pres & CEO)
Adam Gottlieb (Exec VP-Sls & Procurement)
Gary Oswald (Controller)
Kevin Fitzpatrick (CFO)

CONTINENTAL CONSTRUCTION CO.

5646 Shelby Oaks Dr, Memphis, TN 38134
Tel.: (901) 382-4070
Web Site:
https://www.continentalconst.com
Sales Range: $10-24.9 Million
Emp.: 170
Dock Construction
N.A.I.C.S.: 236210
Joe McGaugh (CEO)
Betty Bailey (Treas & Sec)
Shawn Billings (VP)

CONTINENTAL CURRENCY SERVICES INC.
1108 E 17th St, Santa Ana, CA 92701
Tel.: (714) 569-0300
Web Site: http://www.ccurr.com
Year Founded: 1978
Sales Range: $100-124.9 Million
Emp.: 700
Provider of Banking Services
N.A.I.C.S.: 522390
Terrance Murphy (Dir-Marketing)

Subsidiaries:

Continental Express Money Order Company Inc. (1)
1108 E 17th St, Santa Ana, CA 92701-2620
Tel.: (714) 569-0300
Sales Range: $50-74.9 Million
Emp.: 100
Provider of Banking Services
N.A.I.C.S.: 522390

Mobile Money Inc. (1)
7633 Industry Ave, Pico Rivera, CA 90660-4301
Tel.: (562) 948-3916
Sales Range: $25-49.9 Million
Emp.: 40
Provider of Banking Services
N.A.I.C.S.: 522390

CONTINENTAL DATALABEL
1855 Fox Ln, Elgin, IL 60123
Tel.: (847) 742-1600
Web Site: https://www.datalabel.com
Rev.: $15,900,000
Emp.: 120
Tape, Pressure Sensitive: Made From Purchased Materials
N.A.I.C.S.: 322220
Timothy J. Flynn (Pres)
Leslie Lullie (Mgr-Customer Svc)
Max Metz (Mgr-Warehouse)
Rich Filip (Mgr-Mid West Reg)
Pat Hoesel (Supvr-Pre-Press)
Thomas Brand (CFO)

CONTINENTAL DESIGN & ENGINEERING, INC.
1524 Jackson St, Anderson, IN 46016
Tel.: (765) 778-9999
Web Site:
https://www.continentalinc.com
Year Founded: 1985
Sales Range: $10-24.9 Million
Emp.: 300
Design, Engineering, Executive & Technical Staffing Services
N.A.I.C.S.: 561320
Judy Nagengast (CEO)
Bill Nagengast (COO)

CONTINENTAL DEVELOPMENT CORP.
2041 Rosecrans Ave Ste 200, El Segundo, CA 90245
Tel.: (310) 640-1520
Web Site:
https://www.continentaldev.com
Year Founded: 1969
Sales Range: $50-74.9 Million
Emp.: 50

Commercial & Office Building, New Construction
N.A.I.C.S.: 236220
Richard C. Lundquist (Pres)
Robert E. Tarnofsky (Dir-Real Estate)
Carol Sutor (Dir-Mktg)
Marcia Helfer (Sr VP-Admin)
Michael Curran (CFO & Treas)
Leonard E. Blakesley (Gen Counsel & Exec VP)
Lianne M. Ibarra (Dir-Property Mgmt)
Alex J. Rose (Sr VP-Dev)
Michael Simon (Dir-Acctg)
Sherry A. Kramer (Dir-Community Affairs)
Paul D. Holling (Dir-Construction)
Scott Peters (Mgr-Leasing)
Bob Inch (VP-Mktg)

CONTINENTAL DISTRIBUTORS, INC.
35710 Mound Rd, Sterling Heights, MI 48310
Tel.: (586) 939-3600
Web Site:
http://www.continentalserves.com
Year Founded: 1989
Sales Range: $50-74.9 Million
Emp.: 300
Catering Services
N.A.I.C.S.: 722320
Jim Belisle (VP-Corp Fin)

CONTINENTAL DIVIDE ELECTRIC COOPERATIVE INC
200 E High St, Grants, NM 87020
Tel.: (505) 285-6656
Web Site: https://www.cdec.coop
Sales Range: $25-49.9 Million
Emp.: 60
Distribution, Electric Power
N.A.I.C.S.: 221122
Corriena Sandiball (Asst Mgr)
Robert Castillo (Gen Mgr)

CONTINENTAL ELECTRIC CONSTRUCTION COMPANY
815 Commerce Dr, Oak Brook, IL 60523
Tel.: (630) 288-0200
Web Site: https://www.cecco.com
Year Founded: 1912
Sales Range: $10-24.9 Million
Emp.: 80
Electrical Construction Services
N.A.I.C.S.: 238210
David Witz (Pres)
Steven Witz (VP)

CONTINENTAL ESTATES INC.
12052 US 20A, Wauseon, OH 43567
Tel.: (419) 337-5100
Web Site:
http://www.continentalhomes.us
Sales Range: $10-24.9 Million
Emp.: 45
Mobile Home Dealers
N.A.I.C.S.: 459930
Phillip D. Cain (Pres)

CONTINENTAL FIELD SYSTEMS INC.
23 Westgate Blvd, Savannah, GA 31405
Tel.: (912) 232-8121
Web Site:
http://www.continentalfield.com
Year Founded: 1979
Sales Range: $10-24.9 Million
Emp.: 100
Machine Shop, Jobbing & Repair
N.A.I.C.S.: 332710

Eric Christoph (Pres)
Kay McElveen (Controller)
Wayne Hutsell (Mgr-QC)
Bert Scholl (Project Mgr)

CONTINENTAL FINANCE
707 S Polk St, Amarillo, TX 79101-2309
Tel.: (806) 372-3861
Web Site:
http://www.continentalfinance.net
Consumer Lending
N.A.I.C.S.: 522291
Arlene Henry (Mgr)
Stephen McSorley (Pres)

Subsidiaries:

Today Card, LLC   (1)
PO Box 101687, Fort Worth, TX 76185
Web Site: http://www.todaycard.com
Finance & Banking Services
N.A.I.C.S.: 541611

CONTINENTAL FINANCIAL LTD
555 Skokie Blvd, Northbrook, IL 60062
Tel.: (847) 291-3700
Sales Range: $50-74.9 Million
Emp.: 20
Real Estate Development Services
N.A.I.C.S.: 237210
Joseph Rosen (Chm & CEO)

CONTINENTAL FLORAL GREENS
1777 NE Loop 410 Ste 623, San Antonio, TX 78217
Tel.: (210) 654-6543
Web Site: http://www.cfgfloral.com
Sales Range: $10-24.9 Million
Emp.: 110
Nursery Stock
N.A.I.C.S.: 424930
Roger Kilgore (Asst Mgr-Transportation)

CONTINENTAL GRAIN COMPANY
767 Fifth Ave 15th Fl, New York, NY 10153-0015
Tel.: (212) 207-5100   DE
Web Site:
http://www.continentalgrain.com
Year Founded: 1813
Sales Range: Less than $1 Million
Holding Company; Food, Agribusiness & Commodities
N.A.I.C.S.: 551112
Ari Gendason (Chief Investment Officer)
Stephen R. Volk (Vice Chm)
Frank W. Baier (CFO)
Nick Rosa (Mng Dir-Asia)
Stephanie Warner (Chief People Officer)
Ryan Oksenhendler (Principal)
Peter Webel (Principal)
Daniel Weiner (Principal)
Guillermo Bilbao (Mng Dir-Latin America)
Paul J. Fribourg (Chm & CEO)
Michael J. Zimmerman (Vice Chm)

Subsidiaries:

Arlon Group LLC   (1)
767 5th Ave 15th Fl, New York, NY 10153
Tel.: (212) 207-5200
Web Site: http://www.arlongroup.com
Food & Agriculture Equity Investment Firm
N.A.I.C.S.: 523999
Benjamin D. Fishman (Mng Dir)
Guillermo Bilbao (Mng Principal)
David Dryerman (VP-Fin)
Peter Webel (Principal)
Daniel Weiner (Principal)

Holding (Domestic):

Alico, Inc.   (2)
10070 Daniels Interstate Ct Ste 200, Fort Myers, FL 33913   **(50.6%)**
Tel.: (239) 226-2000
Web Site: https://www.alicoinc.com
Rev.: $39,846,000
Assets: $428,353,000
Liabilities: $177,976,000
Net Worth: $250,377,000
Earnings: $1,835,000
Emp.: 194
Fiscal Year-end: 09/30/2023
Land Development Services
N.A.I.C.S.: 115116
John E. Kiernan (Pres & CEO)
Chris Moore (VP-Logistics)
James E. Sampel (CIO)
Janet Barber (Asst Controller)
Glen Blake (Production Mgr-Citrus-Corkscrew)
Dana Campbell (Dir-Citrus-North)
Erle Hatch (Controller)
Carisa Keller (Dir-Sustainability)
David Kemeny (Production Mgr-Citrus-TRB)
Lindsay Krill (Mgr-IT)
Bradley Lawhorn (Dir-Plng & Analysis)
Mary Molina (Mgr-Project & Admin)
Mike Moore (Mgr-Ranch Ops & Real Estate)
Johany Rosario (Dir-HR)
Lynn Steward (Mgr-Nursery)
Richard Strickland (Dir-Citrus-Central)
Tommy Walker (Dir-Citrus-South)
Joby Sherrod (Dir)
Bradley Heine (CFO)

Subsidiary (Domestic):

Alico Citrus Nursery, LLC   (3)
10070 Daniels Interstate Ct Ste 100, Fort Myers, FL 33913
Tel.: (863) 673-4774
Nursery Whslr
N.A.I.C.S.: 444240
Marta Francis (Dir-Plant Breeding & Res)

Alico Fruit Company, LLC   (3)
2001 Thompson Nursery Rd, Lake Wales, FL 33859   **(100%)**
Tel.: (863) 299-1183
Web Site: http://www.alicoinc.com
Emp.: 15
Citrus Fruit Harvesting & Hauling Services
N.A.I.C.S.: 111320
Chris Moore (Pres)

Alico Land Development, Inc.   (3)
10070 Daniels Interstate Ct Ste 100, Fort Myers, FL 33913   **(100%)**
Tel.: (239) 226-2000
Web Site: http://www.alicoinc.com
Emp.: 17
Subdividing, Development & Sale of Real Estate
N.A.I.C.S.: 531390

Alico-Agri, Ltd.   (3)
640 S Main St, Labelle, FL 33935-4606
Tel.: (863) 675-2966
Real Estate Manangement Services
N.A.I.C.S.: 531390

Holding (Domestic):

CiCi Enterprises, LP   (2)
1080 W Bethel Rd, Coppell, TX 75019
Tel.: (972) 745-4200
Web Site: http://www.cicis.com
Pizza Buffet Restaurant
N.A.I.C.S.: 722511

Idaho Pacific Corporation   (2)
4723 E 100 N, Rigby, ID 83442
Tel.: (208) 538-6971
Web Site: http://www.idahopacific.com
Dehydrated Potato Products Mfr
N.A.I.C.S.: 311423
Todd Sutton (VP-Ops)
Wally Browning (Pres & CEO)
Jeanne Harrison (Sls Mgr-Indus & Baking)
Jon Schodde (VP-Sls & Mktg & Mgr-Export Sls)
Chuck Mastruserio (Mgr-Sls & Food Svc-Eastern Reg)
Glade Williams (Mgr-Sls & Food Svc-Western Reg)
Julian Awdry (Mgr-Export Sls)
Paul Eatinger (Mgr-Quality Assurance)

The Coastal Companies   (2)
9001 Whiskey Bottom Road, Laurel, MD 20763
Tel.: (301) 617-4343
Food Service Distr
N.A.I.C.S.: 722310

Subsidiary (Domestic):

Coastal Sunbelt Produce, LLC   (3)
8704 Bollman Pl, Savage, MD 20763-9747
Tel.: (301) 617-4343
Web Site: http://www.coastalsunbelt.com
Fresh Fruit, Vegetable & Dairy Product Distr
N.A.I.C.S.: 424480
Bob Lahmann (CFO)
John Corso (CEO)
Tracy Moore (VP-Customer Care)
Jason Lambros (VP-Pur)
Jim McWhorter (VP-Sls)
John Tenerowicz (VP-HR)
Dave Zeleznik (VP-Safety & Loss Prevention)
Larry Brown (Exec VP-Sls)
Stacy Ward (Dir-Accts Natl)

Lancaster Foods, Inc.   (3)
7700 Conowingo Ave, Jessup, MD 20794-9423   **(100%)**
Tel.: (410) 799-0010
Web Site: http://www.lancasterfoods.com
Produce, Frozen Foods & Floral Products Distr
N.A.I.C.S.: 424480
John Gates (Co-Founder & Pres)
Kevin Jones (Exec VP)
Will Lum (Dir-Quality Assurance)
Alisha Lang (Dir-Office Ops)
Dave Gates (Co-Founder & Dir-Procurement)

ContiAsia   (1)
705 Union Plaza 20 Chaowai Avenue, Chao Yang District, Beijing, 100020, China
Tel.: (86) 10 6588 3388
Web Site: http://www.contiasia.com
Emp.: 40
Investment Management Service
N.A.I.C.S.: 523940
Nicholas W. Rosa (Sr VP & Mng Dir)

ContiLatin   (1)
277 Park Ave, New York, NY 10172-0003   **(100%)**
Tel.: (212) 207-5316
Web Site: http://www.contigroup.com
Poultry Production & Processing, Feed & Flour Milling, Oilseed Crushing & Commodity Supply
N.A.I.C.S.: 311615

Sanderson Farms, Inc.   (1)
127 Flynt Rd, Laurel, MS 39443
Tel.: (601) 649-4030
Web Site: http://www.sandersonfarms.com
Rev.: $4,799,653,000
Assets: $2,345,033,000
Liabilities: $494,794,000
Net Worth: $1,850,239,000
Earnings: $455,089,000
Emp.: 17,662
Fiscal Year-end: 10/31/2021
Production of Fresh Ice Pack Poultry, Whole Birds & Parts, Frozen Frying Chicken Parts, Corn Dogs & Prepared Entrees
N.A.I.C.S.: 311615
Timothy F. Rigney (Chief Acctg Officer & Sec)

Division (Domestic):

Sanderson Farms, Inc. - Foods Division   (2)
4418 Magum Dr Flodde, Jackson, MS 39232
Tel.: (601) 939-9790
Web Site: http://www.sandersonfarms.com
Production of Prepared Foods
N.A.I.C.S.: 311412

Sanderson Farms, Inc. - Processing Division   (2)
PO Box 988, Laurel, MS 39441-0988
Tel.: (601) 649-4030
Web Site: http://www.sandersonfarms.com
Emp.: 3,000
Processing of Fresh & Frozen Poultry
N.A.I.C.S.: 311615

David Michael Cockrell (CFO & Treas)
Lampkin Butts (Pres & COO)
Joe Frank Sanderson Jr. (Chm & CEO)

Wayne Farms LLC   (1)
4110 Continental Dr, Oakwood, GA 30566
Tel.: (770) 538-2120
Web Site: http://www.waynefarms.com
Sales Range: $1-4.9 Billion
Emp.: 9,000
Poultry Production & Processing
N.A.I.C.S.: 311615
Elton H. Maddox (Chm)
Steve Clever (VP-Fresh Sls)
Courtney E. Fazekas (CFO & Treas)
John Flood (VP & Gen Mgr-Prepared Foods)
David Malfitano (Chief HR Officer)
Bryan Miller (VP-Quality Assurance & Food Safety)
Tom Bell (VP-Further Processed Sls)
Clint Rivers (Pres & CEO)
Jeremy Kilburn (Gen Counsel & Sec)
Kevin McDaniel (V P & Gen Mgr-Fresh Ops)

CONTINENTAL HEAT TREATING, INC.
10643 S Norwalk Blvd, Santa Fe Springs, CA 90670
Tel.: (562) 944-8808
Web Site:
https://www.continentalht.com
Sales Range: $10-24.9 Million
Emp.: 62
Metal Heat Treating Services
N.A.I.C.S.: 332811
James Stull (Pres)
Shaun Radford (Gen Mgr)
Laura Rubio (Controller)
Ken Nelson (Mgr-Quality)
Dennis Hugie (Mgr-Ops)
Roberta Cortez (Mgr-Sls)

CONTINENTAL HOLDING COMPANY
PO Box 811, Spartanburg, SC 29304
Tel.: (864) 582-8193
Web Site: http://www.security-finance.com
Rev.: $15,854,122
Emp.: 110
Investment Holding Company
N.A.I.C.S.: 551111
A. R. Biggs (Pres)
Trisha Pendegrass (Controller)

Subsidiaries:

Old Spartan Life Insurance Co.   (1)
PO Box 811, Spartanburg, SC 29304
Tel.: (864) 582-8193
Web Site: http://www.security-finance.com
Rev.: $260,000
Emp.: 3
Insurance Agents, Nec
N.A.I.C.S.: 524210

Professional Bankers Corp   (1)
204 E Main St, Spartanburg, SC 29306
Tel.: (864) 582-2556
Web Site: http://www.security-finance.com
Sales Range: $25-49.9 Million
Emp.: 3
Personal Credit Institutions
N.A.I.C.S.: 522291

Security Finance Corp. Spartanburg   (1)
181 Security Pl, Spartanburg, SC 29307
Tel.: (864) 582-8193
Web Site: http://www.security-finance.com
Licensed Loan Companies, Small
N.A.I.C.S.: 522291
Carla Martin (Mgr)
Patricia Long (Mgr)

Security Finance Corporation   (1)
204 E Main St, Spartanburg, SC 29307
Tel.: (864) 582-8193
Web Site: http://www.security-finance.com
Sales Range: $10-24.9 Million
Emp.: 100
Personal Credit Institutions
N.A.I.C.S.: 522291

Continental Holding Company—(Continued)

Ryan DeYoung (Coord-Recruiting)
Joey Hilliard (Mgr-Network Engrg)

Sunbelt Credit Inc. (1)
1812 W Gore Blvd, Lawton, OK 73501
Tel.: (580) 248-8867
Web Site: http://www.security-finance.com
Rev.: $130,000
Emp.: 2
Financing: Automobiles, Furniture, Etc., Not
A Deposit Bank
N.A.I.C.S.: 522291

CONTINENTAL HOSTS LTD.
1329 N Ave Ste 101, New Rochelle,
NY 10804
Tel.: (914) 576-3300
Year Founded: 1967
Sales Range: $10-24.9 Million
Emp.: 300
Caterers
N.A.I.C.S.: 722320
Vincent Cascione (Controller)

CONTINENTAL INTERIORS INC.
1210 E Maple Rd, Troy, MI 48083
Tel.: (248) 616-6600
Web Site: http://www.continental-interiors.com
Year Founded: 1980
Rev.: $11,000,000
Emp.: 75
Flooring Contractors
N.A.I.C.S.: 238330
Richard Krupske (Pres)
Len Niemiec (Project Mgr)
Matt Forton (Project Mgr)
Matt Genuise (Project Mgr)
Rick Paavola (Project Mgr)
Ron Bosak (Project Mgr)
Scott McConnell (Project Mgr)

CONTINENTAL LABOR RE-SOURCES INC.
900 Mohawk St Ste 120, Bakersfield,
CA 93309-7441
Tel.: (661) 635-0335
Web Site:
http://www.continentallabor.com
Year Founded: 1993
Sales Range: $25-49.9 Million
Emp.: 2,885
Temporary Help Service
N.A.I.C.S.: 561320
Shannon Smith (Owner & CEO)
Karen Cain (Owner, Treas & Sec)

CONTINENTAL LINEN SER-VICES INC.
4200 Manchester Rd, Kalamazoo, MI
49001
Tel.: (269) 762-6143
Web Site: https://www.clsimage.com
Year Founded: 1899
Sales Range: $10-24.9 Million
Emp.: 100
Renter, Leaser & Sales of Uniforms,
Linen & Mat Services
N.A.I.C.S.: 812331
Ronald J. Vander Meer (Chm & CEO)
Kurt Vander Meer (Pres)
Brian Gleason (Controller)

CONTINENTAL MARKETING
15381 E Proctor Ave, City of Industry,
CA 91745
Tel.: (626) 582-8360
Year Founded: 1986
Sales Range: Less than $1 Million
Emp.: 20
Sports Bags, Fanny Packs, Lunch &
Duffle Bags, Other Travel Related
Accessories.
N.A.I.C.S.: 423610

Dawn Du (Gen Mgr)
Mylinh Hang (Acct Exec)
Jasen Huynh (Project Mgr)

CONTINENTAL MILLS, INC.
18100 Andover Park W, Tukwila, WA
98188-4704
Web Site:
http://www.continentalmills.com
Year Founded: 1932
Sales Range: $200-249.9 Million
Emp.: 661
Prepared Flour Mfr
N.A.I.C.S.: 311824
John M. Heily (Chm & CEO)
Andy Heily (Pres)
Liz Castro (Sr VP-HR)
Mike Meredith (Sr VP-Ops)

CONTINENTAL MORTGAGE BANKERS
1025 Old Country Rd Ste 100, West-
bury, NY 11590
Tel.: (516) 876-8500
Web Site:
http://www.financialequities.com
Sales Range: $75-99.9 Million
Emp.: 50
Mortgage Banker
N.A.I.C.S.: 522292
Walter Stashin (Pres)

CONTINENTAL MOTOR CO. INC.
4900 Old Seward Hwy, Anchorage,
AK 99503
Tel.: (907) 562-2722
Web Site:
http://www.continentalvolvo.com
Rev.: $53,200,000
Emp.: 200
Automobiles, New & Used
N.A.I.C.S.: 441110
Peter W. Adolf (Pres)
Eric Wetherington (Dir-Fixed Ops)

CONTINENTAL OFFICE ENVI-RONMENTS
5061 Freeway Dr E, Columbus, OH
43229
Tel.: (614) 262-5010
Web Site:
https://www.continentaloffice.com
Year Founded: 1965
Sales Range: $25-49.9 Million
Emp.: 220
Retailers of Office & Household Fur-
niture
N.A.I.C.S.: 423210
Quinn Gibson (Coord-CSC & Bid)
Amy Relli (Dir-Mktg)
Phil Roberts (Dir-Project Mgmt &
Field Svcs)
Nick Magoto (Exec VP-Design)
Gary Vipperman (Project Mgr)
John Gibbons (Project Mgr)
Joe Griffith (Project Mgr)
Tony Kirchner (Project Mgr)
Rene Phipps (VP-Customer Svcs &
Procurement)
Lisa Welch (VP-Education & Govt)
Jeff Leary (VP-Sls Dev & Natl Accts)
Rob Owens (VP-Sls Dev)
Kent Beightler (VP-Ops)
Marsha Morris (Coord-Ops)
Sara McKinniss (Mgr-Mktg)
Matthew Freedman (Sr VP-Branding)

CONTINENTAL PAPER GRAD-ING CO. INC.
1623 S Lumber St, Chicago, IL
60616-1117
Tel.: (312) 226-2010
Web Site: http://www.cpgco.com
Year Founded: 1951
Sales Range: $10-24.9 Million

Emp.: 40
Provider of Scrap & Waste Services
N.A.I.C.S.: 423930
Tony Aukett (CFO)

CONTINENTAL PLASTIC CARD COMPANY
1801 Green Rd, Pompano Beach, FL
33064
(954) 794-0040
Web Site:
http://www.continentalplasticco.com
Year Founded: 1972
Sales Range: $75-99.9 Million
Emp.: 75
Mfr of Plastic Cards & Security IDs
N.A.I.C.S.: 326199
Debbie Devinney (Dir-Adv)

CONTINENTAL PLASTICS CO. INC.
33525 Groesbeck Hwy, Fraser, MI
48026
Tel.: (586) 294-4600
Web Site:
http://www.continentalplastic.com
Year Founded: 1957
Sales Range: $25-49.9 Million
Emp.: 520
Thermoplastic Injection Molded Inte-
rior & Exterior Decorative Compo-
nents for the Automotive Industry
N.A.I.C.S.: 326199

Subsidiaries:

Continental Coatings (1)
4662 Puttygut Rd, China, MI
48054 (100%)
Tel.: (810) 326-2500
Web Site: http://www.morgankeegan.com
Sales Range: $25-49.9 Million
Emp.: 125
Head Lamps; Tail Lamps
N.A.I.C.S.: 238320

CONTINENTAL PRECISION CORP
25 Howard St, Piscataway, NJ 08854
Tel.: (908) 754-3030
Web Site:
http://www.montrosemolders.com
Rev.: $15,700,000
Emp.: 75
Injection Molding Of Plastics
N.A.I.C.S.: 326199
William B. Wilson (Pres & CEO)

CONTINENTAL PREMIUM CORPORATION
1315 Butterfield Rd Ste 216, Down-
ers Grove, IL 60515
Tel.: (630) 515-0800
Web Site:
http://www.continentalpremium.com
Sales Range: $10-24.9 Million
Emp.: 4
Services Related to Advertising
N.A.I.C.S.: 541890
Debbie Bertram (Pres)

CONTINENTAL PRESS INC.
520 E Bainbridge St, Elizabethtown,
PA 17022
Tel.: (717) 367-1836
Web Site:
http://www.continentalpress.com
Year Founded: 1942
Sales Range: $10-24.9 Million
Emp.: 125
Printers & Publishers of Educational
Materials for Students, Teachers &
Administrators
N.A.I.C.S.: 513130
Gene McFail (CFO)
Eric Beck (Pres)
Megan Bergonzi (VP)
Robyn Matus (VP-Mktg)

Subsidiaries:

Innovative Technologies in Print (1)
200 S Chestnut St, Elizabethtown, PA
17022
Tel.: (717) 367-3670
Web Site: http://www.itpofusa.com
Commercial Printing Services
N.A.I.C.S.: 323111

Seedling Publications (1)
520 E Bainbridge St, Elizabethtown, PA
17022
Tel.: (717) 367-1836
Web Site: http://www.seedlingpub.com
Sales Range: $10-24.9 Million
Emp.: 50
Publishing Company
N.A.I.C.S.: 513130

CONTINENTAL PRODUCTS
2000 W Blvd, Mexico, MO 65265-
1209
Tel.: (573) 581-5438
Web Site:
http://www.continentalproducts.com
Year Founded: 1964
Sales Range: $25-49.9 Million
Emp.: 150
Mfr & Distributor of Plastic Bags
N.A.I.C.S.: 326111
Thad Fisher (Mgr-Sls-Natl)

CONTINENTAL PROPERTY GROUP, INC.
1907 Wayzata Blvd E Ste 250,
Wayzata, MN 55391
Tel.: (952) 473-1700
Web Site:
https://www.leasespace.com
Year Founded: 1985
Sales Range: $75-99.9 Million
Emp.: 5
Commercial Real Estate Developer
N.A.I.C.S.: 531210
Bradley A. Hoyt (Owner & Pres)
Traci Tomas (Exec VP)

CONTINENTAL REAL ESTATE COMPANIES INC.
150 E Broad St, Columbus, OH
43215-3644
Tel.: (614) 221-1800
Web Site: https://www.continental-realestate.com
Year Founded: 1979
Sales Range: $10-24.9 Million
Emp.: 100
Provider of Nonresidential Construc-
tion Services
N.A.I.C.S.: 236220
Mike Hudec (VP-Dev-Pittsburgh)
Frank Kass (Principal)
Jack Lucks (Principal)
David L. Royer (Exec VP-Dev & Fin)

CONTINENTAL REALTY COR-PORATION
1427 Clarkview Rd Ste 500, Balti-
more, MD 21209-0016
Tel.: (410) 296-4800
Web Site: https://www.crcrealty.com
Year Founded: 1960
Sales Range: $10-24.9 Million
Emp.: 60
Real Estate Brokerage Services
N.A.I.C.S.: 531210
J. M. Schapiro (CEO)
Maura Howard (Reg Mgr)
Gene C. Parker (Pres)
David P. Donato (Sr VP-Comml Div)
Anne Angel (VP-Residential Div)
Debra Goldstein (VP-Fin & Capital
Markets)
Steve Roenick (Dir-Acctg & Taxation)
Adam Cook (Mgr-Property)
Jessica Williams (Mgr-Property)
Maggie Sumutka (Mgr-Ops)

Jenny Nguyen *(Mgr-Property)*
Ashley Singley *(Asst Mgr-Property)*
Alisha Covington-Jackson *(Sr Mgr-Property)*
Paul Kang *(VP-Retail Acq)*
Lauren Wayne *(Controller-Fund Investments)*
Belinda Torres *(Dir-Mktg)*
Blake Dickinson *(Sr Mgr-Leasing-Comml Div)*
Haley Gallagher *(Mgr-Asset)*
Kate S. Gayhardt *(Dir-Residential Fund Ops)*
Lawrence Rief *(Partner)*
Matt McNeeley *(Dir-Talent Mgmt)*
Richard M. Berkowitz *(VP-Construction)*
Scott Hamlin *(Dir-Property Mgmt-Multifamily Div)*
Matthew Johnson *(VP-Asset Mgmt)*
J. D. Brakefield *(Dir-Property Mgmt-Comml Div)*
Joshua Kaska *(Project Mgr-Construction)*

CONTINENTAL REFINING COMPANY
300 Refinery Rd, Somerset, KY 42501-2908
Tel.: (606) 679-6301　　　　　IL
Web Site:
　　http://www.continentalrefiningco.com
Year Founded: 1932
Sales Range: $25-49.9 Million
Emp.: 55
Petroleum Refining
N.A.I.C.S.: 324110
Kristopher W. Gibson *(Plant Mgr)*
Demetrios E. Haseotes *(Pres & CEO)*
Amber Vickery *(Mgr-HR)*
Steve Morris *(CFO & Controller)*

CONTINENTAL RESOURCES, INC.
20 N Broadway, Oklahoma City, OK 73102
Tel.: (405) 234-9000　　　　　OK
Web Site: https://www.clr.com
Year Founded: 1967
CLR—(NYSE)
Rev.: $9,473,708,000
Assets: $20,878,350,000
Liabilities: $13,748,742,000
Net Worth: $7,129,608,000
Earnings: $4,024,558,000
Emp.: 1,404
Fiscal Year-end: 12/31/22
Crude Petroleum Extraction Services
N.A.I.C.S.: 211120
Harold G. Hamm *(Founder & Chm)*
John D. Hart *(CFO & Exec VP-Strategic Plng)*
Jeffrey B. Hume *(Vice Chm-Strategic Growth Initiatives)*
Blu Hulsey *(Sr VP-HSE, Govt & Regulatory Affairs)*
Diane Montgomery *(Treas & VP-Corp Fin)*
Robert Doug Lawler *(Pres & COO)*
Shelly Lambertz *(Chief Culture & Admin Officer & Exec VP)*
Joe Davis *(CIO & VP)*
Heather Scott *(VP-Corp & Admin Initiatives)*
Robert Hagens *(Sr VP-Land)*
Chad Elliott *(VP-Drilling)*
Ryan Baker *(VP)*
Jeff Cook *(VP)*
Michael Edmonds *(VP)*
Sean Flynn *(VP)*
Damon Metcalf *(Chief Acctg Officer)*
James Roberts *(VP)*
Robert Douglas Lawler *(Pres & CEO)*

Subsidiaries:

Continental Resources Illinois,
Inc.　　　　　　　　　　　　　　(1)

20 N Broadway Ave, Oklahoma City, OK 73102
Tel.: (580) 233-8955
Web Site: http://www.clr.com
Sales Range: $75-99.9 Million
Emp.: 110
Exploration, Exploitation, Development & Acquisition of Oil & Gas Reserves; Owner & Operator of 700 Miles of Natural Gas Pipelines, Gas Gathering Systems & Gas Processing Plants
N.A.I.C.S.: 211120

CONTINENTAL SALES COMPANY OF AMERICA, LTD.
180 Westgate Dr, Watsonville, CA 95076
Tel.: (831) 763-6931
Web Site: https://www.csclabs.com
Rev.: $22,000,000
Emp.: 225
Eyeglasses Mfr
N.A.I.C.S.: 339115

CONTINENTAL SECRET SERVICE BUREAU
419 N Huron St, Toledo, OH 43604-1405
Tel.: (419) 243-2515
Web Site: https://www.cssb-inc.com
Year Founded: 1919
Sales Range: $10-24.9 Million
Emp.: 450
Security Guards & Patrol Services
N.A.I.C.S.: 561612
Scott Wunder *(CEO)*

CONTINENTAL SERVICES, INC.
700 Stephenson Hwy, Troy, MI 48083
Tel.: (248) 414-1700
Web Site:
　　http://www.continentalserves.com
Year Founded: 1989
Event Management Services; Cafeteria Management Services; Vending Machine Services
N.A.I.C.S.: 722320
Jim Bardy *(CEO)*

Subsidiaries:

Metro Vending Service, Inc.　　(1)
16545 Eastland St, Roseville, MI 48066
Tel.: (586) 779-7710
Web Site: http://www.metrovending.com
Vending Machine Operators
N.A.I.C.S.: 445132

CONTINENTAL TICKING CORPORATION AMERICA
Tel.: (336) 570-0091
Web Site: https://www.ctnassau.com
Year Founded: 1991
Rev.: $14,200,000
Emp.: 100
Narrow Fabric Mills
N.A.I.C.S.: 313220

CONTINENTAL TRADING & HARDWARE INC.
400 Delancey St, Newark, NJ 07105-3812
Tel.: (973) 589-3929
Web Site:
　　http://www.continentaltrading.com
Sales Range: $10-24.9 Million
Emp.: 20
Lumber & Other Building Materials
N.A.I.C.S.: 423310
Joseph Pimentel *(Pres & CEO)*
Melanie Agostinho *(Controller)*

CONTINENTAL TRUCK BROKERS INC.
8890 SW Holly Ln Ste A, Wilsonville, OR 97070
Tel.: (503) 682-1822
Rev.: $11,184,996

Emp.: 8
Truck Transportation Brokers
N.A.I.C.S.: 488510

CONTINENTAL VAN LINES INC.
4501 W Marginal Way SW, Seattle, WA 98106
Tel.: (206) 937-2261
Web Site:
　　http://www.continentalvan.com
Sales Range: $10-24.9 Million
Emp.: 125
Contract Haulers
N.A.I.C.S.: 484121
John G. Blaine *(Pres)*
Brad Fransen *(Dir-Sls & Mktg)*
LaMonica Hummel *(Dir-Bus Dev)*
Darlene Clarke *(Coord-Move)*
Dennise Mustain *(Gen Mgr)*
Christopher Rambo *(Mgr-IT)*

CONTINENTAL VITAMIN CO., INC.
4510 S Boyle Ave, Los Angeles, CA 90058-2488
Tel.: (323) 581-0176
Web Site: http://www.cvc4health.com
Year Founded: 1968
Sales Range: $10-24.9 Million
Emp.: 60
Drugs Whslr
N.A.I.C.S.: 424210
Matthew Supkoff *(VP-Ops)*

CONTINENTAL WEB PRESS, INC.
1430 Industrial Dr, Itasca, IL 60143-1848
Tel.: (630) 773-1903　　　　　IL
Web Site:
　　https://www.continentalweb.com
Year Founded: 1973
Sales Range: $150-199.9 Million
Emp.: 450
Web Offset Printer of Commercial Magazines & Catalogs
N.A.I.C.S.: 323111
Kenneth W. Field *(Founder & VP)*
Diane Field *(Founder, Pres & CEO)*
Jim Arnold *(VP-Sls)*

Subsidiaries:

Continental Web Press of
Kentucky　　　　　　　　　　　(1)
125 Richwood Rd, Walton, KY
41094-8399　　　　　　　　　(100%)
Tel.: (859) 485-1500
Web Site: http://www.continentalweb.com
Sales Range: $25-49.9 Million
Emp.: 200
Catalog Printer
N.A.I.C.S.: 323111
Jim Arnold *(VP-Sls)*
Bill Caldwell *(Dir-Procurement)*
Jerry Haywood *(COO & Exec VP)*
Michele Krahn *(Dir-HR)*
Kenneth W. Field Sr. *(VP)*

CONTINENTAL WESTERN CORPORATION
2950 Merced St Ste 200, San Leandro, CA 94577
Tel.: (510) 352-3133
Web Site: http://www.cwestern.com
Year Founded: 1952
Sales Range: $25-49.9 Million
Emp.: 60
Supplier of Rope, Twine, Rubber Bands, Strapping, Gloves & Tarp Products for the Agricultural, Fishing, Marine, Industrial, Hardware, Utility & Packaging Markets
N.A.I.C.S.: 423840
Donn Mouw *(Branch Mgr)*
Lauren Keba *(Mgr-Mktg)*

CONTINENTAL WORSTEDS INC.
45 N Station Plz Ste 402, Great Neck, NY 11021
Tel.: (516) 472-2000
Sales Range: $10-24.9 Million
Emp.: 6
Textile Mfr
N.A.I.C.S.: 424310
Joseph Jangana *(Pres)*
Eze Bashi *(Controller)*

CONTINUING CARE INC
1100 S Curry Pike, Bloomington, IN 47403
Tel.: (812) 339-1657　　　　　IN
Web Site:
　　http://www.gardenvillahealth.com
Year Founded: 1996
Sales Range: $10-24.9 Million
Health Care Srvices
N.A.I.C.S.: 623110
Tammy Cain *(Dir-Nursing)*

CONTINUUM OF CARE, INC.
67 Trumbull St, New Haven, CT 06510
Tel.: (203) 562-2264　　　　　CT
Web Site: http://www.continuumct.org
Year Founded: 1966
Sales Range: $10-24.9 Million
Emp.: 720
Community Action Services
N.A.I.C.S.: 624190
James Farrales *(Exec VP)*
Monica O'Connor *(VP-Facilities Mgmt)*

CONTOUR DATA SOLUTIONS
8 Neshaminy Interplex Ste 102, Trevose, PA 19053
Tel.: (484) 235-5143
Web Site: http://www.contourds.com
Year Founded: 2005
Sales Range: $1-9.9 Million
Emp.: 20
IT Consulting, Implementation & Managed Services
N.A.I.C.S.: 541618
Rocco Guerriero *(Founder & CEO)*
Jeff Hutchins *(CIO)*
James Sine *(Engr-Implementation)*
Sean Wolf *(Acct Mgr)*
Jesse Trott *(Engr-Multi Sys Support)*

CONTOUR STEEL INC
7254 Southwestern Blvd, Eden, NY 14057
Tel.: (716) 627-1140
Web Site:
　　https://www.contoursteel.com
Rev.: $17,621,339
Emp.: 70
Bridge Construction
N.A.I.C.S.: 237310
Jean Vandermeer *(CFO)*

CONTOURS EXPRESS, INC.
156 Imperial Way, Nicholasville, KY 40356
Tel.: (877) 227-2282
Web Site:
　　http://www.contoursexpress.com
Year Founded: 1998
Sales Range: $1-9.9 Million
Emp.: 8
Franchised Chain of Women-Only Fitness Facilities
N.A.I.C.S.: 713940
Bill Helton *(Pres)*

CONTRA COSTA WATER DISTRICT INC.
1331 Concord Ave, Concord, CA 94520-4907
Tel.: (925) 688-8000

Contra Costa Water District Inc.—(Continued)

Web Site: https://www.ccwater.com
Year Founded: 1936
Sales Range: $100-124.9 Million
Emp.: 323
Water Utility Services
N.A.I.C.S.: 221310
John Burgh (VP-Div 2)
Jerry D. Brown (Gen Mgr)
Lisa M. Borba (Pres-Div 1)
Bette Boatmun (Dir-Div 4)
Connstance Holdaway (Dir-Div 5)
Ron Jacobsma (Asst Gen Mgr-
Admin)

**CONTRACK INTERNATIONAL
INC.**
6862 Elm St Fl 5, McLean, VA 22101-
3838
Tel.: (703) 358-8800　　　　　DC
Web Site: http://www.contrack.com
Year Founded: 1985
Sales Range: $25-49.9 Million
Emp.: 230
Provider of Nonresidential Construc-
tion Services
N.A.I.C.S.: 236220
Assem Iskander (Dir-Procurement &
Logistics)
Frank McConnell (Dir-Contracting &
Controls)
Jacqualin Schermerhorn (Mgr-Payroll)

**CONTRACT CONVERTING
LLC**
W6580 Quality Dr, Greenville, WI
54942
Tel.: (920) 757-4000
Web Site:
　https://www.contractconverting.com
Rev.: $12,300,000
Emp.: 45
Industrial & Personal Service Paper
N.A.I.C.S.: 323120
William Schnettler (Mng Dir)

CONTRACT EXTERIORS LLC
124 Elk Dr, Murrells Inlet, SC 29576
Tel.: (843) 357-9234
Web Site:
　http://www.contractexteriors.com
Year Founded: 2009
Sales Range: $25-49.9 Million
Emp.: 69
Building Exterior Contractor Services
N.A.I.C.S.: 238190
Randy Hann (Co-Owner)
William McCourt (Co-Owner)

**CONTRACT FURNISHERS OF
HAWAII**
50 S Beretania St Ste C208B, Hono-
lulu, HI 96813
Tel.: (808) 599-2411
Web Site:
　http://www.officepavilionhawaii.com
Sales Range: $10-24.9 Million
Emp.: 35
Office Furniture
N.A.I.C.S.: 423210
Sean Mccully (Controller)
Windy Shewalter (Pres & Mgr-Sls)

CONTRACT FURNITURE INC.
4526 Transport Dr, Tampa, FL 33605
Tel.: (813) 247-6622
Web Site:
　https://www.contractfurniturefl.com
Year Founded: 1998
Sales Range: $1-9.9 Million
Emp.: 18
Office Furniture Dealer
N.A.I.C.S.: 423210
Darla Vegenski (Co-Foudner & Pres)
Mike Vegenski (Co-Founder)

CONTRACT HARDWARE INC.
1260 Collier Rd NW, Atlanta, GA
30318
Tel.: (404) 350-9408
Web Site: https://www.contract-
　hardware.com
Sales Range: $10-24.9 Million
Emp.: 30
Hardware, Hollow Metal & Doors Mfr
N.A.I.C.S.: 423710
Mike Perdue (VP)

**CONTRACT INDUSTRIAL
TOOLING, INC.**
2351 Production Ct, Richmond, IN
47374
Tel.: (765) 966-1134
Web Site: https://www.c-i-t.com
Sales Range: $10-24.9 Million
Emp.: 80
Industrial Machinery Mfr
N.A.I.C.S.: 333248

CONTRACT LUMBER INC.
3245 Hazelton Etna Rd SW, Pa-
taskala, OH 43062-8532
Tel.: (740) 927-4242　　　　OH
Web Site:
　https://www.contractlumber.com
Year Founded: 1989
Sales Range: $25-49.9 Million
Emp.: 200
Building Services
N.A.I.C.S.: 238130
Rick Hiegel (Pres)
Tom Bieser (Owner)
Jane Henthorn (Project Mgr)
Patrick McKenney (VP-
Transportation)

**CONTRACT OFFICE GROUP,
INC.**
1731 Technology Dr Ste 100, San
Jose, CA 95110
Tel.: (408) 262-6400
Web Site: http://www.cog.com
Year Founded: 1976
Sales Range: $10-24.9 Million
Emp.: 60
Fiscal Year-end: 12/31/15
Retailer of Office Furniture
N.A.I.C.S.: 423210
Timothy Fritz (Mgr-Ops)

**CONTRACT PHARMACAL
CORP**
135 Adams Ave, Hauppauge, NY
11788
Tel.: (631) 231-4610
Web Site: http://www.cpc.com
Year Founded: 1971
Sales Range: $10-24.9 Million
Emp.: 1,000
Pharmaceutical Preparations
N.A.I.C.S.: 325412
John L. Wolf (Pres)
Matt Wolf (CEO)

**CONTRACT PHARMACY SER-
VICES**
125 Titus Ave, Warrington, PA 18976-
2424
Tel.: (267) 487-9000
Web Site: http://www.contractrx.com
Rev.: $29,582,148
Emp.: 150
Pharmaceuticals
N.A.I.C.S.: 424210
Wayne Shafer (CEO)
Ann Burrell (Pres)
Kimberly Griego (Mgr-Clinical Phar-
macy)

**CONTRACT PROFESSIONALS
INC.**

4141 W Walton Blvd, Waterford, MI
48329
Tel.: (248) 673-3800　　　　MI
Web Site: https://www.cpijobs.com
Year Founded: 1982
Sales Range: $25-49.9 Million
Emp.: 612
Help Supply Services
N.A.I.C.S.: 561920
Steven E. York (Chm & CEO)
Michael Borg (Officer-Facility Security
& VP-Infrastructure)
Tricia Wilson (VP-Fin)
Jay Vorobel (VP)
James Cowper (Pres)

Subsidiaries:

Contract Professionals　　　　(1)
32200 Solon Rd, Solon, OH　　(60%)
44139-3535
Tel.: (440) 248-8550
Web Site: http://www.cpijobs.com
Sales Range: $10-24.9 Million
Emp.: 10
Technical Staffing & Publications
N.A.I.C.S.: 541330

**CONTRACT PURCHASING &
DESIGN INC.**
6530 W Rogers Cir Ste 28, Boca Ra-
ton, FL 33487
Tel.: (561) 994-4555
Web Site: https://www.cpdboca.com
Rev.: $15,000,000
Emp.: 10
Furniture Merchant Whslr
N.A.I.C.S.: 423210
Sylvia D. Patton (VP)

**CONTRACT STEEL SALES
INC.**
1807 E Wendover Ave, Greensboro,
NC 27405
Tel.: (336) 273-9704
Year Founded: 1974
Rev.: $22,468,301
Emp.: 30
Fabricated Structural Metal
N.A.I.C.S.: 332312
John Larry Bundren (Pres)
Philip A. Hutson (Chm)
Mike N. Wagoner (VP-Engrg)
Tim Needham (Mgr-Sls)
Mark Turman (Mgr-Drafting)

CONTRACT TRANSPORT INC.
1440 Vermont St, Des Moines, IA
50314
Tel.: (515) 243-5499
Sales Range: $10-24.9 Million
Emp.: 250
Provider of Contract Hauling Services
N.A.I.C.S.: 484121
Wesley Nible (Pres)

**CONTRACTED LABOR SER-
VICES INC.**
2605 S Miller St Ste 107, Santa Ma-
ria, CA 93455
Tel.: (805) 928-5725
Web Site: https://www.ypp.com
Rev.: $24,000,000
Emp.: 25
Provider of Labor Contractor Services
N.A.I.C.S.: 561311
Cindy McKellar (CEO)

**CONTRACTOR'S SUPPLIES,
INC.**
304 Webber St, Lufkin, TX 75904
Tel.: (936) 634-3341　　　　TX
Web Site:
　https://www.csiconcrete.com
Year Founded: 1947
Sales Range: $25-49.9 Million
Emp.: 100

Ready-Mixed Concrete & Masonry
Supply Mfr
David Butler (Pres)

Subsidiaries:

Contractor's Supplies, Inc. -
LONGVIEW PLANT　　　　(1)
417 Calvin Blvd, Longview, TX 75602
Tel.: (903) 753-5766
Web Site: http://www.csiconcrete.com
Emp.: 20
Readymix Concrete Mfr
N.A.I.C.S.: 327320
Paul Sellers (Plant Mgr)

Contractor's Supplies, Inc. - LUFKIN
PLANT　　　　(1)
303 Webber St, Lufkin, TX 75904
Tel.: (936) 634-3341
Web Site: http://www.csiconcrete.com
Readymix Concrete Mfr
N.A.I.C.S.: 327320
Matthew Johnson (Plant Mgr)
Shawn Kaemmerling (Plant Mgr)
James Pickle (Mgr-Maintenance)

Contractor's Supplies, Inc. - MAR-
SHALL PLANT　　　　(1)
905 Lake St, Marshall, TX 75670
Tel.: (903) 938-2092
Emp.: 5
Readymix Concrete Mfr
N.A.I.C.S.: 327320

Contractor's Supplies, Inc. - TYLER
PLANT　　　　(1)
1601 John Carney Dr, Tyler, TX 75701
Tel.: (903) 597-1308
Web Site: http://www.csiconcrete.com
Emp.: 30
Readymix Concrete Mfr
N.A.I.C.S.: 327320
Chris Sonnamaker (Plant Mgr)

**CONTRACTORS HEATING-
COOLING SUPPLY, LLC**
1433 W 130 S, Orem, UT 84058-
5259
Tel.: (801) 224-1020　　　　UT
Web Site: https://www.chcs-ut.com
Year Founded: 1976
Sales Range: $10-24.9 Million
Emp.: 100
Heating, Ventilation & Air Condition-
ing Equipment Whslr
N.A.I.C.S.: 423730
Blaine Hyde (Pres)
Mike Jensen (Mgr-Sls)

**CONTRACTORS NORTHWEST
INC.**
3731 N Ramsey Rd, Coeur D'Alene,
ID 83815
Tel.: (208) 667-2456　　　　WA
Web Site:
　http://www.contractorsnorthwest.com
Year Founded: 1975
Sales Range: $50-74.9 Million
Emp.: 75
Provider of Nonresidential Construc-
tion Services
N.A.I.C.S.: 236220
D. Dean Haagenson (Chm & CEO)
Bryan Taylor (Pres & COO)
Laura Lachapelle (Office Mgr)
Russ Twardowski (Project Mgr)

**CONTRACTORS PIPE & SUP-
PLY CORP.**
24895 N Industrial Dr, Farmington
Hills, MI 48335
Tel.: (248) 888-5840　　　　MI
Web Site:
　http://www.contractorpipesupply.com
Year Founded: 1964
Sales Range: $10-24.9 Million
Emp.: 30
Pipe, Plumbing Fittings & Supplies
Distr
N.A.I.C.S.: 423720

Albert J. D'Angelo *(Chm)*
David D'Angelo *(Pres)*

CONTRACTORS RENTAL CORPORATION
600 AIS Dr, Grand Rapids, MI 49548
Tel.: (616) 538-2400
Web Site: http://www.aisequip.com
Year Founded: 1963
Sales Range: $300-349.9 Million
Emp.: 300
Provider of Heavy Construction
Equipment Rental Services
N.A.I.C.S.: 532412
James Behrenwald *(Pres)*
Dave TerBeek *(VP-Rental Ops)*
Matt Rinckey *(Mgr-Sls)*

CONTRAN CORPORATION
3 Lincoln Ctr Ste 1700 5430 LBJ
Fwy, Dallas, TX 75240-2694
Tel.: (972) 233-1700   DE
Year Founded: 1968
Emp.: 600
Holding Company; Chemicals, Titanium Metals, Hardware Products, Steel Rod, Wire & Wire Products Mfr
N.A.I.C.S.: 551112
Gregory M. Swalwell *(CFO, Chief Acctg Officer & Exec VP)*
Steven L. Watson *(Vice Chm & Pres)*
Michael S. Simmons *(Pres & CEO)*
Robert D. Graham *(Pres & CEO)*
Courtney J. Riley *(Sr VP)*
Michael S. Simmons *(Pres & CEO)*
James M. Buch *(Sr VP)*
John Sunny *(VP-IT)*

Subsidiaries:

Keystone Consolidated Industries, Inc.   **(1)**
5430 LBJ Fwy, Dallas, TX
75240-2697   **(100%)**
Tel.: (972) 458-0028
Web Site: http://www.kci-corp.com
Mfr of Steel-Fabricated Wire Products, Industrial Wire & Rods
N.A.I.C.S.: 332618
Chris Armstrong *(CEO)*

Subsidiary (Domestic):

Engineered Wire Products, Inc.   **(2)**
1200 N Warpole St, Upper Sandusky, OH 43351-9093
Tel.: (419) 294-3817
Web Site: http://www.ewpinc.com
Sales Range: $50-74.9 Million
Emp.: 100
Welded Wire Reinforcement Mfr
N.A.I.C.S.: 332618
Jeff Babcock *(VP-Sls)*

Keystone Steel & Wire Co.   **(2)**
7000 SW Adams St, Peoria, IL 61641
Tel.: (309) 697-7020
Web Site: http://www.keystonesteel.com
Sales Range: $50-74.9 Million
Mfr of Steel Rods, Wire Mesh Products & Fencing
N.A.I.C.S.: 331221
David L. Cheek *(CEO)*
Vic Stirnaman *(COO)*
Richard Webb *(VP-Sls & Mktg)*
Aaron Williams *(VP)*
Kevin Shake *(VP)*

Sherman Wire Company   **(2)**
428 Gibbons Rd, Sherman, TX 75092-8390
Tel.: (903) 893-0191
Mfr of Steel Wire & Fabricated Wire Products
N.A.I.C.S.: 332618

Valhi, Inc.   **(1)**
5430 LBJ Fwy Ste 1700, Dallas, TX
75240-2620   **(94.4%)**
Tel.: (972) 233-1700
Web Site: https://www.valhi.net
Rev.: $2,266,200,000
Assets: $2,835,700,000
Liabilities: $1,528,900,000
Net Worth: $1,306,800,000

Earnings: $90,200,000
Emp.: 2,266
Fiscal Year-end: 12/31/2022
Holding Company; Chemicals, Refined Sugar, Integrated Forest Products, Fast Food & Hardware Products
N.A.I.C.S.: 551112
Michael S. Simmons *(Vice Chm, Pres & CEO)*
Courtney J. Riley *(Exec VP)*
Michael S. Simmons *(Vice Chm, Pres & CEO)*
Patty S. Brinda *(VP & Controller)*

Subsidiary (Domestic):

Basic Remediation Company
LLC   **(2)**
875 W Warm Springs Rd, Henderson, NV 89011-4063
Tel.: (702) 567-2632
Web Site: http://www.landdwellco.com
Emp.: 25
Management Consulting Services
N.A.I.C.S.: 541618
Mark Paris *(Pres)*

Basic Water Company   **(2)**
875 W Warm Springs Rd, Henderson, NV 89011-4063
Tel.: (702) 567-0463
Web Site: http://www.landdwellco.com
Emp.: 50
Water Supply Services
N.A.I.C.S.: 221310

Kronos Worldwide, Inc.   **(2)**
5430 LBJ Fwy Ste 1700, Dallas, TX
75240-2620   **(50%)**
Tel.: (972) 233-1700
Web Site: https://www.kronosww.com
Rev.: $1,930,200,000
Assets: $1,934,400,000
Liabilities: $977,200,000
Net Worth: $957,200,000
Earnings: $104,500,000
Emp.: 2,266
Fiscal Year-end: 12/31/2022
Specialty Coating Pigments, Rheological Additives & Titanium Dioxide Pigments Producer & Marketer
N.A.I.C.S.: 325510
Michael S. Simmons *(Vice Chm)*
Robert D. Graham *(Vice Chm)*
Courtney J. Riley *(chief transformation officer & Exec VP)*
Michael S. Simmons *(Vice Chm)*
James M. Buch *(Pres & CEO)*

Subsidiary (Domestic):

Kronos International, Inc.   **(3)**
5430 LBJ Freeway Ste 1700, Dallas, TX 75240-2697   **(100%)**
Tel.: (972) 233-1700
Web Site: http://www.kronostio2.com
Sales Range: $1-4.9 Billion
Emp.: 1,985
Chemical Products Mfr & Sales
N.A.I.C.S.: 325510

Subsidiary (Non-US):

Kronos B.V.   **(4)**
Guldenwaard 133 B, 3078 AJ, Rotterdam, Netherlands
Tel.: (31) 104136310
Web Site: http://www.kronostio2.com
Sales Range: $75-99.9 Million
Emp.: 4
Mining Nonmetallic Minerals
N.A.I.C.S.: 212390
Joe De Trimerie *(Mng Dir)*

Kronos Canada, Inc.   **(4)**
1255 University Ave Ste 1102, Montreal, H3B 3W7, QC, Canada
Tel.: (514) 397-3501
Web Site: http://www.kronostio2.com
Sales Range: $50-74.9 Million
Emp.: 16
Titanium Dioxide Mfr
N.A.I.C.S.: 325180

Kronos Chemie GmbH   **(4)**
Peschsprase 5, PO Box 100720, Leverkusen, 100720, Germany
Tel.: (49) 2143560
Web Site: http://www.kronostio2.com

Sales Range: $125-149.9 Million
Mfr of Chemical Products
N.A.I.C.S.: 325998
Ulfert Fiand *(Gen Mgr)*

Kronos Europe S.A./N.V.   **(4)**
Langerbruggekaai 10, Gent, 9000, Belgium
Tel.: (32) 92540311
Web Site: http://www.kronostio2.com
Sales Range: $75-99.9 Million
Emp.: 300
Chemicals Mfr
N.A.I.C.S.: 325998
Marnix Mahieu *(Plant Mgr)*

Kronos Limited   **(4)**
Barons Ct Manchester Rd, Wilmslow, SK9 1BQ, Cheshire, United Kingdom
Tel.: (44) 1625547200
Web Site: http://www.kronostio2.com
Sales Range: $50-74.9 Million
Emp.: 7
Distribution of Chemical Products
N.A.I.C.S.: 424690
Jeffrey Kelly *(Gen Mgr)*

Kronos Titan A/S   **(4)**
Titangaten 1, Gamle, 1630, Fredrikstad, Norway
Tel.: (47) 69309000
Web Site: http://www.kronos.de
Sales Range: $125-149.9 Million
Emp.: 190
Holding Company for Norwegian Subsidiaries
N.A.I.C.S.: 551112
Per Thoen *(Mng Dir)*

Kronos Titan GmbH   **(4)**
Peschstase No 5, PO Box 100720, 41373, Leverkusen, Germany
Tel.: (49) 2143560
Web Site: http://www.kronostea2.com
Sales Range: $125-149.9 Million
Emp.: 650
Mfr of Titanium Dioxide
N.A.I.C.S.: 325180
Ulrich Kablac *(Mgr-Fin)*

Societe Industrielle Du Titane, S.A.   **(4)**
45 rue de Courcelles, 75008, Paris, France
Web Site: http://www.kronosww.com
Rev.: $38,269,000
Emp.: 12
Steel Wiredrawing & Steel Nails & Spike Mfr
N.A.I.C.S.: 332618

Subsidiary (Domestic):

Kronos Louisiana, Inc.   **(3)**
3330 Bayoo Dinde Rd, Westlake, LA 70669-8102
Tel.: (337) 882-1774
Dye & Pigment Mfr
N.A.I.C.S.: 325130

Subsidiary (Non-US):

Kronos Norge A/S   **(3)**
PO Box 1415, 1602, Fredrikstad, Norway
Tel.: (47) 69309000
Inorganic Dye & Pigment Mfr
N.A.I.C.S.: 325130

Subsidiary (Domestic):

Louisiana Pigment Company L.P. **(3)**
3300 Bayou Dinde Rd, Westlake, LA 70669-8102
Tel.: (337) 882-7000
Web Site: http://www.lapigment.com
Sales Range: $250-299.9 Million
Emp.: 450
Inorganic Dye & Pigment Mfr
N.A.I.C.S.: 325130

Subsidiary (Domestic):

NL Industries, Inc.   **(2)**
5430 LBJ Fwy Ste 1700, Dallas, TX
75240-2620   **(83%)**
Tel.: (972) 233-1700
Web Site: https://www.nl-ind.com
Rev.: $166,562,000
Assets: $609,867,000
Liabilities: $207,120,000
Net Worth: $402,747,000
Earnings: $33,844,000
Emp.: 2,818

Fiscal Year-end: 12/31/2022
Holding Company; Precision Ball Bearing Slides, Security Products & Ergonomic Computer Support Systems Mfr; Titanium Dioxide Pigments Producer & Marketer
N.A.I.C.S.: 551112
Michael S. Simmons *(Vice Chm)*
Courtney J. Riley *(Pres & CEO)*
Michael S. Simmons *(Vice Chm)*
Amy Allbach Samford *(CFO & Sr VP)*
Amy E. Ruf *(VP & Controller)*
Thomas P. Stafford *(Bd of Dirs, Executives)*

Holding (Domestic):

CompX International Inc.   **(3)**
5430 LBJ Fwy Ste 1700, Dallas, TX
75240-2620   **(86%)**
Tel.: (972) 448-1400
Web Site: https://www.compxinternational.com
Rev.: $140,815,000
Assets: $192,452,000
Liabilities: $19,364,000
Net Worth: $173,088,000
Earnings: $16,568,000
Emp.: 570
Fiscal Year-end: 01/02/2022
Ergonomic Computer Support Systems, Ball Bearing Slides & Locks Mfr
N.A.I.C.S.: 331314
Michael S. Simmons *(Vice Chm)*
Michael S. Simmons *(Vice Chm, CFO & Sr VP)*
Amy E. Ruf *(VP & Controller)*
Scott C. James *(Pres & CEO)*
Amy A. Samford *(CFO)*
Bryan A. Hanley *(Treas & Sr VP)*
Jane R. Grimm *(Gen Counsel, Sec & VP)*
Bart W. Reichert *(VP-Internal Audit)*
Kristin B. McCoy *(Exec VP-Tax)*

Subsidiary (Domestic):

CompX Fort   **(4)**
715 Ctr St, Grayslake, IL 60030
Tel.: (847) 752-2500
Sales Range: $50-74.9 Million
Emp.: 210
Cam, Switch & Specialty Locks Mfr
N.A.I.C.S.: 332510

CompX National, Inc.   **(4)**
26 Old Mill Rd, Greenville, SC 29607
Tel.: (864) 297-6655
Sales Range: $50-74.9 Million
Emp.: 300
Security Hardware Mfr
N.A.I.C.S.: 332510

CompX Security Products Inc. **(4)**
26 Old Mill Rd, Greenville, SC 29607
Tel.: (864) 297-6655
Web Site: http://www.compx.com
Lock Webcam & Security Product Mfr
N.A.I.C.S.: 332510

Subsidiary (Non-US):

CompX Waterloo   **(4)**
501 Manitou Drive, Kitchener, N2C 1L2, ON, Canada   **(100%)**
Tel.: (519) 748-5060
Sales Range: $50-74.9 Million
Emp.: 300
Mfr of Components for Office Furniture
N.A.I.C.S.: 335999

Subsidiary (Domestic):

Custom Marine Inc.   **(4)**
1315 County Rd G, Neenah, WI 54956
Tel.: (920) 720-4225
Web Site: http://www.custommarine.com
Header & Tailpipe Mfr
N.A.I.C.S.: 332996

Livorsi Marine Inc.   **(4)**
715 Center St, Grayslake, IL 60030
Tel.: (847) 752-2700
Web Site: http://www.livorsi.com
Measuring & Controlling Device Mfr
N.A.I.C.S.: 334519
Mike Livorsi *(Founder & Pres)*

Subsidiary (Domestic):

NL Environmental Management Services, Inc.   **(3)**
5430 LBJ Freeway Ste 1700, Dallas, TX 75240-2697

Contran Corporation—(Continued)

Tel.: (972) 233-1700
Emp.: 10
Inorganic Dye & Pigment Mfr
N.A.I.C.S.: 325130
Patty Kropp (Mgr-HR)

Subsidiary (Domestic):

The Landwell Company LP   (2)
875 W Warm Springs Rd, Henderson, NV 89011
Tel.: (702) 567-0400
Web Site: http://www.landwellco.com
Emp.: 25
Property Management Services
N.A.I.C.S.: 531390
Mark Paris (Pres & CEO)

CONTRAVEST MANAGEMENT COMPANY

237 S Westmonte Dr Ste 140, Altamonte Springs, FL 32714
Tel.: (407) 333-0066   FL
Web Site:
    https://www.contravest.com
Year Founded: 1986
Sales Range: $50-74.9 Million
Emp.: 150
Residential Real Estate Development, Construction & Management Services
N.A.I.C.S.: 237210
John Schaffer (Pres, CFO & Principal)
Mark Ogier (Pres & Principal-Dev)
Steven Ogier (Pres & Principal-Construction)
Christin Tenpenny (VP-Mgmt)
Beth Buckman (Mgr-Admin)
Vickie Keene (Dir-HR & Mgr-Property Acctg)
Wendy Manning (CIO)
Bonnie McAllister (Controller)
Walt McCully (Sr Project Mgr)
Moriah Kosch Worth (Project Mgr)
Chris Pinckney (Project Mgr)
Gregg Hendershot (VP-Builders)
Keith Campbell (Project Mgr)

CONTROL AIR CONDITIONING CORPORATION

5200 E La Palma Ave, Anaheim, CA 92807-2019
Tel.: (714) 777-8600
Web Site:
    http://www.controlaircorp.com
Emp.: 1,200
Warm Air Heating & Air Conditioning Contractor
N.A.I.C.S.: 238220
Kendrick G. Ellis (Pres)
Edward Romero (Mgr-Production)
Marcus Terry (Project Mgr)
Chris Winter (Project Mgr)

CONTROL BUILDING SERVICES INC.

333 Meadowlands Pkwy, Secaucus, NJ 07094-1804
Tel.: (201) 864-1900   NJ
Web Site: http://www.controlsg.com
Year Founded: 1975
Sales Range: $200-249.9 Million
Emp.: 8,000
Building Maintenance Services
N.A.I.C.S.: 561720
Edward D. Turen (Chm & CEO)
Neal L. Turin (Exec VP)
Nick Vataj (Exec VP)

CONTROL CABLE INC.

7261 Ambassador Rd, Baltimore, MD 21244
Tel.: (410) 298-4411
Web Site:
http://www.controlcable.com

Year Founded: 1975
Rev.: $8,800,000
Emp.: 53
Computer Mfr
N.A.I.C.S.: 334118
Michael McDonald (Mgr-IT & Internet Support)
Richard Meltzer (Pres & CEO)
Joe Hart (Dir-Mfg Ops)

CONTROL CHIEF HOLDINGS, INC.

200 Williams St, Bradford, PA 16701-1411
Tel.: (814) 362-6811   NY
Web Site:
    https://www.controlchief.com
Year Founded: 1959
Sales Range: $1-9.9 Million
Emp.: 43
Mfr of Remote Controls for Industrial Machines
N.A.I.C.S.: 335314
Douglas S. Bell (Pres & CEO)
Allison Ambrose (Coord-Mktg & Graphics)

Subsidiaries:

Control Chief Corp.   (1)
200 Williams St, Bradford, PA 16701-1411
Tel.: (814) 362-6811
Web Site: http://www.controlchief.com
Mfr of Wireless Remote Control Units & Systems
N.A.I.C.S.: 335314
Douglas S. Bell (CEO)
Jackie Gregg (Controller)

CONTROL CONTRACTORS, INC.

800 SW 34th St Ste A, Renton, WA 98057
Tel.: (206) 328-1730
Web Site:
    http://www.controlcontractors.com
Year Founded: 1975
Sales Range: $25-49.9 Million
Emp.: 200
Environmental System Control Installation
N.A.I.C.S.: 238210
Amy Smith (Mgr-HR)

CONTROL FLOW INC.

9201 Fairbanks N Houston Rd, Houston, TX 77064-6206
Tel.: (281) 890-8300
Web Site:
    https://www.controlflow.com
Year Founded: 1975
Sales Range: $10-24.9 Million
Emp.: 80
Oil Field Machinery & Equipment
N.A.I.C.S.: 333132
William D. Laird (Pres & CEO)
Jim Adams (Mng Dir-Westech HMD & Corp Sls & Bus Devel Dir)
Gary Egbert (Mgr-Engrg-Pressure Control)
Mollie Laird (VP)

Subsidiaries:

Control Flow Incorporated S. de R. L. de C.V.   (1)
Calle 33 No 58 entre 42 X 44, Colonia Tila, Mexico, CP 24170, Campeche, Mexico
Tel.: (52) 9383825599
Web Site: http://www.controlflow.com
Sales Range: $10-24.9 Million
Emp.: 30
Oil Machinery Mfr
N.A.I.C.S.: 333132
Raul Cullingford (Gen Mgr)

CONTROL HOLDINGS CORPORATION

1700 S Hanley St, Saint Louis, MO 63144
Tel.: (314) 647-6680
Web Site:
    http://www.controlconsultants.com
Sales Range: $100-124.9 Million
Emp.: 5
Warm Air Heating & Air Conditioning
N.A.I.C.S.: 423730
Guy S. McClellan (Chm)
John McClellan (Pres)

CONTROL INSTALLATIONS OF IOWA, INC.

6200 Thornton Ave Ste 190, Des Moines, IA 50321
Tel.: (515) 558-9300
Web Site: http://www.ci3.com
Year Founded: 1983
General Electrical Contractor
N.A.I.C.S.: 238210
Brian Aller (VP)
Jim Suedmeier (Project Manager)
Randy Ballard (Project Mgr)
Vince Stefanski (Mgr-Purchasing)

CONTROL MODULE, INC.

89 Phoenix Ave, Enfield, CT 06082-2625
Tel.: (860) 745-2433   DE
Web Site:
    https://www.controlmod.com
Year Founded: 1969
Sales Range: $50-74.9 Million
Emp.: 100
Mfr of Electronic Bar Code Data Collection Systems
N.A.I.C.S.: 334118
James W. Bianco (VP-Sls & Mktg)
Jeffrey Delton (Engr-Software)

CONTROL SOLUTIONS, INC.

1 Merrin Rd, York, PA 17402-5028
Tel.: (908) 526-9083
Web Site: http://www.consolut.com
Year Founded: 1984
Factory Automation & Supply Chain Management Solutions & Services
N.A.I.C.S.: 541512

Subsidiaries:

Compsee, Inc.   (1)
5775 Soundview Dr Ste 101 E, Gig Harbor, WA 98335
Tel.: (253) 851-6500
Web Site: http://www.compsee.com
Sales Range: $10-24.9 Million
Emp.: 20
Computerized Optical Data Collecting Services
N.A.I.C.S.: 334118
Billy Graham (Pres)

CONTROL SOUTHERN INC.

3850 Lakefield Dr, Suwanee, GA 30024
Tel.: (770) 495-3100
Web Site:
    https://www.controlsouthern.com
Rev.: $12,000,000
Emp.: 70
Process Control Equipment Sales
N.A.I.C.S.: 423830
Harley Jeffery (Mgr-Engrg)

CONTROL SUPPLY CORP.

6 Ditomas Ct, Copiague, NY 11726
Tel.: (631) 789-5100   NY
Web Site:
    http://www.controlsupplycorp.com
Year Founded: 1976
Industrial Machinery & Equipment Whslr
N.A.I.C.S.: 423830
Debra Herbst (Co-Owner & CFO)
Gary Herbst (Co-Owner)
Lewis Finn (COO)

CONTROL TOWER TRUCK STOP INC.

6162 US Hwy 51, De Forest, WI 53532-2958
Tel.: (608) 246-3040
Year Founded: 1976
Sales Range: $10-24.9 Million
Emp.: 15
Retailer of Prepared Food & Gasoline
N.A.I.C.S.: 457120
Dean Mantel (Pres)
Angela Lisi (Mng Dir)

CONTROLLED AIR, INC.

21210 Eaton Ave, Farmington, MN 55024-7917
Tel.: (651) 460-6022   MN
Web Site: http://www.controlledair.net
Year Founded: 1978
Emp.: 10
Heating, Ventilation & Air-Conditioning Services
N.A.I.C.S.: 238220
Jerry Brockman (Co-Owner)

CONTROLLED ENVIRONMENT SYSTEMS, LLC

137 High St, Mansfield, MA 02048-2159
Tel.: (508) 339-4237
Web Site: http://www.cesweb.com
Motor Vehicle Parts Mfr
N.A.I.C.S.: 336390
Don Roussinos (Pres & CEO)

Subsidiaries:

Western Environmental Corp.   (1)
6820 Roosevelt Ave Ste A, Franklin, OH 45005
Tel.: (513) 422-4088
Web Site:
    http://www.westernenvironmental.com
Nonresidential Construction
N.A.I.C.S.: 236220
Mike White (Pres)
Jim Sibcy (Co-Founder)
Scott Flick (Co-Founder)

CONTROLLED POWER COMPANY

1955 Stephenson Hwy, Troy, MI 48083
Tel.: (248) 528-3700
Web Site:
    https://www.controlledpwr.com
Year Founded: 1968
Rev.: $11,430,293
Emp.: 100
Power Conversion Units, A/C To D/C, Static-Electric & Unenterable Power Unit
N.A.I.C.S.: 335999
Chris Tazzia (Pres)
Jeffrey Stemp (Controller)
Tim Schultz (Engr-Production)

CONTROLLED SYSTEMS OF WISCONSIN, INC.

N44 W3 Watertown Plank Rd, Nashotah, WI 53058
Tel.: (262) 367-4400   WI
Year Founded: 1974
Sales Range: $50-74.9 Million
Emp.: 8
Provider of Heating, Air Conditioning & Ventilating Contracting Services
N.A.I.C.S.: 811412
Jeffrey E. Spence (Chm, Pres, CEO & CFO)

CONTROLLER SERVICE & SALES CO INC

13 Robbie Rd, Avon, MA 02322
Tel.: (508) 513-1000
Web Site:
    https://www.controllerservice.com

Year Founded: 1926
Rev.: $11,100,000
Emp.: 45
Electrical Apparatus & Equipment
N.A.I.C.S.: 423610
Scott O'Day (VP-Sls & Mktg)
Mark M. O'Day (Pres)
James Long (Controller)

CONTROLS FOR MOTION AUTOMATION INC.
3265 Gateway Rd Ste 300, Brookfield, WI 53045
Tel.: (262) 781-1815
Web Site:
   http://www.controlsformotion.com
Sales Range: $10-24.9 Million
Emp.: 20
Industrial Machinery & Equipment
N.A.I.C.S.: 423830
Harry C. Aghjian (CEO & Mgr-Sls-Wisconsin)
Tom Machac (Controller)

CONUNDRUM TECHNOLOGIES
5735 W 6th Ave, Denver, CO 80214
Tel.: (303) 308-1400
Web Site:
   https://www.conundrumtech.com
Year Founded: 1999
Construction & Design Services
N.A.I.C.S.: 238210
Jason Perez (Pres & CEO)
Matt McKenzie (Project Mgr)
Stephanie Becker (COO)
David Goldenberg (Gen Mgr)
Tom Vanderstel (CFO)
Pam Bristol (Controller)

CONVENE, INC.
6983 E Fowler Ave, Temple Terrace, FL 33617
Tel.: (813) 344-1889   FL
Web Site: http://www.convene-tech.com
Emp.: 200
Information Technology Services
N.A.I.C.S.: 541519
Karthik Viswanathan (Pres)

CONVENTION DATA SERVICES
107 Waterhouse Rd, Bourne, MA 02532
Tel.: (508) 759-8205
Web Site:
   http://www.conventiondata.com
Year Founded: 1986
Rev.: $13,000,000
Emp.: 127
Data Processing & Preparation
N.A.I.C.S.: 518210
John Kimball (Pres & CEO)
David Lawton (Exec VP-Sls)
John Spencer (Acct Exec)
John Hawley (CTO)
Jim Nugent (Acct Exec-Sls)
Becky Hansen (Exec VP-Event Svcs)
Sharon Keane (Mgr-Sls & Exhibitor Svcs)
Dave Wuethrich (COO)

CONVENTION MODELS & TALENT, INC
1417 Dutch Vly Pl Ste A, Atlanta, GA 30324
Tel.: (404) 233-4644
Web Site: http://www.cmtagency.com
Year Founded: 2001
Rev.: $2,900,000
Emp.: 8
Actor & Brand Management Services
N.A.I.C.S.: 711410
Shelly Justice (Owner)

CONVERGED COMMUNICATION SYSTEMS, LLC
2930 Central St, Evanston, IL 60201
Tel.: (847) 424-0311
Web Site:
   http://www.convergedsystems.com
Year Founded: 2001
Sales Range: $1-9.9 Million
Emp.: 44
Nationwide Telephone & Other Telecommunications Services
N.A.I.C.S.: 517810
Steve Melchiorre (CEO)
Kevin Rubin (Pres & COO)
Jesse Miller (Dir-Telephony Infrastructure)

CONVERGED SECURITY SOLUTIONS LLC
11800 Sunrise Vly Dr Ste 900, Reston, VA 20191
Tel.: (888) 742-4090   DE
Web Site: https://www.cssoperations.com
Year Founded: 2018
Managed Security Services
N.A.I.C.S.: 561621
Mike Santelli (CEO)

Subsidiaries:

Evolver, Inc.   (1)
1943 Isaac Newton Sq Ste 260, Reston, VA 20190
Tel.: (703) 742-4090
Web Site: http://www.evolverinc.com
Rev.: $18,900,000
Emp.: 300
Computer Related Services
N.A.I.C.S.: 541519
Claudio S. Borgiotti (VP)

Subsidiary (Domestic):

Solutions By Design II, LLC   (2)
8614 Westwood, Vienna, VA 22182
Tel.: (703) 286-1880
Web Site: http://www.sbd.com
Rev.: $9,200,000
Emp.: 60
Computer System Design Services
N.A.I.C.S.: 541512
Cida Goldbach (CEO)
Ricardo Silva (Dir-Bus Dev)

CONVERGENCE CONSULTING GROUP, INC.
2502 N Rocky Point Dr Ste 650, Tampa, FL 33607
Tel.: (813) 968-3238   FL
Web Site:
   http://www.convergenceconsul
   tinggroup.com
Year Founded: 2002
Sales Range: $1-9.9 Million
Emp.: 71
Information Technology Systems Integration & Consultancy Services
N.A.I.C.S.: 541690
Daniel R. Rodriguez (Founder, Partner & Dir-Enterprise Bus Intelligence & Analytics)
Brian A. Rimes (Dir-Bus Dev)
Daniel W. Phelps (Dir-Enterprise Info Mgmt Practice)
John Bastone (Dir-Customer Analytics)
Craig Holman (Dir-Customer Success)
Trey Warren (Principal)

CONVERGENCE PARTNERS, INC.
103 E 18th Ave N, Kansas City, MO 64116
Tel.: (816) 581-6300   MO
Web Site:
   http://www.convergerep.com
Electrical & Lighting Products Mfr
N.A.I.C.S.: 335999

Peter Kurtz (Pres)
Scott Denney (Exec VP)
Mark Denney (VP-Projects & Quotations)

Subsidiaries:

Foley Group, Inc.   (1)
333 N 6th St, Kansas City, KS 66101
Tel.: (913) 342-3336
Web Site: http://www.foley-group.com
Rev.: $2,400,000
Emp.: 15
Electrical Apparatus & Equipment, Wiring Supplies & Related Equipment Merchant Whslr
N.A.I.C.S.: 423610
Mark S. Denney (VP)
Scott S. Denney (Pres)

CONVERGENCE TECHNOLOGY CONSULTING, LLC
808 Landmark Dr Ste 213, Glen Burnie, MD 21061
Tel.: (301) 860-1960
Web Site:
   http://www.convergencetech.us
Year Founded: 2002
Sales Range: $10-24.9 Million
Emp.: 24
Network Engineering & Integration Services
N.A.I.C.S.: 541512
Larry Letow (Pres & CEO)
Tiernan Wallace (Chief Sls Officer)

CONVERGENT CAPITAL PARTNERS LLC
4600 W Cypress St Ste 120, Tampa, FL 33607
Tel.: (813) 936-5100
Web Site:
   http://www.convergentcap.com
Year Founded: 2008
Emp.: 10
Real Estate Investment Services
N.A.I.C.S.: 523999
Santosh Govindaraju (CEO & Portfolio Mgr)
Paul Beraquit (Mng Dir)
Nik Sachdev (Mng Dir)
Michelle Dy (Principal)

CONVERGENT NETWORKS INC.
9 Executive Park Dr, North Billerica, MA 01862-1318
Tel.: (978) 323-3300
Rev.: $13,460,710
Emp.: 143
Provider of Broadband Voice Infrastructure Solutions
N.A.I.C.S.: 334290
Frank Gangi (Pres & CEO)
Carl Baptiste (Mng Dir-Mktg)
Dave Scarborough (VP-Systems)

CONVERGENZ, LLC
8260 Greensboro Dr 5th Fl, McLean, VA 22102
Tel.: (703) 584-3700
Web Site: http://www.conv.com
Year Founded: 2000
Sales Range: $25-49.9 Million
Emp.: 400
IT & Finance & Accounting Consulting Services & Staffing
N.A.I.C.S.: 541512
Amanda Greathouse (Exec VP-Ops)
William Hsiung (CFO)
Jacqueline Lago (VP-HR)
Jennifer Kaiman (Chief Admin Officer)
Mike Boyles (Gen Mgr)
Jim Boyd (Exec VP-Southwest Reg)

CONVERMAT CORPORATION
111 Ste 514, Great Neck, NY 11021-5011

Tel.: (516) 472-2410
Web Site: http://www.convermat.com
Year Founded: 1976
Sales Range: $50-74.9 Million
Emp.: 30
Industrial & Personal Paper Sales
N.A.I.C.S.: 424130
Shaw Shahery (Pres & Founder)

CONVERSE MARKETING
1125 Main St, Peoria, IL 61606
Tel.: (309) 672-2100
Web Site:
   http://www.conversemarketing.com
Sales Range: $10-24.9 Million
Emp.: 10
N.A.I.C.S.: 541810
Jane Converse (Principal)
Amy Converse Schlicksup (Project Mgr & Leader-Acct Svc)
Becky Krohe (Dir-Design)
Jason Saylers (Writer)
Kerri Johnston (Writer)
Ted Converse (Designer)
Toni Tripp (Sr Acct Dir)
Allison West (Office Mgr)

CONVERSEON, INC.
85 Broad St Ste 27 141, New York, NY 10004
Tel.: (212) 213-4297
Web Site:
   http://www.converseon.com
Year Founded: 2001
Sales Range: $10-24.9 Million
Emp.: 30
Marketing Consulting Services
N.A.I.C.S.: 541613
Robert Key (Pres & CEO)
Jane Quigley (Chief Client Officer)

Subsidiaries:

Converseon Nordics   (1)
Baunegaardvej 10 B, 2820, Gentofte, Denmark
Tel.: (45) 31201040
Web Site: http://www.converseon.dk
Marketing Consulting Services
N.A.I.C.S.: 541613

CONVERSION INTERACTIVE AGENCY, LLC
5210 Maryland Way Ste 301, Brentwood, TN 37027-5065   TN
Web Site:
   http://www.conversionia.com
Year Founded: 1989
Sales Range: $10-24.9 Million
Advetising Agency
N.A.I.C.S.: 541810
Steve Sichterman (VP-Client Service)
Erin Young (VP-Client Service)

CONVERSIONPOINT TECHNOLOGIES, INC.
840 Newport Ctr Dr Ste 450, Newport Beach, CA 92660
Tel.: (888) 706-6764   DE
Web Site:
   http://www.conversionpoint.com
Year Founded: 2016
Sales Range: $25-49.9 Million
E-commerce & Online Marketing Services
N.A.I.C.S.: 541810
Robert Tallack (CEO)
Tom Furukawa (Chief Product Officer)
Haig Newton (CTO)

CONVERTIBLE CASTLE, INC.
308 E Main St, Norton, MA 02766
Tel.: (508) 286-4000   MA
Web Site:
   http://www.bernieandphyls.com
Year Founded: 1983
Furniture Retailer
N.A.I.C.S.: 449110

Convertible Castle, Inc.—(Continued)

Larry Rubin *(CEO)*
Nick Peryclear *(Gen Mgr)*

CONVEYCO MANUFACTURING COMPANY

15151 SE Industrial Way, Clackamas, OR 97015
Tel.: (503) 657-1158
Web Site: http://www.can-amchains.com
Rev.: $12,000,000
Emp.: 40
Industrial Supplies
N.A.I.C.S.: 423840
Robert B. Gibb *(Pres)*

CONVEYCO TECHNOLOGIES INC.

47 Commerce Dr, Bristol, CT 06010
Tel.: (860) 589-8215
Web Site: https://www.conveyco.com
Sales Range: $10-24.9 Million
Emp.: 30
Materials Handling Machinery
N.A.I.C.S.: 423830
Beth Wollenberg *(Controller)*
Raymond Cocozza *(Pres)*
Ben Plourde *(Engr-Design)*
Ronald Lavoie *(Mgr-Sys Engrg)*
Craig Kiernan *(Engr-Design Sys)*
Chris Benevides *(Acct Exec)*
Bob Lutz *(Acct Exec)*
Scott Busher *(Mgr-Controls Engrg)*
Curt Cooper *(Project Mgr)*
Tim Garoutte *(Project Mgr)*
Terry McAlister *(Project Mgr)*
Matt Cabana *(Sr Project Mgr)*

CONVEYOR HANDLING COMPANY, INC.

6715 Santa Barbara Ct, Elkridge, MD 21075-5830
Tel.: (410) 379-2700
Web Site: https://www.conveyorhandling.com
Sales Range: $10-24.9 Million
Emp.: 49
Industrial Machinery & Equipment
Merchant Whslr
N.A.I.C.S.: 423830
Alan Carey *(Treas & Sec)*
Jean Rittermann *(Pres)*
Richard Rittermann *(VP)*
Heather Connors *(Dir-Mktg)*

CONVEYOR TECHNOLOGIES INC.

5313 Womack Rd, Sanford, NC 27330
Tel.: (919) 776-7227
Web Site: http://www.conveyortechnologies.com
Rev.: $12,000,000
Emp.: 50
Conveyors & Conveying Equipment
N.A.I.C.S.: 333922
Tim Pilson *(Co-Founder & Pres)*
Ed Metcalf *(VP)*

CONVEYORS & DRIVES, INC.

1850 C MacArthur Blvd, Atlanta, GA 30318
Tel.: (404) 355-1511
Web Site: https://www.condrives.com
Year Founded: 1969
Sales Range: $10-24.9 Million
Emp.: 94
System Integrator & Provider of Material Handling Equipment
N.A.I.C.S.: 423840
L. Gary Ashley *(Pres)*
Eric Ragan *(Dir-Sls)*

CONVEYORS & MATERIALS

HANDLING INC.

460 Eagle Dr, El Paso, TX 79912
Tel.: (915) 584-5729
Web Site: http://www.conveyorselpaso.com
Year Founded: 1988
Sales Range: $10-24.9 Million
Emp.: 6
Conveyor Systems
N.A.I.C.S.: 423830
Robert La Belle *(Chm & CEO)*
Juan Carlos Martinez *(Pres & Mgr)*
Larry Peterson *(VP & Mgr-Sls)*
Beth Herman *(Mgr-Fin)*

CONVIBER INC.

644 Garfield St, Springdale, PA 15144-0301
Tel.: (724) 274-6300
Web Site: https://www.conviber.com
Year Founded: 1977
Sales Range: $10-24.9 Million
Emp.: 40
Whslr of Rubber Products & Conveyor Components
N.A.I.C.S.: 423840
Thomas Licker *(VP)*
Frank J. Pucciarelli *(Pres)*

CONVOY OF HOPE, INC.

330 S Patterson Ave, Springfield, MO 65802
Tel.: (417) 823-8998
Web Site: http://www.convoyofhope.org
Year Founded: 1984
Sales Range: $75-99.9 Million
Emp.: 120
Community Food Services
N.A.I.C.S.: 624210
Hal Donaldson *(Pres)*
Court Durkalski *(Vice Chm)*

CONVOY SERVICING COMPANY INC.

3323 Jane Ln, Dallas, TX 75247-6523
Tel.: (214) 638-3050
Web Site: https://www.convoyservicing.com
Year Founded: 1960
Sales Range: $10-24.9 Million
Emp.: 95
Provider of Refrigeration Equipment & Supply Services
N.A.I.C.S.: 423740
William Niesman *(Pres)*

CONWAY CORPORATION

1307 Prairie St, Conway, AR 72033
Tel.: (501) 450-6000
Web Site: http://www.conwaycorp.com
Year Founded: 1928
Sales Range: $200-249.9 Million
Emp.: 180
Provider of Electric Services, Water Supply, Cable & Other Pay Television Services
N.A.I.C.S.: 221118
Brent Carroll *(CEO)*
Jason Hansen *(CTO)*
Michael Chapman *(Asst Dir-Power Supply & Major Accts)*
Steve Conner *(Chm)*
Greg Murry *(Vice Chm)*
Greg Dell *(COO)*
Tracy Moore *(CFO)*
Tom Makara *(Coord-Inventory Control)*

CONWAY HEATON, INC.

810 N 3rd St, Bardstown, KY 40004
Tel.: (502) 348-3929
Web Site: http://www.conway-heaton.com

Year Founded: 1919
Sales Range: $10-24.9 Million
Emp.: 37
Car Whslr
N.A.I.C.S.: 441110
Dick Heaton *(VP)*
Bill P. Conway Jr. *(Pres)*

CONWAY IMPORT CO. INC.

11051 Addison Ave, Franklin Park, IL 60131-1401
Tel.: (847) 455-5600
Web Site: http://www.conwaydressings.com
Year Founded: 1910
Sales Range: $75-99.9 Million
Emp.: 90
Condiment French Dressing Mayonnaise & Processed Oil Mfr
N.A.I.C.S.: 311941
Bob Burns *(VP-Mktg)*

Subsidiaries:

Conway Import Co. Inc.   **(1)**
4 Warehouse Ln, Elmsford, NY 10523-1542
Tel.: (914) 592-1311
Web Site: http://www.conwaydressings.com
Sales Range: $10-24.9 Million
Emp.: 4
Salad Dressing Mfr
N.A.I.C.S.: 311941

CONWAY MACKENZIE, INC.

401 S Old Woodward Ave Ste 340, Birmingham, MI 48009
Tel.: (248) 433-3100
Web Site: http://www.conwaymackenzie.com
Year Founded: 1987
Sales Range: $10-24.9 Million
Emp.: 85
Corporate Restructuring & Financial Advisory Services
N.A.I.C.S.: 541611
John H. Groustra *(Exec Dir)*
William J. Storen *(Exec Dir)*
Kevin J. Hand *(Mng Dir)*
John P. Kotas *(Mng Dir)*
Glenn M. Kushiner *(Mng Dir)*
Carl J. Sekely *(Mng Dir)*
Steven R. Wybo *(Sr Mng Dir)*
Paul R. Share *(Mng Dir)*
Brad Tillett *(Dir-Valuation & Opinion Svcs)*
Dan Johnson *(Dir-Valuation & Opinion Svcs)*
Donald MacKenzie *(Founder & Sr Mng Dir)*
Jeffrey A. Addison *(Mng Dir)*
Alpesh A. Amin *(Mng Dir)*
Matthew J. Davidson *(Mng Dir)*
Aurelio Garcia-Miro *(Sr Mng Dir)*
Kenneth A. Garnett *(Mng Dir)*
Joseph M. Geraghty *(Sr Mng Dir)*
Christopher L. Good *(Mng Dir)*
Brian J. Grant *(Mng Dir)*
Donald E. Harer *(Mng Dir)*
Frederick L. Hubacker *(Mng Dir)*
Maria T. Jao *(Mng Dir)*
Matthew D. Mason *(Mng Dir)*
Justin M. McCarty *(Mng Dir)*
John P. Pencak *(Mng Dir)*
John B. Pidcock *(Mng Dir)*
David B. Piejak *(Mng Dir)*
John T. Young *(Sr Mng Dir)*
Jeffrey A. Zappone *(Sr Mng Dir)*
Kevin Barrentine *(Sr Mng Dir-Atlanta)*
Sig Huber *(Sr Mng Dir)*

Subsidiaries:

Conway MacKenzie Atlanta, LLC   **(1)**
1075 Peachtree St 4675, Atlanta, GA 30305
Tel.: (770) 394-9905
Web Site: http://www.conwaymackenzie.com
Emp.: 7

Corporate Restructuring & Financial Advisory Services
N.A.I.C.S.: 541611
Gregory Charleston *(Sr Mng Dir)*
Robert Barnett *(Mng Dir)*

Conway MacKenzie Chicago, LLC   **(1)**
77 W Wacker Dr Ste 4000, Chicago, IL 60601
Tel.: (312) 220-0100
Web Site: http://www.conwaymackenzie.com
Corporate Restructuring & Financial Advisory Services
N.A.I.C.S.: 541611
Timothy B. Stallkamp *(Sr Mng Dir)*
Timothy A. Turek *(Mng Dir)*

Conway MacKenzie Houston, LLC   **(1)**
1301 McKinney St Ste 2025, Houston, TX 77010
Tel.: (713) 650-0500
Web Site: http://www.conwaymackenzie.com
Emp.: 8
Corporate Restructuring & Financial Advisory Services
N.A.I.C.S.: 541611
Taylor W. Bradshaw *(Dir-Energy Advisory Svcs Team)*

Conway MacKenzie Los Angeles, LLC   **(1)**
333 S Hope St 3625, Los Angeles, CA 90071
Tel.: (213) 416-6200
Web Site: http://www.conwaymackenzie.com
Corporate Restructuring & Financial Advisory Services
N.A.I.C.S.: 541611
Jeffery Perea *(Mng Dir)*

Conway MacKenzie New York, LLC   **(1)**
600 5th Ave 25th Fl, New York, NY 10020
Tel.: (212) 586-2200
Web Site: http://www.conwaymackenzie.com
Emp.: 15
Corporate Restructuring & Financial Advisory Services
N.A.I.C.S.: 541611
Donald S. MacKenzie *(CEO)*
Michael Correra *(Sr Mng Dir)*
Kenneth T. Latz *(Sr Mng Dir)*

Variant Capital Advisors LLC   **(1)**
401 S Old Woodward Ave Ste 340, Birmingham, MI 48009
Tel.: (248) 433-3694
Web Site: http://www.variant-capital.com
Investment Banking & Financial Advisory Services
N.A.I.C.S.: 523150

CONWAY ORGANIZATION

39 W 37 St 3rd Fl, New York, NY 10018
Tel.: (212) 967-5300
Web Site: http://www.conwaystores.com
Sales Range: $10-24.9 Million
Emp.: 1,700
Discount Department Store Operator
N.A.I.C.S.: 455110
Morris Cohen *(Pres)*

CONWAY, DIERKING & HILLMAN, INC.

15 Ionia Ave SW Ste 270, Grand Rapids, MI 49503
Tel.: (616) 776-1600
Web Site: http://www.cdh.com
Year Founded: 1990
Sales Range: $10-24.9 Million
Business Management Software & Consulting Services
N.A.I.C.S.: 561499
Mark Becker *(VP)*
Susan Cotts *(Pres)*

Subsidiaries:

Blue Sphere Solutions, Inc. (1)
3300 Eagle Run NE, Grand Rapids, MI 49525
Tel.: (616) 682-1266
Web Site: http://www.bluesphereinc.com
Business Management Software Developer & Publisher
N.A.I.C.S.: 513210
Chris Hashley (Co-Founder & Dir-Software Dev)

CONXTECH, INC.

24493 Clawiter Rd, Hayward, CA 94545
Tel.: (510) 264-9111
Web Site: http://www.conxtech.com
Year Founded: 2004
Sales Range: $10-24.9 Million
Emp.: 75
Fabricated Structural Metal Mfr
N.A.I.C.S.: 332312
Robert J. Simmons (Founder)
Howard M. Franklin (CFO)
Raymond G. Kitasoe (VP-Engrg)
Michel Luttrell (Co-Founder & Sr VP-Bus Dev)
Travis Simmons (Sr VP-Production Ops)
Michael Lampley (VP-Sls)
Donald M. Bernard (Pres-Industrial)
Adam L. Browne (Chief Structural Engrg Officer)
Gilles Caussade (CEO)

COOK ASSOCIATES, INC.

212 W Kinzie St, Chicago, IL 60654
Tel.: (312) 329-0900
Web Site:
http://www.cookassociates.com
Year Founded: 1961
Sales Range: $1-9.9 Million
Emp.: 55
Executve Search Services & Mergers & Acquisitions Consulting
N.A.I.C.S.: 541612
John Kins (Chm & CEO)
Corby Neumann (VP-Fin)
Cary Morrill (VP-Boston)
Harry Wilson (Mng Dir-Charlotte)

Subsidiaries:

Cook M&A Advisory Services (1)
212 W Kinzie St Ste 600, Chicago, IL 60654
Tel.: (312) 755-5750
Web Site:
http://www.cookmergersacquisitions.com
Emp.: 15
Merger & Acquisition Advisory Services
N.A.I.C.S.: 541611
Arnis Kins (Pres)
Sven A. Kins (Owner & Mng Dir)
Brian A. Gross (Founder & Mng Dir)
Joseph Bilanzic (VP-Bus Dev)
Keith Seebeck (Exec VP-Sls, Strategy & Ops)

Executive Search Division (1)
212 W Kinzie St, Chicago, IL 60654
Tel.: (312) 329-0900
Web Site: http://www.cookassociates.com
Executive Search Service
N.A.I.C.S.: 541612
Mary Kier (CEO)
Walter Rach (Mng Dir)

COOK AUTOMOTIVE

1136 S Philadelphia Blvd, Aberdeen, MD 21001-3911
Tel.: (410) 575-6932
Year Founded: 1962
Sales Range: $25-49.9 Million
Emp.: 41
Home Supply Whslr
N.A.I.C.S.: 441330
Robert Cook (Pres)
Pete Manzo (Mgr-Sls-New Car)

William G. Mosca (Gen Mgr)
Kirsten Mosca (Mgr-F&I)
Tony Mosca (Mgr-F&I)

COOK BROS., INC.

1740 N Kostno Ave, Chicago, IL 60639
Tel.: (773) 770-1200   IL
Web Site:
https://www.cookbrothers.com
Rev.: $15,952,407
Emp.: 60
Discount Department Stores
N.A.I.C.S.: 455110
Carl K. Tickman (Pres)

COOK COMMUNICATIONS MINISTRIES

4050 Lee Vance Dr, Colorado Springs, CO 80918-7102
Tel.: (719) 536-0100   IL
Web Site: http://www.davidccook.com
Year Founded: 1875
Sales Range: $75-99.9 Million
Emp.: 300
Publishers of Christian Educational Materials & Christian Trade Books
N.A.I.C.S.: 813110
Cris Doornbos (Pres & CEO)

COOK GM SUPERSTORE

1193 W Saginaw Rd, Vassar, MI 48768
Tel.: (989) 823-8523
Web Site: http://www.cookgm.com
Sales Range: $10-24.9 Million
Emp.: 46
Automobiles, New & Used
N.A.I.C.S.: 441110
Steve Cook (Pres)
Rhonda Williams (Mgr-Fin)
Janine Gehrig (Office Mgr)

COOK GROUP INCORPO-RATED

750 Daniels Way, Bloomington, IN 47402-0489
Tel.: (812) 339-2235   IN
Web Site:
https://www.cookgroup.com
Year Founded: 1963
Sales Range: $1-4.9 Billion
Emp.: 12,000
Offices of Other Holding Companies
N.A.I.C.S.: 551112
Cynthia Kretz (Gen Counsel & VP)
Pete Yonkman (Pres)
Allison Giles (VP-Federal & Intl Govt Affairs-Washington)

Subsidiaries:

CFC, Inc. (1)
320 W 8th St Showers Plz Ste 200, Bloomington, IN 47404-3700
Tel.: (812) 332-0053
Web Site: http://www.cfcincorporated.com
Emp.: 60
Real Estate Development Services
N.A.I.C.S.: 531390
Jim Murphy (Pres)
Chris Cockerham (VP-Comml Real Estate)
Nikki Johnson (VP-Residential Real Estate)
Kris Ward (Dir-HR)
Robert Jones (Controller)

Cook Aviation Inc. (1)
970 S Kirby Rd, Bloomington, IN 47403-9392
Tel.: (812) 825-2392
Web Site: http://www.cookaviation.com
Emp.: 10
Oil Transportation Services
N.A.I.C.S.: 488190
Rex Hinkle (Gen Mgr)
Steve Capps (Asst Mgr)

Cook Family Health Center Inc. (1)
402 N Rogers St, Bloomington, IN 47404
Tel.: (812) 330-9944

Web Site:
http://www.cookfamilyhealthcenter.com
Emp.: 75
Health Care Srvices
N.A.I.C.S.: 621999
Michelle Gaither (Office Mgr)

Cook Incorporated (1)
750 Daniels Way, Bloomington, IN 47404
Tel.: (812) 339-2235
Web Site: http://www.cookmedical.com
Sales Range: $1-4.9 Billion
Emp.: 10,000
Surgical & Medical Instruments Developer, Mfr & Distr
N.A.I.C.S.: 339112
Rusty Burns (VP-Logistics & Pur-Global)
John A. DeFord (Executives)
Rob Dorocke (VP-eComm-Global)
Bruce Gingles (VP-Global Technology Assessment & Health Policy)
Walter Ryan (Dir-Bus Dev)

Subsidiary (Non-US):

Cook (Canada) Inc. (2)
165 Mostar Street Unit 1, Stouffville, L4A 0Y2, ON, Canada
Tel.: (905) 640-7110
Sales Range: $25-49.9 Million
Emp.: 30
Medical Instruments Mfr & Distr
N.A.I.C.S.: 339112
Bill Bobbie (Pres)

Cook Ireland Ltd. (2)
O'Halloran Road, National Technology Park, Limerick, Ireland
Tel.: (353) 61 239 252
Web Site: http://www.cookmedical.com
Sales Range: $50-74.9 Million
Emp.: 500
Medical Device Mfr
N.A.I.C.S.: 339112

Subsidiary (Domestic):

Cook Medical Incorporated (2)
1025 Acuff Rd, Bloomington, IN 47404
Tel.: (812) 339-2235
Web Site: http://www.cookmedical.com
Medical Device Distribution Services
N.A.I.C.S.: 423450
Pete Yonkman (Pres)
Jason Rager (Dir-Global Tax)
Jean-Marc Creissel (VP & Dir-Asia-Pacific)
Marsha Lovejoy (Gen Mgr-External Corp Comm)
Dan Kaiser (VP-Bus Dev)
Ross Harvey (Dir-Customer Support & Delivery-Global)
Barbara Yeung (Mgr-Corp Brand & Comm-Asia Pacific)

Subsidiary (Non-US):

Cook (China) Medical Trading Co., Ltd. (3)
Room 1503 Ascendews Plaza No 333 Tian Yao Qiao Road, Shanghai, 200030, China
Tel.: (86) 21 5451 9599
Medical Device Wholesale Trade Distr
N.A.I.C.S.: 425120

Cook Asia Ltd. (3)
40 Fl AIA Tower 183 Electric Rd Northpoint, 8 Fleming Road Wan Chai, Hong Kong, China (Hong Kong)
Tel.: (852) 3472 1688
Medical Device Distr
N.A.I.C.S.: 423450

Cook Japan Incorporated (3)
Glass City Moto-Yoyogi Bldg 30-13 Moto-Yoyogi, Shibuya-ku, Tokyo, 151-0062, Japan
Tel.: (81) 3 3468 9911
Medical Device Distr
N.A.I.C.S.: 423450

Cook Medical (Thailand) Co., Ltd. (3)
19th Floor Athenee Tower 63 Wireless Road, Lumpini Pathumwan, Bangkok, 10330, Thailand
Tel.: (66) 2168863031
Medical Device Distr
N.A.I.C.S.: 423450

Cook Medical Europe Ltd. (3)

Europe Shared Service Centre O'Halloran Road, National Technology Park, Limerick, Ireland
Tel.: (353) 61 334 440
Web Site: http://www.cookmedical.com
Emp.: 800
Medical Device Distr
N.A.I.C.S.: 423450

Cook Taiwan Ltd. (3)
11F No 207 Sec 3 Beisin Road, Sindian District, Taipei, 231, Taiwan
Tel.: (886) 266281800
Medical Device Distr
N.A.I.C.S.: 423450

Subsidiary (Domestic):

Cook MyoSite Incorporated (2)
105 Delta Dr, Pittsburgh, PA 15238
Tel.: (412) 963-7380
Web Site: http://www.cookmyosite.com
Emp.: 75
Biotechnology Research & Development Services
N.A.I.C.S.: 541714
Ron Jankowski (VP-Scientific Affairs)
Ryan Pruchnic (VP)
Carl Cook (Pres)

Cook Vascular Incorporated (2)
1186 Montgomery Ln, Vandergrift, PA 15690-0529
Tel.: (724) 845-8621
Cardiac Rhythm Management & Vascular Access Medical Devices Developer & Mfr
N.A.I.C.S.: 334510

Subsidiary (Non-US):

William A. Cook Australia Pty. Ltd. (2)
Brisbane Technology Park 95 Brandl Street, Eight Mile Plains, Brisbane, 4113, QLD, Australia
Tel.: (61) 7 3841 1188
Sales Range: $25-49.9 Million
Emp.: 350
Medical Products & Equipment Mfr & Distr
N.A.I.C.S.: 339112
Barry Thomas (Mng Dir & Reg Dir-Asia Pacific)

William Cook Europe ApS (2)
Sandet 6, DK 4632, Bjaeverskov, Denmark
Tel.: (45) 56868686
Sales Range: $50-74.9 Million
Emp.: 650
Medical Device Mfr & Distr
N.A.I.C.S.: 339112
Kian Olsen (Mgr-Mktg & Sls)

Cook Polymer Technology (1)
3800 Constitution Ave, Bloomington, IN 47402
Tel.: (812) 323-4500
Web Site: http://www.cookgroup.com
Sales Range: $25-49.9 Million
Emp.: 350
Preformed Medical Plastic Tubing & Molded Parts Mfr
N.A.I.C.S.: 326199
David Lessard (CEO)

K-Tube Corporation (1)
13400 Kirkham Way, Poway, CA 92064-7134
Tel.: (858) 513-9229
Web Site: http://www.k-tube.com
Emp.: 120
Medical & Industrial Stainless Steel Tubing Mfr
N.A.I.C.S.: 331210
Terry McCune (CFO)
Greg May (Pres)

Medical Engineering & Development Institute, Inc. (1)
1 Geddes Way, West Lafayette, IN 47906
Tel.: (765) 463-7537
Web Site: http://www.cookmedical.com
Sales Range: $25-49.9 Million
Emp.: 200
New Medical Product Identification, Prototype Development, Testing, Trial Management & Data Analysis Services
N.A.I.C.S.: 541715
Neal Fearnot (Chm)
Steve Charlebois (Dir-Product Discovery)
Matthew S. Waninger (Pres)

Cook Group Incorporated—(Continued)

Star Travel Services, Inc. (1)
1025 Acuff Rd 4th Fl, Bloomington, IN 47404
Tel.: (812) 336-6811
Web Site: http://www.startravelservices.com
Emp.: 12
Travel Arrangement Services
N.A.I.C.S.: 561599
Juli Forrest (Sr Mgr-Corp Travel)

COOK INLET REGION, INC.
725 E Fireweed Ln Ste 800, Anchorage, AK 99503-2633
Tel.: (907) 274-8638   AK
Web Site: http://www.ciri.com
Year Founded: 1972
Sales Range: $250-299.9 Million
Emp.: 1,100
Native American Investment Holding Company
N.A.I.C.S.: 551112
Barbara A. Donatelli (Sr VP)
Sophie Minich (Pres & CEO)
Gregory P. Razo (VP-Govt Contracting)
Thomas P. Huhndorf (Chm)
Douglas W. Fifer (Vice Chm)
Jeffrey A. Gonnason (Sec)
Michael R. Boling (Treas)
Penny L. Carty (Asst Treas)
Bruce Anders (Gen Counsel & VP)
Stig Colberg (CFO)
Chad Nugent (VP-Real Estate)
Thomas Holder (VP-Bus Dev & Ops)
Louis Nagy Jr. (Asst Sec)

Subsidiaries:

ANC Research & Development LLC (1)
360 Command View, Colorado Springs, CO 80915
Tel.: (719) 474-8222
Web Site: http://www.ancrd.com
Emp.: 5
Engineering Research & Development Services
N.A.I.C.S.: 541715
Dave Slaughter (Pres & COO)
Greg Razo (VP)
Matt Holmstrom (VP-Construction Div)

Division (Domestic):

ANC Research & Development LLC - Construction Division (2)
2627 C St Ste 302, Anchorage, AK 99503
Tel.: (907) 727-2824
Construction Engineering Services
N.A.I.C.S.: 541330

CIRI Land Development Company (1)
2525 C St, Anchorage, AK 99503-2639
Tel.: (907) 263-5152
Web Site: http://www.cirilanddevelopment.com
Sales Range: Less than $1 Million
Emp.: 3
Subdividers & Developers
N.A.I.C.S.: 237210

Subsidiary (Domestic):

Pacific Tower Properties Inc. (2)
1231 Gambell St Ste 200, Anchorage, AK 99501
Tel.: (907) 279-0541
Web Site: http://www.pacifictower.com
Real Estate Management Services
N.A.I.C.S.: 531390
Kevin English (VP)
Mike Leonard (Mgr-Property)
Sheila Sparks (Mgr-Property)

Subsidiary (Domestic):

PTP Management Inc. (3)
1231 Gambell St Ste 200, Anchorage, AK 99501
Tel.: (907) 561-4010
Real Estate Management Services
N.A.I.C.S.: 531390
Kevin English (VP)

CIRI Services Corporation (1)
561 E Steel Loop, Palmer, AK 99645
Tel.: (907) 274-8638
Web Site: http://www.ciri.com
Emp.: 100
Real Estate Management Services
N.A.I.C.S.: 531390

Subsidiary (Domestic):

Weldin Construction LLC (2)
561 E Steel Loop, Palmer, AK 99645
Tel.: (907) 746-3200
Web Site: http://www.weldin.com
Construction Engineering Services
N.A.I.C.S.: 541330
Brian Vance (Project Mgr-Electrical)

Cruz Energy Services LLC (1)
10944 27D St SW, Dickinson, ND 58601-8310
Tel.: (701) 483-3016
Web Site: http://www.cruzenergyservices.com
Drilling Rig Transportation Services
N.A.I.C.S.: 488490
Jeff Miller (Sr VP-Ops)
Tony Lamping (Mgr-Ops)
Greg Miller (Mgr-Ops)

Cruz Marine LLC (1)
7000 E Palmer-Wasilla Hwy, Palmer, AK 99645
Tel.: (907) 746-3144
Web Site: http://www.cruzmarine.com
Emp.: 20
Marine Construction Services
N.A.I.C.S.: 237990
Kevin Weiss (Gen Mgr)

North Wind, Inc. (1)
1425 Higham St, Idaho Falls, ID 83402
Tel.: (208) 528-8718
Web Site: http://northwindgrp.com
Sales Range: $150-199.9 Million
Emp.: 820
Holding Company; Environmental Management, Engineering & Construction Services
N.A.I.C.S.: 551112
James Furr (Pres)
Christopher P. Leichtweis (Grp Pres & CEO)

Subsidiary (Domestic):

North Wind Services, LLC 330420 (2)
1425 Higham St, Idaho Falls, ID 83402-1513
Tel.: (208) 528-8718
Web Site: http://www.northwindgrp.com
Environmental Management, Engineering & Construction Services
N.A.I.C.S.: 541330
James Furr (Pres)

Portage, Inc. (2)
1075 S Utah Ave Ste 200, Idaho Falls, ID 83402
Tel.: (208) 528-6608
Web Site: http://www.portageinc.com
Emp.: 250
Environmental, Engineering & Technical Services
N.A.I.C.S.: 541330
Roy McKinney (Pres & Gen Mgr)

Peak Oilfield Services Company (1)
5015 Business Park Blvd Ste 4000, Anchorage, AK 99503
Tel.: (907) 263-7000
Web Site: http://www.peakalaska.com
Sales Range: $75-99.9 Million
Drilling Oil & Gas Wells
N.A.I.C.S.: 811310
Tom Dolan (Pres & CEO)
Ian McCool (VP-North Slope Ops & Dev)

Stone Horn Ridge, LLC (1)
2525 C St Ste 500, Anchorage, AK 99503   (70%)
Tel.: (907) 274-8638
Web Site: http://www.stonehornridge.com
Natural Gas Distribution Services
N.A.I.C.S.: 221210

COOK INLET TRIBAL COUNCIL, INC.

3600 San Jeronimo Dr, Anchorage, AK 99508
Tel.: (907) 793-3600   AK
Web Site: http://www.citci.org
Year Founded: 1983
Sales Range: $25-49.9 Million
Emp.: 345
Youth Development Services
N.A.I.C.S.: 624110
Gloria O'Neill (Pres & CEO)
Jerry Kung (Dir-Tech)
Kelly Hurd (Sr Dir-Dev)
Rebecca Ling (Dir-Recovery Svcs)

COOK JEEP CHRYSLER, INC.
901 Main St, Little Rock, AR 72202
Tel.: (501) 374-4848
Year Founded: 1914
Sales Range: $10-24.9 Million
Emp.: 19
New Car Whslr
N.A.I.C.S.: 441110
Ethel Cook (Partner)
Roger Cook (Partner)

COOK MOVING SYSTEMS, INC.
1845 Dale Rd, Buffalo, NY 14225-4909
Tel.: (716) 897-0700   NY
Web Site: http://www.cookmoving.com
Year Founded: 1912
Sales Range: $100-124.9 Million
Emp.: 250
Moving & Storage of Household Goods, Electronics, Art & Special Products
N.A.I.C.S.: 484210
Gregory Fierle (Pres & CEO)
Debra R. Fierle (Mgr-HR)
Sharon Melius (Coord-Move)
George Griesbaum (Mgr-Ops)

Subsidiaries:

Cook Moving Systems, Inc. (Illinois Corporation) (1)
2195 Arthur Ave, Elk Grove Village, IL 60007-6008   (100%)
Moving & Storage Services
N.A.I.C.S.: 484121

COOK PAVING & CONSTRUCTION CO.
4545 Spring Rd, Brooklyn Heights, OH 44131
Tel.: (216) 267-7705
Web Site: https://www.cookpaving.com
Sales Range: $10-24.9 Million
Emp.: 75
Asphalt Paving
N.A.I.C.S.: 238110
Linda Fletcher (Pres)

COOK TRACTOR CO. INC.
Hwy 7 NW, Clinton, MO 64735
Tel.: (660) 885-3387
Web Site: http://www.cooktractorinc.com
Sales Range: $10-24.9 Million
Emp.: 50
Farm Implements
N.A.I.C.S.: 423820
David Schnoor (Gen Mgr)

COOK'S COLLISION
2990 Lava Ridge Ct Ste 190, Roseville, CA 95661
Tel.: (916) 786-2943
Web Site: http://www.cookscollision.com
Rev.: $15,000,000
Emp.: 85
Auto Body Repair Services
N.A.I.C.S.: 811121

Rick Wood (Co-Pres & Co-CEO)
Valerie Decatur (Dir-HR)
Frankie Quadrato (Area Mgr)
Jaime Villarreal (Mgr)
Kirk Minami (CFO)
Alissa Posedel (Mgr-HR)
Ron Warren (Reg Mgr-Refinish)
Mike Barber (VP-Ops)
Don Wood (Co-Pres & Co-CEO)

COOK-ILLINOIS CORP.
2100 Clearwater Dr, Oak Brook, IL 60523
Tel.: (708) 560-9840   IL
Web Site: https://www.cookillinois.com
Year Founded: 1970
Sales Range: $10-24.9 Million
Emp.: 20
School Bus Transportation Services
N.A.I.C.S.: 485410
John Benish (CEO)
Roger Bannerman (Mgr-Fleet)
Tom O'Sullivan (VP-Contracts & Bids)
Anthony Benish (Gen Counsel)
Douglas Sikora (Dir-IT)
Greg Fischer (CFO)
Jeff Barnes (Dir-Ops-South Reg)
John Knoelke (VP-Ops)

Subsidiaries:

Alpha School Bus Company Inc. (1)
2100 Clearwater Dr Ste 250, Oak Brook, IL 60523
Tel.: (708) 560-9840
Rev.: $3,600,000
Emp.: 2
School Buses
N.A.I.C.S.: 485410
Jeff Barnes (Dir-Ops-South Reg)

Chicago Bus Sales Inc. (1)
4845 167th St Fl 300, Oak Forest, IL 60452-4550
Tel.: (708) 560-9840
Sales Range: $1-9.9 Million
Emp.: 2
Automobiles & Other Motor Vehicles
N.A.I.C.S.: 423110

Cook County School Bus Inc. (1)
2100 Clearwater Dr, Oak Brook, IL 60523
Tel.: (708) 560-9840
Web Site: http://www.cookillinois.com
Sales Range: $10-24.9 Million
Emp.: 10
School Buses
N.A.I.C.S.: 485410

Grand Prairie Transit (1)
18962 Airport Rd, Lockport, IL 60441   (100%)
Tel.: (815) 838-1012
Web Site: http://www.cookillinois.com
School Buses
N.A.I.C.S.: 485410

Illinois School Bus Co. Inc. (1)
4845 167th St Fl 300, Oak Forest, IL 60452-4550
Tel.: (708) 560-9840
Rev.: $3,400,000
Emp.: 2
School Buses
N.A.I.C.S.: 485410

Kickert School Bus Lines, Inc. (1)
20575 Torrence Ave, Lynwood, IL 60411-6911
Tel.: (708) 758-4740
Bus Charter Service, Except Local
N.A.I.C.S.: 485510
Phil Paige (Gen Mgr)

Lakeside Transportation Inc. (1)
2794 Northwestern Ave, Waukegan, IL 60087
Tel.: (847) 263-7619
Bus Transportation Services
N.A.I.C.S.: 485210
Denise Quezada (Mgr-Ops)
Peggy Passe (Mgr-Ops)

North Shore Transit, Inc. (1)
3211 W Howard St, Skokie, IL 60076

Tel.: (847) 677-9700
Bus Transportation Services
N.A.I.C.S.: 485210
Tanisha Flowers *(Mgr-Ops)*

Paige Bus Enterprises Inc.   **(1)**
610 W 138th St, Riverdale, IL 60827
Tel.: (708) 201-9900
Bus Transportation Services
N.A.I.C.S.: 485210
P. J. Lewis *(Mgr-Ops)*

Richlee Vans Inc.   **(1)**
100 E Hill St, Villa Park, IL 60181-1805
Tel.: (630) 279-0080
Web Site: http://www.cookillinois.com
Provide Buses & Vans To Schools On
Rental
N.A.I.C.S.: 485410
Mary Fox *(Office Mgr)*

Westway Coach Inc.   **(1)**
100 E Hill St, Villa Park, IL
60181-1805   **(100%)**
Tel.: (630) 279-2720
Web Site: http://www.cookillinois.com
School Buses
N.A.I.C.S.: 485410
Teri Flanagan *(Mgr-Ops)*

COOKBOOK PUBLISHERS INC.
9825 Widmer Rd, Lenexa, KS 66215
Tel.: (913) 492-5900
Web Site:
     http://www.cookbookpublishers.com
Rev.: $16,000,000
Emp.: 10
Book Publishing & Printing
N.A.I.C.S.: 513130
Kevin Naughton *(Pres)*

COOKE & BIELER, LP
1700 Market St Ste 3222, Philadel-
phia, PA 19103-3912
Tel.: (215) 567-1101   **PA**
Web Site: http://www.cooke-
bieler.com
Year Founded: 1949
Sales Range: $25-49.9 Million
Emp.: 30
Investment & Asset Management
Services
N.A.I.C.S.: 523940
John J. Medveckis *(Partner & Portfo-
lio Mgr-High Net Worth)*
Michael M. Meyer *(Partner & Portfolio
Mgr)*
Bruce A. Smith *(Partner-Trading &
Ops)*
Linda N. Perna *(Partner & Chief
Compliance Officer)*
Thad Fletcher *(Partner-Client Svcs &
Bus Dev)*
John S. Hamblett *(Partner-Client
Svcs & Bus Dev)*
Edward O'Connor *(Partner & Portfolio
Mgr)*
Mehul Trivedi *(Partner & Portfolio
Mgr)*
Theresa M. Weiss *(Sr Mgr-Mktg &
Client Svcs)*
John Pickering *(Partner & Portfolio
Mgr-High Net-Worth & Taxable In-
vesting)*
Andrew B. Armstrong *(Principal &
Portfolio Mgr)*
Steve Lyons *(Partner & Portfolio Mgr)*
William Weber *(Partner & Portfolio
Mgr)*
Frank X. Kinsella *(Dir-IT)*
Wesley Lim *(Principal & Portfolio
Mgr)*
Patrick McDonnell *(Principal-
Consultant Rels)*

COOKE COMMUNICATIONS FLORIDA, LLC
3420 Northside Dr, Key West, FL
33040

Tel.: (305) 292-7777   DE
Web Site:
     http://www.cookecommunica
tions.com
Sales Range: $10-24.9 Million
Newspaper Publishers
N.A.I.C.S.: 513110
John Kent Cooke Jr. *(Exec VP &
Pres-North Carolina Newspapers)*
Paul Clarin *(CFO)*
Thomas K. Cooke *(Pres)*
John Kent Cooke Sr. *(Owner, Chm &
CEO)*

Subsidiaries:

Cooke Communications North Caro-
lina, LLC   **(1)**
1150 Sugg Pkwy, Greenville, NC
27834-9077   **(100%)**
Tel.: (252) 329-9500
Web Site: http://www.reflector.com
Newspaper Publishers
N.A.I.C.S.: 513110
Rubie Smith *(Acct Exec-Adv)*
Betty Williams *(Mgr-Retail Adv)*
Mariann McQueen *(CFO)*
Keven Zepezauer *(Dir-Circulation)*
J. Tim Holt *(Gen Mgr)*
Pat Wilkins *(Mgr-Customer Care)*

COOKE TRUCKING COMPANY INC.
1759 S Andy Griffith Pkwy, Mount
Airy, NC 27030
Tel.: (336) 786-5181
Web Site:
     https://www.cooketrucking.com
Year Founded: 1958
Sales Range: $10-24.9 Million
Emp.: 150
Trucking Services
N.A.I.C.S.: 484121
Paige Smith *(Pres)*
David Smith *(VP)*
Rodney F. Jessup *(CFO)*

COOKES FOOD STORE INC.
3400 Keith St NW, Cleveland, TN
37312
Tel.: (423) 479-8208
Web Site:
     http://www.cookeshometown
grocer.com
Sales Range: $25-49.9 Million
Emp.: 105
Grocery Stores
N.A.I.C.S.: 445110
Dan S. Cooke *(Pres)*

COOKIE KINGDOM INC.
1201 E Walnut St, Oglesby, IL 61348
Tel.: (815) 883-3331
Web Site:
     https://www.cookiekingdom.com
Sales Range: $10-24.9 Million
Emp.: 100
Cookie & Cracker Mfr
N.A.I.C.S.: 311821
Cliff Sheppard *(Pres)*
Quentin G. Pierce *(Chm)*

COOKIE TREE BAKERIES
4010 W Advantage Cir, Salt Lake
City, UT 84104
Tel.: (801) 268-2253   UT
Web Site:
     https://www.cookietree.com
Year Founded: 1981
Sales Range: $100-124.9 Million
Emp.: 135
Gourmet Cookie & Brownie Bakery
N.A.I.C.S.: 311812
Greg F. Schenk *(Owner)*
Sam McLaughlin *(VP-Opers)*
Greg Pannier *(Mgr-Natl Sls)*

Jared Olschewski *(Mgr-Quality &
Sanitation)*
Bob Frank *(VP-Ops)*

COOKIES BY DESIGN, INC.
1865 Summit Ave Ste 605, Plano, TX
75074
Tel.: (972) 398-9536
Web Site:
     http://www.cookiesbydesign.com
Sales Range: $10-24.9 Million
Emp.: 25
Cookie Products Mfr & Distr
N.A.I.C.S.: 533110
Clarice Forrest *(Mgr-Procurement)*
Gwen Willhite *(Founder)*

COOKING ENTHUSIAST, LLC
242 Branford Rd, North Branford, CT
06471
Web Site:
     http://www.artisantable.com
Year Founded: 1993
Sales Range: $1-9.9 Million
Emp.: 27
Online Kitchen & Food Retail
N.A.I.C.S.: 459999
Terri Alpert *(Owner & CEO)*
Diane Humphrey *(Mgr-HR)*

COOKSEY COMMUNICA-TIONS, INC.
5525 N MacArthur Blvd Ste 530, Ir-
ving, TX 75038
Tel.: (972) 580-0662   TX
Web Site: https://www.cookseypr.com
Year Founded: 1994
Sales Range: $1-9.9 Million
Emp.: 14
Public Relations Agency
N.A.I.C.S.: 541820
Gail Cooksey *(Founder, Chm & CEO)*
Colby Walton *(Sr VP & Acct Mgr)*
Jason Meyer *(Sr VP)*
Michael Landon *(Dir-Creative Svcs
Div)*
Kevin Nolan *(Acct Mgr)*
Tyler Bailey *(Acct Exec)*
Michelle Hargis *(VP & Mgr-Acct)*
Karen Berlin Cooperstein *(Sr VP &
Acct Mgr)*
Randy Pruett *(VP & Acct Mgr)*
Mallory Wendel *(Sr Acct Exec)*
Allison Chvojan *(Acct Exec)*
Jennifer Janicki *(Acct Coord)*
Ashley Sears *(Acct Supvr)*
Joel Rowe *(Creative Dir)*

COOKSON HILLS ELECTRIC COOP
1002 E Main St, Stigler, OK 74462
Tel.: (918) 967-4614
Web Site:
     https://www.cooksonhills.com
Year Founded: 1945
Sales Range: $10-24.9 Million
Emp.: 24
Electric Power Distr
N.A.I.C.S.: 221122
William T. Mills *(Pres)*
Kendal Beck *(Gen Mgr)*
Eric Johnson *(Asst Gen Mgr)*

COOL ROOFING SYSTEMS INC.
1286 Dupont Ct, Manteca, CA 95336-
6003
Tel.: (209) 825-0818
Web Site: http://www.cool-
roofing.com
Year Founded: 1999
Sales Range: $10-24.9 Million
Emp.: 55
Roofing Installation Services
N.A.I.C.S.: 238390
Jamie Billman *(CEO)*

COOLANTS PLUS, INC.
2570 Van Hook Ave, Hamilton, OH
45015
Tel.: (513) 892-4000
Web Site:
     http://www.coolantsplus.com
Year Founded: 2000
Chemical & Allied Products Merchant
Whslr
N.A.I.C.S.: 424690
Kurt Deimer *(Pres & CEO)*

COOLERADO CORP
3980 Quebec St, Denver, CO 80207
Tel.: (303) 375-0878
Web Site: http://www.coolerado.com
Year Founded: 2004
Sales Range: $1-9.9 Million
Emp.: 40
Commercial Air Conditioning Systems
N.A.I.C.S.: 333415
Tom Teynor *(CEO)*
Dixie Kauffman *(Mgr-Fulfillment)*
Alan Gillan *(Co-Founder, Vice Chm &
VP-Global Dev)*
Bob Finley *(VP-Mfg)*
Fabio Diaz *(VP-Sls-Intl)*
Steve Slayzak *(VP-Tech)*

COOLEY GROUP, INC.
50 Esten Ave, Pawtucket, RI 02860-
4840
Tel.: (401) 724-9000
Web Site:
     http://www.cooleygroup.com
Year Founded: 1926
Sales Range: $100-124.9 Million
Emp.: 150
Coated Fabrics Mfr
N.A.I.C.S.: 541618
Steve Siener *(VP & Bus Mgr)*

COOLEY GROUP, INC.
1000 Pittsford Victor Rd 2nd Fl, Pitts-
ford, NY 14534
Tel.: (585) 385-1880   NY
Web Site:
     https://www.cooleybrand.com
Year Founded: 1946
Sales Range: $10-24.9 Million
Emp.: 2,000
Stationery & Office Supplies Mer-
chant Wholesalers
N.A.I.C.S.: 424120

COOLEY INDUSTRIES INC.
1930 W Broadway Rd, Phoenix, AZ
85041
Tel.: (602) 243-4288
Rev.: $29,279,282
Emp.: 120
Lumber Mfr
N.A.I.C.S.: 423310
Dean L. Cooley *(Pres)*

COOLEY LLP
3175 Hanover St, Palo Alto, CA
94304-1130
Tel.: (650) 843-5000   CA
Web Site: http://www.cooley.com
Emp.: 700
Law firm
N.A.I.C.S.: 541110
Joseph Conroy *(Chm & CEO)*
John C. Dwyer *(Partner)*
Lynn Kirk *(CMO)*
Mark Pitchford *(Partner-Admin & Le-
gal Practice)*
Michael Attanasio *(Chm-Global Litiga-
tion Dept)*
Craig E. Dauchy *(Partner)*
Kathleen H. Goodhart *(Partner)*
Eric C. Jensen *(Partner)*
Frank Pietrantonio *(Partner)*
Christine Johnston *(Dir-HR & Travel
Svcs)*
Lisanne Morales *(CFO & COO-
Global)*

Cooley LLP—(Continued)

Divakar Gupta *(Partner)*
Fred Muto *(Partner)*
Pang Lee *(Partner)*
Robert W. Phillips *(Partner)*
Garth Osterman *(Partner)*
Daniel Goldberg *(Partner)*
William Haddad *(Partner)*
Yvan-Claude Pierre *(Partner)*
Matthew Pavao *(Partner)*
Seth Van Aalten *(Partner)*
Tali Sealman *(Partner)*
Steven Tonsfeldt *(Partner)*
Patrick Gibbs *(Partner)*
Laura Berezin *(Partner)*
Andy Roth *(Partner)*
Eric Schwartzman *(Partner)*
Stephen Rosen *(Partner)*
Ron Hopkinson *(Partner-New York)*
Brian Sakala *(Dir-Acctg & Fin-Global)*
Carrie Wagner *(Chief Legal Talent Officer)*
Julie Delay *(Dir-Benefits)*
Luke Cadigan *(Partner)*
Paul Roberts *(Partner)*
Alan Hambleton *(Partner)*
Ben Beerle *(Partner)*
Matthew Caplan *(Partner)*
Jonie Kondracki *(Partner)*
Siana Lowrey *(Partner)*
Lowell Mead *(Partner)*
Seth Gottlieb *(Partner)*
Carlton Fleming *(Partner)*
Ray LaSoya *(Partner)*
Ryan Sansom *(Partner)*
Patrick Flanagan *(Partner)*
Rod Freeman *(Partner-London)*
Justin Stock *(Mng Partner-London)*
William O'Connor *(Partner-Litigation-San Diego)*
Kenneth Juster *(Partner)*
Alfred Browne *(Partner)*
Angela Dunning *(Partner)*
Calise Cheng *(Partner)*
Charlie Cameron *(Sr VP-Bus Dev)*
Erik Edwards *(Partner)*
Gordon Ho *(Partner)*
John Clendenin *(Partner)*
John Dado *(Partner)*
John Hale *(Partner)*
Jon Avina *(Partner)*
Jon Gavenman *(Partner)*
Lila Hope *(Partner)*
Matthew Bartus *(Partner)*
Matthew Brigham *(Partner)*
Matthew Hemington *(Partner)*
Maureen Alger *(Partner)*
Nicole Brookshire *(Partner)*
Peter Burns *(Partner)*
Renee Deming *(Partner)*
Reuben Chen *(Partner)*
Robert L. Jones *(Partner)*
Shane Goudey *(Partner)*
Shannon Eagan *(Partner)*
T. J. Graham *(Partner)*
Wendy Brenner *(Partner)*
John Hemann *(Partner-San Francisco)*
Jeff Grossman *(Chief Strategy & Legal Practice Officer)*
William P. Donovan Jr. *(Partner)*

Subsidiaries:

Cooley LLP - Reston   (1)
Reston Town Center 11951 Freedom Dr 14th Fl, Reston, VA 20190-5640
Tel.: (703) 456-8000
Web Site: http://www.cooley.com
Emp.: 130
Law Firm Services
N.A.I.C.S.: 541110
Frank Pietrantonio *(Partner)*
Lisanne Morales *(CFO & COO-Global)*
Brian Sakala *(Dir-Global Acctg & Fin)*
Brian Burke *(Partner)*
Robert Cahill *(Partner-Comml Igitation)*
Darren DeStefano *(Partner)*

Katherine Ferguson *(Sr VP-Bus Dev)*
Colleen Gillis *(Partner)*
Jonathan Graves *(Partner)*
Christopher Hutter *(Partner)*
Kenneth Krisko *(Partner)*
Elizabeth Lewis *(Partner)*
Brian Leaf *(Partner)*
Douglas P. Lobel *(Partner)*
Mark Looney *(Partner)*
Erik Milch *(Partner)*
Christian Plaza *(Partner)*
Scott Talbot *(Partner)*
David Walsh *(Partner)*
Carl N. Grant III *(Exec VP-Bus Dev)*

Cooley LLP - Washington, DC   (1)
1299 Pennsylvania Ave NW Ste 700, Washington, DC 20004
Tel.: (202) 842-7800
Web Site: http://www.cooley.com
Emp.: 254
Law firm
N.A.I.C.S.: 541110
Micheal Tuscan *(Partner)*
Adam Chase *(Partner)*
Robert McDowell *(Partner)*
Adam Pivovar *(Partner)*
Aaron Binstock *(Partner)*
Fraser Brown *(Partner)*
Travis LeBlanc *(Partner)*

COOLEY'S GARDENS INC.

11553 Silverton Rd Ne, Silverton, OR 97381-9652
Tel.: (503) 873-5463   OR
Web Site:
    http://www.cooleysgardens.com
Year Founded: 1928
Sales Range: Less than $1 Million
Emp.: 4
Iris Plants Whslr & Mail Order
N.A.I.C.S.: 111421
Richard C. Ernst *(Pres)*
Catherine Ernst *(Treas & Sec)*

COOLFIRE MEDIA, LLC

1101 Lucas Ave, Saint Louis, MO 63101
Tel.: (314) 421-2665   MO
Web Site: http://www.coolfire.com
Year Founded: 2002
Emp.: 33
Video Production Services
N.A.I.C.S.: 512110
Jeff Keane *(Founder & CEO)*
Joshua Feldt *(CIO)*
Ashley Green *(Mgr-HR)*
Brendan Schmidt *(Coord-Production)*
Eric Stanley *(Editor)*
Jeremy Corray *(VP-Digital Entertainment)*
Maurianna Randazzo *(Mgr-Content)*
Mike Rohlfing *(Editor)*
Pete Salsich *(Gen Counsel)*
Roxanne Henry *(Mgr-Media Asset)*
Steve Luebbert *(VP-Dev)*
Tim Breitbach *(VP-Story Dev)*
Alicia Vega *(Dir-Post & Production)*
Andre De Matheu *(Editor)*
Tia Liston *(Acct Mgr)*

Subsidiaries:

Coolfire Media Originals, LLC   (1)
1101 Lucas 6 flr, Saint Louis, MO 63101
Tel.: (314) 421-2665
Web Site: http://www.coolfire.com
Emp.: 35
Video Content Development, Writing, Independent Film Production & Financing Services
N.A.I.C.S.: 512199
Jeff Keane *(Founder & CEO)*
Steve Luebbert *(Dir-Dev)*
David Johnson *(Pres)*

Subsidiary (Domestic):

Coolfire West   (2)
1021 Aviation Blvd, Hermosa Beach, CA 90254
Tel.: (310) 937-2853

Web Site:
   http://www.wildeyesproductions.com
Sales Range: $1-9.9 Million
Video Production Services
N.A.I.C.S.: 512110
David Keane *(Pres)*
Arcadia Berjonneau *(VP)*

Coolfire Solutions LLC   (1)
1101 lucas Ave, Saint Louis, MO 63101
Tel.: (314) 421-2665
Web Site: http://www.coolfiresolutions.com
Emp.: 25
Custom Software Developer & Interactive Technical Services
N.A.I.C.S.: 541511
Jeff Keane *(Founder & CEO)*
John Dames *(CTO)*
Michael Leopold *(Exec VP-Sls)*
Doh Sharp *(CEO)*

COOLIBAR, INC.

2401 Edgewood Ave S, Minneapolis, MN 55426
Tel.: (952) 922-1445
Web Site: http://www.coolibar.com
Year Founded: 2001
Sales Range: $1-9.9 Million
Emp.: 35
Sun Protective Clothing & Accessories Designer & Mfr
N.A.I.C.S.: 315250
John Barrow *(Founder & Pres)*
Ann Danaher *(VP-Customer Rels)*
Alan Higley *(VP-Mktg)*
G. Michael Hubsmith *(Exec VP)*
Kendra Reichenau *(CEO)*

COOLRAY HEATING & AIR CONDITIONING

1787 Williams Dr, Marietta, GA 30066-6223
Tel.: (770) 421-8400
Web Site: https://www.coolray.com
Year Founded: 1966
Sales Range: $10-24.9 Million
Emp.: 150
Plumbing Services
N.A.I.C.S.: 238220
Eric Evans *(Mgr-Svc)*
Ken Haines *(Pres & CEO)*

COOLWEAR INC.

530 7th Ave Ste 2804, New York, NY 10018
Tel.: (212) 575-1881
Web Site: http://www.coolwear.com
Year Founded: 1985
Sales Range: $25-49.9 Million
Emp.: 150
Womens Clothing
N.A.I.C.S.: 315250
Oded Nachmani *(Co-Founder)*

COON RAPIDS CHRYSLER, INC.

10541 Woodcrest Dr NW, Coon Rapids, MN 55433-6535
Tel.: (763) 421-8000
Web Site:
   http://www.coonrapidschrysler.net
Sales Range: $25-49.9 Million
Emp.: 125
Car Whslr
N.A.I.C.S.: 441110
Deb Aasen *(Controller)*
Bruce Kittlestedt *(Gen Mgr)*
Jack Shimota *(Owner)*

COONEN INC.

1043 Ivory St, Seymour, WI 54165
Tel.: (920) 833-2391
Sales Range: $10-24.9 Million
Emp.: 30
Petroleum Bulk Stations
N.A.I.C.S.: 424710
D. Robert Coonen *(CEO)*

COONER WIRE COMPANY

9265 Owensmouth Ave, Chatsworth, CA 91311
Tel.: (818) 882-8311
Web Site:
   https://www.coonerwire.com
Sales Range: $10-24.9 Million
Emp.: 30
Silo Mfr
N.A.I.C.S.: 423510
Brian Bouchard *(Reg Mgr-Sls)*

COONEY BROTHERS COAL CO.

1207 4th St, Cresson, PA 16630
Tel.: (814) 886-7655
Sales Range: $25-49.9 Million
Emp.: 12
Strip Mining Services
N.A.I.C.S.: 212114
Paul Cooney *(Partner)*

COONROD & ASSOCIATES CONSTRUCTION CO., INC.

3550 S Hoover Rd, Wichita, KS 67215-1213
Tel.: (316) 942-8430
Web Site: https://www.coonrod.com
Sales Range: $10-24.9 Million
Emp.: 125
Commercial & Institutional Building Construction Services
N.A.I.C.S.: 236220
Randall R. Coonrod *(Pres)*
Scot E. Wolfington *(VP)*
Mary T. Joerg *(Controller)*

COOPACA

Calle Captan Abreu Esq J Adorno, Arecibo, PR 00612
Tel.: (787) 878-2095
Web Site: http://www.coopaca.com
Rev.: $18,500,000
Emp.: 208
Personal Credit Institutions
N.A.I.C.S.: 522291
Carlos Villahermosa *(Pres)*

COOPER & COMPANY INC.

10179 Commerce Park Dr, Cincinnati, OH 45246-1335
Tel.: (513) 942-6066   OH
Web Site:
   http://www.dakotawatch.com
Year Founded: 1945
Sales Range: $100-124.9 Million
Emp.: 1,000
Jewelry Stores
N.A.I.C.S.: 458310
Marty Cooper *(Pres)*

COOPER ALLOY CORPORATION

201 Sweetland Ave, Hillside, NJ 07205
Tel.: (908) 688-4216
Web Site: http://www.vanton.com
Sales Range: $10-24.9 Million
Emp.: 35
Pumps & Pumping Equipment
N.A.I.C.S.: 333914
Stuart Cooper *(Chm & Pres)*

COOPER BARNETTE & PAGE

1928 Executive Park Dr, Barrow, GA 30666
Tel.: (770) 725-7400
Web Site:
   http://www.cooperbarnettepage.com
Sales Range: $10-24.9 Million
Emp.: 75
Highway, Street & Bridge Construction Services
N.A.I.C.S.: 237310
Ronald Cooper *(Pres)*
Bruce Page *(Exec VP)*

Lee Barnett *(VP)*
Larry Barnette *(Sec & Treas)*
Mark Allen *(VP-Ops)*
Dustin McNally *(VP)*
Katie Gamblin *(Asst Project Mgr)*
Gabriel J. Leach *(Dir-Tech)*

COOPER CARRY, INC

50 W 17th St 12, New York, NY
10011
Tel.: (212) 691-0271
Web Site:
    http://www.coopercarry.com
Year Founded: 1960
Emp.: 360
Architectural Services
N.A.I.C.S.: 541310
Ben Wauford *(Partner & Principal)*
Janet Diercks *(Mgr-Specifications)*
Sunggu Lee *(Project Mgr)*
Bill Abballe *(Mgr-Technical Svcs)*
Andrea Schaub *(Principal)*
Manny Dominguez *(Principal)*
Bill Halter *(Principal)*
Robert Just *(Principal)*
Brian Campa *(Principal-Higher Education Studio)*
Kyle Reis *(Assoc Principal & Dir-Plng)*
Ray Bouley *(Chief Growth Officer)*
Kerry Blind *(Dir-Landscape Architecture)*
Alexandra Lopatynsky *(Mng Dir & Principal)*
Columb Mahoney *(Mgr-Studio)*

Subsidiaries:

505Design Charlotte, Inc. **(1)**
2520 Broadway St, Boulder, CO 80304-4111
Tel.: (415) 421-9900
Web Site: http://www.505design.com
Architectural Services
N.A.I.C.S.: 541310
John Ward *(Mgr)*

COOPER COMMUNICATIONS

4447 Highway 17 Business, Murrells
Inlet, SC 29576
Tel.: (843) 357-3098
Web Site: https://www.cooper-communications.com
Year Founded: 1999
Sales Range: $1-9.9 Million
Emp.: 4
Advertising Agencies
N.A.I.C.S.: 541810
Elizabeth Cooper *(Owner)*

COOPER COMMUNITIES, INC.

903 N 47th St Ste 101, Rogers, AR
72756
Tel.: (479) 246-6500 DE
Web Site:
    http://www.coopercommunities.com
Year Founded: 1954
Sales Range: $200-249.9 Million
Emp.: 800
Real Estate Developers of Residential Building Construction Management; Engineering
N.A.I.C.S.: 237210
Belinda Jones *(Mgr-Cash)*
William Kennedy *(Gen Counsel & Sr VP)*
Thomas Oppenheim *(VP)*
John A. Cooper III *(Pres)*

Subsidiaries:

Cooper Building Materials **(1)**
1451 Bella Vista Way, Bella Vista, AR
72714 **(100%)**
Tel.: (479) 855-3053
Sales Range: $10-24.9 Million
Emp.: 11
Hardware & Building Materials
N.A.I.C.S.: 423310

Jonathan Kennedy *(Pres)*

Cooper Land Development, Inc. **(1)**
903 N 47th St, Rogers, AR
72715-2395 **(100%)**
Tel.: (479) 246-6500
Sales Range: $10-24.9 Million
Emp.: 4
Land Developer
N.A.I.C.S.: 237210

Cooper Realty Investment Inc. **(1)**
903 N 47th St, Rogers, AR 72756 **(100%)**
Tel.: (479) 246-6700
Web Site: http://www.cooper-realty.com
Sales Range: $10-24.9 Million
Emp.: 17
Commercial Property Developing Services
N.A.I.C.S.: 236115
Gene Groseclos *(Sr VP)*

Escapes! **(1)**
903 N 47th St, Rogers, AR 72756 **(100%)**
Tel.: (479) 246-6500
Web Site: http://www.escapesresorts.com
Sales Range: $10-24.9 Million
Emp.: 125
Timeshare Sales
N.A.I.C.S.: 561990

COOPER FARMS INC.

3310 State Route 49 N, Fort Recovery, OH 45846-0339
Tel.: (419) 375-4619
Web Site:
    https://www.cooperfarms.com
Year Founded: 1984
Sales Range: $10-24.9 Million
Emp.: 130
Producer of Prepared Animal Feeds
N.A.I.C.S.: 311119
Neil Diller *(CFO)*
Chuck Staugler *(VP-Sls & Mktg)*
Janice Fiely *(Controller)*
Dianne Cooper *(VP-PR)*
Jim Cooper *(CEO)*
Tonya Huber *(Mgr-HR)*

COOPER HEALTH SYSTEMS

1 Cooper Plz, Camden, NJ 08103
Tel.: (856) 342-2000
Web Site:
    https://www.cooperhealth.org
Rev.: $370,000,000
Emp.: 4,000
Provider of Healthcare Services
N.A.I.C.S.: 622110
Gary S. Young *(Exec VP-Govt Rels & Pub Policy)*
Jayashree Raman *(CIO & Sr VP)*
William G. Smith *(Chief Acctg Officer & Sr VP)*
Beth Green *(Chief HR Officer & Sr VP)*
Terry Ricca *(Chief Experience Officer & Sr VP)*

COOPER JOHNSON SMITH ARCHITECTS, INC.

102 S 12th St, Tampa, FL 33602
Tel.: (813) 273-0034 FL
Web Site: http://www.cjsarch.com
Year Founded: 1986
Sales Range: $1-9.9 Million
Emp.: 10
Architectural Services
N.A.I.C.S.: 541310
Donald S. Cooper *(Principal)*

COOPER PEST SOLUTION, INC.

351 Lawrence Sta Rd, Lawrenceville,
NJ 08648
Tel.: (609) 799-1300 NJ
Web Site: http://www.cooperpest.com
Year Founded: 1955
Rev.: $5,300,000
Emp.: 80
Pest Services
N.A.I.C.S.: 561710

Nancy Kintner *(Dir-IT)*
Phillip D. Cooper *(CEO)*
David Burgess *(VP)*
Lisa Montgomery *(Mgr-Bus Dev)*

COOPER PETROLEUM INC.

12780 S Caledonia Rd Hwy 501 S,
Laurinburg, NC 28352
Tel.: (910) 276-7474
Web Site: http://cooperpetro.com
Sales Range: $10-24.9 Million
Emp.: 63
Lp Gas
N.A.I.C.S.: 722513
Robert C. Cooper Sr. *(Pres)*

COOPER TANK & WELDING CORP

123 Varick Ave Brooklyn, Brooklyn,
NY 11206
Tel.: (718) 497-4431
Web Site: http://www.coopertank.com
Sales Range: $25-49.9 Million
Emp.: 70
Industrial Tank Mfr
N.A.I.C.S.: 562920
Adrienne Cooper *(CEO)*
David Hillcoat *(Pres)*

COOPER TRADING, INC.

10450 Route 30 E, Irwin, PA 15642
Tel.: (724) 861-8830
Web Site: https://www.ctipa.com
Sales Range: $10-24.9 Million
Emp.: 22
Construction Materials Whslr
N.A.I.C.S.: 444110
Peter Cooper *(Pres)*

COOPER ZIETZ ENGINEERS, INC.

620 SW 5th Ave Ste 1225, Portland,
OR 97204
Tel.: (503) 253-5429
Web Site: http://www.coopercm.com
Year Founded: 1990
Sales Range: $10-24.9 Million
Emp.: 30
Engineeering Services
N.A.I.C.S.: 541330
Fred C. Cooper *(Pres)*
Alan Heiman *(Mgr-Engrg)*
Carl Zietz *(Sr VP)*

Subsidiaries:

Cascade Design Professionals, Inc. **(1)**
6400 SE Lake Rd Ste 270, Portland, OR
97222
Tel.: (503) 652-9090
Web Site: http://www.cascadedesign.net
Sales Range: $1-9.9 Million
Emp.: 10
Engineering Services
N.A.I.C.S.: 541330
Paul Kluvers *(VP & Gen Mgr)*

Cooper Zietz Engineers, Inc. - Battle Ground **(1)**
PO Box 2135, Battle Ground, WA 98604
Tel.: (360) 666-0055
Web Site: http://www.coopercm.com
Sales Range: $1-9.9 Million
Engineeering Services
N.A.I.C.S.: 541330
Ken Valder *(Mgr-Seattle Ops)*
Timothy Oliver *(VP)*

COOPER/T. SMITH CORPORATION

118 N Royal St Ste 1100, Mobile, AL
36602
Tel.: (251) 431-6100
Web Site:
    http://www.coopertsmith.com
Sales Range: $50-74.9 Million
Emp.: 100
Stevedoring Services

N.A.I.C.S.: 488320
Susan D. Bates *(Sec)*
Tim Mire *(Mng Dir)*
David J. Cooper Sr. *(Vice Chm)*
Angus R. Cooper III *(Pres)*

Subsidiaries:

C P & O, LLC **(1)**
4200 Colley Ave Ste B, Norfolk, VA 23508
Tel.: (757) 640-2580
Business Support Services
N.A.I.C.S.: 561499

CSA Equipment Company LLC **(1)**
PO Box 1566, Mobile, AL 36633
Tel.: (251) 431-6100
Business Support Services
N.A.I.C.S.: 561499
Dan Wilkins *(VP-Ops)*

CSA Services **(1)**
PO Box 2891, Mobile, AL 36652
Tel.: (251) 431-7682
Sales Range: $10-24.9 Million
Emp.: 2
Business Support Services
N.A.I.C.S.: 561499
Mike Davis *(Mgr-Ops)*

Cooper Consolidated **(1)**
3027 Hwy 75, Darrow, LA 70725
Tel.: (225) 473-4288
Web Site:
    http://www.cooperconsolidated.com
Emp.: 25
Business Support Services
N.A.I.C.S.: 561499
Billy Fitzpatrick *(Mng Dir-Sls & Logistics)*

Cooper Marine & Timberlands **(1)**
118 N Royal St, Mobile, AL 36602
Tel.: (251) 434-5000
Web Site: http://www.coopermarine.com
Business Support Services
N.A.I.C.S.: 561499
Greg Klix *(Reg Dir-Loss Control)*
Randy Vick *(Reg Dir-Loss Control)*
Teri Lolley *(Supvr-Personnel)*

Cooper-Wilkins Welding & Machine Co., Inc. **(1)**
919 N Water St, Mobile, AL 36602
Tel.: (251) 431-6100
Web Site: http://www.coopertsmith.com
Sales Range: $10-24.9 Million
Emp.: 18
Business Support Services
N.A.I.C.S.: 561499

Cooper/T. Smith Mooring **(1)**
1240 Patterson St, New Orleans, LA 70114
Tel.: (504) 366-1521
Web Site: http://www.coopertsmith.com
Sales Range: $10-24.9 Million
Emp.: 25
Business Support Services
N.A.I.C.S.: 561499

Cooper/T. Smith Stevedoring **(1)**
2030 Hayter St, Charleston, SC 29405
Tel.: (843) 744-1613
Sales Range: $10-24.9 Million
Emp.: 15
Business Support Services
N.A.I.C.S.: 561499
Ronnie Turner *(Mgr-Ops)*

Cooper/T. Smith Stevedoring **(1)**
3027 Hwy 75, Darrow, LA 70725
Tel.: (225) 289-4489
Web Site: http://www.coopertsmith.com
Sales Range: $10-24.9 Million
Emp.: 50
Business Support Services
N.A.I.C.S.: 561499

Cooper/T. Smith Stevedoring **(1)**
6761 Cane Run Rd, Louisville, KY 40258
Tel.: (502) 935-7226
Web Site: http://www.nscorp.com
Business Support Services
N.A.I.C.S.: 561499
Darrell Mahone *(VP-Ops)*

Cooper/T. Smith Stevedoring **(1)**
118 N Royal St, Mobile, AL 36602
Tel.: (251) 431-6100
Web Site: http://www.coopertsmith.com
Business Support Services

Cooper/T. Smith Corporation—(Continued)

N.A.I.C.S.: 561499
Angus R. Cooper III (Pres)

Cooper/T. Smith Stevedoring (1)
365 Canal St Ste 1450, New Orleans, LA 70130
Tel.: (504) 569-2160
Web Site: http://www.coopertsmith.com
Sales Range: $10-24.9 Million
Emp.: 10
Business Support Services
N.A.I.C.S.: 561499
Eric Hansen (Mng Dir)

Cooper/T. Smith Stevedoring - California (1)
Berth 207, Long Beach, CA 90802
Tel.: (562) 436-2259
Web Site: http://www.coopertsmith.com
Business Support Services
N.A.I.C.S.: 561499
Ed Viner (Asst VP & Mgr-Ops)

Cooper/T. Smith Stevedoring - Texas (1)
2315 McCarty Dr, Houston, TX 77029
Tel.: (713) 675-0017
Web Site: http://www.coopertsmith.com
Business Support Services
N.A.I.C.S.: 561499
Britton Cooper (Pres)

International Logistics Company, Inc. (1)
11925 Pearl Rd Ste 410, Cleveland, OH 44136-3343
Tel.: (225) 474-8195
Business Support Services
N.A.I.C.S.: 561499
Karen Conroy (Reg Mgr)

COOPERATIVA DE AHORRO Y CEDITO DE BARRANQUITAS
PO Box 686, Barranquitas, PR 00794-0686
Tel.: (787) 857-3500   PR
Web Site:
    http://www.credicentro.coop
Year Founded: 1967
Sales Range: $10-24.9 Million
Financial Support Services
N.A.I.C.S.: 522130
Luis A. Sato (VP-Fin)
Angel Ortiz (Mgr)

COOPERATIVA DE AHORRO Y CREDITO AGUADA
PO Box 543, Aguada, PR 00602
Tel.: (787) 868-2115   PR
Web Site:
    http://www.coopaguada.coop
Year Founded: 1948
Sales Range: $10-24.9 Million
Emp.: 70
Financial Support Services
N.A.I.C.S.: 523999
Juan Figueroa Ruiz (Co-Pres)
Angela L. Aviles Gonzalez (Exec VP)

COOPERATIVA DE AHORRO Y CREDITO DE CAMUY
300 Baltazar Jimenez Ave, Camuy, PR 00627
Tel.: (787) 898-4970   PR
Web Site:
    http://www.camuycoop.com
Year Founded: 1954
Sales Range: $10-24.9 Million
Credit Union Operator
N.A.I.C.S.: 522130
Michele Franqui Baquero (Pres)
Alvin A. Atiles Tosado (VP-Fin)
Pastor Santiago Toledo (Chm)

COOPERATIVA DE AHORRO Y CREDITO DE ISABELA
21 Calle Barbosa Ste 1, Isabela, PR 00662
Tel.: (787) 872-2265

Web Site:
    http://www.isabelacoop.com
Year Founded: 1953
Sales Range: $10-24.9 Million
Financial Services
N.A.I.C.S.: 522130
Luis A. Perez Hernandez (CEO)
Enrique Carrillo Acevedo (Supvr-Fin)

COOPERATIVA DE SEGUROS DE VIDA
400 Ave Americo Miranda, San Juan, PR 00927
Tel.: (787) 751-5656
Web Site: http://www.cosvi.com
Sales Range: $125-149.9 Million
Emp.: 560
Cooperative Life Insurance Organizations
N.A.I.C.S.: 524113
Ricardo Rivera-Cardona (Pres)

COOPERATIVE DE AHORRO Y CREDITO SAN RAFAEL
Rafael Rodriguez Canals No 1 Urb Avila, Quebradillas, PR 00678-1531
Tel.: (787) 895-2050   PR
Web Site: http://www.sanrafael.coop
Year Founded: 1956
Sales Range: $10-24.9 Million
Savings & Credit Cooperative
N.A.I.C.S.: 522130
Luis A. Velazquez Vera (Pres)
Jaime R. Chaves Munoz (VP)
Hector Velez de Jesus (Sec)
Ana H. Cubero Alicea (Asst Sec)
Rafael Mercado Ramos (Treas)
Edwin A. Cortes Estremera (Asst Treas)

COOPERATIVE ELECTRIC ENERGY UTILITY SUPPLY, INC.
101 Enterprise Pkwy, West Columbia, SC 29170-2249
Tel.: (803) 822-8100
Web Site: https://www.ceeus.com
Year Founded: 1974
Electrical Apparatus & Equipment Mfr
N.A.I.C.S.: 423610
Don McCord (Pres & CEO)
Ronnie Taylor (VP-Fin & Ops)
Scott Bryant (VP-Bus Dev)

COOPERATIVE ELEVATOR ASSOCIATION
823 Main St, Ocheyedan, IA 51354
Tel.: (712) 758-3621
Web Site: http://www.ceacoop.com
Sales Range: $25-49.9 Million
Emp.: 100
Marketer of Grain Elevators
N.A.I.C.S.: 424510
Ron Jacobs (Gen Mgr)
Howard Randy (Coord-Feed)
Jeff Otto (Mgr-Feed Mill)

COOPERATIVE ELEVATOR CO., INC.
7211 E Michigan Ave, Pigeon, MI 48755
Tel.: (989) 453-4500
Web Site: https://www.coopelev.com
Rev.: $10,000,000
Emp.: 150
Postharvest Crop Activities
N.A.I.C.S.: 115114
Kurt Ewald (Chm)
Michael Wehner (VP-Fin)
Barry Albrecht (VP-IT & Asst Sec)
Mike Janowicz (VP)
Tim Sielaff (VP)
Scott Gordon (CEO)
Les Roth (Sec)

COOPERATIVE GAS & OIL CO

153 N Main Ave, Sioux Center, IA 51250
Tel.: (712) 722-2501   IA
Web Site:
    https://www.coopgassc.com
Sales Range: $10-24.9 Million
Emp.: 35
Petroleum Bulk Stations & Terminals
N.A.I.C.S.: 424710
Randy Bos (Gen Mgr)

COOPERATIVE HOLDINGS INC.
210 Clay Ave, Lyndhurst, NJ 07071
Tel.: (973) 759-8100
Web Site:
    http://www.cooperativenet.com
Year Founded: 1988
Sales Range: $10-24.9 Million
Emp.: 80
Local & Long Distance Telephone Communications Services; Internet & Data Services
N.A.I.C.S.: 517121
Jay M. Brzezanski (CFO & Sec)
Michael Lombardi (VP-Fin)
Louis A. Lombardi Sr. (Chm, Pres & CEO)
Louis A. Lombardi Jr. (COO & VP)

Subsidiaries:

Cooperative Communications Inc. (1)
210 Clay Ave, Lyndhurst, NJ 07071
Tel.: (973) 759-8100
Web Site: http://www.cooperativenet.com
Sales Range: $10-24.9 Million
Local & Long Distance Telephone Communications, Data Services, Internet Connections & Web Hosting
N.A.I.C.S.: 517121

Eastern Computer Service Inc. (1)
412 Washington Ave, Belleville, NJ 07109
Tel.: (201) 997-5500
Rev.: $2,000,000
Emp.: 25
Custom Computer Programming Services
N.A.I.C.S.: 541511
Michael Lombardi (CFO)
Louis Lombardi Sr. (Pres)

COOPERATIVE HOME HEALTH CARE OF ATLANTIC COUNTY INC.
6550 Delilah Rd Ste 304, Egg Harbor Township, NJ 08234
Tel.: (609) 484-7300   NJ
Year Founded: 2001
Sales Range: $10-24.9 Million
Emp.: 141
Women Healthcare Services
N.A.I.C.S.: 621610
George Zoyac (Mgr-Physical Therapy)
Robert Pelikoski (Fin Dir)
Ellen Wolownik (Exec Dir)

COOPERATIVE OF AMERICAN PHYSICIANS
333 S Hope St 8th Fl, Los Angeles, CA 90071
Tel.: (213) 473-8600
Web Site: http://www.cap-mpt.com
Year Founded: 1975
Rev.: $48,100,000
Emp.: 230
Medical Liability Insurance Protection Services
N.A.I.C.S.: 813920
Gordon Ownby (Gen Counsel)
John Donaldson (CFO)
Cynthia Belcher (COO)
Nancy Brusegaard Johnson (Sr VP-HR & Ops)
Bela S. Kenessey (Chm & Pres)
Jeffrey Stoner (Sr VP-Claims & Risk Mgmt Svcs)

Ann Whitehead (VP-Risk Mgmt & Patient Safety)
Carole Lambert (VP-Practice Optimization & Program Dir-Residents)

COOPERATIVE OF AMERICAN PHYSICIANS, INC.
333 S Hope St Fl 8, Los Angeles, CA 90071-3001
Tel.: (213) 473-8600
Web Site:
    http://www.capphysicians.com
Year Founded: 1988
Sales Range: $10-24.9 Million
Emp.: 200
Direct Property & Casualty Insurance Services
N.A.I.C.S.: 524126
Thomas Andre (VP-MIS)
Cindy Belcher (COO)
Nancy Brusegaard Johnson (Sr VP-HR & Ops)
John Donaldson (CFO)
Cindy Farrington (Sr VP-Ops)
Gordon Ownby (Gen Counsel)
Jeff Stoner (Sr VP-Claims & Risk Mgmt Svcs)
Deidri Hoppe (Pres/CEO-CAP Physicians Insurance Agency, Inc.)
Mitch Temple (VP-Bus Dev-Assurance Risk Pur Grp)
Sarah E. Scher (CEO)
Alyson Lewis (Chief Underwriting Officer & Sr VP)

COOPERATIVE OPTICAL SERVICES
2424 E 8 Mile Rd, Detroit, MI 48234
Tel.: (313) 366-5100
Web Site:
    http://www.coopoptical.com
Year Founded: 1960
Sales Range: $10-24.9 Million
Emp.: 150
Optical Goods Stores
N.A.I.C.S.: 456130
Benjamin Edwards (Chm)
Barbara McGee (Mgr)
Robert Evangelista (Chm)

COOPERATIVE PRODUCERS, INC.
265 N Showboat Blvd, Hastings, NE 68901
Tel.: (402) 463-5148   NE
Web Site: https://www.cpicoop.com
Year Founded: 1906
Sales Range: $100-124.9 Million
Emp.: 600
Grain, Animal Feed & Farm Supplies Whslr
N.A.I.C.S.: 424510
Mark Hueftle (Dir-Safety)
David L. Nall (Mgr-Automotive Ops)
Eric Werth (Branch Mgr-Funk)
Allan Zumpfe (CEO)

COOPERATIVE PRODUCTION, INC.
455 Somerset Ave, North Dighton, MA 02764-0506
Tel.: (508) 824-1717   MA
Web Site:
    http://www.cooperativeproduction.org
Year Founded: 1976
Sales Range: $10-24.9 Million
Emp.: 378
Developmentally Disabled People Care Services
N.A.I.C.S.: 623210
Eva T. Gaffney (Vice Chm)
Philip C. Vecchio (Treas)
William J. Corbett (Pres & CEO)

COOPERATIVE REGIONS OF ORGANIC PRODUCER POOLS
1 Organic Way, La Farge, WI 54639
Tel.: (608) 625-3025
Web Site:
  http://www.organicvalley.coop
Year Founded: 1988
Sales Range: $200-249.9 Million
Emp.: 350
Organic Food Producer & Marketer
N.A.I.C.S.: 311999
Eric Newman *(VP-Sls)*
Joseph Eagleeye *(CFO)*
Nicole Rakobitsch *(Dir-Sustainability)*

COOPERATIVE RESOURCES INTERNATIONAL INC.
100 MBC Dr, Shawano, WI 54166-6095
Tel.: (715) 526-2141   WI
Web Site: http://www.crinet.com
Year Founded: 1993
Sales Range: $75-99.9 Million
Emp.: 1,200
Livestock Services
N.A.I.C.S.: 115210
Doug Wilson *(CEO)*
Tom Bjelland *(VP-Domestic Mktg)*
Pete Giacomini *(Sr VP-Bus Dev)*
Dave Mellinger *(Sr VP-Fin)*
Huub te Plate *(Sr VP-Mktg-Intl)*
Keith Heikes *(COO)*
Terri Dallas *(VP-Info & PR)*
Troy Klement *(VP-IT)*

Subsidiaries:

Agsource Cooperative Services   (1)
135 Enterprise Dr, Verona, WI
53593-9122   (100%)
Tel.: (608) 845-1900
Web Site: http://www.agsource.com
Sales Range: $10-24.9 Million
Emp.: 42
Provider of Livestock Services
N.A.I.C.S.: 115210
Pat Baier *(COO)*
Robert Fourdraine *(VP-Product Svcs & Dev)*

Central Livestock Association,   (1)
Inc.
953 S Concord St, South Saint Paul, MN
55075
Tel.: (651) 451-1844
Web Site: http://www.centrallivestock.com
Sales Range: $1-9.9 Million
Emp.: 160
Livestock Selling Agency Co-Op Distr
N.A.I.C.S.: 424520
Jeffrey Reed *(Mgr)*

Genex Inc.   (1)
100 MBC Dr, Shawano, WI 54166-6095
Tel.: (715) 526-2141
Web Site: http://www.crinet.com
Sales Range: $10-24.9 Million
Emp.: 75
Provider of Livestock Services
N.A.I.C.S.: 115210
Keith Heikes *(COO)*
Paul Greene *(Pres)*

Subsidiary (Non-US):

Genex Canada   (1)
143 Dennis Street Unit C, Rockwood, N0B
2K0, ON, Canada   (100%)
Tel.: (519) 766-4622
Web Site: http://www.genexcanada.ca
Sales Range: $10-24.9 Million
Emp.: 6
Livestock Breeding Services
N.A.I.C.S.: 115210
Patty Lafty *(Mng Dir)*

COOPERATIVE SUPPLY INC.
239 Frnt St, Dodge, NE 68633
Tel.: (402) 693-2261
Web Site: http://www.coopsupply.com
Rev.: $25,453,109
Emp.: 43
Grains

N.A.I.C.S.: 424510
David Reichmuth *(VP)*
Rick Brune *(Sec)*

COOPERATIVE SYSTEMS, LLC
80 Lamberton Rd, Windsor, CT 06095
Tel.: (860) 523-1000
Web Site: http://www.coopsys.com
Year Founded: 1993
Computer & Computer Peripheral Equipment & Software Merchant Whslr
N.A.I.C.S.: 423430
Robert Delisa *(Pres & CEO)*
Scott Spatz *(VP-Sls & Admin)*
Steve Martocchio *(VP-Ops)*

Subsidiaries:

Fandotech, LLC   (1)
893 Main St, Manchester, CT 06040
Tel.: (860) 432-4745
Web Site: http://www.fandotech.com
Rev.: $4,100,000
Emp.: 28
Computer Services
N.A.I.C.S.: 811210
Jeffrey Heidtman *(CEO)*
Joseph Bucceri *(CTO)*
John W. Boyd Jr. *(Pres)*

COOPERRIIS HEALING COMMUNITY, INC.
101 Healing Farm Ln, Mill Spring, NC 28756
Tel.: (828) 894-5557   NC
Web Site: http://www.cooperriis.org
Year Founded: 2000
Sales Range: $10-24.9 Million
Emp.: 194
Community Care Services
N.A.I.C.S.: 622210
Mary Strickland Kreider *(Dir-Integrative Health)*
Lisa Schactman *(Mng Dir)*
Laurie Rovin *(Chief Dev Officer)*
Kimberly Nelson *(Coord-Outreach-Natl)*
Mary Flora *(Dir-Clinical-Mill Spring)*
Donald R. Cooper *(Co-Founder)*
Lisbeth Riis Cooper *(Co-Founder)*

COOPERS STEEL FABRICATORS INC.
503 N Hillcrest Dr, Shelbyville, TN 37160
Tel.: (931) 684-7962
Web Site:
  https://www.coopersteel.com
Sales Range: $25-49.9 Million
Emp.: 95
Structural Steel Erection & Fabrication
N.A.I.C.S.: 238120
James Kenneth Cooper *(Pres)*
Barry Cooper *(Treas)*
Gary Cooper *(VP)*

COORDINATED BUSINESS SYSTEMS, LTD.
851 W 128th St, Burnsville, MN 55337
Tel.: (952) 894-9460   MN
Web Site:
  https://www.coordinated.com
Year Founded: 1983
Sales Range: $1-9.9 Million
Emp.: 70
Document Imaging & Information Management Technology Services
N.A.I.C.S.: 517810
Jim Oricchio *(Pres)*

COORDINATED CARE CORP.
205 W Boutz Rd Bldg 2, Las Cruces, NM 88005-3262
Tel.: (575) 526-1333

Year Founded: 1983
Sales Range: $10-24.9 Million
Emp.: 1,500
Women Healthcare Services
N.A.I.C.S.: 621610
Lila Roberts *(Pres)*

COORDINATED RESOURCES, INC. OF SAN FRANCISCO
130 Sutter St 3rd Fl, San Francisco, CA 94104
Tel.: (415) 989-0773   CA
Web Site: https://www.cri-sf.com
Year Founded: 1986
Sales Range: $10-24.9 Million
Emp.: 54
Office Furniture Whslr
N.A.I.C.S.: 423210
William Watson *(Pres & CEO)*
Jennifer Wong *(CFO)*
Jaimee Arent *(VP)*
Kristen McKenzie *(VP-Sls & Mktg)*
Janet McNamara *(VP & Acct Mgr)*
Veronica Ratcliff *(Head-HR)*

COORDINATED SYSTEMS INC.
165 Burnside Ave, East Hartford, CT 06108
Tel.: (860) 289-2151
Web Site: http://www.csiworld.com
Year Founded: 1972
Sales Range: $1-9.9 Million
Emp.: 20
Custom Computer Programming Services
N.A.I.C.S.: 541511
Ryan McCormick *(Mgr-Sls)*
David R. Brower *(Pres)*

COORSTEK, INC.
14143 Denver West Pkwy Ste 400, Golden, CO 80401
Tel.: (303) 271-7100   DE
Web Site: https://www.coorstek.com
Year Founded: 1911
Pottery, Ceramics & Plumbing Fixture Mfr
N.A.I.C.S.: 327110
Irma Lockridge *(Chief People Officer)*
Jonathan Coors *(Co-CEO)*
Michael Coors *(Co-CEO)*
Timothy Coors *(Co-CEO)*
Andrew Filson *(COO)*
Randel Mercer *(CTO)*
Jay Voncannon *(CFO)*

Subsidiaries:

ADJ Industries Inc.   (1)
2068 Piper Lane, London, N5V 3N6, ON, Canada
Tel.: (519) 455-4065
Web Site: http://www.amti.ca
Machining, Welding & Fabrication Services; Locomotive Components Mfr
N.A.I.C.S.: 332999

Subsidiary (Domestic):

CoorsTek Engineered Metals
ULC   (2)
2068 Piper Lane, London, N5V 3N6, ON, Canada
Tel.: (519) 455-4065
Industrial Machinery Mfr
N.A.I.C.S.: 333248

CoorsTek Armor Solutions, Inc.   (1)
14143 Denver W Pkwy Ste 400, Golden, CO 80401
Tel.: (303) 271-7100
Vehicle Armor & Survivability System Mfr
N.A.I.C.S.: 336992

CoorsTek KK   (1)
Osaki Wiz Tower 11-1 Osaki 2-chome, Shinagawa-ku, Tokyo, 141-0032, Japan
Tel.: (81) 3 5437 8411
Web Site: http://www.coorstek.co.jp
Engineered Ceramics & Glass Products Mfr
N.A.I.C.S.: 327110

Yoshinaga Ikemoto *(Exec VP & Sr Dir-Acctg & Fin)*
Hiroshi Ito *(Sr Dir-Ops)*
Megan E. Hale *(Auditor)*
Jonathan D. Coors Sr. *(Pres)*

Plant (Domestic):

CoorsTek KK - Hadano Facility   (2)
30 Soya, Hadano, 257-8566, Kanagawa, Japan
Tel.: (81) 463 81 1050
Industrial Machinery Equipment Mfr & Whslr
N.A.I.C.S.: 333248

CoorsTek KK - Kariya Facility   (2)
1 Minami-Fuji Ogakie-cho, Kariya, 448-8665, Aichi, Japan
Tel.: (81) 566 21 2851
Industrial Machinery Equipment Mfr & Whslr
N.A.I.C.S.: 333248

CoorsTek KK - Oguni Facility   (2)
378 Oguni-machi Oaza, Nishiokitamagun, Oguni, 999-1351, Yamagata, Japan
Tel.: (81) 238 62 5902
Industrial Machinery Equipment Mfr & Whslr
N.A.I.C.S.: 333248

Subsidiary (Domestic):

CoorsTek Machinery Corporation   (2)
378 Oguni-machi Oaza Oguni-machi, Nishiokitamagun, Oguni, 999-1351, Yamagata, Japan
Tel.: (81) 238 62 5942
Industrial Machinery Equipment Mfr & Whslr
N.A.I.C.S.: 333248

CoorsTek Nagasaki Corporation   (2)
296 Kawatana-cho Momozugo, Higashisonogi-gun, Nagasaki, 859-3605, Japan
Tel.: (81) 956 82 3111
Optical Functional Components & Refractories & Other Semiconductor Related Materials Mfr
N.A.I.C.S.: 327120

Subsidiary (Non-US):

CoorsTek Taiwan Corp.   (2)
16F-4 No 295 Sec 2 Kuang-Fu Road, Hsin-chu, 30017, Taiwan
Tel.: (886) 3 575 1238
Ceramic Product Mfr & Whslr
N.A.I.C.S.: 327110

Subsidiary (Domestic):

CoorsTek Tokuyama Corporation   (2)
2-1-32 Eguchi, Shunan, 745-0862, Yamaguchi, Japan
Tel.: (81) 834 32 3400
Quartz Glass Product Mfr
N.A.I.C.S.: 334419

CoorsTek, Inc. - CoorsTek Lauf
Facility   (1)
Am Winkelsteig 1, D-91207, Lauf an der Pegnitz, Germany
Tel.: (49) 91231810
Ceramic Components, Industrial Adhesive & Other Electronic Circuit Substrates Mfr
N.A.I.C.S.: 327110

CoorsTek, Inc. - CoorsTek Monchengladbach Facility   (1)
Nobelstrasse 6, Postfach 401254, 41189, Monchengladbach, Germany
Tel.: (49) 2166 5509 0
Silicon Carbide Ring & Seal Components Mfr
N.A.I.C.S.: 327999

CoorsTek, Inc. - CoorsTek New
Hampshire Facility   (1)
47 Powers St, Milford, NH 03055
Tel.: (603) 673-7560
Electric Device Mfr
N.A.I.C.S.: 335999

CoorsTek, Inc. - CoorsTek New Mills
Facility   (1)
Watford Bridge, New Mills High Peak, Stockport, SK22 4HJ, United Kingdom
Tel.: (44) 1663745976
Pump & Valve Mfr
N.A.I.C.S.: 333914

CoorsTek, Inc.—(Continued)

CoorsTek, Inc. - CoorsTek Oregon Operations Facility (1)
555 NE 53rd Ave, Hillsboro, OR 97124
Tel.: (503) 648-3183
Semiconductor Mfr
N.A.I.C.S.: 334413

CoorsTek, Inc. - CoorsTek Paris Facility (1)
45 Curtis Avenue N, Paris, N3L 3T6, ON, Canada
Tel.: (519) 442-7792
Ceramic Components for Molten Metal Filtration Mfr
N.A.I.C.S.: 327110

CoorsTek, Inc. - CoorsTek San Luis Potosi Facility (1)
Eje 114 113 Zona Industrial del Potosi, CP 78395, San Luis Potosi, Mexico
Tel.: (52) 4448246539
Ceramic Components & Industrial Adhesive Mfr
N.A.I.C.S.: 327110

CoorsTek, Inc. - CoorsTek Sweden Facility (1)
Fabriksvagen, S-91532, Robertsfors, Sweden
Tel.: (46) 93417200
Ceramic Plunger & Valve Mfr
N.A.I.C.S.: 327110

CoorsTek, Inc. - CoorsTek Tennessee Facility (1)
1100 Commerce Park Dr, Oak Ridge, TN 37830
Tel.: (865) 481-2021
Ceramic Materials Mfr
N.A.I.C.S.: 334413

CoorsTek, Inc. - CoorsTek Vinhedo Facility (1)
Rua Antonio Matheus Sobrinho 150, Jardin Sao Matheous, Vinhedo, 13280-000, Sao Paulo, Brazil
Tel.: (55) 1933997514
Ceramic Materials Mfr
N.A.I.C.S.: 327910

CoorsTek, Inc. - CoorsTek Vista Facility (1)
2065 Thibodo Rd, Vista, CA 92081
Tel.: (760) 542-7065
High-Strength Ceramic Specialty Materials Mfr
N.A.I.C.S.: 325211

CoorsTek, Inc. - CoorsTek Vista Facility (1)
2065 Thibodo Rd, Vista, CA 92081
Tel.: (760) 542-7065
Ceramic Materials Mfr
N.A.I.C.S.: 334413

CoorsTek, Inc. - CoorsTek Worcester Facility (1)
5 Norton Dr, Worcester, MA 01606
Tel.: (774) 317-2600
Ceramic Materials Mfr
N.A.I.C.S.: 334413

Coorstek, Inc. - CoorsTek Tulsa Facility (1)
7700 Bryant St, Oklahoma City, OK 73149
Tel.: (405) 601-4371
Petroleum Pumps & Industrial Crankshaft Mfr
N.A.I.C.S.: 333248

DEW Engineering and Development ULC (1)
3429 Hawthorne Rd, Ottawa, K1G 4G2, ON, Canada
Tel.: (613) 736-5100
Web Site: http://www.dewengineering.com
Defence & Armour Security Products Mfr
N.A.I.C.S.: 336419

EmiSense Technologies, LLC (1)
999 Corporate Dr Ste 180, Ladera Ranch, CA 92694
Tel.: (949) 542-7121
Web Site: http://www.emisense.com
Sensor Developing Services
N.A.I.C.S.: 334413

COP COMMUNICATIONS

---

620 W Elk Ave, Glendale, CA 91204-1404
Tel.: (818) 291-1100 CA
Web Site: https://www.copprints.com
Year Founded: 1962
Sales Range: $100-124.9 Million
Emp.: 150
Holding Company
N.A.I.C.S.: 323111
William R. Rittwage (Pres & CEO)

Subsidiaries:

California Offset Printers, Inc. (1)
620 W Elk Ave, Glendale, CA 91204
Tel.: (818) 291-1100
Web Site: http://www.copprints.com
Sales Range: $10-24.9 Million
Emp.: 100
Publication Printers Tabloids, Magazines, Directories
N.A.I.C.S.: 323111
William R. Rittwage (Pres & CEO)

Computer Graphics World (1)
620 W Elk Ave, Glendale, CA 91204-1404
Tel.: (603) 432-7568
Web Site: http://www.cgw.com
Computer Graphic Design Services
N.A.I.C.S.: 541430
Mari Kohn (Dir-Sls)

COP CONSTRUCTION CO.
242 S 64th St W, Billings, MT 59106
Tel.: (406) 656-4632
Web Site: https://www.copconstruction.com
Rev.: $25,000,000
Emp.: 35
Bridge Construction
N.A.I.C.S.: 237310

COPA DI VINO
901 E 2nd St, The Dalles, OR 97058
Tel.: (541) 298-8900
Web Site: http://www.copadivino.com
Sales Range: $25-49.9 Million
Emp.: 70
Wine In The Glass Mfr
N.A.I.C.S.: 312130
James Martin (Founder & Owner)

COPA INC.
1900 E Hobson Way, Blythe, CA 92225
Tel.: (760) 922-6800
Web Site: http://www.quikchekmarkets.com
Sales Range: $10-24.9 Million
Emp.: 20
Convenience Store
N.A.I.C.S.: 445131
Barbara Gregg (Office Mgr)
G. Barrett Covington (VP)

COPAC, INC.
1750 Deweerry Rd, Spartanburg, SC 29307
Tel.: (864) 579-2554 SC
Web Site: http://www.copacinc.com
Year Founded: 1970
Sales Range: $10-24.9 Million
Emp.: 100
Offset Printing
N.A.I.C.S.: 323111
Smith Lanford (Controller)
Jerry Lux (Pres)
Ed Benson (Mgr-Mktg-Nutraceuticals)
Sarah Selig (Acct Mgr)
Phillip Ayers (Mgr-Prepress)

COPACINO + FUJIKADO, LLC
1425 4th Ave Ste 700, Seattle, WA 98101-2265
Tel.: (206) 467-6610
Web Site: https://www.copacino.com
Year Founded: 1998
Sales Range: $25-49.9 Million
Emp.: 32
Advertising Agencies

N.A.I.C.S.: 541810
Tim O'Mara (Dir-Engagement Strategy)
Mike Hayward (Exec Dir-Creative)
Jim Copacino (Co-Founder & Exec Dir-Creative)
Tonya Murphy (Dir-Media)
Scott Foreman (Mng Dir)

COPASAT, LLC
12501 71st Ct N, Largo, FL 33773
Tel.: (727) 325-1426
Web Site: http://www.copasat.com
Year Founded: 2014
Sales Range: $10-24.9 Million
Emp.: 12
Telecommunication Servicesb
N.A.I.C.S.: 517810
Obie Johnson (CEO)

COPAZ PACKING CORPORATION
PO Box 40268, Cincinnati, OH 45240
Tel.: (513) 671-1676
Sales Range: $10-24.9 Million
Emp.: 260
Sausage, Luncheon Meat & Frankfurter Mfr
N.A.I.C.S.: 311615
Charles Finkel (Pres)
Harold Wilt (VP-Ops)
Mike Romero (Controller)
Dorothy Finkel (Treas & Sec)

COPE BESTWAY EXPRESS INC.
1875 Harlem Rd, Buffalo, NY 14212
Tel.: (716) 875-6565
Web Site: http://www.bestwaycompanies.com
Sales Range: $10-24.9 Million
Emp.: 70
Trucking Except Local
N.A.I.C.S.: 484121

COPE COMMUNITY SERVICES, INC.
82 S Stone Ave, Tucson, AZ 85701
Tel.: (520) 792-3293 AZ
Web Site: http://www.copecommunityservices.org
Year Founded: 1979
Sales Range: $25-49.9 Million
Emp.: 495
Community Health Care Services
N.A.I.C.S.: 621498
Khalid Al-Maskari (CIO)
Rodney Cook (CFO & COO)

COPE PLASTICS INCORPORATED
4441 Industrial Dr, Alton, IL 62002
Tel.: (618) 466-0221
Web Site: https://www.copeplastics.com
Sales Range: $100-124.9 Million
Emp.: 350
Plastics Sheets & Rods
N.A.I.C.S.: 424610
John Theen (CFO)
John Lee (VP-Sls)

COPELAND CHEVROLET
1555 Main St, Brockton, MA 02301
Tel.: (508) 586-7900
Web Site: http://www.copelandchevrolet.com
New & Used Car Retailer
N.A.I.C.S.: 441110
Todd Copeland (Owner)
Jason Pappas (Gen Mgr)
Dave Turner (CFO)
Ed Cushing (Sls Mgr)
Tom Cullinan (Gen Sls Mgr)
Ivan Greenblatt (Dir-Bus Dev)

Kelly Brand (Office Mgr)
Rich Grondell (Mgr-Svc)
Ed Donato (Assoc Mgr-Parts)
Steve Buchanan (Bus Mgr)
Laura Williams (Bus Dir)

COPELAND OIL & GAS CO. OF MBL
327 Hwy 43 N, Saraland, AL 36571
Tel.: (251) 679-0330
Rev.: $13,840,587
Emp.: 3
Gasoline Mfr
N.A.I.C.S.: 424720
Maxine Copeland (Pres)

COPELANDS OF NEW ORLEANS INC.
1001 Harimaw Ct, Metairie, LA 70001
Tel.: (504) 830-1000
Web Site: http://www.alcopeland.com
Rev.: $54,200,000
Emp.: 20
Franchiser of Fast-Food Restaurants
N.A.I.C.S.: 722511
Alvin C. Copeland (Pres & CEO)

COPEN ASSOCIATES, INC.
37 W 39th St Rm 603, New York, NY 10018-0597
Tel.: (212) 819-0008 NY
Web Site: http://www.copenuni.com
Year Founded: 1976
Sales Range: $25-49.9 Million
Emp.: 175
Broadwoven Fabric Mill Services
N.A.I.C.S.: 313210
Karen Trundle (Pres)
Barry Emanuel (Owner)

COPENHAGEN IMPORTS INC.
1701 E Camelback Rd, Phoenix, AZ 85016
Tel.: (602) 266-8060
Web Site: https://www.copenhagenliving.com
Sales Range: $25-49.9 Million
Emp.: 300
Owner & Operator of Furniture Stores
N.A.I.C.S.: 449110

COPIA SCIENTIFIC, INC.
245 Constitution Dr, Taunton, MA 02780
Tel.: (877) 267-4272 DE
Web Site: http://www.copiasci.com
Year Founded: 2021
Laboratory Equipment Mfr
N.A.I.C.S.: 334516
Bill VanDeWeghe (CEO)
Richard Tula (Pres)
Bryan Hoffman (Chief Revenue Officer)

Subsidiaries:

BioSurplus, Inc. (1)
10805 Vista Sorrento Pkwy Ste 200, San Diego, CA 92121
Tel.: (858) 550-0800
Web Site: http://www.biosurplus.com
Rev.: $1,500,000
Emp.: 14
Laboratory Equipment Distr
N.A.I.C.S.: 334516
Reid Hjalmarson (Dir-Mktg)
Debra Inger (Dir-Bus Dev-Northeast)

Biodirect Inc. (1)
245 Constitution Dr, Taunton, MA 02780
Tel.: (508) 884-5010
Web Site: http://www.biodirectusa.com
Rev.: $2,300,000
Emp.: 15
Bio Technology Services
N.A.I.C.S.: 541714
Francine Tula (CFO)
Jim OK (VP-Sls & Mktg)

COPIC TRUST

7351 E Lowry Blvd Ste 400, Denver, CO 80230
Tel.: (720) 858-6000   CO
Web Site: http://www.callcopic.com
Year Founded: 1981
Sales Range: $50-74.9 Million
Emp.: 100
Provider of Surety Insurance Services
N.A.I.C.S.: 524126
Ted J. Clarke *(Chm & CEO)*
Janel Loud-Mahany *(VP-Underwriting & Policyholder Svc)*
Beverly Razon *(VP-Pub Affairs)*
Kristin Stepien *(VP-Sls & Bus Dev)*
Gerry Lewis-Jenkins *(COO)*
Steven A. Rubin *(Pres)*
Mark Fogg *(Gen Counsel)*
Alan Lembitz *(Chief Medical Officer)*

COPIERSUPPLYSTORE
6511 Nova Dr Ste 147, Davie, FL 33317
Tel.: (954) 584-8497
Web Site:
http://www.copiersupplystore.com
Year Founded: 2007
Sales Range: $1-9.9 Million
Emp.: 5
Supplier Office Machine Consumable Products
N.A.I.C.S.: 424120
Bruce Cooperman *(CEO, Owner & Dir-Online Mktg)*

COPLAND FABRICS, INC.
1714 Carolina Mill Rd, Burlington, NC 27217-7837
Tel.: (336) 226-0272   NC
Web Site:
http://www.coplandfabrics.com
Year Founded: 1941
Sales Range: $150-199.9 Million
Emp.: 400
Mfr of Broad Woven Synthetic Fabrics
N.A.I.C.S.: 313210
Timms Clapp *(Sec & VP)*
Glenn R. Gehlbach *(VP & Mgr-Sls)*
Larry Hulighan *(VP-Sls & Mgr-Hospitality)*
James Coble *(VP-Quality)*
Ross Whitt *(VP)*

COPLEY EQUITY PART-NERS,LLC
150 Newport Ave Extension 3rd fl, Quincy, MA 02171
Tel.: (617) 249-5097
Web Site:
http://www.copleyequity.com
Year Founded: 2012
Privater Equity Firm
N.A.I.C.S.: 523999
Andy Miller *(Co-Founder & Mng Dir)*
Peter Trovato *(Mng Partner)*

Subsidiaries:

Aeromed Group LLC   (1)
1422 S Tryon St Ste 300, Charlotte, NC 28203
Tel.: (704) 412-2666
Web Site: http://www.aeromedgroup.com
Aerospace Management & Investment Services
N.A.I.C.S.: 523999
Bob Spence *(CEO)*

Subsidiary (Domestic):

ETA Global, Inc.   (2)
5500 W Oak St, Palestine, TX 75801
Tel.: (903) 729-3131
Web Site: http://www.etaglobal.com
Sales Range: $1-9.9 Million
Emp.: 41
Whol Transportation Equipment
N.A.I.C.S.: 423860

Douglas Russell *(Pres)*
Janie Richmond *(Mgr-Sls)*
Michael Santangelo *(Dir-Bus Dev)*

COPLEY PROFESSIONAL SERVICES GROUP, INC.
66 Morrisville Plz, Morrisville, VT 05661
Tel.: (802) 851-8608   VT
Web Site: http://www.chslv.org
Year Founded: 1998
Sales Range: $10-24.9 Million
Emp.: 136
Community Health Services
N.A.I.C.S.: 621498
Kevin J. Kelley *(Pres & CEO)*
David Coddaire *(Exec Dir-Medical)*
Vicki Emerson *(Dir-HR)*
Jose Zirena *(CFO)*
Stephanie Frederick *(Dir-Nursing)*

COPPER CLAD MULTILAYER PRODUCTS INC.
1150 N Hawk Cir, Anaheim, CA 92807
Tel.: (714) 237-1388
Web Site: http://www.ccmpinc.com
Year Founded: 1994
Rev.: $12,095,199
Emp.: 50
Printed Circuit Boards
N.A.I.C.S.: 334412
Fred Ohanion *(Pres)*
Dell Schwerter *(VP)*

COPPER RIVER SEAFOODS, INC.
4000 W 50th Ave, Anchorage, AK 99502
Tel.: (907) 522-7806
Web Site:
http://www.copperriverseafood.com
Rev.: $3,135,000
Emp.: 5
Fish & Seafood Markets
N.A.I.C.S.: 445250
Scott Blake *(Owner)*

COPPER STATE BOLT & NUT CO. INC.
3602 N 35th Ave, Phoenix, AZ 85017
Tel.: (602) 455-9141
Web Site: http://www.csbn.com
Sales Range: $250-299.9 Million
Emp.: 250
Miscellaneous Fasteners
N.A.I.C.S.: 423710
Brian Cates *(CFO)*
Martin Calfee *(Chm)*
Robert M. Calfee III *(Pres)*

COPPER VALLEY ELECTRIC ASSOCIATION
Mile 187 Glenn Hwy, Glennallen, AK 99588-0045
Tel.: (907) 822-3211
Web Site: http://www.cvea.org
Year Founded: 1954
Sales Range: $10-24.9 Million
Emp.: 35
Nonprofit Electric Services Cooperative
N.A.I.C.S.: 221118
Travis Million *(COO)*
Jaime Matthews *(CFO)*
Sharon Crisp *(Dir-Comm)*
John Duhamel *(CEO)*
Dan Stowe *(Sec)*
Mary Odden *(VP)*
Will Stark *(Co-Treas)*
Lon Rake *(Pres)*
Brad Honerlaw *(Co-Treas)*

COPPER VALLEY TELE COOP INC.
329 Fairbanks Dr, Valdez, AK 99686

Tel.: (907) 835-2231
Web Site: http://www.cvinternet.net
Sales Range: $10-24.9 Million
Emp.: 40
Local Telephone Communications
N.A.I.C.S.: 517121
Pam Murphy *(CFO)*
Robin Chaffin *(Treas & Sec)*
Dave Dengel *(CEO & Gen Mgr)*
Chris Mishmash *(Mgr-Facilities-CVTC)*
Mitch Vieu *(Plant Mgr-CVTC)*

COPPER VALLEY TELEPHONE COOPERATIVE, INC.
329 Fairbanks Dr, Valdez, AK 99686
Tel.: (907) 835-2231   AK
Web Site: http://www.cvinternet.net
Year Founded: 1961
Sales Range: $10-24.9 Million
Emp.: 57
Communications Services Provider
N.A.I.C.S.: 517810
Mitch Vieu *(Sr Mgr-Telecom Ops)*
Joanne Winney *(Mgr-Mktg)*
Tabitha Gregory *(Chief Customer Rels Officer)*
Pam Murphy *(CFO)*
Michael Rego *(VP)*
Bill Bryson *(VP)*

COPPERMINE CAPITAL, LLC
30 Monument Sq Ste 220, Concord, MA 01742
Tel.: (781) 786-0500
Web Site:
https://www.copperminecapital.com
Year Founded: 2002
Emp.: 7
Privater Equity Firm
N.A.I.C.S.: 523999
Grant Gund *(Mng Partner)*
Zachary Gund *(Mng Partner)*
Ralph Vogel *(Mng Dir)*
David Jones *(Mng Dir)*
Catherine Bird *(CFO)*
G. Zachary Gund *(Founder & Mng Partner)*

Subsidiaries:

U.S. Underwater Services, LLC   (1)
123 Sentry Dr, Mansfield, TX 76063-3601
Tel.: (817) 447-7321
Web Site:
http://www.usunderwaterservices.com
Commercial Diving & Underwater Inspection Services
N.A.I.C.S.: 561990
Michael Hale *(CFO)*
Ashley Johnson *(Mgr-Admin & Fin)*

COPPERPOINT MUTUAL IN-SURANCE HOLDING COM-PANY
3030 N 3rd St, Phoenix, AZ 85012-3068
Tel.: (602) 631-2300   AZ
Web Site:
http://www.copperpoint.com
Year Founded: 2018
Holding Company; Property & Casualty Insurance Products & Services
N.A.I.C.S.: 551112
Dave Kuhn *(Reg Pres-PacificComp & Exec VP-Enterprise Distr)*
Marc E. Schmittlein *(Pres & CEO)*
Mark L. Joos *(CFO & Exec VP)*
Scott L. Shader *(COO & Exec VP)*
Sara Begley *(Chief Compliance Officer, Gen Counsel & Exec VP)*
Rachel Davis-Schultz *(Chief HR Officer & Sr VP)*
Ginny Arnett Caro *(Chief Claims Officer & Sr VP)*
Tom Collins *(Chief Underwriting Officer & Sr VP)*

Bob Roland *(Exec VP)*
Barb Fuchs *(Sr VP-Data Mgmt)*
Joe Fox *(VP-Pay as You Go)*

Subsidiaries:

CopperPoint Insurance Company   (1)
3030 N 3rd St, Phoenix, AZ 85012-3068
Tel.: (602) 631-2300
Web Site: http://www.copperpoint.com
Workers Compensation, Property & Casualty Insurance
N.A.I.C.S.: 524126
Marc E. Schmittlein *(Pres & CEO)*
Scott L. Shader *(COO & Exec VP)*
Bob Roland *(Chief Admin Officer & Exec VP)*
Mark L. Joos *(CFO & Exec VP)*
Sara Begley *(Chief Compliance Officer, Gen Counsel & Sr VP)*
Ginny Arnett Caro *(Sr VP-Claims Svcs)*
David Kuhn *(Exec VP-Enterprise Distr-CopperPoint Family of Insurance Cos.)*
Rachel Davis-Schultz *(Chief HR Officer & Sr VP)*
Ken Kirk *(Chm)*
Stephen Tully *(Vice Chm)*
Brad Lontz *(CIO & Sr VP)*
Michael Goldman *(Sr VP-Corp Dev)*
Barb Fuchs *(Sr VP-Data Mgmt)*
Tom Collins *(Chief Underwriting Officer & Sr VP)*
Jennifer Carrick *(Chief Risk Officer & Sr VP)*
Gina Norris *(Dir-Distr & Bus Dev)*

Pacific Compensation Insurance Company   (1)
1 Baxter Way Ste 170, Thousand Oaks, CA 91362
Tel.: (818) 575-8500
Web Site: http://www.pacificcomp.com
Workers Compensation Insurance Products & Services
N.A.I.C.S.: 524126
Dave Kuhn *(Reg Pres & Exec VP-Enterprise Distr)*
Marc E. Schmittlein *(Pres & CEO)*
Kris J. Mathis *(Sr VP-Claims)*
David Skaggs *(VP-Legal)*
Wayne Phillips *(VP-Fin & Controller)*
Ronnie O'Dell *(VP-Bus Dev & Distr-California)*
Mark Mooney *(VP & Head-Underwriting-California)*
Stephanie Flores *(Asst VP-Mktg & Go to Market Strategy)*
Wendy Lee *(Asst VP-Fin & Asst Controller)*

COPPERSMITH CORPORA-TION
3100 S 176th St Ste 120, Seatac, WA 98188
Tel.: (206) 242-6181
Web Site:
https://www.coppersmith.com
Rev.: $26,521,264
Emp.: 145
Customhouse Brokers
N.A.I.C.S.: 488510
Jeff M. Coppersmith *(Pres)*

COPPES-NAPANEE CO.
455 E Lincoln St, Nappanee, IN 46550-2121
Tel.: (574) 773-4141
Year Founded: 1876
Sales Range: $50-74.9 Million
Emp.: 20
Custom Built Kitchens & Furniture Mfr
N.A.I.C.S.: 337110
Paul Helord *(Owner)*

COPY SOLUTIONS, INC.
919 S Fremont Ave, Alhambra, CA 91803
Tel.: (323) 307-0900
Web Site:
https://www.copysolution.com
Year Founded: 1995
Sales Range: $10-24.9 Million
Emp.: 20

Copy Solutions, Inc.—(Continued)

Stationery & Office Supplies Merchant Whslr
N.A.I.C.S.: 424120
Roger Zhao (Owner & Pres)

COPYPRO INC.

3103 Landmark St, Greenville, NC 27834
Tel.: (252) 756-3175
Web Site: https://www.copypro.net
Year Founded: 1971
Sales Range: $10-24.9 Million
Emp.: 100
Computers, Peripherals & Software, Copier Machines, Fax Machines
N.A.I.C.S.: 423430
Lang Getsinger (COO)
Anita Sutton (Coord-Payroll & Benefits)
Brett Sweigart (Asst Mgr-Parts)
Donnie Skinner (Dir-After Market)
Glenda Whitehurst (Sec-Maintenance)

COPYTALK, LLC

500 Tellevast Rd Ste 102, Sarasota, FL 34243
Tel.: (941) 894-0007
Web Site: https://www.copytalk.com
Year Founded: 2001
Emp.: 375
Secure Transcription Services
N.A.I.C.S.: 513210
Maree Moscati (CEO)
Baird Juckett (VP-Tech)
Brian Johnson (Chief Technologist)
Deanna Faris (Mgr-Sls)
Michael Jacob (Mgr-Sls)

COQUILLE ECONOMIC DEVELOPMENT

3201 Tremont Ave, North Bend, OR 97459
Tel.: (541) 756-8800   OR
Web Site: http://www.cedco.net
Year Founded: 1995
Sales Range: $10-24.9 Million
Emp.: 395
Operates Casino Hotel
N.A.I.C.S.: 721120
Judy Metcalf (CEO)

COR BUSINESS DEVELOPMENT COMPANY LLC

233 Wilshire Blvd Ste 830, Santa Monica, CA 90401
Tel.: (310) 526-8400
Investment Services
N.A.I.C.S.: 523999
Steven A. Sugarman (CEO)

COR365 INFORMATION SOLUTIONS

3302 Old Lexington Rd, Winston Salem, NC 27107
Tel.: (336) 499-6020
Web Site: http://www.cor365.com
Data Storage & Protection Service
N.A.I.C.S.: 519290
Chris Kelley (CEO)
Andy Brown (Pres)

Subsidiaries:

SC Data, Inc.   (1)
2200 New Bern Ave, Raleigh, NC 27610
Tel.: (919) 231-8994
Web Site: http://www.scdatainc.com
Rev.: $2,700,000
Emp.: 60
All Other Support Services
N.A.I.C.S.: 561990
Nicole Sarrocco (VP)

CORA SERVICES, INC.

8540 Verree Rd, Philadelphia, PA 19111
Tel.: (215) 342-7660   PA
Web Site:
  https://www.coraservices.org
Year Founded: 1971
Sales Range: $10-24.9 Million
Emp.: 248
Child & Youth Care Services
N.A.I.C.S.: 624110
J. Michael Schell (VP-Fin & Ops)
Robert McElhenney (VP-HR)

CORA TEXAS MANUFACTURING CO., LLC

32505 Hwy 1, White Castle, LA 70788-3638
Tel.: (225) 545-3679   LA
Web Site: https://www.coratexas.com
Year Founded: 1927
Sales Range: $50-74.9 Million
Emp.: 130
Provider of Raw Sugar & Blackstrap Molasses
N.A.I.C.S.: 311314
Paul Buckley Kessler (CEO)
Charles Schudmak (COO)

CORACENT INC.

3837 Northdale Blvd Ste 294, Tampa, FL 33624
Tel.: (800) 385-1730
Web Site: http://www.coracent.com
Sales Range: $1-9.9 Million
Software Publisher
N.A.I.C.S.: 513210
Ron Rule (CEO)

CORAGGIO DESIGN, INC.

1750 132nd Ave NE, Bellevue, WA 98005
Tel.: (425) 462-0035
Web Site: https://www.coraggio.com
Rev.: $13,541,594
Emp.: 25
Broadwoven Fabrics
N.A.I.C.S.: 424310

CORAL CADILLAC

5101 N Federal Hwy, Pompano Beach, FL 33064
Tel.: (954) 426-1800
Web Site:
  http://www.coralcadillac.com
Sales Range: $10-24.9 Million
Emp.: 106
Used Car Whslr
N.A.I.C.S.: 441120
Tom Sheehan (Owner)

CORAL CHEMICAL COMPANY

1915 Industrial Ave, Zion, IL 60099
Tel.: (847) 246-6666   IL
Web Site: http://www.coral.com
Year Founded: 1953
Sales Range: $10-24.9 Million
Emp.: 30
Industrial Chemical Products Mfr
N.A.I.C.S.: 325612
Mike Stark (COO & CFO)
Peter Dority (VP-Sls & Mktg)

Subsidiaries:

Coral Seas - Consumer Products Division   (1)
2755 Miller Park N, Garland, TX 75042
Tel.: (972) 278-7753
Web Site: http://www.yellowout.com
Emp.: 10
Chemical Products Mfr
N.A.I.C.S.: 325199
Les Potter (Office Mgr)

Coral Technologies   (1)
135 LeBaron St, Waukegan, IL 60085
Tel.: (847) 246-6666
Emp.: 20
Facility Systems Mngmt

N.A.I.C.S.: 561790
Scott Taylor (Plant Mgr)

CORAL CONSTRUCTION COMPANY

10780 SW Clutter Rd, Sherwood, OR 97140
Tel.: (503) 682-2252   OR
Web Site:
  https://www.coralconstruction.com
Year Founded: 1979
Sales Range: $10-24.9 Million
Emp.: 50
Provider of Highway & Street Construction
N.A.I.C.S.: 237310
Marc Roberts (Mgr)
John Weisner (Pres)

CORAL GRAPHIC SERVICES, INC.

840 S Broadway, Hicksville, NY 11801-5017
Tel.: (516) 576-2100
Web Site:
  http://www.coralgraphics.com
Year Founded: 1981
Sales Range: $10-24.9 Million
Emp.: 248
Provider of Commercial Printing & Lithographic Services
N.A.I.C.S.: 323111
Dave Leiss (CEO)
Jared Verano (CFO & VP-Fin)
Jim Luginsland (Dir-Pre-Press)
Anthony Justice (Mgr-IT)

CORAL HOSPITALITY, LLC

9180 Galleria Ct Ste 600, Naples, FL 34109
Tel.: (239) 449-1800
Web Site:
  https://www.coralhospitality.com
Year Founded: 1998
Sales Range: $10-24.9 Million
Emp.: 30
Resort & Hotel Management
N.A.I.C.S.: 541611
Lee R. Weeks (CEO)
John E. Ayres (Founder & Partner)
Christopher Schaeffer (Pres)
Ralph Cioffi (Partner)
Michael D. Cloutier (VP-Food & Beverage-Resort Ops)
Bill Januska (VP-Engrg & Property Svcs)
James Mason (Dir-Golf & Club Ops)
Augustin Lucio (Dir-Agronomics)
Christina Jurek (Dir-HR & Trng)
Mark Osterhaus (Sr VP-Ops, Sls & Mktg)
Gary Hyre (VP)

Subsidiaries:

Riverwood Golf Club   (1)
4100 Riverwood Dr, Port Charlotte, FL 33953
Tel.: (941) 764-6661
Web Site: http://www.riverwoodgc.com
Sales Range: $1-9.9 Million
Golf Course & Country Club Operator
N.A.I.C.S.: 713910

The Angler's Boutique Resort   (1)
660 Washington Ave, Miami Beach, FL 33139
Tel.: (305) 534-9600
Web Site:
  http://www.anglershotelmiami.com
Emp.: 40
Hotel
N.A.I.C.S.: 721110
Jacqueline Ploettner (Gen Mgr)

The Perry South Beach Hotel   (1)
2341 Collins Ave, Miami Beach, FL 33139
Tel.: (305) 604-1000
Web Site: http://www.1hotels.com
Hotel

N.A.I.C.S.: 721110
Phil Dailey (Gen Mgr)

The Savoy Hotel   (1)
425 Ocean Dr, Miami Beach, FL 33139
Tel.: (305) 532-0200
Web Site: http://www.savoymiami.com
Hotel
N.A.I.C.S.: 721110
Jim Anderson (Gen Mgr)

CORAL INDUSTRIES, INC.

3010 Rice Mine Rd NE, Tuscaloosa, AL 35406-1506
Tel.: (205) 345-1013   AL
Web Site: https://www.coralind.com
Year Founded: 1982
Sales Range: $25-49.9 Million
Emp.: 245
Glass Products Mfr
N.A.I.C.S.: 327215
Eric Bilings (Controller)
Grant McAllister (CFO & Exec VP)
Peter Bittle (Mgr-IS Ops)
Tim McKinley (VP-Sls & Mktg)
Deven Segers (Mgr-Pur)

Subsidiaries:

Central Alabama Transport, Inc.   (1)
3010 Rice Mine Rd NE, Tuscaloosa, AL 35406-1506   (100%)
Tel.: (205) 345-1013
Web Site: http://www.coralind.com
Sales Range: $10-24.9 Million
Emp.: 30
Trucking Service
N.A.I.C.S.: 484121
Grant McAllister (CFO & Exec VP)
L. L. McAllister Jr. (CEO)

Coraglass, Inc.   (1)
3010 Rice Mine Rd NE, Tuscaloosa, AL 35406
Tel.: (205) 345-1013
Web Site: http://www.coraglass.com
Sales Range: $25-49.9 Million
Supplier of Flat Glass
N.A.I.C.S.: 327211

CORAL RIDGE MINISTRIES MEDIA INC.

5555 N Federal Hwy Ste 1, Fort Lauderdale, FL 33308
Tel.: (954) 772-0404
Web Site: http://www.tiam.org
Sales Range: $25-49.9 Million
Emp.: 130
Religious Television Broadcasting Stations
N.A.I.C.S.: 516120
Frank Wright (Gen Mgr)

CORAL SPRINGS AUTOMALL

9400 W Atlantic Blvd, Coral Springs, FL 33071
Tel.: (954) 755-7400
Web Site:
  http://www.coralspringsautomall.com
Year Founded: 1985
Automobiles, New & Used Vehicle Dealer
N.A.I.C.S.: 441110
Jack Jackintelle (COO)
Chris Hayek (Gen Sls Mgr)
Dan Praznik (Dir-Pre-Owned)
Philip Valles (Mgr-VIP)
Andres Llanos (Mgr-Fleet)
Chuck Trosch (Dir-Internet)
Steven Morales (Sls Mgr)
Steven Damon (Sls Mgr)
Lauren Prindle (Sls Mgr)

CORAZON CAPITAL V838 MONOCEROS CORP.

222 W Merchandise Mart Plaza Box Ste 2982, Chicago, IL 60654
Tel.: (872) 215-4602   Ky
Year Founded: 2021

CRZNU—(NASDAQ)
Rev.: $7,864,840
Assets: $207,688,104
Liabilities: $214,683,004
Net Worth: ($6,994,900)
Earnings: $9,708,074
Emp.: 3
Fiscal Year-end: 12/31/22
Investment Services
N.A.I.C.S.: 523999
Sam Yagan (Co-Founder & Mng Partner)
Steve Farsht (Co-Founder & Mng Partner)
Phil Schwarz (Partner)
Greg Johnston (VP)
Nina Essandoah (VP)
Tendai Brais (Chief Compliance Officer & Head-Fin)

CORBEL MANAGEMENT LLC
11777 San Vicente Blvd Ste 777, Los Angeles, CA 90049
Tel.: (310) 299-2490
Web Site: http://www.corbelcap.com
Investment Services
N.A.I.C.S.: 523999
Jeffrey Schwartz (Mng Partner)
Jeffrey Serota (Vice Chm & Cio)

CORBELIS MANAGEMENT, LLC
Riverside Ctr 275 Grove St Ste 3-103, Newton, MA 02466
Tel.: (617) 307-5850
Web Site: http://www.corbelis.com
Emp.: 2
Property Development
N.A.I.C.S.: 237210
Garrett Solomon (CEO)

Subsidiaries:

Corbelis Development SWFL, LLC   (1)
10600 Chevrolet Way Ste 102, Estero, FL 33928
Tel.: (239) 908-6400
Property Developer
N.A.I.C.S.: 237210
Anthony Solomon (Reg Pres)

CORBIN PACIFIC INCORPORATED
2360 Technology Pkwy, Hollister, CA 95023
Tel.: (831) 634-1100
Web Site: https://www.corbin.com
Year Founded: 1968
Rev.: $10,000,000
Emp.: 200
Mfr of Motorcycle & Bicycle Accessories
N.A.I.C.S.: 336991
Mike Corbin (Pres)

CORBIN-HILL, INC.
PO Box 28139, Santa Ana, CA 92799
Tel.: (714) 966-6695
Web Site:
    http://corbinhill.openfos.com
Sales Range: $10-24.9 Million
Emp.: 100
Bakery Products Mfr
N.A.I.C.S.: 311812
A. Moreno (Pres)
R. W. Carlyle (CFO & VP)
Jl Corbin (Chm & CEO)
Karen Kelley (Sec)
Chris Nelson (Mgr-Acctg)

CORBIN-HILLMAN COMMUNICATIONS
1776 Broadway Ste 1610, New York, NY 10019
Tel.: (212) 246-6515   NY
Web Site: http://www.corbinpr.com
Year Founded: 1978

Sales Range: $1-9.9 Million
Emp.: 12
Public Relations Services
N.A.I.C.S.: 541820
Michelle Corbin Hillman (CEO & Founder)

CORBY INDUSTRIES, INC.
812 N Gilmore St, Allentown, PA 18109
Tel.: (610) 433-1412   DE
Web Site: https://www.corby.com
Year Founded: 1972
Sales Range: $10-24.9 Million
Emp.: 30
Card & Digital Access Controls for Security Industry, Security Software Packages & Time & Attendance Software Turnkey Systems Mfr
N.A.I.C.S.: 335314
Kathleen S. Matz (CEO & VP-Fin)

CORCENTRIC, INC.
200 Lake Dr E Ste 200, Cherry Hill, NJ 08002
Tel.: (800) 608-0809   DE
Web Site: http://www.corcentric.com
Year Founded: 1996
Procurement & Finance Services
N.A.I.C.S.: 522320
Tom Spencer (Sr VP & Head-Acct Payable Solutions-Sls)
Douglas W. Clark (Founder, Chm & CEO)
Mark P. Joyce (CFO & Exec VP)
James Guice (Exec VP)
Kate Freer (Sr VP-Mktg)
Nancy D. Pearson (CMO)
Matt Clark (Pres & COO)
Daniel Andrew (Sr VP-Sls)
David Gevanthor (VP-Sls Ops)
Buffi Gibbons (VP-HR)
Kevin Harrison (VP-Ops)
Fredrick Smith (Chief Revenue Officer)
Sunil Padiyar (CTO)
Ed Benack (Chief Customer Officer)
Manish Jaiswal (Chief Product Officer)
Brent Kinman (Sr VP-Sls-North America)
Alex Green (Gen Counsel & Sr VP)
Stacy Bronstein (Dir-Comm)

Subsidiaries:

Corcentric, LLC   (1)
200 Lake Dr E Ste 200, Cherry Hill, NJ 08002
Tel.: (800) 608-0809
Web Site: http://www.corcentric.com
Computer Software
N.A.I.C.S.: 541519
Doug Clark (Founder, Pres & CEO)

Subsidiary (Domestic):

Determine, Inc.   (2)
200 Lake Dr E Ste 200, Cherry Hill, NJ 08002
Tel.: (800) 608-0809
Web Site: http://www.determine.com
Rev.: $28,119,000
Assets: $42,064,000
Liabilities: $37,124,000
Net Worth: $4,940,000
Earnings: ($9,948,000)
Emp.: 153
Fiscal Year-end: 03/31/2018
Software Publishing & Internet Related Services
N.A.I.C.S.: 513210
Alan Bradley Howe (Vice Chm)
Jeffrey H. Grosman (COO)
Eric Faulkner (CTO)
Rose Lee (Chief Customer Officer)
Patrick Stakenas (Pres & CEO)
John K. Nolan (CFO & Sec)
Julien Nadaud (Chief Product Officer)
Stephen Potts (Chief Revenue Officer)

Sean Regan (VP-Global Alliances)
Kevin Grande (Gen Counsel)
Gerard Dahan (CMO & Sr VP-EMEA)

Subsidiary (Non-US):

Determine SAS   (3)
33 Rue la Fayette, 75009, Paris, France
Tel.: (33) 183640310
Software Development Services
N.A.I.C.S.: 541511

Subsidiary (Domestic):

Vendorin, Inc.   (2)
120 Regency Pkwy Ste 115, Omaha, NE 68114
Tel.: (402) 206-2060
Web Site: http://www.vendorin.com
Information Technology Services
N.A.I.C.S.: 541511
Darren Blakely (Co-Founder & CEO)
John Petersson (Co-Founder & Pres)
Srinivas Gaddam (Co-Founder & CTO)
Renee Blanchard (VP-Product Mgmt)
Durea Falkner (VP-Enablement)
Robert Johnson (COO)

CORCORAN & JOHNSTON
21748 State Rd 54 Ste 102, Lutz, FL 33549
Tel.: (813) 527-0172
Web Site:
    http://www.corcoranfirm.com
Sales Range: $1-9.9 Million
Emp.: 6
Governmental Consulting Services
N.A.I.C.S.: 541618
Michael Corcoran (Partner)
Jessica Corcoran (Partner)

CORCORAN TRUCKING INC.
221 Lomond Ln, Billings, MT 59101-7350
Tel.: (406) 245-6065   MT
Web Site:
    https://www.corcorantrucking.com
Year Founded: 1971
Sales Range: $75-99.9 Million
Emp.: 100
Long Distance Refrigeration Trucking & Hauling Services
N.A.I.C.S.: 484121
John E. Corcoran (Pres)

CORD CAMERA CENTERS INC.
745 Harrison Dr, Columbus, OH 43204
Tel.: (614) 824-2673
Web Site:
    http://www.cordcamera.com
Sales Range: $10-24.9 Million
Emp.: 45
Cameras
N.A.I.C.S.: 449210
Howard Rosenzweig (Sr Mgr-Store)

CORD MEYER DEVELOPMENT LLC
111-15 Queens Blvd, Forest Hills, NY 11375
Tel.: (718) 268-2500
Web Site:
    https://www.cordmeyer.com
Sales Range: $10-24.9 Million
Emp.: 12
Commercial & Industrial Building Operation
N.A.I.C.S.: 531120
Anthony Colletti (COO)
Kevin Schmidt (VP-Fin)
Mary Hughes (VP)
Matthew Whalen (Pres & CEO)
Richard W. Meyer Jr. (Chm)

CORD MOVING & STORAGE CO.
4101 Rider Trl N, Earth City, MO 63045

Tel.: (314) 291-7440
Web Site:
    https://www.cordmoving.com
Rev.: $13,000,000
Emp.: 180
Furniture Moving & Storage, Local
N.A.I.C.S.: 484220
Martin Ryan (CEO)

CORDAROY'S ORIGINALS, INC.
3417 W University Ave, Gainesville, FL 32607
Tel.: (352) 332-1837
Web Site: https://www.cordaroys.com
Year Founded: 1998
Sales Range: $1-9.9 Million
Beanbag Furniture Mfr & Sales
N.A.I.C.S.: 337121
Byron Young (Founder)

CORDERO & DAVENPORT ADVERTISING
800 W Ivy St Ste B, San Diego, CA 92101
Tel.: (619) 233-3830
Web Site:
    http://www.corderoanddavenport.com
Year Founded: 1991
Brand Development & Integration, Outdoor, Print, Radio, T.V.
N.A.I.C.S.: 541810
J.C. Cordero (Principal & Dir-Client Svcs)
Kevin Davenport (Principal & Dir-Creative)
Patti Mentch (Dir-Mktg)
Jeanne Abueg (Dir-Art)
Delores Chavez (Acct Mgr)
Christine Zykwa (Acct Coord)

CORDEV INC.
146 Hillwood Ave Ste 146B, Falls Church, VA 22046
Tel.: (703) 237-2802
Web Site: https://www.cordev.net
Sales Range: $10-24.9 Million
Emp.: 130
Telephone Communication, Except Radio
N.A.I.C.S.: 541618
Pham Chopra (CEO)
Glenda Brenner (Controller)
John Ressa (Pres & COO)

CORDILLERA CORPORATION
7800 E Dorado Pl Ste 250, Greenwood Village, CO 80111-2306
Tel.: (303) 779-8811   UT
Year Founded: 1971
Sales Range: $25-49.9 Million
Emp.: 150
Investment Holding Company
N.A.I.C.S.: 551112
Joseph E. Maskalenko (Gen Mgr)
Bart Bundage (Exec VP)

Subsidiaries:

jetCenters, Inc.   (1)
7800 E Dorado Pl Ste 250, Greenwood Village, CO 80111
Tel.: (303) 779-8811
Web Site: http://www.jetcenters.com
Sales Range: $25-49.9 Million
Emp.: 40
Holding Company; Airport & Flying Field Support Services
N.A.I.C.S.: 551112

Subsidiary (Domestic):

Colorado jetCenter, Inc.   (2)
1575 Aviation Way, Colorado Springs, CO 80916-2709
Tel.: (719) 591-2288
Sales Range: $25-49.9 Million
Emp.: 25
Airport & Flying Field Services
N.A.I.C.S.: 488119

Cordillera Corporation—(Continued)

Aaron Wood *(Gen Mgr)*
Ian Erickson *(Mgr-Line)*

Denver jetCenter, Inc. (2)
7625 S Peoria St, Englewood, CO 80112-4171
Tel.: (303) 790-4321
Web Site: http://www.jetcenter.com
Sales Range: $25-49.9 Million
Provider of Jet Fuel
N.A.I.C.S.: 488119
Chuck Halderman *(Pres)*
Amber Channel *(Office Mgr)*

CORDOVA CONCRETE INC.
4622 Clarke Rd, Memphis, TN 38141
Tel.: (901) 369-9909
Sales Range: $10-24.9 Million
Emp.: 90
Ready Mixed Concrete
N.A.I.C.S.: 327320
Ricky Brown *(Pres)*
Jay McAlpin *(Dir-Environmental & Safety)*

CORE ASSURANCE PARTNERS, INC.
300 32nd St Ste 400, Virginia Beach, VA 23451
Tel.: (757) 965-8900
Web Site:
http://www.coreassurance.com
Year Founded: 2017
Real Estate, Construction & Maritime Industry Insurance Services
N.A.I.C.S.: 524298
Zachary F Brandau *(Exec VP)*
Sheri Bond *(Exec Admin Asst)*
Roxanne Sayre *(Controller)*
Cornel Pendergrass *(VP-Sr Client Exec)*

CORE CAPITAL PARTNERS
1717 K St Ste 920, Washington, DC 20006
Tel.: (202) 589-0090 DE
Web Site: http://www.core-capital.com
Year Founded: 1999
Sales Range: $350-399.9 Million
Privater Equity Firm
N.A.I.C.S.: 523999
Mark Levine *(Mng Dir)*
Will Dunbar *(Co-Founder & Mng Dir)*
Pascal Luck *(Mng Dir)*
Randy Klueger *(CFO)*
James Keeratisakdawong *(VP)*

CORE CONSTRUCTION
3036 E Greenway Rd, Phoenix, AZ 85032-4414
Tel.: (602) 494-0800
Web Site:
https://www.coreconstruction.com
Year Founded: 1937
Sales Range: $125-149.9 Million
Commercial Building Services
N.A.I.C.S.: 236220

Subsidiaries:

CORE Construction Indiana, LLC (1)
833 Lincoln Hwy Ste 120 W, Schererville, IN 46375
Tel.: (219) 961-4325
Web Site: http://www.coreconstruction.com
Emp.: 50
Construction Engineering Services
N.A.I.C.S.: 541330
Joe Mancusi *(Project Mgr)*

CORE Construction Services of Nevada, Inc. (1)
7150 Cascade Valley Ct, Las Vegas, NV 89128
Tel.: (702) 794-0550
Construction Engineering Services
N.A.I.C.S.: 541330
Jim Miller *(Dir-Ops)*

CORE Construction Services of Texas, Inc. (1)
10625 N County Rd, Frisco, TX 75034-3831
Tel.: (972) 668-9340
Web Site: http://www.coreconstruction.com
Construction Engineering Services
N.A.I.C.S.: 541330
Gary Frazier *(Pres)*

CORE Construction Services, LLC (1)
3131 N I-10 Service Rd East Ste 401, Metairie, LA 70002
Tel.: (504) 733-2212
Construction Engineering Services
N.A.I.C.S.: 541330
Kyle Culverhouse *(VP & Dir-Preconstruction)*

Core Construction Services of Florida, LLC (1)
8027 Cooper Creek Blvd, University Park, FL 34201
Tel.: (941) 552-0240
Web Site: http://www.coreconstruct.com
Sales Range: $50-74.9 Million
Emp.: 45
Commercial, Residential & Industrial New Construction
N.A.I.C.S.: 236115
John P. Wiseman *(Pres)*
Matt Wiseman *(Dir-Comm)*
Brent Elliott *(Dir-Ops)*
Brian Jones *(Dir-Dev)*

CORE CONSULTING LLC
107 Bunt Ave, Thiensville, WI 53092
Tel.: (262) 242-2673
Web Site: https://www.core-usa.com
Year Founded: 2007
Sales Range: $1-9.9 Million
Emp.: 65
Engineering & Technical Staffing
N.A.I.C.S.: 541690
Matthew Buerosse *(Partner)*
Jesse Daily *(Mng Partner)*
Andy Langlois *(Mgr-Client Svcs)*

CORE HEALTH & FITNESS LLC
4400 NE 77th Ave Ste 300, Vancouver, WA 98662
Tel.: (360) 326-4090
Web Site: http://www.corehandf.com
Fitness Equipment Mfr
N.A.I.C.S.: 339920
Erin O'Brien *(Dir-Marketing)*

Subsidiaries:

Nautilus Commercial Fitness (1)
709 Powerhouse Rd, Independence, VA 24348-3782 (100%)
Tel.: (276) 773-2881
Web Site: http://www.nautilusstrength.com
Sales Range: $10-24.9 Million
Emp.: 185
Conditioning & Rehabilitation Equipment, Fitness Systems Mfr
N.A.I.C.S.: 339920
Greg Webb *(VP-Mfg & Engrg)*

Star Trac - Irvine (1)
14410 Myford Rd, Irvine, CA 92606
Tel.: (714) 669-1660
Web Site: http://www.startrac.com
Emp.: 71
Sporting & Athletic Goods Mfr
N.A.I.C.S.: 339920
Michael Carranza *(Mgr-Mktg)*
Renald Cox *(Mgr-Bus Dev)*
Mark Shade *(Mgr-Sls-Export)*

CORE INDUSTRIAL PARTNERS, LLC
150 N Riverside Plz Ste 2050, Chicago, IL 60606
Tel.: (312) 566-4880 DE
Web Site: http://www.coreipfund.com
Year Founded: 2016
Privater Equity Firm
N.A.I.C.S.: 523999
Tzan-Jin Chung *(Co-Founding Partner & Sr Partner)*

Roch B. Lambert *(Operating Partner)*
John May *(Founder & Mng Partner)*
Frank Papa *(Sr Partner)*
T. J. Chung *(Sr Partner)*
Stephen Lee *(Co-Founding Partner & Chief Talent, Strategy & Technology Officer)*
Adam Miller *(VP-Bus Dev)*
Matthew Puglisi *(Partner)*
Carissa DeJacimo Walker *(Principal-Bus Dev)*

Subsidiaries:

Cadrex Manufacturing Solutions
275 Innovation Dr, Romeoville, IL 60446
Tel.: (815) 221-5307
Web Site: https://cadrex.com
Complex Sheet Metal & Machined Production Parts Mfr
N.A.I.C.S.: 333248
Tom McNulty *(CFO)*
Brian Steel *(CEO)*

Subsidiary (Domestic):

CGI Automated Manufacturing, Inc. (2)
275 Innovation Dr, Romeoville, IL 60446
Tel.: (815) 221-5307
Web Site: http://www.cgiautomatedmanufacturing.com
All Other Miscellaneous Fabricated Metal Product Mfr
N.A.I.C.S.: 332999
Carey Chen *(CEO)*
Janice Nieman *(Pres)*
TJ Chung *(Chm)*

Subsidiary (Domestic):

DFF Corp. (3)
79 Abrams Dr, Agawam, MA 01001-2956
Tel.: (413) 786-8880
Web Site: http://www.dffcorp.com
Motor Vehicle Parts Mfr
N.A.I.C.S.: 336390
Ernest Denby *(CEO)*
William Marganti *(Pres)*

Elite Manufacturing Technologies, Inc. (3)
333 Munroe Dr, Bloomingdale, IL 60108
Tel.: (630) 351-5757
Web Site: http://www.emt333.com
Sheet Metal Work Mfg
N.A.I.C.S.: 332322
Craig Kral *(Mgr-Estimating)*
Tom Swier *(Acct Mgr)*
Jim Conlon *(Pres)*

Richlind Metal Fabricators, Inc. (3)
4155 Peavey Rd, Chaska, MN 55318
Tel.: (952) 448-4862
Web Site: http://www.richlindmetals.com
Machine Retailer
N.A.I.C.S.: 332710
Mike Lind *(Pres)*

Tenere Inc. (3)
700 Kelly Ave, Dresser, WI 54009
Tel.: (715) 247-4242
Web Site: http://www.tenere.com
Sheet Metal Work Mfg
N.A.I.C.S.: 332322
Brian Steel *(CEO)*

Subsidiary (Domestic):

Protogenic, Inc. (4)
7401 W Church Ranch Blvd Ste 206, Westminster, CO 80021
Tel.: (303) 252-0212
Web Site: http://www.protogenic.com
Sales Range: $10-24.9 Million
Custom Casting & Prototyping Services
N.A.I.C.S.: 326199
Bob Olsen *(Mgr-Sls)*
Jason Boh *(Dir-Ops)*

Subsidiary (Domestic):

D&R Machine Company, Inc. (2)
1330 Industrial Hwy, Southampton, PA 18966-4013
Tel.: (215) 526-2080
Web Site: http://www.drmachine.com
Sales Range: $1-9.9 Million
Emp.: 35

Commercial & Service Industry Machinery Mfr
N.A.I.C.S.: 333310
Nelson Redante *(Mgr-Bus Dev)*
Paul Redante *(Pres)*

IDL Precision Machining, Inc. (2)
11600 49th Pl W Ste B, Mukilteo, WA 98275
Tel.: (425) 315-8080
Web Site: http://www.idlprecision.com
Sales Range: $1-9.9 Million
Emp.: 15
Machine Shops
N.A.I.C.S.: 332710
Ira Kaplan *(Pres)*

Fathom Digital Manufacturing Corporation (1)
1050 Walnut Ridge Dr, Hartland, WI 53029 (100%)
Tel.: (262) 367-8254
Web Site: https://www.fathommfg.com
Rev.: $161,141,000
Assets: $370,515,000
Liabilities: $318,751,000
Net Worth: $51,764,000
Earnings: ($1,110,488,000)
Emp.: 708
Fiscal Year-end: 12/31/2022
Software Development Services
N.A.I.C.S.: 541511
Carey Chen *(CEO)*
Caprice Perez *(Chief HR Officer)*
Mark Frost *(CFO)*

Fleco Industries, LLC (1)
2055 Luna Rd Ste 142, Carrollton, TX 75006
Tel.: (972) 247-3171
Web Site: https://www.saylite.com
Electrical Apparatus & Equipment, Wiring Supplies & Related Equipment Merchant Whslr
N.A.I.C.S.: 423610
Shannon Kelley *(VP)*
Jon Sayah *(CEO)*

General Converting, Inc. (1)
250 W Crossroads Pkwy, Bolingbrook, IL 60440-3546
Tel.: (630) 378-9800
Web Site: http://www.generalconverting.com
Rev.: $4,400,000
Emp.: 60
Folding Paperboard Box Mfr
N.A.I.C.S.: 322212
Robert F. Ruebenson *(CEO)*

GoProto, Inc. (1)
3940 Ruffin Rd Ste A, San Diego, CA 92123
Web Site: http://www.goproto.com
Sales Range: $1-9.9 Million
Emp.: 200
Additive Mfr
N.A.I.C.S.: 339999
Jesse Lea *(Pres & CEO)*
Mark Baysinger *(Dir-Western Sls)*
Jonathan Wilke *(Dir-Western Sls)*
Matt Lucas *(VP-Mfg)*
Miguel Diaz *(VP-Additive Ops)*

Incodema Holdings LLC (1)
407 Cliff St, Ithaca, NY 14850
Tel.: (607) 277-7070
Web Site: http://www.incodema.com
Sales Range: $1-9.9 Million
Emp.: 40
Sheet Metal Work Mfg
N.A.I.C.S.: 332322
Sean E. Whittaker *(Pres)*
Illa Burbank *(Controller)*
Jeremy Woodman *(Mgr-Quality)*
Carey Chen *(CEO)*

Subsidiary (Domestic):

Majestic Metals, Inc. (2)
7770 Washington St, Denver, CO 80229
Tel.: (303) 288-6855
Web Site: http://www.majesticmetals.com
Sales Range: $1-9.9 Million
Emp.: 120
Sheet Metal Work Mfg
N.A.I.C.S.: 332322
Charlie Ellsworth *(Controller)*
David Roberts *(Owner & Partner)*
Chip Roberts *(Pres)*

Mark Two Engineering, Inc. (2)

14000 NW 58th Ct, Hialeah, FL 33014
Tel.: (305) 889-3280
Web Site: http://www.marktwo.com
Sales Range: $10-24.9 Million
Emp.: 100
Medical Device Mfr
N.A.I.C.S.: 339112
Engracia Gonzalez (VP-Quality Assurance)

Midwest Composite Technologies,
LLC   (1)
1050 Walnut Ridge Dr, Hartland, WI 53029
Tel.: (262) 367-8254
Web Site: https://www.fathommfg.com
Prototype Mfr
N.A.I.C.S.: 339999

Subsidiary (Domestic):

Kemeera Inc.   (2)
620 3rd St, Oakland, CA 94607
Tel.: (510) 281-9000
Web Site: https://www.fathommfg.com
Printing Material Mfr
N.A.I.C.S.: 339999

Subsidiary (Domestic):

Summit Tooling Inc.   (3)
1207 Adams Dr, McHenry, IL 60051
Tel.: (815) 385-7500
Web Site: http://www.summittooling.com
Rev.: $1,400,000
Emp.: 19
Machine Tool, Metal Forming Types, Mfr
N.A.I.C.S.: 333517
Dan Martin (Pres)

Prototek Sheetmetal Fabrication,
LLC   (1)
244 Burnham Intervale Rd, Contoocook, NH
03229
Tel.: (603) 746-2001
Web Site: http://www.prototek.com
Sheet Metal Fabrication Services
N.A.I.C.S.: 332322
Joshua Isabelle (VP)

Subsidiary (Domestic):

Cal-X Incorporated   (2)
900 Cheyenne Ave, Grafton, WI 53024
Tel.: (805) 987-1640
Metal Fabrication & Precision Machining
Services
N.A.I.C.S.: 332322

CORE MEDICAL GROUP
3000 Goffs Falls Rd, Manchester, NH
03103
Web Site:
   http://www.coremedicalgroup.com
Year Founded: 1989
Sales Range: $10-24.9 Million
Emp.: 39
Healthcare Staffing Services
N.A.I.C.S.: 561311
Sue Gentile (Dir-Intl Recruitment)
Aram Hampoian (VP-Healthcare
Travel Svcs)
Greg Henrichon (VP-Permanent
Placement & IT Svcs)
Monique Ricker (VP)
Patrick Shea (Dir-Physician Staffing
Svcs)
Susan Dezurick (Mgr)
Karen Nicolls (Mgr)
Martin Paeplow (Mgr-Recruiting-
Permanent Nursing Div)
Daniel Ryan (Mgr-Sls Dev & Mktg)
Danille Malayandy (Mgr-Sls-
Permanent Nursing Div)
Joshua Bourdon (Mgr-Travel Allied
Div)
Vincent Batza (Mgr-Travel Nurse Div)
Jo Newell (VP-Fin)
Armand L. Circharo Jr. (Pres & CEO)

CORE PIPE INC.
170 Tubeway Dr, Carol Stream, IL
60188
Tel.: (630) 690-7000
Web Site: https://www.corepipe.com
Sales Range: $10-24.9 Million

Emp.: 150
Mfr of Flange, Valve & Pipe Fitting
Forgings
N.A.I.C.S.: 332111
Bill Burn (CFO)
Joseph P. Romanelli Sr. (Chm &
CEO)

CORE PRODUCTS INTERNA-
TIONAL, INC.
808 Prospect Ave, Osceola, WI
54020
Tel.: (715) 294-2050
Web Site:
   https://www.coreproducts.com
Surgical Appliance & Supplies Mfr
N.A.I.C.S.: 339113
Philip Mattison (Pres)

CORE SECURITY SDI CORPO-
RATION
1000 Holcomb Woods Pkwy Ste 401,
Roswell, GA 30076
Tel.: (678) 304-4500
Web Site:
   http://www.coresecurity.com
Year Founded: 1996
Software Publisher
N.A.I.C.S.: 513210
Venkat Rajaji (Sr VP-Mktg)
Chris Sullivan (CTO & Chief Informa-
tion Security Officer)
Curtis Cain (CFO)
Ron Wilson (Sr VP-Global Sls & Cus-
tomer Svc)
Stephen Newman (VP-Product Mgmt)
Edgardo Artusi (Sr VP-Engrg)

CORE SPECIALTY INSUR-
ANCE HOLDINGS, INC.
201 E 5th St Ste 1200, Cincinnati,
OH 45202
Tel.: (281) 538-4844
Web Site: https://corespecialty.com
Property & Casualty Insurance Ser-
vices
N.A.I.C.S.: 524126
Joseph E. Consolino (Founder, Pres
& CEO)

Subsidiaries:

Standard Life & Accident Insurance
Company   (1)
1 Moody Plz, Galveston, TX 77573
Tel.: (281) 538-4844
Web Site: http://slaico.americannational.com
Sales Range: $25-49.9 Million
Emp.: 40
Life, Accident & Health Insurance
N.A.I.C.S.: 524114

CORE STRATEGY GROUP
3000 Old Alabama Rd Ste 119-332,
Alpharetta, GA 30022
Tel.: (404) 381-8565
Web Site:
   http://www.corestrategygroup.com
Year Founded: 1999
Sales Range: $10-24.9 Million
Emp.: 90
Brand Marketing, Communications,
Research & Strategy Consulting Ser-
vices
N.A.I.C.S.: 541613
Craig Binkley (Chief Consulting Offi-
cer)
Scott Miller (CEO)
David Morey (Vice Chm)
Michael Harbert (Mng Dir-CSG-West)

CORE SYSTEMS LLC
787 Renaissance Pkwy, Painesville,
OH 44077
Tel.: (440) 357-8000
Rev.: $34,000,000
Emp.: 260
Injection Molding Of Plastics

N.A.I.C.S.: 326199
Eric Sholtz (CFO)
Chris Day (Pres)
David Zundel (Mgr-Matls)
Gil Burchett (Engr-Process Automa-
tion)
Keith Wittler (Mgr-Tech)

CORE-CREATE INC.
100 Franklin Sq Dr Ste 201, Somer-
set, NJ 08873-1128
Tel.: (732) 748-0433   NJ
Web Site: http://www.core-
create.com
Year Founded: 1991
Rev.: $60,000,000
Emp.: 30
Advetising Agency
N.A.I.C.S.: 541810
Ken Ribotsky (Owner)
Dorene Weisenstein (Chief Creative
Officer & Exec VP)
Jennifer Philburn (Mgr-Editorial)
Paul Moorcroft (Grp Fin Controller)
Donna Diefenbach (Dir-Traffic)

Subsidiaries:

Core-Create Ltd.   (1)
20-22 Stukeley St, London, WC2B 5LR,
United Kingdom
Tel.: (44) 20 7400 6700
Web Site: http://www.core-create.com
Advetising Agency
N.A.I.C.S.: 541810

COREBRAND, LLC
122 W 27th St 9th Fl, New York, NY
10001
Tel.: (212) 329-3030
Web Site:
   http://www.tenetpartners.com
Year Founded: 1980
Sales Range: $10-24.9 Million
Emp.: 43
Advertising Agencies
N.A.I.C.S.: 541810
Andrew Bogucki (Exec Dir-Creative)
Larry Oakner (Mng Dir-Strategy)
Renee Malfi (Brand Dir)
Brad Puckey (Dir-Intelligence)
Matthew Eaton (Brand Dir)
Hampton Bridwell (CEO)

COREFIRST BANK & TRUST
3035 SW Topeka Blvd, Topeka, KS
66611
Tel.: (785) 267-8900   KS
Web Site: https://www.cbtks.com
Year Founded: 1977
Sales Range: $100-124.9 Million
Emp.: 370
Banking Services
N.A.I.C.S.: 522110
Kirk L. Johnson (Sr VP & Dir-Trust &
Investment Svcs)
Joseph Valenciano (Sr VP)
Nancy Goodall (Officer-Trust & Sr
VP)
Aaron Anderson (Officer-Trust & Sr
VP)
Bill Kanaga (Officer-Trust & Invest-
ment)
Ryan Hellmer (Officer-Trust & Invest-
ment)

CORENET GLOBAL, INC.
133 Peachtree St NE Ste 3000, At-
lanta, GA 30303
Tel.: (404) 589-3200
Web Site:
   https://www.corenetglobal.org
Year Founded: 2002
Sales Range: $10-24.9 Million
Emp.: 40
Professional Organizations
N.A.I.C.S.: 813920

Jim Scannell (Sr VP-Admin Svcs)
Angela Cain (CEO)
Larry Bazrod (COO)
Tim Venable (Sr VP)
Matt Dirks (VP-Global Corp Rels)
Steven Quick (Exec VP)
Erica Chapman (VP-Real Estate &
Facilities)
Fred Hernandez (Dir-Client Rels)
Janet Carter (Dir-Mktg)
John Davis (Controller)
John Gilleard (Dir-Learning-Asia Pa-
cific & EMEA)
Kathy Godwin (Dir-Member Svcs-
Global)
Sonali Tare (Dir-Res)

COREPHARMA, LLC
215 Wood Ave, Middlesex, NJ 08846
Tel.: (732) 893-5942   NJ
Web Site:
   http://www.corepharma.com
Solid Dose Generic Pharmaceuticals
N.A.I.C.S.: 325412
Vithalbhai D. Dhaduk (Chm & Pres)
Arpit Patel (CEO)
Payal Dhaduk (CFO)
Srinivasulu Ale (Dir-Quality & Analyti-
cal R&D)
Rajendra Nagamalla (Dir-Product Dev
& Tech Svcs)
Chintan Joshi (Dir-Ops)
Bhavesh Patel (Dir-Facilities & Engrg)

CORESCO, INC.
1407 Airport Rd, Monroe, NC 28110
Tel.: (704) 296-5600   NC
Web Site: http://www.coresco.com
Year Founded: 1979
Rev.: $15,500,000
Emp.: 30
N.A.I.C.S.: 541810
Jeanne E. Corwin (CEO)
Tom Corwin (CEO)
JoAnn Webb (VP-Fin)
Donna Martin (VP-Ops)
William Webb (Mgr-Office)
Donna Whitley (Acct Servicing Rep)
Dennise Nicholson (Mgr-Customer
Svc)
Alan Seidman (Mgr-Mktg & Sls)

CORESTATES CAPITAL ADVI-
SORS, LLC
1010 Stony Hill Rd Ste 315, Yardley,
PA 19067
Tel.: (267) 759-5000
Web Site: http://www.corestates.us
Privater Equity Firm
N.A.I.C.S.: 523999
William T. Spiropoulos (Pres & CEO)
Kenneth C. Coniglio (Sr VP)
Michael D. Carlucci (First VP & Port-
folio Mgr)
William Bromley (First VP & Head-
Alternative Investments)
Lucy A. Steitz (VP)

Subsidiaries:

Sundial Beach and Golf Resort   (1)
1451 Middle Gulf Dr, Sanibel, FL 33957
Tel.: (239) 472-4151
Web Site: http://www.sundialresort.com
Sales Range: $1-9.9 Million
Emp.: 80
Resort & Golf Course
N.A.I.C.S.: 721110

CORESTATES, INC.
4191 Pleasant Hill Rd NW, Duluth,
GA 30096
Tel.: (770) 242-9550
Web Site: http://www.core-eng.com
Year Founded: 1999
Sales Range: $10-24.9 Million
Emp.: 113

CoreStates, Inc.—(Continued)

Land Development,Civil Engineering Services & Commercial Building Design
N.A.I.C.S.: 541330
Andy Shaw (Principal & Dir-Fuel Designs)
Glenn M. Phillips (COO & VP)
John M. Scheffey (Founder, Pres & CEO)
Linda S. Allen (Principal & Dir-Fin & Admin)
Dick Cote (Principal & Dir-Construction Svcs)
Steffen Ricken (Mng Dir & Head-Global Capital Raising)

CORESYS CONSULTING
2121 Eisenhower Ave Ste 403, Alexandria, VA 22314
Tel.: (703) 831-4140
Web Site:
    http://www.coresysconsulting.com
Year Founded: 1998
Sales Range: $1-9.9 Million
Emp.: 50
Design, Development, Test, Implementation & Enhancement of Information Technology Systems
N.A.I.C.S.: 541715
Brian Cordle (Pres & CEO)

CORETEK SERVICES
38505 Country Club Dr Ste 210, Farmington Hills, MI 48331
Tel.: (248) 684-9400
Web Site:
    http://www.coretekservices.com
Year Founded: 2005
Sales Range: $10-24.9 Million
Emp.: 85
It Consulting
N.A.I.C.S.: 541690
Ron Lisch (CEO)
Bill Deighton (COO)

COREY BROTHERS INC.
1410 Lewis St, Charleston, WV 25301
Tel.: (304) 344-3602
Rev.: $10,800,000
Emp.: 55
Fresh,Fruit & Vegetable Merchant Whslr
N.A.I.C.S.: 424480
Robert Corey (VP)
Brenda Hand (Asst Mgr-Sls)

COREY DELTA INC.
PO Box 5547, Concord, CA 94524
Tel.: (707) 747-7500   CA
Web Site: http://www.coreydelta.com
Year Founded: 1974
Sales Range: $10-24.9 Million
Emp.: 260
Plumbing, Heating & Air-Conditioning
N.A.I.C.S.: 238220
Jim Holz (Pres)

COREY NURSERY CO. INC.
1650 Monte Vista Ave, Claremont, CA 91711
Tel.: (909) 621-6886
Sales Range: $10-24.9 Million
Emp.: 70
Nursery Stock Mfr
N.A.I.C.S.: 424930
Gene Corey (Owner)
Sandy Frick (VP-Sls & Mktg)

COREY OIL LTD
W 314 W 7807 Kilddouin Rd, North Lake, WI 53064
Tel.: (262) 966-0868
Web Site: http://www.coreyoil.com
Sales Range: $10-24.9 Million

Emp.: 20
Distributing Gasoline
N.A.I.C.S.: 493110
Valerie Schweitzer (Pres)
E. J. Schweitzer (VP)

CORFACTS, INC.
2323 Hway 9 N, Howell, NJ 07731
Tel.: (732) 780-1188   NJ
Year Founded: 1989
Sales Range: $1-9.9 Million
Emp.: 300
Telemarketing Bureaus
N.A.I.C.S.: 561422
Ariel Freud (Pres & CEO)

CORINTH COCA-COLA BOT-TLING WORKS, INC.
601 Washington St, Corinth, MS 38834
Tel.: (662) 287-1433   MS
Web Site:
    https://www.corinthcoke.com
Sales Range: $25-49.9 Million
Emp.: 300
Soft Drink Bottling Services
N.A.I.C.S.: 312111
Kenneth W. Williams Sr. (Pres)

CORINTHIAN CAPITAL GROUP, LLC
601 Lexington Ave 59th Fl, New York, NY 10022
Tel.: (212) 920-2300
Web Site:
    http://www.corinthiancap.com
Year Founded: 2005
Sales Range: $1-9.9 Million
Emp.: 20
Privater Equity Firm
N.A.I.C.S.: 523999
Peter Van Raalte (Founder, Pres & CEO)
Adam Fitzner (Principal)
Tony Pucillo (Sr Mng Dir, Chief Admin Officer & Operating Partner)
Gerson R. Guzman (Mng Dir & Chief Compliance Officer)
Jason B. Ghoshhajra (Principal)

CORINTHIAN MEDIA, INC.
500 8th Ave 5th Fl, New York, NY 10018
Tel.: (212) 279-5700   DE
Web Site:
    https://www.mediabuying.com
Year Founded: 1974
Sales Range: $300-349.9 Million
Emp.: 55
Media Buying Services
N.A.I.C.S.: 541830
Larry Miller (Owner & Pres)
Tina Snitzer (Exec VP-Buying)
Ellen Carry (Exec VP-Acct Svcs)
Larry Schneiderman (Exec VP-Direct Response)
Bob Klein (Exec VP-New Bus & Trade)
Mary Cannon (Sr VP-Buying)
Ann Mazzini (Sr VP-Acct Svcs)

CORIX BIOSCIENCE, INC.
16772 W Bell Rd Ste 110-471, Surprise, AZ 85374
Tel.: (623) 551-5808   MD
Year Founded: 2007
Sales Range: $1-9.9 Million
Real Estate Investment & Management Services
N.A.I.C.S.: 531190
Michael Lee Ogburn (CEO)

CORK DISTRIBUTORS, LLC
950 Pilot Road e, Las Vegas, NV 89119
Tel.: (702) 485-3894

Web Site: https://www.cork-distributors.com
Emp.: 100
Wine & Spirits Distr
N.A.I.C.S.: 424820
Richard Cox (Founder & CEO)

Subsidiaries:
Encore Beverage, LLC   (1)
8550 W 4th St Ste 400, Reno, NV 89523-8993
Tel.: (775) 747-1759
Web Site: http://www.encorebeverage.com
Grocery & Related Products Merchant Whslr
N.A.I.C.S.: 424490

CORKEN STEEL PRODUCTS COMPANY
7920 Kentucky Dr, Florence, KY 41042
Tel.: (859) 291-4664
Web Site:
    https://www.corkensteel.com
Rev.: $30,000,000
Emp.: 55
Furnaces, Warm Air
N.A.I.C.S.: 423730
Andrea Schmidt (Office Mgr-Fab Shop)
Andy Bucher (Mgr-Sls)
Jason Schmidt (Mgr-Fabrication)
Jay Kaiser (Dir-Sls & Mktg)
Randy Martina (Branch Mgr)

CORKY'S BAR-B-Q
5255 Poplar Ave, Memphis, TN 38119
Tel.: (901) 685-9344
Web Site: http://www.corkysbbq.com
Year Founded: 1984
Sales Range: $50-74.9 Million
Emp.: 120
Barbeque Cuisine Restaurants & Mail Order Gift Packages
N.A.I.C.S.: 722511
Barry Pelts (Co-Owner & Pres)

CORLAND, CO.
327 Isis Ave, Inglewood, CA 90301-2007
Tel.: (310) 670-3720
Web Site: https://www.corland.com
Year Founded: 1954
Sales Range: $10-24.9 Million
Emp.: 25
Fastener Distr
N.A.I.C.S.: 423860
Brian Hopkins (Owner)

CORLE BUILDING SYSTEMS
114 Rosemont Ln, Imler, PA 16655
Tel.: (814) 276-9611
Web Site: http://www.corle.com
Year Founded: 1972
Sales Range: $10-24.9 Million
Emp.: 100
Prefabricated Metal Building & Component Mfr
N.A.I.C.S.: 332311
John Corle (Pres)

CORLEY MANUFACTURING CO.
2900 Crescent Cir, Chattanooga, TN 37407
Tel.: (423) 698-0284   TN
Web Site: https://www.corleymfg.com
Year Founded: 1905
Sales Range: $50-74.9 Million
Emp.: 15
Saw Mill Machinery & Related Supplies
N.A.I.C.S.: 333243
A. J. Corley (Pres)
Wayne Hicks (Sec & Controller)

Subsidiaries:
Lewis Controls, Inc.   (1)
260 N 26th Ave, Cornelius, OR 97113
Tel.: (503) 648-9119
Web Site: http://www.lewiscontrols.com
Wood Products Mfr
N.A.I.C.S.: 321999
Marv Bernhagen (COO & VP)

CORMETECH, INC.
5000 International Dr, Durham, NC 27712-8909
Tel.: (919) 620-3000
Web Site: http://www.cormetech.com
Sales Range: $50-74.9 Million
Emp.: 300
Environmental Technology Solutions
N.A.I.C.S.: 334512
Tom Dow (Dir-Finance & Treas)
Mike Mattes (Pres & CEO)

CORMIER RICE MILLING COMPANY, INC.
PO Box 152, De Witt, AR 72042-0152
Tel.: (870) 946-3561   AR
Sales Range: $75-99.9 Million
Emp.: 50
Rice Milling Services
N.A.I.C.S.: 311212
J.T. Ferguson (Pres & CEO)
Julie Gilbert (VP)
Jim Byers (VP)

CORN BELT ENERGY CORPO-RATION
1 Energy Way, Bloomington, IL 61705
Tel.: (309) 662-5330   IL
Web Site:
    https://www.cornbeltenergy.com
Year Founded: 1938
Sales Range: $25-49.9 Million
Emp.: 100
Electric & Gas Utilities Administration Organization
N.A.I.C.S.: 926130
Mike Nelson (Mgr-Northern)
Ronald Hopkins (Engr-Special Projects)
Hillary Cherry (Dir-Comm)
Joe Priestley (Mgr-IT)
Kacy Wickenhauser (Dir-HR)
Michael Volker (VP-Utility Svcs)
Ryan Campbell (Mgr-Construction & Maintenance)
Steve Hancock (VP-Electric Distr)
Lynn Oleson (Dir-Acct & Fin)

CORN BELT POWER COOP-ERATIVE
1300 13th St N, Humboldt, IA 50548
Tel.: (515) 332-2571
Web Site: https://www.cbpower.coop
Year Founded: 1947
Sales Range: $25-49.9 Million
Emp.: 90
Electric Services
N.A.I.C.S.: 221118
Jennifer Arndorfer (Dir-HR)
Mike Thatcher (VP)
Jim Vermeer (VP-Bus Dev)
Ken Kuyper (Exec VP & Gen Mgr)

CORN REFINERS ASSOCIA-TION
1701 Pennsylvania Ave NW Ste 950, Washington, DC 20006
Tel.: (202) 331-1634   DE
Web Site: http://www.corn.org
Year Founded: 1982
Sales Range: $25-49.9 Million
Emp.: 13
Business Associations
N.A.I.C.S.: 813910

CORNELL & COMPANY, INC.
PO Box 807, Woodbury, NJ 08096
Tel.: (856) 742-1900
Web Site:
http://www.cornellcranesteel.com
Year Founded: 1925
Sales Range: $25-49.9 Million
Emp.: 350
Nonresidential Construction Services
N.A.I.C.S.: 236220
Kevin Brockway (CFO)

CORNELL CAPITAL LLC
499 Park Ave 21st Fl, New York, NY
10022
Tel.: (212) 818-8980
Web Site: http://cornellcapllc.com
Year Founded: 2013
Rev.: $3,000,000,000
Privater Equity Firm
N.A.I.C.S.: 523999
Henry L. Cornell (Sr Partner)

Subsidiaries:

Advantek Inc.   (1)
11010 Prairie Lakes Dr Ste 155, Eden Prairie, MN 55344
Tel.: (510) 623-1877
Web Site: http://www.advantek.com
Plastic Packaging Tape Mfr
N.A.I.C.S.: 326112
Michael Miller (VP-Sls & Mktg)
Wim Goossens (COO)

Subsidiary (Domestic):

CornerStone Research & Development, Inc.   (2)
900 S Depot Dr, Ogden, UT 84404
Tel.: (801) 337-9400
Web Site: http://www.capstonenutrition.com
Sales Range: $25-49.9 Million
Emp.: 400
Research & Development of Nutritional & Herbal Dietary Supplements
N.A.I.C.S.: 541715
Jared Leishman (CEO)
Mark Pedersen (VP-R&D)

S.i. Systems ULC   (1)
Suite 309 401 9th Avenue SW, Calgary,
T2P 3C5, AB, Canada
Tel.: (403) 263-1200
Web Site: https://www.sisystems.com
Staffing & Recruiting Services
N.A.I.C.S.: 561311
Derek Bullen (CEO)

Subsidiary (Domestic):

Annex Consulting Group Inc.   (2)
Suite 950 555 Burrard Street Two Bentall
Centre, Vancouver, V7X 1M9, BC, Canada
Tel.: (604) 638-8878
Web Site: http://www.annexgroup.com
Business Consulting Services
N.A.I.C.S.: 541611
Stacey Cerniuk (CEO)

Eagle Professional Resources
Inc.   (2)
170 Laurier Avenue W Suite 902, Ottawa,
K1P 5V5, ON, Canada
Tel.: (613) 234-1810
Web Site: http://www.eagleonline.com
Employment & Consulting Agencies
N.A.I.C.S.: 561311
Kevin Dee (Chm)
Janis Grantham (Co-Founder & CEO)
Jonah Laist (Co-Founder & CFO-Toronto)
Frances McCart (VP-Bus Dev-Exec & Mgmt Consulting Div-Toronto)
Morley Surcon (VP)
David O'Brien (VP & Gen Mgr-Govt Svcs)
Brendhan Malone (VP & Gen Mgr-Central Canada-Toronto)

Cameron McCallum (VP & Gen Mgr-Edmonton)
Kelly Benson (Mgr-Calgary)

Spectrum Automotive Holdings
LLC   (1)
499 Park Ave 21st Fl, New York, NY 10022
Tel.: (877) 470-6171
Web Site: http://spectrumautoholdings.com
Privater Equity Firm
N.A.I.C.S.: 523901
Justin LaRocque (Mgr-Mktg)

Holding (Domestic):

C.A.R.S. Protection Plus, Inc.   (2)
4431 William Penn Hwy, Murrysville, PA
15668
Tel.: (724) 387-2327
Web Site:
http://www.carsprotectionplus.com
Rev.: $4,800,000
Emp.: 80
Other Direct Insurance, except Life, Health & Medical, Carriers
N.A.I.C.S.: 524128
Rick Tudor (Dir-Ops)

Cal-Tex Protective Coatings Inc. (2)
7455 Natural Bridge Caverns Rd, Schertz,
TX 78154-3210
Tel.: (210) 564-3200
Web Site: http://ww.caltexus.com
Polishes & Sanitation Goods
N.A.I.C.S.: 325612
Matt Ramsey (CFO)
Rande Hawkinson (Pres & COO)
Tim Akard (Exec VP-Sls)

CORNELL CAPITAL MANAGEMENT LLC
6020 Fairlane Dr, Clarence Center,
NY 14032-9733
Tel.: (716) 741-0149   DE
Web Site:
https://www.cornellcapital.com
Year Founded: 1999
Portfolio Management
N.A.I.C.S.: 523940
David C. Hartzell Jr. (Pres & CEO)

Subsidiaries:

Corelle Brands Holdings Inc.   (1)
9525 W Bryn Mawr Ave Ste 300, Rosemont, IL 60018
Tel.: (847) 233-8600
Web Site: http://www.corelle.com
Holding Company
N.A.I.C.S.: 551112

Subsidiary (Domestic):

Corelle Brands LLC   (2)
9525 W Bryn Mawr Ave Ste 300, Rosemont, IL 60018
Tel.: (847) 678-8600
Web Site: http://corellebrands.com
Kitchen & Barbeque Tools, Bar Accessories,
Bathroom Fittings, Closet Hardware, Tableware, Household Tinware & Microwave Accessories Mfr
N.A.I.C.S.: 332215
MaryKay Kopf (CMO)
Michael Scheffki (VP-Mktg & Branding)

Subsidiary (Domestic):

Olfa North America   (3)
9525 W Bryn Mawr Ave Ste 300, Rosemont, IL 60018
Tel.: (847) 678-8600
Web Site: http://www.olfa.com
Utility Knives, Specialty Cutters & Blades
Mfr & Distr
N.A.I.C.S.: 332216
Cassie Donnelly (Sr Mgr-Brand)

Subsidiary (Non-US):

Corelle Brands Manufacturing (M)
Sdn. Bhd.   (2)
Plo 315 Jalan Perak Kawasan Perindustrian, 81700, Pasir Gudang, Johor, Malaysia
Tel.: (60) 64682008
Glassware Mfr
N.A.I.C.S.: 327212

CORNELL FORGE COMPANY
6666 W 66th St, Chicago, IL 60638-4904
Tel.: (708) 458-1582   IL
Web Site:
https://www.cornellforge.com
Year Founded: 1930
Sales Range: $25-49.9 Million
Emp.: 65
Provider of Steel Drop & Press Forgings
N.A.I.C.S.: 332111
William Brewer (Owner)
Rob Adelman (Dir-Matls)
Ken Mathas (Pres)
Micheal Davis (Mgr-Sls)

CORNELL PAPER & BOX INC.
162 Van Dyke St 180, Brooklyn, NY
11231
Tel.: (718) 875-3202
Web Site:
http://www.cornellrobbins.com
Rev.: $18,000,000
Emp.: 49
Corrugated & Solid Fiber Boxes
N.A.I.C.S.: 424130
Marc Robbins (Pres)

CORNELL SCOTT-HILL HEALTH CENTER
400 Columbus Ave, New Haven, CT
06519
Tel.: (203) 503-3000   CT
Web Site:
http://www.hillhealthcenter.com
Year Founded: 1968
Sales Range: $25-49.9 Million
Emp.: 583
Health Care Srvices
N.A.I.C.S.: 622110
Felipe Ordonez (Dir-Dental Svcs)
Stewart Joslin (CFO)
Clark Woodruff (Dir-IT)
Michael Taylor (COO)
Jai Henderson (CEO)
Angel Fernandez-Chavero (Pres)
Mabel Carroll (Sec)
Rober A. Cole (Treas)
Nathan Jones (VP)
Tom McNamee (Chief Medical Officer-Interim)
Jan Martin (Officer-Compliance)

CORNELL UNIVERSITY PRESS
Sage House 512 E State St, Ithaca,
NY 14850-4412
Tel.: (607) 253-2338
Web Site:
https://www.cornellpress.cornell.edu
Year Founded: 1868
Sales Range: $75-99.9 Million
Emp.: 80
General Non-Fiction & Scholarly
Books Publisher
N.A.I.C.S.: 513130
Martyn Beeny (Dir-Mktg)

CORNER OFFICE INC.
125 Mitchell Blvd, San Rafael, CA
94903-2051
Tel.: (415) 472-5531
Web Site:
https://www.corneroffice.com
Sales Range: $800-899.9 Million
Emp.: 8
Office Furniture Retail & Contract
N.A.I.C.S.: 423210
Randy Hershkowitz (Pres)
Kyle Lavin (Controller)

CORNER PANTRY INC.
1001 Idlewilde Blvd, Columbia, SC
29201
Tel.: (803) 254-4806

Web Site:
https://www.cornerpantry.com
Sales Range: $10-24.9 Million
Emp.: 30
Convenience Store
N.A.I.C.S.: 445131
David A. Tucker (Pres)

CORNERSTONE ADVISORS, INC.
7272 E Indian School Rd Ste 400,
Scottsdale, AZ 85251
Tel.: (480) 423-2030   AZ
Web Site: https://www.crnrstone.com
Year Founded: 2002
Sales Range: $1-9.9 Million
Emp.: 15
Management Consulting Services
N.A.I.C.S.: 541611
Bill McFarland (Mng Dir)
Marie Mack (Dir-Client Dev)
Scott Sommer (Pres & CEO)

CORNERSTONE ADVISORS, INC.
1075 Hendersonville Rd Ste 250,
Asheville, NC 28803
Tel.: (828) 210-8184   NC
Investment Management Service
N.A.I.C.S.: 523940
Ralph W. Bradshaw (Co-Founder)
Gary A. Bentz (Chm & CFO)
Daniel W. Bradshaw (Chief Investment Officer)

CORNERSTONE BUSINESSES INC.
3936 Paul S Buchman Hwy, Zephyrhills, FL 33542
Tel.: (813) 715-0808
Web Site: http://www.cornerstonezhill.com
Rev.: $26,000,000
Emp.: 12
Guardrail Construction, Highways
N.A.I.C.S.: 237310
Mary Jane Hubbard (Pres)

Subsidiaries:

Cornerstone of North Florida   (1)
3936 S Paul Buchman Hwy, Zephyrhills, FL
33540
Tel.: (850) 942-1704
Web Site: http://www.cornerstone.com
Underground Utilities Contractor
N.A.I.C.S.: 237110

CORNERSTONE CARE, INC.
7 Glassworks Rd, Greensboro, PA
15338
Tel.: (724) 943-3308   PA
Web Site:
https://www.cornerstonecare.com
Year Founded: 1978
Sales Range: $10-24.9 Million
Emp.: 235
Community Health Care Services
N.A.I.C.S.: 621498
Berardi Hugo (CFO)
Rich Rinehart (COO)

CORNERSTONE COMMUNITIES CORPORATION
4365 Executive Dr Ste 600, San Diego, CA 92121-2128
Tel.: (858) 458-9700
Web Site:
https://www.cornerstonecommunities.com
Year Founded: 1994
Sales Range: $10-24.9 Million
Emp.: 50
Provider of Subdivision & Developer
Services
N.A.I.C.S.: 237210

Cornerstone Communities
Corporation—(Continued)

Ure Kretowicz *(CEO)*
Jay W. Zimmer *(CFO & Controller)*
Michael Sabourin *(Pres & COO)*
Jack E. Robson *(VP-Land Plng-Development)*

CORNERSTONE CONSULTING, INC.
5550 W Executive Dr Ste 240, Tampa, FL 33609
Tel.: (813) 321-1300
Web Site:
http://www.cornerstoneone.com
Year Founded: 1983
Sales Range: $1-9.9 Million
Emp.: 15
Software Publisher; Technology Consulting
N.A.I.C.S.: 513210
David M. Boos *(Pres)*
Ashley Edwards *(VP-Bus Dev)*
Henry Pavlik *(Dir-Software Engrg)*

CORNERSTONE CONTROLS INC.
7131 E Kemper Rd, Cincinnati, OH 45249-1030
Tel.: (513) 489-2500
Web Site:
https://www.cornerstonecontrol.com
Year Founded: 1935
Sales Range: $10-24.9 Million
Emp.: 120
Process Control Information Solutions & Industrial Supplies
N.A.I.C.S.: 423840
Guy Titler *(Bus Mgr-FCS)*

CORNERSTONE DENTAL LABORATORIES, LLC
1800 Byberry Rd Ste 800, Huntingdon Valley, PA 19006
Tel.: (215) 293-9760
Web Site:
http://www.cornerstonedl.com
Emp.: 25
Dental Laboratory
N.A.I.C.S.: 339116
Jay Collins *(Owner)*
Katie Goldstein *(Office Mgr)*
Andy Alonge *(Mgr-Lab)*
Kimberley Grasty *(Controller)*
Dave Grove *(Mgr-Sls)*
Drew Fosater *(Mgr-Digital)*

Subsidiaries:

Jaslow Dental Laboratory, Inc.   **(1)**
261 Old York Rd Ste A-100, Jenkintown, PA 19046
Tel.: (215) 887-6886
Sales Range: Less than $1 Million
Emp.: 20
Dental Laboratory
N.A.I.C.S.: 339116
Edward Jaslow *(Pres)*

CORNERSTONE DETENTION PRODUCTS, INC.
14000 Hwy 20, Madison, AL 35756
Tel.: (877) 374-7311
Web Site:
http://www.cornerstonedetention.com
Year Founded: 1998
Equipment Contractor, Security Controls Integrator & Locking Systems Mfr
N.A.I.C.S.: 238990
C. Mitch Claborn *(Pres & CEO)*
Stephen Claborn *(Exec VP-Strategic Dev)*
Joe Hargrove *(VP-Admin, Electronics & Mfg)*
Phil Mullins *(VP-Construction)*

Don Rochon *(Exec VP-Svc, Supply & Warranty)*
David Watts *(Exec VP-Fin)*

CORNERSTONE DEVELOPERS, INC.
PO Box 111777, Naples, FL 34108
Tel.: (239) 594-7985
Web Site: http://www.cornerstone-swfl.com
Sales Range: $25-49.9 Million
Emp.: 2
New Multifamily Housing Construction Services
N.A.I.C.S.: 236116
Pat Musumano *(Owner & Pres)*
Donna Musumano *(Owner & Exec VP)*

CORNERSTONE EQUITY INVESTORS, LLC
281 Tresser Blvd 12th Fl, Stamford, CT 06901
Tel.: (212) 753-0901
Web Site: http://www.cornerstone-equity.com
Year Founded: 1984
Sales Range: $150-199.9 Million
Emp.: 7
Provider of Investment Services
N.A.I.C.S.: 523999
Robert A. Knox *(Sr Mng Dir)*
Stephen L. Larson *(Mng Dir)*
Robert Hinman Getz *(Co-Founder)*
Mark Alan Rossi *(Sr Mng Dir)*

CORNERSTONE FINANCIAL CREDIT UNION
1701 21st Ave S, Nashville, TN 37212
Tel.: (615) 385-6866
Web Site:
http://www.cornerstonefinancial.org
Year Founded: 1955
Sales Range: $10-24.9 Million
Emp.: 110
Credit Union Operator
N.A.I.C.S.: 522130
Joe Spivey *(Pres)*
Gary Cowen *(Chm)*
Julie Williams *(Sec)*
Frank Ruckman *(Treas)*
Lelan Statom *(Vice Chm)*
Roderick Payne *(VP-Info Sys)*
William Frye *(VP-Mktg)*

CORNERSTONE GROUP DEVELOPMENT CORPORATION
2100 Hollywood Blvd, Hollywood, FL 33020
Tel.: (305) 443-8288
Web Site:
http://www.cornerstonegrp.com
Sales Range: $250-299.9 Million
Emp.: 460
Hotel/Motel & Multi-Family Home Construction
N.A.I.C.S.: 236220
Jorge Lopez *(Co-Founder & Pres)*
Bruce Adams *(CFO)*

CORNERSTONE INFORMATION SYSTEM, INC.
800 S Main St, Hopkinsville, KY 42240
Tel.: (270) 885-9011
Web Site: https://www.cornerstone.us
Year Founded: 1984
Custom Computer Programming Services
N.A.I.C.S.: 541511
David Smith *(Co-Owner & CEO)*
Philip Tillman *(CTO)*

CORNERSTONE INFORMA-

TION TECHNOLOGIES, LLC
1180 Ave of the Americas 8th Fl, New York, NY 10036
Tel.: (646) 530-8900
Web Site: https://www.cornerstone.it
Information Management Design Services
N.A.I.C.S.: 541512
Jim Moreo *(Principal)*
Thomas Moreo *(Principal)*
Neil Failla *(Mgr-Ops)*
Jeff Harris *(Architect)*
Vidit Desai *(Architect)*
Adriana Vitale *(Mgr-Customer Success)*
Amy Russo *(Mgr-HR)*
Teena Katz *(Mgr-Sls)*

CORNERSTONE INVESTMENT CAPITAL HOLDINGS CO.
11450 SE Dixie Hwy, Hobe Sound, FL 33455
Tel.: (772) 545-9079
Year Founded: 2021
Investment Services
N.A.I.C.S.: 523999
Robert Greifeld *(Chm & CEO)*
Thomas Mosimann *(CFO)*

CORNERSTONE MANAGEMENT PARTNERS, INC.
3100 Falling Leaf Ct, Columbia, MO 65201
Tel.: (573) 817-2481
Web Site:
http://www.cornerstonenational.com
Year Founded: 1995
Sales Range: $10-24.9 Million
Emp.: 99
Direct Property & Casualty Insurance Services
N.A.I.C.S.: 524126
Roger Walker *(Exec Dir)*

CORNERSTONE MEDIA
1640 N Major Dr, Beaumont, TX 77713-8506
Tel.: (409) 866-4804
Web Site:
http://www.cornerstoneadgroup.com
Year Founded: 1982
Sales Range: $25-49.9 Million
Emp.: 25
Advertising Agencies
N.A.I.C.S.: 541810
Kent Houp *(Gen Mgr)*
Larry O'Keefe *(Mgr-Corp Video)*
Daryl Fant *(Publr)*

CORNERSTONE MORTGAGE CO.
1177 West Loop South Ste 200, Dallas, TX 75209
Tel.: (713) 621-4463
Web Site: http://www.houseloan.com
Rev.: $9,000,000
Emp.: 18
Mortgage & Nonmortgage Loan Brokers
N.A.I.C.S.: 522310
Mary Dinkins *(Exec VP)*
Jay Wilson *(Mgr-Greenwood)*
Scott Almy *(CEO)*

Subsidiaries:

The Roscoe State Bank   **(1)**
117 Cypress St, Roscoe, TX 79545
Tel.: (325) 766-3311
Web Site: http://www.rsb.bank
Commercial Banking Services
N.A.I.C.S.: 522110
Bryan Studdard *(Officer-Loan & Exec VP)*
John W. Jay *(Pres & CEO)*
Kristie Fox *(Sec & VP)*
Dawna Fullwood *(Sr VP-Lobby Svcs)*

CORNERSTONE PHARMACY, INC.
4220 N Rodney Parham Rd, Little Rock, AR 72212
Tel.: (501) 223-2224
Web Site:
http://www.cornerstonepharmacy.com
Year Founded: 2002
Sales Range: $10-24.9 Million
Pharmacies Owner & Operator
N.A.I.C.S.: 456110
Kenneth Harrison *(Pres)*
Tracee Harrison *(Owner & CFO)*
Leigh Anne Jewart *(Dir-Ops)*

CORNERSTONE PROFESSIONAL LIABILITY CONSULTANTS, INC.
1500 Liberty Ridge Dr, Wayne, PA 19087
Tel.: (610) 296-3700
Web Site:
http://www.cornerstoneplic.com
Year Founded: 2002
Sales Range: $1-9.9 Million
Emp.: 15
Insurance Agencies & Brokerages
N.A.I.C.S.: 524210
Catherine Hayden *(Acct Exec)*
Jennifer Negley *(Sr Acct Exec)*
Michael Henry *(VP)*
Regina Wintz *(VP-Ops)*

CORNERSTONE PROMOTION, INC.
71 W 23rd St Fl 13, New York, NY 10010
Tel.: (212) 741-7100
Web Site:
http://www.cornerstonepromotion.com
Year Founded: 1997
Sales Range: $10-24.9 Million
Emp.: 94
Public Relations, Publicity/Promotions
N.A.I.C.S.: 541820
Anthony Holland *(Gen Mgr)*

CORNERSTONE RESEARCH GROUP, INC.
2750 Indian Ripple Rd, Dayton, OH 45440
Tel.: (937) 320-1877
Web Site: http://www.crgrp.net
Year Founded: 1997
Sales Range: $10-24.9 Million
Emp.: 110
Research & Development
N.A.I.C.S.: 541715
Melissa Aldridge *(Bus Dir-Commercialization Center)*
Stewart Mayhew *(VP)*
Vandy Howell *(Sr VP)*
Matthew Lynde *(Sr VP)*
Andrea Shepard *(Sr VP)*

CORNERSTONE RPO, LLC
5378 Twin Hickory Rd, Glen Allen, VA 23059
Web Site:
http://www.cornerstonerpo.com
Year Founded: 2007
Sales Range: $1-9.9 Million
Emp.: 77
Recruitment Services
N.A.I.C.S.: 561311
Rodney Ashby *(Principal, Co-Owner & Dir-Recruitment)*
Jeff Edwards *(COO)*
David Kenworth *(VP-Bus Dev & Co-Owner)*

CORNERSTONE SOLUTIONS GROUP
14620 Bellamy Brothers Blvd, Dade City, FL 33525

Tel.: (866) 617-2235
Web Site:
http://www.cornerstonesolution.com
Sales Range: $1-9.9 Million
Emp.: 250
Landscaping, Architectural, Construction, Environmental & Nursery Services
N.A.I.C.S.: 561730
Eric A. Meister *(Co-Owner & CEO)*
Fred Ingram *(Mgr-Ops-Landscape)*
Scott B. Meister II *(Co-Owner & Pres)*

CORNERSTONE STAFFING SOLUTIONS, INC.
7041 Koll Center Pkwy Ste 200, Pleasanton, CA 94566
Tel.: (925) 426-6900
Web Site: http://www.cornerstone-staffing.com
Year Founded: 2003
Sales Range: $75-99.9 Million
Emp.: 200
Human Resource Consulting Services
N.A.I.C.S.: 541612
Steve Drexel *(Pres & CEO)*

CORNERSTONE SYSTEMS, INC.
3250 Players Club Pkwy, Memphis, TN 38125
Tel.: (901) 842-0660   TN
Web Site: https://www.cornerstone-systems.com
Year Founded: 1997
Freight Transportation Services
N.A.I.C.S.: 488510
Rick Rodell *(Founder & Chm)*
Tim Clay *(Pres & CEO)*
Pat Nieman *(CFO & COO)*
Guy Wallace *(Sr VP-Sales)*
Nan Hutchins *(Mgr-Pricing)*

CORNET TECHNOLOGY INC.
6800 Versar Ctr Ste 216, Springfield, VA 22151
Tel.: (703) 658-3400
Web Site: https://www.cornet.com
Year Founded: 1989
Sales Range: $100-124.9 Million
Emp.: 100
Intercommunication Systems
N.A.I.C.S.: 334290
Nat Kumar *(CEO)*
Pravin Dand *(Controller)*
Thomas Bennett *(Pres-Comm)*
Sunil Mehta *(VP-Mktg)*

Subsidiaries:

Cornet Technology (India) Private Limited   (1)
A Wing II Floor New Plot No 10/A-16, SIP-COT Information Technology Park Kancheepuram District, Chennai, 603103, India
Tel.: (91) 44 49024500
Web Site: http://www.cornetindia.com
Intercommunication System Mfr
N.A.I.C.S.: 334290

Cornet Technology GmbH   (1)
Jahnstrasse 64, Heusenstamm, 63150, Germany
Tel.: (49) 6104 955 65-00
Web Site: http://www.cornet.de
Emp.: 10
Intercommunication Systems
N.A.I.C.S.: 334290
Ravi Sharma *(Mng Dir)*

Nihon Cornet Technology K.K.   (1)
Higashi-Ueno Kanto Building 6F, 12-2 Higashi-Ueno 1-Chome, Taito-Ku, Tokyo, 110-0015, Japan
Web Site: http://www.nihon-cornet.co.jp
Intercommunication Systems
N.A.I.C.S.: 334290

CORNETT INTEGRATED MARKETING SOLUTIONS
330 E Main St Ste 300, Lexington, KY 40507-1525
Tel.: (859) 281-5104   KY
Year Founded: 1984
Rev.: $8,650,000
Emp.: 25
Fiscal Year-end: 12/31/04
N.A.I.C.S.: 541810
Kip Cornett *(Pres)*
Lenora Rather *(Accountant)*
Paul Blodgett *(Principal & Dir-Creative Svcs)*
Jeff Hancock *(VP & Dir-Creative)*
Tracie Schlich *(Principal & Dir-Acct Svcs)*
Molly Powell *(Acct Mgr)*
Christy Hiler *(Acct Mgr)*
Bill M. Rice *(Dir-Interactive Art)*
Liz Fenner *(Acct Coord)*
Lee Boone *(Dir-Comm Design)*
Teresa Vander Molen *(Dir-Art)*

CORNHUSKER AUTO CENTER INC.
700 E Norfolk Ave, Norfolk, NE 68701
Tel.: (402) 371-3765
Web Site:
http://www.cornhuskerauto.com
Sales Range: $25-49.9 Million
Emp.: 50
Automobiles, New & Used
N.A.I.C.S.: 441110
Al Rajaee *(Pres)*
Chantel Bynum *(Mgr-Fin & Lease)*
Julie Rajaee *(VP)*

CORNHUSKER GROWTH CORPORATION
PO Box 80009, Lincoln, NE 68501-0009
Tel.: (402) 434-2265
Web Site:
http://www.cornhuskerbank.com
Year Founded: 1903
Bank Holding Company
N.A.I.C.S.: 551111
John Dittman *(Chm)*
Perry Haralson *(CFO)*
Barry J. Lockard *(Pres & CEO)*
Stephen Lindgren *(Exec VP)*
Kevin Deaver *(Exec VP)*
David Shiffermiller *(Exec VP-Lending)*
Crystal Wichita *(COO)*
Sherla Post *(Sr VP-HR)*
Carissa Bullock *(VP-Mktg)*
Teresa Elliott *(VP-Comm)*
Audrie Bates *(VP-Retail Experience)*

CORNING BUILDING CO. INC.
346 Park Ave, Corning, NY 14830
Tel.: (607) 936-9921
Web Site:
http://www.corningbuilding.com
Sales Range: $10-24.9 Million
Emp.: 100
Home Center Operator
N.A.I.C.S.: 444110
Matt Smith *(Pres)*
Dennis Mryglot *(VP-Ops)*
Lori Glover *(Mgr-Lumber & Building Matls)*
Jeannie Paulhamus *(Mgr-Kitchen Design Center)*
Bill Raymond *(Mgr)*
Tim Rice *(Mgr)*
Sally Sokira *(Mgr)*
Kirk Dyke *(Asst Mgr)*
Allen Bailey *(Mgr-Store)*
James Smith Jr. *(VP-Comml & Contractor Sls)*

CORNING DATA SERVICES INC.
139 Wardell St, Corning, NY 14830
Tel.: (607) 936-4241
Web Site:
http://www.corningdata.com
Year Founded: 1980
Sales Range: $10-24.9 Million
Emp.: 80
Office Computer Automation Systems Integration
N.A.I.C.S.: 541512
Scott J. Peterson *(Pres)*

CORNING FORD, INC.
2280 Short Dr, Corning, CA 96021-2309
Tel.: (530) 824-5434
Web Site:
https://www.corningford.com
Sales Range: $10-24.9 Million
Emp.: 80
Car Whslr
N.A.I.C.S.: 441110
Benny Brown *(Pres)*
Paul Sutfin *(Gen Mgr)*

CORNWALL MANOR
1 Boyd St, Cornwall, PA 17016
Tel.: (717) 273-2647   PA
Web Site:
https://www.cornwallmanor.org
Year Founded: 1949
Sales Range: $10-24.9 Million
Emp.: 370
Lifecare Retirement Community Operator
N.A.I.C.S.: 623311
Anne Peiffer *(VP-PR & Dev)*
Ed Peiffer *(VP-Ops)*
Paul Weidman *(VP-Plant Ops)*
Steve Hassinger *(Pres)*
Lee Stickler *(VP-Fin)*

CORNWELL CORP.
107 Riverdale Rd Ste 1, Riverdale, NJ 07457
Tel.: (973) 831-9800   IL
Web Site:
http://www.cornwellcorporation.com
Year Founded: 1982
Sales Range: $1-9.9 Million
Emp.: 24
Miscellaneous Intermediation
N.A.I.C.S.: 523910
John Cornwell *(CEO)*

CORO REALTY ADVISORS LLC
3715 Northside Pkwy, Atlanta, GA 30327
Tel.: (404) 846-4000
Web Site: http://www.cororealty.com
Sales Range: $10-24.9 Million
Emp.: 25
Shopping Centers
N.A.I.C.S.: 531210
Patti Pearlberg *(Partner & VP-Asset Mgmt)*
Adam Holland *(Mgr-Property)*
Karmen Haub *(Sr Mgr-Property)*
Michael Salisbury *(CFO)*
Robert Fransen *(CIO & Partner)*
Curtis McLeod *(Mgr-Acctg)*
Steve Cooper *(Mgr-Asset)*
Kerry Farr *(Mgr-Dev)*
Trina Joseph *(Dir-Property)*
Vickie Smith *(Mgr-Property)*
Bart Cross *(VP)*
Andrea Kenney *(VP-Leasing)*
Crissy Hart *(Sr Mgr-Property)*
Keirah Palmer *(Dir-Property Mgmt)*
John W. Lundeen III *(Pres)*

CORONA LABS INC.
1900 Embarcadero Rd Ste 207, Palo Alto, CA 94303
Tel.: (408) 372-7263   DE
Web Site: http://www.coronalabs.com
Mobile Application Development Platform Software Publisher
N.A.I.C.S.: 513210
Surojit Niyogi *(CEO & Owner)*

CORONADO COAL LLC
57 Danbury Rd Ste 201, Wilton, CT 06897
Tel.: (203) 761-1291   DE
Web Site:
http://www.coronadocoal.com
Year Founded: 2011
Coal Mining
N.A.I.C.S.: 212114
James Campbell *(Co-Founder)*
Garold R. Spindler *(Co-Founder)*

CORONET PAPER PRODUCTS ENTERPRISES OF FLORIDA LLC.
3200 NW 119th St, Miami, FL 33167-2904
Tel.: (305) 688-6601
Web Site:
https://www.coronetpaper.com
Rev.: $13,900,000
Emp.: 15
Printing & Writing Paper Merchant Whslr
N.A.I.C.S.: 424110

COROVAN CORPORATION
12302 Kerran St, Poway, CA 92064-6801
Tel.: (858) 762-8100   CA
Web Site: https://www.corovan.com
Year Founded: 1994
Sales Range: $10-24.9 Million
Emp.: 140
Trucking & Storage Distr
N.A.I.C.S.: 484210
Torrie Nguyen *(Mgr-Marketing)*

Subsidiaries:

Corovan Moving & Storage Co.   (1)
12375 Kerran St, Poway, CA 92064-6801
Tel.: (858) 748-1100
Sales Range: $10-24.9 Million
Emp.: 100
Provider of Trucking & Storage Services
N.A.I.C.S.: 484210

CORPAC STEEL PRODUCTS CORP.
20803 Biscayne Blvd Ste 502, Aventura, FL 33180-1432
Tel.: (305) 918-0540
Web Site:
https://www.corpacsteel.com
Metal Service Centers & Other Metal Merchant Whslr
N.A.I.C.S.: 423510
Idel Woldenberger *(Pres & Sec)*

Subsidiaries:

Pipe Exchange Inc.   (1)
13831 NW Fwy Ste 525, Houston, TX 77040
Tel.: (713) 934-9480
Web Site: http://www.pipexch.com
Other Building Material Dealers
N.A.I.C.S.: 444180
Dolty Cheramie *(Pres)*
Mark Bihm *(VP-Sls & Ops)*
Mary Carson *(VP-Fin)*
Jeff Crabtree *(VP-Mktg & Bus Dev)*

CORPDIRECT AGENTS, INC.
515 E Park Ave, Tallahassee, FL 32301
Tel.: (850) 222-1173
Web Site: http://www.corpdirect.com
Year Founded: 1994
Sales Range: $1-9.9 Million
Emp.: 21
Investigation Services
N.A.I.C.S.: 561611

CorpDirect Agents, Inc.—(Continued)

Patricia Tadlock *(VP-Ops)*
Karen Parker *(Office Mgr)*
Lynne Roberts *(VP-Admin)*
Kevin Roberts *(Chm & Pres-Dev & Mktg)*
Katie Wonsch *(Mgr-Corp Svcs)*

CORPORACION LOS HERMANOS

243 Calle Paris, San Juan, PR 00917
Tel.: (787) 763-1879
Rev.: $10,564,920
Emp.: 12
Department Stores
N.A.I.C.S.: 445110
Rosinin Rodriguez *(Pres)*

CORPORATE AIR

1001 S 24th St W, Billings, MT 59102
Tel.: (406) 247-3131   MT
Web Site:
  https://www.corporateair.net
Year Founded: 1981
Sales Range: $10-24.9 Million
Emp.: 180
Provider of Air Courier Services
N.A.I.C.S.: 492110
Linda Overstreet *(Pres & CEO)*
Mike Overstreet *(VP-Intl Rels)*
Robert McIver *(Dir-Operations & VP)*

CORPORATE ALLOCATION SERVICES, INC.

12110 Pecos St Ste 210, Westminster, CO 80234
Tel.: (303) 920-4725
Web Site:
  http://www.corporateallocation.com
Year Founded: 1997
Rev.: $2,100,000
Emp.: 34
Administrative & General Management Consulting Services
N.A.I.C.S.: 541611
Barbara Erisman *(Pres)*

CORPORATE AMERICA FAMILY CREDIT UNION

2075 Big Timber Rd, Elgin, IL 60123
Tel.: (847) 214-2000   IL
Web Site: http://www.cafcu.org
Year Founded: 1939
Sales Range: $25-49.9 Million
Emp.: 223
Credit Union
N.A.I.C.S.: 522130
Ellen Meehan *(Sr VP)*
Paula McCarthy *(Sr VP)*
Andrew Bowen *(VP-Tech)*
Peter Paulson *(Pres & CEO)*

CORPORATE ASSET BACKED CORPORATION

68 S Service Rd Ste 120, Melville, NY 11747
Tel.: (631) 587-4700   DE
Financial Investment Services
N.A.I.C.S.: 523940
Lee Thompson *(VP)*

CORPORATE BANK TRANSIT

415 N McKinley St Ste 850, Little Rock, AR 72205
Tel.: (501) 666-3278
Web Site:
  http://www.corporatebanktransit.com
Year Founded: 1992
Rev.: $20,000,000
Emp.: 300
Messenger Service
N.A.I.C.S.: 561499
James C. Foster *(Chm)*
Miles E. Hilliard *(Pres & CEO)*

CORPORATE BROKERS LLC

170 Jennifer Rd Ste 230, Annapolis, MD 21401
Tel.: (410) 573-0003
Web Site:
  http://www.corporatebrokers.com
Year Founded: 2003
Sales Range: $1-9.9 Million
Emp.: 500
Staffing Services
N.A.I.C.S.: 541612
Shane Ireland *(CEO)*

CORPORATE BUSINESS INTERIORS, INC.

19000 MacArthur Blvd, Irvine, CA 92612
Tel.: (949) 225-3900
Web Site: http://www.cbihq.com
Sales Range: $1-9.9 Million
Emp.: 25
Furniture Merchant Whslr
N.A.I.C.S.: 423210
Hice Stiles *(Founder & Principal)*
Darren Stiles *(CEO)*

Subsidiaries:

Corporate Spaces, Inc.   (1)
696 E Colorado Blvd 220, Pasadena, CA 91101
Tel.: (626) 447-3314
Web Site: https://csifullmer.com
Rev.: $3,997,000
Emp.: 7
Furniture Distr
N.A.I.C.S.: 423210
Bill Baquet *(CEO)*

CORPORATE CENTRAL CREDIT UNION

6262 S Lowell Pl, Muskego, WI 53150
Tel.: (414) 425-5555   WI
Web Site: https://www.corpcu.com
Year Founded: 1947
Sales Range: $1-9.9 Million
Emp.: 41
Credit Union Operator
N.A.I.C.S.: 522130
Nicholas A. Fanning *(Co-CFO & Sr VP)*
Chris Felton *(Pres & CEO)*
Nancy Morgan *(COO & Sr VP)*
Eric Chrisinger *(Chm)*
Sally Dischler *(Vice Chm)*
Dawn Beyer *(Mgr-Admin)*
Fred Blask *(VP-Risk Strategy & Execution)*
Karen Christie *(VP-Member Svcs)*
John Hickey *(VP-Investments)*
Jesse Kohl *(VP-Corp Dev)*
Linda Resler *(Mgr-Acctg)*
John Rice *(VP-Strategic Initiatives)*
Cherie Spargur *(VP-Acctg)*
Michele Vukovic *(Mgr-HR)*
Mark Hopkins *(Mgr-Bus Dev)*
Gail Kearney *(Dir-Member Solutions)*
Lisa Wolfram *(Officer-Relationship Dev)*
Todd Brown *(Co-CFO)*
Kevin P. Chiappetta *(Sr VP-Investment Svcs)*
John Ehmann *(Co-CFO)*
Danny McIntyre *(VP-Investment Svcs)*
David Powers *(Co-CFO)*
Gregg Tushaus *(CIO & Sr VP)*
Julie Woloszyn *(Dir-Brand Awareness)*

CORPORATE CLAIMS MANAGEMENT, INC.

1 Ivybrook Blvd Ste 140, Ivyland, PA 18974
Tel.: (215) 396-1991   PA

Web Site:
  http://www.ccmservices.com
Insurance Claims Management Services
N.A.I.C.S.: 524291
Robert Martines *(Pres & CEO)*
Tara Martines *(Mng Dir)*
Brian Colvin *(VP-Ops)*
Rich Tillotson *(Dir-Bus Dev)*
Jim Van Buren *(Dir-IT)*

CORPORATE COACHES, INC.

1050 S Flower St Ste 501, Los Angeles, CA 90014
Tel.: (424) 299-4545   NV
Web Site:
  http://www.corpcoaches.com
Year Founded: 2014
Emp.: 2
Business Consulting Services
N.A.I.C.S.: 541611
Christopher Mussallem *(Chm, CEO, CFO & Acctg Officer)*
Andre Brown *(Sec & VP)*

CORPORATE CONSTRUCTION LTD

7617 Mineral Point Rd, Madison, WI 53717
Tel.: (608) 827-6001
Web Site: http://www.corporate-construction.com
Rev.: $34,797,547
Emp.: 35
Commercial & Office Building, New Construction Retail
N.A.I.C.S.: 236220
Frederick D. Ruegsegger *(Pres)*

CORPORATE CULINARY SERVICE INC.

400 Atlantic St, Stamford, CT 06901
Tel.: (203) 348-1199
Web Site:
  http://www.corporateculinary.com
Rev.: $12,000,000
Emp.: 20
Cafeterias
N.A.I.C.S.: 722514
Nicholas Simeone *(CEO & Dir-Client Svcs)*
Frederick Laist *(Exec Dir)*

CORPORATE DIRECT APPAREL LLC

121 Cheshire Ln N Ste 100, Minneapolis, MN 55305
Web Site:
  http://www.merchology.com
Year Founded: 2013
Sales Range: $25-49.9 Million
Emp.: 96
Online Shopping Services
N.A.I.C.S.: 423420
Richard Ward *(Co-Founder & CEO)*
Nolan Goodman *(Co-Founder)*
Ally Delgado *(Co-Founder & CMO)*
Andrew Ward *(Co-Founder & Chief Revenue Officer)*
Mark Cherrey *(VP-Fin)*

CORPORATE DISK COMPANY

4610 Prime Pkwy, McHenry, IL 60050
Tel.: (815) 331-6000
Web Site: https://www.disk.com
Sales Range: $10-24.9 Million
Emp.: 80
Disk & Cd Duplication
N.A.I.C.S.: 541519
Bill Mahoney *(Pres)*

CORPORATE DISPLAY SPECIALTIES, INC.

60 Watson Blvd, Stratford, CT 06615
Tel.: (203) 386-0750

Web Site:
  http://www.cdsdisplays.com
Year Founded: 1983
Sales Range: $1-9.9 Million
Emp.: 15
Showcase, Partition, Shelving & Locker Mfr
N.A.I.C.S.: 337215
Joseph Bottone *(Pres)*

CORPORATE DOCUMENT SOLUTIONS, INC.

11120 Ashburn Rd, 45240, Cincinnati, OH
Tel.: (513) 595-8200
Web Site: http://www.cdsprint.com
Year Founded: 1992
Marketing Research & Public Opinion Polling
N.A.I.C.S.: 541910
James Yim *(Pres)*

Subsidiaries:

Alliance Printing & Publishing, Inc.   (1)
6730 Roosevelt Ave Ste 100, 45005, Middletown, OH
Tel.: (513) 423-7768
Web Site: http://www.allianceprinting.net
Lithographic Commercial Printing & Publication Services
N.A.I.C.S.: 323111

CORPORATE ENVIRONMENTS OF GEORGIA INC.

1636 NE Expy NE, Atlanta, GA 30329-2003
Tel.: (404) 679-8999
Web Site: http://www.ceofga.com
Year Founded: 1990
Sales Range: $25-49.9 Million
Emp.: 50
Sale of Furniture
N.A.I.C.S.: 449110
Karen Hughes *(Owner & Pres)*
Bill Hayzlett *(Dir-Ops)*
Timothy A. O'Connell *(COO)*
T. J. Larson *(Controller)*
Marcus Tate *(Mgr-Sls)*
Bill Worthington *(Acct Mgr)*
Keli Burns *(Sr Mgr-A&D & Mktg)*

CORPORATE ESSENTIALS, LLC.

2 Cranberry Rd Ste A2, Parsippany, NJ 07054
Tel.: (973) 402-1088
Web Site:
  https://www.drinkcoffee.com
Year Founded: 1996
Sales Range: $1-9.9 Million
Emp.: 32
Kitchen Supplies
N.A.I.C.S.: 561990
Ivan Mann *(Founder)*
Judson Kleinman *(Founder, Pres & CEO)*
Tim Morgan *(Founder)*
Joe Simonovich *(Chief Growth Officer)*

CORPORATE FACILITIES INC.

2129 Chestnut St, Philadelphia, PA 19103
Tel.: (215) 279-9999
Web Site: http://www.cfi-knoll.com
Year Founded: 1985
Sales Range: $10-24.9 Million
Emp.: 40
Office Furniture Whslr
N.A.I.C.S.: 423210
Robert J. Chevalier *(Owner & Chm)*
Michael Yekenchik *(VP-Sls)*
George Connaghan *(Controller)*

CORPORATE FAMILY NET-WORK
60 E 42nd St Ste 2401, New York, NY 10165
Tel.: (212) 557-8660　　　　NY
Web Site:
　http://www.moretolifeonline.com
Year Founded: 1996
Sales Range: $1-9.9 Million
Emp.: 15
Manages Employee Assistance Programs
N.A.I.C.S.: 923130
Elaine Tragni (Mgr-Mktg)
Zoe Klein (Dir-Ops & Quality)

CORPORATE FITNESS WORKS, INC.
1200 16th St N, Saint Petersburg, FL 33705
Web Site:
　https://www.corporatefitness.com
Year Founded: 1988
Sales Range: $10-24.9 Million
Emp.: 250
Corporate Fitness Consulting & Management
N.A.I.C.S.: 541611
Sheila Drohan (Co-Founder)
Brenda Loube (Co-Founder)

CORPORATE FLIGHT MAN-AGEMENT INC.
276 Doug Warpoole Rd, Smyrna, TN 37167
Tel.: (615) 220-1761
Web Site: http://www.flycfm.com
Year Founded: 1982
Sales Range: $10-24.9 Million
Emp.: 180
Nonscheduled Chartered Passenger Air Transportation
N.A.I.C.S.: 481211
David Augustin (VP-Asst Mgmt)
Leon Custers (Exec VP-Maintenance & FBO Svcs)
Ryan Donahue (VP-Maintenance)
Shad Holloman (Mgr-Piston Engine Svc)
Timothy Wade (Mgr-Managed Fleet Svc)
Matt Chaifetz (CEO)

CORPORATE FLOORS INC.
1712 Minters Chapel Rd Ste 100, Grapevine, TX 76051
Tel.: (817) 329-7100
Web Site:
　http://www.corporatefloors.com
Year Founded: 1997
Sales Range: $10-24.9 Million
Emp.: 53
Flooring Contractors
N.A.I.C.S.: 238330
David Douthit (CFO)
John Davern (Dir-Maintenance Sls)
Rebecca Pollard (Mgr-HR)
Erik Lind (Dir-Strategic Accts)
Mark Cannon (COO)
Jim Burns (Pres)

CORPORATE HEALTH GROUP, LLC
7 Brayton Meadow, East Greenwich, RI 02818
Tel.: (401) 886-5588
Web Site:
　http://www.corporatehealth.com
Year Founded: 1988
Sales Range: $10-24.9 Million
Emp.: 30
Health Care Consulting Services
N.A.I.C.S.: 541611
Carolyn Merriman (Founder & Pres)

CORPORATE INK PUBLIC RE-LATIONS, LTD.
90 Washington St, Newton, MA 02458
Tel.: (617) 969-9192
Web Site:
　http://www.corporateink.com
Year Founded: 1989
Sales Range: $1-9.9 Million
Emp.: 16
Integrated Marketing & Public Relations
N.A.I.C.S.: 541820
Amy Bermar (Pres & Founder)
Corinne Sheehan (VP)
Greg Hakim (VP)
Erin Caldwell (Dir-Acct)

CORPORATE INSTALLATION SERVICES
10421 Ford Rd, Dearborn, MI 48126
Tel.: (313) 582-0800
Rev.: $21,336,619
Emp.: 225
Office Furniture Installation
N.A.I.C.S.: 238990

Subsidiaries:

Rose Moving and Storage Co.　　(1)
41775 Ecorse Ste 190, Belleville, MI 48111
Tel.: (734) 957-8000
Web Site: http://www.allieddetroit.com
Rev.: $21,000,000
Emp.: 190
Local & Long Distance Trucking With Storage & Furniture Installation
N.A.I.C.S.: 484110
Robert E. Maczka (Pres)

CORPORATE INTERIOR SYS-TEMS
3311 E Broadway Rd, Phoenix, AZ 85040
Tel.: (602) 304-0100
Web Site: https://www.cisinphx.com
Sales Range: $10-24.9 Million
Emp.: 30
Sales of Office Furniture
N.A.I.C.S.: 423210
Lisa K. Johnson (Pres)
Pam Harrell (Project Mgr)
Elisabeth Harris (Mgr-Mktg)
Lisa Tinnion (Sr Acct Mgr)
Noel Palmer (Acct Mgr)
Michelle Blaisdell (Project Mgr-Architectural Solutions)
Stephanie Bourland (VP-Sls)

CORPORATE INTERIORS INC.
223 Lisa Dr, New Castle, DE 19720
Tel.: (302) 323-9100
Web Site: https://www.corporate-interiors.com
Sales Range: $25-49.9 Million
Emp.: 150
Office & Public Building Furniture
N.A.I.C.S.: 423210
Janice Leone (Pres & Principal)
Rich Defrancesco (Project Mgr)
Paula McCullin (Controller)
Jeff Ecret (Dir-Workplace Svcs & Sls)
Ned Peterson (Project Mgr)
Kevin Ennis (Mgr-Production)

CORPORATE INTERIORS, INC.
12115 28th St N, Saint Petersburg, FL 33716
Tel.: (727) 539-7544　　　　FL
Web Site:
　http://www.corporateinteriorsinc.com
Year Founded: 1994
Sales Range: $25-49.9 Million
Emp.: 40
Furniture Merchant Whslr
N.A.I.C.S.: 423210
Drew Marshall (Pres)

CORPORATE PARTNERS LLC
45 Rockefeller Plz 19th Fl, New York, NY 10111
Tel.: (212) 332-5601　　　　DE
Web Site:
　http://www.corporatepartnersllc.com
Year Founded: 2005
Sales Range: $150-199.9 Million
Emp.: 10
Privater Equity Firm
N.A.I.C.S.: 523999
Jonathan H. Kagan (Mng Principal)
Ali E. Wambold (Mng Principal)

Subsidiaries:

Universal Trailer Corporation　　(1)
11590 Century Blvd Ste 103, Cincinnati, OH 45246
Tel.: (513) 671-3880
Web Site: http://www.universaltrailer.com
Sales Range: $75-99.9 Million
Cargo Trailer Mfr
N.A.I.C.S.: 336212
Cliff Stewart (Mgr-Plant)

Subsidiary (Domestic):

Exiss Aluminum Trailers, Inc　　(2)
900 E Trail Blvd, El Reno, OK 73036
Tel.: (405) 262-6471
Web Site: http://www.exiss.com
Sales Range: $25-49.9 Million
Specialty Trailer Mfr
N.A.I.C.S.: 336214

Featherlite, Inc.　　(2)
Hwy 63 & Hwy 9 PO Box 320, Cresco, IA 52136
Tel.: (563) 547-6000
Web Site: http://www.fthr.com
Sales Range: $50-74.9 Million
Specialty Trailer Mfr
N.A.I.C.S.: 336214
Craig Powers (Engr-Maintenance)

HMIN, Inc.　　(2)
13927 Country Rd 4, Bristol, IN 46507
Tel.: (574) 825-5867
Web Site: http://www.haulmark.com
Sales Range: $1-9.9 Million
Specialty Trailer Mfr
N.A.I.C.S.: 336214
Kevin Page (Pres)

Sooner Trailer Manufacturing Company　　(2)
900 Exiss Blvd, El Reno, OK 73036
Tel.: (405) 262-6471
Web Site: http://www.soonertrailer.com
Sales Range: $25-49.9 Million
Specialty Trailer Mfr
N.A.I.C.S.: 336214
Don Moreau (VP-Sls & Mktg)

Wells Holdings, Inc.　　(2)
1503 McNaughton Ave, Elkhart, IN 46514-2243
Tel.: (574) 264-9661
Web Site: http://www.wellscargo.com
Sales Range: $125-149.9 Million
Holding Company; Mobile Homes & Trailers Mfr
N.A.I.C.S.: 551112

Subsidiary (Domestic):

Wells Cargo Trailer Sales, LLC　　(3)
1775 E 4th St, Reno, NV 89512
Tel.: (775) 329-0061
Web Site: http://www.wellscargo.com
Sales Range: $10-24.9 Million
Mobile Homes & Trailers Dealership
N.A.I.C.S.: 441210

Plant (Domestic):

Wells Industries　　(3)
1741 W 2550 S, Ogden, UT 84401-3247　　　　(100%)
Tel.: (801) 621-3637
Web Site: http://www.wellscargo.com
Sales Range: $50-74.9 Million
Mfr of Truck Trailers
N.A.I.C.S.: 336212
Roger Shuman (Gen Mgr)

CORPORATE PRESS INC.
9700 Philadelphia Ct, Lanham, MD 20706
Tel.: (301) 499-9200　　　　MD
Web Site:
　http://www.corporatepress.com
Year Founded: 1982
Rev.: $28,000,000
Emp.: 100
Commercial Printing, Lithographic
N.A.I.C.S.: 323111
Michael Marcian (CEO)
Wesley Kopp (Dir-Digital Media)
Stan Ritter (Gen Mgr)

Subsidiaries:

ColorCraft of Virginia, Inc.　　(1)
22645 Sally Ride Dr, Sterling, VA 20164
Tel.: (703) 709-2270
Emp.: 30
Commercial Printing Services
N.A.I.C.S.: 323111
Bryan Koons (VP-Sls)
Scott Shure (Gen Mgr)

Corporate Color, Inc.　　(1)
500 Monocacy Blvd, Frederick, MD 21701
Tel.: (301) 662-1195
Web Site: http://www.cpcolor.com
Rev.: $3,666,666
Emp.: 45
Other Commercial Printing
N.A.I.C.S.: 323111
John Marcian (Gen Mgr)
Charles Cook (Mgr-Fin)

Corporate Direct Inc.　　(1)
9700 Philadelphia Ct, Lanham, MD 20706
Tel.: (301) 499-9200
Web Site: http://www.corppress.com
Sales Range: $10-24.9 Million
Commercial Printing, Lithographic
N.A.I.C.S.: 323111
Michael Marcian (Pres)

JobOn Corporation　　(1)
1422 Brenwoode Rd, Annapolis, MD 21401
Tel.: (410) 604-2040
Web Site: http://www.jobon.com
Data Processing Services
N.A.I.C.S.: 518210

CORPORATE PROPERTY AS-SOCIATES 18 GLOBAL INC
ONE MANHATTAN WEST, 395 9TH AVENUE, 58TH FLOOR, New York, NY 10001
Tel.: (212) 492-1100　　　　MD
N.A.I.C.S.: 525990

CORPORATE PROTECTIVE SECURITY INC.
5100 Popler Ste 811, Memphis, TN 38137
Tel.: (901) 766-7540
Web Site: http://www.corp-security.com
Rev.: $18,000,000
Emp.: 60
Security Guard Services
N.A.I.C.S.: 812990
Tommy R. Young (CEO)

CORPORATE REALTY IN-COME FUND 1 LP
475 5th Ave, New York, NY 10017
Tel.: (212) 696-0772　　　　DE
Sales Range: $10-24.9 Million
Emp.: 17
Management Company
N.A.I.C.S.: 531210
Madeline Matlak (Fund Administrator)

CORPORATE RESEARCH IN-TERNATIONAL
129 E Crawford, Findlay, OH 45840
Tel.: (419) 422-3196
Web Site:
　http://www.mysteryshops.com
Sales Range: $1-9.9 Million
Emp.: 60
Market Research Services

Corporate Research International—(Continued)

N.A.I.C.S.: 541910

CORPORATE RESULTS INC

8219 Leesburg Pike Ste 402, Vienna, VA 22182
Tel.: (703) 893-0919
Web Site: http://www.cri4results.com
Sales Range: $1-9.9 Million
Emp.: 25
Business Management Consulting Services
N.A.I.C.S.: 541611
Dana McMillan (Mgr-Acctg)
Maureen Collins (Mgr-Contracts)

CORPORATE RISK HOLDINGS LLC

600 3rd Ave, New York, NY 10016
Tel.: (703) 448-0178
Web Site: http://www.corprisk.com
Year Founded: 2009
Sales Range: $1-4.9 Billion
Emp.: 10,500
Security Solutions & Law Enforcement Training Services
N.A.I.C.S.: 561611
Adrian Butler (Sr VP & Chief HR Officer)
Jeffrey S. Campbell (Sr VP & CFO)
David R. Fontaine (Sr VP, Gen Counsel & Sec)
Glenn Pinnel (VP & CIO)
Keith Bernius (Treas & VP-Fin)
Carole Yanofsky (VP & Chief Ethics & Compliance Officer)
Ray Howell (Dir-Corp Comm)

Subsidiaries:

Altegrity Risk International, Inc.   (1)
11440 Commerce Park Dr Ste 501, Reston, VA 20191
Tel.: (877) 230-9082
Web Site: http://www.altegrityrisk.com
Emp.: 100
Risk Managemeng Srvices
N.A.I.C.S.: 561611
Heidi Painter (Office Mgr)

Subsidiary (Domestic):

HireRight, Inc.   (2)
3349 Michelson Dr Ste 150, Irvine, CA 92612
Tel.: (949) 428-5800
Web Site: http://www.hireright.com
Sales Range: $50-74.9 Million
Emp.: 407
Internet-Based Pre-Employment Screening & Assessment Services
N.A.I.C.S.: 541612
Catherine Aldrich (VP-Ops)
Steve Girdler (Mng Dir-EMEA & APAC)
Thomas Spaeth (CFO)
Gregg Freeman (VP & Deputy Gen Counsel)
Mary O'Loughlin (VP-Global Customer Experience)
Steven Spencer (Mng Dir-Transportation & Healthcare)
Kathleen Delaney (VP-Mktg & Product)
Guy Abramo (CEO)
Chelsea Pyrzenski (Chief HR Officer)
Brian D. Ward (CMO)
Scott Collins (Chief Revenue Officer)
Dennis Thomas (COO)

Subsidiary (Non-US):

HireRight Canada Corporation   (3)
70 University Avenue Suite 710, Toronto, M5J 2M4, ON, Canada
Tel.: (416) 956-5000
Web Site: http://www.hireright.com
Background Screening Services
N.A.I.C.S.: 561611

HireRight Estonia AS   (3)
Liivalaia 13, Tallinn, 10118, Estonia
Tel.: (372) 6 976 600
Web Site: http://www.hireright.com
Employee Background Verification Services
N.A.I.C.S.: 541990

HireRight Poland Sp. z. o.o.   (3)
Ul Sobieskiego 11, 40-084, Katowice, Poland
Tel.: (48) 32 7288 200
Security Consulting Services
N.A.I.C.S.: 541690

HireRight Pte Ltd   (3)
391A Orchard Road 17-09 Ngee Ann City Tower A, Singapore, 238873, Singapore
Tel.: (65) 6631 2680
Web Site: http://www.hireright.com.sg
Management Consulting Services
N.A.I.C.S.: 541612
Ed Hickey (Mng Dir-Asia Pacific)

Subsidiary (Domestic):

HireRight Solutions, Inc.   (3)
4500 S 129th East Ave Ste 200, Tulsa, OK 74134-5885
Tel.: (918) 664-9991
Security Consulting Services
N.A.I.C.S.: 541690
Carol Richardson (Supvr-Collections)
Amanda J. Mason (Supvr-Project Coordination)
James Harney (Engr-IT Tech Support)

US Investigations Services, LLC   (1)
7799 Leesburg Pk Ste 1100 N, Falls Church, VA 22043-2413
Tel.: (703) 448-0178
Web Site: http://www.usis.com
Sales Range: $1-4.9 Billion
Emp.: 6,000
Information & Security Services
N.A.I.C.S.: 561611
Michael G. Fraser (Pres-Natl Security Div)

Subsidiary (Domestic):

Labat-Anderson Inc.   (2)
8000 Westpark Dr Ste 400, McLean, VA 22102-3105
Tel.: (703) 506-9600
Sales Range: $50-74.9 Million
Emp.: 650
Management Consulting Services
N.A.I.C.S.: 541618
Sandy Laboon (Mgr-HR)
Claudia Conlon (Mgr-Web Analyst & Liaison)
Joe Strange (Project Mgr)
Al Buoni (Sr VP-Ops)
Joshua Elstad (Supvr-Help Desk)

US Investigations Services Professional Services Division, Inc.   (2)
7799 Leesburg Pike Ste 400, Falls Church, VA 22043-2408
Tel.: (703) 448-0178
Management Consulting Services
N.A.I.C.S.: 541618

USIS Commercial Services   (2)
7799 Leesburg Pike Ste 1100 N, Falls Church, VA 22043-2413
Tel.: (703) 448-0178
Web Site: http://www.usis.com
Investigation Services
N.A.I.C.S.: 561611
Phillip C. McVey (Pres)

USIS Intelligence and Investigations Services   (2)
7799 Leesburg Pike Ste 1100 N, Falls Church, VA 22043-2413
Tel.: (703) 448-0178
Web Site: http://www.usis.com
Investigation Services
N.A.I.C.S.: 561613
Christopher D. Tillery (Pres-Investigations Svcs Div)
Thomas Hartley (CEO)

CORPORATE SERVICE CENTER, INC.

5190 Neil Rd Ste 430, Reno, NV 89502
Tel.: (775) 329-7721
Web Site: http://www.corporateservices.com
Year Founded: 1989
Sales Range: $1-9.9 Million
Emp.: 20
Incorporation Services to Clients Forming New Businesses Worldwide

N.A.I.C.S.: 813910
Cort Christie (Founder & Pres)

CORPORATE SERVICES INC.

208 Kishwaukee St, Rockford, IL 61104
Tel.: (815) 962-8367
Web Site: https://www.corpserv.com
Sales Range: $10-24.9 Million
Emp.: 29
Employment Agencies
N.A.I.C.S.: 561311
Roger Buck (Pres)
Sandy Lightner (Acct Mgr)

CORPORATE SUITES, LLC

1180 Ave of Americas, New York, NY 10036
Tel.: (212) 512-0500
Web Site: http://www.csbcenters.com
Year Founded: 1998
Sales Range: $10-24.9 Million
Emp.: 28
Full Service Office Center Rentals
N.A.I.C.S.: 561990
Oleg Dolinko (Coord-IT)
Robin Sanatar (Controller)

CORPORATE SYNERGIES GROUP, LLC

5000 Dearborn Cir Ste 100, Mount Laurel, NJ 08054
Tel.: (856) 813-1500
Web Site: http://www.corpsyn.com
Sales Range: $10-24.9 Million
Emp.: 250
Employee Benefits & Insurance Consulting Services
N.A.I.C.S.: 541612
John A. Turner (Pres & CEO)
Andrew Bloom (Exec VP-Ops)
Eileen Fogarty (Sr VP-HR)
Brian Feeley (Sr VP-Mktg)
Anthony DiLallo (VP-Fin)
Daniel Kuperstein (Sr VP-Compliance)
Lisa Granfors-Hunt (Dir-Acct Mgmt)
Corey Backstrom (VP-Florida)
Christian Giordano (Dir-Acct Mgmt)
Andrew Brickman (Dir-Benefits Admin)
Ellen Hosafros (Sr Mgr-Comm)
Gary Cassidy (Dir-Employee Education, Comm & Wellness)
Greg Andrews (Sr VP)
John Crable (Sr VP)
Raymond Depaola (Dir-Underwriting)
Randy Shaw (Sr VP-Sls Trng & Dev)
Matthew D. Strain (VP)
Travis Turner (VP-Acct Mgmt)
James W. Gow Jr. (Sr VP-Property & Casualty Practice)

CORPORATE TRAVEL MANAGEMENT GROUP

450 E 22nd St Ste 100, Lombard, IL 60148-6175
Tel.: (630) 691-9100
Web Site: http://www.corptrav.com
Year Founded: 1976
Sales Range: $10-24.9 Million
Emp.: 170
Provider of Travel Agency Services
N.A.I.C.S.: 561510
Bonnie Lorefice (CEO)
Jane Batio (Pres)
Lisa Donovan-Berry (Sr VP)

CORPORATE UNITED, INC.

24651 Center Ridge Rd Ste 527, Westlake, OH 44145
Tel.: (440) 895-0938
Web Site: http://www.corporateunited.com
Year Founded: 1997
Sales Range: $10-24.9 Million

Emp.: 20
Outsourced Group Purchasing
N.A.I.C.S.: 541618
Gregg Mylett (Founder)
David Clevenger (VP)
Gary Como (VP)

CORPORATION FOR EDUCATION NETWORK INITIATIVES IN CALIFORNIA

16700 Valley View Ave Ste 400, La Mirada, CA 90638
Tel.: (714) 220-3400
Web Site: https://www.cenic.org
Year Founded: 1997
Sales Range: $50-74.9 Million
Emp.: 64
Educational Support Services
N.A.I.C.S.: 611710
Sherilyn Evans (COO & VP)
Brian Court (Dir-Network Engrg & Design)
Bill Paik (CFO)
Deborah Ludford (Treas)
Louis Fox (Pres & CEO)
Tom Andriola (Sec)
John Dundas III (CTO & VP)

CORPORATION FOR ENTERPRISE DEVELOPMENT CFED

1200 G St NW Ste 400, Washington, DC 20005
Tel.: (202) 408-9788
Web Site: http://www.cfed.org
Year Founded: 1979
Sales Range: $10-24.9 Million
Emp.: 66
Low Income Housing Services
N.A.I.C.S.: 624229
Jennifer Brooks (VP-Field Engagement)
Parker Cohen (Sr Program Mgr-Savings & Fin Capability)
Megan Bolado (Program Mgr-Savings & Fin Capability)
Adnan Bokhari (CFO)
Karianna Barr (Mgr-Database & Sponsorships)

CORPORATION FOR PUBLIC BROADCASTING

401 9th St NW, Washington, DC 20004-2129
Tel.: (202) 879-9600
Web Site: https://www.cpb.org
Year Founded: 1967
Sales Range: $400-449.9 Million
Emp.: 131
Television Broadcasting Services
N.A.I.C.S.: 516120
Patricia De Stacy Harrison (Pres & CEO)
Ted Krichels (Sr VP-System Dev & Media Strategy)
Bruce Ramer (Chm)
Michael Levy (COO & Exec VP)
Patricia Cahill (Vice Chm)
Steven J. Altman (Chief Policy & Bus Affairs Officer & Exec VP)
Teresa Safon (Sec & Sr VP)
Kathy Merritt (Sr VP-Journalism & Radio)
Maja Mrkoci (Sr VP-Television Content & Innovation)
Anne Brachman (Sr VP-Govt Affairs)
Deborah Carr (VP-Media Strategy Ops)
Letitia King (Sr VP-Comm)
Debra Tica Sanchez (Sr VP-Education & Children's Content Ops)
William P. Tayman Jr. (CFO & Treas)

CORPORATION SERVICE COMPANY

251 Little Falls Dr, Wilmington, DE
19808-1645
Tel.: (302) 636-5400   DE
Web Site: http://www.cscglobal.com
Year Founded: 1899
Sales Range: $350-399.9 Million
Emp.: 1,600
Public Record Document Filing, Retrieval & UCC Services; Litigation;
Domain Name & Entity Mgmt; Registered Agent
N.A.I.C.S.: 541199
E. J. Dealy *(Mgr-Corp Dev)*
Kent Priestley *(Mgr-PR)*
Jackie Smetana *(VP-Ops-Global)*
Jennifer Kenton *(Sr VP-Svcs-Global)*
Rodman Ward III *(Pres & CEO)*

Subsidiaries:

CSC Digital Brand Services   (1)
2560 Mission College Blvd Ste 200, Santa
Clara, CA 95054
Tel.: (866) 907-3267
Web Site: http://www.melbourneitdbs.com
Sales Range: $10-24.9 Million
Emp.: 50
Online Brand Monitoring & Protection Services
N.A.I.C.S.: 541618

CSC Digital Brand Services
Limited   (1)
1st Floor 2-5 Benjamin Street, London,
EC1M 5QL, United Kingdom
Tel.: (44) 2075494100
Web Site: http://www.melbourneitdbs.com
Online Brand Monitoring & Protection Services
N.A.I.C.S.: 541618

Corporation Service Company (UK)
Limited   (1)
Unit 20/21 Elysium Gate, 126-128 New
Kings Rd, London, SW6 4LZ, United Kingdom
Tel.: (44) 2075654090
Web Site: http://www.cscglobal.com
Emp.: 15
Corporate Legal & Risk Management Services
N.A.I.C.S.: 561499
Marie Le Maitre *(Mgr-Mktg)*
Justin Hartland *(Reg Dir)*

Internet Names Wordwide Espana
SL   (1)
Calle Jorge Juan 8 3A, Madrid, 28001,
Spain
Tel.: (34) 91 426 1951
Web Site: http://www.inww.es
Online Brand Monitoring & Protection Services
N.A.I.C.S.: 541618

Intertrust B.V.   (1)
Prins Bernhardplein 200, 1097 JB, Amsterdam, Netherlands
Tel.: (31) 205214777
Web Site: http://www.intertrustgroup.com
Rev.: $693,303,405
Assets: $2,532,111,334
Liabilities: $1,598,263,267
Net Worth: $933,848,067
Earnings: $25,596,522
Emp.: 4,076
Fiscal Year-end: 12/31/2020
Holding Company; Trust & Corporate Services
N.A.I.C.S.: 551112

Subsidiary (Domestic):

Intertrust Group B.V.   (2)
Basisweg 10, 1043 AP, Amsterdam, Netherlands
Tel.: (31) 205214777
Web Site: https://www.intertrustgroup.com
Holding Company
N.A.I.C.S.: 551112

Subsidiary (Non-US):

Intertrust Group Holding S.A.   (3)
Place des Alpes 4, 1201, Geneva, Switzerland
Tel.: (41) 223178000
Web Site: https://www.intertrustgroup.com

Holding Company; Trust, Corporate, Administrative & Wealth Management Services
N.A.I.C.S.: 551112
Jurgen M.J. Borgt *(Mng Dir)*
Boudewijn Korten *(Comml Dir)*

Subsidiary (Non-US):

Intertrust (Belgium) NV/SA   (4)
Avenue Marnix 23 5th floor, 1000, Brussels,
Belgium
Tel.: (32) 22092200
Web Site: https://www.intertrustgroup.com
Emp.: 18
Trust, Corporate & Wealth Management Services
N.A.I.C.S.: 523991
Christophe Tans *(Mng Dir)*
Irene Florescu *(Dir-Fin)*
Christine Michel *(Mgr-Customer Rels)*
Alain Smets *(Sr Mgr-Fin Acct)*

Intertrust (Curacao) BV   (4)
Zeelandia Office Park Kaya W F G Jombi
Mensing 14 2nd Floor, PO Box 3889,
Willemstad, Curacao
Tel.: (599) 94331000
Web Site: https://www.intertrustgroup.com
Trust, Corporate, Administrative & Wealth
Management Services
N.A.I.C.S.: 523991
Nacha de Jesus *(Dir-Bus Unit)*
Sonja Hartsuijker *(Mng Dir)*
Arriela Boelijn *(Mgr-Bus Unit)*
Valery Gomez-Trapenberg *(Dir-Bus Unit)*
Yvo Peters *(Acct Mgr-Legal)*
Mireille Clarinda *(Sr Acct Mgr-Legal)*
Vaynith Bonafasia *(Mgr-Bus Unit)*

Intertrust (Denmark) A/S   (4)
Harbour House Sundkrogsgade 21, 2100,
Copenhagen, Denmark   (100%)
Tel.: (45) 33189000
Web Site: https://www.intertrustgroup.com
Trust & Wealth Management Services
N.A.I.C.S.: 523991
Jacob Smed *(Mng Dir-Nordics & Jersey)*
Niels Christian Wedell-Wedellsborg *(Mng
Dir)*
Ken Tellefsen *(Dir-Bus Dev)*
Jesper Ruvald *(Dir-Compliance-Nordic)*
Dorte Thomsen *(Dir-Bus Unit-Fund Admin)*
Kimmie Tronborg *(Dir-Bus Unit & Corp
Svcs)*
Claus Frosch *(Sr Mgr-Payroll & HR)*
Torben Harder *(Acct Mgr-Fund)*
Paolo Castaneda *(Mgr-Bus Unit-Payroll &
HR Svcs)*

Intertrust (Dubai) Limited   (4)
Unit 1306 Level 13 Tower II Al Fattan Currency House DIFC, Dubai, United Arab
Emirates
Tel.: (971) 43780600
Web Site: https://www.intertrustgroup.com
Trust, Corporate & Wealth Management Services
N.A.I.C.S.: 523991
Alia Haskouri *(Mgr-Bus Dev)*
David McVeigh *(Sr Mgr-Fin Acct)*
Patricia't Hart-van Rooijen *(Mng Dir)*

Intertrust (Guernsey) Limited   (4)
Martello Court Admiral Park, PO Box 119,
Saint Peter Port, GY1 3HB, Guernsey
Tel.: (44) 1481211000
Web Site: http://www.intertrustgroup.com
Trust, Corporate & Wealth Management Services
N.A.I.C.S.: 523991
Sue Trebert *(Mgr-Mktg & Comm)*
Grant Howitt *(Dir-Trust & Corp Svcs)*
Mick Cahill *(CEO)*
Paul Schreibke *(Mng Dir)*
Neil Dorey *(Dir-Taxation Svcs)*
Andrew Niles *(Dir-Fin)*
Chris Adkins *(Mgr-Trust & Corp Svcs)*
Chris Bourgaize *(Dir-Risk & Compliance)*
Julia Church *(Dir-Trust & Corp Svcs)*
Tina Coutanche *(Mgr-Taxation Svcs)*
Steven De Jersey *(Assoc Dir)*
Melanie Duquemin *(Mgr-Fund Admin Svcs)*
Mark Fouracre *(Dir-Trust & Corp Svcs)*
Peter Griffin *(Dir-Trust & Corp Svcs)*
Rebecca Settle *(Asst Mgr-Corp Svcs)*
Sarah Willis *(Mgr-Risk Solution)*
David Hutchins *(Dir-Legal Svcs)*
Andrew Maiden *(Dir-Fund Svcs)*
Jane Le Maitre *(Dir-Taxation Svcs)*
Kees Jager *(Dir-Fund Svcs)*
Alison Parry *(Head-Private Wealth)*

Intertrust (Luxembourg) S.a.r.l.   (4)
Vertigo Naos Building 6 rue Eugene Ruppert, 2453, Luxembourg, Luxembourg
Tel.: (352) 264491
Web Site: https://www.intertrustgroup.com
Emp.: 500
Trust, Corporate & Wealth Management
Services
N.A.I.C.S.: 523991
Bram Eijsbouts *(Comml Dir)*
Gaelle Attardo-Kontzler *(Dir-Capital Markets)*
Veronique Bastin *(Dir-Compliance & Risk)*
Franck Beth *(Dir-Bus Unit)*
Nellie Esparza *(Mgr-Bus Unit-Corp & Legal)*
Anja Grenner *(Dir-Funds)*
Maelle Lenaers *(Head-Legal-AIFM)*
Douwe Terpstra *(Mng Dir)*
Frank Welman *(Mng Dir)*
Hui Gao *(Comml Dir)*

Intertrust (Netherlands) B.V.   (4)
Basisweg 10, 1043 AP, Amsterdam, Netherlands
Tel.: (31) 205214777
Web Site: https://www.intertrustgroup.com
Trust, Corporate, Administrative & Wealth
Management Services
N.A.I.C.S.: 523991
Veronica Gunther *(Dir-Legal)*
Jurjen Hardeveld *(Dir-Svc Line)*
Evert Wind *(Head-Corp Client Svcs-Global)*
Joost Broekhuis *(Exec Dir-Capital Markets
& Fund Svcs)*
Marcelo Delfos *(Dir-Bus Dev)*
Rene Blokker *(Dir-Client)*
David Braat *(Dir-Legal)*
Liselotte Heine *(Dir-Legal)*

Intertrust (Spain) S.L.   (4)
Serrano 41 4, 28001, Madrid, Spain
Tel.: (34) 917811671
Web Site: https://www.intertrustgroup.com
Trust, Corporate & Wealth Management
Services
N.A.I.C.S.: 523991
Carmen Rozpide *(Mng Dir)*
Alberto Osacar *(Mgr-Bus Dev)*
Jaime J. Azcona San Julian *(Chm)*

Subsidiary (Domestic):

Intertrust (Suisse) S.A.   (4)
Place des Alpes 4, 1201, Geneva, Switzerland
Tel.: (41) 223178000
Web Site: https://www.intertrustgroup.com
Trust, Corporate, Administrative & Wealth
Management Services
N.A.I.C.S.: 561499
Boudewijn Korten *(Comml Dir)*
Nicole Kourouma *(Dir-Risk & Compliance)*
Jurgen M. J. Borgt *(Mng Dir)*

Subsidiary (Domestic):

Intertrust Services (Schweiz) AG   (5)
Zahlerweg 6, 6300, Zug, Switzerland
Tel.: (41) 417268200
Web Site: https://www.intertrustgroup.com
Trust & Wealth Management Services
N.A.I.C.S.: 523991
Arno Bijl *(Mng Dir)*
Sean Bresin *(Dir-Private Client Svcs)*

Subsidiary (Non-US):

Intertrust (Sweden) AB   (4)
Sveavagen 9 10th Floor, 111 57, Stockholm, Sweden
Tel.: (46) 84027200
Trust & Corporate Management Services
N.A.I.C.S.: 523991

Intertrust Cayman Islands   (4)
One Nexus Way, Camana Bay, KY1-9005,
Grand Cayman, Cayman Islands
Tel.: (345) 9433100
Web Site: https://www.intertrustgroup.com
Trust, Corporate & Wealth Management
Services
N.A.I.C.S.: 523991
Mary Willmot *(Dir-Bus Dev & Content)*
Colin MacKay *(Reg Dir-Caribbean)*
Lesley Connolly *(Head-Compliance & Regulatory Ops)*
Mary Willmot *(Dir-Bus Dev & Content)*
Carl Brenton *(Head-Fund Svcs)*
Evert Brunekreef *(Dir-Capital Markets)*

Christopher Bryan *(Assoc Dir-Capital
Markets-Americas)*
Kim Charaman *(VP-Hedge Funds)*
Susan Craig *(Mgr-Bus Unit-Capital Markets-
Ireland)*
Ellen Christian *(Dir-Capital Markets)*
Brian Eden *(VP-Fiduciary Svcs)*
Neil Gray *(Dir-Fiduciary Svcs)*
Jennifer Chailler *(Sr VP-Private Equity)*
Helen Dombowsky *(Dir)*
Jennifer Stein *(Sr VP-Hedge Funds)*
Nadine Watler *(Mng Dir)*

Intertrust Danismanlik AS   (4)
Cecen Sokak Akasya Kent Business Tower
Floor 28 Suite No 172, Acibadem Uskudar,
34660, Istanbul, Turkiye
Tel.: (90) 2165105465
Web Site: http://www.intertrustgroup.com
Trust, Corporate & Wealth Management
Services
N.A.I.C.S.: 523991
Duygu Takiloglu *(Mng Dir)*

Intertrust Fiduciary Services (Jersey)
Limited   (4)
44 Esplanade, Saint Helier, JE4 9WG, Jersey
Tel.: (44) 1534504000
Web Site: http://www.intertrustgroup.com
Trust, Fund & Company Administration Services
N.A.I.C.S.: 523991
Simon Mackenzie *(Head-Rels Mgmt)*
Cheryl Heslop *(Assoc Dir-Capital Markets)*
Shane Hugill *(Dir-Performance & Reward
Mgmt)*
Laura Butler *(Dir-Performance & Reward
Mgmt)*
Nicola Giraud *(Fin Dir)*
Alma Dauru *(Client Dir-Corp Svcs)*
Chris Bowden *(Dir-Corp Svcs)*

Intertrust Holdings (UK) Limited   (4)
1 Bartholomew Lane, London, EC2N 2AX,
United Kingdom
Tel.: (44) 2073986300
Web Site: https://www.intertrustgroup.com
Trust, Corporate & Wealth Management
Services
N.A.I.C.S.: 523991
Daniel Jaffe *(Mng Dir-Market Offices)*
Claudia Wallace *(Mng Dir)*
Maurice Kalsbeek *(Dir-Corp Svcs)*
Sue Abrahams *(Dir-London)*
Amy LeJune *(Bus Unit Mgr-Fin)*
Debra Parsall *(Dir)*
Neil Townson *(Mng Dir)*
Helena Whitaker *(Dir)*

Subsidiary (Non-US):

Intertrust Management Ireland
Limited   (5)
2nd Floor 1-2 Victoria Buildings Haddington
Road, Dublin, 4, Ireland
Tel.: (353) 16686152
Web Site: https://www.intertrustgroup.com
Trust, Corporate & Wealth Management
Services
N.A.I.C.S.: 523991
Imelda Shine *(Country Mgr)*
Anne Flood *(Mng Dir)*
Anna Alves *(Relationship Mgr)*
Audrey Behan *(Head-Risk AIFMD)*
Brian Buckley *(Mng Dir)*
Brendan Byrne *(Fin Dir)*
Elizabeth Dawson *(Relationship Mgr)*
Seamus Fox *(Mgr-Bus Dev)*
David Greene *(Bus Unit Mgr)*
Paul Griffith *(Sr Relationship Mgr)*
Aine Hickey *(Assoc Dir)*
Neasa Moloney *(Bus Unit Mgr)*
Colm O. Murchadha *(Sr Fin Accountant
Mgr)*
Mark O'Hare *(Relationship Mgr)*
Lelia O'Hea *(Bus Unit Mgr-Corp)*
Ronan O'Neill *(Bus Unit Mgr)*
Anne-Marie Sexton *(Sr Mgr-Fin Acct)*

Subsidiary (Non-US):

Intertrust Hong Kong Limited   (4)
3806 Central Plaza 18 Harbour Road, Wanchai, China (Hong Kong)
Tel.: (852) 28027711
Web Site: https://www.intertrustgroup.com
Trust, Corporate, Administrative & Wealth
Management Services

Corporation Service Company—(Continued)

N.A.I.C.S.: 523991
Alice Lau *(Head-Private Wealth Svcs & Exec Dir)*
James Donnan *(Mng Dir)*
Fang Ling Khor *(Head-Fund Svcs & Exec Dir)*
Larry Lai *(Dir-Taxation-Corp Svcs)*
Jennifer Pau *(Dir-Comml Dev)*
Quinten Kah *(Sr Mgr-Comml Dev)*
Jessica Tsang *(Sr Mgr-Payroll & Visa)*
Emily Wu *(Dir-Fund Svcs)*

Subsidiary (Non-US):

Intertrust (Shanghai) Consultants Limited   (5)
Unit 01 3rd Floor 100 Bund Square No 100 Zhong Shan Road South, Huangpu District, Shanghai, 200010, China
Tel.: (86) 2150988686
Web Site: https://www.intertrustgroup.com
Trust, Corporate & Wealth Management Services
N.A.I.C.S.: 523991
Felix Deng *(Assoc Dir-Bus Dev)*
John Ma *(Gen Mgr)*

Branch (Domestic):

Intertrust China - Guangzhou Office   (6)
Room 708 International Finance Centre No 5 Zhujiang West Road, Tianhe District, Guangzhou, 510623, China
Tel.: (86) 2038858686
Web Site: https://www.intertrustgroup.com
Trust, Corporate & Wealth Management Services
N.A.I.C.S.: 523991
Linda Chen *(Head-Office)*

Subsidiary (Non-US):

Intertrust (Singapore) Ltd.   (5)
77 Robinson Road 13-00 Robinson 77, Singapore, 068896, Singapore
Tel.: (65) 65006400
Web Site: https://www.intertrustgroup.com
Trust, Corporate, Administrative & Wealth Management Services
N.A.I.C.S.: 523991
Sharon Chow *(Dir-Acctg & Payroll)*
Lauren Murphy *(Dir-Private Wealth)*
Charlotte Paauwe *(Mgr-Bus Dev & Capital Markets)*
Lynette Chuah *(Dir-HR)*
Kelly Han *(Mgr-Corp Secretarial)*
Dianie Samad *(Mgr-Fund Svcs)*
Christine Tan *(Dir-Fund Svcs)*
Raj Keloth *(Sr Dir-Corp Secretarial)*
Jennifer Lee *(Assoc Dir-Corp Secretarial)*
Juliana Loh *(Assoc Dir-Corp Secretarial)*
Jon Barratt *(Mng Dir)*

MLM Information Services, LLC   (1)
780 3rd Ave 30th Fl, New York, NY 10017
Tel.: (212) 245-5310
Corporate Tax Software Solutions
N.A.I.C.S.: 513210

Subsidiary (Domestic):

Corptax, Inc.   (1)
1751 Lake Cook Rd Ste 100, Deerfield, IL 60015
Tel.: (847) 236-8000
Web Site: http://www.corptax.com
Sales Range: $50-74.9 Million
Emp.: 500
Computer Software Development
N.A.I.C.S.: 513210
Dave Shea *(CEO)*
Chris Salafatinos *(CFO)*
Steve Buck *(CTO)*
Ted Pacheco *(VP-Sls & Mktg)*
Lloyd Howlett *(VP-Support & Customer Ops)*

Tax Compliance, Inc.   (2)
10089 Willow Creek Rd Ste 300, San Diego, CA 92131
Tel.: (858) 547-4100
Web Site: http://www.taxcomp.com
Tax Software Solutions
N.A.I.C.S.: 513210
Scott Strauss *(Pres & CEO)*
Shannon Cynkin *(Mgr-Client Relationship)*
Ashley Hassler *(Project Mgr-Implementation & Trng)*

The Company Corporation   (1)
251 Little Falls Dr, Wilmington, DE 19808-1660
Tel.: (302) 636-5430
Web Site: http://www.incorporate.com
Sales Range: $10-24.9 Million
Emp.: 100
Business Incorporation Services
N.A.I.C.S.: 561499
David Gilardi *(Gen Mgr)*

CORPORATION TO DEVELOP COMMUNITIES OF TAMPA, INC.
1907 E Hillsborough Ave Ste 100, Tampa, FL 33610
Tel.: (813) 231-4362   FL
Web Site:
  https://www.cdcoftampa.org
Year Founded: 1992
Sales Range: $1-9.9 Million
Emp.: 26
Individual & Family Services
N.A.I.C.S.: 624190
Tammy Haylock-Moore *(Chm)*
Ernest Coney Jr. *(COO)*

CORPOREX COMPANIES, INC.
100 E Rivercenter Blvd Ste 1100, Covington, KY 41011-1555
Tel.: (859) 292-5500   KY
Web Site: https://www.corporex.com
Year Founded: 1965
Sales Range: $200-249.9 Million
Emp.: 65
Commercial & Industrial Operative Builders & Developers
N.A.I.C.S.: 525990
William P. Butler *(Founder, Chm & CEO)*
Thomas E. Banta *(Mng Dir)*
Brett N Blackwell *(CFO)*
Amy Middendorf *(Sls Dir-Ovation)*
Anthony Salants *(Mgr-Interior Design-Ovation)*
Nick Heekin *(COO)*
Heather Harris *(Sr VP-Sls & Mktg)*

Subsidiaries:

Corporex Development   (1)
100 E Rivercenter Blvd Ste 1100, Covington, KY 41011-1602   (100%)
Tel.: (859) 292-5500
Web Site: http://www.corporex.com
Sales Range: $10-24.9 Million
Emp.: 50
Finance And Investment
N.A.I.C.S.: 561110
William P. Butler *(Chm & CEO)*
Thomas E. Banta *(Mng Dir)*
Mark R. Arstingstall *(Treas & Exec VP)*
Leigh R. Judd *(Sec & Asst Treas)*

CORPUS MEDIA LABS, INC.
14160 Dallas Pkwy Ste 100, Dallas, TX 75254
Tel.: (972) 746-4600
Web Site:
  http://corpusmedialabs.com
Sales Range: $10-24.9 Million
Emp.: 270
Computer System Design Services
N.A.I.C.S.: 541512

CORR TECH, INC.
4545 Homestead Rd, Houston, TX 77028
Tel.: (713) 674-7887
Web Site: http://www.corr-tech.com
Year Founded: 1969
Sales Range: $10-24.9 Million
Emp.: 25
Distr of Corrosion Resistant & High Purity Fluid & Air Handling Products
N.A.I.C.S.: 423720
James E. Gottesman *(Founder)*

CORR WIRELESS INC.

600 3rd Ave E, Oneonta, AL 35121
Tel.: (205) 237-3581
Web Site:
  http://www.corrwireless.com
Sales Range: $10-24.9 Million
Emp.: 90
Cellular Telephone Services
N.A.I.C.S.: 517810
Thomas J. Buchanan *(Gen Counsel)*
Tim Knight *(Mgr-MSC)*

CORR-WILLIAMS COMPANY
110 Airport Rd S Ste B, Pearl, MS 39208
Tel.: (601) 420-5121
Web Site:
  https://www.corrwilliams.com
Sales Range: $25-49.9 Million
Emp.: 120
Groceries, General Line
N.A.I.C.S.: 424410
William Becker *(Owner)*
Harold Niebanck *(Owner)*

CORRADO'S FAMILY AFFAIR
1578 Main Ave, Clifton, NJ 07011
Tel.: (973) 340-8590
Web Site:
  https://www.corradosmarket.com
Year Founded: 1950
Owner & Operator of Grocery Stores
N.A.I.C.S.: 445110
Cadell Singh *(Mgr-Front End)*

CORRECT CRAFT, INC.
14700 Aerospace Pkwy, Orlando, FL 32832
Tel.: (407) 855-4141   FL
Web Site: http://www.nautique.com
Year Founded: 1925
Sales Range: $150-199.9 Million
Emp.: 660
Boat Building & Repairing
N.A.I.C.S.: 336612
Angela Pilkington *(VP-Admin)*
Ken Meloon *(Chm)*
Bill Yeargin *(Pres & CEO)*

Subsidiaries:

Bryant Boats, Inc.   (1)
306 East North St., Sweetwater, TN 37874
Tel.: (423) 337-3639
Web Site: http://www.bryantboats.com
Rev.: $3,333,333
Emp.: 38
Boat Building
N.A.I.C.S.: 336612
Joseph Bryant *(Founder)*

Pleasurecraft Engine Group   (1)
1737 US-76, Little Mountain, SC 29075
Tel.: (803) 345-1337
Web Site: http://www.pleasurecraft.com
Gasoline Powered Inboard Motors Mfr
N.A.I.C.S.: 333618
Mark McKinney *(Pres)*
Mark Schneider *(Mgr-Warranty)*
John Valvano *(Mgr)*
Jon Lowe *(Mgr-Engrg)*

Southeast Marine Sales and Services, Inc.   (1)
7576 S Orange Ave, Orlando, FL 32809
Tel.: (407) 851-1965
Web Site:
  http://www.southeastmarinesales.com
Boat Dealers
N.A.I.C.S.: 423910
Gary Meloon *(Gen Mgr)*

CORRECTION PRODUCTS CO.
5802 Rocky Point, San Antonio, TX 78249
Tel.: (210) 829-7951   DE
Web Site:
  https://www.correctionsproducts.com
Sales Range: Less than $1 Million
Emp.: 9

Designer, Producer & Marketer of High Quality Detention Locking Devices for Use in Correctional Facilities
N.A.I.C.S.: 423710
Sandy Watson *(Controller)*

CORRIDOR CAPITAL, LLC
12400 Wilshire Blvd Ste 645, Los Angeles, CA 90025
Tel.: (310) 442-7000
Web Site:
  https://www.corridorcapital.com
Year Founded: 2005
Privater Equity Firm
N.A.I.C.S.: 523999
Craig L. Enenstein *(Founder & Mng Partner)*
Cameron Reilly *(Mng Dir)*
Shaun Wright *(Principal-Bus Dev)*
Jessamyn Davis *(CFO)*
Iman Navi *(VP)*
Tim Thacher *(VP)*
Rohit Bassi *(Mng Dir-Ops)*

Subsidiaries:

Association Headquarters, LLC   (1)
1120 Rte 73 Ste 200, Mount Laurel, NJ 08054
Tel.: (856) 439-0500
Web Site:
  http://www.associationheadquarters.com
Sales Range: $1-9.9 Million
Emp.: 100
Administrative Management & General Management Consulting Service
N.A.I.C.S.: 541611
Shannon Fagan *(Mgr-Exhibit)*
Denise Jackson *(Mng Dir-Washington & VP-Bus Dev)*
Kelly Mariotti *(VP-Client Svcs)*
Amy Williams *(VP-Bus Dev & Consulting)*
Jodi Araujo *(VP-Organizational Dev)*
Sue Pine *(VP-Professional Dev)*
George Rears *(VP-Tech Solutions)*

CORRIGAN BROS., INC.
3545 Gratiot St, Saint Louis, MO 63103-2921
Tel.: (314) 771-6200   MO
Web Site:
  https://www.corriganco.com
Year Founded: 1896
Sales Range: $50-74.9 Million
Emp.: 400
Warm Air Heating & Air Conditioning Contractor; Sheet Metal Work; Rental of Heavy Construction Equipment
N.A.I.C.S.: 238220
Jeff Coulson *(Mgr-Plumbing Div)*
Dawn Wallace *(Dir-HR)*
Michael McAuliffe *(Pres)*

Subsidiaries:

Corrigan Company Mechanical Contractors   (1)
3545 Gratiot St, Saint Louis, MO 63103-2921
Tel.: (314) 771-6200
Sales Range: $25-49.9 Million
Emp.: 320
Mechanical Contracting Works
N.A.I.C.S.: 238220
James A. Corrigan *(Pres)*

CORRIGAN FINANCIAL INC.
747 Aquidneck Ave, Middletown, RI 02842
Tel.: (401) 849-9313
Web Site:
  https://www.corriganfinancialinc.com
Year Founded: 1989
Financial Planning Advice & Investment Management Services
N.A.I.C.S.: 541219
Daniel Corrigan *(Founding Principal)*

CORRIGAN KRAUSE CPA
2055 Crocker Rd Ste 300, Westlake, OH 44145

Tel.: (440) 471-0800   OH
Web Site: http://corrigankrause.com
Year Founded: 1989
Accounting Services
N.A.I.C.S.: 541211

CORRIGAN MOVING SYSTEMS
23923 Research Dr, Farmington Hills, MI 48335
Tel.: (248) 471-4000
Web Site:
   https://www.corriganmoving.com
Rev.: $20,849,120
Emp.: 500
Long Haul Shipping
N.A.I.C.S.: 484121
Paul A. Corrigan *(Chm & CEO)*
David Corrigan *(Pres & COO)*
Michael Corrigan *(Founder & Exec VP)*
Mark Elliot *(Controller)*

CORRIGAN OIL CO.
775 N 2nd St, Brighton, MI 48116
Tel.: (810) 229-6323   MI
Web Site:
   https://www.corriganoil.com
Year Founded: 1958
Sales Range: $10-24.9 Million
Emp.: 40
Gas Stations Operator & Home Heating Oil Services
N.A.I.C.S.: 457120
Michael Corrigan *(Pres)*
Jon DeAngelis *(Gen Mgr)*
Dwayne Janke *(Mgr-Fleet)*
Chrissy Termalaj *(Supvr-Customer Svc)*
Dave Metevier *(Mgr-Sls)*
William Bird *(Dir-Special Projects)*

CORRISOFT LLC
1648 McGrathiana Pkwy Ste 225, Lexington, KY 40511
Tel.: (859) 271-1190
Web Site: https://www.corrisoft.com
Emp.: 100
Electronic Monitoring Technology & Software for Corrections Industry
N.A.I.C.S.: 513210
Alan Eargle *(Co-CEO)*
Jim Webb *(Pres & Co-CEO)*
Nathan McConathy *(CTO)*

Subsidiaries:

iSECUREtrac Corp.   (1)
5078 S 111th St, Omaha, NE 68137
Tel.: (402) 537-0022
Web Site: http://www.isecuretrac.com
Sales Range: $1-9.9 Million
Emp.: 58
Electronic Monitoring & Tracking Products Mfr
N.A.I.C.S.: 334419

CORROHEALTH, INC.
6509 Windcrest Dr Ste 165, Plano, TX 75024
Tel.: (844) 392-4222   DE
Web Site: https://corrohealth.com
Year Founded: 2012
Collection Agencies
N.A.I.C.S.: 561440
Pat Leonard *(CEO)*

Subsidiaries:

Xtend Healthcare LLC   (1)
500 W Main St, Hendersonville, TN 37075-7075
Web Site: https://xtendhealthcare.net
Collection Agencies
N.A.I.C.S.: 561440
Jamie Franks *(Project Dir)*
Mike Morris *(CEO)*

CORROSION FLUID PRODUCTS CORP.

24450 Indoplex Cir, Farmington Hills, MI 48335-2526
Tel.: (248) 478-0100
Web Site:
   https://www.corrosionfluid.com
Year Founded: 1968
Sales Range: $10-24.9 Million
Emp.: 85
Industrial Machinery & Equipment
N.A.I.C.S.: 423830
Joseph V. Andronaco *(Pres)*
Devin Conlin *(Asst Controller)*
David Pedersen *(Controller)*

CORROSION PRODUCTS & EQUIPMENT, INC.
110 Elmgrove Park, Rochester, NY 14624
Tel.: (585) 247-3030   NY
Web Site: https://www.corrosion-products.com
Year Founded: 1988
Sales Range: $10-24.9 Million
Emp.: 45
Plumbing Fixture Mfr
N.A.I.C.S.: 332999
Peter J. Tortorella *(Pres)*
Robert A. Tortorella *(Chm)*
David Nassivera *(COO)*
Michael Codi *(Mgr-Technical Svcs Grp)*
Robert Metz *(Mgr-Engineered Flow Grp)*
Laura Catalano *(Project Coord)*
Douglas Wade *(CEO)*

Subsidiaries:

Corrosion Products & Equipment, Inc. - Albany   (1)
35 Maplewood Ave, Albany, NY 12205
Tel.: (518) 458-7252
Web Site: http://www.corrosion-products.com
Sales Range: $25-49.9 Million
Emp.: 20
Industrial Supplies Merchant Whslr
N.A.I.C.S.: 423840
Peter J. Tortorella *(VP)*

CORRUGATED CONTAINER CORP
6405 Commonwealth Dr, Roanoke, VA 24018
Tel.: (540) 774-0500
Web Site: http://www.cccbox.com
Rev.: $18,777,844
Emp.: 120
Corrugated Box Mfr
N.A.I.C.S.: 322211
David D. Higginbotham *(Pres)*
Peggy Underwood *(Mgr-Graphic Design)*

CORRUGATED METALS, INC.
6550 Revlon Dr, Belvidere, IL 61008-6307
Tel.: (815) 323-1310   IL
Web Site: https://www.corrugated-metals.com
Year Founded: 1954
Sales Range: $50-74.9 Million
Emp.: 18
Corrugated Roofing & Siding Mfr
N.A.I.C.S.: 332322
Edward S. Carlton *(Pres)*
Manuela Martinez *(Mgr-Traffic)*

CORRUGATED SUPPLIES CORP.
5043 W 67th St, Bedford Park, IL 60638-6409
Tel.: (708) 458-5525
Web Site: https://www.csclive.com
Sales Range: $10-24.9 Million
Emp.: 75
Corrugated Box Mfr
N.A.I.C.S.: 322211

John Dopocsnak *(VP)*
Wei Xu *(Engr-Sys)*

CORRY MANUFACTURING COMPANY
519 W Main St, Corry, PA 16407
Tel.: (814) 664-9611
Web Site: https://corrymfg.com
Rev.: $31,413,150
Emp.: 300
Aircraft & Gas Turbine Components Mfr
N.A.I.C.S.: 336412
Debbie Ayers *(Mgr-Accts Payable)*
Mike Biedrgycki *(Pres)*
Steve Johnson *(Controller)*

CORRY MEMORIAL HOSPITAL
965 Shamrock Ln, Corry, PA 16407
Tel.: (814) 664-4641   PA
Web Site:
   https://www.corryhospital.com
Year Founded: 1894
Sales Range: $10-24.9 Million
Emp.: 264
Health Care Srvices
N.A.I.C.S.: 622110
Terry DeLellis *(Dir-Nursing)*
Kim K. Wolfe *(VP-Quality Mgmt)*
Gary R. Webb *(Dir-HR)*
Michael Heller *(CFO)*

CORSA PERFORMANCE EXHAUSTS
140 Blaze Industrial Pkwy, Berea, OH 44017
Tel.: (440) 891-0999
Web Site:
   https://www.corsaperformance.com
Emp.: 200
Exhaust System& Air Intakes Mfr
N.A.I.C.S.: 811114
Brent Noward *(Mgr-Mktg)*
Jim Browning Sr. *(Founder)*

CORSAIR CAPITAL, LLC
717 5th Ave 24th Fl, New York, NY 10022
Tel.: (212) 224-9400   NY
Web Site: http://www.corsair-capital.com
Year Founded: 1992
Privater Equity Firm
N.A.I.C.S.: 523999
D. T. Ignacio Jayanti *(Mng Partner)*
Raja Hadji-Touma *(Partner)*
Hari R. Rajan *(Partner)*
Marwan Karam *(Partner)*
Marwan El-Asmar *(Principal)*
Amy M. Knapp *(Partner & COO)*
Jimmy Wang *(Chief Compliance Officer & Gen Counsel)*
E. Mervyn Davies *(Chm)*
Paul Cabral *(CFO)*
Tony Ling *(Principal)*

Subsidiaries:

Corsair Capital LLP   (1)
4th Floor The Economist Building 25 Saint James's Street, London, SW1A 1HG, United Kingdom
Tel.: (44) 207 152 6530
Web Site: http://www.corsair-capital.com
Emp.: 15
Privater Equity Firm
N.A.I.C.S.: 523999
Derrick R. Estes *(Principal)*

DP World Australia Limited   (1)
Level 21 400 George Street, Sydney, 2000, NSW, Australia
Tel.: (61) 292708800
Web Site:
   http://www.dpworldaustralia.com.au
Marine Terminal Operations & Logistics Services
N.A.I.C.S.: 488310
Jason Varsamidis *(CFO)*
David Owen *(Sec)*

Jessica Blomfield *(Gen Counsel & Sec)*
Max Kruse *(COO)*
Caroline Galibert *(Exec Mgr)*
Craig Thomson *(Chief HR Officer)*
Mark Hulme *(Chief Safety, Innovation & Integration Officer)*
Martin McManus *(CIO)*
Andrews Towers *(Dir-Engrg)*
Nicole Holyer *(Mgr-Natl Comm)*
Ray Lee *(Gen Mgr-Ops-Terminal)*
Ben Moke *(Gen Mgr)*

First Eagle Holdings, Inc.   (1)
1345 Ave of the Americas, New York, NY 10105-4300
Tel.: (212) 698-3300
Holding Company; Asset Management Advisory Services
N.A.I.C.S.: 551112
Mehdi A. Mahmud *(Pres & CEO)*
Mehdi Mahmud *(Pres & CEO)*
Katherine Lynn Perkins *(CFO & Treas)*

Subsidiary (Domestic):

First Eagle Investment Management, LLC   (2)
1345 Avenue of the Americas, New York, NY 10105-4300   (100%)
Tel.: (212) 698-3300
Web Site: https://www.firsteagle.com
Rev.: $102,000,000,000
Asset Management Advisory Services
N.A.I.C.S.: 523940
Mehdi A. Mahmud *(Pres & CEO)*
Mehdi Mahmud *(Pres & CEO)*
Melanie Dow *(Chief Admin Officer)*
Jon Dorfman *(CIO)*
Brian Margulies *(CFO)*
Kimball Brooker Jr. *(Deputy Head-Global Value Team & Portfolio Mgr)*

Subsidiary (Domestic):

First Eagle Private Credit, LLC   (3)
500 Boylston St Ste 1250, Boston, MA 02116
Tel.: (617) 848-2500
Web Site: http://www.feim.com
Commercial Lending & Equipment Financing Services
N.A.I.C.S.: 522299
Timothy J. Conway *(Pres & Head-Private Credit)*
Robert K. Brown *(Mng Dir & Head-Corp Dev)*
Daniel D. McCready *(Mng Dir & Head-Credit Risk Mgmt)*
Jeffrey R. Greene *(Portfolio Mgr)*
Walter J. Marullo *(Portfolio Mgr)*
Patrick F. McAuliffe *(Mng Dir & Head-Direct Origination)*
Robert F. Milordi *(Sr Portfolio Mgr)*
Brian A. Senatore *(Portfolio Mgr)*
E. Scott Trefry *(Portfolio Mgr)*
Paul Horton *(Mng Dir-Middle Market Direct Lending)*
Jason A. Wendorf *(Mng Dir-Middle Market Direct Lending)*
Kevin T. Mulcahy *(Portfolio Mgr)*
Joseph E. Sileo *(Mng Dir & Head-Capital Markets)*
Matthew R. Colucci *(Mng Dir-Middle Market Direct Lending)*
Matthew R. Colucci *(Mng Dir-Middle Market Direct Lending)*

THL Credit Advisors LLC   (3)
100 Federal St, Boston, MA 02110
Tel.: (212) 829-3100
Web Site: http://www.thlcredit.com
Trust, Fiduciary & Custody Activities
N.A.I.C.S.: 523991
Christopher J. Flynn *(CEO)*
Brian Murphy *(Head-Capital Markets)*
Christopher Todisco *(Dir-Bus Dev-New York)*
Michael Herzig *(Mng Dir & Head-Bus Dev)*

CORSETTI STRUCTURAL STEEL INC.
2515 New Lenox Rd, Joliet, IL 60433
Tel.: (815) 726-4083
Web Site: http://www.corsettico.com
Sales Range: $10-24.9 Million
Emp.: 63
Structural Steel & Precast Concrete Contractors

Corsetti Structural Steel Inc.—(Continued)
N.A.I.C.S.: 238120
Anthony Corsetti *(VP)*
Edward Corsetti *(Treas & Sec)*
Nino Corsetti *(Pres)*

CORSICA IMPLEMENT INC.
525 S Hwy 281, Corsica, SD 57328
Tel.: (605) 946-5444   SD
Web Site:
   http://www.corsicaimplement.com
Sales Range: $10-24.9 Million
Emp.: 210
Sales of Farm Implements
N.A.I.C.S.: 423820
George Veenstra *(Controller)*
Mike Noteboom *(Co-Owner & VP)*

CORSICAN FURNITURE, INC.
2437 E 24th St, Los Angeles, CA
90058
Tel.: (323) 587-3101   CA
Web Site: http://www.corsican.com
Year Founded: 1957
Sales Range: $10-24.9 Million
Emp.: 20
Mfr of Iron Furniture & Accessories
N.A.I.C.S.: 337126
Martin Joseph Perfit *(Pres)*

CORSICANA BEDDING, LLC
2700 E Hwy 31, Corsicana, TX 75110
Tel.: (903) 872-2591
Web Site:
   https://www.corsicanamattress.com
Sales Range: $25-49.9 Million
Emp.: 117
Mattresses, Innerspring or Box Spring
N.A.I.C.S.: 337910
Chad Reinsel *(Mgr-Ops)*
Jose Luna *(Asst Mgr)*
Robin Ferguson *(Mgr-Safety)*
Spencer Richardson *(Reg Mgr-Sls)*
Eric Rhea *(CEO)*
Roger Pritchard *(Reg Mgr-Sls)*

CORSTONE CORPORATION
6707 Democracy Blvd Ste 905,
Bethesda, MD 20817   DE
Web Site:
   https://www.corstonecapital.com
Investment Advisory & Asset Man-
agement Services
N.A.I.C.S.: 523940
Albert Hawk *(Chm & Mng Partner)*
John Herring *(Partner)*
Cindy Stark *(Dir-Bus Dev)*

Subsidiaries:

Corstone Asia Co., Ltd.   (1)
2F 203 Shin-A B/D 39-1 Seosomoon Dong,
Jung-gu, Seoul, 100-813, Korea (South)
Tel.: (82) 2 319 1206
Web Site: http://www.corstonecapital.com
Investment Advisory, Private Equity Invest-
ment & Asset Management Services
N.A.I.C.S.: 523940
Sunho Choi *(Co-CEO & Gen Partner)*
Thomas Cho *(Co-CEO & Gen Partner)*
Duke Chung *(Mng Dir)*
Jin Park *(Mng Dir)*
Sungyong Chae *(Officer-Compliance)*
Soyeon Moon *(Officer-Risk Mgmt)*

Holding (Domestic):

KH Electron Co., Ltd.   (2)
52 Samjak-ro 107beon-gil, Ojeong-Gu, Bu-
cheon, 421-810, Gyeonggi-Do, Korea
(South)   (58.62%)
Tel.: (82) 326837300
Web Site: https://khmirae.co.kr
Rev.: $9,599,629
Assets: $174,004,509
Liabilities: $47,436,934
Net Worth: $126,567,575
Earnings: $71,318,547)
Emp.: 39
Fiscal Year-end: 12/31/2022
Audio Device Svc

N.A.I.C.S.: 334310
Bae Bo-Seong *(CEO)*

Subsidiary (Non-US):

Sambon (H.K.) Electronics
Limited   (3)
No 5-10 17 Fl Mega Trade Centre 1 Mei
Wan Street, Tsuen Wan, N.T., China (Hong
Kong)
Tel.: (852) 24981686
Web Site: http://www.esambon.com
Audio Device & Keypad Mfr
N.A.I.C.S.: 334310

**CORTE CONSTRUCTION CO.
INC.**
Rural Route 460, Bluefield, VA 24605
Tel.: (276) 322-5491
Sales Range: $10-24.9 Million
Emp.: 60
General Contractors
N.A.I.C.S.: 236220
R. Schwartz *(CEO)*

CORTEC CORPORATION
4119 White Bear Pkwy, Saint Paul,
MN 55110
Tel.: (651) 429-1100
Web Site: http://www.cortecvci.com
Year Founded: 1977
Sales Range: $10-24.9 Million
Emp.: 125
Metal Protection & Anti-Corrosion
System Mfr
N.A.I.C.S.: 325998
Boris Miksic *(Co-Pres)*
Eric Uutala *(Mgr-Tech Svcs)*
Cliff Cracauer *(VP-Sls)*
Markus Bieber *(Dir-Sls)*
Karen Brasile *(Gen Mgr)*
Dijana Zrinski *(Gen Mgr)*
Melyssa Mogdans *(Mgr-Customer
Svc)*
Tim Taylor *(Mgr-Aerosol Sls)*
Joe Yach *(Project Mgr-Svcs-Global)*
Ivana Radic Borsic *(VP-Sls-Europe)*
Mike Gabor *(VP-Sls-Midwest)*
Jessi Meyer *(VP-Sls)*
Dario Dell Orto *(VP-Intl Sls-South
America & Africa)*
Sonny Reeves *(Mgr-Preservation)*
Jeff Lipsitz *(Co-Pres)*

Subsidiaries:

CorteCros d.o.o.   (1)
Nova Ves 57, 10000, Zagreb, Croatia
Tel.: (385) 14669280
Web Site: https://www.cortecros.com
Anti-Corrosion & Spill Containment Systems
Mfr; Owned by INA-Industrija nafte, d.d. &
Cortec Corporation
N.A.I.C.S.: 332812

Cortec Advanced Films   (1)
410 E 1st Ave, Cambridge, MN 55008
Tel.: (763) 689-4100
Web Site:
   http://www.cortecadvancedfilms.com
Plastics Films Mfr
N.A.I.C.S.: 326113
Tim Bliss *(Mgr-Production)*

**CORTEC GROUP MANAGE-
MENT SERVICES, LLC**
140 E 45th St 43rd Fl, New York, NY
10017
Tel.: (212) 370-5600   NY
Web Site:
   https://www.cortecgroup.com
Year Founded: 1984
Private Equity Investment Firm
N.A.I.C.S.: 523999
Michael E. Najjar *(Mng Partner)*
Jeffrey A. Lipsitz *(Mng Partner)*
Jonathan A. Stein *(Partner)*
Jeffrey Shannon *(Partner)*
Eugene P. Nesbeda *(Sr Mng Dir)*
David L. Schnadig *(Mng Partner)*

Robert Whipple *(Mng Dir)*
Jack Miner *(VP)*
Scott Schafler *(Mng Partner)*

Subsidiaries:

Center for Vein Restoration   (1)
7300 Hanover Dr Ste 303, Greenbelt, MD
20770
Web Site: http://www.centerforvein.com
Vein Treatment Scientific Technology Center
N.A.I.C.S.: 621111
Sanjiv Lakhanpal *(Founder, Pres & CEO)*
Bob Howell *(Assoc VP-Growth & Dev)*
Khanh Q. Nguyen *(Chief Medical Officer)*
Ken Abod *(CFO)*
Neil Collier *(COO)*

Subsidiary (Domestic):

Southeast Vein & Laser Center,
P.C.   (2)
3280 Ross Clark Cir, Dothan, AL 36303-
3040
Tel.: (334) 467-9494
Web Site: http://www.theveinspecialist.com
Vein Laser Treatment Center
N.A.I.C.S.: 621111
Darlene Beech *(Office Mgr)*

E&B Giftware LLC   (1)
4 Executive Plz, Yonkers, NY 10701-6812
Tel.: (914) 964-5200
Web Site: http://www.ebgift.com
Sales Range: $50-74.9 Million
Mfr of Nondurable Goods
N.A.I.C.S.: 424990
Tricia Norton *(Pres-Fitness Div)*
Herbie Calves *(VP-Mktg)*

Rotating Machinery Services,
Inc.   (1)
2760 Baglyos Cir, Bethlehem, PA 18020
Tel.: (484) 821-0702
Web Site: http://www.rotatingmachinery.com
Engineering Services
N.A.I.C.S.: 541330
Jerry Hallman *(Pres)*
Kathy Ehasz *(Dir-HR)*
John Bartos *(CEO)*
Charles G. Smith Jr. *(Dir-Bus Dev-Ops &
Field Svc)*

**CORTEC PRECISION SHEET
METAL, INC.**
2231 Will Wool Dr, San Jose, CA
95112
Tel.: (408) 278-8540
Web Site:
   https://www.cortecprecision.com
Year Founded: 1972
Sales Range: $10-24.9 Million
Emp.: 200
Sheet Metal Work Mfg
N.A.I.C.S.: 332322
Tony Corrales *(Gen Mgr)*
Tom Curtis *(Mgr-Quality)*

CORTECH SOLUTIONS, INC.
1409 Audubon Blvd Ste B1, Wilming-
ton, NC 28403
Tel.: (910) 362-1143
Web Site:
   https://www.cortechsolutions.com
Year Founded: 2001
Sales Range: $1-9.9 Million
Emp.: 12
Professional Equipment & Supplies
Merchant Whslr
N.A.I.C.S.: 423490
Lloyd Smith *(Pres)*
Jennifer Smith *(Treas & Sec)*

**CORTELCO SYSTEMS HOLD-
ING CORP.**
1703 Sawyer Rd, Corinth, MS 38834
Tel.: (662) 287-5281   DE
Web Site: http://www.cortelco.com
Sales Range: $10-24.9 Million
Emp.: 70
Holding Company; Commercial Tele-
phones & Other Telecommunications
Equipment Designer, Mfr & Whslr

N.A.I.C.S.: 551112
Lee M. Bowling *(CFO & VP)*
Robert Schnabl *(COO)*

Subsidiaries:

Cortelco Systems Puerto Rico,
Inc.   (1)
Parque Indus Caguas Oeste Edificio
M-1384-8-86 Sec 04 Carr 156 Km 58 2,
Caguas, PR 00726
Tel.: (787) 704-0000
Web Site: http://www.cortelcopr.net
Emp.: 60
Commercial Telephones & Other Telecom-
munications Equipment Whslr
N.A.I.C.S.: 423610
Juan Carlos Ramos *(Pres & CEO)*
Nancy Gonzalez *(Dir-Admin & HR)*
Josue Lopez *(Mgr-Svc)*

Cortelco, Inc.   (1)
1703 Sawyer Rd, Corinth, MS 38834
Tel.: (662) 287-5281
Web Site: http://www.cortelco.com
Sales Range: $10-24.9 Million
Emp.: 55
Commercial Telephones & Other Telecom-
munications Equipment Designer, Mfr &
Whslr
N.A.I.C.S.: 334210
Lee M. Bowling *(CFO & VP)*
Robert Schnabl *(COO)*

CORTESE DODGE INC.
2400 W Henrietta Rd, Rochester, NY
14623
Tel.: (585) 424-3000
Web Site:
   http://www.corteseautogroup.com
Sales Range: $25-49.9 Million
Emp.: 92
Automobiles, New & Used
N.A.I.C.S.: 441110
John C. Cortese *(Pres)*

CORTESE FORD
2400-2500 W Henrietta Rd, Roches-
ter, NY 14623
Tel.: (585) 475-1211
Web Site:
   https://www.corteseauto.com
Year Founded: 2001
Sales Range: $10-24.9 Million
Emp.: 71
Car Whslr
N.A.I.C.S.: 441110
John Cortese *(Principal)*
Don Heelon *(Mgr-Parts)*
Larry Musson *(Mgr-Used Car)*

CORTEZ GAS COMPANY INC.
1811 SE Main St, Roswell, NM 88203
Tel.: (575) 622-5400
Web Site: http://www.zianet.com
Rev.: $14,534,700
Emp.: 11
Propane Gas, Bottled
N.A.I.C.S.: 457210
Betty Hase *(Dir-Admin)*
Patricia Turner *(Asst Dir)*
Harvielee Moore *(Dir-Personnel)*
Bernie Joplin *(Mgr-Production)*
Dennis Davis *(Dir-HR)*

**CORTEZ HEATING & AIR CON-
DITIONING, INC.**
5928 21st St E, Bradenton, FL 34203
Tel.: (941) 755-5211
Web Site: http://www.cortez-ac.com
Year Founded: 1991
Sales Range: $1-9.9 Million
Emp.: 40
Plumbing, Heating & Air-Conditioning
Contractor
N.A.I.C.S.: 238220
Mark M. Anderson *(Owner & Pres)*
Jerry Brave *(Project Mgr)*
Joe Yount *(VP)*
Ray Crane *(Mgr-HVAC Svc)*

CORTINA LEARNING INTERNATIONAL, INC.
7 Hollyhock Rd, Wilton, CT 06897-4414
Tel.: (203) 762-2510
Web Site: http://www.cortina-languages.com
Year Founded: 1882
Sales Range: $1-9.9 Million
Emp.: 10
Foreign Language, ESL Courses & Educational Services
N.A.I.C.S.: 611710
Robert E. Livesey *(Pres)*
Magdalen B. Livesey *(Mng Editor)*
George G. Bollas *(Gen Mgr)*

Subsidiaries:

Cortina Institute of Languages **(1)**
7 Hollyhock Rd, Wilton, CT 06897 **(100%)**
Tel.: (203) 762-2510
Web Site: http://www.cortinalanguages.com
Foreign Language Instruction
N.A.I.C.S.: 611710

Famous Artist School **(1)**
7 Hollyhock Ln, Wilton, CT 06897
Tel.: (203) 762-2510
Web Site: http://www.famous-artists-school.com
Commercial Art, Fine Painting & Young People's Art
N.A.I.C.S.: 513130
Robert E. Livesey *(Mng Dir)*

Famous Writers School **(1)**
7 Hollyhock Rd, Wilton, CT 06897
Tel.: (203) 762-2510
Web Site: http://www.cortinalearning.com
Fiction/Non Fiction, Advertising, TV & Business Writing
N.A.I.C.S.: 513130
Robert Livesey *(Pres)*

Institute for Language Study **(1)**
9 Hollyhock Rd, Wilton, CT 06897-4414
Tel.: (203) 762-2510
Web Site: http://www.cortinalanguages.com
Foreign Language Instruction & Sales
N.A.I.C.S.: 449210
Madeleine Moret *(Owner)*

CORTINA SOLUTIONS, LLC
8 Parade St NW Ste 201, Huntsville, AL 35806
Tel.: (256) 319-2024
Web Site: http://www.cortinasolutions.com
Year Founded: 2012
Sales Range: $1-9.9 Million
Emp.: 23
Management Consulting Services
N.A.I.C.S.: 541618
Edwina Musante *(Founder, Pres & CEO)*

CORTLAND HARDWOOD PRODUCTS, LLC.
124 Pearl St, Cortland, OH 44410
Tel.: (330) 638-3232
Web Site: https://www.cortlandhardwood.com
Year Founded: 1997
Sales Range: $10-24.9 Million
Emp.: 25
Millwork Services
N.A.I.C.S.: 321918
Keith Denman *(CEO)*

CORTLAND LINE COMPANY, INC.
3736 Kellogg Rd, Cortland, NY 13045-8818
Tel.: (607) 756-2851   NY
Web Site: https://www.cortlandline.com
Year Founded: 1915
Sales Range: $75-99.9 Million
Emp.: 60
Mfr & Distr of Sport Fishing Lines

N.A.I.C.S.: 314994
Brooks Robinson *(Mgr-Social Media)*
Clay Norris *(Dir-Sls & Mktg-Natl)*

CORTLAND PARTNERS, LLC
3424 Peachtree Rd NE Ste 300, Atlanta, GA 30326
Tel.: (404) 965-3988
Web Site: http://www.cortlandpartners.com
Year Founded: 2005
Sales Range: $75-99.9 Million
Real Estate Investment & Management
N.A.I.C.S.: 531390
Steven DeFrancis *(CEO)*
Clyde Stutts *(COO)*
Ned Stiker *(CFO)*
Mike Altman *(Chief Investment Officer)*
Brad Brown *(Chief Acq Officer)*
J. Clayton Landers *(Exec VP-Construction)*
Melanie French *(Exec VP-Ops)*
Paul Wrights *(Exec VP-Fin & Dev)*
Scott Moore *(Exec VP-Strategy & Innovation)*
Amy McCullough *(Chief Acctg Officer)*
Juan Bueno *(Pres-Ops)*

Subsidiaries:

Pure Multi-Family REIT LP **(1)**
Suite 910-925 West Georgia Street, Vancouver, V6C 3L2, BC, Canada
Tel.: (604) 681-5959
Web Site: http://www.puremultifamily.com
Rev.: $109,612,000
Assets: $1,191,368,000
Liabilities: $656,474,000
Net Worth: $534,894,000
Earnings: $46,026,000
Emp.: 183
Fiscal Year-end: 12/31/2018
Real Estate Investment Trust
N.A.I.C.S.: 525990
Robert W. King *(Chm)*
Scott B. Shillington *(CFO)*
Stephen J. Evans *(Founder & CEO)*
Samantha Adams *(Sr VP)*
Andrew Greig *(VP-IR)*
Lee Ann Neumann *(Exec VP-Ops-US)*

CORTLAND PRODUCE COMPANY INC.
150 Johnson Rd, Freeville, NY 13068
Tel.: (607) 708-8029
Web Site: https://www.cortlandproduce.com
Year Founded: 1929
Sales Range: $10-24.9 Million
Emp.: 25
Food Service Products Distr
N.A.I.C.S.: 424410
Felicia Furgison *(Mgr-Fin)*

CORTLAND REGIONAL MEDICAL CENTER
134 Homer Ave, Cortland, NY 13045
Tel.: (607) 756-3500   NY
Web Site: http://www.cortlandregional.org
Year Founded: 1892
Sales Range: $75-99.9 Million
Emp.: 1,141
Community Health Care Services
N.A.I.C.S.: 621498
Brian Mitteer *(Pres & CEO)*

CORTRONIX BIOMEDICAL ADVANCEMENT TECHNOLOGIES INC.
8200 NW 41st St Ste 145B, Doral, FL 33166
Tel.: (786) 859-3585   NV
Web Site: http://www.cor-tronix.com
Year Founded: 2006
Emp.: 2
Investment Services

N.A.I.C.S.: 523999
Richard A. Hull *(Pres, CEO, CFO & Treas)*

CORVAL CONSTRUCTORS, INC.
1633 Eustis St, Saint Paul, MN 55108-1219
Tel.: (651) 645-0451   MN
Web Site: https://www.corvalgroup.com
Year Founded: 1921
Sales Range: $50-74.9 Million
Emp.: 50
Mechanical Contracting Service
N.A.I.C.S.: 238220
Todd Dougan *(Pres)*

CORVALLIS NEIGHBORHOOD HOUSING SERVICES, INC.
212 Main St, Springfield, OR 97477
Tel.: (541) 345-7105   OR
Web Site: http://devnw.org
Community Housing Services
N.A.I.C.S.: 624229
Emily Reiman *(CEO)*
Brigette Olson *(COO)*
Cori Riley *(CFO)*
Erin Dey *(Dir-Real Estate Dev)*
Lynn Meyer *(Dir-Leasing)*
Bett Schmidt *(Pres)*
Matthew Bromley *(VP)*
Ali Coddington *(Treas)*
Chrystal Shearer *(Sec)*

Subsidiaries:

Willamette Neighborhood Housing Services **(1)**
257 SW Madison Ave Ste 113, Corvallis, OR 97333
Tel.: (541) 752-7220
Community Housing Services
N.A.I.C.S.: 624229

CORWIN BEVERAGE COMPANY
219 S Timm Rd, Ridgefield, WA 98642
Tel.: (360) 696-0766
Web Site: https://www.corwinbevco.com
Sales Range: $10-24.9 Million
Emp.: 100
Distr of Soft Drinks
N.A.I.C.S.: 424490
Keith Richards *(CEO)*

CORWIN CHRYSLER DODGE JEEP
301 38th St S, Fargo, ND 58103
Tel.: (701) 282-8425
Sales Range: $10-24.9 Million
Emp.: 80
Car Whslr
N.A.I.C.S.: 441110
Drew Corwin *(Mgr-Ops)*
Timothy F. Corwin *(Pres)*
Bob Kietzer *(Gen Mgr-Sls)*

CORWIN FORD
5707 E Gate Blvd, Nampa, ID 83687
Tel.: (208) 546-3559
Web Site: https://www.corwinfordnampa.com
Sales Range: $50-74.9 Million
Emp.: 150
Car Dealership Owner & Operator
N.A.I.C.S.: 441110
Kevin Neagle *(Mgr-Parts)*
Jason Wilkey *(Mgr-Sls)*
Rory Needs *(Controller)*
Tanner Corwin *(Gen Mgr)*
Leo Carreno *(Mgr-Sls)*
Aandy Coombs *(Mgr-Sls)*
Les Salsman *(Mgr-Used Cars)*
Richard Tolsma *(Mgr-Internet)*

Bill Blazek *(Mgr-Fin)*
John Whitney *(Mgr-Sls-Fleet)*
Tom Browning *(Mgr-Svc)*
Blake Kezar *(Mgr-Fin)*
Couri Inwards *(Mgr-Fin)*
Joey Parke *(Mgr-Sls)*
Sonya Schoger *(Mgr-Fin)*

CORWIN HONDA
3215 Missouri Blvd, Jefferson City, MO 65109
Tel.: (573) 893-7676
Web Site: http://www.corwinhondajeffcity.com
Sales Range: $10-24.9 Million
Emp.: 200
Car Dealership
N.A.I.C.S.: 441110
Drew Corwin *(Pres)*
Jeff Conrad *(Gen Mgr)*

CORY FAIRBANKS MAZDA INC.
400 Hwy 17/92 N, Longwood, FL 32750
Tel.: (407) 339-4777
Web Site: http://www.bigmazda.com
Rev.: $26,300,000
Emp.: 100
New Car Dealers
N.A.I.C.S.: 441110
Terry Taylor *(Pres)*
Michele Ault *(Mgr-HR)*

COSBY OIL COMPANY, INC.
12902 E Park St, Santa Fe Springs, CA 90670
Tel.: (562) 946-4404
Web Site: http://www.cosbyoil.com
Rev.: $83,300,000
Emp.: 35
Petroleum & Petroleum Products Merchant Whslr
N.A.I.C.S.: 424720
Mary Ann Clanton *(Owner)*
Terry L. Clanton *(Exec VP)*
Larry Clanton *(Owner)*
Raul Diaz *(Mgr)*

COSCAN WATERWAYS INC.
5555 Anglers Ave Ste 1, Fort Lauderdale, FL 33312
Tel.: (954) 620-1000
Rev.: $70,000,000
Emp.: 100
Subdividers & Developers
N.A.I.C.S.: 237210
Albert Piazza *(Pres)*
Michael Neil *(VP)*

COSENTINO USA
2245 Texas Ave Ste 600, Sugar Land, TX 77479
Tel.: (281) 494-7277
Web Site: http://www.silestoneusa.com
Year Founded: 1998
Sales Range: $150-199.9 Million
Emp.: 550
Silestone Natural Quartz Surfaces Mfr, Distr & Marketer
N.A.I.C.S.: 327991
Eduardo Cosentino *(CEO)*

COSENTINO'S FOOD STORES
3901 W 83rd St, Prairie Village, KS 66208
Tel.: (816) 523-3769
Web Site: http://www.mypricechopper.com
Supermarkets & Other Grocery Stores
N.A.I.C.S.: 445110
John Cosentino *(VP)*
Gary Crain *(Mgr)*

Cosentino's Food Stores—(Continued)

Whitney Havelka *(Office Mgr)*
Mike Clemons *(CFO)*
Linda Stomboly *(Dir-Front End Ops)*

COSERV UTILITY HOLDINGS, L.P.
7701 S Stemmons, Corinth, TX 76210
Tel.: (940) 321-7800   TX
Web Site: https://www.coserv.com
Sales Range: $450-499.9 Million
Emp.: 250
Holding Company; Electric & Gas Utilities Cooperative Organizations
N.A.I.C.S.: 551112
Richard Muir *(Treas & Sec)*

Subsidiaries:

Denton County Electric Cooperative, Inc.   (1)
7701 S Stemmons Fwy, Denton, TX 76210-1842
Tel.: (940) 321-7800
Web Site: http://www.coserv.com
Sales Range: $400-449.9 Million
Electrical Utilities Administration Organization
N.A.I.C.S.: 926130

COSI, INC.
500 Rutherford Ave Ste 130, Charlestown, MA 02129
Tel.: (866) 580-2674   DE
Web Site: http://www.getcosi.com
Year Founded: 1996
Sales Range: $75-99.9 Million
Sandwich Deli, Restaurant, Delivery & Catering Services
N.A.I.C.S.: 722511
Vicki Baue *(Chief Compliance & Legal Officer, Gen Counsel, VP & Asst Sec)*
William Nicolini *(VP-Ops Support)*

COSIMO'S MANAGEMENT, INC.
1089 Little Britain Rd, Newburgh, NY 12553-7215
Tel.: (845) 564-5571
Year Founded: 1985
Sales Range: $10-24.9 Million
Emp.: 4
Provider of Management Services
N.A.I.C.S.: 561110
Cosimo Dibrizzi *(Pres)*

COSKATA, INC.
4575 Weaver Pkwy, Warrenville, IL 60555
Tel.: (630) 657-5800   DE
Web Site: http://www.coskata.com
Sales Range: Less than $1 Million
Emp.: 61
Renewable Fuels & Bio-Based Chemicals Mfr
N.A.I.C.S.: 324199
William J. Roe *(Pres & CEO)*
David J. Blair *(CFO & Treas)*
Richard Troyer *(Chief Bus Officer)*
Jeffrey E. Burgard *(VP-Engrg & Ops)*
Richard E. Tobey *(VP-R&D)*

COSMETIC EXECUTIVE WOMEN, INC.
159 W 25th St 8th Fl, New York, NY 10001
Tel.: (646) 929-8000   NY
Web Site: http://www.cew.org
Year Founded: 1959
Cosmetics Industry Professional Organization
N.A.I.C.S.: 813920
Heidi J. Manheimer *(Vice Chm)*
Barbara Kotlikoff *(Vice Chm)*
Carlotta Jacobson *(Pres)*

Kelly McPhilliamy *(Treas)*
Lisa Klein *(Sr VP)*
Andrea Nagel *(VP-Content)*
Claudia Flowers *(COO)*
Roch Minieri *(Controller)*
Un Sin Yavanian *(Dir-Dev & Strategic Projects)*
Martin Barfield *(Dir-Tech)*
My Tran *(Assoc Dir-Programs & Events)*
Shari Beck *(Sr Mgr-Member Ops)*
Landree Bower *(Sr Mgr-Dev)*

Subsidiaries:

The Cosmetic Executive Women Foundation Ltd.   (1)
286 Madison Ave 19th Fl, New York, NY 10017
Tel.: (646) 929-8000
Web Site: http://www.cew.org
Charity Organization
N.A.I.C.S.: 813219
Kate Sweeney *(Exec Dir)*
Christine Brennan *(Assoc Dir-Programs)*
Alicia Chin *(Assoc Dir-Dev & Comm)*
Kristin Finn *(Assoc Dir-Membership & Events)*
Martin Barfield *(Dir-Tech)*
Peter Sangiorgio *(Dir-Fin)*
Rachel Becker *(Asst Dir-Programs)*
Sarah Goodell *(Mgr-Programs)*
Lindsay Keane *(Mgr-Mktg)*
Nicole Shaffer *(Mgr-Programs)*

COSMETIQUE, INC.
859 W End Ct Unit 102, Vernon Hills, IL 60061-3171
Tel.: (847) 913-9099   IL
Web Site: https://www.cosmetique.com
Year Founded: 1974
Sales Range: $25-49.9 Million
Emp.: 15
Mail Order Cosmetics
N.A.I.C.S.: 424210
June Giugni *(Pres)*
Rosann Clifton *(VP & Controller)*

COSMO CORPORATION
30201 Aurora Rd, Cleveland, OH 44139
Tel.: (440) 498-7500
Web Site: https://www.cosmocorp.com
Year Founded: 1945
Unsupported Plastics & Profile Shapes Mfr
N.A.I.C.S.: 326121
Andrew W. Hoffmann *(VP)*

COSMO VENTURES INC.
112 North Curry St, Carson City, NV 89703   NV
Year Founded: 2013
Assets: $103
Liabilities: $59,902
Net Worth: ($59,799)
Earnings: ($23,108)
Emp.: 1
Fiscal Year-end: 03/31/19
Overstocked Inventory Items Online Distr
N.A.I.C.S.: 541611
Ashok Kumar *(Pres, CEO, CFO, Treas & Sec)*

COSMOPOLITAN DECORATING CO.
1011 John St Ste 1700, New York, NY 10038
Tel.: (212) 586-6438
Sales Range: $10-24.9 Million
Emp.: 80
Painting & Paper Hanging
N.A.I.C.S.: 238320
Leon J. Gerstle *(Pres)*
Davie Ansbacher *(VP)*

COSMOPOLITAN TRADING CORP.
566 7th Ave Rm 602A, New York, NY 10018
Tel.: (212) 391-2600
Sales Range: $50-74.9 Million
Textile Import & Export Services
N.A.I.C.S.: 424310
Mark Cassuto *(Pres)*

COSMOS CLUB
2121 Massachusetts Ave NW, Washington, DC 20008
Tel.: (202) 387-7783   DC
Web Site: https://www.cosmosclub.org
Year Founded: 1878
Sales Range: $10-24.9 Million
Emp.: 161
Social Club Operator
N.A.I.C.S.: 713910
Gilles Syglowski *(Asst Gen Mgr)*
William T. Caldwell *(Gen Mgr)*

COSMOS COMMUNICATIONS
11-05 44th Dr, Long Island City, NY 11101-5107
Tel.: (718) 482-1800   NY
Web Site: http://www.cosmosinc.net
Year Founded: 1933
Sales Range: $50-74.9 Million
Emp.: 200
Commercial Printing & Prepress Services
N.A.I.C.S.: 323111
Ed Hackett *(VP-Sls)*
Jeff King *(Exec VP)*
Derek Lambert *(Dir-Prepress Svcs & IT)*
Eric Nierenberg *(Acct Dir)*
Richard Quarto *(VP-Sls)*
Ken Taylor *(Co-CEO)*
Jeff Weiss *(Owner & Treas)*

COSMOS INTERNATIONAL, INC.
501 Industrial Dr Ste 101, Richardson, TX 75081
Tel.: (972) 699-1683
Web Site: https://www.cosmosus.com
Sales Range: $10-24.9 Million
Emp.: 3
Machinery & Equipment Whslr
N.A.I.C.S.: 423120
Meng-Lian L Chen *(Sec)*
Bao-Chan Chen *(Pres)*

COSSMA INC.
PO Box 1330, Cidra, PR 00739
Tel.: (787) 739-8182   PR
Web Site: http://www.cossma.org
Year Founded: 1987
Sales Range: $25-49.9 Million
Emp.: 271
Health Care Srvices
N.A.I.C.S.: 622110
Claribel Lara *(Dir-Fin)*
Edgardo Soto *(Dir-Medical)*
Isolina Miranda *(Exec Dir)*

COST MANAGEMENT SERVICES, INC.
2737 78th Ave SE Ste 203, Mercer Island, WA 98040
Tel.: (206) 236-8808
Web Site: http://www.cmsnaturalgas.com
Year Founded: 1989
Sales Range: $25-49.9 Million
Emp.: 7
Energy Consulting Services
N.A.I.C.S.: 541690
Doug Betzold *(CEO)*
Beth Beatty *(Pres)*
Rich Greenwell *(Mgr-Bus Dev)*
Ted Lehmann *(Dir-Sls)*

Laura Rheaume *(Office Mgr)*
Vivian Melekh *(Coord-Acct)*
Erin Pochman *(Coord-Acct)*

COST OF WISCONSIN, INC.
4201 Hwy P, Jackson, WI 53037
Tel.: (262) 677-6060
Web Site: https://www.costofwisconsin.com
Sales Range: $10-24.9 Million
Emp.: 70
Concrete Contractor
N.A.I.C.S.: 238990
Mike Schmuhl *(Dir-Field Ops)*
Jason Burnie *(Project Mgr)*

COSTA BROTHERS MASONRY
2 Lambeth Park Dr, Fairhaven, MA 02719-4734
Tel.: (508) 991-7634
Web Site: https://www.costabrothersmasonry.com
Year Founded: 1989
Sales Range: $10-24.9 Million
Emp.: 85
Masonry Contracting Services
N.A.I.C.S.: 238140
Domingos DaCosta *(Co-Founder)*
Fernando DaCosta *(Co-Founder)*

COSTA FARMS, LLC
21800 SW 162 Ave., Miami, FL 33170
Web Site: http://www.costafarms.com
Year Founded: 2005
General Line Grocery Merchant Whslr
N.A.I.C.S.: 424410
Nadine Costa *(Owner)*

Subsidiaries:

Battlefield Farms Inc.   (1)
23190 Clarks Mtn Rd, Rapidan, VA 22733-2733
Web Site: http://www.battlefieldfarms.com
Farming
N.A.I.C.S.: 111421
Julie Brooks *(Dir-HR)*

COSTA FRUIT & PRODUCE INC.
18 Bunker Hill Industrial Park, Boston, MA 02129-1621
Tel.: (617) 241-8007   MA
Web Site: https://www.freshideas.com
Year Founded: 1949
Sales Range: $25-49.9 Million
Emp.: 250
Fresh Fruits, Vegetables & Other Food Related Items Supplier & Whslr
N.A.I.C.S.: 424480
Kevin Linnehan *(CFO)*

Subsidiaries:

Fresh Ideas Inc.   (1)
18 Bunker Hill Industrial Park, Boston, MA 02129-1645
Tel.: (617) 241-8007
Web Site: http://www.freshideas.com
Sales Range: $10-24.9 Million
Emp.: 60
Suppliers of Fresh Fruits & Vegetables
N.A.I.C.S.: 424480

COSTA RICAN GOLD COFFEE CO.
1425 Park Ln S, Jupiter, FL 33458-8081
Tel.: (561) 746-8110
Web Site: http://www.goldcoffee.com
Sales Range: $10-24.9 Million
Emp.: 10
Coffee, Green Or Roasted
N.A.I.C.S.: 424490
John M. Parry *(Owner)*

COSTA SECURITY SERVICES, LLC

1500 S Christopher Columbus Blvd Ste 6 2nd Fl, Philadelphia, PA 19147
Tel.: (215) 607-8742   PA
Web Site:
  http://www.opssecuritygroup.com
Year Founded: 2012
Sales Range: $1-9.9 Million
Emp.: 291
Security Services
N.A.I.C.S.: 561612
Daniel Costa *(Co-Founder & CEO)*
Mitch Gyger *(Co-Founder & Pres)*
Ian Poush *(Partner & Dir-Private Investigations)*
Kevin Ford *(VP-Sls)*
Michael Krupa *(Dir-Strategic Dev)*

COSTA VIDA MANAGEMENT, INC.

2989 W Maple Loop Dr Ste 100, Lehi, UT 84043
Tel.: (801) 797-2374
Web Site: http://www.costavida.net
Year Founded: 2003
Sales Range: $25-49.9 Million
Emp.: 1,081
Restaurant Operators
N.A.I.C.S.: 722511
Jeff Jefferson *(Pres)*

COSTAMAR TRAVEL, CRUISE & TOURS INC.

531 E Oakland Park Blvd, Oakland Park, FL 33334-2151
Tel.: (954) 630-0060
Web Site: http://www.costamar.com
Rev.: $151,300,000
Emp.: 500
Travel Agencies
N.A.I.C.S.: 561510
Geraldo Concas *(Pres)*

COSTANOA VENTURE CAPITAL MANAGEMENT LLC

160 Forest Ave, Palo Alto, CA 94301
Tel.: (650) 388-9310
Web Site:
  https://www.costanoavc.com
Venture Capital Firm
N.A.I.C.S.: 523150
Greg Sands *(Founder & Mng Partner)*

COSTAR INTERNATIONAL ENTERPRISES, INC.

2200 E 27th St, Vernon, CA 90058
Tel.: (323) 585-2088
Web Site: http://www.costarinc.com
Year Founded: 2000
Sales Range: $10-24.9 Million
Emp.: 32
Importer & Whslr in High-Quality Costume Jewelry & Custom Fashion Accessories
N.A.I.C.S.: 423940
Jay Kim *(Pres)*

COSTELLO DISMANTLING COMPANY, INC.

45 Kings Hwy, West Wareham, MA 02576
Tel.: (508) 291-2324
Web Site:
  http://www.costellodismantling.com
Year Founded: 1985
Sales Range: $10-24.9 Million
Emp.: 40
Wrecking & Demolition Work
N.A.I.C.S.: 238910
Daniel Costello *(Pres)*
Joan Costello *(Sec)*

COSTELLO INDUSTRIES INC.

123 Costello Rd, Newington, CT 06111
Tel.: (860) 666-3311
Web Site:
  http://www.costelloindustries.com
Sales Range: $25-49.9 Million
Emp.: 35
Highway & Street Paving Contractor
N.A.I.C.S.: 237310
John Costello *(Pres)*
Jim Burke *(Superintendent-Equipment)*

COSTUME CRAZE, LLC

350 W Center St, Pleasant Grove, UT 84062
Tel.: (801) 796-1053
Web Site:
  http://www.costumecraze.com
Year Founded: 2001
Sales Range: $1-9.9 Million
Emp.: 20
Online Costumes & Accessories Retailer
N.A.I.C.S.: 459999
Matthew Maloney *(Co-Founder & Pres)*
Kathryn Maloney *(Co-Founder & CEO)*

COSWAY CO INC.

20633 S Fordyce Ave, Carson, CA 90810-1019
Tel.: (310) 603-0297
Web Site: http://www.coswayco.com
Drugs & Druggists' Sundries Merchant Whslr
N.A.I.C.S.: 424210
Richard L. Hough *(Chm)*
Rick Kornbluth *(Pres & CEO)*
Tim Abney *(Dir-Education-Global)*

Subsidiaries:

ColorProof Haircare LLC   (1)
24 Corporate Plz Dr Ste 180, Newport Beach, CA 92660-7989
Tel.: (949) 706-8300
Web Site: http://www.colorproof.com
Beauty Salons
N.A.I.C.S.: 812112
Maureen Saenz *(VP-Mktg)*

COTA & COTA INC.

4 Green St, Bellows Falls, VT 05101
Tel.: (802) 463-0000
Web Site: https://www.cotaoil.com
Year Founded: 1941
Sales Range: $10-24.9 Million
Emp.: 45
Fuel Oil Dealers
N.A.I.C.S.: 457210

COTON COLORS EXPRESS, LLC

2718 Centerville Rd, Tallahassee, FL 32308
Tel.: (850) 383-1111
Web Site: http://www.coton-colors.com
Year Founded: 1995
Sales Range: $1-9.9 Million
Emp.: 25
Colorful, Handcrafted Pottery, Giftware & Seasonal Pieces Designer & Mfr
N.A.I.C.S.: 327110
Ashley Trafton *(Dir-Ops & Customer Svc)*
Brian Bachman *(Engr-Logistics)*
Kristin Hendrix *(Dir-Natl Sls)*
Laura L. Johnson *(Founder & CEO)*

COTT INDEX CO.

2800 Corporate Exchange Dr Ste 300, Columbus, OH 43231
Tel.: (614) 847-4405

Web Site:
  http://www.cottsystems.com
Sales Range: $10-24.9 Million
Emp.: 70
Looseleaf Binders & Devices
N.A.I.C.S.: 323111
Karen L. Bailey *(Owner & Treas)*

COTTAGE GROVE PLACE

2115 1st Ave SE, Cedar Rapids, IA 52402
Tel.: (319) 363-2420   IA
Web Site:
  http://www.cottagegroveplace.com
Year Founded: 1996
Sales Range: $10-24.9 Million
Emp.: 241
Elder Care Services
N.A.I.C.S.: 623312
Bill Jacobson *(Chm)*

COTTAGE HOSPITAL

90 Swiftwater Rd, Woodsville, NH 03785
Tel.: (603) 747-9000   NH
Web Site:
  http://www.cottagehospital.org
Year Founded: 1903
Sales Range: $25-49.9 Million
Emp.: 250
Medical Care Services
N.A.I.C.S.: 622110
Maryanne Aldrich *(Dir-Community Rels & Fund Dev)*
Steven Plant *(CFO)*
Lori Hughes *(Chief Nursing Officer & VP-Ops & Patient Care Svcs)*
Mike Simpson *(Dir-HR)*
Teresa Puffer *(Sec)*
Jim Flynn *(CEO)*
Mark Blackburn *(Chm)*
Holly McCormack *(Chief Nursing Officer)*

COTTAGE SHEET METAL, LLC

6646 W 99th St, Chicago Ridge, IL 60415
Tel.: (708) 599-2992
Web Site:
  https://www.cottagesheetmetal.com
Sales Range: $1-9.9 Million
Emp.: 20
Plumbing Services
N.A.I.C.S.: 238220
Donald Van Witzenburg *(Owner)*

COTTAGES & CASTLES, INC.

2371 Linwood Ave Ste 101, Naples, FL 34112
Tel.: (239) 263-0234
Web Site:
  http://www.certainsomething.com
Sales Range: $1-9.9 Million
Emp.: 2
Interior Design Services
N.A.I.C.S.: 541410
Lisa Anastasia Reisman *(Pres)*

COTTER CONSULTING, INC.

100 S Wacker Dr Ste 920, Chicago, IL 60606
Tel.: (312) 696-1200
Web Site:
  https://www.cotterconsulting.com
Year Founded: 1990
Sales Range: $1-9.9 Million
Emp.: 69
Industrial Building Construction
N.A.I.C.S.: 236210
Joseph Hoerner *(COO)*
Anne Edwards-Cotter *(Pres)*
Carma Wood *(VP-Transportation)*
Nahid Afsari *(VP-Wisconsin Grp)*
Doug Blanchard *(VP-Aviation Grp)*

Joseph Hunn *(VP & Mgr-Transportation Grp)*
Deeta Bernstein *(Mgr-Sustainable Svc Grp)*
Bill Cotter *(Gen Counsel & Mgr-Admin)*
Dave Crowell *(Mng Dir)*
Terri Danko *(VP-Mktg & Bus Dev)*

COTTI FOODS CORPORATION

29889 Santa Margarita Pkwy, Rancho Santa Margarita, CA 92688-3609
Tel.: (949) 858-9191
Sales Range: $25-49.9 Million
Emp.: 15
Franchise Owner of Fast-Food Restaurants
N.A.I.C.S.: 722513
Steve Dees *(COO)*
Peter Capriotti II *(Pres)*

COTTMAN TRANSMISSION SYSTEMS, LLC

201 Gibraltar Rd, Horsham, PA 19044
Tel.: (215) 643-5885   DE
Web Site: http://www.cottman.com
Year Founded: 1962
Automotive Transmission Repair Centers; Starters & Ignition Systems, Radiators & Franchise
N.A.I.C.S.: 811114
Joe Josko *(Sr Ops Mgr)*

COTTON CREEK CAPITAL MANAGEMENT LLC

3700 N Capital of Texas Hwy Ste 520, Austin, TX 78746
Tel.: (512) 412-3300
Web Site:
  http://www.cottoncreekcapital.com
Privater Equity Firm
N.A.I.C.S.: 523999
James E. Braden *(Partner)*
Antonio J. DiGesualdo *(Mng Dir)*
Joseph Lee Rash *(Partner)*
John S. Gault *(VP)*
Stephen Barnish *(CFO)*
Smith S. Brownlie III *(Partner)*

Subsidiaries:

Royal Baths Manufacturing Co. Ltd.   (1)
14635 Chrisman Rd, Houston, TX 77039
Tel.: (281) 442-3400
Web Site: http://www.royal-mfg.com
Whirlpool Baths & Hydrotherapy Equipment Mfr
N.A.I.C.S.: 327110
Bo Hudson *(Pres)*
Lane Jeffryes *(CEO)*

Seatex, LLC   (1)
445 Texas 36, Rosenberg, TX 77471
Tel.: (713) 868-1461
Web Site: http://www.seatexcorp.com
Sales Range: $10-24.9 Million
Emp.: 50
Cleaning Polishing Preparations
N.A.I.C.S.: 325612
Kathy Boykin *(Mgr-HR)*

Subsidiary (Domestic):

ChemQuest Chemicals LLC   (2)
9730 Bay Area Blvd, Pasadena, TX 77507
Tel.: (281) 291-9966
Web Site:
  http://www.chemquestchemicals.com
Sales Range: $1-9.9 Million
Emp.: 20
Miscellaneous Chemical Product & Preparation Mfr
N.A.I.C.S.: 325998

Sterling Foods, LLC   (1)
1075 Arion Pkwy, San Antonio, TX 78216-2883
Tel.: (210) 490-1669
Web Site: http://www.sterling-fd.com
Commercial Bakery

Cotton Creek Capital Management
LLC—(Continued)

N.A.I.C.S.: 311812
John D. Likovich (Chm & CEO)
Fred J. Friend (Sr VP & Gen Mgr-Govt &
Specialty Div)
Liz Thomas (VP-Sls)

Young's Communications Co,
Inc.   (1)
424 West Dr, Melbourne, FL 32904
Tel.: (321) 723-6025
Web Site: http://www.ycominc.com
Electrical Contractor
N.A.I.C.S.: 238210
Gary Young (VP)
Steve Young (Pres)

COTTON ELECTRIC COOP-ERATIVE, INC.
226 N Broadway St, Walters, OK
73572-1226
Tel.: (580) 875-3351   OK
Web Site:
  https://www.cottonelectric.com
Year Founded: 1938
Sales Range: $150-199.9 Million
Emp.: 96
Distribution of Electric Power
N.A.I.C.S.: 221122
Jennifer Meason (CEO)

Subsidiaries:

Cotton Electric Services, Inc.   (1)
127 W Colorado St, Walters, OK 73572
Tel.: (580) 875-4296
Web Site: http://www.cottonservices.com
Electrical Testing Laboratory Services
N.A.I.C.S.: 541380

COTTON HOLDINGS, INC.
840 W Sam Houston Pkwy N 2nd Fl,
Houston, TX 77024
Tel.: (713) 849-9300
Web Site: http://cottonholdings.com
Holding Company
N.A.I.C.S.: 551112
Pete Bell (Founder & CEO)

Subsidiaries:

Full Circle Restoration & Construction
Services, Inc.   (1)
4325 River Green Pkwy, Duluth, GA 30096
Tel.: (770) 232-9797
Web Site:
  http://www.fullcirclerestoration.com
Residential Remodeler
N.A.I.C.S.: 236118
Alana Archer (Mgr-Comm & Mktg)
Daniel Duke (CFO & Exec VP-Ops)
Orlando Ojeda (Founder & Pres)

COTTON INCORPORATED
6399 Weston Pkwy, Cary, NC 27513
Tel.: (919) 678-2220
Web Site: https://www.cottoninc.com
Year Founded: 1971
Sales Range: $100-124.9 Million
Emp.: 175
Importer, Promoter & Producer of US
Cotton
N.A.I.C.S.: 541820
J. Berrye Worsham (Pres & CEO)
Mark A. Messura (Sr VP-Global Sup-
ply Chain Mktg)
Janet O'Regan (Mgr-Nonwovens
Mktg)
Kater Hake (VP-Agricultural & Envi-
ronmental Res)
Jesse Daystar (Chief Sustainability
Officer & VP)
Dahlen Hancock (Chm)
Kimberley S. Kitchings (Sr VP-
Consumer Mktg)

Subsidiaries:

Cotton Incorporated Consumer Marketing Headquarters   (1)
909 3rd Ave, New York, NY 10022 **(100%)**

Tel.: (212) 413-8300
Web Site: http://www.cottoninc.com
Sales Range: $10-24.9 Million
Emp.: 24
Cotton Promotional Services
N.A.I.C.S.: 541613

COTTONS POINT DESIGN
1381 Calle Avanzado, San Clemente,
CA 92673-6351
Tel.: (714) 897-9299
Year Founded: 1988
Sales Range: $10-24.9 Million
Emp.: 4
Electrical Equipment Distr
N.A.I.C.S.: 334419
Curt Vikan (Pres)

COTTONTREE HOSPITALITY GROUP
1030 N 400 E, North Salt Lake, UT
84054
Tel.: (801) 292-7666
Web Site: http://www.cottontree.net
Rev.: $15,300,000
Emp.: 25
Hotel
N.A.I.C.S.: 531210
David J. Petersen (Pres)

COTTONWOOD ACQUISI-TIONS LLC
1700 Ocean Ave St 2, Ronkonkoma,
NY 11779
Tel.: (646) 807-8674
Web Site:
  https://cottonwoodacquisitions.com
Financial Services
N.A.I.C.S.: 523999

Subsidiaries:

Pacific Register Co. Inc   (1)
98 Donald Ave, Newbury Park, CA 91320-
4410
Web Site: http://www.pacificregisterco.com
All Other Miscellaneous Mfr
N.A.I.C.S.: 339999
Mike Pettet (Owner)

COTTONWOOD CO-OP OIL COMPANY
147 Barstad Rd N, Cottonwood, MN
56229
Tel.: (507) 423-6282
Web Site:
  http://www.cottonwoodcoopoil.com
Sales Range: $10-24.9 Million
Emp.: 8
Petroleum Bulk Stations & Terminals
N.A.I.C.S.: 424710
Brad Rosa (Gen Mgr)

COTTONWOOD COMMUNI-TIES, INC.
1245 Brickyard Rd Ste 250, Salt Lake
City, UT 84106
Tel.: (801) 278-0700   MD
Web Site:
  https://www.cottonwoodcommu
  nities.com
Year Founded: 2016
Rev.: $138,302,000
Assets: $1,955,637,000
Liabilities: $1,345,738,000
Net Worth: $609,899,000
Earnings: ($15,649,000)
Emp.: 308
Fiscal Year-end: 12/31/22
Real Estate Investment Services
N.A.I.C.S.: 531210
Enzio A. Cassinis (Pres & CEO)
Adam Larson (CFO)
Susan Hallenberg (Chief Acctg Offi-
cer & Treas)
Gregg Christensen (Chief Legal Offi-
cer & Sec)

Paul Fredenberg (Chief Investment
Officer)
Daniel Shaeffer (CEO)
Chad Christensen (Exec Chm)
Eric Marlin (Exec VP-Capital Markets-
Southeast)
Michelle Langer (Sr VP-Capital Mar-
kets)
Jeremy Lyman (Sr VP-Capital
Markets-Northwest)
Tony Neves (Sr VP-Capital Markets-
Northeast)
Jordon Plapinger (Dir-Capital
Markets-Northwest)
Whitney Fisher (Dir-Capital Markets-
Northeast)
Saul Dougherty (Sr VP-Capital
Markets-Southwest)
Declan Marmion (Dir-Capital Markets-
Southeast)
Preston Corman (Dir-Capital Markets-
Southwest)
Thayer Gallison (Sr VP-Capital Mar-
kets & Head-Product Strategy)

COTTONWOOD FINANCIAL LTD
Ste 200 1901 Gateway Dr, Irving, TX
75038-2425
Tel.: (972) 753-0822
Web Site:
  http://www.cottonwoodfinancial.com
Rev.: $27,700,000
Emp.: 40
Consumer Finance Companies
N.A.I.C.S.: 522291
Triver Ahlverg (Pres)
Rocio Lopez (Coord-Facilities & Con-
struction)
Paul Whitworth (Mgr-Bus Intelligence)
Trevor Ahlberg (Owner)
Laura Louis (Area Mgr)

COTTONWOOD INCORPO-RATED
2801 W 31st St, Lawrence, KS 66047
Tel.: (785) 842-0550   KS
Web Site: https://www.cwood.org
Year Founded: 1972
Sales Range: $10-24.9 Million
Emp.: 451
Disability Assistance Services
N.A.I.C.S.: 624120
Janet Fouche-Schack (Dir-Support
Svcs)
Dennis Meier (Dir-HR)
Heather Thies (Dir-Life Enrichment)
Jessica Wood (CFO)
Kara Walters (Dir-Residential Svcs)
Sharon Spratt (CEO)
J. R. Condra (Dir-Cottonwood Indus)
Phil Bentzinger (Dir-JobLink)
Peggy Wallert (Dir-Community Rels &
Dev)
Angela Drake (Dir-CDDO Admin)
Zak Bolick (Treas)
Doug Gaumer (Chm)
Luke Livingston (Sec)
Tom Mulinazzi (VP)

COTTONWOOD REALTY SER-VICES LLC
2855 Cottonwood Pkwy Ste 560, Salt
Lake City, UT 84121
Tel.: (214) 691-8500
Web Site:
  http://www.cottonwoodpartners.com
Sales Range: $10-24.9 Million
Emp.: 35
Real Estate Agents & Managers
N.A.I.C.S.: 531210
John L. West (CEO)
Scott Collins (CFO)
Steven W. Baer (Sr VP-Dev)

COTTRELL CONTRACTING CORP
328 Battlefield Blvd N, Chesapeake,
VA 23320
Tel.: (757) 547-9611
Web Site:
  https://www.cottrellcontracting.com
Sales Range: $10-24.9 Million
Emp.: 100
Dredging Contractor
N.A.I.C.S.: 236210
Joe Polis (Sec)
Michael Kay (Project Mgr)
Benjamin G. Cottrell IV (Chm)

COUDAL PARTNERS
400 N May St Ste 301, Chicago, IL
60622
Tel.: (312) 243-1107
Web Site: http://www.coudal.com
Year Founded: 1993
Sales Range: $25-49.9 Million
Emp.: 6
Advertising Services
N.A.I.C.S.: 541810
Jim Coudal (Pres)

COUGAR OIL INC.
1411 Water Ave, Selma, AL 36701
Tel.: (334) 875-2023
Web Site: https://www.cougaroil.com
Year Founded: 1971
Sales Range: $10-24.9 Million
Emp.: 125
Petroleum Bulk Station Services
N.A.I.C.S.: 424710
Larry J. Jones (Pres)
Natasha Reynolds (Dir-IT)

COUGH INC.
201 Woodstock Ave, Rutland, VT
05701
Tel.: (802) 747-3365
Rev.: $10,782,945
Emp.: 6
Fast-Food Restaurant, Chain
N.A.I.C.S.: 722513
Charles Coughlin (Chm)

COUGHLAN COMPANIES, INC.
1710 Roe Crest Dr, North Mankato,
MN 56003
Tel.: (507) 345-8100
Web Site: http://www.coughlan-
  companies.com
Sales Range: $25-49.9 Million
Emp.: 135
Holding Company; Book Publishing
N.A.I.C.S.: 551112
G. Thomas Ahern (CEO)
Robert J. Coughlan (Co-Owner &
Principal)
William R. Rouse (COO)
James P. Coughlan (Co-Owner &
Principal)
Steve Robinson (CFO)
Scott Sustacek (Pres)

Subsidiaries:

Buncee, LLC   (1)
170 Montauk Hwy, Speonk, NY 11972
Tel.: (631) 591-1390
Web Site: http://www.buncee.com
Software Publisher
N.A.I.C.S.: 513210
Marie Arturi (Founder & CEO)

Capstone Press, Inc.   (1)
1710 Roe Crest Dr, North Mankato, MN
56003
Tel.: (507) 388-6650
Web Site: http://www.capstonepub.com
Sales Range: $100-124.9 Million
Emp.: 173
Book Publishers
N.A.I.C.S.: 513130
G. Thomas Ahern (CEO)
Eric S. Fitzgerald (VP-Sls & Education)
Matthew A. Keller (VP-Bus Dev)
Gail S. Beer (VP-Customer Rels & Fulfill-
ment)

Division (Domestic):

Heinemann-Raintree (2)
1 N LaSalle Ste 1800, Chicago, IL 60602
Tel.: (312) 324-5200
Web Site:
http://www.heinemannraintree.com
Sales Range: $25-49.9 Million
Emp.: 15
PreKindergarten-Secondary Nonfiction
Books Publisher
N.A.I.C.S.: 513130
Miles E. Stevens-Hoare (Mng Dir)

COUGLE COMMISSION COMPANY, INC.
345 N Aberdeen St, Chicago, IL 60607-1226
Tel.: (312) 666-7861   IL
Web Site:
http://www.couglecommission.com
Year Founded: 1873
Sales Range: $75-99.9 Million
Emp.: 40
Producer & Retailer of Fresh & Frozen Meats & Poultry
N.A.I.C.S.: 424440
Alison Freidheim (VP-Sls & Procurement)
George Fuchs (Dir-Bus Dev)
Lee Freidheim (Pres & CEO)

COULEE TECH, INC.
1111 Linden Rd Ste 201, Holmen, WI 54636
Tel.: (608) 783-8324
Web Site: http://www.coulee.tech
Year Founded: 2008
Sales Range: $1-9.9 Million
Emp.: 11
Software Development Services
N.A.I.C.S.: 541511
Rodney Holum (Founder, CEO, Chief Transition Officer & Specialist-Bus Solution)

COULTER & JUSTUS, P.C.
9717 Cogdill Rd Ste 201, Knoxville, TN 37932
Tel.: (865) 637-4161
Web Site: http://www.cj-pc.com
Year Founded: 1952
Accounting Services
N.A.I.C.S.: 541211
Sam Coulter (Co-Founder)
Ron Justus (Co-Founder)
Mike Parton (Mng Principal)

COULTER CADILLAC INCORPORATED
1188 E Camelback Rd, Phoenix, AZ 85014-3270
Tel.: (602) 264-1188
Web Site:
http://www.coultercadillac.com
Year Founded: 1923
Rev.: $110,000,000
Emp.: 130
New & Used Car Dealers
N.A.I.C.S.: 441110
William R. Coulter (Chm)
Dick Sidabras (CFO)
John McQueen (Asst Mgr-Parts)
Kevin Kish (Mgr-Sls)

COULTER MOTOR COMPANY LLC.
7780 S Autoplex Loop, Tempe, AZ 85284
Tel.: (480) 940-6000
Web Site:
http://www.coultertempe.com
Year Founded: 1994
Sales Range: $10-24.9 Million
Emp.: 100
Car Whslr
N.A.I.C.S.: 441110

Bill Coulter (Owner)

COUNCIL CAPITAL
30 Burton Hills Blvd Ste 576, Nashville, TN 37215
Tel.: (615) 255-3707
Web Site:
https://www.councilcapital.com
Emp.: 7
Venture Capital Investment Firm
N.A.I.C.S.: 523999
Katie H. Gambill (Co-Founder & Partner)
Eric H. Keen (Partner)
Grant A. Jackson (Mng Partner)
John W. Davis (VP)
Tyler L. Augusty (Dir-Council & & Enhanced Tennessee Fund)
Jon L'Heureux (Sr VP-Bus Dev)
Dennis C. Bottorff (Co-Founder & Partner)

COUNCIL FOR CHRISTIAN COLLEGES & UNIVERSITIES
321 8th St NE, Washington, DC 20002
Tel.: (202) 546-8713   DC
Web Site: https://www.cccu.org
Year Founded: 1982
Sales Range: $10-24.9 Million
Emp.: 117
Educational Support Services
N.A.I.C.S.: 611710

COUNCIL FOR OPPORTUNITY IN EDUCATION
1025 Vermont Ave NW Ste 900, Washington, DC 20005-3516
Tel.: (202) 347-7430   DC
Web Site: http://www.coenet.us
Year Founded: 1980
Sales Range: $10-24.9 Million
Emp.: 33
Educational Support Services
N.A.I.C.S.: 611710
Nicole Norfles (Dir-Program Practice & Innovation)
Wendell Fabul (Mgr-Grants & Fin)
Karen Dohvoma (Accountant)
Alvin K. Phillips (Sr VP-Membership & HR)
Jesse Baker (Sr VP-Membership & HR)
Jorge Antonio Martinez Santiago (Treas)
Maureen Hoyler (Pres)
Tracy Karasinski (Sec)
John P. Hernandez (Assoc VP-Tech)
Patricia Mahomond (Mgr-Bus Dev)
Angelica Vialpando (VP-Program & Prof Dev)
Michelle A. Danvers Foust (Chm)
Kimberly A. Jones (VP-Pub Policy & Comm)

COUNCIL ON AGING OF SOUTHWESTERN OHIO
175 Tri County Pkwy, Cincinnati, OH 45246
Tel.: (513) 721-1025   OH
Web Site:
http://www.help4seniors.org
Year Founded: 1971
Sales Range: $75-99.9 Million
Emp.: 255
Elder Care Services
N.A.I.C.S.: 623312

COUNCIL ON FOREIGN RELATIONS
58 E 68th St, New York, NY 10065
Tel.: (212) 434-9400
Web Site: https://www.cfr.org
Year Founded: 1921
Sales Range: $75-99.9 Million

Foreign Policy Information Services; Non-Profit Independent National Organization
N.A.I.C.S.: 541720
Gideon Rose (Editor-Foreign Affairs)
Jonathan Tepperman (Mng Editor-Foreign Affairs)
Richard N. Haass (Pres)
Jeffrey A. Reinke (Chief Staff & Sec)
Lisa Shields (VP-Global Comm & Media Rels)
Neftali F. Alvarez (Dir-Facility, Event & Security Mgmt)
Lynda Hammes (Publr-Foreign Affairs)
Irina A. Faskianos (VP-Outreach Programs-Natl)
Amy R. Baker (Dir-Studies Admin)
Janine Hill (Dir-Fellowship Affairs & Studies Strategic Plng)
Valerie Post (Dir-Special Events)
Anya Schmemann (Dir-Task Force Program)
Jan Mowder Hughes (VP-HR & Admin)
Suzanne E. Helm (VP-Philanthropy & Corp Rels)
Nancy D. Bodurtha (VP-Meetings & Membership)
James Lindsay (Sr VP & Dir-Studies)
Lilita Gusts (Dir-Library & Res Svcs)
Keith Olson (Exec VP, CFO & Treas)
Mia Higgins (Gen Counsel)
Christopher M. Tuttle (Mng Dir-Washington & Task Force Programs)
Veronica Chiu (Asst Dir-Task Force Program)
Emilie Harkin (Dir-Mktg-Publ)
Edward Walsh (Dir-Adv-Publ)
Caroline Netchvolodoff (VP-Education)
Charles Landow (Dir-Education Content)
Lily Cabrera (Dir-Corp Member Rels)
Betsy Gude (Dir-Dev)
Sharon R. Herbst (Dir-Special Projects)
Vera Ranola (Dir-Membership)
Maria Casa (Dir-Natl Program & Outreach Admin)
Iva Zoric (Dir-Global Comm & Media Rels)
Jennifer Perez (Dir-Fin)
Jean-Michel Oriol (Dir-Grants & Budget Admin)
Jeffrey Meade (Dir-HR)
Jayson Frum (Dir-Ops & Project Mgmt-Washington)
Rachel Lumpkin (Dir-Event Mgmt & Special Events-Washington)
Blair Effron (Co-Vice Chm)
Judith A. Miscik (Co-Vice Chm)
David M. Rubenstein (Chm)

COUNCIL ON FOUNDATIONS
2121 Crystal Dr Ste 700, Arlington, VA 22202
Tel.: (800) 673-9036   NY
Web Site: http://www.cof.org
Year Founded: 1949
Emp.: 47
Grantmaking Services
N.A.I.C.S.: 813219

COUNCIL ON RURAL SERVICES
201 RM Davis Pkwy Ste B, Piqua, OH 45356
Tel.: (937) 778-5220   OH
Web Site:
https://www.councilonruralser
vices.org
Year Founded: 1972
Sales Range: $10-24.9 Million
Emp.: 426
Individual & Family Support Services

N.A.I.C.S.: 624190
Dan Schwanitz (CEO & CFO-Interim)
Michael Hormann (Mgr-Facilities & Transportation)
Liz Schoonover (Dir-Early Childhood)
Millie Woryk (Chief Admin Officer & Chief HR Officer)
Dustin Michael Davis (Vice Chm)
Randy Fisher (Chm)
William Lutz (Sec)

COUNSEL ON CALL
112 Westwood Pl 350, Brentwood, TN 37027
Tel.: (615) 467-2388
Web Site:
http://www.counseloncall.com
Sales Range: $25-49.9 Million
Emp.: 30
Contract Placement Services for Attorneys & Paralegals
N.A.I.C.S.: 561320
Jane H. Allen (Founder & Chm)
Chad Schmidt (Dir-Mktg & Comm)
Dennie McKinnie (Pres)
Celeste Flippen (Exec Dir-Talent Dev)
Barry Dark (CEO)
Eric Schultenover (VP-Bus Dev)

COUNSELING & RECOVERY SERVICES OF OKLAHOMA
7010 S Yale Ave, Tulsa, OK 74136
Tel.: (918) 492-2554   OK
Web Site: https://www.crsok.org
Year Founded: 1979
Sales Range: $10-24.9 Million
Emp.: 190
Mental Health Services
N.A.I.C.S.: 621420
Bryan K. Blankenship (Exec Dir)
Martha Hauser (Dir-Ops, Admin & Bus Dev)
Taylor Shorb (Dir-Resource Dev)

COUNSELING & RESEARCH ASSOCIATES
130 W Victoria St, Gardena, CA 90248
Tel.: (310) 715-2020   CA
Web Site:
http://www.masadahomes.org
Year Founded: 1966
Sales Range: $10-24.9 Million
Emp.: 233
Foster Care Services
N.A.I.C.S.: 624110
Sharon Igi (Dir-HR)
George K. Igi (Exec Dir)
Bernard Smith (COO)

COUNSELING & SUPPORT SERVICES FOR YOUTH
544 Valley Way, Milpitas, CA 95035-4106
Tel.: (408) 493-5289   CA
Web Site:
https://www.cassybayarea.org
Year Founded: 2009
Sales Range: $1-9.9 Million
Emp.: 40
Education Awareness & Mental Health Services
N.A.I.C.S.: 813319
Christy Rodgers (Exec Dir)
Cheryl Serna (Dir-Ops)
Lindsay Austin Louie (Pres)
Dana Fenwick (Treas)
Gina Maya (Sec)

COUNSELING ASSOCIATES, INC.
350 Salem Rd Ste 1, Conway, AR 72034

Counseling Associates, Inc.—(Continued)
Tel.: (501) 336-8300   AR
Web Site: http://www.caiinc.org
Year Founded: 1972
Sales Range: $10-24.9 Million
Emp.: 222
Behavioral Healthcare Services
N.A.I.C.S.: 623210
Brian Lutz (CFO)
Steve Newsome (Pres & CEO)

COUNSELING INTERNATIONAL, INC.
2333 Boone Ave, Venice, CA 90291
Tel.: (310) 510-6401   NV
Web Site:
    http://www.livechatcounseling.com
Online Counseling Services
N.A.I.C.S.: 513199
Layla Stone (Pres, CEO & CFO)

COUNSELOR REALTY INC.
951 Hillwind Rd, Fridley, MN 55432
Tel.: (763) 786-0600
Web Site:
    http://www.counselorrealty.com
Sales Range: $10-24.9 Million
Emp.: 25
Real Estate Brokers & Agents
N.A.I.C.S.: 531210
Nick Dreher (Dir-Growth-
Development)

COUNT'S KUSTOMS
2714 Highland Dr, Las Vegas, NV
89109
Tel.: (702) 733-6216
Web Site:
    http://www.countskustoms.com
Sales Range: $10-24.9 Million
Emp.: 20
Motorcycle Dealer & Repair Services
N.A.I.C.S.: 441227
Danny Koker (Owner)

COUNT'S VAMP'D
6750 W Sahara Ave, Las Vegas, NV
89146
Tel.: (702) 220-8849
Web Site:
    https://www.vampdvegas.com
Sales Range: $1-9.9 Million
Emp.: 10
Bar & Grill
N.A.I.C.S.: 722410
Danny Koker (Owner)

COUNTERPOINT CAPITAL PARTNERS, LLC
555 W 5th St 35th Fl, Los Angeles,
CA 90013
Tel.: (424) 259-2228   DE
Web Site:
    http://www.counterpointcp.com
Year Founded: 2010
Privater Equity Firm
N.A.I.C.S.: 523999
Eric M. Willis (Mng Partner)
Cindy Song (VP)

Subsidiaries:

Artcobell Corporation   (1)
1302 Industrial Blvd, Temple, TX 76504
Tel.: (254) 778-1811
Web Site: http://www.artcobell.com
School Furniture, Tables, Desks & Computer Furniture Mfr
N.A.I.C.S.: 337127
Richard Parker (Pres)

Division (Domestic):

Artco-Bell Corporation   (2)
1302 Industrial Blvd, Temple, TX
76504   (100%)
Tel.: (254) 773-1776
Web Site: http://www.artcobell.com
Rev.: $9,000,000

Mfr of Office & School Furniture
N.A.I.C.S.: 337127

POP Displays USA, LLC   (1)
555 Tuckahoe Rd, Yonkers, NY 10710
Tel.: (914) 771-4200
Web Site: http://www.popdisplaysusa.com
Holding Company; Point-of-Purchase Displays Designer & Mfr
N.A.I.C.S.: 551112
John Hegedus (Dir-Fin & Demand Plng)
Alex Prophet (Mgr-Production)
Mony Vann (Controller)
Roseanne Alletto (VP-Sls Ops)

Parts Now LLC   (1)
3150 Pleasant View Rd, Middleton, WI
53562
Tel.: (608) 203-1500
Web Site: http://www.partsnow.com
Sales Range: $75-99.9 Million
Emp.: 250
Printer Parts Distr & Training & Technical
Services
N.A.I.C.S.: 423430
Michael Cox (CEO)
Matt McLeish (VP-Sls & Mktg)
Jennifer Boyd (Dir-Mktg)
Bob Banke (VP-Ops)

COUNTERTOPS INC.
6111 Alter Rd, Eau Claire, WI 54703
Tel.: (715) 876-6744
Web Site:
    http://www.countertopsinc.com
Sales Range: $10-24.9 Million
Emp.: 150
Counter & Sink Tops
N.A.I.C.S.: 337110
Jessica LaPoint (Mgr-HR)

COUNTRY BANK FOR SAVINGS
75 Main St, Ware, MA 01082-2003
Tel.: (413) 967-6221
Web Site:
    https://www.countrybank.com
Sales Range: $1-4.9 Billion
Emp.: 280
Banking Services
N.A.I.C.S.: 522180
Paul Scully (Pres & CEO)
Shelley M. Regin (First VP & Dir-
Mktg)
Blair Robidoux (Mgr-West Street)
Elise Kowal (Mgr-Retail Banking)
Melissa Mann (Mgr-Retail Banking)
Jodie Gerulaitis (VP-Community Rels)
Miriam Siegel (Sr VP-HR)
Mark Phillips (First VP-Internal Audit)
Sarah Yurkunas (Portfolio Mgr-
Comml)
Russell Fontaine (First VP-Sls & Market Mgmt)
Yvonne Santos (VP-Market Dev)
Angela Barahona (VP-Bus Dev &
Cash Mgmt-Comml Div)

COUNTRY BANK SHARES, INC.
617 1st St, Milford, NE 68405
Tel.: (402) 761-7600   NE
Web Site: http://www.bankfmb.com
Year Founded: 1989
Bank Holding Company
N.A.I.C.S.: 551111
Gerry A. Dunlap (Pres & CEO)

Subsidiaries:

Farmers and Merchants Bank   (1)
617 1st St, Milford, NE 68405
Tel.: (402) 761-7600
Web Site: http://www.bankfmb.com
Commericial Banking
N.A.I.C.S.: 522110
Gerry A. Dunlap (Pres & CEO)
Justina Roth (COO)
Scott Boyles (Chief Lending Officer)

COUNTRY CHEVROLET, INC.

299 E State Rd 155, Herscher, IL
60941
Tel.: (815) 426-6311   IL
Web Site:
    http://www.gmchevydealer.com
Year Founded: 2005
Sales Range: $10-24.9 Million
Emp.: 15
New & Used Car Dealer
N.A.I.C.S.: 441110
Scott Irps (Pres)
Rob Kempen (Mgr-Sls)

COUNTRY CHEVROLET, INC.
1400 W Wilson St, Borger, TX
79007-4420
Tel.: (806) 275-9122   TX
Web Site:
    https://www.countrychevrolet.net
Year Founded: 1997
Sales Range: $10-24.9 Million
Emp.: 45
New & Used Car Dealer
N.A.I.C.S.: 441110
Jeffrey Scott Whittington (Pres)

COUNTRY CLUB AUTO GROUP
55 Oneida St, Oneonta, NY 13820
Tel.: (607) 432-2800
Web Site:
    http://www.countryclubimports.com
Sales Range: $10-24.9 Million
Emp.: 35
Automobiles, New & Used
N.A.I.C.S.: 441110
Peter Armao (Owner)

COUNTRY CLUB BANK
414 Nichols Rd, Kansas City, MO
64112
Tel.: (816) 931-4060
Web Site:
    http://www.countryclubbank.com
Sales Range: $10-24.9 Million
Emp.: 400
State Commercial Banks
N.A.I.C.S.: 531210
Timothy J. Thompson (Gen Counsel)
Joe Close (Pres-Reg Comml Banking
Div)
Linda Cole (Exec VP)
Toni Walsh (Exec VP-HR)
Jennifer Fenton (Controller)
Marla Youk (Dir-Mktg)
Alexandra Kuebler (Coord-
Relationship Dev)
Sheila Stokes (Mgr-Private Banking
Relationship)
Charlie R. Hill (Sr VP)
Dwayne K. White (Chief Investment
Officer & Exec VP)
Christee Highbarger (Chief Risk Officer)
Terence Fitzpatrick (Assoc Gen
Counsel)
Angela Stewart (Dir-Consumer Banking)
Robert Healy (Chief Credit Officer)
David Caffrey (Chief Lending Officer)

COUNTRY CLUB OF BIRMINGHAM
3325 Country Club Rd, Birmingham,
AL 35213
Tel.: (205) 879-4611   AL
Web Site: https://www.ccbham.org
Year Founded: 1922
Sales Range: $10-24.9 Million
Emp.: 393
Country Club
N.A.I.C.S.: 713910
Jeff Orkus (Gen Mgr)

COUNTRY COACH CORPORATION

125 E 4th Ave, Junction City, OR
97448-1461
Tel.: (541) 234-2167   OR
Web Site:
    http://www.countrycoach.com
Year Founded: 1973
Emp.: 35
Motor Homes Parts Manufacturing,
Servicing & Sales
N.A.I.C.S.: 336390

COUNTRY EGGS INC.
333 N Mission Rd, Los Angeles, CA
90033
Tel.: (323) 980-4488
Rev.: $22,000,000
Emp.: 42
Producer of Eggs
N.A.I.C.S.: 424440
Joseph Zaritsky (Pres)

COUNTRY FINANCIAL
1701 Towanda Ave, Bloomington, IL
61701-2057
Tel.: (309) 821-3000   IL
Web Site:
    http://www.countryfinancial.com
Year Founded: 1925
Sales Range: $1-4.9 Billion
Emp.: 3,600
Insurance & Financial Services
N.A.I.C.S.: 524210
Doyle J. Williams (CMO)
Steve Denault (COO & Exec VP)
Gabriel Carrillo (Sr VP-Property &
Casualty)
Brad Hildestad (CIO & Exec VP)
Kelvin Schill (Sr VP-Fin Svcs)
Rachael Sklamberg (Sr VP-HR)
Jim Jacobs (CEO)

Subsidiaries:

CC Services, Inc.   (1)
1701 N Towanda Ave, Bloomington, IL
61701-2057
Tel.: (309) 821-3000
Web Site: http://www.countryfinancial.com
Sales Range: $100-124.9 Million
Emp.: 2,000
Life Health Insurance Annuities
N.A.I.C.S.: 541611

COUNTRY Capital Management
Company   (1)
1705 N Towanda Ave, Bloomington, IL
61702-2222
Tel.: (309) 821-5228
Web Site: http://www.countryfinancial.com
Investment Management Service
N.A.I.C.S.: 523940

COUNTRY Financial   (1)
1711 GE Rd, Bloomington, IL
61704   (100%)
Tel.: (309) 821-3000
Web Site: http://www.countryfinancial.com
Sales Range: $125-149.9 Million
Emp.: 300
Life Health Insurance, Annuities
N.A.I.C.S.: 524210
Brian Beaver (Mgr-Web Svcs & Corp
Forms)
Ryan Thomas (Supvr-Claims)
Kristi Rabenberg (Project Mgr-Model Audit
Rule)
Shelly Prehoda (Dir-Compensation & Employee Rels)
Tom Joseph (Mgr-IT Svcs)

COUNTRY Financial - Central
Region   (1)
1705 Towanda Ave, Bloomington, IL 61702
Tel.: (651) 631-7000
Web Site: http://www.countryfinancial.com
Sales Range: $150-199.9 Million
Emp.: 350
Insurance Agents, Brokers & Service
N.A.I.C.S.: 524210

COUNTRY Investors Life Assurance
Company   (1)
1705 N Towanda Ave, Bloomington, IL
61701-2040

Tel.: (309) 557-3000
Fire Insurance Services
N.A.I.C.S.: 524113

COUNTRY Life Insurance
Company **(1)**
1701 Towanda Ave, Bloomington, IL 61702-2000
Tel.: (309) 821-3000
Fire Insurance Services
N.A.I.C.S.: 524113

COUNTRY Mutual Insurance
Company **(1)**
1701 Towanda Ave, Bloomington, IL 61701
Tel.: (309) 821-3000
Web Site: http://www.countryfinancial.com
Sales Range: $250-299.9 Million
Emp.: 2,000
General Insurance Services
N.A.I.C.S.: 524210

Subsidiary (Domestic):

COUNTRY Preferred Insurance
Company **(2)**
1701 N Towanda Ave, Bloomington, IL 61701
Tel.: (309) 821-3000
Fire & Casualty Insurance Services
N.A.I.C.S.: 524128

COUNTRY Trust Bank **(1)**
1705 Towanda Ave, Bloomington, IL 61702-2901
Tel.: (309) 821-4600
Investment Management Service
N.A.I.C.S.: 523999
Laurel Beth Donovan *(Mgr-Retirement & Investment Svcs)*

Country Medical Plans, Inc. **(1)**
PO Box 2000, Bloomington, IL 61702
Tel.: (309) 821-3000
Web Site: http://www.countryfinancial.com
Medical Insurance With HMOs
N.A.I.C.S.: 524210

Middlesex Mutual Assurance
Company **(1)**
213 Court St, Middletown, CT 06457
Tel.: (860) 347-4621
Web Site: http://www.middlesexmutual.com
Sales Range: $75-99.9 Million
Emp.: 210
Auto, Home, Fire, Marine & Casualty Insurance
N.A.I.C.S.: 524126

COUNTRY FLOORS INC.
15 E 16th St, New York, NY 10003
Tel.: (212) 627-8300   NY
Web Site:
https://www.countryfloors.com
Year Founded: 1964
Sales Range: $25-49.9 Million
Emp.: 120
Tiles Mfr
N.A.I.C.S.: 444180

COUNTRY FLORAL SUPPLY INC.
77 Duesenberg Dr Thousand Oaks, Simi Valley, CA 91362
Tel.: (805) 520-8026
Web Site:
http://www.thedecorstore.com
Rev.: $16,677,362
Emp.: 45
Artificial Flowers
N.A.I.C.S.: 424930
Mark Reese *(Pres)*

COUNTRY FORD TRUCKS INC.
1720 Herndon Rd, Ceres, CA 95307
Tel.: (209) 541-3673
Web Site:
http://www.countryfordtrucks.com
Rev.: $35,747,956
Emp.: 30
Trucks, Tractors & Trailers: New & Used
N.A.I.C.S.: 441110

Jeff Shipman *(Mgr-Sls & Fin)*

COUNTRY FRESH BATTER INC.
221 King Manor Dr, King of Prussia, PA 19406
Tel.: (610) 272-4673
Web Site:
http://www.hopescookies.com
Sales Range: $10-24.9 Million
Emp.: 70
Mfr of Frozen Cookie Dough: Cookies
N.A.I.C.S.: 311821
Hope Spivak *(Pres)*

COUNTRY HOUSES, LLC
370 Main St, New London, NH 03257
Tel.: (603) 526-4020   NH
Web Site:
http://www.cblifestylesre.com
Year Founded: 1939
Emp.: 150
Real Estate Agency
N.A.I.C.S.: 531210
Joe Burns *(Partner)*
Stefan Timbrell *(Partner)*

COUNTRY LIFE HOMES INC.
610 Marshall St, Milford, DE 19963
Tel.: (302) 265-2257
Web Site:
https://www.countrylifehomes.com
Sales Range: $10-24.9 Million
Emp.: 20
Single-Family Housing Construction
N.A.I.C.S.: 236115
Elmer Fannin *(Co-Founder)*

COUNTRY MAID, INC.
213 4th Ave NE, West Bend, IA 50597
Web Site:
https://www.countrymaid.net
Year Founded: 1991
Dessert Food Mfr
N.A.I.C.S.: 311999
Ken Banwart *(Co-CEO)*
Darin Massner *(Co-CEO)*
Marlene Banwart *(Mgr-Tech)*
Jim Schonert *(COO)*
Amy Emery Tijerina *(Mgr-Bus Dev)*

COUNTRY MALT GROUP
16 Beeman Way, Champlain, NY 12919
Tel.: (518) 572-4505
Web Site:
http://www.countrymaltgroup.com
Year Founded: 1995
Sales Range: $1-9.9 Million
Emp.: 50
Brewing & Distilling Products Supplier
N.A.I.C.S.: 311213
Michael Saklad *(Sls Mgr-East)*

COUNTRY MUSIC FOUNDATION, INC.
222 5th Ave S, Nashville, TN 37203
Tel.: (615) 416-2043   TN
Web Site:
http://countrymusichalloffame.org
Year Founded: 1964
Sales Range: $25-49.9 Million
History Museum Operator
N.A.I.C.S.: 712110
Earl Bentz *(VP)*
Vince Gill *(Pres)*
Al Giombetti *(Exec VP)*
Steve Turner *(Chm)*
Keel Hunt *(Sec)*
Ernie Williams *(Treas)*
Tim Wipperman *(VP)*

COUNTRY PARTNERS COOPERATIVE

310 E Railroad Ave, Spalding, NE 68665
Tel.: (308) 497-2266
Web Site:
https://www.countrypartners.com
Sales Range: $10-24.9 Million
Emp.: 100
Agricultural Supply & Grain Management Services
N.A.I.C.S.: 424510
Linda Doughty *(Controller)*
Dan Bloom *(Mgr-Fin)*

COUNTRY PRIDE CO-OPERATIVE
648 W 2nd St, Winner, SD 57580
Tel.: (605) 842-2711
Web Site:
http://www.countrypridecoop.com
Rev.: $47,037,947
Emp.: 200
Grains
N.A.I.C.S.: 424510
Mike Trosen *(CEO)*
Mike Barfuss *(VP-Energy)*

COUNTRY PRIDE SERVICES CO-OPERATIVE
144 9th St, Bingham Lake, MN 56118
Tel.: (507) 831-2580
Web Site:
https://www.countrypride.com
Sales Range: $10-24.9 Million
Emp.: 50
Retailer Of Agricultural Chemicals
N.A.I.C.S.: 424910
Kevin Jackson *(Gen Mgr)*
Sue Horn *(Office Mgr)*

COUNTRY ROAD ASSOCIATES, LTD.
5 Milltown Rd, Holmes, NY 12531
Tel.: (845) 677-6041
Web Site:
https://www.countryroadassocs.com
Sales Range: Less than $1 Million
Emp.: 2
Antique Flooring & Furniture Mfr
N.A.I.C.S.: 449110
Dave Dunning *(Owner)*

COUNTRY SQUIRE FARM PRODUCTS
931 SW 5th St, Oklahoma City, OK 73109
Tel.: (405) 232-9404
Sales Range: $10-24.9 Million
Emp.: 20
Poultry & Poultry Products
N.A.I.C.S.: 424440
Denise Wilson *(Pres)*

COUNTRY VISIONS COOPERATIVE
709 Mill St PO Box 460, Reedsville, WI 54230
Tel.: (920) 754-4321   WI
Web Site:
http://www.countryvisionscoop.com
Year Founded: 1923
Dairy, Grain & Other Farm Products Whslr & Storage Services
N.A.I.C.S.: 493130
Joe Holschbach *(Chm)*
David Schneider *(Vice Chm)*
Wes Hedrich *(Sec)*

COUNTRY-WIDE INSURANCE COMPANY
40 Wall St, New York, NY 10005-1304
Tel.: (212) 514-7000
Web Site: https://www.cwico.com
Year Founded: 1963
Property Casualty Insurance
N.A.I.C.S.: 524126

Jayson Harrington *(CIO)*
Ron Canton *(Compliance Officer)*

COUNTRYMARK COOPERATIVE, INC.
225 SE St Ste 144, Indianapolis, IN 46202-4002
Tel.: (317) 692-8500   DE
Web Site:
https://www.countrymark.com
Year Founded: 1938
Sales Range: $100-124.9 Million
Emp.: 275
Petroleum Products for Agriculture Distr
N.A.I.C.S.: 424720
Charles Smith *(CEO)*
Jo Biggers *(VP-Fin & Admin)*
Thomas Tucker *(Chm)*

Subsidiaries:

Countrymark Energy Resources, LLC **(1)**
7116 Eagle Crest Blvd Ste C, Evansville, IN 47715
Tel.: (812) 759-9440
Web Site: http://www.countrymark.com
Emp.: 110
Oil Exploration & Refining Services
N.A.I.C.S.: 324110
Wes Stover *(Mgr-Infrastructure)*
Frank Lindsey *(Mgr-Regulatory Compliance)*

Countrymark Refining and Logistics, LLC **(1)**
1200 Refinery Rd, Mount Vernon, IN 47620
Tel.: (800) 832-5490
Oil Extraction & Refining Services
N.A.I.C.S.: 211120
Keith Symanski *(Engr-Maintenance)*
Nathaniel Robertson *(Supvr-Laboratory)*
Matt Smorch *(VP-Supply & Optimization)*

COUNTRYSIDE COOPERATIVE, INC.
514 E Main St, Durand, WI 54736-1258
Tel.: (715) 672-8947
Web Site:
http://www.countrysidecoop.com
Year Founded: 1956
Sales Range: $25-49.9 Million
Emp.: 250
Farm Supplies Whslr
N.A.I.C.S.: 424910
Gregory Clyde Kruger *(Pres)*
Sue Birtzer *(Dir-Safety)*
Carole Baier *(Sec)*

COUNTRYSIDE MARTS INC.
6138 Duanesburg Rd, Duanesburg, NY 12056
Tel.: (518) 895-2303
Web Site:
http://www.countrysidemarts.com
Sales Range: $10-24.9 Million
Emp.: 25
Owner & Operator of Convenience Stores
N.A.I.C.S.: 445131
David Vincent *(Pres & CEO)*

COUNTRYWIDE BROADBAND, LLC
35 Brentmoor Park, Saint Louis, MO 63105
Tel.: (314) 448-1235
Web Site: http://www.cwbinc.net
Year Founded: 2013
Broadband Telecommunication Services
N.A.I.C.S.: 517121
Grier Raclin *(Pres & CEO)*
Sam Valencia *(CFO & Sr VP)*
Dan Kennedy *(COO & Sr VP)*
Michael Whitaker *(Exec VP-Sls & Bus Dev)*

Countrywide Transportation, Inc.—(Continued)

COUNTRYWIDE TRANSPORTATION, INC.
211 W Chicago Ave Ste 219, Hinsdale, IL 60521
Tel.: (630) 325-7177
Web Site:
http://www.countrywidetransportation.com
Year Founded: 1984
Sales Range: $1-9.9 Million
Emp.: 14
Truck & Railroad Freight Transportation Arrangement
N.A.I.C.S.: 484121
Andrew Dalpini (Acct Exec)
Denise Press (CEO)
Marcy Robbins (Pres & CFO)

COUNTRYWIDE TRUCK INSURANCE AGENCY
3930 S 147 St Ste 101, Omaha, NE 68144
Tel.: (402) 895-0555
Rev.: $17,500,000
Emp.: 11
Insurance Agents
N.A.I.C.S.: 713290
Dick Bower (Pres)

COUNTY BANK
19227 Shuttle Rd, Rehoboth Beach, DE 19971
Tel.: (302) 226-9800
Web Site:
https://www.countybankdel.com
Year Founded: 1990
Sales Range: $10-24.9 Million
Emp.: 150
Commercial Banking Services
N.A.I.C.S.: 522110
Joe Shopley (Pres)
David E. Gillan (Chm & CEO)
Brian Gottschalk (VP)
Kelly R. Sylvester (VP)
Clayton Serman (Asst VP)
Terry M. Brewster (Asst VP & Mgr-Long Neck)

COUNTY CONCRETE CORPORATION
50 Railroad Ave, Kenvil, NJ 07876
Tel.: (973) 584-7122
Web Site:
https://www.countyconcretenj.com
Sales Range: $10-24.9 Million
Emp.: 150
Ready Mixed Concrete
N.A.I.C.S.: 327320
John C. Crimi (Pres)
Kim Schenck (Mgr-Credit)

COUNTY DISTRIBUTING COMPANY
1800 Eagleview Dr, Sedalia, MO 65301
Tel.: (660) 826-5189
Web Site:
http://www.countydistributing.com
Sales Range: $10-24.9 Million
Emp.: 40
Beer & Other Fermented Malt Liquors
N.A.I.C.S.: 424810
Robert Paul Beykirch (Pres)
Ray Smith (Controller)
Joe Beykirch (Mgr-Sls)

COUNTY HOME IMPROVEMENT CENTER
2625 E Terra Ln, Saint Peters, MO 63366
Tel.: (636) 278-5080
Web Site:
https://www.chiclumber.com
Rev.: $15,000,000

Emp.: 27
Hardware
N.A.I.C.S.: 423710
David Hendrix (Pres)

COUNTY MATERIALS CORP.
205 N St, Marathon, WI 54448-0100
Tel.: (715) 848-1365
Web Site:
https://www.countymaterials.com
Year Founded: 1946
Concrete Products Mfr
N.A.I.C.S.: 327390
William Sonnentag (VP & Mgr-Corp Aggregate)
Rebecca Sonnentag (VP-Promotions & Comms)

COUNTY SANITATION DISTRICTS OF LOS ANGELES COUNTY
1955 Workman Mill Rd, Whittier, CA 90601
Tel.: (562) 908-4288
Web Site: https://www.lacsd.org
Sales Range: $10-24.9 Million
Emp.: 1,900
Refuse System
N.A.I.C.S.: 924110
Grace Chan (Pres & CEO)
Dan Schmolesky (Superintendent-JWPCP Ops)

COUNTY SANITATION DISTRICTS OF ORANGE COUNTY INC.
10844 Ellis Ave, Fountain Valley, CA 92708-7018
Tel.: (714) 962-2411
Web Site: http://www.ocsd.com
Year Founded: 1954
Sales Range: $25-49.9 Million
Emp.: 600
Provider of Refuse System Services
N.A.I.C.S.: 562119
John Nielsen (Chm)
Gregory Sebourn (Vice Chm)
Jim Herberg (Gen Mgr)

COUNTY SUPER SPUDS, INC.
16 Industrial St, Mars Hill, ME 04758
Tel.: (207) 429-9449
Web Site:
https://www.countysuperspuds.com
Year Founded: 1972
Sales Range: $10-24.9 Million
Emp.: 226
Farm Operator
N.A.I.C.S.: 111998
Jon McCrum (Supvr-Crop Production)
Robert Lunney (Supvr-Crop Production)

COUPON EXPRESS, INC.
303 5th Ave Rm 206, New York, NY 10016
Tel.: (914) 371-2441
Web Site:
http://www.couponexpressinc.com
Year Founded: 1990
Sales Range: Less than $1 Million
Placement & Management Services
N.A.I.C.S.: 561311
Alan Schor (Interim CFO)

COURIER GRAPHICS CORP.
2621 S 37th St, Phoenix, AZ 85034
Tel.: (602) 437-9700
Web Site:
https://www.couriergraphics.com
Sales Range: $10-24.9 Million
Emp.: 80
Commercial Printing Services
N.A.I.C.S.: 323111
Pamela Carritt (Pres)
Larry Babka (Exec VP)

Jim Nielsen (Coord-Production)
Matt Aldrich (Supvr-Prepress)
Rodger Myers (Supvr-Production)
Scott Hudson (Supvr-Finishing)
Valerie Coffin (Mgr-Fin)
David Thompson (Supvr-Shipping)

COURIER PLUS, INC.
2728 NW Potts Ct Ste 100, Bend, OR 97703
Tel.: (866) 838-8244
Web Site: http://www.courierplus.com
Year Founded: 1991
Sales Range: $1-9.9 Million
Emp.: 25
Software Publisher for Cannabis Industry
N.A.I.C.S.: 541519
Robert E. Monroe (CFO & COO)
Ross Lipson (Founder & CEO)

Subsidiaries:

Green Bits, Inc.   (1)
75 E Santa Clara St Fl 6, San Jose, CA 95113
Web Site: http://www.greenbits.com
Sales Range: $1-9.9 Million
Emp.: 80
Cannabis Product Retailer
N.A.I.C.S.: 424210
Ben Curren (Founder & Chm)
Barry Saik (CEO)
Charlie Wilson (Chief Revenue Officer)
Sarvesh Mathur (CTO)
Bridgett Thurston (VP-Fin)

COURIER SYSTEM INC.
30 Pulaski St, Bayonne, NJ 07002
Tel.: (201) 432-0550
Web Site: http://www.csweb.biz
Sales Range: $10-24.9 Million
Emp.: 150
General Warehousing & Storage & Trucking
N.A.I.C.S.: 493110
Richard Murad (Founder)

COURISTAN INC.
2 Executive Dr Ste 400, Fort Lee, NJ 07024-3308
Tel.: (201) 585-8500
Web Site: http://www.couristan.com
Year Founded: 1926
Sales Range: $50-74.9 Million
Emp.: 200
Oriental Design Rugs & Fine Broadloom Mfr & Importer
N.A.I.C.S.: 314110
Ronald J. Couri (Pres & CEO)
George Couri (Chm)
Mark Ferullo (VP-Natl Accts)
Matt Tollison (Exec VP-Area Rugs-Residential Div)

COURT SQUARE CAPITAL PARTNERS, L.P.
299 Park Ave 35th Fl, New York, NY 10171
Tel.: (212) 752-6110
Web Site:
http://www.courtsquare.com
Privater Equity Firm
N.A.I.C.S.: 523999
Kurt J. Hilzinger (Partner)
Michael A. Delaney (Mng Partner)
John P. Civantos (Mng Partner)
Christopher D. Bloise (Mng Partner)
Ian D. Highet (Mng Partner)
Thomas F. McWilliams (Mng Partner)
Anthony P. Mirra (CFO & Chief Compliance Officer)
David T. Nguyen (Partner)
John D. Weber (Mng Partner)
Jeffrey F. Vogel (Mng Partner)
David M. Thomas (Mng Partner)
Kevin A. White (Partner)
William Ty Comfort III (Mng Partner)

Subsidiaries:

AFS Technologies, Inc.   (1)
2141 E Highland Ave Ste 100, Phoenix, AZ 85016
Tel.: (602) 522-8282
Web Site: http://www.afsi.com
Emp.: 60
Food & Beverage Business Automation Solutions
N.A.I.C.S.: 513210
Richard Nicholas (CEO)
Stephane Gauthier (CTO)
Tom Zauli (Sr VP)

Big Red Ltd.   (1)
720 Jewell Dr, Waco, TX 76712-6616
Tel.: (254) 772-7791
Web Site: http://www.bigredltd.com
Sales Range: $25-49.9 Million
Emp.: 26
Beverages Mfr & Distribution
N.A.I.C.S.: 312111

Broadplex LLC   (1)
100 E Meeting St, Morganton, NC 28655-3549
Tel.: (828) 843-4506
Web Site: http://www.broadplex.com
Telecommunications
N.A.I.C.S.: 517810
Rocco Di Santo (Owner)

Data Blue LLC   (1)
1117 Perimeter Center W Ste W406, Atlanta, GA 30338
Tel.: (800) 317-9775
Web Site: http://www.data-blue.com
Information Technology Solutions
N.A.I.C.S.: 541512
Stephen Ayoub (CEO)

Division (Domestic):

LPS Integration Inc.   (2)
5300 Virginia Way, Brentwood, TN 37027
Tel.: (615) 564-5954
Web Site: http://www.lpsintegration.com
Sales Range: $25-49.9 Million
Emp.: 55
Information Technology & Services
N.A.I.C.S.: 541512
Todd Sanford (CEO)
Frank Pulliza (COO)
Chris McMillen (Pres)
Dylan Hedges (VP-Sls)
Theresa R. Chester (CFO)
Jay Hitt (VP-Tech Solutions & Svcs)

Drew Marine USA, Inc.   (1)
100 S Jefferson Rd, Whippany, NJ 07981
Tel.: (973) 526-5700
Web Site: http://www.drew-marine.com
Marine Water Treatment, Fuel Management & Vessel Maintenance Services
N.A.I.C.S.: 336611
Daniel Kelleher (Sr VP-Mktg)
Len Gelosa (CEO)

Subsidiary (Domestic):

Alexander/Ryan Marine and Safety LLC   (2)
2000 Wayside Dr, Houston, TX 77011
Tel.: (713) 923-1671
Web Site: http://www.alexanderryan.com
Emp.: 50
Marine Safety Equipment Whslr
N.A.I.C.S.: 423990
Tom Jelson (Gen Mgr-Houston)
Jamie Matte (Pres)
Bob Kahak (Mgr-New Survival Craft & Engineered Products)
Mark Dunlap (Mgr-Survival Craft Svc)

Subsidiary (Non-US):

Drew Ameroid (Singapore) Pte. Ltd.   (2)
27 Tanjong Penjuru, Jurong, 609025, Singapore
Tel.: (65) 626165449
Web Site: http://www.drew-marine.com
Marine Support Services
N.A.I.C.S.: 488390

Drew Marine Germany GmbH
Stenzelring 8, 21107, Hamburg, Germany
Tel.: (49) 40 7524650
Web Site: http://www.drew-marine.com

Emp.: 20
Marine Support Services
N.A.I.C.S.: 488390
Jens Turner *(Gen Mgr)*

Drew Marine International B.V. **(2)**
Pesetastraat 5, 2991 XT, Barendrecht,
Netherlands
Tel.: (31) 10 497 5700
Web Site: http://www.drew-marine.com
Marine Support Services
N.A.I.C.S.: 488390

Drew Marine Japan G.K. **(2)**
7th Floor Bashamichi 450 Building 4-50
Ota-machi, Naka-ku, Yokohama, 231 0011,
Japan
Tel.: (81) 45 2124741
Web Site: http://www.drew-marine.com
Marine Support Services
N.A.I.C.S.: 488390

**Drew Marine Signal and Safety UK
Ltd** **(2)**
Suite Westbourne Building 6000 Langstone
Technology Park, Langstone Road, Havant,
PO9 1SA, Hants, United Kingdom **(100%)**
Tel.: (44) 2392 415700
Web Site: http://www.comet-marine.com
Sales Range: $25-49.9 Million
Emp.: 6
Marine Pyrotechnic Signal, Rockets & Line
Thrower Explosive Products Mfr
N.A.I.C.S.: 325920
Keith Bradford *(Product Mgr)*
Claire Newland *(VP-Bus Dev & Gen Mgr)*

Dynata, LLC **(1)**
5800 Tennyson Pkwy, Plano, TX 75024
Tel.: (214) 365-5000
Web Site: http://www.dynata.com
Market Research Sampling Services
N.A.I.C.S.: 541910
Bob Fawson *(Exec VP-Bus Ops)*
Gary S. Laben *(CEO)*
Kalyan Raman *(CTO)*
Hugh Davis *(Pres-Dynata Solutions)*

Branch (Domestic):

Dynata, LLC - Lehi **(2)**
3300 N Ashton Blvd Ste 350, Lehi, UT
84043
Tel.: (801) 373-7735
Web Site: http://www.dynata.com
Market Research Sampling Services
N.A.I.C.S.: 541910

Go Engineer, Inc. **(1)**
1787 E Fort Union Blvd Ste 200, Salt Lake
City, UT 84121
Tel.: (801) 359-6100
Web Site: http://www.goengineer.com
Sales Range: $10-24.9 Million
Commercial Product Design Technology
Products Whslr, User Training & Support
Services
N.A.I.C.S.: 423430
Kevin Douglas *(VP-Sls)*
Ken Coburn *(Founder, Pres & CEO)*
Brad Hansen *(CEO)*
Joel Thomas *(COO)*
Jennifer Douglas *(VP-Mktg)*
Mike Coleman *(VP-Product Lifecycle Mgmt)*

Subsidiary (Domestic):

Computer Aided Technology Inc. **(2)**
165 N Arlington Hts R Ste 101, Buffalo
Grove, IL 60089
Tel.: (888) 308-2284
Web Site: http://www.cati.com
Rev.: $14,500,000
Emp.: 65
Computer, Computer Peripheral Equipment
& Software Merchant Whslr
N.A.I.C.S.: 423430
Richard Werneth *(Pres)*
Rod Levin *(Partner)*
Adrian Fanjoy *(Sr VP-Ops)*
Tony Bustos *(Sr VP-Sls)*

Subsidiary (Domestic):

Fisher Unitech LLC **(3)**
404 E 10 Mile Rd, Pleasant Ridge, MI
48069
Web Site: http://www.fisherunitech.com
Computer Systems Mfr
N.A.I.C.S.: 541512

Subsidiary (Domestic):

Prism Engineering LLC **(4)**
1150 Glenlivet Dr Ste A 13, Allentown, PA
18106
Tel.: (610) 336-9304
Web Site: http://www.prismeng.com
Sales Range: $1-9.9 Million
Emp.: 26
Software Reproducing
N.A.I.C.S.: 334610
Lynne Ewell *(Co-Founder)*
John Ewell *(Co-Founder, Pres & CEO)*
Deborah Kubas *(Controller)*
Chris Tarka *(VP-Sls)*

**Information Planning & Management
Service, Inc.** **(1)**
21592 Atlantic Blvd, Sterling, VA 20166
Tel.: (703) 421-5500
Web Site: http://www.infoplanning.com
Sales Range: $1-9.9 Million
Emp.: 20
Administrative Management & General
Management Consulting Services Specializ-
ing in Engineering
N.A.I.C.S.: 541611
Alastair Gregory *(VP)*

Momentum Telecom, Inc. **(1)**
1 Concourse Pkwy NE Ste 600, Atlanta, GA
30328
Tel.: (877) 251-5554
Web Site:
http://www.momentumtelecom.com
Telephone Communication Services
N.A.I.C.S.: 926130
Scott Helms *(Chief Info Security Officer &
Sr VP-Advanced Solutions)*
Chuck Piazza *(Exec VP-Sls & Mktg)*
Todd Zittrouer *(CEO)*
Robert Hagan *(CFO)*
Mark Marquez *(Exec VP-Tech)*
Ande Hornig *(Exec VP-Network Svcs)*
Jennifer Jacobs *(Exec VP-Customer Experi-
ence)*
Heather Dromgoole *(Exec VP-HR)*
Phillip Roland *(Sr VP-Dev)*

National Seating & Mobility, Inc. **(1)**
320 Premier Court Ste 220, Franklin, TN
37067
Tel.: (615) 595-1115
Web Site: http://www.nsm-seating.com
Convalescent Equipment & Supplies
N.A.I.C.S.: 423450
William C. Mixon *(CEO)*
Charles Sargeant *(Sr VP-Funding Ops)*
Doug McDaniel *(VP-Bus Dev)*
John Bertone *(Sr VP-Filed Ops)*
Kevin Harmon *(VP-Fin Ops)*
Ann Mahaffey *(VP-HR)*
Ryan Peebles *(Dir-Govt Affairs)*
Isaac Rodriguez *(VP-East Reg)*
Brendan Swift *(VP-National Workers' Com-
pensation Program Svc)*
Bart Witteveen *(CFO)*
Kalen McKenzie *(VP)*
Derek Miller *(Vp-Central Reg)*
Katie Stevens *(VP-West Reg)*
David Pietrzak *(Vp-Supply Chain & Vendor
Mgmt)*
Stephanie Buckley *(VP-Mktg)*
Jeremy Stone *(VP-Payer Rels)*
Mark Marschke *(CIO)*
Jeff Matukewicz *(Gen Counsel & Sec)*
Damaris Robles *(Dir-Operational Excel-
lence)*
Karen Shell *(Dir-Compliance)*
Chris Yule *(Sr VP-Payer Rels & Govt Af-
fairs)*
Cynthia Petito *(Program Mgr-Workers'
Compensation & Centralized Access)*
Robert Davies *(Gen Mgr-Home Access So-
lutions)*

Unit (Domestic):

**National Seating & Mobility, Inc. -
Dunbar** **(2)**
200 Roxalana Business Par, Dunbar, WV
25064
Tel.: (304) 766-9317
Web Site: http://www.nsm-seating.com
Sales Range: $10-24.9 Million
Emp.: 10
Convalescent Equipment & Supplies
N.A.I.C.S.: 423450
Dena Paxton *(Branch Mgr)*

North Coast Medical Supply, Inc. **(1)**
390 Oak Ave Ste N, Carlsbad, CA 92008
Tel.: (760) 434-9887
Web Site: http://www.northcoastmed.com
Sales Range: $1-9.9 Million
Emp.: 19
Pharmacies & Drug Stores
N.A.I.C.S.: 456110
Mark Howard *(CEO)*

Subsidiary (Domestic):

**United States Medical Supply,
Inc.** **(2)**
8260 NW 27th St Ste 401, Doral, FL 33122
Tel.: (305) 436-6033
Web Site: http://www.usmed.com
Sales Range: $50-74.9 Million
Emp.: 300
Medical Supplies & Prescriptions
N.A.I.C.S.: 456110
Zachary Schiffman *(Pres)*
Bill Monast *(CEO)*

Offen Petroleum, LLC **(1)**
5100 E 78th Ave, Commerce City, CO
80022
Tel.: (303) 297-3835
Web Site: http://offenpetro.com
Petroleum Products; Fuel, Lubricants & Lo-
gistics Services
N.A.I.C.S.: 424720
Bill Gallagher *(CEO)*
Karen Stanley *(CFO)*
Aaron Hackerott *(Pres & COO)*
Sean Rutherford *(Exec VP-Supply, Pricing
& Logistics)*
Kaleb Hoffer *(VP-Fleet Ops)*

PlayCore Holdings, Inc. **(1)**
544 Chestnut St, Chattanooga, TN 37402
Tel.: (877) 762-7563
Web Site: http://www.playcore.com
Holding Company; Commercial & Con-
sumer Playground Equipment & Institutional
Furniture Designer, Mfr & Marketer
N.A.I.C.S.: 551112
Roger Posacki *(Pres & CEO)*
Richard E. Ruegger *(CFO & Sr VP)*
Brenda Grant *(Gen Counsel)*
Jim Underwood *(Sr VP-Mfg & Ops)*
Lisa Moore *(Sr VP-Corp Strategic Svcs)*
Tom Norquist *(Sr VP-Innovation & Bus Dev)*
Joni Manley *(VP-Corp Fin & Acctg)*
Mike Love *(VP-Talent Mgmt)*
Shay Mahone *(VP-Global Sourcing)*
Randy Beckum *(VP-Natl Accts)*

Subsidiary (Domestic):

PlayCore, Inc. **(2)**
401 Chestnut St Ste 410, Chattanooga, TN
37402
Tel.: (423) 265-7529
Web Site: http://www.playcore.com
Sales Range: $150-199.9 Million
Commercial & Consumer Playground
Equipment Designer, Mfr & Marketer
N.A.I.C.S.: 339920
Mark Burgess *(Pres-Recreation Brands,
Surfacing, Site Amenities & Structure Grp)*
Spencer Cheak *(Pres-GameTime & South-
ern Fulfillment Center Grp)*
Richard E. Ruegger *(CFO & Sr VP)*
Mike McWilliams *(VP-Mfg Svcs)*
Lisa Moore *(Sr VP-Corp Strategic Svcs)*
Mike Hawkins *(VP-Corp Risk Mgmt, Insur-
ance & Legal Affairs)*
James Underwood *(Sr VP-Mfg & Ops)*
Anita Sayed *(Pres-Aquatic Solutions Grp)*
Roger Posacki *(Pres & CEO)*
Mike Love *(VP-Talent Mgmt)*
Joni Manley *(VP-Fin & Acctg)*
Ines M. Palacios *(Dir-Recreation-Programs,
Partnerships & Pro Dev)*
Anne-Marie Spencer *(VP-Mktg & Comm)*
Jennie Sumrell *(Dir-Education-Programs,
Partnerships & Pro Dev)*
Brenda Grant *(Gen Counsel & VP)*
Randy Beckum *(VP-Natl Accts)*

Subsidiary (Domestic):

APC Brands, Inc. **(3)**
230 E Hunt St Ste 200, McKinney, TX
75069
Tel.: (972) 347-6446
Web Site: http://www.apcbrands.com
Holding Company; Play & Recreational Am-
menities Design, Construction & Installation
Services

N.A.I.C.S.: 551112
Chad McNeill *(Pres)*

Subsidiary (Domestic):

American Parks Company **(4)**
230 E Hunt St Ste 200, McKinney, TX
75069-4336
Web Site:
http://www.americanparkscompany.com
Playground Design, Construction & Equipment Installation Services
N.A.I.C.S.: 238990
Martin McNeill *(Mgr)*

Subsidiary (Domestic):

BigToys, Inc. **(3)**
7721 New Market St SW, Olympia, WA
98501
Tel.: (360) 528-8697
Web Site: http://www.bigtoys.com
Sales Range: $10-24.9 Million
Emp.: 8
Playground Equipment Mfr
N.A.I.C.S.: 339920
Mark Burgess *(Pres)*
Lindsay Richardson *(Sr VP & Gen Mgr)*
Jesse Taylor *(Sr VP-Fin)*

Everlast Climbing Industries, Inc. **(3)**
1335 Mendota Heights Rd, Mendota
Heights, MN 55120
Tel.: (651) 665-9131
Web Site: http://www.traversewall.com
Emp.: 50
Recreational Climbing Wall Products De-
signer, Mfr & Distr
N.A.I.C.S.: 339920
Tim Sudeith *(Sr VP & Gen Mgr)*

Freenotes Harmony Park, Inc. **(3)**
171 Suttle St Ste B, Durango, CO 81303-
8210
Tel.: (970) 375-7825
Web Site:
http://www.freenotesharmonypark.com
Playground Equipment Mfr
N.A.I.C.S.: 339920
Richard Cooke *(Founder)*

GameTime LLC **(3)**
150 Gametime Dr, Fort Payne, AL 35967
Tel.: (256) 845-5610
Web Site: http://www.gametime.com
Mfr & Marketer of Modular & Custom Com-
mercial Outdoor & Indoor Playground
Equipment
N.A.I.C.S.: 321992
Spencer Cheak *(Pres)*
Mike McWilliams *(VP-Quality, Global Sourc-
ing & Logistics)*
Don King *(Dir-Sls Admin)*
Anne-Marie Spencer *(Dir-Mktg)*
Bob Barron *(Corp VP-Sls)*

Knorr Systems Inc. **(3)**
2221 Standard Ave, Santa Ana, CA 92707
Tel.: (714) 754-4044
Web Site: http://www.knorrsystems.com
Emp.: 60
Swimming Pools, Equipment & Supplies
N.A.I.C.S.: 423910
Mike Smith *(Dir)*
Joe Fleuette *(Dir-Tech Svcs)*

Unit (Domestic):

Play & Park Structures **(3)**
Park 44 Chestnut 3, Chattanooga, TN
37402
Tel.: (423) 756-0015
Web Site: http://www.playandpark.com
Sales Range: $10-24.9 Million
Emp.: 100
Playground Equipment Designer & Mfr
N.A.I.C.S.: 339920
Mark Burgess *(VP)*

Subsidiary (Domestic):

PlayCore Wisconsin, Inc. **(3)**
1212 Barberry Dr, Janesville, WI 53545
Tel.: (608) 755-4777
Web Site: http://www.swing-n-slide.com
Sales Range: $10-24.9 Million
Emp.: 65
Consumer Playground Equipment Mfr
N.A.I.C.S.: 339920
Dave Biancofiore *(Sr VP & Gen Mgr)*
Scott Gadd *(VP-Sls)*

Court Square Capital Partners, L.P.—(Continued)

Robertson Industries, Inc. (3)
4401 E Baseline Rd Ste 105, Phoenix, AZ
85042
Tel.: (602) 340-8873
Web Site: http://www.totturf.com
Commercial Playground Surface Products
Mfr & Installation Services
N.A.I.C.S.: 238990
Mark Burgess (Pres)
Richard Hawley (VP & Gen Mgr)

Spectrum Products LLC (3)
7100 Spectrum Ln, Missoula, MT 59808
Tel.: (406) 542-9781
Web Site: http://www.spectrumproducts.com
Sales Range: $10-24.9 Million
Emp.: 50
Swimming Pool Equipment Mfr
N.A.I.C.S.: 339902
Nabil Khaled (Dir-Sls & Mktg)

Ultra Play Systems, Inc. (3)
1675 Locust St, Red Bud, IL 62278
Tel.: (618) 282-8200
Web Site: http://www.ultraplay.com
Park Amenities, Benches, Picnic Tables &
Bleachers Mfr & Whslr
N.A.I.C.S.: 332999
Mark Burgess (Pres)
Mike Moll (Gen Mgr & VP-PlayCore)

Subsidiary (Domestic):

GT Grandstands, Inc. (4)
2810 Sydney Rd, Plant City, FL 33566-1173
Tel.: (813) 305-1415
Web Site: http://www.gtgrandstands.com
Sales Range: $50-74.9 Million
Emp.: 40
Institutional Bench Bleacher Grandstand &
Press Box Mfr
N.A.I.C.S.: 337127
Gregory L. Buckner (VP & Gen Mgr)

Subsidiary (Domestic):

Wacky World Studios, LLC (3)
391 Roberts Rd, Oldsmar, FL 34677-4914
Tel.: (813) 818-8277
Web Site:
    http://www.wackyworldstudios.com
Sales Range: $1-9.9 Million
Animation Studio
N.A.I.C.S.: 512191
Bruce Barry (Founder)

Worlds of Wow, LLC (3)
1800 Shady Oaks Dr, Denton, TX 76205
Tel.: (817) 380-4215
Web Site: http://www.worldsofwow.com
Indoor Recreation Environment Designer &
Contractor
N.A.I.C.S.: 238990
Reagan Hillier (Pres)

Subsidiary (Domestic):

Porter Corp. (2)
4240 136th Ave, Holland, MI 49424
Tel.: (616) 888-3500
Web Site: http://www.portercorp.com
Exterior Structures & Insulated Building En-
velopes Design & Mfr
N.A.I.C.S.: 332312

RailPros, Inc. (1)
1320 Greenway Dr Ste 490, Irving, TX
75038
Tel.: (682) 223-6897
Web Site: http://www.railpros.com
Engineering Services
N.A.I.C.S.: 541330
Eric Hankinson (Pres)
Ken Koff (CEO)

Thrive Operations, LLC (1)
25 Forbes Blvd Ste 3, Foxborough, MA
02035
Tel.: (978) 461-3999
Web Site: https://thrivenextgen.com
Information Technology Solutions & Ser-
vices
N.A.I.C.S.: 519290
Michael Gray (CTO)
Rob Stephenson (CEO)
Jay Adams (CFO)
Marc Pantoni (Mng Partner)
William Burke (VP-Revenue Integration)

Bill McLaughlin (Pres)
John Holland (Chief Revenue Officer)
Marc Capobianco (COO)

Subsidiary (Domestic):

4it, Inc. (2)
13501 SW 128th St, Miami, FL 33186
Tel.: (305) 278-7100
Web Site: http://www.4it-inc.com
Sales Range: $1-9.9 Million
Emp.: 11
Scientific & Technical Consulting Services
N.A.I.C.S.: 541690
Adam Nash (Mgr)
William Condon (Mgr-Technical Sls & Mktg)

**DSM Technology Consultants
LLC** (2)
6810 New Tampa Hwy Ste 600, Lakeland,
FL 33815
Tel.: (863) 802-8888
Web Site: http://www.dsm.net
Sales Range: $1-9.9 Million
Emp.: 30
Consulting & Technology Services
N.A.I.C.S.: 541690
J. David Robinson (Founder & CEO)

Edge Technology Group, LLC (2)
1 American Ln, Greenwich, CT 06831-2560
Tel.: (203) 742-7800
Web Site: http://www.edgetg.com
Rev.: $5,500,000
Emp.: 17
Computer System Design Services
N.A.I.C.S.: 541512
James Nekos (CEO & Mng Partner)
John Pecoraro (COO)
Tom Woollard (Mng Dir & Head-Europe)

IT Freedom, LLC (2)
8711 Burnet Rd Ste E55, Austin, TX 78757
Tel.: (512) 419-0070
Web Site: http://www.itfreedom.com
Sales Range: $1-9.9 Million
Emp.: 22
Information Retrieval Services
N.A.I.C.S.: 517810
Brian Camp (Dir-Tech)
Matt Miller (Mgr-Engrg)

SouthTech Solutions Inc. (2)
2801 Fruitville Rd Ste 250, Sarasota, FL
34237
Tel.: (941) 953-7455
Web Site: http://www.southtech.com
IT Consulting Services
N.A.I.C.S.: 541690
Chad Goble (CTO)
Paul Hoffman (CEO)
Nathan Bailey (COO)
Jackson Haskins (Mgr-Bus Dev)

Virtium Technology, Inc. (1)
30052 Tomas, Rancho Santa Margarita, CA
92688
Tel.: (949) 888-2444
Web Site: http://www.virtium.com
Memory Module Solutions Designer, Mar-
keter & Mfr
N.A.I.C.S.: 334413
Phu Hoang (Founder, Pres & CEO)
Chinh Nguyen (VP)
Gary Drossel (CTO)
David Quarles (Sr VP-Worldwide Sls)

COURT SQUARE GROUP
1350 Main St 5th Fl, Springfield, MA
01103
Tel.: (413) 746-0054
Web Site:
    https://www.courtsquaregroup.com
Year Founded: 1995
Rev.: $11,200,000
Emp.: 69
Information Technology Services
N.A.I.C.S.: 541512
Keith M. Parent (CEO)
Pam O'Donnell (Comptroller)

**COURTESY AUTOMOTIVE
CENTER**
2520 Cohasset Rd, Chico, CA 95973-
1307
Tel.: (530) 345-9444

Web Site:
    https://www.chicocourtesy.com
New & Used Car Dealers
N.A.I.C.S.: 441110
Jerry Pajouh (CEO, Pres & Gen Mgr)

COURTESY BUICK GMC, INC.
1857 Edwards Lake Rd, Birmingham,
AL 35235-2762
Tel.: (205) 836-2000
Web Site:
    http://www.courtesybirmingham.com
Year Founded: 1996
Sales Range: $25-49.9 Million
Emp.: 96
Car Whslr
N.A.I.C.S.: 441110
Drew Lolley (Gen Mgr)

COURTESY CAR CITY
2301 39th Ave, Moline, IL 61265
Tel.: (309) 764-6700
Web Site:
    https://www.courtesycarcity.com
Rev.: $17,500,000
Emp.: 50
Automobiles, New & Used
N.A.I.C.S.: 532111
Dale Zude (Pres)
Mike Wolf (Gen Mgr-Sls)

**COURTESY CHEVROLET CEN-
TER**
750 Camino Del Rio N, San Diego,
CA 92108-3296
Tel.: (619) 297-4321
Web Site:
    https://www.courtesysandiego.com
Year Founded: 1961
Sales Range: $50-74.9 Million
Emp.: 150
New Car Dealers
N.A.I.C.S.: 441110
Scott Hasted (Dir-Svc)
Mark Gruwell (Owner)

COURTESY FORD INC.
1636 Dogwood Dr SE, Conyers, GA
30013
Tel.: (770) 922-2700
Web Site:
    http://www.courtesyatlanda.com
Sales Range: $10-24.9 Million
Emp.: 125
Automobiles, New & Used
N.A.I.C.S.: 441110
Randolph Barksdale (Owner)
Jay Barksdale (Gen Mgr)

COURTESY GLASS INC.
14115 NE 189th St, Woodinville, WA
98072
Tel.: (425) 487-6899
Web Site:
    http://www.courtesyglass.com
Rev.: $12,000,000
Emp.: 70
Mfr & Installer of Mirror & Shower
Door Products
N.A.I.C.S.: 423390

**COURTESY LINCOLN MER-
CURY INC.**
3305 Boston Rd, Bronx, NY 10469
Tel.: (718) 547-7400
Web Site: http://www.courtesylincoln
    mercury.com
Rev.: $20,500,000
Emp.: 50
Automobiles, New & Used
N.A.I.C.S.: 441110
Robert Federico (Pres)

COURTESY MITSUBISHI
260 N Gibson Rd, Henderson, NV
89014

Tel.: (702) 567-8000
Web Site:
    http://www.hendersonmitsubishi.com
Sales Range: $100-124.9 Million
Emp.: 96
Automobiles, New & Used
N.A.I.C.S.: 441110
Chris Rashbaum (Mgr-Internet & Sls)

COURTESY SPORTS INC.
301 Green Ave N, Stevens Point, WI
54481
Tel.: (715) 341-2440
Web Site:
    http://www.courtesycorner.com
Year Founded: 1976
Sales Range: $10-24.9 Million
Emp.: 60
Car Dealership
N.A.I.C.S.: 441110
Peter D. Kopecko (Owner & Pres)
Jeri Kopecko (Sec & VP)

COURTLAND HOMES INC.
5333 N 7th St Ste 305, Phoenix, AZ
85014
Tel.: (602) 265-9467
Web Site:
    http://www.courtlandhomes.com
Rev.: $53,000,000
Emp.: 38
New Construction, Single-Family
Houses
N.A.I.C.S.: 236115
Alan Hamberlin (Pres)

COURTNEY MARKETING, INC.
301 W Deer Valley Rd, Phoenix, AZ
85027-2117
Tel.: (623) 434-1113
Web Site:
    http://www.courtneymarketing.com
Year Founded: 1988
Sales Range: $10-24.9 Million
Emp.: 10
Commercial Equipment Whslr
N.A.I.C.S.: 423440
Nancy Yvon (Office Mgr)
Alan Zeman (Mgr-Sls)

COURTS FOR KIDS
PO Box 873786, Vancouver, WA
98687
Tel.: (360) 521-0592   WA
Web Site:
    http://www.courtsforkids.org
Year Founded: 2006
Rev.: $1,001,061
Assets: $437,836
Liabilities: $365
Net Worth: $437,471
Earnings: $186,110
Emp.: 3
Fiscal Year-end: 08/31/14
Sport Event Organizer
N.A.I.C.S.: 711310
Derek Nesland (Pres)
Selene Nesland (Founder)
Brett Wilkerson (Chm)
Kevin Ryan (Treas)
Mary Weishaar (Sec)
Chris Cobb (Dir-East Coast)
Anibal Cardenas (Dir-Panama In-
Country)
Stacey Cooper (Dir-Dominican Re-
public In-Country)

**COURTSMART DIGITAL SYS-
TEMS, INC.**
51 Middlesex St, North Chelmsford,
MA 01863
Tel.: (978) 251-3300
Web Site: http://www.courtsmart.com
Year Founded: 1997
Sales Range: $1-9.9 Million
Emp.: 35

Audio & Video Equipment Mfr
N.A.I.C.S.: 334310
Andrew Treinis *(Pres)*
James Barrick *(Project Mgr)*
Kevin J. Boyd *(Mgr-Ops)*

COURY MOSS INC.
1407 Surrey St, Lafayette, LA 70501
Tel.: (337) 235-9086
Web Site:
  http://www.mossisboss.com
Sales Range: $75-99.9 Million
Emp.: 142
New & Used Car Dealers
N.A.I.C.S.: 441110
Sharon K. Moss *(Pres & CFO)*

COUSIN CORPORATION OF AMERICA
12333 Enterprise Blvd, Largo, FL 33773
Tel.: (727) 536-3568
Web Site: https://www.cousin.com
Year Founded: 1970
Sales Range: $25-49.9 Million
Emp.: 100
Beads, Jewelry, Wearable Art Supplies & General Crafts Supplier & Wholesaler
N.A.I.C.S.: 424990
Sharon Ellingwood *(Mgr-Quality Assurance)*
Marty Dimura *(VP-Ops)*
Denny King *(Pres)*

COUSINEAU INC.
845 Route 2 East, Wilton, ME 04294
Tel.: (207) 645-4448   ME
Web Site:
  http://www.cousineaus.com
Year Founded: 1973
Sales Range: $10-24,9 Million
Emp.: 40
Construction Services & Landscaping Products Mfr
N.A.I.C.S.: 423310
Randy Cousineau *(Pres)*
Brody Cousineau *(Owner)*

Subsidiaries:

Cousineau Forest Products, Inc.   **(1)**
1310 Old Concord Rd, Henniker, NH 03242
Tel.: (603) 428-7155
Web Site: http://www.cousineau.com
Emp.: 13
Wood Products Whslr
N.A.I.C.S.: 423990
Curt Richmond *(Gen Mgr)*

Cousineau Properties   **(1)**
845 US Route 2 E, East Wilton, ME 04294
Tel.: (207) 645-4448
Web Site: http://www.cousineaus.com
Real Estate Manangement Services
N.A.I.C.S.: 531390

Cousineau Henniker   **(1)**
1310 Old Concord Rd, Henniker, NH 03242   **(100%)**
Tel.: (603) 428-7155
Web Site: http://www.cousineaus.com
Sales Range: $10-24.9 Million
Emp.: 10
Lumber Mill
N.A.I.C.S.: 321912
John Baker *(Mgr-Ops)*
Curtis Richmond *(Gen Mgr)*

COUSINS FOOD MARKET INC.
233 W Lehigh Ave, Philadelphia, PA 19133
Tel.: (215) 203-5100   PA
Web Site:
  http://cousinssupermarket.com
Year Founded: 1980
Sales Range: $10-24.9 Million
Emp.: 50
Grocery Retailer
N.A.I.C.S.: 445110
Fozan Ehmedi *(Pres)*

COUSINS HOME LENDING, INC.
1 New Hampshire Ave Ste 125, Portsmouth, NH 03801
Tel.: (603) 433-2223   NH
Web Site:
  http://www.cousinshomelending.com
Year Founded: 2002
Sales Range: $1-9.9 Million
Emp.: 14
Real Estate Credit
N.A.I.C.S.: 522292
Anna-Lisa Cousins *(Founder)*

COUSINS SUBMARINES, INC.
N83 W13400 Leon Rd, Menomonee Falls, WI 53051-3306
Tel.: (262) 253-7700   WI
Web Site:
  https://www.cousinssubs.com
Year Founded: 1972
Sales Range: $50-74.9 Million
Emp.: 850
Sub Sandwiches & Fast Food Franchiser
N.A.I.C.S.: 722513

COVALENT METROLOGY SERVICES, INC.
921 Thompson Pl, Sunnyvale, CA 94085
Tel.: (408) 498-4611
Web Site:
  http://www.covalentmetrology.com
Metrology & Analytical Services
N.A.I.C.S.: 513210
Craig Hunter *(CEO)*

Subsidiaries:

Riga Analytical Lab Inc.   **(1)**
3375 Scott Blvd 132, Santa Clara, CA 95054
Tel.: (408) 496-6944
Web Site: http://www.rigalab.com
Testing Laboratories
N.A.I.C.S.: 541380
Giorgio Riga *(Owner)*

COVANTAGE CREDIT UNION
723 6th Avenue, Antigo, WI 54409-0107
Tel.: (715) 627-4336
Web Site:
  https://www.covantagecu.org
Year Founded: 1953
Emp.: 419
Financial Services
N.A.I.C.S.: 523999
Charlie Zanayed *(Pres)*

COVARIO, INC.
9255 Towne Center Dr Ste 600, San Diego, CA 92121
Tel.: (858) 397-1500
Web Site: http://www.covario.com
Year Founded: 2006
Sales Range: $10-24.9 Million
Emp.: 140
Search Engine Marketing & Optimization
N.A.I.C.S.: 541890
Jeff Johnson *(Chief Client Officer)*
Mike Gullaksen *(COO)*
Collin Cornwell *(Sr VP-Products & Svcs Delivery)*
Jeff MacGurn *(Sr VP)*
Matt Kropp *(Mng Dir-Midwest & Sr VP)*
Kim Sivillo *(Mng Dir & Sr VP-East)*
Max Cheprasov *(Sr VP-Ops)*
Sam Huston *(Chief Strategy Officer)*

Subsidiaries:

Covario China   **(1)**
15/F China World Tower 3, 1 Jianguomenwai Avenue, Beijing, 100004, China
Tel.: (86) 10 5737 2452

Search Engine Marketing & Optimization
N.A.I.C.S.: 541890

Covario Europe   **(1)**
Portland House Bressenden Place, London, SW1E 5RS, United Kingdom
Tel.: (44) 207 869 8299
Search Engine Marketing & Optimization
N.A.I.C.S.: 541890

Covario Japan   **(1)**
14F ARCA Central 1-2-1Kinshi Sumida-ku, Tokyo, 130-0013, Japan
Tel.: (81) 3 6853 6744
Search Engine Marketing & Optimization
N.A.I.C.S.: 541890

Covario Singapore   **(1)**
3 Church Street 08-00, Regus Samsung Hub, Singapore, 49483, Singapore
Tel.: (65) 6408 3300
Search Engine Marketing & Optimization
N.A.I.C.S.: 541890

COVE FOUR-SLIDE & STAMPING CORP.
195 E Merrick Rd, Freeport, NY 11520
Tel.: (516) 379-4232   NY
Web Site: http://www.covefour.com
Year Founded: 1960
Sales Range: $10-24.9 Million
Emp.: 75
Miscellaneous Fabricated Wire, Spring & Assembly Products Mfr
N.A.I.C.S.: 332618
Barry Jaffe *(Chm & Pres)*

COVE HILL PARTENRS, L.P.
888 Boylston St Ste 1410, Boston, MA 02199
Tel.: (857) 245-6060   DE
Web Site:
  http://www.covehillpartners.com
Privater Equity Firm
N.A.I.C.S.: 523999
Yvonne Hao *(Co-Founder)*
Andrew B. Balson *(Mng Partner)*

COVELLI ENTERPRISES LLC
3900 E Market St, Warren, OH 44484
Tel.: (330) 856-3176
Web Site: http://wifi.covelli.com
Sales Range: $400-449.9 Million
Fast Food Restaurant Franchise Owner & Operator
N.A.I.C.S.: 722513
Sam Covelli *(Owner)*

COVENANT BANK
206 Sharkey Ave, Clarksdale, MS 38614
Tel.: (662) 621-1869
Web Site:
  http://www.covenantbank.net
Sales Range: $10-24.9 Million
Emp.: 53
Commercial Bank
N.A.I.C.S.: 522110
Linda Ashmore *(Exec VP-Ops)*
Sheila Riddick *(Exec VP-Credit Admin)*
Deborah Wimberly *(CFO & Exec VP)*
Willis L. Frazer *(Chm)*
Dawn Carraway *(Sr VP-Teller Ops)*
Paul Flowers *(Mgr-Clarksdale)*
Mike Wimberly *(Mgr-Clarksdale)*
Monty Wiggins *(Mgr-Tunica)*
Frances Young *(Mgr-Southaven)*
John Burchfield *(Mgr-Batesville)*
Blair T. Rush *(Pres/COO-Doylestown)*
John C. Spier *(Co-Pres & CEO)*
Robert S. Kile *(Sr VP)*
Earl Clevenstine *(Sr VP)*
Cynthia Zamroz *(VP)*
Patrick Tramontano *(Asst VP)*
Roberta Herald *(VP & Mgr-Deposit Relationship)*

Meghan E. Yarnall *(Asst VP)*
Charles R. Burnett III *(Exec VP-Branch Admin)*

COVENANT CAPITAL GROUP, LLC
4515 Harding Rd Ste 210, Nashville, TN 37205
Tel.: (615) 250-1616
Web Site:
  https://www.covenantcapgroup.com
Rev.: $1,300,000,000
Real Estate Investment Services
N.A.I.C.S.: 523999
Frederic A. Scarola *(Co-Founder & Mng Partner)*
Govan D. White *(Co-Founder & Mng Partner)*
Briana Succop *(VP-Relationship Dev)*
Molly Viola *(VP-Asset Mgmt)*
Eugene Woods Weathersby Jr. *(Sr VP-Acq & Disposition)*

COVENANT EYES, INC.
1525 W King St, Owosso, MI 48867
Tel.: (989) 720-8000
Web Site:
  http://www.covenanteyes.com
Year Founded: 2000
Sales Range: $1-9.9 Million
Emp.: 70
Mfr of Web-Site Accountability Software & Filters
N.A.I.C.S.: 513210
Ron DeHaas *(Founder & CEO)*
Jared Burkeen *(Engr-Software)*
Scott Hammersley *(VP-Tech)*
Rick Finn *(Mgr-QA)*
John Lauro *(Engr-Sys)*

COVENANT HEALTH
100 Fort Sanders W Blvd, Knoxville, TN 37922
Tel.: (865) 374-1000
Web Site:
  http://www.covenanthealth.com
Year Founded: 1996
Sales Range: $900-999.9 Million
Emp.: 10,000
Acute Care & Psychiatric Hospitals
N.A.I.C.S.: 622210
Jim VanderSteeg *(Exec VP-Hospital Ops)*
John Geppi *(CFO & Exec VP)*
Mike Belbeck *(Exec VP-Ops)*
Carol Pahde *(Pres & Chief Admin Officer)*
Dedra Whitaker *(Pres & Chief Admin Officer)*
Jason Pilant *(Pres & Chief Admin Officer)*
Jennifer DeBow *(Pres & Chief Admin Officer)*
Jeremy Biggs *(Pres & Chief Admin Officer)*
Liz Clary *(Pres & Chief Admin Officer)*
Patti Ketterman *(Pres & Chief Admin Officer)*

COVENANT HEALTH, INC.
100 Ames Pond Dr Ste 102, Tewksbury, MA 01876-1240
Tel.: (978) 312-4300   MA
Web Site:
  http://www.covenanthealth.net
Health Care Srvices
N.A.I.C.S.: 621999
Stephen J. Grubbs *(Pres & CEO)*

COVENANT MEDICAL CENTER INC
1447 N Harrison, Saginaw, MI 48602
Tel.: (989) 583-0000   MI
Web Site:
  https://www.covenanthealthcare.com

Covenant Medical Center Inc—(Continued)
Year Founded: 1997
Sales Range: $500-549.9 Million
Emp.: 4,262
Healtcare Services
N.A.I.C.S.: 622110
Mark Gronda (CFO & VP)
John Kosanovich (VP)
Terry Neiderstadt (Chm)
Daniel George (VP)

COVENANT SERVICES WORLDWIDE, LLC
400 Quadrangle Dr Ste A, Boling-brook, IL 60440
Tel.: (630) 771-0800
Web Site:
http://www.covenantsecurity.com
Rev.: $15,052,540
Emp.: 1,000
Security Services
N.A.I.C.S.: 928110
Robert L. Coe (Pres & CEO)

COVENTRY FIRST LLC
7111 Valley Green Rd, Fort Washing-ton, PA 19034
Tel.: (215) 233-5100
Web Site: https://www.coventry.com
Year Founded: 1999
Sales Range: $150-199.9 Million
Emp.: 180
Operator of Secondary Market for Life Insurance Policies
N.A.I.C.S.: 523999
Alan H. Buerger (Co-Founder & Chm)

COVENTRY LUMBER INC.
2030 Nooseneck Hill Rd, Coventry, RI 02816-6708
Tel.: (401) 821-2800
Web Site:
https://www.coventrylumber.com
Year Founded: 1969
Sales Range: $10-24.9 Million
Emp.: 50
Sales of Lumber & Building Materials
N.A.I.C.S.: 423310
Michael Durand (Owner & Pres)
Sue Bullock (Office Mgr)
Brian Vandal (Mgr-Sls)
Bill Finnegan (Mgr-Ops)

COVERALL NORTH AMERICA, INC.
350 SW 12th Ave, Deerfield Beach, FL 33442
Tel.: (561) 922-2500
Web Site: http://www.coverall.com
Year Founded: 1985
Sales Range: $10-24.9 Million
Emp.: 60
Commercial Cleaning Franchises & Support Centers
N.A.I.C.S.: 533110
Rick Ascolese (Chm)
Shirley Klein (COO)
Charlie Daniel (CEO)

COVERCRAFT DIRECT, LLC
100 Enterprise Blvd, Pauls Valley, OK 73075
Web Site: https://www.covercraft.com
Year Founded: 1965
Automotive Seat Cover & Accesso-ries Mfr
N.A.I.C.S.: 811420
Bob Lichtmann (Founder)

Subsidiaries:
Carver Industries, Inc.   (1)
212 N Lyles Ave, Landrum, SC 29356
Tel.: (864) 457-5820
Web Site: http://www.carvercovers.com
Canvas And Related Products
N.A.I.C.S.: 314910

GT Covers   (1)
13550 Smith Rd Ste 100, Aurora, CO 80011-2046
Web Site: http://www.gtcovers.com
Automotive Seat Cover Mfr
N.A.I.C.S.: 811420

COVERICA, INC.
5999 Summerside Dr Ste 200, Dal-las, TX 75252
Tel.: (972) 490-8800   TX
Web Site: http://www.coverica.com
Year Founded: 1983
Insurance Related Activities
N.A.I.C.S.: 524298
Rhonda Cox (Mgr-Ops)
John Sutter (Pres)
Mike Sterlacci (COO)
Andy Bracken (Chief Revenue Offi-cer)
Chris Sterlacci (COO-Agency Alli-ance)

Subsidiaries:
Agape Healthcare Partners, LP   (1)
552 Silicon Dr Ste 100, Southlake, TX 76092
Tel.: (817) 329-4200
Web Site: http://www.agapeins.com
Insurance Services
N.A.I.C.S.: 524298

COVEROS, INC.
4000 Legato Rd Ste 1100, Fairfax, VA 22033
Tel.: (929) 341-0139
Web Site: https://www.coveros.com
Year Founded: 2008
Sales Range: $1-9.9 Million
Emp.: 11
Software Development Services
N.A.I.C.S.: 541511
Jeffery Payne (Founder & CEO)
David Burke (COO & Partner)
Thomas Stiehm (CTO & Partner)

COVERT BUICK INC.
11750 Research Blvd, Austin, TX 78759
Tel.: (512) 298-0426
Web Site: http://www.covertauto.com
Rev.: $75,000,000
Emp.: 500
Automobiles, New & Used
N.A.I.C.S.: 441110
Duke Covert (Pres)
Janet Sopronyi (CFO)

COVERYS
1 Financial Ctr 13th, Boston, MA 02111
Web Site: http://www.coverys.com
Year Founded: 1975
Rev.: $486,746,000
Earnings: $86,900,000
Fiscal Year-end: 12/31/18
Medical Malpractice Insurance Ser-vices
N.A.I.C.S.: 524126
Noreen Fiore-Sarno (VP-HR)
Eric Crockett (Sr VP-IT)
Tara Gibson (Sr VP-Claims)
Robert Hanscom (VP-Risk Mgmt & Analytics)
Stephen Langlois (VP-Actuarial)
Michael Miller (VP-Underwriting)
Joseph G. Murphy (Pres & CEO)
Brenda E. Richardson (Chm)
Brian York (VP-Underwriting-Convergys Custom Accts)
Wayne T. Zack (Sr VP-Claims)
William Chapdelaine (Sr VP-Bus Dev, Distr & Mktg)
Todd Mills (CFO)
Kevin Kelly (VP-Bus Dev)
Veronica G. Matejko (VP-Workers Compensation Svcs)

Stephanie Sheps (VP-Claims)
Elizabeth Brodeur (Gen Counsel & Sr VP)
Michael Murawski (Dir-Legal & Assoc Gen Counsel)
Erwin A. Stuebner Jr. (Vice Chm)

Subsidiaries:
FinCor Holdings, Inc.   (1)
Bl 1 Ste 200 E, Lansing, MI 48823
Tel.: (517) 323-6198
Sales Range: $75-99.9 Million
Emp.: 100
Holding Company; Risk Management Ser-vices to Health Care Industry
N.A.I.C.S.: 551112
Gegg Hanson (CEO)
Verne Rambo (Mgr-Fin Ops)

COVEY-ODELL ADVERTISING LTD.
330 Schneider St SE, North Canton, OH 44720-3652
Tel.: (330) 499-3441
Web Site: http://www.covey-odell.com
Year Founded: 1944
Sales Range: $10-24.9 Million
Emp.: 6
Advertising Agencies
N.A.I.C.S.: 541810
Dane Llewellyn (Acct Exec)
Rod A. Covey (Pres)

COVIA HOLDINGS CORPORA-TION
3 Summit Park Dr Ste 700, Indepen-dence, OH 44131
Tel.: (203) 966-8880   DE
Web Site: http://www.coviacorp.com
Year Founded: 1970
Rev.: $1,595,446,000
Assets: $2,446,518,000
Liabilities: $2,269,354,000
Net Worth: $177,164,000
Earnings: ($1,290,102,000)
Emp.: 2,633
Fiscal Year-end: 12/31/19
Mining-Specializing in Industrial Min-erals
N.A.I.C.S.: 212322
Richard A. Navarre (Chm)
Richard A. Navarre (Chm)
Christopher L. Nagel (CFO & Exec VP)
Campbell J. Jones (COO & Exec VP)
Andrew D. Eich (Pres & CEO)
Brian J. Richardson (Chief Transfor-mation Officer & Exec VP)
Chadwick P. Reynolds (Chief Legal Officer, Sec & Exec VP)
Paolo Gennari (Exec VP-Industrial)
Cameron J. Berry (Exec VP-Energy)
Matthew Schlarb (Dir-IR)
Shawn D. Williams (Exec Chm)
Rory F. O'Donnell Jr. (Chief Acctg Officer, Sr VP & Controller)

Subsidiaries:
Fairmount Santrol Holdings Inc.   (1)
8834 Mayfield Rd, Chesterland, OH 44026
Tel.: (800) 255-7263
Sales Range: $900-999.9 Million
Oilfield Sand-Based Proppant Mining & Quarrying Services
N.A.I.C.S.: 212321

Subsidiary (Domestic):
Fairmount Santrol Inc.   (2)
8834 Mayfield Rd, Chesterland, OH 44026
Tel.: (440) 285-3132
Web Site: http://www.fairmountsantrol.com
Sales Range: $50-74.9 Million
Emp.: 1,000
Industrial Sand Production
N.A.I.C.S.: 212322

Subsidiary (Domestic):
Best Sand Corporation   (3)
11830 Ravenna Rd, Chardon, OH 44024-7006   (100%)
Tel.: (440) 285-3132
Web Site: http://www.fairmountminerals.com
Sales Range: $25-49.9 Million
Industrial Sand
N.A.I.C.S.: 212322
Charles D. Fowler (Pres & CEO)

Black Lab, LLC   (3)
2727 FM 521, Fresno, TX 77545
Tel.: (281) 431-0670
Construction Materials Whslr
N.A.I.C.S.: 423320

Technisand, Inc.   (3)
300 Vermillion St, Troy Grove, IL 61372
Tel.: (815) 538-2645
Resin-Coated Sands Mfr
N.A.I.C.S.: 212322
Lori Krieger (Mgr)

Subsidiary (Domestic):
Alpha Resins, LLC   (4)
17350 Ryan Rd, Detroit, MI 48212
Tel.: (313) 366-2096
Web Site: http://www.fairmountminerals.com
Sales Range: $1-9.9 Million
Resin Mfr
N.A.I.C.S.: 325211

Subsidiary (Non-US):
Santrol (Yixing) Proppant Co. Ltd   (4)
East Tongli Road, Yixing, 214221, Jiangsu, China   (70%)
Tel.: (86) 510 87438118
Resin Mfr
N.A.I.C.S.: 325211
James Xia (Gen Mgr)

Subsidiary (Domestic):
Wisconsin Industrial Sand Company, LLC   (4)
W3302 Hwy 35 S, Maiden Rock, WI 54750
Tel.: (715) 448-3006
Sales Range: $25-49.9 Million
Industrial Sand Production
N.A.I.C.S.: 212322

Subsidiary (Domestic):
Wedron Silica Company   (3)
3450 E 2056th Rd, Wedron, IL 60557
Tel.: (815) 433-2449
Industrial Sand Production
N.A.I.C.S.: 212322
Charles D. Fowler (CEO)

Grupo Materias Primas S. de R. L. de C. V.   (1)
Loma Larga 2621 Colonia Obispado, 64060, Monterrey, Mexico
Tel.: (52) 8181512800
Web Site: http://www.gmp.com.mx
Household Chemical Distr
N.A.I.C.S.: 424690

Unimin Corporation   (1)
7003 Chadwick Dr Ste 100, Brentwood, TN 37027-5288   (100%)
Tel.: (615) 373-7348
Sales Range: $25-49.9 Million
Emp.: 4
Mineral Processing Services
N.A.I.C.S.: 212322

COVICH & WILLIAMS CO. INC.
4800 20th Ave NW, Seattle, WA 98107
Tel.: (206) 784-0171
Web Site:
http://www.covichwilliams.com
Sales Range: $10-24.9 Million
Emp.: 15
Petroleum Products
N.A.I.C.S.: 424720
Mason Williams (Pres)

COVINGTON & BURLING LLP
850 10th St NW, Washington, DC 20001-4956
Tel.: (202) 662-6000

Web Site: https://www.cov.com
Year Founded: 1919
Sales Range: $550-599.9 Million
Emp.: 1,000
Law firm
N.A.I.C.S.: 541110
Stephen P. Anthony *(Partner)*
Lanny A. Breuer *(Partner)*
Sarah Franklin *(Partner)*
Alexander Berengaut *(Partner)*
Jason Fowler *(Partner)*
Denise Esposito *(Partner)*
Ashley E. Bass *(Partner)*
Bruce C. Bennett *(Partner)*
Simon Amies *(Partner)*
Thomas O. Barrett *(Partner)*
Arlo Devlin-Brown *(Partner-White Collar Defense & Investigations Practice)*
Timothy C. Hester *(Partner)*
Tom DeFilipps *(Partner)*
Carolyn Kubota *(Partner-Litigation, White Collar Defense & Investigations)*
Tom Cosgrove *(Partner)*
Joseph A. Tato *(Partner)*

COVINGTON ELECTRIC CO-OPERATIVE

Hwy 84 E, Andalusia, AL 36421
Tel.: (334) 222-4121
Web Site: http://www.covington.coop
Rev.: $28,042,097
Emp.: 62
Electric Power Distribution
N.A.I.C.S.: 221122
Charles E. Short *(Pres, CEO & Gen Mgr)*
Bert Champion *(Mgr-Tech Svcs)*
Greg Fleming *(Mgr-Member Svcs)*
Steven Walker *(Engr-Sys)*

COVINGTON FLOORING COMPANY

709 1st Ave N, Birmingham, AL
35203-3005
Tel.: (205) 328-2330
Web Site: https://www.covington.com
Sales Range: $10-24.9 Million
Emp.: 75
Wood Floor Installation & Refinishing
N.A.I.C.S.: 238330
Richard Johnson *(CFO)*
Edward Covington *(Exec VP-Comml Flooring Sls)*

COVINGTON GROUP, INC.

14180 Dallas Pkwy Ste 730, Dallas,
TX 75254
Web Site:
https://www.covingtongroupinc.com
Industrial Real Estate Investment,
Development & Leasing Services
N.A.I.C.S.: 531390
Kenneth Sheer *(Co-Founder, Partner & Pres-Investments)*
Barry Lang *(Co-Founder & Partner)*
Mark Milakovich *(Partner)*

COVINGTON HEAVY DUTY PARTS

1000 W Bypass, Andalusia, AL 36420
Tel.: (334) 222-4153
Web Site: http://www.worldpages-ads.com
Sales Range: $10-24.9 Million
Emp.: 22
Truck Parts & Accessories
N.A.I.C.S.: 423120
Jay Everage *(Mgr-Sls)*

COVIS PHARMACEUTICALS INC.

1513 Walnut St Ste 270, Cary, NC
27511-5971
Tel.: (919) 535-3049

Web Site:
http://www.covispharma.com
Drugs & Druggists' Sundries Merchant Whslr
N.A.I.C.S.: 424210
Mike Kelly *(Pres)*
Rajiv Kanishka Liyanaarchchie De Silva *(Chm)*

COVIUS HOLDINGS, INC.

710 S Ash St Ste 200, Glendale, CO
80246
Tel.: (877) 516-8121
Web Site: http://www.covius.com
Year Founded: 2014
Holding Company
N.A.I.C.S.: 551112
Rob Clements *(Chm & CEO)*
John S. Surface *(CEO-Covius Svcs)*

Subsidiaries:

Clayton Services, LLC   **(1)**
100 Beard Sawmill Rd Ste 200, Shelton, CT
06484
Tel.: (203) 926-5600
Loan Purchase, Portfolio Analysis, Compliance, Operational Management & Due Diligence Services
N.A.I.C.S.: 522320

Subsidiary (Domestic):

Quantum Servicing Corporation   **(2)**
2 Corporate Dr, Shelton, CT 06484
Tel.: (877) 817-3266
Web Site: http://www.quantum-servicing.com
Sales Range: $75-99.9 Million
Emp.: 150
Home Loan Servicing
N.A.I.C.S.: 522390

Covius Document Services, LLC   **(1)**
27398 Via Industria, Temecula, CA 92590-3699
Tel.: (951) 491-6800
Web Site: http://www.walzpostal.com
Regulatory Compliance Solutions, Critical Data Management, Letter Fulfillment & Certified Mail Automation Services
N.A.I.C.S.: 491110

Nationwide Title Clearing, LLC   **(1)**
2100 Alt 19 N, Palm Harbor, FL 34683
Tel.: (727) 771-4000
Web Site: http://www.nwtc.com
Mortgage Closing Services
N.A.I.C.S.: 522310
Michael O'Connell *(COO)*
Debbie Lastoria *(VP-Bus Dev)*
Jeremy Pomerants *(VP-Bus Dev)*
John Hillman *(CEO)*
Danny Byrnes *(VP-Sls & Mktg)*
Gina Morales *(VP-Bus Dev)*
Meaghan Hunter *(Asst VP-Bus Dev)*
Doug King *(Asst VP-Bus Dev)*
Lindsey Trebian *(Asst VP-Bus Dev)*
Greg McCoskey *(Gen Counsel)*
Amie McCarthy *(VP-Bus Dev-Capital Markets)*
Star Kezsbom *(VP-Compliance & Risk)*
Todd Kugler *(CFO)*

reQuire LLC   **(1)**
5029 Corporate Woods Dr Ste 225, Virginia Beach, VA 23462
Tel.: (757) 552-0306
Web Site: http://www.gorequire.com
Real Estate Services
N.A.I.C.S.: 531390
Randy Cruz *(Mgr-Bus Svcs)*
Nicole Culver *(VP-Ops)*
Linda Aparo *(Natl Dir-Sls)*

COWABUNGA INC.

3585 Trotter Dr, Alpharetta, GA
30004
Tel.: (678) 473-0441
Web Site:
http://www.cowabungainc.com
Rev.: $10,900,000
Emp.: 11
Pizzeria Chain
N.A.I.C.S.: 722513

COWAN SYSTEMS INC.

4555 Hollins Ferry Rd, Baltimore, MD
21227-4501
Tel.: (410) 247-0800
Web Site:
https://www.cowansystems.com
Year Founded: 1994
Sales Range: $50-74.9 Million
Emp.: 250
Trucking Service
N.A.I.C.S.: 484121
Dennis Morgan *(Pres)*
Joseph W. Cowan *(Chm)*

COWBOY CHEVROLET BUICK PONTIAC GMC CADILLAC

1415 Hwy 96 Bypass, Silsbee, TX
77656
Tel.: (409) 385-5221
Web Site:
http://www.cowboyautoplex.com
Sales Range: $50-74.9 Million
Emp.: 100
Automobiles, New & Used
N.A.I.C.S.: 441110
Morris H. Moore *(Pres)*

COWBOY MALONEY APPLIANCE, AUDIO, VIDEO CENTERS, INC.

1313 Harding St, Jackson, MS
39202-3409
Tel.: (601) 948-5600   MS
Web Site:
http://www.cowboymaloney.com
Year Founded: 1952
Sales Range: $25-49.9 Million
Emp.: 250
Electronics, Home Entertainment & Household Appliances Retailer
N.A.I.C.S.: 449210
Eddie Maloney *(Pres & CEO)*
John A. Maloney *(Treas, Sec & VP)*
James C. Maloney Jr. *(Chm)*

COWBOY TOYOTA

9525 E R L Thornton Fwy, Dallas, TX
75228-5617
Tel.: (214) 414-7406
Web Site:
https://www.cowboytoyota.com
Sales Range: $10-24.9 Million
Emp.: 81
Car Whslr
N.A.I.C.S.: 441110
Ron Gallagher *(Mgr-Customer Rels)*
Liane Mann *(Mgr-Internet Sls)*
Tommy Stock *(Controller)*

COWEN CONSTRUCTION INC.

2200 S Utica Pl Ste 100, Tulsa, OK
74114
Tel.: (918) 582-2220
Web Site:
https://www.cowenconstruction.com
Rev.: $50,000,000
Emp.: 80
General Contractors
N.A.I.C.S.: 236210
John S. Cowen *(Pres)*
David Carter *(CFO)*

COWET-FYTTE ELECTRIC MEMBERSHIP CORP.

807 Collingsworth Rd, Palmetto, GA
30268
Tel.: (770) 502-0226
Web Site: http://www.utility.org
Sales Range: $75-99.9 Million
Emp.: 200
Distribution, Electric Power
N.A.I.C.S.: 221122
William Coach *(VP-Fin)*
Christopher Stephens *(Pres & CEO)*

COWETA-FAYETTE ELECTRIC

MEMBERSHIP CORPORATION

807 Collinsworth Rd, Palmetto, GA
30268
Tel.: (770) 502-0226   GA
Web Site: https://www.utility.org
Year Founded: 1947
Sales Range: $150-199.9 Million
Emp.: 200
Electric Power Distribution Services
N.A.I.C.S.: 221122
Chris Stephens *(CEO)*
William Couch *(CFO & VP-Fin & Office Svcs)*
Wendell Webb *(VP-Ops)*
Stanley Sitzler *(COO)*
Mary Ann Bell *(Sr VP-PR)*
Jimmy Adams *(VP-Energy Svcs)*
Dan Hart *(Pres & CEO)*
J. Neal Shepard *(Treas & Sec)*
Therol Brown *(Vice Chm)*
James Fulton *(Chm)*

COWIN & COMPANY, INC.

301 Industrial Dr, Birmingham, AL
35211-4443
Tel.: (205) 945-1300   AL
Web Site: https://www.cowin-co.com
Year Founded: 1924
Sales Range: $125-149.9 Million
Emp.: 175
Provider of Mine Construction Services
N.A.I.C.S.: 236210
John Moore *(Dir-Safety)*
Frank O. Stevens *(Project Mgr)*

COWLES COMPANY

999 W Riverside Ave, Spokane, WA
99201-1006
Tel.: (509) 459-5000   WA
Sales Range: $25-49.9 Million
Emp.: 800
Multimedia Holding Company
N.A.I.C.S.: 551112
William Stacey Cowles *(Pres & CEO)*
Connie Bantz *(Mgr-HR)*

Subsidiaries:

Centennial Properties, Inc.   **(1)**
999 W Riverside Ave, Spokane, WA 99201
Tel.: (509) 459-5220
Emp.: 16
Real Estate Management Services
N.A.I.C.S.: 531390
Elizabeth A. Cowles *(Pres)*

Cowles Publishing Company   **(1)**
999 W Riverside Ave, Spokane, WA 99201-1006
Tel.: (509) 459-5000
Web Site: http://www.spokesman.com
Sales Range: $25-49.9 Million
Emp.: 650
Newspaper Publishers
N.A.I.C.S.: 513110
Amy Tolzmann *(Mgr-Mktg Events)*

Inland Empire Paper Company
Inc.   **(1)**
3320 N Argonne Rd, Spokane, WA
99212-2099   **(100%)**
Tel.: (509) 924-1911
Web Site: http://www.iepco.com
Sales Range: $25-49.9 Million
Emp.: 135
Paper Mills
N.A.I.C.S.: 322120
Kevin Raler *(Pres)*

KCOY-TV   **(1)**
1211 W McCoy Ln, Santa Maria, CA 93455
Tel.: (805) 925-1200
Web Site: http://www.kcoy.com
Television Broadcasting Station
N.A.I.C.S.: 516120
Tracy Reiner *(Sls Mgr-Local)*

KHQ, Incorporated   **(1)**
1201 W Sprague, Spokane, WA 99201-0600
Tel.: (509) 448-6000
Web Site: http://www.khq.com

Cowles Company—(Continued)
Sales Range: $10-24.9 Million
Emp.: 110
Television Broadcasting Station
N.A.I.C.S.: 516120

Northwest Business Press Inc. (1)
429 E 3rd Ave, Spokane, WA
99202-1414 (100%)
Tel.: (509) 456-5257
Web Site: http://www.spokanejournal.com
Sales Range: Less than $1 Million
Emp.: 22
Publishing Newspaper Services
N.A.I.C.S.: 513110
Dana Cunningham *(Acct Exec)*
Kathy Minor *(Mgr-Circulation)*
JoNelle Opitz *(Mgr-Bus)*
Paul Read *(Publr)*

Print Marketing Concepts Inc. (1)
10590 Westoffice Dr Ste 250, Houston, TX
77042-5327
Tel.: (713) 780-7055
Web Site: http://www.printmkt.com
Sales Range: $10-24.9 Million
Emp.: 43
Publishing & Television Broadcasting
N.A.I.C.S.: 513120

COWLEY ASSOCIATES, INC.
235 Walton St, Syracuse, NY 13202
Tel.: (315) 475-8453 **NY**
Web Site: http://www.cowleyweb.com
Year Founded: 1975
Sales Range: Less than $1 Million
Emp.: 6
Direct Marketing, Internet/Web Design, Public Relations, Strategic
Planning/Research
N.A.I.C.S.: 541810
Paul Cowley *(Pres & Dir-Creative)*
Gail Cowley *(Exec VP)*
Martha Swann *(Coord-Mktg)*
Erin Zacholl *(Partner)*

COWLEY DISTRIBUTING INC.
732 Heisinger Rd, Jefferson City, MO
65109
Tel.: (573) 636-6511
Rev.: $19,000,000
Emp.: 43
Books
N.A.I.C.S.: 424920
Jeff Meyer *(Supvr-Route)*
John Cowley II *(Pres)*

**COWLITZ COUNTY PUBLIC
UTILITY DISTRICT**
961 12th Ave, Longview, WA 98632
Tel.: (360) 423-2210
Web Site: https://www.cowlitzpud.org
Sales Range: $150-199.9 Million
Emp.: 150
Distribution, Electric Power
N.A.I.C.S.: 221122
Heather Allen *(Treas & Mgr-Risk)*
Chris Roden *(Gen Mgr)*

COWORKRS LLC
55 Broadway 8th Fl, New York, NY
10006 **NY**
Web Site:
http://www.bondcollective.com
Year Founded: 2013
Sales Range: $10-24.9 Million
Emp.: 32
Environmental Consulting Services
N.A.I.C.S.: 541620
Elie Deitsch *(Co-Founder & Pres)*
Shlomo Silber *(Co-Founder & CEO)*
Meghan Jacobs *(Gen Mgr)*
Elide Rathborne *(Dir-Design)*
Ashley Riggs *(Head-Communtiy &
Culture)*

**COWORX STAFFING SER-
VICES LLC**

1375 Plainfield Ave, Watchung, NJ
07069
Tel.: (908) 757-5300
Web Site:
http://www.coworxstaffing.com
Year Founded: 1974
Full-Service Staffing Services
N.A.I.C.S.: 561311
Jenny Castro *(Acct Mgr)*
Catherine Joiner *(VP-Sls)*
Kara Rogan *(CEO)*

COWTOWN BOOT COMPANY
11401 Gateway Blvd W, El Paso, TX
79936-6499
Tel.: (915) 593-2929 **TX**
Web Site:
http://www.cowtownboots.com
Year Founded: 1962
Sales Range: $1-9.9 Million
Emp.: 75
Mfr & Retailer of Western Boots &
Accessories
N.A.I.C.S.: 316210
Paul Calcattera *(Pres)*
Joe Calcattera *(VP)*

COX & COMPANY, INC.
1664 Old Country Rd, Plainview, NY
11803-5013
Tel.: (212) 366-0200 **NY**
Web Site: http://www.coxandco.com
Year Founded: 1944
Sales Range: $75-99.9 Million
Emp.: 170
Mfr of Aircraft Parts & Equipment
N.A.I.C.S.: 336413
Ray Bozek *(Mktg Mgr)*
John Smith *(Dir-Engrg)*

COX AUTOMOTIVE LLC
2900 Cortez Rd W, Bradenton, FL
34207
Tel.: (941) 749-2690 **FL**
Web Site: https://www.coxauto.com
Year Founded: 2002
Sales Range: $100-124.9 Million
Emp.: 150
New Car Dealers
N.A.I.C.S.: 441110
Gary Cox *(Co-Owner)*

Subsidiaries:

Xtime, Inc. (1)
1400 Bridge Pkwy Ste 200, Redwood
Shores, CA 94065
Tel.: (650) 508-4300
Web Site: http://www.xtime.com
Sales Range: $1-9.9 Million
Emp.: 20
Customer Relationship Management &
Scheduling Solutions Software
N.A.I.C.S.: 513210
Adam Galper *(CTO)*
Neal East *(CEO)*
Chris Howie *(VP-Intl Sls)*
Gary Martin *(COO & Gen Mgr)*
John Grace *(Sr VP-Production & Support)*
Chris Ice *(VP-Product Mktg)*
Adam Springer *(Sr VP-Engrg)*
Warren Webermin *(Sr VP-Strategic Accts &
Bus Dev)*
Steve Knier *(VP-Bus Dev)*
Jim Roche *(Sr VP-Mktg & Managed Svcs)*
Corey Roberts *(Sr VP-Sls)*

COX CHEVROLET INC.
2900 Cortez Rd W, Bradenton, FL
34207
Tel.: (941) 749-2699
Web Site: http://www.coxchevy.com
Sales Range: $100-124.9 Million
Emp.: 150
Car Dealership
N.A.I.C.S.: 441110
Tammy Cox-Leavell *(CFO)*
Chris Cox *(Owner & Pres)*

COX ENGINEERING COMPANY

35 Industrial Dr, Canton, MA 02021
Tel.: (781) 302-3300
Web Site:
http://www.coxengineering.com
Sales Range: $150-199.9 Million
Emp.: 280
Plumbing, Heating & Air-Conditioning
Contracting Services
N.A.I.C.S.: 238220
Jack Desmond *(CEO)*
Mike Donovan *(CFO & Exec VP)*
Leonard McAlister *(Pres-
Construction)*
Brett O'Brien *(VP-Cambridgeport
Custom)*

COX ENTERPRISES, INC.
6205-A Peachtree Dunwoody Rd, At-
lanta, GA 30328
Tel.: (678) 645-6256 **DE**
Web Site:
https://www.coxenterprises.com
Year Founded: 1996
Sales Range: $15-24.9 Billion
Emp.: 50,000
Newspaper Publishers
N.A.I.C.S.: 513110
Sanford Schwartz *(CEO, CEO & VP-
Bus Dev)*
Dallas S. Clement *(Pres & CFO)*
J. Lacey Lewis *(Sr VP-Fin)*
Robert I. Jimenez *(Sr VP-Corp Af-
fairs)*
S. Taylor Glover *(Vice Chm)*
Maria Friedman *(Exec VP-Fin)*
David A. Blau *(VP-Corp Strategy &
Investments)*
Sonji Jacobs *(VP-Corp Comm & PR)*
Alexander C. Taylor *(Chm & CEO)*
Mary Vickers *(VP-Tax)*
Charles Odom *(Treas & Sr VP-Corp
Fin)*
Duncan O'Brien *(Sr VP & Gen Mgr-
Corp Strategy & Investments)*
Mark Dawson *(VP-IT Bus Solutions)*
David Blau *(VP-Corp Strategy & In-
vestments)*
Keith Mask *(VP-Environmental Sus-
tainability)*
Nancy Rigby *(Pres-Cox Foundations)*
Joe Salazarte *(Dir-Bus Travel &
Meeting Svcs)*
Karen Bennett *(Chief People Officer
& Exec VP)*
Paul Scolese *(VP-Govt Affairs)*
Andre Reese *(VP-Info Sys Ops)*
Maury Z. Wolfe *(VP-Corporate Re-
sponsibility & Social Impact)*
John Hatfield *(VP-Aviation)*
John Kovac *(Sr VP-Brand, Mktg &
creative)*
Richard Cox Jr. *(CIO & Sr VP)*
Connie Walters *(VP-Employment
Law)*
Jennifer Hightower *(Gen Counsel,
Sec & Sr VP)*
Patrick Waite *(VP-Audit Svcs)*
Carolyn Pleiss *(CIO & Sr VP)*
Scott LeTourneau *(Sr VP-Corp Dev)*
Cody Partin *(Sr VP-Enterprise Secu-
rity & Corp Svcs)*
Patrick O'Boyle *(Sr VP-Corp Dev)*
Rob Huting *(VP-Corp Dev)*
Shereta D. Williams *(Sr VP-Ops-
Growth)*
Andrew S. Davis *(Sr VP-Strategy &
Investments)*
Joab M. Lesesne III *(Sr VP-Govt Af-
fairs & Public Policy)*

Subsidiaries:

Cox Automotive, Inc. (1)
3003 Summit Blvd Ste 200, Atlanta, GA
30319
Tel.: (404) 568-8000
Web Site: http://www.coxautoinc.com

Emp.: 24,000
Vehicle Remarketing Services & Digital
Marketing & Software Solutions for Automo-
tive Dealers & Consumers
N.A.I.C.S.: 513210
Keith Jezek *(Pres-Retail Solutions Grp)*
Shirley Powell *(Sr VP-Comm & Industry
Rels)*
Stephen E. Anthony *(Partner)*
Shane O'Dell *(Pres-Financial Solutions)*
Amy Mills *(Chief Strategy Officer & Sr VP)*
Philip Nothard *(Head-External Rels-UK)*
Patrick Brennan *(Sr VP-Inventory Solutions
Marketplace)*
Grace Huang *(Pres-Inventory Solutions
Grp)*
Mark Bowser *(CFO & Exec VP)*
Angus Haig *(Gen Counsel & Sr VP)*
David Brooks *(Chief Tech Officer)*
Dale Pollak *(Exec VP)*
Joe George *(Pres-Mobility Solutions Grp)*
Mitch Gersten *(CIO & Sr VP)*
Brodie Taylor *(Dir-Media Partnerships-
Media Solutions)*
Maddie Harris *(Grp Sls Mgr-Media
Solutions-Victoria & South Australia)*
Carl Davies *(Sls Dir-Media Solutions-Natl)*
Martin Forbes *(Pres-Intl)*
Steve Rowley *(Pres)*
Michele Parks *(Chief People Officer)*
Marianne Johnson *(Chief Product Officer &
Exec VP)*

Subsidiary (Domestic):

Dealertrack, Inc. (2)
3400 New Hyde Pk Rd, New Hyde Park,
NY 11040
Tel.: (516) 734-3600
Web Site: http://www.dealertrack.com
Sales Range: $75-99.9 Million
Emp.: 500
Automotive Retail Industry Software & Data
Solutions
N.A.I.C.S.: 513210
Keith Jezek *(Pres)*
Paul Whitworth *(Sr VP-Ops-Dealertrack
DMS)*
Jay Nieman *(VP-Sls-Dealertrack F&I)*

Subsidiary (Domestic):

Dealer Dot Com, Inc. (3)
1 Howard St, Burlington, VT 05401
Tel.: (802) 658-0965
Web Site: http://www.dealer.com
Emp.: 1,000
Internet Marketing Solutions for Automotive
Industry
N.A.I.C.S.: 541519
Rick Gibbs *(CTO)*
Mike Rother *(Gen Mgr)*

Dealertrack Digital Services, Inc. (3)
4070 Willow Lake Blvd, Memphis, TN
38118
Tel.: (901) 565-7900
Web Site: http://www.dealertrack.com
Emp.: 100
Software Development Services
N.A.I.C.S.: 513210
Roy Wood *(Dir-Ops)*

Dealertrack Registration & Titling
Services-Louisiana, LLC (3)
3445 N Causeway Blvd Ste103, Metairie,
LA 70002
Tel.: (504) 456-7438
Web Site: http://us.dealertrack.com
Sales Range: $1-9.9 Million
Emp.: 60
Automobile Registration & Title Solutions
N.A.I.C.S.: 513210

Dealertrack Registration and Titling
Solutions, Inc. (3)
115 Poheganut Dr Ste 201, Groton, CT
06340
Tel.: (860) 448-3177
Web Site: http://www.us.dealertrack.com
Automotive Registration & Title Services
N.A.I.C.S.: 513210

Dealertrack Systems, Inc. (3)
10757 S River Front Pkwy Ste 400, South
Jordan, UT 84095-3907
Tel.: (801) 501-7100
Web Site: http://www.dealertrack.com
Sales Range: $25-49.9 Million
Emp.: 470

Business Management Software for Automobile Dealers
N.A.I.C.S.: 513210
Paul Whitworth *(Sr VP-Ops)*

Subsidiary (Domestic):

Dickinson Fleet Services LLC (2)
4709 W 96th St, Indianapolis, IN 46268-1118
Tel.: (317) 872-4542
Web Site: http://www.dickinsonfleetllc.com
Rev.: $30,000,000
Emp.: 350
Truck Repair
N.A.I.C.S.: 811111
David Henchon *(CFO)*
Larry Fowler *(Mgr-Fleet Svc)*
Alyce Hammond *(Mgr-HR)*
Whitney Mayhill *(Supvr-Billing)*

Subsidiary (Domestic):

Bridgestone Americas Tire Operations, LLC (3)
200 4th Ave S, Nashville, TN 37201   (100%)
Tel.: (615) 937-1000
Web Site: http://www.truckpmplus.com
Tire Mfr & Sales
N.A.I.C.S.: 326211

Subsidiary (Domestic):

Bridgestone Americas Center for Research and Technology, LLC (4)
1659 S Main St, Akron, OH 44301
Tel.: (330) 379-7570
Web Site: http://www.ba-thecenter.com
Tire Polymer Research & Development Services
N.A.I.C.S.: 541715

Plant (Domestic):

Bridgestone Americas Tire Operations, LLC - Abilene Manufacturing Facility (4)
4750 FM 18, Abilene, TX 79602
Tel.: (325) 677-1861
Web Site: http://www.bridgestone-firestone.com
Sales Range: $50-74.9 Million
Emp.: 150
Tread Rubber & Retreading Materials Mfr
N.A.I.C.S.: 326299
Chris Daniel *(Gen Mgr)*

Division (Domestic):

Bridgestone Americas Tire Operations, LLC - Agricultural Tire, U.S. & Canada Commercial Tire Sales Division (4)
730 E 2nd St, Des Moines, IA 50309
Tel.: (515) 283-1440
Automotive Tire Mfr
N.A.I.C.S.: 326211

Plant (Domestic):

Bridgestone Americas Tire Operations, LLC - Aiken County Manufacturing Facility (4)
1 Bridgestone Pkwy, Graniteville, SC 29829
Tel.: (803) 232-2000
Automotive Tire Mfr
N.A.I.C.S.: 326211

Bridgestone Americas Tire Operations, LLC - Akron Manufacturing Facility (4)
10 E Firestone Blvd, Akron, OH 44317
Tel.: (330) 379-7000
Web Site: http://www.bridgestone-firestone.com
Racing Tire Mfr
N.A.I.C.S.: 326211

Division (Domestic):

Bridgestone Americas Tire Operations, LLC - Akron Technical Center Division (4)
10 E Firestone Blvd, Akron, OH 44317
Tel.: (330) 379-6640
Web Site:
  http://www.bridgestoneamericas.com
Emp.: 550

Tire Research & Development Services
N.A.I.C.S.: 541715

Plant (Domestic):

Bridgestone Americas Tire Operations, LLC - Bloomington-Normal Manufacturing Facility (4)
1600 Jesse Rd & Veterans Pkwy, Normal, IL 61761
Tel.: (309) 452-4411
Web Site: http://www.bridgestone-firestone.com
Off Road Tire Mfr
N.A.I.C.S.: 326211
Monty Greutman *(Plant Mgr)*

Division (Domestic):

Bridgestone Americas Tire Operations, LLC - Bridgestone Bandag Tire Solutions Division (4)
2000 Bandag Dr, Muscatine, IA 52761
Tel.: (563) 262-1400
Emp.: 200
Automobile Tire Mfr & Whslr
N.A.I.C.S.: 326211
Kurt Danielson *(Pres)*

Bridgestone Americas Tire Operations, LLC - Des Moines (4)
4600 NW 2nd Ave Ste 100, Des Moines, IA 50313
Tel.: (515) 283-1440
Web Site: http://www.bridgestone-firestone.com
Sales Range: $500-549.9 Million
Agricultural & Forestry Tire Mfr
N.A.I.C.S.: 423130

Plant (Domestic):

Firestone Agricultural-Des Moines (5)
2nd Ave Hoffman Rd, Des Moines, IA 50313
Tel.: (515) 243-1211
Web Site: http://www.firestone.com
Sales Range: $350-399.9 Million
Emp.: 1,600
Agricultural Tire Mfr
N.A.I.C.S.: 326211

Plant (Domestic):

Bridgestone Americas Tire Operations, LLC - Des Moines Manufacturing Facility (4)
2nd Ave & Hoffman Rd, Des Moines, IA 50313
Tel.: (515) 243-1211
Web Site: http://www.bridgestone-firestone.com
Tractor Tire Mfr
N.A.I.C.S.: 326211

Bridgestone Americas Tire Operations, LLC - Griffin Manufacturing Facility (4)
801 Greenbelt Pkwy, Griffin, GA 30223
Tel.: (770) 233-8000
Web Site: http://www.bridgestone-firestone.com
Sales Range: $50-74.9 Million
Emp.: 150
Tread Rubber & Retreading Material Mfr
N.A.I.C.S.: 326299

Plant (Non-US):

Bridgestone Americas Tire Operations, LLC - Joliette Manufacturing Facility (4)
1200 Firestone Blvd, Joliette, J6E 2W5, QC, Canada
Tel.: (450) 756-1061
Automotive Tire Mfr
N.A.I.C.S.: 326211

Plant (Domestic):

Bridgestone Americas Tire Operations, LLC - LaVergne Manufacturing Facility (4)
1201 Bridgestone Pkwy, La Vergne, TN 37086
Tel.: (615) 793-7581
Automotive Tire Mfr
N.A.I.C.S.: 326211

Michael Best *(Mgr-Standards Driven Process)*

Bridgestone Americas Tire Operations, LLC - Long Beach Manufacturing Facility (4)
2500 E Thompson St, Long Beach, CA 90805
Tel.: (562) 531-3880
Web Site: http://www.bridgestone-firestone.com
Sales Range: $25-49.9 Million
Emp.: 60
Tread Rubber & Retreading Material Mfr
N.A.I.C.S.: 326299

Bridgestone Americas Tire Operations, LLC - Muscatine Manufacturing Facility (4)
2000 Bandag Dr, Muscatine, IA 52761
Tel.: (563) 262-1400
Emp.: 200
Retreading Machinery Mfr
N.A.I.C.S.: 333248
Gordon Knapp *(CEO)*

Division (Domestic):

Bridgestone Americas Tire Operations, LLC - Off Road Tire, U.S. & Canada Tire Sales Division (4)
535 Marriott Dr, Nashville, TN 37214
Tel.: (615) 937-1000
Automotive Tires Distr
N.A.I.C.S.: 423130

Bridgestone Americas Tire Operations, LLC - Original Equipment, U.S. & Canada Consumer Tire Sales Division (4)
39500 High Pointe Blvd Ste 150, Novi, MI 48375
Tel.: (248) 348-2202
Web Site: http://www.bridgestone-firestone.com
Automotive Tire Mfr
N.A.I.C.S.: 326211

Plant (Domestic):

Bridgestone Americas Tire Operations, LLC - Oxford Manufacturing Facility (4)
505 W Industry Dr, Oxford, NC 27565
Tel.: (919) 693-8855
Web Site: http://www.bridgestone-firestone.com
Sales Range: $50-74.9 Million
Emp.: 186
Tread Rubber & Retreading Materials Mfr
N.A.I.C.S.: 326299
Mark Highland *(Gen Mgr)*

Division (Domestic):

Bridgestone Americas Tire Operations, LLC - Replacement Tire Sales, U.S. & Canada Consumer Tire Sales Division (4)
535 Marriott Dr, Nashville, TN 37214
Tel.: (615) 937-1000
Automotive Tire Whslr
N.A.I.C.S.: 423130

Plant (Non-US):

Bridgestone Americas Tire Operations, LLC - Sao Paulo Facility (4)
Av Queiros dos Santos 1717, Sao Paulo, 09015-901, Brazil
Tel.: (55) 11 4433 1666
Web Site: http://www.bridgestone-firestone.com
Emp.: 300
Automotive Tire Mfr
N.A.I.C.S.: 326211

Division (Domestic):

Bridgestone Americas Tire Operations, LLC - Texas Proving Ground Division (4)
199 Firestone Rd, Fort Stockton, TX 79735
Tel.: (432) 336-4800
Web Site: http://www.bridgestone-firestone.com
Sales Range: $25-49.9 Million
Emp.: 20
Automobile Testing Ground Operator

N.A.I.C.S.: 541380
Juan De Hoyos *(Gen Mgr)*

Plant (Domestic):

Bridgestone Americas Tire Operations, LLC - Warren County Manufacturing Facility (4)
725 Bridgestone Dr, Morrison, TN 37357
Tel.: (931) 668-5500
Web Site: http://www.bridgestone-firestone.com
Truck & Bus Tires Mfr
N.A.I.C.S.: 326211

Bridgestone Americas Tire Operations, LLC - Wilson Manufacturing Facility (4)
3001 Firestone Pkwy, Wilson, NC 27893
Tel.: (252) 291-4275
Light Truck Tire Mfr
N.A.I.C.S.: 326211

Division (Domestic):

Bridgestone Americas, Inc. - Akron (4)
10 E Firestone Blvd, Akron, OH 44317-0001
Tel.: (330) 379-7000
Web Site: http://www.bf.usa.com
Sales Range: $25-49.9 Million
Emp.: 500
Tire Research & Product Development Services
N.A.I.C.S.: 541715
Heidi Perry *(Supvr-Payroll)*
Chris Dickens *(Mgr-Ops & Facilities)*
John Sabistina *(Mgr-PLTD Section)*

Bridgestone Americas, Inc. - Business Technology Group Division (4)
535 Marriott Dr, Nashville, TN 37214
Tel.: (615) 937-1000
Software Management Services
N.A.I.C.S.: 541511

Bridgestone/Firestone Off Road Tire Division (4)
535 Marriott Dr Ste 800, Nashville, TN 37214-5039
Tel.: (615) 937-5700
Heavy-Duty Tire Distr
N.A.I.C.S.: 441340
Shawn Rasey *(Pres)*

Bridgestone/Firestone Original Equipment Division (4)
39500 High Pointe Blvd Ste 200, Novi, MI 48375-5505
Tel.: (248) 348-2030
Web Site: http://www.bridgestone-firestone.com
Sales Range: $25-49.9 Million
Emp.: 30
Tire Sales to Automotive Manufacturing Businesses
N.A.I.C.S.: 441340

Firestone Tube Division (4)
2700 E Main St, Russellville, AR 72801
Tel.: (479) 968-1443
Web Site: http://www.firestonetubes.com
Sales Range: $25-49.9 Million
Emp.: 75
Tire Tube Mfr
N.A.I.C.S.: 326211
Scott Gately *(Gen Mgr)*

Subsidiary (Domestic):

Kendon Corporation (4)
3904 S Hoyt Ave, Muncie, IN 47302
Tel.: (765) 282-1515
Web Site: http://www.kendon-national.com
Emp.: 40
Hub Assemblies & Rim Mfr
N.A.I.C.S.: 336390
Robert Cook *(Plant Mgr)*
Josh Canada *(Plant Mgr)*

U.S., Canada and Monterrey Manufacturing Group (4)
535 Marriott Dr, Nashville, TN 37214
Tel.: (615) 937-1000
Web Site: http://www.bridgestone-firestone.com
Automotive Tire Mfr
N.A.I.C.S.: 326211

Cox Enterprises, Inc.—(Continued)

White Tire (4)
1615 2nd Ave, Muscatine, IA 52761
Tel.: (563) 288-2200
Automobile Tire Retreading Services
N.A.I.C.S.: 326212

Subsidiary (Domestic):

FleetNet America, Inc. (2)
300 Commerce Dr, Cherryville, NC 28021-8969
Tel.: (704) 435-7156
Web Site: https://www.fleetnetamerica.com
Commercial Truck & Fleet Repair & Maintenance Services
N.A.I.C.S.: 811111
Gary Cummings (CEO)
Jim Buell (Exec VP-Sls & Mktg)
John Wood (Pres)
Bryan Johnson (Exec VP-IT)
Don Doty (VP-Roadside Ops)
Paul Gildenhorn (VP-Sls)
Tim Moore (VP-TMcare Ops)
Evan Costner (Sr Dir-Roadside Quality Solutions)
Jeremy Mikell (Exec VP & Customer Engagement)
Jane Stafford (Dir-HR)
Jeffrey Godwin (VP-Software Solutions)
Misty Bryant (Dir-Invoice Processing)
Steve Cochran (Dir-IT Technical Svcs)
Leah Aikey (VP & Controller)
Lloyd Faulkner (Dir-Software Dev)

Manheim Auctions, Inc. (2)
6205 Peachtree Dunwoody Rd, Atlanta, GA 30328 (90%)
Tel.: (678) 645-0000
Web Site: http://www.manheimauctions.com
Sales Range: $10-24.9 Million
Emp.: 30
Wholesale Automobile Auctions
N.A.I.C.S.: 423110
Janet Barnard (Pres-North America)
Grace Huang (Sr VP-Inventory Svcs)
Stephen Smith (VP-Product Mgmt)
Kevin Chartier (VP-Comml Sls)
Doug Keim (Sr VP-Client Experience)
Anthony Baker (Gen Mgr & Ops Mgr-Washington)
Julie Picard (VP-Industry Partnerships)
Patrick Brennan (Sr VP-Marketplace)

Subsidiary (Domestic):

Arena Auto Auction (3)
200 W Old Chicago Dr, Bolingbrook, IL 60440-3511 (100%)
Tel.: (630) 759-3800
Automobile Auction Services
N.A.I.C.S.: 423110
Mike Meyer (Gen Mgr)

Arizona Auto Auction (3)
3420 S 48th St, Phoenix, AZ 85040-1949 (100%)
Tel.: (480) 894-2400
Wholesale Automobile Auctions
N.A.I.C.S.: 423110

Atlanta Auto Auction, Inc. (3)
4900 Buffington Rd, College Park, GA 30349 (100%)
Tel.: (404) 762-9211
Web Site: http://www.manheim.com
Automobile Auction Services
N.A.I.C.S.: 423110
Pete Palmer (Gen Mgr)

AutoTrader Group, Inc. (3)
3003 Summit Blvd, Atlanta, GA 30319
Tel.: (404) 568-8000
Web Site: http://www.autotrader.com
Sales Range: $1-4.9 Billion
Automotive ECommerce, Marketing & Software
N.A.I.C.S.: 423110
Edward D. Smith (CTO)
Clark Wood (CMO)
Peter C. Cassat (Gen Counsel & VP)
Jimmy W. Hayes (Chm)
Alexander C. Taylor (COO & VP)

Subsidiary (Domestic):

AutoTrader.com Inc. (4)
3003 Summit Blvd, Atlanta, GA 30319 (100%)

Tel.: (404) 568-8000
Web Site: http://www.autotrader.com
Sales Range: $125-149.9 Million
Emp.: 1,400
Online Automobile Buying & Selling Services
N.A.I.C.S.: 441120
Clark Wood (CMO)
Dave Amundsen (VP-Fin)
Jim Franchi (COO & Sr VP-Ops)
Melanie Kovach (Gen Mgr-Private Seller Svc & Sls)
David Pyle (VP-Sls-West Div)
Julie Zorn Shipp (Mgr-PR)
Ed Smith (CIO)

Subsidiary (Domestic):

HomeNet Automotive LLC (5)
220 Willowbrook Ln, West Chester, PA 19382
Tel.: (610) 738-3313
Web Site: http://www.homenetauto.com
Sales Range: $10-24.9 Million
Emp.: 135
Web-Based Applications for the Automotive Industry
N.A.I.C.S.: 513210
Robert Landers (VP & Gen Mgr)

Kelley Blue Book Co., Inc. (5)
195 Technology Dr, Irvine, CA 92618-2402
Tel.: (949) 770-7704
Web Site: http://www.kbb.com
Sales Range: $125-149.9 Million
Emp.: 500
Vehicle Pricing Information
N.A.I.C.S.: 513210
Steve Lind (Pres)

Subsidiary (Domestic):

CDMdata, Inc. (6)
15333 N Pima Rd Ste 370, Scottsdale, AZ 85260
Tel.: (866) 379-2361
Web Site: http://www.cdmdata.com
Inventory Marketing & Management Services
N.A.I.C.S.: 811111

Subsidiary (Domestic):

VinSolutions, Inc. (5)
5700 Broadmoor, Mission, KS 66202
Tel.: (913) 825-6124
Web Site: http://www.vinsolutions.com
Sales Range: $25-49.9 Million
Emp.: 250
Automotive Software Solution Services
N.A.I.C.S.: 513210
Lori Wittman (Sr VP & Gen Mgr)
Chase Abbott (VP-Sls)
Sean Garrett (Sr Dir-Fin)
James Maynard (Sr VP-Product)
Mark Vickery (Sr Dir-Performance Mgmt)

vAuto, Inc. (5)
1901 S Meyers Rd Ste 700, Oakbrook Terrace, IL 60181
Tel.: (630) 590-2000
Web Site: http://www.vauto.com
Sales Range: $10-24.9 Million
Emp.: 78
Software Solutions for Used Vehicles Inventory
N.A.I.C.S.: 513210
Dale Pollak (Founder)
Michael Chiovari (VP-IT Ops)
Michelle Drinnan (VP-Performance Mgmt & Trng)
Mandi Fang (VP-Product Mgmt)
Randy Kobat (VP & Gen Mgr)
Joseph Dougherty (VP-Ops)
David Rice (VP-Res & Dev)
Tom Richards (VP-Sls)

Subsidiary (Domestic):

Big H Auto Auction Services, Inc. (3)
14450 W Rd, Houston, TX 77041-1103 (100%)
Tel.: (281) 890-4300
Wholesale Automobile Auctions
N.A.I.C.S.: 423110

Subsidiary (Domestic):

Fort Worth Vehicle Auction (4)

12101 Trinity Blvd, Euless, TX 76040-6924 (100%)
Tel.: (817) 626-5494
Web Site: http://www.manheim.com
Sales Range: $25-49.9 Million
Emp.: 50
Wholesale Automobile Auctions
N.A.I.C.S.: 423110

Subsidiary (Domestic):

Central Florida Auto Auction (3)
9800 Bachman Rd, Orlando, FL 32824-8005 (100%)
Tel.: (407) 438-1000
Web Site: http://www.manheim.com
Wholesale Used Cars
N.A.I.C.S.: 423110

Colorado Auto Auction (3)
6955 E 50th Ave, Commerce City, CO 80022-4711 (100%)
Tel.: (303) 287-8077
Wholesale Auto Auction
N.A.I.C.S.: 425120

Dallas Auto Auction Inc. (3)
5333 W Kiest Blvd, Dallas, TX 75236-1055 (100%)
Tel.: (214) 330-1800
Web Site: http://www.manheim.com
Automobile Auction
N.A.I.C.S.: 423110
Barry Roop (VP)

Denver Auto Auction (3)
17500 E 32nd Ave, Aurora, CO 80011 (100%)
Tel.: (303) 343-3443
Web Site: http://www.manheim.com
Wholesale Automobile Auctions
N.A.I.C.S.: 423110

Fredericksburg Auto Auction (3)
120 Auction Dr, Fredericksburg, VA 22406-1206 (100%)
Tel.: (540) 368-3400
Web Site: http://www.manheim.com
Emp.: 150
Automobile Auction
N.A.I.C.S.: 423110
Eddie Windsor (Asst Gen Mgr)
Debra Sliver (Mgr-HR)
Steve Mason (Gen Mgr)

Fresno Auto Dealers Auction (3)
278 N Marks Ave, Fresno, CA 93706-1136 (100%)
Tel.: (559) 268-8051
Wholesale Automobile Auctions
N.A.I.C.S.: 423110

Greater Chicago Auto Auction (3)
20401 Cox Ave, Matteson, IL 60443-1856 (100%)
Tel.: (815) 806-4222
Web Site: http://www.cox.com
Wholesale Automobile Auction
N.A.I.C.S.: 423110
Mike Sisto (Gen Mgr)

Harrisonburg Auto Auction (3)
Interstate 81 3560 Early Rd, Harrisonburg, VA 22801 (100%)
Tel.: (540) 434-5991
Wholesale Automobile Auction
N.A.I.C.S.: 441330

Kansas City Auto Auction Inc. (3)
3901 N Skiles Ave, Kansas City, MO 64161 (100%)
Tel.: (816) 452-4084
Web Site: http://www.manheim.com
Wholesale Automobile Auction
N.A.I.C.S.: 488410
Peggy Springer (Gen Mgr)

Lakeland Auto Auction (3)
8025 N State Rd 33, Lakeland, FL 33809 (100%)
Tel.: (863) 984-1551
Web Site: http://www.2.manheim.com
Wholesale Automobile Auction Services
N.A.I.C.S.: 423110
Todd Janego (Gen Mgr)

Lauderdale-Miami Auto Auction Inc. (3)
5353 S State Rd 7, Davie, FL 33314-6403 (100%)
Tel.: (954) 791-3520

Web Site: http://www.publish.manheim.com
Automobile Auction Distr
N.A.I.C.S.: 423110
Jeff Modjeski (Gen Mgr)

Manheim Albany (3)
459 Route 146, Clifton Park, NY 12065-0440 (100%)
Tel.: (518) 371-7500
Web Site: http://www.manheim.com
Automobile Auction
N.A.I.C.S.: 423110
Jay Waterman (Gen Mgr)
Lauren Sokolowski (Asst Gen Mgr)

Subsidiary (Non-US):

Manheim Asia Pacific Ltd. (3)
33/8 Moo 1 On-nuch Road Prawet, Bangkok, 10250, Thailand (100%)
Tel.: (66) 2329 1155
Web Site: http://www.manheimthailand.com
Logistics Management Services
N.A.I.C.S.: 541614

Manheim Auto Auctions Limited (3)
8277 Lawson Rd, Milton, ON, Canada (100%)
Tel.: (905) 275-3000
Web Site: http://www.manheim.com
Used Car & Truck Sales for Dealers
N.A.I.C.S.: 441120
Ken Morin (Asst Gen Mgr)

Subsidiary (Domestic):

Manheim Baltimore-Washington (3)
7120 Dorsey Run Rd, Elkridge, MD 21075-6884 (100%)
Tel.: (410) 796-8899
Web Site: http://www.manheim.com
Vehicle Auctions
N.A.I.C.S.: 423110
Brian Seabrease (Mgr-Arbitration)
Ryan Cluney (Supvr-TRA)
John Eriksen (Gen Mgr)

Manheim California (3)
1320 N Tustin Ave, Anaheim, CA 92807-1619 (100%)
Tel.: (714) 996-2400
Web Site: http://www.manheim.com
Wholesale Automobile Auction
N.A.I.C.S.: 425120
Mike Watrous (Mgr-Arbitration)
Steve Shaangelyan (Mgr-Dealer Svcs)

Subsidiary (Domestic):

Bay Cities Auto Auction (4)
29900 Auction Way, Hayward, CA 94544-6914 (100%)
Tel.: (510) 786-4500
Web Site: http://www.manheim.com
Sales Range: $50-74.9 Million
Emp.: 345
Wholesale Automobile Auctions
N.A.I.C.S.: 423110
Greg Beck (Gen Mgr)

Subsidiary (Domestic):

Manheim Cincinnati (3)
4969 Mulhauser Rd, Hamilton, OH 45011-9789 (100%)
Tel.: (513) 874-9310
Web Site: http://www.publish.manheim.com
Automobile Auction Services
N.A.I.C.S.: 423110

Manheim Darlington (3)
1111 Harry Byrd Hwy, Darlington, SC 29532-3507 (100%)
Tel.: (843) 393-2861
Web Site: http://www.manheim.com
Wholesale Automobile Auctions
N.A.I.C.S.: 423110
Matt Laughridge (Mgr-Field Sls)
Ryan Mason (Gen Mgr)
Bobby Clark (Mgr-Arbitration)
Danny Anderson (Mgr-Ops)
Ellen Westpfahl (Asst Gen Mgr)
John Ericksen (Asst Gen Mgr)
Mike Johnson (Mgr-Sys Support)
Noel Kitsch (Asst Gen Mgr)
Snow Cahill (Mgr-Promotions)
Tony Caraway (Mgr-Vehicle Entry)
Wade Bailey (Controller)

Manheim Georgia (3)

7205 Campbellton Rd SW, Atlanta, GA
30331-8144 **(100%)**
Tel.: (404) 349-5555
Web Site: http://www.manheim.com
Wholesale Automobile Auctions
N.A.I.C.S.: 423110
Mike Benfield *(Gen Mgr)*
Rusty Caston *(Asst Gen Mgr)*
Jamie Masdon *(Mgr-Ops)*

Subsidiary (Domestic):

Bishop Brothers Auto Auction **(4)**
2244 Metropolitan Pkwy SW, Atlanta, GA
30315-6229 **(100%)**
Tel.: (404) 767-3652
Wholesale Automobile Auction
N.A.I.C.S.: 425120

Subsidiary (Domestic):

Manheim Hawaii **(3)**
1001 Ahua St, Honolulu, HI 96819 **(100%)**
Tel.: (808) 840-8900
Web Site: http://www.publish.manheim.com
Vehicle Auction Services
N.A.I.C.S.: 425120
Dewey Hess *(Gen Mgr)*

Manheim Imperial Florida **(3)**
3300 County Line Rd, Lakeland, FL
33811 **(100%)**
Tel.: (863) 607-6000
Wholesale Auto Auctioneer
N.A.I.C.S.: 423110

Subsidiary (Non-US):

Manheim Italia S.r.l. **(3)**
Strada del Drosso, 10135, Turin, Italy
Tel.: (39) 0113406250
Web Site: http://www.manheim.it
Automobile Auction & Whslr
N.A.I.C.S.: 425120

Subsidiary (Domestic):

Manheim Louisville Auto Auction **(3)**
5425 Hwy 31 E, Clarksville, IN
47129 **(100%)**
Tel.: (812) 283-0734
Web Site: http://www.manheim.com
Automobile Auction Services
N.A.I.C.S.: 425120

Manheim Metro Dallas **(3)**
2717 E Main St, Grand Prairie, TX
75050-6214 **(100%)**
Tel.: (972) 339-4100
Web Site: http://www.manheim.com
Automobile Auction Services
N.A.I.C.S.: 423110

Manheim New England **(3)**
123 Williams St, North Dighton, MA
02764-0001 **(100%)**
Tel.: (508) 823-6600
Web Site: http://www2.manheim.com
Automobile Auction
N.A.I.C.S.: 423110
Timothy Hoegler *(Gen Mgr)*
Michael Schaefer *(Asst Gen Mgr)*
Jeff Jackson *(Controller)*
Pat Thompson *(Mgr-MAFS)*

Manheim New Jersey **(3)**
730 Route 68, Bordentown, NJ
08505-0188 **(100%)**
Tel.: (609) 298-3400
Web Site: http://www.manheim.com
Wholesale Automobile Auctions
N.A.I.C.S.: 423110
Peter Sauber *(Gen Mgr)*
Gary George *(Asst Gen Mgr-Ops, Dealer
Svcs & Promos)*
Ben Lasala *(Mgr-Reconditioning)*
Gary Calabro *(Supvr-Post Sale Inspection)*
Jeanna Haas *(Supvr-Comml Accts)*
John Aquaro *(Supvr-Vehicle Entry)*
Rich Shashaty *(Mgr-Arbitration & Post Sale
Inspection)*
Tristan Borcsik *(Mgr-Vehicle Entry)*

Manheim New Mexico **(3)**
3411 Broadway Blvd SE, Albuquerque, NM
87105-0405 **(100%)**
Tel.: (505) 242-9191
Web Site: http://www2.manheim.com
Sales of Wholesale Automobiles
N.A.I.C.S.: 423110
Travis Clark *(Asst Gen Mgr)*

Manheim Northstar Minnesota **(3)**
4908 Valley Industrial Blvd N, Shakopee,
MN 55379 **(100%)**
Tel.: (952) 445-5544
Web Site: http://www.manheim.com
Automobile Auction Services
N.A.I.C.S.: 425120
Gerald Aman *(Gen Mgr)*

Manheim Ohio **(3)**
3905 Jackson Pke, Grove City, OH
43123-9731 **(100%)**
Tel.: (614) 871-2771
Web Site: http://www.ohioautoauction.com
Wholesale Automobile Auctions
N.A.I.C.S.: 423110
Greg Chesko *(Asst Gen Mgr)*
John Deck *(Gen Mgr)*

Manheim Orlando **(3)**
11801 W Colonial Dr, Ocoee, FL
34761-0220 **(100%)**
Tel.: (407) 656-6200
Web Site: http://www.manheim.com
Automobile Auctioneer
N.A.I.C.S.: 423110
Butch Herdegen *(Gen Mgr)*
Iris Arenas *(Mgr-Acctg)*
Lisa Kirk *(Mgr-HR)*
Tim Sherk *(Asst Gen Mgr)*
Robert Zakaib *(Asst Gen Mgr)*

Manheim Philadelphia **(3)**
2280 Bethlehem Pike, Hatfield, PA
19440-0309 **(100%)**
Tel.: (215) 822-1935
Automobile Auction Services
N.A.I.C.S.: 423110
Charles Polina *(Gen Mgr)*
Michael Kriebel *(Mgr-Tech)*
Scott Mulligan *(Asst Gen Mgr)*

Manheim Pittsburgh **(3)**
21095 Route 19 N, Cranberry Township, PA
16066-5907 **(100%)**
Tel.: (724) 452-5555
Automobile Auction
N.A.I.C.S.: 811114
Lisa Ferrari *(Asst Controller)*

Manheim Portland **(3)**
3000 N Hayden Is Dr, Portland, OR
97217-8257 **(100%)**
Tel.: (503) 286-3000
Web Site: http://www2.manheim.com
Wholesale Automobile Auction
N.A.I.C.S.: 423110
Brenda Callahan *(Coord-Quadrant)*
Craig Boughn *(Mgr-Dealer Svcs)*
Teri O'Rourke *(Coord-Transportation)*
Jake Dockter *(Mgr-Promos & Mktg)*

Manheim San Antonio **(3)**
2042 Ackerman Rd, San Antonio, TX
78219-3506 **(100%)**
Tel.: (210) 661-4200
Web Site: http://www.manheim.com
Wholesale Automobile Auctions
N.A.I.C.S.: 423110
Rebecca Robbins *(Office Mgr)*
Laura Goins *(Mgr-Lot Ops)*

Manheim Seattle **(3)**
19711 77th Ave S, Kent, WA
98032-2147 **(100%)**
Tel.: (253) 872-6800
Web Site: http://www.manheim.com
Automobile Auction Services
N.A.I.C.S.: 423110
Ray Priest *(Gen Mgr-Denver)*

Manheim Southern California **(3)**
10700 Beech Ave, Fontana, CA
92337-7205 **(100%)**
Tel.: (909) 822-2261
Web Site: http://www.manheim.com
Wholesale Automobile Auctions
N.A.I.C.S.: 441120
Teresa Borsheim *(Asst Gen Mgr)*
Chad Ruffin *(Gen Mgr)*
David Thompson *(Asst Gen Mgr)*
Lauren Self *(Mgr-HR)*
Lorraine Rambeau *(Office Mgr)*

Manheim Tampa **(3)**
401 S 50th St, Tampa, FL
33619-3651 **(100%)**
Tel.: (813) 247-1666
Web Site: http://www.manheim.com
Automobile Auction

N.A.I.C.S.: 441120
Donna Wright *(Mgr-Front Office)*
Shei Slowey *(Mgr-Mktg)*
Dave Rathjens *(Gen Mgr)*
Roger Shaw *(Mgr-Dealer Svcs)*

Subsidiary (Non-US):

Manheim Toronto **(3)**
8277 Lawson Road, Milton, L9T 5C7, ON,
Canada **(100%)**
Tel.: (905) 875-2915
Web Site: http://www.manheim.com
Wholesale Auto Auction
N.A.I.C.S.: 425120
Don Wallace *(Mng Dir)*

Subsidiary (Domestic):

Manheim of Phoenix **(3)**
201 N 83rd Ave, Tolleson, AZ
85353-3323 **(100%)**
Tel.: (623) 907-7000
Web Site: http://www.greaterpxaa.com
Automobile Auction & Exchange Services
N.A.I.C.S.: 561499
Danny Brawn *(Asst Gen Mgr)*
Gus Jones *(Asst Gen Mgr)*
Scott Domine *(Mgr-Arbitration)*
Todd Luedeker *(Mgr-Comml Accts)*
Jay Neal *(Mgr-Field Sls)*
Shaunna Ryan *(Office Mgr)*

**Manheim's Greater Pensacola
Auction** **(3)**
6359 N W St, Pensacola, FL
32505 **(100%)**
Tel.: (850) 477-3063
Web Site: http://www.manheim.com
Automobile Auction Services
N.A.I.C.S.: 425120
Dustin Ruffin *(Gen Mgr)*
Scott Hollingsworth *(Mgr-Comml)*
Peggy Dirk *(Office Mgr)*

Subsidiary (Non-US):

**Manheim's Oshawa Dealers
Exchange** **(3)**
8277 Lawson Road, Milton, L9T 5C7, ON,
Canada **(100%)**
Tel.: (905) 404-6633
Web Site: http://www.manheim.com
Auto Auction Services
N.A.I.C.S.: 425120

Subsidiary (Domestic):

**Manheim's The Motor City Auto
Auction** **(3)**
29500 Gateway Dr, Flat Rock, MI
48134-1396 **(100%)**
Tel.: (734) 783-3799
Web Site: http://www.manheim.com
Automobile Auction Services
N.A.I.C.S.: 423110
Mike McKinney *(Gen Mgr)*
Joe Maltese *(Mgr-Ops)*

Metro Milwaukee Auto Auction **(3)**
561 27th St, Caledonia, WI
53108-9785 **(100%)**
Tel.: (262) 835-4436
Wholesale Automobile Auctions
N.A.I.C.S.: 423110

Minneapolis Auto Auction **(3)**
8001 Jefferson Hwy, Maple Grove, MN
55369-4902 **(100%)**
Tel.: (763) 425-7653
Web Site:
  http://www.minneapolisautoauction.com
Emp.: 100
Wholesale Automobile Auctions
N.A.I.C.S.: 423110
Jerry Aman *(Gen Mgr)*

Mississippi Auto Auction Inc. **(3)**
7510 US Hwy 49 N, Hattiesburg, MS
39402-9104 **(100%)**
Tel.: (601) 268-7550
Automobile Auction Services
N.A.I.C.S.: 423110
Bo Beason *(Gen Mgr)*

Nashville Auto Auction **(3)**
8400 Eastgate Blvd, Mount Juliet, TN
37122-3141 **(100%)**
Tel.: (615) 773-3800
Automobile Auction

N.A.I.C.S.: 441330

Newburgh Auto Auction **(3)**
2000 Dealer Dr, Newburgh, NY
12550 **(100%)**
Tel.: (845) 567-8400
Web Site: http://www.manheim.com
Wholesale Automobile Auctions
N.A.I.C.S.: 423110
Mark Pester *(Gen Mgr)*

Omaha Auto Auction **(3)**
9201 S 144th St, Omaha, NE
68138-3634 **(100%)**
Tel.: (402) 896-8000
Web Site: http://www.manheim.com
Automobile Auction
N.A.I.C.S.: 423110
Steve Robinson *(Gen Mgr)*

San Diego Auto Auction Inc. **(3)**
4691 Calle Joven, Oceanside, CA
92057-6042 **(100%)**
Tel.: (760) 754-3600
Web Site: http://www2.manheim.com
Vehicle Auction Services
N.A.I.C.S.: 425120

Skyline Auto Exchange **(3)**
100 US Hwy 46, Fairfield, NJ
07004-3217 **(100%)**
Tel.: (973) 227-0100
Automobile Auction Services
N.A.I.C.S.: 423110
Kim Dittow *(Gen Mgr)*

St. Louis Auto Auction **(3)**
13813 Saint Charles Rock Rd, Bridgeton,
MO 63044-3824 **(100%)**
Tel.: (314) 739-1300
Web Site: http://www.manheim.com
Wholesale Automobile Auctions
N.A.I.C.S.: 423110
Jason Blake *(Asst Gen Mgr)*

St. Pete Auto Auction **(3)**
14950 Roosevelt Blvd, Clearwater, FL
33762-3501 **(100%)**
Tel.: (727) 531-7717
Web Site: http://www.manheim.com
Wholesale Automobile Auctions
N.A.I.C.S.: 423110
Brad Burns *(Gen Mgr)*

Statesville Auto Auction **(3)**
Interstate 77 & Hwy 21N, Statesville, NC
28625 **(100%)**
Tel.: (704) 876-1111
Automobile Auction Services
N.A.I.C.S.: 425120

Utah Auto Auction **(3)**
1650 W 500 S, Woods Cross, UT
84087 **(100%)**
Tel.: (801) 298-7900
Wholesale Auto Auctions
N.A.I.C.S.: 423110

West Palm Beach Auto Auction **(3)**
600 Sansbury Way, West Palm Beach, FL
33411 **(100%)**
Tel.: (561) 790-1200
Web Site: http://www.manhien.com
Automobile Auction
N.A.I.C.S.: 423110
Jeff Modjeski *(Gen Mgr)*

Subsidiary (Non-US):

incadea GmbH **(2)**
F-W-Raiffeisenstr 1b, Elsbethen, 5061,
Salzburg, Austria
Tel.: (43) 662 857600 0
Web Site: http://www.incadea.com
Automotive Software Publisher & Informa-
tion Technology Consulting Services
N.A.I.C.S.: 513210
Allan Stejskal *(CEO)*

Corporate Headquarters (Non-US):

incadea GmbH **(3)**
St-Martin-Strasse 61, 81669, Munich, Ger-
many
Tel.: (49) 89 69 33 80
Web Site: http://www.incadea.com
Automotive Software Publisher & Informa-
tion Technology Consulting Services
N.A.I.C.S.: 513210
Allan Stejskal *(CEO)*
Alexandros Tsaparas *(CFO)*

Cox Enterprises, Inc.—(Continued)

Rafal Jacaszek (VP-Sls & Mktg-Software Intl)
Patrick Katenkamp (Pres-Software Intl)
Karsten Rudolph (CTO)
Eric Sentuc (VP-Aftersales & Aftermarket)
Panos Gikas (VP-Ops-Global)

Subsidiary (Non-US):

incadea (Beijing) ITC Ltd. **(4)**
B2003 TYG Center No 2C North Dong San Huan Rd, Chaoyang District, Beijing, 100020, China
Tel.: (86) 10 65915 393
Web Site: http://www.incadea.com.cn
Emp.: 109
Automotive Software Publisher & Information Technology Consulting Services
N.A.I.C.S.: 513210
Ronnie Xu (Gen Mgr)

incadea Greece Informatics Systems S.A. **(4)**
64 Kifissias Avenue, 15125, Maroussi, Greece
Tel.: (30) 214 4169 100
Web Site: http://www.incadea.gr
Automotive Software Publisher & Information Technology Consulting Services
N.A.I.C.S.: 513210
Pantelis Kolias (Dir-Svcs)

incadea India Private Limited **(4)**
Brigade Tech Park Block A Nr ITPL Whitefield Road, Krishnarajapuram Hobli, Bengaluru, 560 066, India
Tel.: (91) 80 49395 400
Web Site: http://www.incadea.in
Automotive Software Publisher & Information Technology Consulting Services
N.A.I.C.S.: 513210
Kumar Pulivarthi (Head-Dev Svcs-Global)

incadea New Zealand Limited **(4)**
Level 1 22 Dundonald Street, Eden Terrace, Auckland, 1021, New Zealand
Tel.: (64) 9 623 6020
Web Site: http://www.incadea.co.nz
Emp.: 15
Automotive Software Publisher & Information Technology Consulting Services
N.A.I.C.S.: 513210
David Blackford (Gen Mgr-Asia Pacific)

Branch (Non-US):

incadea Taiwan **(5)**
4F-6 No 316 Wenchang Street, Xinyi District, Taipei, 11074, Taiwan
Tel.: (886) 2 2723 0660
Automotive Software Publisher & Information Technology Consulting Services
N.A.I.C.S.: 513210

Subsidiary (Non-US):

incadea SL **(4)**
Av De Bruselas 13 3E, 28108, Alcobendas, Madrid, Spain
Tel.: (34) 91 246 76 00
Web Site: http://www.es.incadea.com
Emp.: 20
Automotive Software Publisher & Information Technology Consulting Services
N.A.I.C.S.: 513210
Paloma Verdera (Mgr-Fin & HR)

Cox Communications, Inc. **(1)**
6205 B Peachtree Dunwoody Rd NE, Atlanta, GA 30328 **(100%)**
Tel.: (404) 843-5000
Web Site: http://www.cox.com
Sales Range: $1-4.9 Billion
Emp.: 22,530
Telecommunication Servicesb
N.A.I.C.S.: 516210
Karen Bennett (Chief People Officer & Exec VP)
Patrick J. Esser (Pres)
Len Barlik (COO)
Larry Coval (VP-Bus-West)
Duane Cameron (VP-San Diego)
Perley McBride (CFO & Exec VP)

Joint Venture (Domestic):

Canoe Ventures LLC **(2)**
200 Union Blvd Ste 590, Lakewood, CO 80228

Tel.: (212) 364-3600
Web Site: https://www.canoeventures.com
Television Advertising Services
N.A.I.C.S.: 541890
Tom Huber (COO)
Joel Hassell (CEO)
Chris Pizzurro (Sr VP-Sls & Mktg-Global)
Ed Knudson (Chief Revenue Officer)
Sid Gregory (CTO)
David Porter (Sr VP & Gen Mgr-Addressable)

Unit (Domestic):

Cox Communications - Middle Georgia **(2)**
6601 Hawkinsville Rd, Macon, GA 30319-1464 **(100%)**
Tel.: (478) 784-8000
Web Site: http://www.cox.com
Cable Television Services & Advertising Sales
N.A.I.C.S.: 516210

Cox Communications Cleveland Area **(2)**
12221 Plz Dr, Parma, OH 44130
Tel.: (216) 535-3500
Web Site: http://www.coxenterprises.com
Sales Range: $25-49.9 Million
Emp.: 165
Cable Television Services
N.A.I.C.S.: 516210
Stacie Schafer (Sr Mgr-PR)
Pat Esser (Pres)
Perley McBride (CFO & Exec VP)
Len Barlik (COO & Exec VP)
Sujata Gosalia (Chief Strategy Officer & Exec VP)
Mark Greatrex (CMO, Chief Sls Officer & Exec VP)
Kevin Hart (CTO, Chief Product Officer & Exec VP)
Karen Bennett (Chief HR Officer & Exec VP)

Cox Communications Gainesville/Ocala **(2)**
6020 NW 43rd St, Gainesville, FL 32653-3338
Tel.: (888) 269-9693
Web Site: http://www.cox.com
Sales Range: $25-49.9 Million
Emp.: 250
Cable Television
N.A.I.C.S.: 516210

Subsidiary (Domestic):

Cox Communications Gulf Coast, LLC **(2)**
320 Racetrack Rd NW, Fort Walton Beach, FL 32547-1554
Tel.: (850) 862-4142
Web Site: http://ww2.cox.com
Sales Range: $50-74.9 Million
Emp.: 400
Cable Television Services
N.A.I.C.S.: 516210

Cox Communications Kansas, LLC **(2)**
901 S George Washington Blvd, Wichita, KS 67211-3505 **(100%)**
Tel.: (316) 262-4270
Web Site: http://www.cox.com
Sales Range: $50-74.9 Million
Emp.: 400
Cable Television Services
N.A.I.C.S.: 516210
Coleen Jennison (VP)
Megan Bottenberg (Mgr-Govt & Regulatory Affairs)
John Salem (Natl Sls Mgr)

Cox Communications Las Vegas, Inc. **(2)**
1700 Vegas Dr, Las Vegas, NV 89106-4309 **(100%)**
Tel.: (702) 383-4000
Web Site: http://www.cox.com
Sales Range: $50-74.9 Million
Emp.: 900
Cable & Other Pay Television Services
N.A.I.C.S.: 516210
Gayle Porterfield (VP-Construction)

Cox Communications Louisiana, LLC **(2)**

2121 Airline Dr, Metairie, LA 70001 **(100%)**
Tel.: (504) 304-7345
Web Site: http://www.cox.com
Cable Television Services
N.A.I.C.S.: 516210

Unit (Domestic):

Cox Communications Northern Virginia **(2)**
3080 Centerville Rd, Herndon, VA 20171
Tel.: (703) 378-8400
Web Site: http://www.cox.com
Sales Range: $100-124.9 Million
Emp.: 1,000
Cable Television Broadcasting
N.A.I.C.S.: 516210
Gary McCollum (VP & Mgr)

Subsidiary (Domestic):

Cox Communications Omaha, LLC **(2)**
11505 W Dodge Rd, Omaha, NE 68154-2536 **(100%)**
Tel.: (402) 933-2000
Web Site: http://www.cox.com
Sales Range: $125-149.9 Million
Emp.: 1,200
Cable Television Services
N.A.I.C.S.: 516210

Unit (Domestic):

Cox Communications Phoenix **(2)**
1550 W Data Vly Rd, Phoenix, AZ 85027
Tel.: (623) 594-0505
Web Site: http://www.cox.com
Sales Range: $350-399.9 Million
Emp.: 3,500
Cable Television Services
N.A.I.C.S.: 516210
Steve Rivley (Gen mgr)
John Wolfe (Sr VP & Mgr-Southwest)
Marisol Ruiz (Mgr-Product Mktg)

Cox Communications Roanoke **(2)**
4760 Valley View Blvd Ste 40, Roanoke, VA 24012
Tel.: (540) 266-7077
Web Site: http://www.cox.com
Sales Range: $25-49.9 Million
Emp.: 165
Cable Television Services
N.A.I.C.S.: 516210

Cox Communications Santa Barbara **(2)**
22 S Fairview Ave, Goleta, CA 93117-3324
Tel.: (805) 683-6651
Web Site: http://ww2.cox.com
Sales Range: $25-49.9 Million
Emp.: 150
Cable Television Services
N.A.I.C.S.: 516210
Kirsten McLaughlin (Mgr-Pub Affairs)
Chanelle Hawken (VP-Pub Affairs)

Joint Venture (Domestic):

Music Choice **(2)**
650 Dresher Rd, Horsham, PA 19044
Tel.: (215) 784-5840
Web Site: http://www.musicchoice.com
Emp.: 60
Music Video Cable Television Programming, Online & Mobile Publishing Services
N.A.I.C.S.: 516210
David Del Beccaro (Founder, Co-Pres & CEO)
Christina Tancredi (Co-Pres & COO)
Jeremy Rosenberg (Co-Founder)

Subsidiary (Domestic):

Unite Private Networks, LLC **(2)**
7200 NW 86th St Ste M, Kansas City, MO 64153 **(66%)**
Tel.: (816) 903-9400
Web Site: http://www.uniteprivatenetworks.com
Wired Telecommunications Carriers
N.A.I.C.S.: 517111
Jason W. Adkins (CEO)
Kevin Anderson (Founder & Chm)
Jennifer Bergman (CFO)
Chad Senglaub (Pres & COO)

OpenGov, Inc. **(1)**

955 Charter St, Redwood City, CA 94063
Tel.: (650) 336-7167
Web Site: http://www.opengov.com
Financial Performance Assessment Services
N.A.I.C.S.: 513210
Joe Lonsdale (Co-Founder & Chm)
David Reeves (Pres)
Ammiel Kamon (Chief Product Officer)
Paul Denton (CFO)
Boaz Maor (Sr VP-Customer Success)

Subsidiary (Domestic):

Ontodia, Inc. **(2)**
137 Varick St Fl 2, New York, NY 10013-1110
Tel.: (646) 484-9311
Web Site: http://www.ontodia.com
Custom Computer Programming Services
N.A.I.C.S.: 541511
Sami Baig (Co-Founder & Pres)

COX INDUSTRIES, INC.
860 Cannon Bridge Rd, Orangeburg, SC 29115
Tel.: (803) 534-7467 **SC**
Web Site: http://www.coxwood.com
Year Founded: 1954
Sales Range: $50-74.9 Million
Emp.: 415
Pressure Treated Lumber & Related Wood Products Mfr & Sales
N.A.I.C.S.: 321114
Michael Johnson (CEO)
Matt Yaun (Chief Admin Officer)
Richard Lackey (Gen Counsel)
Greg Campbell (COO)
Jane House (Dir-Environmental, Health & Safety)
Pam Bedenbaugh (Dir-HR)
Phil Tetterton (CFO)

COX INTERIOR INC.
1751 Old Columbia Rd, Campbellsville, KY 42718-9309
Tel.: (270) 789-3129
Web Site:
https://www.coxinterior.com
Year Founded: 1978
Sales Range: $25-49.9 Million
Emp.: 385
Millwork
N.A.I.C.S.: 321918
Lilian Lawhorn (CFO)
Lillian Smith (CFO)
Lucy Cox (Atty)

COX OIL COMPANY
2034 W Woodland St, Springfield, MO 65807
Tel.: (417) 886-3866
Year Founded: 1997
Sales Range: $10-24.9 Million
Emp.: 50
Petroleum Products Mfr
N.A.I.C.S.: 424720
Paul Cox (Pres)

COX TRUCK BROKERAGE INC.
10448 Dow Gil Rd, Ashland, VA 23005
Tel.: (804) 798-1477
Web Site:
https://www.truckingforamerica.com
Sales Range: $25-49.9 Million
Emp.: 250
Truck Transportation Brokers
N.A.I.C.S.: 488510

COX'S FOODARAMA INC.
10810 S Post Oak Rd, Houston, TX 77035
Tel.: (713) 723-8948
Web Site:
http://www.foodaramatexas.com
Rev.: $80,702,000
Emp.: 75

Grocery Stores, Independent
N.A.I.C.S.: 445110
Carrol Cox *(Pres)*

**COX'S WHOLESALE SEA-
FOOD INC.**
5806 N Occident St, Tampa, FL
33614
Tel.: (813) 888-9800
Web Site:
   https://www.coxseafood.com
Sales Range: $50-74.9 Million
Emp.: 100
Whslr of Seafood & Related Products
N.A.I.C.S.: 424460
David Cordy *(Pres)*

COYNE & BLANCHARD, INC.
110 Constitution Dr, Menlo Park, CA
94025
Tel.: (650) 326-6040   CA
Web Site: https://www.commarts.com
Year Founded: 1986
Sales Range: $10-24.9 Million
Emp.: 20
Periodical Publishers
N.A.I.C.S.: 513120
Eric Coyne *(VP)*
Patrick Coyne *(Pres)*

**COYNE ADVERTISING & PUB-
LIC RELATIONS**
3030 Annandale Dr, Nevillewood, PA
15142
Tel.: (412) 787-3500
Year Founded: 1975
Sales Range: Less than $1 Million
Emp.: 6
Advetising Agency
N.A.I.C.S.: 541810
Jack P. Coyne *(Pres)*
Kathleen Beck *(VP-Client Svcs)*
Corinne Zielinski *(VP & Media Dir)*
K.P. Coyne *(Dir-Pub Rels)*

**COYNE INTERNATIONAL EN-
TERPRISES CORP.**
140 Cortland Ave, Syracuse, NY
13202-3411
Tel.: (315) 475-1626   NY
Web Site:
   http://www.coynetextileservices.com
Year Founded: 1929
Sales Range: $50-74.9 Million
Emp.: 1,800
Provider of Industrial Laundry Ser-
vices
N.A.I.C.S.: 812332
Jennifer Clenoms *(CFO)*
Thomas Coyne *(Chm)*

Subsidiaries:

Blue Ridge Textile Manufacturing,
Inc.   (1)
PO Box 4854, Syracuse, NY 13221-4854
Tel.: (706) 632-6700
Sales Range: $10-24.9 Million
Emp.: 60
Mfr Of Broadwoven Manmade Fabrics
N.A.I.C.S.: 313210

Coyne Textile Service Inc.   (1)
215 Commerce Ct, Duncan, SC 29334
Tel.: (770) 451-6080
Web Site:
   http://www.coynetextileservices.com
Sales Range: $10-24.9 Million
Emp.: 20
Provider of Linen Uniforms Towels & Other
Supplies
N.A.I.C.S.: 812332
Sean Dotson *(Gen Mgr)*

COYNE OIL CORPORATION
914 W Pickard Rd, Mount Pleasant,
MI 48858-0009
Tel.: (989) 772-2270
Web Site: https://www.coyneoil.com

Year Founded: 1976
Sales Range: $10-24.9 Million
Emp.: 50
Petroleum Bulk Station & Terminal
Operating Services
N.A.I.C.S.: 424710
David Coyne *(Owner)*

COYNE PUBLIC RELATIONS
14 Walsh Dr 2nd Fl, Parsippany, NJ
07054
Tel.: (973) 316-1665
Web Site: http://www.coynepr.com
Sales Range: $1-9.9 Million
Emp.: 78
Public Relations Agency
N.A.I.C.S.: 541820
Rich Lukis *(Co-Pres)*
John Gogarty *(Co-Pres)*
Kevin Lamb *(Sr VP)*
Joe Gargiulo *(Exec VP)*
Tim Schramm *(Exec VP)*
Deborah Kelco Sierchio *(Sr VP)*
Brian Murphy *(VP)*
David Cooper *(VP)*
Rob Schnapp *(Exec Dir-Creative)*
Luis Hernandez *(Chief Digital Officer
& Sr VP)*
Ann Smith *(VP)*
Geoff Phelps *(VP)*
Jennifer Denick *(VP)*
Jennifer Kamienski *(Exec VP)*
Kate McShane *(VP)*
Lauren Mackiel Gory *(VP)*
Linda Bernstein Jasper *(VP)*
Michael Salzillo *(VP)*
Reggie Dance *(VP)*
Kelly Dencker *(Exec VP)*
Lisa Wolleon *(Exec VP)*
Christopher Brienza *(Sr VP)*
Beth Kimmerling *(VP)*
Chris Vancheri *(VP)*
Norman Booth *(VP)*
Stacy Bataille *(VP)*
Susan Murphy *(VP)*

**COYOTE GRAVEL PRODUCTS,
INC.**
2124 Coors Blvd SW, Albuquerque,
NM 87121
Tel.: (505) 225-1099
Web Site:
   http://www.coyotegravelproduct.com
Year Founded: 1991
Sales Range: $10-24.9 Million
Emp.: 77
Readymix Concrete Mfr
N.A.I.C.S.: 327320
Anthony Villegas *(Pres)*

COZEN O'CONNOR
1 Liberty Pl 1650 Market St Ste 2800,
Philadelphia, PA 19103
Tel.: (215) 665-2000   PA
Web Site: http://www.cozen.com
Year Founded: 1970
Emp.: 700
Law firm
N.A.I.C.S.: 541110
Vincent R. McGuinness *(Pres & Mng
Partner)*
Elliott R. Feldman *(Chm-Litigation
Section)*
Lisa Calvo Haas *(CMO)*
David W. Ellman *(COO)*
Mark L. Alderman *(Chm-Pub Strate-
gies)*
Patrick J. O'Connor *(Vice Chm)*
Erin Bushnell *(Chief HR Officer)*
Lori C. Rosenberg *(Chm-Partner Re-
cruitment & Integration)*
Mindy J. Herczfeld *(Chief Legal Tal-
ent Officer)*
Melinda deLisle *(Dir-Pro Bono En-
gagement)*
Neeraj Aggarwal *(CFO)*

Michael J. Heller *(CEO)*
Joseph Tilson *(Mng Partner-Chicago)*
Tia Ghattas *(Mng Partner-Chicago)*
Scott Bettridge *(Chm-Immigration
Practice)*
Brad W. Breslau *(Chm-Subrogation &
Recovery-Rocky Mountain)*
John T. Carroll *(Chm-Bankruptcy, In-
solvency & Restructuring)*
Natalie Cooksammy *(Chm-
Subrogation & Recovery)*
Raj K. Datt *(Chm-Subrogation & Re-
covery)*
Steven J. Dickinson *(Chm-Intl Prac-
tice)*
J. C. Ditzler *(Chm-London Market)*
Jeffrey D. Feldman *(Chm-Intellectual
Property Litigation)*
Robert I. Friedman *(Chm-Private Cli-
ent Svcs)*
James A. Gale *(Chm-Intellectual
Property Litigation)*
Brian Gillam *(CIO)*
Eugene A. Giotto *(Chm-Long Term
Care Practice)*
Thomas S. Giotto *(Chm-Labor & Em-
ployment)*
Joshua Ross Goodman *(Chm-
Subrogation & Recovery)*
Josh M. Greenbaum *(Chm-Gen Liti-
gation Practice Grp)*
Stephen M. Halbeisen *(Chm-
Subrogation & Recovery)*
Kenneth M. Hildebrandt *(Chief Ana-
lytics Officer)*
Howard D. Maycon *(Chm-
Subrogation & Recovery)*
Suzanne S. Mayes *(Chm-Pub & Proj-
ect Fin)*
Anthony J. Morrone *(Chm-
Subrogation & Recovery)*
James R. Potts *(Chm-Insurance Corp
& Regulatory)*
R. Christopher Raphaely *(Chm-
Health Care)*
Angelo G. Savino *(Chm-Pro Liability
Practice Grp)*
Richard J. Silpe *(Chm-Tax)*
James I. Tarman *(Chm-Intl Practice)*
Susan Eisenberg *(Mng Partner-
Miami)*
Lynnette Espy-Williams *(Chief Diver-
sity Officer-Washington)*
Alexandra Campau *(Principal/Dir-
Health Policy-Washington)*
Jeremy Glenn *(Mng Partner-Chicago)*
Matthew T. Glavin *(Principal-Pub
Strategies Grp-Chicago)*
Katheryn A. Gettman *(Atty-
Minneapolis)*
Michael J. Heller *(Executives)*

COZUMEL CORPORATION
24351 Pasto Rd Ste B, Dana Point,
CA 92629
Tel.: (949) 489-2400   DE
Year Founded: 1994
Yacht Purchasing, Refitting & Resell-
ing
N.A.I.C.S.: 441222
Jehu Hand *(Pres, CFO & Sec)*

COZZOLI MACHINE COMPANY
50 Schoolhouse Rd, Somerset, NJ
08873-1289
Tel.: (732) 564-0400
Web Site: https://www.cozzoli.com
Sales Range: $50-74.9 Million
Emp.: 60
Packaging Machinery
N.A.I.C.S.: 333993
Joan Cozzoli Rooney *(Pres)*

CP FRANCHISING, LLC.

3300 N University Dr Ste 1, Coral
Springs, FL 33065
Tel.: (954) 344-8060
Web Site:
   http://www.cruiseplanners.com
Year Founded: 1994
Sales Range: $25-49.9 Million
Emp.: 52
Travel Tour Operator
N.A.I.C.S.: 561520
Michelle Fee *(CEO & Founder)*
Scott Koepf *(VP-Strategic Develop-
ment)*

CP OF BOZEMAN, INC.
32 Baldeagle Dr, Madison, MT
59740-0207
Tel.: (406) 682-7989
Web Site:
   http://www.maintenancepatrol.com
Sales Range: $10-24.9 Million
Emp.: 165
New Multifamily Housing Construction
Services
N.A.I.C.S.: 236116
Raul Luciani *(Owner & Pres)*

CP SHADES INC.
403 Coloma Str, Sausalito, CA 94965
Tel.: (415) 331-4581   CA
Web Site: http://www.cpshades.com
Year Founded: 1973
Sales Range: $25-49.9 Million
Emp.: 330
Womens & Misses Outerwear
N.A.I.C.S.: 315250
David Weinstein *(Pres)*

CP SOFTWARE GROUP, INC.
716 Figueroa St, Folsom, CA 95630-
2514
Tel.: (916) 985-4445   CA
Web Site:
   https://www.cpsoftwaregroup.com
Year Founded: 1992
Rev.: $30,000,000
Emp.: 147
Custom Computer Programming Ser-
vices
N.A.I.C.S.: 541511
David M. Saykally *(CEO)*

Subsidiaries:

Island Software, Inc.   (1)
716 Figueroa St, Folsom, CA 95630-2514
Tel.: (916) 454-3742
Web Site: http://www.islandsoft.com
Sales Range: $10-24.9 Million
Emp.: 12
Prepackaged Software
N.A.I.C.S.: 513210

Uniplex Software, Inc.   (1)
715 Sutter St, Folsom, CA 95630-2546
Tel.: (916) 985-4445
Web Site: http://www.uniplex.com
Rev.: $11,900,000
Emp.: 150
Office Automation, Groupware & Messaging
Distr
N.A.I.C.S.: 423430

CP WARD INC.
100 W River Rd, Scottsville, NY
14546
Tel.: (585) 889-8800
Web Site: https://www.cpward.com
Sales Range: $10-24.9 Million
Emp.: 122
General Contractor; Heavy Highway;
Utilities; Sitework Construction
N.A.I.C.S.: 237310
Richard Ash *(Pres)*
Ken Stewart *(VP)*

CPA SITE SOLUTIONS
130 W Canal St, Winooski, VT 05404
Web Site:
   http://www.cpasitesolutions.com

CPA Site Solutions—(Continued)
Year Founded: 1999
Sales Range: $1-9.9 Million
Emp.: 25
Complete Web Suite, Secure Client Portal, Email Marketing Systems & Email Solutions for Small Accounting Firms
N.A.I.C.S.: 541219
Brian O'Connell (Founder)
Kathy O'Connell (CFO)

CPALEAD, LLC
6845 S Escondido St Ste 107, Las Vegas, NV 89119
Tel.: (702) 489-4786
Web Site: http://www.cpalead.com
Year Founded: 2006
Sales Range: $25-49.9 Million
Emp.: 22
Marketing Consulting Services
N.A.I.C.S.: 541613
Robert Reynolds (CEO)

CPAMERICA, INC.
11801 Research Dr, Alachua, FL 32615
Tel.: (386) 418-4001
Web Site: http://www.cpamerica.org
Year Founded: 1978
Sales Range: $1-9.9 Million
Emp.: 28
Professional Organizations
N.A.I.C.S.: 813920
Joyce Arthur (Mgr-Svcs)
Lisa Browne (Mgr-Events)
Grace Horvath (VP-Svcs)
Art Winstead (Dir-A&A)

Subsidiaries:

Meepos & Co.   (1)
409 Washington Blvd, Marina Del Rey, CA 90292-5213
Tel.: (310) 827-2525
Web Site: http://www.meeposcpa.com
Other Accounting Services
N.A.I.C.S.: 541219
Bob Meepos (Owner)

CPC LOGISTICS INC.
14528 S Outer Forty Rd Ste 210, Chesterfield, MO 63017
Tel.: (314) 542-2266   MO
Web Site: http://www.callcpc.com
Year Founded: 1973
Sales Range: $150-199.9 Million
Emp.: 4,000
Provider of Transportation Services
N.A.I.C.S.: 561320
John T. Bickel (Pres)
Robert J. Boyich (Exec VP-Ops)
Bill Steimel (VP-IT)

CPCM, LLC
1910 Fairview Ave E Ste 200, Seattle, WA 98102
Tel.: (206) 728-9063   WA
Web Site:
http://www.columbiapacificwm.com
Year Founded: 1989
Investment & Wealth management Services
N.A.I.C.S.: 523940
Alex Washburn (Co-Founder & Mng Partner)
Brian Orton (Mng Partner & Mgr-Relationships)
Tyler Gaspard (Mng Partner & Mgr-Relationships)
Jeremy Kiefer (Co-Founder, Mng Partner & Co-Chief Investment Officer)
Joseph Strecker (Mng Partner & Mgr-Relationships)
Taylor Koivu (Mng Partner & Mgr-Relationships)

Peder Schmitz (Co-Founder, Mng Partner & Mgr-Relationships)
Alan Spragins (Mng Partner & COO)
Rod Bench (Mng Partner & Mgr-Relationships)
Keith Capasso (Mng Partner & Mgr-Relationships)
Derek Crump (Mng Partner & Co-Chief Investment Officer)
Kory Lackey (Sr Portfolio Mgr)
Matthew Kane (Mng Partner & Mgr-Relationships)
Vera Minar (Chief Investment Officer)

Subsidiaries:

Kibble & Prentice Holding Company   (1)
Two Union Sq 601 Union St Ste 1000, Seattle, WA 98101
Tel.: (206) 441-6300
Web Site: http://www.kpcom.com
Insurance, Risk Management, Employee Benefit, Retirement Plan & Business Continuation Planning Services
N.A.I.C.S.: 524126
Arnie Prentice (Chm)
Chris Prentice (CEO)
Dave Ross (Pres & COO)
William Whitaker (Sr VP-Private Client Svcs)
Joe Strecker (Sr VP)
Marty Andrews (Exec VP-Employee Benefits)
Angie Tonnon (VP-Comml Insurance)
Todd McMahon (Chief Compliance Officer)

CPF DENTAL, LLC
2505 21st Ave S Ste 204, Nashville, TN 37212
Tel.: (615) 620-5990   DE
Web Site:
http://www.marqueedental.com
Dental Professional Organization Investment & Support Services
N.A.I.C.S.: 561110
Jim Usdan (CEO)
Fred Ward (COO)
Matt Earnest (Chief Acctg Officer & VP-Fin Ops)
Nathan Cox (Chief Dev Officer & VP-Bus Dev)

Subsidiaries:

Embassy Dental Professionals, P.C.   (1)
2505 21st Ave S Ste 204, Nashville, TN 37212
Tel.: (615) 620-5990
Web Site: http://www.embassydental.com
Emp.: 75
Dental Professional Organization
N.A.I.C.S.: 813920
Warren Melamed (Founder)

Save-On Dental Care   (1)
1518 N Brindlee Mtn Pkwy, Arab, AL 35016
Tel.: (256) 586-3117
Web Site: http://www.save-ondentalcare.com
Emp.: 7
Offices of Dentists
N.A.I.C.S.: 621210
John Denton (Co-founder)

Signature Smile   (1)
2247 Helton Dr, Florence, AL 35630
Tel.: (256) 767-6453
Web Site:
http://www.signaturesmileflorence.com
Offices of Dentists
N.A.I.C.S.: 621210
Sadricia Wilson (Office Mgr)

CPG SALES & MARKETING INC.
1454 Rte 22 Ste A202, Brewster, NY 10509
Tel.: (845) 278-2677   NY
Year Founded: 1987
Sales Range: $125-149.9 Million
Emp.: 2

General Line Groceries Whslr
N.A.I.C.S.: 424410

CPH HOLDING, LLC
4100 MacArthur Blvd Ste 300, Newport Beach, CA 92660-2064
Tel.: (949) 622-8400
Web Site:
http://www.capitalpacifichomes.com
Residential Real Estate Developer
N.A.I.C.S.: 236115

CPI COOPERATIVE
Hwy 6 & 34, Funk, NE 68940
Tel.: (308) 263-2441   DE
Web Site: http://www.cpicoop.com
Year Founded: 1942
Sales Range: $25-49.9 Million
Emp.: 580
Farm Supplies
N.A.I.C.S.: 424510

CPI WIRECLOTH & SCREENS, INC.
2425 Roy Rd, Pearland, TX 77581
Tel.: (281) 485-2300   TX
Web Site:
https://www.cpiwirecloth.com
Year Founded: 1968
Sales Range: $10-24.9 Million
Emp.: 55
Wire Screening Products Mfr
N.A.I.C.S.: 423510
Glen T. Lillie (Pres)
Steve Votny (VP-Sls)
Jay Jenkins (VP-Mktg)

Subsidiaries:

CPI-Louisiana Inc.   (1)
221 Burgess Dr, Broussard, LA 70518
Tel.: (337) 837-2931
Web Site: http://www.cpiwirecloth.com
Sales Range: $10-24.9 Million
Emp.: 6
Miscellaneous Fabricated Wire Products
N.A.I.C.S.: 332618
Bobby Comeaux (Gen Mgr)

CPI-THE ALTERNATIVE SUPPLIER
5580 Skylane Blvd, Santa Rosa, CA 95403
Tel.: (707) 525-5788
Web Site: http://www.colitag.com
Year Founded: 1996
Sales Range: $10-24.9 Million
Emp.: 50
Analytical Instruments
N.A.I.C.S.: 423490
David Hejl (Pres & CEO)
Brad Droubay (Mgr-Sls)
Robin Huff (Controller)
Yu Hou (Mgr-Laboratory)
Jarrett Wendt (Pres)

CPL ARCHITECTS, ENGINEERS & LANDSCAPE ARCHITECT D.P.C.
30 Century Hill Dr Ste 104, Latham, NY 12110
Tel.: (518) 463-4107
Web Site: https://cplteam.com
Architectural Planning & Services
N.A.I.C.S.: 541310

Subsidiaries:

Makovich & Pusti Architects Inc.   (1)
111 Frnt St, Berea, OH 44017-1912
Tel.: (440) 891-8910
Web Site: http://www.mparc.com
Architectural Services
N.A.I.C.S.: 541310
Sherri Varner (Project Mgr)

CPM EDUCATIONAL PROGRAM

9498 Little Rapids Way, Elk Grove, CA 95758
Tel.: (209) 745-2055   CA
Web Site: https://www.cpm.org
Year Founded: 1993
Sales Range: $10-24.9 Million
Emp.: 154
Educational Support Services
N.A.I.C.S.: 611710
Christine Mikles (Dir-Teacher Education)

CPM INDUSTRIES INC.
210 Wilson Bldg 3511 Silverside Rd, Wilmington, DE 19810
Tel.: (302) 478-8200
Web Site:
https://www.cpmindustries.com
Sales Range: $10-24.9 Million
Emp.: 7
Industrial Chemicals
N.A.I.C.S.: 424690
Leonard L. Yowell (Pres)

CPMEDIA & MARKETING SERVICES, INC.
6479 Reflections Dr Ste 150, Dublin, OH 43017
Tel.: (614) 717-4910   OH
Web Site: http://www.cpmedia.com
Year Founded: 1993
Sales Range: $10-24.9 Million
Emp.: 5
Media Buying Services
N.A.I.C.S.: 541810
Betty J. Clark (Mng Partner)

CPR TOOLS, INC.
905 Industrial Blvd, Labelle, FL 33935
Tel.: (863) 674-0120
Web Site: http://www.cprtools.net
Sales Range: $1-9.9 Million
Emp.: 30
Data Security Products
N.A.I.C.S.: 513210
John Benkert (CEO)
Patrick Morrow (Engr-Computer)
Robert Higginbotham (Engr-Computer)

CPS CARDS
7520 Morris Ct Ste 100, Allentown, PA 18106
Tel.: (610) 231-1860
Web Site: https://www.cpscards.com
Year Founded: 1998
Sales Range: $10-24.9 Million
Emp.: 100
Plastics Product Mfr
N.A.I.C.S.: 326199
Jim Cooney (VP & Gen Mgr)
Ethan Stehman (Gen Mgr)
Lisa Burkart (Acct Mgr)
Denise Clark (Acct Mgr)

CPS DISTRIBUTORS INC.
6024 Parretta Dr, Kansas City, MO 64120
Tel.: (816) 241-2552
Web Site:
https://www.cpsdistributorsinc.com
Rev.: $11,456,547
Emp.: 15
Installers & Distributors of Radios, Motor Vehicle
N.A.I.C.S.: 423620
Sara Shandy (VP)

CPS DISTRIBUTORS, INC.
1105 W 122nd Ave, Westminster, CO 80234-3419
Tel.: (303) 394-6040   NY
Web Site:
https://www.cpsdistributors.com
Sales Range: $1-9.9 Million

Emp.: 35
Irrigation Equipment Mfr & Distr
N.A.I.C.S.: 221310
Lowell Kaufhold (Pres & CEO)

CPS ENERGY
145 Navarro St, San Antonio, TX 78205
Tel.: (210) 353-2000
Web Site: http://www.cpsenergy.com
Sales Range: $1-4.9 Billion
Emp.: 4,000
Electric & Natural Gas Utility
N.A.I.C.S.: 221118
Carolyn E. Shellman (Gen Counsel & Exec VP)
Jonathan Tijerina (Sr Dir-Corp Comm, Mktg & Smart Cities Outreach)
Frank Almaraz (Chief Power, Sustainability & Bus Dev Officer)
Rudy D. Garza (Pres & CEO)
Willis Mackey (Chm)
Janie Gonzalez (Vice Chm)

CPS PROFESSIONAL SERVICES
8260 Willow Oaks Corporate Dr Ste 350, Fairfax, VA 22031
Tel.: (571) 282-4024
Web Site: http://www.cps-ps.com
Year Founded: 2006
Sales Range: $10-24.9 Million
Emp.: 40
Management Consulting Services & Support to Various Government Agencies
N.A.I.C.S.: 541618
Phil Panzarella (CEO)
Tom Arnsmeyer (COO)
Jennifer Jackson (Project Mgr)

CPS TECHNOLOGY SOLUTIONS INC.
3949 County Rd 116, Hamel, MN 55340
Tel.: (763) 553-1514
Web Site: https://www.cpsts.com
Year Founded: 1983
Rev.: $10,995,412
Emp.: 18
Mid-Range Integrator
N.A.I.C.S.: 449210
Darren Anderson (Pres)

CPT NETWORK SOLUTIONS
1062 Thorndale Ave, Bensenville, IL 60106
Tel.: (630) 735-7000
Web Site:
    http://www.cptnetworks.com
Year Founded: 2006
Sales Range: $10-24.9 Million
Emp.: 54
Information Technology Consulting Services
N.A.I.C.S.: 541512
Chris Cary (VP-Sales)

CPT SC TITLE HOLDING CORPORATION
533 S Fremont Ave, Los Angeles, CA 90071
Year Founded: 1997
Sales Range: $10-24.9 Million
Title Holding Company
N.A.I.C.S.: 541191

CPWR-THE CENTER FOR CONSTRUCTION RESEARCH AND TRAINING
8484 Georgia Ave Ste 1000, Silver Spring, MD 20910
Tel.: (301) 578-8500
Web Site: https://www.cpwr.com
Year Founded: 1979
Sales Range: $10-24.9 Million

Emp.: 40
Construction Worker Safety & Welfare Services
N.A.I.C.S.: 813930
Linda Goldenhar (Dir-Evaluation & Res)
Eileen Betit (Dir-Res to Practice-Safety & Health Res Dept)
Bruce Lippy (Dir-Safety Res)
Mary Watters (Dir-Comm)

CPX INC.
1400 East Buckeye St, North Vernon, IN 47265
Tel.: (812) 346-8567
Web Site: http://www.cpxinc.com
Year Founded: 1983
Sales Range: $10-24.9 Million
Emp.: 350
Plastics Product Mfr
N.A.I.C.S.: 326199
Michael Sanders (Pres)

CQENS TECHNOLOGIES INC.
5550 Nicollet Ave, Minneapolis, MN 55419
Tel.: (612) 812-2037   DE
Web Site: https://www.cqens.com
Year Founded: 2009
Assets: $2,282,630
Liabilities: $1,336,664
Net Worth: $945,966
Earnings: ($4,303,550)
Emp.: 3
Fiscal Year-end: 12/31/23
E-Cigarettes & Wellness Products Mfr
N.A.I.C.S.: 312230
Alexander Chong (Co-Founder, Chm & CEO)
William P. Bartkowski (Co-Founder, Pres & COO)
Daniel Markes (CFO, Chief Acctg Officer & VP)
Roger Nielsen (Sec & VP)

CQG, INC.
Independence Plz 1050 17th St Ste 2000, Denver, CO 80265
Tel.: (303) 573-1400
Web Site: http://www.cqg.com
Year Founded: 1979
Sales Range: $25-49.9 Million
Emp.: 180
Real-Time Stock Quotes Service
N.A.I.C.S.: 517810
Rod Giffen (Chief Experience Officer)
Tim Mather (Founder & Owner)
Lori Fairbanks (Mgr)
John Arvanites (CTO)
Mike Glista (Sr VP)
Ryan Moroney (CEO)
Steven Luebbering (CFO)
Benjamin Soong (Pres-Asia Pasific)
Rick Chang (Head-Greater Chiina)

CQUEST
500 S 9th St, Springfield, IL 62701
Tel.: (217) 541-7460   IL
Web Site: https://www.cquest.us
Year Founded: 1999
Sales Range: $10-24.9 Million
Emp.: 67
Technology Consulting Services
N.A.I.C.S.: 541618
Adam Bruns (CFO)
Kevin Davis (Pres & CEO)
Diane Decker (VP-Business Development)
William Roth (Sr Dir-System Dev)

CR DYNAMICS & ASSOCIATES
7 E Redwood St 6th Fl, Baltimore, MD 21202
Tel.: (410) 347-5600

Web Site:
    http://www.crdynamics.com
Year Founded: 1994
Rev.: $3,100,000
Emp.: 50
Telemarketing Bureaus
N.A.I.C.S.: 561422
Charles Ramos (Pres & CEO)

CR METAL PRODUCTS INC.
10655 Gateway Blvd, Saint Louis, MO 63132
Tel.: (314) 994-9550
Web Site: https://www.crmetal.com
Sales Range: $200-249.9 Million
Emp.: 100
Sheet Metal Specialties
N.A.I.C.S.: 332322
Steve Walters (Pres)
Mark Chadwick (VP)

CRA
8901 E Pima Center Pkwy Ste 230, Scottsdale, AZ 85258
Tel.: (480) 889-9900
Web Site: http://www.craltd.com
Sales Range: $125-149.9 Million
Emp.: 8
Administrative Management & General Management Consulting Services
N.A.I.C.S.: 541611
Michael Martindale (Principal)

CRABTREE BUICK GMC, INC.
2311 Lee Hwy, Bristol, VA 24202
Tel.: (276) 669-3141
Web Site:
    http://www.crabtreegmc.com
Year Founded: 1962
Sales Range: $10-24.9 Million
Emp.: 44
New Car Dealers
N.A.I.C.S.: 441110
Keith Crabtree (Gen Mgr)

CRACKEN, HARKEY & CO., LLC
12200 North Stemmons Freeway Ste 100, Dallas, TX 75234-5877
Tel.: (972) 241-5500   TX
Year Founded: 1967
Sales Range: $125-149.9 Million
Emp.: 80
Investment Firm
N.A.I.C.S.: 551112
John D. Harkey Jr. (Mng Dir)
John R. W. Cracken (Co-Founder & Vice Chm)
E. Gene Street (Partner)

Subsidiaries:

Consolidated Restaurant Operations, Inc.   (1)
12200 N Stemmons Fwy Ste 100, Dallas, TX 75234-5877
Tel.: (972) 241-5500
Web Site: http://www.croinc.com
Sales Range: $25-49.9 Million
Providers of Restaurant Holding Services
N.A.I.C.S.: 722511
John D. Harkey Jr. (Chm & CEO)
Mark Lann (Pres)
Wendy Hackemack (Controller)
JoseLuis Magana (Pres-Concept)
Kerry Kreitzer (Project Dir-Design)

Subsidiary (Domestic):

El Chico Restaurants, Inc.   (2)
13937 N Central Expy, Dallas, TX 75243
Tel.: (972) 238-0011
Web Site: http://www.elchico.com
Full-Service Mexican Restaurants Operator & Franchiser
N.A.I.C.S.: 482111

Good Eats Holding Company Inc.   (2)
3888 Oak Lawn #101, Dallas, TX 75219

Tel.: (214) 522-3287
Web Site: http://www.goodeatsgrill.com
Rev.: $17,000,000
Emp.: 100
Holding Company; Eating Places
N.A.I.C.S.: 551112

Spaghetti Warehouse, Inc.   (2)
5525 N Macarthur Blvd Ste 665, Irving, TX 75038-2624
Tel.: (972) 536-1901
Web Site: http://www.meatballs.com
Sales Range: $50-74.9 Million
Family Style Italian Restaurants Operator & Franchiser
N.A.I.C.S.: 722511

Holding (Non-US):

Old Spaghetti Factory (Canada) Ltd.   (3)
53 Water Street, Vancouver, V6B 1A1, BC, Canada   (100%)
Tel.: (604) 684-1287
Web Site: http://www.oldspaghettifactory.ca
Sales Range: $25-49.9 Million
Emp.: 120
Restaurant
N.A.I.C.S.: 722511

CRADDOCK OIL CO. INC.
1 Berthadale Rd, McComb, MS 39648
Tel.: (601) 684-5641
Web Site:
    http://www.craddockoil.com
Rev.: $25,431,580
Emp.: 15
Diesel Fuel
N.A.I.C.S.: 424720
Ronald D. Craddock (Pres)

CRADLE SOLUTION INC.
10101 SW Fwy Ste 315, Houston, TX 77074
Tel.: (713) 776-8510
Web Site:
    http://www.cradlesolution.com
Year Founded: 2004
Sales Range: $1-9.9 Million
Emp.: 20
Software Developer
N.A.I.C.S.: 513210
Michael Hoskins (CTO)

CRAFT EQUIPMENT COMPANY
1820 Massaro Blvd Ste 100, Tampa, FL 33619
Tel.: (813) 621-4971
Web Site: http://www.craftequip.com
Year Founded: 1986
Sales Range: $10-24.9 Million
Emp.: 100
Industrial Machinery & Equipment Merchant Whslr
N.A.I.C.S.: 423830
Donald Mays (Pres)
Buddy Chadwell (VP-Sls)
Mike Davis (CFO & VP)

CRAFT MACHINE WORKS INC.
2102 48th St, Hampton, VA 23661
Tel.: (757) 380-8615
Web Site:
    https://www.craftmachine.com
Year Founded: 1970
Sales Range: $25-49.9 Million
Emp.: 100
Custom Machinery
N.A.I.C.S.: 333998
Mike Cobb (Exec VP)

CRAFT MARKETING
112 W 20th St 7th Fl, New York, NY 10011
Tel.: (212) 994-6695
Sales Range: $100-124.9 Million
Emp.: 10

Craft Marketing—(Continued)

Advertising Agencies
N.A.I.C.S.: 541810
Paula Keriazes (Acct Exec)

CRAFT3
203 Howerton Way SE, Ilwaco, WA
98624
Tel.: (360) 642-4265   WA
Web Site: http://www.craft3.org
Year Founded: 1994
Sales Range: $10-24.9 Million
Financial Services
N.A.I.C.S.: 522320
Roni Monteith (Chief Credit Officer)
Adam Zimmerman (Pres & CEO)
Mark Stevenson (CFO)

CRAFTCORPS INC.
3401 Manor Rd, Austin, TX 78723
Tel.: (512) 476-8886
Web Site: https://www.craftcorps.com
Year Founded: 1984
Sales Range: $25-49.9 Million
Emp.: 200
Provider of Renovation, Remodeling
& Repair Services
N.A.I.C.S.: 236220
Sam Griswold (Pres & CEO)
Jerry Perkins (Controller)

CRAFTEX MILLS INC. OF PENNSYLVANIA
450 Sentry Pkwy E, Blue Bell, PA
19422-2319
Tel.: (610) 941-1212   PA
Web Site: http://www.craftex.com
Year Founded: 1903
Sales Range: $100-124.9 Million
Emp.: 255
Mfr of Upholstery Materials & Fabrics
N.A.I.C.S.: 313210
Robert M. Blum (Pres)
Robert Proske (CFO & Sr VP)
Carol Proske (Controller)
Terri Blum (VP-Design)

CRAFTMADE INTERNA-TIONAL, INC.
650 S Royal Ln Ste 100, Coppell, TX
75019-1037
Tel.: (972) 393-3800   DE
Web Site: http://www.craftmade.com
Year Founded: 1985
Sales Range: $125-149.9 Million
Ceiling Fans, Light Kits & Accesso-
ries Designer & Distr
N.A.I.C.S.: 335132
Brad D. Heimann (Pres & COO)

Subsidiaries:

Design Trends, LLC   (1)
650 S Royal Ln Ste 100, Coppell, TX
75019-3836   (50%)
Tel.: (972) 393-3800
Web Site: http://www.craftmade.com
Sales Range: $50-74.9 Million
Emp.: 75
Provider of Marketing Services for Indoor
Lighting
N.A.I.C.S.: 423610
Brad Heimann (Pres)

Durocraft Design Manufacturing
Inc.   (1)
650 S Royal Ln Ste 100, Coppell, TX
75019-3836
Tel.: (972) 393-3800
Sales Range: $25-49.9 Million
Emp.: 110
Assembler of Lamps & Wholesaler of Pe-
ripheral Wire & Cable
N.A.I.C.S.: 811412

Prime/Home Impressions, LLC   (1)
650 S Royal Ln Ste 100, Coppell, TX
75019-3836   (50%)
Tel.: (972) 393-3800
Web Site: http://www.primehome.com

Provider of Marketing Services for Various
Fan Accessories
N.A.I.C.S.: 423610
Brad Hemainn (CEO)

Trade Source International, Inc.   (1)
650 S Royal Ln Ste 100, Coppell, TX
75019-3710
Tel.: (972) 393-3800
Web Site: http://www.tsiprime.com
Sales Range: $50-74.9 Million
Emp.: 100
Design, Distribution & Marketing Services of
Outdoor Lighting Fixtures to Major Retail
Home Improvement Chains
N.A.I.C.S.: 423610
Brad Heimann (COO & CEO)

Woodard, LLC   (1)
650 South Royal Ln, Coppell, TX 75019
Tel.: (972) 393-3800
Web Site: http://www.woodard-furniture.com
Emp.: 125
Handcrafted Wrought Iron, Aluminum &
Steel Furniture
N.A.I.C.S.: 423210
Brad Heimann (VP)

CRAFTMARK HOMES INC.
1355 Beverly Rd Ste 330, McLean,
VA 22101
Tel.: (703) 734-9855
Web Site:
      http://www.craftmarkhomes.com
Rev.: $24,343,155
Emp.: 30
New Construction, Single-Family
Houses
N.A.I.C.S.: 236115
Ken Malm (Pres)
John Pavlik (Project Mgr)
Matt Pollock (Project Mgr)
Sarah Wetzel (Coord-Ops)
Barbara Stoehr (Mgr-Sls)
Chris Schwindt (Mgr-Contracts)
Dan Crowley (Mgr-IT)
David Pastva (VP-Sls & Mktg)

CRAFTMASTER FURNITURE CORP.
221 Craftmaster Rd, Hiddenite, NC
28636-9309
Tel.: (828) 632-9786   NC
Web Site: http://www.cmfurniture.com
Year Founded: 1972
Sales Range: $25-49.9 Million
Emp.: 500
Mfr & Sales of Upholstered House-
hold Furniture
N.A.I.C.S.: 337121
Todd Smithey (Asst Dir-Supply Chain)
Judy Shook (Mgr-Customer Svc)
Ken Babcock (Mgr-Shipping)
Suzanne Henson (Dir-Mdsg & Mktg)
Roy Calcagne (Pres & CEO)

CRAFTMATIC INDUSTRIES, INC.
2500 Interplex Dr, Trevose, PA
19053-6943
Tel.: (215) 639-1310   DE
Web Site: http://www.craftmatic.com
Sales Range: $125-149.9 Million
Emp.: 250
Adjustable Beds Mfr
N.A.I.C.S.: 449110
Stanley A. Kraftsow (Chm & Pres)

Subsidiaries:

Craftmatic Organization, Inc.   (1)
2500 Interplex Dr, Trevose, PA
19053-6943   (100%)
Tel.: (215) 639-1310
Web Site: http://www.craftmaticbed.com
Sales Range: $25-49.9 Million
Emp.: 150
Retail Beds
N.A.I.C.S.: 423210

CRAFTS INC.

3403 Menasha Ave, Manitowoc, WI
54220
Tel.: (920) 682-7707
Web Site:
      http://www.craftsroofing.com
Rev.: $10,000,000
Emp.: 60
Roofing Contractors
N.A.I.C.S.: 238160
Robert S. Weinert (Chm)
Steve Weinert (Pres)
Michael Schutz (VP-Ops & Mgr)
Tom Owens (VP)

CRAFTSMAN CAPITAL PART-NERS, LLC
8117 Preston Rd Ste 300, Dallas, TX
75225
Tel.: (214) 402-0022   TX
Web Site:
      http://www.craftsmancapital.com
Privater Equity Firm
N.A.I.C.S.: 523999
Barrett Dean (Co-Founder & Partner)
Paul Thompson (Co-Founder & Oper-
ating Partner)
Will Walters (Co-Founder & Partner)

Subsidiaries:

BOXX Technologies, LLC   (1)
4616 W Howard Ln, Ste 105, Austin, TX
78728
Tel.: (512) 835-0400
Web Site: http://www.boxx.com
Workstations & Rendering Systems Mfr &
Whslr
N.A.I.C.S.: 334118
Rick Krause (Pres & CEO)
Tim Lawrence (Founder & VP-Engrg &
Ops)
Bill Leasure (VP-Mktg & Sls)

Subsidiary (Domestic):

Cirrascale Corporation   (2)
5775 Kearny Villa Rd, San Diego, CA
92123
Tel.: (858) 874-3800
Web Site: http://www.cirrascale.com
Cloud Infrastructure Developer
N.A.I.C.S.: 541512
David Driggers (CEO)
Mike LaPan (VP-Mktg-Cirrascale Cloud
Svcs)

Pacific Alliance Capital, Inc.   (2)
27141 Aliso Creek Rd Ste 225, Aliso Viejo,
CA 92656
Tel.: (949) 360-1796
Web Site: http://www.pacdata.com
Computer & Computer Peripheral Equip-
ment & Software Merchant Whslr
N.A.I.C.S.: 423430

CRAFTSMEN INDUSTRIES, INC.
3101 Elm Point Industrial Dr, Saint
Charles, MO 63301
Tel.: (636) 940-8400
Web Site:
      https://www.craftsmenind.com
Year Founded: 1982
Sales Range: $10-24.9 Million
Emp.: 140
Advertising Related Services
N.A.I.C.S.: 541890
Tim Matejka (Engr-Design)
Mark Berte (Mgr-Engrg)
Dave Winkler (Project Mgr)
Joe Helmsing (Chm)
Laura Kress (Project Mgr-Graphics)
Mike Henthorn (Dir-Estimating)
Deb Dougherty (Mgr-Payroll)
Jaclyn Nikodym (Mgr-Social Media)

CRAFTSY INC.
999 18th St Ste 240, Denver, CO
80202
Tel.: (888) 979-6769
Web Site: http://www.craftsy.com

Sales Range: $25-49.9 Million
Online Education Website Operator
N.A.I.C.S.: 513199
John Levisay (Co-Founder & CEO)
Josh Scott (Co-Founder)
Todd Tobin (Co-Founder & CTO)
Bret Hanna (Co-Founder & VP-
Engrg)
Catherine Balsam-Schwaber (Gen
Mgr)

CRAFTY BEAVER HOME CEN-TERS
4810 Oakton St, Skokie, IL 60077
Tel.: (847) 673-3000   IL
Web Site:
      https://www.craftybeaver.com
Year Founded: 1934
Building & Related Products Retailer
N.A.I.C.S.: 423310
Gary Beres (CEO)

CRAIG & LANDRETH LEAS-ING, INC.
6424 W Hwy 146, Louisville, KY
40014
Tel.: (502) 447-3450
Web Site:
      http://www.craiglandrethcars.com
Sales Range: $10-24.9 Million
Emp.: 50
New Car Dealers
N.A.I.C.S.: 441110
Larry Craig (Co-Owner & Partner)
Joey Craig (Co-Owner & Partner)
Andy Hall (Gen Mgr)
Kevin House (Dir-Fin)

CRAIG ELECTRIC CORPORA-TION
4314 Stadium Blvd, Jonesboro, AR
72404
Tel.: (870) 932-8301
Web Site: http://www.cecc-ark.com
Rev.: $21,900,000
Emp.: 100
Distribution, Electric Power
N.A.I.C.S.: 221122
Bryan Duncan (CEO)

CRAIG FRAMES, INC.
140 Industrial Pkwy, Ithaca, MI 48847
Tel.: (989) 875-8600   MI
Web Site:
      http://www.craigframes.com
Year Founded: 1971
Sales Range: $1-9.9 Million
Emp.: 60
Miscellaneous Mfr
N.A.I.C.S.: 339999
Alan Kommel (Pres)

Subsidiaries:

Frame USA, Inc.   (1)
225 Northland Blvd, Cincinnati, OH 45246
Tel.: (513) 577-7107
Web Site: http://www.frameusa.com
Rev.: $3,333,333
Emp.: 60
All Other Miscellaneous Wood Product Mfr
N.A.I.C.S.: 321999
Dana Bares (Pres)
Dan Regenold (CEO)
Ron Forbus (Mgr-Production)
Ruby Singh (Mgr-HR)

CRAIG HOSPITAL
3425 S Clarkson St, Englewood, CO
80113
Tel.: (303) 789-8000   CO
Web Site:
      https://www.craighospital.org
Year Founded: 1910
Sales Range: $75-99.9 Million
Emp.: 818
Health Care Srvices
N.A.I.C.S.: 622110

Jacque Howard (Controller)
Thomas E. Balazy (Dir-Medical)
Dana Polonsky (VP-Clinical Svcs)
Stacy Abel (VP-People-Culture)
Diane Reinhard (VP)
Jandel Allen-Davis (Pres & CEO)
Daniel Frank (CFO)

CRAIG INDUSTRIES INC.
401 Delaware St, Quincy, IL 62301
Tel.: (217) 641-1492
Web Site:
  https://www.craigindustries.com
Year Founded: 1986
Sales Range: $10-24.9 Million
Emp.: 65
Metal Building & Component Mfr
N.A.I.C.S.: 332311
Lucas K. Craig (Pres)

CRAIG MURRAY PRODUCTIONS LLC
2717 W Olive Ave, Burbank, CA 91505
Tel.: (818) 729-0800
Sales Range: $10-24.9 Million
Emp.: 25
Video Tape Production Services
N.A.I.C.S.: 512110

CRAIG PAVING INC.
118 Hump Rd, Hagerstown, MD 21740
Tel.: (301) 739-9814
Web Site:
  https://www.craigpaving.com
Rev.: $12,528,447
Emp.: 100
Surfacing & Paving
N.A.I.C.S.: 237310
Ollen O. Craig (Founder)
Roger Craig (Pres)
Evelyn Monnett (VP)

CRAIG SCOTT REALITY INC.
706 Autopark Blvd, West Chester, PA 19382
Tel.: (610) 692-6000
Web Site: http://www.scotthonda.com
Year Founded: 1984
Sales Range: $50-74.9 Million
Emp.: 125
Dealer of New & Used Automobiles
N.A.I.C.S.: 441110
Craig Scott (Owner)
Duke Scott (VP)

CRAIG SHEFFIELD & AUSTIN INC.
2314 McAllister Rd, Houston, TX 77092
Tel.: (713) 686-8868
Web Site:
  http://www.csaconstruction.com
Sales Range: $50-74.9 Million
Emp.: 100
Waste Water & Sewage Treatment
Plant Construction
N.A.I.C.S.: 237110
Rich Austin (Chm & Pres)

CRAIG STEIN BEVERAGE
4719 Market St, Boise, ID 83705
Tel.: (208) 378-0550
Web Site:
  http://www.csbeverage.com
Year Founded: 1990
Soft Drinks Mfr
N.A.I.C.S.: 312111
Rob Schneider (CFO)
Craig Stein (CEO)
Dennis Mcauliff (Pres & COO)

Subsidiaries:

Click Wholesale Distributing, Inc. **(1)**

1825 Raymond Ave SW, Renton, WA 98057
Tel.: (206) 763-3200
Grocery & Related Products Merchant Whslr
N.A.I.C.S.: 424490
John Guinasso (Sls Mgr)

CRAIG TAYLOR EQUIPMENT COMPANY
733 Whitney Rd, Anchorage, AK 99501
Tel.: (907) 276-5050   AK
Web Site:
  https://www.craigtaylorequip
  ment.com
Year Founded: 1954
Sales Range: $10-24.9 Million
Emp.: 28
Construction Equipment Dealer & Rental Services
N.A.I.C.S.: 532412
Lonnie G. Parker (Pres)

CRAIG TECHNOLOGIES
7177 N Atlantic Ave, Cape Canaveral, FL 32920
Tel.: (321) 752-0394
Web Site:
  http://www.craigtechinc.com
Year Founded: 1999
Sales Range: $25-49.9 Million
Emp.: 300
Computer System Design Services
N.A.I.C.S.: 541512
Carol Craig (CEO & CFO)
Shaun Deeming (Dir-IT)
Mark Mikolajczyk (Pres)
Dean Rosenquist (COO)
Greg Sheppard (Dir-Bus Dev)

CRAIG TECHNOLOGIES, INC.
103 Davis Dr, Seaford, DE 19973
Tel.: (302) 628-9900
Web Site:
  https://www.craigtechnologies.com
All Other Plastics Product Mfr
N.A.I.C.S.: 326199
Don Hollenbeck (Pres)

Subsidiaries:

Manufacturing Support Industries, Inc.   **(1)**
2414 Northgate Dr Ste 2, Salisbury, MD 21801
Tel.: (410) 334-6140
Web Site: http://www.mfg-support.com
All Other Miscellaneous Fabricated Metal Product Mfr
N.A.I.C.S.: 332999
Kirk Franks (Mgr-Plng)

CRAIG TRANSPORTATION CO.
26699 Eckel Rd, Perrysburg, OH 43551
Tel.: (419) 872-3333
Web Site:
  http://www.craigtransport.com
Sales Range: $10-24.9 Million
Emp.: 35
Trucking Except Local
N.A.I.C.S.: 484121
Lance C. Craig (Pres & CEO)

CRAIGMICHAELS, INC.
75 Broad St 26th Fl, New York, NY 10004
Tel.: (212) 232-8700   NY
Web Site:
  http://www.craigmichaelsinc.com
Year Founded: 2002
Sales Range: $1-9.9 Million
Emp.: 25
Develops & Manages Executive Summits, Conferences & Corporate Retreats
N.A.I.C.S.: 561920

Craig Lehmann (Co-Founder, Pres & COO)
Michael P. Owens (Dir-Production)
June McCarthy (Dir-Ops)

CRAIN BROTHERS INC.
2715 Grand Chenier Hwy, Grand Chenier, LA 70643
Tel.: (337) 538-2411
Web Site:
  http://www.crainbrothers.com
Rev.: $11,613,508
Emp.: 74
Construction, Repair & Dismantling Services
N.A.I.C.S.: 237120

CRAIN COMMUNICATIONS, INC.
1155 Gratiot Ave, Detroit, MI 48207-2732
Tel.: (313) 446-6000   IL
Web Site: http://www.crain.com
Year Founded: 1916
Sales Range: $700-749.9 Million
Emp.: 1,000
Business, Trade & Consumer Magazines, Newspapers & Internet Publisher
N.A.I.C.S.: 513120
Keith E. Crain (Chm)
K. C. Crain (CEO)
Bob Recchia (CFO)
Nikki Kallek (Chief People Officer & Chief HR Officer)
Christopher Crain (Chief Investment Officer, Sr Exec VP, Exec VP & Dir-Strategic Ops)
Josh Freed (Head-Strategy Automotive News)
Peter Grantz (Gen Counsel & VP)
Veebha Mehta (COO)
Chrissy Taylor (Sr VP-Editorial Ops Automotive News & Global Polymer)
Ursula Williams (Pres-Staffing Industry Analysts)

Subsidiaries:

AutoWeek   **(1)**
1155 Gratiot Ave, Detroit, MI 48207-2997   **(100%)**
Tel.: (313) 446-6000
Web Site: http://www.autoweek.com
Sales Range: $10-24.9 Million
Emp.: 200
Car Enthusiasts Magazine & Internet Publisher
N.A.I.C.S.: 513120
Lauren Melesio (Dir-Reprints & Licensing)

Automotive News   **(1)**
1155 Gratiot Ave, Detroit, MI 48207-2997   **(100%)**
Tel.: (313) 446-6000
Web Site: http://www.automotivenews.com
Sales Range: $10-24.9 Million
Emp.: 300
Automotive Industry Newspaper & Internet Publisher
N.A.I.C.S.: 513110
Karen Faust O'Rourke (Editor-News & Copy)
Rick Kranz (Editor-Product)
Victor Galvan (Editor-Web)
Richard Johnson (Editor-Automotive News Print)
David Versical (Dir-Editorial Ops)
Philip Nussel (Editor-Automotive News Online)
James B. Treece (Editor-News)
Rick Greer (Dir-Sls)
Sharon Silke Carty (Editor-News)
Diana T. Kurylko (Office Mgr)
Ursula Zerilli (Mgr-Info Center)
Georgia Chapman (Dir-European Mktg & Events)
Mary Raetz (Dir-Automotive News Data Center)
Nicole Wrobel (Dir-Online Bus & CRM)
Thomas Heringer (Dir-Adv)
Krishnan M. Anantharaman (Editor-News)

Paul McVeigh (Mng Editor)
Sarah Soentgen (Mgr-CRM & Digital Media)
Tim Good (Editor-Graphics & Copy)
Jerry Hirsch (Editor-News)

Unit (Non-US):

Crain Communications, Inc. - Automotive News China Unit   **(2)**
Room 1303 Building 2 Lane 99 South Hongcao Road, Shanghai, 200233, China
Tel.: (86) 139 1851 5816
Web Site: http://www.autonewschina.com
Emp.: 1'
Automotive News Publisher
N.A.I.C.S.: 513110
Ying Jin (Mng Editor)

Unit (Domestic):

Crain Communications, Inc. - Automotive News Europe Unit   **(2)**
1155 Gratiot Ave, Detroit, MI 48207-2997
Tel.: (877) 812-1584
Web Site: http://www.europe.autonews.com
Book Publishers
N.A.I.C.S.: 513130
Douglas A. Bolduc (Mng Editor)
Paul McVeigh (Mng Editor)
Mary Raetz (Dir-Automotive News Data Center)
Nicole Wrobel (Dir-CRM & Online Bus)
Rick Greer (Dir-Sls)
Steve Massie (Dir-Design)
Dave Guilford (Editor-News)
Sarah Soentgen (Mgr-CRM & Digital Media)
James B. Treece (Editor-News)
Ursula Zerilli (Mgr-Info Center)
Keith Crain (Dir-Editorial Ops)

Crain Communications GmbH   **(1)**
Technopark Oberpfaffenhofen Argelsrieder Feld 13, 82234, Oberpfaffenhofen, Germany   **(100%)**
Tel.: (49) 8153907400
Web Site: http://www.automobilwoche.de
Sales Range: $10-24.9 Million
Emp.: 25
Automotive Trade & Consumer Newspaper Publishing Services
N.A.I.C.S.: 513110
Helmut Kluger (Mng Dir)

Unit (Domestic):

Automobilwoche   **(2)**
Argelsrieder Feld 13 Technopark, 82234, Oberpfaffenhofen, Germany   **(100%)**
Tel.: (49) 8153907400
Web Site: http://www.automobilwoche.de
Sales Range: $10-24.9 Million
Emp.: 13
Automotive Newspaper & Internet Publisher
N.A.I.C.S.: 513110
Helmut Kluger (Publr)
Klaus-Dieter Florecke (Editor)
Bettina John (Editor)
Gerhard Mauerer (Editor-Online)
Thomas Heringer (Head-Sls, Mktg & Publ)
Burkhard Reiring (Editor-in-Chief)

Crain Communications Ltd.   **(1)**
21 Saint Thomas Street 3rd Floor, London, SE1 9RY, United Kingdom   **(100%)**
Tel.: (44) 2074571400
Sales Range: $10-24.9 Million
Emp.: 60
Trade Magazines & Internet Publisher
N.A.I.C.S.: 513120

Unit (Domestic):

European Rubber Journal   **(2)**
21st St. Thomas St 3rd Fl, London, SE1 9RY, United Kingdom   **(100%)**
Tel.: (44) 2074571408
Web Site: http://www.european-rubber-journal.com
Sales Range: $10-24.9 Million
Emp.: 10
Rubber Industry Trade Magazine & Internet Publisher
N.A.I.C.S.: 513120
Paul Mitchell (Publr)
Patrick Raleigh (Editor)

Urethanes Technology International   **(2)**
21 Saint Thomas Street 3rd Floor, London, SE1 9RY, United Kingdom   **(100%)**

Crain Communications, Inc.—(Continued)
Tel.: (44) 2074571400
Sales Range: $10-24.9 Million
Emp.: 10
Polyurethanes Industry Trade Magazine & Internet Publisher
N.A.I.C.S.: 513120
Paul Mitchell *(Mng Dir)*

Crain Communications, Inc. - Akron   **(1)**
1725 Merriman Rd Ste 300, Akron, OH
44313-9006   **(100%)**
Tel.: (330) 836-9180
Web Site: http://www.crain.com
Sales Range: $10-24.9 Million
Emp.: 15
Trade & Consumer Magazines & Internet Publisher
N.A.I.C.S.: 513120
David E. Zielasko *(Publr & VP)*
Keith Crain *(Chm)*
Christopher Crain *(Exec VP & Dir-Strategic Ops)*
K. C. Crain Jr. *(Pres & COO)*

Unit (Domestic):

Plastics News   **(2)**
1155 Gratiot Ave, Detroit, MI
48207   **(100%)**
Tel.: (330) 836-9180
Web Site: http://www.plasticsnews.com
Sales Range: $10-24.9 Million
Emp.: 60
Plastics Industry Trade Newspaper & Internet Publisher
N.A.I.C.S.: 513110
Don Loepp *(Editor)*
Joseph Pryweller *(Dir-Conference)*
Patrick Cannon *(Grp Dir-Sls)*
John Hickey *(Reg Sls Mgr-Western & Midwestern)*

Rubber & Plastics News   **(2)**
1725 Merriman Rd Ste 300, Akron, OH
44313-9006   **(100%)**
Tel.: (330) 836-9180
Web Site: http://www.rubbernews.com
Sales Range: $10-24.9 Million
Emp.: 16
Rubber & Plastics Newspaper & Internet Publisher
N.A.I.C.S.: 513110
Brent Weaver *(Mgr-Sls-Classified)*
Bruce Meyer *(Exec Editor)*
David E. Zielasko *(Publr)*
Donald Detore *(Mng Editor)*

Waste News   **(2)**
1725 Merriman Rd Ste 300, Akron, OH
44313-9006   **(100%)**
Tel.: (330) 836-9180
Web Site:
    http://www.wasterecylingnews.com
Sales Range: $10-24.9 Million
Emp.: 65
Environmental Waste Management Newspaper & Internet Publisher
N.A.I.C.S.: 513110

Crain Communications, Inc. - Chicago   **(1)**
150 N Michigan Ave, Chicago, IL
60601   **(100%)**
Tel.: (312) 649-5200
Web Site: http://www.chicagobusiness.com
Sales Range: $25-49.9 Million
Emp.: 11
Business, Trade & Consumer Magazines, Newspapers & Internet Publisher
N.A.I.C.S.: 513120
Charles R. Thompson *(Publr-Trade Magazines Div & VP)*
Cassie Walker Burke *(Asst Mng Editor)*
Steve Reiss *(Mng Editor)*
Ann Dwyer *(Deputy Mng Editor)*
Alexandra Trumbull *(Coord-Social Media)*

Unit (Domestic):

Crain's Chicago Business   **(2)**
150 N Michigan Ave 16 Fl, Chicago, IL
60601   **(100%)**
Tel.: (312) 649-5200
Web Site: http://www.chicagobusiness.com
Sales Range: $10-24.9 Million
Business Newspaper & Internet Publisher
N.A.I.C.S.: 513110

Thomas J. Linden *(Dir-Art)*
Jason McGregor *(Editor-Digital Design)*
Ann Dwyer *(Mng Editor)*
Aly Brumback *(Mng Dir)*

Crain Communications, Inc. - New York   **(1)**
685 3rd Ave 10th Fl, New York, NY
10017-4024   **(100%)**
Tel.: (212) 210-0100
Web Site: http://www.crain.com
Sales Range: $50-74.9 Million
Emp.: 300
Business Trade & Consumer Magazines Newspaper & Internet Publisher Services
N.A.I.C.S.: 513120

Unit (Domestic):

Advertising Age   **(2)**
685 3rd Ave, New York, NY 10017 **(100%)**
Tel.: (212) 210-0100
Web Site: http://www.adage.com
Sales Range: $10-24.9 Million
Emp.: 40
Advertising, Marketing & Media Newspaper & Internet Publisher
N.A.I.C.S.: 513110
Brian Braiker *(Editor)*

BtoB   **(2)**
685 3rd Ave Fl 9, New York, NY
10017   **(100%)**
Tel.: (212) 210-0100
Web Site: http://www.btobonline.com
Sales Range: $10-24.9 Million
Emp.: 35
Business-to-Business Marketing Magazine & Internet Publisher
N.A.I.C.S.: 513120
Robert Felsenthal *(Publr & VP)*
David Bernstein *(Assoc Publr)*
Jeff Buddle *(Dir-Website)*
John Obrecht *(Editor)*
Kate Maddox *(Exec Editor)*
Bob Felsenthal *(Exec Editor-Media Bus)*

Business Insurance   **(2)**
685 3rd Ave, New York, NY
10017-4036   **(100%)**
Tel.: (212) 210-0100
Web Site:
    http://www.businessinsurance.com
Sales Range: $10-24.9 Million
Emp.: 50
Commercial Insurance & Risk Management Newspaper & Internet Publisher
N.A.I.C.S.: 513110

Crain's New York Business   **(2)**
685 3rd Ave, New York, NY
10017-4036   **(100%)**
Tel.: (212) 210-0100
Web Site: http://www.crainsnewyork.com
Sales Range: $10-24.9 Million
Emp.: 125
Business Newspaper & Internet Publisher
N.A.I.C.S.: 513110
Robert Hordt *(Editor)*
Carolyn McClain *(Dir-Art)*
Courtney Williams *(Dir-Conferences & Events)*
Patty Oppenheimer *(Dir-Custom Content)*
Mary Kramer *(Publr)*
Fred Gabriel *(Publr & Exec Editor)*

Pensions & Investments   **(2)**
685 3rd Ave, New York, NY
10017-4036   **(100%)**
Tel.: (212) 210-0100
Web Site: http://www.pionline.com
Sales Range: $25-49.9 Million
Emp.: 200
Investment Management Newspaper & Internet Publisher
N.A.I.C.S.: 513110
Elizabeth Karier *(Mng Editor)*
Paul D. Margolis *(Dir-Enterprise Licensing)*
Christopher Battaglia *(Grp Publr & VP)*
Richard Scanlon *(Dir-Adv Sls)*
Michelle DeMarco *(Dir-Promos)*
Amy Resnick *(Editor)*
Aaron Cunningham *(Dir-Res & Analytics)*
Anthony Scuderi *(Mgr-Directory)*
Greg Crawford *(Dir-Content Solutions)*
Gregg A. Runburg *(Dir-Art)*
Joel Hauer *(Dir-Conference Sls)*
Julie A. Parten *(Head-Sls)*
Laura Picariello *(Mgr-Reprint Sls)*

Mark Goodrich *(Gen Mgr-Digital)*
Tammy Scholtes *(Dir-Conference Programming)*
Veronica Dominguez-Garcia *(Mgr-Conference Mktg)*
Nikki Pirrello *(Assoc Grp Publr)*
Erin Arvedlund *(Editor-Enterprise)*
Anthony DeRosa *(Dir-Digital Content)*

Crain Communications, Inc. - Staffing Industry Analysts Unit   **(1)**
1975 W El Camino Real Ste 304, Mountain View, CA 94040
Tel.: (650) 390-6200
Web Site: http://www.staffingindustry.com
Emp.: 35
Staffing & Management Consulting Services
N.A.I.C.S.: 541618
Barry Asin *(Pres)*
Diana Gabriel *(Sr VP-Strategy & Solutions-Global)*
John Nurthen *(Exec Dir-Global Res)*
Ursula Williams *(COO)*

Crain's Cleveland Business   **(1)**
700 W Saint Clair Ave Ste 310, Cleveland, OH 44113-1230   **(100%)**
Tel.: (216) 522-1383
Web Site: http://www.crainscleveland.com
Sales Range: $10-24.9 Million
Emp.: 26
Business Newspaper & Internet Publisher
N.A.I.C.S.: 513110
Scott Suttell *(Mng Editor)*
Craig Mackey *(Mgr-Production)*
Nicole Mastrangelo *(Dir-Adv Sls)*
Elizabeth McIntyre *(Publr & Editor)*

Crain's Detroit Business   **(1)**
1155 Gratiot, Detroit, MI 48207 **(100%)**
Tel.: (313) 446-6000
Web Site: http://www.crainsdetroit.com
Sales Range: $10-24.9 Million
Emp.: 35
Business Newspaper & Internet Publisher
N.A.I.C.S.: 513110
Michael Lee *(Mng Editor)*
Beth Reeber Valone *(Editor-News)*
Kacey Anderson *(Mgr-Events)*
K. C. Crain *(Publr)*
Frank Sennett *(Dir-Digital Products & Strategy-Chicago, Cleveland, Detroit &)*

Genomeweb, LLC   **(1)**
1 Battery Park Plz, 8th Fl, New York, NY
10004
Tel.: (212) 269-4747
Web Site: http://www.genomeweb.com
Sales Range: $1-9.9 Million
Emp.: 17
Periodical Publishing
N.A.I.C.S.: 513120
Dennis Waters *(Chm)*
Allan Nixon *(Dir-Bus Dev)*
Andrew Masterson *(Mgr-Premium Content Acct)*
Ben Butkus *(Mng Editor)*
Carla Lira *(Mgr-Sls-Midwest)*
Greg Anderson *(COO & Publr)*
Geoff O'Connor *(Controller)*
Victoria Maher *(Dir-East Coast Media Sls)*

TelevisionWeek   **(1)**
6500 Wilshire Blvd Ste 2300, Los Angeles, CA 90048-4947
Tel.: (323) 370-2400
Web Site: http://www.tvweek.com
Sales Range: $10-24.9 Million
Emp.: 30
Television Broadcast Media Newspaper & Internet Publisher
N.A.I.C.S.: 513110
Chuck Ross *(Mng Dir)*

Workforce Management   **(1)**
4 Executive Cir Ste 185, Irvine, CA
92614   **(100%)**
Tel.: (949) 255-5340
Web Site: http://www.workforce.com
Sales Range: $10-24.9 Million
Emp.: 15
Human Resources Magazine & Internet Publisher
N.A.I.C.S.: 513120
Mike Prokopeak *(VP)*
Norman B. Kamikow *(Pres)*

CRAMCO INC.

2200 E Ann St, Philadelphia, PA
19134
Tel.: (215) 427-9500
Web Site: http://www.cramco.net
Rev.: $23,716,957
Emp.: 241
Dining Room Furniture: Wood
N.A.I.C.S.: 337122
Paul Cramer *(Pres)*
Kathy Augustyn *(Mgr-Credit)*

CRAMER PRODUCTIONS INC.

425 University Ave, Norwood, MA
02062
Tel.: (781) 278-2300
Web Site: https://www.cramer.com
Year Founded: 1982
Sales Range: $25-49.9 Million
Emp.: 160
Advetising Agency
N.A.I.C.S.: 541810
Tim Martin *(Exec VP-Ops)*
T. J. Martin *(Exec VP)*
Richard Sturchio *(Pres)*
Ann Cave *(Sr Dir-Tech)*
Julie Walker *(Exec VP-Corp Dev)*
Greg Martin *(Sr VP-Fin)*
Thom Faria *(CEO)*
Mark Wilson *(Creative Dir)*
Lindsay Nie *(Head-Creative Tech)*
Timothy Owens *(Head-Activations)*
Chris Martin *(Sr VP)*
Angel Micarelli *(VP & Creative Dir-Content)*
Brent Turner *(Sr VP-Solutions)*

CRAMER ROSENTHAL MCGLYNN LLC

520 Madison Ave Fl 20, New York,
NY 10022
Tel.: (212) 326-5300
Web Site: http://www.crmllc.com
Year Founded: 1973
Sales Range: $5-14.9 Billion
Emp.: 60
Investment Advisory Services
N.A.I.C.S.: 523940
Ronald H. McGlynn *(Co-Founder & Chm)*
Jay B. Abramson *(CEO, Chief Investment Officer & Portfolio Mgr)*
Christopher C. Barnett *(Pres & Dir-Mktg)*
Carlos A. Leal *(CFO & Exec VP)*
Steven A. Yadegari *(COO & Gen Counsel)*
Harris Swenson *(VP & Head-Sls & Consultant Rels-Global)*
Jeffrey B. Reich *(VP & Portfolio Mgr)*
Thomas P. Cook *(VP)*
Thaddeus D. Pollock *(VP & Portfolio Mgr)*
Brian M. Harvey *(VP, Dir-Res & Portfolio Mgr)*
Robert Maina *(VP & Portfolio Mgr)*
Andrey A. Belov *(VP & Portfolio Mgr)*
Bernard C. Frojmovich *(VP)*
Bianca Giannetta *(Asst VP)*
Brittain Ezzes *(VP & Portfolio Mgr)*
James D. Brown *(VP & Head-Global Funds Distr)*
Jason Yellin *(VP)*
Jonathan Ruch *(VP)*
Maria Vasiliades *(Asst VP)*
Rebecca E. Brown *(Asst VP & Dir-Mktg & Client Svc)*
Ian Bitner *(VP)*
Isabelle Sajous *(VP)*
Jeffrey Yanover *(VP)*
Martin Teng *(VP)*
Tyler Mixter *(VP)*
Michelle Kaufmann *(VP & Controller)*
Carmine Cerasuolo *(VP & Head-Ops)*
Nicholas Socha *(VP & Mgr-Information Sys)*
Mimi B. Morris *(VP & Portfolio Mgr)*
Sackett S. Cook *(VP & Portfolio Mgr)*

CRAMER TOYOTA OF VENICE
900 US Hwy 41 Bypass S, Venice, FL 34285-4333
Tel.: (941) 484-9000
Web Site:
  http://www.cramertoyota.com
Year Founded: 1990
Sales Range: $10-24.9 Million
Emp.: 100
Car Whslr
N.A.I.C.S.: 441110

CRAMER'S HOME CENTERS, INC.
320 N Courtland St, East Strouds-burg, PA 18301
Tel.: (570) 424-5953
Web Site: https://www.cramers.com
Year Founded: 1915
Sales Range: $10-24.9 Million
Emp.: 120
Home Center Operator
N.A.I.C.S.: 444110
Kenneth Cramer *(Pres)*
Michael Carmella *(VP & Dir-Mktg)*
Steve Giannetto *(Mgr-Credit)*
Kyle Nasatka *(Mgr-Store)*

CRAMP & ASSOCIATES, INC.
1327 Grenox Rd, Wynnewood, PA 19096-2402
Tel.: (610) 649-6002
Web Site: http://www.cramp.com
Year Founded: 1988
Rev.: $30,000,000
Emp.: 10
N.A.I.C.S.: 541810
Jeff Cramp *(Pres & Dir-Creative)*
Arlene J. Hausman *(VP & Controller)*

CRANDALL FORD
2175 Rasmussen Rd, Park City, UT 84098
Tel.: (435) 647-3673
Web Site:
  http://www.crandallford.com
Sales Range: $10-24.9 Million
Emp.: 25
Car Dealership Owner & Operator
N.A.I.C.S.: 441110
Robert Crandall *(Gen Mgr)*
Jill Sargent *(Office Mgr)*
George A. Crandall Jr. *(Pres & Princi-pal)*

CRANE CONSTRUCTION CO.
343 Wainwright Dr Ste B, Northbrook, IL 60062-1928
Tel.: (847) 291-3400   IL
Web Site:
  https://www.craneconstruction.com
Sales Range: $75-99.9 Million
Emp.: 45
Provider of Contracting & Construc-tion Services
N.A.I.C.S.: 236220
Jeffrey D. Crane *(Pres)*

CRANE CREDIT UNION
1 W Gate Dr, Odon, IN 47562
Web Site: http://www.cranecu.org
Bank Holding Company & Services
N.A.I.C.S.: 551111
Kevin Sparks *(Pres & CEO)*

Subsidiaries:

Our Community Bank   (1)
279 E Morgan St, Spencer, IN 47460
Tel.: (812) 829-2095
Web Site: http://www.ocbconnect.com
Rev.: $4,191,000
Assets: $69,567,000
Liabilities: $61,604,000
Net Worth: $7,963,000
Earnings: $535,000
Emp.: 22
Fiscal Year-end: 12/31/2013
Banking Services

N.A.I.C.S.: 522180
Kurt D. Rosenberger *(Pres & CEO)*
Jenny Knapp *(Mgr-Cloverdale)*

CRANE GROUP CO.
330 W Spring St Ste 200, Columbus, OH 43215
Tel.: (614) 754-3000   OH
Web Site:
  https://www.cranegroup.com
Year Founded: 1947
Sales Range: $500-549.9 Million
Emp.: 1,330
Holding & Management Company
N.A.I.C.S.: 551112
Ann B. Crane *(Pres & CEO)*
Michael S. Crane *(Pres)*
Timothy T. Miller *(VP & Gen Counsel)*
Chad M. Utrup *(CFO)*
Eric Van Buskirk *(Dir-Crane Family Offices)*
Andrea Thomas *(VP-Leadership & Dev)*
Hope Sharett *(Dir-Community Stew-ardship)*

Subsidiaries:

Crane Investment Co.   (1)
330 W Spring St Ste 200, Columbus, OH 43215   (100%)
Tel.: (614) 754-3000
Web Site: http://www.cranegroup.com
Sales Range: $25-49.9 Million
Emp.: 36
Real Estate, Private Equity & Other Invest-ments
N.A.I.C.S.: 525990
Andy Hackett *(Pres)*

Crane Materials International (CMI)   (1)
4501 Cir 75 Pkwy Ste E-5370, Atlanta, GA 30339
Tel.: (770) 933-8166
Web Site: http://www.cmiwaterfront.com
Sales Range: $25-49.9 Million
Emp.: 50
Mfr of Marine Products for Home Construc-tion & Engineering Projects
N.A.I.C.S.: 237990
John E. Irvine *(Co-Founder & Pres)*
John Yeosock *(Co-Founder & VP)*
Brendan Sheppard *(Dir-Engrg)*
Jon Ridgway *(VP-Sls & Mktg)*

CRANE INSPECTION & CERTI-FICATION BUREAU L.L.C.
11112 Boggy Creek Dr, Orlando, FL 32824
Tel.: (407) 277-0884   FL
Web Site: https://www.cicb.com
Year Founded: 1969
Sales Range: $50-74.9 Million
Emp.: 25
Training & Inspection Services
N.A.I.C.S.: 541990
Jerry Longtin *(Gen Mgr)*

CRANE JOHNSON LUMBER COMPANY INC.
3320 Main Ave, Fargo, ND 58103
Tel.: (701) 237-0612
Web Site: http://www.cjlumber.com
Year Founded: 1883
Sales Range: $10-24.9 Million
Emp.: 130
Lumber & Other Building Materials
N.A.I.C.S.: 423310
Wayne Briggs *(Pres)*

CRANE PLASTICS HOLDING COMPANY
2141 Fairwood Ave, Columbus, OH 43207
Tel.: (614) 542-1100   DE
Web Site:
  http://www.craneplasticsmfg.com
Year Founded: 1947
Sales Range: $125-149.9 Million

Emp.: 750
Mfr of Vinyl House Siding; Custom Extruded Thermoplastics
N.A.I.C.S.: 326199
Randolph J. Fortener *(CFO & VP)*
Mike Crane *(Pres & CEO)*
John Previte *(Mgr-Mktg)*

CRANE TECH SOLUTIONS, LLC
2030 Ponderosa St, Portsmouth, VA 23701
Tel.: (757) 405-0311   DE
Web Site:
  https://www.cranetechsolutions.com
Year Founded: 1990
Sales Range: $1-9.9 Million
Emp.: 25
Specialty POT Tending Cranes & Various Crane Operations
N.A.I.C.S.: 333923
Manfred Kohler *(CEO)*
Frank Hegan *(Pres)*
Libet Anderson *(Mng Dir-Advisory & Plng)*

CRANE WORLDWIDE LOGIS-TICS LLC
1500 Rankin Rd, Houston, TX 77073
Tel.: (281) 443-2777   DE
Web Site: https://www.craneww.com
Year Founded: 2008
International Supply Chain & Trans-portation Logistics Solutions
N.A.I.C.S.: 488999
Tim Zubradt *(Chief Sls Officer)*
Keith Winters *(CEO)*
Chad Taylor *(Exec VP-Ops-Global)*
Tracey Abram-Anthony *(VP & Chief Compliance Officer)*
Megan Soltura *(VP-HR-Global)*
Marco Nazzari *(VP-EMEIA-Reg)*
Jeff LeBlanc *(VP-Asia Pacific-Reg)*
Chris Monica *(VP-West-Reg)*
Rob Keuten *(VP-East)*
Larry Hack *(Sr VP-Tech)*
Dylan Ross *(CFO)*
Eric Brandt *(VP-Sls-New York)*

Subsidiaries:

DAVACO, Inc.   (1)
4050 Valley View Ln Ste 150, Dallas, TX 75038
Tel.: (214) 373-4700
Web Site: http://www.davacoinc.com
Retail, Restaurant & Hospitality Brand Lo-gistics Consulting & Customer-Facing De-sign Support Services
N.A.I.C.S.: 541614
Richard Loren Davis *(Founder)*
J. Lamar Roberts *(CFO)*
Shelly Vandeven *(CMO)*
Paul Hamer *(Exec VP-Bus Dev)*
Jordan Handel *(Exec VP-Bus Dev)*
Don Williams *(Sr VP-Ops)*

Pacorini Forwarding S.r.l.   (1)
Via Pietro Chiesa 9, Torri Piane 12 piano, 16149, Genoa, Italy
Tel.: (39) 0104698111
Freight Transportation Arrangement
N.A.I.C.S.: 488510

CRANEL INCORPORATED
8999 Gemini Pkwy, Columbus, OH 43240-2010
Tel.: (614) 431-8000   OH
Web Site: http://www.cranel.com
Year Founded: 1985
Sales Range: $25-49.9 Million
Emp.: 137
Provider of Computers & Computer Equipment
N.A.I.C.S.: 423430
James H. Wallace *(Chm)*
Bill Schuman *(VP-Sls)*

Leslie Duff *(VP-HR)*
Scott Slack *(VP-Mktg)*
Craig Wallace *(Pres & COO)*

CRANESVILLE BLOCK CO., INC.
1250 Riverfront Ctr, Amsterdam, NY 12010
Tel.: (518) 684-6400
Web Site:
  https://www.cranesville.com
Year Founded: 1947
Sales Range: $25-49.9 Million
Emp.: 45
Blocks, Ready-Mix Concrete & Aggre-gates Mfr
N.A.I.C.S.: 327331
Mark Silverman *(Mgr)*
Mike Pickering *(Mgr-Environmental Health & Safety)*

CRANFORD JOHNSON ROB-INSON WOODS, INC.
300 Main St, Little Rock, AR 72201-3531
Tel.: (501) 975-6251   DE
Web Site: https://www.cjrw.com
Year Founded: 1961
Emp.: 75
Advertising Agency
N.A.I.C.S.: 541810
Brian Kratkiewicz *(Sr VP & Dir-Media & Innovation)*
Chuck Robertson *(Sr VP-Travel & Tourism)*
Shanon Williams *(Dir-Adv Acct Svcs)*
Stephen Allen *(CFO)*
Bryan Jones *(Dir-Interactive Svcs)*
Annie Holman *(Sr Acct Exec & Supvr-Media)*
Darin Gray *(Chm & CEO)*
Caroline Reddmann *(Mgr-Social Me-dia)*
Kelly McLarty *(Sr Dir-Art-Creative Div)*
Lukas Arnold *(Jr Dir-Art-Creative Div)*
Wade McCune *(Dir-Creative)*
Kelsey Hook *(Coord-Traffic)*
Bob Johnston *(VP & Dir-IT)*
Brian Clark *(Sr VP-Brand Mktg Strat-egist)*
Dan Sawyer *(VP & Dir-Special Events)*
Debbie Grace *(VP & Dir-Brdcst)*
Jill Joslin *(Pres)*
Mark Raines *(VP & Dir-PR)*
Tanya Whitlock *(Sr VP & Dir-Media & Consumer)*
Keegan Wright *(Mgr-Digital Media)*

Subsidiaries:

CJRW Northwest   (1)
4100 Corporate Center Dr Ste 300, Spring-dale, AR 72762
Tel.: (479) 442-9803
Web Site: http://www.cjrw.com
Rev.: $10,000,000
Emp.: 12
Advertising Agency
N.A.I.C.S.: 541810
Brian Rudisill *(VP-Mktg Svcs)*
Rebecca Kirkpatrick Bahn *(Assoc Acct Exec-Little Rock)*
Andrea Ritchie *(Acct Exec)*

Heathcott Associates, Inc.   (1)
303 W Capitol Ave, Little Rock, AR 72201
Tel.: (501) 975-6251
Web Site: http://www.heathcott.com
Advertising & Marketing Services
N.A.I.C.S.: 541810
Gary Heathcott *(Pres)*
Jeremy Henderson *(Sr Dir-Art & Mechanic)*

CRANKY SIGNS & ADVERTIS-ING
456 Wentworth Rd, Brookfield, NH 03872-7106

Cranky Signs & Advertising—(Continued)

Tel.: (919) 596-5588
Web Site:
http://www.crankycreative.com
Year Founded: 2003
Sales Range: $10-24.9 Million
Emp.: 6
Advetising Agency
N.A.I.C.S.: 541810
Barbara Bannon (Pres & CEO-
Cranky Creative Grp)
Keri KIng (Office Mgr)

CRANSTON PRINT WORKS COMPANY
1381 Cranston St, Cranston, RI
02920-6789
Tel.: (401) 943-4800   RI
Web Site: https://www.cpw.com
Year Founded: 1824
Sales Range: $125-149.9 Million
Emp.: 531
Textile Printing & Converting
N.A.I.C.S.: 313310
Fraioli John (Mgr-Sls)
Kerri Dacey (Mgr-Sys Dev)
Mike Emmett (Mgr)
Scott Hoyle (Mgr-IT)
Jodi Beckett (Exec VP)
Anita Pedchenko (Mgr-Customer Svc)
Frederic L. Rockefeller Jr. (Pres &
CEO)

Subsidiaries:

Bercen Inc.   (1)
30140 Eden Church Rd, Denham Springs,
LA 70726   (100%)
Tel.: (225) 664-7167
Web Site: http://www.bercen.com
Sales Range: $25-49.9 Million
Emp.: 65
Chemicals
N.A.I.C.S.: 325510
John Miller (Dir-Sls-Anhydrides-Global)

CRASSOCIATES, INC.
8580 Cinderbed Rd Ste 2400, New-
ington, VA 22122
Tel.: (703) 550-8145
Web Site: http://www.crassoc.com
Year Founded: 1997
Sales Range: $50-74.9 Million
Emp.: 65
Provider of Healthcare Services
N.A.I.C.S.: 561320
Charles B. Robbins (Sr VP-Dev)
John R. Wetherell (CFO)
Kathleen M. Arlinsky (Exec VP-HR)

CRATEX MANUFACTURING CO., INC.
828 Encinitas Blvd Ste 200, Encini-
tas, CA 92024
Tel.: (760) 942-2877
Web Site: https://www.cratex.com
Year Founded: 1935
Sales Range: $75-99.9 Million
Emp.: 60
Mfr of Abrasive Products
N.A.I.C.S.: 327910
Allen McCasland (Chm)
R. M. McCasland (Pres)
Ron Liesch (Dir-Sls)

CRAVATH, SWAINE & MOORE LLP
Worldwide Plz 825 8th Ave, New
York, NY 10019-7475
Tel.: (212) 474-1000
Web Site: https://www.cravath.com
Year Founded: 1819
Sales Range: $550-599.9 Million
Emp.: 1,000
Legal Advisory Services
N.A.I.C.S.: 541110

Craig F. Arcella (Partner)
Philip J. Boeckman (Partner)
Stephen L. Burns (Partner)
Alyssa K. Caples (Partner)
James D. Cooper (Partner)
Thomas E. Dunn (Partner)
LizabethAnn R. Eisen (Partner)
William V. Fogg (Partner)
Michael S. Goldman (Partner)
Mark I. Greene (Partner)
Richard Hall (Partner)
Joel F. Herold (Partner)
David J. Kappos (Partner)
Stephen M. Kessing (Partner)
Tatiana Lapushchik (Partner)
Gary A. Bornstein (Partner-Litigation)
John D. Buretta (Partner-Litigation)
Lauren Angelilli (Partner-Tax)
Robert H. Baron (Partner-Litigation)
D. Scott Bennett (Partner)
Deirdre Stanley (Atty)

CRAVEN POTTERY INC.
6640 Hwy 52, Gainesville, GA 30543
Tel.: (770) 869-3675
Web Site:
https://www.cravenpottery.com
Sales Range: Less than $1 Million
Emp.: 12
Gifts & Novelties
N.A.I.C.S.: 424990
Billy Joe Craven (Pres)

CRAW-KAN TELEPHONE CO-OPERATIVE
200 N Ozark St, Girard, KS 66743
Tel.: (620) 724-8235
Web Site: https://www.ckt.net
Sales Range: $10-24.9 Million
Emp.: 70
Local Telephone Communications
N.A.I.C.S.: 517121
Craig Wilbert (Gen Mgr)
Daniel Droessler (Mgr-Broad & Ops)

CRAWFORD ADVERTISING ASSOCIATES, LTD.
216 Congers Rd, New City, NY
10956
Tel.: (845) 638-0051
Web Site:
http://www.crawfordadv.com
Year Founded: 1992
Sales Range: Less than $1 Million
Emp.: 3
N.A.I.C.S.: 541810
Howard Wolfe (Chm & Pres)
Wendy Wolfe (Treas)

CRAWFORD BROADCASTING CO.
725 Skippack Park 210, Blue Bell, PA
19422
Tel.: (215) 628-3500
Web Site:
http://www.crawfordbroadcas
ting.com
Year Founded: 1959
Rev.: $32,100,000
Emp.: 250
Radio Broadcasting Stations
N.A.I.C.S.: 516110
Donald B. Crawford (Pres)
Laura Scotti (Dir-Sls & Gen Mgr)
Michael Cary (CFO)

CRAWFORD COMPANY
1306 Mill St, Rock Island, IL 61201
Tel.: (309) 788-4573
Web Site: https://www.crawford-
company.com
Year Founded: 1952
Sales Range: $10-24.9 Million
Emp.: 86
Plumbing, Heating & Air-Conditioning
Services

N.A.I.C.S.: 238220
Robert Frink (Owner)
Ian Frink (Owner & Pres)
Larry Anderson (CFO)
Jim Maynard Jr. (Owner & VP)

CRAWFORD FURNITURE MANUFACTURING CORPORA-TION
1021 Allen St, Jamestown, NY
14701-2301
Tel.: (716) 661-9100
Web Site:
http://www.crawfordfurniture.com
Year Founded: 1983
Sales Range: $25-49.9 Million
Emp.: 200
Provider of Wood Furniture
N.A.I.C.S.: 337122
Michael R. Cappa (Pres & CEO)
Vicky McQueen (CFO)

CRAWFORD HEATING & COOLING CO.
1306 Mill St, Rock Island, IL 61201
Tel.: (309) 788-4573
Web Site: https://www.crawford-
company.com
Year Founded: 1952
Sales Range: $10-24.9 Million
Emp.: 86
Plumbing, Heating & Air-Conditioning
Services
N.A.I.C.S.: 238220
Bob Frink (Pres)
Jim Maynard (VP)
Ian Frink (VP)
Larry Anderson (Controller)

CRAWFORD OIL CO. INC.
416 E Wisconsin St, Portage, WI
53901
Tel.: (608) 742-2414
Web Site:
http://www.crawfordoilgasdiesel.com
Sales Range: $10-24.9 Million
Emp.: 20
Petroleum Bulk Stations
N.A.I.C.S.: 424710
James Crawford (Pres)
David Grimes (CFO-Green Valley
Grocery)

CRAWFORD RENOVATION
1050 N Post Oak Rd Ste 140, Hous-
ton, TX 77055-7233
Tel.: (713) 463-8600
Year Founded: 2002
Rev.: $16,600,000
Emp.: 26
Residential Construction
N.A.I.C.S.: 236220
Ben Crawford (Pres)
Shawna Roorda (VP)
Melissa Devore (Project Mgr)
Rusty Pelt (Mgr-Pur & Estimating)

CRAWFORD SALES COM-PANY
1377 S Hamilton Cir, Olathe, KS
66061
Tel.: (913) 782-0801
Web Site: http://www.gandginc.com
Sales Range: $25-49.9 Million
Emp.: 70
Beer & Other Fermented Malt Liquors
N.A.I.C.S.: 424810
Richard G. Rossman (Pres)
Bill McCort (CFO)
Jamie Harrison (Office Mgr)

CRAWFORD SUPPLY COM-PANY
8150 Lehigh Ave, Morton Grove, IL
60053

Tel.: (847) 380-8299   IL
Web Site:
https://www.crawfordsupply.com
Year Founded: 1950
Sales Range: $10-24.9 Million
Emp.: 75
Plumbing & Heating Equipment Distr
N.A.I.C.S.: 423720
Steve Feiger (VP)
Shirley Goldstein (CFO)
Bob McVay (Office Mgr)

Subsidiaries:

Crawford Supply   (1)
751 N Rohlwing Rd, Itasca, IL 60143
Tel.: (630) 487-5949
Web Site: http://www.crawfordsupply.com
Plumbing & Heating Equipment Distr
N.A.I.C.S.: 423720
Sig Feiger (Founder)

CRAWFORD TRUCKS & EQUIPMENT, INC.
3601 6th Ave SE, Aberdeen, SD
57401
Tel.: (605) 225-6200
Web Site:
https://www.crawfordtrucks.com
Sales Range: $10-24.9 Million
Emp.: 20
New Car Dealers
N.A.I.C.S.: 441110
Marie Crawford (Treas & Sec)
Leon Crawford (VP)

CRAWFORDSVILLE ELECTRIC LIGHT & POWER
808 Lafayette Rd, Crawfordsville, IN
47933
Tel.: (765) 362-1900
Web Site: https://www.celp.com
Sales Range: $10-24.9 Million
Emp.: 60
Generation, Electric Power
N.A.I.C.S.: 221118
Phil Goode (Pres)

CRAWLEY & COMPANY IN-CORPORATED
288 Grove St Ste 362, Braintree, MA
02184
Tel.: (781) 749-0011
Year Founded: 1960
Sales Range: $100-124.9 Million
Emp.: 2
Advetising Agency
N.A.I.C.S.: 541810
Lawrence T. Davis (Gen Mgr)

CRAYON
488 Madison Ave 4th Fl, New York,
NY 10022-5731
Tel.: (631) 458-0560
Advertising Agencies
N.A.I.C.S.: 541810
Gary Krivin (Partner & COO)

CRAZY DOG TSHIRTS
316 Good St N Ste 100, Rochester,
NY 14607
Tel.: (585) 271-6740
Web Site:
http://www.crazydogtshirts.com
Year Founded: 2004
Sales Range: $25-49.9 Million
Emp.: 15
Online T-shirt Retailer
N.A.I.C.S.: 424350
Bill Kingston (Founder & CEO)

CRB INSURANCE AGENCY
1400 Newman Rd Fl 2, Racine, WI
53406
Tel.: (262) 886-0900
Web Site: http://www.crbins.com
Rev.: $17,000,000
Emp.: 35
Insurance Agents

N.A.I.C.S.: 524210
Bill Mutchler (VP-Comml Dept)
Beth AlderseBaes (VP-Grp Sls)
Martha Christensen (VP-Ops)

CRC INTERNATIONAL INC.
331 E 50th St, New York, NY 10022
Tel.: (212) 906-1000
Web Site: https://www.crc.net
Rev.: $21,354,767
Emp.: 40
Computer Related Consulting Services
N.A.I.C.S.: 541512
Joshua Wurzburger (Pres)

CRC MARKETING SOLUTIONS
6321 Bury Dr Ste 10, Eden Prairie, MN 55346-1739
Tel.: (952) 937-6000   MN
Web Site: http://www.crc-inc.com
Year Founded: 1979
Sales Range: $1-9.9 Million
Emp.: 15
Sales Promotion
N.A.I.C.S.: 541810
Michael Lundeby (Owner)
Elizabeth Petrangelo (Owner & Exec VP)

CRC PUBLIC RELATIONS
2760 Eisenhower Ave 4th Fl, Alexandria, VA 22314
Tel.: (703) 683-5004
Web Site:
http://www.crcpublicrelations.com
Year Founded: 1989
Sales Range: $1-9.9 Million
Emp.: 30
Public Relations Services
N.A.I.C.S.: 541820
Greg Mueller (Pres)
Leif Noren (Chm)

CRC-EVANS INTERNATIONAL, INC.
7011 High Life Dr, Houston, TX 77066
Tel.: (832) 249-3100   DE
Web Site: https://www.crc-evans.com
Year Founded: 1933
Holding Company; Pipeline Construction Equipment Mfr, Automatic Welding Systems Mfr & Miscellaneous Oil & Gas Support Services
N.A.I.C.S.: 551112
Paul Evans (Chm)
Tim Carey (CEO)
Brenden Logue (CFO)

Subsidiaries:

CRC-Evans Automatic Welding, Inc.   (1)
7011 Highlise Dr, Houston, TX 77066
Tel.: (832) 249-3100
Web Site: http://www.crc-evans.com
Sales Range: $10-24.9 Million
Emp.: 75
Automated Welding Systems Mfr
N.A.I.C.S.: 333992
Kevin Allen (Dir-Sls)

CRC-Evans B.V.   (1)
Galvanistraat 6, 3861 NJ, Nijkerk, Netherlands
Tel.: (31) 332534369
Web Site: http://www.crc-evans.nl
Sales Range: $10-24.9 Million
Emp.: 20
Weighting Systems Mfr
N.A.I.C.S.: 333998

CRC-Evans Canada Ltd.   (1)
13040 25th St NE, Edmonton, T6S 0A4, AB, Canada
Tel.: (780) 440-2005
Web Site: http://www.crc-evans.com
Emp.: 20
Automated Welding Systems Mfr
N.A.I.C.S.: 332996

Ed Bohuch (VP & Gen Mgr)

Pipeline Induction Heat Limited   (1)
Pipeline Centre Farrington Road, Rossendale Rd Industrial Est, Burnley, BB11 5SW, United Kingdom
Tel.: (44) 1282415323
Web Site: http://www.sbdinc.com
Sales Range: $25-49.9 Million
Emp.: 80
Pipeline Construction Equipment Mfr
N.A.I.C.S.: 332996
Adam Wynne Hughes (Mng Dir)

CREAGER MERCANTILE
4900 Acoma St, Denver, CO 80216
Tel.: (303) 293-0210
Web Site:
https://www.creagermerc.com
Year Founded: 1958
Rev.: $19,767,175
Emp.: 28
Tobacco & Liquor Products Whslr
N.A.I.C.S.: 424820
Chip Creager (Owner)
Justin Jones (Head-Buyer)
Derek Wilde (Gen Mgr)

CREAGRI, INC.
25565 Whitesell St, Hayward, CA 94545
Tel.: (510) 732-6478
Web Site: http://www.creagri.com
Year Founded: 1998
Sales Range: $10-24.9 Million
Emp.: 10
Pharmaceutical Preparation Mfr
N.A.I.C.S.: 325412
Roberto Crea (Founder)
Paolo Pontoniere (Dir-Comm)
Mark P. Linder (Dir-Strategic Partnerships)

CREAM-O-LAND DAIRY INC.
529 Cedar Ln, Florence, NJ 08518-2511
Tel.: (609) 499-3601   NJ
Web Site:
https://www.creamoland.com
Year Founded: 1946
Sales Range: $75-99.9 Million
Emp.: 200
Producer of Dairy Products
N.A.I.C.S.: 424430
Jay Schneier (CEO)

CREAMISTRY FRANCHISE, INC.
22755 Savi Ranch Pkwy Ste G, Yorba Linda, CA 92887
Tel.: (657) 224-9602
Web Site: http://www.creamistry.com
Year Founded: 2013
Sales Range: $10-24.9 Million
Emp.: 1,100
Food & Beverage Product Distr
N.A.I.C.S.: 445298
Jay Yim (Pres)

CREATE FOUNDATION
213 W Main St Ste 100, Tupelo, MS 38804
Tel.: (662) 844-8989
Web Site:
https://www.createfoundation.com
Year Founded: 1972
Sales Range: $1-9.9 Million
Emp.: 7
Research & Development in the Social Sciences & Humanities
N.A.I.C.S.: 541720
Michael K. Clayborne (Pres)

Subsidiaries:

Journal Publishing Co. Inc.   (1)
1242 S Green St, Tupelo, MS 38804
Tel.: (662) 842-2611
Web Site: http://www.djournal.com

Emp.: 250
Newspaper Publishers
N.A.I.C.S.: 513110
William H. Bronson III (CEO & Publr)

CREATELIVE, INC.
757 Thomas St, Seattle, WA 98109
Tel.: (206) 403-1395
Web Site: http://www.creativelive.com
Sales Range: $50-74.9 Million
Emp.: 85
Online Education Website Operator
N.A.I.C.S.: 513199
Craig Swanson (Co-Founder & Head-Curriculum Dev)
Rick Silvestrini (VP-Mktg)
Megan Acree Zengerle (VP-People Ops)

CREATING RESULTS, LLC-STRATEGIC MARKETING
14000 Crown Ct Ste 211, Woodbridge, VA 22193
Tel.: (703) 494-7888
Web Site:
https://www.creatingresults.com
Year Founded: 1993
Sales Range: $1-9.9 Million
Emp.: 12
Full-Service Marketing Agency that Develops Integrated Marketing Plans & Programs
N.A.I.C.S.: 541613
Judy Harff (Owner & Founder)
Todd Harff (Pres)
Erin Read (Dir-Strategic Plng)
Jessica Ruhle (Dir-Client Svcs)
Mike Stakem (Dir-Creative Svcs)
Beth Spohn (Dir-Bus Dev)
Beth Mickey (Dir-Senior Client Services)
Martha Schultz (Art Dir)
Kimberly Hulett (Owner & Pres)
Patrick McShane (VP)

CREATION EVIDENCE MUSEUM OF TEXAS
3102 FM 205, Glen Rose, TX 76043-0309
Tel.: (254) 897-3200
Web Site:
https://www.creationevidence.org
Sales Range: $1-9.9 Million
Educational Museum
N.A.I.C.S.: 712110
Carl E. Baug (Pres)

CREATION GARDENS, INC.
725 E Market St, Louisville, KY 40202
Tel.: (502) 587-9012
Web Site:
http://www.whatchefswant.com
Year Founded: 1904
Sales Range: $1-9.9 Million
Emp.: 19
Fresh Fruit & Vegetable Whslr
N.A.I.C.S.: 424480
Ron Turnier (Pres & CFO)
Mollie Turnier (Chm & CEO)

Subsidiaries:

Freshpack Produce, Inc.   (1)
5151 Bannock St Ste 12, Denver, CO 80216-1846
Tel.: (303) 412-6232
Web Site: http://www.freshpackproduce.com
Sales Range: $1-9.9 Million
Emp.: 100
Fruit & Vegetable Whslr
N.A.I.C.S.: 424480
Chris Wisekal (CEO)
Heidi Robertson (Mgr-Customer Svc & Sls)
Jim Hagen (COO)
Tim Ray (Exec VP)

Mattingly Foods Inc.   (1)
302 State St, Zanesville, OH 43701

Tel.: (740) 454-0136
Web Site:
http://www.mattinglycashncarry.com
Sales Range: $150-199.9 Million
Frozen Food Whslr
N.A.I.C.S.: 424420
Rusty Deaton (CFO)

CREATIONS, INC.
1185 Ave of the Americas 31th Fl, New York, NY 10036
Tel.: (212) 930-9700   DE
Web Site:
https://www.creationsfin.com
Year Founded: 2019
Rev.: $13,000
Assets: $2,272,000
Liabilities: $912,000
Net Worth: $1,360,000
Earnings: ($26,000)
Fiscal Year-end: 12/31/22
Holding Company
N.A.I.C.S.: 551112
Shmuel Yelshevich (Interim CFO)

CREATIVE AGENCY SERVICES TEAM, INC.
4440 Fruitville Rd, Sarasota, FL 34232
Tel.: (941) 554-8366
Web Site: http://www.castretail.com
Year Founded: 2007
Sales Range: $10-24.9 Million
Emp.: 50
Retail Management Software
N.A.I.C.S.: 513210
John Paul Orr (Pres & CEO)

CREATIVE ALIGNMENTS, LLC
4760 Walnut St Ste 106, Boulder, CO 80301
Web Site:
http://www.creativealignments.com
Year Founded: 2010
Sales Range: $1-9.9 Million
Emp.: 26
Time Based Recruiting Services
N.A.I.C.S.: 561312
Peggy Shell (Founder & CEO)
Chuck Mccoy (Sr Partner & Mng Dir-Tech)
Frank Milianti (Mng Dir)
Alison Peterson (Dir-Client Svc)
Courtney Ogren (Dir-Ops)

CREATIVE ALTERNATIVES, INC.
2855 Geer Rd, Turlock, CA 95382
Tel.: (209) 668-9361   CA
Web Site: http://www.creative-alternatives.org
Year Founded: 1976
Sales Range: $10-24.9 Million
Emp.: 313
Family Welfare Services
N.A.I.C.S.: 624190
Rene Salazar (Dir-Foster Family Agency Program)

CREATIVE BATH PRODUCTS INC.
250 Creative Dr, Central Islip, NY 11722-4404
Tel.: (631) 582-8000
Web Site:
https://www.creativebath.com
Year Founded: 1973
Sales Range: $25-49.9 Million
Emp.: 350
Plastic Bathroom Accessories Mfr
N.A.I.C.S.: 327110
Bob Weiss (COO)
Henny Lakin (VP-Design)
Gary Ball (VP)

CREATIVE BRANCH

Creative Branch—(Continued)

7246 Wynnwood Ln, Houston, TX 77008
Tel.: (713) 861-5551
Web Site:
https://www.creativebranch.com
Sales Range: Less than $1 Million
Emp.: 14
Silk Floral, Tree, Greenery & Christmas Designs Mfr
N.A.I.C.S.: 541490
Melinda Conley *(Dir-Artistic)*
Vickie Lupher *(Office Mgr)*

CREATIVE BROADCAST CONCEPTS
180 Pool St, Biddeford, ME 04005-2833
Tel.: (207) 283-9191
Web Site: http://www.cbcads.com
Year Founded: 1983
Rev.: $32,000,000
Emp.: 25
Fiscal Year-end: 12/31/00
N.A.I.C.S.: 541810
James Boldebook *(Founder)*
Barry Morgan *(Partner, Exec VP, Acct Exec & New Bus Contact)*
Frank Drigotas *(Partner, Exec VP & Acct Exec)*
Sandy Barry *(Dir-Media)*
Faith Logan *(Dir-Res)*
Brian Watkinson *(Acct Exec)*
Bill Park *(Acct Exec)*
Dana Snyder *(Acct Exec)*
Matt Haywood *(Acct Exec)*
Lil Normand *(Controller)*
Sharon DeAguilar *(Mgr-Traffic)*
Devin Robinson *(Dir-Production)*
Todd Randolph *(Mgr-Art Dept)*
Amy Wheeler *(Media Buyer)*
Della Anderson *(Media Buyer)*
Greg Johnson *(Acct Exec)*
Kirk Stockhaus *(Graphic Designer)*
Stacy Lundberg *(Media Buyer)*

CREATIVE BUS SALES INC.
14740 Ramona Ave, Chino, CA 91710
Tel.: (909) 465-5528
Web Site:
https://www.creativebussales.com
Year Founded: 1980
Sales Range: $10-24.9 Million
Emp.: 45
New & Used Car Dealers
N.A.I.C.S.: 441110
Keith Grube *(Dir-Parts-Purchasing)*

Subsidiaries:

Alliance Bus Group, Inc. (1)
1926 Hyannis Ct, College Park, GA 30337-6614
Tel.: (770) 305-0060
Web Site: http://www.alliancebusgroup.com
Transit & Ground Passenger Transportation
N.A.I.C.S.: 485999
Nick Corley *(Dir-Mktg)*

National Bus Sales & Leasing, Inc. (1)
800 Pickens Industrial Dr, Marietta, GA 30062 (100%)
Tel.: (770) 422-8920
Web Site: http://www.nationalbussales.com
Rev.: $5,800,000
Emp.: 100
Commercial Bus Dealers
N.A.I.C.S.: 485510
John T. Smith *(Chm)*
John Noyd *(CFO)*
Keith Parker *(Mgr-Pub Transportation)*

CREATIVE BUSINESS INTERIORS
1535 S 101st St, Milwaukee, WI 53214
Tel.: (414) 545-8500

Web Site:
https://www.creativebusinessinteriors.com
Year Founded: 1991
Sales Range: $10-24.9 Million
Emp.: 80
Commercial & Office Building Contractors
N.A.I.C.S.: 236220
Mai Xiong *(Mgr-Furniture Project)*
Lauren Medina *(Coord-Mktg)*
Diane Petfalski *(Dir-Bus Dev)*
Rebecca Schliesman *(Program Mgr-Furniture)*
Elizabeth White *(Program Mgr-Furniture)*

CREATIVE CARE FOR REACHING INDEPENDENCE
2903 15th St S, Moorhead, MN 56560
Tel.: (218) 236-6730
Web Site: http://www.creativecare.org
Year Founded: 1977
Sales Range: $10-24.9 Million
Emp.: 617
Disability Assistance Services
N.A.I.C.S.: 624120
Mark McGuigan *(Bus Mgr)*
Andrea Ryan *(Dir-HR)*
Jody Hudson *(Dir-Dev)*
Lynette Weber *(Dir-Options)*
Sue Lopez *(Dir-Supported Living Svcs)*

CREATIVE CHILD CARE, INC.
621 Market St, Stockton, CA 95202
Tel.: (209) 941-9100
Web Site: http://www.cccisj.com
Year Founded: 1992
Sales Range: $10-24.9 Million
Emp.: 36
Child Development Services
N.A.I.C.S.: 624110

CREATIVE CIVILIZATION AN AGUILAR/GIRARD AGENCY
106 Auditorium Cir 2nd Fl, San Antonio, TX 78205-1310
Tel.: (210) 227-1999
Web Site:
http://www.creativecivilization.com
Year Founded: 1999
Sales Range: $25-49.9 Million
Emp.: 27
Hispanic Marketing
N.A.I.C.S.: 541810
Gisela Girard *(Pres, Co Founder & COO)*
Bob Loalbo *(CFO)*
Jennifer Gallegos *(Acct Exec)*
Lisa Martin *(Acct Exec-PR)*
Patty Perez *(Mgr-Ops)*
Amanda Herman *(Acct Supvr)*
Justine Hall *(Sr Acct Exec)*
Adolfo Aguilar Jr. *(Chm & CEO)*

CREATIVE COMMUNICATION ASSOCIATES
16 Sage Estate, Albany, NY 12204-2237
Tel.: (518) 427-6600
Web Site:
http://www.ccanewyork.com
Rev.: $30,000,000
Emp.: 20
Advertising Agency
N.A.I.C.S.: 541810
Edward J. Sirianno *(Pres & Dir-Creative)*
Dan Kehn *(Exec VP)*
Vicki Clark *(Controller)*
Richard Langdon *(Sr Dir-Client Svcs)*
Darcy Sokolewicz *(Dir-Mktg)*
Jim Maximowicz *(Assoc Creative Dir)*

CREATIVE COMMUNICATIONS CONSULTANTS, INC.
1277 N Morningside Dr Ne, Atlanta, GA 30306-3372
Tel.: (404) 898-0423
Web Site:
http://www.creativecomminc.com
Year Founded: 1998
Sales Range: Less than $1 Million
Emp.: 2
Public Relations Services
N.A.I.C.S.: 541820
Claudia Brooks D'Avanzo *(Founder & Pres)*
Arielle D'Avanzano *(Acct Mngr)*

CREATIVE COMMUNICATIONS CONSULTANTS, INC.
111 3rd Ave S Ste 390, Minneapolis, MN 55401-2553
Tel.: (612) 338-5098
Year Founded: 1978
Rev.: $7,500,000
Emp.: 10
Fiscal Year-end: 04/30/04
N.A.I.C.S.: 541910
Susan McPherson *(Pres)*
Jim Mackin *(Controller)*
Deb Hyden *(Dir-Media)*
Robert Sheldon *(Dir-PR)*
Mary K. Jones *(Acct Exec)*
Linda Franey *(Mgr-Production)*
Grant Thornburg *(Dir-Art)*
Chris Thron *(Acct Exec)*
Lynette Paulson *(Coord-PR)*

CREATIVE CONTRACTORS INC.
620 Drew St, Clearwater, FL 33755
Tel.: (727) 461-5522
Web Site:
http://www.creativecontractors.com
Year Founded: 1974
Sales Range: $50-74.9 Million
Emp.: 60
Industrial, Commercial & Multi-Family Construction Services
N.A.I.C.S.: 236210
Alan C. Bomstein *(Founder & CEO)*
Jerry Siminski *(Sr VP)*
James C. Cacini *(VP)*
Joshua M. Bomstein *(Pres)*
Gary R. Richter *(VP)*
H. Alan Holderith Sr. *(COO)*

CREATIVE DESIGN INTERIORS INC.
737 Del Paso Rd, Sacramento, CA 95834-1106
Tel.: (916) 641-1121
Web Site:
http://www.creativedesigninteriors.com
Rev.: $12,000,000
Emp.: 100
Ceramic Floor Tile Installation
N.A.I.C.S.: 238330
Jeff Barth *(Gen Mgr)*

CREATIVE DESIGN INTERIORS OF NEVADA, LLC.
9748 S Virginia St Ste A, Reno, NV 89511-5900
Tel.: (775) 852-1200
Web Site:
http://www.creativedesigninteriors.com
Year Founded: 2004
Sales Range: $10-24.9 Million
Emp.: 75
Fence Installation Services
N.A.I.C.S.: 238990
Craig Bender *(Owner)*
Ron Lapp *(Principal)*

CREATIVE DINING SERVICES, INC.
1 Royal Park Dr Ste 3, Zeeland, MI 49464
Tel.: (616) 748-1700					MI
Web Site:
https://www.creativedining.com
Year Founded: 1990
Administrative Management & General Management Consulting Services
N.A.I.C.S.: 541611
Chuck Melchiori *(VP-Bus Dev)*
Jim Eickhoff *(Pres & CEO)*
Kenneth Ivory *(VP-Ops)*
Jane Newton *(Dir-HR)*

CREATIVE ENTERTAINMENT SERVICES
7009 Valjean Ave, Van Nuys, CA 91406
Tel.: (818) 267-2560					CA
Web Site:
http://www.acreativegroup.com
Year Founded: 1985
Sales Range: $1-9.9 Million
Emp.: 8
Advertising Services
N.A.I.C.S.: 541810
Robert Douglas Woodruff *(Chm)*
Richard P. Storrs *(CEO)*
Kathy Findling *(Pres)*

CREATIVE EXTRUDED PRODUCTS
1414 Commerce Park Dr, Tipp City, OH 45371
Tel.: (937) 667-4485
Web Site:
http://www.creativeextruded.com
Sales Range: $25-49.9 Million
Emp.: 180
Extruded Finished Plastics Products Mfr
N.A.I.C.S.: 326199
Brian A. Wenrick *(CEO)*
Tim Schlater *(Dir-Engrg)*
Rick Douglas *(Dir-Quality)*
Jeff Patrick *(Engr-Design)*
Rick Terry *(Mgr-Process Engrg)*
Jack Young *(VP-Ops)*
Michael Green *(Mgr-Ops)*
R. Thomas Struewing *(Controller & Treas)*

CREATIVE FEED
36 Cooper Sq, New York, NY 10003
Tel.: (212) 966-3025
Web Site: http://www.creativefeed.net
Year Founded: 2006
Sales Range: $1-9.9 Million
Emp.: 20
Advetising Agency
N.A.I.C.S.: 541810
Arthur Ceria *(Founder & CEO)*
Michael Quinn *(Mng Partner)*

CREATIVE FINANCIAL STAFFING LLC
1 Beacon St 26 Fl, Boston, MA 02108
Tel.: (617) 753-6012
Web Site: http://www.cfstaffing.com
Year Founded: 1994
Sales Range: $25-49.9 Million
Emp.: 30
Temporary Staffing Services
N.A.I.C.S.: 561320
Dan J. Casey *(Pres)*
Adria Reed *(Mgr-Bus Dev & Social Media)*

CREATIVE FOODS CORP.
200 Garden City Plz Ste 105, Garden City, NY 11530-3341
Tel.: (516) 746-6800					NY
Web Site:
http://www.creativefoodscorp.com

Year Founded: 1976
Emp.: 1,000
Fast Food Franchise
N.A.I.C.S.: 722513
Jay Della Monica *(Owner)*

CREATIVE GARAGE
1308 Chisholm Trail Rd Ste 111,
Round Rock, TX 78681
Tel.: (512) 799-7065
Web Site:
http://www.creativegarage.com
Year Founded: 1999
Sales Range: Less than $1 Million
Emp.: 3
Print
N.A.I.C.S.: 541810
Mike Kastens *(Creative Dir)*
Martha Hallman *(Dir-Client Svc)*

CREATIVE GROUP, INC.
619 N Lynndale Dr, Appleton, WI
54914-3022
Tel.: (920) 739-8851   WI
Web Site:
http://www.creativegroupinc.com
Sales Range: $75-99.9 Million
Emp.: 120
Vacation Vans
N.A.I.C.S.: 541612
Bob Carlson *(Acct Dir)*
Maritza Zaenger *(Sr VP-Employee Svcs)*
Paul Hebert *(Sr Dir-Solution Architecture)*
Jerry J. Murphy *(VP-Customer Experience)*
Krista Washburn *(Pres)*
Tim O'Neill *(Acct Exec-Bus Dev)*
Glenn Darlington *(Exec VP-Bus Dev)*
Jamie Schwartz *(Sr Dir-Individual Performance Solutions)*
Melissa Van Dyke *(VP-Design & Insights)*
Manon Dicaire *(Sr VP-Bus Dev)*
Karen Hudson *(Acct Exec-Bus Dev)*
Craig Seymour *(VP-Bus Dev)*

CREATIVE INFORMATION TECHNOLOGY, INC.
1110 N Glebe Rd Ste 710, Arlington,
VA 22201
Tel.: (703) 647-1060   MD
Web Site: http://www.citi-us.com
Year Founded: 1996
Sales Range: $10-24.9 Million
Emp.: 150
Application Development, Enterprise
Services & IT Support
N.A.I.C.S.: 541512
Sunil Kolhekar *(Co-Founder, Pres & CEO)*
Mauro Binda *(Dir-SharePoint Practice)*
Melanie Foss *(Mgr-Contract)*
Ramki Uppuluri *(VP)*
Alankar Joshi *(VP)*
Paul Schapiro *(Chief Innovation Officer)*

CREATIVE INSURANCE MARKETING CO.
208 2nd Ave, Belmar, NJ 07719
Tel.: (732) 681-0700
Web Site: http://www.cim-co.com
Rev.: $10,000,000
Emp.: 5
Advetising Agency
N.A.I.C.S.: 541810
Kimberly Paterson *(Principal)*
Shelley Karins *(Creative Dir)*
Angela Martine *(Office Mgr)*
Fred G. Marziano *(Principal)*

CREATIVE LABEL INC.

2450 Estes Ave, Elk Grove Village, IL
60007
Tel.: (847) 956-6960
Sales Range: $10-24.9 Million
Emp.: 100
Gold Stamping On Books
N.A.I.C.S.: 323120
Jerry Koril *(CFO)*
Gloria Matuszewski *(Controller)*

CREATIVE LEATHER FURNITURE INC.
450 N McClintock Dr, Chandler, AZ
85226
Tel.: (602) 337-7054
Web Site:
https://www.creativeleather.com
Sales Range: $75-99.9 Million
Emp.: 150
Household Furniture Mfr
N.A.I.C.S.: 337126
Lubertus Hayenga *(CEO)*
Michael Gregory *(Pres)*
Randy Rodgers *(VP)*
Victoria Beaman *(Mgr-Production)*
Wesley Suderman *(Dir-IT, Distr & Customer Rels)*

CREATIVE LINK ADVERTISING
142 Chula Vista Ste 200, San Antonio, TX 78232
Tel.: (210) 979-8080   TX
Year Founded: 1993
Sales Range: $10-24.9 Million
Emp.: 18
Advertising Agencies, Brand Development, Communications, Event Marketing, Full Service, Hispanic Marketing, Logo & Package Design, Public Relations, Sports Marketing
N.A.I.C.S.: 541810
Kevin Larue *(CEO)*
Randy Cave *(Dir-Art)*
Mike Connor *(Partner & Pres-Creative Link Studios Inc)*

CREATIVE MAILBOX DESIGNS, LLC
12801 Commodity Pl, Tampa, FL
33626
Tel.: (813) 818-7100
Web Site:
http://www.creativemailboxde
signs.com
Rev.: $10,000,000
Emp.: 80
Mailbox & Sign Designs Mfr
N.A.I.C.S.: 238990
Kim McGinnis *(Mgr-Production)*
Paul Wilbur *(Officer-Fin)*
Kelly Crandall *(Co-Owner & Dir-Sls)*
Jamie Harden *(Pres & CEO)*

CREATIVE MANUFACTURING INC.
11191 Calabash Ave, Fontana, CA
92337
Tel.: (909) 357-8295
Web Site: http://www.coronado.com
Rev.: $11,505,000
Emp.: 300
Siding, Precast Stone
N.A.I.C.S.: 327390
Melton Bacon *(Owner)*

CREATIVE MARKETING ALLIANCE INC.
191 Clarksville Rd, Princeton Junction, NJ 08550
Tel.: (609) 297-2222
Web Site:
http://www.cmasolutions.com
Year Founded: 1987
Rev.: $30,000,000
Emp.: 30
Advetising Agency

N.A.I.C.S.: 541810
Jeffrey E. Barnhart *(Pres & CEO)*
Burton W. Lambert *(CFO & Exec VP-Ops)*
Dave Sherwood *(VP & Dir-Creative)*
Christian Horn *(VP-Mktg Comm)*
Rob Jones *(Sr VP & Gen Mgr)*
Albert Vrancart *(VP-Mktg)*
Lynn McCullough *(Dir-Association Meeting & Event Plng)*
Kaitlin Friedman *(Acct Exec)*
Diane Galante *(Assoc Mgr)*
Jennifer Thayer *(Assoc Mgr)*
Christian Amato *(COO & Chief Bus Dev Officer)*

CREATIVE MARKETING RESOURCE, INC.
325 W Huron St, Chicago, IL 60654
Tel.: (312) 943-6266   IL
Year Founded: 1965
Sales Range: $10-24.9 Million
Emp.: 15
N.A.I.C.S.: 541810
Jacqueline Wagner *(Pres)*
Lynn Goodwin *(Controller)*
Ben Molinaro *(Assoc Dir-Creative)*
Alicia Geller *(VP-Client Svcs)*
Lyn Wolfson *(Media Dir)*
Adrianne Sell *(Assoc Dir-Creative)*
Kitty Ciske *(VP-Bus Dev)*

CREATIVE MARKETING RESOURCES
1858 S Wadsworth Blvd Ste 315,
Lakewood, CO 80232-6840
Tel.: (303) 985-8777
Year Founded: 1994
Sales Range: Less than $1 Million
Emp.: 4
N.A.I.C.S.: 541810
Trent Thornton *(Pres & Acct Exec)*
Dan Andrews *(Art Dir)*

CREATIVE MARKETING SPECIALISTS, INC.
1093 A1A Beach Blvd PMB 292,
Saint Augustine, FL 32080
Tel.: (904) 461-6600
Year Founded: 1992
Sales Range: $25-49.9 Million
Emp.: 5
N.A.I.C.S.: 541810
B.J. Fisher *(PR Dir)*
Jacquelyn Zeichner *(Designer & Typesetter)*
Tina Berry *(Controller)*

CREATIVE MEDIA MARKETING INC.
594 Broadway Ste 500, New York,
NY 10012
Tel.: (212) 979-8884
Web Site: https://www.cmmpr.com
Sales Range: $1-9.9 Million
Emp.: 25
Integrated Communications Agency
Services
N.A.I.C.S.: 541820
Stacey Miyamoto *(Founder)*

CREATIVE OFFICE ENVIRONMENT, LLC
11798 N Lakeridge Pkwy, Ashland,
VA 23005
Tel.: (804) 329-0400
Web Site: https://www.creative-
va.com
Year Founded: 1995
Sales Range: $25-49.9 Million
Emp.: 170
Provider of Furnishing Services
N.A.I.C.S.: 423210
Bob De Lille *(CEO)*
Rick Carr *(Pres)*

CREATIVE OFFICE INTERIORS INC.
1 Design Ctr Pl Ste 734, Boston, MA
02210-0734
Tel.: (617) 956-4100
Web Site:
http://www.creativeofficepavilion.com
Year Founded: 1986
Sales Range: $150-199.9 Million
Emp.: 80
Office Furniture
N.A.I.C.S.: 423210
Joseph Gardner *(Pres)*
Angelo DeBenedictis *(CFO)*

CREATIVE OFFICE PAVILION LLC
44 Thomson Pl, Boston, MA 02210
Tel.: (617) 956-4100
Web Site:
https://www.creativeoffices.com
Emp.: 100
Furniture & Home Furnishings Mfr
N.A.I.C.S.: 337211
Denise Horn *(CEO & Partner)*
Karen Krasnomowitz *(Sr VP-Sls)*
Kim Pinkerton *(Mng Principal)*

Subsidiaries:

De Clercq Office Group, Ltd.   (1)
1227 Whitney Ave, Hamden, CT 06517-
2801
Tel.: (203) 230-9144
Web Site: http://www.dog-office.com
Furniture Merchant Whslr
N.A.I.C.S.: 423210

CREATIVE PARTNERS
1 Stamford Landing, 62 Southfield
Ave Ste 110, Stamford, CT 06902
Tel.: (203) 705-9203
Year Founded: 1986
Rev.: $20,000,000
Emp.: 30
N.A.I.C.S.: 541810
Peter Schelfhaudt *(Chm & CEO)*
Laura Saggese *(VP-Client Svcs)*
Jason Martin *(Dir-Web Dev)*
Jason Kannon *(VP)*
Scott Greenley *(Sr Dir-Creative)*
John Meagle *(VP)*
Price Carter *(VP & Dir-Consumer Mktg)*
Tara Clark *(Dir-Digital Strategy)*

CREATIVE PARTNERS GROUP, INC.
409 Via Corta, Palos Verdes Estates,
CA 90274
Tel.: (310) 378-8043
Web Site:
http://www.creativepartners.com
Sales Range: $10-24.9 Million
Emp.: 4
Advetising Agency
N.A.I.C.S.: 541810
Greg Sparkman *(VP)*

CREATIVE PLANNING, LLC
5454 W 110th St, Overland Park, KS
66211
Web Site: http://creativeplanning.com
Year Founded: 1983
Miscellaneous Financial Investment
Activities
N.A.I.C.S.: 523999
Mark Henke *(Mgr-Wealth)*
Molly Rothove *(Mgr-Wealth)*
Craig Seiler *(Partner)*
Beth Sharpe *(Partner)*
Peter Mallouk *(Pres & CEO)*

Subsidiaries:

Coe Financial Services Inc.   (1)
8100 E 22nd St N Ste 1400-2, Wichita, KS
67226-2314

Creative Planning, LLC—(Continued)
Tel.: (316) 689-0900
Web Site:
http://www.coefinancialservices.com
Investment Advice
N.A.I.C.S.: 523940
J. Richard Coe (Mng Principal)

Daniels Tansey LLP (1)
1013 Centre Rd Ste 220, Wilmington, DE 19805-1265
Tel.: (302) 425-3523
Web Site: http://www.danielstansey.com
Investment Banking & Securities Dealing
N.A.I.C.S.: 523150
Susan Benson (Partner)

Emery Howard Portfolio Management, Inc. (1)
577 Airport Blvd, Burlingame, CA 94010
Tel.: (650) 579-7100
Web Site: http://www.emeryandhoward.com
Rev.: $2,075,000
Emp.: 5
Portfolio Management
N.A.I.C.S.: 523940

Heritage Way Advisors, LLC (1)
6833 Stalter Dr Ste 203, Rockford, IL 61108-2582
Tel.: (815) 397-0900
Web Site:
http://www.heritagewayadvisors.com
Emp.: 100
Investment Advice
N.A.I.C.S.: 523940

Lenox Wealth Management, Inc. (1)
8044 Montgomery Rd Ste 420, Cincinnati, OH 45236-2920
Tel.: (513) 618-7080
Web Site: http://www.lenoxwealth.com
Investment Advice
N.A.I.C.S.: 523940
Jane Shank (Pres)
John Lame (CEO)

Stratford Consulting LLC (1)
15303 Dallas Pkwy Ste 460, Addison, TX 75001-6730
Tel.: (972) 960-3780
Web Site: http://www.stratfordllc.com
Intermediation
N.A.I.C.S.: 523910
Mike Hemp (Mng Principal)

Sullivan, Bruyette, Speros & Blayney, LLC (1)
8444 Westpark Dr Ste 610, McLean, VA 22102
Tel.: (703) 734-9300
Web Site: http://www.sbsbllc.com
Financial Planning, Investment Management & Tax Preparation Services
N.A.I.C.S.: 522320
Gregory Sullivan (Founder & Co-CEO)
Amy Adams (Sr Mgr-Tax)

Sunrise Advisors, Inc. (1)
3710 W 135th St, Leawood, KS 66224-7611
Tel.: (913) 681-0215
Web Site: http://www.sunriseadvisors.com
Investment Advice
N.A.I.C.S.: 523940
David P. Scott (Owner)

CREATIVE PLAYTHINGS LTD.
33 Loring Dr, Framingham, MA 01702
Tel.: (508) 620-0900   MA
Web Site:
https://www.creativeplaythings.com
Year Founded: 1951
Sales Range: $100-124.9 Million
Emp.: 175
Mfr & Retailer of Playground Equipment
N.A.I.C.S.: 339920
Donald Hoffman (Pres & CEO)
Brian Dillon (Controller)
Mike Dupras (Mgr-Distr)
Vito Parisi (VP-Sls)
Kakridas Peter (Pres-Retail)

CREATIVE PRODUCTIONS
5030 E 2nd St, Long Beach, CA 90803

Tel.: (562) 985-1363
Web Site:
https://www.creativeproduction.com
Year Founded: 1981
Sales Range: $10-24.9 Million
Emp.: 30
Digital/Interactive, Print & Production Promotions
N.A.I.C.S.: 541890
Deborah Golian Castro (Pres & CEO)

CREATIVE RESOURCE GROUP, LLC
12859 N Hwy 146, Dayton, TX 77535
Tel.: (713) 947-0721   DE
Web Site: http://www.crg-us.net
Year Founded: 2005
Plant Logistic Support & Safety Services
N.A.I.C.S.: 561990
Brian Bourque (CEO)
Timothy Long (Dir-Bus Dev)
Clint Sanders (Dir-Corp Safety)
Tricia Beckman (Controller)
Sal Nunez (Dir-Field Ops)
Chad Robl (VP-Ops & Labor Svcs)
Stewart Records (VP-Safety Svcs)
Keith Dillard (VP-Personnel Busing Ops)
Eric Klenk (VP-HR & Admin)

CREATIVE SALES & MARKETING ASSOCIATES
1401 Air Rail Ave, Virginia Beach, VA 23455
Tel.: (757) 363-9000
Web Site: http://www.creative-displays.com
Rev.: $10,000,000
Emp.: 6
Hobby Goods
N.A.I.C.S.: 423920
Emily Palmer (VP)

CREATIVE SALES GROUP, INC.
598 Byrne Industrial Dr NE, Rockford, MI 49341
Tel.: (616) 245-9781
Rev.: $10,000,000
Emp.: 5
Golf Accessories Sales
N.A.I.C.S.: 424990
Steve Pate (Chm)

CREATIVE SALES INC.
1819 Waterbury Dr SE, Grand Rapids, MI 49508
Tel.: (616) 455-0198
Rev.: $10,000,000
Emp.: 3
Marketing Consulting
N.A.I.C.S.: 541613
Robert Mallory (VP)

CREATIVE SERVICES, INC.
PO Box 6008, High Point, NC 27262
Tel.: (336) 889-3010
Sales Range: $25-49.9 Million
Emp.: 100
Fertilizer Mfr
N.A.I.C.S.: 325314
Christina J. Qubein (Sec & Treas)
Ramsey R. Qubein (VP)
Deena V. Qubein (Pres)

CREATIVE SIGN DESIGNS
12801 Commodity Pl, Tampa, FL 33626
Tel.: (813) 818-7100
Web Site:
https://www.creativesigndesign.com
Year Founded: 1986
Sales Range: $10-24.9 Million
Emp.: 90
Sign Designer & Mfr

N.A.I.C.S.: 339950
Jamie Harden (Pres & CEO)
Larry Morgan (Chm)
Kelly Crandall (VP-Sls)
Paul Wilbur (CFO)
Kim Mcginnis (Dir-Production)
Melanie Harden (Exec VP)
Sean Sheedy (Dir-Installation & Project Mgmt)
Glen Welden (Dir-Design)
Adam Wold (Dir-Project Svcs)
Kris Kay (Acct Mgr)
Linda Prusiecki (Acct Mgr)
Luke Minton (Acct Mgr)
Rick Houston (Acct Mgr-Sls)
Susan Barrett (Acct Mgr)
Tom Hughes (VP & Dir-Ops)
Sam Feldstein (COO)
Jon McDade (Mgr-Environmental Graphics & Wayfinding Studio-Longwood)

CREATIVE SOLUTIONS CONSULTING INC
8225 E 56th St, Indianapolis, IN 46216
Tel.: (317) 757-8764
Web Site:
http://www.csciconsulting.com
Year Founded: 2002
Sales Range: $10-24.9 Million
Emp.: 75
It Consulting
N.A.I.C.S.: 541690
Debra Magnuson (Mgr-HR)
Stacia Fortune-Schoeneman (Dir-Govt Solutions)

CREATIVE SOLUTIONS GROUP, INC.
1250 N Crooks Rd, Clawson, MI 48017
Tel.: (248) 288-9700   MI
Web Site: https://www.csgnow.com
Year Founded: 1998
Sales Range: $10-24.9 Million
Emp.: 100
Advertising Promotional Trade Show Services; Partitions & Fixtures Mfr
N.A.I.C.S.: 541890
Debbie Kierdorf (Mgr-Event Svcs)
Jack McCoy (Mgr-Graphics)
Jason Cooperman (Dir-Multimedia)

CREATIVE STAGE LIGHTING CO.
149 Route 28 N, North Creek, NY 12853
Tel.: (518) 251-3302
Web Site:
http://www.creativestagelighting.com
Sales Range: $10-24.9 Million
Emp.: 50
Lighting Fixtures, Commercial & Industrial
N.A.I.C.S.: 423610
Tracey Cosgrove (VP-Sls & Ops)
George B. Studnicky III (Pres)

CREATIVE TEACHING PRESS INC.
6262 Katella Ave, Cypress, CA 90630
Tel.: (714) 895-5047
Web Site:
https://www.creativeteaching.com
Sales Range: $25-49.9 Million
Emp.: 120
Books, Publishing Only
N.A.I.C.S.: 513130
Jim Connelly (Pres)
Luella Connelly (Founder)

CREATIVE TECHNOLOGIES CORP.

170 53rd St, Brooklyn, NY 11232-4391
Tel.: (718) 492-8400
Rev.: $15,714,000
Emp.: 7
Electric Household Cooking Appliances
N.A.I.C.S.: 335210
David Guttmann (Chm)
Subsidiaries:

Ace Janitorial Supply Co., Inc. (1)
1365 61st St Top Fl, Brooklyn, NY 11219
Tel.: (718) 492-7200
Web Site: http://www.acejan.com
Sales Range: $10-24.9 Million
Emp.: 16
Janitorial Supplies Distr
N.A.I.C.S.: 423850
David Guttmann (Chm)

CREATIVE TESTING SOLUTIONS
2424 W Erie Dr, Tempe, AZ 85282   AZ
Web Site: https://www.mycts.org
Year Founded: 2009
Sales Range: $200-249.9 Million
Emp.: 300
Testing Laboratory
N.A.I.C.S.: 541380
Sally Caglioti (Pres)
German Leparc (Chief Medical Officer)

CREATIVE VISION ALLIANCE CORP.
210 White Wing Dr #B, Columbia, SC 29229
Tel.: (980) 202-2822   SC
Advertising Related Services
N.A.I.C.S.: 541890
Roland Chambers (Owner)

CREATIVEHUB
330 W 38th St Ste 1208, New York, NY 10018
Tel.: (312) 576-0032
Web Site:
http://www.creativehub.com
Sales Range: Less than $1 Million
Emp.: 5
Advetising Agency
N.A.I.C.S.: 541810
Neel Premkumar (CEO)
Eva Weiss (Mgr-Tech Project)

CREDENCE MANAGEMENT SOLUTIONS
1 Metro Ctr 700 12th St NW Ste 700, Washington, DC 20005
Tel.: (202) 903-0330
Web Site: http://www.credence-llc.com
Year Founded: 2005
Sales Range: $1-9.9 Million
Emp.: 32
Business Management & Technology Consulting Services
N.A.I.C.S.: 541611
Jeetendra Ahuja (Principal)
Radhakrishnan Srinivasan (Principal)
Prashant Gaur (Pres)
Siddhartha Chowdhary (CEO)
David Beveridge (Mgr-Practice)
Tiera Kendle (Dir-Credence)

CREDENT TECHNOLOGIES LLC.
30 Brookfield St Ste A, South Windsor, CT 06074
Tel.: (860) 436-6391
Web Site:
https://www.credenttech.com
Year Founded: 2003
Rev.: $6,700,000
Emp.: 85
Business Consulting Services

N.A.I.C.S.: 541618
Dinesh B. Movv *(CEO)*

CREDERA

15303 Dallas Pkwy Ste 300, Addison, TX 75001
Tel.: (972) 692-0010
Web Site: https://www.credera.com
Year Founded: 1999
Sales Range: $10-24.9 Million
Emp.: 200
Information Technology Consulting Services
N.A.I.C.S.: 541512
Matt Levy *(Co-Founder & Mng Dir)*
Justin Bell *(Pres)*
Trent Sutton *(VP)*
Justin Bauer *(Mgr-Infrastructure Practice)*
Derek Knudsen *(Partner & VP)*
Jake Carter *(Principal-Mgmt Consulting Practice)*
Cody Case *(Principal)*

CREDIT ANSWERS, LLC

6200 Tennyson Pkwy Ste 200, Plano, TX 75024-6099
Tel.: (972) 202-4366
Web Site:
    http://www.CreditAnswers.com
Year Founded: 1988
Sales Range: $25-49.9 Million
Emp.: 34
Credit Card Debt Negotiation & Settlement Services
N.A.I.C.S.: 561440
Rick Burton *(Dir-Customer Svcs)*
Bill Loughborough *(Pres)*

CREDIT COLLECTIONS BUREAU COLLECTION AGENCY

3550 E Rosser Ave, Bismarck, ND 58502-0778
Tel.: (701) 250-1390
Web Site: http://www.ccbinet.com
Year Founded: 1987
Sales Range: $25-49.9 Million
Emp.: 90
Credit Collections Services
N.A.I.C.S.: 561440
Dean Bradley *(Gen Mgr)*

CREDIT CONTROL SERVICES INC.

2 Wells Ave, Newton, MA 02459
Tel.: (617) 965-2000
Web Site: http://www.ccsusa.com
Rev.: $40,000,000
Emp.: 700
Collection Agency, Except Real Estate
N.A.I.C.S.: 561440
Gerald Sands *(Chm)*

CREDIT CONTROL, LLC

5757 Phantom Dr Ste 330, Hazelwood, MO 63042
Tel.: (314) 442-7400
Web Site: http://www.credit-control.com
Year Founded: 2006
Collection Agency
N.A.I.C.S.: 561440
Steve Gerow *(CIO)*
Rick Saffer *(CEO)*
Jesse Meade *(Dir-Ops)*
Judy Joyce *(Controller)*
Paul Farinacci *(CMO & Exec VP)*
Tony Pirotta *(Chief Compliance Officer)*
Joe Dibello *(Exec VP-Specialty Ops)*
Robert Hall *(Exec VP-Ops)*

CREDIT GUARD OF FLORIDA INC.

1 Progress Plz Ste 2100, Saint Petersburg, FL 33701
Tel.: (727) 821-4440
Year Founded: 1977
Rev.: $10,000,000
Emp.: 30
Inspection & Investigation Services, Insurance
N.A.I.C.S.: 524298
Dean Kucera *(Pres)*

CREDIT LENDERS SERVICE AGENCY

7 Foster Ave Ste 200, Gibbsboro, NJ 08026
Tel.: (856) 787-9005
Web Site:
    https://www.creditlenders.com
Year Founded: 1982
Sales Range: $10-24.9 Million
Emp.: 165
Consumer Credit Reporting Bureau
N.A.I.C.S.: 561450
Thomas R. Swider *(Pres)*
Rich Scozzari *(VP-Acctg & Fin)*

CREDIT SERVICE INT'L CORP.

512 2nd St Ste 6, Hudson, WI 54016
Tel.: (715) 386-0424
Web Site:
    http://www.upgradeyourcollections.com
Year Founded: 1962
Sales Range: $1-9.9 Million
Emp.: 25
Financial Consulting Services
N.A.I.C.S.: 541611
John Erickson *(Pres & CEO)*

CREDIT SOLUTIONS, INC.

12700 Park Central Dr 21st Fl, Dallas, TX 75251
Tel.: (972) 763-7042
Web Site:
    http://www.creditsolutions.com
Year Founded: 2004
Sales Range: $75-99.9 Million
Emp.: 924
Debt Counselors
N.A.I.C.S.: 561499
Silvestre Luna *(Mgr)*

CREDIT UNION 1

200 E Champaign Ave, Rantoul, IL 61866-2930
Tel.: (217) 893-9112
Web Site:
    https://www.creditunion1.org
Rev.: $37,200,000
Emp.: 250
Credit Union
N.A.I.C.S.: 522130
Brenda Crane *(COO & Sr VP-Lending)*
Ellie Krcmar *(Sr VP-Branch Ops)*
Donna Robinson *(Sec)*
Daniel A. Ricci *(VP)*
Pa Yang *(Mgr-Fairbanks)*
Rich Broaddus *(Sr VP-Fin)*
Steele Hendrix *(Sr VP-Mktg & Bus Dev)*
Jim McNeil *(Sr VP-Risk Mgmt & Strategy)*
Mark Burgess *(CTO)*
Robert L. Larson Jr. *(Vice Chm)*

Subsidiaries:

Emory Alliance Credit Union   **(1)**
1237 Clairmont Rd, Decatur, GA 30030
Tel.: (404) 329-6415
Web Site: http://www.emoryacu.com
Sales Range: $1-9.9 Million
Emp.: 43
Credit Union Operator
N.A.I.C.S.: 522130

CREDIT UNION EXECUTIVES SOCIETY, INC.

5510 Research Park Dr, Madison, WI 53711-5377
Tel.: (608) 271-2664   WI
Web Site: http://www.cues.org
Year Founded: 1980
Sales Range: $10-24.9 Million
Emp.: 53
Professional Association
N.A.I.C.S.: 813920
Dawn Poker *(Chief Sls & Member Rels Officer & Sr VP)*
Kathy Wright *(Dir-HR)*
Erin Templer *(Dir-Mktg)*
Kristina Mattson-Grimm *(VP-Membership)*
Christopher Stevenson *(Chief Learning Officer & Sr VP)*
Karin Sand *(VP-Strategic Partnerships & Solutions)*
Joette Mitchell *(VP-Executive Education & Meetings)*
Jerry Saalsaa *(Chief Admin Officer & Sr VP)*
Stu Ramsey *(Chm)*
Russell Evans *(VP-Sls & Member Rels-Northeast)*
Tony Hill *(CMO & Sr VP)*
Kelly Marshall *(Vice Chm)*
Erin Mendez *(Treas)*
Curt Weier *(VP-Fin)*
Kris P. VanBeek *(Sec)*

CREDIT UNION OF AMERICA

PO Box 47528, Wichita, KS 67201-7528
Tel.: (316) 265-3272   KS
Web Site:
    http://www.cuofamerica.com
Year Founded: 1935
Sales Range: $25-49.9 Million
Emp.: 228
Credit Union
N.A.I.C.S.: 522130
Paul Meissner *(CFO & Sr VP)*
Robert Thurman *(CEO)*
Lea Ann Gabbert *(Chief Admin Officer & Sr VP)*
Gina Evans *(VP-HR & Talent Dev)*
Dan Umscheid *(VP-Support Svcs)*
Sam Grove *(VP-Fin & Data Analytics)*
Shannon Lauber *(Mgr-Deposit Svc)*
Jeremy Holt *(Asst Mgr-West Douglas)*
Glenda Burkett *(Dir-Corp Giving, Comm & Mktg Compliance)*
Matt Schenk *(VP-Enterprise Architecture)*
Tim Dunham *(Asst VP-Consumer Loan Ops)*
Ernest Warren *(Chief Lending Officer & Sr VP)*
Eileen Phelps *(COO & Sr VP)*
Eric Scott *(Asst VP-Real Estate Lending)*
Kym Money *(VP-Mktg & Bus Dev)*
Cassie Bolander *(Asst Branch Mgr)*
Steve Beachum *(Mgr-Goddard)*
Blake Penner *(Mgr-IT Security)*
Melissa Gattenby *(Asst VP-Support Svcs)*
Bert Jones *(Mgr-Svc Center)*
Jesse Foreman *(Mgr-Delano)*
David Germann *(Sr VP-Retail Ops)*
Gavin Hirsh *(Mgr-Automated Teller Svcs)*
Roy Mansch *(VP-Branch Ops)*
Robert Hoyle *(CIO & Sr VP-IT)*
Tim Duhnam *(VP-Consumer Lending)*
Amanda Gish *(Asst VP-Mktg)*
Judy Schoenecker *(Asst VP-Collections)*
Patrick Harms *(Asst VP-Data Analytics)*
Sarah Kueser *(Asst VP-Comml Svcs)*

Nicole El-Chami *(Asst VP-Electronic Svcs)*
Jim Jacobs *(VP-Risk Mgmt)*
Jason Mayer *(Asst VP-IT Infrastructure)*
Brian Isham *(Mgr-Member Experience)*
Cody Blasi *(Mgr-TAP Center)*
Tonya Loper *(Asst VP-Branch Ops & Mgr-Delano)*
Mitch Crouch *(Dir-Real Estate Bus Dev)*
Thomas Henning *(Mgr-IT Support)*

CREDIT UNION OF DENVER

9305 W Alameda Ave, Lakewood, CO 80226
Tel.: (303) 234-1700
Web Site: https://www.cudenver.com
Year Founded: 1931
Rev.: $20,843,378
Emp.: 100
Banking Services
N.A.I.C.S.: 522110
Keith M. Cowling *(Pres & CEO)*
Donna Riley *(Pres)*

CREDIT UNION OF GEORGIA

3048 Eagle Dr, Woodstock, GA 30189
Tel.: (678) 486-1111   GA
Web Site: https://www.cuofga.org
Year Founded: 1960
Sales Range: $10-24.9 Million
Emp.: 73
Credit Union
N.A.I.C.S.: 522130
Frances Roberson *(Chm)*

CREDIT UNION OF SOUTHERN CALIFORNIA

PO Box 200, Whittier, CA 90608-0200
Tel.: (562) 945-2214   CA
Web Site: http://www.cusocal.org
Year Founded: 1954
Sales Range: $25-49.9 Million
Emp.: 202
Credit Union Operator
N.A.I.C.S.: 522130
Dave Gunderson *(Pres & CEO)*

Subsidiaries:

Pacific Transportation Federal Credit Union   **(1)**
501 W 190th St, Gardena, CA 90248
Tel.: (424) 233-3091
Web Site: http://www.ptfcu.org
Federal Credit Unions
N.A.I.C.S.: 522130
Michael Bare *(CEO)*

CREDIT UNION ONE, INC.

400 E 9 Mile Rd, Ferndale, MI 48220-1774
Web Site: http://www.cuone.org
Year Founded: 1937
Rev.: $38,278,696
Assets: $1,190,826,264
Liabilities: $1,082,001,378
Net Worth: $108,824,886
Earnings: $10,799,685
Fiscal Year-end: 12/31/18
Credit Union
N.A.I.C.S.: 522130
Paul W. Stuart *(Chm)*
Guadalupe G. Lara *(Vice Chm)*
Joan Stefanski *(Sec & Treas)*
Gary Moody *(Pres & CEO)*

CREDIT UNION WEST

PO Box 7600, Glendale, AZ 85312-7600
Tel.: (602) 631-3200   AZ
Web Site: https://www.cuwest.org
Year Founded: 1951
Sales Range: $25-49.9 Million
Emp.: 237
Credit Union Operator
N.A.I.C.S.: 522130

Credit Union West—(Continued)

Karen Roch (Exec VP)
Bob Birr (Chief Lending Officer & VP)
Diana Cruz (VP-Support Svcs)

CREDIT-BASED ASSET SERVICING & SECURITIZATION LLC
335 Madison Ave Fl 19, New York, NY 10017-4632
Tel.: (212) 850-7700   DE
Year Founded: 1996
Sales Range: $50-74.9 Million
Emp.: 200
Residential Mortgage Investment & Servicing
N.A.I.C.S.: 523999
Bruce Williams (Founder & Co-CEO)
Saul Sanders (Co-CEO)

Subsidiaries:

Note World   (1)
1001 Pacific Ave Ste 200, Tacoma, WA 98402-4440   **(100%)**
Tel.: (253) 620-7040
Web Site: http://www.noteworld.com
Rev.: $9,000,000
Emp.: 50
Provider of Real Estate Contract Services
N.A.I.C.S.: 522310

Pledged Property LLC   (1)
335 Madison Ave Fl 19, New York, NY 10017-4636
Tel.: (212) 850-7700
Sales Range: Less than $1 Million
Emp.: 50
Purchasing of Mortgage Loans
N.A.I.C.S.: 522310

CREDITCARDS.COM, INC.
13809 Research Blvd Ste 906, Austin, TX 78750
Tel.: (512) 996-8663   DE
Web Site: http://www.creditcards.com
Year Founded: 2002
Sales Range: $25-49.9 Million
Emp.: 30
Online Credit Card Marketplace
N.A.I.C.S.: 522210
Christopher J. Speltz (CEO)
Jeff Whitmire (VP-Ops)
Cesar Gonzalez (VP-Dev)
Jody Farmer (VP-Strategic Mktg)
Kamelia Dianati (CTO)
Veronica Swinson (VP-Sls)

CREDITECH, INC.
50 N 7th St, Bangor, PA 18013
Tel.: (800) 555-5695   PA
Web Site: https://www.creditech-usa.com
Year Founded: 1936
Collection Services
N.A.I.C.S.: 561440
Chad Pulaski (Chief Revenue Officer)

Subsidiaries:

Central Credit Audit, Inc.   (1)
100 N 3rd St, Sunbury, PA 17801
Tel.: (570) 286-7742
Web Site: http://www.centralcreditaudit.com
Rev.: $1,800,000
Emp.: 25
Collection Agencies
N.A.I.C.S.: 561440
Karen Michaels (Treas)
David Woodring (Pres)

CREDITMAX LLC
1555 Palm Beach Lakes Blvd Ste 200, West Palm Beach, FL 33401-2339
Tel.: (561) 352-2200   NY
Sales Range: $150-199.9 Million
Emp.: 20
Mortgage Banking
N.A.I.C.S.: 522292

Michael Bernstein (Pres & COO)
Stephen B. Kass (Chm & CEO)
Scott Manganelli (VP-Sls)

CREDITORS INTERCHANGE RECEIVABLES MANAGEMENT LLC
80 Holtz Dr, Cheektowaga, NY 14225
Tel.: (716) 614-7500
Web Site: http://www.creditorsinterchange.com
Year Founded: 1960
Sales Range: $25-49.9 Million
Emp.: 700
Adjustment & Collection Services
N.A.I.C.S.: 561440
Lance Della Mea (COO)
Pamela Brewer (CFO)

CREDO REFERENCE, INC.
201 South St 4th Fl, Boston, MA 02111
Tel.: (617) 292-6125   DE
Web Site: http://www.credoreference.com
Educational Reference Solutions
N.A.I.C.S.: 513210
Mike Sweet (CEO)

CREED-MONARCH, INC.
1 Pucci Pk, New Britain, CT 06051
Tel.: (860) 826-4000   CT
Web Site: https://www.creedmonarch.com
Year Founded: 1953
Sales Range: $25-49.9 Million
Emp.: 300
Metal Component Mfr
N.A.I.C.S.: 332710
Holly Bulger (Project Mgr)
Paul Stawarz (Mgr-Production & Bus Mgr)
Anna Pesarik (Mgr-HR)
Larry Lubomski (Mgr)
Allen Hilliard (Engr-Control Sys)

CREEK INDIAN ENTERPRISES
100 Brookwood Rd, Atmore, AL 36502
Tel.: (251) 368-0819
Web Site: http://www.creekindianenterprises.org
Sales Range: $25-49.9 Million
Emp.: 48
Investment Holding Company
N.A.I.C.S.: 551112
David Gibbs (Sec)
Linda Brooks (Vice Chm & Co-Treas)
Richard K. Stanley (Chm)
Chad Klinck (CFO)
Tim Manning (COO)
Cody Williamson (Pres & CEO)

Subsidiaries:

Southern Media Communications Inc.   (1)
1318 S Main St, Atmore, AL 36502
Tel.: (251) 368-2511
Web Site: http://www.muskogeemetalworks.com
Rev.: $95,000
Emp.: 4
Country
N.A.I.C.S.: 516110

CREEK SYSTEMS, INC.
25 Enterprise, Aliso Viejo, CA 92656
Tel.: (949) 600-7778
Web Site: http://www.creeksystems.com
Year Founded: 2003
Sales Range: $1-9.9 Million
Emp.: 36
Custom Computer Programming Services
N.A.I.C.S.: 541511

Jean Borden-Aycock (VP-HR)
Ryan Peterson (CTO)
Mike Cook (Dir-Mktg)
Hugh Brown (VP-Bus Dev)

CREEKSIDE INDUSTRIES
1177 W Loop S Ste 1400, Houston, TX 77027-9705
Tel.: (713) 296-7500   TX
Year Founded: 1977
Sales Range: $50-74.9 Million
Emp.: 10
Mfr of Organic Chemicals
N.A.I.C.S.: 561320
Mark Davis (Pres)
Troy Gaddie (CFO)
Peter Buenz (Chm)

CREEL TRACTOR COMPANY
3771 Palm Beach Blvd, Fort Myers, FL 33916
Tel.: (239) 694-2185
Web Site: https://www.creeltractor.com
Sales Range: $10-24.9 Million
Emp.: 30
Garden Machinery & Equipment Whslr
N.A.I.C.S.: 423820
Mark Creel (Pres)
Brian Creel (Mgr-Sls)
Beth Murphy (Office Mgr)
Erik Cintron (Mgr-Parts)

CREGGER COMPANY INC.
637 N 12th St, West Columbia, SC 29169-6336
Tel.: (803) 791-5195   SC
Web Site: http://www.creggercompany.com
Year Founded: 1978
Sales Range: $10-24.9 Million
Emp.: 110
Plumbing Fixtures & Related Equipment Mfr
N.A.I.C.S.: 423720
Mike Cregger (Gen Mgr)

CREIGHTON BROTHERS L.L.C.
4217 W Old Rd 30, Warsaw, IN 46580
Tel.: (574) 267-3101   IN
Web Site: https://www.creightonbrothers.com
Year Founded: 1925
Sales Range: $10-24.9 Million
Emp.: 250
Producer of Chicken Eggs
N.A.I.C.S.: 112310
Ronald D. Truex (Pres & Gen Mgr)

Subsidiaries:

Creighton Brothers   (1)
4217 W Old Rd 30, Warsaw, IN 46580
Tel.: (574) 267-3101
Web Site: http://www.creightonbrothers.com
Sales Range: $10-24.9 Million
Emp.: 15
Crop Farming
N.A.I.C.S.: 112310
Diane Lancaster (Gen Mgr)

CRELLIN HANDLING EQUIPMENT INC
12 Commercial Way, East Providence, RI 02914
Tel.: (401) 438-6400   RI
Web Site: http://www.crellin.com
Year Founded: 1956
Sales Range: $10-24.9 Million
Emp.: 70
Provider of Industrial Equipment & Supplies
N.A.I.C.S.: 423830

Richard Crellin (Pres)
Cheryl Moroni (Dir-HR)
Douglas Crellin (VP)

CREME LURE CO., INC.
5401 Kent Dr, Tyler, TX 75711-6162
Tel.: (903) 561-0522
Web Site: http://www.cremelure.com
Sales Range: $50-74.9 Million
Emp.: 50
Fishing Lures Mfr
N.A.I.C.S.: 339920
Wayne Kent (Pres)

CREMES UNLIMITED INC.
600 Holiday Plz Dr Ste 520, Matteson, IL 60443
Tel.: (708) 748-1336
Sales Range: $10-24.9 Million
Emp.: 4
Non Dairy Products
N.A.I.C.S.: 424430

CRENDO
750 Van Buren Dr NW, Salem, OR 97304-3547
Tel.: (503) 399-4774
Web Site: http://www.crendo.com
Year Founded: 1995
Sales Range: $10-24.9 Million
Emp.: 2
N.A.I.C.S.: 541810
Tamra Heathershaw-Hart (Partner)
Bruce M. Hart (Owner)

CREOKS BEHAVIORAL HEALTH SERVICES
323 W 6th St, Okmulgee, OK 74447
Tel.: (918) 756-9411   OK
Web Site: http://www.creoks.org
Year Founded: 1980
Sales Range: $10-24.9 Million
Emp.: 257
Behavioral Healthcare Services
N.A.I.C.S.: 623220
Paul Bowker (VP-Fin)
Mike Wise (VP-HR)
Chris Perry (VP-Clinical Svcs)
Erin Wambold (VP-Dev)
Brandi Smith (Sr Dir-Creek County)
Brent Black (CEO)
Deborah Barnes (Dir-Wagoner Site)
Jonathan Pierce (Dir-Sapulpa Site)
Marcia Keesee (Sr Dir-Children's Svcs)
Mark Ingram (Dir-Fiscal Mgmt)
Phil Black (CEO)
Rachel Couey (Asst Dir-Sapulpa Site)
Rachel Lindemann (Dir-Okemah Site)
Sheryl Zumwalt (Dir-Clinical Auditing)
Travis Wolff (Sec)
Donnie Nero (Vice Chm)
Mary Smith (Chm)

CREOSALUS, INC.
1044 E Chestnut St, Louisville, KY 40204
Tel.: (502) 515-1100
Web Site: https://www.creosalus.com
Year Founded: 1998
Drugs, Fine Chemicals & Human Medical Devices Developer & Mfr
N.A.I.C.S.: 325412
David Young Phelps (Pres & CEO)

Subsidiaries:

Advanced ChemTech   (1)
5609 Fern Vly Rd, Louisville, KY 40228
Tel.: (502) 969-0000
Web Site: http://www.advancedchemtech.com
Sales Range: $25-49.9 Million
Emp.: 50
Mfr of Chemicals for Pharmaceutical Market
N.A.I.C.S.: 325998
David Phelps (Pres)

CREPS UNITED PUBLICATIONS
1163 Water St, Indiana, PA 15701
Tel.: (724) 463-8522
Web Site:
http://www.crepsunited.com
Rev.: $24,000,000
Emp.: 200
Offset Printing
N.A.I.C.S.: 323111
Jacob Crep *(Partner)*
Jim Shotts *(Mgr-Maintenance)*
Kevin Dittmar *(Supvr-Second Shift)*

CRES-COR
5925 Heisley Rd, Mentor, OH 44060-1833
Tel.: (440) 350-1100   OH
Web Site: http://www.crescor.com
Year Founded: 1936
Sales Range: $100-124.9 Million
Emp.: 200
Mfr & Distr of Mobile Food Service Related Equipment
N.A.I.C.S.: 333241
Cliff Baggott *(Pres & CEO)*
Rio DeGennaro *(VP)*
Jim Miller *(Mgr-Bus Dev-Education)*
Jonathan Stacey *(Mgr-Distr)*
Larry Gage *(Mgr-Engrg)*

CRESA
200 State St Fl 13, Boston, MA 02109
Tel.: (617) 758-6000
Web Site:
http://www.cresapartners.com
Year Founded: 1985
Sales Range: $10-24.9 Million
Emp.: 700
Management Consulting Services
N.A.I.C.S.: 541611
Brandon Leitner *(VP)*
Barry Dube *(Principal-Project Mgmt)*
Christopher Crooks *(Principal)*
Steven Stefanski *(VP)*
James Underhill *(CEO)*
Jonathan C. Rudes *(Sr VP)*
Jon C. Olmstead *(Principal)*
Scott Dumler *(Mng Principal)*
Jack Glasgow *(Mng Principal)*
Jay Neikirk *(VP)*
Leslie Keidan *(VP-Transaction Mgmt-New York City)*
Richard Selig *(Mng Principal-New York)*
Paul Delaney *(Principal)*
John Coakley *(Principal)*
Dan Sullivan *(Mng Principal)*
Adam Subber *(Mng Principal)*
Matt George *(Principal)*
James Errante *(Sr VP-Project Mgmt-New York)*
Kris Woodard *(VP)*

CRESAPARTNERS LLC
280 Congress St Fl 10, Boston, MA 02210
Tel.: (617) 758-6000
Web Site: https://www.cresa.com
Sales Range: $25-49.9 Million
Emp.: 800
Real Estate & Foreign Trade Consulting
N.A.I.C.S.: 541611
William W. Goade *(Mng Principal)*
Edward Fothergill *(Mng Principal)*
David Nuss *(Sr VP-IT)*
Jack Burns *(Mng Principal)*
Matthew J. Feeney *(Chm)*
Matthew Miller *(Mng Principal)*
Gwen Schultz *(Mng Principal)*
Jeff Estep *(Dir-Consulting Grp-Global)*
William D. Tidwell *(Principal)*
Aaron B. Berkey *(Principal)*

Jonathan E. Harms *(Principal)*
Tara Davis *(Dir-Creative Svcs-Washington)*
Carlo Brignardello *(Principal)*
Craig Castor *(Principal)*
Christopher Crooks *(Principal)*
Brian Davies *(Principal)*
Wendy Doumas *(COO)*
Chris J. Finley *(Principal)*
Christian Frers *(Mng Principal)*
Dan Gallup *(Principal)*
Anthony Huygen *(Principal)*
Robert Leigh *(Co-CEO)*
Bob Misdom *(Principal)*
Bob Palffy *(Principal)*
James A. Pirot *(Mng Principal-Project Mgmt)*
Brandon Podolski *(Principal)*
David Price *(Principal)*
David Ross *(Principal)*
Dave Smith *(Principal)*
Adam Subber *(Principal)*
Daniel Sullivan *(Principal)*
Kathryn I. Thomas *(Mng Principal-Project Mgmt)*
David Toomey *(Principal)*
Allen Trowbridge *(Principal)*
James M. Underhill *(Co-CEO)*
Joe Vazquez *(Mng Principal-Project Mgmt)*
Jason Wery *(Mng Principal-Project Mgmt)*
Ross Rikkers *(Mng Principal)*
Greg Albright *(Sr VP)*
Paul Anderson *(Mng Principal)*
Matt Apter *(Mng Principal)*
Robert Badagliacco *(Sr VP)*
Jeff Baker *(Mng Principal)*
Eric Baugh *(Sr VP-Project Mgmt)*
Rod Beach *(Principal)*
Peter Bechunas *(Principal-Project Mgmt)*
John Behm *(Mng Principal)*
Mark Bennett *(Mng Principal)*
Ralph Benzakein *(Sr VP)*
Douglas Bibby *(Sr VP-Project Mgmt)*
Lisa Black *(Sr VP)*
Brian Black *(Sr VP)*
Robert Anderson III *(Principal)*

CRESCEND TECHNOLOGIES, L.L.C.
140 E State Pkwy, Schaumburg, IL 60173
Tel.: (847) 908-5400
Web Site:
http://www.crescendtech.com
Year Founded: 1995
Sales Range: $10-24.9 Million
Emp.: 51
Radio Frequency Amplifier Mfr
N.A.I.C.S.: 334220
James Hougo *(Pres)*

CRESCENDO VENTURE MANAGEMENT, LLC
405 El Camino Real Ste 126, Menlo Park, CA 94025
Tel.: (650) 470-1200   DE
Web Site:
https://www.crescendoventures.com
Sales Range: $1-4.9 Billion
Equity Investment Firm
N.A.I.C.S.: 523999
Wayne C. Cantwell *(Gen Partner)*

CRESCENT BOX CORP.
5 Neshaminy Interplex Ste 301, Trevose, PA 19053-6941
Tel.: (215) 639-3000
Web Site:
http://www.crescentbox.com
Year Founded: 1912
Corrugated Boxes & Other Packaging Materials Mfr

N.A.I.C.S.: 322219
Bob McNeill *(Pres)*
Robert J. Mcneill III *(VP)*

CRESCENT CAPITAL FINANCE GROUP, INC.
11100 Santa Monica Blvd Ste 2000, Los Angeles, CA 90025
Tel.: (310) 235-5900
Web Site:
http://www.crescentcap.com
Investment Services
N.A.I.C.S.: 523999
John A. Fekete *(Mng Dir)*
Christine Vanden Beukel *(Mng Dir-Europe & Head-European Credit Markets)*
Jared Adler *(VP-Capital Markets strategies)*
Kimberly S. Bartholomew *(Asst VP-IR)*
Raymond Barrios *(Sr VP-Mezzanine)*
Jason A. Breaux *(Mng Dir-Special Situations)*

CRESCENT CREDIT UNION
PO Box 4290, Brockton, MA 02303-4290
Tel.: (508) 580-6511   MA
Web Site:
http://www.crescentcredit.org
Year Founded: 1919
Sales Range: $10-24.9 Million
Emp.: 147
Credit Union
N.A.I.C.S.: 522130
Paul Pijanowski *(Sr VP)*

CRESCENT CROWN DISTRIBUTING LLC
5900 Almonaster Ave, New Orleans, LA 70126-7138
Tel.: (504) 240-5900
Web Site:
http://www.crescentcrown.com
Sales Range: $25-49.9 Million
Emp.: 235
Liquor Whslr
N.A.I.C.S.: 424810
William Pananos *(Gen Mgr)*
John Todaro *(Acct Mgr-Red Bull)*
Angela Parchman *(Controller)*
James R. Moffett Jr. *(Pres & CEO)*

Subsidiaries:

Crescent Crown Distributing LLC   **(1)**
402 S 54th Pl, Phoenix, AZ 85034
Tel.: (602) 346-5500
Sales Range: $50-74.9 Million
Liquor Whslr
N.A.I.C.S.: 424810

CRESCENT ELECTRIC SUPPLY COMPANY
7750 Dunleith Dr, East Dubuque, IL 61025
Tel.: (815) 747-3145   DE
Web Site: http://www.cesco.com
Year Founded: 1919
Sales Range: $450-499.9 Million
Emp.: 1,700
Electrical Equipment & Accessories Distr
N.A.I.C.S.: 423610
Alice R. Vontalge *(VP-Fin)*
Dan Philippi *(Sr VP-HR)*
Ronald D. Schlader *(VP-Ops & Quality)*
Richard Cody *(VP-Supplier Mgmt)*
Carol M. Hoffman *(Treas & Sec)*
Dan Hill *(VP & Gen Mgr)*
Dennis DeSousa *(Sr VP-Bus Dev)*
Jacob Pole *(Mgr-Energy Bus Dev-Nebraska & Iowa)*
Jeff Jolly *(VP-West)*
Erich Lemke *(CIO & VP)*

Jeff Byrd *(VP-Central Reg)*
Rob Onorato *(COO)*
Jerry Tucker *(VP-West Reg)*
John Wallace *(VP-Central Reg)*
Mark Rizzetto *(VP-Realty)*
Joe McDermott *(VP-Central)*
Tim Rooney *(VP-Construction Sls)*
John Hammer *(VP-Mktg)*
Scott Teerlinck *(Pres & CEO)*
Kristi Dahlke *(CFO)*

Subsidiaries:

National Electric Supply Co., Inc.   **(1)**
2200 Midtown Pl NE, Albuquerque, NM 87107
Tel.: (505) 345-3577
Web Site: http://www.nationalelectric.com
Electrical Apparatus & Equipment
N.A.I.C.S.: 423610
Rocklan E. Lawrence *(Pres & CEO)*

Stoneway Electric Supply Inc.   **(1)**
402 N Perry St, Spokane, WA 99202-2921
Tel.: (509) 535-2933
Web Site: http://www.stoneway.com
Sales Range: $125-149.9 Million
Emp.: 210
Provider of Electrical Apparatus & Related Equipment Services
N.A.I.C.S.: 423610
Jeff Corrick *(Pres)*

Womack Electric Supply Co., Inc.   **(1)**
186 Towerview Ct, Cary, NC 27513-3595
Tel.: (434) 793-5134
Web Site: http://www.womackelectric.com
Electrical Apparatus Whslr
N.A.I.C.S.: 423610

CRESCENT FOODS INC.
615 N Breazeale Ave, Mount Olive, NC 28365
Tel.: (919) 658-9628
Rev.: $12,000,000
Emp.: 155
Grocery Stores
N.A.I.C.S.: 445110
Moses King *(Pres)*

CRESCENT HEIGHTS OF AMERICA INC.
2200 Biscayne Blvd, Miami, FL 33137
Tel.: (305) 374-5700
Web Site:
https://www.crescentheights.com
Sales Range: $10-24.9 Million
Emp.: 130
Land Subdividers & Developers
N.A.I.C.S.: 237210
Sonny Kahn *(Co-Pres)*
Bruce Menini *(Co-Pres)*
Russell W. Galbut *(Mng Principal)*

CRESCENT HILL CAPITAL CORPORATION
100 Crescent Dr Ste 700-1000, Dallas, TX 75201
Tel.: (972) 564-8820   TX
Web Site:
https://www.crescenthillcapital.com
Private Equity & Venture Capital Investment Firm
N.A.I.C.S.: 523999
Rafael Pinedo *(Pres)*

CRESCENT HOSIERY MILLS INC.
1902 Hwy 11 N, Niota, TN 37826-3040
Tel.: (423) 568-2101
Web Site:
http://www.crescenthosiery.com
Year Founded: 1902
Sales Range: $25-49.9 Million
Emp.: 425
Mfr of Hosiery
N.A.I.C.S.: 315120

Crescent Hosiery Mills Inc.—(Continued)

Bob Yo (Pres)

CRESCENT HOTELS & RE-SORTS

10306 Eaton Pl Ste 430, Fairfax, VA 22030
Tel.: (703) 279-7820
Web Site: http://www.chrco.com
Emp.: 300
Owns, Manages & Co-Invests in Hotel Real Estate; Operator of Hotels, Resorts & Golf Clubs
N.A.I.C.S.: 721110
Michael George (Founder, Pres & CEO)
Michael J. Metcalf (Exec VP)
Anthony Cohen (Partner & Exec VP)
Maricarmen Cardenas (Sr VP-Revenue & Digital Strategy)
Paul Conkle (VP-Fin-Hotel Acctg)
Caroline George (Gen Counsel)
Laura Warner (Sr VP-HR)
Rob Smith (CFO)
Andrea Sorensen (VP-Sls & Mktg)
Evan Studer (Exec VP-Ops)
Dawn Gallagher (Chief Comml Officer)
John Robinson (Sr VP-Fin)
Greg Griffie (Sr VP-Food & Beverage)
Paul Filla (Sr VP-Ops)
Raul Moronta (Sr VP-Revenue Mgmt)
Sheryl Lang (Sr VP-Sls-Lifestyle Hotels)
Troy F. Allvord (VP-Acctg)
Ariel Freeman Sanett (VP-Bus Dev)
Rich Garcia (VP-Culinary)
Delana Meyer (VP-Digital Strategy)
Clarence Jordan (VP-Fin)
Gustavo Serbia (VP-HR)
Kristi Miller (VP-HR & Assoc Rels)
Cynthia Fuller (VP-HR & Organizational Learning)
Markus Kohn (VP-Ops)
Michael Broadhurst (VP-Ops)
Mike Rose (VP-Ops)
Carrie Wells (VP-Revenue Strategy)
Craig Perch (VP-Revenue Strategy)
Tim Bowes (VP-Sls)
Kathryn Bryant (VP-Sls Transitions)
Maureen Mackey (VP-Sls-Global)
Lorraine Park (VP-Spa, Retail & Wellness)
Jackie King (Dir-Sls & Mktg)
Kathleen Barone (VP-Global Sls)

Subsidiaries:

Adolphus Hotel   (1)
1321 Commerce St, Dallas, TX 75202-4211   (100%)
Tel.: (214) 742-8200
Web Site: http://www.hoteladolphus.com
Sales Range: $25-49.9 Million
Hotel & Resort
N.A.I.C.S.: 721110
Craig Scott (Mng Dir)
Tamara Bayo (Dir-Catering & Conference Svcs)
Tauseen Malik (Gen Mgr)
Jodi Doughty (Dir-Sls & Mktg)

CRESCENT MANUFACTURING COMPANY

1310 Majestic Dr, Fremont, OH 43420-9142
Tel.: (419) 332-6484   OH
Web Site: https://www.crescentblades.com
Year Founded: 1898
Sales Range: $50-74.9 Million
Emp.: 130
Precision Disposable Industrial Blades Mfr
N.A.I.C.S.: 332216

Michael Waleryszak (Pres)
Jeff Miller (Dir-Sls & Mktg)
Lisa Adams (Controller)

CRESCENT MARKETING, INC.

8322 Artesia Blvd Ste B, Buena Park, CA 90621
Tel.: (714) 443-3280   CA
Web Site: http://www.gamequestdirect.com
Year Founded: 1994
Sales Range: $10-24.9 Million
Emp.: 16
Retailer of Video Games & Software
N.A.I.C.S.: 449210
Khalid Baqai (Pres)

CRESCENT PARTS & EQUIPMENT COMPANY

5121 Manchester Ave, Saint Louis, MO 63110
Tel.: (314) 647-5511
Web Site: http://www.crescentparts.com
Year Founded: 1944
Sales Range: $10-24.9 Million
Emp.: 80
Warm Air Heating & Air Conditioning
N.A.I.C.S.: 423730

CRESCENT PLUMBING SUP-PLY CO

640 Rosedale Ave, Saint Louis, MO 63112
Tel.: (314) 727-4200
Web Site: http://www.cresentsupply.com
Rev.: $10,000,000
Emp.: 25
Plumbing & Hydronic Heating Supplies
N.A.I.C.S.: 423720
Joe Rotskoff (VP)

CRESCENT PRIVATE CREDIT INCOME CORP.

11100 Santa Monica Blvd Ste 2000, Los Angeles, CA 90025
Tel.: (310) 235-5900   MD
Web Site: https://www.crescentprivatecredit.com
Year Founded: 2022
Rev.: $4,042,000
Assets: $143,722,000
Liabilities: $39,864,000
Net Worth: $103,858,000
Earnings: $3,833,000
Fiscal Year-end: 12/31/23
Investment Management Service
N.A.I.C.S.: 523999

CRESCENT PROCESSING COMPANY, LP

12700 Park Central Dr Ste 1100, Dallas, TX 75251
Tel.: (214) 271-8081
Web Site: http://www.crescentprocessing.com
Year Founded: 2005
Sales Range: $75-99.9 Million
Emp.: 211
Data Processing, Hosting & Related Services
N.A.I.C.S.: 518210
Chris Dierks (CFO)
David S. Kesler (CEO)
Jim Davis (VP-Mktg Centers)

CRESCENT RESOURCES, LLC

227 W Trade St Ste 1000, Charlotte, NC 28202
Tel.: (980) 321-6000   SC
Web Site: http://www.crescent-resources.com
Year Founded: 1969

Sales Range: $200-249.9 Million
Emp.: 200
Real Estate Development & Land Management
N.A.I.C.S.: 531390
Jason Holwerda (Dir-Leasing)
Nina Shor (Gen Counsel)
Alice Zwahlen (VP-HR)
Andrew Carmody (Pres-Residential Div)
Tyler Niess (CMO & VP)
Kevin H. Lambert (CFO)
Brian Natwick (Pres-Multifamily Div)
Robert Whitney Duncan (Pres-Comml Div)
Brenda M. Lenaburg (VP & Controller)
Dean Spencer (VP-IT)
Joseph K. McGorrey (Sr VP-Comml Div)
C. Ford Cox (Sr VP-Multifamily Construction)
Margaret H. Jennesse (Sr VP-Residential Div)
James L. Page (Sr VP-Residential Div)
Stephen Yetts (Sr VP-Residential Div)
John S. Bell (Reg Sr VP-Comml Div)
Laurie Rogers (Div Controller)
Jaime Pou (VP-Investments)
Don Weaver (Mgr-Dev-Multifamily)
Jenny Vallimont (Dir-Innovation & Sustainability)
James Short Jr. (Pres-Land Mgmt Div)
Todd W. Mansfield (Pres & CEO)

Subsidiaries:

Landmar Group L.L.C.   (1)
245 Riverside Ave Ste 410, Jacksonville, FL 32202-4926
Tel.: (904) 998-8300
Sales Range: $10-24.9 Million
Emp.: 44
Residential Land Subdividers & Developers
N.A.I.C.S.: 237210

CRESCENT SOLUTIONS

17871 Mitchell Ave N Ste 100, Irvine, CA 92614
Tel.: (561) 585-1700
Web Site: https://www.crescentsolutions.net
Year Founded: 2001
Sales Range: $25-49.9 Million
Emp.: 380
Employment Agency Specializing in Information Technology, Engineering & Finance Professionals
N.A.I.C.S.: 561311
Brian Albano (VP)
Bob Steuernagel (COO)

CRESCO LINES INC.

15220 S Halsted St, Harvey, IL 60426-2344
Tel.: (708) 596-8310   MS
Web Site: https://www.crescolines.com
Year Founded: 1959
Sales Range: $10-24.9 Million
Emp.: 260
Trucking Service
N.A.I.C.S.: 484121
Robert Stranczek (Pres)

CRESCO UNION SAVINGS BANK INC.

111 N Elm St, Cresco, IA 52136
Tel.: (563) 547-2040
Web Site: https://www.cusb.com
Year Founded: 1888
Sales Range: $10-24.9 Million
Emp.: 98
Savings Bank
N.A.I.C.S.: 522180

Douglas Krabbe (Specialist-Loan)
Scott J. Thomson (Pres)

CRESENT ENTERPRISES INC.

350 Maple St, Gallatin, TN 37066-3639
Tel.: (615) 452-1671   TN
Web Site: http://www.cresent.com
Year Founded: 1984
Sales Range: $10-24.9 Million
Emp.: 40
Retail of Wood Household Furniture
N.A.I.C.S.: 337122
Charles R. Tomkins III (Chm)

CRESLINE PLASTIC PIPE CO., INC.

600 Cross Pointe Blvd, Evansville, IN 47715
Tel.: (812) 428-9300   IN
Web Site: http://www.cresline.com
Year Founded: 1949
Sales Range: $100-124.9 Million
Emp.: 150
Mfr of Plastic Pipe & Fittings
N.A.I.C.S.: 326122
Richard Schroeder (Pres)
Belle Fahrer (Controller)
Bruce Abbott (VP-Engrg)
Jana Laufer (Mgr-IT)

Subsidiaries:

Crescent Plastics, Inc.   (1)
955 E Diamond Ave, Evansville, IN 47711
Tel.: (812) 428-9305
Web Site: http://www.crescentplastics.com
Sales Range: $10-24.9 Million
Emp.: 120
Thermoplastic Material Mfr
N.A.I.C.S.: 325211
John Sthroeder (Pres)

Cresline-West, Inc.   (1)
1930 W Whitesbridge Rd, Fresno, CA 93706
Tel.: (559) 486-1840
Web Site: http://www.cresline.com
Sales Range: $10-24.9 Million
Emp.: 100
Plastic Tank Mfr
N.A.I.C.S.: 326122

CRESSET ASSET MANAGE-MENT, LLC

444 W Lk St Ste 4700, Chicago, IL 60606
Tel.: (312) 429-2400   DE
Web Site: http://www.cressetcapital.com
Year Founded: 2017
Wealth Management Firm
N.A.I.C.S.: 523999
Jack Ablin (Chief Investment Officer & Founding Partner)
Eric Becker (Co-Founder & Co-Chm)
Michael Cole (CEO)
Michael Deasey (Regional Mng Dir-Minneapolis)
Robert B. Dunkin (Regional Mng Dir-West Palm Beach)
Linda Litner (Regional Mng Dir-Chicago)
Kevin Long (Partner, Sr Mng Dir & Head-Sls)
David Mills (CFO)
Martim de Arantes Oliveira (Regional Mng Dir-Northern California)
Bob Pagliuco (Chief Compliance Officer)
Nimesh Patel (CTO)
Doug Regan (Founding Partner & Co-Chm)
Bill Rudnick (Sr Partner, Gen Counsel & Co-Head-Family Office Svcs)
Jeremy Shevlin (Mng Dir-Mountain Reg)
Avy Stein (Co-Founder & Co-Chm)

Aron Grodinsky *(Mng Dir-Investment Strategy-Mountain Reg)*
Dave Jackson *(Chief Experience Officer)*
Michael Costabile *(CFO)*
Barbara Young *(Co-Head-Family Office Svcs)*
Gabriel Garcia *(Mng Dir-Corp Dev)*
Matt Mongia *(Mng Dir-Private Capital)*

Subsidiaries:

Cypress Wealth Advisors, LLC **(1)**
101 California St Ste 1025, San Francisco, CA 94111
Tel.: (415) 489-2100
Web Site: http://www.cypresswealth.com
Investment Management
N.A.I.C.S.: 523940
Barbara Young *(Founder, CEO & CIO)*
Sophia Lee *(COO & Principal)*
Vince Colabianchi *(CFO & Founding Principal)*

EA, Inc. **(1)**
1300 E Woodfield Rd Ste 300, Schaumburg, IL 60173
Tel.: (847) 397-3000
Investment Advice
N.A.I.C.S.: 523940

The Connable Office, Inc. **(1)**
136 E Michigan Ave, Kalamazoo, MI 49007
Tel.: (269) 382-5800
Web Site: https://connableoffice.com
Sales Range: $1-9.9 Million
Emp.: 14
Investment Advice
N.A.I.C.S.: 523940
David Kruis *(Treas)*

True Capital Management, LLC **(1)**
101 Montgomery St Ste 2150, San Francisco, CA 94104-4157
Tel.: (415) 538-3600
Web Site: http://www.truecapitalmgmt.com
Office Administrative Services
N.A.I.C.S.: 561110
Heather Goodman *(Mgr)*

CRESSEY & COMPANY, LP
155 N Wacker Dr Ste 4500, Chicago, IL 60606
Tel.: (312) 945-5700
Web Site: http://www.cresseyco.com
Year Founded: 2008
Privater Equity Firm
N.A.I.C.S.: 523999
Bryan C. Cressey *(Partner)*
Steven Dildine *(Principal)*
William H. Frist *(Partner)*
David Rogero *(Partner)*
Merrick Axel *(Partner)*
Scott Maskalunas *(CFO & Mng Dir)*
Bary Bailey *(Operating Partner)*
Frank Fritsch *(Operating Partner)*
Melissa Mueller *(Mgr-Acctg)*
Ryan Moseley *(VP)*
Peter Ehrich *(Partner)*
Brennan Murray *(Principal-Talent)*
Andy Hurd *(Operating Partner)*
David Lourie *(Dir-Compliance & Chief Compliance Officer)*

Subsidiaries:

HealthDrive Corporation **(1)**
100 Crossing Blvd Ste 300, Framingham, MA 01702
Tel.: (617) 964-6681
Web Site: https://www.healthdrive.com
On-Site Medical Care Services
N.A.I.C.S.: 621610
Daniel B. Baker *(Pres & CEO)*
Rory Kallfelz *(Chief Admin Officer)*
John S. Sepe *(VP-Corp Dev)*
Gean Carlo Padilla *(CFO)*

PurFoods, LLC **(1)**
3210 SE Corporate Woods Dr, Ankeny, IA 50021
Tel.: (515) 963-0641
Web Site: http://www.purfoods.com
Sales Range: $25-49.9 Million
Emp.: 250
Food Products Mfr

N.A.I.C.S.: 311999
Rick Anderson *(Co-Founder & Pres)*
Michael Anderson *(Sr VP-Sls & Bus Dev)*
Chris Choi *(CFO)*
Traci Thompson *(Dir-Mktg)*
Dan Mandolfo *(VP-Client Svcs)*

The InterMed Group, Inc. **(1)**
13301 US Highway 441, Alachua, FL 32615
Web Site: https://intermed1.com
Sales Range: $1-9.9 Million
Emp.: 25
Sells & Services New & Used Biomedical Equipment
N.A.I.C.S.: 423450
Rick Staab *(Pres)*

Subsidiary (Domestic):

Horizon CSA LLC **(2)**
265 Pitt Rd, Mooresville, NC 28115-6783
Tel.: (704) 799-8661
Web Site: http://www.horizonbiomedicalservices.com
All Other Miscellaneous Ambulatory Health Care Services
N.A.I.C.S.: 621999
Mike Marrow *(Owner)*

InterMed Nuclear Medicine, Inc. **(2)**
13351 Progress Blvd, Alachua, FL 32615 **(100%)**
Tel.: (386) 462-5220
Web Site: http://www.intermednucmed.com
Nuclear Medicine Machinery Parts & Services
N.A.I.C.S.: 339112
Danny Hamm *(VP-Sls)*
Rick Staab *(Pres)*
Dave Bauerle *(VP)*
Dave Fox *(COO)*
Theresa Smith *(Treas)*
Don MacLaren *(Mgr-Svc)*
Yvette Graham *(Mgr-Svc)*

InterMed Ultrasound **(2)**
13351 Progress Blvd, Alachua, FL 32615 **(100%)**
Tel.: (386) 462-5220
Web Site: http://www.intermedultrasound.com
Sales Range: $1-9.9 Million
Emp.: 70
Sales & Services of Ultrasound Machines Parts & Services
N.A.I.C.S.: 339113
Rick Staab *(Pres)*
Don Fletcher *(Controller-Quality)*
Dave Fox *(COO)*
Theresa Smith *(Controller)*

InterMed X-Ray, Inc. **(2)**
14000 NW 126th Ter, Alachua, FL 32615
Tel.: (386) 462-5220
Web Site: http://www.intermedxray.com
Sales Range: $1-9.9 Million
Emp.: 18
Medical Imaging Equipment
N.A.I.C.S.: 423450
David Bauerle *(Pres)*

Modern Biomedical Services, Inc. **(2)**
600 E John Carpenter Fwy Ste 284, Irving, TX 75062
Tel.: (214) 217-3700
Web Site: http://www.modernbiomedical.com
Sales Range: $1-9.9 Million
Emp.: 100
Healthcare Technology Management Services
N.A.I.C.S.: 541618
Randy Bullard *(CEO)*

Verisys Corp. **(1)**
1001 N Fairfax St, Alexandria, VA 22314-1797
Tel.: (888) 837-4797
Web Site: http://www.verisys.com
Healthcare Technology Services
N.A.I.C.S.: 541519
Amy Roberson *(VP-Ops)*
Jamie A. Harper *(COO)*
John P. Benson *(Founder & CEO)*
Jennifer Gillespie *(Officer-Compliance)*
Chris Stabile *(CFO)*
Dustin Faultner *(Dir-HR)*
Srini Chillara *(CTO)*

CRESSWELL BROTHERS GENERAL CONTRACTORS, INC.
129 W 2nd Mountain Rd, Pottsville, PA 17901
Tel.: (570) 385-2393
Web Site: https://www.cresswellbrothers.com
Year Founded: 1961
Sales Range: $1-9.9 Million
Emp.: 21
General Construction
N.A.I.C.S.: 236220

CREST AUTO GROUP
2701 N Central Expy, Plano, TX 75075
Tel.: (972) 578-7511
Web Site: http://www.crestcars.com
Rev.: $10,000,000
Emp.: 250
Automobiles, New & Used
N.A.I.C.S.: 441110
Cecil Van Tuyl *(Owner)*
Christopher Willis *(Mgr-Internet Sls)*
Duncan McPhail *(Gen Mgr-Sls)*

CREST CADILLAC INC.
12800 W Capitol Dr, Brookfield, WI 53008
Tel.: (262) 781-2800
Web Site: http://www.crestmotors.com
Rev.: $13,000,000
Emp.: 45
New Car Dealers
N.A.I.C.S.: 441110
Thomas J. Hartigan *(VP-Admin)*
William J. Hartigan *(Owner)*
Ken Kroll *(Office Mgr)*
Patti Karpinski *(Office Mgr)*
Dave Cesel *(Mgr)*
Brady Brown *(Gen Mgr)*
Ross Thimm *(Mgr-Sls)*

CREST CADILLAC OF BIRMINGHAM, INC.
1677 Montgomery Hwy, Birmingham, AL 35216
Tel.: (205) 588-4493
Web Site: http://www.crestcadillacbirmingham.com
Year Founded: 1982
Sales Range: $10-24.9 Million
Emp.: 75
New Car Dealers
N.A.I.C.S.: 441110
Gary Ivey *(Pres)*

CREST CHEVROLET
909 W 21st St, San Bernardino, CA 92405
Tel.: (909) 883-8833
Web Site: http://www.crestchevy.com
Year Founded: 1958
Sales Range: $75-99.9 Million
Emp.: 170
Car Dealership
N.A.I.C.S.: 441110
Doug Bader *(Gen Mgr-Sls)*
Robert Bader *(Owner & Pres)*
Paul Scafide *(Dir-Svcs)*
Adrian Rodriguez *(Mgr-Internet Sls)*
Jonathan Romero *(Mgr-Internet Sls)*

CREST DISTRIBUTING INC.
595 S 200 E, Provo, UT 84606
Tel.: (801) 373-7970
Web Site: https://www.christensenoil.com
Rev.: $11,900,000
Emp.: 25
Petroleum Bulk Stations
N.A.I.C.S.: 424710
Todd Christensen *(Pres)*

CREST FORD, INC.
26333 Van Dyke, Center Line, MI 48015
Tel.: (586) 755-2100
Web Site: http://www.crestford.com
Rev.: $20,500,000
Emp.: 60
Automobile Dealership
N.A.I.C.S.: 441110
Tim Rotarius *(Bus Mgr)*

CREST FURNITURE INC.
30 Tower Rd, Dayton, NJ 08810-1571
Tel.: (732) 355-9200
Web Site: http://www.valuecitynj.com
Rev.: $22,818,831
Emp.: 45
Furniture Retailer
N.A.I.C.S.: 449110
Sidney Rechtman *(Pres)*
Diane Mitnitsky *(Dir-HR, Office Mgr & Mgr-Acctg)*
Krystal Hayes *(Mgr-Accts Payable)*
Larry Young *(COO)*

CREST GROUP INC.
Scotch Rd, Trenton, NJ 08628
Tel.: (609) 883-4000 NJ
Web Site: http://www.crest-ultrasonics.com
Year Founded: 1961
Sales Range: $100-124.9 Million
Emp.: 500
Distr of Electrical Equipment & Supplies
N.A.I.C.S.: 551112
J. Michael Goodson *(CEO & Chm)*

Subsidiaries:

Advanced Ceramics Technology (M) Sdn. Bhd. **(1)**
1536 Jalan Peru Sahaan Kawasan Peru Sahaan, 14000, Penang, Penanag, Malaysia
Tel.: (60) 4 507 0018
Web Site: http://www.act.crestm.com
Emp.: 200
Ultrasonic Equipment Mfr
N.A.I.C.S.: 334510
Harison Omar *(Mgr-HR)*
Jie Wen Tjung *(Mng Dir)*
Zulkiflee Mahamud *(Engr-Mechanical)*
Lim Eng Guan *(Mgr-Ops)*

Artech Ultrasonic Systems AG **(1)**
Seestrasse 46, 8598, Bottighofen, Switzerland
Tel.: (41) 71 460 22 41
Web Site: http://www.artech-systems.com
Ultrasonic Equipment Mfr
N.A.I.C.S.: 334510

CC Hydrosonics Ltd. **(1)**
Units 1-6 Italstyle Estate Harlow Road, Harlow, CM20 2HE, Essex, United Kingdom
Tel.: (44) 1279 418 942
Web Site: http://www.cchydrosonics.com
Ultrasonic Cleaning Equipment Mfr
N.A.I.C.S.: 335999
Brad Underwood *(Engr-Svc)*
Lee Casey Jr. *(Sr Engr-Design)*

Crest Ultrasonics (Thailand) Ltd. **(1)**
898/9 S V City Office Tower 2 7th Floor Rama III Rd, Bangpongpang Yannawa, Bangkok, 10120, Thailand
Tel.: (66) 2 682 6506
Web Site: http://www.crestthai.com
Ultrasonic Cleaning Equipment Mfr
N.A.I.C.S.: 335999

Crest Ultrasonics Shanghai Ltd. **(1)**
Grnd Fl W N Blk Wei Xin Tian Xian Bldg 56 Dhong Xin Rd Suzhou Tech PK, No 56 Zhong Xin Road, Suzhou, 215021, China
Tel.: (86) 512 88184907
Web Site: http://www.crestcn.com
Ultrasonic Cleaning Equipment Mfr
N.A.I.C.S.: 335999
Emma Wang *(Mgr-Fin)*

Custom Blends, Inc. **(1)**
9951 Global Rd, Philadelphia, PA 19115
Tel.: (215) 934-7080

Crest Group Inc.—(Continued)

Emp.: 6
Chemical Products Distr
N.A.I.C.S.: 424690
Charles Kazoreck (Gen Mgr)

Forward Technology, Inc. (1)
260 Jenks Ave SW, Cokato, MN 55321
Tel.: (320) 286-2578
Web Site: http://www.forwardtech.com
Sales Range: $1-9.9 Million
Ultrasonic Welding & Testing Equipment Mfr
N.A.I.C.S.: 333992

KLN Ultraschall AG (1)
Odenwaldstrasse 8, 64646, Heppenheim, Germany
Tel.: (49) 6252 140
Web Site: http://www.kln.de
Emp.: 300
Ultrasonic Welding & Cleaning Equipment Mfr
N.A.I.C.S.: 335999
Herbert Benker (Mgr-Sls)

Subsidiary (Non-US):

KLN Ultrasonics (Shanghai) Co., Ltd. (2)
Building 10 No 388 San Bang Road Chedun Industrial Park, Songjiang, Shanghai, 201611, China
Tel.: (86) 21560 9807
Web Site: http://www.klnchina.com
Ultrasonic Welding & Cleaning Equipment Mfr
N.A.I.C.S.: 335999

Martin Walter Ultrasonics AG (1)
Hardtstrasse 13, 75334, Straubenhardt, Germany
Tel.: (49) 7082 7915 0
Web Site: http://www.walter-ultraschall.de
Ultrasonic Welding & Cleaning Equipment Mfr
N.A.I.C.S.: 335999
Bojan Sasek (Head-Production)
Dieter Schief (Head-Electronical Dev)
Dieter Schwammle (Head-Acctg)
Stefan Wind (Mng Dir)

Mecasonic SA (1)
Technosite Altea 234 Rue Georges Charpak, 74100, Annemasse, France
Tel.: (33) 450 877 300
Web Site: http://www.mecasonic.fr
Emp.: 49
Ultrasonic Welding Equipment Mfr
N.A.I.C.S.: 333992
Andre Verdan (Officer-Data Protection)

Subsidiary (Non-US):

Mecasonic Espana SA (2)
Avda dels Alps 56, Cornella de LLobregat, 08940, Barcelona, Spain
Tel.: (34) 93 473 52 11
Web Site: http://www.mecasonic.es
Ultrasonic Welding Equipment Mfr
N.A.I.C.S.: 333992

Mecasonic UK Ltd (2)
Unit 18 Business Centre West Avenue One, Letchworth, SG6 2HB, Hertfordshire, United Kingdom
Tel.: (44) 1462 678784
Web Site: http://www.mecasonic.co.uk
Ultrasonic Welding Equipment Mfr
N.A.I.C.S.: 333992

Piezo Kinetics Inc. (1)
660 E Rolling Ridge Dr, Bellefonte, PA 16823
Tel.: (814) 355-1593
Web Site: http://www.piezo-kinetics.com
Emp.: 50
Ceramic Materials Mfr
N.A.I.C.S.: 327910
Lea Graffi (Mgr-Shipping)

Rinco Ultrasonics AG (1)
Industriestrasse 4, 8590, Romanshorn, Switzerland
Tel.: (41) 71 466 41 00
Web Site: http://www.rincoultrasonics.com
Emp.: 80
Ultrasonic Welding & Cutting Equipment Mfr
N.A.I.C.S.: 333992
Beatrix Thoma (Mgr-HR)

Subsidiary (Non-US):

AB Rinco Ultrasonics Sverige (2)
Junogatan 9, 451 17, Uddevalla, Sweden
Tel.: (46) 522 64 28 50
Web Site: http://www.rincoultrasonics.se
Ultrasonic Welding Equipment Mfr
N.A.I.C.S.: 333992

Rinco Ultrasonics (India) Private Limited (2)
Plot No 260-A SIDCO Industrial Estate 6th Cross Street, Thirumudivakkam, Chennai, 600 044, India
Tel.: (91) 44 4285 2028
Web Site: http://www.rincoindia.com
Emp.: 12
Ultrasonic Welding & Cleaning Equipment Mfr
N.A.I.C.S.: 333992
Govindan Suresh (Country Mgr)

Rinco Ultrasonics (Shanghai) Co., Ltd. (2)
Building 10 No 388 San Bang Road Chedun Industrial Park, Songjiang, Shanghai, 201611, China
Tel.: (86) 2158680853
Web Site: http://www.rincochina.com
Ultrasonic Welding & Cutting Equipment Mfr
N.A.I.C.S.: 333992

Rinco Ultrasonics Danmark A/S (2)
A Knudsens Vej 9A, 8400, Ebeltoft, Denmark
Tel.: (45) 86 34 31 99
Web Site: http://www.rincoultrasonics.com
Ultrasonic Welding & Cutting Equipment Mfr
N.A.I.C.S.: 333992

Rinco Ultrasonics GmbH (2)
Hardstr 13, 75334, Straubenhardt, Germany
Tel.: (49) 7082 79 185 0
Web Site: http://www.rincoultrasonics.de
Ultrasonic Welding & Cutting Equipment Mfr
N.A.I.C.S.: 333992
Stefan Wind (Mng Dir)

Rinco Ultrasonics Italia S.r.l. (2)
Corso Unione Sovietica 373/B, 10135, Turin, Italy
Tel.: (39) 011 1970 6759
Web Site: http://www.rincoultrasonics.it
Ultrasonic Welding & Cutting Equipment Mfr
N.A.I.C.S.: 333992

Subsidiary (US):

Rinco Ultrasonics USA Inc. (2)
87B Sand Pit Rd, Danbury, CT 06810
Tel.: (203) 744-4500
Web Site: http://www.rinco-usa.com
Emp.: 4
Ultrasonic Welding & Cutting Equipment Mfr
N.A.I.C.S.: 333992

Uthe Technology, Inc. (1)
PO Box 7266, Trenton, NJ 08628
Tel.: (609) 883-4000
Web Site: http://www.uthe.com
Sales Range: $10-24.9 Million
Emp.: 2
Mfr of Bonding Power Supplies & Transducers
N.A.I.C.S.: 334419
Michael Goodson (CEO)

Subsidiary (Non-US):

Uthe Japan Co., Ltd. (2)
4F Shinyokohama Urban Square Building 1-3-1 Shinyokohama Kohoku-ku, Yokohama, Japan
Tel.: (81) 45 470 3747
Web Site: http://www.uthe.co.jp
Ultrasonic Generator & Transducer Mfr
N.A.I.C.S.: 335999
Shiromasa Tonozuka (Gen Mgr)

Uthe Singapore Pte Ltd (2)
970 Toa Payoh North 03-03/05, Singapore, 318992, Singapore
Tel.: (65) 62522072
Web Site: http://www.uthesin.com
Ultrasonic Generator & Transducer Mfr
N.A.I.C.S.: 335999

CREST INDUSTRIES, LLC
4725 Hwy 28 E, Pineville, LA 71360-4730

Tel.: (318) 448-8287   LA
Web Site: https://www.crestoperations.com
Year Founded: 1973
Sales Range: $25-49.9 Million
Emp.: 750
Holding Company
N.A.I.C.S.: 551112
Tim Adam (Coord-Safety)
John Doggett (Gen Counsel)

Subsidiaries:

Crest Natural Resources LLC (1)
4725 Hwy 28 E, Pineville, LA 71360
Tel.: (318) 448-8794
Web Site:
   http://www.crestnaturalresources.com
Lumber Mfr
N.A.I.C.S.: 321113
David Grassi (Pres)
Tracy Blalock (Office Mgr)
Luke Lazarone (Mgr-Real Estate)
Rob Keady (Mgr)
Todd Springer (Mgr-North Unit)

Crest Operations LLC (1)
4725 Howard Hwy 28 E, Pineville, LA 71360-4715
Tel.: (318) 448-8287
Rev.: $39,695,340
Emp.: 8
Electrical Equipment & Supplies
N.A.I.C.S.: 221118
Scott Robison (Owner)

Subsidiary (Domestic):

Beta Engineering LLC (2)
4725 Hwy 28 E, Pineville, LA 71360-3221
Tel.: (318) 487-9599
Web Site: http://www.betaengineering.com
Provider of Turnkey Engineering, Procurement & Construction of High-Voltage Substation & Transmission Projects
N.A.I.C.S.: 238210
Chris Wilson (Mgr-Substation Design)
Andrew Tullos (Project Mgr)
David Chatelain (Engr-Civil)
Jacob Luttgeharm (Project Coord)
Walter Bourgoyne (Mgr-Construction)

DIS-TRAN Packaged Substations, LLC (2)
4725 Hwy 2080, Pineville, LA 71360-4715
Tel.: (318) 448-0274
Web Site: http://www.distran.com
Rev.: $620,000
Emp.: 42
Power, Distribution & Specialty Transformers
N.A.I.C.S.: 541330
Tommy Harless (VP-Projects)

DIS-TRAN Steel Fabrication, LLC (2)
529 Cenla Dr, Pineville, LA 71360-4172
Tel.: (318) 448-0274
Web Site: http://www.distran.com
Sales Range: $1-9.9 Million
Fabricated Structural Metal
N.A.I.C.S.: 332312

DIS-TRAN Steel Pole, LLC (2)
529 Cenla Dr, Pineville, LA 71360-4172
Tel.: (318) 448-0274
Web Site: http://www.distran.com
Sales Range: $10-24.9 Million
Emp.: 25
Mfr & Engineer of Tapered Tubular Folded Plate Steel Substation Structures
N.A.I.C.S.: 331110
Pat Bordelon (Pres)

DIS-TRAN Wood Products, LLC (2)
529 Cenla Dr, Pineville, LA 71360-4172
Tel.: (318) 448-0274
Web Site: http://www.distran.com
Rev.: $750,000
Emp.: 10
Distr of Crossarms, Transmission Timbers & Braces
N.A.I.C.S.: 321215
Pat Bordelon (Pres)
Jerry George (Sr Exec VP)
Mike Ruoppoli (VP-Bus Dev)
Pat Smith (VP)

Mid State Supply Co., LLC (2)

3323 Broadway Ave, Alexandria, LA 71302-4412
Tel.: (318) 448-3411
Web Site: http://www.midstatesupply.net
Rev.: $15,000,000
Emp.: 30
Electrical Apparatus & Equipment
N.A.I.C.S.: 423610
Mike Erwin (VP-Project Sls)
Eddie Milliner (Pres)

CREST LINCOLN MERCURY, INC.
36200 Van Dyke Ave, Sterling Heights, MI 48312
Tel.: (586) 939-6000
Web Site:
   http://www.crestlincolnsterling
   heights.com
Sales Range: $10-24.9 Million
Emp.: 45
New Car Dealers
N.A.I.C.S.: 441110
Scott Kerr (Mgr-New Cars)

CREST NATIONAL FILM LABORATORIES
1000 N Highland Ave, Hollywood, CA 90038
Tel.: (323) 860-1300
Sales Range: $10-24.9 Million
Emp.: 50
Film, Video, Audio & Replicating Services
N.A.I.C.S.: 512191
Rob Stein (Pres)
Jerry Schauer (CFO & COO)

CREST VIEW CORPORATION
4444 Reservoir Blvd NE, Columbia Heights, MN 55421
Tel.: (763) 782-1601
Web Site:
   https://www.crestviewcares.org
Rev.: $11,533,526
Emp.: 171
Senior Citizen Care Services
N.A.I.C.S.: 623312
Joanne Jefferson (Dir-Admissions & Health Info)
Darcy Winsor (Dir-Social Svcs)
Robert Lyndes (Dir-Spiritual Care Svcs)
Ken Svor (CFO)
Shirley Barnes (CEO)
Deb Kaminski (Coord-HR & Payroll)
Pat Hayes (Dir-Dining Svcs)
Dale Kaminski (Dir-Environmental Svcs)
Kristine Backman (Dir-Home Care Svcs)
Kathy Davis (Dir-Life Enrichment)
Cindy Glynn (Mgr-Housing)
Diane Danford (Mgr-Ops)
Kevin Wood (Officer-HIPAA, Dir-IT & Mgr-Independent Living Housing)
Lori Doehne (Co-CFO)

CREST/GOOD MANUFACTURING CO.
90 Gordon Dr Ste A, Syosset, NY 11791
Tel.: (516) 921-7260
Web Site: https://www.crestgood.com
Sales Range: $10-24.9 Million
Emp.: 25
Plumbing & Hydronic Heating Supplies
N.A.I.C.S.: 423720
Ronald B. Goerler (Chm)
Phil Goerler (Pres)

CRESTLINE FUNDING CORP.
18851 Bardeen Ave, Irvine, CA 92612-1520
Tel.: (949) 558-2859   CA
Web Site:
   https://www.crestlinefunding.com

Year Founded: 1994
Sales Range: $10-24.9 Million
Emp.: 50
Full-Service Mortgage Company
N.A.I.C.S.: 522310
Scott Brown (Pres & CEO)
Brad Helman (CFO)
Eric Paluncich (Controller-Audit)

CRESTLINE INVESTORS, INC.
201 Main St Ste 1900, Fort Worth, TX 76102
Tel.: (817) 339-7600
Web Site:
   http://www.crestlineinvestors.com
Year Founded: 1997
Investment Management Firm
N.A.I.C.S.: 523999
Keith Williams (Mng Partner-Credit Strategies)
Douglas K. Bratton (Partner & Chief Investment Officer)
Frank Jordan (Mng Dir & Head-Bus Dev & Client Partnerships)
John Cochran (COO & Partner)
William Palmer (Mng Dir)
Andrey Panna (Mng Dir)
Sanjeev Sarkar (Mng Dir)
Chris Semple (Partner-US Credit)
Susan Yun (Chief People Officer)
Kyle Armbrester (CEO)

Subsidiaries:

CarePayment Technologies, Inc.   (1)
4015 Hillsboro Pike, Nashville, TN 37215
Tel.: (866) 625-8532
Web Site: http://www.carepayment.com
Hospital Software Development Services
N.A.I.C.S.: 541511
Craig S. Hodges (CEO)
Ed Caldwell (Chief Revenue Officer)
Wes Pass (Chief Strategy Officer)
Steve Kukulka (CTO)
james Oliff (CFO)

CRESTMONT CADILLAC CORPORATION
26000 Chagrin Blvd, Beachwood, OH 44122-4298
Tel.: (216) 831-5300
Web Site:
   https://www.crestmontcadillac.com
Year Founded: 1973
Sales Range: $10-24.9 Million
Emp.: 80
New Car Dealers
N.A.I.C.S.: 441110
Kevin Gillespie (Mgr-Sls)
Mike Gutowitz (Mgr-Sls)

CRESTMONT FABRICS, LTD.
75 Laser Ct, Hauppauge, NY 11788
Tel.: (631) 851-0950
Rev.: $14,400,000
Emp.: 23
Mfr of Woven Textiles
N.A.I.C.S.: 424310
Paul Harris (Pres)

CRESTON ADVERTISING & MARKETING INC.
315 Madison Ave Ste 901, New York, NY 10017
Tel.: (212) 400-8698
Year Founded: 1987
Sales Range: $10-24.9 Million
Emp.: 5
Advetising Agency
N.A.I.C.S.: 541810
Diane T. Creston (Pres & Creative Dir)
Mario Stasolla (Art Dir)
Ron Small (Dir, Producer, Writer & Radio Personality)

CRESTONE GROUP BAKING COMPANIES

5927 Farnsworth Ct, Carlsbad, CA 92008
Tel.: (760) 444-9800
Web Site: https://www.crestone-group.com
Year Founded: 1998
Sales Range: $10-24.9 Million
Emp.: 300
Baked Goods Mfr
N.A.I.C.S.: 311811
Charles Bass (COO)
David Shepherd (VP)
James Pettit (Pres)
Patricia Mitchell (Dir-R&D)
Bob Hamill (Exec VP-Facilities Mgmt)

CRESTONE SERVICES GROUP LLC
6145 Broadway Unit 40, Denver, CO 80216
Tel.: (720) 599-4801
Web Site:
   http://crestoneservices.com
Utility & Communication Installation Services
N.A.I.C.S.: 238210
Rick Barrett (CEO)
Michael Walker (CFO)

Subsidiaries:

Americom Technology, Inc.   (1)
5305 W 2400 S England Ct, West Valley City, UT 84120
Tel.: (801) 892-0500
Web Site: http://www.americomtech.com
Sales Range: $10-24.9 Million
Emp.: 85
Telephone & Communication Line Construction Services
N.A.I.C.S.: 237130
Patrick J. Richter (Pres & CEO)
Ron Richter (Co-Owner)
Tim Ray (Mgr-IT)
Randy Hawks (Dir-Utility Svcs)
Barry Papenfuss (CFO)

Dillie & Kuhn, Inc.   (1)
2875 Akers Dr, Colorado Springs, CO 80922
Tel.: (719) 591-9900
Web Site: http://www.dillieandkuhn.com
Sales Range: $1-9.9 Million
Emp.: 20
Electrical Work, Nsk
N.A.I.C.S.: 238210
Brad Kuhn (Co-Founder)
Bryan Crawford (General Mgr)
Brian Erker (Ops Mgr)
Larry Dillie (Co-Founder)

Underground Specialties Inc.   (1)
8890 W Hampden Ave, Denver, CO 80235
Tel.: (303) 877-5004
Web Site:
   http://www.undergroundspecialties.com
Plumbing, Heating & Air-Conditioning Contractors
N.A.I.C.S.: 238220
John Atkins (Pres)

CRESTRON ELECTRONICS INC.
15 Volvo Dr, Rockleigh, NJ 07647-2507
Tel.: (201) 767-3400
Web Site: https://www.crestron.com
Year Founded: 1971
Sales Range: $250-299.9 Million
Emp.: 2,800
Provider of Electronic Controlled & Audio Visual Integration Solutions
N.A.I.C.S.: 334111
George Feldstein (Pres & CEO)
Fred Bargetzi (VP-Tech)
Randy Klein (Exec VP)
Phil Breitschadel (Mgr-Sls-Cobham)
Daniel Brady (VP-Mfg)
Rupert Denoon (Dir-South Africa)
Robin Van Meeuwen (Pres/CEO-EMEA)

CRESTVIEW BUILDERS, INC.
3956 Caliente Circle, Naperville, IL 60564-1140
Tel.: (630) 922-0511
Web Site:
   http://crestviewbuilders.com
Sales Range: $10-24.9 Million
Emp.: 9
Housing Construction Services
N.A.I.C.S.: 236117
Mike Steck (COO)

CRESTVIEW CADILLAC CORPORATION
717 W Genesee St, Syracuse, NY 13204-2350
Tel.: (315) 422-2231
Web Site:
   https://www.crestcadillac.com
Rev.: $16,300,000
Emp.: 70
New & Used Car Dealers
N.A.I.C.S.: 441110
Dave Thompson (Mgr-Fin)
Craig Bunch (Mgr-New Car Sls)
Art Wiley (Mgr-Parts)
Shawn Wolfe (Mgr-Svc)

CRESTVIEW PARTNERS, L.P.
590 Madison Ave 42nd Fl, New York, NY 10022
Tel.: (212) 906-0700   DE
Web Site: http://www.crestview.com
Year Founded: 2004
Privater Equity Firm
N.A.I.C.S.: 523999
Daniel G. Kilpatrick (Partner, Head-financial services strategy & Dir-portfolio companies AutoLenders)
Brian P. Cassidy (Co-Pres, Partner & Head-Media & Communications strategy)
Thomas S. Murphy (Co-Founder & Partner)
Thomas S. Murphy Jr. (Co-Founder & Partner)
Bob Hurst (Vice Chm)
Alex Rose (Co-Pres & Partner)
Richard M. DeMartini (Vice Chm)
Bob Delaney (Partner)
Heather Walker (VP-Fin & Dir-Tax)
Evelyn Pellicone (Partner & CFO)
Adam J. Klein (Partner)
Barry S. Volpert (Co-Founder, CEO & Partner)
Lindsey King (Partner & Head-IR)
Ross Oliver (Partner & Gen Counsel)
Bradford Williams (Principal)
Ben Rhyne (VP)
Lindsay Rosenstein (VP & Head-ESG)
Karen Graham (Office Mgr)
Jeffrey A. Marcus (Vice Chm)
Richard M. DeMartini (Vice Chm)

Subsidiaries:

Accuride Corporation   (1)
7140 Office Cir, Evansville, IN 47715
Tel.: (812) 962-5000
Web Site: http://www.accuridecorp.com
Commercial Vehicles Wheel-end Systems & Components Solutions Mfr & Supplier
N.A.I.C.S.: 336211
Craig Kessler (Sr VP-Engrg)
Robin Kendrick (Pres & CEO)
Robin Kendrick (Pres & CEO)
Drew Hofley (Sr VP-Sls)
Chad Monroe (Sr VP-Admin & Bus Dev)
Scott D. Hazlett (Pres-Accuride Wheels-Europe & Asia)
Robin Kendrick (Pres & CEO)
Fritz Nelson (CFO & Sr VP)
Paul Wright (CIO & Sr VP-IT)
Matt Freeman (Gen Counsel & VP)

Subsidiary (Non-US):

Accuride Canada, Inc.   (2)

31 Firestone Blvd, London, N5W 6E6, ON, Canada   (100%)
Tel.: (519) 453-0880
Web Site: http://www.accuridecorp.com
Motor Vehicle Component Mfr
N.A.I.C.S.: 336390
Rob Jozwiak (Dir-Ops)

Subsidiary (Domestic):

Accuride Erie, L.P.   (2)
1015 E 12th St Ste 200, Erie, PA 16503-1520
Tel.: (814) 480-6400
Web Site: http://www.accuridecorp.com
Motor Vehicle Component Mfr
N.A.I.C.S.: 336390
Greg Dauer (Dir-Ops)

Accuride Henderson Limited Liability Company   (2)
2315 Adams Ln, Henderson, KY 42420
Tel.: (270) 826-5000
Web Site: http://www.accuridecorp.com
Motor Vechicle Components Mfr
N.A.I.C.S.: 336390
Mike Waller (Dir-Ops)

Subsidiary (Non-US):

Accuride Wheels Europe & Asia GmbH   (2)
Weyerstrasse 112-114, 42697, Solingen, Germany
Tel.: (49) 2127011
Emp.: 500
Automotive Wheel Mfr
N.A.I.C.S.: 336110

Subsidiary (Domestic):

Kronprinz GmbH   (3)
Weyerstrasse 112 114, Solingen, 42697, Germany
Tel.: (49) 2127011
Web Site: http://www.kronprinz-raederport.com
Motor Vehicle Parts Mfr
N.A.I.C.S.: 336110
Andreas Wolfsholz (Gen Mgr)

Subsidiary (Non-US):

mefro wheels TURKEY Jant Sanayi A.S.   (4)
Baglarbasi Kisikli Cad Oymaci Sk No 2 Altunizade, 34662, Istanbul, Turkiye
Tel.: (90) 216 474 57 15
Web Site: http://www.mefro-wheels.com
Automotive Parts Mfr & Distr
N.A.I.C.S.: 336390

Subsidiary (Domestic):

Mefro Raderwerk Ronneburg GmbH   (3)
Weidaer Strasse 3, 07580, Ronneburg, Germany
Tel.: (49) 3 66 02 8 0
Web Site: http://www.aw-ronneburg.de
Steel Wheel Mfr
N.A.I.C.S.: 336390

Subsidiary (Non-US):

OOO mefro wheels RUSSIA   (3)
Avtozavodskaya 11, 423520, Zainsk, Tatarstan, Russia
Tel.: (7) 85558 72 667
Web Site: http://www.mefro-wheels.com
Steel Sheet Distr
N.A.I.C.S.: 423510
Deavydov Ilya (Gen Dir)

Subsidiary (Domestic):

Sudrad GmbH Radtechnik   (3)
Strutzstrasse 21, 73061, Ebersbach, Germany
Tel.: (49) 71 63 1 64 0
Web Site: http://www.suedrad.de
Emp.: 280
Steel Wheel Mfr
N.A.I.C.S.: 336390
Alfred Fischbacher (CEO)

Subsidiary (Non-US):

mefro wheels CHINA Co., Ltd.   (3)
Hongyuan Industrial Park Kangtai Road High Technology Zone, Jining, 272000,

Crestview Partners, L.P.—(Continued)

Shandong, China
Tel.: (86) 537 2488 778
Web Site: http://www.mefro-wheels.cn
Steel Sheet Distr
N.A.I.C.S.: 423510
Jack Zhou (Mgr-Quality)

mefro wheels FRANCE S.A.S.   (3)
5 avenue du President Rene Coty, 10601,
La Chapelle-Saint-Luc, Cedex, France
Tel.: (33) 3 25 71 48 00
Web Site: http://www.mefro-wheels.fr
Emp.: 360
Steel Wheel Mfr
N.A.I.C.S.: 336390

mefro wheels Panamerica S.A.   (3)
Av Ovidio Lagos 4480, S2004GMP, Rosa-
rio, Santa Fe, Argentina
Tel.: (54) 341 4664282
Web Site: http://www.mefro-wheels.com.ar
Steel Wheel Mfr & Distr
N.A.I.C.S.: 336390
Mariangel Montes (Mgr-Sls & Logistic)

mefro wheels RUSSIA Plant Togliatti
OOO   (3)
Yuzhnoye shosse 36 Building 46, 445024,
Togliatti, Samara, Russia
Tel.: (7) 8482 270 708
Web Site: http://www.mefro-wheels.com
Steel Wheel Mfr
N.A.I.C.S.: 336390
Aleksei Volnov (Dir-Sls)

Subsidiary (US):

mefro wheels US Services, Inc.   (3)
York Executive Ctr 2555 Kingston Rd Ste
225, York, PA 17402
Tel.: (717) 430-4605
Steel Sheet Distr
N.A.I.C.S.: 423510
Mike Connor (Head-Sls & Gen Mgr)

Subsidiary (Non-US):

Accuride de Mexico, S.A. de
C.V.   (2)
Avenida Internacional 301, Parque Indus-
trial Vynmsa Escobedo, Escobedo, 66062,
Nuevo Leon, Mexico
Tel.: (52) 81 8158 8808
Web Site: http://www.accuridecorp.com
Motor Vehicle Component Mfr
N.A.I.C.S.: 336390

Subsidiary (Domestic):

Assemblies on Time, Inc.   (2)
4800 Gateway Blvd, Springfield, OH 45502
Tel.: (937) 323-9669
Web Site: http://www.accuridecorp.com
Motor Vehicle Component Mfr
N.A.I.C.S.: 336390
Katie Magoteaux (Gen Mgr)

Gunite Corporation   (2)
302 Peoples Ave, Rockford, IL 61104-7035
Tel.: (815) 490-6245
Web Site: http://www.accuridecorp.com
Commercial Vehicle Components Mfr &
Distr
N.A.I.C.S.: 336340
Eric Pansegrau (Dir-Ops)

Advanced Marketing & Processing,
Inc.   (1)
570 Carillon Pkwy Ste 300, Saint Peters-
burg, FL 33716
Tel.: (800) 253-2850
Web Site: http://www.protectmycar.com
Automobile Insurance Services
N.A.I.C.S.: 524126
Craig Rubino (Vice Chm)

Congruex LLC   (1)
2595 Canyon Blvd Ste 400, Boulder, CO
80302
Tel.: (720) 749-2318
Web Site: http://www.congruex.com
Telecommunication, Engineering & Con-
struction Services
N.A.I.C.S.: 541330
Bill Beans (Co-Founder, Pres & CEO)
Kevin O'Hara (Co-Founder & Exec Chm)
Andy Carlson (Exec VP-Corp Dev & M&A)
Neel Dev (CFO & Chief Revenue Officer)

Subsidiary (Domestic):

C.C.L.D. Technologies, Inc.   (2)
3435 Lake Seminole Pl, Buford, GA 30519-
1304
Tel.: (404) 427-8430
Web Site: http://www.ccldtech.com
Telecommunication Servicesb
N.A.I.C.S.: 517112
Nancy Burke (CFO)

CHC Consulting LLC   (2)
1845 W Orangewood Ave Ste 300, Orange,
CA 92868
Tel.: (949) 250-0004
Web Site: http://www.chcconsulting.com
Scientific & Technical Consulting Services
N.A.I.C.S.: 541690
Chris Cook (CEO)
Ryan Matthews (Sr VP-Gen Mgr & Ops)
Lorrie Pope (Pres-Bus Dev & Training)
James Jiranek (Sr VP-AT&T Ops)
Heather Waldenmayer (VP-Fin)
Will Christen (Sr VP-Tech Svcs-AT&T)

Gudenkauf Corporation   (2)
2679 McKinley Ave, Columbus, OH 43204
Tel.: (614) 488-1776
Web Site: http://www.gudenkauf.com
Telephone & Communication Line Construc-
tion
N.A.I.C.S.: 237130
Jeffrey Gudenkauf (Chm & Co-Founder)
Leigh-Anne Duncan (Controller)
Josh Bowman (Mgr-Sys Div)
Sean Leist (Project Mgr)
Sid Hale (Mgr-Civil Projects Div)
Vince Paxton (Asst VP-Ops)
Mark Rogers (COO & VP-Ops)
Bill Adkins (Reg Mgr-OSP)
Dave Robinson (VP-Ops-East)

HHS Construction, Inc.   (2)
2042 S Grove Ave, Ontario, CA 91761
Tel.: (909) 393-3322
Web Site: https://www.congruex.com
Commercial & Institutional Building Con-
struction
N.A.I.C.S.: 236220

Southeast Utilities of Georgia,
LLC   (2)
1020 Franke Industrial Dr, Augusta, GA
30909
Tel.: (706) 733-3053
Web Site:
    http://southeastutilitiesofgeorgia.com
Sales Range: $1-9.9 Million
Emp.: 30
Utility Contractor Services
N.A.I.C.S.: 237110

White Construction Company   (2)
613 Crescent Cir Ste 100, Ridgeland, MS
39157
Tel.: (601) 898-5180
Web Site: http://www.whiteconst.com
Rev.: $26,500,000
Emp.: 160
Commercial & Institutional Building Con-
struction
N.A.I.C.S.: 236220
Charles N. White (Founder)
David Holliman (CFO, Treas & Sr VP)
Neel White (Chm)
Guy H. White (CEO)
Tracy B. Bailey (Dir-Preconstruction Svcs)
Jim Snyder (VP)
Rob Baugher (Sr VP)
Steve Burch (Pres & COO)
Gary Jones (Exec Dir-IT)
Bob Higgins (Sr VP)
Ken Harrison (Sr VP-Estimating)
Tom Howard (VP)
Chad Pippin (VP)
John Wilke (VP)
Bill Farnum (VP-Preconstruction Svcs)
Dominic Padilla (Dir-Relationship Mgmt)
Morgan Pare (Coord-Mktg & Proposal)
Travis Chaney (Asst Superintendent)
Scott Davidson (Superintendent)
David Frame III (VP)

Crestview Advisors, L.L.C.   (1)
590 Madison Ave 36th Fl, New York, NY
10022
Tel.: (212) 906-0700
Web Site: http://www.crestview.com
Privater Equity Firm

N.A.I.C.S.: 523999

Elo Touch Solutions, Inc.   (1)
301 Constitution Dr, Menlo Park, CA 94025
Tel.: (650) 361-4800
Web Site: http://www.elotouch.com
Sales Range: $400-449.9 Million
Emp.: 500
Touch Screens & Touch Monitors Mfr
N.A.I.C.S.: 334118
Craig A. Witsoe (CEO)
Trent Waterhouse (CMO)
Jim Melton (VP-Ops & Quality)
Dan Ludwick (VP-America)
Mike Moran (VP-Ops)
Niklas Fallgren (VP-OEM Bus Unit)
Randi Moran (VP-HR)
Roxi Wen (CFO)
Chris Sullivan (VP-Sls-Americas)
John Lamb (VP-Mktg)
Jenny Cheng (Mgr-Mktg)

Subsidiary (Non-US):

Elo Touch Solutions (Belgium)
NV   (2)
Kolonel Begaultlaan 1C11, 3012, Leuven,
Belgium
Tel.: (32) 16 704 500
Touch Screen Monitor Mfr
N.A.I.C.S.: 334118

Elo Touch Solutions Argentina
SA   (2)
Saavedra 2950, El Talar de Pacheco,
B1618ACP, Buenos Aires, Argentina
Tel.: (54) 11 47332200
Touch Screen Monitor Distr
N.A.I.C.S.: 423430

Elo Touch Solutions Singapore Pte
Ltd   (2)
2 Ang Mo Kio Street 64 Ste 05-02B Econ
Building, Singapore, 569084, Singapore
Tel.: (65) 6483 6216
Web Site: http://www.elotouch.com
Sales Range: $10-24.9 Million
Emp.: 4
Computer Terminal Mfr
N.A.I.C.S.: 334118
Yewhee Tan (Office Mgr)

Branch (Domestic):

Elo Touch Solutions, Inc. -
Rochester   (2)
2245 Brighton-Henrietta Town Line Rd,
Rochester, NY 14623
Tel.: (585) 475-1110
Web Site: http://www.elotouch.com
Sales Range: $25-49.9 Million
Emp.: 35
Turnkey Vendors Computer Systems
N.A.I.C.S.: 334118

Emerald Technologies   (1)
2243 Lundy Ave, San Jose, CA 95131
Tel.: (603) 681-2494
Web Site:
    https://www.emeraldtechnologies.com
Electronic Parts & Equipment Mfr
N.A.I.C.S.: 423690
Ron Menigoz (CTO)
Hartmut Liebel (CEO)
Raul Tejada (CFO)

Subsidiary (Domestic):

Ascentron, Inc.   (2)
994 Antelope Rd, White City, OR 97503
Tel.: (541) 826-2405
Web Site: http://www.ascentron.com
Storage Battery Mfr
N.A.I.C.S.: 335910
Amanda Brewer (Pres)

Optimum Design Associates, Inc.   (2)
1075 Serpentine Ln Ste B, Pleasanton, CA
94566
Tel.: (925) 401-2004
Web Site: http://www.optimumdesign.com
Sales Range: $10-24.9 Million
Emp.: 62
Printed Circuit Board Assemblies
N.A.I.C.S.: 334418
Nick Barbin (Co-Founder & Pres)
Roger Hileman (Co-Founder & CFO)

Saline Lectronics, Inc.   (2)
710 N Maple Rd, Saline, MI 48176

Tel.: (734) 944-2120
Web Site: http://www.lectronics.net
Rev.: $8,611,400
Emp.: 98
Bare Printed Circuit Board Mfr
N.A.I.C.S.: 334412
Mario Sciberras (Pres & CEO)

Hanson Systems, LLC   (1)
9850 Red Arrow Hwy, Bridgman, MI 49106
Tel.: (269) 465-6986
Web Site: https://www.eagletehnologies.com
Sales Range: $1-9.9 Million
Emp.: 45
Measuring & Controlling Device Mfr
N.A.I.C.S.: 334519
Brandon Fuller (Pres)

Modern Wealth Management,
LLC   (1)
30200 Telegraph Ste 210, Bingham Farms,
MI 48025
Tel.: (248) 828-8000
Web Site: https://www.modwm.com
Investment Advisory Firm
N.A.I.C.S.: 523940
Gary L. Roth (Co-CEO & Co-Founder)
Jason Gordo (Pres & Co-Founder)
Mike Capelle (Co-CEO & Co-Founder)

Subsidiary (Domestic):

Barber Financial Group   (2)
13550 W 95th St, Lenexa, KS 66215
Tel.: (913) 825-5900
Web Site:
    http://www.barberfinancialgroup.com
Rev.: $1,300,000
Emp.: 19
Administrative Management & General
Management Consulting Service
N.A.I.C.S.: 541611
Dean Barber (CEO & Partner)
Bud Kasper (Pres & Partner-Lee's Summit)
Bruce Godke (Partner)
Eric Sheerin (Partner)
Shane Barber (Partner)
Tom Clough (Pres)
Amy Ricker (Chief Mktg Officer)

Beltz Ianni & Associates   (2)
240 Kenneth Dr, Rochester, NY 14623
Tel.: (585) 340-5200
Web Site: http://www.beltz-ianni.com
Financial Investment Activities
N.A.I.C.S.: 523999
Fred Beltz (Partner)

Munder Capital Management
Inc.   (1)
480 Pierce St, Birmingham, MI 48009
Tel.: (248) 647-9200
Web Site: http://www.vcm.com
Sales Range: $200-249.9 Million
Investment Advisory Services
N.A.I.C.S.: 523940
Michael P. Gura (Sr Portfolio Mgr)
Tony Y. Dong (Vice Chm & Sr Portfolio Mgr)
Stephen Bradley Fush (Dir-Res)
Edward Goard (Chief Investment Officer-
Fixed Income Grp)

Subsidiary (Domestic):

Victory Capital Management, Inc.   (2)
4900 Tiedeman Rd 4th Fl, Brooklyn, OH
44144
Tel.: (216) 898-2400
Web Site: http://www.vcm.com
Rev.: $20,000,000,000
Investment Management Service
N.A.I.C.S.: 523940
Lawrence Babin (Portfolio Mgr)
Scott Kefer (Sr Portfolio Mgr)
David C. Brown (Chm & CEO)
Paul G. Pasicznyk (Head-Institutional)
Gregory J. Ewald (Chief Legal Officer)
Kevin Schmeits (Head-Intermediary & Re-
tirement Sls)
Lori A. Swain (Head-HR)
Derrick A. MacDonald (Chief Tech & Ops
Officer)
Mannik Dhillon (Head-Product Dev & Strat-
egy)
Caroline Churchill (CMO)
Allison Smith (Head-Sls, Distr, Intermediary
& Retirement)
Mark J. Van Meter (Head-Capital Markets &
Trading)
Michael D. Policarpo (CFO & COO)

SyBridge Technologies, Inc. (1)
20700 Civic Ctr Dr Ste 430, Southfield, MI 48076
Tel.: (909) 476-2555
Web Site: http://www.sybridgetech.com
Industrial Molding Products Mfr
N.A.I.C.S.: 333511
Tony Nardone (CEO)

Subsidiary (Domestic):

Cavaform, Inc. (2)
2700 72nd St N, Saint Petersburg, FL 33710
Tel.: (727) 384-3676
Web Site: http://www.cavaform.com
Sales Range: $1-9.9 Million
Emp.: 50
Industrial Mold Mfr
N.A.I.C.S.: 333511
David Massie (Pres)
Chris Outlaw (Mgr-Engrg)
Chuck Doerner (Engr)
Cliff Pope (Mgr-Quality)
Clyde Henderson (Mgr-Pur)
Dave Woodward (Engr)
John Heintz (Mgr-Mktg)
John Homzak (Mgr-Mfg)
Mike Buhler (Plant Mgr)
Mike Gelineau (Engr)
Nick Scalamogna (Controller)

Pyramid Mold & Tool (2)
10155 Sharon Cir, Rancho Cucamonga, CA 91730
Tel.: (909) 476-2555
Web Site: http://www.pyramidmold.com
Sales Range: $1-9.9 Million
Emp.: 35
Industrial Mold Mfr
N.A.I.C.S.: 333511
Steve Hoare (Owner)
Anthony May (Dir-Sls & Mktg)

TenCate Grass Holding BV (1)
G van der Muelenweg 2, 7443 RE, Nijverdal, Netherlands
Tel.: (31) 548 633 944
Web Site: http://www.tencategrass.com
Holding Company; Synthetic Turf Components Mfr
N.A.I.C.S.: 551112
Brian P. Cassidy (Chm)

Subsidiary (Domestic):

Ten Cate Thiolon B.V. (2)
G van der Muelenweg 2, 7443 RE, Nijverdal, Netherlands
Tel.: (31) 548633944
Web Site: http://www.tencategrass.com
Artificial Turf Fibers & Backing Mfr
N.A.I.C.S.: 325220

Subsidiary (US):

Ten Cate Thiolon USA Inc. (2)
1131 Broadway St, Dayton, TN 37321-1802
Tel.: (423) 775-0792
Web Site: http://www.tencategrass.com
Artificial Turf Fibers & Backing Mfr
N.A.I.C.S.: 325220
Rob Block (VP-Ops)

X-Cell Tool & Mold, Inc. (1)
7701 Klier Drive S, Erie, PA 16506
Tel.: (814) 474-9100
Web Site: http://www.xctam.com
Other Personal & Household Goods Repair & Maintenance
N.A.I.C.S.: 811490
Ronald J. Novel (CEO)
Rachel Ellis (Office Mgr)

CRESTWOOD ASSOCIATES LLC
240 E Lincoln St, Mount Prospect, IL 60056
Tel.: (847) 394-8820 IL
Web Site: http://www.crestwood.com
Year Founded: 1998
Business Software & Services
N.A.I.C.S.: 513210
Brian J. McGuckin (Partner)
Tim J. Thompson (Co-Founder Partner)
Melissa Ryba (Dir-Ops)
Angela Stuart Mills (Dir-Product Dev)

CRESTWOOD INC.
601 E Water Well Rd, Salina, KS 67401
Tel.: (785) 827-0317
Web Site: https://www.crestwood-inc.com
Year Founded: 1969
Sales Range: $10-24.9 Million
Emp.: 180
Mfr of Fine Custom Cabinetry & Related Wood Products
N.A.I.C.S.: 337110
Tyler Bogart (Dir-Sls)
Sharon Burt (VP-HR)

CRESTWOOD TECHNOLOGY GROUP
1 Odell Plz Ste 139, Yonkers, NY 10701
Tel.: (914) 779-3500
Web Site: https://www.ctg123.com
Year Founded: 2001
Sales Range: $10-24.9 Million
Emp.: 35
Commercial Physical Research
N.A.I.C.S.: 541715
Joseph Mancino (COO)
Krista Raia (Acct Exec)
Donald LaRocco (Exec VP-Govt Programs)

CRESTWOOD TUBULARS INC.
3107 S Noland Rd, Independence, MO 64055
Tel.: (314) 842-8604
Web Site: https://www.crestwoodtubulars.com
Rev.: $11,000,000
Emp.: 6
Metal Service Centers & Other Metal Merchant Whslr
N.A.I.C.S.: 423510
Thomas Ferguson (VP)

CRETCHER HEARTLAND LLC
4551 West 107th St 3rd Fl, Overland Park, KS 66207
Tel.: (913) 341-8998 MO
Web Site: http://www.cretcherheartland.com
Year Founded: 2010
Rev.: $439,000,000
Emp.: 158
Insurance & Employee Benefits Consulting Services
N.A.I.C.S.: 524298
Mark Avery (Chief Strategy Officer)
Jeff Wipperman (Sr VP-Sls)
Steven Nicholson (CEO)
Chandler Cullor (Pres)
Jason Patchen (CMO)

Subsidiaries:

Power Group Company, LLC (1)
12721 Metcalf Ave, Overland Park, KS 66213
Tel.: (913) 491-3280
Web Site: http://www.pgcompanies.com
Sales Range: $10-24.9 Million
Emp.: 95
Corporate Risk Consulting Services
N.A.I.C.S.: 541618
Mark Avery (Pres & CEO)
Jeff Wipperman (Principal)

CRETE CARRIER CORP.
400 NW 56th St, Lincoln, NE 68528
Tel.: (402) 475-9521 NE
Web Site: http://www.cretecarrier.com
Year Founded: 1966
Sales Range: $150-199.9 Million
Emp.: 650
Provider of Transportation Services
N.A.I.C.S.: 484230
Tonn M. Ostergard (Chm & CEO)
Tim Aschoff (Pres & COO)

Subsidiaries:

Hunt Transportation, Inc. (1)
10770 I St, Omaha, NE 68127
Tel.: (402) 339-3003
Web Site: http://www.hunttransportationjobs.com
Sales Range: $25-49.9 Million
Emp.: 250
Food Transportation Services
N.A.I.C.S.: 488490
Mark D. Swanson (Co-Pres)
Erick Kutter (Pres-Shaffer Trucking)

Shaffer Trucking Company (1)
400 NW 56th St, Lincoln, NE 68528
Tel.: (402) 475-9521
Web Site: http://www.shaffertrucking.com
Sales Range: $50-74.9 Million
Refrigerated Transportation; Trucking Services
N.A.I.C.S.: 484121
Erick Kutter (Pres)

Shaffer Trucking Company (1)
49 E Main St, New Kingstown, PA 17072
Tel.: (717) 766-4708
Web Site: http://www.shaffertrucking.com
Sales Range: $50-74.9 Million
Trucking Services; Refrigerated Transportation
N.A.I.C.S.: 484121
Raymond Dunn (Pres & CEO)

CRETE MECHANICAL GROUP, INC.
2701 N Rocky Point Blvd. Ste 660, Tampa, FL 33607
Tel.: (833) 273-8364
Web Site: https://cretemechanical.com
Emp.: 200
Specialty Trade Contractors
N.A.I.C.S.: 238990
Michael Cox (CEO)

Subsidiaries:

C & C Service, LLC. (1)
17 Davenport St, Stamford, CT 06902
Tel.: (203) 323-2866
Web Site: http://www.ccservicellc.com
Sales Range: $1-9.9 Million
Emp.: 30
Plumbing, Heating & Air-Conditioning Contracting Services
N.A.I.C.S.: 238220

CREVE COEUR CAMERA INC.
1155 N Warson Rd, Saint Louis, MO 63132-1803
Tel.: (314) 872-7557
Web Site: http://www.cccamera.com
Year Founded: 1974
Sales Range: $10-24.9 Million
Emp.: 20
Camera & Photographic Supply Stores
N.A.I.C.S.: 449210
Stephen Weiss (Pres)

CREW CREATIVE ADVERTISING, LLC.
7966 Beverly Blvd, Los Angeles, CA 90048
Tel.: (323) 468-3636
Year Founded: 1999
Sales Range: $10-24.9 Million
Emp.: 165
Advertising Agency Services
N.A.I.C.S.: 541810
Damon Wolf (Pres & CEO)

CREW CUTS INC.
28 W 44th St, New York, NY 10036
Tel.: (212) 302-2828
Web Site: http://www.crewcuts.com
Rev.: $13,260,312
Emp.: 40
TV Tape Services: Editing, Transfers, Etc.
N.A.I.C.S.: 512191

Clayton Hemmert (Pres)
Sherri Margulies (Partner)
Craig Rohrer (Editor)

CREW TECHNICAL SERVICES
7768 Zionsville Rd Ste 150, Indianapolis, IN 46268
Tel.: (317) 713-7777
Web Site: http://www.crewtech.com
Sales Range: $10-24.9 Million
Emp.: 75
Technical Services
N.A.I.C.S.: 541990
Kathy G. Reehling (Pres & CEO)

CREW2, INC.
2650 Minnehaha Ave, Minneapolis, MN 55406-1591
Tel.: (612) 276-1600
Web Site: https://www.crew2.com
Sales Range: $10-24.9 Million
Emp.: 100
Flooring Installation Services
N.A.I.C.S.: 238330
Denise Firkus (Principal)

CREWS BANKING CORPORATION
106 E Main St, Wauchula, FL 33873
Tel.: (863) 773-4151
Bank Holding Company
N.A.I.C.S.: 551111
Beth Marshall (Dir-DP)
Don Martin (Sr Dir-Mktg)
Josh Haley (Supvr-Help Desk)
Matt Opalach (Dir-IT)
Mike Giguere (CIO)
J.W. Crews Jr. (Chm)

Subsidiaries:

Charlotte State Bank & Trust (1)
1100 Tamiami Trl, Port Charlotte, FL 33953
Tel.: (941) 624-5400
Web Site: http://www.charlottestatebank.com
Sales Range: $50-74.9 Million
Emp.: 81
Banking Services
N.A.I.C.S.: 522110
Craig Deyoung (Co-Pres)
Ann Banting (VP & Controller)
Michael Aloian (Co-Pres & Chief Investment Officer)
Samuel A. Kiburz (VP & Portfolio Mgr)
Lory Weisensee (Exec VP)
Brittney Seymour (Officer-Investment Acct)
Christine Hause (Officer-Investment Mgmt Svcs Dev & VP-Trust)
Cindee Murphy (Officer-Trust & VP)
Patrice A. White (Officer-Trust & VP)
Rich Emch (Officer-Trust Admin & VP)

Englewood Bank & Trust (1)
1111 S McCall Rd, Englewood, FL 34223
Tel.: (941) 475-6771
Web Site: http://www.englewoodbank.com
Sales Range: $25-49.9 Million
Emp.: 43
Commericial Banking
N.A.I.C.S.: 522110
Amy Prestia (Sr VP-Retail Banking & HR)
J. W. Crews (Chm)
Charlene Dorio (Officer-Retail Banking & Branch Mgr)
Liz M. Jarvis (VP)
Kristina Watts (Officer-Bus Dev & Asst VP)
Tamra Britton (Officer-Retail Banking & Branch Mgr)
Stacey F. Goff (Asst VP-Loan Ops)
Michelle Ravagni (Officer-Retail Banking & Branch Mgr)
Kerry Hunter (Officer-Bus Dev Trust)
Lory Weisensee (Exec VP)
Bryan Pennybacker (CFO)
Kevin Casey (Sr VP)
Michael Aloian (Chief Investment Officer & Pres-Trust & Investment Mgmt Svcs)
Sheila Roberts (Chief Compliance Officer)

CRF INC.
4000 Chemical Rd Ste 400, Plymouth Meeting, PA 19462

CRF Inc.—(Continued)

Tel.: (781) 250-4400
Web Site: http://www.crfhealth.com
Sales Range: $10-24.9 Million
Emp.: 110
Electronic Patient-Reported Outcomes & Wireless Data Collection Solutions for the Biopharmaceutical Industry
N.A.I.C.S.: 517810
Timo Ahopelto (Founder)
Chris Clancy (Dir-Bus Dev)
Debi Maloney (VP-Corp Accts)
Rachael King (CEO)

CRG HOLDING COMPANY, INC.
6443 SW Beaverton Hillsdale Hwy Ste 200, Portland, OR 97221
Tel.: (503) 297-8401 OR
Web Site:
http://www.crginsurance.com
Year Founded: 1982
Sales Range: $1-9.9 Million
Holding Company; Employee Benefits, Human Resources & Payroll Consulting Services
N.A.I.C.S.: 551112
Rupert Reinstadler (Mng Partner)
Carol Dobbs (Partner)

CRG INC.
4000 Piedmont Pkwy Ste 300, High Point, NC 27265
Tel.: (336) 875-3110
Web Site: https://www.getcrg.com
Year Founded: 1994
Sales Range: $10-24.9 Million
Emp.: 200
Computer Related Consulting Services
N.A.I.C.S.: 541512
Tim Sessoms (CEO)
Joe Nix (CFO)
Natalie Smith (Mgr-Ops & Projects)
Harlan F. Weisman (Partner)

CRH CATERING CO., INC.
1600 Morrell Ave, Connellsville, PA 15425
Tel.: (724) 628-8100
Web Site: http://www.crh-catering.com
Sales Range: $25-49.9 Million
Emp.: 300
Operator of Candy & Snack Food Vending Machines
N.A.I.C.S.: 445132
Joseph M. Cordaro (Pres)
William B. Hall (VP-Food Svcs)
Joe Parisi (Controller)

CRI HOTEL INCOME PARTNERS, L.P.
11200 Rockville Pike, Rockville, MD 20852
Tel.: (301) 468-9200
Year Founded: 1986
Sales Range: $1-9.9 Million
Emp.: 2
Investment Management Service
N.A.I.C.S.: 523999
Bradford H. Dockser (Pres)

CRICKET MEDIA GROUP LTD.
13625-A Dulles Technology Dr, Herndon, VA 20171
Tel.: (703) 885-3400 ON
Web Site:
http://www.cricketmedia.com
Year Founded: 2010
Sales Range: $10-24.9 Million
Holding Company; Educational Media Publisher
N.A.I.C.S.: 551112

Miles Gilburne (Chm)
Aric Holsinger (CFO)
Nina Zolt (Chief Learning Officer)
Katherine Dunn Andresen (CEO)
Andrew Berman (Chief-Staff)
Jon Zeitler (Exec VP-Corp Dev & Legal Affairs)
Maggie Hatfield (Sr VP-Mktg)
Stephanie Sharis (Co-CEO)
Victor Block (COO)

Subsidiaries:

Cricket Media, Inc. (1)
13625A Dulles Technology Dr, Herndon, VA 20171
Tel.: (703) 885-3400
Web Site: http://www.cricketmedia.com
Educational Media Publisher
N.A.I.C.S.: 513199
Katya Andresen (CEO)
Aric Holsinger (CFO)
Jon Zeitler (Exec VP-Corp Dev & Legal Affairs)
Maggie Hatfield (Sr VP-Mktg)

Subsidiary (Domestic):

Carus Publishing Company (2)
140 S Dearborn St Ste 1450, Chicago, IL 60603
Tel.: (312) 701-1720
Web Site: http://www.cricketmag.com
Magazine & Book Publisher
N.A.I.C.S.: 513130
Jason Patenaude (Pres & COO)
Andre Carus (CEO)

Group (Domestic):

Cricket Magazine Group (3)
30 Grove St Ste C, Peterborough, NH 03458
Tel.: (603) 924-7209
Web Site: http://www.cricketmag.com
Magazine Publisher
N.A.I.C.S.: 513120

CRICKET TECHNOLOGIES, LLC
12310 Pinecrest Rd, Reston, VA 20191
Tel.: (703) 391-1020
Web Site:
http://www.crickettechnologies.com
Year Founded: 2001
Rev.: $11,500,000
Emp.: 5
E-Forensics Software & Litigation Technology Services
N.A.I.C.S.: 513210
Arthur C. Blades (Pres)

CRIDER INC.
1 Plant Ave, Stillmore, GA 30464
Tel.: (912) 562-4435
Web Site: http://www.criderinc.com
Year Founded: 1983
Sales Range: $25-49.9 Million
Emp.: 600
Provider of Poultry Slaughtering & Processing Services
N.A.I.C.S.: 311615
M. M. Harrel (CFO)
Randel Baggett (Controller)
W. A. Crider Jr. (CEO)

CRIGLER ENTERPRISES, INC.
6721 Discovery Blvd, Mableton, GA 30126
Tel.: (404) 874-4401
Web Site: https://www.crigler.com
Year Founded: 1972
Sales Range: $1-9.9 Million
Emp.: 19
Industrial Machinery & Equipment Whslr
N.A.I.C.S.: 423830
Julian Hailey (VP)
Kathryn Renzi (Pres)
Wayne Crigler (CEO)

CRILLON IMPORTERS LTD.
The Atrium 80 Route 4 E, Paramus, NJ 07652
Tel.: (201) 368-8878
Web Site:
http://www.crillonimporters.com
Year Founded: 1999
Sales Range: $1-9.9 Million
Emp.: 50
Importers of Alcoholic Beverages
N.A.I.C.S.: 424820
Michel P. Roux (Chm & CEO)
Jerry Ciraulo (Pres & COO)

CRIME PREVENTION INC.
4200 Sandy Porter Rd, Charlotte, NC 28273
Tel.: (704) 527-4070
Web Site: http://www.cpisecurity.com
Year Founded: 1976
Sales Range: $10-24.9 Million
Emp.: 320
Alarm Signal Systems Designing, Installing & Monitoring
N.A.I.C.S.: 561621
Kenneth J. Gill (Pres)

CRIMSON CONSULTING GROUP, INC.
530 Lytton Ave, Palo Alto, CA 94301
Tel.: (650) 960-3600 CA
Web Site:
http://www.crimsonmarketing.com
Year Founded: 1993
Sales Range: $10-24.9 Million
Emp.: 21
Marketing Consulting Services
N.A.I.C.S.: 541613
Glenn Gow (Founder & CEO)

CRIMSON FOREST ENTERTAINMENT GROUP INC.
8335 Sunset Blvd Ste #238, West Hollywood, CA 90069
Tel.: (323) 337-9089 NV
Web Site:
http://crimsonforestfilms.com
Year Founded: 2010
Theatrical & Home Entertainment Distribution Label
N.A.I.C.S.: 512120
Jonathan Lim (Mgr)

Subsidiaries:

Hannover House, Inc. (1)
1722 N College Ave C303, Fayetteville, AR 72703
Tel.: (818) 481-5277
Web Site: https://www.hannoverhouse.com
Motion Picture, Home Video & On-Demand Production & Distribution
N.A.I.C.S.: 512110
Eric Parkinson (Chm & CEO)

CRIMSON INSULATIONS CO INC.
12309 Bethany Ln, Duncanville, AL 35456
Tel.: (205) 752-6777
Sales Range: $10-24.9 Million
Emp.: 45
Roofing, Siding & Insulation Material Merchant Whslr
N.A.I.C.S.: 423330
Randy Holcomb (VP)
William Woolbright (Exec VP)
Nancy Woolbright (Pres)
Delana Holcomb (Sec)

CRIMSON INVESTMENT
1000 Marina Blvd Ste 105, Brisbane, CA 94005
Tel.: (650) 233-6900
Web Site:
http://www.crimsoninvestment.com
Year Founded: 1993
Privater Equity Firm

N.A.I.C.S.: 523999
John-Paul Ho (Mng Partner)

Subsidiaries:

Aqua-Chem, Inc. (1)
3001 E Governor John Sevier Hwy, Knoxville, TN 37914
Tel.: (865) 544-2065
Web Site: http://www.aqua-chem.com
Water Treatment Equipment Mfr
N.A.I.C.S.: 221310
David Gensterblum (Pres & CEO)
David Hansard (VP-Quality Mgmt)
David Keever (Pres-Ops-China)
Robert C. Brunetti (CFO)
Ronnie Shook (VP-Life Sciences, Beverage & Water Reuse)
Dave Patterson (VP-Govt Sls)
Frank Keeper (VP-Ops-US)

Tyden Group Inc. (1)
28181 River Dr, Circleville, OH 43113
Tel.: (740) 420-6777
Web Site: http://www.tydengroup.com
Emp.: 100
Security, Identification, Traceability & Utility Product Mfr
N.A.I.C.S.: 334519
Ashot Mesropyan (CEO)

Subsidiary (Domestic):

Brooks Utility Products Group (2)
23847 Industrial Park Dr, Farmington Hills, MI 48335-2860
Tel.: (248) 477-0250
Web Site: http://www.ekstrom-metering.com
Sales Range: $10-24.9 Million
Emp.: 100
Metering Equipment Mfr
N.A.I.C.S.: 334519
Karl Loehr (Mgr-Quality)

Telesis Technologies Inc. (2)
28181 River Dr, Circleville, OH 43113
Tel.: (740) 477-5000
Web Site: http://www.telesistech.com
Emp.: 125
Laser Marking System Mfr
N.A.I.C.S.: 334419
Ashot Mesropyan (Pres)

TydenBrooks Security Products Group (2)
2727 Paces Ferry Rd, Atlanta, GA 30339
Web Site: http://www.tydenbrooks.com
Sales Range: $25-49.9 Million
Plastic/Metal Security Seals & Locking Devices Mfr
N.A.I.C.S.: 332510

Subsidiary (Non-US):

Precintia International, S.A. (3)
Vic St 26-28, E 08120, Barcelona, La Llagosta, Spain
Tel.: (34) 935446450
Web Site: http://www.precintia.com
Sales Range: $10-24.9 Million
Seals, Locking Devices, Security Bags & Modular Mail Sorting Products Retail & Mfr
N.A.I.C.S.: 561621

Tyden (Suzhou) Security Seal Co., Ltd. (3)
Bldg 11 Workshop Wujiang Export Processing Zone, 215200, Wujiang, Jiangsu, China
Tel.: (86) 51263496166
Web Site: http://www.tydenbrooks.com
Plastic/Metal Security Seals & Locking Devices Mfr
N.A.I.C.S.: 332510

Unit (Domestic):

TydenBrooks Security Products Group (3)
409 Hoosier Dr, Angola, IN 46703
Tel.: (260) 665-3178
Web Site: http://www.tydenbrooks.com
Sales Range: $10-24.9 Million
Cargo Security Seal Mfr
N.A.I.C.S.: 332510

Subsidiary (Domestic):

TydenBrooks Stoffel Seals Corporation (3)
400 High Ave, Nyack, NY 10960

Tel.: (845) 353-3800
Web Site: http://www.stoffel.com
Sales Range: $50-74.9 Million
Security Seals, Printed Packaging Materials, Promotional Products, Identification Cards & Badges Mfr
N.A.I.C.S.: 322220

CRIMSON RESOURCE MANAGEMENT
410 17th St Ste 1010, Denver, CO 80202
Tel.: (303) 892-9333
Web Site:
https://www.crimsonrm.com
Rev.: $37,584,016
Emp.: 7
Crude Petroleum & Natural Gas Production
N.A.I.C.S.: 211120
Andy Wurst (CFO)
Greg Soukup (Mgr-Engrg)
Nick Amicone (Mgr-HR)
Gary Buntmann (Pres)

CRIMSON SOLUTIONS, LLC
3021-B Griffith St, Charlotte, NC 28203
Tel.: (877) 727-3548   NC
Holding Company
N.A.I.C.S.: 551112
Cortland Ouzts (CEO)

Subsidiaries:

POS Nation   (1)
3021 B Griffith St, Charlotte, NC 28203
Tel.: (704) 405-5089
Web Site: http://www.posnation.com
Customized Point-of-Sale Solutions Provider
N.A.I.C.S.: 513210
Cortland Ouzts (CEO)

Subsidiary (Domestic):

Chuck Atkinson, Inc.   (2)
4100 International plz, Fort Worth, TX 76109
Tel.: (817) 560-8139
Web Site: http://www.capautomation.com
Software Publisher
N.A.I.C.S.: 513210
Chuck Atkinson (CEO)

CRIO INC.
1386 W 70 S, Lindon, UT 84042
Tel.: (801) 462-2377
Web Site: http://www.criobru.com
Sales Range: $1-9.9 Million
Cocoa Bean Brewed Beverages
N.A.I.C.S.: 311999
Jon Fotheringham (Pres & CEO)
Eric Durtsch (COO)

CRIPPEN AUTO MALL
8300 W Saginaw Hwy, Lansing, MI 48917-9769
Tel.: (517) 627-8411
Web Site:
https://www.crippencars.com
Sales Range: $10-24.9 Million
Emp.: 92
Car Whslr
N.A.I.C.S.: 441110
Jeff Crippen (Principal)

CRIPPMANN
8300 W Saginaw Hwy, Lansing, MI 48917
Tel.: (517) 627-8411
Web Site:
http://www.crippencars.com
Sales Range: $10-24.9 Million
Emp.: 95
New Car Retailer
N.A.I.C.S.: 441110
Jeff Crippen (Pres)
Chris Erickson (Gen Mgr-Sls)
Chad Eley (Dir-Fin)

Chris Harder (Mgr-Fin)
Heather Plunkett Johnston (Mgr-Customer Rels)
Shawn Cyrocki (Asst Mgr-Body Shop)
Bill Garrett (Gen Mgr-Motors Parts)
Phil Murphy (Mgr-Body Shop)

CRISAK INC.
37174 Devon Wick Ln, Purcellville, VA 20132
Tel.: (540) 751-0606
Rev.: $10,820,443
Emp.: 20
Commercial & Office Buildings; Renovation & Repair
N.A.I.C.S.: 236220
Steve Spiewak (Pres)

CRISP COUNTY POWER COMMISSION INC.
202 S 7th St, Cordele, GA 31010
Tel.: (229) 273-3811
Web Site:
https://www.crispcountypower.com
Sales Range: $10-24.9 Million
Emp.: 65
Eletric Power Generation Services
N.A.I.C.S.: 221118
Marcus Waters (Mgr-Resource)
Steve Rentfrow (Gen Mgr)

CRISP MARKETING
110 E Broward Blvd Ste 1600, Fort Lauderdale, FL 33301
Tel.: (954) 537-3380
Web Site: http://www.crisp-marketing.com
Year Founded: 2007
Sales Range: $1-9.9 Million
Emp.: 35
Custom Marketing Programs & Consultation Services
N.A.I.C.S.: 541613
Justin Ferreira (Mng Dir)
Chris Henry (Pres)
Dawne Garcia (Office Mgr)
John Pereira (Mgr)

CRISTOFOLI KEELING, INC.
32245 Gilbert Ave Ste 206 The Cable House, Cincinnati, OH 45206
Tel.: (513) 381-3248
Web Site:
http://www.cristofolikeeling.com
Sales Range: Less than $1 Million
Emp.: 10
Public Relations
N.A.I.C.S.: 541820
Tyrese Cristofoli (Partner)
Ann M. Keeling (Principal-Mktg Comm)

CRISWELL ACURA
1701 W St, Annapolis, MD 21401-3246
Tel.: (443) 482-3200
Web Site:
https://www.criswellacura.com
Year Founded: 1990
Sales Range: $50-74.9 Million
Emp.: 85
New Car Retailer
N.A.I.C.S.: 441110
George Criswell (Owner & Pres)
Michael O'Neill (Mgr)

CRISWELL PERFORMANCE CARS LLC.
19525 Amaranth Dr, Germantown, MD 20874
Tel.: (301) 212-4450
Sales Range: $50-74.9 Million
Emp.: 190
Car Whslr
N.A.I.C.S.: 441110
Kevin Szot (Gen Mgr)

CRITCHFIELD MEATS INC.
2285 Danforth Dr, Lexington, KY 40511
Tel.: (859) 255-6021
Web Site:
https://www.critchfieldmeats.com
Sales Range: $10-24.9 Million
Emp.: 65
Whslr of Meats & Meat Products
N.A.I.C.S.: 424470
Mark Critchfield (Pres)
Larry McMillan (CEO)

CRITCHFIELD MECHANICAL INC.
1901 Junction Ave, San Jose, CA 95131
Tel.: (408) 437-7000   CA
Web Site: https://www.cmihvac.com
Year Founded: 1977
Sales Range: $75-99.9 Million
Emp.: 500
Provider of Plumbing, Heating & Air Conditioning
N.A.I.C.S.: 238220
Joe Critchfield (Chm)
Steve Gustafson (VP)
Steve Poe (VP)
Eric Anderson (CFO)

CRITERION CAPITAL MANAGEMENT LLC
Four Embarcadero Ctr 34th Fl, San Francisco, CA 94111
Tel.: (415) 834-3500
Web Site:
http://www.criterionmgt.com
Emp.: 25
Investment Management Service
N.A.I.C.S.: 523999
Christopher H. Lord (Sr Partner)
Matt Perona (Controller-Hedge Fund)
Scott Freeman (Partner)

CRITERION EXECUTIVE SEARCH, INC.
550 N Reo St Ste 101, Tampa, FL 33609
Tel.: (813) 286-2000   FL
Web Site:
http://www.criterionsearch.com
Year Founded: 1981
Sales Range: $1-9.9 Million
Emp.: 18
Executive Search Service
N.A.I.C.S.: 561312
Richard James (Pres)
Chris Planeta (Partner & VP)
Glenn Winograd (Partner & VP-Insurance)

CRITERION GLOBAL
605 Lincoln Rd Unit 205, Miami Beach, FL 33139
Tel.: (646) 330-4673
Web Site:
http://www.criterionglobal.com
Sales Range: $25-49.9 Million
Emp.: 12
Media Buying Services
N.A.I.C.S.: 541810
David Halperin (Principal)

CRITERION SYSTEMS, INC.
8330 Boone Blvd Ste 400, Vienna, VA 22182
Tel.: (703) 942-5800
Web Site: http://www.criterion-sys.com
Year Founded: 2005
Sales Range: $10-24.9 Million
Emp.: 110
Government Services
N.A.I.C.S.: 921190
Promod Sharma (Pres & CEO)
David H. Coxe (Officer-Dev & Sr VP)

Steven Mast (CFO & Exec VP)
Charlie Doyle (COO)
Marcie Cheney (Chief Strategy Officer)
Joe Scott (Sr VP-Contracts & Pricing)
Jerry Black (Acct Exec-Civilian)
Bob Heckman (CIO)
Rodger Jones (CTO)
Rick Williams (VP)
Corionna Canada (VP)

CRITICAL CARE & VETERINARY SPECIALISTS OF SARASOTA LLC
4937 S Tamiami Trl, Sarasota, FL 34231
Tel.: (941) 929-1818
Web Site:
http://www.criticalvetcare.com
Sales Range: $10-24.9 Million
Emp.: 15
Veterinary Services
N.A.I.C.S.: 541940
Anne Elisabeth Chauvet (Founder)
Martyna McDonnell (Dir-PR & Mktg)

CRITICAL CARE SERVICES, INC.
3010 Broadway St NE, Minneapolis, MN 55413
Tel.: (612) 638-4900   MN
Web Site: http://www.lifelinkiii.com
Year Founded: 1985
Sales Range: $25-49.9 Million
Emp.: 114
Medical Care & Transportation Services
N.A.I.C.S.: 622110
Robert Sannerud (CFO)
Jim Leste (Treas & Sec)
Steve Sterner (Chm)
Josh Howell VI (Pres-Ops)

CRITICAL IMAGING, LLC
2306 Bleecker St, Utica, NY 13501
Tel.: (315) 732-1544   NY
Web Site:
http://www.criticalimaging.net
Year Founded: 2003
Sales Range: $1-9.9 Million
Emp.: 23
Photographic Equipment And Supplies
N.A.I.C.S.: 333310
Richard Evans (Gen Mgr)

CRITICAL MENTION, INC.
521 5th Ave 16th Fl, New York, NY 10175
Tel.: (212) 398-1141
Web Site:
http://www.criticalmention.com
Year Founded: 2002
Emp.: 70
Web-Based TV Search & Monitoring Service
N.A.I.C.S.: 519290
Sean Morgan (Founder & Chm)
Steve Shannon (Sr VP-Sls & Mktg)
Don Yount (Pres & CEO)
Nancy Ellma (Sr VP)
Matthew Maul (VP-Engrg)

CRITICAL POWER EXCHANGE LLC
15918 E Euclid Ave, Spokane Valley, WA 99216
Tel.: (509) 228-0178
Web Site:
http://www.criticalpower.com
Rev.: $12,000,000
Emp.: 45
New & Refurbished Back-up Power & Environmental Equipment to Critical Data Centers Nationwide
N.A.I.C.S.: 238990

Critical Power Exchange LLC—(Continued)

Tyler Harbour (Dir-Large Projects)

CRITICAL PR
27 Stony Hill Rd, Burlington, CT
06013-2601
Tel.: (860) 255-7524
Web Site: http://www.criticalpr.com
Year Founded: 1997
Sales Range: Less than $1 Million
Emp.: 5
Public Relations & Marketing Solutions
N.A.I.C.S.: 541820
Jon Crane (Principal)

CRITICAL PROJECT SERVICES, LLC
17000 Dallas Pkwy Ste 104, Dallas,
TX 75248
Tel.: (214) 842-6183
Web Site: http://www.cps-llc.com
Year Founded: 2009
Sales Range: $10-24.9 Million
Emp.: 50
Energy Consulting Services
N.A.I.C.S.: 541690
Matthew Koerner (Principal)
Brandon McDaniel (Principal)
Tommy Neuman (Principal)

CRITICALPOINT CAPITAL, LLC
1230 Rosecrans Ave Ste 170, Manhattan Beach, CA 90266
Tel.: (310) 321-4400
Web Site:
http://www.criticalpointcapital.com
Year Founded: 2012
Privater Equity Firm
N.A.I.C.S.: 523999
Matt Young (Founder & CEO)
Brad Holtmeier (Partner)
Laurie Hunter (CFO & Controller)

Subsidiaries:

Arlon EMD LLC   (1)
9433 Hyssop Dr, Rancho Cucamonga, CA
91730
Tel.: (909) 987-9533
Web Site: http://www.arlonemd.com
Printed Circuit Laminate Mfr
N.A.I.C.S.: 334419
Mike Gardner (Mgr-Lean)

Shoebuy.com, Inc.   (1)
1 Constitution Wharf, Charlestown, MA
02129-2025
Tel.: (617) 451-2880
Web Site: http://www.shoes.com
Online Shoe Retailer
N.A.I.C.S.: 458210
Trisha Sweeney (Exec VP-Mdsg)
Paras Mehta (CTO)
John Foristall (Pres, CFO & Exec VP)

The Running Specialty Group,
Inc.   (1)
231 Milwaukee St Ste 200, Denver, CO
80206
Tel.: (303) 847-4123
Sports Wear Apparel
N.A.I.C.S.: 458110

CRITICALTOOL INC.
3005 Broadhead Rd Ste 286, Bethlehem, PA 18020
Web Site: http://www.criticaltool.com
Year Founded: 1998
Sales Range: $1-9.9 Million
Emp.: 10
Safety Equipment including Disposable Clothing & Gloves
N.A.I.C.S.: 458101
Rathi Niyogi (Owner)

CRITTENDEN BOULEVARD HOUSING COMPANY, INC.
249 Norton Village Ln, Rochester, NY
14609

Tel.: (585) 467-2442
Year Founded: 1969
Rev.: $2,958,712
Assets: $9,295,649
Liabilities: $1,191,503
Net Worth: $8,104,146
Earnings: $705,835
Fiscal Year-end: 03/31/14
Community Housing Services
N.A.I.C.S.: 624229
Michael C. Goonan (VP)
Scott Procious (Treas)
John Desiato (Asst Sec)
Elizabeth A. Dudman (Pres)
Margaret J. Hill (Sec)

CRITTENDEN HOSPITAL ASSOCIATION
200 W Tyler, West Memphis, AR
72301
Tel.: (870) 735-1500
Year Founded: 1953
Sales Range: $50-74.9 Million
Emp.: 643
Patient Wellness Services
N.A.I.C.S.: 813212
Donna Lanier (VP)
Gene Cashman (CEO)
Brad McCormick (CFO)

CRITZAS INDUSTRIES, INC.
4041 Park Ave, Saint Louis, MO
63110-2319
Tel.: (314) 773-8510
Web Site:
https://www.goophandcleaner.com
Year Founded: 1949
Towels, Soaps & Hand Lotion Mfr
N.A.I.C.S.: 325612
Blake Critzas (Owner & Pres)
Dianna Critzas Tate (VP)

CRIUS ENERGY, LLC
535 Connecticut Ave 6th Fl, Norwalk,
CT 06854
Tel.: (203) 663-5089
Web Site:
http://www.criusenergy.com
Year Founded: 2012
Energy Solutions Company
N.A.I.C.S.: 221122
Jake Albert (Gen Counsel)
Kamran Qamar (VP-IT)

Subsidiaries:

U.S. Gas & Electric, Inc.   (1)
3700 Lakeside Dr 6th Fl, Miramar, FL
33027
Tel.: (305) 947-7880
Web Site: http://www.usgande.com
Gas & Electric Supplier
N.A.I.C.S.: 221210
Kevin McMinn (Chief Sls Officer)
James Ganter (VP-Mass Market Sls)
Michael Fallquist (CEO)
Roop Bhullar (COO)
Christian McArthur (COO)
Barbara Clay (Chief Legal Officer)

Verengo Inc.   (1)
20285 S W Ave Ste 200, Torrance, CA
90501
Tel.: (714) 453-2000
Solar Photovoltaic Systems & Products
N.A.I.C.S.: 221114

CRIVELLI FORD INC.
2085 Brodhead Rd, Aliquippa, PA
15001
Tel.: (724) 857-0400
Web Site: https://www.crivelliford.com
Year Founded: 1992
Sales Range: $25-49.9 Million
Emp.: 35
Car Whslr
N.A.I.C.S.: 441110
Kathy Wagler (Pres)

CRM DEVELOPMENT COMPANY
145 Rose St, Lexington, KY 40507
Tel.: (859) 225-3680
Web Site: http://www.crmco.com
Sales Range: $10-24.9 Million
Emp.: 400
Provider of Subdividers & Developers
N.A.I.C.S.: 237210
Wayne Wellman (Pres & Principal)

CRM LEARNING LP
2218 Faraday Ave Ste 110, Carlsbad,
CA 92008
Tel.: (760) 431-9800
Web Site:
http://www.crmlearning.com
Year Founded: 1971
Sales Range: Less than $1 Million
Emp.: 12
Educational Motion Picture Production Services
N.A.I.C.S.: 512110
Peter Jordan (Pres & CEO)
Jackie McGuinness (Controller)

CRM METRIX, INC.
700 Plz Dr 2nd Fl, Secaucus, NJ
07094
Tel.: (201) 617-7500
Web Site: http://www.crmmetrix.com
Year Founded: 2000
Sales Range: $10-24.9 Million
Emp.: 16
Digital Marketing Research & Public
Opinion Polling
N.A.I.C.S.: 541910
Hemmen Patel (VP)
Christophe LeYoanc (Mng Dir)
Laurent Flores (Pres & CEO)

CRN INTERNATIONAL, INC.
1 Circular Ave, Hamden, CT 06514-
4002
Tel.: (203) 288-2002
Web Site: https://www.crnradio.com
Year Founded: 1973
Sales Range: $25-49.9 Million
Emp.: 75
Media Buying Services
N.A.I.C.S.: 541830
Jennifer A. Anderson (VP-HR)
Kelly Travers (Dir-Podcast Ops)
Christina Upton (Dir-Client Svcs)
Katie Geddes (Dir-Media Rels)
Rob O'Mara (Mng Dir)

CROAKIES
1240 Huff Ln, Jackson, WY 83001
Tel.: (307) 733-2266
Web Site: http://www.croakies.com
Rev.: $14,400,000
Emp.: 150
Sporting & Athletic Goods Mfr
N.A.I.C.S.: 339920
A. J. Krisik (Treas & Sec)
Chris McCullough (VP-Mktg)
John Krisik (Pres)

CROCHET & BOREL, INC.
14345 Northwest Fwy, Houston, TX
77040-4927
Tel.: (409) 722-9697
Year Founded: 1995
Sales Range: $25-49.9 Million
Emp.: 85
Disaster Restoration & Remediation
Services
N.A.I.C.S.: 561499

Subsidiaries:

C&B Services, Inc.   (1)
14345 Northwest Fwy, Houston, TX 77040-
4927
Tel.: (409) 722-9697
Web Site: http://www.candbservices.com

Disaster Restoration & Remediation Services
N.A.I.C.S.: 561499

CROCKER & WINSOR SEAFOODS INC.
21 Highland Cir, Needham, MA
02494
Tel.: (617) 269-3100
Web Site:
https://www.crockerwinsor.com
Year Founded: 1895
Sales Range: $25-49.9 Million
Emp.: 25
Distr of Frozen Seafood
N.A.I.C.S.: 424460
John Parker (Pres)
Chris Stegman (Controller)

CROCKER ART MUSEUM ASSOCIATION
216 O St, Sacramento, CA 95814
Tel.: (916) 808-7000
Web Site:
http://www.crockerartmuseum.org
Year Founded: 1885
Sales Range: $10-24.9 Million
Emp.: 85
Art Museum
N.A.I.C.S.: 712110
Celestine Syphax (VP)
David Townsend (Pres)
Randy Getz (Treas)

CROCKER PARTNERS LLC
225 NE Mizner Blvd Ste 200, Boca
Raton, FL 33432
Tel.: (561) 447-1801
Web Site:
http://www.crockerpartners.com
Year Founded: 1993
Sales Range: $1-9.9 Million
Emp.: 80
Real Estate Investment & Management
N.A.I.C.S.: 531390
Thomas J. Crocker (Founder & Mng
Partner)
Angelo J. Bianco (Mng Partner)
Christopher D. Eachus (Partner)
Todd J. Amara (CFO & Partner)
John Osborne (VP)
Jeremy M. Beer (Dir-Fin)
Rachel Tvaroch (Controller)
Rick Pugatch (Sr VP-Dev & Construction)
Fred W. Taeger (Dir-Fin Reporting)
Josh Edwards (VP & Reg Mgr-Asset)
Ryan Zader (Sr VP-Denver & Phoenix)

CROCKER VENTURES LLC
2825 E Cottonwood Pkwy Ste 330,
Salt Lake City, UT 84121
Tel.: (801) 702-8580
Web Site:
https://www.crockerventures.com
Sales Range: $25-49.9 Million
Emp.: 8
Investment Firm
N.A.I.C.S.: 523999
Gary L. Crocker (Pres & Mng Dir)

Subsidiaries:

Nexus CMF, L.L.C.   (1)
2825 E Cottonwood Pkwy Ste 330, Salt
Lake City, UT 84121
Tel.: (801) 702-8595
Web Site: http://www.nexuscmf.com
Medical Device Mfr
N.A.I.C.S.: 339112
Jonathan Crocker (Sls Mgr)

Rejuvenation Labs   (1)
6952 S High Tech Dr Ste C, Midvale, UT
84047
Tel.: (801) 486-4940
Web Site: http://www.rejuvenationlabs.com

Develops, Manufactures & Markets Biotech Products
N.A.I.C.S.: 325414
Gary L. Crocker (Chm)
Kevin Passey (CEO)

CROCKETT FACILITIES SERVICES, INC.
4901 Tesla Dr Ste J, Bowie, MD 20715-4407
Tel.: (202) 600-2787
Web Site: http://www.crockett-facilities.com
Year Founded: 2000
Sales Range: $25-49.9 Million
Emp.: 175
Air Conditioning Installation Services
N.A.I.C.S.: 238220
Cynthia Esparza Crockett (Pres)
Mark Crockett (VP)

CROCKETT HOMES, INC.
5060 Navarre Rd SW, Canton, OH 44706
Tel.: (330) 479-8944
Web Site: https://www.crocketthomesinc.com
Year Founded: 1977
Rev.: $2,800,000
Emp.: 5
New Single-Family Housing Construction
N.A.I.C.S.: 236115
David Hayes (Pres)

CROFT LLC
107 Oliver Emerich Dr, McComb, MS 39648
Tel.: (601) 684-6121   MS
Web Site: http://www.croftllc.com
Year Founded: 1927
Sales Range: $150-199.9 Million
Emp.: 400
Aluminum Building Products Windows, Doors, Hardware Items
N.A.I.C.S.: 331313
James Bitz (Mgr-Engrg)
Susan Bellipanni (Controller)
Vic Donati (VP-Admin)

CROHN'S & COLITIS FOUNDATION OF AMERICA
733 3rd Ave Ste 510, New York, NY 10017-3204
Tel.: (212) 685-3440   NY
Web Site: http://www.ccfa.org
Year Founded: 1965
Sales Range: $50-74.9 Million
Disease Research Services
N.A.I.C.S.: 813212
Caren Heller (Chief Scientific Officer)
Michael Osso (Pres & CEO)
Judi Brown (Chief Dev Officer)
Robert Territo (CFO & COO)
Vance A. Gibbs (Chm)
Andrew Stern (Sec)
Harriet Patterson (Exec Dir)
Allison Coffey (VP-Advancement)
Sheri Markus-Kennell (Sr VP-Bus Dev)

CROIX CONNECT
8130 Boone Blvd Ste 230, Vienna, VA 22182-2640
Tel.: (703) 584-0284
Web Site: http://www.croixconnect.com
Year Founded: 2001
Sales Range: $1-9.9 Million
Emp.: 7
Internet Information Services
N.A.I.C.S.: 517810
Brian Roberts (Founder & CEO)

CROIX OIL COMPANY
1749 S Greeley St, Stillwater, MN 55082
Tel.: (651) 439-5755
Web Site: http://www.croixoil.com
Gasoline Stations with Convenience Stores Owner & Operator; Fuel Dealer
N.A.I.C.S.: 457110
Michele Smith (Brand Mgr-BP)
Mark J. Ogren (Owner & Pres)
Deb Vandinburg (Controller)
Kevin Koenig (Gen Mgr-Wholesale)
Dreux B. Shopbell (Gen Mgr-Retail)
Michael Miller (Dir-Fin)

CROMAN CORPORATION
801 Avenue C, White City, OR 97501
Tel.: (541) 826-4455
Web Site: https://www.croman.net
Sales Range: $25-49.9 Million
Emp.: 147
Logging
N.A.I.C.S.: 113310
Bud L. Kaufman (Pres)
Arnold Cross (VP)

CROMWELL GROUP INC.
1824 Murfreesboro Pike Ste 2, Nashville, TN 37217
Tel.: (615) 361-7560
Web Site: https://www.cromwellradio.com
Sales Range: $10-24.9 Million
Emp.: 150
Owner & Operator of Radio Broadcasting Stations
N.A.I.C.S.: 516110
Bayard Walters (Pres)

CRONIC CHRYSLER JEEP DODGE RAM
2515 N Expy, Griffin, GA 30223-7200
Tel.: (770) 227-4271
Web Site: https://www.cronicchrysler.com
Sales Range: $10-24.9 Million
Emp.: 62
New Car Whslr
N.A.I.C.S.: 441110
Lee Howell (Dir-Adv & PR)
Wanda Howell (Principal)

CRONIN & COMPANY, INC.
50 Nye Rd, Glastonbury, CT 06033-1280
Tel.: (860) 659-0514   CT
Web Site: http://www.cronin-co.com
Year Founded: 1947
Sales Range: $50-74.9 Million
Emp.: 70
Advertising Agencies
N.A.I.C.S.: 541810
Steve Wolfberg (Chief Creative & Growth Officer & Principal)
Kimberly Manning (CEO & Principal)
AnnMarie Kemp (VP-Engagement & Influence)
Wayne Raicik (Sr VP & Dir-Creative)
Jeffrey Mullaly (CFO)
Gary Capreol (Sr VP-Media & Analytics)
Lester Ayala (VP & Dir-Integrated Production)
Betsey Gainey (Sr VP-Brand Strategy & Mgmt)
Mia Walters (Sr VP-Digital Strategy & Tech)
Rick McKenna (Sr VP-Boston)
Mark Demuro (Principal)

CRONIN CO.
5230 N Basin, Portland, OR 97217
Tel.: (503) 226-3508
Web Site: http://www.cronincompany.com
Sales Range: $25-49.9 Million

Emp.: 200
Floor Coverings
N.A.I.C.S.: 423220
Patrick M. Cronin (Chm & CEO)
Jim Gunter (Pres & COO)
Guy Freeman (Exec VP)
Heidi Mandell (VP-Ops)
Rob Novak (Product Mgr)
Tim Rogich (Branch Mgr-Ops-Washington)
Bob Hendren (Product Mgr)
Paul Pfeifer (Mgr-Distr Center)

CRONLAND LUMBER CO. INC.
PO Box 74, Lincolnton, NC 28093
Tel.: (704) 736-2691
Web Site: http://www.cronlandlumber.com
Sales Range: $10-24.9 Million
Emp.: 50
Whslr of Lumber & Related Products
N.A.I.C.S.: 423310
Mike Marsh (VP-Sls)

CROOK MOTOR CO. INC.
1483 N 1st St, Albemarle, NC 28001
Tel.: (704) 982-8188
Web Site: http://www.crookmotors.com
Sales Range: $50-74.9 Million
Emp.: 40
Trucks, Tractors & Trailers- Used
N.A.I.C.S.: 441120
David Horton (VP)

CROOKER CONSTRUCTION, LLC
103 Lewiston Rd, Topsham, ME 04086
Tel.: (207) 729-3331   ME
Web Site: https://www.crooker.com
Highway & Street Paving Contractor
N.A.I.C.S.: 237310
Franklin Crooker (Pres)
Carl Graffam (Controller)
Harry Crooker (Owner)

CROOKHAM COMPANY INC.
301 W Warehouse, Caldwell, ID 83605-3948
Tel.: (208) 459-7451   ID
Web Site: https://www.crookham.com
Year Founded: 1911
Sales Range: $10-24.9 Million
Emp.: 100
Mfr of Farm Supplies
N.A.I.C.S.: 424910
Mary Crookham (Owner)

CROP QUEST AGRONOMIC SERVICES
1204 W Frontview St, Dodge City, KS 67801
Tel.: (620) 225-2233
Web Site: http://www.cropquest.com
Year Founded: 1992
Sales Range: $10-24.9 Million
Emp.: 90
Crop & Agricultural Production Management Consulting
N.A.I.C.S.: 541620
Ron O'Hanlon (CEO)
Tracy Smith (Coord-Event)
Cody Hurdt (Mgr-Retail Acct)

CROPLAND CO-OP, INC.
1125 W Oklahoma Ave, Ulysses, KS 67880-2362
Tel.: (620) 356-1241   KS
Web Site: http://www.unitedfreitag.com
Year Founded: 1930
Sales Range: $10-24.9 Million
Emp.: 89
Grain & Field Beans
N.A.I.C.S.: 424510

Gerald Feltz (Pres)

CROPP-METCALFE CO.
8421 Hilltop Rd, Fairfax, VA 22031-4301
Tel.: (703) 698-8855
Web Site: http://www.croppmetcalfe.com
Year Founded: 1979
Sales Range: $25-49.9 Million
Emp.: 210
HVAC & Plumbing Services
N.A.I.C.S.: 238220
Mitchell Cropp (CEO)

Subsidiaries:

Cropp-Metcalfe Co.   (1)
5301 Holland Dr, Beltsville, MD 20705
Tel.: (301) 937-5100
Web Site: http://www.croppmetcalfe.com
Sales Range: $10-24.9 Million
Emp.: 129
HVAC Contracting Services
N.A.I.C.S.: 238220

CROSBY & OVERTON, INC.
1610 W 17th St, Long Beach, CA 90813-1217
Tel.: (562) 432-5445   CA
Web Site: https://www.crosbyoverton.com
Year Founded: 1950
Sales Range: $50-74.9 Million
Emp.: 45
Provider of Hazardous Waste Treatment & Disposal Services
N.A.I.C.S.: 562211
Michael Shloub (Pres)
Linda Alonzo (Controller)
Dayoan Arturo (Dir-Laboratory)

CROSBY ELECTRIC COMPANY, INC.
6012 E Shirley Ln, Montgomery, AL 36117
Tel.: (334) 272-2085
Web Site: https://www.crosbyelectric.com
Year Founded: 1967
Sales Range: $10-24.9 Million
Emp.: 75
Electrical Contracting Services
N.A.I.C.S.: 238210
Melissa Jane Green-Talley (Office Mgr)
Charlie Meyling (Mgr-Svc)
Kevin Hill (Project Mgr)
Randy Baxter (VP)
K. Alton Crosby II (Pres)

CROSBY INSURANCE INC.
8181 E Kaiser Blvd, Anaheim, CA 92809
Tel.: (714) 221-5200
Web Site: https://www.crosbyinsurance.com
Rev.: $32,000,000
Emp.: 4
Insurance Agents
N.A.I.C.S.: 524210
Chris Hopper (Pres)

CROSBY MARKETING COMMUNICATIONS
705 Melvin Ave Ste 200, Annapolis, MD 21401-1540
Tel.: (410) 626-0805   MD
Web Site: http://www.crosbymarketing.com
Year Founded: 1973
Rev.: $58,000,000
Emp.: 50
Advetising Agency
N.A.I.C.S.: 541810
Ralph W. Crosby (Founder & Chm)
Denise Aube (Exec VP)
Ron Ordansa (Dir-Creative)

Crosby Marketing Communications—(Continued)

Pam Atkinson (*VP & Dir-Connection Plng*)
Elise A. Kolaja (*Creative Dir*)
Amy Hitt (*VP & Dir-Print & Broadcast Production*)
Joel Machak (*Exec Dir-Creative*)
Gillian Pommerehn (*Sr VP*)
Julian Hernandez (*VP-Health Practice*)
Scott Rasmussen (*Dir-Creative*)
Raymond S. Crosby (*Pres & CEO*)
Suresh John (*Exec VP-Digital Strategy & Analytics*)
Meredith Williams (*Exec VP*)
Anna Zawislanski (*Exec VP*)
Amy Inglesby (*VP & Dir-Integration Mgmt*)
Lee Gatchel (*VP-Experience Design*)
Kat Friedman (*Sr VP*)
Anna Morrison (*Assoc Mgr-Integration*)
Caroline Morelock (*Assoc Mgr-Integration*)
Lacey Sladky (*Dir-Integration*)
Anya Karavanov (*Sr VP & Dir-Research & Insights*)
Kara Joyce (*Mgr-Integration & PR*)
Janae David (*Coord-Multimedia & Digital Mktg*)
Carrie Dooher (*Sr VP-Washington*)
Bridget Stockdale (*VP*)
Julia Krahe (*VP-Washington, D.C.*)
Danielle Fox (*Mgr-Social Media*)
Sydney Brown (*Designer-Digital*)
Megan Humphries (*Exec VP*)
Alexx Weincek (*Designer-Sr Multimedia*)
Donald Ritchey (*Dir-IT Svcs*)

Subsidiaries:

Low + Associates   (1)
4550 Montgomery Ave Ste 790 N,
Bethesda, MD 20814
Tel.: (301) 951-9200
Web Site: http://www.lowassociates.com
Rev.: $18,000,000
Emp.: 15
N.A.I.C.S.: 541810
Mike Cosgrove (*Exec VP*)
Andrew Bellows (*Acct Exec*)
Maura McCarthy (*Acct Supvr*)
James Burt (*Dir-Creative*)
Crystal Myers (*VP & Acct Dir*)
Tim Labus (*Pres*)
Victoria Sheer (*Sr Dir-Art*)
Madeline Beck (*Sr Acct Exec*)

CROSBY ROCK LLC
3 Greenwich Office Park 2nd Fl,
Greenwich, CT 06831
Tel.: (203) 552-6679
Web Site:
   https://www.crosbyrock.com
Year Founded: 2015
Private Equity Investment Firm
N.A.I.C.S.: 523150
Robert B. Goergen Jr. (*Principal*)

Subsidiaries:

Silver Star Brands, Inc.   (1)
250 City Ctr, Oshkosh, WI 54901
Tel.: (920) 231-3800
Web Site: http://www.silverstarbrands.com
Consumer Gifts & Household Products Online & Catalog Marketer & Publisher
N.A.I.C.S.: 513191
Kathy Hecht (*CMO*)
Lynne Whitehorn (*Chief Security Architect*)

Subsidiary (Domestic):

Exposures Online   (2)
250 City Ctr, Oshkosh, WI 54906
Tel.: (920) 231-3800
Web Site: http://www.exposuresonline.com
Photographic Albums & Supplies Mfr
N.A.I.C.S.: 513191

CROSBY-NOONAN CO-OP EL-EVATOR COMPANY
202 S Main St, Crosby, ND 58730
Tel.: (701) 965-6371
Rev.: $14,315,677
Emp.: 6
Grain Elevators
N.A.I.C.S.: 424510

CROSBYS MARKETS INC.
125 Canal St, Salem, MA 01970
Tel.: (978) 745-4272
Web Site:
   http://www.crosbysmarkets.com
Sales Range: $25-49.9 Million
Emp.: 125
Independent Supermarket
N.A.I.C.S.: 445110
Dyke Williams (*Mgr-Facilities*)

CROSMAN SEED CORPORATION
511 W Comml St, East Rochester,
NY 14445
Tel.: (585) 586-1928   NY
Web Site:
   http://www.crosmanseed.com
Year Founded: 1838
Sales Range: Less than $1 Million
Emp.: 5
Whslr of Flower & Vegetable Packet Seeds, Lawn Seed Mixture, Grass Seed Mixture & Seed Packing Machines
N.A.I.C.S.: 424910
Justine A. Mapstone (*Dir-Ops*)
Craig H. Mapstone (*Dir-Ops*)
William R. Mapstone Jr. (*Dir-Ops*)

CROSNO CONSTRUCTION, INC.
819 Sheridan Rd, Arroyo Grande, CA 93420
Tel.: (805) 343-7437
Web Site:
   https://www.crosnoconstruction.com
Year Founded: 2004
Sales Range: $10-24.9 Million
Emp.: 45
Fabricated Structural Metal Mfr
N.A.I.C.S.: 332312
Michael Whitney (*VP*)

CROSS BROTHERS IMPLE-MENT INC.
926 E McDonald Bldg 2, Mount Pulaski, IL 62548
Tel.: (217) 792-5086
Web Site:
   http://www.crossbrothers.com
Year Founded: 1978
Sales Range: $10-24.9 Million
Emp.: 40
Farm & Garden Machinery Retailer
N.A.I.C.S.: 423820
Thomas W. Cross (*Pres*)

CROSS CLICK MEDIA INC.
8275 S Eastern Ave Ste 200-661,
Las Vegas, NV 89123   NV
Web Site:
   http://www.crossclickmedia.com
Year Founded: 2010
Sales Range: Less than $1 Million
Marketing Consulting Services
N.A.I.C.S.: 541613

CROSS COMPANY
4400 Piedmont Pkwy, Greensboro,
NC 27410-8121
Tel.: (855) 889-0092   NC
Web Site: http://www.crossco.com
Year Founded: 1954
Emp.: 700
Industrial Machinery & Equipment
N.A.I.C.S.: 423830

Jerry Bohnsack (*CFO*)
John King (*CEO*)
Jason Hicks (*Pres-Process Solutions*)

Subsidiaries:

Flow-Tech, Inc.   (1)
10940 Beaver Dam Rd, Hunt Valley, MD 21030-2211
Tel.: (410) 666-3200
Web Site: http://www.flowtechonline.com
Sales Range: $1-9.9 Million
Emp.: 12
Process Instrumentation & Calibration Equipment Distr
N.A.I.C.S.: 423830
Rick Gayo (*Mgr-Environmental Sls*)

CROSS COUNTY BANCSHARES INC.
1 Cross County Plz, Wynne, AR 72396
Tel.: (870) 238-8171
Web Site:
   http://www.crosscountybank.com
Year Founded: 1981
Sales Range: $10-24.9 Million
Emp.: 50
Bank Holding Company
N.A.I.C.S.: 551111
Willard G. Burks (*Chm*)
David Dowd (*Pres & CEO*)

CROSS COUNTY FEDERAL SAVINGS BANK
79-21 Metropolitan Ave, Middle Village, NY 11379
Tel.: (718) 326-6300
Web Site:
   https://www.crosscounty.com
Rev.: $16,399,000
Emp.: 35
Federal Savings Bank
N.A.I.C.S.: 522110
Anthony Milone (*Pres*)

CROSS CREEK SUBARU, INC.
497 N McPherson Church Rd, Fayetteville, NC 28303
Tel.: (910) 864-5240
Web Site:
   https://www.crosscreeksubaru.com
Sales Range: $10-24.9 Million
Emp.: 60
New Car Dealers
N.A.I.C.S.: 441110
Jason Wells (*Mgr-Sls*)
Sanden Woodham (*Mgr-Internet Sls*)
Sam Johnson Jr. (*Gen Mgr*)

CROSS ENTERPRISES INC.
4321 Oakwood Blvd, Melvindale, MI 48122
Tel.: (313) 386-8005
Web Site:
   https://www.crosspump.com
Year Founded: 1969
Sales Range: $10-24.9 Million
Emp.: 15
Heavy Construction Equipment Rental
N.A.I.C.S.: 532412
Charles E. Cross (*Pres*)

CROSS FINANCIAL CORPO-RATION
491 Main St, Bangor, ME 04401
Tel.: (207) 947-7345   ME
Web Site:
   http://www.crossagency.com
Year Founded: 1954
Holding Company; Insurance Brokerage & Related Services
N.A.I.C.S.: 551112

Subsidiaries:

Colt Insurance Agency, Inc.   (1)
101 South St, Pittsfield, MA 01201

Tel.: (413) 445-5648
Web Site: http://www.coltinsurance.com
Insurance Agency Services
N.A.I.C.S.: 524210
Kelly Collins (*Pres*)
Jenifer Powers (*Mgr-Comml Lines*)
Heidi Gingras (*Mgr-Personal Lines*)
Kim Knights (*Office Mgr*)

Cross Insurance Inc.   (1)
491 Main St, Bangor, ME 04401
Tel.: (800) 999-7345
Web Site: http://www.crossagency.com
Insurance & Financial Services
N.A.I.C.S.: 524210
Joshua Doolan (*Account Executive*)
Timothy Moriarity (*CIO*)

Subsidiary (Domestic):

A.E. Barnes Insurance Agency, Inc.   (2)
141 Pleasant St, South Weymouth, MA 02190
Tel.: (781) 335-1589
Web Site: http://www.aebarnes.com
Insurance Agencies & Brokerages
N.A.I.C.S.: 524210

Woodrow W. Cross Agency   (1)
74 Gilman Rd, Bangor, ME 04401
Tel.: (207) 947-7345
Web Site: http://www.crossagency.com
Sales Range: $1-9.9 Million
Insurance Agents & Brokers
N.A.I.C.S.: 524210
Allice Dyer (*Mgr-HR*)
Royce M. Cross (*Chm*)
Abram Treadwell (*Acct Exec-Personal Lines-Lewiston*)
Sean Doyle (*Acct Exec-Comml Lines-Lewiston*)
Eric Jermyn (*Pres-Cross Employee Benefits-Portland*)
Jonathan Cross (*Pres & CEO*)

Subsidiary (Domestic):

Appleby & Wyman Insurance Agency, Inc.   (2)
152 Conant St, Beverly, MA 01915
Web Site: http://www.applebywyman.com
Emp.: 25
Insurance Agents
N.A.I.C.S.: 524210
Mary McNab (*Sr Acct Mgr & Coord-Mktg*)
Lauren French (*Acct Mgr-Comml*)

BGA Insurance Agency, Inc.   (2)
2331 Congress St Ste 2, Portland, ME 04102
Tel.: (207) 772-4311
Web Site: http://www.bgafinancial.com
Insurance Agents
N.A.I.C.S.: 524210

Corcoran & Havlin Insurance Group   (2)
287 Linden St, Wellesley, MA 02482
Tel.: (781) 235-3100
Web Site: http://www.chinsurance.com
Insurance Services
N.A.I.C.S.: 524210
Mark Sawyer (*Sr VP*)
George Doherty (*Pres*)
Diane Benoit (*Mgr*)
Denise Donohue (*Mgr-Comml Lines*)
Linda Hooper (*Office Mgr*)

Subsidiary (Domestic):

Lougee Insurance Agency, LLC   (3)
24 Bay Rd, Duxbury, MA 02332-5000
Tel.: (781) 934-6500
Web Site: http://www.lougee.net
Emp.: 5
Insurance Agents
N.A.I.C.S.: 524210
Lori Regan (*Acct Mgr & Supvr*)

Subsidiary (Domestic):

Cross Insurance TPA, Inc.   (2)
60 Pineland Dr, New Gloucester, ME 04260
Tel.: (207) 688-1201
Web Site: http://crossagency.com
Insurance Agency & Brokerage Services
N.A.I.C.S.: 524210
Jennifer Reckmeyer (*Sr Acct Mgr-Comml Lines*)

Vuthi Roeun *(Mgr-Claims-Portland)*
Shane Riley *(Acct Mgr-Personal Lines)*
Jessica Reed *(Acct Mgr-Personal Lines-Portland)*
Melissa Sousa *(Sr Acct Mgr-Comml Lines)*
Kari Cyr *(Asst Mgr-Personal Lines)*
Kim Perreault *(Acct Mgr-Small Bus Accts)*

Cross Surety, Inc. **(2)**
485 Main St, Lewiston, ME 04240
Tel.: (207) 786-6750
Web Site: http://www.crossinsurance.com
Emp.: 8
Insurance Agency & Brokerage Services
N.A.I.C.S.: 524210
Blair Torelli *(Sr VP)*

Infantine Insurance, Inc. **(2)**
203 Meetinghouse Rd, Manchester, NH 03101
Tel.: (603) 669-0704
Web Site: http://www.infantine.com
Sales Range: $1-9.9 Million
Emp.: 125
Insurance Services
N.A.I.C.S.: 524210
Royce Cross *(Partner)*

Knapp Schenck & Co. Insurance Agency, Inc. **(2)**
1 India St Ste 204, Boston, MA 02109
Tel.: (617) 742-3366
Web Site: http://www.knappschenck.com
Insurance Agents
N.A.I.C.S.: 524210
Chris Schenck *(Principal)*
David Winship *(Principal)*

SSI Cross, Inc. **(2)**
103 Park St 2nd Fl, Lewiston, ME 04240
Tel.: (207) 753-7300
Web Site: http://www.ssasurety.com
Insurance Agents
N.A.I.C.S.: 524210
Heidi Rodzen *(Sr Acct Exec)*

Schonning Insurance Services, Inc. **(2)**
90 Airport Rd, Westerly, RI 02891
Tel.: (401) 348-2000
Web Site:
    http://www.schonninginsurance.com
Emp.: 5
Insurance Services
N.A.I.C.S.: 524210
Stephen C. Schonning *(Owner & Pres)*

TSA, Inc. **(2)**
43 Cottage St, Bar Harbor, ME 04609
Tel.: (207) 288-5044
Web Site:
    http://www.swanagencyinsurance.com
Insurance Agents
N.A.I.C.S.: 524210
Chris Swan *(Mgr)*

The Driscoll Agency, Inc. **(2)**
93 Longwater Cir, Norwell, MA 02061
Tel.: (781) 681-6656
Web Site: http://www.driscollagency.com
Emp.: 35
Insurance Brokerage Services
N.A.I.C.S.: 524210
Jane Driscoll Henesey *(CFO & Mgr-Personal Lines)*
Jay Driscoll *(Pres)*
Dennis W. Driscoll *(VP)*
Sally M. Driscoll *(VP)*

The Insurance Exchange, Inc. **(2)**
30 Buxton Farm Rd Ste 120, Stamford, CT 06905
Tel.: (203) 321-0001
Web Site: http://www.insurexchg.com
Sales Range: $1-9.9 Million
Emp.: 10
Insurance Agencies & Brokerages
N.A.I.C.S.: 524210
Michael Wiederlight *(Pres)*

CROSS IMPLEMENT INC.
703 S Minier Ave, Minier, IL 61759
Tel.: (309) 392-2150
Web Site: http://www.crossimp.com
Sales Range: $25-49.9 Million
Emp.: 25
Farm Equipment Parts & Supplies
N.A.I.C.S.: 423820

Richard L. Cross *(Pres)*

CROSS INTERNATIONAL
600 SW 3rd St Ste 2201, Pompano Beach, FL 33060
Tel.: (954) 657-9000   FL
Web Site:
    http://www.crossinternational.org
Year Founded: 2001
Sales Range: $75-99.9 Million
Emp.: 114
Christian Ministry Services
N.A.I.C.S.: 813110
Jimmy Dodd *(Chm)*
Joe White *(Sec)*
Kelly Miller *(CEO)*

CROSS KEYS ADVERTISING & MARKETING, INC.
651 N Main St, Doylestown, PA 18901
Tel.: (215) 345-5435
Year Founded: 1981
Sales Range: Less than $1 Million
Emp.: 1
N.A.I.C.S.: 541810
Laura T. Barnes *(Pres)*

CROSS KEYS CAPITAL LLC
200 S Andrews Ave Ste 602, Fort Lauderdale, FL 33301
Tel.: (954) 779-2600
Web Site:
    http://www.crosskeyscapital.com
Sales Range: $75-99.9 Million
Emp.: 15
Investment Banking, Advisory & Real Estate Brokerage Services
N.A.I.C.S.: 523150
Richard Becker *(Mng Dir)*
William Britton *(Mng Dir)*
David Burns *(Mng Dir)*
Marjorie Chang *(VP)*
Victor Kalafa *(VP)*
Roger Schoenfeld *(Mng Dir-Chicago)*

CROSS MANUFACTURING INC.
11011 King St Ste 210, Shawnee Mission, KS 66210
Tel.: (913) 451-1233
Web Site: http://www.crossmfg.com
Sales Range: $10-24.9 Million
Emp.: 100
Fluid Power Actuators, Hydraulic or Pneumatic Mfr
N.A.I.C.S.: 333995
John H. Cross *(Pres)*
Michael Worley *(VP)*

CROSS MEDIAWORKS, INC.
15849 N 77th St, Scottsdale, AZ 85260
Tel.: (480) 596-6320
Web Site: http://www.cross-mediaworks.com
Rev.: $3,800,000
Emp.: 60
Media Representatives
N.A.I.C.S.: 541840
Marc Krigsman *(CEO)*
Mary L. Cloonan *(CFO)*
Stephanie Mitchko-Beale *(CTO)*
Barry Baker *(Chm)*

Subsidiaries:

Cadent Technology, Inc.   **(1)**
65 N San Pedro St, San Jose, CA 95110
Tel.: (408) 292-6369
Web Site: http://cadenttech.tv
Advertising Technology & Solutions
N.A.I.C.S.: 513210
Joe Matarese *(CTO)*
Tricia Iboshi *(COO)*
Chris Hock *(Sr VP-Strategy & Bus Dev)*
Keith Kryszczun *(Sr VP-Sls)*

CROSS MOTORS CORP.
1501 Gardiner Ln, Louisville, KY 40218-4550
Tel.: (502) 459-9900   KY
Web Site:
    http://www.crossmotors.com
Year Founded: 1934
Sales Range: $75-99.9 Million
Emp.: 50
Sales of Automobiles
N.A.I.C.S.: 441110
David L. Moser *(Treas, Sec & Gen Mgr)*
Joe D. Cross Jr. *(Pres)*

CROSS OIL COMPANY INC.
6291 Suburban Ave, Saint Louis, MO 63133-2023
Tel.: (314) 726-6666
Year Founded: 1958
Sales Range: $10-24.9 Million
Emp.: 120
Operator of Gasoline Service Stations
N.A.I.C.S.: 424720
Bob Cross *(Pres & CEO)*

Subsidiaries:

Froesel Oil Company Inc.   **(1)**
15407 Clayton Rd, Ballwin, MO 63011-3125
Tel.: (636) 227-5355
Sales Range: $10-24.9 Million
Emp.: 40
Distr of Petroleum Products
N.A.I.C.S.: 424720
William A Cross *(Pres)*

CROSS OIL REFINING & MARKETING COMPANY
484 E 6th St, Smackover, AR 71762
Tel.: (317) 766-1273
Web Site: https://www.crossoil.com
Sales Range: $50-74.9 Million
Emp.: 200
Oils & Greases, Blending & Compounding
N.A.I.C.S.: 324191
Denman Shaffer *(Dir-Sls)*
Kevin Schettler *(Mgr-Natl Accts)*

CROSS PETROLEUM
6920 Lockheed Dr, Redding, CA 96002
Tel.: (530) 221-2588
Web Site:
    http://www.crosspetroleum.com
Sales Range: $10-24.9 Million
Emp.: 50
Petroleum Products Distr
N.A.I.C.S.: 424710
James L. Cross *(Pres)*
Jimm Cross *(VP)*

CROSS RAPIDS CAPITAL LP
12 E 49th St Fl 40, New York, NY 10017
Tel.: (212) 301-7700
Web Site:
    https://www.crossrapids.com
Holding Company
N.A.I.C.S.: 551112

Subsidiaries:

Wholesale Produce Supply, LLC **(1)**
752 Kasota Cir, Minneapolis, MN 55414
Tel.: (612) 378-2025
Web Site: http://www.wholesaleproduce.cc
Sales Range: $10-24.9 Million
Produce Wholesale Distr
N.A.I.C.S.: 424480
Brian Hauge *(Pres & CEO)*

Subsidiary (Domestic):

Bandwagon Brokerage LLC   **(2)**
4550 Seville Ave, Vernon, CA 90058
Tel.: (323) 983-0670
Web Site: https://www.bandwagoninc.com
Fresh Fruit & Vegetable Merchant Whslr
N.A.I.C.S.: 424480

Dennis Berman *(Pres & Treas)*

CROSS STREET SERVICE INC.
3809 Roundtop Dr, North Little Rock, AR 72117
Tel.: (501) 945-0778
Sales Range: $25-49.9 Million
Emp.: 700
Provider of Mail Hauling Services for the Federal Government
N.A.I.C.S.: 484220

CROSS, FERNANDEZ & RILEY, LLP
201 S Orange Ave Ste 800, Orlando, FL 32801
Tel.: (407) 841-6930
Web Site: http://www.cfrcpa.com
Year Founded: 1963
Sales Range: $1-9.9 Million
Emp.: 90
Accounting, Auditing & Bookkeeping
N.A.I.C.S.: 541211
James B. Cross *(Mng Partner)*
Melanie B. Fernandez *(Partner & Dir-Assurance Svcs)*
Laura L. Hathaway *(Partner & Asst Dir-Assurance Svcs)*
Raymond J. Bersch Jr. *(Partner)*

CROSS-DILLON TIRE INC.
4101 W O St, Lincoln, NE 68528
Tel.: (402) 438-3000
Web Site: http://www.crossdillon.com
Year Founded: 1980
Sales Range: $25-49.9 Million
Emp.: 150
Distr of Tires & Tubes
N.A.I.C.S.: 423130
Michael Dillon *(Owner)*
Joel Edwards *(Mgr-IT)*
Shawn Wilkening *(VP-Ops)*

CROSS-MIDWEST TIRE, INC.
401 S 42nd St, Kansas City, KS 66106-1005
Tel.: (913) 321-3003
Web Site:
    http://www.crossmidwest.com
Rev.: $27,000,000
Emp.: 300
Supplier of Commercial Truck Tires
N.A.I.C.S.: 441340
Lon Baldwin *(Mgr)*
Jeromy Jones *(Mgr-Svc-OTR)*
Sandi Kuder *(Mgr-Retread)*

CROSS-SOUND FERRY SERVICES
2 Ferry St, New London, CT 06320
Tel.: (860) 443-5281
Web Site:
    https://www.longislandferry.com
Sales Range: $10-24.9 Million
Emp.: 100
Ferries
N.A.I.C.S.: 483212
John P. Wronowski *(Pres)*
Julie Hinson *(Mgr)*
Stan Mickus *(Dir-Pub Affairs & Mktg)*
Kristina Hansen *(Supvr-Ticket Agent)*
David Riley *(Asst Mgr-Ops)*

CROSSBOW GROUP, LLC
136 Main St, Westport, CT 06880
Tel.: (203) 222-2244   CT
Web Site:
    http://www.crossbowgroup.com
Year Founded: 1984
Sales Range: $10-24.9 Million
Emp.: 15
Advetising Agency
N.A.I.C.S.: 541810
Jay Bower *(Pres & CEO)*
Mary Plamieniak *(COO)*

Crosscom National Inc.—(Continued)

CROSSCOM NATIONAL INC.
900 Deerfield Pkwy, Buffalo Grove, IL 60089-4528
Tel.: (847) 520-9200
Web Site:
http://www.crosscomnational.com
Year Founded: 1980
Sales Range: $25-49.9 Million
Emp.: 200
Mfr of Electronic Parts & Equipment
N.A.I.C.S.: 423690
Greg Miller (CEO)
Paul Russell (Exec VP-Sls)

CROSSCOUNTRY CONSULTING LLC
1650 Tysons Blvd Ste 720, McLean, VA 22102
Tel.: (866) 945-4462
Web Site: http://www.crosscountry-consulting.com
Year Founded: 2011
Sales Range: $25-49.9 Million
Financial Advisory Services
N.A.I.C.S.: 523940
David Kay (Mng Partner)
Erik Linn (Founder & Mng Partner)
Roderick Carmody (Partner)
Neil Smith (Partner)
P. J. Warwick (Partner)
Nav Makol (Partner)
James Medeiros (Principal)
Adam Washecka (Principal)
Amy Bjarnason (COO)
David Arnold (Dir-Mktg)
Juliana Mastroianni (Dir-Human Capital)
John Hoebler (Partner)
Bruce Klein (Partner)
Kati Penney (Partner)
Keith Linhart (Partner)
Alex Bogopolsky (Principal)
Henry Hilbert (Partner-San Francisco)
Steven F. Strandberg (Dir-Intelligent Automation & Data Analytics Practice)
Heather Stewart (Partner-Risk & Compliance Practice-West Coast)
Amy Seibel (CFO)
Jay Spencer (Partner-Boston)
Jill Jones (Partner)

Subsidiaries:

SCS Software, Inc.   (1)
1130 Cleveland St Ste 260, Clearwater, FL 33755
Web Site: http://www.scscloud.com
Sales Range: $1-9.9 Million
Emp.: 50
Management Consulting Services
N.A.I.C.S.: 541611
Derek Hitchman (CEO)
Josh LaSov (VP-Ops)
Joshua Bone (VP-Professional Svcs)
Brooks Flanagan (Mktg Dir)

CROSSCOUNTRY COURIER
1841 Hancock Dr, Bismarck, ND 58502
Tel.: (701) 222-8498
Web Site:
http://www.crosscountryfreight.com
Year Founded: 1979
Sales Range: $10-24.9 Million
Emp.: 350
Provider of Courier Services, Except By Air
N.A.I.C.S.: 492110
Janeanne Bischke (Owner & Pres)
Ken Becker (Dir-Ops)

CROSSCOUNTRY FREIGHT SOLUTIONS, INC.
1929 Hancock Dr. PO Box 4030, Bismarck, ND 58502

Tel.: (800) 521-0287
Web Site: https://beta.shipcc.com
Truck Transportation
N.A.I.C.S.: 484110

Subsidiaries:

Express 2000, Inc.   (1)
164 NW Industrial Ct, Bridgeton, MO 63044
Tel.: (314) 209-7333
Web Site: http://www.express-2000.com
Sales Range: $1-9.9 Million
Emp.: 50
Local Trucking Operator Trucking Operator-Nonlocal
N.A.I.C.S.: 484110
Chuck Quigle (VP)
Mark Basler (Pres)

CROSSCOUNTRY MORTGAGE, LLC
6850 Miller Rd, Brecksville, OH 44141
Tel.: (440) 845-3700
Web Site:
https://crosscountrymortgage.com
Year Founded: 2004
Sales Range: $10-24.9 Million
Emp.: 158
Mortgage Loan Brokerage Services
N.A.I.C.S.: 522310
Ron Leonhardt (Pres)
Chuck Dindia (Mgr)
Jamie Fiore (Mgr)
Vince Nappi (CFO)
Karen Voytek (Branch Mgr)
Laura J. Soave (Chief Brand Officer)
Gavin Ekstrom (VP-Centennial)
Scott Harshman (Sls Mgr)
Joey Abdullah (Sls Mgr-Producing)

Subsidiaries:

Amcap Mortgage Ltd.   (1)
9999 Bellaire Blvd Ste 700, Houston, TX 77036
Tel.: (281) 860-2533
Web Site: https://myamcap.mymortgage-online.com
Real Estate Credit
N.A.I.C.S.: 522292
Jason Turner (Mgr)
Brian Short (Mgr-Tennessee)

First Choice Loan Services Inc.   (1)
1 Tower Center Fl 18, East Brunswick, NJ 08816
Web Site: http://www.fcloans.com
Loan Services
N.A.I.C.S.: 522390

CROSSETT INC.
201 S Carver St, Warren, PA 16365
Tel.: (814) 723-2200
Web Site:
https://www.crossettinc.com
Sales Range: $10-24.9 Million
Emp.: 135
Liquid Petroleum Transport, Non-Local
N.A.I.C.S.: 484230
Rich Cook (Mgr-Parts)
Sarah Marano-Korbar (Mgr-Payroll)
Eric Ahl (Mgr-Safety)
Jack Martin (Owner & Pres)

CROSSFIELD PRODUCTS CORPORATION
3000 E Harcourt St, Rancho Dominguez, CA 90221
Tel.: (310) 886-9100
Web Site:
https://www.crossfieldproducts.com
Rev.: $17,000,000
Emp.: 40
Plastics Materials & Resins
N.A.I.C.S.: 325211
W. Brad Watt (Pres)
Ronald Borum (VP)
David Johnston (CFO)

CROSSFIRE SOUND PRODUCTIONS, LLC
276 Meserole St, Brooklyn, NY 11206
Web Site:
http://www.crossfiresound.com
Year Founded: 2013
Sales Range: $1-9.9 Million
Emp.: 60
Sound & Lighting Equipment Rental Services
N.A.I.C.S.: 532490
Kyle Malenfant (Founder & CEO)

CROSSGATE PARTNERS, LLC
7320 McGinnis Ferry Rd, Suwanee, GA 30024
Tel.: (678) 672-6240
Web Site:
https://www.crossgatepartners.com
Year Founded: 2002
Sales Range: $10-24.9 Million
Emp.: 3
Real Estate Investment Services
N.A.I.C.S.: 523999
Randy Moore (Mng Partner)
Jeff Neuber (Mng Partner)
John Scott (CFO)
Jeff Fulbright (Corp Counsel)

CROSSING RIVERS HEALTH
37868 US Hwy 18, Prairie Du Chien, WI 53821
Tel.: (608) 357-2000
Web Site:
https://www.crossingrivers.org
Year Founded: 1957
Sales Range: $25-49.9 Million
Health Care Srvices
N.A.I.C.S.: 622110
Paul Ginkel (VP)
Katie Garrity (Pres)

CROSSLAKE SALES INC.
34076 County Rd 3, Crosslake, MN 56442
Tel.: (218) 297-0747
Web Site:
http://www.crosslakesales.com
Year Founded: 2006
Sales Range: $1-9.9 Million
Emp.: 12
Retailer of Sporting Goods & Apparel
N.A.I.C.S.: 423910
Thomas Maschhoff (Owner)

CROSSLAND ASSOCIATES INC.
1410 Broadway Rm 508, New York, NY 10018
Tel.: (212) 730-5157
Sales Range: $10-24.9 Million
Emp.: 10
Women's & Children's Clothing
N.A.I.C.S.: 424350
Alvin Tai (Pres)
Marie Chen (Controller)

CROSSLAND CONSTRUCTION CO. INC.
833 SE Ave, Columbus, KS 66725
Tel.: (620) 429-1414
Web Site:
http://www.crosslandconstruction.com
Sales Range: $100-124.9 Million
Emp.: 1,000
Commercial & Office Building, New Construction
N.A.I.C.S.: 236220
Ivan Crossland (CEO)
Michelle Phelps (CFO)
Bennie Crossland (Co-Owner & Chm)
Randy Nance (Mgr-Oklahoma)
John Crumley (Project Mgr-Natl Accts Div)
John Cross (COO)

Willa Ball (VP-Corp Comm & Plng)
David Allison (Chief Admin Officer)
Patrick Crossland (Co-Owner & Pres-Kansas City)
Curt Crossland (Co-Owner & Pres-Midwest)
Mike Crossland (Co-Owner & Pres-Texas)
John Priest (Pres)
Chris Schnurbusch (Pres-Southeast)
Todd Ketterman (VP)
Danny Langerot (VP-Midwest)
Rachel Treanor (Dir-Bus Dev-Kansas City)

CROSSLANDS CONSTRUCTION CO., INC.
5750 DTC Pkwy Ste 145, Greenwood Village, CO 80111
Tel.: (303) 346-1444   CO
Web Site: http://www.crosslands.us
Year Founded: 1995
Sales Range: $10-24.9 Million
Emp.: 12
Construction Services
N.A.I.C.S.: 236220
Jeff Durbon (Pres)

CROSSLIN & ASSOCIATES PC
3803 Bedford Ave Ste 103, Nashville, TN 37215
Tel.: (615) 320-5500
Web Site: https://www.crosslinpc.com
Year Founded: 1987
Sales Range: $1-9.9 Million
Emp.: 60
Accounting & Consulting Services
N.A.I.C.S.: 541219
Mark Loftis (Dir-State & Local Tax)
Bryan White (Principal)
David M. Hunt (Principal-Audit)
Kevin E. Hickman (Principal-Tax)
Richard M. Winstead (Principal-Tax)
Rodney Brower (Principal-Tax)
Justin D. Crosslin Jr. (Mng Principal)

CROSSLINK CAPITAL, INC.
2 Embarcadero Center Ste 2200, San Francisco, CA 94111
Tel.: (415) 617-1800   DE
Web Site:
http://www.crosslinkcapital.com
Year Founded: 2000
Sales Range: $25-49.9 Million
Emp.: 35
Equity Investment Firm
N.A.I.C.S.: 523999
Michael J. Stark (Co-Founder & Gen Partner)
Eric Chin (Gen Partner)
James McDowell Preston Feuille (Gen Partner)
Tom Bliska (Gen Partner)
Stephen Perkins (Gen Partner)
Joel Hausman (Partner-Mktg & Client Rels)
Maureen Offer (Controller)
Matt Bigge (Partner)
Robert Bernshteyn (CEO-Coupa)

CROSSMAN & COMPANY INC.
3333 S Orange Ave Ste 201, Orlando, FL 32806
Tel.: (407) 423-5400
Web Site:
http://www.crossmanco.com
Year Founded: 1990
Sales Range: $1-9.9 Million
Emp.: 50
Real Estate Brokerage
N.A.I.C.S.: 531210
John Zielinski (Pres)
Bruce D. Lyons (Sr Mng Dir)
Christie Alexander (Dir-Brokerage Svcs)
Megan B. Bobiak (Dir-Mktg)
Craig Katterfield (Dir-Investment Sls)

Rachel Slater *(Mgr-Asset)*
Marc Cook *(Sr VP-Client Svcs & Ops)*
Michael Rautbord *(Reg Dir-Leasing)*
Patrick Hughes *(Dir-Acctg)*
Daphne Colverton *(Mgr-Acctg)*
Michelle Kidd *(Dir-Client Svcs)*
Malia Hayner *(Dir-HR)*

CROSSMARK GRAPHICS INC.

16100 W Overland Dr, New Berlin, WI 53151
Tel.: (262) 821-1343
Web Site:
https://www.crossmarkgraphics.com
Rev.: $10,500,000
Emp.: 55
Commercial Lithographic Printing
N.A.I.C.S.: 323111
James Dobrzynski Sr. *(Founder)*
Mark Dobrzynski *(VP-Sls)*
Tammy Rechner *(Pres & CEO)*
Greg Sterwald *(Mgr-Prepress)*

CROSSOVER CREATIVE GROUP

2643 Appian Way Ste J, Pinole, CA 94564
Tel.: (510) 222-5030
Web Site:
http://www.crossovercreative.com
Year Founded: 1996
Rev.: $10,000,000
Emp.: 12
N.A.I.C.S.: 541810
Steve Climons *(Founder, Pres & Dir-Creative)*
Greg Wood *(VP-Client Svcs-Bus Dev)*
Jay Beverly *(Copywriter)*
Mauricio Escruceria *(Dir-Creative)*
Sharyn O'Keefe *(Dir-Bus Dev)*

CROSSPLANE CAPITAL MANAGEMENT LP

750 N St Paul St Ste 1200, Dallas, TX 75201
Tel.: (805) 324-4072   DE
Web Site:
http://www.crossplanecapital.com
Year Founded: 2018
Privater Equity Firm
N.A.I.C.S.: 523999
Ben Eakes *(Partner)*
Brian Hegi *(Partner)*
Ingrid West *(Operating Partner)*
Mike Sullivan *(Mng Dir)*
Katie Oswald *(Dir-Bus Dev)*

Subsidiaries:

Griffin Dewatering Corporation   (1)
5306 Clinton Dr, Houston, TX 77020
Tel.: (713) 676-8000
Web Site: http://www.griffindewatering.com
Construction Site Dewatering Services
N.A.I.C.S.: 238910
David Singleton *(CEO)*

Subsidiary (Domestic):

Foothill Engineering & Dewatering, Inc.   (2)
7000 Jurupa Ave, Riverside, CA 92504
Tel.: (909) 986-4498
Web Site: http://www.foothilleng.com
Drilling & Dewatering of Drilled Wells Contractor; Construction Equipment Rental & Sales
N.A.I.C.S.: 532490

Griffin Pump & Equipment, Inc.   (2)
5306 Clinton Dr, Houston, TX 77020
Tel.: (713) 675-6441
Web Site: http://www.griffindewatering.com
Sales Range: $1-9.9 Million
Pumping Equipment Distr
N.A.I.C.S.: 532490

Power Associates International, Inc   (2)

13117 Green River Dr, Houston, TX 77044-2451
Tel.: (281) 458-9124
Web Site: http://www.paiinc.com
Pump & Pumping Equipment Mfr
N.A.I.C.S.: 333914
James Hodde *(CEO)*

Slead Construction, Inc.   (2)
9021 Waller Rd E, Tacoma, WA 98446
Tel.: (253) 531-2409
Web Site: http://www.sleadnow.com
Sales Range: $1-9.9 Million
Emp.: 25
Specialty Trade Contractors
N.A.I.C.S.: 238990
Charles Slead *(CEO)*

Hynes Industries Inc.   (1)
3760 Oakwood Ave, Youngstown, OH 44515-3041
Tel.: (330) 799-3221
Web Site: https://www.hynesindustries.com
Sales Range: $125-149.9 Million
Emp.: 200
Mfr of Steel & Rolled Wire Products
N.A.I.C.S.: 423510
William W. Bresnahan *(Chm)*
Timothy T. Bresnahan *(Reg Mgr-Sls)*
Richard S. Evans *(VP-Matl)*
Patrick A. Montana *(Sr VP-Ops)*
James R. Blair *(Pres & CEO)*
Michael G. Giambattista *(Sr VP-Mktg & Sls)*
D. R. Golding *(VP-Strategic Dev)*
Mark Cornman *(Dir-Fin & HR)*

TransAxle LLC   (1)
2501 Rte 73 S, Cinnaminson, NJ 08077
Tel.: (856) 665-4445
Web Site: http://www.transaxle.com
Sales Range: $25-49.9 Million
Emp.: 100
Trailer Parts & Accessories
N.A.I.C.S.: 423120
John Ferry *(Gen Mgr)*
David Gorden *(Controller)*
Matt Douglass *(Dir-Bus Dev)*
Doug Everett *(VP-Sls)*
Dave Olsen *(CEO)*

CROSSPOINT CAPITAL PARTNERS LP

2995 Woodside Rd Ste 150, Woodside, CA 94062
Tel.: (650) 530-2567
Web Site:
http://www.crosspointcapital.com
Privater Equity Firm
N.A.I.C.S.: 523999
Stephen J. Luczo *(Mng Partner)*
Greg Clark *(Mng Partner)*

Subsidiaries:

Absolute Software Corporation   (1)
Suite 1400 Four Bentall Centre 1055 Dunsmuir Street, PO Box 49211, Vancouver, V7X 1K8, BC, Canada
Tel.: (604) 730-9851
Web Site: https://www.absolute.com
Rev.: $197,311,000
Assets: $555,618,000
Liabilities: $552,419,000
Net Worth: $3,199,000
Earnings: ($24,880,000)
Emp.: 740
Fiscal Year-end: 06/30/2022
Endpoint Security Development; Data Risk Management Solution
N.A.I.C.S.: 518210
Mark Grace *(Chief Revenue Officer)*
Nicko van Someren *(CTO)*
Karen Reynolds *(Chief Comm Officer)*
William Morris *(Exec VP-Engrg)*
Robert Booker *(Exec VP-HR)*
Edward Choi *(Sr VP-Alliances-Global)*
Jim Lejeal *(CFO)*
John Herrema *(Exec VP)*
Joe Savarese *(Exec VP)*
Peter Chess *(Gen Counsel)*
Alice Hansen *(CMO)*
Samir Sherif *(Chief Information Security Officer)*

Subsidiary (Non-US):

Absolute Software EMEA Limited   (2)
AbbeyGate 57-75 Kings Road, Reading,

RG1 3AB, Berkshire, United Kingdom
Tel.: (44) 1189022000
Software Development Services
N.A.I.C.S.: 541511
James Pattinson *(VP-Sls)*

Subsidiary (US):

Absolute Software, Inc.   (2)
11401 Century Oaks Ter Ste 430, Austin, TX 78758
Tel.: (512) 600-7400
Web Site: http://www.absolute.com
Sales Range: $50-74.9 Million
Emp.: 50
Laptop Computer Security System Mfr
N.A.I.C.S.: 561621

Subsidiary (Domestic):

NetMotion Software Canada, Inc.   (2)
700-730 View Street, Victoria, V8W 1J8, BC, Canada
Tel.: (250) 412-5719
Software Solutions Services
N.A.I.C.S.: 541511

Subsidiary (US):

NetMotion Software, Inc.   (2)
1505 Westlake Ave N Ste 500, Seattle, WA 98109
Tel.: (866) 262-7626
Web Site:
http://www.netmotionsoftware.com
Mobile Productivity & Management Software Publisher
N.A.I.C.S.: 513210
Joe Savarese *(Founder & CTO)*
Christopher Kenessey *(CEO)*
Dan Pagel *(Chief Revenue Officer)*
Joel Windels *(CMO)*
Erik Helms *(Sr VP-Intl)*
John Knopf *(Sr VP-Product)*
Christina Balam *(VP-HR)*
Clarence Foster *(VP-Information Security & IT)*
Jay Klauser *(VP-Strategic Alliances & Sls Engrg)*

Subsidiary (Non-US):

NetMotion Wireless GmbH   (3)
Brossstrasse 6, D 60487, Frankfurt, Germany
Tel.: (49) 6997961250
Web Site: http://www.netmotionwireless.com
Mobile Productivity & Management Software Publisher
N.A.I.C.S.: 513210

NetMotion Wireless, Ltd.   (3)
4 Mandelbrote Drive, Oxford, OX4 4XG, United Kingdom
Tel.: (44) 1865714814
Web Site: http://www.nmwco.eu
Mobile Productivity & Management Software Publisher
N.A.I.C.S.: 513210

DigiCert, Inc.   (1)
2801 N Thanksgiving Way Ste 500, Lehi, UT 84043
Tel.: (801) 701-9600
Web Site: http://www.digicert.com
Software Publisher
N.A.I.C.S.: 513210
Flavio Martins *(COO)*
Chris Call *(Engr-Support)*
Jeremy Rowley *(Exec VP-Emerging Markets)*
John Merrill *(CEO)*
Sue Allen *(Office Mgr)*
Eric Porter *(VP-Fin & Admin)*
Mike Nelson *(VP-Healthcare Solutions)*
Michael Olson *(CFO)*
Jeff Chandler *(Dir-PR)*
Alan Raymond *(VP-Sls)*
Jason Sabin *(CTO)*
Benjamin T. Wilson *(VP-Compliance & Indus Rels)*
Mark Packham *(VP-Mktg)*
Mike Johnson *(Gen Counsel)*
Amit Sinha *(Pres & CEO)*

Subsidiary (Domestic):

Mocana Corporation   (2)
1735 N 1st St Ste 306, San Jose, CA 94104

Tel.: (415) 617-0055
Web Site: http://www.mocana.com
Software Publisher
N.A.I.C.S.: 513210
Brian Nugent *(Chm)*
Dave Smith *(Chief Revenue Officer)*
Hope Frank *(CMO & Chief Digital Officer)*
Jeanne Pardo *(CFO)*
W. William Diotte *(CEO)*
Srinivas Kumar *(CTO)*

Subsidiary (Non-US):

Mocana Solutions Private Limited   (3)
10 Shreeniwas Classic 273/1/1+2/1 Baner, Pune, 411 045, Maharashtra, India
Tel.: (91) 20 27291608
Software Publisher
N.A.I.C.S.: 513210

McAfee, LLC   (1)
2821 Mission College Blvd, Santa Clara, CA 95054
Tel.: (408) 970-5151
Web Site: http://www.mcafee.com
Emp.: 7,330
Computer Security Software, Products & Services
N.A.I.C.S.: 513210
Steve Grobman *(CTO & Sr VP)*
Gagan Singh *(Exec VP & Chief Product & Revenue Officer)*
Dawn Smith *(Chief Legal Officer & Exec VP)*
Allison Cerra *(CMO & Sr VP)*
Rajiv Gupta *(Sr VP-Cloud Security Bus Unit)*
Aneel Jaeel *(Sr VP-Customer Success Grp)*
Chatelle Lynch *(Chief HR Officer & Sr VP)*
Gregory N. Johnson *(Pres & CEO)*
Bruce Chizen *(Chm)*

Subsidiary (Non-US):

McAfee Co., Ltd.   (2)
Shibuya Mark City West 16/20th Fl 1-12-1 Dougenzaka, Shibuya-ku, Tokyo, 150 0043, Japan
Tel.: (81) 3 5428 1100
Web Site: http://www.mcafee.com
Computer Security Software, Products & Services
N.A.I.C.S.: 513210
Sanjay Manohar *(Mng Dir-India)*
Craig Nielsen *(VP-Asia Pacific)*

McAfee International BV   (2)
Boeingavenue 30, 1119 PE, Schiphol-Rijk, Netherlands
Tel.: (31) 205863800
Web Site: http://www.mcafee.com
Data Security, Protection & Encryption Software Services
N.A.I.C.S.: 513210

CROSSPOINT VENTURE PARTNERS

670 Woodside Rd, Redwood City, CA 94061
Tel.: (650) 851-7600
Web Site: http://www.cpvp.com
Sales Range: $25-49.9 Million
Emp.: 7
Venture Capital Investment Firm
N.A.I.C.S.: 523999
John Breese Mumford *(Partner)*
Seth D. Neiman *(Mng Partner)*
Andrew Alcon *(CFO)*
Dede Barsotti *(Partner-Admin)*

CROSSROAD FUEL SERVICE INC.

1441 Fentress Rd, Chesapeake, VA 23322
Tel.: (757) 482-2179
Web Site:
http://www.crossroadfuel.com
Sales Range: $25-49.9 Million
Emp.: 40
Gasoline
N.A.I.C.S.: 424720
H. Lynn Keffer *(Pres)*
Ryan Keffers *(Mgr-Fleet)*

Crossroad Fuel Service Inc.—(Continued)

Ronnie Keffers *(Mgr-Propane Sls & Svc-Chesapeake)*
Ricky Keffers *(Mgr-Safety)*

CROSSROADS AG LLC
N6055 State Rd 40, Elk Mound, WI 54739
Tel.: (715) 879-5454
Web Site:
http://www.cedarcountrycoop.com
Rev.: $15,700,000
Emp.: 60
Farm Supplies Merchant Whslr
N.A.I.C.S.: 424910

CROSSROADS AUTOMOTIVE GROUP
2333 Walnut St, Cary, NC 27518
Tel.: (919) 460-5600
Web Site:
http://www.crossroadscars.com
Year Founded: 1996
Sales Range: $250-299.9 Million
Holding Company; New & Used Car Dealerships Owner & Operator
N.A.I.C.S.: 551112
Glenn A. Boyd *(Owner & Pres)*
Gary Gearner *(Mgr-Svcs)*
Leonard Tigney *(Mgr)*
Richard Haines *(Gen Mgr)*

Subsidiaries:

Crossroads Ford, Inc.   (1)
2333 Walnut St, Cary, NC 27518
Tel.: (919) 467-1881
Web Site: http://www.crossroadsford.com
New & Used Car Dealer
N.A.I.C.S.: 441110
Tim May *(Pres)*
Tim Nelson *(Gen Mgr)*

Crossroads Nissan of Hickory, Inc.   (1)
840 Hwy 70 SE, Hickory, NC 28602
Tel.: (828) 324-5040
Web Site: http://www.crossroads-nissan.com
Sales Range: $10-24.9 Million
Emp.: 33
New & Used Car Dealer
N.A.I.C.S.: 441110
Steve Yeager *(Gen Mgr-Sls)*

CROSSROADS CAPITAL, INC.
128 N 13th St Ste 1100, Lincoln, NE 68508
Tel.: (402) 261-5345   MD
Web Site: http://www.xroadscap.com
Year Founded: 2008
Rev.: $175,316
Assets: $28,723,562
Liabilities: $423,993
Net Worth: $28,299,569
Earnings: ($1,890,600)
Fiscal Year-end: 12/31/16
Portfolio Management & Investment Services
N.A.I.C.S.: 523940
Stephanie L. Darling *(Chief Compliance Officer)*
David M. Hadani *(CFO, Treas & Sec)*
Ben H. Harris *(Pres)*

CROSSROADS COOPERATIVE ASSOCIATION
800 Greenwood Rd, Sidney, NE 69162
Tel.: (308) 254-4230
Web Site:
http://www.crossroadscoop.com
Sales Range: $25-49.9 Million
Emp.: 30
Grain Elevators
N.A.I.C.S.: 424510
Deb Brauer *(CEO)*

CROSSROADS FILM INC.

1722 Whitley Ave, Los Angeles, CA 90028
Tel.: (310) 659-6220
Web Site:
http://www.crossroadsfilms.com
Sales Range: $10-24.9 Million
Emp.: 17
Commercials, Television: Tape or Film
N.A.I.C.S.: 512110
Wayne Isham *(Dir)*
Harvey B. Brown *(Dir)*
Trudy Bellinger *(Dir)*
Vadim Perelman *(Dir)*
Norman Hafezi *(Dir)*
Lino Russell *(Dir)*
Jeremy Bartel *(Dir)*

CROSSROADS FORD INC.
4210 2nd Ave, Kearney, NE 68847
Tel.: (308) 237-2171
Web Site: http://www.crossroads-ford.com
Sales Range: $10-24.9 Million
Emp.: 52
Automobiles, New & Used
N.A.I.C.S.: 441110
Jeff Seyler *(Pres)*
Dave Lenz *(Treas & Sec)*
Mark Hutsell *(Mgr-Sls)*

CROSSROADS FORD LTD
2033 Laporte Rd, Waterloo, IA 50702
Tel.: (319) 234-4200
Web Site: http://www.dickwitham.net
Year Founded: 1973
Sales Range: $25-49.9 Million
Emp.: 100
Sales of New & Used Automobiles.
N.A.I.C.S.: 441110
Jason Witham *(Pres & Mgr)*

CROSSROADS FORD TRUCK SALES INC.
3401 E Clear Lake Ave, Springfield, IL 62702-6242
Tel.: (217) 528-0770   IL
Web Site:
https://www.landmarkfordtrucks.net
New & Used Cars Sls
N.A.I.C.S.: 423110
Lisa Piatt *(Mgr-Svcs)*
Jim Dambacher *(Mgr-Parts)*
Keith Redd *(Gen Sls Mgr)*
Gary Pate Jr. *(Gen Sls Mgr)*

CROSSROADS HOUSING DEVELOPMENT CORP
201 NE 7th St, Big Spring, TX 79721
Tel.: (432) 267-2206   TX
Year Founded: 1999
Sales Range: $1-9.9 Million
Community Housing Services
N.A.I.C.S.: 624229
Stacy Swisher *(Exec Dir)*

CROSSROADS OF WESTERN IOWA, INC.
1851 Madison Ave Ste 718, Council Bluffs, IA 51503
Tel.: (712) 256-7888   IA
Web Site:
http://www.explorecrossroads.com
Year Founded: 1975
Disability Personal Care & Support Services
N.A.I.C.S.: 812199
Brent Dillinger *(CEO)*
Matt Zima *(CFO)*
Matt Smith *(COO)*
Chris Blake *(Chief HR Officer)*
Pat Kocour *(Pres)*
Beth Morrissette *(Tres & Sec)*

Subsidiaries:

Ida Services, Inc.   (1)

651 1st St, Battle Creek, IA 51006
Tel.: (712) 365-4339
Rev.: $822,803
Assets: $178,982
Liabilities: $168,839
Net Worth: $10,143
Earnings: ($18,557)
Emp.: 32
Fiscal Year-end: 06/30/2014
Disability Assistance Services
N.A.I.C.S.: 624120
Margaret Johnson *(Exec Dir)*
Mike Hittle *(Co-Chm)*
Hank Jessen *(Chm)*
Vicki Dausel *(Sec)*
Kevin Freese *(Treas)*

CROSSROADS TRAILER SALES & SERVICE
2501 Crossroads Blvd, Albert Lea, MN 56007
Tel.: (507) 373-4443
Web Site:
http://www.crossroadstrailer.com
Sales Range: $10-24.9 Million
Emp.: 40
Trailers For Trucks, New & Used
N.A.I.C.S.: 423110
Darvin R. Habben *(Pres & CEO)*
Todd Wayne *(CFO & VP)*
Steve Flaa *(Controller)*

CROSSROADS YOUTH & FAMILY SERVICES, INC.
1333 W Main St, Norman, OK 73069
Tel.: (405) 292-6440   OK
Web Site:
https://www.crossroadsyfs.org
Year Founded: 1985
Sales Range: $10-24.9 Million
Emp.: 377
Youth & Family Care Services
N.A.I.C.S.: 624190
Lisa Winters *(Exec Dir)*
Joer Luper *(Dir-Fin)*
Terrie Vickner *(Program Dir-Head Start)*

CROSSTATES INSURANCE CONSULTANTS
108 S 5th St, Reading, PA 19602-1602
Tel.: (215) 757-3900
Rev.: $13,000,000
Emp.: 7
Insurance Agents
N.A.I.C.S.: 524210
William J. Loose *(Pres & CEO)*

CROSSWELL INTERNATIONAL CORP
101 Madeira Ave, Coral Gables, FL 33134-4515
Tel.: (305) 648-0777
Web Site: http://www.crosswell.com
Rev.: $50,119,695
Emp.: 15
Hospital Equipment & Supplies
N.A.I.C.S.: 423450
Hector Lans *(Pres)*

CROSSWINDS FURNITURE COMPANY
730 Taylor Ave, High Point, NC 27260
Tel.: (336) 882-3565
Web Site:
https://www.frenchheritage.com
Sales Range: $10-24.9 Million
Emp.: 20
Household Furniture Mfr
N.A.I.C.S.: 337126
Jacques Wayser *(VP)*
Henessy Wayser *(Pres)*

CROSWELL BUS LINES, INC.
975 W Main St, Williamsburg, OH 45176-1147

Tel.: (513) 724-2206   OH
Web Site: https://gocroswell.com
Year Founded: 1922
Sales Range: $10-24.9 Million
Emp.: 80
Bus Charter Service & Tour Operator
N.A.I.C.S.: 485510
John W. Croswell *(Pres)*
Scott Croswell *(VP)*
John Croswell *(Pres)*
Susan Mahan III *(VP)*

CROTON AUTO PARK
1 Municipal Pl, Croton on Hudson, NY 10520-2649
Tel.: (914) 862-7403
Web Site:
https://www.crotonautopark.com
Sales Range: $10-24.9 Million
Emp.: 38
New Car Retailer
N.A.I.C.S.: 441110
Jason Giordano *(Mgr-Used Car)*
Vinny DeLuca *(Mgr-Gen Sls)*
Jane Cantone *(Office Mgr)*
Anthony Giordano *(Dir-Svc)*
Harry Losey *(Mgr-Parts)*

CROTON HOLDING COMPANY
8199 McKnight Rd, Pittsburgh, PA 15237
Tel.: (412) 364-2200   PA
Year Founded: 2012
Holding Company; Convenience Stores & Retailer, Whslr & Distr of Petroleum Products
N.A.I.C.S.: 551112
Milo C. Ritton *(Pres)*

Subsidiaries:

Countrywide Petroleum Co.   (1)
5171 Wallings Rd STe 140, North Royalton, OH 44133
Tel.: (440) 237-4448
Gasoline Stations & Petroleum Products Distr & Whslr
N.A.I.C.S.: 457120

Par Mar Oil Company   (1)
114 Westview Ave Unit A, Marietta, OH 45750-9404
Tel.: (740) 373-7406
Web Site: http://www.parmarstores.com
Operator of Convenience Stores & Gasoline Stations
N.A.I.C.S.: 445131

Ravenna Oil Co.   (1)
102 E Lake St, Ravenna, OH 44266-3617
Tel.: (330) 296-9618
Web Site: http://www.ravennaoil.com
Supplier of Liquid Fuels, Heating, Ventilation & Cooling Services & Engine & Industrial Oils & Grease; Transport Services of Petroleum Products
N.A.I.C.S.: 424720
Doug Kolt *(Mgr-Sls)*

CROUCH SUPPLY COMPANY, INC.
305 S Main St, Fort Worth, TX 76104-1226
Tel.: (817) 332-2118   TX
Web Site: http://www.crouchinc.com
Year Founded: 1944
Sales Range: $75-99.9 Million
Emp.: 50
Distr of Food Product Machinery & Chemicals
N.A.I.C.S.: 424690
Bradford Barnes *(Chm & CEO)*
Michael L. Davis *(Treas & Sec)*
Rodney Woodson *(Gen Mgr)*

CROUNSE CORPORATION
400 Marine Way, Paducah, KY 42003
Tel.: (270) 444-9611   KY
Web Site: https://www.crounse.com
Year Founded: 1948

Sales Range: $10-24.9 Million
Emp.: 270
Provider of Freight Transportation Services
N.A.I.C.S.: 483211
Steven Little (Pres)

CROUSE FORD SALES INC.
11 Antrim Blvd, Taneytown, MD 21787
Tel.: (410) 756-6655
Web Site:
https://www.crouseford.com
Sales Range: $25-49.9 Million
Emp.: 41
Automobiles, New & Used
N.A.I.C.S.: 441110
Kenneth Crouse (Pres)
Tom Cross (Pres & Gen Mgr)
Bob Reecher (Mgr-Parts)
David Crouse (Mgr-Sls)

CROW FAMILY HOLDINGS REALTY PARTNERS, L.P.
3819 Maple Ave, Dallas, TX 75219
Tel.: (214) 661-8000   TX
Web Site:
https://www.crowholdings.com
Year Founded: 1998
Sales Range: $25-49.9 Million
Emp.: 100
Holding Company; Real Estate Investment & Asset Management Services
N.A.I.C.S.: 551112
Harlan R. Crow (Chm)
Kevin Bryant (Gen Counsel)
James Don Carreker (Pres)
Joel E. Ehrenkranz (Mng Partner)
Philip J. Prassas (Sr Mng Dir & Head-Los Angeles-Indus)
Ken Valach (CEO-Indus)
Michael Levy (CEO)
Anne L. Raymond (Mng Dir)

CROW WING COOPERATIVE POWER & LIGHT COMPANY
17330 Hwy 371 N, Brainerd, MN 56401
Tel.: (218) 829-2827
Web Site: https://www.cwpower.com
Rev.: $25,474,742
Emp.: 79
Distribution, Electric Power
N.A.I.C.S.: 221122
Bruce Kraemer (CEO)
Kay Blais (Sec)
Gordon Martin (Pres)

CROWDER CONSTRUCTION COMPANY
6425 Brookshire Blvd, Charlotte, NC 28216
Tel.: (704) 372-3541   NC
Web Site: http://www.crowdercc.com
Year Founded: 1947
Sales Range: $350-399.9 Million
Emp.: 850
Heavy Construction Services
N.A.I.C.S.: 237310
Ottis A. Crowder (Co-Pres)
Lynn Hansen (Co-Pres)
William T. Crowder Jr. (Exec VP)

CROWE GROUP LLP
330 E Jefferson Blvd, South Bend, IN 46601
Tel.: (574) 232-3992
Web Site:
http://www.crowehorwath.com
Sales Range: $100-124.9 Million
Emp.: 2,300
Holding Company; Accounting, Consulting, Financial Planning & Professional Staffing Services
N.A.I.C.S.: 551112

Kevin McGrath (COO)
Charles Allen (CEO)
Marilee Hopkins (Partner)

CROWE HORWATH INTERNATIONAL
488 Madison Ave Ste 1200, New York, NY 10022-5722
Tel.: (212) 808-2000   DE
Web Site:
http://www.crowehorwath.net
Accounting & Advisory Services Organization
N.A.I.C.S.: 813920
Kamel Abouchacra (COO)
David Mellor (CEO)

CROWE HORWATH LLP
330 E Jefferson Blvd, South Bend, IN 46601-2314
Tel.: (574) 232-3992   IN
Web Site:
http://www.crowehorwath.com
Accounting & Consulting Services
N.A.I.C.S.: 541211
Doug Schrock (Mng Partner-Mfg & Distr Svcs)
Derek A. Bang (Chief Strategy & Innovation Officer)
Fred J. Bauters (Chief Risk Officer)
Joseph P. Santucci (COO)
Julie K. Wood (Chief People Officer)
Stephen Keeley (Gen Counsel)
Todd Welu (CFO)
Chris Mower (Mng Partner-Springfield)
Gary A. Fox (Mng Partner-Tax Svcs)
Sydney K. Garmong (Mng Partner-Washington)
Josh P. Cole (Mng Principal-Performance Consulting)
Ann Lathrop (CMO & Mng Partner-Indianapolis)
Sal A. Inserra (Mng Partner-Atlanta)
Mark A. Baer (Mng Partner-Audit Svcs)
Stuart J. Miller (Mng Partner-Chicago & Oak Brook)
Gregory J. McClure (Mng Partner-Cleveland)
Chris J. Barrett (Mng Partner-Columbus)
Larry A. Mackowiak (Mng Partner-Construction & Real Estate Svcs)
Dickie L. Heathcott (Mng Partner-Dallas)
Michael Percy (Mng Partner-Fin Svcs)
Mark Adair (Mng Partner-Fort Wayne)
Rhonda Huismann (Mng Partner-Grand Rapids)
Richard A. Buggy (Mng Partner-Hartford & Burlington)
Bill Hoving (Mng Partner-Livingston)
Justin Baxter (Mng Partner-London & Cheltenham)
Jay Mangel (Mng Partner-Los Angeles & Orange County)
Marty C. Lewter (Mng Partner-Nashville)
Wendy L. Cama (Mng Partner-New York)
John Kurkowski (Mng Partner-Private Equity Svcs)
Robert W. Lazard (Mng Partner-Pub Sector Svcs)
Tony Klaich (Mng Partner-San Francisco & San Jose)
Jim Powers (CEO)
Jason Whitmer (Partner & Principal)
Violet Goodheart (Mng Dir-Tax Svcs)
Justin Bass (Chief Data Science Officer)

CROWE LLP

225 W Wacker Dr Ste 2600, Chicago, IL 60606-1224
Tel.: (312) 899-7000
Web Site: https://www.crowe.com
Emp.: 100
Public Accounting & Consulting Services
N.A.I.C.S.: 541219

CROWELL & COMPANY INC.
924 Stevens Creek Rd, Augusta, GA 30907
Tel.: (706) 855-1099
Web Site:
https://www.buildkeystone.com
Rev.: $12,968,379
Emp.: 10
Housing Developers
N.A.I.C.S.: 236115
Mark Gilliam (Pres)

CROWELL & MORING LLP
1001 Pennsylvania Ave NW, Washington, DC 20004-2595
Tel.: (202) 624-2500
Web Site: https://www.crowell.com
Year Founded: 1979
Sales Range: $300-349.9 Million
Emp.: 500
Legal Services, Antitrust & Government Contracts
N.A.I.C.S.: 541199
Ellen Moran Dwyer (Partner)
John Oliverio (CFO)
Joseph J. Palermo (COO)
Mary Anne Mason (Partner)
Larry F. Eisenstat (Partner)
Richard Lehfeldt (Partner)
Evan D. Wolff (Partner-Washington)
Cari N. Stinebower (Partner-Washington)
Andrew Kaplan (Partner)
David Ervin (Partner)
Todd D. Rosenberg (Partner-Washington)
Jennifer A. Ray (Partner-Washington)
Stephen J. McBrady (Partner-Washington)
Karen C. Hermann (Partner)
Leslie A. Davis (Partner-Washington)
W. Scott Douglas (Sr Dir-Policy-Washington)
James G. Flood (Partner)
Elliot Hinds (Partner-Los Angeles)
Lorraine M. Campos (Partner-Washington)
Thomas A. Lorenzen (Partner-Washington)
Angela B. Styles (Partner)
Dwight N. Mersereau (Partner)
Jonathan Lisle (Partner)
Jodi G. Daniel (Partner)
Joseph M. Miller (Partner)
Carlton Greene (Partner)
Michelle Gillette (Partner-San Francisco)
David B. Robbins (Partner)
Robert A. Burton (Partner)
Simon Evers (Partner-London)
Laura Foggan (Partner)
William C. O'Neill (Partner)
Daniel L. Zelenko (Chm-White Collar & Regulatory Enforcement Grp)
Jeffrey L. Poston (Chm-Privacy & Cybersecurity Grp)
Daniel R. Forman (Chm-Govt Contracts Grp)
An Pham (Mgr-Media PR & Comm)
Paul M. Rosen (Partner-White Collar, Regulatory Enforcement, Privacy, Cybersecur)
Jim Dixon (COO)
Melanie Zaletsky (Chief Client Dev & Practice Mgmt Officer)
William S. W. Chang (Partner-Health Care, White Collar & Regulatory Enforcement GrP)

Philip T. Inglima (Chm)
Chris Flynn (Co-Chm-Health Care Grp & Health Care Litigation Team)
David R. Stepp (Partner-Trade Grp-Intl)
Jason C. Murray (Chm-Antitrust Grp-Global, Partner-Litigation & Head-Los Angeles)
Holly A. Melton (Partner-New York)
Glen G. McGorty (Mng Partner-New York)
Jacinta Alves (Partner)
Rebecca Baden Chaney (Partner)
Jenny Cieplak (Partner)
David Wolff (Partner)
Renee Delphin-Rodriguez (Partner-Corp & Health Care grp-Los Angeles)
Kevin Kroeker (Co-Chm-Health Care Group)
Alma Asay (Chief Innovation & Value Officer)
Carmen C. Barboza (Chief HR Officer)
Maura Connell Brandt (CMO)
Joel Gustafson (CIO)
Don Smith (Chief Talent & Inclusion Officer)
Christine K. Lane (Co-Chm-Tax Grp)
Jennifer K. Grady (Chm-Transactional Dept)
S. Starling Marshall (Co-Chm-Tax Grp)

CROWELL ADVERTISING, MARKETING AND PR
12 S 400 W 2nd Fl, Salt Lake City, UT 84101
Tel.: (801) 531-0533
Year Founded: 1987
Rev.: $10,000,000
Emp.: 30
N.A.I.C.S.: 541810
Tracy Crowell (Pres)
Charles Haskell (VP & Dir-Creative)
Melanie Mulvey (Dir-Media)
Rhonda Greenwood (Dir-PR)
Malena Johnson (Dir-Acct Svcs)
Cher Callaway (Dir-Ops)
Rebecca Merrill (Sr Mgr-Production)
Dallas Browning (Dir-Web Dev)
Chris Wells (Assoc Dir-Creative)
Adam T. Bramwell (Acct Coord)
Summer Fredrickson (Sr Acct Mgr)
Travis Gray (Dir-Art)

CROWL, MARKETING & CREATIVE, INC.
713 S Main St, North Canton, OH 44720-8691
Tel.: (330) 494-6999   OH
Web Site: https://www.crowlinc.com
Year Founded: 1959
Advertising Services
N.A.I.C.S.: 541810
Jeff Crowl (CEO)
Rod McGregor (Pres)
Chuck Seeley (Supvr-Acctg)
Frank Scassa (Dir-Creative)
Rod Covey (Exec VP)
Harry Knotts (Supvr-Acctg)
Drew McGregor (Mgr-Acctg)
Anne Morrow (Dir-Art)
Julie Safreed (Gen Mgr)
Chris Sirgo (Dir-Art)

CROWLEY MARITIME CORPORATION
9487 Regency Square Blvd, Jacksonville, FL 32225
Tel.: (904) 727-2200   DE
Web Site: http://www.crowley.com
Year Founded: 1892
Sales Range: Less than $1 Million
Marine & Chemical Transportation & Energy Support Services
N.A.I.C.S.: 483111

Crowley Maritime Corporation—(Continued)

William A. Pennella *(Vice Chm & Exec VP)*
John C. Calvin *(Sr VP & Controller)*
Daniel L. Warner *(CFO)*
Rockwell E. Smith *(Sr VP & Gen Mgr-Petroleum Distr & Marine Svcs)*
Michael Roberts *(Gen Counsel & Sr VP)*
Todd Busch *(Sr VP & Gen Mgr-Technical Svcs)*
Bryan C. Smith *(Asst Treas & VP)*
Rudy Leming *(VP-Marine & Terminal Ops)*
Parker Harrison *(Chief Legal & Risk Officer)*
Kerri McClellan *(VP & Deputy Gen Counsel)*
Susan Michel *(VP-HR & Learning)*
Daniel Vargas *(VP-Bus Dev-Intl)*
Jeffrey de la Combe *(Dir-Logistics-St. Maarten)*
Ken Black *(VP-Miami)*
Ketra Anderson *(VP-Safety, Security, Quality & Environmental Stewardship)*
Tim Bush *(VP/Deputy Gen Counsel-Houston)*
Jose Ayala *(Gen Mgr-Ops-Liner Svcs Grp-Puerto Rico)*
Tiffany King *(VP-People Svcs)*
Jeannie Stewart *(VP-People Svcs)*
Bob Goldenberg *(VP-Comml Ops)*
Brett Bennett *(Sr VP & Gen Mgr-Logistics)*
Ray Fitzgerald *(COO)*
Alisa Praskovich *(VP-Sustainability-Orchestrate Environmental Social Responsibility)*
Deepak Arora *(VP-Corp Strategy)*
Trish Skoglund *(Dir-M&A)*
John Claybrooks *(CMO)*
Jim Pennella *(Sr VP-Corp Svcs)*
Massimo Messina *(VP-Mergers & Acq)*
Megan Davidson *(Chief People Officer)*
Bob Karl *(Sr VP & Gen Mgr-Wind Svcs)*
Erika Graziuso *(CIO)*
Clay Heil *(VP--Global Govt Rels & Global Govt Rels)*
John P. Hourihan Jr. *(Sr VP & Gen Mgr-Puerto Rico & Caribbean Svcs)*
Thomas B. Crowley Jr. *(Chm & CEO)*

Subsidiaries:

Marine Transport Corporation   (1)
9487 Regency Square Blvd, Jacksonville, FL 32225-8126
Tel.: (904) 727-2200
Sales Range: $200-249.9 Million
Emp.: 70
Bulk Shipping
N.A.I.C.S.: 483111

Tamarind Consolidated, Inc.   (1)
3400 MacIntosh Rd, Fort Lauderdale, FL 33316-4223
Tel.: (954) 763-2234
Web Site:
   http://www.tamarindconsolidated.com
Freight Transportation Arrangement
N.A.I.C.S.: 488510

Titan Maritime, LLC   (1)
15894 Diplomatic Plz Dr, Houston, TX 77032
Tel.: (954) 545-4143
Web Site: http://www.titansalvage.com
Marine Salvaging Services
N.A.I.C.S.: 488390
Richard Habib *(Mng Dir)*
Chandran Mathavan *(Gen Mgr)*
Gordon Amos *(Dir-Ops)*
Jason Bennett *(Dir-Comml)*
Jorge Ponce *(Mgr-Ops)*

CROWLEY MICROGRAPHICS, INC.

5111 Pegasus Ct Ste M, Frederick, MD 21704-8318
Tel.: (240) 215-0224
Web Site:
   https://www.crowleycompany.com
Year Founded: 1980
Sales Range: $10-24.9 Million
Emp.: 85
Digital & Analog Solution Mfr & Distr
N.A.I.C.S.: 423420
Christopher Crowley *(Pres)*
Matthew McCabe *(VP-Sls & Mktg)*
Patrick Crowley *(VP)*
Cheri Baker *(Dir-Comm)*
Debbie Harris *(Dir-Admin)*
Lars Christensen *(Dir-Imaging Ops)*
Harvey Hicks *(Dir-Technical Support)*
Chris Stanley *(Mgr-Resale Channel)*
Vicki Sample *(Project Mgr)*
Kris Sheckels *(Project Mgr)*
Phil Westcott *(Project Mgr)*
Andrew Fertig *(Sr Project Mgr)*

CROWN AUTO DEALERSHIPS, INC.

5237 34th St N, Saint Petersburg, FL 33714
Tel.: (727) 498-1424
Web Site:
   https://www.crowngmcbuick.com
Sales Range: $500-549.9 Million
Emp.: 755
New & Used Car Dealership Owner & Operator
N.A.I.C.S.: 441110
Jim Myers *(Pres)*

Subsidiaries:

Crown Motors of Clearwater, Inc.   (1)
18911 US Hwy 19 N, Clearwater, FL 33764
Tel.: (727) 507-8866
Web Site: http://www.crowncars.com
Sales Range: $10-24.9 Million
Emp.: 50
New Car Dealers
N.A.I.C.S.: 441110
Dwayne Hawkins *(Pres)*

CROWN AUTOMOBILE COMPANY INC.

1800 Montgomery Hwy S, Birmingham, AL 35244
Tel.: (205) 985-4200
Web Site:
   http://www.crownautomobile.com
Sales Range: $100-124.9 Million
Emp.: 116
New & Used Automobiles
N.A.I.C.S.: 441110
June B. Willey *(Owner)*
Tommy Dunlap *(Pres)*
Louis H. Anders *(Sec & VP)*

CROWN AUTOMOTIVE SALES CO. INC.

83 Enterprise Dr, Marshfield, MA 02050-0607
Tel.: (781) 319-3100
Web Site:
   http://www.crownautomotive.net
Year Founded: 1963
Rev.: $16,622,769
Emp.: 100
Automotive Supplies & Parts
N.A.I.C.S.: 423120
Herbert J. Gerber *(Pres)*

CROWN BATTERY MANUFACTURING CO. INC.

1445 Majestic Dr, Fremont, OH 43420-0990
Tel.: (419) 334-7181   OH
Web Site:
   https://www.crownbattery.com
Year Founded: 1926
Battery Mfr
N.A.I.C.S.: 335910

Hal Hawk *(Pres)*
Mark Kelley *(VP-Sls-Industrial Products Grp)*

CROWN BAUS CAPITAL CORP.

9107 Wilshire Blvd Ste 450, Beverly Hills, CA 90210
Year Founded: 2011
Asset Management Services
N.A.I.C.S.: 523940

CROWN BUICK GMC

2121 Clearview Pkwy, Metairie, LA 70001-2450
Tel.: (504) 455-6666   LA
Web Site:
   http://www.crownbuickgmc.com
Year Founded: 1975
Sales Range: $100-124.9 Million
Emp.: 90
Retailer of New & Used Automobiles
N.A.I.C.S.: 441110
Gerry Groetsch *(VP)*
Josef Cermak *(Controller)*
Robert Meredith *(Mgr-Comml & Fleet Sls)*
Craig Blacklidge *(Gen Mgr)*
Larry Oggs Jr. *(Pres)*

CROWN CAPITAL INVESTMENTS LLC

1 Buckhead Plz 3060 Peachtree Rd NW Ste 1550, Atlanta, GA 30305
Tel.: (404) 389-4989
Web Site: https://www.crown-inv.com
Year Founded: 2014
Private Equity
N.A.I.C.S.: 523940
Christopher Graham *(CEO)*

Subsidiaries:

Ace-Tex Enterprises Inc.   (1)
7601 Central St, Detroit, MI 48210
Tel.: (313) 834-4000
Web Site: https://www.ace-tex.com
Sales Range: $10-24.9 Million
Emp.: 90
Cleaning & Maintenance Equipment & Supplies
N.A.I.C.S.: 423850
Martin Laker *(Owner)*

CROWN CHRYSLER JEEP, KIA, & EUROCARS - MERCEDES BENZ

6400 Perimeter Loop Rd, Dublin, OH 43017
Tel.: (614) 652-6542
Year Founded: 1992
Sales Range: $50-74.9 Million
Emp.: 75
Car Whslr
N.A.I.C.S.: 441110
Marc Wigler *(Pres & Gen Mgr)*

CROWN COAL & COKE CO. INC.

3 Pkwy Ctr Ste 375, Pittsburgh, PA 15220
Tel.: (412) 921-1950   PA
Web Site:
   http://www.crowncoalandcokeco.org
Year Founded: 1920
Sales Range: $75-99.9 Million
Emp.: 15
Provider of Energy Services
N.A.I.C.S.: 423520
Albert C. Muse *(Pres & CEO)*
Charles H. Muse Jr. *(Treas)*

CROWN COCO INC.

1717 Broadway St NE, Minneapolis, MN 55413
Tel.: (612) 331-9344
Sales Range: $10-24.9 Million

Emp.: 50
Convenience Store
N.A.I.C.S.: 445131
Domenic Losurto *(Pres)*
David Miller *(VP)*

CROWN COMMUNITIES, LLC

1712 Pioneer Ave Ste 2117, Cheyenne, WY 82001
Tel.: (307) 777-7311
Web Site:
   https://crowncommunities.com
Emp.: 100
Property Management Services
N.A.I.C.S.: 531311
Alexander Cabot *(Founder)*

Subsidiaries:

Fawn Creek Court Sales Ltd.   (1)
1900 Highway 64 E, Anamosa, IA 52205
Tel.: (319) 462-6155
Web Site: http://www.fawncreekhomes.com
Rev.: $7,633,000
Emp.: 17
Land Subdivision
N.A.I.C.S.: 237210
Winifred Williams *(Owner)*

CROWN CONSULTING, INC.

1400 Key Blvd Ste 1100, Arlington, VA 22209
Tel.: (703) 650-0663
Web Site: https://www.crownci.com
Year Founded: 1989
Sales Range: $10-24.9 Million
Emp.: 88
Analytics, Information Solutions, Management & Engineering Services
N.A.I.C.S.: 561499
Catherine Myers *(Acct Exec)*
David Budin *(VP-Bus Dev)*
Michael O'Hara *(VP-Bus Dev)*

CROWN CORR, INC.

7100 W 21st Ave, Gary, IN 46406
Tel.: (219) 949-8080
Web Site: https://www.crowncorr.com
Sales Range: $10-24.9 Million
Emp.: 300
Roofing Contractors
N.A.I.C.S.: 238160
Richard Pellar *(Pres)*
Jolaine Boudart *(CFO)*
Jeff McNabb *(Engr-Drafting)*
Scott Swanson *(Project Mgr)*
Steven Otwinowski *(Project Mgr)*

CROWN DISTRIBUTING INC.

1117 59th Ave NE, Arlington, WA 98223
Tel.: (425) 252-4192
Web Site:
   http://www.crowndistributing.com
Sales Range: $25-49.9 Million
Emp.: 130
Beer & Other Fermented Malt Liquors
N.A.I.C.S.: 424810
Peter Bargreen *(Pres & CEO)*

CROWN DIVERSIFIED INDUSTRIES

1065 Executive Pkwy Ste 300, Saint Louis, MO 63141
Tel.: (314) 542-0105
Sales Range: $10-24.9 Million
Emp.: 120
Door Mfr
N.A.I.C.S.: 332321
Gigi Gladson *(Dir-Ops)*
Joe H. Scott Sr. *(Pres)*

CROWN DODGE

6300 King, Ventura, CA 93003-8586
Tel.: (805) 656-6669
Web Site:
   http://www.4crowndodge.com
Rev.: $66,525,584

Emp.: 150
Automobiles, New & Used
N.A.I.C.S.: 441110
Robert Crown (Pres)
Matt Belzano (Mgr-Body Shop)
Richard Schwartz (Mgr)

CROWN DODGE OF FAYETTE-VILLE
436 N McPherson Church Rd, Fay-etteville, NC 28303-4408
Tel.: (910) 745-7806
Web Site:
https://www.dodgefayetteville.com
Year Founded: 2002
Sales Range: $10-24.9 Million
Emp.: 79
Car Whslr
N.A.I.C.S.: 441110
Paul Failor (Gen Mgr)

CROWN ENTERPRISES INC.
52410 Clarke Rd, White Castle, LA 70788
Tel.: (225) 545-3040
Web Site:
http://www.crownenterprises.com
Rev.: $120,000,000
Emp.: 250
Industrial Buildings & Warehouses
N.A.I.C.S.: 236220
Ross Campesi Jr. (Pres)

Subsidiaries:

Cooling Tower Technologies   (1)
52410 Clarke Rd, White Castle, LA 70788
Tel.: (225) 545-2230
Web Site: http://www.crownenterprises.com
Rev.: $23,000,000
Emp.: 200
Industrial Buildings & Warehouses
N.A.I.C.S.: 236220
Pat Campesi (Pres)

CROWN EQUIPMENT CORPO-RATION
151 Greenlawn Dr, Columbia, SC 29209
Tel.: (803) 695-0149
Web Site:
http://www.cmhservices.net
Year Founded: 1973
Sales Range: $10-24.9 Million
Emp.: 85
New & Used Lift Trucks Sales, Rent-als, Parts & Service
N.A.I.C.S.: 441227
Grady Smith (CEO)

CROWN EQUIPMENT CORPO-RATION
44 S Washington St, New Bremen, OH 45869-0097
Tel.: (419) 629-2311   OH
Web Site: https://www.crown.com
Year Founded: 1945
Sales Range: $50-74.9 Million
Emp.: 18,100
Industrial Truck, Tractor, Trailer & Stacker Machinery Manufacturing
N.A.I.C.S.: 333924
John G. Maxa (Gen Counsel & VP)
Kent W. Spille (CFO & VP)
Mark A. Manuel (VP-Dev & Informa-tion Svcs)
Timothy S. Quellhorst (Sr VP)
Randall W. Niekamp (VP-HR)
Michael P. Gallagher (VP-Design Center)
John E. Tate (Sr VP)
Craig D. Seitz (VP)
Kathy A. Doseck (Asst Sec)
James R. Mozer (Sr VP)
James F. Dicke III (Pres)
David J. Besser Sr. (Sr VP)

Subsidiaries:

Crown Equipment Pty Ltd   (1)
15 Cooper St, Smithfield, 2164, NSW, Aus-tralia
Tel.: (61) 1300 072 752
Web Site: http://www.crown.com
Sales Range: $50-74.9 Million
Emp.: 500
Forklift Truck Distr
N.A.I.C.S.: 423830
Greg Simmonds (Gen Mgr)

Crown Gabelstapler GmbH & Co. KG   (1)
Philipp-Hauck-Strasse 12, Feldkirchen, 85622, Germany
Tel.: (49) 89 93 002 0
Web Site: http://www.crown.com
Forklift Truck Mfr & Distr
N.A.I.C.S.: 423830
Kenneth J. Dufford (VP-Europe)

Crown Lift Trucks   (1)
860 Vandalia St, Saint Paul, MN 55114
Tel.: (651) 645-8668
Web Site: http://www.crownminnesota.com
Sales Range: $25-49.9 Million
Emp.: 62
Industrial Machinery & Equipment Whslr
N.A.I.C.S.: 423830
Sue Sherman (Mgr-Ops)
Jon Willman (Mgr-Acct)
Simon Barkworth (Mng Dir-UK)

CROWN FENCE COMPANY
12118 Bloomfield Ave, Santa Fe Springs, CA 90670-4703
Tel.: (562) 864-5177   CA
Web Site:
http://www.crownfence.com
Year Founded: 1923
Sales Range: $10-24.9 Million
Emp.: 135
Provider of Fence Contracting Ser-vices
N.A.I.C.S.: 238990
Cecil Gates (Pres)
Eric W. Fiedler (VP-Sls & Mktg)
Steve Long (Controller)

CROWN FOODS LLC
5243 Manchester Ave, Saint Louis, MO 63110-2015
Tel.: (314) 645-5300   DE
Web Site:
http://www.crownfoods.com
Year Founded: 1975
Sales Range: $75-99.9 Million
Emp.: 90
Whslr of Fresh Meats, Poultry & Fro-zen Foods; Retailer of Meats & Pro-duce
N.A.I.C.S.: 424440
Larry Stein (Pres)
Bill Moss (Controller)

CROWN FORD INC.
420 Merrick Rd, Lynbrook, NY 11563
Tel.: (516) 209-2303
Web Site:
https://crownfordlynbrook.com
Year Founded: 1972
Sales Range: $25-49.9 Million
Emp.: 41
Car Whslr
N.A.I.C.S.: 441110
Edward Anderson (Pres)

CROWN FORD LINCOLN MER-CURY, INC.
3853 Youngstown Rd SE, Warren, OH 44484
Tel.: (330) 369-4444
Year Founded: 1984
Sales Range: $25-49.9 Million
Emp.: 70
Car Whslr
N.A.I.C.S.: 441110

Joseph Filipovich (Coord-Customer Care)
Michael Klaben Sr. (Pres)

CROWN HARDWARE, INC.
9045 Adams Ave, Huntington Beach, CA 92646-3401
Tel.: (714) 962-4160   CA
Web Site:
http://www.crownhardware.com
Year Founded: 1949
Sales Range: $50-74.9 Million
Emp.: 300
Hardware Stores Owner & Operator
N.A.I.C.S.: 444140
Frank Rogers (VP)
Mark Schulein (Pres)

CROWN LABORATORIES, INC.
349 Lafe Cox Dr, Johnson City, TN 37604
Tel.: (423) 926-4413
Web Site:
http://www.crownlaboratories.com
Year Founded: 2000
Sales Range: $10-24.9 Million
Emp.: 82
Mfr of Prescriptions & Over The Counter Medications & Cosmetics
N.A.I.C.S.: 325620
Jeff Bedard (Founder, Pres & CEO)
Thomas Hitchcock (Chief Science Officer)

CROWN LINEN SERVICE IN-CORPORATED
15 Technology Way, Nashua, NH 03060
Tel.: (603) 598-7000
Web Site:
https://www.crownuniform.com
Sales Range: $10-24.9 Million
Emp.: 48
Linen Supply
N.A.I.C.S.: 812331
Arthur P. Spilios (CEO)

CROWN LIQUORS OF BRO-WARD INC.
910 NW Tenth Pl, Fort Lauderdale, FL 33311-6132
Tel.: (954) 763-6831   FL
Web Site:
http://www.crownwineandspirits.com
Year Founded: 1955
Sales Range: $10-24.9 Million
Emp.: 175
Liquor Stores
N.A.I.C.S.: 445320
Stanley Kassao (Pres)

CROWN MARKETING GROUP, INC.
245 Newtown Road Ste 103, Plain-view, NY 11803
Tel.: (516) 470-2700   NY
Web Site: http://www.crownad.com
Year Founded: 1992
Rev.: $45,000,000
Emp.: 11
N.A.I.C.S.: 541810
Tom Cullen (Pres & CEO)

CROWN MOTORS LTD.
196 Regent Blvd, Holland, MI 49423
Tel.: (616) 396-5268
Web Site:
https://www.crownmotors.com
Year Founded: 1986
Rev.: $108,000,000
Emp.: 70
Sales of Automobiles
N.A.I.C.S.: 441110
Craig Eaas (Pres)

Subsidiaries:

Crown Motors II Llc   (1)
11260 Chicago Dr, Holland, MI 49424
Tel.: (616) 393-0400
Web Site: http://www.crownmotors2.com
Rev.: $7,700,000
Emp.: 42
Automobiles, New & Used
N.A.I.C.S.: 441110
Craig Werida (Pres)
Michaele Beaton (Controller)

CROWN MOTORS OF RED-DING
555 Cypress Ave, Redding, CA 96001-2819
Tel.: (530) 241-4321
Web Site:
http://www.crownmotorsredding.com
Year Founded: 1996
Sales Range: $50-74.9 Million
Emp.: 120
Dealer in New & Used Automobiles
N.A.I.C.S.: 441110
David Burch (Sls Mgr-Dodge Ram)
Diane Hill (Dir-Fin)

CROWN PACKAGING CORP.
17854 Chesterfield Airport Rd, Ches-terfield, MO 63005
Tel.: (636) 681-9400
Web Site:
https://www.crownpack.com
Year Founded: 1969
Sales Range: $50-74.9 Million
Emp.: 402
Distr of Industrial & Personal Service Paper
N.A.I.C.S.: 424130
Ray L. Hunt (CFO)
Don Hoffmann (VP)
Rich Benkelman (VP)
John Anthon (VP)

CROWN PACKAGING INTER-NATIONAL INC.
8919 Colorado St, Merrillville, IN 46410-7208
Tel.: (219) 738-1000
Web Site: https://crownpolycon.com
Year Founded: 1947
Sales Range: $10-24.9 Million
Emp.: 250
Mfr of Packaging Products
N.A.I.C.S.: 423840
Berle Littstein (CEO)
William Hansen (CFO)
Jill Contro (Controller)

Subsidiaries:

Polycon Industries Inc.   (1)
8919 Colorado St, Merrillville, IN 46410-7208
Tel.: (219) 738-1000
Mfr of Plastics Bottles
N.A.I.C.S.: 326160
Bill Zick (Mgr-Shipping)

West-Hub Building Corp.   (1)
8919 Colorado St, Merrillville, IN 46410-7208
Tel.: (773) 374-5500
Sales Range: $10-24.9 Million
Emp.: 3
Manager of Real Estate
N.A.I.C.S.: 423840

CROWN PARTS AND MA-CHINE INC.
1733 US Hwy 87 E, Billings, MT 59101
Tel.: (406) 252-6682
Web Site:
http://www.crownpartsmachine.com
Rev.: $10,036,738
Emp.: 57
Machine Shop, Jobbing & Repair
N.A.I.C.S.: 332710

Crown Parts and Machine Inc.—(Continued)

Jacquie Preeshl *(Mgr-Pur)*

**CROWN POWER & EQUIP-
MENT CO.**
1881 E Prathersville Rd, Columbia,
MO 65202
Tel.: (573) 443-4541
Web Site: https://www.crown-
power.com
Sales Range: $25-49.9 Million
Emp.: 40
Agricultural Machinery & Equipment
N.A.I.C.S.: 459999
Harold Chapman *(Gen Mgr)*
Neil Eddingfield *(Mgr-Svc)*
Jeff Tucker *(Mgr)*

CROWN PRINCE, INC.
18581 Railroad St, City of Industry,
CA 91748
Tel.: (626) 912-3700   **CA**
Web Site:
https://www.crownprince.com
Year Founded: 1948
Sales Range: $10-24.9 Million
Emp.: 50
Canned Seafood Importer
N.A.I.C.S.: 424490
Robert Hoffman *(Owner)*
Dustan Hoffman *(Pres)*
Gary Gruettner *(Mgr-Sls-Natl)*
Denise Hines *(Mgr-Mktg)*
Lawrence DeMarco *(Mgr-North Cen-
tral Reg)*
Ed Leavister *(Mgr-Sls-Eastern Reg)*

**CROWN PRODUCTS COM-
PANY INC.**
6390 Philips Hwy, Jacksonville, FL
32216
Tel.: (904) 737-7144
Web Site:
https://www.crownproductsco.com
Rev.: $21,619,322
Emp.: 250
Flues & Pipes Mfr
N.A.I.C.S.: 332322
Peter Tuggle *(Pres)*

**CROWN REALTY OF KANSAS
INC.**
102 S Silver St, Paola, KS 66071
Tel.: (913) 557-4333
Web Site:
http://www.crownrealty.com
Sales Range: $10-24.9 Million
Emp.: 50
Real Estate Brokers & Agents
N.A.I.C.S.: 531210
Katie Casey *(CIO)*

CROWN RESORTS, LTD.
412 Inverness Ct, Ocean Springs,
MS 39564
Tel.: (228) 875-0020   **TX**
Web Site:
http://www.crownresortsltd.com
Resort Properties & Timeshare Ex-
change System Operator
N.A.I.C.S.: 721110
Richard W. Dickson *(Partner)*

Subsidiaries:

Hiawatha Manor Association at Lake
Tansi   **(1)**
8007 Cherokee Trl, Crossville, TN 38572-
6331
Tel.: (931) 788-6724
Web Site: http://www.crownresortsltd.com
Sales Range: Less than $1 Million
Emp.: 10
Resort Management & Hospitality Services
N.A.I.C.S.: 531311
Gail Boles *(Gen Mgr)*

Westwind Manor Resort Association,
Inc.   **(1)**
110 Private Rd 1509, Runaway Bay, TX
76426
Tel.: (940) 575-4913
Web Site: http://www.westwind-manor.com
Sales Range: Less than $1 Million
Emp.: 6
Resort Management & Hospitality Services
N.A.I.C.S.: 531311

CROWN ROLL LEAF INC.
91 Illinois Ave, Paterson, NJ 07503-
1722
Tel.: (973) 742-4000
Web Site:
https://www.crownrollleaf.com
Year Founded: 1973
Sales Range: $10-24.9 Million
Emp.: 230
Mfr of Metal Foil Products
N.A.I.C.S.: 332999
Ramon Cinquino *(Product Mgr)*

CROWN SERVICES INC.
2800 Corporate Exchange Dr Ste
120, Columbus, OH 43231
Tel.: (614) 844-5429
Web Site:
http://www.crownservices.com
Year Founded: 1968
Sales Range: $50-74.9 Million
Emp.: 10
Temporary Help Service
N.A.I.C.S.: 561320
Richard Diana *(Pres & CEO)*
Vickie Ogletree *(Gen Mgr)*

**CROWN STEEL SALES IN-
CORPORATED**
3355 W 31st St, Chicago, IL 60623
Tel.: (773) 376-1700
Web Site: http://www.crownsteel.com
Sales Range: $10-24.9 Million
Emp.: 45
Metals Service Centers & Offices
N.A.I.C.S.: 423510
Lynne McCutcheon *(CEO)*

**CROWN WORLDWIDE MOV-
ING & STORAGE COMPANY**
14826 Wicks Blvd, San Leandro, CA
94577-6606
Tel.: (510) 895-8050
Web Site:
https://www.crownwms.com
Year Founded: 1972
Sales Range: $25-49.9 Million
Emp.: 250
Provider of Freight Transportation
Arrangement Services
N.A.I.C.S.: 488510
Robert Bowen *(Owner)*
Cynthia Allen *(VP-Customer Svc)*

CROWNE GROUP LLC
Key Tower 127 Public Sq Ste 5110,
Cleveland, OH 44114
Tel.: (216) 589-0198
Automotive & Industrial Products Mfr
N.A.I.C.S.: 333995
Steve Graham *(CFO)*
Gregory Flake *(Pres & CEO)*

Subsidiaries:

First Brands Group, LLC   **(1)**
3255 W Hamlin Rd, Rochester Hills, MI
48309-3231
Tel.: (248) 371-1700
Web Site: http://www.tricoproducts.com
Wiper Blades Mfr
N.A.I.C.S.: 336390

Subsidiary (Domestic):

ASC Industries Inc.   **(2)**
2100 International Pkwy, North Canton, OH
44720
Tel.: (330) 899-0340

Web Site: http://www.airtexasc.com
Automobile Parts Mfr
N.A.I.C.S.: 336310
Airtex Products, LP   **(2)**
407 W Main St, Fairfield, IL 62837-1622
Tel.: (618) 842-2111
Automobile Parts, Fuel Pumps, Water
Pumps & Parts, Water Outlets & Fan
Clutches
N.A.I.C.S.: 423120

CWD LLC   **(2)**
14528 Bonelli St, City of Industry, CA 91746
Tel.: (626) 961-5775
Web Site: http://www.centricparts.com
Emp.: 500
Aftermarket Automotive Replacement Parts
N.A.I.C.S.: 441330
Dan Lelchuk *(Pres)*
Sal Bora *(VP-Ops)*
John Beale *(Mgr-Sls-Central)*
Andrea Schultz *(Mgr-Sls-East)*
Dan Billie *(Exec VP-Sls & Mktg)*
Charlie Kirkland *(VP-Traditional Sls)*
Brian Schweinhagen *(Dir-Quality)*
Don Bales *(Mgr-Corp Logistics)*
Division (Domestic):

Qualis Automotive LLC   **(3)**
29380 John R Rd, Madison Heights, MI
48071
Tel.: (248) 740-3510
Web Site: http://www.qualisautomotive.com
Automotive Replacement Parts
N.A.I.C.S.: 441330
Subsidiary (Domestic):

Horizon Global Corporation   **(2)**
3255 W Hamlin Rd, Rochester Hills, MI
48309
Tel.: (734) 656-3000
Web Site: https://www.horizonglobal.com
Rev.: $782,120,000
Assets: $438,920,000
Liabilities: $479,170,000
Net Worth: ($40,250,000)
Earnings: ($31,720,000)
Emp.: 3,800
Fiscal Year-end: 12/31/2021
High-Quality, Custom-Engineered Towing,
Trailering, Cargo Management & Other Re-
lated Accessory Products Designer, Mfr &
Distr
N.A.I.C.S.: 336999
James F. Sistek *(Chief Admin Officer)*
Jian James Zhou *(CFO)*
Subsidiary (Domestic):

Cequent Consumer Products,
Inc.   **(3)**
29000-2 Aurora Rd, Solon, OH 44139
Tel.: (440) 498-0001
Web Site:
http://www.cequentconsumerproducts.com
Emp.: 100
Vehicle Accessories Designer & Mfr
N.A.I.C.S.: 336390

Cequent Performance Products,
Inc.   **(3)**
47912 Halyard Dr Ste 100, Plymouth, MI
48170
Tel.: (440) 498-0001
Web Site: http://www.cequentgroup.com
Sales Range: $300-349.9 Million
Aftermarket Towing & Trailer Accessory
Products Mfr
N.A.I.C.S.: 336390
Michael Finos *(Sr VP-Ops)*
Branch (Domestic):

Cequent Performance Products -
Trailer Division   **(4)**
1050 Indianhead Dr, Mosinee, WI 54455
Tel.: (877) 208-2548
Sales Range: $75-99.9 Million
Emp.: 200
Mfr of Marine, Agricultural & Industrial
Trailer Components; Lights, Wire Har-
nesses, Hub & Grease Caps & Boat Lad-
ders
N.A.I.C.S.: 336999
John Aleva *(Pres)*
Subsidiary (Non-US):

Trico Automotive Systems Co.,
Ltd   **(2)**

No 57 Xinglin Street, Suzhou Industrial
Park, Suzhou, 215126, China
Tel.: (86) 51262831688
Web Site: http://www.tricoproducks.com.cn
Wiper Blades Whslr
N.A.I.C.S.: 423710

Trico Componentes S.A. de C.V.   **(2)**
Ave Michigan 200, Matamoros, Mexico
Tel.: (52) 9565440342
Wiper Blades Mfr
N.A.I.C.S.: 336390

Trico Latinoamericana SA   **(2)**
Calle 10 y 11 Frac 2 Parcela 14, Pilar,
1629, Buenos Aires, Argentina
Tel.: (54) 2322496305
Web Site: http://www.tricoproducts.com.ar
Wiper Blades Mfr
N.A.I.C.S.: 336390

Trico Latinoamericana do Brasil
Ltda   **(2)**
Geraldo Scavone Highway 2080, Jacarei,
12305-490, Sao Paulo, Brazil
Tel.: (55) 12 3954 6522
Web Site: http://www.tricoproducts.com.br
Wiper Blades Mfr
N.A.I.C.S.: 336390

Trico Limited   **(2)**
Skewfields Torfaen, Pontypool, NP4 0XZ,
South Wales, United Kingdom
Tel.: (44) 1495 767700
Web Site: http://www.trico.eu.com
Wiper Blades Mfr
N.A.I.C.S.: 336390

Trico Pty. Limited   **(2)**
Unit 1 80 Fairbank Road Clayton South,
Victoria, 3169, VIC, Australia
Tel.: (61) 392713288
Web Site: http://www.tricoproduct.com.au
Wiper Blades Mfr
N.A.I.C.S.: 336390
Robert Patman *(Mgr-Supply Chain)*

Parthenon Metal Works, Inc.   **(1)**
5018 Murfreesboro Rd, La Vergne, TN
37086
Tel.: (615) 793-6801
Web Site:
http://www.parthenonmetalworks.com
Welded Steel Tubing Mfr
N.A.I.C.S.: 331210

Vari-Form Corporation   **(1)**
17199 N Laurel Park Ste 322, Livonia, MI
48152
Tel.: (248) 879-7656
Web Site: http://www.vari-form.com
Motor Vehicle Body Mfr
N.A.I.C.S.: 336211
Steve Greer *(Program Mgr)*
Nick Callow *(Mgr-Mfg & Engrg)*

**CROWNPEAK TECHNOLOGY,
INC.**
707 17th St Fl 38, Denver, CO 80202
Tel.: (720) 800-9600
Web Site: http://www.crownpeak.com
Year Founded: 2001
Sales Range: $1-9.9 Million
Emp.: 13
Software Development Services
N.A.I.C.S.: 513210
Adrian Newby *(CTO)*
Allan Stewart *(VP-Sls-Global)*
Tim Vollman *(Co-CEO)*
Ravi Kumaraswami *(Co-CEO)*
Suman Raju *(CFO)*
Al Mays *(Sr VP-Engrg)*
Darren Guarnaccia *(Chief Strategy
Officer & Chief Product Officer)*

Subsidiaries:

ATTRAQT Group plc   **(1)**
236 Grays Inn Road, London, WC1X 8HB,
United Kingdom
Tel.: (44) 2036757800
Web Site: http://www.attraqt.com
Rev.: $31,041,552
Assets: $71,466,308
Liabilities: $19,433,046
Net Worth: $52,033,261
Earnings: ($4,794,109)

Emp.: 164
Fiscal Year-end: 12/31/2021
Software Publisher
N.A.I.C.S.: 513210
Nick Habgood (Chm)
John Raap (Chief Strategy & Partner Officer)
Peter Thomas (Co-CTO)
Allyson Barclay (Sr VP-Global)
Jonathan Schradi (VP-Customer Success)
Andrea Nicol (Head)
Mark Adams (CEO)
Nicolas Mathon (VP)
David Newberry (Chief Customer Officer)
Paul Tough (Co-CTO)
Terence Tsang (Gen Counsel)
Kevin Abbott (Sr VP)
Tom Crawford (Chm)

Subsidiary (Non-US):

Early Birds S.A.S.   (2)
18 Rue De Londres, 75009, Paris, France
Tel.: (33) 185090377
E-Commerce Technology Solutions Services
N.A.I.C.S.: 541519

Fredhopper BV   (2)
Weesperstraat 61, 1018 VN, Amsterdam,
Netherlands   (100%)
Tel.: (31) 203 675 7800
Web Site: http://www.fredhopper.com
Online Marketing Software Development
Services
N.A.I.C.S.: 541511

CrownPeak Technology UK   (1)
5 Abbeylands, Cobbetts Hill, Weybridge,
KT13 0UB, Surrey, United Kingdom
Tel.: (44) 203 384 6598
Software Publisher
N.A.I.C.S.: 513210

Evidon, Inc.   (1)
10 E 39th St, New York, NY 10016
Tel.: (917) 262-2530
Web Site: http://www.evidon.com
Online & Mobile Consent & Monitoring Marketing Application Developer & Services
N.A.I.C.S.: 541511
Scott Meyer (Founder)

CROZER-KEYSTONE HEALTH SYSTEM INC.
100 W Sproul Rd 3rd Fl, Springfield,
PA 19064
Tel.: (610) 338-8200   PA
Web Site: http://www.crozer.org
Year Founded: 1990
Sales Range: $500-549.9 Million
Emp.: 7,100
Health Care Srvices
N.A.I.C.S.: 541611
Eileen Young (Chief Nursing Officer &
VP)
Sharif Omar (CEO)

CRP INDUSTRIES INC.
35 Commerce Dr, Cranbury, NJ
08512-1104
Tel.: (609) 578-4100
Web Site:
     http://www.crpindustries.com
Year Founded: 1954
Sales Range: $10-24.9 Million
Emp.: 100
Importer, Fabricator & Distributor of
Motor Vehicle Supplies & New Parts
N.A.I.C.S.: 423120
George H. Schildge (Chm)
Kevin Stock (VP-Fin)
Dan Schildge (Pres & CEO)
P. T. Muldoon (Dir-Engrg)
Scott Shea (COO)

Subsidiaries:

CRP Industries of California Inc.   (1)
4900 Hannover Pl, Fremont, CA 94538
Tel.: (510) 657-8080
Web Site: http://www.crpindustries.com
Sales Range: $10-24.9 Million
Emp.: 8
Providing Warehousing Facilities

N.A.I.C.S.: 423840

CRP de Mexico S.A. de C.V.   (1)
Ricardo Flores Magon No 92, San Jeronimo
Caleras, Puebla, 91700, Mexico
Tel.: (52) 222 2242170
Automobile Parts Distr
N.A.I.C.S.: 423120
Salvador Domingo Ueb (Dir-Comml)

CRS ONE SOURCE
2803 Tamarack Rd, Owensboro, KY
42302
Tel.: (270) 684-1469
Web Site:
     https://www.crsonesource.com
Sales Range: $10-24.9 Million
Emp.: 130
Groceries & Related Products Whslr
N.A.I.C.S.: 424420
Steve Clark (Pres)
Kim Clark (Founder)
J. R. Riney (Mgr-Sls)

CRST INTERNATIONAL, INC.
3930 16th Ave SW, Cedar Rapids, IA
52404-2332
Tel.: (319) 396-4400   IA
Web Site: http://www.crst.com
Year Founded: 1978
Sales Range: $1-4.9 Billion
Emp.: 2,300
Long Distance Trucking Services
John M. Smith (Chm)
David Souza (CFO)
Hugh Ekberg (Pres & CEO)
Jerry Kilgore (CIO)
Michael Gannon (COO)

Subsidiaries:

CRST Flatbed Inc.   (1)
1901 Floyd Bradford Rd, Trussville, AL
35173-3140
Tel.: (205) 951-1900
Web Site: http://www.crstrecruiting.com
Sales Range: $10-24.9 Million
Emp.: 70
Provider of Long Distance Trucking Services
N.A.I.C.S.: 484121

CRST Flatbed, Inc.   (1)
3420 S 11th Ave, Eldridge, IA 52748
Tel.: (563) 285-6750
Sales Range: $10-24.9 Million
Emp.: 20
Provider of Long Distance Trucking Services
N.A.I.C.S.: 484121
Ron Maynard (Mgr-Ops)

CRST Logistics Inc.   (1)
3930 16th Ave SW, Cedar Rapids, IA
52404-2332   (100%)
Tel.: (319) 396-4400
Web Site: http://www.crstlogistics.com
Sales Range: $100-124.9 Million
Emp.: 1,000
Provider of Freight Transportation Arrangement Services
N.A.I.C.S.: 488510
Michael Gannon (Pres-Strategic Growth)
Kimberly Maes (Pres)

CRST Malone Inc.   (1)
1901 Floyd Bradford Rd, Trussville, AL
35173
Tel.: (205) 951-5960
Web Site: http://www.crstmalone.com
Logistics Consulting Servies
N.A.I.C.S.: 541614
Chuck Haffenden (VP-Safety)

Gardner Trucking, Inc.   (1)
PO Box 747, Chino, CA 91708-0747
Tel.: (909) 563-5606
Web Site: http://www.gardnertrucking.com
Sales Range: $25-49.9 Million
Emp.: 600
Trucking Service
N.A.I.C.S.: 484121
Andrea Martinez (Mgr-Billing & Payroll)
Bruce Rodriguez (Mgr-Parts)
Ivan Moret (Supvr-Night Dispatch)
Steven Miller (Mgr-Fleet Maintenance)

Pegasus Transportation, Inc.   (1)
2903 S English Station Rd, Louisville, KY
40299
Tel.: (502) 212-5510
Web Site:
     http://www.pegasustransportation.com
Sales Range: $1-9.9 Million
Emp.: 520
General Freight Trucking Services
N.A.I.C.S.: 484121

Rapid Leasing, Inc.   (1)
3930 16th Ave SW, Cedar Rapids, IA
52404-2332
Tel.: (319) 396-4400
Sales Range: $25-49.9 Million
Emp.: 220
Provider of Truck Rental & Leasing Services
N.A.I.C.S.: 532120

Specialized Transportation, Inc.   (1)
5001 US Hwy 30 W, Fort Wayne, IN 46818-
9701
Tel.: (800) 443-0940
Web Site: http://www.stidelivers.com
Logistics Consulting Servies
N.A.I.C.S.: 541614

The BESL Transfer Co. Inc.   (1)
5700 Este Ave, Cincinnati, OH 45232-1435
Tel.: (513) 242-3456
Web Site: http://www.besl.com
Sales Range: $10-24.9 Million
Emp.: 50
Trucking Service
N.A.I.C.S.: 484121
Mike Meyer (Controller)
Michael Gannon (Pres-Strategic Growth)
John M. Smith (Chm)

CRT CUSTOM PRODUCTS, INC.
7532 Hickory Hills Ct, Whites Creek,
TN 37189
Tel.: (615) 876-5490
Web Site:
     http://www.crtcustomproducts.com
Year Founded: 1979
Sales Range: $1-9.9 Million
Emp.: 50
Custom Audio, Video, Software &
Packaging Materials Mfr
N.A.I.C.S.: 333310
Jeff Pomeroy (Head-Prepress Dept)
Gnol Long (Mgr-Computer Tech)

CRT PARTNERS INC.
2343 E Broadway Blvd Ste 102, Tucson, AZ 85719
Tel.: (520) 327-7055
Sales Range: $10-24.9 Million
Emp.: 700
Fast Food Restaurant Operator
N.A.I.C.S.: 722513
Norma Hammock (Office Mgr)
Laura Olguin (Owner & CEO)

CRTS INC.
3301 Integrity Dr, Garner, NC 27529
Tel.: (919) 773-4000
Web Site: https://www.crtsinc.com
Year Founded: 1971
Sales Range: $10-24.9 Million
Emp.: 120
Trailers For Trucks, New & Used
N.A.I.C.S.: 423110
Thomas F. Crowder (CEO)
Paula Goodsell (Mgr-Parts)
Steve Eger (Mgr-Svc)

CRU DATA SECURITY GROUP, LLC
1000 SE Tech Center Dr, Vancouver,
WA 98683
Tel.: (360) 816-1800
Web Site: http://www.cru-inc.com
Year Founded: 1986
Security System Services
N.A.I.C.S.: 561621

Randal Barber (Pres & CEO)
Chris Kruell (Dir-Mktg)
Dan Bovee (VP-Strategic & Global
Alliances)
Robin Wessel (Exec VP)
Dave Kaysen (Mgr-Quality & Dir-
Engrg)

Subsidiaries:

Sunland International, LLC   (1)
1400 Dell Ave Ste A, Campbell, CA 95008
Tel.: (408) 796-5140
Sales Range: $1-9.9 Million
Emp.: 11
Computer & Computer Peripheral Equipment & Software Merchant Whslr
N.A.I.C.S.: 423430

ioSafe, Inc.   (1)
10600 Industrial Ave Ste 120, Roseville, CA
95678
Tel.: (530) 820-3090
Web Site: http://www.iosafe.com
Computer Storage Device Mfr
N.A.I.C.S.: 334112

CRUCIAL VACUUM
415 Hamburg Tpke, Wayne, NJ
07470
Tel.: (877) 750-9239
Web Site:
     http://www.crucialvacuum.com
Year Founded: 2008
Sales Range: $1-9.9 Million
Emp.: 17
Manufactures & Retails Vacuum
Cleaner Bags, Filters & Accessories
Directly to Consumers Via the Internet
N.A.I.C.S.: 335220
Kristin Leishman (Supvr-Ops & Creative)
Chad Rubin (Founder)
Cindy Yuk (Mgr-Mktg & Bus Dev)

CRUCIBLE INDUSTRIES LLC
575 State Fair Blvd, Solvay, NY
13209   NY
Web Site: https://www.crucible.com
Year Founded: 1876
Steel Mfrs
N.A.I.C.S.: 331110
Lorna E. Carpenter (VP-Admin)

CRUDUP OIL COMPANY INC.
3237 Hwy 29 N, Belton, SC 29627
Tel.: (864) 226-1585
Sales Range: $25-49.9 Million
Emp.: 8
Petroleum Bulk Stations; Convenience Stores
N.A.I.C.S.: 424710
T. G. Madden (Pres)

CRUISE AMERICA, INC.
11 W Hampton Ave, Mesa, AZ
85210-5258
Tel.: (480) 464-7300   FL
Web Site:
     https://www.cruiseamerica.com
Year Founded: 1972
Sales Range: $75-99.9 Million
Emp.: 275
Rental & Sale of Recreational Vehicles
N.A.I.C.S.: 532120
Robert A. Smalley (Pres)
Randall S. Smalley (Chm & CEO)
Eric R. Bensen (VP)

Subsidiaries:

Cruise Canada, Inc.   (1)
2980 26th St Northeast, Calgary, T1Y 6R7,
AB, Canada   (100%)
Tel.: (403) 291-4963
Web Site: http://www.cruisecanada.com
Sales Range: $10-24.9 Million
Emp.: 12
Rental of Recreation Vehicles

Cruise America, Inc.—(Continued)

N.A.I.C.S.: 532120

System Management Group   (1)
11 W Hampton Ave, Mesa, AZ
85210-5258   **(100%)**
Tel.: (480) 464-7300
Web Site: http://www.cruiseamerica.com
Sales Range: $10-24.9 Million
Emp.: 90
RV Rentals & Sales
N.A.I.C.S.: 441210

CRUISE CAR INC.
6265 E Sawgrass Rd, Sarasota, FL
34240
Tel.: (941) 929-1630
Web Site:
  http://www.cruisecarinc.com
Year Founded: 2004
Sales Range: $1-9.9 Million
Emp.: 50
Solar Powered Vehicle Mfr
N.A.I.C.S.: 336999
Adam Sulimirski (Pres)

CRUISE LINES INTERNA-TIONAL ASSOCIATION
2111 Wilson Blvd 8th Fl, Arlington, VA
22201
Tel.: (754) 444-2542   DC
Web Site: http://www.cruising.org
Year Founded: 1990
Sales Range: $10-24.9 Million
Emp.: 44
Tourism Support Services
N.A.I.C.S.: 561591
Bud Darr (Sr VP-Technical & Regula-tory Affairs)
Tom Fischetti (CFO)
Mike McGarry (Sr VP-Pub Affairs & Govt Rels)
Melissa Juelich (Mgr-Membership Ops-Australasia)
Joel Katz (Mng Dir-Australasia)
Bo Larsen (Sr VP-Strategic Partner-ships)
John Mancuso (VP-IT)
Marla Phaneuf (VP-Industry Rels)
Christian Savel (VP-Res & Bus Ana-lytics)
Peter Kollar (Head-Training & Dev-Intl)
Troy Ashman (Mgr-Training & Dev-Australasia)
Megan King (Sr VP-Strategic Comm)
Ross Walker (Dir-Digital & Social Strategy-Global)
Louise Prior (Dir-PR-London)
Kelly Craighead (Pres & CEO)
Pierfrancesco Vago (Chm-Global)
Jason Park (Sr VP-Global Govt Af-fairs & Mng Dir-North America)

CRUISERS GRILL
319 23rd Ave S, Jacksonville Beach,
FL 32250
Tel.: (904) 270-0356
Web Site:
  https://www.cruisersgrill.com
Year Founded: 1996
Sales Range: $1-9.9 Million
Emp.: 120
Fast-Food Burgers & Tex-Mex Res-taurant
N.A.I.C.S.: 722513
Robert Handmaker (Owner & CEO)
Michelle Baum (Mgr)

CRUM ELECTRIC SUPPLY CO., INC.
1165 W English Ave, Casper, WY
82601-1618
Tel.: (307) 266-1278   WY
Web Site: https://www.crum.com
Year Founded: 1976
Sales Range: $10-24.9 Million

Emp.: 110
Supplier of Electrical Equipment & Part to Electrical Contractor Industrial User Utility & Equipment Builder Distr
N.A.I.C.S.: 423610
David H. Crum (CEO)
Jeff Hockin (Pres)
Jim Roden (VP-Ops)
Chuck Anfinson (Mgr-Credit)
Kent Nelson (Mgr-Cody)
Mark Harkins (Mgr-Inventory)
Cheryl Yarkosky (Branch Mgr)
Andy Schroeder (Dir-Project Sls)
Kevin Collins (Mgr-Casper)

CRUMBLEY PAPER CO. INC.
1227 N 1st Ave, Laurel, MS 39440
Tel.: (601) 649-3431
Sales Range: $10-24.9 Million
Emp.: 40
Distribute Dry Goods
N.A.I.C.S.: 424490
Louis S. Crumbley Jr. (Pres)

CRUNCH PAK
300 Sunset Hwy, Cashmere, WA
98815
Tel.: (509) 782-2807
Web Site:
  https://www.crunchpak.com
Year Founded: 2000
Sales Range: $25-49.9 Million
Emp.: 300
Postharvest Crop Activity Related Services
N.A.I.C.S.: 115114
Tony Freytag (Founder & Dir-Natl Mktg)

CRUNCHY LOGISTICS
379 W Michigan St Ste 206, Orlando,
FL 32806
Tel.: (407) 476-2044
Web Site: http://www.crunchy.co
Year Founded: 2008
Sales Range: $1-9.9 Million
Emp.: 15
Technology Firm
N.A.I.C.S.: 541690
Neil Dufva (CEO)
Adi Khanna (CFO)
Leo Moretti (COO)

CRUSHING EQUIPMENT SO-LUTIONS, LLC
226 County Rd 3341, Paradise, TX
76073
Tel.: (720) 580-6824
Web Site: https://www.cesrock.com
Commercial & Industrial Equipment Whslr
N.A.I.C.S.: 423830
Bruce Wagner (Pres & CEO)

Subsidiaries:

Bayne Mineral Systems, Inc.   (1)
6829 K Ave Ste 102, Plano, TX 75074-2542
Tel.: (972) 578-8591
Sales Range: $1-9.9 Million
Emp.: 5
Construction & Mining Machinery Whslr
N.A.I.C.S.: 423810

CRUSOE ENERGY SYSTEMS LLC
1641 California St, Denver, CO
80202
Tel.: (720) 327-8070   DE
Web Site:
  https://www.crusoeenergy.com
Year Founded: 2018
Emp.: 170
Information Technology Consulting Services
N.A.I.C.S.: 519290
Chase Lochmiller (Founder & CEO)

Subsidiaries:

Easter-Owens Electric Company   (1)
6692 Fig St, Arvada, CO 80004
Tel.: (303) 431-0111
Web Site: http://www.easter-owens.com
Sales Range: $1-9.9 Million
Emp.: 48
Current-Carrying Wiring Devices
N.A.I.C.S.: 335931
William Easter (Chm & CEO)
David A. Easter (CEO & Pres)

CRUSTBUSTER-SPEED KING, INC.
2300 E Trial St, Dodge City, KS
67801-9023
Tel.: (620) 227-7106   KS
Web Site: http://www.crustbuster.com
Year Founded: 1960
Sales Range: $100-124.9 Million
Emp.: 95
Retailer & Whslr of Farm Tillage, Seeding & Other Farming Equipment
N.A.I.C.S.: 423820
Donald F. Hornung (Pres)
Walter Ludt (Sec & Controller)
Eric Dawson (Engr-Mechanical)

CRUTCHFIELD CORPORATION
1 Crutchfield Park, Charlottesville, VA
22911-9097
Tel.: (434) 817-1000
Web Site:
  https://www.crutchfield.com
Year Founded: 1974
Sales Range: $200-249.9 Million
Emp.: 500
Mail Order & E-Commerce Services
N.A.I.C.S.: 449210
Rick Souder (Exec VP-Mdsg)
Travis Bingler (Acct Mgr-Comml)
Jay McCartney (Dir-Internet Mktg)
Keri Crum (Dir-Web IT & Design)

CRUTTENDEN PARTNERS, LLC
4600 Campus Dr, Newport Beach,
CA 92660-1801
Tel.: (949) 399-9000   CA
Web Site:
  http://www.cruttendenpartners.com
Year Founded: 1998
Private Equity & Venture Capital Firm
N.A.I.C.S.: 523150
Rian Cruttenden (CFO)
Jeffrey Cruttenden (Partner)
Alexander Cruttenden (Mgr)
Chris Cruttenden (Mgr)
Walter W. Cruttenden III (Pres)

CRUX CAPITAL LTD
3838 Oak Lawn Ave Ste 430, Dallas,
TX 75219
Tel.: (469) 389-1244
Web Site: https://www.crux-cap.com
Emp.: 100
Investment Services
N.A.I.C.S.: 523999

Subsidiaries:

Superscapes, Inc.   (1)
1500 Capital Dr, Carrollton, TX 75006
Tel.: (972) 712-0353
Web Site: https://superscapes.net
Landscaping Services
N.A.I.C.S.: 561730

Subsidiary (Domestic):

Newman Lawn Care Inc.   (2)
2771 FM 36 N, Merit, TX 75458
Tel.: (903) 355-0983
Web Site: http://www.newmanlawncare.com
Landscaping Services
N.A.I.C.S.: 561730
Brandon Newman (Owner)

CRUZ CONTRACTORS LLC

952 Holmdel Rd, Holmdel, NJ 07733
Tel.: (732) 946-8400
Web Site:
  http://www.cruzcontractors.com
Sales Range: $50-74.9 Million
Emp.: 120
Sewer Line Construction Services
N.A.I.C.S.: 237110
Tony Cardoso (Mgr-Field Ops)
Joe Salgado (Project Mgr)

CRUZ MANAGEMENT INC.
434 Massachusetts Ave Ste 300,
Boston, MA 02118-3522
Tel.: (617) 247-2389
Rev.: $11,900,000
Emp.: 35
Land Subdividers & Developers, Residential
N.A.I.C.S.: 531110
John Cruz (Pres)

CRUZ/KRAVETZ:IDEAS
26 W Olive Ave Ste 910, Burbank,
CA 91505
Tel.: (310) 312-3630   CA
Year Founded: 1991
Rev.: $20,000,000
Emp.: 25
Advetising Agency
N.A.I.C.S.: 541810
Carl J. Kravetz (Chm)
Maite Quilez D'Amico (Pres)
Melissa Diaz (Controller & Mgr-Fin)
Cynthia Lardizabal (Mgr-HR)
Susan Perez (Dir-Media)

CRW CORPORATION
795 Marshall Ave, Williston, VT
05495
Tel.: (802) 658-1700
Web Site: https://www.woodscrw.com
Sales Range: $50-74.9 Million
Emp.: 40
Cranes & Earth Moving Equipment
N.A.I.C.S.: 333120
Chris Palmer (Pres-Mobile Cranes & Lifts Sls-Earth Moving Equipment)
Mike Sylvia (VP-Crane Sls)
Steve McKnight (Mgr-Parts)
Joe Baccari (Mgr-Svc)
Tom Gion (Mgr-Parts)
Bobby Wood (COO-Product Support)
Jonathan Beckwith (Mgr-Svcs)
Andy Racine (Mgr-Rental & Traffic)

CRW PARTS INC.
1211 68th St, Baltimore, MD 21237
Tel.: (410) 866-3306
Web Site: https://www.crwparts.com
Rev.: $20,600,000
Emp.: 130
Automotive Supplies & Parts
N.A.I.C.S.: 423120
David Norris Willis (Pres)

CRW, INC.
3716 S Elyria Rd, Shreve, OH 44676
Tel.: (330) 264-3785   OH
Web Site:
  http://www.crwfreightmgmt.com
Year Founded: 1988
Holding Company; General Freight Trucking Services
N.A.I.C.S.: 551112

Subsidiaries:

CRW Freight Management Services,
Inc.   (1)
3716 S Elyria Rd, Shreve, OH 44676
Tel.: (330) 264-3785
Web Site: http://www.crwfreightmgmt.com
General Freight Trucking Services
N.A.I.C.S.: 484121

CRY -TECHINC
85 Winter St, Hanover, MA 02339

Tel.: (781) 826-5600
Sales Range: $25-49.9 Million
Emp.: 40
Mfr of Fluoro Rubbers
N.A.I.C.S.: 325212
Bob Berg *(Gen Mgr)*

CRYE-LEIKE INC.
6525 Quail Hollow Rd, Memphis, TN
38120-1325
Tel.: (901) 756-8900
Web Site: https://www.crye-leike.com
Year Founded: 1976
Sales Range: $50-74.9 Million
Emp.: 504
Provider of Real Estate Agency Services
N.A.I.C.S.: 531210
Harold E. Crye *(Chm & CEO)*
Gurtej Sodhi *(Chief Info & Ops Officer)*
Steve Brown *(Pres-Residential Sls)*
Joyce Friedman *(VP)*

CRYOGENIC INDUSTRIAL SO-LUTIONS, INC.
25918 Hardin Store Rd, Magnolia, TX
77354
Tel.: (281) 470-2512
Web Site:
   http://www.cryoindsolutions.com
Transport Trailers Equipment Repairs
& Lease Fleet Services
N.A.I.C.S.: 488999
Edward Leon *(Pres)*

Subsidiaries:

Alloy Custom Products, LLC   **(1)**
9701 State Rd 25 N, Lafayette, IN 47905
Tel.: (765) 564-4684
Web Site: http://www.cryoindsolutions.com
Cryogenic Trailer Mfr
N.A.I.C.S.: 333924
Edward Leon *(Pres)*

CRYOGENIC VESSEL ALTER-NATIVES
1301 Transport Dr, Baytown, TX
77523-7523
Tel.: (281) 738-2863
Web Site: http://www.cvatanks.com
Metal Tank Mfr
N.A.I.C.S.: 332420
Keith Hall *(Mgr-Engrg-LNG & Specialty Products)*

CRYPTOSIGN INC.
626 E 1820 N, Orem, UT 84097
Tel.: (801) 592-3000   DE
Web Site: http://www.cryptosign.com
Rev.: $2,931
Assets: $406,556
Liabilities: $115,225
Net Worth: $291,331
Earnings: ($822,876)
Fiscal Year-end: 06/30/15
Investment Services
N.A.I.C.S.: 523999
Soren Jonassen *(Chm)*
Robert K. Bench *(Pres & CFO)*
Lars Nielsen *(COO & VP)*
Stephen Abu *(VP-Corp Dev)*
Brian Palm Svaneeng Mertz *(CEO)*
Morten Krarup *(Chief Bus Dev Officer)*

CRYSTAL CABINET WORKS, INC.
1100 Crystal Dr, Princeton, MN
55371-3350
Tel.: (763) 389-4187   MN
Web Site: https://crystalcabinets.com
Year Founded: 1947
Sales Range: $25-49.9 Million
Emp.: 345
Mfr of Custom Cabinets
N.A.I.C.S.: 337110

Jeffrey R. Hammer *(Pres)*
Robert Nordland *(CFO)*
Peggy Talberg *(VP-Sls & Mktg)*
Sandy Niergarten *(Dir-Mktg)*

CRYSTAL CATHEDRAL MINIS-TRIES INC.
12921 Lewis St, Garden Grove, CA
92840
Tel.: (714) 971-4000   CA
Web Site:
   http://www.crystalcathedral.org
Year Founded: 1970
Sales Range: $600-649.9 Million
Emp.: 200
Motion Picture, Video Production &
Church Ministry Services
N.A.I.C.S.: 512110
Robert H. Schuller *(Founder)*

Subsidiaries:

New Hope Counseling   **(1)**
12141 Lewis St, Garden Grove, CA
92840-4627   **(100%)**
Tel.: (714) 639-4673
Web Site: http://www.newhopenow.org
Rev.: $290,000
Emp.: 4
Provider of Counseling Services
N.A.I.C.S.: 624190

CRYSTAL CLEAR DIGITAL MARKETING, LLC
5750 Major Blvd Ste 500, Orlando,
FL 32819
Web Site:
   http://www.crystalcleardigital.com
Year Founded: 2013
Sales Range: $1-9.9 Million
Emp.: 61
Digital Marketing Services
N.A.I.C.S.: 541810
Adam DeGraide *(Co-Founder & CEO)*
Tim Sawyer *(Co-Founder & Pres)*
Joe Amaral *(Co-Founder & COO)*
Jacob Horn *(Sr VP-Software Ops)*
Audrey Neff *(Mktg Dir)*

CRYSTAL CLEAR TECHNOLO-GIES, INC.
5555 Central Ave, Saint Petersburg,
FL 33710
Tel.: (727) 321-8888
Web Site:
   https://www.crystalcleartec.com
Year Founded: 2002
Sales Range: $10-24.9 Million
Emp.: 31
Environmental & Technology Consulting Services
N.A.I.C.S.: 541620
Crystal Culberston *(CEO)*
Jeremy Martin *(VP-Pro Svcs)*
John Lescarbeau *(COO & VP-Bus Dev)*
Joseph Culbertson III *(Pres & VP-Strategic Product Sourcing)*

CRYSTAL DISTRIBUTION SER-VICES
1656 Sycamore St, Waterloo, IA
50703
Tel.: (319) 274-4555
Web Site: https://www.crystaldist.com
Sales Range: $75-99.9 Million
Emp.: 50
Warehousing, Cold Storage or Refrigerated
N.A.I.C.S.: 493120
Tom Poe *(Pres)*
Don Johnston *(VP-Ops)*

CRYSTAL FINISHING SYS-TEMS, INC.
2610 Ross Ave, Schofield, WI 54476

Tel.: (715) 355-5351
Web Site:
   http://www.crystalfinishing.com
Sales Range: $10-24.9 Million
Emp.: 750
Metal Coating Engraving & Allied Services Mfr
N.A.I.C.S.: 332812
Mark Matthiae *(Pres)*
Denis Crevier *(CEO)*

CRYSTAL FLASH LP OF MICHIGAN
1754 Alpine Ave NW, Grand Rapids,
MI 49504
Tel.: (616) 363-4851   MI
Web Site:
   https://www.crystalflash.com
Year Founded: 1932
Emp.: 250
Marine Fueling, Pump Out Services &
Diesel, Gasoline & Propane Bulk
Delivery
N.A.I.C.S.: 457210
Tom Olive *(Pres & CEO)*
Charles Kroll *(CFO)*

CRYSTAL KOBE LTD. INC.
1407 Broadway 7 Fl, New York, NY
10018-5007
Tel.: (212) 391-2229
Web Site:
   http://www.kblgroupinc.com
Year Founded: 1985
Sales Range: $10-24.9 Million
Emp.: 50
Clothing for Women, Children, Juniors & Infants Mfr
N.A.I.C.S.: 424350
Steven Begleiter *(CEO)*

CRYSTAL MOTOR CAR CO. INC.
1035 S Suncoast Blvd, Homosassa,
FL 34448
Tel.: (352) 795-1515
Web Site:
   http://www.crystalautos.com
Rev.: $55,800,000
Emp.: 200
Automobiles, New & Used
N.A.I.C.S.: 441110
Steve Lamb *(Pres)*
Mark Pickett *(CFO)*
Jewel Lamb *(VP)*

CRYSTAL MOTOR EXPRESS INC.
10 Kimball Ln, Lynnfield, MA 01940
Tel.: (781) 245-6988
Web Site:
   http://www.crystalmotorexpress.com
Rev.: $12,101,513
Emp.: 115
Local Trucking without Storage
N.A.I.C.S.: 484110
Ronald Masiello *(Pres)*
Jen Bokav *(Dir-Sls & Mktg)*
Paul Amico *(Supvr-Ops)*
Sue Pinkham *(Mgr-AR)*
Debra Farrell *(Mgr-HR)*

CRYSTAL OAKS
1500 Calvary Church Rd, Festus, MO
63028
Tel.: (636) 933-1818   MO
Web Site:
   https://www.crystaloaks.org
Year Founded: 2006
Sales Range: $10-24.9 Million
Emp.: 349
Elder Care Services
N.A.I.C.S.: 623312
Jennifer Barnes *(Asst Dir-Nursing)*
Linda Twomey *(CFO)*
Paul Poss *(Mgr-Building Ops)*

Amy Basler *(Dir-Housekeeping)*
Amy Daniels *(Dir-Social Svcs)*
Cheryl Sazama *(Dir-Rehab Svcs)*
Jim Arnold *(CEO)*
Kelly Anderson *(Dir-Activities)*
Paula Thurman *(Dir-Dietary)*
Tammy Cashion *(Dir-Nursing)*
Bill Dodson *(Chm)*

CRYSTAL PALMS BEACH RE-SORT
11605 Gulf Blvd, Treasure Island, FL
33706
Tel.: (727) 360-0037
Web Site:
   http://www.crystalpalmsbeach.com
Sales Range: $1-9.9 Million
Hotel Operations
N.A.I.C.S.: 721110
Pete Chenhall *(Gen Mgr)*

CRYSTAL PROMOTIONS INC.
1820 S Grand Ave, Los Angeles, CA
90015
Tel.: (213) 746-4740
Web Site:
   http://www.crystalpromotions.com
Rev.: $18,693,409
Emp.: 30
Electrical Appliances, Television &
Radio
N.A.I.C.S.: 423620
Melanie Lleonart *(Mgr)*

CRYSTAL RUN VILLAGE, INC.
601 Stony Ford Rd, Middletown, NY
10941
Tel.: (845) 692-4444   NY
Web Site: http://www.crvi.org
Year Founded: 1978
Sales Range: $25-49.9 Million
Emp.: 1,005
Intellectual Disability Assistance Services
N.A.I.C.S.: 623210
Michael J. Flynn *(Pres)*

CRYSTAL SODA WATER CO.
425 Franklin Ave, Scranton, PA
18503
Tel.: (570) 347-5661
Rev.: $22,600,000
Emp.: 48
Iced Tea & Fruit Drinks, Bottled &
Canned
N.A.I.C.S.: 312111

CRYSTAL SPRINGS APPAREL LLC
216 Bellewether Pass, Ridgeland, MS
39157-8762
Tel.: (601) 892-4551
Rev.: $25,000,000
Emp.: 27
Men's & Boys' Sports & Polo Shirts
N.A.I.C.S.: 315250
Michael Nigro *(VP)*

CRYSTAL SPRINGS RESORT
2 Chamonix Dr & State Rte 94, Vernon, NJ 07462
Tel.: (973) 827-5996
Web Site:
   http://www.crystalgolfresort.com
Golf, Skiing, Water Park & Spa Resort Developer, Owner & Operator
N.A.I.C.S.: 721110
Andrew Mulvihill *(Pres)*
Chelsea Vander Groef *(Mgr-PR & Social Media)*
Alissa Winters *(Mktg Mgr)*
Natasha Wright *(Mgr-Website Dev)*

Subsidiaries:

Mountain Creek Resort, Inc.   **(1)**
200 State Rte 94, Vernon, NJ 07462

Crystal Springs Resort—(Continued)

Tel.: (973) 827-2000
Web Site: http://www.mountaincreek.com
Sales Range: $125-149.9 Million
Ski Resort Operator
N.A.I.C.S.: 713920
Bill Benneyan (Pres & COO)
Hugh Reynolds (Dir-Sls & Mktg)
Julie Koop (Dir-Resort Svcs)

CRYSTAL STAIRS, INC.
5110 W Goldleaf Cir Ste 150, Los
Angeles, CA 90056-1282
Tel.: (323) 299-8998   CA
Web Site:
   https://www.crystalstairs.org
Year Founded: 1980
Sales Range: $75-99.9 Million
Emp.: 274
Child Care Services
N.A.I.C.S.: 624110
Karen Hill Scott (Co-Founder)

CRYSTAL VALLEY COOPERA-TIVE
721 W Humphrey, Lake Crystal, MN
56055
Tel.: (507) 726-6455
Web Site:
   http://www.crystalvalley.coop
Year Founded: 1927
Sales Range: $75-99.9 Million
Emp.: 150
Grains
N.A.I.C.S.: 424510
Roger Kienholz (Pres & CEO)
Todd Wihlm (Controller)
Ashley Leivermann (Chief HR Officer)
Tim Lewer (Sec)
Paul Lange (Dir-Safety)
Randy Hulke (Mgr-Credit)
Jon Langland (CTO)
Dan Jones (Chm)
Mark Eggimann (Vice Chm)

CRYSTAL WINDOW & DOOR SYSTEMS
31-10 Whitestone Expy, Flushing, NY
11354
Tel.: (718) 961-7300
Web Site:
   https://www.crystalwindows.com
Sales Range: $25-49.9 Million
Emp.: 280
Sales of Window Glass, Clear & Col-
ored
N.A.I.C.S.: 327211
Thomas Chen (Founder & Chm)
Steve Chen (Pres)
Mason Wang (Dir-Mgmt Info Sys)
Julian Tu (Engr)

CRYSTAL-PIERZ MARINE INC.
5712 Lakeland Ave N, Crystal, MN
55429
Tel.: (952) 533-1655
Year Founded: 1956
Sales Range: $25-49.9 Million
Emp.: 225
Boat Dealers
N.A.I.C.S.: 441222
Myron Kujawa (CEO)
Paul Lauer (Bus Mgr)
Tim Daniels (Controller)

CRYSTEEL TRUCK EQUIP-MENT, INC.
52248 Ember Rd, Lake Crystal, MN
56055
Tel.: (507) 726-6041   MN
Web Site:
   https://www.crysteeltruck.com
Year Founded: 1974
Sales Range: $10-24.9 Million
Emp.: 52

Truck Parts, Accessories & Equip-
ment Distr
N.A.I.C.S.: 423120
Chad Wiens (Pres & CEO)

CS AUTO, LTD.
4220 W Expy 83, McAllen, TX 78501-
7435
Tel.: (956) 687-5286   TX
Web Site:
   http://www.southtexasgmc.com
Sales Range: $10-24.9 Million
Emp.: 50
New & Used Car Dealer
N.A.I.C.S.: 441110
Victor Pardo (Gen Mgr)
Shelby Longoria (Owner)

CS BUSINESS SYSTEMS INC.
1236 Main St, Buffalo, NY 14209
Tel.: (716) 886-6521
Web Site: http://www.csbusiness.com
Sales Range: $50-74.9 Million
Emp.: 45
Computers, Peripherals & Software
N.A.I.C.S.: 423430
Michael I. Choo (Pres)
Carl Adolf (Sr Acct Mgr)
Gina Gabryszak (Mgr-Acctg)
Peter Bartula (Sr Acct Exec)
kevin Pietersen (Dir-Enterprise Pro-
grams)

CS MANUFACTURING, INC.
299 W Cherry St, Cedar Springs, MI
49319
Tel.: (616) 696-2772
Web Site: https://csmanufacturing.us
Year Founded: 1986
Sales Range: $10-24.9 Million
Emp.: 105
Plastics Product Mfr
N.A.I.C.S.: 326199
Tim Mabie (Pres)
Brendan Fitzgerald (VP)
Todd McNeil (Mgr-Engrg)
Jeremy Casarez (Mgr-Matls)
Tracy Bongard (Mgr-Quality)
Wil McClurken (Mgr-Production)
Steve Brott (Mgr-HR)
Jason Johnson (Mgr-IT)

CS MYERS & SON INC.
650 W Cherry Ln, State College, PA
16803
Tel.: (814) 238-3081   PA
Web Site:
   https://www.csmyersandson.com
Year Founded: 1985
Sales Range: $10-24.9 Million
Emp.: 42
Provider of Heating, Cooling & Petro-
leum
N.A.I.C.S.: 457210
Gary E. Myers (Pres)

CS TECHNOLOGY, INC.
1 Penn Plz 54th Fl, New York, NY
10119
Tel.: (646) 473-2400
Web Site:
   http://www.cstechnology.com
Year Founded: 1992
Sales Range: $50-74.9 Million
Emp.: 152
Scientific & Technical Consulting Ser-
vices
N.A.I.C.S.: 541690
John P. Rosato (Founder, Chm &
CEO)
David Murray (Chief Advisory Officer)
William R. Angle (Dir-Mission Critical
Engrg)

CS2 ADVERTISING

400 Union Ave, Memphis, TN 38103-
3216
Tel.: (901) 526-6220
Web Site:
   http://www.cs2advertising.com
Year Founded: 1987
Rev.: $18,000,000
Emp.: 40
Advetising Agency
N.A.I.C.S.: 541810
Donna Gordy (Pres)
Eric Melkent (Exec VP)
David Maddox (Art Dir)
Walter Rose (Sr VP & Dir-Creative)
Troy McCall (Art Dir)
Wil Huh (Dir-Media)
Kenny Patrick (Dir-Art)
Josh Harper (Copywriter)

CSA FRATERNAL LIFE
2050 Finley Rd Ste 70, Lombard, IL
60148
Tel.: (630) 472-0500   IL
Web Site: https://www.csalife.com
Year Founded: 1911
Sales Range: $10-24.9 Million
Emp.: 19
Fraternity Organization
N.A.I.C.S.: 813410
Matthew Koski (Sec)

CSA HOLDINGS INC.
137 Benchmark Rd Ste 218, Avon,
CO 81620
Tel.: (720) 536-5824   CO
Sales Range: $1-9.9 Million
Security Systems for Cannabis Indus-
try
N.A.I.C.S.: 561621
Thomas Sciliano (Pres)

CSA SERVICE SOLUTIONS, LLC
9208 Waterford Ctr Blvd Ste 150,
Austin, TX 78758
Tel.: (877) 228-6533
Nationwide Technical Services & Pro-
fessional Solutions Provider; Labora-
tory & Healthcare, Self-Service &
Critical Power Sectors
N.A.I.C.S.: 561491

Subsidiaries:

CSA Franchising, LLC   (1)
270 Davids Dr, Wilmington, OH 45177-2491
Web Site: https://www.emsar.com
Professional, Scientific & Technical Services
N.A.I.C.S.: 541990

CSBH LLC
2442 New Dorset Cir, Powhatan, VA
23139
Tel.: (804) 598-9101   DE
Holding Company
N.A.I.C.S.: 551112
Douglas Mitchell (Mgr)
F. Edward Urbine Jr. (Chm)

Subsidiaries:

New Horizon Bank, N.A.   (1)
2501 Anderson Hwy, Powhatan, VA 23139-
7508
Tel.: (804) 302-4849
Web Site: http://www.newhorizonbank.com
Commercial Banking
N.A.I.C.S.: 522110
Douglas Mitchell (Pres & CEO)
Brian K. Grizzard (Chief Lending Officer)
F. Edward Urbine Jr. (Chm)

CSC GENERATION HOLD-INGS, INC.
8450 Broadway, Merrillville, IN
46410   DE
Web Site:
   https://www.cscgeneration.com
Year Founded: 2017

Holding Company; Online Retail
Brand Investor & Operator
N.A.I.C.S.: 551112
Justin Yoshimura (Co-Founder, Chm
& CEO)

CSE CORPORATION
600 Seco Rd, Monroeville, PA 15146
Tel.: (412) 856-9200
Web Site:
   http://www.csecorporation.com
Sales Range: $10-24.9 Million
Emp.: 100
Mfr of Safety Products
N.A.I.C.S.: 335314
Vince Trotnick (Engr-Electrical)
Paul Ream (Mgr-Chem Lab)
Karl Baumgart (Supvr-Inventory Con-
trol)
Matthew Sudak (Engr-Mechanical)

CSE INSURANCE GROUP
2121 N California Blvd Ste 900, Wal-
nut Creek, CA 94596-3501
Tel.: (415) 274-7800   DE
Web Site:
   http://www.cseinsurance.com
Year Founded: 1951
Sales Range: $25-49.9 Million
Emp.: 130
Insurance Holding Company
N.A.I.C.S.: 524126
David Carmany (Sr VP-Product &
Underwriting)
Marcus Linden (Pres & CEO)
Mark Chequer (CIO)
Randy Farless (Sr VP-Sls & Mktg)
Ryan McAllister (Chief Actuary & Asst
VP)

Subsidiaries:

CSE Safeguard Insurance
Company   (1)
2121 N California Blvd Ste 555, Walnut
Creek, CA 94596-3501
Tel.: (925) 817-6300
Property & Casualty Insurance Services
N.A.I.C.S.: 524210

Civil Service Employees Insurance
Company   (1)
2121 N California Blvd Ste 555, Walnut
Creek, CA 94596-3501   (100%)
Tel.: (925) 817-6300
Web Site: http://www.cseinsurance.com
Property & Casualty Insurance
N.A.I.C.S.: 524126
David Brinker (Exec VP-Products & Sup-
port)
David Carmany (Sr VP-Technical Ops)
Mark Chequer (CIO)
Randy Farless (Sr VP-Sls & Mktg)
Richard Rey (Pres & CEO)
Michael Suzuki (VP-Technical Ops)
James Van Farowe (VP-Claims)
Patrick Wong (Gen Counsel & Sec)

CSENGE ADVISORY GROUP, LLC
4755 E Bay Dr, Clearwater, FL 33764
Tel.: (727) 437-6000
Web Site: https://www.csenge.com
Sales Range: $25-49.9 Million
Emp.: 15
Investment Advisory Services
N.A.I.C.S.: 523940
John Csenge (Founder & Mng Dir)
Stephen J. Csenge (Partner)
Eric Caisse (Dir-Investments)
Kelly Annenos (Dir-Client Svcs)

Subsidiaries:

Csenge Advisory Group, LLC   (1)
470 Johnson Rd Ste 140, Washington, PA
15301
Tel.: (724) 228-9910
Investment Advisory Services
N.A.I.C.S.: 523940
Kristin Barr (Mgr-Ops & Compliance)

CSG GLOBAL
450 Colwell Ln, Conshohocken, PA 19428
Web Site: http://www.csggc.com
Year Founded: 2004
Sales Range: $1-9.9 Million
Emp.: 28
Voice & Data Consulting
N.A.I.C.S.: 541690
Cate Weaver (Co-Founder)
Stephen Maleno (Co-Founder)

CSHQA, INC.
CW Moore Plz Bldg 250 S 5th St, Boise, ID 83702
Tel.: (208) 343-4635
Web Site: http://www.cshqa.com
Rev.: $17,600,000
Emp.: 200
Architectural Svcs
N.A.I.C.S.: 541310
Kent Allen Hanway (Pres)
John D. Maulin (Exec VP)
K. K. Lipsey (Dir-Bus Dev)
Jim Otradosky (Sec)
Amy K. Dockter (Treas)
Andrea Kier (Sr Coord-Mktg)

CSI ACQUISITION CORP.
645 W 200 N, North Salt Lake, UT 84054
Tel.: (801) 936-8082
Web Site:
https://www.companionsystem.com
Year Founded: 1980
Rev.: $20,900,000
Emp.: 120
Computer Peripheral Equipment Mfr
N.A.I.C.S.: 334118
John Hansen (VP)
Al Tiley (Pres)
Diane Williams (CFO)
Sally Tiley (CEO)

CSI HOLDINGS INC.
4850 E St Rd Ste 230 Feasterville, Trevose, PA 19053-6655
Tel.: (215) 357-4400
Web Site: http://www.ceinetwork.com
Sales Range: $10-24.9 Million
Emp.: 350
Holding Company
N.A.I.C.S.: 551112
Wayne G. Smolda (CEO)
Claudia B. Smolda (Treas)
James A. Tornetta (Pres)

Subsidiaries:

Collision Services International Inc. **(1)**
1864 Chews Landing Rd, Blackwood, NJ 08012-5039 **(100%)**
Tel.: (609) 228-1200
Rev.: $1,200,000
Emp.: 9
Top & Body Repair & Paint Shops
N.A.I.C.S.: 811121

CollisionMax of Cinnaminson **(1)**
811 Route 130 S, Cinnaminson, NJ 08077 **(100%)**
Tel.: (856) 829-1982
Web Site: http://www.collisionmax.com
Sales Range: $10-24.9 Million
Emp.: 12
Auto Body Repair & Maintenance Services
N.A.I.C.S.: 811121
Paul Cardoso (Reg VP)
Jim DiPasquale (Reg VP)

East Coast Fleet Service Corporation **(1)**
1840 Grant Ave, Philadelphia, PA 19115-4305 **(100%)**
Tel.: (215) 676-9800
Sales Range: $10-24.9 Million
Emp.: 12
Top & Body Repair & Paint Shops
N.A.I.C.S.: 811121

First And Ten Inc. **(1)**

2034 Grant Ave, Philadelphia, PA 19115-4355 **(100%)**
Tel.: (215) 676-7400
Sales Range: $10-24.9 Million
Emp.: 15
Top & Body Repair & Paint Shops
N.A.I.C.S.: 811121

The CEI Group Inc. **(1)**
4850 E St Rd Ste 200, Feasterville Trevose, PA 19053-6646 **(100%)**
Tel.: (215) 364-8237
Web Site: http://www.ceinetwork.com
Sales Range: $25-49.9 Million
Emp.: 250
Collision Mangement Services
N.A.I.C.S.: 524292
Wayne Smolda (Owner)
Bob Glose (Sr VP)
James Pritz (Dir-Application Dev)
Steve Colonnello (Dir-Risk & Safety Applications)
Bob Marriott (Dir-Technical Infrastructure & Sys)
Ken Latzko (VP-Sls & Mktg)
Carol Gillespie (Sr Dir-Ops & Trng Dev)
Kathy Latzko (VP-Human Capital Ops)
Jen Redanauer (Dir-HR & Facilities)
Eliot Bensel (VP-Acct Dev)
Randy Denmyer (VP-Accident Mgmt Svcs)
Chris Villella (VP-Strategic Relationship Mgmt)

CSI POWERLINE
2221 W Pecos Rd Ste 2, Chandler, AZ 85224
Tel.: (480) 820-8663
Web Site:
http://www.csipowerline.com
Year Founded: 2004
Sales Range: $10-24.9 Million
Emp.: 100
Electrical Contractor
N.A.I.C.S.: 238210
Phil Panek (CEO)

CSI WORLDWIDE INC.
40 Regency Plz, Glen Mills, PA 19342
Tel.: (610) 558-4500
Web Site: http://www.planetcsi.com
Sales Range: $10-24.9 Million
Emp.: 10
Trade Show Arrangement
N.A.I.C.S.: 561920
Stephen F. Cahill (Pres)
Brian Panza (Mgr-Dallas, San Antonio & Houston)
Michael Santarpia (Mgr-Trade Show Div)
Jeff Centrowitz (Mgr-Miami)
Doug Haynes (Mgr-Washington, Baltimore & Philadelphia)
Karen Clove (Mgr-Las Vegas)
Alex Hill (Mgr-Los Angeles, Anaheim & San Diego)
John Abernathy (Mgr-Atlanta)
Dorothy Navera (Mgr)

CSL CAPITAL MANAGEMENT, LLC
700 Louisiana St Ste 2700, Houston, TX 77002
Tel.: (281) 407-0686
Web Site: http://www.cslenergy.com
Year Founded: 2008
Privater Equity Firm
N.A.I.C.S.: 523999
Charles S. Leykum (Founder)
Gerald C. Cimador (CFO)
Andrew F. Gould (Partner)

Subsidiaries:

Vericor Power Systems LLC **(1)**
3625 Brookside Pkwy Ste 500, Alpharetta, GA 30022
Tel.: (770) 569-8800
Web Site: http://www.vericor.com
Sales Range: $25-49.9 Million
Emp.: 35
Marine Gas Turbines Mfr & Distr

N.A.I.C.S.: 333611
Troy Hoyte (CFO)
Richard S. Clinton (Pres & CEO)
Umberto Marseglia (CMO & VP-Oil & Gas)
Shannon Rogers (VP-Programs & Aftermarket)
Glenn Duffard Jr. (VP-Supply Chain)

CSM COMPANIES, INC.
5100 Eastpark Blvd Ste 210, Madison, WI 53718
Tel.: (608) 241-5616
Web Site:
http://www.csmcompaniesinc.com
Year Founded: 1978
Sales Range: $150-199.9 Million
Emp.: 190
New & Used Truck Sales, Rental, Leasing, Fleet Maintenance & Financial Services
N.A.I.C.S.: 423110
Brett Nelson (Mgr-Svc)
Todd Blomberg (Mgr-Svc)
Tim Johnson (VP)
Dennis R. Petzke (VP & Gen Mgr)
Walter Hoefs (Mgr-Svc)
James Miller (Pres)

CSM CORPORATION
500 Washington Ave S Ste 3000, Minneapolis, MN 55415
Tel.: (612) 395-7000
Web Site: https://www.csmcorp.net
Year Founded: 1976
Rev.: $598,000,000
Emp.: 125
Acquisition, Development, Leasing, Management & Ownership of Real Estate Assets
N.A.I.C.S.: 531110
Gary Holmes (Pres & CEO)
John Ferrier (VP-Architecture)
Michael C. Coolidge (Sr VP-Real Estate & Lodging Dev)
Chris Fodor (CFO)
Scott Moe (VP-Leasing & Dev)
Brian Averbeck (Dir-Comml Properties)
Brian Schwarz (VP-Residential & ExecuStay Corp Housing)
Steve Schlundt (Pres-Lodging & Residential)
Peter Kilbourne (VP-Ops)
Barb Ward (VP-Sls & Mktg)
Joel Rietz (Gen Counsel)
Lisa Perez (VP-HR)
Matt Van Slooten (Pres-Comml Properties)
Ryan Bartley (Dir-Comml Dev & Investments)
Dan Ullom (Dir-Construction)
Justin Wing (Dir-Comml Leasing)
Matthew Weiner (VP-Corp Strategy & Bus Analytics)
Robb Hall (VP-Ops)
Julie Watkin (VP-HR)

CSMI
60 Island St, Lawrence, MA 01840-1835
Tel.: (978) 989-9460
Web Site: http://www.csmi.com
Sales Range: $10-24.9 Million
Emp.: 40
Security Technologies & Communications Systems
N.A.I.C.S.: 561621
Michael Thompson (Co-Founder, COO & Exec VP)
Randall Kaminsky (Co-Founder & CEO)

CSP MOBILE PRODUCTIONS, LLC
15 Willey Rd, Saco, ME 04072
Tel.: (207) 282-9680
Web Site: https://www.cspmobile.com

Sales Range: $10-24.9 Million
Emp.: 12
Television Broadcasting Services
N.A.I.C.S.: 516120
Len Chase (Pres)
Andrew MacVane (VP-Ops)
Brian Dyer (Supvr-Engrg)
Bonnie Barclay (Office Mgr)

CSR COMPANY INC.
11701 Centennial Rd Ste 2 & 3, La Vista, NE 68128
Tel.: (402) 731-9600   DE
Web Site:
http://www.omahavaccine.com
Year Founded: 1995
Sales Range: $150-199.9 Million
Emp.: 80
Distr of Vaccines & Vet Supplies
N.A.I.C.S.: 424210
Scott Remington (CEO)

Subsidiaries:

American Veterinary Pharmaceuticals **(1)**
11701 Centennial Rd, La Vista, NE 68128 **(100%)**
Tel.: (402) 731-9600
Web Site:
http://www.americanvetsupply.com
Sales Range: $10-24.9 Million
Emp.: 55
Distr of Vaccine And Veterinary Supplies
N.A.I.C.S.: 424210
Scott Remington (Pres)

CSRA PROBATION SERVICES, INC.
802-D Oakhurst Dr, Evans, GA 30809
Tel.: (706) 210-7071
Web Site:
https://www.csraprobation.com
Probation Services
N.A.I.C.S.: 561311
Michael Popplewell (Pres)

Subsidiaries:

Sentinel Offender Services, LLC **(1)**
220 Technology Dr Ste 200, Irvine, CA 92618
Tel.: (949) 453-1550
Web Site: http://www.sentrak.com
Rev.: $12,000,000
Emp.: 50
Confinement Surveillance Systems Maintenance & Monitoring
N.A.I.C.S.: 561621
Robert Contestabile (Founder & Pres)
Mark Contestabile (Chief Bus Dev Officer & Pres-Div)
Julie Hunt (Dir-HR)
Tim Lewis (VP-Ops)
Dennis Fuller (CFO)
Darryl Martin (COO & Pres-Div)
Melissa Starr (VP-Field Ops)
Glen Huang (VP-IT)

CSS DISTRIBUTION GROUP, INC.
10801 Electron Dr Ste 208, Louisville, KY 40299
Tel.: (502) 423-1011
Web Site:
http://www.customersourcings.com
Year Founded: 2006
Sales Range: $10-24.9 Million
Emp.: 13
Packing & Shipping Outsourcer
N.A.I.C.S.: 488991
Mindy Withrow (Co-Founder & CEO)
Daniel Withrow (Co-Founder & Pres)
Walter Blecha (VP-Bus Dev)

CSS FARMS INC.
1200 33rd St SE, Watertown, SD 57201-5639
Tel.: (605) 886-2577
Web Site: https://www.cssfarms.com
Year Founded: 1985

CSS Farms Inc.—(Continued)

Sales Range: $10-24.9 Million
Emp.: 100
Potato Growers
N.A.I.C.S.: 531210
Milt Carter (Owner)
Robin Stamp (CFO)

CSS HOTELS SERVICES INC.
205 Hilltop View Dr, Seymour, TN
37865
Tel.: (865) 573-5430
Sales Range: $10-24.9 Million
Emp.: 25
Motel, Franchised
N.A.I.C.S.: 561110
Pace Cooper (Pres)

CSS LABORATORIES INC.
17173 Gillette Ave Ste A, Irvine, CA
92614-7602
Tel.: (949) 852-8161
Web Site: http://www.csslabs.com
Year Founded: 1984
Sales Range: $10-24.9 Million
Emp.: 110
Provider of Computers, Peripherals &
Software
N.A.I.C.S.: 423430
Edward Chiu (Pres)
Amy Fu (Mgr-HR)
Siew Yeung (VP)

CSSI INC.
425 3rd St SW Ste 700, Washington,
DC 20024
Tel.: (202) 863-2175
Web Site: http://www.cssiinc.com
Sales Range: $10-24.9 Million
Emp.: 78
Systems Engineering, Computer Related
N.A.I.C.S.: 541512
Cynthia Castillo (CEO)
Kelly Caccetta (Pres)

CSSS.NET
3906 Raynor Pkwy Ste 201, Bellevue, NE 68123
Tel.: (402) 393-8059
Web Site:
http://www.constellationwest.com
Sales Range: $25-49.9 Million
Emp.: 195
Information Technology Services
N.A.I.C.S.: 541512
Lisa N. Wolford (Pres & CEO)
Joel Merriman (Sr Vp)

CSU LLC
9261 Cody St, Shawnee Mission, KS
66214
Tel.: (913) 541-0960
Sales Range: $10-24.9 Million
Emp.: 100
Photocopy Machine Repair Services
N.A.I.C.S.: 811210
Doug Fisher (CFO)
Mike Valenti (VP-Natl Sls)

CSUBS
155 Chestnut Ridge Rd, Montvale,
NJ 07645
Tel.: (201) 307-9900
Web Site: http://www.csubs.com
Year Founded: 2003
Sales Range: $10-24.9 Million
Emp.: 17
Subscription Management Services
for Businesses
N.A.I.C.S.: 541611
Julie Sue Auslander (Owner)
David Rifkin (VP)
Leianne Eskinazi (Dir-HR & Fin)
Peggy Kelly (Sr Acct Mgr & Mgr-Ops)

CSW, INC.
45 Tyburski Rd, Ludlow, MA 01056
Tel.: (413) 589-1311
Web Site:
http://www.cswgraphics.com
Year Founded: 1937
Sales Range: $10-24.9 Million
Emp.: 104
Platemaking Services
N.A.I.C.S.: 332313
Laura Wright (Pres)
Jim Mootz (Gen Mgr)

CSWW INC.
5109 Alaska Trl, Great Falls, MT
59405
Tel.: (406) 761-6623
Web Site: http://www.bigrstore.com
Sales Range: $10-24.9 Million
Emp.: 550
Sales of Farm Equipment & Supplies
N.A.I.C.S.: 459999
Chuck Schmidt (Owner & Pres)
Wayne Wicke (Treas & Sec)

CT ASSIST LLC
237 E Market St, Harrisonburg, VA
22801
Web Site: http://www.ct-assist.com
Year Founded: 2013
Sales Range: $10-24.9 Million
Emp.: 70
Health Care Srvices
N.A.I.C.S.: 621610
Daryl Bert (CEO)
Minnette Hostetler (COO)

CT GROUP
900 Montgomery St, Laurel, MD
20707
Tel.: (240) 554-6500
Web Site:
https://www.ctmanagement.com
Year Founded: 1981
Sales Range: $25-49.9 Million
Emp.: 400
Provider of Trucking Services
N.A.I.C.S.: 484121
Marsha S. Jackson (Exec VP)
Charles A. Tini (Owner)
Andrew J. Lasky (Sr Mgr-Property)
Christopher Wood (Reg Mgr-Property)
David Katz (Mgr-Compliance & Trng)
Derek Lee (Dir-Mgmt Info Sys)
Fred Killian (Reg Mgr-Property)
Karen Fletcher (Reg Mgr-Property)
Pamela Kirby (Controller)
Rhiannon Dunn (Dir-Compliance & Trng)
Tanya Daye-Holt (Reg Mgr-Property)

Subsidiaries:

Cargo Consolidation Services (1)
3350 N Oxford St, Claremont, NC 28610
Tel.: (828) 459-3160
Web Site: http://www.ctgrp.com
Sales Range: $25-49.9 Million
Provider of Trucking Services
N.A.I.C.S.: 484121

Cargo Transporters, Inc. (1)
3390 N Oxford St, Claremont, NC 28610
Tel.: (828) 459-3282
Web Site: http://www.cargotransporters.com
Sales Range: $25-49.9 Million
Emp.: 250
Trucking Service
N.A.I.C.S.: 484121
John Pope (Chm)
Dennis Dellinger (Pres & CEO)
Jerry Sigmon (Exec VP)
Shawn R. Brown (VP-Safety & Recruiting)

Catawba Truck Rental (1)
3350 N Oxford St, Claremont, NC 28610-0339
Tel.: (828) 459-3200
Web Site: http://www.ctgrp.com
Provider of Truck Rental Services

N.A.I.C.S.: 484121

CTA MANUFACTURING, INC.
1160 California Ave, Corona, CA
92881
Tel.: (951) 280-2400
Web Site:
https://www.bagmasters.com
Year Founded: 1922
Sales Range: $10-24.9 Million
Emp.: 50
Textile Bags, Covers & Soft Cases
Mfr
N.A.I.C.S.: 314910
Richard Whittier (Pres)

Subsidiaries:

Bagmasters (1)
1160 California Ave, Corona, CA 92881-3324
Tel.: (951) 280-2400
Web Site: http://www.bagmasters.com
Promotional Bag Mfr & Distr
N.A.I.C.S.: 314910
Rick Whittier (Pres)

CTC FOOD INTERNATIONAL
50 W Ohio Ave, Richmond, CA 94804
Tel.: (650) 873-7600
Web Site:
http://www.asianfoodgrocer.com
Rev.: $24,000,000
Emp.: 50
Specialty Food Items
N.A.I.C.S.: 424490
Hideki Otani (Chm)
Larry Tanita (CFO)
Ike Sukumoto (CEO)

CTE LOGISTICS
4103 C St NE Ste 100, Auburn, WA
98390
Tel.: (866) 990-3090
Web Site: http://www.ctelogistics.com
Year Founded: 2009
Sales Range: $1-9.9 Million
Emp.: 10
Transportation Services Throughout
The U.S. & Canada
N.A.I.C.S.: 488510
Todd Lytle (Pres)
Kimm Lytle (VP)
Blair Grant (VP-Operations)
Milo Davis (Mgr-Warehouse)

CTF HOLDINGS INC.
1155 Connecticut Ave NW, Washington, DC 20036
Tel.: (202) 533-1200
Sales Range: $25-49.9 Million
Emp.: 10
Hotel Operating Services
N.A.I.C.S.: 721110
K. Daniel Heininger (Exec VP)
Patrick Gassney (CFO)

CTG US LLC
3740 Nw 124 Ave, Coral Springs, FL
33065
Tel.: (305) 394-9446
Web Site: http://www.ctg.us
Year Founded: 2006
Sales Range: $1-9.9 Million
Emp.: 10
Global Supply Chain Management
Solutions
N.A.I.C.S.: 488510
Michael Cornish (Founder & Pres)

CTI CORP.
11105 N Casa Grande Hwy, Rillito,
AZ 85654
Tel.: (520) 624-2348
Web Site: https://www.cti-az.com
Year Founded: 1947
Sales Range: $25-49.9 Million
Emp.: 450

Trucking Service
N.A.I.C.S.: 484121
Gregg L. Gibbons (CEO)
Tom Jones (Pres)
Mike Nakayama (Controller)

Subsidiaries:

CTI Leasing Inc. (1)
11105 N Casa Grande Hwy, Rillito, AZ
85654
Tel.: (520) 624-2348
Web Site: http://www.cti-az.com
Sales Range: $10-24.9 Million
Emp.: 57
Heavy Construction Equipment Rental
N.A.I.C.S.: 532412

CTI MEDIA
6120 Powers Ferry Rd NW Ste 140,
Atlanta, GA 30339
Tel.: (404) 843-8717
Web Site: http://www.ctimedia.com
Rev.: $20,000,000
Emp.: 20
Advetising Agency
N.A.I.C.S.: 541810
Toni Augustine-Dwyer (Pres & CEO)
Lori Krinsky (Sr VP-Media)

CTI RESOURCE MANAGEMENT SERVICES, INC.
4800 Spring Park Rd Ste 200, Jacksonville, FL 32207
Tel.: (904) 722-6500
Web Site: http://www.ctirms.com
Year Founded: 2003
Sales Range: $10-24.9 Million
Emp.: 115
Business Support Services
N.A.I.C.S.: 561499
Christopher Imbach (Founder, Pres &
CEO)
Chris Getz (VP-Ops)
Robin Norton (Dir-HR)

CTIA-THE WIRELESS ASSOCIATION
1400 16th St NW Ste 600, Washington, DC 20036
Tel.: (202) 785-0081
Web Site: https://www.ctia.org
Year Founded: 1984
Sales Range: $50-74.9 Million
Emp.: 105
Wireless Communication Industry
Association
N.A.I.C.S.: 813910
Rocco Carlitti (CFO & Sr VP)
Scott Bergmann (VP-Regulatory Affairs)
Meredith Attwel Baker (Pres & CEO)
Kelly Cole (Sr VP-Govt Affiars)
Bret Comolli (Treas)
Jamie Hastings (Sr VP-External-State
Affairs)
John Marinho (VP-Cybersecurity &
Tech)
Tom Power (Sr VP)
Robert Roche (VP-Res Pub Affairs)
Mark Sargent (VP-Certification Programs)
Tom Sawanobori (CTO & Sr VP)
Jim Schuler (VP-External-State Affairs)
Marcelo Claure (Chm)

CTL AEROSPACE INC.
5616 Spellmire Dr, Cincinnati, OH
45246-4898
Tel.: (513) 874-7900
Web Site:
https://www.ctlaerospace.com
Year Founded: 1946
Sales Range: $10-24.9 Million
Emp.: 300
Aircraft Parts & Equipment
N.A.I.C.S.: 336413

James C. Irwin *(Owner)*
James Allen *(Engr-Quality)*
Craig Rollins *(Dir-Mfg)*
Brian Riestenberg *(Engr-Repair Dev)*
Bill Schmidt *(Engr-Repair)*
Tim Eads *(Supvr-Quality Assurance)*
Jim Conaty *(Mgr)*
Mit Tonsaly *(Mgr-Pur)*

CTL ENGINEERING, INC.
2860 Fisher Rd, Columbus, OH
43204
Tel.: (614) 276-8123
Web Site: https://www.ctleng.com
Year Founded: 1927
Engineeering Services
N.A.I.C.S.: 541510
CK Satyapriya *(Pres)*
Chiranjiv Zutshi *(CIO)*
David A. Breitfeller *(VP)*
Pawan Sigdel *(Engr-Geotechnical)*
George Hummeldorf *(Sr Project Mgr-Environmental)*

CTM MEDIA GROUP, INC.
11 Largo Dr S, Stamford, CT 06907
Tel.: (203) 323-5161   NY
Web Site:
   https://www.ctmmediagroup.com
Year Founded: 1983
Sales Range: $25-49.9 Million
Advertising Equipment Distr
N.A.I.C.S.: 541870
Peter Magaro *(Pres)*
Ed Wiemeler *(Reg Dir-Sls & Mktg-Midwest)*
Steven Guerrini *(VP-Sls)*
Jerry McConnell *(Vp-Ops)*
Maria Tedesco *(Dir-HR)*
Cricket Jiranek *(Exec VP-Sls)*
Diane Salvo *(Dir-Mktg)*
Ira Nicoll *(Dir-Acctg)*

Subsidiaries:

CTM Media Group - Canadian
Division   (1)
1011 Haultain Ct Unit 2, Mississauga, L4W
1W1, ON, Canada
Tel.: (905) 624-8950
Web Site: http://www.ctmmedia.com
Sales Range: $10-24.9 Million
Emp.: 14
Brochure Rack Distr
N.A.I.C.S.: 541870
Durrell Martin *(Mgr-Ops)*

CTR SYSTEMS INC.
555 Keystone Dr, Warrendale, PA
15086
Tel.: (724) 772-2400
Web Site: http://www.ctrsystems.com
Year Founded: 1964
Sales Range: $25-49.9 Million
Emp.: 100
Time & Attendance, Labor Management, Payroll & Human Resources,
Parking Revenue & Access Control
Services
N.A.I.C.S.: 238290
Dru W. Duffy *(CEO)*
Ken Russo *(Exec VP-Ops)*
Mark Pitchford *(VP-Sls)*

CTS ADVANTAGE LOGISTICS INC.
2071 Ringwood Ave, San Jose, CA
95131
Tel.: (408) 943-6300
Web Site:
   http://www.ctsadvantage.com
Year Founded: 1981
Rev.: $30,000,000
Emp.: 250
Trucking Service
N.A.I.C.S.: 484110
Dave Wilson *(Exec VP)*
Nick Karloff *(Mgr-Acct)*

CTS FLOORING
319 W Rdg Pike, Limerick, PA 19468
Tel.: (610) 489-6270
Web Site: http://www.ctsflooring.com
Sales Range: $10-24.9 Million
Emp.: 18
Flooring Contract Services
N.A.I.C.S.: 238330
Drew Guinan *(COO & Exec VP)*
Ken Brown *(CFO)*
Fran Guinan *(Mgr-Mktg & Sls)*
Al Schwartz *(Mgr-Sls-Western Reg)*
Joe Purcell *(VP-Ops)*

CTT INC.
241 E Java Dr, Sunnyvale, CA 94089
Tel.: (408) 541-0596
Web Site: http://www.cttinc.com
Year Founded: 1981
Sales Range: $10-24.9 Million
Emp.: 105
Microwave Communication Equipment
N.A.I.C.S.: 334220
David Tai *(Pres)*
Gordon Graham *(Reg Mgr-Sls)*
Russell Wong *(Controller)*
Alvin Chan *(Engr)*

CTW GROUP INCORPORATED
4820 Minnetonka Blvd Ste 303, Minneapolis, MN 55416
Tel.: (612) 808-6767
Web Site:
   http://www.homesteadroad.com
Year Founded: 2012
Sales Range: $25-49.9 Million
Emp.: 23
Real Estate Services
N.A.I.C.S.: 531390
Andrey Sokurec *(CEO)*
Alex Delendik *(COO)*
David O'Neil *(VP-Acquisitions)*
Diann Tilden *(Sr Mgr-Acquisition)*
Sunil Bawa *(Sr Mgr-Acquisition)*

CTW GROUP, INC.
4820 Minnetonka Blvd Ste 303, Minneapolis, MN 55416
Tel.: (612) 808-6767
Web Site:
   http://www.homesteadroad.com
Year Founded: 2012
Sales Range: $1-9.9 Million
Real Estate Investment Services
N.A.I.C.S.: 531210
Andrey Sokurec *(CEO)*
Alex Delendik *(COO)*
David Nix *(CMO)*
David O'Neil *(VP-Sls)*

CU COOPERATIVE SYSTEMS, INC.
9692 Haven Ave, Rancho Cucamonga, CA 91730   CA
Web Site: https://www.co-opfs.org
Year Founded: 1981
Financial Industry Network Support
Services
N.A.I.C.S.: 561499
Kari Wilfong *(CFO & Chief Admin Officer)*
James Hanisch *(Pres-CO-OP Network)*
Christopher Todd Clark *(Pres & CEO)*
Bill Prichard *(Dir-PR)*
Todd Clark *(CEO)*
Bruce Dragt *(Chief Product Officer)*
Cheryl Middleton Jones *(Chief People Officer)*
Nicholas Calcanes *(COO)*
Mathew Kardell *(Chief Revenue Officer)*
Dean Michaels *(Chief Strategy Officer)*
Samantha Expanson *(Chief Experience Officer)*

Subsidiaries:

AMC FS, Inc.   (1)
7745 Office Plza Dr North Ste 170, West
Des Moines, IA 50266
Tel.: (866) 596-3060
Web Site: http://www.affiliatesmgt.com
Financial Services
N.A.I.C.S.: 522210
Matt Oakley *(VP-Mktg)*
Murray Williams *(Chm & CEO)*
Michael Powers *(CFO)*
Michelle Barker *(Gen Counsel)*
Carrie Kompelien *(VP-HR)*
Miriam De Dios Woodward *(Sr VP & CEO-PolicyWorks, LLC)*
Justin Hupfer *(Sr VP & CEO-PolicyWorks Iowa)*
Deb M Madison-Levi *(Dir-Admin)*

CO-OP Network   (1)
3500 Porsche Way Ste 300, Ontario, CA
91764-4937
Tel.: (909) 948-2500
Web Site: http://www.co-opfs.org
Mfr Of Automatic Teller Machines
N.A.I.C.S.: 522390

CU Ventures Inc.   (1)
9692 Haven Ave, Rancho Cucamonga, CA
91730
Tel.: (909) 948-2500
Web Site: http://www.coopfs.org
Sales Range: $10-24.9 Million
Business Support Services
N.A.I.C.S.: 561499

CU DIRECT CORPORATION
2855 E Guasti Rd Ste 500, Ontario,
CA 91761   NV
Web Site: https://www.cudirect.com
Consumer Lending Solutions Services
N.A.I.C.S.: 522291
Tony Boutelle *(Pres & CEO)*
Bob Child *(COO)*
Neetu Bhagat *(CFO)*
Phil DuPree *(Chief Revenue Officer)*
Brian Hendricks *(Chief Product Officer)*
Jeff Shood *(CTO)*
Erin Wilson *(Gen Counsel)*
Laurel Levine *(Chief People Officer-Engagement Officer)*

Subsidiaries:

Origence Lending Services   (1)
5680 Greenwood Plz Blvd Ste 400, Greenwood Village, CO 80111
Tel.: (720) 974-1311
Web Site:
   https://origencelendingservices.com
Sales Range: $1-9.9 Million
Emp.: 52
Consumer Lending
N.A.I.C.S.: 522291

CU*ANSWERS
6000 28th St, Grand Rapids, MI
49546-6927
Tel.: (616) 285-5711
Web Site:
   https://www.cuanswers.com
Year Founded: 1970
Sales Range: $10-24.9 Million
Emp.: 75
Data Processing Services
N.A.I.C.S.: 518210
Randy Karnes *(CEO)*
Bob Frizzle *(CFO)*
Jody Karnes *(CIO)*
Dave Wordhouse *(VP-Network Tech)*
Karen Chesbro *(VP-Item Processing)*
Jack Carpenter *(VP-Programming)*
Scott Page *(Bus Mgr-Developer's Help Desk)*
Vickie Schmitzer *(Vice Chm)*
Esteban Camargo *(Mgr-Content Mktg)*
Keegan Daniel *(VP-Professional Svcs)*

CUADRILLA CAPITAL LLC
2984 San Marcos Ave, Los Olivos,
CA 93441
Tel.: (310) 741-7098   DE
Web Site:
   https://www.cuadrillacapital.com
Year Founded: 2021
Investment Services
N.A.I.C.S.: 523999
Jonah Sulak *(Co-Founder & Mng Partner)*
Vikram Abraham *(Co-Founder & Mng Partner)*

Subsidiaries:

Chartbeat Inc.   (1)
826 Broadway 12th St 6th Fl, New York, NY
10003
Tel.: (646) 786-8472
Web Site: http://www.chartbeat.com
Software Publisher
N.A.I.C.S.: 513210
Tony Haile *(CEO & Gen Mgr)*

InfoDesk, Inc.   (1)
660 White Plains Rd, Tarrytown, NY 10591
Tel.: (914) 332-5940
Web Site: http://www.infodesk.com
Information Retrieval Services, Nsk
N.A.I.C.S.: 517810
Sterling Stites *(CEO)*

CUATTRO, LLC
150 Capital Dr Ste 280, Golden, CO
80401-5611
Tel.: (970) 775-2247   CO
Web Site: http://www.cuattro.com
Year Founded: 2007
Medical Digital Imaging Equipment &
Software Developer & Mfr
N.A.I.C.S.: 551112
Kevin S. Wilson *(Owner & CEO)*

Subsidiaries:

Cuattro Medical, LLC   (1)
3760 Rocky Mountain Ave, Loveland, CO
80538
Tel.: (970) 775-2247
Web Site: http://med.cuattro.com
Medical Imaging Equipment Designer & Mfr
N.A.I.C.S.: 334517
Kevin S. Wilson *(CEO)*

Cuattro Software, LLC   (1)
3760 Rocky Mountain Ave, Loveland, CO
80538   (100%)
Tel.: (970) 775-2247
Medical Imaging Equipment Software Developer
N.A.I.C.S.: 541511
Kevin S. Wilson *(CEO)*

CUBA MEMORIAL HOSPITAL, INC.
140 W Main St, Cuba, NY 14727
Tel.: (585) 968-2000   NY
Web Site:
   https://www.cubamemorialhos
   pital.com
Year Founded: 1925
Sales Range: $10-24.9 Million
Emp.: 293
Health Care Srvices
N.A.I.C.S.: 622110

CUBAN CLUB FOUNDATION, INC.
2010 Avenida Republica de Cuba,
Tampa, FL 33605
Tel.: (813) 248-2954   FL
Web Site:
   http://www.thecubanclubybor.com
Year Founded: 1993
Sales Range: $1-9.9 Million
Emp.: 2
Membership Organization
N.A.I.C.S.: 813410
Patrick Manteiga *(Mgr)*

CUBBISON COMPANY

Cubbison Company—(Continued)

380 Victoria Rd, Youngstown, OH 44515
Tel.: (330) 793-2481　　　　OH
Web Site: https://www.cubbison.com
Year Founded: 1971
Sales Range: $1-9.9 Million
Emp.: 70
Product Identification Solutions
N.A.I.C.S.: 561910
Tim Merrifield (Pres)
Sheila Scheel (COO)

Subsidiaries:

Drake Industries, Inc.　　　　　　(1)
1916 Hydro Dr, Austin, TX 78728
Tel.: (512) 251-2231
Web Site: http://www.drake.com
Commercial Printing Services
N.A.I.C.S.: 323111
Timothy Moore (Pres & CEO)

CUBBY'S INC.
9230 Mormon Bridge Rd, Omaha, NE 68152-1959
Tel.: (402) 453-2468　　　　NE
Year Founded: 1985
Sales Range: $25-49.9 Million
Emp.: 180
Grocery Stores
N.A.I.C.S.: 445131
Phil Morrison (Owner)
Tom Gruidel (VP-Fin)

CUBE 3 STUDIO
360 Merrimack St Ste 337, Lawrence, MA 01843
Tel.: (978) 989-9900
Web Site:
　http://www.cube3studio.com
Year Founded: 2003
Sales Range: $10-24.9 Million
Emp.: 60
Architecture & Interior Design
N.A.I.C.S.: 541310
Nicholas Adam Middleton (CEO & Partner)
Doug Carr (Principal)
John Harding (Assoc Principal)
Keith Boyle (Assoc Principal)
Peter Bartash (Assoc Principal)

CUBIC ENERGY, LLC
9870 Plano Rd, Dallas, TX 75238
Tel.: (972) 686-0369　　　　TX
Web Site:
　http://www.cubicenergyinc.com
Year Founded: 1999
Sales Range: $10-24.9 Million
Crude Oil & Natural Gas Development, Production & Exploration Services
N.A.I.C.S.: 211120
Jon Stuart Ross (Sec & Exec VP)

CUBICLE NINJAS LLC
800 Roosevelt Rd Ste D 115, Glen Ellyn, IL 60137
Tel.: (630) 469-4850
Web Site:
　https://www.cubicleninjas.com
Sales Range: $1-9.9 Million
Emp.: 14
Graphic Design, Advertising & Marketing Services
N.A.I.C.S.: 541430
Josh Farkas (Founder & Pres)

CUBIX CORPORATION
2800 Lockheed Way, Carson City, NV 89706-0719
Tel.: (775) 888-1000　　　　NV
Web Site: http://www.cubix.com
Year Founded: 1975
Rev.: $5,000,000
Emp.: 15

Fiscal Year-end: 12/31/14
Mfr of High-Density, Multi-Server Computer Platforms
N.A.I.C.S.: 334111
Donald A. Lehr (Chm, CEO, Treas & Sec)
Allan G. Fiegehen (Pres & COO)
Bob Eichenberger (Gen Mgr)

CUBRC, INC.
4455 Genesee St Ste 106, Buffalo, NY 14225-1955
Tel.: (716) 204-5100　　　　NY
Web Site: https://www.cubrc.org
Year Founded: 1983
Sales Range: $25-49.9 Million
Scientific Research Services
N.A.I.C.S.: 541720
Tracy E. Gertz (CFO & Sr VP-Fin, HR & Admin)
David J. Mangino (VP-Chemical, Biological & Medical Sciences Sector)
Michael S. Holden (VP-Aeronautics Sector)
Michael Moskal (CIO & VP-Info Exploitation Sector)
Tom McMahon (Pres & CEO)
Richard Aubrecht (Chm)

CUCAMONGA VALLEY WATER DISTRICT
10440 Ashford St, Rancho Cucamonga, CA 91730-2799
Tel.: (909) 987-2591
Web Site:
　https://www.cvwdwater.com
Sales Range: $75-99.9 Million
Emp.: 119
Water & Wastewater Services
N.A.I.C.S.: 221310
John Bosler (CEO & Gen Mgr)
Luis Cetina (VP)
James V. Curatalo Jr. (Pres)

Subsidiaries:

Fontana Union Water Company　　(1)
15966 Arrow Blvd, Fontana, CA 92335-3891　　　　　　　(100%)
Tel.: (909) 822-9199
Web Site: http://www.fontanawater.com
Water Resources
N.A.I.C.S.: 221310
Kathleen J. Tiegs (Chm)

CUETER CHRYSLER JEEP DODGE
2448 Washtenaw Rd, Ypsilanti, MI 48197
Tel.: (734) 434-2424
Web Site:
　http://www.cueterchryslerjeep.com
Year Founded: 1992
Sales Range: $10-24.9 Million
Emp.: 55
Car Whslr
N.A.I.C.S.: 441110
Steve Demers (Gen Mgr)

CUFFLINKS.COM
3699 McKinney Ave Ste 303, Dallas, TX 75204
Tel.: (214) 780-0333
Web Site: http://www.cufflinks.com
Sales Range: $1-9.9 Million
Emp.: 13
Jewelry Stores
N.A.I.C.S.: 458310
Ravi Raton (Owner)
Kate Lashley (Coord-Exec Sls)
Paul Song (VP-Mktg)

CUFFY CO. INCORPORATED
721 Main St, West Dennis, MA 02670-2201
Tel.: (508) 398-5162
Web Site: http://www.cuffys.com
Rev.: $10,435,597

Emp.: 12
Men's & Boys' Clothing Stores
N.A.I.C.S.: 458110
Adrienne Adams (Office Mgr)
Laurie McNamara (Mgr-Product Dev & Sourcing)
Dominick J. Albano Jr. (Pres)

CUHACI & PETERSON ARCHITECTS LLC
1925 Prospect Ave, Orlando, FL 32814
Tel.: (407) 661-9100
Web Site: http://www.c-p.com
Year Founded: 1978
Sales Range: $10-24.9 Million
Emp.: 125
Architectural, Engineering & Landscaping Services
N.A.I.C.S.: 541310
Lonnie Peterson (Principal)
Michael Lynch (Exec VP)
Norberto Campos (VP-Design)
Greg Simpson (CEO)
Brett Rylands (VP-Structural Engrg)
Jay Adkinson (Dir-Tech)
Betsy Englert (Dir-Fin)
Tina Kennedy (Dir-HR)
Steven Blevins (Principal)
Bo Newman (CFO)
Stephen Roberts (Dir-Bus Dev)
Casey Duranczyk (Mgr-Bus Dev)
Chris Renegar (Principal)
Dale Ulmer (Dir-Architecture)
Jaison Moras (VP-Electrical Engrg)
Keith Harwell (Principal)
Leigh Paull (Principal)
Wess Luke (Principal)
Steven Duffy (VP-Grocery)
Jeff Suchan (Chief Dev Officer)
David Mayer (Principal)
Jose Diaz (VP-Mechanical Engrg)

CUIVRE RIVER ELECTRIC COOPERATIVE INC.
PO Box 160, Troy, MO 63379-0160
Tel.: (636) 528-8261　　　　MO
Web Site: http://www.cuivre.com
Year Founded: 1941
Sales Range: $25-49.9 Million
Emp.: 111
Electronic Services
N.A.I.C.S.: 221122
Doug Tracy (Mgr)
Keith Stone (Mgr)

CULBERSON STOWERS, INC.
805 N Hobart St, Pampa, TX 79065-5201
Tel.: (806) 665-1665
Web Site:
　http://www.culbersonstowers.com
Year Founded: 1927
Sales Range: $10-24.9 Million
Emp.: 35
Car Whslr
N.A.I.C.S.: 441110
Richard H. Stowe (Mgr-GMC)

CULBERT HEALTHCARE SOLUTIONS
800 W Cummings Park Ste 6000, Woburn, MA 01801
Tel.: (781) 935-1002
Web Site:
　http://www.culberthealth.com
Sales Range: $10-24.9 Million
Emp.: 100
Health Care Srvices
N.A.I.C.S.: 621491
Rob Culbert (CEO)
Brad Boyd (Pres)
Kristene McLaughlin (Dir-HR)
Joe Ali (COO)
Jaffer Traish (Dir-Epic Practice)

Johanna Epstein (VP-Mgmt Consulting Svcs)
Randy Jones (Sr VP-Consulting Svcs-West)
Alan Worsham (Dir-Mgmt Consulting Svcs)
Scott Griffin (VP-Consulting Svcs)
Nancy Gagliano (Chief Medical Officer)

CULINAIRE INTERNATIONAL INC.
2100 Ross Ave Ste 3100, Dallas, TX 75201-2739
Tel.: (214) 754-1880　　　　TX
Web Site: http://www.culinaireintl.com
Year Founded: 1993
Sales Range: $50-74.9 Million
Emp.: 2,000
Food & Beverage Management Services
N.A.I.C.S.: 541618
Richard N. Gussoni (Founder & CEO)
David Wood (Sr VP-Sls & Mktg)
Bill Thompson (Pres & COO)
Kimberly Larsen (VP-HR)
Scott Thompson (Reg VP-Ops)
William Lenoir (VP-Projects & Pur)

CULINARY CONCEPTS INC.
2215 Tradeport Dr, Orlando, FL 32824
Tel.: (407) 228-0069
Web Site:
　http://www.chefcreations.com
Year Founded: 1986
Sales Range: $10-24.9 Million
Emp.: 100
Soup & Sauce Mfr
N.A.I.C.S.: 311941
Hall Valdes (Pres)
Bill Roccio (CIO)

CULINARY DEPOT, INC.
2 Melnick Dr, Monsey, NY 10952
Web Site:
　http://www.culinarydepotinc.com
Year Founded: 1999
Sales Range: $50-74.9 Million
Emp.: 100
Commercial Kitchen Equipment Distr
N.A.I.C.S.: 423440
Michael Lichter (CEO)
Sholem Potash (Pres)

CULINARY EYE, INC
1501 Cortland Ave, San Francisco, CA 94110
Tel.: (415) 824-1225
Web Site:
　http://www.culinaryeye.com
Year Founded: 2010
Sales Range: $1-9.9 Million
Emp.: 64
Catering Services
N.A.I.C.S.: 722320
John Silva (Founder)

CULINARY HOLDINGS INC.
567 San Nicolas Dr Ste 400, Newport Beach, CA 92660
Tel.: (949) 718-4631
Rev.: $14,700,000
Emp.: 8
Eating Place
N.A.I.C.S.: 722511
John E. Martin (Chm)

Subsidiaries:

Culinary Adventures, Inc.　　　　(1)
567 San Nicolas Dr Ste 410, Newport Beach, CA 92660
Tel.: (949) 718-4631
Sales Range: $10-24.9 Million
Owner & Operator of Restaurant Family Chain

N.A.I.C.S.: 722511

CULINARY VENTURES VEND-ING
1835 Burnet Ave Ste 2, Union, NJ 07083-4282
Tel.: (908) 624-9940
Web Site: http://www.cvv.biz
Year Founded: 1994
Sales Range: $10-24.9 Million
Emp.: 60
Contract Food Services
N.A.I.C.S.: 532289
Jack Yuppa (Pres)
Michael Ricca (CFO)
Douglas P. Longworth (Dir-Tech)

CULINEX
1802 1st Ave S, Fargo, ND 58103
Tel.: (701) 232-4428
Web Site: http://www.goculinex.com
Sales Range: $10-24.9 Million
Emp.: 49
Restaurant Equipment & Supplies
N.A.I.C.S.: 423440
Kevin Bouma (Pres & CEO)
Mark Howes (VP-Mktg & Sls)
Kathy Stephenson (Mktg Dir)
Lucinda Salinas (Sr Dir-Bus Dev)

CULLEN & DYKMAN LLP
100 Quentin Roosevelt Blvd, Garden City, NY 11530-4850
Tel.: (516) 357-3700
Web Site:
　http://www.cullenanddykman.com
Year Founded: 1850
Law firm
N.A.I.C.S.: 541110
Kenneth S. Buffaloe (Partner-Manhattan)
Elizabeth M. Aboulafia (Partner)
Thomas S. Baylis (Partner)
Marna E. Bernstein (Partner)
Christopher H. Palmer (Mng Partner)
Michael H. Traison (Partner-Bankruptcy & Creditors Rights Dept-Wall Street)

CULLEN & WHIM INC.
231 W 39th St Ste 1016, New York, NY 10018
Tel.: (212) 575-1178
Web Site: http://www.cullenusa.com
Sales Range: $10-24.9 Million
Emp.: 10
Men's & Boys' Sweaters
N.A.I.C.S.: 424350
Barry Pfeiffer (Pres)
Paul Levine (CFO)

CULLIGAN SOFT WATER SER-VICE CO.
6030 Culligan Way, Minnetonka, MN 55345-5917
Tel.: (952) 933-7200
Web Site:
　https://www.culliganwater.com
Year Founded: 1946
Sales Range: $25-49.9 Million
Emp.: 376
Business Services
N.A.I.C.S.: 561990
John Packard (Chm, Pres & CEO)

Subsidiaries:

Susquehanna Valley Water Condition-ing Co.　　　　　　　　　　　　(1)
1316 College Ave Ste 3, Elmira, NY 14901
Tel.: (607) 737-2748
Web Site: http://www.culliganwater.com
Sales Range: $10-24.9 Million
Emp.: 20
Business Services
N.A.I.C.S.: 561990
Jim Davis (Mgr)

Unco Data Systems, Inc.　　　　(1)
6030 Culligan Way, Minnetonka, MN 55345
Tel.: (952) 908-2222
Web Site: http://www.uncodata.com
Sales Range: $10-24.9 Million
Emp.: 5
Data Processing Services
N.A.I.C.S.: 518210
John Packard (Pres)
Craig Larson (Gen Mgr)

CULLIGAN WATER COMPANY OF NEW JERSEY, INC.
18 Northfield Ave, West Orange, NJ 07052-5305
Tel.: (973) 731-7110　　　　　NJ
Web Site: https://www.culligannj.com
Year Founded: 1986
Water Softening & Filtration Products
Installation & Services
N.A.I.C.S.: 238220

CULLIGAN WATER CONDI-TIONING SERVICE
2703 Airport Rd, Plant City, FL 33567
Tel.: (813) 759-6060
Web Site: http://www.culligan.com
Rev.: $14,200,000
Emp.: 65
Water Softener Systems Distr
N.A.I.C.S.: 221310
Dale Mast (Pres)
Brian Kennedy (Gen Mgr)
Frank Riker (Branch Mgr)

CULLINAN PROPERTIES, LTD.
420 North Main St, East Peoria, IL 61611
Tel.: (309) 999-1700
Web Site:
　http://www.cullinanproperties.com
Year Founded: 1988
Sales Range: $50-74.9 Million
Emp.: 125
Provider of Commercial Real Estate Development & Acquisitions
N.A.I.C.S.: 531210
Janet Frietsch (Mgr-HR, Ops & Mktg)
Christopher M. West (Partner)
Ginger Benz (VP-Ops & Mktg)
Kathleen Cullinan Brill (VP & Dir-Leasing)
Scott D. Fitzgerald (VP-Leasing & Dev)
Sean Garrett (Pres-Acq & Dir-Community Rels)
Anaise Berry (VP-Ops & Mktg)
Stephanie Webster (Sr VP-Dev)
Brian Morrissey (CFO-Chicago)
Tim Hogenkamp (CFO)
Matthew Beverly (CEO)
Diane Cullinan Oberhelman (Chm & Partner)

CULLMAN ELECTRIC CO-OPERATIVE INC.
1749 Eva Rd NE, Cullman, AL 35055
Tel.: (256) 737-3200　　　　　AL
Web Site: https://www.cullmanec.com
Year Founded: 1936
Sales Range: $25-49.9 Million
Emp.: 96
Electronic Services
N.A.I.C.S.: 221122
Kyle Baggett (VP-Engrg-Ops)
Gail Neal (VP-HR)
Grady Smith (Pres & CEO)
Jerry Weathersby (VP-Acctg & Fin)
Kim Arndt (Mgr-Member Svc)
Dennis Reid (Mgr-Mktg & Energy Svcs)
Melissa Cartee (VP)
Daniel Stricklin (Mgr-IT Svcs)
Jan Sutton (Mgr-Acctg)
Pat Weissend (Mgr-Pur & Stores)

Wade Yarbrough (Superintendent-Field Svcs)
Leonard Romine (Superintendent-Technical Svcs)

CULLMAN JEFFERSON COUNTIES GAS DISTRIBU-TION
1550 County Rd 715, Hanceville, AL 35077
Tel.: (256) 734-1911
Web Site: https://www.cjgas.com
Year Founded: 1952
Sales Range: $25-49.9 Million
Emp.: 50
Natural Gas Distribution
N.A.I.C.S.: 221210
Mark Bussman (CEO)
Brian Dove (CEO)

CULLMAN REGIONAL MEDI-CAL CENTER
1912 Alabama Hwy 157, Cullman, AL 35058
Tel.: (256) 737-2000　　　　　AL
Web Site:
　http://www.crmchospital.com
Year Founded: 1939
Sales Range: $100-124.9 Million
Emp.: 1,075
Health Care Srvices
N.A.I.C.S.: 622110
Susan Copeland (VP-Ambulatory Svcs)
Nesha Donaldson (COO)
Charna Brown (Chief Quality Control Officer)
James Clements (CEO)
Cheryl Bailey (Chief Nursing Officer)
Kimberly Albright (Interim CFO)

CULLUM & BROWN INC.
1200 Burlington, Kansas City, MO 64116
Tel.: (816) 842-7711
Web Site:
　https://www.cullumandbrown.com
Sales Range: $10-24.9 Million
Emp.: 40
Industrial Pumps; Air Compressors; Blowers; Engines; Industrial Vehicles & Related Equipment
N.A.I.C.S.: 423830
Greg Chapman (Acct Mgr)

CULLUM CONSTRUCTION COMPANY
6440 N Central Expwy, Dallas, TX 75206
Tel.: (972) 271-9333
Sales Range: $10-24.9 Million
Emp.: 50
Sewer Line Construction
N.A.I.C.S.: 237110
G. Mark Cullum (Pres)

CULLUM MECHANICAL CON-STRUCTION, INC.
3325 Pacific St, North Charleston, SC 29418
Tel.: (843) 554-6645
Web Site: https://www.culluminc.com
Year Founded: 1972
Sales Range: $25-49.9 Million
Emp.: 250
Plumbing, Process Piping, Heating, Ventilation, Air-Conditioning, Electri-cal, Construction, Engineering & Maintenance Services
N.A.I.C.S.: 238220
Shealee Harmon (Sec & Controller)
Christopher Cullum (Chm)

CULLUM SEEDS LLC
316 N Hawthorne St, Fisher, AR 72429
Tel.: (870) 328-7222
Web Site: http://www.armorseed.com
Sales Range: $10-24.9 Million
Emp.: 50
Processor & Sales of Seeds
N.A.I.C.S.: 111422
Kelly Phipps (Pres)
Carl Phipps (VP)
Catina Hollingsworth (Office Mgr)

CULP CONSTRUCTION CO.
2320 S Main St, Salt Lake City, UT 84115
Tel.: (801) 486-2064
Web Site: https://www.culpco.com
Sales Range: $25-49.9 Million
Emp.: 75
Commercial & Office Building; New Construction
N.A.I.C.S.: 236220
Charles H. Culp (Pres)
Debra Platis (Controller)
Michael Vance (VP-Ops)
Richard Dunn (Treas & Sec)
Jon Easter (VP-California)
Jeff Morgan (Mgr-Project & Ops-California)
Travis Goldston (Project Mgr-California)

CULPEPER FARMERS COOP-ERATIVE INC
15172 Brandy Rd, Culpeper, VA 22701
Tel.: (540) 825-2200
Web Site:
　http://www.cfcfarmhome.com
Sales Range: $10-24.9 Million
Emp.: 150
Farm Supplies
N.A.I.C.S.: 424910
David Durr (Gen Mgr)
Lydia Utz (Mgr-HR)

CULPEPPER & ASSOCIATES SECURITY SERVICES, INC.
1810 Water Pl, Atlanta, GA 30339
Tel.: (770) 916-0060
Web Site: http://www.cassecurity.com
Year Founded: 1992
Sales Range: $10-24.9 Million
Emp.: 300
Security Services & Products
N.A.I.C.S.: 561621
Louis Culpepper (Founder, Pres & CEO)
Vera Culpepper (Exec VP)
Pam Cooper (Dir-Fin & HR)

CULT360
225 Varick St 3rd Fl, New York, NY 10014
Tel.: (212) 463-9300
Web Site: http://www.cult360.com
Sales Range: $10-24.9 Million
Emp.: 15
N.A.I.C.S.: 541810
Joe Jelic (Partner & Dir-Creative)
Daniel Armyn (Assoc Dir-Creative)
Jeff Rothstein (Partner & Strategist-Mktg)

CULTIVA LLC
4780 W Harmon Ave Ste 6, Las Ve-gas, NV 89103
Web Site: http://www.cultiva.com
Year Founded: 2011
Sales Range: $1-9.9 Million
Emp.: 11
Agriculture Technology Development Services
N.A.I.C.S.: 541715
Luis Hernandez (CEO)
Chad Christopherson (Sls Dir)

Cultural Data Project—(Continued)

CULTURAL DATA PROJECT
400 Market St Ste 600, Philadelphia, PA 19106
Tel.: (215) 383-0700   **PA**
Web Site: http://www.culturaldata.org
Year Founded: 2012
Sales Range: $10-24.9 Million
Emp.: 40
Art & Cultural Promotion Services
N.A.I.C.S.: 711310
Ken Dinitz (Dir-Development)

CULTURAL EXPERIENCES ABROAD
2999 N 44th St, Phoenix, AZ 85018
Tel.: (480) 557-7900
Web Site: http://www.gowithcea.com
Year Founded: 1996
Sales Range: $10-24.9 Million
Emp.: 70
International Study & Education Opportunities Abroad for US Students
N.A.I.C.S.: 923110
Brian Boubek (Chm & CEO)
Caroline Walsh (Partner-Program Ops & VP-Dev)

CULVER CITY MOTOR CARS, INC.
11201 Washington Blvd, Culver City, CA 90230-4621
Tel.: (310) 391-0445
Web Site: https://www.culvercityvolvo.com
Sales Range: $25-49.9 Million
Emp.: 50
New Car Dealers
N.A.I.C.S.: 441110
Leigh Balcher (Mgr-Sls)
Florence Benjamin (Mgr-Customer Rels)
Richard Diaz (Asst Mgr-Internet)
Guy Garner (Mgr-Overseas Delivery)
Augie Gonzales (Dir-Svc & Parts)
Tony Tehrani (Portfolio Mgr)
Will Saunders (Mgr-Fin)
Steve Irons (Dir-Parts)

CULVER FRANCHISING SYSTEM, INC.
1240 Water St, Prairie Du Sac, WI 53578
Tel.: (608) 643-7980
Web Site: http://www.culvers.com
Year Founded: 1984
Sales Range: $10-24.9 Million
Emp.: 200
Fast Food Franchise Operator
N.A.I.C.S.: 722511
Craig C. Culver (Founder & Chm)
Jeff Bonner (COO)
Enrique Silva (CEO)

CULVER GLASS COMPANY
2619 NW Industrial St, Portland, OR 97210
Tel.: (503) 226-2520
Web Site: https://www.culver-glass.com
Sales Range: $10-24.9 Million
Emp.: 36
Glass & Glazing Work
N.A.I.C.S.: 238150
Terry Burns (Pres)
Craig Nauck (Project Mgr)
Culver Glass (VP)
Todd Barnes (VP)

CUMBERLAND AMERICA DEVELOPMENT COMPANY INC.
6928 Lupton Dr, Dallas, TX 75225
Tel.: (214) 750-7744
Year Founded: 1994
Sales Range: $10-24.9 Million

Emp.: 20
Subdividers & Developers of Real Estate
N.A.I.C.S.: 237210

CUMBERLAND CHRYSLER CENTER
1540 Interstate Dr, Cookeville, TN 38501
Tel.: (931) 526-5600
Web Site: http://www.cumberland-auto.com
Year Founded: 1991
Sales Range: $10-24.9 Million
Emp.: 110
Automobiles New & Used Service & Parts
N.A.I.C.S.: 441110
William Lanny Dunn (Owner)

CUMBERLAND CONSULTING GROUP, LLC
720 Cool Springs Blvd Ste 550, Franklin, TN 37067
Tel.: (615) 373-4470
Web Site: http://www.cumberlandcg.com
Year Founded: 2004
Rev.: $8,000,000
Emp.: 265
Management Consulting Services
N.A.I.C.S.: 541618
Jim Lewis (Chm)
Matt Abrams (CIO)
Brian Junghans (Mng Partner)
Christopher Miller (Partner-Provider)
Greg Varner (Partner)
Mike Penich (Partner)
Jennifer Montlary (Dir-Mktg & Comm)
Terrell Warnberg (Partner)
Pete Biagioni (Mng Partner)
Matthew Good (Partner)
Tom Howard (Partner)
Brian Cahill (CEO)
Brian Cahill (CEO)

CUMBERLAND COUNTY GUIDANCE CENTER
2038 Carmel Rd, Millville, NJ 08332
Tel.: (856) 825-6810   **NJ**
Web Site: https://www.ccgcnj.org
Year Founded: 1964
Sales Range: $10-24.9 Million
Emp.: 235
Behavioral Healthcare Services
N.A.I.C.S.: 623220
Josephine White (Dir-Clinical)
Gary Moellers (Dir-Community Svcs)
David G. Bartels (CFO)
H. Dieter Hovermann (Exec Dir)
George R. LoBiondo (Dir-HR)
Robin Daplyn (VP)
Wayne Lewis (Dir-Quality Improvement)
Anita Brady (Treas)
Donna Vertolli (Sec)

CUMBERLAND COUNTY HOSPITAL ASSOCIATION INC.
299 Glasgow Rd, Burkesville, KY 42717
Tel.: (270) 864-2511   **KY**
Web Site: https://www.cchospital.org
Year Founded: 1964
Sales Range: $1-9.9 Million
Emp.: 222
Health Care Srvices
N.A.I.C.S.: 622110
Richard Neikirk (CEO)
Richie Capps (CFO)
Samuel Rice (Dir-Inpatient Svcs)

CUMBERLAND DAIRY INCORPORATED

899 Landis Ave, Rosenhayn, NJ 08352
Tel.: (856) 451-1300
Web Site: https://www.cumberlanddairy.com
Rev.: $47,391,168
Emp.: 100
Milk Drinks, Flavored
N.A.I.C.S.: 311511
Don Richman (Mgr-Production)
Carmine Catalana III (Pres)

CUMBERLAND ELECTRIC MEMBERSHIP CORPORATION
1940 Madison St, Clarksville, TN 37043-6521
Tel.: (931) 645-2481   **TN**
Web Site: https://www.cemc.org
Year Founded: 1938
Sales Range: $25-49.9 Million
Emp.: 195
Electronic Services
N.A.I.C.S.: 221122
James Codd (Gen Mgr)

CUMBERLAND ELECTRONICS INC.
2501 Sycamore St, Harrisburg, PA 17111
Tel.: (717) 233-5883
Web Site: http://www.cumb.com
Rev.: $11,661,000
Emp.: 45
Electronic Parts
N.A.I.C.S.: 423690
Don Smoths (Pres)

CUMBERLAND INSURANCE GROUP
633 Shiloh Pike, Bridgeton, NJ 08302
Tel.: (800) 232-6992
Web Site: http://www.cumberlandgroup.com
Year Founded: 1844
Sales Range: $125-149.9 Million
Emp.: 110
Property & Casualty Insurance Services
N.A.I.C.S.: 524126
David F. Raczenbek (Chief Legal Officer & Sec)
Harold P. Gunning (Sr VP-Casualty Claims)
Keith A. Maxfield (Chief Underwriting Officer & Exec VP)
William F. Fowler (VP-Underwriting)
Glenn W. Watkins (VP-Mktg)
Cheryl G. Oswald (VP-Mktg)
Adam Lamanteer (Controller)
Richard M. Ritter (COO & Exec VP)
Steve J. Catranis (Sr VP-Mktg)
Lisa C. Koelln (Asst VP-CL Product Mgmt)
Rob L. Musick (CIO & Sr VP)
Neal G. Pierce (CFO & Treas)
Linda M. May (VP-Product Dev)
Kenneth M. Mailley (Sr VP-Property Claims)
Patrick Padalik (Sr VP-Product & Pricing)
Jeanette Metzenroth (Asst VP-CL Underwriting)
Paul J. Ritter III (Pres & CEO)
Lawrence A. Pepper Jr. (Chm)

CUMBERLAND INTERNATIONAL TRUCKS, INC.
1901 Lebanon Pike, Nashville, TN 37210
Tel.: (615) 256-4633
Web Site: http://www.cumberlandtrucks.com
Sales Range: $25-49.9 Million
Emp.: 85
Heavy & Medium Duty Trucks Sales & Rentals

N.A.I.C.S.: 423110
Terry Minor (Pres)

CUMBERLAND MATERIALS
1710 61st Ave N, Nashville, TN 37209
Tel.: (615) 350-8888
Web Site: http://www.cumberlandmaterials.com
Sales Range: $25-49.9 Million
Emp.: 35
Drywall Materials
N.A.I.C.S.: 423320
Ron Hodges (Pres)
Freeman Payne (Mgr)
Heather Markum (Controller)

Subsidiaries:

3 Rivers Materials Inc   **(1)**
1441 Sunshine Ln, Lexington, KY 40505
Tel.: (859) 225-8801
Rev.: $5,000,000
Emp.: 8
Drywall Materials
N.A.I.C.S.: 423320

CUMBERLAND PACKING CORP.
2 Cumberland St, Brooklyn, NY 11205-1040
Tel.: (718) 858-4200   **NY**
Web Site: http://www.sweetnlow.com
Sales Range: $50-74.9 Million
Emp.: 350
Sugar & Salt Substitutes Mfr
N.A.I.C.S.: 325199
Frank Guglielmo (Mgr-Facility)
Claire Irizarry (Mgr-HR)
Marie Stigall (Supvr-AR)
Tulio Espinola (Dir-Pur)
Al Shea (Engr-Maintenance)
Sara Slivon (Mgr-Mktg)

Subsidiaries:

Butter Buds Food Ingredients   **(1)**
2330 Chicory Rd, Racine, WI 53403
Tel.: (262) 598-9900
Web Site: http://www.bbuds.com
Sales Range: $10-24.9 Million
Emp.: 70
Powered Diary Flavoring Concentrates Mfr
N.A.I.C.S.: 311512
William Buhler (Gen Mgr)

CUMBERLAND RECYCLING CORPORATION OF SOUTH JERSEY
702 S West Blvd, Vineland, NJ 08360
Tel.: (856) 825-4153
Web Site: https://www.cumberlandrecycling.com
Sales Range: $10-24.9 Million
Emp.: 43
Recycling, Waste Materials
N.A.I.C.S.: 562920
George Scholl Jr. (Pres)

CUMBERLAND TECHNOLOGIES, INC.
1501 E 2nd Ave, Tampa, FL 33605-5005
Tel.: (813) 885-2112   **FL**
Web Site: http://www.cumberlandtech.com
Year Founded: 1988
Sales Range: $25-49.9 Million
Emp.: 34
Holding Company
N.A.I.C.S.: 551112
Joseph R. Williams (Pres, CEO & Treas)

Subsidiaries:

Cumberland Casualty & Surety
Company   **(1)**
4311 W Waters Ave Ste 401, Tampa, FL 33614

Tel.: (813) 885-2112
Web Site: http://www.cumberlandtech.com
Sales Range: $25-49.9 Million
Emp.: 11
Provider of Casualty & Surety Insurance Services
N.A.I.C.S.: 524210

Qualex Consulting Group, Inc. **(1)**
4311 W Waters Ave Ste 304, Tampa, FL 33614-1901
Tel.: (813) 881-1162
Sales Range: $10-24.9 Million
Emp.: 15
Consulting Services
N.A.I.C.S.: 541618
Edward Mackowiak *(Pres)*

CUMBERLAND VALLEY FINANCIAL CORPORATION
100 Main St, London, KY 40741
Tel.: (606) 878-7010
Web Site: https://www.cvnb.com
Year Founded: 1983
Sales Range: $50-74.9 Million
Emp.: 220
Bank Holding Company
N.A.I.C.S.: 551111
James Tatum *(Pres & CEO)*
Tim Edwards *(COO)*

Subsidiaries:

Cumberland Valley National Bank & Trust Company **(1)**
100 Main St, London, KY 40741 **(100%)**
Tel.: (606) 878-7010
Web Site: http://www.cvnb.com
Sales Range: $50-74.9 Million
Emp.: 260
Savings Bank
N.A.I.C.S.: 522180
James Tatum *(CEO)*

CUMBEY & FAIR, INC.
2463 Enterprise Rd, Clearwater, FL 33763-1790
Tel.: (727) 797-8982   FL
Web Site:
   https://www.cumbeyfair.com
Year Founded: 1975
Sales Range: $1-9.9 Million
Emp.: 40
Engineering & Land Surveying Services
N.A.I.C.S.: 541330

CUMMING CONSTRUCTION MANAGEMENT, INC.
523 W 6th St Ste, Los Angeles, CA 90014
Tel.: (213) 408-4518   CA
Web Site: http://www.ccorpusa.com
Year Founded: 1996
Construction Management & Consulting Services
N.A.I.C.S.: 236220
Mike Jensen *(COO)*
Derek Hutchison *(Pres)*
Adam T. Todd *(Dir)*

Subsidiaries:

Project One Integrated Services LLC **(1)**
88 Inverness Cir E Bldg G Ste 101, Englewood, CO 80112
Tel.: (303) 771-0396
Web Site: http://www.p1cumming.com
Project Management & Owner Representation Firm
N.A.I.C.S.: 541611
Steve Howard *(Mng Principal)*
Kristen Pyle *(VP)*
Steve Sciscione *(VP-Ops)*
Daniel Pomfrett *(Reg Dir)*
Jack Christensen *(Dir)*
Patrick Chambers *(Dir)*

Zubatkin Owner Representation, LLC **(1)**
333 W 52nd St, New York, NY 10019
Tel.: (212) 271-4700

Web Site: http://www.zubatkin.com
Sales Range: $1-9.9 Million
Emp.: 16
Management Consulting Services
N.A.I.C.S.: 541618
Andrew J. Bast *(Principal)*
Martin S. Zubatkin *(Mng Principal)*
Jason B. Zubatkin *(VP)*
Laurie-Anne Haller *(Mgr-Comm)*
Erica Tishman *(VP)*

CUMMINGS ADVERTISING, INC.
5301 E State St Ste 301, Rockford, IL 61108
Tel.: (815) 398-4289
Web Site: http://www.42en.com
Sales Range: $1-9.9 Million
Emp.: 9
Advetising Agency
N.A.I.C.S.: 541810
Rick Belinson *(Pres)*
Carol Merry *(Sr Dir-Art)*
Amanda Nyen *(Dir-Media)*

CUMMINGS GROUP
New Towne Plz II 5301 E State St Ste 301, Rockford, IL 61108
Tel.: (815) 394-0184   IL
Year Founded: 1906
Sales Range: $1-9.9 Million
Emp.: 20
Advetising Agency
N.A.I.C.S.: 541810
Larry Schubert *(Sr Acct Exec)*

CUMMINGS MCGOWAN & WEST INC.
8668 Olive Blvd, Saint Louis, MO 63132
Tel.: (314) 993-1336
Web Site: https://www.cmw-equip.com
Sales Range: $10-24.9 Million
Emp.: 22
General Construction Machinery & Equipment
N.A.I.C.S.: 423810
Lee Newton *(VP)*
Lawrence F. Glynn Jr. *(Pres)*

CUMMINGS OIL CO. INC.
1389 Savannah Hwy, Hampton, SC 29924
Tel.: (803) 943-3921
Sales Range: $10-24.9 Million
Emp.: 18
Petroleum Bulk Stations
N.A.I.C.S.: 424710
H. V. Cummings *(Pres)*

CUMMINGS OIL INC.
42430 State Hwy 210, Aitkin, MN 56431-5107
Tel.: (218) 927-2909   MN
Year Founded: 1946
Sales Range: $25-49.9 Million
Emp.: 50
Oil Distr
N.A.I.C.S.: 424710
Kent Cummings *(Pres)*

CUMMINGS TRANSFER CO.
3015 Salem Ave SE, Albany, OR 97321
Tel.: (541) 928-3385
Rev.: $103,325,694
Emp.: 169
Trucking Service
N.A.I.C.S.: 493190
Don Arroyo *(Pres)*

Subsidiaries:

Cummings Moving Systems L.L.C. **(1)**
740 29th Ave SW, Albany, OR 97321
Tel.: (541) 928-3385

Web Site: http://www.ctcmovers.com
Rev.: $8,000,000
Emp.: 25
Movers of Household Goods
N.A.I.C.S.: 488991

Subsidiary (Domestic):

Cummings Moving Systems **(2)**
915 International Way, Springfield, OR 97477-1082
Tel.: (541) 688-5211
Moving & Storage Company-Mayflower Agent
N.A.I.C.S.: 484121

CUMMINGS-BACCUS INTERESTS
9606 N Mopac Expy Ste 125, Austin, TX 78759
Tel.: (512) 459-7100
Web Site:
   https://www.cummingsbaccus.com
Year Founded: 1992
Sales Range: $25-49.9 Million
Emp.: 3
Real Estate Agents & Brokerage Services
N.A.I.C.S.: 531210
Ross M. Cummings *(Gen Partner)*
M. Buckner Baccus *(Gen Partner)*

CUMMINS-WAGNER CO., INC.
10901 Pump House Rd, Annapolis Junction, MD 20701-1200
Tel.: (301) 490-9007   MD
Web Site: https://www.cummins-wagner.com
Year Founded: 1960
Sales Range: $10-24.9 Million
Emp.: 100
Supplier of Industrial Machinery & Equipment
N.A.I.C.S.: 423830

Subsidiaries:

Siewert Equipment Co. Inc. **(1)**
175 Akron St, Rochester, NY 14609
Tel.: (585) 482-9640
Web Site: http://www.siewertequipment.com
Rev.: $13,693,350
Emp.: 48
Industrial Machinery & Equipment
N.A.I.C.S.: 423830
Gregg Chalmers *(VP-Ops)*
Jerry Connolly *(VP-Sls)*
Ed Lewis *(Controller)*

CUNNINGHAM BUTANE GAS COMPANY
5301 Hwy 49, West Helena, AR 72390
Tel.: (870) 572-5912
Rev.: $10,000,000
Emp.: 14
Gasoline
N.A.I.C.S.: 424720

CUNNINGHAM CHILDREN'S HOME
1301 N Cunningham Ave, Urbana, IL 61802
Tel.: (217) 367-3728   IL
Web Site:
   https://www.cunninghamhome.org
Year Founded: 1921
Sales Range: $25-49.9 Million
Emp.: 340
Child Care Services
N.A.I.C.S.: 624110
Pat Ege *(VP-Programs)*
Daniel Holmer *(VP-Fin & Ops)*
Marlin Livingston *(Pres & CEO)*
Rhonda Whitaker *(Pres)*

CUNNINGHAM FARMS INC.
102 Main St, Craig, MO 64437
Tel.: (660) 683-5631

Web Site: https://www.craiggrain.com
Rev.: $10,000,000
Emp.: 7
Fertilizer & Fertilizer Materials
N.A.I.C.S.: 424910

CUNNINGHAM FIELD & RESEARCH SERVICE
3 Signal Ave Ste A386, Ormond Beach, FL 32174
Tel.: (386) 677-5644
Web Site:
   https://www.crgglobalinc.com
Rev.: $15,664,568
Emp.: 40
Market Analysis Or Research
N.A.I.C.S.: 541910
Mary Cunningham *(Pres)*

CUNNINGHAM MOTORS, INC.
2516 Memorial Blvd, Springfield, TN 37172
Tel.: (615) 212-2263
Web Site:
   http://www.cunninghamgm.com
Sales Range: $10-24.9 Million
Emp.: 40
New & Used Automobile Dealer
N.A.I.C.S.: 441110
Calvin Cothron *(Owner)*
Roy Drusky *(Mgr-Sls)*
Bob Stroud *(Mgr-Used Cars)*

CUNNINGHAM SUPPLY INCORPORATED
674 Oakwood Ave, West Hartford, CT 06110
Tel.: (860) 953-2101
Web Site:
   http://www.cunninghamsupply.net
Sales Range: $10-24.9 Million
Emp.: 33
Provider of Plumbing & Hydronic Heating Supplies
N.A.I.C.S.: 423720
Kevin Cunningham *(Pres)*
Dale Duby *(Mgr)*

CUNNINGHAM-LIMP COMPANY
28970 Cabot Dr Ste 100, Novi, MI 48377
Tel.: (248) 489-2300   MI
Web Site:
   https://www.cunninghamlimp.com
Year Founded: 1940
Sales Range: $75-99.9 Million
Emp.: 12
Holding Company; Contracting Services
N.A.I.C.S.: 236220
John Packovich *(Controller)*
Donald R. Kegley Jr. *(Pres)*

CUPID FOUNDATIONS, INC.
475 Park Ave S, New York, NY 10016-3903
Tel.: (212) 686-6224
Web Site:
   http://www.cupidintimates.com
Sales Range: $75-99.9 Million
Emp.: 35
Brassieres, Girdles & Undergarments Mfr
N.A.I.C.S.: 315250
Bella Rozenfeld *(Mgr-Credit)*

CUPPLES' J & J COMPANY INCORPORATED
1063 Whitehall, Jackson, TN 38302
Tel.: (731) 424-3621
Web Site:
   https://www.cupplesjandj.com
Sales Range: $100-124.9 Million
Emp.: 120
Special Dies, Tools, Jigs & Fixtures

Cupples' J & J Company Incorporated—(Continued)

N.A.I.C.S.: 333514
James Cupples (Owner & Pres)
Lee Davies (CFO)

CUPRIC CANYON CAPITAL LLC

7377 E Doubletree Ranch Rd Ste A-180, Scottsdale, AZ 85258
Tel.: (480) 607-6771   DE
Web Site:
  http://www.cupriccanyon.com
Year Founded: 2010
Copper Asset Investment Holding Company
N.A.I.C.S.: 551112
Timothy R. Snider (Founder, Founder, Chm & Chm)
Dennis M. Bartlett (CEO)
Lowell A. Shonk (Founder)
Rodney A. Prokop (CFO)
Catherine Knight (VP-Exploration & Resource Dev)
Johan Ferreira (Mng Dir-Khoemacau Copper Mining & Head-Ops-Africa)
Dale Quaker (CFO)

CUR MEDIA INC.

2217 New London Tpke, South Glastonbury, CT 06073
Tel.: (211) 8604301520   DE
Year Founded: 2011
CURM—(OTCBB)
Emp.: 100
Internet & Mobile Music Streaming Application
N.A.I.C.S.: 513210

CURAE HEALTH, INC.

1721 Midpark Rd, Knoxville, TN 37921
Tel.: (865) 269-4074   TN
Web Site: http://www.curaehealth.org
Health Care Services Organization
N.A.I.C.S.: 813910
Tim Brown (CFO)
Vince Jamagin (CIO)

Subsidiaries:

Amory HMA, LLC   (1)
1105 Earl Frye Blvd, Amory, MS 38821
Tel.: (662) 256-7111
Web Site:
  https://www.gilmorememorialhospital.org
Hospital Operator
N.A.I.C.S.: 622110
J. Allen Tyra (CEO)

Batesville HMA Medical Group, LLC   (1)
303 Medical Ctr Dr, Batesville, MS 38606-8608
Tel.: (662) 563-5611
Web Site:
  http://www.panolamedicalcenter.org
Hospital Operator
N.A.I.C.S.: 622110

Clarksdale HMA, LLC   (1)
1970 Hospital Dr, Clarksdale, MS 38614
Tel.: (662) 627-3211
Web Site:
  http://www.northwestmsmedicalcenter.org
Hospital Operator
N.A.I.C.S.: 622110

Lakeland Community Hospital, Inc.   (1)
42024 State Hwy 195 E, Haleyville, AL 35565
Tel.: (205) 486-5213
Web Site: http://www.lakelandcommunityhospital.com
Hospital Operator
N.A.I.C.S.: 622110
Debbie Pace (CEO)

Northwest Medical Center, Inc.   (1)
1530 US Hwy 43, Winfield, AL 35594
Tel.: (205) 487-7000

Web Site:
  http://www.northwestmedcenter.net
Hospital Operator
N.A.I.C.S.: 622110
Glenda Reyes (CFO)
Theresa Lawrence (Dir-Nursing)
Danna Hardin (Dir-HR)
Robert Henger (CEO)
Jim L. Dickinson (Chm)
Russell Carothers (Vice Chm)

Russellville Hospital, Inc.   (1)
15155 Hwy 43, Russellville, AL 35653
Tel.: (256) 332-1611
Web Site: http://www.russellvillehospital.com
Hospital Operator
N.A.I.C.S.: 622110
Pam Welborn (Dir-Nursing)
Diane Myrick (Dir-Quality Resource Mgmt)

CURAEGIS TECHNOLOGIES, INC.

1999 Mt Read Blvd Bldg 3, Rochester, NY 14615
Tel.: (585) 254-1100   NY
Web Site: http://www.curaegis.com
Year Founded: 1996
CRGS—(OTCBB)
Rev.: $15,000
Assets: $251,000
Liabilities: $12,454,000
Net Worth: ($12,203,000)
Earnings: ($4,494,000)
Emp.: 7
Fiscal Year-end: 12/31/19
Holding Company; Automotive Parts Designer & Mfr
N.A.I.C.S.: 551112

CURAMED STAFFING, LLC

1825 S Pinellas Ave, Tarpon Springs, FL 34689
Tel.: (727) 938-7485
Web Site:
  http://www.curamedstaffing.com
Sales Range: $1-9.9 Million
Emp.: 35
Nursing & Healthcare Professional Staffing Services
N.A.I.C.S.: 561311
Shannon Sutton (CEO)

CURAS, INC.

1676 Bryan Rd Ste 111, Dardenne Prairie, MO 63368
Tel.: (636) 980-1310
Web Site: http://www.curas.net
Year Founded: 2004
Sales Range: $1-9.9 Million
Emp.: 25
Health Information Technology Consulting
N.A.I.C.S.: 541690
Num Pisutha-Arnond (Mng Partner)

CURATIVE CARE NETWORK, INC.

1000 N 92nd St, Milwaukee, WI 53226
Tel.: (414) 259-1414   WI
Web Site: https://www.curative.org
Year Founded: 1919
Sales Range: $10-24.9 Million
Emp.: 532
Residential Rehabilitation Services
N.A.I.C.S.: 623210
Maureen Collins (VP-Quality)
Julie Rogers (VP-Mktg & Comm)
Sandy Modahl (Dir-Birth To Three Program)
Janine Overeem (VP-Therapy Svcs)
Barbara Tice (CFO)
Patricia Fabian (Dir-Adult Day Ops)
Karin Langsdorf (Dir-IT)
Candace Hennessy (Pres & CEO)

CURATORS OF THE UNIVERSITY OF MISSOURI

One Hospital Dr, Columbia, MO 65212
Tel.: (573) 882-4141
Web Site: https://www.muhealth.org
Emp.: 100
General Medical & Surgical Hospital
N.A.I.C.S.: 622110

Subsidiaries:

Capital Region Medical Center Inc.   (1)
1125 Madison St, Jefferson City, MO 65101-5227
Tel.: (573) 632-5000
Web Site: https://www.crmc.org
Sales Range: $75-99.9 Million
Emp.: 1,200
Provider of General Medical & Surgical Hospital Services
N.A.I.C.S.: 622110
Janet Weckenborg (VP-Ops)
Robert A. Mazur (VP-HR)
Jason Cecil (CIO)
Tom Luebbering (VP-Fin)
Randall Haight (VP-Medical Affairs)
Thomas Niekamp (VP-Physician Rels & Clinics)
Jason Schwartz (Chm)
Rod Smith (Sec)
Steve Price (Vice Chm & Treas)

CURB RECORDS, INC.

48 Music Sq E, Nashville, TN 37203
Tel.: (615) 321-5080
Web Site: http://www.curb.com
Year Founded: 1962
Music Publisher & Distr
N.A.I.C.S.: 512230
Dennis Hannon (Gen Mgr)
Jeffrey Edmonson (Controller)
Mike Curb (Owner)
Jim Ed Norman (CEO-Recorded Music & Publ-Word Entertainment)
Cheryl Broz (Sr VP-Pop Promotion & Radio Mktg)
Laurel Kittleston (VP-Artist Dev & A&R)

Subsidiaries:

Word Entertainment LLC   (1)
25 Music Sq W, Nashville, TN 37203-3205   (100%)
Tel.: (615) 251-0600
Web Site:
  http://www.wordentertainment.com
Holding Company; Music & Entertainment Media Recording, Publishing & Distribution Services
N.A.I.C.S.: 551112
Rod Riley (Pres & CEO)

CURBELL, INC.

7 Cobham Dr, Orchard Park, NY 14127-4101
Tel.: (716) 667-3377   NY
Web Site: http://www.curbell.com
Year Founded: 1942
Emp.: 450
Holding Company; Plastic & Medical Products Mfr
N.A.I.C.S.: 551112
Thomas E. Leone (CEO & Chm)
Tina Sabuda (Vice Chm)

Subsidiaries:

Curbell Medical Products, Inc.   (1)
7 Cobham Dr, Orchard Park, NY 14127
Tel.: (716) 667-2520
Web Site: http://www.curbellmedical.com
Medical Products Mfr & Whslr
N.A.I.C.S.: 334510
Keith Hechtel (Sr Dir-Bus Dev)

Curbell Plastics, Inc.   (1)
7 Cobham Dr, Orchard Park, NY 14127
Tel.: (716) 667-3377
Web Site: http://www.curbellplastics.com
Plastic Product Distr
N.A.I.C.S.: 424610

Garry Helbig (Pres)
Peter Delgado (Sr Dir-Sls & Customer Svc)
Keith Hechtel (Sr Dir-Bus Dev)
Charlie Riley (Mktg Dir)

Subsidiary (Domestic):

Nationwide Plastics, Inc.   (2)
2001 Timberlake Dr, Arlington, TX 76010
Tel.: (214) 239-3870
Web Site: http://www.nationwideplastics.net
All Other Plastics Product Mfr
N.A.I.C.S.: 326199
Ron Hopton-Jones (Pres & CEO)

CURBS PLUS, INC.

8767 Alabama Hwy, Ringgold, GA 30736
Tel.: (706) 858-1188
Web Site: https://www.curbs-plus.com
Year Founded: 1996
Sales Range: $10-24.9 Million
Emp.: 105
Sheet Metal Work Mfg
N.A.I.C.S.: 332322
Jon Steed (Pres)
Steve Rodman (VP-Pur & Ops)
Bill Noble (Controller)

CURE 4 THE KIDS FOUNDATION

3121 S Maryland Pkwy Ste 220, Las Vegas, NV 89109
Tel.: (702) 732-0232   NV
Web Site:
  http://www.cure4thekids.org
Year Founded: 2007
Sales Range: $10-24.9 Million
Emp.: 34
Child Health Care Services
N.A.I.C.S.: 622310
Annette Logan (Founder & Pres)
Catherine Laska (Treas)
Alan Ikeda (Chief Medical Officer-Children's Specialty Center-Nevada)
Kanyalakshmi Ayyanar (Dir-Oncology-Children's Specialty Center-Nevada)
Danielle Bello (Dir-Long-Term Follow-Up Clinic-Childhood Cancer Survivors)
Rose Sarti (Mgr-Special Events & Donor Rels)

CURE STARTS NOW

10280 Chester Rd, Cincinnati, OH 45215
Tel.: (513) 772-4888   OH
Web Site:
  https://www.thecurestartsnow.org
Year Founded: 2007
Sales Range: $1-9.9 Million
Emp.: 3
Cancer Treatment Services
N.A.I.C.S.: 622310
Keith Desserich (Chm)

CURI HOLDINGS, INC.

7650 Edinborough Way Ste 525, Minneapolis, MN 55435
Tel.: (800) 328-5532
Web Site: https://curi.com
Emp.: 100
Holding Company; Insurance Services
N.A.I.C.S.: 551112
Jason Sandner (CEO)
Ryan Crawford (CEO-Insurance)

Subsidiaries:

Constellation, Inc.   (1)
7701 France Ave S Ste 500, Edina, MN 55435
Tel.: (952) 838-6700
Web Site:
  https://www.constellationmutual.com
Mutual Insurance Holding Company; Medical Liability Insurance Products & Services
N.A.I.C.S.: 551112

William J. McDonough *(Pres & CEO)*
Deb Penrod *(CIO & VP-IT)*
Jay Koepsell *(VP & Controller)*
John Woodward *(VP-Bus Dev)*
Julie Stafford *(Pres-MMIC)*
Laurie Drill-Mellum *(Chief Medical Officer)*
Steve Lacke *(COO & CFO)*
Lori Trygg *(Chief Legal Officer & Sr VP)*
Nicholas Ghiselli *(VP-Legal)*
Jeff Pearson *(VP-Underwriting)*
Tim Schultz *(VP-Claims)*
Heidi Thom *(Sr VP-Corp Strategy)*

Subsidiary (Domestic):

Midwest Medical Insurance
Company   **(2)**
7701 France Ave S, Minneapolis, MN
55435
Tel.: (952) 838-6700
Web Site: http://www.mmicgroup.com
Medical Insurance Products & Services
N.A.I.C.S.: 524114
Julie Stafford *(Pres)*
Jeff Pearson *(VP-Underwriting)*

Curi Wealth Management, LLC   **(1)**
700 Spring Forest Rd, Ste 235, Raleigh, NC
27609
Tel.: (984) 202-2800
Web Site: https://curicapital.com
Financial Services
N.A.I.C.S.: 523999
Dimitri P. Eliopoulos *(CEO)*

Subsidiary (Domestic):

RMB Capital Management, LLC   **(2)**
115 S LaSalle 34th Fl, Chicago, IL 60603
Tel.: (312) 993-5800
Web Site: http://www.rmbcap.com
Financial Investment Management Services
N.A.I.C.S.: 523940
Frederick Paulman *(Co-Founder, Pres & Partner)*
Jeffrey C. Pearsall *(Partner & Mng Dir-Family Office Svcs-Chicago)*
Christopher M. Graff *(Co-Chief Investment Officer, Partner & Mng Dir-Asset Mgmt-Chicago)*
Jay Krause *(Mgr-Client Relationship-Denver)*
Kate Demet *(Partner & CMO)*
Donald A. Bechter *(Partner & Mng Dir-M&A-West Denver)*
Katherine Lester *(VP & Mgr-Training & Dev)*
Erica Tarantur *(VP)*
Sean Conway *(VP & Mgr-Integrations)*
Trevor Isham *(VP-Milwaukee)*
Andrew Baker *(Partner & Portfolio Mgr)*
Gretchen T. McLaughlin *(VP-Client Dev-Denver)*
Maher Hrb *(CFO & Partner)*
Jennifer A. Rydwelski *(Chief HR Officer & Partner)*
Michelle Francisco *(Partner)*
Richard M. Burridge Jr. *(Co-Founder, CEO, Co-Chief Investment Officer)*

Subsidiary (Domestic):

Greenwood Investment Management
Inc.   **(3)**
6430 S Quebec St Bldg 6, Centennial, CO
80111-4628   **(100%)**
Tel.: (303) 366-5799
Web Site:
    http://www.greenwoodinvestment.com
Emp.: 12
Investment & Portfolio Advice
N.A.I.C.S.: 523940
Ken James *(VP & Advisor)*

CURIODYSSEY
1651 Coyote Point Dr, San Mateo,
CA 94401
Tel.: (650) 342-7755   **CA**
Web Site: http://www.curiodyssey.org
Year Founded: 1953
Sales Range: $1-9.9 Million
Emp.: 67
Science & Wildlife Center Operator
N.A.I.C.S.: 813312
Joan Martel *(Dir-Fin & Ops)*
Nikii Finch-Morales *(Dir-Wildlife)*
Eric Maschwitz *(Dir-Exhibits)*
Rachel Meyer *(Exec Dir)*

Ann Aristides *(Vice Chm)*
Amy Ramsey *(Vice Chm)*
Tara Samuels *(Sec)*
Connie Sevier *(Chm)*
Patricia Jenkins *(Dir-Mktg & Comm)*
Carl Oosterman *(Dir-Education)*
Ryan Polley *(Vice Chm)*

CURRAN & CONNORS, INC.
3455 Peachtree Rd NE 5th Fl, At-
lanta, GA 30326-3236
Tel.: (404) 239-3979
Web Site: http://www.curran-
connors.com
Year Founded: 1965
Sales Range: $10-24.9 Million
Emp.: 50
Advertising, Graphic Design,
Internet/Web Design, Local Market-
ing, Nonprofit/Social Marketing, Stra-
tegic Planning/Research
N.A.I.C.S.: 541810
Henry L. Morris *(Chm)*
Paul Cammarata *(VP-Production)*
Barbara Koontz *(Reg VP)*

CURRAN GROUP, INC.
286 Memorial Ct, Crystal Lake, IL
60014
Tel.: (815) 455-5100   **DE**
Web Site:
    http://www.currangroup.com
Year Founded: 1930
Sales Range: $200-249.9 Million
Emp.: 1,200
Highway & Street Paving Contractor;
Ceramic Wall & Floor Tile; Railroad
Equipment & Supplies
N.A.I.C.S.: 327120
Timothy J. Curran *(Co-Pres)*
Michael Curran *(Co-Pres)*
Catherine Curran *(Sec)*
Jim Lancaster *(Controller)*

Subsidiaries:

Curran Contracting Company   **(1)**
286 Memorial Ct, Crystal Lake, IL
60014-6277   **(100%)**
Tel.: (815) 455-5100
Web Site: http://www.currancontracting.com
Sales Range: $25-49.9 Million
Emp.: 35
N.A.I.C.S.: 237310
Rick Noe *(Pres)*
Jim Lancaster *(Controller)*
Bill Curran *(VP)*

Plant (Domestic):

Curran Contracting Company, Inc. -
Lake Bluff Plant   **(2)**
941 Skokie Hwy, Lake Bluff, IL 60044-1118
Tel.: (847) 689-1181
Hot Mix Asphalt Mfr
N.A.I.C.S.: 324121

Curran Contracting Company, Inc. -
McHenry Plant   **(2)**
1819 N Dot St, McHenry, IL 60050-6586
Tel.: (815) 385-6310
Hot Mix Asphalt Mfr
N.A.I.C.S.: 324121

Subsidiary (Domestic):

G.A. Blocker Grading Contractor,
Inc.   **(2)**
18 Stonehill Rd, Oswego, IL 60543
Tel.: (630) 554-1665
Web Site: http://www.gablocker.com
Site Preparation Contractor
N.A.I.C.S.: 238910
Matt Blocker *(Pres)*

Curran Contracting Inc   **(1)**
2220 County Farm Rd, Dekalb, IL 60115-
9429
Tel.: (815) 758-8113
Web Site: http://www.currancontracting.com
Sales Range: $10-24.9 Million
Emp.: 55
N.A.I.C.S.: 237310

Mike Leopardo *(Mgr-DeKalb)*
Rick Noe *(Pres)*

Global Finishing Solutions LLC   **(1)**
12731 Norway Rd, Osseo, WI
54758-0250   **(100%)**
Tel.: (715) 597-3168
Web Site: http://www.globalfinishing.com
Sales Range: $25-49.9 Million
Emp.: 400
Paint Booth Equipment Mfr
N.A.I.C.S.: 333248
Jack Vold *(Mgr-Bus Unit)*
Vicki Hagberg *(Mgr-Sls & Support)*
Brian Antczak *(Project Mgr)*
James Faragher *(Pres)*
Steve Love *(Mgr-Parts & Filters Sls Dept)*
Sal Parente *(Exec VP-Ops)*
Dustin Warren *(Sr Acct Mgr-Automotive Re-
finish Sls Team)*

Holland LP   **(1)**
1000 Holland Dr, Crete, IL 60417-2120
Tel.: (708) 672-2300
Web Site: http://www.hollandco.com
Sales Range: $25-49.9 Million
Emp.: 300
Mfr Of Railway Products
N.A.I.C.S.: 238990

CURRAX PHARMACEUTICALS
LLC
10 N Park Pl Ste 201, Morristown, NJ
07960
Web Site:
    http://www.curraxpharma.com
Pharmaceutical Products Distr
N.A.I.C.S.: 424210
Eckard Weber *(CEO)*

CURRENT BUILDERS OF
FLORIDA INC.
2251 Blount Rd, Pompano Beach, FL
33069-5114
Tel.: (954) 977-4211   **FL**
Web Site:
    http://www.currentbuilders.net
Year Founded: 1985
Rev.: $94,300,000
Emp.: 150
Residential Construction
N.A.I.C.S.: 236220
Michael C. Taylor *(CEO)*
Charlene Faber *(COO)*
Scott Remer *(VP-Ops)*
Aaron Buttress *(VP-Construction)*
Ryan Kelley *(VP-Construction)*
Chip Angenendt *(Partner)*
Darrell Turner *(Dir-Mktg-West Coast)*
Mike Gillette *(Partner)*
Brett Schreiber *(Partner)*

CURRENT CAPITAL LLC
555 Madison Ave 19th Fl, New York,
NY 10022
Tel.: (212) 737-3671   **DE**
Web Site: http://www.currentcap.com
Year Founded: 2008
Sales Range: $1-9.9 Million
Private Equity & Investment Manage-
ment Firm
N.A.I.C.S.: 523999
Jonathan F. Foster *(Founder & Mng
Dir)*

CURRENT, INC.
30 Tyler Street Ext, East Haven, CT
06512
Tel.: (203) 469-1337   **CT**
Web Site:
    http://www.currentcomposites.com
Year Founded: 1962
Plastics Product Mfr
N.A.I.C.S.: 326130
Albert Prinz Jr. *(VP-Sls)*

CURRIER CONSTRUCTION
INC.
36 N 56th St, Phoenix, AZ 85034
Tel.: (602) 274-4370

Web Site: https://www.currierinc.com
Rev.: $11,933,618
Emp.: 15
Industrial Plant Construction
N.A.I.C.S.: 237990
Scott A. Currier *(Founder & Pres)*
Michael Rivera *(Mgr)*
Jason Boelke *(Project Mgr)*

CURRIER MCCABE & ASSOCI-
ATES
700 Troy Schenectady Rd, Latham,
NY 12110
Tel.: (518) 783-9003
Web Site: http://www.cma.com
Sales Range: $10-24.9 Million
Emp.: 175
Computer Software Development
N.A.I.C.S.: 541511
Kay Stafford *(Pres & CEO)*
Kenneth Romanski *(Exec VP)*
Tom Mullen *(VP)*
Gary Davis *(Exec VP-Ops)*
Peter Chynoweth *(Sr VP)*
Steve Zizzi *(CTO & Dir-Program)*

CURRY AUTOMOTIVE, LLC.
767 Memorial Dr, Chicopee, MA
01020-5022
Tel.: (413) 593-6721
Web Site:
    https://www.curryhondamass.com
Year Founded: 1998
Sales Range: $25-49.9 Million
Emp.: 125
Car Whslr
N.A.I.C.S.: 441110
Richard Conrad *(Gen Mgr)*
Bernard Curry III *(Owner)*

CURRY CONTROLS COMPANY
INC.
4245 S Pipkin Rd, Lakeland, FL
33811
Tel.: (863) 646-5781
Web Site:
    http://www.currycontrols.com
Year Founded: 1972
Sales Range: $10-24.9 Million
Emp.: 45
Computerized Controls Installation
N.A.I.C.S.: 238210
David L. Curry *(Pres & CEO)*
Alex Curry *(Controller)*
Ben Matthews *(Mgr-Estimate)*
Mike Brown *(Engr-Application)*

CURRY CORPORATION
727 Central Park Ave, Scarsdale, NY
10583
Tel.: (914) 725-3500
Web Site: https://www.curryauto.com
Year Founded: 1919
Rev.: $132,300,000
Emp.: 15
Car Dealership Owner & Operator
N.A.I.C.S.: 441110
Howard Mirchin *(CFO)*
Bernard F. Curry III *(Owner & CEO)*

Subsidiaries:

Curry Acura   **(1)**
685 Central Ave, Scarsdale, NY 10583
Tel.: (914) 472-6800
Web Site: http://www.curryacura.com
Sales Range: $100-124.9 Million
Retailer of New & Used Vehicles
N.A.I.C.S.: 441110
Michael D. Miele *(Gen Mgr)*
Dimitry Davidoff *(Mgr-Fin)*
Whitney Bonilla *(Coord-Loaner)*
Yuri Abramov *(Mgr-Bus)*
Parm Singh *(Mgr-Bus)*

Curry Honda   **(1)**
767 Memorial Dr, Chicopee, MA 01020
Tel.: (413) 593-1155
Web Site: http://www.3cars.com

Curry Corporation—(Continued)

Sales Range: $25-49.9 Million
Automobile Dealers
N.A.I.C.S.: 441110
Joe Adamowicz (Mgr-IT & HR)

Curry Honda (1)
3845 Crompond Rd Rt 202, Yorktown
Heights, NY 10598
Tel.: (914) 739-7600
Web Site: http://www.curryhonda.com
Sales Range: $25-49.9 Million
Automobile Dealers
N.A.I.C.S.: 441110
Nicole Bruder (Office Mgr)

CURRY INVESTMENT COMPANY
2700 NE Kendallwood Pkwy, Gladstone, MO 64119-2083
Tel.: (816) 414-5200
Web Site: https://www.curryre.com
Sales Range: $10-24.9 Million
Emp.: 50
Real Estate Brokers & Agents
N.A.I.C.S.: 531210
Ellen Tod (Pres)

CURRY UP NOW
2640 5th St, Alameda, CA 94501
Tel.: (510) 217-8191
Web Site:
   http://www.curryupnow.com
Year Founded: 2009
Indian Street Food, Restaurant &
Food Trucks
N.A.I.C.S.: 722513
Akash Kapoor (CEO)

CURRY'S AUTO SERVICE
5611 Wellington Rd Unit 115, Gainesville, VA 20155
Tel.: (571) 382-2200
Web Site: http://www.currysauto.com
Sales Range: $10-24.9 Million
Emp.: 118
Automotive Tire Sales & Maintenance
Services
N.A.I.C.S.: 423130
Matt Curry (Pres & CEO)
Judy Curry (CMO)
Bob Curry (Reg Mgr)
Vernon Abel (Reg Mgr)

CURT G. JOA, INC.
100 Crocker Ave, Sheboygan Falls,
WI 53085-1141
Tel.: (920) 467-6136   WI
Web Site: https://www.joa.com
Year Founded: 1932
Sales Range: $10-24.9 Million
Emp.: 340
Mfr of Paper Converting Machinery
N.A.I.C.S.: 333243
Kevin Zeinemann (Mng Dir)
Brian Jankuski (Mgr-Bus Dev)
Richard Michaletz (Pres)

Subsidiaries:

Curt G. Joa Europe GmbH (1)
Strassenbahnring 13, 20251, Hamburg,
Germany
Tel.: (49) 40 80 60 99 33
Web Site: http://www.joa.com
Paper Mill Machinery Mfr
N.A.I.C.S.: 333243
Stephan Knobloch (Dir-Sls)

CURT WARNER CHEVROLET INC.
3712 NE 66th Ave, Vancouver, WA
98661
Tel.: (360) 892-0900
Web Site:
   http://www.alanwebbautogroup.com
Sales Range: $10-24.9 Million
Emp.: 100
New Car Whslr

N.A.I.C.S.: 441110
Jim Johnson (CEO)

CURTCO MEDIA LABS LLC
29160 Heathercliff Rd Ste 200,
Malibu, CA 90265-6105
Tel.: (310) 589-7700   CA
Web Site: http://www.curtco.com
Magazine & Periodical Publishing
N.A.I.C.S.: 513120
William J. Curtis (CEO)
Chris Fabian (CFO & Sr VP)
Lauren Coniglio (Sr VP-Circulation)
Charles Gawartin (Sr VP-Fin)
Colette Alderson (Sr VP)
Melinda Lyon (VP-HR)

Subsidiaries:

Worth Group, LLC (1)
1271 Ave Of The Americas 7th Fl, New
York, NY 10028
Tel.: (917) 934-2800
Web Site: http://www.worth.com
Magazine Publisher
N.A.I.C.S.: 513120
James Dimonekas (Pres)
Soledad O'Brien (Editor)
Eric Sinoway (CEO)
Richard Bradley (Chief Content Officer &
Editor-in-Chief)
Dean Sebring (Creative Dir)
Kirk Posmantur (Chm)

CURTIS C. GUNN, INC.
227 Broadway St, San Antonio, TX
78205-1923
Tel.: (210) 472-2501   DE
Web Site: http://www.gunnauto.com
Year Founded: 1955
Sales Range: $200-249.9 Million
Emp.: 900
Automobile Dealership
N.A.I.C.S.: 441110
Kelly Collins (CFO)
Curtis C. Gunn Jr. (Chm)

Subsidiaries:

Gunn Pontiac GMC, Inc. (1)
12526 Interstate Hwy 35 N, San Antonio,
TX 78233   (100%)
Tel.: (210) 599-5600
Web Site: http://www.gunnauto.com
Sales Range: $25-49.9 Million
Emp.: 210
Automobile Dealership
N.A.I.C.S.: 441110
Charlie O'Daniel (Gen Mgr)

CURTIS CIRCULATION COMPANY
730 River Rd, New Milford, NJ
07646-3048
Tel.: (201) 634-7400
Web Site: http://www.curtiscirc.com
Year Founded: 1946
Sales Range: $1-4.9 Billion
Magazine Distr
N.A.I.C.S.: 424920
Dennis F. Porti (Pres & CEO)
Michelle P. Ingenito (Sr VP-Publ Svcs
& Sls Dev)
Domenic A. Crocetti (CFO & Exec
VP)
Scott Largey (Sr VP-Sls & Mktg)
Brett Savio (COO & Exec VP)

CURTIS CORPORATION
44 Berkshire Rd, Sandy Hook, CT
06482
Tel.: (203) 426-5861
Web Site:
   https://www.curtispackaging.com
Sales Range: $25-49.9 Million
Emp.: 150
Folding Paperboard Boxes
N.A.I.C.S.: 322212
Donald Droppo (Pres)

Subsidiaries:

Curtis Packaging Corporation (1)
44 Berkshire Rd, Sandy Hook, CT 06482-
1499
Tel.: (203) 426-5861
Web Site: http://www.curtispackaging.com
Sales Range: $25-49.9 Million
Folding Paperboard Box Mfr
N.A.I.C.S.: 322212
Kerry Brown (VP-Ops)
Donald R. Droppo Jr. (Pres & CEO)

CURTIS H STOUT INC.
2400 Cantrell Rd Ste 100, Little
Rock, AR 72202
Tel.: (501) 372-2555
Web Site: https://www.chstout.com
Sales Range: $10-24.9 Million
Emp.: 61
Electrical Construction Materials
N.A.I.C.S.: 423610
David Payne (CFO)
Ron C. Smith (Pres & CEO)
Mark Elmore (Dir-Sls)

CURTIS INSTRUMENTS INC.
200 Kisco Ave, Mount Kisco, NY
10549
Tel.: (914) 666-2971
Web Site: http://www.curtisinst.com
Rev.: $109,810,000
Emp.: 170
Speed Indicators & Recorders, Vehicle
N.A.I.C.S.: 334514
Anne Papaelias (VP-HR)
David Ryan (Engr-Electrical)
Frank Fiumara (CFO)
Joe Mezzone (Engr-Mfg)
Steve Waite (Dir-Sls)

CURTIS LUMBER COMPANY, INC.
885 State Route 67, Ballston Spa,
NY 12020
Tel.: (518) 885-5311   NY
Web Site:
   https://www.curtislumber.com
Year Founded: 1949
Sales Range: $200-249.9 Million
Emp.: 450
Lumber & Building Supplies Whslr
N.A.I.C.S.: 444110
Jay S. Curtis (Pres)

CURTIS MEDIA GROUP
3012 Highwoods Blvd Ste 200, Raleigh, NC 27604-1031
Tel.: (919) 790-9392   NC
Web Site:
   https://www.curtismedia.com
Year Founded: 1991
Sales Range: $100-124.9 Million
Emp.: 200
Radio Broadcasting Stations
N.A.I.C.S.: 516110
Rick Martinez (VP-News & Info Programming)

Subsidiaries:

WBBB-FM (1)
3012 Highwoods Blvd Ste 200, Raleigh, NC
27604
Tel.: (919) 790-9392
Web Site: http://www.96rockonline.com
Sales Range: $10-24.9 Million
Emp.: 22
Radio Broadcasting Stations
N.A.I.C.S.: 516110

WGBR-AM (1)
2581 US 70 W, Goldsboro, NC 27530-1934
Tel.: (919) 734-3336
Web Site: http://www.wgbr.com
Sales Range: $10-24.9 Million
Emp.: 12
Radio Broadcasting Stations
N.A.I.C.S.: 516110
Bill Johnston (Gen Mgr)

WPCM-AM (1)
1109 Tower Dr, Burlington, NC 27215-4425
Tel.: (336) 584-0126
Web Site: http://www.920wpcm.com
Radio Broadcasting Stations
N.A.I.C.S.: 516110
Bill Whitley (Gen Mgr)

WPTF-AM (1)
3012 Highwoods Blvd Ste 201, Raleigh, NC
27604
Tel.: (919) 860-9783
Web Site: http://www.wptf.com
Sales Range: $10-24.9 Million
Emp.: 100
Radio Broadcasting Station Services
N.A.I.C.S.: 516110
Donald W. Curtis (Chm & CEO)
Trip Savery (Pres)
David Lewis (Gen Mgr)

WQDR-FM (1)
3012 Highwoods Blvd, Raleigh, NC 27604-
1037
Tel.: (919) 790-9392
Web Site: http://www.947qdr.com
Sales Range: $10-24.9 Million
Emp.: 100
Radio Broadcasting Stations
N.A.I.C.S.: 516110
Donald W. Curtis (CEO)
Lisa Mckay (Dir-Program)
Adam Maisano (Sr VP & Dir-Sls)
Seodt Taylor (Controller)
David Stuckey (Gen Mgr)
Tammy Odell (Mgr-Sls-Natl)

CURTIS OIL CO. INC.
4985 Miller Trunk Hwy, Hermantown,
MN 55811-1491
Tel.: (218) 729-8241
Web Site: http://www.curtisoil.com
Rev.: $25,328,631
Emp.: 45
Gasoline
N.A.I.C.S.: 424720
Frederick J. Curtis (Pres)
Tim Gross (CFO)
Olivia Johnston (Mgr-Food Svc)

CURTIS PACKING CO., INC.
2416 Randolph Ave, Greensboro, NC
27406-2910
Tel.: (336) 275-7684   NC
Web Site:
   https://www.curtispackingco.com
Year Founded: 1915
Sales Range: $10-24.9 Million
Emp.: 80
Provider of Meat Packing Services
N.A.I.C.S.: 311611
Doug Curtis (Pres)

CURTIS PARTITION CORP.
505 8th Ave Rm 201, New York, NY
10018
Tel.: (212) 695-5575
Web Site:
   http://www.curtispartition.com
Sales Range: $10-24.9 Million
Emp.: 40
Plastering, Drywall & Insulation
N.A.I.C.S.: 238310
Chris Mertz (VP-Ops)
Michael Fifelski (Superintendent)

CURTIS PRODUCTS INC.
401 N Bendix Dr, South Bend, IN
46628
Tel.: (574) 289-4891
Web Site:
   http://www.curtisproducts.com
Sales Range: $10-24.9 Million
Emp.: 150
Tube Fabricating (Contract Bending &
Shaping)
N.A.I.C.S.: 332996
David Heckaman (Pres)
John Heckaman (Pres)
Becky Papai (Mgr-Admin)
Greg Cheak (Mgr-IT)

CURTIS RESTAURANT EQUIP-MENT INC.
555 Shelley St, Springfield, OR 97477
Tel.: (541) 746-7480
Web Site:
https://www.curtisresteq.com
Year Founded: 1963
Rev.: $21,000,000
Emp.: 50
Whslr of Restaurant Equipment & Supplies
N.A.I.C.S.: 423440
Daniel E. Curtis *(Pres)*
Donna Lee *(Office Mgr)*
Sue Simonton *(Mgr-Acctg)*
Travis Yates *(Mgr-Warehouse)*

CURTIS SCREW CO., INC.
10 Industrial Rd, Prospect, CT 06712
Tel.: (203) 758-4441   DE
Web Site: http://www.curtisscrew.com
Year Founded: 1905
Sales Range: $150-199.9 Million
Emp.: 50
Holding Company; Precision Machined Metal Components Mfr & Whslr
N.A.I.C.S.: 551112
James A. Piatek *(Gen Mgr-Ops)*
John Hoskins Jr. *(Exec VP)*

Subsidiaries:

Curtis Screw Company, LLC   (1)
10 Industrial Rd, Prospect, CT 06712
Tel.: (203) 758-4441
Web Site: http://www.sheldonprecision.com
Precision Machined Metal Components Mfr & Whslr
N.A.I.C.S.: 332721
James A. Piateck *(Gen Mgr)*

CURTIS STEEL COMPANY
6504 Hurst St, Houston, TX 77008-6217
Tel.: (713) 861-4621   TX
Web Site:
https://www.curtissteelco.com
Year Founded: 1976
Sales Range: $25-49.9 Million
Emp.: 100
Provider of Steel Metals Services
N.A.I.C.S.: 423510
Mike Boriack *(Pres)*
Chris Vacek *(Controller)*
Tom Boriack *(Pres)*

CURTIS TRACTOR CAB, INC.
111 Higgins St, Worcester, MA 01606
Tel.: (508) 853-2200
Web Site: http://www.curtiscab.com
Year Founded: 1969
Sales Range: $25-49.9 Million
Emp.: 120
Mfr of Tractor & Truck Cabs
N.A.I.C.S.: 336211
Fred J. Curtis Jr. *(Founder)*

CURTIS TRAILERS INC.
10177 SE Powell Blvd, Portland, OR 97266
Tel.: (503) 760-1363
Web Site:
https://www.curtistrailers.com
Rev.: $10,000,000
Emp.: 40
Truck Mounted Camper Mfr
N.A.I.C.S.: 441210
Cammy Pierson *(VP)*

CURTIS V. COOPER PRIMARY HEALTH CARE, INC.
106 E Broad St, Savannah, GA 31401
Tel.: (912) 527-1000   GA
Web Site: https://www.cvcphc.net
Year Founded: 1979

Sales Range: $10-24.9 Million
Emp.: 159
Health Care Srvices
N.A.I.C.S.: 622110
Reginald Franklin *(Chm)*
Deborah Wright *(Treas)*
Mary Hill *(Sec)*
Larry Jackson *(Vice Chm)*
Albert B. Grandy Jr. *(CEO)*

CURTIS, MALLET-PREVOST, COLT & MOSLE LLP
101 Park Ave, New York, NY 10178
Tel.: (212) 696-6000   NY
Web Site: https://www.curtis.com
Year Founded: 1830
Sales Range: $125-149.9 Million
Emp.: 250
Law firm
N.A.I.C.S.: 541110
Evan S. Borenstein *(Partner)*
Jeffrey N. Ostrager *(Partner)*
Joseph D. Pizzurro *(Mng Partner)*
Eric L. Gilioli *(Partner)*
Mark H. O'Donoghue *(Partner)*
Marty L. Forman *(Partner)*
Miriam K. Harwood *(Partner)*
Nancy E. Delaney *(Partner)*
Theresa A. Foudy *(Partner)*
Valarie A. Hing *(Partner)*
Shaya Rochester *(Partner)*
David Bayrock *(Partner)*
Gabriela Alvarez-Avila *(Partner)*
Luis Maria Ayarragaray *(Partner)*
Marco A. Blanco *(Partner)*
Peter J. Behmke *(Partner)*
Roman A. Bninski *(Partner)*
Sabrina Ainouz *(Partner)*
William H. Barringer *(Partner)*

CURTIS-LAYER CONSTRUC-TION CO.
340 Harris Dr, Aurora, OH 44202
Tel.: (330) 562-5269
Web Site: http://www.curtislayer.com
Sales Range: $10-24.9 Million
Emp.: 5
Industrial Building Construction Services
N.A.I.C.S.: 236210
Michael J. Curtis *(Pres)*
Bob Ready *(VP)*
Mike Alexander *(Project Mgr)*

CURTS GAINES HALL JONES ARCHITECTS, INC.
1213 E 6th Ave Ybor City, Tampa, FL 33605
Tel.: (813) 228-8000   FL
Web Site:
https://www.cghjarchitects.com
Year Founded: 1987
Sales Range: $1-9.9 Million
Emp.: 18
Architectural Services
N.A.I.C.S.: 541310
Charles A. Jones *(Principal & Dir-Architecture)*
Gerald G. Curts *(Chm & Dir-Architecture)*
Stephanie December Gaines *(CFO & Dir-Architecture)*
Robert D. Hall *(Pres, CEO & Dir-Architecture)*
Joan Miller *(Office Mgr)*

CUSH ENTERPRISES INC.
1700 Auto Park Way N, Escondido, CA 92029
Tel.: (760) 737-3202
Year Founded: 1979
Sales Range: $125-149.9 Million
Emp.: 525
Dealer of New & Used Automobiles
N.A.I.C.S.: 441110

CUSHING AND COMPANY INC.
420 W Huron St, Chicago, IL 60654
Tel.: (312) 266-8228
Web Site: http://www.cushingco.com
Sales Range: $10-24.9 Million
Emp.: 50
Blueprinting Service
N.A.I.C.S.: 323111
Cathleen Cushing Duff *(Pres)*
Jorge Galvan *(Sr Mgr-Digital Production)*
Joe Cushing *(Exec VP-Ops)*
Brian Burke *(VP-Ops)*

CUSHING TERRELL
1185 W Grove St, Boise, ID 83702
Tel.: (208) 336-4900
Web Site: http://www.ctagroup.com
Rev.: $5,134,000
Emp.: 34
Architectural Services
N.A.I.C.S.: 541310

Subsidiaries:

Eclipse Engineering, P.C.   (1)
229 E Front St, Missoula, MT 59802
Tel.: (406) 721-5733
Web Site:
http://www.eclipse-engineering.com
Rev.: $1,200,000
Emp.: 14
Engineeering Services
N.A.I.C.S.: 541330
Tom Sullivan *(Pres)*

CUSHING TRANSPORTATION INC.
3756 S Cicero Ave, Chicago, IL 60804
Tel.: (708) 656-5050
Web Site:
http://www.cushingtrans.com
Rev.: $18,000,000
Emp.: 90
Provider of Local Trucking Services
N.A.I.C.S.: 484110
John Rocco Pacella *(Pres)*
Jerry Grosz *(Mgr-Ops)*
David Parkes *(Dir-IT)*
Eric Hermosillo *(VP-Ops)*
Dominic J. Pacella *(COO)*
Jim Pacella *(CEO)*
Joseph Pacella *(CFO)*
Vince Pacella *(VP-IT)*

CUSITECH, LLC
833 Green Crest Dr, Westerville, OH 43081
Tel.: (614) 212-4155
Web Site: http://www.cusitech.com
Emp.: 25
Electrical Equipment Mfr & Hardware Installation Services
N.A.I.C.S.: 335999
Craig Kalie *(Pres & CEO)*
Brent Pastorek *(VP-Fin)*

Subsidiaries:

Peak Professional Contractors Inc.   (1)
1029 S Sierra Madre St Ste A, Colorado Springs, CO 80903-4260
Tel.: (719) 578-0091
Web Site: http://peakprocontractors.com
Sales Range: $1-9.9 Million
Emp.: 30
Nonresidential Construction Services
N.A.I.C.S.: 236220
David Brinker *(Pres)*
Kelly Levar *(Comptroller)*
Mark Carlos *(VP-Field Ops)*
John Eldridge *(VP-Hotel Div)*
Bryon Hoewisch *(VP-Construction)*

CUST-O-FAB, INC.
8888 W 21st St, Sand Springs, OK 74063
Tel.: (918) 245-6685
Web Site: https://www.custofab.com

Year Founded: 1972
Sales Range: $10-24.9 Million
Emp.: 160
Plate Work Mfr
N.A.I.C.S.: 332313
Tony Phillips *(VP-Mfr)*
Dennis Barnett *(Dir-Plant Safety)*
Danny O'Brian *(VP-Sls & Mktg)*
Paul Stokes *(Mgr-Mfr)*

CUSTARD INSURANCE AD-JUSTERS INC.
4875 Avalon Ridge Pkwy, Peachtree Corners, GA 30071-4712
Tel.: (770) 263-6800   IN
Web Site: https://www.custard.com
Year Founded: 1962
Sales Range: $10-24.9 Million
Emp.: 430
Provider of Insurance Services
N.A.I.C.S.: 524291
Rick Custard *(Founder)*
Dave White *(Exec VP)*
Rick Linville *(Chm)*
Charles Peek *(CEO)*
Joe Wiggins *(Sr VP)*
Susan Meadows *(Sr VP)*
Alan Cooper *(Asst VP)*
Belinda Clay *(CFO)*
Michael Arendt *(Sr VP)*
Brian Goud *(VP)*

CUSTER CITY FARMERS COOP EXCHANGE
518 W Broadway Ave, Custer City, OK 73639
Tel.: (580) 593-2531
Web Site: http://www.custercoop.com
Sales Range: $10-24.9 Million
Emp.: 10
Grain Elevators
N.A.I.C.S.: 424510
Jet Tharp *(Gen Mgr)*
Lorri Jones *(Office Mgr)*

CUSTER OFFICE ENVIRON-MENTS INC.
217 Grandville Ave SW Ste 100, Grand Rapids, MI 49503-2602
Tel.: (616) 458-6322   MI
Web Site:
http://www.custeroffice.com
Year Founded: 1981
Rev.: $43,702,746
Emp.: 170
Design & Create Office Environments
N.A.I.C.S.: 449110

CUSTINO ENTERPRISES
1710 S Amphlett Blvd Ste 250, San Mateo, CA 94402
Tel.: (650) 638-3300
Web Site:
https://www.custinoenterprises.com
Rev.: $23,700,000
Emp.: 249
Transportation Agents & Brokers
N.A.I.C.S.: 488510
Ben Davies *(VP-Ops)*

CUSTODIAN VENTURES LLC
1185 Ave of the Americas 3rd Fl, New York, NY 10036
Tel.: (646) 768-8417   WY
Investment Fund
N.A.I.C.S.: 523999

CUSTOM ACCESSORIES INC.
5900 Ami Dr, Richmond, IL 60071
Tel.: (815) 678-1600   IL
Web Site: http://www.causa.com
Year Founded: 1974
Sales Range: $100-124.9 Million
Emp.: 160
Interior & Exterior Automotive Accessories Distr

Custom Accessories Inc.—(Continued)
N.A.I.C.S.: 423120
Vince Alesi (VP)

Subsidiaries:

Custom Accessories Asia Ltd.   (1)
Room 604 6 F 9 Chong Yip St Kwun Tong,
Kowloon, China (Hong Kong)   **(100%)**
Tel.: (852) 27230723
Emp.: 15
N.A.I.C.S.: 441330
David Li (Gen Mgr)

Custom Accessories Europe Ltd.   (1)
The Granary Standen Manor, Hungerford,
RG17 0RB, Berkshire, United
Kingdom   **(100%)**
Tel.: (44) 1488662770
Web Site: https://www.caeurope.co.uk
Sales Range: $10-24.9 Million
Emp.: 25
Automobile Parts Distr
N.A.I.C.S.: 441330

Custom Accessories Scandinavia
Oy   (1)
Tyyrpuurinkaput 4A 1819, Lahti, 15140,
Finland   **(70%)**
Tel.: (358) 37834417
Sales Range: $1-9.9 Million
Emp.: 2
N.A.I.C.S.: 441330

CUSTOM AIR, INC.
6384 Tower Ln, Sarasota, FL 34240
Tel.: (941) 371-0833
Web Site:
    http://www.customairinc.com
Year Founded: 1986
Sales Range: $10-24.9 Million
Emp.: 99
HVAC Contractors
N.A.I.C.S.: 238220
Gerald L. Kurtz (Owner, Pres & CEO)
Brad Schlabach (Dir-Sls & Mktg)
Larry Zeller (Mgr-Svc & Installation)
Rod Shrock (CFO)
Stephen Heinz (Mgr-Svc Contract)

CUSTOM ALLOY SCRAP SALES, INC.
2730 Peralta St, Oakland, CA 94607-
1707
Tel.: (510) 893-6476   CA
Web Site:
    https://www.customalloy.com
Year Founded: 1969
Ferrous & Non-ferrous Metals Pro-
cessor; Metal Recycling & Secondary
Aluminum Ingot Mfr
N.A.I.C.S.: 423930
Chal Sulprizio (Founder & CEO)
Carmen Zeng (CFO)

CUSTOM ALUMINUM PRODUCTS INC.
414 Division St, South Elgin, IL
60177-1110
Tel.: (847) 741-6333
Web Site: https://www.custom-
    aluminum.com
Year Founded: 1960
Sales Range: $25-49.9 Million
Emp.: 400
Aluminum Extruded Products
N.A.I.C.S.: 331318
James Castoro (Owner)
Walter Michael Dander (Engr-Quality)
Steve Dillett (Pres)

CUSTOM BILT METALS
4522 Parker Ave Ste 400, McClellan,
CA 95652
Tel.: (916) 333-5680   CA
Web Site:
    https://www.custombiltmetals.com
Year Founded: 1974
Sales Range: $25-49.9 Million
Emp.: 1,000

Whslr of Metalworking Machinery
N.A.I.C.S.: 423830
Joel Ramirez (Gen Mgr)

CUSTOM BUILDER SUPPLY COMPANY
4556 John Tyler Hwy, Williamsburg,
VA 23185
Tel.: (757) 229-5150
Web Site:
    https://www.custombuilders.com
Year Founded: 1988
Sales Range: $10-24.9 Million
Emp.: 32
Sale of Lumber, Plywood & Millwork
Products
N.A.I.C.S.: 423310
Randall Cooper (Pres)

CUSTOM BUILDING PRODUCTS
13001 Seal Beach Blvd, Seal Beach,
CA 90740-2753
Tel.: (562) 598-8808   CA
Web Site:
    http://www.custombuildingprod.com
Year Founded: 1953
Sales Range: $50-74.9 Million
Emp.: 600
Provider of Adhesives & Sealants
N.A.I.C.S.: 423840
Michael Chang (Dir-Engrg)
Steve Taylor (Dir-Architecture & Tech
Mktg)
Bruce Burton (Mgr-Bus Dev)

CUSTOM BUSINESS SOLUTIONS INC.
12 Morgan, Irvine, CA 92618-2003
Tel.: (949) 380-7674
Web Site:
    http://www.cbsnorthstar.com
Year Founded: 2001
Sales Range: $10-24.9 Million
Emp.: 70
Cash Registers
N.A.I.C.S.: 423420
Michael Block (CFO)
Art Julian (Founder & CEO)
Rom V. Krupp (VP-Bus Dev)
Jeremy Julian (VP-Pro Svcs)
Gary Stotko (VP-Sls & Mktg)
Joseph Castillo (VP-Software Dev)
Brian Wesley (Dir-Support Svcs)
Michael Crouse (Dir-Channel Sls-
Compass Dealer Network)

CUSTOM CABLE SERVICES, INC.
3518 Decatur Hwy, Fultondale, AL
35068
Tel.: (800) 227-1266   AL
Web Site:
    http://www.customcableservices.net
Year Founded: 1989
Sales Range: $1-9.9 Million
Emp.: 30
Cable & Other Pay Television Ser-
vices
N.A.I.C.S.: 516210
John Pait (Pres)
Gary Park (CEO)
Dan Shoop (VP-Ops)
John Westrich (Dir-Construction)
Steve Vickers (VP-Safety & Compli-
ance)
Melody Lott (Controller)
Richard Steffen (Reg Mgr)
Scott Pait (Dir-Tech)

CUSTOM CHEMICAL FORMULATORS, INC.
8707 Millergrove Dr, Santa Fe
Springs, CA 90670
Tel.: (562) 699-5070   CA

Web Site:
    https://www.customchem.com
Year Founded: 1964
Sales Range: $10-24.9 Million
Emp.: 45
Cleaning Preparations & Industrial
Chemicals Mfr
N.A.I.C.S.: 325612
Stacy Roselli (Dir-Mktg & Sls)

CUSTOM COMPUTER CABLES
2364 Merritt Dr Ste A, Garland, TX
75041
Tel.: (972) 638-9309
Web Site: http://www.cccoa.com
Year Founded: 1982
Sales Range: $1-9.9 Million
Emp.: 66
Fiber Optic Cable Mfr & Distr
N.A.I.C.S.: 335921
Jay Chenault (Pres & CEO)
Robbie Chenault (VP-Ops)
Kenneth Atkins (Exec VP)
Vince Schlueter (VP-Sls & Mktg)

CUSTOM COMPUTER SPECIALISTS, LLC
70 Suffolk Ct, Hauppauge, NY 11788
Tel.: (631) 864-6699
Web Site:
    https://www.customonline.com
Rev: $20,800,000
Emp.: 300
Systems Integration
N.A.I.C.S.: 541512
Irira Berk (Dir-IT)
Thomas Nejezchleba (Assoc Dir-
Project Mgmt Office)
Kenneth Wygand (Dir-Bus Dev)
Kyriakos Kaimis (Dir-Tech)
Laura Gavey (Mgr-Program & Ops)
Alan Lacher (Pres-CustomTech Soft-
ware)
Dennis Callagy (Pres-IT Div)

Subsidiaries:

Net Activity, Inc.   (1)
9535 Midwest Ave Ste 114, Garfield
Heights, OH 44125
Tel.: (216) 503-5150
Web Site: http://www.netactivity.us
Rev.: $1,000,000
Emp.: 14
Computer & Office Machine Repair & Main-
tenance
N.A.I.C.S.: 811210

CUSTOM CONTROL SENSORS, INC.
21111 Plummer St, Chatsworth, CA
91311-4905
Tel.: (818) 341-4610   CA
Web Site:
    https://www.ccsdualsnap.com
Year Founded: 1958
Sales Range: $100-124.9 Million
Emp.: 250
Pressure Flow & Temperature
Switches Mfr
N.A.I.C.S.: 335313
Rodger Benjamins (Controller)
Savitur Badhwar (Mgr-IT)
Ruiz Jorge (Mgr-Lean Mfg)
Eric FLOYD (Mgr)

CUSTOM CONTROL SOLUTIONS, INC.
1520 Power Blvd, Cantonment, FL
32533
Tel.: (850) 937-8902
Web Site: http://www.ccsinc-
    florida.com
Sales Range: $1-9.9 Million
Emp.: 20
Control Systems, Equipment Skids,
Analyzer Systems & Electrical Con-
trols Mfr

N.A.I.C.S.: 334513
Manfred Laner (Pres)
Glenn Miller (VP-Production)

CUSTOM DECOR, INC.
1585 McKee Rd Ste 1, Dover, DE
19904
Tel.: (302) 735-7600   DE
Web Site:
    https://www.customdecornet.com
Year Founded: 1974
Sales Range: $75-99.9 Million
Emp.: 28
Whslr of Mats & Flags
N.A.I.C.S.: 424990
William P. Scotton (Pres)
Angela Rigsby (Gen Mgr)

CUSTOM DECORATORS, INC.
12006 SW Garden Pl, Portland, OR
97223
Tel.: (503) 655-4114
Web Site:
    http://www.customdecorators.com
Sales Range: $75-99.9 Million
Emp.: 180
Interior Design Services
N.A.I.C.S.: 541410
Stephen Zimmer (Pres)
Curt Hopkins (Coord-Installation)

CUSTOM DESIGN & CONSTRUCTION
2001 E Mariposa Ave, El Segundo,
CA 90245
Tel.: (310) 815-4815
Web Site:
    https://www.visitcustomdesign.com
Year Founded: 1986
Sales Range: $1-9.9 Million
Emp.: 9
Home Design & Construction Ser-
vices
N.A.I.C.S.: 236115
Bill Simone (Pres)
Randy Ricciotti (VP)
Santos Mejia (Supvr-Field)

CUSTOM DRAPERY COMPANY INC.
3402 E TC Jester Blvd, Houston, TX
77082
Tel.: (713) 225-9211
Web Site: http://www.cdbas.com
Sales Range: $10-24.9 Million
Emp.: 20
Floor Coverings
N.A.I.C.S.: 423220
Allan R. Klein (Pres)
Elma Klein (VP)

CUSTOM FABRICATING & REPAIR INC
1932 E 26th St, Marshfield, WI 54449
Tel.: (715) 387-6598
Web Site: https://www.gotocfr.com
Year Founded: 1984
Rev.: $21,000,000
Emp.: 75
Dairy Equipment Mfr
N.A.I.C.S.: 333111
Steve Isenberg (Pres)
Joe Bugni (Engr-Controls)
Judd Brandl (Engr-Controls)

CUSTOM FIBERGLASS MANUFACTURING CO. INC.
1711 Harbor Ave, Long Beach, CA
90183
Tel.: (562) 432-5454   CA
Web Site: http://www.snugtop.com
Year Founded: 1959
Sales Range: $10-24.9 Million

Emp.: 350
Fiberglass Truck Caps & Tonneau
Covers Mfr & Distr
N.A.I.C.S.: 336390
Hartmut W. Schroeder *(Pres & CEO)*

CUSTOM FOOD GROUP, L.P.
1903 Anson Rd, Dallas, TX 75235
Tel.: (214) 637-0899
Web Site:
    http://www.customfoodgroup.com
Rev.: $31,000,000
Emp.: 275
Automated & Custom Food Vending
Machines
N.A.I.C.S.: 445132
Terry Rinck *(Controller)*
Ron Brown *(Mgr-Pur-Warehouse)*

CUSTOM HBC, CORP.
888 Industrial Blvd, Waconia, MN
55387
Tel.: (952) 442-8241   MN
Web Site: http://www.customhbc.com
Year Founded: 2000
Sales Range: $1-9.9 Million
Emp.: 80
Health & Beauty Care Promotional
Products
N.A.I.C.S.: 456120
Larry Wilhelm *(Owner & Pres)*
Mark Larned *(Dir-Sls-East)*

CUSTOM INDEX INC.
8 Vreeland Ave, Totowa, NJ 07512
Tel.: (973) 890-2414
Web Site:
    http://www.customindex.com
Year Founded: 1982
Sales Range: $10-24.9 Million
Emp.: 170
Die-Cut Index Cards
N.A.I.C.S.: 531120
Nafees Rahman *(CEO)*
Liam Downward *(Mgr-IT)*

CUSTOM INDUSTRIES INC.
215 Aloe Rd, Greensboro, NC 27409-
2105
Tel.: (336) 299-2885
Web Site:
    http://www.customindustries.com
Sales Range: $10-24.9 Million
Emp.: 90
Textile Machinery & Store Fixtures
N.A.I.C.S.: 333248
James E. Nagel *(Pres)*

CUSTOM MAGNETICS, INC.
801 W Main St, North Manchester, IN
46962
Tel.: (260) 982-8508
Web Site:
    https://www.custommag.com
Year Founded: 1974
Sales Range: $1-9.9 Million
Emp.: 45
Mfr of Custom-Designed Transform-
ers & Coils for Electrical/Electronics
Industries
N.A.I.C.S.: 334416
Kirti P. Shah *(Founder & Pres)*

Subsidiaries:

James Electronics Inc.   (1)
4050 N Rockwell St, Chicago, IL 60618
Tel.: (773) 463-6500
Web Site: http://www.custommag.com
Electronic Coils & Transformers
N.A.I.C.S.: 334416

CUSTOM MANUFACTURING &
ENGINEERING, INC.
3690 70th Ave N, Pinellas Park, FL
33781-4603
Tel.: (727) 547-9799

Web Site: http://www.custom-mfg-
    eng.com
Year Founded: 1997
Sales Range: $10-24.9 Million
Emp.: 65
Mfr & Engineering Services
N.A.I.C.S.: 339999
Nancy P. Crews *(Pres)*

CUSTOM METAL CRAFTERS,
INC.
815 N Mtn Rd, Newington, CT 06111
Tel.: (860) 953-4210
Web Site: http://www.custom-
    metal.com
Nonferrous Metal Die-Casting Found-
ries
N.A.I.C.S.: 331523
Stephen Rosner *(Pres)*

Subsidiaries:

Waterbury Style, Inc.   (1)
815 NMountain Road, Newington, CT 06111
Tel.: (860) 953-3100
Web Site: http://www.custom-metal.com
Buckles & Accessories Mfr
N.A.I.C.S.: 339993

CUSTOM METALCRAFT INC.
2332 E Division St, Springfield, MO
65808
Tel.: (417) 862-0707
Web Site: https://www.custom-
    metalcraft.com
Sales Range: $10-24.9 Million
Emp.: 157
Food Products Machinery
N.A.I.C.S.: 333241
Dwayne A. Holden *(Pres)*
Jerry Cowan *(VP)*
Sharon Saunders *(Controller)*

CUSTOM MIRRORED WALLS
485 Kennedy Rd, Buffalo, NY 14227
Tel.: (716) 892-7981
Rev.: $12,900,000
Emp.: 6
Whslr of Mirrors & Pictures, Framed
& Unframed
N.A.I.C.S.: 423220

CUSTOM MOBILITY INC.
7199 Bryan Dairie Rd, Largo, FL
33777
Tel.: (727) 539-8119
Web Site: https://www.custom-
    mobility.com
Rev.: $10,000,000
Emp.: 75
Medical Apparatus & Supplies
N.A.I.C.S.: 456199
Bruce Bayes *(Pres)*
Gary Bayes *(VP)*
Angie Bolds *(Mgr-Funding)*
Janice Mullins *(Dir-Medical & Fund-
ing)*
Robert Garguilo *(Mgr)*

CUSTOM PACKAGING INC.
1315 W Baddour Pkwy, Lebanon, TN
37087
Tel.: (615) 444-6025
Web Site:
    http://www.custompackaging.com
Year Founded: 1968
Sales Range: $25-49.9 Million
Emp.: 147
Corrugated & Solid Fiber Boxes Mfr
N.A.I.C.S.: 322211
Lonnie Dillard *(Dir-Quality Programs)*
Stephanie Shelton *(Mgr-Graphics)*

Subsidiaries:

Custom Packaging Inc.   (1)
20 Beale Rd, Arden, NC
28704-9213   (100%)
Tel.: (828) 684-5060

Web Site: http://www.custompackaging.com
Sales Range: $10-24.9 Million
Emp.: 45
Mfr of Industrial & Personal Service Paper
N.A.I.C.S.: 424130

CUSTOM PINE STRAW, INC.
2669 NW CR 138, Branford, FL
32008
Tel.: (386) 935-6933
Web Site:
    http://www.custompinestraw.com
Year Founded: 1997
Sales Range: $10-24.9 Million
Emp.: 53
Postharvest Crop Farming Services
N.A.I.C.S.: 115114
Amber Schwab *(Mgr-Sls)*
Melissa Lamb *(Mgr-Custom Storage)*
Laurie Nazworth *(Office Mgr)*
Manny Espinosa *(Dir-Driver Safety)*
Blaine Thompson *(Supvr-Field)*

CUSTOM PLASTIC DEVELOP-
MENTS, INC.
2710 N John Young Pkwy, Kissim-
mee, FL 34741
Tel.: (407) 847-3054   FL
Web Site: http://www.cpdfl.com
Year Founded: 1972
Sales Range: $1-9.9 Million
Emp.: 58
Plastics Product Mfr
N.A.I.C.S.: 326199
Cal Sanforn *(Owner)*
Richard Hord *(Pres)*
Scott Mills *(Mgr-Engrg)*

CUSTOM POLYMERS INC.
700 Tuckaseegee Rd, Charlotte, NC
28208
Tel.: (704) 332-6070
Web Site:
    http://www.custompolymers.com
Year Founded: 1996
Sales Range: $10-24.9 Million
Emp.: 25
Recycling of Waste Materials
N.A.I.C.S.: 562920
Patricia Sims *(Coord-Intl Logistics)*

Subsidiaries:

Custom Polymers Inc. - Latin & South
America   (1)
4700 Eastpark Dr, Houston, TX 77028
Tel.: (713) 673-2468
Web Site: http://www.custompolymers.com
Sales Range: $10-24.9 Million
Emp.: 20
Plastic Scrap Material Recycling Services
N.A.I.C.S.: 562920

CUSTOM PRINT NOW
10015 Old Columbia Rd Ste B-215,
Columbia, MD 21046
Web Site:
    http://www.customprintnow.com
Year Founded: 2004
Sales Range: $1-9.9 Million
Emp.: 10
Online & On-Demand Platforms in
Custom Printing & Marketing Materi-
als
N.A.I.C.S.: 323111
Willie Brennan *(Founder)*

CUSTOM PRINTED PROD-
UCTS
4924 Hazel Jones Rd, Bossier City,
LA 71111
Tel.: (318) 747-7460
Web Site: https://www.cpp-flexo.com
Year Founded: 1971
Sales Range: $10-24.9 Million
Emp.: 110
Paper Labels
N.A.I.C.S.: 322299

Glenn McAllister *(Mgr-Ops)*
Jenny O'Quinn *(Mgr-Customer Svc)*
Paul Miley *(Dir-Art)*
Richard Nicholson *(CEO)*

CUSTOM PRINTING INC.
3700 Mac Lee Dr, Alexandria, LA
71302-3347
Tel.: (318) 445-2124
Year Founded: 1973
Sales Range: $10-24.9 Million
Emp.: 6
Lithographic Commercial Printing
N.A.I.C.S.: 323111
James Bonnette *(Owner)*

CUSTOM PRO LOGISTICS,
LLC
1707 Race St, Cincinnati, OH 45202
Web Site:
    http://www.customprologistics.com
Year Founded: 2013
Sales Range: $25-49.9 Million
Emp.: 27
Refrigerated Logistics & Transport
Services
N.A.I.C.S.: 484230
Devin Reilly *(CEO)*

CUSTOM PROTEIN CORPORA-
TION
3453 N Farm Rd 151, Springfield,
MO 65803
Tel.: (417) 833-1214   AR
Sales Range: $10-24.9 Million
Emp.: 37
Oils & Greases Mfr
N.A.I.C.S.: 424990
Thomas L. Carter *(Pres)*

Subsidiaries:

National Commodity Exchange,
Inc.   (1)
3453 N Farm Rd 151, Springfield, MO
65803
Tel.: (417) 833-1129
Sales Range: Less than $1 Million
Emp.: 10
Contract Haulers
N.A.I.C.S.: 484121
Thomas L. Carter *(Pres)*

CUSTOM TOOL AND MANU-
FACTURING COMPANY
1031 Industry Rd, Lawrenceburg, KY
40342
Tel.: (502) 839-9541
Web Site: http://www.customtool.org
Rev.: $10,000,000
Emp.: 30
Special Dies, Tools, Jigs & Fixtures
N.A.I.C.S.: 333514
Rodney N. Cunningham *(Owner)*

CUSTOM TRUSS LLC
1890 W Atlantic Ave, Delray Beach,
FL 33444
Tel.: (954) 786-8800
Web Site:
    http://www.customtrussllc.com
Year Founded: 1978
Sales Range: $10-24.9 Million
Emp.: 60
Trusses & Wooden Roofs
N.A.I.C.S.: 321215
Iva Kutlova *(Owner)*
Josh Altug *(Gen Mgr)*

CUSTOM UNDERGROUND
INC.
9907 W US Hwy 150, Edwards, IL
61528
Tel.: (309) 683-3677
Web Site: https://www.custommug.com
Sales Range: $10-24.9 Million
Emp.: 200

Custom Underground Inc.—(Continued)

Underground Utilities Contractor
N.A.I.C.S.: 237110
James B. Feuchter (Sr VP)

CUSTOM VAULT CORP

4 Research Dr, Bethel, CT 06801
Tel.: (203) 403-4205
Web Site:
  http://www.customvault.com
All Other Miscellaneous Nonmetallic
Mineral Product Mfr
N.A.I.C.S.: 327999
Thomas P. Brennan (Pres & CEO)
Greg Navin (VP-Engrg)
Mike Elliot (Exec VP-Sls)
Rebecca Cicarelli (Dir-Mktg & Bus Dev)
Michael Iadarola (COO)
Matthew B. Gifford (Sr Dir-Sls)
Todd Michalka (CFO)

Subsidiaries:

BranchServ Systems Integration
LLC   (1)
4 Research Dr, Bethel, CT 06801-1040
Tel.: (203) 403-4200
Web Site: http://www.branchserv.com
Electrical Apparatus & Related Equipment
Merchant Whslr
N.A.I.C.S.: 423610
Thomas Brennan (CEO)
David Pepin (Pres)

Subsidiary (Domestic):

SafePak Corporation   (2)
4 Research Dr, Bethel, CT 06801
Tel.: (800) 215-0361
Web Site: http://www.safepakcorp.com
Electrical Apparatus & Related Equipment
Merchant Whslr
N.A.I.C.S.: 423610

CUSTOM WHOLESALE FLOORS INC.

2655 Dawin Rd N, Jacksonville, FL
32207
Tel.: (904) 281-0303
Web Site:
  http://www.customwholesale
  floors.com
Year Founded: 1973
Sales Range: $10-24.9 Million
Emp.: 60
Wood Flooring
N.A.I.C.S.: 423220
Dharma Martinez (Controller)

CUSTOM WHOLESALE SUPPLY CO. INC.

2324 Kermit Hwy, Odessa, TX
79761-1141
Tel.: (432) 580-4009
Web Site:
  http://www.johnstonesupply.com
Rev.: $10,478,687
Emp.: 12
Air Conditioning Equipment
N.A.I.C.S.: 423730
Eddie Rhodes (Pres)
Jason Akin (Mgr-Acctg & IT)

CUSTOM WOOD PRODUCTS INC.

415 E Bertrand, Saint Marys, KS
66536
Tel.: (785) 437-6533
Web Site: https://www.cwponline.com
Rev.: $11,497,300
Emp.: 150
Wood Kitchen Cabinets
N.A.I.C.S.: 337110
Willie Mergenmeier (Controller)

CUSTOM-METAL FABRICATORS, INC.

PO Box 286, Herington, KS 67449

Tel.: (785) 258-3744
Web Site: http://www.cmfmfg.com
Air Blasting & Pneumatic Conveying
Equipment Provider
N.A.I.C.S.: 333922

CUSTOM-PAK, INC.

86 16th Ave N, Clinton, IA 52732
Tel.: (563) 242-1801   IA
Web Site: https://www.custom-
pak.com
Year Founded: 1974
Sales Range: $150-199.9 Million
Emp.: 1,000
Blow Molded Finished Plastic Products Mfr
N.A.I.C.S.: 326199
Louise Laurent (VP-Fin)
Mark Rutenbeck (VP)
Lonnie Adrian (VP/Gen Mgr-Grp A
Mfg Facility)
Jeff Anderson (Pres & CEO)

Subsidiaries:

Custom-Pak de Mexico S. de R.L. de
C.V.   (1)
Blvd Circuito Siglo XXI 1960, 21290, Mexicali, BC, Mexico
Tel.: (52) 686 565 5888
Web Site: http://www.custompak.com
Blow Molded Plastic Products Mfr
N.A.I.C.S.: 326199
Fernando Barba (Gen Mgr)

Custom-Pak, Inc. - Dewitt Plant   (1)
1401 Lake St, DeWitt, IA 52742
Tel.: (563) 659-2100
Blow Molded Product Mfr
N.A.I.C.S.: 333248

Custom-Pak, Inc. - Walnut Ridge
Plant   (1)
160 S Miller Dr, Walnut Ridge, AR 72476
Tel.: (870) 886-7400
Sales Range: $25-49.9 Million
Emp.: 130
Industrial Plastic Blow Mold Mfr
N.A.I.C.S.: 326199
Andrew McDonnough (Gen Mgr)

Midwest Poly   (1)
901 S 3rd St, Clinton, IA 52732
Tel.: (563) 243-4858
Web Site: http://www.custom-pak.com
Sales Range: $25-49.9 Million
Emp.: 10
Custom Poly Bag Mfr
N.A.I.C.S.: 326111
David West (Gen Mgr)

CUSTOMER 1 ONE INC.

1000 W State St, Bristol, TN 37620
Tel.: (423) 764-5121
Web Site: http://www.billgatton.com
Sales Range: $50-74.9 Million
Emp.: 70
New & Used Automobiles
N.A.I.C.S.: 441110
David Meade (Gen Mgr)
Chris Lee (Pres)

CUSTOMER COMMUNICATIONS GROUP, INC. (CCG)

165 S Union Blvd Ste 260, Lakewood, CO 80228
Tel.: (303) 986-3000
Web Site: http://www.customer.com
Year Founded: 1977
Sales Range: $1-9.9 Million
Emp.: 15
Full-Service Customer Relationship
Marketing (CRM) Agency
N.A.I.C.S.: 541613
Sandra Gudat (Pres & CEO)
Lane Ware (Sr VP-Consulting & Acct
Svcs)
Greg Sultan (Sr VP & Strategist-Fin)
Becky O'Brien (VP & Assoc Creative
Dir)
Jerry White (VP & Dir-Ops)

CUSTOMER CONTACT SERVICES CCS

7525 Mitchell Rd Ste 315, Eden Prairie, MN 55344
Tel.: (952) 936-4000
Web Site:
  http://www.yourccsteam.com
Year Founded: 1972
Sales Range: $1-9.9 Million
Emp.: 60
Inbound Call Center Offering Virtual
Telephone Reception & Customer
Service Solutions
N.A.I.C.S.: 561421
Erik O'Borsky (Owner)
Janet Livingston (Pres)
Andrea Godsave (Controller)

CUSTOMER VALUE PARTNERS

3701 Pender Dr Ste 200, Fairfax, VA
22030-6045
Tel.: (703) 267-6999
Web Site: http://www.cvpcorp.com
Year Founded: 2002
Sales Range: $10-24.9 Million
Emp.: 110
Customer Service Focused Business
& Technology Consulting Services
N.A.I.C.S.: 561499
Anirudh Kulkarni (CEO & Mng Principal)
Douglas Taphouse (Principal)
Gus Vazquez (Principal-Delivery Ops)
Lee Canterbury (Dir-Bus Dev)
Cheree Hodges (Dir-Contracts)
Abdullah Monawer (Dir-Fin)
Kirthi Anantharam (Chief Growth Officer)
Raelene Wagoner (Dir-HR)
Linda Skelton (Dir-Proposal Ops)
Andrew Vanjani (Dir-Pub Sector Solutions)
Keith Kapp (Dir-Tech Innovation)
Lisa Brown (Principal-Performance
Mgmt)
Joseph Kostakis (Program Dir-CMS)
Todd Pantezzi (Chief Strategy Officer)

CUSTOMERSTREAM

113 Seaboard Ln Ste 170B, Franklin,
TN 37067
Tel.: (704) 227-0709
Web Site:
  http://www.customerstream.net
Year Founded: 2006
Sales Range: $1-9.9 Million
Emp.: 10
Marketing Consulting
N.A.I.C.S.: 541613
Dan Roselli (CEO)

CUSTOMINK, LLC

7902 Westpark Dr, McLean, VA
22102-4202
Tel.: (703) 891-2259
Web Site: http://www.customink.com
Year Founded: 2000
Sales Range: $10-24.9 Million
Emp.: 113
Custom Apparel Website Operator
N.A.I.C.S.: 315990
Marc Katz (Co-Founder, Chm, Pres &
CEO)

CUSTOMIZED DISTRIBUTION SERVICES

20 Harry Shupe Blvd, Wharton, NJ
07885
Tel.: (973) 366-5090   NJ
Web Site: http://www.dsdcds.com
Year Founded: 1983
Sales Range: $10-24.9 Million
Emp.: 100

Provider of Full Service Industrial
Real Estate Development & Contract
Warehousing
N.A.I.C.S.: 493120
John Sanacore (Pres)
Angelo Laporta (Mgr-Facility)
Dan Tullo (Mgr-Fleet Svc)
Luis Rivera (Supvr-Shipping & Receiving)
Rafael Menendez (Mgr-Ops)
Ryan Kurth (Mgr-Ops)
Stacey Kunsman (Supvr-Customer
Svc)
Carlos Jose Guerra (Mgr-Ops)
Joseph Kurian (Project Mgr-IT)
Ben Mera (Dir-HR)
John Jasionowicz (Dir-Ops)

CUSTOMIZED ENERGY SOLUTIONS LTD.

1528 Walnut St 22nd Fl, Philadelphia,
PA 19102
Tel.: (215) 875-9440
Web Site: https://www.ces-ltd.com
Year Founded: 1998
Rev.: $10,600,000
Emp.: 50
Management Consulting Services
N.A.I.C.S.: 541618
Sharon Barra (Controller)
Nancy Chafetz (Dir-Market
Intelligence-New England)
Jacquie DeRosa (VP-Emerging Technologies)
Stephen Fernands (Pres)
Jim Krajecki (Dir-Wholesale Svcs-
Southwest)
Ariel Lager (VP-Renewable Energy
Svcs)
Rick Mancini (Dir-Wholesale Svcs-
Northeast)
Erik Paulson (VP-Wholesale Market
Svcs)
David Sapper (Dir-Market
Intelligence-Midcontinent)
William Schofield (VP-Corp Dev)
Harveyetta Stone (Mgr-Benefits)
Ed Toppi (VP-Integrated Solutions)
Apoorve Bhatnagar (Sr Mgr-India
Markets)
Barbara Clemenhagen (VP-Market
Intelligence)
Bill Dagan (Dir-Tech Dept)
Dharmest Bharathan (Dir-Scheduling
Svcs)
Gustav H. Beerel (VP-Market Dev)
Markus Brunner (VP-Congestion
Mgmt)
Rob Abraham (Dir-Retail Ops)
Rahul Walawalkar (Pres & Mng Dir-
Customized Energy Solutions India)
Jedidiah Trott (VP-Demand Response)

CUSTOMWEATHER, INC.

230 California St Ste 420, San Francisco, CA 94111
Tel.: (415) 777-3303
Web Site:
  http://www.customweather.com
Year Founded: 2000
Rev.: $2,100,000
Emp.: 20
Custom Computer Programing
N.A.I.C.S.: 541511
Susan Kreuz Flint (Mgr-Bus)
Geoff Flint (Pres & CEO)
Kevin Levey (VP-Ops)
Murray Armstrong (VP-Sls & Bus
Dev)
Richard Reed (Sr Mgr-Bus Dev)

CUT LOOSE

101 Williams Ave, San Francisco, CA
94124
Tel.: (415) 822-2031

Web Site: https://www.cutloose.com
Sales Range: $10-24.9 Million
Emp.: 60
Mfr & Sales of Women's Clothing
N.A.I.C.S.: 315250
Will Wenham (CEO)

CUTCO CORPORATION
1116 E State St, Olean, NY 14760-3814
Tel.: (716) 372-3111
Web Site: http://www.cutco.com
Year Founded: 1982
Sales Range: $75-99.9 Million
Emp.: 700
Cutlery Whslr
N.A.I.C.S.: 332215
Kathleen Donovan (Coord-PR)
James E. Stitt (Chm, Pres & CEO)

Subsidiaries:

CUTCO International Inc. (1)
1116 E State St, Olean, NY 14760-3814 (100%)
Tel.: (716) 372-3111
Web Site: http://www.cutco.com
Emp.: 800
Cutlery Marketing & Sales
N.A.I.C.S.: 423220
James E. Stitt (Chm, Pres & CEO)

Cutco Cutlery Corporation (1)
1116 E State St, Olean, NY 14760-3814
Tel.: (716) 372-3111
Web Site: http://www.cutco.com
Sales Range: $25-49.9 Million
Emp.: 800
Cutlery Mfr
N.A.I.C.S.: 332215

KA-BAR Knives, Inc. (1)
200 Homer St, Olean, NY 14760-3813
Tel.: (716) 372-5952
Web Site: http://www.ka-bar.com
Sales Range: $10-24.9 Million
Emp.: 15
Sporting Knives Mfr
N.A.I.C.S.: 423910
Kim Johnson (Mgr-Customer Svc)

Schilling Forge, Inc. (1)
606 Factory Ave, Syracuse, NY 13208
Tel.: (315) 454-4421
Web Site: http://www.schillingforge.com
Precision Equipment Mfr
N.A.I.C.S.: 332111

Vector Marketing Corporation (1)
1116 E State St, Olean, NY 14760-3814
Tel.: (302) 888-8888
Web Site: http://www.vectormarketing.com
Sales Range: $50-74.9 Million
Emp.: 800
Direct Selling Establishment Distr
N.A.I.C.S.: 423220
Albert T. DiLeonardo (Pres/CEO-Vector East)
John W. Whelpley (Pres & COO)
Mark D. Heister (CFO)
Amar Dave (Exec VP-Eastern Reg)

CUTLER ASSOCIATES INC.
43 Harvard St, Worcester, MA 01609-0049
Tel.: (508) 757-7500
Web Site: https://www.cutlerdb.com
Year Founded: 1972
Sales Range: $100-124.9 Million
Emp.: 75
Builder & Designer of Industrial Buildings & Warehouses; Elder Care; Private School
N.A.I.C.S.: 236220
Frederic Mulligan (Chm)
Bill Bocchino (Exec VP-Southeast Reg)
Ed O'Brien (Pres)
Tony Ricciardi (Exec VP-Mid Atlantic Reg)

CUTLER REAL ESTATE, INC.
4618 Dressler Rd NW, Canton, OH 44718

Tel.: (330) 493-9323   OH
Web Site: http://www.cutlerhomes.com
Year Founded: 1947
Real Estate Services
N.A.I.C.S.: 531210
Jay Cutler (Co-Owner)
Jim Camp (Owner)
Vinny DeFrancisco (Office Mgr)
Deb Saczawa (Office Mgr)
Andy Camp (Co-Owner & Pres)
Art Travis (Office Mgr)
Chris Rosen (Office Mgr)
Don Johnson (Office Mgr)
Emily Levitt (Office Mgr)
Jim Hinton (Office Mgr)
Joe Mock (Office Mgr)
Tricia Reed (Office Mgr)

CUTLER-DICKERSON COMPANY
507 College Ave, Adrian, MI 49221
Tel.: (517) 265-5191
Web Site: http://www.cutlerdickerson.com
Sales Range: $10-24.9 Million
Emp.: 25
Provider of Feed & Farm Supplies
N.A.I.C.S.: 459999
Jack Patterson (Pres)

CUTRUBUS MOTORS INC.
895 W Riverdale Rd, Ogden, UT 84405
Tel.: (801) 627-1300
Web Site: http://www.cutrubus.com
Sales Range: $10-24.9 Million
Emp.: 38
New & Used Automobile Sales
N.A.I.C.S.: 441110
Phidia Cutrubus (Pres)
Karen Schmertz (Office Mgr)

CUTSHAW CHEVROLET, INC.
10116 US Hwy 287N, Grapeland, TX 75844-2042
Tel.: (936) 687-2014
Web Site: http://cutshawchevrolet.com
Sales Range: $10-24.9 Million
Emp.: 14
Car Whslr
N.A.I.C.S.: 441110
Michael Cutshaw (Pres)

CUTTER & COMPANY BROKERAGE, INC.
15415 Clayton Rd, Ballwin, MO 63011
Tel.: (636) 537-8770   MO
Web Site: https://www.cutterco.com
Year Founded: 1988
Sales Range: $1-9.9 Million
Emp.: 18
Investment & Insurance Advice for Retail Clients
N.A.I.C.S.: 523940
Deborah Castiglioni (CEO)
William L. Meyer (Pres)

CUTTER DODGE CHRYSLER JEEP OF PEARL CITY INC.
905 Kamehameha Hwy, Pearl City, HI 96782-2501
Tel.: (808) 400-6370
Web Site: https://www.cutterdodgechryslerjeepofpearlcity.com
Sales Range: $10-24.9 Million
Emp.: 77
Car Whslr
N.A.I.C.S.: 441110
Marc Cutter (Pres)

CUTTER HOLDING CO.

2802 E Old Twr Rd, Phoenix, AZ 85034
Tel.: (602) 273-1237   AZ
Web Site: http://www.cutteraviation.com
Year Founded: 1998
Sales Range: $50-74.9 Million
Emp.: 320
Holding Company; Aircraft Maintenance, Sales & Aviation Support Services
N.A.I.C.S.: 551112
William W. Cutter (Pres & CEO)
Steven C. Prieser (CFO & VP)
Mike Livezey (Dir-Special Projects)
Lowell Whitten (VP)
Matt Sorace (Mgr-Flight-Phoenix Sky Harbor Airport)
David Clifton (Dir-Technical & Flight Support Svcs)

Subsidiaries:

Cutter Aviation Albuquerque, Inc. (1)
2502 Clark Carr Loop SE, Albuquerque, NM 87106-5606 (100%)
Tel.: (505) 842-4184
Web Site: http://www.cutteraviation.com
Sales Range: $25-49.9 Million
Emp.: 85
Aircraft Maintenance, Sales & Aviation Support Services
N.A.I.C.S.: 488190
Jessica Rowden (Gen Mgr)
Matthew Olguin (Mgr-Line Svc)

Cutter Aviation Colorado Springs, LLC (1)
5763 Camper View, Colorado Springs, CO 80916-2714 (100%)
Tel.: (719) 591-2065
Web Site: http://www.cutteraviation.com
Sales Range: $25-49.9 Million
Emp.: 15
Aircraft Maintenance, Sales & Aviation Support Services
N.A.I.C.S.: 488190
Calvin Martin (Gen Mgr-Colorado Springs)

Cutter Aviation Dallas-Addison, LLC (1)
4500 Claire Chennault Dr, Addison, TX 75001 (100%)
Tel.: (469) 518-5770
Web Site: http://cutteraviation.com
Sales Range: $25-49.9 Million
Emp.: 27
Aircraft Maintenance Sale & Aviation Support Services
N.A.I.C.S.: 488190
Christopher Gradisar (Mgr-Aircraft Svcs)

Cutter Aviation Deer Valley, Inc. (1)
732 W Deer Vly Rd, Phoenix, AZ 85027-2136 (100%)
Tel.: (623) 581-1444
Web Site: http://www.cutteraviation.com
Sales Range: $25-49.9 Million
Emp.: 15
Aircraft Maintenance, Sales & Aviation Support Services
N.A.I.C.S.: 488190
Michael Brasier (Gen Mgr)

Cutter Aviation El Paso Limited Partnership (1)
1771 Shuttle Columbia Dr, El Paso, TX 79925
Tel.: (915) 779-0270
Web Site: http://www.cutteraviation.com
Sales Range: $25-49.9 Million
Emp.: 30
Aircraft Maintenance, Sales & Aviation Support Services
N.A.I.C.S.: 488190
Scott Andre (Gen Mgr)
William Moreno (Mgr-Line Svc)

Cutter Aviation Phoenix, Inc. (1)
2802 E Old Tower Rd, Phoenix, AZ 85034-6000
Tel.: (602) 273-1237
Web Site: http://www.cutteraviation.com
Emp.: 50
Aircraft Maintenance, Sales & Aviation Support Services
N.A.I.C.S.: 488190

Steven C. Prieser (CFO & VP)
William W. Cutter (Pres & CEO)
David Clifton (Mgr-Aircraft Svcs-Phoenix)
Genaro Sanchez (Dir-Mktg & Comm)
Heather Wahl (Dir-HR)
Nels Peterson (Mgr-Customer Rels-Phoenix)
Kevin Reedy (Dir-Safety)
Sam Perez (Reg Sls Mgr-MRO)
Richard P. Campbell Jr. (Gen Mgr-PHX)

Cutter Aviation San Antonio, Inc. (1)
367 Sandau Rd, San Antonio, TX 78216-3620
Tel.: (210) 340-6780
Web Site: http://www.cutteraviation.com
Emp.: 22
Aircraft Maintenance, Sales & Aviation Support Services
N.A.I.C.S.: 488190
Kirk Wood (Mgr-Aircraft Svcs)
Mike Livezey (Dir-Special Projects)
Steven Prieser (CFO & VP)
Genaro Sanchez (Dir-Mktg & Comm)
Heather Wahl (Dir-HR)

Cutter Holding Co. - Cutter Aviation - Dallas-Addison Facility (1)
4500 Claire Chennault Dr, Addison, TX 75001
Tel.: (469) 518-5770
Aircraft Sales & Maintenance Services
N.A.I.C.S.: 423860

CUTTER OF MAUI, INC.
1100 Alakea St Ph 2, Honolulu, HI 96813
Tel.: (808) 564-9000   HI
Web Site: http://www.cuttercars.com
Holding Company; New & Used Car Dealerships Owner & Operator
N.A.I.C.S.: 551112
Nick S. Cutter (Pres & CEO)
Marc J. Cutter (VP)

Subsidiaries:

Cutter Management Co. (1)
1100 Alakea St Ph 2, Honolulu, HI 96813-4513 (100%)
Tel.: (808) 564-9000
Web Site: http://www.cuttercars.com
Automobile Dealership Operator
N.A.I.C.S.: 561110

Unit (Domestic):

Cutter Buick GMC (2)
94-119 Farrington Hwy, Waipahu, HI 96797-2202
Tel.: (808) 564-9500
Web Site: http://www.cutterbuickwaipahu.com
Sales Range: $50-74.9 Million
Emp.: 95
New & Used Car Dealer
N.A.I.C.S.: 441110

Cutter Mazda Waipahu (2)
94-245 Farrington Hwy, Waipahu, HI 96797
Tel.: (808) 564-9500
Web Site: http://www.cuttermazdawaipahu.com
Sales Range: $50-74.9 Million
Emp.: 40
New & Used Car Dealer
N.A.I.C.S.: 441110
Ronald Wright (Gen Mgr)
Charnell Kainoa (Mgr-Svc)
Chris Wong (Mgr-Internet Sls)
Joe Lui-Kwan (Dir-Internet)
John Woodman (Mgr-Internet Sls)
Matt Shiraki (Mgr-Internet Sls)
Scott Nelson (Gen Mgr-Sls)
Sean Sadaoka (Mgr-Parts)
Tylor Duarte (Mgr-Internet Sls)
Tim Nolan (Mgr-Internet Sls)
Jess Hong (Mgr-Fin)
Kevin Kim (Asst Mgr-Sls)
Levi Kunukau (Asst Mgr-Svc)
Maima Tulimaiau (Mgr-Customer Rels)

Cutter Mitsubishi - Aiea (2)
98-015 Kamehameha Hwy, Aiea, HI 96701
Tel.: (808) 564-9777
Web Site: http://www.cuttermitsubishi.com
Sales Range: $50-74.9 Million
Emp.: 60
New & Used Car Dealer
N.A.I.C.S.: 441110

Cutter of Maui, Inc.—(Continued)

Barry Eisen (Gen Mgr-Sls)
Anthony Guevara (Mgr-Fin)
Ernie Salazar (Mgr-Fin)
Guy Takamiya (Mgr-Used Car Sls)

CUTTING CORNERS INC.
13720 Midway Ste 200, Dallas, TX
75244-4345
Tel.: (972) 233-4503
Web Site:
  https://www.fabricresource.com
Rev.: $14,320,047
Emp.: 2
Draperies
N.A.I.C.S.: 449122
Kelli Boler (Office Mgr)

CUTTING LOOSE SALON AND SPA
8429 Honore Ave, University Park, FL
34201
Tel.: (941) 358-6000
Web Site:
  https://www.cuttingloose.net
Year Founded: 2008
Sales Range: $1-9.9 Million
Emp.: 40
Hair Salon & Spa
N.A.I.C.S.: 812112
Coral Pleas (Owner)

CUTTING TOOLS INC.
4050 Shelbyville Rd, Louisville, KY
40207-3107
Tel.: (502) 896-2353 KY
Web Site:
  http://www.cuttingtoolsinc.net
Year Founded: 1969
Sales Range: $10-24.9 Million
Emp.: 30
Provider of Industrial Tools
N.A.I.C.S.: 423840
Curtis Coombs (Bus Mgr)
Walter H. Grell III (Pres)

CUYAHOGA VENDING CO. INC.
14250 Industrial Ave S No 104,
Cleveland, OH 44137
Tel.: (216) 663-1457
Web Site:
  http://www.cuyahogagroup.com
Sales Range: $10-24.9 Million
Emp.: 65
Service Vending Machine
N.A.I.C.S.: 532289
James N. Variglotti (Pres)
Susan Brett (Controller)

CV HOLDINGS, LLC.
1030 Riverfront Ctr, Amsterdam, NY
12010
Tel.: (518) 627-0051
Year Founded: 2002
Sales Range: $1-9.9 Million
Emp.: 140
Plastics Product Mfr
N.A.I.C.S.: 326199
Robert Abrams (CEO)

CV INDUSTRIES INC.
401 11th St NW, Hickory, NC 28601
Tel.: (828) 328-1851 NC
Web Site:
  https://www.centuryfurniture.com
Year Founded: 1947
Sales Range: $75-99.9 Million
Emp.: 2,100
Holding Company; Wood Household
Furniture
N.A.I.C.S.: 551112
Snyder Garrison (Chm)

Subsidiaries:

Century Furniture Industries (1)

401 11th St NW, Hickory, NC 28601
Tel.: (828) 328-1851
Web Site: http://www.centuryfurniture.com
Furniture Mfr
N.A.I.C.S.: 337121
Kevin Boyle (VP-Mfg)
Brandon Hucks (CFO)
Roger Jones (VP-Global Logistics)
Chris Ward (VP-Fin)

First Plaza Inc. (1)
1985 Tate Blvd SE, Hickory, NC
28602-1433 (100%)
Tel.: (828) 328-8817
Rev.: $710,000
Emp.: 3
Nonresidential Building Operators
N.A.I.C.S.: 531110

Shuford Development Co. Inc. (1)
1985 Tate Blvd SE, Hickory, NC 28602-
1433
Tel.: (828) 328-8817
Sales Range: Less than $1 Million
Emp.: 4
Apartment Building Operator
N.A.I.C.S.: 322220

Valdese Weavers, LLC (1)
1000 Perkins Rd SE, Valdese, NC 28690
Tel.: (828) 874-2181
Web Site: http://www.valdeseweavers.com
Sales Range: $50-74.9 Million
Emp.: 544
Broadwoven Fabric Mills, Cotton
N.A.I.C.S.: 313210
Michael Shelton (Pres & CEO)
Scott George (VP-Sls & Mktg-Contract)
Blake Millinor (CMO & Sr VP)
Janet Kuck (CFO)
Joel Crisp (Sr VP-Global Ops)
Scott A. Malcolm (Sr VP-Ops)
Carson Copeland (COO)
Ray Barnette (VP-Info Sys)
Roger Berrier (VP-Supply Chain & Procurement)
Jennifer Gwynn (VP-Product Assurance)
Todd Irvin (VP-Logistics)

CV INTERNATIONAL, INC.
1128 W Olney Rd, Norfolk, VA 23507
Tel.: (757) 466-1170
Web Site:
  https://www.cvinternational.com
Year Founded: 1991
Sales Range: $1-9.9 Million
Emp.: 20
International Freight Forwarder
N.A.I.C.S.: 488510
B. Wayne Coleman (Owner & CEO)
Michael W. Coleman (Pres)
Venetia Huffman (VP-Ops & Compliance)
Michael King (CFO)

CV PRODUCTS, INC.
42 High Tech Blvd, Thomasville, NC
27360
Tel.: (336) 472-2242
Web Site: http://www.cvproducts.com
Sales Range: $10-24.9 Million
Emp.: 68
Automotive Supplies & Parts Services
N.A.I.C.S.: 423120
Clyde Vickers (Founder)
Rob Celendano (Mng Dir)
Stephen L. Lineberger (Pres & CEO)
Jason Siler (Mgr-IT)

CV'S FAMILY FOOD INC.
124 Hwy 71 N, Alma, AR 72921
Tel.: (479) 632-0471
Web Site:
  http://www.cvsfamilyfoods.com
Sales Range: $25-49.9 Million
Emp.: 30
Supermarket
N.A.I.C.S.: 445110
CV Combs (Pres)

CV'S FOODLINER INCORPORATED

1004 E Walnut St, Paris, AR 72855
Tel.: (479) 471-1212
Web Site:
  http://www.cvsfamilyfoods.com
Sales Range: $1-9.9 Million
Emp.: 50
Independent Supermarket
N.A.I.C.S.: 445110
C. V. Combs Jr. (Pres)

CVA ADVERTISING & MARKETING, INC.
5030 E University Ste B401, Odessa,
TX 79762
Tel.: (432) 368-5483 TX
Web Site: http://www.cvaadv.com
Year Founded: 1993
Emp.: 12
Advertising Services
N.A.I.C.S.: 541810
Lila Evans (Media Buyer)

CVF CAPITAL PARTNERS, INC.
1590 Drew Ave Ste 110, Davis, CA
95618
Tel.: (530) 757-7004 DE
Web Site:
  https://www.cvfcapitalpartners.com
Year Founded: 2005
Emp.: 100
Privater Equity Firm
N.A.I.C.S.: 523999
Jose Blanco (Mng Partner)
Edward McNulty (Mng Partner)
Brad Triebsch (Mng Partner)
Chris Carleson (VP)
Stefan Okhuysen (Principal)

Subsidiaries:

Waterman Industries, LLC (1)
25500 Rd 204, Exeter, CA 93221-9655
Tel.: (559) 562-4000
Web Site: http://www.watermanusa.com
Sales Range: $10-24.9 Million
Emp.: 60
Water Control & Irrigation Equipment Mfr
N.A.I.C.S.: 332911
Kevin Bense (Pres)

CVS SYSTEMS INC.
1139 S Baldwin Ave, Marion, IN
46953-1526
Tel.: (765) 662-0037 IN
Web Site:
  http://www.cvssystems.com
Year Founded: 1980
Rev.: $50,000,000
Emp.: 65
Electrical Apparatus & Equipment
N.A.I.C.S.: 423610
John Collins (Pres)
Mike Roberts (Partner)
John Kirkwood (VP-Mktg)
Patty Dailey (Asst Mgr)
Scott Wilson (VP-Sls)

CW BROWER INC.
413 S Riverside Dr, Modesto, CA
95354
Tel.: (209) 523-5447
Rev.: $64,741,792
Emp.: 200
Groceries, General Line
N.A.I.C.S.: 424410
Libby Pomeroy (Pres)
William Harris (Gen Mgr & Dir-Mktg)
Diana Gardner (Mgr-Acctg)

CW HAYES CONSTRUCTION COMPANY
821 Executive Dr, Oviedo, FL 32765
Tel.: (407) 366-1564
Web Site:
  https://www.cwhayesconstruction.com
Rev.: $16,300,000

Emp.: 30
Commercial & Institutional Building
Construction
N.A.I.C.S.: 236220
Kelly Cavett (Office Mgr)
William R. Dillworth (VP)
C. Wayne Hayes (Pres)

CW ROEN CONSTRUCTION CO.
40 Oak Ct, Danville, CA 94526
Tel.: (925) 837-5501
Web Site: http://www.cwroen.com
Sales Range: $10-24.9 Million
Emp.: 60
Waste Disposal Plant Construction
N.A.I.C.S.: 236210
Steve Mann (VP)

CWDKIDS INC.
3607 Mayland Ct, Henrico, VA 23233-
1453
Tel.: (804) 270-7401
Web Site: http://www.cwdkids.com
Year Founded: 1987
Sales Range: $25-49.9 Million
Emp.: 20
Children's Clothing Catalog & Mail
Order
N.A.I.C.S.: 458110
James Klaus (CEO)

CWM, LLC
14600 Branch St, Omaha, NE 68154
Web Site:
  http://www.carsongroup.com
Year Founded: 1983
Sales Range: $1-9.9 Million
Wealth Management Services
N.A.I.C.S.: 522180
Ron Carson (Founder & CEO)
Teri Shepherd (Co-Pres)
Aaron Schaben (Co-Pres)
Nick Engelbart (CFO)
Dan Tobin (Chief Risk Officer)
Mary Kate Gulick (CMO)
Samantha Allen (VP-Digital Mktg)
Jamie Hopkins (Mng Partner-Wealth
Solutions)

CWPS ONLINE
917 S Fifth St, Saint Charles, MO
63301
Tel.: (636) 946-7227
Web Site: http://www.cwpsstl.com
Year Founded: 2003
Rev.: $2,000,000
Emp.: 10
Business Products & Services
N.A.I.C.S.: 423850
Don Guenther (Pres)

CWPS, INC.
14120A Sullyfield Cir, Chantilly, VA
20151-1660
Tel.: (703) 263-9539
Web Site: http://www.cwps.com
Year Founded: 1980
Sales Range: $25-49.9 Million
Emp.: 45
IT Solutions & Services
N.A.I.C.S.: 541512
Jason Waldrop (CEO)
Frank Lusko (Exec VP-Sls)
Christine Waldrop (Owner)
Dan Smith (COO)

CWR CONSTRUCTION, INC.
1312 Main, North Little Rock, AR
72115
Tel.: (501) 375-9047
Web Site: http://cwrconstruction.com
Sales Range: $10-24.9 Million
Emp.: 75
Commercial & Institutional Building
Construction Services
N.A.I.C.S.: 236220

Joey Stoll (Project Mgr)

CWS CAPITAL PARTNERS, LLC
14 Corporate Plz Ste 210, Newport Beach, CA 92660-7928
Tel.: (949) 640-4200   DE
Web Site:
   https://www.cwscapital.com
Year Founded: 1998
Sales Range: $25-49.9 Million
Emp.: 25
Real Estate Investment & Management
N.A.I.C.S.: 531110
Steve Sherwood (Chm & CEO)
Gary Carmell (Pres & Partner)
Mike Engels (Partner & Chief Investment Officer)
Mark Ruggles (COO & Chief Compliance Officer-Newport Beach)
Michael Brittingham (Principal-Investments-Austin)

Subsidiaries:

CWS Apartment Homes LLC   (1)
9606 N Mopac Expy Ste 500, Austin, TX 78759
Tel.: (512) 837-3028
Web Site: http://www.cwsapartments.com
Real Estate Manangement Services
N.A.I.C.S.: 531390
Kimberly Fisher (Dir-Property)
Jessica Howes (Dir-Community)

CWS CORPORATE HOUSING
9606 N Mopac Expy Ste 500, Austin, TX 78759
Tel.: (512) 837-3028
Web Site:
   http://www.cwshousing.com
Year Founded: 1996
Rev.: $20,400,000
Emp.: 58
Real Property Lessor
N.A.I.C.S.: 531190
Gary Carmell (CIO)
Jenny Garza (Mgr-HR)
Sue Mills (VP-Personnel)

CWU, INC.
19321C US Hwy 19 N Ste 602B, Clearwater, FL 33764
Tel.: (727) 442-8400   FL
Web Site: http://www.cwuinc.us
Year Founded: 2004
Sales Range: $10-24.9 Million
Emp.: 474
Temporary Help Service
N.A.I.C.S.: 561320
Charles Jenkins (Founder, Owner & Pres)

CXM INC.
1601 S 54th Ave, Cicero, IL 60804-1898
Tel.: (708) 656-7900
Web Site: https://www.cxm.com
Year Founded: 1923
Sales Range: $75-99.9 Million
Emp.: 100
Brass Smelting & Refining (Secondary)
N.A.I.C.S.: 331420
Patrick Balson (Pres & CEO)

CXTEC
5404 S Bay Rd, Syracuse, NY 13212-3801
Tel.: (315) 476-3000   NY
Web Site: https://www.cxtec.com
Year Founded: 1978
Sales Range: $25-49.9 Million
Emp.: 260
Computers, Peripherals & Software
N.A.I.C.S.: 334210

Barbara Ashkin (COO & VP)
Peter E. Belyea (VP-Bus Dev)
Ray Oliver (Dir-IT)

CY-FAIR VOLUNTEER FIRE DEPARTMENT
9630 Telge Rd, Houston, TX 77095
Tel.: (281) 550-6663   TX
Web Site: http://www.cyfairvfd.com
Year Founded: 1955
Sales Range: $10-24.9 Million
Emp.: 521
Fire Protection Services
N.A.I.C.S.: 922160
Jennifer Walls (Pres)
Tom Jackovich (VP)
Melissa Bierwirth (Sec)
Bob Fitzgerald (Treas)
David Manley (Pres)

CYAN PARTNERS, LP
1251 Avenue of the Americas 28th Fl, New York, NY 10020
Tel.: (212) 218-1621
Year Founded: 2008
Middle Market Direct Lender
N.A.I.C.S.: 522390
David Milich (COO)
Brennan McCaw (CFO)
Arnold Wong (Mng Dir)
Jonathan Tunis (Mng Dir)
Ashok Nayyar (Partner & Chief Investment Officer)

CYBER ADAPT, INC.
14755 Preston Rd Ste 405, Dallas, TX 75254   DE
Web Site:
   https://www.cyberadapt.com
Year Founded: 2014
Mobile-Enabled Network Security Platform Software Developer, Publisher & Services
N.A.I.C.S.: 513210
Devin Jones (Sr VP-Product)
Michael Weinberger (Sr VP-Product Dev)
Sam Stover (Sr VP-Res)
Dan Dunkel (Sr VP-Worldwide-Sls)
Alex McKenzie (Sr Dir-Mktg)
Kevin Patterson (Dir-Svc Ops)
Reuben Richards (Chm)

CYBER DIGITAL, INC.
400 Oser Ave Ste 200, Hauppauge, NY 11788
Tel.: (631) 231-1200
Year Founded: 1983
Software Development Services
N.A.I.C.S.: 541511
J. C. Chatpar (Pres, CEO & CFO)

CYBER OPERATIONS, INC.
1449 Court Pl, Pelham, AL 35124
Tel.: (205) 733-0901
Web Site:
   https://www.cyberoperations.com
Rev.: $4,885,958
Emp.: 25
Computer System Design Services
N.A.I.C.S.: 541512
James A. Massey (Founder & Chm)
Kevin Etheridge (CTO)
Mary Nelson (Gen Counsel)

CYBER RESOURCE GROUP
208 N Ctr Dr, North Brunswick, NJ 08902
Tel.: (732) 422-4060
Web Site: http://www.cyberrg.com
Year Founded: 2003
Rev.: $13,400,000
Emp.: 135
Computer Programming Services
N.A.I.C.S.: 541511
Suresh Reddy (Pres)

CYBERADVISORS, INC.
11324 86th Ave N, Maple Grove, MN 55369
Tel.: (952) 924-9990   MN
Web Site:
   http://www.cyberadvisors.com
Year Founded: 1997
Sales Range: $1-9.9 Million
Emp.: 43
Computer Software & Hardware
N.A.I.C.S.: 449210
Igor Bogachev (CTO & Mng Partner)
Darin Ringuette (Sr Acct Mgr)
Will Cattrysse (Engr-Network)
Christopher Mezera (Engr-Network)
Michael Schultz (Engr-Network)
Ryan Vinje (VP-Managed Svcs)

Subsidiaries:

eDot LLC   (1)
3075 Tollview Dr, Rolling Meadows, IL 60008
Tel.: (847) 847-4500
Web Site: https://www.edotsolutions.com
Sales Range: $1-9.9 Million
Emp.: 24
Extensive IT Consulting & Managed Services
N.A.I.C.S.: 541613
Melvin Thoede (Pres)
Steve Jaffe (CEO)
Patrick Torney (VP-Ops)
Todd Hepler (Sr VP-e-Dot Low Voltage)

CYBERGRANTS, LLC
300 Brickstone Sq Ste 601, Andover, MA 01810
Tel.: (978) 824-0300   DE
Web Site:
   https://www.cybergrants.com
Year Founded: 1999
Employee Engagement & Grants Management Software Developer & Publisher
N.A.I.C.S.: 513210

Subsidiaries:

J.K. Group, Inc.   (1)
650 College Rd E Ste 4100, Princeton, NJ 08540
Tel.: (609) 799-7830
Web Site: http://www.jk-group.com
Corporate Philanthropy Management Software & Data Services
N.A.I.C.S.: 513210
Martin Johnson (VP-Ops)
Jon-Marc Patton (VP-Pro Svcs)
Hesha Patel (Dir-Sls & Mktg)
Susanne Hart (Dir-Product Mgmt)
Nita Kirby (Dir-Client Mgmt)

CYBERGY HOLDINGS, INC.
10333 E Dry Creek Rd Ste 200, Englewood, CO 80112
Tel.: (303) 856-3232   NV
Web Site:
   http://www.cybergypartners.com
Year Founded: 2006
Sales Range: $25-49.9 Million
Emp.: 100
Holding Company; Technology Products
N.A.I.C.S.: 551112
Mark E. Gray (Chm & CEO)
Jennifer Williamson Cockrum (Chief Admin Officer)
Wyly T. Wade (CTO)
William Michael Gregorak (CFO & Chief Acctg Officer)
Terrence DiVittorio (Pres/COO-Cybergy Partners)

Subsidiaries:

Binary Group, Inc.   (1)
1911 Fort Myer Dr Ste 300, Arlington, VA 22209
Tel.: (571) 480-4444
Web Site: http://www.binarygroup.com

Corporate & Government IT Consulting & Engineering Services
N.A.I.C.S.: 541690
Rose Wang (Exec VP-Strategy & Corp Dev)
Kawaljit Singh (Pres & CEO)
Kelly M. Boehringer (Chief Compliance Officer & Gen Counsel)

CYBERRESEARCH INC.
25 Business Park Dr, Branford, CT 06405
Tel.: (203) 483-8815
Web Site:
   http://www.cyberresearch.com
Year Founded: 1983
Sales Range: $10-24.9 Million
Emp.: 10
Rack-Mount PCs, Motion Control Systems, Industrial & Scientific Computers Specialists
N.A.I.C.S.: 423430
Robert C. Molloy (Founder & Pres)

CYBERSETTLE, INC.
1700 E Putnam Ave, Old Greenwich, CT 06870
Tel.: (914) 286-5600   NY
Web Site: http://www.cybersettle.com
Year Founded: 1996
Sales Range: $1-9.9 Million
Emp.: 9
Software Solutions for the Resolution of Claims Settlements
N.A.I.C.S.: 541990
MaryAnn Jennings (Gen Counsel & Sr VP)
Michael S. Carey (Sr VP)

CYBERSHIELD, INC.
308 Ellen Trout Dr, Lufkin, TX 75904
Tel.: (936) 633-6387   DE
Web Site:
   https://www.cybershieldinc.com
Year Founded: 1987
Sales Range: $50-74.9 Million
Emp.: 100
Paint, Plating & Coating Application Services
N.A.I.C.S.: 332812
Jim Skelly (Owner & CEO)

CYBERTECH SYSTEMS INC.
1301 W 22nd St Ste 308, Oak Brook, IL 60523-2094
Tel.: (630) 472-3200   DE
Web Site: https://www.cybertech.com
Year Founded: 1992
Sales Range: $50-74.9 Million
Emp.: 390
Computer Integrated Systems Design
N.A.I.C.S.: 541512
Steven Jeske (CFO & VP)
C. N. Rao (Exec Dir)

Subsidiaries:

CyberTech Information Services Ltd. UK   (1)
Park House 1 Sarbir Industrial Park, Cambridge Road, Harlow, CM20 2EU, Essex, United Kingdom
Tel.: (44) 1279 425384
N.A.I.C.S.: 541512

CyberTech Systems & Software Inc.   (1)
1210 Northbrook Dr Ste 400, Trevose, PA 19053-6944
Tel.: (215) 494-2702
Web Site: http://www.cybertech.com
Sales Range: $10-24.9 Million
Emp.: 125
It Consulting
N.A.I.C.S.: 541512

CyberTech Systems & Software Ltd.   (1)
                                              (49%)
Tel.: (91) 2242839200
Web Site: https://www.cybertech.com

CyberTech Systems Inc.—(Continued)
Sales Range: $25-49.9 Million
Emp.: 485
Provider of Computer Services
N.A.I.C.S.: 541511
S. Ramasubramanian (COO)
Vish Tadimety (Founder, Chm & CEO)
Sarita Leelaramani (Officer-Compliance & Sec)
Praveen Agarwal (CFO)

CYBERTEX INSTITUTE OF TECHNOLOGY
6300 La Calma Dr, Austin, TX 78752
Tel.: (512) 454-6116
Web Site: https://www.cybertex.edu
Year Founded: 1999
Sales Range: $1-9.9 Million
Emp.: 20
Vocational Institute Providing Training in IT & Medical Fields
N.A.I.C.S.: 611519
Iqbal Shaikh (Pres)
Ivan Seduinot (Engr-Network)

CYBERTHINK, INC.
1125 US Hwy 22 W Ste 1 685 Rte 202/206 Ste 101, Bridgewater, NJ 08807-9837
Tel.: (908) 429-8008
Web Site: http://www.cyberthink.com
Year Founded: 1996
Sales Range: $25-49.9 Million
Emp.: 300
Provider of IT Services
N.A.I.C.S.: 541511
Ravinder S. Thind (Pres & CEO)
Bhavesh Adani (Exec VP)
James Lombardo (Exec VP)

CYBERTROL ENGINEERING, LLC
2950 Xenium Ln N Ste 130, Minneapolis, MN 55441
Tel.: (763) 559-8660   MN
Web Site: http://www.cybertrol.com
Year Founded: 1996
Computer System Design Services
N.A.I.C.S.: 541512
Ben Durbin (Pres)
Clinton Graunke (Mgr-Support Sys)
Greg Stadden (Engr-Controls)
Ben Durbin (Pres)
Tim Barthel (VP-Automation Solutions)
Alexei Sacks (VP-Integration)
Jeff Reust (VP-Fin, Admin & Ops)

CYBRDI, INC.
143 Crofton Hill Ln, Rockville, MD 20850
Tel.: (301) 838-8966
Web Site: http://www.cybrdi.com
Year Founded: 1966
Life Science Equipment Mfr
N.A.I.C.S.: 334516
Yonghong Ren (COO & Treas)

CYCLE BARN INC.
5711 188th St SW, Lynnwood, WA 98037
Tel.: (425) 774-3538
Web Site: http://www.cyclebarn.com
Sales Range: $25-49.9 Million
Emp.: 130
Motorcycles
N.A.I.C.S.: 441227
James Boltz (Pres)
Gary Harper (CFO)
Garrett Johnson (Gen Mgr)

CYCLE COUNTRY, INC.
4764 Portland Rd NE, Salem, OR 97305-7336
Tel.: (971) 600-3000

Web Site: https://www.cyclecountry.net
Sales Range: $10-24.9 Million
Emp.: 33
Car Whslr
N.A.I.C.S.: 441110
Jimmie L. Smith (Principal)

CYCLONE DRILLING, INC.
5800 Mohan Rd, Gillette, WY 82718
Tel.: (307) 682-4161
Web Site: https://www.cyclonedrilling.com
Rev.: $43,200,000
Emp.: 600
Drilling Oil & Gas Wells
N.A.I.C.S.: 213111
Paul Hladky (Engr)
Colan Hulse (Mgr-Ops)

CYCLONE URANIUM CORPORATION
2186 S Holly St Ste 104, Denver, CO 80222
Tel.: (303) 800-0678   NV
Web Site: http://www.cycloneuranium.com
Sales Range: Less than $1 Million
Emp.: 1
Mining & Mineral Exploration
N.A.I.C.S.: 212290
James G. Baughman (Chm, Pres & CEO)

CYCLOPS TECHNOLOGIES, INC.
640 Booker Creek Blvd Ste 465, Oldsmar, FL 34677
Tel.: (813) 749-0892
Web Site: http://www.platesmart.com
Sales Range: $1-9.9 Million
Emp.: 30
License Plate Recognition Software
N.A.I.C.S.: 513210
John Chigos (CEO)
Kathleen Chigos (Pres)
Webb Wang (CTO)

CYDCOR, INC.
30699 Russell Rnch, Westlake Village, CA 91362
Tel.: (818) 706-9500   NY
Web Site: http://www.cydcor.com
Year Founded: 2007
Sales Range: $10-24.9 Million
Emp.: 100
Direct Selling Establishments
N.A.I.C.S.: 541613
Gary Polson (Chm & CEO)
Bobby Park (Sr VP-Campaign Dev)
Jim Majeski (Vice Chm)
Ron Nathanson (CFO)
Vera Quinn (Pres & Chief Revenue Officer)
Jeannie Finkel (Chief People Officer)
Stephen Semprevivo (Chief Strategy & Growth Officer)
Dwight Coates (CIO)
Chris Laurence (COO)
Brooke Levy (Sr VP & Gen Mgr)
Ramy Rizkana (Sr VP-Fin)
Rich Mangafas (VP & Gen Mgr-Retail)
Anthony Ottaviano (VP & Gen Mgr-Residential)
Lalo Burgos (VP & Gen Mgr-Canada)
Uwe Kneile (VP-Natl Accounts)
Harold Unroth (Gen Counsel-Global)
Gail Michalak (VP-Mktg)
Joe Wolfe (VP-Bus Dev)
James Mccarthy (VP-Bus Dev-Europe)
Sean Devine (VP-Bus Dev)
Kim Schram (VP-Bus Dev)

CYGER MEDIA

321 High School Rd NE Ste D3 #281, Bainbridge Island, WA 98110
Tel.: (206) 922-5314
Web Site: http://www.cygermedia.com
Online Publishing, Social, Mobile Applications Development & Digital Publishing
N.A.I.C.S.: 513199
Michael Cyger (Chm)

Subsidiaries:

CTQ Media   (1)
321 High School Rd NE Ste D3 #434, Bainbridge Island, WA 98110
Tel.: (206) 922-5314
Web Site: http://www.ctqmedia.com
Business-to-Business Products Including Internet Portals, E-Commerce Stores, Magazines, Research, Marketing Services, Conferences & Custom Publishing
N.A.I.C.S.: 561499

Web X.0 Media   (1)
321 High School Rd NE Ste D3 281, Bainbridge Island, WA 98110
Tel.: (206) 347-0977
Web Site: http://www.webxmedia.com
Social Applications Developer
N.A.I.C.S.: 513210
Michael Cyger (Publr)

CYGNET STAMPING & FABRICATING, INC.
613 Justin Ave, Glendale, CA 91201
Tel.: (818) 240-7574   CA
Web Site: https://www.cygnetstamping.com
Year Founded: 1974
Sales Range: $10-24.9 Million
Emp.: 32
Metal Stamping
N.A.I.C.S.: 332119
Marko Swan (Mgr-Ops)

CYGNUS MANUFACTURING CO.
491 Chantler Dr, Saxonburg, PA 16056
Tel.: (724) 352-8000
Web Site: https://www.cmc-usa.com
Rev.: $17,672,235
Emp.: 100
Custom Machinery
N.A.I.C.S.: 333998
Jodi Ricketts (VP-Sls)
Craig K. Harding (Owner & Chm)
John J. Maholtz (Pres & CEO)
Rudy Oblak (Mgr-Mfg)

CYMBAL DEVELOPMENT
3470 N Miami Ave Upper Ste, Miami, FL 33127
Tel.: (305) 573-8700
Web Site: http://www.cymbaldevelopment.com
Sales Range: $1-9.9 Million
Real Estate Development & Construction
N.A.I.C.S.: 237210
Asi Cymbal (Owner & Pres)
Ziva Nitzan (Comptroller)

CYN OIL CORPORATION
100 Tosca Dr, Stoughton, MA 02072
Tel.: (781) 341-5108
Web Site: https://www.cynenv.com
Rev.: $25,000,000
Emp.: 200
Environmental Cleanup Services
N.A.I.C.S.: 562910
Albert A. Tucci (Chm)
Steve Cucci (Pres)

CYNERGIES CONSULTING, INC.
26301 Curtiss Wright Pkwy Ste 400, Richmond Heights, OH 44143

Tel.: (440) 918-9341
Web Site: http://www.cynergies.net
Year Founded: 1997
Sales Range: $1-9.9 Million
Emp.: 40
Temporary Staffing of Programmers, Project Managers & Business Analysts
N.A.I.C.S.: 561320
Debbie Holy (Co-Owner & Pres)
Ellie Chalko (Owner & Exec VP)

CYNERGY PROFESSIONAL SYSTEMS, LLC
23187 La Cadena Dr Ste 102, Laguna Hills, CA 92653
Web Site: http://www.cynergy.pro
Year Founded: 2009
Sales Range: $25-49.9 Million
Emp.: 18
Telecommunication Servicesb
N.A.I.C.S.: 517810
Cynthia Mason (Pres)
Denton Browning (VP-Sls & Mktg)
Jesse Lake (VP-Ops)

CYPRESS COVE AT HEALTHPARK FLORIDA
10200 Cypress Cove Dr, Fort Myers, FL 33908
Tel.: (239) 481-6605   FL
Web Site: https://www.cypresscoveliving.org
Year Founded: 1995
Sales Range: $10-24.9 Million
Emp.: 347
Lifecare Retirement Community Operator
N.A.I.C.S.: 623311
Kevin Mannix (Dir-Dining)
Michele S. Wasserlauf (Exec Dir)
Vasyl Kasiyan (Dir-Campus Medical)
Melody Desilets (Officer-Community Advancement)

CYPRESS CREEK RENEWABLES, LLC
3250 Ocean Park Ste 355, Santa Monica, CA 90405
Tel.: (310) 581-6299
Web Site: http://www.ccrenew.com
Year Founded: 2014
Eletric Power Generation Services
N.A.I.C.S.: 221114
Ben Van De Bunt (Chm)
Sarah Slusser (CEO)
Michael Cohen (Pres)
Jerome O'Brien (Chief Admin Officer & Gen Counsel)
Jon Buttles (CFO)
Brad Bauer (Chief Capital Markets Officer)
Patrick McConnell (Chief Structured Finance Officer)
Jaime Carlson (Exec VP-Ops)
Kevin Knee (Co-Founder)
David Riester (Mng Dir)
Pete Farlekas (Pres-Engrg, Procurement & Construction)
Evan Riley (VP-Dev)
Chris Quarterman (Vp-Market Strategy)
Noah Hyte (VP-Strategy & Origination)
Geoff Fallon (Sr Dir-Dev)
Steve Levitas (Sr VP-Regulatory Affairs & Strategy)
Cassidy DeLine (Dir-Project Fin)
Jeffrey Meigel (Chief Investment Officer)
Jeremy Wodakow (Chief Revenue Officer)
Bennet Van De Bunt (Executives)

CYPRESS EQUIPMENT FUND A, LLC

188 The Embarcadero Ste 420, San
Francisco, CA 94105 **CA**
Year Founded: 2011
Investment Services
N.A.I.C.S.: 523999
Stephen Harwood *(Pres)*
Ken Park *(CFO)*

CYPRESS HUMAN CAPITAL MANAGEMENT, LLC.
221 Main St Ste 920, San Francisco,
CA 94105
Tel.: (415) 394-6400
Web Site:
http://www.cypresshcm.com
Year Founded: 2005
Sales Range: $1-9.9 Million
Emp.: 111
Information Technology Staffing Services
N.A.I.C.S.: 561330
Brian J. Vesce *(Mng Dir)*

CYPRESS LAKE COUNTRY CLUB INC.
6767 Winkler Rd, Fort Myers, FL
33919
Tel.: (239) 481-1333
Web Site:
http://www.cypresslakecc.com
Sales Range: $1-9.9 Million
Emp.: 80
Golf Course & Country Club
N.A.I.C.S.: 713910
Ed Rodgers *(Gen Mgr)*
Bryce Koch *(Superintendent-Golf Course)*
Kris Antonacci *(Dir-Food & Beverage)*

CYPRESS MEDIA GROUP
3105 S Martin Luther King Blvd Ste
231, Lansing, MI 48910
Tel.: (770) 640-9918
Web Site:
http://www.cypressmedia.net
Year Founded: 1978
Sales Range: Less than $1 Million
Emp.: 5
Web Design, Public Relations, Video
Production, Training Seminars
N.A.I.C.S.: 541820
Randall P. Whatley *(Pres)*

CYPRESS MEDICAL PRODUCTS LTD.
1400 S Wolf Rd Ste 200, Wheeling,
IL 60090
Tel.: (815) 385-0100
Web Site:
http://www.cypressmed.com
Sales Range: $10-24.9 Million
Emp.: 100
Medical Equipment & Supplies
N.A.I.C.S.: 423450
Shannon Krizka *(Mgr-HR)*

CYPRESS PARTNERS, LLC
116 Intercoastal Pointe Dr, Jupiter,
FL 33477
Tel.: (561) 744-9122 **FL**
Web Site:
http://www.cypresspartners.com
Year Founded: 2000
Holding Company; Diagnostic Imaging Centers Owner & Operator
N.A.I.C.S.: 551112
Joseph A. Paul *(Co-Founder & Pres)*
Paul Cote *(Co-Founder & COO)*
Sam Burke *(Dir-Asset Mgmt)*

Subsidiaries:

Griffin Imaging, Inc. **(1)**
220 Rock St, Griffin, GA 30224
Tel.: (770) 229-4660
Web Site:
http://www.griffinimagingradiology.com

Radiological Services
N.A.I.C.S.: 621111
Ron Gay *(Dir-Medical)*

CYPRESS PROPERTY & CASUALTY INSURANCE COMPANY
12926 Gran Bay Pkwy W Ste 200,
Jacksonville, FL 32258
Tel.: (904) 992-4492
Web Site: http://www.cypressig.com
Year Founded: 1999
Sales Range: $75-99.9 Million
Emp.: 75
Property & Casualty Insurance Services
N.A.I.C.S.: 524126
Dianne Stebbins *(Mgr-HR)*
L. G. Lugo *(Exec VP-Texas)*
Jay Rine *(Pres)*
Trevor Hillier *(CFO & Treas)*

CYPRESS TECHNOLOGIES CORP.
17301 FM 1431, Leander, TX 78641
Tel.: (512) 267-9973
Web Site: http://www.cypresstech.net
Year Founded: 1987
Sales Range: $10-24.9 Million
Emp.: 45
Computer Peripheral Equipment
N.A.I.C.S.: 334118
Jacqueline L. Child *(Pres)*
Phillip Pavelka *(Mgr-Logistics)*

CYPRESS TRUCK LINES, INC.
1414 Lindrose Rd, Jacksonville, FL
32206
Tel.: (904) 356-9322 **FL**
Web Site:
http://www.cypresstruck.com
Rev.: $18,408,857
Emp.: 300
General Freight Trucking Services
N.A.I.C.S.: 484121
David V. Penland Sr. *(Pres)*

Subsidiaries:

Cypress Truck Leasing Company,
Inc. **(1)**
1414 Lindrose St, Jacksonville, FL 32206
Tel.: (904) 353-8641
Web Site: http://www.cypresstruck.com
Sales Range: $1-9.9 Million
Emp.: 40
Truck Rental And Leasing; Freight Delivery
N.A.I.C.S.: 484110
Cynthia Penland *(Treas)*

Sunbelt Transport, LLC **(1)**
1414 Lindrose St, Jacksonville, FL 32206
Tel.: (904) 353-8641
Web Site:
http://www.sunbelttransportllc.com
Sales Range: $150-199.9 Million
Emp.: 275
Freight Truck Delivery
N.A.I.C.S.: 484110

CYPRIUM INVESTMENT PARTNERS LLC
200 Public Sq Ste 2020, Cleveland,
OH 44114
Tel.: (216) 453-4500 **DE**
Web Site: https://www.cyprium.com
Year Founded: 2011
Sales Range: $50-74.9 Million
Emp.: 18
Private Equity & Investment Management Firm
N.A.I.C.S.: 523999
John Sinnenberg *(Chm & Co-Founder)*
Cindy Babitt *(Mng Partner)*
Daniel Kessler *(Principal)*
Beth Laschinger *(Principal)*
Patrick Rond *(VP)*
Nick Stone *(Principal)*

Ted Laufik *(CFO & Chief Compliance Officer)*
Leland Lewis *(Mng Partner)*
Mike Conaton *(Mng Partner)*
Drew Molinari *(VP)*

Subsidiaries:

Cyprium Investment Partners LLC -
New York **(1)**
461 Fifth Ave 26th Fl, New York, NY 10017
Tel.: (646) 571-1620
Web Site: http://www.cyprium.com
Private Equity & Investment Management Firm
N.A.I.C.S.: 523999

Plastival Inc. **(1)**
3055 Anderson, Terrebonne, J6Y 1W5, QC, Canada
Tel.: (450) 965-3231
Web Site: http://www.plastival.com
Sales Range: $25-49.9 Million
Emp.: 150
Vinyl & Aluminum Railing & Fencing Systems Mfr & Distr
N.A.I.C.S.: 332323
Jack White *(Pres & CEO)*

CYQUENT, INC.
5410 Edson Ln Ste 210C, Rockville,
MD 20852
Tel.: (240) 292-0230
Web Site: http://www.cyquent.com
Year Founded: 2001
Sales Range: $10-24.9 Million
Emp.: 35
Information Technology Services
N.A.I.C.S.: 541512
Sagar I. Sawant *(Founder & CEO)*
Niraj Jaipuria *(Pres-Offshore Ops)*
Kiran T *(Mgr-Delivery)*

CYRACOM INTERNATIONAL, INC.
5780 N Swan Rd Ste 100, Tucson,
AZ 85718
Tel.: (520) 232-1640
Web Site: http://www.cyracom.com
Year Founded: 1995
Sales Range: $25-49.9 Million
Emp.: 350
Interpretation & Translation Services
N.A.I.C.S.: 541930
Jeremy Woan *(Chm & CEO)*
Best Ihegborow *(VP-Contact Center Ops)*
Austin Wade *(VP-Client Satisfaction)*
Todd Torman *(Sr VP-Sls)*
Don Oliver *(CFO)*

CYRQ ENERGY, INC.
Kearns Bldg Ste 600 136 S Main St,
Salt Lake City, UT 84101
Tel.: (801) 875-4200 **UT**
Web Site: http://www.cyrqenergy.com
Sales Range: $1-9.9 Million
Emp.: 27
Geothermal Power Plant Operations
N.A.I.C.S.: 221116
Nicholas Goodman *(CEO)*
Scott Rhees *(VP-Transmission & Utility Rels)*
Steven R. Brown *(VP-Bus Dev)*
Mike Gipson *(Mgr-Geothermal Ops)*
John T. Perry *(CFO)*

CYRUS CAPITAL PARTNERS, L.P.
65 E 55th St 6th Fl, New York, NY
10022
Tel.: (212) 380-5800
Web Site:
https://www.cyruscapital.com
Year Founded: 2005
Sales Range: $1-4.9 Billion
Emp.: 39
Privater Equity Firm
N.A.I.C.S.: 523999

Stephen Cyrus Freidheim *(Co-Founder)*
Daniel John Bordessa *(Partner)*
James Tucker *(Mng Dir)*
Jose Santiago *(Dir-Security)*
Robert Swenson *(Dir-Ops)*
Roger Sherman *(Dir-Bus Dev)*
Ember Shmitt *(Dir-IR)*
Soohyung Kim *(Co-Founder)*

Subsidiaries:

Tandberg Data GmbH **(1)**
Feldstrasse 81, 44141, Dortmund, Germany
Tel.: (49) 23154360
Web Site: http://www.tandbergdata.com
Business Data Storage & Protection Solutions
N.A.I.C.S.: 513210
Nils Hoff *(Mng Dir)*
Kurt Kalbfleisch *(Mng Dir)*

Subsidiary (US):

Tandberg Data **(2)**
10225 Westmoor Dr Ste 125, Westminster, CO 80021
Tel.: (303) 442-4333
Web Site: http://www.tandbergdata.com
Sales Range: $75-99.9 Million
Business Data Storage & Protection Solutions
N.A.I.C.S.: 513210

Subsidiary (Non-US):

Tandberg Data (Japan) Inc. **(2)**
Eitaibashi Eco-Piazza Bldg 8th floor 29-13, Shinkawa 1-chome Chuo-ku, Tokyo, 104-033, Japan
Tel.: (81) 355662871
Web Site: http://www.tandberg.co.jp
Sales Range: $25-49.9 Million
Emp.: 11
Business Data Storage & Protection Solutions
N.A.I.C.S.: 513210

Tandberg Data Norge AS **(2)**
Okernveien 94, 0579, Oslo, Norway
Tel.: (47) 22 18 90 90
Business Data Storage & Protection Solutions
N.A.I.C.S.: 513210

Toys "R" Us S.A.R.L. **(1)**
La Remise 2 Rue Thomas Edison, 91044, Lisses, France
Tel.: (33) 160768300
Web Site: http://www.toysrus.fr
Sales Range: $75-99.9 Million
Toy Retailer
N.A.I.C.S.: 459120

CYRUS INNOVATION
200 Varick St Ste 902, New York, NY
10014
Tel.: (212) 647-7186
Web Site:
http://www.cyrusinnovation.com
Year Founded: 2003
Sales Range: $1-9.9 Million
Emp.: 35
Software Development Consulting Services
N.A.I.C.S.: 541618
Bruce Eckfeldt *(Founder, CEO & Mng Dir)*

CYRUS OLEARYS PIES INC.
1528 S Hayford Rd, Airway Heights,
WA 99001-9001
Tel.: (509) 624-5000
Web Site: http://www.cyruspies.com
Commercial Bakeries
N.A.I.C.S.: 311812
Ken Hazelton *(Mgr-Sls)*

CYSTIC FIBROSIS FOUNDATION
4550 Montgomery Ave Ste 1100 N,
Bethesda, MD 20814
Tel.: (301) 951-4422

Cystic Fibrosis Foundation—(Continued)

Web Site: http://www.cff.org
Rev.: $135,604,341
Assets: $4,013,935,956
Liabilities: $238,572,484
Net Worth: $3,775,363,472
Earnings: ($418,822,593)
Emp.: 470
Fiscal Year-end: 12/31/18
Health Care Srvices
N.A.I.C.S.: 622110
Vera H. Twigg (Exec VP)
David A. Mount (Treas)
K. C. Bryan White (Chm)
Louis A. DeFalco (Vice Chm)
Marc S. Ginsky (Exec VP)
Jack Mahler (Chief Investment Officer)
Michael P. Boyle (Pres & CEO)
Robert H. Niehaus (Vice Chm)
Theodore J. Torphy (Vice Chm)
Kathryn Brown (Chief Comm & Mktg Officer)
Yvonne Massenburg (Chief People Officer)
Irena Barisic (Chief Operating & Fin Officer & Exec VP)

CYTON INDUSTRIES INC.
5558 Bill Cody Rd, Hidden Hills, CA 91302-1101
Tel.: (818) 768-7330
Rev.: $11,300,000
Emp.: 80
Automotive Supplies & Parts
N.A.I.C.S.: 423120

Subsidiaries:

Prime Plating Inc   (1)
11321 Goss St, Sun Valley, CA 91352
Tel.: (818) 768-9100
Web Site: http://www.prime-plating.com
Sales Range: $1-9.9 Million
Electroplating Of Metals Or Formed Products
N.A.I.C.S.: 332813

CYWEB HOLDINGS INC.
70 Middle Neck Rd Ste 5, Great Neck, NY 11021
Tel.: (516) 467-4518
Web Site:
    https://www.cywebholdings.com
Sales Range: $1-9.9 Million
Emp.: 10
Web-Based Information Services
N.A.I.C.S.: 551112
Ian Aronovich (Pres & CEO)
Michael Pesochinsky (VP & Gen Counsel)

Subsidiaries:

GovernmentAuctions.org   (1)
70 Middle Neck Rd Ste 5, Great Neck, NY 11021
Tel.: (516) 773-9844
Web Site:
    http://www.governmentauctions.org
Emp.: 3
Online Government Auction Services
N.A.I.C.S.: 561990
Ian Aronovich (Pres & CEO)

CZ-USA
3327 N 7th St Trafficway, Kansas City, KS 66115
Tel.: (913) 321-1811
Web Site: http://www.cz-usa.com
Sales Range: $25-49.9 Million
Emp.: 20
Sporting Goods Whslr
N.A.I.C.S.: 459110
Angus Hobdell (Principal)

CZARNOWSKI EXHIBIT SERVICE INC.

2287 S Blue Island Ave, Chicago, IL 60608-4344
Tel.: (773) 247-1500
Web Site:
    https://www.czarnowski.com
Year Founded: 1973
Sales Range: $50-74.9 Million
Emp.: 200
Business Services; Exhibition Industry
N.A.I.C.S.: 561990
Mark Nagle (Pres)
Laurie Ciesla (Acct Exec)

D & D BUILDING, INC.
3264 Union St SE, Wyoming, MI 49548-2312
Tel.: (616) 243-5633
Web Site:
    https://www.dndbuilding.com
Year Founded: 1968
Sales Range: $10-24.9 Million
Emp.: 80
Civil Engineering Services
N.A.I.C.S.: 237310
Scott Gibson (Pres)

D & E MITSUBISHI
6220 Market St, Wilmington, NC 28405
Tel.: (910) 799-4210
Web Site:
    https://www.demitsubishi.com
Year Founded: 1971
Sales Range: $10-24.9 Million
Emp.: 25
Used Car Retailer
N.A.I.C.S.: 441120
Jeff DuBose (Pres)
Carol Holbrook (Controller)

D & G BRICE CONTRACTORS, INC.
4900 Wetheredsville Rd Bldg 3, Baltimore, MD 21207-6669
Tel.: (410) 448-2100
Sales Range: $10-24.9 Million
Emp.: 32
Readymix Concrete Mfr
N.A.I.C.S.: 327320
Gerald Brice (Owner)

D & H MASONRY, INC.
5719 Edward Dr, Houston, TX 77032
Tel.: (281) 442-6666
Web Site:
    http://www.dhmasonryinc.com
Sales Range: $10-24.9 Million
Emp.: 150
Masonry Services
N.A.I.C.S.: 238140
David Knight (Pres)

D & J TILE COMPANY, INC.
1045 Terminal Way, San Carlos, CA 94070
Tel.: (650) 632-4000
Web Site: https://www.djtile.com
Year Founded: 1989
Sales Range: $10-24.9 Million
Emp.: 100
Tile & Terrazzo Contracting Services
N.A.I.C.S.: 238340
David Newman (Owner)

D & K IMPLEMENT LLC
507 S E St, Pomeroy, IA 50575
Tel.: (712) 468-2217
Web Site:
    http://www.dandkimplement.com
Sales Range: $10-24.9 Million
Emp.: 18
Farm Implements Whslr
N.A.I.C.S.: 423820
Dennis Lenz (Owner)

D & M INDUSTRIES, INC.
4205 30th Ave S, Moorhead, MN 56560
Tel.: (218) 287-3100
Web Site:
    https://www.weselldoors.com
Year Founded: 1982
Sales Range: $10-24.9 Million
Emp.: 110
Metal Window & Door Mfr
N.A.I.C.S.: 332321
Tom Boyle (Pres)
Gail Borowicz (VP-Fin & Admin)

D & R GENERAL CONTRACTING & DESIGN, INC.
133 W Lake Mead Pkwy Ste 120, Henderson, NV 89015
Tel.: (702) 558-3815
Sales Range: $1-9.9 Million
Emp.: 10
Commercial & Institutional Building Construction Services
N.A.I.C.S.: 236220
Roy Phillips (Pres)

D & W MANUFACTURING CO., INC.
3237 W Lake St, Chicago, IL 60624-2004
Tel.: (773) 533-1542
Web Site: https://www.dwmfg.com
Year Founded: 2004
Sales Range: $10-24.9 Million
Emp.: 45
Tubular Product Whslr
N.A.I.C.S.: 423510
Ed Przybyla (Mgr)
Michael Leavitt (Pres)

D & W PAINTING INC.
1000 S West Dr, Leander, TX 78641
Tel.: (512) 259-1411
Web Site: http://www.dwpainting.com
Year Founded: 1994
Sales Range: $10-24.9 Million
Emp.: 350
Painting & Wall Covering Contractor Services
N.A.I.C.S.: 238320
Duke Williams (Pres)
Jodi Pepper (VP)

D A E INDUSTRIES
501 S 15th St, Louisville, KY 40203
Tel.: (502) 589-1445
Web Site: http://www.daeind.com
Sales Range: $10-24.9 Million
Emp.: 50
Machine Shop Operator
N.A.I.C.S.: 332710
Jeff Owen (Dir-Pur)

D CUBED GROUP LLC
590 Madison Ave 21st Fl, New York, NY 10022
Tel.: (212) 605-4910
Web Site:
    https://www.dcubedgroup.com
Investment Services
N.A.I.C.S.: 523999
Glenn B. Kaufman (Mng Dir)

D EXPOSITO & PARTNERS, LLC
875 Ave of the Americas 25th Fl, New York, NY 10001
Tel.: (646) 747-8800
Year Founded: 2005
Sales Range: $10-24.9 Million
Emp.: 25
N.A.I.C.S.: 541810
Fernando Fernandez (Partner & Chief Client Officer)
Gloria Constanza (Partner & Chief Contact Strategist)

Daisy Exposito-Ulla (Chm & CEO)
Louis Maldonado (Mng Dir)
Jorge Ulla (Partner & Chief Ideation Officer)
Danilo Alvarez (Dir-Creative)
John Ross (CFO & Partner)
Mary Miqueli (Partner-Client Svc)
Orlando Millian (Partner & Reg Dir)

D L BECK INC.
2860 W 5200 S, Rexburg, ID 83440
Tel.: (208) 656-9344
Web Site: http://www.dlbeck.com
Year Founded: 2005
Construction Services
N.A.I.C.S.: 237310
Pam Beck (Co-Founder)
David Beck (Co-Founder)

D SQUARE ENERGY LLC
1546 Boalch Ave NW Ste 70, North Bend, WA 98045
Tel.: (425) 888-2882
Web Site: http://www.d2energy.com
Year Founded: 1990
Sales Range: $1-9.9 Million
Emp.: 23
Electrical Equipment Whslr
N.A.I.C.S.: 423610
Don Dunavant (Pres)

D&B CONSTRUCTION GROUP
D&B Construction Group, Sinking Spring, PA 19608
Tel.: (610) 927-6494
Web Site:
    http://www.dbconstructiongrp.com
Year Founded: 2010
Sales Range: $1-9.9 Million
Emp.: 50
Construction Services
N.A.I.C.S.: 236116
Dan Gring (CEO)
Brennan Brennan (COO & VP-Reading Market)
Mark Keever (VP-Preconstruction)
Drew Bell (VP-Bus Dev)
Jessica Nelis (Ops Mgr)

D&B MACHINE, INC.
1855 61st St, Sarasota, FL 34243
Tel.: (941) 335-8002
Web Site:
    https://www.dandbmachine.com
Sales Range: $1-9.9 Million
Emp.: 30
Contract Machining
N.A.I.C.S.: 332710
David Frostad (Pres)
Betty Frostad (CEO)
James Bock (Mgr-Ops)

D&B SUPPLY COMPANY INC.
3303 E Linden St, Caldwell, ID 83605
Tel.: (208) 459-7446
Web Site: http://www.dbsupply.com
Year Founded: 1959
Rev.: $84,100,000
Emp.: 300
Farm Supplies
N.A.I.C.S.: 424910
Mark Schmidt (CFO)
Kelly Hendricks (Owner)
Christopher J. Coughlin (Chm)

D&B TILE DISTRIBUTORS
14200 NW 4th St, Sunrise, FL 33325
Tel.: (954) 846-2663
Web Site: http://www.dbtile.com
Year Founded: 1968
Sales Range: $25-49.9 Million
Emp.: 140
Ceramic Tile Whslr
N.A.I.C.S.: 423320

David A. Yarborough (Pres)
Janis List (Mgr)
Maddy Diaz (Branch Mgr)
Richard Favreau (Mgr)
Rudy Llerena (COO & VP)
Martha Alvarez (Mgr)

D&C CONSTRUCTION CO. INC.
415 VFW Dr, Rockland, MA 02370
Tel.: (781) 871-8200
Web Site:
http://www.dandcconstruction.com
Sales Range: $10-24.9 Million
Emp.: 45
Provider of Water Main Construction
N.A.I.C.S.: 237110
Bradford S. Cleaves (Pres)
Douglas Tillotson (Project Mgr)
Duncan Peterson (VP)
Ben Cleaves (Office Mgr)

D&C HONDA CO. INC.
28 County Rd, Tenafly, NJ 07670
Tel.: (201) 569-5515   NJ
Web Site: http://www.dcautos.com
Year Founded: 1932
Sales Range: $50-74.9 Million
Emp.: 80
Sales of New & Used Automobiles
N.A.I.C.S.: 441110
Norman Dorf (Owner)

D&C INC.
1915 S St, Duluth, MN 55812
Tel.: (218) 728-6349
Sales Range: $10-24.9 Million
Emp.: 64
Convenience Store
N.A.I.C.S.: 445131
Catherine T. Letourneau (Owner)

D&D COMMODITIES LTD.
PO Box 359, Stephen, MN 56757
Tel.: (218) 478-3308
Web Site:
http://www.ddcommodities.com
Sales Range: $10-24.9 Million
Emp.: 40
Mfr of Pet Food & Related Products
N.A.I.C.S.: 311119
Dick Hebert (Owner & Pres)
Jennifer Deere (VP-Ops)

D&D DISTRIBUTION SER-VICES
789 Kingsmill Rd, York, PA 17403
Tel.: (717) 845-1646
Web Site: https://www.dd-dist.com
Year Founded: 1978
Sales Range: $10-24.9 Million
Emp.: 30
General Warehousing
N.A.I.C.S.: 493110
Sandra Green (Mgr-Sls)
Tanja Gray (Mgr-CSR)
Kurt Feltenberger (Mgr-IT)

D&D INTERACTIVE
215 Presidential Blvd, Bala Cynwyd, PA 19004
Tel.: (610) 667-4200
Year Founded: 1996
Sales Range: $10-24.9 Million
Emp.: 20
N.A.I.C.S.: 541810

D&D MANAGEMENT INC.
606 Green Bay Rd, Winnetka, IL 60093
Tel.: (847) 446-6707
Sales Range: $10-24.9 Million
Emp.: 150
Grocery Stores
N.A.I.C.S.: 445110
Dave Ruehlman (Pres)

Subsidiaries:

Grand Food Center   (1)
341 Hazel Ave, Glencoe, IL 60022
Tel.: (847) 835-2842
Web Site: http://www.grandfoodcenter.com
Rev.: $7,100,000
Emp.: 69
Grocery Stores, Independent
N.A.I.C.S.: 445110
Dan Klebba (Pres)

D&D OF LEE COUNTY INC.
2545 Estero Blvd, Fort Myers Beach, FL 33931
Tel.: (239) 463-7979
Rev.: $11,100,000
Emp.: 50
Supermarket
N.A.I.C.S.: 445110
David Carney (Pres)

D&D OIL CO. INC.
120 Bridge Ave, Murfreesboro, TN 37129
Tel.: (615) 896-2354
Web Site: https://ddoilco.com
Sales Range: $10-24.9 Million
Emp.: 20
Gases
N.A.I.C.S.: 424720
Doyle Scott (Pres)

D&D TEXAS OUTFITTERS INC.
516 E Interstate 10, Seguin, TX 78155-1417
Tel.: (830) 379-7340
Web Site:
https://www.ddtexasoutfitters.com
Year Founded: 1972
Sales Range: $50-74.9 Million
Emp.: 55
Farm Supply & Clothing Whslr
N.A.I.C.S.: 424910
Kevin Ferrell (Pres & Owner)
Lisa Murphy (Dir-Adv)

D&D TOOLING MANUFACTUR-ING, INC.
500 Territorial Dr, Bolingbrook, IL 60440
Tel.: (630) 759-0015
Web Site: https://www.ddmfg.com
Year Founded: 1987
Sales Range: $10-24.9 Million
Emp.: 120
Supplier of Precision Stampings
N.A.I.C.S.: 332119
William Diedrick (Pres)
Lawrence Diedrick (VP)

D&D TRANSPORTATION SER-VICES
1735 Main St, Gooding, ID 83330
Tel.: (208) 934-4451
Web Site: https://www.ddtsi.com
Sales Range: $10-24.9 Million
Emp.: 150
Truck Transportation Brokers
N.A.I.C.S.: 488510
Calvin Kuntz (Pres)
Jennifer Graves (VP)
Darlene Kuntz (Treas & Sec)
Dena Freeman (Mgr-Billing)

D&E PLUMBING & HEATING INC.
1112 N Falconcrest Ct, Nixa, MO 65714
Tel.: (417) 725-5300
Sales Range: $10-24.9 Million
Emp.: 38
Excavation & Grading, Building Construction
N.A.I.C.S.: 238910
Bill Collison (Office Mgr)

D&F CONSTRUCTION, INC.
4017 Penn Belt Pl, Forestville, MD 20747
Tel.: (301) 516-8460
Web Site:
http://www.dandfconstruction.com
Sales Range: $10-24.9 Million
Emp.: 80
Highway Street & Bridge Construction
N.A.I.C.S.: 237310
Joaquim Duartes (Pres)
Edite D. Florencio (Sec)
Luis Slavian (Gen Mgr)

D&F EQUIPMENT SALES INC.
8641 Hwy 227, Crossville, AL 35962
Tel.: (256) 528-7842
Web Site: https://www.dfequip.com
Sales Range: $10-24.9 Million
Emp.: 120
Sales of Poultry Brooders, Feeders & Waterers
N.A.I.C.S.: 333111
Larry Fortenberry (Owner)
Gary Cambron (Engr-Design)
Gene Pledger (Mgr-Pur)

D&G EQUIPMENT CO., INC.
69 Wesley St, South Hackensack, NJ 07606-1598
Tel.: (201) 343-2255
Year Founded: 1917
Sales Range: $75-99.9 Million
Emp.: 2
Distr of Roofing & Road Maintenance Equipment
N.A.I.C.S.: 423330
Douglas E. Butler Jr. (Owner)

D&G EQUIPMENT INC.
2525 E Grand River Rd, Williamston, MI 48895
Tel.: (517) 655-4606
Web Site:
http://www.dgequipment.com
Sales Range: $10-24.9 Million
Emp.: 55
Farm Equipment & Supplies
N.A.I.C.S.: 459999
Elden E. Gustafson (Pres)
Dale Koven (Mgr-Svcs)
Patti Norton (Office Mgr)

D&G MACHINE PRODUCTS INC.
50 Eisenhower Dr, Westbrook, ME 04092
Tel.: (207) 854-1500
Web Site:
https://www.dgmachine.com
Year Founded: 1967
Sales Range: $10-24.9 Million
Emp.: 115
Provider of Industrial Machinery Services
N.A.I.C.S.: 332710
Steven Sullivan (VP-Sls, Mktg & New Bus Dev)
Charlie Tarling (Pres)
Kevin Wormwood (Mgr-Welding Tech Plant)
Dan Sullivan (Engr-Sls)
Rick Green (Project Engr)
Bryant Oja (Mgr-Quality Control)
Bob Smith (Mgr-HR)
John Doran (Mgr-Sls)

D&H DISTRIBUTING CO., INC.
100 Tech Dr, Harrisburg, PA 17112
Tel.: (717) 236-8001   PA
Web Site: https://www.dandh.com
Year Founded: 1918
Sales Range: $1-4.9 Billion
Emp.: 1,628

Computer & Computer Peripheral Equipment & Software Merchant Wholesalers
N.A.I.C.S.: 423430
Daniel Schwab (Co-Pres)
Michael Schwab (Co-Pres)
Mary Campbell (VP-Mktg)
Matthew Nolan (CFO)
Michael Everly (CIO)
Timmothy Billing (Sr VP-Vendor Mgmt & Pur)
Michelle Biase (Gen Mgr-Canada)

Subsidiaries:

D&H Canada ULC   (1)
570 Matheson Boulevard East, Mississauga, L4Z 4G3, ON, Canada   (100%)
Tel.: (905) 890-8320
Computer & Home Office Electronic Products Distr
N.A.I.C.S.: 423430
Greg Tobin (Gen Mgr)
Shawn Snobelen (Natl Mgr-Retail & Online Sls)

D&H UNITED FUELING SOLU-TIONS, INC.
12100 Crownpoint Dr Ste 110, San Antonio, TX 78233
Tel.: (210) 651-3882   DE
Web Site: https://www.dh-united.com
Year Founded: 1939
Emp.: 200
Gasoline Service Station Equipment Installation, Maintenance & Repair Services
N.A.I.C.S.: 238990
John Farrell (COO)
BJ Moore (Dir-Construction)
Craig Bush (CTO)
Travis Williams (CFO)
Bolling H. Sasnett III (Owner & CEO)

D&J CONSTRUCTION COM-PANY INC.
101 Blazier Ln, West Monroe, LA 71292
Tel.: (318) 388-2764
Web Site: http://www.djcon.com
Year Founded: 1967
Sales Range: $25-49.9 Million
Emp.: 160
Highway & Street Paving Contracting Services
N.A.I.C.S.: 212321
Steve Hackworth (Sr VP-Ops)
James Hays (VP-Asphalt Plants)

D&J ENTERPRISES INC.
3495 Lee Rd 10, Auburn, AL 36832
Tel.: (334) 821-1249
Web Site:
http://www.dandjenterprises.net
Year Founded: 1965
Rev.: $15,200,000
Emp.: 150
Convenience Store & Gasoline Service Station Distr
N.A.I.C.S.: 445131
David Vining (Pres)
Joanna Vining (Treas, Sec & VP)
Larry Jones (Dir-Pur)
Martin K. Conroy (Dir-Construction)
Patrick Kirkpatrick (Mgr-Pur)
J. Copeland (Mgr-Engrg)

D&J SALES CO. LLC
8 Newport Dr, Forest Hill, MD 21050-2616
Tel.: (410) 893-1116
Web Site:
https://www.dandjmedical.com
Medical Equipment Whslr
N.A.I.C.S.: 423450
Shana O'Neil (CFO)

D&J Sales Co, LLC—(Continued)

Subsidiaries:

Maryland Orthotics & Prosthetics Co., Inc.   **(1)**
8517 Loch Raven Blvd, Baltimore, MD 21286
Tel.: (410) 665-8200
Web Site: http://www.mdop.com
Sales Range: $1-9.9 Million
Emp.: 10
Orthotic & Prosthetic Device Mfr
N.A.I.C.S.: 339999
Linda Schofield (Pres)
Denise Moore (Chief Compliancy Officer)

D&K GROUP, INC.
1795 Commerce Dr, Elk Grove Village, IL 60007-2119
Tel.: (847) 956-0160
Web Site: https://www.dkgroup.com
Year Founded: 1978
Sales Range: $25-49.9 Million
Emp.: 200
Adhesives & Sealant Mfr
N.A.I.C.S.: 325520
Karl Singer (Pres)
Tom Pidgeon (VP-Sls & Mktg)
James Broz (CFO)

Subsidiaries:

D&K Coating Technologies, Inc.   **(1)**
1400 Venture Dr, Janesville, WI 53546
Tel.: (608) 741-6520
Thermal Film Mfr
N.A.I.C.S.: 326112

D&K Custom Machine Design Inc.   **(1)**
80 Bond St 1795 Commerce Dr, Elk Grove Village, IL 60007-1217   **(100%)**
Tel.: (847) 956-4757
Web Site: http://www.dkgroup.com
Sales Range: $10-24.9 Million
Emp.: 25
Mfr of Printing Trades Machinery
N.A.I.C.S.: 333248
James Broz (CFO)
Tom Pidgeon (VP-Sls & Mktg)
Silvia Arroyo (Acct Exec)
Fernando Morales (Mgr-Sls-Canada & Latin America)

D&K Europe Ltd.   **(1)**
38-39 Crossgate Road Park Farm, Redditch, B98 7SN, Worcestershire, United Kingdom
Tel.: (44) 1527 520 073
Web Site: http://www.dkeurope.co.uk
Emp.: 20
Lamination Equipment Mfr
N.A.I.C.S.: 333310
John Hancock (Mgr-Sls)
Robin French (Mng Dir)

D&K International Inc.   **(1)**
1795 Commerce Dr, Elk Grove Village, IL 60007-2005   **(100%)**
Tel.: (847) 956-0160
Sales Range: $10-24.9 Million
Emp.: 50
Mfr of Adhesives & Sealants
N.A.I.C.S.: 325520
Karl Singer (Pres)

D&L FOUNDRY, INC.
12970 Wheeler Rd NE, Moses Lake, WA 98837
Tel.: (509) 765-7952
Web Site: http://www.dlfoundry.us
Sales Range: $10-24.9 Million
Emp.: 170
Iron Foundries
N.A.I.C.S.: 331511
Linda Cooper (Pres)
Russ Goodsell (Sec & Treas)

D&L PARTS CO. INC.
2100 Freedom Dr, Charlotte, NC 28208
Tel.: (704) 374-0400
Web Site: https://www.dlpartsco.com
Sales Range: $10-24.9 Million

Emp.: 90
Household Appliance Parts
N.A.I.C.S.: 423620
Ralph B. Brackett (Owner, Pres & CEO)
Barbara Thomas (Mgr-Fayetteville)
Michael Murray (Mgr-Durham)
Robert Turner (Mgr-Florence)
Tom May (Mgr-Distr)
Lisa Johnson (Branch Mgr-Raleigh-Trane)
Glenn Barbour (Reg Mgr-East & Branch Mgr-Raleigh)
Steve Padgett (Branch Mgr-Greenville)
Peter Schmitz (Branch Mgr-Wilmington)
Pam Butler (CFO & Sec)
David Walker (Dir-Sls)
Toney McCuen (Mgr-Hickory)
Orlando Rodriguez (Mgr-Greenville)
Jaime Perez (Dir-IT)
Ryan Brookover (Mgr-Greensboro)
Rachel Brackett (VP)
Mark Williams (VP-Ops)

D&L SUPPLY INC.
880 W 150 N, Lindon, UT 84042
Tel.: (801) 785-5015
Web Site: http://www.dlfoundry.us
Sales Range: $10-24.9 Million
Emp.: 37
Iron Or Steel Flat Products
N.A.I.C.S.: 423510
Linda Cooper (Pres)

D&M GENERAL CONTRACTING, INC.
814 W Diamond Ave Ste 200, Beltsville, MD 20878
Tel.: (301) 258-7385
Web Site: http://www.dmgeneralcontracting.com
Sales Range: Less than $1 Million
Emp.: 30
Commercial & Institutional Building Construction
N.A.I.C.S.: 236220
Dave Wimsatt (Chm & Pres)

D&N ELECTRIC COMPANY
3015 R N Martin St, East Point, GA 30344
Tel.: (404) 768-3150
Web Site: http://www.dnelectric.com
Year Founded: 1970
Sales Range: $50-74.9 Million
Emp.: 150
Providers of Electrical Services
N.A.I.C.S.: 238210

D&R BOATS INC.
271 US Highway 22, Green Brook, NJ 08812
Tel.: (732) 968-2600
Web Site: http://www.dnrboats.com
Year Founded: 1956
Sales Range: $1-9.9 Million
Emp.: 25
Sales & Services of Boats
N.A.I.C.S.: 441222
Robert Barone (Pres)

D&R LATHIAN LLC
745 Hope Rd 2nd Fl, Eatontown, NJ 07724
Tel.: (732) 460-2500
Web Site: http://www.drlathian.com
Year Founded: 1999
Sales Range: $1-9.9 Million
Emp.: 20
Multichannel Marketing Services; Consulting Services
N.A.I.C.S.: 541613

Reide Rosen (Partner)
Chris Teo (VP-Tech)
David Schoonmaker (Partner)
Jennifer Nuzzo (VP-Ops)
Scott Miller (VP-Fin)
Damon Smith (VP-Bus Dev & Strategy)

Subsidiaries:

Lathian Systems, Inc.   **(1)**
2250 Hickory Rd, Plymouth Meeting, PA 19462
Tel.: (949) 798-1000
Sales Range: $10-24.9 Million
Marketing Services
N.A.I.C.S.: 541618

D&S CAR WASH EQUIPMENT CO.
4200 Brandi Ln, High Ridge, MO 63049
Tel.: (636) 677-3442
Web Site: https://www.dscarwash.com
Year Founded: 1972
Sales Range: $25-49.9 Million
Emp.: 100
Car Washing Equipment Mfr
N.A.I.C.S.: 333310
Jon Jansky (Pres & CEO)
Lynette Geno (Mgr-Customer Svc)
Tim Huntington (COO)

D&S DISTRIBUTION INC.
3500 Old Airport Rd, Wooster, OH 44691-7951
Tel.: (330) 264-7400
Web Site: https://www.dsdistribution.com
Year Founded: 1986
Rev.: $41,600,000
Emp.: 582
Transportation & Distribution
N.A.I.C.S.: 484121
William DeRodes (CEO)
Kevin Trent (VP-Fin)

D&W DIESEL INC.
1503 Clark St Rd, Auburn, NY 13021
Tel.: (315) 253-5300
Web Site: http://www.dwdiesel.com
Sales Range: $10-24.9 Million
Emp.: 105
Motor Vehicle Supplies & New Parts
N.A.I.C.S.: 423120
Douglas Wayne (Co-Founder)

D'ADDARIO & COMPANY, INC.
595 Smith St, Farmingdale, NY 11735
Tel.: (631) 439-3255
Web Site: https://www.daddario.com
Sales Range: $25-49.9 Million
Emp.: 815
Musical Instruments & Accessories Mfr
N.A.I.C.S.: 339992
James D'Addario (Chm & CEO)

Subsidiaries:

Rico International   **(1)**
8484 San Fernando Rd, Sun Valley, CA 91352-0456
Tel.: (818) 394-2700
Web Site: http://www.ricoreeds.com
Sales Range: $10-24.9 Million
Emp.: 120
Mfr & Sales of Musical Instruments
N.A.I.C.S.: 339992

D'ADDARIO INDUSTRIES INC.
10 Middle St, Bridgeport, CT 06604
Tel.: (203) 333-9488
Web Site: http://www.daddario.com
Sales Range: $75-99.9 Million
Emp.: 50
Bridge Construction Services
N.A.I.C.S.: 237310

Lawrence D'Addario (COO)
David F. D'Addario (Chm & CEO)
Sue Conte (VP & Controller)
Nick Vitti (Pres)

Subsidiaries:

Hi-Ho Petroleum Co.   **(1)**
39 Salt St, Bridgeport, CT 06605-2126
Tel.: (203) 335-0101
Web Site: http://www.hihopetroleum.com
Sales Range: $10-24.9 Million
Emp.: 3
Petroleum Products & Services
N.A.I.C.S.: 457210

D'AGOSTINO SUPERMARKETS INC.
790 Greenwich St, New York, NY 10014
Tel.: (212) 691-9198
Web Site: https://www.dagnyc.com
Year Founded: 1932
Operator of Supermarkets
N.A.I.C.S.: 445110
Kevin Kelly (Mgr-Loss Prevention & Security)
Nicholas D'Agostino Jr. (Pres)

D'AMBROSIO EYE CARE, INC.
255 Park St Ste 606, Worcester, MA 01609
Tel.: (508) 753-1032
Web Site: https://www.dambrosio-eye-care-boston.com
Year Founded: 1984
Eye Care Service
N.A.I.C.S.: 622110
Wilma Stone (Office Mgr)

D'AMICO & SONS INC.
211 N 1st Str, Minneapolis, MN 55401
Tel.: (612) 374-1776
Web Site: https://www.damicoandsons.com
Rev.: $17,400,000
Emp.: 1,000
Restaurant Operators
N.A.I.C.S.: 722511
Richard D'Amico (CEO)
Larry D'Amico (Pres)

D'ARCY & PARTNERS, LLC
18 E 67 Studio 3A, New York, NY 10021
Tel.: (212) 988-0718
Web Site: http://www.darcyandpartners.com
Year Founded: 2003
Sales Range: Less than $1 Million
Emp.: 6
N.A.I.C.S.: 541810
Shelagh D'Arcy Hinds (Founder & Chief Creative Dir)
Kristin Roony (Dir-Graphic Design)
Terry Kidder (Copy Writer)

D'ARCY BUICK GMC, INC.
2022 Essington Rd, Joliet, IL 60435-1769
Tel.: (815) 439-5500
Web Site: https://www.darcybuickgmc.com
Sales Range: $10-24.9 Million
Emp.: 68
Car Whslr
N.A.I.C.S.: 441110
Mark Holzapfel (Principal)
Mike Kastrati (Gen Mgr)

D'ARCY HYUNDAI
2521 W Jefferson St, Joliet, IL 60435-6430
Tel.: (815) 725-5200
Web Site: https://www.darcyhyundai.com
Year Founded: 2000

Sales Range: $10-24.9 Million
Emp.: 53
New Car Retailer
N.A.I.C.S.: 441110
Guy Campobasso *(Gen Mgr)*
Terry D'Arcy *(Owner)*

D'ARRIGO BROS. COMPANY
21777 Harris Rd, Salinas, CA 93908
Tel.: (831) 455-4500   CA
Web Site: https://www.andyboy.com
Year Founded: 1927
Sales Range: $25-49.9 Million
Emp.: 900
Vegetables & Melons Producer
N.A.I.C.S.: 111219
Andrew A. D'Arrigo *(Chm)*
John D'Arrigo *(Pres)*
Dave Martinez *(Dir-Sls)*

D'LAURO & RODGERS, INC.
465 Maryland Dr Ste 400, Fort Washington, PA 19034
Tel.: (215) 542-0100
Web Site: http://www.dandrinc.com
Sales Range: $10-24.9 Million
Emp.: 15
Commercial & Office Buildings Construction Services
N.A.I.C.S.: 236220
Alfred P. Ferraro *(Pres)*
John Cantone *(CFO)*
Rick Mariani *(Gen Counsel-Retail Construction Div)*
Gregory Sabatino *(Project Mgr)*

D'ONOFRIO & SON LAND-SCAPING, INC.
47 Van Ness Ter, Maplewood, NJ 07040
Tel.: (973) 763-8911
Web Site:
    https://www.donofrioandsonland
    scaping.com
Year Founded: 1984
Rev.: $2,200,000
Emp.: 32
Landscaping Services
N.A.I.C.S.: 561730
Diane D'Onofrio *(Pres)*

D'VONTZ
7208 E 38th St, Tulsa, OK 74145
Tel.: (918) 622-3600
Web Site: https://www.dvontz.com
Year Founded: 2004
Sales Range: $10-24.9 Million
Emp.: 100
Fashion Plumbing Products Designer & Mfr
N.A.I.C.S.: 332913
Greg Hoff *(Principal)*
John F. Kellerstrass *(Principal)*

D-A LUBRICANT COMPANY
801 Edwards Dr, Lebanon, IN 46052
Tel.: (317) 923-5321
Lubricating Oils & Greases Whslr
N.A.I.C.S.: 324191

D-C ELEVATOR CO., INC.
124 Venture Ct Ste 1, Lexington, KY 40511
Tel.: (859) 254-8224
Web Site: http://www.dcelevator.com
Year Founded: 1977
Emp.: 48
Elevator Installation & Maintenance Services
N.A.I.C.S.: 238990
Dale Howard *(Sr Project Mgr)*

Subsidiaries:

D-C Elevator Co., Inc. -
Louisville   **(1)**
140 E Woodlawn Ave, Louisville, KY 40214

Tel.: (502) 363-5961
Web Site: http://www.dcelevatorco.com
Emp.: 15
Elevator Installation & Maintenance Services
N.A.I.C.S.: 238990
Rick Hardin *(Mgr-Area)*

D-K TRADING CORP.
900 Battle St, Scranton, PA 18508
Tel.: (570) 586-9662   PA
Web Site: https://www.dk-t.com
Year Founded: 1965
Sales Range: $10-24.9 Million
Emp.: 13
Paper Services
N.A.I.C.S.: 424130
David L. Kirtland *(Pres)*
Suzanne Tully *(Controller)*

D-PATRICK INC.
200 N Green River Rd, Evansville, IN 47715
Tel.: (812) 473-6500   IN
Web Site: https://www.dpat.com
Year Founded: 1949
Sales Range: $25-49.9 Million
Emp.: 190
New & Used Automobiles Dealers
N.A.I.C.S.: 441110
Raymond Farabaugh *(Pres)*

D-URSO ENTERPRISES INC.
8725 Lefferts Blvd, Richmond, NY 11418
Tel.: (718) 850-4302
Rev.: $16,700,000
Emp.: 5
Supermarket
N.A.I.C.S.: 445110
Steven Kaufman *(Controller)*

D. BENEDETTO INC.
280 Madison Ave Rm 900, New York, NY 10016
Tel.: (212) 532-9191
Sales Range: $10-24.9 Million
Emp.: 15
Industrial & Personal Service Paper
N.A.I.C.S.: 424130
Peter Benedetto *(Pres)*

D. CARR INVESTMENTS INC.
200 Main St PO Box 280, Cassville, MO 65625
Tel.: (417) 847-2533
Rev.: $29,000,000
Emp.: 10
Fast-Food Restaurant, Chain
N.A.I.C.S.: 722513
Mike Carr *(CEO)*
Bernie Quintero *(Dir-Ops)*

D. CONSTRUCTION
1488 S Broadway, Coal City, IL 60416-9443
Tel.: (815) 634-2555
Web Site:
    http://www.dconstruction.net
Year Founded: 1982
Sales Range: $150-199.9 Million
Emp.: 40
Highway & Street Construction Services
N.A.I.C.S.: 237310
Kenneth Sandeno *(Owner)*

D. DAHLE MAZDA OF MUR-RAY
4595 S State St, Salt Lake City, UT 84107-3813
Tel.: (801) 266-0033
Web Site:
    http://www.ddahlemazda.com
Year Founded: 2002
Sales Range: $10-24.9 Million
Emp.: 40

New Car Whslr
N.A.I.C.S.: 441110
Robert Meyer *(Owner)*

D. E. SHAW & CO., L.P.
1166 Avenue of the Americas 9 Fl, New York, NY 10036
Tel.: (212) 478-0000   DE
Web Site: https://www.deshaw.com
Year Founded: 1988
Sales Range: $100-124.9 Million
Emp.: 1,200
Equity Investment Firm
N.A.I.C.S.: 523999
David E. Shaw *(Founder)*
Max Stone *(Mng Dir)*
Julius Gaudio *(Mng Dir)*
Eric Wepsic *(Mng Dir)*
Eddie Fishman *(Mng Dir)*

Subsidiaries:

D. E. Shaw & Co. (Asia Pacific)
Limited   **(1)**
19th Floor York House The Landmark 15 Queen's Road Central, Hong Kong, China (Hong Kong)
Tel.: (852) 3521 2500
Web Site: http://www.deshaw.com
Financial Management Services
N.A.I.C.S.: 523999

D. E. Shaw & Co. (Bermuda),
Ltd.   **(1)**
44 Church Street West, Hamilton, Bermuda
Tel.: (441) 294 6650
Financial Management Services
N.A.I.C.S.: 523999
Rachel Hutchings *(Office Mgr)*

D. E. Shaw & Co. (London), LLP **(1)**
Seventh Floor 55 Baker Street, London, W1U 8EW, United Kingdom
Tel.: (44) 20 7409 4300
Financial Management Services
N.A.I.C.S.: 523999
Kevin Krist *(Chief Legal Officer & Chief Compliance Officer)*

D. E. Shaw India Securities Private
Limited   **(1)**
Fortune 2000 3rd Floor B Wing Bandra Kurla Complex Bandra East, Mumbai, 400 051, Maharashtra, India
Tel.: (91) 22 4267 1000
Financial Management Services
N.A.I.C.S.: 523999
Nirav Tanna *(Head-Ops)*

D. E. Shaw India Software Private
Limited   **(1)**
Sanali Infopark 8-2-120/113 Road No 2, Banjara Hills, Hyderabad, 500 034, Telangana, India
Tel.: (91) 40 6639 0000
Web Site: http://www.deshawindia.com
Financial Management Services
N.A.I.C.S.: 523999
Namrata Shah *(Mgr-Talent Acq)*

D. E. Shaw Private Equity Investment Management (Shanghai) Co.,
Limited   **(1)**
Suite 20 20/F Mirae Asset Tower 166 Lujiazui Ring Road, Pudong, Shanghai, 200120, China
Tel.: (86) 21 5174 8830
Financial Management Services
N.A.I.C.S.: 523999

D. E. Shaw Research, LLC   **(1)**
120 W 45th St 39th Fl, New York, NY 10036
Tel.: (212) 849-0080
Web Site: http://www.deshawresearch.com
Research & Development Services
N.A.I.C.S.: 541715

Embrace Group Limited   **(1)**
Two Parklands Business Park Birmingham Great Park, Rubery, Birmingham, B45 9PZ, W Midlands, United Kingdom
Tel.: (44) 844 980 3666
Web Site: http://www.embracegroup.co.uk
Emp.: 70
Holding Company; Health & Social Care Services

N.A.I.C.S.: 551112
Trish Lee *(CEO)*
David Manson *(CFO)*
Amanda Morgan-Taylor *(Dir-Quality Dev)*
Shane Gidman *(Dir-IT)*
Roger Poynton *(Dir-Property)*

Subsidiary (Domestic):

Embrace (UK) Limited   **(2)**
Two Parklands Business Park Birmingham Great Park, Rubery, Birmingham, B45 9PZ, W Midlands, United Kingdom
Tel.: (44) 844 980 3666
Web Site: http://www.embracegroup.co.uk
Health & Social Care Services
N.A.I.C.S.: 623110
Ted Smith *(Chm)*
Trish Lee *(CEO)*
Amanda Morgan-Taylor *(Dir-Quality Dev)*
Alison Whelan *(Dir-Trng & Dev)*
Roger Poynton *(Dir-Property)*

James River Group Holdings,
Ltd.   **(1)**
Tel.: (441) 2951422
Web Site: https://jrvrgroup.com
Rev.: $812,009,000
Assets: $5,317,250,000
Liabilities: $4,782,629,000
Net Worth: $534,621,000
Earnings: $61,209,000
Emp.: 649
Fiscal Year-end: 12/31/2023
Insurance Holding Company
N.A.I.C.S.: 551112
Richard J. Schmitzer *(Pres-Excess & Surplus Lines & CEO-Excess & Surplus Lines)*
Sarah C. Doran *(CFO & Grp CFO)*
Frank N. D'Orazio *(CEO)*
Brett Shirreffs *(Sr VP-Fin, Investments, and IR)*
Michael J. Hoffmann *(Grp Chief Underwriting Officer)*
Jeanette L. Miller *(Chief Legal Officer)*
Thomas E. Peach *(CIO & Grp CIO)*
Angela J. Burnett *(Chief HR Officer & Grp Chief HR Officer)*

Subsidiary (US):

James River Group, Inc.   **(2)**
3600 Glenwood Ave Ste 310, Raleigh, NC 27612
Tel.: (919) 883-4171
Web Site: http://www.james-river-group.com
Property & Casualty Insurance Services
N.A.I.C.S.: 524126

Subsidiary (Domestic):

James River Insurance
Company   **(3)**
PO Box 27648, Richmond, VA 23261-7648
Tel.: (804) 289-2700
Web Site: http://www.jamesriverins.com
Sales Range: $100-124.9 Million
Excess & Surplus Lines Insurance Services
N.A.I.C.S.: 524298
Richard J. Schmitzer *(Pres & CEO)*
John G. Clarke *(Sr VP & Dir-Mktg)*
Raju S. Sodhi *(CIO & Sr VP)*
Richard H. Seward *(Chief Actuary & Sr VP)*
Anthony R. Owens *(Mgr-Property Div)*
Christy Miller *(Mgr-Regulatory Compliance & Product Dev)*
Crileen Kixmoeller *(VP-Excess Casualty, Life Sciences, Mfg & Contractors)*
David S. Weisenberger *(VP & Mgr-Allied Healthcare & Pro Liability Div)*
Eric Taylor *(VP-Gen Casualty, Sports Entertainment & Small Acct-Casualty)*
Richard A. Kern *(Mgr-Energy & Environmental Div)*
Angela J. Burnett *(Sr VP-HR & Ops)*

Stonewood Insurance Company **(3)**
7721 Six Forks Rd, Raleigh, NC 27615
Tel.: (919) 882-3500
Web Site: http://www.stonewoodins.com
Sales Range: $50-74.9 Million
Insurance Company
N.A.I.C.S.: 524114
Sallie Mercer *(Dir-Claims)*
Cindy A. Sullivan *(Dir-Policy Svcs)*
Ann M. Person *(COO & VP)*
Steven J. Hartman *(Pres & CEO)*
Wes Cunningham *(Dir-Loss Control)*
Thomas R. Fauerbach *(CFO)*
Joseph Raia *(Controller)*

D. E. Shaw & Co., L.P.—(Continued)

Multigestion Iberia 2014, S.L. (1)
Avenida de la Albufera 153 3 Planta Izqda,
28038, Madrid, Spain
Tel.: (34) 91 444 48 00
Web Site: http://www.multigestioniberia.com
Emp.: 400
Debt Collection Services
N.A.I.C.S.: 561440

D. H. GRIFFIN CO.
PO Box 7657, Greensboro, NC,
27417-0657
Tel.: (336) 855-7030
Web Site: http://www.dhgriffin.com
Sales Range: $10-24.9 Million
Emp.: 500
Construction Engineering Services
N.A.I.C.S.: 237310
David Griffin Sr. *(Pres)*

D. HILTON ASSOCIATES, INC.
9450 Grogans Mill Rd Ste 200, The
Woodlands, TX 77380
Tel.: (281) 292-5088
Web Site: http://www.dhilton.com
Year Founded: 1985
Rev.: $10,000,000
Emp.: 48
Fiscal Year-end: 12/31/06
Advertising, Brand Development &
Integration, Email, Internet/Web De-
sign, Market Research, Merchandis-
ing, Newspaper, Outdoor, Print, Ra-
dio, Retail, Strategic
Planning/Research, T.V.
N.A.I.C.S.: 541810
David Hilton *(Pres & CEO)*
Janice Shisler *(Sr VP-Exec Recruit-
ing)*
Brian Kidwell *(Exec VP-Mktg Res)*
Marcus Cotton *(VP-Exec Recruiting)*
John Andrews *(Exec VP-
Compensation)*
Debbie Hilton *(Exec VP-Retention &
Retirement)*

**D. HONORE CONSTRUCTION,
INC.**
383 Highlandia Dr, Baton Rouge, LA
70810
Tel.: (225) 751-3078
Web Site: https://www.dhonore.com
Year Founded: 1998
Rev.: $15,600,000
Emp.: 15
Nonresidential Construction
N.A.I.C.S.: 236220
Dwayne G. Honore *(Pres)*

**D. L. FALK CONSTRUCTION
INC.**
3526 Investment Blvd, Hayward, CA
94545
Tel.: (510) 887-6500
Web Site: https://www.dlfalk.com
Sales Range: $10-24.9 Million
Emp.: 25
Housing Construction Services
N.A.I.C.S.: 236117
David Falk *(Owner)*

**D. L. KENNEY GENERAL CON-
TRACTORS INC.**
3114 Bath Pike, Nazareth, PA 18064
Tel.: (610) 837-0644
Web Site: https://www.dlkeeney.com
Year Founded: 1974
Sales Range: $1-9.9 Million
Emp.: 18
General Contractors, Demolition &
Excavation
N.A.I.C.S.: 238190
George Kenney *(Pres)*

D. WALDNER COMPANY, INC.

125 Route 110, Farmingdale, NY
11735
Tel.: (631) 844-9300   **NY**
Web Site: https://www.waldners.com
Year Founded: 1939
Sales Range: $100-124.9 Million
Emp.: 100
Retailer of Office Furniture
N.A.I.C.S.: 449110
Stephen Waldner *(Chm)*
John Marsicano *(CFO)*
Mike Cuellar *(VP-Ops)*

D.A. DAVIDSON COMPANIES
8 3rd St N, Great Falls, MT 59401
Tel.: (406) 727-4200   **MT**
Web Site:
  http://www.dadavidson.com
Year Founded: 1935
Sales Range: $350-399.9 Million
Emp.: 1,318
Holding Company; Investment Bank-
ing, Securities Brokerage, Asset Man-
agement & Investment Advisory Ser-
vices
N.A.I.C.S.: 551112
James Kerr *(Chm & CEO)*
Thomas Nelson *(CFO & Exec VP)*
William A. Johnstone *(Chm)*
Monte Giese *(Pres-Equity Capital
Markets)*
Michael Purpura *(Pres-Individual In-
vestor Grp)*
Michael Lupin *(Sr VP-Institutional Sls)*
Lawrence Martinez *(CEO)*
Timothy Austin *(COO & Sr VP)*
Ranee Chew-Hopkins *(Sr VP & Dir-
Human Capital)*
Nataleah Dietzman *(Sr VP & Dir-
Mktg)*
Andrew E. Crowell *(Vice Chm-IIG)*
Steven Condon *(Pres-Asset Mgmt &
Trust)*
Dean Hall *(Chief Compliance Officer
& VP)*
Jackie Beauprez *(Gen Counsel & Sr
VP)*
Peter Raphael *(Sr VP & Mng Dir-Pub
Fin Team-Chicago)*
T. J. Brudzinski *(Sr VP-Institutional
Sls)*
Steven Conn *(Sr VP-Institutional Sls)*
George Dulcich *(Sr VP-Institutional
Sls)*
Mike Franz *(Sr VP-Institutional Sls)*
Donald Ginnetti *(Sr VP-Institutional
Sls)*
Thomas Hofacker *(Sr VP-Institutional
Sls)*
Paul Manganelli *(Sr VP-Institutional
Sls)*
Eric Meulenberg *(Sr VP-Institutional
Sls)*
Tyler Morten *(Sr VP-Institutional Sls)*
Marcus Nield *(Sr VP-Institutional Sls)*
Trini Rodriguez *(Mng Dir-Pub Fin &
Sr VP)*
Jamie Royce *(Sr VP-Institutional Sls)*
Jeff Stanley *(COO & Sr VP-Risk &
Strategy)*
Tom Thompson *(Mng Dir)*
Greg Tucker *(Sr VP-Institutional Sls)*
Joseph Wilson *(Sr VP-Institutional
Sls)*
Mark Aquilino *(Mng Dir-Institutional
Trading)*
Christopher Brendler *(Mng Dir)*
Gil Luria *(Head-Institutional Res)*
Joey Speyrer Jr. *(Sr VP-Trading)*
Subsidiaries:
D.A. Davidson & Co. (1)
8 3rd St N, Great Falls, MT 59401
Tel.: (406) 727-4200
Web Site:
  http://www.davidsoncompanies.com

Investment Banking & Securities Brokerage
N.A.I.C.S.: 523150
James Kerr *(Chm & CEO)*
Ramsey Gregg *(Mng Dir)*
Rory McKinney *(Mng Dir)*
Brad Gevurtz *(Mng Dir-Investment Banking)*
Brien Rowe *(Mng Dir-Investment Banking)*
Michael Purpura *(Pres-Wealth Mgmt)*
James Ragan *(Dir-Wealth Mgmt)*
Jeffrey Cleveland *(Mng Dir)*
James Lykins *(VP)*
Kevin Reevey *(Mng Dir)*
Andrew Crowell *(Vice Chm-Wealth Mgmt)*
Danielle Prewett *(Assoc VP)*
Joe Morgan *(Mng Dir-Costa Mesa)*
Michael Jackson *(Sr VP & Branch Mgr)*
Daryl Geffken *(Assoc VP & Program Dir-
Plng Resource Center)*
Michael Anderson *(Assoc VP & Branch
Mgr)*
Grady McConnell *(Dir-Tech Investment
Banking-Costa Mesa)*
Scott Isherwood *(Mng Dir-Diversified Indus
Investment Banking-New York)*
Carmen Jacobs *(Co-COO & Sr VP)*
Chris Barone *(Sr VP & Reg Dir)*
Dave Pollock *(Sr VP & Reg Dir)*
Jim Layden *(Sr VP & Reg Dir)*
Marc Dispense *(Pres-Fixed Income Capital
Markets)*
Scott Witeby *(CFO)*
Steve O'Donnel *(Mng Dir-Boston)*
Chuck Stubbs *(Mng Dir-Fin Institutions In-
vestment Banking Grp)*
Jonathan Lejuez *(Mng Dir-Tech Investment
Banking Grp)*
Greg Thomas *(Mng Dir & Head-Tech)*
Sokol Cano *(Mng Dir-Paper & Packaging
Practice-Diversified Industrials Investment
Banking Grp)*
Tim Sznewajs *(Mng Dir & Head-Diversified
Industrials Investment Banking Grp)*
Andreea Popa *(Head-Mktg-Equity Capital
Markets)*
Clinton Miyazono *(Mng Dir-Debt Advisory
Grp-Chicago)*
Amy Johnson *(Head-Debt Advisory)*

Subsidiary (Domestic):
Crowell, Weedon & Co. (2)
1 Wilshire Blvd 26th Fl, Los Angeles, CA
90017-3876
Tel.: (213) 620-1850
Web Site: http://www.crowellweedon.com
Sales Range: $100-124.9 Million
Emp.: 312
Investment Services
N.A.I.C.S.: 523150
Andrew E. Crowell *(COO & Mng Partner)*
James L. Cronk *(COO)*
Antonios Karantonis *(Controller)*
Alan Griffin *(Partner)*

Group (Domestic):
**D.A. Davidson & Co. - Equity Capital
Markets** (2)
2 Centerpointe Dr Ste 400, Lake Oswego,
OR 97035-8629
Tel.: (503) 603-3000
Web Site:
  http://www.davidsoncompanies.com
Emp.: 75
Investment Banking
N.A.I.C.S.: 523150
Rich O'Connor *(Sr VP-Institutional Sls)*
Timothy Austin *(COO & Sr VP)*
Lawrence Martinez *(Chief Admin Officer &
Sr VP)*
Thomas Nelson *(CFO & Sr VP)*
Brit Stephens *(Head-Sls, Trading & Capital
Markets)*
Monte Giese *(Pres)*

**D.A. Davidson & Co. - Fixed Income
Capital Markets** (2)
1600 Broadway Ste 1100, Denver, CO
80202
Tel.: (303) 764-6000
Web Site:
  http://www.davidsoncompanies.com
Fixed Income Banking & Public Finance
Services
N.A.I.C.S.: 523150
Sam Doyle *(Pres)*
David Cheung *(COO & Sr VP-Sls & Trad-
ing)*
Eric Duran *(Mng Dir-Pub Fin)*

Mark Kendle *(Sr VP-Pub Fin)*
Rick Turnage *(Sr VP & Mgr-Sls)*
Bradley Fawcett *(Sr VP-Institutional Sls)*
David Freie *(Sr VP-Institutional Sls)*
Henry Jenkins *(Sr VP-Institutional Sls)*
Chris Muilenburg *(Sr VP-Institutional Sls)*
Raoul Clark *(Mng Dir & Head-Institutional
Sls)*
Brandon DeBenedet *(Sr VP)*
Marcus Lambert *(Sr VP)*
Michael Cullinane *(Sr VP-Trading)*
Kirk Haines *(VP-Institutional Sls)*
John Banks *(Mng Dir-Pub Fin)*
Zachary Bishop *(Mng Dir-Special District
Grp)*
Matthew DeAngelis *(Sr VP-Pub Fin)*
Kreg Jones *(Mng Dir & Sr VP)*
Andy Kane *(Mng Dir-Pub Fin)*
Dan Smith *(Mng Dir-Pub Fin)*
Crystal Vogl *(VP-Pub Fin)*

Subsidiary (Domestic):
**Smith Hayes Financial Services
Corporation** (2)
1225 L St Ste 200, Lincoln, NE 68508
Tel.: (402) 476-3000
Web Site: http://www.smithhayes.com
Secondary Market Financing
N.A.I.C.S.: 522299
John Decker *(Pres & CEO)*

**Davidson Fixed Income Management,
Inc.** (1)
1550 Market St Ste 300, Denver, CO 80202
Tel.: (303) 764-6000
Web Site:
  http://www.davidsoncompanies.com
Emp.: 60
Investment Management Service
N.A.I.C.S.: 523940
Christopher B. Johns *(Sr VP & Portfolio
Mgr)*
Timothy Iltz *(VP)*

**Davidson Investment Advisors,
Inc.** (1)
8 3rd St N, Great Falls, MT 59401 (100%)
Tel.: (406) 727-6111
Web Site:
  http://www.davidsoncompanies.com
Sales Range: $25-49.9 Million
Emp.: 9
Investment Advisory & Asset Management
Services
N.A.I.C.S.: 523940
Andrew I. Davidson *(Pres)*
Edward P. Crotty *(Chief Investment Officer,
Sr VP & Portfolio Mgr)*
Brian P. Clancy *(Sr VP & Portfolio Mgr)*
Michael P. Kubas *(VP & Portfolio Mgr)*
Paul G. Condrat *(VP & Portfolio Mgr)*
Bill Holevoet *(VP & Portfolio Mgr)*
Bob Kern *(VP & Portfolio Mgr)*
Heather Kubas *(COO & VP)*
Gino DiLello *(VP-Bus Dev)*
Erica Lynn *(Assoc VP & Mgr-Ops)*
Andrew Elofson *(VP & Portfolio Mgr)*

Davidson Trust Co. (1)
8 3rd St N, Great Falls, MT
59403-2309 (100%)
Tel.: (406) 791-7320
Web Site:
  http://www.davidsoncompanies.com
Sales Range: $25-49.9 Million
Emp.: 20
Trust Company
N.A.I.C.S.: 523991
Arthur P. Sims *(Pres)*
Darcy MacLaren *(Mng-Investment)*
Holli Rozinka *(VP, Trust Officer & Branch
Mgr)*
Lisa Martin *(Asst VP & Trust Officer)*
Evelyn Forsyth *(VP & Dir-Trust Ops)*

**Seattle Capital Management
Company** (1)
701 5th Ave Ste 6710, Seattle, WA 98104
Tel.: (206) 654-0480
Investment Management Service
N.A.I.C.S.: 523940

Wells Nelson & Associates, LLC (1)
105 N Hudson Ave Ste 600, Oklahoma City,
OK 73102
Tel.: (405) 239-9000
Investment Advice
N.A.I.C.S.: 523940

D.A. WHITACRE CONSTRUCTION, INC.
1108 Greenfield Dr, El Cajon, CA 92021
Tel.: (619) 444-4350
Web Site:
https://www.dawhitacre.com
Year Founded: 1976
Sales Range: $25-49.9 Million
Emp.: 325
Carpentry Services
N.A.I.C.S.: 238130
William Whitacre *(Pres)*
Terri Heald *(Mgr-Payroll)*
Glenn Stewart *(VP-Ops)*
Dave Kapalla *(Project Mgr)*
David Blackston *(Project Mgr)*
Angela Dean *(Mgr)*

D.A.G. CONSTRUCTION CO., INC.
4924 Winton Rd, Cincinnati, OH 45232
Tel.: (513) 542-8597   OH
Web Site: https://www.dag-cons.com
Year Founded: 1990
Sales Range: $10-24.9 Million
Emp.: 30
Commercial & Office Building New Construction
N.A.I.C.S.: 236220
Dave Zins *(Mgr-Ops)*
Dale S. White Sr. *(Founder, Pres & CEO)*
Albert P. Owens Jr. *(Controller)*

D.C. CAPITAL PARTNERS, LLC
11 Canal Center Plz Ste 350, Alexandria, VA 22314
Tel.: (202) 737-5220   VA
Web Site:
http://www.dccapitalpartners.com
Year Founded: 2007
Privater Equity Firm
N.A.I.C.S.: 523999
Thomas J. Campbell *(Founder, Pres & Partner)*
T. Gail Dady *(Partner)*
Douglas T. Lake Jr. *(Partner)*

Subsidiaries:

Hill Technical Solutions, Inc.   (1)
3077-I Leeman Ferry Rd, Huntsville, AL 35801
Tel.: (256) 970-1258
Web Site: http://www.htsi-al.com
Sales Range: $1-9.9 Million
Emp.: 48
Engineeering Services
N.A.I.C.S.: 541330
Daniel Lowery *(Project Mgr)*
David Diaddario *(Pres)*

Subsidiary (Domestic):

Valkyrie Enterprises, LLC   (2)
4460 Corporation Ln Ste 130, Virginia Beach, VA 23462
Tel.: (757) 962-2545
Web Site: http://www.valkyrie.com
Sales Range: $10-24.9 Million
Emp.: 147
Engineeering Services
N.A.I.C.S.: 541330
Gary Lisota *(Founder & Vice Chm)*
Danny R. Redmon *(Exec VP)*
David Streett *(Pres & CEO)*
Tom Hayes *(Asst VP & Dir-Technical)*
Shirley Jahn *(Sr Mgr-Consulting)*
Mike Lombardo *(Mgr-Ops-DC)*
Scott Mattingly *(Sr Mgr-Consulting)*
Bill Boudouris *(VP-Engrg & Technical Svcs Ops)*
Kathleen Daniels *(Chief Admin Officer & VP)*
David Klinedinst *(VP-Bus Dev)*
Christine Miller *(VP & Controller)*
Jeff Stermer *(VP & Deputy Dir-Ops)*
Dale Hopper *(Sr VP-Sustainment & Modernization)*

Michael Baker International, LLC   (1)
100 Airside Dr, Moon Township, PA 15108
Tel.: (412) 269-6300
Web Site: http://www.mbakercorp.com
Sales Range: $1-4.9 Billion
Emp.: 5,000
Holding Company; Information Technology, Enterprise Systems & Communication Support Services; Engineering, Technical Support & Professional Services
N.A.I.C.S.: 541330
Thomas J. Campbell *(Chm)*
David Schaarsmith *(Project Mgr)*
Ronald Schirato *(Asst VP-DoD Market Sector)*
Rick Bernet *(Asst VP)*
Jim McKnight *(Gen Counsel & Exec VP)*
Bill Shiderly *(Mgr-Tech)*
Jeff Baker *(Sr VP & Dir-Mountain Reg)*
Dave Thompson *(Dir-Mid Atlantic)*
Harold Honey *(Mgr-Technical)*
David Mueller *(Mgr-Surface Water Dept)*
Jim Katsafanas *(Assoc VP)*
John Tricini *(Assoc VP)*
Mary Rosick *(Assoc VP)*
Scott Vannoy *(Assoc VP)*
J. Brad Homan *(Assoc VP)*
Max Heckman *(Assoc VP)*
Carl Jeffreys *(Assoc VP)*
Richard Baich *(Mgr-Corp Fleet)*
Harold Chappell *(VP & Dir-Specialized Construction Bus)*
Kevin Abel *(Project Mgr-Transportation)*
Craig Churchward *(Mgr-Transportation Plng)*
Bonnie D. Shepherd *(Chief Practice Officer & Exec VP)*
James Twomey *(Exec VP)*
Jennifer Lewis *(Dir-Southeast)*
Brian A. Lutes *(CEO)*
Justin Falce *(Mgr-PR)*
Frederick Jones *(Sr Project Mgr-Community & Mobility Plng)*
Kenton Zinn *(Pres-Infrastructure)*
Todd Potter *(Engr-Transportation)*
Steven Rushmore *(Mgr-BIM & CAD)*
Daniel Baic *(Sr Engr-Structural)*
Jeffrey McKendree *(Sr Engr-Fire Protection)*
Penny Mercadante *(Chief HR Officer & Exec VP)*
Darcie Zeliesko *(VP-Talent Mgmt)*
Beth Steimle *(VP)*
Alfred Murillo *(VP)*
Juan Contreras *(Dir-Gulf Coast)*
Danielle Smith *(Mgr-Transportation Dept-Denver)*
Leanna Anderson *(Chief Comm Officer & Exec VP)*
Frank Holzmann *(Assoc VP-San Antonio)*
Elese Roger *(CIO & Exec VP)*
Bryan Rerko *(Mgr-Construction Engrg & Inspection-Florida)*
Ted Coffey *(VP-Chicago)*
Dwain Hathaway *(VP)*
Michael J. Conaboy *(Dir-West)*
Jeff Clevenger *(Sr VP-Denver)*
H. Daniel Cessna *(Sr VP)*
Don Sepulveda *(VP)*
Rick Robyak *(Sr VP)*
Rebecca Schwartz *(Mgr-Architecture Technical)*
Brad Shelton *(Dir-Engrg-Richmond)*
Anna Lantin *(Sr VP-Bus Dev)*
Laura Weis *(VP-Dallas)*
Malcolm Dougherty *(Sr VP & Reg Dir-West)*
Ralph Hennessy *(Head-Aviation Svcs Grp-Baton Rouge)*
Chuck Duggar *(VP-Baton Rouge)*
Brad Thoburn *(VP)*
Michael J. Hall *(VP)*
Michael Brescia *(Sr VP & Dir-Northeast)*
Joseph R. Catalano *(VP)*
David Boone *(Chief Growth Officer)*
Jake K. Watson *(Sr VP-Federal Ops)*
Alfonso Riera *(VP-Gulf Coast & West)*
Dan Kieny *(CTO)*
Frank Russo *(Natl Dir-Technical-Bridge Practice)*
Amy Davis *(CFO & Exec VP)*
Gil Bosque *(VP-Hamilton)*
Magdy M. Hagag *(Reg Dir-Northeast)*
Mohamed A. Bagha *(VP-Water Practice)*
John Tedder *(Chief Legal Officer, Gen Counsel & Exec VP)*
Stephen Browning *(Sr VP-Federal Markets)*
James E. Koch *(COO & Exec VP)*
George Guszcza *(Sr VP & Natl Dir-Federal)*
David Liebgold *(VP-Newark)*

Sirish Peyyeti *(VP-New York)*
Elizabeth Bradford *(VP)*
Malcolm Dougherty *(Sr VP & Reg Dir-West)*
Eric Ostfeld *(Pres-Design-Build Svcs)*
Dennis Berlien *(Pres-Sustainable & Resilient Solutions)*

Subsidiary (Domestic):

Catapult Technology, Ltd.   (2)
7500 Old Georgetown Rd 11th Fl, Bethesda, MD 20814
Tel.: (301) 986-8577
Web Site:
http://www.catapulttechnology.com
Sales Range: $25-49.9 Million
Emp.: 300
Information Technology Support, Enterprise Systems Engineering & Strategic Consulting Services
N.A.I.C.S.: 541519
Mark E. Hunker *(Pres & CEO)*
David Lyons *(CTO & Exec VP-Tech & Mgmt Solutions)*
Tony Myers *(VP-Tech & Mgmt Solutions)*
Grant Williams *(Sr Mgr-Proposal)*

Computer Security Solutions, LLC   (2)
1356 Beverly Rd Ste 100, McLean, VA 22101
Tel.: (703) 956-5700
Web Site: http://www.compsecinc.com
Emp.: 15
Government Information Technology Support Services
N.A.I.C.S.: 541519
Charlie Suter *(VP-Sls)*

KS International LLC   (2)
3601 Eisenhower Ave Ste 600, Alexandria, VA 22304
Tel.: (703) 676-3200
Web Site: http://www.mbakerintl.com
Emp.: 1,200
Government Engineering, Training, Professional & Support Services
N.A.I.C.S.: 561499
Thomas J. Campbell *(Chm)*
Kurt C. Bergman *(CEO)*
Brian Arsenault *(CFO)*
Nick Gross *(COO)*
James S. Rogers *(VP-Contracts & Compliance)*
Douglas Magee *(Sr VP-Support Svcs)*
Ellen A. Dwyer *(Dir-Bus Dev)*
John L. Whisler Jr. *(VP & Dir-Engrg & Construction)*

Strategic Intelligence Group LLC   (2)
11320 Random Hills Rd Ste 350, Fairfax, VA 22030
Tel.: (703) 273-0003
Web Site: http://www.sigusa.com
Sales Range: $25-49.9 Million
Emp.: 120
Management & Technical Consulting Services
N.A.I.C.S.: 541611

Tidal Basin Government Consulting, LLC   (2)
300 N Washington St Ste 505, Alexandria, VA 22314-2544
Tel.: (703) 683-8551
Web Site: https://www.tidalbasingroup.com
General Management Consulting Services
N.A.I.C.S.: 541611
Daniel Craig *(CEO)*
Heather Stickler *(VP-Mktg)*
Luis Avila *(Asst VP-Mitigation Practice)*
James K. Joseph *(VP-Response)*

Owl Cyber Defense Solutions, LLC   (1)
38A Grove St Ste 101, Ridgefield, CT 06877
Tel.: (203) 894-9342
Web Site: http://www.owlcyberdefense.com
Emp.: 200
Data Transfer Security Technology Services
N.A.I.C.S.: 561621
Dennis Lanahan *(Dir-Sls & Customer Svc)*
Michael Timan *(Pres & CEO)*
Sal Morlando *(COO)*
Scott W. Coleman *(Dir-Mktg & Product Mgmt)*
Jerry B. Chernock *(VP)*
Ray Kunzmann *(CFO)*

Steve Staubly *(Dir-Product Dev)*
Andy Holmes *(Dir-Technical Svcs)*
Kathleen Gallagher *(Dir-HR)*

D.C. PLASTICS INC.
70 Hobart Ave, Bayonne, NJ 07002
Tel.: (201) 339-0111
Web Site:
http://www.dcplasticsinc.com
Year Founded: 1984
Sales Range: $10-24.9 Million
Emp.: 40
Plastics Bag Mfr
N.A.I.C.S.: 326111
Janice Chambers *(Mgr)*

D.C. TAYLOR CO.
312 29th St NE, Cedar Rapids, IA 52402
Tel.: (319) 363-2073   IA
Web Site: http://www.dctaylorco.com
Year Founded: 1949
Sales Range: $50-74.9 Million
Emp.: 200
Roofing Contracting Services
N.A.I.C.S.: 238160
William W. Taylor *(Chm & CEO)*
Greg Thirnbeck *(VP-Contract Admin)*
Bob Pence *(VP-Matls)*
Wielka Cosgrove *(VP-HR)*

D.C. VIENT INC.
1556 Cummins Dr, Modesto, CA 95358
Tel.: (209) 578-1224
Web Site: http://www.dcvient.com
Sales Range: $10-24.9 Million
Emp.: 70
Commercial Painting
N.A.I.C.S.: 238320
Douglas J. Vient *(VP)*

D.C.R. SERVICES
502 County Rd 640 E, Mulberry, FL 33860
Tel.: (863) 904-1077
Web Site:
http://www.dcrservices.com
Sales Range: $25-49.9 Million
Emp.: 150
Enginering Procurement & Construction
N.A.I.C.S.: 541330
Dale Rossman *(Owner)*

D.D. BEAN & SONS CO.
207 Peterborough St, Jaffrey, NH 03452-5868
Tel.: (603) 532-8311   NH
Web Site: https://www.ddbean.com
Year Founded: 1938
Sales Range: $75-99.9 Million
Emp.: 53
Paper Book Matches
N.A.I.C.S.: 325998

D.D. WILLIAMSON & CO., INC.
1901 Payne St, Louisville, KY 40206
Tel.: (502) 895-2438
Web Site: http://www.caramel.com
Year Founded: 1865
Sales Range: $10-24.9 Million
Emp.: 60
Caramel Color Mfr for the Food Industry
N.A.I.C.S.: 311999
Theodore H. Nixon *(Chm & CEO)*
Thomas Dotter *(Mgr-North American-West)*
Danny Srour *(Mgr-Caribbean & Latin America)*
Mark Murphy *(Mgr-Sls-North American-East)*

D.E. RICE CONSTRUCTION CO., INC.

D.E. Rice Construction Co., Inc.—(Continued)

PO Box 3344, Borger, TX 79007
Tel.: (806) 274-7187
Web Site: http://www.derice.com
Heavy & Civil Engineering Construction
N.A.I.C.S.: 237990
Mike Williams *(Bus Mgr)*

Subsidiaries:

Panhandle Valve, Fabrication &
Machine (1)
1400 Hemlock St, Borger, TX 79007-6106
Tel.: (806) 274-2151
Web Site: http://www.panhandlevalve.com
Industrial Machinery Repair & Maintenance
Services
N.A.I.C.S.: 811310

D.F. CHASE INC.
3001 Armory Dr Ste 200, Nashville,
TN 37204-3711
Tel.: (615) 777-5900   TN
Web Site: https://www.dfchase.com
Year Founded: 1986
Sales Range: $10-24.9 Million
Emp.: 25
Provider of General Contracting Services
N.A.I.C.S.: 236220

D.F. PRAY INC.
25 Anthony St, Seekonk, MA 02771
Tel.: (508) 336-3366
Web Site: http://www.dfpray.com
Year Founded: 1959
Sales Range: $10-24.9 Million
Emp.: 50
Commercial & Office Building, New
Construction
N.A.I.C.S.: 236220
Scott W. Pray *(Pres)*
Michael Burke *(Exec VP)*
Ronald H. Laprise *(Sr VP)*
Mark E. Conley *(VP-Construction &
Dev)*
Philip G. Kominsky *(VP-Construction)*

**D.G. JENKINS DEVELOPMENT
CORP.**
3575 Koger Blvd Ste 200, Duluth, GA
30096-4958
Tel.: (770) 614-3101
Rev.: $43,727,140
Emp.: 50
Subdividers & Developers
N.A.I.C.S.: 237210
David Jenkins *(CEO)*

Subsidiaries:

Winmark Homes Inc. (1)
395 Brogdon Rd, Suwanee, GA 30024
Tel.: (770) 614-3101
Web Site:
    http://www.winmarkhomesatlanta.com
Rev.: $35,985,560
Emp.: 25
Residential Construction
N.A.I.C.S.: 236115

**D.G. YUENGLING & SON IN-
CORPORATED**
500 Mahantongo St, Pottsville, PA
17901
Tel.: (570) 622-4141
Web Site: http://www.yuengling.com
Sales Range: $100-124.9 Million
Emp.: 280
Producer of Beer
N.A.I.C.S.: 312120
David Casinelli *(COO)*
Richard L. Yuengling Jr. *(Pres)*

Subsidiaries:

Yuengling Beer Company of Tampa,
Inc. (1)
3751 E Fowler Ave, Tampa, FL 33612

Tel.: (813) 867-2878
Web Site: http://www.yuengling.com
Sales Range: $1-9.9 Million
Emp.: 80
Breweries Mfr
N.A.I.C.S.: 312120
Andy Pickerell *(Plant Mgr)*
Santo Lazzara *(Mgr-Plant Engrg)*

D.H. ADAMS COMPANY, INC.
100 Thomas St, Worcester, MA
01608
Tel.: (508) 753-1491
Web Site: http://www.dhadams.net
Plumbing & Heating Equipment &
Supplies, Hydronics, Merchant Whslr
N.A.I.C.S.: 423720
Robert A. McManus *(Chm)*
John McManus *(Pres)*

Subsidiaries:

D.H. Adams Company, Inc. -
Leominster (1)
435 Lancaster St, Leominster, MA 01453
Tel.: (978) 534-8894
Web Site: http://www.dhadams.net
Sales Range: $1-9.9 Million
Emp.: 6
Plumbing & Heating Equipment & Supplies,
Hydronics, Merchant Whslr
N.A.I.C.S.: 423720
Tom Sambito *(Mgr)*

**D.H. GRIFFIN WRECKING CO.
INC.**
4716 Hilltop Rd, Greensboro, NC
27407-5217
Tel.: (336) 855-7030   NC
Web Site: http://www.dhgriffin.com
Year Founded: 1959
Sales Range: $100-124.9 Million
Emp.: 1,000
Wrecking & Demolition Work
N.A.I.C.S.: 238910
David H. Griffin Sr. *(CEO & Founder)*

Subsidiaries:

D H Griffin Construction Co. LLC (1)
431 Raleigh View Rd, Raleigh, NC 27610-
4623
Tel.: (919) 835-3655
Web Site: http://www.dhgc.com
Sales Range: $10-24.9 Million
Emp.: 100
General/Commercial Construction
N.A.I.C.S.: 236115
Bill Sinclair *(Dir-Bus Dev)*
Gary A. Rogers *(Pres)*

D. H. Griffin Contracting Co., Inc. (1)
974 Berry Shoals Rd, Duncan, SC 29334
Tel.: (864) 848-1885
Construction Engineering Services
N.A.I.C.S.: 541330

D.H. Griffin Wrecking Co. Inc. - Ashe-
ville Division (1)
125 Sweeten Creek Rd Bldg A, Asheville,
NC 28802
Tel.: (828) 274-4520
Environmental Engineering Services
N.A.I.C.S.: 541330

D.H. Griffin Wrecking Co. Inc. -
Crushing Division (1)
11205 Reames Rd, Charlotte, NC 28269
Tel.: (704) 598-6969
Construction Engineering Services
N.A.I.C.S.: 541330

D.H. Griffin of Texas, Inc (1)
8690 Lambright Rd, Houston, TX 77075
Tel.: (713) 991-4444
Web Site: http://www.dhgt.com
Building Demolition Services
N.A.I.C.S.: 238910
John F. Angelina *(Pres)*
John W. Angelina *(VP-Estimating & Bus
Dev)*
William L. Holt *(VP-Environmental Affairs)*

D.J. BRONSON INC.

5401 Telegraph Rd, Los Angeles, CA
90040
Tel.: (323) 278-5440
Rev.: $11,300,517
Emp.: 14
Women's, Junior's & Girls" Dresses
Mfr
N.A.I.C.S.: 315250
Bruce Bronson *(Pres)*
Beth Dizon *(Controller)*
Justin Ding *(COO)*

D.J. POWERS COMPANY INC.
5000 Business Center Dr Ste 1000,
Savannah, GA 31405
Tel.: (912) 234-7241
Web Site: https://www.djpowers.com
Year Founded: 1930
Rev.: $10,000,000
Emp.: 90
Freight Transportation Services
N.A.I.C.S.: 488510
Bill Conaway *(Exec VP)*

**D.L. COUCH WALLCOVERING,
INC.**
499 E County Rd 300 S, New Castle,
IN 47362
Tel.: (765) 521-9500
Web Site: http://www.dlcouch.com
Year Founded: 1993
Sales Range: $10-24.9 Million
Emp.: 60
Wallcoverings & Supplies Whslr
N.A.I.C.S.: 424950
Dennis L. Couch *(Pres)*
Shari Spera *(VP-Ops)*

D.L. EVANS BANCORP
375 N Overland Ave, Burley, ID
83318
Tel.: (208) 678-2552   ID
Web Site: https://www.dlevans.com
Year Founded: 1994
Sales Range: $50-74.9 Million
Emp.: 271
Bank Holding Company
N.A.I.C.S.: 551111
H. Scott Horsley *(Chief Credit Officer
& Exec VP)*
Brenda Sanford *(CFO)*
Larry Hogg *(VP-Fruitland)*
John V. Evans Jr. *(Pres & CEO)*
John V. Evans III *(Exec VP)*
Don S. Evans Jr. *(Chm)*

Subsidiaries:

D.L. Evans Bank (1)
375 N Overland Ave, Burley, ID 83318
Tel.: (208) 678-8615
Web Site: http://www.dlevans.com
Sales Range: $50-74.9 Million
Emp.: 341
Commericial Banking
N.A.I.C.S.: 522110
Amy Kesner *(VP)*
Jerry Smith *(Sr VP & Reg Mgr-West)*
James P. Evans *(VP)*
Brenda Sanford *(Chief Admin Officer)*
Jim Reames *(Sr VP)*
Curtis Smith *(CFO)*
Matthew E. Gilgen *(VP)*
Jessica Aguilar *(Asst VP-Corp Real Estate
& Construction-Boise)*
Ben Nelson *(Sr VP-Residential Mortgage
Lending)*
Jerri Richardson *(VP)*
Michael Combs *(Mgr-Fairview)*
Christian Griffith *(VP & Mgr-Nampa)*
Duane Alexander *(VP-Caldwell)*
Dan Gammon *(VP)*
Amy Durfee *(Asst VP/Asst Mgr-Rupert
Branch)*
Monica Swan *(Mgr-Mortgage Loan Ops)*
Wendy Parkinson *(Asst VP)*
Dirk Stanger *(VP-Rigby)*
Joshua Vincent *(Branch Mgr-Retail-South
Meridian)*
Kelley Edinger *(Mgr-Retail-Downtown Twin
Falls)*

Juanita Villa *(VP & Sls Mgr-South Idaho)*
Ron Wolfe *(Sr VP)*
John V. Evans Jr. *(Pres & CEO)*
Don S. Evans Jr. *(Chm)*

D.L. LEE & SONS INC.
927 Hwy 32 E, Alma, GA 31510
Tel.: (912) 632-4406
Web Site: https://www.dllee.com
Sales Range: $50-74.9 Million
Emp.: 250
Beef Products Distr
N.A.I.C.S.: 311611
W. David Lee *(Pres)*
Jerry Lee *(CEO)*
Diwakar Furtado *(Mgr-Quality Assur-
ance)*
Kevin Moore *(Mgr-HR)*

**D.L. PORTER CONSTRUC-
TORS INC.**
6574 Palmer Park Cir, Sarasota, FL
34238
Tel.: (941) 929-9400
Web Site: https://www.dlporter.com
Year Founded: 1977
Sales Range: $10-24.9 Million
Emp.: 12
Commercial & Office Building Con-
tractor
N.A.I.C.S.: 236220
Gary A. Loer *(Pres)*

D.M. FIGLEY CO. INC.
10 Kelly Ct, Menlo Park, CA 94025
Tel.: (650) 329-8700
Web Site: http://www.dmfigley.com
Sales Range: $10-24.9 Million
Emp.: 30
Sealants Distr
N.A.I.C.S.: 424690
Janet Dgioia *(Pres)*
Gary DiGioia *(VP-Ops)*

D.M. STOLTZFUS & SON INC.
330 Quarry Rd, Leola, PA 17540
Tel.: (717) 656-2411
Rev.: $14,667,912
Emp.: 54
Limestones, Ground
N.A.I.C.S.: 212312

**D.S. WOLF GROUP INTERNA-
TIONAL, LLC**
100 Park Ave Ste 1600, New York,
NY 10017
Tel.: (212) 692-9400
Web Site: https://www.dswolf.com
Year Founded: 1987
Sales Range: $10-24.9 Million
Emp.: 30
Executive Search Service
N.A.I.C.S.: 541612
Susan Stack *(Mng Dir & CFO)*
Jon Friedman *(Mng Dir & Head-Sls &
Mktg)*
Gary Obler *(Mng Dir & COO)*
Edward A. Merhige III *(Mng Dir)*

**D.T. CARSON ENTERPRISES
INC.**
42882 Ivy St, Murrieta, CA 92562
Tel.: (909) 684-9585
Web Site:
    http://www.completecoach.com
Rev.: $12,494,248
Emp.: 200
Transportation Repair Services &
Parts Remanufacturing
N.A.I.C.S.: 811121
Floyd Holland *(Sr VP)*
Macy Neshati *(VP-Sls & Mktg-
Complete Coach Works)*

D.T. MCCALL & SONS
101 Water St, Carthage, TN 37030

Tel.: (615) 735-0165
Web Site: https://www.dtmccalls.com
Sales Range: $10-24.9 Million
Emp.: 178
Furniture Retailer
N.A.I.C.S.: 449110
Albert B. McCall *(Partner)*
Tom Morris *(Mgr-Store)*
Samantha Key *(Atty)*

D.V. BROWN & ASSOCIATES, INC.
567 Vickers St, Tonawanda, NY 14150
Tel.: (716) 695-5533
Web Site: https://www.dvbrown.com
Sales Range: $25-49.9 Million
Emp.: 99
Plumbing, Heating & Air-Conditioning Contracting Services
N.A.I.C.S.: 238220
Omar J. Abdallah *(VP-Construction)*
Erik Deglopper *(VP-Svc)*
Kevin Bitikofer *(Mgr-Svc Ops)*
Donald V. Brown Jr. *(Pres & CEO)*

D.V.F. STUDIO
440 W 14th St, New York, NY 10014-1723
Tel.: (212) 741-6607   NY
Web Site: https://www.dvf.com
Sales Range: $75-99.9 Million
Emp.: 50
Beauty Product Distr
N.A.I.C.S.: 533110
Paula Sutter *(Pres)*

Subsidiaries:

Diane Von Furstenberg Couture   (1)
440 W 14th St, New York, NY 10014
Tel.: (212) 753-1111
Web Site: http://www.dvf.com
Couture Designer
N.A.I.C.S.: 315210
Von Furstenberg *(Chm)*
Nathan Jenden *(Chief Design Officer & VP-Creative)*

D.W. CAMPBELL, INC.
3217 S Cherokee Ln Ste 720, Woodstock, GA 30188-7053
Tel.: (770) 620-2000   GA
Web Site:
http://www.dwcampbelltire.com
Year Founded: 1985
Sales Range: $50-74.9 Million
Emp.: 15
Holding Company; Tire & General Automotive Repair Centers Owner & Operator
N.A.I.C.S.: 551112
Brian Campbell *(CEO & Gen Mgr)*
Arlene Campbell *(Owner & CFO)*
Tina Henderson *(Sec)*

Subsidiaries:

D.W. Campbell of Atlanta, Inc.   (1)
1921 Howell Mill Rd NW, Atlanta, GA 30318
Tel.: (404) 352-0001
Sales Range: $25-49.9 Million
Emp.: 12
Tire & General Automotive Repair Center
N.A.I.C.S.: 811111

D.W. Campbell of Dunwoody, Inc.   (1)
8445 Roswell Rd, Atlanta, GA 30350   (100%)
Tel.: (770) 518-1611
Web Site: http://www.dwcampbelltire.com
Rev.: $560,000
Emp.: 10
Tire & General Automotive Repair Center
N.A.I.C.S.: 811111
Brian Campbell *(CEO)*

D.W. Campbell of Kennesaw, Inc.   (1)
2970 George Busbee Pkwy, Kennesaw, GA 30144

Tel.: (770) 792-2982
Web Site: http://www.dwcampbelltire.com
Emp.: 5
Tire & General Automotive Repair Center
N.A.I.C.S.: 811111
Brian Campbell *(Gen Mgr)*

D.W. Campbell of Marietta, Inc.   (1)
3330 Canton Rd, Marietta, GA 30066-2680   (100%)
Tel.: (770) 427-0234
Web Site: http://www.dwcampbelltire.com
Sales Range: Less than $1 Million
Emp.: 9
Tire & General Automotive Repair Center
N.A.I.C.S.: 811111
Brian Campbell *(Gen Mgr)*

D.W. Campbell-Cobb Pkwy, Inc.   (1)
1930 Cobb Pkwy, Marietta, GA 30060-9257   (100%)
Tel.: (770) 980-1811
Web Site: http://www.dwcampbelltire.com
Tire & General Automotive Repair Center
N.A.I.C.S.: 811111
Brian Campbell *(Gen Mgr)*

D.W. DICKEY & SONS INC.
512 E Washington St, Lisbon, OH 44432-9391
Tel.: (330) 424-1922   OH
Web Site: https://www.dwdickey.com
Year Founded: 1948
Sales Range: $25-49.9 Million
Emp.: 185
Ready Mix Concrete & Builders' Supplies Distr
N.A.I.C.S.: 424690
Dick Cope *(Mgr-Concrete Dispatch)*

Subsidiaries:

D.W. Dickey & Sons Inc. - Columbiana Plant   (1)
169 Duquesne St, Columbiana, OH 44408
Tel.: (330) 482-3833
Web Site: http://www.dwdickey.com
Emp.: 13
Concrete Block Mfr
N.A.I.C.S.: 327331
Todd Ramsey *(Mgr-Div)*

D.W. Dickey & Sons Inc. - East Liverpool Concrete Plant   (1)
700 River Rd, East Liverpool, OH 43920
Tel.: (330) 386-8226
Concrete Block Mfr
N.A.I.C.S.: 327331

D.W. Dickey & Sons Inc. - Lisbon Concrete Plant   (1)
512 E Washington St, Lisbon, OH 44432
Tel.: (330) 424-1922
Concrete Block Mfr
N.A.I.C.S.: 327331
Dick Rose *(Gen Mgr)*

D.W. Dickey & Sons Inc. - Steubenville Plant   (1)
1088 Labelle Ave, Steubenville, OH 43952
Tel.: (740) 284-1960
Concrete Block Mfr
N.A.I.C.S.: 327331

Hilltop Energy Inc.   (1)
PO Box 189, Lisbon, OH 44432-9391
Tel.: (330) 859-2108
Web Site: http://www.dwdickey.com
Sales Range: $10-24.9 Million
Emp.: 50
Explosives & Blasting Services
N.A.I.C.S.: 424690
Timothy G. Dickey *(Pres)*

Lisbon Builders Supply   (1)
9016 SR 164, Lisbon, OH 44432
Tel.: (330) 424-5008
Building Materials Distr
N.A.I.C.S.: 423390
Rick Pittenger *(Mgr-Concrete Quality Control)*

D.W. NICHOLSON CORPORATION
24747 Clawiter Rd, Hayward, CA 94545
Tel.: (510) 887-0900

Web Site:
https://www.dwnicholson.com
Year Founded: 1935
Sales Range: $25-49.9 Million
Emp.: 200
Other Building Equipment Contracting Services
N.A.I.C.S.: 238290
John L. Nicholson *(Chm & CEO)*
Thomas S. Reed *(Pres)*
Clifford A. Schuch *(CFO & Treas)*

D1 CAPITAL PARTNERS L.P.
9 W 57th St 36th Fl, New York, NY 10019
Tel.: (212) 390-9100
Investment Services
N.A.I.C.S.: 523999
Daniel Sundheim *(Founder & CIO)*

Subsidiaries:

Collectors Universe Inc.   (1)
1610 E Saint Andrew Pl, Santa Ana, CA 92705
Tel.: (949) 567-1234
Web Site: http://www.collectorsuniverse.com
Rev.: $78,891,000
Assets: $55,482,000
Liabilities: $30,470,000
Net Worth: $25,012,000
Earnings: $10,786,000
Emp.: 446
Fiscal Year-end: 06/30/2020
Authentication, Grading, Appraisal, Information & Exchange Services
N.A.I.C.S.: 561990
Joseph J. Wallace *(CFO & Sr VP)*
Nataniel S. Turner *(Chm)*

D2 REALTY SERVICES INC.
701 S Wells Unit 3401, Chicago, IL 60607
Tel.: (312) 663-4300
Web Site: http://www.d2realty.com
Sales Range: $10-24.9 Million
Emp.: 6
Full-Service Real Estate Firm Engaged in Residential & Commercial Development, Property Management, Construction & Real Estate Brokerage
N.A.I.C.S.: 812220
David Kleiman *(Co-Founder & Principal)*
David Crawford *(Co-Founder & Principal)*

D2C STORES INC.
1 Broadway 14th Fl, Cambridge, MA 02142
Tel.: (989) 656-8517   DE
Emp.: 6
Internet Publishing & Broadcasting & Web Search Portal
N.A.I.C.S.: 516210
Chris Litster *(CEO)*

Subsidiaries:

Cuddle Clones LLC   (1)
445 Baxter Ave Ste 150, Louisville, KY 40204
Web Site: http://www.cuddleclones.com
Sales Range: $1-9.9 Million
Emp.: 50
Pet Care Product Mfr
N.A.I.C.S.: 339930
Jennifer Williams *(Founder)*

D3 LOGIC, INC.
89 Commercial Way, East Providence, RI 02915
Tel.: (401) 435-4300   RI
Web Site: https://www.d3-inc.com
Commercial Marketing Services
N.A.I.C.S.: 541613
Ralph R. Delmonico Jr. *(Pres)*

D4 CREATIVE GROUP

4646 Umbria St, Philadelphia, PA 19127
Tel.: (215) 483-4555
Web Site: http://www.d4creative.com
Year Founded: 1990
Sales Range: $10-24.9 Million
Emp.: 30
N.A.I.C.S.: 541810
Kurt Shore *(Pres)*
Sara Stuard *(VP-Acct Svcs)*

DA KINE HAWAII INC.
603 Portway Ave Ste 103, Hood River, OR 97031
Tel.: (541) 386-3166
Web Site: http://www.dakine.com
Sales Range: $10-24.9 Million
Emp.: 200
Sporting & Athletic Goods
N.A.I.C.S.: 339920
Chico Bukovansky *(VP-Sls & Mdsg)*
Tim Weisser *(Mgr-Natl Sls-US)*

DA-LY REALTY & INSURANCE INC.
2514 S Locust St, Grand Island, NE 68801-8226
Tel.: (308) 384-1101
Web Site:
http://www.jackiebeltzer.com
Lessors of Residential Buildings & Dwellings
N.A.I.C.S.: 531110
Robert Clymer *(Pres)*

Subsidiaries:

First Brokers Real Estate   (1)
1515 N Webb Rd, Grand Island, NE 68803-2318
Tel.: (308) 227-9146
Web Site: http://www.first-brokers.com
Offices of Real Estate Agents & Brokers
N.A.I.C.S.: 531210
Coad Miller *(Pres)*

DA-PRO RUBBER INC.
601 N Poplar Ave, Broken Arrow, OK 74012
Tel.: (918) 258-9386
Web Site:
http://www.daprorubber.com
Rev.: $22,900,000
Emp.: 225
Molded Rubber Products
N.A.I.C.S.: 326299
C. B. Daubenberger *(Chm)*

DA-RUE OF CALIFORNIA, INC.
14102 S Broadway St, Los Angeles, CA 90061
Tel.: (310) 323-1350   CA
Web Site:
http://www.darueofcalifornia.com
Year Founded: 1945
Sales Range: $75-99.9 Million
Emp.: 40
Women's Clothing Designer, Mfr & Retailer
N.A.I.C.S.: 315250
Richard McElrath *(Pres & CEO)*

DABECCA NATURAL FOODS INC.
PO Box 15, Clifton, TX 76634
Tel.: (254) 675-2563
Web Site:
http://www.dabeccafoods.com
Sales Range: $10-24.9 Million
Emp.: 86
Processed Meat Mfr
N.A.I.C.S.: 311612
David Pederson *(Pres)*

DABURN ELECTRONICS & CABLE CORP.
44 Richboynton Rd, Dover, NJ 07801
Tel.: (973) 328-3200

Daburn Electronics & Cable
Corp.—(Continued)

Web Site: https://www.daburn.com
Power Supply Products & Custom
Electronics Mfr
N.A.I.C.S.: 334419
Ed Flaherty *(Pres & CEO)*

Subsidiaries:

EMSE, Inc. (1)
10 Plog Rd, Fairfield, NJ 07004
Tel.: (973) 227-9221
Web Site: http://www.emse.com
Sales Range: $1-9.9 Million
Emp.: 13
Laboratory Apparatus And Furniture
N.A.I.C.S.: 333248

Precise Circuits Inc. (1)
1411 LeMay Dr Ste 203, Carrollton, TX
75007
Tel.: (972) 242-7398
Web Site: http://www.precisecircuits.com
Electric Equipment Mfr
N.A.I.C.S.: 335999
David McClung *(Gen Mgr & Engr)*

DAC GROUP/BROOME MARKETING
455 S 4th St Ste1045, Louisville, KY
40202
Tel.: (502) 582-3565
Web Site: http://www.dacgroup.com
Year Founded: 1993
Rev.: $19,000,000
Emp.: 30
Interactive Agencies, Yellow Pages
Advertising
N.A.I.C.S.: 541810
Michelle Mabry *(Owner)*
Colleene Masters *(Acct Dir)*
Brian Blandford *(VP-Client Svcs)*
Norm Hagarty *(CEO & Mng Partner)*
Wayne Fulcher *(Founder)*

DAC REALTY GROUP, INC.
7026 Old Katy Rd Ste 303, Houston,
TX 77024
Tel.: (713) 973-2100
Web Site: http://www.dacrealty.com
Year Founded: 1987
Sales Range: $1-9.9 Million
Real Estate Brokerage
N.A.I.C.S.: 531210
Don Czarneski *(Pres & Founder)*

DACO CORPORATION
1761 E Brooks Rd, Memphis, TN
38116-3605
Tel.: (901) 332-4000
Web Site:
http://peterbiltofmemphis.com
Year Founded: 1982
Sales Range: $75-99.9 Million
Emp.: 275
Holding Company: Trucking Services
N.A.I.C.S.: 551112
Hoyt Rogers *(Pres)*

Subsidiaries:

Peterbilt of Memphis (1)
1761 E Brooks Rd, Memphis, TN 38116-
3605
Tel.: (901) 332-4000
Web Site:
http://www.peterbiltofmemphis.com
Sales Range: $10-24.9 Million
Emp.: 40
Provider of Truck Rental Services
N.A.I.C.S.: 532120
Patt Ellis *(Gen Mgr)*

Trans-Carriers Inc. (1)
5135 Lamar Ave, Memphis, TN 38118-7819
Tel.: (901) 368-2900
Web Site: http://www.transcarriers.com
Sales Range: $25-49.9 Million
Emp.: 200
Provider of Trucking Services
N.A.I.C.S.: 484121

DACOTAH PAPER CO.
3940 15th Ave N, Fargo, ND 58102
Tel.: (701) 281-1734
Web Site:
http://www.dacotahpaper.com
Sales Range: $25-49.9 Million
Emp.: 130
Industrial & Personal Service Paper
N.A.I.C.S.: 424130
Wayne Chadwick *(Asst Territory Mgr-
Bemidji Paper Div)*

DACRA DEVELOPMENT CORP.
3841 NE 2nd Ave Ste 400, Miami, FL
33137
Tel.: (305) 531-8700
Web Site: https://www.dacra.com
Year Founded: 1987
Sales Range: $1-9.9 Million
Emp.: 50
Real Estate Development & Investment
N.A.I.C.S.: 531390
Craig Robins *(Pres & CEO)*
Anna Williams *(VP-Mktg)*
David Holtzman *(VP)*
Jonathan Levin *(Controller)*
Linda Ebin *(Gen Counsel)*
Steven Gretenstein *(COO)*
Jen Roberts *(CEO-Design Miami)*

DADANT & SONS INC.
51 S 2nd St, Hamilton, IL 62341
Tel.: (217) 847-3324
Web Site: https://www.dadant.com
Sales Range: $10-24.9 Million
Emp.: 60
Beekeeping Supplies
N.A.I.C.S.: 339999
Mack Dadant *(VP)*

DADDY'S JUNKY MUSIC STORES
1015 Candia Rd, Manchester, NH
03109
Tel.: (603) 623-7900
Rev.: $34,143,574
Emp.: 120
Musical Instrument Stores
N.A.I.C.S.: 459140
Frederick Bramante *(Founder &
CEO)*
Bobby Baker *(Exec VP)*
Scott Maser *(Controller)*

DAEDALUS BOOKS, INC.
9645 Gerwig Ln, Columbia, MD
21046
Tel.: (410) 309-2700
Web Site:
http://www.daedalusbooks.com
Year Founded: 1980
Sales Range: $25-49.9 Million
Emp.: 150
Retailer of Books & Music
N.A.I.C.S.: 424920
Robin Moody *(Pres)*
Helaine Harris *(VP)*
Keith Blocker *(Mgr-Facilities)*

DAFFIN'S, INC.
496 E State St, Sharon, PA 16146-
2056
Tel.: (724) 342-2892
Web Site: https://www.daffins.com
Year Founded: 1947
Sales Range: $10-24.9 Million
Emp.: 100
Candy & Confectionery Retailer
N.A.I.C.S.: 445292
Diane Daffin *(Pres)*
Stan Lefes *(Dir-Sls)*
Stacy Turner *(Office Mgr)*

DAG VENTURES, LLC

251 Lytton Ave Ste 200, Palo Alto,
CA 94301
Tel.: (650) 543-8180 DE
Web Site:
https://www.dagventures.com
Venture Capital Investment & Management Services
N.A.I.C.S.: 523999
John Cadeddu *(Mng Dir)*
Young Chung *(Mng Dir)*
Nick Pianim *(Mng Dir)*
Greg Williams *(Mng Dir)*
Joe Zanone *(CFO)*
Tom Goodrich *(Mng Dir)*
Deberah Stark *(Controller-Admin)*
Monika Chen *(Office Mgr)*

DAGE-MTI OF MICHIGAN CITY, INC.
701 N Roeske Ave, Michigan City, IN
46360
Tel.: (219) 872-5514
Web Site: https://www.dagemti.com
Year Founded: 1952
Closed Circuit TV & Video Cameras;
Monitors & Signal Processors Mfr
N.A.I.C.S.: 333998
Peggy Moore *(Owner)*

DAGGETT VENTURES, LLC
720 Hwy 7 W, Hutchinson, MN 55350
Tel.: (320) 587-4653 MN
Web Site: http://www.hutchmfg.com
Emp.: 100
Holding Company
N.A.I.C.S.: 551112
Thomas E. Daggett *(Owner & Pres)*

Subsidiaries:

Hutchinson Manufacturing, Inc. (1)
720 Hwy 7 W, Hutchinson, MN 55350
Tel.: (320) 587-4653
Web Site: http://www.hutchmfg.com
Sales Range: $50-74.9 Million
Emp.: 120
Custom Metal Fabrication & Machining Services
N.A.I.C.S.: 332999
Thomas E. Daggett *(Pres)*
Michael J. Dickerman *(VP-Sls & Mktg)*
Scott Bandas *(VP-Health, Safety, Quality &
Environment)*
Isaac Marceau *(VP-Ops)*
Kathy Silvernale *(VP-Fin)*
Todd Drahos *(Sr Mgr-Acct)*
James Garvin *(COO)*

Moxie Media MN, LLC (1)
1007 Broadway St, Cleveland, MN
56017 (50%)
Tel.: (320) 587-0587
Web Site: http://www.moxiemediamn.com
Sales Range: $50-74.9 Million
Emp.: 15
Promotional Products Graphic Design,
Printing & Marketing Services
N.A.I.C.S.: 541430
Ellen Dickie *(Owner & Pres)*
Deb Ely *(Project Mgr)*
Dan Sowers *(Designer-Graphic)*
Lee Huebner *(Principal)*

Pride Solutions, LLC (1)
120 E Gate Dr SE, Hutchinson, MN 55350
Tel.: (320) 587-0760
Web Site: http://www.pridesolutions.us
Sales Range: $25-49.9 Million
Emp.: 25
Compression Molding Plastic Products Mfr
N.A.I.C.S.: 326199
Thomas E. Daggett *(Pres)*
Justin Eggert *(Gen Mgr)*

DAGIT GROUP
2701 Renaissance Blvd 4th Fl, King
of Prussia, PA 19406
Tel.: (610) 205-1595
Web Site: http://www.dagitgroup.com
Year Founded: 2006
Sales Range: $1-9.9 Million
Emp.: 9

Remodeling & Construction
N.A.I.C.S.: 236220
Timothy Dagit *(Pres)*
Stephen Callaghan *(Project Mgr)*

DAHL FORD-LA CROSSE INC.
711 3rd St S, La Crosse, WI 54601
Tel.: (608) 791-6400
Web Site: https://www.dahlauto.com
Rev.: $41,000,000
Emp.: 104
New & Used Automobiles Dealer
N.A.I.C.S.: 441110
Harry J. Dahl *(Owner)*
Will Pape *(Controller)*

DAHL'S FOOD MART INC.
4343 Merle Hay Rd, Des Moines, IA
50310-1411
Tel.: (515) 276-4845 IA
Web Site: http://www.dahlsfoods.com
Year Founded: 1951
Sales Range: $100-124.9 Million
Emp.: 1,600
Grocery Supermarkets
N.A.I.C.S.: 424940
Craig Moore *(CEO)*

DAHL-BECK ELECTRIC CO.
2775 Goodrick Ave, Richmond, CA
94801
Tel.: (510) 237-2325
Web Site: http://www.dahl-beck.com
Sales Range: $10-24.9 Million
Emp.: 35
Electrical Apparatus & Related Equipment
N.A.I.C.S.: 423610
William Beck *(Chm)*
Jim Ross *(CFO)*
Roger Beck *(Gen Mgr)*

DAHLEM COMPANIES, INC.
1531 Ormsby Station Ct, Louisville,
KY 40223
Tel.: (502) 479-0200 KY
Web Site: http://www.dahlem.com
Year Founded: 1963
Sales Range: $75-99.9 Million
Emp.: 16
Commercial Real Estate Development & Acquisition Services
N.A.I.C.S.: 531120
Bernard A. Dahlem *(Chm)*
Charlie J. Dahlem *(Pres)*

Subsidiaries:

Dahlem Enterprises, Inc. (1)
1531 Ormsby Station Ct, Louisville, KY
40223
Tel.: (502) 479-0200
Web Site: http://www.dahlem.com
Real Estate Management Services
N.A.I.C.S.: 531390

Dahlem Realty Company, Inc. (1)
6200 Dutchmans Ln Ste LI1, Louisville, KY
40205
Tel.: (502) 479-0200
Real Estate Management Services
N.A.I.C.S.: 531390
Wes Elmore *(Mgr-Property)*

DAHLHEIMER DISTRIBUTING COMPANY, INC.
3360 Chelsea Rd W, Monticello, MN
55362
Tel.: (763) 295-3347
Web Site: http://www.dahlh.com
Sales Range: $10-24.9 Million
Emp.: 30
Beer & Ale Whslr
N.A.I.C.S.: 424810
Paul O'Donnel *(Branch Mgr)*
John Berg *(Mgr-Sls)*
Rod Deters *(Mgr-Merchandiser)*

DAHN CORPORATION

4675 Macarthur Ct Ste 500, Newport Beach, CA 92660
Tel.: (949) 752-1282
Web Site: http://www.dahncorp.com
Sales Range: $10-24.9 Million
Emp.: 15
Operative Builders
N.A.I.C.S.: 236117
Jeffrey L. Swanson (VP)
Kimberlee Drenk (VP)
Robert Bradley (Exec VP)

DAI HOLDING, LLC

42 Thomas Patten Dr, Randolph, MA 02368
Tel.: (781) 437-9880
Web Site: http://www.chadwicks.com
Year Founded: 2011
Online & Catalog Women's Apparel Retailer
N.A.I.C.S.: 458110
Jason Bates (Dir-Ops)

Subsidiaries:

Chasing Fireflies, LLC   (1)
350 Midland Ave, Seattle, WA 98188
Tel.: (206) 574-4500
Web Site: http://www.chasing-fireflies.com
Children & Babies Clothing, Home Items, Toys, Costumes & Novelties Sales
N.A.I.C.S.: 459999

TravelSmith Outfitters, Inc.   (1)
5568 W Chester Rd, West Chester, OH 45069
Tel.: (800) 770-3387
Web Site: http://www.travelsmith.com
Travel Clothing & Travel Accessories Retailer
N.A.I.C.S.: 458110

DAIBES BROTHERS INC.

1000 Portside Dr, Edgewater, NJ 07020
Tel.: (201) 840-0050
Sales Range: $25-49.9 Million
Emp.: 15
Residential Construction
N.A.I.C.S.: 236115
Fred A. Daibes (Founder)
Fred Assad (Co-CEO)

DAIDONE ELECTRICAL INC.

200 Raymond Blvd, Newark, NJ 07105-4608
Tel.: (973) 690-5216   NJ
Web Site:
  https://www.daidoneelectric.com
Sales Range: $25-49.9 Million
Emp.: 150
Electrical Contractor
N.A.I.C.S.: 238210
John Daidone (Pres)
Victor Daidone (VP)
Patrick Young (Project Mgr)

DAIEI TRADING CO. INC.

1450 128th St, College Point, NY 11356
Tel.: (718) 539-8100
Web Site: https://www.daiei-trading.com
Rev.: $20,000,000
Emp.: 35
Groceries & Related Products
N.A.I.C.S.: 424490
Yoshio Takeda (Pres)

DAIGLE & HOUGHTON INC.

130 Market St, Fort Kent, ME 04743
Tel.: (207) 834-6186
Web Site:
  http://www.daigleandhoughton.com
Sales Range: S25-49.9 Million
Emp.: 60
Commercial Trucks
N.A.I.C.S.: 423110

Scott Rice (Mgr-Parts Dept)
Daniel Freeman (Mgr-Parts)
Andre Landry (Mgr-Svcs)
David Saucier (Controller)
Dave Madore (Mgr-Shipping & Receiving)
Bill Lewis (Mgr-Svc Dept)

DAIGLE OIL COMPANY

155 W Main St, Fort Kent, ME 04743-1231
Tel.: (207) 834-5027   ME
Web Site: https://www.daigleoil.com
Year Founded: 1955
Sales Range: $75-99.9 Million
Emp.: 100
Whslr & Retailer of Petroleum Products
N.A.I.C.S.: 457210
Beverly Jandreau (Exec Sec)
Richard G. Daigle (Pres)

DAILEY & WELLS COMMUNICATIONS

3440 E Houston St, San Antonio, TX 78219
Tel.: (210) 893-6500
Rev.: $40,000,000
Emp.: 51
Amateur Radio Communications Equipment
N.A.I.C.S.: 423690
Richard A. Wells (Pres)
Joanne Wells (CFO)
Dan Meyer (Mgr-Ops)

DAILY BREAD MINISTRIES

6351 Rittiman Rd, San Antonio, TX 78218
Tel.: (210) 223-4707   TX
Web Site:
  http://www.dailybreadministries.org
Year Founded: 1997
Sales Range: $10-24.9 Million
Emp.: 14
Donation Collection & Distribution Services
N.A.I.C.S.: 813211
Marcus Walker (Program Dir)
Donna Hoyack (Dir-Dev)
Joey Cooper (Mgr-Warehouse)
Randy Lindsey (Mgr-Facilities)
Seth Kuehn (Founder)

DAILY EXPRESS, INC.

1072 Harrisburg Pike, Carlisle, PA 17013-1615
Tel.: (717) 243-5757   PA
Web Site: https://www.dailyexp.com
Year Founded: 1958
Sales Range: $100-124.9 Million
Emp.: 200
Nationwide Trucking Company
N.A.I.C.S.: 484121
Erik Thompson (Dir-Recruiting)
Michael McGeoy (VP-Fin)

DAILY GAZETTE CO. INC.

2345 Maxon Rd Ext, Schenectady, NY 12301
Tel.: (518) 374-4141
Web Site:
  https://www.dailygazette.com
Rev.: $25,000,000
Emp.: 235
Newspapers
N.A.I.C.S.: 513110
John DeAugustine (Publr)
Erin O'Neill (Editor-Web)
Mark Mahoney (Editor-Editorial Page)
Randy Lewis (Dir-Adv)
Judy Patrick (Editor)
Lance Geda (VP-Fin)
Miles Reed (Mng Editor)
Bob O'Leary (VP-Revenue Diversification)

DAILY INSTRUMENTS INC.

5700 Hartsdale Dr, Houston, TX 77036
Tel.: (713) 780-8600
Web Site: http://www.dailyinst.com
Year Founded: 1973
Sales Range: $10-24.9 Million
Emp.: 100
Thermocouples
N.A.I.C.S.: 334519
Jeffrey N. Daily (Pres & CEO)
Don Fulton (Controller)

DAILY NEWS, L.P.

450 W 33rd St, New York, NY 10001
Tel.: (212) 210-6336   NY
Web Site:
  http://www.nydailynews.com
Year Founded: 1919
Sales Range: $400-449.9 Million
Emp.: 1,500
Daily & Sunday General Circulation Newspaper
N.A.I.C.S.: 513110
Colin Myler (Pres & Editor-in-Chief)
Tom Wolf (Dir-Procurement)

DAINGERFIELD HOLDING COMPANY

107 Webb St, Daingerfield, TX 75638
Tel.: (903) 645-2251   TX
Web Site: http://www.texashnb.com
Year Founded: 1973
Sales Range: $1-9.9 Million
Emp.: 34
Bank Holding Company
N.A.I.C.S.: 551111

Subsidiaries:

Texas Heritage National Bank   (1)
107 Webb St, Daingerfield, TX 75638
Tel.: (903) 645-2251
Web Site: http://www.texashnb.com
Sales Range: $1-9.9 Million
Commericial Banking
N.A.I.C.S.: 522110
Brenda Howard (Sr VP)
Dwyatt Bell (Pres & CEO)
John A. Bryan Sr. (Chm)

DAIRY BARN STORES INC.

544 Elwood Rd, East Northport, NY 11731-4826
Tel.: (631) 368-8050
Web Site: https://www.dairybarn.com
Year Founded: 1962
Rev.: $42,000,000
Emp.: 425
Dairy Products Stores
N.A.I.C.S.: 445298
Stephen Valdini (Mgr-Retail)

DAIRY CONVEYOR CORPORATION

38 Mount Ebo Rd S, Brewster, NY 10509
Tel.: (845) 278-7878
Web Site:
  https://www.dairyconveyor.com
Sales Range: $25-49.9 Million
Emp.: 100
Conveyors & Conveying Equipment
N.A.I.C.S.: 333922
Gary Freudenberg (Pres)
Frank Fink (Mgr-Warehouse)
Karl Horberg (CFO)
Roland Debald (Mgr-Production)
Tony Gomez (Partner)
Csaba Tilger (Engr-Electrical)

DAIRY FARMERS OF AMERICA, INC.

PO Box 909700, Kansas City, MO 64190-9700
Tel.: (816) 801-6455   KS
Web Site: http://www.dfamilk.com
Year Founded: 1998

Sales Range: $5-14.9 Billion
Emp.: 4,000
Dairy Marketing Services
N.A.I.C.S.: 926140
John J. Wilson (Chief Fluid Mktg Officer & Sr VP-Kansas City)
Randy Mooney (Chm)
Kent Herman (Vice Chm)
Doug Nuttelman (Vice Chm)
Jeff Raney (Vice Chm)
Case Van Steyn (Vice Chm)
Monica Massey (Exec VP)
Renee Cool (Chief Compliance & Integrity Officer & VP-Legal-Kansas City)
Dennis Rodenbaugh (Pres & CEO)
Kevin O'Donnell (Sr VP-Sustainability)

Subsidiaries:

Agri-Services Agency, LLC   (1)
5001 Brittenfield Pkwy, East Syracuse, NY 13057   (100%)
Tel.: (315) 433-1238
Web Site: http://www.agri-servicesagency.com
Sales Range: $10-24.9 Million
Emp.: 30
Insurance Services for Farm & Agricultural Businesses
N.A.I.C.S.: 524298
Julia Newman (Dir-Sls & Svcs)
Paula Kulpa (VP-Market & Product Dev)
Brandi Franklin (Mgr-Acct)
Janil Wilson (Dir-Health Underwriting)

Subsidiary (Domestic):

Agri-Edge Development, LLC   (2)
5001 Britainfield Pkwy, East Syracuse, NY 13057   (100%)
Tel.: (315) 433-0100
Web Site: http://www.agri-edge.com
Economic Development & Consulting for Agricultural Businesses
N.A.I.C.S.: 541618

Agri-Max Financial Services, L.P. (2)
5001 Brittonfield Pkwy, East Syracuse, NY 13057   (60%)
Tel.: (315) 433-0100
Web Site: http://www.agri-maxfinancial.com
Agricultural Financial Services
N.A.I.C.S.: 522299
Li Yong (Chm & Gen Mgr)

Gladle Associates, Inc.   (2)
216 Washington St, Watertown, NY 13601-6487   (100%)
Tel.: (315) 785-8700
Web Site: http://www.gladle.com
Emp.: 3
Insurance Agents
N.A.I.C.S.: 524114
Don Gladle (Pres)
Gregory I. Wickham (VP-Sls)
Edward W. Bangel (Treas & Sec)

Castro Cheese Company Inc.   (1)
4006 Campbell Rd, Houston, TX 77080
Tel.: (713) 460-0329
Web Site: http://www.castrocheese.com
Sales Range: $25-49.9 Million
Emp.: 50
Mfr, Marketer & Distr of Hispanic Cheeses & Creams
N.A.I.C.S.: 311513
Elizabeth Castro (VP-Sls & Mktg)

Central Area Council   (1)
10220 N Ambassador Dr, Kansas City, MO 64153-1155
Tel.: (816) 801-6200
Web Site: http://www.dfamilk.com
Sales Range: $25-49.9 Million
Emp.: 300
Milk Marketing Cooperative
N.A.I.C.S.: 311511
Randy McGinnis (COO)

DairiConcepts, L.P.   (1)
3253 E Chestnut Expy, Springfield, MO 65802-2584
Tel.: (417) 829-3400
Web Site: http://www.dairiconcepts.com
Sales Range: $50-74.9 Million
Emp.: 500
Mfr of Cheese & Dairy Powders

Dairy Farmers of America, Inc.—(Continued)
N.A.I.C.S.: 311513

Dairy Farmers of America - Reading Plant (1)
100 McKinley Ave, Reading, PA 19605
Tel.: (610) 929-5736
Web Site: http://www.dfamilk.com
Sales Range: $25-49.9 Million
Emp.: 80
Industrial Food Ingredients Mfr
N.A.I.C.S.: 311514
Audrey Connolly (Gen Mgr)

Dairy Marketing Services, LLC (1)
5001 Brittonfield Pkwy, East Syracuse, NY 13057
Tel.: (315) 433-0100
Web Site:
    http://www.dairymarketingservices.com
Sales Range: $25-49.9 Million
Emp.: 100
Milk Marketing Services for Dairy Industry
N.A.I.C.S.: 541613
Tim Virgil (VP-Member Rels)
Sharad Mathur (COO)

Eagle Dairy Direct LLC (1)
5001 Brittonfield Pkwy, East Syracuse, NY 13057
Tel.: (866) 591-2925
Web Site: http://www.dfafarmsupplies.com
Sales Range: $10-24.9 Million
Emp.: 20
Farm Supplies Distr
N.A.I.C.S.: 424590
Jeff McIntyre (Pres)
Bill Taylor (Dir-Sls)
Tom Rausch (Dir-Ops)

Empire Livestock Marketing LLC (1)
5001 Brittonfield Park 13057, Syracuse, NY 13221-4844 (100%)
Tel.: (315) 433-9129
Web Site: http://www.empirelivestock.com
Sales Range: $50-74.9 Million
Emp.: 90
Livestock Marketing Services
N.A.I.C.S.: 424520
Jack Bero (Mgr)
Dannielle Cornelius (Mgr)
Lonnie Kent (Mgr)
Jonathan Lubic (Mgr-Bath)
Tim Miller (Mgr)
Sue Rudgers (Mgr)
David Sherwood (Mgr-Vernon)

Hiland Dairy Foods Company, LLC (1)
1133 E Kearney, Springfield, MO 65803
Tel.: (417) 862-9311
Web Site: http://www.hilanddairy.com
Dairy Foods & Beverages Mfr & Distr
N.A.I.C.S.: 311511

Kemps LLC (1)
1270 Energy Ln, Saint Paul, MN 55108-5225
Tel.: (651) 379-6500
Web Site: http://www.kemps.com
Sales Range: $10-24.9 Million
Emp.: 75
N.A.I.C.S.: 311513
Rachel A. Kyllo (VP-Mktg)
Craig Kurr (CEO)
Cindy Trousdale (VP-Bus Svcs)

Mideast Area Council (1)
1035 Medina Rd, Medina, OH 44256
Tel.: (330) 670-7800
Web Site: http://www.dsamilk.com
Sales Range: $25-49.9 Million
Emp.: 75
N.A.I.C.S.: 445298

Mountain Area Council (1)
1140 S 3200 W, Salt Lake City, UT 84104-4561
Tel.: (801) 977-3000
Web Site: http://www.appletoncorp.net
Rev.: $3,975,000
Emp.: 200
Milk Marketing Cooperative
N.A.I.C.S.: 424130

Northeast Area Council (1)
5001 Brittonfield Pkwy, East Syracuse, NY 13057
Tel.: (315) 433-0100

Sales Range: $10-24.9 Million
Emp.: 50
N.A.I.C.S.: 445298
Gregory I. Wickham (CEO)

Southeast Area Council (1)
830 Cordood Parl Ste200, Knoxville, TN 37932-3353
Tel.: (865) 218-8500
Web Site: http://www.dfamilk.com
Sales Range: $10-24.9 Million
Emp.: 25
Milk Marketing Cooperative
N.A.I.C.S.: 459110
Bob Shipley (Area Mgr)
John Bebermeyer (Dir-Ops)

Western Area Council (1)
170 N Maple Ste 106, Corona, CA 92880
Tel.: (951) 493-4900
Web Site:
    http://www.dairyfarmersofamerica.com
Sales Range: $10-24.9 Million
Emp.: 15
Milk Marketing Cooperative
N.A.I.C.S.: 813410
Denise Rodenbaugh (CEO)

DAIRY FEEDS INC.
1901 NW 9th St, Okeechobee, FL 34972
Tel.: (863) 763-0258
Sales Range: $10-24.9 Million
Emp.: 5
Feed Premixes
N.A.I.C.S.: 311119
Louis E. Larson Jr. (Pres)

DAIRY FRESH FARMS INC.
9636 Blomberg St SW, Olympia, WA 98512
Tel.: (360) 357-9411
Web Site:
    https://www.dairyfreshfarms.com
Sales Range: $10-24.9 Million
Emp.: 20
Dairy Products
N.A.I.C.S.: 424440
Jerry Clark (Owner)
Deborah Eide (Mgr-Accts Revceivable)

DAIRY FRESH FOODS, INC.
21405 Trolley Industrial Dr, Taylor, MI 48180-1811
Tel.: (313) 295-6300
Web Site:
    http://www.dairyfreshfoods.com
Year Founded: 1933
Sales Range: $100-124.9 Million
Emp.: 200
Whslr of Dairy Products & Frozen Foods
N.A.I.C.S.: 424430
Alan Must (Co-Pres)
Joel Must (Co-Pres)
James A. Mrowka (Controller)

DAIRY ONE COOPERATIVE INC.
730 Warren Rd, Ithaca, NY 14850
Tel.: (607) 257-1272
Web Site: https://www.dairyone.com
Rev.: $17,600,000
Emp.: 270
Support Activities for Animal Production
N.A.I.C.S.: 115210
Beverley Whittier (Acct Mgr)
Jamie Zimmerman (Gen Mgr)

DAIRY SERVICE & MANUFACTURING INC.
4630 W Florissant Ave, Saint Louis, MO 63115
Tel.: (952) 941-2944
Web Site: http://www.dsiprocess.com
Sales Range: $10-24.9 Million
Emp.: 41

Food Product Manufacturing Machinery
N.A.I.C.S.: 333241
Jack Luechtefeld (Pres)
Charlie Siebert (Controller)
Gary Rinck (VP)
Scott Studley (Acct Mgr)
Gordon Gosejohan (Acct Mgr)
John Dougherty (Acct Mgr)
Georgia Pilla (Mgr-Customer Svcs)

DAIRY, LLC
3801 Parkwood Blvd Ste 300, Frisco, TX 75034
Tel.: (214) 360-0061
Web Site: https://www.dairy.com
Year Founded: 2000
Sales Range: $1-9.9 Million
Emp.: 52
Dairy Industry Software Development Services
N.A.I.C.S.: 541511
Ryan Mertes (Chief Solutions Officer)

Subsidiaries:

Data Specialists, Inc. (1)
1021 Proctor Dr, Elkhorn, WI 53121
Tel.: (262) 723-5726
Web Site: http://www.dataspecialists.com
Computers, Peripherals, And Software, Nsk
N.A.I.C.S.: 423430

Ever.Ag Corporation (1)
4400 State Hwy 121 Ste 520, Lewisville, TX 75056
Tel.: (214) 360-0061
Web Site: https://www.ever.ag
Software Publr
N.A.I.C.S.: 513210
Scott Sexton (CEO)

Subsidiary (Domestic):

Prairie Systems, LLC (2)
1803 Hwy Blvd, Spencer, IA 51301
Tel.: (712) 580-3311
Web Site: http://www.prairiesystems.com
Emp.: 6
Software Development Services
N.A.I.C.S.: 541511

DAIRY-MIX, INC.
3020 46th Ave N, Saint Petersburg, FL 33714-3863
Tel.: (727) 525-6101
Web Site: https://www.dairymix.com
Year Founded: 1948
Sales Range: $10-24.9 Million
Emp.: 20
Ice Cream Mix Producer
N.A.I.C.S.: 311520
Edward Coryn (Pres)
John Coryn (VP)
Ann Coryn (Sec)

DAIRYAMERICA, INC.
7815 N Palm Ave Ste 250, Fresno, CA 93711
Tel.: (559) 251-0992
Web Site:
    http://www.dairyamerica.com
Sales Range: $10-24.9 Million
Emp.: 20
Production of Dairy Products
N.A.I.C.S.: 424430
Jean McAbee (Controller)
Dan Block (CEO)

DAIRYFOOD USA INCORPORATED
2819 County Rd F, Blue Mounds, WI 53517
Tel.: (608) 437-5598
Web Site:
    http://www.dairyfoodusa.com
Rev.: $24,200,000
Emp.: 100
Cheese Mfr
N.A.I.C.S.: 311513

Dan Culligan (Pres)
Judd Batterman (Controller)

DAIRYLAND POWER COOPERATIVE
3200 E Ave S, La Crosse, WI 54601-0218
Tel.: (608) 788-4000
Web Site: http://www.dairynet.com
Year Founded: 1941
Sales Range: $300-349.9 Million
Emp.: 586
Generation & Transmission of Electrical Energy
N.A.I.C.S.: 221118
Mary Lund (Exec VP-HR)
Brian Rude (VP-External & Member Rels)
Phil Moilien (CFO & VP)
Robert Palmberg (VP-Strategic Plng)
John Carr (VP-Strategic Plng)
Ben Porath (VP-Power Delivery)
Jennifer Shilling (Mgr-Govt Rels)
Brent Ridge (Pres & CEO)
Ed Gullickson (Chm)

DAIRYLAND SEED CO. INC.
PO Box 958, West Bend, WI 53095-0958
Tel.: (262) 626-3080
Web Site:
    http://www.dairylandseed.com
Rev.: $22,900,000
Emp.: 35
Developer & Supplier of Corn, Soybeans & Alfalfa Seeds
N.A.I.C.S.: 111191
Barry Sutton (Reg Mgr)
Tom Strachota (CEO & Gen Mgr)
Gary Freiburger (Reg Mgr)
Fred Reckner (Controller)

DAIRYMAN'S SUPPLY COMPANY INC.
Us Hwy 45 S, Mayfield, KY 42066
Tel.: (270) 247-5642
Web Site:
    http://www.dairymanssupply.com
Year Founded: 1925
Sales Range: $10-24.9 Million
Emp.: 90
Provider of Building Materials
N.A.I.C.S.: 423310
Gregg Cook (VP)

Subsidiaries:

Dairyman's Supply Company Inc. (1)
2816 S Jean Ave, Inverness, FL 34450-7456
Tel.: (352) 726-7204
Lumber, Plywood & Millwork
N.A.I.C.S.: 423390

Dairymans Supply Company Inc. (1)
407 McElroy Ave, Gadsden, AL 35903-1174 (100%)
Tel.: (256) 492-9560
Sales Range: $10-24.9 Million
Emp.: 43
Provider of Metals Service Centers & Offices
N.A.I.C.S.: 423510
Mike Kilcoyne (Gen Mgr)

DAISY BRAND INC.
12750 Merit Dr Ste 600, Dallas, TX 75251
Tel.: (972) 726-0800
Web Site:
    https://www.daisybrand.com
Year Founded: 1917
Rev.: $70,000,000
Emp.: 60
Milk Processing Services
N.A.I.C.S.: 311511
Debra Storgaard (Supvr-Acctg)

DAKIN DAIRY FARMS, INC.

30771 Betts Rd, Myakka City, FL 34251
Tel.: (941) 322-2802
Web Site:
https://www.dakindairyfarms.com
Sales Range: $1-9.9 Million
Emp.: 70
Dairy Products
N.A.I.C.S.: 112120
Karen Dakin *(Owner)*
Scott Cagle *(Gen Mgr)*

DAKOTA BROTHERS INC.

10122 Bandley Dr, Cupertino, CA 95014
Tel.: (408) 255-2648
Web Site:
http://www.marinafoodusa.com
Sales Range: $10-24.9 Million
Emp.: 110
Grocery Stores, Independent
N.A.I.C.S.: 445110

DAKOTA COMMUNITY BAN-SHARES, INC.

609 Main St, Hebron, ND 58638
Tel.: (701) 878-4416   ND
Web Site:
http://www.dakotacommunity
bank.com
Year Founded: 1994
Emp.: 162
Bank Holding Company
N.A.I.C.S.: 551111
Dale Pahlke *(Pres & CEO)*
Stan Sayler *(Exec VP)*

Subsidiaries:

Dakota Community Bank & Trust, N.A.   (1)
609 Main St, Hebron, ND 58638
Tel.: (701) 878-4416
Web Site:
http://www.dakotacommunitybank.com
Sales Range: $25-49.9 Million
Commercial Banking
N.A.I.C.S.: 522110
Dale Pahlke *(Pres & CEO)*
Heather Haag *(Acct Exec)*
Stan Sayler *(Exec VP)*

DAKOTA CRAFT INC.

2135 Dakota Craft Dr, Rapid City, SD 57701
Tel.: (605) 341-6100
Web Site: http://www.dakotacraft.com
Sales Range: $10-24.9 Million
Emp.: 100
Lumber, Plywood & Millwork
N.A.I.C.S.: 423310
Brett McManigal *(Gen Mgr)*

DAKOTA CREEK INDUSTRIES, INC.

820 4th St, Anacortes, WA 98221
Tel.: (360) 293-9575
Web Site:
http://www.dakotacreek.com
Rev.: $17,500,000
Emp.: 250
Boat Building
N.A.I.C.S.: 336612
Michael Nelson *(Founder & VP)*
Lynne Vorhees *(Mgr-Payroll)*
Aga Samsel *(Mgr-HR)*

DAKOTA DRUG, INC.

28 Main St N, Minot, ND 58703-3104
Tel.: (701) 852-2141   ND
Web Site: http://www.dakdrug.com
Sales Range: $75-99.9 Million
Emp.: 85
Mfr & Retailer of Drugs & Drug Proprietaries
N.A.I.C.S.: 424210

Ted Scherr *(Pres & Gen Mgr)*
Jim Edwards *(CEO)*

DAKOTA ELECTRIC ASSOCIATION

4300 220th St W, Farmington, MN 55024
Tel.: (651) 463-6201   MN
Web Site:
http://www.dakotaelectric.com
Year Founded: 1937
Rev.: $204,037,000
Assets: $335,802,000
Liabilities: $162,651,000
Net Worth: $173,151,000
Earnings: $7,027,000
Fiscal Year-end: 12/31/18
Electric Services; Electric Distribution Cooperative
N.A.I.C.S.: 221122
Greg Miller *(Pres & CEO)*
Jim Sheldon *(Treas)*
Paul Trapp *(Sec)*
David Jones *(Chm)*
Paul Bakken *(Vice Chm)*

Subsidiaries:

Midwest Energy Services, Inc.   (1)
4300 W 220th St, Farmington, MN
55024   (100%)
Tel.: (651) 463-6212
Sales Range: $10-24.9 Million
Emp.: 10
Holding Company
N.A.I.C.S.: 238210
Greg Miller *(Pres)*

Subsidiary (Domestic):

Energy Alternatives, Inc.   (2)
17685 Juniper Path Ste 301, Lakeville, MN
55044-9821   (100%)
Tel.: (651) 460-6100
Web Site: http://www.energyalternative.com
Standby Generator Sales & Installations
N.A.I.C.S.: 238210

DAKOTA GRANITE COMPANY

48391 150th St, Milbank, SD 57252
Tel.: (605) 432-5580
Web Site: http://www.dakgran.com
Year Founded: 1925
Sales Range: $10-24.9 Million
Emp.: 100
Monuments, Cut Stone & Granite Mfr
N.A.I.C.S.: 327991
Kevin Wright *(Dir-Sls-Intl & Comml)*

DAKOTA KING INC.

3800 W 53rd St, Sioux Falls, SD 57106
Tel.: (605) 361-7714
Sales Range: $25-49.9 Million
Emp.: 500
Fast Food Restaurants
N.A.I.C.S.: 722513
Dieter Maiwald *(Mgr-Projects)*
Mike Leslie *(Dir-Ops)*
Cindy L. Walsh *(Sec)*
Jeffrey Oliver *(CFO)*
Tom Walsh Jr. *(Pres & Treas)*
Thomas P. Walsh Sr. *(VP)*

DAKOTA LAYERS, LLP.

22252 SD Hwy 13, Flandreau, SD 57028
Tel.: (605) 997-2271
Web Site:
https://www.dakotalayers.com
Year Founded: 1999
Sales Range: $10-24.9 Million
Emp.: 60
Egg Producing Services
N.A.I.C.S.: 112330
Scott Ramsdell *(Pres)*

DAKOTA LINE, INC.

11 E Main St, Vermillion, SD 57069

Tel.: (605) 624-5228   SD
Web Site:
https://www.dakotalines.com
Year Founded: 1989
Rev.: $13,000,000
Emp.: 9
Trucking Services
N.A.I.C.S.: 484121
Robert Fields *(Pres)*

DAKOTA MANUFACTURING CO. INC.

323 Quince St, Mitchell, SD 57301
Tel.: (605) 996-5571
Web Site: https://www.traileze.com
Sales Range: $10-24.9 Million
Emp.: 100
Mfr Of Truck Trailers
N.A.I.C.S.: 336212
Brent Hohman *(Reg Mgr-Sls)*
Brian Goergen *(Reg Mgr-Sls)*
Don Huber *(Reg Mgr-Sls)*
Reggie Davenport *(Reg Mgr-Sls)*
Zac Appletoft *(Coord-Parts Sls & Warranty)*
Tim Wermers *(Coord-Parts Sls & Warranty)*
Rick Heying *(Mgr-Parts, Svc & Warranty-TRAIL-EZE)*
Jeff Hruby *(Reg Mgr-Sls)*

Subsidiaries:

TRAIL-EZE Trailers   (1)
1909 S Rowley, Mitchell, SD 57301
Tel.: (605) 996-5571
Web Site: http://www.traileze.com
Mfr of Custom-built Semi-trailers
N.A.I.C.S.: 336212
Armond Dean Oehlerking *(Pres)*
Cynthia Barjun *(VP)*

DAKOTA NEWS INC.

221 S Petro Ave, Sioux Falls, SD 57107
Tel.: (605) 336-3000
Sales Range: $10-24.9 Million
Emp.: 55
Magazines
N.A.I.C.S.: 424920
Terry Bourne *(Pres)*
Gary Widmann *(Owner)*

DAKOTA PLAINS AGRICULTURAL CENTER LLC

41055 282nd St, Parkston, SD 57366
Tel.: (605) 935-6791
Web Site:
http://www.dakotaplains.net
Rev.: $35,000,000
Emp.: 14
Grains
N.A.I.C.S.: 424510
Bill Beukema *(Gen Mgr)*

DAKOTA PLAINS COOPERATIVE

151 9th Ave NW, Valley City, ND 58072
Tel.: (701) 845-0812
Web Site:
http://www.dakotaplains.coop
Year Founded: 1929
Sales Range: $25-49.9 Million
Emp.: 65
Farm Supplies & Diesel Fuel Whlsr
N.A.I.C.S.: 424910
Ken Astrup *(Gen Mgr)*
Gary Wieck *(Mgr-Crop Nutrients)*
Casey Wieck *(Mgr-Safety & Compliance)*
Daniel Olson *(Mgr-Agronomy)*

Subsidiaries:

Dakota Plains
Cooperative-Lisbon   (1)
715 Main St, Lisbon, ND 58054
Tel.: (701) 683-4183

Web Site: http://www.dakotaplains.coop
Sales Range: $10-24.9 Million
Emp.: 6
Farm Supplies, Feed & Fuel Whlsr
N.A.I.C.S.: 424910
Ken Astrup *(Mgr)*

DAKOTA SPECIALTY MILLING COMPANY

4014 15th Ave NW, Fargo, ND 58102
Tel.: (701) 282-9656
Web Site:
https://www.dakotaspecialtymilling.com
Year Founded: 1969
Sales Range: $10-24.9 Million
Emp.: 100
Mfr of Cereal Breakfast Foods
N.A.I.C.S.: 311230
William L. Matthaei *(Pres & CEO)*
Bob Meyer *(Dir-Tech Svcs)*
Brian Sorenson *(VP-Mfg Ops)*
Bob Waters *(Mgr-Mill)*

DAKOTA SUPPLY GROUP INC.

2601 3rd Ave, Fargo, ND 58108
Tel.: (701) 237-9440
Web Site:
http://www.dakotasupplygroup.com
Rev.: $93,311,230
Emp.: 73
Electrical Apparatus & Equipment
N.A.I.C.S.: 423610
Tom Rosendahl *(Pres)*
Todd Eber *(Mgr-East Reg-La Crosse)*
Ryan Tracy *(Mgr-Sls)*
John Gearman *(Mgr-Electrical Segment)*
Malcolm MacDonald *(Mgr-Waterworks Segment)*
Phil Baumel *(Mgr-Plumbing Segment)*
Tracy Koenig *(CIO)*
Brent Rudser *(CFO-Plymouth & Minnesota)*
Mike Meiresonne *(COO)*
Melissa Lunak *(Chief HR Officer)*
Matt Burke *(Mgr-Bozeman)*
Paul Kennedy *(CEO)*
Travis Klitzke *(Mgr-Dickinson)*
Rod Hicks *(VP-Ops)*
Wayne Trosen *(Gen Mgr-North)*
Brandon Swenson *(Mgr-Bismarck)*
T. J. Bedell *(Gen Mgr-Minnesota)*
Brent Moldenhauer *(Mgr-La Crosse)*

Subsidiaries:

MT Waterworks, LLC   (1)
7128 Commercial Ave, Billings, MT 59101
Tel.: (406) 294-4455
Web Site: http://www.mtwaterworks.com
Sales Range: $1-9.9 Million
Emp.: 6
Metal Services & Whslr
N.A.I.C.S.: 423510
Kent Boos *(Branch Mgr)*
Terry Sather *(Office Mgr)*
Carli Boos *(Coord-Office)*

Western Steel & Plumbing Inc.   (1)
901 S 26th St, Bismarck, ND 58504
Tel.: (701) 223-3130
Web Site: http://www.western-steel.com
Rev.: $11,958,998
Emp.: 30
Furnaces, Except Electric & Warm Air
N.A.I.C.S.: 423720
Mike Swanberg *(CEO)*
Todd Blasy *(CFO)*

DAKOTA TUBE INC.

221 Airport Dr, Watertown, SD 57201
Tel.: (605) 882-2156
Web Site:
https://www.dakotatube.com
Year Founded: 1961
Rev.: $20,000,000
Emp.: 210
Hydraulic Tubing Mfr
N.A.I.C.S.: 333998
John Steinbauer *(Pres)*

Dakota Valley Electric Coorperative Inc.—(Continued)

DAKOTA VALLEY ELECTRIC COORPERATIVE INC.
14051 Hwy 13, Milnor, ND 58060
Tel.: (701) 427-5242
Web Site:
http://www.dakotavalley.com
Sales Range: $10-24.9 Million
Emp.: 45
Distr of Electric Power
N.A.I.C.S.: 221122
Craig Rysavy (Mgr-Ops)

DAKOTA WEALTH MANAGEMENT LLC
11376 N Jog Rd Ste 101, Palm Beach Gardens, FL 33418
Tel.: (561) 774-8101
Web Site: http://www.dakotawm.com
Year Founded: 2018
Investment Management, Wealth & Estate Planning & Full-service Tax Planning Firm
N.A.I.C.S.: 523940
Kurt Durrwachter (Mng Dir)
James K. Tonrey (Sr Mng Dir)
Gina K. Bartell (Mng Dir)
Bryan Keller (Chief Strategic Officer)
Peter Raimondi (Founder & CEO)
Greg Horn (Chief Development Officer)

Subsidiaries:

Ledge Wealth Management, Inc. (1)
1637 4th Ave N Ste 110, Sauk Rapids, MN 56379
Tel.: (320) 281-3203
Web Site: http://www.ledgewealth.com
Secondary Market Financing
N.A.I.C.S.: 522299
Kurt Durrwachter (Founder)

Loveless Wealth Management LLC (1)
2615 Saint Johns Ave Ste A, Billings, MT 59102-4663
Tel.: (406) 656-9212
Web Site: http://www.lovelesscapital.com
Investment Advice
N.A.I.C.S.: 523940

Persimmon Capital Management, LP (1)
1777 Sentry Pkwy W Ste 102, Blue Bell, PA 19422-2232
Tel.: (484) 572-0500
Web Site: http://www.persimmoncapital.com
Investment Advice
N.A.I.C.S.: 523940
Gregory Horn (Pres & Mng Partner)

Pineno Levin & Ford Asset Management, Inc. (1)
7204 Glen Forest Dr Ste 103, Richmond, VA 23226-3778
Tel.: (804) 288-3772
Web Site: http://www.pinenolevinford.com
Investment Advice
N.A.I.C.S.: 523940
Francis A. Pineno (Principal)

Stillwater Investment Management, LLC (1)
423 Main St S #E1, Stillwater, MN 55082
Tel.: (651) 275-9380
Web Site: https://www.dakotawm.com
Investment Counseling & Consulting Services
N.A.I.C.S.: 523940

DALACO MATERIALS LLC
4805 Hamilton Middletown Rd, Hamilton, OH 45011
Tel.: (513) 893-5483
Web Site: http://www.dalaco.com
Year Founded: 1986
Sales Range: $10-24.9 Million
Emp.: 40
Concrete Building Products Whslr
N.A.I.C.S.: 423320

Mike Salyers (Pres)
Dane Margrume (Mgr-Sls)

DALAND CORPORATION
9313 E 34th St N Ste 100, Wichita, KS 67226-2638
Tel.: (316) 681-1081
Web Site: http://www.dalandcorp.com
Rev.: $12,320,014
Emp.: 35
Pizzeria Chain
N.A.I.C.S.: 722513
Dee Custer (Sr Mgr-Risk)
Mark Rucas (Sr Dir-Field Sys)
Dale Wiggins (Chm)

Subsidiaries:

Mackinaw Food Service Corp. (1)
9313 E 34th St N Ste 100, Wichita, KS 67226-2638
Tel.: (316) 681-1081
Sales Range: $1-9.9 Million
Pizzeria Chain
N.A.I.C.S.: 722513
Larry Payne (Chm)
Darcy Smith (Office Mgr)

Peru Pizza Co. Inc. (1)
9313 E 34th St N Ste 100, Wichita, KS 67226-2638
Tel.: (316) 681-1081
Rev.: $10,375,661
Emp.: 13
Pizzaria Resturant Chains
N.A.I.C.S.: 722513
William Walsh (Pres)

Virginia Pizza Co., Inc. (1)
9313 E 34th St N Ste 100, Wichita, KS 67226-2638
Tel.: (316) 681-1081
Pizzeria Chain
N.A.I.C.S.: 722513
William Walsh (Pres)

DALB, INC.
73 Industrial Blvd, Kearneysville, WV 25430
Tel.: (304) 725-0300
Web Site: https://www.dalb.com
Rev.: $11,300,000
Emp.: 154
Commercial Printing
N.A.I.C.S.: 323111
Linda Barr (Sec)
Kevin Steeley (Pres)
Cathy Windsor (Mgr-Fin)
Brent Yost (CFO)

DALBANI CORPORATION
4225 NW 72nd Ave, Miami, FL 33166
Tel.: (305) 716-1016
Web Site: http://www.dalbani.com
Sales Range: $10-24.9 Million
Emp.: 15
Electric Household Appliances
N.A.I.C.S.: 423620
Mohammed Imad Dalbani (Pres)

DALCO INDUSTRIES INC.
3730 Salem St, Denver, CO 80239
Tel.: (303) 371-3950
Web Site:
http://www.dalcoindustries.com
Sales Range: $25-49.9 Million
Emp.: 65
Expansion Joints Mfr
N.A.I.C.S.: 332312
Ramsey Cross (Mgr-Sls)

Subsidiaries:

Dalco Industries Inc. (1)
3730 Salem St, Denver, CO 80239 (100%)
Tel.: (303) 371-3950
Web Site: http://www.dalco.com
Sales Range: $10-24.9 Million
Emp.: 7
Metal Doors, Sash & Trim
N.A.I.C.S.: 332321
David L. Dickerson Sr. (Pres)

Teton Steel Co. (1)
5008 Paige St, Casper, WY 82604
Tel.: (307) 234-0715
Sales Range: $1-9.9 Million
Steel Mfrs
N.A.I.C.S.: 331110

DALCO METALS, INC.
857 Walworth Ave, Walworth, WI 53184-9595
Tel.: (262) 275-6175
Web Site:
https://www.dalcometals.com
Rev.: $20,500,000
Emp.: 40
Metal Service Centers & Other Metal Merchant Whslr
N.A.I.C.S.: 423510
James Conners (VP)
John Ring (Treas)
Bill Ring (Pres)

DALE & MAXEY, INC.
915 6th Ave S, Nashville, TN 37203
Tel.: (615) 254-3454
Web Site: http://www.daleinc.net
Year Founded: 1947
Sales Range: $10-24.9 Million
Emp.: 62
Lumber Product Whslr
N.A.I.C.S.: 423310
Andy Dale (VP)
Jackson Dale (Mgr-Sls)

DALE CARNEGIE & ASSOCI-ATES, INC.
290 Motor Pkwy, Hauppauge, NY 11788-5105
Tel.: (631) 415-9300 NY
Web Site:
http://www.dalecarnegie.com
Year Founded: 1912
Sales Range: $50-74.9 Million
Emp.: 100
Business Courses & Seminars; Sales & Communication Training
N.A.I.C.S.: 611699
Michael A. Crom (Chief Learning Officer)
Donna Dale Carnegie (Owner & Chm)
Joseph Hart (Pres & CEO)
Kara Hankins (Mgr-Pub Sls-Nashville)
Christine Buscarino (CMO)

Subsidiaries:

DC Berlin Training GbR (1)
Friedrichstrasse 200, 10117, Berlin, Germany
Tel.: (49) 3376 222 8555
Web Site: http://www.berlin.dalecarnegie.de
Professional Training Services
N.A.I.C.S.: 611430

DCD Training GmbH (1)
Stefan-George-Ring 24, 81929, Munich, Germany
Tel.: (49) 180 20 40 400
Web Site: http://www.dalecarnegie.de
Emp.: 9
Professional Training Services
N.A.I.C.S.: 611430

Dale Carnegie Denmark (1)
Ravnsgaardsvej 109, DK 7000, Fredericia, Denmark
Tel.: (45) 70107050
Web Site: http://www.dalecarnegie.dk
Leadership Training Services
N.A.I.C.S.: 611430
Thomas Dybvad (CEO)
Rikke Illum (Mgr-PR)
Ole Stampe (Accountant)
Annette Thiesen (Partner)

Dale Carnegie Institute of Long Island (1)
290 Motor Pkwy, Hauppauge, NY 11788-5105 (100%)
Tel.: (631) 435-2800
Web Site: http://www.dalecarnegie.com

Sales Range: $10-24.9 Million
Emp.: 80
Training of Self Development
N.A.I.C.S.: 611699
David Fagiano (COO)
Christopher Noonan (CFO)
Peter V. Handal (Chm & CEO)

DALE EARNHARDT, INC.
1675 Dale Earnhardt Hwy 3, Mooresville, NC 28115
Tel.: (704) 662-8000 NC
Web Site:
http://www.daleearnhardtinc.com
Year Founded: 1980
Sales Range: $10-24.9 Million
Emp.: 150
Professional Motorsports Organization
N.A.I.C.S.: 711211
Teresa Earnhardt (Pres & CEO)
Melanie Whitfield (Coord-Mktg)
Pamela Middlemiss (Coord-Safety)

DALE GROUP INC.
30 Vreeland Rd, Florham Park, NJ 07932
Tel.: (973) 377-7000
Web Site: http://www.dalegroup.com
Rev.: $10,000,000
Emp.: 35
Insurance Agents, Brokers & Service
N.A.I.C.S.: 524210
Lee Jorge (Founder)
Maureen Cupo (VP-Ops & HR)
Charles Sanfilippo (VP-Bus Dev)
Gary Vicaro (Mgr-Acct)
Sarah Eshiwani (Dir-Media Mktg)

DALE INCORPORATED
915 6th Ave S, Nashville, TN 37203
Tel.: (615) 254-3454
Web Site: http://www.daleinc.net
Year Founded: 1947
Sales Range: $10-24.9 Million
Emp.: 50
Residential & Commercial New Construction & Remodeling Contractors
N.A.I.C.S.: 238190

DALE K. EHRHART, INC.
100 W Venice Ave Ste A, Venice, FL 34285
Tel.: (941) 485-8220 FL
Web Site: http://www.dkeinc.com
Year Founded: 1950
Sales Range: $800-899.9 Million
Emp.: 8
Investment Banking & Advisory Services
N.A.I.C.S.: 523150
Byron A. Sanders (Pres)
Michael T. Hartley (Chm & CEO)
Michael W. Hartley (VP-Ops)
James H. Moore (VP)
Robert C. Keyser (VP)
Brian Pope (VP-Private Client Grp)

DALE KIRK AUTOMOTIVE
2955 N Main St, Crossville, TN 38555-5411
Tel.: (931) 484-5151
Web Site: https://www.davekirk.com
Sales Range: $10-24.9 Million
Emp.: 76
New Car Whslr
N.A.I.C.S.: 441110
Charlie Strayer (Mgr-Fixed Ops)

DALE L PRENTICE CO.
26511 Harding St, Oak Park, MI 48237
Tel.: (248) 399-5500
Web Site: http://www.prenticeco.com
Sales Range: $10-24.9 Million
Emp.: 32

Distr of Valves & Fittings
N.A.I.C.S.: 423830
Lawrence M. Prentice *(Pres)*
Mike Prentice *(VP-Ops & Controller)*
Jane Sondergaard *(Gen Mgr)*

DALE MEDICAL PRODUCTS INC.
7 Cross St, Plainville, MA 02762
Tel.: (508) 695-9316
Web Site: http://www.dalemed.com
Sales Range: $10-24.9 Million
Emp.: 110
Surgical Appliances & Supplies
N.A.I.C.S.: 339113
John W. Brezack *(Pres)*

DALE ROGERS TRAINING CENTER, INC.
2501 N Utah Ave, Oklahoma City, OK 73107
Tel.: (405) 946-4489   OK
Web Site: https://www.drtc.org
Year Founded: 2004
Sales Range: $10-24.9 Million
Emp.: 760
Disabled People Assistance Services
N.A.I.C.S.: 624120
Connie Thrash McGoodwin *(Exec Dir)*
Gayle McGuire *(Dir-HR)*
Lillian Hobbs *(CFO)*
Mark Woods *(COO)*
Bob Hale *(Sec)*
Cheryl Moore *(VP)*
Frank Stone *(Treas)*
Rebecca Cook *(Pres)*

DALE TIFFANY INC
14765 Firestone Blvd, La Mirada, CA 90638
Tel.: (714) 739-2700
Web Site: https://www.daletiffany.com
Sales Range: $10-24.9 Million
Emp.: 25
Floor, Bedroom & Desk Lamps
N.A.I.C.S.: 423220
Ye Chung *(Pres)*

DALE TILE COMPANY
6007 Cullitan Way, Minnetonka, MN 55345
Tel.: (763) 488-1880   MN
Year Founded: 1930
Sales Range: $10-24.9 Million
Emp.: 5
Stone & Tile Product Mfr
N.A.I.C.S.: 327991
Alan Dale *(Pres & CEO)*

Subsidiaries:

Pollux Manufacturing, Inc.   (1)
650 Taft St NE, Minneapolis, MN 55413
Tel.: (612) 362-4565
Sales Range: $1-9.9 Million
Stone Countertop Mfr
N.A.I.C.S.: 327991

DALE WILLEY PONTIAC-CADILLAC
2840 Iowa St, Lawrence, KS 66046
Tel.: (785) 843-5200
Web Site: http://www.dalewilleyauto.com
Rev.: $13,400,000
Emp.: 60
New & Used Automobiles
N.A.I.C.S.: 441110
Greg Maurer *(Pres)*

DALES AUTO MART INC.
13474 Harbor Blvd, Garden Grove, CA 92843
Tel.: (714) 534-3200
Web Site: http://www.dalesautomart.com

Sales Range: $10-24.9 Million
Emp.: 2
Automobiles
N.A.I.C.S.: 423110
Dale H. Brown *(Pres)*

DALES TIRE & RETREADING INC.
3200 Cambell St, Rapid City, SD 57701-0109
Tel.: (605) 348-1244
Web Site: https://www.dalestire.com
Sales Range: $10-24.9 Million
Emp.: 60
Tire Recapping
N.A.I.C.S.: 811198
Dale H. Rovere *(Pres)*
Brennan Pruss *(CFO & Gen Mgr)*

DALEVILLE CHRISTIAN CHURCH DAY CARE CENTER
PO Box 49, Daleville, IN 47334
Tel.: (765) 378-7722
Web Site: http://www.dalevillechristian.org
Sales Range: $10-24.9 Million
Emp.: 9
Child Care & Development Services
N.A.I.C.S.: 624410
Jill Adkins *(Sec)*
Linnet Stafford *(Chm)*
Steve Selby *(Treas)*

DALEY & ASSOCIATES, LLC.
1 Financial Center 4th Fl, Boston, MA 02111
Tel.: (617) 832-2040
Web Site: https://www.daleyaa.com
Year Founded: 2006
Sales Range: $1-9.9 Million
Emp.: 25
Human Resource Consulting Services
N.A.I.C.S.: 541612
Mike Dale *(Pres)*
Shawn Flaherty *(Partner)*
Christyn Thatcher *(CFO)*
Brian Daley *(Mgr-Contract Staffing Div)*
Alexandra Powell *(Mgr-Life Sciences)*

DALFORT CAPITAL PARTNERS, LLC
3963 Maple Ave Ste 260, Dallas, TX 75219
Tel.: (214) 396-8880   TX
Web Site: http://www.dalfortcapital.com
Privater Equity Firm
N.A.I.C.S.: 523999
Bryan Bailey *(Mng Partner)*

Subsidiaries:

Key Polymer Corporation   (1)
17 Shepard St, Lawrence, MA 01843-1023
Tel.: (978) 683-9411
Web Site: http://www.keypolymer.com
Chemicals Mfr
N.A.I.C.S.: 325998
Robert Baker *(Pres)*

DALHART CONSUMERS FUEL ASSOCIATION INC.
Hwy 87 N, Dalhart, TX 79022-0610
Tel.: (806) 249-5695
Web Site: http://www.dalhartconsumers.com
Sales Range: $25-49.9 Million
Emp.: 48
Grains
N.A.I.C.S.: 424510
Jim T. Turner *(Gen Mgr)*
Tami Buck *(Comptroller)*

DALLAS 1 CORP.

10328 Main St, Thonotosassa, FL 33592
Tel.: (813) 986-1922
Web Site: https://www.d1cd.com
Year Founded: 1985
Sales Range: $10-24.9 Million
Emp.: 130
Sewer Line & Related Structure Construction Services
N.A.I.C.S.: 237110
Bart Azzarelli *(Founder & CEO)*
Jan Azzarelli *(Treas & Sec)*
Paul Lancaster *(Chief Ministry Officer)*
Tim Smith *(VP)*
B. J. Azzarelli *(Pres)*
Shirley Wiley *(Asst VP)*

DALLAS AREA RAPID TRANSIT INC.
1401 Pacific Ave, Dallas, TX 75202-2714
Tel.: (214) 749-3278   TX
Web Site: http://www.dart.org
Year Founded: 1983
Sales Range: $75-99.9 Million
Emp.: 3,579
Local & Suburban Transit
N.A.I.C.S.: 485113
Albert J. Bazis *(Dir-Internal Audit)*
Michael C. Hubbell *(VP-Maintenance)*
Doug Douglas *(VP-Mobility Mgmt Svcs)*
Timothy H. McKay *(Exec VP-Growth & Reg Dev)*
John Adler *(VP-Procurement)*
Stephen Salin *(VP-Rail Plng)*
Todd Plesko *(VP-Plng & Dev)*
Scott Carlson *(Gen Counsel)*
Richard Carrizales *(vice Chm)*
Jerry Christian *(Asst Sec)*
Nancy K. Johnson *(Dir-Bd Support Office)*
Nevin Grinnell *(CMO & VP)*
Gary Slagel *(Sec)*
Jesse Oliver *(Deputy Exec Dir)*
Michael Miles *(VP-Govt Rels)*
Carol Wise *(Exec VP)*
Tim Newby *(VP-Transportation)*
David Schulze *(VP-Policy & Strategy)*
Michael Muhammed *(VP-Diversity & Innovative Svcs)*
Joseph G. Costello *(Sr VP-Fin)*
Nicole O. Fontayne *(CIO & VP)*
Maureen McCole *(VP-Commuter Rail)*
Cheryl D. Orr *(VP-HR)*
John M. Rhone *(VP-Capital Design & Construction)*
Nicole O. Fontayne-Bardowell *(Chief Admin Officer & Exec VP)*
Gregory Elsborg *(Chief Innovation Officer & VP)*
Bernard Jackson *(COO)*
Nadine S. Lee *(Pres & CEO)*
Michele Wong Krause *(Chm)*
Elizabeth Reich *(CFO)*
Jeamy Molina *(Chief Comm Officer)*

DALLAS CONTAINER CORPORATION
8330 Endicott Ln, Dallas, TX 75227
Tel.: (214) 381-7148
Web Site: http://www.dallascontainer.net
Rev.: $10,000,000
Emp.: 70
Corrugated & Solid Fiber Boxes
N.A.I.C.S.: 322211
Rod Turnipseed *(Pres)*
Mom Paschall *(Mgr-Customer Svc)*

DALLAS COUNTRY CLUB
4155 Mockingbird Ln, Dallas, TX 75205
Tel.: (214) 521-2151   TX

Web Site: https://www.thedallascc.org
Year Founded: 1896
Sales Range: $10-24.9 Million
Emp.: 292
Country Club Operator
N.A.I.C.S.: 713910
J. Kyle Ayers *(CFO)*
G. Michael Thomas *(Gen Mgr)*

DALLAS COUNTY INDIGENT CARE CORPORATION
PO Box 655999, Dallas, TX 75265-5999
Tel.: (214) 947-4581   TX
Year Founded: 2007
Sales Range: $150-199.9 Million
Health Care Srvices
N.A.I.C.S.: 622110
Michael J. Schaefer *(Chm)*
Kathleen Sweeny *(Sec)*

DALLAS COWBOYS FOOTBALL CLUB, LTD.
1 Cowboys Way Ste 100, Frisco, TX 75034
Tel.: (972) 556-9900   TX
Web Site: https://www.dallascowboys.com
Year Founded: 1960
Sales Range: $75-99.9 Million
Emp.: 300
Professional Football Franchise
N.A.I.C.S.: 711211
Charlotte Jones Anderson *(Pres-Charities & Exec VP-Brand Mgmt)*
George Mitchell *(CFO)*
Dave Frey *(Controller)*
Robin Woith *(Sr Dir-Sls & Mktg)*

DALLAS FAN FARES, INC.
5485 Beltline Rd Ste 270, Dallas, TX 75254
Tel.: (972) 239-9969
Web Site: http://www.fanfares.com
Year Founded: 1980
Sales Range: $50-74.9 Million
Emp.: 35
Hospitality Services Including Destination Management & Special Events Planning
N.A.I.C.S.: 711310
Kaye Burkhardt *(Founder & Pres)*
Andra Craven *(VP-Ops)*
Emily Sager *(Sr Acct Mgr)*

DALLAS INDUSTRIES, INC.
103 Park Dr, Troy, MI 48083
Tel.: (248) 583-9400
Web Site: http://www.dallasindustries.com
Year Founded: 1988
Sales Range: $1-9.9 Million
Emp.: 25
Machine Tool (Metal Forming Types) Mfr
N.A.I.C.S.: 333517
Joseph A. Gentilia *(Pres)*
Willie Chacko *(CEO)*
Cliff Bernor *(Chief Engr)*
Dave Laws *(Mgr-Sls)*
Warren Gideon *(Mgr-Sls)*
Warren Hawley *(Plant Mgr)*

Subsidiaries:

Dixie Machine & Fabricating Co.   (1)
11333 Dixie Hwy, Holly, MI 48442
Tel.: (810) 695-3460
Rev.: $4,380,000
Emp.: 20
Fabricated Structural Metal Mfr
N.A.I.C.S.: 332312
Bob Harris *(Owner)*

Dallas Jewish Community Foundation—(Continued)

DALLAS JEWISH COMMUNITY FOUNDATION
12700 Hillcrest Rd Ste 201, Dallas, TX 75230
Tel.: (214) 615-9351   TX
Web Site: https://www.djcf.org
Year Founded: 1999
Sales Range: $10-24.9 Million
Emp.: 11
Community Action Services
N.A.I.C.S.: 813410
Jerry Blair *(CFO)*
Cynthia P. Hendricks *(Sr Dir-Res & Controller)*
Paula Shoemaker *(Mgr-Fundholder Svcs)*

DALLAS MARKET CENTER COMPANY
2100 N Stemmons Freeway 1000, Dallas, TX 75207
Tel.: (214) 655-6100
Web Site: http://www.dallasmarketcenter.com
Sales Range: $100-124.9 Million
Emp.: 200
Commercial & Industrial Building Operation
N.A.I.C.S.: 531120
Cindy Morris *(Pres & CEO)*
Amy Galindo *(VP-Market Svcs)*
Babs Blair *(Dir-Leasing)*
Laura Van Zeyl *(VP-Lighting Tech Dev & Mktg)*
Nicole Bowling *(Editor-in-Chief-Residential Lighting & Home Fashion Forecast)*
Kristina Johnson *(VP-Tradeshows)*
Penni Barton *(Exec VP-Mktg)*
Joan Ulrich *(Exec VP-Leasing)*
Kelly Bristol *(VP-Trade Show Bus Dev)*

DALLAS MAVERICKS
The Pavilion 2909 Taylor St, Dallas, TX 75226
Tel.: (214) 747-6287
Web Site: http://www.mavs.com
Year Founded: 1980
Sales Range: $100-124.9 Million
Emp.: 100
Professional Basketball Team
N.A.I.C.S.: 711211
George Killebrew *(Sr VP-Corp Sponsorships)*
Floyd Jahner *(CFO & VP)*
Buddy Pittman *(Sr VP-HR)*
Donnie Nelson *(Pres-Basketball Ops & Gen Mgr)*
George Prokos *(VP-Ticket Sls & Svc)*
Steve Letson *(VP-Ops & Arena Dev)*
Mark Cuban *(Owner)*
Keith Grant *(Asst Gen Mgr)*
Sarah Melton *(Dir-Comm-Basketball)*
Scott Tomlin *(Mgr-Basketball Comm)*
Derek Earls *(Dir-Security)*
Mike Procopio *(Dir-Player Dev)*
Cynthia G. Marshall *(CEO)*

DALLAS RETIREMENT VILLAGE
377 NW Jasper St, Dallas, OR 97338
Tel.: (503) 623-5581   OR
Web Site: https://www.dallasretirementvillage.com
Year Founded: 1947
Sales Range: $10-24.9 Million
Emp.: 280
Community Retirement Care Services
N.A.I.C.S.: 623311
Lavonne Wilson *(Chm)*

DALLAS SYMPHONY ASSOCIATION INC.

2301 Flora St, Dallas, TX 75201
Tel.: (214) 692-0203
Web Site: http://www.dallassymphony.com
Sales Range: $25-49.9 Million
Emp.: 68
Symphony Orchestra
N.A.I.C.S.: 711130
Jaap van Zweden *(Dir-Music)*
Joshua Habermann *(Dir-Dallas Symphony Chorus)*

DALLAS TOURISM PUBLIC IMPROVEMENT DISTRICT
325 N Saint Paul St Ste 700, Dallas, TX 75201
Tel.: (214) 571-1005   TX
Web Site: http://www.dtpid.com
Year Founded: 2012
Sales Range: $10-24.9 Million
Tourism & Convention Bureau
N.A.I.C.S.: 561591
Brad Kent *(Chief Sales Officer)*
Mark Woelffer *(Sec)*
Fred Euler *(Chm)*
Harold Rapoza *(Vice Chm & Treas)*

DALLO & CO. INC.
5075 Federal Blvd, San Diego, CA 92102
Tel.: (619) 527-3385
Year Founded: 1981
Sales Range: $50-74.9 Million
Emp.: 180
Grocery Stores
N.A.I.C.S.: 445110
Mike Dallo *(Pres)*
Terrie Huckins *(Controller)*

DALMAC CONSTRUCTION PARTNERS LTD.
600 S. Sherman St Ste 124, Richardson, TX 75081
Tel.: (972) 234-0700
Year Founded: 1988
Rev.: $250,000,000
Emp.: 200
Nonresidential Construction
N.A.I.C.S.: 236220
Fred Bennett *(VP)*

Subsidiaries:

DalMac Development Corp.   (1)
111 W Spring Valley Rd, Richardson, TX 75081
Tel.: (972) 275-3400
Rev.: $20,100,000
Emp.: 110
Commercial & Office Building, New Construction
N.A.I.C.S.: 236220

DALMATIAN FIRE INC.
5670 W 73rd St, Indianapolis, IN 46278
Tel.: (317) 299-3889
Web Site: https://www.dalmatianfire.net
Sales Range: $10-24.9 Million
Emp.: 75
Fire Sprinkler System Installation
N.A.I.C.S.: 238220
Jon Ackley *(Pres)*

DALMATIAN PRESS LLC
113 Seaboard Ln Ste C 250, Franklin, TN 37067
Tel.: (615) 370-9922
Web Site: http://www.bendonpub.com
Sales Range: $10-24.9 Million
Emp.: 80
Children's Book Publishers
N.A.I.C.S.: 513130
Ben Ferguson *(Owner)*

DALRYMPLE HOLDING CORP.

2105 S Broadway, Pine City, NY 14871
Tel.: (607) 737-6200
Web Site: http://www.dalrymplegravel.com
Emp.: 120
Heavy Highway & Street Construction Services
N.A.I.C.S.: 237310
Paul Collins *(VP-Admin)*

DALSON FOODS INC.
642 Brakke Dr, Hudson, WI 54016-7968
Tel.: (715) 381-1043   MN
Year Founded: 1980
Sales Range: $10-24.9 Million
Emp.: 5
Trading of Packaged Meat
N.A.I.C.S.: 424470
Martin J. Ryan *(Pres & CEO)*

DALTON BEARING SERVICE, INC.
PO Box 1363, Dalton, GA 30722
Tel.: (706) 226-2022
Web Site: http://www.daltonbearing.com
Year Founded: 1946
Sales Range: $10-24.9 Million
Emp.: 25
Industrial Supplies Whslr
N.A.I.C.S.: 423840
Gerry Lewis *(Owner & Pres)*

DALTON CARPET ONE FLOOR & HOME
3690 Atlanta Hwy, Athens, GA 30606
Tel.: (706) 353-0547
Web Site: https://www.daltoncarpetone.com
Year Founded: 1978
Emp.: 200
Hardwoods, Carpets & Flooring Sales
N.A.I.C.S.: 449121
Mike R. Blanton *(Owner, Pres & CEO)*
J.R. Allred *(COO)*
Mike Boyd *(Sls Mgr-Retail & Comml)*
Lee Stinchcomb *(Controller & Mgr)*
Keith Guest *(Mgr-Customer Svc)*

DALTON INVESTMENTS LLC
1601 Cloverfield Blvd Ste 5050 N, Santa Monica, CA 90404
Tel.: (424) 231-9100
Web Site: https://www.daltoninvestments.com
Year Founded: 1998
Sales Range: $75-99.9 Million
Emp.: 37
Investment Management Service
N.A.I.C.S.: 551112
Steven D. Persky *(Co-Founder & COO)*
Gifford Combs *(Mng Dir & Portfolio Mgr-Equities-Global)*
Belita Ong *(CEO)*
Rory Donald *(VP-Legal & Compliance Counsel)*
Janet Hunpadongrat *(VP-Fin & Controller)*
Erin Lavelle *(CFO)*
Bart Maeda *(Mng Dir-Client Relationships)*
James B. Rosenwald III *(Co-Chm, Mng Partner & Portfolio Mgr)*

DALTON PETROLEUM INC.
206 W Washington St, Hayti, MO 63851
Tel.: (573) 359-0130
Sales Range: $10-24.9 Million
Emp.: 23
Petroleum Terminal

N.A.I.C.S.: 424710
Neal A. Gibbons Sr. *(Pres)*

DALTON TRUCKING INC.
13560 Whittram Ave, Fontana, CA 92335
Tel.: (909) 823-0663
Web Site: https://www.daltontrucking.com
Rev.: $29,342,084
Emp.: 295
Local Trucking without Storage
N.A.I.C.S.: 484110
Terry Klenske *(Pres)*
Matt Klenske *(VP-Lowbed Flatbed Div)*
Jim Swegles *(Mgr-Asset)*
Al Leon *(Mgr-Compliance)*

DALTON'S BEST MAID PRODUCTS INC.
1400/1401 S Riverside Dr, Fort Worth, TX 76104-5840
Tel.: (817) 335-5494   TX
Web Site: http://www.bestmaidproducts.com
Year Founded: 1926
Sales Range: $25-49.9 Million
Emp.: 350
Mfr of Pickles, Sauces & Salad Dressings
N.A.I.C.S.: 311421
Gary Dalton *(Chm & CEO)*
Brian Dalton *(Pres)*
Paula Clay *(Controller)*

DALY COMPUTERS INC.
22521 Gateway Ctr Dr, Clarksburg, MD 20871
Tel.: (301) 670-0381
Web Site: http://www.daly.com
Year Founded: 1987
Sales Range: $25-49.9 Million
Emp.: 110
Computer Terminals Mfr & Distr
N.A.I.C.S.: 334118
Diane Levant *(Mgr-Mktg)*
Mike Farmer *(Engr-Customer)*
Paul Hill *(Engr-Sys)*
David Whipp *(Project Mgr)*

DALYN CORPORATION
2386 Abutment Rd Whitfield, Dalton, GA 30721
Tel.: (706) 277-2909
Web Site: http://www.dalyn.com
Year Founded: 1979
Sales Range: $10-24.9 Million
Rugs Mfr & Distr
N.A.I.C.S.: 423220
William L. Adams *(CEO)*
Judith S. Adams *(CFO & Sec)*

DAMAGE CONTROL, INC.
16655 W Glendale Dr, New Berlin, WI 53151
Tel.: (414) 672-3409   WI
Web Site: http://www.damage-control.com
Year Founded: 1992
Sales Range: $10-24.9 Million
Emp.: 30
Restoration Contractor
N.A.I.C.S.: 238990
Eva Zipf-Isenhour *(Exec VP)*
John Ortenblad *(Mgr-Bus Dev)*
Sarah Smith *(Office Mgr & Mgr-HR)*
Paul Winter *(Owner & CEO)*

DAMAGE CONTROL, LLC
422 S Drew St, Mesa, AZ 85210
Tel.: (480) 892-3855   AZ
Web Site: http://www.damagecontrolaz.com
Year Founded: 2002

Sales Range: $10-24.9 Million
Emp.: 85
Emergency & Restoration Services
N.A.I.C.S.: 624230
Sonny Goodman *(Dir-Loss-Western States)*
Tyson Smith *(Dir-Loss-Southwestern Reg)*
Tony Fowler *(Dir-Loss-Natl)*

DAMAR SERVICES, INC.
6067 Decatur Blvd, Indianapolis, IN 46241
Tel.: (317) 856-5201
Web Site: http://www.damar.org
Year Founded: 1967
Continuing Care Retirement Communities
N.A.I.C.S.: 623311
Jim Dalton *(Pres & CEO)*
Shannon Bess *(VP-Community Living & Support Svcs)*
Carla Bill *(VP-Youth Svcs-Admissions & Transitions)*
Donna Stutler *(Dir-Dev)*
Tifini McClyde *(VP-Performance Mgmt)*
Jennifer Maggard *(VP-Outpatient & Behavior Support Svcs)*
Jenny Peters *(VP-Comm & Mktg)*
Brad Linville *(Chm)*
Grant Jenkins *(Vice Chm)*
Stephen D. Price *(Treas)*
Nick Andersen *(Dir-Facilities & Assets)*
Karen Causey *(Dir-Medicaid Grp Homes)*
Erin Crick *(Dir-Education Svcs)*
Dottie Gilliam *(Dir-Dietary Svcs)*
Tammy Henninger *(Dir-Volunteer Resources)*
Arnetta Jackson *(Dir-Bus Initiatives-Community Living & Support Svcs)*
Guenevere Kalal *(Dir-Foster Care Svcs)*
Angel Knapp Reese *(Sr Dir-External Initiatives & Quality Svcs)*
Donnie McCoy *(Dir-Ops)*
Nina Suntzeff *(Dir-Grant Administration)*
Donna Hammock *(Dir-Parent Voices)*
Jesseca Hartman *(Dir-Clinical Ops-ABA Autism Svcs)*
Octavius Molton *(CFO)*

DAMASCUS MOTOR COMPANY INC.
26100 Woodfield Rd, Damascus, MD 20872
Tel.: (301) 253-2151
Web Site: https://www.damascusmotors.com
Sales Range: $10-24.9 Million
Emp.: 50
Car Whslr
N.A.I.C.S.: 441110
H. D. Warfield *(Pres)*

DAMERON ALLOY FOUNDRIES
927 S Santa Fe Ave, Compton, CA 90221
Tel.: (310) 631-5165
Web Site: http://www.dameron.net
Rev.: $10,000,000
Emp.: 170
Commercial Investment Castings
N.A.I.C.S.: 331512
John Dameron *(CEO)*
Roger Duenes *(Mgr-Comml Bus Unit)*
Dave Franco *(Mgr-Comml Bus Unit)*
Andrea Viola *(Mgr-Comml Bus Unit)*
Francisco Montes *(Mgr-Glass Bus Unit)*
Ian Domingo *(Mgr-Sls & Mktg-Global)*

DAMERON HOSPITAL ASSOCIATION
525 W Acacia St, Stockton, CA 95203
Tel.: (209) 944-5550   CA
Web Site: https://www.dameronhospital.org
Year Founded: 1912
Sales Range: $150-199.9 Million
Emp.: 1,177
Health Care Srvices
N.A.I.C.S.: 622110
Bradley Reinke *(Chief Medical Officer & VP-Medical Affairs)*
David Kerrins *(CIO & VP-Info Svcs)*
Chad Davis *(Mgr-Clinical Nurse)*
Maria Villarreal *(Asst Mgr-Clinical)*
Elizabeth Propp *(CFO & VP-Fin)*

DAMES CHEVROLET INC.
525 High St, Pottstown, PA 19464
Tel.: (610) 323-5100   PA
Web Site: http://www.dameschevrolet.com
Year Founded: 1947
Sales Range: $10-24.9 Million
Emp.: 26
Sales of New & Used Automobiles
N.A.I.C.S.: 441110
Gerald W. Dames Sr. *(Pres)*
Gerald W. Dames Jr. *(VP)*
Jerry Dames Jr. *(Gen Mgr)*

DAMSKY PAPER COMPANY
3501 1st Ave N, Birmingham, AL 35222
Tel.: (205) 521-9840
Web Site: http://www.damskypaper.com
Rev.: $14,000,000
Emp.: 28
Industrial & Personal Service Paper Merchant Whslr
N.A.I.C.S.: 424130
Martin D. Damsky *(Pres)*

DAMUTH TRANE
1100 Cavalier Blvd, Chesapeake, VA 23323
Tel.: (757) 558-0200
Web Site: https://www.damuth.com
Year Founded: 1970
Sales Range: $10-24.9 Million
Emp.: 185
Warm Air Heating & Air Conditioning Services
N.A.I.C.S.: 423730
Don R. Damuth *(Chm)*
Clint Damuth *(Pres & Gen Mgr)*
Bill Mitchell *(CFO)*

DAMY CORP.
9353 Seymour Ave, Schiller Park, IL 60176
Tel.: (847) 233-0515
Web Site: http://www.atlasscreensupply.com
Year Founded: 2002
Sales Range: $10-24.9 Million
Emp.: 14
Commercial Screen Printing Services
N.A.I.C.S.: 323113
David Gayton *(Pres)*

DAN A. HUGHES COMPANY
208 E Houston St, Beeville, TX 78102
Tel.: (361) 358-3752
Sales Range: $50-74.9 Million
Emp.: 25
Producer of Crude Petroleum & Natural Gas
N.A.I.C.S.: 211120
Jim Scotten *(Mgr-Acctg)*

DAN CALLAGHAN ENTERPRISES INC.
1301 44th Ave E, Bradenton, FL 34203
Tel.: (941) 751-1577
Web Site: http://www.callaghantire.com
Sales Range: $25-49.9 Million
Emp.: 135
Truck Tires Distr & Retreading
N.A.I.C.S.: 423130
Daniel C. Callaghan *(CEO)*
Todd Severson *(Pres)*

DAN CUMMINS CHEVROLET-BUICK-PONTIAC, INC.
1020 Martin Luther King Jr Blvd, Paris, KY 40361-2210
Tel.: (859) 987-4345
Web Site: http://www.dancummins.com
Sales Range: $25-49.9 Million
Emp.: 175
Car Whslr
N.A.I.C.S.: 441110
Jessica Coleman *(Mgr-Ops)*
Joshua Cummins *(Owner)*
Dusty Cummins *(CEO)*

DAN DEERY MOTOR CO. OF WATERLOO, INC.
3900 Alexandra Dr, Cedar Falls, IA 50613-0099
Tel.: (319) 233-5000
Web Site: http://www.dandeerymotor.com
Sales Range: $10-24.9 Million
Emp.: 40
Car Whslr
N.A.I.C.S.: 441110
Dan Deery *(Owner)*
Blaine Nichols *(Mgr-Svc)*
Jamie Thompson *(Gen Mgr)*
Jeff Zaputil *(Comptroller)*

DAN DEERY TOYOTA
7404 University Ave, Cedar Falls, IA 50613-5026
Tel.: (319) 242-3083
Web Site: https://www.dandeerytoyota.com
Year Founded: 1992
Sales Range: $10-24.9 Million
Emp.: 100
Car Whslr
N.A.I.C.S.: 441110
Brian Jensen *(Mgr-Svc)*
Shane McCollow *(Mgr-Internet Sls)*

DAN HEMM AUTO GROUP
2594 W Michigan St, Sidney, OH 45365
Tel.: (937) 492-8005
Year Founded: 1984
Sales Range: $10-24.9 Million
Emp.: 35
Car Whslr
N.A.I.C.S.: 441110
Scott Crawford *(Gen Mgr)*
Daniel J. Hemm *(Pres)*

DAN PERKINS AUTO GROUP
1 Boston Post Rd, Milford, CT 06460
Tel.: (203) 878-4621
Web Site: http://www.danperkins.com
Sales Range: $25-49.9 Million
Emp.: 30
Holding Company; New & Used Car Dealer
N.A.I.C.S.: 551112
Evan Perkins *(Pres)*

Subsidiaries:

Dan Perkins Leasing Inc.   (1)
1 Boston Post Rd, Milford, CT 06460
Tel.: (203) 878-4621

Web Site: http://www.danperkinssubaru.com
Sales Range: Less than $1 Million
Emp.: 2
Passenger Car Leasing
N.A.I.C.S.: 532112
Danzil S. Perkins *(Pres)*

Dan Perkins Subaru   (1)
1 Boston Post Rd, Milford, CT 06460
Tel.: (203) 878-4621
Web Site: http://www.danperkinssubaru.com
Sales Range: $50-74.9 Million
New & Used Car Dealer
N.A.I.C.S.: 441110
Danzil S. Perkins *(Pres)*
Avrom Sevell *(Gen Mgr)*
Nick Aquilina *(Mgr-Bus)*
Anthony Aveni *(Mgr-Parts)*
Marc Mesidor *(Dir-Svc)*
Paul Dempsey *(Mgr-Used Cars)*
John Correa *(Mgr-Wholesale Parts)*
Gary Seidner *(Mgr-ECommerce)*
Shawn Hayden *(Mgr-New Car Sls)*
Jeff Watkins *(Asst Mgr-Sls)*

DAN PORTER MOTORS INC.
2391 Interstate 94 Business Loop E, Dickinson, ND 58601
Tel.: (701) 227-1272
Web Site: http://www.dpmotors.com
Sales Range: $10-24.9 Million
Emp.: 35
New & Used Automobile & Recreational Vehicle Dealers
N.A.I.C.S.: 441110
Daniel Porter *(Pres)*

DAN RYAN BUILDERS, INC.
64 Thomas Johnson Dr, Frederick, MD 21702
Tel.: (301) 696-0200   MD
Web Site: http://www.danryanbuilders.com
Sales Range: $50-74.9 Million
Emp.: 150
New Construction, Single-Family Houses
N.A.I.C.S.: 236115
Tim Cowan *(Pres-Washington West)*
Ronny Salameh *(COO)*
Paul J. Yeager *(CFO & Sr VP)*
Adam Schueftan *(Pres-Washington Metro)*
Chris Rusch *(Pres-Morgantown)*
Shaun Seydor *(Mgr-Pittsburgh)*
Curt Wegner *(Pres-Charleston)*
Marv McDaris *(Pres-Greenville)*
Edwin Woods *(Pres-South Reg)*

DAN T. MOORE CO.
127 Public Square Suite 2700, Cleveland, OH 44114
Tel.: (216) 771-8444
Web Site: http://www.dantmoore.com
Private Equity Group
N.A.I.C.S.: 523999
Nancy Keene *(CFO)*

Subsidiaries:

Team Wendy, LLC   (1)
17000 Saint Clair Ave, Cleveland, OH 44110
Tel.: (216) 738-2518
Web Site: http://www.teamwendy.com
Sales Range: $1-9.9 Million
Emp.: 33
Mfg Sporting/Athletic Goods
N.A.I.C.S.: 339920
Jose Rizo-Patron *(CEO)*

DAN TOBIN BUICK GMC, INC.
2539 Billingsley Rd, Columbus, OH 43235
Tel.: (614) 889-6300
Web Site: http://www.dantobin.com
Sales Range: $10-24.9 Million
Emp.: 85
Car Whslr
N.A.I.C.S.: 441110

Dan Tobin Buick GMC, Inc.—(Continued)

Jimmy Snyder *(Gen Mgr)*
Dan Tobin *(Pres)*

DAN VADEN CHEVROLET CA-DILLAC

121 Altama Connector, Brunswick, GA 31525
Tel.: (912) 265-3540
Web Site:
   http://www.danvadenchevrolet-cadillac.com
Year Founded: 1995
Sales Range: $10-24.9 Million
Emp.: 60
Car Whslr
N.A.I.C.S.: 441110
Dot Algie *(Principal)*

DAN VALLEY FOODS INC.

615 Kentuck Rd, Danville, VA 24540
Tel.: (434) 792-4311
Web Site: http://www.dvffoods.com
Rev.: $12,000,000
Emp.: 65
Groceries
N.A.I.C.S.: 424410
Donnie H. Stevens *(Pres & CEO)*
William Ray *(VP)*
Christi Oakes *(Controller)*

DAN WILLIAMS COMPANY

1826 Kramer Ln Ste L, Austin, TX 78758
Tel.: (512) 320-1410
Web Site:
   http://www.danwilliamscompany.com
Sales Range: $25-49.9 Million
Emp.: 176
Highway, Street & Bridge Construction Services
N.A.I.C.S.: 237310
Steve Cardwell *(VP)*

DAN WOLF INCORPORATED

1515 W Ogden Ave, Naperville, IL 60540
Tel.: (630) 596-1189
Web Site: http://www.danwolf.com
Sales Range: $25-49.9 Million
Emp.: 75
Holding Company; New & Used Car Dealerships Owner & Operator
N.A.I.C.S.: 551112
Daniel A. Wolf *(Owner & Pres)*

Subsidiaries:

Dan Wolf Motors of Naperville, Inc.   (1)
2480 Aurora Ave, Naperville, IL 60540
Tel.: (630) 570-7900
Web Site: http://www.lexusofnaperville.com
New & Used Car Dealer
N.A.I.C.S.: 441110
Daniel A. Wolf *(Pres)*

Dan Wolf's Chevrolet of Naperville, Inc.   (1)
1515 W Ogden Ave, Naperville, IL 60540
Tel.: (630) 246-4639
Web Site:
   http://www.chevroletofnaperville.com
New & Used Car Dealer
N.A.I.C.S.: 441110

DAN WYLIE'S DREAM ENTERPRISES, INC.

6120 E State Rd 64, Bradenton, FL 34208
Tel.: (941) 748-8889
Web Site: http://www.dreamrvfl.com
Year Founded: 1998
Sales Range: $1-9.9 Million
Emp.: 10
Recreational Vehicle Dealers
N.A.I.C.S.: 441210
Dan Wylie *(Pres)*

DAN'S CEMENT, INC.

29400 25 Mile Rd, Chesterfield, MI 48051
Tel.: (586) 749-9027
Year Founded: 1990
Sales Range: $1-9.9 Million
Emp.: 30
Mfr of Concrete Products
N.A.I.C.S.: 327390
Cora Vollmar *(VP)*

DAN'S CHOCOLATES

289 College St, Burlington, VT 05402
Web Site:
   http://www.danschocolates.com
Year Founded: 1995
Sales Range: $10-24.9 Million
Emp.: 10
Online Chocolate Retailer
N.A.I.C.S.: 445292
Dan Cunningham *(Founder)*

DAN'S FAN CITY INC.

300 Dunbar Ave, Oldsmar, FL 34677
Tel.: (813) 855-7384
Web Site:
   https://www.dansfancity.com
Sales Range: $10-24.9 Million
Emp.: 25
Fans, Electric
N.A.I.C.S.: 449210
Ed Veclooth *(CFO)*
Daniel Hibbeln Jr. *(Pres)*

DAN'S FEED & SEED INC.

240 E 4th St, Perris, CA 92570
Tel.: (951) 657-5111
Web Site:
   https://www.dansfeedandseed.com
Sales Range: $10-24.9 Million
Emp.: 33
Farm Supplies
N.A.I.C.S.: 424910
John Harrison *(Pres)*

DAN'S SUPERMARKET INC.

835 S Washington St Ste 4, Bismarck, ND 58504-5477
Tel.: (701) 258-2127
Web Site:
   http://www.dansupermarket.com
Year Founded: 1949
Sales Range: $50-74.9 Million
Emp.: 800
Provider of Grocery Services
N.A.I.C.S.: 445110
Terrance M. Rockstad *(Chm & CEO)*
Keith Mantz *(VP-Fin)*
Dennis Bosch *(Pres)*

DAN'S SUPREME SUPER MARKETS INC.

474 Fulton Ave, Hempstead, NY 11550-4101
Tel.: (516) 483-2400
Sales Range: $150-199.9 Million
Emp.: 1,000
Grocery Stores
N.A.I.C.S.: 445110
Donald Gross *(Chm)*
Richard Grobman *(Pres & CEO)*
Sam Cardiello *(VP)*
Frank Grobman *(VP)*
Ira Gross *(Treas)*
Frank Condurso *(Dir-Store Opers)*

DAN-ED CORPORATION

PO Box 513, Pottsville, PA 17901-0513
Tel.: (570) 277-6611
Sales Range: $10-24.9 Million
Emp.: 50
Fluid Milk Mfr
N.A.I.C.S.: 311511
Daniel W. Guers *(CEO)*

DANA B. KENYON COMPANY, INC.

5772 Timuquana Rd, Jacksonville, FL 32210
Tel.: (904) 777-0833
Web Site: https://www.dbkenyon.com
Sales Range: $25-49.9 Million
Emp.: 60
Commercial & Institutional Building Construction Services
N.A.I.C.S.: 236220
Matthew E. Kenyon *(Pres & CEO)*
Joe G. Bajalia *(COO & Exec VP-Construction Ops)*
Bob Gillander *(Exec VP-Bus Dev)*
Thorn Himel *(VP)*
Brian Whitmire *(COO & Exec VP)*

DANA TRANSPORT INC.

210 Essex Ave E, Avenel, NJ 07001
Tel.: (732) 750-9100   NJ
Web Site:
   http://www.danacompanies.com
Year Founded: 1972
Sales Range: $25-49.9 Million
Emp.: 375
Trucking Service
N.A.I.C.S.: 484121
Ronald B. Dana *(Pres)*

Subsidiaries:

Dana Container Inc.   (1)
210 Essex Ave E, Avenel, NJ 07001
Tel.: (732) 750-9100
Web Site: http://www.danacontainer.com
Rev.: $21,000,000
Emp.: 20
Truck Rental & Leasing, No Drivers
N.A.I.C.S.: 532120

Dana Railcare, Inc.   (1)
1280 RailCar Ave, Wilmington, DE 19802
Tel.: (302) 652-8550
Emp.: 25
Railcar Repair Services
N.A.I.C.S.: 488210
Jennings Nichols *(Plant Mgr)*

Liquid Transport Corp.   (1)
8470 Allison Pointe Blvd Ste 400, Indianapolis, IN 46250-4365
Tel.: (317) 841-4200
Web Site: http://www.liquidtransport.com
Sales Range: $10-24.9 Million
Emp.: 40
Local Non-Storage Trucking Services
N.A.I.C.S.: 484121
Keith Lewis *(Pres & COO)*

Liquid Transport Inc.   (1)
2930 Quant Ave N, Stillwater, MN 55082-1626
Tel.: (651) 439-5773
Sales Range: $10-24.9 Million
Emp.: 85
Local Non-Storage Trucking Services
N.A.I.C.S.: 484121
John Shaleen *(Dir-Safety)*

Suttles Truck Leasing Inc.   (1)
2460 US Hwy 43 S, Demopolis, AL 36732
Tel.: (334) 289-0670
Web Site: http://www.danacompanies.com
Sales Range: $25-49.9 Million
Emp.: 60
Trucking Service
N.A.I.C.S.: 484121
Ronald Dana *(Pres)*

DANA'S HOUSEKEEPING PERSONNEL SERVICES

Ste 345 10535 Foothill Blvd, Rancho Cucamonga, CA 91730-3829
Tel.: (925) 944-9867
Web Site:
   http://www.danashousekeeping.com
Rev.: $11,000,000
Emp.: 100
Maid Registry
N.A.I.C.S.: 561311

DANA-FARBER CANCER INSTITUTE

450 Brookline Ave, Boston, MA 02215
Tel.: (617) 632-3000
Web Site: http://www.dana-farber.org
Year Founded: 1947
Sales Range: $1-4.9 Billion
Emp.: 4,274
Cancer Research & Care for Adults & Children
N.A.I.C.S.: 541715
William G. Kaelin Jr. *(Professor)*
Richard S. Boskey *(Sr VP & Gen Counsel)*
Craig A. Bunnell *(Chief Medical Officer)*
Deborah Hicks *(Sr VP-HR)*
Joseph Jacobson *(Chief Quality Officer)*
Maria Megdal *(Sr VP-Institute Ops)*
Elizabeth A. Liebow *(Sr VP-Bus Dev, Clinical Plng & Community Site Ops)*
Drew Memmott *(Sr VP-Res)*
Lee M. Nadler *(Sr VP-Experimental Medicine)*
Anne Gross *(Chief Nursing Officer & Sr VP-Patient Care Svcs)*
Goldie Taylor *(Chief Comm & Mktg Officer & Sr VP)*

DANARA INTERNATIONAL, LTD.

8101 Tonnelle Ave, North Bergen, NJ 07047
Tel.: (201) 295-1448
Sales Range: $10-24.9 Million
Emp.: 75
Women & Children Clothing Whslr
N.A.I.C.S.: 424350
Lyle Kluesner *(Mgr-Ops)*

DANBURY AEROSPACE, INC.

9503 Middlex Dr, San Antonio, TX 78217-5915
Tel.: (210) 820-2400   DE
Web Site: http://www.danbury.aero
Year Founded: 2008
Sales Range: $25-49.9 Million
Emp.: 175
Holding Company; Aircraft Engines & Engine Parts Mfr & Repair Services
N.A.I.C.S.: 551112
Ty Stoller *(Pres)*
Gary H. Garvens *(CEO)*
Johnny Doo *(Gen Counsel & Sr VP)*
Ken Suda *(Exec VP-Global Ops)*
Shan Tian *(Sr VP-Intl Bus Dev)*
Stephen Ginger *(Gen Counsel & Sr VP)*
Susan Ames *(VP-HR)*

Subsidiaries:

Engine Components, Inc.   (1)
9503 Middlex Dr, San Antonio, TX 78217-5915   (100%)
Tel.: (210) 820-8101
Web Site: http://www.eci.aero
Emp.: 8
Aircraft Engine & Engine Parts Mfr & Distr, Repair & Engineering Services
N.A.I.C.S.: 336412
Gary H. Garvens *(CEO)*
James K. Ball *(Gen Mgr)*

Unit (Domestic):

Air Cooled Motors   (2)
9503 Middlex Dr, San Antonio, TX 78217-5915   (100%)
Tel.: (210) 820-8150
Web Site: http://www.aircooledmotors.aero
Aircraft Engine Components Mfr
N.A.I.C.S.: 336412

Airmotive Engineering Corp.   (2)
9503 Middlex Dr, San Antonio, TX 78217-5915   (100%)
Tel.: (210) 820-2450
Web Site: http://www.aecorp.aero
Aircraft Engine & Engine Parts Engineering & Quality Assurance Services

N.A.I.C.S.: 541330
Hope Valentine (Mgr-Quality-AEC)
Bob Rasmussen (CEO)

EC Services (2)
9503 Middlex Dr, San Antonio, TX
78217-5915 (100%)
Tel.: (210) 820-8170
Aircraft Engine & Engine Parts Repair &
Maintenance Services
N.A.I.C.S.: 488190

DANBURY KIA
100A Federal Rd, Danbury, CT
06810
Tel.: (203) 730-5737
Web Site: https://danburykia.com
Year Founded: 2010
Sales Range: $10-24.9 Million
Emp.: 75
Used Car Whslr
N.A.I.C.S.: 441120
Susan Eway (Mgr-Bus Dev)
William Sabatini Jr. (Owner & Gen
Mgr)

DANCE BIOPHARM INC.
150 N Hill Dr Ste 24, Brisbane, CA
94005
Tel.: (415) 769-4200   DE
Web Site:
http://www.dancebiopharm.com
Year Founded: 2009
Biopharmaceutical Mfr
N.A.I.C.S.: 325412
John S. Patton (Chm)
Lisa E. Porter (Chief Medical Officer)
Truc Le (Exec VP-Ops & Quality)
Mei-chang Kuo (Sr VP-
Pharmaceutics)
Blaine Bueche (Dir-Pharmaceutics)
Lisa Molloy (Sr Dir-Device Dev)
Ben Stedman (VP-Mfg)

DANCIN' DOGG GOLF
400 W Front St Ste 200, Traverse
City, MI 49684
Tel.: (231) 421-2380
Web Site:
http://www.dancindogg.com
Year Founded: 2005
Sales Range: $1-9.9 Million
Emp.: 12
Portable Infrared Home Golf Simula-
tor
N.A.I.C.S.: 423910
Russell Edens (Pres)

**DANCKER, SELLEW & DOUG-
LAS, INC.**
291 Evans Way, Somerville, NJ
08876
Tel.: (908) 231-1600   NY
Web Site: http://www.dancker.com
Year Founded: 1829
Architectural, Furniture & Technology
Solutions & Facility Management
Support
N.A.I.C.S.: 459410
Mary Snyder (VP-HR)
Steven Lang (Pres & CEO)
William Hendry (CFO)
Robert J. Culvert (VP-Ops)
Tony Cianciola (VP-Sls-Architectural
Solutions)
Kevin Klier (Sr Exec VP & Gen Mgr)
Don Kolterjahn (VP-Sls-Furniture)
Ted Grillo (Sr Exec VP)
Rob Newell (CTO)

DANCO INC.
704 Fellowship Rd, Mount Laurel, NJ
08054
Tel.: (856) 234-6620
Web Site: http://www.danco-inc.com
Sales Range: $10-24.9 Million
Emp.: 20

Plumbing & Hydronic Heating Sup-
plies
N.A.I.C.S.: 423720
Barb Campbell (Sec)

DANCO TRANSMISSION
5221 Dixie Hwy, Fairfield, OH 45014
Tel.: (513) 540-2142
Web Site:
https://www.dancotransmission.com
Year Founded: 1971
Sales Range: $1-9.9 Million
Emp.: 18
Transmission & Auto Repair Services
N.A.I.C.S.: 811111
Donna Stewart (Mgr-Ops)
Dan Stewart (Owner)
Marty Human (Mgr)

DANDREA PRODUCE, INC.
3665 N Mill Rd, Vineland, NJ 08360
Tel.: (856) 205-1830
Web Site:
https://www.dandreaproduce.com
Year Founded: 1917
Emp.: 150
Fruits & Vegetables Producer, Im-
porter & Distr
N.A.I.C.S.: 424480
Steven Dandrea (VP-Sls & Mktg)
Peter Dandrea (Dir-Direct Store De-
livery)

DANDRIDGE EQUIPMENT INC.
11495 US Hwy 64, Somerville, TN
38068-6017
Tel.: (901) 465-9811   TN
Web Site:
http://www.dandridgeequipment.com
Year Founded: 1967
Sales Range: $10-24.9 Million
Emp.: 35
Distr of Farm & Garden Maintenance
Equipment
N.A.I.C.S.: 423820
Mike Cotton (Controller)
W.C. Dandridge Jr. (Pres)

DANDY OIL CO. INC.
1346 W Sunset Ave, Springdale, AR
72764
Tel.: (479) 751-8131
Rev.: $12,000,000
Emp.: 20
Whslr of Petroleum Products
N.A.I.C.S.: 424720
Marvin Dandy (Pres)
Gary Dandy (Treas & Sec)
Christine Dandy (Gen Mgr)

DANE CONSTRUCTION INC.
280 Mooresville Blvd, Mooresville,
NC 28115
Tel.: (704) 664-5042   NC
Web Site:
https://www.daneconstruction.com
Year Founded: 1995
Sales Range: $10-24.9 Million
Emp.: 70
General Contractors
N.A.I.C.S.: 237310
Michael E Dane (Pres)
Amber Covington (VP-Acctg)
Peter Weber (VP-Estimating)
Denise Luther (Dir-Safety & Mgr-HR)
Kristin Drinka (Office Mgr)
Adam Holcomb (VP-Ops)

Subsidiaries:

Dane Equipment Llc (1)
201 N Church St, Mooresville, NC 28115
Tel.: (704) 664-5042
Web Site: http://www.daneconstruction.com
Equipment Rental & Leasing
N.A.I.C.S.: 532490

DANE EXPLORATION INC.
500 McLeod Trail E #5178, Belling-
ham, WA 98226   NV
Web Site:
http://www.daneexplorationinc.com
Year Founded: 2010
Gold & Silver Exploration Services
N.A.I.C.S.: 212220
G. Dale Murray II (Pres, CEO, CFO,
Treas & Sec)

**DANE GOUGE'S ASTORIA
FORD**
1809 SE Ensign Ln, Warrenton, OR
97146
Tel.: (503) 325-6411
Web Site: http://www.astoriaford.com
Year Founded: 1999
Sales Range: $10-24.9 Million
Emp.: 100
New Car Dealers
N.A.I.C.S.: 441110
Dane Gouge (Owner)

**DANE MANUFACTURING
COMPANY**
115 Dane St, Dane, WI 53529
Tel.: (608) 849-5921   WI
Web Site: http://www.danemfg.com
Year Founded: 2001
Sales Range: $10-24.9 Million
Emp.: 55
Metal Fabrication & Stamping
N.A.I.C.S.: 332322
Troy Berg (Pres)

DANE STREET
3815 Washington St Ste 4, Boston,
MA 02130
Tel.: (888) 920-4440
Web Site: http://www.danestreet.com
Year Founded: 2008
Sales Range: $1-9.9 Million
Emp.: 81
Medical Peer Review Services
N.A.I.C.S.: 541611
Will Fulton (Founder & CEO)
C. Joseph Gasparoni (COO)
Greg Powers (CMO & Sr VP-Sls)
Jennifer Kaburick (VP-Natl Acct
Mgmt)
Christian Whitney (Assoc Dir-Medical-
Pharmacy)
David Gordon (Dir-Medical-Natl)
Kelly N. Hunt (Sr VP-Regulatory &
Legal Affairs)
Lawrence S. Burstein (VP-Ops)

**DANERICA ENTERPRISES,
INC.**
6345 Balboa Blvd Ste 285 Bldg IV,
Encino, CA 91316
Tel.: (818) 774-1813   CA
Web Site:
http://www.taxresolution.com
Year Founded: 1998
Sales Range: $10-24.9 Million
Emp.: 100
Tax Return Preparation Services
N.A.I.C.S.: 541213
Michael Rozbruch (CEO)
Shelly Murad (Dir-Ops)
Brian Compton (Pres)

**DANFORTH ASSOCIATES,
INC.**
1 Hollis St Ste 206, Wellesley, MA
02482
Tel.: (781) 235-9100
Web Site:
http://www.danforthassociates.com
Year Founded: 1936
Sales Range: Less than $1 Million
Emp.: 4
Investment Management Service
N.A.I.C.S.: 523999

Peter Alhart (Pres & CIO)

DANIEL B. HASTINGS INC.
13378 Port Dr, Laredo, TX 78045
Tel.: (956) 723-7431
Web Site: http://www.dhastings.com
Year Founded: 1994
Sales Range: $10-24.9 Million
Emp.: 92
Customhouse Brokers
N.A.I.C.S.: 488510
Dalia Moncivais (Mgr-Autmotive &
Compliance)
Franz Brunner (Mgr-Customer Svc)
Guadalupe Luciano (Mgr-IT)
Fernando Martinez (Supvr-Intl Traffic)
Fatima Perez (Mgr-Exports)
David Trevino (VP)
Gloria M. Hastings (Owner)

DANIEL CORPORATION
3660 Grandview Pkwy Ste 100, Bir-
mingham, AL 35243
Tel.: (205) 443-4500
Web Site:
http://www.danielrealty.com
Sales Range: $10-24.9 Million
Emp.: 65
Subdividers & Developers
N.A.I.C.S.: 237210
Charles Tickle (Chm, CEO & Princi-
pal)
Pat Henry (Pres)
Jim Adams (Sr VP)
Cameron Conner (Principal)
John P. Dobbins (VP-Fin)
John Knutsson (VP-Dev)
Scott Martin (VP-Investments)
Scott Pulliam (Chief Investment Offi-
cer & Principal)
Fred Roddy (Exec VP-Atlanta)
Chris Schmidt (VP-Office Leasing &
Sls)
Christine Strange (VP-Ops)
Justin Weintraub (Exec VP)
Burgoyne McClendon (Mgr-Mktg)
Jim Spahn (Dir-Multifamily Ops)

Subsidiaries:

Daniel Realty Corporation (1)
3660 Grandview Pkwy Ste 100, Birming-
ham, AL 35243
Tel.: (205) 443-4500
Web Site: http://www.danielcorp.com
Sales Range: $1-9.9 Million
Emp.: 50
Real Estate Managers
N.A.I.C.S.: 531210
Margi Ingram (VP-Sls & Mktg)

DANIEL DEFENSE
101 Warfighter Way, Black Creek, GA
31308
Web Site:
https://www.danieldefense.com
Year Founded: 2002
Sales Range: $10-24.9 Million
Emp.: 130
Small Arms Mfr & Sales of Parts &
Accessories
N.A.I.C.S.: 332992
Marty Daniel (Pres & CEO)
Thomas Carlson (Dir-Mktg Comm)
Patrick Kisgen (VP-Sls)
Steve Reed (VP-Mktg)

DANIEL F. YOUNG, INC.
1235 Westlakes Dr Ste 305, Berwyn,
PA 19312-2413
Tel.: (610) 524-4000   NY
Web Site: https://www.dfyoung.com
Year Founded: 1903
Sales Range: $400-449.9 Million
Emp.: 200
Freight Transportation, Forwarding &
Logistics Services
N.A.I.C.S.: 488510

Daniel F. Young, Inc.—(Continued)

Denise Traynor *(CFO)*
Chris Carpenter *(COO)*
Wesley A. Wyatt IV *(Pres & CEO)*

Subsidiaries:

DF Young Australia Pty Ltd (1)
33 Abeadeen St, Port Adelaide, 5015, SA,
Australia
Tel.: (61) 882405183
Web Site: http://www.dfyoung.com
Emp.: 2
Freight Transportation & Logistics Services
N.A.I.C.S.: 488510
Daniel Osborne *(Mgr-Ops)*

DANIEL G. SCHUSTER INC.

3717 Crondall Ln Ste B, Owings
Mills, MD 21117
Tel.: (410) 363-9620
Web Site:
https://www.schusterconcrete.com
Year Founded: 1975
Sales Range: $25-49.9 Million
Emp.: 1,000
Concrete Work
N.A.I.C.S.: 238110
Daniel G. Schuster *(Owner & Pres)*
Cindy Eckenrode *(Project Coord)*

DANIEL J QUIRK INC.

444 Quincy Ave, Braintree, MA 02184
Tel.: (781) 843-4800
Web Site: http://www.quirkcars.com
Rev.: $140,600,000
Emp.: 100
Automobiles, New & Used
N.A.I.C.S.: 441110
Daniel J. Quirk *(Pres)*

DANIEL J. EDELMAN HOLD-INGS, INC.

250 Hudson St, New York, NY 10013
Tel.: (212) 768-0550
Web Site:
http://www.djeholdings.com
Holding Company
N.A.I.C.S.: 551112
Catherine L. Burke *(Executives)*
Richard Edelman *(Chm)*
Lisa Kimmel *(Global Mng Dir-Sector
Specialty Agencies)*

Subsidiaries:

Mustache, LLC (1)
20 Jay St Ste 1100, Brooklyn, NY 11201
Tel.: (212) 226-3493
Web Site: http://www.mustacheagency.com
Advertising Services
N.A.I.C.S.: 541810
John Limotte *(Founder, CEO & Exec Cre-
ative Dir)*

DANIEL J. EDELMAN, INC.

200 E Randolph St Fl 63, Chicago, IL
60601-6705
Tel.: (312) 240-3000 DE
Web Site: http://www.edelman.com
Year Founded: 1952
Sales Range: $500-549.9 Million
Emp.: 3,200
Public Relations & Advertising
Agency
N.A.I.C.S.: 541820
Richard W. Edelman *(CEO)*
Matthew J. Harrington *(Global COO)*
Kevin Cook *(Pres)*
Ann Glynn *(Mgr-Mktg)*
Dan Cornell *(VP-Grp Strategy)*
Victor Malanga *(Worldwide CFO)*
Bob Grove *(COO-Asia Pacific)*
Kym White *(Vice Chm-Health)*
Alan VanderMolen *(Vice Chm-DJE
Holdings & Pres/CEO-Global Prac-
tices)*
David Brain *(Pres/CEO-Asia Pacific,
Middle East & Africa)*

Lisa Sepulveda *(Pres-Global Client
Relationship Mgmt)*
Julianna Richter *(COO-US)*
Cricket Wardein *(Pres-West)*
Robert Holdheim *(CEO-South Asia,
Middle East & Africa)*
Russell Dubner *(CEO-US)*
Rakesh Thukral *(Mng Dir-India)*
Trisch Smith *(Mng Dir-Diversity & In-
clusion)*
Steve Behm *(Pres-South)*
Helen Vollmer *(Chm-South)*
Kelly Schwager *(Gen Mgr-Silicon Val-
ley)*
Will Collie *(Gen Mgr-Health)*
Carol Potter *(CEO-Europe & CIS)*
Nick Barron *(Mng Dir-Corp & Fin
Practice)*
Kent Hollenbeck *(Sr VP-Corp Comm-
Portland)*
Raymond Siva *(Head-Indonesia)*
Jamie Kieffer *(Exec VP)*
Tod Donhauser *(CEO-UAE)*
Holly McGavock *(VP-Plng, Corp &
Pub Affairs)*
Sachin Talwalkar *(Exec Dir-Creative-
South Asia, Middle East & Africa)*
Gavin Coombes *(Mng Dir-Digital-Asia
Pacific, Middle East & Africa)*
Rupen Desai *(Vice Chm-Asia Pacific,
Middle East & Africa)*
John Larsen *(Gen Mgr-Calgary)*
Megan Spoore *(Deputy Gen Mgr)*
Katie Spring *(Gen Mgr)*
Tantri Kadiman-Beekelaar *(Head-
Indonesia)*
Harry Deje *(Dir-Bus)*
Bobby Arthawan *(Head-Brands-
Indonesia)*
Geeta Ramachanran *(Dir-Bus-Brand-
Indonesia)*
Feargal Purcell *(Dir-Pub Affairs)*
Kevin Coleman *(Gen Mgr-Health)*
Kate DuBois *(Gen Mgr-Digital)*
Hitesh Balwada *(Exec VP-Fin Comm)*
Michael Arndt *(Exec Editor-Editorial
Team)*
Holly Wallace *(Sr Acct Exec-Middle
East)*
Patrick Hillmann *(Exec VP-Crisis &
Risk)*
Rico Ricketson *(Exec VP-Health)*
Antoine Calendrier *(Head-Reputation-
North Asia)*
Stephen Kehoe *(CEO-Asia Pacific)*
Ian McCabe *(VP-Public Affairs)*
Theresa LaMontagne *(Head-Data &
Tech Svcs-US)*
Jacob Loban *(Haed-Performance
Mktg-US)*
Jon Flannery *(Chief Creative Officer)*
Dave Samson *(Vice Chm-Corp
Affairs-Global)*
Yvonne Koh *(Head-Corp-Asia-Pacific)*
Chris Gee *(Mng Dir-Digital-Corp &
Advisory Svcs Grp-US)*
Jim O'Leary *(Chm-Corp Practice-
Global)*

Subsidiaries:

AMI Communications (1)
Tyn 4/641, 110 00, Prague, Czech Republic
Tel.: (420) 234 124 112
Web Site: http://www.amic.cz
Sales Range: $75-99.9 Million
Emp.: 70
Public Relations Agency
N.A.I.C.S.: 541820
Milan Hejl *(Founder & Mng Partner)*
Marek Stransky *(Mng Partner)*
Pavel Novak *(Sr Acct Dir)*

Branch (Non-US):

AMI Communications Slovakia (2)
Grosslingova 7, 811 09, Bratislava, Slovakia
Tel.: (421) 2 52498549
Web Site: http://www.amic.sk

Emp.: 9
Public Relations Agency
N.A.I.C.S.: 541820
Karen Ovseyevitz *(Partner & Reg Dir)*
Peter Chilmoovqi *(Acct Dir)*

Blue Worldwide (1)
1875 Eye St NW Ste 900, Washington, DC
20006
Tel.: (202) 326-1721
Public Relations Agency
N.A.I.C.S.: 541820

Communique (1)
Kromprimsesse No 80, 2900, Copenhagen,
Denmark
Tel.: (45) 36983400
Web Site: http://www.communique.com
Sales Range: $75-99.9 Million
Emp.: 16
Public Relations Agency
N.A.I.C.S.: 541820
Frans Grandjean *(Partner)*
Michael Buksti *(Mng Dir)*
Christian Bentsen *(Partner)*
Ole Brandt *(Partner)*

Edelman (1)
250 Hudson St 16th Fl, New York, NY
10013
Tel.: (212) 768-0550
Web Site: http://www.edelman.com
Emp.: 600
Public Relations Agency
N.A.I.C.S.: 541820
Lex Suvanto *(Global Mng Dir-Fin Comm &
Capital Markets)*
Peter Landau *(Global CEO)*
Tyler Gray *(Dir-Editorial)*
Freya Williams *(Exec VP & Grp Head-Bus
& Social Purpose)*
Liz Lee *(Head-Digital Practice)*
Andrew Foote *(Gen Mgr-Digital)*
Martin O'Reilly *(Global Chief Info & Tech
Officer)*
Jennifer Simon *(Sr VP-Bus & Social Pur-
pose)*
Nadia Damouni *(Sr VP-Fin Comm & Spe-
cial Situations)*
Blain Rethmeier *(Mng Dir-Crisis & Risk
Practice-West Coast)*
Francesca Trainor Alt *(Exec VP & Grp
Head-Crisis & Risk)*
Kristine Boyden *(Pres-West)*
Lucy Allen *(Head-Bay Area)*
Laurie Hays *(Exec VP-Fin Comm & Capital
Markets)*
Joanna Poulton *(Dir-Media Ops-Asia-
Pacific, Middle East & Africa)*
Diarmid Farquhar *(Head-Paid Media-
Australia)*
Ben Naparstek *(Dir-Digital & Content)*
Kevin Goldman *(Exec VP)*

Edelman (1)
1875 I St NW Ste 900, Washington, DC
20006-5422
Tel.: (202) 371-0200
Web Site: http://www.edelman.com
Emp.: 160
Public Relations Agency
N.A.I.C.S.: 541820
Sarah Swinehart *(VP-Media Svcs & Strate-
gies)*
Joe Lockhart *(Vice Chm-Pub Affairs)*
Darci L. Vetter *(Gen Mgr-Public Affairs &
Vice Chm-Agriculture, Food, Trade)*
Lisa Osborne Ross *(COO-US)*

Edelman (1)
5900 Wilshire Blvd 24th & 25th Fl, Los An-
geles, CA 90036
Tel.: (323) 857-9100
Web Site: http://www.edelman.com
Emp.: 130
Public Relations Agency
N.A.I.C.S.: 541820
Amy Kavanaugh *(Global Chair-Pub En-
gagement & Exec VP)*
J. P. Schuerman *(Exec VP-Digital)*
Jeremy Tunis *(VP-Pub Affairs Practice)*
Sara Jones *(Mng Dir-Pub Affairs, Crisis &
Risk Mgmt Practices-Western Reg)*
Deb Kazenelson Deane *(Exec VP & Grp
Head-Corp Practice)*
James Williams *(Gen Mgr)*
Catherine Heath *(Exec VP-West)*

Edelman (1)
525 Market St Ste 1400, San Francisco, CA
94105

Tel.: (415) 222-9944
Web Site: http://www.edelman.com
Emp.: 80
Public Relations Agency
N.A.I.C.S.: 541820
Sanjay Nair *(Chm-Tech-Global)*
Dave Samson *(Vice Chm-Corp Affairs-
Global)*

Edelman (1)
Block 2 Harcourt Centre Harcourt Street,
Dublin, D02 DX37, Ireland
Tel.: (353) 16789333
Web Site: http://www.edelman.ie
Emp.: 30
Marketing Management Services
N.A.I.C.S.: 327910
Joe Carmody *(Mng Dir)*

Edelman (1)
Level 26 Centrepoint North Mid Valley City,
Lingkaran Syed Putra, 59200, Kuala Lum-
pur, Malaysia
Tel.: (60) 3 2287 8689
Web Site: http://www.edelman.com
Emp.: 11
Public Relations Agency
N.A.I.C.S.: 541820
Maha Dhurairaj *(Dir-Client Svcs)*
Sahana Prabhakar *(Sr Mgr-Health Practice)*
Christine Chang *(Dir-Integrated Brand &
Digital Practice)*
Robert Kay *(CEO)*

Edelman (1)
15 Beach Road Beach Centre No 04-01,
Singapore, 189677, Singapore
Tel.: (65) 6733 1110
Web Site: http://www.edelman.com
Emp.: 110
Public Relations Agency
N.A.I.C.S.: 541820
Jamie Read *(Mng Dir-Sectors)*
Amanda Goh *(CEO)*
Celevel Butler *(Mng Dir-Integrated Brand)*
Delicia Tan *(Mng Dir-Client Growth & Inno-
vation)*
Ranjit Jathanna *(Chief Strategy Officer-
Client Programming-Asia Pacific)*
Remona Duquesne *(Chief Strategy Officer)*
Nisha Sivan *(Dir-Strategy-Brand)*
Logan Smith *(Dir-Strategy-Digital)*
Matt Collette *(Vice Chm-Digital-Asia Pacific)*

Edelman (1)
Southside 105 Victoria Street, London,
SW1E 6QT, United Kingdom
Tel.: (44) 2030472000
Web Site: http://www.edelman.com
Sales Range: $25-49.9 Million
Emp.: 260
Public Relations Agency
N.A.I.C.S.: 541820
Alex Bigg *(Gen Mgr)*
Susan Eastoe *(COO-Europe & CIS)*
Jo Sheldon *(Exec Dir-Media Strategy)*
Jackie Cooper *(Vice Chm & Dir-Creative-
UK)*
Matt Hurst *(COO)*
Steve Spurr *(Chm-Health)*
Michael Stewart *(Pres/CEO-Europe & CIS)*
Niaz Samadizadeh *(Head-Sponsored Con-
tent & Media Partnerships)*
Justin Westcott *(Mng Dir-Tech Practice)*
Claudia Patton *(Chief Talent Officer)*
Matt Groves *(Mng Dir-Digital)*
Bronwen Andrews *(Grp Dir-New Bus)*
Toby Gunton *(Gen Mgr-Digital Ops)*
Ed Williams *(CEO)*
Kate Hawker *(Mng Dir-Healthcare)*

Edelman (1)
Level 7 1 York Street, Sydney, 2000, NSW,
Australia
Tel.: (61) 2 9241 3131
Web Site: http://www.edelman.com
Emp.: 35
Public Relations Agency
N.A.I.C.S.: 541820
Matthew Gain *(COO)*
Tim Riches *(CEO)*
Max Hegerman *(Mng Dir-Digital)*
Carl Moggridge *(Head-Strategy)*
Jamal Hamidi *(Exec Dir-Creative)*
Alex Lefley *(Natl Head-Social Media & Digi-
tal Engagement)*
Jamil Bhatti *(Dir-Creative)*

Edelman (1)

Niddastrasse 91, 60329, Frankfurt, Germany
Tel.: (49) 69 75 61 990
Web Site: http://www.edelman.com
Emp.: 50
Public Relations Agency
N.A.I.C.S.: 541820
Ernst Primosch (CEO)

Edelman (1)
150 Bloor Street West Suite 300, Toronto, M5S 2X9, ON, Canada
Tel.: (416) 979-1120
Web Site: http://www.edelman.com
Emp.: 150
Public Relations Agency
N.A.I.C.S.: 541820
Lisa Kimmel (Chm & CEO)

Edelman (1)
201 Baldwin Ave, San Mateo, CA 94401-3914
Tel.: (650) 762-2800
Web Site: http://www.edelman.com
Emp.: 170
Public Relations Agency
N.A.I.C.S.: 541820
Andrea Mueller (Acct Supvr)
Katie Sue Ambellan (Sr Acct Exec-Digital)
Rebecca Andreassen (Sr Acct Exec)
Kelly Schwager (Gen Mgr-Silicon Valley)
Bridgitte Anderson (Gen Mgr-Vancouver)

Edelman (1)
46 rue Notre Dame des Victoires, 75008, Paris, France
Tel.: (33) 1 56 69 75 00
Web Site: http://www.edelman.com
Emp.: 40
Public Relations Agency
N.A.I.C.S.: 541820
Michael Stewart (Pres & CEO-Edelman Europe & CIS)
Frederic-Gerard Leveque (Sr VP-Digital)

Edelman (1)
Felix Cuevas 6 Office 601 Tlacoquemecatl del Valle, 03200, Mexico, DF, Mexico
Tel.: (52) 55 5350 1500
Web Site: http://www.edelman.com.mx
Emp.: 35
Public Relations Agency
N.A.I.C.S.: 541820
Luz Vazquez (Gen Mgr)
Sergio Sanchez (VP-Strategic Plng)
Eduardo Cisneros (VP-Creative)

Edelman (1)
1075 Peachtree St NE Ste 3100, Atlanta, GA 30309
Tel.: (404) 262-3000
Web Site: http://www.edelman.com
Emp.: 104
Public Relations Agency
N.A.I.C.S.: 541820
Marilynn Mobley (Sr VP-Strategic counsel)
Courtney Harkness (VP-Corp Practice)

Edelman (1)
921 11th St Ste 250, Sacramento, CA 95814
Tel.: (916) 442-2331
Web Site: http://www.edelman.com
Emp.: 18
Public Relations Agency
N.A.I.C.S.: 541820
Tom Knox (VP)
Matt Notley (VP)
Kierstan DeLong (Sr VP)

Edelman (1)
Avenue Marnixlaan 28 2nd Floor, 1000, Brussels, Belgium
Tel.: (32) 2 227 6170
Web Site: http://www.edelman.be
Sales Range: $50-74.9 Million
Emp.: 17
Public Relations Agency
N.A.I.C.S.: 541820
Rob Regh (Pres)
Martin Porter (Gen Mgr)

Edelman (1)
Room 707 Dongshan Plaza 69 Xianlie Zhong Road, Guangzhou, 510095, China
Tel.: (86) 20 8732 2111
Web Site: http://www.edelman.com
Emp.: 11
Public Relations Agency
N.A.I.C.S.: 541820

Mark Wang (CEO)
Melinda Po (Chief Growth Officer)

Edelman (1)
3F Want Want Plaza, 211 Shi Men Yi Lu, Shanghai, 200041, Shanghai, China
Tel.: (86) 21 6193 7588
Web Site: http://www.edelman.com
Emp.: 42
Public Relations Agency
N.A.I.C.S.: 541820
Mikko He (Dir-Creative)
Jeffrey Yu (Pres)
Alex Lam (Gen Mgr-Digital-Shanghai & Guangzhou)
Jesse Lin (CEO-Asia Pacific)
Melinda Po (Mng Dir)

Edelman (1)
Paseo de la Castellana 91-5A Pta, Edificio Centro 23, Madrid, 28046, Spain
Tel.: (34) 91 556 0154
Web Site: http://www.edelmanspain.com
Emp.: 28
Public Relations Agency
N.A.I.C.S.: 541820
Jordi Ballera (Dir-Edeman Madrid)

Edelman (1)
Medienpark Kampnagel Barmbeker Strasse 4, 22303, Hamburg, Germany
Tel.: (49) 40 37 47 980
Web Site: http://www.edelman.com
Emp.: 35
Public Relation Agency Services
N.A.I.C.S.: 541820
Cornelia Kunze (Gen Mgr)

Edelman (1)
Paraguay 610 Piso 29, C1057AAH, Buenos Aires, Argentina
Tel.: (54) 11 4315 4020
Web Site: http://www.edelman.com.ar
Emp.: 35
Public Relations Agency
N.A.I.C.S.: 541820
Allan McCrea Steele (CEO-Latin America)
Natalia Martinez (Grp Dir-Buenos Aires & Reg Dir-Tech)

Edelman (1)
Rua Joaquim Floriano N 820 20 andar, Sao Paulo, 04534-003, SP, Brazil
Tel.: (55) 11 3017 5300
Web Site: http://www.edelman.com.br
Emp.: 50
Public Relations Agency
N.A.I.C.S.: 541820

Edelman (1)
10F No 36 Pateh Road Sec 3, Taipei, 105, Taiwan
Tel.: (886) 2 2570 7588
Web Site: http://www.edelman.com
Emp.: 20
Public Relations Agency
N.A.I.C.S.: 541820

Edelman (1)
18th Fl Ferrum Tower, Suha Dong Jungu, Seoul, 100-210, Korea (South)
Tel.: (82) 2 725 2001
Web Site: http://www.edelman.co.kr
Emp.: 45
Public Relations Agency
N.A.I.C.S.: 541820
S.B. Jang (Mng Dir)

Edelman (1)
1221 Brickell Ave, Miami, FL 33131
Tel.: (305) 358-9500
Web Site: http://www.edelman.com
Emp.: 25
Public Relations Agency
N.A.I.C.S.: 541820
Carla Santiago (Gen Mgr)

Edelman (1)
Passeig de Gracia 86 3a Planta, 08008, Barcelona, Spain
Tel.: (34) 93 488 1290
Web Site: http://www.edelman.com
Emp.: 20
Public Relation Agency Services
N.A.I.C.S.: 541820
Miguel Angel Aguirre (Gen Mgr)

Edelman (1)
Westlake Tower 1601 5th Ave Ste 2300, Seattle, WA 98101
Tel.: (206) 223-1606

Web Site: http://www.edelman.com
Emp.: 200
Public Relations Agency
N.A.I.C.S.: 541820
Will Ludlum (Gen Mgr)
Michael Ann Thomas (Sr VP-Tech)
Gina Avila (Sr VP & Grp Dir-Digital-Pacific Northwest)
Katie Goldberg (Sr VP-Food Accts-West Coast)

Edelman (1)
Gustav Mahlerlaan 2970, Amsterdam, 1081 LA, Netherlands
Tel.: (31) 20 30 10 980
Web Site: http://www.edelman.com
Emp.: 40
Public Relations Agency
N.A.I.C.S.: 541820
Annemieke Kievit (Gen Mgr-Benelux)

Edelman (1)
Rosenlundsgatan 29A, Stockholm, 118 63, Sweden
Tel.: (46) 8 54 54 55 70
Web Site: http://www.edelmandeportivo.com
Sales Range: $10-24.9 Million
Emp.: 40
Public Relations Agency
N.A.I.C.S.: 541820
Mattias Ronge (Gen Mgr)

Edelman (1)
Landshuter Allee 10, Munich, 80637, Germany
Tel.: (49) 89 41 30 16
Web Site: http://de.edelman.com
Emp.: 30
Public Relations Agency
N.A.I.C.S.: 541820
Martina Pennekamp (Deputy Mng Dir)

Edelman (1)
3rd Floor Toranomon 45 MT Bldg, 5-1-5 Toranomon Minato-ku, Tokyo, 105-001, Japan
Tel.: (81) 3 6403 5200
Web Site: http://www.edelman.jp
Public Relations Agency
N.A.I.C.S.: 541820
Ross Rowbury (Pres)
Yosuke Miyazaki (Dir-Strategy)

Edelman (1)
1500 West Georgia Street Suite 1400, Vancouver, V6G 2Z6, BC, Canada
Tel.: (604) 623-3007
Web Site: http://www.edelman.com
Emp.: 40
Public Relations Services
N.A.I.C.S.: 541820
Rhonda Trenholm (Dir-Client Svcs)

Edelman Beijing (1)
Room 1001 Building 2 World Profit Center No16 Tianzelu, Chaoyang District, Beijing, 100015, China
Tel.: (86) 10 5676 8888
Web Site: http://www.edelman.com
Public Relations Agency
N.A.I.C.S.: 541820
Mark Wang (Mng Dir)

Edelman Hong Kong (1)
701 Central Plaza 18 Harbour Rd, Hong Kong, China (Hong Kong)
Tel.: (852) 2804 1338
Web Site: http://www.edelman.com
Emp.: 60
Public Relations & Branding Agency
N.A.I.C.S.: 541820
Adrian Warr (Mng Dir)

Edelman Russia (1)
3rd ulitsa Yamskogo-Polya Bldg 18, 125040, Moscow, Russia
Tel.: (7) 4957852255
Web Site: http://www.edelman.com
Sales Range: $75-99.9 Million
Emp.: 30
Public Relations Agency
N.A.I.C.S.: 541820
Kerry Irwin (Gen Mgr)

Edelman S.R.L. (1)
Via Varese 11, 20121, Milan, Italy
Tel.: (39) 02631161
Web Site: http://www.edelman.com
Public Relations Agency
N.A.I.C.S.: 541820

Fiorella Passoni (Gen Mgr)
Anna Capella (Deputy Gen Mgr & Dir-Consumer)

Edelman South Africa (1)
Hutton Court 8 Summit Road Dunkeld West, Blairgowrie, 2196, Randburg, South Africa
Tel.: (27) 832726373
Web Site: http://www.edelman.com
Sales Range: $75-99.9 Million
Emp.: 25
Public Relation Agency Services
N.A.I.C.S.: 541820
Francois Baird (Chm)
Peter Mageza (Vice Chm)
Jordan Rittenberry (Mng Dir)
Craig Atherfold (Grp Acct Dir)

Edelman Southwest (1)
1201 Louisiana St Ste 830, Houston, TX 77002
Tel.: (713) 970-2100
Web Site: http://www.edelman.com
Sales Range: $10-24.9 Million
Emp.: 53
Public Relations Agency
N.A.I.C.S.: 541820
David Roznowski (Sr VP)

Unit (Domestic):

Edelman Southwest - Dallas (2)
825 Old Trail Rd, Dallas, TX 75201
Tel.: (214) 520-3555
Web Site: http://www.edelman.com
Rev.: $50,000,000
Sales Range: $50,000,000
Emp.: 20
Public Relations Agency
N.A.I.C.S.: 541820
Chris Manzini (Gen Mgr)

IndoPacific Edelman (1)
Recapital Bldg 3rd Fl Jl Adityawarman Kav 55, Kebayoran Baru, Jakarta, 12160, Indonesia
Tel.: (62) 21 721 59000
Web Site: http://www.indopacedelman.com
Emp.: 90
Public Relations Agency
N.A.I.C.S.: 541820

Jackie Cooper Public Relations (1)
SouthSide 105 Victoria St, London, SW1E 6QT, United Kingdom
Tel.: (44) 2072087208
Web Site: http://www.jcpr.com
Sales Range: $10-24.9 Million
Emp.: 70
Public Relations Agency
N.A.I.C.S.: 541820

Pegasus Communications (1)
Room No 801 MapleTree Tower No 108, Chaoyang District, Beijing, 100022, China
Tel.: (86) 1058693376
Web Site: http://www.realpegasus.com
Sales Range: $75-99.9 Million
Emp.: 25
Public Relations Agency
N.A.I.C.S.: 541820
Steven Cao (Mng Dir)
Michael Du (Acct Dir)

Saunders Unsworth Limited (1)
Level 4 Solnet House 70 The Terrace, PO Box 10-200, Wellington, 6011, New Zealand
Tel.: (64) 4 914 1750
Web Site: http://www.sul.co.nz
Emp.: 5
Public Relations Agency
N.A.I.C.S.: 541820
Mark Unsworth (Owner)
Melisa Webster (Office Mgr)

Wolf Press & Public Relations (1)
65 Yigal Alon St, Tel Aviv, 67443, Israel
Tel.: (972) 35610808
Web Site: http://www.wolfppr.com
Sales Range: Less than $1 Million
Emp.: 10
Public Relations Agency
N.A.I.C.S.: 541820
Erez Banks (CEO)

DANIEL J. KEATING CONSTRUCTION COMPANY, LLC
134 N Narberth Ave, Narberth, PA 19072

Daniel J. Keating Construction Company, LLC—(Continued)

Tel.: (610) 664-4550 — DE
Web Site: http://www.djkeating.com
Year Founded: 1909
Construction Services
N.A.I.C.S.: 236210
Pierce J. Keating *(Chrm, Pres & CEO)*
Nina Keating Fisher *(Gen Counsel)*
Thomas Broadhurst *(VP-Ops)*
Michael Messina *(Treas)*
Anthony Bell *(Dir-Safety)*
Craig Hunt *(Dir-Project)*
Pierce Keating Jr. *(Exec VP)*

DANIEL K INC.

555 Madison Ave, New York, NY 10022
Tel.: (212) 759-7604
Web Site: http://www.danielk.net
Year Founded: 1999
Sales Range: $1-9.9 Million
Emp.: 15
Jewelry Whslr
N.A.I.C.S.: 423940

DANIEL L. JACOB & CO. INC.

2403 E High St, Jackson, MI 49203
Tel.: (517) 782-7191
Web Site: https://www.dlj-bud.com
Year Founded: 1980
Sales Range: $25-49.9 Million
Emp.: 120
Distr of Beer & Other Fermented Malt Liquors
N.A.I.C.S.: 424810
Daniel L. Jacob *(CEO)*
Larry O. Dunn *(VP)*
Joff Marcanten *(VP & Gen Mgr)*

DANIEL M. POWERS & ASSOCIATES LTD.

575 W Crossroads Pkwy, Bolingbrook, IL 60440
Tel.: (630) 685-8400
Web Site: http://www.powersinet.com
Sales Range: $10-24.9 Million
Emp.: 45
Store Fixtures; Milwork Manufacturer
N.A.I.C.S.: 423440
Daniel M. Powers *(Founder & CEO)*
Pam Newman *(CFO)*

DANIEL P. O'REILLY & COMPANY

8755 W Higgins Rd, Chicago, IL 60631
Tel.: (815) 245-3073
Web Site: http://www.dpoandco.com
Year Founded: 2017
Strategy & Operations Consulting Services
N.A.I.C.S.: 541618
Daniel P. O'Reilly *(Pres)*

Subsidiaries:

Circuits West, Inc. (1)
410 S Sunset Ste D, Longmont, CO 80501
Tel.: (303) 772-9261
Web Site: http://www.circuitswest.com
Sales Range: $1-9.9 Million
Emp.: 23
Printed Circuits Mfr
N.A.I.C.S.: 334412
Chuck Anderson *(Pres)*
Jack Jeffries *(Mgr-Sls-Natl)*
Charles Anderson *(CEO)*

DANIEL SMITH, INC.

4150 1st Ave S, Seattle, WA 98134
Tel.: (206) 223-9599
Web Site: http://www.danielsmith.com
Year Founded: 1976
Sales Range: $25-49.9 Million
Arts & Crafts Equipment & Supplies Mfr

N.A.I.C.S.: 459920
John Cogley *(Owner)*
Gerg Marks *(Brand Mgr)*

DANIEL'S OF ALBION, INC.

4048 Oak Orchard Rd, Albion, NY 14411
Tel.: (585) 589-7056
Year Founded: 1980
Sales Range: $10-24.9 Million
Emp.: 23
Car Whslr
N.A.I.C.S.: 441110
Heidi Schumacher *(Gen Mgr)*

DANIEL, BURTON, DEAN ADVERTISING & DESIGN, INC.

225 Court St, Evansville, IN 47708
Tel.: (812) 426-0551 — IN
Web Site: http://www.dbd15.com
Year Founded: 1976
Sales Range: $10-24.9 Million
Emp.: 10
Advertising Agencies
N.A.I.C.S.: 541810
Phillip Dean Mowrey *(Dir-Creative)*
Julie Mitchell *(Dir-Tech)*
David Wright *(Mgr-Creative)*
Jill Schuler *(Mgr-Digital Media)*

DANIELS & ROBERTS, INC.

209 N Seacrest Blvd Ste 2, Boynton Beach, FL 33435
Tel.: (561) 241-0066
Web Site: http://www.danielsandroberts.com
Year Founded: 1986
Sales Range: $1-9.9 Million
Emp.: 25
Advetising Agency
N.A.I.C.S.: 541810
Daniel A. Muggeo *(Founder & CEO)*
Anthony Hanna *(Dir-Mgmt Info Sys)*
Amy Scharf *(VP-Client Svcs)*
Frank Coffy *(Mgr-Production)*
Mary Dundore *(Controller)*

DANIELS BMW

4600 Crackersport Rd, Allentown, PA 18104
Tel.: (610) 820-2950
Web Site: https://www.danielsbmw.com
Sales Range: $50-74.9 Million
Emp.: 70
New & Used Car Dealers
N.A.I.C.S.: 441110
Gary Daniels *(Pres)*

DANIELS BUILDING & CONSTRUCTION, INC.

2898 W Cedar St, Beaumont, TX 77702
Tel.: (409) 838-3006
Web Site: https://www.danielsinc.com
Year Founded: 1957
Sales Range: $10-24.9 Million
Emp.: 75
Commercial & Institutional Building Construction Services
N.A.I.C.S.: 236220
Janet Daniels Houston *(CFO & Exec VP)*

DANIELS CADILLAC, INC.

4600 Crackersport Rd, Allentown, PA 18104
Tel.: (610) 820-2950
Year Founded: 1961
Sales Range: $25-49.9 Million
Emp.: 62
Car Whslr
N.A.I.C.S.: 441110
Gary Daniels *(Pres)*

DANIELS ENTERPRISES INC.

4683 Mill Landing Rd, Wanchese, NC 27981
Tel.: (252) 473-5001
Rev.: $31,510,525
Emp.: 30
Holding Company
N.A.I.C.S.: 551112
Kim Daniels *(Pres)*

Subsidiaries:

Wanchese Fish Company, Inc. (1)
2000 Northgate Commerce Pkwy, Suffolk, VA 23435
Tel.: (757) 673-4500
Web Site: http://www.wanchese.com
Sales Range: $25-49.9 Million
Seafood Whslr
N.A.I.C.S.: 424460
Samuel C. Daniels *(Dir-Sls & Mktg)*
Ross Butler *(CEO)*
Betsey Crockett *(Office Mgr)*
Dallas Daniels *(Mgr)*
Faron Daniels *(Mgr)*
Joey Daniels *(Plant Mgr)*
Richard Kim *(Mgr-Quality)*

DANIELS FAMILY CUTLERY CORPORATION

507 Chestnut St, Titusville, PA 16354-1209
Tel.: (814) 827-3673 — PA
Year Founded: 2012
Pocket & Hunting Knives Designer, Mfr & Distr
N.A.I.C.S.: 332215
Kenneth Ryan Daniels *(Owner & Pres)*

DANIELS GROUP INC.

609 Penn Ave, Pittsburgh, PA 15222
Tel.: (412) 355-0780
Year Founded: 1974
Sales Range: $25-49.9 Million
Emp.: 2
Bits For Use On Lathes, Planers, Shapers, Etc.
N.A.I.C.S.: 333515
Nathan K. Parker Jr. *(Chm)*

DANIELS MANUFACTURING CORPORATION

526 Thorpe Rd, Orlando, FL 32824-8133
Tel.: (407) 855-6161 — FL
Web Site: https://www.dmctools.com
Year Founded: 1949
Sales Range: $10-24.9 Million
Emp.: 150
Mfr of Hand & Edge Tools; Power-Driven Handtools
N.A.I.C.S.: 332216
Loretta Ring *(Mgr-HR)*
Michelle Zink *(Controller)*
Erik Francoforte *(Mgr-Engrg)*

DANIELS MOTORS INC.

670 Automotive Dr, Colorado Springs, CO 80905
Tel.: (719) 632-5591
Web Site: http://www.danielschevrolet.com
Rev.: $51,489,000
Emp.: 70
New & Used Car Dealers
N.A.I.C.S.: 441110
Elizabeth Daniels *(Owner & Pres)*

DANIELS SENTRY FOODS INC.

681 Kenosha St, Walworth, WI 53184
Tel.: (262) 275-0458
Web Site: http://www.sentryfoods.com
Rev.: $30,000,000
Emp.: 90
Supermarkets, Chain
N.A.I.C.S.: 445110
Ken Riley *(Gen Mgr)*

DANIELS TIRE SERVICE INC.

11850 E Slauson Ave, Santa Fe Springs, CA 90670-2228
Tel.: (562) 698-9401
Web Site: https://www.danielstireservice.com
Year Founded: 1911
Sales Range: $25-49.9 Million
Emp.: 150
Automotive Tires
N.A.I.C.S.: 441340
Douglas A. Daniels *(Pres)*
Brent Cole *(VP-Consumer Sls)*

DANIELSON DESIGNS, LTD.

36750 Constitution Dr, Trinidad, CO 81082
Tel.: (719) 846-4149
Year Founded: 2000
Sales Range: $1-9.9 Million
Emp.: 85
Picture Frame Mfr & Distr
N.A.I.C.S.: 321999
Elizabeth Danielson *(Pres)*
Erik Jacobson *(Mgr-Mktg)*

DANIELSON OIL COMPANY OF OKLAHOMA

18700 County Rd 3590, Ada, OK 74820
Tel.: (580) 332-8008
Rev.: $24,155,252
Emp.: 15
Gasoline
N.A.I.C.S.: 424720
Jerry Danielson *(Pres)*
Mike Lawson *(Controller)*

DANIS BUILDING CONSTRUCTION COMPANY INC.

3233 Newmark Dr, Miamisburg, OH 45342-4978
Tel.: (937) 228-1225 — OH
Web Site: https://www.danis.com
Year Founded: 1916
Sales Range: $150-199.9 Million
Emp.: 350
Provider of General Construction & Construction Services
N.A.I.C.S.: 236220
John Danis *(CEO)*
Tim Carlson *(CFO)*
Aaron Phillips *(Dir-Virtual Design & Construction)*
Bill Root *(Mgr-Medical Equipment & IT Project)*
Kevin Appling *(Mgr-Preconstruction)*
Buck Smoak *(VP-Bus Dev)*
Cory Farmer *(VP)*
Dustin Rohrbach *(VP)*
Gordon Steadman *(VP-Bus Dev)*
Neil Winland *(VP-Ops)*
Tony Suttles *(VP)*

Subsidiaries:

Danis Builders, LLC (1)
852 Chanterelle Way, Jacksonville, FL 32259
Tel.: (904) 826-0614
Building Contractors
N.A.I.C.S.: 236115

Danis Construction Company LLC (1)
5511 Capital Center Dr Ste 100, Raleigh, NC 27606
Tel.: (919) 468-6240
Commercial Building Construction Services
N.A.I.C.S.: 236220
Mark Moeller *(Dir-Bus Dev)*
Steve Sefton *(Pres)*
Brian Ross DiDiano *(VP)*
Ken Powell *(Superintendent)*

R.N. Rouse & Co. Inc. (1)
1101 Pkwy Dr, Goldsboro, NC 27534
Tel.: (919) 778-8800
Web Site: http://www.rnrouse.com

Sales Range: $75-99.9 Million
Emp.: 10
Institutional Building Construction Services
N.A.I.C.S.: 236220
Troy Erbes *(Dir-Bus Dev)*
Ray N. Rouse III *(Chm)*

DANISH INSPIRATIONS CORPORATION
8648 Glenmont Dr, Houston, TX
77036-1930
Tel.: (713) 782-6448   TX
Web Site:
   http://www.danishinspirations.com
Year Founded: 1982
Sales Range: $1-9.9 Million
Emp.: 25
Furniture Distr
N.A.I.C.S.: 449110
Jan Christiansen *(Pres)*

Subsidiaries:

Danish Inspirations, Showroom   (1)
2775 Fondren Rd, Houston, TX
77063   (100%)
Tel.: (713) 782-4911
Web Site: http://www.danishinspirations.com
Furniture Showroom
N.A.I.C.S.: 449110

DANJAQ LLC
11400 W Olypmic Ste 1700, Los Angeles, CA 90064
Tel.: (310) 449-3185
Web Site: http://www.007.com
Year Founded: 1962
Rev.: $2,000,000
Emp.: 10
Motion Picture Producer
N.A.I.C.S.: 512110
Michael Wilson *(Pres)*
Barbara Brockley *(VP)*
Michael Tavares *(VP-Mktg)*

DANKER FURNITURE INC.
1000 Township Line Rd Ste 6, Phoenixville, PA 19460-2269
Tel.: (301) 258-8160
Web Site: http://www.danker-furniture.com
Sales Range: $10-24.9 Million
Emp.: 35
Furniture Retailer
N.A.I.C.S.: 449110
Gerard Kvasnovsky *(Pres)*

DANKER LABORATORIES INC.
6805 33rd St E, Sarasota, FL 34243-4144
Tel.: (941) 758-7711   NY
Web Site: http://www.dankerlabs.com
Year Founded: 1958
Sales Range: Less than $1 Million
Emp.: 10
Contact Lenses & Ophthalmic Cleaning Solutions Mfr
N.A.I.C.S.: 339115
Frederick J. Danker *(CEO)*
Jeri Struve *(Pres)*

DANLAW, INC.
41131 Vincenti Ct, Novi, MI 48375
Tel.: (248) 476-5571   MI
Web Site: https://www.danlawinc.com
Year Founded: 1984
Sales Range: $75-99.9 Million
Emp.: 300
Holding Company; Software Engineering, Information Technology Consulting & Project Management Services
N.A.I.C.S.: 551112
Tom Rzeznik *(Pres & CEO)*

Subsidiaries:

Danlaw Technologies India
Limited   (1)

Unit 201 & 202 & 203 Gowra Fountainhead
Huda Techno Enclave, Patrikanagar Madhapur, Hyderabad, 500 081, Telangana,
India   (49.74%)
Tel.: (91) 4023542499
Web Site:
   https://www.danlawtechnologies.com
Rev.: $20,130,532
Assets: $13,486,170
Liabilities: $9,182,423
Net Worth: $4,303,747
Earnings: $869,720
Emp.: 108
Fiscal Year-end: 03/31/2023
Software Engineering, Information Technology Consulting & Project Management Services
N.A.I.C.S.: 513210
Raju Satyanarayana Dandu *(Chm)*
B. V. Ramana *(COO)*
A. V. R. K. Varma *(CFO)*
Gaurav Padmawar *(Sec)*

Subsidiary (US):

Danlaw Technologies, Inc.   (2)
23700 Research Dr, Farmington Hills, MI
48335-2624   (100%)
Tel.: (248) 476-5571
Web Site:
   http://www.danlawtechnologies.com
Sales Range: Less than $1 Million
Software Engineering, Information Technology Consulting & Project Management Services
N.A.I.C.S.: 541519
Raju S. Dandu *(Chm & Mng Dir)*
Tim Morris *(Mgr-Bus Dev)*
B. V. Ramana *(COO)*
E. U. S. Prabhakar *(VP)*
G. Govardhan Rao *(Exec VP)*
Y. V. Subramanyam *(VP)*
A. V. R. K. Varma *(CFO)*

Micromax, Inc.   (1)
5840 N Canton Center Rd, Canton, MI
48187-2614
Tel.: (734) 354-0400
Web Site: http://www.mrmx.com
Sales Range: $10-24.9 Million
Emp.: 45
Embedded Software Solutions
N.A.I.C.S.: 513210
Michael McCormack *(CEO)*
Larry Thiede *(Sr Acct Mgr)*

DANLEY LUMBER CO. INC.
612 Academy Dr, Northbrook, IL
60062-2424
Tel.: (847) 562-9390
Web Site:
   http://www.danleysgarageworld.com
Sales Range: $10-24.9 Million
Emp.: 32
Garage Construction
N.A.I.C.S.: 236220
Paul Fisher *(Pres)*

DANMAR INDUSTRIES, INC.
2303 Oil Ctr Ct, Houston, TX 77073
Tel.: (281) 230-1000
Web Site:
   https://www.danmarind.com
Year Founded: 1980
Sales Range: $10-24.9 Million
Emp.: 50
Industrial Machinery & Equipment
Whslr
N.A.I.C.S.: 423830
Mark Depauw *(VP)*
Ben Giusti *(Acct Mgr)*

DANMER, INC.
21001 Nordhoff St, Chatsworth, CA
91311
Tel.: (800) 684-3434   CA
Web Site: http://www.danmer.com
Year Founded: 1976
Window Shutters & Wood Mfr
N.A.I.C.S.: 321911
Sandy Spellman *(Sls Dir)*

DANNY & CLYDE'S FOOD STORE
1401 Kuebel St, New Orleans, LA
70123-2254
Tel.: (504) 833-5438
Web Site:
   http://www.dannyandclydes.com
Sales Range: $25-49.9 Million
Emp.: 100
Independent Convenience Store
N.A.I.C.S.: 445131
Kristal Gautreaux *(Controller)*
Chris Rittiner *(Pres)*

DANNY BECK CHEVROLET, INC.
8300 New Sapulpa Rd, Tulsa, OK
74131
Tel.: (918) 227-1070
Web Site:
   http://www.dannybeckchevy.com
Emp.: 80
Car Whslr
N.A.I.C.S.: 441110
Danny Beck *(Owner)*

DANNY HERMAN TRUCKING INC.
339 Cold Springs Rd, Mountain City,
TN 37683-4023
Tel.: (423) 727-9061
Web Site:
   https://www.dannyherman.com
Sales Range: $25-49.9 Million
Emp.: 50
Trucking
N.A.I.C.S.: 484121
Joe Herman *(Pres)*

DANNY NICHOLSON INC.
339 City Lk Rd, Lexington, NC 27295
Tel.: (336) 249-7204
Year Founded: 1995
Sales Range: $10-24.9 Million
Emp.: 150
Trucking Except Local
N.A.I.C.S.: 484121
Judy Moore *(Controller)*
Danny Nicholson Sr. *(Pres)*

DANNY ZECK FORD LINCOLN MERCURY
4501 S 4th St Trafficway, Leavenworth, KS 66048
Tel.: (913) 727-1650
Web Site: http://www.dzford.com
Sales Range: $25-49.9 Million
Emp.: 85
Automobiles, New & Used
N.A.I.C.S.: 441110
Gene Triplett *(Controller)*
Thomas Tomrell *(Mgr-Svc)*

DANNY'S CONSTRUCTION CO., INC.
1066 3rd Ave W, Shakopee, MN
55379
Tel.: (952) 445-4143
Web Site:
   https://www.dannysconstruction.com
Year Founded: 1970
Rev.: $35,000,000
Emp.: 100
Provider of Structural Steel Erection
Contracting Services
N.A.I.C.S.: 238120

DANNY'S FAMILY COMPANIES, LLC
15509 N Scottsdale Rd, Scottsdale,
AZ 85254
Tel.: (480) 348-2223   AZ
Web Site:
   http://www.dannysfamily.com

Year Founded: 2003
Sales Range: $25-49.9 Million
Emp.: 20
Holding Company; Carwash, Automotive Maintenance, Gas Station & Convenience Store Owner & Operator
N.A.I.C.S.: 551112
Daniel L. Hendon *(Pres & CEO)*
Jack Edlund *(Gen Mgr)*

Subsidiaries:

Danny's Family Carousel, Inc.   (1)
15509 N Scottsdale Rd, Scottsdale, AZ
85254
Tel.: (480) 348-2223
Web Site: http://www.dannysfamily.com
Rev.: $11,000,000
Emp.: 1,000
Carwash Holding Company
N.A.I.C.S.: 551112

DANOS & CUROLE MARINE CONTRACTORS INC.
3878 West Main St, Gray, LA 70359
Tel.: (985) 693-3313   LA
Web Site: http://www.danos.com
Year Founded: 1947
Rev.: $50,328,644
Emp.: 1,000
Oil & Gas Field Services
N.A.I.C.S.: 213112
Hank Danos *(Pres)*
John Bigler *(Gen Mgr)*
James Callahan *(VP-Projects)*
Mark Danos *(VP-Project Svcs)*
Stacy Gisclair *(VP-HR)*
Reed Pere *(VP-Production Svcs)*
Jerry Knight *(Gen Mgr-Project Svcs)*
Nicole Williams *(Mgr-Mktg & Comm)*
Paul Danos *(CEO)*

DANRIC HOMES
89 Durand Rd, LaGrange, GA 30241
Tel.: (706) 882-7773
Web Site: https://www.danric.com
Year Founded: 1974
Rev.: $12,088,909
Emp.: 30
Single-Family House Construction
N.A.I.C.S.: 236115
Darby Durand Pippin *(Pres)*

DANSER, INC.
US 50 E Murphytown Rd, Parkersburg, WV 26104
Tel.: (304) 679-3666
Web Site: http://www.danserinc.com
Year Founded: 1930
Sales Range: $10-24.9 Million
Emp.: 130
Fabricated Structural Metal Mfr
N.A.I.C.S.: 332312
Tim Buckley *(Engr-Mechanical)*

DANSKO INC.
8 Federal Rd, West Grove, PA 19390
Tel.: (610) 869-8335
Web Site: http://www.dansko.com
Year Founded: 1991
Sales Range: $10-24.9 Million
Emp.: 150
Footwear Distr
N.A.I.C.S.: 424340
Mimi Curry *(COO)*
Mark Diehl *(Sr VP-Sls)*
Scott Schwartz *(Gen Counsel)*
Jim Fox *(CEO)*

DANT CLAYTON CORPORATION
1500 Bernheim Ln, Louisville, KY
40210
Tel.: (502) 634-3626
Web Site:
   http://www.dantclayton.com
Sales Range: $10-24.9 Million
Emp.: 150

Dant Clayton Corporation—(Continued)

Stadium Furniture
N.A.I.C.S.: 337127
Bruce C. Merrick (Chm)
Billy Prather (Coord-Production & Matls)
Bryan Carey (Coord-Matl & Pur)
Cy Duvall (Mgr-Construction)
Joseph Price (Supvr-Shipping)
Kimberly Martin (Mgr-Pur)
Rick Bowman (Mgr-Network)
Keith Williams (Pres & CEO)
Tate Hutton (VP)
William Block (Reg Mgr)
Ylonda Davis (Controller)

DANTONE INC.
1200 Ridge Pike, Conshohocken, PA 19428
Tel.: (610) 825-7085   PA
Web Site: https://www.carriagetrade.com
Year Founded: 1977
Sales Range: $25-49.9 Million
Emp.: 175
Provider of Automobile Auctions
N.A.I.C.S.: 423110
Dominick Connicelli (CEO)
Robert Mazzola (Controller)
Brian McNally (Pres)
Brian McNally (Pres)

DANTZLER LUMBER & EXPORT CO., INC.
54 SW 6th St Ste 200, Hialeah, FL 33130.
Tel.: (305) 828-9666   FL
Web Site: http://www.dantzler1865.com
Year Founded: 1865
Sales Range: $10-24.9 Million
Emp.: 85
Provider of Lumber, Plywood & Millwork Services
N.A.I.C.S.: 423310
Antonio Godinez (Pres)
Vaughn Potter (Controller)

DANUSER MACHINE COMPANY, INC.
500 E 3rd St, Fulton, MO 65251-1679
Tel.: (573) 642-2246   MO
Web Site: https://www.danuser.com
Year Founded: 1910
Sales Range: $75-99.9 Million
Emp.: 65
Mfr of Digger Tractor Attachments, Earth Drills, Specialized OEM Metal Components & Construction Diggers
N.A.I.C.S.: 333111
Jerry Danuser (Pres)
Glen Danuser (VP)
Betty Smola (Mgr-Acctg)

DANVERS MOTOR COMPANY, INC.
106 Sylvan St, Danvers, MA 01923
Tel.: (978) 774-0727
Web Site: https://www.danversmotors.com
Year Founded: 1933
Sales Range: $10-24.9 Million
Emp.: 40
New Car Retailer
N.A.I.C.S.: 441110
Timothy Guinee (Pres)

DANVILLE COOPERATIVE ASSOCIATION INC.
1 Rail Rd Ave, Danville, KS 67036
Tel.: (620) 962-5238
Web Site: http://www.danvillecoop.com
Sales Range: $1-9.9 Million
Emp.: 22

Grains
N.A.I.C.S.: 424510
Mark McCoy (VP)
David R. Wedman (Pres)
Wayne Drouhard (Sec)

DANVILLE METAL STAMPING CO. INC.
20 Oakwood Ave, Danville, IL 61832
Tel.: (217) 446-0647
Web Site: http://www.danvillemetal.com
Sales Range: $25-49.9 Million
Emp.: 398
Engine Mount Parts, Aircraft
N.A.I.C.S.: 336412
Judd Peck (Pres & CEO)
Tom Neal (VP-Mfg)
Tim Scarlett (VP)
Rich George (CFO & VP-Fin)

DAPAT INC.
428 6th Ave NW, Dyersville, IA 52040
Tel.: (563) 875-8706   IA
Web Site: http://www.speccast.com
Year Founded: 1974
Sales Range: $10-24.9 Million
Emp.: 15
Mfr of Die-Cast & Pewter Collectibles
N.A.I.C.S.: 423920
Dave Bell (Pres)
Jennifer Gehrum (Controller)

DAPHNE UTILITY DEPT
900 Daphne Ave, Daphne, AL 36526
Tel.: (251) 626-2628
Web Site: https://www.daphneutilities.com
Year Founded: 1953
Sales Range: $10-24.9 Million
Emp.: 100
Sewage Treatment Facility Services
N.A.I.C.S.: 221320
Bob Segalla (Chm)
Rob McElroy (Gen Mgr)
Danny Lyndall (Gen Mgr)
Drew Klumpp (Mgr-Admin Svcs)
Teresa Logiotatos (Mgr-Fin)
Billy Mayhand (Treas & Sec)

DAQ ELECTRONICS, INC.
262 Old New Brunswick Rd Ste B, Piscataway, NJ 08854-3756
Tel.: (732) 981-0050   NJ
Web Site: https://www.daq.net
Year Founded: 1975
Sales Range: $25-49.9 Million
Emp.: 38
Mfr, Designer, Engineer & Field Supporter of Integrated Security & Communication Systems
N.A.I.C.S.: 334513
James Recchia (VP-Mktg & Sls)
David Green (Pres)
Roy Davies (VP-Design & Dev)
Robert J. Musumeci (VR-Ops)
Dave Bellina (Sr Mgr-Comm)

DAR CARS TOYOTA
12210 Cherry Hill Rd, Silver Spring, MD 20904
Tel.: (301) 622-0300
Web Site: http://www.darcars.com
Year Founded: 1973
Sales Range: $250-299.9 Million
Emp.: 350
New & Used Automobiles
N.A.I.C.S.: 441110
John R. Darvish (Pres)
Joe Moorman (Dir-Parts)

DAR-MEL INC.
4650 E Thomas Rd, Phoenix, AZ 85018
Tel.: (602) 840-0853
Sales Range: $10-24.9 Million

Emp.: 4
Fast-Food Restaurant, Chain
N.A.I.C.S.: 722513

DAR-TECH INC.
16485 Rockside Rd, Cleveland, OH 44137
Tel.: (216) 663-7600   OH
Web Site: http://www.dar-techinc.com
Year Founded: 1951
Sales Range: $10-24.9 Million
Emp.: 12
Specialty Raw Materials & Laboratory Equipment Distr
N.A.I.C.S.: 424690
Jim Benduhn (Sr VP)
Thomas Kramer (CFO)
Brett Walburn (Pres)
Pete Marek (VP-Distr)
Gina M. Tabasso (Mktg Dir)

DAR/RAN FURNITURE INDUSTRIES
2402 Shore St, High Point, NC 27263
Tel.: (336) 861-2400
Web Site: https://www.darran.com
Sales Range: $10-24.9 Million
Emp.: 150
Mfr of Wood Office Furniture
N.A.I.C.S.: 337211
Jennifer Hollingsworth (Pres)
Michael Darnell (Mgr-Admin Svcs)

DARANT DISTRIBUTING CORP.
1832 E 68th Ave, Denver, CO 80229
Tel.: (303) 289-2220
Web Site: https://www.darant.com
Year Founded: 1982
Sales Range: $10-24.9 Million
Emp.: 30
Whslr of Sliding Doors
N.A.I.C.S.: 423390
Robert C. Grant (Pres)

DARBY BUICK-GMC INC.
1455 Tamiami Trl S, Venice, FL 34285-4145
Tel.: (941) 488-3667
Web Site: http://www.darbyauto.com
Emp.: 68
Car Dealership
N.A.I.C.S.: 441110
Scott Frost (Owner & Pres)
Joe Mazur (Mgr-New Cars)
Mark Brandafino (Mgr-Used Cars)
Patrick Amboyan (Bus Mgr)
Brooks Crawford (Mgr-Parts)
Mary Frost (VP)
Ken Roberts (Mgr-Wholesale)
Geoffrey Lynch (Mgr-Svc)
Rachel Wallace (Office Mgr-Body Shop)
Travis Richolson (Mgr-Body Shop)

DARBY GROUP COMPANIES, INC.
300 Jericho Quadrangle Ste 200, Jericho, NY 11753
Tel.: (516) 683-1800   NY
Web Site: http://www.darbygroup.com
Year Founded: 1948
Sales Range: $650-699.9 Million
Emp.: 1,400
Medical, Dental, Veterinary Supplies, Dental Laboratory Equipment & Pharmaceutical Products Distr
N.A.I.C.S.: 423450
Carl Ashkin (CEO)
Michael Ashkin (Chm)
Laura Kahn (VP-Corp Mktg)
Justina Sorraci (CFO)

Subsidiaries:

Darby Dental Supply, LLC   (1)

300 Jericho Quadrangle, Jericho, NY 11753-2704
Tel.: (516) 683-1800
Web Site: http://www.darbydental.com
Sales Range: $50-74.9 Million
Emp.: 500
Dental Supplies
N.A.I.C.S.: 423450
Carl Ashkin (CEO)
Scott Walsh (VP-Sls)

Prima Dental Group   (1)
Stephenson Drive Waterwells Business Park, Gloucester, GL2 2HA, United Kingdom
Tel.: (44) 1452 729751
Web Site: http://www.primadental.com
Year Founded: 1976
Sales Range: $10-24.9 Million
Emp.: 150
Dental Product Mfr
N.A.I.C.S.: 339114
Daniel Hodgson (Mgr-Sls)
Annette John (Gen Mgr)

DARC CORPORATION
2500 W Higgins Rd Ste 1080, Hoffman Estates, IL 60169
Tel.: (847) 519-3150
Web Site: http://www.darc.com
Sales Range: $10-24.9 Million
Emp.: 100
Computer Software Systems Analysis & Design
N.A.I.C.S.: 541511
Brian J. Connolly (Founder, Pres & COO)
Donald E. Kidwell (Sr VP-Bus Dev)
Sheila B. Quinn (VP-Risk Mgmt & Gen Counsel)

DARCARS AUTOMOTIVE GROUP
12511 Prosperity Dr, Silver Spring, MD 20904
Tel.: (888) 808-1431
Web Site: http://www.darcars.com
Year Founded: 1977
Sales Range: $10-24.9 Million
Emp.: 400
Car Dealerships Owner & Operator
N.A.I.C.S.: 441110
John R. Darvish (Pres)
Gary Amey (VP)
Dan Noell (VP)
Ramin Robinson (Gen Mgr-Sls)
Terry Ferguson (Mgr-Sls)
Lalin Gallart (Gen Mgr)
Oscar Bonilla (Mgr-Fin)
Henry Marin (Mgr-Fin)
James Walker (Mgr-Fin)
Tim Williams (Mgr-Fin)
Jose Alvarado (Mgr-Used Vehicle)

Subsidiaries:

Darcars Ford   (1)
9020 Lanham Severn Rd, Lanham, MD 20706-2922
Tel.: (301) 459-1100
Web Site: http://www.darcarsford.com
Sales Range: $10-24.9 Million
Emp.: 12
Automobile Dealership
N.A.I.C.S.: 441110

DARCARS TOYOTA SCION
15625 Frederick Rd, Rockville, MD 20855
Tel.: (301) 340-0900
Web Site: http://www.darcarstoyota.com
Sales Range: $10-24.9 Million
Emp.: 50
Car Whslr
N.A.I.C.S.: 441110
Jorge Gallert (Gen Mgr)

DARCO ENTERPRISES INC.
5200 W 73rd St, Chicago, IL 60638-6616
Tel.: (312) 243-3000

Web Site: http://www.northern-container.com
Sales Range: $25-49.9 Million
Emp.: 6
Metals Service Centers & Offices
N.A.I.C.S.: 423510
John Friedman *(Pres)*

DARE PRODUCTS INCORPORATED
860 Betterly Rd, Springfield, MI 49037
Tel.: (269) 965-2307
Web Site:
https://www.dareproducts.com
Sales Range: $10-24.9 Million
Emp.: 40
Insulators & Insulation Materials, Electrical
N.A.I.C.S.: 335932
Brad Wilson *(VP)*
Robert M. Wilson Jr. *(Founder)*

DARET INC.
33 Daret Dr, Ringwood, NJ 07456
Tel.: (973) 962-6005
Web Site: http://www.daret.com
Year Founded: 1972
Sales Range: $10-24.9 Million
Emp.: 100
Plastic Color Molds & Products
N.A.I.C.S.: 322220
Howard Pitts *(Pres)*
Theresa Mulligan *(Mgr-Payroll)*

DARI-MART STORES INC.
125 E 6th Ave, Junction City, OR 97448-1807
Tel.: (541) 998-2388
Web Site: https://www.darimart.com
Sales Range: $25-49.9 Million
Emp.: 400
Convenience Store
N.A.I.C.S.: 445131
Charlie Box *(Mgr-IT)*
Cory Brown *(Engr-Network)*

DARIC CORPORATION
234 Marshall St, Redwood City, CA 94059
Tel.: (650) 218-4287   DE
Web Site: http://www.daric.com
Year Founded: 2011
Sales Range: $10-24.9 Million
Emp.: 3
Internet-Based Peer-To-Peer Lending
N.A.I.C.S.: 522291
Vasant Ramachandran *(CTO)*

DARK HORSE COMICS, INC.
10956 SE Main St, Milwaukie, OR 97222-7644
Tel.: (503) 652-8815   OR
Web Site: https://www.darkhorse.com
Year Founded: 1986
Sales Range: $75-99.9 Million
Emp.: 80
Comic Books & Multimedia Publisher
N.A.I.C.S.: 513120
Mike Richardson *(Founder & CEO)*
Neil Hankerson *(Exec VP)*
Amy Huey *(Mgr-Adv & Clearances)*
Chris Gaslin *(Dir-Product Dev)*
Nick McWhorter *(VP-Media Licensing)*
Sarah Robertson *(Dir-Sls)*
Kari Yadro *(Dir-Custom Programs)*
Melissa Lomax *(Dir-Mktg)*
Vanessa Todd-Holmes *(VP-Production & Scheduling)*

DARK HORSE CONSULTING
1255 Treat Blvd, Suite 230, Walnut Creek, CA 94597
Tel.: (408) 326-0303
N.A.I.C.S.: 541611

Subsidiaries:

BioTechLogic, Inc.   (1)
717 Indian Rd, Glenview, IL 60025
Tel.: (847) 730-3475
Web Site: http://www.biotechlogic.com
Biopharmaceutical Product Mfr
N.A.I.C.S.: 325412
Patrick Giljum *(Head-Ops)*

DARK HORSE MARKETING
455 Main St Ste 102, New Rochelle, NY 10801
Tel.: (914) 632-1584
Web Site:
http://www.darkhorsemarketing.com
Year Founded: 2002
Sales Range: Less than $1 Million
Emp.: 5
N.A.I.C.S.: 541810
Belinda Brouder Hayes *(Owner)*

DARLAND PROPERTIES
4115 S 133rd St, Omaha, NE 68137-1105
Tel.: (402) 330-1440   NE
Web Site: https://www.darland.com
Year Founded: 1974
Sales Range: $75-99.9 Million
Emp.: 35
Provider of Real Estate Services
N.A.I.C.S.: 236220
Erik Wagner *(Exec VP)*
Kevin Amick *(VP)*
Lisa Clapp *(Mgr-Property)*

DARLENE JEWELRY MANUFACTURING COMPANY
93 Park Pl, Pawtucket, RI 02860
Tel.: (401) 728-3300   RI
Web Site:
http://www.darlenegroup.com
Sales Range: $1-9.9 Million
Emp.: 20
Mfr of Costume Jewelry
N.A.I.C.S.: 339910
Maria Baccari *(Pres)*

DARLIND
1540 Route 55, Lagrangeville, NY 12540
Tel.: (845) 223-5115
Web Site:
https://www.darlindconstruction.com
Year Founded: 1977
Sales Range: $25-49.9 Million
Emp.: 250
Commercial & Institutional Building Construction Services
N.A.I.C.S.: 236220
Jason Pettit *(Project Mgr)*

DARLING BOLT CO.
2941 E 10 Mile Rd, Warren, MI 48091
Tel.: (586) 757-4100
Web Site: http://www.darlingbolt.com
Rev.: $10,115,189
Emp.: 39
Industrial Fasteners
N.A.I.C.S.: 423840
Timothy P. Heacock *(Pres)*

DARLING HOMES
2500 Legacy Dr Ste 100, Frisco, TX 75034
Tel.: (469) 252-2200   TX
Web Site:
http://www.darlinghomes.com
Year Founded: 1998
Sales Range: $10-24.9 Million
Emp.: 120
Home Construction Services
N.A.I.C.S.: 236115

William Darling *(Pres)*
Shannon Vining *(Mgr-Mktg-Houston)*
Amy Haywood-Rino *(Pres-Houston)*
Karla Horton *(VP-Sls & Mktg)*

Subsidiaries:

Darling Interests, Inc.   (1)
2500 Legacy Dr Ste 100, Frisco, TX 75034-5984
Tel.: (469) 252-2200
Web Site: http://www.darlinghomes.com
Single-Family Housing Construction
N.A.I.C.S.: 236115

DARLING'S INC.
96 Pkwy S Unit 1, Brewer, ME 04412
Tel.: (207) 992-1740   ME
Web Site: http://www.darlings.com
Year Founded: 1976
Sales Range: $125-149.9 Million
Emp.: 400
Retailer of New & Used Automobiles; Whslr & Distr of Motor Vehicle Parts
N.A.I.C.S.: 441110
John B. Darling *(Principal & Consultant)*
Charles Rohn *(Exec VP)*
Timothy Daugherty *(Treas)*
Jay Darling *(Pres)*
Bob Jonah *(Gen Mgr-Darlings Honda Nissan Volvo)*
Kerry Galeaz *(Mgr-Sls-Darlings Auto Mall)*

DARLINGTON VENEER COMPANY
225 4th St, Darlington, SC 29532-4025
Tel.: (843) 393-3861   SC
Web Site:
http://www.darlingtonveneer.com
Year Founded: 1918
Sales Range: $600-649.9 Million
Emp.: 210
Hardwood & Plywood
N.A.I.C.S.: 321918
Reginald H. Hubbard *(Treas & VP)*
H. M. Reynolds *(Mgr-Sls)*

DARR FAMILY FOUNDATION
2870-D S Ingram Mill Rd, Springfield, MO 65804
Tel.: (417) 888-1495
Web Site: http://www.darrff.org
Year Founded: 2002
Financial Resources Agency
N.A.I.C.S.: 525990
Heather Zoromski *(Exec Dir)*

DARRAGH CO
4801 Wheeler Ave, Fort Smith, AR 72901
Tel.: (479) 648-3930
Web Site:
http://www.darraghcompany.com
Rev.: $4,075,000
Emp.: 100
Construction & Mining, except Oil Well, Machinery & Equipment Merchant Whslr
N.A.I.C.S.: 423810
Loretta Collins *(Mgr)*
Rich Dunlap *(CEO)*

Subsidiaries:

Service Construction Supply, Inc.   (1)
2516 6th Ave S, Birmingham, AL 35233
Tel.: (205) 252-3158
Web Site:
http://www.serviceconstructionsupply.com
Sales Range: $1-9.9 Million
Emp.: 45
Lumber, Plywood, Millwork & Wood Panel Merchant Whslr
N.A.I.C.S.: 423310
Gil Roberts *(Pres)*

DARRAGH COMPANY

1401 E 6th St, Little Rock, AR 72202
Tel.: (501) 372-2112
Web Site:
https://www.darraghcompany.com
Rev.: $15,000,000
Emp.: 45
Construction Supplies
N.A.I.C.S.: 423320
Rich Dunlup *(VP)*
Mitchell Forbush *(Sec)*
Scott Trammel *(Dir-Retail Ops)*
F. Kramer Darragh III *(Pres)*

DARRELL DINSMORE GRADING INC.
1995 Dr Bramblett Rd, Cumming, GA 30028
Tel.: (770) 781-4347   GA
Web Site:
https://www.dinsmoregrading.com
Year Founded: 1993
Sales Range: $10-24.9 Million
Grading Services
N.A.I.C.S.: 237310
Darrell Dinsmore *(Owner)*
Stan Pyles *(Ops Mgr-Residential Div)*
Mike Burke *(Ops Mgr-Comml Div)*
Chet Mirabal *(Sls Mgr)*

DARRELL WALTRIP HONDA-VOLVO
1450 Murfreesboro Rd, Franklin, TN 37067
Tel.: (615) 791-1101
Web Site:
http://www.darrellwaltriphonda.com
Sales Range: $10-24.9 Million
Emp.: 60
Car Whslr
N.A.I.C.S.: 441110
John Gallagher *(Gen Mgr)*
Kelly Harrell *(Acct Mgr)*
Darrell L. Waltrip *(Pres)*

DARRELL'S SIGN COMPANY
10965 Hwy 242, Conroe, TX 77385
Tel.: (936) 321-4888
Web Site: http://www.darrellsign.com
Custom Sign Services
N.A.I.C.S.: 541490
Anthony Tinsley *(Mgr)*

Subsidiaries:

AdCorP Sign Systems, LLC   (1)
10965 Hwy 242, Conroe, TX 77385
Tel.: (936) 321-4888
Web Site: http://www.adcorp-usa.com
Custom Sign Mfr
N.A.I.C.S.: 339950

DART APPRAISAL.COM, INC.
2600 W Big Beaver Rd Ste 540, Troy, MI 48084-4754   MI
Web Site:
http://www.dartappraisal.com
Year Founded: 1993
Offices of Real Estate Appraisers
N.A.I.C.S.: 531320
Michael Dresden *(Pres)*
Christie Visconti *(VP-Fin)*
Darton Case *(Owner & CEO)*
Tracey Vollatrauer *(VP-Compliance & Process Control)*

Subsidiaries:

MaxVantage LLC   (1)
PO Box 460, 08750, Sea Girt, NJ
Tel.: (732) 556-4000
Web Site: http://www.maxvantageamc.com
Professional, Scientific & Technical Services
N.A.I.C.S.: 541990

DART BANK
368 S Park St, Mason, MI 48854
Tel.: (517) 676-3661
Web Site: http://www.dartbank.com
Sales Range: $50-74.9 Million

Dart Bank—(Continued)

Emp.: 84
National Commercial Banks
N.A.I.C.S.: 522110
Kim Harless (Officer-Treasury Mgmt & VP)
Devin Lavengood (VP & Mgr-Comml Relationship)
Sally Rae (Exec VP)
Nanette Listing (Officer-Ops & VP)
Karla Spoor (Sr VP-HR)
Danielle Bull (VP & Controller)
Scott Cornell (Officer-IT & VP)
John Morris (VP & Mgr-Comml Relationship)
Bryan Clark (Sr VP-Mortgage Banking & Mktg Div)
Dann Small (Sr VP)
David Farhat (Mgr-Quality Assurance-Mktg Div)
Debra Mack (CFO & Sr VP)
Joseph A. Joseph (Sr VP-Mortgage Banking & Mktg Div)
Susan Webster (Officer-Loan Ops & VP)
Adam Goss (VP & Mgr-Comml Relationship)
Dan Wilkinson (Mgr-Comml Relationship)
Kassie Rhodes (VP & Mgr-Comml Relationship)
Colleen Briggs (Officer-Consumer Loan & CRA & Asst VP)
John Blossey (Officer-Credit & VP)
Carol Ann Henson Lee (Officer-BSA & Auditor)
William Hufnagel (Pres & CEO)
Gerald Sambaer (CFO-Mortgage Banking Ops & Mktg Div)
Kevin Waldie (Chief Risk Officer, Officer-Audit, Compliance & BSA & VP)

DART CONTAINER CORPORATION
500 Hogsback Rd, Mason, MI 48854-9541
Tel.: (517) 248-5960   MI
Web Site:
   https://www.dartcontainer.com
Year Founded: 1937
Sales Range: $1-4.9 Billion
Emp.: 13,500
Polystyrene Foam Product Manufacturing
N.A.I.C.S.: 326140
Robert Novak (Exec VP-Sls)
Christine Waltz (CFO & Exec VP-Fin)
Mike Lonsway (Exec VP-Engrg & Machinery Mfg)
Tom Jewell (Exec VP-Bus Dev)
Keith Clark (Exec VP-Mfg)

Subsidiaries:

Dart Cup Ltd   (1)
2121 Markham Road, Toronto, M1B 2W3, ON, Canada
Tel.: (705) 653-2877
Web Site: http://www.container.com
Sales Range: $10-24.9 Million
Emp.: 50
Plastic Cup Mfr
N.A.I.C.S.: 322219
Jess Hamilton (Plant Mgr)

Dart Products Ltd   (1)
Garretts Ln, Cradley Heath, B64 5RE, W Midlands, United Kingdom
Tel.: (44) 01215591414
Web Site: http://www.dart.biz
Sales Range: $10-24.9 Million
Emp.: 75
Plastic Cup Mfr
N.A.I.C.S.: 322219

Dart Sudamericana S.A.   (1)
Calle 9 y 15 Fraccion I Lote 16 Parque Industrial Pilar, Buenos Aires, 1269, Argentina

Tel.: (54) 2322496600
Web Site: http://www.dart.biz
Sales Range: $10-24.9 Million
Emp.: 70
Plastics Product Mfr
N.A.I.C.S.: 326199

Phoenix Manufacturing Services Pty. Ltd.   (1)
118 Long St, Smithfield, 2164, NSW, Australia
Tel.: (61) 2 9757 1488
Foam Cup Mfr
N.A.I.C.S.: 326140

Solo Cup Company   (1)
300 Tri State Intl Ste 200, Lincolnshire, IL 60069
Tel.: (847) 444-5000
Web Site: http://www.solocup.com
Sales Range: $1-4.9 Billion
Emp.: 250
Paper & Plastic Cups Mfr & Distr
N.A.I.C.S.: 326199

Subsidiary (Domestic):

Solo Cup Operating Corporation   (2)
10100 Reisterstown Rd, Owings Mills, MD 21117-3815
Tel.: (410) 363-1111
Web Site: http://www.solocup.com
Sales Range: $900-999.9 Million
Paper, Foam & Plastic Disposable Foodservice Products Mfr
N.A.I.C.S.: 326199

Branch (Domestic):

Solo Cup Company   (3)
1550 Wrightsboro Rd, Augusta, GA 30904-4079
Tel.: (706) 737-7000
Web Site: http://www.sweetheart.com
Sales Range: $25-49.9 Million
Emp.: 250
Mfr of Disposable Foodservice Products
N.A.I.C.S.: 722511

Solo Cup Company   (3)
PO Box 2090, Springfield, MO 65801-2090
Tel.: (417) 862-2744
Web Site: http://www.solocup.com
Sales Range: $75-99.9 Million
Emp.: 350
Mfr of Disposable Foodservice Products
N.A.I.C.S.: 423830

Solo Cup Company   (3)
2260 Delray Rd, Thomaston, GA 30286-1413
Tel.: (706) 647-2205
Web Site: http://www.solocup.com
Sales Range: $25-49.9 Million
Emp.: 35
All Other Plastics Product Mfr
N.A.I.C.S.: 326199

Sweetheart Cup Company Inc.   (3)
1455 Hwy 138 Northeast, Conyers, GA 30013-1267
Tel.: (770) 483-9556
Web Site: http://www.sweetheart.com
Sales Range: $50-74.9 Million
Emp.: 550
Mfr of Disposable Foodservice Products
N.A.I.C.S.: 722511

DART INTERNATIONAL
1430 S Eastman Ave, Los Angeles, CA 90023
Tel.: (323) 264-1011
Web Site:
   http://www.dartinternational.com
Sales Range: $25-49.9 Million
Emp.: 500
Long Haul & Local Trucking With Storage
N.A.I.C.S.: 484110
Terence Dedeaux (Chm)
Steve Okamura (CFO)
Joseph M. Medlin (VP-Bus Dev)
Don Brown (VP)
Rich Vitek (Gen Mgr)

DART TRANSIT COMPANY

800 Lone Oak Rd, Eagan, MN 55121-2212
Tel.: (651) 688-2000   MN
Web Site: https://www.dart.net
Year Founded: 1934
Sales Range: $150-199.9 Million
Emp.: 400
Freight & Transportation Services
N.A.I.C.S.: 484121
Donald G. Oren (Chm)

Subsidiaries:

Dart Portable Storage, Inc.   (1)
800 Lone Oak Rd, Eagan, MN 55121
Tel.: (651) 683-1667
Web Site:
   http://www.dartportablestorage.com
Metal Container Mfr
N.A.I.C.S.: 332439

Dartco, Inc.   (1)
2800 Sawnee Ave, Buford, GA 30518
Tel.: (800) 333-5500
Web Site: http://www.dartcoinc.com
Food Transportation Services
N.A.I.C.S.: 488490

Pro Stop Truck Service Inc.   (1)
800 Lone Oak Rd, Eagan, MN 55121-2212
Tel.: (651) 452-8137
Web Site: https://www.dart.net
Rev.: $10,000,000
Emp.: 200
Diesel Engine Repair: Automotive
N.A.I.C.S.: 811111
David Oren (Pres)

DART WAREHOUSE CORPORATION
1430 S Eastman Ave, Los Angeles, CA 90023
Tel.: (323) 264-1011
Sales Range: $250-299.9 Million
Emp.: 250
General Warehousing
N.A.I.C.S.: 493110
Robert Santag (Pres)
Perry Dedeaux (Chm)
Philip Feldman (Dir-Corp Security)
Raj Dhami (Project Mgr)

DARTMOUTH BOOKSTORE INC.
33 S Main St, Hanover, NH 03755
Tel.: (603) 643-3616
Web Site:
   http://www.dartmouthbooks.bn
college.com
Sales Range: $10-24.9 Million
Emp.: 10
Book Sales
N.A.I.C.S.: 459210
Bernadette Farrell (Gen Mgr)

DARTMOUTH BUILDING SUPPLY INC.
958 Reed Rd, North Dartmouth, MA 02747-1520
Tel.: (508) 990-2389   MA
Web Site:
   https://www.dartmouthbuilding
supply.com
Year Founded: 1984
Sales Range: $10-24.9 Million
Emp.: 80
Provider of Lumber, Plywood & Millwork Services
N.A.I.C.S.: 423310
Joseph Delgado (Founder & CEO)
Tim Patenaude (Gen Mgr)

DARTNELL ENTERPRISES INC.
1400 Blossom Rd, Rochester, NY 14610-2220
Tel.: (585) 224-9000   DE
Web Site: http://www.dartnell.com
Year Founded: 1985
Sales Range: $10-24.9 Million

Emp.: 3
Provider of Computer Integrated Systems Design Services
N.A.I.C.S.: 541512
Ronald E. Wilson (Pres)
Peggy Wright (Office Mgr)

DARVIN FURNITURE
15400 S La Grange Rd, Orland Park, IL 60462-4799
Tel.: (708) 460-4100
Web Site: https://www.darvin.com
Year Founded: 1920
Sales Range: $25-49.9 Million
Emp.: 300
Furniture Whslr
N.A.I.C.S.: 449110
Marty Darvin (Owner)

DARWILL PRESS, INC.
11900 Roosevelt Rd, Hillside, IL 60162
Tel.: (708) 236-4900
Web Site: https://www.darwill.com
Year Founded: 1951
Sales Range: $25-49.9 Million
Emp.: 150
Printing & Direct Marketing Services
N.A.I.C.S.: 323111
Troy Van Dyke (Co-CEO)
Brandon Van Dyke (Co-CEO)
Beth Gill (Dir-Rels)
Debbie Bills (Controller)
Gus Gutierrez (Dir-Technical Svcs)
Jim Antis (Gen Mgr)
Jon Romano (VP-Sls)
Mark DeBoer (Dir-Customer Experience)
Mark Pageau (VP-Sls)

DARYL FLOOD RELOCATION & LOGISTICS
450 Airline Dr, Coppell, TX 75019
Tel.: (972) 471-1496
Web Site: https://www.darylflood.com
Year Founded: 1982
Sales Range: $25-49.9 Million
Moving & Relocation Services
N.A.I.C.S.: 484210
Daryl Flood (Founder, Pres & CEO)
Jason Smith (Dir-Fleet Svcs)
J. Kelly O'Connor (VP-Sls & Mktg)
Linda Carithers (Coord-Customer Svc)

DAS ACQUISITION COMPANY, LLC
12140 Woodcrest Executive Dr Ste 150, Saint Louis, MO 63141
Tel.: (314) 628-2000
Web Site: http://www.usa-mortgage.com
Sales Range: $5-14.9 Billion
Emp.: 200
Mortgage Loans & Services
N.A.I.C.S.: 522310
Douglas Schukar (Pres & CEO)
Linda Pring (Exec VP)
Stephanie Todd (Mgr-Mktg)

DAS DISTRIBUTORS INC.
724 Lawn Rd, Palmyra, PA 17078
Tel.: (717) 964-3642   PA
Web Site: https://www.dasinc.com
Year Founded: 1978
Sales Range: $25-49.9 Million
Emp.: 500
Provider of Electrical Appliance Services
N.A.I.C.S.: 423620
Steve Birli (VP-Travel Centers)
Wendy Stoviak (VP-Brands & Mktg)
Chuck White (VP-Brands & Mktg)

DAS GLOBAL CAPITAL CORP.
1785 E Sahara Ave Ste 490, Las Vegas, NV 89104

Tel.: (281) 914-8635   NV
Web Site:
     http://www.dasglobalcapital.com
Year Founded: 2011
Sales Range: $10-24.9 Million
Emp.: 1
Real Estate Services
N.A.I.C.S.: 531390
Darrell A. Calloway *(Treas & Sec)*

DAS HEALTH VENTURES, INC.
1000 N Ashley Dr Ste 300, Tampa,
FL 33602
Tel.: (813) 774-9800
Web Site: http://www.dashealth.com
Year Founded: 2003
Health Care Srvices
N.A.I.C.S.: 456199
David Schlaifer *(Founder & Chm)*
Kyle Mynatt *(Sr VP-Technology Solutions)*
Julianne Porter *(Sr VP-Business Solutions)*
Eric Fudge *(Sr VP-Fin)*
Michelle Jaeger *(Pres & CEO)*
Emile Clifford *(Sr VP-HR & Admin)*
Adam Kravatz *(Gen Counsel & VP)*
Marc Porupsky *(VP-Growth)*

Subsidiaries:

Automated Medical Systems Inc. **(1)**
2310 N Patterson St Ste H, Valdosta, GA
31602
Tel.: (229) 253-9526
Software Development Services
N.A.I.C.S.: 513210
David Lingefelt *(Pres)*

DAS, INC.
1717 Route 6, Carmel, NY 10512
Tel.: (845) 282-7859   NV
Web Site: http://www.dastrader.com
Year Founded: 2007
Sales Range: Less than $1 Million
Emp.: 4
Securities Trading Software Publisher
N.A.I.C.S.: 513210
Karen Gentile *(Treas & Sec)*

DASCO HOME MEDICAL EQUIPMENT
375 N West St, Westerville, OH
43082-1400
Tel.: (614) 901-2226
Web Site: https://www.godasco.com
Year Founded: 1987
Sales Range: $10-24.9 Million
Emp.: 110
Medical Equipment Mfr
N.A.I.C.S.: 339112
Rachel Mazur *(CEO)*
Jason Seeley *(Pres)*

DASEKE, INC.
15455 Dallas Pkwy Ste 550, Addison,
TX 75001-6785
Tel.: (972) 248-0412   DE
Year Founded: 2008
DSKE—(NASDAQ)
Rev.: $1,773,300,000
Assets: $1,195,400,000
Liabilities: $1,002,400,000
Net Worth: $193,000,000
Earnings: $44,500,000
Emp.: 4,123
Fiscal Year-end: 12/31/22
Holding Company; Freight Trucking &
Logistics Services
N.A.I.C.S.: 551112
Brian A. Bonner *(Executives)*

Subsidiaries:

Alabama Carriers, Inc.   **(1)**
3800 Industrial Dr, Birmingham, AL 35217
Web Site: https://alabamacarriers.com
Truckload Transportation Provider
N.A.I.C.S.: 484121

Aveda Transportation and Energy
Services Inc.   **(1)**
300 435 - 4th Avenue SW, Calgary, T2P
3A8, AB, Canada
Tel.: (403) 264-4950
Web Site: https://www.avedaenergy.com
Sales Range: $150-199.9 Million
Oilfield Transportation Services
N.A.I.C.S.: 484220
Mark Ackerman *(Mgr-Terminal)*

Bed Rock, Inc.   **(1)**
8141 E 7th St, Joplin, MO 64801
Tel.: (417) 624-3131
Freight Truck Transportation Services
N.A.I.C.S.: 484220

Belmont Enterprises, Inc.   **(1)**
935 83rd Ave SW, Tumwater, WA 98512
Tel.: (360) 628-8237
Web Site: https://www.belmonttrucking.com
Trucking Service
N.A.I.C.S.: 484121

Boyd Logistics, LLC   **(1)**
3275 Hwy 30, Clayton, AL 36016
Tel.: (334) 775-1240
Web Site: https://boydlogisticsllc.com
Logistic Services
N.A.I.C.S.: 488510
Scott Orazine *(Gen Mgr-Birmingham)*
Tobi Carter *(Coord-Logistics)*

Builders Transportation Co., LLC **(1)**
Po Box 16369 3710 Tulane Rd, Memphis,
TN 38116
Tel.: (800) 238-6803
General Freight Trucking, Long-Distance,
Truckload
N.A.I.C.S.: 484121

Bulldog Hiway Logistics, LLC   **(1)**
3390 Buffalo Ave N, Charleston, SC 29418
Tel.: (843) 744-1651
Web Site: https://www.bulldoghiway.com
Freight Truck Transportation Services
N.A.I.C.S.: 484220

Daseke Companies, Inc.   **(1)**
15455 Dallas Pkwy Ste 550, Addison, TX
75001
Tel.: (972) 248-0412
Holding Company; Freight Trucking & Logistics Services
N.A.I.C.S.: 551112

Subsidiary (Non-US):

Big Freight Systems Inc.   **(2)**
10 Hutchings Street, Winnipeg, R2X 2X1,
MB, Canada
Tel.: (204) 632-0025
Web Site: https://www.bigfreight.com
Freight Management & International Transport Services
N.A.I.C.S.: 488510

Subsidiary (Domestic):

Boyd Bros. Transportation Inc.   **(2)**
3275 Hwy 30, Clayton, AL 36016
Tel.: (334) 775-1400
Web Site: https://boydbros.com
General Trucking Services
N.A.I.C.S.: 484121
Nick Walker *(Dir-Ops)*
Jeff Hopkins *(Dir-Safety)*
Jay Fenn *(Dir-Ops)*
Kevin Spivey *(Mgr-Fleet)*
Ruth Brummitt *(Mgr-Fleet)*
Leigh Pody *(Mgr-Auto Liability Claims)*

Subsidiary (Domestic):

Mid Seven Transportation Co.   **(3)**
2323 Delaware Ave, Des Moines, IA 50317
Tel.: (515) 266-5181
Web Site: https://www.mid7.com
Transportation Services
N.A.I.C.S.: 488490
Rick Burroughs *(Dir-Safety)*

Subsidiary (Domestic):

Bulldog Hiway Express Inc.   **(2)**
3390 Buffalo Ave, North Charleston, SC
29418
Tel.: (843) 744-1651
Web Site: https://www.bulldoghiway.com
Trucking Service
N.A.I.C.S.: 484121

Central Oregon Truck Company,
Inc.   **(2)**
394 NE Hemlock Ave, Redmond, OR 97756
Tel.: (541) 504-4016
Web Site:
     https://www.centraloregontruck.com
Trucking Service
N.A.I.C.S.: 488490
Rick Williams *(Founder)*
Paul Coil *(CFO)*
Phil Taylor *(VP-Fleet Maintenance)*
Luke Williams *(Pres)*
Jessica Frey *(Controller)*
Lane Lyons *(Sls Dir)*
Brad Aimone *(Dir-Safety)*
Matt Ellsworth *(Dir-Operations)*
Jessica Arnold *(Dir-Human Resources)*
Dylan Stott *(Dir-Operations)*
Jessica Frey *(Controller)*
Lane Lyons *(Sls Dir)*
Brad Aimone *(Dir-Safety)*
Matt Ellsworth *(Dir-Operations)*
Jessica Arnold *(Dir-Human Resources)*
Dylan Stott *(Dir-Operations)*

Hornady Transportation, LLC   **(2)**
1736 Hwy 21 By-Pass, Monroeville, AL
36461
Tel.: (251) 575-4811
Web Site:
     http://www.hornadytransportation.com
Trucking Service
N.A.I.C.S.: 484121
Brad Bridges *(VP-Sls)*
Johnny Clardy *(Mgr-Terminal-Birmingham)*

J. Grady Randolph, Inc.   **(2)**
541 Concord Rd, Gaffney, SC 29341
Tel.: (864) 488-9030
Web Site: http://www.jgr-inc.com
Emp.: 200
Trucking & Logistics Services
N.A.I.C.S.: 484121
Mark S. Randolph *(Pres & CEO)*
Jimmy Randolph *(CFO)*
Mike Harlan *(Dir-Safety & HR)*
Ted Payne *(CFO)*
Jeff Vassey *(Controller)*

LoneStar Transportation, LLC   **(2)**
1100 Northway Dr, Fort Worth, TX 76131
Web Site: http://www.lonestar-llc.com
Trucking Service
N.A.I.C.S.: 561110

Moore Freight Service   **(2)**
2000 Eastbridge Blvd, Mascot, TN 37806
Tel.: (865) 932-2660
Web Site:
     http://www.moorefreightservice.com
Freight Transportation Arrangement
N.A.I.C.S.: 488510
Grant Mize *(CEO & COO)*
Julie Reasonover *(CFO)*

Schilli Transportation Services,
Inc.   **(2)**
6358 W US-24, Remington, IN 47977
Tel.: (219) 261-2101
Transportation Brokerage Services
N.A.I.C.S.: 488510

Subsidiary (Domestic):

Schilli Leasing, Inc.   **(3)**
1919 W Western Ave, South Bend, IN
46619
Tel.: (888) 233-1919
Web Site: http://www.nationalease.com
Truck Rental Services
N.A.I.C.S.: 532120

Scilli Specialized Flatbed Division,
Inc.   **(3)**
6358 W US 24, Remington, IN 47977
Tel.: (219) 261-2101
Web Site: http://www.schillispecialized.com
Flatbed Trucking & Transportation Services
N.A.I.C.S.: 484121

Subsidiary (Domestic):

Schilli Distribution Services, Inc. **(4)**
1560 Kepner Dr, Lafayette, IN 47905
Tel.: (765) 448-4888
Web Site: http://www.sdsscs.com
Supply Chain Management Services
N.A.I.C.S.: 541614
Vince Williamson *(Gen Mgr)*

Schilli Specialized, Inc.   **(4)**
6358 W US Hwy 24, Remington, IN 47977
Tel.: (219) 261-2101
Web Site: http://www.schillispecialized.com
Trucking Service
N.A.I.C.S.: 488490

Subsidiary (Domestic):

Smokey Point Distributing, Inc. **(2)**
19201 63rd Ave NE, Arlington, WA 98223
Web Site: https://www.spdtrucking.com
Trucking & Logistics Services
N.A.I.C.S.: 484122

Subsidiary (Domestic):

E.W. Wylie Corporation   **(3)**
2500 43rd St N, Fargo, ND 58102
Web Site: https://www.wylietrucking.com
Trucking & Logistics Services
N.A.I.C.S.: 484110
Scott Hoppe *(Pres & CEO)*

Subsidiary (Domestic):

Tennessee Steel Haulers, Inc.   **(2)**
2607 Brick Church Pike, Nashville, TN
37207
Tel.: (615) 271-2400
Web Site: https://www.tenh.com
Trucking Service
N.A.I.C.S.: 484121
Sid Stanley *(CEO)*
Gregg Stanley *(Co-CEO)*
Michael Sheehan *(Chief Bus Dev Officer)*
Scott Sheehan *(VP-Ops)*
Dan Smith *(Dir-Safety)*
Mike Morgan *(Dir-Equipment & Maint)*
Dan Waltz *(Asst VP-Fin)*
Natasha Chichester *(Mgr-Settlements & Billing)*
Jon Bagwell *(Dir-Fin Ops)*
Anthony VanArsdale *(Mgr-Freight-Southeast)*
Matthew Schroeder *(Mgr-Freight-Midwest)*

Fleet Movers, Inc.   **(1)**
2280 Cainhoy Rd, Huger, SC 29450
Tel.: (843) 529-0050
Web Site: https://www.fleetmoversinc.com
Flatbed Trucking Services
N.A.I.C.S.: 484121

Group One, Inc.   **(1)**
1445 Taney St N, Kansas City, MO 64116
Tel.: (816) 283-9500
Web Site:
     https://www.grouponetransport.com
Trucking Service
N.A.I.C.S.: 484121

Hornady Truck Line, Inc.   **(1)**
1736 Hwy 21 By-Pass, Monroeville, AL
36461
Tel.: (251) 575-4811
Freight Truck Transportation Services
N.A.I.C.S.: 484220
Susan Andress *(VP-Admin)*

Kelsey-Trail Trucking Ltd.   **(1)**
3914 Thatcher Ave, Saskatoon, S7R 1A4,
SK, Canada
Tel.: (306) 518-8733
Web Site: https://www.kelseytrail.com
Transportation Services
N.A.I.C.S.: 484230

Leavitts Freight Service, Inc.   **(1)**
3855 Marcola Rd, Springfield, OR 97477
Tel.: (541) 204-1902
Web Site: http://www.leavitts.com
Freight Services
N.A.I.C.S.: 484230
Ron Riddle *(Pres & CEO)*
Don Redding *(Ops Mgr)*

Lone Star Transportation, LLC   **(1)**
1100 Northway Dr, Fort Worth, TX 76131
Web Site: https://www.lonestar-llc.com
Transportation Services
N.A.I.C.S.: 488999

Roadmaster Transportation, Inc. **(1)**
1640 Stone Rdg Dr, Stone Mountain, GA
30083
Tel.: (770) 934-8555
Web Site: https://www.roadmastertrans.com
Trucking Service
N.A.I.C.S.: 484122

Daseke, Inc.—(Continued)

Edward Weeks (Pres)
Gary Stephens (VP)
Jim Holliday (VP & Gen Mgr)

SPD Trucking, LLC (1)
1660 240th St, Manchester, IA 52057
Tel.: (319) 310-3626
Emp.: 1
Freight Truck Transportation Services
N.A.I.C.S.: 484220

**Schilli National Truck Leasing &
Sales, Inc.** (1)
6358 W Us Hwy 24, Remington, IN 47977
Tel.: (219) 261-2100
Emp.: 50
Freight Truck Transportation Services
N.A.I.C.S.: 484220

Schilli Specialized of Texas, Inc. (1)
2401 N 4th St, Crockett, TX 75835
Tel.: (936) 544-7322
Freight Truck Transportation Services
N.A.I.C.S.: 484220

**Schilli Transportation Services,
Inc.** (1)
6358 Us 24 W, Remington, IN 47977
Tel.: (877) 724-4554
Freight Truck Transportation Services
N.A.I.C.S.: 484220

Steelman Transportation, Inc. (1)
2160 N Burton, Springfield, MO 65803
Tel.: (417) 831-6300
Web Site:
   https://www.steelmantransport.com
Trucking Service
N.A.I.C.S.: 484121
Josh White (Ops Mgr)
Kevin Corban (Gen Mgr)
Brett Sheets (CEO)
Cathy Clendening (CFO)
Mike Freese (Mgr-Accounting)
Tim Davis (Dir-Information Technology)
Ange Young (Mgr-Fleet)
Phillip Matney (Mgr-Fleet)
Timothy McCandless (Mgr-Hazmat & Over-
size)
Donna Underwood (Dir-Safety-Human Re-
sources)
Brad Crain (Mgr-Accounting)
Glen Beck (Dir)

WTI Transport, Inc. (1)
7300 Commerce Dr, Tuscaloosa, AL 35401
Web Site: https://www.wtitransport.com
Driving School Operator
N.A.I.C.S.: 611519
Jack Potthoff (Pres)
Jem Blair (VP-Safety)
Alan Martin (VP-Maintenance)
Josh King (VP-Ops)
Derek Hines (VP-Sls)
Larry Baker (VP)

XE.com Inc. (1)
1145 Nicholson Rd Ste 200, Newmarket,
L3Y 9C3, ON, Canada
Tel.: (416) 214-5606
Web Site: http://www.xe.com
Foreign Currency Exchange Services
N.A.I.C.S.: 523160

DASH ENTERPRISES INC.
2015 W Saint Paul Ave, Milwaukee,
WI 53233
Tel.: (414) 933-0808
Sales Range: $10-24.9 Million
Emp.: 50
Light Bulbs & Related Supplies
N.A.I.C.S.: 423610
Henry S. Albert (Pres)
Marty Brand (Mgr-Bus Dev)

DASHAMERICA INC.
101 S Taylor Ave, Louisville, CO
80027
Tel.: (303) 460-8888
Web Site: http://www.pearlizumi.com
Sales Range: $10-24.9 Million
Emp.: 115
Sportswear & Athletic Clothing
N.A.I.C.S.: 315250
Peggy Barrett (VP-Fin)

DASHER TECHNOLOGIES
INC.
655 Campbell Technology Pkwy Ste
150, Campbell, CA 95008
Tel.: (408) 409-2858
Web Site: http://www.dasher.com
Year Founded: 1982
Sales Range: $10-24.9 Million
Emp.: 35
Technology Solutions
N.A.I.C.S.: 423430
Laurie Dasher (CEO)
Angela Armstrong (Dir-Mktg)
Al Chien (Pres)
John Galatea (VP-Sls)

DASI CORPORATION
9716 Old Annapolis Rd, Ellicott City,
MD 21042
Tel.: (410) 730-7993
Rev.: $25,400,000
Emp.: 5
Dry, Condensed & Evaporated Dairy
Products
N.A.I.C.S.: 311514

DASI SOLUTIONS, LLC
31 Oakland Ave Ste 100, Pontiac, MI
48342
Tel.: (248) 333-2996
Web Site:
   http://www.dasisolutions.com
Emp.: 90
Computer Systems & Graphic Design
N.A.I.C.S.: 541512
David Darbyshire (Co-founder &
Owner)
Richard Darbyshire (CEO & Owner)
Scott Byrne (Dir-Bus Dev)
Bryon Morell (Mgr-Sls)
Laura Cominotto (Mgr-Mktg)
Connie Jaracz (Dir-HR)
Eric Endlich (Dir-IT)

Subsidiaries:

Digital Dimensions, Inc. (1)
3934 Murphy Canyon Rd B100, San Diego,
CA 92123
Tel.: (858) 279-2557
Web Site: http://www.ddicad.com
Sales Range: $1-9.9 Million
Emp.: 27
Computer & Computer Peripheral Equip-
ment & Software Merchant Whslr
N.A.I.C.S.: 423430
Brain Findley (Mgr-Ops)

DASIGN SOURCE & CO. INC.
11500 Overseas Hwy, Marathon, FL
33050
Tel.: (305) 743-7130
Web Site:
   https://www.dasignsource.com
Sales Range: $10-24.9 Million
Emp.: 100
Single-Family Housing Construction
N.A.I.C.S.: 236115
Anthony D'ascanio (Owner)

DASP GROUP LLC
760 Oak Glen Rd, Howell, NJ 07731
Tel.: (732) 523-1432
Web Site: http://www.savewize.com
Year Founded: 2011
Sales Range: $10-24.9 Million
Emp.: 4
Household Product Distr
N.A.I.C.S.: 423620
David Pinter (CEO)

DASWANI V. I. INC.
5175 Dronningens Gade Ste 2, Saint
Thomas, VI 00802
Tel.: (340) 776-4110
Web Site:
   http://www.royalcaribbeanvi.com
Sales Range: $25-49.9 Million

Emp.: 120
Jewelry /Camera Store
N.A.I.C.S.: 458310
Prem Daswani (Pres)

DATA AGE BUSINESS SYS-
TEMS, INC.
10225 Ulmerton Rd Ste 10-A, Largo,
FL 33771
Tel.: (727) 582-9100
Web Site: http://www.dataage.com
Year Founded: 1988
Sales Range: $1-9.9 Million
Emp.: 35
Financial Transactions Software &
Solutions
N.A.I.C.S.: 513210
Tom Streng (Co-Founder & Chm)
Randy Peffly (Co-Founder & Exec
VP)
Len Summa (CEO)
Bill Reinacher (Dir-Ops)
Vanessa Gray (CFO)
Kari Rinehart (Dir-Sls & Ops)
Dave Larson (Dir-Sls-Global)
Bill Booth (VP-Product Dev)
Bill Brannan (Dir-Software Dev)
Anthony Parise (Acct Mgr-Technical
Enterprise)

DATA ANALYSIS, INC.
12655 Beatrice St, Los Angeles, CA
90066-7300
Tel.: (310) 448-6800   CA
Web Site:
   http://www.oneilsecurities.com
Sales Range: $100-124.9 Million
Emp.: 600
Investor Business Information
N.A.I.C.S.: 523150
Justin Nielson (Chm)

DATA BUSINESS SYSTEMS
INC.
156 Business Park Dr, Virginia
Beach, VA 23462
Tel.: (757) 490-1294
Web Site: https://www.1dbs.com
Year Founded: 1977
Rev.: $14,000,000
Emp.: 70
Cash Registers
N.A.I.C.S.: 423420
Larry Harmon (Pres)
Bob Doxey (Controller)

DATA CAPTURE SOLUTIONS
INC.
160 West Rd, Ellington, CT 06029
Tel.: (860) 812-0008
Web Site:
   http://www.datacapturesolution.com
Rev.: $12,547,493
Emp.: 49
Broker Services
N.A.I.C.S.: 541990
Joe Teixeira (Pres)
Mark Lonabaugh (Mgr-IT)
Carole Burbank (Mgr-Natl Sls)

DATA CENTER INC.
20 W 2nd Ave, Hutchinson, KS
67501
Tel.: (620) 694-6800
Web Site:
   http://www.datacenterinc.com
Year Founded: 1964
Sales Range: $10-24.9 Million
Emp.: 300
Data Processing & Preparation
N.A.I.C.S.: 518210
John H. Jones (CEO)
Candace Wolke (Pres-Market)
Sarah Fankhauser (Pres & COO)
Dennis Queal (CFO & Exec VP)

Susan Flores (Sr VP-Customer Sup-
port)
Tanna Faulkner (Sr VP-Sls & Digital
Comm)
Paul Jones (VP-Pro Svcs)
Mark Harris (VP-Mktg)
Daren Fankhauser (Chief Dev Officer
& Sr VP)
Sencer Tasan (CTO)

DATA COMPUTER CORPORA-
TION OF AMERICA
5310 Dorsey Hall Dr, Ellicott City, MD
21042
Tel.: (410) 992-3760
Web Site: https://www.dcca.com
Sales Range: $10-24.9 Million
Emp.: 150
Computer Related Consulting Ser-
vices
N.A.I.C.S.: 541512
David E. Bower (CEO)
Sharon Villeger (VP)

DATA CORE SYSTEMS INC.
1880 John F Kennedy Blvd Fl 15,
Philadelphia, PA 19103
Tel.: (215) 243-1983
Web Site: http://www.dclgroup.com
Rev.: $13,000,000
Emp.: 34
Computer Software Development &
Applications
N.A.I.C.S.: 541511
Pradeep Banerjee (Exec Dir)
Sandip Ghosh (Mng Dir)
Ganesh C. Nundy (Vice Chm & Mng
Dir)
Subir K. Dasgupta (Vice Chm)
Anil C. Banerjee (Chm)
Shyamal Choudhury (CEO)

Subsidiaries:

Biz-Core (1)
111 Sinclair Rd, Bristol, PA 19007-1522
Tel.: (215) 633-5900
Web Site: http://www.biz-core.com
Data Processing & Preparation
N.A.I.C.S.: 518210

DATA DIMENSIONS CORP.
400 Midland Ct, Janesville, WI 53546
Tel.: (608) 757-1100
Web Site:
   https://www.datadimensions.com
Sales Range: $10-24.9 Million
Emp.: 300
Data Processing & Preparation
N.A.I.C.S.: 518210
Karin Hallett (VP-HR)
Cindi Benson (VP-Fin)
Amanda Kilburg (VP-Implementation)
Brian Maag (VP-Application Dev)
John Boumstein (Chm)
Constantine Moshos (Exec VP-Bus
Dev)
Kathy Miller (VP-Ops)
Michael Effner (Chief Information Se-
curity Officer)

DATA DISTRIBUTING, LLC
107 Dakota Ave Ste 3, Santa Cruz,
CA 95060
Tel.: (831) 457-3537
Web Site:
   http://www.datadistributing.com
Year Founded: 1984
Sales Range: $10-24.9 Million
Emp.: 30
Image-Intensive Digital Storage;
Computer Disks
N.A.I.C.S.: 334112
Nancy Fisher (Pres & CEO)

DATA EXCHANGE CORPORA-
TION

3600 Via Pescador, Camarillo, CA
93012-5051
Tel.: (805) 388-1711   CA
Web Site: http://www.dex.com
Year Founded: 1980
Sales Range: $10-24.9 Million
Emp.: 300
Computer Maintenance & Repair
N.A.I.C.S.: 811210
Sheldon Malchicoff *(Founder)*

Subsidiaries:

DEX Supply Chain Services Cooper-
atie N.V.   (1)
Cooperatie UA Zwenkgras 3, 5986 PM, Ber-
inge, Netherlands
Tel.: (31) 11 322767 1613
Logistics Consulting Servies
N.A.I.C.S.: 541614

DEX Supply Chain Services
Limited   (1)
Tongwell Street Opal Drive, Fox Milne, Mil-
ton Keynes, United Kingdom
Tel.: (44) 1908 606266
Logistics Consulting Servies
N.A.I.C.S.: 541614

Data Exchange Europe, Ltd   (1)
IDA Business & Technology Park, Clon-
shaugh, Dublin, Ireland
Tel.: (353) 1 848 6555
Logistics Consulting Servies
N.A.I.C.S.: 541614
Thomas Humphry *(Mgr-Bus Dev)*

DATA IMAGING & ASSOCI-
ATES
224 9th St NW, Hickory, NC 28601
Tel.: (828) 322-8295
Web Site: http://www.datai.com
Year Founded: 1973
Rev.: $12,000,000
Emp.: 20
Business Forms Distr
N.A.I.C.S.: 424120
Dent Guarino *(CFO)*
Sherry Reinheardt *(Controller)*

DATA INDUSTRIES LTD.
1370 Broadway Ste 519, New York,
NY 10018
Tel.: (212) 747-9166
Web Site: http://www.dataind.com
Rev.: $35,000,786
Emp.: 15
Computer Related Consulting Ser-
vices
N.A.I.C.S.: 541512
Charles Duval *(Founder & Pres)*

DATA LABEL INC.
1000 Spruce St, Terre Haute, IN
47807
Tel.: (812) 232-0408
Web Site: https://www.data-label.com
Year Founded: 1980
Rev.: $10,000,000
Emp.: 140
Pressure Sensitive Labels Mfr
N.A.I.C.S.: 323111
George Snyder *(Pres)*

DATA NETWORKS OF
AMERICA INC.
309 Intl Cir Ste 120, Hunt Valley, MD
21030
Tel.: (410) 823-3000
Web Site:
   http://www.datanetworks.com
Sales Range: $75-99.9 Million
Emp.: 150
Value-Added Resellers, Computer
Systems
N.A.I.C.S.: 541512
Patrick M. Regan *(Pres & CEO)*

DATA PAPERS INC.

468 Industrial Park Rd, Muncy, PA
17756
Tel.: (570) 546-2201   PA
Web Site: http://www.datapapers.com
Year Founded: 1969
Sales Range: $10-24.9 Million
Emp.: 95
Custom Products Mfr
N.A.I.C.S.: 323111
Jerry Wertz *(Pres & CEO)*
Rick Pasco *(Mgr-Sls)*
Frank Michael *(Plant Mgr)*

DATA PATH
318 McHenry Ave, Modesto, CA
95354
Tel.: (209) 521-0055
Web Site:
   http://www.mydatapath.com
Sales Range: $1-9.9 Million
Emp.: 38
Information Technology Services
N.A.I.C.S.: 541512
James Bates *(Co-Founder)*
David Darmstandler *(Co-Founder &
CEO)*
Brian Jump *(Mgr-Procurement, Stra-
tegic Partnerships & R&D)*
Laurie Fleming *(Mgr-Bus)*
Devin Peterson *(Mgr-Support Svcs)*

DATA PRO ACCOUNTING
SOFTWARE, INC.
111 2nd Ave NE Ste 1200, Saint Pe-
tersburg, FL 33701
Tel.: (727) 803-1550
Web Site: https://www.dpro.com
Sales Range: $1-9.9 Million
Emp.: 15
Accounting Software
N.A.I.C.S.: 513210
Joel A. Brodk *(Pres)*
Patricia Hartsock *(Mgr-Acctg)*

DATA PROCESSING AIR
CORP.
5226 S 40th St, Phoenix, AZ 85040
Tel.: (602) 438-4747
Web Site: https://www.dpair.com
Rev.: $24,728,464
Emp.: 30
Air Conditioning Repair Services
N.A.I.C.S.: 811412
Arnie Evdokimo *(Pres)*
Jennifer Harler *(Controller)*

DATA PROCESSING SCI-
ENCES CORPORATION
10810 Kenwood Rd, Cincinnati, OH
45242-2812
Tel.: (513) 791-7100   OH
Web Site: http://www.dpsciences.com
Year Founded: 1961
Sales Range: $10-24.9 Million
Emp.: 125
Computer Network Integrator & Re-
Seller; Installs & Leases Electronic
Data Communications Equipment;
Network Consulting & E-Architecture
for Business
N.A.I.C.S.: 541512
Scott Nesbitt *(Chm & CEO)*
Kurt Loock *(Pres)*
Tim Shelton *(CFO)*
Stephen Vandegriff *(VP-Sls)*
Jerry Harden *(VP-Pro Svcs)*

DATA PROCESSING SER-
VICES
3495 Lawrenceville Suwanee Rd, Su-
wanee, GA 30024-2402
Tel.: (770) 368-1300
Web Site: http://www.dpservices.com
Year Founded: 1995
Sales Range: $10-24.9 Million
Emp.: 35

N.A.I.C.S.: 541810
Bryan Galloway *(Pres)*

DATA PROCESSING SOLU-
TIONS, INC.
9160 Red Branch Rd Ste W-1, Co-
lumbia, MD 21045-2002
Tel.: (410) 720-3300
Web Site:
   http://www.dpsolutions.com
Year Founded: 1971
Emp.: 60
Information Technology Services
N.A.I.C.S.: 541519
Karyn Schell *(Pres)*
Clay Westbrook *(VP-Technical Svcs)*
Richard Carey *(Dir-Technology)*
Jefferson Eckles *(Dir-Strategic
Growth)*
Melissa Bryant *(Mgr-Client Experi-
ence)*
Michael Ande Kear *(VP-Sls & Mktg)*

DATA RECOGNITION CORPO-
RATION
13490 Bass Lake Rd, Maple Grove,
MN 55311-3634
Tel.: (763) 268-2000   MN
Web Site:
   https://www.datarecognition.com
Year Founded: 1976
Sales Range: $25-49.9 Million
Emp.: 635
Data Processing & Preparation
N.A.I.C.S.: 518210
Susan Engeleiter *(Pres & CEO)*
Doug Russell *(Sr VP-Strategic Mktg
& Surveys)*
Russ Hagen *(Founder & Chm)*
Sandra Wiese *(Gen Counsel & Sr
VP-Govt Affairs)*
David Chayer *(Sr VP-Res)*
Lisa Peterson-Nelson *(Chief Quality
Officer)*
Patricia McDivitt *(Sr VP-Curriculum,
Instruction & Assessment)*

Subsidiaries:

REDA International, Inc.   (1)
11141 Georgia Ave Ste 517, Wheaton, MD
20902-4680
Tel.: (301) 946-9790
Web Site: http://www.redainternational.com
Research & Evaluation Services
N.A.I.C.S.: 541720

DATA SALES CO.
3450 W Burnsville Pkwy, Burnsville,
MN 55337-4203
Tel.: (952) 890-8838   MN
Web Site: https://www.datasales.com
Year Founded: 1973
Rev.: $73,900,000
Emp.: 120
Computers, Peripherals & Software
N.A.I.C.S.: 423430
Ronald Breckner *(Chm)*
Gary Meyer *(Controller)*
Paul Breckner *(Pres)*

DATA SEARCH NY INC.
27500 Riverview Ctr Blvd, Bonita
Springs, FL 34134   NY
Web Site:
   http://www.trakamerica.com
Year Founded: 1996
Sales Range: $10-24.9 Million
Emp.: 100
Debt Recovery Management & Data
Services
N.A.I.C.S.: 518210
Vincent P. Iacono *(Pres & CEO)*

DATA SECURITY DEVELOP-
MENT, INC

13201 Data Vault Dr, Louisville, KY
40223-1390
Tel.: (502) 244-1151
Web Site:
   http://www.thedatavault.com
Rev.: $2,600,000
Emp.: 31
General Warehousing & Storage
N.A.I.C.S.: 493110
Richard Gladden *(Pres)*

DATA SOURCE MEDIA INC.
3505 N 48th St, Lincoln, NE 68504
Tel.: (402) 466-3342
Web Site: https://www.dsmedia.com
Year Founded: 1983
Sales Range: $10-24.9 Million
Emp.: 15
Computers, Peripherals & Software
N.A.I.C.S.: 423430
Mark Tallman *(Pres)*

DATA SPECIALTIES INC.
8400 Kass Dr, Buena Park, CA
90621
Tel.: (714) 523-8489
Web Site:
   http://www.dataspecialtiesinc.com
Year Founded: 1991
Rev.: $18,152,912
Emp.: 40
Electrical Work
N.A.I.C.S.: 238210
Phil Rafferty *(Co-Founder & Pres)*
Rick Maxson *(Co-Founder & VP)*
Tina Myers *(Mgr-Acctg & HR)*
Don Walton *(Project Mgr)*

DATA SYSTEMS ANALYSTS
INC. (DSA)
8 Neshaminy Interplex Ste 209, Tre-
vose, PA 19053-6980
Tel.: (215) 245-4800
Web Site: http://www.dsainc.com
Year Founded: 1963
Sales Range: $100-124.9 Million
Emp.: 125
IT Solutions
N.A.I.C.S.: 519290
Frances R. Pierce *(Chm, Pres &
CEO)*
Bill Jones *(VP & Gen Mgr-Integrated
Solutions Grp)*
Kathleen Kirk *(COO)*
John Foley *(CFO)*
Cynthia Scott *(Sr Dir-Contracts & Bus
Strategy)*
Marie Meyers *(VP-HR)*
Robert Wheeler *(Sr VP-Enterprise
Solutions Grp)*
Alvie Johnson *(Sr VP-Bus Dev)*
Mike Donovan *(Sr VP-Strategic Solu-
tions)*

DATA SYSTEMS OF TEXAS,
INC.
720 N 64th St, Waco, TX 76710
Tel.: (254) 772-6301   TX
Web Site: http://www.datasystx.com
Year Founded: 1974
Sales Range: $1-9.9 Million
Emp.: 17
Software Solutions
N.A.I.C.S.: 513210
Bob McEachern *(Chm)*
Greg McEachern *(Pres)*
Jan Franklin *(Mgr-Project & Installa-
tion)*
Vance Lawson *(COO)*
Foy Burns *(VP-Dev)*
Brian Hoppe *(CTO)*

Subsidiaries:

Data Systems Technology
Solutions   (1)

Data Systems of Texas, Inc.—(Continued)

801 Washington Ave Ste 115, Waco, TX
76701-1282
Tel.: (254) 230-0380
Web Site: http://www.egm-tech.com
IT Infrastructure & Technology Solutions
N.A.I.C.S.: 541519
Gus Welter (Exec VP)

DATA VISION, INC.
18124 Wedge Pkwy Ste 1050, Reno,
NV 89511
Tel.: (778) 995-1267   NV
Web Site: http://www.datavision-
inc.com
Year Founded: 2017
Assets: $31,401
Liabilities: $50
Net Worth: $31,351
Earnings: ($56,341)
Fiscal Year-end: 12/31/19
Software Development Services
N.A.I.C.S.: 541511
Xinwei Zhang (Pres, CEO & Sec)
Juan Zhang (CFO, Chief Acctg Offi-
cer & Treas)

DATA-STITCH INC.
113 Dennis Junction Rd, Weather-
ford, TX 76088
Tel.: (817) 594-9577
Web Site: https://www.datastitch.com
Sales Range: $10-24.9 Million
Emp.: 6
Embroidery Machines & Software
Distr
N.A.I.C.S.: 423830
Larry Lawley (Pres)

DATA2 CORPORATION
222 Turner Blvd, Saint Peters, MO
63376
Tel.: (636) 278-8888
Web Site: http://www.data2.com
Sales Range: $10-24.9 Million
Emp.: 80
Label Printing & Sealing
N.A.I.C.S.: 561910
Jack M. Delo (Pres)

Subsidiaries:

Data2 Inc.   (1)
1470 Enea Cir Ste 1550, Concord, CA
94520
Tel.: (925) 603-7575
Web Site: http://www.datapage.com
Rev.: $2,500,000
Emp.: 22
Labels (Unprinted), Gummed: Made From
Purchased Materials
N.A.I.C.S.: 322220

DATA41
13681 Newport Ave Ste 8 613, Tu-
stin, CA 92780
Tel.: (714) 505-3028
Web Site: https://www.data41.com
Year Founded: 2006
Sales Range: $1-9.9 Million
Emp.: 18
Software Development Services
N.A.I.C.S.: 541511
Hans Mize (Founder & Pres)

DATAART SOLUTIONS, INC.
475 Park Ave S Fl 15, New York, NY
10016
Tel.: (212) 378-4108   NY
Web Site: https://www.dataart.com
Year Founded: 1997
Sales Range: $25-49.9 Million
Emp.: 800
Custom Computer Programming Ser-
vices
N.A.I.C.S.: 541511
Michael Zaitsev (Chm)
Alexei Miller (Mng Dir)
Dennis Afanassiev (Sr VP-Engrg)

Eugene Goland (Pres)
Luba Kabrits (CFO)
Tanya Andrianova (Sr VP-HR)
Vica Miller (Sr VP-Global Comm)
Gregory Abbott (Sr VP & Head-Travel
& Hospitality Practice)
Dmitry Andrianov (Sr VP-Engrg)
Julia Zavileyskaya (Sr VP-Integrated
Comm)
Eugene Sedov (Pres-Odessa)
Alexey Filimonov (COO)
Alistair Wandesforde (Sr VP-
Engagement Mgmt)
Allan Wellenstein (Sr VP)
Peter Vaihansky (Sr VP-Engagement
Mgmt & Fin Practice)
Dmitry Bagrov (Mng Dir-London)
Alexander Khizha (Pres-Dnipro)
Nikolay Snizhko (Pres-Kyiv)
Denis Baranov (Principal)
Sergey Bludov (Sr VP-Media & Enter-
tainment)
Daniel Piekarz (Sr VP-Healthcare &
Life Sciences-New York)
Yury Kabrits (Sr VP-Engrg-Saint Pe-
tersburg)
Alexey Utkin (Head-Data & Analytics)
Alexander Makeyenkov (Head-
European Bus Dev-Zug-Switzerland
& Dir-Switzerland)
Gregory Gor (Sr VP-New York)
Michael Lazar (Sr VP-Telecom)
Steve Pscheid (VP)
Mike Brett (VP-Bus Dev & Sls-
Europe)
Dmitry Stillermann (Head-Delivery &
Fin Practice)
Dmitry Yakovlev (VP-Engrg-Saint Pe-
tersburg)
Charlotte Lamp Davies (VP-Travel &
Hospitality-Europe-DataArt UK)
David Tossell (VP-Travel &
Hospitality-Texas)

DATABANK, LTD.
400 S Akard St Ste 100, Dallas, TX
75202
Tel.: (214) 720-2266
Web Site: https://www.databank.com
Year Founded: 2005
Web Hosting & Associated Informa-
tion Technology Services
N.A.I.C.S.: 518210
Raul K. Martynek (CEO)
Kevin Ooley (Pres & CFO)
Vlad Friedman (CTO)
Stephen Callahan (Sr VP-Sls)
Jerry Blair (Founder)
Mark Houpt (Chief Info Security Offi-
cer)
Justin Puccio (Exec VP-Strategy)

Subsidiaries:

Edge Hosting, LLC   (1)
120 E Baltimore St Ste 1900, Baltimore,
MD 21202
Tel.: (410) 246-8800
Web Site: http://www.edgehosting.com
Sales Range: $10-24.9 Million
Emp.: 62
Web Hosting Services
N.A.I.C.S.: 518210
Mike Altman (COO)
Michael Deamer (VP-Client Svcs)
Robb Goetz (Controller)
Mark Houpt (Chief Info Security Officer)
Stacey Levas (VP-Mktg)

DATABASE MARKETING GROUP
5 Peters Canyon Rd Ste 380, Irvine,
CA 92606
Tel.: (714) 836-8373
Web Site: http://www.dbmgroup.com
Year Founded: 1991
Sales Range: $10-24.9 Million
Emp.: 28

Direct Marketing Solutions
N.A.I.C.S.: 541613

DATABASE PUBLISHING CON-SULTANTS, INC.
1560 Broadway Ste 810, New York,
NY 10036
Tel.: (212) 575-5609   NY
Web Site:
http://www.databasepublish.com
Year Founded: 1999
Sales Range: $1-9.9 Million
Emp.: 15
Software Consulting Services
N.A.I.C.S.: 513210
Joseph Bachana (Founder & Pres)
Tracy Gardner (VP-Client Svcs)
Joozer Tohfafarosh (VP-Tech)
Samuel Wilson (Dir-Ops)

DATABIT, INC.
200 Route 17, Mahwah, NJ 07430
Tel.: (201) 529-8050
Web Site:
https://www.databitmsp.com
Year Founded: 2004
PC-based Computer Data Storage,
Client/Server, Networking Solutions,
Hardware & Software Mfr
N.A.I.C.S.: 423430
Joseph Engelson (Acct Mgr)

DATACARD CORPORATION
11111 Bren Rd W, Minnetonka, MN
55343-9015
Tel.: (952) 933-1223   DE
Web Site: http://www.datacard.com
Year Founded: 1969
Sales Range: $400-449.9 Million
Emp.: 1,400
Secure ID & Financial Card Personal-
ization Solutions
N.A.I.C.S.: 333310
Mike Schnaus (VP-Corp Dev)
Todd G. Wilkinson (Pres & CEO)
Jeffrey Smolinski (Sr VP-Ops)
Kurt Ishaug (CFO)
Timothy Cheung (Pres-China)
John Di Leo (Sr VP-Global Sls &
Svc)
Lynette Heath (Sr VP-HR)
Chris Pelletier (Sr VP-Strategy Ex-
ecution & Bus Process)
Lisa Tibbits (Gen Counsel & Sec)
Siddharth N. Mehta (Chm)
Siddharth N. Mehta (Chm)

Subsidiaries:

Datacard (Shanghai) Trading Co.,
Ltd.   (1)
Room 2305B Hua Xia Bank Tower 256 Pu-
dong Road South, Shanghai, 200120,
China
Tel.: (86) 21 6886 6033
Web Site: http://www.com.cn
Secure Card Mfr
N.A.I.C.S.: 326199

Datacard Asia Pacific Limited   (1)
27/F Asia Orient Tower Town Place 33
Lockhart Road, Wanchai, China (Hong
Kong)
Tel.: (852) 2866 2613
Secure Card Mfr
N.A.I.C.S.: 326199
Timothy Cheung (Pres)

Datacard Asia Pacific Limited   (1)
152 Beach Road 12-05 08 Gateway East,
Singapore, 189721, Singapore
Tel.: (65) 66323320
Web Site: http://www.datacard.com
Sales Range: $10-24.9 Million
Emp.: 18
Secure Card Mfr
N.A.I.C.S.: 326199

Datacard Canada, Inc.   (1)
120 Woodstream Blvd Unit 17, Vaughan,
L4L 7Z1, ON, Canada   (100%)

Tel.: (800) 368-3996
Web Site: http://www.datacard.com
Sales Range: $10-24.9 Million
Emp.: 18
Secure ID & Financial Card Personalization
Solutions
N.A.I.C.S.: 333310
Tony Rakun (VP-Sls & Svc Delivery-US &
Canada Reg)

Datacard Deutschland GmbH   (1)
Euro Ctr 2 Emanuel-Leutze-St 4, Dussel-
dorf, 40547, Germany   (100%)
Tel.: (49) 21159520
Web Site: http://www.datacard.de
Sales Range: $1-9.9 Million
Emp.: 14
Secure ID & Financial Card Personalization
Solutions
N.A.I.C.S.: 333310
Todd Wilkinson (Mng Dir)

Datacard Equipment   (1)
11111 Bren Rd W, Minnetonka, MN 55343-
9015
Tel.: (952) 933-1223
Web Site: http://www.datacard.com
Sales Range: $50-74.9 Million
Emp.: 900
Secure ID & Financial Card Personalization
Solutions
N.A.I.C.S.: 333310
Todd G. Wilkinson (Pres & CEO)

Datacard France S.A.   (1)
ZAC les Chateliers 200 Rue Leonnard De
Vinci, Fleury les Aubrais, 45404, Semoy,
Cedex, France   (100%)
Tel.: (33) 238607600
Web Site: http://www.datacard.com
Sales Range: $10-24.9 Million
Emp.: 70
Secure ID & Financial Card Personalization
Solutions
N.A.I.C.S.: 333310
Benoit Brtht (Mng Dir)

Datacard Iberica, S.L.   (1)
Parque Empresarial La Finca Po Club De-
portivo 1 Bloque 3 Bajo, Pozuelo de Alar-
con, Madrid, 28223, Spain
Tel.: (34) 91 799 74.74
Web Site: http://www.datacard.es
Sales Range: $10-24.9 Million
Emp.: 17
Secure Card Mfr
N.A.I.C.S.: 326199
Fernando Exposito (Mgr-Sls)

Datacard Japan Ltd.   (1)
Nishi Building, 1 6 3 Ohsaki Shinagawa Ku,
Tokyo, 1410032, Japan   (100%)
Tel.: (81) 334946111
Web Site: http://www.datacard.co.jp
Sales Range: $25-49.9 Million
Emp.: 100
Secure ID & Financial Card Personalization
Solutions
N.A.I.C.S.: 333310
Junko Takei (Mgr-HR)

Datacard Ltd.   (1)
Forum 3 Solent Bus Pk, Whiteley, Fareham,
PO15 7FH, Hampshire, United
Kingdom   (100%)
Tel.: (44) 1489555600
Web Site: http://www.datacard.com
Sales Range: $10-24.9 Million
Emp.: 66
Secure ID & Financial Card Personalization
Solutions
N.A.I.C.S.: 333310

Datacard Service   (1)
11111 Bren Rd W, Minnetonka, MN 55343-
9015
Tel.: (952) 933-1223
Web Site: http://www.datacard.com
Sales Range: $50-74.9 Million
Emp.: 700
Secure ID & Financial Card Personalization
Solutions
N.A.I.C.S.: 333310

Datacard South Pacific (Nz) Ltd.   (1)
Unit 16E 14-22 Triton Drive, Albany, 632,
New Zealand
Tel.: (64) 9 451 9555
Web Site: http://www.datacard.com
Emp.: 3

Secure Card Mfr
N.A.I.C.S.: 326199
Dorath Chia *(Mgr-HR)*

Datacard South Pacific Pty. Ltd. (1)
56A Bld 5 195 Wellington Road, Clayton,
3168, VIC, Australia
Tel.: (61) 3 9535 0300
Web Site: http://www.datacard.com.au
Sales Range: $10-24.9 Million
Emp.: 20
Identification Card Distr
N.A.I.C.S.: 424130
Michael Robinson *(Mng Dir)*

Entrust, Inc. (1)
1187 Park Pl, Minneapolis, MN
55379 **(100%)**
Tel.: (952) 933-1223
Web Site: http://www.entrust.com
Sales Range: $75-99.9 Million
Emp.: 411
Secure Digital Identity Software Publisher
N.A.I.C.S.: 513210

Subsidiary (Domestic):

CygnaCom Solutions, Inc. (2)
7925 Jones Branch Dr Ste 5400, McLean,
VA 22102-3322 **(100%)**
Tel.: (703) 848-0883
Web Site: http://www.cygnacom.com
Sales Range: $25-49.9 Million
Emp.: 36
Public Key Infrastructure, Cryptography,
Evaluation of Security Products & Computer
Security
N.A.I.C.S.: 541511
William Conner *(Chm)*
Peter Bello *(Pres)*
Wendy Murphy *(Sr Dir-Sls)*

Subsidiary (Non-US):

Entrust (Europe) Ltd. (2)
Unit 4 Napier Court 1st Floor, Napier Road,
Reading, RG1 8BW, Berkshire, United
Kingdom **(100%)**
Tel.: (44) 1189533000
Web Site: http://www.entrust.com
Sales Range: $25-49.9 Million
Emp.: 25
Secure Digital Identity Software Publisher
N.A.I.C.S.: 513210

Subsidiary (Domestic):

HyTrust, Inc. (2)
1975 W El Camino Real Ste 203, Mountain
View, CA 94040
Tel.: (650) 681-8100
Web Site: http://www.hytrust.com
Software Development Services
N.A.I.C.S.: 513210
John De Santis *(Chm & CEO)*
Eric Chiu *(Co-Founder & Pres)*
Mercedes Caprara *(CFO)*
Wayne Lewandowski *(Sr VP/Gen Mgr-Govt Bus)*
Chris Moore *(Sr VP/Gen Mgr-North America)*
Pat Conte *(VP/Gen Mgr-Bus-Intl)*
Jason Cowie *(VP-Channels-Global)*
John Rafter *(Sr VP-Customer Success)*
Tushar Tambay *(Sr VP-Products)*

Subsidiary (Domestic):

DataGravity, Inc. (3)
100 Innovative Way 4th Fl Ste 3410,
Nashua, NH 03062
Tel.: (844) 681-8100
Web Site: http://www.datagravity.com
Computer Technology Development Services
N.A.I.C.S.: 541511
Paula Long *(CEO)*
John Joseph *(Founder & Pres)*
Andrew Hay *(Chief Info Security Officer)*
Becky Zehr *(CFO)*

DATACEDE LLC
2 Research Way, Princeton, NJ
08540
Tel.: (877) 789-2333
Web Site: http://www.datacede.com
Property & Casualty Insurance Consulting & Outsourced Processing Services

N.A.I.C.S.: 524298
Joseph Zarandona *(CEO)*

DATACOM SYSTEMS INC.
9 Adler Dr, East Syracuse, NY 13057
Tel.: (315) 463-9541
Web Site:
   https://www.datacomsystems.com
Sales Range: $25-49.9 Million
Emp.: 35
Switches, Electronic Applications
N.A.I.C.S.: 335314
Samuel J. Lanzafame *(Chm)*
Gilbert Kaufman *(VP-Engrg)*
Kevin Formby *(Pres & CEO)*
Andy Mather *(VP-Intl Sls-London)*

DATACOMM NETWORKS, INC.
6801 N 54th St, Tampa, FL 33610
Tel.: (813) 873-0674   FL
Web Site: http://www.datacomm.com
Year Founded: 1984
Sales Range: $1-9.9 Million
Emp.: 40
Computer System Design Services
N.A.I.C.S.: 541512
Douglas P. Sliman *(Dir-Ops)*
Lee Williams *(Mgr-Customer Svc)*
Brian C. Boyer *(Pres & CEO)*
Travis E. Norris *(COO & VP)*

DATACOR, INC.
25 Hanover Rd Ste 300B, Florham
Park, NJ 07932
Tel.: (973) 822-1551   NJ
Web Site: http://www.datacorinc.com
Year Founded: 1981
Sales Range: $1-9.9 Million
Emp.: 45
Custom Computer Programming Services, Nsk
N.A.I.C.S.: 541511
Richard Bartley *(Controller & Mgr-HR)*
Baker Bartley *(Controller & Mgr-HR)*
Richard Watanabe *(Controller & Mgr-HR)*
Tom Jackson *(Pres)*
Caitlin O'Donnell *(Head-Mktg)*

Subsidiaries:

Chemstations, Inc. (1)
11000 Richmond Ave Ste 580, Houston, TX
77077
Tel.: (713) 978-7700
Web Site: http://www.chemstations.com
Chemical Engineering Software
N.A.I.C.S.: 513210
Mingder Lu *(CTO & Sr VP)*
Steve Brown *(CEO)*

DATACORE SOFTWARE CORP.
1901 Cypress Creek Rd Ste 200,
Fort Lauderdale, FL 33309
Tel.: (954) 377-6000
Web Site: http://www.datacore.com
Rev.: $7,291,000
Emp.: 37
Computer Facilities Management Services
N.A.I.C.S.: 541513
Christian Hagen *(VP-EMEA Bus Dev & Strategic Initiatives)*
George Teixeira *(Co-Founder & Chm)*
Jamie Humphrey *(VP-Asia Pacific)*
Roni Putra *(Co-Founder & CTO)*
Rosario Perri *(Dir-Strategic Partners & Alliances-EMEA)*
Amanda Bedborough *(Sr VP-EMEA)*
Dave Zabrowski *(CEO)*
Gerardo A. Dada *(Chief Mktg Officer)*
Abhijit Dey *(Chief Product Officer)*
Gregg Machon *(VP-Sls-Americas)*
Alex Grossman *(VP-Product Mgmt & Mktg)*

Subsidiaries:

Caringo, Inc. (1)
6801 N Capital of Texas Hwy Bldg 2 Ste
200, Austin, TX 78731
Tel.: (512) 782-5127
Web Site: http://www.caringo.com
Software & Technology Development Services
N.A.I.C.S.: 513210
Jeff Mims *(CFO)*
Mark Goros *(Co-Founder)*
Jonathan Ring *(Co-Founder & Chief Technical Officer)*
Brandon Canaday *(VP-Channels)*
Adrian J. Herrera *(VP-Mktg)*
Cornelius Economou *(VP-Global Sls)*
T. W. Cook *(VP-Engrg & Product Mgmt)*
Tony Barbagallo *(Pres & CEO)*
Vivek Mohindra *(Chm)*
Charles Portnoy *(Mgr-Sls-Federal & Southeast)*

DATADIRECT NETWORKS INC.
9351 Deering Ave, Chatsworth, CA
91311
Tel.: (818) 700-7600
Web Site: http://www.ddn.com
Year Founded: 1988
Sales Range: $25-49.9 Million
Emp.: 600
Computer Data Storage
N.A.I.C.S.: 334112
Alex Bouzari *(Co-Founder & CEO)*
Paul Bloch *(Co-Founder & Pres)*
Ian Angelo *(CFO)*
Robert Triendl *(Sr VP-Sls, Mktg & Field Svcs)*
Michael King *(Sr Dir-Mktg)*
Bret Costelow *(VP-Global Sls)*
Jessica Popp *(Gen Mgr-Infinite Memory Engine)*
Eric Barton *(CTO-Software-Defined Storage)*
James Coomer *(Sr VP-Products)*
Sven Began *(Chief Res Officer)*

Subsidiaries:

Tintri Inc. (1)
303 Ravendale Dr, Mountain View, CA
94043
Tel.: (650) 810-8200
Rev.: $125,904,000
Assets: $76,247,000
Liabilities: $167,957,000
Net Worth: ($91,710,000)
Earnings: ($157,659)
Emp.: 722
Fiscal Year-end: 01/31/2018
Software Development Services
N.A.I.C.S.: 541511

DATADIRECT TECHNOLOGIES, INC.
14 Oak Park Dr, Bedford, MA 01730
Tel.: (919) 461-4200
Web Site: http://www.datadirect.com
Rev.: $42,546,194
Emp.: 350
Software Services
N.A.I.C.S.: 513210
Carlo Innocenti *(Sr Mgr-XML Program)*
Asher Arembandd *(Sr Dir-Shadow Dev)*
Charles Gold *(VP-Mktg-Worldwide)*
Lindsey Anderson *(VP-Sls)*
Christopher Larsen *(VP-Intl Sls)*

DATAFLOW BUSINESS SYSTEMS, INC.
540 Work St Ste E, Salinas, CA
93901
Tel.: (831) 759-8760   CA
Web Site: http://www.startdbs.com
Year Founded: 2006
Sales Range: $10-24.9 Million
Office Equipment Merchant Whslr
N.A.I.C.S.: 423420
Oly Gomez *(Owner & Pres)*

Subsidiaries:

Copy Duplicating Systems (1)
9727 Business Park Dr Ste C, Sacramento,
CA 95827
Tel.: (916) 366-8003
Rev.: $2,331,000
Emp.: 7
Office Supplies & Stationery Stores
N.A.I.C.S.: 459410
Richard Reese *(Owner)*

DATALAB USA
20261 Goldenrod Ln, Germantown,
MD 20876-4063
Tel.: (301) 972-1430
Web Site: http://www.datalabusa.com
Sales Range: $10-24.9 Million
Emp.: 51
Database Marketing Services
N.A.I.C.S.: 518210
Hans Aigner *(Pres & CEO)*
Ryder Warehall *(CIO)*
Jay Kim *(Dir-Client Svcs)*
Larissa Warehall *(CFO)*
Alex Aigner *(COO)*
Nino Ajami *(Dir-Client Svcs)*
David Flam *(COO)*
Olga Aigner *(COO)*

DATALINE LLC
7918 Jones Branch Dr Ste 650,
McLean, VA 22102
Tel.: (703) 847-7412
Web Site: http://www.dataline.com
Sales Range: $25-49.9 Million
Emp.: 120
Computers, Peripherals & Software
N.A.I.C.S.: 423430
Denise M. Robinson *(Pres)*
Casey Robinson *(COO)*

DATALINK BANKCARD SERVICES, CO.
3505 Token Dr, Richardson, TX
75082
Tel.: (214) 343-4242
Web Site:
   https://www.datalinkonline.net
Year Founded: 1989
Sales Range: $10-24.9 Million
Emp.: 125
Credit & Gift Card Processor
N.A.I.C.S.: 561450
Ruben Pizana *(Dir-Risk)*
Andrew Tate *(CTO)*
Dawnita Hines *(Dir-HR)*

DATALUX CORPORATION
155 Aviation Dr, Winchester, VA
22602-4589
Tel.: (540) 662-1500
Web Site: https://www.datalux.com
Sales Range: $10-24.9 Million
Emp.: 30
Cathode Ray Tube (Crt), Computer Terminal
N.A.I.C.S.: 334118
Robert H. Twyford *(CEO)*
Marilynn Lose *(Controller)*
David Clark *(Mgr)*

DATAMANUSA, LLC
6890 S Tucson Way Ste 100, Centennial, CO 80112
Tel.: (720) 248-3110
Web Site:
   https://www.datamanusa.com
Year Founded: 2000
Sales Range: $1-9.9 Million
Emp.: 34
Consulting & Information Systems Services Specializing in Information Technology Staff Augmentation & Software Design & Development
N.A.I.C.S.: 541690

DatamanUSA, LLC—(Continued)

Gyan Saxena (CIO)
Anuj Saksena (Mgr-Recruiting)

DATAMARK INC.
2305 Presidents Dr, Salt Lake City, UT 84120-7230
Tel.: (801) 886-2002   UT
Web Site: http://www.datamark.com
Year Founded: 1987
Rev.: $35,000,000
Emp.: 250
N.A.I.C.S.: 541810
Tom Dearden (CEO)
Sherrie Martin (VP-Media Svcs)
Rick Bentz (Sr VP-Bus Intelligence)
Ed Patterson (Sr Acct Exec)
Jeff Adams (VP-Bus Dev)
Kristine Rasmussen (CFO)
Paul Reddy (Pres)
Kim Carter (Dir-Creative & VP)
Deborah Richman (VP)

Subsidiaries:

Datamark Inc.   (1)
157 S Howard St Ste 309, Spokane, WA 99201
Tel.: (509) 777-0357
Web Site: http://www.datamark.com
Sales Range: $10-24.9 Million
Emp.: 4
N.A.I.C.S.: 541810
Sheila Swofford (Office Mgr)

DATAMARK INC.
43 Butterfield Cir, El Paso, TX 79906
Tel.: (915) 778-1944
Web Site: http://www.datamark.net
Rev.: $25,712,178
Emp.: 300
Data Entry Services
N.A.I.C.S.: 518210
Bill Randag (Pres)
Nina Brown (VP-Sls & Mktg)
Matt Lochausen (VP-IT)
Ceasar Casas (VP-Global Ops)
John Holmes (Sr VP)
Stephen Darling (Dir-Sls & Mktg)
Martin Rocha (Mgr-Mktg)

DATAMATICS CONSULTANTS INC.
3505 Duluth Pk Ln Ste 200, Duluth, GA 30096
Tel.: (770) 232-9460
Web Site: http://www.datamatics.us
Year Founded: 1993
Sales Range: $10-24.9 Million
Emp.: 70
Computer Related Consulting Services
N.A.I.C.S.: 541512
Jeetan Singh (Pres)
Frank Kulendran (Exec VP)
Udai Shanker (VP-Resourcing)

Subsidiaries:

Cognix Group Ltd.   (1)
Level 3 Microsoft Hse, 11 Hunter Street, Wellington, New Zealand
Tel.: (64) 44701697
Computer Related Consulting Services
N.A.I.C.S.: 541512

DATAMAXX GROUP, INC.
2001 Drayton Dr, Tallahassee, FL 32311
Tel.: (850) 558-8000
Web Site: https://www.datamaxx.com
Year Founded: 1991
Sales Range: $10-24.9 Million
Emp.: 80
Law Enforcement Software Applications
N.A.I.C.S.: 513210
Kay Stephenson (Pres & CEO)
Jonathan Waters (CTO)

DATAMEER INC.
1550 Bryant St Ste 490, San Francisco, CA 94103
Tel.: (415) 817-9558
Web Site: http://www.datameer.com
Year Founded: 2009
Sales Range: $10-24.9 Million
Emp.: 75
End-to-End Big Data Analytics Application Purpose-Built for Hadoop Systems
N.A.I.C.S.: 513210
Frank Henze (VP-Innovation)
Monique Sherman (Mgr-PR-Global)
Linda Esperance (VP-People Ops)
Matt McManus (VP-Engrg)
Jon Oslowski (VP-Fin)
Christian Rodatus (CEO)
George Shahid (CFO)
Jeff Gallagher (Sr VP-Sls)
Raghu Thiagarajan (VP-Product Mgmt)
Erin Hitchcock (Mgr-PR)
Susan O'Brien (VP-Mktg)
Tarlock Sagoo (VP-Svcs-Global & Customer Success)

DATAMENTORS, LLC
2319-104 Oak Myrtle Ln, Wesley Chapel, FL 33544
Tel.: (813) 960-7800   FL
Web Site: http://www.datamentors.com
Year Founded: 1998
Sales Range: $1-9.9 Million
Emp.: 32
Data Quality & Business Analytics Solutions
N.A.I.C.S.: 513210
Anders Ekman (CEO)
Michelle Taves (Sr VP-Strategy & Product Mgmt)
Bob Ort (Vice Chm)
Kelly Idol (Exec VP-Data Sls)
Peg Kuman (Chief Privacy Officer & Exec VP)
Andy Pappas (Sr VP-Database Mktg & Analytics)
Linda Chiodo (Sr VP-Fin)
Scott Busby (COO & CTO)
Tommy Bardinas (VP-Tech)
Brent Cosgrove (CFO)
Thomas Green (Sr VP-Data Strategy Svcs)
Graham Line (Exec VP)
Karen Mascott (CMO)
Edward C. Williams III (Chm)

DATAMETRIX
310 E 4500 S Ste 660, Salt Lake City, UT 84107
Tel.: (866) 977-1001
Web Site: http://www.data-metrix.com
Year Founded: 2005
Sales Range: $1-9.9 Million
Emp.: 70
Consulting Services to Health Insurance Companies
N.A.I.C.S.: 541690
Mary Jane LaBelle (Co-Founder & Chm)
Brent Anderson (Co-Founder & Pres)
Chad J. Charles (CIO)
Gary G. Twigg (CFO)
Cindy A. Machowski (Exec VP-Bus Dev)

DATAMINR INC.
99 Madison Ave 3rd Fl, New York, NY 10016
Tel.: (212) 292-8160
Web Site: http://www.dataminr.com
Year Founded: 2009
Emp.: 150
Data Analytic Services
N.A.I.C.S.: 518210

Ted Bailey (Co-Founder, Chm & CEO)
Jeff Kinsey (Co-Founder & CTO)
Peter Bailey (Chief Strategy Officer)
Jay Naik (Sr VP-Product & Ops)
Julio Pekarovic (CFO)
Steven Schwartz (Pres-Comml Markets)
Nicole Miles (VP-Ops Engrg)
Neil Steinberg (VP-PR & Crisis Comm Sls)

DATANOMICS INC.
0991 US Hwy 22 W, Bridgewater, NJ 08807
Tel.: (732) 981-0192
Web Site: http://www.datanomics.com
Year Founded: 1982
Sales Range: $25-49.9 Million
Emp.: 500
Provider of Computer Related Services
N.A.I.C.S.: 541512
John Proske (Pres)

DATAPOINTLABS
95 Brown Rd Ste 102, Ithaca, NY 14850
Tel.: (607) 266-0405
Web Site: http://www.datapointlabs.com
Year Founded: 1995
Sales Range: $1-9.9 Million
Emp.: 18
Plastic & Rubber Testing Services
N.A.I.C.S.: 541380
Hubert Lobo (Founder)

DATASAFE, INC.
574 Eccles Ave, South San Francisco, CA 94080
Tel.: (650) 875-3800   CA
Web Site: https://www.datasafe.com
Year Founded: 1998
Sales Range: $10-24.9 Million
Emp.: 83
Provider of Management & Storage of Document Office Records
N.A.I.C.S.: 493190
Tom Reis (Pres & CEO)
Debra Pierce (VP-Corp Svcs)

DATASERV LLC
1630 Des Peres Rd Ste 301, Saint Louis, MO 63131
Tel.: (314) 842-1155   MO
Web Site: http://www.dataserv.us
Year Founded: 1994
Sales Range: $1-9.9 Million
Emp.: 56
Document & Process Automation Services
N.A.I.C.S.: 541519
Jeffrey L. Haller (Founder & CEO)
Kathi Haller (Co-Founder, CFO & Partner)
Michael Casey (Acct Mgr-Bus Dev)
Shane Freeman (Dir-Mktg & Product Mgmt)
Julie King (Acct Mgr-Client Success)

DATASIFT INC.
100 1st St Ste 360, San Francisco, CA 94105
Tel.: (415) 795-9393
Web Site: http://www.datasift.com
Year Founded: 2007
Emp.: 100
Social Data Processing Services
N.A.I.C.S.: 518210
Nick Halstead (Founder)
Steven Pease (CFO & COO)
Tim Barker (Chief Product Officer)
Andrew Jackson (VP-Engrg)
Lorenzo Alberton (CTO)

Jason Rose (Sr VP-Mktg)
Zuzanna Pasierbinska-Wilson (VP-Mktg)
Jeff Horing (Mng Dir)

Subsidiaries:

DataSift Ltd.   (1)
Reading Enterprise Centre University of Reading Earley Gate Whiteknigh, Earley, RG6 6BU, Reading, United Kingdom
Tel.: (44) 845 643 0673
Social Data Processing Services
N.A.I.C.S.: 518210
Toby Potter (Reg VP-Sls-EMEA)

DATASIGHT CORPORATION
2451 S Buffalo Dr Ste 105, Las Vegas, NV 89117
Tel.: (702) 442-0996   DE
Investment Services
N.A.I.C.S.: 523999
Lyle L. Probst (CEO)

DATASTAX, INC.
3975 Freedom Circle, Santa Clara, CA 95054
Tel.: (650) 389-6000
Web Site: http://www.datastax.com
Emp.: 360
Database Management Software Developer
N.A.I.C.S.: 513210
Jonathan Ellis (Co-Founder)
Matt Pfeil (Co-Founder & COO)
Clint Smith (Gen Counsel)
Martin Van Ryswyk (Exec VP-Product & Engrg)
Robin Schumacher (VP-Products)
Debbie Murray (VP-HR)
Robert O'Donovan (CFO)
Alan Anderson (Mgr-Japan)
Deirdre Toner (Sr VP-Sls-Worldwide)
Cate Lochead (CMO)
Chet Kapoor (CEO)
Harry Ault (Chief Revenue Officer)

DATASTREAM MARKET INTELLIGENCE, INC.
PO Box 1348, Owasso, OK 74055
Tel.: (978) 376-2724
Web Site: https://www.ds-mi.com
Year Founded: 2000
Sales Range: $1-9.9 Million
Emp.: 4
Retail Data Collection & Related Services
N.A.I.C.S.: 519290

DATATEL RESOURCES CORPORATION
1729 Pennsylvania Ave, Monaca, PA 15061
Tel.: (724) 775-5300
Web Site: http://www.datatelcorp.com
Sales Range: $10-24.9 Million
Emp.: 79
Business Forms
N.A.I.C.S.: 323111
Mark Zurick (VP-Admin)
Frank Blaskowitz (VP-Mfg)
Allen Simon (Pres)

DATATRAX PUBLISHING SYSTEMS, INC.
10 Executive Dr, Farmington, CT 06032
Tel.: (860) 677-5577
Web Site: https://www.datatrax.net
Sales Range: $1-9.9 Million
Emp.: 8
Advertising Software Publisher
N.A.I.C.S.: 513210
Michael Symolon (Pres & CEO)
Diana Barbieri (VP)

DATAVIZ, INC.

Merritt Corporate Woods 612 Wheelers Farms Rd, Milford, CT 06461
Tel.: (203) 874-0085   **CT**
Web Site: http://www.dataviz.com
Year Founded: 1984
Sales Range: $10-24.9 Million
Emp.: 100
File Compatibility & Wireless Computer Software Developer
N.A.I.C.S.: 541511
Kathleen McAneany *(Mgr-Documents To Go Bus)*

DATAWIZ CORPORATION
8605 Westwood Center Dr Ste 303, Vienna, VA 22182
Tel.: (703) 288-5258
Web Site: http://www.datawiz.net
Sales Range: $1-9.9 Million
Emp.: 40
Computer System Design Services
N.A.I.C.S.: 541512
Waseem Haider *(Pres)*
Tahir Rameez *(VP)*

DATCU CREDIT UNION
225 W Mulberry St, Denton, TX 76202
Tel.: (940) 387-8585   **TX**
Web Site: http://www.datcu.org
Year Founded: 1936
Sales Range: $50-74.9 Million
Emp.: 221
Credit Union
N.A.I.C.S.: 522130
James Henderson *(CIO & Exec VP)*
Melanie Vest *(CFO & Exec VP)*
Becky Sylvera *(Sr VP-HR)*
Glen McKenzie *(Pres)*

DATEL SYSTEMS INCORPORATED
5636 Ruffin Rd, San Diego, CA 92123
Tel.: (858) 571-3100
Web Site: http://www.datelsys.com
Sales Range: $10-24.9 Million
Emp.: 30
Personal Computers
N.A.I.C.S.: 449210
Larry Piland *(Pres & CEO)*
Heidi Groves *(Acct Mgr)*
Michael Warner *(Dir-Pur)*
Sean Yost *(Sr Acct Mgr)*

DATIX, INC.
9666 Olive Blvd Ste 580, Saint Louis, MO 63132   **MO**
Web Site: https://www.datixinc.com
Year Founded: 1997
Software Solutions Developer
N.A.I.C.S.: 513210
Matt Schuval *(CEO)*
Jessica Staley *(COO)*
Thomas Falteich *(Chief Innovation Officer)*
Mark Chinsky *(CTO)*
Chris Young *(CFO)*
Candice Evertowski *(Chief Mktg & Bus Dev Officer)*

Subsidiaries:

Accuvar, Inc.   (1)
670 N Beers St Ste 4, Holmdel, NJ 07733
Tel.: (732) 970-1450
Web Site: http://www.clientsfirst-us.com
Sales Range: $1-9.9 Million
Emp.: 25
Custom Computer Programing
N.A.I.C.S.: 541511
Mark Chinsky *(Mng Dir)*
Ahmed Elfeky *(Engr-Sys)*
Thomas Falteich *(Pres)*

DATREK PROFESSIONAL BAGS, INC.

835 Bill Jones Industrial Dr, Springfield, TN 37172
Tel.: (615) 384-1286   **TN**
Web Site: http://www.datrek.com
Year Founded: 1981
Sales Range: $50-74.9 Million
Emp.: 100
Golf Bags, Head Covers, Tote Bags & Golf Accessories Mfr
N.A.I.C.S.: 339920
Lori Breedlove *(Controller)*
Karen Seabolt *(Mgr-Customer Svc)*
Mike Fox *(Engr-Devel)*

DATROSE
660 Basket Rd, Webster, NY 14580
Tel.: (585) 265-1780
Web Site: https://www.datrose.com
Year Founded: 1976
Rev.: $73,100,000
Emp.: 777
Staffing & Business Outsourcing
N.A.I.C.S.: 561311
Wendy Jones *(Dir-Shared Svcs)*
Cheryl Keck *(Pres & COO)*
William W. Rose *(Chm & CEO)*

DATS TRUCKING INC.
321 N Old Hwy 91, Hurricane, UT 84737
Tel.: (435) 673-1886
Web Site:
    http://www.datstrucking.com
Rev.: $115,613,083
Emp.: 100
Contract Haulers
N.A.I.C.S.: 484110
Don L. Ipson *(Pres & CEO)*

DATUM CORPORATION
6009 Business Blvd, Sarasota, FL 34240
Tel.: (941) 799-3100
Web Site:
    http://www.datumcorporation.com
Year Founded: 2003
Sales Range: $10-24.9 Million
Emp.: 60
Business Consulting Services
N.A.I.C.S.: 541611
Thomas Frost *(CEO)*
Scott Eshelman *(Pres & COO)*
Larry Boyd *(VP-Tech Svcs)*
Nick Guy *(Dir-Bus Tech Solutions)*
Lori Robinson *(Dir-Fin)*
Andrew Wilkins *(Dir-Independent Restaurant Solutions)*
Hector Rojas *(Dir-Project Mgmt)*
Jason Levinson *(VP-Restaurant Tech)*

DATZ
2616 S MacDill Ave, Tampa, FL 33629
Tel.: (813) 831-7000
Web Site:
    https://www.datztampa.com
Sales Range: $1-9.9 Million
Restaurant
N.A.I.C.S.: 722511
Roger Perry *(Co-Owner)*
Suzanne Perry *(Co-Owner)*
Morgan Buch *(Gen Mgr)*

DAUBERT INDUSTRIES, INC.
1333 Burr Ridge Pkwy Ste 150, Burr Ridge, IL 60527-0833
Tel.: (630) 203-6800   **DE**
Web Site: http://www.daubert.com
Year Founded: 1935
Sales Range: $125-149.9 Million
Emp.: 150
Holding Company; Corrosion Prevention Products Mfr
N.A.I.C.S.: 424690

Peter Fischer *(Chm)*
J.R. Cosbey *(Treas, Sec & VP)*
Donald G. Lubin *(Principal)*
Fritz Fischer *(Vice Chm)*

Subsidiaries:

Daubert Chemical Company, Inc.   (1)
4700 S Central Ave, Chicago, IL 60638-1531   (100%)
Tel.: (708) 496-7350
Web Site: http://www.daubertchemical.com
Sales Range: $25-49.9 Million
Corrosion Prevention Products Mfr
N.A.I.C.S.: 424690
Mike Duncan *(Pres & CEO)*
Tim Henderson *(CFO & VP)*
Matthew McGinnis *(VP-Comml Dev)*
Aaron Sanders *(VP-Tech)*
Greg Merchen *(VP-Ops)*

Daubert Cromwell, LLC   (1)
12701 S Ridgeway Ave, Alsip, IL 60803   (100%)
Tel.: (708) 293-7750
Web Site: http://www.daubertcromwell.com
Sales Range: $10-24.9 Million
Emp.: 30
Mfr of Non-Rust Volatile Corrosion Inhibitor (VCI) Protective Packaging for Metal Surfaces
N.A.I.C.S.: 326113
Luis Jacome *(Mgr-Mexico)*

ECP Incorporated   (1)
11210 Katherines Crossing Ste 100, Woodridge, IL 60517   (100%)
Tel.: (630) 754-4200
Web Site: http://www.ecpinc.net
Sales Range: $10-24.9 Million
Emp.: 26
Automobile Protection Coating Mfr & Distr
N.A.I.C.S.: 325510
John Vesely *(Product Mgr)*
Michael Heraty *(VP & Gen Mgr)*

DAUGHERTY & COMPANY LLC
90 S 7th St Ste 4300, Minneapolis, MN 55402-4105
Tel.: (612) 376-4000
Web Site:
    http://www.doughertymarkets.com
Rev.: $12,000,000
Emp.: 150
Brokers Security
N.A.I.C.S.: 523150
Pam Ziermann *(VP-Compliance)*
Jeff Jacobson *(Exec VP)*
David B. Juran *(Exec VP)*

DAUGHERTY SYSTEMS INC.
3 Cityplace Ste 400, Saint Louis, MO 63141-7066
Tel.: (314) 432-8200   **MO**
Web Site: https://www.daugherty.com
Year Founded: 1984
Rev.: $31,877,079
Emp.: 500
Computer Related Services For Software
N.A.I.C.S.: 541512
Ron Daugherty *(Pres)*
Mike Garofalo *(CFO)*

DAUGHTERS OF CHARITY HEALTH SYSTEM
26000 Altamont Rd, Los Altos, CA 94022-4317
Tel.: (650) 917-4500   **CA**
Web Site: http://www.dochs.org
Year Founded: 2002
Sales Range: $900-999.9 Million
Emp.: 7,000
Hospital & Medical Center Operator
N.A.I.C.S.: 561110
Carol Padilla *(VP-Mission Integration)*
Robert K. Cook *(VP-Risk Mgmt)*
Stephanie Battles *(VP-HR)*
Andrei Soran *(Pres & COO)*
Mitchell Creem *(CEO)*

Subsidiaries:

O'Connor Hospital   (1)
2105 Forest Ave, San Jose, CA 95128
Tel.: (408) 947-2500
Web Site: http://www.oconnorhospital.org
Sales Range: $75-99.9 Million
Emp.: 1,000
Health Care Srvices
N.A.I.C.S.: 622110
Bruce Blackfield *(Dir-Fin)*
Pamela Brotherton-Sedano *(VP-Patient Safety)*
Julie Hatcher *(VP-HR)*
Michele Randall *(VP-Mission Integration)*
James F. Dover *(Pres & CEO)*
David W. Carroll *(CFO & Sr VP)*
Donna Cumming *(Dir-Mktg)*

Robert F. Kennedy Medical Center   (1)
3663 Martin Luther King Jr Blvd, Lynwood, CA 90262-3506
Tel.: (310) 349-4000
Web Site:
    http://www.robertfkennedymedctr.org
Sales Range: $25-49.9 Million
Emp.: 650
Healtcare Services
N.A.I.C.S.: 622110

Saint Louise Regional Hospital   (1)
9400 No Name Uno, Gilroy, CA 95020
Tel.: (408) 848-2000
Web Site: http://www.saintlouisehospital.org
Rev.: $1,927,225
Emp.: 200
Health Care Srvices
N.A.I.C.S.: 622110
Costa Slrh *(Dir-Environmental Svcs)*

Seton Medical Center   (1)
1900 Sullivan Ave, Daly City, CA 94015
Tel.: (650) 992-4000
Web Site:
    http://www.setonmedical.org
Sales Range: $75-99.9 Million
Emp.: 1,600
Health Care Srvices
N.A.I.C.S.: 622110
Kim Pardini-Kiely *(COO)*
John H. Velyvis *(Dir-Medical-Robotic Orthopedic Surgery)*
Mark Brown *(Chief Nursing Officer)*
Mark S. Fratzke *(Pres & CEO)*
Thomas A. Nuris *(Chm)*

Division (Domestic):

Seton Medical Center Coastside   (2)
600 Marine Blvd, Moss Beach, CA 94038
Tel.: (650) 563-7100
Web Site: http://www.setoncoastside.org
Health Care Srvices
N.A.I.C.S.: 622110
Judy Cook *(Dir-Nursing)*
Mark Brown *(Chief Nursing Officer)*

St. Francis Medical Center   (1)
3630 E Imperial Hwy, Lynwood, CA 90262
Tel.: (310) 900-8900
Web Site:
    http://www.stfrancismedicalcenter.org
Sales Range: $75-99.9 Million
Emp.: 1,634
Health Care Srvices
N.A.I.C.S.: 622110
Maria Lariccia Brennan *(Chief Nursing Officer & VP-Patient Care Svcs)*
David Ricci *(Interim Pres)*
Jerry Kozai *(Pres & CEO)*
Jeremy Rogers *(CFO)*

DAUGHTERS OF MIRIAM CENTER
155 Hazel St, Clifton, NJ 07011
Tel.: (973) 772-3700   **NJ**
Web Site:
    http://www.daughtersofmiriamcenter.org
Year Founded: 1920
Sales Range: $25-49.9 Million
Emp.: 432
Elder Care Services
N.A.I.C.S.: 623312
Frank Dasilva *(COO)*

DAUGHTERS OF SARAH SE-

DAUGHTERS OF SARAH SE—(CONTINUED)

NIOR COMMUNITY
180 Washington Ave Ext, Albany, NY 12203
Tel.: (518) 456-7831 **NY**
Web Site:
http://www.daughtersofsarah.org
Year Founded: 1942
Sales Range: $10-24.9 Million
Emp.: 397
Lifecare Retirement Community Operator
N.A.I.C.S.: 623311
Courtney Mulson (CFO)
Mark L. Koblenz (CEO)
Mike Regan (Dir-Building Svcs & Facilities Plng)
Sharon Rosenblum (Exec Dir-The Massry Residence)
Ruth Schulman (Dir-Philanthropy-Daughters of Sarah Jewish Foundation)
Nicole Graham (Dir-Resident Life)

DAUSIN ELECTRIC CO.
16294 IH 35 N, Selma, TX 78154
Tel.: (210) 651-5204
Web Site:
http://www.dausinelectric.com
Year Founded: 1985
Sales Range: $10-24.9 Million
Emp.: 100
Electronic Services
N.A.I.C.S.: 238210
Ronnie Dausin (Pres)
Irene Dausin (VP)
Gina Holstein (Coord-Construction)
Todd Persyn (Mgr-Construction)
James Arce (Mgr-Small Projects)
Eric Zablosky (Mgr-Svc-Columbus)

DAV PRODUCTIONS, INC.
711 Pilot Rd, Las Vegas, NV 89119
Tel.: (702) 795-8805 **NV**
Year Founded: 1999
Sales Range: $1-9.9 Million
Emp.: 37
Multimedia Event Planning & Video Production Services
N.A.I.C.S.: 561499
Ryan Legue (Dir-Sls & Exec Producer)
Jae Thiele (Acct Exec & Sr Producer)
Josh Meeter (Dir-Art)
Jeffrey Lowney (Sr Mgr-Production)
Rob Erickson (Acct Exec)
Greg Mireles (Acct Exec)

DAVALEN, LLC
104 Archway Court, Lynchburg, VA 24502
Web Site: http://www.davalen.com
Year Founded: 1993
Sales Range: $1-9.9 Million
Emp.: 25
Collaborative Software Consulting, Design & Implementation Services for IBM's Suite of Enterprise Products
N.A.I.C.S.: 513210
Len Barker (Mng Partner)

DAVCO ACQUISITION HOLDING INC.
1657 Crofton Blvd, Crofton, MD 21114
Tel.: (410) 721-3770 **DE**
Year Founded: 1997
Sales Range: $200-249.9 Million
Emp.: 6,000
Holding Company; Franchise Fast Food Restaurants Owner & Operator
N.A.I.C.S.: 551112
Harvey Rothstein (Chm & CEO)
David J. Norman (Pres & Gen Counsel)

Subsidiaries:
DavCo Restaurants LLC (1)
1657 Crofton Blvd, Crofton, MD 21114-1305
Tel.: (410) 721-3770
Sales Range: $200-249.9 Million
Emp.: 5,000
Franchise Fast-Food Restaurants Operator
N.A.I.C.S.: 722513
Dave Carpenter (VP-HR)

DAVE BREWER INC.
4155 St Johns Pkwy Ste 2000, Sanford, FL 32771
Tel.: (407) 330-9901
Web Site:
http://www.davebrewer.com
Sales Range: $10-24.9 Million
Emp.: 71
New Single-Family Housing Construction
N.A.I.C.S.: 236115
Matt Trask (VP)
Darla Sutrich (Coord-Design)

DAVE CANTIN GROUP, LLC
45 Rockefeller Plz 20th Fl, New York, NY 10111
Tel.: (212) 787-5466 **DE**
Web Site:
https://www.davecantingroup.com
Holding Company
N.A.I.C.S.: 551112

DAVE CARTER & ASSOCI-ATES, INC.
3530 SW 7th St, Ocala, FL 34474-1953
Tel.: (352) 732-2992 **FL**
Web Site:
https://www.davecarter.com
Year Founded: 1976
Sales Range: $10-24.9 Million
Emp.: 100
Electrical Apparatus & Equipment, Molding, Electronics, Mobile Home Products
N.A.I.C.S.: 423610
John Curran (CFO)

DAVE DENNIS CHRYSLER JEEP DODGE
4232 Colonel Glenn Hwy, Dayton, OH 45431-1604
Tel.: (937) 429-5566
Web Site:
https://www.davedennis.com
Sales Range: $10-24.9 Million
Emp.: 60
Car Whslr
N.A.I.C.S.: 441110
J. B. Davis (Gen Mgr)
Julie A. Parrott (CFO)
Sarafina Buchanan (Asst Mgr-Internet)
Jerry Hecht (Mgr-Fin)
Jimmy Thornton (Mgr-Fin)
Jason Bergman (Mgr-Internet)
Pat Triola (Mgr-Pre-Owned Sls)
Kevin Brown (Mgr-Sls)
Matt Langford (Mgr-Sls)
Billy Sutterlin (Mgr-Sls)

DAVE HAMILTON CHEVROLET-OLDS-JEEP INC.
2067 N Hwy 97, Redmond, OR 97756
Tel.: (541) 548-1064
Web Site:
http://www.davehamiltonmotors.com
Rev.: $14,300,000
Emp.: 43
Automobiles, New & Used
N.A.I.C.S.: 441110
Nancy Hamilton (Pres)
Hector Bijarro (Office Mgr)

DAVE JONES, INC.
2225 Kilgust Rd, Madison, WI 53713
Tel.: (608) 222-8490
Web Site:
https://www.davejonesinc.com
Year Founded: 1979
Sales Range: $10-24.9 Million
Emp.: 105
Plumbing, Heating & Air-Conditioning Contracting Services
N.A.I.C.S.: 238220
Holly M. Kellesvig (COO)
David D. Jones (Owner & Pres)
Elissa Glebs (Mgr-Payroll)
Sharon Wagner (Dir-Fin)

DAVE KNAPP FORD LINCOLN INC.
500 Wagner Ave, Greenville, OH 45331
Tel.: (937) 547-9401
Web Site:
https://www.daveknappford.com
Sales Range: $10-24.9 Million
Emp.: 51
New Car Retailer
N.A.I.C.S.: 441110
Jake Cabay (Gen Mgr-Sls)
Bryan Knapp (Gen Mgr)
Rodney Fisher (Mgr-Fin)
Jeff Bixler (Mgr-Inventory)
Vera Houpt (Office Mgr)
Dale Mansfield (Dir-Parts & Svc)
Joe Wyant (Mgr-Collision Center)
Craig Dill (Asst Mgr-Collision Center)
Allen Coffman (Coord-Svc & Sls)
Kasi Gregson (Coord-Svc & Sls)
Trudy Matthew (Mgr-Bus Dev)
Chris Heidenreich (Mgr-Sls)

DAVE KRING CHEVROLET CA-DILLAC
1861 N US Hwy 31, Petoskey, MI 49770-9319
Tel.: (231) 347-2585
Web Site: https://www.davekring.com
Year Founded: 1975
Sales Range: $10-24.9 Million
Emp.: 53
Car Dealer
N.A.I.C.S.: 441110
David Kring (Pres)

DAVE REISDORF INC.
16 Clinton St, Batavia, NY 14020
Tel.: (585) 343-4453
Web Site: https://www.reisdorfoil.com
Year Founded: 1953
Rev.: $11,000,000
Emp.: 25
Retailer of Fuel & Oil
N.A.I.C.S.: 457210
Kirk Reisdorf (Pres)

DAVE SINCLAIR FORD INC.
7466 S Lindbergh, Saint Louis, MO 63125
Tel.: (314) 892-2600
Web Site:
http://www.davesinclair.com
Sales Range: $125-149.9 Million
Emp.: 175
New & Used Car Dealers
N.A.I.C.S.: 441110
Chris Flippo (Mgr-Body Shop)
James Sinclair (Pres)

DAVE SINCLAIR LINCOLN MERCURY ST. PETERS INC.
4760 N Service Rd, Saint Peters, MO 63376
Tel.: (800) 416-0341
Web Site:
http://www.davesinclairstpeters.com
Rev.: $13,800,000
Emp.: 45

New Car Dealers
N.A.I.C.S.: 441110
James Sinclair (Pres)
Brian Day (Mgr-Internet Sls)
Mike Lautner (Mgr-Fin)
Terry Overkamp (Gen Mgr)

DAVE STEEL COMPANY INC.
40 Meadow Rd, Asheville, NC 28803
Tel.: (828) 252-2771
Web Site: https://www.davesteel.com
Sales Range: $10-24.9 Million
Emp.: 85
Fabricated Structural Metal
N.A.I.C.S.: 332312
Jeff Dave (Pres)
William Luman (VP-Fin)
Tim C. Heffner (VP-Sls & Mktg)

DAVE SYVERSON INC.
2310 E Main St, Albert Lea, MN 56007-0251
Tel.: (507) 373-1438 **MN**
Web Site:
https://www.davesyverson.com
Year Founded: 1967
Sales Range: $100-124.9 Million
Emp.: 65
Retailer of New/Used Automobiles & Trucks; Repair Shops; Truck Leasing
N.A.I.C.S.: 441110
Lea Ann Hovland (Controller)

Subsidiaries:
Dave Syverson Truck Center, Inc. (1)
7 County Rd 16 SE, Rochester, MN 55904
Tel.: (507) 280-3080
Web Site: http://www.syversontruck.com
Sales Range: $25-49.9 Million
Emp.: 30
Truck Distr
N.A.I.C.S.: 441110
Aaron Smith (Gen Mgr)
Andrew Peterson (Coord-Sls)

DAVE WHITE CHEVROLET, INC.
5880 Monroe St, Sylvania, OH 43560
Tel.: (419) 910-2014
Web Site:
https://www.davewhitechevy.com
Year Founded: 1960
Sales Range: $50-74.9 Million
Emp.: 110
New Car Retailer
N.A.I.C.S.: 441110
Tracy Stack (Mgr-Used Vehicle Dept Sls)
Jon Dunphy (Mgr-Used Vehicle Internet Sls)

DAVE WILSON NURSERY, INC.
19701 Lake Rd, Hickman, CA 95323
Tel.: (209) 874-1821
Web Site:
https://www.davewilson.com
Year Founded: 1938
Rev.: $3,484,700
Emp.: 50
Nursery & Tree Production
N.A.I.C.S.: 111421
Chris Tarry (Mgr-Wholesale Div)
Bill Reid (CEO)

DAVE'S SPORTS CENTER, INC.
1127 N Easton Rd, Doylestown, PA 18901
Tel.: (215) 766-8000
Sporting Goods
N.A.I.C.S.: 459110
Diane Louden (Owner)

Subsidiaries:
Mainstream Outfitters (1)
1121 N Easton Rd, Doylestown, PA 18901

Tel.: (215) 766-1244
Web Site:
http://www.mainstreamoutfitters.com
Fishing Tackle & Fly Fishing Products Sales
N.A.I.C.S.: 114119
Diane Louden *(Owner)*

DAVE'S SUPERMARKET INC.
3301 Payne Ave, Cleveland, OH 44114
Tel.: (216) 361-5130   OH
Web Site:
http://www.davesmarkets.com
Year Founded: 1932
Sales Range: $50-74.9 Million
Emp.: 800
Provider of Grocery Services
N.A.I.C.S.: 445110
Burton Saltzman *(Pres)*
Dan Saltzman *(VP)*
Steve Saltzman *(VP)*

DAVENPORT & COMPANY LLC
1 James Ctr 901 E Cary St Ste 1100, Richmond, VA 23219
Tel.: (804) 780-2000   VA
Web Site:
http://www.davenportllc.com
Year Founded: 1863
Sales Range: $100-124.9 Million
Emp.: 350
Provider of Security Broker Services
N.A.I.C.S.: 523150
Sean J. Allburn *(Mng Dir-Investments-Williamsburg)*
John D. Gammon *(VP-Corp Svcs)*
Kyle A. Laux *(Sr VP-Pub Fin)*
Garrett S. Nelson *(Assoc VP-Res)*
Michael Denton *(Sr VP-Investments-Private Wealth Mgmt)*
Coleman Wortham III *(Chm & CEO)*

DAVENPORT ENERGY INC.
108 S Main St, Chatham, VA 24531
Tel.: (434) 432-0251
Web Site:
http://www.davenportenergy.com
Year Founded: 1941
Sales Range: $25-49.9 Million
Emp.: 100
Petroleum Product Mfr
N.A.I.C.S.: 324199
Herold Thorton *(VP)*
Lewis Wall *(Pres & CEO)*

DAVENPORT UNION WAREHOUSE COMPANY
10th Jefferson St, Davenport, WA 99122
Tel.: (509) 725-7081
Web Site:
http://www.davenportunion.com
Sales Range: $10-24.9 Million
Emp.: 7
Grains
N.A.I.C.S.: 424510
Tom Scharff *(Pres)*
Beau Duff *(CEO)*

DAVID & GOLIATH, INC.
1419 S Martin Luther King Jr Ave, Clearwater, FL 33756
Tel.: (727) 462-6205   FL
Web Site:
http://www.davidandgoliathtees.com
Year Founded: 2000
Sales Range: $10-24.9 Million
Emp.: 25
T-Shirts, Sleepwear & Accessories Retailer
N.A.I.C.S.: 458110
Lenor Goldman *(VP)*
Billy Campisciano *(Exec VP)*
Dean Martin *(Dir-Mktg)*
Todd Goldman *(Founder & Pres)*

Peter Bassett *(Mng Dir-Integrated Production & Tech Svcs)*
Tim Knock *(VP-Sls)*

DAVID A. BRAMBLE, INC.
705 Morgnec Rd, Chestertown, MD 21620-3110
Tel.: (410) 778-3023   MD
Web Site:
https://www.davidabrambleinc.com
Year Founded: 1959
Sales Range: $25-49.9 Million
Emp.: 240
Provider of Excavation, Paving & Utility Services
N.A.I.C.S.: 236210
David C. Bramble *(Pres & COO)*
R. Preston Jacquette *(CFO & Treas)*
Chuck Breeding *(VP & Project Mgr)*
Debbie Glebe *(Mgr-Payroll-Accts Receivable)*
Megan Bramble Owings *(Sec)*

Subsidiaries:

David A. Bramble, Inc. - Massey Facility   (1)
32559 Bramble Way, Massey, MD 21650
Tel.: (410) 928-3893
Emp.: 6
Highway Construction Services
N.A.I.C.S.: 237310
Mike Thrift *(Plant Mgr)*

DAVID A. CAMPBELL CORPORATION
3060 Adam St, Riverside, CA 92504
Tel.: (951) 785-4444
Web Site:
http://www.bmwriverside.com
Sales Range: $25-49.9 Million
Emp.: 205
Automobiles, New & Used
N.A.I.C.S.: 441110
R. J. Romero *(Pres)*

DAVID A. NOYES & COMPANY
209 S La Salle St Fl 12, Chicago, IL 60604
Tel.: (312) 782-0400
Web Site: http://www.danoyes.com
Sales Range: $10-24.9 Million
Emp.: 150
Investment Firm General Brokerage
N.A.I.C.S.: 523150
L. H. Bayley *(Chm)*
Sharon Wierzba *(Dir-Ops-Noyes)*
Matthew Reynolds *(Chief Operating & Compliance Officer)*
Jim Huse *(VP-Capital Markets)*
Robert Welch Jr. *(Sr Mng Dir-Capital Markets)*

DAVID A. STRAZ JR. CENTER FOR THE PERFORMING ARTS
1010 N MacInnes Pl, Tampa, FL 33602
Tel.: (813) 222-1000
Web Site: http://www.strazcenter.org
Sales Range: $25-49.9 Million
Emp.: 350
Theatrical Productions & Entertainment Venues
N.A.I.C.S.: 711110
Julie Britton *(VP-Dev)*
Summer Bohnenkamp *(Sr Dir-Mktg)*
Brad Hudson *(Dir-Video & Documentary Projects)*
Judith Lisi *(Dir-Opera Tampa)*
Paul B. Bilyeu *(Sr Dir-Comm)*
Marc Brechwald *(Dir-Corp Rels & Sponsorship)*
Georgiana Young *(CMO & Chief Programming Officer)*
Lorrin Shepard *(COO)*

Jeanne Piazza *(Mgr-Programming Rentals)*
Patrick Leahy *(Dir-Programming)*

DAVID ALLEN COMPANY INC.
150 Rush St, Raleigh, NC 27603-3594
Tel.: (919) 821-7100   NC
Web Site: https://www.davidallen.com
Year Founded: 1920
Sales Range: $25-49.9 Million
Emp.: 200
Provider of Terrazzo, Tile, Marble & Mosaic Services
N.A.I.C.S.: 238340
Robert Roberson *(Owner)*

DAVID BIRNBAUM/RARE 1 CORPORATION
589 5th Ave Ste 710, New York, NY 10017
Tel.: (212) 575-0266
Web Site:
http://www.davidbirnbaum.com
Year Founded: 2001
Sales Range: $125-149.9 Million
Emp.: 6
Jeweler in Precious & Rare Gems
N.A.I.C.S.: 458310
David Birnbaum *(Pres)*

DAVID BOLAND, INC.
219 Indian River Ave Ste 201, Titusville, FL 32796-3558
Tel.: (321) 269-1345   FL
Web Site: https://www.dboland.com
Year Founded: 1976
Sales Range: $75-99.9 Million
Emp.: 65
Contracting Services
N.A.I.C.S.: 236210
Jeff Duguid *(Mgr-Proposal)*
Luca Fucito *(Engr-Electrical Project)*

DAVID BRUCE AUTO CENTER INC.
555 William Latham Dr, Bourbonnais, IL 60914
Tel.: (815) 933-7700
Web Site: http://www.davidbruce.com
Rev.: $16,700,000
Emp.: 54
New Car Dealers
N.A.I.C.S.: 441110
Bruce Dickstein *(Owner & Pres)*
Dan Ballard *(Gen Mgr-Sls)*
Ken Ballard *(Mgr-Used Cars)*
Janelle Hindmand *(Mgr-Toyota Sls)*
Dave Sosnowski *(Mgr-Internet Sls)*
Jason Connor *(Mgr-New Car Sls)*
Rhonda Thomas *(Comptroller & Office Mgr)*
Rick Elroy *(Dir-Parts)*
Brent Dolliger *(Mgr-Used Car)*

DAVID C. GREENBAUM CO. INC.
1490 Victoria Ct, San Bernardino, CA 92408
Tel.: (909) 824-9070
Sales Range: $10-24.9 Million
Emp.: 13
Whslr of Industrial Supplies
N.A.I.C.S.: 423840
David C. Greenbaum *(Pres)*
Robert Kruse *(Treas & VP)*

DAVID C. POOLE COMPANY INC.
6 Arborland Way, Greenville, SC 29615
Tel.: (864) 271-9935   SC
Web Site:
https://www.poolecompany.com
Year Founded: 1973
Sales Range: $50-74.9 Million

Emp.: 20
Sales of Nondurable Goods
N.A.I.C.S.: 424990
David C. Poole *(Pres & Treas)*

DAVID CLARK COMPANY INCORPORATED
360 Franklin St, Worcester, MA 15054
Tel.: (508) 751-5800   MA
Web Site:
https://www.davidclarkcompany.com
Year Founded: 1935
Sales Range: $100-124.9 Million
Emp.: 300
Headset Communication System Mfr
N.A.I.C.S.: 334220
Robert A. Vincent *(Pres)*
Bob Daigle *(Product Mgr-Fire, Marine, Airline & Wireless)*
Dennis Buzzell *(Mgr-Aviation Market)*
John Tasi *(Mgr-Govt & Military Product)*
Aaron Simmons *(Mgr-Sls-North East)*
Bob Carroll *(Mgr-Sls-South East)*
Bryce Clark *(Mgr-Technical Product-OEM & Special Markets)*
Bob Zajdel *(Mgr-Sls-North Central)*
Keith Liu *(Mgr-Sls-Asia-Pacific & Middle East)*
Ralph Chance *(Mgr-Sls-South Central)*
Ron Lassing *(Mgr-Sls-Europe & Africa)*

Subsidiaries:

Air-Lock Incorporated   (1)
108 Gulf St, Milford, CT 06460-4845
Tel.: (203) 301-6060
Web Site: http://www.airlockinc.com
Rev.: $4,400,000
Emp.: 40
Aircraft Parts & Equipment Mfr
N.A.I.C.S.: 336413
Michael H. McCarthy *(Pres & Gen Mgr)*

DAVID DOBBS ENTERPRISES INC.
4600 US 1 N, Saint Augustine, FL 32095
Tel.: (904) 824-6171
Web Site:
http://www.dobbsapparel.com
Sales Range: $50-74.9 Million
Emp.: 150
N.A.I.C.S.: 323120
David Dobbs *(Pres)*
Terry Sechen *(Controller)*
Gladys Morales *(Engr-Prototype)*
Lisa Preble *(Dir-HR)*
Mike Snyder *(Dir-Sls)*
Susan Fina *(Coord-Payroll)*

Subsidiaries:

Dobbs Apparel   (1)
4600 US 1 N, Saint Augustine, FL 32095
Tel.: (904) 824-6171
Web Site: http://www.menudesigns.com
Sales Range: $25-49.9 Million
Emp.: 100
Mfr of Apparel
N.A.I.C.S.: 323120
Jason Poland *(Mgr-Mktg)*

Dobbs Business Products   (1)
4600 US 1 N, Saint Augustine, FL 32095
Tel.: (904) 824-6171
Web Site: http://www.menudesigns.com
Sales Range: $25-49.9 Million
Emp.: 100
Mfr of Binders, Checkbook Covers, Organizers, Pads, Slip Cases, Address Books, Bank Deposit Bags, Diploma Holders, Business Card Holders, Hotel Guest Directories, Tote Bags, Telephone Book Covers
N.A.I.C.S.: 323120

DAVID DRYE COMPANY LLC

David Drye Company LLC—(Continued)

175 Davidson Hwy, Concord, NC
28027
Tel.: (704) 786-6181
Web Site:
http://www.daviddryecompany.com
Sales Range: $50-74.9 Million
Emp.: 14
Apartment Building Operator
N.A.I.C.S.: 531110
John Edward Littlefield (CEO)

DAVID E. HARVEY BUILDERS INC.

3630 Westchase Dr, Houston, TX
77042-5224
Tel.: (713) 783-8710   TX
Web Site:
http://www.harveybuilders.com
Year Founded: 1958
Sales Range: $150-199.9 Million
Emp.: 300
Nonresidential Construction
N.A.I.C.S.: 236220
David E. Harvey Jr. (Pres)
Rodney Finkey (Controller)
Jim Cecil (Sr Project Mgr)
Joseph A. Cleary Jr. (Exec VP)

Subsidiaries:

Harvey-Cleary Builders   (1)
6710A Rockledge Dr Ste 430, Bethesda,
MD 20817
Tel.: (301) 519-2288
Web Site: http://www.harveycleary.com
Sales Range: $10-24.9 Million
Emp.: 40
Nonresidential Construction
N.A.I.C.S.: 236220
Michael Bellusci (Dir-Repositioning & Renovations)
Catherine Hall (Office Mgr)
Jondell Shives (VP-San Antonio)

Harvey-Cleary Builders   (1)
8107 Springdale Rd Ste 105, Austin, TX
78724-2437
Tel.: (512) 928-9300
Web Site: http://www.harvey-cleary.com
Sales Range: $10-24.9 Million
Emp.: 50
Nonresidential Construction
N.A.I.C.S.: 236220
Mike Bellusci (Dir-Repositioning & Renovations)
Rusty Gorman (VP)
Kevin Rogge (VP)
Ed Green (Sr Project Mgr)
Joseph LaFonte Jr. (VP)

DAVID ENERGY SYSTEMS, INC.

417 Grand St, Brooklyn, NY 11211
Tel.: (203) 246-9205
Web Site:
http://www.davidenergy.com
Oil & Energy Distr
N.A.I.C.S.: 237120
James McGinniss (Co-Founder & CEO)

Subsidiaries:

R3 Energy Management Audit & Review LLC   (1)
417 Grand St Unit 1, Brooklyn, NY 11211
Tel.: (914) 909-3940
Web Site: http://www.r3energy.com
Scientific & Technical Consulting Services
N.A.I.C.S.: 541690
Rudy Scholl (Pres)

DAVID GOODING INC.

173 Sparks St, Brockton, MA 02302
Tel.: (508) 894-2000
Web Site: https://www.goodingd.com
Sales Range: $25-49.9 Million
Emp.: 64
Plumbing & Hydronic Heating Supplies
N.A.I.C.S.: 423720

David Gooding (Pres)
Jim Partridge (VP-Fin)
George Gooding (VP-Sls & Ops)

DAVID H. FELL & COMPANY INCORPORATED

6009 Bandini Blvd, City of Commerce, CA 90040
Tel.: (323) 722-9992
Web Site: https://www.dhfco.com
Rev.: $31,760,611
Emp.: 20
Secondary Precious Metals
N.A.I.C.S.: 331492
David H. Fell (Founder & Chm)

DAVID HOBBS HONDA

6100 N Green Bay Ave, Glendale, WI
53209
Tel.: (414) 352-6100
Web Site:
https://www.davidhobbs.com
Year Founded: 1987
Sales Range: $10-24.9 Million
Emp.: 61
New Car Retailer
N.A.I.C.S.: 441110
Jeremy Olson (Dir-F&I)
Greg Hobbs (Exec VP)
Bruce Kolz (Gen Mgr)
Wolfgang Miller (Mgr-BDC)

DAVID HOCKER & ASSOCIATES, INC.

620 Park Plz Dr, Owensboro, KY
42301-5483
Tel.: (270) 926-2616
Web Site:
https://www.davidhocker.com
Year Founded: 1964
Sales Range: $25-49.9 Million
Emp.: 150
Land Subdivision Services
N.A.I.C.S.: 237210
David E. Hocker (Chm & CEO)
Scott D. Hornaday (Pres, COO & Gen Counsel)
Philip L. Purdom (Sr VP-Dev & Mall Leasing)
David W. Conkright (CFO)
H. Ted Belcher (CFO)

DAVID I. PETERSON INC.

1621 W Oakridge Dr, Albany, GA
31706
Tel.: (229) 435-8233
Web Site:
http://www.davidipetersoninc.net
Sales Range: $10-24.9 Million
Emp.: 40
Petroleum Bulk Stations
N.A.I.C.S.: 424710
Debbie Logan (Pres)

DAVID J. FRANK LANDSCAPE CONTRACTING, INC.

N 120 W 21350 Freistadt Rd, Germantown, WI 53022
Tel.: (262) 255-4888
Web Site:
https://www.davidjfrank.com
Sales Range: $10-24.9 Million
Emp.: 150
Landscape Contractors
N.A.I.C.S.: 561730
David J. Frank (Chm & CEO)
Lynn Brummond (Sec)
David R. Frank (Pres & CFO)

DAVID J. STANTON AND ASSOCIATES

714 W Michigan Ave, Jackson, MI
49201
Tel.: (517) 784-4094
Sales Range: $50-74.9 Million
Emp.: 2,000

Fast-Food Restaurant, Chain
N.A.I.C.S.: 722513
Mark Behm (Pres)

DAVID JAMES GROUP LTD.

1 Trans Am Plz Dr Ste 300, Oakbrook Terrace, IL 60181
Tel.: (630) 305-0003
Web Site:
http://www.davidjamesgroup.com
Year Founded: 2002
Sales Range: $1-9.9 Million
Emp.: 12
Advetising Agency
N.A.I.C.S.: 541810
Ron Zywicki (VP-Creative Svcs)
David Laurenzo (Pres)

DAVID JOHN GLUCKLE INSURANCE AGENCY LLC

4452 Heatherdowns Blvd, Toledo, OH
43614
Tel.: (419) 741-4051
Web Site:
http://www.gluckleinsurance
agency.com
Insurance & Financial Services
N.A.I.C.S.: 524210
David Gluckle (Principal Agent)
Matt Brown (Office Mgr)

DAVID K. BURNAP ADVERTISING AGENCY, INC.

36 S Main St, Dayton, OH 45458
Tel.: (937) 439-4800   OH
Web Site: http://www.dkburnap.com
Year Founded: 1959
Sales Range: Less than $1 Million
Emp.: 9
Advetising Agency
N.A.I.C.S.: 541810
Dennis R. Hays (VP-Creative Svcs)
E.B. Terhune (VP & Dir-Media Svcs Dir)
David Baker (Mgr-Electronic Mktg)
David K. Burnap Jr. (Pres)

DAVID KURLAN & ASSOCIATES, INC.

114 Turnpike Rd, Westborough, MA
01581
Tel.: (508) 389-9350
Web Site:
http://www.salesdevelopment
specialists.com
Year Founded: 1985
Rev.: $2,300,000
Emp.: 13
Management Consulting Services
N.A.I.C.S.: 541613
Dave Kurlan (Pres & CEO)
Chris Mott (Pres-Corp Trng)

DAVID LERNER ASSOCIATES INC.

477 Jericho Tpke, Syosset, NY
11791-9006
Tel.: (516) 921-4200   NY
Web Site:
https://www.davidlerner.com
Year Founded: 1968
Sales Range: $50-74.9 Million
Emp.: 292
Provider of Security Broker Services
N.A.I.C.S.: 523150
David Lerner (Owner & Pres)
Alan Chodosh (CFO)
John Dempsey (Sr VP-Sls)
William Mason (Mng Dir-Trading)
Larry Maverick (VP-Recruitment)

DAVID LEWIS & ASSOCIATES INC.

10 Suntree Pl, Melbourne, FL 32940
Tel.: (321) 435-6000

Web Site:
https://www.davidlewis.com
Rev.: $10,000,000
Emp.: 15
Computer Software Development
N.A.I.C.S.: 541511
David Lewis (Pres)

DAVID LYNG & ASSOCIATES, INC.

2170 41st Ave, Capitola, CA 95010
Tel.: (831) 464-4424   CA
Web Site: http://www.davidlyng.com
Year Founded: 1980
Sales Range: $25-49.9 Million
Emp.: 260
Real Estate Agency
N.A.I.C.S.: 531210
David A. Lyng (Founder, Pres & CEO)
Sally Lyng (VP & Mktg Mgr)
Morgan Lyng Lukina (Gen Mgr)
Megan Lyng (Dir-Social Media-Special Events)
Jenny Putney (Mgr-Human Resources)

DAVID MARTIN & ASSOCIATES

1201 Buck Jones Rd, Raleigh, NC
27606
Tel.: (919) 467-7200
Web Site: http://www.martinprop.biz
Sales Range: $10-24.9 Million
Emp.: 10
Shopping Center, Property Operation Only
N.A.I.C.S.: 531120
David J. Martin (Founder & Pres)
Bob Dascombe (Sr VP)

DAVID MCDAVID AUTOMOTIVE GROUP

3700 W Airport Fwy, Irving, TX 75062
Tel.: (469) 405-3340
Web Site:
https://www.mcdavidhondairving.com
Sales Range: $25-49.9 Million
Emp.: 300
New & Used Automobiles
N.A.I.C.S.: 441110

Subsidiaries:

David McDavid Acura   (1)
4051 W Plano Pkwy, Plano, TX 75093
Tel.: (972) 964-6000
Web Site: http://www.mcdavidacura.com
Sales Range: $10-24.9 Million
Emp.: 200
New & Used Automobile Dealers
N.A.I.C.S.: 811111
Peggy Kohler (Controller)
Charles Sokolash (Gen Mgr-Sls)

David McDavid Acura of Austin   (1)
13553 Research Blvd, Austin, TX 78750
Tel.: (512) 335-5555
Web Site: http://www.mcdavid.com
New & Used Automobile Dealers
N.A.I.C.S.: 441110
Clifton Goldsmith (Gen Mgr)

David McDavid GMC   (1)
3600 W Airport Freeway, Irving, TX 75062-5903
Tel.: (972) 790-6000
Web Site: http://www.mcdavid.com
New & Used Automobile Dealers
N.A.I.C.S.: 517112

David McDavid Honda   (1)
3700 W Airport Fwy, Irving, TX 75062
Tel.: (972) 790-6000
Web Site:
http://www.mcdavidhondafrisco.com
Sales Range: $10-24.9 Million
Emp.: 50
New & Used Automobile Dealers
N.A.I.C.S.: 441110
Ty Patterson (Mgr-Phone)

David McDavid Nissan (1)
11911 Gulf Fwy, Houston, TX 77034
Tel.: (713) 941-0600
Web Site:
https://www.nissanhouston.mcdavid.com
Sales Range: $25-49.9 Million
Emp.: 150
New & Used Automobile Dealers
N.A.I.C.S.: 441110
Randy Foust (Gen Mgr)

David McDavid Plano Lincoln (1)
3333 W Plano Pkwy, Plano, TX 75075
Tel.: (972) 964-5000
Web Site: http://www.mcdavidlincoln.com
Sales Range: $10-24.9 Million
Emp.: 100
New & Used Automobile Dealers
N.A.I.C.S.: 441110
Will Palasota (Gen Mgr)

McDavid Honda (1)
11200 Gulf Freeway, Houston, TX 77034
Tel.: (713) 948-1900
Web Site: http://www.mcdavidhonda.com
Sales Range: $25-49.9 Million
Emp.: 200
New & Used Automobile Dealers
N.A.I.C.S.: 441110
Allen Paul (Gen Mgr)

DAVID MONTOYA CONSTRUCTION, INC.
315 Alameda Blvd NE, Albuquerque,
NM 87113
Tel.: (505) 898-6330
Web Site:
https://www.montoyaconstruct.com
Year Founded: 1985
Sales Range: $25-49.9 Million
Emp.: 35
Construction Contractor
N.A.I.C.S.: 236220
Evalyn Hodgdon (Controller)
Richard Brooks (Mgr-HR)
Robert Watson (Project Mgr)
Eli Morfin (Project Mgr)
Vincent Martinez (Project Mgr)
Bobby Gonzales (Project Mgr)
Pamela Montoya (VP)
David Montoya (Pres)
Alex Atencio (Project Mgr)
Paul Montoya (Mgr-HR)
Phil Plante (Mgr-Safety)
Leroy Hoak (Mgr-Warehouse)
Mark Cavasos (Mgr-Equipment)
David Dodson (Engr-Field)

DAVID MORSE & ASSOCIATES
330 N Brand Blvd Ste 230, Glendale,
CA 91203
Tel.: (323) 342-6800
Web Site:
https://www.davidmorse.com
Rev.: $24,000,000
Emp.: 140
Provider of Insurance Adjustment &
Investigation Services
N.A.I.C.S.: 524291

DAVID O'KEEFE STUDIOS INC.
615 Channelside Dr, Tampa, FL
33602
Tel.: (813) 254-5056
Web Site:
https://www.davidokeefe.com
Sales Range: $1-9.9 Million
Art Gallery & Store
N.A.I.C.S.: 712110
David O'Keefe (Pres)
Cheryl Schmidt (Bus Mgr)

DAVID PEARSON ASSOCIATES
1390 S Dixie Hwy Ste 2117, Coral
Gables, FL 33146
Tel.: (305) 967-8225
Web Site:
http://www.davidpearsonasso
ciates.com

Year Founded: 1966
Sales Range: $1-9.9 Million
Emp.: 5
Public Relations Agency
N.A.I.C.S.: 541820
David Pearson (Founder & Co-
Principal)
Chris Pearson (Co-Principal)

DAVID PEYSER SPORTS-WEAR INC.
88 Spence St, Bay Shore, NY 11706-
2230
Tel.: (631) 273-8020 NY
Web Site: https://mvsport.com
Year Founded: 1948
Sales Range: $100-124.9 Million
Emp.: 200
Sportswear & Athletic Clothing Sup-
plier & Mfr
N.A.I.C.S.: 315250
Paul Peyser (Owner)

DAVID R. MCGEORGE CAR CO. INC.
9319 W Broad St, Richmond, VA
23294
Tel.: (804) 755-9200
Web Site:
http://www.mcgeorgetoyota.com
Sales Range: $10-24.9 Million
Emp.: 141
Automobiles, New & Used
N.A.I.C.S.: 441110
Linda Swaim (Mgr-HR)

DAVID RICE AUTO SALES
12654 N US Highway 131, School-
craft, MI 49087-9401
Tel.: (269) 679-4371
Web Site:
https://www.davidriceautosales.com
Rev.: $10,000,000
Emp.: 2
Used Car Dealer & Trader
N.A.I.C.S.: 441120
David Rice (Pres)

DAVID S. DE LUZ SR ENTER-PRISES
811 Kanoelehua Ave, Hilo, HI 96720
Tel.: (808) 935-2258
Sales Range: $50-74.9 Million
Emp.: 150
Automobiles, New & Used
N.A.I.C.S.: 441110
David S. DeLuz Sr. (Pres)

Subsidiaries:

Big Island Toyota Inc (1)
811 Kanoelehua Ave, Hilo, HI 96720
Tel.: (808) 935-2920
Web Site: http://www.bigislandtoyota.com
Rev.: $25,000,000
Emp.: 70
New & Used Car Dealers
N.A.I.C.S.: 441110
David S. De Luz Sr. (Owner)

DAVID WEEKLEY HOMES, LP
1111 N Post Oak Rd, Houston, TX
77055-7211
Tel.: (713) 963-0500 TX
Web Site:
http://www.davidweekleyhomes.com
Year Founded: 1976
Sales Range: $1-4.9 Billion
Emp.: 1,052
Custom Home Builder
N.A.I.C.S.: 236115
Chad Durham (Div Pres)
Joe Rentfro (Pres-Div)

DAVID WILSON AUTOMOTIVE GROUP
1400 Tustin St, Orange, CA 92867-
3902

Tel.: (714) 639-6750 CA
Web Site:
https://www.toyotaoforange.com
Year Founded: 1966
Sales Range: $350-399.9 Million
Emp.: 1,000
Automobile Dealership
N.A.I.C.S.: 441110
David W. Wilson (Owner)
Ren Rooney (Pres)
Vickie Murphy (VP)
Glen Quintos (CFO)

DAVID X. MANNERS CO., INC.
64 Post Rd W, Westport, CT 06880-
4208
Tel.: (203) 227-7060 CT
Web Site:
http://www.hubmagazine.com
Year Founded: 1966
Sales Range: $1-9.9 Million
Emp.: 4
Public Relations Agency
N.A.I.C.S.: 541820
Timothy G. Manners (Pres)
Peter F. Eder (COO)

DAVID Z INTERNET, INC.
384 5th Ave, New York, NY 10018
Tel.: (212) 274-9044
Web Site: http://www.davidz.com
Year Founded: 2003
Rev.: $10,700,000
Emp.: 140
Shoes & Boots Retailer
N.A.I.C.S.: 458210
David Zaken (Pres)

DAVID-EDWARD COMPANY LTD.
1407 Parker Rd, Baltimore, MD
21227
Tel.: (410) 242-2222
Web Site:
http://www.davidedward.com
Year Founded: 1986
Sales Range: $10-24.9 Million
Emp.: 160
Mfr of Wood Office Furniture
N.A.I.C.S.: 337211
David E. Pitts (Pres)
Gregory Pitts (Dir-Sls & Mktg-Intl)

DAVIDON HOMES LTD.
1600 S Main St Ste 150, Walnut
Creek, CA 94596
Tel.: (925) 945-8000
Web Site:
http://www.homesbydavidon.com
Sales Range: $10-24.9 Million
Emp.: 100
Residential Land Subdividers & De-
velopers
N.A.I.C.S.: 237210
Diana Fox (VP)
Dave James (Mgr-Computer Sys
Ops)
Steve Abbs (VP)

DAVIDS SUPERMARKETS INC.
103 E Criner St, Grandview, TX
76050
Tel.: (817) 866-2651
Sales Range: Less than $1 Million
Emp.: 3
Grocery Stores, Independent
N.A.I.C.S.: 445110
Robert Waldrip (CEO)

DAVIDSON CHEVROLET
18579 US Rte 11, Watertown, NY
13601
Tel.: (315) 836-4621
Web Site:
https://www.davidsongmsuper
center.com

Sales Range: $25-49.9 Million
Emp.: 100
Car Whslr
N.A.I.C.S.: 441110
Dwight Davidson (Pres & Gen Mgr)
Cathy Dickenson (Asst VP)

DAVIDSON CHEVROLET INC.
5871 Rome Taberg Rd, Rome, NY
13440
Tel.: (315) 371-4138
Web Site:
https://www.davidsongmrome.com
Sales Range: $10-24.9 Million
Emp.: 40
Car Whslr
N.A.I.C.S.: 441110
Dennis Peresegti (Bus Mgr)

DAVIDSON ENGINEERING, INC.
3530 Kraft Rd Ste 301, Naples, FL
34105
Tel.: (239) 434-6060 FL
Web Site:
http://www.davidsonengineering.com
Year Founded: 1997
Sales Range: $1-9.9 Million
Emp.: 20
Engineeering Services
N.A.I.C.S.: 541330
Jeff Davidson (Pres)
Andrew Rath (Project Mgr)
Josh Fruth (VP)
Ryan White (Mgr-Engrg Production)

DAVIDSON HEALTH CARE, INC.
250 Hospital Dr, Lexington, NC
27292-6792
Tel.: (336) 248-5161 NC
Web Site:
http://www.lexingtonmemorial.com
Year Founded: 1985
Sales Range: $50-74.9 Million
Emp.: 700
Retailer of Pharmaceutical & Propri-
etary Items
N.A.I.C.S.: 456110
Steve Schultz (CEO)

Subsidiaries:

Lex Properties Inc. (1)
250 Hospital Dr, Lexington, NC 27292-6792
Tel.: (336) 248-5161
Web Site:
http://www.lexingtonmemorial.com
Sales Range: $50-74.9 Million
Operator of Apartment Buildings
N.A.I.C.S.: 531110

Lexington Memorial Hospital Inc. (1)
250 Hospital Dr, Lexington, NC 27292-6792
Tel.: (336) 248-5161
Web Site:
http://www.lexingtonmemorial.com
Sales Range: $25-49.9 Million
Providers of Medical Services
N.A.I.C.S.: 622110

DAVIDSON HOLDING CO.
1200 Rte 22 E, Bridgewater, NJ
08807
Tel.: (908) 707-3888
Web Site:
http://www.davidsonholdings.co.uk
Rev.: $44,000,000
Emp.: 400
Owner & Operator of Supermarkets
N.A.I.C.S.: 445110
Robert Davidson (Chm)
William Davidson (Pres)

DAVIDSON INSULATION & ACOUSTICS
2200 Murphy Ct, North Port, FL
34289-9302
Tel.: (941) 429-3600 FL
Web Site:
https://www.davidsoninsulation.com

Davidson Insulation & Acoustics—(Continued)

Year Founded: 1977
Rev.: $12,138,321
Emp.: 25
Insulation, Buildings
N.A.I.C.S.: 238310
Constance Blanchard *(Sec)*
Heather B. Henson *(Treas)*
Ted Blanchard *(Mgr-Insulation)*
Fred Schmidt *(Mgr-Acoustics)*
Russ Joseph *(Mgr-Shelving)*
Jim Stoner *(Office Mgr)*
Constance Blanchard *(Sec)*
John Ridgeway *(Mgr-Spray Foam)*
Judy Barth *(Mgr-Port St. Lucie Office)*
Edward E. Blanchard III *(Pres)*
Edward E. Blanchard IV *(VP)*

DAVIDSON KEMPNER CAPITAL MANAGEMENT LP
520 Madison Ave 30th Fl, New York, NY 10022
Tel.: (212) 446-4000　DE
Web Site:
　https://www.davidsonkempner.com
Year Founded: 1983
Alternative Asset Management Services
N.A.I.C.S.: 523940
Anthony Sabatino *(Controller)*
Robert Melnyk *(Mng Dir)*

Subsidiaries:

Nature Energy Biogas A/S　**(1)**
Orbaekvej 260, DK-5220, Odense, Denmark
Tel.: (45) 70224000
Web Site: http://www.natureenergy.dk
Emp.: 250
Biogas Production Services
N.A.I.C.S.: 221117
Peter Gaemelke *(Chm)*
Steen Parsholt *(Vice Chm)*
Kim Kragelund *(CFO)*

Subsidiary (Domestic):

Nature Energy Construction A/S　**(2)**
Hermesvej 1, DK-9530, Stovring, Denmark
Tel.: (45) 99351600
Web Site: http://www.natureenergy.dk
Biomass Energy Services
N.A.I.C.S.: 221117
Jesper Bundgaard *(Dir-Construction)*

DAVIDSON OIL COMPANY INC.
202 S Arthur St, Amarillo, TX 79102
Tel.: (806) 374-6022　TX
Web Site:
　https://www.davidsonoil.com
Year Founded: 1975
Sales Range: $10-24.9 Million
Emp.: 64
Distr of Oil Products
N.A.I.C.S.: 484220
Chan Davidson *(CEO & CFO)*

Subsidiaries:

Flying Star Transport LLC　**(1)**
1201 N Forest, Amarillo, TX 79102-3221
Tel.: (806) 372-4620
Web Site: http://www.goflyingstar.com
Sales Range: $10-24.9 Million
Emp.: 19
Provider of Transport Services
N.A.I.C.S.: 484230

DAVIDSON ORGANICS, LLC
665 Spice Island Dr Ste 101, Sparks, NV 89431
Tel.: (775) 356-1690
Web Site:
　http://www.davidsonstea.com
Year Founded: 1976
Sales Range: $1-9.9 Million
Emp.: 200
Organic Product Mfr
N.A.I.C.S.: 325199
Kunall Patel *(Owner)*

DAVIDSON REALTY, INC.
100 E Town Pl Ste 100, Saint Augustine, FL 32092
Tel.: (904) 940-5000
Web Site:
　https://www.davidsonrealtyinc.com
Year Founded: 1989
Sales Range: $10-24.9 Million
Emp.: 50
Real Estate Brokerage Services
N.A.I.C.S.: 531210
Sherry Davidson *(Co-Founder & Pres)*
Shirley Barber *(Coord-Transaction & Mktg)*

DAVIDSON TECHNOLOGIES, INC.
530 Discovery Dr NW, Huntsville, AL 35806-2810
Tel.: (256) 922-0720
Web Site: https://www.davidson-tech.com
Year Founded: 1996
Emp.: 151
Scientific Management & Technical Services
N.A.I.C.S.: 541690
Dorothy Davidson *(Chm & CEO)*
Linda Knapp *(CFO & VP)*
Paul Hastings *(VP-NASA & Space Sys)*

DAVIDSON WATER INC.
7040 Old US Hwy 52, Welcome, NC 27374
Tel.: (336) 731-2341
Web Site:
　https://www.davidsonwater.com
Year Founded: 1967
Rev.: $10,972,771
Emp.: 60
Irrigation Systems
N.A.I.C.S.: 221310
Robert Walters *(Asst Mgr)*
Ron Sink *(Gen Mgr)*

DAVIDSON'S INC.
6100 Wilkinson Dr, Prescott, AZ 86301-6162
Tel.: (928) 776-8055　NC
Web Site:
　http://www.davidsonsinc.com
Year Founded: 1932
Sales Range: $100-124.9 Million
Emp.: 50
Supplier of Sporting & Recreation Goods
N.A.I.C.S.: 423910
Bryan Tucker *(Pres & CEO)*

DAVIDSON'S OF DUNDEE
28421 Hwy 27, Dundee, FL 33838
Tel.: (863) 439-2284
Web Site:
　https://www.dundeegroves.com
Year Founded: 1967
Sales Range: $1-9.9 Million
Emp.: 20
Confectionery & Fruit Basket Merchant Whslr
N.A.I.C.S.: 424450
Tom Davidson *(Pres)*

DAVIDSON-KENNEDY CO.
800 Industrial Park Dr, Marietta, GA 30062
Tel.: (770) 427-9467
Web Site:
　http://www.equipmentinnovator.com
Sales Range: $10-24.9 Million
Emp.: 25
Truck Bodies; Manufacturer
N.A.I.C.S.: 333922
Joe Rubis *(Pres)*

DAVIES
808 State St, Santa Barbara, CA 93101
Tel.: (805) 963-5929
Web Site:
　http://www.daviespublicaffairs.com
Year Founded: 1983
Sales Range: $1-9.9 Million.
Emp.: 48
Public Affairs, Crisis Communication Support & Issues Management Services
N.A.I.C.S.: 541820
John Davies *(Chm & CEO)*
Robb Rice *(Exec VP-Pub Affairs)*

DAVIES, PACHECO & MURPHY ADVERTISING AGENCY, INC.
1 Parkview Plz Ste 150, Oakbrook Terrace, IL 60181
Tel.: (630) 570-4800
Web Site: http://www.moveo.com
Year Founded: 1987
Sales Range: $10-24.9 Million
Emp.: 42
Advertising Agencies
N.A.I.C.S.: 541810
Bob Murphy *(Mng Partner)*
Brian Davies *(Mng Partner)*
Dave Cannon *(VP-Creative Tech)*
Kevin Randall *(VP-Strategy & Plng)*
Angela Costanzi *(VP-Creative Tech)*
Sheri Granholm *(VP-Consulting & Engagement)*
Julie Rechlicz *(Dir-Media Svcs)*
Irene Westcott *(Dir-Creative Svcs)*
Jiani Zhang *(Dir-Data & Insights)*
Stephanie Hides *(Mgr-Resource)*

DAVIESMOORE
277 N Sixth St Ste 3B, Boise, ID 83702
Tel.: (208) 472-2129　ID
Web Site:
　http://www.daviesmoore.com
Year Founded: 1953
Rev.: $3,200,000
Emp.: 9
Fiscal Year-end: 07/31/04
N.A.I.C.S.: 541810
Jeffrey L. Nielsen *(VP-Client Svcs)*
Vicki L. Ward *(Controller)*
Ernie Monroe *(VP-Creative Svcs)*
Edward Moore *(Partner)*
Brooke Smith *(Media Dir-Buying & Coord-PR)*
Carolyn Sali *(VP-Ops)*
Jason Sievers *(Creative Dir-Svcs)*
Michael Reagan *(VP-Brand Plng)*
Nikki Reynolds *(Media Dir-Plng)*
Roger Finch *(Fin Dir)*
Tyler LaDouceur *(Acct Mgr & Media Buyer)*
Aaron Grable *(Designer)*
Katie Johnson *(Acct Exec)*
Tanya Vaughan *(VP-Digital Strategies)*
Jay Bowen *(Dir-Digital Content)*

DAVIESS-MARTIN COUNTY RURAL ELECTRIC MEMBERSHIP CORPORATION
12628 E 75 N, Loogootee, IN 47553
Tel.: (812) 295-4200
Web Site: https://www.dmremc.com
Sales Range: $25-49.9 Million
Emp.: 25
Electric Power Distribution Services
N.A.I.C.S.: 221122
John Crays *(Mgr-Ops)*
Rob Powell *(Mgr-Engrg)*
Chuck Wichman *(Coord-Svc)*
Robert Wilson *(Mgr-Fin)*

DAVINCI SELECTWORK
900 Tower Dr 6th Fl, Troy, MI 48098
Tel.: (248) 925-5086
Sales Range: $10-24.9 Million
Emp.: 50
N.A.I.C.S.: 541810
Alex Crowther *(CEO-Americas & Asia Pacific)*
Dirk Fromm *(CEO-Europe)*
Mike Elms *(Dir-Non Exec)*

DAVIS & ASSOCIATES, INC.
2852 N Webster Ave, Indianapolis, IN 46219
Tel.: (317) 263-9947
Web Site:
　https://www.davisassocindy.com
Sales Range: $10-24.9 Million
Emp.: 50
Commercial & Institutional Building Construction
N.A.I.C.S.: 236220
Gary Davis *(Pres & CEO)*
Mark Smith *(VP)*

DAVIS & COMPANY
1705 Baltic Ave, Virginia Beach, VA 23451
Tel.: (757) 627-7373　VA
Year Founded: 1976
Sales Range: $10-24.9 Million
Emp.: 25
N.A.I.C.S.: 541810
Jerome R. Davis *(Pres)*
Tracey Alexander *(Creative Dir)*
Brantley Davis *(Exec VP)*
Andy Kostecka *(VP-Client Svcs)*
Sarah Nicosia *(Sr Acct Exec)*
Lee O'Neil *(Media Dir)*

Subsidiaries:

Davis & Co. Inc.　**(1)**
1220 19th St NW Ste 210, Washington, DC 20036
Tel.: (202) 775-8181
N.A.I.C.S.: 541810
Brantley Davis *(Exec VP)*
Andy Kostecka *(VP-Client Svcs)*
Kim Powell *(Bus Mgr)*
Lee O'Neill *(Media Dir-Svcs)*
Tracey Alexander *(Dir-Creative Svcs)*

DAVIS & FLOYD, INC.
1319 Highway 72 221 E, Greenwood, SC 29649
Tel.: (864) 229-5211
Web Site: http://www.davisfloyd.com
Year Founded: 1954
Emp.: 173
Engineeering Services
N.A.I.C.S.: 541330
Roland L. Powell *(Pres & COO-Environmental & Laboratory)*
Jerry R. Timmons *(CEO & COO)*
J. Donovan Dukes *(Sr VP)*
Brent P. Robertson *(VP)*
Danny M. Ware *(VP)*
Eric S. Dickey *(VP)*
Jason P. Eppley *(COO)*
Jennifer L. Bragg *(VP)*
Thomas G. Jordan *(VP)*
Stephen L. Davis *(Pres)*
Emmett I. Davis III *(VP)*

Subsidiaries:

The Andrews Engineering Company Incorporated　**(1)**
40A Shanklin Rd Ste A, Beaufort, SC 29906
Tel.: (843) 466-0369
Sales Range: $1-9.9 Million
Emp.: 30
Engineeering Services
N.A.I.C.S.: 541330
Steven W. Andrews *(Pres)*

DAVIS & SONS CONSTRUCTION CO. LLC

20725 SW 46th Ave, Newberry, FL 32669
Tel.: (352) 472-7773
Web Site:
    http://www.davisandsons.com
Sales Range: $25-49.9 Million
Emp.: 6
Apartment Building Construction
N.A.I.C.S.: 236117
Stefan Davis *(Principal & Dir-Dev)*
Kevin J. Bzoch *(Partner & Mgr-Acq & Dev)*

DAVIS ADVERTISING, INC.
306 Main St, Worcester, MA 01608-1550
Tel.: (508) 752-4615   MA
Web Site: http://www.davisad.com
Year Founded: 1948
Rev.: $45,000,000
Emp.: 45
Fiscal Year-end: 06/30/05
N.A.I.C.S.: 541810
Andrew Davis *(Pres)*
Alan Berman *(Exec VP)*
Donna Chase *(Office Mgr)*
Paul Murphy *(Art Dir)*
Tisha Geeza *(Sr Acct Exec)*
Jeff Wolff *(Creative Dir)*
Benjamin Thaler *(Supvr-Media)*
Steven Salloway *(Sr Acct Exec)*
Adam Levine *(Acct Exec)*
Ashley Haddad *(Acct Exec)*
Barbie Bell *(Acct Exec)*
Jeff Carbonneau *(Sr Videographer & Editor)*
Travis Spiva *(Acct Exec)*
Nicole Tadgell *(Asst Dir-Art)*

DAVIS AUTOMOTIVE GROUP
6135 Kruse Dr, Solon, OH 44139
Tel.: (440) 542-0600
Year Founded: 1991
Sales Range: $75-99.9 Million
Emp.: 100
Car Whslr
N.A.I.C.S.: 441110
Jeff Davis *(Pres)*
Chris Balentine *(Mgr-Svc)*

DAVIS BARONE AGENCY
4566 S Lake Dr, Boynton Beach, FL 33436
Tel.: (561) 733-5025
Web Site:
    http://www.davisbarone.com
Year Founded: 1994
Rev.: $3,500,000
Emp.: 6
Fiscal Year-end: 12/31/03
N.A.I.C.S.: 541810
J. Paul Davis *(Pres & Dir-Mktg)*

DAVIS BEWS DESIGN GROUP, INC.
150 State St E, Oldsmar, FL 34677
Tel.: (813) 925-1300   FL
Web Site:
    https://www.davisbews.com
Year Founded: 1994
Sales Range: $1-9.9 Million
Emp.: 20
Architectural Services
N.A.I.C.S.: 541310
John Bews *(Mng Partner)*
Melissa Bradley *(Controller)*
Rory Braine *(Project Mgr)*
Bill Kendrick *(Mng Partner)*
Bradley Poisson *(Project Mgr)*
Larry Rash *(Project Mgr-Quality Assurance)*
John Wagner *(Partner)*

DAVIS BOAT WORKS INC.
99 Jefferson Ave, Newport News, VA 23607

Tel.: (757) 247-0101   VA
Web Site: http://www.davisboat.com
Year Founded: 1958
Sales Range: $10-24.9 Million
Emp.: 85
Boat Building & Repairing
N.A.I.C.S.: 336612
Barbara Savering *(CFO)*
Jimmy Heath *(Mgr-Production)*
Al Spurlock *(Mgr-Contracts)*
Glenn Hudgins *(Mgr-MIS)*
Sharone Lewis *(Mgr-HR)*
Donna Daugherty *(Mgr-Quality Assurance Environmental & Coord-Trng)*
Bruce McCrickard *(VP-Ops)*

DAVIS CARGO LLC
6100 Lake Ellenor Dr ste 261, Orlando, FL 32809
Tel.: (314) 441-3740
Web Site: http://www.daviscargo.com
Year Founded: 2014
Sales Range: $25-49.9 Million
Emp.: 50
Logistic Services
N.A.I.C.S.: 488510
Timur Mirzaev *(Founder & CEO)*

DAVIS CARTAGE CO.
230 Earl Sleeseman Dr, Corunna, MI 48817
Tel.: (989) 743-5335
Web Site:
    https://www.daviscartage.com
Sales Range: $10-24.9 Million
Emp.: 85
Trucking Except Local
N.A.I.C.S.: 484121
Glen Merkel *(Chm & Pres)*
Gregg Janicek *(VP & Dir-Trucking Ops)*
Patricia Forsyth *(Mgr-HR & Safety)*
Kelly Reynolds *(CFO)*
Kevin Nevison *(Mgr-Bus Dev)*
Timothy Ryan *(Dir-Global Logistics)*
Al Wells *(Coord-Safety)*

DAVIS COMPANY INC.
904 Jernigan St, Perry, GA 31069-3436
Tel.: (478) 987-2443   GA
Web Site: http://www.davis-company.com
Year Founded: 1981
Sales Range: $25-49.9 Million
Emp.: 130
Petroleum Products
N.A.I.C.S.: 424720
David Cosey *(CEO)*
Robert Sexton *(Pres)*

DAVIS CONSTRUCTION, INC.
5236 Dumond Ct Ste A, Lansing, MI 48917
Tel.: (517) 322-3800   MI
Web Site:
    https://www.davisconstruction.us
Year Founded: 1968
Sales Range: $10-24.9 Million
Emp.: 100
Provider of Construction Services
N.A.I.C.S.: 236220
Michael H. Davis *(Pres)*
Terri Neumann *(Office Mgr)*
Scott Miller *(VP-Bridge Div)*
Rob Kaliniak *(VP-Concrete Div & Gen Contracting)*

DAVIS COUNTY CO-OPERATIVE SOCIETY
20 Century Park Way, Salt Lake City, UT 84115
Tel.: (801) 466-3361
Rev.: $17,100,000
Emp.: 25
Grocery Stores

N.A.I.C.S.: 445110
Kimberly Moreau *(Mgr-Mktg)*

DAVIS DEVELOPMENT, INC.
1050 Eagles Landing Pkwy Ste 300, Stockbridge, GA 30281
Tel.: (770) 474-4345
Web Site:
    http://www.davisdevelopment.info
Sales Range: $10-24.9 Million
Emp.: 30
Multi-Family Development & Management
N.A.I.C.S.: 236116
Mike Davis *(Pres)*

DAVIS ENTERPRISES
8000 Sagemore Dr Ste 8201, Marlton, NJ 08053
Tel.: (856) 985-1200
Web Site:
    http://www.daviscommunities.com
Year Founded: 1962
Rev.: $35,000,000
Emp.: 20
Apartment Building Operator
N.A.I.C.S.: 531120
Mitchell Davis *(Owner)*

DAVIS FOODTOWN INC.
830 E Main St, Dayton, OH 45426
Tel.: (937) 837-2658
Rev.: $12,800,000
Emp.: 45
Grocery Stores, Independent
N.A.I.C.S.: 445110
James E. Davis *(VP)*

DAVIS FURNITURE, INC.
2401 S College Dr, High Point, NC 27260
Tel.: (336) 889-2009
Web Site:
    http://www.davisfurniture.com
Year Founded: 1945
Sales Range: $10-24.9 Million
Emp.: 150
Mfr & Wholesaler of Office Furniture
N.A.I.C.S.: 337211
Daniel Davis *(Pres)*
Charles Kennedy *(CFO & VP-Fin)*
Rob Easton *(VP-Design & Dev)*
Robert Stewart *(Mgr-Pur Sys & Product Engr-Costing)*
Rusty Morris *(Mgr-Inside Sls)*

DAVIS H. ELLIOT COMPANY, INC.
1920 Progress Dr, Roanoke, VA 24013
Tel.: (540) 992-2865   VA
Web Site: http://www.davishelliot.com
Year Founded: 1946
Sales Range: $50-74.9 Million
Emp.: 700
Electrical Construction
N.A.I.C.S.: 238210
William D. Elliot *(Chm & Mng Dir)*
David Haskins *(Pres & CEO)*

Subsidiaries:

Davis H. Elliot Construction Company, Inc.   (1)
673 Blue Sky Pkwy, Lexington, KY 40509
Tel.: (859) 263-5148
Web Site: https://dhec.com
Engineeering Services
N.A.I.C.S.: 541330

Elliot Electric Company Inc.   (1)
1920 Progress Dr SE, Roanoke, VA 24013-2912
Tel.: (540) 427-5459
Web Site: http://www.davishelliot.com
Sales Range: $1-9.9 Million
Emp.: 25
Provider of Electric Services
N.A.I.C.S.: 423830

Elliot Engineering, Inc.   (1)
673 Blue Sky Pkwy, Lexington, KY 40509
Tel.: (859) 263-5148
Web Site: https://dhec.com
Engineering Services
N.A.I.C.S.: 541330
Patrick Wells *(Pres)*

Subsidiary (Domestic):

Wells Engineering, Psc   (2)
5900 Houston Rd Ste 38, Florence, KY 41042
Tel.: (859) 282-7538
Web Site: http://www.wellsengineering.com
Rev.: $1,500,000
Emp.: 4
Engineeering Services
N.A.I.C.S.: 541330

DAVIS HARRISON DION, INC.
333 N Michigan Ave Ste 2300, Chicago, IL 60601-4109
Tel.: (312) 332-0808   IL
Web Site:
    http://www.dhdchicago.com
Year Founded: 1982
Sales Range: $1-9.9 Million
Emp.: 25
Advetising Agency
N.A.I.C.S.: 541810
P. Susan Harrison *(Partner)*
Robert E. Dion *(Partner)*

DAVIS HYUNDAI
1655 N Olden Ave, Ewing, NJ 08638
Tel.: (609) 883-3500
Web Site:
    http://www.davishyundai.com
Year Founded: 2010
Sales Range: $50-74.9 Million
Emp.: 65
Car Whslr
N.A.I.C.S.: 441110
Jeffrey Feldman *(CEO)*

DAVIS INDUSTRIES II, LLC
1224 W Melinda Ln, Phoenix, AZ 85027
Tel.: (818) 980-6178   AZ
Web Site: http://www.dimfg.com
Year Founded: 1969
Sheet Metal Work Mfg
N.A.I.C.S.: 332322

DAVIS JEFFERSON ELECTRIC COOP
906 N Lake Arthur Ave, Jennings, LA 70546
Tel.: (337) 824-4330
Web Site: https://www.jdec.org
Rev.: $14,870,981
Emp.: 32
Transmission, Electric Power
N.A.I.C.S.: 221121
Michael Heinen *(Gen Mgr)*

DAVIS LANDSCAPE, LLC
4347 Brogdon Place Cove, Suwanee, GA 30024
Tel.: (770) 781-9041
Web Site: http://www.davis-landscape.com
Year Founded: 1994
Sales Range: $1-9.9 Million
Emp.: 75
Retail Nurseries & Garden Stores
N.A.I.C.S.: 444240
Jay Stephens *(Pres)*

DAVIS MINING & MANUFACTURING INC.
Miners Professional Bldg 613 Frnt St W, Coeburn, VA 24230
Tel.: (276) 395-3354   VA
Year Founded: 1985
Sales Range: $400-449.9 Million
Emp.: 1,600

Davis Mining & Manufacturing Inc.—(Continued)

Mfr & Distr of Construction & Mining Equipment
N.A.I.C.S.: 325920
William Jack Davis (Pres)

Subsidiaries:

Austin Powder Company (1)
25800 Science Park Dr, Cleveland, OH 44122-7311
Tel.: (216) 464-2400
Web Site: http://www.austinpowder.com
Sales Range: $100-124.9 Million
Emp.: 1,000
Industrial Explosives Mfr
N.A.I.C.S.: 325920
David True (Pres)

Rish Equipment Company (1)
6384 Airport Rd, Bluefield, WV 24701
Tel.: (304) 327-5124
Web Site: http://www.rish.com
Sales Range: $10-24.9 Million
Emp.: 35
Construction & Mining Machinery Distr
N.A.I.C.S.: 423810
Dale Hall (VP-Ops)

DAVIS MOORE AUTO GROUP, INC.
3501 N 14th St, Ponca City, OK 74601
Tel.: (580) 765-2511   OK
Web Site:
    http://www.davismoore.com
Year Founded: 1998
Sales Range: $10-24.9 Million
Emp.: 30
New & Used Automobile Dealership & Repair Services
N.A.I.C.S.: 441110
Steve Peresko (Owner & Gen Mgr)
Travis Bush (Mgr-Svc)
Darren Wells (Mgr-Sls)
Whitney Anthony (Mgr-Customer Rels & Internet)

DAVIS PAINT COMPANY
1311 Iron St, Kansas City, MO 64116-4010
Tel.: (816) 471-4447   MO
Web Site: https://www.davispaint.com
Year Founded: 1921
Sales Range: $10-24.9 Million
Emp.: 45
Paints Mfr
N.A.I.C.S.: 325510
Kevin C. Ostby (Pres)
Jeff Lee (VP)
James L. Davis (Chm)

DAVIS POLK & WARDWELL LLP
450 Lexington Ave, New York, NY 10017
Tel.: (212) 450-4000
Web Site: http://www.davispolk.com
Year Founded: 1849
Sales Range: $800-899.9 Million
Emp.: 750
Law firm
N.A.I.C.S.: 541110
Monica L. Holland (Partner-Credit Grp)
Brian S. Lichter (Partner-Real Estate Practice)
Neil MacBride (Partner)
David H. Schnabel (Partner)
Ronald Cami (Partner-Menlo Park)
Tenley Laserson Chepiga (Dir-Bus Dev)
Daniel G. Kelly Jr. (Co-Founder-Silicon Valley office)
Ken Lebrun (Partner-Tokyo)
Adam Kaminsky (Partner-Exec Compensation Grp-Washington)

Daniel Stipano (Partner-Fin Institutions & Regulation Grp-Washington DC)
Katie Moss (Dir-PR & Comm)
Neil Barr (Mng Partner)
Meg Tahyar (Head-Fin Institutions & Regulation Grp)

DAVIS SELECTED ADVISORS, L.P.
2949 E Elvira Rd Ste 101, Tucson, AZ 85756
Tel.: (520) 806-7600   CO
Web Site:
    http://www.davisadvisors.com
Year Founded: 1987
Sales Range: $50-74.9 Million
Emp.: 154
Management Investment Advisors
N.A.I.C.S.: 523940
Christopher Cullom Davis (Chm & CEO)
Gary P. Tyc (CFO)

Subsidiaries:

Davis Distributors, LLC (1)
2949 E Elvira Rd Ste 101, Tucson, AZ 85706
Tel.: (520) 806-7659
Web Site: http://www.davisfunds.com
Financial Management Services
N.A.I.C.S.: 523999

Davis Selected Advisers-NY, Inc. (1)
620 5th Ave 3rd Fl, New York, NY 10020
Tel.: (212) 207-3500
Emp.: 60
Financial Management Services
N.A.I.C.S.: 523999

DAVIS STRATEGIC INNOVATIONS, INC.
6767 Old Madison Pike Ste 285, Huntsville, AL 35806
Tel.: (256) 489-0550
Web Site: http://www.davisdsi.com
Sales Range: $1-9.9 Million
Emp.: 15
Engineeering Services
N.A.I.C.S.: 541330
Jim A. Davis (Pres)

DAVIS TRANSFER CO. INC.
520 Busha Rd, Carnesville, GA 30521
Tel.: (706) 384-2030
Web Site:
    https://www.davistransfer.com
Rev.: $17,201,567
Emp.: 125
Provider of Trucking Services
N.A.I.C.S.: 484121
Gary Davis (Pres)

DAVIS TRANSPORT INC.
216 Trade St, Missoula, MT 59808
Tel.: (406) 728-5510
Web Site:
    https://www.davistransport.com
Sales Range: $10-24.9 Million
Emp.: 37
Long Haul Trucking
N.A.I.C.S.: 484121
Jim Dunn (Exec VP)
Brian Miller (Controller)
Jim McKinny (Pres)

DAVIS TRUCKING, LLC
7365 Mission Gorge Rd Ste B, San Diego, CA 92120
Tel.: (619) 229-9997
Web Site:
    http://www.davistrucking.com
Year Founded: 1996
Sales Range: $10-24.9 Million
Emp.: 40
Freight Transportation Services
N.A.I.C.S.: 484121

Gary Davis (Pres)
Ken Taylor (Controller)
Omar Ortiz (COO)
Rosibel Benavides (Mgr-Billing)

DAVIS WHOLESALE ELECTRIC INC.
11581 Vanowen St, North Hollywood, CA 91605
Tel.: (818) 392-2400
Web Site:
    http://www.daviswholesale.com
Rev.: $17,000,000
Emp.: 100
Electrical Supplies
N.A.I.C.S.: 423610
Howard Davis (Pres)

DAVIS WHOLESALE SUPPLY INC.
5845 W 82nd St Ste 108, Indianapolis, IN 46278
Tel.: (317) 876-9212
Web Site: http://www.dws-salt.com
Sales Range: $10-24.9 Million
Emp.: 12
Whslr of Salt & Bottled Water
N.A.I.C.S.: 424690
Janis Davis (Controller)

DAVIS WOOD PRODUCTS, INC.
1 Davis St, Hudson, NC 28638
Tel.: (828) 728-8444   NC
Web Site:
    http://www.daviswoodproducts.com
Year Founded: 1949
Sales Range: $50-74.9 Million
Emp.: 50
Mfr of Furniture Parts, Plywood, Veneer & Particle Board
N.A.I.C.S.: 321211
Marc C. Davis (Pres)
Wallace J. Davis (COO)

Subsidiaries:

Davis Wood Products, Inc.-Mississippi Division (1)
PO Box 1727, New Albany, MS 38652-1727   (100%)
Tel.: (662) 534-2211
Web Site:
    http://www.daviswoodproducts.com
Rev.: $10,000,000
Emp.: 5
Mfr of Furniture Parts, Plywood, Veneer & Particle Board
N.A.I.C.S.: 321211

DAVIS WRIGHT TREMAINE LLP
1201 3rd Ave Ste 2200, Seattle, WA 98101
Tel.: (206) 622-3150
Web Site: http://www.dwt.com
Year Founded: 1908
Sales Range: $250-299.9 Million
Emp.: 490
Law firm
N.A.I.C.S.: 541110
Robert A. Blackstone (Partner)
Wendy Kearns (Co-Chm-Tech, Comm & Privacy & Security Practice)
David W. Gee (Partner)
Craig Gannett (Partner)
Clifford DeGroot (Partner)
Evan M. Shapiro (Partner)
Kelsey M. Sheldon (Partner)
Jane Eckels (Partner)
Arne Wellman Lewis (Partner)
Mark Usellis (Chief Strategy Officer)
Martinelle Cole (Dir-Pro Dev-Seattle)
Jaime Drozd Allen (Partner)
Andrew J. Schultheis (Partner)
Broady R. Hodder (Partner)
Nicholas A. Kampars (Partner)
Benjamin J. Byer (Partner)

Peter G. Finch (Partner)
Warren W. Tock (Partner)
Jonathan A. DeMella (Partner)
James Howard (Partner)
Traeger Machetanz (Partner)
Lisa M. Marchese (Partner)
Dipa N. Sudra (Partner)
John A. Goldmark (Partner)
Patrick J. Ferguson (Partner)
Judy Deng (Partner)
John Reed (Partner)
Keith Gorder (COO)
Kelli Kohout (Chief Admin Officer)
Joseph R. Rodriguez (Partner)
Leah C. Lively (Partner-Employment Svcs Grp-Portland)
Jonathan Engel (Partner)
Robin Nunn (Partner)
Nancy Libin (Co-Chm-Tech, Comm & Privacy & Security Practice)
Ryan Maughn (Partner-Portland)
Christie Totten (Partner-Portland)
James Parker (Partner-Portland)
Stephen Cazares (Partner)
Ryan Richardson (Partner-Fin Svcs Practice-New York)
Bradford Hardin (Co-Chm-Fin Svcs Practice)
Elizabeth Davis (Co-Chm-Fin Svcs Practice)
Lafayette M. Greenfield II (Partner-Washington-DC)

DAVIS-ELEN ADVERTISING, INC.
865 S Figueroa St Ste 1200, Los Angeles, CA 90017-2543
Tel.: (213) 688-7000   CA
Web Site: http://www.daviselen.com
Year Founded: 1925
Emp.: 115
Advetising Agency
N.A.I.C.S.: 541810
Terry Sullivan (CFO, COO & Partner)
Marcos Arroyo (Dir-IT & Office Svcs)
Melissa Ojeda (Mgr-HR)
Debbie Zimmerman (Dir-Bus Dev)
Brett Bandow (Sr VP & Dir-Acct)
Malu Santamaria (Partner & Mng Dir)
Marianne Turner (Sr VP & Dir-Acct)
Tracy Sanders (Sr VP & Dir-Acct)

Subsidiaries:

Davis-Elen Advertising, Inc. (1)
236 S Sierra Ave Ste 300 Solana Beach, San Diego, CA 92075
Tel.: (858) 847-0789
Web Site: http://www.daviselen.com
Emp.: 5
N.A.I.C.S.: 541810

Davis-Elen Advertising, Inc. (1)
1200 NW Naito Pkwy Ste 500, Portland, OR 97209
Tel.: (503) 241-7781
Web Site: http://www.daviselen.com
Emp.: 10
Advetising Agency
N.A.I.C.S.: 541810

DAVIS-FROST INC.
3416 Candlers Mountain Rd, Lynchburg, VA 24502-2214
Tel.: (434) 522-3562   MN
Web Site:
    http://www.jamestdavis.com
Year Founded: 1936
Sales Range: $25-49.9 Million
Emp.: 160
Paint Products
N.A.I.C.S.: 325510
Calvin C. Henning (Pres & CEO)

DAVIS-MOORE AUTOMOTIVE, INC.
11220 E Kellogg Dr, Wichita, KS 67207

Tel.: (316) 618-2000   KS
Web Site: http://www.davis-moore.com
Year Founded: 1969
Sales Range: $150-199.9 Million
Emp.: 400
New & Used Automobile Dealership & Repair Services
N.A.I.C.S.: 441110
Michelle Hill *(Controller)*
Tara Clary *(Mgr-Mktg)*

Subsidiaries:

Davis-Moore Chevrolet, Inc.   (1)
8200 W Kellogg Dr, Wichita, KS
67209   **(100%)**
Tel.: (316) 768-4874
Web Site: http://www.davis-moorechevrolet.com
Sales Range: $50-74.9 Million
Emp.: 75
New & Used Automobile Dealership & Repair Services
N.A.I.C.S.: 441110
Dawson Grimsley *(Pres)*

DAVISCO INTERNATIONAL INC.

704 N Main St, Le Sueur, MN 56058-1403
Tel.: (507) 665-8811   MN
Web Site:
    http://www.daviscofoods.com
Year Founded: 1943
Sales Range: $25-49.9 Million
Emp.: 500
Mfr of Natural & Processed Cheese
N.A.I.C.S.: 311513
Mark Davis *(Pres & CEO)*
Pauline Olson *(VP-Sls)*

DAVISDENNY ADVERTISING & RELATED SERVICES, INC.

2545 Highland Ave, Birmingham, AL 35205
Tel.: (205) 933-0355   AL
Year Founded: 1989
Sales Range: $10-24.9 Million
Emp.: 10
N.A.I.C.S.: 541810
David M. Davis *(Owner, Pres, Partner)*
Tim Denny *(VP & Dir-Creative)*
Steva Austill *(Dir-Media)*
Dana McGough *(Acct Exec & Mgr-PR)*
Ben Burford *(Partner & Sr Dir-Art)*
Margriet Linthout *(Office Mgr)*

DAVISON OIL COMPANY INC.

8450 Tanner Williams Rd, Mobile, AL 36608
Tel.: (251) 633-4444
Web Site: https://www.davisonoil.com
Sales Range: $10-24.9 Million
Emp.: 50
Engine Fuels & Oils
N.A.I.C.S.: 424720
Todd Davison *(Pres)*
David Padgett *(Pres-Fuels)*
Jeff Ladnier *(Controller)*

DAVISON TRANSPORT INC.

2000 Farmerville Hwy, Ruston, LA 71270-3010
Tel.: (318) 255-3850   LA
Year Founded: 1968
Sales Range: $25-49.9 Million
Emp.: 300
Provider of Trucking Services
N.A.I.C.S.: 484230
Chad A. Landry *(VP & Gen Mgr-Refinery Svcs)*
Garland G. Gaspard *(VP-Corp Technical Svcs & Offshore Ops)*
Grant E. Sims *(CEO)*
Karen N. Pape *(Sr VP & Controller)*

Kristen O. Jesulaitis *(Gen Counsel)*
Michael A. Barber *(VP-Trucking)*
Paul A. Davis *(Sr VP-Bus Dev)*
Rick R. Alexander *(VP & Gen Mgr-Marine)*
Robert V. Deere *(CFO)*
Stephen M. Smith *(VP & Gen Mgr-Supply & Logistics)*

DAVLER MEDIA GROUP, LLC

498 7th Ave 10th Fl, New York, NY 10018
Tel.: (212) 315-0800
Web Site:
    http://www.davlermedia.com
Year Founded: 2004
Sales Range: $10-24.9 Million
Periodical & Tourism Materials Publisher
N.A.I.C.S.: 513120
David L. Miller *(CEO)*

Subsidiaries:

Metrosource Publishing, Inc.   (1)
498 7th Ave 10th Fl, New York, NY 10018-3322
Tel.: (212) 315-0800
Web Site: http://www.metrosource.com
Sales Range: $1-9.9 Million
Periodical Publishers
N.A.I.C.S.: 513120
Paul Hagen *(Editor-in-Chief)*

DAVOIL INC.

6300 Ridglea Pl Ste 1208, Fort Worth, TX 76116-5738
Tel.: (817) 737-6678   TX
Year Founded: 1976
Sales Range: $25-49.9 Million
Emp.: 10
Provider of Crude Petroleum & Natural Gas
N.A.I.C.S.: 211120
Debbie Singleton *(VP-Ops)*
William S. Davis Sr. *(Pres)*

Subsidiaries:

Tarantula Corporation   (1)
6300 Ridglea Pl Ste 1200, Fort Worth, TX 76116-5738
Tel.: (817) 763-8297
Web Site: http://www.fwwr.net
Railroads Controller
N.A.I.C.S.: 482112

Subsidiary (Domestic):

Fort Worth & Western Railroad Inc.   (2)
6300 Ridglea Pl Ste 1200, Fort Worth, TX 76116-5738
Tel.: (817) 763-8297
Web Site: http://www.fortworthsouth.org
Sales Range: $10-24.9 Million
Emp.: 8
Provider of Switching & Terminal Services
N.A.I.C.S.: 482112

Tarantula Mercantile Corporation   (1)
6300 Ridglea Pl Ste 1200, Fort Worth, TX 76116-5738
Tel.: (817) 763-8297
Sales Range: $10-24.9 Million
Provider of Tour Operators
N.A.I.C.S.: 482112

DAW CONSTRUCTION GROUP, LLC

12552 S 125th W, Draper, UT 84020-8409
Tel.: (801) 553-9111
Web Site: http://www.dawcg.com
Year Founded: 1951
Sales Range: $75-99.9 Million
Emp.: 50
Plastering, Drywall & Insulation Services
N.A.I.C.S.: 238310
Mike Skalla *(Pres)*

DAW TECHNOLOGIES, INC.

1600 W 2200 S Ste 201, Salt Lake City, UT 84119
Tel.: (801) 977-3100   UT
Web Site: http://www.dawtech.com
Controlled Environmental Solutions & Cleanroom Supplier
N.A.I.C.S.: 334413

DAWE'S LABORATORIES

3355 N Arlington Heights Rd, Arlington Heights, IL 60004-7706
Tel.: (847) 577-2020
Web Site:
    https://www.dawesnutrition.com
Year Founded: 1920
Sales Range: $75-99.9 Million
Emp.: 10
Mfr of Vitamin Products for Animal Nutrition
N.A.I.C.S.: 311119
Charles R. Dawe *(Pres & CEO)*
Doug Foss *(Mgr-QC)*

DAWN ASSOCIATES INC.

14516 John Humphrey Dr, Orland Park, IL 60462
Tel.: (708) 460-8878
Rev.: $17,100,000
Emp.: 5
Iron Or Steel Flat Products
N.A.I.C.S.: 423510
Loyal L. Lightfoot *(Pres)*

DAWN ENTERPRISES INCORPORATED

16 Rd 5860, Farmington, NM 87401
Tel.: (505) 327-6314
Web Site:
    http://www.dawntrucking.com
Sales Range: $10-24.9 Million
Emp.: 200
Provider of Trucking Services
N.A.I.C.S.: 484121

DAWN FOOD PRODUCTS, INC.

3333 Sargeant Rd, Jackson, MI 49201-3473
Tel.: (517) 789-4400   IN
Web Site: http://www.dawnfoods.com
Year Founded: 1920
Mfr & Distr of Bakery Mixes, Ingredients & Supplies
N.A.I.C.S.: 311824
Carrie Jones-Barber *(CEO)*
Bob Howland *(Chief Digital Officer)*
John Schmitz *(Pres-North America)*
Karl Brown *(CFO)*
Emilio Castillo *(Pres-LATAM)*
Jason Lioy *(Chief HR Officer)*
Eric Metzendorf *(Chief Corp Affairs & Strategic Partnership Officer)*
John Sanders *(Chief Product Officer)*
Scott Thayer *(Chief Legal Officer & Sec)*
Steven Verweij *(Pres-Europe & AMEAP)*
Michelle Vickers *(Sr VP-Global Labor, Employment, Diversity & Compliance)*

Subsidiaries:

Countryside Baking Company, Inc.   (1)
1722 Kettering St, Irvine, CA 92614
Tel.: (949) 851-9654
Cookies & Sweet Goods Mfr
N.A.I.C.S.: 311821

Dawn Food Products (Canada), Ltd.   (1)
75 Vickers Road, Etobicoke, M9B 6B6, ON, Canada   **(100%)**
Tel.: (416) 233-5851
Web Site: http://www.dawnfoods.com
Sales Range: $10-24.9 Million
Emp.: 120
Dried & Glazed Fruits, Nuts, Cereal & Health Foods, Flowers, Nuts & Spices Mfr

N.A.I.C.S.: 311230

Dawn Foods B.V.   (1)
Handelsweg 59D, 1181 ZA, Amstelveen, Netherlands
Tel.: (31) 20 808 1225
Web Site: http://www.dawnfoods.eu
Bakery Mixes, Ingredients & Supplies Mfr & Distr
N.A.I.C.S.: 311824
Janet Spiering *(Cluster Dir)*
Tim Clarkson *(Dir-Cluster-UK & Ireland)*
Vince Frye *(VP-West)*
Bob Howland *(Chief Digital Officer)*
Kristin Pados *(Sr Dir-Product Mgmt)*
Gireesh Sahukar *(Sr Dir-Digital Tech)*

DAWN OF HOPE, INC.

500 E Oakland Ave, Johnson City, TN 37601
Tel.: (423) 434-5600   TN
Web Site:
    https://www.dawnofhope.com
Year Founded: 1968
Sales Range: $10-24.9 Million
Emp.: 609
Developmental Disability Assistance Services
N.A.I.C.S.: 623210
Rodney Conduff *(Chm)*
Jill Grayson Stott *(Sec)*
John Somich *(Treas)*
Rob Sampson *(Vice Chm)*

DAWN PATROL PARTNERS, LLC

28382 Constellation Rd, Valencia, CA 91355
Tel.: (661) 775-9399
Web Site:
    https://www.dawnpatrolpartners.com
Emp.: 100
Investment Services
N.A.I.C.S.: 523999

Subsidiaries:

Midwest Trading Group, Inc.   (1)
Tel.: (866) 815-4714
Web Site: https://www.mtradinggroup.com
Rev.: $1,400,000
Emp.: 10
Piece Goods, Notions & Other Dry Goods Merchant Whslr
N.A.I.C.S.: 424310
Carrie Weiss *(Controller)*
Rashid Aziz *(Founder & Pres)*

DAWS MANUFACTURING INC.

8811 Grow Dr, Pensacola, FL 32514-7051
Tel.: (850) 478-3298   FL
Web Site:
    http://www.dawsbetterbuilt.com
Year Founded: 1989
Rev.: $38,000,000
Emp.: 360
Metal Stampings; Truck Accessories
N.A.I.C.S.: 332119
Clint Daws *(Pres)*

DAWSON BUILDING CONTRACTORS, INC.

106 Rainbow Indus Blvd, Rainbow City, AL 35906-8901
Tel.: (256) 442-7280   FL
Web Site:
    http://www.dawsonbuilding.com
Year Founded: 1994
Sales Range: $10-24.9 Million
Emp.: 116
General Contractors
N.A.I.C.S.: 236220
Jud Dawson *(CEO & Co-Owner)*
William Thomas Dawson *(Chm)*
Denise McCullars *(CFO)*

DAWSON CONSTRUCTION INC.

Dawson Construction Inc.—(Continued)

405 32nd St Ste 110, Bellingham, WA
98225
Tel.: (360) 756-1000
Web Site: https://www.dawson.com
Sales Range: $10-24.9 Million
Emp.: 30
Commercial & Institutional Building
Construction
N.A.I.C.S.: 236220
Gary Hovde (Project Mgr)
Peter C. Dawson (Pres & VP-
Construction-Alaska)
Lee Kadinger (COO)

DAWSON COUNTY PUBLIC POWER DISTRICT
75191 Rd 433, Lexington, NE 68850
Tel.: (308) 324-2386
Web Site:
https://www.dawsonpower.com
Sales Range: $10-24.9 Million
Emp.: 75
Electric Power Distr
N.A.I.C.S.: 221122
Paul Neil (Pres)
Tracy Gordon (Mgr-IT)
Para Natrspeck (Mgr-Fin & Admin)

DAWSON LOGISTICS
122 Eastgate Dr, Danville, IL 61834
Tel.: (217) 292-7329
Web Site:
https://www.dawsonlogistics.com
Year Founded: 2000
Supply Chain Management & Logistics Services
N.A.I.C.S.: 541614
Douglas M. Dawson (CEO)
Josh A. Hobick (Pres & COO)
Erica Bash (Gen Counsel)
Mike Torma (VP-Ops)
Jeff OBrien (Dir-Ops)
Andrea Pohlmann (Mgr-HR)

DAWSON MANUFACTURING COMPANY
1042 N Crystal Ave, Benton Harbor,
MI 49022
Tel.: (269) 925-0100
Web Site:
https://www.dawsonmfg.com
Rev.: $62,508,311
Emp.: 130
Automotive Rubber Goods (Mechanical)
N.A.I.C.S.: 326291
Bob Trivedi (Pres & CEO)

DAWSON METAL COMPANY INC.
825 Allen St, Jamestown, NY 14701
Tel.: (716) 664-3815
Web Site:
https://www.dawsonmetal.com
Rev.: $13,322,868
Emp.: 150
Custom Metal Fabrications, Metal
Cutting, Bending, Welding & Finishing
Mfr
N.A.I.C.S.: 333992
David Dawson (Pres & CEO)
Ken Ullman (Sr Project Engr)
Rick Carlson (COO & Sr VP)

DAWSON OIL CO., INC.
2282 W State Rd 44, Rushville, IN
46173-9247
Tel.: (765) 932-2613
Web Site:
https://www.dawsonoilco.com
Year Founded: 1967
Sales Range: $10-24.9 Million
Emp.: 50
Provider of Petroleum Services
N.A.I.C.S.: 424710

Chris Laker (CEO)

DAWSON RESOURCES, INC.
1114 Dublin Rd, Columbus, OH
43215
Tel.: (614) 255-1400
Web Site:
https://www.dawsoncareers.com
Year Founded: 2004
Sales Range: $50-74.9 Million
Staffing Agency
N.A.I.C.S.: 561311
Christopher DeCapua (Co-Owner)
Emily Marshall (Mgr-Office & Call
Center Div)
Jeff Miller (Pres)
Matt Backiewicz (VP-Bus Dev)
Phil Freeman (Sr VP)
Becky Staub (Mgr-IT Div)
Steve Chieffo (Mgr-Creative Div)
Tina Hoffman (Mgr-Acctg & Fin Div)
Linda Mounts (Mgr-Warehouse &
Light Indus Div)
David DeCapua (Co-Owner)

DAXCON ENGINEERING, INC.
5607 S Washington St, Bartonville, IL
61607
Tel.: (309) 697-5975
Sales Range: $10-24.9 Million
Emp.: 180
Engineeering Services
N.A.I.C.S.: 541330
Mike Daxenbichler (CEO)

DAY AIR CREDIT UNION, INC.
3501 Wilmington Pike, Kettering, OH
45429
Tel.: (937) 643-2160
Web Site: https://www.dayair.org
Year Founded: 1945
Credit Union
N.A.I.C.S.: 522130
William Burke (Pres & CEO)
Joe Eckley (Dir-Mktg)
Jannell Eichstaedt (Sr VP-Member
Svc)

DAY AUTOMATION SYSTEMS, INC.
7931 Rae Blvd, Victor, NY 14564-
8931
Tel.: (585) 924-4630
Web Site:
https://www.dayautomation.com
Year Founded: 1926
Sales Range: $75-99.9 Million
Emp.: 90
Mfr, Installer & Servicer of Temperature Control, Process Control & Building Automation Systems, Including
Security Systems
N.A.I.C.S.: 541330
Eric Orban (Pres)
Ronald Harper (Controller)
Robert Ormsby (VP)

DAY ENTERPRISES INC.
1912 S Rdg Ave, Kannapolis, NC
28083
Tel.: (704) 933-2218
Web Site: http://www.dayent.com
Sales Range: $25-49.9 Million
Emp.: 700
Chicken Restaurant
N.A.I.C.S.: 722513
Eric Overcash (Pres)
Linda Day Huie (VP)

DAY FORD
3696 William Penn Hwy, Monroeville,
PA 15146
Tel.: (412) 856-0600
Web Site: http://www.dayford.net
Year Founded: 1979
Sales Range: $100-124.9 Million

Emp.: 540
Car Whslr
N.A.I.C.S.: 441110
Newton Da Silva (Coord-Delivery)

DAY KETTERER LTD.
Millennium Ctr 200 Market Ave N Ste
300, Canton, OH 44701-4213
Tel.: (330) 455-0173
Web Site: http://www.day-
ketterer.com
Year Founded: 1872
Emp.: 33
Law firm
N.A.I.C.S.: 541110
Sheila Markley Black (Atty)
Richard W. Arnold (Atty)
John H. Brannen (Atty)
James R. Blake (Atty)
Emily Clevenger (Dir-Client Svcs &
Dev)
Kathy Merritt (Mgr-Acctg)
Jude Belden Streb (Atty)
Daniel E. Clevenger II (Atty)

Subsidiaries:

Goldman & Rosen, Ltd.   (1)
11 S Forge St, Akron, OH 44304
Tel.: (330) 376-8336
Web Site: http://www.goldman-rosen.com
Law firm
N.A.I.C.S.: 541110
Marc P. Gertz (Atty)

DAY MANAGEMENT CORP.
4700 SE International Way, Milwaukie, OR 97222
Tel.: (503) 659-1240
Web Site:
https://www.daywireless.com
Year Founded: 1969
Sales Range: $10-24.9 Million
Intercommunication Equipment Repair & Services
N.A.I.C.S.: 811210
Gordon Day (Owner & Pres)
Mike Ishida (VP-Sls)
Brent McGraw (VP-Ops)
Marty Gant (VP-Rentals)
Mark Hough (CFO)

DAY ONLINE SOLUTIONS, LLC
PO Box 48, Sellersburg, IN 47172-
0048
Tel.: (502) 438-9354
Web Site:
https://www.dayonlinesolutions.com
Year Founded: 2007
Sales Range: $1-9.9 Million
Emp.: 2
Website Development, Coding, Script
Installation, Web Hosting, Promotion
& Domain Sales & Purchasing
N.A.I.C.S.: 541511
Andrew Day (Owner & CEO)

DAY PITNEY LLP
242 Trumbull St, Hartford, CT 06103
Tel.: (860) 275-0100
Web Site: https://www.daypitney.com
Year Founded: 1919
Emp.: 289
Legal Advisory Services
N.A.I.C.S.: 541110
Harold M. Blinderman (Partner)
Christopher John Stracco (Partner)
Craig M. Gianetti (Partner)
Michael K. Furey (Partner)
Paul J. Halasz (Partner)
Peter M. Shapland (Partner)
Daniel L. Gottfried (Partner-Corp &
Bus Law Dept)
Stanley A. Twardy Jr. (Mng Partner)

DAY PITNEY LLP
7 Times Sq Broadway between 41st
& '42nd Streets, New York, NY 10036

Tel.: (212) 297-5800
Web Site: http://www.daypitney.com
Year Founded: 1919
Sales Range: $150-199.9 Million
Emp.: 201
Legal Advisory Services
N.A.I.C.S.: 541110
Michael W. Kaufman (Partner-Fin
Grp-Stamford)
Tom Goldberg (Mng Partner)

DAY SPRING, INC.
3430 Day Spring Ct, Louisville, KY
40213
Tel.: (502) 636-5990
Web Site:
https://www.dayspringky.org
Year Founded: 1992
Sales Range: $1-9.9 Million
Intellectual Disability Assistance Services
N.A.I.C.S.: 623210

DAY STAR RESTAURANT HOLDINGS, LLC
5055 W Park Blvd Ste 500, Plano,
TX 75093
Tel.: (972) 295-8600
Year Founded: 2013
Holding Company; Restaurant Chain
Owner, Operator & Franchisor
N.A.I.C.S.: 551112
Scott Smith (Co-Owner, Chm & CEO)
Tim Dungan (Co-Owner, Pres &
CFO)

Subsidiaries:

Lone Star Steakhouse   (1)
5055 W Park Blvd Ste 500, Plano, TX
75093
Tel.: (972) 295-8600
Restaurants Operator & Franchisor
N.A.I.C.S.: 722511
Tim Dungan (Pres & CFO)
Scott Smith (Chm & CEO)

Texas Land & Cattle Steakhouse   (1)
5055 W Park Blvd Ste 500, Plano, TX
75093
Tel.: (972) 295-8600
Web Site:
http://www.texaslandandcattle.com
Restaurant & Franchisor Operator
N.A.I.C.S.: 722511
Scott Smith (Chm & CEO)
Tim Dungan (Pres & CFO)

DAY VISION MARKETING
2222 S 12th St Ste D, Allentown, PA
18103
Tel.: (610) 403-3999
Web Site: http://www.dayvision.com
Year Founded: 2000
Sales Range: $1-9.9 Million
Emp.: 7
Full Service Marketing Communications
N.A.I.C.S.: 541613
Danny Youssef (Pres)

DAYBREAK FOODS INC.
533 E Tyranena Pk Rd, Lake Mills,
WI 53551-0800
Tel.: (920) 648-8232
Web Site:
http://www.daybreakfoods.com
Year Founded: 1994
Sales Range: $25-49.9 Million
Emp.: 175
Poultry Products Mfr
N.A.I.C.S.: 424440

DAYBROOK HOLDINGS INC.
161 Madison Ave, Morristown, NJ
07962-1931
Tel.: (973) 538-6766
Web Site: http://www.daybrook.com
Year Founded: 1990

Sales Range: $25-49.9 Million
Emp.: 300
Supplier of Fats & Oils
N.A.I.C.S.: 311710
Gregory F. Holt *(Pres & CEO)*
Stephen Morganstein *(CFO)*

Subsidiaries:

Westbank Corporation Inc. **(1)**
161 Madison Ave, Morristown, NJ 07960-7329
Tel.: (973) 538-6766
Sales Range: $10-24.9 Million
Emp.: 2
Supplier of Fish & Seafoods
N.A.I.C.S.: 424460

DAYCARE CLEANING SERVICES, INC.
1909 Fairfax Ave, Cherry Hill, NJ 08003
Tel.: (856) 498-1706
Web Site:
    http://www.daycarecleaningservices.com
Year Founded: 2001
Sales Range: $1-9.9 Million
Emp.: 30
Janitorial Services
N.A.I.C.S.: 561720
Rob Nestore *(Pres)*

DAYCO HOLDING CORP.
8950 SW 74th Ct Ste 2213, Miami, FL 33156
Tel.: (305) 377-8333
Web Site:
    http://www.daycoholding.com
Sales Range: $50-74.9 Million
Emp.: 15
Land Subdividers & Developers, Commercial
N.A.I.C.S.: 237210
Franco D'agostino *(Chm & CEO)*
Richard Liss *(Controller)*
Luis Lamar *(Pres & COO)*

DAYCO LLC
501 John James Audubon Pkwy, Amherst, NY 14228
Tel.: (716) 689-4972   DE
Web Site: http://www.dayco.com
Sales Range: $1-4.9 Billion
Emp.: 3,000
Automobile Parts Mfr
N.A.I.C.S.: 326220
John T. Bohenick *(CEO)*
Thomas Hart *(Sr VP-Production Sys)*
Joao Ramon *(Pres-South America)*
Paul DiLisio *(Sr VP-Automotive & Industrial Original Equipment Sls-Troy)*
Phil Liu *(Gen Mgr-Aftermarket Bus-China)*
Arnold Mouw *(Mng Dir-Southeast Asia, Australia & New Zealand)*

Subsidiaries:

Dayco Canada Corp. **(1)**
216 Chrislea Rd Suite 402, Woodbridge, L4L 8S5, ON, Canada   **(100%)**
Tel.: (905) 760-6900
Web Site: http://www.dayco.com
Sales Range: $50-74.9 Million
Emp.: 200
Automobile Parts Mfr
N.A.I.C.S.: 336340

Dayco Europe Automotive **(1)**
C/ Comte d'Urgell 143 3 1a, 08036, Barcelona, Spain   **(100%)**
Tel.: (34) 932469710
Web Site: http://www.mark-iv.com
Rev.: $14,000,000
Emp.: 400
Mfr of Automotive Components & Tube Components
N.A.I.C.S.: 336340

Dayco Products LLC **(1)**
1650 Research Dr Ste 200, Troy, MI 48083

Tel.: (248) 404-6500
Web Site: http://www.dayco.com
Motor Vehicle Parts Mfr
N.A.I.C.S.: 336390
Bruno Valillo *(Pres-Global Aftermarket)*
Daniel Sheehan *(VP-Aftermarket Sls)*
John Kinnick *(Exec VP-Aftermarket)*
Tom Tecklenburg *(VP-Aftermarket-North America)*
Joel Wiegert *(CEO)*

DAYCON PRODUCTS COMPANY, INC.
16001 Trade Zone Ave, Upper Marlboro, MD 20774-8795
Tel.: (301) 218-1000   DC
Web Site: https://www.daycon.com
Year Founded: 1940
Sales Range: $125-149.9 Million
Emp.: 176
Wholesale Janitorial Products; Sanitation & Hardware
N.A.I.C.S.: 423850
Robert N. Cohen *(CEO)*
Harry Feldman *(Partner)*

Subsidiaries:

Daycon **(1)**
10404 Lakeridge Pkwy Ste 600, Ashland, VA 23005
Tel.: (804) 550-9754
Web Site: http://www.daycon.com
Sales Range: $25-49.9 Million
Emp.: 10
Service Establishment Equipment & Supplies-Wholesale
N.A.I.C.S.: 423850
Mike Shupe *(Mgr-Ops)*

Daycon Products Company, Inc. **(1)**
875 Pk St, Christiansburg, VA 24073-3223
Tel.: (476) 869
Service Establishment Equipment & Supplies-Wholesale
N.A.I.C.S.: 423850

DAYLIGHT DONUT FLOUR COMPANY LLC.
11707 E 11th St, Tulsa, OK 74128
Tel.: (918) 438-0800
Web Site:
    http://www.daylightdonuts.com
Sales Range: $10-24.9 Million
Emp.: 46
Doughnut Mixes
N.A.I.C.S.: 311824
John Bond *(CEO)*
Jimmy Keeter *(CFO)*

DAYLIGHT TRANSPORT
1501 Hughes Way Ste 200, Long Beach, CA 90810
Tel.: (310) 507-8200
Web Site: http://www.dylt.com
Rev.: $113,577,495
Emp.: 200
Provider of Trucking Services
N.A.I.C.S.: 484121
Richard S. Breen *(CEO)*

DAYMARK SOLUTIONS, INC.
23 3rd Ave, Burlington, MA 01803
Tel.: (978) 431-1500
Web Site: http://www.daymarksi.com
Year Founded: 2002
Sales Range: $25-49.9 Million
Emp.: 28
Computer Peripheral Equipment & Software Merchant Whslr
N.A.I.C.S.: 423430
Suzanne Hardy *(Mgr-Sls)*
Tim Donovan *(Pres & CEO)*
Jeff Rushton *(CFO)*
Brian Casey *(COO & Gen Mgr)*
Corey Roberts *(Dir-Tech)*
Jay Sartori *(Mgr-Networking)*
Jon Mehlman *(Dir-Mktg)*
Sean Gilbride *(Dir-Pro Svcs)*

DAYS BEVERAGE INC.
529 Guinevere Dr, Newtown Square, PA 19073
Tel.: (215) 990-0983
Web Site: http://www.dayssoda.com
Sales Range: $50-74.9 Million
Emp.: 52
Soft Drinks
N.A.I.C.S.: 424490
David P. Digirolamo *(CEO)*

DAYSPRING INTERNATIONAL
1062 Laskin Rd, Virginia Beach, VA 23451
Tel.: (757) 428-1092   VA
Web Site:
    https://www.dayspringnational.org
Year Founded: 1979
Sales Range: $10-24.9 Million
Emp.: 20
Individual & Family Support Services
N.A.I.C.S.: 624190
David G. Mercer *(Exec VP)*

DAYTNER CONSTRUCTION GROUP
114 S Main St Ste 202, Mount Airy, MD 21771
Tel.: (301) 829-1772
Web Site:
    http://www.daytnercorp.com
Sales Range: $10-24.9 Million
Emp.: 10
Construction Services
N.A.I.C.S.: 236210
Theresa A. Daytner *(Pres & CEO)*

DAYTON ANDREWS FIVE STAR CHRYSLER PLYMOUTH JEEP, INC.
2388 Gulf to Bay Blvd, Clearwater, FL 33765-4103
Tel.: (727) 799-4539   FL
Web Site:
    http://www.daytonandrews.com
Year Founded: 1964
Sales Range: $75-99.9 Million
Emp.: 50
Retailer of New & Used Automobiles
N.A.I.C.S.: 441110
C. Taylor Andrews *(VP)*
Steve Hagenau *(Controller)*
Charley Flatley *(Dir-Svcs)*

DAYTON BAG & BURLAP CO.
322 Davis Ave, Dayton, OH 45403
Tel.: (937) 258-8000
Web Site: https://www.daybag.com
Sales Range: $25-49.9 Million
Emp.: 100
Automotive Trimmings, Fabric
N.A.I.C.S.: 336360
Samuel Lumby *(Pres)*
Jeff Rutter *(VP)*
Charles Cretcher *(Controller)*

DAYTON CHILDRENS HOSPITAL
1 Children's Plz, Dayton, OH 45404
Tel.: (937) 641-3000   OH
Web Site:
    https://www.childrensdayton.org
Year Founded: 1967
Sales Range: $200-249.9 Million
Emp.: 1,940
Children Healthcare Services
N.A.I.C.S.: 622110
Matt Graybill *(COO)*
Gregory Ramey *(Exec Dir)*
Adam Mezoff *(Chief Medical Officer & VP-Medical Affairs)*
Lisa Coffey *(VP-Physician Svcs)*
Therese McNea-Wiley *(Asst Treas & Sec)*
Michael R. Shane *(Chm)*
Deborah A. Feldman *(Pres & CEO)*

Laurence R. Klaben *(Treas & Sec)*
Derek Theodor *(Exec Dir-Ambulatory Clinics)*
Linda Black-Kurek *(Vice Chm)*

DAYTON FOODS LIMITED PARTNERSHIP
3255 Feyjay Dr, Dayton, OH 45430-1323
Tel.: (937) 431-1662
Web Site:
    http://www.cubfoodsdayton.com
Year Founded: 1995
Sales Range: $50-74.9 Million
Emp.: 700
Provider of Grocery Services
N.A.I.C.S.: 445110
Michael Lofino *(Owner & Pres)*

DAYTON FORGING & HEAT TREATING COMPANY
215 N Findlay St, Dayton, OH 45403
Tel.: (937) 253-4126
Web Site:
    https://www.daytonforging.com
Year Founded: 1919
Sales Range: $25-49.9 Million
Emp.: 67
Iron & Steel Forging Services
N.A.I.C.S.: 332111
Eric Wilson *(Pres)*

DAYTON FREIGHT LINES INC.
6450 Poe Ave, Dayton, OH 45414-2647
Tel.: (937) 264-4060   OH
Web Site:
    https://www.daytonfreight.com
Year Founded: 1981
Sales Range: $100-124.9 Million
Emp.: 2,000
Trucking Services
N.A.I.C.S.: 484121
Thomas Cronin Jr. *(Pres)*

DAYTON HEIDELBERG DISTRIBUTING CO INC.
1247 Leo St, Dayton, OH 45404-1660
Tel.: (937) 220-6451   OH
Web Site:
    http://www.heidelbergdist.com
Year Founded: 1937
Sales Range: $50-74.9 Million
Emp.: 675
Beer & Ale Distr
N.A.I.C.S.: 424810
Vail Miller *(CEO & COO)*
Tom Rouse *(CFO)*
Steve Lowrey *(Pres)*

DAYTON INTERNATIONAL AIRPORT
3600 Terminal Dr Ste 300, Dayton, OH 45377-3313
Tel.: (937) 454-8200
Web Site: https://www.flydayton.com
Year Founded: 1936
Sales Range: $10-24.9 Million
Emp.: 165
Airport & Air Facilities Operator
N.A.I.C.S.: 488119
Tony Branch *(Coord-IT)*
Linda Hughes *(Mgr-PR & Mktg)*

DAYTON NUT SPECIALTIES INC.
919 N Main St, Dayton, OH 45405
Tel.: (937) 223-3225
Web Site: http://www.candyfarm.com
Year Founded: 1923
Sales Range: $10-24.9 Million
Emp.: 46
Confectionery
N.A.I.C.S.: 424450
Stanley Maschino *(Pres)*

Dayton Rogers Mfg. Co.—(Continued)

DAYTON ROGERS MFG. CO.
8401 W 35 W Service Dr, Minneapolis, MN 55449-7260
Tel.: (763) 784-7714   MN
Web Site:
http://www.daytonrogers.com
Year Founded: 1929
Sales Range: $25-49.9 Million
Emp.: 600
Metal Stamping Mfr
N.A.I.C.S.: 332119
Ron Lowry (Chm)
Dayton A. Rogers (Founder)
David Fenske (CEO & Chief Legal Officer)
Chad Koebnick (CFO & COO)

Subsidiaries:

Dayton Rogers of California   (1)
13630 Saticoy St, Van Nuys, CA 91402-6302   (100%)
Tel.: (818) 787-6670
Web Site: http://www.daytonrogers.com
Sales Range: $10-24.9 Million
Emp.: 45
Sheet Metal Fabrication
N.A.I.C.S.: 332119

Dayton Rogers of Minnesota   (1)
8401 W 35 W Service Dr NE, Minneapolis, MN 55449-7260
Tel.: (763) 784-7714
Web Site: http://www.daytonrogers.com
Sales Range: $25-49.9 Million
Emp.: 175
Sheet Metal Fabrication
N.A.I.C.S.: 332119
John Madsen (Gen Mgr)

Dayton Rogers of New York   (1)
150 Fedex Way, Rochester, NY 14624-1174
Tel.: (585) 349-4040
Web Site: http://www.daytonrogers.com
Sales Range: $10-24.9 Million
Emp.: 4
Sheet Metal Fabrication
N.A.I.C.S.: 332119
Tony Harper (Mgr-Mfg)

Dayton Rogers of Ohio   (1)
2309 McGaw Rd, Columbus, OH 43207-4806   (100%)
Tel.: (614) 491-1477
Web Site: http://www.daytonrogers.com
Sales Range: $10-24.9 Million
Emp.: 48
Sheet Metal Fabrication
N.A.I.C.S.: 332119

Dayton Rogers of Texas   (1)
1107 Comml Blvd N, Arlington, TX 76001-7123
Tel.: (817) 467-1261
Web Site: http://www.daytonrogers.com
Sales Range: $25-49.9 Million
Emp.: 42
Sheet Metal Fabrication Mfr
N.A.I.C.S.: 332119
Ron Lowry (Owner & Co-CEO)
Dayton A. Rogers (Founder)
John Seeger Jr. (Co-CEO)

DAYTON SUPERIOR CORPORATION
1125 Byers Rd, Miamisburg, OH 45342-5765
Tel.: (937) 428-6360   OH
Web Site:
http://www.daytonsuperior.com
Year Founded: 1924
Sales Range: $450-499.9 Million
Emp.: 600
Concrete Accessories Masonry Products Welded Dowel Assemblies Paving Products & Corrosive preventing Epoxy Coatings Mfr
N.A.I.C.S.: 331210
Peter Viens (Pres & COO)
Richard Lindstrom (VP-Engrg)
Balaji Viswanathan (Dir-Pricing)
Thomas Chieffe (Chm & CEO)
Daniel T. Dolson (CFO & VP)

Subsidiaries:

Dayton Superior Canada Ltd.   (1)
1366 Ave De La Gare, Mascouche, J7K 2Z2, QC, Canada
Tel.: (450) 433-2107
Web Site: http://www.daytonsuperior.com
Sales Range: $10-24.9 Million
Services For Hardwares For Pre Cast Concrete Markets
N.A.I.C.S.: 423710

Dayton Superior Canada Ltd.   (1)
6650 Pacific Circle, Mississauga, L5T 1V6, ON, Canada
Tel.: (416) 798-2000
Web Site: http://www.daytonsuperior.com
Sales Range: $10-24.9 Million
Emp.: 50
Mfr of Concrete Accessories
N.A.I.C.S.: 327331

Dayton Superior Corporation   (1)
1125 Byers Rd, Miamisburg, OH 45342-5765
Tel.: (937) 866-0711
Web Site: http://www.daytonsuperior.com
Sales Range: $25-49.9 Million
Emp.: 125
Mfr Concrete Accessories
N.A.I.C.S.: 327390
Paul Fisher (Treas & VP)
Jim McRickard (Pres)
Randy Brown (VP-Mktg & Intl Sls)
Richard Lindstrom (VP-Engrg)
Lutz Richter (CFO & VP)
Kenneth Tynes (VP-HR)
Peter Viens (Chief Supply Chain Officer & Sr VP)

Dur-O-Wal Inc.   (1)
30 Rasons Ct, Hauppauge, NY 11788
Tel.: (631) 234-0600
Web Site: http://www.dur-o-wal.com
Sales Range: $10-24.9 Million
Emp.: 12
Mfr Masonry Construction Products
N.A.I.C.S.: 332618

Kodi Klip Corporation   (1)
314 S Cumberland St, Lebanon, TN 37087
Tel.: (615) 449-1880
Web Site: http://www.kodiklip.com
Mining
N.A.I.C.S.: 213114
Jon Kodi (Founder)

Symons Corporation   (1)
2400 Arthur Ave, Elk Grove Village, IL 60007
Tel.: (847) 298-3200
Web Site: http://www.symons.com
Rev.: $100,000,000
Emp.: 360
Pre-Engineered Concrete Forming Systems & Accessories For Walls, Columns & Decks; Fiberglass Column Forms; Flying Systems & Shoring; Liquid, Powder & Epoxy Chemicals
N.A.I.C.S.: 332322
Paul Elvin (Mgr-Tech Svc & Exports)

DAYTON SUPERIOR PRODUCTS CO., INC.
1370 Lytle Rd, Troy, OH 45373-9401
Tel.: (937) 332-1930   OH
Web Site:
http://www.daytonsuperiorprod.com
Year Founded: 1982
Sales Range: $10-24.9 Million
Emp.: 15
Industrial Power Transmission Products
N.A.I.C.S.: 336390
Daniel P. Gleason (Pres)

DAYTON T. BROWN INC.
1175 Church St, Bohemia, NY 11716-5031
Tel.: (631) 589-6300   NY
Web Site: https://www.dtb.com
Year Founded: 1950
Sales Range: $10-24.9 Million
Emp.: 300

Provider of Sheet Metal Work, Engineering, Testing & Technical Communications
N.A.I.C.S.: 332322
Angela Chewning (VP)
Bill Courbanou (Dir-IS)
Mike Ferlini (Supvr-Writing)
Pawel Kulesza (Engr-Data Acq)
Michael Natale (Engr-Electrical)
Donald Schlauraff (Mgr-Engrg)
Frank Scimeca (Engr-Test)
Jag Sookhdeo (Engr-Ballistics)
Hank Funsch (Sr VP)
Robert Single (Sr VP)
Jeffrey Hallstein (Supvr-Creative & Imaging)
Jay Bartholomew (Supvr-Production)
William Bradshaw (VP & Chief Engr)
James F. Maggipinto (VP-Procurement & Facilities)
Joe Deo (Mgr-Bus Dev)

DAYTON-PHOENIX GROUP INC.
1619 Kuntz Rd, Dayton, OH 45404-1240
Tel.: (937) 496-3900   OH
Web Site: https://www.dayton-phoenix.com
Year Founded: 1939
Mfr of Railroad Equipment, Specializing in Electric Motors, Generators & HVACK Units
N.A.I.C.S.: 335312
Gale Kooken (CEO)
Christie Fox (CFO)
Debra Caudill (Mgr-HR)
Grant Root (Mgr-IT)

DAYTONA BR-GD, INC.
451 N Nova Rd, Daytona Beach, FL 32114
Tel.: (386) 255-7475   FL
Web Site:
http://www.daytonatoyota.com
Year Founded: 1974
Sales Range: $25-49.9 Million
New Car Dealers
N.A.I.C.S.: 441110
Kevin Busler (Dir-Bus Dev)
Sean Tinder (Mgr-Inventory)
Steve Spiletic (Mgr-Collision Center)
Manny Cacoilo (Mgr-Svc)
Joseph Darrow (Mgr-Parts)
Joe Donahue (Mgr-Sls)
Jim Kowalak (Dir-Ops)
Tom Kuhn (Gen Mgr-Sls)
James Martens (Dir-Fin)
Mark Mitchell (Dir-Fixed Ops)
Serge Nash (Mgr-Fin)
Natasha Parisho (Coord-Rental)
Steve Piaz (Mgr-Fin)
Monte Asti (Mgr-Fin)
Rodney Rodriguez (Mgr-Fin)
Gilbert Dannehower (Pres)

DAYTONA DODGE CHRYSLER JEEP RAM
1450 N Tomoka Farms Rd, Daytona Beach, FL 32124
Tel.: (386) 777-9822
Web Site:
https://www.daytonachrysler.net
Sales Range: $50-74.9 Million
Emp.: 95
New Car Retailer
N.A.I.C.S.: 441110
Randy Dayne (Owner)

DAYTONA HARLEY DAVIDSON
1635 North US Hwy 1, Ormond Beach, FL 32174
Tel.: (386) 253-2453
Web Site: http://www.daytonahd.com
Rev.: $10,100,000
Emp.: 62

Motorcycle Dealers
N.A.I.C.S.: 441227
Denise Jabaly (Mgr)
Phyllis Barnett (Mgr)

DAZADI INC.
6700 Fallbrook Ave Ste 203A, West Hills, CA 91307
Web Site: http://www.dazadi.com
Year Founded: 2002
Sales Range: $1-9.9 Million
Emp.: 12
Online Supplier of Sporting Goods & Game Room Equipment
N.A.I.C.S.: 423910
Josh Klaristenfeld (Co-Founder & Exec VP-Ops)

DAZOR MANUFACTURING CORP.
2079 Congressional Dr, Saint Louis, MO 63146
Tel.: (314) 652-2400
Web Site: http://www.dazor.com
Year Founded: 1938
Sales Range: $50-74.9 Million
Emp.: 23
Mfr of Portable & Adjustable Lighting Fixtures & Video Microscopes
N.A.I.C.S.: 335132
Stan Hogrebe (Pres & CEO)
Ann Settlage (Mgr-Engrg & New Product Dev)

DB ASSOCIATES ADVERTISING
222 Forbes Rd Ste 204, Braintree, MA 02184-2706
Tel.: (781) 843-0181
Year Founded: 1991
Sales Range: Less than $1 Million
Emp.: 3
N.A.I.C.S.: 541810
David E. Bershad (Pres)
Tom Martin (Dir-Creative)
Susan Nappi (Sr Dir-Art)

DB BEST TECHNOLOGIES, LLC
2763 152nd Ave NE, Redmond, WA 98052
Web Site: http://www.bebest.com
Year Founded: 2002
Sales Range: $1-9.9 Million
Emp.: 100
Developer of Mobile Software & Business Applications
N.A.I.C.S.: 513210
Lior Ribalov (VP-Bus Dev)
Prabhat Varma (VP-Sls)

DB CONSULTING GROUP, INC.
8401 Colesville Rd Ste 300, Silver Spring, MD 20910
Tel.: (301) 589-4020
Web Site:
http://www.dbconsultinggroup.com
Year Founded: 2000
Rev.: $21,069,739
Emp.: 85
Business Consulting Services
N.A.I.C.S.: 541618
Gerald Boyd Jr. (Pres & CEO)

DB PROFESSIONALS, INC.
620 SW 5th Ave Ste 610, Portland, OR 97204
Tel.: (503) 226-6586
Computer Consulting Services
N.A.I.C.S.: 541512
Prabha Ananthanarayana (VP)

DBA KNOWLEDGE, INC.
385 Inverness Pkwy Ste 190, Englewood, CO 80112

Tel.: (720) 475-8600
Web Site: http://www.dbak.com
Year Founded: 2005
Sales Range: $10-24.9 Million
Emp.: 41
Technology Consulting Services
N.A.I.C.S.: 541512
Ed Hut (Co-Founder & CEO)
Frank Bommarito (Co-Founder & Mng Partner)
Pam Malone (VP-Fin & Acctg)

DBH WORLDWIDE, LLC

5 Holland Ste 119, Irvine, CA 92618
Tel.: (855) 333-9836
Web Site:
http://www.designbyhumans.com
Year Founded: 2007
Sales Range: $1-9.9 Million
Online Tee Shirt Retailer
N.A.I.C.S.: 424500
Jeff Sierra (Owner & Mng Partner)
Sage Hagan (Dir-Ops & Product Dev)
Trey Swartz (Dir-Bus Dev-Gaming)

DBI BEVERAGE NAPA

Two Ingram Blvd, La Vergne, TN 37089
Tel.: (707) 462-1697
Web Site:
http://www.mendobrew.com
Sales Range: $25-49.9 Million
Emp.: 60
Beer Brewer & Distr
N.A.I.C.S.: 312120
Jeffrey D. Skinner (CEO)

DBI BUSINESS INTERIORS LLC

912 E Michigan Ave, Lansing, MI 48912
Tel.: (517) 485-3200
Web Site: https://www.dbiyes.com
Year Founded: 1961
Rev.: $20,000,000
Emp.: 59
Office Forms & Supplies
N.A.I.C.S.: 423210
George Snyder (Pres)
Steve Klaver (VP-Ops)

DBM TECHNOLOGIES LLC

140 S Saginaw St Ste 725, Pontiac, MI 48342-2255
Tel.: (248) 836-4800
Year Founded: 1999
Sales Range: $25-49.9 Million
Emp.: 700
Mfr of Plastic Parts for Automobiles
N.A.I.C.S.: 326199

DBS CORPORATION

506 Broad St, Chattanooga, TN 37402
Tel.: (423) 752-1302
Web Site:
http://www.dbscorporation.com
Year Founded: 1994
Sales Range: $50-74.9 Million
Emp.: 35
Commercial & Institutional Building Construction Services
N.A.I.C.S.: 236220
Cary Davis (Pres)
George Bright (Co-Owner)
Doug Stein (VP)

DBSI INCORPORATED

6950 W Morelos Pl Ste 1, Chandler, AZ 85226
Tel.: (602) 264-7263   AZ
Web Site: https://www.dbsi-inc.com
Year Founded: 1998
Sales Range: $50-74.9 Million
Emp.: 138
Construction Services

N.A.I.C.S.: 237990
Debra Dillon (Principal)
John W. Smith (CEO)
Corde Kurtz (Dir-Construction & Facilities)
Joe Kim (COO)
Jim Ransco (Principal)
Todd Brown (CFO)
Ron Suchan (Sr VP-Sls)

DBSI, INC.

12426 W Explorer Dr Ste 220, Boise, ID 83713-1560
Tel.: (208) 955-9800
Web Site: http://dbsi-inc.com
Year Founded: 1979
Holding Company; Real Estate & Technology
N.A.I.C.S.: 551112
Douglas L. Swenson (Founder & Pres)
John Mayeron (Exec VP-Mktg & Product Dev)
Charles E. Hassard (CFO)

Subsidiaries:

DBSI Housing Inc.   (1)
12426 W Explorer Dr Ste 220, Boise, ID 83713-1560
Tel.: (208) 955-9800
Holding Company
N.A.I.C.S.: 551112

Subsidiary (Domestic):

DBSI Development LLC   (2)
8850 W Emerald Ste 164, Boise, ID 83704
Tel.: (208) 489-2500
Real Estate Development
N.A.I.C.S.: 531390

Western Electronics LLC   (1)
1550 S Tech Ln, Meridian, ID 83642
Tel.: (208) 955-9700
Web Site:
http://www.westernelectronics.com
Sales Range: $10-24.9 Million
Emp.: 150
Printed Circuit Board Mfr & Assembly
N.A.I.C.S.: 334412
Brad Grover (CFO)
Rob Subia (Pres & CEO)
Randy Manfull (Plant Mgr)
Dustin Taylor (VP-Bus Dev)

DBTS INC.

11200 Rockville Pike Ste 300, Rockville, MD 20852-7101
Tel.: (202) 393-3287
Web Site: http://www.dbts.com
Year Founded: 2000
Sales Range: $1-9.9 Million
Emp.: 55
IT Staffing & Project Management Services
N.A.I.C.S.: 561320

DC BRANDS INTERNATIONAL, INC.

1685 S Colorada Blvd Unit S291, Denver, CO 80222
Tel.: (720) 281-7143   CO
Web Site:
http://www.hardnutrition.com
Year Founded: 1998
Sales Range: Less than $1 Million
Emp.: 1
Nutritional-Based Water Beverages & Other Specialized Nutritional Products Mfr & Distr
N.A.I.C.S.: 312111
Richard J. Pearce (Founder)
Bob Armstrong (Acting CEO & CFO)

DC BUILDING GROUP LLC

6110 Elton Ave, Las Vegas, NV 89107
Tel.: (702) 434-9991
Web Site:
http://www.buildwithdcbg.com

Year Founded: 2001
Sales Range: $10-24.9 Million
Emp.: 16
Commercial & Institutional Building Construction
N.A.I.C.S.: 236220
Shawn Danoski (CEO)
Bryce Clutts (Pres)
Dave Teator (Sr Project Mgr)
Dale Swinn (Dir-Field Ops)
Charlie Stewart (Dir-Pre Construction Svcs)
Pat Warren (Superintendent)
Gary Siroky (COO)
Brenden Graves (Dir-Client Svcs)

DC DENTAL SUPPLIES, LLC

1133 Greenwood Rd, Baltimore, MD 21208
Tel.: (410) 653-7500
Web Site: https://www.dcdental.com
Year Founded: 2002
Sales Range: $10-24.9 Million
Emp.: 56
Dental Equipment Supplies
N.A.I.C.S.: 423450
Mark Sambrowsky (VP-Natl Acct)

DC ENERGY, LLC.

8065 Leesburg Park Fl 6, Vienna, VA 22182
Tel.: (703) 506-3901
Web Site: http://www.dc-energy.com
Year Founded: 2002
Sales Range: $25-49.9 Million
Emp.: 70
Energy Market Investment & Trade
N.A.I.C.S.: 551112
Dean Wilde (CEO & Mng Dir)
Todd Ramsey (Principal)
William Cliff Brown (Principal)

DC GROUP, INC.

1977 W River Rd N, Minneapolis, MN 55411
Tel.: (612) 529-9516   MN
Web Site: https://www.dc-group.com
Year Founded: 1969
Sales Range: $10-24.9 Million
Emp.: 103
Supplies Uninterrupted Power Maintenance to Data Centers, Telecommunication Companies & Hospitals
N.A.I.C.S.: 221122
Jonathan Frank (Pres & CEO)

DC INTERNATIONAL

701 Robley Dr Ste 115, Lafayette, LA 70503
Tel.: (337) 988-1500
Web Site: https://www.dcint.net
Year Founded: 2002
Sales Range: $10-24.9 Million
Emp.: 125
Oil & Gas Field Operating Services
N.A.I.C.S.: 213112
Linda Earles (CEO)
Russell Earles (Pres)
Al Wambsgans (VP-Ops)
Jim Williams (VP-Sls)
Joseph Hawkins (Dir-Bus & Fin)
Paul Herbert (Dir-Res & Workforce Dev)
Paul Hebert (Dir-Resources & Workforce Dev)

DC VALUE ADDED SERVICE TECHNOLOGY

1319 Butterfield Rd Ste 504, Downers Grove, IL 60515
Tel.: (630) 964-6060
Web Site: http://www.dcvast.com
Year Founded: 1989
Rev.: $22,719,135
Emp.: 20
System Integration Services
N.A.I.C.S.: 541512

Donald M. Swanson (CEO)
Larry Shalzi (CFO & Pres-Ops)

DCA OUTDOOR, INC.

5840 NW Prairie View Rd, Kansas City, MO 64151
Web Site: http://www.dcaoutdoor.com
Year Founded: 2016
Holding Company; Garden Centers & Nurseries
N.A.I.C.S.: 551112
Tory Schwope (Founder & Pres)

Subsidiaries:

Brehob Nursery Inc.   (1)
4316 Bluff Rd, Indianapolis, IN 46217
Tel.: (317) 783-3233
Web Site: http://www.brehobnursery.com
Nursery & Garden Center
N.A.I.C.S.: 424930
Scott Lawson (COO)

DCA/DCPR

441 E Chester St Ste 106, Jackson, TN 38301
Tel.: (731) 427-2080   TN
Web Site: http://www.dca-dcpr.com
Year Founded: 1985
Emp.: 10
Advertising Services
N.A.I.C.S.: 541810
Seth Chandler (CEO)

Subsidiaries:

DCA/DCPR   (1)
609 Beech St, East Lansing, MI 48823
Tel.: (810) 730-0032
Emp.: 1
Public Relations Services
N.A.I.C.S.: 541820

DCA/DCPR Chicago   (1)
1866 N Sheridan Rd Ste 205, Chicago, IL 60035
Tel.: (847) 432-6000
Web Site: http://www.dca-dcpr.com
Emp.: 5
Public Relations
N.A.I.C.S.: 541820

DCC RETOUCHING & PHOTOGRAPHY SERVICES

42 W 39th St 6th Fl, New York, NY 10018
Tel.: (212) 989-4888
Web Site: http://www.dccnyc.com
Year Founded: 1987
Sales Range: $25-49.9 Million
Emp.: 110
Retouching & Pre-Media Print Services
N.A.I.C.S.: 541922
Steve Pandolfi (Founder)
Don Terwilliger (COO)

DCG DEVELOPMENT CO.

240 Clifton Corporate Pkwy, Clifton Park, NY 12065
Tel.: (518) 383-0059
Web Site:
http://www.dcgdevelopment.com
Sales Range: $10-24.9 Million
Emp.: 20
General Real Estate Developers
N.A.I.C.S.: 531110
David S. Congdon (VP)
Donald MacElroy (VP-Comml Dev)

DCI BIOLOGICALS INC.

1019 Fort Salonga Rd, Northport, NY 11768
Tel.: (631) 757-0792
Web Site: http://www.dciplasma.com
Sales Range: $25-49.9 Million
Emp.: 700
Plasma Collection Facilities
N.A.I.C.S.: 621991

DCI Biologicals Inc.—(Continued)

Martin Silver *(Pres)*
David Spink *(Exec VP)*

DCI CONSTRUCTION, LLC.

1354 E Kingsley St, Springfield, MO
65804
Tel.: (417) 832-8382
Sales Range: $10-24.9 Million
Emp.: 10
Nonresidential Construction Services
N.A.I.C.S.: 236220
Denton Cline *(Principal)*
Mark Gardner *(Principal)*
James Smith *(Controller)*

DCI CONSULTING GROUP, INC.

1920 I St NW, Washington, DC
20006
Tel.: (202) 828-6900
Web Site: https://www.dciconsult.com
Administrative Management & General Management Consulting Service
N.A.I.C.S.: 541611
David Cohen *(Pres)*

Subsidiaries:

Human Resource Specialties
Inc.   (1)
3 Monroe Pkwy, Lake Oswego, OR 97035
Tel.: (503) 697-3329
Web Site: http://www.hrspecialties.com
Rev.: $3,060,000
Emp.: 18
Administrative Management & General
Management Consulting Service
N.A.I.C.S.: 541611
Janette L. Kilgore *(Bus Mgr)*
Robin M. Helm *(Dir-Client Svcs)*
Scott W. Mylnechuk *(Gen Mgr)*
Heidi L. Shaw *(Dir-Affirmative Action Svcs)*
Lisa Green *(Project Mgr)*

DCI GROUP

1828 L St NW Ste 400, Washington,
DC 20036
Tel.: (202) 546-4242
Web Site: http://www.dcigroup.com
Government/Political/Public Affairs,
Public Relations
N.A.I.C.S.: 541820
Thomas J. Synhorst *(Chm & Mng Partner)*
Douglas M. Goodyear *(CEO)*
Dan Combs *(Partner)*
Justin Peterson *(Mng Partner)*
Craig Stevens *(VP)*
Ed Patru *(VP)*
Paul Ryan *(Partner)*
Susan Reiche *(Partner)*

DCI, INC.

600 N 54th Ave, Saint Cloud, MN
56303
Tel.: (320) 252-8200   MN
Web Site: https://www.dciinc.com
Year Founded: 1955
Sales Range: $100-124.9 Million
Emp.: 230
Mfr of Stainless Steel Vessels
N.A.I.C.S.: 332313
Jeff Keller *(Pres)*
Wayne Brinkman *(VP-Ops)*

Subsidiaries:

DCI, Inc. - Springfield Division   (1)
1590 E Bain St Ste B, Ozark, MO 65721
Tel.: (417) 581-1224
Stainless Storage Tank Mfr
N.A.I.C.S.: 332420

DCINY

250 W 57th St Ste Fl 19, New York,
NY 10107
Tel.: (212) 707-8566
Web Site: https://www.dciny.org

Year Founded: 2007
Sales Range: $1-9.9 Million
Emp.: 12
Orchestral Backing & Concert Assistance Services
N.A.I.C.S.: 711130
Iris Derke *(Dir Gen)*
Jonathan Griffith *(Dir-Artistic & Principal-Conductor)*

DCK PACIFIC CONSTRUCTION LLC.

707 Richards St Ste 410, Honolulu,
HI 96813
Tel.: (808) 533-5000
Web Site: http://www.dckww.com
Year Founded: 2008
Sales Range: $10-24.9 Million
Emp.: 150
Civil Engineering Services
N.A.I.C.S.: 237310
Wil Ideue *(Owner & Pres)*
Milton T. Mitsui *(Treas & VP)*

DCK WORLDWIDE, LLC

6 Ppg Pl Ste 700, Pittsburgh, PA
15222
Tel.: (412) 384-1000
Web Site: http://www.dckww.com
Sales Range: $100-124.9 Million
Emp.: 500
Commercial, Institutional & Industrial
Building Construction
N.A.I.C.S.: 236220
Stephen D'Angelo *(Pres & CEO)*
Matthew Brodie *(Sr VP & Gen Mgr)*
Eugene V. Bucci *(Exec VP)*
Chris C. Barbe *(Sr VP & Gen Mgr-Sls & Project Dev-Global)*
Charles E. Ostiguy *(Sr VP-IT)*
Laurie H. Bowers *(Sr VP-Org Dev)*
Kelvin J. Osborne *(VP-Ops-Hawaii Reg)*
Felix Pagan *(VP & Controller)*
Rob Sagwitz *(Dir-Mktg)*
Luis Pozo *(Dir-Project Acctg)*

Subsidiaries:

Dck International, LLC   (1)
PO Box 34234, Abu Dhabi, United Arab
Emirates
Tel.: (971) 50 848 5106
Commercial, Institutional & Industrial Building Construction
N.A.I.C.S.: 236220

DCN, LLC

3901 Great Plains Dr S, Fargo, ND
58104
Tel.: (701) 364-1300
Web Site:
https://www.dakotacarrier.com
Year Founded: 1996
Rev.: $17,000,000
Emp.: 30
Fiber Optic Cable Communications
Network Services
N.A.I.C.S.: 517111
Jesse Heck *(Mgr-Ops)*

DCS CORPORATION

6909 Metro Park Dr Ste 500, Alexandria, VA 22310
Tel.: (571) 227-6000   VA
Web Site: http://www.dcscorp.com
Year Founded: 1977
Sales Range: $100-124.9 Million
Emp.: 800
Engineering Services for Defense
Systems
N.A.I.C.S.: 541512
William J. Protzman *(Exec VP & Mgr-Army & Marine Corps)*
Thomas R. Fradette *(CFO, Treas & Exec VP)*
Thomas J. Gallagher *(VP-Contracts)*
Jim Benbow *(CEO)*

Murray B. Anderson *(CTO & VP)*
Larry M. Egbert *(Pres & COO)*
Nancy B. Mahoney *(VP-AWL/IPT SW Engrg Support)*
Timothy H. Phelps *(VP & Controller)*
Raul S. Sagun *(Chief Growth Officer)*
Curtis L. Schehr *(Chief Ethics Officer, Gen Counsel, Sec & Exec VP)*
Michael R. Smith *(VP-Ground Vehicle Sys)*
Alice T. Weadon *(VP)*
Lori Marracino *(VP-Proposal Dev & Strategic Comm)*

Subsidiaries:

Infoscitex Corporation   (1)
303 Bear Hill Rd, Waltham, MA 02451-1016
Tel.: (781) 890-1338
Web Site: http://www.infoscitex.com
Sales Range: $10-24.9 Million
Emp.: 100
Defense & Intelligence Technologies Developer
N.A.I.C.S.: 335999
Mike Gilkey *(Exec VP-Air & Space Tech & Mgr-Air & Space Tech)*

OptiMetrics, Inc.   (1)
3115 Professional Dr, Ann Arbor, MI 48104-5131
Tel.: (734) 330-2190
Web Site: http://www.omi.com
Sales Range: $10-24.9 Million
Emp.: 85
Research & Engineering Services
N.A.I.C.S.: 541330

DCS SANITATION MANAGEMENT

7864 Camargo Rd, Cincinnati, OH
45243
Tel.: (513) 271-9300
Web Site: http://www.dcs.com
Sales Range: $10-24.9 Million
Emp.: 15
Building Cleaning Services
N.A.I.C.S.: 561720
David Cozzens *(CEO)*
Jack Messman *(Chm)*
Chris Belden *(Sr VP-Global Svcs)*
Kyle Messman *(CFO)*
Ralph Mason *(Co-Founder & CTO)*
Susan Heystee *(Exec VP-Worldwide Sls)*
Ted Serentelos *(COO)*
Tim Taylor *(Chief Client Success Officer)*

DCV INC.

2281 N Masch Branch Rd, Denton,
TX 76207
Tel.: (940) 243-8530
Sales Range: $10-24.9 Million
Emp.: 11
Dump Truck Services
N.A.I.C.S.: 484220
Lynn Johnson *(Pres)*

DCX-CHOL ENTERPRISES, INC.

12831 S Figueroa St, Los Angeles,
CA 90061-1157
Tel.: (310) 516-1692   CA
Web Site: https://www.dcxchol.com
Year Founded: 1980
Sales Range: $50-74.9 Million
Emp.: 100
Designer, Developer & Manufacturer
of Cable Assemblies, Wire Harnesses, Electromechanical Devices &
Pneumatic Signal & Control Mechanisms
N.A.I.C.S.: 331524
Neal Castleman *(Pres)*
Brian Gamberg *(VP)*
Lola Herron *(VP-Fin)*

Subsidiaries:

DCX-CHOL Enterprises, Inc. - NEW-
VAC / DCX Division   (1)
9330 DeSoto Ave, Chatsworth, CA 91311-
4926
Tel.: (310) 516-1692
Electronic Connector Mfr
N.A.I.C.S.: 334417
Garrett Hoffman *(VP & Gen Mgr)*

DCX-CHOL Enterprises, Inc. - SMI
Division   (1)
1615 E Wallace St, Fort Wayne, IN 46803
Tel.: (260) 744-2261
Web Site: http://www.dcxchol.com
Electronic Connector Mfr
N.A.I.C.S.: 334417
Gerry Pettit *(Gen Mgr)*

DCX-CHOL, Inc.   (1)
11451 N Settlers Dr, Parker, CO
80138-8031   (100%)
Tel.: (310) 516-1692
Web Site: http://www.dcxchol.com
Sales Range: $10-24.9 Million
Emp.: 50
Cable Assemblies, Wire Harnesses, Electromechanical Devices, Special Application
Fluid, Pneumatic Signal & Control Mechanisms Mfr, Designer, Developer & Tester
N.A.I.C.S.: 331524

ELECSYS Division   (1)
225 Enterprise Dr, Pekin, IL 61554-9311
Tel.: (309) 353-4455
Sales Range: $10-24.9 Million
Emp.: 70
Custom Electrical-Interconnection Systems
& Components
N.A.I.C.S.: 335931
Mike Jamison *(VP & Gen Mgr)*

DD & SF INVESTMENTS, INC.

3020 Highwood Blvd, Raleigh, NC
27604
Tel.: (919) 834-6506   NC
Web Site:
http://www.workplaceoptions.co.uk
Sales Range: $1-9.9 Million
Emp.: 100
Work-Life Employee Benefits Services
N.A.I.C.S.: 561320
Alan Nray *(Pres & Mng Dir)*
Mary Ellen Gornick *(Sr VP-Global Products)*

Subsidiaries:

Network Advantage   (1)
944 Market St Ste 701, San Francisco, CA
94102
Tel.: (919) 834-6506
Employee Assistance Solutions
N.A.I.C.S.: 561320

DD TRADERS, INC.

5000 W 134th St, Leawood, KS
66209-7806
Tel.: (913) 402-6800
Web Site: https://www.demdaco.com
Year Founded: 1991
Sales Range: $50-74.9 Million
Emp.: 285
Vitreous China, Fine Earthenware Mfr
N.A.I.C.S.: 327110
David Kiersznowski *(Pres)*
Steve Fowler *(CFO)*
Frank Davis *(VP-Sls)*

DDB UNLIMITED, INC.

8445 Hwy 77 N, Wynnewood, OK
73098
Tel.: (405) 665-2876
Web Site:
http://www.ddbunlimited.com
Year Founded: 1996
Sales Range: $10-24.9 Million
Emp.: 150
Aluminum Extruded Product Mfr
N.A.I.C.S.: 331318

Dustin Mahorney *(Pres)*
Rolf Davis *(Dir-OEM Sls)*
Steve Adamietz *(Mgr-ISO)*
Tom Winters *(Dir-Engrg Svcs)*
Marvin Saucer *(Dir-CAD Svcs)*
Clark Kawamoto *(Mgr-Production)*
Mike Mahorney *(Gen Mgr-Corp)*
Lester Mahorney *(Sr VP)*
Bryan Campbell *(Mgr-Sls)*

DDFOODSOLUTIONS
4404 Sentry Dr, Tucker, GA 30084
Tel.: (770) 492-1322
Web Site:
   http://www.ddfoodsolutions.com
Year Founded: 2002
Sales Range: $10-24.9 Million
Emp.: 160
Preparation of Fully Cooked Meals
for Food Service Companies, Con-
vention Centers & Club Stores
N.A.I.C.S.: 722310
Avinash Grootens *(CEO)*
Rustico de Jesus *(VP-Fin)*

DDG INC.
910 Skokie Blvd, Northbrook, IL
60062
Tel.: (847) 714-0400
Rev.: $25,000,000
Emp.: 4
Steel Pipe & Tubes
N.A.I.C.S.: 331210

DDH INVESTMENTS OF SOUTH TEXAS
7322 SW Fwy No 1777, Houston, TX
77074
Tel.: (713) 988-2211
Rev.: $34,786,851
Emp.: 15
New & Used Automobiles
N.A.I.C.S.: 441110
Donald W. Hudler *(Pres & CEO)*

DDI CUSTOMER SERVICE, INC.
367 Morganza Rd, Canonsburg, PA
15317-5717
Tel.: (724) 746-3900
Web Site: http://www.ddiworld.com
Sales Range: $10-24.9 Million
Emp.: 80
Stationery & Office Supplies Mer-
chant Whslr
N.A.I.C.S.: 424120
William C. Byham *(Founder & Exec Chm)*
Robert W. Rogers *(Pres)*
Tacy Byham *(CEO)*
Ronald R. Dalesio *(Exec VP)*
Scott Erker *(Sr VP)*
Audrey B. Smith *(Sr VP-Talent Diag-nostics Solutions)*
David Tessmann-Keys *(Sr VP-Intl Ops)*
Richard S. Wellins *(Sr VP)*
Barry Stern *(Sr VP-Accelerated Dev Solutions)*
Douglas Reynolds *(CTO & Sr VP-Assessment Tech)*
Patsy Tsao *(CFO & Sr VP)*

DDP ROOFING SERVICES, INC.
20 Conchester Rd, Glen Mills, PA
19342
Tel.: (610) 361-9337
Web Site:
   https://www.ddproofing.com
Rev.: $15,800,000
Emp.: 150
Roofing Contractors
N.A.I.C.S.: 238160
Marty Fagan *(Mgr-Warehouse)*
Nancy Howard *(Mgr-Svc)*

Dana Daughtery *(Founder & VP)*
Rusty Boyko *(Pres)*
Paul Becker *(Founder & CEO)*

DDR BUILDERS, LLC
923 Village Center Dr Ste 305, Ra-
cine, WI 53406-4091
Tel.: (262) 989-7331   WI
Web Site:
   https://www.ddrbuilders.com
Year Founded: 1994
Residential Real Estate Investment,
Development, Construction & Home
Sales
N.A.I.C.S.: 236117
David Lundberg *(Owner & Pres)*

Subsidiaries:

DDR Realty, LLC   (1)
923 Village Ctr Dr Ste 305, Racine, WI
53406-4089
Tel.: (262) 989-7331
Web Site: http://www.ddrbuilders.com
New Home Sales
N.A.I.C.S.: 531210
David Lundberg *(Pres)*

DDR HOLDINGS INC.
195 Danbury Rd, Wilton, CT 06897
Tel.: (203) 761-9300
Web Site: http://www.dwvd.com
Rev.: $17,800,000
Emp.: 28
Accident & Health Reinsurance Carri-
ers
N.A.I.C.S.: 524130
Donald K. Drelich *(Chm & CEO)*

Subsidiaries:

D. W. Van Dyke & Co. of Connecticut
Inc.   (1)
195 Danbury Rd, Wilton, CT 06897
Tel.: (203) 761-9300
Web Site: http://www.dwvd.com
Rev.: $17,400,000
Life Reinsurance Carriers
N.A.I.C.S.: 524114
Christopher Koehler *(Pres)*
Ronald Charette *(COO)*
Donald K. Drelich *(Chm & CEO)*
Nanette Torres *(VP-Acctg)*
Jonathan Cole *(VP-Structured Fin & IT)*
Kenneth R. Broad *(Asst VP)*

DDW, INC.
100 S Spring St, Louisville, KY
40206-1945
Tel.: (502) 895-2438
Web Site: https://www.ddwcolor.com
Year Founded: 1865
Sales Range: $10-24.9 Million
Emp.: 175
Natural Food Color Mfr
N.A.I.C.S.: 311942
Ted Nixon *(Chm & CEO)*
Elaine Gravatte *(Pres & COO)*

DE AMERTEK CORPORATION INC.
300 Windsor Dr, Oak Brook, IL 60523
Tel.: (630) 572-0800
Web Site: http://www.deamertek.com
Rev.: $15,900,000
Emp.: 205
Electronic Circuits
N.A.I.C.S.: 334419
Jack C. Chen *(Chm)*
Theresa Chen *(CFO)*
Theresa Soria *(Mgr-Quality)*
Dan Anderson *(VP-Mktg)*

DE CAPUA ENTERPRISES INC.
1114 Dublin Rd, Columbus, OH
43215
Tel.: (614) 255-1400
Web Site:
   http://www.dawsoncouriers.com

Sales Range: $10-24.9 Million
Emp.: 60
Employment Agencies
N.A.I.C.S.: 561311
Chris DeCapua *(Owner)*

DE CORMIER MOTOR SALES, INC.
30 Tolland Tpke, Manchester, CT
06042
Tel.: (860) 643-4165
Web Site:
   http://www.decormiernissan.com
Year Founded: 1945
Sales Range: $10-24.9 Million
Emp.: 38
Car Whslr
N.A.I.C.S.: 441110
Carter G. De Cormier *(Gen Mgr)*

DE JAGER CONSTRUCTION, INC.
75 60th St SW, Wyoming, MI 49548-
5761
Tel.: (616) 530-0060
Web Site:
   https://www.dejagerconstruction.com
Sales Range: $10-24.9 Million
Emp.: 50
Nonresidential Construction Services
N.A.I.C.S.: 236220
Dan de Jager *(Pres)*
David de Jager *(Treas & Sec)*
Dan Eisma *(VP)*

DE LA GARZA PUBLIC RELA-TIONS, INC.
5773 Woodway Dr Ste 296, Houston,
TX 77057
Tel.: (713) 622-8818
Web Site: http://www.delagarza-
   pr.com
Sales Range: Less than $1 Million
Emp.: 5
Public Relations Agency
N.A.I.C.S.: 541820
Henry A. de La Garza *(Chm & CEO)*

DE LILLO CHEVROLET
18211 Beach Blvd, Huntington
Beach, CA 92648-1308
Tel.: (714) 847-6087
Web Site: https://www.delillo.com
Year Founded: 1946
Sales Range: $25-49.9 Million
Emp.: 70
New Car Whslr
N.A.I.C.S.: 441110
Sue Harmon *(Principal)*

DE LUCA ENTERPRISES INC.
370 E Maple Ave Ste 101, Lang-
horne, PA 19047-2859
Tel.: (215) 860-6500
Web Site:
   https://www.delucahomes.com
Year Founded: 1958
Sales Range: $10-24.9 Million
Emp.: 60
Single-Family Housing Construction
N.A.I.C.S.: 236115
Jim De Luca *(Pres)*

DE MOULIN BROTHERS & COMPANY
1025 S 4th St, Greenville, IL 62246
Tel.: (618) 664-2000
Web Site: https://www.demoulin.com
Sales Range: $10-24.9 Million
Emp.: 200
Band Uniforms
N.A.I.C.S.: 315250
Don Adamski *(Pres & COO)*

DE MOYA GROUP INC.

14600 SW 136th St, Miami, FL
33186-6762
Tel.: (305) 255-5713
Web Site: https://www.demoya.com
Rev.: $30,000,000
Emp.: 10
Builder of Roads, Highways, Side-
walks, Etc: Concrete Construction
N.A.I.C.S.: 237310
Arnando Demoya *(Pres)*
Jillian de Moya *(Mgr-Payroll)*

DE RONDE CASING INTERNA-TIONAL INC.
95 Rapin Pl, Buffalo, NY 14211
Tel.: (716) 897-6690
Sales Range: $10-24.9 Million
Emp.: 13
Truck Tires & Tubes
N.A.I.C.S.: 423130

DE RONDE TIRE SUPPLY, INC.
2010 Elmwood Ave, Buffalo, NY
14207
Tel.: (716) 897-6690   NY
Web Site: https://www.etrucktire.com
Year Founded: 1986
Sales Range: $50-74.9 Million
Emp.: 12
Tire & Tube Merchant Whslr
N.A.I.C.S.: 423130
Jack D. Nys *(Pres)*
John Cesari Jr. *(VP)*

DE SOTO FUELS INC.
614 N Main St, De Soto, MO 63020
Tel.: (636) 337-5500
Web Site: http://www.desotomo.com
Rev.: $17,000,000
Emp.: 10
Petroleum Bulk Stations
N.A.I.C.S.: 424710
Terry Propst *(Pres)*

DE VONS JEWELERS
1151 Galleria Blvd Ste 1080, Rose-
ville, CA 95678
Tel.: (916) 788-4150   CA
Web Site:
   https://www.devonsjewelers.com
Year Founded: 1929
Sales Range: $125-149.9 Million
Emp.: 150
Retailer of Jewelry
N.A.I.C.S.: 458310
Gerald M. Merksamer *(Owner)*
Jon R. Merksamer *(Pres)*
Larry S. Miller *(CEO)*

DE VROOMEN BULB CO., INC.
3850 Clearview Court, Gurnee, IL
60031
Tel.: (847) 395-9911
Web Site: http://www.devroomen.com
Plant Nursery & Garden Products
N.A.I.C.S.: 444240
Angelo Schultz *(Gen Mgr)*

DEACON JONES AUTO GROUP
1115 N Brightleaf Blvd, Smithfield,
NC 27577-4247
Tel.: (919) 934-8101
Web Site:
   http://www.speakindeacon.com
Year Founded: 1978
Sales Range: $25-49.9 Million
Emp.: 80
New Car Retailer
N.A.I.C.S.: 441110
Gary W. Rhodes *(CFO)*

DEACON JONES AUTO PARK
1115 N Bright leaf Blvd, Smithfield,
NC 27577-4247
Tel.: (919) 934-8101

Deacon Jones Auto Park—(Continued)

Web Site:
https://www.deaconjonesgm.com
Year Founded: 1970
Sales Range: $25-49.9 Million
Emp.: 80
New & Used Car Dealers
N.A.I.C.S.: 811111
Bobby Kenneth Jones (Owner)

DEACONESS ABUNDANT LIFE COMMUNITIES
80 Deaconess Rd, Concord, MA 01742
Tel.: (978) 369-5151   MA
Web Site:
http://www.nedeaconess.com
Year Founded: 1889
Sales Range: $25-49.9 Million
Emp.: 450
Retirement Community Operator
N.A.I.C.S.: 623311
Nancy Marzilli (Dir-HR)
Dorene Glynn (Dir-Dev)

DEAD RIVER COMPANY
73 Pleasant Hill Rd, Scarborough, ME 04074
Tel.: (207) 883-9515   ME
Web Site: https://www.deadriver.com
Year Founded: 1907
Sales Range: $450-499.9 Million
Emp.: 1,000
Petroleum Products; Retailer of Non-durable Goods; Service Stations; Miscellaneous Retail Stores & Real Estate Management Services
N.A.I.C.S.: 531120
Deanna Sherman (Pres & CEO)

Subsidiaries:

DR Power LLC   (1)
82 Running Hill Rd, South Portland, ME 04106
Tel.: (207) 358-5800
Heating Oil & Plumbing Equipment Installation Services
N.A.I.C.S.: 238220

Dead River Company - Country
Oil   (1)
540 Northfield Rd, Bernardston, MA 01337
Tel.: (413) 648-9912
Web Site: http://www.deadriver.com
Emp.: 19
Home Heating Oil & Plumbing Installation Services
N.A.I.C.S.: 238220
John Rider (Gen Mgr)

Dead River Company - Fleming Oil
Division   (1)
1 Putney Rd, Brattleboro, VT 05301
Tel.: (802) 254-6095
Web Site: http://www.flemoil.com
Heating Oil & Plumbing Installation Services
N.A.I.C.S.: 238220

Dead River Company - Webber Energy Fuels Division   (1)
700 Main St, Bangor, ME 04401
Tel.: (207) 942-5505
Web Site: http://www.webberenergy.com
Energy Fuel Distr
N.A.I.C.S.: 457210

Dead River Petroleum Co.   (1)
80 Exchange St, Bangor, ME
04401   (100%)
Tel.: (207) 947-8641
Sales Range: $10-24.9 Million
Emp.: 50
Marketer of Petroleum Products; Gasoline, Fuel Oil & Propane
N.A.I.C.S.: 424720
Guy Langevin (VP-HR)

Dead River Properties   (1)
82 Running Hill Rd Ste 400, South Portland, ME 04106   (100%)
Tel.: (207) 773-5868
Web Site: http://www.deadriver.com

Sales Range: $10-24.9 Million
Emp.: 10
Manager of Commercial Real Estate Properties
N.A.I.C.S.: 531120
Anne Littlefield (Gen Mgr)

Dead River Transport   (1)
133 Main St PO Drawer O, Bucksport, ME 04416-1429   (100%)
Tel.: (207) 469-3143
Web Site: http://www.deadriver.com
Sales Range: $10-24.9 Million
Emp.: 50
Trucking Service
N.A.I.C.S.: 424720
Levi Ross (Gen Mgr)
Gary Thebarge (Mgr-Ops)

DEALER IGNITION, LLC
2 N Main St Ste 510, Greenville, SC 29601
Tel.: (864) 569-5204
Web Site:
http://www.dealerignition.com
Year Founded: 2007
Sales Range: $1-9.9 Million
Emp.: 9
Public Relations Promotional Services
N.A.I.C.S.: 541820
Steven Wagner (Founder)

DEALER IMPORTS INC.
17711 Old Statesville Rd, Cornelius, NC 28031
Tel.: (704) 892-0210
Web Site: https://www.dealer-imports.com
Sales Range: $10-24.9 Million
Emp.: 23
Plywood
N.A.I.C.S.: 423310
Herbert W. Eplee (Pres)

DEALER INFO SYSTEMS CORP.
1315 Cornwall Ave, Bellingham, WA 98225
Tel.: (360) 733-7610
Web Site: http://www.dis-corp.com
Sales Range: $10-24.9 Million
Emp.: 120
Computer Software Development
N.A.I.C.S.: 541511
Randy McIntyre (Pres & CEO)
Wende Sanderson (Sr VP-Svs & Dev)
Wendell Knight (VP-Dealer Svs Keystone)
Phillip Conophy (VP-Dev)

DEALER WORLD LLC
531 Seneca Rd, Lehighton, PA 18235   DE
Web Site:
http://www.mydealerworld.com
Year Founded: 2009
Sales Range: $1-9.9 Million
Emp.: 23
Advertising Agency Services
N.A.I.C.S.: 541810
Troy Spring (Founder & CEO)
Mark Ferguson (Gen Mgr)
Hunter Swift (VP-Sls & Client Rels)

DEALER'S AUTO AUCTION GROUP
6723 Highway 51 N, Horn Lake, MS 38637
Tel.: (662) 393-0500
Web Site:
http://www.dealersauto.com
Rev.: $8,600,000
Emp.: 100
Coastal & Great Lakes Freight Transportation
N.A.I.C.S.: 483113

Subsidiaries:

OKI Auto Auction, Inc.   (1)
120 Citycentre Dr, Cincinnati, OH 45216-1622
Tel.: (513) 679-7910
Web Site: http://www.okiautoauction.com
Professional, Scientific & Technical Services
N.A.I.C.S.: 541990
Lee Schoenling (Gen Mgr)

DEALER.COM, INC.
1 Howard St, Burlington, VT 05401
Tel.: (802) 658-0965
Web Site: http://www.dealer.com
Year Founded: 1997
Sales Range: $25-49.9 Million
Emp.: 350
Automotive Internet Marketing Solutions
N.A.I.C.S.: 541519
Mark Bonfigli (Co-Founder)

DEALERON, INC.
7361 Calhoun Pl Ste 420, Derwood, MD 20855
Web Site: http://www.dealeron.com
Year Founded: 2003
Sales Range: $1-9.9 Million
Emp.: 30
Online Marketing Services to the Retail Automotive Industry
N.A.I.C.S.: 541613
Ali Amirrezvani (Owner, Pres & CEO)
Amir Amirrezvani (Co-Founder)
Mark Firoozfar (CTO)
Jeff Clark (Chief Sls Officer)
Shaun Raines (VP-Mktg)

DEALERRATER
203 Crescent St Ste 503, Waltham, MA 02453
Web Site: http://www.dealerrater.com
Year Founded: 2002
Sales Range: $1-9.9 Million
Emp.: 30
Car Dealership Reviewer Website Enabling Consumers Easier Car Shopping Access
N.A.I.C.S.: 441110
Chip Grueter (Founder & Chief Innovation Officer)
Jamie Oldershaw (Sr VP-Product)
Brad Walker (VP-Tech)
Dana Faughnan (Controller)
Lauren Melton (Dir-HR)
Brian Epro (VP-Bus Dev)
Bobby Gaudreau (VP-Sls & Mktg)

DEALERS ALLIANCE CORPORATION
240 N 5th St Ste 350, Columbus, OH 43215
Tel.: (614) 459-0364
Web Site:
http://www.dealersassurance.com
Year Founded: 1977
Sales Range: $10-24.9 Million
Emp.: 14
Direct Insurance Services
N.A.I.C.S.: 524128
Kristen Gruber (Pres)

DEALERS ELECTRICAL SUPPLY CO.
2320 Columbus Ave, Waco, TX 76701-1041
Tel.: (254) 756-7251   TX
Web Site:
https://www.dealerselectrical.net
Year Founded: 1946
Sales Range: $200-249.9 Million
Emp.: 454
Electrical & Construction Supplies Whslr
N.A.I.C.S.: 423610

Anthony Newberg (VP-Sls & Mktg)
David Bryant (Controller)
Valerie Gauer (Mgr-Mktg)
Scott Bracie (CEO)

DEALERS SUPPLY COMPANY
112 S Duke St, Durham, NC 27701
Tel.: (919) 383-7451
Rev.: $61,757,642
Emp.: 70
Floor Coverings
N.A.I.C.S.: 423220
Steven Barringer (VP)
Russell N. Barringer Jr. (CEO)
Russell Barringer III (Pres)

DEALERS SUPPLY COMPANY INC.
82 Kennedy Dr, Forest Park, GA 30297-1708
Tel.: (404) 361-6800
Web Site:
https://www.dealerssupply.net
Year Founded: 1946
Sales Range: $10-24.9 Million
Emp.: 120
Provider of Air Heating & Air Conditioning
N.A.I.C.S.: 423730
Richard Laurens (Pres)

Subsidiaries:

Aladdin Metal Products Inc.   (1)
82 Kennedy Dr, Forest Park, GA 30297-2536
Tel.: (404) 366-2215
Web Site:
http://www.aladdinmetalproducts.com
Sheet Metal Work Mfg
N.A.I.C.S.: 332322
Clayton Barnes (Gen Mgr)
David Shinn (Asst Mgr-Ops)
Matthew Atkins (Mgr-Design & Engrg)
Pepper Norris (Dir-Natl Sls)
Carl Burts (Production Mgr)

DEALERS TRUCK EQUIPMENT CO. INC.
2460 Midway St, Shreveport, LA 71108
Tel.: (318) 635-7567
Web Site:
https://www.dealerstruck.com
Year Founded: 1943
Sales Range: $10-24.9 Million
Emp.: 50
Truck Equipment Distr
N.A.I.C.S.: 336212
Donnie K. Hornsby (VP)

DEALERS UNITED LLC
1680 Fruitville Rd Unit 401, Sarasota, FL 34236
Tel.: (941) 366-6760
Web Site:
https://www.dealersunited.com
Sales Range: $10-24.9 Million
Emp.: 19
Automotive Dealership Business Services
N.A.I.C.S.: 561499
Matt Buchanan (Co-Founder)
Jesse Biter (Co-Founder)

DEALMED MEDICAL SUPPLIES LLC
2361 Nostrand Ave, Brooklyn, NY 11234-4231
Tel.: (718) 332-5633
Web Site: http://www.dealmed.com
Year Founded: 2003
Medical, Dental & Hospital Equipment & Supplies Merchant Whslr
N.A.I.C.S.: 423450
Michael Einhorn (Pres)

Subsidiaries:

Park Surgical Co, Inc. **(1)**
5001 New Utrecht Ave, Brooklyn, NY 11219
Tel.: (718) 436-9200
Web Site: http://www.parksurgical.com
Whol & Ret Medical & Surgical Equipment & Supplies
N.A.I.C.S.: 423450

Vantage Medical Supplies, Inc. **(1)**
194 Morris Ave, Holtsville, NY 11742-1449
Tel.: (631) 207-3313
Web Site:
  http://www.vantagemedicalsupply.com
Medical & Surgical Equipment Mfr & Distr
N.A.I.C.S.: 423450
Christopher Etts *(Pres)*

DEAN & COMPANY

8065 Leesburg Pike 5th Fl, Vienna, VA 22182
Tel.: (703) 506-3900
Web Site: http://www.dean.com
Year Founded: 1993
Sales Range: $1-9.9 Million
Emp.: 120
Strategy Consulting & Investment Services
N.A.I.C.S.: 541611
James Smist *(Pres)*
Dean L. Wilde II *(CEO)*

DEAN & DRAPER INSURANCE AGENCY, LP

3131 W Alabama Ste 150, Houston, TX 77098
Tel.: (713) 527-0444 **TX**
Web Site:
  http://www.deandraper.com
Year Founded: 1980
Sales Range: $10-24.9 Million
Emp.: 100
Insurance Agents Specializing in Personal & Commercial Insurance, Risk Management & Employee Benefits
N.A.I.C.S.: 524210
Bob Dean *(Founder)*
Kyle Dean *(Pres & CEO)*
Gene Darnell *(Sr VP)*
Jeffery Mace Meeks *(Executives)*

DEAN ARBOUR CHEVROLET CADILLAC

1859 N US Hwy 23, East Tawas, MI 48730
Tel.: (989) 362-3403
Web Site:
  http://www.deanarbour.com
Sales Range: $10-24.9 Million
Emp.: 100
Sales of New & Used Automobiles
N.A.I.C.S.: 441110
Dean Arbour *(Owner)*
Bryan Duford *(Gen Mgr & Mgr-New & Used Car)*

DEAN DORTON ALLEN FORD, PLLC

250 W Main St, Ste 1400, Lexington, KY 40507
Tel.: (859) 255-2341
Web Site:
  http://www.deandorton.com
Accounting Firm
N.A.I.C.S.: 541219
David Bundy *(Pres & CEO)*
Danielle Adair *(Dir-Tax Svcs)*

Subsidiaries:

VonLehman & Co. Inc. **(1)**
250 Grandview Dr Ste 300, Fort Mitchell, KY 41017
Tel.: (859) 331-3300
Web Site: http://www.vlcpa.com
Sales Range: $10-24.9 Million
Emp.: 100
Certified Public Accountant & Management Consulting Firm

N.A.I.C.S.: 541611
Kyle Shumate *(Dir-Mktg)*
Deirdre Bird *(Dir-HR Consulting)*
Kyle Taylor *(Principal)*
Adam Davey *(Pres)*

DEAN EVANS & ASSOCIATES, INC.

5613 DTC Pkwy Ste 1250, Greenwood Village, CO 80111
Tel.: (303) 771-0110
Web Site: http://www.dea.com
Year Founded: 1986
Sales Range: $1-9.9 Million
Emp.: 45
Prepackaged Software & Computer Related Services
N.A.I.C.S.: 513210
Dean Evans *(Pres)*

Subsidiaries:

EmergingSoft Corp. **(1)**
6365 Carlson Dr Ste D, Eden Prairie, MN 55346
Tel.: (952) 842-7444
Web Site: http://www.emergingsoft.com
Sales Range: $1-9.9 Million
Emp.: 15
Software Solutions
N.A.I.C.S.: 541512
Matt Quinn *(CEO)*
Blake Pieper *(Project Mgr)*

DEAN FENCE & GATE, INC.

220 N William Dillard Dr, Gilbert, AZ 85233
Tel.: (480) 969-4995
Web Site: http://www.deanfence.com
Year Founded: 1989
Sales Range: $10-24.9 Million
Emp.: 150
Architectural Metal Work Mfr
N.A.I.C.S.: 332323
Dwayne T. Dean *(Pres)*

DEAN FOODS COMPANY

2711 N Haskell Ave Ste 3400, Dallas, TX 75204
Tel.: (214) 303-3400 **DE**
Web Site: http://www.deanfoods.com
Year Founded: 1925
Rev.: $7,755,283,000
Assets: $2,118,492,000
Liabilities: $1,803,760,000
Net Worth: $314,732,000
Earnings: ($326,900,000)
Emp.: 15,000
Fiscal Year-end: 12/31/18
Milk & Dairy Products, Soymilk & Organic Food Products Mfr & Distr
N.A.I.C.S.: 311520
David Bernard *(CIO & Sr VP)*
Jose A. Motta *(Sr VP-HR)*
Chris Finck *(Chief Sls Officer & Sr VP)*
Eric Beringause *(Pres & CEO)*

Subsidiaries:

Broughton Foods LLC **(1)**
1701 Greene St, Marietta, OH 45750-9816
Tel.: (740) 373-4121
Web Site: http://www.broughtonfoods.com
Dairy & Non-Dairy Foods Processor & Distr
N.A.I.C.S.: 311511

Country Delite **(1)**
1401 Church St, Nashville, TN 37203-3428 **(100%)**
Tel.: (615) 320-1440
Sales Range: $50-74.9 Million
Emp.: 150
Production Of Milk
N.A.I.C.S.: 311511
Jeff Brown *(Gen Mgr-Sls)*

Country Fresh, Inc. **(1)**
3200 Research Forest Dr Ste A5, The Woodlands, TX 77381
Tel.: (281) 453-3300
Web Site: http://www.countryfreshinc.com
Rev.: $375,000,000

Emp.: 300
Mfr & Distr of Milk, Ice Cream, Cottage Cheese & Yogurt
N.A.I.C.S.: 424430
Bill Riley *(Gen Mgr)*

Country Fresh, LLC **(1)**
3200 Research Forest Dr, Spring, TX 77381
Tel.: (281) 453-3300
Web Site: http://www.countryfreshinc.com
Fruit & Vegetable Distr
N.A.I.C.S.: 424480

DF-AP#1, LLC **(1)**
6920 Salashan Pkwy A-102, Ferndale, WA 98248-8320
Tel.: (501) 868-6400
Eletric Power Generation Services
N.A.I.C.S.: 221118

Dairy Fresh, LLC **(1)**
2221 Patterson Ave, Winston Salem, NC 27105 **(100%)**
Tel.: (336) 723-0311
Web Site: http://www.dairyfresh.com
Sales Range: $100-124.9 Million
N.A.I.C.S.: 332439

Dean Dairy Holdings, LLC **(1)**
2711 N Oscar Ave, Dallas, TX 75201
Tel.: (214) 303-3400
Web Site: http://www.deanfoods.com
Sales Range: $250-299.9 Million
Investment Holding Company
N.A.I.C.S.: 551112

Subsidiary (Domestic):

Alta-Dena Certified Dairy, LLC **(2)**
17637 E Valley Blvd, City of Industry, CA 91744 **(100%)**
Tel.: (626) 964-6401
Web Site: http://www.altadenadairy.com
Sales Range: $250-299.9 Million
Emp.: 500
Dairy Products Mfr
N.A.I.C.S.: 311511
Larry Sewell *(Plant Mgr)*

Barber Dairies, Inc. **(2)**
36 Barber Ct, Birmingham, AL 35209
Tel.: (205) 942-2351
Web Site: http://www.barbersdairy.com
Sales Range: $400-449.9 Million
Emp.: 750
Processor & Packager of Milk & Milk Products
N.A.I.C.S.: 311511

Berkeley Farms, LLC **(2)**
25500 Clawiter Rd, Hayward, CA 94545 **(100%)**
Tel.: (510) 265-8600
Web Site: http://www.berkeleyfarms.com
Sales Range: $150-199.9 Million
Emp.: 300
N.A.I.C.S.: 311511

Creamland Dairies, Inc. **(2)**
10 Indian School Rd NW, Albuquerque, NM 87102 **(100%)**
Tel.: (505) 247-0721
Web Site: http://www.creamland.com
Sales Range: $25-49.9 Million
Emp.: 40
Processor & Distributor of Dairy Products
N.A.I.C.S.: 311511

Subsidiary (Domestic):

Creamland Dairies, Inc. **(3)**
PO Box 25067, Albuquerque, NM 87121 **(100%)**
Tel.: (800) 334-3865
Web Site: http://www.creamland.com
Producer of Ice Cream & Dairy Products
N.A.I.C.S.: 311520

Subsidiary (Domestic):

Dean Dairy Products Company, LLC **(2)**
1690 Oneida Ln, Sharpsville, PA 16150 **(100%)**
Tel.: (724) 962-7801
Web Site: http://deandairy.com
Sales Range: $75-99.9 Million
Emp.: 400
Processor & Distributor of Dairy Products

N.A.I.C.S.: 311511
Ralph Scozafava *(CEO)*
Bill Reilly *(Gen Mgr)*

Dean Foods Company of Indiana, LLC **(2)**
1700 Old US 31 N, Rochester, IN 46975 **(100%)**
Tel.: (574) 223-2141
Web Site: http://www.deanfoods.com
Sales Range: $100-124.9 Million
Emp.: 200
N.A.I.C.S.: 311511

Dean Milk Company, LLC **(2)**
4420 Bishop Ln, Louisville, KY 40218 **(100%)**
Tel.: (502) 451-9111
Web Site: http://www.deanfoods.com
Sales Range: $75-99.9 Million
Emp.: 160
Mfr of Fresh Milk, Ice Cream, Cottage Cheese & Related Dairy Products; Powdered Non-Dairy Creamers;
N.A.I.C.S.: 311511

Gandy's Dairies, LLC **(2)**
201 University Ave, Lubbock, TX 79415-3426 **(100%)**
Tel.: (806) 765-8833
Sales Range: $75-99.9 Million
Emp.: 150
Processor & Distributor of Dairy Products
N.A.I.C.S.: 311511
Steve Garish *(Gen Mgr)*

Land-O-Sun Dairies LLC **(2)**
2900 Bristol Hwy, Johnson City, TN 37601-1502
Tel.: (423) 283-5700
Web Site: http://www.petdairy.com
Emp.: 60
Mfr of Ice Cream, Fresh Milk, Other Dairy Products & Fruit Juices, Drinks & Beverages
N.A.I.C.S.: 311511

Mayfield Dairy Farms, LLC **(2)**
806 E Madison Ave, Athens, TN 37303-3858 **(100%)**
Tel.: (423) 745-2151
Web Site: http://www.mayfielddairy.com
Sales Range: $300-349.9 Million
Emp.: 1,700
Mfr Of Fluid Milk & Ice Cream
N.A.I.C.S.: 311511

Branch (Domestic):

Mayfield Dairy Farms **(3)**
1160 Broadway Ave, Braselton, GA 30517
Tel.: (706) 654-9180
Web Site: http://www.mayfielddairy.com
Sales Range: $50-74.9 Million
Emp.: 150
Mfr of Fresh Milk, Ice Cream, Cottage Cheese & Related Dairy Products; Powdered Non-Dairy Creamers;
N.A.I.C.S.: 311511

Subsidiary (Domestic):

McArthur Dairy, LLC **(2)**
240 NE 71st St, Miami, FL 33138 **(100%)**
Tel.: (305) 576-2880
Web Site: http://www.deanfoods.com
Sales Range: $150-199.9 Million
Dairy Products Mfr
N.A.I.C.S.: 112120

Meadow Brook Dairy Company **(2)**
2365 Buffalo Rd, Erie, PA 16510 **(100%)**
Tel.: (814) 899-3191
Web Site:
  http://www.meadowbrookdairy.com
Sales Range: $350-399.9 Million
Mfr of Fresh Milk & Related Dairy Products
N.A.I.C.S.: 311511

Model Dairy **(2)**
500 Guld St, Reno, NV 89502
Tel.: (775) 788-7900
Sales Range: $50-74.9 Million
Emp.: 100
N.A.I.C.S.: 332439
Derek Allbee *(Gen Mgr-Sls)*
Paul Horsley *(Engr-Maintenance)*

Oak Farms/Schepps Dairy **(2)**
3114 S Haskell Ave, Dallas, TX 75223

Dean Foods Company—(Continued)

Tel.: (214) 824-8163
Rev.: $915,000,000
Emp.: 500
Dairy Products Mfr
N.A.I.C.S.: 311511
Tom Davis (VP & Gen Mgr)

Purity Dairies, LLC (2)
360 Murfreesboro Rd, Nashville, TN
37210-2816 (100%)
Tel.: (615) 244-1900
Web Site: http://www.puritydairies.com
Sales Range: $250-299.9 Million
Emp.: 500
Milk Production & Dairy Products Mfr
N.A.I.C.S.: 112120

Plant (Domestic):

Purity Dairies - Hohenwald Plant (3)
320 Summertown Hwy, Hohenwald, TN
38462-1926
Tel.: (931) 796-1238
Web Site: http://www.puritydairies.com
Sales Range: $25-49.9 Million
Emp.: 25
Ice Cream Mfr
N.A.I.C.S.: 311520

Subsidiary (Domestic):

Reiter Dairy, LLC (2)
1961 Commerce Cir, Springfield, OH
45504 (100%)
Tel.: (937) 323-5777
Web Site: http://www.reiterdairy.com
Sales Range: $100-124.9 Million
Emp.: 190
Ice Cream Noveltie Mfr
N.A.I.C.S.: 311511

Branch (Domestic):

Reiter Dairy, LLC (3)
1415 W Waterloo Rd, Akron, OH
44314-1544 (100%)
Tel.: (330) 745-1123
Web Site: http://www.reiterdairy.com
Sales Range: $125-149.9 Million
Emp.: 100
Processor & Distributor of Milk & Ice Cream
N.A.I.C.S.: 311511

Subsidiary (Domestic):

Santee Dairies, Inc. (2)
17851 E Railroad St, City of Industry, CA
91748 (100%)
Tel.: (626) 923-3058
Web Site: http://www.heartlandfarms.com
Sales Range: $100-124.9 Million
Emp.: 400
Dairy & Specialty Food Products
N.A.I.C.S.: 311511

Swiss Premium Dairy, LLC (2)
2401 Walnut St, Lebanon, PA
17042-9444 (100%)
Tel.: (717) 273-2658
Web Site: http://www.deanfoods.com
Sales Range: $75-99.9 Million
Emp.: 160
Mfr of Processed Milk & Fruit Drinks
N.A.I.C.S.: 311511

Dean Foods Company (1)
1126 Kilburn Ave, Rockford, IL 61101
Tel.: (815) 962-0647
Sales Range: $100-124.9 Million
Emp.: 200
N.A.I.C.S.: 311511

Dean Foods Company (1)
11713 Mill St, Huntley, IL 60142
Tel.: (847) 669-5123
Sales Range: $250-299.9 Million
N.A.I.C.S.: 311511

Dean Foods North Central, LLC (1)
1200 W Russell St, Sioux Falls, SD 57104
Tel.: (605) 336-1958
Dairy Products Mfr
N.A.I.C.S.: 311514

Dean's Ice Cream (1)
1253 Kingsland Dr, Batavia, IL
60510-1324 (100%)
Tel.: (630) 879-0800

Sales Range: $75-99.9 Million
Emp.: 100
N.A.I.C.S.: 424430

Friendlys Manufacturing and Retail, LLC (1)
1855 Boston Rd, Wilbraham, MA 01095
Tel.: (800) 966-9970
Web Site: http://www.friendlys.com
Frozen Dessert Mfr
N.A.I.C.S.: 311520
Martha Leyburn (VP-Creamery Ops)

Garelick Farms, LLC (1)
1199 W Central St, Franklin, MA
02038 (100%)
Tel.: (508) 528-9000
Web Site: http://www.garelickfarms.com
Sales Range: $300-349.9 Million
Emp.: 650
Milk Whslr
N.A.I.C.S.: 424430

Subsidiary (Domestic):

Garelick Farms, LLC (2)
626 Lynnway, Lynn, MA
01905-3030 (100%)
Tel.: (781) 599-1300
Web Site: http://www.garelickfarms.com
Sales Range: $300-349.9 Million
Emp.: 650
Milk Processing; Fruit Juices; Ice Cream; Food Preparations; Dairy Products, Except Dried or Canned
N.A.I.C.S.: 311511

Marie's Salad Dressing (1)
201 W Armory Dr, Thornton, IL 60476-1044
Tel.: (708) 877-5150
Sales Range: $25-49.9 Million
Emp.: 47
Mfr Of Food
N.A.I.C.S.: 311941
Jeff Lawson (Plant Mgr)

Midwest Ice Cream Company, LLC (1)
630 Meadow St, Belvidere, IL 61008
Tel.: (815) 544-2105
Emp.: 104
Fluid Milk Mfr
N.A.I.C.S.: 311511
Dale Flotz (Gen Mgr)

Sampson Ventures, LLC (1)
2115 N Hillridge, Mesa, AZ 85207
Tel.: (480) 354-0767
Milk Whslr
N.A.I.C.S.: 424430
Solomon Sampson (Pres)

Uncle Matt's Organic Inc. (1)
PO Box 120187, Clermont, FL 34712
Tel.: (352) 394-1003
Web Site: http://www.unclematts.com
Fruit Beverage Mfr
N.A.I.C.S.: 311421
Matt McLean (Founder & CEO)

DEAN JOHNSTON INC.
207 San Jacinto Blvd, Austin, TX
78701
Tel.: (512) 477-3747
Web Site:
    http://www.deanjohnston.com
Sales Range: $10-24.9 Million
Emp.: 300
Electrical Wiring Services
N.A.I.C.S.: 238210
Judith Hyatt (Principal)

DEAN KURTZ CONSTRUC-TION
1651 Rand Rd, Rapid City, SD 57702
Tel.: (605) 343-6665
Web Site:
    https://www.deankurtzconstruction.com
Year Founded: 1971
Sales Range: $25-49.9 Million
Emp.: 46
Commercial & Institutional Building Construction Services
N.A.I.C.S.: 236220

Bradley D. Kurtz (Pres)
Stephen F. Burgess (VP-Ops)
Rae Simpson (Treas & Sec)
Kasey L. Kurtz (Project Mgr)

DEAN LUMBER & SUPPLY CO.
24425 3 Notch Rd, Hollywood, MD
20636
Tel.: (301) 373-2111
Web Site: http://www.dean-lumber.com
Year Founded: 1920
Sales Range: $10-24.9 Million
Emp.: 60
Lumber Product Whslr
N.A.I.C.S.: 423310
Mike Derby (Gen Mgr)
Eric Dean (Mgr-Sls)

DEAN MARKLEY STRINGS, INC.
3350 Scott Blvd Ste 45, Santa Clara, CA 95054
Tel.: (408) 988-2456
Web Site:
    http://www.deanmarkley.com
Year Founded: 1971
Sales Range: $10-24.9 Million
Emp.: 20
Musical Instrument Mfr
N.A.I.C.S.: 339992
Dean Markley (Owner & Pres)
Jon Rooff (Mgr-Sls)

DEAN OPERATIONS, INC.
5701 E 87th St, Kansas City, MO
64132
Tel.: (816) 753-5300 MO
Year Founded: 1955
Sales Range: $200-249.9 Million
Emp.: 350
Holding Company; Distributor of Construction & Paving Equipment; Commercial Real Estate Subdividers & Developers
N.A.I.C.S.: 551112
Paul Hoffman (CFO)
Bill Jackson (Bus Dev Mgr)
Joyce Hess (Controller)
Michael Claytool (Mgr-Pur)

Subsidiaries:

Dean Realty Co (1)
1201 W 31st St Ste 2, Kansas City, MO
64108
Tel.: (816) 531-0800
Web Site: http://www.deanrealtyco.com
Sales Range: $25-49.9 Million
Emp.: 30
Realty Services
N.A.I.C.S.: 237210
Walt Clements (Pres & CEO)

Foley Equipment Company (1)
5701 E 87th St, Kansas City, MO
64132 (100%)
Tel.: (816) 753-5300
Web Site: http://www.foleyeq.com
Sales Range: $25-49.9 Million
Emp.: 300
Machinery Dealers
N.A.I.C.S.: 423810
Shane Ham (COO)
Joel Burke (CIO)

DEAN ROOFING CO. INC.
5525 Cameron St, Las Vegas, NV
89118
Tel.: (702) 876-2630
Web Site: http://www.dean-roofing.co.uk
Year Founded: 1954
Rev.: $15,000,000
Emp.: 200
Roofing Contracting Services
N.A.I.C.S.: 238160
Jerry Dean (Pres)
Leila Dean (Sec)
Dennis Dean (VP)

DEAN SAUSAGE COMPANY INC.
3750 Pleasant Valley Rd, Attalla, AL
35954
Tel.: (256) 538-6082
Web Site:
    https://www.deansausage.com
Sales Range: $10-24.9 Million
Emp.: 100
Hog Breakfast Sausage Mfr
N.A.I.C.S.: 311612
Marsue D. Lancaster (Pres)

DEAN SELLERS FORD INC.
2600 W Maple Rd, Troy, MI 48084-7133
Tel.: (248) 643-7500 MI
Web Site:
    http://www.deansellersford.com
Sales Range: $10-24.9 Million
Emp.: 100
Sales of Automobiles
N.A.I.C.S.: 441110
Thomas D. Sellers (Pres)
Dean Sellers (Gen Mgr-Sls)
Liz Sellers (Gen Mgr)
Barbara Smith (Comptroller)
Chuck Barr (Mgr-Parts)
Fred Klein (Mgr-Fin Svcs)
Dan Paul (Mgr-Fin Svcs)
Brendt Henry (Mgr-New Car)
Jim Bogdanski (Mgr-New Vehicle Sls & Fleet)
Shareek Asgarally (Mgr-Svc-Columbus)
Steve Miller (Mgr-Used Car)

DEAN SNYDER CONSTRUC-TION COMPANY
913 N 14th St, Clear Lake, IA 50428
Tel.: (641) 357-2283
Web Site:
    http://www.deansnyderconst.com
Year Founded: 1958
Emp.: 230
Provider of Construction Services
N.A.I.C.S.: 236220
Donald Snyder (Pres)
Dale Snyder (CEO, Treas & Sec)
David Snyder (VP)
Brian Carrott (Dir-HR)

DEAN STEEL BUILDINGS INC.
2929 Industrial Ave, Fort Myers, FL
33901
Tel.: (239) 334-1051
Web Site:
    https://www.deansteelbuildings.com
Rev.: $14,341,300
Emp.: 100
Prefabricated Metal Buildings
N.A.I.C.S.: 332311

DEAN WORD COMPANY LTD.
1245 River Rd, New Braunfels, TX
78130
Tel.: (830) 625-2365
Web Site: https://www.deanword.com
Sales Range: $25-49.9 Million
Emp.: 250
General Contractor, Highway & Street Construction
N.A.I.C.S.: 237310
Dean Word (Gen Mgr)

DEAN'S PROFESSIONAL SER-VICES, INC.
11511 Katy Fwy Ste 430, Houston,
TX 77079
Tel.: (713) 785-7483 TX

Web Site:
https://www.deansprofessional
services.com
Year Founded: 1993
Sales Range: $1-9.9 Million
Emp.: 560
Employment Placement & Consulting
N.A.I.C.S.: 561311
Jennifer Dean *(Pres & CEO)*
Mike Dean *(VP)*
Shannon Divers *(Dir-HR & Branch Mgr)*
Tiffany Dean-Wright *(Exec Dir-Mktg)*

DEANCO AUCTION & REAL ESTATE CO, INC.
3664 S Oates St, Dothan, AL 36301
Tel.: (334) 677-3192
Web Site:
https://www.deancoauction.com
Rev.: $25,000,000
Emp.: 12
Automobile & Other Motor Vehicle Merchant Whslr
N.A.I.C.S.: 423110
Holly Roberts *(Office Mgr)*
Donnie W. Dean *(Owner & Pres)*

DEANGELIS DIAMOND CON-STRUCTION, INC.
6635 Willow Park Dr, Naples, FL 34109
Tel.: (239) 594-1994   FL
Web Site:
https://www.deangelisdiamond.com
Year Founded: 1996
Sales Range: $100-124.9 Million
Emp.: 73
Single-Family House & Industrial Construction
N.A.I.C.S.: 236115
David B. Diamond *(Co-Founder & CEO)*
John M. DeAngelis *(Co-Founder)*
Robert Lewis *(Partner-Birmingham)*
David Kovalik *(VP-Project Mgmt)*
Brian Hood *(VP-Field Ops)*
Chris Curran *(VP-Preconstruction & Estimating)*
Reggie Morgan *(COO-Healthcare Grp)*
Jason Sain *(Principal & Exec VP)*
Grant Goebel *(CFO)*
Kaisa Schmidt *(VP-Mktg & PR)*
B. J. Brundage *(VP-Strategic Dev)*
Nick Pair *(Dir-Field Ops)*
Brett Diamond *(Chief Admin Officer)*
Heath Cahoon *(Dir-Preconstruction-Nashville)*

DEANHOUSTON, INC.
625 Eden Park Dr Ste 1000, Cincinnati, OH 45202
Tel.: (513) 421-6622
Web Site:
http://www.deanhouston.com
Year Founded: 1988
Sales Range: $1-9.9 Million
Emp.: 35
Full-Service, Business-to-Business Marketing Communications
N.A.I.C.S.: 541613
Chris Ryan *(VP-Client Svcs)*
Eric Hirth *(Mgr-Publicity & Media)*
Rene Normand *(Mgr-HR)*
Mike Seta *(Dir-Brand Strategy)*
Tim Essex *(Acct Mgr)*
Andrew Yunker *(Mgr-Content)*
Chris Fryburger *(Dir-Digital)*
Cris Davis *(Acct Mgr)*
Jamie Grabert *(Dir-Media)*

DEANNA ENTERPRISES INC.
2125 Biscayne Blvd # 205, Miami, FL 33137
Tel.: (305) 573-0333

Web Site:
http://www.a1aemployment.com
Sales Range: $10-24.9 Million
Emp.: 17
Employment Agencies
N.A.I.C.S.: 561311
Veldrin D. Freemon *(Pres & CEO)*

DEANNES OFFICE & COM-PUTER SUPPLIES
3360 Raymond Diehl Business Ln, Tallahassee, FL 32308
Tel.: (850) 385-5555
Web Site: http://www.docs-usa.com
Year Founded: 1988
Sales Range: $25-49.9 Million
Emp.: 60
Office Supplies Furniture
N.A.I.C.S.: 424120
Michelle Bembry *(VP-Design)*
Susie Maynard *(Founder & Pres)*

DEANS OIL COMPANY INC.
3537 Airport Blvd, Wilson, NC 27896
Tel.: (252) 237-2712
Sales Range: $10-24.9 Million
Emp.: 21
Propane Gas, Bottled
N.A.I.C.S.: 457210
John F. Deans *(Pres)*
Roland Lucas *(Office Mgr)*

DEANS RV SUPERSTORE INC.
9005 E Skelly Dr, Tulsa, OK 74129
Tel.: (918) 664-3333
Web Site: http://www.deansrv.com
Year Founded: 1971
Emp.: 50
Recreational Vehicles, Travel Trailers & Motorhomes Sales & Services
N.A.I.C.S.: 441210
Randy Coy *(Owner)*
Dan Ziemann *(Controller)*
Steve Darnell *(Mgr-Fin)*
Chris Coy *(Mgr-Mktg)*
Tom Morgan *(Dir-Mktg)*

DEAR GARDEN ASSOCIATES, INC.
6746 Old Easton Rd, Pipersville, PA 18947
Tel.: (215) 766-8110
Web Site:
http://www.deargarden.com
Sales Range: $1-9.9 Million
Emp.: 30
Garden Maintenance Services
N.A.I.C.S.: 444240
Bill Dear *(Founder & Principal)*
Darren Sandvik *(Project Mgr)*
Adam Cressman *(Mgr-Landscape Ops)*
Kelly Murphy *(Office Mgr)*

DEARBORN COUNTY HOSPI-TAL
600 Wilson Creek Rd, Lawrenceburg, IN 47025
Tel.: (812) 537-1010   IN
Web Site: http://www.dch.org
Year Founded: 1977
Sales Range: $10-24.9 Million
Emp.: 850
Health Care Srvices
N.A.I.C.S.: 622110
Roger D. Howard *(Pres & CEO)*
Michael Schwebler *(Pres & CEO)*

DEARBORN CRANE & ENGI-NEERING CO.
1133 E 5th St, Mishawaka, IN 46544
Tel.: (574) 259-2444
Web Site:
https://www.dearborncrane.com
Year Founded: 1947
Sales Range: $10-24.9 Million

Bridge Crane Mfr
N.A.I.C.S.: 333923
Joan Mansfield *(VP & Gen Mgr)*
Dan Yeakey *(Mgr-Svc)*
Simon Addicott *(Pres)*

Subsidiaries:

NAI Cranes, LLC   (1)
80 Holton St, Woburn, MA 01801-5205
Tel.: (781) 897-4100
Web Site: http://www.naicranes.com
Industrial Machinery Mfr
N.A.I.C.S.: 333248
George Wheelwright *(VP-Sls & Mktg)*

DEARBORN FEDERAL SAV-INGS BANK
22315 Michigan Ave, Dearborn, MI 48124
Tel.: (313) 565-3100
Sales Range: $25-49.9 Million
Emp.: 40
Federal Savings Bank
N.A.I.C.S.: 522180
William R. White *(Pres)*
Scott Biers *(Loan Officer)*
Bryan Laabs *(Loan Officer)*

DEARBORN MOVING & STOR-AGE INC.
7441 Haggerty Rd, Canton, MI 48187
Tel.: (734) 207-8200
Web Site:
https://www.dmsmoving.com
Rev.: $10,513,083
Emp.: 60
Household Goods Transport
N.A.I.C.S.: 484210

DEARBORN RESOURCES, INC.
2130 Inwood, Houston, TX 77019
Tel.: (713) 521-1950
Year Founded: 2006
Holding Company
N.A.I.C.S.: 551112
Gregory Curran *(Owner & CEO)*

Subsidiaries:

U.S. Pipeline, Inc.   (1)
8100 Washington Ave Ste 200, Houston, TX 77007
Tel.: (281) 531-6100
Web Site: http://www.uspipeline.com
Sales Range: $250-299.9 Million
Emp.: 1,500
Pipelines & Energy Infrastructure Construction
N.A.I.C.S.: 237110
Lowell Brien *(VP-Ops)*
Kelly Osborn *(Pres)*
Ryan Palazzo *(VP-Ops)*
Kevin Franzen *(Dir-Safety)*
Luke Kesner *(Dir-Project Controls)*
Bret Roper *(CFO)*
Brad Vickers *(Dir-Estimating)*

DEARBORN WHOLESALE GROCERS LP
2801 S Western Ave, Chicago, IL 60608-5220
Tel.: (773) 254-4300   IL
Web Site:
http://www.dearbornwholesale.com
Year Founded: 1938
Sales Range: $25-49.9 Million
Emp.: 450
General Line Groceries
N.A.I.C.S.: 424410
Sandra Nunez *(Mgr-Human Resources)*

DEARDEN'S
700 S Main St, Los Angeles, CA 90014-2013
Tel.: (213) 362-9600   CA
Web Site: http://www.deardens.com
Year Founded: 1909

Sales Range: $200-249.9 Million
Emp.: 600
Retailer of Furniture, Appliances, TV & Audio Equipment & Fine Jewelry
N.A.I.C.S.: 449110
Raquel Bensimon *(Chm & CEO)*
Ronny A. Bensimon *(Pres & COO)*
William Opdike *(Sec)*
James S. Anderson *(CFO)*
Salvador Ahumada *(Mgr-LP)*
Angel Lopez *(VP-Sls)*
Frank MacLean Jr. *(Mgr-Wireless Dept)*

DEARDORFF-JACKSON COM-PANY
400 N Lombart St, Oxnard, CA 93030
Tel.: (805) 487-7801   CA
Web Site:
http://www.deardorfffamilyfarms.com
Year Founded: 1947
Sales Range: $100-124.9 Million
Emp.: 200
Grower & Shipper of Fresh Fruits & Vegetables
N.A.I.C.S.: 424480
Tom D. Deardorff *(Pres)*
Scott Deardorff *(Treas)*

DEARING & DEARING
132 S Carroll Ave, Dallas, TX 75226
Tel.: (214) 823-3410
Rev.: $14,000,000
Emp.: 44
Liquor Stores
N.A.I.C.S.: 445320
David Dearing *(Chm)*

DEARYBURY OIL & GAS INC.
2558 Southport Rd, Spartanburg, SC 29302
Tel.: (864) 585-6226
Web Site:
http://www.dearyburylpg.com
Rev.: $57,500,011
Emp.: 19
Petroleum Products Mfr
N.A.I.C.S.: 424720
C. W. Dearybury Jr. *(Pres)*

DEATH VALLEY CONSER-VANCY
PO Box 566, Death Valley, CA 92328
Tel.: (760) 263-4900   CA
Web Site:
http://www.dvconservancy.org
Year Founded: 2008
Sales Range: $10-24.9 Million
Emp.: 2
Nature Reserves
N.A.I.C.S.: 712190
Henry Golas *(Treas & Sec)*
Kari Krusmark *(VP)*
Preston Chiaro *(Pres)*

DEATLEY CRUSHING COM-PANY
4307 Snake River Ave, Lewiston, ID 83501
Tel.: (208) 743-6550
Web Site:
https://www.deatleycrushing.com
Sales Range: $10-24.9 Million
Emp.: 85
Slate, Crushed & Broken-Quarrying
N.A.I.C.S.: 212319
Brian N. Deatley *(Pres)*

DEAUVILLE HOTEL MANAGE-MENT, LLC
6701 Collins Ave, Miami Beach, FL 33141
Tel.: (305) 865-8511   FL
Web Site:
http://www.deauvillebeachresort.com
Sales Range: $10-24.9 Million

Deauville Hotel Management, LLC—(Continued)
Emp.: 250
Hotels (except Casino Hotels) & Motels
N.A.I.C.S.: 721110
Guillermo Tenaglia (Mgr-IT)
Belinda Meruelo (Owner & Pres)

DEB CONSTRUCTION
2230 E Winston Rd, Anaheim, CA 92806
Tel.: (714) 632-6680
Web Site:
https://www.debconstruction.com
Sales Range: $10-24.9 Million
Emp.: 20
Bank Building Construction
N.A.I.C.S.: 236220

DEB WHOLESALE, INC.
1216 American Way, Watertown, WI 53094
Tel.: (920) 261-8094
Web Site:
https://store.debwholesale.com
Sales Range: $10-24.9 Million
Emp.: 40
Confectionery Whslr
N.A.I.C.S.: 424450
Tom Behling (Pres)
Stacey Heinzelman (VP-Ops)

DEBARTOLO CORPORATION
7620 Market St, Youngstown, OH 44512
Tel.: (330) 965-2000
Year Founded: 1944
Sales Range: $200-249.9 Million
Emp.: 12
Holding Company
N.A.I.C.S.: 551112
Marie Denise DeBartolo York (Chm & CEO)
Pamela Vidmar (CFO)
John C. York II (Pres)

Subsidiaries:

San Francisco Forty Niners, Ltd. (1)
4949 Centennial Blvd, Santa Clara, CA 95054-1229
Tel.: (408) 562-4949
Web Site: http://www.49ers.com
Sales Range: $50-74.9 Million
Professional Football Franchise
N.A.I.C.S.: 711211
Jim Mercurio (VP-Stadium Ops)
Paraag Marathe (Pres)
Guy McIntyre (Dir-Alumni Rels)
M. Denise DeBartolo York (Co-Chm)
Jed York (CEO)
Keena Turner (VP-Football Affairs)
Steve Risser (Mgr-Team Logistics)
Bob Sargent (Dir-Brdcst Partnerships)
Trent Baalke (Gen Mgr)
Dan Cory (VP-Security)
Hannah Gordon (Chief Admin Officer & Gen Counsel)
Al Guido (Pres)
Brano Perkovich (Chief Investment Officer)
Scott Sabatino (CFO)
John M. Sobrato (Owner)
Mark Wan (Owner)

DEBARTOLO HOLDINGS, LLC
15436 N Florida Ave Ste 200, Tampa, FL 33613
Tel.: (813) 908-8400
Web Site:
http://www.debartoloholdings.com
Year Founded: 1955
Sales Range: $10-24.9 Million
Emp.: 50
Diversified Holding Company; Real Estate & Property Services
N.A.I.C.S.: 551112
Edward J. DeBartolo Jr. (Founder & CEO)
Cynthia R. DeBartolo (Exec VP)

Lisa M. DeBartolo (Exec VP)
Geza Henni (Pres)
David S. Mallitz (CFO & Exec VP)
James D. Palermo (Gen Counsel & Exec VP)
Linda Pearce (Mgr-HR)
Valerie Panou (VP-Mktg & Comm)

Subsidiaries:

D-Terra Solutions LLC (1)
35 Clairedan Dr, Powell, OH 43065
Tel.: (614) 450-1040
Web Site: http://www.dterrasolutions.com
Supply Chain Management Services
N.A.I.C.S.: 541614
Aaron Dryer (Chief Comml Officer)
Denis Bruncak (CEO)
Mike Billman (Sr VP-Sls & Mktg)
Mike Minichello (CFO)
Shawn Dodson (COO)

DeBartolo Development, LLC (1)
4401 W Kennedy Blvd 3rd Fl, Tampa, FL 33609
Tel.: (813) 676-7677
Web Site:
http://www.debartolodevelopment.com
Emp.: 15
Real Estate Developers
N.A.I.C.S.: 531390
Edward M. Kobel (Pres & COO)
Drew M. Barkett (Exec VP)

DeBartolo Family Foundation (1)
15436 N Florida Ave Ste 200, Tampa, FL 33613
Tel.: (813) 908-8400
Web Site:
http://www.debartolofamilyfoundation.com
Sales Range: $10-24.9 Million
Emp.: 1
Foundation
N.A.I.C.S.: 813211
Mellisa Johnson (Coord-Foundation)

Ed & Eddie's Ice Cream (1)
2227 S Dale Mabry, Tampa, FL 33629
Tel.: (813) 251-6300
Homemade Ice Cream Shop
N.A.I.C.S.: 445298

Famiglia - DeBartolo, LLC (1)
199 Main St 8th Fl, White Plains, NY 10601
Tel.: (914) 328-4444
Web Site: http://www.famousfamiglia.com
Pizza Restaurant Franchise
N.A.I.C.S.: 722511
Giorgio Kolaj (Co-Founder & Global Bus Dev)
John Kolaj (Co-Founder & COO)
Paul Kolaj (Co-Founder & CEO)

Hytec Automotive (1)
11400 NW 34th St, Doral, FL 33178
Tel.: (786) 279-9090
Web Site: http://www.hytecauto.com
Motor Vehicle & Marine Vehicle Water Pump Mfr & Supplier
N.A.I.C.S.: 333914

DEBBIE'S STAFFING SERVICES
4431 N Cherry St, Winston Salem, NC 27105
Tel.: (336) 776-1717
Web Site:
https://www.debbiesstaffing.com
Rev.: $30,400,000
Emp.: 15
Temporary Help Service
N.A.I.C.S.: 561320
Heinz Little (Pres)
Karen Stevens (Reg Mgr)
Linda Smoak (Branch Mgr)
Denny Kallam (Mgr-Safety)
Eddie Bello (Mgr-Onsite)
Patricia Handsome (Branch Mgr)
William Dixon (Coord-Safety)
Patty Bare (Mgr-Payroll)
Ashley Pyatt (Branch Mgr)
Debbie Little (Founder)

DEBEVOISE & PLIMPTON LLP
919 3rd Ave, New York, NY 10022

Tel.: (212) 909-6000
Web Site: http://www.debevoise.com
Year Founded: 1931
Sales Range: $650-699.9 Million
Emp.: 1,400
Legal Advisory Services
N.A.I.C.S.: 541110
Daniel M. Abuhoff (Partner)
Andrew L. Bab (Partner)
Jasmine Ball (Partner)
William B. Beekman (Partner)
David H. Bernstein (Partner)
Paul S. Bird (Partner)
Richard D. Bohm (Partner)
Ezra Borut (Partner)
Craig A. Bowman (Partner)
David A. Brittenham (Partner)
Paul D. Brusiloff (Partner)
Julie M. Riewe (Partner-Washington)
Mark P. Goodman (Partner)
Sarah A. W. Fitts (Partner)
Brian E. Liu (Partner)
Lee Schneider (Head-Broker Dealer & FinTech Practices)
Ted Hassi (Partner-Washington)
John T. Curry III (Chm-Aviation Practice Grp & Partner)

DEBRAND INC.
5608 Coldwater Rd, Fort Wayne, IN 46825
Tel.: (260) 969-8333
Web Site: http://www.debrand.com
Rev.: $10,400,000
Emp.: 100
Chocolate Candy
N.A.I.C.S.: 311352
Cathy Brand Beere (Pres)

DEBRINO CAULKING ASSOCIATES
1304 Route 9, Castleton on Hudson, NY 12033
Tel.: (518) 732-7234
Web Site: https://www.debrino.com
Year Founded: 1945
Sales Range: $10-24.9 Million
Emp.: 150
Caulking (Construction)
N.A.I.C.S.: 238990
Lewis Houghtaling (Owner & Pres)
Charles Dings (VP)
Joe Lazzara (Mgr-Caulking & Waterproofing)
Richard Farnan (Project Mgr)

DEBT FREE ASSOCIATES
2101 Business Center Dr Ste 150, Irvine, CA 92612
Tel.: (877) 425-8332
Web Site:
http://www.debtfreeassociates.com
Year Founded: 2006
Sales Range: $25-49.9 Million
Emp.: 46
Debt & Financial Solutions for Companies & Individuals
N.A.I.C.S.: 525990
Bradley Smith (Founder & CEO)

DEBTMERICA, LLC
3100 S Harbor Blvd Ste 250, Santa Ana, CA 92704
Tel.: (714) 389-4200
Web Site:
https://www.debtmerica.com
Year Founded: 2006
Sales Range: $10-24.9 Million
Emp.: 65
Debt Relief Counseling Services
N.A.I.C.S.: 812990
Jesse E. Torres (Co-Founder, CEO & Mng Partner)
Harry H. Langenberg (Co-Founder, COO & Mng Partner)
Kristen Bemis (Gen Counsel)

DEBTSCAPE, INC.
1304 Concourse Dr Ste 100, Linthicum, MD 21090
Web Site: http://www.debtscape.org
Sales Range: $10-24.9 Million
Emp.: 100
Non-profit Credit & Debt Counseling Services
N.A.I.C.S.: 541618
Dave Hensel (Owner)

DEBUT BROADCASTING CORPORATION, INC.
1011 Cherry Ave Ste B, Nashville, TN 37203
Tel.: (615) 866-0530
Web Site:
http://www.debutbroadcasting.com
Sales Range: $1-9.9 Million
Emp.: 14
Radio Broadcasting Services
N.A.I.C.S.: 516110
Ronald E. Heineman (Chm & CEO)

DECARE DENTAL
3560 Delta Dental Dr, Eagan, MN 55123
Tel.: (651) 994-5275
Web Site: https://www.decare.com
Sales Range: $800-899.9 Million
Emp.: 700
Dental Benefit Management Companies
N.A.I.C.S.: 524114
Norman C. Storbakken (Exec VP-Ops)

DECAROLIS DESIGN & MARKETING, INC.
476 S 1st St, San Jose, CA 95113
Tel.: (408) 947-1411
Web Site: http://www.decdesign.com
Year Founded: 1991
Sales Range: $1-9.9 Million
Emp.: 23
Advetising Agency
N.A.I.C.S.: 541810
Sheila Hatch (Pres)
Regina Damore (VP-Ops)

DECATUR COOPERATIVE ASSOCIATION
305 S York Ave, Oberlin, KS 67749
Tel.: (785) 475-2234
Web Site: http://www.decaturcoop.net
Sales Range: $10-24.9 Million
Emp.: 30
Grain Elevators
N.A.I.C.S.: 424510
Kurt Anderson (Gen Mgr)

DECATUR INDUSTRIAL ELECTRIC
1501 N 22nd St, Decatur, IL 62526
Tel.: (217) 428-6621
Web Site: http://www.elect-mech.com
Sales Range: $10-24.9 Million
Emp.: 78
Electrical Supplies
N.A.I.C.S.: 423610
Claude Thompson (Chm)
Trent Thompson (Pres)
Matt Briggs (Controller)
Kelli Runyon (Mgr-Mktg & Comm)

DECATUR TRUCK & TRACTOR INC.
1850 W US Hwy 224, Decatur, IN 46733
Tel.: (260) 724-2166
Web Site:
https://www.selkinginternational.com
Rev.: $18,000,000
Emp.: 130
Trucks, Tractors & Trailers: New & Used

N.A.I.C.S.: 441110
Reinhard Selking *(Chm)*

DECCA DESIGN & DEVELOPMENT INC.
2852 Palmer Dr, Sierra Vista, AZ 85650-5264
Tel.: (520) 459-7191
Rev.: $12,432,185
Emp.: 5
Distr of Beer
N.A.I.C.S.: 445320
Eli Drakulich *(VP)*

DECHAN II, INC.
9360 W Flamingo Rd Ste 110-170, Las Vegas, NV 89147
Tel.: (702) 873-8478   NV
Web Site: http://www.dechaninc.com
Year Founded: 2007
Sales Range: Less than $1 Million
Emp.: 2
Printing
N.A.I.C.S.: 323111
Carol Ann Dechan *(Pres, CEO & Sec)*
Allison Joyce Harvey *(CFO & Treas)*

DECHERT LLP
Cira Centre 2929 Arch St, Philadelphia, PA 19104-2808
Tel.: (215) 994-4000   PA
Web Site: http://www.dechert.com
Year Founded: 1875
Sales Range: $700-749.9 Million
Emp.: 1,001
Legal Advisory Services
N.A.I.C.S.: 541110
Ethan D. Fogel *(Partner)*
David W. Forti *(Partner)*
Matthew B. Ginsburg *(Partner)*
Justin J. Gdula *(Partner)*
Arif H. Ali *(Partner)*
Camille Abousleiman *(Partner)*
Gavin B. Watson *(Partner)*
Rob Bradshaw *(Partner-London)*
Joachim Kayser *(Partner-Investment-Frankfurt)*
Achim Putz *(Mng Partner)*
Brenden Carroll *(Partner-Washington)*
Erica Franzetti *(Partner-Washington)*
Rani Habash *(Partner-Washington)*
Lucy Lu *(Natl Partner-Beijing)*
Cameron Mitcham *(Partner-Global Fin Practice-London)*
David Passey *(Partner-Global Tax Grp-New York)*
Joshua Milgrim *(Chm-Tax Grp-Global)*
Vincent H. Cohen Jr. *(Partner)*

DECIBEL RESEARCH, INC.
325 Bob Heath Dr, Huntsville, AL 35806
Tel.: (256) 716-0787
Web Site:
    http://www.decibelresearch.net
Year Founded: 2002
Sales Range: $10-24.9 Million
Emp.: 75
Software Systems Designed to Improve Military Radar Equipment
N.A.I.C.S.: 541512
Eric Cochran *(CFO)*
Sally Colocho *(VP-Comm)*
Enrico Poggio *(CTO)*
Bassem Mahafza *(Founder & CEO)*

DECIPHER, INC.
7 River Park Pl E Ste 110, Fresno, CA 93720
Tel.: (559) 436-6940
Web Site:
    http://www.decipherinc.com
Sales Range: $10-24.9 Million
Emp.: 145

Data Processing Services
N.A.I.C.S.: 518210
Jayme Plunkett *(Co-Founder & Co-CEO)*
Jamin Brazil *(CEO)*

Subsidiaries:

decipher, inc.   **(1)**
115 SW Ash St Ste 323, Portland, OR 97204
Tel.: (503) 488-2200
Web Site: http://www.decipherinc.com
Online Survey Programming, Data Collection, Data Processing/Reporting & Custom Technology Development
N.A.I.C.S.: 541511

DECISION BIOMARKERS, INC.
150 Bear Hill Rd, Waltham, MA 02451
Tel.: (781) 890-2006   MA
Year Founded: 2003
Pharmaceutical Development Services & Products Mfr
N.A.I.C.S.: 325412
Jean Montagu *(Founder & Chm)*
Roger Dowd *(Pres & CEO)*
Joe Blanchard *(Sr VP-Bus Dev & Strategic Plng)*
Walter Leslie *(VP-Engrg)*
Peter Maimonis *(VP-Biological Research)*

DECISION DIAGNOSTICS CORP.
2660 Townsgate Rd Ste 300, Westlake Village, CA 91361
Tel.: (805) 446-1973   NV
Web Site:
    https://www.decisiondiagnostics.co
Rev.: $2,235,000
Assets: $4,183,000
Liabilities: $3,093,000
Net Worth: $1,090,000
Earnings: ($2,240,000)
Emp.: 9
Fiscal Year-end: 12/31/18
Diagnostics & Home Testing Products Distr
N.A.I.C.S.: 423450
Keith M. Berman *(CFO & Sec)*

DECISION DISTRIBUTION
33 S Delaware Ave Ste 106H, Yardley, PA 19067
Tel.: (215) 493-4400
Web Site:
    http://www.ddistribution.com
Year Founded: 2004
Sales Range: $10-24.9 Million
Emp.: 6
Construction Trade Products
N.A.I.C.S.: 423390
Dan Goldman *(Pres)*
Kait Frain *(Controller)*

DECISION ECONOMICS, INC.
10 Post Office Sq Ste 615, Boston, MA 02109-4603
Tel.: (617) 994-0500
Web Site:
    http://www.decisioneconomics.com
Year Founded: 1996
Sales Range: $10-24.9 Million
Emp.: 15
Financial Information Services
N.A.I.C.S.: 519290
Allen L. Sinai *(Pres & CEO)*
M. Cary Leahey *(Sr Mng Dir)*

DECISION TECHNOLOGIES, INC.
2711 Jefferson Davis Hwy - Airport Plz 1, Arlington, VA 22202-4015
Tel.: (703) 416-5050
Web Site: http://www.decision-tech.com

Year Founded: 2003
Sales Range: $10-24.9 Million
Emp.: 105
Engineeering Services
N.A.I.C.S.: 541330
Dwayne J. Moses *(Pres & CEO)*
Shanna Moses *(Sec)*

DECISIONPATH CONSULTING
6 Montgomery Vlg Ave Ste 402, Gaithersburg, MD 20879
Tel.: (301) 926-8323
Web Site:
    http://www.decisionpath.com
Year Founded: 1999
Sales Range: $10-24.9 Million
Emp.: 45
Data Management & Business Consulting Services
N.A.I.C.S.: 541618
Steve Williams *(Pres)*
Nancy Williams *(VP-Bus Intelligence & Data Warehousing)*

DECISIONPOINT INTERNATIONAL
3420 Toringdon Way Ste 350, Charlotte, NC 28277
Tel.: (704) 248-1111   OH
Web Site:
    http://www.decisionpointint.com
Year Founded: 1955
Sales Range: $10-24.9 Million
Emp.: 125
M&A Advisory Services for Middle-Market Technology Companies & Venture Capital Firms
N.A.I.C.S.: 523940
Doug Ellis *(Founder & Mng Partner)*

DECKER COAL COMPANY
3555 Farnam St, Omaha, NE 68131
Tel.: (402) 342-2052
Rev.: $141,827,406
Emp.: 5
Bituminous Coal & Lignite-Surface Mining
N.A.I.C.S.: 212114
Tony Ritter *(Mgr)*

DECKER CREATIVE MARKETING
99 Citizens Dr, Glastonbury, CT 06033-1262
Tel.: (860) 659-1311
Web Site: http://www.deckerct.com
Year Founded: 1977
Rev.: $25,000,000
Emp.: 15
Advertising Agency Services
N.A.I.C.S.: 541810
Kathy Boucher *(Pres, CFO & Partner)*
Kim Keller *(Sr Dir-Art & Designer)*
Angel R. Martinez *(Pres, CEO & Chm)*

Subsidiaries:

OnTap   **(1)**
99 Citizens Dr, Glastonbury, CT 06033-1262
Tel.: (860) 659-1311
N.A.I.C.S.: 541810
Kathy Boucher *(Pres)*
Paul Tedeschi *(Dir-Creative)*

DECKER ROSS INTERIORS, INC.
1445 Court St, Clearwater, FL 33756
Tel.: (727) 442-9996
Web Site:
    https://www.deckerross.com
Sales Range: $10-24.9 Million
Emp.: 10
Interior Design Services
N.A.I.C.S.: 541410
Suzan Decker Ross *(Owner & Pres)*

DECKSIDE POOL SERVICE
1612 S Lyon St, Santa Ana, CA 92705
Tel.: (949) 858-0686
Web Site:
    http://www.decksidepool.com
Year Founded: 1981
Sales Range: $1-9.9 Million
Emp.: 25
Commercial Swimming Pool Services
N.A.I.C.S.: 561990
Fred Ross *(Owner & Pres)*
Traci Ross *(Treas & VP)*
Noel Jewell *(Reg Mgr)*

DECO PRODUCTS CO.
506 Sanford St, Decorah, IA 52101
Tel.: (563) 382-4264
Web Site: https://www.decoprod.com
Year Founded: 1960
Sales Range: $100-124.9 Million
Emp.: 275
Mfr of Zinc Die Castings, Mechanical Assemblies, Machining, Powder Coating & Hose Clamps
N.A.I.C.S.: 331523
Lew Storlie *(Gen Mgr)*
Chris Storlie *(Asst Gen Mgr)*
Jim Raptes *(Mgr-Sls-Custom)*
Gary Timp *(Mgr-Sls-Windows & Doors)*

DECOLAV, INC.
424 SW 12th Ave, Deerfield Beach, FL 33442
Tel.: (561) 274-2110
Web Site: http://www.decolav.com
Year Founded: 2000
Sales Range: $10-24.9 Million
Emp.: 60
Bathroom Fixtures
N.A.I.C.S.: 332999
Scott Bourne *(VP-Design & Dev)*
Brian Bringham *(Sr Dir-Mktg)*
Micheal Srankel *(Controller)*
Robert H. Mayer *(Pres & CEO)*

DECOR HOLDINGS, INC.
225 Foxboro Blvd, Foxboro, MA 02035
Tel.: (508) 339-9151
Sales Range: $25-49.9 Million
Emp.: 100
Holding Company
N.A.I.C.S.: 551112
Jeff Cordover *(Owner)*
Ron Cordover *(Owner, Chm & CEO)*

Subsidiaries:

The Robert Allen Group, Inc.   **(1)**
225 Foxboro Blvd, Foxboro, MA 02035
Tel.: (508) 339-9151
Web Site: http://www.robertallendesign.com
Sales Range: $50-74.9 Million
Emp.: 530
Fabrics & Textiles Distr
N.A.I.C.S.: 423220
Judy Fishman *(Sr VP-HR)*
Phillip H. Kowalczyk *(Pres & CEO)*

DECOR INC.
60 Cedar Ln, Englewood, NJ 07631
Tel.: (201) 569-1900
Sales Range: $10-24.9 Million
Emp.: 200
Decorative Glassware
N.A.I.C.S.: 327110
Richard Engel *(Pres)*
Peggy Napolitano *(VP)*

DECORATIVE CASTINGS INC.
3400 Wentworth Dr SW, Grand Rapids, MI 49519

Decorative Castings Inc.—(Continued)
Tel.: (616) 534-4977   MI
Web Site: http://www.brillcast.com
Year Founded: 1995
Sales Range: $25-49.9 Million
Emp.: 90
Mfr of Castings
N.A.I.C.S.: 551112
Les O'Nan (Pres)

Subsidiaries:

Allied Finishing Inc.   (1)
4100 Broadmoor Ave SE, Grand Rapids, MI
49512-3933
Tel.: (616) 698-7550
Web Site: http://www.alliedfinishinginc.com
Sales Range: $25-49.9 Million
Emp.: 150
Plating & Polishing Services Mfr
N.A.I.C.S.: 332813
Biff Kiley (Coord-Project)
Dan Gerke (Supvr-Shipping)
Brad Hirdes (Engr-Plating Process)

Brillcast Inc,   (1)
3400 Wentworth Dr SW, Grand Rapids, MI
49519
Tel.: (616) 534-4977
Web Site: http://www.brillcast.com
Sales Range: $10-24.9 Million
Emp.: 100
Casting Mfr
N.A.I.C.S.: 331523

DECORATIVE CRAFTS, INC.
50 Chestnut St, Greenwich, CT
06830-5952
Tel.: (203) 531-1500   CT
Web Site:
    https://www.decorativecrafts.com
Year Founded: 1928
Sales Range: $75-99.9 Million
Emp.: 50
Wholesale Distributor of Furniture &
Accessories
N.A.I.C.S.: 424990
Richard Cohn (Chm)
Jeffrey Cohn (Pres & CEO)

DECORATIVE SPECIALTIES
4414 Azusa Canyon Rd, Irwindale,
CA 91706
Tel.: (626) 960-7731
Web Site: http://www.decore.com
Sales Range: $100-124.9 Million
Emp.: 1,200
Doors, Wood
N.A.I.C.S.: 238130
Jack Lansford Sr. (CEO)

DECORATOR'S OFFICE FURNITURE INC.
2729 E Adamo Dr, Tampa, FL 33605
Tel.: (813) 241-8551   FL
Web Site: http://www.dofetc.net
Year Founded: 2001
Sales Range: $1-9.9 Million
Emp.: 8
Office Furniture Dealer
N.A.I.C.S.: 449110
John Taylor (Mgr-Ops)

DECORPLANET.COM
18 W 21st St, New York, NY 10010
Web Site:
    http://www.decorplanet.com
Year Founded: 2006
Sales Range: $10-24.9 Million
Emp.: 60
Bathroom Fixtures & Components
N.A.I.C.S.: 459999
Robert Gavartin (Owner)

DECOTY COFFEE COMPANY
1920 Austin St, San Angelo, TX
76903
Tel.: (325) 655-5607
Web Site: http://www.decoty.com

Year Founded: 1929
Sales Range: $10-24.9 Million
Emp.: 71
Coffee, Tea & Spices Mfr & Distr
N.A.I.C.S.: 311920
Mark Sedden (Dir-Ops)
Frankie Marquez (Reg Mgr-Sls)
Danah Osbourn (Dir-Accts)
Bryan Baker (Mgr-Natl Sls & Mktg)
Mike Agan (Owner, Pres & CEO)

Subsidiaries:

LA Creme Coffee & Tea   (1)
438 W Mockingbird Lane, Dallas, TX
75247-6614
Tel.: (214) 352-8090
Web Site:
    http://www.lacremecoffeeandtea.com
Emp.: 7
Specialty Coffee & Fine Tea Purveyor
N.A.I.C.S.: 311920
Mike Agan (Owner)
Samantha Hamilton (Gen Mgr & Dir)

DECRESCENTE DISTRIBUTING CO., INC.
211 N Main St, Mechanicville, NY
12118
Tel.: (518) 664-9866
Web Site:
    https://www.decrescente.com
Year Founded: 1947
Emp.: 134
Beer Product Distr
N.A.I.C.S.: 312120
Kate Otis (Dir-Comm Rels)
Steve Rychcik (Dir-On Premise Sls)
Greg White (Dir-Independent Channel Sls)
Carmine DeCrescente III (VP-Distr Svcs)
C. J. DeCrescente Jr. (Pres)

DECURION CORP.
120 N Robertson Blvd, Los Angeles,
CA 90048-3115
Tel.: (310) 657-8420
Web Site: http://www.decurion.com
Year Founded: 1966
Sales Range: $150-199.9 Million
Emp.: 4,300
Holding Company; Motion Picture
Theater Services
N.A.I.C.S.: 551112
Christopher S. Forman (Pres)
Neil S. B. Haltrecht (COO)
Steven Bedi (Dir-Asset Protection)

Subsidiaries:

Consolidated Amusement Co. Ltd.
Inc.   (1)
120 N Robertson Blvd, Los Angeles, CA
90048
Tel.: (310) 657-8420
Sales Range: $25-49.9 Million
Emp.: 400
Motion Picture Theater Services
N.A.I.C.S.: 512131

Mini-Pac Inc.   (1)
120 N Robertson Blvd, Los Angeles, CA
90048-3115
Tel.: (310) 657-8420
Sales Range: $10-24.9 Million
Emp.: 20
Provider of General Warehousing Services
N.A.I.C.S.: 493110

Pacific Theaters Entertainment
Corp.   (1)
120 N Robertson, Los Angeles, CA 90048
Tel.: (310) 657-8420
Web Site:
    http://www.pacificresidenttheatre.com
Motion Picture Theaters (except Drive-Ins)
N.A.I.C.S.: 512131
Christopher Forman (CEO)

Pacific Theatres Corporation   (1)
120 N Robertson Blvd, Los Angeles, CA
90048-3115

Tel.: (310) 657-8420
Web Site: http://www.pacifictheatres.com
Provider of Management Consulting Services
N.A.I.C.S.: 541611

Worldport LLC   (1)
1891 N Gaffey St, San Pedro, CA 90731
Tel.: (310) 514-5500
Web Site: http://worldportllc.com
Sales Range: $25-49.9 Million
Emp.: 5
Provider of Drive-In Motion Picture Theater
Services
N.A.I.C.S.: 523999

DEDC, INC.
8603 E Adamo Dr, Tampa, FL 33619
Tel.: (813) 626-5195   FL
Web Site:
    https://www.dowtechnologies.com
Year Founded: 1959
Emp.: 150
Electronic Parts & Equipment Distr
N.A.I.C.S.: 423690
Chip Yodzis (Exec Chm)
John Yodzis (Pres & CEO)
Drew Fischer (Dir-Sls)
Mike Hurwitz (Mgr-Strategic Sls)

DEDERT CORPORATION
17740 Hoffman Way, Homewood, IL
60430
Tel.: (708) 747-7000   IL
Web Site: https://www.dedert.com
Year Founded: 1968
Sales Range: $10-24.9 Million
Emp.: 35
Supplier of Evaporators, Liquid Solid
Separation Equipment & Solvent Recovery Systems
N.A.I.C.S.: 333248
Guy Lonergan (Pres)

Subsidiaries:

Dedert (Shanghai) Drying and Evaporating Technology Co., Ltd   (1)
23B China Resources Times Square No
500 Zhangyang Road, Pudong, Shanghai,
200122, China
Tel.: (86) 21 60450890
Web Site: http://www.dedert.com.cn
Industrial Equipment & Machinery Mfr
N.A.I.C.S.: 333994

DEDHAM INSTITUTION FOR SAVINGS INC.
55 Elm St, Dedham, MA 02026-5996
Tel.: (781) 329-6700   MA
Web Site:
    https://www.dedhamsavings.com
Year Founded: 1831
Sales Range: $50-74.9 Million
Emp.: 220
Savings Institutions
N.A.I.C.S.: 522180
Jim Dunn (VP & Mgr-Sls)
Doug Natale (Officer-Loan)

DEDHAM NISSAN, INC.
945 Providence Hwy, Dedham, MA
02026
Tel.: (781) 326-1500
Year Founded: 1955
Sales Range: $10-24.9 Million
Emp.: 65
Car Whslr
N.A.I.C.S.: 441110
Joseph Laham (Pres)

DEDICATED LOGISTICS INC.
2900 Granada Ln N, Oakdale, MN
55128-1134
Tel.: (651) 631-5918   MN
Web Site: https://www.shipdli.com
Year Founded: 1995
Sales Range: $25-49.9 Million
Emp.: 450

Trucking, Except Local & Warehousing
N.A.I.C.S.: 484121
Thomas G. Wintz (Pres)

DEDICATED TRANSPORT LLC
700 W Resource Dr, Brooklyn
Heights, OH 44131
Tel.: (216) 641-2500
Web Site:
    http://www.dedicatedtransport.com
Year Founded: 1995
Sales Range: $10-24.9 Million
Emp.: 130
Trucking Service
N.A.I.C.S.: 484121
Tom McDermott (Pres & CEO)
Tim Jarus (Dir-Ops)
Tom Connolly (Dir-Logistics)
Dave Hartman (Dir-HR & Safety)

DEDOES INDUSTRIES INC.
1060 W West Maple Rd, Walled
Lake, MI 48390
Tel.: (248) 624-7710
Web Site: https://www.dedoes.com
Rev.: $10,600,000
Emp.: 100
Paint Making Machinery
N.A.I.C.S.: 333248
David Pratt (Gen Mgr)

DEDOLA GLOBAL LOGISTICS
3822 Katella Ave, Los Alamitos, CA
90720
Tel.: (562) 594-8988
Web Site: https://www.dedola.com
Sales Range: $10-24.9 Million
Emp.: 20
Freight Transportation Arrangement
N.A.I.C.S.: 488510
John A. Dedola (Founder)
Mark Dedola (Pres)
Steven Dedola (VP)

DEE & DEE OIL CO.
200 E Clarendon Dr, Dallas, TX
75203
Tel.: (214) 943-7447
Sales Range: $10-24.9 Million
Emp.: 6
Convenience Stores, Independent
N.A.I.C.S.: 445131

DEE BROWN, INC.
4101 S Shiloh Rd, Garland, TX
75041-4717
Tel.: (214) 321-6443   TX
Web Site: http://www.deebrown.com
Year Founded: 1955
Sales Range: $25-49.9 Million
Emp.: 340
Masonry Sub Contractor
N.A.I.C.S.: 238140
Michael D. Humphrey (CFO & Exec VP)

Subsidiaries:

DBM/Hatch Inc.   (1)
640 Arrow Hwy, La Verne, CA
91750-5101   (100%)
Tel.: (909) 592-7988
Web Site: http://www.deebrown.com
Sales Range: $10-24.9 Million
Emp.: 90
Masonry & Other Stonework
N.A.I.C.S.: 238140

DEE CRAMER INC.
4221 E Baldwin Rd, Holly, MI 48442-
9328
Tel.: (810) 579-5000   MI
Web Site:
    https://www.deecramer.com
Year Founded: 1939
Sales Range: $25-49.9 Million
Emp.: 180

Plumbing, Heating & Air-Conditioning Services
N.A.I.C.S.: 238220
Matthew Cramer *(Pres)*
Rich Cramer *(VP)*
Steve Hunt *(Mgr-Estimating Support)*
Glenn Lamb *(Mgr-Production)*

DEE ENGINEERING INC.
3560 Cadillac Ave, Costa Mesa, CA 92626
Tel.: (714) 979-4990
Web Site: http://www.deeeng.com
Year Founded: 1991
Rev.: $10,000,000
Emp.: 60
Mfr & Distributor of Motor Vehicle Parts & Accessories
N.A.I.C.S.: 336390
Gary T. Fulton *(Sec & VP)*

DEE PAPER COMPANY
100 Broomall St, Chester, PA 19013-3413
Tel.: (610) 876-9285   PA
Web Site: http://www.deepaper.com
Year Founded: 1921
Sales Range: $10-24.9 Million
Emp.: 82
Mfr of Folding Paper Boxes
N.A.I.C.S.: 322211
George Roland *(Mgr-Customer Svc)*

DEE PEE ELECTRIC MEMBER-SHIP
575 Hwy 52 S, Wadesboro, NC 28170
Tel.: (704) 694-2114
Rev.: $26,127,113
Emp.: 70
Electric Power Distribution
N.A.I.C.S.: 221122
Richard Johnson *(Member-Exec Bd)*
Donnie Spivey *(CEO)*

DEE SIGN COMPANY
6163 Allen Rd, West Chester, OH 45069-3855
Tel.: (513) 779-3333
Web Site:
   http://www.deesigncompany.com
Year Founded: 1967
Sales Range: $75-99.9 Million
Emp.: 50
Real Estate Signs Mfr
N.A.I.C.S.: 339950
Robert C. Huenefeld *(Co-Owner & Co-Pres)*
Brad Huenefeld *(Pres)*
Craig Dixon *(Gen Mgr)*
Joe Kolks *(CFO)*
Will Kriedler *(Mgr-Mktg)*

Subsidiaries:

Dee Sign Company - Anaheim Facility   (1)
1010 E Raymond Way, Anaheim, CA 92801
Tel.: (714) 871-5113
Sign Mfr
N.A.I.C.S.: 339950

Dee Sign Company - Los Angeles Facility   (1)
16250 Stagg St, Van Nuys, CA 91406
Tel.: (818) 904-3400
Sign Mfr
N.A.I.C.S.: 339950

Dee Sign Company - Oakland Facility   (1)
24001 Watkins St, Hayward, CA 94544
Tel.: (510) 885-8760
Sign Mfr
N.A.I.C.S.: 339950

Dee Sign Company - San Diego Facility   (1)
7835 Wilkerson Ct, San Diego, CA 92111
Tel.: (858) 751-2900

Sign Mfr
N.A.I.C.S.: 339950

DEE ZEE, INC.
1572 NE 58th Ave, Des Moines, IA 50313-1622
Tel.: (515) 299-7377   OH
Web Site: https://www.deezee.com
Year Founded: 1977
Sales Range: $250-299.9 Million
Emp.: 600
Aluminum Running Boards & other Pickup & Van Accessories
N.A.I.C.S.: 336390

DEEB CONSTRUCTION & DE-VELOPMENT CO.
9400 River Crossing Blvd Ste 102, New Port Richey, FL 34655
Tel.: (727) 376-6831   FL
Web Site:
   https://www.deebcompanies.com
Year Founded: 1932
Sales Range: $10-24.9 Million
Emp.: 60
Commercial Construction
N.A.I.C.S.: 236220
Thomas Deeb *(Pres)*

DEECO METALS CORPORA-TION
655 N Main St, Travelers Rest, SC 29690
Tel.: (973) 373-0070   NJ
Web Site:
   http://www.deecometals.com
Year Founded: 1986
Sales Range: $75-99.9 Million
Emp.: 15
Custom Bronze Brass Aluminum Stainless Steel & Specialty Alloy Component Distr
N.A.I.C.S.: 423510
Desmond W. Sinclair *(Pres & CEO)*
Coral Sinclair *(VP-Fin)*
Randy Klein *(Mgr-Tech & Sls)*
Tanith Sinclair *(Mgr-Admin & Sls)*
Carrie Sinclair *(VP-Adv & Mktg)*

Subsidiaries:

Siltin Industries, Inc.   (1)
10-16 Renee Pl, Irvington, NJ 07111   (100%)
Tel.: (973) 373-0070
Sales Range: $25-49.9 Million
Emp.: 10
Mfr & Distributor of Metals
N.A.I.C.S.: 423140
Desmond W. Sinclair *(Pres)*

DEEGIT INC.
1900 E Golf Rd Ste 925, Schaum-burg, IL 60173
Tel.: (847) 330-1985
Web Site: https://www.deegit.com
Year Founded: 1993
Rev.: $8,000,000
Emp.: 40
Business Consulting Services
N.A.I.C.S.: 541690
Jaya K. Madipadaga *(CEO)*
Deepak J. Patel *(Pres)*

DEEL VOLVO
3650 Bird Rd, Miami, FL 33133
Tel.: (305) 444-2222
Web Site: http://www.deelvolvo.net
Sales Range: $25-49.9 Million
Emp.: 130
Car Whslr
N.A.I.C.S.: 441110
Cesar Lanuza *(Mgr-Sls)*

DEEL, INC.
995 Market St, San Francisco, CA 94103
Tel.: (415) 915-9803

Web Site: https://www.deel.com
Year Founded: 2019
Emp.: 650
Payroll Solution & Services
N.A.I.C.S.: 541214
Alex Bouaziz *(Founder & CEO)*

Subsidiaries:

PayGroup Limited   (1)
Level 10 440 Collins Street, Melbourne, 3000, VIC, Australia
Tel.: (61) 386927248
Web Site: https://paygroup.global
Rev.: $12,269,569
Assets: $30,404,454
Liabilities: $14,447,672
Net Worth: $15,956,783
Earnings: ($391,291)
Fiscal Year-end: 03/31/2021
Human Resource Consulting Services
N.A.I.C.S.: 541612

Subsidiary (Non-US):

PT Payasia Konsultansi Indonesia   (2)
Centennial Tower 35th Floor JL Jend Gatot Subroto Kav 24-25, Jakarta, Indonesia
Tel.: (62) 2129539500
Information Technology Services
N.A.I.C.S.: 541511

DEEM STEEL
109 Benny St, Longview, TX 75604
Tel.: (903) 236-7800
Year Founded: 2008
Sales Range: $10-24.9 Million
Emp.: 75
Structural Steel Erection Services
N.A.I.C.S.: 238190
David Steel *(Owner)*

DEEN MEAT CO.
813 E Northside Dr, Fort Worth, TX 76102-1017
Tel.: (817) 335-2257   TX
Web Site: https://www.deenmeat.com
Year Founded: 1946
Sales Range: $10-24.9 Million
Emp.: 50
Producer & Retailer of Fresh Meats
N.A.I.C.S.: 424470
Danny Deen *(Pres)*
Craig Deen *(VP)*

DEEP EAST TEXAS ELECTRIC COOPERATIVE, INC.
PO Box 736, San Augustine, TX 75972
Tel.: (936) 275-2314   TX
Web Site: http://www.deepeast.com
Year Founded: 1938
Sales Range: $75-99.9 Million
Emp.: 127
Electric Power Distr
N.A.I.C.S.: 221122
Kelly Parker *(Dir-Ops)*
Gina Evett *(Dir-Admin)*
Doug Turk *(Gen Mgr)*
Ronnie Greer *(Treas & Sec)*
William A. Speights *(VP)*
J. P. Dobbs Jr. *(Pres)*

DEEP FOODS, INC.
1090 Springfield Rd, Union, NJ 07083
Tel.: (908) 810-7500
Web Site:
   https://www.deepfoods.com
Year Founded: 1977
Sales Range: $150-199.9 Million
Emp.: 330
Mfr of Authentic, All Natural Indian Cuisine
N.A.I.C.S.: 445298
Arvind Amin *(Co-Founder)*
Bhagwati Amin *(Founder)*

DEEP IMAGING TECHNOLO-GIES, INC.
990 Vlg Sq Dr, Tomball, TX 30656-4815
Tel.: (281) 290-0492
Web Site:
   http://www.mywasteremoval.com
Business to Business Electronic Markets
N.A.I.C.S.: 425120
Trevor Pugh *(CEO)*

Subsidiaries:

Engineering Seismology Group Canada, Inc.   (1)
20 Hyperion Court, Kingston, K7K 7K2, ON, Canada
Tel.: (613) 548-8287
Web Site: http://www.esgsolutions.com
Oil & Gas Machinery Mfr
N.A.I.C.S.: 333132

DEEP LIQUIDITY, INC.
3225 Smoky Ridge Rd, Austin, TX 78730
Tel.: (512) 585-4589   DE
Web Site:
   http://www.deepliquidity.com
Sales Range: Less than $1 Million
Emp.: 3
Electronic Trading Platform
N.A.I.C.S.: 425120
Sam Balabon *(Founder, Chm, Pres & CEO)*

DEEP SOUTH EQUIPMENT COMPANY
4201 Michoud Blvd, New Orleans, LA 70129
Tel.: (504) 254-2700
Web Site:
   http://www.deepsouthequipment.com
Sales Range: $10-24.9 Million
Emp.: 32
Materials Handling Machinery
N.A.I.C.S.: 423830
John Parsons *(Pres)*
Gerald Boudreaux *(Treas & Sec)*
Lindsey Hernandez *(Mgr-Gen Sls)*
Randy Watkins *(Mgr-Parts)*

DEEP SOUTH INSURANCE
7701 Las Colinas Ridge Ste 600, Ir-ving, TX 75063
Tel.: (214) 493-4200
Web Site: http://www.deep-south.com
Sales Range: $25-49.9 Million
Emp.: 280
Insurance Agents
N.A.I.C.S.: 524210
David Disiere *(Pres)*
Russell Ellers *(CEO-Los Angeles)*
Bennie Hutcheson *(Pres & Gen Mgr-Little Rock)*

DEEP SURPLUS
27671 La Paz Rd Ste 100, Laguna Niguel, CA 92677
Tel.: (949) 643-5004
Web Site:
   http://www.deepsurplus.com
Year Founded: 2002
Sales Range: $1-9.9 Million
Emp.: 16
Online Sales of Surplus, Closeout & Overstocked Cabling Supplies
N.A.I.C.S.: 423430
Sean Griffith *(Engr-Indus)*

DEEP WATER POINT LLC
8300 Greensboro Dr Ste 800, McLean, VA 22102
Tel.: (202) 577-7931
Web Site:
   http://www.deepwaterpoint.com
Year Founded: 2002

Deep Water Point LLC—(Continued)

Sales Range: $1-9.9 Million
Emp.: 25
Management Consulting Firm
N.A.I.C.S.: 541611
Howard Seeger (Mng Partner)
John Przysucha (Partner)
Scott Hastings (Partner)
Stephen Kalish (Partner)
John Johnson (Partner)
Tony Pease (Principal)
Cindy Moran (Principal-DoD)
Doug McGovern (Principal-DoD & IC)
Amy Caro (Partner)
Kim Skvorak (Principal-Intelligence Community Sector Team)
Robert Ashely (Principal)
Thomas Moore (Principal)
Bon Bouchard (Partner)
Charles Hanley III (Partner)

DEEPWATER CORROSION SERVICES, INC.
13813 FM 529 Rd, Houston, TX 77041
Tel.: (713) 983-7117
Web Site: http://www.stoprust.com
Year Founded: 1986
Sales Range: $10-24.9 Million
Emp.: 45
Cathodic Protection Equipment Mfr
N.A.I.C.S.: 335999
James N. Britton (CEO)
Dishundra Turner (Mgr-HSE)

Subsidiaries:

Deepwater EU Limited   (1)
4 8 Frimley Business Park, Frimley, Camberley, GU16 7SG, Surrey, United Kingdom.
Tel.: (44) 1483600482
Web Site: http://www.stoprust.com
Sales Range: $10-24.9 Million
Emp.: 14
Cathodic Protection Equipment Mfr
N.A.I.C.S.: 335999
Geoff Camm (Mgr-Design Centre)

DEER CROSSING, INC.
65 Main St, Warwick, NY 10990
Tel.: (845) 986-6900
Web Site:
   http://www.deercrossinghomes.com
Rev.: $10,700,000
Emp.: 100
Land Subdivision
N.A.I.C.S.: 237210
Alyce Cosgriff (VP)
Rick Cosgriff (Pres)

DEER PARK ROOFING, LLC
7201 Blue Ash Rd, Cincinnati, OH 45236-5236
Tel.: (513) 891-9151
Web Site:
   https://www.deerparkroofing.com
Roofing Contractors
N.A.I.C.S.: 238160
Nick Sabino (Founder & Pres)

DEER STAGS CONCEPTS, INC.
902 Bdwy 3rd Fl, New York, NY 10010
Tel.: (212) 888-2424
Web Site: http://www.deerstags.com
Year Founded: 1929
Footwear Mfr, Retailer & Distr
N.A.I.C.S.: 424340
Rick Muskat (Pres & COO)

DEERFIELD BUILDERS SUPPLY CO.
77 SE 2nd Ave, Deerfield Beach, FL 33441
Tel.: (954) 427-1010
Rev.: $15,800,000

Emp.: 52
Lumber & Other Building Materials
N.A.I.C.S.: 423310
Edward H. Dietrich (Pres)
Brad Wanzenberg (VP)

DEERFIELD COMMUNICATIONS INC.
625 Kenmoor Ave SE Ste 301, Grand Rapids, MI 49546
Tel.: (989) 732-8856
Web Site: http://www.deerfield.net
Sales Range: $10-24.9 Million
Emp.: 10
Electronic Publishing
N.A.I.C.S.: 449210
Mike Courterier (Mgr-Product Dev)

DEERFIELD CONSTRUCTION CO., INC.
8960 Glendale Milford Rd, Loveland, OH 45140-8908
Tel.: (513) 984-4096
Web Site:
   https://www.deerfieldconstruc tion.com
Year Founded: 1981
Sales Range: $10-24.9 Million
Emp.: 50
Contractor of Nonresidential Construction
N.A.I.C.S.: 236220
Steven W. Bitzer (Pres)
John Stewart (CFO & VP)
Dave Knueven (VP)

DEERFIELD CONSTRUCTION GROUP INC.
14927 New Ave, Lockport, IL 60441
Tel.: (815) 588-1099
Web Site: http://www.dcgi1.com
Sales Range: $25-49.9 Million
Emp.: 50
Communication Line & Transmission Tower Construction
N.A.I.C.S.: 237130
Chris Bunch (Pres)
Bob Johnson (Project Mgr)
Gary Wetzel (Project Mgr)
Jason Bay (VP)

DEERFIELD DISTRIBUTING INC.
97 McKee Dr, Mahwah, NJ 07430
Tel.: (201) 512-1400
Web Site: http://www.edist.com
Sales Range: $50-74.9 Million
Emp.: 40
Office Equipment
N.A.I.C.S.: 423420
Quinn Ruelle (Pres)
Mike Wahlen (VP)

DEERFIELD EPISCOPAL RETIREMENT COMMUNITY, INC.
1617 Hendersonville Rd, Asheville, NC 28803
Tel.: (828) 274-1531
Web Site:
   https://www.deerfieldwnc.org
Year Founded: 1955
Sales Range: $25-49.9 Million
Continuing Care Retirement Community Operator
N.A.I.C.S.: 623311
Shirley Burnette (Dir-Human Resources)
Matthew Sharpe (Dir-Resident Svcs)
Robert Chandler (CFO)
Brian King (Dir-Health-Wellness)
Kathy Foster (Dir-Marketing)
Keith Einsmann (Dir-Facility Services)

DEERFIELD MANAGEMENT COMPANY L.P.

780 Third Ave 37th Fl, New York, NY 10017
Tel.: (212) 551-1600
Web Site: http://www.deerfield.com
Emp.: 100
Hedge Fund Management Services
N.A.I.C.S.: 523999
William S. Slattery (Partner)
Steven I. Hochberg (Operating Partner)
James E. Flynn (Gen Partner)
Andrew ElBardissi (Partner)
Jonathan S. Leff (Partner)

Subsidiaries:

Melinta Therapeutics, Inc.   (1)
44 Whippany Rd Ste 280, Morristown, NJ 07960
Tel.: (908) 617-1309
Web Site: http://www.melinta.com
Rev.: $96,430,000
Assets: $441,590,000
Liabilities: $251,526,000
Net Worth: $190,064,000
Earnings: ($157,192,000)
Emp.: 290
Fiscal Year-end: 12/31/2018
Holding Company; Pharmaceutical Developer & Mfr
N.A.I.C.S.: 551112
Kate Farrington (Chief Medical Officer)
Mike McGuire (Sr VP-Comml)
Peter J. Milligan (CFO)
Ryan Lococo (Sr VP & COO)
Jill Massey (Sr VP-Medical Affairs)
Susan Blum (CFO)
Christine Ann Miller (Pres & CEO)
Kristen Allgor (Chief HR Officer)
John Harlow (Chief Comml Officer)
Jisoo Park (Head-Bus Dev, M&A & Strategy)

Subsidiary (Domestic):

Melinta Subsidiary Corp.   (2)
300 George St Ste 301, New Haven, CT 06511
Tel.: (312) 767-0291
Web Site: http://www.melinta.com
Sales Range: $10-24.9 Million
Emp.: 43
Pharmaceutical Developer & Mfr
N.A.I.C.S.: 325412
Erin Duffy (Chief Scientific Officer)
Paul Estrem (CFO)
Lyn Baranowski (Sr VP-Corp Dev & Strategy)
Sue Cammarata (Chief Medical Officer)
Peter DiRoma (Sr VP-Regulatory Affairs & Quality Assurance)
Suzie Paulson (VP-HR)
Kevin Conway (VP-Program Mgmt & Technical Ops)
Daniel Wechsler (Pres & CEO)

DEERPATH CORPORATION
2095 Niles Rd, Saint Joseph, MI 49085
Tel.: (269) 983-7160
Web Site: http://www.scope-services.com
Sales Range: $10-24.9 Million
Emp.: 5
Mechanical Contractor
N.A.I.C.S.: 238220
Lydia Demski (Pres)

DEERWOOD BANCSHARES, INC.
21236 Archibald Rd, Deerwood, MN 56444
Tel.: (218) 534-3111
Web Site:
   https://www.deerwoodbank.com
Year Founded: 1996
Sales Range: $10-24.9 Million
Emp.: 79
Bank Holding Company
N.A.I.C.S.: 551111
John Ohlin (Pres & CEO)

Subsidiaries:

Deerwood Bank   (1)

21236 Archibald Rd, Deerwood, MN 56444
Tel.: (218) 534-3111
Web Site: http://www.deerwoodbank.com
Sales Range: $10-24.9 Million
Commercial Banking
N.A.I.C.S.: 522110
Luke T. Spalj (Owner)
Grant Frenzel (VP-Bus Banking-Blackduck)
John Ohlin (Pres & CEO)
Jerry Moynagh (VP-Bus Banking-Mendota Heights)
Jed Rusk (Coord-Mktg & Product)
Bill Eickhoff (Pres-Central Market)
Jim Schleper (Sr VP-Bus Banking-Waite Park)
Joe Bauer (Pres-Metro Market)
Phil Verchota (Pres-Northern Market)

DEERY BROTHERS CHEVROLET, INC.
6000 E University Ave, Pleasant Hill, IA 50327
Tel.: (515) 285-1000
Web Site: http://www.godeery.com
Year Founded: 1961
Sales Range: $50-74.9 Million
Emp.: 55
New & Used Automobile Sales
N.A.I.C.S.: 441110
Brad Deery (Pres)
Tony Nordman (Dir-Svc)
Heath Lilly (Mgr-Parts)

DEFENDER SECURITY COMPANY
3750 Priority Way S Dr Ste 200, Indianapolis, IN 46240
Tel.: (317) 810-4720
Web Site:
   http://www.defenderdirect.com
Year Founded: 1998
Sales Range: $250-299.9 Million
Emp.: 1,289
Residential Security Systems & Satellite Products Dealer; Heating, Ventilation, Air Conditioning & Plumbing Contractors
N.A.I.C.S.: 561621
Dave Lindsey (Founder)

Subsidiaries:

Zipper Air Conditioning & Heating Company   (1)
1546 Berry Blvd, Louisville, KY 40215
Tel.: (502) 368-5848
Web Site: http://www.ziptozipper.com
Heating & Air Conditioning Contractor
N.A.I.C.S.: 238220

DEFENDER SERVICES, INC.
9031 Garners Ferry Rd, Hopkins, SC 29061
Tel.: (803) 776-4220
Web Site:
   https://www.defenderservices.com
Year Founded: 1958
Sales Range: $75-99.9 Million
Emp.: 6,000
Building Management & Maintenance Services
N.A.I.C.S.: 561720
Rocky Herring (Mgr)
Susan Bennett (Mgr-HR)

DEFENDERS OF WILDLIFE
1130 17th St NW, Washington, DC 20036
Tel.: (202) 682-9400
Web Site: https://www.defenders.org
Year Founded: 1947
Sales Range: $25-49.9 Million
Emp.: 186
Wildlife Conservation Services

N.A.I.C.S.: 813312
Robert Dewey *(VP-Govt Rels)*
Winsome Dunn McIntosh *(Chm)*
Caroline Gabel *(Sec)*
Mark Caylor *(Treas)*
Jamie Rappaport Clark *(Pres & CEO)*
Mari Snyder Johnson *(Exec Dir)*
Mark Salvo *(VP-Landscape Conservation)*
Juan Carlos Cantu *(Mgr-Mexico Programs)*
Ya-Wei Li *(Sr Dir-Endangered Species Conservation)*
Mary Elizabeth Beetham *(Dir-Legislative Affairs)*
Michael Senatore *(Gen Counsel & VP-Conservation Law)*
Nancy Gloman *(VP-Field Conservation Programs)*
James Stofan *(COO)*
Ben Prater *(Dir-Southeast Program)*
Bryan Bird *(Dir-Southwest Program)*
Jonathan Proctor *(Dir-Rockies & Plains Program)*
Karla M. Dutton *(Dir-Alaska Program)*
Kim Delfino *(Dir-California Program)*
Sharon Boland *(Coord-Rockies & Plains Program)*
Shawn Cantrell *(Dir-Northwest Program)*
Tracy Davids *(Coord-Southeast Program)*
Vanessa E. Lopez *(Coord-Northwest Program)*
Jane P. Davenport *(Atty)*
Jason Rylander *(Atty)*
McCrystie Adams *(Atty)*
Bob Dreher *(Sr VP-Conservation Programs)*

DEFENSE CONTRACT SERVICES, INC.
204 Bagdad St, Leander, TX 78641
Tel.: (512) 219-7958
Web Site: http://www.dcsi1.com
Year Founded: 2000
Sales Range: $1-9.9 Million
Emp.: 138
Airport/Airport Services
N.A.I.C.S.: 488119
Frank Brown *(Pres)*
Marilyn Brown *(Treas & Sec)*

DEFI SOLUTIONS, INC.
1026 Texan Trl Ste 150, Grapevine, TX 76051
Web Site:
   http://www.defisolutions.com
Auto Application Solutions Mfr
N.A.I.C.S.: 513210
Kevin Perkins *(Mgr-PR)*
Stephanie Alsbrooks *(Founder)*
Robert Dufalo *(Chief Innovation Officer)*
Keven Sticher *(CIO)*
Deborah L. Kerr *(Chm)*
Lana Johnson *(COO)*
Jason Zubrick *(CTO)*
Charlie Lewis *(Dir-Comm)*
Tom Allanson *(CEO)*

Subsidiaries:
Open Rule Systems Inc.   (1)
1133 Airline Dr Ste 2201, Grapevine, TX 76051-7501
Tel.: (817) 410-9888
Web Site: http://www.openrule.com
Custom Computer Programming Services
N.A.I.C.S.: 541511
Glenn McCallum *(VP)*

DEFIANCE VENTURES LLC
1920 Cleveland Ave Ste B, Charlotte, NC 28203   NC
Web Site: http://defiance.ai
Information Technology Services
N.A.I.C.S.: 519290

Tareq Amin *(Co-Founder & Chm)*
John Espey *(Co-Founder)*
Kevin O'Dell *(CTO)*
Mike Privette *(Chief Info Security Officer)*

Subsidiaries:
Tavve Software Company   (1)
1 Copley Pkwy Ste 480, Morrisville, NC 27560-7423
Tel.: (919) 460-1789
Web Site: http://www.tavve.com
Custom Computer Programming Services
N.A.I.C.S.: 541511
Doug Austin *(VP-Sls-Worldwide)*

DEFIANT REQUIEM FOUNDATION
PO Box 6242, Washington, DC 20015
Tel.: (202) 244-0220   DC
Web Site:
   http://www.defiantrequiem.org
Year Founded: 2008
Sales Range: $1-9.9 Million
Emp.: 5
Grantmaking Services
N.A.I.C.S.: 813211
Mark B. Rulison *(Gen Mgr & Dir-Program)*
David Welch *(Dir-Finance)*
Louisa Hollman *(Exec Dir)*
Stuart E. Eizenstat *(Chm)*
J. Christian Kennedy *(Treas)*
Murry Sidlin *(Founder & Pres)*

DEFILIPPO BROS MOTORCARS AUTO SALES INC
602 Lincoln Ave, Prospect Park, PA 19076-2301
Tel.: (610) 532-8771
Web Site: http://www.ujobucredit.com
Sales Range: $10-24.9 Million
Emp.: 11
Automobile Whslr
N.A.I.C.S.: 423110
Matthew S. Defilippo *(Mgr-Fin)*

DEFINED FINANCIAL PLANNING, LLC
2413 Webb Ave Ste B, 94501, Alameda, CA
Tel.: (510) 200-8655
Web Site:
   https://www.definedplanning.com
Year Founded: 2016
Emp.: 100
Financial Planning Services
N.A.I.C.S.: 523940
Samuel Gaeta *(Principal)*

Subsidiaries:
Annadel Capital Inc.   (1)
899 Northgate Dr Ste 302, San Rafael, CA 94903-3667
Tel.: (415) 499-1901
Web Site: http://www.annadelcapital.com
Investment Advice
N.A.I.C.S.: 523940
Gregg Smith *(Principal)*

DEFINITIVE REST MATTRESS COMPANY
4570 Brooks St, Montclair, CA 91763
Tel.: (909) 923-1620
Web Site:
   http://www.definitiverest.com
Sales Range: Less than $1 Million
Mattress & Bedding Mfr
N.A.I.C.S.: 337910
Juan Carlos Murga *(Chm, Pres, CEO & CFO)*
Claudia Lima *(Treas & Sec)*

DEFINITIVE RESULTS, LLC
202 Church St SE Ste 204, Leesburg, VA 20175-3031

Tel.: (703) 624-7285
Web Site: http://www.definitive-results.com
Emp.: 100
Computer Related Services
N.A.I.C.S.: 541519
Adam Schrager *(Founder & Pres)*

DEFOREST CREATIVE GROUP
300 W Lake St, Elmhurst, IL 60126
Tel.: (630) 834-7200
Web Site:
   http://www.deforestgroup.com
Year Founded: 1965
Sales Range: $10-24.9 Million
Emp.: 15
N.A.I.C.S.: 541810
Lee DeForest *(Partner & VP)*
Jim DeForest *(Partner)*
Joanna Mattix *(Coord-Project)*
Nick Chapman *(Sr Graphic Designer)*

DEFRAN SYSTEMS, INC.
5 E 16th St 6th Fl, New York, NY 10003
Tel.: (212) 727-8342   NY
Web Site: http://www.defran.com
Year Founded: 1984
Sales Range: $10-24.9 Million
Emp.: 40
Software Developer for Social Service Organizations
N.A.I.C.S.: 513210
Boris Kagan *(VP-Dev)*
Julie Ingram *(Dir-Sls)*

DEFY VENTURES INC.
5 Penn Plz 19th Fl, New York, NY 10001
Tel.: (914) 330-9950   NY
Web Site:
   https://www.defyventures.org
Year Founded: 2010
Sales Range: $1-9.9 Million
Emp.: 23
Ex-Offender Employment Support Services
N.A.I.C.S.: 624190
Brian Korb *(Sec)*
Melissa Gelber-O'Dell *(Mgr-Dev & Recruitment)*
John Garofolo *(CFO)*

DEFYSUPPLY
PO Box 47852, Minneapolis, MN 55447
Web Site:
   http://www.DefySupply.com
Year Founded: 2008
Sales Range: $1-9.9 Million
Emp.: 25
Online Discounted Furniture Retailer
N.A.I.C.S.: 449110
Brent Gensler *(CEO)*

DEG
10801 Mastin Blvd Ste 130, Overland Park, KS 66210
Tel.: (913) 498-9988
Web Site: http://www.degdigital.com
Year Founded: 1999
Sales Range: $10-24.9 Million
Emp.: 190
Digital Marketing & Consulting Services
N.A.I.C.S.: 541613
Neal Sharma *(CEO & Principal)*
Jeff Eden *(Chief Sls Officer & Principal)*
Dale Hazlett *(CFO & Principal)*
Jasvindarjit Singh *(CTO & Principal)*
Greg Bustamante *(Mng Dir-Engrg)*
Joe Cromer *(Dir-Enterprise Collaboration)*
Cara Olson *(Dir-Direct Mktg & eCRM)*
Scott Miles *(Dir-Svc Delivery)*

Kyle Johnston *(Dir-Creative)*
David Saul *(Dir-Data Mgmt)*
Quinn Sheek *(Dir-Digital Paid Media)*
Craig Sizemore *(Dir-Project Mgmt)*
Jen Forrest *(Dir-Social Media)*
John Stauffer *(Mng Dir-Strategic Plng & Channel Strategy)*
Paula Burr *(Dir-Analytics & Insight)*

DEGENKOLB ENGINEERS
235 Montgomery St Ste 500, San Francisco, CA 94104-2908
Tel.: (213) 596-5000
Web Site: http://www.degenkolb.com
Emp.: 100
Engineeering Services
N.A.I.C.S.: 541330
Stacy Bartoletti *(Pres & CEO)*
Tricia Ruby *(Principal & Grp Dir)*

Subsidiaries:
Ruby Associates, PC   (1)
30445 Northwstrn Hwy 31, Farmington Hills, MI 48334
Tel.: (248) 865-8855
Web Site: http://www.rubyusa.com
Sales Range: $1-9.9 Million
Emp.: 29
Structural Engineers
N.A.I.C.S.: 541330
David Ruby *(Founder)*

DEGROOD OIL INC.
1419 Division St W, Faribault, MN 55021
Tel.: (507) 334-5151
Sales Range: $10-24.9 Million
Emp.: 15
Convenience Store
N.A.I.C.S.: 445131
Michael E. Degrood *(Pres)*

DEHOFF ENTERPRISES INC.
1 Waters Park Dr Ste 185, San Mateo, CA 94403-1163
Tel.: (650) 572-6020   CA
Year Founded: 1972
Sales Range: $25-49.9 Million
Emp.: 120
Grocery Stores
N.A.I.C.S.: 445110
Chris Dehoff *(Pres)*

DEI WORLDWIDE, INC.
11132 Ventura Blvd 3rd Fl, Studio City, CA 91604
Tel.: (818) 763-9065   CA
Web Site:
   http://www.deiworldwide.com
Year Founded: 2000
Rev.: $2,100,000
Emp.: 25
Fiscal Year-end: 12/31/06
Online Advertising And Marketing
N.A.I.C.S.: 541613
David Reis *(Founder, Pres & CEO)*
Tyler Starrine *(VP-Dev)*

DEIG BROS. LUMBER & CONSTRUCTION CO. INC.
2804 A St, Evansville, IN 47712-4901
Tel.: (812) 423-4201   IN
Web Site: https://www.deigbros.com
Year Founded: 1954
Sales Range: $25-49.9 Million
Emp.: 200
Industrial Buildings & Warehouses
N.A.I.C.S.: 236210
Charles R. Martin *(Pres)*
David Deig *(Dir-Safety)*

DEISTER MACHINE CO. INC.
1933 E Wayne St, Fort Wayne, IN 46803
Tel.: (260) 426-7495

Deister Machine Co. Inc.—(Continued)
Web Site:
　https://www.deistermachine.com
Rev.: $26,253,991
Emp.: 200
Mining Machinery
N.A.I.C.S.: 333131
E. Mark Deister *(Pres)*
Irwin F. Deister Jr. *(Chm)*

DEITER BROTHERS

1226 Stefko Blvd, Bethlehem, PA
18017
Tel.: (610) 868-8566
Web Site: https://www.dbrothers.com
Year Founded: 1929
Sales Range: $10-24.9 Million
Emp.: 40
Heating & Cooling Services
N.A.I.C.S.: 238220
James G. Deiter *(VP)*

DEITSCH PLASTICS COMPANY

14 Farwell St, West Haven, CT
06516-1717
Tel.: (203) 934-6601　　　CT
Web Site:
　https://www.deitschplastic.com
Sales Range: $75-99.9 Million
Emp.: 100
Mfr of Soft Plastics for Furniture
N.A.I.C.S.: 313320
Joseph Deitsch *(Pres)*
Sara Deitsch *(Sec)*
Yases Deitsch *(Mgr-Sls)*
Joshua H. Sandman *(VP)*

DEJEAN CONSTRUCTION COMPANY, INC.

3002 E X St, Deer Park, TX 77536
Tel.: (281) 479-5206　　　TX
Web Site: https://www.dejeanco.com
Year Founded: 1960
Sales Range: $25-49.9 Million
Emp.: 150
Industrial Buildings & Warehouses
Construction
N.A.I.C.S.: 236210
Larry Cunningham *(Pres)*

DEKALB AREA RETIREMENT CENTER

2944 Greenwood Acres Dr, Dekalb,
IL 60115
Tel.: (815) 756-8461　　　IL
Web Site:
　https://www.oakcrestdekalb.org
Year Founded: 1975
Sales Range: $10-24.9 Million
Emp.: 283
Retirement Community Operator
N.A.I.C.S.: 623311
Stephen P. Cichy *(Exec Dir)*
Linda Sherman *(Coord-Resident
Svcs)*
Dave Rourke *(Dir-Maintenance)*
Elizabeth Hoppenworth *(Dir-Resident
Svcs)*
Mary Fleetwood *(Dir-Housekeeping)*
Sharon Cox *(Dir-Nursing)*
Elena Canlas *(Dir-Food Svcs)*
Cheryl Buehler *(Office Mgr)*

DEKALB CHEROKEE COUNTIES GAS DISTRIBUTORS

1405 Gault Ave S, Fort Payne, AL
35967
Tel.: (256) 845-3731
Web Site: https://www.dcgas.org
Sales Range: $25-49.9 Million
Emp.: 60
Natural Gas Distribution
N.A.I.C.S.: 221210
Jason Higdon *(Gen Mgr)*

DEKALB FEEDS INC.

105 Dixon Ave, Rock Falls, IL 61071
Tel.: (815) 625-4546
Web Site:
　http://www.dekalbfeeds.com
Sales Range: $10-24.9 Million
Emp.: 54
Livestock Feeds
N.A.I.C.S.: 311119
Kelly Keaschall *(Pres)*

DEKALB MECHANICAL, INC.

339 Wurlitzer Dr, Dekalb, IL 60115-
2676
Tel.: (815) 756-6528
Web Site:
　https://www.dekalbmechanical.com
Sales Range: $10-24.9 Million
Emp.: 55
Plumbing Services
N.A.I.C.S.: 238220
Steve Doonan *(Owner)*

DEKALB MOLDED PLASTICS INC.

550 W Main St, Butler, IN 46721
Tel.: (260) 868-2105
Web Site:
　https://www.dekalbplastics.com
Sales Range: $10-24.9 Million
Emp.: 90
Molding Compounds & Plastics Structural Gas Assistance Services
N.A.I.C.S.: 325211
Rick Walters *(Pres & CEO)*
Mike Campbell *(Engr-Improvement)*
Max Houser *(Supvr-Maintenance)*
Mark Magnuson *(Supvr-Production)*
Diane Fogle *(Coord-Production
Scheduler & Inventory Control)*
Mick Egly *(Mgr-Molding)*
Richele Orn *(Controller)*
Gerry Schafer *(Mgr-Engrg & Quality)*
Marcia Lee *(Mgr-HR)*
Toni Rose *(Mgr-Matls)*

DEKALB REGIONAL HEALTHCARE SYSTEM, INC.

2701 N Decatur Rd, Decatur, GA
30033
Tel.: (404) 501-5200　　　GA
Web Site:
　http://www.dekalbmedical.org
Year Founded: 1992
Sales Range: $250-299.9 Million
Emp.: 4,575
Health Care Management Services
N.A.I.C.S.: 621491
Cheryl Iverson *(VP-Mktg Comm &
Corp Health-DeKalb Medical)*
Leroy Walker *(VP-HR)*
David L. Jollay *(Chm)*
Daniel J. Thompson *(Sec)*
Charles L. Clifton *(Treas)*
Robert E. Wilson *(Vice Chm)*
John Katsianis *(CFO & Sr VP)*
Jim Forstner *(COO & Exec VP-
DeKalb Medical)*
Elizabeth Patino *(CIO & VP-Info Sys)*
J. Tyler Tippett *(VP-Foundation & Volunteer Svcs)*
Raoul Mayer *(VP-Medical Affairs)*

Subsidiaries:

DeKalb Medical Downtown
Decatur　　　　　　　　　　(1)
450 N Candler St, Decatur, GA 30030-2626
Tel.: (404) 501-6700
Web Site:
　http://www.dekalbmedicalcenter.org
Sales Range: $25-49.9 Million
Emp.: 200
Hospital
N.A.I.C.S.: 621111
Eric Norwood *(Pres & CEO)*
Bill Foley *(Exec Dir-Support Svcs)*
Martin Kelvas *(Dir-Pharmacy Sys)*

Mike Folk *(Dir-Radiation Oncology)*
J. Tyler Tippett *(VP-Foundation & Volunteer
Svcs)*
Sharon Mawby *(Chief Nursing Officer & VP-
Patient Care)*

DEKALB STEEL & COWART IRON

3476 Lawrenceville Hwy, Tucker, GA
30084
Tel.: (770) 939-2300
Rev.: $18,455,253
Emp.: 112
Fabricated Structural Metal
N.A.I.C.S.: 332312
Glenn Bone *(Pres)*

DEKALB TELEPHONE COOPERATIVE

111 High St, Alexandria, TN 37012
Tel.: (615) 529-2955
Web Site: https://www.dtccom.net
Sales Range: $25-49.9 Million
Emp.: 100
Local Telephone Communications
N.A.I.C.S.: 517121
Leslie Greer *(CEO)*

DEKSIA LLC

49 Coldbrook St NE, Grand Rapids,
MI 49503
Tel.: (616) 207-3610　　　MI
Web Site: https://www.deksia.com
Year Founded: 2003
Emp.: 100
Digital Marketing Services
N.A.I.C.S.: 541810
Aaron VanderGalien *(CEO)*

Subsidiaries:

Anvil Media, Inc.　　　　　　(1)
310 NE Failing St, Portland, OR 97212
Tel.: (503) 595-6050
Web Site: http://www.anvilmediainc.com
Sales Range: $1-9.9 Million
Emp.: 16
Media Buying Services
N.A.I.C.S.: 541830
Kent Lewis *(Pres)*
Mike Terry *(VP)*
Josh Breese *(Dir-Strategy)*
Shannon Wolcott *(Mgr-Ops)*

DEL CORPORATION

436 Hwy 93 N, Scott, LA 70583
Tel.: (337) 237-8400
Web Site: https://www.deltank.com
Year Founded: 1979
Sales Range: $10-24.9 Million
Emp.: 60
Construction & Mining Machinery &
Equipment Whslr
N.A.I.C.S.: 423810
Dan Baker *(Mgr-Sls)*

DEL MAR AVIONICS

1601 C Alton Pkwy, Irvine, CA 92606-
4801
Tel.: (949) 250-3200　　　CA
Web Site: http://www.dma.com
Year Founded: 1952
Sales Range: $50-74.9 Million
Emp.: 23
Designer, Developer & Manufacturer
of Precision Load-Positioning Systems, Multi-Media Presentation Systems & Aerospace Electronics.
N.A.I.C.S.: 334419
Jack Hammond *(Sr VP & Gen Mgr)*
Fran Johnson *(Sec)*
Jim Singley *(VP-Sls & Svc)*

DEL MAR DESIGNS, INC.

301 Division Ave Unit 17, Ormond
Beach, FL 32174
Tel.: (386) 767-1997
Web Site: http://www.delmarfans.com
Year Founded: 2003

Sales Range: $125-149.9 Million
Emp.: 5
Other Home Furnishing Services
N.A.I.C.S.: 449129
Ron Harris *(Partner)*

DEL MAR FOOD PRODUCTS CORP.

1720 W Beach Rd, Watsonville, CA
95077
Tel.: (831) 722-3516
Web Site:
　https://www.delmarfoods.com
Sales Range: $10-24.9 Million
Emp.: 300
Process Frozen Fruits & Vegetables
N.A.I.C.S.: 311411
P. J. Mecozzi *(Pres)*
Lee Haskin *(VP-Ops)*
Silvia Lara *(Coord-Local Berries)*
Mike Minuth *(Controller)*

DEL MAR INDUSTRIES INC.

12901 SW Ave, Gardena, CA 90249
Tel.: (323) 321-0600　　　CA
Web Site:
　http://www.delmardiecasting.com
Year Founded: 1968
Rev.: $400,000,000
Emp.: 180
Zinc & Zinc-Base Alloy Die-Castings
Mfr
N.A.I.C.S.: 331523
Louis A. Cuhrt *(VP)*
Richard Trueblood *(VP)*
A. Richard Trueblood *(COO & Exec
VP)*

DEL MAR SEAFOODS INC.

331 Ford St, Watsonville, CA 95076
Tel.: (831) 763-3000
Web Site:
　http://www.delmarseafoods.com
Rev.: $23,000,000
Emp.: 17
Fresh Seafoods
N.A.I.C.S.: 424460
Joe Cappuccio *(Pres)*
Joe Riggio *(CFO)*

DEL MONTE CAPITAL MEAT CO. INC.

948 Arden Way, Sacramento, CA
95815
Tel.: (916) 927-0595
Web Site:
　http://www.delmontemeat.com
Sales Range: $25-49.9 Million
Emp.: 40
Meats, Fresh
N.A.I.C.S.: 424470
David De Benedetti *(Pres)*

DEL MONTE ELECTRIC CO. INC.

6998 Sierra Ct, Dublin, CA 94568-
2662
Tel.: (925) 829-6000
Web Site:
　http://www.delmonteelectric.com
Year Founded: 1938
Emp.: 200
Electrical Work
N.A.I.C.S.: 238210
John Hunter *(Pres)*
Lynn Martin *(Controller)*
Deborah Cota *(Mgr-AP)*

DEL MONTELL MOTORS LIMITED

1127 Santa Monica Blvd, Santa
Monica, CA 90401
Tel.: (310) 829-3535
Web Site: https://www.smbmw.com
Sales Range: $25-49.9 Million
Emp.: 100

Automobiles, New & Used
N.A.I.C.S.: 441110
Del Montell (Gen Mgr-Sls)
Henry Hall (Mgr-Fin)

DEL NORTE CREDIT UNION

PO Box 1180, Los Alamos, NM 87544
Tel.: (505) 455-5356　　　　　　NM
Web Site: http://www.dncu.org
Year Founded: 1954
Sales Range: $10-24.9 Million
Emp.: 151
Credit Union
N.A.I.C.S.: 522130
Clyde Leyba (Chm)
Luis Alba (Treas)

DEL PAPA DISTRIBUTING CO.

6702 Broadway St, Galveston, TX 77554-8906
Tel.: (409) 741-4400　　　　　　TX
Web Site:
　http://www.delpapabud.com
Year Founded: 1947
Sales Range: $50-74.9 Million
Emp.: 215
Distr of Beer & Ale
N.A.I.C.S.: 424810
Larry DelPapa (Pres)
Bill Falkenhagen (CFO & Exec VP)
Mike McAfee (VP-Mktg)
Karla Mock Oates (Coord-Adv)
Alex Guidroz (Exec VP-Sls & Mktg)

DEL REAL FOODS

11041 Inland Ave, Mira Loma, CA 91752
Tel.: (951) 681-0395
Web Site:
　http://www.delrealfoods.com
Year Founded: 1957
Sales Range: $10-24.9 Million
Emp.: 85
Canned Food Mfr
N.A.I.C.S.: 311423
Herb Bowden (VP-Sls & Mktg)
Michael Axelrod (CEO)
Ed Lambert (Chm)
Viviano del Villar (COO)

DEL REY JUICE CO.

5286 S Del Rey Ave, Del Rey, CA 93616
Tel.: (559) 888-8533
Sales Range: $10-24.9 Million
Emp.: 99
Fruit & Vegetable Production Services
N.A.I.C.S.: 311411
Eric Fritz (Pres)

DEL SOL FOOD COMPANY, INC.

PO Box 2243, Brennan, TX 77834
Tel.: (979) 836-5978
Web Site:
　http://www.briannassaladdress.com
Sales Range: $1-9.9 Million
Emp.: 50
Salad Dressing Mfr
N.A.I.C.S.: 311941
Jerry Brown (Pres)
Jay McKeown (Dir-Fin & Tech-BRIANNAS)
Scott Eckert (Pres/CEO-BRIANNAS)
Jenny Van Dorf (Dir-Brand Mktg-BRIANNAS)

DEL TORO LOAN SERVICING, INC.

2434 Southport Way Ste F, National City, CA 91950
Tel.: (619) 474-5400
Web Site:
　http://www.deltoroloanservicing.com

Secondary Market Financing
N.A.I.C.S.: 522299
Drew Louis (Pres)

Subsidiaries:

Evergreen Escrow, Inc.　　　　　(1)
1016 57th St E #100, Sumner, WA 98390
Tel.: (253) 848-5678
Web Site: http://www.evergreenescrow.com
Sales Range: $1-9.9 Million
Emp.: 23
Offices of Real Estate Agents & Brokers
N.A.I.C.S.: 531210
Phil Dryden (Owner)

DEL WEST ENGINEERING INC.

28128 W Livingston Ave, Valencia, CA 91355
Tel.: (661) 295-5700
Web Site: http://www.delwestusa.com
Year Founded: 1973
Sales Range: $25-49.9 Million
Emp.: 150
Race Car Components
N.A.I.C.S.: 336390
Al Sommer (Chm & CEO)

DEL-AIR HEATING, AIR CONDITIONING & REFRIGERATION CORP.

531 Codisco Way, Sanford, FL 32771
Tel.: (407) 831-2665　　　　　　FL
Web Site: https://www.delair.com
Year Founded: 1983
Sales Range: $25-49.9 Million
Emp.: 325
Plumbing, Heating & Air-Conditioning
N.A.I.C.S.: 238220
Bob Dello Russo (Founder & CEO)

Subsidiaries:

American Residential Services LLC　　　　　　　　　　　　　　(1)
965 Rdg Lake Blvd Ste 201, Memphis, TN 38120-9421
Tel.: (901) 271-9700
Web Site: http://www.ars.com
Sales Range: $600-649.9 Million
HVAC & Plumbing Services
N.A.I.C.S.: 238220
Ryan Kaler (Mgr-Pur & Fleet)
Sylvia Respess (Supvr-Cash Mgmt)
Scott Boose (CEO)
Jennifer Hughes (Dir-Comm)
Mike Midgett (Chief Sls & Mktg Officer)

Subsidiary (Domestic):

A. J. Perri, Inc.　　　　　　　　(2)
1162 Pine Brook Rd, Tinton Falls, NJ 07724
Tel.: (732) 733-2548
Web Site: http://www.ajperri.com
Sales Range: $1-9.9 Million
Emp.: 25
Plumbing, Heating & Air-Conditioning Contractors
N.A.I.C.S.: 238220
Greg Johnston (Mgr-Installation)

Aspen Air Conditioning, Inc.　　(2)
3999 N Dixie Hwy, Boca Raton, FL 33431-4520
Tel.: (561) 395-1500
Web Site: http://www.aspenac.com
Plumbing, Heating & Air-Conditioning Contractors
N.A.I.C.S.: 238220
Steven Maguire (Pres & Sec)

Atlas Trillo Heating & Air Conditioning, Inc.　　　　　　　　　(2)
2305 Paragon Dr, San Jose, CA 95131
Tel.: (408) 444-6310
Web Site: http://www.atlastrillo.com
Sales Range: $1-9.9 Million
Emp.: 60
Household & Commercial HVAC Heating & Cooling Services
N.A.I.C.S.: 238220
Steve Trillo (Pres)

Brothers Air & Heat, Inc.　　　　(2)
1320 E Main St, Rock Hill, SC 29730
Tel.: (803) 327-4040

Web Site: http://www.brotherair.com
Sales Range: $10-24.9 Million
HVAC & Plumbing Systems Installation & Repairs
N.A.I.C.S.: 238220
Donald Costner (Gen Mgr)
Roger Costner (Gen Mgr)

East Coast Air & Heat, LLC　　(1)
3435 S Hopkins Ave, Titusville, FL 32780-5656
Tel.: (321) 383-1930
Web Site: http://www.eastcoastairheat.com
Plumbing, Heating & Air-Conditioning Contractors
N.A.I.C.S.: 238220
Bill Burson (Pres)

DEL-CO. WATER CO. INC.

6658 Olentangy River Rd, Delaware, OH 43015
Tel.: (740) 548-7746
Web Site: http://www.delcowater.com
Year Founded: 1969
Rev.: $10,305,724
Emp.: 85
Water Supply
N.A.I.C.S.: 221310
Sandra Terry (Office Mgr)

DEL-MONDE INC.

10107 Toebben Dr Ste 100, Independence, KY 41051
Tel.: (859) 371-7780
Web Site: http://www.delmonde.com
Year Founded: 1986
Sales Range: $10-24.9 Million
Emp.: 60
Heating & Air Conditioning Contractors
N.A.I.C.S.: 238220
Herb Spaeth (Pres)
Daryl Schoulthies (Mgr-Svcs)

DEL-THO INDUSTRIES INC.

6170 S Boyle Ave, Vernon, CA 90058
Tel.: (323) 585-3115　　　　　　CA
Web Site: https://www.del-tho.com
Year Founded: 1959
Rev.: $30,000,000
Emp.: 13
Industrial & Personal Service Paper
N.A.I.C.S.: 424130
Anthony DeLellis Sr. (Chm)
Anthony R. DeLellis Jr. (Pres)

DEL-TRON PRECISION, INC.

5 Trowbridge Dr, Bethel, CT 06801
Tel.: (203) 778-2727
Web Site: https://www.deltron.com
Year Founded: 1974
Rev.: $5,000,000
Emp.: 50
Linear Motion Position Equipment Mfr
N.A.I.C.S.: 332991
Emil Melvin (Dir-Sls & Mktg)
Bill Schule (Mgr-Engrg)

DELACO STEEL CORP.

8111 Tireman Ave, Dearborn, MI 48126
Tel.: (313) 491-1200
Web Site:
　http://www.thediezgroup.com
Year Founded: 1973
Automotive Steel Blanks Mfr
N.A.I.C.S.: 331110
John Favorite (VP-Sls Admin)

Subsidiaries:

Delaco Kasle LLC　　　　　　　(1)
25225 Hall Rd, Woodhaven, MI 48183-5111
Tel.: (734) 692-8000
Web Site: http://www.delacosteel.com
Sales Range: $100-124.9 Million
Emp.: 100
Supplier of Automotive Steel Blanks; Owned 49% by Steel Technologies, Inc & 51% by Delaco Steel Corporation
N.A.I.C.S.: 331110

Ivan Brillhart (Gen Mgr)

DELACY FORD INC.

3061 Transit Rd, Elma, NY 14059
Tel.: (716) 668-1200
Web Site:
　http://www.nickelcityford.com
Sales Range: $50-74.9 Million
Emp.: 60
Automobiles, New & Used
N.A.I.C.S.: 441110
Peter Delacy (VP)
Ed Stiller (Mgr-Parts)
Bryan Cooksey (Mgr-Fleet Accts)
Dennis Beres (Bus Mgr)
Dwayne DeVaughn (Bus Mgr)
Jim Grew (Mgr-Fleet Accts)
Mark Moscato (Bus Mgr)
Patrick Higgins (Gen Mgr-Sls)
Sheryl Fleming (Mgr-Customer Rels)
James Delacy Sr. (Pres)

DELAFIELD CORPORATION

1520 Flower Ave, Duarte, CA 91010
Tel.: (626) 303-0740
Web Site: https://www.dftcorp.com
Sales Range: $25-49.9 Million
Emp.: 120
Flexible Metallic Hose Mfr
N.A.I.C.S.: 332999
Jim Martin (VP)
Henry Custodia (Controller)

DELAN ASSOCIATES, INC.

30S Ocean Ave Ste 104, Freeport, NY 11520
Tel.: (516) 442-0040
Web Site: https://www.delanhq.com
Year Founded: 2002
Sales Range: $10-24.9 Million
Emp.: 155
Training & IT Network & Design Services for the Federal Government
N.A.I.C.S.: 921190
Michael Chung (Founder & Pres)
Rhonda Wheeler (Dir-Southeast Reg)
Charmaine Black (Dir-Northeast Reg)

DELANDE SUPPLY CO. INC.

58 Pulaski St, Peabody, MA 01960-7707
Tel.: (978) 532-5850
Web Site: https://www.delande.com
Sales Range: $10-24.9 Million
Emp.: 30
Electrical Supplies
N.A.I.C.S.: 423610
David Delande (Owner)
Rick Delande (Owner)

DELANO OIL COMPANY

301 W Washington St, Saint James, MO 65559
Tel.: (573) 265-3266
Web Site: http://delanooil.com
Sales Range: $10-24.9 Million
Emp.: 20
Convenience Stores, Independent
N.A.I.C.S.: 445131
William J. Delano Jr. (Pres)

DELANT CONSTRUCTION CO.

7380 NW 77th Ct, Miami, FL 33166
Tel.: (305) 592-2223
Web Site:
　http://www.delantconstruction.com
Rev.: $33,400,000
Emp.: 70
New Housing Operative Builders
N.A.I.C.S.: 236117
Juan M. Delgado (Pres)
James Abbondanza (Project Mgr)
Jorte Pazos (Project Mgr)

DELANY CAPITAL MANAGEMENT CORP.

Delany Capital Management Corp.—(Continued)

6972 SE Harbor Cir, Stuart, FL 34996
Tel.: (772) 334-2451
Web Site: https://www.dcmcorp.com
Holding Company
N.A.I.C.S.: 551112
Logan D. Delany Jr. *(Pres)*
Joel Motley *(Principal)*

Subsidiaries:

DMI Technology Corp. **(1)**
1 Progress Dr, Dover, NH 03820
Tel.: (603) 742-3330
Web Site: http://www.dmitechnology.com
Sales Range: $10-24.9 Million
Emp.: 100
Holding Company; Electromechanical Motors, Actuators & Motion Control Products Mfr
N.A.I.C.S.: 551112

Subsidiary (Domestic):

ElectroCraft, Inc. **(2)**
2 Marin Way Ste 3, Stratham, NH 03885-2578
Tel.: (603) 742-3330
Web Site: http://www.electrocraft.com
Electromechanical Motor Actuators & Motion Control Product Mfr
N.A.I.C.S.: 335312
Logan D. Delany Jr. *(Chm)*
Rob Kerber *(VP-Global Sls & Mktg)*
Daniel Drury *(CFO)*
Tom Dalton *(Pres & CEO)*

Subsidiary (Domestic):

ElectroCraft Arkansas, Inc. **(3)**
1701 S Benton St, Searcy, AR 72143
Tel.: (501) 268-4203
Web Site: http://www.electrocraft.com
Evaporator Fan Motors Mfr, Designer, Distr & Supplier
N.A.I.C.S.: 335312
Doug Cook *(Gen Mgr)*

ElectroCraft Michigan, Inc. **(3)**
4480 Varsity Dr Ste G, Ann Arbor, MI 48108-5007
Tel.: (734) 662-7771
Web Site: http://www.electrocraft.com
Sales Range: $10-24.9 Million
Emp.: 20
Motion Control Technology Mfr
N.A.I.C.S.: 334519

ElectroCraft New Hampshire, Inc. **(3)**
1 Progress Dr, Dover, NH 03820-5450
Tel.: (603) 742-3330
Web Site: http://www.electrocraft.com
Sales Range: $10-24.9 Million
Emp.: 30
Precision Motors, Rotating Components, Blowers & Fans Designer & Mfr
N.A.I.C.S.: 335312
Jack Lemire *(VP-Sls-Americas)*
Mike Karsonovidh *(Pres & CEO)*

Hansen Corporation **(3)**
901 S 1st St, Princeton, IN 47670-2369
Tel.: (812) 385-3415
Web Site: http://www.hansen-motor.com
Sales Range: $100-124.9 Million
Emp.: 300
Synchronous Timing Motors, Stepper Motors, D C Motors, Chart Drives & Related Products Mfr
N.A.I.C.S.: 335312
Dan Hawkins *(Production Mgr)*
John Bertram *(Controller)*

DELAWARE BOOK INC.
5700 Casey Dr, Knoxville, TN 37909
Tel.: (865) 558-8187
Sales Range: $25-49.9 Million
Emp.: 900
Book Stores
N.A.I.C.S.: 459210
David Hinkle *(Pres)*

DELAWARE COUNTY REAL ESTATE

108 Main St, Stamford, NY 12167-1137
Tel.: (607) 652-3311   **NY**
Web Site:
https://www.delcountyrealestate.com
Year Founded: 1973
Sales Range: $10-24.9 Million
Emp.: 11
Real Estate Broker
N.A.I.C.S.: 531210
Michael J. Bergleitner *(Sec)*
George C. Bergleitner Jr. *(Pres)*
George C. Bergleitner III *(Chm)*

DELAWARE COUNTY REGIONAL WATER QUALITY CONTROL AUTHORITY
100 E 5th St, Chester, PA 19013-4508
Tel.: (610) 876-5523   **PA**
Web Site: https://www.delcora.org
Year Founded: 1971
Sales Range: $25-49.9 Million
Emp.: 115
Sewerage Water Waste Managemnet Company
N.A.I.C.S.: 221320
John Pileggi *(Controller)*

DELAWARE ELECTRIC COOPERATIVE
14198 Sussex Hwy, Greenwood, DE 19950
Tel.: (302) 349-9090   **DE**
Web Site: https://www.delaware.coop
Year Founded: 1938
Sales Range: $200-249.9 Million
Emp.: 135
Electric Power Distr
N.A.I.C.S.: 221122
Bruce Henry *(Vice Chm)*
Gary Cripps *(COO)*
Mark Nielson *(VP)*
William J. Wells *(Chm)*

DELAWARE ELECTRO INDUSTRIES INC.
9248 Eton Ave, Chatsworth, CA 91311-5807
Tel.: (818) 786-8111
Web Site: https://www.libertyeng.com
Year Founded: 1986
Sales Range: $25-49.9 Million
Emp.: 46
Electrical Apparatus & Equipment Distr
N.A.I.C.S.: 423610
Steven Hollopeter *(Pres)*

DELAWARE HOSPICE, INC.
3515 Silverside Rd No 100, Wilmington, DE 19810-4924
Tel.: (302) 478-5707   **DE**
Web Site:
http://www.delawarehospice.org
Year Founded: 1982
Sales Range: $25-49.9 Million
Emp.: 479
Health Care Srvices
N.A.I.C.S.: 622110

DELAWARE MOTOR SALES INC.
1606 Pennsylvania Ave, Wilmington, DE 19806
Tel.: (302) 656-3100
Web Site:
http://www.autoteamdelaware.com
Rev.: $47,000,000
Emp.: 120
Automobiles, New & Used
N.A.I.C.S.: 441110
Michael Uffner *(Pres)*

DELAWARE MUSEUM OF

NATURAL HISTORY
4840 Kennett Pike, Wilmington, DE 19807
Tel.: (302) 658-9111
Web Site: http://www.delmnh.org
Sales Range: $10-24.9 Million
Emp.: 20
Museum Services
N.A.I.C.S.: 712110
Jean Woods *(Dir-Collections)*

DELAWARE NORTH COMPANIES, INC.
250 Delaware Ave, Buffalo, NY 14202
Tel.: (716) 858-5000   **DE**
Web Site:
https://www.delawarenorth.com
Year Founded: 1915
Sales Range: $1-4.9 Billion
Emp.: 43,900
Food Service Contractors
N.A.I.C.S.: 722310
Charlie Jacobs *(CEO-Boston)*
Michael Reinert *(VP-Supply Mgmt Svcs)*
Todd Merry *(CMO)*
Kathy Gill *(VP-Mktg & Comm)*
Alexis Becker *(VP-Internal Audit)*
Scott Socha *(Pres-Parks & Resorts)*
James Obletz *(VP-Corp Bus Dev)*
Jack McNeill *(Sr VP-Govt Affairs)*
Stephen Harrington *(Chief Procurement Officer)*
Jill Kelly *(VP-HR)*
Steve Bass *(COO-Travel)*
Jim McGrath *(VP-Lodging-Parks & Resorts)*
Christina Rothenberger *(VP-HR Shared Svcs)*
Paul Adey *(CFO)*
Frank Mendicino *(Chief Admin Officer & Exec VP)*
Doug Tetley *(Mng Dir-UK)*
Lou Jacobs *(Co-CEO)*
Jeremy M. Jacobs Sr. *(Chm)*
Jeremy M. Jacobs Jr. *(Co-CEO)*

Subsidiaries:

American Park 'n Swap **(1)**
3801 E Washington St, Phoenix, AZ 85034
Tel.: (716) 858-5000
Sales Range: $25-49.9 Million
Emp.: 50
Operation of Open-Air Bazaars
N.A.I.C.S.: 722511

Delaware North Companies Gaming & Entertainment **(1)**
250 Delaware Ave, Buffalo, NY 14202 **(100%)**
Tel.: (716) 858-5000
Web Site: http://www.dncinc.com
Sales Range: $25-49.9 Million
Emp.: 350
Owner & Operator of Greyhound & Horse Racecourses
N.A.I.C.S.: 711212

Delaware North Companies International, Ltd. **(1)**
40 Fountain Plz, Buffalo, NY 14202 **(100%)**
Tel.: (716) 858-5000
Web Site: http://www.dncinc.com
Sales Range: $25-49.9 Million
Emp.: 350
Foodservice, Accommodation & Facilities Management & Hospitality Services
N.A.I.C.S.: 722513
Jeremy Jacobs *(Pres)*

Subsidiary (Non-US):

Delaware North Companies (Australia) Pty. Ltd. **(2)**
Level 2 630 Chruch St, Richmond, 3121, VIC, Australia **(100%)**
Tel.: (61) 393265686
Sales Range: $10-24.9 Million
Emp.: 50

Foodservice Accommodation & Facility Management & Hospitality Services
N.A.I.C.S.: 722511

Delaware North Companies International Ltd **(2)**
11th Floor York House Empire Way, Wembley, HA9 0WS, United Kingdom
Tel.: (44) 2087959630
Hospitality & Foodservices Management
N.A.I.C.S.: 713990

Delaware North Companies Parks & Resorts **(1)**
40 Fountain Plz, Buffalo, NY 14202 **(100%)**
Tel.: (716) 858-5768
Web Site: http://www.delawarenorth.com
Sales Range: $10-24.9 Million
Emp.: 150
Hospitality Services & Parks Operations
N.A.I.C.S.: 722511
Kelly Scofield *(Mgr-New Bus)*
Barry Freilicher *(Sr VP-Bus Dev)*
Kevin Quinlivan *(CIO)*
Todd Merry *(CMO)*
Christopher J. Feeney *(CFO)*
Bill Borden *(Dir-Food & Beverage)*
Jim Houser *(Pres)*
Richard Ayson *(Sr VP-Bus Dev-Travel Hospitality)*
Emilio Fortini *(Gen Mgr)*

Subsidiary (Domestic):

Yosemite Concession Services Mail Order Dept **(2)**
9032 Village Dr, Yosemite National Park, CA 95389 **(100%)**
Tel.: (209) 372-1354
Principal Concessioner at Yosemite National Park
N.A.I.C.S.: 445131

Delaware North Companies Sportservice **(1)**
250 Delaware Ave, Buffalo, NY 14202 **(100%)**
Tel.: (716) 858-5000
Web Site:
http://www.delawarenorthcompanies.com
Sales Range: $10-24.9 Million
Emp.: 500
Concessionaire
N.A.I.C.S.: 722513
Rick Abramson *(Pres)*
Barry Freilicher *(VP-Bus Dev)*
Allison Appoloney *(Gen Mgr-First Niagara Center)*
Lateyfa Ali *(VP-Talent & Org Dev)*
Alexis Becker *(VP-Internal Audit)*
John Czwartacki *(VP-Strategic Comm & Governmental Affairs)*
Kathy Gill *(VP-Mktg & Comm)*
Abigail Kozara *(VP & Asst Gen Counsel)*
Todd Merry *(CMO)*
Kevin Quinlivan *(CIO)*
Mike Reinert *(VP-Supply Mgmt Svcs)*
Jeff Sellers *(VP-Hospitality Dev & Construction)*
Yvette Vincent *(VP-IT)*

Delaware North Companies Travel Hospitality Services **(1)**
40 Fountain Plz, Buffalo, NY 14202 **(100%)**
Tel.: (716) 858-5000
Sales Range: $10-24.9 Million
Emp.: 250
Airport & In-Flight Food & Beverage Services, Retail Merchandising
N.A.I.C.S.: 722513
Nicolas Liberto *(VP-Fin)*
Steve Nowaczyk *(VP-Fin)*
Kevin Kelly *(Pres)*

Finger Lakes Racing Association Inc. **(1)**
5857 Rte 96, Farmington, NY 14425
Tel.: (585) 924-3232
Web Site:
http://www.fingerlakesracetrack.com
Sales Range: $25-49.9 Million
Emp.: 425
Thoroughbred Race Track Services
N.A.I.C.S.: 711212
Chris Riegle *(Pres & Gen Mgr)*

New Boston Garden Corp. **(1)**

1 Fleetcenter Pl Ste 200, Boston, MA
02114-1303
Tel.: (617) 624-1050
Web Site: http://www.fleetcenter.com
Sales Range: $10-24.9 Million
Emp.: 250
Operator of a Sports & Entertainment Arena
N.A.I.C.S.: 722511

Patina Restaurant Group LLC **(1)**
120 W 45th St 16th Fl, New York, NY
10036
Tel.: (212) 789-8100
Web Site: http://www.patinagroup.com
Sales Range: $200-249.9 Million
Restaurants Owner & Operator
N.A.I.C.S.: 722511
Nick Valenti *(CEO)*
David Ruede *(VP-Design & Construction)*
Eric Kaplan *(Sr VP-Ops-Rock Center)*
Joachim Splichal *(Founder)*
Joe Polidora *(Sr VP-Ops-Sports & Enter-tainment)*
Laura Santella-Saccone *(Sr VP-Mktg)*
Peter Wyss *(Sr VP-Ops)*
Steve Charron *(VP-Pur)*
Steven Tanner *(CFO)*
Dawn Hernandez *(VP-HR)*
Tanja Yokum *(Dir-PR & Mktg)*
Matthew King *(Pres-Delaware North)*

Subsidiary (Domestic):

Patina Group **(2)**
1150 Olive St Ste Tg25, Los Angeles, CA
90015-2223
Tel.: (213) 239-2500
Web Site: http://www.patinagroup.com
Emp.: 60
Restaurant Management Services
N.A.I.C.S.: 541611
Nick Valenti *(CEO)*
Joachim Splichal *(Founder)*
Julie Van *(Sr Mgr-HR)*
Scott Kleckner *(VP-Ops)*
Leah Smith *(VP-Mktg)*

Unit (Domestic):

Cafe Centro **(3)**
200 Park Ave, New York, NY 10166
Tel.: (212) 818-1222
Web Site: http://www.patinagroup.com
Sales Range: $10-24.9 Million
Restaurant Services
N.A.I.C.S.: 722511
Alexandra Miller *(Mgr)*

Cafe Pinot **(3)**
700 W 5th St, Los Angeles, CA 90071
Tel.: (213) 239-6500
Web Site: http://www.patinagroup.com
Sales Range: $10-24.9 Million
Emp.: 55
Restaurant Services
N.A.I.C.S.: 722511
Chriselda Chew *(Gen Mgr)*

Kendall's Brasserie & Bar **(3)**
135 N Grand Ave, Los Angeles, CA 90012
Tel.: (213) 972-7322
Web Site: http://www.kendallsbrasserie.com
Emp.: 25
Restaurant Services
N.A.I.C.S.: 722511
David Stork *(Exec Dir-Ops)*

Market Cafe **(3)**
550 S Hope St, Los Angeles, CA 90071
Tel.: (213) 412-9900
Web Site: http://www.patinagroup.com
Restaurant Services
N.A.I.C.S.: 722511
Steve Charron *(CFO)*

Nick & Stef's Steakhouse **(3)**
330 S Hope St, Los Angeles, CA 90071
Tel.: (213) 680-0330
Web Site: http://www.patinagroup.com
Sales Range: $10-24.9 Million
Restaurant Services
N.A.I.C.S.: 722511

Patina **(3)**
141 S Grand Ave, Los Angeles, CA 90012
Tel.: (213) 972-3331
Web Site: http://www.patinagroup.com
Emp.: 50
Restaurant Services
N.A.I.C.S.: 722511

Kevin Welby *(Gen Mgr)*

Pinot Provence **(3)**
686 Anton Blvd, Costa Mesa, CA 92626-1920
Tel.: (714) 444-5900
Web Site: http://www.patinagroup.com
Sales Range: $10-24.9 Million
Emp.: 52
Restaurant Services
N.A.I.C.S.: 722511
Christian Muniz *(Dir-Ops)*

DELAWARE OTSEGO CORP.

1 RailRd Ave, Cooperstown, NY
13326-1110
Tel.: (607) 547-2555 NY
Web Site: http://www.nysw.com
Year Founded: 1997
Sales Range: $25-49.9 Million
Emp.: 150
Railroads & Line-Haul Operating
N.A.I.C.S.: 482111
Nathan Fenno *(Pres)*
Richard Hensel *(VP-Engrg)*
John Senton *(VP-Mktg)*
William Bloomfield *(Chief Transportation Officer)*

Subsidiaries:

Susquehanna Properties, Inc. **(1)**
1 Railroad Ave, Cooperstown, NY
13326-1110 **(100%)**
Tel.: (607) 547-2555
Web Site: http://www.nysw.com
Rev.: $1,200,000
Emp.: 100
Nonresidential Building Operators
N.A.I.C.S.: 531120

The New York Susquehanna & West-
ern Railway Corp **(1)**
1 Railroad Ave, Cooperstown, NY
13326-1110 **(100%)**
Tel.: (607) 547-2555
Web Site: http://www.nysw.com
Sales Range: $10-24.9 Million
Emp.: 30
Local & Suburban Transit
N.A.I.C.S.: 485112
Tabetha Rathbone *(CFO)*
Nathan Fenno *(Pres)*
Bill Bloomfield *(Chief Transportation Officer)*

DELAWARE RACING ASSO-CIATION

777 Delaware Park Blvd, Wilmington,
DE 19804
Tel.: (302) 994-2521
Web Site: http://www.delpark.com
Sales Range: $75-99.9 Million
Emp.: 2,000
Horse Race Track Operation & Ca-
sino
N,A,I.C.S.: 711212
William Fasy *(Pres)*
William M. Rickman Jr. *(CEO)*

DELAWARE RIVER & BAY AU-THORITY

Delaware Memorial Bridge Plz Junc-
tion of I 295 U S Rte 9, New Castle,
DE 19720
Tel.: (302) 571-6300
Web Site: https://www.drba.net
Year Founded: 1962
Sales Range: $75-99.9 Million
Emp.: 500
Transportation & Economic Develop-
ment Services
N.A.I.C.S.: 488490
Victor A. Ferzetti *(CFO)*
Charlotte L. Crowell *(Chief HR Offi-cer)*
Geraldine DiNicola-Owens *(CIO)*
Vincent P. Meconi *(COO)*

DELAWARE RIVER JOINT TOLL BRIDGE COMMISSION

110 Wood St, Morrisville, PA 19067

Tel.: (215) 295-5061
Web Site: http://www.drjtbg.org
Year Founded: 1934
Sales Range: $25-49.9 Million
Emp.: 314
Highway Bridge Operation
N.A.I.C.S.: 488490
Frank J. Tolotta *(Acting Exec Dir & Deputy Exec Dir-Ops)*
Joseph J. Resta *(Exec Dir)*
Sean M. Hill *(Deputy Exec Dir-Ops)*
David R. DeGerolamo *(Chm)*

DELAWARE RIVER PORT AU-THORITY OF PENNSYLVANIA & NEW JERSEY

1 Port Ctr 2 Riverside Dr, Camden,
NJ 08101-1949
Tel.: (856) 968-2000
Web Site: http://www.drpa.org
Year Founded: 1919
Rev.: $371,907,000
Assets: $2,525,694,000
Liabilities: $1,745,855,000
Net Worth: $779,839,000
Earnings: $109,840,000
Emp.: 218
Fiscal Year-end: 12/31/18
Regional Waterway Transportation
Agency
N.A.I.C.S.: 926120
John Hanson *(CEO)*
Jeffrey L. Nash *(Vice Chm)*
James M. White *(CFO & Treas)*
Maria J. Wing *(Deputy CEO)*
Raymond J. Santarelli *(Gen Counsel & Sec)*
Toni P. Brown *(Chief Admin Officer)*
Robert P. Hicks *(COO)*
Michael Venuto *(Chief Engr)*
Ryan N. Boyer *(Chm)*

Subsidiaries:

Port Authority Transit Corp. of Penn-
sylvania And New Jersey Inc. **(1)**
PO Box 4262, Lindenwold, NJ
08021 **(100%)**
Tel.: (856) 772-6900
Web Site: http://www.ridepatco.org
Sales Range: $25-49.9 Million
Emp.: 375
Provider of Local & Suburban Transit Ser-
vices
N.A.I.C.S.: 485112
John Matheussen *(Pres & CEO)*

DELAWARE RIVER STEVE-DORES INC.

441 N 5th St Ste 210, Philadelphia,
PA 19123
Tel.: (215) 440-4100
Web Site: https://www.d-r-s.com
Sales Range: $10-24.9 Million
Emp.: 245
Stevedoring
N.A.I.C.S.: 488320
Robert W. Palaima *(Pres)*

DELAWARE RIVER WATER-FRONT CORPORATION

121 N Columbus Blvd, Philadelphia,
PA 19106
Tel.: (215) 922-2386 PA
Web Site:
https://www.delawareriverwater
front.com
Year Founded: 1970
Sales Range: $10-24.9 Million
Emp.: 226
River Waterfront Operator
N.A.I.C.S.: 924110
Joseph A. Forkin *(VP-Ops & Dev)*
Rinku Modi *(Dir-Fin)*
Lavelle Young *(Dir-Ops)*

DELAWARE STATE UNIVER-SITY

1200 N Dupont Hwy, Dover, DE
19901
Tel.: (302) 857-6060
Web Site: http://www.desu.edu
Year Founded: 1891
Colleges & Universities
N.A.I.C.S.: 611310
Irene Chapman-Hawkins *(Assoc VP-HR)*
Denese Lindsey *(VP-Fin & Admin)*
Carolyn Curry *(VP-Institutional Ad-vancement Office)*
Teresa Hardee *(VP-Fin)*
Alton Lavan *(Dir-Dev)*
Angenette Oliver *(Mgr-Enrollment Ops)*
Ayanna Overall *(Dir-Application Dev)*
Anthony Patterson *(Dir-Plng & Con-struction)*
Al Tunnell *(Mgr-Safety & Risk)*
Alexander J. Volpe *(Mgr-Network)*
Ahira Y. Smith *(Dir-Academic Advise-ment)*
Bryant T. Bell *(Dir-Major Gifts)*
Charmaine Babb *(Mgr-User Svcs)*
Christopher D. Garland *(Mgr-Academic Tech Support Center)*
Charity Shockley *(Dir-Grants Mgmt)*
Don Wujtewicz *(Program Mgr-Aquatic Sciences)*
Evelyn Crump *(Mgr-Clinical)*
Jennifer Rickard *(Assoc Dir-Integrated Mktg)*
JoAnn Holmes *(Mgr-Campus Store)*
Jeanel Lofland *(Dir-Budget)*
John Samardza *(Mgr-Theater)*
Jonathan Stewart *(Mgr-Aquatics)*
Jessica Wilson *(Dir-Pur)*
Karla E. Lewis *(Mgr-Clinical)*
Karen Fair *(Dir-Facilities Mgmt)*
Karen Sissons *(Mgr-Intramural Sports)*
Latasha Daniels *(Mgr-Intl Affairs Of-fice)*
Stacey Colton *(Dir-Integrated Mktg)*
Vernice Oney *(Coord-Benefits)*
Vita Pickrum *(Assoc VP-Dev)*
Zafar Chaudhry *(Assoc VP-Fin & Ad-min)*
Wilma Mishoe *(Chm & Interim Pres)*

Subsidiaries:

Wesley College, Inc. **(1)**
120 N State St, Dover, DE 19901
Tel.: (302) 736-2300
Web Site: http://wesley.edu
Graduate & Undergraduate College
N.A.I.C.S.: 611310
William N. Johnston *(Pres)*
Patricia Dwyer *(Provost & VP-Academic Affairs)*
Greg Potts *(VP-Enrollment Mgmt)*
Chris A. Wood *(VP-Institutional Advance-ment)*
Mike Drass *(Exec Dir-Intercollegiate Sports & Recreation)*
Christopher Jester *(Assoc Dir-Admissions)*
Nate Biondi *(Asst Dir-Residence Life)*
George Frunzi *(Dir-Adult Studies)*
Amanda Downes *(Dir-Advancement Svcs)*
Brian Cass *(Dir-Band)*
Elana Baukman *(Dir-Campus Life)*
Jessica Cook *(Dir-Comm & Mktg)*
Cathy Anderson *(Dir-Dev)*
Cassandra Hynson *(Dir-Enrollment Comm)*
Susan Houser *(Dir-Enrollment Ops)*
Kevin Cullen *(Dir-Intl Programs)*
Walter Beaupre *(Dir-Safety & Security)*
J. Michael Hall *(Dir-Student Fin Aid)*
Christine Gibson *(VP-Fin)*
Robert V. A. Harra *(Chm)*
D. Wayne Holden *(Sec)*
William J. Strickland *(Vice Chm)*

DELAWARE SUPERMARKETS INC.

1600 W Newport Pike, Wilmington,
DE 19804
Tel.: (302) 999-1801

Delaware Supermarkets Inc.—(Continued)

Web Site: http://www.shoprite.com
Rev.: $54,000,000
Emp.: 275
Supermarket
N.A.I.C.S.: 445110
Bernard F. Kenny (Pres)
Dan Tanzer (Dir-Admin Svcs)

DELAWARE VALLEY COMMUNITY HEALTH, INC.
1412 Fairmount Ave 2nd Fl, Philadelphia, PA 19130
Tel.: (215) 684-5344   PA
Web Site: https://www.dvch.org
Year Founded: 1977
Sales Range: $10-24.9 Million
Emp.: 310
Community Health Care Services
N.A.I.C.S.: 621498
Alvin Scott McNeal (Chief Medical Officer & VP)
Carla Wimbush (CFO & VP)
Nilsa Gonzales (Chm)
Carmen I. Paris (Vice Chm)
Rick Beaton (Sec)
Mark Macinelli (VP-HR & Info Sys)
Brenda Robles Cooke (COO & VP)

DELAWARE VALLEY CONCRETE CO.
248 E County Line Rd, Hatboro, PA 19040
Tel.: (215) 675-8900
Web Site: http://www.dvc-concrete.com
Year Founded: 1955
Sales Range: $10-24.9 Million
Emp.: 20
Mfr of Ready-Mixed Concrete
N.A.I.C.S.: 327320
Mario DiLiberto (Pres)

DELAWARE VALLEY STEEL CO.
2249 Manor Ave, Upper Darby, PA 19082
Tel.: (610) 449-6100
Web Site: https://delawarevalleysteel.com
Sales Range: $10-24.9 Million
Emp.: 18
Mfr of Black Plate Iron or Steel
N.A.I.C.S.: 423510
Jerry Sharpe (VP)

DELAWARE VALLEY WHOLESALE FLORIST INC.
520 N Mantua Blvd, Sewell, NJ 08080
Tel.: (856) 468-7000
Web Site: https://www.dvflora.com
Sales Range: $25-49.9 Million
Emp.: 550
Flowers & Florists Supplies
N.A.I.C.S.: 424930
Gene Owens (CFO)
Jack Chidester (CEO)
Frank J. Soucek (Dir-Sls-Central)
Vince Tromatore (Dir-Sls-Southern)
William Schimmel (Dir-Sls-Northern)
Colleen Weldon (Mgr-Credit & Collection)
Paul Fowle (Dir-Sls-Natl)

Subsidiaries:

Flower Transfer Inc.   (1)
520 Mantua Blvd, Sewell, NJ
08080   (100%)
Tel.: (856) 468-7000
Web Site: http://www.flowertransfer.com
Sales Range: $10-24.9 Million
Emp.: 15
Local Light Haulage & Cartage
N.A.I.C.S.: 484110
Robert M. Wilkins (Owner & Pres)

DELAWARE.NET, INC.
28 Old Rudnick Ln, Dover, DE 19901
Tel.: (302) 736-5515
Web Site: http://www.delaware.net
Year Founded: 1997
Sales Range: $1-9.9 Million
Emp.: 13
Internet & Computer Related Services
N.A.I.C.S.: 517810
John McKown (Pres)

DELBAR PRODUCTS INCORPORATED
601 W Spruce St, Perkasie, PA 18944
Tel.: (215) 257-6892   PA
Year Founded: 1977
Sales Range: $25-49.9 Million
Emp.: 800
Mfr of Rear Mirrors
N.A.I.C.S.: 327215
Tom Karabinos (Pres)

DELBERT CRAIG FOOD BROKERS
777 Old E End Blvd, Wilkes Barre, PA 18702
Tel.: (570) 825-8200   PA
Year Founded: 1936
Sales Range: $25-49.9 Million
Emp.: 12
Food Retailer
N.A.I.C.S.: 541618

DELCAM HOLDINGS, LLC
50 Mellen St, Hopedale, MA 01747
Tel.: (617) 281-7038   DE
Web Site: https://www.delcamholdings.com
Private Equity Firm
N.A.I.C.S.: 523999
Stephen Trotta (Mng Partner)

Subsidiaries:

Space Age Electronics, Inc.   (1)
58 Chocksett Rd, Sterling, MA 01564
Tel.: (978) 562-2998
Web Site: http://www.1sae.com
Rev.: $6,861,000
Emp.: 25
Fire Alarm Systems Mfr
N.A.I.C.S.: 922160
Nancy Powers (Office Mgr-Customer Svc)
Kristian White (Mgr-Sls-Natl)

DELCO BUILDERS & DEVELOPERS, INC.
3480 Buskirk Ave Ste 260, Pleasant Hill, CA 94523
Tel.: (925) 942-2600
Rev.: $35,000,000
Emp.: 32
Real Estate Services
N.A.I.C.S.: 531210
Christine Charette (Dir-HR)
Alysse Rueckert (Mgr-Acctg)
R. J. Wilson (VP & Dir-Construction Svcs)
Doyle D. Heaton (Pres & CEO)

DELEGARD TOOL COMPANY INC
205 E 78th St, Bloomington, MN 55420
Tel.: (952) 881-8683
Sales Range: $10-24.9 Million
Emp.: 38
Automotive Tools & Equipment
N.A.I.C.S.: 423120
Duane Delegard (Pres)
Curt Delegard (VP)

DELEON GROUP, LLC
20 Kenneth Pl, Staten Island, NY 10309
Tel.: (718) 967-2241

Web Site: http://www.deleongroup.com
Sales Range: $10-24.9 Million
Emp.: 20
N.A.I.C.S.: 541810
Ken DeLeon (Pres & Dir-Creative)
Stephanie Turzanski (Acct Coord-Comcast Bus)

DELESLINE CONSTRUCTION, INC.
320 7th St W, Palmetto, FL 34221
Tel.: (941) 723-6112   FL
Web Site: https://www.deleslinecon.com
Year Founded: 1973
Sales Range: $1-9.9 Million
Emp.: 5
General, Roofing & Underground Utility Contractor
N.A.I.C.S.: 236220
Janet DeLesline (Sec)
John DeLesline (Owner & Pres)

DELFINO MARKETING COMMUNICATIONS, INC.
400 Columbus Ave Ste 120S, Valhalla, NY 10595-1396
Tel.: (914) 747-1400   NY
Web Site: https://www.delfino.com
Year Founded: 1970
Rev.: $26,000,000
Emp.: 25
Advetising Agency
N.A.I.C.S.: 541810
Geno B. Delfino (Founder & Chm)
Lisa A. Delfino (Dir-Creative)
Paul Delfino (Co-Owner & Pres)
Christine Delfino Seneca (Co-Owner, Exec VP & Gen Mgr)
Joseph Harary (Controller)
Maria Garvey (Dir-Media Svcs)
Michael Rosa (Dir-Art)
Donato Dell'Orso (Mgr-Production)

DELGADO TRAVEL AGENCY CORPORATION
79-08 Roosevelt Ave, Jackson Heights, NY 11372-6717
Tel.: (718) 426-0500
Web Site: http://www.velgalcotravelusa.com
Year Founded: 1974
Sales Range: $10-24.9 Million
Emp.: 180
Travel Services
N.A.I.C.S.: 561510
Hector Giletezo (Pres)

Subsidiaries:

Casa De Cambio Delgado Inc.   (1)
7908 Roosevelt Ave, Jackson Heights, NY 11372-6717
Tel.: (718) 426-0500
Sales Range: $10-24.9 Million
Emp.: 30
Business Services
N.A.I.C.S.: 561499
Karina Vacabela (Gen Mgr)

Delgado Communications Inc.   (1)
7908 Roosevelt Ave, Jackson Heights, NY 11372-6717
Tel.: (718) 426-0500
Web Site: http://www.delgadotravelusa.com
Sales Range: $10-24.9 Million
Emp.: 20
Communication Service
N.A.I.C.S.: 561499
Hector Delgado (Gen Mgr)

Delgado Courier Inc.   (1)
7908 Roosevelt Ave, Jackson Heights, NY 11372-6717
Tel.: (718) 426-1900
Web Site: http://www.delgadotravelusa.com
Sales Range: $10-24.9 Million
Emp.: 50
Courier Service
N.A.I.C.S.: 492110

Hector Delgado (Pres)

DELHI HILLS FLOWER & GARDEN CENTER
5843 Harrison Ave, Cincinnati, OH 45248
Tel.: (513) 451-7020
Web Site: http://www.delhigardencenter.com
Sales Range: $10-24.9 Million
Emp.: 195
Lawn & Garden Supplies
N.A.I.C.S.: 444240
Robert Maddux (Pres)

DELI MANAGEMENT INC.
2400 Bdwy St, Beaumont, TX 77702-1904
Tel.: (409) 838-1976   TX
Web Site: http://www.jasonsdeli.com
Year Founded: 1976
Sales Range: $10-24.9 Million
Emp.: 90
Eating Place
N.A.I.C.S.: 722513
Lee Greer (Dir-Mktg)
Joseph V. Tortorice Jr. (Founder & CEO)

DELI, INC.
W6585 County Rd O, Millston, WI 54643-0437
Tel.: (715) 284-2296   WI
Web Site: https://www.mosserlee.com
Year Founded: 1932
Sales Range: $10-24.9 Million
Emp.: 25
Mfr of Baled Sphagnum Moss; Seed Germinator; Spanish Moss; Green Sheet Moss; Plant Supports; Wreath Frames & Spray Bars; Plant Propagators; Bird Feeders & Bird Houses
N.A.I.C.S.: 424590
Guy Huus (Pres)

Subsidiaries:

American Foliage Mart   (1)
PO Box 437, Millston, WI 54643-0437
Tel.: (715) 284-2296
Web Site: http://www.mosserlee.com
Sales Range: $25-49.9 Million
Emp.: 20
Gardening & Craft Products
N.A.I.C.S.: 444240

Cardinal Crest   (1)
PO Box 437, Millston, WI 54643-0437
Tel.: (715) 284-2296
Web Site: http://www.mosserlee.com
Sales Range: $25-49.9 Million
Emp.: 20
N.A.I.C.S.: 444240
John LaCourse (Pres)

Mosser Lee Co.   (1)
PO Box 437, Millston, WI 54643-0437
Tel.: (715) 284-2296
Web Site: http://www.mosserlee.com
Sales Range: $25-49.9 Million
Emp.: 15
Gardening & Craft Products
N.A.I.C.S.: 444240
John LaCourse (Pres)

DELI-BOY INC.
100 Matthews Ave, Syracuse, NY 13209
Tel.: (315) 488-4411
Web Site: https://www.deli-boy.com
Sales Range: $10-24.9 Million
Emp.: 56
Meats & Meat Products Whslr
N.A.I.C.S.: 424470
John Petosa (CFO)
Lon Frocione (Pres)
Jim Wright (VP-Sls)

DELIA ASSOCIATES

456 Rte 22 W, Whitehouse, NJ
08888-0338
Tel.: (908) 534-9044   NJ
Web Site: https://www.delianet.com
Year Founded: 1964
Sales Range: $25-49.9 Million
Emp.: 10
Advertising Agencies
N.A.I.C.S.: 541810
Edward Delia (Pres)
Matthew Taylor (Dir-Program Mgmt)
Jamie Rosen (Dir-Art & Design)

DELIA INC.
4 Laser Ln, Wallingford, CT 06492-
1928
Tel.: (203) 303-2000   CT
Web Site: http://www.deliainc.com
Year Founded: 1965
Sales Range: $75-99.9 Million
Emp.: 75
Distr of Kitchen Appliances
N.A.I.C.S.: 335220
Cal Callahan (Pres)

DELIA'S, INC.
50 W 23rd St, New York, NY 10010
Tel.: (212) 590-6200   DE
Web Site: http://www.delias.com
Year Founded: 1993
Sales Range: $125-149.9 Million
Emp.: 499
Retail Store Owner/Operator & La-
dies Casual Apparel & Related Ac-
cessories Direct Marketer
N.A.I.C.S.: 315210
David Diamond (Sr VP-HR)
Michael Zimmerman (Chm)
Whitney Randall (VP & Gen Mgr-
Mdse)
Daphne Smith (Exec VP-Ops)
Brian Lex Austin-Gemas (COO)
Ryan A. Schreiber (Gen Counsel,
Sec & Sr VP)

DELICATO VINEYARDS
455 Devlin Rd Ste 201, Napa, CA
94558-6274
Tel.: (707) 265-1700   CA
Web Site: https://www.delicato.com
Year Founded: 1924
Sales Range: $50-74.9 Million
Emp.: 60
Winery & Vineyards
N.A.I.C.S.: 111332
Don Allen (CFO)
John Yarborough (VP-Winery Ops)

Subsidiaries:

San Bernabe Vineyards   (1)
53001 Oasis Rd, King City, CA
93930-9667   (100%)
Tel.: (831) 386-5600
Sales Range: $10-24.9 Million
Mfr Wines Brandy & Spirits
N.A.I.C.S.: 111332

DELILLE OXYGEN CO.
772 Marion Rd, Columbus, OH 43207
Tel.: (614) 444-1177
Web Site: https://www.delille.com
Sales Range: $10-24.9 Million
Emp.: 63
Acetylene; Industrial Gases Supply
N.A.I.C.S.: 325120
David Simpson (Controller)

DELIVER MEDIA
5132 Tampa W Blvd Ste B, Tampa,
FL 33634
Tel.: (813) 885-3203
Web Site:
   http://www.delivermedia.com
Sales Range: $10-24.9 Million
Emp.: 45
Direct Mail & Email Marketing
N.A.I.C.S.: 541613

Sean Johnson (CEO)
Jennifer Scott (Dir-Ops)
Tony Agan (Dir-New Bus Dev)
Melissa San Vicente (Dir-Creative)
Emily Walsh (Dir-Mktg)
Jessica Johnson (Office Mgr)

DELIVERY AGENT, INC.
300 California St 3rd Fl, San Fran-
cisco, CA 94104
Tel.: (415) 696-5800   DE
Web Site:
   http://www.deliveryagent.com
Year Founded: 2001
Media Buying Agency
N.A.I.C.S.: 541830
Mike Fitzsimmons (CEO)
David Rudnick (CTO)
Kim Marder (Chief Media Officer)
Mark Smith (Gen Counsel)
Pat Ivers (Exec VP-Adv Sls)
Jeff Combs (Sr VP-ECommerce)
Jeff Banks (VP-Mdsg)
James Peters (Pres & COO)
John Perez (Mgr-Natl Sls-Hispanic
Advanced Adv Sls & TCommerce
Div)
Jeff Hagan (CFO)

DELIZZA, INC.
6610 Corporation Pkwy, Battleboro,
NC 27809
Tel.: (252) 442-0270
Year Founded: 1999
Sales Range: $50-74.9 Million
Emp.: 500
Ice Cream & Pastries Mfr
N.A.I.C.S.: 311520
Brian Hill (VP-Ops, Treas & Co-Sec)
Delizza Pattiserie (Co-Sec)
Frans Castelein (Pres)
Raymond Laruelle (CEO)
Brian Wall (Mgr-IT)

DELKOR SYSTEMS INC.
4300 Round Lake Rd W, Saint Paul,
MN 55112
Tel.: (651) 348-6700
Web Site:
   https://www.delkorsystems.com
Sales Range: $10-24.9 Million
Emp.: 170
Packaging Materials
N.A.I.C.S.: 333993
Dale Andersen (Pres & CEO)
Terry Cook (CFO)

**DELL CAPITAL PARTNERS,
L.P.**
460 Briarwood Dr Ste 415, Jackson,
MS 39206-3026
Tel.: (601) 969-0610
Holding Company
N.A.I.C.S.: 561499

DELL-COMM INC.
4860 Mustang Cir, Saint Paul, MN
55112
Tel.: (763) 783-0035
Web Site: http://www.dell-comm.com
Sales Range: $10-24.9 Million
Emp.: 55
Telephone & Telephone Equipment
Installation
N.A.I.C.S.: 238210
Jim Freichels (Pres)
Marc Johnson (Mgr-Ops)
Karen Aho (Owner)

**DELLA LAMB COMMUNITY
SERVICES**
500 Woodland Ave, Kansas City, MO
64106-9908
Tel.: (816) 842-8040   MO
Web Site: https://www.dellalamb.org
Year Founded: 1897

Sales Range: $10-24.9 Million
Emp.: 165
Community Support Services
N.A.I.C.S.: 624190
Patrick A. Johnston (Chm)
Hal Havens (VP-Property)
Susan J. Fershee (Sec)
Michael B. Roos (Treas)
Judy Aker (Exec VP)

DELLA PONTIAC
293 Quaker Rd, Queensbury, NY
12804
Tel.: (518) 793-3871
Sales Range: $10-24.9 Million
Emp.: 50
Car Whslr
N.A.I.C.S.: 441110
Jim Melleon (Principal)

DELLARIA SALONS
159 Cambridge St, Allston, MA 02134
Tel.: (617) 254-1004
Web Site: https://www.dellaria.com
Rev.: $14,000,000
Emp.: 7
Beauty Shops
N.A.I.C.S.: 812112
Nino Micozzi (Pres)
Crystal Norcross (Mgr)
Cristina Kennedy (Mgr-Salon)

DELLEN AUTOMOTIVE INC.
2527 W Main St, Greenfield, IN
46140
Tel.: (317) 586-4599
Web Site: https://www.dellen.com
Sales Range: $75-99.9 Million
Emp.: 155
Sales of New & Used Cars
N.A.I.C.S.: 441110
Pat Beally (Treas)

DELLENBACH MOTORS
3111 S College Ave, Fort Collins, CO
80525
Tel.: (970) 226-2438
Web Site: http://www.dellenbach.com
Year Founded: 1965
Sales Range: $75-99.9 Million
Emp.: 120
New & Used Automobiles Dealer
N.A.I.C.S.: 423110
John Dellenbach (Mgr-Catalog)
Ron Heusinkveld (Mgr-Fleet)
Brad Laugel (Mgr-Used Cars)
Charles Grant (Mgr-Sls)

DELLING ENTERPRISES
1111 N Post Rd, Midwest City, OK
73130
Tel.: (405) 769-4390
Sales Range: $10-24.9 Million
Emp.: 120
Owner & Operator of Grocery Stores
N.A.I.C.S.: 541219

DELLTRON CO. INC.
3600 Afshari Cir, Florissant, MO
63034
Tel.: (314) 839-0033
Sales Range: $10-24.9 Million
Emp.: 5
Electronic Parts
N.A.I.C.S.: 423690
James P. Garrison (Pres)
Wilma Garrison (CFO)

**DELMAR FINANCIAL COM-
PANY**
1066 Executive Pkwy Ste 100, Saint
Louis, MO 63141
Tel.: (314) 434-7000
Web Site:
   http://www.delmarfinancial.com
Sales Range: $75-99.9 Million

Emp.: 80
Mortgage Banker
N.A.I.C.S.: 522110
Matt Lebison (Pres)

DELMAR SYSTEMS, INC.
8114 W Hwy 90, Broussard, LA
70518-8215
Tel.: (832) 252-7100
Web Site: http://www.delmarus.com
Oil & Gas Operations
N.A.I.C.S.: 213112
Ken Babin (CIO)

Subsidiaries:

Deep Sea Mooring AS   (1)
Trollhaugmyra 15, 5353, Straume, Norway
Tel.: (47) 90760823
Web Site: http://www.deepseamooring.com
Oil & Gas Field Drilling Services
N.A.I.C.S.: 213111
Age Straume (Mng Dir-North Atlantic)
Jan Eide (Mgr-Bus Support)
Jorund Havneras (Mgr-Ops)
Wolfgang Wandl (Chm)
Frode Hoyland (CFO)

**DELMARVA BANCSHARES,
INC.**
304 High St, Cambridge, MD 21613
Tel.: (410) 228-5600   MD
Web Site: http://www.1880bank.com
Year Founded: 1998
DLMV—(OTCBB)
Sales Range: $10-24.9 Million
Bank Holding Company
N.A.I.C.S.: 551111

Subsidiaries:

1880 Bank   (1)
304 High St, Cambridge, MD 21613
Tel.: (410) 228-5600
Web Site: http://www.1880bank.com
Sales Range: $25-49.9 Million
Emp.: 50
Commericial Banking
N.A.I.C.S.: 522110

**DELMARVA COMMUNITY SER-
VICES, INC.**
2450 Cambridge Beltway, Cam-
bridge, MD 21613
Tel.: (410) 221-1900   MD
Web Site: https://www.dcsdct.org
Year Founded: 1974
Sales Range: $10-24.9 Million
Emp.: 403
Developmental Disability Assistance
Services
N.A.I.C.S.: 623210
Santo A. Grande (Pres & CEO)

**DELMARVA RV CENTER IN
SEAFORD**
702 Milford-Harrington Hwy Route 14,
Milford, DE 19963
Tel.: (302) 424-4505
Web Site:
   http://www.delmarvarvcenter.com
Year Founded: 1992
Sales Range: $10-24.9 Million
Emp.: 23
Recreational Vehicle Whslr
N.A.I.C.S.: 441210
Ryan Clough (Pres)

DELOITTE LLP
30 Rockefeller Plz 41st FL, New
York, NY 10112-0015
Tel.: (212) 492-4000   DE
Web Site: http://www2.deloitte.com
Year Founded: 1895
Sales Range: $15-24.9 Billion
Emp.: 5,000
Holding Company; Accounting, Audit-
ing, Tax Preparation & Management
Consulting Services
N.A.I.C.S.: 551112

Deloitte LLP—(Continued)

James Brennan (Mng Partner-Upstate)
Stuart Cottee (Sr Partner-Practice-Yorkshire & The North East)
David Sproul (CEO-UK)
Jon Gonzalez (Partner-Audit & Assurance)
Shaun Reynolds (Partner)
Dan Berner (Mng Partner-North Texas)
Emma Codd (Mng Partner-Talent-UK,North West Europe)
Michael Castle (Mng Partner & Sr Partner)
Graham Hollis (Sr Partner-Aberdeen & Partner-Audit & Assurance)
Linda Pawczuk (Principal & Head-Fin Svcs Indus Blockchain Grp)
Bob Contri (Partner)
Scott Mund (Partner)
Stanley Porter (Vice Chm)
George Simeone (Partner)
Mark Steiger (Partner)
Christian Schelde Jensby (Co-CEO)
Lars Kronow (Co-Chm)
Joseph B. Ucuzoglu (Co-CEO)
Jason Girzadas (Co-CEO)

Subsidiaries:

Deloitte & Touche LLP (1)
30 Rockefeller Plz, New York, NY 10112-0015
Tel.: (212) 618-4000
Web Site: http://www2.deloitte.com
Accounting Services
N.A.I.C.S.: 541211
Nicole Sandford (Partner-Audit)
Yang Chu (Sr Mgr)
Barrett Daniels (Partner)
Bruce Rucks (Partner)
Cynthia Vitters (Mng Dir)
David Cutbill (Principal)
Jade M. Shopp (Mng Partner)
Previn Waas (Partner)
Will Braeutigam (Partner)
Christie Simons (Partner-Audit & Assurance)

Subsidiary (Domestic):

LRA Worldwide, Inc. (2)
5 Walnut Grove Ste 280, Horsham, PA 19044-2263
Tel.: (215) 957-1999
Web Site: http://www.lraworldwide.com
Sales Range: $10-24.9 Million
Emp.: 170
Brand Protection & Customer Experience Measurement Management Consulting Services
N.A.I.C.S.: 541611
Rob Rush (Mng Dir)
Zachary Conen (Sr Mgr-Bus Dev)

Deloitte Consulting LLP (1)
25 Broadway, New York, NY 10004
Tel.: (212) 618-4000
Web Site: http://www.deloitte.com
Sales Range: $100-124.9 Million
Emp.: 1,100
Financial Consultant
N.A.I.C.S.: 541618
Andrew Vaz (Principal & Chief Innovation Officer)
Sandra Shirai (Natl Mng Principal-Tech, Media & Telecom Practice)
Lynn Collyar (Dir-Federal Practice-Defense)
Tim Gross (Principal)
Matt Parker (Partner)
Janet Foutty (Chm & CEO)
Mostafa Noorzay (Mng Dir)
Kevin Mercadante (Principal)
Maunil Mehta (Principal)
Lukas Hoebarth (Principal)
Harry Datwani (Principal)
Derek Polzien (Mng Dir)
Christopher Allen (Mng Dir)
Abby Levine (Principal)
Sharique Ahmed (Principal-Dallas)
Brian Burrus (Principal-Tech Strategy, Architecture & Oil & Gas Practice)
Kevin Gregory (Principal-Analytics & Info Mgmt Practice)

Kashif Rahamatullah (Principal-Digital Practice)
Marc Scheinrock (Principal-Merger & Acq Consulting Practice)
Jeremy Scott (Mng Dir-Sys Integration Practice)
Michelle Peregrine (Mng Dir)
David Wennergren (Mng Dir)
Margaret Anderson (Mng Dir-Federal Health Practice)
Kevin Brault (Principal)

Subsidiary (Domestic):

BIAS Corporation (2)
1100 Abernathy Rd Ste 950, Atlanta, GA 30328
Tel.: (678) 578-4280
Web Site: http://www.biascorp.com
Sales Range: $25-49.9 Million
Emp.: 160
Information Technology Consulting Services
N.A.I.C.S.: 541512
Jeff Harvey (Co-Founder & Pres)
Krishnan Balasubramanian (CTO-Cloud Sys & Svcs)
Dasaradha Chereddy (Dir-Offshore Delivery Center-Hyderabad)
Dinesh Senanayake (CFO)
Pam Fisher (VP-Application Consulting Svcs)
Amin Oteifa (Sr VP-Consulting Svcs-Global)

Unit (Domestic):

Bersin by Deloitte (2)
180 Grand Ave Ste 320, Oakland, CA 94612
Tel.: (510) 251-4400
Web Site: http://www.bersin.com
Sales Range: $10-24.9 Million
Emp.: 57
Research Based People Strategies & Advisory Services
N.A.I.C.S.: 541612
Josh Bersin (Founder & Principal)
Laura Evenson (VP-Mktg & Comm)
Chris Howard (Dir-Consulting)
Allen Keetch (VP-Global Corp Sls)
Suvendu Mahapatra (VP-Engrg)
David Mallon (Head-Res)
Rikard Bandebo (Head-Product Mgmt)
Andrew Huddart (Gen Mgr)
Andrew Potts (CFO)
Keather Snyder (VP-Sls)

Casey Quirk by Deloitte (2)
17 Old Kings Hwy S Ste 200, Darien, CT 06820
Tel.: (203) 899-3000
Web Site: http://www.caseyquirk.com
Corporate Consultancy Services
N.A.I.C.S.: 541511
Kevin P. Quirk (Founder & Principal)
Benjamin F. Phillips (Principal)
Jeffrey A. Levi (Principal)
Jeffrey B. Stakel (Principal)
Jonathan L. Doolan (Principal & Head-EMEA)
Justin R. White (Principal)
Yariv Itah (Mng Principal)

Subsidiary (Domestic):

Deloitte Development LLC (2)
837 N 34th St Ste 100, Seattle, WA 98103
Tel.: (206) 633-1167
Web Site: http://www.deloittedigital.com
Digital Marketing Services
N.A.I.C.S.: 541511
Alicia Hatch (CMO)
Nidal Haddad (Head-Markets)
Gustavo Vampre (CEO-Australia)
Matt Lawson (Chief Creative Officer)

Subsidiary (Domestic):

Heat (3)
1100 Sansome St, San Francisco, CA 94111
Tel.: (415) 477-1999
Web Site: http://www.thisisheat.com
Sales Range: $1-9.9 Million
Emp.: 79
Advetising Agency
N.A.I.C.S.: 541810
Steve Stone (Chief Creative Officer)
John Elder (Owner & CEO)

Subsidiary (Domestic):

Gryphon Scientific, LLC (2)

973 Hale St, Beverly, MA 01915-2235
Tel.: (978) 922-0383
Web Site: http://www.gryphonscientific.com
Scientific & Technical Consulting Services
N.A.I.C.S.: 541690
Kimberly Legrow (Bus Mgr)

National Teleconsultants Inc. (2)
700 N Brand Blvd Ste 10, Glendale, CA 91203-1202
Tel.: (818) 265-4400
Web Site: http://www.ntc.com
Electronics Stores
N.A.I.C.S.: 449210
Elliot Graham (Pres)

Optimal Design Co. (2)
1699 Wall St, Mount Prospect, IL 60056
Tel.: (847) 545-6800
Rev.: $1,500,000
Emp.: 20
Engineeering Services
N.A.I.C.S.: 541330

Deloitte Tax LLP (1)
1633 Broadway, New York, NY 10019
Tel.: (212) 489-1600
Tax Advisory Services
N.A.I.C.S.: 541213
Suzanne Kao (Dir-Export Controls)
Benjamin Elliott (Sr Mgr-Sacramento)
Marcy A. Stulce (Principal-Tax)
Marshal Sulayman (Partner-Tax)
James Petrie (Partner)
Lauren Knapp (Mgr-Multistate Tax Practice)
Steve Chapman (Partner-Investment Mgmt Practice)
Dan Byrne (Partner-Investment Mgmt Practice)
Dave Varley (Principal-Washington Natl Tax Grp Transfer Pricing Practice)
Jeff Anderson (Mng Dir-Dallas)
Niketu Bhatt (Mng Dir)
David Nuernberger (Mng Partner-Tax-Denver)
Robert Stack (Mng Dir-Washington Natl Tax-Intl Tax Practice)
Steve Kimble (Chm & CEO)
Rosemary Sereti (Mng Dir-Tax Controversy Svcs Practice-Natl Tax-Washington)

DELON HAMPTON & ASSOCIATES, CHARTERED
900 7th St NW Ste 800, Washington, DC 20001
Tel.: (202) 898-1999
Web Site:
https://www.delonhampton.com
Rev.: $11,600,000
Emp.: 190
Engineeering Services
N.A.I.C.S.: 541330
James Long (Sr VP-Engrg Ops)
Mamo Assefa (VP)
Loretta Morris (Asst VP)
Pamela V. Prue (Asst VP-Mktg)
Michele T. Nanna (Sr VP-Bus Dev)
J. Douglas Nauman (VP)
Jo Fisher-Hall (VP-HR & Admin)
Carol Holland (VP-Program & Construction Mgmt)
C. Gary Kellogg (VP-Pro Svcs)
Pamela Holmes (CFO)
Jacquelyn Glover (VP-Bus Dev)
Desiree Thomas (Asst VP-Strategic Pursuits & Mktg)

DELONG SPORTSWEAR, INC.
821 5th Ave, Grinnell, IA 50112-1653
Tel.: (641) 236-3106   IA
Web Site:
http://www.delongsports.com
Year Founded: 1930
Sales Range: $100-124.9 Million
Emp.: 200
Team Uniforms, Warm-Ups, Jackets, Outerwear & Caps Mfr
N.A.I.C.S.: 315250
Sharp Lannom (Pres)
Mark Bjorndal (VP-Fin)
Tim Marsho (Dir-Mktg-Sls)
Linda Pirkl (Mgr-Adv)

DELOS CAPITAL, LLC
120 5th Ave 3rd Fl, New York, NY 10011
Tel.: (212) 257-4450   NY
Web Site: http://www.deloscap.com
Year Founded: 2013
Privater Equity Firm
N.A.I.C.S.: 523999
Matthew Constantino (Founder & Partner)
Sanjay Sanghoee (Partner)

Subsidiaries:

FCA, LLC (1)
7601 John Deere Pkwy, Moline, IL 61265
Tel.: (309) 792-3444
Web Site: http://www.fcapackaging.com
Sales Range: $10-24.9 Million
Emp.: 200
Custom Industrial Shipping Containers Mfr
N.A.I.C.S.: 332439
Jeffery Campanga (Founder & Chm)

Subsidiary (Domestic):

Crate Tech, Inc. (2)
8247 South 194th St, Kent, WA 98032
Tel.: (253) 872-6857
Web Site: http://www.cratetech.com
Rev.: $6,666,666
Emp.: 35
Wood Container & Pallet Mfr
N.A.I.C.S.: 321920
Tia Sosa (Mgr)
Tom George (Mgr-Ops)

Timber Creek Resource, LLC. (2)
5059 N 119th St, Milwaukee, WI 53225
Tel.: (414) 466-1645
Web Site: http://www.tcrllc.com
Sales Range: $10-24.9 Million
Emp.: 150
Wood Container & Pallet Mfr
N.A.I.C.S.: 321920
Stephanie Mustin (Mgr-HR)
James Krause (Product Mgr-Dev)
Steve Everett Jr. (Pres)

Transpak Corporation (2)
Two World Packaging Cir, Franklin, WI 53132
Tel.: (414) 855-9200
Web Site: http://transpakusa.com
Packaging Materials Mfr
N.A.I.C.S.: 326112

HOP Energy LLC (1)
4 W Red Oak Ln 3rd Fl, White Plains, NY 10604
Tel.: (914) 304-1300
Web Site: http://www.hopenergy.com
Heating Oil & Heating Equipment Sales & Services
N.A.I.C.S.: 424720
Michael Anton (Pres & CEO)
William H. Weber (Dir-Capital Assets)
Jeff Lucking (Controller)
Matthew J. Ryan (Sr VP-Supply & Logistics)
John Kuebler (VP-Ops-Southern Reg)
Michael Gleave (Dir-HR & Labor Rels)
Tedd Teschner (VP-Ops)
Harry Dohnert (VP-Sls & Mktg)
Victoria French-Sanches (Dir-Mktg)
Brian Chartier (Treas)

Subsidiary (Domestic):

Alliance Express (2)
11 Broadway, Chelsea, MA 02150-2603
Tel.: (844) 859-1148
Web Site: http://www.hopenergy.com
Fuel Oil Delivery
N.A.I.C.S.: 424720
Douglas Goodman (Gen Mgr)

Keyser Energy (2)
77 Grove St Ste G102, Rutland, VT 05701
Tel.: (855) 203-1279
Web Site: http://www.hopenergy.com
Fuel Oil Dealers
N.A.I.C.S.: 457210

Le Sueur Incorporated (1)
1409 Vine St, Le Sueur, MN 56058-1125
Tel.: (507) 665-6204
Web Site: http://www.lesueurinc.com
Sales Range: $25-49.9 Million
Emp.: 450
Provider of Industrial Products

N.A.I.C.S.: 331523
Mark Mueller *(Chm & CEO)*
Mike Jindra *(Controller)*
Dick Seidenstricker *(Pres)*

Subsidiary (Domestic):

Craft Pattern & Mold, Inc.   (2)
1410 County Rd 90 Ste 3, Maple Plain, MN
55359
Tel.: (763) 479-1969
Web Site: http://www.craftpattern.com
Sales Range: $1-9.9 Million
Emp.: 30
Industrial Patterns
N.A.I.C.S.: 332999
Ben Kuehl *(Production Mgr)*
Kurt Lemke *(Mgr-Quality)*
Steve Shade *(Mgr-Project)*
Tony Cremers *(Pres & CEO)*

DELPHI GROWTH CAPITAL CORP.
9 W 57th St43rd Fl, New York, NY
10019
Tel.: (212) 515-3200   DE
Year Founded: 2021
Emp.: 2
Investment Services
N.A.I.C.S.: 523999
Philip Mintz *(CEO)*
James Crossen *(CFO & Chief Acctg Officer)*
John Zito *(Chm)*

DELPHI MANAGEMENT GROUP, INC.
3824 E Roeser Rd, Phoenix, AZ
85040
Tel.: (602) 431-8560
Web Site: https://www.delphimg.com
Retail Dry Cleaner Owner & Operator
N.A.I.C.S.: 812320
Donald J. Lothrop *(Gen Partner, Mng Dir & Mgr)*
Bill Delia *(Pres)*

Subsidiaries:

Delias Cleaners Inc.   (1)
3824 E Roesner Rd, Phoenix, AZ 85040
Tel.: (602) 431-8560
Web Site: http://www.deliacleaners.com
Rev.: $237,300,000
Emp.: 130
Investment Holding Companies
N.A.I.C.S.: 812320
Philip A. Delia *(Pres & CEO)*

DELPHON INDUSTRIES, LLC
31398 Huntwood Ave, Hayward, CA
94544
Tel.: (510) 576-2220
Web Site: http://www.delphon.com
Year Founded: 1997
Sales Range: $1-9.9 Million
Emp.: 200
Microelectronic Packaging & Assembly Solutions
N.A.I.C.S.: 325520
Jennifer Nunes *(Dir-Mktg)*
Jeanne Beacham *(Chm)*
Raj Varma *(CTO)*
Thaddeus Ericson *(CFO)*
Joe Montano *(Pres & CEO)*

Subsidiaries:

UltraTape Industries   (1)
9770 SW Wilsonville Rd Ste 400, Wilsonville, OR 97070
Tel.: (503) 427-2880
Web Site: http://www.cleanroomtape.com
Emp.: 11
Adhesive Tape Mfr
N.A.I.C.S.: 325520
Lance Ochs *(Mgr-Sls)*

DELPHOS COOPERATIVE ASSOCIATION
413 W 1st St, Delphos, KS 67436
Tel.: (785) 523-4213

Web Site:
https://www.delphoscoop.com
Sales Range: $10-24.9 Million
Emp.: 14
Grain & Bean Whslr
N.A.I.C.S.: 424510
Rhonda Kiser *(Office Mgr)*
Steve Hoesli *(Mgr)*
Daniel Ablard *(Mgr)*
David Kiser *(Office Mgr)*

DELPHOS HERALD INC.
405 N Main St, Delphos, OH 45833
Tel.: (419) 695-0015
Web Site:
https://www.delphosherald.com
Year Founded: 1869
Sales Range: $10-24.9 Million
Emp.: 83
Newspapers Publishing & Printing
N.A.I.C.S.: 513110
Murray Cohen *(Chm)*
Ray Geary *(Gen Mgr)*

DELRAY IMPORTS, INC.
4464 Tulane Dr, West Palm Beach,
FL 33406-2147
Tel.: (561) 684-2939
Web Site:
http://www.autoadviceusa.com
Sales Range: $10-24.9 Million
Emp.: 10
Sales Of Used Automobiles
N.A.I.C.S.: 423110
Brandy Santillo *(Controller)*
William Santillo *(Pres)*
Hollie Michael *(Mgr-Fin)*

DELRAY MOTORS
2102 S Federal Hwy, Delray Beach,
FL 33483
Tel.: (561) 454-1800
Web Site:
http://www.delraymotors.com
Sales Range: $10-24.9 Million
Emp.: 35
New Car Dealers
N.A.I.C.S.: 441110
Tim Young *(Pres)*
Tracie Boynton *(Mgr-HR & Payroll)*

DELRAY TIRE & RETREADING INC.
2544 S Cherry Ave, Fresno, CA
93706
Tel.: (559) 485-1761
Web Site: https://www.delraytire.com
Rev.: $11,500,000
Emp.: 25
Retreading Of Automobile Tires &
Tubes
N.A.I.C.S.: 423130
Danny Stevens *(Mgr-Store)*
Kenny Lay *(Mgr-Retail)*
Scott Graham *(Mgr-Sls)*

Subsidiaries:

Atwater Tire Services Inc.   (1)
1040 High St, Atwater, CA 95301-4608
Tel.: (209) 358-6475
Web Site: http://www.atwatertireservice.com
Tire Dealers
N.A.I.C.S.: 441340
George Bianchi *(Owner)*

DELSEA DRIVE SUPERMARKET LLC
1000 N Pearl St, Bridgeton, NJ
08037
Tel.: (856) 691-9395
Sales Range: $10-24.9 Million
Emp.: 147
Supermarket
N.A.I.C.S.: 445110
Richard Ciselli *(Controller)*
James Bottino *(Pres)*

DELSON LUMBER, LLC
1801 W Bay Dr NW #201, Olympia,
WA 98502-4313
Tel.: (360) 740-9400   WA
Web Site:
http://www.delsonlumber.com
Year Founded: 1952
Rev.: $32,000,000
Emp.: 135
Saw Mills & Planing Mills
N.A.I.C.S.: 423310
Tucker Smyth *(Gen Mgr)*

DELTA AREA ECONOMIC OPPORTUNITY CORPORATION
99 Skyview Rd, Portageville, MO
63873-9180
Tel.: (573) 379-3851   MO
Web Site: http://www.daeoc.com
Year Founded: 1965
Sales Range: $10-24.9 Million
Emp.: 440
Economic Development Services
N.A.I.C.S.: 541720
Dan Lape *(Dir-Purchasing-Procurement)*
Joel P. Evans *(Pres & CEO)*

DELTA AUTO SALES SERVICE, INC.
125 US Hwy 51 Byp N, Dyersburg,
TN 38024-3660
Tel.: (731) 882-1042
Web Site:
https://www.deltaautosales.net
Sales Range: $10-24.9 Million
Emp.: 36
Car Whslr
N.A.I.C.S.: 441110
Charles Dunn *(Pres)*
Lori Hamil *(Office Mgr)*

DELTA CONSTRUCTION PARTNERS, INC.
1 Beach Dr SE, Saint Petersburg, FL
33701
Tel.: (727) 822-2048
Web Site:
http://www.deltaconstructionpartners.com
Sales Range: $1-9.9 Million
Emp.: 10
Executive Recruiting for the Construction Industry
N.A.I.C.S.: 561312
Bob Magnan *(Founder & Pres)*
Barbara Montgomery *(VP-Bus Dev)*
Marci Wainwright *(Office Mgr)*

DELTA CONSULTING GROUP, INC.
4330 Prince William Pkwy, Ste 301,
Woodbridge, VA 22192
Tel.: (703) 580-8801
Web Site: http://www.delta-cgi.com
Rev.: $2,600,000
Emp.: 50
Fiscal Year-end: 12/31/06
Management Services
N.A.I.C.S.: 541618
Jeffrey E. Fuchs *(CEO)*

Subsidiaries:

Froese Forensic Partners Ltd.   (1)
55 University Avenue Suite 1000, Toronto,
M5J 2H7, ON, Canada
Tel.: (416) 364-6400
Web Site: http://www.froeseforensic.com
Sales Range: $10-24.9 Million
Emp.: 15
Economic & Financial Analysis, Expert Testimony, Litigation Support & Management
Consulting Services
N.A.I.C.S.: 561499
Sheree Mann *(Mng Dir)*
Ken Froese *(Sr Mng Dir)*
Kevin Lo *(Mng Dir)*

Cyrus F. Khory *(Mng Dir)*
Don Perron *(Mng Dir)*
Mark Vandertoorn *(Mng Dir)*
Scott Porter *(Mng Dir)*

DELTA CORPORATE SERVICES INC.
129 Littleton Rd, Parsippany, NJ
07054
Tel.: (973) 334-6260
Web Site: https://www.deltacorp.com
Sales Range: $10-24.9 Million
Emp.: 200
Custom Computer Programming Services
N.A.I.C.S.: 541511
Michael J. Iovino *(Pres)*
Carl Schulz *(Mgr-Svc)*
Pat Bergamo *(Mgr-Svc)*
Kathy Bannon *(Mgr-Corp Facility)*
Fred Garman *(Mgr-Texas)*
Julie Bilinkas *(VP-Bus Dev)*

DELTA DEFENSE, LLC
N173W21298 NW Passage Way,
Jackson, WI 53037-9124
Tel.: (715) 445-8722
Web Site:
http://www.deltadefense.com
Year Founded: 2004
Sales Range: $1-9.9 Million
Emp.: 40
Publications & Services in the Self-Defense & Personal Protection Industry
N.A.I.C.S.: 513110
Tim Schmidt *(Founder, Pres & CEO)*
Rebecca Ciriacks *(Supvr-Members Svcs)*
Jerry Noskowiak *(CFO)*

DELTA DENTAL OF SOUTH DAKOTA
PO Box 1157, Pierre, SD 57501
Tel.: (605) 244-7345   SD
Web Site:
http://www.deltadentalsd.com
Year Founded: 1963
Sales Range: $125-149.9 Million
Emp.: 80
Dental Care Services
N.A.I.C.S.: 621210
Scott Jones *(Pres & CEO)*
Kirby Scott *(VP-Fin)*
Gene Tetzlaff *(VP-IT)*
Mick Heckenlaible *(VP-Ops)*
Nance Orsbon *(VP-Pro Svcs)*
Dale Gibson *(Chm)*
Greg Gertsen *(Sec)*
John Clausen *(Treas)*
Paul Rezich *(Vice Chm)*
Connie Halverson *(VP-Pub Benefit)*
Jeff Miller *(VP-Underwriting)*

DELTA DENTAL PLAN OF NEW HAMPSHIRE, INC.
1 Delta Dr, Concord, NH 03302
Tel.: (603) 223-1000
Web Site: http://www.nedelta.com
Dental Insurance Services
N.A.I.C.S.: 524298
Thomas Raffio *(Pres & CEO)*
Jodie Hittle *(VP-Sls & Mktg)*
Francis R. Boucher *(Treas)*
David B. Staples *(Chm)*
Mary Ann Aldrich *(Vice Chm)*
Sara M. Brehm *(Sec)*

Subsidiaries:

PreViser Corporation   (1)
20849 Cascade Ridge Dr, Mount Vernon,
WA 98274
Tel.: (360) 941-4715
Web Site: http://www.previser.com
Software Publisher
N.A.I.C.S.: 513210

Delta Dental Plan of New Hampshire, Inc.—(Continued)

Shane Gildnes (VP-Tech)
Carl F. Loeb (CEO)
John Martin (Chief Scientific Officer)

DELTA DENTAL PLAN OF VIRGINIA INC.
4818 Starkey Rd, Roanoke, VA 24018
Tel.: (540) 989-8000   VA
Web Site:
https://www.deltadentalva.com
Year Founded: 1964
Sales Range: $50-74.9 Million
Emp.: 175
Provider of Insurance Services
N.A.I.C.S.: 524210
George A. Levicki (Pres)
Michael Wise (VP-Fin)

DELTA DENTAL PLAN OF WYOMING
6234 Yellowstone Rd, Cheyenne, WY 82009
Tel.: (307) 632-3313   WY
Web Site:
http://www.deltadentalwy.org
Year Founded: 1968
Sales Range: $25-49.9 Million
Emp.: 9
Dental Care Services
N.A.I.C.S.: 621210
Patricia J. Guzman (VP-Administration-Government Relations)

DELTA DENTAL PLANS ASSOCIATION
1515 W 22nd St Ste 450, Oak Brook, IL 60523
Tel.: (630) 574-6853   IL
Web Site: http://www.deltadental.com
Year Founded: 1965
Sales Range: $10-24.9 Million
Emp.: 45
Dental Care Services
N.A.I.C.S.: 621210
Jennifer Elliot (VP-Dental Rels & Pub Policy)
Steve Olson (Pres & CEO)
William Kohn (VP-Dental Science & Policy)
Chuck Stich (VP-Fin & Compliance)
Scott Jessee (CIO)

DELTA DIVERSIFIED ENTERPRISES INC.
425 W Gemini Dr, Tempe, AZ 85283
Tel.: (480) 831-0532
Web Site: https://www.deltadiv.com
Year Founded: 1971
Sales Range: $25-49.9 Million
Emp.: 300
General Electrical Contractor
N.A.I.C.S.: 238210
Larry Donelson (Pres & CEO)
Dale Campbell (Sr Project Mgr)
David Dudding (Sr Project Mgr)
Jon Knoche (Project Mgr)
Alan Hermreck (Asst Mgr-Svc Dept)
Bob Lloyd (Project Mgr)
Claude Tremblay (Project Mgr)
Jim Vance (Dir-Safety)
Don Wagner (VP-Engrg Design)
Karen Smith (Project Mgr)
Jeff Weltsch (Mgr-Pur)
Matt Maxwell (Mgr-Flagstaff)
Paul Savarino (Mgr-Logistics)
John Clayton (Project Mgr-Svc Dept)
Jim McCain (Project Mgr-Svc Dept)

DELTA ELECTRIC POWER ASSOCIATION
1700 Hwy 82, Greenwood, MS 38930
Tel.: (662) 453-6352

Web Site: https://www.deltaepa.com
Sales Range: $25-49.9 Million
Emp.: 75
Electric Power Distribution
N.A.I.C.S.: 221122
Ronnie Robertson (Gen Mgr)

DELTA ENTERPRISE CORPORATION
114 W 26th St, New York, NY 10001
Tel.: (212) 736-7000
Web Site:
http://www.deltaenterprise.com
Year Founded: 1970
Sales Range: $75-99.9 Million
Emp.: 70
Juvenile Furniture & Accessories
N.A.I.C.S.: 449110
Andrea Roberson (Mgr-Acct Svcs)
Robert McCullough (VP-Wood Production)

Subsidiaries:

Simmons Juvenile Furniture   (1)
677 commerce Dr, Hortonville, WI 54944
Tel.: (920) 982-2140
Web Site:
http://www.simmonskidsfurniture.com
Sales Range: $25-49.9 Million
Emp.: 12
Juvenile Furniture Mfr
N.A.I.C.S.: 449110

DELTA FABRICATION & MACHINE, INC.
1379 CR 2110, Daingerfield, TX 75638
Tel.: (903) 645-3458   TX
Web Site: https://www.deltafab.net
Sales Range: $10-24.9 Million
Emp.: 150
Metal Fabrication & Machining Services
N.A.I.C.S.: 332999
Gerald W. Williams (Owner & Pres)

DELTA FLORAL DISTRIBUTORS INC.
6810 W Blvd, Los Angeles, CA 90043
Tel.: (323) 751-8116
Rev.: $13,085,206
Emp.: 70
Flowers & Nursery Stock
N.A.I.C.S.: 424930

DELTA FOREMOST CHEMICAL CORP.
3915 Air Park St, Memphis, TN 38118-6007
Tel.: (901) 363-4340   TN
Web Site:
https://www.deltaforemost.com
Year Founded: 1947
Industrial Cleaning Chemical Mfr
N.A.I.C.S.: 325612
Brenda Martin (Mgr-Sls Admin)

DELTA FUNDING CORPORATION
105 Maxess Rd Ste S-124, Melville, NY 11747
Tel.: (631) 574-4440   DE
Year Founded: 1984
Sales Range: $500-549.9 Million
Emp.: 1,395
Mortgage Services
N.A.I.C.S.: 522310
Richard Schneider (VP)
Debra Ward (VP)

DELTA GEAR CO. INC.
345 Sun Vly Cir, Fenton, MO 63026
Tel.: (636) 343-0311
Web Site: http://www.dgc-atc.com
Sales Range: $1-9.9 Million
Emp.: 35
Machine Shops

N.A.I.C.S.: 332710

DELTA GRANITE AND MARBLE INC.
2011 Sable Ln, San Antonio, TX 78217
Tel.: (210) 829-7171
Web Site:
https://www.deltagranite.com
Rev.: $13,100,000
Emp.: 70
Granite Building Stone
N.A.I.C.S.: 423320
David Rymer (Pres)
France Brantley (Treas)

DELTA GROUP ELECTRONIC INC.
4801 Lincoln Rd NE, Albuquerque, NM 87109
Tel.: (505) 883-7674
Web Site:
http://www.deltagroupinc.com
Rev.: $10,900,000
Emp.: 500
Printed Circuit Boards
N.A.I.C.S.: 334412
Harry C. Mueller (Pres & CEO)
Bill West (Mgr-Plant Ops-California)
Brett R. Greer (Mgr-Southwest)
Ron Reef (Mgr-Plant Ops-Florida)
Tod Cummins (Dir-Corp Quality Assurance)
Carla Tennyson (Mgr-HR)

DELTA GROWERS ASSOCIATION
313 S Hwy 105, Charleston, MO 63834
Tel.: (573) 649-3036
Web Site:
https://www.deltagrowers.com
Sales Range: $25-49.9 Million
Emp.: 75
Feed Fertilizer Chemicals
N.A.I.C.S.: 424910

DELTA HEALTH ALLIANCE
PO Box 277, Stoneville, MS 38776
Tel.: (662) 686-7004   MS
Web Site:
http://www.deltahealthalliance.com
Year Founded: 2001
Sales Range: $10-24.9 Million
Emp.: 141
Health Care Srvices
N.A.I.C.S.: 622110
Elizabeth McCullers (Dir-Sponsored Programs)
Karen Matthews (Pres & CEO)
Bill Kennedy (Chm)
Lisa Percy (Sec)
Marlin Womack (Gen Counsel & VP-Fin & Admin)
Sam Dawkins (VP-Health IT & Healthcare)
Josh Davis II (VP-External Affairs & Programs)

DELTA HOLDINGS, INC.
600 Horizon Dr, Chalfont, PA 18914-3961
Tel.: (215) 997-8850   PA
Year Founded: 1979
Sales Range: $10-24.9 Million
Emp.: 550
Holding Company
N.A.I.C.S.: 551112
John K. Desmond Jr. (Pres & Treas)
Lee Stranburg (Pres)
Vincent DiDomenico Jr. (Founder)

Subsidiaries:

Design & Supply Co., Inc.   (1)
600 Horizon Dr, Chalfont, PA 18914-1448
Tel.: (215) 997-8850

Web Site: http://www.designandsupply.com
Sales Range: Less than $1 Million
Emp.: 12
Furniture Distributor
N.A.I.C.S.: 423210
Lee Stranburg (Pres)

The Desmond Albany Hotel & Conference Center   (1)
660 Albany Shaker Rd, Albany, NY 12211-1056
Tel.: (518) 869-8100
Web Site:
http://www.desmondhotelsalbany.com
Rev.: $270,000
Emp.: 300
Hotel
N.A.I.C.S.: 721110
Jack Roddy (Dir-Sls)
J. Tyler Desmond (Gen Mgr)

The Desmond Great Valley Hotel & Conference Center   (1)
1 Liberty Blvd, Malvern, PA 19355
Tel.: (610) 296-9800
Web Site: http://www.desmondgv.com
Sales Range: $1-9.9 Million
Emp.: 195
Hotel
N.A.I.C.S.: 721110
Michael Chain (Gen Mgr)

Woodmere Management Inc.   (1)
600 Horizon, Chalfont, PA 18914
Tel.: (215) 997-8850
Rev.: $240,000
Emp.: 3
Management Services
N.A.I.C.S.: 561110
Michael Chain (Pres & Treas)

DELTA HOUSING INVESTMENT INC.
1416 W Marshall Ave, Longview, TX 75604
Tel.: (903) 758-2570
Sales Range: $10-24.9 Million
Emp.: 3
Mobile Home Dealers
N.A.I.C.S.: 459930
Wayne Smith (Pres)

DELTA INDUSTRIAL SERVICES, INC.
11501 Eagle St NW, Minneapolis, MN 55448
Tel.: (763) 755-7744   MN
Web Site:
http://www.deltamodtech.com
Year Founded: 1977
Sales Range: $1-9.9 Million
Emp.: 45
General Industrial Machinery, Nec, Nsk
N.A.I.C.S.: 333998
David Schiebout (Founder)
Rob Hattling (Sr Engr-Electrical)

Subsidiaries:

Frontier Industrial Technology   (1)
67 Campbell Rd, Towanda, PA 18848-8093
Tel.: (570) 265-2500
Web Site: http://www.frontierindustrial.com
Commercial & Service Industry Machinery Mfr
N.A.I.C.S.: 333310
Thomas J. Forbes (Owner)

DELTA INDUSTRIES INC.
100 W Woodrow Wilson Dr, Jackson, MS 39213-7643
Tel.: (601) 354-3804
Web Site: https://www.delta-ind.com
Year Founded: 1979
Sales Range: $25-49.9 Million
Emp.: 310
Supplier of Central-Mixed Concrete
N.A.I.C.S.: 327320
Paul Duff (CIO & VP)
Tom Evans (COO & Exec VP)
Dave Robison (Pres & CEO)
Leland R. Speed (Chm)

Pete Hays (*CFO, Treas & Sec*)
Les Howell (*VP, Chief Engr & Dir-Tech Svcs*)
Charlie McLemore (*Dir-Sls & Mktg*)

DELTA INFORMATION SYSTEMS INC.
300 Welsh Ste Road 120 Bldg 3, Horsham, PA 19044
Tel.: (215) 657-5270
Web Site: http://www.delta-info.com
Rev.: $8,000,000
Emp.: 35
Other Communications Equipment Mfr
N.A.I.C.S.: 334290
Gary Thom (*Pres*)

Subsidiaries:

Wideband Systems, Inc. (1)
2409 Linden Ln, Silver Spring, MD 20910
Tel.: (301) 588-8840
Web Site: http://www.wideband-sys.com
Rev.: $1,500,000
Emp.: 15
Audio & Video Equipment Mfr
N.A.I.C.S.: 334310
Marsh J. Dougherty (*Pres*)

DELTA INN INC.
9930 N Whitaker Rd, Portland, OR 97217
Tel.: (503) 285-8601
Web Site: http://www.deltainn.net
Rev.: $10,269,483
Emp.: 150
Hotel
N.A.I.C.S.: 721110
Andre Warren (*Gen Mgr*)
Hung Kim (*Pres*)

DELTA LABORATORIES INC.
3710 W Hwy 326, Ocala, FL 34475
Tel.: (352) 629-8101
Web Site:
http://www.deltalaboratories.com
Rev.: $10,600,000
Emp.: 55
Lacquer: Bases, Dopes, Thinner
N.A.I.C.S.: 325510
Richard E. Pesola (*Pres*)
Jordan Dern (*Mgr-Engrg*)
Aaron Dhawan (*Dir-Mktg*)

DELTA LIFE INSURANCE CO.
4370 Peachtree Rd NE 5th Fl, Atlanta, GA 30319
Tel.: (404) 231-2111
Web Site: http://www.delta-life.com
Sales Range: $25-49.9 Million
Emp.: 250
Provider of Life Insurance Services
N.A.I.C.S.: 524113
Hilton H. Howell Jr. (*Gen Counsel & Exec VP*)
Jeff Donahue (*VP & Dir-Trng & Education*)
Robin Robinson Howell (*VP*)

DELTA LIQUID ENERGY
1960 Ramada Dr, Paso Robles, CA 93446
Tel.: (805) 239-0616
Web Site:
https://www.deltaliquidenergy.com
Sales Range: $10-24.9 Million
Emp.: 95
Propane Gas, Bottled
N.A.I.C.S.: 457210
Bill Platz (*Pres*)
Robert Jacobs (*VP-Retail Ops*)
Richard Steck (*Mgr-Safety*)
Lisa Gerwitz (*Mgr-Logistics*)

DELTA MARINE INDUSTRIES, INC.
1608 S 96th St, Seattle, WA 98108

Tel.: (206) 763-2383
Web Site:
https://www.deltamarine.com
Sales Range: $25-49.9 Million
Boat Building & Repair Services
N.A.I.C.S.: 336612
Jason Jurgensen (*Mgr-HR*)

DELTA MARKETING INC.
1266 Plz Dr, Burlington, NC 27215
Tel.: (336) 229-5155   NC
Web Site:
http://www.burlingtonbrands.com
Year Founded: 1981
Sales Range: $10-24.9 Million
Emp.: 20
Operates Family Clothing Stores
N.A.I.C.S.: 458110
Kevin Fitzgerald (*Pres*)

DELTA MATERIALS HANDLING INC.
4676 Clarke Rd, Memphis, TN 38141
Tel.: (901) 795-7230
Web Site: https://www.deltamat.com
Rev.: $22,009,262
Emp.: 100
Industrial Trucks
N.A.I.C.S.: 423830
Greg Costa (*Pres & Gen Mgr*)
Roy Cochran (*Controller*)
Jerry Rodgers (*Mgr-Customer Svc Sls*)
Jim Colloredo (*Sr VP*)
Frank Fabrie (*VP-Ops*)
Francie Ridley (*Mgr-Mktg & Adv*)

DELTA MAX
PO Box 7188, Newport Beach, CA 92658
Tel.: (949) 759-8529
Web Site: http://www.delta-max.com
Sales Range: $25-49.9 Million
Emp.: 475
IT Consulting & Other Computer Related Services
N.A.I.C.S.: 541690
Robert Swanson (*Pres*)

DELTA MEDICAL SYSTEMS INC.
W 239 N 2890 Pewaukee Rd, Pewaukee, WI 53072
Tel.: (262) 523-2300
Web Site:
http://www.deltamedicalsystem.com
Sales Range: $10-24.9 Million
Emp.: 45
Medical Equipment & Supplies
N.A.I.C.S.: 423450
Tom Grisham (*VP-Fin*)
Jim Ziebart (*Pres*)
Joel Frank (*Coord-Svcs*)
Michelle Kocher (*Mgr-Internal Ops*)

DELTA METALS COMPANY INC.
1388 N 7th St, Memphis, TN 38107-1413
Tel.: (901) 525-5000   TN
Web Site: http://www.delta-metals.com
Year Founded: 1978
Sales Range: $25-49.9 Million
Emp.: 49
Metals Service Centers & Offices
N.A.I.C.S.: 423510
Darren Aghabeg (*Pres*)

DELTA OIL MILL
100 Mill St, Jonestown, MS 38639
Tel.: (662) 358-4481
Web Site: http://www.deltaoilmill.com
Sales Range: $10-24.9 Million
Emp.: 130
Cottonseed Oil Mills

N.A.I.C.S.: 311224
J. Scott Middleton Jr. (*Pres & Gen Mgr*)
John B. Laney Jr. (*Sec & Treas*)

DELTA PILOTS MUTUAL AID
PO Box 20883, Atlanta, GA 30320
Tel.: (404) 559-9421   GA
Web Site: http://www.dpma.org
Year Founded: 1943
Sales Range: $10-24.9 Million
Emp.: 2
Mutual Fund Services
N.A.I.C.S.: 523940
Mark O'Brien (*Treas*)

DELTA POWER CO.
4484 Boeing Dr, Rockford, IL 61109-2931
Tel.: (815) 397-6628   IL
Web Site: https://www.delta-power.com
Year Founded: 1967
Sales Range: Less than $1 Million
Emp.: 90
Mfr of Hydraulic Valves & Hydraulic Control Systems
N.A.I.C.S.: 332912
John Tackes (*Dir-Engrg*)

Subsidiaries:

Tecnord S.r.l. (1)
via Malavolti 36, 41100, Modena, Italy (50%)
Tel.: (39) 059254895
Web Site: http://www.tecnord.com
Rev.: $7,000,000
Emp.: 80
Mfr Hydraulic Valves & Hydraulic Control Systems
N.A.I.C.S.: 332912

DELTA PRODUCE MARKETING INC.
2001 S Laredo St, San Antonio, TX 78207-7023
Tel.: (210) 226-1900   TX
Year Founded: 1980
Sales Range: $50-74.9 Million
Emp.: 150
Fresh Fruits & Vegetables
N.A.I.C.S.: 424480
W. Scott Jensen (*Pres*)

DELTA PROJECTS, INC.
118 Allied Dr, Dedham, MA 02026
Tel.: (781) 449-8545   MA
Web Site:
https://www.deltaprojects.org
Year Founded: 1976
Sales Range: $10-24.9 Million
Emp.: 336
Disability Assistance Services
N.A.I.C.S.: 623210
Kevin McCullough (*Pres*)
Kathryn McNeil (*Chief Admin Officer*)
Pat Johnson (*Dir-Clinical*)

DELTA PURE FILTRATION CORPORATION
11011 Richardson Rd, Ashland, VA 23005
Tel.: (804) 798-2888
Web Site: http://www.deltapure.com
Year Founded: 1983
Sales Range: $1-9.9 Million
Emp.: 30
Mfr of Cartridge Filters for Water & Other Process Fluids
N.A.I.C.S.: 221310
J. Todd Furbee (*Owner & Pres*)
Dan Hall (*Supvr-Ops*)

DELTA RAILROAD CONSTRUCTION
PO Box 1398, Ashtabula, OH 44005-1398

Tel.: (440) 992-2997
Web Site: http://www.deltarr.com
Sales Range: $10-24.9 Million
Emp.: 100
Railroad & Railway Roadbed Construction
N.A.I.C.S.: 236210
Larry Laurello (*Pres*)
Ernesto Scarpitti (*Mgr-Corp Safety*)
Jennette Penna (*Asst Controller*)
Gary Dunbar Jr. (*Superintendent-Shop*)

DELTA REGIONAL MEDICAL CENTER
1400 E Union St, Greenville, MS 38703
Tel.: (662) 378-3783
Web Site:
http://www.deltahealthsystem.org
All Other Miscellaneous Ambulatory Health Care Services
N.A.I.C.S.: 621999
Scott Christensen (*CEO*)
Amy Walker (*Chief Nursing Officer*)
Scott Goodin (*Interim CFO*)
Sam Newsom (*Chm*)
Jamelda Fulton (*Vice Chm*)
Sylvia G. Jackson (*Sec*)

DELTA SAND & GRAVEL, INC.
562 Amherst Rd, Sunderland, MA 01375
Tel.: (413) 665-4051
Web Site: http://www.delta-sand.com
Sales Range: $10-24.9 Million
Emp.: 12
Construction Services
N.A.I.C.S.: 324121
Robert Warner (*Pres*)
Craig Warner (*Pres*)

DELTA SCIENTIFIC CORP.
40355 Delta Ln, Palmdale, CA 93551
Tel.: (661) 575-1100
Web Site:
https://www.deltascientific.com
Rev.: $21,000,000
Emp.: 200
Counter Terrorist System Control Equipment
N.A.I.C.S.: 334290
David G. Dickinson (*Sr VP*)
Keith Bobrosky (*VP-Sls*)
Greg Hamm (*VP-Sls & Mktg*)

DELTA SIGMA THETA SORORITY, INC.
1707 New Hampshire Ave NW, Washington, DC 20009
Tel.: (202) 986-2400   DC
Web Site:
https://www.deltasigmatheta.org
Year Founded: 1913
Sales Range: $25-49.9 Million
Fraternal Organization
N.A.I.C.S.: 813410
Gwendolyn E. Boyd (*Member-Exec Bd*)
Carla A. Harris (*Member-Exec Bd*)
Essie Jeffries (*Member-Exec Bd*)
Dolores Sennette (*Member-Exec Bd*)
Beverly Evans Smith (*Pres-Natl*)
Paulette C. Walker (*Pres-Natl*)
Deborah A. Jones-Buggs (*Treas-Natl*)
Edna Lee Moffitt (*Member-Exec Bd*)
Taylor Ashley (*Second VP-Natl*)
Taylor McCain (*Second VP-Natl*)

DELTA SONIC CAR WASH SYSTEMS INC.
570 Delaware Ave, Buffalo, NY 14202-1207
Tel.: (716) 886-0931   NY
Web Site:
https://www.deltasoniccarwash.com

Delta Sonic Car Wash Systems Inc.—(Continued)

Year Founded: 1967
Sales Range: $75-99.9 Million
Emp.: 800
Car Wash Company
N.A.I.C.S.: 457120
James Elston *(Sr Mgr-Detail Shop)*

DELTA STAR INC.

3550 Mayflower Dr, Lynchburg, VA 24501
Tel.: (434) 845-0921
Web Site: https://www.deltastar.com
Year Founded: 1988
Sales Range: $150-199.9 Million
Emp.: 450
Power, Distribution & Specialty Transformers Mfr
N.A.I.C.S.: 335311
Brenda Fairley *(Dir-HR)*
Jason Greene *(CEO)*

Subsidiaries:

Delta Star West   (1)
270 Industrial Rd, San Carlos, CA 94070-6212
Tel.: (650) 508-2850
Web Site: http://www.deltastar.com
Power Distribution & Specialty Transformer Mfr
N.A.I.C.S.: 335311

DELTA T CONSTRUCTION COMPANY

W 137 N 5732 Williams Pl, Menomonee Falls, WI 53051
Tel.: (262) 781-9243
Web Site:
https://www.deltatconstruction.com
Sales Range: $10-24.9 Million
Emp.: 91
Insulation, Buildings
N.A.I.C.S.: 238310
John Dohogne *(Pres)*

DELTA T EQUIPMENT

8850 Jameel Ste 100, Houston, TX 77040
Tel.: (281) 745-9060
Web Site:
http://www.deltaequipment.com
Sales Range: $1-9.9 Million
Emp.: 11
Air Conditioning Equipment Distr
N.A.I.C.S.: 423730
Paul McCarver *(Pres-Sls)*
Ron Hartman *(VP-Ops)*
Pat McCarver *(VP-Sls)*
Karen Balzi *(CFO & Chief Admin Officer)*

DELTA TOOLING CO. INC.

1350 Harmon Rd, Auburn Hills, MI 48326-1540
Tel.: (248) 391-6800
Web Site:
https://www.deltatechgroup.com
Year Founded: 1953
Sales Range: $10-24.9 Million
Emp.: 260
Special Dies, Tools, Jigs & Fixtures
N.A.I.C.S.: 333511
Peter Mozer *(Pres)*

DELTA-MONTROSE ELECTRIC ASSOCIATION

11925 6300 Rd, Montrose, CO 81401
Tel.: (970) 249-4572
Web Site: https://www.dmea.com
Sales Range: $1-9.9 Million
Emp.: 75
Distribution, Electric Power
N.A.I.C.S.: 221122
Kent Davenport *(VP-Engrg)*
Steve Metheny *(VP-Power & Supply)*

DELTA-V CAPITAL, LLC

1941 Pearl St Ste 200, Boulder, CO 80302
Tel.: (303) 405-7565
Web Site: https://deltavcapital.com
Year Founded: 2009
Privater Equity Firm
N.A.I.C.S.: 523999
Dave Schaller *(Founder & Mng Partner)*

Subsidiaries:

Tquila Automation, Inc.   (1)
310 Comal St, Austin, TX 78702
Tel.: (512) 552-2615
Web Site: https://tquila-automation.com
Artificial Intelligence, Robotic Process Automation & Business Process Management Services
N.A.I.C.S.: 518210
Tom Abbott *(Founder & CEO)*

Subsidiary (Domestic):

Element Blue LLC   (2)
3401 Louisiana St Ste 230, Houston, TX 77002-9546
Tel.: (832) 532-4056
Web Site: http://www.elementblue.com
Internet Publishing & Broadcasting & Web Search Portals
N.A.I.C.S.: 516210
Ian Uriarte *(COO & Mng Partner)*

DELTAPOINT CAPITAL MANAGEMENT, LLC

45 East Ave 6th Fl, Rochester, NY 14604
Tel.: (585) 454-6990   NY
Web Site:
http://www.deltapointcapital.com
Year Founded: 1996
Sales Range: $10-24.9 Million
Emp.: 6
Privater Equity Firm
N.A.I.C.S.: 523999
Stephen C. McCluski *(Dir-Ops)*
David H. Waterman *(Mng Dir)*
Thomas W. Cimino *(Mng Dir)*
Kevin M. Halpin *(VP)*
Thomas Merkel *(Dir-Ops)*
Joseph P. Richardson *(Dir-Ops)*
Michael D. Grosso *(Dir-Operating)*
Hugh Quigley *(Dir-Operating)*
John T. Cordes *(Mng Dir)*
George F. T. Yancey Jr. *(Dir-Ops)*

Subsidiaries:

Climax Manufacturing Company   (1)
7840 State Rte 26, Lowville, NY 13367
Tel.: (315) 376-8000
Web Site: http://www.climaxpkg.com
Sales Range: $150-199.9 Million
Folding Paperboard Cartons & Paperboard Mfr
N.A.I.C.S.: 322212

Subsidiary (Domestic):

Climax Packaging, Inc.   (2)
4515 Easton Rd, Saint Joseph, MO 64503
Tel.: (816) 233-3181
Web Site: http://www.stjpkg.com
Sales Range: $10-24.9 Million
Folding Paperboard Box Mfr
N.A.I.C.S.: 322212
Josh Hamilton *(Mgr-Production)*

SIGMA Marketing Group LLC   (1)
1 Cambridge Pl 1850 Winton Rd S, Rochester, NY 14618-3923
Tel.: (585) 473-7300
Web Site: http://www.sigmamarketing.com
Sales Range: $10-24.9 Million
Emp.: 75
Advertising & Marketing Services
N.A.I.C.S.: 541810
Martha Bush *(Sr VP-Strategy)*
Stefan Willimann *(CEO)*

DELTATHREE, INC.

1 Bridge Plz Ste 275, Fort Lee, NJ 07024
Tel.: (212) 500-4850   DE
Web Site: https://www.deltathree.com
Year Founded: 1996
Sales Range: $10-24.9 Million
Holding Company; Internet Protocol Network Management Services
N.A.I.C.S.: 551112
Yochai Ozeri *(Treas & Dir-Fin)*

Subsidiaries:

deltathree, Ltd.   (1)
Technological Park Building 9, Jerusalem, 96958, Israel
Tel.: (972) 26491222
Sales Range: $200-249.9 Million
Internet Protocol Network Management Services
N.A.I.C.S.: 517121
Effi Baruch *(CEO)*

DELTON RESTAURANTS INC.

373 Timberline Pkwy, Vienna, WV 26105
Tel.: (304) 865-2222
Rev.: $12,851,560
Emp.: 50
Fast-Food Restaurant, Chain
N.A.I.C.S.: 722513

DELTROL CORP.

3001 Grant Ave, Bellwood, IL 60104-1251
Tel.: (708) 547-0500   IL
Web Site:
https://www.deltrolfluid.com
Year Founded: 1963
Sales Range: $25-49.9 Million
Emp.: 100
Relays & Industrial Controls
N.A.I.C.S.: 335314
Paul Goc *(Mgr-Mfg Production)*
Susan Rogers *(Mgr-Sls)*

DELUCA FRIGOLETTO ADVERTISING, INC.

108 N Washington Ave, Scranton, PA 18503
Tel.: (570) 344-8339
Web Site: http://www.dfainc.com
Year Founded: 1993
Sales Range: $10-24.9 Million
Emp.: 7
N.A.I.C.S.: 541810
Paul DeLuca *(Pres)*

DELUCA TOYOTA SCION

1719 SW College Rd, Ocala, FL 34471
Tel.: (352) 732-0770
Web Site:
https://www.delucatoyota.com
Year Founded: 1978
Sales Range: $50-74.9 Million
Emp.: 103
Car Whslr
N.A.I.C.S.: 441110
Frank DeLuca *(Pres)*

DELUCCHI +

1828 L St NW Ste 240, Washington, DC 20036
Tel.: (202) 349-4000
Web Site:
http://www.delucchiplus.com
Sales Range: $10-24.9 Million
Emp.: 22
Advetising Agency
N.A.I.C.S.: 541810
Christine L. Delucchi *(Owner & Pres)*
Joseph Dunne *(Controller)*
Theresa Wasington *(Mgr-Billing)*
Kevin Tomko *(Sr Acct Exec)*
Shay Carson Onorio *(VP)*
David Menda *(Dir-Digital Strategy)*
Joanne Williams *(Dir-Ops)*

DELUVIA INC.

2040 Weaver Park Dr, Clearwater, FL 33765
Tel.: (727) 446-8785
Web Site:
https://www.deluviausa.com
Year Founded: 2002
Sales Range: $1-9.9 Million
Emp.: 90
Mfr of Organic & All Natural Skincare & Cosmetic Products
N.A.I.C.S.: 456120
Matt Webb *(CEO)*

DELUXE BUILDING SYSTEMS, INC.

499 W 3rd St, Berwick, PA 18603
Tel.: (800) 843-7372
Web Site:
http://www.deluxebuildings.com
Year Founded: 1965
Steel-Framed Modular Construction Services
N.A.I.C.S.: 332311
John Erb *(VP-Sls & Mktg)*
Donald E. Meske *(Pres)*
Dan Meske *(VP)*
David Thompson *(Dir-Project Controls)*

DELUXE CORPORATION OMNIBUS PLAN VEBA TRUST

3680 Victoria St N, Shoreview, MN 55126
Tel.: (651) 481-7111
Sales Range: $25-49.9 Million
Dental Association
N.A.I.C.S.: 813910
Hope R. Newland *(Dir-Corp Benefits)*

DELUXE FEEDS INC.

1500 RMT Ave, Sheldon, IA 51201
Tel.: (712) 324-4694
Web Site:
http://www.deluxefeeds.com
Sales Range: $10-24.9 Million
Emp.: 11
Fiscal Year-end: 05/31/15
Feed
N.A.I.C.S.: 424910
Gary Doppenberg *(Pres)*
Doug Perry *(CFO)*
Kirk Hall *(Mgr-Sls)*

DELUXE MARKETING, INC. (DMI)

101 Convention Ctr Dr Ste 700, Las Vegas, NV 89109
Tel.: (831) 245-7968   CA
Web Site:
http://www.deluxemarketinginc.com
Year Founded: 2003
Sales Range: $10-24.9 Million
Emp.: 20
Marketing & Retail Services
N.A.I.C.S.: 541613
Jeremy A. Larson *(Chm & CEO)*
Brad Canepa *(CFO & VP)*

DELYSE, INC.

505 Reactor Way, Reno, NV 89502
Tel.: (775) 857-1811
Web Site: http://www.delyse.com
Sales Range: $10-24.9 Million
Emp.: 50
Cookie & Cracker Mfr
N.A.I.C.S.: 311821
John B. Galvin *(Treas)*
Penny Pulsifer *(Controller)*

DELZER LITHOGRAPH COMPANY

510 S W Ave, Waukesha, WI 53186
Tel.: (262) 522-2600
Web Site: http://www.delzer.com
Year Founded: 1949

Sales Range: $10-24.9 Million
Emp.: 100
Commercial Lithographic Printing
N.A.I.C.S.: 323111
Greg Royal (Dir-DP)
Jim Polzin (Exec VP)
Mike Delzer (Pres & Treas)

DEMA ENGINEERING CO.
10020 Big Bend Rd, Saint Louis, MO
63122
Tel.: (314) 966-3533
Web Site: https://www.demaeng.com
Rev.: $16,000,000
Emp.: 150
Fluid Control Products Mfr
N.A.I.C.S.: 339999
Carl Deutsch (Chm)
Johnathan Deutsch (Pres)
Angela Dudley (Coord-Mktg)

Subsidiaries:

Dema Europe LLC   (1)
Mast 25, 3891 KE, Zeewolde, Netherlands
Tel.: (31) 36 522 7006
Web Site: http://www.demaeng.com
Emp.: 8
Industrial Equipment Distr
N.A.I.C.S.: 423840
Tony Harvey (Gen Mgr)
Rob Parkin (Reg Mgr-Sls)
David Pugh (Reg Mgr-Sls)

Standard Machine & Manufacturing
Co.   (1)
10014 Big Bend Rd, Saint Louis, MO 63122
Tel.: (314) 966-4500
Web Site: http://www.demaeng.com
Sales Range: $25-49.9 Million
Process Control Regulator Valves
N.A.I.C.S.: 332911
Sharon Cordray (Mgr-Customer Svc)

Viking LLC   (1)
512 Industrial Rd, Nesquehoning, PA 18240
Tel.: (570) 645-3633
Web Site: http://www.thevikingbowl.com
Emp.: 13
Dispenser Mfr
N.A.I.C.S.: 332999
Pete Yurchak (Gen Mgr)

DEMAAGD ENTERPRISES,
LLC
333 W Dickman Rd, Battle Creek, MI
49037
Tel.: (269) 963-5538   MI
Web Site:
   http://www.demaagdautogroup.com
Year Founded: 2003
Sales Range: $50-74.9 Million
Emp.: 30
Holding Company; New & Used Car
Dealerships
N.A.I.C.S.: 551112
Matthew Demaagd (Owner)

Subsidiaries:

Demaagd GMC-Nissan, Inc.   (1)
333 W Dickman Rd, Battle Creek, MI 49037
Tel.: (269) 963-5538
Web Site:
   http://www.demaagdgmcnissan.com
Sales Range: $10-24.9 Million
New & Used Car Dealership
N.A.I.C.S.: 441110
James C. Demaagd Jr. (Owner & Mgr-New
Car)

DEMAKES ENTERPRISES INC.
37 Waterhill St, Lynn, MA 01905-
2134
Tel.: (781) 595-1557   MA
Year Founded: 1914
Sales Range: $200-249.9 Million
Emp.: 300
Sausages & Other Prepared Meats
N.A.I.C.S.: 311612
Thomas L. Demakes (Pres)
Ann Conner (Mgr-Benefits)
Carol Langlois (Mgr-Acctg)

DEMAND POOLING, INC.
12720 Hillcrest Rd Ste 750, Dallas,
TX 75230
Tel.: (972) 388-1973   DE
Web Site: http://www.depo.org
Year Founded: 2008
Emp.: 1
Internet-Based Financial Services
N.A.I.C.S.: 525990
Kai Cheng Tang (CEO & CFO)
Philip S. Lanterman (COO)
Daniel L. Conrad (Sec)

DEMAND SCIENCE GROUP,
LLC
222 Rosewood Dr, Danvers, MA
01923
Tel.: (857) 770-1744
Web Site:
   https://demandscience.com
Year Founded: 2012
Business Support Services
N.A.I.C.S.: 561499
Peter Cannone (Chm & CEO)

Subsidiaries:

Terminus Software, Inc.   (1)
3340 Peachtree Rd NE Ste 300, Atlanta,
GA 30326
Web Site: http://www.terminus.com
Sales Range: $10-24.9 Million
Emp.: 162
Software Development Services
N.A.I.C.S.: 541511
Tim Kopp (CEO)
Oliver Bell (CFO)
Bryan Wade (Chief Customer Officer)
Tim Satterwhite (Chief Revenue Officer)
Natalie Cunningham (CMO)
Carter Lassy (Chief Product Officer)

DEMANDBASE, INC.
680 Folsom Ste 400, San Francisco,
CA 94107
Tel.: (415) 683-2660
Web Site:
   http://www.demandbase.com
Year Founded: 2006
B2B Marketing & Advertising Services
N.A.I.C.S.: 541613
Chris Golec (Founder & Chief Strat-
egy Officer)
David Lieberman (VP-Customer Suc-
cess)
Peter Isaacson (CMO)
Phil Hollrah (VP-Product Mktg)
George Rekouts (Sr VP-Engrg)
Aman Naimat (Sr VP-Tech)
Tony Russo (CFO)
Dom Lindars (VP-Product & Mktg So-
lutions)
Kelly Cook (VP-Product & Adv Solu-
tions)
Fatima Khan (Chief Privacy Officer)
Trish Sparks (Chief Customer Officer)
Gabe Rogol (CEO)
Brian Babcock (CTO)
Jon Miller (Chief Product Officer)
Umberto Milletti (Gen Mgr)

Subsidiaries:

InsideView Technologies, Inc.   (1)
444 De Haro St Ste 210, San Francisco,
CA 94107
Tel.: (415) 728-9300
Web Site: http://www.insideview.com
Marketing Consulting Services
N.A.I.C.S.: 541613
Umberto Milletti (Founder & CEO)
Gordon T. Anderson (VP-Content)
Heidi Tucker (VP-Alliances & Bus Dev)
Jason Muldoon (VP-Tech)
Loree Farrar (VP-HR)
Tracy Eiler (CMO)
Adam Shulman (CFO)

Subsidiary (Non-US):

InsideView Technologies (India) Pvt
Ltd.   (2)

Ascendas Mariner Building Block B 4th
Floor Plot No 17, Hyderabad, 500081, India
Tel.: (91) 40 4011 5200
Web Site: http://www.insideview.com
Emp.: 180
Customer Relationship Management Solu-
tions
N.A.I.C.S.: 513210
Sesha Rao (Mng Dir)

DEMANDDRIVE, LLC
135 Beaver St Ste 308, Waltham, MA
02452
Tel.: (508) 283-5350
Web Site:
   http://www.demanddrive.com
Year Founded: 2011
Sales Range: $1-9.9 Million
Marketing Services
N.A.I.C.S.: 541613
Lindsay Frey (Co-Founder & Pres)
Dan Paul (Co-Founder & Mng Dir)
Sarah Fotos (VP-Client Success)
Brad Losurdo (Mgr-Client Success)
Jon Hanman (VP-Sls)

DEMANDG, LLC
2801 Buford Hwy Druid Chase Ste
375, Atlanta, GA 30329
Tel.: (404) 929-0091
Web Site: http://www.arketi.com
Year Founded: 2005
Sales Range: $1-9.9 Million
Emp.: 14
Advetising Agency
N.A.I.C.S.: 541810
Rory Carlton (Principal)
Jacqueline Parker (VP)

DEMARIA BUILDING COM-
PANY INC.
45500 Grand River Ave, Novi, MI
48374-1305
Tel.: (248) 348-8710   MI
Web Site:
   http://www.demariabuild.com
Year Founded: 1969
Sales Range: $75-99.9 Million
Emp.: 100
Contracting & Construction Services
N.A.I.C.S.: 236220
Rick Flynn (CFO)
Darren Murray (Exec VP)
Mark Brimmeier (Exec VP)
Tony Demaria (Pres)
Joseph A. Demaria Jr. (CEO)
Mike Joseph V (VP-Estimating)

DEMATTIA GROUP
46321 Five Mills Rd, Plymouth, MI
48170
Tel.: (734) 453-2000
Web Site: http://www.demattia.com
Year Founded: 1977
Sales Range: $25-49.9 Million
Emp.: 75
Commercial & Institutional Building
Construction Services
N.A.I.C.S.: 236220
Gary D. Roberts (Pres & CEO)
Bob Demattia (Founder)

DEMBO JONES, P.C.
6010 Executive Blvd Ste 900, Rock-
ville, MD 20852-3874
Tel.: (301) 770-5100   MD
Web Site:
   http://www.dembojones.com
Year Founded: 1954
Accounting, Auditing, Tax & Consult-
ing Services
N.A.I.C.S.: 541211
Neil Berger (Mgr)
Nikki Boyadzhieva (Mgr)
Marcy Del Grosso (Mgr)
Cheryl Finkelstein (Mgr)
Christopher J. Guay (Mgr)

Nancy Guerra (Mgr)
Christopher A. Andracsek (Dir)
Russell G. Bregman (Dir)
Brent A. Croghan (Dir)
Robert L. Falk (Dir)
Jay Fielding (Dir)
Michael B. Hendrix (Dir)

DEMCO INC.
238 Lein Rd, Buffalo, NY 14224
Tel.: (716) 674-0883
Web Site: http://www.demcoinc.com
Sales Range: $10-24.9 Million
Emp.: 180
Wrecking & Demolition Work
N.A.I.C.S.: 238910
Chad Edwards (Pres)

DEMENT CONSTRUCTION
COMPANY INC.
403 N Pkwy Ste 201, Jackson, TN
38305
Tel.: (731) 424-6306   TN
Web Site:
   http://www.dementconstruction.com
Year Founded: 1977
Sales Range: $10-24.9 Million
Emp.: 150
Bridge, Tunnel & Elevated Highway
Construction
N.A.I.C.S.: 237310
James Newmon (Treas & Sec)

DEMETER LP
98 S 100 E Ste A, Fowler, IN 47944
Tel.: (765) 884-9320
Web Site: http://www.demeterlp.com
Sales Range: $50-74.9 Million
Emp.: 35
Farm Elevators
N.A.I.C.S.: 424510
Joanne Brouillet (Pres & CEO)

Subsidiaries:

Demeter-Chemung/ Harvard
Division   (1)
23619 Route 173, Harvard, IL 60033
Tel.: (815) 943-7424
Web Site: http://www.demeterlp.com
Farm Elevators
N.A.I.C.S.: 424510

Demeter-Ridgefield Division   (1)
8550 Ridgefield Rd, Crystal Lake, IL 60012
Tel.: (815) 459-1600
Web Site: http://www.demeterlp.com
Sales Range: $10-24.9 Million
Farm Elevators
N.A.I.C.S.: 541940
Robert Seegers Jr. (Mgr)

Demeter-South Beloit Division   (1)
4739 Prairie Hill Rd, South Beloit, IL 61080
Tel.: (815) 389-3737
Web Site: http://www.demeterlp.com
Sales Range: $50-74.9 Million
Emp.: 8
Farm Elevators
N.A.I.C.S.: 522220

DEMMER ENGINEERING &
MACHINE CO.
1600 N Larch, Lansing, MI 48906
Tel.: (517) 321-3600
Web Site:
   http://www.demmercorp.com
Sales Range: $25-49.9 Million
Emp.: 500
Tooling & Component Parts for Auto-
motive; Aerospace & Defense Indus-
tries Mfr
N.A.I.C.S.: 333514
Bill Demmer (Pres)

DEMOCRACY NOW!
207 W 25th St Fl 11, New York, NY
10001
Tel.: (212) 431-9090   NY

Democracy Now!—(Continued)

Web Site:
https://www.democracynow.org
Year Founded: 2002
Sales Range: $1-9.9 Million
Emp.: 35
News Publisher
N.A.I.C.S.: 516120
Isis Phillips *(Mgr-Finance)*
Julie Crosby *(Gen Mgr)*
Simin Farkhondeh *(Dir-Education)*

DEMOCRACY WORKS INC.
20 Jay St Ste 824, Brooklyn, NY
11201-8306
Tel.: (718) 923-1400   MA
Year Founded: 2010
Sales Range: $1-9.9 Million
Emp.: 27
Civic & Social Services
N.A.I.C.S.: 813410
Seth E. Flaxman *(Pres)*
Kathryn Peters *(Treas)*
Luis Lozada *(Gen Counsel)*

**DEMOCRAT PRINTING &
LITHOGRAPH COMPANY**
6401 Lindsey Rd, Little Rock, AR
72206
Tel.: (501) 374-0271   AR
Web Site:
https://www.democratprinting.com
Year Founded: 1871
Sales Range: $25-49.9 Million
Emp.: 250
Commercial Printing of Publications &
Catalogs
N.A.I.C.S.: 323111
Frank H. Parke *(Exec VP)*
David Smith *(Controller)*
Bert Parke *(Chm)*
John Parke *(COO & VP)*
Thomas Whitney *(VP)*
Haynes Whitney Jr. *(Pres)*

**DEMONTROND AUTO COUN-
TRY, INC.**
888 I 45 S, Conroe, TX 77304
Tel.: (281) 443-2500
Web Site:
http://www.demontrondauto.com
Year Founded: 1993
Sales Range: $75-99.9 Million
Emp.: 130
New Car Dealers
N.A.I.C.S.: 441110
George A. DeMontrond *(Pres)*

**DEMONTROND AUTOMOTIVE
GROUP**
14101 N Fwy, Houston, TX 77090
Tel.: (281) 872-7200
Web Site:
http://www.demontrond.com
Sales Range: $75-99.9 Million
Emp.: 250
New & Used Car Sales & Recre-
ational Vehicles
N.A.I.C.S.: 441110

**DEMOULAS SUPER MAR-
KETS, INC.**
875 E St, Tewksbury, MA 01876
Tel.: (978) 851-8000   MA
Web Site:
https://www.shopmarketbasket.com
Year Founded: 1917
Sales Range: $1-4.9 Billion
Emp.: 27,500
Supermarkets & Other Grocery Re-
tailers (except Convenience Retail-
ers)
N.A.I.C.S.: 445110
William J. Shea *(Chm)*
Donald Mulligan *(CFO, Treas & VP)*

DEMPEWOLF FORD LINCOLN
2530 US 41 North, Henderson, KY
42420
Tel.: (270) 827-3566
Web Site: http://www.dempewolf.com
Year Founded: 1968
Sales Range: $25-49.9 Million
Emp.: 55
Car Whslr
N.A.I.C.S.: 441110
Tommy Dempewolf *(Principal)*
Rick Tappan *(Gen Mgr-Sls)*

**DEMPSEY CONSTRUCTION,
INC.**
5937 Darwin Ct 103, Carlsbad, CA
92008
Tel.: (760) 918-6900
Web Site:
http://www.dempseyconstruct.com
Sales Range: $10-24.9 Million
Emp.: 50
Construction Services
N.A.I.C.S.: 236210
John Dempsey *(Pres)*
Bryce Raleigh *(VP)*
Nick Alford *(VP)*
Darla Kooiman *(Office Mgr)*

Subsidiaries:

Legacy Building Services, Inc.   (1)
2505 Congress St, San Diego, CA 92110
Tel.: (619) 298-1828
Web Site: http://www.legacybldg.com
Sales Range: $10-24.9 Million
Emp.: 36
Janitorial Services
N.A.I.C.S.: 561720

**DEMPSEY UNIFORM & LINEN
SUPPLY, INC.**
1200 Mid Valley Dr, Jessup, PA
18434-1823
Tel.: (570) 307-2300   PA
Web Site:
https://www.dempseyuniform.com
Year Founded: 1959
Sales Range: $10-24.9 Million
Emp.: 125
Linen Supply
N.A.I.C.S.: 812331
Patrick J. Dempsey *(Chm)*

DEN COL SUPPLY CO.
4630 N Washington St, Denver, CO
80216
Tel.: (303) 295-1683
Web Site: https://www.dencol.com
Rev.: $13,627,153
Emp.: 57
Steel
N.A.I.C.S.: 423510
Dewayne Deck *(Pres)*

**DENALI ADVANCED INTEGRA-
TION, INC.**
17735 NE 65th St Ste 130, Red-
mond, WA 98052
Tel.: (425) 885-4000
Web Site: http://www.denaliai.com
Sales Range: $75-99.9 Million
Emp.: 400
Computer Systems Design & Related
Services
N.A.I.C.S.: 541512
Majdi Daher *(Founder & CEO)*
Michael Leeper *(CTO)*
Jennifer Sprague *(Dir-HR)*
Lisanne Schliemann *(VP-Ops)*
Tracy Smith *(VP-Pro Svcs)*
Jamison Marra *(Exec VP-Enterprise
Application Dev)*
Trevor Greenaway *(Mng Dir-Europe)*

DENALI FAMILY SERVICES
6411 A St, Anchorage, AK 99518

Tel.: (907) 274-8281   AK
Web Site: http://www.denalifs.org
Year Founded: 1995
Sales Range: $10-24.9 Million
Emp.: 219
Behavioral Healthcare Services
N.A.I.C.S.: 623220
Dan Bigley *(Dir-Clinical)*

DENALI FLAVORS, INC.
4666 Leighton Lakes Dr, Wayland, MI
49348
Tel.: (616) 877-4625
Web Site:
http://www.moosetracks.com
Sales Range: $1-9.9 Million
Frozen Snack Food Mfr
N.A.I.C.S.: 311919
Wally Blume *(Co-Owner)*
June Blume *(Co-Owner)*
Jerry Trancik *(VP)*

**DENALI WATER SOLUTIONS
LLC**
3308 Bernice Ave, Russellville, AR
72802
Tel.: (479) 498-0500   DE
Web Site:
http://www.denaliwater.com
Waste & Environmental Services
N.A.I.C.S.: 562998
Andy McNeill *(Chm)*
Jeffrey LeBlanc *(Chief Growth Offi-
cer)*
Todd Mathes *(CEO)*
Samuel Liebl *(Dir-Sustainability &
Comm)*

Subsidiaries:

WeCare Denali, LLC   (1)
3308 Bernice Ave, Russellville, AR 72802
Tel.: (479) 498-0500
Web Site: http://www.WeCareDenali.com
Compost, Mulch & Soil Mfr
N.A.I.C.S.: 115112

Subsidiary (Domestic):

Swanson Bark & Wood Products,
Inc.   (2)
240 Tennant Way, Longview, WA 98632
Tel.: (360) 414-9663
Web Site: http://www.swansonbark.com
Wood Products Mfr
N.A.I.C.S.: 321999
Steve Liffers *(Co-Pres)*
Jeff Jackson *(Co-Pres)*

DENAPLES AUTO PARTS INC.
400 Mill St, Dunmore, PA 18512
Tel.: (570) 346-7673
Web Site: http://www.denaples.com
Rev.: $13,500,000
Emp.: 60
Automotive Parts
N.A.I.C.S.: 441330
Louis A. DeNaples Sr. *(Pres)*
Dominick L. DeNaples *(VP)*

**DENARK CONSTRUCTION,
INC.**
1635 Western Ave, Knoxville, TN
37921
Tel.: (865) 637-1925
Web Site: https://www.denark.com
Year Founded: 1985
Sales Range: $25-49.9 Million
Emp.: 160
Nonresidential Construction Services
N.A.I.C.S.: 236220
Frank Rothermel *(CEO)*
Raja J. Jubran *(Founder & CEO)*

**DENAULTS HARDWARE-
HOME CENTERS**
23281 Antonio Pkwy, Rancho Santa
Margarita, CA 92688
Tel.: (949) 888-5200

Web Site: https://www.denaults.com
Rev.: $23,241,145
Emp.: 36
Builders' Hardware
N.A.I.C.S.: 444140
Tom Denault *(VP)*

DENCAP DENTAL PLANS, INC.
45 E Milwaukee St, Detroit, MI 48202
Tel.: (313) 972-1400
Web Site: https://dencap.com
Dental Plans
N.A.I.C.S.: 524113

Subsidiaries:

Golden Dental Plans, Inc.   (1)
29377 Hoover Rd, Warren, MI 48093
Tel.: (586) 573-8118
Health Practitioners
N.A.I.C.S.: 621399
Gary Bingaman *(VP & Dir-Mktg)*

DENCHELS INCORPORATED
630 Wine Country Rd, Prosser, WA
99350
Tel.: (509) 786-2155
Web Site: http://www.fordcountry.com
Sales Range: $10-24.9 Million
Emp.: 50
Automobiles, New & Used
N.A.I.C.S.: 441110
Tom Denchel *(Pres)*

DENCO SALES CO.
55 S Yuma St, Denver, CO 80223
Tel.: (303) 733-0607
Web Site:
https://www.dencosales.com
Rev.: $13,000,000
Emp.: 150
Signmaker Equipment & Supplies
N.A.I.C.S.: 423840
Kenneth R. Von Wald *(Pres & CEO)*
Craig Kunde *(Branch Mgr)*
David Beyer *(Mgr-Distr-Natl)*
Kris Kliewer *(Mgr-Accts-Natl)*
Todd Castillo *(Mgr-Ops-Reg)*
Tanya Meacham *(Branch Mgr-Ops)*
Jerry Hicks *(Mgr-Bridgeport)*
Brad Watkins *(Mgr-Bridgeport)*
Ken Mehler *(Mgr-Customer Svc)*
Dave Smith *(Mgr-Ecommerce)*
David Orliss *(Mgr-Product Mktg)*
Joe House *(Mgr-Technical Svcs)*

**DENHAM CAPITAL MANAGE-
MENT LP**
185 Dartmouth St 7th Fl, Boston, MA
02116
Tel.: (617) 531-7200   MA
Web Site:
https://www.denhamcapital.com
Year Founded: 2004
Rev.: $7,900,000,000
Emp.: 65
Energy & Resources-Focused Private
Equity Firm
N.A.I.C.S.: 523999
John Collins *(Mng Dir & CFO)*
Michael Sigman *(Mng Dir & Head-
Risk Grp)*
Tim Smith *(Mng Dir-IR)*
Wallace Varga *(Mng Dir-Tax)*
Robert Warburton *(Operating Partner)*
Paul Winters *(Mng Dir, Chief Compli-
ance Officer & Gen Counsel)*
Scott Mackin *(Partner-London)*
Jordan Marye *(Partner-Houston)*
Riaz Siddiqi *(Partner-Houston)*
Carl Tricoli *(Partner-Houston)*
Tony Fiore *(Dir-Legal & Assoc Gen
Counsel)*
William A. Zartler *(Founder)*
Caroline Donally *(Mng Dir)*
Geer Blalock *(Mng Dir)*
Jason Craig *(Mng Dir)*

Saurabh Anand *(Mng Dir)*
Stuart Porter *(CEO, Mng Partner & Chief Investment Officer)*

Subsidiaries:

Auctus Minerals Pty. Ltd. **(1)**
Suite 15 58 Kishorn Road, Mount Pleasant, 6153, Western Australia, Australia
Tel.: (61) 86243 2801
Resource Development Services
N.A.I.C.S.: 212290
Steve Murdoch *(Mng Dir)*

Greenleaf Power, LLC **(1)**
2600 Capitol Ave, Sacramento, CA 95816
Tel.: (916) 596-2500
Web Site: http://www.greenleaf-power.com
Sales Range: $50-74.9 Million
Owner & Operator of Green Energy Plants
N.A.I.C.S.: 221118
Charles Abbott *(Pres & CEO)*
Russell Huffman *(VP-Ops-CA)*

Subsidiary (Domestic):

Colmac Energy, Inc. **(2)**
62300 Gene Welmas Dr, Mecca, CA 92254
Tel.: (760) 396-2554
Rev.: $70,386,000
Emp.: 52
Biomass Green Energy Power Plant
N.A.I.C.S.: 221118
Graeme Donaldson *(VP)*
Rick Kruzel *(Mgr-Ops)*

DENHOLTZ MANAGEMENT CORP.
14 Cliffwood Ave, Matawan, NJ 07047
Tel.: (732) 381-1115
Web Site:
http://www.denholtzassociates.com
Year Founded: 1983
Sales Range: $10-24.9 Million
Emp.: 75
Industrial Buildings & Warehouses
N.A.I.C.S.: 236220
Brian MacMurray *(Dir-HR)*
Kristine Hurlbut *(Sr VP-Leasing)*
Charlene Lemoine *(Mgr-Property)*

DENIER ELECTRIC CO. INC.
10891 State Rte 128, Harrison, OH 45030
Tel.: (513) 738-2641   OH
Web Site: https://www.denier.com
Year Founded: 1942
Sales Range: $25-49.9 Million
Emp.: 240
Provider of Power Systems & Services
N.A.I.C.S.: 238210
Mary Hurd *(Controller)*
Jeff Hecker *(CEO)*
Mike Kallmeyer *(Sr VP-Construcion)*

DENIHAN HOSPITALITY GROUP, LLC
551 5th Ave, New York, NY 10176
Tel.: (212) 465-3700
Web Site: https://www.denihan.com
Hotels Owner & Operator
N.A.I.C.S.: 721110
Patrick Benjamin Denihan *(Co-CEO)*
Brook Barrett *(Co-CEO)*
Glenn Wasserman *(CFO)*
Carl L. Cohen *(Chief Experience Officer)*
Gul Turkmenoglu *(Gen Mgr-The Benjamin)*
Edward Maynard *(Exec VP-Ops)*
Vera Manoukian *(Pres & COO)*
Paul Cardona *(Gen Mgr-The James Chicago)*
Von Fabella *(Dir-Sls-The James Chicago)*
John Chan *(Sr VP-Dev)*
Garine Ferejian-Mayo *(Sr VP-Market Strategy & Revenue Mgmt)*

DENISON INC.
36 S Pennsylvania St Ste 200, Indianapolis, IN 46204
Tel.: (317) 633-4003
Web Site:
http://www.denisonparking.com
Year Founded: 1934
Sales Range: $10-24.9 Million
Emp.: 15
Parking Lots
N.A.I.C.S.: 812930
Perry Griffith *(Chm)*
Mark Davis *(VP-Acctg & Fin)*
Jeff Line *(Pres)*
Mark Pryor *(Dir-Reg Ops)*
Kathy Richardson *(VP-Auditing)*

Subsidiaries:

Denison Parking Inc. **(1)**
36 S Pennsylvania St 200, Indianapolis, IN 46204
Tel.: (317) 633-4003
Web Site: http://www.denisonparking.com
Parking Garage
N.A.I.C.S.: 812930
Kathy L. Richardson *(VP-Auditing)*
Jeff Line *(COO & Exec VP)*
Mark Pryor *(VP-Bus Dev & Special Projects)*
Kosta Sofianopoulos *(Project Mgr-Boston)*

Denison Properties Inc. **(1)**
36 S Pennsylvania St Ste 200, Indianapolis, IN 46204-7757
Tel.: (317) 633-4003
Rev.: $3,600,000
Emp.: 2
Subdividers & Developers
N.A.I.C.S.: 237210
Harry F. McNaught Jr. *(Pres)*

DENISON-CANNON CO.
PO Box 20, North Billerica, MA 01862
Tel.: (978) 663-8711
Web Site:
http://www.denisoncannon.com
Year Founded: 1920
Sales Range: $10-24.9 Million
Emp.: 23
Lumber, Flooring & Building Product Distr
N.A.I.C.S.: 423310
John Belanger *(Treas)*

DENMAR ASSOCIATES LLC
740 E Lincoln Ave, Myerstown, PA 17067
Tel.: (717) 866-7555
Web Site:
http://www.martinwater.com
Rev.: $15,000,000
Emp.: 125
Electric Household Appliances
N.A.I.C.S.: 449210

DENNEY ELECTRIC SUPPLY
61 Butler Ave, Ambler, PA 19002
Tel.: (215) 628-8880
Web Site: https://www.denneyelectric
supply.com
Rev.: $19,752,000
Emp.: 50
Electrical Supplies Distributors
N.A.I.C.S.: 423610
David Chelstowski *(Dir-Inventory)*
Don Griffith *(CIO)*
Steve Thornton *(CEO)*
Charles Childers *(Coord-Inventory)*
Kelly Stefanik *(Controller)*

DENNIS DILLON AUTO PARK TRUCK CENTER
2777 S Orchard St, Boise, ID 83705
Tel.: (208) 336-6000
Web Site:
http://www.dennisdillon.com
Sales Range: $25-49.9 Million
Emp.: 140
Automobiles, New & Used

N.A.I.C.S.: 441110
Dennis E. Dillon *(CEO)*

DENNIS K. BURKE INC.
284 Eastern Ave, Chelsea, MA 02150-3308
Tel.: (617) 884-7800   MA
Web Site: http://www.burkeoil.com
Year Founded: 1961
Sales Range: $10-24.9 Million
Emp.: 100
Supplier of Petroleum Products
N.A.I.C.S.: 424720
Jimmy Logan *(Mgr-Operations)*

DENNIS M. MCCOY & SONS
74 Union Chapel Rd, Gillette, WY 82718-7469
Tel.: (307) 687-0382   Ca
Web Site:
http://www.mccoyandsons.com
Year Founded: 1994
Sales Range: $10-24.9 Million
Contract Mining Services
N.A.I.C.S.: 212321
Dennis Mccoy *(Pres)*

DENNIS PAPER COMPANY
910 Acorn Dr, Nashville, TN 37210
Tel.: (615) 883-9010   TN
Web Site:
https://www.dennispaper.com
Year Founded: 1969
Sales Range: $10-24.9 Million
Emp.: 35
Distr of Fine Paper
N.A.I.C.S.: 424110
Morris Dennis *(Pres)*
Ronald Dennis *(Exec VP)*
Jerry Dennis *(VP)*
Steve Dennis *(Treas & VP)*
Agnes Dennis *(Sec)*

DENNIS PR GROUP
41 Crossroads Ste 228, West Hartford, CT 06117
Tel.: (860) 523-7500
Web Site: http://www.dennispr.com
Year Founded: 2000
Sales Range: $1-9.9 Million
Emp.: 6
Public Relations Agency
N.A.I.C.S.: 541820
Ron Dresner *(Pres)*
Craig King *(VP-Acct Svcs)*
Victoria Stevens *(Mgr-Acct Svcs)*
Jessica O'Reilly *(Mgr-Acct Svcs)*

DENNIS SALES CO. INC.
146 5th St, Raymond, WA 98577
Tel.: (360) 942-2427
Web Site:
http://www.denniscompany.com
Rev.: $12,254,539
Emp.: 47
Department Stores
N.A.I.C.S.: 455110
Brent B. Dennis *(Pres)*

DENNIS SUPPLY COMPANY
300 W 7th St, Sioux City, IA 51103
Tel.: (712) 255-7637   IA
Web Site:
http://www.dennissupply.com
Year Founded: 1975
Sales Range: $10-24.9 Million
Emp.: 50
Whslr of Refrigeration, Heating & Air Conditioning Equipment & Supplies
N.A.I.C.S.: 423740
Carter R. Dennis *(Pres)*

DENNIS, GARTLAND & NIERGARTH, CPA
415 Munson Ave Ste 201, Traverse City, MI 49686

Tel.: (231) 946-1722   MI
Web Site: http://www.dgncpa.com
Year Founded: 1973
Emp.: 100
Accounting, Auditing & Bookkeeping Services
N.A.I.C.S.: 541211
Brad Neirgarth *(Sr Partner)*
Laurie A. Bamberg *(Partner)*
Thomas E. Gartland *(Founding Partner)*
James G. Shumate *(Sr Partner)*
Shelly K. Bedford *(Mng Partner)*
Mary F. Krantz *(Partner)*
Heidi M. Wendel *(Partner)*
Shelly A. Ashmore *(Tax Partner)*
James M. Taylor *(Partner)*
Trina B. Ochs *(Partner)*
John A. Blair *(Partner)*

DENNISON CORPORATION
1508 Morrissey Dr, Bloomington, IL 61701
Tel.: (309) 663-1331
Web Site:
http://www.dennisonford.com
Rev.: $46,000,000
Emp.: 125
Owner & Operator of Car Dealerships
N.A.I.C.S.: 441110
Robert Dennison *(Pres)*

DENNISON LUBRICANTS
102 Charles Eldridge Rd, Lakeville, MA 02347-1377
Tel.: (508) 946-0500
Web Site: https://www.denlube.com
Year Founded: 1988
Rev.: $40,300,000
Emp.: 63
Petroleum Product Whslr
N.A.I.C.S.: 424720
Tom Dellisandrew *(Controller)*
Frank Glasby *(Mgr-HR)*
Timothy Dennison *(Pres)*
Brian Dennison *(Mgr-Sls)*

DENNY MENHOLT FRONTIER CHEVROLET
3000 King Ave W, Billings, MT 59102
Tel.: (406) 896-3000   MT
Web Site:
http://www.dennymenholtchevy.com
Year Founded: 1970
Sales Range: $25-49.9 Million
Emp.: 160
New & Used Car Dealer
N.A.I.C.S.: 441110
Dennis Menholt *(Pres)*
Wendy Ray *(Controller)*

DENOOYER CHEVROLET INC.
127 Wolf Rd, Albany, NY 12205-1105
Tel.: (518) 458-7700   NY
Web Site:
http://www.denooyerchevrolet.com
Year Founded: 1971
Sales Range: $75-99.9 Million
Emp.: 130
Retailer of Automobiles
N.A.I.C.S.: 441110
Doreen Vogt *(Controller)*
Joel DeNooyer *(Pres)*
Tim Rigney *(Mgr-Sls)*
Tom Denooyer *(Gen Mgr)*

DENRON PLUMBING & HVAC, LLC.
605 Front St, Manchester, NH 03102-2698
Tel.: (603) 627-4186
Web Site: http://www.denronph.com
Year Founded: 1973
Sales Range: $10-24.9 Million
Emp.: 130
Plumbing Services

Denron Plumbing & HVAC, LLC.—(Continued)
N.A.I.C.S.: 238220

DENS PARTNERS, INC.
31 Route 13, Brookline, NH 03033
Tel.: (603) 673-2200
Web Site:
  http://www.denspartners.com
Sales Range: $50-74.9 Million
Emp.: 1
Plumbing, Heating & Air-Conditioning
Contracting Services
N.A.I.C.S.: 238220
Roy Greenwald *(Pres & CEO)*

DENSON OIL COMPANY, INC.
2571 Hwy 11 N, Laurel, MS 39440
Tel.: (601) 764-9870   **MS**
Rev.: $25,973,000
Emp.: 12
Petroleum Whslr
N.A.I.C.S.: 424720
William Lloyd Denson *(VP & Gen Mgr)*
Gary Allen Gordon *(Pres)*

DENT ENTERPRISES INC.
1161 E Clark Rd Ste 124 126 &
128, Dewitt, MI 48820
Tel.: (517) 668-9488
Web Site:
  http://www.theoutsideguys.com
Sales Range: $10-24.9 Million
Emp.: 50
Provider of Lawn & Garden Mainte-
nance Services
N.A.I.C.S.: 561730
Gregory Dent *(Pres)*
Kevin Dent *(CEO)*
Brian Wooton *(CFO)*
Scott Milnes *(COO)*
Teresa Phelps *(Dir-Sls)*

DENTAL BURS USA
824 W Superior St Ste 605, Chicago,
IL 60642
Tel.: (847) 414-3595
Web Site: http://www.bursusa.com
Year Founded: 2005
Sales Range: $1-9.9 Million
Emp.: 7
Dental Equipment & Supplies
N.A.I.C.S.: 339114
Boris Lehtman *(Pres)*

**DENTAL EQUIPMENT LIQUI-
DATORS, INC.**
16720 Bachmann Ave, Hudson, FL
34667
Tel.: (727) 863-5500
Web Site:
  http://www.useddentalequipment.net
Sales Range: $1-9.9 Million
Emp.: 12
Dental Equipment Distr
N.A.I.C.S.: 423450
Greg Brown *(Pres)*
Leanne Brown *(VP)*

**DENTAL HEALTH MANAGE-
MENT SOLUTIONS (DHMS)**
2001 Windy Ter Ste F, Cedar Park,
TX 78613
Tel.: (512) 989-6990
Web Site:
  https://www.usdentalsolutions.com
Year Founded: 2003
Sales Range: $10-24.9 Million
Emp.: 50
Quality, Affordable Dental Services
N.A.I.C.S.: 339116
Shane Stevens *(Co-Founder & CEO)*
Jennifer Stevens *(Co-Founder, Chm
& Pres)*

John Babineau *(Owner & Chief Den-
tal Officer)*
Cathy Stevens *(Dir-Clinical Hygiene)*
Chris Holmes *(VP-Military Ops)*

**DENTAL HEALTH PRODUCTS
INC.**
2614 N Sugar Bush Rd, New Fran-
ken, WI 54229
Tel.: (920) 866-9001
Web Site: http://www.dhpi.net
Sales Range: $10-24.9 Million
Emp.: 114
Dental Equipment & Supplies
N.A.I.C.S.: 423450
Heath Miller *(Sr Acct Mgr)*
Bill Michales *(Sr Acct Mgr)*
Chlorissa Kramer *(Mgr-Mktg)*
Steve Ward *(Sr Acct Mgr)*
Chris Larsen *(Acct Mgr)*
Kimberly Nelsen *(Mgr-Sls Acct)*
Jim Ness *(Coord-Equipment)*
Lisa Benson *(Mgr-HR)*
Patricia Donovan *(Sr Acct Mgr)*

DENTAL INTELLIGENCE, INC.
2100 W Grove Blvd Ste 400, Pleas-
ant Grove, UT 84062
Web Site: http://www.dentalintel.com
Year Founded: 2015
Sales Range: $1-9.9 Million
Emp.: 84
Dental Care Services
N.A.I.C.S.: 621399
Dan Geraty *(CEO)*
Marty Ostermiller *(CFO)*
Jeff Adams *(Chief Revenue Officer)*
James Grover *(Chief Product Officer)*

**DENTAL NETWORK OF
AMERICA INC.**
2 Transam Plz Dr, Oakbrook Terrace,
IL 60181-4823
Tel.: (630) 691-1133
Web Site: http://www.dnoa.com
Year Founded: 1985
Sales Range: $10-24.9 Million
Emp.: 110
Administrative Services Consultant
N.A.I.C.S.: 541611
Rachel Derrico *(Exec VP-HR)*
Mike Miller *(VP-Dental Networks)*
Christopher H. Stevens *(Chief Actu-
ary & VP-Risk Mgmt)*

DENTAL SALON
939 W North Ave Ste 890, Chicago,
IL 60642
Tel.: (312) 642-3370
Web Site:
  https://www.dentalsalon.com
Year Founded: 2003
Sales Range: $1-9.9 Million
Emp.: 70
Dental Practice Offering Complete
Range of Services Including Financial
Assistance
N.A.I.C.S.: 339116
Nicholas Dallas *(Principal)*
Darleen Alberts *(Coord-Insurance)*

DENTAL SELECT
5373 S Green St 4th Fl, Salt Lake
City, UT 84123
Tel.: (801) 495-3000
Web Site:
  http://www.dentalselect.com
Year Founded: 1989
Sales Range: $10-24.9 Million
Emp.: 93
Insurance Agents & Brokers Dentist
Office Business Consulting Service
N.A.I.C.S.: 524210
Brent Williams *(Founder & CEO)*
Suzette Musgrove *(Chief Growth Offi-
cer)*

Mike Nelson *(Chief Underwriting Offi-
cer)*
Jeff Van Leeuwen *(VP-Sls)*
Thomas Nehren *(Dir-Mktg)*
Mark Coyne *(Pres)*
LaTonya Pegues *(Sr Mgr-Ops)*
Michele Flood *(Mgr-Sls-Texas, Okla-
homa, New Mexico, Louisiana &
Arkansas)*

**DENTALCARE PARTNERS
INC.**
6200 Oak Tree Blvd Ste 200, Inde-
pendence, OH 44131
Tel.: (440) 684-6940   **OH**
Web Site: http://www.dcpartners.com
Year Founded: 1989
Sales Range: $150-199.9 Million
Emp.: 850
Dental Services
N.A.I.C.S.: 621210
Doug Brown *(CEO)*
Carole Shaull *(Sr Dir-HR)*

**DENTCARE DELIVERY SYS-
TEMS, INC.**
333 Earle Ovington Blvd, Uniondale,
NY 11553-3608
Tel.: (516) 542-2200   **NY**
Web Site:
  https://www.dentcaredelivery.org
Year Founded: 1977
Sales Range: $25-49.9 Million
Dental Care Services
N.A.I.C.S.: 339116
Glenn J. Sobel *(Pres)*

DENTEL BANCORPORATION
201 W Jackson, Corydon, IA 50060
Tel.: (641) 872-2212   **IA**
Year Founded: 1985
Sales Range: $10-24.9 Million
Multi-Bank Holding Company
N.A.I.C.S.: 551111
Robert V. Dentel *(Pres & CEO)*
Mary P. Howell *(Treas, Sec & VP)*

Subsidiaries:

Corydon State Bank   **(1)**
201 W Jackson St, Corydon, IA 50060
Tel.: (641) 872-2212
Web Site: http://www.corydonstatebank.com
Sales Range: $1-9.9 Million
Commericial Banking
N.A.I.C.S.: 522110

Maxwell State Bank   **(1)**
122 Main St, Maxwell, IA 50161
Tel.: (515) 387-1175
Web Site: http://www.maxwellstatebank.com
Commericial Banking
N.A.I.C.S.: 522110
Ronald Ingram *(Chm)*

Pocahontas State Bank   **(1)**
233 N Main St, Pocahontas, IA 50574-1636
Tel.: (712) 335-3567
Web Site:
  http://www.pocahontasstatebank.com
Sales Range: $1-9.9 Million
Commericial Banking
N.A.I.C.S.: 522110
Robert O'Donald *(Pres)*

DENTINO MARKETING
515 Executive Dr, Princeton, NJ
08540
Tel.: (609) 454-3202   **NJ**
Web Site:
  http://www.dentinomarketing.com
Year Founded: 1987
Rev.: $10,000,000
Emp.: 10
Direct Response Marketing
N.A.I.C.S.: 541810
Karl Dentino *(Pres)*
Joel Rubinstein *(Sr Dir-Creative)*
Rosalba De Meo *(Dir-Creative)*

**DENTON COUNTY TERMITE &
HOUSE LEVELING, INC.**
902 N Elm St, Denton, TX 76201
Tel.: (940) 387-6049   **TX**
Web Site:
  https://www.dentontermitepest.com
Year Founded: 1940
Sales Range: $1-9.9 Million
Emp.: 13
Pest Control & Foundation Repair
Services
N.A.I.C.S.: 561710
Sylvia Baird *(Treas)*

DENTON ENTERPRISES INC.
22003 Harper Ave, Saint Clair
Shores, MI 48080-1815
Tel.: (586) 777-9444   **MI**
Web Site:
  http://www.dentoncompanies.net
Year Founded: 1941
Sales Range: $25-49.9 Million
Emp.: 100
Highway & Street Construction
N.A.I.C.S.: 237310

Subsidiaries:

Denton Concrete Services Inc.   **(1)**
22203 Harper Ave, Saint Clair Shores, MI
48080-1815   **(100%)**
Tel.: (586) 777-9444
Web Site: http://www.denton.com
Highway & Street Construction
N.A.I.C.S.: 237310

**DENTON HINES PROPERTIES,
INC.**
500 N Akard St Ste 1900, Dallas, TX
75201
Tel.: (214) 220-1011
Year Founded: 1979
Sales Range: $1-9.9 Million
Emp.: 7
Real Estate Property Developers
N.A.I.C.S.: 531210
Lee Fikes *(Pres)*

DENTON VACUUM INC.
1259 N Church St Bldg 3, Moores-
town, NJ 08057
Tel.: (856) 439-9100
Web Site:
  https://www.dentonvacuum.com
Year Founded: 1964
Sales Range: $10-24.9 Million
Emp.: 110
Vacuum Pumps, Laboratory
N.A.I.C.S.: 334516
Ellen Carson *(Controller & Dir-Fin)*

DENTON-RENFROE, INC.
PO Box 65634, Lubbock, TX 79464-
5634
Tel.: (806) 368-5071   **TX**
Year Founded: 1999
Sales Range: $1-9.9 Million
Emp.: 12
Nonresidential Construction & Archi-
tectural Services
N.A.I.C.S.: 236220
Dennis Rocha *(Pres)*

DENTONS GROUP
1900 K St NW Ste 100 E Twr, Wash-
ington, DC 20005-3364
Tel.: (202) 408-6400
Web Site: http://www.dentons.com
Legal Services Association
N.A.I.C.S.: 813910
Joe Andrew *(Chm-Global)*
Elliott I. Portnoy *(CEO-Global)*
Federico Sutti *(Mng Partner-Italy)*
Aldo Calza *(Partner)*
Pier Francesco Faggiano *(Partner)*
Matteo Falcione *(Partner)*
Maria Sole Insinga *(Partner)*

Iacopo Aliverti Piuri *(Partner)*
Federico Vanetti *(Partner)*
Jennifer R. Williams *(Partner)*
Marc Burgat *(Principal-Nationally Ranked Public Policy & Regulation Practice)*
Scott DeMartino *(Partner-Real Estate Practice)*
Brian Raftery *(Partner-Trusts, Estates & Wealth Preservation)*
Nick Kappas *(Partner)*
Jennifer Simmons *(Partner)*
Sharon Gay *(Mng Partner-Atlanta)*
Jeff Haidet *(Chm)*
Thurbert Baker *(Partner)*
Gordon Giffin *(Partner)*
Brian P. McGowan *(Principal-Public Policy & Regulation Practice)*
Steven Labovitz *(Sr Partner-Global Law Practice)*
Edward Lindsey *(Partner-Public Policy & Regulation Practice)*
Noor Kapdi *(CEO-Africa & Mng Partner-South Africa)*
Oleg V. Batyuk *(Mng Partner-Ukraine)*
Bernardo Cardenas *(Mng Partner-Colombia)*
Jeremy Cohen *(CEO-UK & Middle East & Partner)*
Philip Jeyaretnam *(Vice Chm-Global & CEO-Singapore)*
John C. Koski *(Chief Legal Officer-Global)*
Siang Pheng Lek *(Deputy Mng Partner)*
Matthew Hanslip Ward *(Partner)*
Mark G. Trigg *(Partner-Litigation & Dispute Resolution Practice-Atlanta)*
Gianpaolo Garofalo *(Partner-Structured Fin Grp-Banking & Fin Practice-Italy)*
Alessandro Fosco Fagotto *(Head-Banking & Fin Practice-Italy)*
Julien Bacus *(Partner-Paris)*
Michael Huertas *(Partner-Frankfurt)*
Arne Kluwer *(Partner-Germany)*
Matthias Eggert *(Partner-Germany)*
Mortimer Bertlet *(Partner-Germany)*
Rene Dubois *(Partner-Munich)*
Amanda Jones *(Dir-Women's Advancement)*
Florian Schneider *(Partner)*
Mark Withey *(Partner-Moscow)*
Tomasz Dabrowski *(CEO-Europe)*
Severine Hotellier *(Mng Partner-France)*
Alexei Zakharko *(Mng Partner-Russia)*
Marc Fornacciari *(Partner)*
Mike McNamara *(CEO-US)*
Eric Tanenblatt *(Chm-Pub Policy Practice-Global)*
Ashley Bell *(Partner)*

Subsidiaries:

Dentons Canada LLP   **(1)**
77 King Street West Suite 400 Toronto-Dominion Centre, Toronto, M5K 0A1, ON, Canada
Tel.: (416) 863-4511
Web Site: http://www.dentons.com
Emp.: 514
Law firm
N.A.I.C.S.: 541110
Carman McNary *(Mng Partner-Edmonton)*
Chris Pinnington *(Chm)*
Gary R. Sollis *(Partner)*

Dentons UKMEA LLP   **(1)**
One Fleet Place, London, EC4M 7WS, United Kingdom
Tel.: (44) 20 7242 1212
Web Site: http://www.dentons.com
Law firm
N.A.I.C.S.: 541110
Jeremy Cohen *(CEO & Partner)*
Justin Hill *(Partner)*
Alex Tostevin *(Partner)*
Darren Acres *(Partner)*

Gordon Aitken *(Partner)*
Akin Akinbode *(Partner)*
Daren Allen *(Partner)*
Virginia K. Allen *(Partner)*
Celyn Armstrong *(Partner)*
Catherine Astruc *(Partner)*
Howard Barrie *(Partner)*
Yusuf Battiwala *(Partner)*
Alistair Black *(Partner)*
Cristiano Bortolotti *(Partner)*
Dan Burge *(Partner)*
Bonnie Calnan *(Partner)*
Jonathan Cantor *(Partner)*
Ryan Carthew *(Partner)*
Nick Chandler *(Partner)*
Helen Cleaveland *(Partner)*
David Cohen *(Partner)*
Nik Colbridge *(Partner)*
David Collins *(Partner)*
Ted Craig *(Partner)*
Lucille De Silva *(Partner)*
Deepa Deb *(Partner)*
Humphry Douglas *(Partner)*
Rupert Dowdell *(Partner)*

Subsidiary (Non-US):

Dentons Europe LLP   **(2)**
Thurn-und-Taxis-Platz 6, Frankfurt, 60313, Germany
Tel.: (49) 69 4500 120
Web Site: http://www.dentons.com
Law firm
N.A.I.C.S.: 541110

Subsidiary (Non-US):

Dentons Boekel N.V.   **(3)**
Gustav Mahlerplein, 1082 MA, Amsterdam, Netherlands
Tel.: (31) 20 795 39 53
Web Site: http://www.boekel.com
Law firm
N.A.I.C.S.: 541110
Wendela Raas - de Lange *(Co-Partner)*

Subsidiary (Non-US):

Rodyk & Davidson LLP   **(2)**
Republic Plaza 9 Raffles Place 55-01, Singapore, 048619, Singapore
Tel.: (65) 6 2252626
Web Site: http://www.rodyk.com.sg
Emp.: 39
Law firm
N.A.I.C.S.: 541110
Ai Ming Lee *(Partner & Atty)*
Govindarajalu Asokan *(Partner)*
Norman Ho *(Partner-Real Estate)*
Philip Jeyaretnam *(Mng Partner)*

Dentons US LLP   **(1)**
233 S Wacker Dr Ste 5900, Chicago, IL 60606-6361
Tel.: (312) 876-8000
Sales Range: $700-749.9 Million
Emp.: 5,001
Law firm
N.A.I.C.S.: 541110
Rob Adam *(CFO)*
Eric P. Berlin *(Partner)*
Joanne Caceres *(Partner)*
Brian E. Cohen *(Partner)*
Amberlee Cook *(Partner)*
Jacqueline A. Giannini *(Partner)*
John Grossbart *(Partner)*
Susan M. Hughes *(Partner)*
Jonathan M. Kaden *(Partner)*
Thomas A. Labuda Jr. *(Partner)*
Steven M. Levy *(Partner)*
Patrick C. Maxcy *(Partner)*
Andrew T. McClain *(Partner)*
Sulema Medrano *(Partner)*
Jordan G. McCarthy *(Partner)*
Adam Docks *(Partner)*
Michael M. Froy *(Partner)*
Mark L. Hanover *(Partner)*
Katharine E. Mellon *(Partner)*
Jeffrey C. Fort *(Partner)*
David R. Metzger *(Partner)*
Samuel Fifer *(Partner)*

Subsidiary (Domestic):

Cohen & Grigsby, P.C.   **(2)**
625 Liberty Ave, Pittsburgh, PA 15222-3152
Tel.: (412) 297-4900
Web Site: http://www.cohenlaw.com
Emp.: 113
Law firm

N.A.I.C.S.: 541110
Charles R. Brodbeck *(Atty)*
Charles C. Cohen *(Co-Founder, Chm & Atty)*
Mark I. Baseman *(Atty)*
John S. Brendel *(Atty)*
Ronald J. Andrykovitch *(Atty)*
Matthew Clark *(Dir-Bus Svcs Grp)*
Steven Taibl *(Dir-Bus Svcs Grp)*
James Cinque *(Controller)*
Kimberly Connell *(Dir-HR & Mgmt Svcs)*
David Kearney *(Dir-Tech Svcs)*
Christine Mazza *(CMO)*
Joseph P. Sharp *(CFO)*
Kevin Sullivan *(Dir-Tech)*
Todd Normane *(Head-Energy Practice)*
Andrew M. Paris *(Sr Mgr-Policy)*
Roberta D. Anderson *(Dir-Data Security & Insurance Recovery Practice Grps)*

Durham Jones & Pinegar, P.C.   **(1)**
111 E Broadway Ste 900, Salt Lake City, UT 84111
Tel.: (801) 415-3000
Web Site: http://www.djplaw.com
Law firm
N.A.I.C.S.: 541110
Mark L. Astling *(Atty)*
David L. Arrington *(Atty)*
Gregory N. Barrick *(Atty)*
Philip Ballif *(Atty)*
Thomas J. Burns *(Atty)*

DENTSABLE, INC.
576 Main St, Woburn, MA 01801
Tel.: (781) 933-2107
Web Site: http://www.dentsable.com
Sales Range: $10-24.9 Million
Emp.: 60
Dental Equipment Mfr
N.A.I.C.S.: 339114
Carmichael Roberts *(Chm)*
Marcus Lovell Smith *(CEO)*

DENVER ART MUSEUM
100 W 14th Ave Pkwy, Denver, CO 80204
Tel.: (720) 865-5000   CO
Web Site:
     https://www.denverartmuseum.org
Year Founded: 1897
Sales Range: $75-99.9 Million
Emp.: 524
Art Museum Operator
N.A.I.C.S.: 712110
Andrea Kalivas Fulton *(CMO)*
Melora McDermott-Lewis *(Chief Learning & Engagement Officer)*
Arpie Chucovich *(Dir-Dev)*
Curtis L. Woitte *(CFO)*

DENVER BOTANIC GARDENS
1007 York St, Denver, CO 80206
Tel.: (720) 865-3500   CO
Web Site:
     https://www.botanicgardens.org
Year Founded: 1951
Sales Range: $10-24.9 Million
Emp.: 229
Botanical Garden
N.A.I.C.S.: 712130
Brian Vogt *(CEO)*
Patricia Lepiani *(Sec)*
Richard Clark *(Vice Chm)*

DENVER CENTER FOR THE PERFORMING ARTS INC.
1101 13th St, Denver, CO 80204-2154
Tel.: (303) 893-4000   CO
Web Site:
     https://www.denvercenter.org
Year Founded: 1972
Sales Range: $10-24.9 Million
Emp.: 285
Theatrical Producers & Services
N.A.I.C.S.: 711310
Donald R. Seawell *(Founder)*
Jeff Hovorka *(Dir-Media & Mktg)*
Vicky Miles *(CFO)*

Daniel L. Ritchie *(Chm)*
John Ekeberg *(Exec Dir-Broadway & Cabaret)*
Charles Varin *(Mng Dir)*
Clay Courter *(VP-Facilities & Event Svcs)*
Jennifer Nealson *(VP-Ops)*
Janice Sinden *(Pres & CEO)*
Deanna Haas *(Chief Dev Officer)*
Lisa Mallory *(VP-Mktg & Sls)*
Chris Coleman *(Dir-Artistic)*
Yovani Pina *(VP-IT)*
Shaunda Van Wert *(VP-HR)*
Allison Watrous *(Exec Dir-Education)*

DENVER DRYWALL CO. INC.
3251 S Zuni St, Englewood, CO 80110
Tel.: (303) 761-0515
Web Site:
     http://www.denverdrywall.com
Sales Range: $10-24.9 Million
Emp.: 295
Drywall
N.A.I.C.S.: 238310
Bruce L. Miller *(Pres)*
Terri Miller *(VP & Treas)*

DENVER FOUNDATION
55 Madison St 8th Fl, Denver, CO 80206
Tel.: (303) 300-1790   CO
Web Site:
     http://www.denverfoundation.org
Year Founded: 1925
Sales Range: $50-74.9 Million
Emp.: 77
Grantmaking Services
N.A.I.C.S.: 813211
Daniel Lee *(VP-Fin & Admin)*
Brian Van Vleet *(Dir-IT)*
Dace West *(VP-Community Impact)*

DENVER PARENT CORPORATION
370 17th St Ste 3900, Denver, CO 80202-1370
Tel.: (303) 626-8300   DE
Year Founded: 1992
Sales Range: $50-74.9 Million
Emp.: 162
Oil & Natural Gas Exploration Services
N.A.I.C.S.: 213112
Timothy M. Marquez *(CEO)*
Mark A. DePuy *(Interim Pres & Interim COO)*

DENVER RESCUE MISSION
Administration & Education Bldg 6100 Smith Rd, Denver, CO 80216
Tel.: (303) 297-1815   CO
Web Site:
     https://www.denverrescuemission.org
Year Founded: 1892
Rev.: $35,854,795
Assets: $33,131,054
Liabilities: $2,604,799
Net Worth: $30,526,255
Earnings: $9,840,120
Emp.: 273
Fiscal Year-end: 06/30/14
Emergency Care Services
N.A.I.C.S.: 624230
Brad Meuli *(Pres & CEO)*
Steve Walkup *(VP-Programs)*
Griff Freyschlag *(VP-Dev)*
Hugh Burns *(VP-Ops)*
David Schunk *(VP-Fin & Admin)*
Linda Brown *(Dir-HR)*
Chris Darr *(Controller)*
Joseph Shehata *(Asst Controller)*
Lisette Williams *(Mgr-Community Events)*
Bryan Smith *(Mgr-IT)*
Paul Anderson *(Mgr-Grant)*

Denver Rescue Mission—(Continued)

Chris Gallamore (Dir-Comm)
Joseph Hayes (Dir-Major Gifts)
Michaelann Pineda (Mgr-Phone Outreach & Donor Rels)
Alexxa Gagner (Dir-PR)
Logan Hoffman (Mgr-Direct Mail & Donor Database)
Ryan Wickstrom (Mgr-Special Events)
Amy Fletcher (Program Dir-Champa House)
Josh Geppelt (Dir-Lawrence Street Shelter)
Lon Gregg (Dir-Spiritual)
Duncan Shaw (Program Dir-Harvest Farm)
Mark Plaza (Program Dir-Family & Senior Homeless Initiative)
Tom Leavitt (Dir-Family Svcs)
Mark S. Miller (Program Dir)
Mark Siegrest (Dir-Education)
Brian Dale (Dir-Facility)
Sean Degroat (Mgr-Facilities)
Mike Garza (Asst Dir-Facility-The Crossing)
Kyle Petrie (Dir-Ops)
Richard Yochim (Supvr-Warehouse)
Tanner Cogsdil (Mgr-Client Svcs)
Joseph Fortna (Chm)
Don Manuell (Vice Chm)
Scott Harris (Treas)
Sherri Heronema (Sec)
John P. Boucher (Sec)
May Thomsen (Officer-Corp Philanthropy)
Alice Cavanaugh (Officer-Legacy Giving)
Sarah Waite (Officer-Major Gifts)
Ashley Miltgen (Officer-Major Gifts)
Susan Bond (Officer-Major Gifts)
Shannon Carlson (Dir-HR)
Lisa Cooper (Dir-Ops)
Ed Kerr (Chm)
Aric Wauzzinski (Mgr-Client Svcs)

DENVER SIGN SUPPLY CO., INC.
26929 Hagen Dr, Slaughter, LA 70777
Tel.: (225) 654-3693
Web Site:
  http://www.denversignsupply.com
Year Founded: 1977
Sales Range: $10-24.9 Million
Emp.: 18
Durable Goods Whslr
N.A.I.C.S.: 423990
Larry M. Powenski (Pres)

DENVER WHOLESALE FLORISTS COMPANY
4800 Dahlia St, Denver, CO 80216-3121
Tel.: (303) 399-0970   CO
Web Site:
  http://www.dwfwholesale.com
Year Founded: 1909
Sales Range: $25-49.9 Million
Emp.: 300
Carnations, Roses, Cut Flowers & Florist Supplies Whslr
N.A.I.C.S.: 424930
David A. Lisowski (Pres)
Debbie Barber (VP-HR)
David L. Gaul (VP-Sls & Mktg)
Joel L. Kramer (Dir-Natl Mass Market)
Dave R. Legge (CFO)

Subsidiaries:

DWF Seatac   (1)
7327 S 228th St, Kent, WA 98032 (100%)
Tel.: (253) 854-5800
Web Site: http://www.dwfwholesale.com

Sales Range: $10-24.9 Million
Emp.: 45
Flowers & Florist Supplies
N.A.I.C.S.: 424930
Pat Layhon (Mgr)

DWF of Boise   (1)
1623 W River St, Boise, ID 83702-6806 (100%)
Tel.: (208) 336-5275
Sales Range: $10-24.9 Million
Emp.: 10
Wholesale of Flowers & Florist Supplies
N.A.I.C.S.: 424930
Tim Harrigfeld (Mgr)

DWF of Cincinnati, Inc.   (1)
4725 Ashley Dr, Hamilton, OH 45011 (100%)
Tel.: (513) 874-5183
Web Site: http://www.dwfwholesale.com
Sales Range: $10-24.9 Million
Emp.: 35
Flowers & Florist Supplies
N.A.I.C.S.: 459310
John Muennich (Mgr)
Debbie Barber (VP-HR)
David L. Gaul (VP-Sls & Mktg)
Dave R. Legge (CFO)

DWF of Dallas   (1)
2430 Converse St, Dallas, TX 75207-6008 (100%)
Tel.: (303) 399-0970
Web Site: http://www.dwfwholesale.com
Sales Range: $10-24.9 Million
Emp.: 16
Flowers & Florist Supplies
N.A.I.C.S.: 424930
Pete Neme (Mgr)

DWF of Flint Inc.   (1)
5100 Exchange Dr, Flint, MI 48507-2929 (100%)
Tel.: (810) 733-5100
Web Site: http://www.dwfwholesale.com
Sales Range: $10-24.9 Million
Emp.: 35
Flowers & Florist Supplies
N.A.I.C.S.: 424930

DWF of Milwaukee, Inc.   (1)
425 W Walnut St, Milwaukee, WI 53212-3836 (100%)
Tel.: (414) 263-8400
Web Site: http://www.dwfwholesale.com
Sales Range: $10-24.9 Million
Emp.: 15
Flowers & Florist Supply Services
N.A.I.C.S.: 424930

DWF of North Kansas City   (1)
21 W 13th Ave, Kansas City, MO 64116-4017
Tel.: (816) 474-9705
Web Site: http://www.dwfwholesale.com
Sales Range: $10-24.9 Million
Emp.: 15
Flowers & Florist Supplies
N.A.I.C.S.: 424930
Debbie Barber (VP-HR)
David L. Gaul (VP-Sls & Mktg)
Dave R. Legge (CFO)

DWF of Omaha   (1)
10923 Olive St, La Vista, NE 68128-2981 (100%)
Tel.: (402) 339-5080
Web Site: http://www.dwfwholesale.com
Sales Range: $10-24.9 Million
Emp.: 15
Flowers & Florist Supplies
N.A.I.C.S.: 424210

DWF of Saint Louis, Inc.   (1)
2715 Lasalle St, Saint Louis, MO 63104-1917 (100%)
Tel.: (314) 772-0254
Web Site: http://www.dwfwholesale.com
Sales Range: $10-24.9 Million
Emp.: 10
Flowers & Florist Supplies
N.A.I.C.S.: 424930
David A. Lasouski (Pres & CEO)
Larry Hagen (CFO)
David L. Gaul (VP-Sls & Mktg)
Dave R. Legge (CFO)

DWF of Salt Lake, Inc.   (1)
601 W 4330 South, Salt Lake City, UT 84123 (100%)

Tel.: (801) 904-4800
Web Site: http://www.dwfwholesale.com
Sales Range: $10-24.9 Million
Emp.: 14
Flowers & Florist Supplies
N.A.I.C.S.: 424930
Kelly Cheshire (Mgr)

DWF of Toledo   (1)
14 N Erie St, Toledo, OH 43624-1940 (100%)
Tel.: (419) 241-7241
Web Site: http://www.dwfwholesale.com
Sales Range: $10-24.9 Million
Emp.: 25
Flowers & Florist Supplies
N.A.I.C.S.: 424930
John Smith (Mgr)

Denver Wholesale Florists of Albuquerque   (1)
4717 Lumber Ave NE, Albuquerque, NM 87109-2144 (100%)
Tel.: (505) 888-2636
Web Site: http://www.dwfwholesale.com
Sales Range: $10-24.9 Million
Emp.: 14
Flowers & Florist Supplies
N.A.I.C.S.: 424910

DENVER ZOOLOGICAL FOUNDATION
2300 Steele St, Denver, CO 80205
Tel.: (303) 376-4800   CO
Year Founded: 1950
Sales Range: $25-49.9 Million
Emp.: 450
Zoo
N.A.I.C.S.: 712130
Kyle Burks (COO & VP)
Jacque Taylor (VP-Education & Volunteer Svc)
George Pond (VP-Plng)
Ana Bowie (VP-Strategic Initiatives & External Affairs)
Pat Moredock (Asst Sec)
Tamra Ward (Chief External Rels Officer)
D. Lance King (Chief Dev Officer)
Andrew Rowan (Dir-Public Affairs)

DEPARTURE
533 F St Ste 207, San Diego, CA 92101
Tel.: (619) 326-0288
Web Site:
  http://departureadvertising.com
Year Founded: 2007
Rev.: $10,000,000
Emp.: 24
Advetising Agency
N.A.I.C.S.: 541810
Emily Rex (Principal)

DEPAUL
1931 Buffalo Rd, Rochester, NY 14624
Tel.: (585) 426-8000   NY
Web Site: https://www.depaul.org
Year Founded: 1986
Sales Range: $25-49.9 Million
Emp.: 1,394
Adult Care Services
N.A.I.C.S.: 623312
Mark H. Fuller (Pres)
Jill Bateman (Mgr-Accounting)

DEPAUL COMMUNITY SERVICES, INC.
1931 Buffalo Rd, Rochester, NY 14624
Tel.: (585) 426-8000   NY
Web Site: https://www.depaul.org
Year Founded: 1958
Sales Range: $10-24.9 Million
Emp.: 470
Behavioral Healthcare Services
N.A.I.C.S.: 623220

Chris Syracuse (Exec Dir)
Kevin Mucci (Sec)
Mark Fuller (Pres)

DEPAULA CHEVROLET - HUMMER
785 Central Ave, Albany, NY 12206
Tel.: (518) 417-2564
Web Site: https://www.depaula.com
Sales Range: $75-99.9 Million
Emp.: 100
Car Whslr
N.A.I.C.S.: 441110
Tom Restino (Gen Mgr)

DEPCOM POWER, INC.
9185 E Pima Ctr Pkwy Ste 100, Scottsdale, AZ 85258
Tel.: (480) 270-6910   DE
Web Site:
  http://www.depcompower.com
Year Founded: 2013
Solar Panels & Related Equipment Customization & Installation Services
N.A.I.C.S.: 238290
Jim Lamon (Chm)
Johnnie Taul (CEO)
Bill Judge (CFO)
York Tsuo (CTO)
Jeff Dewit (Chief Investment Officer)
Robert Rynar (Chief Engr)
Charlotte Scaglione (Gen Counsel & Sec)

DEPECHE MODE COMPANY
230 W 38th St Fl 12, New York, NY 10018-9052
Tel.: (212) 643-6633   NY
Web Site: http://www.depecheco.com
Year Founded: 1976
Sales Range: $25-49.9 Million
Emp.: 35
Women's, Juniors' & Misses' Dresses
N.A.I.C.S.: 315250
Leo Rosenthal (Pres)
Maria Sidow (Controller)
Ruth Ann Stanley (Dir-Design)

DEPENDABLE AUTO SHIPPERS, INC.
3020 E Hwy 80, Mesquite, TX 75149-1207
Tel.: (214) 381-0181   TX
Web Site:
  http://www.dependableautoshippers.com
Year Founded: 1954
Motor Vehicle & Other Specialized Freight Transportation Services
N.A.I.C.S.: 484230
John C. Roehll (Partner & Exec VP)
Chris R. Chalk (Dir-Corp Accts)
Erin Almand (VP-Corp Bus)
Tim Higgins (Exec VP)
Kenneth Phillips (Mng Partner)

DEPENDABLE CLEANERS INC.
320 Quincy Ave Fl 2, Quincy, MA 02169
Tel.: (617) 471-1900
Web Site:
  https://www.dependablecleaner.com
Rev.: $10,000,000
Emp.: 250
Drycleaning Plants, Except Rugs
N.A.I.C.S.: 812320
Christa Hagearty (Pres)
Donald C. Fawcett Jr. (CEO)

DEPENDABLE COMPONENT SUPPLY CORP.
1003 E Newport Ctr Dr, Deerfield Beach, FL 33442-7724
Tel.: (954) 283-5800   FL

Web Site:
http://www.dependonus.com
Year Founded: 1986
Sales Range: $10-24.9 Million
Emp.: 50
Distr Of Electronic Parts & Equipment
N.A.I.C.S.: 423690
Susan Ryan *(Treas & Sec)*
William Miller *(COO & VP)*
Diana Meagher *(Controller)*
Matt Mccauley *(VP-Sls & Mktg)*

DEPENDABLE HEALTH SER-VICES, INC.
118 Broadway Ste 528, San Antonio, TX 78205
Tel.: (210) 736-4300
Web Site:
http://www.dependablehealthser
vices.com
Year Founded: 1996
Sales Range: $1-9.9 Million
Emp.: 70
Health & Administrative Staffing Services to the Federal Government's Department of Defense
N.A.I.C.S.: 561320
Joe Urby *(Owner)*
Karen Sponseller *(COO)*

DEPENDABLE HIGHWAY EXPRESS INC.
2555 E Olympic Blvd, Los Angeles, CA 90023-2605
Tel.: (323) 526-2222
Web Site:
http://www.godependable.com
Year Founded: 1950
Sales Range: $75-99.9 Million
Emp.: 800
Trucking Services Local & Long Distance; Freight Forwarding Services
N.A.I.C.S.: 484121
Ronald Massman *(CEO)*
Bob Massman *(VP)*
Michael Dougan *(CFO)*
Joe Finney *(COO)*

Subsidiaries:

Dependable Distribution Centers **(1)**
2555 E Olympic Blvd, Los Angeles, CA 90023
Tel.: (323) 526-2200
Web Site: http://www.godependable.com
Sales Range: $10-24.9 Million
Emp.: 100
Warehousing & Distribution
N.A.I.C.S.: 493110

Dependable Global Express **(1)**
19201 S Susana Rd, Rancho Dominguez, CA 90221
Tel.: (310) 537-2000
Web Site: http://www.dgxshipping.com
Sales Range: $50-74.9 Million
Emp.: 130
Ocean/Air Freight, Logistics, Transcontinental, Intermodal Services, Import & Export Services
N.A.I.C.S.: 488510
Ronald Massman *(Chm)*

Dependable Hawaiian Express **(1)**
19201 S Susana Rd, Rancho Dominguez, CA 90221
Tel.: (310) 537-2000
Web Site: http://www.dhx.com
Sales Range: $50-74.9 Million
Emp.: 150
Ocean & Air Freight Forwarding
N.A.I.C.S.: 488510
Ralph T. Merolla *(Exec VP)*

Dependable Logistics Solutions **(1)**
2555 E Olympic Blvd, Los Angeles, CA 90023
Tel.: (323) 526-2288
Web Site: http://www.godependable.com
Freight Management Services
N.A.I.C.S.: 541614
Ronald Massman *(CEO)*

DEPENDABLE MAIL SER-VICES INC.
850 Aquila Way Ste 120, Austell, GA 30168
Tel.: (404) 349-6389
Web Site:
http://www.dependablemailser
vices.com
Year Founded: 1989
Sales Range: $10-24.9 Million
Emp.: 150
Provider of Advertising Services
N.A.I.C.S.: 541860
Charles Smith *(Pres)*

DEPOSITORS INSURANCE FUND
1 Linscott Rd, Woburn, MA 01801-2000
Tel.: (781) 938-1984   **MA**
Web Site: https://www.difxs.com
Year Founded: 1932
Sales Range: $10-24.9 Million
Emp.: 11
Loan Provider
N.A.I.C.S.: 522310
David Elliott *(Pres & CEO)*
John J. D'Alessandro *(Sr VP)*
Kara McNamara *(Sr VP)*

DEPOT INTERNATIONAL INC.
1495 Hwy 34, Farmingdale, NJ 07727
Tel.: (732) 919-0209
Web Site: http://www.depot-america.com
Sales Range: $10-24.9 Million
Emp.: 200
Computer Maintenance & Repair
N.A.I.C.S.: 811210
John Tiano *(Pres)*
Chris Sinibaldi *(VP-Sls & Ops-Mid Market)*
Tom O'Donnell *(VP-Ops)*

DEQUE SYSTEMS, INC.
2121 Cooperative Way Ste 210, Herndon, VA 20171
Tel.: (703) 225-0380
Web Site: http://www.deque.com
Year Founded: 1999
Sales Range: $1-9.9 Million
Emp.: 80
Offers Digital Accessibility Solutions for People with Disabilities
N.A.I.C.S.: 541511
Preety Kumar *(Co-Founder & CEO)*
Michael Farrell *(Principal)*
Anik Ganguly *(Co-Founder & Exec VP)*
Dylan Barrell *(VP-Product Dev)*

DERA, ROSLAN & CAMPION PUBLIC RELATIONS
Rm 619 132 Nassau St, New York, NY 10038-2432
Tel.: (212) 966-4600   **NY**
Web Site:
http://www.drcpublicrelations.com
Year Founded: 1989
Sales Range: $10-24.9 Million
Emp.: 13
N.A.I.C.S.: 541820
Joseph Dera *(CEO)*
Chris Roslan *(CFO)*
Eileen Campion *(Pres & Mng Partner)*

DERBIGUM AMERICAS, INC.
4800 Blue Pkwy, Kansas City, MO 64130
Tel.: (816) 921-0021
Web Site: http://www.derbigum.us
Year Founded: 1979
Sales Range: $10-24.9 Million
Emp.: 60
Roofing Materials Mfr
N.A.I.C.S.: 324122
Robert Seeley *(Pres & CEO)*

DERBY INDUSTRIES, LLC
4451 Robards Ln, Louisville, KY 40218-4513
Tel.: (502) 451-7373   **KY**
Web Site: https://www.derbyllc.com
Year Founded: 1977
Sales Range: $75-99.9 Million
Emp.: 340
Integrated Supply Chain Services
N.A.I.C.S.: 488510
Dianna Herold *(Pres)*
Renee Hunt *(VP-HR)*

DERECKTOR GUNNELL INC.
775 Taylor Ln, Dania Beach, FL 33004
Tel.: (954) 920-5756
Web Site: https://www.derecktor.com
Year Founded: 1947
Sales Range: $10-24.9 Million
Emp.: 150
Provider of Yacht Building & Repairing Services
N.A.I.C.S.: 336612
Paul E. Derecktor *(Pres & CEO)*

DEREK AND CONSTANCE LEE CORP.
19355 San Jose Ave, City of Industry, CA 91748
Tel.: (909) 595-8831
Rev.: $11,100,000
Emp.: 40
Food Preparations
N.A.I.C.S.: 311999
Derek Lee *(Pres)*

DERFLAN INC
55 SE 2 Ave, Delray Beach, FL 33444-3615
Tel.: (425) 284-3072
Web Site: https://www.derflan.com
Year Founded: 2002
Sales Range: $1-9.9 Million
Emp.: 60
Marketing Consulting
N.A.I.C.S.: 541613
Ellen Sova *(Principal)*
Shanaz Diefendorf *(Principal)*
John Diefendorf *(Principal)*

DERIGO SALES INC.
3780 Harlem Rd, Buffalo, NY 14215
Tel.: (716) 834-7578   **NY**
Year Founded: 1978
Sales Range: $10-24.9 Million
Emp.: 15
Distr of Confectionery Products
N.A.I.C.S.: 424450
John Derigo *(Pres)*
Derrick Derigo *(Controller)*
Cathy Sundeen *(Office Mgr)*

DERING ELLIOTT & ASSOCIATES
1887 Gold Dust Ln Ste 101, Park City, UT 84060
Tel.: (435) 645-7500
Year Founded: 1983
Sales Range: Less than $1 Million
Emp.: 8
N.A.I.C.S.: 541810
Steve Dering *(Founder & Pres)*
Conrad Elliott *(Owner)*
Kimberly Page *(Acct Mgr)*

DERINGER-NEY INC
616 Atrium Dr Ste 100, Vernon Hills, IL 60061
Tel.: (847) 566-4100
Web Site:
http://www.deringerney.com
Sales Range: $25-49.9 Million
Emp.: 210
Contacts Electrical Precious Metals
N.A.I.C.S.: 335931
Roderick W. Lamm *(Chm)*
John Wallace *(Pres)*
Joseph Kain *(Mgr-Engineered Matls Product)*

DERIVE TECHNOLOGIES
110 William St 14th Fl, New York, NY 10038
Tel.: (212) 363-1111
Web Site: http://www.derivetech.com
Year Founded: 1987
Sales Range: $50-74.9 Million
Emp.: 70
Reseller of Computer Software
N.A.I.C.S.: 423430
Kirit Desai *(CEO)*
Mitch Martinez *(Exec VP-Sls)*
John Wood *(Sr VP-Mktg & Bus Dev)*

DERLE FARMS INC.
5 Grumman Rd, Long Island, NY 11433-1040
Tel.: (718) 257-2040
Web Site: http://www.derle.com
Year Founded: 1954
Sales Range: $50-74.9 Million
Emp.: 80
Dairy Products Distr
N.A.I.C.S.: 424430
Nathan Abramson *(Pres)*
Rabin Rehe *(Controller)*
Gerald Shaber *(Mgr)*

DERMA GLISTEN, INC.
14260 W Newberry Rd Ste 328, Newberry, FL 32669-0276
Tel.: (755) 321-8226   **NV**
Web Site:
http://www.dermaglisten.com
Year Founded: 2017
Personal Care Product Distr
N.A.I.C.S.: 424210
Jessica Foster *(Pres, CEO, CFO, Treas & Sec)*

DERMA HEALTH
2905 W Warner Rd Ste 17, Chandler, AZ 85224
Tel.: (480) 470-5747
Web Site:
https://www.dermahealthinstitute.com
Year Founded: 2004
Sales Range: $1-9.9 Million
Emp.: 35
Specialists in Noninvasive & Minimally Invasive Cosmetic Dermatology Treatments
N.A.I.C.S.: 622110
Trish Gulbranson *(Pres & CEO)*
Gina Long *(VP-Client Rels)*

DERMADOCTOR, LLC
4346 Belgium Blvd, Riverside, MO 64150
Tel.: (816) 472-5700   **DE**
Web Site:
http://www.dermadoctor.com
Year Founded: 1998
Sales Range: $1-9.9 Million
Emp.: 21
Skin Care Product Mfr & Distr
N.A.I.C.S.: 325620
Audrey Kunin *(Chief Creative Officer)*
Jeff Kunin *(Pres)*
Andrea Bielsker *(CFO)*

DERMATOLOGY & SKIN SURGERY CENTER
210 Village Center Pkwy, Stockbridge, GA 30281-9044
Tel.: (770) 474-5952

Dermatology & Skin Surgery
Center—(Continued)

Web Site:
https://www.dermandskin.com
All Other Outpatient Care Centers
N.A.I.C.S.: 621498
Juan A. Mujica *(CEO)*

DERMAZONE SOLUTIONS, INC.
2440 30th Ave N, Saint Petersburg, FL 33713
Tel.: (727) 446-6882
Web Site:
https://www.dermazone.com
Year Founded: 2001
Sales Range: $10-24.9 Million
Emp.: 37
Skin Care Product Mfr
N.A.I.C.S.: 325620
Deborah Duffey *(Pres & Chief Product Dev Officer)*
Karalyn Schuchert *(Founder & Chm)*
Robin McCarthy *(Dir-Bus Dev-DermaCM)*
Maya Ivanjesku *(Dir-Formulation Dev & R&D)*
Rob Miller *(Controller)*

Subsidiaries:

Kara Vita, Inc.   (1)
2440 30th Ave N, Saint Petersburg, FL 33713
Tel.: (727) 456-7560
Web Site: http://www.karavita.com
Skin Care Products
N.A.I.C.S.: 325620
Deborah Duffey *(Pres & Chief Product Dev Officer)*
Karalyn Schuchert *(Chm)*

DERMODY PROPERTIES INC.
5500 Equity Ave, Reno, NV 89502
Tel.: (775) 858-8080   NV
Web Site:
http://www.partnerwithdp.com
Year Founded: 1959
Sales Range: $25-49.9 Million
Emp.: 15
Nonresidential Building Operators
N.A.I.C.S.: 531120
Michael C. Dermody *(Chm & CEO)*
Bruce D. Storey *(Co-Founder)*
C. Douglas Lanning *(CFO)*
Brendan P. Egan *(Dir-Dev-West Reg)*
Casey Kreck *(Sr VP-Fin)*
Elizabeth Teske *(Sr VP-Property Mgmt)*
Jeffrey Zygler *(Sr VP-Capital Deployment-East Chatham)*
Shelagh Danna *(Asst Mgr-Dev-West)*
Becky Moody *(Controller)*
Jenna Sulprizio *(Mgr-Corp Acctg)*
Megan Rahn *(Sr VP-Dev)*
Nancy E. Shultz *(Sr VP-Capital Deployment-Southwest)*
Steven A. Karpf *(Chief Acquisition Officer & Partner)*
Timothy F. Walsh *(Chief Acquisition Officer-Dermody Properties & Partner)*
Pearce Dermody *(VP & Mgr-Investment)*
John Ramous *(Partner)*
Kathleen S. Briscoe *(Partner & Chief Capital Officer)*
Douglas A. Kiersey Jr. *(Pres)*

DERMTECH, LLC
12340 El Camino Real, San Diego, CA 92130
Tel.: (858) 450-4222
Web Site: https://dermtech.com
Melanoma Testing Instrument Developer & Mfr
N.A.I.C.S.: 339112

Subsidiaries:

DermTech, Inc.   (1)
12340 El Camino Real, San Diego, CA 92130
Tel.: (858) 450-4222
Web Site: https://dermtech.com
Rev.: $15,296,000
Assets: $121,930,000
Liabilities: $64,755,000
Net Worth: $57,175,000
Earnings: ($100,888,000)
Emp.: 206
Fiscal Year-end: 12/31/2023
Holding Company; Melanoma Testing Instrument Developer & Mfr
N.A.I.C.S.: 551112
Kevin Sun *(CFO, Treas & Sec)*
Ray Akhavan *(Gen Counsel)*
Mark Aguillard *(Chief Comml Officer)*

Subsidiary (Domestic):

DermTech Operations, Inc.   (2)
12340 El Camino Real, San Diego, CA 92130
Tel.: (858) 450-4222
Web Site: https://www.dermtech.com
Melanoma Testing Instrument Developer & Mfr
N.A.I.C.S.: 339112

DEROSA CORPORATION
7613 W State St, Wauwatosa, WI 53213
Tel.: (414) 771-3100
Web Site:
https://www.derosacorp.com
Sales Range: $10-24.9 Million
Emp.: 700
Full-Service Restaurants
N.A.I.C.S.: 722511
Joseph DeRosa *(Pres)*
George Flees *(Gen Mgr)*
Jeff Martin *(Dir-IT)*
Bob Frederickson *(Gen Mgr)*

DEROYAL INDUSTRIES INC.
200 Debusk Ln, Powell, TN 37849-4703
Tel.: (865) 938-7828
Web Site: https://www.deroyal.com
Year Founded: 1973
Sales Range: $25-49.9 Million
Emp.: 350
Mfr of Surgical & Medical Instruments
N.A.I.C.S.: 339112
Autrey O. DeBusk *(Co-Owner & Co-Chm)*
Pete DeBusk *(Co-Owner & Co-Chm)*
Marcia Kilby *(VP-Legal Svcs)*
Angie Sewell *(VP-IT)*
Greg Hodge *(VP-Continuum & Bus Dev)*
Brian C. DeBusk *(CEO)*
Mario Gaztambide *(VP-Sls-Intl)*
Christian Schulz *(Chief Sls Officer)*
Tim Knisley *(CFO)*

Subsidiaries:

Demedco Inc.   (1)
851 Old Emory Rd, Clinton, TN 37716-6065
Tel.: (865) 457-4077
Sales Range: $10-24.9 Million
Emp.: 21
Mfr of Industrial Machinery
N.A.I.C.S.: 332312

HD Hospital Disposables Incorporated   (1)
104 Wheeler St, Portland, TN 37148-1202   (100%)
Tel.: (615) 325-9278
Sales Range: $10-24.9 Million
Emp.: 44
Mfr of Plastic Products
N.A.I.C.S.: 326199
Autrey O. DeBusk *(Pres)*

DERR FLOORING CO. INC.
525 Davisville Rd, Willow Grove, PA 19090-1525

Tel.: (215) 657-6300   PA
Web Site:
https://www.derrflooring.com
Year Founded: 1912
Sales Range: $25-49.9 Million
Emp.: 150
Homefurnishings
N.A.I.C.S.: 423220
Tom Clayton *(Product Mgr)*

DERRICK CORPORATION
590 Duke Rd, Buffalo, NY 14225-5102
Tel.: (716) 683-9010   NY
Web Site: http://www.derrickcorp.com
Year Founded: 1951
Rev.: $50,000,000
Emp.: 300
Sales of Mining Machinery
N.A.I.C.S.: 333131
William W. Derrick *(Founder)*
Michael Schwec *(Engr-Electrical)*
Frank Russom *(Mgr-Adv)*
John Guarnieri *(Engr-R&D)*
Shanahan Terry *(Dir-Safety)*
Baojie Zhang *(Mgr-Product Application)*
James Colgrove *(VP-R&D)*
Linda Lussier *(Mgr-Export)*

DERRICK PUBLISHING CO.
1510 W 1st St, Oil City, PA 16301
Tel.: (814) 676-7444
Web Site: http://www.thederrick.com
Rev.: $14,000,000
Emp.: 130
Newspapers, Publishing & Printing
N.A.I.C.S.: 513110
Patrick C. Boyle *(Owner)*
Paul Hess *(Mgr-Adv Sls)*

DERRY ENTERPRISES INC.
9883 N Alpine Rd, Machesney Park, IL 61115
Tel.: (815) 637-9002
Web Site:
https://www.fieldfastener.com
Sales Range: $25-49.9 Million
Emp.: 55
Fastener Distr
N.A.I.C.S.: 423840
Chad Olson *(Dir-IT)*
Tim Firm *(Dir-HR)*
Adam Derry *(Dir-Sls & Mktg)*
Doug Warner *(VP-Ops & Logistics)*
Mark Andrews *(VP-Supply Chain)*

Subsidiaries:

HRS Logistics, Inc.   (1)
13182 Rte 110 S, Tyler, TX 75707
Tel.: (903) 581-5767
Web Site: http://www.hrslogisticsinc.com
Sales Range: $1-9.9 Million
Emp.: 12
Fastener Products Importer & Distr
N.A.I.C.S.: 423840
Jim Derry *(Pres)*

DERSCH ENERGIES INCORPORATED
620 Oak St, Mount Carmel, IL 62863
Tel.: (618) 262-5181
Sales Range: $10-24.9 Million
Emp.: 12
Petroleum Bulk Stations
N.A.I.C.S.: 424710
Thomas Dersch *(Owner & Pres)*

DERSE INC.
3800 W Canal St, Milwaukee, WI 53208-2916
Tel.: (414) 257-2000   WI
Web Site: http://www.derse.com
Year Founded: 1989
Rev.: $47,029,003
Emp.: 325

Exhibit & Environmental Design Marketing Strategies
N.A.I.C.S.: 541613
Russ Fowler *(VP-Mktg Environments)*
David Sherman *(VP-Creative Svcs)*
Michelle MacRae *(Acct Dir)*
Pete Riddell *(Exec Dir-Creative)*
Brett Haney *(CEO)*
Colleen Chianese *(VP-Corp Ops)*
Rick Stoner *(VP-Sls & Client Strategy)*
Todd Sussman *(VP-Creative)*
Dan Loaskie *(VP-Dallas)*
Julia Haas *(Dir-Mktg)*
Eric Preston *(Pres)*

DES COMPANIES
1300 Cummins Rd, Des Moines, IA 50315
Tel.: (515) 288-2300
Web Site: http://www.desstaffing.com
Year Founded: 1999
Rev.: $19,800,000
Emp.: 32
Employment Placement Agencies
N.A.I.C.S.: 561311
Dan Sethi *(Pres & CEO)*
Shane Sorenson *(Mgr-Dival)*

DES INC.
1752 B Rte 9, Clifton Park, NY 12065
Tel.: (518) 373-2167
Web Site:
http://www.dunkindonuts.com
Sales Range: $10-24.9 Million
Emp.: 100
Retailer of Doughnuts
N.A.I.C.S.: 311811
Willie Arruda *(Pres)*

DES MOINES SYMPHONY ASSOCIATION
1011 Locust St Ste 200, Des Moines, IA 50309
Tel.: (515) 280-4000
Web Site:
https://www.dmsymphony.org
Emp.: 100
Symphony Orchestra
N.A.I.C.S.: 711130
Joseph Giunta *(Dir-Music)*
Richard L. Early *(Exec Dir)*

DES MOINES WATER WORKS
2201 George Flagg Pkwy, Des Moines, IA 50321
Tel.: (515) 283-8755
Web Site: http://www.dmww.com
Year Founded: 1871
Sales Range: $25-49.9 Million
Emp.: 215
Water Supply
N.A.I.C.S.: 221310
Ted Corrigan *(CEO & Gen Mgr)*
Graham Gillette *(Chm)*
Leslie A. Gearhart *(Vice Chm)*

DESAI CAPITAL MANAGEMENT INCORPORATED
410 Pk Ave Ste 830, New York, NY 10022-3224
Tel.: (212) 838-9191   NY
Year Founded: 1984
Sales Range: $150-199.9 Million
Emp.: 4
Investment Management
N.A.I.C.S.: 523940
Andre J. McSherry *(VP-Fin & Admin)*
Rohit M. Desai *(Chm, Pres & Chief Compliance Officer)*

DESAI SYSTEMS INC.
199 Oakwood Ave, West Hartford, CT 06119
Tel.: (860) 233-0011
Web Site: http://www.desai.com

Sales Range: Less than $1 Million
Emp.: 2
Computer Integrated Systems Design
N.A.I.C.S.: 541512
Jatin DeSai (CEO)
Fal Desai (Founder & COO)
Rob Berman (Sr Partner)
Srinivas Raghavan (Sr Partner)

DESANCTIS INSURANCE AGENCY, INC.
100 Unicorn Park Dr Ste 2, Woburn, MA 01801
Tel.: (781) 935-8480
Web Site:
https://www.desanctisins.com
Sales Range: $1-9.9 Million
Emp.: 23
Insurance Services
N.A.I.C.S.: 524210
Adam DeSanctis (Pres)
Marc Bergeron (Asst Mgr-Comml Dept)

DESANTIS BREINDEL
30 W 21st St, New York, NY 10010
Tel.: (212) 994-7680
Web Site:
https://www.desantisbreindel.com
Year Founded: 2002
Sales Range: $1-9.9 Million
Emp.: 30
Advetising Agency
N.A.I.C.S.: 541810
Dru DeSantis (Co-Founder & Partner)
Howard S. Breindel (Co-Founder & Partner)
Jonathan Paisner (Mng Dir)
Dayna McAnnally (Controller)
Sara Hashim (Dir-Design)
Robert Schroeder (Dir-Creative)

DESARROLLOS METROPOLITANOS, LLC.
207 Diez de Andino St, San Juan, PR 00912
Tel.: (787) 727-8666
Web Site: https://www.dmse.com
Year Founded: 1970
Sales Range: $10-24.9 Million
Emp.: 300
Commercial & Institutional Building Construction Services
N.A.I.C.S.: 236220
Jose R. Vizcarrondo (Pres & CEO)
Ismael Sanchez (Project Mgr)
Ramon Vazquez (Project Mgr)
Francisco Colon (Project Mgr)
Richard Lopez (Project Mgr)
Isaac Suarez (Mgr-Equipment)
Edwin Ramos (Comptroller)
Julio E. Vizcarrondo Jr. (Chm)
Milton Miro Jr. (Project Mgr)

DESAUTEL HEGE COMMUNI-CATIONS
315 W Riverside Ste 200, Spokane, WA 99201
Tel.: (509) 444-2350
Web Site:
http://www.desautelhege.com
Year Founded: 1996
Sales Range: $25-49.9 Million
Emp.: 14
Advetising Agency
N.A.I.C.S.: 541810
James M. Desautel (Partner)
Michelle Hege (Pres & CEO)
Sara Johnston (Partner)
Andrei Mylroie (Partner)
Stephanie Bast (Mgr-Ops)
Searri Shipman (Mgr-Acctg)
Lisa Cargill (Acct Dir)
Sarah Schwering (Acct Dir)
Sara Desautel (Acct Dir)
Casey Barratt (Acct Exec)

Kristen Paul (Acct Exec)
Casey Fielder (Acct Exec)
Emily Easley (Acct Coord)
Todd Zeidler (Acct Exec)
Hayley Graham (Acct Exec)
Jessica Wade (Acct Exec)

DESBUILD INCORPORATED
4744 Baltimore Ave, Hyattsville, MD 20781-2231
Tel.: (301) 864-4095
Web Site: https://www.desbuild.com
Rev.: $50,700,000
Emp.: 45
Commercial & Institutional Building Construction
N.A.I.C.S.: 236220
Prakash Hosadurga (VP-Ops)
Ananth Badrinath (VP-Tech)
Candace Dickerson (Mgr-Proposal & Admin Contract)

DESCCO DESIGN & CON-STRUCTION
1 Willow St Industrial Park, Fleetwood, PA 19522
Tel.: (610) 944-0404
Web Site: https://www.descco.com
Year Founded: 1976
Sales Range: $1-9.9 Million
Emp.: 19
Project & Construction Management & General Contractors
N.A.I.C.S.: 236210
Nicholas D. Stoltzfus (Pres)
Eric J. Peterson (VP)
Timothy M. Heffner (VP & Sr Mgr-Projects)

DESCHUTES BREWERY INC.
901 SW Simpson Ave, Bend, OR 97702
Tel.: (541) 385-8606
Web Site:
http://www.deschutesbrewery.com
Year Founded: 1988
Sales Range: $10-24.9 Million
Emp.: 500
Producer & Distr of Alcoholic Beverages
N.A.I.C.S.: 312120
Gary D. Fish (Founder)
Michael Lalonde (Pres & CEO)
Amanda Benson (Coord-Sensory Panel)
Eddie Anderson (Mgr-Market Sls-Ohio & Kentucky)
Mark Fischer (Dir-Ops)
Neal Stewart (VP-Mktg)

Subsidiaries:

Boneyard Beer LLC   (1)
1955 NE Division St, Bend, OR 97701
Tel.: (541) 323-2325
Web Site: http://www.boneyardbeer.com
Breweries
N.A.I.C.S.: 312120
Clay Storey (Controller)

DESCO CORPORATION
7795 Walton Pkwy Ste 175, New Albany, OH 43054
Tel.: (614) 888-8855   OH
Web Site:
https://www.descocorporation.com
Year Founded: 1992
Sales Range: $350-399.9 Million
Emp.: 1,100
Mfr of Measuring, Controlling & Counting Devices; Timers; Oil & Natural Gas Producers
N.A.I.C.S.: 332321
Arnold B. Siemer (CEO)

Subsidiaries:

Desco Acquisition LLC   (1)
230 Commerce Dr, Berthoud, CO 80513

Tel.: (970) 532-0600
Web Site:
http://www.blackeagleenergyservices.com
Oil & Gas Field Engineering Services
N.A.I.C.S.: 213112
Joe Colletti (Chm & CEO)
Scott Yenzer (Sr VP-Corp Dev)

Desco Capital   (1)
7795 Walton Pkwy Ste 175, New Albany, OH 43054
Tel.: (614) 888-8855
Web Site: http://www.descocorporation.com
Emp.: 11
Investment Management Service
N.A.I.C.S.: 523940
Arnold B. Siemer (CEO)
Roger D. Bailey (CFO)

MDT Software   (1)
3480 Preston Ridge Rd Ste 450, Alpharetta, GA 30005
Tel.: (678) 297-1000
Web Site: http://www.mdt-software.com
Change Management Software Publisher
N.A.I.C.S.: 511210
Greg Pysher (Dir-Sls)

Marsh Bellofram Corporation   (1)
8019 Ohio River Blvd, Newell, WV 26050
Tel.: (304) 387-1200
Web Site: http://www.marshbellofram.com
Sales Range: $25-49.9 Million
Emp.: 300
Component, Instrumentation & Control Mfr
N.A.I.C.S.: 335311
Dwight Nafziger (VP-Sls & Mktg)

Division (Domestic):

Automatic Timing & Controls   (2)
8019 Ohio River Blvd, Newell, WV 26050
Tel.: (304) 387-1200
Web Site: http://www.automatictiming.com
Sales Range: $25-49.9 Million
Emp.: 300
Digital Panel Meters, Timers & Counters Mfr
N.A.I.C.S.: 335314
Dean Garwick (Product Mgr)
Jeff Gamble (Mgr-Sls-Natl)
Dwight D. Nafziger (VP-Sls & Mktg)

Division (Domestic):

WestCon   (3)
8019 Ohio River Blvd, Newell, WV 26050
Tel.: (304) 387-1200
Web Site: http://www.marshbellofram.com
Digital Thermal & Electronic Devices for Motor Vehicles Mfr
N.A.I.C.S.: 335314

Subsidiary (Non-US):

Bellofram Instruments (India) Pvt. Ltd.   (2)
Survey No 83 2/3 Old NDA Road Near Vidyut Controls, At Post Shivane Taluka-Haveli, Pune, 411023, India
Tel.: (91) 20 64701076
Web Site: http://www.marshbellofram.com
Sales Range: $25-49.9 Million
Emp.: 6
Industrial Measurement & Control Device Distr
N.A.I.C.S.: 423830

Division (Domestic):

Marsh Bellofram   (2)
State Rte 2, Newell, WV 26050
Tel.: (304) 387-1200
Web Site: http://www.marshbellofram.com
Rev.: $3,500,000
Emp.: 300
Mfr of Temperature Sensors
N.A.I.C.S.: 335311
Joe Colletti (Pres)
Tom Cigolle (Mgr-Quality Assurance)

Subsidiary (Non-US):

Marsh Bellofram Europe Ltd   (2)
9 Castle Park Queens Drive, Nottingham, NG2 1AH, United Kingdom
Tel.: (44) 1159 933300
Web Site: http://www.marshbellofram.co.uk
Emp.: 15
Industrial Measurement & Control Device Distr
N.A.I.C.S.: 423830

Chris Reynolds (Mgr-UK)

Marsh Bellofram Shanghai Trading Co. Ltd.   (2)
4th Floor Building B No 1281 Jinhu Road, Shanghai, 201206, China
Tel.: (86) 21 5031 3725
Pressure Regulator Mfr
N.A.I.C.S.: 334519

Tek-Air Systems, Inc.   (1)
41 Eagle Rd, Danbury, CT 06810
Tel.: (203) 791-1400
Web Site: http://www.tek-air.com
Airflow Control Device Mfr
N.A.I.C.S.: 334519

DESCO INC.
1205 Lincolnton Rd, Salisbury, NC 28147-1347
Tel.: (704) 633-6331   NC
Web Site: https://www.descoinc.com
Year Founded: 1960
Rev.: $30,000,000
Emp.: 72
Electrical Apparatus & Equipment
N.A.I.C.S.: 423610
Gary Pinkston (Branch Mgr-Mooresville & Pres)

DESCO INDUSTRIES INC.
3651 Walnut Ave, Chino, CA 91710
Tel.: (909) 627-8178
Web Site: http://www.desco.com
Year Founded: 1979
Sales Range: $25-49.9 Million
Emp.: 175
Static Elimination Equipment, Industrial
N.A.I.C.S.: 335999
Wayne Hunter (Pres)
Fernando Amorim (Mgr-IT)
Dave Bermani (Coord-Corp Mktg)
Alex Hernandez (Engr-Design)
Bob West (Mgr-Engrg)
Gene Felder (Product Mgr)

DESCO, LLC
44 Barkley Cir, Fort Myers, FL 33907
Tel.: (239) 275-1991
Web Site: http://www.desco-soft.com
Sales Range: $1-9.9 Million
Emp.: 30
Air-Conditioner & Heating Contractor Software
N.A.I.C.S.: 513210
Dean Schreiner (Pres)
Charles Cubbage (Mgr-Software)
Eric Rausin (VP)
Steve Gordon (Mgr-IT & Support)
Alexey Sednev (Engr-Software)

DESE RESEARCH INC.
315 Wynn Dr Ste 2, Huntsville, AL 35805
Tel.: (256) 837-8004   AL
Web Site: https://www.dese.com
Year Founded: 1982
Commercial Physical Research
N.A.I.C.S.: 541715
Wallace Kirkpatrick (CEO)
Michael Kirkpatrick (Pres)

DESERET BIOLOGICALS
469 W Parkland Dr, Sandy, UT 84070-6403
Tel.: (801) 563-7448
Web Site: https://www.desbio.com
Year Founded: 1987
Sales Range: $1-9.9 Million
Emp.: 16
Supplier of Homeopathic, Herbal, Mineral & Enzyme Supplements to Healthcare Practitioners
N.A.I.C.S.: 456191
Jacob Carter (Partner)

Deseret Biologicals—(Continued)

DESERET FIRST CREDIT UNION INC.
143 Social Hall Ave, Salt Lake City, UT 84111
Tel.: (801) 538-0894
Web Site: https://www.dfcu.com
Rev.: $17,149,475
Emp.: 90
State Credit Union Services
N.A.I.C.S.: 522130
Susan Rather (Sec)
Jim Tidwell (Chm)
Doug Martin (Co-Chm)

DESERET GENERATION & TRANSMISSION COOPERATIVE, INC.
10714 S Jordan Gateway, South Jordan, UT 84095
Tel.: (801) 619-6500
Web Site:
http://www.deseretpower.com
Sales Range: $200-249.9 Million
Emp.: 300
Generation, Electric Power
N.A.I.C.S.: 221118
Kimball Rasmussen (Pres)
Robert Dalley (CFO & VP)

DESERET LABORATORIES, INC.
1414 E 3850 S, Saint George, UT 84790
Tel.: (435) 628-8786
Web Site:
https://www.deseretlabs.com
Year Founded: 1983
Sales Range: $1-9.9 Million
Emp.: 120
Medicinal & Botanical Mfr
N.A.I.C.S.: 325411
Scott A. Gubler (Pres & CEO)
Mark H. Gubler (CFO & COO)

DESERET MANAGEMENT CORPORATION
55 N 300 W Ste 800, Salt Lake City, UT 84101
Tel.: (801) 538-0651   UT
Web Site:
http://www.deseretmanagement.com
Year Founded: 1966
Rev.: $778,000,000
Emp.: 30
Holding Company
N.A.I.C.S.: 551112
Keith B. McMullin (Pres & CEO)
Kirby Brown (CFO)
Sheri Dew (VP)
Gary B. Porter (Sr VP)

Subsidiaries:

Beneficial Life Insurance
Company   (1)
150 E Social Hall Ave, Salt Lake City, UT 84145
Tel.: (801) 531-7979
Web Site:
http://www.beneficialfinancialgroup.com
Sales Range: $550-599.9 Million
Emp.: 18
Life Insurance
N.A.I.C.S.: 524113
Kirby Brown (Pres & CEO)

Bonneville International
Corporation   (1)
55 N 300 West, Salt Lake City, UT 84180-1109   (100%)
Tel.: (801) 575-7500
Web Site: http://www.bonneville.com
Sales Range: $25-49.9 Million
Radio & Television Broadcasting Services
N.A.I.C.S.: 516110
Gerrell Brown (Pres & CEO)
Darrell Brown (Pres)
Bob Call (VP & Mgr-Mktg)

Mike Dowdle (Gen Counsel & Sr VP-Bus Affairs)
Carl Gardner (VP & Mgr-Mktg)
Kent Nate (CFO & Sr VP)
Scott Sutherland (VP & Mgr-Mktg)
Tanya Vea (VP & Mgr-Mktg)
Melanie Miltz (Dir-Mktg & Promos-DENVER)

Unit (Domestic):

Bonneville International Corp. - Phoenix   (2)
7740 N 16th St, Phoenix, AZ 85020
Tel.: (602) 274-6200
Web Site: http://www.ktar.com
Radio Broadcasting Stations
N.A.I.C.S.: 221118
Ryan Hatch (VP-Content & Ops)

Bonneville International Corp. - Sacramento   (2)
280 Commerce Cir, Sacramento, CA 95815
Tel.: (916) 923-6800
Web Site: http://www.mix96sac.com
Radio Broadcasting Stations
N.A.I.C.S.: 516110
Chad Rufer (Program Dir)

Unit (Domestic):

KNCI-FM   (3)
280 Commerce Cir, Sacramento, CA 95815
Tel.: (916) 923-6800
Web Site: http://www.kncifm.com
Radio Broadcasting Stations
N.A.I.C.S.: 516110

Unit (Domestic):

Bonneville International Corp. - San Francisco   (2)
2001 Junipero Serra Blvd Ste 350, Daly City, CA 94014
Tel.: (415) 546-8300
Web Site: http://www.kblx.com
Radio Broadcasting Stations
N.A.I.C.S.: 516110

Unit (Domestic):

KOIT-FM   (3)
2001 Junipero Serra Blvd Ste 350, Daly City, CA 94014
Tel.: (415) 546-8300
Web Site: http://www.koit.com
Radio Broadcasting Stations
N.A.I.C.S.: 516110

Unit (Domestic):

KIRO Radio   (2)
1820 Eastlake Ave E, Seattle, WA 98102-3711
Tel.: (206) 726-7000
Web Site: http://www.mynorthwest.com
Radio Broadcasting Stations
N.A.I.C.S.: 516110

KSL-TV   (2)
55 N 300 W, Salt Lake City, UT 84180
Tel.: (801) 575-5555
Web Site: http://www.ksl.com
Sales Range: $50-74.9 Million
Emp.: 300
Television Broadcasting Station
N.A.I.C.S.: 516120
Steve Poulsen (VP-Mktg & Promo)
Randy Ochsenbein (Coord-Satellite)
Danny Andreason (Engr-Transmitter)
Bob Brown (Pres)
Darrell Brown (Gen Mgr)

Deseret Book Co.   (1)
57 W South Temple St, Salt Lake City, UT 84101
Tel.: (801) 534-1515
Web Site: http://www.deseretbook.com
Sales Range: $25-49.9 Million
Emp.: 150
Publication of General Trade Hardcovers & Paperbacks, Juveniles, Bibles, Cookbooks, Religion & General Non-Fiction
N.A.I.C.S.: 424920
Keith Hunter (VP-Ops)
Ryan Wilson (Mgr-Help Desk)

Deseret Digital Media   (1)
55 N 300 W Ste 500, Salt Lake City, UT 84101-3502
Tel.: (801) 333-7400

Web Site: http://www.deseretdigital.com
Online Publishing Services
N.A.I.C.S.: 513199
Patrick Reeve Boyd (Mgr-Acct)
Stephan Bergen (Dir-Content & Design)
Russell Banz (VP-Product)
Jeff Barton (CFO)
Dale Z. Darling (VP-Sls)
Lori Pugh (Sr Dir-HR)

Deseret Morning News   (1)
55 N 300 W Fl 6th, Salt Lake City, UT 84101-3506
Tel.: (801) 236-6000
Web Site: http://www.deseretnews.com
Sales Range: $25-49.9 Million
Emp.: 196
Publishes Sunday Evening, Saturday Deseret News & Sunday Deseret News
N.A.I.C.S.: 513110
Michael Todd (CFO)
Burke Olsen (Gen Mgr)
Scott Taylor (Mng Editor)

Temple Square Hospitality
Corporation   (1)
50 W North Temple St, Salt Lake City, UT 84150
Tel.: (801) 531-1000
Web Site:
http://www.templesquarehospitality.com
Sales Range: $25-49.9 Million
Emp.: 500
Hospitality Services
N.A.I.C.S.: 721110
Clark Stenquist (VP & Controller)
Neil Wilkinson (Dir-Tourism & Mktg)
Juan Canals (Dir-Support Svcs)

Utah Property Management Associates, LLC   (1)
51 S Main St Ste 301, Salt Lake City, UT 84111
Tel.: (801) 321-8700
Web Site: http://www.utpma.com
Sales Range: $25-49.9 Million
Rental Property
N.A.I.C.S.: 531210
Mark Gibbons (Pres)

DESERET RANCHES OF FLORIDA
13754 Deseret Ln, Saint Cloud, FL 34773-9381
Tel.: (407) 892-3672
Web Site:
http://www.deseretranchflorida.com
Year Founded: 1947
Sales Range: $25-49.9 Million
Emp.: 90
Cattle, Citrus, Sod, Forestry & Seashells
N.A.I.C.S.: 112111
Erik Jacobsen (VP)

DESERT COASTAL TRANSPORT INCORPORATION
10686 Banana Ave, Fontana, CA 92337-0131
Tel.: (909) 357-3395
Web Site:
http://www.desertcoastal.com
Sales Range: $10-24.9 Million
Emp.: 100
Trucking
N.A.I.C.S.: 484121
Tim Wyant (Pres)
Chuck Waynt (Sec)

DESERT COMMUNICATIONS, INC.
7100 Westwind Dr Ste 300, El Paso, TX 79912
Tel.: (915) 584-1287
Web Site: http://www.descominc.com
Year Founded: 1994
Rev.: $13,100,000
Emp.: 52
Electrical Contractor
N.A.I.C.S.: 238210
Chuck Mosely (VP-Fin)

DESERT ELECTRIC SUPPLY
74875 Velie Dr, Palm Desert, CA 92260
Tel.: (760) 568-5991
Web Site:
https://www.desertelectric.com
Year Founded: 1972
Rev.: $10,484,879
Emp.: 40
Electrical Apparatus & Equipment
N.A.I.C.S.: 423610
Eric Stevens (Pres)

DESERT ENERGY EQUIPMENT, INC.
3341 NW Loop 338, Odessa, TX 79768-3290
Tel.: (432) 381-3321
Web Site:
http://www.desertenergy.com
Year Founded: 1978
Sales Range: $10-24.9 Million
Emp.: 10
Construction & Mining Machinery & Equipment Whslr
N.A.I.C.S.: 423810
Ed Barham (CEO)
Brett Barham (Pres)
Charles McGuire (Mgr-Sls)

DESERT EUROPEAN MOTORCARS, LTD.
71387 Hwy 111, Rancho Mirage, CA 92270-4110
Tel.: (760) 773-5000
Web Site:
http://www.deserteuropean.com
Rev.: $90,000,000
Emp.: 100
Car Dealership
N.A.I.C.S.: 441110
Austin Lewis (Mgr-Sls)
Lisa Hamilton (Mgr-Fin)
Sandi Sheffield (Office Mgr)

DESERT FIRE PROTECTION LP
505 Valley Rd, Reno, NV 89512
Tel.: (775) 329-1926
Sales Range: $10-24.9 Million
Emp.: 200
Fire Sprinkler System Installation
N.A.I.C.S.: 238220
Joe Reghetti (Pres)
Bob Audenried (Gen Mgr)

DESERT FRESH, INC.
PO Box 878, Coachella, CA 92236
Tel.: (760) 398-1808
Sales Range: $150-199.9 Million
Emp.: 40
Fruit & Vegetable Canning Services
N.A.I.C.S.: 311421
Anthony Bianco (Owner)
Blaine Carian (VP & Gen Mgr)

DESERT HAWK GOLD CORP.
1290 Holcomb Ave, Reno, NV 89502
Tel.: (775) 837-0557   NV
Web Site:
http://www.deserthawkgoldcorp.com
Year Founded: 1957
Rev.: $4,631,531
Assets: $13,752,054
Liabilities: $24,796,111
Net Worth: ($11,044,057)
Earnings: ($6,489,405)
Emp.: 17
Fiscal Year-end: 12/31/22
Gold Mining Services
N.A.I.C.S.: 212220
Richard Havenstrite (Pres & CEO)

DESERT JET
56600 Invader Blvd, Thermal, CA 92274

Tel.: (760) 399-1000
Web Site: https://www.desertjet.com
Sales Range: $1-9.9 Million
Emp.: 60
Aircraft Charter & Private Jet Charter Services
N.A.I.C.S.: 481212
Denise Wilson *(Pres & Dir-Ops)*

DESERT MOUNTAIN CLUB, INC.
10550 E Desert Hills Dr, Scottsdale, AZ 85262
Tel.: (480) 595-4000   AZ
Web Site:
   http://www.desertmountain.com
Year Founded: 2010
Emp.: 958
Country Club
N.A.I.C.S.: 713910
Michael J. Scully *(Dir-Golf)*
Shawn Emerson *(Dir-Agronomy)*
Kelly Rausch *(CFO)*
Christophe Hermine *(Dir-Ops)*
Jackie Wooldridge *(Dir-Talent & Culture)*
Damon DiOrio *(CEO)*
Robert Ejones II *(COO & Gen Mgr)*

DESERT MOUNTAIN PROPERTIES LIMITED PARTNERSHIP
10550 E Desert Hills Dr, Scottsdale, AZ 85262-3438
Tel.: (480) 595-4000   AZ
Web Site:
   https://www.desertmountain.com
Year Founded: 1983
Sales Range: $75-99.9 Million
Emp.: 700
Subdividers & Developers
N.A.I.C.S.: 237210
Robert Jones *(Gen Mgr)*

DESERT PAVING, INC.
900 S Meadow Ave, Odessa, TX 79761
Tel.: (432) 332-0939   TX
Year Founded: 1963
Sales Range: $1-9.9 Million
Emp.: 25
Highway, Street & Home Paving & Construction
N.A.I.C.S.: 237310
Roger Clayton *(Pres)*

DESERT PEAK MINERALS INC.
1144 15th St Ste 2650, Denver, CO 80202
Tel.: (720) 640-7620   DE
Web Site:
   https://www.desertpeak.com
Year Founded: 2019
Mineral Mining Services
N.A.I.C.S.: 213114
Christopher L. Conoscenti *(CEO)*
Carrie L. Osicka *(CFO)*
Brett S. Riesenfeld *(Gen Counsel)*
Britton L. James *(VP)*
Jarret J. Marcoux *(VP-Engineering)*

DESERT PUBLICATIONS INC.
303 N Indian Canyon Dr, Palm Springs, CA 92262
Tel.: (760) 325-2333
Web Site:
   http://www.desertpublications.com
Sales Range: $10-24.9 Million
Emp.: 65
Publisher of Magazines
N.A.I.C.S.: 513120
Milton W. Jones *(Pres & Publr)*
Frank W. Jones *(Assoc Publr)*
Tom Brown *(Dir-Creative)*

DESERT SPRINGS POOLS & SPAS
8130 S Vly View Blvd, Las Vegas, NV 89139
Tel.: (702) 436-1500
Web Site:
   http://www.desertspringspool.com
Rev.: $15,000,000
Emp.: 12
Spa & Hot Tub Installation
N.A.I.C.S.: 238990
Ron Stewart *(Gen Mgr)*

DESERT SUN MOTORS
2600 N White Sands Blvd, Alamogordo, NM 88310
Tel.: (505) 437-7530
Rev.: $34,533,573
Emp.: 68
Automobiles, New & Used
N.A.I.C.S.: 441110
Robert A. Martinez *(Pres)*
Steve Irick *(Gen Mgr-Sls)*
Herman Smith *(Dir-Dealer Dev)*
Susan Wilton *(Controller)*

DESHANO CONSTRUCTION COMPANY
325 Commerce CT, Gladwin, MI 48624
Tel.: (989) 426-2521
Web Site: https://www.deshano.com
Year Founded: 1966
Sales Range: $10-24.9 Million
Emp.: 40
Builder of Single Family Homes, Condominiums, Multi-Family Projects & Small Commercial Buildings
N.A.I.C.S.: 531120
Gary L. Deshano *(Founder)*
Chad Deshano *(Pres)*

DESHAZO SERVICE COMPANY, LLC
3850 Pinson Valley Pkwy, Birmingham, AL 35217-1854   AL
Web Site: http://www.deshazo.com
Year Founded: 2003
Rev.: $9,600,000
Emp.: 55
Commercial & Industrial Machinery & Equipment (except Automotive & Electronic) Repair & Maintenance
N.A.I.C.S.:
David B. Hovey *(Fin-Other)*

Subsidiaries:

Integrated Machinery Solutions, LLC   (1)
1121 Cantrell Sansom Rd, Fort Worth, TX 76131-1411
Tel.: (817) 659-2398
Web Site: http://www.team-ims.com
Overhead Traveling Crane, Hoist & Monorail System Mfr
N.A.I.C.S.: 333923
Rick Reeves *(VP)*

DESHLER FARMERS ELEVATOR CO.
114 West Maple St, Deshler, OH 43516
Tel.: (419) 278-3015
Web Site:
   http://www.deshlerfarmers.com
Sales Range: $10-24.9 Million
Emp.: 10
Grain Elevators
N.A.I.C.S.: 424510
Mark Sunderman *(Gen Mgr)*
Lisa Christman *(Controller)*

DESICCARE, INC.
985 Damonte Ranch Pkwy Ste 320, Reno, NV 89521-4870
Tel.: (909) 444-8272
Web Site: http://www.desiccare.com

Year Founded: 1994
Sales Range: $10-24.9 Million
Emp.: 90
Treated Mineral & Earth Mfr
N.A.I.C.S.: 327992
Ken Blankenhorn *(Pres & CEO)*

DESIGN CENTER INC.
546 46th Ave, Long Island City, NY 11101
Tel.: (718) 784-4800
Web Site: http://www.plaxall.com
Sales Range: $10-24.9 Million
Emp.: 100
Thermoformed Finished Plastics Products
N.A.I.C.S.: 326199
James M. Pfohl *(Pres)*
Ray Schiffner *(Controller)*

DESIGN CONCEPTS
11 Norton Ave, West Babylon, NY 11704-6618
Tel.: (631) 321-8200
Year Founded: 1971
Sales Range: Less than $1 Million
Emp.: 4
Advetising Agency
N.A.I.C.S.: 541810
Angelo V. Giovanniello *(Pres)*
Eugene A. Mora *(Dir-Creative)*
Joanne Giovanniello *(Media Dir)*

DESIGN CONTEMPO INC.
265 S Main St, Lisbon, NH 03585-6217
Tel.: (603) 838-6544
Web Site: https://www.dcifurn.com
Year Founded: 1973
Sales Range: $10-24.9 Million
Emp.: 270
Mfr of Institutional & Residential Wooden Furniture & Fixtures
N.A.I.C.S.: 337127

DESIGN DISPLAY GROUP INC.
105 Amor Ave, Carlstadt, NJ 07072
Tel.: (201) 438-6000
Web Site:
   http://www.designdisplaygroup.com
Year Founded: 1985
Sales Range: $10-24.9 Million
Emp.: 165
Plastics Product Mfr
N.A.I.C.S.: 326199
Andrew Freedman *(CEO)*
Henry Lee *(Dir-Engrg)*
Jonathon Loew *(Exec VP-Design & Engrg)*
Tim Santana *(Project Mgr)*

DESIGN ELECTRIC INC.
1307 Carlton Ave, Charlottesville, VA 22902
Tel.: (434) 293-7740
Web Site:
   https://www.designelectricinc.com
Sales Range: $10-24.9 Million
Emp.: 210
Electrical Contractor
N.A.I.C.S.: 238210
David Kirby *(Project Mgr)*
Gregory Smith *(Pres)*
Daniel Martino *(Treas & Sec)*

DESIGN EXTENSIONS, LLC
701 Market St Unit 101, Saint Augustine, FL 32095
Tel.: (904) 299-8150
Web Site:
   http://www.designextensions.com
Year Founded: 1999
Sales Range: $1-9.9 Million
Emp.: 15
Advertising Agency Services
N.A.I.C.S.: 541810

Jay Owen *(Founder & CEO)*
Travis Sutphin *(Dir-Dev)*
Ashley Swanson *(Creative Dir)*
Ali Guy *(Acct Mgr)*
Brandon Lowe *(Project Mgr-Digital)*

DESIGN HOMES INC.
600 N Marquette Rd, Prairie Du Chien, WI 53821-1127
Tel.: (608) 326-6041
Web Site:
   https://www.designhomes.com
Year Founded: 1968
Sales Range: $25-49.9 Million
Emp.: 300
Prefabricated Homes & Radio & TV Equipment Mfr
N.A.I.C.S.: 321992
Franklin A. Weeks *(Pres & CEO)*
Martin MacEachern *(Gen Mgr)*
Brian Groom *(Mgr)*

DESIGN INTERACTIVE, INC.
1221 E Broadway St Ste 110, Oviedo, FL 32765
Tel.: (407) 706-0977
Web Site:
   http://www.designinteractive.net
Year Founded: 1998
Sales Range: $1-9.9 Million
Emp.: 25
Data Processing, Hosting & Related Services
N.A.I.C.S.: 518210
John P. Stanney *(Sr VP-Fin & Admin)*
Kelly S. Hale *(Sr VP-Technical Ops)*
Kay M. Stanney *(Founder & Pres)*
Matt Archer *(Sr VP-Software Dev)*

DESIGN LABORATORY, INC.
14711 NE 29th Pl Ste 220, Bellevue, WA 98007
Tel.: (425) 952-4300
Web Site: https://www.dli.com
Year Founded: 1995
Sales Range: $1-9.9 Million
Emp.: 75
Business Management Consulting Services
N.A.I.C.S.: 541611
Erik Knutsona *(Pres & CEO)*
Tina Knutson *(COO)*
Brian Ruffoa *(Acct Mgr)*
Dawn Gilmore *(Dir-Ops)*
Lyndsy Atkins *(Dir-Personnel)*

DESIGN MARKETING GROUP, INC.
4391 Independence Ct, Sarasota, FL 34234
Tel.: (941) 377-6709
Web Site:
   https://www.dmgsarasota.com
Year Founded: 1992
Sales Range: $1-9.9 Million
Emp.: 10
Advertising & Public Relations
N.A.I.C.S.: 541810
Sanford Cohen *(Pres)*
Michael Weber *(Art Dir)*

DESIGN MATERIALS INCORPORATED
10498 E 49th Ave, Denver, CO 80238
Tel.: (303) 256-2800
Web Site:
   http://www.designmaterials.com
Rev.: $11,000,000
Emp.: 60
Ceramic Wall & Floor Tile, Nec
N.A.I.C.S.: 423320
Sue Ann Guth *(Pres)*

DESIGN ON STAGE HAIR, INC.
178 S Dowlen, Beaumont, TX 77707

Design On Stage Hair, Inc.—(Continued)

Tel.: (409) 866-0560   **TX**
Web Site:
   https://www.onstagehairdesign.com
Year Founded: 1983
Sales Range: $1-9.9 Million
Emp.: 50
Hair Salon & Day Spa
N.A.I.C.S.: 812112
Paul Traylor (Pres)

DESIGN OPTIONS

5455 W Waters Ave Ste 214, Tampa,
FL 33634-1208
Tel.: (813) 885-4950   **FL**
Web Site:
   http://www.designoptions.com
Year Founded: 1981
Sales Range: $75-99.9 Million
Emp.: 100
Office Furniture Mfr
N.A.I.C.S.: 337211

DESIGN PACKAGING COM-PANY INC.

100 Hazel Ave, Glencoe, IL 60022-1731
Tel.: (773) 486-8100
Sales Range: $10-24.9 Million
Emp.: 7
Polyethylene Film
N.A.I.C.S.: 326113
Myron Horvitz (CEO)

DESIGN PICKLE, LLC

16414 N 91st St, Scottsdale, AZ
85260
Tel.: (480) 696-8558
Web Site:
   http://www.designpickle.com
Year Founded: 2015
Sales Range: $1-9.9 Million
Emp.: 230
Graphic Design Services
N.A.I.C.S.: 541430
Russ Perry (CEO)
Dave Ball (Dir-Growth)
Alex Guevara (Dir-Customer Experience)
Kate Rooney (Dir-Brand)
Nico Moore (Dir-Global Ops)

DESIGN RESOURCES GROUP ARCHITECTS, A.I.A., INC.

371 Hoes Ln Ste 301, Piscataway,
NJ 08854-4143
Tel.: (732) 560-7900
Web Site: http://www.drgaia.com
Emp.: 100
Architectural Services
N.A.I.C.S.: 541310
Hany Y. Salib (CEO & Principal)

Subsidiaries:

The Vaughn Collaborative Inc   (1)
42 W Lafayette St, Trenton, NJ 08608
Tel.: (609) 695-7411
Rev.: $1,300,000
Emp.: 12
Architectural Services
N.A.I.C.S.: 541310
Lewis J. Delosso (Pres)

DESIGN STRATEGY CORPO-RATION

805 3rd Ave 11th Fl, New York, NY
10022-2001
Tel.: (212) 370-0000
Web Site:
   http://www.designstrategy.com
Year Founded: 1980
Sales Range: $25-49.9 Million
Emp.: 150
Provider of Data Processing & Preparation Services
N.A.I.C.S.: 518210

Michelle Shriver (Mgr-Recruiting)
Bob Cooke (Sr VP)
Charles Wehrle (Dir-IT)
Jay Sherwood (VP)
Mario Carreira (VP)
Michael Darbin (COO)

DESIGN STYLES INC.

1708 E Columbus Ave, Tampa, FL
33605
Tel.: (813) 241-6700
Web Site:
   https://www.designstylesarchitecture.com
Year Founded: 1998
Sales Range: $1-9.9 Million
Emp.: 20
Architectural Services
N.A.I.C.S.: 541310
Andy Dohmen (CEO & Partner)
Craig Smith (Mgr-Sys)
Jim Fisher (Project Mgr)
Jenny Callahan (Project Mgr)

DESIGN SYSTEMS INC.

38799 W 12 Mile Rd, Farmington
Hills, MI 48331
Tel.: (248) 489-4300
Web Site: https://www.dsidsc.com
Rev.: $12,700,000
Emp.: 125
Computer Software Development
N.A.I.C.S.: 541511
Dan Birchmeier (VP-Sls & Mktg)
Brian Lynn (Engr-Simulation)
Mark Yanalunas (Mng Partner)
Nick Kleinow (Project Mgr)
Rick Ogg (Project Mgr)
William Yoder (Project Mgr)
Larry Pope (Gen Mgr)
Gabriel Valdes (Supvr-Acct)

DESIGN TOSCANO, INC.

1400 Morse Ave, Elk Grove Village,
IL 60007
Tel.: (847) 952-0100
Web Site:
   https://www.designtoscano.com
Year Founded: 1989
Sales Range: $10-24.9 Million
Emp.: 85
Home Furnishings Retailer
N.A.I.C.S.: 449129
Michael Stopka (Pres)

DESIGN+BUILD GROUP

211 N Robinson Ave Ste 210, Oklahoma City, OK 73102
Tel.: (405) 601-2700
Web Site:
   http://www.DesignBuildOK.com
Sales Range: $1-9.9 Million
Emp.: 16
Building Construction Services
N.A.I.C.S.: 236115
Deemah Ramadan (Mng Partner)
Frey Radfar (Mng Partner)
Sheila Wicker (Office Mgr)

DESIGNATRONICS, INC.

250 Duffy Ave, Hicksville, NY 11801
Tel.: (516) 328-3300   **NY**
Web Site: https://www.sdp-si.com
Year Founded: 1960
Sales Range: $150-199.9 Million
Emp.: 150
Mechanical & Electro-Mechanical
Components Mfr
N.A.I.C.S.: 334514
Robert Kufner (Pres & CEO)
Charles Comstock (Gen Mgr-Wybur Tools)

Subsidiaries:

Designatronics, Inc. - Advanced Anti-vibration Components Division   (1)

2101 Jericho Tpke, New Hyde Park, NY
11040
Tel.: (516) 328-3662
Web Site: http://www.vibrationmounts.com
Sales Range: $25-49.9 Million
Emp.: 300
Electro-mechanical Motion Control Component Mfr
N.A.I.C.S.: 334519
Dorothena Bonham (Asst VP & Gen Mgr)

Designatronics, Inc. - All Metric Small
Parts Division   (1)
2101 Jericho Tpke, New Hyde Park, NY
11040
Tel.: (516) 302-0152
Web Site:
   http://www.allmetricsmallparts.com
Sales Range: $10-24.9 Million
Emp.: 288
Electronic Components Mfr
N.A.I.C.S.: 334419
Bryan Bengel (Mgr)

Designatronics, Inc. - Quality Bearings & Components Division   (1)
2101 Jericho Turnpike, New Hyde Park, NY
11040
Tel.: (516) 616-0436
Web Site: http://www.qbcbearings.com
Sales Range: $50-74.9 Million
Bearing Equipments Mfr
N.A.I.C.S.: 332991

Designatronics, Inc. - Quality Transmission Components Division   (1)
125 Railroad Ave Garden City Park, New
York, NY 11040
Tel.: (516) 437-6700
Web Site: http://www.qtcgears.com
Gear Product Mfr
N.A.I.C.S.: 333612

Sterling Instrument Div.   (1)
250 Duffy Ave, Hicksville, NY
11801   **(100%)**
Tel.: (516) 328-3300
Web Site: http://www.sdp-si.com
Sales Range: $50-74.9 Million
Emp.: 320
Mfr of Mechanical & Electronic Components
N.A.I.C.S.: 334514
Joseph Sackman (Controller)
Robert Kufner (Pres)

Stock Drive Products   (1)
250 Duffy Ave, Hicksville, NY
11801   **(100%)**
Tel.: (516) 328-3300
Web Site: http://www.sdp-si.com
Sales Range: $50-74.9 Million
Emp.: 240
Mechanical Component Mfr
N.A.I.C.S.: 333613
Robert Kufner (Pres & CEO)

Stock Drive Products Div.   (1)
250 Duffy Ave, Hicksville, NY
11801   **(100%)**
Tel.: (516) 328-3300
Web Site: http://www.sdp-si.com
Sales Range: $10-24.9 Million
Emp.: 200
Counting Device Mfr
N.A.I.C.S.: 334514
Robert Kufner (Pres)
Steve Safranek (Mgr-Bus Dev)
Doug Kerester (VP-Sls & Mktg)

Techno Div.   (1)
2101 Jericho Tpke, New Hyde Park, NY
11040-4702   **(100%)**
Tel.: (516) 328-3970
Sales Range: $25-49.9 Million
Emp.: 200
Mfr Of Power Transmission Equipment
N.A.I.C.S.: 334514

DESIGNED ALLOYS INC.

601 W New York St, Aurora, IL 60506
Tel.: (630) 906-2750
Web Site:
   http://www.designedalloys.com
Sales Range: $10-24.9 Million
Emp.: 20
Metals Service Centers & Offices
N.A.I.C.S.: 423510
Moises Angel (Controller)

DESIGNED MOBILE SYSTEMS INDUSTRIES, INC.

800 S Hwy 33, Patterson, CA 95363
Tel.: (209) 892-6298
Web Site: http://www.dmsi-inc.com
Year Founded: 1973
Sales Range: $10-24.9 Million
Emp.: 130
Commercial & Institutional Building
Construction Services
N.A.I.C.S.: 236220
David Smith (Pres)
Trina Morton (Coord-Sls & Customer
Svc)
Edward Smith (VP-Ops & Engrg)

DESIGNED STAIRS INC.

1251 6th St, Sandwich, IL 60548
Tel.: (815) 786-7600
Web Site:
   http://www.designstairs.com
Sales Range: $10-24.9 Million
Emp.: 50
Staircases, Stairs & Railings
N.A.I.C.S.: 321918
Michelle Ducharme (Pres)
Brent Peterson (Mgr-Acctg)
Diane Gregoire (Acct Coord)
John Ressler (Mng Partner)

DESIGNER APPLIANCES

208 Bellevue Ave, Montclair, NJ
07043
Tel.: (973) 559-0888
Web Site:
   https://www.designerappliances.com
Sales Range: $10-24.9 Million
Emp.: 16
Discount Kitchen Appliances
N.A.I.C.S.: 449210
Metin Ozkuzey (Founder)

DESIGNER DOORS, INC.

702 Troy St, River Falls, WI 54022
Tel.: (715) 426-1100
Web Site:
   http://www.designerdoors.com
Year Founded: 1980
Sales Range: $10-24.9 Million
Emp.: 85
Wood Window & Door Mfr
N.A.I.C.S.: 321911
Kent Forsland (Founder)

DESIGNER GREETINGS INC.

1 Executive Ave, Edison, NJ 08817
Tel.: (718) 981-7700
Web Site:
   http://www.designergreetings.com
Rev.: $9,080,000
Emp.: 20
Stationery & Office Supplies Merchant Whslr
N.A.I.C.S.: 424120
Steven Gimbelman (Pres & CEO)
Mary Soliven (Dir-HR)

Subsidiaries:

Expressions Unlimited, Inc.   (1)
300 Rdg Rd Bldg D, Lafayette, LA 70506
Tel.: (337) 269-1006
Web Site:
   http://expressionsunlimitedinc.com
Rev.: $9,500,000
Emp.: 71
Stationery & Office Supplies Merchant
Whslr
N.A.I.C.S.: 424120
Mike Declouet (Dir-Sls)

DESIGNER IMPORTS INTER-NATIONAL

6931 Stanford Ave, Los Angeles, CA
90001
Tel.: (323) 753-5448
Web Site:
   http://www.designersimports.com

Sales Range: $1-9.9 Million
Emp.: 25
Office & Public Building Furniture
N.A.I.C.S.: 423210
Joubin Torkan (Pres)
Phillip Elga (CEO)

DESIGNER SASH & DOOR SYSTEMS, INC.
18890 Seaton Ave, Perris, CA 92570-8720
Tel.: (951) 657-4179
Web Site:
http://www.renewyourhome.com
Year Founded: 1988
Sales Range: $10-24.9 Million
Emp.: 91
Plastics Product Mfr
N.A.I.C.S.: 326199
Ken McBride (Owner)

DESIGNERS FOUNTAIN
20101 S Santa Fe Ave, Rancho Dominguez, CA 90221
Tel.: (310) 886-5143
Web Site:
https://www.designersftn.com
Year Founded: 1982
Sales Range: $10-24.9 Million
Emp.: 110
Mfr & Distributor of Lighting Fixtures
N.A.I.C.S.: 335139
Irene L. Wang (Pres)

DESIGNING HEALTH, INC.
28410 Witherspoon Pkwy, Valencia, CA 91355-4167
Tel.: (661) 257-1705
Web Site:
http://www.designinghealth.com
Sales Range: $10-24.9 Million
Emp.: 25
Food, Vitamins & Nutritional Supplements
N.A.I.C.S.: 325411
Robert Collett (Pres)
Nate Armstrong (COO & VP)
Mike Melia (VP)

DESIGNS FOR HEALTH, INC.
980 S St, Suffield, CT 06078
Tel.: (860) 623-6314
Web Site:
http://www.designsforhealth.com
Year Founded: 1989
Sales Range: $10-24.9 Million
Emp.: 100
Nutritional Supplements Mfr
N.A.I.C.S.: 325412
Linda Lizotte (Co-Founder)
Jonathan Lizotte (Co-Founder)
Phil Lizotte (CEO)
Gail Lizotte (Chief Admin Officer)
David M. Brady (Chief Medical Officer)
Jose A. Llobrera (VP-Res & Production Education)
Michael Jurgelewicz (Mng Dir-Clinical R&D)
Robert J. Nicolosi (Chief Science Officer)

Subsidiaries:

Ashley-Martin Manufacturing LLC   (1)
90160 US Hwy 93, Arlee, MT 59821
Tel.: (406) 726-3700
Nutritional Supplements Mfr
N.A.I.C.S.: 325412
Mindy Fyant (Gen Mgr)

DESIGNWORKS ADVERTISING INC.
109 Twin Oaks Dr, Syracuse, NY 13206
Tel.: (315) 431-0808

Web Site:
http://www.designworksadv.com
Year Founded: 1992
Sales Range: $10-24.9 Million
Emp.: 15
Collateral, Print, Production, Publicity/Promotions, Sales Promotion
N.A.I.C.S.: 541810
David Bellso (Pres)
Olivia Erwin (Mgr-Production)
Janina Miller (Accountant)
Darcy DiBiase (VP)
Scott Herron (Dir-Creative)

DESILVA GATES CONSTRUCTION
11555 Dublin Blvd, Dublin, CA 94568-2854
Tel.: (925) 829-9220   CA
Web Site:
https://www.desilvagates.com
Year Founded: 1995
Sales Range: $25-49.9 Million
Emp.: 200
Highway & Street Construction Services
N.A.I.C.S.: 237310
Richard B. Gates (Pres)
Edwin O. DeSilva (Chm)
David DeSilva (Exec VP)
J. Scott Archibald (VP)
Chris Hallun (Controller)
Pete Davos (VP-Construction Ops)

DESILVA+PHILLIPS LLC
475 Park Ave S 22nd Fl, New York, NY 10016
Tel.: (212) 686-9700
Web Site:
http://www.desilvaphillips.com
Year Founded: 1996
Sales Range: $1-9.9 Million
Emp.: 16
Investment Banking
N.A.I.C.S.: 523150
Roland A. DeSilva (Co-Founder, Chm & Mng Partner)
Jeffrey L. Dearth (Partner)
Lillian Liu (Mng Dir)
Jessica Luterman Naeve (Mng Dir)
Jack Noble (Partner)
Ken Sonenclar (Mng Dir)
Lon Williams (Mng Dir)
Robin Warner (Mng Dir)
Dow Jones (Dir-Strategic Plng)
Thomson Learning (VP-Strategy & Dev)
Kerry Hatch (Mng Dir)
Danny Phillips (Mng Dir-Events)
Reed Phillips III (Co-Founder, CEO & Mng Partner)
John Kaiser Jr. (Mng Dir)

DESK TOP GRAPHICS INC.
65 Bay St, Boston, MA 02125
Tel.: (617) 350-8837
Web Site: http://www.digipress.net
Sales Range: $10-24.9 Million
Emp.: 100
Graphics Communications
N.A.I.C.S.: 323120
Rick Dyer (Pres)
Skip Dyer (VP)
Rick Theder (VP)
Julie Daffie (Controller)

DESKS INC.
225 W Ohio St Ste 500, Chicago, IL 60654
Tel.: (312) 334-3375   IL
Web Site: http://www.desksinc.com
Year Founded: 1956
Sales Range: $25-49.9 Million
Emp.: 50
Mfr & Sales of Furniture

N.A.I.C.S.: 423210
Jim Ford (Pres)
Greg Erazmus (CFO)

DESOTO AUTOMOTIVE ENTERPRISES INC
3039 SE Hwy 70, Arcadia, FL 34266
Tel.: (863) 494-4848
Web Site:
http://www.desotoautomall.com
Sales Range: $25-49.9 Million
Emp.: 70
Automobile Sales, New & Used
N.A.I.C.S.: 441110
Mark Schlundt (Pres)
Matt Kratzer (Gen Mgr-Sls)
Morey Browning (Controller)

DESOTO HOSPITAL ASSOCIATION
207 Jefferson St, Mansfield, LA 71052
Tel.: (318) 872-4610   LA
Web Site:
http://www.desotoregional.com
Year Founded: 1949
Sales Range: $10-24.9 Million
Emp.: 257
Health Care Srvices
N.A.I.C.S.: 622110
Daniel Campbell (VP-Ancillary Svcs)
Todd Eppler (CEO)
Johhny May (Sec)
Jill Heard (Chm)
Deborah Dees (Treas)
John Freeman (Vice Chm)
Sandra Anderson (CFO)
Christopher Davis (VP)

DESOTO SALES INC.
20945 Osborne St, Canoga Park, CA 91304
Tel.: (818) 998-0853
Web Site:
https://www.desotosales.com
Rev.: $10,900,000
Emp.: 125
Wholesale Flooring Supplies
N.A.I.C.S.: 423710
James Keenan (Pres)
Mark McNeely (Mgr-Sls)

DESRI INC.
1166 Avenue of the Americas 9th Fl, New York, NY 10036
Tel.: (212) 478-0000   DE
Year Founded: 2021
Holding Company
N.A.I.C.S.: 551112
Bryan Martin (Co-Founder & Chm)
David Zwillinger (CEO & Co-Founder)
Chris Clevenger (COO)
Thomas de Swardt (Chief Comml Officer)
Stan Krutonogiy (CFO)

DESSIN/FOURNIR, INC.
308 W Mill St, Plainville, KS 67663
Tel.: (785) 434-2777
Web Site:
http://www.dessinfournir.com
Rev.: $4,400,000
Emp.: 80
Nonupholstered Wood Household Furniture Mfr
N.A.I.C.S.: 337122
Charles Comeau (Pres)

Subsidiaries:

Kenneth Meyer Co Inc.   (1)
325 Vermont St, San Francisco, CA 94103
Tel.: (415) 861-0118
Web Site: http://www.kennethmeyer.com
Rev.: $3,590,000
Emp.: 5
Piece Goods, Notions & Other Dry Goods Merchant Whslr

N.A.I.C.S.: 424310

DESTINATION CINEMA INC.
4155 Harrison Blvd Ste 201, Ogden, UT 84403
Tel.: (801) 392-5881
Web Site:
http://www.destinationcinema.com
Sales Range: $10-24.9 Million
Emp.: 12
Motion Picture Distribution Services
N.A.I.C.S.: 512110
Bob Perkins (CEO)

DESTINATION CONCEPTS, INC.
4241 Jutland Dr Ste 200, San Diego, CA 92117
Tel.: (858) 274-7979   CA
Web Site:
http://www.destinationconcepts.com
Year Founded: 1998
Sales Range: $1-9.9 Million
Emp.: 25
Corporate Event & Meeting Planning, Management & Logistics
N.A.I.C.S.: 711320
Ana Reilly (Principal & VP-Sls & Mktg)
Brittany Boysel (Coord-Design)
Jenny Avery Bradshaw (Sr Acct Mgr)
Stacy Ruffell (Acct Mgr)

DESTINATION HARLEY DAVIDSON LLC
2302 Pacific Hwy E, Tacoma, WA 98424
Tel.: (253) 922-3700
Web Site:
http://www.destinationharley
davidson.com
Sales Range: $25-49.9 Million
Emp.: 60
Motorcycles
N.A.I.C.S.: 441227
Ed Wallace (Owner & Chm)
Jane Herzog (Controller)

DESTINATION MARKETING
6808 220th St SW Ste 300, Mountlake Terrace, WA 98043
Tel.: (425) 774-8343
Web Site: http://www.destmark.com
Rev.: $12,000,000
Emp.: 20
Advertising, Brand Development & Integration, Graphic Design, Interactive, Media Buying Services, Public Relations, Radio, Strategic Planning/Research, T.V.
N.A.I.C.S.: 541810
Dan Voetmann (Pres & CEO)
Maureen O'Hanlon (VP)
Tim Hunter (Dir-Creative)
Thomas Saladin (VP)
Chris Settle (Sr VP & Dir-Creative Svcs)
Cliff Skillings (Dir-Brdcst Buying & Promos)

DESTINATION PACKWOOD ASSOCIATION
13011B US Hwy 12, Packwood, WA 98361
Tel.: (360) 492-7365
Web Site:
http://www.destinationpackwood.com
Year Founded: 1998
Tourism Promotion Services
N.A.I.C.S.: 813910
CJ Neer (Exec Dir)

DESTINATIONS UNLIMITED, INC.
419 1st St SE, Cedar Rapids, IA 52401

Destinations Unlimited, Inc.—(Continued)

Tel.: (319) 393-1359
Web Site: http://duagency.com
Travel Agency
N.A.I.C.S.: 561510
Duane Jasper *(Owner & CEO)*

**DESTINY CORPORATE EN-
TERPRISES, INC.**
81 Dow Jones St #8, Henderson, NV
89074
Tel.: (702) 466-3333   DE
Year Founded: 2011
Investment Services
N.A.I.C.S.: 523999
Nicole Anderson *(Pres, CEO, CFO,
Chief Acctg Officer & Sec)*

DESTINY ORGANICS, LLC.
16 Forest Pkwy Bldg E, Forest Park,
GA 30297
Tel.: (404) 366-7006
Web Site: http://www.destiny-
organics.com
Sales Range: $10-24.9 Million
Emp.: 65
Fresh Fruit & Vegetable Whslr
N.A.I.C.S.: 424480
Jason Waters *(Mgr-Sls)*

**DESTRA U.S. LIQUIDITY AL-
PHA AND INCOME FUND**
901 Warrenville Rd Ste 15, Lisle, IL
60532
Tel.: (630) 853-3300
Web Site:
    http://www.destracapital.com
Sales Range: $25-49.9 Million
Emp.: 20
Investment Services
N.A.I.C.S.: 523999
Nicholas Dalmaso *(CEO, CFO &
Chief Investment Officer)*

**DET DISTRIBUTING COMPANY
INC.**
301 Great Cir Rd, Nashville, TN
37228-1703
Tel.: (615) 244-4113   TN
Web Site: https://detdistributing.com
Year Founded: 1951
Sales Range: $50-74.9 Million
Emp.: 165
Distr of Beer & Ale
N.A.I.C.S.: 424810
Fred Detwiller *(Pres)*
Vicky Victory *(Controller)*
John Curley *(COO & Gen Mgr)*
Mike Anderson *(Mgr-Warehouse)*
Pete Pirtle *(VP-Sls)*

DETECT, INC.
1022 West 23rd St Ste 620, Panama
City, FL 32405
Tel.: (850) 763-7200
Web Site: http://www.detect-inc.com
Sales Range: $25-49.9 Million
Emp.: 100
Radar Detection Device Mfr
N.A.I.C.S.: 334511
Jonathan M. Rothberg *(Founder &
Chm)*
Gary W. Andrews *(Chm & CEO)*
Ron L. Merritt *(Pres)*
T. Adam Kelly *(CTO)*
Melissa Adams *(Mgr-Acctg & Fin)*

Subsidiaries:

DeTect Canada   (1)
2600 Rue Saint-Jacques, Montreal, H3J
T24, QC, Canada
Tel.: (438) 401-0471
Radar Detection Device Mfr
N.A.I.C.S.: 334511
Carolyn Matkovich *(Gen Mgr)*

DeTect EU Ltd.   (1)
Afon House Worthing Road, Horsham,
RH12 1TL, West Sussex, United Kingdom
Tel.: (44) 1403 788 315
Web Site: http://www.detect-inc.com
Emp.: 2
Radar Detection Device Mfr
N.A.I.C.S.: 334511
Edward Zakrajsek *(Gen Mgr)*

DeTect, Inc. - Aviation & Security
Systems Group   (1)
1902 Wilson Ave, Panama City, FL 32405
Tel.: (850) 763-7200
Radar Detection Device Mfr
N.A.I.C.S.: 334511
Karen Voltura *(Dir-Aviation & Wind Energy
Sys)*
Doug McElwain *(Mgr-Engrg & Ops)*
Jesse Lewis *(Mgr-Data Sys & Svcs)*

DeTect, Inc. - International
Division   (1)
5801 Lee Hwy, Arlington, VA 22207
Tel.: (703) 533-8555
Radar Detection Device Retailer
N.A.I.C.S.: 423690

DeTect, Inc. - Meteorological Radar
Group   (1)
117L S Sunset Syt, Longmont, CO 80501
Tel.: (303) 848-8090
Web Site: http://www.detect-inc.com
Emp.: 25
Radar Detection Device Mfr
N.A.I.C.S.: 334511
Scott McLaughlin *(VP-Meteorological Sys)*

DETER MOTOR CO.
100 E 2nd St, Atlantic, IA 50022
Tel.: (712) 243-4514
Web Site:
    https://www.determotor.com
Rev.: $12,000,000
Emp.: 30
Automobiles, New & Used
N.A.I.C.S.: 441110
Donald Deter *(Owner & Pres)*
Julie Fischer *(Mgr-Svc)*
Doug Gifford *(Mgr-Parts)*

**DETERING COMPANY OF
HOUSTON LP**
6800 Helmers St, Houston, TX 77022
Tel.: (713) 869-3761
Web Site: https://www.detering.com
Rev.: $16,000,000
Emp.: 50
Building Materials, Interior
N.A.I.C.S.: 423310
Carl A. Detering Jr. *(Pres)*

DETERLING COMPANY, INC.
4323 S Dr, Houston, TX 77053
Tel.: (832) 399-9393
Web Site:
    http://www.swformseal.com
Year Founded: 1975
Sales Range: $1-9.9 Million
Emp.: 28
Packaging Solutions
N.A.I.C.S.: 322220
John Deterling *(Pres)*

DETERMINA INC.
3401 Hillview Ave, Palo Alto, CA
94304-1320
Tel.: (650) 637-5500
Year Founded: 2003
Sales Range: $1-9.9 Million
Emp.: 25
Host Intrusion Prevention Solutions
for Servers & Desktops
N.A.I.C.S.: 561621
Matthew Powell *(Pres & CEO)*
Paul Denton *(CFO)*

**DETERRENT TECHNOLOGIES
INC.**
1750 Brielle Ave Ste 1A, Asbury
Park, NJ 07712

Tel.: (732) 918-0800
Web Site: http://www.deterrent.com
Rev.: $17,615,815
Emp.: 60
Safety & Security Specialization
N.A.I.C.S.: 561621
David Hersh *(Pres)*
John Maguire *(VP)*
Jeffry Glassman *(VP-Ops)*
Paul Midura *(Acct Exec-Global)*

DETEX CORPORATION
302 Detex Dr, New Braunfels, TX
78130-3045
Tel.: (830) 629-2900   TX
Web Site: https://www.detex.com
Year Founded: 1923
Sales Range: $10-24.9 Million
Emp.: 120
Watchclock Mfr & Distr
N.A.I.C.S.: 334519
John Blodgett *(Pres)*
Jeff Addis *(Principal)*
Ken Kuehler *(Gen Mgr)*
Tim Shafer *(Mktg Mgr)*

Subsidiaries:

Design Security Inc.   (1)
1402 Hawthorne St, Bastrop, TX 78602-
2654
Tel.: (512) 321-4426
Web Site: http://www.dsigo.com
Sales Range: $10-24.9 Million
Emp.: 30
Mfr of Security Systems
N.A.I.C.S.: 335999

**DETHMERS MANUFACTURING
COMPANY**
4010 320th St, Boyden, IA 51234
Tel.: (712) 725-2311
Web Site: https://www.demco-
products.com
Sales Range: $25-49.9 Million
Emp.: 300
Trailers & Trailer Equipment
N.A.I.C.S.: 333111
Robert Koerselman *(Pres)*
Kevin Ten Haken *(Exec VP)*

**DETROIT EDGE TOOL COM-
PANY**
6570 E Nevada St, Detroit, MI 48234
Tel.: (313) 366-4120
Web Site:
    https://www.detroitedge.com
Sales Range: $10-24.9 Million
Emp.: 50
Machine Knives, Metalworking
N.A.I.C.S.: 333515
Raymond R. Ebbing *(Pres)*
John Ebbing *(VP)*

**DETROIT ELECTRO-
COATINGS CO, LLC**
2599 22nd St, Detroit, MI 48216-1076
Tel.: (313) 897-2277   MI
Web Site: http://www.decnow.com
Year Founded: 1996
Sales Range: $75-99.9 Million
Emp.: 120
Electro Coat Painting Services
N.A.I.C.S.: 332812
John Sinanis *(Pres)*

**DETROIT RESCUE MISSION
MINISTRIES**
150 Stimson St, Detroit, MI 48201
Tel.: (313) 993-4700   MI
Web Site: https://www.drmm.org
Year Founded: 1909
Sales Range: $25-49.9 Million
Emp.: 394
Substance Abuse Rehabilitation Ser-
vices
N.A.I.C.S.: 623220

Barbara Willis *(COO)*
C. Paschal Eze *(Dir-Media & Com-
munity Rels)*
Belinda Flowers *(Dir-HR)*
Esther Gwilly *(Dir-Fin)*
Chad Audi *(Pres)*
Aurine Moore *(VP-Dev)*
Luke Elliott *(Vice Chm)*
Randall Pentiuk *(Chm)*
Nina Simone *(Sec)*

**DETROIT SHOREWAY COM-
MUNITY DEVELOPMENT OR-
GANIZATION**
6516 Detroit Ave, Cleveland, OH
44102
Tel.: (216) 961-4242   OH
Web Site: http://www.dscdo.org
Year Founded: 1976
Sales Range: $1-9.9 Million
Emp.: 45
Community Development Services
N.A.I.C.S.: 813319
Adam Davenport *(Mgr-Project & Ops)*
Greg Baron *(Dir-Real Estate Dev)*
Adam Rosen *(Dir-Economic Dev)*
Donna Gonyon *(Vice Chm)*

DETROIT STOKER CO.
1510 E 1st St, Monroe, MI 48161-
1915
Tel.: (800) 786-5374
Web Site:
    http://www.detroitstoker.com
Year Founded: 1898
Industrial Stokers Mfr
N.A.I.C.S.: 333414
Thomas Giaier *(Pres)*

**DETROIT SYMPHONY OR-
CHESTRA, INC.**
3711 Woodward, Detroit, MI 48201
Tel.: (313) 576-5100
Web Site: http://www.dso.org
Sales Range: $10-24.9 Million
Emp.: 250
Symphony Orchestra
N.A.I.C.S.: 711130
Eric Woodhams *(Mgr-Digital Media &
Engagement)*
Paul Hogle *(Exec VP)*
Phillip Fisher *(Chm)*
Emily Lamoreaux *(Sr Dir-Education &
Artistic)*
Jader Bignamini *(Dir-Music)*

DETROIT TRADING COMPANY
2000 Town Ctr Ste 1300, Southfield,
MI 48075
Tel.: (248) 352-1313   MI
Web Site:
    https://www.detroittrading.com
Sales Range: $10-24.9 Million
Emp.: 16
Online Automotive Marketing Ser-
vices
N.A.I.C.S.: 541810
Pete Bonner *(Co-Founder & Exec
VP)*
Jeff Bonner *(VP-Dealer Sls)*

DETROW & UNDERWOOD
12 W Main St, Ashland, OH 44805-
2218
Tel.: (419) 289-0265
Year Founded: 1945
Sales Range: $1-9.9 Million
Emp.: 10
Advertising Agencies
N.A.I.C.S.: 541810
Gary D. Underwood *(Pres)*
Don Hubacher *(VP & Graphic Svcs
Dir)*
Todd Whitmer *(Creative Dir)*
George Callas *(Promotion One Dir)*
Randy Boyd *(Art Dir)*

DETYENS SHIPYARDS INC.
1670 Dry Dock Ave Ste 236, North Charleston, SC 29405-2121
Tel.: (843) 308-8000
Web Site: https://www.detyens.com
Sales Range: $50-74.9 Million
Emp.: 400
Shipbuilding & Repairing
N.A.I.C.S.: 336611
Richard Stokes *(Exec VP)*
Larry Reynolds *(VP-Ops)*
Roy Caraway *(Mgr-Pur)*
Leo Fary *(CFO & VP)*
Bradley Kerr *(Dir-Sls & Mktg)*
Jimmy Lamb *(Mgr-Plng)*
Jim Youker *(Dir-HR)*
Ken Richardson *(Mgr-Contracts')*
Peter Browne *(VP-Estimating)*
D. Loy Stewart Jr. *(Pres & Chm)*

DEUCE ENTERTAINMENT, LLC
1154 S Robertson Blvd, Los Angeles, CA 90035
Tel.: (310) 807-0660
Web Site: https://www.deuce-ent.com
Year Founded: 2006
Sales Range: $10-24.9 Million
Emp.: 30
Distr of Closeout Home Entertainment Games & Movies
N.A.I.C.S.: 512120
Amir Ahdoot *(Pres)*

DEUTSCHES ALTENHEIM, INC.
2222 Centre St, West Roxbury, MA 02132-4097
Tel.: (617) 325-1230
Web Site:
https://www.germancentre.org
Year Founded: 1932
Sales Range: $10-24.9 Million
Emp.: 330
Elder Care Services
N.A.I.C.S.: 624120
Gregory Karr *(CEO)*
Steven Kolodziej *(Dir-Clinical Svcs)*
Kathy Ellard *(Dir-Nursing)*
David W. Chen *(Dir-Medical)*

DEV DIGITAL LLC
162 Rosa L Parks Blvd 1, Nashville, TN 37203
Tel.: (615) 257-1490
Web Site: http://www.devdigital.com
Year Founded: 2008
Web Design & Software Application Development Services
N.A.I.C.S.: 541512
Mitch Ballard *(Partner)*
Turner Nashe *(Partner & Pres-IDS)*
Brittany Wegusen *(Partner & Dir-Ops)*
Thomas Ross *(Partner & Mgr-Enterprise Project)*
Debby Dickens *(Partner & VP-Fin)*
Jay Daniel *(Partner & CTO)*
Viren Bhavsar *(Partner & Dir-Ops)*
Daniel Mcmahan *(Project Mgr)*
Grant Owens *(Project Mgr)*
Ambrish Vadnerkar *(Mgr-PMP Team)*
Ritesh Pancholi *(Mgr-PHP Team)*
Tofique Shaikh *(Mgr-SEO Team)*
Nirav Darji *(Mgr-Design Team)*
Manoj Ginoya *(Mgr-PHP Team)*
Vrajesh Parmar *(Mgr-Design Team)*

DEVAN LOWE INC.
1151 Gault Ave S, Fort Payne, AL 35967
Tel.: (256) 845-0922
Web Site:
http://www.devanlowegm.com
Rev.: $85,244,982
Emp.: 30
Automobiles, New & Used
N.A.I.C.S.: 441110

Devan Lowe *(Pres)*
Barbara Murks *(Office Mgr)*

DEVANEY ENERGY INC.
177 Wells Ave, Newton, MA 02459-9120 — MA
Web Site:
https://www.devaneyenergy.com
Year Founded: 1934
Fuel Oil & Heating & Cooling Products Sales
N.A.I.C.S.: 457210
Bob Duffy *(Mgr-Sls)*

DEVAR, INC.
706 Bostwick Ave, Bridgeport, CT 06605-2396
Tel.: (203) 368-6751 — CT
Web Site: https://www.devarinc.com
Year Founded: 1961
Sales Range: $75-99.9 Million
Emp.: 120
Process Instruments, Temperature Transmitters, Data Loggers & Telemetry Mfr
N.A.I.C.S.: 335314
Anthony J. Ruscito *(Chm, Pres & CEO)*
Jeffery C. Head *(VP-Ops)*
Diane Billings *(VP-Acctg)*

DEVBRIDGE GROUP LLC
343 W Erie St Ste 600, Chicago, IL 60654
Tel.: (312) 635-4228 — IL
Web Site: http://www.devbridge.com
Year Founded: 2008
Sales Range: $1-9.9 Million
Emp.: 50
Technology Consulting Services
N.A.I.C.S.: 541690
Aurimas Adomavicius *(Pres)*
Martin Stasaitis *(Co-Founder & CEO)*
Viktoras Gurgzdys *(VP-Engineering)*

DEVCARE SOLUTIONS
131 N High St Ste 640, Columbus, OH 43215
Tel.: (614) 221-2277
Web Site: http://www.devcare.com
Year Founded: 2005
Sales Range: $1-9.9 Million
Emp.: 42
IT Solutions
N.A.I.C.S.: 519290

DEVCON (TCI) LTD.
3165 SW 10th St, Deerfield Beach, FL 33442
Tel.: (954) 429-1500 — TC
Web Site: http://www.devconltd.com
Year Founded: 1951
Sales Range: $10-24.9 Million
Emp.: 6
Construction & Marine Engineering Services
N.A.I.C.S.: 237990
John Chellgren *(Pres)*

DEVCON CONSTRUCTION INCORPORATED
690 Gibraltar Dr, Milpitas, CA 95035-6317
Tel.: (408) 942-8200 — CA
Web Site: https://www.devcon-const.com
Year Founded: 1976
Sales Range: $400-449.9 Million
Emp.: 500
Commercial & Institutional Building Construction
N.A.I.C.S.: 236220
Gary Filizetti *(Pres)*
Bret Sisney *(VP-Acctg, Fin & Investment)*
Catherine Cote *(Project Mgr)*

John Dunn *(Superintendent-Construction)*
Peter Copriviza *(VP-Construction)*
Jonathan Harvey *(VP-Construction)*
Daisy Pereira *(VP-Construction)*
Justine Pereira *(Sec)*

DEVELOPMENT ALTERNATIVES, INC.
7600 Wisconsin Ave Ste 200, Bethesda, MD 20814-2960
Tel.: (301) 771-7600
Web Site: https://www.dai.com
Year Founded: 1970
Sales Range: $10-24.9 Million
Emp.: 300
Provider of Business Consulting Services
N.A.I.C.S.: 541690
James Boomgard *(Pres & CEO)*
Jean Gilson *(Sr VP-Strategy & IT Grp)*
Helle Weeke *(Gen Counsel & Sr VP)*
Michael Jakobowski *(CFO)*
Bobby Jefferson *(CTO & VP-Global Health)*
Susan Scribner *(VP-Health Sys Solutions & Dir-Preparedness and Response Project)*
Chris LeGrand *(Pres-Global Health)*

DEVELOPMENT CORPORATION FOR ISRAEL
575 Lexington Ave Fl 11, New York, NY 10022
Tel.: (212) 644-2663
Web Site:
http://www.israelbonds.com
Year Founded: 1951
Rev.: $195,000,000
Emp.: 207
Securities Broker & Dealer Services
N.A.I.C.S.: 523150
Marisa Brahms *(Asst Gen Counsel)*
Feldstein Alan *(Gen Counsel)*
Stuart Garawitz *(Head-Sls-Natl)*

DEVELOPMENT COUNSELLORS INTERNATIONAL, LTD.
215 Park Ave S 10th Fl, New York, NY 10003
Tel.: (212) 725-0707 — NY
Web Site: http://www.aboutdci.com
Year Founded: 1960
Sales Range: $25-49.9 Million
Emp.: 40
Public Relations, Travel & Tourism
N.A.I.C.S.: 541810
Andrew T. Levine *(Pres & Chief Creative Officer)*
Patricia T. Levine *(VP)*
Peggy Bendel *(Sr VP-Travel Mktg)*
Millicent Brown *(VP)*
Julie Curtin *(Partner)*
Robert DeRocker *(Partner & Exec VP)*
Karyl Leigh Barnes *(Pres-Tourism Practice)*
Malcolm Griffiths *(Acct Dir)*
Neilia Stephens *(Acct Dir)*
Carrie Nepo *(CFO & Partner)*
Intisar Wilson *(Acct Dir & Coord)*
Erin Bodine *(Acct Supvr)*
Susan Brake *(Acct Dir-Denver)*
Dariel Curren *(VP)*
Tara Morrill *(Sr Acct Exec)*
Annette Henriques *(Coord-Accts Payable)*
Ashley Fenton *(Asst Acct Exec)*
Jessica Herring *(Mgr-Promos-North America)*
Luminita Hilchey *(Coord-Mktg)*
Maureen Haley *(Acct Supvr)*
Ryan Shell *(Dir-Social & Digital Media)*
Steve Duncan *(VP-Denver)*
Kayla Leska *(VP-PR)*

Subsidiaries:

DCI-West (1)
19594 E Ida Pl, Aurora, CO 80015
Tel.: (303) 627-0272
Web Site: http://www.aboutdci.com
Emp.: 3
Public Relations, Travel & Tourism
N.A.I.C.S.: 541820
Julie Curtin *(Partner, Exec VP & Reg Director-Denver)*
Karyl Leigh Barnes *(VP)*
Brittani Wood *(Asst Acct Exec)*
Elissa Doyle *(Sr Acct Exec)*
Peggy Bendel *(Sr VP-Travel Mktg)*
Milosh J. Cerevka *(Assoc Dir)*
Dariel Curren *(VP)*
Rob DeRocker *(Sr Counsellor)*
Malcolm Griffiths *(Acct Dir)*
Erin Bodine *(Acct Supvr)*
Iain Watt *(Sr Acct Exec)*
Jordan Robinson *(Acct Exec)*
Katie Webster *(Acct Exec)*
Kara Steible *(Acct Coord)*
Jessica Tuquero *(Acct Supvr)*
Tara Morrill *(Asst Acct Exec)*
Rafael Perez *(Acct Exec)*
Nathaniel Stumpf *(Dir-PDQ)*
Maria Mantz *(Acct Supvr)*
Mary Rachelle Cherpak *(Acct Supvr)*
Katrina DeBor *(Acct Exec)*
Kristie Pendleton *(Acct Coord)*
Susan Brake *(Sr Acct Exec)*
Steve Duncan *(Acct Supvr)*
Intisar Wilson *(Dir-Acct Coordination)*
Dudhie Michel *(Acct Exec-PDQ)*
Annette Henriques *(Coord-Accts Payable)*
Amalia Meliti *(Mgr-Travel Trade)*
Michael Kubelle *(Mgr)*
Ryan Shell *(Dir-Social & Digital Media)*

DEVELOPMENT DIMENSIONS INTERNATIONAL INC.
1225 Washington Pike, Bridgeville, PA 15017-2838
Tel.: (412) 257-0600 — PA
Web Site: https://www.ddiworld.com
Year Founded: 1970
Sales Range: $100-124.9 Million
Emp.: 1,200
Management Consulting Services
N.A.I.C.S.: 541612
William C. Byham *(Founder & Chm)*
Richard S. Wellins *(Sr VP)*
Scott Erker *(Sr VP-US Ops)*
Audrey B. Smith *(Sr VP-Talent Diagnostics Solutions)*
Steven Lau *(Mng Dir)*
David Tessmann-Keys *(Pres)*
Elmar Kronz *(VP-Global Bus Dev)*
Dipali Naidu *(Head-Consulting-India)*
Amogh Deshmukh *(Mng Dir-India)*
Tacy M. Byham *(CEO)*
Barry Stern *(Sr VP-Accelerated Dev Solutions)*
Patsy Tsao *(CFO & Sr VP)*

DEVELOPMENT HOMES, INC.
3880 S Columbia Rd, Grand Forks, ND 58201
Tel.: (701) 335-4000 — ND
Web Site:
https://www.developmenthomes.org
Year Founded: 1974
Sales Range: $10-24.9 Million
Emp.: 518
Disability Assistance Services
N.A.I.C.S.: 624120
Cindy Holweger *(Dir-Quality Enhancement)*
Gordon R. Johnson *(Dir-Ops)*
Janelle Mitzel *(Dir-Gaming)*
Scott Anderson *(Dir-Program Svcs)*
Sandra J. Marshall *(CEO)*

DEVELOPMENTAL PATHWAYS, INC.
325 Inverness Dr S, Englewood, CO 80112
Tel.: (303) 360-6600 — CO

Developmental Pathways, Inc.—(Continued)

Web Site:
http://www.developmentalpath
ways.org
Year Founded: 1964
Sales Range: $25-49.9 Million
Emp.: 425
Developmental Disability Assistance
Services
N.A.I.C.S.: 623210
Deb Bosch *(Dir-Mktg & Dev)*
Chris Becze *(Treas)*
Beth Klein *(Sec)*
Melanie Worley *(CEO)*
Tim Batz *(Pres)*

DEVELOPMENTAL RE-SOURCES CORPORATION
1130 US Hwy 202, Raritan, NJ
08869-1490
Tel.: (908) 707-8844   NJ
Web Site: http://www.drcweb.org
Year Founded: 1980
Sales Range: $10-24.9 Million
Emp.: 300
Educational & Religious Trusts
N.A.I.C.S.: 813211
John Komisor *(Dir-Facilities)*

DEVELOPMENTAL SERVICES OF NORTHWEST KANSAS, INC.
2703 Hall St Ste 10, Hays, KS 67601
Tel.: (785) 625-5678   KS
Web Site: http://www.dsnwk.org
Year Founded: 1967
Sales Range: $10-24.9 Million
Emp.: 694
Developmental Disability Assistance
Services
N.A.I.C.S.: 623210
Gerard L. Michaud *(Pres)*
Alice Goscha *(Treas & Sec)*
Galen Huffman *(Chm)*

DEVELOPMENTAL STUDIES CENTER
1250 53rd St Ste 3, Emeryville, CA
94608
Tel.: (510) 533-0213   CA
Web Site: http://www.devstu.org
Year Founded: 1975
Sales Range: $10-24.9 Million
Emp.: 130
Educational Support Services
N.A.I.C.S.: 611710
Kelly Stuart *(Dir-Dissemination)*
Nazar Yousif *(CTO)*
Lana Costantini *(Dir-Program Dev)*
Peter Brunn *(Dir-Strategic Partner-ships)*
Linda Davis *(Chm)*

DEVERE CONSTRUCTION COMPANY INC.
1030 DeVere Dr, Alpena, MI 49707
Tel.: (989) 356-4411
Web Site: http://www.devere.tv
Rev.: $111,800,000
Emp.: 100
Nonresidential Building Construction
N.A.I.C.S.: 236210
Richard L. Crittenden *(Pres)*
Cynthia Gabara *(Sec)*
Cheryl Lumsden *(Treas)*

DEVEREAUX MOTOR SALES INCORPORATED
230 Buffalo St, Freeport, PA 16229
Tel.: (724) 295-2171
Web Site:
http://www.devyautopark.com
Sales Range: $10-24.9 Million
Emp.: 25
Sales of New & Used Automobiles

N.A.I.C.S.: 441110
Philip S. Devereaux *(Pres)*
Carol Schall *(Office Mgr)*

DEVICEANYWHERE
1730 S Amphlett Blvd Ste 300, San
Mateo, CA 94402
Tel.: (650) 655-6400
Web Site:
http://www.deviceanywhere.com
Year Founded: 2003
Sales Range: $10-24.9 Million
Emp.: 160
Online Mobile Device Application
Software Tester
N.A.I.C.S.: 334220
Faraz A. Syed *(Co-Founder & CEO)*
David J. Marsyla *(Co-Founder & CTO)*
Christopher C. Callahan *(Sr VP-Global Sls & Mktg)*
Mark A. Dirsa *(VP-Fin & Admin)*
Rachel Obstler *(VP-Product Mgmt)*
Leila Modarres *(VP-Mktg)*
Mike McHale *(Mng Dir-Sls-EMEA)*
Robert Kleinschmidt *(VP-Engrg)*

DEVILLE INVESTMENT, INC.
1212 W Moore Ave, Terrell, TX 75160
Tel.: (972) 524-2663   TX
Year Founded: 1995
Sales Range: $1-9.9 Million
Emp.: 50
Automotive Financing
N.A.I.C.S.: 522291
Wylie Musser *(Pres)*

DEVILS HOLDINGS, LLC
Prudential Ctr 25 Lafayette St, New-ark, NJ 07102
Tel.: (973) 757-6000   DE
Year Founded: 2013
Holding Company; Professional
Hockey Team & Sports Arena Owner
& Operator
N.A.I.C.S.: 551112
Hugh Weber *(Pres)*
Joshua J. Harris *(Co-Owner)*
Scott M. O'Neil *(CEO)*
David S. Blitzer *(Co-Owner)*
Louis Lamoriello *(Pres-New Jersey Devils)*
Kerry Graue *(Mgr-PR)*
Brad Shron *(Gen Counsel & Exec VP)*
Gracie Mercado *(VP-HR)*
Adam Davis *(Exec VP-Corp Partner-ships)*
David Collins *(CFO & Exec VP)*
Subsidiaries:

Devils Arena Entertainment LLC   (1)
Prudential Ctr 25 Lafayette St, Newark, NJ
07102
Tel.: (973) 757-6000
Web Site: http://www.prucenter.com
Sports & Entertainment Arena Operator
N.A.I.C.S.: 711310
Hugh Weber *(Pres)*
Frank Perrone *(Dir-Events)*
Brian Gale *(VP-Booking)*
James Crann *(Dir-Security)*
Mark A. Gheduzzi *(Sr VP-Facility Mgmt & Strategic Plng)*
Adam Davis *(Chief Revenue Officer)*
Donna Daniels *(Sr VP-Bus Svcs)*
Adam Cross *(VP-Corp Partnerships)*
Fatima Saliu *(VP-Mktg Partnerships)*
Joyce Jelks *(VP-HR)*
Leonard Edwards *(Sr Dir-Corp Partner-ships)*
Brad Shron *(Gen Counsel & Exec VP)*
Dan Spiegel *(VP-Mktg)*
Starr Butler *(Dir-Special Events)*
Jason Gonella *(VP-Premium Partnerships)*
Michelle McCarthy *(Dir-Entertainment Mktg)*

New Jersey Devils LLC   (1)

Prudential Center 25 Lafayette St, Newark,
NJ 07102
Tel.: (973) 757-6100
Web Site: http://devils.nhl.com
Professional Hockey Franchise
N.A.I.C.S.: 711211
Hugh Weber *(Pres-New Jersey Devils & Prudential Center)*
Joshua J. Harris *(Chm & Mng Partner)*
Scott M. O'Neil *(CEO)*
Peter Albietz *(VP-Hockey Comm & Team Ops)*
Adam Davis *(Chief Revenue Officer)*
Ray Shero *(Exec VP & Gen Mgr)*
Tom Fitzgerald *(Asst Gen Mgr)*
Donna Daniels *(Sr VP-Bus Ops)*
Adam Cross *(Sr VP-Corp Partnerships)*
Leo Edwards *(Sr Dir-Corp Partnerships)*
David Blitzer *(Co-Mng Partner)*
Martin Brodeur *(Exec VP-Bus Dev)*
David Abrams *(Exec VP-Investment & Strat-egy)*
Chad Biggs *(Sr VP-Mktg Partnerships)*
Jillian Frechette *(Sr VP-Mktg)*
Gabe Harris *(VP-Strategy)*
Sasha Puric *(CTO)*
Jake Reynolds *(Chief Revenue Officer)*
Sean Saadeh *(Exec VP-Entertainment)*

DEVIN OIL CO. INC.
733 Riverside St, Heppner, OR
97836
Tel.: (541) 481-4876
Sales Range: $10-24.9 Million
Petroleum Bulk Stations
N.A.I.C.S.: 424710
Richard G. Devin *(Pres)*

DEVINE & PETERS INTER-MODAL
3870 Channel Dr, West Sacramento,
CA 95691
Tel.: (916) 371-4430
Web Site:
https://www.devineintermodal.com
Sales Range: $25-49.9 Million
Emp.: 60
Trucking, Rail & Ocean Logistics
N.A.I.C.S.: 484121
John F. Drewes *(CEO)*
Carl Dolk *(Controller)*
Dick Coyle *(Pres)*
Kathie Baker *(Mgr-Admin-Sacramento)*

DEVINE COMMUNICATIONS CORP.
9300 5th St N, Saint Petersburg, FL
33702
Tel.: (727) 573-2575
Web Site:
https://www.devineads.com
Year Founded: 1982
Sales Range: $1-9.9 Million
Emp.: 10
Advetising Agency
N.A.I.C.S.: 541810
Barry Devine *(Founder & Pres)*
Tim Devine *(VP-Acct Svcs)*
Jim Kenefick *(Dir-Creative)*
Debbie Devine *(Acct Mgr)*

DEVINE, MILLIMET & BRANCH PROFESSIONAL ASSOCIA-TION
111 Amherst St, Manchester, NH
03101
Tel.: (603) 669-1000
Web Site:
http://www.devinemillimet.com
Year Founded: 1947
Emp.: 53
Law firm
N.A.I.C.S.: 541110
Paul C. Remus *(Atty)*
David H. Barnes *(Atty)*
Anu R. Mullikin *(Atty)*
Robert C. Dewhirst *(Atty)*
Steven Cohen *(Atty)*

Kevin Baum *(Atty)*
Kristin Mendoza *(Atty)*
Linda M. Engstrand *(Dir-Fin)*
Charles Giacopelli *(Pres)*

DEVINEY CONSTRUCTION CO., INC.
PO Box 6717, Jackson, MS 39282-6717
Tel.: (601) 372-3121   MS
Web Site:
https://www.devineyconstruction.com
Year Founded: 1946
Sales Range: $200-249.9 Million
Emp.: 800
Telecommunication & Utility Services
N.A.I.C.S.: 237110
Richard Black *(Pres)*
Dana Deviney Lomax *(CFO)*
William C. Deviney Jr. *(CEO)*

DEVITA INTERNATIONAL, INC.
1616 W Williams Dr, Phoenix, AZ
85027
Web Site:
http://www.devitaskincare.com
Year Founded: 1998
Sales Range: $1-9.9 Million
Emp.: 15
Manufactures, Distributes, Markets &
Retails Aloe Vera Based All-Natural
Skin Care, Anti-Aging Products &
Color Cosmetics
N.A.I.C.S.: 456120
Cherylanne DeVita *(Pres & CEO)*

DEVITO GROUP
151 W 19th St 4th Fl, New York, NY
10011-5511
Tel.: (212) 924-7430
Web Site:
http://www.devitogroup.com
Year Founded: 1997
Sales Range: $10-24.9 Million
Emp.: 15
Advertising Agencies
N.A.I.C.S.: 541810
Frank Devito *(Pres & Partner)*
Chris DeVito *(Partner & Dir-Creative)*

DEVITO/VERDI
100 5th Ave 16th Fl, New York, NY
10011
Tel.: (212) 431-4694   NY
Web Site: http://www.devitoverdi.com
Year Founded: 1991
Rev.: $140,000,000
Emp.: 45
Full Service
N.A.I.C.S.: 541810
Ellis Verdi *(Pres)*
Sal DeVito *(Dir-Creative)*
Preeya Vyas *(Chief Strategy & Inno-vation Officer)*
Erin Boyer *(CMO)*

DEVMYND SOFTWARE INC.
2035 W Wabanasia Ave 2nd Fl, Chi-cago, IL 60647
Tel.: (773) 492-0209
Web Site: http://www.devmynd.com
Sales Range: $1-9.9 Million
Software Developer
N.A.I.C.S.: 513210
J. C. Grubbs *(CEO)*

DEVOE AUTOMOTIVE GROUP
1410-1411 Solana Rd, Naples, FL
34103
Tel.: (239) 649-1400
Web Site:
https://www.devoeauto.com
Dealer of Automobiles
N.A.I.C.S.: 441110
Chris Rozsas *(Gen Mgr)*
Bill Gresh *(CFO)*
Grant Brosseau *(Dir-IT)*

Larry Ward (Dir-HR)
Vincent Caltagirone (Mgr-Internet Sls)
Emily Reed (Dir-Social Media)

Subsidiaries:

Dick DeVoe Buick Cadillac (1)
4100 Tamiami Trl N, Naples, FL 34103
Tel.: (239) 261-1234
Web Site: http://www.devoecadillac.com
Sales Range: $200-249.9 Million
Emp.: 50
Automobile New & Used Distr
N.A.I.C.S.: 441110
Mark Klahm (Gen Mgr)
Tim Blaskovich (Mgr-Cadillac New Car Sls)
Tony Desimone (Mgr-Bus)
Pete Weidner (Mgr-Cadillac Pre-owned Sls)
Steve Whittaker (Mgr-Svc)

DEVON BANK

6445 N Western Ave, Chicago, IL 60645
Tel.: (773) 465-2500
Web Site: https://www.devonbank.com
Year Founded: 1945
Sales Range: $25-49.9 Million
Emp.: 100
State Commercial Banks
N.A.I.C.S.: 522110

DEVSOURCE TECHNOLOGY SOLUTIONS, LLC

310 S 4th St, Murray, KY 42071
Tel.: (270) 753-8708
Web Site: http://www.dev-source.com
Year Founded: 2001
Business Technology Services
N.A.I.C.S.: 513210
Mike Hopkins (CEO)
Trent Ballard (VP)

Subsidiaries:

Upright Technologies LLC (1)
803A Country Club Ln, Hopkinsville, KY 42240
Tel.: (270) 874-1560
Web Site: http://www.uprighttechnologies.com
Computer & Office Machine Repair & Maintenance
N.A.I.C.S.: 811210
Rambabu Vadapu (Owner)

DEWAYNE'S QUALITY METAL COATINGS, LLC.

205 N Industrial Dr, Lexington, TN 38351
Tel.: (731) 968-0763
Web Site: https://www.dqmc.net
Sales Range: $10-24.9 Million
Emp.: 150
Metal Coating, Engraving & Allied Services
N.A.I.C.S.: 332812
Mark Brown (Supvr-Shipping)
Mike Joyner (Gen Mgr)
Jim Terry (Pres)
Tommy Tyler (Controller)

DEWBERRY LLC

8401 Arlington Blvd, Fairfax, VA 22031-4666
Tel.: (703) 849-0100
Web Site: http://www.dewberry.com
Year Founded: 1956
Sales Range: $400-449.9 Million
Emp.: 1,840
Planning, Engineering, Architectural, Program Management, Surveying & Mapping Services
N.A.I.C.S.: 541330
Sidney O. Dewberry (Founder)
Barry K. Dewberry (Chm)
James Draheim (Mgr-Practice Area & Architect)
Rachel Vandenberg (Sr VP)

Amar Nayegandhi (Sr VP & Sr Project Mgr)
John Teeter (Mgr-Mechanical Dept-Raleigh)
David Maxwell (Mgr-Operating Unit-Southeast)
Gib Jones (Assoc VP)
Jeff Gangai (Assoc VP)
Cynthia Chen (CFO)
Catherine Bohn (Assoc VP)
Dan Southwick (Pres-Design Build Practice-Natl)
Mark Unterkofler (Assoc VP)
Jeremy Beck (Asst VP)
Christopher Simon (Assoc VP)
Dustin O'Brien (Principal)
Nicole Stalder (Assoc VP-Orlando)
Thomas Christensen (Assoc VP)
Steve Tarallo (Asst VP/Mgr-Water & Wastewater Practice-Baltimore)
Dave Huey (Pres-Architectural Practice)
Jean O'Toole (Mgr-Bus Unit)
David Mahoney (Mgr-Operating Unit)
Elese Adele Roger (CIO)
Steve Kuntz (Mgr-Transportation Bus Unit)
Phil Thiel (Exec VP)
Carol Holland (Assoc VP)
Christian Volz (Sr Project Mgr-Charlotte Area Water Practice)
Jerry Sparks (Sr VP)
Dave Francis (Chief Compliance & HR Officer)
Shannon Brewer (Assoc VP/Mgr-Dept-Atlanta)
Peter Garvey (VP/Mgr-Bus Unit-Boston)
Kate Gallagher (Assoc VP)
Siavosh Agahy (Assoc VP)
Elizabeth Scarce (Mktg Dir-Engrg Svcs-Natl)
Mark Safran (Assoc VP & Sr Mgr-Program)
Donald E. Stone Jr. (CEO)
Larry Melton Jr. (Vice Chm)

Subsidiaries:

Dewberry & Davis, Inc. (1)
8401 Arlington Blvd, Fairfax, VA 22031 (100%)
Tel.: (703) 849-0100
Web Site: http://www.dewberry.com
Sales Range: $25-49.9 Million
Emp.: 800
Architectural & Engineering Services
N.A.I.C.S.: 541330
Sidney O. Dewberry (Chm)
Thomas L. Dewberry (CEO)
Dave Francis (Dir-HR)
Mark H. Reiner (CFO)
Craig N. Thomas (Gen Counsel)
Henry J. Tyler (CIO)

Dewberry Technologies, Inc. (1)
8401 Arlington Blvd, Fairfax, VA 22031-4619 (100%)
Tel.: (703) 876-4760
Web Site: http://www.dewberry.com
Sales Range: $10-24.9 Million
Emp.: 12
Information Technology Solutions
N.A.I.C.S.: 561990

Dewberry-Goodkind, Inc. (1)
200 Broadacres Dr 4th Fl, Bloomfield, NJ 07003
Tel.: (973) 338-9100
Web Site: http://www.dewberry.com
Rev.: $12,000,000
Emp.: 100
Bridges, Roads, Transportation Facilities, Urban Infrastructures & Flood Control Designer & Inspector
N.A.I.C.S.: 541330
Tony Pecci (Branch Mgr)

PSA Dewberry (1)
1350 S Boulder Ave Ste 600, Tulsa, OK 74119-3203
Tel.: (918) 587-7283
Web Site: http://www.dewberrydesign.com
Rev.: $15,000,000

Emp.: 50
Engineers, Architects, Planners
N.A.I.C.S.: 541330

DEWEY COMMUNICATIONS, INC.

5411 Mt Normandale Dr, Bloomington, MN 55437-1011
Tel.: (952) 451-1488   MN
Web Site: http://www.deweycomm.com
Year Founded: 1976
Sales Range: $10-24.9 Million
Emp.: 2
Electronic Media, Engineering, High Technology, Industrial, Publicity/Promotions, Technical Advertising
N.A.I.C.S.: 541810
Thomas Dewey (Pres)

DEWEY CORPORATION

5500 Hwy 80 W, Jackson, MS 39209
Tel.: (601) 922-8331   MS
Web Site: http://www.millert.com
Year Founded: 1986
Sales Range: $150-199.9 Million
Emp.: 750
Common & Contract Carrier
N.A.I.C.S.: 484230
Lee Miller (Pres)
H. D. Miller Jr. (Treas & Sec)

Subsidiaries:

Miller Intermodal Logistics Services, Inc. (1)
5500 Hwy 80 W, Jackson, MS 39209-3507 (100%)
Tel.: (601) 922-8331
Web Site: http://www.mils3pl.com
Sales Range: $10-24.9 Million
Emp.: 100
Logistics & Transportation Management Services
N.A.I.C.S.: 541614
Steve Haskins (Pres)

Miller Transporters, Inc. (1)
5500 Hwy 80 W, Jackson, MS 39209-3507 (100%)
Tel.: (601) 922-8331
Web Site: http://www.millert.com
Sales Range: $10-24.9 Million
Emp.: 100
Freight Trucking Services
N.A.I.C.S.: 484230
Joe Hegi (VP-Fin)
Lee D. Miller (Pres)
Terry Malone (VP-HR & Insurance)
Larry Bagwell (VP-Ops)
Steven Tapscott (VP-Sls & Mktg)
Brent Cobb (VP-Safety & Quality)
David Bass V (VP-Ops)

DEWEY FORD INC.

3055 SE Delaware Ave, Ankeny, IA 50021
Tel.: (515) 518-6918
Web Site: https://www.deweyford.com
Sales Range: $50-74.9 Million
Emp.: 1,500
Car Dealership
N.A.I.C.S.: 441110
Thomas Duffy (Mgr-Collision Center)
Holly Bearden (CFO)
Teri Seanz (Gen Mgr)

DEWEY JORDAN INC.

6309 Monocacy Blvd, Frederick, MD 21701
Tel.: (301) 662-3389
Sales Range: $10-24.9 Million
Emp.: 45
Bridge Construction
N.A.I.C.S.: 237310
Kenneth Jordan (Pres)
Karen Mack (Office Mgr)

DEWEY SERVICES INCORPORATED

939 E Union St, Pasadena, CA 91106-1716
Tel.: (626) 568-9248
Web Site: https://www.deweypest.com
Sales Range: $10-24.9 Million
Emp.: 500
Pest Control Services
N.A.I.C.S.: 561710
Brock Dewey (VP)

DEWILS INDUSTRIES

11012 NE 4th Plain, Vancouver, WA 98662
Tel.: (360) 892-0300
Web Site: http://www.dewils.com
Year Founded: 1959
Sales Range: $25-49.9 Million
Emp.: 180
Mfr of Wood Kitchen Cabinets
N.A.I.C.S.: 337110
Tracy S. Wilson (Pres)

DEWITT HOSPITAL & NURSING HOME

1641 S Whitehead Dr, De Witt, AR 72042
Tel.: (870) 946-3571   AR
Web Site: http://www.dhnh.org
Year Founded: 2002
Sales Range: $10-24.9 Million
Emp.: 259
Health Care Srvices
N.A.I.C.S.: 622110
Darren Caldwell (CEO)

DEWITT ROSS & STEVENS S.C.

2 E Mifflin St Ste 600, Madison, WI 53703
Tel.: (608) 255-8891
Web Site: http://www.dewittross.com
Year Founded: 1903
Sales Range: $10-24.9 Million
Emp.: 130
Law firm
N.A.I.C.S.: 541110
Michelle Friedman (Dir-Mktg)
Keith Halleland (Chm-Health Care Practice Grp)
Christopher Scherer (Atty-Intellectual Property)
Shannon Allen (Atty)

Subsidiaries:

DeWitt Mackall Crounse & Moore S.C. (1)
1400 AT&T Tower 901 Marquette Ave, Minneapolis, MN 55402
Tel.: (612) 305-1400
Web Site: http://www.mcmlaw.com
Emp.: 29
Law firm
N.A.I.C.S.: 541110
Leslie H. Novak (Atty)
Denis E. Grande (Atty)
Robert W. Due (Atty)
Lawrence R. Commers (Atty)
Timothy D. Moratzka (Atty)
Al Christy (Atty)
Patrick Steinhoff (Atty)
William O'Brien (Atty)
Keith Halleland (Chm-Health Care Practice Grp)
Catherine Krisik (Atty-Family Law)
John Thomas (Atty)

Thomsen & Nybeck, P.A. (1)
3600 American Blvd W Ste 400, Bloomington, MN 55431
Tel.: (952) 835-7000
Web Site: http://www.dewittllp.com
Law firm
N.A.I.C.S.: 541110
Dennis Patrick (Atty)

DEWOLF CHEMICAL INC.

DeWolf Chemical Inc.—(Continued)

300 Jefferson Blvd, Warwick, RI
02888
Tel.: (401) 434-3515
Web Site:
https://www.dewolfchem.com
Year Founded: 1942
Sales Range: $25-49.9 Million
Emp.: 25
Supplier of Specialty Chemicals
N.A.I.C.S.: 424690
Steven Pettigrew *(VP-Sls)*
Michael Ayles *(CFO)*
Christopher Nork *(VP-Sls)*

**DEWOLFF, BOBERG & ASSO-
CIATES INC.**
12750 Merit Dr Ste 250, Dallas, TX
75251-1266
Tel.: (972) 233-5209   SC
Web Site:
http://www.dewolffboberg.com
Year Founded: 1987
Sales Range: $50-74.9 Million
Emp.: 230
Management Consulting Services
N.A.I.C.S.: 541611
Michael Owens *(Pres & CEO)*

DEWPOINT, INC.
300 S Washington Sq Ste 200, Lan-
sing, MI 48933
Tel.: (517) 316-2860
Web Site: https://www.dewpoint.com
Sales Range: $25-49.9 Million
Emp.: 150
Computer Integrated Systems Design
N.A.I.C.S.: 541512
Andy Kotarba *(Pres & CEO)*
Robert Piecuch *(Mgr-Agile Transfor-
mation)*
Brian Beeckman *(Engr-Sys)*
Renee Roth *(Dir-HR)*
Don Patterson *(Engr-Sys-Grand Rap-
ids)*
Brett Cagney *(Engr-Network-Grand
Rapids)*
Martin Clason *(Engr-Network-Grand
Rapids)*
Angela Doede *(Engr-Sys-Grand Rap-
ids)*
David Henshaw *(Engr-Network-Grand
Rapids)*
Kat Shroyer *(Engr-Sys-Grand Rapids)*
Carl Strickland *(Engr-Network-Grand
Rapids)*

DEXCLUSIVE
8362 Pines Blvd Ste 137, Pembroke
Pines, FL 33024
Tel.: (954) 862-3900
Web Site: http://www.dexclusive.com
Sales Range: $10-24.9 Million
Emp.: 9
Watch Retailer
N.A.I.C.S.: 458310
Danyl Herron *(Mgr-Affiliate Program)*

DEXIA CREDIT
445 Park Ave, New York, NY 10022
Tel.: (212) 515-7000
Web Site: http://www.dexia.com
Sales Range: $25-49.9 Million
Emp.: 200
Foreign Trade & International Banks
N.A.I.C.S.: 522299
Igor Balagulov *(Asst VP & Sr Engr-
Sys)*

**DEXTER APACHE HOLDINGS,
INC.**
2211 W Grimes Ave, Fairfield, IA
52556
Tel.: (641) 472-5131   IA

Web Site:
https://www.dexterapache.com
Year Founded: 1894
Sales Range: $75-99.9 Million
Emp.: 750
Commercial Laundry Machinery &
Equipment & Foundry Operations
N.A.I.C.S.: 333310
Patrick D. Albregts *(Pres)*
Frank D. Fritz *(Treas)*

Subsidiaries:

Crystal Group, Inc.   (1)
850 Kacena Rd, Hiawatha, IA 52233
Tel.: (319) 378-1636
Web Site: http://www.crystalrugged.com
Sales Range: $10-24.9 Million
Emp.: 120
System Integration & Rugged Server Mfr
N.A.I.C.S.: 541512
Scott Kongable *(Pres)*
Jim Shaw *(Exec VP-Engrg)*
Mike Kruger *(VP-Ops)*
Britni Gookin *(VP-Fin)*
Chad Hutchinson *(Sr Mgr-Engrg)*
Troy Jensen *(Mgr-Matls)*
Chris Cargin *(Dir-Technical)*
Chip Thurston *(Chief Architect & Dir-
Technical)*
David Chase *(Mgr-Mktg)*
Justin Pegump *(Mgr-Pur)*
Andrew Friend *(Dir-Technical)*
Bill Maly *(Dir-Technical)*
Micah Snodgrass *(Dir-Technical)*
Toni Hogan *(Dir-Program Mgmt)*
Allison Barnes *(Mgr-Sls Support)*
Christine Davis *(Mgr-Sls Support)*
Barb Jones *(Mgr-Sls Support)*
Todd Prouty *(Mgr-Bus Dev)*

Dexter Financial Services, Inc.   (1)
5001 J St Sw, Cedar Rapids, IA 52404-
4916
Tel.: (319) 363-3769
Web Site: http://www.dexterfinancial.com
Equipment Financing Services
N.A.I.C.S.: 522220
Jim Freeze *(Pres)*
Leo Frazier *(Dir-Portfolio Dev)*
Judy Burghart *(Coord-Sls)*

Dexter Laundry Inc.   (1)
2211 W Grimes Ave, Fairfield, IA 52556
Tel.: (641) 472-5131
Web Site: http://www.dexter.com
Drycleaning & Laundry Services
N.A.I.C.S.: 812320
Andrew Kretz *(Pres)*

Leer Inc.   (1)
206 Leer St, New Lisbon, WI 53950-1123
Tel.: (608) 562-3161
Web Site: http://www.leerinc.com
Sales Range: $25-49.9 Million
Emp.: 165
Ice Merchandising Machine Mfr
N.A.I.C.S.: 333415

DEXTER FIELD SERVICES
1844 IH 10 S Ste 202, Beaumont, TX
77707
Tel.: (409) 838-4800
Web Site: http://www.dexterfs.com
Year Founded: 2006
Sales Range: $1-9.9 Million
Emp.: 75
Environmental Air Sampling
N.A.I.C.S.: 541620
Brett Kriley *(CFO)*
Nicole Morrow *(Mgr-Client Svcs)*
Judah Fontenot *(Mgr-Client Svc)*

**DEYA ELEVATOR SERVICES,
INC.**
PO Box 364211, San Juan, PR
00936-2411
Tel.: (787) 268-8777
Web Site: http://www.deya.com
Year Founded: 1969
Sales Range: $10-24.9 Million
Emp.: 122
Building Equipment Installation Ser-
vices

N.A.I.C.S.: 238290
Jose Deya *(VP)*
Jose G. Deya Jr. *(VP)*

DEYTA LLC.
7400 New LaGrange Rd Ste 200,
Louisville, KY 40222
Tel.: (502) 896-8438
Web Site: http://www.deyta.com
Year Founded: 1993
Sales Range: $1-9.9 Million
Emp.: 63
Health Care Satisfaction Surveying
Services
N.A.I.C.S.: 541910
Sarah Balmer *(VP-Bus Dev)*
Steve Sablan *(VP-IT)*
Liz Silva *(Dir-Hospice)*
David Donenburg *(CFO)*
Jack Draughon *(Chief Dev Officer)*
Robin Finkelstein *(Dir-Implementation
& Consulting)*
Chip Carroll *(Dir-Sls)*
Gina Volpe *(Mgr-Clinical)*
Sue Zimmerman *(Product Mgr)*

DEZER PROPERTIES, INC.
89 5th Ave 11th Fl, New York, NY
10003
Tel.: (212) 929-1285
Web Site:
https://www.dezerproperties.com
Year Founded: 1996
Sales Range: $10-24.9 Million
Emp.: 15
Commercial Buildings Lessor & Man-
ager
N.A.I.C.S.: 531120
Richard Angel *(Dir-Property Mgmt)*
Trevor Matwey *(Mgr-Property)*
John Harvey *(Dir-Construction)*
George G. Schreiner *(Dir-Security &
Life Safety)*
Howard Dubs *(Legal Counsel)*
Michael Dezer *(Founder)*

DF RICHARD INC.
124 Broadway, Dover, NH 03820
Tel.: (603) 742-2020   NH
Web Site: https://www.dfrichard.com
Year Founded: 1930
Sales Range: $10-24.9 Million
Emp.: 40
Provider of Energy Systems
N.A.I.C.S.: 457210
Robert Richard *(Pres)*
Rick Racardo *(Gen Mgr)*

DF SHUMPERT OIL CO.
814 Pine St, Pelion, SC 29123
Tel.: (803) 894-3131
Sales Range: $10-24.9 Million
Emp.: 65
Petroleum Bulk Stations & Terminals
N.A.I.C.S.: 424710
Frank Shumpert *(Owner)*

**DFB PHARMACEUTICALS,
INC.**
3909 Hulen St, Fort Worth, TX 76107
Tel.: (817) 900-4050
Web Site: http://www.dfb.com
Sales Range: $125-149.9 Million
Emp.: 1,700
Licensing Opportunities & Outsourc-
ing Services to the Healthcare Indus-
try
N.A.I.C.S.: 325412
H. Paul Dorman *(Chm & CEO)*
Mark A. Mitchell *(Mng Dir & Chief
Legal Officer)*
Marc A. Iacobucci *(Mng Dir)*

Subsidiaries:

Phyton Biotech, Inc.   (1)

279 Princeton-Hightstown Rd, East Wind-
sor, NJ 08520-1401
Tel.: (604) 777-2340
Web Site: http://www.phytonbiotech.com
Rev.: $15,500,000
Emp.: 56
Pharmaceutical & Plant Cell Research
N.A.I.C.S.: 541715
Tim Cowan *(Sr Dir-Quality & Regulatory
Affairs)*
Gilbert Gorr *(Chief Scientific Officer)*
Kai Schutte *(Mng Dir)*
Michael Von Gonner *(Head-Quality Mgmt)*
Michael Woudenberg *(Mng Dir)*
Colin Marr *(Pres)*

Subsidiary (Non-US):

Phyton Biotech GmbH   (2)
Alter Postweg 1, D 22926, Ahrensburg,
Germany
Tel.: (49) 410249060
Web Site: http://www.phytonbiotech.com
Sales Range: $25-49.9 Million
Emp.: 50
Pharmaceutical & Plant Cell Research
N.A.I.C.S.: 541715

DFG CONFECTIONARY LLC.
60 Revere Dr Ste 750, Northbrook, IL
60062-1593
Tel.: (847) 412-1961
Sales Range: $25-49.9 Million
Emp.: 740
Frozen Food Product Mfr
N.A.I.C.S.: 311412
Phillip Gay *(COO)*

DFS FLOORING, INC.
15651 Saticoy St, Van Nuys, CA
91406-3234
Tel.: (818) 374-5200
Web Site:
https://www.dfsflooring.com
Sales Range: $10-24.9 Million
Emp.: 110
Floor Laying Services
N.A.I.C.S.: 238330
Catherine Bong *(Mgr)*
Brian Hydar *(Mgr-Ops)*

**DFT COMMUNICATIONS COR-
PORATION**
40 Temple St, Fredonia, NY 14063
Tel.: (716) 673-3031   DE
Web Site:
http://www.dftcommunications.com
Year Founded: 1898
Sales Range: $25-49.9 Million
Emp.: 100
Telecommunication Servicesb
N.A.I.C.S.: 517121
Mark R. Maytum *(Pres & COO)*
Dan Siracuse *(Dir-Mktg & PR)*

DFW CAMPER CORRAL INC.
808 E Division St, Arlington, TX
76011
Tel.: (817) 461-8663
Web Site:
http://www.truckaccessorystore.com
Sales Range: $10-24.9 Million
Emp.: 15
Campers (Pickup Coaches) For
Mounting On Trucks
N.A.I.C.S.: 423110
Ed Abbott *(Co-Founder)*
Mellisa Funk *(Sec)*
Kevin Moore *(Mgr-Store-Arlington)*
Charles Matocha *(Gen Mgr)*
Bob Abbott *(CFO)*

DFW CAPITAL PARTNERS
300 Frank W Burr Blvd Glenpointe
Centre East 5th Fl, Teaneck, NJ
07666
Tel.: (201) 836-6000
Web Site: http://www.dfwcapital.com
Private Equity Investment Firm
N.A.I.C.S.: 523999

Keith W. Pennell *(Mng Partner)*
Brett L. Prager *(Partner)*
Donald F. DeMuth *(Partner)*
Douglas H. Gilbert *(Partner)*
Brian C. Tilley *(Partner)*
Angela Nobre *(Controller)*
Cheri Lieberman *(CFO)*

Subsidiaries:

Restoration + Recovery Services,
LLC   **(1)**
2510 Meridian Pkwy Ste 350, Durham, NC
27713
Tel.: (855) 257-8328
Web Site: http://www.rrstormwater.com
Stormwater Management
N.A.I.C.S.: 562998
Richard Matero *(CEO)*

Subsidiary (Domestic):

DGC Environmental Services,
Inc.   **(2)**
853 S Kings Hwy, Fort Pierce, FL 34945
Tel.: (772) 467-9224
Web Site: http://www.dgcenvironmental.com
Stormwater Management
N.A.I.C.S.: 562998
Tripp Dunagan *(Mgr)*

Sev1Tech, LLC   **(1)**
12700 Black Forest Ln Ste 306, Wood-
bridge, VA 22192
Tel.: (703) 496-3776
Web Site: http://www.Sev1Tech.com
Sales Range: $1-9.9 Million
Emp.: 85
Management Consulting Services
N.A.I.C.S.: 541611
Martin Wright *(CIO & VP-Engrg)*
Joseph Montoya *(COO)*
Kristin Lohfeld *(CFO)*
Tara Berman *(VP-DHS Law Enforcement)*
Valerie Bryce Gauthier *(VP-US Coast
Guard Acct)*
Andy Cohen *(VP-Bus Dev)*
Lisa Anderson *(Chief HR Officer)*
Yogesh Khanna *(Chief Tech & Strategy Offi-
cer)*
Tim Hays *(VP-Health IT)*
William Zito *(VP-Mission Solutions Grp)*
Zhenia Klevitsky *(Chief Growth Officer)*
Hector Collazo *(CTO)*
Michael Fry *(Deputy CTO)*
Robert E. Lohfeld Jr. *(Founder & CEO)*

Subsidiary (Domestic):

Geocent, LLC   **(2)**
111 Veterans Memorial Blvd Ste 1600,
Metairie, LA 70005
Tel.: (504) 831-1900
Web Site: http://www.geocent.com
Sales Range: $10-24.9 Million
Emp.: 160
Information Technology Services
N.A.I.C.S.: 541512
Robert A. Savoie *(CEO)*
Rick Gremillion *(Pres & COO)*
Jeff Tomeny *(CFO & Exec VP)*
Keith Alphonso *(CTO & VP)*
Torrie Hebert *(Dir-Ops-Federal Bus Unit)*
Brett Camet *(VP-Bus Dev)*
Wayne Eldridge Bourgeois *(VP-Enterprise
Tech Solutions)*
Cooper Jumonville *(Coord-Mktg)*
Dax Thibodeaux *(Sr Engr-Software)*
Patrick Scheuermann *(Chief Strategy Offi-
cer & Exec VP)*

DFW MOVERS & ERECTORS INC.
3201 N Sylvania Ave Ste 115, Fort
Worth, TX 76111
Tel.: (817) 222-3200
Web Site:
   https://www.dfwmovers.com
Year Founded: 1980
Sales Range: $10-24.9 Million
Emp.: 81
Building Equipment Installation Ser-
vices
N.A.I.C.S.: 238290
Joanne Ingle *(CEO)*

DG FOODS, LLC
1449 E Goodrich Ln, Milwaukee, WI
53217-2950
Tel.: (414) 351-2221   **WI**
Year Founded: 1956
Sales Range: $25-49.9 Million
Emp.: 120
Holding Company for Manufacturers
of Specialty Food Products
N.A.I.C.S.: 311941

Subsidiaries:

J.L. DeGraffenreid & Sons, Inc.   **(1)**
2848 N Lecompte Rd, Springfield, MO
65803   **(100%)**
Tel.: (417) 862-9411
Web Site: http://www.jldpickle.com
Sales Range: $25-49.9 Million
Emp.: 100
Mfr of Pickles & Relishes for Food Service
Industries
N.A.I.C.S.: 311421

DG TECHNOLOGY CONSULT-ING, LLC
3317 Jean Cir, Tampa, FL 33629
Tel.: (813) 258-0488
Web Site: http://www.dgtechllc.com
Sales Range: $1-9.9 Million
Technology Consulting Services
N.A.I.C.S.: 541690
Deborah Gannaway *(Pres & CEO)*

DGB LUGGAGE & LEATHER LLC
4340 Almaden Expy Ste 100, San
Jose, CA 95118
Tel.: (408) 266-5398
Year Founded: 1927
Sales Range: $25-49.9 Million
Emp.: 175
Online Luggage, Business Cases &
Travel Accessories Retailer
N.A.I.C.S.: 458320

DGMB CASINO, LLC
1133 Boardwalk, Atlantic City, NJ
08401
Tel.: (800) 772-9000
Web Site: http://www.resortsac.com
Year Founded: 1978
Resorts, Casino & Hotels
N.A.I.C.S.: 721120
Mark Giannantonio *(Pres & CEO)*

DGT ASSOCIATES, INC.
803 Summer St 1st Fl, Boston, MA
02127
Tel.: (617) 275-0541   **MA**
Web Site:
   http://www.dgtassociates.com
Surveying & Engineering Services
N.A.I.C.S.: 541370
Bassam Sam Taleb *(Mgr-Survey)*
Michael A. Clifford *(Co-Founder &
Principal)*

DGWB
217 N Main St Ste 200, Santa Ana,
CA 92701
Tel.: (714) 881-2300
Web Site: http://www.dgwb.com
Year Founded: 1988
Rev.: $88,000,000
Emp.: 60
Business-To-Business, Consumer
Marketing, Food Service
N.A.I.C.S.: 541810
Michael Weisman *(Co-Founder)*
Mandi Dossin *(Co-Founder)*
Jon Gothold *(Partner & Exec Dir-
Creative)*
Cathy Sosa *(Dir-Media)*
Mark Weinfeld *(Dir-Strategic Plng)*

DH REALTY PARTNERS INC.
801 N Saint Mary's, San Antonio, TX
78205-1325
Tel.: (210) 222-2424
Web Site: https://dhrp.us
Year Founded: 1965
Commercial Real Estate Manage-
ment & Brokerage Company
N.A.I.C.S.: 531210
Steves Rosser *(Sr VP)*
Michael D. Hoover *(CEO)*
John Cannon *(Pres)*
Charles L. Jeffers *(Sr VP)*
Terri Rubiola *(Sr VP)*
Darrell Keller *(VP)*
Gilles Ghez *(Sr VP)*
Matthew Baylor *(VP)*
Clint Hennessey *(VP)*
Trish Hoover *(Sec)*
Jaymes Sagistano *(Office Mgr)*
Angela Lincoln *(Controller)*
Elie Young *(Dir-Mktg)*

DHALIWAL LABS
11910 Shiloh Rd Ste 130, Dallas, TX
75228
Tel.: (214) 446-5862
Web Site:
   http://www.dhaliwallabs.com
Year Founded: 2008
Sales Range: $1-9.9 Million
Emp.: 49
Personal Care Product Laboratory
Testing Services
N.A.I.C.S.: 541380
Nancy Juarez *(Mgr)*
Tehsel Dhaliwal *(Owner)*
Jackie Wade *(Dir-Ops)*

DHC SUPPLIES INC.
3790 Omec Cir, Rancho Cordova, CA
95742
Tel.: (916) 383-2024
Web Site:
   http://www.dhcsupplies.com
Sales Range: $1-9.9 Million
Emp.: 50
General Construction Machinery &
Equipment
N.A.I.C.S.: 423810
Donald G. Smith Jr. *(Pres)*

DHCU COMMUNITY CREDIT UNION
PO Box 1550, Moline, IL 61265
Tel.: (309) 796-7500   **IL**
Web Site: http://www.dhcu.org
Year Founded: 1935
Sales Range: $10-24.9 Million
Emp.: 161
Credit Union
N.A.I.C.S.: 522130
Jay England *(CFO & Exec VP)*
Denise Carothers *(VP-HR)*
Cheryl Frame *(VP-Mktg &
E-Commerce)*
Matthew McCombs *(Pres & COO)*
Kevin Pieper *(Chief Risk Officer &
Exec VP)*

DHI ACQUISITION CORP.
5205 W Donges Bay Rd, Mequon, WI
53092
Tel.: (262) 242-5205   **WI**
Web Site:
   http://www.todaysdesignhouse.com
Year Founded: 1872
Sales Range: $125-149.9 Million
Emp.: 190
Lighting & Fans Distr
N.A.I.C.S.: 423220
Todd Witte *(Pres & CEO)*

DHI COMPUTING SERVICE IN-CORPORATED
1525 W 820 N, Provo, UT 84601
Tel.: (801) 373-8518

Web Site: http://www.dhiprovo.com
Year Founded: 1954
Sales Range: $10-24.9 Million
Emp.: 300
Computer Integrated Systems Design
N.A.I.C.S.: 541512
B. Lynn Crandall *(Pres)*
Brent Shuldberg *(Exec VP)*
Dirk Jolley *(Acct Mgr)*
Anna Silveira *(Acct Mgr)*
Leslie Brost *(Acct Mgr)*
Steven Smith *(VP-Svcs)*

DHR INTERNATIONAL, INC.
71 S Wacker Dr Ste 2700, Chicago,
IL 60606
Tel.: (312) 782-1581   **DE**
Web Site:
   http://www.dhrinternational.com
Executive Search & Consulting Ser-
vices
N.A.I.C.S.: 561312
Geoffrey Hoffmann *(CEO)*
Douglas Black *(CFO)*
Lauren Finch *(Dir-Mktg & PR-Global)*
Ken Takai *(Partner-Consumer & Re-
tail Practice)*
Jayme Willie *(Dir-Strategic Accts)*
David Hoffmann *(Chm)*
Vince Saunders *(Co-Mng Partner-
Real Estate)*
Martin Nass *(Vice Chm & Co-
Managing Partner-Real Estate)*
Christine Greybe *(Pres-Advisory)*
Rob Tillman *(Mng Partner-Fin Officer
Practice-Global)*

Subsidiaries:

DHR International, Inc. -
Milwaukee   **(1)**
1200 N Mayfair Rd Ste 307, Milwaukee, WI
53226
Tel.: (414) 456-0850
Web Site: http://www.dhrinternational.com
Executive Search & Consulting Services
N.A.I.C.S.: 561312
Dennis Hood *(Exec VP & Mng Dir)*

DHR International, Inc. - New
York   **(1)**
280 Park Ave 43rd Fl, New York, NY 10017
Tel.: (212) 883-6800
Web Site: http://www.dhrinternational.com
Executive Search & Consulting Services
N.A.I.C.S.: 561312
James DiFilippo *(Partner)*
Mike Magsig *(CEO)*
Olivia Quatrone *(Partner)*
Lawrence R. Noble *(Partner)*
David Madden *(Partner)*
Louis M. Hipp III *(Partner)*

DHX INCORPORATED
19201 S Susana Rd, Rancho
Dominguez, CA 90221
Tel.: (310) 537-2000
Web Site: http://www.dhx.com
Rev.: $52,000,000
Emp.: 127
Freight Forwarding
N.A.I.C.S.: 488510
Ronald Massman *(Owner & Chm)*
Cammie Laster *(VP-Corp Trng)*

DI CANIO ORGANIZATION INC.
720 Smithtown Byp, Smithtown, NY
11787
Tel.: (631) 366-4000
Web Site:
   https://www.dicaniobuilders.com
Rev.: $10,000,000
Emp.: 5
Single-Family Housing Construction
N.A.I.C.S.: 236115
Vincent Dicanio *(Pres)*

Subsidiaries:

Di Canio Residential Communities
Inc   **(1)**

Di Canio Organization Inc.—(Continued)

720 Smithtown Byp Ste A, Smithtown, NY 11787
Tel.: (631) 366-4000
Web Site: http://www.dicaniobuilders.com
Rev.: $120,000
Single-Family Housing Construction
N.A.I.C.S.: 236115

DI CARLO DISTRIBUTORS INC.
1630 N Ocean Ave, Holtsville, NY 11742
Tel.: (631) 758-6000
Web Site:
　https://www.dicarlofood.com
Year Founded: 1963
Sales Range: $25-49.9 Million
Emp.: 200
Distr of Packaged Frozen Goods
N.A.I.C.S.: 424420
Vincent Di Carlo (Pres)
Bill Schlageter (Dir-Mgmt Info Sys)
Joanne Hitchcock (Coord-Safety & Trng)

DIABETES RESEARCH & WELLNESS FOUNDATION
1832 Connecticut Ave NW Ste 420, Washington, DC 20009
Tel.: (202) 298-9211
Web Site:
　http://www.diabeteswellness.net
Year Founded: 1993
Sales Range: $10-24.9 Million
Emp.: 7
Diabetic Research Services
N.A.I.C.S.: 813212
Valerie Jeremiah (Coord-Program)
Andrea G. Stancik (Exec Dir)

DIABETICSUPPLIES.COM, INC.
2210 W Main St Ste 107, Battle Ground, WA 98604
Tel.: (360) 723-9001
Web Site:
　http://www.diabeticsupplies.com
Sales Range: $1-9.9 Million
Emp.: 8
Diabetic Supplies Online Retailer
N.A.I.C.S.: 456199
Pam Luna (Pres & CEO)

DIABLO FOODS
3615 Mt Diablo Blvd, Lafayette, CA 94549
Tel.: (925) 283-0737
Web Site: https://diablofoods.com
Sales Range: $10-24.9 Million
Emp.: 85
Owner & Operator of Grocery Stores
N.A.I.C.S.: 445110

DIABLO MEDIA LLC
2641 Walnut St, Denver, CO 80205
Tel.: (303) 305-4052
Web Site:
　http://www.diablomedia.com
Year Founded: 2006
Sales Range: $10-24.9 Million
Emp.: 21
Advertising Agency Services
N.A.I.C.S.: 541810
Ben Smith (CEO)
Mike Schuster (CFO)
Justin Cline (Dir-Art)
Rochelle Emerson (Dir-Bus Dev)
Aaron Peterson (VP-Sls)
Alyssa Dickerson (Acct Exec)
Gordon Riegel (Dir-Adv)
Rachel Escobar (Dir-Bus Dev)
Ashley Farr (VP-Affiliate Rels)

DIABLO SUBARU

2646 N Main St, Walnut Creek, CA 94597
Tel.: (925) 937-6900
Web Site:
　https://www.diablosubaru.com
Sales Range: $25-49.9 Million
Emp.: 36
New Car Retailer
N.A.I.C.S.: 441110
Scott McAllister (Gen Mgr)
Jim Thomas (Mgr-Sls)
Gino Genrikh (Mgr-Internet Sls)

DIAGNOSTIC CLINIC MED GROUP
1301 2nd Ave SW, Largo, FL 33770
Tel.: (727) 581-8767
Web Site: http://www.dc-fl.com
Sales Range: $25-49.9 Million
Emp.: 500
Medical Group
N.A.I.C.S.: 531120
H. Charlie Campbell (CEO)
Ed Buyers (Dir-IT)

DIAGNOSTIC CONSULTING NETWORK, INC.
6354 Corte Del Abeto Ste B, Carlsbad, CA 92011-1555
Tel.: (760) 804-3886
Web Site: http://www.dcndx.com
Emp.: 100
Chemicals Mfr
N.A.I.C.S.: 325413
Brendan O'Farrell (Co-Founder & Pres)

Subsidiaries:

BioMed Diagnostics, Inc.　　　　(1)
1388 Antelope Road, White City, OR 97503
Tel.: (541) 830-3000
Web Site:
　http://www.biomeddiagnostics.com
Rev.: $3,370,346
Emp.: 100
Surgical & Medical Instrument Mfr
N.A.I.C.S.: 339112
Robert Hall (Chm)

DIAGNOSTICS & DESIGNS INC.
16840 Edwards Rd, Cerritos, CA 90703-2418
Tel.: (562) 926-7373
Web Site: http://www.trihaircare.com
Year Founded: 1972
Sales Range: $10-24.9 Million
Emp.: 20
Hair Preparations
N.A.I.C.S.: 424210
Joe Oliveri (CEO & Founder)

DIAL COMPANIES CORPORATION
11506 Nicholas St Ste 200, Omaha, NE 68154
Tel.: (402) 493-2800
Web Site:
　http://www.dialcompanies.com
Property Operation, Retail Establishment, Management In Commercial Property
N.A.I.C.S.: 531120
Bob Furley (CFO & Controller)

Subsidiaries:

Dial Equities Inc.　　　　(1)
10703 J St Ste 103, Omaha, NE 68127
Tel.: (402) 392-1200
Web Site: http://www.dialequities.com
Rev.: $1,459,947
Emp.: 135
Real Estate Brokers & Agents
N.A.I.C.S.: 531110
Daniel Clantanoff (CEO)

Dial Realty Corp　　　　(1)
11506 Nicholas St Ste 100, Omaha, NE 68154

Tel.: (402) 493-2800
Real Estate Investment Services
N.A.I.C.S.: 531210
Christopher Held (Partner)
Lisa Naylon (VP)
Robert Welstead (Pres)

DIAL INDUSTRIES INCORPORATED
25 S 51st Ave, Phoenix, AZ 85043
Tel.: (602) 278-1100
Web Site: http://www.dialmfg.com
Sales Range: $10-24.9 Million
Emp.: 100
Air Conditioning & Ventilation & Duct Work Contractor
N.A.I.C.S.: 423730
Duane K. Johnston (Pres)

Subsidiaries:

Dial Manufacturing Inc.　　　　(1)
25 S 51st Ave, Phoenix, AZ 85043
Tel.: (602) 278-1100
Web Site: http://www.dialmfg.com
Designer & Mfr of Replacement Parts for Evaporative Coolers
N.A.I.C.S.: 423730

DIAL TEMPORARY HELP SERVICE
12540 SW 69th Ave, Tigard, OR 97223
Tel.: (503) 639-1400
Web Site:
　http://www.employersoverload.com
Year Founded: 1947
Sales Range: $10-24.9 Million
Emp.: 35
Temporary Help Service
N.A.I.C.S.: 561320
Pete J. Szambelan (Chm & CEO)
Thomas P. Szambelan (Pres)

DIAL800
9911 Pico Blvd Ste 1200, Los Angeles, CA 90035
Web Site: http://www.dial800.com
Year Founded: 1996
Sales Range: $1-9.9 Million
Emp.: 25
Marketing Optimization Tools, Including Phone Call Tracking Software, Toll Free Numbers & Call Routing
N.A.I.C.S.: 517810
Scott Richards (Chm)
James Diorio (CEO)
Chris Lowe (Dir-Telecom & Tech)
Eddie Treizman (Dir-Ops)
Barry Ross (Dir-Bus Dev)
Gordon Cowie (Dir-Application Dev)
Jennifer Powell (Dir-Mktg)
Laurence DeMers (CFO)
Megan Andersen (Mgr-Digital Mktg)
Tim Wald (COO)

DIALOGUE MARKETING, INC.
300 E Big Beaver Rd 4th Fl, Troy, MI 48083
Tel.: (248) 836-2600
Web Site: http://www.dialogue-marketing.com
Year Founded: 1977
Sales Range: $25-49.9 Million
Emp.: 1,073
Business Process Outsourcing Services
N.A.I.C.S.: 561499
Peter Schmitt (CEO)

DIALOGUE SYSTEM INC.
Ste 202 313 Speen St, Natick, MA 01760-1538
Tel.: (212) 475-8377
Rev.: $13,900,000
Emp.: 80
Books, Publishing Only
N.A.I.C.S.: 513130

DIALYSIS CLINIC, INC.
1633 Church St Ste 500, Nashville, TN 37203
Tel.: (615) 327-3061
Web Site: https://www.dciinc.org
Year Founded: 1971
Sales Range: $550-599.9 Million
Renal Dialysis Services
N.A.I.C.S.: 621492
William E. Wood (Treas)
James E. Attrill (Pres)

DIAMANTE FILMS
13095 San Fernando Rd, Sylmar, CA 91342
Tel.: (818) 362-2264
Web Site:
　http://www.diamantefilms.com
Year Founded: 2000
Sales Range: $1-9.9 Million
Emp.: 15
Motion Picture & Video Production
N.A.I.C.S.: 512110
Blanca Ramos (Principal)

DIAMOND B CONSTRUCTION CO., LLC
2090 Industrial Park Rd, Alexandria, LA 71303
Tel.: (318) 443-5686
Web Site: https://www.diamondb.com
Rev.: $19,100,000
Emp.: 400
General Contractor, Highway & Street Construction
N.A.I.C.S.: 237310
Greg Cox (Reg Mgr)

DIAMOND BRAND CANVAS PRODUCTS CO., INC.
145 Cane Creek Industrial Park Rd Ste 100, Fletcher, NC 28732
Tel.: (828) 209-0322
Web Site:
　http://www.diamondbrand.com
Year Founded: 1881
Sales Range: $75-99.9 Million
Emp.: 100
Tents & Backpacks Whlsr
N.A.I.C.S.: 314910
William Gay (Pres & Owner)

DIAMOND BRANDS INCORPORATED
1800 Cloquet Ave, Cloquet, MN 55720
Tel.: (218) 879-6700
Year Founded: 1881
Sales Range: $100-124.9 Million
Emp.: 680
Wood Products Mfr
N.A.I.C.S.: 321999
Naresh K. Nakra (CEO)
Thomas W. Knuesel (CFO)
Peter R. Lynn (CIO)
Scott Strudwick (Mgr-Mgmt Info Sys-Network Sys)
Robert Manfredonia (Founder)

DIAMOND CASTLE HOLDINGS, LLC
366 Madison Ave 4th Fl, New York, NY 10017
Tel.: (212) 300-1900
Web Site: http://www.dchold.com
Year Founded: 1985
Sales Range: $25-49.9 Million
Emp.: 10
Privater Equity Firm
N.A.I.C.S.: 523999
Ari J. Benacerraf (Sr Mng Dir)
Michael W. Ranger (Sr Mng Dir)

DIAMOND CHEMICAL CO., INC.

Union Ave & DuBois St, East Ruther-
ford, NJ 07073
Tel.: (201) 935-4300   NJ
Web Site:
   https://www.diamondchem.com
Year Founded: 1930
Sales Range: $25-49.9 Million
Emp.: 300
Chemical Specialty Detergent &
Cleaning Products Mfr & Whslr
N.A.I.C.S.: 325611
Harold Diamond *(Pres)*

Subsidiaries:

Spectrum Services   (1)
Union Ave & DuBois St, East Rutherford,
NJ 07073
Tel.: (201) 935-4300
Web Site: http://www.diamondchem.com
Sales Range: $25-49.9 Million
Emp.: 100
Chemical Specialty Products & Equipment
Distr
N.A.I.C.S.: 423440
Harold Diamond *(Pres)*

Starco Chemical   (1)
Union Ave & DuBois St, East Rutherford,
NJ 07073
Tel.: (201) 935-4300
Web Site: http://www.diamondchem.com
Sales Range: $25-49.9 Million
Emp.: 200
Specialty Chemical Detergents & Cleaning
Products Mfr
N.A.I.C.S.: 325611
Harold Diamond *(Pres)*
Barbara Riehle *(Mgr-Midwest)*

**DIAMOND COACH CORPORA-
TION**
2300 W 4th St, Oswego, KS 67356
Tel.: (620) 795-2191
Web Site:
   https://www.diamondcoach.com
Sales Range: $10-24.9 Million
Emp.: 50
Mid Size Busses
N.A.I.C.S.: 336120

**DIAMOND COMIC DISTRIBU-
TORS, INC.**
150 York Rd Ste 300, Cockeysville,
MD 21030
Tel.: (410) 560-7100   MD
Web Site:
   http://www.diamondcomics.com
Year Founded: 1982
Sales Range: $200-249.9 Million
Emp.: 540
Comic Books & Related Products
Distr
N.A.I.C.S.: 424920
Steve Geppi *(Founder, Pres & CEO)*
Cindy Anderson *(Mgr-Mktg Produc-
tion)*
Tim Lenaghan *(VP-Pur)*

**DIAMOND DETECTIVE
AGENCY INC.**
1651 S Halsted St, Chicago Heights,
IL 60411
Tel.: (708) 754-9884
Rev.: $12,469,738
Emp.: 350
Detective Agency
N.A.I.C.S.: 561611
James P. Vock *(CFO)*
Christopher D. Adzia *(VP-HR)*
John J. Jordan Sr. *(Founder)*

DIAMOND DRUGS, INC.
645 Kolter Dr, Indiana, PA 15701-
3570
Tel.: (724) 349-1111
Web Site:
   https://www.diamondpharmacy.com
Year Founded: 1979
Sales Range: $200-249.9 Million

Emp.: 775
Pharmaceutical Services to Prisons
N.A.I.C.S.: 456110
Joan R. Zilner *(Owner & Pres)*
Mark J. Zilner *(Owner & COO)*
Louann C. Bowser *(CFO)*
Gilbert Zilner *(Owner & VP)*

**DIAMOND ENGINEERING
COMPANY**
1521 W Anna St, Grand Island, NE
68802
Tel.: (308) 382-8362
Web Site:
   https://www.diamondeng.com
Sales Range: $50-74.9 Million
Emp.: 130
Telephone & Communication Line
Construction
N.A.I.C.S.: 237130
Douglas Sass *(Treas & Sec)*
James L. Harder *(Pres)*

DIAMOND EQUIPMENT INC.
1060 E Diamond Ave, Evansville, IN
47711-3902
Tel.: (812) 425-4428   IN
Web Site:
   https://www.diamondequipment.com
Year Founded: 1969
Sales Range: $10-24.9 Million
Emp.: 57
Provider of Construction & Mining
Machinery Services
N.A.I.C.S.: 423810
Dave Clement *(Co-Pres)*
Stan Henyon *(CFO)*

**DIAMOND FOOD MARKETS
INC.**
150 Industrial Ave, Azle, TX 76020-
2955
Tel.: (817) 444-5525   TX
Web Site:
   http://www.diamondfood.com
Year Founded: 1959
Sales Range: $50-74.9 Million
Emp.: 11
Grocery Stores
N.A.I.C.S.: 445110
Lisa Geer *(Pres)*
Edmond Geer *(VP)*

**DIAMOND FRUIT GROWERS
INC.**
3515 Chevron Dr, Hood River, OR
97041
Tel.: (541) 354-5300   OR
Web Site:
   https://www.diamondfruit.com
Year Founded: 1913
Sales Range: $25-49.9 Million
Emp.: 100
Crop Preparation Services for Market
N.A.I.C.S.: 115114
Ronald K. Girardelli *(Pres)*
David Garcia *(VP-Fin)*
Wes Bailey *(Coord-Pur)*

DIAMOND FURNITURE INC.
3400 Kensington Ave, Philadelphia,
PA 19134
Tel.: (215) 423-8020   PA
Web Site:
   https://www.diamondfurniture.com
Year Founded: 1927
Sales Range: $25-49.9 Million
Emp.: 35
Home Furnishing Sales
N.A.I.C.S.: 449110
Jerry Robinson *(Dir-Ops)*
Bev Gatti *(VP)*

DIAMOND GROUP INC.
11424 Pulaski Hwy, White Marsh, MD
21162

Tel.: (410) 335-4000
Rev.: $14,116,146
Emp.: 28
Trucking Except Local
N.A.I.C.S.: 484121
Robert W. Muir Jr. *(Partner)*

Subsidiaries:

H & K Equipment Company Inc.   (1)
4200 Casteel Dr, Coraopolis, PA 15108
Tel.: (412) 490-5300
Web Site: http://www.hkequipment.com
Rev.: $2,900,000
Emp.: 21
Truck Leasing, Without Drivers
N.A.I.C.S.: 532120

**DIAMOND HONDA OF GLEN-
DALE**
138 S Glendale Ave, Glendale, CA
91205
Tel.: (818) 244-8674
Web Site:
   http://www.diamondhondaof
   glendale.com
Year Founded: 1953
Sales Range: $25-49.9 Million
Emp.: 80
Car Dealership Owner & Operator
N.A.I.C.S.: 441110
Philip Keung *(Gen Mgr)*
Paul Pituch *(Gen Mgr-Sls)*
Patty Alonzo *(Office Mgr)*

DIAMOND LANE, INC.
2501 E Aragon Blvd Ste 1, Sunrise,
FL 33313
Tel.: (954) 800-5825   FL
Year Founded: 2013
Real Time Weather & Traffic Informa-
tion Software for Mobile Devices
N.A.I.C.S.: 513210
Dronix Suarez *(Pres, CEO, CFO,
Treas & Sec)*

**DIAMOND MANUFACTURING
COMPANY**
243 W 8th St, Wyoming, PA 18644
Tel.: (570) 693-0300
Web Site:
   https://www.diamondman.com
Rev.: $56,000,000
Emp.: 200
Perforated Metal, Stamped
N.A.I.C.S.: 332119
David Simpson *(Pres)*
Keith Zinn *(CFO)*

DIAMOND MIND INC.
10220 River Rd Ste 306, Potomac,
MD 20854
Tel.: (240) 898-1817
Web Site:
   http://www.diamondmindinc.com
Year Founded: 2004
Sales Range: $1-9.9 Million
Emp.: 7
Electronic Payment Services
N.A.I.C.S.: 525990
Katherine Novikov *(Founder & CEO)*
Vladimir Novikov *(Pres, CFO & COO)*

DIAMOND NATION, LLC
129 River Rd, Flemington, NJ 08822
Tel.: (908) 284-1778
Web Site:
   http://www.diamondnation.com
Emp.: 100
Sporting & Recreational Goods &
Supplies Merchant Whslr
N.A.I.C.S.: 423910
Nick Massari *(Asst Gen Mgr)*

**DIAMOND P ENTERPRISES,
INC.**
2800 Morris Sheppard Dr, Brownwood, TX 76801

Tel.: (325) 643-5629
Web Site:
   http://www.diamondpenterprises.com
Year Founded: 1995
Sales Range: $50-74.9 Million
Emp.: 46
Electrical Contractor
N.A.I.C.S.: 238210
Domingo Perez *(Owner & Pres)*
Tim Goodwin *(Mgr-Logistics)*

**DIAMOND PAPER BOX COM-
PANY**
111 Commerce Dr, Rochester, NY
14623
Tel.: (585) 334-8030
Web Site:
   http://www.diamondpkg.com
Year Founded: 1911
Sales Range: $25-49.9 Million
Emp.: 250
Folding Paperboard Boxes
N.A.I.C.S.: 322212
Kalla Vichter *(Owner)*

**DIAMOND PARKING SER-
VICES LLC**
605 1st Ave Ste 600, Seattle, WA
98104-1099
Tel.: (206) 284-3100
Web Site:
   http://www.diamondparking.com
Year Founded: 1922
Sales Range: $75-99.9 Million
Emp.: 1,000
Automobile Parking Facilities Opera-
tor
N.A.I.C.S.: 812930
Jonathon Diamond *(Pres)*
Robert Turley *(CFO)*
Dan Geiger *(Reg VP)*
Mike Poirier *(VP-Ops-British Colum-
bia)*
Jeff Sandborn *(VP-Real Estate-
Hawaii)*
Dave Watson *(Sr VP-Ops)*
Greg Matous *(Controller)*
Joel Diamond *(Chm & CEO)*

Subsidiaries:

Automated Equipment Company
Inc.   (1)
10847 E Marginal Way S, Seattle, WA
98168-1931
Tel.: (206) 767-9080
Web Site: http://www.aegates.com
Sales Range: $10-24.9 Million
Emp.: 20
Gates & Access Control
N.A.I.C.S.: 332323
Brian Thorp *(Gen Mgr)*

Diamond Parking Inc.   (1)
3151 Elliott Ave Ste 100, Seattle, WA
98121-1152
Tel.: (206) 284-6303
Web Site: http://www.diamondparking.com
Sales Range: $10-24.9 Million
Emp.: 5
Concrete Contracting Services
N.A.I.C.S.: 812930
Joel Diamond *(Pres)*

**DIAMOND PLASTICS CORPO-
RATION**
1212 Johnstown Rd, Grand Island,
NE 68803-5011
Tel.: (308) 384-4400   NE
Web Site: https://www.dpcpipe.com
Year Founded: 1984
Rev.: $136,000,000
Emp.: 80
Plastics Pipe Mfr
N.A.I.C.S.: 326122
Dennis Bauer *(VP-Sls & Mktg)*

DIAMOND PUBLIC RELATIONS
4770 Biscayne Blvd Ste 503, Miami,
FL 33137

Diamond Public Relations—(Continued)

Tel.: (305) 854-3544
Web Site:
    https://www.diamondpr.com
Year Founded: 2007
Sales Range: Less than $1 Million
Emp.: 15
Public Relations
N.A.I.C.S.: 541820
Jody Diamond *(Pres)*
Kara Rosner *(VP)*
Liz Eads *(Dir-Lifestyle-US & Intl Div)*

DIAMOND S SHIPPING GROUP, INC.
33 Benedict Pl, Greenwich, CT 06830
Tel.: (203) 413-2000   MH
Web Site:
    http://www.diamondsshipping.com
Year Founded: 2011
Rev.: $595,910,000
Assets: $1,961,843,000
Liabilities: $732,407,000
Net Worth: $1,229,436,000
Earnings: $23,317,000
Emp.: 36
Fiscal Year-end: 12/31/20
Deep Sea Freight Transportation Arrangement
N.A.I.C.S.: 488510
Sanjay Sukhrani *(COO)*
Florence Ioannou *(CFO)*
Michael G. Fogarty *(Sr VP-Comml)*
Craig Stevenson Jr. *(Pres & CEO)*

DIAMOND SERVICES CORPORATION
503 S Degravelle Rd, Amelia, LA 70340
Tel.: (985) 631-2187
Web Site:
    http://www.diamondservices.com
Rev.: $23,000,000
Emp.: 161
Dredging, Pile Driving, Salvage Work, Fabrication, General Oilfield Construction & Marine Transportation
N.A.I.C.S.: 236210
James Furlette *(VP-Ops)*
Wallace Carline *(Pres)*
Earl J. Hebert *(Treas & Sec)*
Mike Swiber *(Mgr-Pur & Safety)*

DIAMOND SOFTWARE, INC.
84315 Hwy 437, Covington, LA 70435
Tel.: (985) 892-2710   LA
Web Site: https://www.diamond-soft.com
Year Founded: 1985
Sales Range: $10-24.9 Million
Custom Software & Support Services
N.A.I.C.S.: 541511
Elizabeth G. Long *(Treas & Sec)*
Tommy J. Tastet *(Pres)*

DIAMOND SOLUTIONS, INC.
12150 Monument Dr Ste 100, Fairfax, VA 22033
Tel.: (703) 356-5550
Web Site:
    https://www.diamondsolutions.com
Year Founded: 2002
Sales Range: $1-9.9 Million
Emp.: 112
Business Management Consulting Services
N.A.I.C.S.: 541611
Earl Brown *(Pres & CEO)*
Gaile Hyman *(Supvr-Compliance Inspection)*

DIAMOND STATE VENTURES, LLC

200 River Market Ave Ste 400, Little Rock, AR 72201
Tel.: (501) 374-9247
Web Site:
    http://diamondstateventures.com
Year Founded: 1999
Privater Equity Firm
N.A.I.C.S.: 523940
Joe T. Hays *(Mng Dir)*

DIAMOND TECHNOLOGY ENTERPRISES, INC.
37 W 47th St 1301, New York, NY 10036
Tel.: (212) 382-2104   DE
Year Founded: 2013
Emp.: 5
Diamond Processor & Mfr
N.A.I.C.S.: 339910
Eduard Musheyev *(Chm, Pres, CEO & Sec)*
Jordan Friedberg *(CFO & Treas)*

DIAMOND TRANSPORTATION SYSTEMS
5021 21st St, Racine, WI 53406
Tel.: (262) 554-5400
Web Site:
    https://www.diamondtrans.net
Sales Range: $10-24.9 Million
Emp.: 32
Heavy Hauling
N.A.I.C.S.: 484121
Chad Thur *(Controller)*

DIAMOND V MILLS, INC.
2525 60th Ave SW, Cedar Rapids, IA 52404
Tel.: (319) 366-0745
Web Site: https://www.diamondv.com
Year Founded: 1943
Sales Range: $10-24.9 Million
Emp.: 120
Animal Feed Mfr
N.A.I.C.S.: 311119
Jeff Cannon *(Pres & CEO)*
Paul R. Faganel *(COO & Exec VP)*
C. W. Bloomhall *(Founder)*
David Lusson *(CFO & VP)*

DIAMOND VALLEY HONDA GROUP, LLC.
300 Carriage Cir, Hemet, CA 92545
Tel.: (951) 389-7582
Web Site: https://www.diamondvalley
    honda.com
Sales Range: $10-24.9 Million
Emp.: 50
Car Whslr
N.A.I.C.S.: 441110
Sam Massoud *(Mgr-Sls)*

DIAMOND VOGEL PAINT, INC.
1110 Albany Pl SE, Orange City, IA 51041-1982
Tel.: (712) 737-8880   IA
Web Site:
    https://www.diamondvogel.com
Year Founded: 1926
Sales Range: $10-24.9 Million
Emp.: 500
Paint Mfr & Retailer
N.A.I.C.S.: 325510
Drew Vogel *(Chm & CEO)*
Mark Vogel *(VP-Corp Bus Dev & Strategic Relationships)*
Jeff Powell *(Pres)*

Subsidiaries:

Diamond Products Company   **(1)**
1110 Albany Pl SE, Orange City, IA 51041
Tel.: (712) 737-8880
Web Site: http://www.diamondvogel.com
Mfr of Paints
N.A.I.C.S.: 444120
Drew Vogel *(Pres)*
Mark Vogel *(VP)*

Vogel West Inc.   **(1)**
1110 Albany Pl SE, Orange City, IA 51041
Tel.: (712) 737-8880
Web Site: http://www.diamondvogel.com
Paint & Painting Supplies
N.A.I.C.S.: 444120
Drew Vogel *(Pres)*

DIAMOND WIPES INTERNATIONAL, INC.
4651 Schaefer Ave, Chino, CA 91710
Tel.: (909) 230-9888
Web Site:
    http://www.diamondwipes.com
Year Founded: 1994
Sales Range: $10-24.9 Million
Emp.: 150
Hot & Cold Disposable Wet Wipe Mfr
N.A.I.C.S.: 325620
Jessica Lum *(Pres)*
Steve Gallo *(CEO)*
Peter Nolan *(Chm)*
Eve Yen *(Founder & Owner)*

DIAMOND WIRE SPRING COMPANY
1479 Glenn Ave, Glenshaw, PA 15116-2310
Tel.: (412) 492-8280
Web Site:
    https://www.diamondwire.com
Sales Range: $10-24.9 Million
Emp.: 75
Torsion & Die Spring Mfr
N.A.I.C.S.: 332613
Paul S. Cocheres *(Gen Mgr)*
Donald S. Fazio *(Pres)*
Becky L. Bernarding *(Asst Mgr-Acctg)*

DIAMOND/TRIUMPH AUTO GLASS INC.
2400 Farmers Dr, Columbus, OH 43235-2762
Tel.: (570) 287-9915   DE
Web Site:
    http://www.diamondglass.com
Year Founded: 1987
Sales Range: $200-249.9 Million
Emp.: 1,826
Automotive Glass Replacement Shops
N.A.I.C.S.: 811111
Kenneth Levine *(Chm)*
Richard Wooditch *(CFO)*

DIAMONDBACK AUTOMOTIVE ACCESSORIES INC.
354 Enterprise Dr, Philipsburg, PA 16866
Tel.: (814) 343-2500
Web Site:
    https://diamondbackcovers.com
Year Founded: 2003
Sales Range: $1-9.9 Million
Emp.: 58
Retail Patented DiamondBack HD Truck Cover Mfr
N.A.I.C.S.: 336110
Ethan Wendle *(Co-Founder)*
Matt Chverchko *(Co-Founder)*

Subsidiaries:

DiamondBack Truck Covers   **(1)**
354 Enterprise Dr, Philipsburg, PA 16866
Tel.: (814) 343-2500
Web Site:
    http://www.diamondbackcovers.com
Sales Range: $1-9.9 Million
Emp.: 45
Design Market & Retail its Patented DiamondBack HD Truck Covers & Utility Tonneau Covers for Pickup Truck Mfr
N.A.I.C.S.: 336110
Ethan Wendle *(Co-Founder)*
Matt Chverchko *(Co-Founder & Engr)*

DIAMONDS DIRECT ONLINE USA, LLC
5037 France Ave S, Minneapolis, MN 55410-2046
Tel.: (612) 929-0054
Web Site:
    https://www.diamondsdirectmn.com
Diamond & Jewelry Store
N.A.I.C.S.: 458310
Itay Berger *(Pres)*

Subsidiaries:

Diamonds Direct USA of Indianapolis, Inc.   **(1)**
8555 N River Rd, Indianapolis, IN 46240
Tel.: (317) 575-8555
Web Site:
    http://www.distinctivediamondsinc.com
Diamond & Other Jewelry Stores
N.A.I.C.S.: 458310

DIANA E. KELLY, INC.
820 Bell Rd Unit B, Sarasota, FL 34240
Web Site: http://www.dianaekelly.com
Sales Range: $1-9.9 Million
Women's Shoes & Handbags Designer & Retailer
N.A.I.C.S.: 316210
Diana E. Kelly *(Pres)*
Stephanie Hannum *(VP-Ops)*

DIANAS MEXICAN FOOD PRODUCTS
16330 Pioneer Blvd, Norwalk, CA 90650
Tel.: (562) 926-5802
Web Site: https://www.dianas.net
Rev.: $25,100,000
Emp.: 300
Food Preparations
N.A.I.C.S.: 311999
Samuel Magana *(Pres)*

DIANE SAUER CHEVROLET, INC.
700 Niles Rd, Warren, OH 44483-5951
Tel.: (330) 373-1600
Web Site:
    https://www.dianesauerchevy.com
Sales Range: $10-24.9 Million
Emp.: 80
Car Whslr
N.A.I.C.S.: 441110
Diane R. Sauer *(Pres)*

DIANI CONSTRUCTION
351 N Blosser, Santa Maria, CA 93456-0636
Tel.: (805) 925-9533
Web Site: https://www.diani.com
Year Founded: 1949
Sales Range: $10-24.9 Million
Emp.: 100
Nonresidential Construction Services
N.A.I.C.S.: 236220
Andy Moynagh *(Dir-Sls)*

DIASPARK INC.
200 Metroplex Dr, Edison, NJ 08817
Tel.: (732) 248-8333
Web Site: http://www.diaspark.com
Year Founded: 1993
Rev.: $30,100,000
Emp.: 250
Custom Computer Programming Services
N.A.I.C.S.: 541511
Sanjay Phanda *(VP-Fin)*
Dushyant Pahare *(Gen Mgr-Fin)*
Sarvesh Jain *(VP-HR)*
Vinay Chhajlani *(Founder & Grp Chm)*
Vipin Bhardwaj *(Pres-Global Ops)*
Prashun Amin *(Sr VP-Consulting Practice)*

Parvindar S. Gujral (*VP-Enterprise Solution*)
Prashant Raghuvanshi (*VP-HR-India*)

DIAZ FRITZ ISABEL GENERAL CONTRACTORS

13075 Telecom Pkwy N, Temple Terrace, FL 33637
Tel.: (813) 254-0072
Web Site: https://www.diazfritz.com
Year Founded: 1985
Sales Range: $10-24.9 Million
Emp.: 16
Commercial & Industrial Construction
N.A.I.C.S.: 236220
Bob Dance (*VP-Ops*)
Joe Furlong (*Controller*)
Delvis H. Diaz (*CEO*)
Holly R. Calhoun (*Sec & Dir-Admin Svcs*)

DIAZ WHOLESALE & MANU-FACTURING CO., INC.

5501 Fulton Industrial Blvd, Atlanta, GA 30336
Tel.: (404) 344-5421
Web Site: https://www.diazfoods.com
Year Founded: 1980
Sales Range: $50-74.9 Million
Emp.: 200
Whslr of Groceries & Dairy Products
N.A.I.C.S.: 424410
Rene M. Diaz (*Chm, Pres & CEO*)
Eric Newberg (*CFO*)
Judy Henderson (*Controller*)

Subsidiaries:

La Cena Fine Foods Ltd.   (1)
4 Rosol Ln, Saddle Brook, NJ 07663
Tel.: (201) 797-4600
Web Site: http://www.lacenafoods.com
Food Products Distr & Whslr
N.A.I.C.S.: 424410

DIBERT VALVE & FITTING CO. INC.

4716 Richneil Rd, Henrico, VA 23231
Tel.: (804) 275-7871
Web Site: http://www.swagelok.com
Sales Range: $10-24.9 Million
Emp.: 25
Valves & Fittings
N.A.I.C.S.: 423830
David E. O'Connor (*VP-Distr Support Svcs*)
Frank J. Roddy (*Exec VP-Fin & Admin*)
Matthew P. LoPiccolo (*CIO & VP-IS*)
Michael F. Neff (*VP-Ops*)
Nick Ezzone (*VP-Customer Svc & Supply Chain*)
Sally Turner (*VP-HR*)
Timothy G. Rosengarten (*VP-Continuous Improvement & Quality*)
Jill Whelan (*VP-Corp Comm*)
Robert G. Wilson (*VP-Mktg*)

DIBONA, BORNSTEIN & RANDOM, INC.

46 Waltham St, Boston, MA 02118
Tel.: (617) 267-6262   MA
Web Site: http://www.dbrnet.com
Year Founded: 1989
Rev.: $3,000,000
Emp.: 20
Fiscal Year-end: 12/31/03
Full Service
N.A.I.C.S.: 541810
Stanley Bornstein (*Owner*)
Nik Barkley (*Dir-Creative*)
Tami Gauvreau (*Dir-Media*)
Jacqueline Holland (*Dir-Art*)

DICAPTA CORP.

900 Fox Valley Dr Ste 204, Longwood, FL 32779-2552
Tel.: (407) 389-0712
Web Site: http://www.dicapta.com
Sales Range: $1-9.9 Million
Emp.: 10
Caption Insertion (Electronic Closed Subtitles), Video Description, Subtitling, Dubbing, Live Dubbing & CART (Putting Words Into Text In Real Time)
N.A.I.C.S.: 512199
Maria Diaz (*CEO & Founder*)

DICAR, INC.

10 Bloomfield Ave, Pine Brook, NJ 07058
Tel.: (973) 575-1174
Web Site: http://www.dicar.com
Sales Range: $10-24.9 Million
Emp.: 30
Mfr & Supplier of Urethane Products
N.A.I.C.S.: 325212
Steve Warll (*VP-Intl Sls*)

DICCICCO BATTISTA COMMU-NICATIONS

1200 River Rd Ste 300 E, Conshohocken, PA 19428
Tel.: (215) 957-0300   PA
Year Founded: 1968
Rev.: $30,000,000
Emp.: 35
Advetising Agency
N.A.I.C.S.: 541810
Michael Diccicco (*Pres & CEO*)
Scott Keegel (*Dir-New Bus Plng*)
Sam Fiorella (*Sr VP-Integrated Strategies*)
Marc Traub (*CFO*)
Sean Donahue (*Sr VP & Dir-Creative*)
Tim Cifelli (*Sr VP & Gen Mgr-PR*)
Michelle Freed-Gold (*Pres-Intellimedia-DBC*)
Rob Burkholder (*Acct Mgr*)
Chris Kalin (*Mgr-Production*)

Subsidiaries:

IntelliMedia-DBC   (1)
1200 River Rd Ste 300 E, Conshohocken, PA 19428
Tel.: (215) 957-0300
Emp.: 15
N.A.I.C.S.: 541810
Michelle Freed-Gold (*Pres*)
Renee Rozniatoski (*Dir-Pub Rel*)

Reverb-DBC   (1)
1200 River Rd Ste 300 E, Conshohocken, PA 19428
Tel.: (484) 342-3600
Emp.: 20
N.A.I.C.S.: 541810
Tim Cifelli (*Sr VP & Gen Mgr*)
Sean Donahue (*Dir-Creative*)

DICK ANDERSON CONSTRUC-TION

3424 Highway 12 E, Helena, MT 59601
Tel.: (406) 443-3225
Web Site: https://www.daconstruction.com
Sales Range: $25-49.9 Million
Emp.: 160
Commercial & Office Building Contractors
N.A.I.C.S.: 236220
Richard G. Anderson (*CEO*)
Marty Schuma (*Pres*)
Tony Stonehouse (*Mgr-Resource*)
Bob Heberly (*VP*)
Evan Peacock (*Project Mgr*)
Regan Meredith (*Treas & Sec*)
Kirk Scheel (*Project Mgr*)
Tom Tubbs (*Mgr-Safety*)
Josh de Vos (*Project Mgr*)
A. J. Harmon (*Project Mgr*)
Bobbi Foran (*Accountant*)
Bree Bishop (*Dir-Mktg*)
Brett Welker (*Project Mgr*)
Brian Bolton (*VP*)
Carol Machalk (*Project Mgr*)
Caryn Johnson (*Project Mgr*)
Corey McGreevey (*CFO*)
Kevin Hintt (*VP*)
Travis Neil (*Project Mgr*)

DICK BLICK HOLDINGS INC.

PO Box 1267, Galesburg, IL 61402-1267
Tel.: (309) 343-6181
Web Site: https://www.dickblick.com
Year Founded: 1911
Holding Company; Art Supplies Mail Order & Retail Store Operator
N.A.I.C.S.: 551112
Robert Buchsbaum (*CEO*)

Subsidiaries:

Dick Blick Company   (1)
1849 Green Bay Rd Ste 310, Highland Park, IL 60035
Tel.: (847) 681-6800
Web Site: http://www.dickblick.com
Sales Range: $10-24.9 Million
Emp.: 50
Art Supplies Mail Order & Retail Store Operator
N.A.I.C.S.: 459999
Robert Buchsbaum (*CEO*)
John Polillo (*VP-Ops*)

Utrecht Manufacturing Corp.   (1)
6 Corp Dr, Cranbury, NJ 08512
Tel.: (609) 409-8001
Web Site: http://www.utrecht.com
Sales Range: $25-49.9 Million
Emp.: 225
Art Materials Mfr
N.A.I.C.S.: 339940

DICK BROWNING, INC.

18827 Studebaker Rd, Cerritos, CA 90703-5332
Tel.: (562) 924-1414   CA
Web Site: https://www.browningautogroup.com
Year Founded: 1960
Sales Range: $125-149.9 Million
Emp.: 600
Holding Company; New & Used Car Dealership Owner & Operator
N.A.I.C.S.: 551112
Kent C. Browning (*Owner & Pres*)
Scott Dickinson (*VP*)

Subsidiaries:

Browning Mazda   (1)
18827 Studebaker Rd, Cerritos, CA 90703
Tel.: (562) 924-1414
Web Site: http://www.browningmazda.com
New & Used Car Dealer
N.A.I.C.S.: 441110
Henry Loza (*Gen Mgr*)
Sam Gomez (*Mgr-Sls*)
Carl Hegge (*Mgr-Svc*)
Steve Brodkin (*Mgr-Svc*)
Rosemarie Cuevas (*Mgr-Customer Rels*)
Wendy Diep (*Mgr-Fin*)
Dudley Gamino (*Asst Mgr-Sls*)
Deandre Jacocks (*Mgr-Internet Sls*)
Tom Kirby (*Mgr-Parts*)
Alan Kok (*Mgr-Fin*)
Jasmine Martinez (*Mgr-Internet Sls*)
Jose Uscanga (*Mgr-Internet Sls*)

Cerritos Dodge Chrysler Jeep   (1)
18803 Studebaker Rd, Cerritos, CA 90703
Tel.: (562) 402-5335
Web Site: http://www.cerritosdodge.com
New & Used Car Dealer
N.A.I.C.S.: 441110
Jack Ameen (*Gen Mgr*)

Valley-Hi Automotive Group   (1)
14612 Valley Center Dr, Victorville, CA 92395
Tel.: (760) 241-6484
Web Site: http://www.valleyhi.com
Holding Company; New & Used Car Dealerships
N.A.I.C.S.: 551112

Kent C. Browning (*Owner*)

Unit (Domestic):

Valley-Hi Honda   (2)
15710 Vly Park Ln, Victorville, CA 92394
Tel.: (760) 962-9600
Web Site: http://www.valleyhihonda.com
New & Used Car Dealer
N.A.I.C.S.: 441110
Christopher Justice (*Gen Mgr-Sls*)
Chris Justis (*Gen Mgr*)

Valley-Hi Nissan   (2)
15722 Valley Park Ln, Victorville, CA 92394
Tel.: (760) 241-1700
Web Site: http://www.valleyhinissan.com
New & Used Car Dealer
N.A.I.C.S.: 441110
Todd Stokes (*Gen Mgr-Toyota*)
Christopher Justice (*Gen Mgr-Sls-Honda*)

Valley-Hi Toyota   (2)
14644 Vly Ctr Dr, Victorville, CA 92395
Tel.: (760) 241-6484
Web Site: http://www.valleyhitoyota.com
Sales Range: $50-74.9 Million
Emp.: 200
New & Used Car Dealer
N.A.I.C.S.: 441110
Edward Chavez (*Mgr-Parts*)
Todd Stokes (*Gen Mgr*)
Robert Ball (*Gen Mgr-Sls*)
Alex Atalla (*Mgr-Fin*)
Evelyn Brown (*Dir-Customer Rels*)
Larry Ojeda (*Mgr-Fin*)
Mojibul Hague (*Asst Mgr-Sls*)
Mike Petite (*Mgr-Sls*)
Sandy Wherry (*Asst Mgr-Used Car*)
Sal Jamili (*Mgr-Fin*)
Tim Clark (*Mgr-Vehicle Exchange*)

DICK BRUHN INCORPORATED

300 Main St, Salinas, CA 93901-2706
Tel.: (831) 758-4684   CA
Year Founded: 1950
Sales Range: $200-249.9 Million
Emp.: 368
Retailer of Mens & Ladies Clothing; Renter of Uniforms
N.A.I.C.S.: 532281

DICK CAMPAGNI'S CAPITAL FORD

3660 S Carson St, Carson City, NV 89701
Tel.: (775) 882-5353
Web Site: http://www.capitalfordonline.com
Rev.: $18,200,000
Emp.: 75
Automobiles, New & Used
N.A.I.C.S.: 441110
Richard Campagni (*Owner*)

DICK DEAN ECONOMY CARS INC.

15121 Manchester Rd, Ballwin, MO 63011
Tel.: (636) 227-0100
Web Site: http://www.deanteam.com
Rev.: $16,400,000
Emp.: 50
Automobiles, New & Used
N.A.I.C.S.: 441110
Patrick C. Dean (*Pres*)
Tom Perry (*Controller*)

DICK DYER & ASSOCIATES, INC.

5825 2 Notch Rd, Columbia, SC 29223
Tel.: (803) 828-6952
Web Site: https://www.dickdyeronline.com
Year Founded: 1969
Sales Range: $100-124.9 Million
Emp.: 125
New Car Dealers
N.A.I.C.S.: 441110
Jerry Greene (*Sls Mgr*)
Scott Mims (*Mgr-Sls*)

Dick Dyer & Associates, Inc.—(Continued)

Cooper Wall (Mgr-Sls)
Jack Derrick (Mgr-Internet)
Neal Bray (Mgr-Internet Sls)

DICK DYER TOYOTA

240 Killian Commons Pkwy, Columbia, SC 29203-9131
Tel.: (803) 786-4111
Web Site:
http://www.dickdyertoyota.com
Year Founded: 1988
Sales Range: $50-74.9 Million
Emp.: 100
New Car Whslr
N.A.I.C.S.: 441110
Bruce Dyer (Pres)
Adam Berman (Gen Mgr)
Bishme Foster (Mgr-Fin)
Sharaz Hassan (Gen Mgr-Sls)

DICK EDWARDS FORD LINCOLN MERCURY

7920 E US Hwy 24, Manhattan, KS 66502
Tel.: (785) 776-4004
Web Site: http://dickedwards.net
Sales Range: $25-49.9 Million
Emp.: 100
Automobiles, New & Used Sales & Service
N.A.I.C.S.: 441110
Tanice Edwards (Mgr-Fin)
Don Glaspie (Mgr-Sls)

DICK GENTHE CHEVROLET

15600 Eureka Rd, Southgate, MI 48195
Tel.: (734) 250-9240
Web Site: https://www.genthe.com
Year Founded: 1967
Sales Range: $25-49.9 Million
Emp.: 93
Car Whslr
N.A.I.C.S.: 441110
Richard S. Genthe (Pres)
Jim Lewis (Mgr-Auto Body)

DICK GORE'S RV WORLD INC.

14590 Duval Pl W, Jacksonville, FL 32218
Tel.: (904) 741-5100
Web Site:
http://www.dickgoresrvworld.com
Sales Range: $25-49.9 Million
Emp.: 70
Recreational Vehicle Dealers
N.A.I.C.S.: 441210
Dick Gore (Pres)
Dana Drake (Gen Mgr)
Ronnie Devane (Mgr-RV Parts)
Tom Ansley (Mgr)

DICK GREENFIELD DODGE INC.

2700 Brunswick Pike, Lawrenceville, NJ 08648
Tel.: (609) 882-1000
Web Site:
http://www.dickgreenfield.com
Sales Range: $25-49.9 Million
Emp.: 49
Automobiles, New & Used
N.A.I.C.S.: 441110

DICK HUVAERE'S RICHMOND CHRYSLER DODGE INC.

67567 S Main St, Richmond, MI 48062
Tel.: (586) 727-7577
Web Site: https://www.driveenvy.com
Rev.: $63,000,000
Emp.: 110
Owner & Operator of Car Dealerships
N.A.I.C.S.: 441110

Tom Tessmer (Mgr-Sls)
Richard Huvaere (Pres)
Kim Jugowicg (VP & Gen Mgr)

DICK MASHETER FORD, INC.

1090 S Hamilton Rd, Columbus, OH 43227
Tel.: (614) 861-7150
Web Site:
https://www.masheterford.net
Year Founded: 1967
Sales Range: $75-99.9 Million
Emp.: 100
Car Whslr
N.A.I.C.S.: 441110
Robert Masheter (Owner & CEO)
Jeremy McNutt (Gen Mgr)

DICK MOORE INC.

6565 US Highway 51 N, Millington, TN 38053
Tel.: (901) 873-4663
Web Site:
https://www.dickmoorehousing.com
Year Founded: 1958
Sales Range: $10-24.9 Million
Emp.: 50
Mobile Home Dealers
N.A.I.C.S.: 459930
R. E. Crawford (Pres)
Richard C. Moore Jr. (Owner & CEO)

DICK MYERS CHRYSLER DODGE JEEP

1711 S Main St, Harrisonburg, VA 22801
Tel.: (540) 534-0388
Web Site:
https://www.dickmyerschrysler
dodgejeep.net
Emp.: 50
Automobiles, New & Used
N.A.I.C.S.: 441110
Andy Myers (Gen Mgr)
Eric Myers (Mgr-Ops-Variable)
Sam Lee (Sls Mgr)
Jim Lowe (Mgr-Used Car)
Darrel Baker (Mgr-Fin)

DICK NORRIS BUICK PONTIAC GMC

30777 United States Hwy 19 N, Palm Harbor, FL 34684
Tel.: (727) 787-8663
Web Site: http://www.dicknorris.com
Sales Range: $50-74.9 Million
Emp.: 90
Automobiles, New & Used
N.A.I.C.S.: 441110
Richard Norris (Owner)
Doug Norris (Gen Mgr)
James Ballou (Dir-Fin)
Steve Newcomer (Mgr-Sls)
Dan Small (Mgr-Sls)

DICK POE CHRYSLER-PLYMOUTH INC.

6501 Montana Ave, El Paso, TX 79925-2128
Tel.: (915) 206-4489
Web Site: https://www.dickpoe.com
Sales Range: $50-74.9 Million
Emp.: 100
Automobile Sales New & Used
N.A.I.C.S.: 441110
Dick Poe (Owner & Pres)
Jerry Rickelbus (Gen Mgr)

DICK POE MOTORS LP.

6501 Montana Ave, El Paso, TX 79925
Tel.: (915) 778-9331
Year Founded: 1928
Sales Range: $25-49.9 Million
Emp.: 100
Car Whslr

N.A.I.C.S.: 441110
Gery Reckelbus (Gen Mgr)

DICK SCOTT MOTOR MALL INC.

3030 N Fowlerville Rd, Fowlerville, MI 48836
Tel.: (517) 223-3721
Web Site:
http://www.dickscottchrysler.com
Sales Range: $10-24.9 Million
Emp.: 30
New & Used Car Dealers
N.A.I.C.S.: 441110
Richard L. Scott (Pres)
Jud Scott (Gen Mgr)

Subsidiaries:

Dick Scott Dodge Inc.   (1)
684 W Ann Arbor Rd, Plymouth, MI 48170
Tel.: (734) 451-2110
Web Site:
http://www.dickscottchryslerdodge.com
Emp.: 100
Sells New & Used Automobiles
N.A.I.C.S.: 441110
Richard L. Scott (Owner)
Jason Scott (Gen Mgr)

DICK SMITH AUTOMOTIVE GROUP

9940 2 Notch Rd, Columbia, SC 29223-4381
Tel.: (803) 256-6600
Web Site: http://www.dicksmith.com
Rev.: $115,600,000
Emp.: 420
New & Used Car Dealer
N.A.I.C.S.: 441110
Brian Smith (Pres)
Tommy Dale (Controller)
Bill Goodwin (COO)

Subsidiaries:

Columbia Nissan Inc.   (1)
3670 Fernandina Rd, Columbia, SC 29210
Tel.: (803) 772-8700
Web Site: http://www.humidity.com
Rev.: $16,100,000
Emp.: 50
New & Used Car Dealers
N.A.I.C.S.: 441110

Dick Smith Auto Sales Inc.   (1)
9940 2 Notch Rd, Columbia, SC 29223
Tel.: (803) 256-6600
Web Site: http://www.dicksmith.com
Sales Range: $50-74.9 Million
Emp.: 400
New & Used Car Dealers
N.A.I.C.S.: 441110
Eddie Maracich (Gen Mgr)

Dick Smith Ford   (1)
7201 Garners Ferry Rd, Columbia, SC 29209
Tel.: (803) 254-4000
Web Site: http://www.dicksmith.com
Sales Range: $25-49.9 Million
Emp.: 100
Provider of Automobile & Truck Sales, Parts & Service
N.A.I.C.S.: 441110
Harold Wray (VP)
Jeremy Winters (Asst Mgr-Svc)

Dick Smith Infiniti Inc.   (1)
3670B Fernandina Rd, Columbia, SC 29210
Tel.: (803) 750-6500
Web Site: http://www.dicksmith.com
Sales Range: $1-9.9 Million
Emp.: 20
New & Used Automobiles
N.A.I.C.S.: 441110
Brian Smith (Pres)

Dick Smith Nissan Inc.   (1)
3670 Fernandina Rd, Columbia, SC 29210
Tel.: (803) 772-8700
Web Site: http://www.dicksmith.com
Rev.: $16,100,000
Emp.: 75
New & Used Car Dealers
N.A.I.C.S.: 441110

Calvin Legette (Pres)

Dick Smith Nissan of Lexington   (1)
5536 Sunset Blvd, Lexington, SC 29072
Tel.: (803) 957-7760
Web Site: http://www.dicksmith.com
Rev.: $16,100,000
Emp.: 49
New & Used Car Dealers
N.A.I.C.S.: 441110
Brian Smith (Pres & CEO)
Bill Goodwin (CFO)
Selena Wise (Office Mgr)

DICK VANDYKE INCORPORATED

3800 W Wabash, Springfield, IL 62711
Tel.: (217) 544-8180
Web Site:
http://www.applianceworld.com
Rev.: $13,607,498
Emp.: 50
Electric Household Appliances
N.A.I.C.S.: 449210
Dennis Riekes (Pres)
John Shepherd (VP)
Lynn Rieken (CFO)

DICK'S COUNTRY CHRYSLER JEEP DODGE

767 SW Baseline St, Hillsboro, OR 97123-3816
Tel.: (503) 640-1050
Web Site:
http://www.dickscountrydodge.com
Sales Range: $10-24.9 Million
Emp.: 40
New Car Whslr
N.A.I.C.S.: 441110
Jose Wojahn (Mgr-Svc)

DICKENS BOOKS LTD.

219 N Milwaukee St, Milwaukee, WI 53202-5818
Tel.: (414) 270-3434
Web Site:
http://www.800ceoread.com
Sales Range: $1-9.9 Million
Emp.: 12
Owner & Operator of Book Stores
N.A.I.C.S.: 459210
Carol Grossmeyer (Co-Owner & Chm-800-CEO-READ)
Sally Haldorson (Gen Mgr)
Rebecca Schwartz (Co-Owner, Pres & CEO)

DICKERSON & NIEMAN REALTORS, INC.

6277 E Riverside Blvd Ste 2, Rockford, IL 61114
Tel.: (815) 893-7401
Web Site:
https://www.dickersonnieman.com
Year Founded: 1964
Real Estate Services
N.A.I.C.S.: 531390

Subsidiaries:

Pioneer Real Estate Services Inc.   (1)
631 N Longwood St Ste 202, Rockford, IL 61107
Tel.: (940) 569-1493
Web Site: http://www.pioneer-rockford.com
Offices of Real Estate Agents & Brokers
N.A.I.C.S.: 531210
Margaret Ford (Partner)

DICKEY INC.

401 E 4th St, Packwood, IA 52580
Tel.: (319) 695-3601
Web Site:
http://www.dickeytransport.com
Sales Range: $10-24.9 Million
Emp.: 105
Trucking Except Local
N.A.I.C.S.: 484121
Doug Dickey (Pres)

DICKEY'S BARBECUE RESTAURANTS, INC.

4514 Cole Ave Ste 1015, Dallas, TX 75205
Web Site: https://www.dickeys.com
Year Founded: 1941
Sales Range: $150-199.9 Million
Emp.: 78
Texas Barbecue, Dine-In, Take-Out, Catering Services & Franchising Opportunities
N.A.I.C.S.: 722511
Laura Rea Dickey (CEO)
Steve Hawter (VP-Trng)
Christie Finley (Chief Brand Officer)
Diana Larocca (CMO)
Christine Johnson (Gen Counsel)
Michelle Frazier (Chief Admin Officer)
Renee Roozen (Pres)
Kenn Miller (Sr VP-Ops)
Jared Madry (VP-Construction)
John Geyerman (VP-Franchise Sls)
Barry M. Barron Sr. (COO)
Roland Dickey Jr. (CEO-Capital Grp)

DICKINSON BRANDS, INC.

31 E High St, East Hampton, CT 06424
Tel.: (888) 860-2279
Web Site:
http://www.dickinsonsusa.com
Drugs & Druggists' Sundries Merchant Whslr
N.A.I.C.S.: 424210
Edward C. Jackowitz (Pres)

DICKINSON CAMERON CONSTRUCTION COMPANY, INC.

6184 Innovation Way, Carlsbad, CA 92009
Tel.: (760) 438-9114   CA
Web Site:
http://www.dickinsoncameron.com
Year Founded: 1994
Emp.: 60
Commercial Construction Management Services
N.A.I.C.S.: 236220
Frank Naliboff (Co-Founder, Pres & CEO)
Ronald Gordines (Dir-Bus Dev)
Eddy Barth (Sr Project Mgr)
Chris Nightingale (Sr Project Mgr-Restaurant Div)
Maryam Samady (Controller)
Gerrry Harbinson (Sr Project Mgr-East Coast)

DICKINSON CENTER, INC.

43 Servidea Dr, Ridgway, PA 15853
Tel.: (814) 776-2145   PA
Web Site: http://www.dmhc.org
Year Founded: 1958
Sales Range: $10-24.9 Million
Emp.: 276
Behavioral Healthcare Services
N.A.I.C.S.: 621420
Tim Lowe (Dir-Mgmt-Information Systems)
Jim Prosper (COO)
Leona Hoohuli (Controller)
Lynne Childs (Mgr-Compliance-Risk)
Sara Mercer (Dir-Billing)

DICKINSON FINANCIAL CORPORATION

1111 Main St Ste 1600, Kansas City, MO 64105-5114
Tel.: (816) 472-5244
Bank Holding Company
N.A.I.C.S.: 551111
Dan L. Dickinson (Sr Exec VP)
Paul P. Holewinski (Pres & CEO)
Jane Dickinson Kress (Gen Counsel & Sr Exec VP)
Ann K. Dickinson (Chm)

Amy Dickinson Holewinski (Vice Chm)
Burt K. Dickinson (Head-Mktg)
Teresa Ascencio (Chief People Officer)

Subsidiaries:

Academy Bank, N.A.   (1)
8551 N Boardwalk Ave, Kansas City, MO 64154
Tel.: (816) 216-5890
Web Site: http://www.academybank.com
Savings Bank
N.A.I.C.S.: 522180
Paul P. Holewinski (Pres & CEO)
Jane Dickinson Kress (Chief Legal Officer)
Richard DeWire (Sr VP)
Dawn Tubbesing (VP)
Robert Holt (Sr VP)
Bret Duston (Sr VP & Dir-Comml Banking Div)
Matthew Cammer (Dir-Bus Banking & Treasury Mgmt)
Michael Haynes (Sr VP & Dir-Valuation Svcs)
Bobbie McCauley (VP-Treasury Mgmt Sls)
Tim Steves (VP)
Shawn Watts (VP & Mgr-Natl Sls)
Ronald Hendrickson (Sr VP & Mgr-Consumer Loan Dept)
Jeff Sullivan (VP)
Bob Sellers (Sr VP-Comml Banking)
Morgan Johnson (Mgr-Comm Processing)
Robert Owens (Sr VP & Dir-Community Banking)
Teresa Ascencio (Chief People Officer)
Grant Killion (VP/Sr Portfolio Mgr-Comml Banking-Kansas City)
Joe Houlehan (Sr VP-Comml Banking-Kansas City)
Tim David (Sr VP & Dir-Pub Fin)
Shane Mahoney (Sr VP)
Richard Morgan (Sr VP)
Carlos Molina (Mng Dir-Comml Banking-Arizona)

Armed Forces Bank, N.A.   (1)
320 Kansas Ave, Fort Leavenworth, KS 66027-3400
Tel.: (913) 682-9090
Web Site: http://www.afbank.com
Sales Range: $100-124.9 Million
Emp.: 100
Commercial Banking Services
N.A.I.C.S.: 522110
Diane Bales (VP)
David Neice (VP-Comml Lending)

DICKINSON PRESS, INC.

5100 33rd St SE, Grand Rapids, MI 49512-2062
Tel.: (616) 957-5100   MI
Web Site:
http://www.dickinsonpress.com
Year Founded: 1884
Sales Range: $25-49.9 Million
Emp.: 120
Provider of Book Publishing Services
N.A.I.C.S.: 323117
Steve DeWeerd (Mgr-Customer Svc)

DICKINSON THEATRES INC.

6801 W 107th St, Overland Park, KS 66212
Tel.: (913) 432-2334
Web Site: http://www.dtmovies.com
Year Founded: 1920
Rev.: $39,000,000
Emp.: 500
Motion Picture Theaters Owner & Operator
N.A.I.C.S.: 512131
Edward Carl (VP)
Kevin White (Dir-Concessions)

DICKINSON WRIGHT PLLC

500 Woodward Ave Ste 4000, Detroit, MI 48226-3425
Tel.: (313) 223-3500
Web Site: http://www.dickinsonwright.com
Year Founded: 1878

Sales Range: $125-149.9 Million
Emp.: 254
Legal Advisory Services
N.A.I.C.S.: 541110
W. Anthony Jenkins (Chief Diversity Officer)
James A. Samborn (Chm)
Harlan Robins (Mgr-Real Estate, Environmental, Energy & Sustainability Practices)
Michelle Murad (CMO)
Dustin Kovacic (Atty)
Scot Crow (Mgr-Practice Dept)
Philip Rettig (Mgr-Practice Dept)
David A. Judson (Partner)
Michael C. Hammer (CEO)
Jake R. McMillian (Dir-Diversity & Inclusion)
William P. Shield Jr. (Mgr-Practice Dept)

DICKINSON, MACKAMAN, TYLER & HAGEN, P.C.

699 Walnut St Ste 1600, Des Moines, IA 50309-3986
Tel.: (515) 244-2600
Web Site:
http://www.dickinsonlaw.com
Year Founded: 1936
Emp.: 100
Law firm
N.A.I.C.S.: 541110
Jeffrey A. Krausman (Atty)
Mary A. Zambreno (Atty)
Howard O. Hagen (Atty)
Jill R. Jensen-Welch (Atty)
Joan M. Fletcher (Atty)

Subsidiaries:

Bradshaw, Fowler, Proctor & Fairgrave, PC   (1)
801 Grand Ave Ste 3700, Des Moines, IA 50309-8004
Tel.: (515) 243-4191
Web Site: https://www.bradshawlaw.com
Sales Range: $10-24.9 Million
Emp.: 100
Law firm
N.A.I.C.S.: 541110
Sandra Dodson (Principal)

DICKMAN SUPPLY INCORPORATED

1991 Saint Marys Rd, Sidney, OH 45365
Tel.: (937) 492-6166   OH
Web Site: http://www.electro-controls.com
Year Founded: 1975
Sales Range: $25-49.9 Million
Emp.: 100
Provider of Complete Engineered Turn-Key Solutions
N.A.I.C.S.: 423610
Mario Nova (Mgr-Sls)

DICKSON INDUSTRIES, LLC

7015 Grand Blvd, Houston, TX 77054
Tel.: (713) 747-1167
Sales Range: $10-24.9 Million
Emp.: 100
Furniture Whslr
N.A.I.C.S.: 423210
Douglas Mueller (Pres)

DICOCCO FAMILY'S ST. JUDE SHOP, INC.

21 Brookline Blvd, Havertown, PA 19083
Tel.: (610) 789-1300
Web Site:
https://www.stjudeshop.com
Year Founded: 1965
Rev.: $10,000,000
Emp.: 70
Supplier of Religious Goods & Church Restoration Services

N.A.I.C.S.: 423490
Norma DiCocco (Founder)
Louis DiCocco III (Founder)

DICOM, INC.

12412 Powers Ct Dr Ste 110, Saint Louis, MO 63131-1851
Tel.: (314) 909-0900
Web Site: http://www.dicominc.com
Year Founded: 1989
Sales Range: $1-9.9 Million
Emp.: 20
Media Buying Services
N.A.I.C.S.: 541810
Jim Steward (Partner-Media Plng, Buying & Media Auditing)
David B. Travers (Partner)

DICON FIBEROPTICS, INC.

1689 Regatta Blvd, Richmond, CA 94804
Tel.: (510) 620-5000
Web Site: http://www.diconfiber.com
Year Founded: 1986
Sales Range: $50-74.9 Million
Emp.: 343
Fiberoptic Component Mfr
N.A.I.C.S.: 334419
Ho-Shang Lee (Pres & CEO)
Paul Lo (VP-Ops & Mfg)
Robert Schleicher (VP-Product Dev)
Gilles Corcos (Chm)

DICTOR CAPITAL CORPORATION

910 Evergreen Rd, Chester Springs, PA 19425
Tel.: (610) 827-2110
Sales Range: $10-24.9 Million
Emp.: 6
Brokers, Business: Buying & Selling Business Enterprises
N.A.I.C.S.: 541990

DIDION MILLING INC.

520 Hartwig Blvd, Johnson Creek, WI 53038
Tel.: (920) 699-3633
Web Site:
http://www.didionmilling.com
Year Founded: 1972
Sales Range: $25-49.9 Million
Emp.: 140
Flour & Other Grain Mill Products
N.A.I.C.S.: 311211
John A. Didion (Co-Founder & CEO)
Dow A. Didion (Co-Founder & COO)
Luke Burmeister (CFO)
Riley Didion (Pres)
Derrick Clark (VP-Ops)

DIDIT.COM, INC.

330 Old Country Rd Ste 206, Mineola, NY 11501
Tel.: (516) 255-0500   DE
Web Site: http://www.didit.com
Year Founded: 1996
Full-Service Online & Marketing Services Firm & Search Engine Marketing
N.A.I.C.S.: 541890
Kevin Lee (Chm)
Ashleigh Harvey (Acct Mgr)

Subsidiaries:

Bridge Global Strategies, LLC   (1)
276 5th Ave Ste 205, New York, NY 10001
Tel.: (212) 583-1043
Web Site: http://www.bridgeny.com
Advetising Agency
N.A.I.C.S.: 541810
Lucy B. Siegel (Pres & CEO)
Keiko Okano (VP)
Carinna Gano (Acct Exec)
Alex Varney (Acct Exec)

JB Cumberland PR   (1)
276 Fifth Ave Ste 206, New York, NY 10001

Didit.com, Inc.—(Continued)
Tel.: (646) 230-6940
Web Site: http://www.jbcumberlandpr.com
Public Relations Agency
N.A.I.C.S.: 541820
Joanna Cumberland (Pres)

LVM Group, Inc.   (1)
276 Fifth Ave Ste 205, New York, NY 10001
Tel.: (212) 499-6500
Web Site: http://www.lvmgroup.com
Emp.: 3
Public Relations & Marketing Communications Services
N.A.I.C.S.: 541820
Jeannette M. Boccini (Exec VP)
Rachel Antman (VP)

Laser Image Corporation   (1)
1 Fairchild Ct Ste 400, Plainview, NY 11803   (100%)
Tel.: (516) 349-9700
Sales Range: $1-9.9 Million
Emp.: 10
Digital Printing & Direct Mail Services
N.A.I.C.S.: 323120
Michael Regan (Pres)

DIDLAKE, INC.
8641 Breeden Ave, Manassas, VA 20110
Tel.: (703) 361-4195
Web Site: https://www.didlake.org
Year Founded: 1965
Sales Range: $50-74.9 Million
Emp.: 386
Disability Assistance Services
N.A.I.C.S.: 624120
Joseph Pascale (Chm)
Pamela N. Moody (Vice Chm)
Sarah Pitkin (Sec)
Nathan Gilbert (Treas)
John Craig (VP-Rehabilitation)
Bruce Gross (Gen Counsel & VP)
Trisha Juerling (VP-HR)
Denee Fortune Mcknight (CFO & VP-Fin)
Mike Payne (VP-Contract Ops)
Ivy Tetreault (VP-Info Tech)

DIDRICK MEDICAL, INC.
999 Vanderbilt Beach Rd Ste 200, Naples, FL 34108
Tel.: (877) 343-7425
Web Site: http://www.didrickmedical.com
Sales Range: $1-9.9 Million
Emp.: 2
Medical Device Mfr
N.A.I.C.S.: 339112
Dan Didrick (CEO)

DIE CUTS WITH A VIEW
2250 N University Pkwy Ste 486, Provo, UT 84604
Tel.: (801) 224-6766
Web Site: http://www.diecutswithaview.com
Sales Range: $10-24.9 Million
Emp.: 110
Decorative Paper Products
N.A.I.C.S.: 424110
Nancy M. Hill (Founder & Pres)

DIE SERVICES INTERNATIONAL, LLC
45000 Van Born Rd, Belleville, MI 48112-0339
Tel.: (734) 699-3400
Web Site: http://www.dieservicesinternational.com
Year Founded: 2010
Sales Range: $50-74.9 Million
Emp.: 20
Mfr of Automotive Sheet Metal Stampings & Dies
N.A.I.C.S.: 333514
Michael Rosochacki (Gen Mgr)

DIE-TECH INDUSTRIES, INC.
102 Automation Dr, Carrollton, GA 30017
Tel.: (770) 836-1042
Web Site: https://www.1dietech.com
Year Founded: 1987
Sales Range: $25-49.9 Million
Emp.: 85
Stamping Die Mfr
N.A.I.C.S.: 333514
Jerry Wysoczynski (Co-Founder)
Tom Wysoczynski (Co-Founder)

DIEBOLD GLASCOCK ADVERTISING, INC.
10100 Lantern Rd Ste 225, Fishers, IN 46037
Tel.: (317) 813-2222
Web Site: https://www.dgsmarketingengineers.com
Year Founded: 1985
Sales Range: $1-9.9 Million
Emp.: 10
Advetising Agency
N.A.I.C.S.: 541810
Marc Diebold (Founder & Chm)
Leslie Galbreath (CEO)
Justin Brown (Sr Dir-Art)
Chuck Bates (Dir-PR)

DIEDRICHS & ASSOCIATES, INC.
915 Center St, Cedar Falls, IA 50613
Tel.: (319) 266-0549
Web Site: http://www.iowaengineer.com
Sales Range: $1-9.9 Million
Emp.: 22
Engineeering Services
N.A.I.C.S.: 541330
Robert Diedrichs (Pres)
Randy Rigdon (Mgr-Shop)
Dennis Padget (Owner & Mgr-HR)

DIEFENTHAL HOLDINGS, LLC
1750 S Ln Ste 1, Mandeville, LA 70471
Tel.: (985) 867-1801
Sales Range: $25-49.9 Million
Emp.: 20
Holding Company
N.A.I.C.S.: 551112
James R. Diefenthal (Pres & CEO)
Peter Beach (Controller)

Subsidiaries:

PET Processors, LLC   (1)
1350 Bacon Rd, Painesville, OH 44077-4718
Tel.: (440) 354-4321
Web Site: http://www.petus.com
Sales Range: $25-49.9 Million
Mfr of Plastics Materials Or Resins
N.A.I.C.S.: 325211
Ken Berlin (Acct Mgr)

Premium Valve Services, LLC   (1)
16220 Interstate 10 E, Channelview, TX 77530
Tel.: (281) 457-2565
Web Site: http://www.premiumvalveservices.com
Sales Range: $25-49.9 Million
Emp.: 10
Industrial Valves
N.A.I.C.S.: 332911
Rodney Payne (VP & Gen Mgr)

DIEGO PLUS EDUCATION CORPORATION
42455 10th St W Ste 105, Lancaster, CA 93534
Tel.: (661) 272-1225
Year Founded: 2009
Sales Range: $1-9.9 Million
Emp.: 93
Educational Support Services

N.A.I.C.S.: 611710
Steve Gocke (CFO)
Dante R. Simi (CEO)
Skip Hansen (VP)
Mary Jane Almandoz (Pres)
Robert Harenski (Sec)

DIEHL FORD INC.
1820 James St, Bellingham, WA 98225
Tel.: (360) 734-2640
Web Site: http://www.diehlford.com
Rev.: $26,000,000
Emp.: 68
Automobiles, New & Used
N.A.I.C.S.: 441110
Robert C. Diehl (Pres)
Mike Diehl (Gen Mgr-Sls)
Randy Larsen (Mgr-Used Cars)

DIEHL WOODWORKING MACHINERY, INC.
981 S Wabash St, Wabash, IN 46992-4125
Tel.: (260) 563-2102
Web Site: https://www.diehlmachines.com
Year Founded: 1909
Woodworking Machinery Mfr
N.A.I.C.S.: 333243

DIELECTRIC CORPORATION
W141 N9250 Fountain Blvd, Menomonee Falls, WI 53051
Tel.: (262) 255-2600
Web Site: http://www.dielectriccorp.com
Year Founded: 1966
Sales Range: $10-24.9 Million
Emp.: 94
Plastic Parts & Components Mfr & Custom Fabricator
N.A.I.C.S.: 326199
Robert Collins (VP-Sls-Strategic Accts)
Michael Esser (Pres & CEO)
Perry Pabich (VP-Sls & Mktg)
Todd Zimdars (CFO)
Thomas Gardner (Mgr-Product Dev & Application Engrg)
Daryl Groe (Gen Mgr)

Subsidiaries:

Centerline Machine, Inc.   (1)
777 S Industrial Dr, Waupaca, WI 54981
Tel.: (715) 258-5229
Web Site: http://www.centerlinemachine.com
Sales Range: $1-9.9 Million
Emp.: 45
Precision Machining & Fabrication Services
N.A.I.C.S.: 332999
Beth Brown (Office Mgr)
Todd Zimdars (CFO)

DIELECTRICS INDUSTRIES INC.
300 Burnett Rd, Chicopee, MA 01020
Tel.: (413) 594-8111
Web Site: http://www.dielectrics.com
Year Founded: 1997
Sales Range: $25-49.9 Million
Emp.: 180
Mfr of Unsupported Plastics Film & Sheet
N.A.I.C.S.: 326113
Eric C. Stahl (Pres & CEO)
John Kelser (COO)

DIEMOLDING CORPORATION
125 Rasbach St, Canastota, NY 13032-1430
Tel.: (315) 697-2221
Web Site: http://www.diemolding.com
Year Founded: 1920
Sales Range: $75-99.9 Million
Emp.: 100

Mfr of Plastics & Proprietary Products for Medical & Automotive Industries
N.A.I.C.S.: 326199
John Pinard (Mgr-Special Projects)
Jim Morin (Gen Mgr)
Cindy Ondriezek (Mgr-Quality)
Sandra Stage (Engr-Quality)
Greg Guignard (Mgr-Engrg)
Joal Vanderwerken (Mgr-Maintenance & Facilities)

DIENER BRICK COMPANY
W Cuthbert Blvd & Park Ave, Collingswood, NJ 08108
Tel.: (856) 858-2000
Web Site: https://www.dienerbrick.com
Year Founded: 1925
Rev.: $16,000,000
Emp.: 12
Construction Materials Mfr
N.A.I.C.S.: 423320
Mike Mignogna (Mgr-Dispatch)

DIEPHOLZ CHEVROLET CADILLAC INC.
631 W Lincoln Ave, Charleston, IL 61920
Tel.: (217) 348-0141
Web Site: https://www.diepholzchevrolet.com
Sales Range: $10-24.9 Million
Emp.: 50
New Car Dealers
N.A.I.C.S.: 441110
Kenneth R. Diepholz (Treas)
Ronald Diepholz (Pres)

DIERBERGS MARKETS INC.
16690 Swingley Ridge Rd, Chesterfield, MO 63017-0758
Tel.: (636) 532-8884
Web Site: https://www.dierbergs.com
Year Founded: 1854
Sales Range: $550-599.9 Million
Emp.: 4,000
Supermarket
N.A.I.C.S.: 445110
Andrew J. Pauk (COO & Sr VP)
Gary Engelhardt (Dir-Store)

DIESEL FORWARD, INC.
15 International Dr Ste E, East Granby, CT 06026-9718
Tel.: (860) 844-8465
Web Site: http://www.dieselforward.com
General Automotive Repair
N.A.I.C.S.: 811111
Ken Roberts (Mgr)
Houman Kashanipour (Pres)
Robert Breunig (CEO)

Subsidiaries:

Dipaco, Inc.   (1)
105 East Parr Blvd, Reno, NV 89512
Tel.: (775) 329-7511
Web Site: http://www.dipaco.com
Rev.: $3,333,333
Emp.: 25
Gasket, Packing & Sealing Device Mfr
N.A.I.C.S.: 339991
Rick Bumgardner (Mgr-Product)
John Walker (Pres & CEO)

DIESEL INJECTION SERVICE CO., INC.
4710 Allmond Ave, Louisville, KY 40209
Tel.: (502) 357-7803
Web Site: http://www.dieselusa.com
Year Founded: 1950
Sales Range: $50-74.9 Million
Emp.: 125
Engines & Parts Diesel
N.A.I.C.S.: 423830

Steve Bailey *(Pres & COO)*
Renee Glasscock *(Controller)*

DIESEL MACHINERY INC.
4301 N Cliff Ave, Sioux Falls, SD
57104-5517
Tel.: (605) 336-0411   SD
Web Site:
  http://www.dieselmachinery.com
Year Founded: 1965
Sales Range: $25-49.9 Million
Emp.: 55
Construction & Mining Machinery
N.A.I.C.S.: 423810
Dan Healy *(Pres)*
Don Mosey *(VP & Gen Mgr)*
Steve Ward *(Mgr-Svcs)*
Kate Hansen *(Mgr-Parts)*

DIESEL PERFORMANCE INC.
2804 E Tremont St, Stockton, CA
95205
Tel.: (209) 946-0233
Web Site:
  https://www.dieselperformance.com
Sales Range: $10-24.9 Million
Emp.: 32
Sales of Truck Equipment & Parts
N.A.I.C.S.: 441330
Lori Shields *(Controller)*

DIESEL POWER EQUIPMENT COMPANY INCORPORATED
13619 Industrial Rd, Omaha, NE
68137
Tel.: (402) 330-5100
Web Site:
  http://www.dieselpower.com
Sales Range: $10-24.9 Million
Emp.: 50
Engines & Parts, Air-Cooled
N.A.I.C.S.: 423830
Brian Rehberger *(Mgr-Parts & Svcs)*
Ken Womack *(Mgr-Parts)*

DIESEL RADIATOR CO.
1990 Janice Ave, Melrose Park, IL
60160
Tel.: (708) 345-9244
Web Site:
  https://www.dieselradiator.com
Rev.: $18,700,000
Emp.: 42
All Other Motor Vehicle Parts Mfr
N.A.I.C.S.: 336390
Humberto Suarez *(Co-Pres)*
Brian Light *(CFO)*
Lisa Burkhart *(VP)*

DIETZ & KOLODENKO CO.
2404 S Wolcott Ave Ste 24, Chicago,
IL 60608-5300
Tel.: (312) 666-6320
Rev.: $15,500,000
Emp.: 16
Fresh Fruit & Vegetable Merchant
Whslr
N.A.I.C.S.: 424480
Angela Margaris *(Mgr)*
Nicholas Gaglione *(Pres-Fin)*

DIETZ & WATSON INC.
5701 Tacony St, Philadelphia, PA
19135-4311
Tel.: (215) 831-9000   NJ
Web Site:
  http://www.dietzandwatson.com
Year Founded: 1939
Sales Range: $200-249.9 Million
Deli Products Mfr, Processor & Distr
N.A.I.C.S.: 311611
Ruth Eni *(Chm)*
Louis Eni *(CEO)*
Christopher Eni *(COO)*

DIETZGEN CORPORATION

121 Kelsey Ln Ste G, Tampa, FL
33619
Tel.: (813) 286-4767   FL
Web Site: http://www.dietzgen.com
Year Founded: 1885
Converted Paper Mfr & Distr
N.A.I.C.S.: 322299
Tony Muscatelli *(VP-Sls)*

DIFIORE GROUP
155 Pool St, Rochester, NY 14606
Tel.: (585) 235-2310
Web Site:
  https://www.difioregroup.com
Year Founded: 1919
Sales Range: $10-24.9 Million
Emp.: 80
Highway, Street & Bridge Construction Services
N.A.I.C.S.: 237310
Brian Difiore *(VP)*

DIGAGOGO VENTURES CORP.
645 Griswold St Ste 3500, Detroit, MI
48226-4120
Tel.: (704) 246-8073   DE
Year Founded: 2010
Light Bulb Power Products Mfr
N.A.I.C.S.: 335139
Brian Teed *(CFO)*
Kenneth A. Williams *(CEO)*

DIGALOG SYSTEMS INC.
3180 S 166th St, New Berlin, WI
53151
Tel.: (262) 797-8000
Web Site:
  https://www.digalogsystems.com
Year Founded: 1973
Sales Range: $10-24.9 Million
Emp.: 20
Test Equipment For Electronic &
Electrical Circuits
N.A.I.C.S.: 334515
Justin Thompto *(Engr-Electrical)*

DIGENNARO COMMUNICATIONS
18 W 21st St 6th Fl, New York, NY
10010
Tel.: (212) 966-9525
Web Site: https://www.digennaro-
usa.com
Sales Range: $1-9.9 Million
Emp.: 26
Public Relation Agency Services
N.A.I.C.S.: 541820
Samantha DiGennaro *(Founder & CEO)*
Robert Osmond *(Exec VP-Client Svc)*
Michael Burgi *(Sr VP-Content & News)*
Megan McIlroy *(Sr VP)*
Stephanie Agresta *(Sr VP-Client Svc & Bus Dev)*

DIGERATI GROUP, LLC.
230 W Monroe Ste 350, Chicago, IL
60606
Tel.: (312) 360-1900
Web Site:
  http://www.digeratigroup.com
Year Founded: 2005
Sales Range: $1-9.9 Million
Emp.: 13
Computers Dealers
N.A.I.C.S.: 423430
John Kampas *(Pres)*

DIGI-KEY CORPORATION
701 Brooks Ave S, Thief River Falls,
MN 56701
Tel.: (218) 681-6674
Web Site: https://www.digikey.com
Year Founded: 1972
Sales Range: $1-4.9 Billion

Emp.: 5,135
Other Electronic Parts & Equipment
Merchant Wholesalers
N.A.I.C.S.: 423690
Dave Doherty *(Pres)*

DIGI-TEL COMMUNICATIONS, LLC
11215 Lee Hwy Ste L, Fairfax, VA
22030-5660
Tel.: (703) 352-0203   VA
Web Site:
  http://www.adcommdigitel.com
Year Founded: 1997
Rev.: $12,000,000
Emp.: 65
Telephone Communication, Except
Radio
N.A.I.C.S.: 517121
Stephen Finch *(CEO)*

DIGICELL INTERNATIONAL, INC.
6101 Washington Blvd Ste 201, Culver City, CA 90232-7472
Tel.: (310) 836-8600
Web Site: http://www.digicellintl.com
Sales Range: $10-24.9 Million
Emp.: 55
Miscellaneous Product Whslr
N.A.I.C.S.: 456120
Dony Ebized *(Pres)*

DIGICON CORPORATION
510 Spring St Ste 100, Herndon, VA
20170
Tel.: (703) 621-1000
Web Site: http://www.digicon.com
Year Founded: 1985
Sales Range: $25-49.9 Million
Emp.: 300
Computer Programming Services
N.A.I.C.S.: 541511
John J. Wu *(Chm, Pres & CEO)*

DIGILAB, INC.
100 S St, Hopkinton, MA 01748
Tel.: (508) 893-3130
Web Site:
  http://www.digilabglobal.com
Mfr of Spectrometers & Accessories
N.A.I.C.S.: 334516
Sidney Braginsky *(Exec Chm)*
John Moore *(CEO & COO)*

DIGILANT, INC.
2 Oliver St Ste 901, Boston, MA
02109
Tel.: (617) 849-6900
Web Site: http://www.digilant.com
Year Founded: 2009
Software Developer
N.A.I.C.S.: 513210
Krishna Boppana *(Chief Strategy Officer)*
Ricky McClellen *(CTO)*
Miguel Prieto *(CFO)*
Eduardo Arevalo *(Dir-Comml & Mgr-Chile)*
Alexis Reategui *(Dir-Comml & Mgr-Peru)*
Patrick Robson *(Dir-Comml & Mgr-UK)*
Juan Rodes *(Gen Counsel)*
Ester Pascual *(CMO)*
Raquel Rosenthal *(CEO)*
Todd Heger *(Chief Revenue Officer)*
Abhinav Bondalapati *(Co-CTO)*
Chris McCourt *(Co-CFO)*
Colin Brown *(COO)*
Shaun Gibbons *(Sr VP-Campaign Solutions)*

Subsidiaries:

Digilant B.V.   **(1)**

Prinseniland 57, 1013 LM, Amsterdam,
Netherlands
Tel.: (31) 20 7795943
Software Developer
N.A.I.C.S.: 513210

Digilant Brasil   **(1)**
Rua Luigi Galvani 42 cj 123/124, CEP
04575-020, Sao Paulo, Brazil
Tel.: (55) 11 5507 7007
Software Developer
N.A.I.C.S.: 513210

Digilant Madrid   **(1)**
Avenida de Brasil 17 entreplanta A, Madrid,
28020, Spain
Tel.: (34) 91 770 46 99
Software Developer
N.A.I.C.S.: 513210
Pedro Robert *(Mng Dir)*

Digilant Mexico   **(1)**
Galileo 20 Suite 102 Col Polanco Chapultepec, Delegacion Miguel Hidalgo, CP 11560,
Mexico, Mexico
Tel.: (52) 55 5281 7339
Web Site: http://www.digilant.com
Emp.: 5
Software Developer
N.A.I.C.S.: 513210
Mauricio Vazquez *(Mng Dir)*

DIGILITI MONEY GROUP, INC.
18671 Lake Dr E dellFive Business
Park G, Minneapolis, MN 55317
Tel.: (952) 698-6980   DE
Web Site:
  http://www.digilitimoney.com
Year Founded: 2010
Cloud-based, SaaS Technology Services
N.A.I.C.S.: 518210
Bryan D. Meier *(Interim CEO, CFO & Exec VP)*

DIGIMEDICAL SOLUTIONS, INC
5400 Rustic Trail Ste B, Colleyville,
TX 76034
Tel.: (817) 503-8880
Year Founded: 2005
Pharmaceuticals Product Mfr
N.A.I.C.S.: 325412
David A. Lee *(Pres & CEO)*

DIGINEER, INC.
505 Hwy 169 N Ste 750, Minneapolis, MN 55441
Tel.: (763) 210-2300
Web Site: https://www.digineer.com
Year Founded: 1998
Sales Range: $10-24.9 Million
Emp.: 100
IT Consulting Services
N.A.I.C.S.: 541690
Michael Lacey *(Pres)*

DIGITAL AIR STRIKE INC.
6991 E Camelback Rd Ste B111,
Scottsdale, AZ 85251
Web Site: https://digitalairstrike.com
Year Founded: 2007
Social Media Technology, Online
Reputation & Consumer Engagement
Company
N.A.I.C.S.: 541613
Michael Pordon *(CFO)*
Rich Brown *(CTO)*
Glenn Hardy *(COO)*
Dave Venneri *(Chief Revenue Officer)*
Bill Taylor *(Sr VP-Partnerships)*
Erica Sietsma *(Sr VP-Consumer Engagement & Strategy)*
Deke Keating *(Sr VP-People & Programs)*
Christina Wofford *(VP-Mktg & Comm)*
Alexi Venneri *(Founder & CEO)*

Subsidiaries:

3 Birds Marketing LLC   **(1)**

Digital Air Strike Inc.—(Continued)

321 W Rosemary St Ste 110, Chapel Hill,
NC 27514
Web Site: http://www.3birdsmarketing.com
Services Related to Advertising
N.A.I.C.S.: 541890
Barron Meade (VP-Bus Dev)

Target Media Partners   (1)
5200 Lankershim Blvd #350, North Holly-
wood, CA 91601
Tel.: (323) 930-3123
Web Site:
    http://www.targetmediapartners.com
Advertising & Periodical Publisher
N.A.I.C.S.: 513120
Mark Schiffmacher (Founder & Co-CEO)
Susan Humphreville (CFO)
Andie Smith (Coord-AP)
Gerri Copeland (Dir-Trng)
Karen Heinze (Dir-HR)
Cerise Hultberg (Supvr-Help Desk)
Boris Bronshteyn (VP-Tech)
Mario Alvarez (Mgr-Sys Support)
Dave Duckwitz (Co-CEO)
Jim Sington (COO & Exec VP)
Robert Izzy Izquierdo (Head-Product Mgmt)
Kevin Aylmer (VP-Digital Sls)
Tom Minogue (VP-Digital Sls)
Bobby Ralston (VP-Fin)
Jane Zhang (VP-Monetization)
Linda Coffman (VP-Ops)
Ed Leader (VP-Ops)

Subsidiary (Domestic):

Buy & EZ Sell Recycler
Corporation   (2)
4954 Van Nuys Blvd, Sherman Oaks, CA
91403
Tel.: (818) 772-3590
Web Site: http://www.recycler.com
Sales Range: $10-24.9 Million
Emp.: 40
Classified Newspaper Publisher
N.A.I.C.S.: 513120
Brenda Madena (Gen Mgr)

Unit (Domestic):

Nickel Nik, Wheel Deals &
Driveline   (2)
13026 W McFarlane Rd Bldg D2 Unit 1,
Airway Heights, WA 99001
Tel.: (509) 244-8200
Web Site: http://www.recycler.com
Sales Range: $10-24.9 Million
Emp.: 50
Advertising Newspaper
N.A.I.C.S.: 513110
Kristen Bryant (Reg Mgr)

Steals N Deals   (2)
1010 C M Fagan Dr Ste 102, Hammond,
LA 70403
Tel.: (504) 468-8684
Web Site: http://www.newsonwheels.com
Sales Range: $10-24.9 Million
Emp.: 20
Publishing of Periodicals
N.A.I.C.S.: 513120
Toya Domineck (Gen Mgr)

Subsidiary (Domestic):

Trucker Publications Inc.   (2)
1123 S University Ave Ste 320, Little Rock,
AR 72204-1609
Tel.: (501) 666-0500
Web Site: http://www.thetrucker.com
Newspaper Publishing
N.A.I.C.S.: 513120
Lyndon Finney (Editor)

DIGITAL BLUE DOG, INC.
2147 Porter Lake Dr Ste E, Sarasota,
FL 34240
Tel.: (941) 755-5686   **FL**
Web Site:
    http://www.digitalbluedog.com
Year Founded: 2011
Sales Range: Less than $1 Million
Digital Out of Home Advertising &
Digital Signage
N.A.I.C.S.: 541850
John R. Boyle (Pres & CEO)

DIGITAL BOARDWALK, INC.
1457 N 9th Ave, Pensacola, FL
32503
Tel.: (850) 456-2225
Web Site:
    https://www.digitalboardwalk.com
Year Founded: 2008
Sales Range: $10-24.9 Million
Emp.: 7
IT Support Services
N.A.I.C.S.: 541519
Tim Shoop (Pres & CEO)
Brian Wilkey (Sr VP)

DIGITAL CHECK CORP.
630 Dundee Rd Ste 210, Northbrook,
IL 60062
Tel.: (847) 446-2285
Web Site:
    https://www.digitalcheck.com
All Other Personal Services
N.A.I.C.S.: 812990
Thomas P. Anderson (Pres & CEO)
Chris Ellinas (Dir-Sls-EMEA)
Alex Trombetta (VP-Intl Sls)
Eric Gearding (Mgr-Bus Dev-North
America)
John Gainer (Dir-Strategy)
Jeff Hempker (Exec VP)
Paul Slager (CIO)
Merrick Hatcher (Gen Counsel &
Exec VP-Corp Dev)

Subsidiaries:

Nextscan Inc.   (1)
690 S Industry Way, Meridian, ID 83642-
7899
Tel.: (208) 514-4000
Web Site: http://www.nextscan.com
Photographic & Photocopying Equipment
Mfr
N.A.I.C.S.: 333310
Kurt Breish (Pres & CEO)

DIGITAL CHOCOLATE, INC.
1855 S Grant St 2nd Fl, San Mateo,
CA 94402
Tel.: (650) 372-1600   **DE**
Web Site:
    http://www.digitalchocolate.com
Year Founded: 2003
Sales Range: $10-24.9 Million
Emp.: 65
Social Media Game Publishing
N.A.I.C.S.: 513210
W. M. Hawkins (CEO)

DIGITAL COLOR GRAPHICS
105 James Way Rear Buld, South-
ampton, PA 18966
Tel.: (215) 942-7500
Web Site: http://www.digital-
color.com
Year Founded: 1997
Sales Range: $1-9.9 Million
Emp.: 40
Commercial Printing
N.A.I.C.S.: 323111
John Rosenthal (Pres)

DIGITAL CONNECTIONS, INC.
152 Molly Walton Dr, Hendersonville,
TN 37075
Tel.: (615) 826-5000
Web Site:
    http://www.digitalconnections.com
Year Founded: 1992
Sales Range: $25-49.9 Million
Emp.: 40
Systems Integration
N.A.I.C.S.: 541512
Lee Williams (Chm & CEO)
Duke Gatlin (COO)
Sarah Jones (Exec VP-HR & Admin)

**DIGITAL CURRENCY SER-
VICES INC.**

500 E Carson Plz Dr 203, Carson,
CA 90745
Tel.: (310) 518-9441
Rev.: $12,100,000
Emp.: 88
Check Cashing Agencies
N.A.I.C.S.: 522390
Daniel Roberts (Pres)

DIGITAL ENERGY WORLD
4809 Ave N, Brooklyn, NY 11234
Tel.: (718) 251-0096
Web Site:
    http://www.digitalenergyworld.com
Year Founded: 2001
Sales Range: $10-24.9 Million
Emp.: 16
Cell Phone & Laptop Accessories
N.A.I.C.S.: 449210
Zach Kalatsky (Art Dir)

DIGITAL FINANCIAL GROUP
4970 S 900 E Ste J, Salt Lake City,
UT 84117
Tel.: (801) 327-9422
Web Site: https://www.digitalfg.com
Year Founded: 2002
Sales Range: $1-9.9 Million
Emp.: 40
Credit, Debit & Prepaid Card Pro-
cessing, Payroll, Check Management
& Payment Services
N.A.I.C.S.: 522390
Cory Gray (Owner & CEO)
Dave Parson (VP-Sls)
Tina Suazo (Acct Mgr)

DIGITAL FUEL, LLC
339 Auburn St Ste 12, Newton, MA
02466
Tel.: (617) 274-8400   **DE**
Web Site: http://digitalfuelcapital.com
Year Founded: 2013
Equity Investment Firm
N.A.I.C.S.: 523999
Carson Biederman (Founder & Pres)
Stephen Owen (VP)

DIGITAL GATEWAY INC.
4626 N 300 W Ste 200, Provo, UT
84604
Tel.: (801) 492-3576
Web Site:
    http://www.digitalgateway.com
Year Founded: 2001
Rev.: $9,300,000
Emp.: 60
Computer & Software Stores
N.A.I.C.S.: 449210
Lance Terrell (Mgr-Support)
Duane Walker (Dir-Implementation
Svcs)
Jim Phillips (Owner)

DIGITAL HANDS, LLC
400 N Ashley Dr Ste 900, Tampa, FL
33602
Tel.: (813) 229-8324
Web Site:
    http://www.digitalhands.com
Year Founded: 2001
Sales Range: $1-9.9 Million
Emp.: 25
Cloud Security Solutions, Application
Management & Managed IT Services
N.A.I.C.S.: 541512
Charlotte Baker (CEO)
Mark T. Geary (Chief Svcs Officer)
Jeff Foresman (Chief Info Security
Officer & VP-Security Ops)
Jeff Multz (Chief Revenue Officer)
Jason Allen (CTO)
Kim Bilderback (Assoc VP-Channel
Sls)
Dewayne Alford (VP-Ops)
Charlotte Kibert (Chief Customer
Officer)

**DIGITAL INTELLIGENCE SYS-
TEMS, LLC**
8270 Greensboro Dr Ste 1000,
McLean, VA 22102
Tel.: (703) 752-7900   **DE**
Web Site: http://www.disys.com
Year Founded: 1994
Sales Range: $400-449.9 Million
Emp.: 3,500
Information Technology Staffing &
Consulting Services
N.A.I.C.S.: 541690
Mahfuz Ahmed (CEO)
Ahmar Abbas (VP-Global Svcs)
Maruf Ahmed (Pres)
Curry Nichols (VP-Tech Consulting
Svcs)
Laura Smith (VP-Global HR)
Lily Yeh (VP-Strategy, Programs &
Plng)
Alex Baldwin (Gen Counsel & Sec)
Tim Kirby (VP-High Tech & Health-
care Svcs)
Scott Evans (VP-Fin & Acctg Staffing)
Steve Matas (VP-Healthcare & Life
Sciences Consulting Svcs)
Firas Al-Hindi (VP-Ops)
Ashish Srivastava (VP-Ops-Intl)
Shabbir Alibhai (Dir-Intelligent Pro-
cess Automation)
Paul Pinto (VP-Global Svc Sls)
Sandra Schwartzman (VP-PR)
Mike Leroy (CFO)

Subsidiaries:

Princeton Information Ltd.   (1)
727 N Broadway Ste C-1, North Massa-
pequa, NY 11758-2348
Tel.: (516) 710-7712
Web Site:
    http://www.princetoninformation.com
Sales Range: $10-24.9 Million
Emp.: 1,500
Information Technology Staffing & Consult-
ing Services
N.A.I.C.S.: 541690
Justin Marcus (COO)
Maryjo Terranova (Acct Mgr)
Michael Rand (Reg Mgr-Recruiting)
Nina Beckford (Mgr-Billing)
Noel Marcus (Founder)

Signature Consultants LLC   (1)
200 Cypress St Rd, Fort Lauderdale, FL
33309-3047
Tel.: (954) 677-1020
Web Site: http://www.sigconsult.com
Sales Range: $25-49.9 Million
Emp.: 1,000
IT Services
N.A.I.C.S.: 561320
Nancy Tarchis (Mgr-Benefits)
Philip Monti (CFO & Treas)

DIGITAL LIGHTWAVE, INC.
1780 102nd Ave N, Saint Petersburg,
FL 33716
Tel.: (727) 442-6677   **DE**
Web Site: http://www.lightwave.com
Year Founded: 1991
Sales Range: $10-24.9 Million
Emp.: 39
Design, Develop, Market & Support
Diagnostic Products for Monitoring,
Maintaining & Managing Fiber Optic
Networks
N.A.I.C.S.: 334220
Bryan J. Zwan (Chm)
Mo Karimi (Dir-Ops)
Thomas L. Newhart (VP-Sls)
Sharon Bayly (Mgr-Bus Dev)
Michael L. Martin (Exec VP)

**DIGITAL PERIPHERAL SOLU-
TIONS, INC.**

8015 E Crystal Dr, Anaheim, CA
92807
Tel.: (714) 998-3440
Web Site: http://www.q-c.com
Sales Range: $10-24.9 Million
Emp.: 40
Mfr of Computers, Peripherals & Software
N.A.I.C.S.: 423430
Priti Sharma (Pres)
Long Nghiem (Mgr-Sls)

DIGITAL PROSPECTORS CORP.
100 Domain Dr Ste 103, Exeter, NH
03833
Tel.: (603) 772-2700
Web Site:
   https://digitalprospectors.com
Year Founded: 1999
Custom Computer Programing Management Consulting Services
N.A.I.C.S.: 541511
Jessica Catino (Pres)
Chris Roos (Co-Founder & Principal)
Don Catino (Co-Founder & Principal)
Jessica Catino (Pres)
Corey Miller (VP-Sls)
Emma Charney (Acct Exec)
Janet S. Walsh (Dir-HR)
Jon Rostler (Mgr-Bus Dev)
Justin Pleadwell (Mktg Mgr)
Kevin Shea (VP-Recruiting Ops)
Lisa Wolanski (Acct Exec)
Peter Roos (Acct Mgr-R&D)
Sabrina Dugas (Officer-Facility Security, Office Mgr & Mgr-HR)
Steve Iannessa (Mng Dir-ERP & BI Div)
Steve Merriman (Acct Mgr-R&D)

DIGITAL PULP
220 E 23rd St Ste 900, New York, NY
10010
Tel.: (212) 679-0676   NY
Web Site: http://www.digitalpulp.com
Year Founded: 1996
Sales Range: $10-24.9 Million
Emp.: 20
Advertising Agencies
N.A.I.C.S.: 541810
Ron Fierman (Pres, CEO & Partner)
Gene Lewis (Partner & Dir-Creative)
Sarah Blecher (Partner & Exec Producer-Web)
Susan Reiter (Acct Dir)
Franco Fiore (Exec Dir-Creative)
Bruce Goodman (Founder)
Christopher Daly (Dir-User Experience)

DIGITAL STORM, INC.
448 Kato Ter, Fremont, CA 94539
Tel.: (510) 656-1122
Web Site:
   http://www.digitalstormonline.com
Year Founded: 2001
Sales Range: $10-24.9 Million
Emp.: 37
Gaming Computers Mfr
N.A.I.C.S.: 541519
Paramjit Chana (Pres)

DIGITAL VIDEO SYSTEMS, INC.
357 Castro St Ste 5, Mountain View,
CA 94041-1258
Tel.: (650) 938-8815   DE
Web Site: http://www.dvsystems.com
Year Founded: 1992
Sales Range: $75-99.9 Million
Emp.: 225
Developer of Digital Video Technologies
N.A.I.C.S.: 334310
Douglas T. Watson (COO)

DIGITAL VOICE SYSTEMS, INC.
234 Littleton Rd, Westford, MA 01866
Tel.: (978) 392-0002   MA
Web Site: https://www.dvsinc.com
Year Founded: 1988
Sales Range: $1-9.9 Million
Voice Compression Technologies Developer, Mfr & Marketer
N.A.I.C.S.: 334413
John C. Hardwick (Co-Founder & Pres)
Jae S. Lim (Co-Founder & Chm)
Dan W. Griffin (Dir-R&D)

DIGITALBRAINZ INC.
17892 US Hwy 41, Lutz, FL 33549
Tel.: (813) 406-0999
Web Site:
   http://www.digitalbrainz.com
Sales Range: $1-9.9 Million
IT Solutions
N.A.I.C.S.: 541519
Brad Savage (VP)
Dale Savage (Pres)

DIGITALPOST INTERACTIVE, INC.
4040 Barranca Pkwy Ste 220, Irvine,
CA 92604
Tel.: (949) 333-7500   NV
Web Site: http://www.dglp.com
Sales Range: $1-9.9 Million
Emp.: 6
Digital Media Sharing Applications
N.A.I.C.S.: 513210
Brian Goss (CTO)

DIGITEK SOFTWARE, INC.
650 Radio Dr, Lewis Center, OH
43035
Tel.: (614) 764-8875
Web Site:
   https://www.digiteksoftware.com
Year Founded: 1994
Sales Range: $10-24.9 Million
Emp.: 40
IT Consulting & Outsourcing Services
N.A.I.C.S.: 541519
Chetan Bhuta (Founder, Pres & CEO)
Vivek Kanakia (Acct Mgr)
Bharat Gandhi (VP-Fin)
Sonal Shah (VP-Overseas Ops)
Theodore Agranat (VP-Mktg)
Pankaj Oza (Acct Mgr)
Deepak Chavan (Dir-Offshore-Projects)

DIGITEL CORPORATION
2600 School Dr, Atlanta, GA 30360
Tel.: (770) 451-1111
Web Site: http://www.digitel.net
Sales Range: $10-24.9 Million
Emp.: 68
Mfr & Distribution Of Communication Equipment
N.A.I.C.S.: 459999
Luis Simonet (Chief Info Security Officer)
Jason Asbury (Pres)

DIGITY COMPANIES, LLC
701 Northpoint Parkway Ste 500,
West Palm Beach, FL 33407
Tel.: (561) 616-4600
Web Site: http://www.digity.me
Radio Station Operator
N.A.I.C.S.: 516110
Dean Goodman (CEO)

Subsidiaries:

KTGL-FM   (1)
3800 Cornhusker Hwy, Lincoln, NE 68504
Tel.: (402) 466-1234
Web Site: http://www.ktgl.com

Sales Range: $10-24.9 Million
Emp.: 35
Radio Stations
N.A.I.C.S.: 516110
Joy Patten (Dir-Sls)

DIGNITAS TECHNOLOGIES, LLC
3504 Lk Lynda Dr Ste 170, Orlando,
FL 32817
Tel.: (407) 601-7847
Web Site:
   http://www.dignitastechnologies.com
Year Founded: 2004
Sales Range: $1-9.9 Million
Emp.: 60
Application Software Publisher
N.A.I.C.S.: 513210
Elizabeth Burch (Co-Owner, Pres & CEO)
Jon Watkins (Founder, Co-Owner, CTO & VP)
Bob Burch (CTO)
Marlo Verdesca (Program Dir)

DILGARD FROZEN FOODS INC.
830 Hayden St, Fort Wayne, IN
46803
Tel.: (260) 422-7531
Web Site:
   http://www.dilgardfoods.com
Sales Range: $10-24.9 Million
Emp.: 40
Retailer of Packaged Frozen Goods
N.A.I.C.S.: 424420
Kevin L. Geesaman (Pres)
Jeff Crosby (VP-Info Sys)

DILIGENT DELIVERY SYSTEMS
9200 Derrington Road Suite 100 &
200, Houston, TX 77064
Tel.: (888) 374-3354
Web Site: http://www.diligentusa.com
Year Founded: 1994
Emp.: 2,500
General Freight Trucking
N.A.I.C.S.: 484121
Darlene Sharbonow (Mgr)

Subsidiaries:

Express Courier International,
Inc.   (1)
3440 Briley Park Blvd. N, Nashville, TN
37207
Tel.: (615) 333-8531
Web Site: http://www.expressdelivers.net
Emp.: 185
Courier Service
N.A.I.C.S.: 492110
Terry Douglas (CEO)

DILL INVESTMENTS, LLC
1836 W Virginia St Ste 105, Mc-
Kinney, TX 75069-7868
Tel.: (972) 342-5408
Web Site:
   http://www.dillinvestments.com
Lessors of Nonresidential Buildings
N.A.I.C.S.: 531120
Chris Dill (Mgr-Property)

DILLING MECHANICAL CONTRACTORS, INC.
111 E Mildred St, Logansport, IN
46947-4961
Tel.: (574) 753-3182
Web Site:
   http://www.dillingmechanical.com
Rev.: $25,600,000
Emp.: 275
Plumbing, Heating & Air-Conditioning Contractors
N.A.I.C.S.: 238220

Frank Freeman (VP)
Pat Clark (Treas & Sec)
Richard L. Dilling Jr. (Pres)

DILLMAN & UPTON, INC.
607 Woodward Ave, Rochester, MI
48307
Tel.: (248) 651-9411
Web Site:
   https://www.dillmanupton.com
Year Founded: 1908
Sales Range: $10-24.9 Million
Emp.: 28
Lumber & Building Material Whslr
N.A.I.C.S.: 444110
Brad Upton (CEO)

DILLMAN FARM
4955 W State Rd 45, Bloomington, IN
47403-9362
Tel.: (812) 825-5525
Web Site:
   https://www.dillmanfarm.com
Year Founded: 1970
Sales Range: $10-24.9 Million
Emp.: 56
Fruit & Vegetable Canning Services
N.A.I.C.S.: 311421
Cary Dillman (Pres)
Rebecca Obley (Mgr-Warehouse)

DILLON PROVISION COMPANY INC.
408 N 1st Ave, Dillon, SC 29536
Tel.: (843) 774-9491
Rev.: $11,713,510
Emp.: 20
Meats & Meat Products
N.A.I.C.S.: 424470
Dan Bozard (Pres)

DILLON TRANSPORT INC.
901 McClintock Dr Ste 300, Burr
Ridge, IL 60527
Tel.: (630) 281-7093
Web Site:
   http://www.dillonlogistics.com
Year Founded: 1984
Sales Range: $10-24.9 Million
Emp.: 800
Local Trucking
N.A.I.C.S.: 484110
Jeffrey T. Dillon (Owner)
Sue Crofts (VP-Admin)
Charles Musgrove (Pres & COO)
Eric Peterson (VP-Maintenance)

Subsidiaries:

Dillon Transport Inc   (1)
1603 Huey Rd, Douglasville, GA 30134
Tel.: (770) 577-3260
Rev.: $1,500,000
Emp.: 15
Trucking Except Local
N.A.I.C.S.: 484121

DILLON YARN CORPORATION
53 E 34th St, Paterson, NJ 07514-
1307
Tel.: (973) 684-1600   NJ
Web Site: http://www.dillonyarn.com
Year Founded: 1986
Sales Range: $150-199.9 Million
Emp.: 50
Textile Processing & Distribution
N.A.I.C.S.: 313110
Deirdra Gallenagh (Dir-Human Resources)

DILMAR OIL COMPANY INC.
1951 W Darlington St, Florence, SC
29501-2050
Tel.: (843) 662-4179   SC
Web Site: https://www.dilmar.com
Year Founded: 1932
Sales Range: $50-74.9 Million
Emp.: 85

Dilmar Oil Company Inc.—(Continued)

Distr of Gasoline, Fuel & Lubricants
N.A.I.C.S.: 457120
R. Earle Atkinson Jr. *(Founder)*

Subsidiaries:

Atkinson Investment Corporation **(1)**
1951 W Darlington St, Florence, SC 29501-
2050
Tel.: (843) 662-4179
Web Site: http://www.dilmar.com
Sales Range: $10-24.9 Million
Emp.: 3
Provider of Lubricants
N.A.I.C.S.: 531120
R. E. Atkinson *(Pres)*

Dilmar Oil Company Inc. - Atlanta
Plant **(1)**
273 Industrial Park Dr, Lawrenceville, GA
30046
Tel.: (866) 818-7226
Petroleum Product Distr
N.A.I.C.S.: 424720

Dilmar Oil Company Inc. - Charleston
Plant **(1)**
7120 Cross County Rd, Charleston, SC
29418
Tel.: (800) 922-2893
Petroleum Product Distr
N.A.I.C.S.: 424720

Dilmar Oil Company Inc. - Charlotte
Plant **(1)**
3531 Dallas High Shoals Rd, Dallas, NC
28034
Tel.: (888) 922-8628
Petroleum Product Distr
N.A.I.C.S.: 424720

Dilmar Oil Company Inc. - Columbia
Plant **(1)**
1959 Bluff Rd, Columbia, SC 29201
Tel.: (866) 885-7978
Petroleum Product Distr
N.A.I.C.S.: 424720

Dilmar Oil Company Inc. - Henderson
Plant **(1)**
615 W US 158 Bypass Rd, Henderson, NC
27536
Tel.: (888) 922-8626
Petroleum Product Distr
N.A.I.C.S.: 424720

Dilmar Oil Company Inc. - Latta
Plant **(1)**
401 S Marion St, Latta, SC 29565
Petroleum Product Distr
N.A.I.C.S.: 424720

Dilmar Oil Company Inc. - Wilmington
Plant **(1)**
1325 Castle Hayne Rd, Wilmington, NC
28401
Petroleum Product Distr
N.A.I.C.S.: 424720

DILON TECHNOLOGIES LLC

12050 Jefferson Ave, Newport News,
VA 23606
Tel.: (757) 269-4910
Web Site: http://www.dilon.com
Clinical & Aerial Imaging Products Mfr
N.A.I.C.S.: 334114
Bob Moussa *(Chm)*

Subsidiaries:

Dune Medical Devices **(1)**
6120 Windward Pkwy Ste 160, Alpharetta,
GA 30005
Tel.: (855) 597-3863
Web Site: http://www.dunemedical.com
Medical & Surgical Equipment Mfr
N.A.I.C.S.: 339112
Amos Goren *(Chm)*
Dan Hashimshony *(Founder)*
Gil Cohen *(Chief Scientific Officer)*
Lior Zrihan *(CFO)*
Lori Chmura *(CEO)*
Skip Ashmore *(Chief Comml Officer)*
Susan Turner *(VP-Healthcare Economics &
Reimbursement)*
Avihai Lachman *(VP-R&D)*

DILWORTH MANUFACTURING COMPANY

6051 Division Hwy, Narvon, PA
17555
Tel.: (717) 354-8956
Web Site:
https://www.windowbubble.com
Year Founded: 1965
Sales Range: $25-49.9 Million
Emp.: 30
Glass Products Mfr
N.A.I.C.S.: 327215
Bill Dilworth *(Pres)*
Jan Dilworth *(Owner)*

DIMAGI, INC.

585 Massachusetts Ave Ste 3, Cam-
bridge, MA 02139
Tel.: (617) 649-2214
Web Site: https://www.dimagi.com
Year Founded: 2002
Sales Range: $1-9.9 Million
Emp.: 21
Software Development Services
N.A.I.C.S.: 541511
Jonathan Jackson *(Co-Founder &
CEO)*
Vikram Sheel Kumar *(Co-Founder &
Chief Medical Officer)*
Cory Zue *(CTO)*
Neal Lesh *(Chief Strategy Officer)*
Carter Powers *(COO)*
Amelia Sagoff *(Product Mgr)*
Daniel Roberts *(VP-Dev & Ops)*
Julie Odette *(Dir-Ops)*
Audrey Philippot *(Dir-Bus Innovation)*
Jason Kass *(Dir-Fin)*
Courtney Kelly *(Dir-Global Svcs)*
Stella Luk *(Dir-India)*
Arya Shekar *(Dir-Legal Affairs)*
Krishna Swamy *(Dir-Ops-India)*
Ryan Hartford *(Dir-Partnerships &
Sls)*
Devika Sarin *(Dir-Partnerships-Asia)*
Lucina Tse *(Mgr-Engrg)*
Clayton Sims *(VP-Mobile Dev)*

DIMAR MANUFACTURING CORPORATION

10123 Main St, Clarence, NY 14031-
2050
Tel.: (716) 759-0351 NY
Web Site: https://www.dimarmfg.com
Year Founded: 2003
Sales Range: $1-9.9 Million
Emp.: 100
Contract Mfr Specializing in Fabri-
cated Metal Products
N.A.I.C.S.: 332999
Gregory A. Fry *(Owner & Pres)*
Thomas J. Kowalski *(CFO & VP)*
Charles Russell *(Dir-Mktg)*
Patrick McQuillen *(Plant Mgr)*

DIMARE FRESH, INC.

4029 Diplomacy Rd, Fort Worth, TX
76155
Tel.: (817) 385-3000
Web Site:
https://www.dimarefresh.com
Year Founded: 1928
Sales Range: $10-24.9 Million
Emp.: 100
Shipper, Grower, Packer & Repacker
of Fresh Produce
N.A.I.C.S.: 424480
Paul J. DiMare *(Pres)*
Nancy Blakney *(Mgr-HR)*

Subsidiaries:

DiMare Fresh **(1)**
4050 Pell Cir, Sacramento, CA 95838
Tel.: (714) 529-9255
Web Site: http://www.dimareinc.com

Sales Range: $10-24.9 Million
Emp.: 3
Fresh Fruits & Vegetables
N.A.I.C.S.: 424480

DIMCO-GRAY CORP.

900 Dimco Way, Centerville, OH
45458-2710
Tel.: (937) 433-7600 OH
Web Site:
https://www.dimcogray.com
Year Founded: 1924
Electric Timing Devices, Molded Plas-
tic Knobs, Handles & Snap Slide Fas-
teners Sls & Mfr
N.A.I.C.S.: 326199
Jim Daulton *(Pres & CEO)*

DIME BANK

290 Salem Tpke, Norwich, CT 06360
Tel.: (860) 859-4300 CT
Web Site: http://www.dime-bank.com
Year Founded: 1869
Sales Range: $25-49.9 Million
Emp.: 250
Provider of State Savings Banks
N.A.I.C.S.: 522180
Brian McNamara *(Chief Lending Offi-
cer & Sr VP)*
Joan M. Nagle *(VP-Retail Banking)*
Karen C. Roman *(VP-Residential
Lending)*
Nicholas Caplanson *(Pres & CEO)*
David Stanland *(CFO, Treas & Sr
VP)*
Ted Burrows *(Asst VP-Foreclosed
Properties)*
Cheryl A. Calderado *(Sr VP-HR &
Trng)*
Shalin Peck *(Asst VP-Deposit Ops &
e-Banking)*
Christopher Gauthier *(VP-Comml
Lending)*
John V. Estelle *(VP-Comml Lending)*
Robert Buckley *(VP-Comml Lending)*
Todd Bower *(Asst VP & Branch Mgr)*

DIMELING, SCHREIBER & PARK

1629 Locust St, Philadelphia, PA
19103-6304
Tel.: (215) 546-8585 PA
Web Site:
http://www.dsppartners.com
Year Founded: 1982
Sales Range: $10-24.9 Million
Emp.: 7
Investment Firm Services
N.A.I.C.S.: 525910
Steven G. Park *(Principal)*
Peter D. Schreiber *(Partner & Princi-
pal)*

Subsidiaries:

Dana Classic Fragrances, Inc. **(1)**
400 Yester Ave, Saddle Brook, NJ 07663
Tel.: (201) 881-8550
Web Site: http://www.danaclassic.com
Sales Range: $25-49.9 Million
Nail Care Products & Fragrances Mfr
N.A.I.C.S.: 325620

Martin Color-Fi, Inc. **(1)**
320 Neeley St, Sumter, SC 29150 **(100%)**
Tel.: (803) 436-4200
Web Site: http://www.colorfi.com
Sales Range: $50-74.9 Million
Mfr & Retailer of Plastic Pellets & Polyester
Fibers
N.A.I.C.S.: 325220

DIMENSION CONSTRUCTION INC.

3776 New Getwell Rd, Memphis, TN
38118
Tel.: (901) 794-9292
Web Site: http://www.dimconst.com
Year Founded: 1993

Sales Range: $10-24.9 Million
Emp.: 10
Restaurant Construction
N.A.I.C.S.: 236220
Mark Wofford *(Pres)*
Amber Wofford *(Controller)*

DIMENSION DESIGN

3400 W Lake Ave, Glenview, IL
60026
Tel.: (847) 564-5033
Web Site:
https://www.dimensiondesign.com
Year Founded: 2002
Sales Range: $10-24.9 Million
Emp.: 92
Display Advertising & Interior Design
Services
N.A.I.C.S.: 541850
Jeremy Biewer *(Acct Mgr-
Relationship)*
Linda Soucy *(Acct Mgr-Relationship)*
Tom Schowater *(Project Mgr)*
Marc Butvilas *(Project Mgr)*
Chris Grant *(Dir-Project Mgmt)*
Heather Haney-King *(Dir-Ops-Las
Vegas)*
Mike Rogers *(Founder & Owner)*
John Hernandez *(Dir-Ops)*
Larry Roberts *(Dir-Engrg)*
Adam Klyber *(Dir-Fabrication)*
Paul Kloeckner *(Dir-Graphics)*

DIMENSION DEVELOPMENT COMPANY

401 Keyser Ave, Natchitoches, LA
71457
Tel.: (318) 352-8238
Web Site: http://www.dimdev.com
Rev.: $18,000,000
Emp.: 34
Hotels & Motels
N.A.I.C.S.: 721110
Sam Friedman *(Founder & CEO)*
Bobby Mancil *(CFO & Comptroller)*
Eric Arender *(VP-Construction)*
Tim Horton *(Exec VP-Hotel Ops)*
Greg Friedman *(Pres & Gen Coun-
sel)*
Shirley Walker *(Sr VP-Pur, Design &
Construction Grp)*
Sharon Raue *(Dir-Sls & Mktg-Eastern
Reg)*
Virginia Moore *(Dir-MIS)*
Jeff Cole *(Dir-Revenue Mgmt)*
Gigi Siemsen *(Dir-Sls & Mktg-
Western Reg)*
Kevin Holder *(Mgr-Revenue)*
Angie Sanchez *(Mgr-Revenue)*
Edie McPolin *(Mgr-Revenue)*
Craig Stechman *(Sr VP-Sls & Mktg)*
Samuel Cueva *(VP-HR & Trng)*
James Kurt Weber *(VP-Ops-Central
Reg)*
Michael Hildum *(VP-Ops-Eastern
Reg)*
Bridget McEowen *(VP-Ops-Mountain
Reg)*
Tim Bristol *(VP-Ops-Western Reg)*

DIMENSION ENERGY CO. LLC

1010 Lamar St Ste 720, Houston, TX
77002
Tel.: (713) 651-1588
Sales Range: $10-24.9 Million
Emp.: 4
Oil & Gas Exploration & Production
N.A.I.C.S.: 213112

DIMENSION X CORPORATION

1000 Clay Ave Ext, Jeannette, PA
15644-3466
Tel.: (724) 522-9990
Year Founded: 1994
Sales Range: Less than $1 Million

Emp.: 10
N.A.I.C.S.: 541810
Brennan Wright *(Mgr-Bus Dev)*
Charles Matone Jr. *(Partner & CEO)*
Norman Wright Jr. *(Partner, Chief Creative Officer & Pres)*

DIMENSIONAL FUND ADVISORS LP
1299 Ocean Ave, Santa Monica, CA 90401-1038
Tel.: (310) 395-8005   DE
Web Site:
   https://www.us.dimensional.com
Year Founded: 1981
Sales Range: $25-49.9 Million
Emp.: 1,300
Management Investment
N.A.I.C.S.: 525910
David G. Booth *(Founder & Chm)*
Catherine L. Newell *(Gen Counsel)*
Christopher S. Crossan *(Chief Compliance Officer-Global)*
Stephen A. Clark *(Head-Institutional Svcs-Global)*
David P. Butler *(Co-CEO)*
Gerard K. O'Reilly *(Co-CEO & Chief Investment Officer)*
Aaron M. Marcus *(Head-HR-Global)*

Subsidiaries:

DFA Australia Limited   (1)
Level 29 Gateway, One Macquarie Pl, Sydney, 2000, NSW, Australia   (100%)
Tel.: (61) 292477822
Web Site: http://www.dfaus.com
Sales Range: $50-74.9 Million
Emp.: 30
Investment Services
N.A.I.C.S.: 523940
David G. Booth *(Chm)*

DFA Investment Dimensions Group
Inc.   (1)
6300 Bee Cave Rd Bldg 1, Austin, TX 78746
Tel.: (512) 306-7400
Investment Management Service
N.A.I.C.S.: 525910

Dimensional Fund Advisors Canada
Inc.   (1)
1500 W Georgia Street Suite 1520, Vancouver, V6G 2Z6, BC, Canada
Tel.: (604) 685-1633
Web Site: http://www.dfacanada.com
Sales Range: $25-49.9 Million
Emp.: 6
Investment Services
N.A.I.C.S.: 523940

Dimensional Fund Advisors Ltd. (1)
20 Triton Street, Regents Place, London, NW1 3BF, United Kingdom   (100%)
Tel.: (44) 2030333300
Web Site: http://www.dimensional.com
Sales Range: $1-9.9 Million
Investment Advisor
N.A.I.C.S.: 523940
David G. Booth *(Founder & Chm)*
Christopher S. Crossan *(Chief Compliance Officer-Global & VP)*
John S. Romiza *(CEO)*

Dimensional Japan Ltd.   (1)
3-1-1 Marunouchi Kokusai Building Suite 808, Tokyo, Japan
Tel.: (81) 3 6267 1600
Web Site: http://www.japan.dimensional.com
Investment Management Service
N.A.I.C.S.: 525910
John Alkire *(CEO)*

DIMENSIONAL GRAPHICS CORPORATION
325 N Jackson Ave, Mason City, IA 50401-2626
Tel.: (641) 423-8931   IA
Web Site:
   http://www.dimensionalgroup.com
Year Founded: 1987
Rev.: $3,300,000

Emp.: 45
Lithographic Coml Print Mfg Nonconductv Wire Dvc M
N.A.I.C.S.: 323111
Paul Gold *(Pres)*

DIMENSIONAL INSIGHT, INC.
60 Mall Rd, Burlington, MA 01803
Tel.: (781) 229-9111
Web Site: https://www.dimins.com
Year Founded: 1989
Rev.: $10,000,000
Emp.: 120
Database & File Management Software Development & Sales
N.A.I.C.S.: 513210
Frederick A. Powers *(Co-Founder & CEO)*
Ed O'Brien *(VP-Healthcare)*
Stanley R. Zanarotti *(Co-Founder & CTO)*

DIMENSIONAL MERCHANDISING, INC.
86 N Main St, Wharton, NJ 07885
Tel.: (973) 328-1600   NJ
Web Site: https://www.dminj.com
Year Founded: 1973
Sales Range: $100-124.9 Million
Emp.: 200
Contract Packaging Services
N.A.I.C.S.: 561910
Eugene R. Sylva *(CEO)*
Douglas Sylva *(Pres)*
Daniel Cohen *(Sr Acct Exec)*
Stephen Maun *(Mgr-Cosmetic Maintenance)*
Jose Correa *(Mgr-QA)*
Mayra Patrick *(Mgr-QA)*
Edward Mabey *(Engr-Pkg Dev)*

DIMENSIONS HEALTHCARE CORPORATION
7300 Van Dusen Rd, Laurel, MD 20707
Tel.: (301) 725-4300   MD
Web Site:
   http://www.dimensionshealth.org
Year Founded: 1982
Sales Range: $350-399.9 Million
Emp.: 3,020
Healtcare Services
N.A.I.C.S.: 622110
Neil J. Moore *(CEO)*
Barbara Frush *(Sec)*
Benjamin Stallings *(Treas)*
Tawanna P. Gaines *(Vice Chm)*
Trudy Hall *(Pres)*
C. Philip Nichols Jr. *(Chm)*

DIMEO CONSTRUCTION COMPANY
75 Chapman St, Providence, RI 02905-5405
Tel.: (401) 781-9800   RI
Web Site: https://www.dimeo.com
Year Founded: 1930
Sales Range: $125-149.9 Million
Emp.: 250
Contracting & Construction Services
N.A.I.C.S.: 236220
Bradford S. Dimeo *(Pres)*
Stephen F. Rutledge *(COO & Exec VP)*
Doug Peckham *(VP-Boston)*
Anthony Dematteo *(VP-Bus Dev)*
Steven B. Avery *(CFO)*
Paul Aballo *(VP-Construction)*
Lori Corsi *(VP-Admin)*

DIMMIT REGIONAL HOSPITAL
704 Hospital Dr, Carrizo Springs, TX 78834
Tel.: (830) 876-2424   TX
Web Site: https://www.dimmitregional hospital.com

Year Founded: 2008
Sales Range: $10-24.9 Million
Emp.: 234
Health Care Srvices
N.A.I.C.S.: 622110
Alma Melendez *(CFO)*
Carmen P. Esquivel *(Chief Nursing Officer)*
Jim Buckner *(CEO)*

DIMMITT AUTOMOTIVE GROUP
25191 US Hwy 19 N, Clearwater, FL 33763
Tel.: (727) 797-7070
Web Site: http://www.dimmitt.com
Sales Range: $25-49.9 Million
Emp.: 120
Automobiles, New & Used
N.A.I.C.S.: 441110
Richard Dimmitt *(Pres & CEO)*
Kris Jordan *(CFO)*
Scott Larguier *(COO & Gen Mgr)*
Cory Allen *(Engr-Maintenance)*

DIN GLOBAL CORP.
18701 S Figueroa St, Gardena, CA 90248
Tel.: (310) 337-5200
Web Site: http://www.enpointe.com
Holding Company
N.A.I.C.S.: 551112
Attiazaz Din *(Owner)*

Subsidiaries:

En Pointe Technologies, Inc.   (1)
18701 S Figueroa St, Gardena, CA 90248-4506
Tel.: (310) 337-5200
Web Site: http://www.enpointe.com
Sales Range: $300-349.9 Million
Emp.: 1,200
Computer Products Mfr & Services
N.A.I.C.S.: 334112
Javed Latif *(CFO)*
Michael Rapp *(Pres)*
Bob Bogle *(Sr VP-Sls)*

Subsidiary (Domestic):

En Pointe Gov, Inc.   (2)
18701 S Figueroa St, Gardena, CA 90248-4506
Tel.: (310) 337-5200
Web Site: http://www.enpointegov.com
Sales Range: $25-49.9 Million
Emp.: 200
Government IT Services
N.A.I.C.S.: 541512
Majid Jilani *(Head-Federal Sls)*
Rebecca Lauber *(Mgr-Brand Dev)*

DINAIR AIRBRUSH MAKE-UP SYSTEM, INC.
6215 Laurel Canyon Blvd, North Hollywood, CA 91606
Tel.: (818) 308-8500
Web Site:
   http://www.airbrushmakeup.com
Year Founded: 1985
Sales Range: $10-24.9 Million
Emp.: 60
Toilet Preparation Mfr
N.A.I.C.S.: 325620
George Lampman *(CEO)*
Dina Ousley *(Founder & Pres)*

DINDON FOODS CORP.
12207 Los Nietos Rd Ste G, Santa Fe Springs, CA 90670
Tel.: (562) 946-8501
Web Site:
   http://www.dindonfoods.com
Sales Range: $1-9.9 Million
Emp.: 33
Candy & Confectionery Mfr
N.A.I.C.S.: 311340
Lee L. Lin *(Pres)*
Lily Lin *(VP-Mktg)*

DINE DEVELOPMENT CORPORATION
8840 E Chaparral Rd Ste 145, Scottsdale, AZ 85250
Tel.: (717) 262-9750
Web Site: https://ddc-dine.com
Year Founded: 2004
IT, Professional & Environmental Services
N.A.I.C.S.: 541990
Austin Tsosie *(CEO)*

Subsidiaries:

Spin Systems Inc.   (1)
100 Carpenter Dr, Sterling, VA 20164
Tel.: (703) 318-0803
Web Site: http://www.spinsys.com
Rev.: $7,113,300
Emp.: 30
Data Processing, Hosting & Related Services
N.A.I.C.S.: 518210
Wael Al-Ali *(Pres)*

DINI SPHERIS
2727 Allen Pkwy Ste 1650, Houston, TX 77019
Tel.: (713) 942-1248
Web Site:
   https://www.dinispheris.com
Year Founded: 1969
Management Consulting Services
N.A.I.C.S.: 541618

DINOCO OIL, INC.
100 NW Loop 410 Ste 700-134, San Antonio, TX 78213
Tel.: (210) 414-3092   DE
Year Founded: 2013
Oil & Gas Exploration
N.A.I.C.S.: 211120
Dorothy Scaringe *(Pres, CEO & CFO)*

DINOCRATES GROUP LLC
1 Research Ct Ste 450, Rockville, MD 20850
Tel.: (240) 403-4103
Web Site: http://dinocrates.com
Year Founded: 2014
Boutique Strategy & Technology Advisory Firm
N.A.I.C.S.: 523940
Thomas R. Prokop *(Founder, Pres & CEO)*
Jim St. Clair *(CTO)*
Karen Wynn *(Chief People Officer)*

Subsidiaries:

Global Management Systems
Inc.   (1)
1 Research Ct Ste 450, Rockville, MD 20850
Tel.: (202) 471-4674
Web Site: http://www.gmsi.com
Systems Integration Services & Voice & Data Communication Support
N.A.I.C.S.: 541512
Hilton H. Augustine Jr. *(CEO)*

DINSMORE & SHOHL LLP
255 E 5th St Ste 1900, Cincinnati, OH 45202
Tel.: (513) 977-8200
Web Site: https://www.dinsmore.com
Year Founded: 1908
Sales Range: $200-249.9 Million
Emp.: 650
Law Firm
N.A.I.C.S.: 541110
George H. Vincent *(Chm & Mng Partner)*
Christopher A. Benintendi *(Partner-Cincinnati)*
Thomas J. Bonasera *(Partner-Columbus)*
Michael S. Glassman *(Partner-Cincinnati)*

Dinsmore & Shohl LLP—(Continued)

Jennifer A. Davenport (CMO)
Stephanie Higgins (Chief HR Officer)
Mary Jo Merkowitz (Dir-Library Svcs)
Peter Pepiton (Dir-e-Discovery & Litigation Support)
Jennifer L. Stark (Dir-Recruiting & Legal Personnel)
Juanene L. Wong (CIO)
Bobby Lucas (Chm-Corp Dept)
Gregory A. Harrison (Partner-Cincinnati)
Timothy D. Hoffman (Partner-Dayton)
Joshua A. Lorentz (Partner-Cincinnati)
R. Kenyon Meyer (Partner-Louisville)
Charles M. Roesch (Partner-Cincinnati)
John E. Selent (Partner & Atty)
Brian S. Sullivan (Partner-Cincinnati)
Richard H. C. Clay (Partner)
Chauncy S. R. Curtz (Partner-Lexington)
Anna M. Dailey (Partner-Charleston)
Anthony A. Ditka (Partner-Pittsburgh)
Jeffrey P. Hinebaugh (Partner-Cincinnati)
Thomas A. Wilson (Partner-Columbus)
Matthew S. Arend (Partner-Cincinnati)
Allan R. Daily (Partner)
Allison L. Goico (Partner)
Nicholaus R. Rericha (Partner)
Matthew P. Gunn (Partner)
Clifford H. Daily (Partner)
Barbara W. Menefee (Partner)
Brigette R. Koreny (Atty)
Erin C. Farabaugh (Partner)
Richard J. McNeely (Partner)
Lindsey M. Hoelzle (Partner)
Barbara B. Edelman (Partner)
Carolyn M. Brown (Partner)
Thomas M. Conner (Partner)
April L. Besl (Partner)
Kristin L. Lenhart (Partner)
Faith C. Whittaker (Partner)
Bryan L. Walker (Atty-Washington)
Yongsok Choi (Atty)
Ashley C. Pack (Partner)
Colleen P. Lewis (Partner)
Donna King Perry (Partner)
Erin A. Sutton (Partner)
Jerry S. Sallee (Partner)
Kara M. Stewart (Partner)
Kirk M. Wall (Partner)
Mark A. Carter (Partner)
Michael W. Hawkins (Partner)
Douglas M. Ventura (Partner)
Eric B. Kjellander (Atty-Columbus)
Bryan C. Wisecup (Atty)
Michael J. Bronson (Partner)
Michael S. Jackson (Partner)
Patrick M. Hagan (Partner)
Joseph W. Harper (Partner & Atty)
Laurie A. Witek (Partner)
Govinda M. Davis (Atty)
Leland P. Schermer (Partner)
Elizabeth E. Cary (Atty)
James A. Baldwin (Atty)
Anthony M. Zelli (Partner)
J. Tanner Watkins (Partner)
Matthew J. Wiles (Partner)
Ryan P. Aiello (Partner)
Joshua S. Rogers (Mng Partner-Morgantown)
Mark D. Schneider (Mng Partner)
Fabian Koenigbauer (Atty)
Therese Finan (Partner)
Mark Shanks (Partner)
Toni-Junell Herbert (Partner)
Brian O'Shaughnessy (Atty)
Jason Danks (Atty-Pittsburgh)
John Saccoccia (Atty)
Keith DeMaggio (Atty)
Brett L. Huston (Atty-Pittsburgh)

Joseph Leventhal (Mng Partner-San Diego)
Martine R. Dunn (Partner & Atty)
Thomas W. Hess (Partner & Atty)
Lee M. Stautberg (Partner & Atty)
Edward Carroll (CIO)
Robyn Dow (Chief HR Officer)
Javier Flores (Partner-Boston)
Eric Skelly (Partner-Litigation Dept)
Brian W. Blaesser (Partner)
Thomas W. Dinwiddie (Partner)
Thomas Dinwiddie (Partner)
James R. Carlisle II (Partner)

Subsidiaries:

Mateer & Harbert, P.A. (1)
2 Landmark Ctr 225 East Robinson St Ste 600, Orlando, FL 32801
Tel.: (407) 425-9044
Web Site: http://www.mateerharbert.com
Emp.: 31
Law firm
N.A.I.C.S.: 541110
Steven R. Bechtel (Atty)
Mary A. Edenfield (Atty)
James B. Bogner (Atty)
Chad K. Alvaro (Atty)
Richard L. Allen (Atty)
Lawrence J. Phalin (Atty)
Michael A. Paasch (Atty)
Sharon Duncan (Atty)
Alexander J. Ombres (Atty)

Wooden McLaughlin LLP (1)
1 Indiana Sq 211 N Pennsylvania Ste 1800, Indianapolis, IN 46204-4208
Tel.: (317) 639-6151
Web Site: http://www.woodmclaw.com
Emp.: 34
Law firm
N.A.I.C.S.: 541110
Matthew M. Adolay (Partner & Atty)
Michael C. Cook (Partner & Atty)
James M. Boyers (Partner & Atty)
Mark L. Boos (Partner & Atty)
Kent M. Broach (Partner & Atty)
Misha Rabinowitch (Partner)

DIO, LLC

3111 Farmtrail Rd, York, PA 17406
Tel.: (717) 764-8288
Web Site: http://www.diousa.com
Sales Range: $10-24.9 Million
Emp.: 17
Advertising, Brand Development & Integration, Graphic Design, Public Relations
N.A.I.C.S.: 541810
Regis C. Maher (Founder & Pres)
Roger Monson (CFO)
Joe Easton (Dir-Creative)
Lee M. Karon (Dir-Media)
Glenn Cudaback (Acct Dir)
Elizabeth Shaffer (Dir-Art)
Katy Halter (Acct Exec)
Rick Pace (VP-Experiential Mktg)
David W. Pridgen II (CEO)

DION INTERNATIONAL TRUCKS LLC

5255 Federal Blvd, San Diego, CA 92105
Tel.: (619) 263-2251
Web Site: http://www.diontrucks.com
Sales Range: $25-49.9 Million
Emp.: 70
Trucks, Tractors & Trailers: New & Used
N.A.I.C.S.: 441110
Cary Dion (Pres)
Tony Biong (CFO)

DIONO, INC.

418 Vly Ave NW Ste 100, Puyallup, WA 98371
Tel.: (253) 268-2500
Web Site: http://www.us.diono.com
Year Founded: 1999
Sales Range: $10-24.9 Million
Emp.: 33

Car Seat Accessory Mfr & Distr
N.A.I.C.S.: 337126
Bradley Alan Keller (Pres)

DIOS RIOS PARTNERS, LP

205 Wild Basin Rd S Bldg Ste 100, Austin, TX 78746
Tel.: (512) 298-0801 DE
Web Site: http://dosriospartners.com
Year Founded: 2012
Holding Company
N.A.I.C.S.: 551112
Jay Turner (Partner)
Andres Churin (VP)

Subsidiaries:

Pathfinder Aviation, LLC (1)
1936 Merrill Field Dr, Anchorage, AK 99501
Tel.: (907) 257-1550
Web Site: http://www.pathfinderaviation.com
Remote Aviation Operations & Logistics
N.A.I.C.S.: 541614

DIPASQUA ENTERPRISES, INC.

2277 Lee Rd, Winter Park, FL 32789-1887
Tel.: (407) 644-8578
Web Site:
https://www.subwaydipasqua.com
Sales Range: $50-74.9 Million
Emp.: 700
Limited-Service Restaurants
N.A.I.C.S.: 722513

DIPCRAFT MANUFACTURING COMPANY

111 W Braddock Ave, Braddock, PA 15104-1115
Tel.: (412) 351-2363 DE
Web Site: https://www.dipcraft.com
Year Founded: 1946
Sales Range: $1-9.9 Million
Emp.: 2
Translucent Fiberglass, Reinforced Plastic Building Panels Mfr; Candy Wrappers & Latex Balloons Imprinter
N.A.I.C.S.: 326199
Michael Tobias (Pres)

DIPLOMAT HOTEL CORPORATION

2300 Henderson Mill Rd NE Ste 125, Atlanta, GA 30345
Tel.: (770) 938-2060
Rev.: $22,000,000
Emp.: 15
Motel, Franchised
N.A.I.C.S.: 721110
R. C. Patel (Chm & CEO)
Mukesh Patel (Pres)

Subsidiaries:

Diplomat Risk Services (1)
2100 Park Lk Dr NE, Atlanta, GA 30345
Tel.: (678) 281-0395
Sales Range: $25-49.9 Million
Emp.: 4
Licensed Insurance Agency
N.A.I.C.S.: 524210

Premier Travels, Inc. (1)
2100 Parklake Dr NE, Atlanta, GA 30345-2167
Tel.: (770) 492-1206
Travel Agency
N.A.I.C.S.: 561510

DIRCKS ASSOCIATES

550 N Country Rd Ste A, Saint James, NY 11780-1427
Tel.: (631) 584-2274 NY
Web Site: http://www.dircksny.com
Year Founded: 1995
Rev.: $14,000,000
Emp.: 15
Advetising Agency
N.A.I.C.S.: 541810

David Dircks (CEO)
Gail Keane (Controller)

DIRCKS MOVING SERVICES, INC.

4340 W Mohave St, Phoenix, AZ 85043
Tel.: (602) 243-1205
Web Site: http://www.dircks.com
Rev.: $10,400,000
Emp.: 100
Commercial & Residential Moving & Storage Solutions
N.A.I.C.S.: 484230
Alicia Tobin (Coord-Natl Accts)
Dave Barnett (Mgr-Quality Control & Agency Svcs)
Jeff Chretien (Mgr-Comml Relocations & Logistics)
Brandon Stephens (Dir-Corp Svcs)
Chad Helgemo (Dir-Natl Acct Sls)
Gary Snipes (Mgr-Residential Sls)
Juli Hankins (Mgr-Military)
Matt Dircks (Pres & CEO)
Tim Whalen (Gen Mgr-Logistics)

DIRECT AGENTS, INC.

740 Broadway Ste 701, New York, NY 10003-9574
Tel.: (212) 925-6558 NY
Web Site:
http://www.directagents.com
Year Founded: 2003
Sales Range: $10-24.9 Million
Emp.: 40
Interactive Advertising Services
N.A.I.C.S.: 541613
Josh Boaz (Mng Dir & Co-Founder)
Dinesh Boaz (Mng Dir & Co-Founder)
Lyle Srebnick (Sr VP-Sls)
Megan Conahan (VP-Adv Sls)
Mark Glauberson (VP-Media Buying)
Daniel Owen (VP-Mktg & Tech)
Rachel Nugent (VP-Client Svcs)

DIRECT AUTOMOTIVE GROUP, LLC.

547 Winston Rd, Jonesville, NC 28642
Tel.: (336) 835-1831
Year Founded: 2001
Sales Range: $10-24.9 Million
Emp.: 20
New Car Dealers
N.A.I.C.S.: 441110
Michael Johnson (Owner)

DIRECT CHECK REDEMPTION CENTER, INC.

2641 McCormick Dr Ste 101, Clearwater, FL 33759
Tel.: (727) 536-3399 FL
Web Site:
http://www.directcheckmarketing.com
Year Founded: 1991
Sales Range: $10-24.9 Million
Emp.: 75
Direct Marketing, Graphic Design & Printing Services
N.A.I.C.S.: 541613
Jennifer Polich (Pres)

DIRECT COMPANIES, LLC

2320 W 54th St. N, Sioux Falls, SD 57106
Tel.: (866) 583-3377
Web Site:
https://directcompanies.com
Year Founded: 2012
Software Publisher
N.A.I.C.S.: 513210

Subsidiaries:

Workplace Technology Center, Inc. (1)

2101 W 41st St Ste 39, Sioux Falls, SD 57105
Tel.: (605) 367-3767
Web Site: https://workplace-it.com
Sales Range: $1-9.9 Million
Emp.: 16
Computer And Software Stores, Nsk
N.A.I.C.S.: 449210

DIRECT CONNECT GROUP (DCG) LLC
4401 E Marginal Way S, Seattle, WA 98134
Tel.: (206) 784-6892   WA
Web Site: https://www.dcgone.com
Printing Services
N.A.I.C.S.: 323111
Tammy Peniston (Chief Comml Officer)
Terry Storms (CEO)
Brad Clarke (Pres)

DIRECT CONNECT LLC
3901 Centerview Dr Ste W, Chantilly, VA 20151
Tel.: (800) 747-6273
Web Site: http://directconnectps.com
Year Founded: 1994
Electronic Payment Services
N.A.I.C.S.: 522320

Subsidiaries:

United Payment Services, Inc.   (1)
3537 Old Conejo Rd Ste 113, Newbury Park, CA 91320
Tel.: (866) 886-4833
Credit Card Services
N.A.I.C.S.: 522320

DIRECT DATA CORPORATION
907 Easton Rd Ste 1b, Willow Grove, PA 19090-2051
Tel.: (267) 913-1000
Web Site: http://www.directdata.net
Year Founded: 1996
Sales Range: $10-24.9 Million
Emp.: 25
Technology Solutions
N.A.I.C.S.: 541519
Robert Rao (Pres & CEO)

DIRECT DISTRIBUTORS INC.
100 Partlo St, Garner, NC 27529-3671
Tel.: (919) 772-8625   NC
Web Site: http://www.agrisupply.com
Year Founded: 1970
Sales Range: $25-49.9 Million
Emp.: 100
Farm & Garden Machinery
N.A.I.C.S.: 423820
Barry W. Partlo (Pres)

Subsidiaries:

Agri-Supply Company Inc.   (1)
632 W Hwy 70, Garner, NC 27529
Tel.: (919) 772-9722
Web Site: http://www.agri-supply.com
Sales Range: $10-24.9 Million
Emp.: 25
Farm Equipment & Supplies
N.A.I.C.S.: 423820

DIRECT EATS, INC.
54 Tannery Ln S, Weston, CT 06683
Tel.: (917) 923-5154
Web Site: http://www.directeats.com
Online Grocery & Home Products Service
N.A.I.C.S.: 424490
David Hack (Founder & CEO)
Rocco Strazza (Sr Dir-Fin & Ops)
Lisa Tambini (Sr Dir-Mktg)

DIRECT EDGE CAMPAIGNS, LLC
2000 Glen Echo Rd Ste 207 A, Nashville, TN 37215

Tel.: (615) 236-5083
Web Site: https://www.directedgewins.com
Year Founded: 2013
Management Consulting Services
N.A.I.C.S.: 541618

DIRECT EFFECT MEDIA SERVICES, INC.
1042-B N El Camino Real Ste 329, Encinitas, CA 92024
Tel.: (760) 943-9400
Web Site: http://www.directeffectmedia.com
Year Founded: 1990
Sales Range: $1-9.9 Million
Emp.: 7
Media Buying Services
N.A.I.C.S.: 541810
Bernard Ryan (Pres & CEO)
Allison Tahara (Acct Exec)

DIRECT EXTERIORS, INC.
10550 County Rd 81 Ste 209, Maple Grove, MN 55369
Tel.: (612) 623-4245
Year Founded: 2003
Sales Range: $1-9.9 Million
Emp.: 15
Natural Disaster Home Restoration Services Focusing on Insurance Restoration
N.A.I.C.S.: 238190
Mike McAlpin (Pres)

DIRECT IMPACT, INC.
655 Craig Rd Ste 240, Saint Louis, MO 63141
Tel.: (314) 336-1300   MO
Web Site: https://www.directimpactinc.com
Year Founded: 1995
Sales Range: $10-24.9 Million
Emp.: 90
Marketing & Advertising Services
N.A.I.C.S.: 541810
Barb Montanye (Sr Dir-Art)
Sam Myers (Pres)

DIRECT INNOVATIONS
5455 Dashwood Ste 600, Bellaire, TX 77401
Tel.: (713) 780-1387
Web Site: http://www.dimarketing.net
Year Founded: 2005
Sales Range: $1-9.9 Million
Emp.: 8
Advertising & Marketing Agency Services
N.A.I.C.S.: 541810
Jackie Trevathan (Office Mgr)
Jacqueline Wallace (Mgr-Ops)

DIRECT INVESTMENT HOLDINGS GROUP, INC.
150 S Pine Island Rd Ste 300, Plantation, FL 33324
Tel.: (469) 522-4200   NV
Year Founded: 1996
Rev.: $4,017
Assets: $625,764
Net Worth: $625,764
Earnings: ($104,307)
Fiscal Year-end: 12/31/22
Investment Services
N.A.I.C.S.: 523999
R. Neil Crouch II (Pres & Treas)

DIRECT LINE COMMUNICATIONS
917 Union St, Mishawaka, IN 46544
Tel.: (574) 272-9814
Web Site: http://www.directlineonline.com
Sales Range: $10-24.9 Million
Emp.: 50

Communications Specialization
N.A.I.C.S.: 238210
Peter Corfield (Dir-Mktg)
Kent Bertsch (Controller)

DIRECT MAIL EXPRESS, INC.
2441 Bellevue Ave, Daytona Beach, FL 32114
Tel.: (877) 720-0082
Web Site: http://www.dmecorporate.com
Year Founded: 1982
Direct Mail Advertising Services
N.A.I.C.S.: 541860
Michael J. Panaggio (Co-Founder & CEO)
Kathy Wise (Pres)
Eric Remington (CTO)
Mike Dunn (COO)
Terry Webber (Exec VP-Tech Solutions)
Bart Worley (Mng Partner)
Mark Williams (Mng Partner)
Peter Mollers (Controller)
Joe Lovecchio (Mgr-Market Dev)

DIRECT MARKETING CENTER
21171 S Western Ave Ste 260, Torrance, CA 90501-3449
Tel.: (310) 212-5727
Web Site: http://www.directmarketingcenter.net
Year Founded: 1985
Rev.: $24,793,010
Emp.: 25
Advetising Agency
N.A.I.C.S.: 541810
Craig Huey (Pres)

DIRECT MARKETING SOLUTIONS, INC.
8534 NE Alderwood Rd, Portland, OR 97220
Tel.: (503) 281-1400
Web Site: http://www.teamdms.com
Year Founded: 1982
Business-To-Business, Direct Marketing, Media Buying Services, Production
N.A.I.C.S.: 541860
Steve Sherman (Pres)
Mike Sherman (CEO)
Luke Teboul (Exec VP)
Mary Manning (VP-HR)
Brian Byers (VP-Bus Dev)

Subsidiaries:

Mailing Services of Pittsburgh, Inc.   (1)
155 Commerce Dr, Freedom, PA 15042
Tel.: (724) 774-3244
Web Site: http://www.msp-pgh.com
Direct Mail Marketing Company
N.A.I.C.S.: 541860
Doug Wright (COO)
Richard Bushee III (Pres)

DIRECT ONLINE MARKETING, LLC
4727 Jacob St, Wheeling, WV 26003-3279
Tel.: (304) 214-4850
Web Site: http://www.directom.com
Services Related to Advertising
N.A.I.C.S.: 541890
Heather Campbell (Mgr-Digital Adv)

Subsidiaries:

C-Leveled LLC   (1)
4117 Liberty Ave, Pittsburgh, PA 15224
Tel.: (412) 980-8875
Web Site: http://www.c-leveled.com
Business Consulting Services & Software Mfr
N.A.I.C.S.: 561499
Denise DeSimone (Chm-Growth Strategy & Revenue Enhancement)

DIRECT PARTNER SOLUTIONS, INC.
6386 Nichols Rd, Flowery Branch, GA 30542
Tel.: (678) 828-9831
Web Site: http://www.directpartnersolutions.com
Year Founded: 2000
Sales Range: $1-9.9 Million
Emp.: 10
Direct Response Marketing Services
N.A.I.C.S.: 541890
Deborah Simone-Holmes (Founder & CEO)
Whitney Banta-Simone (Mgr-Bus Admin)
Brennan Holmes (Coord-Mktg)

DIRECT PHARMACY SERVICE, INC.
9332 Annapolis Rd Ste 211, Lanham, MD 20706
Tel.: (301) 918-1711
Web Site: https://www.dpsrx.com
Year Founded: 1994
Sales Range: $10-24.9 Million
Emp.: 17
Pharmaceutical Product Whslr
N.A.I.C.S.: 424210
Rufus J. Williams (Founder & Owner)

DIRECT RESPONSE ACADEMY
140 Lotus Cir, Austin, TX 78737-8728
Tel.: (512) 301-5900
Web Site: http://www.directresponse academy.com
Year Founded: 1999
Sales Range: Less than $1 Million
Emp.: 4
Cable T.V., Consulting, Direct Response Marketing, Education, Media Buying Services, Media Training, T.V., Telemarketing
N.A.I.C.S.: 541810
Greg Sarnow (Founder & CEO)
Beatrice Sarnow (VP-Mktg)
Patricia Mellody (Dir-Response)

DIRECT RESPONSE INSURANCE ADMINISTRATIVE SERVICES, INC.
7930 Century Blvd, Chanhassen, MN 55317-8001
Tel.: (952) 556-5600
Web Site: https://www.driasi.com
Year Founded: 1982
Sales Range: $10-24.9 Million
Emp.: 100
Insurance Services
N.A.I.C.S.: 524298
David Kaldor (CFO & Exec VP)
Scott Allison (Exec VP-IT)

DIRECT SOUTH INC.
3115 Hillcrest Ave, Macon, GA 31201
Tel.: (478) 746-3518
Web Site: http://www.restaurantandkitchen supply.com
Rev.: $10,512,093
Emp.: 30
Restaurant Equipment & Supplies
N.A.I.C.S.: 423440
Nick Adams (Pres)

DIRECT TITLE SOLUTIONS, INC.
12 N Braddock St, Winchester, VA 22601
Tel.: (540) 450-0740
Web Site: http://www.dtsadvantage.com
Year Founded: 2001
Sales Range: $1-9.9 Million
Emp.: 20

Direct Title Solutions, Inc.—(Continued)

Real Estate Title Services
N.A.I.C.S.: 541191
Nathan Laing (VP)

DIRECT WEB ADVERTISING, INC.
1375 Gateway Blvd, Boynton Beach, FL 33426
Tel.: (561) 649-2792
Web Site:
http://www.directwebadv.com
Year Founded: 2002
Sales Range: $10-24.9 Million
Emp.: 12
Advetising Agency
N.A.I.C.S.: 541810
Peter LaBella (COO)

DIRECTBUY, INC.
8450 Broadway, Merrillville, IN 46410-6221
Tel.: (219) 736-1100
Web Site: http://www.directbuy.com
Year Founded: 1971
Discount Home Furnishings Retailer
N.A.I.C.S.: 455211
Mike Bornhorst (CEO)
Curt Hilliard (CMO & Exec VP-Sls)
Dylan Astle (VP-Member Experience)
Jim O'Keefe (VP-Mdsg)

DIRECTEC CORPORATION
1650 Lyndon Farm Ct Ste 202, Louisville, KY 40223
Tel.: (502) 357-5000
Web Site: http://www.directec.com
Sales Range: $25-49.9 Million
Emp.: 15
Computers, Peripherals & Software
N.A.I.C.S.: 423430
David Jarnagin (CEO)
Matthew Wood (Acct Mgr)

DIRECTECH LLC
19 S La Salle Ste 1201, Chicago, IL 60603
Tel.: (800) 622-0034   DE
Web Site: http://www.directech.co
Internet & Broadband Services
N.A.I.C.S.: 517112

Subsidiaries:

Hanson Directory Service, Inc. (1)
1501 N 15th Ave E, Newton, IA 50208
Tel.: (612) 792-2855
Web Site: http://www.hansondirectory.com
Database & Directory Publishers
N.A.I.C.S.: 513140
Shawna Stevenson (Dir-Ops)

DIRECTED CAPITAL RESOURCES, LLC
333 Third Ave N Ste 400, Saint Petersburg, FL 33701-3899
Tel.: (727) 341-8380
Web Site:
http://www.directedcapital.com
Year Founded: 2001
Rev.: $700,000,000
Emp.: 21
Private Equity; Real Estate Investments
N.A.I.C.S.: 523999
Christopher S. Moench (CEO)
Stacy J. Ames (CFO)
Nick W. Griffin (Mng Dir-Capital Formation)
Lance B. Amano (Mng Dir-Asset Dispositions)
Michael P. McGinn (Mng Dir-Portfolio Mgmt)
John W. Savage (Mng Dir-Asset Acq)

DIRECTED ENERGY SOLUTIONS

890 Elkton Dr Ste 101, Colorado Springs, CO 80907
Tel.: (719) 593-7848
Web Site:
http://www.denergysolutions.com
Sales Range: $1-9.9 Million
Emp.: 50
Laser Beam Technology Development
N.A.I.C.S.: 339999
David K. Neumann (CEO)

DIRECTEMPLOYERS ASSOCIATION, INC.
9002 N Purdue Rd Ste 100, Indianapolis, IN 46268
Tel.: (317) 874-9000   IN
Web Site:
http://www.directemployers.org
Year Founded: 2001
Sales Range: $10-24.9 Million
Emp.: 61
Employment Placement Services
N.A.I.C.S.: 561311
Candee Chambers (Exec Dir)
Tom Eckhart (VP-Membership Dev)
Hal Cooper (VP-Product Development)
Dan Jordan (Treas & Sec)

DIRECTFX SOLUTIONS INC.
601 N 3rd St, Memphis, TN 38107
Tel.: (901) 344-8169
Web Site:
https://www.directfxsolutions.com
Year Founded: 2003
Sales Range: $1-9.9 Million
Emp.: 20
Digital Printing, Direct Mail, List Services, Graphic Design, Fulfillment & Data Management
N.A.I.C.S.: 323111
Chris Warner (Co-Owner)
Kush Shah (Co-Owner)

DIRECTIONAL CAPITAL LLC
355 Richmond Rd, Cleveland, OH 44143
Tel.: (216) 261-3000
Web Site:
http://www.directionalaviation.com
Year Founded: 1981
Sales Range: $25-49.9 Million
Emp.: 2,200
Privater Equity Firm
N.A.I.C.S.: 523999
Kenneth C. Ricci (Principal)
Michael A. Rossi (Principal)

Subsidiaries:

Corporate Wings Inc. (1)
355 Richmond Rd, Richmond Heights, OH 44143
Tel.: (216) 261-3000
Web Site: http://www.corporatewings.com
Rev.: $109,018,211
Emp.: 75
Aircraft Support Services, Maintenance & Transportation Services
N.A.I.C.S.: 488190
Ed McDonald (Gen Mgr)
Mike Rossi (CFO)
Kenneth C. Ricci (CEO)

Subsidiary (Domestic):

Corporate Wings (2)
6060 S Aviation Ave Ste 99 Charleston AFB/Intl Airport, North Charleston, SC 29406
Tel.: (843) 746-7600
Sales Range: $25-49.9 Million
Emp.: 40
Aircraft Services
N.A.I.C.S.: 488119
Joanna Grennci (Acct Mgr)

Corporate Wings Services Corp. (2)
355 Richmond Rd, Richmond Heights, OH 44143-1453

Tel.: (216) 261-3000
Web Site: http://www.flightoptions.com
Airports, Flying Fields & Services
N.A.I.C.S.: 488190

Flexjet, LLC (1)
26180 Curtiss Wright Pkwy, Cleveland, OH 44143
Tel.: (216) 261-3500
Web Site: http://www.flexjet.com
Private Aviation Charter Services
N.A.I.C.S.: 481211
Kenn Ricci (Chm)
Eli Flint (Pres-Private Helicopter Div)
Michael Silvestro (CEO)
Jay Heublein (Sr VP-Maintenance)

Subsidiary (Non-US):

FlairJet Limited (2)
Business Aviation Centre Terminal Road, Birmingham International Airport, Birmingham, B26 3QN, United Kingdom
Tel.: (44) 121 663 1910
Web Site: http://www.flair-jet.com
Private Aviation Charter Services
N.A.I.C.S.: 481211

Flying Colours Corporation (2)
901-120 Airport Road, Peterborough, K9J 0E7, ON, Canada
Tel.: (705) 742-4688
Web Site: http://www.flyingcolourscorp.com
Aircraft Completion & Maintenance
N.A.I.C.S.: 488119
John Gillespie (Pres & CEO)
Eric Gillespie (Exec VP-Sls & Mktg)
Sean Gillespie (Exec VP-Sls & Mktg)
Graham Dickie (CFO)

Plant (Non-US):

Flying Colours Corporation - Singapore Facility (3)
10 Seletar Aerospace Heights Seletar Aerospace Park, Singapore, 797546, Singapore
Tel.: (65) 60866610
Aircraft Repair & Maintenance Services
N.A.I.C.S.: 488190
Paul Dunford (Gen Mgr)
Catherine Chew (Office Mgr)
Kevin Chan (Coord-Interior Project)

Subsidiary (US):

JetCorp Technical Services Inc. (3)
657 N Bell Ave, Chesterfield, MO 63005
Tel.: (314) 602-5366
Web Site: http://www.flyingcolourscorp.com
Sales Range: $10-24.9 Million
Emp.: 200
Aviation Services Including Maintenance, Fuel & Refurbishments
N.A.I.C.S.: 488119

Flight Options LLC (1)
26180 Curtiss Wright Pkwy, Cleveland, OH 44143-1453
Tel.: (216) 261-3500
Web Site: http://www.flightoptions.com
Flight Equipment Rental & Leasing
N.A.I.C.S.: 532411
Kenneth Ricci (Chm)
David H. Davies (CIO)
Joseph Salata (VP-Flight Ops)

Simcom, Inc. (1)
6989 Lee Vista Blvd, Orlando, FL 32822   (50%)
Tel.: (407) 275-1050
Web Site: https://www.simulator.com
Sales Range: $25-49.9 Million
Flight Training Services
N.A.I.C.S.: 611512
Eric Hinson (CEO)

Subsidiary (Domestic):

PrestoSIM, Inc. (2)
1000 Nolen Dr Ste 400, Grapevine, TX 76051-8622
Tel.: (817) 488-4870
Flight Training Services
N.A.I.C.S.: 611512

DIRECTORS INVESTMENT GROUP INC.
955 S Virginia St Ste 116, Reno, NV 89502-0413

Tel.: (775) 329-3311   NV
Web Site: http://www.dig-inc.net
Year Founded: 1992
Sales Range: $50-74.9 Million
Emp.: 150
Life Insurance
N.A.I.C.S.: 524113

Subsidiaries:

Directors Air Corporation (1)
955 S Virginia St Ste 116, Reno, NV 89502-2472
Tel.: (775) 329-3311
Web Site: http://www.dig-inc.net
Sales Range: Less than $1 Million
Emp.: 3
Air Transportation, Nonscheduled
N.A.I.C.S.: 481211

Directors Holding Corporation (1)
955 S Virginia St Ste 116, Reno, NV 89502-0413
Tel.: (775) 329-3311
Sales Range: Less than $1 Million
Life Insurance
N.A.I.C.S.: 524113

Funeral Directors Capital Ventures Inc. (1)
6550 Directors Pkwy, Abilene, TX 79606-5854
Tel.: (325) 695-3412
Sales Range: $25-49.9 Million
Emp.: 5
Life Insurance
N.A.I.C.S.: 524113

Funeral Directors Life Insurance Co. Inc. (1)
6550 Directors Pkwy, Abilene, TX 79606-5854
Tel.: (325) 695-3412
Web Site:
http://www.funeraldirectorslife.com
Sales Range: $50-74.9 Million
Emp.: 100
Life Insurance
N.A.I.C.S.: 524113
Kris Seale (Chm, Pres & CEO)
Jeff Stewart (CMO & VP)
Dawson Rodriguez (CIO & Exec VP)
Paul Lovelace (VP-Corp Dev)
Mark France (Chief Actuary & Exec VP)
Todd Carlson (Chief Sls Officer & Exec VP-Sls)
Terry Groban (CFO & Exec VP)
Chris Welch (Dir-Sls Dev)
Amy Biggs (Supvr-Policy Svcs)
Anissa Minatra (Supvr-Claims & Policy Svcs)
Charles Rohus (Engr-Software-MIS)
D. J. Jons (Dir-Learning & Dev Programs)
Don Strickland (Specialist-Implementation, Trng, Learning & Dev)

Texas Directors Life Insurance Company Inc. (1)
6550 Directors Pkwy, Abilene, TX 79606-5854
Tel.: (325) 695-3412
Web Site:
http://www.funeraldirectorslife.com
Sales Range: $50-74.9 Million
Emp.: 100
Life Insurance
N.A.I.C.S.: 524113
Terry Groban (CFO & Exec VP)

DIRKSEN SCREW PRODUCTS CO.
14490 23 Mile Rd, Utica, MI 48315
Tel.: (586) 247-5400
Web Site:
http://www.dirksenscrew.com
Sales Range: $10-24.9 Million
Emp.: 90
Screw Machine Products
N.A.I.C.S.: 332711
Clifford S. Dirksen (Pres)
Rita Dziersk (Controller)
Eric McDowell (Engr-Automation Process)

DIRSON ENTERPRISES, INC.

7175 W Post Rd, Las Vegas, NV
89113-6611
Tel.: (702) 385-5200
Web Site:
   http://www.gamingtoday.com
Book, Periodical & Newspaper Merchant Whslr
N.A.I.C.S.: 424920
Bill Paulos *(Publr)*

DISABATINO CONSTRUCTION COMPANY INC.
1 S Cleveland Ave, Wilmington, DE
19805-1426
Tel.: (302) 652-3838
Web Site:
   https://www.disabatino.com
Sales Range: $25-49.9 Million
Emp.: 300
Residential Remodeler
N.A.I.C.S.: 236118
Lawrence J. DiSabatino *(Pres)*

DISABILITY MANAGEMENT SERVICES INC.
1350 Main St, Springfield, MA 01103-
1641
Tel.: (413) 747-0990   MA
Web Site:
   http://www.disabilitymanagement
   services.com
Year Founded: 1995
Sales Range: $25-49.9 Million
Emp.: 135
Disability Health Insurance Services
N.A.I.C.S.: 524114
Andrew J. Cohen *(Gen Counsel & Sec)*
Timothy J. O'Connor *(VP-Claim Ops)*
Steve A. Miller *(COO & Exec VP)*
Paul Ziobrowski *(Chief Actuary & VP)*
Richard Robinson *(CFO & Treas)*
Robert A. Bonsall Jr. *(Chm, Pres & CEO)*

DISABILITY RIGHTS CALIFORNIA
1831 K St, Sacramento, CA 95811-
4114
Tel.: (916) 504-5800   CA
Web Site:
   https://www.disabilityrightsca.org
Year Founded: 1978
Sales Range: $10-24.9 Million
Emp.: 254
Disability Assistance Services
N.A.I.C.S.: 624120
Rick Guidara *(Dir-IT)*
Clarisa Anderson *(Mgr-HR)*
Milanka Radosavljevic *(Dir-Admin Svcs)*
Catherine Blakemore *(Exec Dir)*
Izetta Jackson *(Pres)*
Katana Austin-Burell *(Mgr-Admin Svcs)*
Diana Lynn Nelson *(Chm)*
Herb Anderson *(CFO)*

DISABILITY RIGHTS TEXAS
2222 W Braker Ln, Austin, TX 78758
Tel.: (512) 454-4816   TX
Web Site:
   http://www.disabilityrightstx.org
Year Founded: 1977
Sales Range: $10-24.9 Million
Emp.: 169
Intellectual Disability Assistance Services
N.A.I.C.S.: 623210
Richard Lavallo *(Dir-Legal)*
Karen Rucker *(Dir-Finance)*

DISABILITY SERVICES OF THE SOUTHWEST
6243 IH-10 W Ste 430, San Antonio,
TX 78201

Tel.: (210) 798-3779   TX
Web Site: http://www.dsswtx.org
Year Founded: 1993
Sales Range: $25-49.9 Million
Emp.: 1,891
Elderly & Disabled People Assistance Services
N.A.I.C.S.: 624120
Laurie Lyssy *(CFO)*

DISABLED VETERANS NATIONAL FOUNDATION
1020 19th St NW Ste 475, Washington, DC 20036
Tel.: (202) 737-0522   DC
Web Site: http://www.dvnf.org
Year Founded: 2007
Sales Range: $25-49.9 Million
Emp.: 7
Disabled Veteran Support Services
N.A.I.C.S.: 624120
Patrick Heron *(Mgr-Direct Mail)*
Leander Brereton *(Dir-Operations)*
Joseph VanFonda *(CEO)*

DISASTER RESTORATION SERVICES
544 5th St Ext, Trafford, PA 15085
Tel.: (412) 362-7000
Web Site:
   http://www.disasterrestoration
   servicespa.com
Sales Range: $10-24.9 Million
Emp.: 100
Commercial & Residential Restoration Services
N.A.I.C.S.: 236118
John Botti *(Pres)*

DISCMAKERS, INC.
7905 N Crescent Blvd, Pennsauken,
NJ 08110-1402
Tel.: (856) 663-9030   NJ
Web Site:
   http://www.discmakers.com
Year Founded: 1988
Sales Range: $50-74.9 Million
Emp.: 350
Business Services
N.A.I.C.S.: 512290
Stephen Cunnion *(Mgr-Sls Dev)*

DISCOUNT CAR WASH INC.
9721 Lanham Severn Rd, Lanham,
MD 20706
Tel.: (301) 577-2900
Sales Range: $10-24.9 Million
Emp.: 30
Carwash
N.A.I.C.S.: 811192
Harvey Blonder *(Pres)*

DISCOUNT CLEANING PRODUCTS
10 Ridge Ct, Manahawkin, NJ 08092
Web Site:
   http://www.discountcleaning
   products.com
Year Founded: 2008
Sales Range: $1-9.9 Million
Emp.: 10
Office Supplies & Cleaning Products Whslr
N.A.I.C.S.: 423840
Michael Kawula *(Owner)*

DISCOUNT COFFEE.COM, INC.
501 N Service Rd, Saint Peters, MO
63376-5614
Tel.: (636) 278-1900   MO
Web Site:
   https://www.discountcoffee.com
Year Founded: 1999
Sales Range: $1-9.9 Million
Emp.: 10

Coffee & Related Products Online Whslr
N.A.I.C.S.: 424490
Kirby Newbury *(Co-Founder & CEO)*
Cherri Newbury *(Co-Founder & Pres)*

DISCOUNT DANCE SUPPLY
5065 E Hunter Ave, Anaheim, CA
92807
Tel.: (714) 970-0462
Web Site:
   http://www.discountdance.com
Sales Range: $10-24.9 Million
Emp.: 150
Clothing Stores
N.A.I.C.S.: 458110
Brian Hill *(CEO)*

DISCOUNT DRUG MART INC.
211 Commerce Dr, Medina, OH
44256-1331
Tel.: (330) 725-2340   OH
Web Site: https://www.discount-
   drugmart.com
Year Founded: 1969
Sales Range: $1-4.9 Billion
Emp.: 4,000
Drug Store
N.A.I.C.S.: 455219
Parviz Boodjeh *(Founder)*

DISCOUNT ELECTRONICS
1011 W Anderson Ln, Austin, TX
78757
Tel.: (512) 983-9989
Web Site:
   https://www.discountelectronics.com
Sales Range: $10-24.9 Million
Emp.: 101
Consumer Electronics Sales
N.A.I.C.S.: 449210
Rick Culleton *(Pres & CEO)*
Eugene Terrell *(Mgr-Ops)*

DISCOUNT EMPORIUM INC.
1601 Kanawha Blvd W Ste 200,
Charleston, WV 25312-2539
Tel.: (304) 345-4836   WV
Web Site: http://www.drugemp.com
Year Founded: 1988
Sales Range: $25-49.9 Million
Emp.: 225
Drug Stores & Proprietary Stores
N.A.I.C.S.: 456110
Robert Petryszuk *(Pres)*

DISCOUNT FENCE SUPPLY, INC.
10050 Wellman Rd, Streetsboro, OH
44241
Tel.: (330) 650-9226
Web Site:
   http://www.discountfence.com
Year Founded: 1983
Sales Range: $1-9.9 Million
Emp.: 15
Fences, Gates & Entry Access Equipments Whslr & Distr
N.A.I.C.S.: 423390
Scott Moore *(Dir-IT)*
John Ridley *(Partner & VP)*
Corey Stoffer *(Mgr-Warehouse)*

DISCOUNT FOODS INC.
2413 Hwy 202, Anniston, AL 36201-
5349
Tel.: (256) 236-0533   AL
Year Founded: 1985
Sales Range: $25-49.9 Million
Emp.: 200
Grocery Stores
N.A.I.C.S.: 445110
Trae Fite *(Pres)*

DISCOUNT SMOKE SHOP MISSOURI INC.

4400 Woodson Rd, Saint Louis, MO
63134
Tel.: (314) 447-0282
Web Site:
   http://www.discountsmokeshop.com
Sales Range: $10-24.9 Million
Emp.: 10
Tobacco Stores & Stands
N.A.I.C.S.: 459991
Jon Rand *(Pres)*

DISCOUNT TOBACCO OUTLET INC.
1231 Salem Park Ct, Murfreesboro,
TN 37128
Tel.: (615) 867-5070
Sales Range: $10-24.9 Million
Emp.: 20
Tobacco Products Supplier & Retailer
N.A.I.C.S.: 459991
James Keith Watts *(Pres & CEO)*
Aaron Watts *(CFO)*

DISCOUNT TWO WAY RADIO CORPORATION
1430 240th St, Harbor City, CA
90710
Tel.: (310) 224-5100   CA
Web Site: http://www.discounttwo-
   wayradio.com
Year Founded: 1997
Sales Range: $10-24.9 Million
Emp.: 32
Radio & Electronic Communication Equipment Distr
N.A.I.C.S.: 423690
Ben Burns *(Owner)*
Kenneth Klyberg *(COO)*
Tony Varbanov *(Dir-Mktg & Sls)*
Alex Thompson *(Dir-IT)*

DISCOVERX CORP.
42501 Albrae St, Fremont, CA 94538
Tel.: (510) 979-1415   DE
Web Site: http://www.discoverx.com
Year Founded: 1999
Sales Range: $10-24.9 Million
Emp.: 40
Pharmaceutical Reagents & Assay Kits Mfr
N.A.I.C.S.: 541715
Sailaja Kuchibhatla *(Sr VP & Gen Mgr-Products Div)*
David Martz *(Sr VP-Sls & Distr)*
Theresa Schaub *(Sr VP-Comml Ops)*

Subsidiaries:

BioSeek LLC   (1)
310 Utah Ave Ste 100, South San Francisco, CA 94080
Tel.: (650) 416-7600
Web Site: http://www.bioseekinc.com
Sales Range: $10-24.9 Million
Emp.: 30
Pharmaceutical Research & Development Services
N.A.I.C.S.: 541715
Alison O'Mahony *(Sr Dir-Biology Res)*
Ellen Berg *(Co-Founder & Gen Mgr)*
Sailaja Kuchibhatla *(Sr VP-Bus Dev)*

DISCOVERY BEHAVIORAL HEALTH, INC
4281 Katella Ave Ste 111, Los Angeles, CA 90720
Tel.: (844) 670-4785
Web Site:
   http://www.discoverybehavioral.com
Year Founded: 2018
Mental Health Care Services
N.A.I.C.S.: 621112
John Peloquin *(Pres & CEO)*
Corey Procunier *(VP-HR)*
Chris Diamond *(VP-Bus Dev)*
Sandra Sellani *(VP-Mktg)*

Subsidiaries:

New Hope Ranch LLC   (1)
11908 Sparks Rd, Manor, TX 95648-0758
Tel.: (512) 298-4379

Discovery Behavioral Health, Inc—(Continued)

Web Site: http://www.newhoperanch.com
Animal Production
N.A.I.C.S.: 115210
Diane Knight (Owner)

Prosperity Wellness Center (1)
122201 Pacific Ave, Tacoma, WA 98446-5307
Tel.: (253) 536-6425
Web Site:
http://www.prosperitywellnesscenter.com
Graphic Design Services
N.A.I.C.S.: 541430
David Laws (Owner)

DISCOVERY HOMES
4061 Port Chicago Hwy, Concord, CA 94520
Tel.: (925) 682-6419
Web Site:
http://www.discoveryhomes.com
Year Founded: 1938
Sales Range: $10-24.9 Million
Emp.: 80
Operative Builder Services
N.A.I.C.S.: 236117
Jennifer Johansen (Principal)
Lewis Parsons (Pres)

DISCOVERY LIFE SCIENCES, LLC
1236 Los Osos Vly Rd Ste T, Los Osos, CA 93402-3360
Tel.: (805) 528-4341
Web Site:
http://www.discoverylifescience.com
Research & Development in Biotechnology Services
N.A.I.C.S.: 541714
Michael Pisano (Exec VP-Proteomics)
Glenn Bilawsky (CEO)
Thomas Halsey (Exec VP-Genomic Sequencing & Bioinformatics Svcs Div)
Dominic Clarke (CTO-Cell & Gene Therapy)
Katelyn Petti Hokenberg (Chief HR Officer)
Suso J. Platero (Chief Scientific Officer)

Subsidiaries:

AllCells, LLC. (1)
5858 Horton St Ste 360, Emeryville, CA 94608
Tel.: (510) 450-3900
Web Site: http://www.allcells.com
Sales Range: $1-9.9 Million
Emp.: 48
Hematopoietic Cell Product Research & Development Services
N.A.I.C.S.: 541715
Jay Tong (Pres & CEO)
Wayne E. Vaz (VP-Corp & Bus Dev)
Jack Zhai (VP-Sls & Mktg)

Qualtek Molecular Laboratories (1)
6483 Calle Real Ste A, Santa Barbara, CA 93117
Tel.: (215) 504-7402
Web Site: http://www.qmlabs.com
Chemicals Mfr
N.A.I.C.S.: 325998
Frank Lynch (COO)
Steve Bernstein (CEO)

DISCOVERY PLACE, INC.
301 N Tryon St, Charlotte, NC 28202
Tel.: (704) 372-6261   NC
Web Site:
https://www.discoveryplace.org
Year Founded: 1947
Sales Range: $10-24.9 Million
Emp.: 233
Science & Technology Museum Operator
N.A.I.C.S.: 712110

Christopher Perri (Chm)
Rich Campbell (Vice Chm)
Sean O'Neil (Sec)
Victor Fields (Treas)

DISCOVERY SERVICES LLC
1100 17th St NW Ste 604, Washington, DC 20036
Web Site:
http://www.discoveryservicesllc.com
Year Founded: 2008
Sales Range: $10-24.9 Million
Emp.: 307
Litigation Support Services
N.A.I.C.S.: 541199
Ashish Prasad (CEO)
Ashley Kumar (COO & CFO)

DISCOVERY TECHNOLOGY INTERNATIONAL, INC.
6968 Professional Pkwy E, Sarasota, FL 34240
Tel.: (941) 907-4444
Web Site: http://www.dtimotors.com
Sales Range: $10-24.9 Million
Emp.: 12
Ultrasonic Standing Wave-Type Piezoelectric Motor Mfr
N.A.I.C.S.: 334519
Mark P. Broderick (Co-Founder & CEO)
Valentin Zhelyaskov (Co-Founder, CTO & Chief Scientific Officer)
Sergey Petrenko (Dir-R&D)

DISCOVERY WORLD TRAVEL, INC.
1045 Pennsylvania Ave, Sheboygan, WI 53081
Tel.: (920) 459-2963
Web Site:
https://www.tldiscovery.com
Rev.: $12,400,000
Emp.: 39
Travel Agencies
N.A.I.C.S.: 561510
Dale Rauwerdink (Mgr)
David Prigge (Mgr-Mktg)

DISCOVERY-THE FINANCIAL INFORMATION GROUP, INC.
12 Christopher Way Ste 202, Eatontown, NJ 07724
Tel.: (732) 933-1899
Web Site:
http://www.discoveryco.com
Year Founded: 2001
Sales Range: $1-9.9 Million
Emp.: 34
Online Investment & Financial Services
N.A.I.C.S.: 523150
Robert Hemann (CEO)

DISCTRONICS TEXAS INC.
2800 Summit Ave, Plano, TX 75074-7444
Tel.: (972) 881-8800   TX
Year Founded: 1990
Sales Range: $25-49.9 Million
Emp.: 175
Prerecorded Records & Tapes
N.A.I.C.S.: 334610
David Littlefield (Pres)
Michael Brassil (Gen Mgr)

DISHONE SATELLITE
2601 N Canyon Rd Ste 201, Provo, UT 84604
Tel.: (801) 705-5353
Web Site: http://www.dishone.net
Year Founded: 2004
Sales Range: $1-9.9 Million
Emp.: 140
Satellite Retailer for DirectTV & Dish Network

N.A.I.C.S.: 517410
Mike Hammond (Owner & Founder)
Ben Callis (Exec Dir-Ops)
Jon Clifton (VP-Ops)

DISITRON INDUSTRIES, INC.
3381 NW 168th St, Miami Gardens, FL 33056
Tel.: (951) 324-9752
Web Site: http://www.disitron.com
Year Founded: 2002
Sales Range: $10-24.9 Million
Emp.: 12
Satellite Systems Mfr
N.A.I.C.S.: 517410
Ricardo P. Dias (Pres)
Renato G. Dias (VP-Bus Dev)

DISMAS CHARITIES, INC.
2500 S 7th St, Louisville, KY 40208
Tel.: (502) 636-2033   KY
Web Site: https://www.dismas.com
Year Founded: 1979
Sales Range: $25-49.9 Million
Emp.: 969
Residential Care Services
N.A.I.C.S.: 623990
Jan M. Kempf (COO & Exec VP)
Raymond J. Weis (Pres & CEO)

DISORDERLY KIDS, LLC
6100 S Malt Ave, Commerce, CA 90040-3508
Tel.: (323) 581-3511
Rev.: $30,890,173
Emp.: 69
Girls & Childrens Clothing Mfr
N.A.I.C.S.: 458110
Elliot Schutzer (Pres)
Susan Fisher (Controller & Office Mgr)
Jason Schutzer (VP)

DISOSWAY, INC.
942 Old Liverpool Rd, Liverpool, NY 13088-5552
Tel.: (315) 457-3110
Sales Range: $50-74.9 Million
Emp.: 1
Hydraulic & Pneumatic Control Valves Mfr
N.A.I.C.S.: 551112
Dudley Disosway Johnson (Pres)
David Hutton (CFO)

DISPATCH TECHNOLOGIES, INC.
123 N Washington St 2nd Fl, Boston, MA 02114
Tel.: (617) 580-0607   MA
Web Site: http://www.dispatch.me
Year Founded: 2012
Sales Range: $1-9.9 Million
Emp.: 65
Information Technology Services
N.A.I.C.S.: 541512
Avi Goldberg (CEO)
David Morland (CFO)
Scott Rudberg (CTO)
Rob Simons (VP-Sls)
Nahi Simon (VP-Professional Svcs)

DISPATCH TRANSPORTATION INC.
14032 Santa Ana Ave, Fontana, CA 92337
Tel.: (909) 355-5531
Web Site:
http://www.dispatchtrans.com
Sales Range: $10-24.9 Million
Emp.: 200
Truck Transportation Brokers
N.A.I.C.S.: 488510
Bruce Degler (Co-Owner & Pres)
Kim Pugmire (Co-Owner & VP)
Brian Bolton (Mgr-Ops)

DISPENSER BEVERAGES INC.
2090 Farallon Dr, San Leandro, CA 94577
Tel.: (510) 346-2200
Web Site:
http://www.dispenserbeverages.com
Sales Range: $10-24.9 Million
Emp.: 20
Beverage Concentrates
N.A.I.C.S.: 424490
Scott Riel (Exec VP)
Bryan Bunch (Dir-Sls & Mktg)

DISPENSER SERVICES INC.
4273 Domino Ave, North Charleston, SC 29405
Tel.: (843) 554-6854   SC
Web Site:
https://www.dispenserservices.com
Year Founded: 1970
Beverage Dispenser Equipment & Services
N.A.I.C.S.: 445132
Steven Harth (Owner)

DISPENSERS OPTICAL SERVICE CORPORATION
1815 Plantside Dr, Louisville, KY 40299
Tel.: (502) 491-3440
Year Founded: 1951
Sales Range: $10-24.9 Million
Emp.: 5
Optical Laboratories Operator & Opthalmic Lens Mfr
N.A.I.C.S.: 339115
Charles S. Arensberg (Pres)

DISPENSING DYNAMICS INTERNATIONAL
1020 Bixby Dr, City of Industry, CA 91745
Tel.: (626) 961-3691
Web Site:
http://www.dispensingdynamics.com
Year Founded: 1932
Sales Range: $10-24.9 Million
Emp.: 75
Plastic Dispensing Products Mfr & Distr
N.A.I.C.S.: 326199
Dean deBuhr (Chm & CEO)
Joel Keily (Chief Technical Officer)
Michael Severyn (Exec VP-Sls & Mktg)
Chris Sigmon (Pres & COO)
Andrew Sterkowitz (CFO)
Alex Mora (VP-Ops)
Barnabas Shanti (Plant Dir)
Greg Hunter (Co-CEO)
Arne Pike (Pres)

DISPLAY BOYS
17032 Murphy Ave, Irvine, CA 92614
Tel.: (949) 833-0100
Web Site:
http://www.displayboys.com
Year Founded: 1989
Sales Range: $1-9.9 Million
Emp.: 40
Advetising Agency
N.A.I.C.S.: 541810
John Riley (Co-Founder & VP)
Mike Mikyska (VP-Bus Dev)
Darin Rasmussen (Co-Founder, Pres & Chief Creative Officer)

DISPLAY INDUSTRIES, LLC
5850 Peachtree Industrial Blvd, Norcross, GA 30071
Tel.: (404) 350-4800
Web Site:
http://www.displayindustries.com
Sales Range: $10-24.9 Million
Emp.: 100
Wood Products Mfr

N.A.I.C.S.: 321999
Mark Higgins *(Pres)*
Dean Wu *(Engr-Mechanical)*
Michael Mills *(Engr-Logistics)*
Joe Barker II *(Mgr-Pur)*

DISPLAY PACK INC.
1340 Monroe Ave NW, Grand Rapids, MI 49505-4604
Tel.: (616) 451-3061   MI
Web Site:
   http://www.displaypack.com
Year Founded: 1967
Rev.: $39,803,456
Emp.: 200
Plastics Product Mfr
N.A.I.C.S.: 326199

DISPUTESUITE.COM, LLC
6619 State Rd 54, New Port Richey, FL 34652
Tel.: (727) 842-9999
Web Site:
   http://www.disputesuite.com
Year Founded: 2007
Sales Range: $1-9.9 Million
Emp.: 14
Credit Repair Software Mfr
N.A.I.C.S.: 513210
Michael Citron *(CEO)*
Carmen Lopez *(Dir-Bus Rels)*

DISTEK INTEGRATION, INC.
6612 Chancellor Dr Ste 600, Cedar Falls, IA 50613
Tel.: (319) 859-3600
Web Site: https://www.distek.com
Year Founded: 1992
Sales Range: $1-9.9 Million
Emp.: 110
Software Development Services
N.A.I.C.S.: 541511
Matt Dickinson *(Founder & Pres)*
Dillon Glissmann *(Engr-Test)*
Jeremy Yoder *(VP-Engrg)*
Beth Hallett *(Engr-Software)*
Edwin Dickens *(Engr-Sys)*
Ian Abbott *(Engr-Software)*

DISTINCTIVE FOODS LLC.
654 S Wheeling Rd, Wheeling, IL 60090
Tel.: (847) 459-3600
Web Site:
   https://www.distinctivefoods.com
Year Founded: 1976
Sales Range: $10-24.9 Million
Emp.: 100
Bakery Products Mfr
N.A.I.C.S.: 311812

DISTORTIONS UNLIMITED CORP.
517 13th St, Greeley, CO 80631
Tel.: (970) 351-0100
Web Site:
   https://www.distortionsunlimited.com
Sales Range: $1-9.9 Million
Emp.: 20
Movie Props, Displays, Sculptures, Masks & Costumes Mfr
N.A.I.C.S.: 541490
Ed Edmunds *(Pres)*
Marsha Edmunds *(VP)*

DISTRIBUTION & MARKING SERVICES, INC.
2127 Earsley Town Blvd Ste 301, Charlotte, NC 28273
Tel.: (704) 587-3674
Web Site: https://www.dmsi.net
Year Founded: 1987
Sales Range: $25-49.9 Million
Emp.: 800
General Warehousing Services
N.A.I.C.S.: 493110

Nicholas Santella *(Pres)*

DISTRIBUTION 2000 INC.
1165 W Crossroads Pkwy, Romeoville, IL 60446
Tel.: (630) 633-6100
Web Site: http://www.dist2000.com
Year Founded: 1995
Warehousing Services
N.A.I.C.S.: 493190
Cheryl LaCorte *(VP)*

Subsidiaries:

Starlite Services, Inc.   (1)
1165 W Crossroads Pkwy, Romeoville, IL 60446
Tel.: (630) 679-2840
Web Site: http://www.dist2000.com
Freight Transportation Arrangement
N.A.I.C.S.: 488510
Judy Zerial *(Pres)*

DISTRIBUTION ALTERNATIVES, INC.
435 Park Ct, Lino Lakes, MN 55014-2073
Tel.: (651) 636-9167   MN
Web Site: http://www.daserv.com
Year Founded: 1935
Sales Range: $150-199.9 Million
Emp.: 180
Third-Party Warehousing, Distribution & Fulfillment Services
N.A.I.C.S.: 493110
Keith T. Bailey *(VP-Warehouse Ops)*

DISTRIBUTION AMERICA, INC.
11301 Carmel Commons Blvd Ste 111, Charlotte, NC 28226
Tel.: (704) 940-4800
Web Site: http://www.daonline.com
Year Founded: 1991
Hardware & Paint Sundries Whslr & Distr
N.A.I.C.S.: 423710
David W. Christmas *(Pres & CEO)*

DISTRIBUTION COOPERATIVE INC
5356 E Ponce De Leon Ave Ste 100, Stone Mountain, GA 30083
Tel.: (770) 496-5900   GA
Year Founded: 2005
Sales Range: $50-74.9 Million
Hospital Supplies Warehousing & Distribution Services
N.A.I.C.S.: 493190
Christopher Pope *(Sec)*
Roy Gilleland *(Pres)*
Thomas McBride *(CFO)*

DISTRIBUTION ROYALTY INC.
3753 Howard Hughes Pkwy Ste 200, Las Vegas, NV 89169
Tel.: (702) 425-7825   NV
Year Founded: 2010
Feature Films, Film Scripts & Theatrical Musicals Licensing
N.A.I.C.S.: 533110
Stephen F. McKernan *(Pres & CEO)*
Bernard Faibish *(CFO)*

DISTRIBUTION SERVICES OF AMERICA, INC.
208 North St, Foxboro, MA 02035
Tel.: (508) 543-9700   MA
Web Site: http://www.dsa-inc.com
Year Founded: 1917
Rev.: $18,200,000
Emp.: 170
General Warehousing & Storage
N.A.I.C.S.: 493110
Joe Gualtieri *(VP)*
Paul Lestan *(Chm & Pres)*

Subsidiaries:

DSA-Software, Inc.   (1)
34 School St Ste 201, Foxboro, MA 02035
Tel.: (508) 543-0400
Web Site: http://www.dsasoft.com
Emp.: 5
Software Development Services
N.A.I.C.S.: 541511
Boris Henkin *(Dir-Sys Dev)*
Lee Petri *(Pres)*
Michael Barad *(VP-Sls & Bus Dev)*
Ted Long *(Dir-Client Svcs)*
David L. Petri *(Chm)*

Foxboro Terminals Co. Inc.   (1)
208 N St, Foxboro, MA 02035
Tel.: (508) 543-6363
Rev.: $7,700,000
Emp.: 86
General Warehousing
N.A.I.C.S.: 493110

DISTRIBUTION VIDEO & AUDIO, INC.
31541 US Hwy 19 N, Palm Harbor, FL 34684
Tel.: (727) 447-4147
Web Site: http://www.dva.com
Year Founded: 1988
Sales Range: $10-24.9 Million
Emp.: 30
Audio & Video Products Whslr
N.A.I.C.S.: 512120
Brad S. Kugler *(Co-Owner & CEO)*
Ryan J. Kugler *(Co-Owner & Pres)*
Carol Kurak *(VP-Sls)*
Jim Grimes *(VP-Warehouse Ops)*
Nathalie Manecchia *(VP-Ops)*

DISTRIBUTIVE EDUCATION CLUBS OF AMERICA, INC.
1908 Association Dr, Reston, VA 20191
Tel.: (703) 860-5000
Web Site: http://www.deca.org
Year Founded: 1946
Sales Range: $10-24.9 Million
Emp.: 11
Employment Placement Services
N.A.I.C.S.: 611430
Julie Kandik *(Dir-Images)*
Christopher Young *(Dir-High School Div)*
Cindy Allen *(Dir-Corp Affairs)*
Shane Thomas *(Dir-Competitive Events)*
Michael Mount *(Dir-Data Mgmt)*

DISTRIBUTOR CORPORATION OF NEW ENGLAND INC.
767 Eastern Ave, Malden, MA 02148-5910
Tel.: (781) 322-8800
Web Site: http://www.dcne.com
Year Founded: 1963
Sales Range: $10-24.9 Million
Emp.: 92
Warm Air Heating & Air Conditioning Supplies Distr
N.A.I.C.S.: 423730
Nancy R. Kolligian *(CEO)*
Brendan Curran *(Mgr-Customer Assurance)*
Michael Morse *(Mgr-Svc)*

DISTRIBUTOR SERVICE INC.
1 Dorrington Rd, Carnegie, PA 15106-1600
Tel.: (412) 279-7824   PA
Web Site: http://www.maildsi.com
Year Founded: 1968
Rev.: $39,273,138
Emp.: 124
Lumber, Plywood & Millwork
N.A.I.C.S.: 423310
William Delaney *(Pres)*

DISTRIBUTORS WAREHOUSE INC.
1900 N 10th St, Paducah, KY 42001
Tel.: (270) 442-8201
Web Site: http://www.btbauto.com
Sales Range: $10-24.9 Million
Emp.: 40
Automotive Supplies & Parts
N.A.I.C.S.: 423120
Walter Korte *(Chm)*
Steve Korte *(Pres)*
Lisa Pullen *(Controller)*

DISTRICT MEDICAL GROUP INC.
2929 E Thomas Rd, Phoenix, AZ 85016
Tel.: (602) 470-5000   AZ
Year Founded: 2006
Emp.: 792
Medical Care Services
N.A.I.C.S.: 621511
Craig Jones *(Treas & CFO)*
Peg Loos *(COO)*
Carol Olson *(Chm-Psychiatry)*
Daniel Caruso *(Chm-Surgery)*
Iman Feizerfan *(Dir-Neurosurgery)*
Kote Chundu *(Pres & CEO)*
Dean Coonrod *(Chm-OBGYN & Sec)*
David Wisinger *(Chm-Medicine & CMO)*
Phyllis Biedess *(Vice Chm)*
Dan Hobohm *(Chm, Chm-Path & VP-Quality)*

DISTRICT OF COLUMBIA PRIMARY CARE ASSOCIATION
1620 I St NW Ste 300, Washington, DC 20006
Tel.: (202) 638-0252   DC
Web Site: http://www.dcpca.org
Year Founded: 1996
Sales Range: $10-24.9 Million
Emp.: 44
Community Health Care Services
N.A.I.C.S.: 621498
Donna Ramos-Johnson *(CTO)*
Saida Z. Durkee *(Coord-Policy, External Affairs & Comm)*
Gwendolyn O. Young *(Dir-Quality Improvement & Ops)*
Alicia Wilson *(Vice Chm)*
Tamara Smith *(CEO)*
Maria S. Gomez *(Pres & CEO)*

DISTRICT PHOTO INC.
10501 Rhode Island Ave, Beltsville, MD 20705-2317
Tel.: (301) 937-5300   MD
Web Site:
   http://www.districtphoto.com
Year Founded: 1949
Sales Range: $150-199.9 Million
Emp.: 700
Photo Finisher
N.A.I.C.S.: 812921
Bob Friend *(Exec VP & Gen Mgr)*
Neil D. Cohen *(Pres & CEO)*

Subsidiaries:

Harrier LLC   (1)
Brunel Road, Newton Abbot, TQ12 4UH, Devon, United Kingdom
Tel.: (44) 1626 322022
Web Site: http://www.harrierllc.co.uk
Sales Range: $25-49.9 Million
Emp.: 144
Digital Photo Printing Services
N.A.I.C.S.: 323111
Chris Hughes *(Mng Dir)*

Mystic Color Lab, Inc.   (1)
10619 Baltimore Ave, Beltsville, MD 20705   (100%)
Tel.: (301) 937-5300
Web Site: http://www.districtphoto.com

District Photo Inc.—(Continued)
Sales Range: $50-74.9 Million
Emp.: 400
Online Photofinishing Services
N.A.I.C.S.: 812921
Bob Friend (VP)

DIT CORPORATION
2201 N 90th St Ste 121, Omaha, NE 68134
Tel.: (402) 393-0828
Web Site: http://www.ditcorp.com
Sales Range: $10-24.9 Million
Emp.: 26
Computer & Software Stores
N.A.I.C.S.: 449210
Dyon Tang (Founder & Chm)
Bob Bally (District Mgr)

DITCH WITCH EQUIPMENT OF TENNESSE INC.
10732 Dutchtown Rd, Knoxville, TN 37932
Tel.: (865) 970-2840
Web Site:
http://www.ditchwitchtn.com
Sales Range: $10-24.9 Million
Emp.: 30
Construction Equipment Distr
N.A.I.C.S.: 423810
Ray Romano (Pres & CEO)

DITCH WITCH MINNESOTA INC.
12826 Emery Way, Shakopee, MN 55379
Tel.: (952) 445-3066
Web Site:
http://www.ditchwitchmn.com
Year Founded: 1965
Sales Range: $10-24.9 Million
Emp.: 21
General Construction Machinery & Equipment Whslr
N.A.I.C.S.: 423810
Warren Peiffer (Pres & CEO)
Louis Gardeski (Controller)

DITCH WITCH SALES INC.
1617 S Service Rd PO Box 429, Sullivan, MO 63080
Tel.: (573) 468-8012
Web Site:
http://www.ditchwitchsales.com
Emp.: 135
Underground Construction & Utility Equipment Dealer
N.A.I.C.S.: 423830
Mark Jones (Sls Mgr)
Kent Cudney (Gen Mgr & CFO)
Laura DeClue (Controller)

DITECH HOLDING CORPORATION
1100 Virginia Dr Ste 100, Fort Washington, PA 19034
Tel.: (844) 714-8603 MD
Web Site:
http://www.walterinvestment.com
Year Founded: 1989
Rev.: $658,940,000
Assets: $11,284,526,000
Liabilities: $11,302,649,000
Net Worth: ($18,123,000)
Earnings: ($205,094,000)
Emp.: 2,900
Fiscal Year-end: 12/31/18
Real Estate Investment Services
N.A.I.C.S.: 523999
Elizabeth F. Monahan (Chief HR Officer)
John J. Haas (Chief Legal Officer, Gen Counsel & Sec)
Gerald A. Lombardo (CFO)

Thomas F. Marano (Chm, Pres & CEO)
Alfred W. Young Jr. (Chief Risk & Compliance Officer)

Subsidiaries:

Green Tree Servicing LLC   (1)
345 Saint Peter St, Saint Paul, MN 55102
Tel.: (651) 293-3400
Web Site:
http://www.greentreecreditsolutions.com
Sales Range: $400-449.9 Million
Emp.: 1,800
Loan Services
N.A.I.C.S.: 522291

DITEK CORPORATION
1 DITEK Ctr 1720 Starkey Rd, Largo, FL 33771
Tel.: (727) 812-5000
Web Site: http://www.ditekcorp.com
Sales Range: $10-24.9 Million
Emp.: 90
Surge Protection Products Mfr
N.A.I.C.S.: 335311
Robert McIntyre (Co-Owner)
Anne Miles (Mgr-Production & Inventory Control)
Roy VanNostran (VP-Ops)
Tony Cuda (Mgr-Mfg)

DITO, LLC
9913 Sugarwood Lane, Manassas, VA 20110
Tel.: (855) 937-3486
Web Site: http://www.ditoweb.com
Year Founded: 2007
Sales Range: $1-9.9 Million
Emp.: 30
Google Apps Authorized Reseller
N.A.I.C.S.: 513210
Dan McNelis (CEO & Founder)

DITTMAR LUMBER CORP.
500 Seguin St, San Antonio, TX 78208
Tel.: (210) 226-3141
Sales Range: $10-24.9 Million
Emp.: 45
Lumber & Building Materials Whslr
N.A.I.C.S.: 423310
John J. Jenschke (Pres)
Michael Lily (Controller)

DITTO SALES INC.
2332 Cathy Ln, Jasper, IN 47546
Tel.: (812) 482-3043
Web Site: http://www.dittosales.com
Year Founded: 1975
Sales Range: $10-24.9 Million
Emp.: 200
Furniture Parts Whslr & Distr
N.A.I.C.S.: 332999
Scott G. Schwinghammer (Pres)
Bruce Reinhart (Dir-Procurement)
Donna Stetter (Dir-IT)
Gene Hostetter (VP)
Diane Denk (Dir-HR & Employee Dev)

DITTOE PUBLIC RELATIONS, INC.
2815 E 62nd St Ste 300, Indianapolis, IN 46220-2983
Tel.: (317) 202-2280
Web Site: http://www.dittoepr.com
Sales Range: $1-9.9 Million
Emp.: 7
Public Relations Agency
N.A.I.C.S.: 541820
Chris Dittoe (Co-Founder & Pres)
Lauren Sanders (Partner & VP-Client Success)
Ashley Eggert (Sr Acct Mgr)
Christy Chen (Partner & VP-Acct Svcs)
Liza Dittoe (Co-Founder & Principal)

Greta Snell (Sr Acct Mgr)
Eric Kokonas (Partner)
Britny Kalule (Acct Exec)
Kalyn Long (Acct Exec)
Mallory Sturgeon (Dir-Accts)
Megan Custodio (Partner & Sr VP)
Michelle Bower (Sr Acct Mgr)
Sophie Maccagnone (Acct Exec)
Madisen Petrosky (Sr Acct Mgr)
Lauryn Gray (Dir-Bus Dev)

DIVA LIMOUSINE LTD.
11132 Ventura Blvd Ste 100, Studio City, CA 91604
Tel.: (310) 278-3482
Web Site: http://www.divalimo.com
Rev.: $12,115,190
Emp.: 51
Chaffeured Ground Transportation
N.A.I.C.S.: 485320
Bijan Zoughi (Pres & CEO)
Israel Juarez (COO)

DIVAL SAFETY EQUIPMENT INC.
1721 Niagara St, Buffalo, NY 14207
Tel.: (716) 874-9060
Web Site: http://www.divalsafety.com
Year Founded: 1977
Sales Range: $25-49.9 Million
Emp.: 130
Safety Equipment & Supplies
N.A.I.C.S.: 423990
C. J. Vallone (Pres)
Chris Werner (Exec VP)
Michael Arcara (Mgr-Construction & Oil & Gas Sls)
Tim Devin (Mgr-Sls)
Jay Spencer (Gen Mgr)
Dale Lesinski (VP)

DIVALL INSURED INCOME PROPERTIES 2 LIMITED PARTNERSHIP
1900 W 75th St Ste 100 Prairie Village, Kansas City, MO 66208
Tel.: (816) 421-7444 WI
Web Site:
https://www.divallproperties.com
Year Founded: 1987
Rev.: $1,611,173
Assets: $3,550,689
Liabilities: $144,144
Net Worth: $3,406,545
Earnings: $2,069,792
Fiscal Year-end: 12/31/22
Financial & Insurance Management Services
N.A.I.C.S.: 524298
Bruce A. Provo (Pres & CEO)

DIVANE BROS. ELECTRIC COMPANY
2424 N 25th Ave, Franklin Park, IL 60131-3323
Tel.: (847) 455-7143 IL
Web Site: http://www.divanebros.com
Year Founded: 1920
Sales Range: $10-24.9 Million
Emp.: 250
Electrical Contracting Services
N.A.I.C.S.: 238210
John T. Raiche (Treas & Sec)
Daniel Divane III (Pres)
William T. Divane Jr. (Chm & CEO)

DIVAR CHEMICALS, INC.
12603 SW Fwy Ste 572, Stafford, TX 77477
Tel.: (281) 451-6880 TX
Web Site:
https://www.impexcolors.com
Year Founded: 2003
Pigments, Resins, Polymers & Other Chemical Products Mfr & Whslr
N.A.I.C.S.: 325130

Anurag Gupta (Pres)

DIVCO CONSTRUCTION CORP.
6628 Willow Park Dr, Naples, FL 34109
Tel.: (239) 592-7222
Web Site:
https://www.divcohomes.com
Sales Range: $10-24.9 Million
Emp.: 16
Residential Construction
N.A.I.C.S.: 236115
Alan Foster (VP-Sls & Mktg)
Mark Eastman (Pres)
Stephen Kauffman (CEO)
Ron Glace (COO)

DIVE N SURF
504 N Broadway, Redondo Beach, CA 90277
Tel.: (310) 372-8423
Web Site: https://www.divensurf.com
Sales Range: $10-24.9 Million
Emp.: 50
Surfing Equipment & Supplies Distr
N.A.I.C.S.: 423910
Robert W. Meistrell (CEO)
Russell Lesser (Pres)
Randy Meistrell (VP)
Scott Daley (Dir-Mktg)

DIVERSANT, LLC
331 Newman Springs Rd Bldg 3 2nd Fl Ste 350, Red Bank, NJ 07701
Tel.: (732) 222-1250
Web Site: http://www.diversant.com
Year Founded: 2005
Sales Range: $75-99.9 Million
Emp.: 100
IT Staffing Services
N.A.I.C.S.: 561320
John Goullet (Chm)
Gene C. Waddy (CEO)
Marilyn Phillips (Mgr-Billing)
Yaniv Simpson (VP-Bus Dev)
Matt Schreier (Mng Dir-Minneapolis)
Charlean Parks (Mktg Mgr)
Gregg Schmedding (Exec VP)

Subsidiaries:

Atrilogy Solutions Group, Inc.   (1)
23052-H Alicia Pwy Ste 620, Mission Viejo, CA 92692
Tel.: (949) 777-4700
Web Site: http://www.atrilogy.com
Sales Range: $10-24.9 Million
Emp.: 15
Enterprise Resource Application Installation & Maintenance Services
N.A.I.C.S.: 541519
David Charest (Founder, Pres & CEO)
Paige Goff Doerr (Dir-IT Sls)
Kimberly Ladany (Dir-IT Sls)

DIVERSE DEVELOPMENT GROUP, INC.
4819 Wood Pointe Way, Sarasota, FL 34233
Tel.: (617) 510-1777 DE
Web Site:
http://www.diversedevelopment group.com
Year Founded: 2016
Assets: $104
Liabilities: $115,859
Net Worth: ($115,755)
Earnings: ($72,951)
Emp.: 1
Fiscal Year-end: 12/31/18
Real Estate Asset Management Services
N.A.I.C.S.: 531390
Christopher Kiritsis (Chm, Pres, CEO, CFO & Sec)

DIVERSE LYNX, LLC

300 Alexander Park Ste 200, Princeton, NJ 08540
Tel.: (732) 452-1006
Web Site:
https://www.diverselynx.com
Year Founded: 2002
Rev.: $15,400,000
Emp.: 145
Computer Related Services
N.A.I.C.S.: 541512
Ashok Srivastava (Exec VP-Clinical Ops & Chief Scientific Officer)
Myron B. Peterson (Dir-Medical)
Shubhendra Varma (Pres)

DIVERSE OPTICS, INC.
10310 Regis Ct, Rancho Cucamonga, CA 91730
Tel.: (909) 593-9330
Web Site:
http://www.diverseoptics.com
Year Founded: 2011
Precision Polymer Optic Components Mfr
N.A.I.C.S.: 333310
Erik Fleming (Pres & CEO)
Letty Ortega-Trevino (Sls Engr)

DIVERSEID PRODUCTS OF FLORIDA LLC
11111 N 46th St, Tampa, FL 33617
Tel.: (877) 446-2374
Web Site: http://www.diverseid.com
Sales Range: $10-24.9 Million
Emp.: 3
Signs, Printing Products & Office Supplies Mfr
N.A.I.C.S.: 339950
Mark Govin (Pres)

DIVERSIFIED AERO SERVICES, INC.
11920 SW 128th St, Miami, FL 33186
Tel.: (305) 234-2333
Web Site: http://www.dasi.com
Emp.: 110
Aftermarket Commercial Aircraft Parts & Supplies
N.A.I.C.S.: 336412
Andrea Dziuba (VP-Customer Svcs)
John Dziuba (Founder, Pres & CEO)
J. C. Banderas (Dir-Logistics, Exchanges & Repairs)
Ernie Sanchez (CFO)
Lou Bongiovi (Dir-Quality)
Sunil Pathi (Dir-IT)
Harp Brar (Reg VP-EMEA)
Collin Trupp (Mng Dir-Asia Pacific)
Kevin Brownstein (VP-Asset Mgmt)
Andrew Pye (Exec VP)
Claus Schnau (Reg VP-Sls-Americas)
Chris Glascock (VP-Pur)
Rhod Gibson (Pres)
Nick Chambers (COO)

DIVERSIFIED AIR SYSTEMS INC.
4760 Van Epps Rd, Cleveland, OH 44131
Tel.: (216) 741-1700
Web Site:
https://www.diversifiedair.com
Rev.: $10,300,000
Emp.: 34
Industrial Equipments Whslr & Distr
N.A.I.C.S.: 423830
Vince Lisi (Pres)

DIVERSIFIED AUTOMOTIVE INC.
6 Ramland Rd, Orangeburg, NY 10962
Tel.: (845) 359-2500
Web Site:
http://www.diversifiedauto.com
Rev.: $10,626,924

Emp.: 50
Freight Shipping & Trucking Services
N.A.I.C.S.: 484110
Michael Lewis (VP)
Randy Beggs (Exec VP)

DIVERSIFIED CAPITAL CREDIT CORP.
550 Mtn Ave, Gillette, NJ 07933
Tel.: (908) 647-4500
Web Site: http://www.dicapcredit.com
Rev.: $10,000,000
Emp.: 6
Equipment Rental & Leasing
N.A.I.C.S.: 532490
Bruce Smith (Pres & CEO)
Jacob Cutler (Sr Acct Mgr)

DIVERSIFIED CHEMICAL TECHNOLOGIES INC.
15477 Woodrow Wilson St, Detroit, MI 48238-1586
Tel.: (313) 867-5444
Web Site: https://www.dchem.com
Year Founded: 1971
Sales Range: $25-49.9 Million
Emp.: 240
Adhesives & Sealants Mfr
N.A.I.C.S.: 325520
Arnold Joseff (Co-Founder)

Subsidiaries:

Adhesive Systems Inc.   (1)
14410 Woodrow Wilson St, Detroit, MI 48238-1508
Tel.: (313) 865-4448
Web Site:
http://www.diversifiedchemicalinc.com
Sales Range: $10-24.9 Million
Emp.: 50
Adhesives & Sealants Mfr
N.A.I.C.S.: 325520

Coat-It Inc.   (1)
15400 Woodrow Wilson St, Detroit, MI 48238-1564
Tel.: (313) 869-8500
Sales Range: $10-24.9 Million
Emp.: 25
Adhesives & Sealants Mfr
N.A.I.C.S.: 325520
Roy Jacob (Mgr-Tech)
Yushin Ahn (Product Dir-Tech & Plng)
Rajan Eadara (VP-R&D)

Diversified Chemical Technologies Operating Company Inc.   (1)
15477 Woodrow Wilson St, Detroit, MI 48238-1586
Tel.: (313) 867-5444
Web Site:
http://www.diversifiedchemicalinc.com
Sales Range: $10-24.9 Million
Emp.: 35
Cyclic Crudes & Intermediates Mfr
N.A.I.C.S.: 325520

Diversitak, Inc.   (1)
15400 Woodrow Wilson St, Detroit, MI 48238
Tel.: (313) 869-8500
Chemical Products Mfr
N.A.I.C.S.: 325998

Paperworks Inc.   (1)
350 Midland St, Highland Park, MI 48203   (100%)
Tel.: (313) 867-5600
Web Site: http://www.pwi-inc.com
Sales Range: $10-24.9 Million
Emp.: 30
Printing & Writing Paper Whslr & Distr
N.A.I.C.S.: 424110
David Gray (Dir-Bus Dev)

Recycled Polymeric Materials, Inc.   (1)
6031 Joy Rd, Detroit, MI 48204
Tel.: (313) 957-6373
Web Site: http://www.rpmpolymer.com
Plastics Product Mfr
N.A.I.C.S.: 325211

DIVERSIFIED CLINICAL SERVICES, INC.
4225 E La Palma Ave, Anaheim, CA 92807
Tel.: (714) 579-8400
Web Site:
http://www.sechristusa.com
Year Founded: 2006
Sales Range: $1-9.9 Million
Emp.: 85
Health Care Srvices
N.A.I.C.S.: 621999
Dan Nguyen (CFO)
Veronica Lau (Program Dir)

DIVERSIFIED COATINGS INC.
224 River Rd, Ridgway, PA 15853
Tel.: (814) 772-3850
Web Site:
http://www.alleghenycoatings.com
Rev.: $12,500,000
Emp.: 70
Rust Preventive Coating Mfr
N.A.I.C.S.: 332812
Steve Quinn (Pres)

DIVERSIFIED COMMUNICATIONS
121 Free St, Portland, ME 04112-7437
Tel.: (207) 842-5500   ME
Web Site: http://www.divcom.com
Year Founded: 1949
Multi-Media Holding Company; Broadcasting, Publishing, Exhibitions & Emerging Media
N.A.I.C.S.: 551112
Janice Rogers (VP-HR)
Ted Wirth (Pres & CEO)
Rick Watson (CEO-DBC Pri Med)
Oakley Dyer (VP-Strategy & Corp Dev)
Whit Mitchell (VP-Fin)
Mary Larkin (Pres-Diversified Comm USA)
Carsten Holm (Mng Dir-Diversified Comm UK)
David Longman (Mng Dir-Diversified Comm Australia)
Liz Plizga (Grp VP)

Subsidiaries:

Diversified Business Communications   (1)
121 Free St, Portland, ME 04101-3919
Tel.: (207) 842-5500
Web Site: http://www.divbusiness.com
Sales Range: $25-49.9 Million
Emp.: 170
Convention & Trade Shows Organizer, Publisher & eMedia Services
N.A.I.C.S.: 561920
Kendra Lavigne (Coord-Bus Dev)
Oakley Dyer (VP-Strategy & Corp Dev)
Kavin Kittiboonya (Mng Dir-Diversified Comm-Thailand)
Mary Larkin (Exec VP)
Mike Lodato (Exec VP)
Bob MacGregor (Mng Dir-Diversified Comm-Canada)
Janice Rogers (VP-HR)
Bill Springer (Exec VP)
Kathy Willing (CFO)
Ted Wirth (Pres & CEO)

Diversified Business Communications Canada   (1)
Unit 1-110 Cochrane Drive, Markham, L3R 9S1, ON, Canada
Tel.: (905) 948-0470
Web Site: http://www.divbusiness.com
Sales Range: $10-24.9 Million
Emp.: 40
Trade Show & Event Organizer
N.A.I.C.S.: 561920
Carsten Holm (Mng Dir)
Janice Rogers (VP-HR)

Diversified Business Communications UK   (1)

Blenheim House 120 Church Str, Brighton, BN1 1UD, East Sussex, United Kingdom
Tel.: (44) 1273 645110
Web Site: http://www.divcom.co.uk
Sales Range: $10-24.9 Million
Emp.: 37
Event Planning & Management Services
N.A.I.C.S.: 926110
Carsten Holm (Mng Dir)
Ami Giles (Coord-Office)
Amy Muddle (Mgr-Mktg)
Carol Dunning (Mgr-Event-Natural & Organic Products Europe)
Caroline Hobden (Mgr-Event-Ocean Bus)
Cheri Arvonio (Mgr-Event-Marelec, Ocean Bus & Offshore Survey)
Chris Brazier (Mgr-Grp Event-Lunch)
Emma Crane (Mgr-Ops-Ocean Bus)
Emma-Louise Jones (Mgr-PR)

Diversified Communications India   (1)
6/C-5 Sangeeta Apartments Juhu Tara Road, Santa Cruz West, Mumbai, 400049, India
Tel.: (91) 2226604560
Web Site: http://www.divcom.in
Emp.: 40
Telecommunication Servicesb
N.A.I.C.S.: 517810
Anil Chopra (Mng Dir)
Ramesh Chetwani (Dir-Exhibition)
Ninja Monga (Sr Mgr-Sls & Mktg)
Jyoti Singh (Mgr-Advertising)
Mamta Pandey (Mgr-Advertising)

Diversified Events Hong Kong   (1)
Unit B 32/F Convoy 169 Electric Road, North Point, China (Hong Kong)
Tel.: (852) 31053970
Web Site: http://www.divcom.com.hk
Sales Range: $10-24.9 Million
Emp.: 40
Event Management Services
N.A.I.C.S.: 517810
Stuart Bailey (Mng Dir)

Diversified Exhibitions Australia   (1)
Level 5 636 St Kilda Rd, Melbourne, 3004, VIC, Australia
Tel.: (61) 392614500
Web Site: http://www.divcom.net.au
Event Planning & Management Services
N.A.I.C.S.: 711310

The Sleeter Group, Inc.   (1)
5776 Stoneridge Mall Rd Ste 120, Pleasanton, CA 94588-2860
Tel.: (925) 416-6300
Web Site: http://www.sleeter.com
Accounting Services
N.A.I.C.S.: 541211
Douglas Sleeter (Founder)
Jeannie Ruesch (Mgr-Mktg)

DIVERSIFIED COMPUTER SUPPLIES
4435 Concourse Dr, Ann Arbor, MI 48108
Tel.: (734) 677-7878
Web Site: https://www.dcsbiz.com
Year Founded: 2003
Sales Range: $75-99.9 Million
Emp.: 45
Computer Peripheral Equipment & Software Merchant Whslr
N.A.I.C.S.: 423430
Benjamin Harpster (Acct Mgr)
Mike McClure (Dir-Bus Dev)

DIVERSIFIED CONTROLS & SYSTEMS, INC.
645 Persons St, East Aurora, NY 14052
Tel.: (716) 652-5255
Web Site:
http://www.diversifiedcontrols.com
Sales Range: $25-49.9 Million
Emp.: 8
Custom Power Supplies & Custom Control Systems Mfr, Designer & Services
N.A.I.C.S.: 221122
Joseph Purcell (Pres)

Diversified Data Communications—(Continued)

DIVERSIFIED DATA COMMUNI-CATIONS
10811 Northend Ave, Ferndale, MI 48220
Tel.: (248) 399-0715
Web Site: http://www.divdat.com
Year Founded: 1971
Sales Range: $25-49.9 Million
Emp.: 60
Electronic Mail
N.A.I.C.S.: 517111
Alfred Bierkle (Owner)
Jason Bierkle (Pres)

DIVERSIFIED DYNAMICS COR-PORATION
1681 94th Ln NE, Minneapolis, MN 55449-4324
Tel.: (763) 780-5440   MN
Web Site: http://www.catpumps.com
Year Founded: 1968
Sales Range: $75-99.9 Million
Emp.: 110
Reciprocating Pumps & Systems Mfr & Distr
N.A.I.C.S.: 423830
Steve Bruggeman (Pres)
Darla Jean Thompson (Mgr-Mktg)
William L. Bruggeman Jr. (CEO)

Subsidiaries:

Cat Pumps (UK) Ltd.   (1)
1 Fleet Business Park Sandy Ln, Church Crookham, Fleet, GU52 8BF, Hampshire,
United Kingdom   (100%)
Tel.: (44) 252622031
Web Site: http://www.catpumps.co.uk
Sales Range: $10-24.9 Million
Emp.: 11
Pumps Mfr
N.A.I.C.S.: 333914

Cat Pumps Deutschland GmbH   (1)
Buchwiese 2, 65510, Idstein,
Germany   (100%)
Tel.: (49) 612693030
Web Site: http://www.catpumps.de
Sales Range: $10-24.9 Million
Emp.: 18
Pumps Mfr
N.A.I.C.S.: 333914
Bernhard Klink (Mgr)

Cat Pumps International N.V.   (1)
Heiveld Kens 6A, Kontich, 2550,
Belgium   (100%)
Tel.: (32) 34507150
Web Site: http://www.catpumps.be
Sales Range: $10-24.9 Million
Emp.: 17
Pumps Retailer & Marketer
N.A.I.C.S.: 423830
Alein Robenet (Gen Mgr)

Cat Pumps-International Division   (1)
1681 94th Ln NE, Minneapolis, MN 55449-4324
Tel.: (763) 780-5440
Web Site: http://www.catpumps.com
Sales Range: $10-24.9 Million
Emp.: 100
Pump Equipment Mfr
N.A.I.C.S.: 333914

Home Right   (1)
1770 Fernbrook Ln, Plymouth, MN 55447
Tel.: (763) 780-5115
Web Site: http://www.homeright.com
Sales Range: $25-49.9 Million
Emp.: 35
Painting Equipment & Home Care Product Distr
N.A.I.C.S.: 423830

DIVERSIFIED ELECTRONICS INC.
309 C Agnew Dr, Forest Park, GA 30297
Tel.: (404) 361-4840
Web Site: https://www.diversifiedelectronics.com

Sales Range: $10-24.9 Million
Emp.: 60
Communication Equipment Mfr
N.A.I.C.S.: 423690
John V. Thornton (CEO)
Chad Thornton (Mgr-Sales)

Subsidiaries:

Aplus Products LLC   (1)
88 Inverness Cir E Ste L 104, Englewood, CO 80111-1933
Tel.: (303) 755-3402
Web Site: http://www.aplusproducts.com
Sales Range: $10-24.9 Million
Emp.: 15
Electronic Components Mfr
N.A.I.C.S.: 334419

DIVERSIFIED EXECUTIVE SYSTEMS, INC.
2649 Valleydale Rd Ste B, Birmingham, AL 35244
Tel.: (205) 408-0922
Web Site: http://www.dessolutions.com
Year Founded: 1995
Sales Range: $10-24.9 Million
Emp.: 90
Business Consulting Services
N.A.I.C.S.: 541611
Walter J. DeCastro (Pres & CEO)

DIVERSIFIED FASTENING SYSTEMS
501 Richings St, Charles City, IA 50616
Tel.: (641) 228-1162
Web Site: https://www.dfsusa.com
Rev.: $17,400,000
Emp.: 75
Metal Component Parts Mfr
N.A.I.C.S.: 423710
Dan Crawford (Pres)
Trevor Crawford (Mgr-Sls-Natl)

DIVERSIFIED FOOD & SEA-SONING INC.
1115 N Causeway Ste 200, Mandeville, LA 70471
Tel.: (985) 809-3600   CA
Web Site: http://www.diversifiedfoodsandseasonings.com
Year Founded: 1981
Rev.: $42,400,000
Emp.: 457
Food Mfr
N.A.I.C.S.: 311999
Rick Chapman (Pres & CEO)

DIVERSIFIED GLASS SER-VICES
715 S Blvd E, Rochester Hills, MI 48307
Tel.: (248) 829-4800
Web Site: http://www.diversifiedglass.com
Sales Range: $25-49.9 Million
Emp.: 145
Automotive Glass Distr & Services
N.A.I.C.S.: 811122
Adam Ostdiek (Pres & CEO)

DIVERSIFIED GLOBAL GRAPHICS GROUP, LLC
100 Burma Rd, Jersey City, NJ 07305
Tel.: (201) 793-5000
Web Site: https://www.dg3.com
Year Founded: 2004
Sales Range: $125-149.9 Million
Print & Graphic Communications Services
N.A.I.C.S.: 323111
Joe Lindfeldt (Pres-Tech & Advisory Svcs)

Tom Saggiomo (Pres & CEO)
Steven Babat (Co-CFO)
Mike Roth (Co-CFO)

Subsidiaries:

DG3 Asia Limited   (1)
9th Floor Haking Tung Shing Industrial Building 34 Lee Chung Street, Chai Wan, Hong Kong, China (Hong Kong)
Tel.: (852) 29656777
Web Site: http://www.dg3.com
Emp.: 160
Print & Graphic Communications Services
N.A.I.C.S.: 323111
Victor Lee (Mng Dir)

DG3 Europe Ltd.   (1)
Unit 11 Thames Gateway Park Chequers Lane, Dagenham Dock, London, RM9 6FB, United Kingdom
Tel.: (44) 2075310500
Web Site: http://www.dg3.com
Sales Range: $10-24.9 Million
Emp.: 160
Print & Graphic Communications Services
N.A.I.C.S.: 323111
Barry Page (Mng Dir)

DG3 Japan Limited   (1)
Kyobashi Nagaoka Bldg 3-6-1 Hatchobori, Chuo-ku, Tokyo, 104-0032, Japan
Tel.: (81) 335235901
Web Site: http://www.dg3.com
Sales Range: $10-24.9 Million
Emp.: 6
Print & Graphic Communications Services
N.A.I.C.S.: 323111

DG3 Manila Ltd.   (1)
Unit 2604 Union Bank Plaza Building Meralco Avenue, cor Onyx and Sapphire Sts Ortigas Center, Pasig, Manila, Philippines
Tel.: (63) 26382676
Web Site: http://www.dg3.com
Emp.: 119
Print & Graphic Communications Services
N.A.I.C.S.: 323111
Cesar Cudiamat Jr. (Pres)

DG3 North America, Inc.   (1)
100 Burma Rd, Jersey City, NJ 07305-4623
Tel.: (201) 793-5000
Sales Range: $50-74.9 Million
Emp.: 400
Financial & Commercial Printing Services
N.A.I.C.S.: 323111
Gordon Mays (Exec VP-Pharmaceutical Solutions)
Joe Lindfeldt (Exec VP-Sls & Mktg)
Michael D'Onofrio (Sr VP-Comml Sls)
Fred Gorra (Sr VP-Sls)
Patrick Carhelion (Sr VP-Client Ops & Sr VP-Mfg)

Digital Publishing Solutions, Inc.   (1)
46 Third Ave, Somerville, MA 02143
Tel.: (617) 241-5600
Web Site: http://www.dpsicorp.com
Rev.: $1,500,000
Emp.: 50
Digital Publishing Services
N.A.I.C.S.: 513199
David Pompeo (Exec VP)
Ira Penner (CEO & Principal)
Eric Genova (Exec VP)
Art Baggot (Mng Dir-Bus Dev)
Robert Collins (Mng Dir-Asset Mgmt Div)

DIVERSIFIED GROUP LLC
5801 Citrus Blvd, Harahan, LA 70123-1680
Tel.: (504) 733-2800   LA
Year Founded: 1967
Sales Range: $25-49.9 Million
Emp.: 80
Holding Company; Power Line Construction & Maritime Repairs
N.A.I.C.S.: 336611
Vicki Kihnemann (VP)
H.D. Hughes II (Chm, Pres & CEO)

DIVERSIFIED INDUSTRIAL STAFFING
1441 E Maple Rd Ste 103, Troy, MI 48083

Tel.: (248) 519-4025
Web Site: http://www.diversifiedindustrialstaffing.com
Sales Range: $1-9.9 Million
Emp.: 6
Personnel & Human Resource Consulting Services
N.A.I.C.S.: 541612
Todd Palmer (Pres)

DIVERSIFIED INSURANCE SO-LUTIONS, INC.
100 N Corp Dr Ste 100, Brookfield, WI 53045
Tel.: (262) 439-4700
Web Site: http://www.div-ins.com
Year Founded: 1982
Emp.: 130
Insurance Brokerage Services
N.A.I.C.S.: 524210
Karl Cumblad (COO & Member-Mgmt Bd)
Beth Sczerzen (Sr Acct Mgr)
Crystal Benson (Mgr-Property & Casualty Svcs)
Kristy Banaszak (Acct Mgr-Employee Benefits)
John Stahl (Acct Mgr-Employee Benefits)
Katie Donovan (Mgr-Employee Benefit Svcs)
Dan Gahlman (Dir-Ops)
Skip Hansen (Co-Founder & Sr VP)
Jim McCormack (Co-Founder & Chm-Mgmt Bd)
Tom Jocz (Pres-Employee Benefit Grp)
Chris Lie (CEO)
Bob Sowinski (Vice Chm & Member-Mgmt Bd)
David Stark (Sr VP)
Matt Wallace (Sls Dir)
Matt Weimer (Dir-Strategic Solutions)
Donna Finch (Coord-Bus Dev)
Margaret Fieldbinder (Coord-Event)
Sally Keppert (Mgr-Acctg)
Cindy Frechett (Acct Mgr)
Tami Hesthaven (Sr Acct Mgr)
Dirk Mlachnik (Acct Exec)
Kristin Cox (Acct Mgr)
Debbie Devine (Acct Mgr)
Claudia Gavin (Acct Exec-Strategic Bus Unit)
Roger Green (Acct Exec)
Beth Heal (Dir-HR Tech & Consulting)
Sandy Kirchenberg (Acct Exec-Strategic Bus Unit)
Julie Sosnay (Lead Acct Exec)
Dan Vanden Boogard (Acct Mgr)
Tammy Lewis (Acct Exec)

DIVERSIFIED INTERIORS OF EL PASO INC.
4750 Ripley Dr, El Paso, TX 79922
Tel.: (915) 585-0030
Web Site: https://www.diversifiedinteriors.com
Rev.: $22,000,000
Emp.: 400
Drywall & Acoustical Installation Services
N.A.I.C.S.: 238310
Ed Anderson (Pres)

DIVERSIFIED INTERNATIONAL SCIENCES CORPORATION
4550 Forbes Blvd Ste 300, Lanham, MD 20706
Tel.: (301) 731-9070
Web Site: http://www.discmd.com
Rev.: $14,000,000
Emp.: 100
Scientific & Technical Consulting Services
N.A.I.C.S.: 541690
William Attick (Controller)

DIVERSIFIED LABELING SO-LUTIONS, INC.
1285 Hamilton Pkwy, Itasca, IL 60143
Tel.: (630) 625-1225
Web Site:
http://www.teamdlsolutions.com
Year Founded: 1985
Sales Range: $25-49.9 Million
Emp.: 120
Labels & Tapes Design Services
N.A.I.C.S.: 541430
Robert Hakman *(Pres)*
Dan Petersen *(Gen Mgr)*
Ken Bozelka *(Mgr-Maintainance)*
Jim Kersten *(CEO)*
Nancy Grisanzio *(Controller)*
Bill Johnstone *(COO)*

DIVERSIFIED LIGHTING ASSO-CIATES INC.
825 Mearns Rd, Warminster, PA 18974
Tel.: (610) 434-4733   PA
Web Site:
http://www.diversifiedlighting.com
Year Founded: 1967
Sales Range: $50-74.9 Million
Emp.: 200
Electrical Apparatus & Equipment Whslr
N.A.I.C.S.: 423610
Joe Burkart *(Project Mgr)*

DIVERSIFIED MAINTENANCE SYSTEMS, LLC
5110 Einsenhower Blvd Ste 250, Tampa, FL 33634
Tel.: (813) 383-0238
Web Site:
http://www.diversifiedm.com
Year Founded: 1973
Sales Range: $200-249.9 Million
Janitorial Services
N.A.I.C.S.: 561720
Peter Belusic *(Pres)*
Jeremy Dieterle *(COO)*
Andrea Kiehl *(Gen Counsel)*
Patrick J. Sheil *(CFO)*
Burney Veazey *(Sr VP-Ops)*
Ed Turner *(VP-Sls & Mktg)*
Jon Jordan *(VP-Bus Dev)*
Angie Bennett *(VP-Bus Dev)*
Paul Gargagliano *(VP-Fin)*
Tommy Balkus *(VP-Natl Accts)*
Amy Chasse *(VP-Acct Mgmt)*
Kelly Devlin *(VP-Corp Ops)*
Tony Valdez *(VP-Ops)*
Frank Donato *(VP-Ops)*
Bob Duncan *(VP-Ops)*
Maheen Zaidi *(VP-Mktg)*
Neal Pomroy *(CEO)*
J. Tyler Bruce *(VP-HR)*

Subsidiaries:

Rite Way Service Inc.   (1)
325 1st Ave N, Birmingham, AL 35204-4904
Tel.: (205) 251-9249
Web Site: http://www.ritewayservice.com
Sales Range: $250-299.9 Million
Commercial Facility Maintenance Services
N.A.I.C.S.: 561720
Rob Fournier *(Dir-Info Sys)*
Doug O'Shields *(Mgr)*
Glynis Schoch *(Dir-HR)*

DIVERSIFIED MARKETING GROUP, INC.
8225 Village Harbor Dr, Cornelius, NC 28031
Tel.: (704) 817-2900   NC
Web Site: http://www.dmggroup.org
Year Founded: 1986
Sales Range: $10-24.9 Million
Emp.: 15
Marketing Consulting Services

N.A.I.C.S.: 541613
David Goodman *(Owner)*
Barbara Goodman *(VP-Tech)*

DIVERSIFIED MEDICAL STAFFING, LLC
2025 E Beltline SE Ste 310, Grand Rapids, MI 49546
Web Site: http://www.dmshome.com
Year Founded: 1985
Sales Range: $1-9.9 Million
Emp.: 10
Medical & Administrative Staffing Services
N.A.I.C.S.: 561311
Charles Ferro *(Pres)*

DIVERSIFIED MEMBERS CREDIT UNION
1480 E Jefferson Ave, Detroit, MI 48207
Tel.: (313) 568-5000   MI
Web Site: https://www.dmcu.com
Year Founded: 1929
Credit Union Operator
N.A.I.C.S.: 522130
Kevin Finneran *(Exec VP)*
Kathie Trembath *(Pres & CEO)*
Francis Allen *(Sec)*
Carl Jarboe *(Vice Chm)*
Andrew Pollock *(Treas)*
Monique Dunbar *(COO)*
Albert Patrick Jr. *(Chm)*

DIVERSIFIED MORTGAGE, INC.
101 Old Mammoth Rd, Mammoth Lakes, CA 93546
Tel.: (760) 924-7552
Web Site: http://www.dmortgage.biz
Year Founded: 2001
Sales Range: $1-9.9 Million
Emp.: 4
Mortgage Services
N.A.I.C.S.: 522310
Margot Zen *(Pres & CEO)*

DIVERSIFIED PARATRANSIT INC.
1400 E Mission Blvd, Pomona, CA 91766
Tel.: (909) 622-1313
Sales Range: $10-24.9 Million
Emp.: 65
Taxi Service
N.A.I.C.S.: 485310
Chris Lamb *(Gen Mgr)*

DIVERSIFIED PLASTICS COR-PORATION
120 W Mount Vernon St, Nixa, MO 65714-9105
Tel.: (417) 725-2622   MO
Web Site: http://www.dpcap.com
Year Founded: 1969
Rev.: $30,300,000
Emp.: 300
Plastics & Foam Products Mfr
N.A.I.C.S.: 326150
Randy Kerns *(Controller)*
John Emfinger *(Mgr-Ops)*
Larry Clark *(Plant Mgr)*
Shane Bostian *(Dir-Sls & Engrg)*
Kevin G. Hogan *(CEO)*
Vincent Pope *(Mgr-Engrg)*

Subsidiaries:

Accurate Mold & Plastics Corp.   (1)
202 W Mount Vernon St, Nixa, MO 65714-9105
Tel.: (417) 724-3955
Web Site: http://www.dpcap.com
Sales Range: $10-24.9 Million
Emp.: 35
Plastics Product Mfr
N.A.I.C.S.: 326199
Kenney Magers *(Pres)*

DIVERSIFIED SEARCH, LLC
2005 Market St, Philadelphia, PA 19103-7079
Tel.: (215) 732-6666
Web Site:
http://www.diversifiedsearch.com
Year Founded: 1974
Emp.: 200
Executive Search Service
N.A.I.C.S.: 561312
J. Veronica Biggins *(Mng Partner-Atlanta office)*
Beth Reeves *(VP)*
Neysa Dillon-Brown *(Mng Dir-Healthcare Practice-Atlanta)*
Guy Sava *(Mng Partner)*
Stephen S. Morreale *(COO)*
Judith M. von Seldeneck *(Founder & Chm)*
Lyn Brennan *(Mng Dir-Healthcare Svcs Practice)*
Chris Berger *(Mng Dir)*
Cynthia Price Heckscher *(Mng Dir)*
Euris E. Belle *(Mng Dir)*
Gene E. Head *(Mng Dir)*
Hugo Fueglein *(Mng Dir)*
James A. Langston *(Mng Dir)*
Jason D. Leon *(Mng Dir)*
Judy Boreham *(Partner & Mng Dir)*
Julie Kanak *(Mng Dir)*
Karen Bertrand *(Mng Dir)*
Ken Hirshman *(Mng Dir-Private Equity & Industrial Practices)*
Kevin B. Kelly *(Mng Dir)*
Kim Ennis *(Mng Dir)*
Lionel Anderson *(Mng Dir)*
Lorena Keough *(Mng Dir)*
Marjorie Kean *(Mng Dir)*
Martha C. Hauser *(Mng Dir)*
Peter J. Gillin *(Mng Dir-Education, Nonprofit, Arts & Culture Practice)*
Roger Anderson *(Mng Dir)*
Sara Connolly *(Mng Dir-Healthcare Svcs Practice)*
Sean Lee *(Mng Dir)*
Tony Leng *(Mng Dir)*
Victor Arias *(Mng Dir)*
Kim Dukes *(Mng Dir-Nonprofit Practice)*
Anne C. Malmud *(Dir-PR)*
Katie Bouton *(Pres)*
Aileen K. Alexander *(CEO)*
Karen Yetman Rea *(Mng Dir-Nonprofit Practice)*
Molly Brennan *(Mng Partner-Nonprofit Practice-Global)*
Gerard F. Cattie Jr. *(Mng Dir)*

Subsidiaries:

Alta Associates, Inc.   (1)
8 Bartles Corner Rd, Flemington, NJ 08822
Tel.: (908) 806-8442
Web Site: http://www.altaassociates.com
Exterminating & Pest Control Services
N.A.I.C.S.: 561710

BioQuest, Inc.   (1)
101 Mission St Ste 700, San Francisco, CA 94105   (100%)
Tel.: (415) 777-2422
Web Site: http://www.bioquestinc.com
Emp.: 100
Executive Search Services for Healthcare Professionals
N.A.I.C.S.: 561312
Roger Anderson *(Co-Founder & Mng Partner-San Francisco)*
Karen Bertrand *(Partner)*
Jo Mahaney *(VP)*
Brad Buehler *(VP)*
Heather Linehan *(VP)*
Dave Mildrew *(Partner)*
Gale Richards *(Partner)*
Kim Ennis *(Partner)*
Molly A. Robb *(Mng Dir-Boston)*

Grant Cooper & Associates, LLC   (1)
1 N Brentwood Blvd Ste 950, Saint Louis, MO 63105
Tel.: (800) 886-4690

Web Site:
https://diversifiedsearchgroup.com
Employment Agencies
N.A.I.C.S.: 541612

DIVERSIFIED SPECIALTIES, INC.
37 Market St, Kenilworth, NJ 07033
Tel.: (908) 245-4833
Web Site:
http://www.diversifiedus.com
Year Founded: 1993
Sales Range: $1-9.9 Million
Emp.: 600
Full-Service Systems & Media Technology Integration
N.A.I.C.S.: 541512
Fred D'Alessandro *(Founder & CEO)*
Bruce Herman *(Exec VP & CFO)*
Kevin Collins *(Pres)*
Johan Claassen *(COO)*

Subsidiaries:

Sensory Technologies, LLC   (1)
6951 Corporate Cir, Indianapolis, IN 46278
Tel.: (317) 347-5252
Web Site:
http://www.sensorytechnologies.com
Photographic Equipment & Supplies Merchant Whslr
N.A.I.C.S.: 423410
Derek Paquin *(Principal)*

Technical Innovation, LLC   (1)
2975 Northwoods Pkwy, Atlanta, GA 30071-1537
Tel.: (770) 447-1001
Web Site: http://www.technical-innovation.com
Emp.: 200
Communication Equipment Mfr
N.A.I.C.S.: 334290
Kevin Powers *(Pres)*
Andy Jackson *(VP-Sls-Brdcst Solutions Grp & Blue Hat Design)*
Michael Wright *(Pres-TI Brdcst Solutions Grp)*

DIVERSIFIED SUPPLY INC.
210 N Highland Park Ave, Chattanooga, TN 37404
Tel.: (423) 698-1551
Web Site:
https://www.diversifiedsupply.com
Sales Range: $25-49.9 Million
Emp.: 60
Electrical Supplies Mfr & Whslr
N.A.I.C.S.: 423610
Dan K. Anderson *(Pres & CEO)*
Pam Waugh *(VP-Electrical Div)*
Ralph Russaw *(Acct Mgr)*

DIVERSIFIED TECHNOLOGY CONSULTANTS, INC.
2321 Whitney Ave Ste 301, Hamden, CT 06518
Tel.: (203) 239-4200
Web Site: https://www.teamdtc.com
Rev.: $16,800,000
Emp.: 70
Engineeering Services
N.A.I.C.S.: 541330
Murali Atluru *(Chm & CEO)*

DIVERSIFIED UTILITY SER-VICES, INC.
3105 Unicorn Rd, Bakersfield, CA 93308
Tel.: (661) 325-3212
Web Site:
https://www.diversifiedutility services.com
Year Founded: 1997
Sales Range: $25-49.9 Million
Emp.: 272
Water & Sewer Line Structures Construction Services
N.A.I.C.S.: 237110
Leigh Ann Anderson *(CEO)*

Diversified Utility Services, Inc.—(Continued)

DIVERSIS CAPITAL, LLC
1100 Glendon Ave Ste 920, Los Angeles, CA 90024
Tel.: (310) 396-4200
Web Site:
   http://www.diversiscapital.com
Year Founded: 2013
Privater Equity Firm
N.A.I.C.S.: 523999
Ron Nayot (Co-Founder & Mng Dir)
Kevin Ma (Co-Founder & Mng Dir)
Mike Garland (Dir)
Dave Muscatel (Sr Operating Partner)
Joseph Lok (VP)
Ryan Tanaka (VP)
Rachel Park (Office Mgr)
Devin Scott (VP)
Jeffrey Hsiang (VP)
Abe Bordon (Dir)
Oded Noy (Sr Operating Partner)

Subsidiaries:

Caligor Rx, Inc.   (1)
801 Penhorn Ave Unit 4, Secaucus, NJ 07094
Tel.: (212) 988-0590
Web Site: http://www.caligorrx.com
Sales Range: $1-9.9 Million
Emp.: 16
Pharmaceutical Product Retailer
N.A.I.C.S.: 456110
Tammy Bishop (CEO)
Joseph E. Safdie (VP-Fin & Legal)
Stephanie Smith (Dir-Global Access Programs)
Kelly Fearn (Global Head-Regulatory Affairs-Global Access Programs)
Phil Joyce (Dir-Ops)
Lianne Kloppenburg (Dir-Client Svcs)
Karen Frascello (VP-Bus Dev & Mktg)
Michael Dallman (Dir-Strategic Plng)
Andrea Chopek (Head-Bus Dev-Clinical Trial Svcs Bus Unit-Global)
Craig LaMarca (Head-Bus Dev-TrialAssist-Global)
Alex Shvartsburg (CFO & COO)

Dari-Farms Ice Cream Co., Inc.   (1)
1 Dairy Farms Way, Tolland, CT 06084
Tel.: (860) 872-8313
Web Site: http://www.darifarms.com
Rev.: $64,800,000
Emp.: 20
Ice Cream & Ices
N.A.I.C.S.: 424430
Christopher Ciotola (Controller)
Kevin Simons (Mgr)
Tim Platt (Mgr-Credit)

Marketron Broadcast Solutions, LLC   (1)
101 Empty Saddle Trl, Hailey, ID 83333
Tel.: (208) 788-6800
Web Site: http://www.marketron.com
Software Solutions Services
N.A.I.C.S.: 541512
Todd Kalman (Sr VP-Sls)
Jim Howard (CEO)
Jimshade Chaudhari (Sr VP-Product)
Mike Jackson (Sr VP-Engrg)
Jeff London (Sr VP-Client Svcs)
Matt Wellner (CFO)

Nylon, LLC   (1)
110 Greene St Ste 607, New York, NY 10012
Tel.: (212) 226-6454
Web Site: http://www.nylonmag.com
Sales Range: $1-9.9 Million
Emp.: 25
Periodical Publishers
N.A.I.C.S.: 513120
Ryland McIntyre (Dir-Creative-TV & Video)
Allison Stock (Acct Exec-Digital)
Tile Wolfe (Dir-Social Media)

Performance Designed Products, LLC   (1)
9179 Aero Dr, San Diego, CA 92123
Tel.: (323) 234-9911
Web Site: http://www.pdp.com
Sales Range: $1-9.9 Million
Emp.: 20
Graphic Design Services

N.A.I.C.S.: 541430
Tom Roberts (CTO)
Brad Wildes (CEO)

Pure Auto LLC   (1)
1447 Peachtree St NE #900, Atlanta, GA 30309
Web Site: http://www.PureCars.com
Sales Range: $1-9.9 Million
Emp.: 81
Advertising & Marketing Services
N.A.I.C.S.: 541810
Jeremy Anspach (Founder & Chm)
Don DeLillo (CFO)
Sam Mylrea (CEO)
Mac White (Dir-Dev)
Adam Phillips (Chief Product Officer & Chief Strategy Officer)
Jeff Ranalli (Chief Revenue Officer)

ServicePower Technologies LTD   (1)
Petersgate House, St Petersgate, Stockport, SK1 1HE, United Kingdom
Tel.: (44) 1614762277
Web Site: http://www.servicepower.com
Sales Range: $10-24.9 Million
Scheduling Software for Field-Service Workforces
N.A.I.C.S.: 513210
Joe Wang (Chief Customer Officer)
Brad Hawkins (Sr VP-Product Mgmt)
Samir Gulati (CMO)
Sam Sippl (CFO)
Frank Gelbart (CEO)
Marc Specher (Sr VP-Sls)
Eric Marking (VP-Pro Svcs & Support)

Subsidiary (Domestic):

ServicePower Business Solutions Limited   (2)
Petersgate House, Saint Petersgate, Stockport, SK1 1HE, United Kingdom
Tel.: (44) 1614762277
Software Development Services
N.A.I.C.S.: 541511

Subsidiary (US):

ServicePower, Inc   (3)
8180 Greensboro Dr Ste 600, McLean, VA 22102
Tel.: (703) 287-8900
Web Site: http://www.servicepower.com
Software Development Services
N.A.I.C.S.: 541511
Frank Gelbart (CEO)
Marc Sprecher (Sr VP-Sls-Global)

WorldAPP, Inc.   (1)
161 Forbes Rd, Braintree, MA 02184
Tel.: (781) 849-8118
Web Site: http://www.worldapp.com
Rev.: $4,300,000
Emp.: 200
Computer Peripheral Equipment & Software Merchant Whslr
N.A.I.C.S.: 423430
Oleg Matsko (CEO)

DIVI HOTELS, INC.
6320 Quadrangle Dr Ste 210, Chapel Hill, NC 27517
Tel.: (919) 419-3484   DE
Web Site:
   https://www.diviresorts.com
Sales Range: $50-74.9 Million
Emp.: 55
Hotel Timeshare & Casino Services
N.A.I.C.S.: 721110
Mike Walsnovich (CFO)

DIVIHN INTEGRATION INC.
2500 W Higgins Rd Ste 870, Hoffman Estates, IL 60169
Tel.: (847) 882-0585
Web Site: http://www.divihn.com
Year Founded: 2002
Sales Range: $10-24.9 Million
Emp.: 100
Computer Peripheral Equipment & Software Merchant Whslr
N.A.I.C.S.: 423430
Balaji Padmanabhan (CTO)
Herald P. Manjooran (Pres)
Vijay Mohan (VP)

DIVINE CORPORATION
203 W 3rd Ave, Spokane, WA 99201
Tel.: (509) 455-8622
Web Site: http://www.divinecorp.com
Rev.: $27,407,267
Emp.: 100
General Automotive Repair Shops
N.A.I.C.S.: 811111
James Redmon (CEO)
Debbie Divine Cornell (Gen Mgr)

DIVIRGILIO INSURANCE & FINANCIAL GROUP
270 Broadway, Lynn, MA 01904
Tel.: (781) 592-5220
Web Site:
   http://www.divirgilioinsurance.com
Insurance Agencies & Brokerages
N.A.I.C.S.: 524210
Matthew DiVirgilio (Pres)

Subsidiaries:

On-Time Payroll, Inc.   (1)
2 Winter St Ste 101, Waltham, MA 02451
Tel.: (781) 209-1188
Web Site: http://www.on-timepayroll.com
Offices of Certified Public Accountants
N.A.I.C.S.: 541211
Cynthia Spencer (Pres)

DIVURGENT
4445 Corporation Ln Ste 232, Virginia Beach, VA 23462
Tel.: (757) 213-6875
Web Site: http://www.divurgent.com
Year Founded: 2007
Sales Range: $10-24.9 Million
Emp.: 36
Health Care Srvices
N.A.I.C.S.: 621999
Colin Konschak (CEO & Mng Partner)
Philip Felt (Mng Partner)
Dan Frietze (Partner & VP-Client Svcs)
Paul Anderson (VP-Advisory Svcs)
Stephen Eckert (Pres & Chief Revenue Officer)
Bert Reese (VP-Portfolio Mgmt & Innovation)
Brittany Williams (Dir-Mktg & Comm)
Shaun Sangwin (Sr VP-Bus Dev)
Shane Danaher (COO)

DIX & EATON INCORPORATED
200 Public Sq Ste 1400, Cleveland, OH 44114
Tel.: (216) 241-0405   DE
Web Site: http://www.dix-eaton.com
Year Founded: 1952
Emp.: 75
Public Relations Agency
N.A.I.C.S.: 541820
Scott Chaikin (Chm)
Chas D. Withers (CEO)
Lisa M. Zone (Mng Dir)
Karin Bonev (VP)
Kevin M. Poor (Mng Dir)
James A. Brown (CFO)
David Hertz (Mng Dir)
Amy McGahan (Sr VP)
Sarah Hihn (Dir-HR)
Gregg LaBar (Mng Dir)
Matt Barkett (Chief Client Officer)
Angela Rodenhauser (VP)
Lisa Rose (Pres)
Jon Barnes (VP)
Joanne Darrah (Art Dir)
Ann Lentz (Sr VP-Creative & Program Mgmt)
David Loomis (CMO)
Kellie Friery (VP-MSACC)
Theresa Allen (Accountant)
Cheri Walczak (Acct Coord)
Donna Harlan (Dir-Admin Svcs)
Brady Cohen (Chief Digital Officer)

Tim Dewald (Sr Acct Exec-Media Rels)
Kris Fiocca (Asst Acct Exec)
Allison Wood (Acct Exec)

DIX 1898, INC
212 E Liberty St, Wooster, OH 44691-0918
Tel.: (330) 264-1125   OH
Web Site: http://www.dixcom.com
Year Founded: 1890
Holding Company; Newspaper, Trade Magazine & Digital Media Products Publisher; Radio Broadcasting Stations Operator; Advertising & Marketing Consulting Services
N.A.I.C.S.: 551112
Todd Whetstone (CFO)
Andrew S. Dix (Publr-The Daily Jeffersonian, The Daily Record & Times-Gazette)
David E. Dix (Publr-Record Publ Company)
Ronald Waite (Sr VP-Sls & Reg Gen Mgr-Record Publ & Alliance Publ)
Josh Gordon (Pres-Full Spectrum Mktg)
Jim Robertson (Pres-Radio Div)
Heather Veney (Controller)
Betty Lentz (VP-Audience Retention & Dev)
Andrei Turchyn (Dir-IT)
Brian Zerrer (Dir-Production-Joint Printing Facility)
Anthony Krajcik (Mgr-Web Dev)
G. Charles Dix II (Pres)

Subsidiaries:

Ocala Broadcasting Corporation, LLC   (1)
3602 NE 20th Pl, Ocala, FL 34470
Tel.: (352) 622-9500
Web Site: http://www.windfm.com
Sales Range: $1-9.9 Million
Radio Broadcasting Stations
N.A.I.C.S.: 516110
Jim Robertson (VP & Gen Mgr)
Holly Kreienbrink (Bus Mgr)
Shanna McCoy (Bus Mgr)
Chelsea Allen (Dir-Digital Media & Promos)
Cheree Carr (Mgr-Traffic)

DIXIE BEDDING CORPORATION
4800 NW 37th Ave, Miami, FL 33142
Tel.: (305) 634-1505
Rev.: $10,700,000
Emp.: 75
Mattresses, Innersprings & Box Springs Mfr
N.A.I.C.S.: 337910
Dan Kamis (Pres)

DIXIE BRANDS, INC.
4990 Oakland St, Denver, CO 80239
Tel.: (720) 361-4100
Web Site: http://www.dixieelixirs.com
Cannabis Product Distr
N.A.I.C.S.: 424590
Greg Robbins (CFO)

DIXIE BUICK GMC TRUCK INC.
14565 S Tamiami Trl, Fort Myers, FL 33912-1947
Tel.: (239) 489-0600
Web Site:
   http://www.dixiebuickgmc.com
Year Founded: 1934
Rev.: $19,500,000
Emp.: 50
New Car Dealers
N.A.I.C.S.: 441110
Lynn Adkins-Springs (Mgr)
Robert C. Adkins (Pres)
Marilyn Adkins (Treas & Sec)

DIXIE CONSTRUCTION PRODUCTS INC.
970 Huff Rd NW, Atlanta, GA 30318
Tel.: (404) 351-1100
Web Site:
https://www.dixieconstruction.com
Rev.: $19,000,000
Emp.: 45
Industrial & Construction Tools Whslr
N.A.I.C.S.: 423710
Shannon Worthington (*Pres*)

DIXIE DIAMOND MANUFACTURING, INC.
205 Buxton Ct NW, Lilburn, GA 30047
Tel.: (770) 921-2464
Sales Range: $1-9.9 Million
Emp.: 25
Diamond Saw Blade & Handsaw Mfr
N.A.I.C.S.: 332216
Garret Wolters (*CEO*)

Subsidiaries:

Concut, Inc.   (1)
6815 S 220th St, Kent, WA 98032
Tel.: (253) 872-3507
Web Site: http://www.ddmconcut.com
Sales Range: $1-9.9 Million
Emp.: 14
Diamond Saw Blade & Associated Cutting
Tool Mfr
N.A.I.C.S.: 333515
Jim Mayer (*Pres*)

DIXIE ELECTRIC COOPERATIVE
402 E Blackmon St, Union Springs, AL 36089-1627
Tel.: (334) 738-2500   AL
Web Site: https://www.dixie.coop
Year Founded: 1938
Sales Range: $50-74.9 Million
Emp.: 90
Electric Utility Services
N.A.I.C.S.: 221122
R. Gary Harrison (*Pres & CEO*)
Ernie Faulkner (*VP-Member Svcs, Mktg & Economic Dev*)
Mike Barlow (*CFO*)
Tom James (*Chm*)

DIXIE ELECTRIC MEMBERSHIP CORP.
16262 Wax Rd, Greenwell Springs, LA 70739
Tel.: (225) 261-1221
Web Site:
http://www.demcoenergy.com
Rev.: $90,000,000
Emp.: 200
Electric Utility Services
N.A.I.C.S.: 221122
Carl Westbrook (*Mgr-GIS*)

DIXIE ELECTRIC POWER ASSOCIATION
1863 Hwy 184 E, Laurel, MS 39443
Tel.: (601) 425-2535
Web Site: https://www.dixieepa.com
Sales Range: $75-99.9 Million
Emp.: 94
Electric Power Distribution Services
N.A.I.C.S.: 221122
Lydia Walters (*Mgr-Comm & HR*)
Jim Grantham (*Mgr-IT*)
Pat McCarthy (*Mgr-Ops*)

DIXIE ESCALANTE RURAL ELECTRIC ASSOCIATION, INC.
71 E Hwy 56, Vineyard, UT 84714
Tel.: (435) 439-5311
Web Site: http://www.dixiepower.com
Sales Range: $10-24.9 Million
Emp.: 54
Electric Power Distribution Services
N.A.I.C.S.: 221122

Rebecca Jensen (*Vice Chm*)
Mike Brown (*Chm*)
Robyn Serage (*Sec*)

DIXIE GAS & OIL CORPORATION
229 Lee Hwy, Verona, VA 24482
Tel.: (540) 248-6273
Web Site: http://www.dixiegas.com
Rev.: $17,757,855
Emp.: 33
Convenience Stores & Petroleum Distr
N.A.I.C.S.: 445131
Chris Earhart (*Pres*)
Nick Alexander (*Mgr-Lexington & Covington*)

DIXIE HEALTH, INC.
2161 New Market Pkwy SE Ste 222, Marietta, GA 30067-8768
Tel.: (770) 951-9232
Web Site: http://www.dixiehealth.com
Year Founded: 1988
Sales Range: $75-99.9 Million
Emp.: 25
Health Care Products Mfr
N.A.I.C.S.: 424210
Lois Bruce (*Gen Counsel*)

DIXIE HOMECRAFTERS INC.
3100 Medlock Bridge Rd Ste 370, Norcross, GA 30071-1481
Tel.: (770) 455-6450
Rev.: $12,000,000
Emp.: 40
Telemarketing Services
N.A.I.C.S.: 561422

DIXIE LANDSCAPE CO. INC.
12950 NW 113th Ct, Miami, FL 33178
Tel.: (305) 884-5700
Web Site:
http://www.dixielandscape.com
Sales Range: $10-24.9 Million
Emp.: 100
Landscape Contractors
N.A.I.C.S.: 561730
Jeffrey Reamer (*Pres*)
Luis Aponte (*Mgr-HR*)
Howard Nehls (*Mgr-Credit*)

DIXIE MEDICAL INC.
175 Pagemont Dr, Medina, TN 38355-8764
Tel.: (731) 664-9973
Web Site:
http://www.dixiemedical.com
Year Founded: 1999
Rev.: $10,200,000
Emp.: 12
Medical, Hospital Equipment & Supplies Merchant Whslr
N.A.I.C.S.: 423450
Ruth Spencer (*Sec*)
Julie Spencer (*VP*)
Matt Spencer (*Pres*)

DIXIE METAL PRODUCTS INC.
442 SW 54th Ct, Ocala, FL 34474
Tel.: (352) 873-2554
Web Site:
https://www.dixiemetals.com
Sales Range: $10-24.9 Million
Emp.: 160
Metal Products Mfr
N.A.I.C.S.: 332323
Philip Schnorr (*Pres*)
David Kmieciak (*Sr VP*)
Rita Winkler (*Mgr-Credit*)
Troy Girouex (*Project Mgr*)
Eric Hutton (*Project Mgr*)
Howard Dano (*Mgr-Pur*)

DIXIE MOTORS, INC.

10241 Destination Dr, Hammond, LA 70403
Tel.: (985) 542-0324
Web Site: http://www.dixierv.com
Year Founded: 1984
Sales Range: $25-49.9 Million
Emp.: 100
New Car Dealers
N.A.I.C.S.: 441110
Gregory Lala (*Owner*)
Steven Guidry (*Pres*)
Carol Kronlage (*Comptroller*)

DIXIE NUMERICS LLC
5286 Cir Dr, Morrow, GA 30260
Tel.: (404) 366-7427
Web Site:
http://www.dixienumerics.com
Sales Range: $25-49.9 Million
Emp.: 150
Automotive Metal Stampings & Molded Plastic Products Mfr
N.A.I.C.S.: 326199
Juan Garcia (*CEO*)

DIXIE OIL COMPANY
1284 US Hwy 82 E, Tifton, GA 31794-9444
Tel.: (229) 382-2700   GA
Year Founded: 1946
Sales Range: $25-49.9 Million
Emp.: 3
Petroleum & Gasoline Products Whslr
N.A.I.C.S.: 424720
Fred W. Lindsey (*Chm*)
Bob Lindsey (*Pres*)

DIXIE PAPER COMPANY
148 Country Club Cir, Minden, LA 71055
Tel.: (318) 371-1954
Web Site:
http://www.dixiepaperco.com
Sales Range: $10-24.9 Million
Emp.: 30
Janitorial & Office Supplies Whslr & Distr
N.A.I.C.S.: 424130
Charles Horn (*Pres*)

DIXIE PIPE SALES, LP
2407 Brollier St, Houston, TX 77054-4505
Tel.: (713) 796-2021   TX
Web Site: http://www.dixiepipe.com
Year Founded: 1952
Sales Range: $10-24.9 Million
Emp.: 74
Metal Pipes Whslr & Distr
N.A.I.C.S.: 423510
Charles McGuire (*Pres*)
Scott Tritt (*VP-Sales*)

DIXIE PLYWOOD AND LUMBER COMPANY
PO Box 2328, Savannah, GA 31402-2328
Tel.: (912) 447-7000
Web Site: https://www.dixieply.com
Year Founded: 1944
Sales Range: $10-24.9 Million
Plywood & Lumber Products Distr
N.A.I.C.S.: 423310
Dewey Evans (*Branch Mgr*)
Rollie Mowery (*Gen Mgr*)

DIXIE POLY DRUM CORPORATION
28 Dixie Poly Dr, Yemassee, SC 29945
Tel.: (843) 589-6660
Web Site:
http://www.dixiepolydrum.com
Year Founded: 1951
Sales Range: $1-9.9 Million
Emp.: 41

Plate Work Mfr
N.A.I.C.S.: 332313
Pete G. Hamiker (*Pres*)
Seymour Zilbert (*Founder*)

DIXIE RESTAURANTS INC.
1215 Rebsamen Park Rd, Little Rock, AR 72202-1819
Tel.: (501) 666-3494   AR
Web Site: http://www.dixiecafe.com
Year Founded: 1986
Sales Range: $10-24.9 Million
Emp.: 8
Restaurant Operators
N.A.I.C.S.: 722511
Frank Battisto (*Pres*)

DIXIE RV SUPERSTORE
11963 Jefferson Ave, Newport News, VA 23606
Tel.: (757) 249-1257
Web Site:
http://www.dixiervsuperstore.com
Year Founded: 1961
Sales Range: $10-24.9 Million
Emp.: 65
Recreational Vehicle Whslr
N.A.I.C.S.: 441210
Dennis Dalheim (*Gen Mgr*)
Crosby C. Forrest (*Owner & Pres*)

DIXIE SALES COMPANY INC.
5920 Summit Ave, Browns Summit, NC 27214
Tel.: (336) 375-7500
Web Site: http://www.dixiesales.com
Sales Range: $25-49.9 Million
Emp.: 125
Lawn Machinery & Equipment Whslr & Distr
N.A.I.C.S.: 423820
Mike Rounsavall (*Co-Pres*)

DIXIE STAMPEDE LP
PO Box 58 3849 Pkwy, Pigeon Forge, TN 37868-0058
Tel.: (865) 453-9473   TN
Web Site:
http://www.dixiestampede.com
Year Founded: 1991
Sales Range: $25-49.9 Million
Emp.: 450
Amusement & Recreation Services
N.A.I.C.S.: 712190
Jim Rule (*CEO*)

DIXIELAND PRODUCE INC.
2501 3rd Pl W, Birmingham, AL 35204
Tel.: (205) 252-9816
Rev.: $15,000,000
Emp.: 45
Fruit & Vegetables Whslr
N.A.I.C.S.: 424480
Dale Derieux (*Mgr*)
Neal Angrisano (*Pres-Ops-Mfg*)
Virginia Angrisano (*Sec*)

DIXON BROS. INC.
100 Pocono Rd, Mountain Lakes, NJ 98119
Tel.: (973) 265-2914
Web Site: https://www.dixonbros.com
Rev.: $20,460,957
Emp.: 30
Fuel Oil Dealers
N.A.I.C.S.: 457210
Sally Pierson (*VP*)
Catherine Vecchiarelli (*Mgr-Credit*)
David Levitt (*Gen Mgr*)

DIXON BROTHERS INC.
5093 E Hwy 16, Newcastle, WY 82701
Tel.: (307) 746-2788
Sales Range: $10-24.9 Million
Emp.: 140

Dixon Brothers Inc.—(Continued)

Trucking Service
N.A.I.C.S.: 484121
Jim Dixon (CEO)

DIXON FISHERIES INC.
1807 N Main St, East Peoria, IL
61611
Tel.: (309) 694-6823
Web Site:
  https://www.dixonsseafood.com
Sales Range: $10-24.9 Million
Emp.: 65
Fish & Seafoods Whslr
N.A.I.C.S.: 424460
Jason Livingston (Mgr-Sls)
Jim Dixon (Pres)

DIXON MIDLAND LIGHTING CO.
180 N Lasalle St Ste 3820, Chicago,
IL 60601
Tel.: (312) 364-0150
Rev.: $34,200,000
Emp.: 2
Lighting Fixtures Whslr
N.A.I.C.S.: 423610

DIXON SCHWABL ADVERTIS-ING
1595 Moseley Rd, Victor, NY 14564
Tel.: (585) 383-0380
Web Site:
  http://www.dixonschwabl.com
Year Founded: 1987
Sales Range: $10-24.9 Million
Emp.: 85
N.A.I.C.S.: 541810
Lauren Dixon (Owner & CEO)
Jessica Savage (VP)
Mike Schwabl (Owner & Pres)
Kathy Phelps (Supvr-PR)
Nellie Hedegard (Acct Mgr)
David Lyttle (CFO & Mng Partner)
Vicki Alva (Acct Supvr)
Jennifer Lynn (Dir-First Impressions)
Kellie Adami (Mng Partner-Acct Svcs)
Kim Allen (VP-PR)
Bill Colburn (VP-Creative Svcs)
Liz Corcoran (Mng Partner-Acct Svcs)
Howie Jacobson (Mng Partner)
Tom Martin (VP-Media Svcs)
Megan Connor Murphy (VP-Emerging Tech, Economic Dev & PR)
Greg Kamp (Assoc Dir-PR)
Jon Alhart (Mgr-PR)
Rosi Lamanna (Mgr-PR)
Mary Scott (Mgr-Pub Rels)
Jimmy Gonzalez (Sr Dir-Art)
Melissa Lord (Acct Supvr)
Connor Dixon-Schwabl (Acct Coord)
Marshall Statt (Assoc Dir-Creative)
Ann McAllister (Assoc Dir-Creative)
Mark Stone (Chief Creative Officer & Mng Partner)
Sarah Picciotto (Coord-Media)
Abha Dhakal Bowers (Acct Supvr)
Tracy Moyer (Coord-Interactive)
Jaclyn Garrett (Dir-Client Rels)
David Brodsky (Acct Exec-Client Rels)

DIXON SCHWABL INC.
1595 Moseley Rd, Victor, NY 14564
Tel.: (585) 383-0380
Web Site:
  https://www.dixonschwabl.com
Year Founded: 1987
Sales Range: $25-49.9 Million
Emp.: 90
Marketing, Advertising & Public Relations Services
N.A.I.C.S.: 541820

Kim Allen (Mng Partner-PR)
Lauren Dixon (CEO)
Michael Schwabl (Pres)
Laurie Bennett (Assoc Dir-Media)
Andrew Knoblauch (Supvr-Social Media & Digital Media)
Brian Moore (VP-Acct Svc)
Jake Ziegler (Mgr-Social & Digital Media)
Nadine General (VP-Agency Non-profit Svcs)
Suzanne Komenski (Coord-Media)
Rob Meacham (Acct Exec)
Pete Wayner (Mgr-Content)
David Crist (Mgr-Digital Media)
Tyler Chauncey (Acct Coord)
Randy Zajonczkoski (Dir-IT)
Diana Osgood (Dir-Customer Insights)
Kala Gorelick (Coord-Digital Media)
Michael Reed (Mgr-Analytics & Automated Mktg)
Kevin Berliner (Dir-Art)
Ryan Moore (Dir-Design)
Cassandra Nickels (Acct Dir)
Rosi Statt (Acct Dir)
Jenna Van Thof (Assoc VP-Special Events-Events Div)
Christine DeNering (Acct Supvr)
David Brodsky (Acct Exec-Client Rels)
Merritt Ward (Acct Supvr)
Kellie Adami (Mng Partner-Client Rels)
Jon Alhart (VP-Social & Digital Media)
Bill Colburn (VP-Creative Svcs)
Liz Corcoran (Mng Partner-Acct Svcs)
Scott Ensign (VP-Digital Media)
Shane Grant (VP-Acct Svcs)
Britton Lui (VP-People & Dev)
David Lyttle (CFO & Mng Partner)
Jewel Mastrodonato (Dir-First Impressions)
Kathy Phelps (VP-Special Events & PR)
Jessica Savage (Mng Partner-Acct Svcs)
Mark Stone (Chief Creative Officer & Mng Partner)
Nick Vernetti (Sr Art Dir-Interactive)
Nikki Nisbet (Acct Supvr)
Elizabeth Bennett (Art Dir)
Chris Grant (VP-Mktg Insights)
Michele Diehl (Sr Acct Supervisor)
Cathleen Wells (VP-Martech Strategy & Solutions)
Malorie Benjamin (VP-Media Svcs)
Amanda Satterwhite (Project Mgr-Digital)

DIXON VALVE & COUPLING COMPANY
800 High St, Chestertown, MD 21620
Tel.: (410) 778-2000
Web Site: http://www.dixonvalve.com
Year Founded: 1916
Sales Range: $150-199.9 Million
Emp.: 900
Valve & Hose Coupling Mfr
N.A.I.C.S.: 332912
Richard L. Goodall (Chm & CEO)

Subsidiaries:

Dixon Group Canada Limited   (1)
2200 Logan Ave, Winnipeg, R2R OJ2, MB, Canada
Tel.: (204) 633-5650
Web Site:
  http://www.dixongroupcanada.com
Hose Fitting Whslr
N.A.I.C.S.: 423830

Dixon Group Europe Ltd   (1)
350 Walton Summit Centre Bamber Bridge,

Preston, PR5 8AS, Lancashire, United Kingdom
Tel.: (44) 1772 323529
Web Site:
  http://www.europe.dixonvalve.com
Sales Range: $10-24.9 Million
Emp.: 100
Hose Coupling & Fitting Mfr
N.A.I.C.S.: 332912

Dixon Valve & Coupling Company - Dixon Brass Division   (1)
40 Chestnut Ave, Westmont, IL 60559
Tel.: (800) 323-4440
Web Site: http://www.dixonbrass.com
Brass Hose Fitting Mfr
N.A.I.C.S.: 332912
Jim Jablonsky (Gen Mgr)

Dixon Valve & Coupling Company Dixon Powhatan Division   (1)
800 High St, Chestertown, MD 21620
Tel.: (410) 778-2008
Web Site: http://www.dixonpowhatan.com
Sales Range: $10-24.9 Million
Emp.: 10
Fire Protection Hose Fitting & Valve Mfr
N.A.I.C.S.: 332912
Hazen Arnold (Mgr)

Dixon Valve & Coupling Company - Dixon Quick Coupling Division   (1)
2925 Chief Ct, Dallas, NC 28034
Tel.: (704) 334-9175
Web Site: http://www.dixonvalve.com
Hydraulic & Pneumatic Coupling Distr
N.A.I.C.S.: 423830

Dixon Valve & Coupling Company - Dixon Sanitary Division   (1)
N25 W23040 Paul Rd, Pewaukee, WI 53072
Tel.: (800) 789-1718
Web Site: http://www.bradfordfittings.com
Emp.: 30
Metal Valve Mfr
N.A.I.C.S.: 332919
Dick Goodall (Gen Mgr)

Dixon Valve & Coupling Company - Dixon Specialty Hose Division   (1)
151 Dixon Dr, Chestertown, MD 21620
Tel.: (888) 226-4673
Web Site: http://www.dixonvalve.com
Emp.: 50
Hose Fitting Mfr
N.A.I.C.S.: 332912
Tony Reed (Mgr-Ops)

Hydrasearch Company, Inc.   (1)
100 Log Canoe Cir, Stevensville, MD 21666
Tel.: (410) 643-8900
Web Site: http://www.hydrasearch.com
Sales Range: $10-24.9 Million
Emp.: 50
Fluid Power Valves & Hose Fittings Mfr
N.A.I.C.S.: 332510

Yardley Products Corporation   (1)
10 W College Ave, Yardley, PA 19067-1517
Tel.: (215) 493-2723
Web Site: http://www.yardleyproducts.com
Sales Range: $10-24.9 Million
Emp.: 15
Threaded Inserts for Fastening Applications Mfr
N.A.I.C.S.: 332510
Tim E. Bailey (Pres)
Ken Grady (VP)

DIY GROUP, INC.
2401 W 26th St, Muncie, IN 47302-9548
Tel.: (765) 284-7652
Web Site: https://www.diygroup.com
Year Founded: 1983
Emp.: 131
Packaging Product Storage & Distr
N.A.I.C.S.: 423840
Brian Lough (Dir-Sls & Mktg)

DJ INTERNATIONAL INCORPORATED
600 Stuart St Ste 1350, Seattle, WA 98101
Tel.: (206) 343-5800

Sales Range: $25-49.9 Million
Emp.: 27
Office Furniture Whslr
N.A.I.C.S.: 423210
Dick Petrait (Pres)

Subsidiaries:

Facility Services Inc.   (1)
7048 S 190th St, Kent, WA 98032
Tel.: (253) 236-0220
Web Site: http://www.mbiseattle.com
Rev.: $3,900,000
Emp.: 20
Office Furniture Warehouse
N.A.I.C.S.: 423210

DJ LEASING LLC
6507 Preston Hwy, Louisville, KY 40219
Tel.: (502) 367-0231
Web Site:
  http://www.thriftycarsales.com
Year Founded: 1967
Sales Range: $10-24.9 Million
Emp.: 90
Truck Rental & Leasing Services
N.A.I.C.S.: 532110
Steven Sternberg (Pres & CEO)

DJ ROOFING SUPPLY INC.
2143 W Vista St, Springfield, MO 65807
Tel.: (417) 882-3254
Web Site:
  http://www.djroofingsupply.com
Sales Range: $25-49.9 Million
Emp.: 80
Roofing & Siding Materials Distr
N.A.I.C.S.: 423330
T. Piddington (Exec VP)
Daniel Piddington (Exec VP)

DJ-LA LLC
11400 W Olympic Blvd Ste 200, Los Angeles, CA 90064-1644
Tel.: (310) 473-1000   CA
Web Site: http://www.dj-la.com
Year Founded: 1974
Rev.: $12,000,000
Emp.: 12
N.A.I.C.S.: 541810
Dennis Horlick (Pres)
Jackie Horlick (CEO)
Jimmy Ringhofer (Mgr-Acct Svcs)
Scott C Doughty (Exec VP & Creative Dir)
Ian Sambor (Mgr-Acct Svcs)
Pam McNeely (Exec VP & Media Dir)

DJD/GOLDEN ADVERTISING, INC.
145 W 28th St Ste 12f, New York, NY 10001-6114
Tel.: (212) 366-5033   NY
Web Site: http://www.djdgolden.com
Year Founded: 1990
Sales Range: $10-24.9 Million
Emp.: 7
Advetising Agency
N.A.I.C.S.: 541810
Courtney St. Clement (Dir-Creative)
Malcolm Petrook (Dir-Pub Rels)
Joseph Milner (Dir-Telemarketing & Prospect Rels Mngmt)

DJM SALES & MARKETING
129 E 50th St, Boise, ID 83714
Web Site: http://www.yourdjm.com
Year Founded: 1997
Sales Range: $1-9.9 Million
Emp.: 90
Lead Generation, Event Services, Partnership Development & Customer Data Services
N.A.I.C.S.: 541613
Deborah J. Marlor (Founder & CEO)

DJR HOLDING CO.
815 W 10th St, Pella, IA 50219
Tel.: (641) 628-3153
Web Site: http://www.stctire.com
Year Founded: 1941
Sales Range: $10-24.9 Million
Emp.: 50
Automobile Tires & Tubes Whslr
N.A.I.C.S.: 423130
Dewey Veenstra (Pres)

DJS ADVERTISING
2398 S Dixie Hwy, Miami, FL 33133
Tel.: (305) 860-9500
Web Site: http://www.djs-marketing.com
Year Founded: 1987
Sales Range: $10-24.9 Million
Emp.: 21
Advetising Agency
N.A.I.C.S.: 541810
Deborah J. Scarpa (Owner)

DK CONSULTING, LLC
10380 Old Columbia Rd Ste 100, Columbia, MD 21046
Tel.: (443) 552-5851
Web Site: http://www.dkconsult.net
Year Founded: 2003
Sales Range: $1-9.9 Million
Emp.: 40
Management & Technology Services
N.A.I.C.S.: 541618
Dana Kerr (Pres & CEO)

DK FOOT & CASUAL, INC.
3427 Trinity Mills Rd Ste 900, Dallas, TX 75287-6279
Tel.: (972) 306-9105
Web Site: http://www.dkfc3.com
Sales Range: $1-9.9 Million
Emp.: 50
Apparel Whslr
N.A.I.C.S.: 424350
Omar Kuzbare (Owner)

DKH, INCORPORATED
55 E Monroe St Ste 3900, Chicago, IL 60603
Tel.: (312) 346-8600
Year Founded: 1893
Real Estate Brokers & Agents
N.A.I.C.S.: 531210
Todd Bancroft (Pres & CEO)
James Hayes (CFO)

Subsidiaries:

Draper & Kramer, Incorporated   (1)
55 W Monroe St Fl 19th, Chicago, IL 60603
Tel.: (312) 346-8600
Web Site: http://www.draperandkramer.com
Real Estate Brokers & Agents
N.A.I.C.S.: 531210
Forrest D. Bailey (CEO)
James R. Love (VP-Mktg)
Ian Novak (VP & Dir-Condominium Mgmt Svcs)
Jay Howell (Dir-Ops & Mgr-Ops-Condominium Mgmt Svcs Grp)
Julie Johnson (Sr VP & Dir-Mgmt Svcs)
Ed Polich (Chief Dev Officer)
Blas Puzon (Sr VP-Acq, Dev & Asset Mgmt)
David Newton (Mgr-Property-1350 1360 N. Lake Shore Drive & 1130 S. Michigan)

Subsidiary (Domestic):

Draper & Kramer Realty Advisors, Inc.   (2)
33 W Monroe St Ste 1900, Chicago, IL 60603
Tel.: (312) 346-8600
Web Site: http://www.draperandkramer.com
Pension & Retirement Plan Consultants
N.A.I.C.S.: 524298
Forrest D. Bailey (Pres & CEO)

Unit (Domestic):

Draper & Kramer Retirement Property Services   (2)
33 W Monroe St Fl 19, Chicago, IL 60603
Tel.: (312) 346-8600
Web Site: http://www.draperandkramer.com
Real Estate Manangement Services
N.A.I.C.S.: 531210
Forrest D. Bailey (Pres & CEO)

DKN HOTEL LLC
42 Corporate Park Ste 200, Irvine, CA 92606
Tel.: (714) 427-4320
Web Site: https://www.dknhotels.com
Home Management Services
N.A.I.C.S.: 721110
Ana Almada (Dir-Ops)

Subsidiaries:

Pierpont Inn, Inc.   (1)
550 Sanjon Rd, Ventura, CA 93001
Tel.: (805) 643-0245
Web Site: http://www.pierpontinn.com
Sales Range: $10-24.9 Million
Emp.: 54
Hotel & Restaurant Services
N.A.I.C.S.: 721191
Mauline Patel (VP)

DKR CAPITAL INC.
1281 E Main St Fl 3, Stamford, CT 06902
Tel.: (203) 324-8400
Sales Range: $10-24.9 Million
Emp.: 100
Management Investment Services
N.A.I.C.S.: 525910
Gary Davis (CEO)

DKS SYSTEMS, LLC
8401 Wayzata Blvd Ste 220, Golden Valley, MN 55426
Tel.: (952) 476-7443
Web Site:
   http://www.dkssystems.com
Year Founded: 2001
Sales Range: $1-9.9 Million
Emp.: 16
Management Consulting Services
N.A.I.C.S.: 541618
Mike Sowada (CEO)
Colin Dockry (Pres & CEO)

DKT INTERNATIONAL, INC.
1701 K St NW Ste 900, Washington, DC 20006
Tel.: (202) 223-8780
Web Site:
   http://www.dktinternational.org
Year Founded: 1984
Sales Range: $100-124.9 Million
Emp.: 26
Family Planning Support Services
N.A.I.C.S.: 621410

DKW COMMUNICATIONS INC.
1900 M St NW Ste 800, Washington, DC 20036
Tel.: (202) 355-7400
Web Site:
   http://www.dkwcommunications.com
Year Founded: 2000
Rev.: $17,100,000
Emp.: 180
Computer System Design Services
N.A.I.C.S.: 541512
Kevin McKinstrie (Mgr-Contract)
Darryl L. Washington (Founder, Pres & CEO)
Cliff Andrews (Dir-Enterprise Solutions)
John Holman III (Sr VP)

DL MARTIN CO.
25 Harbaugh Dr, Mercersburg, PA 17236

Tel.: (717) 328-2141
Web Site: https://www.dlmartin.com
Rev.: $18,581,616
Emp.: 175
Jacks & Hydraulic Mfr
N.A.I.C.S.: 333998
Roy Brake (Acct Mgr)
Michael A. White (Mgr-Quality & En-grg)
Terry Stine (Supvr-Quality)

DLB INC.
371 Expansion Dr, Hillsville, VA 24343
Tel.: (276) 728-2137
Rev.: $14,500,000
Emp.: 120
Highway & Street Paving Contractors
N.A.I.C.S.: 237310
Donald L. Branscome (Pres)
Peer Segelke (Gen Counsel)

DLC MANAGEMENT CORP.
565 Taxter Rd Ste 400, Elmsford, NY 10523
Tel.: (914) 631-3131
Web Site: https://www.dlcmgmt.com
Year Founded: 1991
Sales Range: $150-199.9 Million
Emp.: 125
Shopping Center Owner, Operator & Manager
N.A.I.C.S.: 531312
Adam W. Ifshin (Pres & CEO)
Stephen Ifshin (Chm)
William Comeau (CFO & Exec VP)
Jonathan Wigser (Chief Investment Officer & Exec VP-IR)
Patrick Tandy (Sr VP-Construction Mgmt)
Michael Desmarais (Sr VP-Property Mgmt)
Basil Donnelly (Sr VP-Legal Affairs)
Christopher Ressa (Sr VP-Natl Leasing)
Michael Puline (Sr VP-Leasing-Southeast & Mid-Atlantic)
Matt McCarthy (Assoc Dir-Southeast)

DLP REAL ESTATE CAPITAL INC.
95 Highland Ave Ste 300, Bethlehem, PA 18017
Web Site:
   http://www.dlprealestate.com
Year Founded: 2010
Sales Range: $75-99.9 Million
Emp.: 296
Real Estate Investment Services
N.A.I.C.S.: 531390
Don Wenner (Founder & Co-CEO)
Robert Peterson (Co-CEO & Partner)
Richard Delgado (Mng Dir)
Dominique Song (Mng Dir)
Patrick O'Donnell (Chief Experience Officer)
Gary Cho (VP-Ops-DLP Lending)
Bonnie Habyan (CMO)
Brad Bernstein (Sr Dir-Real Estate Fin)
Sandy Jacolow (CIO)

DLR HOLDING, LLC
6457 Frances Ste 200, Omaha, NE 68106-3778
Tel.: (402) 393-4100
Web Site: http://www.dlrgroup.com
Holding Company; Architectural & Planning Services
N.A.I.C.S.: 551112
Brooke Grammier (CIO & Principal)
Rebecca Schnack (CFO & Principal)
Juliana Norvell (Principal)
Peter Rutti (Sr Principal)

Subsidiaries:

DLR Group Inc.   (1)
6457 Frances Ste 200, Omaha, NE 68106
Tel.: (402) 393-4100
Web Site: http://www.dlrgroup.com
Design Firm; Architecture, Engineering, Interiors & Planning Services
N.A.I.C.S.: 541310
Griff Davenport (CEO & Mng Principal)
Charles D. Dalluge (Pres & COO)
Jesse Kook (Dir-Talent Mgmt & Dev)
John Fuller (Mng Principal)
Noah Greenberg (Principal)
Bob Watkins (CTO & Principal)
Sandra Schutt (Principal)
Staci Patton (Principal)
Stanley Meradith (Principal)
Troy Thompson (Principal)
Rebecca S. Schnack (CFO)
Chris McGiff-Brown (Principal)
Mary Ruppenthal (Principal)
Justin Stranzl (Principal)
Robert Esau (Principal)
Erica Loynd (Principal & Architect)
Rico Quirindongo (Principal & Architect)
Jim Beckett (Principal & Architect)
Steve McKay (Mng Principal)
Jim French (Sr Principal)
David Almany (Principal)

Subsidiary (Domestic):

Brayton & Hughes Design Studio   (2)
639 Howard St Ste 2, San Francisco, CA 94105
Tel.: (415) 291-8100
Web Site: http://www.bhdstudios.com
Sales Range: $1-9.9 Million
Emp.: 45
Interior Design Services
N.A.I.C.S.: 541410
Richard Brayton (Principal)
Janea Nakagawa (Principal)

Subsidiary (Non-US):

DLR Group (Shanghai) Architectural Design Consulting Co., Ltd.   (2)
Suite 304 Building 2 283 West Jianguo Rd, Shanghai, 200031, China
Tel.: (86) 21 6418 3277
Architectural Design Services
N.A.I.C.S.: 541310
Leon L. Qiu (Gen Mgr)

Subsidiary (Domestic):

Kwan Henmi Architecture & Planning, Inc.   (2)
456 Montgomery St Ste 300, San Francisco, CA 94104
Tel.: (415) 777-4770
Web Site: http://www.kwanhenmi.com
Fiscal Year-end: 12/31/2010
Architectural & Planning Services
N.A.I.C.S.: 541310

Rossdruliscusenbery Architecture, Inc.   (2)
18294 Sonoma Hwy, Sonoma, CA 95476
Tel.: (707) 996-8448
Web Site: https://www.rdcarchitecture.com
Sales Range: $1-9.9 Million
Emp.: 22
Architectural Services
N.A.I.C.S.: 541310

Signa Development Services, Inc.   (2)
10404 Essex Ct Ste 300, Omaha, NE 68114-3752
Tel.: (402) 393-2288
Sales Range: $25-49.9 Million
Emp.: 7
Property Development Services
N.A.I.C.S.: 237210

DLSM INCORPORATED
7801 N 73rd St, Milwaukee, WI 53223
Tel.: (414) 354-4530
Rev.: $44,000,000
Emp.: 250
Metal Stamping
N.A.I.C.S.: 332119

DLSM Incorporated—(Continued)

James Bryant *(CFO & Treas)*
Lisa Hill *(Mgr-HR)*
Scott Moon *(Chm)*
John Schliesmann *(Sec)*

DLVA, INC.
5217 103 Raeford Rd, Fayetteville,
NC 28304
Tel.: (910) 484-6565
Web Site: http://www.NearU.Services
HVAC Services
N.A.I.C.S.: 333415
Ashish Achlerkar *(Founder & CEO)*

Subsidiaries:

Bass Air Conditioning Co, Inc. (1)
3261 Natal St, Fayetteville, NC 28306
Tel.: (910) 778-1536
Web Site: http://www.bass-air.com
Plumbing, Heating & Air-Conditioning Contractors
N.A.I.C.S.: 238220
Allen E. Bass *(Pres)*

Carolina Heating Service of Green-
ville, Inc. (1)
1326 Piedmont Hwy, Piedmont, SC 29673
Tel.: (864) 232-5684
Web Site: http://www.carolinaheating.com
Plumbing, Heating & Air-Conditioning Contractors
N.A.I.C.S.: 238220
Scott W. Kelly *(Pres)*

Mark-Air Inc. (1)
5217 103 Raeford Rd, Fayetteville, NC
28304-3209
Tel.: (910) 484-6565
Web Site: http://www.mark-air.com
Plumbing, Heating, Ventilation & Air-
Conditioning Contractors
N.A.I.C.S.: 238220
Ken McMullen *(Gen Mgr)*

Mountain Air Mechanical Contractors,
Inc. (1)
27 Loop Rd, Arden, NC 28704
Tel.: (828) 654-0001
Web Site:
http://www.mountainairmechanical.com
Rev.: $3,760,000
Emp.: 20
Site Preparation Contractor
N.A.I.C.S.: 238910
John Graham *(Pres)*
Brian McDonald *(Mgr-Svc)*

DM SHIVTEX, INC.
PO Box 631970, Irving, TX 75063
Tel.: (972) 869-0998
Web Site: https://www.shivtex.com
Sales Range: $10-24.9 Million
Emp.: 2
Poultry & Poultry Product Whslr
N.A.I.C.S.: 424440
Nisha Bhojwani *(VP)*

DM TRANS, LLC
7701 Metropolis Dr Bldg 15, Austin,
TX 78744   **TX**
Web Site:
http://www.arrivelogistics.com
Year Founded: 2014
Sales Range: $350-399.9 Million
Emp.: 1,000
Logistics Consulting Servies
N.A.I.C.S.: 541614
Matt Pyatt *(Co-Founder)*
Eric Dunigan *(Co-Founder)*

DMA ENTERPRISES
2255 Union Pl, Simi Valley, CA 93065
Tel.: (805) 520-2468
Web Site: http://www.thermasol.com
Sales Range: $10-24.9 Million
Emp.: 44
Hot Tubs
N.A.I.C.S.: 339999
Mitchell Altman *(Pres & CEO)*
Michael Straw *(Mgr-Sls)*

DMA HOLDINGS, INC.
233 N US Hwy 701 Bypass, Tabor
City, NC 28463
Tel.: (910) 653-7101
Web Site: http://www.dma-sales.com
Year Founded: 2008
Sales Range: $50-74.9 Million
Emp.: 84
Car Part Distr
N.A.I.C.S.: 423120
John Treece *(Pres & CEO)*
Steve Bertling *(CFO & COO)*
Maria Treece *(Chief Process Integra-
tion Officer)*
Olga McIntyre *(CIO)*
Larry Clark *(Dir-Product Mgmt)*
Gary Hertzog *(VP-Automotive After-
market Sls)*
Ray Glunz *(VP-Supply Chain)*

DMB PROPERTY VENTURE LP
7600 E Doubletree Ranch Rd Ste
300, Scottsdale, AZ 85258
Tel.: (480) 367-7000
Web Site: http://www.dmbinc.com
Rev.: $30,400,000
Emp.: 3
Land Development
N.A.I.C.S.: 531120
D. Brown *(Pres)*

DMBM LLC
2445 E 12th St, Los Angeles, CA
90021
Tel.: (323) 981-1600
Sales Range: $10-24.9 Million
Emp.: 5
Women's & Girls' Apparel Mfr
N.A.I.C.S.: 315250
David Chong *(Pres)*

**DMC ADVERTISING & DIRECT
MARKETING, INC.**
1 Creative Way, Pewaukee, WI
53072
Tel.: (262) 523-2000   **WI**
Year Founded: 1987
Rev.: $38,000,000
Emp.: 30
Advetising Agency
N.A.I.C.S.: 541810
Jeffrey G. Nowak *(Pres)*
Mary Konkel *(Dir-Admin)*
Clay Altman *(Dir-Creative)*
Karen Vande Zande *(Dir-Media)*
Tom Dietrich *(Dir-Production)*

DMC BEVERAGE CORP.
19563 E Mainstreet Ste 206, Parker,
CO 80138
Tel.: (720) 206-4411   **DE**
Web Site: http://www.cooljuice.com
Year Founded: 2002
Sales Range: Less than $1 Million
Juice Beverage Products Mfr
N.A.I.C.S.: 311411
Donald G. Mack *(CEO & CFO)*
Yankel Rosenthal *(Chm)*
George H. Palmer *(Sec)*
John S. Wittler *(CFO)*

DMC CONSTRUCTION, INC.
13500 Foley St, Detroit, MI 48227
Tel.: (313) 491-1815
Web Site:
https://www.DMCGroupUSA.com
Year Founded: 2005
Sales Range: $1-9.9 Million
Emp.: 25
Roof Contract Services
N.A.I.C.S.: 238160
Mike Chaudhary *(Pres)*

DMC ENTERPRISES INC.
1525 E Interstate 65 Service Rd S,
Mobile, AL 36606

Tel.: (251) 471-3326
Web Site:
http://www.deanmccrary.com
Rev.: $20,674,254
Emp.: 70
New & Used Automobiles
N.A.I.C.S.: 441110
Dean Mccrary *(Pres)*

DMCS/SOURCELINK INC.
5 Olympic Way, Madison, MS 39110-
9045
Tel.: (601) 898-8700   **DE**
Web Site: http://www.sourcelink.com
Year Founded: 1984
Sales Range: $10-24.9 Million
Emp.: 111
Direct Mail Advertising Services
N.A.I.C.S.: 518210
Phil Graben *(COO)*

DMD DATA SYSTEMS, INC.
208 Steele St, Frankfort, KY 40601
Tel.: (859) 296-5780
Web Site:
http://www.dmddatasystems.com
Sales Range: $10-24.9 Million
Emp.: 14
Information Technology Services
N.A.I.C.S.: 334610
Dave Sevigny *(Founder & Exec VP-
Ops)*
Harley Butler *(VP-Svcs & Consulting)*
Marshall Butler *(Pres)*

DMD PRODUCTS, LLC
9973 FM 521 Rd, Rosharon, TX
77583
Tel.: (281) 778-2051
Web Site: http://www.lovehandle.com
Year Founded: 2014
Sales Range: $1-9.9 Million
Smartphone Accessory Distr
N.A.I.C.S.: 423690
Mike Watts *(Founder & Pres)*

DMEP CORPORATION
139 E 63rd St Ste 14, New York, NY
10065
Tel.: (212) 840-3900   **DE**
Web Site:
https://www.haleglobal.com
Technology Holding Company
N.A.I.C.S.: 551112
Charles C. Hale *(Pres)*

Subsidiaries:

Market News International Inc. (1)
212 W 29th St, New York, NY 10001
Tel.: (212) 669-6400
Web Site: http://mninews.marketnews.com
News Services & Publisher
N.A.I.C.S.: 516210
Terry Alexander *(CEO)*
Ian Stannard *(Head-Markets & Data-Global)*
Nick Shamim *(Head-Editorial Ops-Global)*
Kevin Woodfield *(Head-Policy/Connect-
Global)*

QL2 Software, LLC (1)
Waterstone Bldg 4751 Best Rd Ste 400M,
Atlanta, GA 30337
Tel.: (404) 401-9571
Web Site: http://www.ql2.com
Sales Range: $10-24.9 Million
Emp.: 100
Real Time Search Technology & Analytical
Tools Offer Business Intelligence Solutions
for Day-to-Day Situations
N.A.I.C.S.: 513210
Paul Campbell *(Chief Comml Officer)*
Justin Hill *(VP-Pro Svcs & Support)*
Sochieta Moth *(CFO)*
Dan Pohl *(Chief Product Officer)*
Samir Bhakta *(VP-Ops)*
Sarah McKenna *(VP-Quality Assurance &
Delivery)*
Thomas Laveau *(VP-Sls-Americas)*
Carl Wartzack *(CEO)*

DMF INC.
7915 E Elm St, Houston, TX 77012
Tel.: (713) 926-4780
Rev.: $10,200,000
Emp.: 18
Lubricating Oils & Greases
N.A.I.C.S.: 424720
Dennis M. Frauenberger *(Pres)*

DMG BANCSHARES, INC.
2 Park Plz Ste 550, Irvine, CA 92614
Web Site: https://www.libertybk.com
Bank Holding Company
N.A.I.C.S.: 551111
Don M. Griffith *(Chm & CEO)*

Subsidiaries:

Liberty Bank, N.A. (1)
2 Park Plz Ste 550, Irvine, CA 92614
Web Site: https://www.libertybk.com
Commericial Banking
N.A.I.C.S.: 522110
Don M. Griffith *(Chm & CEO)*

DMG CORPORATION
2603 Pacific Park Dr, Whittier, CA
90601-1612
Tel.: (562) 692-1277
Web Site: http://www.dmg-la.com
Year Founded: 1967
Sales Range: $10-24.9 Million
Emp.: 40
Provider of Warm Air Heating & Air
Conditioning Services
N.A.I.C.S.: 423730
John Goodwin *(Mgr)*
Allen Hampton *(Mgr)*
Bill Aldrich *(Mgr)*
Brian Burg *(Mgr)*
Victor Murphy *(Mgr)*

DMG INCORPORATED
809 W Russell St, Sioux Falls, SD
57104
Tel.: (605) 336-3693
Web Site:
https://www.malloyelectric.com
Year Founded: 1945
Rev.: $13,800,000
Emp.: 56
Supplier of Electric Motors
N.A.I.C.S.: 423610
Gary Jacobson *(Pres)*
Steve Klein *(Controller)*

DMI CORP.
1002 KCK Way, Cedar Hill, TX 75104
Tel.: (972) 291-9907
Web Site:
http://www.deckermechanical.com
Sales Range: $25-49.9 Million
Emp.: 150
Mechanical Contractor
N.A.I.C.S.: 238220
Wade Decker *(Owner & Pres)*
Roy McMurrary *(Controller)*

DMI DISTRIBUTION INC.
990 Industrial Port Dr, Winchester, IN
47394
Tel.: (765) 584-3234
Web Site:
http://www.dmidistribution.com
Rev.: $10,800,000
Emp.: 14
General Warehousing & Storage
N.A.I.C.S.: 321920
Jerry Franke *(Owner)*

DMI TILE & MARBLE CO. INC.
3012 5th Ave S, Birmingham, AL
35233
Tel.: (205) 322-8473
Sales Range: $25-49.9 Million
Emp.: 160
Tile Installation
N.A.I.C.S.: 238340

Quinn Sanders (Exec VP-Ops)
Joe Floyd (Project Mgr)

DMJ & CO., PLLC
703 Green Vly Rd Ste 201, Greensboro, NC 27408
Tel.: (336) 275-9886   NC
Web Site: http://www.dmj.com
Year Founded: 1949
Sales Range: $1-9.9 Million
Emp.: 50
Accounting, Tax & Wealth Advisory Services
N.A.I.C.S.: 541211
Michael R. Gillis (Mng Partner)
Susan Miller (Partner-Tax)
Kimberly Cossaart (Mgr-Tax)

Subsidiaries:

DMJ & Co., PLLC   (1)
3620 Shannon Rd Ste 200, Durham, NC 27707-6332
Tel.: (919) 489-3393
Web Site: http://www.dmj.com
Accounting Services
N.A.I.C.S.: 541211
Jeff Markov (Mgr-Tax)
Philip W. Hutchings III (Principal)

DMK ASSOCIATES, INC.
421 Commercial Ct Ste C, Venice, FL 34292
Tel.: (941) 412-1293
Web Site: https://www.dmkassoc.com
Sales Range: $1-9.9 Million
Emp.: 30
Civil Engineering, Planning & Designing
N.A.I.C.S.: 541330
Karl Kokomoor (Pres & CEO)
Barry McLeod (Principal & Sr VP)

DMN3
2010 N Loop W Ste 240, Houston, TX 77018
Tel.: (713) 868-3000
Web Site: http://www.dmn3.com
Year Founded: 1992
Sales Range: $10-24.9 Million
Emp.: 30
Direct Marketing
N.A.I.C.S.: 541810
Pamela Lockard (Pres & CEO)
Charles Eldred (Dir-Creative)
Kent Bartholomew (Mgr-Online Media)
Beth Howard (Dir-Interactive Svcs)
James Wilkins (Dir-Client Svcs)

Subsidiaries:

DMN3/Dallas   (1)
2710 Swiss Ave, Dallas, TX 75204
Tel.: (214) 826-7576
Sales Range: Less than $1 Million
Emp.: 5
N.A.I.C.S.: 541810
Charles Eldred (Dir-Creative)
Lisa Moscarelli (Creative Dir-Brdcst)

DMR MECHANICAL, LLC.
6150 W Bert Kouns Industrial Loop, Shreveport, LA 71129
Tel.: (318) 629-6800
Web Site: https://www.dmrmechanical.com
Year Founded: 2004
Sales Range: $10-24.9 Million
Emp.: 75
Air System Balancing & Testing Services
N.A.I.C.S.: 238220
Danny Danny (Founder)
Mark Ross (Founder)
Rick Barr (Founder)

DMS FACILITY SERVICES INC.

417 E Huntington Dr, Monrovia, CA 91016   CA
Web Site: http://www.dmsfacilityservices.com
Year Founded: 1967
Sales Range: $75-99.9 Million
Emp.: 3,800
Building Maintenance Services
N.A.I.C.S.: 561720
Richard E. Dotts (Pres)

DMS HEALTH TECHNOLOGIES, INC.
1351 Page Dr S Ste 300, Fargo, ND 58103
Tel.: (701) 237-9073   ND
Web Site: http://www.dmshealth.com
Year Founded: 1972
Electro Medical & Electrotherapeutic Apparatus Mfr
N.A.I.C.S.: 334510
Tom Andersson (Pres)

DMT SERVICES INC.
995 S Lincoln, Siloam Springs, AR 72761
Tel.: (479) 524-2351
Web Site: https://www.dmtservicesinc.com
Sales Range: $10-24.9 Million
Emp.: 75
Local Trucking Services
N.A.I.C.S.: 484110
Dale Moten (Pres)

DMW WORLDWIDE LLC
701 Lee Rd Ste 210, Chesterbrook, PA 19087-5612
Tel.: (484) 276-4701   DE
Web Site: http://www.dmwdirect.com
Year Founded: 1981
Emp.: 80
Advetising Agency
N.A.I.C.S.: 541810
Bill Spink (Chief Creative Officer & Exec VP)
Josie B. Clippinger (CFO & Exec VP)
Linda Armstrong (Exec VP)
Renee Mezzanotte (Exec VP-Client Engagement)
Mark S. Mandia (Pres & CEO)
George A. Price (VP-Bus Dev)

DMW&H
253 Passaic Av, Fairfield, NJ 07004
Tel.: (201) 635-3493
Web Site: http://www.whsystems.com
Year Founded: 1964
Warehouse Consulting, Material Handling Systems Implementation & Automated Picking & Packing Operations
N.A.I.C.S.: 238290
Ken Knapp (COO)
Paul Laman (VP-Food & Beverage Grp)
Jim McLafferty (Dir-Pro Svcs Grp)
Joe Colletti (Pres)
Jim Huston (Mgr-Sys Engrg)

DN TANKS, INC.
11 Teal Rd, Wakefield, MA 02108
Tel.: (781) 246-1133   MA
Web Site: https://www.dntanks.com
Year Founded: 1972
Sales Range: $25-49.9 Million
Emp.: 200
Prestressed Concrete Liquid Storage Tanks Mfr
N.A.I.C.S.: 333120
Joe Manzi (VP-Concrete Tank Svcs-Eastern Reg)

DNA BRAND MECHANICS
1301 5th Ave Ste 2600, Seattle, WA 98101-3100

Tel.: (206) 770-9615
Web Site: http://www.dnaseattle.com
Year Founded: 1998
Rev.: $13,000,000
Emp.: 37
N.A.I.C.S.: 541810
Alan Brown (Mng Dir & Principal)
Dan Gross (Principal & Exec Dir-Creative)
Melissa Davis (Dir-Media)
Dave Echenoz (Dir-Production)
Caroline Bellaine (Dir-Brand Stratergy)
Lauren Stephens (Acct Mgr & Media Buyer)
Jenny Storey (Dir-Art)
Melissa Durfee-Davis (Dir-Media)
Chris Witherspoon (Principal & Dir-Client Svc)
Gretchen Anderson (Acct Supvr)
Eric Petersen (Assoc Dir-Creative)
Roxanne Tolnas (Acct Dir)
Jenny Lee (Sr Dir-Art)

DNA MODEL MANAGEMENT LLC
555 W 25th St Fl 6, New York, NY 10001-5542
Tel.: (212) 226-0080
Web Site: https://www.dnamodels.com
Sales Range: $1-9.9 Million
Emp.: 15
Modeling Agency
N.A.I.C.S.: 711410
Wayne Spivack (CFO)

DNE GROUP LTD.
222 W 37th St, New York, NY 10018
Tel.: (212) 967-5222
Web Site: http://www.demetriosbride.com
Sales Range: $10-24.9 Million
Emp.: 60
Dress Designer & Retailer
N.A.I.C.S.: 424350
Maria Golias (VP-HR)
John Vlahoyianis (Pres)
Demetrios James Elias (Owner)

DNI CORP.
711 Spence Ln, Nashville, TN 37217
Tel.: (615) 313-7000
Web Site: http://dnicorp.com
Year Founded: 1984
Rev.: $1,800,000
Emp.: 34
Data Processing, Hosting & Related Services
N.A.I.C.S.: 518210
Jono Huddleston (Owner & CEO)
Robert Cook (Pres)

Subsidiaries:

Mailer's Choice, Inc.   (1)
1924 Air Ln Dr, Nashville, TN 37210-3810
Tel.: (615) 883-0070
Web Site: http://www.mailerschoice.com
Direct Mail Advertising
N.A.I.C.S.: 541860
David Hedges (CEO)
Jordan Watkins (Associate Project Mgr)

DNP INTERNATIONAL CO. INC.
14241 E Firestone Blvd Unit 31, Miranda, CA 90638
Tel.: (562) 293-4018
Web Site: http://www.dnpint.com
Year Founded: 1994
Sales Range: $25-49.9 Million
Emp.: 80
Raw Ingredient Importer & Distr
N.A.I.C.S.: 311999

DNS CAPITAL, LLC

400 N Michigan Ave Ste S1700, Chicago, IL 60611
Tel.: (312) 982-0047
Web Site: http://www.dnscap.com
Year Founded: 2015
Private Investment Firm
N.A.I.C.S.: 523999
Michael A. Pucker (Chm & CEO)
Charles Tollinche (Mng Dir)

Subsidiaries:

Industrial Magnetics, Inc.   (1)
1385 S M 75, Boyne City, MI 49712
Tel.: (800) 662-4638
Web Site: http://www.magnetics.com
Industrial Magnets & Electromagnets Mfr
N.A.I.C.S.: 333248
Casey House (Dir-Ops)
Bud Shear (CEO)
Nathan Bell (Mgr-Mtls & Logistics)
Aaron Evans (Mgr-Southwest)

Subsidiary (Domestic):

Sterling Controls, Inc.   (2)
24711 Emerson Rd, Sterling, IL 61081
Tel.: (815) 625-0852
Web Site: http://www.sterlingcontrols.com
Emp.: 15
Industrial Automation Systems Design
N.A.I.C.S.: 541420
Don Goshert (VP)

La Force LLC   (1)
1060 W Mason St, Green Bay, WI 54303-1863
Tel.: (920) 497-7100
Web Site: http://www.laforceinc.com
Sales Range: $25-49.9 Million
Emp.: 220
Provider of Hardware
N.A.I.C.S.: 423710
Brian Mannering (CEO)
Jill Pruski (Treas)

Subsidiary (Domestic):

Collins Door and Hardware Inc.   (2)
394 Delozier Dr, Fort Collins, CO 80524
Tel.: (970) 221-2396
Rev.: $1,400,000
Emp.: 7
Lumber, Plywood, Millwork & Wood Panel Merchant Whslr
N.A.I.C.S.: 423310
James Merritt (Pres)

DNT CONSTRUCTION, LLC.
1014 N Lamar Blvd, Austin, TX 78753
Tel.: (512) 837-6700
Web Site: http://www.dntconstruction.com
Sales Range: $10-24.9 Million
Emp.: 150
Housing Construction Services
N.A.I.C.S.: 236117
Jason Gray (VP-Ops)

DNT CORPORATION
140 Wharton Rd, Bristol, PA 19007-4060
Tel.: (215) 364-0240   PA
Web Site: http://www.ewkaufmann.com
Year Founded: 1977
Sales Range: $10-24.9 Million
Emp.: 25
Producer of Chemicals & Allied Products
N.A.I.C.S.: 424690
Robin Connor (Controller)
Brian O'Connor (Pres)

DO IT BEST CORP.
6502 Nelson Rd, Fort Wayne, IN 46803-1920
Tel.: (260) 748-5300   IN
Web Site: http://www.doitbestcorp.com
Year Founded: 1945
Sales Range: $1-4.9 Billion

Do It Best Corp.—(Continued)

Emp.: 1,432
Lumber, Building Materials & Hardware Distr
N.A.I.C.S.: 423710
Dan Starr (Pres & CEO)
Tim Miller (VP-Logistics)
Mike Altendorf (VP-IT)
Steve Markley (VP-Mdsg)
Doug Roth (CFO & VP-Fin)
Gary Furst (Gen Counsel & VP-HR)
Karena Reusser (Sec)
Brad McDaniel (Chm)
Rich Lynch (VP-Mktg)
Gary Nackers (VP-Lumber & Building Matls)
Nick Talarico (VP-Sls & Bus Dev)
John Wade (Mgr-Natl Product Sls & New Bus Dev)
Lauren Wilson (Mgr-Mdse)
Dent Johnson (VP-Mdsg)
Eerik Hale (Mgr-Territory Sls & Bus Dev)
Derek Opliger (Assoc Mgr-Mdse-Global Sourcing)
Amy McCaw (Asst Mgr-Credit)
Vince Riddle (Engr-Sys)
Mike Melchi (Sls Mgr-Indiana, Michigan & Ohio)
Russ Kathrein (Mgr-Lumber & Building Matls-Bus Dev)

DO MORE GOOD LLC

2 N Nevada Ave Ste 1120, Colorado Springs, CO 80903
Tel.: (719) 434-5250
Web Site: http://domoregood.com
Advertising, Marketing & Brand Consulting Services
N.A.I.C.S.: 541810
Steve Maegdlin (Co-Founder & Pres)
Cheryl Farr (Co-Founder)
Keith Brock (Co-Founder)
Thomas McMillan (Dir-Brand Strategy)
Scott Appel (Dir-Mktg Svcs)
Cristina Schuett (Dir-Strategic Design)

DO MY OWN PEST CONTROL

4260 Communications Dr, Norcross, GA 30093
Tel.: (770) 840-8831
Web Site:
   http://www.domyownpestcontrol.com
Year Founded: 2004
Sales Range: $10-24.9 Million
Emp.: 23
Online Pest Control Marketing Services
N.A.I.C.S.: 541613
Michael Gossling (Pres)
Jim Sawtelle (Mgr-Warehouse)
Michael Hasson (Dir-SEO & Inbound Mktg)

DO-IT CORPORATION

1201 Blue Star Hwy, South Haven, MI 49090
Tel.: (269) 637-1121
Web Site: http://www.do-it.com
Year Founded: 1973
Sales Range: $10-24.9 Million
All Other Plastics Product Mfr
N.A.I.C.S.: 326199
Mark T. McClendon (Pres)
John Deschaine (Dir-Mktg)
Ron McIntyre (VP-Sls & Mktg)

Subsidiaries:

Tower Tag & Label, LLC   (1)
1300 E Empire, Benton Harbor, MI 49022
Tel.: (269) 927-1065
Web Site: http://www.towertag.com
Plastics Product Mfr
N.A.I.C.S.: 326199

Thomas Miller (Pres)

DOALL COMPANY

1480 S Wolf Rd, Wheeling, IL 60090
Tel.: (847) 495-6800   IL
Year Founded: 1927
Machine Tools, Cutting Tools, Industrial Supplies, Precision Gauges, Measuring Equipment & Cutting Fluids Distr & Mfr
N.A.I.C.S.: 423840
Michael L. Wilkie (Chm & Pres)
David Crawford (Sr VP)
Jon Henricks (Vice Chm)
Timothy Moran (Gen Counsel)
William Henricks (COO)
Steve Lund (VP-Fin & Acctg)
Mickey Davis (VP-Sls & Mktg)

Subsidiaries:

Continental Machines, Inc.   (1)
5505 123rd St W, Savage, MN 55378
Tel.: (952) 890-3300
Web Site:
   http://www.continentalmachines.com
Sales Range: $25-49.9 Million
Emp.: 165
Mfr of Band Saws, Gaging Equipment, Hydraulic Pumps, Valves & Power Units
N.A.I.C.S.: 333517
Tom Esterl (Engr-Mfg)

DGI Supply   (1)
1480 S Wolf Rd, Wheeling, IL 60090
Tel.: (847) 495-6800
Web Site: http://www.dgisupply.com
Sales Range: $25-49.9 Million
Emp.: 70
Hardware, Tools & Industrial Supplies Distr
N.A.I.C.S.: 423840
Michael L. Wilkie (Chm-Mgmt Bd)
David Crawford (Exec VP-Sls)
Bill Henricks (Treas)
Jon Henricks (Vice Chm)
Steve Lund (VP-Fin & Acctg)
Todd Mills (Dir-Market Intelligence)
Tim Moran (CFO)
Bruce Ott (Sr VP-Ops)
Jim Rudolph (VP-Info Tech)
Jim Hobbs (Pres & CEO)

Subsidiary (Domestic):

Anich Industries, Inc.   (2)
1408 SW 15th Ave, Ocala, FL 34474
Tel.: (352) 620-8080
Web Site: http://www.dgisupply.com
Sales Range: $1-9.9 Million
Emp.: 15
Hardware, Tools & Industrial Supplies Distr
N.A.I.C.S.: 423840
Mary-Helen Anich (Gen Mgr)

K & H Sales, Inc.   (2)
1977 Davis St, San Leandro, CA 94577
Tel.: (510) 352-2600
Web Site: http://www.dgisupply.com
Sales Range: $1-9.9 Million
Emp.: 35
Hardware, Tools & Industrial Supplies Distr
N.A.I.C.S.: 423840
Gary Walker (Mgr-Pricing)

Merwin-Stoltz Co., Inc.   (2)
N52 W13325 Falls Creek Ct, Menomonee Falls, WI 53051
Tel.: (262) 781-8870
Web Site: http://www.merwin-stoltz.com
Sales Range: $10-24.9 Million
Emp.: 32
Hardware, Tools & Industrial Supplies Distr
N.A.I.C.S.: 423840
Leroy Chris (Mgr-Warehouse Shipping)

Tool & Abrasive Supply, Inc.   (2)
2906 Leonis Blvd, Los Angeles, CA 90058-2991
Tel.: (323) 589-9171
Web Site: http://www.toolandabrasive.com
Sales Range: $1-9.9 Million
Emp.: 13
Hardware, Tools & Industrial Supplies Distr
N.A.I.C.S.: 423840

DOAN BUICK

4477 W Ridge Rd, Rochester, NY 14626
Tel.: (585) 227-1900
Web Site: http://www.doanbuick.net
Year Founded: 1980
Sales Range: $10-24.9 Million
Emp.: 78
Car Whslr
N.A.I.C.S.: 441110
Mike Sofia (Mgr-Sls)

DOAN CHEVROLET LLC

5035 Ridge Rd W, Spencerport, NY 14559
Tel.: (585) 352-3434
Web Site: http://www.doanchevy.net
Rev.: $29,200,000
Emp.: 80
Automobile Dealers
N.A.I.C.S.: 441110
Ray Atlfrich (Pres)

DOAN PYRAMID LLC

5069 Corbin Dr, Cleveland, OH 44128-5413
Tel.: (216) 518-2432
Mobile Phone Shops & Electrical Work Services
N.A.I.C.S.: 531210
Michael Forlani (Pres)
Thomas Simek (Project Mgr)

DOAR COMMUNICATIONS INC.

170 Earle Ave, Lynbrook, NY 11563
Tel.: (516) 823-4000
Web Site: http://www.doar.com
Year Founded: 1989
Sales Range: $10-24.9 Million
Emp.: 50
Technology-Based Systems & Services for the Judicial Court, Litigation & Alternative Dispute Resolution Markets
N.A.I.C.S.: 541618
Paul Neale (CEO)
Gene Klimov (CTO)
Scott C. Allen (Pres)
Michael Ferrara (COO)
Rebecca Hunt (Mgr-Bus Dev)
Rick Johnson (Sr Mgr-Case)
Julie Blackman (Sr VP)
Maria Obregon (VP)
Evan Lieberman (Mng Dir)

DOBA LLC

3401 N Thanksgiving Way Ste 150, Lehi, UT 84043
Tel.: (801) 765-6101
Web Site: http://www.doba.com
Year Founded: 2002
Sales Range: $1-9.9 Million
Emp.: 87
Software Developer
N.A.I.C.S.: 513210
Brandon Williams (Pres & CEO)
Ben Reece (CTO)
David Niccum (VP-Product)
Tyson Wanlass (Dir-Ops)

DOBBS BROTHERS MANAGEMENT

5170 Sanderlin Ave, Memphis, TN 38117-4360
Tel.: (901) 685-8881
Sales Range: $50-74.9 Million
Emp.: 5
Provider of Management Services
N.A.I.C.S.: 541614
John C. Dobbs (VP)
Jim Carr (Controller)
James K. Dobbs III (Pres)

DOBBS TEMPORARY SERVICES, INC.

50 South 10th St Ste 500, Minneapolis, MN 55403
Tel.: (612) 373-2600   MN
Web Site: http://www.prostaff.com
Year Founded: 1982
Sales Range: $10-24.9 Million
Emp.: 1,080
Employment Staffing
N.A.I.C.S.: 561320
Kevin Roberg (Dir)

DOBBS TIRE & AUTO CENTERS, INC.

1983 Brennan Plz, High Ridge, MO 63049-1893
Tel.: (636) 677-2101   MO
Web Site:
   https://www.gotodobbs.com
Year Founded: 1976
Sales Range: $50-74.9 Million
Emp.: 650
Provider of Auto & Home Supply Store Services
N.A.I.C.S.: 441340
Darrell Schelp (VP-Mktg)
Patrick McEwen (Mgr-Store)
Nick Wade (Mgr-Store)

DOBER CHEMICAL CORP.

11230 Katherine's Crossing Ste 100, Woodridge, IL 60517
Tel.: (708) 388-7700   IL
Web Site: http://www.dober-group.com
Year Founded: 1957
Sales Range: $125-149.9 Million
Emp.: 175
Industrial Chemicals Mfr
N.A.I.C.S.: 325998
Jim Harper (CFO)

Subsidiaries:

Dober Chemical Corp. - Glenwood Plant   (1)
333 W 195th St, Glenwood, IL 60425
Tel.: (708) 755-5545
Web Site: http://www.dober.com
Emp.: 50
Chemical Products Mfr
N.A.I.C.S.: 325998

Dober Chemical Corp. - Midlothian Plant   (1)
14461 S Waverly Ave, Midlothian, IL 60445
Tel.: (708) 388-7700
Web Site: http://www.dobergroup.com
Chemical Products Mfr
N.A.I.C.S.: 325998

DOBLER CONSULTING INC.

8270 Woodland Ctr Blvd, Tampa, FL 33614
Tel.: (813) 322-3240
Web Site:
   http://www.doblerconsulting.com
Sales Range: $1-9.9 Million
IT Consulting Services
N.A.I.C.S.: 541690
Peter Dobler (Pres & CEO)
Raju Chidambaram (Mng Partner)
Alan Roeder (VP-Sls)

DOBRINSKI OF KINGFISHER, INC.

2600 Frontage Rd, Kingfisher, OK 73750
Tel.: (405) 375-3155
Web Site:
   http://www.dobrinskiofkingfisher.com
Sales Range: $10-24.9 Million
Emp.: 25
Car Whslr
N.A.I.C.S.: 441110
Kirk Milligan (Gen Mgr)

DOBSON FLOORS INC.

2010 Eastgate Dr, Garland, TX
75041
Tel.: (972) 270-8741
Web Site:
　　http://www.dobsonfloors.com
Sales Range: $10-24.9 Million
Emp.: 35
Floor Covering Stores
N.A.I.C.S.: 449121
Sue Brown *(Pres)*
Jessica Fierro *(Acct Mgr-Comml Div)*
Michelle Rios *(Mgr-Installation)*

DOC POPCORN FRANCHISING, INC.

3200 Carbon Pl Ste 103, Boulder,
CO 80301
Tel.: (866) 599-9744
Web Site:
　　http://www.docpopcorn.com
Year Founded: 2003
Sales Range: $1-9.9 Million
Emp.: 20
Retails Natural Flavored Popcorn
N.A.I.C.S.: 311919
Rob Israel *(Co-Founder)*
Renee Israel *(Co-Founder)*

DOCEO OFFICE SOLUTIONS, LLC

325 Cottage Hill Rd, York, PA 17401-
3003
Tel.: (717) 718-8190
Web Site: http://www.mydoceo.com
Office Equipment Merchant Whslr
N.A.I.C.S.: 423420
John Lewis *(Owner)*

Subsidiaries:

Document Essentials LLC　　　**(1)**
2605 Lord Baltimore Dr Ste K, Baltimore,
MD 21244-2652
Tel.: (410) 298-3336
Web Site:
　　http://www.documentessentials.com
Communication Equipment Repair & Maintenance
N.A.I.C.S.: 811210
Phil Sporer *(VP)*

DOCHTER LUMBER & SAWMILL, INC.

201 W Indiana Ave, Trinidad, CO
81082
Tel.: (719) 846-2110
Sales Range: $10-24.9 Million
Emp.: 18
Resawing Lumber & Planning Services
N.A.I.C.S.: 321912
Ken Dochter *(Pres)*
Mike Dochter *(Sec & Treas)*
Richard Dochter *(VP)*

DOCIRCLE INC.

2544 W Woodland Dr, Anaheim, CA
92801
Tel.: (714) 229-8300
Web Site: https://www.trumpia.com
Year Founded: 2004
Sales Range: $1-9.9 Million
Emp.: 50
Marketing Software
N.A.I.C.S.: 513210
Ken Rhie *(CEO)*

DOCK LEVELER MANUFACTURING

1215 Industrial Ln, Malvern, AR
72104
Tel.: (501) 332-5495
Web Site: https://www.dlmdocks.com
Sales Range: $10-24.9 Million
Emp.: 100
Mfr of Dock Equipment & Supplies
N.A.I.C.S.: 339999
Ed McGuire *(Pres)*

DOCK-N-LOCK LLC

11524 Providence Rd Ste 208-C,
Charlotte, NC 28277-0233
Tel.: (980) 339-8572
Web Site: http://www.dock-n-
　　lock.com
Sales Range: $1-9.9 Million
Automotive Safety Product
N.A.I.C.S.: 336320
Ron Pothul *(Chm)*
John Arciero *(CEO)*

DOCKER, INC.

475 Brannan Ste 330, San Francisco,
CA 94107
Tel.: (650) 224-5969
Web Site: http://www.docker.com
Emp.: 70
Software Publisher
N.A.I.C.S.: 513210
David Messina *(Sr VP-Mktg)*
Solomon Hykes *(Founder, CTO & Chief Product Officer)*
Scott Johnston *(Sr VP-Product)*
Eric Bardin *(Sr VP-Fin & Bus Ops)*
Sam Alba *(Sr Dir-Engrg)*
Iain Gray *(Sr VP-Customer Success)*
Kal De *(CTO)*
Neil Charney *(CMO)*
Brian Camposano *(CFO)*
Victor Raisys *(Exec VP/Gen Mgr-New Markets)*
Debbie Anderson-Brooke *(Sr VP-Corp Mktg)*
Papi Menon *(VP-Product)*

DOCKING BANCSHARES, INC.

127 S Summit, Arkansas City, KS
67005
Tel.: (620) 442-5200　　　　**KS**
Web Site:
　　http://www.myunionstate.com
Year Founded: 2001
Bank Holding Company
N.A.I.C.S.: 551111
William R. Docking *(Chm, Pres & CEO)*
David B. Marshall *(CFO & Treas)*
Eric J. Kurtz *(Pres/CEO-Union State Bank)*

Subsidiaries:

The Union State Bank　　　　**(1)**
127 S Summit St, Arkansas City, KS 67005
Tel.: (620) 442-5200
Web Site: http://www.myunionstate.com
Commercial Banking
N.A.I.C.S.: 522110
William R. Docking *(Chm)*
David B. Marshall *(CFO & Exec VP)*
Eric J. Kurtz *(Pres & CEO)*
Steve A. MoSpadden *(Vice Chm)*
David W. Harris *(Reg Pres-Kansas)*

DOCMAGIC, INC.

1800 W 213th St, Torrance, CA
90501
Tel.: (310) 323-1994　　　　**CA**
Web Site: https://www.docmagic.com
Year Founded: 1987
Sales Range: $10-24.9 Million
Electronic Loan Document Preparation Products & Data Management Services
N.A.I.C.S.: 518210
Dominic A. Iannitti *(Pres & CEO)*
Tim Anderson *(Dir-e-Services)*
Steve Ribultan *(Dir-Bus Dev)*
Jeremy Boyd *(Dir-IT)*
Melanie Feliciano *(Chief Legal Officer)*
Ron Carrillo *(Mgr-Trng Dept)*
Gavin T. Ales *(Chief Compliance Officer)*
Jim Pao *(CEO)*
Lori Johnson *(Dir-Client Svcs)*

Subsidiaries:

Doc-Tech, Inc.　　　　　　　**(1)**
1226 W Northwest Hwy, Palatine, IL 60067
Tel.: (847) 654-1500
Web Site:
　　http://www.documentexpressinc.com
Electronic Loan Document Preparation & Data Management Services
N.A.I.C.S.: 518210
Lori Johnson *(Grp Dir-Client Svcs)*

eSignSystems　　　　　　　　**(1)**
3108 N Swan Rd, Tucson, AZ 85712
Tel.: (602) 840-1199
Web Site: http://www.esignsystems.com
Electronic Signature & Verification Software Developer, Publisher & Whslr
N.A.I.C.S.: 513210
Kelly Purcell *(Exec VP-Sls & Mktg-Global)*

DOCO CREDIT UNION

107 N Westover Blvd, Albany, GA
31708
Tel.: (229) 435-1715　　　　**GA**
Web Site: http://www.dococu.com
Year Founded: 1959
Sales Range: $10-24.9 Million
Emp.: 113
Credit Union
N.A.I.C.S.: 522130
Tom Pollock *(Chm)*
Seaborn Jackson *(Treas)*
Rochelle Bush *(Sec)*
J. Derryl Quinn *(Vice Chm)*
Tammy Howell *(Mgr-Lee County)*

DOCS DRUGS LTD.

455 E Reed St, Braidwood, IL 60408-
2037
Tel.: (815) 458-6104　　　　**IL**
Web Site: http://www.docsdrugs.com
Year Founded: 1978
Sales Range: $25-49.9 Million
Emp.: 238
Drug Store Services
N.A.I.C.S.: 456110
Anthony Sartoris *(Pres)*
Jeff Haran *(Controller)*
Christy Enz *(Dir-Pharmacy)*

DOCS FOOD STORES INC.

15028 S Memorial Dr, Bixby, OK
74008
Tel.: (918) 366-8238
Rev.: $11,284,574
Emp.: 100
Grocery Stores
N.A.I.C.S.: 445110
James Roy Brown *(Pres)*
Kevin Caskey *(Mgr-Store)*

DOCTOR'S ASSOCIATES INC.

325 Bic Dr, Milford, CT 06461-3072
Tel.: (203) 877-4281　　　　**FL**
Web Site: http://www.subway.com
Year Founded: 1965
Sales Range: $5-14.9 Billion
Emp.: 730
Holding Company; Fast Food Restaurants Franchiser
N.A.I.C.S.: 551112
Karlin Linhardt *(Sr VP-Mktg-North America)*
Carissa Ganelli *(Chief Digital Officer)*
David Worrell *(CFO)*
Michele DiNello *(VP-PR, Comm & Special Events)*
Alan Marcus *(Sr Dir-Global PR)*
John Chidsey *(CEO)*
Mike Kappitt *(Chief Operating & Insights Officer)*

Subsidiaries:

Subway Restaurants　　　　　**(1)**
325 Bic Dr, Milford, CT 06461　　**(100%)**
Tel.: (203) 877-4281
Web Site: http://www.subway.com

Sales Range: $25-49.9 Million
Emp.: 900
Franchisor of Individually-Owned & Operated Deli-Style, Fast Food Restaurants
N.A.I.C.S.: 722513
John W. Chidsey *(CEO)*
Tracy Steinwand *(Dir-Ops-Global)*
Carissa Ganelli *(Chief Digital Officer)*
Carrie Walsh *(CMO-North America)*
Robin Seward *(Sr VP-Mktg Strategy & Plng)*
Aidan Hay *(VP-Ops-North America)*
Bill McCane *(VP-Global Dev)*
Trevor Haynes *(CEO)*

Subsidiary (Domestic):

Subway Real Estate Corp.　　　**(2)**
325 Bic Dr, Milford, CT 06461
Tel.: (203) 877-4281
Web Site: http://www.subway.com
Sales Range: $75-99.9 Million
Emp.: 700
Franchising Services
N.A.I.C.S.: 531390

DOCTOR'S CHOICE HOME CARE, INC.

7250 Beneva Rd, Sarasota, FL
34238
Tel.: (941) 925-5900
Web Site:
　　http://www.doctorschoicefl.com
Sales Range: $10-24.9 Million
Emp.: 160
Women Healthcare Services
N.A.I.C.S.: 621610
Timothy Beach *(Pres)*

DOCTOR'S NATURAL

400 Fifth Ave S Ste 203, Naples, FL
34102
Web Site:
　　http://www.doctorsnatural.com
Year Founded: 1989
Sales Range: $1-9.9 Million
Nutritional Supplements
N.A.I.C.S.: 325411
Bo Nielsen *(Founder)*

DOCTORS ADMINISTRATIVE SOLUTIONS, LLC

3414 W Bay to Bay Blvd Ste 100,
Tampa, FL 33629
Tel.: (813) 774-9800
Web Site: http://www.dr-
　　solutions.com
Year Founded: 2003
Sales Range: $1-9.9 Million
Emp.: 20
Healthcare Providers Management & Business Consulting Solutions
N.A.I.C.S.: 541611
David Schlaifer *(Pres & CEO)*
Mallory Taylor *(Dir-Mktg, Govt Affairs & Client Svcs)*
Alison Talleri *(Mgr-Sls)*
Melissa Combs *(Mgr-Implementation)*
Dana Pope *(Mgr-Bus Support)*
Kyle Mynatt *(Mgr-Support)*
Nicole Bures *(Project Mgr)*
Brooke Evans *(CFO)*

DOCTORS' MEMORIAL HOSPITAL INC.

333 N Byron Butler Pkwy, Perry, FL
32347
Tel.: (850) 584-0800
Web Site:
　　https://www.doctorsmemorial.com
Year Founded: 1992
Rev.: $26,800,000
Emp.: 320
General Medical & Surgical Hospitals
N.A.I.C.S.: 622110
Amanda Gregory *(Dir-Pur)*
Dewayne Lanier *(Chm)*
Glenda Hamby *(Sec)*
Ken Arnold *(Treas)*

Doctors' Memorial Hospital Inc.—(Continued)

DOCUGRAPHICS, LLC
2408A Ashley River Rd, Charleston, SC 29414-4619
Tel.: (843) 573-0011
Web Site: http://www.docu-
graphics.com
Office Equipment Merchant Whslr
N.A.I.C.S.: 423420
Thomas Fimian (CEO)
Brian Marshall (Mgr)

Subsidiaries:

Quality Quickly, Inc.   (1)
945 3rd Ave NW, Hickory, NC 28601
Tel.: (828) 832-8339
Web Site: http://www.qualityquickly.com
Computer & Office Machine Repair & Maintenance
N.A.I.C.S.: 811210
David T. Wagner (Sec & VP)

DOCUMENT CAPTURE TECHNOLOGIES INC.
4255 Burton Dr, Santa Clara, CA 95054
Tel.: (408) 436-9888
Web Site: http://www.docucap.com
Sales Range: $10-24.9 Million
Emp.: 28
Optical Scanning Devices
N.A.I.C.S.: 334118
Richard Dietl (Chm)
M. Carolyn Ellis (CFO)
Karl Etzel (Pres & CEO)
Pim Blom (VP-Bus Dev-EMEA)
Edward M. Straw (Vice Chm)

DOCUPLEX, INC.
725 E Bayley St, Wichita, KS 67211
Tel.: (316) 262-2662
Web Site: http://www.docuplex.com
Sales Range: $10-24.9 Million
Emp.: 20
Commercial Lithographic Printing
N.A.I.C.S.: 323111
Gerald K. Ewy (Pres)

Subsidiaries:

Color Impressions, Inc.   (1)
3550 Comotara St, Wichita, KS 67226
Tel.: (316) 636-5505
Web Site: http://www.colorimpressions.biz
Sales Range: $1-9.9 Million
Emp.: 18
Commercial Lithographic Printing
N.A.I.C.S.: 323111

DOCUSOURCE INC.
12100 Wilshire Blvd Ste 150, Los Angeles, CA 90025-7137
Tel.: (310) 478-8322
Web Site:
http://www.docusource.com
Sales Range: $10-24.9 Million
Emp.: 80
Sales & Leases of Photocopy Machines & Other Office Machinery
N.A.I.C.S.: 449110
Lester A. Walker (CEO)
John Rashap (Pres)
Gene Kim (VP-Sls-Solutions Grp)

DOCUSOURCE OF NC, LLC
2800 Slater Rd, Morrisville, NC 27560
Tel.: (919) 459-5900
Web Site:
https://www.docusourceofnc.com
Year Founded: 2001
Rev.: $4,800,000
Emp.: 37
Commercial Printing Services
N.A.I.C.S.: 323111
Adele C. Fine (Founder)
Derek Dorroh (Mgr)

DOCUSOURCE PRINT MANAGEMENT
15575 SW Sequoia Pkwy Ste 180, Portland, OR 97224
Tel.: (503) 906-4046
Web Site: http://www.docu-
source.com
Year Founded: 1969
Sales Range: $10-24.9 Million
Emp.: 50
Print & Promotional Management Services
N.A.I.C.S.: 561439
Keith Walkiewicz (Sr Acct Exec)
Ken Kountz (Mgr-Warehouse)
Ray Alen (Mgr-IS)
Amy Tiller (Pres-Growth)

DOCUTREND
575 8th Ave Fl 10, New York, NY 10018
Tel.: (212) 382-0300
Web Site: http://www.docutrend.com
Year Founded: 2002
Sales Range: $1-9.9 Million
Emp.: 40
Document & Print Management Services
N.A.I.C.S.: 323111
Aaron Rubin (Pres)

DODD DIESEL INC.
4600 Highway 50, Whitewater, CO 81527
Tel.: (970) 243-3422
Web Site: https://www.ddiequip.com
Sales Range: $10-24.9 Million
Emp.: 10
Engine & Motor Equipment & Supplies
N.A.I.C.S.: 459999
David Dodd (Pres)

DODGE CHRYSLER JEEP OF WINTER HAVEN, INC.
299 Cypress Garden Blvd, Winter Haven, FL 33880-4331
Tel.: (863) 299-1243
Web Site:
https://www.dodgeofwinterhaven.net
Year Founded: 1991
Sales Range: $10-24.9 Million
Emp.: 100
Car Whslr
N.A.I.C.S.: 441110
Ralph Mahalak (Pres)
Alex Mahalak (Mgr-Sls)
Jp Mahalak (VP)

DODGE CITY COOPERATIVE EXCHANGE INC.
710 W Trail St, Dodge City, KS 67801-5419
Tel.: (620) 225-4193
Web Site: http://www.prideag.com
Year Founded: 1915
Sales Range: $75-99.9 Million
Emp.: 150
Production of Grain & Field Beans
N.A.I.C.S.: 424510
Jerald Kemmerer (Gen Mgr)

DODGE COMPANY INC.
165 Cambridge Pk Dr, Cambridge, MA 02140
Tel.: (617) 661-0500
Web Site: http://www.dodgeco.com
Sales Range: $10-24.9 Million
Emp.: 60
Embalming Fluids
N.A.I.C.S.: 325199
George Dodge (Treas)

DODGE MOVING & STORAGE COMPANY INCORPORATED
13390 Lakefront Dr, Earth City, MO 63045
Tel.: (314) 344-4300   MO
Web Site:
https://www.dodgemoving.com
Year Founded: 1902
Sales Range: $10-24.9 Million
Emp.: 175
Provider of Transportation Services
N.A.I.C.S.: 484121
John Clerc (Pres)

DODGE OF BURNSVILLE, INC.
12101 Hwy 35W S, Burnsville, MN 55337-1693
Tel.: (952) 894-9000
Web Site:
https://www.dodgeofburnsville.com
Sales Range: $10-24.9 Million
Emp.: 50
Car Whslr
N.A.I.C.S.: 441110
John Adamich (Pres)

DODGEN INDUSTRIES INC.
1505 13th St N, Humboldt, IA 50548
Tel.: (515) 332-3755
Web Site: http://www.dodgen-
bornfree.com
Sales Range: $10-24.9 Million
Emp.: 40
Mfr of Self-Contained Motor Homes
N.A.I.C.S.: 336120
Dennis Day (VP-Comml Div)

DODSON ADVERTISING
1910 S Highland Ave Ste 250, Lombard, IL 60148-6161
Tel.: (630) 495-7766
Year Founded: 1978
Sales Range: Less than $1 Million
Emp.: 2
Advertising Agency
N.A.I.C.S.: 541810
Dale A. Dodson (Chm & Pres)

DODSON BROTHERS EXTERMINATING COMPANY, INC.
3712 Campbell Ave, Lynchburg, VA 24501
Tel.: (434) 847-9051   VA
Web Site:
https://www.dodsonbros.com
Year Founded: 1944
Sales Range: $25-49.9 Million
Emp.: 500
Exterminating & Pest Control Services
N.A.I.C.S.: 561710
Bert F. Dodson Jr. (Pres & CEO)

DODSON INTERNATIONAL, INC.
2155 Vermont Rd, Rantoul, KS 66079
Tel.: (785) 878-8077
Web Site: https://www.dodson.com
Year Founded: 1984
Sales Range: $10-24.9 Million
Emp.: 75
Aircraft Parts & Related Product Mfr
N.A.I.C.S.: 423860

Subsidiaries:

Dodson Aviation Incorporated   (1)
2110 Montana Rd, Ottawa, KS 66067
Tel.: (785) 242-4000
Web Site: http://www.dodsonaviation.com
Rev.: $2,800,000
Emp.: 8
Aircraft & Avionic Sales
N.A.I.C.S.: 423860
Robert Lee Dodson Sr. (Pres)

Dodson International Parts Inc.   (1)
2155 Vermont Rd, Rantoul, KS 66079
Tel.: (785) 878-8000
Web Site: http://www.dodson.com
Rev.: $20,632,584

Emp.: 69
Aircraft Parts Distr
N.A.I.C.S.: 423860
Tim Meir (CFO)
Robert Lee Dodson Jr. (Pres)

DODSON STEEL PRODUCTS INC.
5650 E Ponce Deleon Ave, Stone Mountain, GA 30083
Tel.: (404) 363-8900
Year Founded: 1972
Sales Range: $10-24.9 Million
Emp.: 21
Pipe & Tubing, Steel
N.A.I.C.S.: 423510
Paul Clark (Chm & CEO)
Barbara McMichen (Mgr-Acctg)
Rodney Fulmer (Mgr-Inventory)
Joe Huddle (Mgr-Warehouse)
Robert Elliott (Pres)

DOE & INGALLS, INC.
2525 Meridian Pkwy Ste 400, Durham, NC 27713
Tel.: (919) 598-1986
Web Site: http://www.doeingalls.com
Sales Range: $25-49.9 Million
Emp.: 90
Mfr of Industrial Chemicals
N.A.I.C.S.: 424690
Torey Payne (Dir-Sls)

DOE-ANDERSON
620 W Main St, Louisville, KY 40202-2933
Tel.: (502) 589-1700   KY
Web Site:
http://www.doeanderson.com
Year Founded: 1915
Sales Range: $75-99.9 Million
Emp.: 100
Advertising Agency
N.A.I.C.S.: 541810
Daniel Burgess (Sr VP & Dir-PR)
Stephanie Massler (Exec VP)
Todd Spencer (Pres & CEO)
Michael Littman (CMO)
David Vawter (Chief Creative Officer & Exec VP)
Brittany Campisano (Accountant)
Amy McNatt (VP & Dir-Strategic Plng)
Melanie Whitham (VP)
Tom Walthall (Sr VP)
Stacey Cauley (Mgr-Traffic)
Jack McIntyre (Acct Mgr)
Loni Knight (Acct Mgr-Carrier Team)
Laura Esselman (Acct Mgr)
Mendy Mulberry (Acct Mgr)
Amber Fowler (Asst Acct Mgr)
Kevin Price (VP & Dir-Digital Creative)

DOEREN MAYHEW & CO., P.C.
305 W Big Beaver Rd Ste 200, Troy, MI 48084   MI
Web Site: http://www.doeren.com
Year Founded: 1932
Accounting & Consulting Services
N.A.I.C.S.: 541211
Mark A. Crawford (Chm)
Joseph A. Amine (Head-Intl Practice)
Joseph C. DeGennaro (Head-Tax Grp)
Robin D. Hoag (Head-Fin Institutions Grp)
John T. Scollin (Head-Bus Advisory Grp)
Tina Parmar (Mgr-Tax)
Clark Whitley (Mgr-Bus Dev)
Mary Torres (Dir-Tax)
Amyn Jinnah (Mgr-Tax Grp)
Rolando Garcia (Dir-Tax Grp)
Earl Hersh (Dir-Bus Dev)

DOERFER CORPORATION

1801 E Bremer Ave, Waverly, IA 50677
Tel.: (319) 483-4716   IA
Web Site: http://www.doerfer.com
Sales Range: $25-49.9 Million
Emp.: 150
Design, Engineer & Manufacture of Machinery; Packaging & Medical Machinery
N.A.I.C.S.: 541330
David L. Takes *(Pres & CEO)*

Subsidiaries:

Advanced Automation Inc.   (1)
17 Haywood Rd, Greenville, SC 29607
Tel.: (800) 640-0760
Web Site: http://www.aautomation.com
Emp.: 70
Industrial Supplies Whslr
N.A.I.C.S.: 423840
Ramin Pourmand *(Engr-Applications)*
Don Roberts *(Engr-Controls)*
Neil Bultz *(Mgr-Controls & Software Engrg)*
Kevin Wilson *(VP-Ops)*

PSB Technologies Pte Ltd   (1)
Advanex Building 2306 Bedok Reservoir Rd
1st Floor, Singapore, 479224, Singapore
Tel.: (65) 6671 4899
Web Site: http://www.psb-technologies.com
Emp.: 100
Industrial Supplies Whslr
N.A.I.C.S.: 423840
Han Meng-Kwang *(Gen Mgr)*

TDS Automation, Inc.   (1)
1801 E Bremer Ave, Waverly, IA 50677
Tel.: (877) 483-4700
Emp.: 130
Industrial Supplies Whslr
N.A.I.C.S.: 423840
Rob Meusel *(Mgr-Svcs)*
Tim Bodine *(Project Mgr)*

Votaw Precision Technologies, Inc.   (1)
13153 Lakeland Rd, Santa Fe Springs, CA 90670-4520
Tel.: (562) 944-0661
Web Site: http://www.votaw.com
Machine & Other Job Shop Work
N.A.I.C.S.: 333514
Scott Wallace *(Pres)*
Mike Carlson *(Program Mgr)*

Williams White & Company   (1)
600 River Dr, Moline, IL 61265-1122
Tel.: (309) 797-7650
Web Site: http://www.williamswhite.com
Sales Range: $10-24.9 Million
Emp.: 55
Heavy Machinery, Custom Hydraulic Presses & Machinery Mfr
N.A.I.C.S.: 333517
Sunder Subbaroyan *(Chm & Pres)*

Wright Industries, Inc.   (1)
1520 Elm Hill Pike, Nashville, TN 37210
Tel.: (888) 542-4111
Industrial Supplies Whslr
N.A.I.C.S.: 423840
Bobby Veach *(Acct Mgr)*
Brenda McCourt *(Coord-Travel)*
W. Hunter Spurgeon *(Engr-Applications)*
Bill Haddock *(Engr-Nuclear Applications)*

DOERING COMPANY, LLC
6343 River Rd Se, Clear Lake, MN 55319
Tel.: (320) 743-2276
Web Site: http://www.doering.com
Year Founded: 1969
Mechanical Power Transmission Equipment Mfr
N.A.I.C.S.: 333613
Russell Doering *(Pres)*
Marty Dombroske *(VP)*

Subsidiaries:

Metro Machine & Engineering Corp.   (1)
8001 Wallace Rd, Eden Prairie, MN 55344-2224
Tel.: (952) 937-2800
Web Site: http://www.metromachine.com

Designer & Builder of Hydraulic Couplers, Lock Valves, Selector Valves, Restrictors, Check Valves, Hydraulic Components & Directional Control Valves
N.A.I.C.S.: 333519
Joray Dunlavy *(VP-Sls & Engrg)*
Paul Sivula *(VP-Engrg & Sls)*

DOERR ASSOCIATES
31 Church St, Winchester, MA 01890
Tel.: (781) 729-9020
Web Site: http://www.mdoerr.com
Sales Range: $10-24.9 Million
Emp.: 4
Public Relations
N.A.I.C.S.: 541820
Maureen Doerr *(Pres)*

DOERS EDUCATION ASEAN LIMITED
9454 Wilshire Blvd Ste 612, Beverly Hills, CA 90212
Tel.: (310) 888-1870   DE
Year Founded: 2016
Assets: $3,376
Liabilities: $119,668
Net Worth: ($116,292)
Earnings: ($17,547)
Fiscal Year-end: 12/31/20
Holding Company
N.A.I.C.S.: 551112
Wei-Hsien Lin *(Founder, Pres, CFO, Treas & Sec)*

DOG DOG BOY
50 N Alvernon Way, Tucson, AZ 85711
Tel.: (520) 547-3381
Year Founded: 2004
Rev.: $13,000,000
Emp.: 15
Advertising Agencies, Consumer Marketing, Entertainment, Event Marketing, Hispanic Marketing, Magazines, Newspaper, Outdoor, Print, Production, Radio, T.V.
N.A.I.C.S.: 541810
Alan Alexander *(Pres)*
Taby Olague *(VP & Dir-Direct Response)*
Jim Brasher *(CFO & Exec VP)*
Adrienne Leary *(VP & Dir-Agency Svcs)*
Dale Halfaker *(VP & Dir-Creative)*
Morgan O'Crotty *(Acct Exec)*

DOG EAT DOG ADVERTISING
67 W Chippewa St Ste 100, Buffalo, NY 14202
Tel.: (716) 856-0142   NY
Year Founded: 1993
Sales Range: $10-24.9 Million
Emp.: 10
Full Service, Print, Radio, T.V.
N.A.I.C.S.: 541810
Kenneth Andrewlavage *(Pres & Creative Dir)*
Tony Hoffman *(Sec & VP)*

DOG LAKE CONSTRUCTION, INC.
18225 Kadrmas Rd, Lakeview, OR 97630
Tel.: (541) 947-2265
Sales Range: $10-24.9 Million
Emp.: 15
Utility Contractor Services
N.A.I.C.S.: 237110
Sharon M. Briggs *(Pres & Sec)*

DOGGETT EQUIPMENT SERVICES, LTD.
9111 N Fwy, Houston, TX 77037
Tel.: (210) 351-9500
Web Site:
http://www.doggettgroup.com

Emp.: 100
Holding Company; Industrial & Construction Equipment Dealer & Rental Services
N.A.I.C.S.: 551112
William Doggett *(Pres, CEO & Gen Counsel)*
Brian McLemore *(CFO)*

Subsidiaries:

Carruth-Doggett Inc.   (1)
7110 N Fwy, Houston, TX 77076
Tel.: (713) 675-7000
Web Site: http://www.toyotaforklift.com
Rev.: $26,421,258
Emp.: 75
New & Used Industrial Equipment Distr
N.A.I.C.S.: 423830
Alan McKnight *(Controller)*

Doggett Heavy Machinery Services   (1)
4355 W Cardinal Dr, Beaumont, TX 77705
Tel.: (409) 600-9290
Web Site: http://www.doggett.com
Sales Range: $10-24.9 Million
Emp.: 49
New & Used Heavy Construction Vehicles & Equipment Dealer & Rental Services
N.A.I.C.S.: 532412
Mike Ortiz *(VP & Head-Construction & Forestry Div)*

Doggett Machinery Services   (1)
10110 Daradale Ave, Baton Rouge, LA 70816
Tel.: (225) 291-3750
Web Site:
   http://www.doggettmachineryservices.com
Sales Range: $10-24.9 Million
Emp.: 40
New & Used Construction & Forestry Equipment Dealer
N.A.I.C.S.: 532412
Mike Ortiz *(VP)*
Fay Ramey *(Mgr-Acctg)*

Toyota Lift of South Texas   (1)
4001 N Pan Am Expy, San Antonio, TX 78219   (100%)
Tel.: (210) 351-9500
Web Site: http://www.toyotalift.com
New & Used Industrial Equipment Dealer
N.A.I.C.S.: 423830
Ken Townsend *(Sr VP & Gen Mgr)*
John Borgmann *(Mgr-Rental)*

Truck Enterprises, Inc.   (1)
13675 Gateway W, El Paso, TX 79928
Tel.: (915) 858-4464
Web Site: https://www.vernongenes.com
Motor Vehicle Transmission & Power Train Parts Mfr
N.A.I.C.S.: 336350

DOGTOPIA
4920 Wyaconda Rd N, Bethesda, MD 20852
Tel.: (240) 514-0210
Web Site:
   http://www.dogdaycare.com
Year Founded: 2002
Rev.: $2,600,000
Emp.: 35
Pet Care Services
N.A.I.C.S.: 812910
Taylor James *(Owner)*
Alex Samios *(Dir-Fin)*
Charlie Rhoads *(CFO)*
Kim Hamm *(Dir-Ops)*
Neil Gill *(Pres & CEO)*
Peter Thomas *(Chm)*

DOHENY ENTERPRISES INC.
6950 51st St, Kenosha, WI 53144-1740
Tel.: (262) 605-1060   IL
Web Site: http://www.doheny.com
Year Founded: 1980
Sales Range: $10-24.9 Million
Emp.: 50
Provider of Catalog & Mail-Order Services

N.A.I.C.S.: 424690
John Doheny *(Pres)*

DOHERTY EMPLOYMENT GROUP, INC.
7625 Parklawn Ave, Edina, MN 55435-5123
Tel.: (952) 832-8383   MN
Web Site:
   http://www.dohertyemployment.com
Year Founded: 1980
Sales Range: $100-124.9 Million
Emp.: 140
HR Outsourcing
N.A.I.C.S.: 561320
Tim Doherty *(Co-Owner & Chm)*
Valerie Doherty *(Co-Owner & CEO)*
Joe Willie *(Mgr-Sys)*
David James *(Dir-Payroll)*

Subsidiaries:

Doherty Staffing Solutions   (1)
7645 Metro Blvd, Edina, MN 55439
Tel.: (952) 832-8363
Web Site: http://www.dohertystaffing.com
Temporary Help Service
N.A.I.C.S.: 561320
Valerie K. Doherty *(Co-Owner & CEO)*
Amy Giessinger *(Dir-Mktg)*
Dan Gronseth *(Dir-IT)*
Gauher Mohammad *(VP)*
Lisa Koll *(VP)*
Lisa Stinespring *(VP)*
Pat Robertson *(VP-Trng & Dev)*
Scott Foley *(VP)*
Tim Doherty *(Co-Owner & Chm)*
William Doherty *(Gen Counsel)*

DOHERTY ENTERPRISES, INC.
7 Pearl Ct, Allendale, NJ 07401
Tel.: (201) 818-4669
Web Site:
   https://www.dohertyinc.com
Year Founded: 1985
Sales Range: $500-549.9 Million
Emp.: 9,500
Restaurant Operators
N.A.I.C.S.: 722511
Edward Doherty *(Chm & CEO)*
Jerry Marcopoulos *(CFO & Exec VP)*
Kurt Pahlitzsch *(VP-Specialty Restaurants)*
David DiBartolo *(VP-Ops-Applebee's)*
Gregory K. George *(VP-Ops-Panera Bread)*
Kathleen Coughlin *(VP-HR & Trng)*
Mike Veneziano *(VP-Fin)*
Shannon Portell *(VP-New Concept Dev)*
Tim Doherty *(Pres & COO)*
T. J. Stallone *(VP-IT)*

DOHERTY FORD
4223 Pacific Ave, Forest Grove, OR 97116-2227
Tel.: (503) 357-3114
Web Site:
   http://www.dohertyford.com
Year Founded: 1948
Sales Range: $10-24.9 Million
Emp.: 50
New Car Whslr
N.A.I.C.S.: 441110
Michael Doherty *(Pres)*

DOHMEN CO.
215 N Water Str Ste 300, Milwaukee, WI 53202
Tel.: (414) 501-5273   WI
Web Site: http://www.dohmen.com
Year Founded: 1858
Sales Range: $1-4.9 Billion
Emp.: 200
Prescription Benefits Management, Healthcare Management Software Supplier & Health Insurance Management Services

Dohmen Co.—(Continued)

N.A.I.C.S.: 456110
Cynthia A. LaConte (CEO)
Carole Pfeil (VP-Comm)
Mike O'Neil (Chief Legal Officer)
Kathy Koshgarian (COO)

Subsidiaries:

Centric Health Resources, Inc. (1)
17877 Chesterfld, Chesterfield, MO 63005
Tel.: (636) 519-2400
Web Site:
    http://www.centrichealthresources.com
Sales Range: $10-24.9 Million
Emp.: 102
Health Care Srvices
N.A.I.C.S.: 423450
Warwick Charlton (Chief Medical Officer)
Penny Bemus (VP-Bus Dev)

ChemWare Inc. (1)
900 Ridgefield Dr, Raleigh, NC 27609
Tel.: (919) 855-8716
Web Site: http://www.chemware.com
Emp.: 25
Laboratory Information Management Solutions
N.A.I.C.S.: 513210
Robert J. Whitehead (VP & Gen Mgr)

DDN (1)
190 N Milwaukee St, Milwaukee, WI 53202
Tel.: (414) 434-4600
Web Site: http://www.ddnnet.com
Logistics Management Consulting Services
N.A.I.C.S.: 541614
Dan Johnson (Pres)
Pat McGinn (VP-Client Initiatives)
Janett Gray (VP-Regulatory & Quality Assurance)
Steve Gilmore (Dir-Supply Chain & Logistics)

Dohmen Investment Group, LLC (1)
215 N Water St No 300, Milwaukee, WI 53202
Tel.: (414) 299-4900
Healthcare Product Distr
N.A.I.C.S.: 424210

MedComm Solutions, LLC (1)
2200 Powell St Ste 800, Emeryville, CA 94608
Tel.: (510) 595-8289
Web Site:
    http://www.medcommsolutions.com
Call Center Operator
N.A.I.C.S.: 561422

PlanIT, Incorporated (1)
800 Woodland Prime W127N7564 Flint Dr Ste 101, Menomonee Falls, WI 53051
Tel.: (262) 251-8970
Web Site: http://www.planitcenter.com
Healtcare Services
N.A.I.C.S.: 621999
Brian Behnken (Principal)
Terrance Adams (Principal)

Siren Interactive, LLC (1)
626 W Jackson Blvd Ste 100, Chicago, IL 60661
Tel.: (312) 204-6700
Web Site: http://www.sireninteractive.com
Rare Disease Marketing Agency
N.A.I.C.S.: 541613
Frieda Hernandez (VP-Bus Dev)
Suzanne Tsuchiya (Pres)

The Dohmen Company Foundation (1)
190 N Milwaukee St, Milwaukee, WI 53202
Tel.: (414) 299-4914
Web Site:
    http://www.dohmencompanyfoundation.org
Health Care Srvices
N.A.I.C.S.: 621999
Michael Italiano (Chief Fin & Investment Officer)
Rachel Roller (Pres & CEO)

DOHRN TRANSFER COMPANY
6253rd Ave, Rock Island, IL 61201
Tel.: (309) 794-0723
Web Site: https://www.dohrn.com
Rev.: $39,146,245
Emp.: 305

Trucking Except Local
N.A.I.C.S.: 484121
Gary C. Dohrn (Pres)

DOIG CORPORATION
7400 Quail Ct, Cedarburg, WI 53012
Tel.: (262) 376-3644   WI
Web Site: https://www.doigcorp.com
Sales Range: $10-24.9 Million
Emp.: 19
Industrial Automation Component Distr
N.A.I.C.S.: 423830
Robert D. Doig (CEO)

DOING STEEL, INC.
2125 N Golden Ave, Springfield, MO 65803-2221
Tel.: (417) 866-5020
Web Site:
    https://www.doingsteel.com
Year Founded: 1987
Emp.: 100
Residential Building Services
N.A.I.C.S.: 236115
Monty M. Doing (Pres)
Richard Trussell (Treas, Sec & VP)
Jerry D. Freeman (VP-Mktg)
Tim Doing (Project Mgr)
Mike Downing (Project Mgr)
Derek Todd (Project Mgr)
Kelly Todd (Mgr-Pur)
Paul Murdaugh (Mgr-IT)

DOLA INTERNATIONAL CORP.
501 Royalston Ave, Minneapolis, MN 55405
Tel.: (612) 339-7521
Rev.: $10,700,000
Emp.: 2
Screw Machine Products
N.A.I.C.S.: 332721

DOLAN CONSTRUCTION INC.
401 S 13th St, Reading, PA 19602-2027
Tel.: (610) 372-4664
Web Site:
    https://www.dolanconstruction.com
Year Founded: 1977
Sales Range: $50-74.9 Million
Emp.: 33
Site Analysis, Commercial Development & Project Budget Development
N.A.I.C.S.: 236220
Patrick J. Dolan (Pres & COO)
Maureen Dolan (Owner)

DOLAN NORTHWEST LLC
1919 NW 19th Ave, Portland, OR 97209-1735
Tel.: (503) 225-9009
Web Site:
    https://www.seattlelighting.com
Year Founded: 1917
Sales Range: $125-149.9 Million
Emp.: 300
Lighting Fixtures & Related Products Mfr & Distr
N.A.I.C.S.: 423610
Dan Dolan (Pres)
Dave McKee (COO)
Pat Dolan (Exec VP)
Susan McFarlan (Controller)

DOLAN'S OF CONCORD
4563 E 2nd St, Benicia, CA 94510-1032
Tel.: (707) 746-6131
Web Site:
    http://www.dolanlumber.com
Rev.: $16,200,000
Emp.: 40
Lumber & Other Building Materials Sales
N.A.I.C.S.: 444140
Gene Dolan (CEO)

DOLEAC ELECTRIC COMPANY INCORPORATED
1120 Finlo Dr, Hattiesburg, MS 39401
Tel.: (601) 544-2052
Web Site: https://www.doleac.com
Sales Range: $10-24.9 Million
Emp.: 85
General Electrical Contractor
N.A.I.C.S.: 238210
Donald L. Doleac (Pres)
John A. Doleac (VP)

DOLESE BROS. CO.
20 NW 13th St, Oklahoma City, OK 73103
Tel.: (405) 235-2311
Web Site: http://www.dolese.com
Rev.: $95,000,000
Emp.: 150
Ready Mixed Concrete
N.A.I.C.S.: 327320
Mark Helm (Pres & CEO)
Bill Schlittler (CFO)
Gaylan Towle (Dir-Occupational Health & Safety Dept)
Jon Yarbrough (Supvr-Shop)
Kevin Mueggenborg (Mgr-Ops-Masonry Div)
Kristin Freeman (Supvr-Fixed Assets)
Pam Pettigrew (Asst Mgr-Pur)
Robert Stillwell (Area Mgr)
Roger Teel (Mgr-Pur)
Scott Brewer (Mgr-Tech Svcs)
Stacy Foley (Plant Mgr)
Steve Bowen (Gen Mgr-Concrete Products)
Tom Dupuis (Mgr-Environmental Dept)
Craig Groat (Supvr-Lab)
Dan Mayen (Mgr-Quality)
George Dumont (Gen Mgr-Aggregates)
M. Britt Burrows (Engr-Concrete Matls)
Randall Daniel (Mgr-Internal Audit)
Richard Chesley (Dir-IT Dept)
Jim Clymer (Area Mgr)
Troy Banks (Asst Gen Mgr)

Subsidiaries:

The Quapaw Company (1)
3224 N Perkins Rd, Stillwater, OK 74075   (100%)
Tel.: (405) 377-9240
Construction Services
N.A.I.C.S.: 212319

DOLL CAPITAL MANAGEMENT
2420 Sand Hill Rd Ste 200, Menlo Park, CA 94025
Tel.: (650) 233-1400
Web Site: https://www.dcm.com
Year Founded: 1996
Sales Range: $10-24.9 Million
Emp.: 50
Investment Services
N.A.I.C.S.: 523999
Rudolph J. Rehm (Partner-Fin)
Carl Amdahl (Partner)
Tom Blaisdell (Gen Partner)
Hurst Lin (Gen Partner)
Peter Moran (Gen Partner)
Matthew Bonner (Partner-Legal & Ops)
Osuke Honda (Gen Partner)
Ruby Rong Lu (Partner)
Jason Krikorian (Gen Partner)
Jeff Lee (Principal-Venture)
Andre Levi (Partner & CFO)
Kyle Lui (Partner)
Ray Zhao (Partner-China)
Ramon Zeng (Gen Partner)
David K. Chao (Gen Partner)

DOLLAR DAZE INC.

1828 N Saginaw Rd, Midland, MI 48640
Tel.: (989) 948-1561
Web Site:
    https://www.dollardazemi.com
Sales Range: $10-24.9 Million
Emp.: 64
Gift, Novelty & Souvenir Stores
N.A.I.C.S.: 459420
Chris Ralph (CEO)

DOLLAR MUTUAL BANCORP
401 Liberty Ave, Pittsburgh, PA 15222
Web Site: http://www.dollar.bank
Holding Company
N.A.I.C.S.: 551111
James J. McQuade (Pres & CEO)

Subsidiaries:

Dollar Bank, Federal Savings Bank (1)
2700 Liberty Ave, Pittsburgh, PA 15222
Tel.: (412) 261-4900
Web Site: http://www.dollarbank.com
Sales Range: $250-299.9 Million
Emp.: 1,236
Mutual Savings Bank
N.A.I.C.S.: 522180
Joseph Smith (Sr VP-Mktg)
Thomas Kobus (Treas)
Brian Tucker (VP & Dir-Corp Affairs)
Andrew D. Devonshire (Pres-Ohio)
James J. McQuade (Pres & CEO)
Jerry Ritzert (CFO)
Lisa Griffith (Exec VP)

Subsidiary (Domestic):

Colton Enterprises, Inc. (2)
401 Liberty Ave, Pittsburgh, PA 15222   (100%)
Tel.: (412) 261-4900
Real Estate Agency
N.A.I.C.S.: 531210
John S. Shelley III (Pres)

Dollar Bank Insurance Agency, Inc. (2)
3 Gateway Center Lbby 401 Liberty Ave, Pittsburgh, PA 15222
Tel.: (412) 261-3098
General Insurance Services
N.A.I.C.S.: 524210

Dollar Bank Leasing Corp. (2)
3 Gateway Ctr, Pittsburgh, PA 15222
Tel.: (412) 261-4900
Web Site: http://www.dollarbank.com
Sales Range: $25-49.9 Million
Emp.: 12
Provider of Equipment Rental & Leasing Services
N.A.I.C.S.: 522180
Robert Oeler (Pres)
Mark Marusic (Asst VP-Bus Banking)
Ray Garofalo (Asst VP-Community Dev)
Stephanie Herring-Myers (Asst VP-HR)
William Marnell (Branch Mgr)
Linda Ulrich (Portfolio Mgr)

Standard Bank, PaSB (2)
2640 Monroeville Blvd, Monroeville, PA 15146
Tel.: (412) 856-0350
Web Site: http://www.standardbankpa.com
Sales Range: $25-49.9 Million
Savings Bank
N.A.I.C.S.: 522180
Timothy K. Zimmerman (COO & Sr Exec VP)
Sheila D. Crystaloski (CTO & Sr VP)
Susan A. Parente (CFO & Exec VP)
Andrew W. Hasley (Pres & CEO)
Christian Chelli (Chief Credit Officer & Sr VP)
John P. Kline (Chief Lending Officer & Exec VP)
Susan Deluca (Chief Risk Officer & Sr VP)
James J. McQuade (CEO)

DOLLY INC.
2770 Golden Fox Trl, Lebanon, OH 45036-8955

Tel.: (937) 667-5711
Web Site: http://www.dolly.com
Year Founded: 1923
Sales Range: $75-99.9 Million
Emp.: 100
Wall Decor, Nursery Lamps, Mobiles & Diaper Bags Mfr
N.A.I.C.S.: 339930
Dennis J. Sullivan *(Pres)*
Carolyn Taylor *(VP)*
Mike Howell *(CEO)*
Kristin Toth Smith *(COO)*

DOLPHIN INTERNATIONAL INC.

1125 W Hillcrest Blvd, Inglewood, CA 90301
Tel.: (310) 645-2046
Web Site: http://www.dolphin-int.com
Sales Range: $10-24.9 Million
Emp.: 50
Tropical Fish
N.A.I.C.S.: 424990
Steven Lunblad *(Pres)*

DOLPHIN LINE INCORPORATED

4521 Higgins Rd, Mobile, AL 36619-9559
Tel.: (251) 666-2057
Web Site:
https://www.dolphinline.com
Rev.: $11,626,553
Emp.: 140
Contract Haulers
N.A.I.C.S.: 484121
Nancy Ellison *(Mgr-HR)*

DOLPHINS ENTERPRISES, LLC

7500 SW 30th St, Davie, FL 33314
Tel.: (954) 452-7000   FL
Web Site:
http://www.miamidolphins.com
Year Founded: 2005
Sales Range: $50-74.9 Million
Emp.: 50
Holding Company; Professional Football Team & Stadium Owner & Operator
N.A.I.C.S.: 551112
H. Wayne Huizenga *(Partner)*
Stephen Millard Ross *(Chm & Mng Gen Partner)*
George Torres *(VP-Sun Life Stadium Events)*
Tery Howard *(CTO & Sr VP)*
Tom Garfinkel *(Pres & CEO)*
Harvey Greene *(VP-Historical Affairs)*
Jason Jenkins *(Sr VP-Comm & Community Affairs)*
Jeremy Walls *(VP-Mktg Partnerships & New Media)*

Subsidiaries:

Miami Dolphins, Ltd.   (1)
347 Don Shula Dr, Miami Gardens, FL 33056
Tel.: (954) 452-7000
Web Site: http://www.miamidolphins.com
Sales Range: $25-49.9 Million
Professional Football Franchise
N.A.I.C.S.: 711211
Stephen Millard Ross *(Chm & Mng Gen Partner)*
Bill Galante *(VP-Guest & VIP Svcs)*
Jorge M. Perez *(Vice Chm & Partner)*
Donald F. Shula *(Vice Chm)*
Harvey Greene *(VP-Historical Affairs)*
Tery Howard *(CTO & Sr VP)*
George Torres *(VP-Sun Life Stadium Events)*
Chris Grier *(Gen Mgr)*
Joe Cimino *(Mgr-Equipment)*
Scott Stone *(Sr Dir-Digital & Print Media)*
Emilio Estefan *(Partner)*
Gloria Estefan *(Partner)*
Marc Anthony *(Partner)*
Serena Williams *(Partner)*

Venus Williams *(Partner)*
Yolanda Barreto *(Sr Dir-HR)*
Bob Lynch *(VP-Corp Partnerships)*
Dawn Aponte *(Exec VP-Football Admin)*
Nat Moore *(Sr VP-Special Project & Alumni Rels)*
Todd Boyan *(Sr VP-Ops)*
Stuart Weinstein *(Dir-Team Security)*
Kaleb Thornhill *(Dir-Player Engagement)*
Scott Bullis *(Sr Dir-Team Ops)*
Ryan Herman *(Dir-Football Admin)*
Heather Pearson *(Mgr-Brdcst Distr)*
Jason Jenkins *(Sr VP-Comm & Community Affairs)*
Chris Clements *(CFO & Sr VP)*
Tom Garfinkel *(Pres & CEO)*
Mike Tannenbaum *(Exec VP-Football Ops)*
Todd Kline *(Chief Comml Officer & Sr VP)*
Jeremy Walls *(CMO & Sr VP)*
Wayne Diesel *(Dir-Sports Performance)*
Dennis Lock *(Dir-Analytics)*
Nicole Bienert *(VP-Partnership Activation & Retention)*
Myles Pistorius *(Gen Counsel & Sr VP)*
Ryan Norys *(Sr Dir-Corp Partnerships)*
Samantha Coghill *(Sr Dir-HR & Performance Mgmt)*
Sydney Wade *(Coord-Comm)*
Ryan Stiehler *(Acct Mgr-Premium Sls)*
David Baldwin *(Sr Dir-Bus Dev & Premium Sls)*
Joe Cicini *(Sr Dir-Security)*
Jason Green *(Sr Dir-Membership & Premium Svcs)*
Dorie Grogan *(Sr Dir-Brand Impact & Entertainment)*
David Helfman *(Sr Dir-New Stadium Partnerships)*
Matt Higgins *(Vice Chm)*
Twan Russell *(Sr Dir-Community Affairs)*
Brandon Shore *(Sr Dir-HR)*
Alan Sigwardt *(Sr Dir-Grounds)*
Marvin Allen *(Asst Gen Mgr)*
Laura Sandall *(VP-Mktg)*

Sun Life Stadium   (1)
2269 Dan Marino Blvd, Miami, FL 33056
Tel.: (305) 623-6100
Web Site: http://www.sunlifestadium.com
Sales Range: $25-49.9 Million
Emp.: 125
Sports & Entertainment Stadium Operator
N.A.I.C.S.: 711310
Yolanda Barreto *(Sr Dir-HR)*
Tom Garfinkle *(CEO)*

DOM CAMERA & COMPANY, LLC

630 3rd Ave 12th Fl, New York, NY 10017-6705
Tel.: (212) 370-1130   DE
Web Site: http://www.domcameracompany.com
Year Founded: 1985
Sales Range: $75-99.9 Million
Emp.: 12
Media Buying Services
N.A.I.C.S.: 541810
Dom Camera *(Mng Gen Partner)*
Jeanine Domich *(Partner)*

DOMAIN ASSOCIATES LLC

1 Palmer Sq E Ste 515, Princeton, NJ 08542
Tel.: (609) 683-5656
Web Site: http://www.domainvc.com
Year Founded: 1985
Sales Range: $10-24.9 Million
Emp.: 24
Venture Capital Company
N.A.I.C.S.: 523910
James C. Blair *(Gen Partner)*
Nimesh Shah *(Partner)*
Kim Puloma Kamdar *(Mng Partner)*
Brian H. Dovey *(Partner)*

DOMAIN INC.

156 High St, New Richmond, WI 54017
Tel.: (715) 246-6525
Web Site: http://www.domaininc.com
Rev.: $22,000,000
Emp.: 45

Livestock Feeds
N.A.I.C.S.: 311119
William Buell *(Pres)*
Bruce Werner *(Mgr-Sls)*
Delroy Rutledge *(Plant Mgr)*

DOMAIN MEDIA CORP.

3100 West Ray Rd Ste 201, Chandler, AZ 85226
Tel.: (480) 659-4907   NV
Web Site:
http://www.domainmediacorp.com
Sales Range: Less than $1 Million
Emp.: 1
Website Domain Owner & Operator
N.A.I.C.S.: 513199
Christopher J. Kern *(Pres & CEO)*
Ashley Minchin *(Dir-Agency Sls-New South Wales)*
Burzin Mehta *(Grp Mgr-Sls)*
Andrew Knowles *(Dir-Agency Sls-Natl)*
Monty Hanger *(Dir-Sls-Victoria)*
Peter Tyrrell *(CTO)*

DOMAINMARKET.COM LLC

600 Jefferson Plz Ste 320, Rockville, MD 20850
Web Site:
http://www.domainmarket.com
Year Founded: 2007
Sales Range: $1-9.9 Million
Emp.: 10
Online Marketplace for Domain Names as Well as Revenue-Sharing & Brand Development Services
N.A.I.C.S.: 425120
Michael Mann *(CEO & Founder)*

DOMARI & ASSOCIATES, INC.

135 Triple Diamond Blvd Unit 100, North Venice, FL 34275
Tel.: (941) 488-4440
Web Site: http://www.domarijobs.com
Sales Range: $1-9.9 Million
Emp.: 30
Employment Placement Services
N.A.I.C.S.: 561311
Michelle M. Olivo *(Pres)*

DOME CORPORATION NORTH AMERICA

5450 E Rd, Saginaw, MI 48601
Tel.: (989) 777-2050
Web Site: https://www.dome-corp-na.com
Sales Range: $10-24.9 Million
Emp.: 20
Stadium Construction
N.A.I.C.S.: 236220
Ross Lake *(Pres)*
Jeromy Estes *(VP)*

Subsidiaries:

Enviro Tech   (1)
5450 E Rd, Saginaw, MI 48601
Tel.: (989) 777-3456
Web Site: http://www.dome-corp-na.com
Sales Range: $1-9.9 Million
Service Station Construction
N.A.I.C.S.: 236220
Theresa Bakke *(Office Mgr)*

DOME EQUITIES, LLC

400 Park Ave Ste 810, New York, NY 10022
Tel.: (212) 867-4520
Web Site: http://www.domeeq.com
Rev.: $860,000,000
Private Equity Real Estate Services
N.A.I.C.S.: 523999
Eric D. Jones *(Chief Investment Officer)*
Jeremy P. Klein *(Mng Dir-Portfolio Mgmt)*
Todd M. Cather *(COO)*

Daniel C. Bourla *(Mng Dir-Acq & Res)*
Richard Angal *(CFO)*
Trevor Baptista *(Controller)*

DOME HEADWEAR CO.

506 3rd St S, Jacksonville Beach, FL 32250
Tel.: (904) 746-3972
Web Site:
http://www.domeheadwear.co
Year Founded: 2010
Sales Range: $1-9.9 Million
Emp.: 8
Hat Mfr & Distr
N.A.I.C.S.: 315990
Jeff Whitaker *(Co-Founder)*
Chris Hetland *(Co-Founder)*

DOME PUBLISHING COMPANY, INC.

10 New England Way, Warwick, RI 02886-6904
Tel.: (401) 738-7900
Web Site:
http://www.thedomecompanies.com
Year Founded: 1940
Payroll Books; Travel Expense Records; Medical Expense Logs & Related Products Publisher
N.A.I.C.S.: 323120

DOMESTIC CASTING COMPANY, LLC

275 N Queen St, Shippensburg, PA 17257-0220
Tel.: (717) 532-6615
Web Site:
http://www.domesticcasting.com
Year Founded: 2003
Sales Range: $10-24.9 Million
Emp.: 115
Iron Foundry
N.A.I.C.S.: 331511
John Varner *(VP-Sls)*

DOMESTIC INDUSTRIES INC.

101 Corliss St, Providence, RI 02904
Tel.: (401) 942-5000
Web Site: http://www.santorooil.com
Year Founded: 1983
Sales Range: $50-74.9 Million
Emp.: 100
Holding Company: Fuel Oil Dealer Services
N.A.I.C.S.: 551112
Joseph Santoro *(Pres)*

Subsidiaries:

Domestic Fuels & Lubes   (1)
204 E Main St, Everetts, NC 27825
Tel.: (252) 792-5131
Web Site: http://www.domesticfuels.com
Petroleum Bulk Station Services
N.A.I.C.S.: 424710
John C. Santoro *(Pres)*

Domestic Industries of Virginia Inc.   (1)
400 Freeman Ave, Chesapeake, VA 23324-1026   (100%)
Tel.: (757) 545-5100
Web Site:
http://www.domesticfuelsandlubes.com
Sales Range: $10-24.9 Million
Emp.: 50
Provider of Fuel Oil Dealer Services
N.A.I.C.S.: 457210
Lisa Wawrzyniak *(Mgr-Comml)*
John Santoro *(Pres)*
Chris Ivey *(VP)*

Santoro Oil Company Inc   (1)
101 Corliss St, Providence, RI 02904-2621
Tel.: (401) 942-5000
Web Site: http://www.santorooil.com
Sales Range: $10-24.9 Million
Emp.: 50
Provider of Fuel Oil Dealer Services
N.A.I.C.S.: 457210

Domestic Industries Inc.—(Continued)

Joseph Santoro (Pres)
Matt Volpe (Office Mgr)

DOMESTIC LINEN SUPPLY & LAUNDRY COMPANY
30555 Northwestern Hwy Ste 300, Farmington Hills, MI 48334-3160
Tel.: (248) 737-2000 — MI
Web Site:
http://www.domesticuniform.com
Year Founded: 1926
Sales Range: $500-549.9 Million
Emp.: 1,000
Supplier of Linens & Garment Rental
N.A.I.C.S.: 812331
George Collet (CFO)
Michael Defortuna (Dir-IT Svcs)
Evan Colton (Mgr-Mktg)

Subsidiaries:

Domestic Uniform Rental Co. (1)
30555 NW Hwy Ste 300, Farmington Hills, MI 48334-3160 (100%)
Tel.: (248) 737-2000
Sales Range: $10-24.9 Million
Emp.: 30
Linen Supply; Garment Rental
N.A.I.C.S.: 812331
Bruce L. Colton (Pres & CEO)
Michael Defortuna (VP-IT)
Leonard H. Colton (Treas)
David J. Colton (Sec)
Jeffrey Weiss (Mgr-Mktg)
George Collet (VP-Fin)
George Pollet (Controller)

DOMINICAN COMMUNICATIONS CORP.
2 Bennett Ave Fl 10, New York, NY 10033
Tel.: (212) 928-4400
Sales Range: $25-49.9 Million
Emp.: 15
Long Distance Telephone Communications
N.A.I.C.S.: 517121

DOMINICAN SISTERS FAMILY HEALTH SERVICE
299 N Highland Ave, Ossining, NY 10562
Tel.: (914) 941-1710 — NY
Web Site: http://www.dsfhs.org
Year Founded: 1974
Sales Range: $25-49.9 Million
Emp.: 497
Health Care Srvices
N.A.I.C.S.: 622110
Mary Zagajeski (Pres & CEO)
Mary Alice Higgins Donius (Sec)
Max Van Gilder (Chm)
John A. Salandra (CFO)
Mary Jean McKeveny (VP-Dev)

DOMINION AIR & MACHINERY CO.
1401 Coulter Dr NW, Roanoke, VA 24012
Tel.: (540) 366-2000
Web Site:
https://www.dominionair.com
Year Founded: 1983
Sales Range: $10-24.9 Million
Emp.: 35
Distr of Machine Tools & Accessories
N.A.I.C.S.: 423830
Richard C. Bishop (Pres)
Bob Stevenson (VP)
Angela Bowling (Mgr-Accts Receivable)

DOMINION CAROLINA SALES INC.
1416 Long St, High Point, NC 27262
Tel.: (336) 882-1132

Web Site:
https://www.dominioncarolina.com
Year Founded: 1950
Sales Range: $10-24.9 Million
Emp.: 5
Industrial Machinery & Equipment
N.A.I.C.S.: 423830
Dale Grimsley (VP)

DOMINION DIGITAL, INC.
210 Ridge Mcintire Rd Ste 200, Charlottesville, VA 22903
Tel.: (434) 984-1112
Web Site:
http://www.dominiondigital.com
Year Founded: 1997
Rev.: $6,800,000
Emp.: 70
Computer System Design Services
N.A.I.C.S.: 541512
Chris Little (Principal & CEO)

DOMINION ELECTRIC SUPPLY COMPANY, INC.
5053 Lee Hwy, Arlington, VA 22207-2513
Tel.: (703) 536-4400 — VA
Web Site:
https://www.dominionelectric.com
Year Founded: 1940
Sales Range: $25-49.9 Million
Emp.: 258
Distr of Electrical Apparatus & Equipment
N.A.I.C.S.: 423610
Richard Williams (Pres & COO)
Tom Culotta (Exec VP-Comml Sls)
Mike O'Donnell (VP-Credit)
Grace Kwong (CFO)
Patricia Jordan (Mgr-Mktg)
Richard Sharlin (Chm)
Liz Erkenbrack (Dir-IT-Computer Ops-Chantilly-Virginia)
John Pishner (Mgr-Warehouse Ops-Arlington-Virginia)
Mike Stombock (VP-Branch Sls)
Sam Stotler (Exec VP-Pur)
Duane Baker (Project Mgr)
Glenn Bickham (Dir-Trng)
Mike Brooks (Mgr-Web Quotes & Counter Sls)
Maria Castillo (Project Mgr)
Kathleen Cunigan (Dir-Comml Sls Ops)
Ben Go (Mgr)
Gerald Jackson (Pres & CEO-Washington)
Ron Allison (Mgr-Switchgear Quotations)
Stephen Krooth (Pres)
James J. Pishner (Exec VP-Ops)
Angela Leach (Pres & CEO)

DOMINION EQUITY LLC
230 W Superior St, Chicago, IL 60654
Tel.: (646) 249-2436
Web Site: https://dominion-equity.com
Emp.: 100
Investment Services
N.A.I.C.S.: 523999
Curtis Hector (Mng Partner)

Subsidiaries:

Readfield Meats Inc. (1)
2130 Willam Joel Bryan Pkwy, Bryan, TX 77802
Tel.: (979) 776-5685
Web Site: http://www.ruffinomeats.com
Sales Range: $10-24.9 Million
Emp.: 35
Meats & Meat Products
N.A.I.C.S.: 424470
Richard L. Ruffino (Pres)

DOMINION HOMES, INC.

600 Stonehenge Pkwy Ste 200, Dublin, OH 43017-6026
Tel.: (614) 356-5000 — OH
Web Site:
http://www.dominionhomes.com
Year Founded: 1952
Sales Range: $125-149.9 Million
Emp.: 193
New Home Builder
N.A.I.C.S.: 236220
William G. Cornely (CFO, COO & Exec VP-Fin)
David S. Borror (Vice Chm)
Michael A. Archer (Sr VP-Sls Ops-Ohio Div)
Mark A. Nelson (Owner)
Mike Biagi (Pres-Centennial Home Mortgage)

DOMINION MINERALS CORP.
3171 US Hwy 9 N Ste 324, Old Bridge, NJ 08857
Tel.: (732) 536-1600 — DE
Year Founded: 1996
Emp.: 2
Copper & Gold Exploration Services
N.A.I.C.S.: 212230
Pinchas Althaus (CEO)

DOMINION PAYROLL SERVICES
306 E Main St, Richmond, VA 23219
Tel.: (804) 355-3430
Web Site:
http://www.dominionpayroll.com
Sales Range: $1-9.9 Million
Emp.: 28
Payroll Processing Services
N.A.I.C.S.: 541214
David A. Gallagher (CEO)
David L. Fratkin (Founder & Pres)

DOMINION PROPERTIES INC.
1034 S Brentwood Blvd Ste 2020, Saint Louis, MO 63117-1224
Tel.: (314) 963-7500
Web Site:
http://www.dominionproperties.com
Sales Range: $25-49.9 Million
Emp.: 220
Subdividers & Developers
N.A.I.C.S.: 237210
Doug Mullenix (VP)

DOMINION VIDEO SATELLITE INC.
1300 Googlette Rd N, Naples, FL 34102
Tel.: (239) 403-9130
Web Site: http://www.skyangel.com
Year Founded: 1981
Sales Range: $10-24.9 Million
Emp.: 125
High-Powered DBS Satellite TV & Radio Programming
N.A.I.C.S.: 516120
Kevin Alexander (Sr VP-Mktg)
Thomas Scott (Pres & COO)
Robert W. Johnson Jr. (CEO)

DOMINIQUE'S LIVESTOCK MARKET
3600 N University, Lafayette, LA 70507
Tel.: (337) 896-6995
Rev.: $15,700,000
Emp.: 70
Auctioning Livestock
N.A.I.C.S.: 424520
Mike Dominique (Pres)
John Dominique (Treas & Sec)

DOMINO DATA LAB, INC.
548 4th St, San Francisco, CA 94107
Tel.: (415) 570-2425

Web Site:
http://www.dominodatalab.com
Year Founded: 2013
Sales Range: $10-24.9 Million
Emp.: 102
Software Development Services
N.A.I.C.S.: 541511
Nick Elprin (Co-Founder & CEO)
Chris Yang (Co-Founder & CTO)
Matthew Granade (Co-Founder)
Natalie McCullough (Pres & COO)

DOMINUS CAPITAL, L.P.
1325 Ave of Americas 26th Fl, New York, NY 10019
Tel.: (212) 784-5440 — DE
Web Site:
http://www.dominuscap.com
Privater Equity Firm
N.A.I.C.S.: 523999
Gary A. Binning (Co-Founder & Mng Partner)
Robert D. Haswell (Co-Founder & Partner)
Ashish B. Rughwani (Co-Founder & Partner)
Lynn J. Horn (CFO)
James R. Adler (VP)
Terence T. Culmone (Principal)
Brian A. Finnie (VP)
Scott Moore (Operating Partner)

Subsidiaries:

Bentley Prince Street, Inc. (1)
14641 E Don Julian Rd, City of Industry, CA 91746
Tel.: (626) 333-4585
Web Site:
http://www.bentleyprincestreet.com
Sales Range: $100-124.9 Million
Textile Fiber Carpets Mfr & Marketer
N.A.I.C.S.: 314110
Ralph Grogan (Pres & CEO)

Koufu Group Limited (1)
1 Woodlands Height No 07-01, Singapore, 737859, Singapore
Tel.: (65) 65060161
Web Site: https://www.koufu.com.sg
Rev.: $145,237,354
Assets: $257,909,077
Liabilities: $181,456,285
Net Worth: $76,452,792
Earnings: $7,277,156
Fiscal Year-end: 12/31/2020
Coffeeshop Operator
N.A.I.C.S.: 722515
Lim Pang (Founder, Chm & CEO)

Lockmasters, Inc. (1)
2101 John C Watts Dr, Nicholasville, KY 40356
Tel.: (800) 654-0637
Web Site: https://www.lockmasters.com
Hardware Mfr
N.A.I.C.S.: 332510

Subsidiary (Domestic):

Hudson Lock, LLC (2)
81 Apsley St, Hudson, MA 01749-1549
Tel.: (978) 562-3481
Web Site: https://www.hudsonlock.com
Sales Range: $75-99.9 Million
Emp.: 150
Metal Lock Mfr
N.A.I.C.S.: 332510
Philip C. Calian (Executives)
Robert J. Sylvia (Pres & Gen Mgr)

Subsidiary (Domestic):

Jacob Holtz Company (3)
10 Industrial Hwy MS 6 Airport Business Complex B, Lester, PA 19029
Tel.: (215) 423-2800
Web Site: http://www.jacobholtz.com
Sales Range: $1-9.9 Million
Emp.: 55
Metal Stamping & Casters Mfr
N.A.I.C.S.: 332119
James V. Piraino (Pres)
Erik Watson (Reg Mgr)

Subsidiary (Domestic):

JLM Wholesale Inc. (2)
3095 Mullins Ct, Oxford, MI 48371-0000
Tel.: (248) 628-6440
Web Site: http://www.jlmwholesale.com
Hardware Merchant Whslr
N.A.I.C.S.: 423710

Strobic Air Corporation (1)
140 W Orvilla Rd, Lansdale, PA 19446
Tel.: (215) 723-4700
Web Site: http://www.strobicair.com
Fumehood Exhaust Systems, Clean Room
Recirculation Systems & Rane Axial & High
Temperature Fans Mfr
N.A.I.C.S.: 333413

Surface Preparation Technologies, Inc. (1)
44 E Main St, New Kingstown, PA 17072
Tel.: (717) 697-1450
Web Site: http://www.rumblestrips.com
All Other Specialty Trade Contractors
N.A.I.C.S.: 238990
Steven R. Burke (Pres & CEO)

DOMINY OIL INC.
1942 Hwy 441 S, Dublin, GA 31021
Tel.: (478) 272-0737
Sales Range: $10-24.9 Million
Emp.: 11
Petroleum Products
N.A.I.C.S.: 457120
Rob Cook (Pres)

DOMO RECORDS, INC.
11340 W Olympic Blvd Ste 270, Los
Angeles, CA 90064
Tel.: (310) 966-4414
Web Site:
http://www.domomusicgroup.com
Year Founded: 1993
Sales Range: $1-9.9 Million
Emp.: 7
New Age & World Music Producer &
Distr
N.A.I.C.S.: 512250
Eiichi Naito (Founder)
Dino Malito (VP)
Howard Sapper (VP-Bus Affairs)

DOMUS INC.
123 S Broad St Ste 1980, Philadelphia, PA 19109
Tel.: (215) 772-2800
Web Site: http://www.domusinc.com
Year Founded: 1993
Rev.: $25,000,000
Emp.: 30
Advetising Agency
N.A.I.C.S.: 541810
Lisa Samara (Pres & COO)
Meghan Becker (Asst Acct Mgr)
Lisa Ross (Sr Acct Mgr)
Elise LeMay (Acct Mgr)
Mara Rueter (Sr Acct Mgr)
Elizabeth K. Tuppeny (CEO)
Samantha Garcia (Acct Mgr)
Maggie Kane (Sr Mgr-Acct & Ops)
Megan Woodruff (Sr Acct Mgr)
Kevin Schluth (Sr Acct Mgr)
Renee Stanzione (Asst Acct Mgr)

DON BESSETTE MOTORS, INC.
1715 N Broadway, Minot, ND 58703-1362
Tel.: (701) 852-3300
Web Site:
http://www.donbessettemotors.com
Sales Range: $10-24.9 Million
Emp.: 45
Car Whslr
N.A.I.C.S.: 441110
Don Besette (Owner & Mgr)
Jason Henke (Dir-Sls)

DON BEYER MOTORS INC.

1231 W Broad St, Falls Church, VA
22046
Tel.: (703) 237-5000
Web Site:
http://www.donbeyervolvo.com
Rev.: $15,000,000
Emp.: 300
Automobiles, New & Used
N.A.I.C.S.: 441110
Jon Holl (Gen Mgr)
Richard Torres (Dir-Svc)

DON BLACKBURN & COMPANY
5060 Langlewood Dr, West Bloomfield, MI 48322-2015
Tel.: (734) 261-9100   MI
Year Founded: 1938
Sales Range: $10-24.9 Million
Emp.: 58
Sellers of Industrial Automation Products
N.A.I.C.S.: 423610
John Mcbride (CEO)
Ron Clark (Pres)
David Pride (VP-Sls)

DON BROWN AUTOMOTIVE GROUP
2244 S Kingshighway Blvd, Saint
Louis, MO 63110-3362
Tel.: (314) 450-7161
Web Site:
http://www.donbrownchevrolet.com
Rev.: $34,800,000
Emp.: 80
Automobiles, New & Used
N.A.I.C.S.: 441110
Don Brown (Co-Owner)

DON C. MUSICK CONSTRUCTION CO., INC.
254 Hanley Industrial Ct, Saint Louis,
MO 63144-1507
Tel.: (314) 781-7005   MO
Web Site:
https://www.musickconstruction.com
Year Founded: 1946
Sales Range: $10-24.9 Million
Emp.: 60
Provider of Nonresidential Construction Services
N.A.I.C.S.: 236220
Don Musick (Chm & CEO)
Thad Pieper (CFO)

Subsidiaries:

West Park Painting Inc. (1)
254 Hanley Industrial Ct, Saint Louis, MO
63144-1507
Tel.: (314) 781-3750
Sales Range: $10-24.9 Million
Emp.: 50
Provider of Painting & Paper Hanging Services
N.A.I.C.S.: 238320

DON CHALMERS FORD INC.
2500 Rio Rancho Dr, Rio Rancho,
NM 87124
Tel.: (505) 897-2500
Web Site:
http://www.donchalmersford.com
Rev.: $58,100,000
Emp.: 200
New & Used Automobile Dealer
N.A.I.C.S.: 441110
Lee Butler (Dir-Performance)
Jim Cartwright (Mgr-Sls)
Andy Strebe (Dir-Svcs)
Gary Housley (Pres)

DON DAVIS AUTO GROUP, INC.
1901 N Collins St, Arlington, TX
76011
Tel.: (817) 461-1000   TX

Web Site:
http://www.dondavisautogroup.com
Sales Range: $125-149.9 Million
Emp.: 700
Holding Company New & Used Car
Dealership Owner & Operator
N.A.I.C.S.: 551112
Robert Howard (Pres)
Don Davis (Founder & Owner)
Jim Brown (CFO)

Subsidiaries:

Don Davis Ford, Inc. (1)
633 N Hwy 360, Arlington, TX 76011
Tel.: (817) 588-5474
Web Site:
http://www.ford.dondavisautogroup.com
New & Used Car Dealer
N.A.I.C.S.: 441110
Robert Howard (Pres)

DON DAVIS DEALERSHIPS, INC.
216 W Hwy 332, Lake Jackson, TX
77566-4013
Tel.: (979) 292-0077   TX
Web Site:
https://www.drivedondavis.com
Sales Range: $25-49.9 Million
Emp.: 200
New & Used Car Dealerships Owner
& Operator
N.A.I.C.S.: 441110
Richard Davis (Pres & CEO)

Subsidiaries:

Don Davis Bay City (1)
5020 7th St, Bay City, TX 77414
Tel.: (979) 245-6391
Web Site: http://www.dondavisbaycity.com
Sales Range: $25-49.9 Million
Emp.: 30
New & Used Car Dealer
N.A.I.C.S.: 441110
Richard Davis (Pres)

Don Davis Motor Co., Inc. (1)
2011 N Mechanic St, El Campo, TX 77437
Tel.: (979) 543-3291
Web Site: http://www.dondavismotor.com
Sales Range: $25-49.9 Million
New & Used Car Dealer
N.A.I.C.S.: 441110
Richard Davis (Pres & Owner)

DON E. KEITH TRANSPORTATION, LLC
3012 Buck Owens Blvd # 101, Bakersfield, CA 93308
Tel.: (661) 321-3111
Year Founded: 1940
Sales Range: $10-24.9 Million
Emp.: 50
Petroleum Trucking Services
N.A.I.C.S.: 484110
Ken Keith (Mgr)

DON ERICKSON INC.
2606 Lee Ave, South El Monte, CA
91733
Tel.: (626) 579-1500
Web Site:
https://www.coastparts.com
Rev.: $25,100,000
Emp.: 85
Appliance Parts, Household
N.A.I.C.S.: 423620
Kirk Coburn (CFO)

DON FRANKLIN FORD LINCOLN LLC
388 KY 192 W, London, KY 40741
Tel.: (606) 864-3555
Web Site:
http://www.donfranklinlondon.com
Sales Range: $10-24.9 Million
Emp.: 25
Car Dealership
N.A.I.C.S.: 441110

Eddie Franklin (Principal)
Neil Brown (Mgr-Parts)
Robby Brown (Mgr-Svc)

DON HALL GM SUPERCENTER
1800 Greenup Ave, Ashland, KY
41101
Tel.: (606) 326-7170
Web Site:
https://www.donhallgmsuper
center.com
Year Founded: 1935
Sales Range: $25-49.9 Million
Emp.: 93
Car Whslr
N.A.I.C.S.: 441110
Jill Hall Rose (Owner)
David Dyer (Mgr-Fixed Ops)
Elmer Dials (Mgr)

DON HATTAN CHEVROLET, INC.
6000 Hattan Dr, Wichita, KS 67219-2110
Tel.: (316) 633-7109
Web Site: https://www.donhattan.com
Year Founded: 1962
Sales Range: $10-24.9 Million
Emp.: 85
Car Whslr
N.A.I.C.S.: 441110
Mike Offutt (Mgr)

DON HEATH'S AUTO HAUS, INC.
110 Manley Ave, Greensboro, NC
27407
Tel.: (336) 852-3056
Year Founded: 1982
Sales Range: $10-24.9 Million
Emp.: 10
New Car Whslr
N.A.I.C.S.: 441110
Donald Heath (Pres)

DON HILL AUTOMOTIVE ASSOCIATES INC.
2525 E Stone Dr, Kingsport, TN
37660
Tel.: (423) 246-6611
Web Site:
http://www.donhillautomotive.com
Sales Range: $10-24.9 Million
Emp.: 70
Automobiles, New & Used
N.A.I.C.S.: 441110
J. Don Hill (Pres)
Brian Griffith (Gen Mgr-Sls)
Robert Culbertson (Mgr-Sls)
Mike Smith (Mgr-Svc)
Jerry Tomlinson (Mgr-Parts)
Greg McClellan (Bus Mgr)
Shawn Thomason (Mgr-Fin)
Jim Overbey (Mgr-Inventory)

Subsidiaries:

Don Hill Pontiac Jeep Inc. (1)
2523 E Stone Dr, Kingsport, TN 37660
Tel.: (423) 246-4455
Web Site: http://www.toyotaofkingsport.com
Rev.: $14,500,000
Emp.: 50
Automobiles, New & Used
N.A.I.C.S.: 441110
J. Don Hill (Pres)

Rick Hill Imports Inc (1)
865 E Stone Dr, Kingsport, TN 37662
Tel.: (423) 246-7421
Automobiles, New & Used
N.A.I.C.S.: 441110

Sentry Leasing Inc (1)
2523 E Stone Dr, Kingsport, TN 37660
Tel.: (423) 246-4455
Rev.: $500,000
Emp.: 5
Passenger Car Leasing
N.A.I.C.S.: 532112

Don Hinds Ford Inc.—(Continued)

DON HINDS FORD INC.

12610 Ford Dr, Fishers, IN 46038
Tel.: (317) 849-9000   IN
Web Site:
   http://www.donhindsford.com
Year Founded: 1955
Sales Range: $25-49.9 Million
Emp.: 100
Sales of New & Used Automobiles
N.A.I.C.S.: 441110
John Colglazier (Mgr-Fleet)
Ed Kleyla (Mgr-Parts)
Brad Zaun (Mgr-Gen Sls)
Marq Boggs (Mgr-Svc)
Bud Colglazier (Owner)
Cam Cornett (Mgr-Comml & Fleet)
Randy Walker (Mgr-Fin)

DON JACOBS AUTOMOTIVE INC.

2689 Nicholasville Rd, Lexington, KY 40503
Tel.: (859) 276-3546
Web Site:
   https://www.donjacobs.com
Sales Range: $50-74.9 Million
Emp.: 200
Automobiles; New & Used
N.A.I.C.S.: 441110
Don Jacobs (Pres)
Scott Brittain (Gen Mgr)

Subsidiaries:

Courtesy Acura   (1)
3701 Nicholasville Rd, Lexington, KY 40503
Tel.: (859) 272-8900
Web Site:
   https://www.courtesyonwheels.com
Sales Range: $10-24.9 Million
Emp.: 55
Car Whslr
N.A.I.C.S.: 441110
Mike Edmondson (Dir-Sls-Acura)
John Tewell (Dir-Pre-Owned)
Burton Legear (Dir-Parts & Svc)
Larry Heath (Asst Mgr-Svc)
Matt Wells (Mgr-Fin)
Stephen Curtis (Mgr-Pre-Owned Sls)
Edward Hogan III (Dir-Fin)
John Tewell III (Mgr-Pre-Owned Sls)

DON JACOBS IMPORTS, INC.

2689 Nicholasville Rd, Lexington, KY 40503-3303
Tel.: (859) 276-5555
Year Founded: 1970
Sales Range: $50-74.9 Million
Emp.: 200
Car Whslr
N.A.I.C.S.: 441110
Michelle Bensberg (Acct Mgr)
Scott Brittain (Mgr-Ops)
Lori DeJesus (Controller)
Don Jacobs (Owner & Pres)

DON JACOBS TOYOTA

5727 S 27th St, Milwaukee, WI 53221
Tel.: (414) 281-3100
Web Site:
   https://www.donjacobstoyota.com
Year Founded: 1977
Sales Range: $25-49.9 Million
Emp.: 86
New Car Retailer
N.A.I.C.S.: 441110
Scott J. Fisler (Dir-Fixed Ops)
Steve Jacobs (Mgr-New Car Sls)
Ron Huber (Mgr-Used Car Sls)

DON JAGODA ASSOCIATES, INC.

100 Marcus Dr, Melville, NY 11747-4229
Tel.: (631) 454-1800   NY
Web Site: http://www.dja.com

Year Founded: 1962
Rev.: $15,000,000
Emp.: 70
N.A.I.C.S.: 541810
Don Jagoda (Owner)
Larry Berney (COO)
Bruce Hollander (Exec VP)
Steve Greco (VP-Creative Svcs)
Andrew Gusman (Controller)
Suzanne Gulbransen (Sr VP)
Jacqueline Lamberti (Sr VP-Promos)

Subsidiaries:

Don Jagoda Associates, Inc.   (1)
717 E Union St, Pasadena, CA 91101
Tel.: (818) 508-3000
Web Site: http://www.dja.com
Emp.: 8
N.A.I.C.S.: 541810
Kitty Dunning (Sr VP)
Becky Schaefer (Sr Dir-Opers)

DON JOHNSON MOTORS INC.

734 W Ave, Rice Lake, WI 54868
Tel.: (715) 234-8161
Web Site:
   http://www.donjohnsonauto.com
Rev.: $39,107,161
Emp.: 55
Automobiles, New & Used
N.A.I.C.S.: 441110
Don Johnson (Pres)

DON JOHNSON MOTORS INC.

2101 Central Blvd, Brownsville, TX 78520
Tel.: (956) 546-2288
Web Site:
   http://www.realdonjohnson.com
Emp.: 50
Automobile Dealership
N.A.I.C.S.: 441110
Sylvia Muniz (Mgr-Fin)
Donald G. Johnson Sr. (Owner)
Donald J. Johnson Jr. (Gen Mgr)

DON JOSEPH INCORPRATED

1111 W Main St, Kent, OH 44240
Tel.: (330) 673-2200
Web Site:
   http://www.donjosephtoyota.com
Sales Range: $25-49.9 Million
Emp.: 50
Sales of New & Used Automobiles
N.A.I.C.S.: 441110
Jeffrey Joseph (Pres)

DON K CHEVROLET INC.

6219 Hwy 93 S, Whitefish, MT 59937-8234
Tel.: (406) 905-1229
Web Site:
   https://www.donkchryslerdodge.com
Sales Range: $10-24.9 Million
Emp.: 70
New & Used Automobiles
N.A.I.C.S.: 441110
Donald Kaltschmidt (Pres)

DON KRUEGER CONSTRUC-TION CO.

205 Profit Dr, Victoria, TX 77901
Tel.: (361) 573-5291   TX
Year Founded: 1965
Sales Range: $10-24.9 Million
Emp.: 80
Commercial & Institutional Building Construction Services
N.A.I.C.S.: 236220
Kevin Krueger (Pres)
Lester Colley (VP)

DON M. BARRON CONTRAC-TORS INC.

408 Cedar St, Farmerville, LA 71241-0399
Tel.: (318) 368-2622   LA

Web Site:
   http://www.donmbarroncontractor.com
Year Founded: 1951
Sales Range: $10-24.9 Million
Emp.: 75
Providers of Heavy Construction Services
N.A.I.C.S.: 237110
David Farrar (VP)

DON MCCUE CHEVROLET

2015 E Main St, Saint Charles, IL 60174-2303
Tel.: (630) 584-9700
Web Site:
   http://www.mccuechevy.com
Year Founded: 1980
Sales Range: $25-49.9 Million
Emp.: 97
New Car Whslr
N.A.I.C.S.: 441110
Don McCue (Owner)
Tim McCue (VP)

DON MCCUE CHEVROLET & GEO INC.

2015 E Main St, Saint Charles, IL 60174
Tel.: (630) 524-2683
Web Site:
   https://www.mccuechevy.com
Sales Range: $25-49.9 Million
Emp.: 97
New Car Dealers
N.A.I.C.S.: 441110
Tim M. Cue (Pres)
Donald W. McCue (Pres & Sec)

DON MCGILL TOYOTA OF HOUSTON

11800 Katy Fwy, Houston, TX 77079
Tel.: (281) 496-9730
Web Site:
   https://www.donmcgilltoyota.com
Year Founded: 1970
Sales Range: $75-99.9 Million
Emp.: 285
Car Whslr
N.A.I.C.S.: 441110
Sahar Askari (Mgr-Customer Rels)

DON MEALEY MAZDA

6239 S Orange Blossom Trl, Orlando, FL 32809-4611
Tel.: (407) 851-8510
Year Founded: 2008
Sales Range: $10-24.9 Million
Emp.: 48
New Car Whslr
N.A.I.C.S.: 441110
John Lumpkin (Principal)

DON MEDLIN CO.

1197 State Hwy D, Caruthersville, MO 63830
Tel.: (573) 333-0663
Web Site:
   https://www.donmedlinco.com
Sales Range: $10-24.9 Million
Emp.: 50
Agricultural Machinery & Equipment
N.A.I.C.S.: 423820
Byron Medlin (Pres)
Lannie Morgan (Mgr-Shop)

DON MILLER SUBARU EAST

5339 Wayne Ter, Madison, WI 53718
Tel.: (608) 258-3636
Web Site:
   http://www.subaru.donmiller.com
Rev.: $32,600,000
Emp.: 100
Automobiles, New & Used
N.A.I.C.S.: 441110

Don W. Miller (Owner)
Peter Hubbard (Gen Mgr)
Jon Morrison (Dir-Parts)

DON MOORE NISSAN

4216 Frederica St, Owensboro, KY 42301
Tel.: (270) 926-2500
Web Site:
   http://www.donmoorenissan.net
Year Founded: 1988
Sales Range: $25-49.9 Million
Emp.: 95
Car Whslr
N.A.I.C.S.: 441110
Don P. Moore III (Pres)

DON PRESLEY AUCTIONS

2202 S Main St, Santa Ana, CA 92707
Tel.: (714) 633-2437
Web Site:
   http://www.donpresleyauction.com
Emp.: 5
Antique Dealer
N.A.I.C.S.: 459510
Don Presley (Owner)

DON REID FORD, INC.

1875 S Orlando Ave, Maitland, FL 32751
Tel.: (407) 644-6111
Web Site:
   http://www.donreidford.com
Sales Range: $25-49.9 Million
Emp.: 145
Car Whslr
N.A.I.C.S.: 441110
Russell L. Reid (Pres)
Michael Vitale (Gen Mgr)

DON RINGLER CHEVROLET CO. INC.

7777 S General Bruce Dr, Temple, TX 76504
Tel.: (254) 778-4285
Web Site:
   http://www.donringlertoyota.com
Rev.: $26,200,000
Emp.: 200
New & Used Car Dealers
N.A.I.C.S.: 441110
Don Al Ringler (Owner & Pres)

DON ROBERTO JEWELERS INC.

1020 Calle Recodo, San Clemente, CA 92673
Tel.: (949) 361-6700
Web Site:
   http://www.donrobertojewelers.com
Sales Range: $25-49.9 Million
Emp.: 600
Jewelry Stores
N.A.I.C.S.: 458310
Robert D. Trette (CEO)
Juan Diego (Mgr)

DON SEBASTIANI & SONS

19150 Sonoma Hwy, Sonoma, CA 95476
Tel.: (707) 933-1704
Web Site:
   http://www.donandsons.com
Year Founded: 2001
Sales Range: $10-24.9 Million
Emp.: 66
Vineyard & Wine Mfr
N.A.I.C.S.: 111332
Donny Sebastiani (Pres & CEO)
John Nicolette (VP-Ops)
Alice Castorena (Office Mgr)
Tom Hawkins (COO)
Omar Percich (CFO)
Andrew Meyer (VP-Wine & Spirits-Sls-Global)

Steve Pearce *(Mgr-Wine & Spirits-Sls-West)*
Marie Brown *(Mgr-Distr & Export Logistics)*
Greg Kitchens *(Dir-Winemaking)*

DON SEELYE FORD INC.
3820 Stadium Dr, Kalamazoo, MI 49008
Tel.: (269) 375-3820
Web Site: http://www.swautonet.com
Sales Range: $25-49.9 Million
Emp.: 150
Sales of New & Used Automobiles
N.A.I.C.S.: 441110
Michael Seelye *(Owner & Pres)*
Barry Broekhuizen *(CFO)*

DON SMALL & SONS OIL DISTRIBUTING CO. INC.
112 3rd St NW, Auburn, WA 98002
Tel.: (253) 833-0430   **WA**
Web Site:
   http://www.smallandsonsoil.com
Year Founded: 1963
Sales Range: $10-24.9 Million
Emp.: 81
Petroleum Oil & Fuel
N.A.I.C.S.: 424710
Steve Small *(Pres)*
Dan Small *(CEO)*

DON THORNTON CADILLAC SAAB, INC.
3939 S Memorial Dr, Tulsa, OK 74145-1332
Tel.: (918) 553-8073
Web Site:
   https://www.donthorntoncadillac.com
Sales Range: $25-49.9 Million
Emp.: 65
Car Whslr
N.A.I.C.S.: 441110
Tom Bloomfield *(Gen Mgr)*

DON WALTER KITCHEN DISTRIBUTORS
260 Victoria Rd, Youngstown, OH 44515
Tel.: (330) 793-9338
Web Site:
   https://www.donwalterkitchen.com
Sales Range: $10-24.9 Million
Emp.: 12
Electrical Appliances, Major
N.A.I.C.S.: 423620
Gary Walter *(Pres)*

DON WENNER HOME SELLING, INC.
710 W Broad St Ste 200, Bethlehem, PA 18018
Tel.: (610) 421-4610   **PA**
Web Site:
   http://www.dreamliveprosper.com
Real Estate Brokerage, Investment, Development & Property Management Services
N.A.I.C.S.: 531390
Donald Wenner *(Owner, Pres & CEO)*
Robert Peterson *(CFO)*
Cindy Lou Temple *(Mgr-HR)*
Stephanie Birster *(Controller)*
Jeffrey Miggins *(Dir-Acctg)*
Barry Degroot *(Corp Counsel-Legal)*
Subsidiaries:

DLP Builders   (1)
701 W Broad St Ste 200, Bethlehem, PA 18018
Tel.: (610) 421-4610
Web Site: http://www.dlpbuilders.com
Construction & Renovation Contractor
N.A.I.C.S.: 236115

Donald Wenner *(Pres & CEO)*
Larry Greenberg *(VP-Construction)*

DLP Capital Advisors   (1)
701 W Broad St Ste 200, Bethlehem, PA 18018
Tel.: (610) 488-2375
Web Site: http://www.dlpcapitaladvisors.com
Real Estate Investment & Development
N.A.I.C.S.: 531390
Donald Wenner *(Pres & CEO)*
Kevin Earnest *(VP-Investments & Lending)*
Patrick Heller *(VP-Lending)*

DLP Interactive Media   (1)
710 W Broad St Ste 200, Bethlehem, PA 18018
Tel.: (610) 421-4610
Web Site: http://www.dlpinteractive.com
Advertising Media Buying Agency
N.A.I.C.S.: 541830
Donald Wenner *(Pres & CEO)*
Brion Yarnell *(VP-Bus Dev)*

DLP Realty   (1)
701 W Broad St Ste 200, Bethlehem, PA 18018
Tel.: (610) 421-4610
Web Site: http://www.dlprealty.com
Sales Range: $1-9.9 Million
Emp.: 20
Real Estate Brokerage Services
N.A.I.C.S.: 531210
Donald Wenner *(Pres & CEO)*
Larry Keiner *(Mktg Dir)*
Cindy Lou Temple *(Mgr-HR)*
Tina Steuer *(Coord-Mktg)*
Amy Godiska *(Coord-Feedback)*
Jonathan Campbell *(Mgr-Sls)*

DLP Realty Property
Management   (1)
701 W Broad St Ste 200, Bethlehem, PA 18018
Tel.: (610) 421-4610
Web Site: http://www.dlpproperty.com
Residential & Commercial Property Management Services
N.A.I.C.S.: 531311
Donald Wenner *(Pres & CEO)*
Jason Battestelli *(Sr VP)*
Bruce Eaton *(Head-Comml Real Estate & Mgr-Property)*
John Przyuski *(Head-Rent Collection & Mgr-Property)*
Ken Gross *(Mgr-Property)*

Direct Lending Partner   (1)
701 W Broad St, Bethlehem, PA 18018
Tel.: (610) 232-7540
Web Site:
   http://www.directlendingpartner.com
Short-Term Real Estate Loan Origination Services
N.A.I.C.S.: 522299
Donald Wenner *(Pres & CEO)*
Patrick Heller *(VP-Lending)*
Kevin Earnest *(VP-Investments & Lending)*

DON WESSEL HONDA
3520 S Campbell Ave, Springfield, MO 65807
Tel.: (417) 882-3900
Web Site: http://www.donwessel.com
Year Founded: 1966
Sales Range: $25-49.9 Million
Emp.: 100
New Car Retailer
N.A.I.C.S.: 441110
Jon Wessel *(Pres)*

DON WILLIAMSON NISSAN
310 Western Blvd, Jacksonville, NC 28546-6339
Tel.: (910) 353-7700
Web Site: https://www.dwnissan.com
Sales Range: $10-24.9 Million
Emp.: 36
New Car Whslr
N.A.I.C.S.: 441110
Alycia Williamson Tomazic *(Gen Mgr)*
Bobby Bourquin *(Mgr-Sls)*
Freddie Haargett *(Mgr-Sls)*

DON YOUNG COMPANY INCORPORATED
8181 Ambassador Row, Dallas, TX 75247
Tel.: (214) 630-0934
Web Site:
   https://www.dycwindows.com
Year Founded: 1978
Rev.: $14,000,000
Emp.: 80
Storm Doors & Windows
N.A.I.C.S.: 332321
Scott Young *(VP)*
Mike Loter *(Exec VP)*

DON'S BROOKLYN CHEVROLET, INC.
4941 Pearl Rd, Cleveland, OH 44109
Tel.: (216) 741-1500
Web Site:
   http://www.donsbrooklyn.com
Sales Range: $10-24.9 Million
Emp.: 45
Car Whslr
N.A.I.C.S.: 441110
Donald J. Petruzzi *(Owner)*
Laura Lee Petruzzi *(VP)*

DON'S FARM SUPPLY, INC.
167 W 1st St, Newell, IA 50568
Tel.: (712) 272-3396
Web Site: http://www.dfsfeed.com
Year Founded: 1970
Sales Range: $10-24.9 Million
Emp.: 62
Animal Feed Mfr
N.A.I.C.S.: 311119
David Kier *(CEO)*
Mike Kinely *(COO)*
Geoff Smith *(Dir-Technical Support)*
Patrick Ryherd *(CFO & Treas)*
Nathan Kier *(Pres)*

DON'S MOBILE GLASS INC.
1424 H St, Modesto, CA 95354
Tel.: (209) 526-9100
Web Site:
   http://www.donsmobileglass.com
Rev.: $15,173,164
Emp.: 15
Glass Construction Materials
N.A.I.C.S.: 423390
Don Monaco *(Founder)*
Stacy Veronese *(Mgr)*
Robert Serpa *(Founder)*

DON'S TRUCK SALES INC.
102 S 1st St, Fairbank, IA 50629
Tel.: (319) 635-2751   **IA**
Web Site:
   http://www.donstrucksales.com
Year Founded: 1959
Sales Range: $10-24.9 Million
Emp.: 30
Sales of Commercial Trucks
N.A.I.C.S.: 423110
Gene Carpenter *(Mgr-Sls)*

DON-A-VEE CHRYSLER JEEP INC.
777 W Orangethorpe Ave, Placentia, CA 92870
Tel.: (714) 528-5337
Web Site: http://www.donavee.com
Sales Range: Less than $1 Million
Emp.: 60
Automobiles, New & Used
N.A.I.C.S.: 457120
Marlon Arana *(Owner & Pres)*

DON-LEE DISTRIBUTORS INC.
5400 Patterson Ave SE, Grand Rapids, MI 49512-9630
Tel.: (616) 698-1900   **MI**
Web Site:
   http://www.abwholesaler.com
Year Founded: 1933
Sales Range: $75-99.9 Million

Emp.: 110
Beer & Ale Products Distr
N.A.I.C.S.: 424810
Keith Klopcic *(Pres)*
Bruce Parkes *(Gen Mgr)*
Karla Grzybowski *(Coord-Promotional Products Grp)*
Donald Klopcic Sr. *(Chm)*
Donald Klopcic Jr. *(CEO)*

DON-MAR CREATIONS INC.
862 Waterman Ave E, Providence, RI 02914
Tel.: (401) 633-1410
Web Site:
   http://www.donmarcreations.com
Rev.: $10,000,000
Emp.: 50
Retailer of Picture Frames
N.A.I.C.S.: 423220
Donald W. Marino *(Pres)*
Beth Marino *(Controller)*
Donald Marino Jr. *(Gen Mgr)*

DONALD B REMMEY INC.
523 Mill Rd, Lehighton, PA 18235
Tel.: (570) 386-5379
Web Site: https://www.remmey.com
Sales Range: $10-24.9 Million
Emp.: 10
Pallet Mfr
N.A.I.C.S.: 321920
Bill Lusignea *(CFO)*
Donald B. Remmey Jr. *(Pres)*

DONALD B. RICE TIRE CO. INC.
909 N E St, Frederick, MD 21701-4621
Tel.: (301) 662-0166   **MD**
Web Site: https://www.ricetire.com
Year Founded: 1938
Sales Range: $25-49.9 Million
Emp.: 200
Provider of Tires
N.A.I.C.S.: 423130
Ken Rice *(CEO)*
Chris Chase *(Pres)*

DONALD B. SMITH INCORPORATED
PO Box 78, Hanover, PA 17331
Tel.: (717) 632-2100
Web Site: http://www.dbsroofing.com
Year Founded: 1952
Sales Range: $10-24.9 Million
Emp.: 48
Roofing Installation Services
N.A.I.C.S.: 238390

DONALD BRUCE & CO.
6323 N Avondale Ave Ste 243, Chicago, IL 60631-4794
Tel.: (773) 477-8100
Rev.: $26,600,000
Emp.: 3
Jewelry, Precious Metal
N.A.I.C.S.: 423940
Gary Solomon *(Pres)*

DONALD DANFORTH PLANT SCIENCE CENTER
975 N Watson Rd, Saint Louis, MO 63132
Tel.: (314) 587-1000   **MO**
Web Site:
   https://www.danforthcenter.org
Year Founded: 1998
Sales Range: $25-49.9 Million
Emp.: 276
Science Research Services
N.A.I.C.S.: 541715
James C. Carrington *(Pres & CEO)*
Todd Hornburg *(VP-Facilities Mgmt)*
Anna Dibble *(VP-Human Resources)*

Donald Danforth Plant Science Center—(Continued)

Elliott Kellner (Sr Program Mgr)
Stephanie Regagnon (Exec Dir-Innovation Partnerships)

DONALD J. FAGER & ASSOCIATES
2 Park Ave Fl 25, New York, NY 10016
Tel.: (212) 576-9800
Web Site: http://www.mlmic.com
Rev.: $40,000,000
Emp.: 150
Insurance Brokers
N.A.I.C.S.: 524210
Donald J. Fager (Pres)
Howard Brush (Supvr-Underwriting)
Timothy Krieg (VP)
Michael Schoppmann (Pres)

DONALD R. HARVEY, INC.
3555 Veterans Memorial Hwy Ste D, Ronkonkoma, NY 11779
Tel.: (631) 467-6200   NY
Web Site: http://www.drhinc.com
Year Founded: 1968
Sales Range: $10-24.9 Million
Emp.: 10
Advertising Agencies
N.A.I.C.S.: 541810
Anthony Vela (VP-Client Svcs)

DONALDSON PLASTIC SURGERY, LLC
92 N High St, Dublin, OH 43017
Tel.: (614) 300-5431
Web Site: http://www.donaldsonplasticsurgery.com
Year Founded: 2008
Sales Range: $1-9.9 Million
Emp.: 10
Plastic Surgery & Aesthetic Services
N.A.I.C.S.: 621111
Olivia Whapham (Comm Mgr)
E. D. Stange (COO)
Carrie Esposito (Dir-Patient Experience)

DONALSONVILLE HOSPITAL, INC.
102 Hospital Cir, Donalsonville, GA 39845
Tel.: (229) 524-5217   GA
Web Site: https://www.donalsonvillehospital.org
Year Founded: 1977
Sales Range: $25-49.9 Million
Emp.: 401
Health Care Srvices
N.A.I.C.S.: 622110
James Moody (CFO)

DONATECH CORPORATION
2094 185th St Ste 110, Fairfield, IA 52556
Tel.: (641) 472-7474
Web Site: http://www.donatech.com
Year Founded: 1987
Sales Range: $25-49.9 Million
Emp.: 250
Computer Software Development Services
N.A.I.C.S.: 541511
Shreyash Nayak (VP-Talent Acq)
Patrick Adam (VP-Bus Dev)

DONATOS PIZZERIA CORPORATION
935 Taylor Station Rd, Columbus, OH 43230-6657
Tel.: (614) 416-7700
Web Site: http://www.donatos.com
Year Founded: 1963

Sales Range: $150-199.9 Million
Emp.: 5,000
Pizza Restaurant Owner, Operator & Franchisor
N.A.I.C.S.: 722513
James E. Grote (Co-Founder)
Doug Kourie (CFO)
Jodie Conrad (CMO)
Steven Graves (CIO)
Kevin King (Pres)
Christina Jackson (Chief People Officer)
Kevin Myers (CMO)

DONATWALD+HAQUE
1316 Third St Ste 301, Santa Monica, CA 90401
Tel.: (310) 394-1717
Year Founded: 1987
Sales Range: Less than $1 Million
Emp.: 50
Brand Development, Consumer Marketing, Direct Marketing, Full Service, Internet/Web Design, Media Buying Services, Print, Production, Radio, T.V.
N.A.I.C.S.: 541810
Lucas Donat (CEO)
Elizabeth Espat (Head-Production)
Amir Haque (Partner)

DONDELINGER CHEVROLET CADILLAC
6720 Pine Beach Rd, Baxter, MN 56425
Tel.: (218) 829-4787
Web Site: http://www.dondelingerauto.com
Sales Range: $25-49.9 Million
Emp.: 70
Car Dealership
N.A.I.C.S.: 532112
Roger H. Dondelinger (Owner)
Deb Mitzel (Controller)

DONDLINGER & SONS CONSTRUCTION CO. INC.
2656 S Sheridan St, Wichita, KS 67201-0398
Tel.: (316) 945-0555   KS
Web Site: https://www.dondlinger.biz
Year Founded: 1898
Sales Range: $25-49.9 Million
Emp.: 250
Provider of Industrial Contracting Services
N.A.I.C.S.: 236210

Subsidiaries:

Dondlinger & Sons Construction Co. Inc.-Texas   (1)
2656 S Sheridan St, Wichita, KS 67217   (100%)
Tel.: (316) 945-0555
Web Site: http://www.dondlinger.biz
Sales Range: $25-49.9 Million
Emp.: 230
Provider of Industrial Contracting Services
N.A.I.C.S.: 236210

DONELAN'S SUPERMARKETS, INC.
236 Great Rd, Littleton, MA 01460
Tel.: (978) 486-8986   MA
Web Site: http://www.donelans.com
Year Founded: 1983
Sales Range: $50-74.9 Million
Emp.: 350
Provider of Grocery Store Services
N.A.I.C.S.: 445110
John Donelan (Founder & Pres)

DONER
25900 Northwestern Hwy, Southfield, MI 48075
Tel.: (248) 354-9700   MI

Web Site: http://www.doner.com
Year Founded: 1937
Rev.: $1,700,000,000
Emp.: 544
Advertising Services
N.A.I.C.S.: 541810
Monica Tysell (Chief Integration Officer)
Sheryll Kollin (Sr VP & Dir-Bus Affairs)
David DeMuth (CEO)
Jim Vassallo (Sr VP-Brand Leadership)
Stephen Bantien (Dir-Creative)
Jason Gaboriau (Chief Creative Officer)
Marcus Collins (Sr VP & Exec Dir-Social Engagement)
Lucy Solomon (Dir-Client Svcs-London)
Charlie Rowe (Head-Design-London)
Nick Constantinou (Mng Dir-London)
Mike Cessario (Dir-Creative)
Naveen Passey (CFO, COO & Exec VP)
Mike Ensroth (Exec VP-Detroit)
Amy Murrin (VP)
Jon Krevolin (Exec Creative Dir)
Ryan McKone (Sr VP & Dir-Digital Strategy)
Carla Butwin (VP & Creative Dir)

Subsidiaries:

Doner   (1)
4675 MacArthur Ct Ste 1000, Newport Beach, CA 92660
Tel.: (949) 623-4300
Web Site: http://www.donerus.com
Sales Range: $10-24.9 Million
Emp.: 25
Advertising Services
N.A.I.C.S.: 541810
Lauren Prince (Pres)
Sue Guise (Exec VP & Dir-Ops)
Jane Goodman (Chief Strategy Officer)

Doner   (1)
600 Six Flags Dr Ste 545, Arlington, TX 76011
Tel.: (817) 695-1705
Web Site: http://www.donerus.com
Sales Range: $10-24.9 Million
Emp.: 3
Advertising Services
N.A.I.C.S.: 541810

Doner   (1)
The Diamond Bldg 1100 Superior Ave 10th Fl, Cleveland, OH 44114
Tel.: (216) 771-5700
Web Site: http://www.doner.com
Advertising Services
N.A.I.C.S.: 541810
Jennifer Deutsh (Exec VP & Gen Mgr)
Larry Deangelis (Sr VP)

Doner Canada, Inc.   (1)
90 Eglinton Avenue East Suite 800, Toronto, M4P 3A5, ON, Canada
Tel.: (416) 485-9901
Web Site: http://www.doner.com
Sales Range: $25-49.9 Million
Emp.: 80
Advertising Services
N.A.I.C.S.: 541810
Dave Carey (Sr Acct Dir)
Michael Reneau (Sr VP & Gen Mgr)
Greg Clausen (Exec VP & Chief Media Officer)
Kevin Weinman (Exec VP-Brand Leadership)
Lisa Nardone (Exec VP-Brand Leadership)

Doner Canada, Inc.   (1)
2075 University Street Ste 920, Montreal, H3A 2L1, QC, Canada
Tel.: (514) 842-3757
Web Site: http://www.donerus.com
Sales Range: $10-24.9 Million
Emp.: 4
Advertising Services
N.A.I.C.S.: 541810
Alison Taubman (Exec VP & Chief Strategy Officer)

Doner Cardwell Hawkins   (1)
26-34 Emerald Street, London, WC1N 3QA, United Kingdom
Tel.: (44) 2077340511
Sales Range: $10-24.9 Million
Emp.: 45
Advertising Services
N.A.I.C.S.: 541810

DONGFANG CITY HOLDING GROUP COMPANY LIMITED
48 Wall St 5th Fl, New York, NY 10005
Tel.: (212) 625-8648   DE
Year Founded: 2019
Assets: $10,100
Liabilities: $200,429
Net Worth: ($190,329)
Earnings: ($190,000)
Fiscal Year-end: 10/31/20
Investment Services
N.A.I.C.S.: 523999
Zhenggui Wang (Chm, Pres, CEO, CFO, Treas & Sec)

DONGILI INVESTMENT GROUP, INC.
5563 Marquesas Cir, Sarasota, FL 34233-3332
Tel.: (941) 359-8477
Sales Range: $25-49.9 Million
Emp.: 10
Commercial Gravure Printing Services
N.A.I.C.S.: 323111
Paul Santostasi (Owner)

DONLEY FORD LINCOLN INC.
1641 Claremont Ave, Ashland, OH 44805
Tel.: (419) 281-3673
Web Site: http://www.donleyfordofashland.com
Rev.: $24,000,000
Emp.: 40
Automobiles, New & Used
N.A.I.C.S.: 441110
Scott Donley (Pres)
Ryan Sponsler (VP)
Damon Hitchcock (Gen Mgr-Sls)

DONLEY'S, INC.
5430 Warner Rd, Cleveland, OH 44125
Tel.: (216) 524-6800   OH
Web Site: https://www.donleyinc.com
Year Founded: 1895
Sales Range: $75-99.9 Million
Emp.: 225
Provider of Contracting & Construction Services
N.A.I.C.S.: 238110
Terrance K. Donley (Chm)
Mac Donley (Pres & CEO)
Patrick J. Powers (CFO & Treas)
Don K. Dreier (Exec VP)

DONNA SAYLERS' FABULOUS-FURS
25 W Robinson St, Covington, KY 41011
Tel.: (859) 291-3300
Web Site: https://www.fabulousfurs.com
Sales Range: $10-24.9 Million
Emp.: 40
Fake Fur Clothing & Accessories Retailer
N.A.I.C.S.: 112930
Donna Saylers (Pres)

DONNELL SYSTEMS INC.
300 S Saint Louis Blvd, South Bend, IN 46617
Tel.: (574) 232-3784   IN
Web Site: http://www.donnell.com
Year Founded: 1989
Sales Range: $10-24.9 Million
Emp.: 30

Computer Software Development
N.A.I.C.S.: 541511
Lynn Donnell (Pres)
Peter Dosch (VP-Ops)
Thomas White (CTO)

DONNELLON MCCARTHY INC.

4141 Turrill St, Cincinnati, OH 45241
Tel.: (513) 681-5617
Web Site:
    http://www.donnellonmccarthy.com
Sales Range: $10-24.9 Million
Emp.: 120
Photocopy Machines
N.A.I.C.S.: 423420
Robert P. Donnellon (Head-Logistics)
Dave Ehlers (VP-Sls)
Jim George (Pres)

DONNERWOOD MEDIA, INC.

620 Folsom St Ste 350, San Francisco, CA 94107
Tel.: (415) 543-6339   DE
Web Site:
    http://www.donnerwood.com
Online Entertainment Services
N.A.I.C.S.: 541511
John Cahill (CEO)

Subsidiaries:

Meez   (1)
620 Folsom St Ste 350, San Francisco, CA
94107
Tel.: (415) 543-6339
Web Site: http://www.meez.com
Social Entertainment Community
N.A.I.C.S.: 516210

DONNINI ENTERPRISES INC.

3501 SW Corporate Pkwy, Palm City,
FL 34990
Tel.: (772) 288-0454   FL
Web Site:
    http://www.donninienterprises.com
Year Founded: 1978
Sales Range: $10-24.9 Million
Emp.: 30
Gasoline Station Services
N.A.I.C.S.: 457120
Gerald Donnini (Pres)
Mary Vinson (Dir-Ops & VP)
Marybeth Kohn (Controller)
Jesse G. Oakley (CFO)

Subsidiaries:

Reliance Petroleum Company
Inc.   (1)
2955 E 11th Ave, Hialeah, FL 33013
Tel.: (772) 288-0454
Petroleum Services
N.A.I.C.S.: 424710

DONOHOO CHEVROLET, LLC

1000 Greenhill Blvd NW, Fort Payne,
AL 35967
Tel.: (256) 273-4752
Web Site:
    https://www.donohoochevrolet.com
Sales Range: $10-24.9 Million
Emp.: 20
Car Dealership Owner & Operator
N.A.I.C.S.: 441110
Chris Donohoo (Principal)

DONOR ALLIANCE, INC.

720 S Colorado Blvd Ste 800-N, Denver, CO 80246
Tel.: (303) 329-4747   CO
Web Site:
    http://www.donoralliance.org
Year Founded: 1985
Sales Range: $25-49.9 Million
Emp.: 128
Organ & Tissue Donation Services
N.A.I.C.S.: 621991
Jennifer Prinz (Pres & CEO)
Grace Harcek (Dir-Quality Sys)

Lorrie Linquist (Dir-Special Projects)
Sarah Snow (Mgr-HR)
Bradley T. Kornfeld (Chm)
Kevin M. Smith (Treas & Sec)
Matt Lovetro (CFO)
Jennifer Muriett (COO)
Paul Lange (Dir-Medical)

DONOR NETWORK OF ARIZONA

201 W Coolidge St, Phoenix, AZ
85013
Tel.: (602) 222-2200   AZ
Web Site: https://www.dnaz.org
Year Founded: 1992
Sales Range: $25-49.9 Million
Emp.: 201
Organ & Tissue Donation Services
N.A.I.C.S.: 621991
Tim Brown (CEO)

DONOVAN ADVERTISING & MARKETING SERVICES

180 W Airport Rd, Lititz, PA 17543
Tel.: (717) 560-1333
Web Site:
    http://www.donovanadv.com
Year Founded: 1992
Rev.: $11,800,000
Emp.: 15
N.A.I.C.S.: 541810
Donna Sheetz (Dir-Acct Svcs)
Matt London (Dir-Ops)
Jean Jones (Dir-Creative)
Chris Renna (Art Dir)
Kevin Harder (Dir-Art)
William J. Donovan Jr. (Owner)

DONOVAN ENTERPRISES

3353 SE Gran Pkwy, Stuart, FL
34997
Tel.: (772) 286-3350
Web Site: http://www.donovan-ent.com
Emp.: 300
Fabric Liners & Covers
N.A.I.C.S.: 314910
Max Owens (Mgr-Customer Svc & Sls)
Scott Klager (Pres)

DONOVAN FARMERS ELEVATOR COOP

201 2nd St, Donovan, IL 60931
Tel.: (815) 486-7327
Web Site:
    http://www.donovanfarmerscoop.com
Sales Range: $10-24.9 Million
Emp.: 30
Chemicals, Agricultural
N.A.I.C.S.: 424910
Tim Fletcher (Pres)
Terry Winger (Gen Mgr)

DONOVAN MARINE INC.

6316 Humphreys St, Harahan, LA
70123
Tel.: (504) 488-5731
Web Site:
    http://www.donovanmarine.com
Rev.: $52,941,303
Emp.: 66
Marine Supplies
N.A.I.C.S.: 423860
J. Benton Smallpage Jr. (Pres)

DONSCO, INC.

N Front St, Wrightsville, PA 17368
Tel.: (717) 252-1561   PA
Web Site: http://www.donsco.com
Year Founded: 1970
Sales Range: $125-149.9 Million
Emp.: 500
Cast Iron Parts Supplier
N.A.I.C.S.: 331511

John Smeltzer (VP-Sls)
H. K. Smith (Founder)

DONUT MANAGEMENT INC.

3 Pluff Ave, North Reading, MA
01864
Tel.: (978) 521-4552
Sales Range: $125-149.9 Million
Emp.: 850
Franchise of Independent Doughnut
Stores
N.A.I.C.S.: 445291
Gus Constantine Skrivanos (Pres)

DOODAD

7990 2nd Flags Dr Ste D, Austell, GA
30168
Tel.: (770) 732-0321   FL
Web Site: https://www.doodad.com
Year Founded: 1969
Sales Range: $25-49.9 Million
Emp.: 150
Commercial Printing Services
N.A.I.C.S.: 323111
Todd Schweitzer (Mgr-Prepress)

DOOLEY OIL INC.

720 Skyline Rd, Laramie, WY 82070
Tel.: (307) 742-5667
Web Site: https://www.dooleyoil.com
Sales Range: $1-9.9 Million
Emp.: 30
Petroleum Products
N.A.I.C.S.: 424720
John Dooley (Pres)
Greg Warren (CFO-Laramie)
Kevin Prahl (Mgr-Warehouse)
Steve Gosbee (Gen Mgr-Cheyenne)
Don Dobrenz (Gen Mgr-Casper &
Fuel Dispatch)
Kelly Smith (Mgr-Sls-Casper)
Mike Flick (Gen Mgr-Gering)

DOOLEY'S PETROLEUM INCORPORATED

304 Main Ave, Murdock, MN 56271
Tel.: (320) 875-2641
Web Site: http://www.dooleydnn.com
Rev.: $33,852,791
Emp.: 60
Petroleum Bulk Stations
N.A.I.C.S.: 424710
Dan Selander (Mgr-HR)

DOOLEYMACK CONSTRUCTORS INC.

4550 Atwater Ct Ste 204, Buford, GA
30518
Tel.: (770) 945-0696   FL
Web Site:
    http://www.dooleymack.com
Year Founded: 1976
Sales Range: $25-49.9 Million
Emp.: 150
Nonresidential Construction Services
N.A.I.C.S.: 236220
Tim Sterritt (Sr VP)
Chris Dooley (VP)

DOOLITTLE DISTRIBUTING INC.

9736 Legler Rd, Lenexa, KS 66219-
1282
Tel.: (913) 888-7820
Web Site: http://www.ddius.com
Sales Range: $10-24.9 Million
Emp.: 22
Electrical Appliances, Major
N.A.I.C.S.: 423620
Jack Doolittle (Pres)
Carla Frew (Office Mgr)

DOOLITTLE OIL CO. INC.

411 Broadway St, Webster City, IA
50595
Tel.: (515) 832-4318   IA

Web Site: https://www.doolittleoil.com
Year Founded: 1963
Sales Range: Less than $1 Million
Emp.: 12
Whslr of Petroleum Products
N.A.I.C.S.: 424720
John Doolittle (Pres & CEO)

DOOLITTLES RESTAURANTS

9201 E Bloomington Fwy Ste GG,
Bloomington, MN 55420
Tel.: (952) 944-6070
Web Site:
    http://www.doolittlesrestaurants.com
Sales Range: $10-24.9 Million
Emp.: 500
Eating Place
N.A.I.C.S.: 722511
Lynn Reimer (Owner & CFO)
John Sheehan (Owner & COO)
Melanie Brudos (Dir-Bus Dev, Mktg &
Trng)
Steve Schroeder (Reg Mgr)
Darin Deboer (Reg Mgr)

DOONAN SPECIALIZED TRAILER, LLC

36 NE Hwy 156 Bldg B, Great Bend,
KS 67530-1988
Tel.: (620) 792-6222   KS
Web Site: https://www.doonan.com
Year Founded: 1973
New & Used Commercial Trucks &
Trailers for Trucks Distr
N.A.I.C.S.: 336212
Michael Gordy (Co-Mgr-Ops)
Elgen Reynolds (Co-Mgr-Fin)
Tom OBrien (Mgr-Plant)
Natalie Towns (Mgr-Office)

DOONAN TRUCK & EQUIPMENT OF WICHITA, INC.

11118 W Kellogg St, Wichita, KS
67209-1229
Tel.: (316) 722-6034
Web Site:
    http://www.doonantruck.com
Year Founded: 1984
Sales Range: $75-99.9 Million
Emp.: 90
New Car Whslr
N.A.I.C.S.: 441110
Kenneth Doonan (Principal)
Shane Palmer (Gen Mgr)
Mike Speer (Mgr-Sls)

DOONEY & BOURKE, INC.

1 Regent St, Norwalk, CT 06855
Tel.: (203) 853-7515
Web Site: http://www.dooney.com
Year Founded: 1975
Sales Range: $400-449.9 Million
Emp.: 500
Handbags & Accessories Retailer &
Mfr
N.A.I.C.S.: 316990
Peter Dooney (Founder & CEO)

DOOR COMPONENTS, INC.

7980 Redwood Ave, Fontana, CA
92336
Tel.: (909) 770-5700
Web Site:
    http://www.doorcomponents.com
Year Founded: 1981
Sales Range: $10-24.9 Million
Emp.: 200
Metal Window & Door Mfr
N.A.I.C.S.: 332321
Bob Briggs (Pres)
Chuck Kiley (VP-Sls & Mktg)

DOOR COUNTY COOPERATIVE INC.

Door County Cooperative Inc.—(Continued)
317 Green Bay Rd, Sturgeon Bay, WI 54235
Tel.: (920) 743-6555
Web Site:
https://www.doorcountycoop.com
Sales Range: $10-24.9 Million
Emp.: 35
Feed
N.A.I.C.S.: 424910
Deanna Frame (CFO)

DOOR GALLERY MFG. INC.
81 Dimmig Rd, Upper Saddle River, NJ 07458-2204
Tel.: (201) 794-9050
Rev.: $4,000,000
Steel Doors & Window Products Mfr & Sales
N.A.I.C.S.: 332321
Andreas Parneros (Pres)

DOOR STORE FURNITURE
100 Enterprise Ave S, Secaucus, NJ 07094
Tel.: (201) 864-6669
Year Founded: 1951
Sales Range: $10-24.9 Million
Emp.: 110
Furniture Retailer
N.A.I.C.S.: 449110
Roberta Billington (VP)

DOOR TO DOOR ORGANICS INC.
282 Century Pl Ste 500, Lafayette, CO 80026
Tel.: (303) 297-3636
Web Site:
http://www.doortodoororganics.com
Year Founded: 1997
Sales Range: $25-49.9 Million
Emp.: 170
Online Grocery Shopping Services
N.A.I.C.S.: 423990
Greg Lems (CTO)
Jeff Ludwin (VP-Mdsg)
Michael Demko (CEO)
Stefan Pepe (Chm)
Scott DeGraeve (COO)

DOORBOT
1523 26th St, Santa Monica, CA 90404
Tel.: (800) 656-1918
Web Site: http://www.getdoorbot.com
Sales Range: $1-9.9 Million
Security Software
N.A.I.C.S.: 513210
James Siminoff (Founder)
Mark Dillon (CTO)
August Cziment (Dir-Ops)

DOORLINK MANUFACTURING, INC.
1501 Taney St, Kansas City, MO 64116
Tel.: (816) 474-3900
Web Site:
http://www.doorlinkmfg.com
Sales Range: $10-24.9 Million
Emp.: 90
Metal Window & Door Mfr
N.A.I.C.S.: 332321
Brad Belcher (Controller)
Tim Link (Owner)

DOORMATION, INC.
552 Central Dr Ste 102, Virginia Beach, VA 23454
Tel.: (757) 481-0888
Web Site: http://www.doormation.com
Year Founded: 2003
Rev.: $2,600,000
Emp.: 13

Automatic & Revolving Door Parts & Services
N.A.I.C.S.: 811210
David Giesen (CEO)
Robin Giesen (Pres)

DOORS INCORPORATED
300 SW 6th St, Des Moines, IA 50309
Tel.: (515) 288-8951
Web Site:
http://www.doorsinciowa.com
Sales Range: $10-24.9 Million
Emp.: 45
Commercial Doors
N.A.I.C.S.: 423310
Dave Dierking (Project Mgr)
Everett Kruger (Project Mgr)
Sandy Firestine (Mgr-Customer Svc)
Hannah Anderson (Project Mgr)
John L. J. Kennelley (Project Mgr)
Kyle Lemberg (Project Mgr)
Hance Throckmorton (Project Mgr)
Roland Kouski (Treas & Branch Mgr)
Paul Eliason (VP & Branch Mgr)
Jon Swanson (VP)

DOOSAN FUEL CELL CO LTD.
195 Governors Hwy, South Windsor, CT 06074-0739
Tel.: (860) 727-2200
Web Site:
http://www.doosanfuelcell.com
Sales Range: $125-149.9 Million
Emp.: 487
Fuel Cell Technologies Mfr
N.A.I.C.S.: 335910
Eric Strayer (VP-Sls & Bus Dev)
Sathya Motupally (COO)
Mark Layaw (Dir-Svc & Installation)
Howie Hooseok Che (CFO)
Sridhar Kanuri (VP-Res & Engrg)
Sookyung Yoo (Chm & CEO)

DOR-MAE INDUSTRIES
4001 Reading Crest Ave, Reading, PA 19605
Tel.: (610) 929-5003
Web Site: https://www.dormae.com
Year Founded: 1967
Sales Range: $10-24.9 Million
Emp.: 75
Machine Shop Operator
N.A.I.C.S.: 332710
Mitzi J. Reitnouer (Pres)
Pam Houck (VP-Acct Payable)

DORADO CORPORATION
1200 Park Pl St 400, San Mateo, CA 94403
Tel.: (650) 227-7300
Web Site: http://www.corelogic.com
Year Founded: 1998
Sales Range: $25-49.9 Million
Emp.: 250
Software Developer & Services to Streamline Loan Origination & Production
N.A.I.C.S.: 513210
Rob Carpenter (CTO)
Dain Ehring (Founder)
Dave Parker (VP-Bus Dev)
Landon V. Taylor (Sr VP-Bus Dev)

DORADO OIL COMPANY
9101 Up River Rd, Corpus Christi, TX 78409
Tel.: (361) 241-3200
Web Site: https://www.doradooil.com
Rev.: $20,000,000
Emp.: 15
Crude Petroleum Production
N.A.I.C.S.: 211120

DORAL BUICK, PONTIAC, GMC

8447 NW 12th St, Doral, FL 33126
Tel.: (305) 436-8400
Year Founded: 2007
Sales Range: $10-24.9 Million
Emp.: 38
New Car Whslr
N.A.I.C.S.: 441110
Richard J. Garber (Pres)
Eric Gasper (Principal)
Yamilka Yadira Socarras (Controller)

DORAL STEEL INC.
1500 Coining Dr, Toledo, OH 43612
Tel.: (419) 470-7070
Web Site: http://www.doralsteel.com
Year Founded: 1975
Sales Range: $10-24.9 Million
Emp.: 120
Steel Service Center
N.A.I.C.S.: 423510
Craig Robertson (Controller)

DORANCO, INC.
81 West St, Attleboro, MA 02703
Tel.: (508) 261-1200
Web Site: https://www.doranco.com
Sales Range: $10-24.9 Million
Emp.: 12
Mfr of Nameplates, Decorative Panels, Mounting Devices & Complete Product Assemblies
N.A.I.C.S.: 334310
David Doran (Pres)

DORCHESTER HOUSE MULTI-SERVICE CENTER
1353 Dorchester Ave, Dorchester, MA 02122
Tel.: (617) 288-3230
Web Site:
https://www.dorchesterhouse.org
Year Founded: 1970
Sales Range: $25-49.9 Million
Emp.: 389
Healtcare Services
N.A.I.C.S.: 622110
John Chambers (Pres)
Mary Irwin (Chief HR Officer)
Michelle Nadow (CEO)
Daniel MacNeil (CIO)
Huy Nguyen (Chief Medical Officer)

DORCHESTER PUBLISHING CO., INC.
200 Madison Ave Ste 2000, New York, NY 10016
Tel.: (212) 725-8811
Web Site:
http://www.dorchesterpub.com
Year Founded: 1971
Sales Range: $10-24.9 Million
Emp.: 50
Book Publishers
N.A.I.C.S.: 513130
John Predich (Pres)
Brooke Borneman (Dir-Sls & Mktg)
Fran Adrian (Dir-Art & Production)

DORCY INTERNATIONAL INC.
2700 Port Rd, Columbus, OH 43217-1136
Tel.: (614) 497-5830
Web Site: https://www.dorcy.com
Sales Range: $10-24.9 Million
Emp.: 50
Mfr & Distr of Flashlights, Lanterns & Batteries
N.A.I.C.S.: 423610
Kathy Verhoeven (VP-Finance-Administration)

Subsidiaries:

Dorcy International H.K LTD (1)
21/F Excel Centre 483A Castle Peak Road, Cheung Sha Wan, Kowloon, China (Hong Kong)

Tel.: (852) 2394 8281
Flashlight & Lantern Distr
N.A.I.C.S.: 423610

Dorcy Pacific Pty Ltd (1)
Unit 2 231 Holt Street, Eagle Farm, 4009, QLD, Australia
Tel.: (61) 7 3268 6506
Web Site: http://www.dorcy.com.au
Flashlight & Lantern Distr
N.A.I.C.S.: 423610

DORE & ASSOCIATES CONTRACTING, INC.
900 Harry S Truman Pkwy, Bay City, MI 48706
Tel.: (989) 684-8358
Web Site:
http://www.doreandassociates.com
Rev.: $10,918,755
Emp.: 134
Demolition, Buildings & Other Structures
N.A.I.C.S.: 238910
Arthur P. Dore (Pres & CEO)
Robert Hutchinson (Controller)
Ed Dore (Sec & VP-Ops)

DOREY ELECTRIC COMPANY
894 Widgeon Rd, Norfolk, VA 23513
Tel.: (757) 855-3381
Web Site:
http://www.doreyelectric.com
Sales Range: $10-24.9 Million
Emp.: 100
Provider of General Electrical Contracting Services
N.A.I.C.S.: 238210
Donald R. Dorey (Pres)
Mark Rosenstock (VP-Fin)
Deborah Lovitt (Office Mgr)
Heark Simpson (Corp VP)

DORFMAN-PACIFIC COMPANY
2615 Boeing Way, Stockton, CA 95206
Tel.: (209) 982-1400
Web Site: http://www.dorfman-pacific.com
Year Founded: 1921
Sales Range: $10-24.9 Million
Emp.: 150
Men's & Boys' Caps Mfr
N.A.I.C.S.: 424350
Scott S. Kent (VP-Accts)
Trudy Nielson (Asst Mgr-Customer Svc)
Elaine Pruneau (Dir-Art)
Jessica Rimington (Dir-Pur & Product Dev)
Bakul Patel (VP-Fin)
Steve Blankenship (VP-Ops)
Valerie Dawson (Mgr-HR)

DORIA ENTERPRISES INC.
1299 2nd Ave, New York, NY 10065
Tel.: (212) 737-0600
Web Site:
https://www.gracesmarketplace.com
Year Founded: 1985
Sales Range: $25-49.9 Million
Emp.: 160
Gourmet Food Stores
N.A.I.C.S.: 445298
Pina Doria Soares (Controller)
Louis Doria (Owner)
Maria Doria Pacheco (Co-Owner & Dir-Catering)
Dino Doria (Owner & Dir-Ops)
Giuseppe Cosenza (Gen Mgr)
Joseph Doria Jr. (Owner & Dir-Ops)

DORIAN DRAKE INTERNATIONAL, INC.
2 Gannett Dr Fl 4, White Plains, NY 10604-3403
Tel.: (914) 640-1531

Web Site:
http://www.doriandrake.com
Year Founded: 1947
Sales Range: $10-24.9 Million
Emp.: 45
Mfr of Industrial Machinery & Equipment
N.A.I.C.S.: 423830
Edward Dorian Jr. *(Pres)*

DORIGNAC'S FOOD CENTER INC.

710 Veterans Memorial Blv, Metairie, LA 70005
Tel.: (504) 837-4650
Web Site: http://www.dorignacs.com
Sales Range: $25-49.9 Million
Emp.: 190
Independent Supermarket
N.A.I.C.S.: 445110
Eddie Moreno *(Mgr-Store)*

DORILTON CAPITAL ADVISORS LLC

32 Ave of the Americas 26th Fl, New York, NY 10013
Tel.: (212) 929-0358   CT
Web Site:
http://www.doriltoncapital.com
Year Founded: 2009
Privater Equity Firm
N.A.I.C.S.: 523999
Michael Landerer *(Exec VP-Investment)*

Subsidiaries:

L-K Industries, Inc.   (1)
1999 Tellepsen St, Houston, TX 77023
Tel.: (713) 926-2623
Web Site: http://www.lk-ind.com
Portable Centrifuges & Sample Heaters Mfr
N.A.I.C.S.: 333998
Frank Ragan *(Mgr-Engrg)*
John Jordan *(Mgr-Production)*

Traditions Health, LLC   (1)
1862 Rock Prairie Rd Ste 201, College Station, TX 77845
Tel.: (979) 704-6547
Web Site: http://www.traditionshealth.com
Holding Company; Healthcare Services
N.A.I.C.S.: 551112
Bryan Wolfe *(Pres & CEO)*
Stuart Young *(COO)*
Chris Anderson *(Chief Compliance Officer)*
Duane Neel *(Pres-HealthCare ConsultLink)*
Russ Ridenhour *(Pres-Texas Div)*
Ronda Van Meter *(Pres-California Div)*
Crystal Mineo Diaz *(VP-HR)*
Ashley Pool *(Dir-Bus Intelligence)*
Chris Fitzgerald *(Dir-Fin)*
Alan Blakeney *(CFO)*

Subsidiary (Domestic):

Family First Hospice Inc.   (2)
15317 Paramount Blvd Ste 205, Paramount, CA 90723
Tel.: (562) 630-5300
Web Site: http://www.familyfirsthospice.net
Securities & Commodity Exchanges
N.A.I.C.S.: 523210

Hospice of America, Inc.   (2)
1N131 County Farm Rd, Winfield, IL 60190
Tel.: (630) 682-3871
Web Site:
http://www.harborlighthospice.com
Nursing Care Facilities
N.A.I.C.S.: 623110
Megan Ostrowski *(Dir-Mktg)*
Greg Thome *(CEO)*

Williams Grand Prix Engineering
Limited   (1)
Grove, Wantage, OX12 0DQ, Oxfordshire, United Kingdom
Tel.: (44) 12 3577 7700
Web Site: http://www.attwilliams.com
Emp.: 900
Race Cars Mfr
N.A.I.C.S.: 336999

DORMAN INDUSTRIES, LLC

40950 Woodward Ave, Bloomfield Hills, MI 48304
Tel.: (248) 723-3007
Sales Range: Less than $1 Million
Emp.: 2
Investment Holding Company
N.A.I.C.S.: 551112
Daniel J. Dorman *(Chm, Pres & CEO)*

DORNER MANUFACTURING CORP.

975 Cottonwood Ave, Hartland, WI 53029
Tel.: (262) 367-7600   WI
Web Site: http://www.dorner.com
Year Founded: 1965
Sales Range: $75-99.9 Million
Emp.: 150
Belt Conveyors Mfr
N.A.I.C.S.: 333922
Brian Baumgart *(CFO)*
Dan Nasato *(VP-Intl Ops)*
Enrico Berlenghi *(Mng Dir-Sls-Europe)*
Ben McGruder *(Dir-Customer Svc & Inside Sls)*

DORNERWORKS, LTD.

3445 Lake Eastbrook Blvd SE, Grand Rapids, MI 49546
Tel.: (616) 245-8369
Web Site:
http://www.dornerworks.com
Year Founded: 2000
Sales Range: $1-9.9 Million
Emp.: 40
Engineeering Services
N.A.I.C.S.: 541330
David K. Dorner *(Pres & CEO)*
Corrin Meyer *(Engr-Embedded Sys)*
Justin Jansen *(Engr-Embedded Electrical)*
Lance Hilbelink *(Dir-Quality Assurance)*
Bruce Wehr *(Engr-Embedded Software)*
Aaron Cornelius *(Engr-Software)*
Dan Rittersdorf *(Engr-Software)*
Steven H. Vanderleest *(COO)*

DORON PRECISION SYSTEMS, INC.

150 Corporate Dr, Binghamton, NY 13904
Tel.: (607) 772-1610   DE
Web Site:
https://www.doronprecision.com
Year Founded: 1973
Sales Range: $100-124.9 Million
Emp.: 50
Driving Simulation & Entertainment Simulation Systems
N.A.I.C.S.: 333310
Michael Stricek *(Sr VP)*

DOROTHY LANE MARKETS INC.

2710 Far Hills Ave, Dayton, OH 45419
Tel.: (937) 299-3561
Web Site:
https://www.dorothylane.com
Rev.: $45,531,938
Emp.: 700
Independent Supermarket
N.A.I.C.S.: 445110
Norman C. Mayne *(CEO)*
Kent Dimbath *(CFO)*
Deb Lackey *(Dir-Cooking)*

DOROTHY LEO INC.

5 S Main St, Englishtown, NJ 07726
Tel.: (732) 792-1010

Web Site:
http://www.nostalgiaoaknj.webs.com
Rev.: $13,757,882
Emp.: 5
Furniture Retailer
N.A.I.C.S.: 449110
Leo Deutsch *(Pres)*

DORSETT & JACKSON INC.

3800 Noakes St, Los Angeles, CA 90023
Tel.: (323) 268-1815
Web Site:
https://www.dorsettandjackson.com
Year Founded: 1973
Sales Range: $10-24.9 Million
Emp.: 35
Distr of Chemicals & Allied Products
N.A.I.C.S.: 424690
Paul E. Grubs *(Chm)*
Donald F. Witteman *(CFO)*
Romer Johnson *(COO & Exec VP)*
Tony Di Giacomo *(Pres)*

DORSETT BROS CONCRETE SUPPLY, INC.

3210 Lilac St, Pasadena, TX 77505
Tel.: (281) 487-0264
Web Site:
http://www.dorsettbrothers.com
Year Founded: 1977
Rev.: $60,000,000
Emp.: 200
Sand, Gravel & Stabilized Material Distr
N.A.I.C.S.: 327320
Bill Dorsett *(Pres)*

DORSEY & WHITNEY LLP

Ste 1500 50 S 6th St, Minneapolis, MN 55402-1498
Tel.: (612) 340-2600   MN
Web Site: http://www.dorsey.com
Year Founded: 1912
Emp.: 473
Legal Advisory Services
N.A.I.C.S.: 541110
Jonathan B. Abram *(Partner)*
Timothy B. Arends *(Partner)*
Shari L. J. Aberle *(Partner)*
Michael J. Ahern *(Chm-Legislative Practice Grp & Partner)*
C. Christopher Bercaw *(Partner)*
William J. Berens *(Partner)*
Theresa Bevilacqua *(Partner)*
Daniel J. Brown *(Partner)*
Elizabeth C. Buckingham *(Partner)*
Robert E. Cattanach *(Partner)*
Marilyn Clark *(Co-Partner)*
Lynnette Slater Crandall *(Co-Partner)*
Ross C. D'Emanuele *(Co-Partner)*
Adam V. Floyd *(Partner-Intellectual Property Litigation Grp-Denver)*
Nicholas A. J. Vlietstra *(Partner-Fin & Restructuring)*
Sarah Iannacone *(Partner)*
Jeffrey Cadwell *(Partner)*
Joel O'Malley *(Partner)*
Eric Rauch *(Partner)*
Jaime Stilson *(Partner)*
Alyson Van Dyk *(Partner)*
Betsy Parker *(Partner)*
Jeffrey M. Bauer *(Partner)*
Bob Seng *(Partner-Benefits & Compensation Grp)*
Joe Sevack *(Partner-Hong Kong)*
Elizabeth Deckman *(Partner-Benefits & Compensation Grp-Seattle)*
I. Daniel Colton *(Partner)*
J. Michael Keyes *(Head-Seattle)*
John R. Marti *(Partner-Govt Enforcement & Corp Investigations Practice Grp)*
Annette Jarvis *(VP-Comm)*
James Rubin *(Partner)*

Jill Ann Fleischer McLeod *(Partner-Corp Grp-Anchorage)*
Kate Demarest *(Partner-Comml Litigation-Anchorage)*
Monica Clark *(Partner-Fin & Restructuring)*
Clint Conner *(Partner-Intellectual Property Litigation)*
Meghan DesLauriers *(Partner-Healthcare Litigation)*
Beth Forsythe *(Partner-Govt Enforcement & Corp Investigation)*
Kirsten Schubert *(Partner-Comml Litigation)*
Nathaniel Longley *(Partner-Patent)*
Noel Spencer *(Partner-Mergers & Acq)*
Adam Jachimowski *(Partner-Fin & Restructuring-New York)*
Aaron Goldstein *(Partner-Labor & Employment-Seattle)*
Rabeha Kamaluddin *(Partner-Regulatory Affairs-Washington)*
Cam Hoang *(Partner-Corp Grp)*
Jenny Lee *(Partner-Trial Grp-Washington)*
Geoffrey Godfrey *(Partner)*
Christopher T. Shaheen *(Partner-Securities & Fin Svcs Litigation Practice Grp)*
B. Andrew Brown *(Partner)*
Gillian Brennan *(Dir-Client Rels)*
Kimberley Anderson *(Partner)*
Robert Rosenbaum *(Partner)*
Sandra Edelman *(Partner)*
Skip Durocher *(Partner)*
Steven Wells *(Partner)*
Marcus A. Mollison *(Partner-Real Estate & Land Use Practice Grp)*
Janet M. Weiss *(Partner-Fin & Restructuring Grp-New York)*
Laura Graf *(Partner-Real Estate & Land Use Practice Grp)*
David Meyer *(Partner)*
L. B. Guthrie *(Partner)*
Molly Sigel *(Dir-Legislative Affairs)*
Simon Chan *(Partner)*
Michael L. Weaver *(Partner-Corp Grp)*
Jay Riffkin *(Partner)*
Diana S. Parks *(Partner)*
Ronnie Stern *(Sr Atty)*
Bob Cordran *(Partner-London)*
Gina Betts *(Partner)*
Jamie Whatley *(Partner)*
Jason DuVall *(Partner)*
Stan Mayo *(Partner)*
Larry Makel *(Partner)*
Jay Kim *(Partner-Banking Industry Grp)*
Benjamin Machlis *(Partner-Regulatory Affairs Grp-Salt Lake City)*
Louisiana W. Cutler *(Partner-Trial Grp-Anchorage)*
Jeremy R. Larson *(Partner-Trial Grp-Seattle)*
Laura Kalesnik *(Partner-Corp Grp-Dallas)*
Robert Hale *(Partner)*
Steven Khadavi *(Partner)*
Michael J. McCarthy *(Partner-Real Estate & Land Use Practice Grp-New York)*
Mark Powell *(Partner-Tax, Trusts & Estates Grp-South California)*
G. Michael Gruber *(Partner-Trial Grp-Dallas)*
Martha F. Coultrap *(Partner-New York)*
Betty Carter Arkell *(Partner-Emerging Companies Grp-Denver)*
Matthew DeArman *(Partner)*
Walter Wu *(Partner-Patent Grp-Palo Alto)*

Dorsey & Whitney LLP—(Continued)

David B. Barlow *(Partner-Trial Grp & Govt Enforcement & Corp Investigations)*
William R. Stoeri *(Mng Partner)*
Sarah Zach *(Partner-Real Estate Grp)*
Jack Sullivan *(Partner)*
Mike Stinson *(Partner)*
Michael Rowe *(Partner-Trial Grp)*
Matthew Peckosh *(Partner)*
Lincoln Loehrke *(Partner-Trial Grp)*
Ben Kappelman *(Partner-Trial Grp)*
Jennifer Ede *(Partner-Tax, Trusts & Estates Grp)*
Robert Webber *(Chm-Immigration Practice Grp & Partner)*
Matthew Bromberg *(Partner-Corp Grp-New York)*
Mackenzie McNaughton *(Sr Atty-Nonprofit & Tax Exemption)*
Katherine Cheung *(Partner-Comml Litigation Grp-Hong Kong)*
Jennifer Coates *(Partner-Comml Litigation Practice Grp)*
Andrew Herr *(Partner-Fin & Restructuring Practice Grp)*
Marc Kushner *(Partner-Cross-Border M&A Grp)*
Michael Budabin *(Partner-Cross-Border M&A Grp)*
Joseph T. Lynyak III *(Partner-Fin & Restructuring Grp)*

DORT FINANCIAL CREDIT UNION
2845 Davison Rd, Flint, MI 48506
Tel.: (810) 767-8390
Web Site: https://www.dortonline.org
Sales Range: $1-9.9 Million
Emp.: 125
Credit Union
N.A.I.C.S.: 522130
Edward C. Sterling *(COO)*
Harry Awdish *(Chm & Chm)*
Wayne Natzke *(Treas & Treas)*
Bruce Allan *(Vice Chm & Vice Chm)*
Douglas Kidd *(Treas)*
Vicki Hawkins *(Pres & CEO)*

Subsidiaries:

Flagler Bank   (1)
1801 Forest Hill Blvd, West Palm Beach, FL 33406
Tel.: (561) 432-2122
Web Site: http://www.flaglerbankusa.com
Rev.: $7,645,000
Emp.: 41
Commericial Banking
N.A.I.C.S.: 522110
James A. Semrad *(Pres)*
David Lumbert *(VP & Branch Mgr)*
Brian McClung *(VP-Credit David Lumbert)*
Craig Crombie *(VP-Bus Dev)*
Janet Yohe *(VP & Branch Mgr)*
Jeannine Brouillet-Murphy *(VP & Officer-BSA)*
Sally Kirk *(VP-Ops)*

DORVIN LEIS COMPANY INC.
202 Lalo St, Kahului, HI 96732
Tel.: (808) 877-3902   CA
Web Site: https://www.leisinc.com
Year Founded: 1961
Mechanical Contractor
N.A.I.C.S.: 238220
Stephen T. Leis *(Pres & CEO)*
Richard Pennington *(Exec VP)*
Nancy Leis Overton *(VP)*
David Parke *(VP-Construction Ops)*
Ward Letvin *(CFO)*
Mandy Moikeha *(Ops Mgr-Maui)*
Jason Blinkhorn *(Mgr-Fire Protection Div)*
Sachin Shah *(Dir-Design Build Div)*
Wayne Yamabe *(Dir-Procurement)*
Byron Tanaka *(Mgr-Oahu Pipe Trades Div)*

DOS GRINGOS INC.
300 Burlington Rd, Saginaw, TX 76179-1304
Tel.: (817) 379-6619   TX
Year Founded: 1974
Sales Range: $25-49.9 Million
Emp.: 410
Restaurant
N.A.I.C.S.: 722511
Don Bowden *(Pres)*

Subsidiaries:

SRD Inc.   (1)
300 Burlington Rd, Saginaw, TX 76179-1304
Tel.: (817) 379-6523   (100%)
Sales Range: $10-24.9 Million
Emp.: 30
Provider of Management Consulting Services
N.A.I.C.S.: 541611

DOSAL CAPITAL, LLC
2894 NW 79th Ave, Doral, FL 33122
Tel.: (786) 641-5432   FL
Web Site:
   http://www.dosalcapital.com
Investment Holding Company
N.A.I.C.S.: 551112
Alberto Dosal *(Chm & CEO)*

Subsidiaries:

Blue Wave Communications, LLC   (1)
2898 NW 79th Ave, Doral, FL 33122
Tel.: (305) 436-8886
Web Site: http://www.bwcfla.com
Telecommunications Systems Network Design, Installation & Support Services
N.A.I.C.S.: 238210
Tim Orr *(Gen Mgr)*

Compuquip Technologies, LLC   (1)
8399 NW 30th Ter, Miami, FL 33122
Tel.: (305) 436-7272
Web Site: http://www.compuquip.com
Sales Range: $1-9.9 Million
Emp.: 50
Commercial Internet Security Services
N.A.I.C.S.: 541519
Alberto Dosal *(Chm)*
Bradford Reed *(Dir-Security Div)*
Eric Dosal *(Pres & CEO)*
Luis Santiago *(Dir-Security Svcs)*
Ivan Rezvoy *(Dir-Fin)*

DOSS, LTD.
112 N Main St, Weatherford, TX 76086-3241
Tel.: (817) 763-9999
Sales Range: $25-49.9 Million
Emp.: 500
Financial Holding Company
N.A.I.C.S.: 237210

Subsidiaries:

Texas Bank Holding Company   (1)
102 N Main St, Weatherford, TX 76086-3241
Tel.: (817) 594-8721
Sales Range: $100-124.9 Million
Emp.: 631
Bank Holding Companies
N.A.I.C.S.: 522110
Frank D. Heuszel *(CEO)*

Subsidiary (Domestic):

Texas Bank   (2)
102 N Main St, Weatherford, TX 76086-3241
Tel.: (817) 560-6400   (100%)
Web Site: http://www.texasbank.com
Rev.: $12,308,000
Emp.: 110
State Commercial Banks
N.A.I.C.S.: 522110

DOSSETT PONTIAC CADILLAC GMC
1058 W Pine St, Hattiesburg, MS 39401

Tel.: (601) 544-7700
Sales Range: $50-74.9 Million
Emp.: 41
Car Dealership
N.A.I.C.S.: 441110
Danny E. Dossett *(Pres)*

DOSTER CONSTRUCTION COMPANY INC.
2100 International Park Dr, Birmingham, AL 35243
Tel.: (205) 443-3800   AL
Web Site:
   http://www.dosterconstruction.com
Year Founded: 1969
Sales Range: $25-49.9 Million
Emp.: 200
Provider of Nonresidential Construction Services
N.A.I.C.S.: 236220
Walton C. Doster *(Pres)*
Ed Smith *(VP & Mgr-Nashville)*
Bob Hardin *(Dir-Preconstruction Svcs)*
Chris Overstreet *(VP & Dir-Client Svcs)*
Elizabeth Goodwin *(Mgr-Bus Dev)*
Stephen Yeatman *(Sr Project Mgr)*
Mitchell Jones *(Sr Project Mgr)*
Denise Owen *(Controller)*
Tom Boyle *(VP & Mgr-Nashville Div)*
Alan Chandler *(Sr VP-Bus Dev)*
Allan Dedman *(COO)*
Jon Elsea *(CFO)*
Tom Reynolds *(Pres-Multifamily Construction)*
Cobey Everett *(VP-Field Ops)*
Michael Booth *(VP & Dir-Client Svcs)*
Dan Wilson *(VP)*
Joe Wall *(Project Dir-Nashville)*
Chance Mitchell *(Mgr-Preconstruction)*

DOSTER WAREHOUSE INC.
933 Ashley St, Rochelle, GA 31079
Tel.: (229) 365-2469
Rev.: $34,325,364
Emp.: 31
Peanuts (Bulk), Unroasted
N.A.I.C.S.: 424590
Jack T. Chastain *(Pres)*

DOT FAMILY HOLDINGS LLC
17050 Baxter Rd, Saint Louis, MO 63005
Tel.: (636) 449-3157
Web Site:
   http://www.dotfamilyholdings.com
Holding Company
N.A.I.C.S.: 551112
John Tracy *(Chm)*

Subsidiaries:

Omni Cable, LLC   (1)
2 Hagerty Blvd, West Chester, PA 19382-7594
Tel.: (610) 701-0100
Web Site: http://www.omnicable.com
Sales Range: $10-24.9 Million
Emp.: 107
Supplier of Electrical & Electronic Cables
N.A.I.C.S.: 423610
Jeff Siegfried *(Chm)*
Cindy Marshall *(Mgr-Acct)*
Jeanine Bilotta *(Dir-IT)*
Adam Biggs *(Mgr-Charlotte)*
Emmett Mauer *(Acct Mgr)*
Darrin Hervieux *(VP-Ops)*
Steve Glinski *(CFO)*
Ryan Bruni *(Mgr-Accts-Natl)*
John Dean *(Dir-Mktg & ECommerce)*
Gregory J. Lampert *(Pres & CEO)*
Brad Cook *(Mgr-Tampa)*
Jim Alton *(Mgr-Los Angeles)*
Greg Donato *(COO)*
Ashley Eckard *(Dir-HR)*
Tony Aimi *(Mgr-Northwest & North California)*
Allen Henry *(VP-West)*

Chip Barrett *(Dir-Bus Dev)*
Bryan Dabruzzi *(VP-East)*
Bell Tran *(Sls Mgr-Seattle)*
Jimmy Moreno *(Dir-Distr)*
Chris Bjorkman *(VP-Central)*
Brittany Guyton *(Mgr-Los Angeles)*
Victor Lewis *(VP-Boston)*
Todd Sweeney *(VP-Bus Dev)*

Subsidiary (Domestic):

Houston Wire & Cable Company   (2)
10201 N Loop E, Houston, TX 77029
Tel.: (713) 609-2100
Web Site: http://www.houwire.com
Rev.: $286,017,000
Assets: $157,712,000
Liabilities: $65,818,000
Net Worth: $91,894,000
Earnings: ($12,582,000)
Emp.: 338
Fiscal Year-end: 12/31/2020
Specialty Wire & Cable Distr
N.A.I.C.S.: 423610
Jerry Zurovchak *(COO & Sr VP)*

Subsidiary (Domestic):

Haynes Wire Rope, Inc.   (3)
1355 Sheffield Blvd, Houston, TX 77015
Tel.: (713) 453-7822
Web Site: http://www.hayneswirerope.com
Rev.: $2,100,000
Emp.: 7
Wire Rope Installation Services
N.A.I.C.S.: 213112

PFI, LLC   (3)
4847 Park 370 Blvd, Hazelwood, MO 63042
Tel.: (314) 310-1345
Web Site: http://www.pfinnovation.com
Emp.: 200
Industrial Fasteners Distr
N.A.I.C.S.: 423840
John Charles Pope *(Chm & CEO)*
Mark Klosek *(Exec VP)*

Southwest Synthetic Systems, Inc.   (3)
1357 Sheffield Blvd, Houston, TX 77015
Tel.: (713) 451-9341
Web Site: http://www.swssi.com
Rev.: $3,300,000
Emp.: 25
Nylon Sling Mfr
N.A.I.C.S.: 314994

Southwest Wire Rope, L.P.   (3)
1902 Federal Rd, Houston, TX 77015
Tel.: (713) 453-8518
Web Site:
   http://www.southwestwirerope.com
Rev.: $50,000,000
Emp.: 45
Wire Rope & Rigging Product Mfr
N.A.I.C.S.: 332618

DOT FOODS, INC.
1 Dot Way, Mount Sterling, IL 62353
Tel.: (217) 773-4411   IL
Web Site: https://www.dotfoods.com
Year Founded: 1960
Sales Range: $1-4.9 Billion
Emp.: 6,300
General Warehousing & Storage
N.A.I.C.S.: 493110
Joe Tracy *(CEO)*
John Tracy *(Chm)*
Dick Tracy *(Pres)*
George Eversman *(Exec VP-Retail & Bus Dev)*
Matt Holt *(VP-HR)*
Anita Montgomery *(CFO)*
Jeff Grever *(VP-Corp Accts)*
Bryan Langston *(VP-Warehousing)*
Ryan P. Jacobsen *(Dir-Grocery Sls)*
Mandi Clark *(Dir-Customer Svc & Dev)*
Devin Fogleman *(Dir-Convenience, Drug & Mass)*

Subsidiaries:

Dot Transportation, Inc.   (1)
1 Dot Way, Mount Sterling, IL 62353
Tel.: (217) 773-3922
Web Site: http://www.dotfoods.com

Truck Fleet Management, Servicing & Logistics Services
N.A.I.C.S.: 541614
Joe Tracy (Pres)

edotfoods, Inc. (1)
17050 Baxter Rd, Chesterfield, MO 63005
Tel.: (636) 537-4002
Web Site: http://www.dotfoods.com
Sales Range: $10-24.9 Million
Emp.: 75
Program Development & Information Technology Services
N.A.I.C.S.: 541519
Joe Tracy (Pres & COO)
Mark Read (VP-IT)

DOT PRINTER, INC.
2424 Mcgaw Ave, Irvine, CA 92614-5834
Tel.: (949) 474-1100   CA
Web Site: http://www.dotprinter.com
Year Founded: 1980
Sales Range: $350-399.9 Million
Emp.: 200
Provider of Lithographic Printing Services
N.A.I.C.S.: 323111
Bruce M. Carson (Pres)
Jim Voss (CFO & Controller)

DOTCMS INC.
3250 Mary St Ste 405, Miami, FL 33133
Tel.: (305) 900-2001
Web Site: http://www.dotcms.com
Year Founded: 2003
Sales Range: $1-9.9 Million
Content Management Software
N.A.I.C.S.: 513210
Will Ezell (CTO)
Timothy Brigham (Chief Revenue Officer)
Ralph Miller (CEO)
Stefan Schinkel (Chief Sls Officer)
Robert Slaughter (cmo)

DOTHAN CHRYSLER DODGE JEEP RAM
4074 Ross Clark Cir, Dothan, AL 36303-5724
Tel.: (334) 500-3861
Web Site: https://www.dothanchrysler.net
Sales Range: $10-24.9 Million
Emp.: 38
Car Whslr
N.A.I.C.S.: 441110
Ted Milanowski (Gen Mgr)

DOTHAN GLASS CO. INC.
655 S Oates St, Dothan, AL 36302-1308
Tel.: (334) 793-1161
Web Site: https://www.pensacolaglass.com
Year Founded: 1931
Sales Range: $25-49.9 Million
Emp.: 150
Glazing Services
N.A.I.C.S.: 238150
Earl Pitman Jr. (Pres)

Subsidiaries:

City Glass Company (1)
16 S W Hollywood Blvd, Fort Walton Beach, FL 32548
Tel.: (850) 243-8167
Web Site: http://www.cityglassco.com
Emp.: 23
Glass Product Distr
N.A.I.C.S.: 444180
Aaron Fogarty (Project Mgr)

Dougherty Glass Company (1)
219 Cedric St, Leesburg, GA 31763
Tel.: (229) 435-8579
Web Site: http://www.doughertyglass.com
Emp.: 30
Glass Product Distr

N.A.I.C.S.: 423220
Jimmy Murphy (Mgr)
Darren King (Mgr-Contract Dept)

Pensacola Glass Company (1)
3901 N Palafox St, Pensacola, FL 32505
Tel.: (850) 433-8348
Web Site: http://www.pensacolaglass.com
Sales Range: $10-24.9 Million
Emp.: 85
Auto & Flat Glass Mfr
N.A.I.C.S.: 327211
Woody Watters (Gen Mgr)

DOTHAN SECURITY INC.
600 W Adams St, Dothan, AL 36302
Tel.: (334) 793-5720
Web Site: https://www.dsisecurity.com
Emp.: 3,000
Security Guard Services
N.A.I.C.S.: 561612
Alan B. Clark (Founder & Pres)
Eddie Sorrells (COO & Gen Counsel)
Tony Earnest (Reg Mgr)

DOTPHOTO, INC.
860 Lower Ferry Rd, West Trenton, NJ 08628
Tel.: (609) 643-0090   NJ
Web Site: http://www.dotphoto.com
Year Founded: 1999
Sales Range: $75-99.9 Million
Emp.: 25
Photo Printing & Image & Sound Archiving Services on the Internet
N.A.I.C.S.: 541511
Lisa Jaffee (Dir-Press)
Tom Juhamo (CFO)

DOTSTER, INC.
PO Box 821066, Vancouver, WA 98682
Tel.: (360) 449-5800
Web Site: http://www.dotster.com
Year Founded: 1999
Sales Range: $10-24.9 Million
Emp.: 500
Domain Registration, Web Hosting & Other Computer Related Services
N.A.I.C.S.: 518210
Clint Page (CEO)

DOTTED LINE COMMUNICATIONS
268 W 84th 4A, New York, NY 10024
Tel.: (646) 596-7502
Web Site: http://www.dottedlinecomm.com
Emp.: 100
Public Relations
N.A.I.C.S.: 541820
Aimee Yoon (Mng Partner)
Darcy Cobb (Founder & Mng Partner)

Subsidiaries:

Dotted Line Communications (1)
1047 Moraga Dr, Los Angeles, CA 90049-1620
Tel.: (310) 472-8600
Web Site: http://www.dottedlinecomm.com
Public Relations & Brand Strategy
N.A.I.C.S.: 541820
Darcy Cobb (Co-Founder & Mng Partner)
Aimee Yoon (Co-Founder & Mng Partner)

DOUBLE 8 FOODS INC.
2201 E 46th St, Indianapolis, IN 46205
Tel.: (317) 253-3417   IN
Web Site: http://www.double8foods.com
Year Founded: 1957
Sales Range: $10-24.9 Million
Emp.: 100
Provider of Independent Grocery Stores
N.A.I.C.S.: 445110

Isaiah Kuperstein (Pres & CEO)
Elana Kuperstein (VP)

DOUBLE A TRAILER SALES INC.
1750 E 5th St, Delphos, OH 45833
Tel.: (419) 692-7626   OH
Web Site: http://www.doubleatrailer.com
Year Founded: 1965
Sales Range: $10-24.9 Million
Emp.: 35
Sales of Trailers
N.A.I.C.S.: 423830
Mark A. Wannemacher (Chm & CEO)
Kendra Stout (Office Mgr)

DOUBLE AA BUILDERS, LTD.
6040 E Thomas Rd, Scottsdale, AZ 85251-7508
Tel.: (480) 994-0400   AZ
Web Site: https://www.doubleaabuilders.com
Year Founded: 1989
Sales Range: $75-99.9 Million
Emp.: 26
General Contracting Services
N.A.I.C.S.: 236220
Geoffrey E. Schwan (Pres)
David G. Pena (VP)
Joseph P. Schwan (Dir-Mktg)

DOUBLE BARREL ENVIRONMENTAL SERVICES INCORPORATED
121 Main St, Riverside, CA 92501
Tel.: (951) 683-6994
Web Site: http://www.doublebarrelenvironmental.com
Year Founded: 2006
Sales Range: $1-9.9 Million
Emp.: 50
Environmental Services Specializing in HAZMAT & Disaster Response, Hazardous Waste Management, Transportation, Remediation, Decontamination & Industrial Cleaning
N.A.I.C.S.: 562211
Erik Ricardo (Pres & Gen Mgr)
Michelle Ricardo (VP-HR)
Jon Toten (Mgr-Ops)

DOUBLE CHECK CO. INC.
4000 Raytown Rd, Kansas City, MO 64129
Tel.: (816) 921-5032
Web Site: https://www.dblchk.com
Rev.: $19,500,000
Emp.: 100
Service Station Equipment Installation, Maintenance & Repair
N.A.I.C.S.: 238990
Phillip Farrell (Pres)
Scott Cross (CFO)

DOUBLE CHEESE CORPORATION
4810 Hardware Dr NE, Albuquerque, NM 87109
Tel.: (505) 883-5285
Web Site: http://www.doublecheese.com
Sales Range: $10-24.9 Million
Emp.: 900
Fast-Food Restaurant, Chain
N.A.I.C.S.: 722513
Tim W. Hogsett (Pres)
Roseann Houlihan (Controller)

DOUBLE CROWN RESOURCES INC.
10120 S Eastern Ave Ste 200, Henderson, NV 89052
Tel.: (707) 961-6016   NV

Web Site: http://www.doublecrownresources.com
Year Founded: 2006
Sales Range: Less than $1 Million
Gold, Other Metal, Oil & Gas Exploration
N.A.I.C.S.: 212220
Jerold S. Drew (Co-Chm, Pres & CEO)
Tricia Oakley (Treas, Sec & Dir-Corp Admin)
Allen E. Lopez (Pres)

DOUBLE DELAWARE INC.
5495 Belt Line Rd Ste 200, Dallas, TX 75254
Tel.: (214) 706-9801   TX
Web Site: https://www.ddresorts.com
Year Founded: 1997
Sales Range: $50-74.9 Million
Emp.: 800
Developer of Real Estate
N.A.I.C.S.: 237210
Mike Ward (Pres)

Subsidiaries:

Double Diamond Companies (1)
5495 Belt Line Rd Ste 200, Dallas, TX 75254
Tel.: (214) 706-9800
Web Site: http://www.ddresorts.com
Sales Range: $10-24.9 Million
Emp.: 50
Developer of Real Estate
N.A.I.C.S.: 237210
Fran Pfeifle (Dir-HR)
Randy Gracy (Sr VP)
Jonathan Hawkins (Assoc Gen Counsel)

DOUBLE DIAMOND DELAWARE INC.
1105 N Market St Ste 1140, Wilmington, DE 19801
Tel.: (302) 427-0386
Web Site: http://www.4cablex.com
Rev.: $60,200,000
Emp.: 2
Jewelry Stores
N.A.I.C.S.: 458310

DOUBLE DOWN HOLDINGS INC.
1135 Terminal Way Ste 209, Reno, NV 89502
Tel.: (775) 352-3936   NV
Web Site: http://www.ticketcorp.com
Year Founded: 2013
Rev.: $11,700
Assets: $247,050
Liabilities: $248,048
Net Worth: ($998)
Earnings: ($132,978)
Emp.: 2
Fiscal Year-end: 12/31/19
Internet Ticket Retailer
N.A.I.C.S.: 722511
Russell Rheingrover (Founder, Chm, Pres, CEO & Sec)
Kristi Ann Nelson (CFO, Principal Acctg Officer & Treas)

DOUBLE L GROUP LTD.
2020 Beltline Rd, Dyersville, IA 52040-0324
Tel.: (563) 875-6257
Web Site: https://www.doublel.com
Sales Range: $10-24.9 Million
Emp.: 25
Farm Equipment
N.A.I.C.S.: 333111
Norbert Borcherding (Pres)
Donna Borcherding (VP)

DOUBLE LINE, INC.
1817 W Braker Ln Ste 100, Austin, TX 78758
Tel.: (512) 646-4929

Double Line, Inc.—(Continued)

Web Site:
http://www.wearedoubleline.com
Year Founded: 2009
Sales Range: $1-9.9 Million
Emp.: 99
Business Management Consulting
Services
N.A.I.C.S.: 541611
Brady Rathgeber *(Sr Project Mgr)*

DOUBLE P CORPORATION
5724 N Pulaski Rd, Chicago, IL
60646
Tel.: (773) 539-0500
Sales Range: $10-24.9 Million
Emp.: 500
Selling or Licensing of Franchises
N.A.I.C.S.: 533110
Phillip J. Patinkin *(Pres)*
Daisy Ramos *(Controller)*
Scott Rubin *(VP)*

DOUBLE R BRAND FOODS LLC.
1500 Oliver St, Houston, TX 77007
Tel.: (281) 342-3749
Web Site:
http://www.holmessmokehouse.com
Year Founded: 1970
Sales Range: $10-24.9 Million
Emp.: 105
Prepared Meat Mfr & Distr
N.A.I.C.S.: 311612
Debbie Frewin *(Dir-Houston Ops)*
Stewart E. Rosenthal *(CFO)*

DOUBLE-COLA CO.-USA
537 Market St Ste 100, Chattanooga,
TN 37402-1229
Tel.: (423) 267-5691   GA
Web Site: http://www.double-
cola.com
Year Founded: 1927
Sales Range: $75-99.9 Million
Emp.: 20
Soft Drinks Mfr
N.A.I.C.S.: 311930
Alnoor Dhanani *(Pres & CEO)*
Gina Dhanani *(COO)*
Keely Anderson *(Mktg Dir)*
Wesley Steele *(Sls Mgr)*

DOUBLE-TEAM BUSINESS PLANS LLC
1725 Ocean Ave Unit 115, Santa
Monica, CA 90404-2791
Tel.: (310) 839-4300
Web Site: http://www.double-team-
bp.com
Marketing Consulting Services
N.A.I.C.S.: 541613
Doug R. Hedlund *(Mng Dir)*

DOUBLELINE CAPITAL LP
333 S Grand Ave 18th Fl, Los Ange-
les, CA 90071
Tel.: (213) 633-8200   DE
Web Site: http://www.doubleline.com
Rev.: $148,000,000,000
Emp.: 269
Investment Management & Advisory
Services
N.A.I.C.S.: 523940
Ronald Robert Redell *(Pres-
DoubleLine Gp)*
Jeffrey Gundlach *(Founder & CEO)*
Henry Chase *(CFO & Controller)*
Casey Moore *(CTO)*
Youse Guia *(Chief Compliance Offi-
cer)*
Jeffrey Sherman *(Deputy Chief In-
vestment Officer)*
Earl Lariscy *(Gen Counsel)*
Leticia Acosta *(Dir-HR)*

Patrick Townzen *(Dir-Ops)*
Barbara VanEvery *(Dir-Investor Svcs)*
Cris Santa Ana III *(Chief Risk Officer)*

Subsidiaries:

DoubleLine Group LP   (1)
333 S Grand Ave Ste 1800, Los Angeles,
CA 90071
Tel.: (213) 633-8200
Investment Management Service
N.A.I.C.S.: 523940
Ronald Robert Redell *(Pres)*
Louis Charles Lucido *(Co-Founder & COO)*

DoubleLine Income Solutions
Fund   (1)
333 S Grand Ave Ste 1800, Los Angeles,
CA 90071
Tel.: (213) 633-8200
Web Site: http://doubleline.com
Sales Range: $200-249.9 Million
Open-Ended Investment Fund
N.A.I.C.S.: 525990
Ronald Robert Redell *(Chm, Pres & CEO)*

DoubleLine Opportunistic Credit
Fund   (1)
333 S Grand Ave 18th Fl, Los Angeles, CA
90071
Tel.: (213) 633-8200
Web Site: http://www.doublelinefunds.com
Sales Range: $25-49.9 Million
Open-Ended Investment Fund
N.A.I.C.S.: 525990
Ronald Robert Redell *(Chm, Pres & CEO)*
Earl A. Lariscy *(VP & Asst Sec)*
Jeffrey J. Sherman *(VP)*
Grace Walker *(Asst Treas)*
David James Kennedy *(VP)*
Patrick A. Townzen *(VP)*
Ken Shinoda *(Portfolio Mgr)*
Andrew Hsu *(Portfolio Mgr)*
Cris Santa Ana III *(VP)*

DOUCETTE HOMES, INC.
3044 N Alvernon Way, Tucson, AZ
85712
Tel.: (520) 622-7373
Web Site: https://doucettehomes.com
Sales Range: $10-24.9 Million
Emp.: 25
Land Subdividing Services
N.A.I.C.S.: 237210
Sheryl A. Doucette *(Principal)*
Thomas L. Doucette *(Founder)*
Brigid Murphy *(Principal)*
Jeffrey Singleton *(Principal)*

DOUG ASHY BUILDING MATE-RIALS INC.
4950 Johnston St, Lafayette, LA
70503-4801
Tel.: (337) 984-2110
Web Site: https://www.dougashy.com
Year Founded: 1960
Sales Range: $50-74.9 Million
Emp.: 200
Lumber, Plywood & Millwork Whslr
N.A.I.C.S.: 423310
Steve Buller *(Mgr-Store)*
Scott Major *(Mgr-Store)*

Subsidiaries:

Doug Ashy Building Materials of
Rayne Inc.   (1)
302 E Texas Ave, Rayne, LA 70578-6433
Tel.: (337) 334-7567
Web Site: http://www.dougashy.com
Sales Range: $10-24.9 Million
Emp.: 40
Lumber, Plywood & Millwork
N.A.I.C.S.: 423310
Doug Ashy *(CEO)*

Doug Ashy Building Materials of Ville
Platte Inc.   (1)
719 Dardo St Parkview Plz, Ville Platte, LA
70586
Tel.: (337) 363-2106
Web Site: http://www.dougashy.com
Sales Range: $10-24.9 Million
Emp.: 26
Lumber & Other Building Materials

N.A.I.C.S.: 423310

DOUG HENRY BUICK GMC, INC.
709 US Hwy 70 E Bypass, Golds-
boro, NC 27534
Tel.: (919) 648-1280
Car Whslr
N.A.I.C.S.: 441110
Bill Welles *(Gen Mgr)*
Jim Carr *(Gen Sls Mgr)*
Jimmy Summer *(Mgr-Inventory)*
Mike Amos *(Mgr-Sls)*
Caitlin Opp *(Mgr-BDC)*
Nick Burroughs *(Dir-Fixed Ops)*
Steve Hawkins *(Mgr-Parts)*
Bhobie Belmonte *(Fin Dir)*
Mike Taylor *(Mgr-Bodyshop)*

DOUG HENRY CHEVROLET INC.
809 W Wilson St, Tarboro, NC
27886-4817
Tel.: (252) 823-3145
Year Founded: 1999
Sales Range: $10-24.9 Million
Emp.: 25
Car Whslr
N.A.I.C.S.: 441110
Douglas Henry *(Owner)*

DOUG HOLLYHAND CON-STRUCTION CO.
527 Main Ave, Northport, AL 35476
Tel.: (205) 345-0955
Web Site: https://www.hollyhand.com
Sales Range: $10-24.9 Million
Emp.: 40
Provider of Commercial & Office
Building Construction Services
N.A.I.C.S.: 236220
Douglas P. Hollyhand *(VP)*

DOUG RILEY ENTERPRISES INC.
444 Regency Pkwy Dr # 306,
Omaha, NE 68114
Tel.: (402) 390-0853
Rev.: $15,000,000
Emp.: 3
Labels & Seals; Printing Services
N.A.I.C.S.: 541611
Doug Riley *(Pres & CEO)*

DOUG VEERKAMP GENERAL ENGINEERING, INC.
2585 Cold Springs Rd, Placerville,
CA 95667
Tel.: (530) 676-0825
Web Site:
https://www.dougveerkamp.com
Year Founded: 1983
Emp.: 112
Engineeering Services
N.A.I.C.S.: 541330
Matt Veerkamp *(VP)*

DOUGHERTY EQUIPMENT CO. INC.
2202 Soabar St, Greensboro, NC
27406-4517
Tel.: (336) 389-1290   NC
Web Site:
http://www.doughertyequipment.com
Year Founded: 1984
Sales Range: $125-149.9 Million
Emp.: 370
Mfr of Industrial Machinery & Equip-
ment
N.A.I.C.S.: 423830
Michael Emmett Dougherty *(Pres)*
Chris Morrow *(Branch Mgr)*

DOUGHERTY FINANCIAL GROUP LLC

90 South 7th St Ste 4300, Minneapo-
lis, MN 55402-4105
Tel.: (612) 376-4000
Web Site:
http://www.doughertymarkets.com
Year Founded: 1977
Rev.: $50,000,000
Emp.: 150
Investment Bankers
N.A.I.C.S.: 523150
Michael Emmett Dougherty *(Chm)*
Bill Dougherty *(Owner & Principal)*
Michael Sandberg *(Sr Mgr-Tax Dept)*

DOUGHERTY'S PHARMACY, INC.
5924 Royal Lane Ste 250, Dallas, TX
75230
Tel.: (972) 250-0945   DE
Web Site:
http://irdoughertys.irpass.com
Year Founded: 2000
Rev.: $36,051,000
Assets: $8,462,000
Liabilities: $10,364,000
Net Worth: ($1,902,000)
Earnings: ($3,528,000)
Emp.: 75
Fiscal Year-end: 12/31/18
Investment Services
N.A.I.C.S.: 523999
Stewart I. Edington *(Pres, CEO &
CFO-Interim)*

Subsidiaries:

Dougherty's Holdings, Inc.   (1)
16250 Dallas Pkwy Ste 111, Dallas, TX
75248-2622
Tel.: (972) 860-0200
Web Site:
http://www.doughertysholdings.com
Sales Range: $25-49.9 Million
Emp.: 238
Pharmacy Operator
N.A.I.C.S.: 456110
Elsie Ulate *(Mgr-Accts Payable)*
Mark Heil *(Pres & CFO)*

Subsidiary (Domestic):

Dougherty's Pharmacy, Inc.   (2)
16250 Dallas Pkwy Ste 111, Dallas, TX
75248-2622
Tel.: (972) 860-0200
Web Site: http://www.doughertys.com
Pharmacy Operator
N.A.I.C.S.: 456110
Stewart Edington *(Pres, CEO & Interim
CFO)*
James C. Leslie *(Chm)*

McCrory's Pharmacy, Inc.   (2)
6151 Dew Dr Ste 100, El Paso, TX 79912
Tel.: (915) 581-9655
Web Site:
http://www.mccroryspharmacy.com
Sales Range: $1-9.9 Million
Emp.: 15
Pharmacies & Drug Stores
N.A.I.C.S.: 456110
Andy Dougherty *(Pres)*

DOUGLAS COMPANIES INC.
2507 E 9th St, Texarkana, AR 71854
Tel.: (870) 773-3633
Web Site:
http://www.douglascompanies.com
Rev.: $76,100,000
Emp.: 110
Tobacco & Tobacco Products
N.A.I.C.S.: 424940
Steve Douglas *(Pres)*

Subsidiaries:

Douglas Tobacco Products Co.   (1)
2507 E 9th St, Texarkana, AR 71854
Tel.: (870) 773-3633
Rev.: $14,900,000
Emp.: 32
Tobacco & Tobacco Products
N.A.I.C.S.: 424940

DOUGLAS CORPORATION
9650 Vly View Rd, Eden Prairie, MN 55344
Tel.: (952) 941-2944
Web Site:
http://www.douglascorp.com
Rev.: $59,400,000
Emp.: 588
Plastic Moldings Mfr
N.A.I.C.S.: 326199
John Ponozzo *(Mgr-Customer Svc-Urethane)*
Steve Montbriand *(Dir-Acctg)*
Mike Buchanan *(Mgr-Ops)*

DOUGLAS COUNTY FARMERS COOP
3171 NE Stephens St, Roseburg, OR 97470
Tel.: (541) 673-0601
Web Site:
https://www.douglascountyfar
merscoop.com
Sales Range: $10-24.9 Million
Emp.: 48
Retail Nurseries & Garden Stores
N.A.I.C.S.: 444240
Melvin Burk *(Gen Mgr)*
Kent Little *(Office Mgr)*

DOUGLAS COUNTY INSUR-ANCE SERVICES
4348 Woodlands Blvd Ste 229, Castle Rock, CO 80104
Tel.: (303) 688-9597
Web Site: https://www.cowest.com
Sales Range: $25-49.9 Million
Emp.: 13
Insurance Agents
N.A.I.C.S.: 524210
Laurie Lewis *(Pres)*

DOUGLAS ELECTRIC COOP-ERATIVE, INC.
1981 NE Stephens St, Roseburg, OR 97470
Tel.: (541) 673-6616   OR
Web Site:
http://www.douglaselectric.com
Year Founded: 1939
Sales Range: $10-24.9 Million
Emp.: 42
Electric Power Distr
N.A.I.C.S.: 221122
Shirley Cairns *(Sec)*
Dick McHaffie *(Treas)*
Robert Poage *(VP)*

DOUGLAS GARDENS COM-MUNITY MENTAL HEALTH CENTER OF MIAMI BEACH
1680 Meridian Ave Ste 501, Miami Beach, FL 33139
Tel.: (305) 531-5341   FL
Web Site: http://www.dgcmhc.org
Year Founded: 1978
Sales Range: $10-24.9 Million
Emp.: 117
Mental Health Care Services
N.A.I.C.S.: 623220
Daniel Brady *(Exec Dir)*
Eleanor Lanser *(Dir-Facility)*

DOUGLAS LABORATORIES
600 Boyce Rd, Pittsburgh, PA 15205
Tel.: (412) 494-0122
Web Site:
https://www.douglaslabs.com
Year Founded: 1955
Rev.: $31,100,000
Emp.: 200
Pharmaceutical Preparation Services
N.A.I.C.S.: 325412

Samuel L. Lioon *(Founder)*
Jeffery D. Lioon *(Pres)*
L. Douglas Lioon *(CEO)*
Naeem Shaikh *(VP-R&D)*

DOUGLAS MACHINE, INC.
3404 Iowa St, Alexandria, MN 56308-3345
Tel.: (320) 763-6587   MN
Web Site: http://www.douglas-machine.com
Year Founded: 1964
Sales Range: $150-199.9 Million
Emp.: 690
Packaging Equipment Mfr
N.A.I.C.S.: 333993
Vernon J. Anderson *(CEO)*
Steve Black *(Gen Mgr)*
Jon Ballou *(Pres)*
Tom Wosepka *(CFO)*

Subsidiaries:

Davis Business Unit   (1)
PO Box 370, Deerwood, MN 56444-0310   (100%)
Tel.: (218) 546-7290
Web Site: http://www.douglasmachine.com
Sales Range: $10-24.9 Million
Emp.: 45
Rebuilder of Packaging Equipment
N.A.I.C.S.: 333993

DOUGLAS MOTORS CORPO-RATION
491 Morris Ave, Summit, NJ 07901
Tel.: (908) 277-3300
Web Site:
http://www.douglasautonet.com
Sales Range: $10-24.9 Million
Emp.: 50
Sales of New & Used Automobiles
N.A.I.C.S.: 441110
Peter T. Liebman *(Pres)*
Joseph Calavano *(CFO)*

DOUGLAS MOTORS INC.
295 Resley St, Hancock, MD 21750
Tel.: (301) 678-6163
Web Site:
http://www.douglasmotors.net
Emp.: 35
Dealers of New & Used Cars
N.A.I.C.S.: 441110
Harold Stephen Douglas *(Pres)*

DOUGLAS N. HIGGINS INC.
3390-A Travis Pointe Rd, Ann Arbor, MI 48108
Tel.: (734) 996-9500
Web Site: http://www.dnhiggins.com
Rev.: $25,334,661
Emp.: 27
Water Main Construction
N.A.I.C.S.: 237110
Daniel Higgins *(VP)*

DOUGLAS STEEL FABRICAT-ING CORPORATION
1312 S Waverly Rd, Lansing, MI 48917-4259
Tel.: (517) 322-2050   MI
Web Site:
https://www.douglassteel.com
Year Founded: 1952
Sales Range: $75-99.9 Million
Emp.: 128
Provider of Steel Fabrication & Erection of Steel Structures
N.A.I.C.S.: 238190
J. Michael Rogers *(Pres)*
Ruth Essenberg *(Mgr)*
Michael M. Gleason *(Plant Mgr)*
Mike Harris *(VP-Fin)*

DOUGLAS STEEL SUPPLY CO.

5764 Alcoa Ave, Los Angeles, CA 90058-3727
Tel.: (323) 587-7676
Web Site:
http://www.douglassteelsupply.com
Year Founded: 1972
Sales Range: $10-24.9 Million
Emp.: 54
Provider of Metal Service Centers
N.A.I.C.S.: 423510
Doug Stein *(Pres)*
Don Beier *(Controller)*

DOUGLAS STEPHEN PLAS-TICS, INC.
22 36 Green St, Paterson, NJ 07501
Tel.: (973) 523-3030   NJ
Web Site:
http://www.douglasstephen.com
Year Founded: 1959
Sales Range: $100-124.9 Million
Emp.: 140
Mfr of Plastic Food Containers & Cutlery Catering Tray Kits
N.A.I.C.S.: 326199
Paul Beshaw *(CEO)*
Kathy Lewis *(Reg Mgr-Sls)*

DOUGLAS TELECOMMUNICA-TIONS
125 E Sir Francis Drake Blvd Ste 400, Larkspur, CA 94939
Tel.: (415) 526-2200
Sales Range: $10-24.9 Million
Emp.: 15
Cellular Telephone Services
N.A.I.C.S.: 551110
Eileen Davis Wheatman *(CFO)*
Timothy Albert McGaw *(Pres)*
Kevin G. Douglas *(CEO)*

DOUGLAS THEATRE CO.
201 N 13th St, Lincoln, NE 68508-1505
Tel.: (402) 474-4909
Web Site:
http://www.dougtheatres.com
Sales Range: $10-24.9 Million
Emp.: 500
Motion Picture Theater
N.A.I.C.S.: 512131
Russell Brehm *(Chm)*
John Decker *(CFO)*

DOUGLAS VIDEO WARE-HOUSE
217 S Madison Ave, Douglas, GA 31533
Tel.: (912) 384-1781
Web Site: http://www.video-warehouse.com
Sales Range: $10-24.9 Million
Emp.: 700
Video Disk/Tape Rental To The General Public
N.A.I.C.S.: 532282
Gerald Pryor *(Pres & CEO)*

DOUGLAS WILSON COMPA-NIES
1620 5th Ave Ste 400, San Diego, CA 92101
Tel.: (619) 641-1141   CA
Web Site:
http://www.douglaswilson.com
Year Founded: 1989
Sales Range: $1-9.9 Million
Emp.: 15
Real Estate & Management Consulting Services
N.A.I.C.S.: 531390
Nancy Cook *(CFO)*
Jennifer Lloyd *(Dir-Mktg-Brokerage Svcs)*
Thomas Olson *(Mng Dir-Brokerage Svcs)*

Terry Plowden *(Sr Mng Dir)*
Alan Scott *(Mng Dir-Brokerage Svcs)*
Michele Vives *(Mng Dir)*
Douglas S. Wilson *(Chm & CEO)*
John Morrell *(Pres)*
Nicholas Wilson *(COO)*
Ryan Baker *(Sr Mng Dir-Los Angeles & Orange County)*
Stephen Walton *(CMO & VP)*

DOUGLAS, KNIGHT & ASSO-CIATES, INC.
1201 6th Ave W Ste 201, Bradenton, FL 34205
Tel.: (941) 744-1042   FL
Web Site:
https://www.douglasknight.com
Year Founded: 2001
Sales Range: $1-9.9 Million
Emp.: 20
Collection Agencies
N.A.I.C.S.: 561440
Emile Amarnek *(Pres)*
David Meketon *(CEO)*
Valerie Bradford *(Mgr-Subrogation)*

DOUGLAS-GUARDIAN SER-VICES CORPORATION
14800 Saint Marys Ln Ste 200, Houston, TX 77079-2936
Tel.: (281) 531-0500   TX
Web Site:
https://www.douglasguardian.com
Year Founded: 1932
Sales Range: $100-124.9 Million
Emp.: 300
Collateral Management Services & Inventory Equipment Verification to Financial Institutions
N.A.I.C.S.: 561499
Bruce E. Lurie *(Pres)*
Jack F. Ryan *(Sr VP)*
Woodley Simon *(Mgr-IT)*

DOUGLASS COLONY GROUP, INC.
5901 E 58 Ave, Commerce City, CO 80022
Tel.: (303) 288-2635
Web Site:
https://www.douglasscolony.com
Year Founded: 1947
Sales Range: $50-74.9 Million
Emp.: 400
Roofing & Construction Services
N.A.I.C.S.: 238160
Gary Degenhart *(Owner)*
Don Hayden *(Mgr-Svcs Dept)*
Dana Hubert *(Coord-Svcs)*
Bradley Joe *(Superintendent)*
Kate Faulkner *(Mgr-Solar Div)*
Larry Lehnerz *(Supvr-Shop)*

DOUGLASS DISTRIBUTING COMPANY INC.
325 E Forest Ave, Sherman, TX 75090-8832
Tel.: (903) 893-1181   TX
Web Site:
https://www.douglassdist.com
Year Founded: 1981
Sales Range: $25-49.9 Million
Emp.: 181
Petroleum Bulk Stations & Terminals
N.A.I.C.S.: 424710

DOUGLASS ORTHOPEDIC & SPINE REHABILITATION, INC.
25241 Elementary Way Ste 200, Bonita Springs, FL 34135
Tel.: (239) 947-4184
Web Site: http://www.douglasspt.com
Year Founded: 2001
Sales Range: $1-9.9 Million
Orthopedist Offices

Douglass Orthopedic & Spine Rehabilitation,
Inc.—(Continued)

N.A.I.C.S.: 621340
Eric Douglass (Owner & Pres)

DOUMAK INC.
1004 Fairway Dr, Bensenville, IL
60106-1317
Tel.: (847) 437-2100   DE
Web Site: http://www.cantfiremarsh
   mallows.com
Year Founded: 1983
Sales Range: $10-24.9 Million
Emp.: 90
Producer of Candy & Other Confec-
tionery Products
N.A.I.C.S.: 311340
Damon Fugate (Plant Mgr)
Eric Lawrence (Mgr-Sls-Natl)
Adela Rada (Mgr-HR)
Gary Conway (VP-Ops)
Timothy Pignato (Mgr-Maintenance)

DOURON, INC.
10 Payners Mill Rd, Owings Mills, MD
21117
Tel.: (410) 363-2600
Web Site: http://www.douron.com
Year Founded: 1969
Sales Range: $25-49.9 Million
Emp.: 150
Supplier of Educational & Office Fur-
niture
N.A.I.C.S.: 423210
Donna Petrelli (Dir-A&D Rels)
Ed Mathews (VP-Sls)
Ronald W. Hux (Co-Owner & Pres)

DOVARRI, INC.
5718 Westheimer Ste 1440, Houston,
TX 77057
Tel.: (713) 273-6880   TX
Web Site: http://www.dovarri.com
Year Founded: 2000
Sales Range: $1-9.9 Million
Emp.: 13
Software Development Services
N.A.I.C.S.: 541511
Geary G. Broadnax (CEO)
Andy Bates (Owner)
Christopher Williams (Acct Exec)
Larry Baty (CFO)
Scott Tartaglia (VP-Sls & Mktg)

DOVE CONTRACTING, INC.
292 S Main St Ste 500, Alpharetta,
GA 30009
Tel.: (770) 777-0055
Web Site:
   https://www.dovecontracting.com
Sales Range: $1-9.9 Million
Emp.: 10
Commercial & Institutional Building
Construction Services
N.A.I.C.S.: 236220
Susan H. Dove (VP)

DOVE DATA PRODUCTS INC.
1819 Range Way, Florence, SC
29501
Tel.: (843) 665-7678
Web Site: http://www.dovedata.com
Sales Range: $25-49.9 Million
Emp.: 130
Toner & Laser Cartridges Mfr & Distr
N.A.I.C.S.: 334118
Richard Coxe (Pres)
Ben D'Souza (Mgr-Lean Mfg Engrg &
Quality)

DOVE ELECTRONIC COMPO-
NENTS
39 Research Way, East Setauket, NY
11733
Tel.: (631) 689-7733   NY

Web Site:
   https://www.doveonline.com
Year Founded: 1983
Rev.: $13,906,584
Emp.: 30
Electronic Parts
N.A.I.C.S.: 423690
Matthew Waite (Owner)
Irma Waite (Treas)
Barry Mcmanus (Dir-Sls)
Sandra Seitz (Product Mgr)

DOVELL & WILLIAMS, INC.
1120 Crains Hwy NW, Glen Burnie,
MD 21061
Tel.: (410) 766-8132
Web Site:
   https://www.dovellandwilliams.com
Sales Range: $10-24.9 Million
Emp.: 43
Car Whslr
N.A.I.C.S.: 441110
Randall G. Williams (VP)

DOVENMUEHLE MORTGAGE
INC.
1501 E Woodfield Rd Ste 400 E,
Lake Zurich, IL 60173
Tel.: (847) 550-7550   IL
Web Site:
   http://www.dovenmuehle.com
Year Founded: 1844
Sales Range: $100-124.9 Million
Emp.: 400
Mortgage & Insurance Services
N.A.I.C.S.: 522292
Corinna Small (Coord-Loss Draft)
Nancy B. Gross (Project Mgr)
Phyllis Carlson (Supvr)
Patricia McCarthy (VP-Insurance Ad-
min)
Glen Braun (Sr VP)

Subsidiaries:

Dovenmuehle Funding Inc.   (1)
1501 E Woodfield Rd, Schaumburg, IL
60173-6052
Tel.: (847) 619-5535
Mortgage Services
N.A.I.C.S.: 522310

Dovenmuehle Insurance Agency
Inc.   (1)
1501 E Woodfield Rd Ste 400 E, Schaum-
burg, IL 60173-6011
Tel.: (847) 619-5535
Sales Range: $25-49.9 Million
Emp.: 8
Insurance Services
N.A.I.C.S.: 522292

DOVETAIL
12 Maryland Plz, Saint Louis, MO
63108-1502
Tel.: (314) 361-9800
Web Site: http://www.dovetail-stl.com
Year Founded: 1979
Rev.: $10,000,000
Emp.: 12
Business-To-Business, Consumer
Marketing
N.A.I.C.S.: 541810
Paul E. Maring (Partner)
Susan Weissman (Pres)
Jeff Stein (Dir-Strategy & New Bus)
Scott Leisler (Partner, Dir-Creative &
Iron Chef)
Thomas Etling (Partner-Strategy &
Innovation)
Jack Curran (VP-Bus Solutions)

DOVETAIL PROMOTION PART-
NERS
14240 Slater St, Overland Park, KS
66221-2144
Web Site: http://www.dovetailpp.com
Year Founded: 1984
Sales Range: $10-24.9 Million

Emp.: 1
Sales Promotion
N.A.I.C.S.: 541810
Richard Hopkins (Owner & Pres)

DOVETAIL PUBLIC RELA-
TIONS
15951 Los Gatos Blvd Ste 16, Los
Gatos, CA 95032
Tel.: (408) 395-3600
Web Site: https://www.dovetailpr.com
Year Founded: 1993
Sales Range: Less than $1 Million
Emp.: 5
Media & Analyst Relations
N.A.I.C.S.: 541820
Corey Oiesen (Pres)
Keri McKie (Mgr-Fin & HR)
Raylene Belcher (Mgr-Res & Office)
Mark Coker (Founder & CEO)

DOVETAIL SOLUTIONS INC.
210 University Blvd Ste 310, Denver,
CO 80206
Tel.: (720) 226-9595   CO
Web Site:
   http://www.dovetailsolutions.com
Year Founded: 2005
Public Relations & Marketing Comu-
nications Services
N.A.I.C.S.: 541820
Andy Boian (Founder & CEO)
Emily Teiffel (Pres & COO)
Summer Wright (Sr VP)
Carri Boian (Dir-Ops & HR)
Dave Farmer (Exec Creative Dir)

Subsidiaries:

Modamedia Communications,
Inc.   (1)
2508 J St, Sacramento, CA 95816
Tel.: (916) 572-7009
Web Site: http://www.modamedia.com
Telecommunications
N.A.I.C.S.: 517810
Jennifer Bulotti (Owner)

DOW LEWIS MOTORS, INC.
2913 Colusa Hwy, Yuba City, CA
95993-8934
Tel.: (530) 923-4867
Web Site:
   https://www.dowlewisbuickgmc.com
Year Founded: 1984
Sales Range: $25-49.9 Million
Emp.: 43
Car Whslr
N.A.I.C.S.: 441110
Ted Lewis (Treas & Sec)

DOW MANAGEMENT COM-
PANY, INC.
1000 Cir 75 Pkwy SE Ste 500, At-
lanta, GA 30339
Tel.: (770) 937-9735
Web Site:
   http://www.downetworks.com
Year Founded: 2001
Sales Range: $1-9.9 Million
Emp.: 50
VoIP Telecommunications Services
N.A.I.C.S.: 517121
David Wise (Founder & CEO)
Weston Edmunds (Exec VP)

DOWD & GUILD, INC.
14 Crow Canyon Ct Ste 200, San
Ramon, CA 94583-1668
Tel.: (925) 820-7222
Web Site:
   http://www.dowdandguild.com
Year Founded: 1986
Sales Range: $10-24.9 Million
Emp.: 30
Chemicals & Allied Products Distr
N.A.I.C.S.: 424690

Thomas Dowd (CEO)
Howard Guild (Pres)

DOWDING INDUSTRIES, INC.
449 Marilin Ave, Eaton Rapids, MI
48827
Tel.: (517) 543-0980
Web Site:
   https://www.dowdingindustries.com
Year Founded: 1965
Sales Range: $10-24.9 Million
Emp.: 150
Automotive Stamping Mfr
N.A.I.C.S.: 336370
G. Chris Dowding (CEO)
Jake Warren (Plant Mgr)
Paula Metts (Mgr-HR)

DOWLING & POPE ADVERTIS-
ING INC.
311 W Superior St, Chicago, IL
60610
Tel.: (312) 573-0600
Year Founded: 1988
Rev.: $19,500,000
Emp.: 25
Recruitment
N.A.I.C.S.: 541810
Garrett Kallenbach (Dir-Creative)

DOWLING CAPITAL MANAGE-
MENT, LLC
190 Farmington Ave, Farmington, CT
06032
Tel.: (860) 676-7300
Web Site:
   http://www.dowlingcapitalpart
   ners.com
Privater Equity Firm
N.A.I.C.S.: 523999
David K. Zwiener (Sr Partner)
Jeffery B. Cappel (Partner)
Vincent J. Dowling Jr. (Partner)

Subsidiaries:

Protector Holdings LLC   (1)
135 Main St 21st Fl, San Francisco, CA
94105
Tel.: (818) 482-6917
Web Site: http://www.protectorholdings.com
Insurance Services
N.A.I.C.S.: 524210
Paul Areida (CEO)
Vince Trapani (CFO)
Paul Woodward (CIO)

Subsidiary (Domestic):

Big Savings Insurance Agency
Inc.   (2)
7838 Stockton Blvd Ste 300, Sacramento,
CA 95823
Tel.: (916) 830-9200
Web Site:
   http://www.bigsavingsinsurance.com
Insurance Agencies & Brokerages
N.A.I.C.S.: 524210
Sunny Singh (Pres)

Premier Insurance Services Inc.   (2)
829 Main St Ste A, Delano, CA 93215
Tel.: (661) 721-8300
Web Site: https://www.prontoinsurance.com
Insurance Services
N.A.I.C.S.: 524210
Rick Genest (Pres)

Subsidiary (Domestic):

Oasis South Insurance Services
Inc.   (3)
1295 Broadway 209, Chula Vista, CA 91911
Tel.: (619) 425-9696
Web Site: http://www.oasissouth.com
Insurance Services
N.A.I.C.S.: 524210
Trey Nelson (Gen Mgr)

DOWLING GRAPHICS INC.
12920 Automobile Blvd, Clearwater,
FL 33762

Tel.: (727) 573-5997
Web Site:
https://www.dowlinggraphics.com
Year Founded: 1982
Sales Range: $1-9.9 Million
Emp.: 40
Commercial Flexographic Printing
N.A.I.C.S.: 323111
Denise C. Dowling (Owner & Pres)

DOWN EAST COMMUNITY HOSPITAL
11 Hospital Dr, Machias, ME 04654
Tel.: (207) 255-3356   ME
Web Site: https://www.dech.org
Year Founded: 1963
Sales Range: $25-49.9 Million
Emp.: 331
Health Care Srvices
N.A.I.C.S.: 622110
Lynnette Parr (VP-Fin)
Ernestine Reisman (VP-HR)
Rob Janssen (Chief Nursing Officer & VP-Patient Care Svcs)
Nicole Shaw (VP-Ops)
Lisa Carr (VP-Physician Practices)

DOWN UNDER ANSWERS, LLC
400 108th Ave Ne Ste 200, Bellevue, WA 98004-5565
Tel.: (425) 460-0895
Web Site: http://www.duatravel.com
Sales Range: $1-9.9 Million
Emp.: 22
Travel Agency
N.A.I.C.S.: 561510
Kirk Demeter (Pres)
Anita Lan (Mgr-Air)

DOWN-LITE PRODUCTS INC.
8153 Duke Blvd, Mason, OH 45040
Tel.: (513) 229-3696
Web Site: http://www.downlite.com
Sales Range: $50-74.9 Million
Emp.: 200
Pillows, Bed: Made From Purchased Materials
N.A.I.C.S.: 314120
Larry Werthaiser (Co-Owner)
Bob Altbaier (Co-Owner)
Chuck Northcutt (VP-Quality Assurance)
David Lueder (Chief Revenue Officer)
Frank Carella (VP-Ops)
Josh Werthaiser (CEO)
Jyl Davis (VP-Mktg & Product Dev)
Marvin Werthaiser (Co-Owner)
Stefan Hunter (VP-ECommerce)
Zach Zellner (VP-Sourcing)

DOWNEAST CONCEPTS INC.
86 Downeast Dr, Yarmouth, ME 04096
Tel.: (207) 846-3726
Web Site:
http://www.downeastconcepts.com
Sales Range: $10-24.9 Million
Emp.: 40
Gifts & Novelties
N.A.I.C.S.: 424990

DOWNEAST TOYOTA BMW INC.
652 Wilson St, Brewer, ME 04412
Tel.: (207) 573-7535
Web Site:
https://www.downeasttoyota.com
Sales Range: $25-49.9 Million
Emp.: 150
Car Whslr
N.A.I.C.S.: 441110
Kevin Kelly (Gen Mgr)

DOWNEY OIL CO. INC.

806 High St, Maryville, TN 37804-5031
Tel.: (865) 982-2192   TN
Web Site:
https://www.kenjomarkets.com
Year Founded: 1988
Sales Range: $10-24.9 Million
Emp.: 30
Provider of Petroleum Bulk Station Services
N.A.I.C.S.: 424710
Charles Carruthers Jr. (VP)
Charles Carruthers Sr. (Pres)

DOWNING CONSTRUCTION, INC.
2500 W 2nd Ave, Indianola, IA 50125
Tel.: (515) 961-5386
Web Site:
http://www.downingconstruct.com
Sales Range: $10-24.9 Million
Emp.: 24
Commercial & Institutional Building Construction
N.A.I.C.S.: 236220
Denis Frischmeyer (Pres)
Christopher Lyon (Dir-Safety)
Debbie McCoy (Mgr-Acctg)
Joe Butler (Project Mgr)

DOWNING DISPLAYS INC.
550 Techne Center Dr, Milford, OH 45150
Tel.: (513) 248-9800
Web Site:
https://www.downingdisplays.com
Sales Range: $25-49.9 Million
Emp.: 70
Signs & Advertising Specialties
N.A.I.C.S.: 339950
Mollie Krumlaw (Controller)
Deanna Haun (Mgr-Acct)
Greg Ward (VP-Sls)
Dan Weber (Dir-Art)
Donnie Wilson (Sr Acct Exec)
Dan Imhoff (Acct Exec-Indiana & Ohio Reg)

Subsidiaries:

Horizon Downing LLC   (1)
1115 E Locust St, Dekalb, IL 60115
Tel.: (815) 758-6867
Web Site: http://www.horizondowning.com
Sales Range: $1-9.9 Million
Emp.: 65
Graphic Design Services
N.A.I.C.S.: 541430
Terry Beckman (VP-Sls)
Mike Thanepohn (Mgr-Ops)

DOWNING-FRYE REALTY, LNC.
180 9th St S, Naples, FL 34102
Tel.: (800) 448-3411
Web Site:
http://www.downingfrye.com
Emp.: 500
Real Estate Broker
N.A.I.C.S.: 531210

DOWNS CRANE & HOIST CO, INC.
8827 S Juniper St, Los Angeles, CA 90002
Tel.: (323) 589-6061
Web Site:
https://www.downscrane.com
Year Founded: 1922
Sales Range: $10-24.9 Million
Emp.: 5
Industrial Machinery Mfr
N.A.I.C.S.: 333923
J.W. Downs III (VP-Fin)
C.M. Downs (Treas & Sec)
H. Horowitz (Mgr-Sls & Mktg)
J.W. Downs Jr. (Pres)

DOWNS FOOD GROUP
54934 210th Ln, Mankato, MN 56001
Tel.: (507) 387-3663   MN
Web Site:
https://www.downsfoodgroup.com
Year Founded: 1947
Sales Range: $200-249.9 Million
Emp.: 460
Producer of Chicken & Other Meat Products
N.A.I.C.S.: 311615
Richard Downs (Chm & CEO)
Patty Anderson (CFO)
Mike Downs (Pres)

Subsidiaries:

Aussie Foods, LLC   (1)
54934 210th Ln, Mankato, MN 56001
Tel.: (507) 387-3663
Frozen Pies Mfr
N.A.I.C.S.: 311412

Double D Foods   (1)
54934 210th Ln, Mankato, MN 56001
Tel.: (507) 345-5677
Cooked Meat Mfr
N.A.I.C.S.: 311612

Tony Downs Foods   (1)
418 Benzel Ave, Madelia, MN 56062
Tel.: (507) 642-3203
Frozen Meat Mfr
N.A.I.C.S.: 311612
Mitch Forstie (VP)
Teresa Schumann (Mgr-HR & Safety)

DOWNTOWN AUTO CENTER
4145 Broadway, Oakland, CA 94611
Tel.: (510) 547-4436
Web Site:
http://www.downtownautocenter.com
Sales Range: $100-124.9 Million
Emp.: 90
Automobiles, New & Used
N.A.I.C.S.: 441110
Ralph Fattore (Owner)
Cynthia Gordon (Mgr-Customer Rels)
David Pipkins (Mgr-Fin)

DOWNTOWN BUSINESS IMPROVEMENT DISTRICT CORPORATION
1275 K St NW Ste 1000, Washington, DC 20005
Tel.: (202) 638-3232   DC
Web Site:
http://www.downtowndc.org
Year Founded: 1997
Rev.: $15,645,117
Assets: $13,578,918
Liabilities: $4,689,724
Net Worth: $8,889,194
Earnings: $1,474,428
Fiscal Year-end: 09/30/21
Property Management & Maintenance Services
N.A.I.C.S.: 531312
Gerry Widdicombe (Dir-Economic Dev)
Chase Rynd (Chm)
Donna Cooper (Sec)
Jalal Chaoui (Mgr-Payroll)
Parker Roach (Mgr-HR)
Scott Frisch (Treas)
Remi Wallace (Mgr-Events & Strategic Partnerships)
Rachel Rose Hartman (Exec Dir-Downtown Foundation)
Neil Albert (Pres & CEO)
Nabavi Oliver (Dir-Admin)
Darlyene Direkston (Program Mgr)
Galin Brooks (Dir-Plng & Placemaking & Infrastructure)
Gerren G. Price (Dir-Pub Space Ops)
Ellouise Johnson (Mgr-Maintenance Svcs)

DOWNTOWN DAYTON SPE-

CIAL IMPROVEMENT DISTRICT INC.
10 W 2nd St Ste 611, Dayton, OH 45402
Tel.: (937) 224-1518   OH
Year Founded: 1994
Sales Range: $1-9.9 Million
Business & Economic Developmental Services
N.A.I.C.S.: 813910
Joey Williams (Treas)
Gary Gottschlich (Sec)
Dan Med (Chm)
Ryan Powell (Vice Chm)

DOWNTOWN FORD SALES INC.
525 N 16th St, Sacramento, CA 95811
Tel.: (916) 442-6931
Web Site:
http://www.downtownfordsales.com
Sales Range: $100-124.9 Million
Emp.: 100
Automobile Dealers
N.A.I.C.S.: 441110
Terry Meadows (Mgr-Bus)
Scott Ikesaki (Mgr-New Vehicle)
Jeff Stubblefield (Dir-Parts & Svc)
Dave C. Sarra (Mgr-Parts)

DOWNTOWN L.A. MOTORS, LP.
1801 S Figueroa St, Los Angeles, CA 90015
Tel.: (213) 748-8951
Web Site: http://www.dtlamotors.com
Sales Range: $50-74.9 Million
Emp.: 200
New Car Dealers
N.A.I.C.S.: 441110
Nicholas Shammas (Owner)

DOWNTOWN LA NISSAN MOTORS
1801 S Figueroa St, Los Angeles, CA 90015
Tel.: (213) 748-8951
Sales Range: $25-49.9 Million
Emp.: 132
Car Whslr
N.A.I.C.S.: 441110
Ken Nakano (Dir-Ops-Downtown Center Bus Improvement)

DOWNTOWN REPORTING LLC
200 S Andrews Ave Ste 604, Fort Lauderdale, FL 33301
Tel.: (954) 522-3376
Web Site:
http://www.downtownreporting.com
Year Founded: 2009
Sales Range: $1-9.9 Million
Emp.: 35
Court Reporting Service
N.A.I.C.S.: 561492
Michael Frost (CEO)

DOXA INSURANCE HOLDINGS LLC
101 E Washington Blvd 10th Fl, 46802, Fort Wayne, IN
Tel.: (888) 747-3692
Web Site: http://doxainsurance.com
Year Founded: 2016
Insurance Services
N.A.I.C.S.: 524210
Matt Sackett (CEO)
Tim Wiggins (COO)
Kevin Wall (CFO)
Stu Holloway (VP & Sls Dir-Southeast)
Bernie Holicky (VP & Sls Dir-Central)
Joe Guerrero (Pres)
Michael Robbins (Reg Dir-Sls-Texas)

DOXA Insurance Holdings LLC—(Continued)

Subsidiaries:

Financial Risk Solutions, Inc.   (1)
180 N LaSalle St Ste 3700, Chicago, IL
60601
Tel.: (630) 986-9676
Web Site: https://chillpro.com
Insurance Services
N.A.I.C.S.: 524210
Jim Wilson (Pres)

Renters Legal Liability LLC.   (1)
60 S 600 E Ste 100, Salt Lake City, UT
84102
Tel.: (801) 994-0237
Web Site: http://www.rllinsure.com
Risk Managemeng Srvices
N.A.I.C.S.: 524298
Welden L. Daines (CFO)
Paul J. Kaliades (Pres)
Nick J. Colessides (Gen Counsel)
Marcellus Q. Barrus (VP-IT)
Constantine J. Colessides (COO)
Jean Smith (Reg Mgr)
John Steffen (VP)

DOYLE CHEVROLET-SUBARU
740 Ridge Rd, Webster, NY 14580
Tel.: (585) 671-5390
Web Site: http://www.doyleauto.com
Year Founded: 1974
Sales Range: $10-24.9 Million
Emp.: 55
Car Whslr
N.A.I.C.S.: 441110
Michael Doyle (Gen Mgr)
Scott Wallace (Mgr-Sls)

DOYLE ELECTRIC SERVICES INC.
3415 Queen Palm Dr, Tampa, FL
33619
Tel.: (813) 630-4600
Web Site: https://www.doyle-electric.com
Year Founded: 1987
Sales Range: $10-24.9 Million
Emp.: 160
Electrical Contractor
N.A.I.C.S.: 238210
Hugh Armstrong (Superintendent)
Lonnie Hatcher (Pres)
Todd Hopkins (Mgr-Sarasota)
Tom Zack (Project Mgr)
Richard Curtis (Mgr-Svc)
Brian Jacinto (Controller)
Paul Blankmann (Mgr-Tampa Pur)
Dennis Fliess (Mgr-Tampa Svc)
Scott Johnson (VP & Reg Mgr)

DOYLE EQUIPMENT COMPANY INC.
20400 Rte N 19, Cranberry Township,
PA 16066-7523
Tel.: (724) 776-3636   **PA**
Year Founded: 1983
Sales Range: $10-24.9 Million
Emp.: 45
Construction & Mining Machines Mfr
N.A.I.C.S.: 423810
Tom Bishop (Mgr-Product-Support)

DOYLE GROUP INC.
792 Cocin Rd, Rochester, NY 14623-
1829
Tel.: (585) 244-3400
Web Site: https://www.godoyle.com
Year Founded: 1919
Sales Range: $10-24.9 Million
Emp.: 100
Security System Services
N.A.I.C.S.: 561621
Kevin Stone (COO & Exec VP)
Todd Julien (Dir-Sls)
Sue Kelley (CFO)
Sara Chaudari (Controller)
Joe Schwartz (Coord-Mktg)

Devon Ritch (Dir-IT)
Ernie Cole (Dir-Ops-Emergency Response Center)
Chris Marsh (Dir-Sls-Doyle Medical Monitoring)
Ed Evans (Gen Mgr-Albany)
Jeremy Daumen (Gen Mgr-Buffalo-NY)
John G. Doyle Jr. (Pres & CEO)

Subsidiaries:

Doyle Security Systems Inc.   (1)
792 Calkins Rd, Rochester, NY 14623-4436
Tel.: (585) 244-3400
Web Site: http://www.godoyle.com
Sales Range: $10-24.9 Million
Emp.: 87
Residential & Commercial Security Systems
Services
N.A.I.C.S.: 561621
John Doyle (Pres & CEO)

DOYLE SYSTEMS
5186 New Haven Cir, Barberton, OH
44203
Tel.: (330) 564-4000
Web Site: https://www.doylesystems.com
Year Founded: 1922
Sales Range: $10-24.9 Million
Emp.: 20
Printing & Packaging Cleaning & Inspection Systems Mfr & Marketer
N.A.I.C.S.: 333248
Joseph M. Lynch (Pres)
Jean Reash (Gen Mgr)
Linda Lynch (VP)

DOYLE WEALTH MANAGEMENT, INC.
333 3rd Ave N Ste 300, Saint Petersburg, FL 33701
Tel.: (727) 898-3063
Web Site: http://www.doylewealth.com
Year Founded: 2005
Rev.: $366,000,000
Emp.: 15
Investment Advisory Services
N.A.I.C.S.: 523940
Robert K. Doyle (Pres)
Jillian D. Doyle (Principal)
Anne Drake McMullen (Exec VP-Bus Dev)
Connie E. Roman (Controller)
Robyn A. Bowman (Mgr-Ops)
Cassandra Smalley (Dir-Fin Plng)
Kimbwely Markiewicz (Mgr-Ops)
Michael Chren (Chief Investment Officer)
Todd B. Youngs (Dir-Portfolio Mgmt)
Scott Connor (Dir-Investment Svcs-Natl)
Matthew Benz (Reg Dir-Client Rels)

DOYON UTILITIES, LLC.
714 4th Ave Ste 101, Fairbanks, AK
99701-4470
Tel.: (907) 455-1500
Web Site: https://www.doyonutilities.com
Sales Range: $10-24.9 Million
Emp.: 120
Electrical Wiring Services
N.A.I.C.S.: 238210

DOYON, LIMITED
1 Doyon Pl Ste 300, Fairbanks, AK
99701-2941
Tel.: (907) 459-2000
Web Site: http://www.doyon.com
Year Founded: 1971
Sales Range: $300-349.9 Million
Emp.: 2,501
Oil & Gas Exploration Services
N.A.I.C.S.: 213112

Miranda Wright (Treas)
Walter Carlo (Chm)
Christopher Simon (Sec)
Patrick W. Duke (CFO & Sr VP)
James Mery (Sr VP-Lands & Natural Resources)
Allen Todd (Gen Counsel & Asst Sec)
Robin Renfroe (VP-HR & Shareholder Svcs)
Kelly Brooks (VP-Fin)
Charlene Ostbloom (VP-Comm)
Richard Woodson (VP-IT)
Sarah Obed (VP-External Affairs)
Julie M. Morman (COO & Sr VP)
Aaron M. Schutt (Pres & CEO)
Tanya Kaquatosh (Sr VP-Admin)

DP FOX VENTURES, LLC
200 Ottawa Ave NW Ste 800, Grand
Rapids, MI 49503
Tel.: (616) 774-4044
Web Site: http://www.dpfox.com
Sales Range: $75-99.9 Million
Emp.: 500
Diversified Holding Company
N.A.I.C.S.: 551112
Daniel G. DeVos (Chm & CEO)
Diane Maher (Pres & COO)
Monica R. Sekulich (Sr VP)
Scott J. Gorsline (Sr VP)

Subsidiaries:

Fox Buick GMC   (1)
5977 Alpine Ave NW, Comstock Park, MI
49321
Tel.: (616) 871-2208
Web Site: http://www.foxgm.com
Sales Range: $25-49.9 Million
Emp.: 35
New & Used Car Dealer Services
N.A.I.C.S.: 441110
John Phillips (Gen Mgr)
Jason Harriman (Mgr-Parts)
Jason Visser (Mgr-F&I)

Fox Ford   (1)
3560 28th St SE, Grand Rapids, MI 49512
Tel.: (616) 956-5511
Web Site: http://www.foxfordusa.com
Sales Range: $25-49.9 Million
Emp.: 100
New & Used Car Dealer
N.A.I.C.S.: 441110
Kim Guiles (Mgr-Parts)
Todd Raible (Mgr)
Steve Scheffler (Mgr)
Duke Macgrayne (Mgr-Sls)
Steve Winters (Gen Mgr)
Jim McCormick (Mgr-Comml Acct)
John Steere (Mgr-Comml Acct)
Tom Scobt (Mgr-Mazda Sls)
Tom Tasker (Mgr-Ford Sls)

Fox Hyundai   (1)
4141 28th St, Grand Rapids, MI 49512
Tel.: (616) 942-5000
Web Site: http://www.foxmotorgroup.com
Sales Range: $10-24.9 Million
Emp.: 60
Car Dealership Owner & Operator
N.A.I.C.S.: 441110
Nick Dieleman (Gen Mgr)
Jack Turske (Gen Mgr)

Grand Rapids Griffins   (1)
130 W Fulton Ste 111, Grand Rapids, MI
49503
Tel.: (616) 774-4585
Web Site: http://griffinshockey.com
Professional Hockey Team
N.A.I.C.S.: 711211
Daniel G. DeVos (Co-Owner & CEO)
David Van Andel (Co-Owner & Chm)
Bob Kaser (VP-Community Rels & Brdcst)
Randy Cleves (Sr Dir-PR)
Lisa Vedder (Dir-Acctg & Tax)
Matt Batchelder (VP-Ticket Sls)
John Hoffa (Dir-Sls)
Diane Maher (Pres & COO-DP Fox)
Phil Cronin (Dir-Game Presentation)
Jason Pearson (Mgr-PR)

Mercedes-Benz of Traverse City   (1)
3258 N US 31 S, Traverse City, MI 49684

Tel.: (231) 938-3800
Web Site: http://www.foxmb.com
Sales Range: $1-9.9 Million
Emp.: 12
New & Used Car Dealer
N.A.I.C.S.: 441110
Tony Jerome (Gen Mgr)

DP+COMPANY
38505 Country Club Dr Ste 110,
Farmington, MI 48331
Tel.: (248) 489-8300
Web Site: https://www.dpplus.com
Year Founded: 1997
Rev.: $10,700,000
Emp.: 60
Advertising & Strategic Marketing
Agency
N.A.I.C.S.: 424990
Mark Petrosky (Co-Founder & CEO)
Jo Bourjaily (Dir-PR)
Jimmy Kollin (Chief Creative Officer)
Julia Francke (Dir-Client Svcs)
Tracie Reihm (Dir-Customer Relationship Mktg)
Paul Murray (Dir-Media)

DPI, INC.
900 N 23rd St, Saint Louis, MO
63106
Tel.: (314) 621-3314   **MO**
Web Site: http://www.dpiinc.com
Year Founded: 1971
Sales Range: $50-74.9 Million
Emp.: 300
Audio & Video Electronic Products
Mfr & Whslr
N.A.I.C.S.: 334310
William L. Fetter (Pres & CEO)
Jeff Dusch (Sr VP-Prod Mngmt, Mktg
& Sls)
Mike McCartney (VP-DP)

DPR CONSTRUCTION
5990 Greenwood Plz Blvd, Englewood, CO 80111
Tel.: (303) 741-0404
Web Site: http://www.dpr.com
Sales Range: $25-49.9 Million
Emp.: 90
Civil Engineering Services
N.A.I.C.S.: 237310
Geoff G. Wormer (Principal)
Chad Monroe (Project Mgr)
Brian Coakley (Mgr-Preconstruction)
Brad Moore (Superintendent)

DPR CONSTRUCTION, INC.
1450 Veterans Blvd, Redwood City,
CA 94063
Tel.: (650) 474-1450   **CA**
Web Site: https://www.dpr.com
Year Founded: 1990
Sales Range: $1-4.9 Billion
Emp.: 10,000
Commercial & Institutional Building
Construction
N.A.I.C.S.: 236220
Doug Woods (Co-Founder)
Ronald J. Davidowski (Co-Founder)
Yumi Clevenger (Dir-Mktg)
Michele Leiva (CFO)

Subsidiaries:

DPR Hardin Construction Company,
LLC   (1)
3301 Windy Rdg Pkwy Ste 500, Atlanta, GA
30339
Tel.: (404) 264-0404
Web Site: http://www.dpr.com
Commercial Contracting Services
N.A.I.C.S.: 236220
Matt Hoglund (Regional Mgr)
Chris Bontrager (Reg Mgr)

DPR GROUP, INC.
7200 Bankcourt Ste 100, Frederick,
MD 20874

Tel.: (240) 686-1000
Web Site: http://www.dprgroup.com
Year Founded: 1998
Sales Range: $10-24.9 Million
Emp.: 8
Public Relations Agency
N.A.I.C.S.: 541820
Dan Demaree (Pres & CEO)

Subsidiaries:

DPR Group, Inc. (1)
200 Cascade Point Ln Ste 104, Cary, NC 27513
Tel.: (919) 678-9200
Web Site: http://www.dprgroup.com
Sales Range: $10-24.9 Million
Emp.: 3
Public Relations Agency
N.A.I.C.S.: 541820
Erin Hatfield (Acct Exec)
Felix Pekar (COO)

DPRA INCORPORATED
121 S 4th St Ste 202, Manhattan, KS 66502
Tel.: (785) 539-3565
Web Site: https://www.dpra.com
Year Founded: 1961
Sales Range: $25-49.9 Million
Emp.: 250
Economic Research
N.A.I.C.S.: 541910
Mary Carter (CFO)
Ivan Eno (Dir-Bus Dev)

DPS TELECOM
4955 E Yale Ave, Fresno, CA 93727
Tel.: (559) 454-1600
Web Site: https://www.dpstele.com
Sales Range: $1-9.9 Million
Emp.: 80
Network Monitoring Solutions
N.A.I.C.S.: 335313
Bob Berry (CEO)
Jeff Kirkpatrick (Mgr)

DPSI INC.
1801 Stanley Rd Ste 301, Greensboro, NC 27407
Tel.: (336) 854-7700
Web Site: http://www.dpsi.com
Year Founded: 1986
Sales Range: $1-9.9 Million
Emp.: 45
Provider of Application Computer Software Services
N.A.I.C.S.: 513210
Carol C. Owens (Pres)
Deedee Gatz (VP-Product Mgmt)
E. Lynn Carriker (Exec VP)
Trevor Miller (VP-Tech)

DPT CONSULTING GROUP, INC.
333 E City Ave Ste 801, Bala Cynwyd, PA 19004
Tel.: (610) 206-0101 **PA**
Web Site: http://www.learnquest.com
Year Founded: 1996
Rev.: $5,100,000
Emp.: 90
Computer Training
N.A.I.C.S.: 611420
Lucy Schneiberg (CEO)
Dimitri Schneiberg (VP)

DR WARREN E SMITH COMMUNITY MENTAL HEALTH MENTAL RETARDATION & SUBSTANCE ABUSE CENTERS
1926 Arch St 2nd Fl, Philadelphia, PA 19103
Tel.: (267) 256-5201 **PA**
Web Site: http://www.drwes.org
Year Founded: 1992
Sales Range: $10-24.9 Million

Emp.: 287
Behavioral Healthcare Services
N.A.I.C.S.: 623220
Abayomi Ige (Chief Medical Officer)
Dave Kittka (CFO)
Dennis E. Cook (Pres & Sec)

DR. JAY'S INC.
Prince St Sta, New York, NY 10012
Tel.: (888) 437-5297
Web Site: http://www.drjays.com
Year Founded: 1991
Sales Range: $25-49.9 Million
Emp.: 300
Sale of Mens & Boys Clothing; Urban Fashions
N.A.I.C.S.: 458110
Elliot Vetesh (Pres)

DR. LEONARD HEALTH CARE CATALOG
100 Nixon Ln, Edison, NJ 08837
Tel.: (732) 225-0100
Web Site: http://www.drleonards.com
Sales Range: $250-299.9 Million
Emp.: 600
Catalog Sales
N.A.I.C.S.: 456199
Joe Albanese (Pres)

DR. PARK AVE.
846 Franklin Ave, Franklin Lakes, NJ 07417
Tel.: (201) 485-8400 **NV**
Web Site: https://www.drparkave.com
Year Founded: 2010
Sales Range: $10-24.9 Million
Emp.: 5
Plastic Surgery Facility Owner & Operator
N.A.I.C.S.: 621498
Paul Fondacaro (Pres)
Thomas Zanardi (CFO)

DR. PEPPER BOTTLING CO. ELK CITY
322 S Jefferson Ave, Elk City, OK 73644
Tel.: (580) 225-3186
Sales Range: $10-24.9 Million
Emp.: 15
Soft Drink Whslr
N.A.I.C.S.: 424490
Jim Schmidt (Gen Mgr)

DR. SHRINK, INC.
315 Washington St, Manistee, MI 49660
Tel.: (231) 723-2685 **MI**
Web Site: https://www.dr-shrink.com
Year Founded: 1992
Sales Range: $10-24.9 Million
Emp.: 17
Premium Shrinkwrap Whslr & Retailer
N.A.I.C.S.: 424610
Michael Stenberg (Pres)
Bart Stenberg (CEO)
Angela Jensen (Mgr-Mktg)
Melissa Spoor (Mgr-HR)

DRA ADVISORS LLC
220 E 42nd St 27th Fl, New York, NY 10017-5806
Tel.: (212) 697-4740
Web Site:
http://www.draadvisors.com
Year Founded: 1986
Rev.: $9,000,000,000
Emp.: 80
Real Estate Investment & Property Management Services
N.A.I.C.S.: 523999
David Luski (Pres & CEO)
Andrew E. Peltz (Mng Dir)
Paul McEvoy (Sr Mng Dir)
Brian T. Summers (Mng Dir & CFO)

David P. Gray (Mng Dir)
Diana Tully (Mng Dir)
Jean Marie Apruzzese (Mng Dir & COO)
Janine Roberts (Mng Dir)
Adam Breen (Mng Dir)
Jason Borreo (Dir-Portfolio Mgmt)
Valla Brown (Dir-Asset Mgmt)
Matthew Shore (Mng Dir)
Dean Sickles (Mng Dir)
Daniel Goldman (Mng Dir)

Subsidiaries:

IRC Retail Centers Inc. (1)
814 Commerce Dr, Oak Brook, IL 60523
Web Site: http://www.ircretailcenters.com
Real Estate Investment Trust
N.A.I.C.S.: 525990
Mark E. Zalatoris (Pres & CEO)
William W. Anderson (Sr VP-Transactions)
D. Scott Carr (Chief Investment Officer & Exec VP)
Beth Sprecher Brooks (Sec, Gen Counsel & Sr VP)
Carol Adams (Chief Compliance Officer & VP)
Anne Arnold (Sr VP-Fin & Portfoilo Mgmt)
Shane Boyle (Chief Acctg Officer & VP)
Rick Lippert (VP-Transactions)
Allison Kuchny Curtin (Reg Mgr-Leasing)
Mike Fitzgerald (Sr VP-Leasing)
Kevin Cianferri (Mgr-Ops)
Shannon Hormanski (Mgr-Leasing)
Donna Osborn (Sr Coord-Tenant Svc)
Robert Boswell (Project Mgr)
John Cresto (Sr Mgr-Ops)
Tina Beilke (Dir-Tax Svcs)
Matt Cavanagh (Mgr-Leasing)
Fawn Le (Sr Mgr-Leasing)
Melissa Skoieczny (Mgr-Comm & Mktg)
Rebekah Buck (Mgr-Property)
Kara Crousore (Mgr-Property)
Nadia Cudele (Mgr-Property)
Pam Daniels (Mgr-Property)
Jeanne Heller (Mgr-Strategic Mktg)
Kristi Rankin (COO)

Lake Cameron, LLC (1)
1000 Cameron Woods Dr, Apex, NC 27523
Tel.: (984) 246-2641
Web Site: https://www.lakecameron.com
Residential Building & Dwelling Leasing Services
N.A.I.C.S.: 531110

DRACO, INC.
165 Waterman Dr, South Portland, ME 04106
Tel.: (207) 799-5591 **ME**
Web Site: http://www.yankeeford.com
Sales Range: $25-49.9 Million
Emp.: 50
Automobiles, New & Used
N.A.I.C.S.: 441110
D. R. Arnold (Pres)
Robert Esposito (VP-Sls & Mktg)

DRAEGER CONSTRUCTION INC.
605 Commercial St, San Jose, CA 95112
Tel.: (408) 536-0420
Rev.: $14,001,258
Emp.: 140
Foundation & Footing Contractor
N.A.I.C.S.: 236118
John Draeger (Pres)
Shawn Draeger (Gen Mgr)

DRAEGER OIL CO. INC.
N 4005 Hwy 45, Antigo, WI 54409
Tel.: (715) 623-4518
Year Founded: 1981
Sales Range: $10-24.9 Million
Emp.: 3
Petroleum Bulk Station Services
N.A.I.C.S.: 424710
James Draeger (Pres)

Subsidiaries:

Draeger Leasing Inc. (1)

N4005 Hwy 45, Antigo, WI 54409-2011 **(100%)**
Tel.: (715) 623-4518
Web Site: http://www.draeger.com
Sales Range: $10-24.9 Million
Provider of Grocery Store Services
N.A.I.C.S.: 532120
James Draeger (Pres)

DRAEGER'S SUPER MARKETS INC.
291 Utah Ave, South San Francisco, CA 94080-6802
Tel.: (650) 244-6500
Web Site: https://www.draegers.com
Year Founded: 1946
Sales Range: $25-49.9 Million
Emp.: 520
Grocery Store Services
N.A.I.C.S.: 561110
James Draeger (Pres & Owner)

DRAGON CLAW USA INC.
16033 Arrow Hwy, Irwindale, CA 91706
Tel.: (626) 480-0068
Web Site: http://www.dcamerica.net
Sales Range: $10-24.9 Million
Emp.: 20
Garden Supplies
N.A.I.C.S.: 424910
Leo C.H. Wang (Pres)

DRAGON ESP, LTD.
1655 Louisiana St, Beaumont, TX 77701
Tel.: (574) 893-1569 **TX**
Web Site:
http://www.dragonproductsltd.com
Year Founded: 1999
Truck/Trailer & Truck Parts Whlsr
N.A.I.C.S.: 532120
Will Crenshaw (Chm & CEO)
Tom Inman (VP-Pumps & Stimulation Equipment)
Johnny Tennison (VP-Southeast Sls, Tanks & Trailers)
Casey Crenshaw (Pres)
Todd Henning (VP-Northwest Sls, Tanks & Trailers)
Jimmy Jones (VP-Rigs Sls & Svcs)

DRAGON POLYMERS INC.
1301 Southwest Blvd, Jefferson City, MO 65109
Tel.: (573) 415-9201 **NV**
Sales Range: Less than $1 Million
Landfill Mining
N.A.I.C.S.: 562212
Daniel Solomita (CEO)

DRAGONEER INVESTMENT GROUP, LLC
101 California St Ste 2840, San Francisco, CA 94111
Tel.: (415) 539-3085 **DE**
Investment Firm
N.A.I.C.S.: 523999
Pat Robertson (Partner, COO & Chief Compliance Officer)
Kelland Reilly (VP)

Subsidiaries:

Arco Platform Limited (1)
Rua Augusta 2840 9th Floor Suite 91, Consolacao, Sao Paulo, 01412-100, Brazil
Tel.: (55) 1130472655
Rev.: $341,325,841
Assets: $1,106,092,688
Liabilities: $741,311,771
Net Worth: $364,780,918
Earnings: $7,591,760
Emp.: 2,935
Fiscal Year-end: 12/31/2022
Educational Software Development Services
N.A.I.C.S.: 541511

Dragoneer Investment Group, LLC—(Continued)

Subsidiary (Domestic):

Nave a Vela Ltda. (2)
R Augusta 2840 - Jardins, Sao Paulo, SP, Brazil
Tel.: (55) 11988828432
Web Site: https://www.naveavela.com.br
Education Training Services
N.A.I.C.S.: 611110
Tadeu Omae (Product Mgr)

SAE Digital S.A. (2)
Rua Joao Domachoski 5 Mossungue, Curitiba, 81200-150, Parana, Brazil
Tel.: (55) 8007259797
Web Site: https://sae.digital
Education Training Services
N.A.I.C.S.: 611110

DRAGOS, INC.
1745 Dorsey Rd Ste R, Hanover, MD 21076
Tel.: (855) 372-4670   DE
Web Site: http://www.dragos.com
Year Founded: 2016
Software Security & Services
N.A.I.C.S.: 513210
Kate Kawalek (VP-Customer Success)
Darren Sankbeil (CFO)
Robert M. Lee (Founder & CEO)
Ben Miller (VP-Svcs)
Jodi Cathey (VP-Engrg)
Jill Samuel (VP-HR)
Meg Kammerud (Gen Counsel)
Jon Lavender (CTO & Head-Product)
Christophe Culine (Chief Revenue Officer & Pres-Global Sls)
Christophe Culine (Chief Revenue Officer & Pres-Global Sls)

DRAHOTA COMMERCIAL LLC.
4700 Innovation Dr Ste C, Fort Collins, CO 80525
Tel.: (970) 204-0100
Web Site: http://www.drahota.com
Year Founded: 1972
Sales Range: $10-24.9 Million
Emp.: 62
Nonresidential Construction Services
N.A.I.C.S.: 236220
Patty Williams (Mgr-Bus)

DRAKE COOPER INC.
416 S 8th St Ste 300, Boise, ID 83702-5471
Tel.: (208) 342-0925   ID
Web Site:
    https://www.drakecooper.com
Year Founded: 1987
Sales Range: $10-24.9 Million
Emp.: 36
Advertising Services
N.A.I.C.S.: 541810
Katie S. Nichols (Sr Dir-Art)
Jeremy Chase (VP-Client Svcs)
Sara A. Chase (Acct Dir)
Jamie Cooper (CEO)
Jennie Myers (Dir-Creative)
John Drake (VP-Brand Plng)
Meghan Rae (Dir-Media)
Malia Cramer (Brand Mgr)
Josh Mercaldo (Dir-Tourism Acct)
Cale Cathey (Art Dir)
Andrew Piron (Pres & COO)
Brad Weigle (Dir-Digital)
Chris Watts (Project Mgr)
Colleen Cahill (Dir-Art)
Dannielle Nicholson (Dir-Art)
Jessica Carter (Mgr-Brand)
Mattie Stanford (Project Mgr)
Michael Wilson (CTO)
Mona Teffeteller (Acct Dir)
Nikson Mathews (Dir-Art)

DRAKE ENTERPRISES LTD.
235 E Palmer St, Franklin, NC 28734

Tel.: (828) 524-8020
Web Site:
    https://www.drakesoftware.com
Year Founded: 1977
Sales Range: $25-49.9 Million
Emp.: 500
Prepackaged Software
N.A.I.C.S.: 513210
Phil Drake (Owner)
Rhonda Stevens (Partner-HR Bus)

DRAKE, INC.
4315 Sheriff Rd NE, Washington, DC 20019
Tel.: (202) 291-3174
Web Site: https://www.drake-inc.com
Year Founded: 2001
Sales Range: $10-24.9 Million
Emp.: 10
Construction Engineering Services
N.A.I.C.S.: 541330
Joseph Wilson (Sr Project Mgr)

DRAKE-WILLIAMS STEEL INC.
2301 Hickory St, Omaha, NE 68108
Tel.: (402) 342-1043
Web Site: https://www.dwsteel.com
Rev.: $40,000,000
Emp.: 150
Fabricated Structural Metal
N.A.I.C.S.: 332312
Chad Jensen (Mgr-Ops)
Matt Cole (Dir-Bus Dev)

DRAKEN INTERNATIONAL INC.
3330 Flightline Dr, Lakeland, FL 33811
Tel.: (800) 936-4079
Web Site: http://www.drakenintl.com
Sales Range: $1-9.9 Million
Tactical Aircrafts
N.A.I.C.S.: 336411

DRAKONTAS LLC
200 Federal St Ste 300, Camden, NJ 08103
Tel.: (856) 283-3327
Web Site: http://www.drakontas.com
Year Founded: 2004
Sales Range: $1-9.9 Million
Emp.: 19
Software & Technology Consulting
N.A.I.C.S.: 541519
Brian Regli (Co-Founder & CEO)
James J. Sim (Co-Founder, Pres & COO)
William Regli (Co-Founder)

DRAPER CHEVROLET COMPANY
4200 Bay Rd, Saginaw, MI 48603
Tel.: (989) 790-0800
Web Site: http://www.draperauto.com
Sales Range: $25-49.9 Million
Emp.: 125
Car Dealership Owner & Operator
N.A.I.C.S.: 441110
Robert G. Draper (Pres)

DRAPER HOLDINGS BUSINESS TRUST
1729 N Salisbury Blvd, Salisbury, MD 21801
Tel.: (410) 749-1111
Web Site: http://www.wboc.com
Sales Range: $10-24.9 Million
Emp.: 100
Television Broadcasting Station
N.A.I.C.S.: 516120
Thomas H. Draper (Owner & Pres)
Laura Baker (CFO & VP)

Subsidiaries:

WBOC Inc. (1)

1729 N Salisbury Blvd, Salisbury, MD 21801
Tel.: (410) 749-1111
Web Site: http://www.wboc.com
Sales Range: $1-9.9 Million
Television Broadcasting Station
N.A.I.C.S.: 516120
Laura Baker (COO & VP)

DRAPER INC.
411 S Pearl St, Spiceland, IN 47385
Tel.: (765) 987-7999
Web Site: https://www.draperinc.com
Sales Range: $100-124.9 Million
Emp.: 500
Projection Screens & Related Products Mfr
N.A.I.C.S.: 334310
Brian Cassley (Mgr-Sls-Europe)
Jed Vardaman (Product Mgr)
Gretchen Gander-Donaldson (Reg Mgr-Sls)
Kathy Greenway (Reg Mgr-Contract Sls)
Brian Kunz (Reg Mgr-Sls)
Jim Judy (Mgr-Architectural Screens Product)
Art Tober (Reg Mgr-Contract Sls)
Matt Schultz (Reg Mgr-Contract Sls)
Leo Nickel (Reg Mgr-Sls)

DRAPER KNITTING CO., INC.
28 Draper Ln, Canton, MA 02021-1693
Tel.: (781) 828-0029   MA
Web Site:
    https://www.draperknitting.com
Year Founded: 1984
Sales Range: $75-99.9 Million
Emp.: 40
Knitted Fabrics, Safety Fabrics & Non-Woven Fabrics Mfr
N.A.I.C.S.: 313240
Kristin Draper (Pres & Mgr-Mktg & Dev)
Robert Vassi (Reg Mgr-Sls)
Connie Kinsella (Mgr-Payroll)

DRAPHIX, LLC
1200B Roberts Industrial Dr, Birmingham, AL 35208
Tel.: (205) 226-0830
Web Site:
    https://www.teacherdirect.com
Year Founded: 2001
Sales Range: $10-24.9 Million
Emp.: 35
Classroom Equipment & Supplies Whslr
N.A.I.C.S.: 423490
Jack Womack (Gen Mgr)

DRAVON MEDICAL, INC.
11465 SE Hwy 212, Clackamas, OR 97015
Tel.: (503) 656-6600   WA
Web Site: https://www.dravon.com
Year Founded: 1974
Sales Range: $10-24.9 Million
Emp.: 25
Disposable Medical Products & Custom Bags Mfr & Contract Services
N.A.I.C.S.: 339112
Michael P. Napoli (Pres & CEO)
Richard W. Parker (VP-Fin)
Alan Crowe (Engr-Sls)

DRAYTON RICHDALE CORP.
6130 W Flamingo Rd 370, Las Vegas, NV 89103
Tel.: (702) 605-7285
Web Site:
    http://www.draytonrichdale.com
Financial Investment Services
N.A.I.C.S.: 523999
Antonio Arnel Maquera (Chm & CEO)

DRC INC.
740 Museum Dr, Mobile, AL 36608
Tel.: (251) 343-3581
Web Site: http://www.drcusa.com
Rev.: $29,473,397
Emp.: 20
General Remodeling Single-Family Houses Reconstruction Services
N.A.I.C.S.: 236118
Mark Stafford (VP-Ops Recovery)
Kristy Fuentes (Chief Exec Compliance Officer, Sec & VP)
Les Flynn (CFO)
Stephen A. Meyer (Asst Dir-Pub Works)
Leo T. Lucchesi (Dir-Pub Works)
Harry Hayes (Dir-Solid Waste Mgmt)
Lisa Garcia (Mgr-Contracts)
Marc Watkins (VP-Estimating)

DRD NORTHWEST LLC
101 E Hopi Dr, Holbrook, AZ 86025
Tel.: (928) 524-3680
Web Site: http://www.myqkinc.com
Sales Range: $10-24.9 Million
Emp.: 3,000
Eating Place
N.A.I.C.S.: 722511
Robbie Qualls (Pres)
Irma Carpenter (Dir-Fin)

DREAM CENTER FOUNDATION, A CALIFORNIA NONPROFIT CORP.
2301 Bellevue Ave, Los Angeles, CA 90026
Tel.: (213) 273-7000   CA
Web Site: https://dreamcenter.org
Year Founded: 2008
Faith-based Charitable Church Organization
N.A.I.C.S.: 813110
Matthew Barnett (Founder)
Jack Carey (Sec)

Subsidiaries:

Education Management Corporation (1)
210 6th Ave 33rd Fl, Pittsburgh, PA 15222-2598
Tel.: (412) 562-0900
Web Site: http://www.edmc.edu
Post-Secondary Education Services
N.A.I.C.S.: 611710
Mark A. McEachen (Pres & CEO)

Subsidiary (Domestic):

Argosy Education Group, Inc. (2)
20 S Clark St Ste 2800, Chicago, IL 60603
Tel.: (312) 899-9900
Educational Support Services
N.A.I.C.S.: 611710

Subsidiary (Domestic):

Argosy University Family Center, Inc. (3)
310 E 38th St, Minneapolis, MN 55409
Tel.: (612) 827-5981
Educational Support Services
N.A.I.C.S.: 611710

Argosy University of Florida, Inc. (3)
1403 N Howard Ave, Tampa, FL 33607
Tel.: (813) 393-5290
Web Site: http://www.argosy.edu
Educational Support Services
N.A.I.C.S.: 611710
Jeff Day (Pres)

The Connecting Link, Inc. (3)
5126 Ralston St, Ventura, CA 93003
Tel.: (888) 550-5465
Web Site: http://www.connectinglink.com
Educational Support Services
N.A.I.C.S.: 611710

Subsidiary (Domestic):

Argosy University (2)

205 N Michigan Ave Ste 1300, Chicago, IL 60601
Tel.: (312) 899-9900
Web Site: http://www.argosyeducation.com
Sales Range: $10-24.9 Million
Emp.: 55
Postgraduate Educational Services
N.A.I.C.S.: 611310

Subsidiary (Domestic):

Argosy University/Atlanta   (3)
980 Hammond Dr Ste 100, Atlanta, GA 30328
Tel.: (770) 671-1200
Rev.: $1,500,000
Emp.: 25
Education Services
N.A.I.C.S.: 611310

Argosy University/Chicago   (3)
225 N Michigan Ave Ste 1300, Chicago, IL 60601
Tel.: (312) 777-7600
Web Site: http://www.argosy.edu
Sales Range: $10-24.9 Million
Emp.: 55
Post-Secondary Education Services
N.A.I.C.S.: 611310
C. Ronald Kimberling (Pres)

Argosy University/Dallas   (3)
5001 Lyndon B Johnson Fwy, Farmers Branch, TX 75244
Tel.: (214) 890-9900
Sales Range: $10-24.9 Million
Emp.: 30
College & University
N.A.I.C.S.: 611310
Ron Hyson (Pres-Dallas Campus)

Argosy University/Honolulu   (3)
10001 Bishop St Ste 400, Honolulu, HI 96813
Tel.: (808) 536-5555
Web Site: http://www.argosyu.edu
Sales Range: $10-24.9 Million
College & University
N.A.I.C.S.: 611310
Warren Evans (Pres)

Argosy University/Orange County   (3)
601 S Lewis St, Orange, CA 92868
Tel.: (714) 338-6200
Sales Range: $10-24.9 Million
Emp.: 50
College & University
N.A.I.C.S.: 611310
Jeb Egbert (Pres)
Marilyn Al-Hassan (Pres)

Argosy University/Phoenix   (3)
2233 W Dunlap Ave Ste 150, Phoenix, AZ 85021
Tel.: (602) 216-2600
Web Site: http://www.argosy.edu
Sales Range: $10-24.9 Million
Emp.: 35
College & University
N.A.I.C.S.: 611310

Argosy University/Sarasota   (3)
5250 17th St, Sarasota, FL 34235
Tel.: (941) 379-0404
Web Site: http://www.argosy.edu
Sales Range: $10-24.9 Million
College & University
N.A.I.C.S.: 611310
Joffrey Suprina (Chm-Program)
Ann Weaver (Chm-Res Program)

Argosy University/Schaumburg   (3)
999 N Plz Dr Ste 111, Schaumburg, IL 60173
Tel.: (847) 969-4900
Web Site: http://www.argosyu.edu
Sales Range: $10-24.9 Million
College & University
N.A.I.C.S.: 611310
Barbara Hochgesang (Coord-Clinical Psychology Support)

Argosy University/Seattle   (3)
2601A Elliott Ave, Seattle, WA 98121-1318
Tel.: (206) 283-4500
Sales Range: $10-24.9 Million
Emp.: 30
College & University
N.A.I.C.S.: 611310

Tom Dyer (Pres)

Argosy University/Tampa   (3)
1403 N Howard Ave, Tampa, FL 33607
Tel.: (813) 393-5290
Web Site: http://www.argosy.edu
Sales Range: $10-24.9 Million
Emp.: 30
Post-Secondary Education Services
N.A.I.C.S.: 611310

Argosy University/Twin Cities   (3)
1515 Central Pkwy, Eagan, MN 55121
Tel.: (651) 846-2882
Web Site: http://www.argosy.edu
Post-Secondary Education Services
N.A.I.C.S.: 611310

Argosy University/Washington DC   (3)
1550 Wilson Blvd Ste 600, Arlington, VA 22209
Tel.: (703) 526-5800
Web Site: http://www.argosy.edu
Post-Secondary Education Services
N.A.I.C.S.: 611310
David Erekson (Pres)

Subsidiary (Domestic):

Brown Mackie College - Atlanta/College Park, Inc.   (2)
4370 Peachtree Rd NE, Atlanta, GA 30319
Tel.: (404) 799-4500
Web Site: http://www.brownmackie.edu
Educational Support Services
N.A.I.C.S.: 611710
C. James (Dir-Admin)

Brown Mackie College - Boise, Inc.   (2)
9050 W Overland Rd Ste 100, Boise, ID 83709
Tel.: (208) 321-8800
Web Site: http://www.brownmackie.edu
Emp.: 40
Educational Support Services
N.A.I.C.S.: 611710
Debbie Jones (Pres)

Brown Mackie College - Dallas/ Ft. Worth LLC   (2)
2200 N Hwy 121 Ste 250, Bedford, TX 76021
Tel.: (817) 799-0500
Web Site: http://www.brownmackie.edu
Emp.: 75
Educational Support Services
N.A.I.C.S.: 611710
Tod M. Gibbs (Pres)

Brown Mackie College - Miami, Inc.   (2)
3700 Lakeside Dr, Miramar, FL 33027-3264
Tel.: (305) 341-6600
Web Site: http://www.brownmackie.edu
Educational Support Services
N.A.I.C.S.: 611710
Julia Denniston (Pres)

Brown Mackie College - San Antonio LLC   (2)
4715 Fredericksburg Rd Ste 100, San Antonio, TX 78229
Tel.: (210) 428-2210
Web Site: http://www.brownmackie.edu
Educational Support Services
N.A.I.C.S.: 611710
Nora Nieto (Mgr-HR)

Brown Mackie College - Tulsa, Inc.   (2)
4608 S Garnett Ste 110, Tulsa, OK 74146
Tel.: (918) 628-3700
Web Site: http://www.brownmackie.edu
Educational Support Services
N.A.I.C.S.: 611710
John Pappas (Pres)

Brown Mackie College-Birmingham LLC   (2)
105 Vulcan Rd Ste 100, Birmingham, AL 35209
Tel.: (205) 909-1500
Web Site: http://www.brownmackie.edu
Educational Support Services
N.A.I.C.S.: 611710
Claire Walker (Pres)

Brown Mackie College-Fort Wayne   (2)

3000 E Coliseum Blvd, Fort Wayne, IN 46805
Tel.: (260) 484-4400
Web Site: http://www.brownmackie.edu
Sales Range: $25-49.9 Million
Emp.: 110
Education Services
N.A.I.C.S.: 611699
Jim Bishop (CEO)

Brown Mackie College-Tucson, Inc.   (2)
4585 E Speedway Blvd Ste 204, Tucson, AZ 85712
Tel.: (520) 319-3300
Web Site: http://www.brownmackie.edu
Educational Support Services
N.A.I.C.S.: 611710
Tim Bush (Pres)

Subsidiary (Domestic):

Brown Mackie College-Albuquerque LLC   (3)
10500 Copper Ave NE, Albuquerque, NM 87123
Tel.: (505) 559-5200
Web Site: http://www.brownmackie.edu
Educational Support Services
N.A.I.C.S.: 611710
Sami Fanek (Pres)

Brown Mackie College-Greenville, Inc.   (3)
75 Beattie Pl Ste 100, Greenville, SC 29601
Tel.: (864) 239-5300
Web Site: http://www.brownmackie.edu
Emp.: 150
Educational Support Services
N.A.I.C.S.: 611710
Karen Burges (Pres)

Brown Mackie College-Phoenix, Inc.   (3)
13430 N Black Canyon Hwy Ste 190, Phoenix, AZ 85029
Tel.: (602) 337-3044
Web Site: http://www.brownmackie.edu
Emp.: 200
Educational Support Services
N.A.I.C.S.: 611710
Mike Fontaine (Pres-Campus)

Brown Mackie College-St. Louis, Inc.   (3)
2 Soccer Park Rd, Saint Louis, MO 63026
Tel.: (636) 651-3290
Web Site: http://www.brownmackie.edu
Emp.: 50
Educational Support Services
N.A.I.C.S.: 611710
Keith Grant (Pres)

Subsidiary (Domestic):

Brown Mackie Education Corporation   (2)
9705 Lenexa Dr, Lenexa, KS 66215-1345
Tel.: (913) 768-1900
Web Site: http://www.brownmackie.edu
Emp.: 25
Educational Support Services
N.A.I.C.S.: 611710
Andrew Spiller (Mgr-HR)

Subsidiary (Domestic):

Brown Mackie College-Salina LLC   (3)
2106 S 9th St, Salina, KS 67401
Tel.: (785) 825-5422
Web Site: http://www.brownmackie.edu
Educational Support Services
N.A.I.C.S.: 611710

Subsidiary (Domestic):

Brown Mackie College-Kansas City LLC   (4)
9705 Lenexa Dr, Lenexa, KS 66215
Tel.: (913) 768-1900
Web Site: http://www.brownmackie.edu
Educational Support Services
N.A.I.C.S.: 611710

Brown Mackie College-Oklahoma City LLC   (4)
7101 NW Expy Ste 800, Oklahoma City, OK 73132
Tel.: (405) 621-8000

Web Site: http://www.brownmackie.edu
Educational Support Services
N.A.I.C.S.: 611710
Don Parker (Office Mgr)

Subsidiary (Domestic):

EDMC Marketing and Advertising, Inc.   (2)
210 6th Ave 33rd Fl, Pittsburgh, PA 15222
Tel.: (412) 562-0900
Educational Support Services
N.A.I.C.S.: 611710

Higher Education Services, Inc.   (2)
4720 Carlisle Pike Ste 200, Mechanicsburg, PA 17050
Tel.: (717) 731-9350
Web Site: http://www.highereducationservices.org
Educational Support Services
N.A.I.C.S.: 611710

South University   (2)
709 Mall Blvd, Savannah, GA 31406-4805
Tel.: (912) 201-8000
Web Site: http://www.southuniversity.edu
Colleges & Universities
N.A.I.C.S.: 611310
Betsy Nolen (Dir-Comm)
Kim Hahn (Mgr-Enrollment)
Marilou Jean Louise (Coord-Clinical)

Branch (Domestic):

South University - Columbia   (3)
9 Science Ct, Columbia, SC 29203
Tel.: (803) 799-9082
Web Site: http://www.southuniversity.edu
Post-Secondary Education Services
N.A.I.C.S.: 611310

South University - Montgomery   (3)
5355 Vaughn Rd, Montgomery, AL 36116
Tel.: (334) 395-8800
Web Site: http://www.southuniversity.edu
Emp.: 175
Post-Secondary Education Services
N.A.I.C.S.: 611310
Victor K. Biebighauser (Pres)

South University - West Palm Beach   (3)
9801 Belvedere Rd, Royal Palm Beach, FL 33411
Tel.: (561) 697-9200
Web Site: http://www.southuniversity.edu
Post-Secondary Education Services
N.A.I.C.S.: 611310
David McGuire (Pres)
Creola Thomas (Pres)

Subsidiary (Domestic):

South University, LLC   (2)
709 Mall Blvd, Savannah, GA 31406-4805
Tel.: (912) 201-8000
Web Site: http://www.southuniversity.edu
Educational Support Services
N.A.I.C.S.: 611710

Subsidiary (Domestic):

South Education - Texas LLC   (3)
7700 W Parmer Ln Bldg A Ste 100A, Austin, TX 78729-8101
Tel.: (877) 659-5706
Web Site: http://www.southuniversity.edu
Sales Range: $10-24.9 Million
Educational Support Services
N.A.I.C.S.: 611710
Shelby Frutchey (Pres)

South University of Alabama, Inc.   (3)
5355 Vaughn Rd, Montgomery, AL 36116-1120
Tel.: (334) 395-8800
Web Site: http://www.southuniversity.edu
Emp.: 100
Educational Support Services
N.A.I.C.S.: 611710
Victor K. Biebighauser (Pres)

South University of Arizona LLC   (3)
1140 N Colombo Ave, Sierra Vista, AZ 85635
Tel.: (520) 458-8278
Web Site: http://www.uas.arizona.edu
Emp.: 50
Educational Support Services

Dream Center Foundation, a California Nonprofit
Corp.—(Continued)

N.A.I.C.S.: 611710
Brian Bates (Mgr-IT)

South University of Carolina, Inc. (3)
9 Science Ct, Columbia, SC 29203
Tel.: (803) 799-9082
Web Site: http://www.southuniversity.edu
Educational Support Services
N.A.I.C.S.: 611710

South University of Florida, Inc. (3)
4401 N Himes Ave Ste 175, Tampa, FL
33614-7095
Tel.: (813) 393-3800
Web Site: http://www.southuniversity.edu
Educational Support Services
N.A.I.C.S.: 611710
Dan Coble (Pres)

**South University of Michigan,
LLC** (3)
41555 Twelve Mile Rd, Novi, MI 48377
Tel.: (248) 675-0200
Web Site: http://www.southuniversity.edu
Educational Support Services
N.A.I.C.S.: 611710

**South University of North Carolina
LLC** (3)
3975 Premier Dr, High Point, NC 27265
Tel.: (336) 812-7200
Web Site: http://www.southuniversity.edu
Emp.: 20
Educational Support Services
N.A.I.C.S.: 611710
Michael Trembley (Pres)

South University of Ohio LLC (3)
4743 Richmond Rd, Warrensville Heights,
OH 44128
Tel.: (216) 755-5000
Web Site: http://www.southuniversity.edu
Sales Range: $10-24.9 Million
Emp.: 50
Educational Support Services
N.A.I.C.S.: 611710
Scott Behmer (Pres)

The Art Institute of Dallas, Inc. (3)
8080 Park Ln Ste 100, Dallas, TX 75231-
5993
Tel.: (214) 692-8080
Web Site: http://www.artinstitutes.edu
Sales Range: $25-49.9 Million
Emp.: 180
Fine Arts School
N.A.I.C.S.: 611610
Leslie C. Baughman (VP-Academic Affairs)
Tommy Newsom (Pres)

Subsidiary (Domestic):

AID Restaurant, Inc. (4)
8080 Park Ln Ste 100, Dallas, TX 75231
Tel.: (214) 692-8080
Web Site: http://www.artinstitutes.com
Emp.: 100
Restaurant Operating Services
N.A.I.C.S.: 722511
Jodie Hall (Mgr-HR)

**The Art Institute of Fort Worth,
Inc.** (4)
7000 Calmont Ave Ste 150, Fort Worth, TX
76116
Tel.: (817) 210-0808
Web Site: http://www.artinstitutes.edu
Sales Range: $25-49.9 Million
Emp.: 50
Educational Support Services
N.A.I.C.S.: 611710

Subsidiary (Domestic):

TAIC- San Diego, Inc. (2)
7650 Mission Valley Rd, San Diego, CA
92108-4423
Tel.: (858) 598-1200
Web Site: http://www.aicasd.artinstitutes.edu
Sales Range: $10-24.9 Million
Emp.: 50
Art School
N.A.I.C.S.: 611610

Subsidiary (Domestic):

**The Art Institute of California - Inland
Empire, Inc.** (3)

674 E Brier Dr, San Bernardino, CA 92408
Tel.: (909) 915-2100
Web Site: http://www.artinstitutes.edu
Emp.: 500
Educational Support Services
N.A.I.C.S.: 611710
Matthew Madrid (Pres)

Subsidiary (Domestic):

TAIC- San Francisco, Inc. (2)
1170 Market St, San Francisco, CA 94102-
4928
Tel.: (415) 865-0198
Web Site: http://www.artinstitutes.edu
Sales Range: $25-49.9 Million
Emp.: 100
Art School
N.A.I.C.S.: 611610

Subsidiary (Domestic):

**The Art Institute of California - Los
Angeles, Inc.** (3)
2900 31st St, Santa Monica, CA 90405-
3035
Tel.: (310) 752-4700
Web Site: http://www.artinstitutes.edu
Fine Arts School
N.A.I.C.S.: 611610
Laura Soloff (Pres)

**The Art Institute of California - Or-
ange County, Inc.** (3)
3601 W Sunflower Ave, Santa Ana, CA
92704-9888
Tel.: (714) 830-0200
Web Site: http://www.aicaoc.artinstitutes.edu
Sales Range: $10-24.9 Million
Emp.: 100
Fine Arts School
N.A.I.C.S.: 611610
Steve Rickard (Dir-Student Affairs)
Siovia Guzman (Dir-Fin & Admin)
Harry Ramos (Sr Dir-Admissions)

**The Art Institute of California - Sacra-
mento, Inc.** (3)
2850 Gateway Oaks Dr Ste 100, Sacra-
mento, CA 95833
Tel.: (916) 830-6320
Web Site: http://www.aii.edu
Emp.: 75
Educational Support Services
N.A.I.C.S.: 611710
John Andersen (Pres)

Subsidiary (Domestic):

**The Art Institutes International
LLC** (2)
420 Blvd of the Allies, Pittsburgh, PA 15222
Tel.: (412) 995-7685
Web Site: http://www.artinstitutes.edu
Art Schools
N.A.I.C.S.: 611310
Charles Restivo (Pres)

Subsidiary (Domestic):

**Miami International University of Art &
Design** (3)
1501 Biscayne Blvd, Miami, FL
33132 (100%)
Tel.: (305) 428-5700
Web Site: http://new.artinstitutes.edu
Emp.: 175
Colleges & Universities
N.A.I.C.S.: 611310
Erika Fleming (Pres)
Devra Pransky (Sr Dir-Comm)
Cherme Lucero (Coord-Featured Program)
Angelina Martin (Coord-Featured Program)
Carol Ashley (Dir-Academic Dept)
Kristy Janigo (Dir-Academic Dept)
Chris Chen Mahoney (Dir-Academic Dept)

The Art Institute of Atlanta, LLC (3)
6600 Peachtree Dunwoody Rd 100 Em-
bassy Row, Atlanta, GA 30328-1649
Tel.: (770) 394-8300
Web Site: http://www.aia.artinstitutes.edu
Sales Range: $25-49.9 Million
Emp.: 300
Fine Arts School
N.A.I.C.S.: 611610

Subsidiary (Domestic):

**The Art Institute of Virginia Beach
LLC** (4)

2 Columbus Ctr 4500 Main St Ste 100, Vir-
ginia Beach, VA 23462
Tel.: (757) 493-6700
Web Site: http://www.artinstitutes.edu
Educational Support Services
N.A.I.C.S.: 611710

Subsidiary (Domestic):

The Art Institute of Austin, Inc. (3)
101 W Louis Henna Blvd Ste 100, Austin,
TX 78728
Tel.: (512) 691-1707
Web Site: http://www.artinstitutes.edu
Educational Support Services
N.A.I.C.S.: 611710
Monica Jeffs (Pres)

**The Art Institute of California - Holly-
wood, Inc.** (3)
5250 Lankershim Blvd, North Hollywood,
CA 91601
Tel.: (818) 299-5100
Web Site: http://www.artinstitutes.edu
Sales Range: $10-24.9 Million
Emp.: 70
Art & Design School
N.A.I.C.S.: 611610
Liz Kok (Acct Dir)

**The Art Institute of California - Sunny-
vale, Inc.** (3)
1120 Kifer Rd Silicon Vly 01, San Fran-
cisco, CA 94086
Tel.: (408) 962-6400
Web Site: http://www.artinstitutes.edu
Fine Arts School
N.A.I.C.S.: 611610
Tim Hansen (Pres)

**The Art Institute of Charleston,
Inc.** (3)
24 N Market St, Charleston, SC 29401-
2623
Tel.: (843) 727-3500
Web Site: http://www.artinstitutes.edu
Educational Support Services
N.A.I.C.S.: 611710
Todd Cunningham (Pres)

**The Art Institute of Charlotte,
LLC** (3)
3 Lake Pointe Plz 2210 Water Rdg Pkwy,
Charlotte, NC 28217-4536
Tel.: (704) 357-8020
Web Site: http://www.artinstitutes.edu
Sales Range: $10-24.9 Million
Emp.: 100
Fine Arts School
N.A.I.C.S.: 611610
Mark M. Martin (Dir-Academics)

Subsidiary (Domestic):

**The Art Institute of Raleigh-Durham,
Inc.** (4)
410 Blackwell St Ste 200, Durham, NC
27701
Tel.: (919) 317-3050
Web Site: http://www.artinstitutes.edu
Educational Support Services
N.A.I.C.S.: 611710
Christopher Mesecar (Pres)

Subsidiary (Domestic):

The Art Institute of Colorado, Inc. (3)
1200 Lincoln St, Denver, CO 80203-2172
Tel.: (303) 837-0825
Web Site: http://www.artinstitutes.edu
Sales Range: $10-24.9 Million
Emp.: 100
Fine Arts School
N.A.I.C.S.: 611610
Janet Day (Pres)

Subsidiary (Domestic):

The Art Institute of St. Louis, Inc. (4)
1520 S 5th St Ste 107, Saint Charles, MO
63303
Tel.: (636) 688-3010
Web Site: http://www.artinstitutes.edu
Educational Support Services
N.A.I.C.S.: 611710

Subsidiary (Domestic):

**The Art Institute of Fort Lauderdale,
Inc.** (3)

1799 SE 17th St, Fort Lauderdale, FL
33316-3000 (100%)
Tel.: (954) 463-3000
Web Site: http://www.artinstitutes.edu
Sales Range: $25-49.9 Million
Emp.: 350
Fine Arts School
N.A.I.C.S.: 611610
Carolyn Pierce (Pres)

The Art Institute of Houston, Inc. (3)
4140 SW Freeway, Houston, TX
77027 (100%)
Tel.: (713) 623-2040
Web Site: http://www.artinstitutes.edu
Sales Range: $25-49.9 Million
Emp.: 200
Fine Arts School
N.A.I.C.S.: 611610

**The Art Institute of Indianapolis,
LLC** (3)
3500 Depauw Blvd Ste1010, Indianapolis,
IN 46268-6124
Tel.: (317) 613-4800
Web Site: http://www.artinstitutes.edu
Emp.: 100
Educational Support Services
N.A.I.C.S.: 611710
Chad Robertson (Sr Dir-Admissions)

**The Art Institute of Jacksonville,
Inc.** (3)
8775 Baypine Rd, Jacksonville, FL 32256-
8528
Tel.: (904) 486-3000
Web Site: http://www.artinstitutes.edu
Sales Range: $10-24.9 Million
Emp.: 75
Educational Support Services
N.A.I.C.S.: 611710
Erika Fleming (Pres)

**The Art Institute of New York City,
Inc.** (3)
11-17 Beach, New York, NY
10013-1917 (100%)
Tel.: (212) 226-5500
Web Site: http://www.artinstitutes.edu
Sales Range: $50-74.9 Million
Emp.: 150
Fine Arts School
N.A.I.C.S.: 611610

**The Art Institute of Philadelphia
LLC** (3)
1622 Chestnut St, Philadelphia, PA
19103-5198 (100%)
Tel.: (215) 567-7080
Web Site: http://www.artinstitutes.edu
Sales Range: $25-49.9 Million
Emp.: 400
Fine Arts School
N.A.I.C.S.: 611610
William V. Larkin (Pres)

**The Art Institute of Pittsburgh
LLC** (3)
420 Blvd of the Allies, Pittsburgh, PA
15219-3203 (100%)
Tel.: (412) 291-6200
Web Site: http://www.artinstitutes.edu
Sales Range: $25-49.9 Million
Emp.: 225
Fine Arts School
N.A.I.C.S.: 611610
Melinda Trempus (Dir-College Affiliate Pro-
grams)
Kathy Ober (Dir-Library Svcs)
George W. Sebolt (Pres)

Division (Domestic):

The Art Institute Online (4)
1400 Penn Ave, Pittsburgh, PA 15222
Tel.: (412) 291-5100
Web Site: http://www.aionline.edu
Online Creative Arts Education
N.A.I.C.S.: 611310

Subsidiary (Domestic):

The Art Institute of Portland, Inc. (3)
1122 NW Davis St, Portland, OR
97209-4907 (100%)
Tel.: (503) 228-6528
Web Site: http://www.artinstitutes.edu
Sales Range: $25-49.9 Million
Emp.: 200
Fine Arts School

28175 Cabot Dr Ste 120, Novi, MI 48377
Tel.: (248) 675-3800
Web Site: http://www.artinstitutes.edu
Emp.: 55
Educational Support Services
N.A.I.C.S.: 611710
Tracey Bass (Pres)

The Art Institute of San Antonio, Inc. (3)
10000 IH 10 W Ste 200 Ste 106, San Antonio, TX 78230
Tel.: (210) 338-7320
Web Site: http://www.artinstitutes.edu
Emp.: 50
Educational Support Services
N.A.I.C.S.: 611710
Brendan Mesch (Pres)

The Art Institute of Seattle, Inc. (3)
2323 Elliott Ave, Seattle, WA
98121-1642 (100%)
Tel.: (206) 448-0900
Web Site: http://www.artinstitutes.edu
Sales Range: $25-49.9 Million
Emp.: 500
Fine Arts School
N.A.I.C.S.: 611610
Elden Monday (Pres)

The Art Institute of Tampa, Inc. (3)
4401 N Himes Ave Ste 150, Tampa, FL
33614 (100%)
Tel.: (813) 873-2112
Web Site: http://www.artinstitutes.edu
Fine Arts School
N.A.I.C.S.: 611610
Karen Habblitz (Pres)

The Art Institute of Tennessee - Nashville, Inc. (3)
100 Centerview Dr Ste 250, Nashville, TN
37214-3439
Tel.: (615) 874-1067
Web Site: http://www.artinstitutes.edu
Emp.: 200
Educational Support Services
N.A.I.C.S.: 611710
Carol Menck (Pres)

The Art Institute of Washington - Dulles LLC (3)
Dulles Town Ctr 21000 Atlantic Blvd Ste
100, Dulles, VA 20166
Tel.: (571) 449-4400
Web Site: http://www.artinstitutes.edu
Educational Support Services
N.A.I.C.S.: 611710
Gregg Crowe (Dir-Campus)

The Art Institute of Washington, Inc. (3)
1820 N Fort Myer Dr, Arlington, VA
22209-1802 (100%)
Tel.: (703) 358-9550
Web Site: http://www.artinstitutes.edu
Sales Range: $10-24.9 Million
Emp.: 102
Art School
N.A.I.C.S.: 611610
Jim Polamo (Pres)
Tiffany Young (Dir-Rels-Arlington)

The Art Institute of York-Pennsylvania LLC (3)
1409 Williams Rd, York, PA 17402-9012
Tel.: (717) 755-2300
Web Site: http://www.artinstitutes.edu
Educational Support Services
N.A.I.C.S.: 611710
Tim Howard (Pres)

The Art Institutes International Minnesota, Inc. (3)
15 S 9th St, Minneapolis, MN
55402-3137 (100%)
Tel.: (612) 332-3361
Web Site: http://www.artinstitutes.edu
Sales Range: Less than $1 Million
Emp.: 200
Art School
N.A.I.C.S.: 611610
Jennifer Sorenson (Pres)

The Illinois Institute of Art, Inc. (3)
350 N Orleans St, Chicago, IL
60654 (100%)
Tel.: (312) 280-3500
Web Site: http://www.artinstitutes.edu
Fine Arts School
N.A.I.C.S.: 611610
John Balester Jenkins (Pres)

Subsidiary (Domestic):

The Art Institute of Michigan, Inc. (4)

The Art Institute of Ohio - Cincinnati, Inc. (4)
8845 Governors Hill Dr Ste 100, Cincinnati,
OH 45249-3317
Tel.: (513) 833-2400
Web Site: http://www.artinstitutes.edu
Fine Arts School
N.A.I.C.S.: 611610
Matthew Madrid (Pres)

The Illinois Institute of Art - Tinley Park LLC (4)
18670 Graphic Dr, Tinley Park, IL 60477
Tel.: (708) 781-4200
Web Site: http://www.artinstitutes.edu
Educational Support Services
N.A.I.C.S.: 611710
Donna L. Gray (Dir-Campus)

The Illinois Institute of Art at Schaumburg, Inc. (4)
1000 N Plz Dr Ste 100, Schaumburg, IL
60173 (100%)
Tel.: (847) 619-3450
Web Site: http://www.ilia.aii.edu
Sales Range: $50-74.9 Million
Emp.: 130
Art School
N.A.I.C.S.: 611610
David W. Ray (Pres)
Julie Spencer (Asst Dir-Admissions)

Subsidiary (Domestic):

The Institute of Post-Secondary Education, Inc. (3)
2233 W Dunlap Ave, Phoenix, AZ 85021-
2859
Tel.: (602) 678-4300
Web Site: http://www.artinstitutes.edu
Sales Range: $10-24.9 Million
Emp.: 35
Fine Arts School
N.A.I.C.S.: 611610

Subsidiary (Domestic):

The Art Institute of Las Vegas, Inc. (4)
2350 Corporate Cir, Henderson, NV
89074-7737 (100%)
Tel.: (702) 369-9944
Web Site: http://www.artinstitutes.edu
Fine Arts School
N.A.I.C.S.: 611610

The Art Institute of Salt Lake City, Inc. (4)
121 W Election Rd Ste 100, Draper, UT
84020-9492
Tel.: (801) 601-4700
Web Site: http://www.artinstitutes.edu
Educational Support Services
N.A.I.C.S.: 611710
Tott Harrison (Pres)

The Art Institute of Tucson, Inc. (4)
5099 E Grant Rd Ste 100, Tucson, AZ
85712
Tel.: (520) 318-2700
Web Site: http://www.artinstitutes.edu
Educational Support Services
N.A.I.C.S.: 611710

The Art Institute of Wisconsin LLC (4)
320 E Buffalo St Ste 100, Milwaukee, WI
53202
Tel.: (414) 978-5000
Web Site: http://www.artinstitutes.edu
Educational Support Services
N.A.I.C.S.: 611710

The Art Institutes International - Kansas City, Inc. (4)
8208 Melrose Dr, Lenexa, KS 66214
Tel.: (913) 217-4600
Web Site: http://www.artinstitutes.edu
Educational Support Services
N.A.I.C.S.: 611710

Natalia Derevyanny (Mgr-PR-North & South
Central Reg)

Subsidiary (Domestic):

The New England Institute of Art, LLC (3)
10 Brookline Pl W, Brookline, MA 02445-
7295
Tel.: (617) 739-1700
Web Site: http://www.artinstitutes.edu
Art School
N.A.I.C.S.: 611610

Subsidiary (Domestic):

Western State University College of Law (2)
1 Banting, Irvine, CA 92618-3601
Tel.: (714) 459-1101
Web Site: http://www.wsulaw.edu
Sales Range: $10-24.9 Million
Emp.: 84
Post-Secondary Education Services
N.A.I.C.S.: 611310
Peg Savala (Dir-HR)

DREAM FINDERS HOMES LLC
360 Corporate Way Ste 100, Orange
Park, FL 32073
Tel.: (904) 644-7670
Web Site:
http://www.dreamfindershomes.com
Year Founded: 2004
Sales Range: $10-24.9 Million
Emp.: 50
New Home Construction
N.A.I.C.S.: 236115
Casey Conner (Coord-Warranty)
John Blanton (VP)
Scott Hayman (Mgr-Ops)

DREAM HOMES LIMITED
314 Route 9, Forked River, NJ 08731
Tel.: (609) 693-8881 NV
Year Founded: 2008
Real Estate Development & Construction Services
N.A.I.C.S.: 531390
Vincent Simonelli (Chm, CEO & CFO)
John Kennedy (VP-Construction)
April Martyn (VP-HR)
Richard Pezzullo (VP-IT)

DREAM POLISHERS, INC.
2701 Ivy Ln, Englewood, FL 34224
Tel.: (941) 473-4180
Web Site:
http://www.dreampolishers.com
Sales Range: Less than $1 Million
Emp.: 4
Furniture & Cabinet Repair, Restoration & Refurnishing
N.A.I.C.S.: 811420
LaDonna Haywood (Pres & Mng Partner)

DREAMBRANDS, INC.
11645 N Cave Creek Rd, Phoenix,
AZ 85020-1325
Tel.: (602) 354-7640
Web Site:
http://www.dreambrands.com
Year Founded: 2004
Sales Range: $1-9.9 Million
Emp.: 15
Develops Natural Health, Diet & Energy Wellness Products
N.A.I.C.S.: 456191
Gary S. Kehoe (CEO)
Jonathan K. Hall (CFO)
Ron Pannuzzo (Pres)
Cecile Kehoe (COO)

DREAMFLY PRODUCTIONS CORPORATION
3107 Cole Ave, Dallas, TX 75204
Tel.: (214) 642-6716 DE

Web Site:
http://www.dreamflyproductions.com
Year Founded: 2002
Emp.: 2
Motion Picture Production Services
N.A.I.C.S.: 512110
Lisa Jenkins (CEO)

DREAMGEAR, LLC
20001 S Western Ave, Torrance, CA
90501
Tel.: (310) 222-5522
Web Site: http://www.dreamgear.net
Year Founded: 2002
Rev.: $35,800,000
Emp.: 63
Electronic Gaming Products
N.A.I.C.S.: 423920
Moe Katouzian (Controller)

DREAMSTYLE REMODELING, INC.
1460 Renaissance Blvd NE, Albuquerque, NM 87107
Tel.: (505) 588-0698
Web Site:
https://www.dreamstyleremodeling.com
Year Founded: 1989
Residential Remodeler
N.A.I.C.S.: 236118
Joyce Hitchner (Founder, Treas & Sec)
Dawn Dewey (Sr VP-Mktg & Bus Dev)
Kellie Linfoot (VP-Consumer Fin)
James Zunno (Gen Mgr-Sls)
Guy W. Bluff (Chief Compliance Officer & Gen Counsel)
Carolyn Fittipaldi (Mgr-Mktg & Comm-New Mexico & Arizona)
Randy Rainey (Gen Mgr-Roofing)
Larry Chavez Jr. (VP-Sls-Sunrooms)

Subsidiaries:

Legacy Custom Building & Remodeling, Inc. (1)
7750 E Gelding Dr Ste 4, Scottsdale, AZ
85260
Tel.: (480) 991-1993
Web Site: http://www.legacyaz.com
Sales Range: $1-9.9 Million
Emp.: 40
Residential Remodeler
N.A.I.C.S.: 236118
Ed Feeney (Production Mgr)

DREAMWEAR, INC.
183 Madison Ave 10th Fl, New York,
NY 10016
Tel.: (212) 684-7799
Web Site: http://www.dreamwear.com
Sales Range: $25-49.9 Million
Emp.: 125
Womens Clothing & Accessories Merchant Whslr
N.A.I.C.S.: 424350
Elliot Franco (Pres)
Felicia Yong (Product Mgr)
Lauren Glover (Product Mgr)

DREDGING SUPPLY COMPANY INC.
156 Airport Rd, Reserve, LA 70084
Tel.: (985) 479-1355
Web Site:
https://www.dscdredge.com
Rev.: $11,062,028
Emp.: 100
Dredging Machinery
N.A.I.C.S.: 333120
William Wetta (CEO)

DREISBACH ENTERPRISES INC.
2530 E 11th St, Oakland, CA 94601
Tel.: (510) 533-6600

Dreisbach Enterprises Inc.—(Continued)

Web Site: https://www.dreisbach.com
Rev.: $10,000,000
Emp.: 40
Real Property Lessor
N.A.I.C.S.: 531190
Ronald Dreisbach (Pres)

DREISILKER ELECTRIC MOTORS INC.
352 Roosevelt Rd, Glen Ellyn, IL 60137
Tel.: (630) 469-7510
Web Site:
   http://www.emotorstore.com
Sales Range: $10-24.9 Million
Emp.: 110
Electrical Motors & Equipment
N.A.I.C.S.: 423610
Steve Ables (Acct Mgr)
Sue Muehlfelt (VP-Fin)

DREISON INTERNATIONAL, INC.
4540 W 160th St, Cleveland, OH 44135-2628
Tel.: (216) 265-8006   OH
Year Founded: 1976
Sales Range: $25-49.9 Million
Emp.: 350
Holding Company
N.A.I.C.S.: 551112
John Berger (Pres & CEO)
Whitney Slaght (CFO)

Subsidiaries:

DCM Manufacturing, Inc.   (1)
4540 W 160th St, Cleveland, OH 44135-2628
Tel.: (216) 265-8006
Web Site: http://www.dcm-mfg.com
Sales Range: $1-9.9 Million
Emp.: 90
Fuel Fired Heaters & Electric Motors Mfr
N.A.I.C.S.: 335312
John Berger (Pres)
Joan France (Mgr-Customer Svc)

KPH Holdings, LLC   (1)
402 E Haven St Ste H, Eaton Rapids, MI 48827
Tel.: (517) 663-4330
Web Site: http://www.vonweise.com
Motors & Generators Mfr
N.A.I.C.S.: 335312
Kevin Hein (Pres)

Maradyne Corporation   (1)
4540 W 160th St, Cleveland, OH 44135-2628
Tel.: (216) 362-0755   (100%)
Web Site: http://www.maradyne.com
Sales Range: $1-9.9 Million
Emp.: 55
Truck & Bus Heaters, Fans, Air Starters, Air Power Steering & Air Dryer Systems Mfr
N.A.I.C.S.: 336320
John Berger (Pres)
John Barrish (Gen Mgr)

Division (Domestic):

Maradyne Corporation - Pow-R-Quik Division   (2)
4540 W 160th St, Cleveland, OH 44135
Tel.: (216) 362-0755
Web Site: http://www.powrquik.com
Motor Vehicle Electrical & Electronic Equipment Mfr
N.A.I.C.S.: 336320
John Barrish (Mgr-Mfg)
Paul Ellsworth (Mgr-Engrg)
Joe Rivera (Mgr-Quality)
John Urbank (Mgr-Product & Sls)

Maradyne Corporation - SuperTrapp Industrial Mufflers Division   (2)
4540 W 160th St, Cleveland, OH 44135
Tel.: (216) 362-0755
Web Site: http://www.maradyne.com
Motor Vehicle Parts Mfr
N.A.I.C.S.: 336390

Marion Fluid Power Division of Maradyne Corp   (2)
4540 West 160th St, Cleveland, OH 44135-2628
Tel.: (216) 362-0755
Web Site: http://www.maradyne.com
Fluid Filters Mfr
N.A.I.C.S.: 336390

Turbo Precleaner Inc   (2)
4540 W 160th St, Cleveland, OH 44135-2628
Tel.: (216) 362-0755
Web Site: http://www.turboprecleaner.com
Off-Road Trucks Air Pre-Cleaners Mfr
N.A.I.C.S.: 333413
John Berger (Owner & Pres)
John Barrish (Gen Mgr)
Tracy Long (Dir-Bus Dev)
Dave Tino (Mgr-Shipping)

Maradyne Mobile Products   (1)
4540 W 160th St, Cleveland, OH 44135
Tel.: (216) 265-8006
Web Site: http://www.maradynemobile.com
Sales Range: $10-24.9 Million
Emp.: 80
Industrial Fan & Blower Mfr
N.A.I.C.S.: 333314
John Berger (Gen Mgr)

SuperTrapp Industries, Inc.   (1)
4540 W 160th St, Cleveland, OH 44135
Tel.: (216) 265-8400
Web Site: http://www.supertrapp.com
Sales Range: $10-24.9 Million
Emp.: 100
Motorcycles & ATVs Exhaust Systems Mfr
N.A.I.C.S.: 336390
Kevin Berger (Pres)

Subsidiary (Domestic):

JayBrake, LLC   (2)
4540 W 160th St, Cleveland, OH 44135-2628
Tel.: (216) 265-8400
Web Site: http://www.jbrake.com
Motorcycle Parts Mfr
N.A.I.C.S.: 336991

DRESNER CORPORATE SERVICES INC.
20 N Clark St Ste 3550, Chicago, IL 60602
Tel.: (312) 726-3600
Web Site:
   http://www.dresnercorp.com
Sales Range: $10-24.9 Million
Emp.: 30
Investor & Public Relations
N.A.I.C.S.: 541820
Steven D. Carr (Mng Dir & Exec VP)
Kristine Walczak (Sr VP-IR)
David E. Gutierrez (Head-PR & Corp Dev)
Rene Caron (Sr VP & Head-California)

Subsidiaries:

Dresner Allen Caron   (1)
2151 Michelson Dr, Irvine, CA 92612
Tel.: (949) 474-4300
Web Site: http://www.dresnerallencaron.com
Public Relations Agency
N.A.I.C.S.: 541820

Branch (Domestic):

Allen & Caron Inc.   (2)
276 5th Ave Ste 604, New York, NY 10001
Tel.: (212) 691-8087
Web Site: http://www.dresnerallencaron.com
Public Relations Agency
N.A.I.C.S.: 541820
Joseph Allen (Head)

DRESS FOR SUCCESS WORLDWIDE
32 E 31st St, New York, NY 10016
Tel.: (212) 532-1922   NY
Web Site:
   https://www.dressforsuccess.org
Year Founded: 2003
Sales Range: $10-24.9 Million

Emp.: 50
Economic Development Services
N.A.I.C.S.: 813410
Joanne Leighton (Controller)
Liz Carey (Chief Affiliate Growth & Sustainability Officer)
Wendy Longwood (COO)

DRESSLER TRUCK SERVICE INC.
409 W Apple St, Freeburg, IL 62243
Tel.: (618) 539-3015
Sales Range: $10-24.9 Million
Emp.: 30
Local Trucking without Storage
N.A.I.C.S.: 424510
Allen B. Dressler (Pres)
Jason Dressler (VP)

DREW CHILD DEVELOPMENT CORPORATION
1770 E 118th St, Los Angeles, CA 90059
Tel.: (323) 249-2950   CA
Web Site: https://www.drewcdc.org
Year Founded: 1987
Sales Range: $10-24.9 Million
Emp.: 171
Child Care & Development Services
N.A.I.C.S.: 624110
Jacqueline Clarke (CFO & COO)
Mike Jackson (Pres & CEO)
Dee Michaelis (Dir-HR)
Diann Fauntleroy (Dir-Education)
Darrell Hills (Dir-Alternative Payment Programs)

DREW OIL COMPANY, INC.
980 1st Ave NE, Cairo, GA 39828
Tel.: (229) 377-9866
Sales Range: $10-24.9 Million
Petroleum Product Whslr
N.A.I.C.S.: 424710
Phillip Drew (Pres)
Melinda Gainous (Sec)
Jenny Drew (CFO)

DREXEL BUILDING SUPPLY
227 W Main St PO Box 510, Campbellsport, WI 53010
Tel.: (920) 533-4412
Web Site:
   http://www.DrexelTeam.com
Year Founded: 1985
Sales Range: $50-74.9 Million
Emp.: 225
Building Materials & Construction Services
N.A.I.C.S.: 238190
Joel Fleischman (Pres)
Julie Korth (CFO)

DREXEL CHEMICAL COMPANY INC.
1700 Channel Ave, Memphis, TN 38106
Tel.: (901) 774-4370   TN
Web Site: https://www.drexchem.com
Year Founded: 1990
Sales Range: $25-49.9 Million
Emp.: 180
Agricultural Chemical Mfr
N.A.I.C.S.: 325320

DREXEL METALS CORPORATION
1234 Gardiner Ln, Louisville, KY 40213
Tel.: (502) 716-7143
Web Site:
   http://www.drexelmetals.com
Year Founded: 1985
Sales Range: $50-74.9 Million
Emp.: 57
Metal Roofing System Mfr & Distr
N.A.I.C.S.: 332322

Brian Partyka (Pres)
Randy McHone (Pres)
Bill Chandler (Exec VP)

DREXEL UNIVERSITY
3141 Chestnut St, Philadelphia, PA 19104
Tel.: (215) 895-2000
Web Site: http://www.drexel.edu
Year Founded: 1891
Colleges & Universities
N.A.I.C.S.: 611310
Mark L. Greenberg (Sr VP-Academic Affairs & Provost)
Helen Y. Bowman (CFO, Treas & Sr VP-Fin)
Lori N. Doyle (Sr VP-University Comm)
Michael J. Exler (Gen Counsel & Sr VP)
James K. Seaman (VP-Internal Audit & Mgmt Consulting Svcs)
Bill G. Shea (Asst VP-Internal Audit & Mgmt Consulting Svcs)
Donald Liberati (Exec Dir-Drexel Bus Svcs)
Diana Mihaylova (Assoc Dir-Retail Mgmt)
Sri Anitha Ramachandran (Coord-Budget)
Bryn Baker (Coord-Budget)
Loretta Sweet Jemmott (VP-Health & Health Equity)
Dana Russo (Assoc Dir-Presidential & Principal Gifts Stewardship)

Subsidiaries:

St. Christopher's Hospital for Children, LLC   (1)
160 E Erie Ave, Philadelphia, PA 19134
Tel.: (215) 427-5000
Web Site:
   http://www.stchristophershospital.com
Children's Hospitals
N.A.I.C.S.: 622110
Ronald Dreskin (CEO-Interim)

Subsidiary (Domestic):

SCHC Pediatric Anesthesia Associates, L.L.C.   (2)
3601 A St, Philadelphia, PA 19134-1043
Tel.: (215) 427-5293
Web Site: http://www.stchristopher.com
Medical Devices
N.A.I.C.S.: 622110

SCHC Pediatric Associates, LLC   (2)
3601 A St, Philadelphia, PA 19134-1095
Tel.: (215) 427-8881
Medical Devices
N.A.I.C.S.: 622110

St. Christopher's Pediatric Urgent Care Center, L.L.C.   (2)
500 Old York Rd Ste 250, Jenkintown, PA 19046
Tel.: (215) 572-5300
Health Care Srvices
N.A.I.C.S.: 621999

DREXELINE FOODS LLP
5004 State Rd, Drexel Hill, PA 19026
Tel.: (610) 622-1520
Web Site:
   http://www.thefreshgrocer.com
Year Founded: 1984
Sales Range: $10-24.9 Million
Emp.: 200
Grocery Store Operator
N.A.I.C.S.: 445110
Mary Pouch (Gen Mgr)

DREYCO INC.
263 Veterans Blvd, Carlstadt, NJ 07072
Tel.: (201) 896-9000
Web Site: http://www.dreycoinc.com
Rev.: $18,000,000
Emp.: 15

Automotive Supplies & Parts
N.A.I.C.S.: 423120
Karen Borghard *(Comptroller)*
Jamie Rubel *(Mgr-Ops)*

DREYER & REINBOLD INC.
9375 Whitley Dr, Indianapolis, IN
46240
Tel.: (317) 573-0200
Web Site:
http://www.dreyerreinboldbmw.com
Year Founded: 1968
Sales Range: $50-74.9 Million
Emp.: 100
Car Dealership
N.A.I.C.S.: 441110
Dennis Reinbold *(Pres)*
Paul Brown *(Gen Mgr)*
Wanda Lamon *(Controller)*

DREYFUS ASHBY INC.
630 3rd Ave 15th Fl, New York, NY
10017
Tel.: (212) 818-0770
Web Site:
https://www.dreyfusashby.com
Year Founded: 1957
Sales Range: $75-99.9 Million
Emp.: 35
Wines & Spirits Whslr
N.A.I.C.S.: 424820
Christopher Ryan *(CEO)*
Kelly Carlos *(Office Mgr)*
John A. Caruso *(Pres)*

**DREYFUS MUNICIPAL INFRA-
STRUCTURE FUND, INC.**
144 Glenn Curtiss Blvd 9 th Fl E
Tower, Uniondale, NY 11556
Tel.: (212) 922-6000   MD
Web Site: https://www.dreyfus.com
Year Founded: 2012
DMB—(NYSE)
Sales Range: $10-24.9 Million
Investment Services
N.A.I.C.S.: 523999
James Windels *(Treas)*

DRFIRST.COM, INC.
9420 Key W Ave Ste 230, Rockville,
MD 20850
Tel.: (301) 231-9510   DE
Web Site: https://www.drfirst.com
Year Founded: 2000
Medical Care Management Platform
Software Developer & Publisher
N.A.I.C.S.: 513210
James F. Chen *(Co-Founder, Chm &
CEO)*
G. Cameron Deemer *(Pres)*
David A. Samuels *(CFO)*
Thomas E. Sullivan *(Chief Strategic
Officer)*
George Pappas *(COO)*
Irene Froehlich *(VP-Corp Dev &
Comm)*
Brad Block *(Gen Mgr-Hospital Mar-
kets)*
Richard Cohan *(Pres-Patient Innova-
tions)*
Meriellen Cain *(CIO)*

Subsidiaries:

Diagnotes, Inc.   (1)
8831 Keystone Crossing, Indianapolis, IN
46240
Tel.: (317) 395-7080
Web Site: http://www.diagnotes.net
Custom Computer Programming Services
N.A.I.C.S.: 541511
Marc Kleinman *(Dir-Bus Dev)*

DRG & ASSOCIATES, INC.
5801 W Alameda Ave Ste A, Lakewood, CO 80226
Tel.: (303) 274-7716
Year Founded: 1993

Sales Range: $10-24.9 Million
Emp.: 25
Civil Engineering Services
N.A.I.C.S.: 237310
Raymond Garcia *(Gen Mgr)*
Diedra Garcia Jr. *(Pres)*

DRG TECHNOLOGIES, INC.
300 East 4th St, Safford, AZ 85546-
2025
Tel.: (928) 428-7450
Web Site: https://www.drgtech.com
Year Founded: 1983
Printing Services
N.A.I.C.S.: 323111
Roger Popovec *(Pres)*

Subsidiaries:

Martes Enterprises, LLC   (1)
6162 W Detroit St, Chandler, AZ 85226-
2632
Tel.: (480) 785-3900
Sales Range: $1-9.9 Million
Emp.: 12
Converted Paper Product Mfr
N.A.I.C.S.: 322299
Charlotte A. Valadez *(Sec & VP)*

DRI COMPANIES
17182 Armstrong Ave, Irvine, CA
92614
Tel.: (949) 266-1990
Web Site:
http://www.dricompanies.com
Sales Range: $75-99.9 Million
Emp.: 500
Commercial Roofing & Waterproofing
Services
N.A.I.C.S.: 238160
Timothy M. Davey *(CEO)*

DRI CORPORATION
13760 Noel Rd Ste 830, Dallas, TX
75240
Tel.: (214) 378-8992   NC
Web Site: http://www.digrec.com
Year Founded: 1983
Sales Range: $75-99.9 Million
Emp.: 275
Transportation & Law-Enforcement
Digital Communication
N.A.I.C.S.: 334290
David L. Turney *(Chm & CEO)*
Veronica B. Marks *(VP-Corp Comm,
Asst Sec & Admin)*
Elaine Rudisill *(Chief Restructuring
Officer)*

Subsidiaries:

RTI, Inc.   (1)
13760 Noel Rd Ste 830, Dallas, TX 75240-
1343
Tel.: (214) 378-8992
Sales Range: $100-124.9 Million
Recording Devices Mfr
N.A.I.C.S.: 334610

DRI ENTERPRISES LTD.
1410 S FM 51, Decatur, TX 76234
Tel.: (940) 627-3949
Web Site: http://www.nrsworld.com
Sales Range: $10-24.9 Million
Emp.: 150
Western Apparel
N.A.I.C.S.: 458110
David Isham *(CEO)*

DRI MARK PRODUCTS, INC.
999 S Oyster Bay Rd Ste 312, Beth-
page, NY 11714
Tel.: (516) 484-6200   NY
Web Site: http://www.drimark.com
Year Founded: 1960
Sales Range: $100-124.9 Million
Emp.: 200
Promotional Products Mfr
N.A.I.C.S.: 339940

Charles Reichmann *(Owner)*
Cathy Williams-Owen *(Pres & CFO)*
Mark Dobbs *(VP-Sls)*

**DRI-THE VOICE OF THE DE-
FENSE BAR**
55 W Monroe St 2000, Chicago, IL
60603
Tel.: (312) 795-1101   WI
Web Site: http://www.dri.org
Year Founded: 1960
Sales Range: $10-24.9 Million
Emp.: 45
Bar Association
N.A.I.C.S.: 813920
Toyja E. Kelley *(First VP-Baltimore)*
Douglas K. Burrell *(Treas & Sec)*

DRIESSEN WATER I INC.
1104 S State St, Waseca, MN 56093
Tel.: (507) 835-1234
Web Site: http://www.culligan.com
Sales Range: $10-24.9 Million
Emp.: 17
Water Purification Equipment
N.A.I.C.S.: 449210
Diane Powell *(Office Mgr)*
Heidi Klinger *(Mgr-Acctg)*

Subsidiaries:

Ultrapure & Industrial Services,
LLC   (1)
4429 Mint Way, Dallas, TX 75236-2011
Tel.: (972) 432-9951
Web Site: http://www.ultrapure.com
Business Support Services
N.A.I.C.S.: 561499
Robert Cappa *(Mgr-Site)*

**DRIFTLESS GLEN DISTILLERY
LLC**
300 Water St, Baraboo, WI 53913
Tel.: (608) 356-4536
Web Site:
http://www.driftlessglen.com
Year Founded: 2014
Sales Range: $1-9.9 Million
Beverage Product Mfr & Distr
N.A.I.C.S.: 312140
Brian Bemis *(Co-Owner)*
Renee Bemis *(Co-Owner)*

DRIFTWOOD CATERING, LLC
1422 Euclid Ave Ste 840, Cleveland,
OH 44115
Tel.: (440) 567-2386
Web Site:
http://thedriftwoodgroup.com
Restaurant & Catering Services
N.A.I.C.S.: 722511
Scott David Kuhn *(Founder & CEO)*
Chris Hodgson *(Pres)*
Toby Heintzelman *(Ops Mgr)*

**DRIFTWOOD GARDEN CEN-
TER**
5051 Tamiami Trl N, Naples, FL
34103
Tel.: (239) 261-0328   FL
Web Site: http://www.driftwoodgarden
center.com
Year Founded: 1983
Sales Range: $1-9.9 Million
Emp.: 32
Nursery & Garden Centers
N.A.I.C.S.: 444240
Mike Gill *(Mgr-Store)*
Gary Hazelett *(Pres)*

**DRIFTWOOD HOSPITALITY
MANAGEMENT, LLC**
11770 US Hwy 1 Ste 202, North
Palm Beach, FL 33408
Tel.: (561) 207-2700
Web Site:
https://www.driftwoodhospitality.com

Sales Range: $1-9.9 Million
Emp.: 3,000
Hotel Owner & Operator
N.A.I.C.S.: 721110
Charles Michael Diaz *(COO)*
Peter Walz *(Exec VP)*
David Buddemeyer *(Pres)*
Steven M. Johnson *(Exec VP)*
Jackie Gerstenfeld *(Dir-Legal Admin)*
Tom Sweeney *(Mgr-Pur)*
Tiffany Cahill *(Dir-Corp HR)*
Teresa M Kramer-Petrone *(VP-Reg
Mktg & Sls)*
Brian LaPlante *(Dir-Reg Ops)*
Rob Auman *(Mgr-Ops Reg)*
Bill Terrill *(Reg Dir-Sls & Mktg)*
Scott Cornelius *(Reg Mgr-Ops)*
Carlos J. Rodriguez Jr. *(Exec VP)*

DRIGGS CORPORATION
8700 Ashwood Dr, Capitol Heights,
MD 20743
Tel.: (301) 336-6700
Web Site: http://www.driggs.net
Sales Range: $10-24.9 Million
Emp.: 50
Excavation & Grading, Building Con-
struction
N.A.I.C.S.: 238910
John Driggs *(Pres)*

DRILLOT CORPORATION
325 Horizon Dr, Suwanee, GA 30024-
3103
Tel.: (770) 932-7282   GA
Web Site: http://www.hadco.net
Year Founded: 1953
Sales Range: $10-24.9 Million
Emp.: 84
Provider of Electrical Appliances &
Television Services
N.A.I.C.S.: 423620
Jon Classon *(VP-Acctg & Fin)*
James Needham *(VP-Sls Support
Svcs)*

DRILLSPOT
5777 Central Ave Ste 230, Boulder,
CO 80301
Tel.: (720) 204-3660
Web Site: http://www.drillspot.com
Year Founded: 2005
Sales Range: $10-24.9 Million
Emp.: 15
Hardware Supplies
N.A.I.C.S.: 444140
Paul Lin *(CEO)*

**DRING AIR CONDITIONING &
HEATING, LP**
2503 Southwell Rd, Dallas, TX 75229
Tel.: (972) 241-1312   TX
Web Site: http://www.dring.com
Year Founded: 1996
Sales Range: $1-9.9 Million
Emp.: 50
Plumbing, Heating, Air-Conditioning
Services
N.A.I.C.S.: 238220
Jennifer Shafer *(Principal)*

Subsidiaries:

Keen Air Services, Inc.   (1)
1000 Jupiter Rd Ste 700, Plano, TX 75074
Tel.: (972) 312-9575
Web Site: http://www.kleenairservices.com
Sales Range: $1-9.9 Million
Emp.: 18
Plumbing, Heating & Air-Conditioning Con-
tractors
N.A.I.C.S.: 238220

DRISCOLL'S, INC
345 Westridge Dr, Watsonville, CA
95076-4169
Tel.: (831) 763-5100   CA
Web Site: http://www.driscolls.com

Driscoll's, Inc—(Continued)

Year Founded: 1953
Sales Range: $25-49.9 Million
Emp.: 300
Fresh Fruit Farming
N.A.I.C.S.: 111333
J. Miles Reiter (Chm, Pres & CEO)
Soren Bjorn (Exec VP-Americas)
Tom O'Brien (Gen Counsel & Sr VP-Governance & External Engagement)

Subsidiaries:

Costa Group Holdings Limited   (1)
Tel.: (61) 383639000
Web Site: https://www.costagroup.com.au
Rev.: $885,150,942
Assets: $1,341,585,056
Liabilities: $809,824,607
Net Worth: $531,760,449
Earnings: $30,645,498
Emp.: 200
Fiscal Year-end: 01/01/2022
Holding Company
N.A.I.C.S.: 551112
David Thomas (Gen Counsel)
Kirsty Deglas (Chief Strategy Officer)
Wayne Johnston (CEO)

Driscoll's of Florida, Inc.   (1)
12880 E US Hwy 92, Dover, FL 33527-4103
Tel.: (813) 659-2551
Web Site: http://www.driscoll.com
Sales Range: $10-24.9 Million
Emp.: 30
Fresh Fruits & Vegetables Whslr
N.A.I.C.S.: 424480
Kristal Lara (Supvr)

DRISHA INSTITUTE FOR JEWISH EDUCATION, INC.
37 W 65th St 5th Fl, New York, NY 10023
Tel.: (212) 595-0307   NY
Web Site: http://www.drisha.org
Year Founded: 1979
Emp.: 100
Jewish Educational Support Services & Scholarships for Women
N.A.I.C.S.: 611710
Dalia Smerka (Office Mgr)
Jordana Golden (Dir-Info Res)
Geri Gindea (Dir-Ops)
David Silber (Founder)
Elissa Shay Ordan (Sec)
Alan Septimus (Treas)

DRISHTICON INC.
39658 Mission Blvd, Fremont, CA 94539-3000
Tel.: (510) 402-4515
Web Site: http://www.drishticon.com
Emp.: 100
Custom Computer Programming Services
N.A.I.C.S.: 541511
Lakshmi Epari (Mgr-Bus Dev)
Manoj Vidyarthi (Pres)

Subsidiaries:

Commercial Programming Systems, Inc.   (1)
4400 Coldwater Canyon Ave Ste 320, Studio City, CA 91604-5039
Web Site: https://www.cpsinc.com
Sales Range: $10-24.9 Million
Emp.: 100
Data Processing & IT Services
N.A.I.C.S.: 541519
Alan Strong (Founder, Chm & CEO)
Phil Sawyer (Pres)
Michelle Stewart (VP-Fin & Admin)
Donna Preston (VP)
Carol Cruz (Accountant)

DRIV-LOK, INC.
1140 Park Ave, Sycamore, IL 60178-2927
Tel.: (815) 315-1004   IL
Web Site: https://www.driv-lok.com

Year Founded: 1933
Sales Range: $50-74.9 Million
Emp.: 80
Press Fit Fasteners Mfr
N.A.I.C.S.: 332510
Gary Seegers (Owner & Pres)
Becky Metcalf (Exec VP)
Jacky Mohr (Coord-QS)
John Miller (Mgr-R&D)
Pat Kline (Mgr-Sls)

DRIVE TRAIN INDUSTRIES, INC.
5555 Joliet St, Denver, CO 80239-2004
Tel.: (303) 292-5176   CO
Web Site:
   http://www.drivetrainindustries.com
Year Founded: 1945
Sales Range: $125-149.9 Million
Emp.: 167
Heavy Duty Truck Parts Mfr & Retailer & General Automotive Repair Services
N.A.I.C.S.: 423120
Bruce Sommerville (Gen Mgr)
Steve Back (Mgr-Sls)
Charity Robinette (Mgr-Gillette)
Chance Karwoski (Mgr-Casper)
Doug Ware (Mgr-Colorado Springs)
Mike Palumbo (Mgr-Store)

DRIVE-O-RAMA INC.
350 Main St, Dennis Port, MA 02639
Tel.: (508) 771-8100   MA
Web Site: https://www.millstores.com
Year Founded: 1958
Sales Range: $10-24.9 Million
Emp.: 15
Furniture Whslr
N.A.I.C.S.: 423210
Philip Baroni (Pres)

DRIVEKORE INC.
101 Wesley Dr, Mechanicsburg, PA 17055
Tel.: (717) 766-7636
Web Site: https://www.drivekore.com
Sales Range: $10-24.9 Million
Emp.: 52
Sales, Rental & Power Repair Tools & Accessories Whslr
N.A.I.C.S.: 423710
Dan Emanuel (Owner)
Kim McLain (Sec)
Mike Amsbaugh (Mgr-Warehouse Ops)
Tom VanWinkle (VP)

DRIVEN, INC.
6400 Arlington Blvd, Falls Church, VA 22042
Tel.: (703) 533-9200
Web Site: http://www.driven-inc.com
Year Founded: 2001
Computer System Design Services
N.A.I.C.S.: 541512
Brian Cunningham (CFO & Exec VP)
Mike Jreige (COO)
Ozzy Jimenez (CEO)
Wynter Grant (Chief Revenue Officer)
Tara S. Emory (Dir-Consulting)

Subsidiaries:

OmniVere, LLC   (1)
208 S LaSalle Ste 1550, Chicago, IL 60604
Tel.: (312) 583-9956
Web Site: http://www.omnivere.com
Data Risk Management Consulting Services
N.A.I.C.S.: 541690
Erik Post (Co-Founder & Pres)
Kevin Byrne (Co-Founder & COO)
Celine Tischler (Controller-Fin Dept)

Subsidiary (Domestic):

Kiersted Systems, L.P.   (2)

1301 Fannin St Ste 750, Houston, TX 77002
Tel.: (713) 739-7883
Web Site: http://www.kiersted.com
Electronic Discovery & Legal Technology Consulting Services
N.A.I.C.S.: 561499
George W. Kiersted (Founder & Pres)
Robert Harris (VP-Tech)
E. Andre Guilbeau (Exec VP)
Linda Gordon (VP-Sls & Mktg)
Amanda Heldt (VP-Consulting)

Update Legal, Inc.   (1)
1040 Ave of the Americas 11th Fl, New York, NY 10018
Tel.: (212) 921-2200
Web Site: http://www.updatelegal.com
Employment Agencies, Nsk
N.A.I.C.S.: 561311
April Pish (CEO)
Julian Brown (Exec VP)
Cheryl Van Tine (COO)
Jennifer O'Sullivan (Exec VP)

DRIVENMEDIA
2009 N 7th St Ste C, Phoenix, AZ 85006
Tel.: (602) 357-4884
Web Site:
   http://www.drivenmediaonline.com
Year Founded: 2008
Sales Range: Less than $1 Million
Emp.: 10
Advertising, Advertising Specialties, Alternative Advertising, Automotive, Outdoor, Out-of-Home Media, Print, Viral/Buzz/Word of Mouth
N.A.I.C.S.: 541810
Brandon Clarke (Founder)

DRIVER PIPELINE COMPANY INC.
1200 N Union Bower Rd, Irving, TX 75061
Tel.: (214) 638-7131   TX
Web Site:
   https://www.driverpipeline.com
Year Founded: 1970
Sales Range: $25-49.9 Million
Emp.: 400
Water, Sewer & Utility Line Services
N.A.I.C.S.: 237120
Jim Driver (Pres)
Jeff Moore (Dir-Safety)
Austin Siler (Project Mgr)

DRIVER-HARRIS COMPANY
200 Madison Ave, Morristown, NJ 07960
Tel.: (973) 267-8100   NJ
Year Founded: 1899
Sales Range: $75-99.9 Million
Emp.: 101
Holding Company
N.A.I.C.S.: 551112
Frank Driver (Chm & CEO)

Subsidiaries:

Irish Driver-Harris Co., Ltd.   (1)
Mill Banks, New Ross, Co Wexford, Ireland   (89%)
Tel.: (353) 51421405
Web Site: http://www.idh.ie
Sales Range: $50-74.9 Million
Emp.: 50
Insulated Electrical Wire & Cable Mfr
N.A.I.C.S.: 332618
Frank Driver (Mng Dir)
Dominic Robinson (Mgr-Ops)
Peter Ryan (Mgr-Comml)
Billy O'Reilly (Controller-Fin)
Trevor Dickerson (Mgr-Sls-UK)

DRIVERGE VEHICLE INNOVATIONS, LLC.
Driverge 4199 Kinross Lakes Pkwy, Ste 300, Richfield, OH 44286
Tel.: (855) 337-9543
Web Site: https://www.driverge.com

Year Founded: 1997
Emp.: 86
Motor Vehicles Mfr
N.A.I.C.S.: 336211
Mark Minatel (Pres)

Subsidiaries:

Inlad Truck & Van Equipment Company, incorporated   (1)
980 N. Lombard Rd, Lombard, IL 60148
Tel.: (630) 652-1200
Web Site: http://www.inlad.com
Motor Vehicle Supplies & New Parts Merchant Whslr
N.A.I.C.S.: 423120
Jim Fuller (Pres)

DRIVERS HISTORY
1 Keystone Ave Unit 700, Cherry Hill, NJ 08003
Tel.: (856) 673-1281
Web Site: http://drivershistory.com
Year Founded: 2007
Sales Range: $1-9.9 Million
Emp.: 20
Automobile Insurance Services
N.A.I.C.S.: 524298
Stephen Esposito (Co-Founder & CEO)
Brian Wolfson (Sr VP-Sls & Bus Dev)
Robert Mayo (CIO)
Bruce Schulkins (VP-Data Quality)
Christopher Mucha (CFO)
Thomas P. Richards (VP-Product Mgmt)

DRIVES & CONVEYORS INC.
3865 Cumberland Falls Hwy, Corbin, KY 40701
Tel.: (606) 528-0500
Sales Range: $10-24.9 Million
Emp.: 13
Industrial Supplies
N.A.I.C.S.: 423840
Alfred Apple (Pres)

DRIVESAVERS DATA RECOVERY, INC.
400 Bel Marin Keys Blvd, Novato, CA 94949-5650
Tel.: (415) 382-2000
Web Site:
   http://www.drivesavers.com
Year Founded: 1985
Sales Range: $10-24.9 Million
Emp.: 100
Data Recovery & Retrieval Services
N.A.I.C.S.: 519290
Jay Hagan (CEO)

DRIVETIME AUTOMOTIVE GROUP, INC.
1720 W Rio Salado Pkwy, Tempe, AZ 85281
Tel.: (602) 852-6600   DE
Web Site: https://www.drivetime.com
Year Founded: 1992
Sales Range: $1-4.9 Billion
Emp.: 3,165
Used Car Dealership & Financing Services
N.A.I.C.S.: 441120
Jon D. Ehlinger (Gen Counsel, Sec & Exec VP)
Mark G. Sauder (CFO, Treas & Exec VP)
Paul I. Kaplan (CIO, Chief Risk Officer & Sr VP)
Don Reese (CEO)

DRM INC.
5324 N 134th Ave, Omaha, NE 68164
Tel.: (402) 573-1216
Web Site: https://www.drmarbys.com
Rev.: $33,091,113
Emp.: 20

Fast-Food Restaurant, Chain
N.A.I.C.S.: 722513
Matthew Johnson *(Co-Pres & CEO)*
Marc Johnson *(Co-Pres & COO)*

DRM PARTNERS, INC.
50 Harrison St Ste 114, Hoboken, NJ
07030
Tel.: (201) 418-0050
Web Site: http://www.drm-partners.com
Year Founded: 2004
Sales Range: $25-49.9 Million
Emp.: 10
Media Buying Services
N.A.I.C.S.: 541830
Mary Ram *(Owner)*
Susan Pensabene *(Pres)*

DROISYS INC.
4800 Patrick Henry Dr, Santa Clara,
CA 95054
Tel.: (408) 329-1761
Web Site: http://www.droisys.com
Year Founded: 2003
Rev.: $7,700,000
Emp.: 159
Consumer Information Services
N.A.I.C.S.: 812990
Sanjiv Goyal *(CEO)*
Amit Kumar *(COO)*
Dean Lane *(CIO)*
Shum Mukherjee *(CFO)*

DRONE SERVICES USA, INC.
1850 S E 17 St Ste 305 Ft, Fort Lau-
derdale, FL 33316
Tel.: (954) 306-6242
Aircraft Components Mfr
N.A.I.C.S.: 336411
Joel Bredow *(Chm, Pres & CEO)*

DRONESEED CO.
Ballard Brewery District, Seattle, WA
98107
Tel.: (917) 716-8555
Web Site: http://droneseed.com
Environemental Sustainability Ser-
vices
N.A.I.C.S.: 813312
Grant Canary *(CEO)*

Subsidiaries:

Silvaseed Co.   (1)
317 James St N, Roy, WA 98580
Tel.: (253) 843-2246
Web Site: http://www.silvaseed.com
Rev.: $6,570,000
Emp.: 30
Flower, Nursery Stock & Florists' Supplies
Merchant Whslr
N.A.I.C.S.: 424930
Mike Gerdes *(VP-HR & IT)*

DRONEUP LLC
160 Newtown Rd Ste 302, Virginia
Beach, VA 23462
Tel.: (877) 932-8357
Web Site: http://www.droneup.com
Year Founded: 2016
Drone Services Provider
N.A.I.C.S.: 336411
John Vernon *(CTO)*

Subsidiaries:

Web Teks, Inc.   (1)
676 Independence Pkwy Ste 120, Chesa-
peake, VA 23320
Tel.: (757) 578-4923
Web Site: http://www.webteks.com
Enterprise Web & Portal Development Ser-
vices
N.A.I.C.S.: 519290
Dyanne Walker *(Founder & CEO)*
Tom Walker *(Pres)*

DROP STOP, LLC

PO Box 34648, Los Angeles, CA
90034
Tel.: (310) 559-7155
Web Site: http://www.dropstop.com
Sales Range: $1-9.9 Million
Automotive Accessory Mfr
N.A.I.C.S.: 326199
Marc Newburger *(Co-Founder)*
Jeffrey Simon *(Co-Founder)*

DROPOFF, INC.
901 S Mopac Expy Ste 250 Bldg 2,
Austin, TX 78746
Web Site: http://www.dropoff.com
Year Founded: 2014
Delivery Service
N.A.I.C.S.: 492110
Sean Spector *(Founder & CEO)*
Warmoth Guillaume *(Reg Gen Mgr)*
Jason Burns Sr. *(Dir-Corp Dev)*

Subsidiaries:

Quick Courier Services, Inc.   (1)
6600 Plz Dr Ste 307, New Orleans, LA
70127
Tel.: (504) 940-6262
Web Site: http://www.qcslogistics.com
Sales Range: $1-9.9 Million
Emp.: 75
Logistics & Transportation Services
N.A.I.C.S.: 541614
Sheila B. Burns *(Co-Founder, Partner & VP-Compliance)*
David Domingue *(Gen Mgr)*
Ronald V. Burns Sr. *(Chm & CEO)*

**DROUBAY AUTOMOTIVE
GROUP INCORPORATED**
348 W Main St, Delta, UT 84624
Tel.: (435) 864-2581
Web Site: http://www.droubaychevrolet.com
Rev.: $14,399,692
Emp.: 25
Automobiles, New & Used
N.A.I.C.S.: 441110
Robert L. Droubay *(Pres)*

DRT MFG. COMPANY
618 Greenmount Blvd, Dayton, OH
45419-2835
Tel.: (937) 298-7391   OH
Web Site: http://www.drtmfgco.com
Year Founded: 1949
Sales Range: $25-49.9 Million
Emp.: 300
Special Dies, Tools, Jigs & Fixtures
N.A.I.C.S.: 333514
Gary L. Van Gundy *(Pres & CEO)*
Gregory S. Martin *(VP-Ops)*
Chad Massie *(Engr-Mfg)*
Steve Smith *(Controller)*

Subsidiaries:

Hovis Precision Products Inc.   (1)
110 Corporate Dr, Simpsonville, SC
29681-2800   (100%)
Tel.: (864) 967-2300
Web Site: http://www.hovispp.com
Sales Range: $25-49.9 Million
Emp.: 45
Machine Tool Accessories & Aerospace
Components Mfr
N.A.I.C.S.: 333515

DRT STRATEGIES, INC.
4245 N Fairfax Dr Ste 800, Arlington,
VA 22203
Tel.: (571) 482-2500
Web Site: http://www.drtstrategies.com
Rev.: $11,100,000
Emp.: 210
Management Consulting Services
N.A.I.C.S.: 541618
Susan M. Kidd *(CEO)*
Michael Duffy *(Exec VP & Dir-Corp Dev)*
Geoffrey McDermott *(Mgr-Contract)*

Kathy Gilmore *(VP-West)*
Clara Hickerson *(Dir-PR & Mktg)*
Dave Potts *(Chief Talent Officer)*

DRT TRANSPORTATION
850 Helen Dr, Lebanon, PA 17042
Tel.: (717) 274-2871
Web Site:
https://www.drttransportation.com
Year Founded: 2007
Sales Range: $10-24.9 Million
Emp.: 30
Logistics & Transportation Services
N.A.I.C.S.: 541614
Rob Kemp *(Pres)*
Terry Ryan *(Owner & VP)*

**DRUG ABUSE AND COMPRE-
HENSIVE COORDINATING OF-
FICE, INC.**
4422 E Columbus Dr, Tampa, FL
33605
Tel.: (813) 384-4000
Web Site: http://www.dacco.org
Year Founded: 1973
Sales Range: $10-24.9 Million
Emp.: 230
Drug Abuse Treatment Services
N.A.I.C.S.: 621420
Ashit Vijapura *(Dir-Medical)*
Mary Lynn Ulrey *(CEO)*
Noel Allen *(VP-Fin)*
Deborah Palaez *(Mgr-Mktg & Comm)*

**DRUG INFORMATION ASSO-
CIATION**
800 Enterprise Rd ste 200, Horsham,
PA 19044-3595
Tel.: (215) 442-6100   MD
Web Site: http://www.diaglobal.org
Year Founded: 1964
Sales Range: $25-49.9 Million
Emp.: 112
Professional Association
N.A.I.C.S.: 813920
Timothy Hess *(Dir-IT-Global)*
Elizabeth Lincoln *(Dir-Engagement-Global)*
Bayard G. Gardineer *(CFO)*
Holger Adelmann *(Mng Dir-EMEA & Sr VP)*
Michelle Rovner *(Sr Mgr-Mktg-Global)*
Marwan Fathallah *(Pres & CEO-Global)*
Cynthia Verst *(Chm)*

**DRUG PLASTICS & GLASS
CO. INC.**
1 Bottle Dr, Boyertown, PA 19512
Tel.: (610) 367-5000   PA
Web Site:
https://www.drugplastics.com
Year Founded: 1963
Sales Range: $25-49.9 Million
Emp.: 500
Plastics Bottle Mfr
N.A.I.C.S.: 326160
Fred N. Biesecker *(Chm & Pres)*

Subsidiaries:

Drug Plastics Closures   (1)
2236 E University Dr, Phoenix, AZ 85034
Tel.: (602) 629-9000
Web Site:
http://www.drugplasticsclosures.com
Sales Range: $10-24.9 Million
Emp.: 70
Mfr Plastic Closures
N.A.I.C.S.: 326199

DRUG TRANSPORT INC.
1939 Forge St, Tucker, GA 30084
Tel.: (770) 938-8700
Web Site: http://www.dticares.com
Year Founded: 1959
Sales Range: $10-24.9 Million

Emp.: 450
International Motor Carrier
N.A.I.C.S.: 484121
Dave Hudson *(Vice Chm)*
Dick Lockwood *(Chm)*
Bob Dortch *(VP-Sls & Mktg)*
Bud Schrilla *(Sr VP-Ops)*
Patrick Ryan *(CFO)*
Scott Briley *(Dir-Ops)*
Arlene Dove *(Dir-Admin Svcs)*
Benny Cordero *(Dir-Remote Ops)*
Stephen Little *(CFO)*

**DRUID CAPITAL PARTNERS,
LLC**
500 Main Ave Ste 201, Northport, AL
35476
Tel.: (205) 349-4464   AL
Web Site:
https://www.druidcapital.com
Investment Services
N.A.I.C.S.: 523999
Randy Allen *(Co-Founder & Sr Mng Partner)*
John Brilbeck *(Co-Founder & Gen Partner)*
Martin A. Holt *(Co-Founder & Mng Partner)*
Hunter Plott *(Co-Founder & Gen Partner)*

Subsidiaries:

Thermex-Thermatron Systems,
LLC   (1)
10501 Bunsen Way Ste 102, Louisville, KY
40299
Tel.: (502) 493-1299
Web Site: http://www.thermex-thermatron.com
Industrial Microwave, Radio Frequency &
Thermal Heating Equipment Mfr
N.A.I.C.S.: 423830
Ray Lund *(Pres & CEO)*
Traci Evling *(Dir-Bus Dev)*
Jens Evling *(Dir & Engr-Electro-Mechanical)*
Dean Mancuso *(Dir-Sls)*

Subsidiary (Domestic):

JTE Machine Systems, Inc.   (2)
80 Industrial Loop N Bldg 4, Orange Park,
FL 32073
Tel.: (904) 278-2388
Web Site: http://www.jtemachine.com
Rev.: $8,496,000
Emp.: 9
Industrial Machinery & Equipment Whslr
N.A.I.C.S.: 423830
Angela Bowling *(VP)*
David Bowling *(VP-Ops)*
Traci Evling *(Pres)*
Jens Evling *(COO)*

DRULEY ENTERPRISES INC.
3305 N Anthony Blvd, Fort Wayne, IN
46805
Tel.: (260) 424-4604   IN
Web Site:
https://www.belmontbev.com
Year Founded: 1971
Sales Range: $50-74.9 Million
Emp.: 25
Liquor Stores
N.A.I.C.S.: 445320
Gary Gardner *(Mgr-Operations)*
Clair McKinley *(Pres)*

DRUM HILL FORD, INC.
1212 Westford St, Lowell, MA 01851
Tel.: (978) 452-3900
Web Site:
http://www.drumhillfordsales.com
Sales Range: $10-24.9 Million
Emp.: 60
New Car Retailer
N.A.I.C.S.: 441110
Steven Twombly *(Gen Mgr)*

**DRUMMOND BANKING COM-
PANY**

Drummond Banking Company—(Continued)
1627 N Young Blvd, Chiefland, FL 32626
Tel.: (352) 493-2277 FL
Web Site:
   http://www.drummondbank.com
Year Founded: 1989
Sales Range: $10-24.9 Million
Emp.: 173
Bank Holding Company
N.A.I.C.S.: 551111
Mike Comer (Chief Lending Officer)

Subsidiaries:

Drummond Community Bank (1)
1627 N Young Blvd, Chiefland, FL 32626
Tel.: (352) 493-2277
Web Site: http://www.drummondbank.com
Sales Range: $10-24.9 Million
Commericial Banking
N.A.I.C.S.: 522110

DRUMMOND COMPANY, INC.
PO Box 10246, Birmingham, AL 35202
Tel.: (205) 945-6300 AL
Web Site:
   http://www.drummondco.com
Year Founded: 1935
Sales Range: $1-4.9 Billion
Coke Mfr
N.A.I.C.S.: 333131
Augusto Jimenez (Pres)
Bruce C. Webster (Exec VP & Gen Counsel)
Richard Mullen (CEO)
Nathaniel Drummond (Sr VP)
Paulo Gonzalez (VP-Corp Social Responsibility)
Ron Damron (Pres-Mining)
Carolina Riano (Chief Sustainability Officer)

Subsidiaries:

Drummond Company, Inc.- ABC Coke Division (1)
900 Huntsville Ave, Tarrant, AL 35217
Tel.: (205) 849-1300
Web Site: http://www.abccoke.com
Foundry Coke Mfr
N.A.I.C.S.: 324199

Perry Supply Inc. (1)
831 1st Ave N, Birmingham, AL 35203
Tel.: (205) 943-7200
Web Site: http://www.perrysupply.com
Emp.: 55
Industrial Equipment & Supplies Whslr
N.A.I.C.S.: 423830
Charles Trimble Beasley (VP)

DRUPAL CONNECT
449 Thames St, Newport, RI 02840
Tel.: (401) 338-2589
Web Site:
   http://www.drupalconnect.com
Year Founded: 2006
Sales Range: $1-9.9 Million
Emp.: 5
Online Marketing Consulting Services
N.A.I.C.S.: 541613
John Florez (Founder, Pres & CEO)
Karen Sironen (Founder)
Jonathon Whitener (CTO)
Nina Samberg (Project Mgr)
Lisa Lohrum (Coord-Sls)
Taylor Zurowski (Mgr-Admin)
Alison Rhea (Mgr-Ops)
Casey Smith (Mgr-Sls & Mktg)
Sarah Blake (Project Mgr)
Melissa Grant (Project Mgr)
Celeste Ludwikowski (Project Mgr)
Vanessa Turke (VP-Digital Strategy)
Chris Sloan (VP-Project Mgmt)

DRURY DEVELOPMENT CORP.
721 Emerson Rd Ste 200, Saint Louis, MO 63141-6755

Tel.: (314) 423-6698
Web Site: http://www.ddimedia.net
Sales Range: $10-24.9 Million
Emp.: 80
Commercial & Industrial Building Operation
N.A.I.C.S.: 531120
Tim Drury (Pres)
Bob Zaegel (Dir-Tax)
Jon Knobloch (Dir-Ops)
Mark Goldman (Mgr-Landscape)
David E. Wilson (Assoc Gen Counsel)
Jacqueline Polivogt (Gen Counsel)
Charles Lee (VP-Construction)

Subsidiaries:

Drury Development (1)
8315 Drury Industrial Pkwy, Saint Louis, MO 63114
Tel.: (314) 423-6698
Rev.: $2,200,000
Emp.: 70
Commercial & Industrial Building Operation
N.A.I.C.S.: 531120
Mark Kohl (VP-Dev)

DRURY INN INC.
200 Farrar Dr, Cape Girardeau, MO 63701-4908
Tel.: (314) 429-2255
Web Site: http://www.druryhotels.com
Year Founded: 1986
Sales Range: $200-249.9 Million
Emp.: 2,750
Lodging Services
N.A.I.C.S.: 721110
Charles L. Drury Jr. (Pres)

Subsidiaries:

D.I. Supply Inc. (1)
1820 County Rd 319, Cape Girardeau, MO 63701
Tel.: (573) 204-0600
Web Site: http://www.druryhotels.com
Sales Range: $10-24.9 Million
Emp.: 15
Furniture Mfr & Whslr
N.A.I.C.S.: 423210

Drury Hotels Company, LLC. (1)
721 Emerson Rd Ste 400, Saint Louis, MO 63141
Tel.: (314) 429-2255
Web Site: http://www.druryhotels.com
General Hotel Management Services
N.A.I.C.S.: 721110
Ken Wilkes (Gen Mgr-Drury Plaza Hotel-Saint Paul)
Jesse Kairy (Sls Mgr-St. Paul)

Drury Inn & Suites Stadium (1)
3830 Blue Rdg Cutoff, Kansas City, MO 64133
Tel.: (816) 923-3000
Web Site: http://www.druryhotels.com
Sales Range: $10-24.9 Million
Emp.: 21
Lodging Services
N.A.I.C.S.: 721110
Chuck Drury (Owner)
Chris Knipp (Gen Mgr)

Drury Inn Poplar Bluff Inc. (1)
2220 N Westward Blvd, Poplar Bluff, MO 63901 (100%)
Tel.: (573) 686-2451
Web Site: http://www.druryhotels.com
Sales Range: $10-24.9 Million
Emp.: 30
Lodging Services
N.A.I.C.S.: 721110
Julie Crosswhite (Gen Mgr)

Drury Inns Inc. (1)
10490 Natural Bridge Rd, Saint Louis, MO 63134 (100%)
Tel.: (314) 423-7700
Web Site: http://www.druryhotels.com
Sales Range: $10-24.9 Million
Emp.: 75
Lodging Services
N.A.I.C.S.: 721110
Michael Galer (Gen Mgr)

Drury Southwest, Inc. (1)
101 S Farrar Dr, Cape Girardeau, MO 63701
Tel.: (573) 335-3134
Web Site: http://www.drurysouthwest.com
Sales Range: $10-24.9 Million
Emp.: 225
Hotels & Motels Managers & Developers
N.A.I.C.S.: 721110
Steve Schmittzehe (Controller)

Subsidiary (Domestic):

Auburn Investments Inc. (2)
101 S Farrar Dr, Cape Girardeau, MO 63701-4905
Tel.: (573) 335-3134
Sales Range: $10-24.9 Million
Emp.: 50
Hotels & Motels Financers
N.A.I.C.S.: 721110
Carolyn Bohnert (Sr VP)

DSW Restaurants Inc. (2)
101S Farrar Dr, Cape Girardeau, MO 63701-4905
Tel.: (573) 335-3134
Sales Range: $10-24.9 Million
Emp.: 30
Public Dining Facilities Services
N.A.I.C.S.: 722513

Drury South, Inc. (2)
101 Farrar Dr, Cape Girardeau, MO 63701-4905 (100%)
Tel.: (573) 335-3134
Web Site: http://www.drurysouthwest.com
Nonresidential Construction Services
N.A.I.C.S.: 721110

West Park Bowling Lanes Inc. (2)
354 S Silver Springs Rd, Cape Girardeau, MO 63703-6312
Tel.: (573) 334-1047
Web Site: http://www.westparklanes.com
Sales Range: $10-24.9 Million
Emp.: 20
Public Bowling Centers Proprietors
N.A.I.C.S.: 713950
Darrell James (Mgr)

DRW HOLDINGS, LLC
540 W Madison St Ste 2500, Chicago, IL 60661
Tel.: (312) 542-1000
Web Site: http://www.drw.com
Investment Banking & Securities Dealing
N.A.I.C.S.: 523150
Donald R. Wilson Jr. (Founder & CEO)

Subsidiaries:

Chopper Trading LLC (1)
141 W Jackson Blvd Ste 2201A, Chicago, IL 60604
Tel.: (312) 628-3500
Web Site: http://www.choppertrading.com
All Other Support Services
N.A.I.C.S.: 561990
Raj Fernando (CEO)

DRW Investments (UK) Ltd. (1)
51-55 Gresham Street 6th Floor, London, EC2V 7HQ, United Kingdom
Tel.: (44) 20 7282 1000
Web Site: http://www.drw.com
Investment Banking & Securities Dealing
N.A.I.C.S.: 523150

Zettics, Inc. (1)
5 Lyberty Way, Westford, MA 01886
Tel.: (978) 254-5329
Data Analytic Services
N.A.I.C.S.: 518210
Sterling Wilson (Pres & CEO)
Asa Kalavade (CTO & Sr VP)
Tal Kedar (CFO)
John Gillespie (Sr VP-Sls)
Ian Herbert-Jones (Sr VP)
Joe Levy (VP-Customer Strategy & Mktg)
Andrew Gibbs (VP-Product Mgmt)
Prasasth Palnati (VP-Engrg)
Stephen Douglas (VP-Tech)
John Thomas (Dir-Res)
Adam Guy (VP-Monetization)

Subsidiary (Domestic):

Velocent Systems, Inc. (2)
1250 E Diehl Rd, Naperville, IL 60563
Tel.: (630) 799-3800
Web Site: http://www.velocent.com
Emp.: 15
Data Processing Services
N.A.I.C.S.: 423430
Ian Herbert Jones (CEO)
Stephen Douglas (CTO)
Tom Smith (COO)
Jagadeesh Dantuluri (VP-Mktg)
Randy Johnson (VP-Engrg)
Eric Hong (Co-Founder)
Philip Stevens (VP-Sls)
Larry Border (Dir-Fin)

DRY CREEK STRUCTURES
9088 N River Rd, Idaho Falls, ID 83402
Tel.: (208) 529-0400
Year Founded: 2005
Sales Range: $10-24.9 Million
Emp.: 40
Highway & Street Construction Services
N.A.I.C.S.: 237310
Stephanie Mickelsen (Owner)

DRY FLY CAPITAL LLC
5901 S Middlefield Rd Ste 100, Littleton, CO 80123
Tel.: (720) 315-5155
Web Site: https://www.dryflycap.com
Emp.: 100
Privater Equity Firm
N.A.I.C.S.: 523999
Dan Ogdon (Mng Partner)

Subsidiaries:

PSA Worldwide Corp. (1)
6645 Delmonico Dr Ste 201, Colorado Springs, CO 80919
Tel.: (719) 471-4228
Web Site: http://www.psacorp.com
Sales Range: $1-9.9 Million
Health Education & Promotional Products Online Retailer
N.A.I.C.S.: 459999
Brad Dombaugh (CEO)

DRY STORAGE CORPORATION
1750 S Wolf Rd, Des Plaines, IL 60018
Tel.: (847) 390-6800
Web Site:
   http://www.dsclogistics.com
Rev.: $26,100,000
Emp.: 224
General Warehousing & Storage
N.A.I.C.S.: 493110

DRY-PRO BASEMENT SYSTEMS, INC.
130 Performance Dr, Belmont, NC 28012
Tel.: (980) 220-5839 NC
Web Site:
   http://www.dryprosystems.com
Year Founded: 1999
Sales Range: $10-24.9 Million
Emp.: 108
Waterproofing Contractor Services
N.A.I.C.S.: 238390
Ron Weatherly (Pres & CEO)

DRYCO CONSTRUCTION, INC.
42745 Boscell Rd, Fremont, CA 94538
Tel.: (510) 438-6500
Web Site: https://www.dryco.com
Sales Range: $10-24.9 Million
Emp.: 130
Highway & Street Construction Services
N.A.I.C.S.: 237310
Daren Young (Owner)

DRYDEN MUTUAL INSURANCE COMPANY
12 Ellis Dr, Dryden, NY 13053
Tel.: (607) 844-8106
Web Site:
https://www.drydenmutual.com
Year Founded: 1860
Sales Range: $10-24.9 Million
Emp.: 60
Direct Property & Casualty Insurance Services
N.A.I.C.S.: 524126
Peter Vercello (Gen Mgr)

DRYMALLA CONSTRUCTION COMPANY
608 Harbert St, Columbus, TX 78934-0698
Tel.: (979) 732-5731
Web Site: https://www.drymalla.com
Sales Range: $75-99.9 Million
Emp.: 145
School Building Construction
N.A.I.C.S.: 236220
Earl W. Pitchford (Pres)
Chris Elder (Engr-Field)

DRYTAC CORPORATION
5601 Eastport Blvd, Henrico, VA 23231-4444
Tel.: (804) 222-3094
Web Site: http://www.drytac.com
Sales Range: $25-49.9 Million
Emp.: 90
Non-Durable Goods Whslr
N.A.I.C.S.: 425120
Wayne Colbath (VP-Sls)
Richard Kelley (Chm)
Darren Speizer (VP-Mktg)
Hayden Kelley (CEO)
Douglas Jackson (Dir-Ops)
Steve Broad (Dir-Sls-European & Asia)
Tadeusz Niedziolka (Mgr-Export Sls)
David Johnson (Mgr-Mfg & Technical)
Phil Webster (Mgr-Technical Sls)
Jean-Francois Labonte (Mgr-Territory Sls-Channel & Custom Sls-Eastern Canada)
Peter Bourgeois (Mgr-Territory Sls-Western Canada)
Olga Bates (Mgr-Brand)
Amanda Brown (Coord-Mktg)
Michelle Kempf (Mgr-Territory Sls-Midwest)
Shaun Holdom (Mgr-Product-Global)
Gilbert Espinosa (Mgr-West Coast)

DRYVE INC.
3627 E Miraloma Ave, Anaheim, CA 92806
Tel.: (714) 577-9611
Web Site: http://www.dryve.com
Sales Range: $10-24.9 Million
Emp.: 32
Dry Cleaning Services
N.A.I.C.S.: 812320

DS CAPITAL, LLC
35 E Wacker Dr Ste 900, Chicago, IL 60601-2120
Tel.: (312) 346-9191 IL
Web Site: http://www.dscapitalllc.com
Year Founded: 1964
Sales Range: $10-24.9 Million
Emp.: 4
Mortgage Banking Services
N.A.I.C.S.: 522292
Andrew Wineburgh (Exec VP)
Amy Rosenblum-Wineburgh (Pres)

DS GRAPHICS INC.
120 Stedman St, Lowell, MA 01851-1253
Tel.: (978) 970-1359
Web Site:
https://www.dsgraphics.com
Year Founded: 1974
Sales Range: $10-24.9 Million
Emp.: 150
Offset Printing
N.A.I.C.S.: 323111
Christine Westerlind (Project Mgr)
Joel White (VP-Print Ops)
Dave Crocker (Controller)
Bill Nethercote (Exec VP)

DS HEALTHCARE GROUP, INC.
1601 Green Rd, Pompano Beach, FL 33064
Web Site: http://dshealthgroup.com
Year Founded: 2007
Sales Range: $10-24.9 Million
Emp.: 131
Skin Care & Personal Care Products Mfr & Marketer
N.A.I.C.S.: 325620
Daniel Khesin (Founder)
Myron Lewis (Chm & Chief Acctg Officer)

DS HULL COMPANY INCORPORATED
3377 SW 2nd Ave, Fort Lauderdale, FL 33315
Tel.: (954) 463-4307
Web Site: http://www.bowboat.com
Sales Range: $10-24.9 Million
Emp.: 65
Marine Parts & Supplies Whslr & Distr
N.A.I.C.S.: 423860
Steven Baum (Pres)

DS MEDIALABS
405 SE Oceola Ave 2nd Fl Ste 209, Ocala, FL 34471
Tel.: (855) 438-3765
Web Site:
http://www.dsmedialabs.com
Year Founded: 2007
Sales Range: $1-9.9 Million
Emp.: 20
Mobile Application Designer & Developer
N.A.I.C.S.: 513210
Michael Sean Dasch (Co-Founder & Pres)
Shane Wooten (CFO & Sr VP-Bus Dev)
Gary Melendez (Sr VP-Engrg)
Duane Schor (Dir-Art)
Ben S. Stahlhood II (Co-Founder & CEO)

DSA ONCORE
50 Pocono Rd, Brookfield, CT 06804
Tel.: (203) 740-4200
Web Site: http://www.dsaencore.com
Rev.: $55,000,000
Emp.: 50
Power Supplies
N.A.I.C.S.: 334419
Rudolph Kraus (Mng Dir)
Ron Croce (Pres & COO)
Steve Freedman (Co-Founder, CEO & Mng Dir)
Mark Schnider (COO)

DSC (DILEONARDO SIANO CASERTA) ADVERTISING
237 Chestnut St, Philadelphia, PA 19106
Tel.: (215) 923-3200
Web Site: http://www.dscadv.com
Year Founded: 2001
Sales Range: $10-24.9 Million
Emp.: 25
Advetising Agency
N.A.I.C.S.: 541810
Joseph Dileonardo (CEO)
Joseph Caserta (Pres & COO)
Karen Brenner (Dir-Media Svcs)
Bruno Circolo (Sr Dir-Art)
Matt Mungan (Dir-Interactive Svcs)
Tony Leone (Dir-Traffic & Production)
Ken Suman (Sr VP-Acct Mgmt)
Rich Caserta (Sr Dir-Art)
Natalie Pantaleo Smoley (VP-Mktg-Pub Rel)

DSC LIMITED
1491 W Jefferson Ave, Trenton, MI 48183-1240
Tel.: (734) 285-1200 MI
Web Site: http://www.dsclimited.com
Year Founded: 1996
Sales Range: $75-99.9 Million
Emp.: 110
Steel Processing Plant
N.A.I.C.S.: 332996
Matthew Wilkinson (VP)
Matthew Zwack (Pres)

DSC/PURGATORY LLC
1 Skier Pl, Durango, CO 81301
Tel.: (970) 247-9000
Web Site:
http://www.durangomountainresort.com
Sales Range: $10-24.9 Million
Emp.: 150
Aerial Tramway & Ski Lift
N.A.I.C.S.: 487990
Gary Derck (Pres & CEO)
Mark Seiter (Sr VP-Fin)

DSCS HOLDINGS LLC
9415 Pioneer Ave Ste 200, Charlotte, NC 28273
Tel.: (803) 547-8888
Web Site:
http://www.vimagetech.com
Year Founded: 2008
Sales Range: $10-24.9 Million
Emp.: 50
Holding Company
N.A.I.C.S.: 551112
Marc McQueen (Co-Owner)
Scott McQueen (Co-Owner)

DSI DISTRIBUTING, INC.
3601 109th St, Urbandale, IA 50322
Tel.: (515) 276-9181 IA
Web Site:
http://www.dsisystemsinc.com
Year Founded: 1998
Sales Range: $25-49.9 Million
Emp.: 242
Electrical Apparatus & Equipment Distr
N.A.I.C.S.: 423610
Craig Anderson (CFO)

DSI, DOCUMENT SOLUTIONS, INC.
414 Union St Ste 1210, Nashville, TN 37219
Tel.: (615) 255-5343
Web Site: http://www.dsicovery.com
Year Founded: 1999
Sales Range: $10-24.9 Million
Emp.: 70
Attorneys Litigation Support Services
N.A.I.C.S.: 541199
John Burchfield (VP-Bus Dev)
Tom Turner (Co-Founder & Pres)
Kevin Tyner (Co-Founder & CFO)
Jason Bradley (Dir-IT)

DSI, INC.
1271 Fayland Dr, Fargo, ND 58102
Tel.: (701) 282-8451 ND
Web Site:
https://www.dsiautomotive.com
Sales Range: $10-24.9 Million
Emp.: 25
Motor Vehicle Parts & Supplies Whslr
N.A.I.C.S.: 423120
Todd Salter (Gen Mgr)

Subsidiaries:

DSI Automotive Products (1)
46895 271st St, Tea, SD 57064
Tel.: (605) 368-5226
Web Site: http://www.dsiautomotive.com
Emp.: 30
Motor Vehicle Parts & Supplies Whslr
N.A.I.C.S.: 423120
Todd Salter (Gen Mgr)

DSI/DYNAMATIC CORPORATION
7900 Durand Ave Bldg 3, Sturtevant, WI 53177
Tel.: (262) 554-7977
Web Site:
https://www.dynamatic.com
Year Founded: 1931
Sales Range: $50-74.9 Million
Emp.: 15
Dynamatic Eddy-Current Brakes & Clutches, Adjustable Speed Drives
N.A.I.C.S.: 323111
Gary Garson (VP-Engrg)
Barb Konicek (Mgr-Pur)
Alan Konieczka (CEO)
Gregory Ostrowski (Mgr-Engrg)
Mike Defranco (Gen Mgr)

DSP BUILDERS INC.
12000 E 47th Ave Ste 201, Denver, CO 80239
Tel.: (303) 289-0666 CO
Web Site:
https://www.dspbuilders.com
Year Founded: 1992
Sales Range: $10-24.9 Million
Emp.: 12
Construction Services
N.A.I.C.S.: 236220
Thomas D. Oxley (Pres)
Chris Lindstrom (Project Mgr)
Leslie Roland (Asst Controller)
Robert Krull (Project Mgr)

DSP CLINICAL RESEARCH
50 Fairfield Rd, Fairfield, NJ 07004
Tel.: (973) 265-1060
Web Site:
https://www.dspclinical.com
Year Founded: 1999
Rev.: $4,400,000
Emp.: 26
Clinical Research
N.A.I.C.S.: 541720
Darlene Panzitta (Founder & Pres)
Cindy Lee (Sr Mgr-Data)
Kathleen Kolsum (Dir-Medical)

DSQUARED INTERNATIONAL, LLC
119 S Main St, Saint Charles, MO 63301
Web Site: http://www.grillaholics.com
Year Founded: 2014
Sales Range: $1-9.9 Million
Grill Accessory Retailer
N.A.I.C.S.: 449129
Devin Dorosh (Founder & CEO)

DSR MANAGEMENT, INC.
500 Davis St Ste 801, Evanston, IL 60201
Tel.: (847) 328-6355
Web Site: http://www.dsrminc.com
Sales Range: $1-9.9 Million
Emp.: 100
IT Professional & Consulting Services
N.A.I.C.S.: 541690
Rahul Shah (Founder & CEO)
Manjari Gupta (CFO)
Shobha Shagle (VP-HR)

DSR Management, Inc.—(Continued)

DSSI LLC
9300 Shelbyville Rd Ste 402, Louisville, KY 40222-5163
Tel.: (502) 326-4300   KY
Web Site:
   http://www.directsourcing.com
Year Founded: 1991
Sales Range: $10-24.9 Million
Emp.: 230
Outsourced Purchasing Services
N.A.I.C.S.: 812910
Bhagwan P. Thacker *(Pres & CEO)*

DST INDUSTRIES, INC.
34364 Goddard Rd, Romulus, MI 48174
Tel.: (734) 941-0300
Web Site:
   http://www.dstindustries.com
Year Founded: 1955
Automotive Suppliers
N.A.I.C.S.: 336390
Breda Lewo *(CEO)*
Scot Schmidt *(Mgr-Pur)*

DSTILLERY
37 E 18th St 9th Fl, New York, NY 10016
Tel.: (646) 278-4929
Web Site: http://www.dstillery.com
Year Founded: 2008
Sales Range: $25-49.9 Million
Emp.: 100
Marketing & Advertising Consulting Services
N.A.I.C.S.: 541613
Michael Beebe *(CEO)*

DSU PETERBILT & GMC TRUCK, INC.
4810 N Basin Ave, Portland, OR 97217-3548
Tel.: (503) 285-7771   OR
Web Site: http://www.dsutrucks.com
Year Founded: 1945
Sales Range: $75-99.9 Million
Emp.: 220
Trucks & Other Vehicle Parts, Sales & Services
N.A.I.C.S.: 441110
Jan Yost *(Pres & CEO)*
Tom Stassens *(VP & Gen Mgr)*
Terry Causgrove *(Sls Mgr)*
Jamie Toman *(VP & Gen Mgr)*

Subsidiaries:

DSU Leasing, Inc.   (1)
4810 N Basin Ave, Portland, OR 97217-3548
Tel.: (503) 285-7771
Sales Range: $10-24.9 Million
Emp.: 6
Trucks & Trailers Leasing Services
N.A.I.C.S.: 532120
Lewis Haddan *(Mgr-Leasing & Rental)*

DSU Rental   (1)
4810 N Basin Ave, Portland, OR 97217-3548   **(100%)**
Tel.: (503) 285-7771
Sales Range: $25-49.9 Million
General Automotive Repair Shops
N.A.I.C.S.: 811198
Jan Yost *(Pres & CEO)*

DSYS INC
12700 Century Dr Ste C, Alpharetta, GA 30009
Tel.: (770) 752-5356
Web Site: https://www.dsysinc.com
Year Founded: 2005
Sales Range: $1-9.9 Million
Emp.: 35
IT Consulting Services
N.A.I.C.S.: 541990

Deepa Telang *(Pres)*
Anoop Nair *(Mgr-Ops)*
Mark Ennis *(Dir-Client Success)*
Sid Kumar *(CEO)*

DTC COMPUTER SUPPLIES, INC.
9033 9th St, Rancho Cucamonga, CA 91730
Tel.: (909) 466-7680
Web Site: https://www.dtc1.com
Sales Range: $50-74.9 Million
Emp.: 20
Computers, Peripherals & Software
N.A.I.C.S.: 423430
Mike Kinsley *(Pres & CEO)*

DTIQ TECHNOLOGIES, INC.
111 Speen St 550, Framingham, MA 01701   CA
Web Site: http://www.dtiq.com
Year Founded: 1998
Security Services
N.A.I.C.S.: 561621
Sam Naficy *(Founder & Chm)*
Lawrence Lee *(VP & Controller)*
Mike Coffey *(CEO)*
Marc Litz *(CFO)*
Jon Mignone *(Chief Customer Officer)*
Ariel Gonzales *(Sr VP-Support)*
John Fice *(VP-Ops)*
Michael Pellicano *(VP-Implementation)*

Subsidiaries:

LP Innovations, Inc.   (1)
111 Speen St 550, Framingham, MA 01701
Web Site: http://www.dtiq.com
Loss Prevention Solution Services
N.A.I.C.S.: 561621

DTL TRANSPORTATION INC.
301 Northstar Ct, Sanford, FL 32771
Tel.: (407) 330-9348
Web Site:
   http://www.dtltransportation.com
Sales Range: $10-24.9 Million
Emp.: 100
Heavy Hauling
N.A.I.C.S.: 484121
Ian Smith *(Engr-Pro Transportation)*
Bonnie Drapeau *(Dir-Safety)*

DTS COMPANIES INC.
1640 Monad Rd, Billings, MT 59101
Tel.: (406) 245-4695
Web Site: https://www.dtsb.com
Year Founded: 1988
Long Haul Trucking Services
N.A.I.C.S.: 484122
Jay Foley *(Pres & CEO)*

Subsidiaries:

DTS Logistics LLC   (1)
1640 Monad Rd, Billings, MT 59101
Tel.: (406) 245-4695
Web Site: http://www.dtslogistx.com
Rev.: $5,158,053
Emp.: 9
Freight Forwarding
N.A.I.C.S.: 488510
Anne Jensen *(Coord-Billing)*

DTS FLUID POWER LLC
3560 Busch Dr SW, Grandville, MI 49418
Tel.: (616) 538-3759
Web Site:
   http://www.dtsfluidpower.com
Year Founded: 1979
Sales Range: $10-24.9 Million
Emp.: 50
Hydraulic Systems Equipment & Supplies Whslr
N.A.I.C.S.: 423830
Al Wilde *(Pres)*

DTSV INC.
739 Thimble Shoals Blvd Ste 101, Newport News, VA 23606-2988
Tel.: (757) 873-0725
Web Site: http://www.dtsvinc.com
Year Founded: 1982
Rev.: $43,400,000
Emp.: 905
Document Processing Services
N.A.I.C.S.: 561410
E. D. David *(CEO)*

DU BELL LUMBER CO.
148 Rte 70 E, Medford, NJ 08055
Tel.: (609) 654-4143
Web Site: http://www.dubell.com
Sales Range: $25-49.9 Million
Emp.: 170
Fiscal Year-end: 12/31/15
Lumber: Rough, Dressed & Finished
N.A.I.C.S.: 423310
Joe Brooks *(Mgr-Shipping)*
Terry Arnold *(Plant Mgr-Truss)*
Jennifer Cain *(Mgr-Sls)*
Bart Withstandley. *(Mgr-Stair Dept)*

DU INTERNATIONAL INC.
30727 Beverly Rd, Romulus, MI 48174
Tel.: (734) 641-6700
Web Site: http://www.qvs.com
Year Founded: 1984
Rev.: $11,000,000
Emp.: 40
Computer & Communication Cables & Connectivity Products Mfr & Distr
N.A.I.C.S.: 423430
Frank Tsou *(Pres)*

DU PAGE AIRPORT AUTHORITY
2700 International Dr Ste 200, West Chicago, IL 60185
Tel.: (630) 584-2211
Web Site:
   https://www.dupageairport.com
Rev.: $11,648,567
Emp.: 50
Airports, Flying Fields & Services
N.A.I.C.S.: 488119
Brian Decoudres *(Gen Mgr)*

DU PAGE PRECISION PRODUCTS CO.
3695 Darlene Ct Ste 101, Aurora, IL 60504-6515
Tel.: (630) 849-2940
Web Site:
   https://www.dupageprecision.com
Rev.: $19,448,062
Emp.: 85
Machine Shop, Jobbing & Repair
N.A.I.C.S.: 332710
Dennis Flynn *(Pres)*
Gary Adams *(Supvr-Quality)*
Mike Schroeder *(VP)*

DU-ART FILM LABORATORIES INC.
245 W 55th St, New York, NY 10019
Tel.: (212) 757-4580
Web Site: https://www.duart.com
Sales Range: $10-24.9 Million
Emp.: 80
Film Processing, Editing & Titling
N.A.I.C.S.: 512191
Irwin Young *(Chm)*
Josestha Gonzalez *(Controller)*

DU-CO CERAMICS COMPANY
155 S Rebecca St, Saxonburg, PA 16056
Tel.: (724) 352-1511
Web Site: https://www.du-co.com
Year Founded: 1949
Technical Ceramic Parts

N.A.I.C.S.: 327120
Tom Arbanas *(Pres)*
Pat D'Angelo *(VP-Sls)*

DU-MONT COMPANY INCORPORATED
7800 N Pioneer Ct, Peoria, IL 61615
Tel.: (309) 692-7240
Web Site: http://www.du-mont.com
Sales Range: $10-24.9 Million
Emp.: 40
Sheet Metal Fabrication Services
N.A.I.C.S.: 332322
Steven P. Graves *(Pres)*
Robert Williams *(Treas & Sec)*
Brady Mann *(VP)*

DUAL TEMP COMPANY, INC.
2050 S 12th St, Allentown, PA 18103
Tel.: (610) 791-9100
Web Site: https://www.dualtemp.com
Sales Range: $10-24.9 Million
Emp.: 100
Plumbing Services
N.A.I.C.S.: 238220
David Noel *(Pres)*
Brad Noel *(VP)*

DUALITE SALES & SERVICE, INC.
1 Dualite Ln, Williamsburg, OH 45176-1121
Tel.: (513) 724-7100   OH
Web Site: https://www.dualite.com
Year Founded: 1947
Sales Range: $25-49.9 Million
Emp.: 295
Illuminated Indoor & Outdoor Signs, Clocks & Menu Signs Mfr & Sales
N.A.I.C.S.: 423990
Greg Schube *(Pres & CEO)*
Patrick Seggerson *(Dir-Design)*
Robert Stephany *(Mgr-Sls-Natl)*
Dennis Emery *(VP-Sls)*
Betty Jewell *(Dir-HR)*

DUANE MORRIS LLP
30 S 17th St, Philadelphia, PA 19103
Tel.: (215) 979-1000
Web Site:
   http://www.duanemorris.com
Year Founded: 1904
Sales Range: $400-449.9 Million
Emp.: 630
Law firm
N.A.I.C.S.: 541110
Kenneth Argentieri *(Mng Partner-Pittsburgh)*
Robert Ruben *(Partner)*
Sean Zabaneh *(Partner)*
Brian P. Kerwin *(Chm-Corp Practice Grp)*
John Baird *(Partner-Washington)*
Roger Goldman *(Partner-Real Estate Practice Grp)*
Marsha Madorsky *(Partner-Wealth Plng Practice Grp)*
Anastasios Kastrinakis *(Partner-Tax Practice)*
William Rohrer *(Partner-Tax Practice)*
Sean Burke *(Partner)*
Gregory R. Haworth *(Mng Partner-Newark)*
Michael Gallagher *(Partner)*
Michael Hardy *(Partner-Baltimore)*
John Gibson *(Partner-IP Practice Grp-Atlanta)*
Karen Kline *(Partner-IP Practice Grp-Boca Raton)*
Christopher Tyson *(Partner-IP Practice Grp-Washington)*
Matthew A. Taylor *(Chm & CEO)*
L. Norwood Jameson *(Chm/Partner-Intellectual Property Practice Grp)*
Katherine Brodie *(Partner-Washington)*

Richard A. Silfen *(Partner-Philadelphia)*
Denis F. Shanagher *(Partner-San Francisco)*
Brian D. Siff *(Partner-New York-New York)*
Brad A. Molotsky *(Partner-Real Estate Dept)*
Robert E. Horwath Jr. *(Partner-Chicago)*
David S. Drobner *(Partner-Miami & Boca Raton)*
Jay Steinman *(Partner-Miami & Boca Raton)*
Robert W. Kadlec *(Partner-Los Angeles-Los Angeles)*
Benton T. Wheatley *(Partner-Austin-Austin)*
Tracy L. McCreight *(Partner-Austin-Austin)*
Hersh Kozlov *(Partner-Marlton)*
Charles J. O'Donnell *(COO)*
Peter J. Cronk *(Partner)*
Michael Bruckner *(CIO)*
James C. Carignan *(Partner)*
Mark P. Messing *(CMO)*
Daniel Sheeran *(CFO)*
Leen Al-Alami *(Partner)*
David Amerikaner *(Partner)*
Caroline M. Austin *(Partner)*
Michael F. Brown *(Partner & Asst Gen Counsel)*
Sharon L. Caffrey *(Partner)*
Timothy B. Collins *(Partner)*
Samuel W. Apicelli *(Partner)*
Ryan E. Borneman *(Partner)*
Robert L. Byer *(Partner)*
Robert L. Archie Jr. *(Partner)*
Richard L. Cohen *(Partner)*
Miles L. Plaskett *(Partner-Miami)*
Michael S. Cohen *(Partner)*
Mark A. Canizio *(Partner-New York & Chm-Construction Grp)*
Jonathan Lourie *(Partner-Boston)*
Jolie-Anne S. Ansley *(Partner-San Francisco)*
John Robert Weiss *(Mng Partner-Chicago)*
John F. L'Esperance *(Partner-Boca Raton)*
Jocelyn Margolin Borowsky *(Partner)*
James J. Holman *(Partner & Chm-Bus Reorganization & Fin Restructuring Practice Grp)*
James L. Beausoleil Jr. *(Partner)*
Jennifer A. Wieclaw *(Partner)*
Harry M. Byrne *(Partner)*
Gregory M. Lefkowitz *(Partner-Boca Raton)*
Gregory P. Duffy *(Partner)*
Gerald J. Schirato *(Partner-Pittsburgh)*
Edward G. Biester III *(Partner)*
Driscoll R. Ugarte *(Partner-Boca Raton & Miami)*
David B. Yelin *(Mng Partner/Partner-Chicago)*
David C. Dotson *(Partner-Intellectual Property Litigation)*
Cyndie M. Chang *(Mng Partner/Partner-Los Angeles)*
Christopher D. Durham *(Partner-Philadelphia)*
Christiane Schuman Campbell *(Partner-Philadelphia)*
Adam Berger *(Partner)*
Valentine A. Brown *(Partner)*
Stephen H. Sutro *(Mng Partner/Partner-San Francisco)*
Richard L. Renck *(Partner-Wilmington)*
Natalie F. Bare *(Partner)*
David R. Augustin *(Partner)*

DUARTE, INC.

3200 Coronado Dr, Santa Clara, CA 95054
Tel.: (650) 625-8200
Web Site: https://www.duarte.com
Year Founded: 1988
Sales Range: $10-24.9 Million
Emp.: 106
Cinema & Literature Visual Techniques & Graphical Designs Services
N.A.I.C.S.: 541430
Nancy Duarte *(Founder & Principal)*
Joe Terry *(CEO)*

DUB PUBLISHING, INC.

11803 Smith Ave, Santa Fe Springs, CA 90670
Tel.: (562) 228-1737   CA
Web Site:
http://www.dubmagazine.com
Year Founded: 1999
Sales Range: $1-9.9 Million
Automotive Lifestyle Enthusiast Magazine Publisher
N.A.I.C.S.: 513120
Myles Kovacs *(Co-Founder & Pres)*
Haythem Haddad *(Co-Founder & Creative Dir)*
John Ramos *(Dir-Events & Promos)*

Subsidiaries:

DUB Publishing, Inc. - DUB Shop   (1)
11803 Smith Ave, Santa Fe Springs, CA 90670
Tel.: (626) 336-3821
Web Site: http://www.dubshop.com
Aftermarket Automotive Products & Accessories Retailer
N.A.I.C.S.: 441330
Myles Kovacs *(Pres)*

DUBILIER & COMPANY, INC.

2187 Atlantic St, Stamford, CT 06902
Tel.: (203) 351-2891   DE
Web Site: http://www.dubilier.com
Sales Range: $150-199.9 Million
Emp.: 5
Private Investment Firm
N.A.I.C.S.: 523150
Michael J. Dubilier *(Mng Partner)*

Subsidiaries:

Bluegrass Dairy and Food, Inc.   (1)
1117 Cleveland Ave, Glasgow, KY 42141
Web Site: http://www.bluegrassdairy.com
Dairy Products Mfr
N.A.I.C.S.: 311514
Patty Howlett *(Gen Mgr)*

DC Safety Sales, Inc.   (1)
40 Commerce Dr, Hauppauge, NY 11788
Tel.: (631) 750-2400
Web Site: http://www.dcsafety.com
First Aid Kit Mfr
N.A.I.C.S.: 339113
Peter Murphy *(Pres & CEO)*

ODC Nimbus Inc   (1)
490 E Princeland Ct Ste 3 & 4, Corona, CA 92879
Tel.: (951) 372-9800
Web Site: http://www.odc-nimbus.com
Optical Disc Mastering Equipment Mfr
N.A.I.C.S.: 334419
Tony Holden *(Pres)*

DUBIN CLARK & COMPANY, INC.

323 Newbury St, Boston, MA 02115
Tel.: (203) 629-2030   DE
Web Site:
https://www.dubinclark.com
Year Founded: 1984
Equity Investment Firm
N.A.I.C.S.: 523999
Thomas J. Caracciolo *(Mng Partner)*

Subsidiaries:

CE Rental, Inc.   (1)
4300 Craftsman Dr, Raleigh, NC 27609

Tel.: (919) 833-9743
Web Site: http://www.cerental.com
Wedding & Boutique Rental Company
N.A.I.C.S.: 532289
Heather Sutton *(Gen Mgr)*

Subsidiary (Domestic):

Capital Party Rentals LLC   (2)
44232 Mercure Cir, Dulles, VA 20166
Tel.: (703) 661-8290
Web Site:
http://www.capitalpartyrentals.com
Sales Range: $1-9.9 Million
Party & Associated Event Planning Equipment Rental Company
N.A.I.C.S.: 532289
Jodi Lee Orndorff *(Dir-Sls)*

M&M Rental Center, Inc.   (1)
493 Mission St, Carol Stream, IL 60188
Tel.: (630) 871-9999
Web Site: http://www.mmspecialevents.com
Sales Range: $1-9.9 Million
Wedding, Party & Corporate Event Furniture & Supplies Rental Services
N.A.I.C.S.: 532289
Scott Berk *(Pres/Gen Mgr-Texas Ops)*
Seth Berk *(Pres)*

Subsidiary (Domestic):

Heiferman, Inc.   (2)
3020 W 167th St, Markham, IL 60428
Tel.: (708) 210-1200
Hospitality Equipment Rental
N.A.I.C.S.: 532284

Trim Parts, Inc.   (1)
2175 Deerfield Rd, Lebanon, OH 45036
Tel.: (513) 934-0815
Web Site: http://www.trimparts.com
Sales Range: $10-24.9 Million
Emp.: 35
Automotive Restoration Parts Mfr
N.A.I.C.S.: 336390

DUBLIN & ASSOCIATES, INC.

3015 San Pedro, San Antonio, TX 78212-4721
Tel.: (210) 227-0221   TX
Web Site:
http://www.dublinandassociates.com
Year Founded: 1982
Sales Range: $1-9.9 Million
Emp.: 6
Public Relations Agency
N.A.I.C.S.: 541820
James R. Dublin *(Chm & CEO)*
Edna Strey *(Controller)*
Rose Marie Eash *(Sr Acct Mgr)*

DUBLIN BUICK GMC

4400 John Monego Ct, Dublin, CA 94568-3165
Tel.: (925) 452-4621   CA
Web Site: http://www.dublinbuick.com
Year Founded: 1999
Sales Range: $10-24.9 Million
Emp.: 70
Car Dealership
N.A.I.C.S.: 441110
Bani Paulus *(Gen Mgr)*
Inder Dosanjh *(Owner)*

DUBLIN CONSTRUCTION COMPANY, INC.

305 S Washington St, Dublin, GA 31021
Tel.: (478) 272-0721
Web Site:
http://www.dublinconstruction.com
Year Founded: 1945
Sales Range: $50-74.9 Million
Emp.: 150
Commercial & Institutional Building Construction Services
N.A.I.C.S.: 236220
William D. Key *(Sr VP)*

DUBLIN SAN RAMON SERVICES DISTRICT

7051 Dublin Blvd, Dublin, CA 94568
Tel.: (925) 828-0515
Web Site: https://www.dsrsd.com
Year Founded: 1953
Sales Range: $10-24.9 Million
Emp.: 100
Water Supply & Irrigation System Services
N.A.I.C.S.: 221310
Michelle Gallardo *(Supvr-HR & Risk)*
D. L. Howard *(Pres)*
Richard M. Halket *(VP)*
Dan McIntyre *(Gen Mgr)*
John Archer *(Interim Gen Mgr)*
Jeff Carson *(Mgr-Ops)*

DUBOIS WOOD PRODUCTS INC.

707 E 6th St, Huntingburg, IN 47542
Tel.: (812) 683-3613
Web Site:
https://www.duboiswood.com
Sales Range: $10-24.9 Million
Emp.: 160
Novelty Furniture Commercial
N.A.I.C.S.: 337122
Brian Meyerholtz *(Pres)*

DUBUG NO 7 INC.

3711 Morrow Ln, Chico, CA 95928
Tel.: (530) 895-1433
Web Site: http://www.paylessbuilding supply.com
Rev.: $10,000,000
Emp.: 30
Lumber & Other Building Materials
N.A.I.C.S.: 423310
Frank Solinsky *(Pres)*

DUBUIS HEALTH SYSTEM, INC.

2707 N Loop W 7th Fl, Houston, TX 77008
Tel.: (281) 936-7343   LA
Web Site: http://www.dubuis.org
Year Founded: 1994
Sales Range: $25-49.9 Million
Emp.: 11
Health Care Srvices
N.A.I.C.S.: 622110
Mathew E. Smith *(Sec)*
Paul Veillon *(VP-Fin)*

DUBUQUE RACING ASSOCIATION LTD.

1855 Greyhound Park Rd, Dubuque, IA 52001
Tel.: (563) 582-3647   IA
Web Site:
http://www.dradubuque.com
Year Founded: 1985
Sales Range: $25-49.9 Million
Emp.: 535
Entertainment Facility Operator
N.A.I.C.S.: 713290
Brian D. Southwood *(VP-Grants & Special Projects)*
Jesus Aviles *(Pres & CEO)*

DUBUQUE STAMPING & MANUFACTURING INC.

32nd & Jackson, Dubuque, IA 52001
Tel.: (563) 583-5716
Web Site: http://www.dbqstamp.com
Rev.: $20,000,000
Emp.: 150
Metal Stampings Mfr
N.A.I.C.S.: 332119
David W. Spahn *(Pres)*
Craig Schmal *(Engr-Mfg)*

DUCATI SEATTLE, LLC

711 9th Ave N, Seattle, WA 98109
Tel.: (206) 298-9995   WA
Web Site:
http://www.ducatiseattle.com

Ducati Seattle, LLC—(Continued)
Year Founded: 1999
Rev.: $4,900,000
Emp.: 15
Motorcycle Dealers
N.A.I.C.S.: 441227
Jon Payne (Mgr-Parts & Accessories)

DUCHATEAU FLOORS
8480 Miralani Dr, San Diego, CA 92126
Tel.: (858) 790-3139
Web Site:
http://www.duchateaufloors.com
Year Founded: 2006
Sales Range: $10-24.9 Million
Emp.: 22
Hardwood Floor Mfr
N.A.I.C.S.: 321918
Misael Tagle (Co-Founder & CEO)
Benjamin Buzali (Co-Founder & Pres)
Joseph Patterson (Mgr-East Coast)
Todd Gates (VP-Residential Sls)
Scott Campbell (CFO)
Doug Robinson (Sls Mgr-Midwest)
Jim Heaton (COO)
Dennis Whitler (Mgr-Customer Svc)
Rick Wagner (Mgr-West Coast)

DUCK RIVER ELECTRIC MEMBERSHIP CORPORATION
1411 Madison St, Shelbyville, TN 37160
Tel.: (931) 684-4621
Web Site: https://www.dremc.com
Rev.: $30,770,384
Emp.: 75
Distribution, Electric Power
N.A.I.C.S.: 221122
Michael Watson (Pres & CEO)
Barry Cooper (Chm)
Shelia Orrell (Dir-Fin)
Steve Oden (Dir-Member Svcs)
Laura L. Willis (Sec)
John Moses (Treas)

DUCKER FSG HOLDINGS LLC
1150 18th St NW Ste 350, Washington, DC 20036
Tel.: (202) 741-1333
Year Founded: 2018
Holding Company; Market Information & Advisory Services
N.A.I.C.S.: 551112
Richard Leggett (CEO)
Joanne Ulnick (Mng Principal-Global Consulting Solutions)

Subsidiaries:

Ducker Worldwide LLC (1)
1250 Maplelawn Dr, Troy, MI 48084
Tel.: (248) 644-0086
Web Site: http://www.ducker.com
Market Research & Consulting
N.A.I.C.S.: 519290
Joanne Ulnick (CEO & Mng Principal)

Frontier Strategy Group LLC (1)
1150 18th St NW Ste 350, Washington, DC 20036
Tel.: (202) 741-1333
Web Site:
http://www.frontierstrategygroup.com
Emerging Market Information & Advisory Services
N.A.I.C.S.: 519290
Neeraj Vohra (CFO)
Jonathan Rubin (Sr VP-Ops & Strategy)
Joel Whitaker (Sr VP & Head-Res-Global)

DUCKETT CREEK SEWER DISTRICT
3550 Hwy K, O'Fallon, MO 63368
Tel.: (636) 441-1244
Web Site:
https://www.duckettcreek.com
Year Founded: 1972
Sales Range: $10-24.9 Million

Emp.: 41
Sewage Treatment Services
N.A.I.C.S.: 221320
Rick Higgins (Dir-Ops)
Jerry Hurlbert (Vice Chm)
Chuck Gross (Exec Dir)
Keith Arbuckle (Dir-Engrg)

DUCKREY ENTERPRISES INC.
3000 3D Lincoln Dr W, Marlton, NJ 08053
Tel.: (856) 983-6351
Sales Range: $10-24.9 Million
Emp.: 2
Fast-Food Restaurant, Chain
N.A.I.C.S.: 722513
Vernon J. Duckrey (Pres)

DUCKS UNLIMITED, INC.
1 Waterfowl Way, Memphis, TN 38120-2350
Tel.: (901) 758-3825
Web Site: https://www.ducks.org
Year Founded: 1937
Sales Range: $1-9.9 Million
Emp.: 510
Wetland Conservation Organization
N.A.I.C.S.: 114210
John W. Newman (First VP)
Chuck Smith (Sec)
Wendell Weakley (Treas)
Andrew Schmidt (Mgr-Agriculture Policy)
Karen Waldrop (Chief Conservation Officer)
Steve Adair (Natl Dir-Conservation Strategies)
Doug Schoenrock (Pres)
Adam H. Putnam (CEO)
Rogers Hoyt Jr. (Chm)

DUCLARKEE, INC.
222 E Robinson St, Knoxville, IA 50138
Tel.: (641) 828-8000
Web Site: http://www.issbank.com
Holding Company
N.A.I.C.S.: 551111

Subsidiaries:

Iowa State Savings Bank (1)
222 E Robinson St, Knoxville, IA 50138
Tel.: (641) 828-8000
Web Site: http://www.issbank.com
Banking Services
N.A.I.C.S.: 522180
Kevin Stuart (Pres)

DUCON TECHNOLOGIES INC.
19 Engineers Ln, Farmingdale, NY 11735
Tel.: (631) 694-1700
Web Site: https://www.ducon.com
Sales Range: $300-349.9 Million
Emp.: 25
Air Pollution Control Equipment Mfr
N.A.I.C.S.: 333413
Aron K. Govil (Pres & CEO)
Renato Dela Rama (Accountant)

DUCTMATE INDUSTRIES INC.
210 5th St, Charleroi, PA 15022-1514
Tel.: (724) 258-0500
Web Site: https://www.ductmate.com
Rev.: $45,000,000
Emp.: 170
Ducts, Sheet Metal
N.A.I.C.S.: 332322
Alvin Jefferson (Engr-Applications)
Dale Kemp (Mgr-Traffic)
Ed Rafalski (Mgr-Sls-Natl)
Tim Omstead (Owner)
Virginia Ferris (Mgr-Product Line)
Darrell Frost (Engr-Maintenance)

Subsidiaries:

Linx Industries, Inc. (1)

2600 Airline Blvd, Portsmouth, VA 23701-2701
Tel.: (757) 488-1144
Web Site: http://www.li-hvac.com
Emp.: 200
HVAC Ductwork & Air Distribution Products Mfr & Marketer
N.A.I.C.S.: 332322

DUCTS UNLIMITED MECHANICAL SYSTEMS, INC.
5156 W 58 Ave Ste A, Arvada, CO 80002
Tel.: (303) 657-5592
Web Site:
https://www.ductsunlimitedinc.com
Year Founded: 2000
Sales Range: $10-24.9 Million
Emp.: 57
Plumbing, Heating & Air Conditioning Contractors
N.A.I.C.S.: 238220
Elissa Leishman (CEO & Sec)
Robert Leishman (Pres)
Clifton Lamont (Principal & VP)

DUDA MOBILE INC.
577 College Ave, Palo Alto, CA 94306
Tel.: (855) 790-0003
Web Site:
http://www.dudamobile.com
Year Founded: 2009
Sales Range: $1-9.9 Million
Emp.: 80
Mobile Applications
N.A.I.C.S.: 513210
Itai Sadan (Co-Founder & CEO)
Amir Glatt (Co-Founder & CTO)
Allan Keller (Chief Revenue Officer)
Oren Zeev (Chm)
Jason Knaut (CFO)

DUDEK & BOCK SPRING MANUFACTURING COMPANY
5100 W Roosevelt Rd, Chicago, IL 60644
Tel.: (773) 379-4100
Web Site: https://www.dudek-bock.com
Year Founded: 1946
Sales Range: $100-124.9 Million
Emp.: 190
Mfr of Steel Springs & Fabricated Wire Products
N.A.I.C.S.: 332613
John Dudek (Pres)
Ron Vojik (VP-Bus Dev)
Raquel Chole (Mgr-Sls & Mktg)
Bob Fashingbauer (Controller)

Subsidiaries:

Dudek & Bock S. de R.L. de C.V. (1)
3490 Blvd Isidro Lopez Zertuche Col La Salle Industrial, Saltillo, 25240, Coahuila, Mexico
Tel.: (52) 84 44 16 2300
Spring & Metal Stamping Mfr
N.A.I.C.S.: 332613
Roberto Solis Abraham (Mgr-Matls)

KHC DUDEK & BOCK LLC (1)
333 E Judd St, Woodstock, IL 60098
Tel.: (815) 337-7630
Spring Mfr
N.A.I.C.S.: 332613

DUDLEY PRODUCTS INC.
4035 Premier Dr Ste 109, High Point, NC 27265
Tel.: (336) 993-8800
Web Site: http://www.dudleyq.com
Year Founded: 1967
Sales Range: $25-49.9 Million
Emp.: 475
Mfr of Cosmetics & Hair Care Products

N.A.I.C.S.: 424210
Ursula Oglesby (CIO)

DUDLEY SUPERMARKET INC.
14 Airport Rd, Dudley, MA 01571
Tel.: (508) 943-1352
Web Site: http://www.parknshop.net
Sales Range: $25-49.9 Million
Emp.: 250
Provider of Grocery Store Services
N.A.I.C.S.: 445110
Charles Pappas (CEO & Treas)
Helen Pappas (VP)
Joe Doherty (Mgr)

DUDNYK ENTERPRISES, LTD.
5 Walnut Grove Dr Ste 280, Horsham, PA 19044
Tel.: (267) 532-1384
Web Site:
http://www.dudnykexchange.com
Holding Company; Advertising Agencies
N.A.I.C.S.: 551112
Laurie Bartolomeo (Exec VP)
John Kemble (Exec VP)
Drew Desjardins (Exec VP)
Dan Zaksas (Sr VP & Dir-Medical & Scientific Affairs)
Brett Amdor (VP & Dir-IT & Bus Solutions)
Ellen Schneider (VP & Dir-Editorial Svcs & Corp Comm)
Scott Harper (VP & Dir-Bus Plng & Ops)
Jahda Hill (Dir-Scientific)
Kathie Carnes (VP-HR)
Katie Rosseau (Sr Dir-Art)
Margaret Sinclair (Mgr-Acctg)
Rick Sutliff (COO)
Sari Schwartz (Sr Mgr-HR)
Tim Anderson (VP & Grp Acct Dir)

Subsidiaries:

Dudnyk Advertising & Public Relations, Inc. (1)
5 Walnut Grove Dr Ste 300, Horsham, PA 19044
Tel.: (215) 443-9406
Web Site: http://www.dudnyk.com
Sales Range: $10-24.9 Million
Emp.: 60
Advertising Agencies, Brand Development, Health Care
N.A.I.C.S.: 541810
Scott Harper (VP & Dir-Bus Plng & Ops)
Heather Wagoner (Dir-Accts)

DUEA MOTOR COMPANY INC.
117 S Main St, Albia, IA 52531-2013
Tel.: (641) 932-5172
Web Site: http://www.dueamotor.com
Year Founded: 1952
Sales Range: $10-24.9 Million
Emp.: 17
Car Whslr
N.A.I.C.S.: 441110
Greg Dorpinghaus (Pres)

DUFFE GRAIN INC.
201 Cedar St, Wilton, IA 52778
Tel.: (563) 732-3310
Web Site: https://www.duffegrain.com
Sales Range: $25-49.9 Million
Emp.: 20
Grain Elevator Services
N.A.I.C.S.: 424510
Ronald D. Duffe (Pres)
Deb Duffe (CFO)

DUFFEK SAND & GRAVEL INC.
1625 W Ctr St, Antigo, WI 54409
Tel.: (715) 623-7616
Web Site:
http://www.duffeksandandgravel.com
Sales Range: $10-24.9 Million

Emp.: 100
Sand, Construction
N.A.I.C.S.: 423320
Calvin Krueger *(Pres)*

DUFFEY COMMUNICATIONS, INC.

3379 Peachtree Rd NE Ste 740, Atlanta, GA 30326
Tel.: (404) 266-2600
Web Site: https://www.duffey.com
Year Founded: 1984
Public Relations Agency
N.A.I.C.S.: 541820
Sherri Fallin Simmons *(Pres & CEO)*
Allen Haynes *(Dir-PR)*

DUFFY & SHANLEY, INC.

10 Charles St, Providence, RI 02904
Tel.: (401) 274-0001   RI
Web Site:
    http://www.duffyshanley.com
Year Founded: 1973
Rev.: $30,000,000
Emp.: 35
Fiscal Year-end: 06/30/03
N.A.I.C.S.: 541810
Karen Shuster *(VP & Media Dir)*
Rae Mancini *(VP)*
Robert Hart *(CFO)*
Peter Marcionetti *(Chief Creative Officer)*
Jonathan D. Duffy *(Pres)*
Carol Cunha *(Studio Mgr)*
Annette Maggiacomo *(VP-PR)*
Jeremy A. Duffy *(VP-Bus Dev)*
Michael Silvia *(Creative Dir)*
Karen Maia *(Office Mgr)*
Doug Burns *(Acct Supvr)*
Shawna Hassett *(Asst Acct Exec)*
Meaghan Wims *(Sr Acct Exec)*
Emily Hollenbeck *(Acct Exec)*
Robert L. Newbert Jr. *(CEO)*

DUFFY'S HOLDINGS INC.

1926 10th Ave N Ste 300, Lake Worth, FL 33461
Tel.: (561) 804-7676
Web Site: http://www.duffysmvp.com
Year Founded: 1985
Sales Range: $75-99.9 Million
Emp.: 950
Restaurant & Sports Bar Services
N.A.I.C.S.: 551112
Sandy Nelson *(Dir-Mktg)*

Subsidiaries:

Duffy's Sports Grill   (1)
4280 Northlake Blvd, Palm Beach Gardens, FL 33410
Tel.: (561) 493-8381
Web Site: http://www.duffysmvp.com
Sales Range: $10-24.9 Million
Emp.: 75
Restaurant & Sports Bar Services
N.A.I.C.S.: 722511
Katie Loren *(Mgr-Northlake)*

DUFOUR ADVERTISING

532 S 8th St, Sheboygan, WI 53081
Tel.: (920) 457-9191
Web Site: http://www.dufour.com
Year Founded: 1980
Sales Range: Less than $1 Million
Emp.: 7
Advetising Agency
N.A.I.C.S.: 541810
Timothy F. DuFour *(Owner)*
Roman Draughon *(Dir-Creative)*
Kathryn Wade DuFour *(Designer & Graphic Artist)*
Pre Priyadarshane *(Acct Mgr)*
Drew Foerster *(Asst Dir-Creative)*
Carol Senkbeil *(Dir-Accts Payable)*

DUGAN OIL CO. INC.

207 Main St, Loami, IL 62661

Tel.: (217) 624-3402
Web Site:
    https://www.duganoilandtire.com
Sales Range: $10-24.9 Million
Emp.: 10
Petroleum Bulk Stations & Terminals
N.A.I.C.S.: 424710
John Norris *(Pres)*

DUGAN PRODUCTION CORP.

709 E Murray Dr, Farmington, NM 87401-6649
Tel.: (505) 325-1821   NM
Year Founded: 1959
Sales Range: $125-149.9 Million
Emp.: 98
Oil & Gas Production Services
N.A.I.C.S.: 211120
Thomas A. Dugan *(Chm, Pres & CEO)*
Eddie Chavez *(Mgr-Safety)*

Subsidiaries:

Atomi Corp.   (1)
PO Box 420, Farmington, NM
87499-0208   (100%)
Tel.: (505) 326-4548
Web Site: http://www.atomi.com
Sales Range: $50-74.9 Million
Emp.: 20
Mfr of Compressors
N.A.I.C.S.: 333912

DUGGAL COLOR PROJECTS INC.

29 W 23rd St, New York, NY 10010-3201
Tel.: (212) 242-7000
Web Site: http://www.duggal.com
Rev.: $15,000,000
Emp.: 300
Photofinish Laboratories
N.A.I.C.S.: 812921
Baldev Duggal *(Founder)*

DUGGAL VISUAL SOLUTIONS, INC.

63 Flushing Ave Bldg 25, Brooklyn, NY 11205
Tel.: (212) 242-7000
Web Site: http://www.duggal.com
Year Founded: 1961
One-Hour Photofinishing
N.A.I.C.S.: 812922
Duggal West *(VP)*
Michael Duggal *(CEO)*

Subsidiaries:

National Communications Group, Inc.   (1)
220 E 23rd St Ste 509, New York, NY 10010
Tel.: (212) 251-0005
Commercial Lithographic Printing
N.A.I.C.S.: 323111
Scott May *(Pres & CEO)*

DUGGAN CONTRACTING CORPORATION

4120 Industrial Dr, Saint Peters, MO 63376
Tel.: (636) 936-1566
Web Site:
    http://dugancontracting.com
Sales Range: $25-49.9 Million
Emp.: 16
Nonresidential Construction Services
N.A.I.C.S.: 236220
Pat Duggan *(Pres)*
Aden Vickrey *(Project Mgr-Construction)*

DUGGAN INDUSTRIES, INC.

3901 S Lamar St, Dallas, TX 75215-4006
Tel.: (214) 428-8336   TX
Web Site: http://www.dimcosteel.com

Year Founded: 1946
Sales Range: $10-24.9 Million
Emp.: 15
Distr of Steel
N.A.I.C.S.: 423510
Evelyn Kay *(Mgr-Credit)*

Subsidiaries:

Ace Iron & Metal   (1)
4603 Irving Blvd, Dallas, TX
75247-5705   (100%)
Tel.: (214) 631-2256
Web Site: http://www.timetorecycle.com
Ferrous Metal Scrap & Waste
N.A.I.C.S.: 423510

DUHIG AND CO. INC.

5071 Telegraph Rd, Los Angeles, CA 90022
Tel.: (323) 263-7161
Web Site: http://www.duhig.com
Rev.: $13,077,365
Emp.: 30
Valves & Fittings
N.A.I.C.S.: 423830
Thomas W. Card *(Chm & CEO)*
Jodi Burton *(Treas)*
Albert Marquez *(Pres-San Diego)*
Ray Espinoza *(Mgr-Los Angeles)*
Dale Ghaner *(VP-Modesto)*
Marie Olivarez *(Mgr-Ops-Los Angeles)*
Jared Despain *(Mgr-Ops-San Diego)*
Rob Davis *(Mgr-Sls-Northern CA)*

DUININCK COMPANIES LLC

408 6th St, Prinsburg, MN 56281
Tel.: (320) 978-6011
Web Site:
    http://www.duininckcompanies.com
Rev.: $100,000,000
Emp.: 380
General Contractor, Highway & Street Construction
N.A.I.C.S.: 237310

DUKAL CORPORATION

2 Fleetwood Ct, Ronkonkoma, NY 11779
Tel.: (631) 656-3800
Web Site: http://www.dukal.com
Year Founded: 1991
Emp.: 50
Medical, Helath & Wellness Products Distr
N.A.I.C.S.: 423450
Gerry LoDuca *(Pres)*
Rick Kinsella *(CFO)*
Lou Campione *(Mgr-Vet Market)*
Jean Swanson *(VP-Health & Beauty)*
Brian Walsh *(Sls Mgr-Intl)*
David Welch *(Mgr-Clinical Support)*
Chris Brooks *(VP-Sls)*

DUKANE CORPORATION

2900 Dukane Dr, Saint Charles, IL 60174
Tel.: (630) 584-2300   DE
Web Site: http://www.dukcorp.com
Year Founded: 1922
Sales Range: $25-49.9 Million
Emp.: 225
Mfr & Marketer of Advanced Technology Products
N.A.I.C.S.: 334220
Michael W. Ritschdorff *(Pres & CEO)*
Mike Johnston *(Pres-Div)*
Terry Goldman *(VP-Admin)*

Subsidiaries:

Dukane Corporation-Audio Visual Division   (1)
2900 Dukane Dr, Saint Charles, IL 60174-3348
Tel.: (630) 584-2300
Web Site: http://www.dukane.com
Sales Range: $10-24.9 Million
Emp.: 25

Audio-Visual Equipment for the Sales Aids, Training & Teaching Fields, Microfilm Readers
N.A.I.C.S.: 334220

Dukane Corporation-Ultrasonics Division   (1)
2900 Dukane Dr, Saint Charles, IL 60174-3348
Tel.: (630) 584-2300
Web Site: http://www.dukane.com
Sales Range: $25-49.9 Million
Emp.: 200
Mfr of Ultrasonic Welding Equipment for Plastics Industry
N.A.I.C.S.: 334220

Dukane Intelligent Assembly Solutions   (1)
2900 Dukane Dr, Saint Charles, IL 60174
Tel.: (630) 797-4900
Web Site: http://www.dukane.com
Welding Equipment & Supplies Distr
N.A.I.C.S.: 423830
Michael Johnston *(Pres & CEO)*
Russ Witthoff *(Dir-Sls & Mktg-Asia & Europe)*
Terry Goldman *(VP-Admin)*
Dan Majewski *(CFO)*

DUKE AUTOMOTIVE CORP.

2016 N Main St, Suffolk, VA 23434
Tel.: (757) 539-8777
Web Site: http://www.dukeauto.com
Sales Range: $25-49.9 Million
Emp.: 48
New & Used Car Dealers
N.A.I.C.S.: 441110
Lydia Duke *(Pres)*
Bruce Blythe *(Mgr-Pre-Owned-Sls)*
Don Kelly *(Mgr-Fin)*
Richard Potts *(Mgr-Svc)*
Dianne Dillow *(Mgr-Parts)*
Eley Duke III *(VP)*

DUKE MANUFACTURING COMPANY, INC.

2305 N Broadway, Saint Louis, MO 63102-1405
Tel.: (314) 231-1130   MO
Web Site: http://www.dukemfg.com
Year Founded: 1923
Sales Range: $150-199.9 Million
Emp.: 500
Foodservice Equipment Mfr
N.A.I.C.S.: 333310
Jack J. Hake *(Chm & CEO)*
Douglas George *(Sr VP)*
Ron Kieffer *(Dir-Tech Svcs)*
David Marvel *(Pres)*
Tom LaMantia *(Exec VP-Global Ops)*

Subsidiaries:

Duke Manufacturing C.R. s.r.o   (1)
Prologis Park D1 West Building 4, Ricany, 251 01, Czech Republic
Tel.: (420) 257741033
Foodservice Equipment Mfr
N.A.I.C.S.: 333241

Duke Manufacturing Company, Inc. - St. Louis Factory   (1)
2305 N Broadway, Saint Louis, MO 63102
Tel.: (314) 231-1130
Web Site: http://www.dukemfg.com
Sales Range: $25-49.9 Million
Emp.: 50
Foodservice Equipment Mfr
N.A.I.C.S.: 333241
Dave Marvel *(Gen Mgr)*

DUKE UNIVERSITY

2138 Campus Dr, Durham, NC 27708
Tel.: (919) 684-8111
Web Site: https://www.duke.edu
Year Founded: 1838
Rev.: $6,446,827,000
Assets: $20,840,677,000
Liabilities: $5,835,996,000
Net Worth: $15,004,681,000
Earnings: $260,553,000
Emp.: 52,994

Duke University—(Continued)

Fiscal Year-end: 06/30/18
Colleges & Universities
N.A.I.C.S.: 611310
Tracy Futhey (CIO & VP-IT)
Laurene Sperling (Vice Chm)
Pamela J. Bernard (Gen Counsel & VP)
Kyle Cavanaugh (VP-Admin)
Richard V. Riddell (Sr VP)
Michael Schoenfeld (VP-Pub Affairs & Govt Rels)
Sally Kornbluth (Provost)
John J. Noonan (VP-Facilities)
Tim Walsh (VP-Fin)
Chris Derickson (Dir-Student Info Sys & Svcs Office)
Vincent E. Price (Pres)
Alec D. Gallimore (Chief Academic Officer)
Tallman Trask III (Treas & Exec VP)
Jack O. Bovender Jr. (Chm)

DUKES ACE HARDWARE INC.
5634 W 87th St, Burbank, IL 60459
Tel.: (708) 422-4000
Web Site:
https://www.dukesacehardware.com
Sales Range: $10-24.9 Million
Emp.: 34
Hardware Stores
N.A.I.C.S.: 444140
Douglas J. Gniadek (Pres)

DUKES LUMBER CO. INC.
28504 Dukes Lumber Rd, Laurel, DE 19956
Tel.: (302) 875-7552
Web Site:
http://www.dukeslumber.com
Year Founded: 1963
Sales Range: $10-24.9 Million
Emp.: 20
Lumber & Other Building Materials
N.A.I.C.S.: 423310
Dale R. Dukes (Owner-Laurel)
Rusty Dukes (VP & Mgr-Laurel)

DULANY INDUSTRIES INC.
1600 E President St, Savannah, GA 31401
Tel.: (912) 944-3740
Web Site: https://www.dulanyind.com
Year Founded: 1901
Sales Range: $10-24.9 Million
Emp.: 55
Mfr of Sulfuric Acid
N.A.I.C.S.: 325312
Katie Joyner (Dir-Rels)
Ginger Dubberly (Mgr-PR)
Subsidiaries:

Champion Machine, LLC (1)
1722 E President St, Savannah, GA 31404
Tel.: (912) 232-4333
Web Site: http://www.champmach.com
Machine Tool Distr
N.A.I.C.S.: 423830

Seagate Handling Inc (1)
1750 E President St, Savannah, GA 31404
Tel.: (912) 944-3744
Web Site: http://www.seagatehandling.com
Rev.: $1,300,000
Emp.: 6
Phosphatic Fertilizers
N.A.I.C.S.: 325312

Southern States Chemical, Inc. (1)
1750 E President St, Savannah, GA 31404
Tel.: (912) 232-1101
Web Site: http://www.sschemical.com
Sulfuric Acid Mfr
N.A.I.C.S.: 325180
Key D. Compton (Pres)

Plant (Domestic):

Southern States Chemical, Inc.
Wilmington Plant (2)

4620 Hwy 421 N, Wilmington, NC 28402
Tel.: (910) 762-5054
Sulfuric Acid Mfr
N.A.I.C.S.: 325180
Randy Moore (Plant Mgr)

DULCICH, INC.
16797 SE 130th Ave, Clackamas, OR 97015
Tel.: (503) 905-4500
Web Site:
http://www.pacseafood.com
Year Founded: 1941
Sales Range: $250-299.9 Million
Emp.: 1,200
Holding Company; Fish & Seafood Processor & Distr
N.A.I.C.S.: 551112
Frank Dominic Dulcich (Pres & CEO)

Subsidiaries:

Bandon Pacific, Inc. (1)
PO Box 5583, Coos Bay, OR 97420
Tel.: (541) 888-9626
Web Site: http://www.pacseafood.com
Seafood Packaging Services
N.A.I.C.S.: 311710
Dave Wright (Gen Mgr)

BioOregon Protein, Inc. (1)
PO Box 429, Warrenton, OR 97146
Tel.: (503) 861-2256
Web Site: http://www.biooregonprotein.com
Pet Food Mfr
N.A.I.C.S.: 311119

Coast Seafoods Company Inc. (1)
14711 NE 29th Pl Ste 111, Bellevue, WA 98007-7666
Tel.: (425) 702-8800
Web Site: http://www.coastseafoods.com
Sales Range: $25-49.9 Million
Emp.: 250
Canned, Cured Fish & Seafoods Mfr
N.A.I.C.S.: 311710

Hoy Bros. Fish & Crab Co. Inc. (1)
604 S Commercial, Garibaldi, OR 97118
Tel.: (503) 322-3500
Sales Range: $10-24.9 Million
Emp.: 25
Supplier of Fresh & Frozen Packaged Fish
N.A.I.C.S.: 311710

Island Seafood Inc. (1)
317 Shelikof St, Kodiak, AK 99615
Web Site: http://www.islandseafoods.com
Seafood Whslr
N.A.I.C.S.: 424460
Judi Thompson (Controller)

Johnny's Seafood Company (1)
1199 Dock St, Tacoma, WA 98401
Tel.: (253) 627-2158
Seafood Whslr
N.A.I.C.S.: 424460

Omega Packing Company (1)
2040 Harrison Avenue, Masset, V0T 1M0, BC, Canada
Tel.: (503) 905-4512
Seafood Packaging Services
N.A.I.C.S.: 311710

Pacific Alaska Shellfish Co (1)
Mile 27 5 Spur Hwy, Nikiski, AK 99635
Tel.: (907) 776-8050
Web Site: http://www.pacseafood.com
Emp.: 30
Shellfish Farming Services
N.A.I.C.S.: 112512
Rusty Roessler (Gen Mgr)

Pacific Aquaculture, Inc. (1)
3378 Columbia River Rd, Nespelem, WA 99155
Tel.: (509) 631-1567
Aquaculture Farming Services
N.A.I.C.S.: 112519
John Bielka (Mgr-Aquaculture)
Demetrios Malamas (Founder)

Pacific Choice Seafood Company (1)
1 Commercial St, Eureka, CA 95501 (100%)
Tel.: (707) 442-2981
Web Site: http://www.pacseafood.com

Sales Range: $10-24.9 Million
Emp.: 35
Fresh & Frozen Packaged Fish & Seafood Distr
N.A.I.C.S.: 424460
Dan Obradovich (Dir-Sls-Natl)

Pacific Coast Seafoods Company, Inc. (1)
450 NE Skipanon Dr, Warrenton, OR 97146 (100%)
Tel.: (503) 861-2201
Sales Range: $100-124.9 Million
Supplier of Fresh & Frozen Packaged Fish
N.A.I.C.S.: 484121
Frank Dominic Dulcich (Owner)

Pacific Fresh Seafood (1)
1420 W National Dr, Sacramento, CA 95834-4677
Tel.: (916) 419-5500
Web Site: http://www.pacseafood.com
Sales Range: $25-49.9 Million
Emp.: 200
Fish & Seafood Distr
N.A.I.C.S.: 424460
Anwar Hider (Gen Mgr)

Pacific Oyster Co., Inc. (1)
5150 Oyster Dr, Bay City, OR 97107
Tel.: (503) 377-2330
Sales Range: $25-49.9 Million
Emp.: 299
Supplier of Shellfish
N.A.I.C.S.: 114112

Pacific Seafood Co., Inc. (1)
16797 SE 130th Ave, Clackamas, OR 97015
Tel.: (503) 905-4500
Web Site: http://www.pacseafood.com
Fish & Seafoods Processor & Distr
N.A.I.C.S.: 311710
Frank Dominic Dulcich (Pres & CEO)

Division (Domestic):

Pacific Group Transport Co., Inc. (2)
16797 S E 130th St, Clackamas, OR 97015
Tel.: (503) 905-4500
Provider of Long Distance Trucking Services
N.A.I.C.S.: 484121

Pacific Marketing Group Inc. (2)
16797 SE 130th Ave, Clackamas, OR 97015
Tel.: (503) 226-2200
Web Site: http://www.pacificmrktg.com
Sales Range: $25-49.9 Million
Emp.: 6
Distr of Packaged Frozen Goods
N.A.I.C.S.: 424420

Pacific Seafood of Washington (1)
4520 107th St SW, Mukilteo, WA 98275 (100%)
Tel.: (425) 347-7994
Web Site: http://www.pacseafood.com
Seafood Distribution Center
N.A.I.C.S.: 445250
Frank Dominic Dulcich (Pres & CEO)

Pacific Shrimp Company (1)
213 SW Bay Blvd, Newport, OR 97365
Tel.: (541) 265-4215
Web Site: http://www.pacificseafood.com
Seafood Packaging Services
N.A.I.C.S.: 311710
Dave Wright (Gen Mgr)

Salmolux, Inc. (1)
34100 9th Ave S, Federal Way, WA 98003
Tel.: (253) 874-2026
Web Site: http://www.salmolux.com
Seafood Packaging Services
N.A.I.C.S.: 311710

Sea Level Seafoods, LLC (1)
PO Box 2085, Wrangell, AK 99929
Tel.: (907) 874-2401
Web Site: http://www.pacseafood.com
Seafood Whslr
N.A.I.C.S.: 424460
Vern Phillips (Gen Mgr)

Washington Crab Producers Inc. (1)
1980 Nyhus St N, Westport, WA 98595
Tel.: (360) 268-9161
Web Site: http://www.pacificseafood.com

Sales Range: $10-24.9 Million
Emp.: 120
Supplier of Fresh & Frozen Packaged Fish
N.A.I.C.S.: 311710
Bill Weidman (Gen Mgr)

DULLES MOTORCARS
107 Catoctin Cir SE, Leesburg, VA 20175
Tel.: (703) 777-7077
Web Site:
https://www.dullesmotorcars.com
Year Founded: 1989
Sales Range: $10-24.9 Million
Emp.: 65
Car Whslr
N.A.I.C.S.: 441110
Jeff Collins (Controller)
Ray Hartley (Mgr-Fleet)

DULUTH CHRYSLER JEEP DODGE & RAM
4755 Miller Trunk Hwy, Duluth, MN 55811-3918
Tel.: (218) 720-6123
Web Site:
http://www.duluthdodge.com
Sales Range: $10-24.9 Million
Emp.: 50
Car Whslr
N.A.I.C.S.: 441110
Tom Jubie (Gen Mgr)
Burleigh Randolph (Gen Mgr)

DULUTH REGIONAL CARE CENTER
5629 Grand Ave, Duluth, MN 55807
Tel.: (218) 722-8180
Web Site: https://www.drccinfo.org
Year Founded: 1970
Sales Range: $10-24.9 Million
Emp.: 756
Disability Assistance Services
N.A.I.C.S.: 624120
Michelle Hooey (Program Mgr)
Sandy DeZeler (Bus Mgr)
Buck Erpestad (Program Mgr)
Michael Mills (CEO)

DUMAC BUSINESS SYSTEMS, INC.
19 Corporate Cir, East Syracuse, NY 13057-1129
Tel.: (315) 463-1010
Web Site: https://www.dumac.com
Year Founded: 1952
Sales Range: $10-24.9 Million
Emp.: 81
Office Equipment Whslr
N.A.I.C.S.: 423420
Shaun O'Brien (VP)
Stephen Kiesa (Mgr-Web Svcs)

DUMAC INC.
280 S Mangum St Ste 210, Durham, NC 27701
Tel.: (919) 668-9995
Year Founded: 2011
Sales Range: $10-24.9 Million
Emp.: 50
Investment Management Service
N.A.I.C.S.: 523940
Robert E. McGrail (Co-Sec)
David R. Shumate (VP)
Neal F. Triplett (Pres)

DUMAS CO-OP
600 Twichell Ave, Dumas, TX 79029
Tel.: (806) 935-6440
Web Site:
https://www.dumascoop.com
Sales Range: $25-49.9 Million
Emp.: 30
Grains
N.A.I.C.S.: 424510

Jed Garrison *(VP)*
Nathan Sargent *(Sec)*
Delena Hays *(Gen Mgr)*

DUMAS CONCEPTS IN BUILD-ING
8711 Epworth St, Detroit, MI 48204
Tel.: (248) 380-8480
Web Site:
    http://www.dumasconcepts.com
Year Founded: 1973
Sales Range: $25-49.9 Million
Emp.: 32
Commercial & Office Building, New
Construction
N.A.I.C.S.: 236220
Junius L. Dumas *(Pres)*
Dorothy Dumas *(Gen Mgr)*
Kent Broughman *(Mgr-Estimating)*
Raymond Stephen *(Owner)*

DUMAS COTTON WARE-HOUSE INC.
400 S Main St, Dumas, AR 71639
Tel.: (870) 382-4801
Web Site: http://www.dumasar.net
Rev.: $10,000,000
Emp.: 45
Cotton Compresses & Warehouses
N.A.I.C.S.: 493130

DUMONT GROUP INCORPO-RATED
985 Farmington Ave, Bristol, CT
06010
Tel.: (860) 582-8161   CT
Web Site:
    http://www.dumontagency.com
Year Founded: 1956
Sales Range: $50-74.9 Million
Emp.: 50
Provider of Insurance Services
N.A.I.C.S.: 524210
Roland J. Dumont *(CEO)*

DUNAVANT ENTERPRISES, INC.
959 Ridgeway Loop Rd Ste 205,
Memphis, TN 38120
Tel.: (901) 369-1500   TN
Web Site: https://www.dunavant.com
Year Founded: 1969
Sales Range: $1-4.9 Billion
Emp.: 2,250
Cotton Merchandising
N.A.I.C.S.: 424590
Clayton Fahey *(Sr VP-Ops-Houston)*
William B. Dunavant Jr. *(Chm)*
William B. Dunavant III *(Pres & CEO)*

Subsidiaries:

Dunavant Enterprises   (1)
959 Ridgeway Loop Rd Ste 200, Memphis,
TN 38120
Tel.: (559) 447-1800
Web Site:
    http://www.dunavantenterprises.com
Sales Range: $25-49.9 Million
Emp.: 30
Domestic & International Cotton Trading
N.A.I.C.S.: 424590
Kelly Lomax *(CFO & Exec VP)*
Woodson Dunavant *(Sr VP & Dir-Mktg &
Bus Dev)*
Russel Cherry *(Gen Counsel, Sec & Sr VP)*

DUNAWAY ASSOCIATES, LLC
550 Bailey Ave Ste 400, Fort Worth,
TX 76107
Tel.: (817) 335-1121
Web Site: https://dunaway.com
Year Founded: 1956
Emp.: 231
Engineeering Services
N.A.I.C.S.: 541330

Subsidiaries:

Criado & Associates, Inc.   (1)
3030 Lyndon B Johnson Fwy, Ste 600, Dal-
las, TX 75234
Tel.: (972) 392-9092
Web Site: http://www.criadoassociates.com
Engineeering Services
N.A.I.C.S.: 541330
Cristina Criado *(Pres)*

DUNBAR STONE COMPANY
901 Lewis Ave, Ash Fork, AZ 86320
Tel.: (928) 637-2592
Web Site:
    http://www.dunbarstoneinc.com
Rev.: $10,700,000
Emp.: 50
Crushed & Broken Stone
N.A.I.C.S.: 327320

DUNCAN AVIATION INC.
3701 Aviation Rd, Lincoln, NE 68524
Tel.: (402) 475-2611
Web Site:
    https://www.duncanaviation.aero
Year Founded: 1956
Sales Range: $150-199.9 Million
Aircraft & Heavy Equipment Repair
Services
N.A.I.C.S.: 811310
Aaron C. Hilkemann *(Pres & CEO)*
Lori Johnson *(Mgr-Mktg Comm)*
Doug Alleman *(VP-Customer Svc)*
Mike Minchow *(VP-Sls)*
Kevin Miesbach *(Mgr-Components &
OEM Bus Dev)*
Lee Bowes *(Mgr-Central US Reg)*
Brian Andrews *(Mgr-Interior)*
Brian Leffers *(Mgr-Component Svcs)*
Mark Cote *(VP-Parts Sls, Avionics,
Accessories & Satellites)*
Johnathan Almeida *(Mgr-Avionics
Satellite-Portland)*
Jeffrey Aman *(Mgr-Avionics Satellite)*
Vincent Antignani *(Mgr-Northeast
Reg)*
Steve Ballard *(Project Mgr)*
Kent Beal *(Mgr-Avionics Satellite)*
Janet Beazley-Okafor *(Project Mgr)*
Jamie Blackman *(Mgr-Rotable)*
Tammie Burns *(Project Mgr)*
Shawn Busby *(Project Mgr)*
Dominic Buschini *(Project Mgr)*
Shawn Carraher *(Mgr-Cert Programs)*
John Biever *(VP-Air Frame Svcs-
Michigan)*
Corey Johnston *(Project Mgr)*
Jarek Jones *(Project Mgr)*
Rich Jones *(Project Mgr)*
John Kelly *(Project Mgr)*
Joe Lacorte *(Mgr-Southeast US Reg)*
Matt Lentell *(Mgr-Bombardier Pro-
gram)*
Tom Lieser *(Mgr-Avionics Satellite)*
Marty Lincoln *(Mgr-Prop & Accesso-
ries)*
Pat Mapes *(Mgr-Avionics Install-
Lincoln)*
Susan Masek *(Sr Mgr-Consignment)*
Gary McClure *(Project Mgr)*
Todd Wright *(Asst Mgr-Interior)*
Mike White *(Mgr-Avionics Satellite-
Seattle)*
Jerry Tollas *(Project Mgr)*
Dustin Thomas *(Project Mgr)*
Phil Suglia *(Mgr-Svc Sls)*
Luke Swager *(Mgr-Customer Svc)*
Terry Stehlik *(Mgr-Govt Contract)*
Terry Stovall *(Mgr-Govt Program)*
Thomas B. Fischer *(Gen Counsel &
VP-Lincoln)*
Michael Cox *(VP-Completions)*
Cindy L. Morris *(VP-Fin & Admin)*
Jeannine Falter *(VP-Bus Dev)*
Andy Richards *(COO & Exec VP)*
Jamie Harder *(CFO & VP)*

Ted Roethlisberger *(Asst Mgr-
Customer Svc-Battle Creek)*
Tim Kelly *(Sls Mgr-Great Lakes)*
Mark Kahle *(Mgr-Avionics Install &
Line Svcs Dept-Battle Creek)*

DUNCAN BOLT
8535 Dice Rd, Santa Fe Springs, CA
90670
Tel.: (562) 698-8800
Web Site:
    https://www.duncanbolt.com
Rev.: $14,400,000
Emp.: 47
Hardware Merchant Whslr
N.A.I.C.S.: 423710
Bill Bernard *(Mgr-Sls)*
Andrew Cohn *(Pres)*
Virginia Cohn *(VP)*
Norris Glantz *(Branch Mgr)*

DUNCAN CHANNON
114 Sansome St 14th Fl, San Fran-
cisco, CA 94104
Tel.: (415) 306-9200   CA
Web Site:
    http://www.duncanchannon.com
Year Founded: 1990
Rev.: $40,000,000
Emp.: 38
Advetising Agency
N.A.I.C.S.: 541810
Robert Duncan *(Partner & Exec Dir-
Creative)*
Parker Channon *(Partner & Exec Dir-
Creative)*
Leslie Diard *(Dir-Comm Plng)*
Anne Elisco-Lemme *(Dir-Creative)*
Renee Phipps *(Controller)*
John Munyan *(Dir-Creative)*
Liddy Parlato *(Sr Acct Mgr)*
Jacqueline Fodor *(Dir-Integrated Pro-
duction)*
Jennifer Corrigan *(Acct Dir)*
Brian Bacino *(Dir-Creative)*
Michael Lemme *(Partner)*
Robbie Whiting *(Dir-Creative Tech &
Production)*
Aaron Smith *(Assoc Dir-Comm Plng-
Digital Media)*
Andrea Bozeman *(Dir-Creative)*
M. J. Deery *(Dir-Purpose Practice)*
Melissa Ploysophon *(Assoc Dir-
Creative)*
Marty Bonacorso *(Assoc Dir-Creative)*
John Kovacevich *(Exec Creative Dir)*
Gary Stein *(Chief Integration Officer)*
Amy Cotteleer *(Partner & Chief Expe-
rience Officer)*
Noel Johnson *(Dir-Mktg & Client En-
gagement)*
Andrew Berkenfield *(CEO, Partner &
Gen Mgr)*
Jamie Katz *(Dir-Acct Mgmt & Ops)*

Subsidiaries:

A Squared Productions Group,
Inc.   (1)
8000 Sunset Blvd Ste 8301, Los Angeles,
CA 90046
Tel.: (310) 432-2650
Web Site: http://www.asquaredgroup.com
Sales Range: $10-24.9 Million
Emp.: 14
Marketing Research & Public Opinion Poll-
ing
N.A.I.C.S.: 541910
Amy Cotteleer *(Chief Creative Officer)*
Jennifer Truc *(Acct Mgr)*
Katie Holden *(Acct Mgr)*

DUNCAN CO.
425 Hoover St NE, Minneapolis, MN
55413
Tel.: (612) 331-1776
Web Site: https://www.duncanco.com
Sales Range: $10-24.9 Million

Emp.: 35
Industrial Supplies
N.A.I.C.S.: 423840
Eric B. Duncan *(Co-Pres)*
Joe Klick *(Co-Pres)*

DUNCAN FINANCIAL CORPO-RATION
5673 E Shields Ave, Fresno, CA
93727-7819
Tel.: (559) 294-3300   CA
Year Founded: 1979
Sales Range: $25-49.9 Million
Emp.: 250
Arts & Crafts Supply Mfr
N.A.I.C.S.: 327420
Larry R. Duncan *(Pres)*
Kerri Ladd *(Dir-HR)*

Subsidiaries:

Duncan Enterprises   (1)
5673 E Shields Ave, Fresno, CA 93727-
7819
Tel.: (559) 291-4444
Web Site: http://www.ilovetocreate.com
Sales Range: $25-49.9 Million
Emp.: 225
Paints & Crafts Mfr
N.A.I.C.S.: 325510
Larry R. Duncan *(Chm)*
Linda Bagby *(Coord-PR)*
Don Laines *(Dir-Fin)*
Larry Hermansen *(Pres & COO)*
Erma Duncan *(Founder)*

DUNCAN OIL COMPANY
416 Old Ranger Rd, Murphy, NC
28906
Tel.: (828) 837-2666
Web Site:
    http://www.duncanoilco.com
Sales Range: $10-24.9 Million
Emp.: 40
Convenience Store
N.A.I.C.S.: 445131
Jim Duncan *(Gen Mgr)*

DUNCAN OIL COMPANY
849 Factory Rd, Beavercreek, OH
45434
Tel.: (937) 426-5945
Web Site: https://www.duncan-
oil.com
Sales Range: $50-74.9 Million
Emp.: 200
Petroleum Products Distr & Retailer
N.A.I.C.S.: 424720
Roger McDaniel *(Pres)*
Ryan McDaniel *(CEO)*

DUNCAN REGIONAL HOSPI-TAL
1407 Whisenant, Duncan, OK 73533
Tel.: (580) 252-5300   OK
Web Site:
    https://www.duncanregional.com
Year Founded: 1976
Sales Range: $100-124.9 Million
Emp.: 1,158
Healtcare Services
N.A.I.C.S.: 622110
Roger L. Neal *(CIO & VP)*
William Stewart *(VP-Solutions Prac-
tice Mgmt)*
Douglas R. Volinski *(CFO & VP)*
Jay R. Johnson *(Pres & CEO)*

DUNCAN SEAWALL, DOCK & BOAT LIFT, LLC
1714 Independence Blvd, Sarasota,
FL 34234
Tel.: (941) 351-1553   FL
Web Site:
    https://www.duncanseawall.com
Year Founded: 1979
Sales Range: $1-9.9 Million
Emp.: 60

Duncan Seawall, Dock & Boat Lift,
LLC—(Continued)

Marine Construction
N.A.I.C.S.: 237990
Scott Myers (Pres)

DUNCAN SUPPLY CO. INC.
910 N Illinois St, Indianapolis, IN
46204-1087
Tel.: (317) 634-1335
Web Site:
https://www.duncansupply.com
Sales Range: $25-49.9 Million
Emp.: 88
Refrigeration, Air Conditioning &
Heating Equipment Distr
N.A.I.C.S.: 423730
Rick Fine (Pres)
Steve Pluckebaum (Controller)
Greg Combs (Mgr-Counter Sls)
Linda Hendricks (Sec & Dir-HR)

DUNCAN-PARNELL, INC.
900 S McDowell St, Charlotte, NC
28204
Tel.: (704) 372-7766
Web Site: https://www.duncan-
parnell.com
Year Founded: 1946
Sales Range: $10-24.9 Million
Emp.: 100
Reprographic & Surveying Products
& Services
N.A.I.C.S.: 561499
Mark Duncan (Pres)

Subsidiaries:

Duncan-Parnell (1)
1478 Dividend Loop, Myrtle Beach, SC
29577-3972
Tel.: (843) 626-3641
Web Site: http://www.duncan-parnell.com
Sales Range: $10-24.9 Million
Emp.: 4
Printing Equipment Distr
N.A.I.C.S.: 423430

Duncan-Parnell (1)
1208 Copeland Oaks Dr, Morrisville, NC
27560
Tel.: (919) 460-8886
Web Site: http://www.duncan-parnell.com
Sales Range: $10-24.9 Million
Emp.: 4
Surveying Products & Services
N.A.I.C.S.: 541370
Chuck Drouillard (Coord-Sls)
Mike Withers (Coord-Sls)
Rick Lusher (Coord-Sls)

Duncan-Parnell (1)
201 Glenwood Ave, Raleigh, NC 27603
Tel.: (919) 833-4677
Web Site: http://www.dunca-parnell.com
Sales Range: $10-24.9 Million
Emp.: 15
Reprographics Solutions & Services
N.A.I.C.S.: 323111
Denise Cooper (Coord-Quality Control)

Duncan-Parnell (1)
8 Beaufain St, Charleston, SC 29401
Tel.: (843) 722-2898
Web Site: http://www.duncan-parnell.com
Sales Range: $10-24.9 Million
Emp.: 4
Reprographic Services
N.A.I.C.S.: 323111
Tommy Faulk (Coord-Production)
Mike Branham (Gen Mgr)
Rob Means (Product Mgr)

Duncan-Parnell (1)
3150 W Montague Ave, Charleston, SC
29418
Tel.: (843) 747-6033
Web Site: http://www.duncan-parnell.com
Emp.: 7
Reprographic Services
N.A.I.C.S.: 323111
Rod Means (Mgr-Production)
Carlton Batts (Coord-Production)
Rick Pastva (Coord-Production)

DUNCAN-WILLIAMS, INC.
6750 Poplar Ave Ste 300, Memphis,
TN 38138
Tel.: (901) 260-6800
Web Site: http://www.duncanw.com
Year Founded: 1969
Sales Range: $25-49.9 Million
Emp.: 169
Investment Banking & Securities
Dealing
N.A.I.C.S.: 523150
Donald A. Malmo (Co-Chm)
Duncan Williams (Pres)
Carolyn Williams (Co-Chm)
Don Clanton (COO)
Frank Reid (CFO)
Jim Pauline (Exec VP-Ops)
Wayne Breunig (Mng Dir & Head-Pub
Fin)
Gary Lendermon (VP-Mktg Comm)
Jack Schlifer (Pres-Debt Capital Mar-
kets)
Jim Cherry (Chief Compliance Offi-
cer)
Buddy Crihfield (Mng Dir-Southeast
Reg)
Dwight Clark (VP)
E. J. Gregory (Sr VP-Southeast)
S. J. Guzzo (Mng Dir-Debt Capital
Markets Sls & Strategies)
Patrick Burnett (Assoc Gen Counsel)

DUNCAN/DAY ADVERTISING
6513 Preston Rd Ste 200, Plano, TX
75024
Tel.: (469) 429-1974
Web Site: http://www.duncanday.com
Year Founded: 1986
Sales Range: $50-74.9 Million
Emp.: 9
N.A.I.C.S.: 541810
Leslie Duncan (Owner)
Stacey Day (Owner & Dir-Creative)
Cris Turman (Dir-New Bus)
Dan Sweeney (Copywriter)

DUNCASTER LIFECARE COMMUNITY
40 Loeffler Rd, Bloomfield, CT 06002
Tel.: (860) 380-5006   CT
Web Site: https://www.duncaster.org
Year Founded: 1984
Sales Range: $10-24.9 Million
Emp.: 332
Lifecare Retirement Community Op-
erator
N.A.I.C.S.: 623311

DUNDEE CITRUS GROWERS ASSOCIATION
PO Box 1739, Dundee, FL 33838
Tel.: (863) 439-1574
Web Site: http://www.dun-d.com
Sales Range: $25-49.9 Million
Emp.: 400
Citrus Farming
N.A.I.C.S.: 111339
Steve Callaham (CEO & Exec VP)
John Mullen (VP-IT)
Melissa McGuinness (VP-HR)
Dawn Hostetler (Mgr-Acctg)

DUNDON CAPITAL ACQUISITION CORPORATION
2100 Ross Ave Ste 800, Dallas, TX
75201
Tel.: (214) 329-9939   TX
Year Founded: 2015
Emp.: 2
Investment Services
N.A.I.C.S.: 523999
Thomas G. Dundon (Chm, Pres &
CEO)
John Zutter (CFO & Sec)

DUNE COMPANY OF YUMA LLC
2948 S Ave 7 E, Yuma, AZ 85365
Tel.: (928) 344-0040
Sales Range: $25-49.9 Million
Emp.: 40
Fertilizer Mfr
N.A.I.C.S.: 444240

DUNES POINT CAPITAL, LLC
411 Theodore Fremd Ave Ste 125,
Rye, NY 10580
Tel.: (914) 269-2020   DE
Web Site:
http://www.dunespointcapital.com
Year Founded: 2013
Privater Equity Firm
N.A.I.C.S.: 523999
Timothy J. White (CEO & CIO)
James Baker (Mng Dir)
Jordan Benyas (Mng Dir)
Ryan Miller (Mng Dir)
Jack Hayden (VP)
Nick Bunn (Principal)
Istvan Nadas (VP)
Erik Minor (CFO & Chief Compliance
Officer)
Jene Elzie (Mng Dir-Investment
Team)

Subsidiaries:

All-Lift Systems, Inc. (1)
1377 Kimberly Dr, Neenah, WI 54956
Tel.: (920) 738-0800
Web Site: http://www.all-liftsystems.com
Industrial Supplies, Nsk
N.A.I.C.S.: 423840
Jim Molitor (Chm)
Robert Molitor (Pres)

Earl W. Johnston Roofing Inc. (1)
5721 Dewey St, Hollywood, FL 33023-1917
Tel.: (954) 989-5666
Web Site: http://www.johnstonroofing.com
Roofing Contractors
N.A.I.C.S.: 238160
Earl W. Johnston (Owner)

Ehrhardt Tool & Machine, LLC (1)
25 Central Industrial Dr, Granite City, IL
62040-6802
Tel.: (314) 436-6900
Web Site: http://www.ehrhardttool.com
Sales Range: $10-24.9 Million
Emp.: 100
Customized Tools, Dies, Special Machines
& Automated Equipment Designer & Mfr
N.A.I.C.S.: 333514
Andy Adams (Estimating & Mktg)

Haysite Reinforced Plastics, LLC (1)
5599 New Perry Hwy, Erie, PA 16509-3562
Tel.: (814) 868-3691
Web Site: http://www.haysite.com
Sales Range: $25-49.9 Million
Emp.: 120
Fiberglass Reinforced Plastics & Thermoset
Composite Materials Mfr
N.A.I.C.S.: 326199
Mark Anderson (Pres)
John Feighner (Coord-Safety & Environ-
mental Compliance)
Tom Gardner (VP-Sls & Mktg)
Scott Besco (VP-Ops & Technical Svcs)
Anthony Lignetta (Dir-Sls)
Alicia Kudlak (Mgr-HR)
Rick Fortune (Mgr-Matls)
Brian Hardy (Mgr-QA, Safety & Compli-
ance)
David Janas (Mgr-Ops)
Pat Comer (Mgr-Quality, Safety & Environ-
mental Compliance)
Geoff Rovegno (Dir-Fin)

Subsidiary (Non-US):

Haysite Reinforced Plastics Ltd. (2)
Greenhill Industrial Estate, Birmingham
Road, Kidderminster, DY10 2RN, United
Kingdom
Tel.: (44) 1562 512 528
Web Site: http://www.haysite.com
Fiberglass Reinforced Plastics & Thermoset
Composite Materials Mfr

N.A.I.C.S.: 326199
Todd Littlehales (Mgr-Sls)

Hy-Tek Material Handling, Inc. (1)
2222 Port Rd, Columbus, OH 43217-1130
Tel.: (614) 497-2500
Web Site: http://www.hy-tek.net
Sales Range: $125-149.9 Million
Emp.: 171
Distr of Material Handling Equipment
N.A.I.C.S.: 423830
Samuel Grooms (CEO)
Jim Ripkey (Pres-Mobile Equipment Div)
Tom Mann (Pres-Integrated Sys)

Subsidiary (Domestic):

Fascor, Inc. (2)
11260 Chester Rd Ste 610, Cincinnati, OH
45246
Tel.: (513) 421-1777
Web Site: http://www.fascor.com
Sales Range: $1-9.9 Million
Emp.: 40
Custom Computer Programming Services
N.A.I.C.S.: 541511
Ian Carrus (Pres)

Johnson Stephens Consulting, (2)
Inc.
100 Hartsfield Ctr Pkwy Ste 5, Atlanta, GA
30354
Tel.: (678) 842-9114
Web Site: http://www.johnsonstephens.com
General Consulting Services
N.A.I.C.S.: 541611
Steve Johnson (Mng Principal)
Sandy Stephens (Mng Principal)

LCS Inc. (2)
411 Stachler Dr, Saint Henry, OH 45883
Tel.: (419) 678-8600
Sales Range: $10-24.9 Million
Emp.: 30
Electrical Contractor
N.A.I.C.S.: 238210
Daniel R. Lennartz (Pres)

John Wood Company, LLC (1)
Highland Business Park 98 Highland Ave,
Oaks, PA 19456-1052
Tel.: (610) 666-1220
Web Site: http://www.johnwood.com
Sales Range: $10-24.9 Million
Emp.: 40
Tank & Pressure Vessel Mfr
N.A.I.C.S.: 332313
David Fix (Pres)

K-1 Packaging Group (1)
17989 Arenth Ave, City of Industry, CA
91748
Tel.: (626) 964-9384
Web Site: http://k1packaging.com
Rev.: $5,000,000
Emp.: 48
Commercial Lithographic Printing
N.A.I.C.S.: 323111
Alice Tsai (Pres)
Eric Tsai (Owner)
Frank Tsai (VP-Sls & Mktg)
Angela Hsu (Controller)
Renee Sun (Project Coord-Overseas)

Miether Bearing Products, LLC (1)
8720 N County Rd W, Odessa, TX 79764-
1926
Tel.: (432) 366-3838
Web Site: http://www.miether.com
Sales Range: $50-74.9 Million
Emp.: 50
Spherical Bearing Housings, Inserts, Adapt-
ers, Parts & Accessories Mfr
N.A.I.C.S.: 332710
Michael Smith (Pres)

Modern Equipment Company, (1)
LLC
401 E South Island St, Appleton, WI 54915
Tel.: (920) 939-2819
Web Site: http://www.moderneq.com
Sales Range: $10-24.9 Million
Emp.: 53
Foundry Melting & Hot Metal Handling
Equipment Mfr
N.A.I.C.S.: 333248
Jim Keller (Exec VP)

Nextgen Security, LLC (1)
770 Pennsylvania Dr Ste 120, Exton, PA
19341

Tel.: (484) 235-5520
Web Site: http://www.nextgensecured.com
Security System Services
N.A.I.C.S.: 561621
Michael Hennessy *(Mgr-Fin)*

Subsidiary (Domestic):

Micro Security Solutions Inc. **(2)**
3070 N Commerce Pkwy, Miramar, FL
33025
Tel.: (855) 620-0600
Rev.: $6,060,000
Emp.: 6
Radio, Television & Other Electronics
Stores
N.A.I.C.S.: 449210
Stephen De Molina *(Owner)*

Professional Plumbing Group,
Inc. **(1)**
2951 Hwy 501 E, Conway, SC 29526
Tel.: (415) 124-5678
Web Site: http://www.professionalplumbing
group.com
Sales Range: $75-99.9 Million
Emp.: 310
Holding Company; Plumbing Supply
N.A.I.C.S.: 551112

Subsidiary (Domestic):

PlumbMaster Inc. **(2)**
2951 E Hwy 501, Conway, SC 29526
Tel.: (610) 459-8600
Web Site: http://www.plumbmaster.com
Emp.: 50
Plumbing Maintenance Specialties
N.A.I.C.S.: 423720
Thomas Penner *(CEO)*

Wolverine Brass, Inc. **(2)**
2951 E Hwy 501, Conway, SC 29526
Tel.: (415) 124-5678
Web Site: http://www.wolverinebrass.com
Plumbing Product Distr
N.A.I.C.S.: 423720

Sonneman Design Group, Inc **(1)**
200 Lexington Ave, New York, NY 10016
Tel.: (914) 834-3600
Web Site: http://sonnemanlight.com
Industrial Design Services
N.A.I.C.S.: 541420

Specialty Products & Insulation
Co. **(1)**
1600 Cloister Dr, Lancaster, PA
17601 **(100%)**
Tel.: (717) 581-0650
Web Site: http://www.spi-co.com
Roofing, Siding & Insulation Mfr
N.A.I.C.S.: 423330

Subsidiary (Domestic):

Amerisafe Inc. **(2)**
3990 Enterprise Ct, Aurora, IL 60504
Tel.: (630) 862-2600
Web Site: http://www.amerisafe.net
Sales Range: $10-24.9 Million
Commercial & Industrial Insulation & Safety
Equipment Distr
N.A.I.C.S.: 423990

Burnham Insulation Sales, Inc. **(2)**
3229 Babcock Blvd, Pittsburgh, PA 15237
Tel.: (412) 348-0356
Web Site: http://www.burnhamins.com
Sales Range: $10-24.9 Million
Emp.: 10
Commercial & Industrial Insulation Supply
Whslr
N.A.I.C.S.: 423330
Mike Burnham *(Pres)*
Sean Burnham *(Chm-Intl Bus)*

Synthane-Taylor (Canada)
Limited **(1)**
50 Rue Sicard 125, Sainte-Therese, J7E
5R1, QC, Canada
Tel.: (450) 430-3030
Web Site: http://www.synthanetaylor.com
Sales Range: $10-24.9 Million
Emp.: 25
Electrical, Mechanical & Thermal Insulation
Materials Mfr
N.A.I.C.S.: 332999
Denise Gopie *(Mgr-Customer Svc)*

Plant (Domestic):

Synthane-Taylor (Canada) Ltd. - Ste.
Therese Facility **(2)**
50 rue Sicard Suite 125, Sainte-Therese,
J7E 5R1, QC, Canada
Tel.: (450) 430-3030
Thermal Insulation Material Mfr
N.A.I.C.S.: 326140
Christopher Di Filippo *(Dir-Ops)*

Warshaw, Inc. **(1)**
893 Shepherd Ave, Brooklyn, NY 11208
Tel.: (718) 257-2111
Web Site: http://www.warshawinc.com
Sales Range: $1-9.9 Million
Emp.: 16
Electrical Apparatus & Equipment, Wiring
Supplies & Related Equipment Merchant
Whslr
N.A.I.C.S.: 423610
Brett Goldman *(Controller)*
Michael Molloy *(VP)*
John Randazzo Jr. *(Mgr-Inside Sls)*

DUNGAN ENGINEERING PA
1574 Highway 98 E, Columbia, MS
39429
Tel.: (601) 731-2600
Web Site: http://www.dunganeng.com
Rev.: $2,600,000
Emp.: 30
Engineeering Services
N.A.I.C.S.: 541330
Jeff J. Dungan *(Co-Founder & Princi-
pal)*
James Lee Mock *(VP)*
Brooks R. Wallace *(Principal)*
Ryan A. Holmes *(Principal)*
H. Les Dungan III *(Co-Founder &
Principal)*

DUNGARVIN, INC.
1444 Northland Dr Ste 100, Mendota
Heights, MN 55120
Tel.: (651) 699-6050
Year Founded: 1998
Emp.: 25
Business Support Services
N.A.I.C.S.: 561499
David Toeniskoetter *(Pres & CEO)*
Debi Allsup *(Dir-HR & Risk Mgmt)*
Jennifer Gulley *(Sr Dir)*
Joe Regenscheid *(CFO, Treas &
Sec)*
Bob Longo *(Dir-Ops-Natl)*
Paul Smith *(Dir-Organizational Dev)*
Lori Kress *(Dir-Central)*
Daniel Griffin *(Dir-East Reg)*
Robert Bachicha *(Dir-West Reg)*

Subsidiaries:

ACI Support Specialists, Inc. **(1)**
1015 Ashes Dr Ste 107, Wilmington, NC
28405
Tel.: (910) 763-7458
Web Site: http://www.acisupport.com
Rev.: $3,300,000
Emp.: 50
Special Needs Support Services
N.A.I.C.S.: 624190

Disability Services, Inc. **(1)**
503 Williams St 16, Gallup, NM 87301
Tel.: (505) 863-9591
Emp.: 75
Disability Services
N.A.I.C.S.: 624310
Ellen Lacayo *(Exec Dir)*

DUNHAM & ASSOCIATES IN-
VESTMENT COUNCIL, INC.
10251 Vista Sorrento Pkwy Ste 200,
San Diego, CA 92121
Tel.: (858) 964-0500
Web Site: https://www.dunham.com
Year Founded: 2000
Sales Range: $25-49.9 Million
Emp.: 50
Investment Advisory Services
N.A.I.C.S.: 523940

Jeffrey A. Dunham *(Founder, Chm &
CEO)*
Salvatore M. Capizzi *(Chief Sls &
Mktg Officer)*
Denise S. Iverson *(CFO)*
Tamara S. Wendoll *(COO)*
William J. Brims *(Dir-IT)*
Hilarey M. Findeisen *(Dir-Ops)*
Dawn Gillard *(Dir-Admin)*
Pamela F. Nichols *(Dir-HR)*
Joseph P. Kelly *(Chief Compliance
Officer & Gen Counsel)*
Ryan J. Dykmans *(Dir-Res)*

DUNHAM EXPRESS CORPO-
RATION
3633 Lexington Ave, Madison, WI
53714
Tel.: (608) 242-1000
Web Site:
http://www.dunhamexpress.com
Year Founded: 1951
Sales Range: $25-49.9 Million
Emp.: 225
Courier Services
N.A.I.C.S.: 492110
Mark McDonald *(Owner & Pres)*
Jim Collins *(Dir-Ops)*

DUNHAM'S ATHLEISURE
CORPORATION
5607 New King Dr Ste 125, Troy, MI
48098
Tel.: (248) 530-6769   DE
Web Site:
https://www.dunhamssports.com
Year Founded: 1937
Sales Range: $400-449.9 Million
Emp.: 2,000
Sporting Goods & Athletic Apparel
Store
N.A.I.C.S.: 459110
John Palmer *(Gen Counsel, Sec & Sr
VP)*

DUNHAM-PRICE INC.
210 Mike Hooks Rd, Westlake, LA
70669
Tel.: (337) 433-3900
Web Site:
https://www.dunhamprice.com
Rev.: $14,000,000
Emp.: 100
Readymix Concrete Mfr
N.A.I.C.S.: 327320
Ryan Price *(Exec VP-Procurement)*
Linda Ash *(Dir-Safety)*
Mike Morris *(Dir-Sls)*
Brent LeJeune *(VP-Concrete Ops)*
Courtney Corner *(Mgr-Admin)*
Shannon Cary *(VP-Indus Ready Mix
Ops)*
Ginny Johnson *(Dir-HR)*
Jody Singletary *(VP-Concrete Prod-
ucts Ops)*
Mike Morris Concrete *(Mgr-Sls)*
Robert W. Price III *(CFO & COO)*
Robert W. Price Jr. *(Pres & CEO)*

DUNHILL HOMES, LLC
4835 Lbj Fwy Ste 700, Dallas, TX
75244
Tel.: (214) 765-0598   TX
Web Site:
http://www.dunhillhomes.com
Emp.: 113
Single-Family Home Construction &
Sales
N.A.I.C.S.: 236117
Richard Dix *(Owner)*

DUNHILL INTERNATIONAL
LIST CO., INC.
6400 Congress Ave Ste 1750, Boca
Raton, FL 33487-2898
Tel.: (561) 998-7800   DE

Web Site: https://www.dunhills.com
Year Founded: 1938
Sales Range: $1-9.9 Million
Emp.: 15
Direct Mail Advertising Services
N.A.I.C.S.: 541860
Robert Dunhill *(Pres)*
Candy Dunhill *(VP-Sls)*
Cindy Dunhill *(VP-Ops)*
Mary Reed *(Mgr-Production)*

DUNK & BRIGHT FURNITURE
CO.
2648 S Salina St, Syracuse, NY
13205
Tel.: (315) 930-4048
Web Site:
https://www.dunkandbright.com
Sales Range: $10-24.9 Million
Emp.: 15
Furniture Retailer
N.A.I.C.S.: 449110
Jim Bright *(Pres)*

DUNKIN & BUSH INC.
8244 122nd Ave NE, Kirkland, WA
98033-8017
Tel.: (425) 885-7064
Web Site:
http://www.dunkinandbush.com
Year Founded: 1943
Sales Range: $10-24.9 Million
Emp.: 130
Industrial Coating & Lining Applica-
tions, Lead Abatement, Fireproofing,
Consulting & Inspection Services
N.A.I.C.S.: 238320
Jody Daugherty *(Mgr-Acctg)*
Martin Horgan *(VP-Ops)*
Mark Rondeau *(Mgr-Bus Dev)*
Rex Bison *(Mgr-Corp Safety & Risk)*
Pete Weese *(VP-Production)*
Deidre Dunkin *(Pres)*
Deanne Donovan *(CFO)*
Sally McInnis *(Coord-Reg Safety)*
Shawn Harju *(Gen Counsel)*
Ashar MacKenzie *(Mgr-Acctg)*
Laura MacDonald *(Mgr-HR)*
Andrew Johnson *(Mgr-IT)*
Charles Carter *(Mgr-Quality)*
Tyler Bishop *(Mgr-Shop Ops)*
Jacob Melton *(Project Mgr)*
Thomas Dunkin II *(Chm)*

DUNKIN'S DIAMONDS INC.
897 Hebron Rd Ste 103, Heath, OH
43056
Tel.: (740) 788-8610
Web Site:
http://www.dunkinsdiamonds.com
Rev.: $25,000,000
Emp.: 150
Jewelry, Precious Stones & Precious
Metals Mfr & Distr
N.A.I.C.S.: 458310
Stuart Dunkin *(Pres)*
Leah Tallman *(Controller)*

DUNLAP & CO., INC.
6325 E 100 S, Columbus, IN 47201
Tel.: (812) 376-3021   IN
Web Site: https://www.dunlapinc.com
Year Founded: 1873
Sales Range: $25-49.9 Million
Emp.: 150
Mechanical, General, Industrial &
Non-Residential Building Contracting
Services
N.A.I.C.S.: 236220
Dennis E. King *(CEO)*
Chuck Corbin *(VP)*
Brian E. King *(Pres)*
Jo Holt *(Controller)*

DUNLAP & KYLE CO. INC.
280 Eureka St, Batesville, MS 38606

Dunlap & Kyle Co. Inc.—(Continued)
Tel.: (662) 563-1143
Web Site:
  https://www.gatewaytire.com
Year Founded: 1929
Sales Range: $50-74.9 Million
Emp.: 1,000
Tires & Tubes
N.A.I.C.S.: 423130
Robert H. Dunlap (Chm)

Subsidiaries:

Hesselbein Tire Co. Inc.   (1)
4299 Industrial Dr, Jackson, MS 39209
Tel.: (601) 974-5912
Sales Range: $25-49.9 Million
Emp.: 80
Whslr & Retailer of Automotive & Truck
Tires
N.A.I.C.S.: 423130
W. D. King (Pres)
Robert Dunlap (Owner)

DUNLAP INDUSTRIES INC.
297 Industrial Park Rd, Dunlap, TN
37327
Tel.: (423) 949-4021
Web Site:
  https://www.dunlapworld.com
Rev.: $15,970,881
Emp.: 100
Zippers, Thread, Hook & Loop Mfr &
Distr
N.A.I.C.S.: 339993
Horace Wayne Reynolds (Chm)
Michael W Kwasnik (Co-Pres)
Robert Kwasnik (Co-Pres)

DUNLAP OIL COMPANY INC.
759 S Haskell Ave, Willcox, AZ
85643-2748
Tel.: (520) 384-2248   AZ
Web Site: http://www.dunlapoil.com
Year Founded: 1956
Sales Range: $10-24.9 Million
Emp.: 90
Petroleum Bulk Station Services
N.A.I.C.S.: 424710
Teddy Dunlap (Pres)

DUNLAP SALES, INC.
208 Bradshaw Pike, Hopkinsville, KY
42240
Tel.: (270) 886-1390
Web Site: https://dsinternational.com
Year Founded: 1968
Sales Range: $10-24.9 Million
Emp.: 150
Needles, Industrial Sewing Machines,
Sewing Machine Parts & Related
Products Supplier
N.A.I.C.S.: 423830
Bruce McInnis (Pres)
Letty Rodriguez (Dir-Mktg)

DUNLAPSLK, P.C.
1300 Horizon Dr Ste 106, Chalfont,
PA 18914-3970
Tel.: (267) 594-3755
Web Site: https://dunlapslk.com
Year Founded: 1998
Accounting Firm
N.A.I.C.S.: 541219
Dennis K Dunlap (Mng Dir)

DUNN & CO. INC.
75 Green St, Clinton, MA 01510
Tel.: (978) 368-8505
Web Site:
  https://www.booktrauma.com
Sales Range: $10-24.9 Million
Emp.: 90
Landscaping Services
N.A.I.C.S.: 561730
Paul Cherubini (VP-Fin)
Rocco Windover (VP)

DUNN BLUE PRINT COMPANY
1009 W Maple Rd, Clawson, MI
48017
Tel.: (248) 288-5600   MI
Web Site: http://www.dunnblue.com
Year Founded: 1941
Sales Range: $10-24.9 Million
Emp.: 100
Blueprinting Services
N.A.I.C.S.: 541440
Bill Dunn (Pres)

**DUNN CONSTRUCTION COM-
PANY, INC.**
3905 Messer Airport Hwy, Birming-
ham, AL 35222-1420
Tel.: (205) 592-8908
Web Site:
  http://www.dunnconstruction.com
Year Founded: 1977
Sales Range: $450-499.9 Million
Emp.: 1,100
Nonresidential Construction
N.A.I.C.S.: 237310
Craig Fleming (Pres)
Michael Estell (Asst Mgr-Ops-ALDOT,
Plants & QAQC)
Wade Edwards (CFO)
Tommy Robinette (Asst
Superintendent-Asphalt Plant Ops)
Courtney Judd (Coord-Project Mgmt)
Sarah Johnson (Mgr-Acctg)
Cody Jackson (Mgr-Safety)
Brian Hibbard (Project Mgr)
Bo Walters (Asst Mgr-Ops-Private
Projects, Trucking & Shop Ops)
Mike Fields (Superintendent-Asphalt
Plant Ops)
Keith Brown (Superintendent-Project)
Barry Evans (Superintendent-Project)
Mark Williamson (Superintendent-
Project)

DUNN ELECTRIC CO.
3796 Plz Dr, Ann Arbor, MI 48108
Tel.: (734) 662-5541   MI
Web Site:
  http://www.dunnelectric.com
Year Founded: 1962
Sales Range: $10-24.9 Million
Emp.: 10
General Electrical Contracts Services
N.A.I.C.S.: 238210
Gary L. Davis (Pres)

**DUNN LUMBER COMPANY IN-
CORPORATED**
3801 Latona Ave NE, Seattle, WA
98105
Tel.: (206) 632-2129
Web Site:
  https://www.dunnlumber.com
Emp.: 200
Lumber & Other Building Materials
Whslr
N.A.I.C.S.: 423310
Mike Dunn (Pres)
Brent Spears (Asst Mgr)
Albert L. Dunn (Founder)

Subsidiaries:

Dunn Lumber Northwest Inc.   (1)
3801 Latona Ave NE, Seattle, WA 98105
Tel.: (206) 632-2129
Rev.: $18,700,000
Emp.: 75
Lumber & Other Building Materials
N.A.I.C.S.: 423310
Mike Dunn (Pres)

**DUNN MANUFACTURING
CORPORATION**
1400 Goldmine Rd, Monroe, NC
28110
Tel.: (704) 283-2147

Web Site: http://www.dunnc.com
Year Founded: 1905
Sales Range: $10-24.9 Million
Emp.: 300
Cotton Narrow Fabrics Supplier
N.A.I.C.S.: 313220
Lance M. Dunn (Pres)

DUNN ROADBUILDERS LLC
411 W Oak St, Laurel, MS 39440-
3948
Tel.: (601) 649-4111
Web Site:
  https://www.dunnroadbuilders.com
Year Founded: 1996
Sales Range: $125-149.9 Million
Emp.: 160
Highway & Street Construction Ser-
vices
N.A.I.C.S.: 237310
Clifton L. Beckman (Pres)
Jason Wooten (Dir-Ops)
Gary Walters (CFO & VP)

DUNN TIRE LLC
475 Cayuga Rd 475, Cheektowaga,
NY 14225
Tel.: (716) 683-3910
Web Site: http://www.dunntire.com
Sales Range: $25-49.9 Million
Emp.: 288
Automotive Tires Distr
N.A.I.C.S.: 441340

DUNN&CO.
202 S 22nd St Ste 202, Tampa, FL
33605
Tel.: (813) 350-7990
Web Site: http://www.dunn-co.com
Year Founded: 2003
Sales Range: $1-9.9 Million
Emp.: 30
Advertising Agencies
N.A.I.C.S.: 541810
Troy Dunn (Pres)
Brittany DeCarolis (Dir-Art)
Seth Allen (Dir-Trade Show)
Sarah Dworak (Acct Exec)
Katharine Bonnet (VP & Dir-Digital)
Kamden Kuhn (Mng Dir & Exec VP-
Strategy)
Chris Corley (Exec Creative Dir)

**DUNN'S SPORTING GOODS
CO. INC.**
8733 Commercial Blvd, Pevely, MO
63070
Tel.: (636) 475-4240
Web Site:
  https://www.shopdunns.com
Sales Range: $10-24.9 Million
Emp.: 35
Fishing & Hunting Equipment & Ap-
parel
N.A.I.C.S.: 459110
Dennis Dunn (Mgr-Store)

DUNN-RITE PRODUCTS, INC.
2200 S J St, Elwood, IN 46036
Tel.: (765) 552-9433
Web Site:
  http://www.dunnriteproducts.com
Year Founded: 1983
Rev.: $3,200,000
Emp.: 30
Sporting & Athletic Goods Mfr
N.A.I.C.S.: 339920
Douglas Dunn (Treas)
Edward Dunn (Pres)

Subsidiaries:

Crescent Moon Snowshoes, Inc.   (1)
5401 Western Ave Ste C, Boulder, CO
80301
Tel.: (303) 494-5506
Web Site:
  http://www.crescentmoonsnowshoes.com

Sporting & Athletic Goods Mfr
N.A.I.C.S.: 339920
Jake Thamm (Pres)
Tanner Dunn (VP)

DUNNAGE ENGINEERING INC.
721 Advance St, Brighton, MI 48116
Tel.: (810) 229-9501
Web Site: https://www.dunnage-
eng.com
Sales Range: $10-24.9 Million
Emp.: 35
Fabricated Structural Metal
N.A.I.C.S.: 332312
David Joseph (Pres)
Kathy Rindle (Mgr-Customer Svc)
Jim Banish (Mgr-Mfg Ops)

DUNNDATA COMPANY
2022 Rte 22, Brewster, NY 10509
Tel.: (845) 278-1200   NY
Web Site: http://www.dunndata.com
Year Founded: 1972
Sales Range: $10-24.9 Million
Emp.: 25
Direct Mail Advertising Services
N.A.I.C.S.: 541860
Stephen Dunn (Pres & CEO)
Rosy Faver (COO)
Sara Blair (Controller)
Jennifer Schmidt (Dir-Sls & Mktg)

DUNNE MANNING INC.
645 W Hamilton St, Allentown, PA
18101
Tel.: (610) 625-8000
Petroleum Products & Convenience
Retail Products Distr
N.A.I.C.S.: 424720
Daniel Robinson (Gen Counsel)
David Hrinak (Pres)
Lowell Brogan (VP)
Howard Krapf (Sec & Treas)

**DUNNING MOTOR SALES,
INC.**
9108 Southgate Rd, Cambridge, OH
43725
Tel.: (740) 439-4465
Web Site:
  https://www.dunningmotorsales.com
Sales Range: $10-24.9 Million
Emp.: 45
Car Whslr
N.A.I.C.S.: 441110
John Dunning (VP)

DUNSIRN PARTNERS LLC
W 6416 Greenville Dr, Greenville, WI
54942
Tel.: (920) 277-3808   WI
Web Site: http://www.dunsirn.com
Year Founded: 1987
Sales Range: $75-99.9 Million
Emp.: 200
Holding & Investment Company
N.A.I.C.S.: 424130
Brian L. Dunsirn (Pres & Partner)

Subsidiaries:

Dura-Fibre, LLC.   (1)
352 6th St, Menasha, WI 54952
Tel.: (920) 969-3600
Web Site: http://www.durafibre.com
Sales Range: $1-9.9 Million
Packaging Paperboard Box Mfr
N.A.I.C.S.: 322212
Brian Dunsirn (CEO)
Debbie Koschmann (Mgr-Bus)
Luke Benrud (Pres)
Scott Gehl (Mgr-Design & Quality)
Stefanie Peterson (Controller)

Oliver Printing & Packaging Co.,
LLC   (1)
1760 Enterprise Pkwy, Twinsburg, OH
44087
Tel.: (330) 425-7890
Web Site: http://www.oliverprinting.com

Sales Range: $1-9.9 Million
Commercial Lithographic Printing Services
N.A.I.C.S.: 323111
Dan Oliver *(Dir-Ops)*
George Oliver *(Pres)*
Rob van Gilse *(Dir-Sls & Mktg)*

Subsidiary (Domestic):

Disc Graphics Inc. **(2)**
10 Gilpin Ave, Hauppauge, NY 11788-4724
Tel.: (631) 234-1400
Web Site: http://www.discgraphics.com
Sales Range: $50-74.9 Million
Emp.: 354
Corrugated & Solid Fiber Box Mfr
N.A.I.C.S.: 322211
Donald Sinkin *(CEO)*
Margaret M. Krumholz *(Pres)*
Brian Hartigan *(VP-Fin)*
Jane Goitia *(Mgr-Credit)*
Fran Kahn *(Acct Mgr)*
Richard Roth *(Chief Strategy Officer)*
John Rebecchi *(Sr VP-Mktg & Bus Dev)*
Nik Blake *(VP-Ops)*
Sam John *(Mgr-Label Div)*

Subsidiary (Domestic):

Disc Graphics Label Group Inc. **(3)**
10 Gilpin Ave, Hauppauge, NY 11788
Tel.: (631) 234-1400
Web Site: http://www.discgraphics.com
Sales Range: $10-24.9 Million
Paperboard Boxes Supplier
N.A.I.C.S.: 561910
Samuel John *(Mgr-Label Dept)*

Graph-Corr **(3)**
4 Corn Rd, Dayton, NJ 08810
Tel.: (732) 355-0088
Paperboard Boxes Supplier
N.A.I.C.S.: 322211
Hugh Murphy *(Gen Mgr)*

Operon Systems, L.L.C. **(1)**
W6240 Greenville Rd, Greenville, WI 54914
Tel.: (920) 882-8720
Web Site: http://www.operonsystems.com
Sales Range: $10-24.9 Million
Emp.: 6
Productivity Solutions
N.A.I.C.S.: 561499

DUNWOODY VILLAGE
3500 W Chester Pike, Newtown
Square, PA 19073-4168
Tel.: (610) 359-4400 PA
Web Site: https://www.dunwoody.org
Year Founded: 1974
Sales Range: $25-49.9 Million
Emp.: 543
Continuing Care Retirement Community Operator
N.A.I.C.S.: 623311
Sherry Smyth *(Pres & CEO)*
Frank Beech *(Exec Dir)*
Elaine Kaiser *(Dir-Mktg & Admissions)*
John W. Lear *(Sec)*

DUO DOGS, INC.
10955 Linpage Pl, Saint Louis, MO
63132
Tel.: (314) 997-2325 MO
Web Site: https://duodogs.org
Year Founded: 1981
Emp.: 100
Dog Support Services
N.A.I.C.S.: 812910

DUO PR
4743 Ballard Ave NW Ste 300, Seattle, WA 98107
Tel.: (206) 706-0508
Web Site: http://www.duopr.com
Year Founded: 2004
Sales Range: Less than $1 Million
Emp.: 12
Communications, Branding, Public Relations
N.A.I.C.S.: 541820

Amanda Foley *(Co-Founder & Co-Partner)*
Rebecca Mosley *(Co-Founder & Co-Partner)*

DUO-FAST, INC.
1595 Ashby Rd, Saint Louis, MO
63132
Tel.: (314) 426-5440
Rev.: $21,598,753
Emp.: 50
Building Material Dealers
N.A.I.C.S.: 444180
Jim Whitley *(Pres)*

DUO-FORM PLASTICS
69836 Kraus Rd, Edwardsburg, MI
49110-9692
Tel.: (269) 663-8525
Web Site:
   https://www.duoformplastics.com
Year Founded: 1968
Plastic Bathroom Tubs Mfr
N.A.I.C.S.: 326191
Mike Gonser *(Sls & Project Mgr-Major Accts)*

DUPACO COMMUNITY CREDIT UNION
PO Box 179, Dubuque, IA 52004-0179
Tel.: (800) 373-7600
Web Site: http://www.dupaco.com
Year Founded: 1948
Financial Services; Wealth Management, Financial Coaching & Budgeting
N.A.I.C.S.: 522320
Joe Hearn *(Pres & CEO)*

DUPAGE CREDIT UNION
1515 Bond St, Naperville, IL 60563
Tel.: (630) 428-3440
Web Site: http://www.dupagecu.com
Rev.: $19,920,027
Emp.: 120
Credit Union
N.A.I.C.S.: 522130
Diane Shelton *(Pres)*

DUPAGE DODGE CHRYSLER JEEP, INC.
1400 E Roosevelt Rd, Wheaton, IL
60187-6804
Tel.: (630) 653-4060
Web Site:
   http://www.dupagedodgechry
   slerjeep.com
Sales Range: $10-24.9 Million
Emp.: 40
Car Whslr
N.A.I.C.S.: 441110
John Kay *(Pres)*
David J. Fritz Sr. *(Sr VP)*

DUPAGE MACHINE PRODUCTS, INC.
311 Longview Dr, Bloomingdale, IL
60108-2640
Tel.: (630) 690-5400
Web Site:
   https://www.dupagemachine.com
Year Founded: 1969
Sales Range: $10-24.9 Million
Emp.: 110
Precision Turned Product Mfr
N.A.I.C.S.: 332721
David R. Knuepfer *(Pres)*

DUPHIL INC.
6608 Interstate 10, Orange, TX
77632-8350
Tel.: (409) 883-8550
Web Site: https://www.duphil.com
Year Founded: 1996
Sales Range: $25-49.9 Million

Emp.: 260
Nonresidential Construction Services
N.A.I.C.S.: 236220
Neal Ledet *(Branch Mgr)*

DUPLESSIS BUICK GMC TRUCK, INC.
2522 S Burnside Ave, Gonzales, LA
70737-4647
Tel.: (225) 621-2164
Web Site:
   http://www.duplessisbuickgmc
Year Founded: 1988
Sales Range: $25-49.9 Million
Emp.: 50
Car Whslr
N.A.I.C.S.: 441110
Ron Duplessis *(Pres)*

DUPLICATOR SALES & SERVICE INC.
831 E Broadway, Louisville, KY
40204
Tel.: (502) 589-5555
Web Site:
   https://www.duplicatorsales.net
Sales Range: $10-24.9 Million
Emp.: 160
Copying Equipment
N.A.I.C.S.: 423420
Mike M. Nash *(Pres)*

DUPLO USA CORPORATION
3050 S Daimler St, Santa Ana, CA
92705
Tel.: (949) 752-8222
Web Site: https://www.duplousa.com
Rev.: $11,400,000
Emp.: 105
Office Equipment Merchant Whslr
N.A.I.C.S.: 423420
Toshiko Christopher *(Pres)*
Juko Shima *(Founder & Sec)*
Peter Tu *(Pres)*
Jesse Yuan *(Project Mgr)*
Tony Lock *(Mng Dir-UK)*

DUPONT COMMUNITY CREDIT UNION
140 Lucy Ln, Waynesboro, VA 22980
Tel.: (540) 946-3200
Web Site: https://www.mydccu.com
Year Founded: 1959
Rev.: $24,738,315
Emp.: 120
Credit Union Services
N.A.I.C.S.: 522130
Q. Maurice Gresham *(Treas)*
Ron L. Harlow *(Sec)*
Lynn Wagner *(Sec)*
Leslie E. Ramsey *(Treas)*
Everett J. Campbell Jr. *(Chm)*

DUPRE ENERGY SERVICES, LLC
510 Bering Dr Ste 455, Houston, TX
77057
Tel.: (713) 231-7132
Web Site: http://www.dupre.com
Emp.: 311
Oil Extraction Supporting Services
N.A.I.C.S.: 213112
David Knight *(Pres)*
Cornelius Dupre *(Chm & CEO)*
Dobie Weise *(VP-Fin)*

DUPRE LOGISTICS, LLC
201 Energy Pkwy, Lafayette, LA
70508
Tel.: (337) 237-8471
Web Site:
   https://www.duprelogistics.com
Year Founded: 1980
Sales Range: $50-74.9 Million
Emp.: 100
Trucking & Transportation Services

N.A.I.C.S.: 541614
Reggie Dupre *(Pres & CEO)*
Tom Voelkel *(COO)*
Raoul Siclait *(CFO)*

Subsidiaries:

Interstate Transport, Inc. **(1)**
324 1st Ave N, Saint Petersburg, FL 33701
Tel.: (727) 822-9999
Web Site: http://www.interstate-transport.com
Logistic Services
N.A.I.C.S.: 541614
Kim Dennis *(Mgr-HR)*
Zach Aufmann *(COO)*
Robert Bedinghaus *(Mgr-IT)*
Gloria Hudson Higham *(Founder, Pres & CEO)*
Colleen Kearney *(Mgr-Acctg)*
Bryan J. Nelson *(Chief Admin Officer & Gen Counsel)*
Rick J. Raimo *(Mgr-Customer Svc)*

DUPREE PLUMBING COMPANY
869 Worley Dr, Marietta, GA 30066-3865
Tel.: (770) 428-2291
Web Site:
   https://www.dupreeplumbing.com
Sales Range: $25-49.9 Million
Emp.: 175
Plumbing Services
N.A.I.C.S.: 238220
Emily Dupree *(CFO)*
R. Michael Dupree *(Pres & CEO)*
Becky Moore *(Mgr-Customer Rels)*

DUPREE, INC.
14395 Ramona Ave, Chino, CA
91710-5740
Tel.: (909) 597-4889
Web Site: https://www.dupreeinc.com
Year Founded: 1958
Rev.: $3,000,000
Emp.: 40
Stake Fasteners & Western Photometric Systems Designer & Mfr
N.A.I.C.S.: 332999
J. D. Dupree *(VP-Engrg)*

Subsidiaries:

Animal Reproduction Systems **(1)**
14395 Ramona Ave, Chino, CA 91710-5740
Tel.: (909) 597-4889
Web Site: http://www.arssales.com
Animal Breeding Supplies Mfr
N.A.I.C.S.: 112990

Stake Fastener Company **(1)**
14395 Ramona Ave, Chino, CA
91710-5740 **(100%)**
Tel.: (909) 597-4889
Web Site: http://www.stakefastener.com
Sales Range: $10-24.9 Million
Fastener Products & Custom Coating Mfr
N.A.I.C.S.: 335139

Western Photometric
Laboratories **(1)**
14395 Ramona Ave, Chino, CA 91710-5740
Tel.: (909) 597-4889
Web Site: http://www.dupreeinc.com
Sales Range: $10-24.9 Million
Lamp Testing Products & Lamp Adaptors Mfr
N.A.I.C.S.: 335139

DURA ART STONE INC.
1265 Montecito Ave Ste 110, Mountain View, CA 94043
Tel.: (650) 965-7100
Web Site:
   http://www.duraartstone.com
Sales Range: $10-24.9 Million
Emp.: 30
Pre-Cast Concrete Products
N.A.I.C.S.: 327390
Sam Diesendruck *(Principal)*

DURA SOFTWARE SERIES A QOF LLC

Dura Software Series A Qof LLC—(Continued)

425 Soledad St, San Antonio, TX
78205
Software Publisher
N.A.I.C.S.: 513210
Paul Salisbury *(CEO)*
Michael Girdley *(Exec Chm)*
Chris Burney *(CFO)*
Joseph Villafranca *(CTO)*
Beki Yorgason *(Controller)*

Subsidiaries:

6Connex Inc.   (1)
6701 Koll Center Pkwy Ste 250, Pleasanton, CA 94566
Tel.: (408) 341-1399
Web Site: http://www.6connex.com
Sales Range: $1-9.9 Million
Emp.: 35
Software Publisher
N.A.I.C.S.: 513210
Marc Goodell *(VP-Environments & Infrastructure)*
Michael Goodell *(Exec VP-Environments & Infrastructure)*
Joakim Jonsson *(Chief Product Officer)*
Matthew Simmons *(Gen Counsel)*
Ruben Castano *(CEO)*
Luiz Martins *(CMO)*
Henry Tran *(CTO)*
Lee Schor *(Chief Revenue Officer)*
Geoffrey Wellen *(Chief Customer Officer)*
Emily Wilson *(CFO)*

Subsidiary (Non-US):

6Connex China   (2)
D-2107 Freetown 58 South Dong San Huan Rd, Chaoyang District, Beijing, 100022, China
Tel.: (86) 10 58679179
Web Site: http://www.6connex.com
Software Publisher
N.A.I.C.S.: 513210

Dura Software, Inc.   (1)
425 Soledad St, San Antonio, TX 78205
Tel.: (210) 201-2053
Web Site: http://www.dura.software
Software Publisher
N.A.I.C.S.: 513210
Paul Salisbury *(CEO)*

Subsidiary (Domestic):

DB Technology, Inc.   (2)
1090 King Georges Post Rd Ste 203, Edison, NJ 08837
Tel.: (732) 882-0200
Web Site: http://www.dbtech.com
Sales Range: $1-9.9 Million
Emp.: 30
Computer System Design Services
N.A.I.C.S.: 541512
Angelo LoBue *(Controller)*
Greg Park *(Dir-Enterprise Solutions)*
Michelle Garron *(Mgr-Implementation)*
Phil Sullivan *(Dir-Mktg & Tech)*
Justin Brady *(CEO)*

It Retail, Inc.   (2)
5041 Lamart Dr Ste 250, Riverside, CA 92507
Tel.: (951) 682-6277
Web Site: http://www.itretail.com
Sales Range: $1-9.9 Million
Emp.: 12
Software Publisher
N.A.I.C.S.: 513210
Martin Goodwin *(Pres & CEO)*
David Rochlin *(Pres)*
Steve Douglas *(Owner)*
Terry Ficklin *(VP-Product Dev)*

Oxlo Systems, Inc.   (2)
11001 W 120th Ave Ste 300, Broomfield, CO 80021
Tel.: (720) 890-7545
Web Site: http://www.oxlo.com
Sales Range: $1-9.9 Million
Emp.: 22
Software Devolopment
N.A.I.C.S.: 541511
Henry Tran *(CEO)*

Paperwise, Inc.   (2)
3171 E Sunshine St, Springfield, MO 65804

Tel.: (417) 886-7505
Web Site: http://www.paperwise.com
Sales Range: $1-9.9 Million
Emp.: 18
Custom Computer Programming Services, Nsk
N.A.I.C.S.: 541511
Bob Black *(Pres)*
Clay Embry *(VP-Admin)*

Satuit Technologies, Inc.   (2)
100 Grossman Dr Ste 302, Braintree, MA 02184
Tel.: (781) 871-7788
Web Site: http://www.satuit.com
Rev.: $4,600,000
Emp.: 32
Management Consulting Services
N.A.I.C.S.: 541611
Josh Weiss *(CTO)*
Karen Maguire *(CEO)*
Mike Shields *(VP & Mgr-Relationship-North America)*
James Plassmann *(VP-Client Rels)*

DURA-BOND INDUSTRIES INC.

2658 Puckety St, Export, PA 15632
Tel.: (724) 327-0782
Web Site: https://www.dura-bond.com
Sales Range: $10-24.9 Million
Emp.: 150
Fabricated Structural Metal
N.A.I.C.S.: 332312
Wayne Norris *(Pres)*
Brad Norris *(VP-Sls & Engrg)*
John Christy *(Controller)*

DURABAG COMPANY INC.

1432 Santa Fe Dr, Tustin, CA 92780
Tel.: (714) 259-8811
Web Site: https://www.durabag.net
Rev.: $23,100,000
Emp.: 80
Food Storage & Frozen Food Bags & Plastic Mfr
N.A.I.C.S.: 326111
Wendy Sue *(Office Mgr)*
Frank J. Huang Jr. *(Co-Pres)*

DURACLEAN INTERNATIONAL, INC.

220 Campus Dr, Arlington Heights, IL 60004-1498
Tel.: (847) 704-7100
Web Site: http://www.duraclean.com
Year Founded: 1930
Sales Range: $75-99.9 Million
Emp.: 20
Cleaning Service
N.A.I.C.S.: 533110
Vince Caffarello *(Pres)*
Wilbur A. Gage *(Exec VP)*

DURAFLAME, INC.

PO Box 1230, Stockton, CA 95201-1230
Tel.: (209) 461-6600   CA
Web Site: http://www.duraflame.com
Year Founded: 1972
Sales Range: $75-99.9 Million
Emp.: 30
Fireplace Logs Mfr & Distr
N.A.I.C.S.: 423990
Mike Taylor *(Controller)*

Subsidiaries:

Wonderfuel, LLC   (1)
344 Arthur Dr, Somerset, KY 42501
Tel.: (606) 451-9174
Fire Log Distr
N.A.I.C.S.: 423720

DURAFLEX INC.

765 Industrial Dr, Cary, IL 60013
Tel.: (847) 462-1007
Web Site:
   https://www.duraflexinc.com
Rev.: $14,000,000

Emp.: 31
Fabricated Pipe & Pipe Fitting Mfr
N.A.I.C.S.: 332996
Dean Dellacecca *(Pres)*
Yvonne Kasper *(Mgr-Acctg)*

DURAGROUP LLC

316 E Woodlawn St 316 E, Ridgeland, SC 29936
Tel.: (843) 726-9225
Web Site: http://www.kwalu.com
Year Founded: 1984
Sales Range: $25-49.9 Million
Emp.: 5
Furniture Mfr; Holding Company
N.A.I.C.S.: 423210
Michael Zusman *(CEO)*

Subsidiaries:

Kwalu   (1)
146 Woodlawn St, Ridgeland, SC 29936
Tel.: (843) 726-9225
Web Site: http://www.duracasegoods.com
Sales Range: $25-49.9 Million
Furniture Mfr
N.A.I.C.S.: 423210
Mark Levine *(Reg Mgr-Sls)*
Jaclyn Vergara *(Sr Mgr-Graphic Design)*
Matthew Chutjian *(VP-Sls-Natl)*

DURALEE MULTIFABRICS, INC.

1775 5th Ave, Bay Shore, NY 11706-1762
Tel.: (631) 273-8800   NY
Web Site: http://www.duralee.com
Year Founded: 1962
Sales Range: $25-49.9 Million
Emp.: 150
Piece Goods Mfr
N.A.I.C.S.: 424310
Martin Rosenberger *(Pres)*
Lenny Silverman *(Owner)*

DURAMERICA BROKERAGE INC

37-14 30th St, Long Island City, NY 11101
Tel.: (718) 626-0700
Web Site: http://www.duramerica.com
Year Founded: 1996
Sales Range: $1-9.9 Million
Emp.: 11
Insurance Brokerage Services
N.A.I.C.S.: 524210
George Douramanis *(Founder & Pres)*

DURAMOLD CASTINGS INC.

1901 N Bendix Dr, South Bend, IN 46628-1603
Tel.: (574) 251-1111
Sales Range: $1-9.9 Million
Emp.: 10
Nonferrous Foundries
N.A.I.C.S.: 331529
Bob A. Lalwani *(Pres)*
K. B. Lalwani *(Sec)*

DURAN OIL CO

426 N Chestnut St, Trinidad, CO 81082
Tel.: (719) 846-9822
Rev.: $17,105,400
Emp.: 150
Petroleum Bulk Stations
N.A.I.C.S.: 424710
Ray E. Duran *(Pres)*

DURAND BUILDERS SERVICE INC.

N6344 State Hwy 25, Durand, WI 54736
Tel.: (715) 672-5941
Web Site:
   https://www.durandbuilders.com
Sales Range: $10-24.9 Million

Emp.: 40
Commercial & Office Building Construction Services
N.A.I.C.S.: 236220
Larry B. Hagness *(CEO)*
Patrick Thayer *(Project Mgr)*

DURAND WAYLAND INC.

101 Durand Rd, LaGrange, GA 30241-2501
Tel.: (706) 882-8161
Web Site: https://www.durand-wayland.com
Sales Range: $10-24.9 Million
Emp.: 150
Fruit & Vegetable Equipment Mfr & Supplier
N.A.I.C.S.: 333111
Ray Perry *(Sr VP-Sls)*
Harold Taylor *(Engr-Sprayer)*
Ricky Ashley *(Supvr-Sheet Metal)*
Gayla Jones *(Mgr-Acctg)*
Nick Lenger *(Mgr-Sls-Packinghouse-Northern)*
Ron Shrum *(Reg Mgr-Sls)*

DURANGO COCA-COLA BOTTLING CO.

75 Girard St, Durango, CO 81303
Tel.: (970) 247-1560
Web Site:
   https://www.durangococacola.com
Sales Range: $10-24.9 Million
Emp.: 55
Soft Drinks
N.A.I.C.S.: 424490
Donald T. Mapel *(Pres)*

DURANT BANCORP, INC.

1400 W Main St, Durant, OK 74701
Tel.: (580) 924-2211   OK
Web Site:
   http://www.firstunitedbank.com
Year Founded: 1978
Bank Holding Company
N.A.I.C.S.: 551111
Greg Massey *(Vice Chm, Pres & CEO)*
John Massey *(Chm)*
William Fahrendorf *(Chief Admin Officer & Exec VP)*
Stephen Phillips *(Chief Banking Officer-Texas & Exec VP)*
George Clark *(CFO & Sr VP)*
Mark Dawson *(Chief Fin Svcs Officer & Exec VP)*
Scott Flowers *(Chief Banking Officer-Oklahoma & Exec VP)*
David Keese *(Gen Counsel & Sr VP)*
Timothy Schneider *(COO, CIO & Exec VP)*

Subsidiaries:

First United Bank & Trust
Company   (1)
1400 W Main St, Durant, OK 74701
Tel.: (580) 924-2211
Web Site: http://www.firstunitedbank.com
Commercial Banking
N.A.I.C.S.: 522110
Greg Massey *(CEO)*
Mark Dawson *(Chief Fin Svcs Officer & Exec VP)*
Scott Flowers *(Chief Banking Officer-Oklahoma & Exec VP)*
Stephen Phillips *(Chief Banking Officer-Texas & Exec VP)*
William Fahrendorf *(Chief Admin Officer & Exec VP)*
Melissa Perrin *(Sr VP & Sr People & Culture Officer)*
George Clark *(CFO & Sr VP)*
David Keese *(Gen Counsel & Sr VP)*
Timothy Schneider *(COO, CIO & Exec VP)*

DURANT PLASTICS & MANUFACTURING, INC.

301 Gerlach Dr, Durant, OK 74701

Tel.: (580) 745-9430   OK
Web Site:
    https://www.durantplastics.com
Year Founded: 2005
Custom Thermoforming Plastic Components Mfr
N.A.I.C.S.: 326199
Glen Barton *(CEO)*

DURASERV CORP
2200 Luna Rd Ste 160, Carrollton, TX 75006
Web Site: http://duraservcorp.com
Year Founded: 2016
Loading Dock, Door & Safety Equipment Installation & Repair Services
N.A.I.C.S.: 811310
David Iliff *(CEO)*
John Brooker *(Pres)*
Jamie Gibbs *(Chm)*

Subsidiaries:

ACME Rolling Steel Door Corp.   (1)
1099 Linden Ave, Ridgefield, NJ 07657
Tel.: (201) 943-7693
Web Site: http://www.acmedoor.com
Rev.: $6,450,000
Emp.: 25
Home Center Operator
N.A.I.C.S.: 444110
Jeff Krautman *(Pres)*

Overhead Door Co of New Orleans, Inc.   (1)
5913 Blessey St., New Orleans, LA 70123
Tel.: (504) 822-0345
Web Site: https://ohdno.com
Facilities Services : Installation, Servicing & Repair
N.A.I.C.S.: 238210

DURATECH INDUSTRIES INC.
3216 Commerce St, La Crosse, WI 54603
Tel.: (608) 781-2570
Web Site: https://www.duratech.com
Year Founded: 1977
Design, Printing & Packaging Services
N.A.I.C.S.: 323111
Peter Johnson *(Pres)*

DURATIONAL CAPITAL MANAGEMENT, LP
107 Grand St 7th Fl, New York, NY 10013
Tel.: (646) 798-0656   NY
Web Site: http://www.durational.com
Investment Services
N.A.I.C.S.: 523940
Susanna Hong *(Partner)*
Deron J Haley *(Founder, Partner & COO)*

Subsidiaries:

Bojangles', Inc.   (1)
9432 Southern Pine Blvd, Charlotte, NC 28273
Tel.: (704) 527-2675
Web Site: http://www.bojangles.com
Sales Range: $550-599.9 Million
Emp.: 9,900
Fast Food Restaurant Operator
N.A.I.C.S.: 722513
Laura Roberts *(Officer-Compliance, Gen Counsel, Sec & VP)*
Kenneth M. Koziol *(Chief Restaurant Support Officer)*
Brian Unger *(COO)*
Keith Vigness *(VP-Fin)*
Reese Stewart *(CFO)*
Jackie Woodward *(CMO)*
Jose R. Costa *(Chief Growth Officer)*
Marshall Scarborough *(VP-Menu & Culinary Innovation)*
Byron Chandler *(Chief Dev Officer)*
Jose Armario *(Pres & CEO)*

Subsidiary (Domestic):

Bojangles' Restaurants, Inc.   (2)

9432 Southern Pine Blvd, Charlotte, NC 28273
Tel.: (704) 527-2675
Web Site: http://www.bojangles.com
Franchised Fast Food Restaurants
N.A.I.C.S.: 722513

DURAWOOD PRODUCTS, INC.
18 Industrial Way, Denver, PA 17517
Tel.: (717) 336-0220
Web Site:
    http://www.durawoodproducts.com
Year Founded: 1986
Sales Range: $10-24.9 Million
Emp.: 110
Millwork Services
N.A.I.C.S.: 321918
Craig McDonald *(Pres)*
Larry Larsen *(Plant Mgr)*

DURAY/J.F. DUNCAN INDUSTRIES, INC.
9301 Stewart & Gray Rd, Downey, CA 90241-5315
Tel.: (562) 862-4269   CA
Web Site:
    https://www.durayduncan.com
Year Founded: 1944
Sales Range: $75-99.9 Million
Emp.: 120
Commercial Cooking Equipment & Foodservice Equipment Dealer, Mfr & Installer
N.A.I.C.S.: 333310
Johnny Wong *(Pres)*
Donald L. Durward *(VP)*
Dan Centurioni *(Gen Mgr)*
Chris Thompson *(COO)*
Barbara Blanchard *(Coord-Job)*
Diane Lomma *(Project Coord)*
Michael Freed *(Partner)*

Subsidiaries:

Baring Industries, Inc.   (1)
3249 SW 42nd St, Fort Lauderdale, FL 33312
Tel.: (954) 327-6700
Web Site: http://www.baring.com
Sales Range: $50-74.9 Million
Emp.: 60
Laundry & Foodservice Equipment & Supplies Mfr
N.A.I.C.S.: 423850
Charles Sperry *(Sr VP)*
Michael Fitzgibbon *(Exec VP)*
Manny Alvarez *(VP-Bus Dev)*
Mike Mackey *(Reg VP-Nashville)*
Michael Perez *(VP-Engrg)*
Helene Durocher *(Mgr-Contract Admin)*
Michael Heim *(VP-Chicago)*
Jennifer Hendrick *(Controller)*
Robert Jones *(Sr Project Mgr-Bus Dev)*

DURDACH BROS. INC.
Main St RR 61, Paxinos, PA 17860
Tel.: (570) 648-5706
Sales Range: $10-24.9 Million
Emp.: 50
Beer & Other Fermented Malt Liquors
N.A.I.C.S.: 424810
Richard J. Durdach *(CEO)*
Jeff Hershey *(Mgr-Sls)*
Scott Herbert *(VP-Sls & Bus Dev)*

DUREX INC.
5 Stahuber Ave, Union, NJ 07083
Tel.: (908) 688-0800
Web Site: http://www.durexinc.com
Sales Range: $25-49.9 Million
Emp.: 150
Metal Stamping Services
N.A.I.C.S.: 332119
Robert Denholtz *(Pres)*
Sherry Falkenberg *(Controller)*
Bill Jensen *(Mgr-Quality)*
Jeffrey Berwick *(Dir-Sls)*
Linda Willoughby *(Office Mgr)*
Mike Danniballe *(Mgr-Production)*

Subsidiaries:

Sternvent Co., Inc.   (1)
5 Stahuber Ave, Union, NJ 07083
Tel.: (908) 688-0807
Web Site: http://www.sternvent.com
Air Purification Equipment Mfr
N.A.I.C.S.: 333413
Peter Levitt *(Product Mgr)*

DURHAM CO.
722 Durham Rd, Lebanon, MO 65536-3405
Tel.: (417) 532-7121
Web Site:
    http://www.durhamcompany.com
Sales Range: $25-49.9 Million
Emp.: 353
Non-Current Carrying Wiring Devices Mfr
N.A.I.C.S.: 335932

Subsidiaries:

GEC Durham Industries, Inc.   (1)
255 Samuel Barnet Blvd, New Bedford, MA 02745
Tel.: (508) 995-2636
Web Site: http://www.gec.ac.in
Sales Range: $10-24.9 Million
Emp.: 40
Transformers Distr
N.A.I.C.S.: 335311

DURHAM COCA COLA BOTTLING CO.
3214 Hillsborough Rd, Durham, NC 27705
Tel.: (919) 383-1531
Sales Range: $50-74.9 Million
Emp.: 105
Soft Drink Bottling Services
N.A.I.C.S.: 312111
Hager Rand *(Pres)*
Arnold Lea *(VP)*

DURHAM GEO-ENTERPRISES INCORPORATED
2175 W Park Ct, Stone Mountain, GA 30087
Tel.: (770) 465-7557
Web Site:
    http://www.durhamgeo.com
Year Founded: 1965
Sales Range: $10-24.9 Million
Emp.: 70
Engineers Equipment & Supplies
N.A.I.C.S.: 423490
Tom Paquette *(Pres)*
Monica Baxter *(Asst Controller)*
David Richardson *(Mgr-Sls-Natl)*

Subsidiaries:

Durham Geo Slope Indicator   (1)
12123 Harbour Reach Dr Ste 106, Mukilteo, WA 98275
Tel.: (425) 493-6200
Web Site: http://www.slopeindicator.com
Rev.: $4,500,000
Emp.: 30
Geo Technical Instrument Mfr
N.A.I.C.S.: 334519
John Rogers *(Plant Mgr)*

DURHAM PECAN COMPANY, INC.
308 S Houston, Comanche, TX 76442
Tel.: (325) 356-5291   TX
Web Site:
    http://www.durhampecan.com
Year Founded: 1928
Pecan & Other Nut Sheller, Packager & Distr
N.A.I.C.S.: 115114
Odie Dollins *(Pres)*
Paul Rich *(Dir-Sls)*
Rickey Jones *(Gen Mgr)*
Clint Welch *(Dir-Pur)*

DURHAM PUMP, INC.
2313 Durham-Dayton Hwy, Durham, CA 95938
Tel.: (530) 891-4821
Web Site:
    https://www.durhampump.com
Year Founded: 1952
Sales Range: $10-24.9 Million
Emp.: 25
Heavy & Civil Engineering Construction Services
N.A.I.C.S.: 237990
John Rhein *(Pres)*
Walt Chrupalo *(Mgr-Sls)*
Keith Drobny *(Acct Mgr-Agriculture)*
Dave Kistle *(Acct Mgr-Agriculture)*

DURITZAS ENTERPRISES INC.
125 W Beau St, Washington, PA 15301
Tel.: (724) 223-5493
Sales Range: $25-49.9 Million
Emp.: 135
Supermarkets, Chain
N.A.I.C.S.: 445110

DURKEE-MOWER, INC.
2 Empire St, Lynn, MA 01902-1815
Tel.: (781) 593-8007
Web Site:
    http://www.marshmallowfluff.com
Year Founded: 1920
Sales Range: $75-99.9 Million
Emp.: 20
Sandwich Spreads & Marshmallow Toppings Mfr
N.A.I.C.S.: 311340
Donald D. Durkee *(Pres)*
Jonathan S. Durkee *(Treas & Exec VP)*
Dan Quirk *(Dir-Sls-Mktg)*

DURO ART INDUSTRIES, INC.
1832 W Juneway Ter, Chicago, IL 60626-1016
Tel.: (773) 743-3430
Web Site: http://www.duroart.com
Sales Range: $50-74.9 Million
Emp.: 25
Art Supplies Mfr
N.A.I.C.S.: 339940
Kurt Rathslag *(Mgr-Key Accts)*
Thomas C. Rathslag Jr. *(Owner)*

DURO DYNE CORPORATION
81 Spence St, Bay Shore, NY. 11706
Tel.: (631) 249-9000   NY
Web Site: https://www.durodyne.com
Year Founded: 1952
Sales Range: $75-99.9 Million
Emp.: 165
Sheet Metal & Accessories for the HVAC Industry & Flexible Duct Connectors & Insulation Fastening Machinery Mfr
N.A.I.C.S.: 333415
Leo White *(Controller)*
Jo Ann Sanacora *(Asst Controller)*

DURO INDUSTRIES INC.
110 Chace St, Fall River, MA 02724-1416
Tel.: (508) 675-0101   MA
Web Site:
    http://www.duroindustries.com
Year Founded: 1985
Sales Range: $100-124.9 Million
Emp.: 1,400
Cotton Broadwoven Fabrics Finisher
N.A.I.C.S.: 313310
Ron Souza *(VP-Bus Ops)*
Peter Ricci *(VP-HR)*
Edward W. Ricci II *(Pres & CEO)*

DURO-LAST ROOFING, INC.

Duro-Last Roofing, Inc.—(Continued)

525 Morley Dr, Saginaw, MI 48601-
9400
Tel.: (989) 753-6486   **MI**
Web Site: http://www.duro-last.com
Year Founded: 1978
Sales Range: $150-199.9 Million
Emp.: 400
Roofing Services
N.A.I.C.S.: 313320
Thomas L. Saeli (CEO)
Andrea Fisher (Dir-Mktg)
Dan Ervin (Dir-Natl Accts)

**DUROCHER AUTO SALES
INC.**
4651 Route 9, Plattsburgh, NY 12901
Tel.: (518) 405-6787   **NY**
Web Site:
   http://www.durocherauto.com
Sales Range: $10-24.9 Million
Emp.: 70
Motor Vehicle Dealers
N.A.I.C.S.: 441110
Lawrence Durocher (Pres)
Robert Durocher (VP)
Bette Durocher (Treas)

**DUROCHER TV & APPLIANCE
INC.**
222 S Monroe St, Monroe, MI 48161
Tel.: (734) 241-7626   **MI**
Web Site: http://www.durochers.com
Year Founded: 1942
Sales Range: $10-24.9 Million
Emp.: 35
Home Funishings & Appliances
N.A.I.C.S.: 449110
Chris Durocher (Pres)

DUROTECH, INC.
11931 Wickchester Ln Ste 205,
Houston, TX 77043
Tel.: (281) 558-6892
Web Site:
   https://www.durotechgc.com
Sales Range: $10-24.9 Million
Emp.: 90
Nonresidential Construction Services
N.A.I.C.S.: 236220
David Rowe (Principal)
Meadows Becky (Mgr-Mktg)
Clarence Stephens (Project Mgr)

**DURR MECHANICAL CON-
STRUCTION INC.**
80 8th Ave Fl 17, New York, NY
10011
Tel.: (212) 627-1313
Web Site: http://www.durrmech.com
Year Founded: 1985
Sales Range: $50-74.9 Million
Emp.: 100
Mechanical Contractor: HSVC
N.A.I.C.S.: 238220
Kenneth A. Durr (Pres)
Robert J. Durr (Chm & Treas)
Frank Heidinger (VP-Construction)
John J. T. Pecoraro (VP-Special
Projects)

DURST CORPORATION
129 Dermody St, Cranford, NJ
07016-3217
Tel.: (908) 653-1100   **NJ**
Web Site: http://www.durstcorp.com
Year Founded: 1901
Sales Range: $75-99.9 Million
Emp.: 25
Specialty Plumbing Products Mfr
N.A.I.C.S.: 423720
Larry Brody (Pres)

Subsidiaries:

Jaclo Industries   (1)

129 Dermody St, Cranford, NJ 07016
Tel.: (908) 653-4433
Web Site: http://www.jaclo.com
Sales Range: $25-49.9 Million
Bathroom Supplies Mfr
N.A.I.C.S.: 423720
Larry Brodey (CEO)

DUSTROL INC.
1200 Main St, Towanda, KS 67144
Tel.: (316) 536-2262
Web Site: https://www.dustrol.com
Year Founded: 1973
Rev.: $40,675,140
Emp.: 80
Concrete Breaking for Streets &
Highways
N.A.I.C.S.: 238910
Tim Murphy (Pres)
Brian Hansen (VP)
Jean Thompson (Dir-Safety)
Ted Dankert (CEO)
Kevin Koehler (Sec)

**DUSTY RHODES FORD SALES
INCORPORATED**
1615 US Hwy 259 N, Kilgore, TX
75662
Tel.: (903) 984-2006
Web Site:
   http://www.autodealerbase.com
Sales Range: $25-49.9 Million
Emp.: 62
New Car Dealers
N.A.I.C.S.: 441110
Gilbert Lopez (Pres)

DUTCH BROS. COFFEE, LLC
PO Box 1929, Grants Pass, OR
97528
Tel.: (541) 471-2969
Web Site: http://www.dutchbros.com
Year Founded: 1992
Sales Range: $100-124.9 Million
Emp.: 2,000
Coffee Retailer & Franchisor
N.A.I.C.S.: 722513
Travis Boersma (Founder & CEO)
Christine Barone (Pres & CFO)
Travis Boersma (Exec Chm)

DUTCH CHEVROLET BUICK
6 Belmont Ave, Belfast, ME 04915
Tel.: (207) 338-1470
Web Site: http://www.dutchchevy.com
Year Founded: 1926
Sales Range: $10-24.9 Million
Emp.: 50
New Car Dealers
N.A.I.C.S.: 441110
Joshua Treat (Mgr-Sls)
Ray Rogers (Mgr-Ops)
Mark Walsh (Mgr-F&I)

DUTCH ENTERPRISES INC.
4832 Old Cape Rd E, Jackson, MO
63755
Tel.: (573) 352-4039
Web Site:
   https://www.dutchenterprises.com
Sales Range: $10-24.9 Million
Emp.: 90
Mechanical Contracting Service
N.A.I.C.S.: 238220
Randy Werner (Pres)
Rob Janet (CEO)

DUTCH GOLD HONEY INC.
2220 Dutch Gold Dr, Lancaster, PA
17601-1941
Tel.: (717) 393-1716   **PA**
Web Site:
   https://www.dutchgoldhoney.com
Year Founded: 1946
Sales Range: $50-74.9 Million
Emp.: 85
Honey & Maple Syrup Mfr & Whslr

N.A.I.C.S.: 424490
Charles Schatzman (VP-Fin & Admin)

Subsidiaries:

McLures Honey & Maple
Products   (1)

46 N Littleton Rd, Littleton, NH
03561-3814   (100%)
Tel.: (603) 444-6246
Web Site: http://www.mclures.com
Sales Range: $25-49.9 Million
Emp.: 26
Honey & Maple Syrup Mfr & Distr
N.A.I.C.S.: 424490

DUTCH HERITAGE GARDENS
11901 E Palmer Divide Ave, Lark-
spur, CO 80118
Tel.: (303) 660-1196
Web Site:
   https://www.dhgardens.com
Sales Range: $1-9.9 Million
Emp.: 25
Nursery & Tree Production Services
N.A.I.C.S.: 111421
Aaron Van Wingerden (Owner)
Rozalia Van Wingerden (Owner)

DUTCH MADE
10415 Roth Rd, Grabill, IN 46741
Tel.: (260) 657-3311
Web Site:
   https://www.dutchmade.com
Rev.: $11,016,773
Emp.: 80
Wood Kitchen Cabinets
N.A.I.C.S.: 337110
Martin Graber (CEO)
Steve Krug (Controller)
Luster Zehr (Pres)

**DUTCH MILLER CHEVROLET
INC.**
1100 Washington Ave, Huntington,
WV 25704
Tel.: (304) 521-4566
Web Site:
   http://www.dutchmillerchevy.net
Rev.: $35,000,000
Emp.: 100
New Car Dealers
N.A.I.C.S.: 441110
Kathy McIlhenny (Office Mgr)
Sam Miller (Owner)
Taylor Allen (Mgr-Internet Sls)

DUTCH MILLER KIA
6400 US Route 60 E, Barboursville,
WV 25504
Tel.: (681) 347-7927
Web Site:
   https://www.dutchmillerkia.com
Sales Range: $10-24.9 Million
Emp.: 18
Car Whslr
N.A.I.C.S.: 441110
Henry M. Kayes (Principal)
Chris Miller (Owner)

DUTCH OIL COMPANY INC.
730 Alabama St, Columbus, MS
39702
Tel.: (662) 327-5202
Web Site:
   http://www.dutchoilcompany.net
Rev.: $40,000,000
Emp.: 28
Petroleum Products
N.A.I.C.S.: 424720
Joe A. Gillis (Pres)
Sue Grantham (Mgr-Ops-Comml
Credit Cards)

DUTCH POINT CREDIT UNION
195 Silas Deane Hwy, Wethersfield,
CT 06109
Tel.: (860) 563-2617   **CT**

Web Site: https://www.dutchpoint.org
Year Founded: 1960
Sales Range: $10-24.9 Million
Emp.: 76
Credit Union
N.A.I.C.S.: 522130
Francis R. N. Proto (Pres & CEO)

DUTCH PRIME FOODS INC.
235 West Ave, Long Branch, NJ
07740
Tel.: (732) 222-0910
Web Site:
   http://www.dutchprimefoods.com
Rev.: $22,662,546
Emp.: 25
Meat Product Whslr
N.A.I.C.S.: 424470
Ronald J. Orzechowski (CFO &
Treas)
Jeffry C. Sherman (COO & VP)

**DUTCH VALLEY AUTO
WORKS**
3331 Columbia Ave, Lancaster, PA
17603
Tel.: (717) 394-6278
Web Site:
   https://www.dutchvalleyauto.com
Year Founded: 2009
Rev.: $2,700,000
Emp.: 21
Automotive Towing Services
N.A.I.C.S.: 488410
Geoff McCollom (Owner)
Ken Trimble (Gen Mgr)

**DUTCHESS COUNTY AGRI-
CULTURAL SOCIETY, INC.**
6550 Spring Brook Ave, Rhinebeck,
NY 12572
Tel.: (845) 876-4000   **NY**
Web Site:
   https://www.dutchessfair.com
Year Founded: 1950
Sales Range: $1-9.9 Million
Emp.: 336
Agricultural Fair Organizer
N.A.I.C.S.: 711310
Vicki Imperati (Mgr-Admin Ops)
Andrew K. Imperati (Pres & CEO)
Donna Zuna (CFO)

DUTCHESS TERMINALS INC.
66 Prospect St, Poughkeepsie, NY
12601
Tel.: (845) 471-3383
Sales Range: $25-49.9 Million
Emp.: 10
Petroleum Terminal
N.A.I.C.S.: 424710
Khosrow Vosoughi (Pres)

**DUTCHMAN HOSPITALITY
GROUP, INC.**
4985 Walnut St, Walnut Creek, OH
44687
Tel.: (330) 893-2926
Web Site: http://www.dhgroup.com
Sales Range: $25-49.9 Million
Emp.: 1,000
Restaurant, Hotel & Gift Shop Owner
& Operator
N.A.I.C.S.: 722511
Mike Palmer (Pres)
Vicki VanNatta (Mgr-Mktg)
Evelon Littleton (Mgr-HR)

**DUTCHWAY FARM MARKET
INC.**
649 E Lincoln Ave, Myerstown, PA
17067
Tel.: (717) 866-5758   **PA**
Web Site:
   https://www.dutchwayfarm.com
Sales Range: $10-24.9 Million.

Emp.: 175
Farm Land Leasing
N.A.I.C.S.: 531190

DUTRAC COMMUNITY CREDIT UNION
3465 Asbury Rd, Dubuque, IA 52004-3250
Tel.: (563) 582-1331   IA
Web Site: http://www.dutrac.org
Year Founded: 1946
Rev.: $25,792,107
Assets: $709,629,061
Liabilities: $4,802,900
Net Worth: $704,826,161
Earnings: $7,792,570
Emp.: 186
Fiscal Year-end: 12/31/18
Credit Union Operator
N.A.I.C.S.: 522130
Andrew Hawkinson (Pres & CEO)
Lee Hoerner (Sr VP-Sls & Svc)
Andy Lassen (Sr VP-IT)
Megan Egan (Sr VP-HR)
Jason Norton (Sr VP-Mktg & Bus Dev)
Daniel Deutmeyer (CFO & Treas)
Scott Neyens (Chm)
David Eggers (Vice Chm)
John Vail (Sec)
Ron Kinsella (Sr VP-Lending)
Kim Adams (Sr VP-Ops & Facilities)
Michelle Ariss (Sr VP-Fin)

DUTRO COMPANY
675 N 600 W Ste 2, Logan, UT 84321-3192
Tel.: (435) 752-3921
Web Site: https://www.dutro.com
Rev.: $20,392,010
Emp.: 50
Barbecues, Grills & Braziers for Outdoor Cooking
N.A.I.C.S.: 335220
William A. Dutro (Pres)

DUTRO FORD LINCOLN MER-CURY INC.
131S 5th St, Zanesville, OH 43701
Tel.: (740) 452-6334
Web Site: https://www.dutros.com
Sales Range: $10-24.9 Million
Emp.: 70
Automobiles, New & Used
N.A.I.C.S.: 441110
James F. Graham (Pres)
Bryan Graham (Gen Mgr)
Mark Clapper (Asst Mgr-Body Shop)

DUTTON-LAINSON COMPANY
451 W 2nd St, Hastings, NE 68901-7529
Tel.: (402) 462-4141   NE
Web Site: https://www.dutton-lainson.com
Year Founded: 1886
Sales Range: $100-124.9 Million
Emp.: 310
Marine, Automotive & Agricultural Products Mfr; Plumbing & Electrical Products Wholesale Distr
N.A.I.C.S.: 333120
Mark Bliss (VP-Sls & Mktg)

DUVENJIAN
650 S Hill St Ste 918, Los Angeles, CA 90014
Tel.: (213) 624-8068
Web Site: http://www.duvenjian.com
Year Founded: 1986
Rev.: $12,500,000
Emp.: 3
Advetising Agency
N.A.I.C.S.: 541810
Dikran Duvenjian (Pres)

DUXBURY HARDWARE CORP.
40 Independence Rd, Kingston, MA 02364
Tel.: (781) 422-0131
Web Site: https://www.goodrichlumber.com
Year Founded: 1906
Sales Range: $10-24.9 Million
Emp.: 20
Lumber & Building Material Whslr
N.A.I.C.S.: 444110
Kevin Medeiros (Mgr)

DVELE, INC.
5521 La Jolla Blvd, La Jolla, CA 92037
Tel.: (604) 358-4272   DE
Web Site: http://www.dvele.com
New Single-Family Housing Construction
N.A.I.C.S.: 236115
Kurt Goodjohn (Co-Founder & CEO)

Subsidiaries:

Blu Homes, Inc   (1)
1245 Nimitz Ave, Vallejo, CA 94592
Tel.: (866) 887-7997
Web Site: http://www.bluhomes.com
Sales Range: $25-49.9 Million
Emp.: 134
Prefabricated Home Mfr
N.A.I.C.S.: 321992
Bill Haney (Co-Founder & Chm)
Maura McCarthy (Co-Founder & VP-Market Dev)
Gary Martell (CFO & Treas)
Kaitlin Burek Haggerty (CEO)
Dan Goodin (VP-Sls)

DVHP INC.
2955 Inca St Ste 1A, Denver, CO 80202
Tel.: (303) 232-3840   CO
Web Site: http://www.deviq.io
Software Publisher
N.A.I.C.S.: 513210
Shawn Davison (CEO)
Denton Crofts (Pres)
Perry Nelson (COO & VP-Delivery)
James Shelby (CTO)

Subsidiaries:

Notion One, LLC   (1)
2630 W Belleview Ave Ste 270, Littleton, CO 80123
Tel.: (303) 536-5200
Web Site: http://www.notionone.com
Software Development Services
N.A.I.C.S.: 513210
Eric Brown (Co-Founder)
Tyler Brinks (Co-Founder)

DVL GROUP, INC.
115 Sinclair Rd, Bristol, PA 19007
Tel.: (215) 785-5950
Web Site: https://www.dvlnet.com
Year Founded: 1985
HVAC & AC/DC Power System Maintenance Services
N.A.I.C.S.: 423730
Michael P. Murphy (Founder)
Christy Magee (Dir-HR)
Bob Gusciora (Pres)
Gary Hill (Chm & CEO)

Subsidiaries:

Energy Transfer Solutions Inc   (1)
425 Mcfarlan Rd Ste 209, Kennett Square, PA 19348
Tel.: (610) 444-0333
Emp.: 20
HVAC Equipment Mfr & Services
N.A.I.C.S.: 423730
Todd Goodstein (Pres & CEO)
Dave Robertson (Dir-Svc & Controls)
Jeff McKee (Dir-Equipment Sls)
Tim Schmidt (Dir-Field Ops)
Bill McQuaide (Engr-Sls)
Jason Roebke (Engr-Sls)
Greg Stoughton (Engr-Sls)

Casey Younkins (Engr-Sls)
Kevin Hanson (Mgr)
Greg Haggarty (Mgr-Sls)
Katherine Bartlett (Coord-Mktg)
Charlene Chandler (Mgr-Svc Sls)
Marissa Donatone (Mgr-Mktg)
Mike Haggarty (COO)
Amy McCoy (VP-Fin)
Tim Winters (District Mgr)
Pete Wolf (Dir-Sls)
Colleen Wood (Coord-Sls)

DVSM LLC
760 SW 9th Av Ste 2300, Portland, OR 97205
Tel.: (503) 223-2721
Web Site: http://www.endeavourcapital.com
Year Founded: 1991
Rev.: $1,500,000,000
Privater Equity Firm
N.A.I.C.S.: 523999
Stephen E. Babson (Mng Dir)
Rocky Dixon (Co-Founder & Mng Dir)
Mark Dorman (Mng Dir)
John von Schlegell (Co-Founder & Mng Dir)
Chad Heath (Mng Dir-Los Angeles)
Leland Jones (Mng Dir-Los Angeles)
Aaron Richmond (Mng Dir-Seattle)
Derek Eve (Principal)

Subsidiaries:

Forrest Machining Inc.   (1)
27756 Ave Mentry, Valencia, CA 91355-3453
Tel.: (661) 257-0231
Web Site: http://www.forrestmachining.com
Aerospace Structures & Assemblies Mfr
N.A.I.C.S.: 336411
Joanie Crawford (Gen Mgr)
Tim Mickael (CEO)

DW RICHARDS SONS INC.
701 Rocky Glen Rd, Avoca, PA 18641
Tel.: (570) 457-5424   PA
Web Site: https://www.dwrichards.net
Year Founded: 1956
Sales Range: $50-74.9 Million
Emp.: 40
Cooking Oils & Shortenings Whslr
N.A.I.C.S.: 424490
Kenneth C. Richards (Pres)

DWA MEDIA
49 Geary St Ste 500, San Francisco, CA 94108
Tel.: (415) 296-8050
Web Site: http://www.dwamedia.com
Year Founded: 1996
Sales Range: $10-24.9 Million
Emp.: 155
Media Planning & Buying
N.A.I.C.S.: 541830
Bob Ray (CEO)
David Wood (Founder & Chm)
Isabelle Kane (VP-Client Svcs)
Kris Garland (Grp Dir-Mktg)
James Miller (Sr VP-Bus Dev)
Pippa Hollebone (Mng Dir-Southeast Asia & India)
Roland Deal (Pres-Americas)
Tiffany Egan (Mng Dir-Australia & New Zealand)
Steve Jones (Chief Comml Officer)

DWA, INC.
506 Maury St, Richmond, VA 23224-4120
Tel.: (804) 233-8371   VA
Web Site: http://www.dwa-inc.com
Year Founded: 1997
Sales Range: $25-49.9 Million
Emp.: 50
Industrial Machinery Mfr
N.A.I.C.S.: 332710

Margaret Maxwell (Office Mgr)
James Miller (Sr VP-Bus Dev)

Subsidiaries:

Richmond Metal Finishing   (1)
506 Maury St, Richmond, VA 23224-4120
Tel.: (804) 233-8372
Web Site: http://www.dwa-inc.com
Sales Range: $10-24.9 Million
Emp.: 3
Metal Polishing & Plating Services
N.A.I.C.S.: 332813
James Stewart (Plant Mgr)

Richmond Pressed Metal Works, Inc.   (1)
506 Maury St, Richmond, VA 23224-4120   (100%)
Tel.: (804) 377-9051
Sales Range: $10-24.9 Million
Emp.: 20
Sheet Metal Fabrication
N.A.I.C.S.: 332813
Richard Westbrook (Owner)

DWAIN TAYLOR CHEVROLET-BUICK-GMC
1307 S 12th St, Murray, KY 42071
Tel.: (270) 767-6476
Web Site: https://www.dwaintaylorchevrolet.com
Year Founded: 1969
Sales Range: $10-24.9 Million
Emp.: 50
Car Whslr
N.A.I.C.S.: 441110
Dwain Taylor (Pres)

DWAYNE LANES CHRYSLER DODGE JEEP RAM
10515 Evergreen Way, Everett, WA 98204
Tel.: (425) 267-9000
Web Site: https://www.dwaynelane.com
Year Founded: 1954
Sales Range: $10-24.9 Million
Emp.: 68
Auto Dealers & Distr
N.A.I.C.S.: 441110
Ken Barczyszyn (Controller)

DWC CONSTRUCTION COM-PANY, INC.
1301- 1303 Division St, Nashville, TN 37203
Tel.: (615) 259-3185
Web Site: http://dwccares.com
Sales Range: $10-24.9 Million
Emp.: 35
Civil Engineering Services
N.A.I.C.S.: 237310
John Arndt (Pres & COO)

DWIGHT CAPITAL LLC
787 11th Ave 10th Fl, New York, NY 10019
Tel.: (212) 960-3750   NY
Web Site: http://www.dwightcapital.com
Commercial Real Estate Finance & Investment Services
N.A.I.C.S.: 522320
Adam Sasouness (Co-CEO)
Josh Sasouness (Co-CEO)
Ryan Miles (Mng Dir-Chief LEAN/Healthcare Underwriter)

Subsidiaries:

Love Funding Corporation   (1)
1250 Connecticut Ave NW Ste 310, Washington, DC 20036
Tel.: (202) 887-8475
Web Site: http://www.lovefunding.com
Emp.: 20
Mortgage Lending Services
N.A.I.C.S.: 522292

Dwolla Inc.—(Continued)

DWOLLA INC.
6661 Walnut St Ste 1830, Des
Moines, IA 50309
Tel.: (515) 280-1000
Web Site: http://www.dwolla.com
Sales Range: $10-24.9 Million
Emp.: 30
Financial Software
N.A.I.C.S.: 513210
Ben Milne *(CEO)*
Charise Flynn *(COO)*

DWWA INC.
8375 E La Palma Ave, Anaheim, CA
92807
Tel.: (714) 777-3300
Web Site:
    http://www.weircanyonacura.com
Sales Range: $10-24.9 Million
Emp.: 40
New & Used Automobiles Dealer
N.A.I.C.S.: 441110
A.J. D'Amato Jr. *(Pres)*

**DWYER PRODUCTS CORPO-
RATION**
1000 Davey Rd # 100, Woodridge, IL
60517-5142
Tel.: (219) 874-5236
Web Site: http://dwyerproducts.com
Year Founded: 1926
Sales Range: $75-99.9 Million
Emp.: 75
Compact Kitchens, Custom Wet Bars
& Under Counter Refrigerators Mfr
N.A.I.C.S.: 337126
Suzanne M. Buelow *(VP-Healthcare
Sls)*
Emily Rudolph *(Mgr-Mktg)*

Subsidiaries:

Dwyer Kitchens   (1)
418 N Calumet Ave, Michigan City, IN
46360
Tel.: (219) 873-0358
Rev.: $1,000,000
Compact Kitchens Mfr
N.A.I.C.S.: 337126

DX HOLDING COMPANY INC.
300 Jackson Hill St, Houston, TX
77007
Tel.: (713) 863-1947
Web Site:
    http://www.dixiechemical.com
Rev.: $158,000,000
Emp.: 50
Industrial Organic Chemicals
N.A.I.C.S.: 325199
S. Reed Morian *(Chm, Pres & CEO)*

Subsidiaries:

DPC Industries Inc.   (1)
300 Jackson Hill St, Houston, TX 77007
Tel.: (713) 863-1947
Rev.: $36,500,000
Emp.: 4
Oil Additives
N.A.I.C.S.: 424690
S. Reed Morian *(Chm)*

DX Distributors Inc.   (1)
300 Jackson Hill St, Houston, TX 77007
Tel.: (713) 863-1947
Sales Range: $10-24.9 Million
Emp.: 42
Chemicals & Allied Products
N.A.I.C.S.: 424690

DX Service Company Inc.   (1)
12711 Blume Rd, Houston, TX 77034
Tel.: (281) 922-1776
Web Site: http://www.dxcharter.com
Rev.: $11,300,000
Emp.: 6
Chemicals & Allied Products
N.A.I.C.S.: 424690

DXI Industries Inc.   (1)

300 Jackson Hill St, Houston, TX 77007
Tel.: (713) 863-1947
Rev.: $8,700,000
Industrial Gases
N.A.I.C.S.: 424690
Rick C. Karm *(Pres)*

Dixie Chemical Company, Inc.   (1)
10601 Bay Area Blvd, Pasadena, TX 77057
Tel.: (281) 474-3271
Web Site: http://www.dixiechemical.com
Chemical Product Mfr & Distr
N.A.I.C.S.: 325199
Gary MacDonell *(Dir-Tech)*
Michael Gromacki *(Sr VP)*
Kelli Gregory *(Dir-Admin)*
Michael Campbell *(CFO & VP-Fin)*
Karana Shah *(VP-Tech)*
Dominic Rende *(Dir-ASA Product Sls)*
William Snyder *(VP-Sls-Fuel & Lubricant)*

DYENOMITE, LLC
3706 Lacon Rd, Hilliard, OH 43026
Tel.: (614) 767-1958
Web Site:
    https://www.dyenomite.com
Year Founded: 2001
Sales Range: $1-9.9 Million
Emp.: 50
Tie-Dyed Clothing Distr & Whslr
N.A.I.C.S.: 458110
Nathan Brown *(Pres)*
Michael Campbell *(Co-Owner)*

Subsidiaries:

Ares Sportswear   (1)
3704 Lacon Rd, Hilliard, OH
43026   (100%)
Tel.: (614) 767-1950
Web Site: http://www.areswear.com
Sportswear Screen-Printing & Embroidery
Mfr
N.A.I.C.S.: 323113
Michael Campbell *(Co-Owner)*
Michael Leibrand *(Co-Owner)*
Jaclyn Miller *(Mgr-Mktg)*

DYER AUTO AUCTION INC.
641 Joliet St, Dyer, IN 46311
Tel.: (219) 865-2361
Web Site:
    http://www.dyerauction.com
Sales Range: $10-24.9 Million
Emp.: 55
Coastal & Great Lake Freight Trans-
portation Services
N.A.I.C.S.: 483113
Buzz Cotton *(Pres)*
Mike Dean *(Gen Mgr)*
Jason Cotton *(Mgr-Fleet & Lease)*
Curt Cable *(Mgr-Lot)*
Rocco Maggiore *(Mgr-Credit)*
Linn Cmelo *(Bus Mgr)*
Terry Anderson *(Dir-IT)*

**DYER CONSTRUCTION COM-
PANY, INC.**
1716 Sheffield Ave, Dyer, IN 46311
Tel.: (219) 865-2961
Web Site:
    https://www.dyerconstruction.com
Rev.: $24,100,000
Emp.: 40
Site Preparation Contractor
N.A.I.C.S.: 238910
Janet Furman *(Pres)*
Greg Furman *(VP)*
Kevin Horn *(Mgr)*
Dave Neises *(Mgr)*

**DYERSBURG ELECTRIC SYS-
TEM**
211 E Ct St, Dyersburg, TN 38024-
4741
Tel.: (731) 287-4600
Web Site: https://www.despower.com
Year Founded: 1902
Sales Range: $25-49.9 Million
Emp.: 44
Eletric Power Generation Services

N.A.I.C.S.: 221118
Stephen M. Lane *(Pres & CEO)*
Robert A. Smith *(VP-Construction)*
Robby N. Richards *(VP-Fin)*

DYKE INDUSTRY, INC.
309 Ctr St, Little Rock, AR 72201-
2603
Tel.: (501) 376-2921   AR
Web Site: http://www.dykeind.com
Year Founded: 1865
Sales Range: $200-249.9 Million
Emp.: 600
Rough, Dressed & Finished Lumber,
Plywood & Millwork Distr & Whslr
N.A.I.C.S.: 423310
James T. Dyke *(Chm)*
Wendy Bush *(Treas)*

DYKEMA ARCHITECTS INC.
807 N Uppr Broadway Ste 101, Cor-
pus Christi, TX 78401
Tel.: (361) 882-8171
Web Site:
    https://www.levydykema.com
Rev.: $1,208,000
Emp.: 100
Architectural Services
N.A.I.C.S.: 541310
Bibiana B. Dykema *(Pres & Architect)*
John R. Dykema Jr. *(VP & Architect)*

Subsidiaries:

Cotera Reed Architects Inc.   (1)
812 San Antonio St Ste 406, Austin, TX
78701-2224
Tel.: (512) 472-3406
Web Site: http://www.coterareed.com
Architectural Services
N.A.I.C.S.: 541310
Juan Cotera *(Founder)*

DYKEMA GOSSETT PLLC
400 Renaissance Ctr, Detroit, MI
48243
Tel.: (313) 568-6800
Web Site: http://www.dykema.com
Year Founded: 1926
Sales Range: $150-199.9 Million
Emp.: 340
Law firm
N.A.I.C.S.: 541110
Peter M. Kellett *(Chm & CEO)*
Lori McAllister *(Gen Counsel)*
Paul R. Boken *(COO-Chicago)*
Laura C. Baucus *(Dir-Automotive In-
dus Grp)*

**DYKES LUMBER COMPANY
INC.**
1899 Park Ave, Weehawken, NJ
07087
Tel.: (201) 867-0391   NJ
Web Site:
    https://www.dykeslumber.com
Year Founded: 1973
Sales Range: $25-49.9 Million
Emp.: 190
Lumber & Other Building Materials
Distr
N.A.I.C.S.: 423310
Hank Clasen *(Mgr)*

DYKNOW
7602 E 88th Pl, Indianapolis, IN
46256
Tel.: (317) 275-5900
Web Site: http://www.dyknow.com
Year Founded: 2003
Sales Range: $1-9.9 Million
Emp.: 22
Custom Computer Programing
N.A.I.C.S.: 449210
David B. Becker *(Founder & CEO)*
Brian Banta *(Mgr-Customer Success)*

Frank Gilbert *(Sr Mgr-Customer Success)*
Michael Vasey *(VP-Customer Experience)*

DYM ENERGY CORPORATION
2591 Dallas Pkwy Ste 102, Frisco,
TX 75034
Tel.: (972) 963-0001   NV
Year Founded: 2006
Sales Range: Less than $1 Million
Oil & Gas Exploration Services
N.A.I.C.S.: 213112
Kevin B. Halter Jr. *(Pres, CEO, CFO,
Chief Acctg Officer, Treas & Sec)*

DYMAX CORP.
318 Industrial Ln, Torrington, CT
06790
Tel.: (860) 482-1010
Web Site: http://www.dymax.com
Rev.: $12,663,735
Emp.: 160
Adhesives
N.A.I.C.S.: 325520
Greg Bachmann *(Chm)*
Dennis Dell'Accio *(Mgr-Equipment)*
Mike Acker *(Dir-Sls-Americas)*
Steven Suzuki *(Global Acct Mgr-
West)*
David Shaskey *(Mgr-Territory Sls)*
Marco Reyes *(Sr Mgr-Sls-West)*
Jason Maupin *(Chief Bus Dev & R&D
Officer)*
Robert Palmer *(Dir-Electronic Bus
Dev-Global)*
Aaron Mambrino *(Pres-Americas)*
Beth Schivley *(Dir-Mktg Comm-
Global)*

DYN
150 Dow St, Manchester, NH 03101
Tel.: (603) 668-4998
Web Site: http://www.dyn.com
Year Founded: 1998
Sales Range: $10-24.9 Million
Emp.: 250
Data Processing Services
N.A.I.C.S.: 518210
Josh Delisle *(VP-Sls-North America)*
Matt Toy *(Sr VP-Customer Experi-
ence)*
Cory von Wallenstein *(CTO)*
Kyle York *(Chief Strategy Officer)*
Paul Heywood *(Dir-Revenue-EMEA)*
Scott Hilton *(Exec VP-Product)*
Brian Hayes *(VP-Fin)*
Dave Allen *(Gen Counsel & Sr VP)*
Chris Brenton *(Sr Dir-Ops & Security)*
Phil Hochmuth *(Head-Market Intelli-
gence)*
Kevin Bisson *(CFO)*
Jeremy P. Hitchcock *(Co-Founder &
Chm)*

DYN365, INC.
500 Technology Dr Ste 200, Irvine,
CA 92618
Tel.: (512) 566-4103   DE
Web Site:
    http://www.restaurant365.com
Year Founded: 2012
Software Publisher
N.A.I.C.S.: 513210
Tony Smith *(Co-Founder & CEO)*
John Moody *(Co-Founder)*
Morgan Harris *(Co-Founder)*

Subsidiaries:

Compeat, Inc.   (1)
9500 Arboretum Blvd Ste 140, Austin, TX
78759
Tel.: (512) 279-0771
Web Site: http://www.compeat.com
Computer Related Services
N.A.I.C.S.: 541519

Paul Dodd *(Sr VP-Sls)*
Carol Dunnigan *(Sr VP-People & Culture)*
Brendan Reidy *(CEO)*

Expand, LLC (1)
4040 Embassy Pkwy Ste 320, Akron, OH
44333-8354
Web Site: https://www.expandshare.com
Professional, Scientific & Technical Services
N.A.I.C.S.: 541990
Eric Harsh *(Co-Founder & CEO)*

DYNA CONTRACTING
1537 NW Ballard Way, Seattle, WA
98107
Tel.: (206) 297-6369
Web Site: https://dyna.builders
Year Founded: 1999
Sales Range: $10-24.9 Million
Emp.: 32
Design, Remodeling & Home Building
N.A.I.C.S.: 541490
Stacey Rains *(Asst Project Mgr)*
Merrylin Zawislak *(Asst Project Mgr)*
Ren Chandler *(Founder & Pres)*
Howard Freeman *(Project Mgr)*
Andy Mroczek *(Project Mgr)*
Gus Poole *(Project Mgr)*

DYNA-BRITE LIGHTING, INC.
200 McElhiney Rd, Dickson, TN
37055
Tel.: (901) 324-5588
Web Site: https://www.dyna-brite.com
Rev.: $10,000,000
Emp.: 7
Lighting Fixtures, Commercial & Industrial
N.A.I.C.S.: 423610
Hardy Hassell *(Pres)*

DYNA-EMPIRE, INC.
1075 Stewart Ave, Garden City, NY
11530
Tel.: (516) 222-2700
Web Site: https://www.dyna-empire.com
Year Founded: 1941
Emp.: 167
Aerospace & Marine Industry Equipment Mfr
N.A.I.C.S.: 334511
Louis David *(Dir-Mfg)*
Richard Bradley *(Dir-QA)*

DYNA-LIFT, INC.
184 Western Blvd, Montgomery, AL
36108-1600
Tel.: (334) 263-1600
Web Site: https://www.dyna-lift.com
Year Founded: 1981
Sales Range: $10-24.9 Million
Emp.: 61
Lift Truck, Handtruck, Industrial Battery & Dock Equipment Whslr
N.A.I.C.S.: 423830
Craig S. Pinson *(Pres)*
David Abbott *(Owner)*

DYNABRADE, INC.
8989 Sheridan Rd, Clarence, NY
14031-1419
Tel.: (716) 631-0100   DE
Web Site: http://www.dynabrade.com
Year Founded: 1965
Sales Range: $50-74.9 Million
Emp.: 150
Portable Abrasive Power Tools Mfr &
Whslr
N.A.I.C.S.: 333991
Walter Welsch *(Founder)*
Michael Buffamonti *(Pres)*
Michael Saraf *(VP-Sls-Global)*

Subsidiaries:

Dynabrade Europe S.a.r.l. (1)
Zone Artisanale Op Tomm 6, 5485,
Wormeldange-Haut, Luxembourg

Tel.: (352) 768 494 1
Web Site: http://www.dynabrade.com
Power-Driven Handtool Mfr
N.A.I.C.S.: 333991
Cengiz Ceylan *(Dir-Mktg & Sls)*

Dynabrade India Abrasive Power
Tools Pvt. Ltd. (1)
EL-54 TTC Industrial Area, M I D C Mahape
Electronic Zone, Navi Mumbai, 400710,
India
Tel.: (91) 22 2763 2226
Emp.: 20
Power-Driven Handtool Mfr
N.A.I.C.S.: 333991
Nischal Sachdev *(Mng Dir)*

Dynabrade International Sales
Corporation (1)
8989 Sheridan Dr, Clarence, NY 14031-
1490
Tel.: (716) 631-0100
Web Site: http://www.dynabrade.com
Sales Range: $10-24.9 Million
Emp.: 100
Industrial Supplies Whslr
N.A.I.C.S.: 423840
Walter Welsch *(Pres)*

Dynabrade do Brasil LTDA. (1)
Rua Martim Francisco 141 2 andar, 09541-
330, Sao Caetano do Sul, Brazil
Tel.: (55) 11 4390 0133
Power-Driven Handtool Mfr
N.A.I.C.S.: 333991

DYNACO INC.
10 E River Park Pl E Ste 104,
Fresno, CA 93720-1534
Tel.: (559) 485-8520
Web Site:
     http://www.dynacofoods.com
Rev.: $15,464,976
Emp.: 35
Groceries, General Line
N.A.I.C.S.: 424410
Dmitri Istomin *(CFO)*

DYNACQ HEALTHCARE, INC.
4301 Vista Rd, Pasadena, TX 77504
Tel.: (713) 378-2000   DE
Web Site: https://www.dynacq.com
Sales Range: $1-9.9 Million
Emp.: 96
Holding Company; Acute Care Hospital Management Services
N.A.I.C.S.: 622310
Hemant Khemka *(CFO)*
Ringo Cheng *(Dir-IT)*
Eric K. Chan *(Pres & CEO)*

Subsidiaries:

Surgery Specialty Hospitals of
America (SSHA) (1)
4301 Vista Rd, Pasadena, TX 77504-2117
Tel.: (713) 378-3000
Web Site: http://www.ssha.us.com
Sales Range: $50-74.9 Million
Hospital Services
N.A.I.C.S.: 622110

DYNALENE INC.
5250 W Coplay Rd, Whitehall, PA
18052
Tel.: (610) 262-9686
Web Site: https://www.dynalene.com
Sales Range: $1-9.9 Million
Emp.: 14
Dental Checkup Plans Services
N.A.I.C.S.: 541611
Daniel Loikits *(Chm)*
David Arcury *(VP-Sls-Latin America &
Mexico)*

DYNAMAC INTERNATIONAL INC.
1901 Research Blvd Ste 220, Rockville, MD 20850-3268
Tel.: (301) 417-9800
Web Site: http://www.dynamac.com
Year Founded: 1974

Sales Range: $10-24.9 Million
Emp.: 35
Facilities Support Services
N.A.I.C.S.: 561210
Diana MacArthur *(Chm & CEO)*
Douglas L. Britt *(Pres & COO)*

Subsidiaries:

Dynamac Corporation (1)
1901 Research Blvd Ste 220, Rockville, MD
20850
Tel.: (301) 417-6145
Web Site: http://www.dynamac.com
Sales Range: $10-24.9 Million
Emp.: 30
Environmental Consulting Services
N.A.I.C.S.: 541690

DYNAMEDIA OF AMERICA, INC.
205 S Hoover Blvd Ste 102, Tampa,
FL 33609-3594
Tel.: (813) 287-8177
Year Founded: 1984
Rev.: $15,000,000
Emp.: 3
Automotive
N.A.I.C.S.: 541810
Cody Lowry *(Owner)*
Don Poole *(Mgr-Production)*
Anthony J. Pesce *(VP-Creative Svcs)*
Diana Tomasello *(Media Buyer)*

DYNAMIC AIR INC.
1125 Willow Lake Blvd, Saint Paul,
MN 55110
Tel.: (651) 484-2900
Web Site:
     https://www.dynamicair.com
Year Founded: 1969
Sales Range: $25-49.9 Million
Emp.: 150
Conveyors & Conveying Equipment
Mfr
N.A.I.C.S.: 333922
James R. Steele *(Pres)*
Carol Steele *(Mgr-Mktg)*
Michael Steele *(VP)*
Gregory Steele *(VP)*
Jeffie Howe *(Controller)*

DYNAMIC AUTOMATION
4525 Runway St, Simi Valley, CA
93063
Tel.: (805) 584-8476
Web Site:
     http://www.dynamicautomation.com
Year Founded: 1986
Rev.: $4,500,000
Emp.: 17
Industrial Machinery & Equipment
N.A.I.C.S.: 423830
Marc Freedman *(Pres)*
Teri Mabry *(Office Mgr)*

DYNAMIC BRANDS
2701 Emerywood Pkwy Ste 101,
Richmond, VA 23294
Tel.: (804) 262-3000
Web Site:
     https://www.dynamicbrands.com
Year Founded: 2004
Sales Range: $25-49.9 Million
Emp.: 75
Holding Company
N.A.I.C.S.: 551112
Craig Ramsbottom *(Pres)*
Caroline Allison *(Asst Product Mgr-
Product Dev Team)*
Ashley Hicks *(Project Mgr-Ops Team)*
Alec Christian *(Project Mgr-IT-Ops
Team)*
Sarah Starke *(Coord-Sls)*
Carlton Mitchell *(Coord-Customer
Svcs)*
Perry Hilbert *(Sls Mgr)*

DYNAMIC BUILDERS INC.
2114 S Hill St, Los Angeles, CA
90007
Tel.: (213) 746-6630
Web Site:
     http://www.dynamicbuilders.com
Sales Range: $25-49.9 Million
Emp.: 9
Build-to-Suit Design & Construction
N.A.I.C.S.: 236210
L. Ramon Bonin *(CEO)*
Ramon Bonin *(Pres)*
Ken Jackson *(Dir-Sls & Acq)*
Ariel Trinidad *(Controller)*

DYNAMIC BUILDING CORP.
51 Pennwood Pl Ste 200, Warrendale, PA 15086
Tel.: (724) 772-9020   PA
Web Site:
     http://www.dynamicbuilding.com
Year Founded: 1991
Sales Range: $10-24.9 Million
Emp.: 30
Nonresidential Construction Services
N.A.I.C.S.: 236220
Joe Zsolcsak *(Controller)*
Larry Kiec *(Dir-Bus Dev)*
T. J. Mattey *(Project Mgr)*

DYNAMIC COMPUTER CORPORATION
23400 Industrial Park Ct, Farmington
Hills, MI 48335
Tel.: (248) 473-2200
Web Site: http://www.dcc-online.com
Year Founded: 1979
Sales Range: $10-24.9 Million
Emp.: 25
IT & Hardware Procurement Services
N.A.I.C.S.: 541519
Fida H. Bohra *(Founder & Chm)*
Farida Ali *(Pres & CEO)*
Casie Melady *(VP-Client Svcs)*
Lori Kasparian *(Sr Acct Mgr)*
Amy Courter *(COO)*

DYNAMIC COMPUTING SERVICES CORP.
115 Wild Basin Rd Ste 107, West
Lake Hills, TX 78746-3305
Tel.: (512) 493-9703
Web Site: http://www.dcshq.com
Custom Computer Programming Services
N.A.I.C.S.: 541511

Subsidiaries:

Coastal Healthcare Consulting,
Inc. (1)
6808 220th St SW Ste 204, Mountlake Terrace, WA 98043
Tel.: (206) 324-6540
Web Site: http://www.coastalhealthcare.com
Sales Range: $1-9.9 Million
Emp.: 50
Health Care Consulting Services
N.A.I.C.S.: 541618
Patricia Oligmueller *(Sr Exec VP)*
Amy Noel *(CEO)*
Shirley Pruitt *(Sr Exec VP)*
Don Darling *(Dir-IT)*
Kae Kamiya *(Dir-Fin & HR)*

DYNAMIC CONCEPTS INC.
1730 17th St NE, Washington, DC
20002
Tel.: (202) 944-8787   DC
Web Site: https://www.dcihq.com
Year Founded: 1979
Sales Range: $10-24.9 Million
Emp.: 60
Network Solutions Services
N.A.I.C.S.: 517121
Pedro Alfonso *(Co-Founder, Chm &
CEO)*
Ronald E. Watkins *(COO)*

Dynamic Concepts Inc.—(Continued)

Craig Fitzgerald *(Gen Mgr-Utility Infrastructure Svcs)*
Gwen Tharpe *(Mgr-HR)*
Renee Martin *(Project Mgr)*
Rolle Chris *(Project Mgr-Comm)*
Nathan Hardy *(CTO & Dir-Enterprise Solutions)*
Kathleen Yadvish *(Mgr-Ops)*
Benjamin Peasant *(Sr VP-Federal Sls)*

DYNAMIC DECISIONS INC.
2709 Hamilton Blvd, South Plainfield, NJ 07080-2515
Tel.: (908) 755-5000   NY
Web Site:
   http://www.ddicomputer.com
Year Founded: 1978
Sales Range: $10-24.9 Million
Emp.: 10
Electronic Computer Services
N.A.I.C.S.: 334111
Alan Fan *(Pres)*
Hui Jin *(Mgr-Pur)*

DYNAMIC DESIGN SOLUTIONS, INC.
11435-A Granite St, Charlotte, NC 28273
Tel.: (803) 548-3609
Web Site:
   http://www.dynamicdesignsolutionsinc.com
Year Founded: 1998
Sales Range: $1-9.9 Million
Emp.: 40
Industrial Machinery Equipment Mfr & Distr
N.A.I.C.S.: 333998
Wayne Smith *(Dir-Engrg)*
Brad DeMarco *(Founder)*

DYNAMIC DIES INC.
1705 Commerce Rd, Holland, OH 43528
Tel.: (419) 865-0249
Web Site:
   https://www.dynamicdies.com
Sales Range: $10-24.9 Million
Emp.: 115
Special Dies & Tools
N.A.I.C.S.: 333248
Tom Bruno *(Mgr-Graphics Production)*
Bud Bigley *(Dir-IT)*
Jim Louy *(Mgr-Transportation-Natl)*
Jean Costilla *(Supvr-Art Dept)*
Kevin Koelsch *(VP-Ops)*

DYNAMIC DISPLAYS, INC.
1625 Westgate Rd, Eau Claire, WI 54703
Tel.: (715) 835-9440   WI
Web Site:
   http://www.dynamicdisplay.com
Year Founded: 1991
Sales Range: $1-9.9 Million
Emp.: 11
Computer Systems Design
N.A.I.C.S.: 541512
Michael R. Conlin *(Pres)*
Kathy White *(Mgr-Acctg)*
Oscar Martinez *(VP-Engrg)*
Tom Padjen *(Mgr-Pur)*

DYNAMIC ENGINEERING INC.
221 Cessna St, Watertown, SD 57201
Tel.: (605) 886-5544
Web Site:
   https://www.dynamicengineering.net
Year Founded: 1972
Sales Range: $10-24.9 Million
Emp.: 140

Machine Shop, Jobbing & Repair
N.A.I.C.S.: 332710
Becky Davis *(CFO)*

DYNAMIC FASTENER SERVICE INC.
9911 E 53rd St, Kansas City, MO 64133
Tel.: (816) 358-9898
Web Site:
   https://www.dynamicfastener.com
Sales Range: $25-49.9 Million
Emp.: 150
Hardware
N.A.I.C.S.: 423710
Kevin Perez *(Chm)*
Paul Smith *(CFO)*

DYNAMIC HEALTHIER CONSULTANT
3359 Main St, Skokie, IL 60076
Tel.: (847) 679-8219
Sales Range: $25-49.9 Million
Emp.: 25
Billing & Bookkeeping Service
N.A.I.C.S.: 541219
Marshall Mauer *(Pres)*
Mauer Aaron *(VP)*
Steve Levy *(CFO)*

DYNAMIC HOMES, INC.
525 Roosevelt Ave, Detroit Lakes, MN 56501-2826
Tel.: (218) 847-2611   MN
Web Site:
   https://www.dynamichomes.com
Year Founded: 1970
Sales Range: $10-24.9 Million
Emp.: 112
Construction & Contracting Services
N.A.I.C.S.: 321992
Ronald Gustafson *(Sec)*
Paul Nord *(Controller)*
Jason Jendrysik *(Mgr-Svc & IT)*

DYNAMIC HYDROCARBONS LTD.
7001 Winterberry Dr, Austin, TX 78750
Tel.: (512) 289-2489   NV
Year Founded: 2009
Oil & Gas Exploration Services
N.A.I.C.S.: 211120
Ronald Petrucci *(Pres, CEO, CFO, Treas & Sec)*

DYNAMIC INTERNATIONAL USA, INC.
2900 69th St, North Bergen, NJ 07047
Tel.: (973) 344-6300
Web Site:
   http://www.dynamiconline.com
Rev.: $22,300,000
Emp.: 126
Trucking, Distribution & Warehousing Services
N.A.I.C.S.: 484110
Thomas Gambino *(Pres & CEO)*
Leif Arntzen *(Sr VP-Bus Dev)*
Richard Morabito *(CFO)*
Andrew D. Rotondi *(COO)*

Subsidiaries:

Dynamic Worldwide West, Inc.   **(1)**
14141 Alondra Blvd, Santa Fe Springs, CA 90670
Tel.: (562) 407-1000
Logistic Services
N.A.I.C.S.: 541614
John Belsito *(Pres)*

DYNAMIC LANGUAGE CENTER, LTD.
15215 52nd Ave S Ste 100, Seattle, WA 98118

Tel.: (206) 244-6709   WA
Web Site:
   https://www.dynamiclanguage.com
Year Founded: 1985
Sales Range: $1-9.9 Million
Emp.: 47
Language Translation Services
N.A.I.C.S.: 541930
Maria Antezana *(CEO)*
Audrey Dubois-Boutet *(Supvr-Quality Control)*

DYNAMIC LIVING, INC.
95 W Dudley Town Rd, Bloomfield, CT 06002
Tel.: (860) 683-4442
Web Site: http://www.dynamic-living.com
Rev.: $1,900,000
Emp.: 7
Mail-Order Houses
N.A.I.C.S.: 332215
Andrea Tannenbaum *(Pres)*

DYNAMIC LOGISTIX, LLC
7220 W 98th Ter, Overland Park, KS 66212
Tel.: (913) 274-3800
Web Site:
   http://www.dynamiclogistix.com
Year Founded: 2015
Sales Range: $50-74.9 Million
Emp.: 50
Logistic Services
N.A.I.C.S.: 541614
Jeff Auslander *(CEO & Mng Partner)*
Jason Yeager *(COO & Partner)*
Casey Schirk *(Chief Revenue Officer)*
Aimee Clardy *(VP-Fin)*

DYNAMIC MANAGEMENT COMPANY LLC
313 E Main St, Hendersonville, TN 37075
Tel.: (615) 277-1234   AZ
Web Site:
   http://www.dynamicusa.com
Sales Range: $900-999.9 Million
Emp.: 6,300
Restaurant Owner & Operator
N.A.I.C.S.: 722511
Robert Langford *(Chm/CEO-Dynamic Hospitality, LLC)*
Ivan Peraza *(Dir-IT)*
Kori Langford *(Dir-Brand Dev)*

Subsidiaries:

Black-eyed Pea Restaurants Inc.   **(1)**
313 E Main St Ste 2, Hendersonville, TN 37075   **(100%)**
Tel.: (615) 277-1234
Web Site: http://www.theblackeyedpea.com
Sales Range: $10-24.9 Million
Emp.: 10
Full-Service Restaurants
N.A.I.C.S.: 722511
Bob Langford *(Chm & Owner)*

DYNAMIC MARKETING, INC.
400 Cabot Dr Unit B, Hamilton, NJ 08690
Tel.: (718) 649-9203   NY
Web Site: https://www.dmiorg.co
Year Founded: 1957
Co-op Business; Electrical Appliances Marketer
N.A.I.C.S.: 423620
Lucina Montalvo *(Supvr-Inventory Control)*
Anthony Lopez *(Mgr-Night Crew)*

DYNAMIC MECHANICAL CONTRACTORS INC.
15 Warren St Ste 31, Hackensack, NJ 07601
Tel.: (201) 488-3400

Web Site:
   http://www.dynamiccontractors.com
Rev.: $18,212,904
Emp.: 4
Mechanical Contractor
N.A.I.C.S.: 238220
Gene Bolla *(Pres)*
Chris Haschak *(VP)*

DYNAMIC METHODS
9070 Irvine Ctr Dr Ste 260, Irvine, CA 92618-4692
Tel.: (949) 579-9522
Web Site:
   http://www.dynamicmethods.com
Process, Physical Distribution & Logistics Consulting Services
N.A.I.C.S.: 541614
John Moody *(Co-Founder & Partner)*

DYNAMIC MOBILE IMAGING
PO Box 17588, Richmond, VA 23226
Tel.: (804) 282-9729
Web Site:
   https://www.dynamicmobileimaging.com
Year Founded: 2005
Sales Range: $1-9.9 Million
Emp.: 70
24HR Mobile X-Ray Services
N.A.I.C.S.: 621512
Debbie Berger *(Owner)*
Tim Forehand *(VP-Ops)*
Pam Overstreet *(Mgr-Sls & Mktg)*

DYNAMIC RECYCLING
N 5549 County Rd Z, Onalaska, WI 54650
Tel.: (608) 781-4030
Web Site:
   http://www.dynamicrecycling.com
Year Founded: 2007
Sales Range: $1-9.9 Million
Emp.: 175
Recycles Electronics, Purchases Electronics Scrap & Provides IT Asset Management Services
N.A.I.C.S.: 423930
Miles Harter *(CEO)*
Curt Greeno *(Pres)*

Subsidiaries:

Minnesota Computers
Corporation   **(1)**
5000 Winnetka Ave N, Minneapolis, MN 55428-3079
Tel.: (763) 577-0803
Web Site:
   http://www.minnesotacomputers.com
Sales Range: $1-9.9 Million
Emp.: 24
Computer Peripheral Equipment Whslr
N.A.I.C.S.: 423430
Jay Faber *(Mgr-Sls)*

DYNAMIC RESOURCE GROUP, INC.
269 S Jefferson, Berne, IN 46711-1138
Tel.: (260) 589-4000   IN
Web Site:
   https://www.drgnetwork.com
Year Founded: 1925
Sales Range: $25-49.9 Million
Emp.: 90
Catalogs & Magazines Publisher
N.A.I.C.S.: 513120
Roger Muselman *(Chm)*
Tyler Kitt *(CEO-EP Graphics & Treas-DRG)*
Thomas C. Muselman *(Pres)*
Charles Croft *(CEO)*
Michele Fortune *(Exec VP)*

Subsidiaries:

Annie's Publishing, LLC   **(1)**
306 E Parr Rd, Berne, IN 46711-1138
Tel.: (260) 589-4000

Web Site: http://www.annies-publishing.com
Emp.: 80
Magazines & Catalogs Publisher
N.A.I.C.S.: 513120
Michelle Thorpe (Dir-Adv)

Subsidiary (Domestic):

Country Sampler, LLC (2)
707 Kautz Rd, Saint Charles, IL 60174
Tel.: (630) 377-8000
Web Site: http://www.countrysampler.com
Magazine Publisher
N.A.I.C.S.: 513120
Margaret B. Kernan (Pres & Publr)
Denise Boba (VP-Circulation & Mktg)

E.P. Graphics, Inc. (1)
169 S Jefferson St, Berne, IN 46711-2157
Tel.: (260) 589-2145
Web Site: http://www.epgraphics.com
Sales Range: $25-49.9 Million
Printing Services
N.A.I.C.S.: 323111
Tyler Kitt (Pres & CEO)
John Richert (Mgr-Quality Control & Customer Svcs)
Jan Simmons (Mgr-Sls)

Strategic Fulfillment Group LLC (1)
111 Corporate Dr, Big Sandy, TX 75755
Tel.: (903) 636-4011
Web Site: http://www.strategicfulfillment.com
Fulfillment Services
N.A.I.C.S.: 561499
Roger Muselman (Chm)
John Trotter (Dir-Info Svcs)
Sally Allen (Dir-Bus Dev)
Nancy White (Dir-Sls)
Eric Wilson (Dir-Decision Mgmt Analytics)
Tony Pytlak (Pres & COO)
Mark Ray (Dir-Customer Svc/Mail Processing)
Pam Prather (Mgr-HR)
Sundi Kissinger (Dir-Fin)
Ken Smith (Dir-Partner Svcs)
Geroge Strub (Mgr-Info Svcs Ops)
Karl Wilson (Mgr-Applications Dev)

DYNAMIC RESOURCES, INC.
25 W 31st St, New York, NY 10001
Tel.: (212) 209-1155
Web Site: http://www.driglobal.com
Year Founded: 1994
Rev.: $15,139,000
Emp.: 20
Site Survey & Retail Stores Installation Services
N.A.I.C.S.: 541370
Evan Giniger (Founder & Pres)
Debra Gambino (VP-Fin)
Anastasia Melnicova (Project Mgr)
Eamonn Kelly (Project Mgr)
Gerry Walsh (Mng Dir)
Jeff Rowe (Supvr-Acct)
Laurie Chalmers (Deputy Mng Dir)
Luciana Alemanno (Project Coord)
Mark Hilzenrath (VP)
Rich Bornheimer (Acct Dir-Natl)
Scott Bernstein (VP)
Selena Bekakis (Mgr-Acct)

DYNAMIC SECURITY INC.
1102 Woodward Ave, Muscle Shoals, AL 35661
Tel.: (256) 383-5798
Web Site: https://www.dynamicsecurity.org
Sales Range: $10-24.9 Million
Emp.: 1,200
Security Guard Services
N.A.I.C.S.: 561612
Scott A. Riddle (Exec VP)
James Donnelly (Gen Mgr-Govt Svcs)
Jim Banta (VP)
John C. Riddle Sr. (Pres & CEO)

DYNAMIC SOLUTIONS GROUP INC.
785 County Rd 1, Palm Harbor, FL 34683

Tel.: (727) 734-4374
Web Site: https://www.dsolutionsgroup.com
Year Founded: 2000
Sales Range: $1-9.9 Million
Emp.: 20
Computer Related Services
N.A.I.C.S.: 541519
James M. Watt (Co-Founder, Pres & CEO)
John P. Connelly (Co-Founder)

DYNAMIC SYSTEMS TECHNOLOGY, INC.
3554 Chain Bridge Rd Ste 200, Fairfax, VA 22030
Tel.: (571) 321-0460
Web Site: http://www.dystech.com
Year Founded: 1995
Rev.: $19,300,000
Emp.: 260
Custom Computer Programming Services
N.A.I.C.S.: 517810
Laxmi Jain (CEO)
Atul Jain (Pres)

DYNAMIC SYSTEMS, INC.
124 Maryland St, El Segundo, CA 90245
Tel.: (310) 337-4400 CA
Web Site: http://www.dynasys.com
Year Founded: 1990
Sales Range: $10-24.9 Million
Emp.: 40
Data Security Storage Solutions
N.A.I.C.S.: 334112
Kristi Giordano (Acct Mgr)
Darlene Mircse Teel (Dir-Fin)

DYNAMIC TEAM SPORTS INC.
454 Acord Ln, Downingtown, PA 19335
Tel.: (610) 518-3300
Web Site: http://www.dynamicteamsports.com
Sales Range: $10-24.9 Million
Emp.: 60
Team Athletic Uniforms Mfr
N.A.I.C.S.: 315250
Scott A. Samter (Pres)

DYNAMICARD, INC.
332 S Juniper St Ste 108, Escondido, CA 92025
Web Site: http://www.dynamicard.com
Year Founded: 2008
Sales Range: $1-9.9 Million
Emp.: 6
Direct Mail & Marketing Services
N.A.I.C.S.: 541860
Ivan Farber (CEO & Founder)

DYNAMICS MARKETING INC.
805 Sunflower Ave, Cooperstown, ND 58425
Tel.: (701) 797-2852
Web Site: https://www.dynamicsmarketing.com
Sales Range: $10-24.9 Million
Emp.: 300
Telemarketing Services
N.A.I.C.S.: 561422
Stacy Somerville (Pres)
Randy Saxberg (CFO)
Patti Bridgeman (Sr Dir-Mktg)

DYNAMICSIGNALS LLC
900 N State St, Lockport, IL 60441
Tel.: (815) 838-0005 IL
Web Site: https://www.dynamicsignals.com
Year Founded: 1970
Sales Range: $50-74.9 Million
Emp.: 20

Data Acquisition & Control Systems Designer, Mfr & Marketer
N.A.I.C.S.: 541512
Steven Krebs (Dir-Engrg-Kinetic Sys Brand)
William A. Boston (Chm & CEO)
Patrick T. Cassady (Exec VP)
Patricia Ramazinski (Dir-HR)
Wayne G. Coppe (Mgr-Pur)
Andre G. Lareau (Pres & COO)
Andrew Dawson (VP & Gen Mgr-GATI)
Natalie Rauworth (Dir-Ops & Mgr-Quality Control)

Subsidiaries:

Preston Kinetic (1)
1450 N Hundley St, Anaheim, CA 92806-1322
Tel.: (714) 632-3700
Sales Range: $10-24.9 Million
Emp.: 6
Computer-Based Data Acquisition & Load Control Systems Mfr
N.A.I.C.S.: 334514

DYNAMIT
274 Marconi Blvd Ste 300, Columbus, OH 43215
Tel.: (614) 538-0095
Web Site: http://www.dynamit.com
Year Founded: 2004
Sales Range: $1-9.9 Million
Emp.: 30
Digital Consultants to Start-Ups & Business-to-Business Companies
N.A.I.C.S.: 541613
Jamie Timm (Partner & Sr Dir-Accts)
Matt Dopkiss (CEO)
Billy Fischer (Dir-Bus Dev)
Sarah Wojta (Acct Coord)
Susan Lauck (Controller)

DYNAMIX GROUP INC.
604 Macy Dr, Roswell, GA 30076
Tel.: (770) 643-8877
Web Site: http://www.dynamixgroup.com
Sales Range: $50-74.9 Million
Emp.: 88
Value-Added Resellers, Computer Systems
N.A.I.C.S.: 541512
Dave Delong (CFO & COO)
Matthew Porreca (Dir-Sls)
Charles Hawkins Jr. (Co-Founder & Pres)

DYNAMIX MECHANICAL, LLC
5910 Benjamin Ctr Dr Ste 120, Tampa, FL 33634
Tel.: (813) 884-5300
Web Site: http://www.dynamixmechanical.com
Year Founded: 2007
Sales Range: $10-24.9 Million
Emp.: 40
Pumping Station Construction Services
N.A.I.C.S.: 237110
Greg Hoch (Office Mgr-HR)
John Hyatt (Project Mgr)

DYNAPATH SYSTEMS, INC.
34155 Industrial Rd, Livonia, MI 48150
Tel.: (248) 488-0440
Web Site: https://www.dynapath.com
Sales Range: $75-99.9 Million
Emp.: 74
CNC Systems & Machine Tools Mfr
N.A.I.C.S.: 423830
Nick Pitsellos (Controller)
Jim McCue (Pres)

DYNAREX CORP

10 Glenshaw St, Orangeburg, NY 10962
Tel.: (845) 365-8200
Web Site: https://www.dynarex.com
Year Founded: 1967
Rev.: $13,000,000
Emp.: 35
Medical Equipment & Supplies
N.A.I.C.S.: 423450
John Moulden (Sr VP-Sls)
Zalman Tenenbaum (CEO)
Bill Roberts (VP-Natl Sls)
John Burns (VP-Mktg)
Mitch Kushner (COO)
Eugene Vorchheimer (CFO-Fin)
Melodi Pomeroy (Sr VP-Mktg)
Ray Ziemba (Sr VP-IT)

DYNARIC, INC.
5740 Bayside Rd, Virginia Beach, VA 23455
Tel.: (757) 460-3794 DE
Web Site: https://www.dynaric.com
Year Founded: 1973
Plastic Strapping Systems Mfr
N.A.I.C.S.: 326199
Joseph Martinez (Pres)

DYNASIL CORPORATION OF AMERICA
200 Baker Ave Ste 301, Concord, MA 01742
Tel.: (978) 759-7201
Web Site: http://www.dynasil.com
Year Founded: 1960
Rev.: $43,701,000
Assets: $30,827,000
Liabilities: $12,039,000
Net Worth: $18,788,000
Earnings: ($370,000)
Emp.: 207
Fiscal Year-end: 09/30/19
Optical Materials, Components, Coatings & Specialized Instruments Mfr
N.A.I.C.S.: 327999
Peter Sulick (Chm, Pres & CEO)
Patricia M. Kehe (Sec)
Gary J. Bishop (Exec VP-Photonics)
Robert J. Bowdring (VP-Financial Integration)
Nirmal Parikh (VP-Mktg)
Holly A. Hicks (CFO & VP)
Patricia Tuohy (VP-Corp Dev)

Subsidiaries:

Dynasil - Synthetic Fused Silica (1)
385 Cooper Rd, West Berlin, NJ 08091
Tel.: (856) 767-4600
Web Site: http://www.dynasil.com
Sales Range: $100-124.9 Million
Synthetic Optical Materials Mfr
N.A.I.C.S.: 327999

Evaporated Metal Films Corporation (1)
239 Cherry St, Ithaca, NY 14850
Tel.: (607) 272-3320
Web Site: http://www.emf-corp.com
Sales Range: $25-49.9 Million
Emp.: 25
Thin Film Coatings Mfr
N.A.I.C.S.: 332812
Paul Schulz (Pres)

Hilger Crystals Ltd. (1)
Unit R1 Westwood Estate, Margate, CT9 4JL, Kent, United Kingdom
Tel.: (44) 1843231166
Web Site: http://www.hilger-crystals.co.uk
Sales Range: $100-124.9 Million
Emp.: 24
Synthetic Crystals Mfr
N.A.I.C.S.: 327999

Optometrics Corporation (1)
8 Nemco Way, Ayer, MA 01432
Tel.: (978) 772-1700
Web Site: http://www.optometrics.com
Sales Range: $25-49.9 Million
Emp.: 55
Optical Component Mfr

Dynasil Corporation of America—(Continued)

N.A.I.C.S.: 333310

RMD Instruments Corporation (1)
44 Hunt St, Watertown, MA 02472
Tel.: (617) 668-6900
Industrial Machinery Mfr
N.A.I.C.S.: 334290

Radiation Monitoring Devices, Inc. (1)
44 Hunt St Ste 2, Watertown, MA 02742
Tel.: (617) 668-6800
Web Site: http://www.rmdinc.com
Sales Range: $10-24.9 Million
Emp.: 78
Radiation, Lead & Chemical Detection Systems Developer & Mfr
N.A.I.C.S.: 334519
Michael R. Squillante (VP-Res)
Joanne Gladstone (VP-Ops)
Kanai Shah (Pres)
Vivek Nagarkar (VP-Imaging Sys)
Patricia McLaughlin (VP-Fin)
Martin Waters (VP-Program Mgmt)

Xcede Technologies, Inc. (1)
1815 14th St NW, Rochester, MN 55901
Tel.: (206) 428-8100
Web Site: http://www.dynasil.com
Biotechnology Research & Development Services
N.A.I.C.S.: 541714

DYNASPLINT SYSTEMS INC.
770 Ritchie Hwy Ste W21, Severna Park, MD 21146
Tel.: (410) 544-9530
Web Site: https://www.dynasplint.com
Rev.: $13,900,000
Emp.: 450
Medical Equipment Rental
N.A.I.C.S.: 532283
George R. Hepburn (Founder & Pres)

DYNASTY CONSOLIDATED INDUSTRIES INCORPORATED
4646 Harry Hines Blvd, Dallas, TX 75235
Tel.: (214) 630-3132
Web Site:
　　http://www.posturebeauty.com
Sales Range: $25-49.9 Million
Emp.: 100
Mattresses & Foundations
N.A.I.C.S.: 337910
Amir Ali Sunderji (Pres)

DYNASTY EQUITY PARTNERS MANAGEMENT, LLC
280 Park Ave 15th Fl, New York, NY 10017
Tel.: (212) 970-9850
Web Site: https://dynastyequity.com
Privater Equity Firm
N.A.I.C.S.: 523999
Jonathan M. Nelson (Co-Founder & Exec Chm)

DYNASTY FASHIONS, INC.
1706 Maple Ave, Los Angeles, CA 90015
Tel.: (213) 748-4380
Sales Range: $25-49.9 Million
Emp.: 32
Women's & Children's Clothing Mfr
N.A.I.C.S.: 424350
Jehuda Abramovich (VP)
Jennifer Chen (Mgr-Production)
Luisa Camarena (Coord-Garment Adv)
Cathy Wong (Coord-Pre-Production)

DYNASTY FOOTWEAR LTD
800 N Sepulveda Blvd, El Segundo, CA 90245
Tel.: (310) 647-6700
Web Site:
　　http://www.dynastyfootwear.com
Rev.: $24,000,000

Emp.: 67
Footwear
N.A.I.C.S.: 424340
Jack E. Silvera (Pres)
Dyn Petersen (Product Mgr-Dev)
Dewi Hartawan (Supvr-AP)

DYNATEC DRILLING, INC.
2200 S 4000 W, Salt Lake City, UT 84120-1235
Tel.: (801) 974-0645
Year Founded: 1988
Sales Range: $10-24.9 Million
Emp.: 400
Fence Installation Services
N.A.I.C.S.: 238990
Noble Larson (Pres)

DYNATECH INTERNATIONAL CORP.
35 Pinelawn Rd Ste 206 E, Melville, NY 11717
Tel.: (631) 243-1700
Web Site:
　　http://www.dynatechintl.com
Year Founded: 1974
Sales Range: $10-24.9 Million
Emp.: 45
Aircraft Engines & Engine Parts Supplier
N.A.I.C.S.: 423860
Issac Robinson (Pres)
Herbert S. Winokur (Chm)
Dixie Newton (CFO & VP-Fin & Admin)

DYNATEX INTERNATIONAL
5577 Skylane Blvd, Santa Rosa, CA 95403-1048
Tel.: (707) 542-4227　　　CA
Web Site: https://www.dynatex.com
Year Founded: 1958
Sales Range: $10-24.9 Million
Emp.: 100
Semiconductor Dicing Equipment Mfr
N.A.I.C.S.: 333515
Kate Henry (CEO)
Leanne Brogan (VP-Mktg)
Leanne Sarcy (CFO)
John Tyler (VP-Mktg)

DYNAXYS LLC
11911 Tech Rd, Silver Spring, MD 20904
Tel.: (301) 622-0900
Web Site: https://www.dynaxys.com
Year Founded: 1982
Rev.: $11,500,000
Emp.: 100
Designer of Customized Data Management Tools: Custom Computer Programming Services
N.A.I.C.S.: 541511
Lisa Miller (Pres)
Catharine Silva (Mgr-HR)
Rodney Wildermuth (VP-Tech)
Cindy Mumford (VP-Tech Svcs)
Kathleen Conley (VP-Ops)

Subsidiaries:

DP Service LLC (1)
11911 Tech Rd, Silver Spring, MD 20904
Tel.: (301) 622-0900
Web Site: http://www.dynaccsys.com
Rev.: $7,000,000
Emp.: 55
Computer Software Development
N.A.I.C.S.: 518210
C. Mumford (VP-Tech Svcs)

DYNIS LLC.
9020 Mendenhall Ct Ste H, Columbia, MD 21045
Tel.: (410) 290-9972
Web Site: http://www.dynis.com
Rev.: $8,500,000
Emp.: 200

Internet Services
N.A.I.C.S.: 517810
Jack Kuchera (Mgr-Quality & Compliance)
Humayun Nasar (Engr-Network)

DYNO OIL CO. INC.
216 E Milwaukee St, Spencer, IA 51301　　　　　　　　　　IA
Tel.: (712) 262-2921
Web Site: http://www.dynooil.com
Year Founded: 1958
Sales Range: $10-24.9 Million
Emp.: 8
Petroleum & Petroleum Products Whslr
N.A.I.C.S.: 424720
Mark W. Nelson (Pres)

DYNOMIGHTY DESIGN
18 Bridge St Ste 4G, Brooklyn, NY 11201
Tel.: (212) 431-3005
Web Site:
　　http://www.Dynomighty.com
Sales Range: $1-9.9 Million
Emp.: 10
Wallets Mfr
N.A.I.C.S.: 316990
Terrence Kelleman (Pres)

DYONYX, L.P.
1235 N Loop W Ste 1220, Houston, TX 77008
Tel.: (713) 830-5900
Web Site: http://www.dyonyx.com
Year Founded: 1996
Rev.: $22,276,000
Emp.: 50
Corporate & Government IT Services
N.A.I.C.S.: 541519
Walter McKinlay (Co-Founder & Dir-Inside)
Chuck Orrico (Pres & CEO)
Patrick Clary (COO & Exec VP)
James Melchor (CTO)
Talbot Theiss (VP-Strategic Acct)

DYSART CORPORATION
60 Elm St, Canal Winchester, OH 43110
Tel.: (614) 837-1201
Web Site: http://www.dysartcorp.com
Sales Range: $25-49.9 Million
Emp.: 30
Custom Packaging
N.A.I.C.S.: 488991
Jeff Jordan (CEO)
Kimberly Basham (Mgr-Safety)

DYSON, DYSON & DUNN INC.
566 Chestnut St Ste 7, Winnetka, IL 60093-2228
Tel.: (847) 441-5517　　　　DE
Web Site:
　　http://www.dysondysondunn.com
Year Founded: 1982
Private Holding Company
N.A.I.C.S.: 551112
Barbara B. Dyson (Principal)
Peter L. Dyson (Principal)

DYSONS INC.
1880 Kimberly Rd, Twin Falls, ID 83301
Tel.: (208) 734-7659
Web Site: http://www.napa.com
Rev.: $18,950,000
Emp.: 35
Automotive Supplies & Parts
N.A.I.C.S.: 423120
Robert Dyson (Owner)

DYVENTIVE INC.
1170 Wheeler Way, Langhorne, PA 19047

Tel.: (215) 354-9200
Web Site: https://www.dyventive.com
Year Founded: 1997
Sales Range: $1-9.9 Million
Emp.: 65
Business Equipment Event Rentals & AV Solutions
N.A.I.C.S.: 532420
Dave Kvalcik (Pres)
Frank Zink (Sr Acct Exec)
Dan Stinziani (Sr Mgr-Production)

DZ SOLUTIONS
12424 Wilshire Blvd 800, Los Angeles, CA 90025
Tel.: (424) 238-7300
Web Site: http://www.dzsolutions.com
Year Founded: 2005
Sales Range: $10-24.9 Million
Emp.: 18
Application Software Development Services
N.A.I.C.S.: 541511
Thomas Gilsenan (Founder)
Justin King (Mgr-Engrg)
Carolyn Kiefer (Mgr-Mktg)
Mike Somich (Mgr-Sls)

E C MOORE COMPANY
13325 Leonard St, Dearborn, MI 48126
Tel.: (313) 581-7878
Web Site: http://www.ecmoore.com
Year Founded: 1898
Sales Range: $10-24.9 Million
Emp.: 35
Precision Product Mfr
N.A.I.C.S.: 332721
George Aho (Pres & CEO)
Rick Steinmetz (VP)

E COMMUNICATIONS SYSTEMS INC.
415 N Prince St Ste 200, Lancaster, PA 17603
Tel.: (717) 299-7100
Web Site: http://www.askecomm.com
Rev.: $11,382,634
Emp.: 100
Sound Equipment, Electronic
N.A.I.C.S.: 423690
Gary S. Ritacco (Pres & CEO)

E CONSTRUCTION GROUP INC.
1300 Pennsylvania Ave NW Reagan Bldg, Washington, DC 20004
Tel.: (202) 216-0077
Web Site:
　　http://econstructiongroupgc.com
Year Founded: 2010
Sales Range: $10-24.9 Million
Emp.: 5
Nonresidential Construction Services
N.A.I.C.S.: 236220
Sharada Sharon Singh (CEO)

E CONTRACTORS USA, LLC
16554 Creek Bend Dr Ste 200, Sugar Land, TX 77478
Tel.: (713) 493-2500
Web Site:
　　http://www.econtractors.com
Year Founded: 2011
Sales Range: $25-49.9 Million
Construction Services
N.A.I.C.S.: 236220
Irfan Abji (Principal)
Alejandra Cobas (Principal)
Manny Garcia (Mng Dir)
Joseph Roemen (Project Mgr)
Stanley Jackson (Project Mgr)

E E HOOD & SONS CONSTRUCTION

17000 Senior Rd, San Antonio, TX 78214
Tel.: (210) 624-2475
Web Site: http://www.eehood.com
Sales Range: $25-49.9 Million
Emp.: 250
Highway & Street Construction Services
N.A.I.C.S.: 237310
E. E. Hood *(Pres)*

E N BISSO & SON INC.
3939 N Causeway Blvd, Metairie, LA 70002
Tel.: (504) 828-3296
Web Site: http://www.enbisso.com
Rev.: $2,872,000
Emp.: 100
Construction Machinery Mfr
N.A.I.C.S.: 333120
Walter Kristiansen *(Pres & CEO)*
William McDonald *(Pres)*
Matt Holzhalb *(COO)*
Timothy Michel *(Mgr-Fleet Ops)*
Connie Sandras *(Chief Admin Officer)*
Ken Skrmetta *(Mgr-Ops)*
Mike Vitt *(Gen Counsel & VP-Ops)*

E PATTI & SONS INC.
8 Berry St, Brooklyn, NY 11249
Tel.: (718) 963-3700   NY
Year Founded: 1992
Sales Range: $10-24.9 Million
Emp.: 100
Structural Concrete Construction Services
N.A.I.C.S.: 238120
Michael Patty *(Pres)*

E REVOLUTION VENTURES, INC.
9 Mason Dr, Selbyville, DE 19975
Tel.: (361) 265-8697
Web Site:
    http://www.thinkfasttoys.com
Year Founded: 1986
Sales Range: $10-24.9 Million
Emp.: 60
Electronic Shopping Services
N.A.I.C.S.: 449210
Stu Eisenman *(Pres & CFO)*

E SYSTEMS TECHNOLOGY
3001 Coronado Dr, Santa Clara, CA 95054
Tel.: (650) 961-0671
Web Site:
    http://www.esystemstechnology.com
Year Founded: 2007
Sales Range: $10-24.9 Million
Emp.: 65
Lean Mfr & Global Product Support Services
N.A.I.C.S.: 339999
Robert de Neve *(CEO)*
Kip Smith *(VP-Ops)*
Peter Gise *(Dir-Mktg)*

E&A INDUSTRIES, INC.
101 W Ohio St Ste 1350, Indianapolis, IN 46204-1996
Tel.: (317) 684-3150   IN
Web Site:
    http://www.eaindustries.com
Year Founded: 1977
Sales Range: $75-99.9 Million
Emp.: 100
Administrative & Financial Services, Property Leasing, Lighting
N.A.I.C.S.: 561110
Robert E. Fuller *(VP-Ops)*
Devin Anderson *(Pres, CEO & Partner)*
Jason Kashman *(CFO)*

Subsidiaries:

Con-Tech Lighting   **(1)**
725 Landwehr Rd, Northbrook, IL 60062
Tel.: (847) 559-5500
Web Site: http://www.con-techlighting.com
Emp.: 150
Retail, Commercial & Industrial Lighting Distr
N.A.I.C.S.: 423220
John Ranshaw *(Pres & CEO)*

Conservation Technology, Ltd.   **(1)**
725 Landwehr Rd, Northbrook, IL 60062   **(100%)**
Tel.: (847) 559-5500
Web Site: http://www.con-techlighting.com
Sales Range: $25-49.9 Million
Commercial & Industrial Lighting Fixtures Mfr & Distr
N.A.I.C.S.: 335132
John R. Ranshaw *(Pres)*
Timothy Brennan *(VP-Sls)*
Mike Lehman *(VP-Mktg)*
Joe Sexton *(VP-Fin)*

Lysse   **(1)**
530 W 36th St, New York, NY 10018
Tel.: (877) 595-9773
Web Site: http://www.lysse.com
Emp.: 25
Leggings Mfr
N.A.I.C.S.: 316990
Bryan Helm *(Office Mgr)*

Ultra Solutions   **(1)**
1137 E Philadelphia St, Ontario, CA 91761
Tel.: (909) 628-1778
Web Site: http://www.ultrasolutions.com
Ultrasound System Repair & Maintenance Services
N.A.I.C.S.: 811210

E&A MARKETS INC.
106 Main St, Westerly, RI 02891
Tel.: (401) 596-2054   RI
Year Founded: 1958
Sales Range: $10-24.9 Million
Emp.: 500
Food Products Services
N.A.I.C.S.: 445110
Michael Mcquade *(Pres)*
Melanie Sexton *(Office Mgr)*

E&B NATURAL RESOURCES
1600 Norris Rd, Bakersfield, CA 93308
Tel.: (661) 679-1700
Web Site:
    http://www.ebresources.com
Year Founded: 1972
Rev.: $154,700,000
Emp.: 110
Crude Petroleum & Natural Gas Production
N.A.I.C.S.: 211120
Bill Moody *(Sr VP-Gulf Coast)*
Steve Layton *(Pres)*
Frank J. Ronkese *(CFO & Treas)*
Jeff Blesener *(Sr VP-LA Basin & Midwest Div)*
Christy Swatzell *(VP-HR)*
Gary Richardson *(VP-Land)*

E&E ACQUIRING LLC
18111 S Santa Fe Ave, Rancho Dominguez, CA 90221
Tel.: (310) 604-9488
Rev.: $26,500,000
Emp.: 100
Generators
N.A.I.C.S.: 423610

E&E CO., LTD.
45875 Northport Loop E, Fremont, CA 94538
Tel.: (866) 456-8852
Web Site: http://www.ee1994.com
Sales Range: $150-199.9 Million
Emp.: 500
Household Textile Product Mfr & Distr
N.A.I.C.S.: 314110

Edmund Jin *(Pres & CEO)*
Subsidiaries:

JLA Home, Inc.   **(1)**
45875 Northport Loop E, Fremont, CA 94538
Tel.: (510) 490-9788
Web Site: http://www.jlahome.com
Household Textile Product Mills
N.A.I.C.S.: 314120
Hellen Xu *(VP-Production)*

E&E ENTERPRISES GLOBAL, INC.
303 Butler Farm Rd Ste 106a, Hampton, VA 23666-1393
Tel.: (757) 826-9532
Web Site:
    http://www.eeenterprisesinc.com
Year Founded: 1997
Sales Range: $1-9.9 Million
Telecommunications Resellers
N.A.I.C.S.: 517121
Ernest Green *(Pres & CEO)*

E&E EXHIBITS
1365 W Auto Dr, Tempe, AZ 85284
Tel.: (480) 966-9873
Web Site:
    https://www.exhibitsusa.com
Year Founded: 1996
Rev.: $4,600,000
Emp.: 15
Support Services
N.A.I.C.S.: 561990
Daniel Chaddock *(Pres)*
Cynthia Chaddock *(VP)*

E&H STEEL CORPORATION
3635 E Hwy 134, Midland City, AL 36350
Tel.: (334) 983-5636
Web Site: https://www.ehsteel.com
Sales Range: $25-49.9 Million
Emp.: 90
Structural Shapes & Pilings Mfr
N.A.I.C.S.: 331110
Jimmy Henderson *(Exec VP)*
Robert Thomas *(Pres)*
Scott Thomas *(Mgr-Acctg)*

E&H TRANSPORT NETWORK INC.
1901 Camino Vida Roble Ste 200, Carlsbad, CA 92008
Tel.: (760) 929-0670
Web Site:
    http://www.ehtransport.com
Sales Range: $10-24.9 Million
Emp.: 113
Transportation Services
N.A.I.C.S.: 484121
Oren Zaslansky *(Pres & CEO)*

E&J LAWRENCE CORP.
43 Hall St 7th Fl, Brooklyn, NY 11205
Tel.: (718) 596-1414
Sales Range: $25-49.9 Million
Emp.: 10
Country General Stores
N.A.I.C.S.: 455219
Joseph Khezrie *(CEO)*

E&M ADVERTISING
462 7th Ave 8th Fl, New York, NY 10018-7606
Tel.: (212) 981-5900   NY
Web Site: http://www.emadv.com
Year Founded: 1981
Rev.: $42,000,000
Emp.: 30
Consulting, Direct Response Marketing, Direct-to-Consumer, Electronic Media, Infomercials, Media Buying Services, Media Planning, Mobile Marketing, New Technologies, T.V.
N.A.I.C.S.: 541810

Michael Medico *(CEO)*
Jeffrey R. Wyant *(Sr VP & Dir-Creative)*
Tom Farrell *(VP & Dir-Fin)*
Beth Devlin *(Acct Exec)*
Nina Maxwell *(VP-Integrated Mktg Svcs)*
Lori A. Capitelli *(Sr VP & Dir-Media)*
Robert Kulka *(VP-Bus Dev & Client Svcs)*
Anthony Medico *(Pres)*
Jennifer Tarsitano *(VP-Bus Dev)*

Subsidiaries:

E&M Media Group   **(1)**
1410 Broadway Ste 1002, New York, NY 10018-3704
Tel.: (212) 455-0177
Web Site: http://www.emtvsales.com
Emp.: 10
N.A.I.C.S.: 541810
Bonnie Schalle *(Owner & Pres)*
Diane Zeit *(Dir-Media)*
David Geller *(Co-VP)*

E&M ELECTRIC & MACHINERY
126 Mill St, Healdsburg, CA 95448
Tel.: (707) 433-5578
Web Site: http://www.enm.com
Rev.: $13,500,000
Emp.: 85
Instruments & Control Equipment
N.A.I.C.S.: 423830
Judy Deas *(Pres)*

E&S INTERNATIONAL ENTERPRISES INC.
7801 Hayvenhurft Ave, Van Nuys, CA 91406
Tel.: (818) 887-0700   CA
Web Site: https://www.esintl.com
Year Founded: 1945
Sales Range: $50-74.9 Million
Emp.: 177
Consumer Electronic Products & Sporting Goods Mfr & Distr; Real Estate Property Lessor
N.A.I.C.S.: 423620
Farshad Asherian *(VP)*
Don Varga *(Sr VP)*
Eddie Garcia *(Controller)*

Subsidiaries:

Compact Power Systems, LLC   **(1)**
5900 Canoga Ave, Woodland Hills, CA 91367
Tel.: (818) 226-5791
Portable Power Solutions Mfr & Distr
N.A.I.C.S.: 335910

E.S.I. Worldwide, Inc.   **(1)**
700 55 Town Center Ct, Scarborough, M1P 4X4, ON, Canada   **(100%)**
Tel.: (416) 296-9926
Sales Range: $10-24.9 Million
Emp.: 1
Durable Goods Mfr
N.A.I.C.S.: 423990

E&T PLASTIC MANUFACTURING CO.
4545 37th St, Long Island City, NY 11102
Tel.: (718) 729-6226
Web Site: https://www.e-tplastics.com
Rev.: $20,285,000
Emp.: 80
Extruded Finished Plastics Products
N.A.I.C.S.: 326199
Gary Thal *(Pres & CEO)*
Pam Aungst *(Mgr-ECommerce-Teterboro)*

E&V ENERGY CORPORATION
11858 W Main St, Wolcott, NY 14590
Tel.: (315) 594-8076

E&V Energy Corporation—(Continued)

Web Site:
https://www.eandvenergy.com
Year Founded: 1913
Sales Range: $10-24.9 Million
Emp.: 75
Petroleum Bulk Station Services
N.A.I.C.S.: 424710
Theodore Marshall *(Pres)*

E'PRIME AEROSPACE COR-PORATION
7637 Leesburg Pike Ste 200, Falls
Church, VA 22043
Tel.: (321) 269-0900
Web Site:
http://www.eprimeaerospace.com
Aerospace & Space Vehicle Mfr
N.A.I.C.S.: 336414
Nick W. Herren Jr. *(Chm, Pres & CEO)*

E*TRADE FINANCIAL CORPO-RATION
671 N Glebe Rd, Arlington, VA 22203
Tel.: (646) 521-4340   DE
Web Site: http://www.etrade.com
Year Founded: 1982
Rev.: $3,145,000,000
Assets: $61,416,000,000
Liabilities: $54,873,000,000
Net Worth: $6,543,000,000
Earnings: $955,000,000
Emp.: 4,122
Fiscal Year-end: 12/31/19
Holding Company; Online Securities
Brokerage & Financial Services
N.A.I.C.S.: 551112
Michael A. Pizzi *(CEO)*
Dirk Wyckoff *(Principal Acctg Officer & Controller)*
Rodger Alan Lawson *(Chm)*
Lori S. Sher *(Gen Counsel & Exec VP)*
Chad E. Turner *(CFO & Exec VP)*
Jolie Fleming *(Sr VP-Mobile, Web, & Investing)*
David Inggs *(COO)*
Christopher Larkin *(Sr VP-Trading)*
Michael Murphy *(Sr VP-Retail Brokerage)*
Alice Milligan *(Chief Customer Officer & Exec VP)*
Mayank Gupta *(Chief HR Officer)*
Matthew Minetola *(CIO)*
Andrea Zaretsky *(CMO)*

Subsidiaries:

Capitol View, LLC   (1)
107 W Cook St Ste A, Springfield, IL 62704
Tel.: (217) 544-7880
Emp.: 4
Professional Consulting Services
N.A.I.C.S.: 541618

E*TRADE Bank   (1)
671 N Glebe Rd Fl 10, Arlington, VA 22203
Tel.: (678) 624-6210
Web Site: http://www.us.etrade.com
Sales Range: $125-149.9 Million
Saving Bank Services
N.A.I.C.S.: 522180
Paul Thomas Idzik *(Pres & CEO)*

E*TRADE Capital Management, LLC   (1)
1271 Ave of The Americas 14th Fl, New York, NY 10020
Tel.: (866) 789-0736
Financial Investment Services
N.A.I.C.S.: 523940

E*TRADE Securities LLC   (1)
Harborside 2 200 Hudson St Ste 501, Jersey City, NJ 07311-1113   (100%)
Tel.: (646) 521-4793
Web Site: http://us.etrade.com
Sales Range: $650-699.9 Million
Online Securities Brokerage & Dealing Services

SP Capital AB   (1)
Slussplan 9 1 Tr, Stockholm, 111 30, Sweden
Tel.: (46) 851510610
Web Site:
http://www.structuredinvestments.se
Financial Investment Services
N.A.I.C.S.: 523150
Jack Johansson *(CEO)*

E-3 ELECTRICAL
4545 S Pinemont Dr, Houston, TX 77041
Tel.: (713) 622-1222
Web Site: https://www.e3electric.com
Sales Range: $25-49.9 Million
Emp.: 185
Electrical Wiring Services
N.A.I.C.S.: 238210
Jim Roberts *(Pres)*

E-B DISPLAY CO., INC.
1369 Sanders Ave SW, Massillon, OH 44647-7632
Tel.: (330) 833-4101
Web Site: http://www.ebdisplay.com
Year Founded: 1952
Rev.: $20,000,000
Emp.: 115
N.A.I.C.S.: 541810
Michael Rotolo *(Pres & CEO)*
Rick Catazaro *(CFO)*
Richard Philyaw *(VP)*

E-BUSINESS INTERNATIONAL INC (E-BI)
15244 NW Greenbrier Pkwy, Beaverton, OR 97006
Tel.: (503) 644-2290
Web Site: https://www.e-bi.com
Year Founded: 1999
Sales Range: $10-24.9 Million
Emp.: 127
Business Outsourcing Services
N.A.I.C.S.: 541618
George Wang *(Pres & CEO)*

E-CHECK HOLDINGS, INC.
6001 NW 153rd St, Miami Lakes, FL 33014
Tel.: (305) 827-8373   NV
Year Founded: 2010
Sales Range: $1-9.9 Million
Investment Services
N.A.I.C.S.: 523999
Ellen Luckman Gardner *(Pres & CEO)*

E-COMMERCE EXCHANGE INC.
Ste 100 26707 Agoura Rd, Calabasas, CA 91302-3827
Web Site: http://www.ecx.com
Sales Range: $25-49.9 Million
Emp.: 100
Credit Card Services
N.A.I.C.S.: 522320

E-COMPLISH LLC
228 Park Ave S Ste 89324, New York, NY 10003-1502
Tel.: (888) 847-7744
Web Site: http://www.e-complish.com
Year Founded: 1999
Payment Processing Solutions Services
N.A.I.C.S.: 522320
Stephen Price *(CEO)*

Subsidiaries:

Regal Technologies LLC   (1)
1125 W St Ste 529, Annapolis, MD 21401
Tel.: (213) 493-0605
Web Site: http://www.regaltek.com
Electronic Payment Solutions Services
N.A.I.C.S.: 522320

Don Pette *(Partner)*

E-CYCLE LLC
4105 Leap Rd, Hilliard, OH 43026-1117
Tel.: (614) 210-1120
Web Site: https://www.e-cycle.com
Sales Range: $1-9.9 Million
Emp.: 100
Computer & Electronic Product Recycling Services
N.A.I.C.S.: 811210
Paulie Anthony *(Dir-Mktg)*
Dave Wine *(Dir-Ops & Distr)*

E-MANAGEMENT
1010 Wayne Ave Ste 1150, Silver Spring, MD 20910
Tel.: (301) 565-2988
Web Site: http://www.e-mcinc.com
Year Founded: 1999
Sales Range: $10-24.9 Million
Emp.: 60
Government Services
N.A.I.C.S.: 921190
Ola Sage *(Chm & CEO)*
Ric Colton *(CIO)*
Dave Thompson *(Sr VP)*
Karen Britton *(COO & Sr VP)*

E-MAX GROUP, INC.
16969 NW 67th Ave, Miami, FL 33015
Tel.: (954) 843-0483
Web Site: http://www.databazaar.com
Year Founded: 1999
Sales Range: $25-49.9 Million
Emp.: 100
Online Office Supplies Retailer
N.A.I.C.S.: 424120
Oney Seal *(Chm & CEO)*

Subsidiaries:

Databazaar India Pvt. Ltd.   (1)
Infinity Tower-II Plot# A3, Block-GP Sector V, Saltlec Electronic Complex, Kolkata, 700091, India
Tel.: (91) 33 23331201
Web Site: http://www.databazaar.biz
Online Office Supplies Retailer
N.A.I.C.S.: 424120

E-MEDIA PLUS INC.
71 Schrieffer St, South Hackensack, NJ 07606
Tel.: (201) 525-0100
Web Site: http://www.e-mediaplus.com
Sales Range: $10-24.9 Million
Emp.: 15
IT Infrastructure Products & Services
N.A.I.C.S.: 423430
Stephen P. Marolda *(Pres)*

E-MERGING TECHNOLOGIES GROUP, INC.
22021 Brookpark Rd Ste 130, Cleveland, OH 44126
Tel.: (440) 779-5680   OH
Web Site: http://etg1.com
Year Founded: 1999
Sales Range: $1-9.9 Million
Emp.: 100
Computer Operations & Program Management Services
N.A.I.C.S.: 541512
Ann E. Katigbak *(Exec VP-Ops)*
Jeremy A. Samide *(CEO)*
Charles Painter *(Sr VP-Intelligence Community Bus Unit)*
Lewis C. Merletti *(Chm)*
Thomas N. Kasza *(Exec VP-Cyber Intelligence & Security Svcs)*

E-PATH COMMUNICATIONS, INC.

5110 Eisenhower Blvd Ste 300, Tampa, FL 33634
Tel.: (813) 840-4160
Web Site:
http://www.epathcommunications.com
Sales Range: $1-9.9 Million
Wireless Broadband Networks Developer
N.A.I.C.S.: 334220
Joseph A. Tortoretti *(Pres)*
Bobby Ceklic *(VP-Sls & Mktg)*

E-POLL MARKET RESEARCH
16133 Ventura Blvd Ste 905, Encino, CA 91436
Tel.: (818) 995-4960
Web Site:
https://www.epollresearch.com
Year Founded: 2000
Rev.: $4,800,000
Emp.: 31
Market Research Services
N.A.I.C.S.: 541910
Gerry Philpott *(Pres & CEO)*
Stephen Anspach *(CTO & Sr VP-Operations)*
Michelle Waxman *(Sr VP-Corporate Development)*
Mary Ann Farrell *(Sr VP-Res)*

E-QURE CORP.
20 W 64th St - Ste 39G, New York, NY 10023
Tel.: (972) 891-6733   DE
Web Site: https://www.e-qure.com
Year Founded: 1988
EQUR—(OTCBB)
Rev.: $35,305
Assets: $81,070
Liabilities: $479,921
Net Worth: ($398,851)
Earnings: ($612,356)
Emp.: 1
Fiscal Year-end: 12/31/20
Medical Device Mfr
N.A.I.C.S.: 334510
Ohad Goren *(CEO)*
Itsik Ben Yesha *(CTO)*
Ron Weissberg *(Chm)*

E-REWARDS, INC.
5800 Tennyson Pkwy Ste 600, Plano, TX 75024-3992
Tel.: (214) 782-2800
Web Site: https://www.e-rewards.com
Year Founded: 1999
Sales Range: $10-24.9 Million
Emp.: 800
Online Market Research Services
N.A.I.C.S.: 541910
Kurt Knapton *(Pres & CEO)*
Donald J. Carty *(Chm)*

Subsidiaries:

Research Now Plc   (1)
1st Floor Elizabeth House, 39 York Road, London, SE1 7NQ, United Kingdom
Tel.: (44) 2079212400
Web Site: http://www.researchnow.co.uk
Market Research Fieldwork Services
N.A.I.C.S.: 541910
Nathan Runnicles *(CFO)*
Michael Bigby *(CTO)*
John Rothwell *(Pres & COO)*
Stephanie Marty *(Dir-Client Dev-Corp, Strategy & Media-France)*
Ed Russo *(Sr VP-Global Mktg)*
Michael Ryan-Todd *(VP-Client Svcs)*
Melanie Courtright *(Exec VP-Global Client Svcs)*
Kathy Rowley *(Chief HR Officer & Gen Counsel)*
Chris Dubreuil *(Mng Dir-EMEA)*
Ben Hogg *(Mng Dir-Sls-Northern Europe)*
Marc Smaluhn *(Mng Dir-Continental Europe)*
Ryan Jantz *(Sr VP-Panels & Partnerships)*

Dirk Hobgood *(Sr VP-Data Privacy & Port-folio Businesses)*
James Burge *(Mng Dir-Asia Pacific)*
Kris Baker *(VP-Client Dev-Plano)*
Bart Roselli *(VP-Client Dev-Cincinnati)*
Mike Gasper *(VP-Bus Dev-New York)*
Chawntae Applegate *(Sr Dir-Client Dev-Cincinnati)*
Tom Greco *(Sr Dir-Consumer Panels & Communities-Cincinnati)*
Aaron Simmons *(Sr VP-Client Dev-Northern Europe)*
Gary S. Laben *(CEO)*
Tom Johnson *(Exec VP-Sls-North America)*
Mayer Danzig *(Sr VP-Product Mgmt)*
George Pappachen *(Exec VP-Corp Dev & Strategy)*
Floriane Locatelli *(Dir-Bus Dev-EMEA)*

E-SOLUTIONS INC.
2 N Market St Ste 400, San Jose, CA 95113
Tel.: (408) 289-8200
Web Site: https://www.e-solutionsinc.com
Year Founded: 2003
Sales Range: $10-24.9 Million
Emp.: 250
Technical Consulting Services
N.A.I.C.S.: 541690
Priyanka Gupta *(Pres)*
Raj Singh *(Mgr-Resource)*

E-SOURCE, INC.
1950 Hurd Dr, Irving, TX 75038
Tel.: (214) 614-0215
Web Site: http://www.esequip.com
Rev.: $42,000,000
Emp.: 25
Commercial Kitchen Equipment Mfr, Distr & Whslr
N.A.I.C.S.: 423440
Harry Starkweather *(Principal)*
Mary Lee Cruz *(Principal)*
Jeff Swindle *(VP-Ops)*

E-STET
1149 S Hill St, Los Angeles, CA 90015
Tel.: (213) 744-1414
Web Site: http://www.e-stet.com
Sales Range: $1-9.9 Million
Emp.: 20
Electronic Litigation Support Services
N.A.I.C.S.: 561499
Salim Elkhou *(Founder)*
Michael Dunn *(Pres)*
Bhuvan Singh *(Dir-Ops)*
Cerbel Cerdeno *(Office Mgr)*
Timothy Kressman *(Coord-Bus Dev)*
Kristin Currey *(Dir-Bus Dev)*
Adam Friedman *(Dir-Corp Solutions)*
Fahd Syed *(Dir-Mktg)*
Bowe Kurowski *(Mgr-Acct)*
Jeremy Krant *(Project Mgr)*
Bradley Roughan *(Project Mgr)*
Thomas Hegelund *(CEO)*
Rhea Frederick *(VP-Bus Dev)*
Bridgette Harris *(Gen Counsel & VP-Managed Review)*
Aria Safar *(Chief Bus Dev Officer)*

E-T-M ENTERPRISES INC.
920 N Clinton St, Grand Ledge, MI 48837
Tel.: (517) 627-8461
Web Site: https://www.etmenterprises.com
Year Founded: 1970
Sales Range: $10-24.9 Million
Emp.: 180
Molded Composite Fiber Glass Mfr, Engineering & Tooling Services
N.A.I.C.S.: 541330

E-VERIFILE.COM, INC.
900 Cir 75 Pkwy Ste 1550, Atlanta, GA 30339

Tel.: (770) 859-9899
Web Site: http://www.e-verifile.com
Year Founded: 1999
Emp.: 48
Risk Assessment & Administrative Support Software Publisher
N.A.I.C.S.: 513210
Mark Wilson *(CEO)*

E-W TRUCK & EQUIPMENT CO., INC.
6336 Federal Blvd, San Diego, CA 92114
Tel.: (619) 263-2111
Web Site: https://www.ewtruck.com
Rev.: $9,100,000
Emp.: 40
Automobile & Other Motor Vehicle Merchant Whslr
N.A.I.C.S.: 423110
Linda Winters *(Pres)*
Karen Bare *(Office Mgr)*

E-WASTE SYSTEMS, INC.
1350 E Flamingo #3101, Las Vegas, NV 89119
Tel.: (650) 283-2907   NV
Web Site: http://www.ewastesystems.com
Year Founded: 2008
Sales Range: Less than $1 Million
Emp.: 35
Computer Equipment Recycling Services
N.A.I.C.S.: 562920
N. Martin Nielson *(Founder & CEO)*
Carolyne Susan Johnson *(Treas, Sec & VP)*

Subsidiaries:

Surf Investments, Ltd.   (1)
17981 Sky Park Cir Ste K, Irvine, CA 92614
Tel.: (949) 250-0744
Web Site: http://www.cpurepair.com
Sales Range: $1-9.9 Million
Emp.: 4
Electronic Waste Management, Mobile Computing Services & Computer Repair Services
N.A.I.C.S.: 541519
Julie Peterson Mindiola *(Founder)*

E-Z MART STORES, INC.
602 W Falvey Ave, Texarkana, TX 75501
Tel.: (903) 832-6502   TX
Web Site: http://www.ezmart.com
Year Founded: 1970
Sales Range: $700-749.9 Million
Emp.: 2,700
Convenience Stores; Gasoline Whslr & Station Equipment Services
N.A.I.C.S.: 445131
Sonja Hubbard *(Pres & CEO)*
Stacy Floyd *(CFO)*
Faellen Yates *(Founder & Chm)*

E-Z-8 MOTEL INC.
4747 Pacific Hwy, San Diego, CA 92110
Tel.: (619) 294-2512
Web Site: https://www.ez8motels.com
Sales Range: $25-49.9 Million
Emp.: 600
Motel, Franchised
N.A.I.C.S.: 721110
Michael S. Morris *(Pres)*

E. & J. GALLO WINERY
600 Yosemite Blvd, Modesto, CA 95354-2760
Tel.: (209) 341-6349   CA
Web Site: https://www.gallo.com
Year Founded: 1933
Sales Range: $1-4.9 Billion
Emp.: 7,593

Winery & Wine Distr
N.A.I.C.S.: 312130
Stephanie Gallo *(CMO & VP-Mktg)*
Roger Nabedian *(Exec VP & Gen Mgr-Premium Wine Div)*

Subsidiaries:

Ballatore Champagne Cellars   (1)
600 Yosemite Blvd, Modesto, CA 95354-2760
Tel.: (209) 341-3111
Web Site: http://www.gallo.com
Sales Range: $400-449.9 Million
Emp.: 3,800
Champagne Mfr
N.A.I.C.S.: 312130
A. P. Fenderson *(Exec VP-Mktg)*

Carlo Rossi Vineyards   (1)
600 Yosemite Blvd, Modesto, CA 95354
Tel.: (209) 341-3111
Web Site: http://www.carlorossi.com
Sales Range: $500-549.9 Million
Emp.: 2,500
Vineyard & Winery
N.A.I.C.S.: 312130

Courtside Cellars   (1)
2425 Mission St, San Miguel, CA 93451
Tel.: (805) 467-2882
Web Site: http://www.courtsidecellars.com
Sales Range: $1-9.9 Million
Emp.: 18
Winery
N.A.I.C.S.: 312130

Edna Valley Vineyard   (1)
2585 Biddle Ranch Rd, San Luis Obispo, CA 93401   (100%)
Tel.: (805) 544-9594
Web Site: http://www.ednavalley.com
Sales Range: $1-9.9 Million
Emp.: 30
Winery
N.A.I.C.S.: 312130

J Vineyards & Winery   (1)
11447 Old Redwood Hwy, Healdsburg, CA 95448-9523
Tel.: (707) 431-5400
Web Site: http://www.jwine.com
Sales Range: $1-9.9 Million
Vineyard & Winery
N.A.I.C.S.: 312130
Brandon Vorst *(Reg Sls Mgr-Southeast Reg)*

McCall Wineries & Distillers   (1)
12 E 49th St, New York, NY 10017-1028
Tel.: (559) 454-1302
Produces & Markets Brandies
N.A.I.C.S.: 312130

Orin Swift Cellars LLC   (1)
1352 Main St, Saint Helena, CA 94574-1905
Tel.: (707) 967-9179
Web Site: http://www.orinswift.com
Wine Production & Sales
N.A.I.C.S.: 312130
Bryan Sandoli *(Pres & Gen Mgr)*
Nathan Bergeron *(Asst Gen Mgr)*

Pahlmeyer, LLC   (1)
811 St Helena Hwy S Ste 202, Saint Helena, CA 94574
Tel.: (707) 255-2321
Web Site: http://www.pahlmeyer.com
Vineyard & Wine Making Services
N.A.I.C.S.: 312130

Rombauer Vineyards, LLC   (1)
3522 Silverado Trl N, Saint Helena, CA 94574
Tel.: (707) 963-5170
Web Site: http://www.rombauer.com
Sales Range: $10-24.9 Million
Emp.: 40
Wine Mfr & Distr
N.A.I.C.S.: 312130
John Cochennette *(Gen Mgr)*
George Kneip *(Mgr-Acctg)*
Jeff Papa *(Mgr-Sls-Southeast)*
Martha Welshans *(Asst Mgr-Retail Ops)*
Richie Allen *(Dir-Viticulture & Winemaking)*
Ingrid Cheng *(Mgr-Digital & Consumer Rels)*
Jim Teegan *(Mgr-Northeast Sls)*
Dale Higgins *(Mgr-Ops-Retail)*

John Egan *(Mgr-Sls Ops)*
Clyde Gilbert *(Mgr-Sls-Midwest)*
Alan Cannon *(Mgr-Sls-Natl)*
Alison Surgeon *(Mgr-Sls-Northern California)*
Bob Knebel *(COO)*
Reagan Rombauer Blackwood *(Mgr-Sls & Mktg Support)*

Stagecoach Vineyard   (1)
3555 Soda Canyon Rd, Napa, CA 94558
Tel.: (707) 259-1198
Web Site: http://www.stagecoachvineyard.com
Vineyard
N.A.I.C.S.: 111332
Jan Krupp *(Founder)*

Talbott Vineyards   (1)
25 Pilot Rd, Carmel Valley, CA 93924
Tel.: (831) 659-3500
Web Site: http://www.talbottvineyards.com
Wineries
N.A.I.C.S.: 312130

The Ranch Winery   (1)
105 Zinfandel Ln, Saint Helena, CA 94574-1631
Tel.: (707) 963-4520
Web Site: http://www.ranchwinery.com
Winery
N.A.I.C.S.: 312130

Tott's Champagne Cellars   (1)
600 Yosemite Blvd, Modesto, CA 95354-2760
Tel.: (209) 341-3111
Sales Range: $400-449.9 Million
Emp.: 4,000
Mfr of Champagne
N.A.I.C.S.: 312130

E. BOINEAU & COMPANY
128 Beaufain St, Charleston, SC 29401
Tel.: (843) 723-1462
Web Site: http://www.eboineauandco.com
Year Founded: 1990
Sales Range: Less than $1 Million
Emp.: 3
Education, Engineering, Environmental, Financial, Health Care, Legal Services, Public Relations, Real Estate, Retail, Travel & Tourism
N.A.I.C.S.: 541820
Elizabeth Boineau *(Founder)*
Melissa Pluta Parker *(Sr Acct Exec)*

E. COHEN AND COMPANY
1 Research Ct Ste 400, Rockville, MD 20850
Tel.: (301) 917-6200
Web Site: http://www.ecohencpas.com
Year Founded: 1989
Rev.: $3,700,000
Emp.: 27
Financial Services
N.A.I.C.S.: 541211
Eric Cohen *(Founder, Pres & CEO)*
Jena Guarino Basiliko *(Supvr-Admin)*
Richard Rawson *(Dir-Mktg)*
Caitlin Migliorini *(Mgr-Tax)*
JoAnn Platt *(Dir-Tax)*
Valeria Parker *(Mgr-Admin)*
Donald Keninitz *(Principal)*
Robin Meisner Cameron *(Principal)*
Kimberly H. Maxwell *(Principal)*

E. ESCHER INC.
1802 Macy Dr, Roswell, GA 30076
Tel.: (770) 642-8299
Web Site: http://www.eescherinc.com
Sales Range: $10-24.9 Million
Emp.: 20
Plumbing, Heating & Air Conditioning Contractor Services
N.A.I.C.S.: 238220
Joseph J. Escher *(CEO)*
Diana L. Escher *(CFO)*
Erica Escher *(Sec)*

E. Gluck Corp.—(Continued)

E. GLUCK CORP.
60-15 Little Neck Pkwy, Little Neck, NY 11362-2929
Tel.: (718) 784-0700   **NY**
Web Site: http://www.egluck.com
Year Founded: 1977
Sales Range: $250-299.9 Million
Emp.: 350
Clock Mfr & Distr
N.A.I.C.S.: 334519
Eugene Gluck (Pres)
Renee Jacobs (Controller)
Bob Nublin (Sr Vp)

Subsidiaries:

Armitron Watch Division   **(1)**
2910 Thomson Ave 60-15 Little Neck Pkwy, Little Neck, NY 11362
Tel.: (718) 784-0700
Web Site: http://www.egluck.com
Sales Range: $50-74.9 Million
Watch Mfr
N.A.I.C.S.: 334519
Eugene Gluck (Pres)
Jerry Dikowitz (VP-Mktg & Adv)
Ron Summers (Dir-Premiums)
Mark Odenheimer (VP)

E. JORDAN BROOKES CO. INC.
10634 Shoemaker Ave, Santa Fe Springs, CA 90670
Tel.: (562) 968-2100
Web Site: http://www.ejbco.com
Sales Range: $25-49.9 Million
Emp.: 68
Copper Based Metals & Engineered Plastics Mfr
N.A.I.C.S.: 423510
Lindsey Fisher (Mgr-Sls)
Martin Kaplan (Mgr-Mktg)
Bob Brookes (Pres & CEO)

E. MISHAN & SONS, INC.
230 5th Ave, New York, NY 10001-7704
Tel.: (212) 689-9094   **NY**
Web Site: https://www.emsoninc.com
Year Founded: 1945
Sales Range: $75-99.9 Million
Emp.: 45
Promotional Products Mfr, Distr & Whlsr
N.A.I.C.S.: 424990
Ike Mishan (Pres)
Jeff Mishan (Dir-Adv)
Bob Brill (Exec VP)
Jennifer Jacobs (Mgr-Import Traffic & Documentation)
Antoinette Ramos (Supvr-Customer Svc)
Jack Guindi (VP)
Nathan Bailey (VP-Sls & Mktg)

E. MORRIS COMMUNICA-TIONS, INC.
820 N Orleans St Ste 402, Chicago, IL 60610
Tel.: (312) 943-2900   **IL**
Web Site: http://www.emorris.com
Year Founded: 1987
Rev.: $48,000,000
Emp.: 20
Advetising Agency
N.A.I.C.S.: 541810
Deborah Easton (Assoc Dir-Creative)
Alvin W. Hawkins (Creative Consultant)
Reginald Ponder (VP & Sr Acct Dir)
Kathleen Smiles (VP, Dir-Production & Creative Svcs)
Regina Dove (Assoc Dir-Commun Svcs)

E. OSTERMAN GAS SERVICE INC.
1 Memorial Sq, Whitinsville, MA 01588
Tel.: (508) 234-9902
Web Site: http://www.ostermangas.com
Sales Range: $25-49.9 Million
Emp.: 180
Liquefied Petroleum Gas Dealers
N.A.I.C.S.: 457210
Ernest Osterman (CEO)
Vincent J. Osterman (Pres)

E. RITTER & COMPANY
106 Frisco St, Marked Tree, AR 72365-2243
Tel.: (870) 358-2200   **AR**
Year Founded: 1958
Sales Range: $25-49.9 Million
Emp.: 220
Holding Company; Telecommunications & Farm Management Services
N.A.I.C.S.: 551112
Charles R. Dickinson Jr. (CEO)

Subsidiaries:

E. Ritter Agribusiness Holdings, Inc.   **(1)**
10 Elm St, Marked Tree, AR 72365
Tel.: (870) 358-7333
Web Site: http://www.ritterag.com
Holding Company; Farm Management Services
N.A.I.C.S.: 551112
Kevin Wright (Pres)

Subsidiary (Domestic):

E. Ritter Farm Management, Inc.   **(2)**
10 Elm St, Marked Tree, AR 72365
Tel.: (870) 358-7333
Web Site: http://www.ritterag.com
Farm Management Services
N.A.I.C.S.: 115116
Kevin Wright (Pres)
Jason Brewer (Gen Mgr)
Phil Negri (Mgr-Farm)
Woody Ray (Project Mgr)

E. Ritter Communications Holdings, Inc.   **(1)**
30 Elm St, Marked Tree, AR 72365
Tel.: (870) 358-4400
Web Site:
http://www.rittercommunications.com
Holding Company; Telecommunications Services
N.A.I.C.S.: 551112
Jeff Chapman (VP/Gen Mgr-Fiber-to-the-Home Bus)
Alan Morse (CEO)

Subsidiary (Domestic):

E. Ritter Communications, Inc.   **(2)**
30 Elm St, Marked Tree, AR 72365
Tel.: (870) 358-4400
Web Site:
http://www.rittercommunications.com
Radio Telephone Communication & Internet Access Services
N.A.I.C.S.: 517112

Subsidiary (Domestic):

E. Ritter Telephone Company   **(3)**
30 Elm St, Marked Tree, AR 72365
Tel.: (870) 358-4400
Web Site:
http://www.rittercommunications.com
Wired Telephone Communication Services
N.A.I.C.S.: 517121

E. SAM JONES DISTRIBUTOR INCORPORATED
4898 S Atlanta Rd, Atlanta, GA 30339
Tel.: (404) 351-3250   **GA**
Web Site:
https://www.esamjones.com
Year Founded: 1970
Sales Range: $25-49.9 Million
Emp.: 140
Electrical Apparatus & Equipment
N.A.I.C.S.: 423610
Kevin Harbin (Mgr-Ops)

E.A. & H. HILDRETH INC.
51-55 Main St, Southampton, NY 11968
Tel.: (631) 283-2300
Web Site: https://www.hildreths.com
Rev.: $10,343,928
Emp.: 30
Department Stores
N.A.I.C.S.: 455110
Henry H. Hildreth (Pres & CEO)
Ann Barry (Mgr-Dept)
David Dempsey (COO)

E.A. SWEEN COMPANY
16101 W 78th St, Eden Prairie, MN 55344-5709
Tel.: (952) 937-9440   **MN**
Web Site: http://www.easween.com
Year Founded: 1955
Sales Range: $100-124.9 Million
Emp.: 300
Sandwich Distr, Mfr & Whslr
N.A.I.C.S.: 311991
Tom E. Sween (Chm & CEO)
John Davis (Controller)
Bryan Virgin (Sr VP-Sls)
Kim Larish (VP-HR)
Rob Linner (Sr VP-Distr Solutions)
Tim Engmark (Sr VP-Ops)

E.B. BERGER INCORPO-RATED
218 W 12650 S, Draper, UT 84020
Tel.: (801) 553-0993
Web Site: http://www.ebberger.com
Sales Range: $10-24.9 Million
Emp.: 120
Plastering Plain Or Ornamental
N.A.I.C.S.: 238310
David Berger (Pres)
Matthew Curtin (Project Mgr)
Mike Muse (Project Mgr-Painting & Special Coatings)

E.B. HORN CO.
429 Washington St, Boston, MA 02108
Tel.: (617) 542-3902   **MA**
Web Site: https://www.ebhorn.com
Year Founded: 1839
Sales Range: $10-24.9 Million
Emp.: 52
Retailer of Jewelry, Precious Stones & Precious Metals
N.A.I.C.S.: 458310
Richard Finn (VP)
Michael Finn (Treas)

E.B. WALL + ASSOCIATES
1520 Harper Ave NW, Lenoir, NC 28645
Tel.: (828) 757-0047
Web Site: http://www.ebwall.com
Year Founded: 1989
Sales Range: Less than $1 Million
Emp.: 2
Advetising Agency
N.A.I.C.S.: 541810
Shawn Bradley (Production Mgr)
Elisabeth Wall (Owner & CEO)
Julie Zoller (Acct Exec)
Kelly Babbs (Designer)
David Wall (CFO)

E.C. BARTON & COMPANY
2929 Browns Ln, Jonesboro, AR 72403
Tel.: (870) 932-6673
Web Site: http://www.ecbarton.com
Year Founded: 1885
Sales Range: $125-149.9 Million
Emp.: 650
Lumber & Building Materials Whslr & Retailer
N.A.I.C.S.: 423310

Niel Crowson (Pres & CEO)
Tom Rainwater (Treas & Sec)
Gary Beasley (Controller)
H. R. McDonough (Dir-Mktg)
Joe Crowson (Mgr-Transportation)
Kevin Wooldridge (Mgr-Inventory)
Jeff Hart (VP-Pur)
Cullen Barbato (VP-Mktg, Real Estate & IT)
Steve Debber (Mgr-Mdsg)
Chris Gardner (Chm)

Subsidiaries:

Builders Material Company   **(1)**
102 N Gee St, Jonesboro, AR 72401
Tel.: (870) 935-3511
Web Site: http://www.ecbarton.com
Sales Range: $10-24.9 Million
Building Materials Whslr
N.A.I.C.S.: 423390

E.C. Barton & Co. Design Center   **(1)**
3023 Browns Ln, Jonesboro, AR 72401
Tel.: (870) 932-6673
Web Site: http://www.ecbarton.com
Sales Range: $10-24.9 Million
Emp.: 10
Kitchen & Bath Designer
N.A.I.C.S.: 541490
Ron Turpin (Mgr-Store)

ECB Brokerage   **(1)**
PO Box 16360, Jonesboro, AR 72403
Tel.: (870) 336-6035
Web Site: http://www.ecbbrokerage.com
Sales Range: $10-24.9 Million
Emp.: 5
Building Material Brokerage Distr
N.A.I.C.S.: 423310
Jack Gockel (Dir-Sls)

Grossmans Bargain Outlet   **(1)**
90 Hawes Way, Stoughton, MA 02072
Tel.: (781) 297-3300
Web Site: http://www.bargain-outlets.com
Sales Range: $10-24.9 Million
Lumber, Building Materials & Other Home Improvement Products Whslr
N.A.I.C.S.: 423310

E.C. COTTLE INC.
256 Lamberts Cove Rd, Vineyard Haven, MA 02568
Tel.: (508) 693-1385
Web Site: https://www.eccottle.com
Sales Range: $10-24.9 Million
Emp.: 23
Distributes Lumber & Other Building Materials
N.A.I.C.S.: 423310
Janet Johnson (CFO-Acctg)
Edmund C. Cottle Sr. (Pres)

E.C. GRIFFITH CO.
1944 Brunswick Ave, Charlotte, NC 28207
Tel.: (704) 332-7173
Web Site:
http://www.griffithrealestateservices.com
Year Founded: 1912
Sales Range: $10-24.9 Million
Emp.: 7
Commerical Land Subdividers & Developers
N.A.I.C.S.: 237210
Preston Griffith (VP)
James Griffith Jr. (Pres)

E.C. ORTIZ & CO., LLP
333 S Desplaines St Ste 2N, Chicago, IL 60661
Tel.: (312) 876-1900
Web Site: http://www.ecortiz.com
Year Founded: 1974
Rev.: $4,100,000
Emp.: 73
Financial Services
N.A.I.C.S.: 541219
Gilda Belmonte (Partner)
Edilberto C. Ortiz (Mng Partner)
Marites Sy (Partner)

Seilani Rodrigo *(Partner)*
Edilberto C. Ortiz *(Mng Partner)*
Leilani Nabo-Rodrigo *(Co-Partner)*
Gilda M. Belmonte *(Co-Partner)*

E.C. STYBERG ENGINEERING CO., INC.
1600 Goold St, Racine, WI 53404
Tel.: (262) 637-9301
Web Site: https://www.styberg.com
Rev.: $26,900,000
Emp.: 200
Mechanical Power Transmission Equipment Mfr
N.A.I.C.S.: 333613
Michael Budish *(VP-Fin)*
Ernest C. Styberg Jr. *(Pres)*
Bernice Styberg *(Sec)*

E.D. BULLARD COMPANY
1898 Safety Way, Cynthiana, KY 41031-9303
Tel.: (859) 234-6611   CA
Web Site: http://www.bullard.com
Year Founded: 1898
Sales Range: $50-74.9 Million
Emp.: 325
Industrial Head Protection, Respiratory Protection & Thermal Imaging Equipment Mfr & Distributor
N.A.I.C.S.: 339113
Edward D. Bullard *(Chm)*

E.D. CRANE & ASSOCIATES
PO Box 260217, Tampa, FL 33685
Tel.: (813) 806-9604
Web Site:
  http://www.cranesalescompany.com
Rev.: $50,000,000
Emp.: 20
Drugs, Proprietaries & Sundries
N.A.I.C.S.: 424210
Herb Nelson *(CEO)*
Joe Murphy *(Pres)*
Nancy Rodewald *(VP & Dir-Retail Svc)*

E.D. SUPPLY CO. INC.
457 Snow Hill Rd, Salisbury, MD 21801
Tel.: (410) 546-2201
Web Site: https://www.edsupply.com
Year Founded: 1975
Sales Range: $10-24.9 Million
Emp.: 44
Provider of Electrical Supplies
N.A.I.C.S.: 423610
Robert F. Brown *(Pres)*
Henry Brown *(CFO & Treas)*
Ed Haenftling *(VP)*

E.E. AUSTIN & SON INC.
1919 Reed St, Erie, PA 16503
Tel.: (814) 454-7147
Web Site: https://www.eeaustin.com
Sales Range: $25-49.9 Million
Emp.: 60
Industrial Buildings, New Construction,
N.A.I.C.S.: 236210
Clemont Austin *(Pres)*
Charles Jenkins *(VP)*
Matthew Sahlmann *(VP)*
Stephen Morvay *(VP)*
Sara Temple *(Controller)*

E.E. NEWCOMER ENTERPRISES INC.
1901 E 119th St, Olathe, KS 66061
Tel.: (816) 221-0543
Web Site: https://www.dhpace.com
Year Founded: 1980
Sales Range: $25-49.9 Million
Emp.: 900
Provider of Repair & Construction Services

N.A.I.C.S.: 811490
Rex E. Newcomer *(Chm, Pres & CEO)*
Thomas S. Palmer *(Sr Exec VP)*

Subsidiaries:

D.H. Pace Company Inc.   **(1)**
1901 E 119th St, Olathe, KS 66061
Tel.: (816) 221-0543
Web Site: http://dhpace.com
Sales Range: $300-349.9 Million
Emp.: 1,457
Mfr of Wood Products
N.A.I.C.S.: 423310
Rex E. Newcomer *(CEO)*
Bradley P. Newcomer *(VP)*
Chris Mann *(CIO)*

Subsidiary (Domestic):

Ankmar, LLC   **(2)**
4200 Monaco St, Denver, CO 80216
Tel.: (303) 321-6051
Web Site: http://www.ankmar.com
Sales Range: $1-9.9 Million
Door Sales & Repair Services
N.A.I.C.S.: 423310
Debby Cuccio *(Dir-HR)*

Overhead Door Company of Albuquerque   **(2)**
5656 Pasadena Ave N E, Albuquerque, NM 87113
Tel.: (505) 344-3667
Web Site: http://www.overheaddoorofalbuquerque.com
Door Sales & Repair Services
N.A.I.C.S.: 423310
Manny Maestas *(Gen Mgr)*

Overhead Door Company of Atlanta   **(2)**
221 Armour Dr, Atlanta, GA 30324
Tel.: (404) 872-3667
Web Site:
  http://www.overheaddooratlanta.com
Door Sales & Repair Services
N.A.I.C.S.: 423310
Tim Smith *(Gen Mgr-Residential Ops)*

Overhead Door Company of Central Arizona   **(2)**
616 W 24th St, Tempe, AZ 85282
Tel.: (480) 968-3667
Web Site:
  http://www.overheaddoorcentralarizona.com
Emp.: 3,500
Door Sales & Repair Services
N.A.I.C.S.: 423310
Michael Waldron *(Reg Mgr)*
Tim Duy *(Gen Mgr)*

Overhead Door Company of Central Missouri   **(2)**
1313 Grand Ave, Columbia, MO 65203
Tel.: (573) 874-3667
Web Site:
  http://www.overheaddoorcentralmo.com
Door Sales & Repair Services
N.A.I.C.S.: 423310
Tim Lower *(VP & Gen Mgr)*

Overhead Door Company of Kansas City   **(2)**
1901 E 119th St, Olathe, KS 66061
Tel.: (816) 221-0072
Web Site:
  http://www.overheaddoorkansascity.com
Abrasive Product Mfr
N.A.I.C.S.: 327910
Chuck Dungan *(Mgr-Fleet)*

Overhead Door Company of Santa Fe   **(2)**
10 Bisbee Ct Unit E, Santa Fe, NM 87508
Tel.: (505) 474-2932
Web Site:
  http://www.overheaddoorofsantafe.com
Door Sales & Repair Services
N.A.I.C.S.: 423310
Dennis Aragon *(Gen Mgr)*

Overhead Door Company of Springfield   **(2)**
707 N Grant Ave, Springfield, MO 65802
Tel.: (417) 862-9339
Web Site: http://www.ohdspringfield.com

Door Sale & Repair Services
N.A.I.C.S.: 423310
Jeff Begley *(Mgr-Ops)*

Overhead Door Company of St. Louis   **(2)**
12046 Lackland Rd, Saint Louis, MO 63146
Tel.: (314) 781-5200
Web Site:
  http://www.overheaddoorstlouis.com
Emp.: 200
Door Sales & Repair Services
N.A.I.C.S.: 423310
Joe Fisher *(VP & Gen Mgr)*

Overhead Door Company of The Four Corners   **(2)**
2798 Inland St, Farmington, NM 87401
Tel.: (505) 327-1282
Web Site:
  http://www.overheaddoorfourcorners.com
Door Sale & Repair Distr
N.A.I.C.S.: 423310

Overhead Door Company of Wichita   **(2)**
3506 W Harry St, Wichita, KS 67213
Tel.: (316) 944-3667
Web Site:
  http://www.overheaddoorswichita.com
Emp.: 35
Door Sales & Repair Services
N.A.I.C.S.: 423310
Justin Carmicheal *(Branch Mgr)*

E.E. REED CONSTRUCTION, L.P.
333 Commerce Green Blvd, Sugar Land, TX 77478
Tel.: (281) 933-4000
Web Site: https://www.eereed.com
Sales Range: $50-74.9 Million
Emp.: 200
Nonresidential Construction
N.A.I.C.S.: 236220
Gene E. E. Reed *(Founder & CEO)*
Mike Den Herder *(CFO)*
Quadros Mike *(Project Mgr)*
Troy Hoffart *(Project Mgr)*
David Rasch *(VP)*
Dan Delforge *(VP)*
Alex Gutenson *(VP)*
Behringer Harvard *(Owner)*

E.E. SCHENCK COMPANY
6000 N Cutter Cir, Portland, OR 97217
Tel.: (503) 284-4124
Web Site:
  https://www.eeschenck.com
Sales Range: $25-49.9 Million
Emp.: 100
Piece Goods & Other Fabrics
N.A.I.C.S.: 424310
Stanley G. Gray *(Pres)*
J. Neff *(Controller)*

E.E. WINE INC.
9108 Centreville Rd, Manassas, VA 20110
Tel.: (703) 368-6568
Web Site:
  http://www.wineenergyva.com
Sales Range: $10-24.9 Million
Emp.: 165
Fuel Oil Dealers
N.A.I.C.S.: 457210
Judy Wine *(VP)*
Donvan V. Wine *(Pres)*
Charles Seltman *(Controller)*

E.F. LACROSSE SALES INC.
3666 Middle Cheshire Rd, Canandaigua, NY 14424
Tel.: (585) 396-0803
Web Site:
  http://www.lacrossesales.com
Rev.: $13,700,000
Emp.: 3
Iron & Steel Castings
N.A.I.C.S.: 423510

Steven LaCrosse *(Pres)*

E.F. MOORE INC.
1119 Fayette St, Conshohocken, PA 19428
Tel.: (610) 825-5600
Web Site: http://efmoore.com
Sales Range: $10-24.9 Million
Emp.: 34
Car Whslr
N.A.I.C.S.: 441110
Dennis F. Moore *(Pres)*

E.G. FORREST COMPANY INC.
1023 N Chestnut St, Winston Salem, NC 27101-1519
Tel.: (336) 723-9151   NC
Web Site: http://www.egforrest.com
Year Founded: 1920
Sales Range: $25-49.9 Million
Emp.: 104
Packaged Frozen Goods
N.A.I.C.S.: 424420
Jamie Swicegood *(Dir-Mktg)*
Rob Heflin *(CFO)*
Jeff Holderfeild *(Pres)*

E.H. HAMILTON TRUCKING SERVICE
2612 W Morris St, Indianapolis, IN 46221
Tel.: (317) 916-2600
Web Site:
  https://www.ehhtrucking.com
Sales Range: $10-24.9 Million
Emp.: 70
Provider of Office & Household Furniture Transport
N.A.I.C.S.: 484210
Byron Bayne *(Pres)*

E.I. MEDICAL IMAGING
110 12th St SW Unit 102, Loveland, CO 80537-6396
Tel.: (970) 669-1793
Web Site: https://www.eimedical.com
Year Founded: 2005
Sales Range: $1-9.9 Million
Emp.: 11
Medical Imaging Equipment Mfr
N.A.I.C.S.: 334510
Charles Maloy *(Pres)*

E.J. BARTELLS CO.
700 Powell Ave SW, Renton, WA 98057-2911
Tel.: (425) 228-4111   WA
Web Site: http://www.ejbartells.com
Year Founded: 1923
Sales Range: $125-149.9 Million
Emp.: 250
Thermal Insulation Products Mfr
N.A.I.C.S.: 423330
Michael Karami *(Dir-IT)*
Kathy Krey *(Mgr-Credit)*

E.J. BRENEMAN, LP.
1119 Snyder Rd, West Lawn, PA 19609
Tel.: (610) 678-1913
Web Site:
  http://www.ejbreneman.com
Sales Range: $10-24.9 Million
Emp.: 80
Highway & Street Construction Services
N.A.I.C.S.: 237310
Rodney Treichler *(Head-Maintenance & Supvr-Shop)*

E.J. DEL MONTE CORP.
909 Linden Ave, Rochester, NY 14625
Tel.: (585) 586-3121
Web Site: http://www.ejdcorp.com
Rev.: $42,738,913

E.J. Del Monte Corp.—(Continued)

Emp.: 900
Construction Services
N.A.I.C.S.: 237210
Mike Mercier (CFO)

E.J. HARRISON & SONS INC.
5275 Colt St, Ventura, CA 93003
Tel.: (805) 647-1414
Web Site: https://www.ejharrison.com
Rev.: $21,900,000
Emp.: 275
Rubbish Collection & Disposal
N.A.I.C.S.: 562111
Ralph Harrison (Pres)

E.J. THOMAS COMPANY
5101 Forest Dr Ste, New Albany, OH
43054
Tel.: (614) 294-3373
Web Site:
http://www.ejthomascompany.com
Sales Range: $10-24.9 Million
Emp.: 19
Provider of Laundry Equipment &
Supplies
N.A.I.C.S.: 423850
John O. Eckhardt (Pres)

**E.J. VESTCO INDUSTRIES,
LLC**
2204 S Exmoor St, Tampa, FL 33629
Tel.: (813) 258-3553
Web Site:
https://www.ejvestcoindustries.com
Emp.: 10
Holding Company
N.A.I.C.S.: 525990
John J. Kaziow (Gen Partner)
Errol J. Menke (Principal)

Subsidiaries:

Powder Processing and Technology,
LLC   (1)
5103 Evans Ave, Valparaiso, IN 46383-
8387
Tel.: (219) 462-4141
Web Site: http://www.pptechnology.com
Sales Range: $10-24.9 Million
Emp.: 80
Ferrites
N.A.I.C.S.: 331221
Kenneth H. Bartelt (Pres & COO)

E.J. VICTOR INC.
110 Wamsutta Mill Rd, Morganton,
NC 28655
Tel.: (828) 437-1991
Web Site: https://www.ejvictor.com
Sales Range: $25-49.9 Million
Emp.: 200
Couches, Sofas & Davenports: Up-
holstered On Wood Frames
N.A.I.C.S.: 337121
Kathy Lockhart (VP-Ops Support)

E.J. WELCH COMPANY INC.
13735 Lakefront Dr, Earth City, MO
63045
Tel.: (314) 739-2273
Web Site: http://www.ejwelch.com
Sales Range: $10-24.9 Million
Emp.: 60
Floor Coverings
N.A.I.C.S.: 423220
Paul Mullen (Controller)
Tony Johnson (Gen Mgr)
Keith Throm (Mgr-Sls-Southern Terri-
tory)
Anthony Capizzi (Branch Mgr)
Mitch Jolley (CEO)
Tressa Samdal (VP-Mktg)
Kavita McCarthy (Pres)

**E.K. BAILEY CONSTRUCTION,
INC.**
1243 N Washington Blvd, Ogden, UT
84404
Tel.: (801) 782-4748
Web Site:
http://www.ekbaileyconstruction.com
Year Founded: 1954
Sales Range: $10-24.9 Million
Emp.: 78
Commercial & Institutional Building
Constructor
N.A.I.C.S.: 236220
Brent Bailey (Owner)

E.K. MACHINE CO., INC.
671 S Main St, Fall River, WI 53932
Tel.: (920) 484-3700
Web Site:
https://www.ekmachine.com
Year Founded: 1970
Sales Range: $10-24.9 Million
Emp.: 85
Sheet Metal Work Mfg
N.A.I.C.S.: 332322
Dan Weinberger (Mgr-Sls)
Gary Errthum (Founder)
Jeff Dykstra (Engr-Mfg)
Ron Hurckman (Dir-Production & En-
grg)
Steven Slack (Dir-Quality Assurance
& Production Plng)

**E.L. HAMM & ASSOCIATES
INC.**
4801 Columbus St, Virginia Beach,
VA 23462-6751
Tel.: (757) 497-5000   DE
Web Site: http://www.elhamm.com
Year Founded: 1980
Sales Range: $10-24.9 Million
Emp.: 100
Engineering Management Services
N.A.I.C.S.: 236220
Beverly Boler (VP)
Debbie Fessler (VP)
Steve Borloz (Project Mgr & Engr-
Civil)
Edward L. Hamm Jr. (Pres)

E.L. HOLLINGSWORTH & CO.
3039 Airpark Dr N, Flint, MI 48507
Tel.: (810) 233-7331
Web Site: https://www.elhc.net
Sales Range: $10-24.9 Million
Emp.: 220
Local Trucking without Storage
N.A.I.C.S.: 484110
Stephen Barr (Chm & CEO)
Jennifer Ward (Mgr-Billing)
Gary House (VP-Ops)
Chris Shepard (Pres)
Jeff Berlin (COO & Exec VP)

E.L. MUSTEE & SONS, INC.
5431 W 164th St, Brook Park, OH
44142
Tel.: (216) 267-3100   OH
Web Site: https://www.mustee.com
Year Founded: 1932
Sales Range: $75-99.9 Million
Emp.: 70
Shower & Bath Stalls, Floors & En-
closures Mfr
N.A.I.C.S.: 326191
Robert J. Mustee (Pres)
Kevin Mustee (VP-Mktg)

**E.L. THOMPSON ASSOCIATES
LLC**
2255 Cumberland Pkwy Ste 1950,
Atlanta, GA 30339
Tel.: (770) 434-6990
Web Site: http://www.elta-ga.com
Sales Range: $10-24.9 Million
Emp.: 15
Plastering, Plain & Ornamental
N.A.I.C.S.: 238310

Dave Steward (Controller)

E.M. GRAY & SON INC.
16440 Industrial Dr, Milford, VA
22514
Tel.: (804) 633-6800
Web Site: https://emgrayandson.com
Rev.: $13,438,444
Emp.: 8
Petroleum Products, Nec
N.A.I.C.S.: 424720
Gary Gray (Pres)

E.M. LAWRENCE LTD.
225 W 37th St Fl 8, New York, NY
10018-6713
Tel.: (201) 319-1955
Sales Range: $10-24.9 Million
Emp.: 40
Women's & Children's Sweaters
N.A.I.C.S.: 424350
Moses Berman (Pres)
Donald Spitzner (CFO)

E.M. THARP INC.
15243 Rd 192, Porterville, CA 93257
Tel.: (559) 782-5800
Web Site: https://www.emtharp.com
Sales Range: $25-49.9 Million
Emp.: 125
Trucks, Tractors & Trailers Whslr
N.A.I.C.S.: 423110
Bruce Greer (Gen Mgr)
Morris A. Tharp (Owner & Pres)
Christina Christina Gomez (Mgr-HR)
Ken Goodwin (VP-Admin)

**E.M. THOMAS MANAGEMENT
INC.**
177 Business Ctr Dr, Corona, CA
92880
Tel.: (951) 817-2525
Sales Range: $10-24.9 Million
Emp.: 12
Fast Food Restaurants Franchisor
N.A.I.C.S.: 722513
Edward Thomas (Pres)

**E.N. BEARD HARDWOOD
LUMBER INC.**
2801 Thurston Ave, Greensboro, NC
27406-4514
Tel.: (336) 378-1265   NC
Web Site:
http://www.beardhardwood.com
Year Founded: 1968
Sales Range: $10-24.9 Million
Emp.: 32
Retailer And Distributor Of Lumber
N.A.I.C.S.: 423310
John Beard (Pres)

**E.O. HABHEGGER COMPANY
INC.**
460 Penn St, Yeadon, PA 19050
Tel.: (610) 622-1977
Web Site:
https://www.habhegger.com
Year Founded: 1929
Emp.: 115
Preventative Maintenance Repairs &
Calibrations for Fueling Trucks & Bulk
Facilities
N.A.I.C.S.: 423830
Kenneth Hagman (Pres & CEO)

**E.O. JOHNSON COMPANY,
INC.**
8400 W Stewart Ave, Wausau, WI
54401
Tel.: (715) 842-9999   WI
Web Site:
https://www.eojohnson.com
Rev.: $22,188,036
Emp.: 170
Copying Equipment

N.A.I.C.S.: 423420
Mary Johnson (CEO)

E.P. GERBER & SONS INC.
4918 Kidron Rd, Kidron, OH 44636
Tel.: (330) 857-2021
Web Site:
https://www.gerberlumber.com
Rev.: $15,165,983
Emp.: 50
Hardware Stores
N.A.I.C.S.: 444140
Elton Gerber (VP)

E.P. HENRY CORPORATION
201 Pk Ave, Woodbury, NJ 08096-
3523
Tel.: (856) 845-6200   NJ
Web Site: http://www.ephenry.com
Year Founded: 1903
Sales Range: $100-124.9 Million
Emp.: 200
Concrete Products & Paving Stones
Mfr; Dealer of Building Supplies
N.A.I.C.S.: 327331
James S. Nash (Head-Fin)
Marianne W. Anzaldo (Sec, Dir-Mktg
& Mgr-Adv)
James C. Henry III (CEO)

**E.R. BERWALD ROOFING
COMPANY**
2440 Charles St N, Saint Paul, MN
55109
Tel.: (651) 777-7411
Web Site:
http://www.berwaldroofing.com
Sales Range: $10-24.9 Million
Emp.: 160
Roofing Contractors
N.A.I.C.S.: 238160
Eugene R. Berwald (Pres)

E.R. JAHNA INDUSTRIES INC.
202 E Stewart Ave, Lake Wales, FL
33853
Tel.: (863) 676-9431
Web Site: https://www.jahna.com
Year Founded: 1950
Sales Range: $25-49.9 Million
Emp.: 130
Sand, Rock & Agriproducts Mining,
Mfr & Distr
N.A.I.C.S.: 212321
Ron Mincey (Mgr-Contract Dredging)

**E.R. STUEBNER CONSTRUC-
TION INC.**
227 Blair Ave, Reading, PA 19601
Tel.: (610) 376-6625
Web Site:
http://www.ersconstruction.com
Year Founded: 1951
Sales Range: $75-99.9 Million
Emp.: 100
Commercial & Institutional Building
Construction Services
N.A.I.C.S.: 236220
Peter Redwanski (Pres)

**E.R. WAGNER MANUFACTUR-
ING CO.**
W130 N8691 Old Orchard Rd,
Menomonee Falls, WI 53051
Tel.: (414) 871-5080   WI
Web Site: https://www.erwagner.com
Year Founded: 1900
Sales Range: $100-124.9 Million
Emp.: 300
Hinge & Stamping Tubular Product &
Coaster & Wheel Mfr
N.A.I.C.S.: 332510
Brad Gador (Pres-Engineered Prod-
ucts Div)

Subsidiaries:

E.R. Wagner Casters and Wheels Div. (1)
331 Riverview Dr, Hustisford, WI 53034
Tel.: (920) 349-3271
Web Site: http://www.erwagner.com
Sales Range: $10-24.9 Million
Emp.: 60
Custom Hinges, Engineered Stampings, Casters, Wheels & Tubular Products Mfr
N.A.I.C.S.: 332510
Lew Schildkraut (CEO)

E.R. Wagner Manufacturing Co. - Engineered Products Division (1)
4611 N 32nd St, Milwaukee, WI 53209-6023
Tel.: (414) 871-5080
Caster & Hinge Mfr
N.A.I.C.S.: 332510

Haydock Caster Company (1)
331 Riverview Dr, Hustisford, WI 53034
Tel.: (920) 349-4350
Sales Range: $10-24.9 Million
Mfr of Casters & Rivets, Wheels, Plastic Plugs & Tips
N.A.I.C.S.: 326199

E.REPUBLIC, INC.
100 Blue Ravine Rd, Folsom, CA 95630
Tel.: (916) 932-1300   CA
Web Site: https://www.erepublic.com
Year Founded: 1983
Sales Range: $10-24.9 Million
Emp.: 200
Periodical & Website Publishing Services
N.A.I.C.S.: 513120
Dennis McKenna (Founder & CEO)
Cathilea Robinett (Pres)
Paul Harney (CFO & COO)
Lisa Harney (Chief Admin Officer)
Paul Taylor (Chief Content Officer)
Kelly Martinelli (Chief Design Officer)
Dustin Haisler (Chief Innovation Officer)
Alan Cox (Exec VP)
Mark Funkhouser (Publr-Governing Magazine)
Steve Towns (Deputy Chief Content Officer)
Stacy Ward-Probst (Sr VP)

Subsidiaries:

Governing Magazine (1)
1100 Connecticut Ave NW Ste 1300, Washington, DC 20036-4101
Tel.: (202) 862-8802
Web Site: http://www.governing.com
Sales Range: $1-9.9 Million
Emp.: 30
National Magazine about Local Government
N.A.I.C.S.: 513120
Mark Funkhouser (Publr)
David Kidd (Dir-Design & Editor-Photo)
Lisa Bernard (CFO)
Alan Cox (Exec VP)
Adam Fowler (Dir-Online Ad Ops)
Kelly Martinelli (CMO)
Dennis McKenna (CEO)
Margaret Mohr (VP-Res)
Cathilea Robinett (Exec VP)
Todd Sander (VP-Res)
Stephan Widmaier (Dir-Production)
Veronika Zubo (Dir-Event-Natl)
Paul Harney (CFO)

E.S. INVESTMENTS, LLC
14055 US Hwy 19 N, Clearwater, FL 33764
Tel.: (727) 536-8822
Web Site:
    https://www.sunmicrostamping.com
Sales Range: $25-49.9 Million
Emp.: 300
Investor; Holding Company; Metal Stampings Mfr
N.A.I.C.S.: 332119

Bryan Clark (Pres & CEO)
Keith Rutherford (Dir-Ops)
Steve McKenzie (VP-Ops)
Phil Ross (VP-Engrg)

Subsidiaries:

Sun Microstamping Technologies (1)
14055 US Hwy 19 N, Clearwater, FL 33764-7239
Tel.: (727) 536-8822
Web Site:
    http://www.sunmicrostamping.com
Sales Range: $25-49.9 Million
Emp.: 250
Computer Products
N.A.I.C.S.: 332119
Phillip Ross (VP-Engrg)
James Brian Clark (CEO)
Charlotte Clarke (Mgr-Mktg)
Bryan Clarke (Pres & CEO)
Matt Dlugosz (Dir-Molding Ops & Production)
Greg Fish (Dir-Quality)
Marilyn Maginnes (Controller-Fin)
Steve McKenzie (VP-Ops)
Keith Rutherford (Mgr-Mexico Ops & Production)

E.S. SUTTON INC.
1400 26 Fl Broadway, New York, NY 10018
Tel.: (212) 944-9494
Rev.: $45,000,000
Emp.: 100
Women's & Children's Sportswear Mfr
N.A.I.C.S.: 424350
Albert Sutton (Pres)
Shalom Braun (Engr-Logistics)
Mordechai Swadron (Mgr-Cost Containment)
Luis Diaz (Mgr-Import & Logistics)
Sarah Sammut (Coord-Production)
Shirley So (Coord-Production)

Subsidiaries:

E.S. Sutton Inc. (1)
115 Kennedy Dr, Sayreville, NJ 08872-1459
Tel.: (732) 721-0022
Sales Range: $25-49.9 Million
Mfr of Women's, Children's & Infants' Clothing
N.A.I.C.S.: 315250

Hi-Rollers Sportswear Ltd. (1)
1400 Broadway Fl 26, New York, NY 10018-5396   (100%)
Tel.: (212) 944-9494
Rev.: $16,700,000
Emp.: 25
Mfr of Women, Children & Infant Clothing
N.A.I.C.S.: 424350
Joseph Sutton (Chm)

E.S. THE THIRD INC.
259 Front St, Bath, ME 04530
Tel.: (207) 442-7994
Web Site: https://www.mwsewall.com
Sales Range: $50-74.9 Million
Emp.: 50
Heating Oil, Kerosene, Propane, Bio-Heat & Gasoline Products
N.A.I.C.S.: 424720
Edward Sewall III (Pres)

E.S.C. ELECTRONICS CORP.
98 Lincoln Ave, Sayville, NY 11782
Tel.: (631) 467-5328   NY
Web Site:
    http://www.custompowersystem.com
Year Founded: 1953
Sales Range: $25-49.9 Million
Emp.: 100
Miniature Delay Lines, Networks & Radio Frequency Interference Filters Mfr
N.A.I.C.S.: 334419
Paul Alessandrini (Pres)

E.S.I. HOLDOING CORP.

Riverview Office Tower Ste 1492 34th Ave S, Bloomington, MN 55425
Tel.: (952) 853-0924
Web Site: http://www.esiholding.com
Holding Company
N.A.I.C.S.: 551112
John West (CFO)

E.T. BROWNE DRUG COMPANY, INC.
440 Sylvan Ave, Englewood Cliffs, NJ 07632
Tel.: (201) 894-9020   DE
Web Site: https://www.palmers.com
Year Founded: 1840
Sales Range: $100-124.9 Million
Emp.: 250
Perfumes, Skin Care, Lotions, Toiletries & Hair Care Products Mfr
N.A.I.C.S.: 325620
Robert Neis (Pres)
Rebecca Brown (VP-Mktg)

Subsidiaries:

Hayward Laboratories (1)
Rte 447, East Stroudsburg, PA 18301-0386   (100%)
Tel.: (570) 424-9512
Web Site: http://www.etbrown.com
Sales Range: $25-49.9 Million
Mfr of Perfumes, Skin Care, Lotions & Toiletries, Hair Care Products
N.A.I.C.S.: 325620
Scott Mount (VP)

Universal Corporation Ltd (1)
Sikkim Commerce House 4/1 Middleton Street, Kolkata, 700071, India
Tel.: (91) 3330587068
Web Site: http://www.uclindia.in
Sales Range: $10-24.9 Million
Emp.: 93
Logistics Consulting Servies
N.A.I.C.S.: 541614
Naraian Sharma (Acct Mgr)

E.T. HORN COMPANY INC.
16050 Canary Ave, La Mirada, CA 90638
Tel.: (714) 523-8050   CA
Web Site: http://www.ethorn.com
Year Founded: 1961
Rev.: $65,000,000
Emp.: 63
Supplier of Chemicals, Raw Materials & Allied Products
N.A.I.C.S.: 424690
Gene Alley (Chm & CEO)
Julie Wubbena (VP-Fin & Ops)
Bob Ahn (Pres-Indus Div)
Jeff Martin (Pres-Admin & Ops)
Kevin Salerno (Pres-Human Nutrition Div)
Roger Clemens (Chief Scientific Officer)

E.T. MACKENZIE COMPANY INC.
4248 W Saginaw Hwy, Grand Ledge, MI 48837-2225
Tel.: (517) 627-8408   MI
Web Site:
    https://www.mackenzieco.com
Year Founded: 1982
Sales Range: $25-49.9 Million
Emp.: 190
Excavation Work, Demolition, Underground Utility Installation, Rehabilitation Site Development
N.A.I.C.S.: 326199
Keith Edgar (Controller)

Subsidiaries:

E T Mackenzie of Florida Inc (1)
6212 33rd St E, Bradenton, FL 34203
Tel.: (941) 756-6760
Emp.: 130
Construction Engineering Services
N.A.I.C.S.: 541330

Melissa Baker (Mgr-HR)

E.T. SIMONDS CONSTRUCTION COMPANY
1500 N Oakland Ave, Carbondale, IL 62902
Tel.: (618) 457-8191   IL
Web Site:
    https://www.etsimonds.com
Year Founded: 1946
Sales Range: $25-49.9 Million
Emp.: 85
Highway & Street Construction
N.A.I.C.S.: 237310
E. K. Simonds (Chm)
Edward T. Simonds (Pres)
Becker Simonds (Mgr-Ops)

E.W. AUDET & SONS, INC.
169 Bay St, Providence, RI 02905
Tel.: (401) 467-3510
Web Site: https://www.ewaudet.com
Year Founded: 1966
Sales Range: $10-24.9 Million
Emp.: 100
Electrical Contractor Services
N.A.I.C.S.: 238210
John Osowa Jr. (VP)

E.W. BULLOCK ASSOCIATES, INC.
730 Bayfront Pkwy Ste 5, Pensacola, FL 32502-6250
Tel.: (850) 438-4015   FL
Web Site: http://www.ewbullock.com
Year Founded: 1982
Sales Range: $25-49.9 Million
Emp.: 12
Advertising Agencies
N.A.I.C.S.: 541810
Sarah Turner (Dir-Art)
Sandy Bartoszewicz (Officer-Finance)
Leslie Perino (COO)
Katie King (Acct Mgr)
Ellis W. Bullock III (Pres & Dir-Creative)

E.W. JAMES & SONS INC.
1308 14 Nailing Dr, Union City, TN 38261
Tel.: (731) 885-0601
Web Site: http://www.ewjames.com
Rev.: $129,900,000
Emp.: 1,300
Grocery Stores
N.A.I.C.S.: 445110
Mike Coley (Dir-Mktg)
Lee Ann James (CEO)
Ken Pink (Pres & COO)

E.W. TOMPKINS COMPANY INC.
124 Sheridan Ave, Albany, NY 12210
Tel.: (518) 462-6577
Web Site:
    http://www.thetompkinsgroup.com
Sales Range: $10-24.9 Million
Emp.: 30
Mechanical Contractor
N.A.I.C.S.: 238220
Thomas Colloton (Pres)
Howard Arnold (VP)

E1 ENTERTAINMENT U.S. LP
22 Harbor Pk Dr, Port Washington, NY 11050
Tel.: (516) 484-1000   NY
Year Founded: 1993
Sales Range: $10-24.9 Million
Emp.: 130
Music, Videos & DVDs Distr
N.A.I.C.S.: 423990
Carolyn Prudente (VP-Fin)
Michael Koch (CEO)
Michael Rosenberg (Pres)
Bill Crowley (VP-Digital & Mobile)

E1 Entertainment U.S. LP—(Continued)

Laura Lombardi *(Dir-Retail Mktg-E1 Music)*
Charles Book *(Dir-Intl Sls & Licensing)*
Rob McDonald *(VP-Sls)*

E2 RECRUITING, INC.
13046 Race Track Rd, Tampa, FL 33626
Tel.: (813) 886-1900
Web Site:
http://www.e2recruiting.com
Sales Range: $10-24.9 Million
Emp.: 25
Recruiting Services
N.A.I.C.S.: 561311
Gary Jacobs *(Owner & Mng Partner)*

E21CORP
47787 Fremont Blvd, Fremont, CA 94538
Tel.: (510) 226-6780
Web Site: http://www.e21mm.com
Year Founded: 1989
Rev.: $15,000,000
Emp.: 150
Brand Development, Full Service, High Technology, Public Relations
N.A.I.C.S.: 541810
Joseph Sun *(CEO)*
James M. Wong *(VP-Global Bus Strategy, Gen Mgr & Comm)*
James Chen *(CTO)*
Agnes Liu *(VP-Asia Pacific Bus)*
Culsin Li *(VP-Asia Pacific Trade Show Bus)*
Jessica Lo Sr. *(COO & VP)*

E2AMP
5354 Denny Ave Unit 126, North Hollywood, CA 91601
Tel.: (818) 252-0090   CA
Year Founded: 2000
Sales Range: $10-24.9 Million
Emp.: 15
Advetising Agency
N.A.I.C.S.: 541810
John C. Anderson *(CEO)*
Michael Chu *(Chief Creative Officer)*
Brock Selig *(Pres)*

E2B TEKNOLOGIES
521 5th Ave, Chardon, OH 44024
Tel.: (440) 352-4700
Web Site: http://www.e2btek.com
Year Founded: 2001
Sales Range: $1-9.9 Million
Emp.: 32
Computer Software Publishers & Developers
N.A.I.C.S.: 513210
William Henslee *(Pres)*
James Mallory *(Dir-Mktg)*

E4E INC.
3979 Freedom Cir Ste 610, Santa Clara, CA 95054
Tel.: (408) 764-5100
Year Founded: 2000
Sales Range: $50-74.9 Million
Emp.: 3,200
Technology & Business Services, Including Transaction Processing, Technical Support & Infrastructure Development
N.A.I.C.S.: 561499
K. B. Chandrasekhar *(Co-Founder & Chm)*
Sridhar Mitta *(Co-Founder)*
Bhaskar Menon *(Pres & CEO)*
Stephen Moseley *(CFO)*
Awanti Agarwala *(Exec VP & Head-Resource & Capacity Mgmt)*
Thomas George *(Exec VP & Head-Sls & Client Rels)*

Nagapriya Asuri *(Exec VP & Head-Solutions & Mktg)*
Viswanathan Balasubramanian *(Exec VP & Head-Total Quality)*
Mohan Krishna *(Pres-Healthcare Bus Svcs)*

Subsidiaries:

e4e Business Solutions India Private Limited   **(1)**
Unit No 1303-1304 13th Floor Prestige Meridian II #30 MG Rd, 560 001, Bengaluru, India   **(100%)**
Tel.: (91) 80 4170 5258
Outsourcing Services-on-Tap for Corporations
N.A.I.C.S.: 561311
Nagapriya Asuri *(Exec VP & Head-Solutions & Mktg)*

Unit (Domestic):

e4e Financial Services   **(2)**
109 Koramangala Industrial Layout, 4th Cross 5th Block, Bengaluru, 560 095, India
Tel.: (91) 8066172295
Web Site: http://www.e4e.com
Financial & Business Services for Corporations
N.A.I.C.S.: 525990

Subsidiary (Domestic):

e4e Healthcare Services Pvt. Ltd.   **(2)**
Fortune Towers 152 Thoraipakkam Pallavaram, Radial Road Kovilambakkam, Chennai, 600 117, India   **(100%)**
Tel.: (91) 4422681240
Web Site: http://www.e4e.com
Outsourced Healthcare Services
N.A.I.C.S.: 621610

E4E SOLUTIONS
3820 Mansell Rd Ste T20, Alpharetta, GA 30022
Tel.: (678) 334-2490
Web Site:
http://www.e4esolutions.com
Year Founded: 2007
Sales Range: $1-9.9 Million
Emp.: 11
Energy Solutions
N.A.I.C.S.: 541620
Josh Long *(Pres & CEO)*
Greg Rupert *(Exec VP-Engrg & Construction)*
Pierpaolo Baldisserotto *(Exec VP-Energy Audits)*
Mike McMurtry *(Exec VP-Sls & Mktg)*

EA ENGINEERING, SCIENCE & TECHNOLOGY, INC.
225 Schilling Cir Ste 400, Hunt Valley, MD 21031
Tel.: (410) 584-7000   DE
Web Site: https://www.eaest.com
Year Founded: 1973
Sales Range: $100-124.9 Million
Emp.: 250
Infrastructure Engineering Services
N.A.I.C.S.: 541690
Loren D. Jensen *(Founder, Chm & CEO)*
Ian D. MacFarlane *(Pres & CEO)*
Peter Ney *(Treas & Sr VP)*
Lee Becker *(VP & Chief Engrg)*
Peggy Derrick *(VP)*

Subsidiaries:

EA Engineering, P.C.   **(1)**
3 Washington Ctr, Newburgh, NY 12550
Tel.: (845) 565-8100
Infrastructure Engineering Services
N.A.I.C.S.: 541330

EA Engineering, Science, and Technology (MI), PLC   **(1)**
455 E Eisenhower Pkwy Ste 50, Ann Arbor, MI 48108
Tel.: (734) 369-3410

Infrastructure Engineering Services
N.A.I.C.S.: 541330

EAB GLOBAL, INC.
2445 M St. NW, Washington, DC 20037
Tel.: (202) 747-1000   DE
Web Site:
http://www.eabresearch.com
Year Founded: 2007
Marketing Consulting Services
N.A.I.C.S.: 541613
Erin Bishop *(Pres)*
David Felsenthal *(CEO)*
Chris Marett *(Pres-EAB Enrollment Svcs)*

Subsidiaries:

Cappex.com LLC   **(1)**
230 W Jackson Blvd Ste 2700, Chicago, IL 60606-4704
Tel.: (847) 859-5621
Web Site: http://www.cappex.com
Educational Support Services
N.A.I.C.S.: 611710
Chris Long *(Pres & Gen Mgr)*
Mark Kantrowitz *(Publr & VP-Strategy)*
Alex Stepien *(CEO)*

EAC NETWORK
50 Clinton St Ste 107, Hempstead, NY 11550
Tel.: (516) 539-0150   NY
Web Site: http://www.eacinc.org
Year Founded: 1969
Sales Range: $10-24.9 Million
Emp.: 458
Community Welfare Services
N.A.I.C.S.: 624190
Lance W. Elder *(Pres & CEO)*
Donna Leto *(Treas)*

EAC PRODUCT DEVELOPMENT SOLUTIONS
14501 Judicial Rd #10, Burnsville, MN 55306
Web Site: http://www.eacpds.com
Year Founded: 1996
Sales Range: $10-24.9 Million
Emp.: 52
Product Development Services
N.A.I.C.S.: 541490
Anthony Bayer *(Mgr-Mktg)*

EACCESS SOLUTIONS, INC.
407 N Quentin Rd, Palatine, IL 60067-4832
Tel.: (847) 991-7190
Web Site: https://www.eaccess.com
Year Founded: 2001
Rev.: $8,500,000
Emp.: 25
Business Consulting Services
N.A.I.C.S.: 541618
David Bean *(Pres)*

EAGLE ASSOCIATES INC.
500 NW 165th St Rd Ste 204, Miami, FL 33169-6306
Tel.: (305) 945-8844   FL
Year Founded: 1971
Sales Range: $10-24.9 Million
Emp.: 4
Sales of Electrical Appliances
N.A.I.C.S.: 423620
George Locke *(Pres)*

EAGLE AVIATION INC.
2861 Aviation Way, West Columbia, SC 29170
Tel.: (803) 822-5555
Web Site: https://www.eagle-aviation.com
Year Founded: 1967
Sales Range: $50-74.9 Million
Emp.: 450
General Aviation Services

N.A.I.C.S.: 532411
David A. Lipski *(Pres)*

EAGLE BANK
466 Broadway, Everett, MA 02149
Tel.: (617) 387-5110
Web Site: http://www.bankeagle.com
Rev.: $21,024,000
Emp.: 100
State Savings Banks, Not Federally Chartered
N.A.I.C.S.: 522180
Angela DiGiacomo *(VP & Branch Mgr)*
Marc J. Whittaker *(Pres & COO)*
Scott Macdonald *(VP-Comml Lending)*
David DiFronzo *(VP-Comml Lending)*
William C. Nolan Jr. *(VP-Comml Lending)*

EAGLE BUICK GMC, INC.
1275 S Suncoast Blvd, Homosassa, FL 34448-1461
Tel.: (352) 436-4797
Web Site:
https://www.eaglebuickgmc.com
Sales Range: $10-24.9 Million
Emp.: 45
New Car Retailer
N.A.I.C.S.: 441110
Ron Elson *(Mgr)*

EAGLE BUSINESS SOLUTIONS INC.
6 Harbison Way, Columbia, SC 29212
Tel.: (803) 732-4300
Web Site:
http://www.ebsisolutions.com
Rev.: $14,100,000
Emp.: 20
Computer & Software Stores
N.A.I.C.S.: 449210
Mike Haigler *(Mgr-Acct)*

EAGLE BUTTON CO., INC.
700-76 Broadway Ste 318, Westwood, NJ 07675
Tel.: (201) 652-4063   NJ
Web Site:
https://www.eaglebutton.com
Year Founded: 1926
Sales Range: $75-99.9 Million
Emp.: 65
Buttons, Buckles, Tabs, Hangers, Toggles, Elbow Paches, Draw Cords & Braids Mfr
N.A.I.C.S.: 424310
Arthur Simon *(Pres & Treas)*

Subsidiaries:

Tho-Ro Products, Inc.   **(1)**
335 Paterson Plank Rd, Carlstadt, NJ 07072-2015
Tel.: (201) 935-3994
Rev.: $7,000,000
Emp.: 35
Cast Polyester
N.A.I.C.S.: 339993

EAGLE COMMUNICATIONS INC.
2703 Hall St Ste 15, Hays, KS 67601
Tel.: (785) 625-4000
Web Site: http://www.eaglecom.net
Sales Range: $10-24.9 Million
Emp.: 270
Radio Broadcasting Stations, Cable TV Stations & Internet Services
N.A.I.C.S.: 516110
Gary D. Shorman *(Chm & CEO)*
Travis Kohlrus *(Gen Mgr-Broadband)*
Mark Trotman *(VP-Radio)*
Terry Drouhard *(Mgr-Hutchinson)*

EAGLE COMTRONICS INC.

7665 Henry Clay Blvd, Liverpool, NY
13088-3507
Tel.: (315) 622-3402
Web Site:
http://www.eaglecomtronics.com
Year Founded: 1975
Sales Range: $10-24.9 Million
Emp.: 210
Radio & Television Communications
Equipment Mfr
N.A.I.C.S.: 334220
Alan Devendorf *(Chm)*

EAGLE CORPORATION
1020 Harris St, Charlottesville, VA
22903-5315
Tel.: (434) 971-2686   VA
Year Founded: 1979
Sales Range: $50-74.9 Million
Emp.: 800
Concrete, Precast & Other Building
Materials Mfr & Supplier
N.A.I.C.S.: 327390
Jay McNeely *(Co-Owner)*
Dave Paulson *(CFO)*
Vince Bush *(Pres)*

Subsidiaries:

Agglite of Virginia Inc.   (1)
3900 Shannon St, Chesapeake, VA 23324
Sales Range: $10-24.9 Million
Emp.: 20
Mfr of Concrete Products
N.A.I.C.S.: 327390

CS Mundy Quarries Inc.   (1)
PO Box 126, Broadway, VA 22815
Tel.: (540) 833-2061
Sales Range: $25-49.9 Million
Emp.: 30
Distr of Crushed & Broken Limestone
N.A.I.C.S.: 212312
David Harrison *(Pres)*

Valley Building Supply Inc.   (1)
210 Stone Spring Rd, Harrisonburg, VA
22801-9651
Tel.: (540) 434-6725
Web Site:
http://www.valleybuildingsupply.com
Sales Range: $25-49.9 Million
Emp.: 250
Mfr of Concrete Products
N.A.I.C.S.: 327390

Valley Building Supply Inc.   (1)
703 Richmond Ave, Staunton, VA 24401
Tel.: (540) 886-3990
Web Site:
http://www.valleybuildingsupply.com
Sales Range: $10-24.9 Million
Emp.: 30
Supplier of Lumber & Other Building Materials
N.A.I.C.S.: 423310
Mitch Moore *(Mgr-Store)*

EAGLE CRUSHER CO. INC.
525 S Market St, Galion, OH 44833
Tel.: (419) 468-2288
Web Site:
http://www.eaglecrusher.com
Sales Range: $10-24.9 Million
Emp.: 85
Crushing, Pulverizing & Screening
Equipment Mfr
N.A.I.C.S.: 333131
Susanne Cobey *(CEO)*
Jay Giltz *(Reg Mgr-Sls)*
Mike Tinkey *(Pres)*

EAGLE DISTRIBUTING CO.
INC.
310 Radford Pl, Knoxville, TN 37917-
4936
Tel.: (865) 637-3311   TN
Web Site: http://www.eaglebud.com
Year Founded: 1983
Sales Range: $25-49.9 Million
Emp.: 190
Beer Distr & Whslr

N.A.I.C.S.: 424810
Raymond Hand *(Pres)*
Betty Carter *(Mgr-Payroll)*

EAGLE DISTRIBUTING OF
SHREVEPORT
900 W 62nd St, Shreveport, LA
71106
Tel.: (318) 868-2708
Web Site:
http://www.eagledistributing.com
Sales Range: $25-49.9 Million
Emp.: 150
Beer & Other Fermented Malt Liquors
Whslr
N.A.I.C.S.: 424810
Mark Ellis *(Mgr)*
Timothy Hawkins *(Mgr-Craft & Import Brand)*
Ray Hand *(Owner & Pres)*

EAGLE FAB
11558 Hartley Rd, Houston, TX
77093
Tel.: (281) 442-8787
Web Site:
http://www.eaglefabsteel.com
Sales Range: $25-49.9 Million
Emp.: 50
Fabricated Structural Metal Mfr
N.A.I.C.S.: 332312
Paul Elizondo Jr. *(Pres)*

EAGLE FOUR EQUITIES LLC
2532 Dupont Dr, Irvine, CA 92612-
1524
Tel.: (949) 863-1344
Web Site:
http://www.eaglefourpartners.com
Privater Equity Firm
N.A.I.C.S.: 523999
Rick Weiner *(Partner)*
Kevin Martin *(Partner)*
Todd Pickup *(Principal)*

Subsidiaries:

The Balboa Bay Club & Resort   (1)
1221 Coast Hwy, Newport Beach, CA
92663
Tel.: (949) 630-4120
Web Site: http://www.balboabayclub.com
Emp.: 500
Resort Hotel Services
N.A.I.C.S.: 721110
Sam El-Rabaa *(Gen Mgr)*
Leticia Rice *(Mgr-Membership Sls)*

The Newport Beach Country   (1)
Club
1 Clubhouse Dr, Newport Beach, CA 92660
Tel.: (949) 644-9550
Web Site: http://www.newportbeachcc.com
Emp.: 60
Golf Country Club
N.A.I.C.S.: 713910
Kevin Martin *(CEO)*

EAGLE GRAPHICS
600 City Pkwy W Ste 600, Orange,
CA 92868
Tel.: (714) 978-2200   CA
Web Site: https://www.eagle411.com
Year Founded: 1975
Sales Range: $10-24.9 Million
Emp.: 27
Printing, Marketing & Promotional
Services
N.A.I.C.S.: 323111
Tim Smith *(Pres)*
Jeff Carte *(VP)*
Jodee Gonzalez *(Acct Mgr)*

EAGLE GROWTH AND IN-
COME OPPORTUNITIES FUND
100 Wall St 11th Fl, New York, NY
10005
Tel.: (212) 701-4500
Investment Fund Services

N.A.I.C.S.: 523999
Joseph L. Morea *(Chm)*
Steven A. Baffico *(Pres & CEO)*
Jennifer Wilson *(CFO, Prinicipal
Acctg Officer & Treas)*

EAGLE HOMES INC.
6454 US Hwy 70 W, La Grange, NC
28551-7916
Tel.: (252) 566-3352
Web Site:
http://www.eaglehomesnc.com
Year Founded: 1990
Sales Range: $10-24.9 Million
Emp.: 30
Mobile Home Dealers
N.A.I.C.S.: 459930
Jesse Miller *(Pres)*

EAGLE INDUSTRIES LLC
625 Raven Ave, Bowling Green, KY
42101
Tel.: (270) 843-3363
Web Site: http://www.eagle-ind.com
Rev.: $33,300,000
Emp.: 300
Home Furniture Mfr
N.A.I.C.S.: 321999
Amado Rivas *(Gen Mgr)*
Cory Jackson *(Mgr-Quality)*

EAGLE INFRASTRUCTURE
SERVICES, INC.
370669 East Hwy 64, Cleveland, OK
74020
Tel.: (918) 358-5735
Web Site: http://www.eagle-infra.com
Year Founded: 1991
Oil Pipeline Mfr
N.A.I.C.S.: 237120
Louis Berezovsky *(CFO & Chief Ad-
min Officer)*
Randy Byer *(Chm & CEO)*
Seth Marsolek *(VP-Bus Dev)*
Matt Cheney *(Pres-Applied Consul-
tants)*
Matt Kesner *(Pres-Cleveland Integrity
Svcs)*
Steven Wright *(Pres-Encompass
Svcs)*
Jeremiah Horne *(Sr VP-Encompass
Svcs)*
David Beckmeyer *(Pres-Perennial
Environmental Svcs)*
Dennis J. Woods *(Pres-Perennial En-
vironmental Services, LLC)*
Laura Villa *(Chief Compliance Officer
& Gen Counsel)*
Jenny Lacy *(Corp Dir-HR)*
Jeff Craig *(Corp Dir-Health Safety &
Environment)*
Glo Hu *(Mgr-E-Bus)*

Subsidiaries:

Perennial Environmental   (1)
Services
13100 NW Fwy Ste 160, Houston, TX
77040-6343
Tel.: (713) 462-7121
Web Site: http://www.perennialenv.com
Research & Development in the Social Sci-
ences & Humanities
N.A.I.C.S.: 541720
Dennis Woods *(Pres)*

EAGLE LEASING COMPANY
1 Irving Eagle Pl, Orange, CT 06477
Tel.: (203) 795-5661
Web Site:
http://www.eagleleasing.com
Sales Range: $10-24.9 Million
Emp.: 65
Trailer Rental Services
N.A.I.C.S.: 532120
Louis Eagle *(Pres)*

EAGLE MANUFACTURING
COMPANY
2400 Charles St, Wellsburg, WV
26070-1000
Tel.: (304) 737-3171   WV
Web Site: http://www.eagle-mfg.com
Year Founded: 1894
Sales Range: $100-124.9 Million
Emp.: 200
Metal Fabricated Products Mfr
N.A.I.C.S.: 332431
John Mitchell *(VP-Sls)*
Joe Eddy *(Pres & CEO)*

EAGLE MANUFACTURING
GROUP
3200 W 84th St, Hialeah, FL 33018-
4908
Tel.: (305) 885-0301   FL
Web Site: https://www.usffab.com
Year Founded: 1937
Rev.: $30,100,000
Emp.: 250
Gray & Ductile Iron Foundries
N.A.I.C.S.: 331511
Alex Debogory *(Pres)*
Dave Brunswick *(CFO & Exec VP)*
Adam W. Solo *(Dir-Tech)*

Subsidiaries:

Eagle Metal Processing & Recycling
Inc   (1)
9599 NW 87 Ave, Medley, FL 33178
Tel.: (305) 364-8350
Web Site:
http://www.eaglemetalprocessing.com
Metal Recycling Services
N.A.I.C.S.: 562920

US Precast Corp.   (1)
8351 NW 93rd St, Miami, FL 33166-2025
Tel.: (305) 885-8471
Sales Range: $10-24.9 Million
Concrete Products
N.A.I.C.S.: 327390
Jamie Rubin *(Gen Mgr)*

USF Fabrication, Inc.   (1)
3200 W 84 St, Hialeah, FL 33018
Tel.: (305) 364-8200
Web Site: http://www.usffab.com
Fabricated Structural Metal Mfr
N.A.I.C.S.: 332312
Nick Conrad *(Mgr-Sls-Western)*
Mark Harrison *(Mgr-Sls-Central Reg)*
Rick Terrill *(Mgr-Sls-Northeast)*

Plant (Domestic):

USF Fabrication, Inc. - Utah
Facility   (2)
2382 Rulon White Blvd, Ogden, UT 84404
Tel.: (800) 258-6873
Fabricated Structural Metal Mfr
N.A.I.C.S.: 332312

United Concrete Products, LLC   (1)
8351 NW 93 St, Medley, FL 33166
Tel.: (305) 885-8471
Web Site:
http://www.unitedconcreteproducts.com
Precast Concrete Pipe Mfr
N.A.I.C.S.: 327332
Joe Tenedine *(VP)*
Shane Debourg *(Gen Mgr)*

Division (Domestic):

United Concrete Products, LLC   (2)
1926 Skees Rd, West Palm Beach, FL
33411-2504
Tel.: (561) 686-4622
Web Site:
http://www.unitedconcreteproducts.com
Sales Range: $1-9.9 Million
Emp.: 75
Concrete Products Mfr
N.A.I.C.S.: 327390

United States Foundry Manufacturing
Inc.   (1)
8351 NW 93rd St, Medley, FL 33166-2025
Web Site: http://www.usfoundry.com
Rev.: $13,600,000
Emp.: 245

Eagle Manufacturing Group—(Continued)

Gray & Ductile Iron Foundries
N.A.I.C.S.: 331511

EAGLE MARINE INDUSTRIES INC.

1 Riverview Ave, East Saint Louis, IL 62201
Tel.: (618) 875-1153
Sales Range: $10-24.9 Million
Emp.: 3
Waterfront Terminal Operation
N.A.I.C.S.: 488320
Richard D. Burke (Pres)
Tim Thomas (VP)

EAGLE MOBILE HOME CENTER INC.

15111 Palmdale Rd, Victorville, CA 92392-2547
Tel.: (760) 241-6468
Web Site:
http://www.highdeserthousing.net
Sales Range: $10-24.9 Million
Emp.: 10
Real Estate Services
N.A.I.C.S.: 459930
Greg Holberg (VP & Gen Mgr)
Debbie J. Stokes (Pres)

EAGLE NATIONAL STEEL LTD

540 Skyline Dr, Hutchins, TX 75141
Tel.: (972) 225-8138
Web Site:
https://www.eaglesteel.com
Year Founded: 1995
Rev.: $19,002,023
Emp.: 25
Metal Building Mfr & Steel Distr
N.A.I.C.S.: 423510

Subsidiaries:

Wylie Steel Inc.   (1)
2001 N Hwy 78, Wylie, TX 75098
Tel.: (972) 442-2568
Web Site: http://www.eaglesteel.com
Rev.: $2,700,000
Emp.: 5
Structural Shapes, Iron Or Steel
N.A.I.C.S.: 423510

EAGLE NEWSPAPERS INC.

4901 Indian School Rd NE, Salem, OR 97305
Tel.: (503) 393-1774
Web Site:
http://www.eaglenewspapers.com
Sales Range: $25-49.9 Million
Emp.: 350
Commercial Printing & Newspaper Publishing
N.A.I.C.S.: 513110
Denny Smith (Chm)

EAGLE POINT SOFTWARE CORPORATION

600 Star Brewery Ste 200, Dubuque, IA 52001
Tel.: (563) 556-8392   IA
Web Site:
https://www.eaglepoint.com
Year Founded: 1983
Sales Range: $10-24.9 Million
Business & Process Improvement Services & Technologies For Land Development Professionals
N.A.I.C.S.: 541511
John Biver (Pres & CEO)

EAGLE POWER & EQUIPMENT CORP.

953 Bethlehem Pike, Montgomeryville, PA 18936-9607
Tel.: (215) 699-5871   PA

Web Site:
https://www.eaglepowerande quipment.com
Year Founded: 1972
Sales Range: $10-24.9 Million
Emp.: 60
Provider of Construction & Mining Machinery Services
N.A.I.C.S.: 423810
Darwin Boe (Controller)
Bridget McDonald (VP)
Matt McDonald (Pres & CEO)

EAGLE PRESS, INC.

640 Instrument Dr, Rocky Mount, NC 27804
Tel.: (252) 451-1825
Web Site: http://www.eaglepress.com
Year Founded: 1989
Rev.: $7,800,000
Emp.: 74
Business Products & Services
N.A.I.C.S.: 323111
Harold Lovell (Mgr-Shipping)
Ken Weatherly (Mgr-Sls-Southeast Reg)
R. Nathan (Mgr-Slitting & Foil Stamping)
Greg McClean (Sls Mgr-Western Reg)
Lance Hancock (Production Mgr)
Carol Dornseif (Mgr-Acctg)
Anthony Sledge (VP-Sls)
David Gooding (CFO)
Tim Shea (COO)
Lane Weatherly (Pres)

EAGLE PRINTING COMPANY

114 W Diamond St, Butler, PA 16001-6003
Tel.: (724) 282-8000
Web Site: http://www.butlereagle.com
Sales Range: $10-24.9 Million
Emp.: 145
Newspapers, Publishing & Printing
N.A.I.C.S.: 513110
Vernon L. Wise (Treas & VP)
Laurie Klutinoty (Controller)
Ron Vodenichar (Gen Mgr & Mgr-HR)

EAGLE PRIVATE CAPITAL, LLC

1 N Brentwood Ste 1550, Saint Louis, MO 63105
Tel.: (314) 754-1400   MO
Web Site:
https://www.eagleprivatecapital.com
Year Founded: 2011
Rev.: $400,000,000
Privater Equity Firm
N.A.I.C.S.: 523999
Scott D. Fesler (Mng Dir)
Matthew J. Kosler (Mng Dir)
Megan M. Macheca (CFO)
Benjamin M. Geis (Mng Dir)
Andrea M. Meyer (Dir)
Wayne L. Smith II (Mng Dir)
James J. Tighe III (Mng Dir)

Subsidiaries:

Cole Information Services, Inc. (1)
17041 Lakeside Hills Plz Ste 2, Omaha, NE 68130-4677
Tel.: (402) 323-3505
Web Site: http://www.coleinformation.com
Insurance, Small Business, Real Estate & Home Services Directory Publisher & Information Services
N.A.I.C.S.: 513140
James Eggleston (Pres & CEO)

Practis Inc. (1)
8720 Red Oak Blvd #220, Charlotte, NC 28217
Tel.: (704) 887-5300
Web Site: http://www.practisinc.com
Landscape Architectural Services
N.A.I.C.S.: 541320

Elizabeth Pettrone (Founder & Mng Partner)

EAGLE PRODUCTIVITY SOLUTIONS

2165 Brighton-Henrietta Townline Rd, Rochester, NY 14623
Tel.: (585) 273-8000
Web Site:
http://www.eagleproductivity.com
Year Founded: 1988
Sales Range: $50-74.9 Million
Emp.: 57
Corporate Consulting & Training Companies
N.A.I.C.S.: 611430
Bob Cannan (CEO)

EAGLE PUBLISHING INC.

1 Massachusetts Ave NW Ste 610, Washington, DC 20001
Tel.: (202) 216-0600   MD
Web Site: http://www.eaglepub.com
Year Founded: 1974
Sales Range: $250-299.9 Million
Emp.: 250
Publisher of Books & Periodicals
N.A.I.C.S.: 513130
Thomas L. Phillips (Chm)
Chris Pascuzzo (Dir-E-Business)
Linda Clark (Dir-HR)
Roger Michalski (VP)

Subsidiaries:

Doctors' Preferred, Inc. (1)
7811 Montrose Rd, Potomac, MD 20854
Tel.: (310) 340-2100
Health Foods Distr
N.A.I.C.S.: 424490

Eagle Publishing Inc. - Eagles Financial Publications Division (1)
1 Massachusetts Ave NW, Washington, DC 20001
Tel.: (202) 216-0600
Financial Magazine Publisher
N.A.I.C.S.: 513130

Eagle Publishing Inc. - The Human Events Group Division (1)
1 Massachusetts Ave NW Ste 600, Washington, DC 20001
Tel.: (202) 216-0601
Web Site: http://www.HumanEvents.com
Emp.: 50
Newspaper Publishers
N.A.I.C.S.: 513110

Eagle Wellness, LLC (1)
300 New Jersy Ave Ste 500, Washington, DC 20001
Tel.: (202) 216-0600
Emp.: 4
Health Care Srvices
N.A.I.C.S.: 621111
Maritza Lizama (Gen Mgr)

IDG Communications, Inc. (1)
5 Speen St 3rd Fl, Framingham, MA 01701
Tel.: (508) 875-5000
Magazine Publisher
N.A.I.C.S.: 513120
John P. O'Malley (COO)
Kumaran Ramanathan (Pres)
Lynn Holmlund (Mktg Dir)
Matt Egan (Dir-Global Editorial)

Subsidiary (Domestic):

Selling Simplified Group, Inc. (2)
7400 E Orchard Rd Ste 350S, Greenwood Village, CO 80111
Tel.: (720) 638-8500
Web Site: http://www.sellingsimplified.com
Sales Range: $1-9.9 Million
Emp.: 200
Software Development Services
N.A.I.C.S.: 541511
Michael White (Pres & CEO)
Jag Sidhu (COO)
Ashok Singh (Sr VP-Software & Data Dev)
Charlie White (VP-Global Sls)
Harman Singh Jaspaul (VP-Data Analytics & Product Dev)
Thomas Koletas (Chief Growth Officer)

EAGLE RIDGE RESORT, LLC

444 Eagle Rdg Dr, Galena, IL 61036
Tel.: (815) 777-2444
Web Site: http://www.eagleridge.com
Year Founded: 1991
Resort & Spa; Hotel & Golf Course
N.A.I.C.S.: 721110
Thomas Ruhs (Gen Mgr)

EAGLE ROCK DISTRIBUTING COMPANY

6205 Best Friend Rd, Norcross, GA 30071
Tel.: (770) 498-5500
Web Site:
https://www.eaglerocks.com
Sales Range: $25-49.9 Million
Emp.: 175
Beer Distr & Whslr
N.A.I.C.S.: 424810
John Economos (Chm)
Fred Millard (VP-Facilities)
Bo Bebeau (VP-Natl Retail Chains)
Keith Palmer (Mgr-Fleet)
Steve Economos (CEO)
Bruce McCall (Mgr-Inventory Control)
Fran Lutz (CFO)
Steven Brand (Dir-Craft & Import Brands)
Max Hannum (Dir-HR)
Nancy Krause (Dir-Pur & Pricing)
Josh Culbreth (Sr Dir-Wine & Spirits)
Larry Kearns (VP & Gen Mgr)
Nick Economos (Pres)

Subsidiaries:

Eagle Rock North Distributing Company (1)
340 Howell Dr, Dalton, GA 30721
Tel.: (706) 226-2194
Beer Distr
N.A.I.C.S.: 424810

EAGLE SALES COMPANY INCORPORATED

5100 Raleigh-Lagrange Rd, Memphis, TN 38134
Tel.: (901) 458-6133
Web Site:
https://www.eaglesales.com
Sales Range: $10-24.9 Million
Emp.: 52
Industrial Supply Whslr
N.A.I.C.S.: 423840
Mark Kobeck (CEO & Exec VP)
Bret Hart (Sr VP-Sls)
Randy Hoard (VP-Electrical Div)
Bill Kobeck (Founder)
Lee Vickers (Mgr-Pur)

EAGLE SUPPORT SERVICES CORPORATION

2705 Artie S Bldg 400 Ste 30, Huntsville, AL 35805
Tel.: (256) 534-2274
Web Site:
http://www.eaglesupport.com
Year Founded: 1996
Sales Range: $25-49.9 Million
Emp.: 350
Management Services
N.A.I.C.S.: 541614
Bob Hauser (Sr VP-Strategic Ops)

EAGLE SYSTEMS & SERVICES, INC.

6221 W Gore Blvd, Lawton, OK 73505-5836
Tel.: (580) 355-6023
Web Site: http://www.esascorp.com
Year Founded: 1986
Sales Range: $10-24.9 Million
Emp.: 316
IT, Logistics, Instructional Design & Program Support Services
N.A.I.C.S.: 561499

Donna Reddout *(Exec VP)*
Mary Ellen *(Dir-HR)*

EAGLE SYSTEMS INC.
230 Grant Rd Ste A1, East
Wenatchee, WA 98802-7721
Tel.: (509) 884-7575
Web Site:
https://www.eaglesystems.net
Year Founded: 1979
Sales Range: $25-49.9 Million
Emp.: 500
Trucking Service
N.A.I.C.S.: 484121
Michael L. Walker *(Owner & Chm)*
Chreston Knutson *(Dir-Info Sys)*

EAGLE TECHNOLOGIES GROUP
9850 Red Arrow Hwy, Bridgman, MI 49106
Tel.: (269) 465-6986   MI
Web Site:
https://www.eagletechnologies.com
Year Founded: 1953
Sales Range: $75-99.9 Million
Emp.: 130
Provider of Systems Integration Products
N.A.I.C.S.: 333998
Gary Reisig *(Project Mgr)*
Dan Riippa *(Engr-Sls)*

EAGLE TRANSPORT CORPORATION
300 S Wesleyan Blvd Ste 202, Rocky Mount, NC 27804
Tel.: (252) 937-2464
Web Site:
https://www.eagletransportcorp.com
Sales Range: $50-74.9 Million
Emp.: 23
Liquid Petroleum Transport
N.A.I.C.S.: 484230
Ron Thomas *(VP-HR)*
Lance Collette *(Pres)*

EAGLE VENEER INC.
2158 NE Industry Dr, Grants Pass, OR 97526-1670
Tel.: (541) 479-3301   OR
Web Site:
http://www.eagleplywood.com
Year Founded: 1984
Sales Range: $25-49.9 Million
Emp.: 95
Softwood Veneer & Plywood Products Mfr
N.A.I.C.S.: 321212
Phil Busch *(Controller)*

EAGLE'S MARK INC.
4200 Papin St, Saint Louis, MO 63110
Tel.: (314) 533-2224
Web Site:
http://www.swissamerican.com
Rev.: $29,000,000
Emp.: 45
Packer, Importer & Wholesale Distributor of Cheese & Fine Foods
N.A.I.C.S.: 424490

EAGLE:XM
5105 E 41st Ave, Denver, CO 80216-4420
Tel.: (303) 320-5411   CO
Web Site: http://www.eaglexm.com
Year Founded: 1956
Sales Range: $1-9.9 Million
Emp.: 100
Fiscal Year-end: 12/31/14
Online Printing & Direct Marketing Production Services
N.A.I.C.S.: 323111

David A. Born *(VP-Database Mktg & Mgmt)*
Joel I. Susel *(Sr VP-Sls & Solution Dev)*
Shell Watt *(VP-IT)*
Mary Kent *(Controller)*

EAGLECARE INC.
6900 Gray Rd, Indianapolis, IN 46237
Tel.: (317) 788-2500
Web Site:
http://www.ascseniorcare.com
Sales Range: $75-99.9 Million
Emp.: 80
Nonresidential Building Operators
N.A.I.C.S.: 531120
Gonna Kelscy *(CEO)*
Gavid Stordy *(COO)*

EAGLELINE ACQUISITION CORP.
595 E Lancaster Ave Ste 300, Radnor, PA 19087
Tel.: (610) 229-9070   DE
Year Founded: 2016
Emp.: 2
Investment Services
N.A.I.C.S.: 523999
Steven E. Fishman *(CEO)*
Joseph Fox *(Pres)*
Arnold Whitman *(Chm)*

EAGLETREE CAPITAL, LP
1185 Ave of the Americas 39th Fl, New York, NY 10036
Tel.: (212) 702-5600   DE
Web Site: http://www.eagletree.com
Year Founded: 2001
Privater Equity Firm
N.A.I.C.S.: 523999
Anup Bagaria *(Co-Mng Partner)*
Robert A. Gray *(Operating Partner)*
Stephanie McCavitt *(Chief Compliance Officer & Gen Counsel)*
Robert Fogelson *(Sr Partner)*
Anup Bagaria *(Co-Mng Partner)*
George L. Majoros Jr. *(Co-Mng Partner)*

Subsidiaries:

AlliedPRA, Inc.   (1)
1 N LaSalle St Ste 1800, Chicago, IL 60602
Tel.: (312) 667-5117
Web Site: http://www.pra.com
Travel Arrangement & Event Planning Services
N.A.I.C.S.: 561599
Mike Fiber *(CEO)*
Laurie Knapp *(Chief Growth Officer)*
Sara Talsma *(Sr VP-People)*
Greg Myles *(CFO)*
Hillary Smith *(Sr VP-Creative & Strategy)*
Michael Costa *(Sr VP-Bus Ops)*
Stan Dzierzega *(Sr VP-Enterprise Project Mgmt)*
Danielle Cirami-Gillis *(VP-Strategic Partnerships)*
Courtney Lohmann *(Dir-Corp Social Responsibility)*
Ally Topp *(Dir-Sls Ops-Global)*
Cosimo Bruzzese *(VP-Bus Dev)*
Dean Altvater *(Sls Dir-Global)*
Mitch MacGregor *(Acct Mgr-Global Sls)*
Hannah Bodine *(Mgr-Global Sales Operation)*

Subsidiary (Domestic):

Kinetic Energy, LLC   (2)
3451 N Dixie Hwy, Oakland Park, FL 33334
Tel.: (954) 390-0898
General Management Consulting Services
N.A.I.C.S.: 541611

One Smooth Stone, Inc.   (2)
5222 Main St, Downers Grove, IL 60515
Tel.: (630) 969-1800
Event Planning Services
N.A.I.C.S.: 561599

Corsair Components, Inc.   (1)

47100 Bayside Pkwy, Fremont, CA 94538
Tel.: (510) 657-8747
Web Site: http://www.corsair.com
Personal Computer & Gaming Hardware High-Performance Components Designer, Mfr & Supplier
N.A.I.C.S.: 334118
Andy J. Paul *(Founder & CEO)*
Thi La *(Pres & COO)*

Subsidiary (Domestic):

ORIGIN PC, LLC   (2)
12400 SW 134th Ct Ste 8, Miami, FL 33186-6499
Tel.: (305) 971-1000
Web Site: http://www.originpc.com
Computer Mfr; Desktops & Laptops
N.A.I.C.S.: 334111
Kevin Wasielewski *(Founder)*

FuseFX, Inc.   (1)
14823 Califa ST., Los Angeles, CA 91411
Tel.: (818) 237-5052
Web Site: http://www.fusefx.com
Emp.: 1,200
Visual Effect Development Service
N.A.I.C.S.: 541430
Tim Jacobsen *(Founder & Chief Dev Officer)*
Jason Fotter *(Co-Founder)*
David Altenau *(Founder & Chm)*
Jon Cowley *(Head-Studio)*

Gaylord Chemical Company LLC   (1)
106 Galeria Blvd, Slidell, LA 70458-1245
Tel.: (985) 649-5464
Web Site: http://www.gaylordchem.com
Chemicals Mfr
N.A.I.C.S.: 325998
Paul Dennis *(CEO)*
Artie McKim *(VP-Tech)*
Marc Smith *(VP-Mfg)*
Dawn Pichon *(VP & Controller)*
Steve Skal *(VP-Sls)*

Invincible Boat Company   (1)
4700 NW 132nd St, Opa-locka, FL 33054
Tel.: (305) 685-2704
Web Site: http://www.invincibleboats.com
Shipbuilding And Repairing
N.A.I.C.S.: 336611
Bill Cordes *(VP-Sls)*
Scott Wood *(Sr VP-Design)*
John Dorton *(CEO)*

Lignetics, Inc.   (1)
1075 E S Boulder Rd Ste 210, Louisville, CO 80027
Tel.: (303) 802-5400
Web Site: http://lignetics.com
Renewable Wood Products Mfr
N.A.I.C.S.: 321999
Brett Jordan *(CEO)*
Casey Hofmann *(CFO)*
Mike Sale *(VP-Ops)*

Subsidiary (Domestic):

Fiber Energy Products AR LLC   (2)
288 Industrial Dr, Mountain View, AR 72560-9085
Tel.: (870) 269-7930
Web Site: https://www.fiberenergy.us
Wood Pellet Mfr
N.A.I.C.S.: 321999

Marth Wood Shaving Supply, Inc.   (2)
6752 State Highway 107, Marathon, WI 54448
Tel.: (715) 842-9200
Web Site: http://www.marthwood.com
Renewable Wood Products Mfr
N.A.I.C.S.: 321999

MMGY Global LLC   (1)
4601 Madison Ave, Kansas City, MO 64112
Tel.: (816) 472-5988
Web Site: http://www.mmgyglobal.com
Sales Range: $100-124.9 Million
Emp.: 120
Advertising Services
N.A.I.C.S.: 541810
Don Montague *(Principal)*
Stewart Colvin *(Exec VP-Creative)*
Lucas Cobb *(CFO & Exec VP-Ops)*
Hugh McConnell *(CFO & Exec VP-Ops)*
Chris Davidson *(Exec VP-Global Strategy)*
Calep Howard *(CIO)*

Chris Pomeroy *(Dir-Global Strategies & Client Svcs)*
Peter Yesawich *(Principal)*
Katie Briscoe *(CEO)*
Craig Compagnone *(Pres & COO)*
Al Merschen *(Partner)*
Julie Freeman *(Exec VP & Mng Dir-NJF)*
Nancy Friedman *(Partner)*
Wes Kubik *(Chief HR Officer & Sr VP)*
Jessica Schultz *(Exec VP-Global Media Strategy)*
Mia R. Wise *(Exec VP-Global HR)*
Karla Flannery *(CMO)*

Subsidiary (Domestic):

D. K. Shifflet & Associates, Ltd.   (2)
1750 Old Meadow Rd Ste 425, McLean, VA 22102
Tel.: (703) 536-0500
Web Site: http://www.dksa.com
Travel-Related Marketing Research & Public Opinion Polling
N.A.I.C.S.: 541910
Jim Caldwell *(VP-Sls & Mktg)*
Douglas Shifflet *(Chm & CEO)*
Jayant Shukla *(CFO)*
Cheryl Schutz *(VP-Acct Svcs)*
Nandini Nadkarni *(VP-Analytical Ops)*

Branch (Domestic):

MMGY Global - New York   (2)
360 Lexington Ave 10 Fl, New York, NY 10017
Tel.: (212) 219-7560
Emp.: 53
Public Relations Services
N.A.I.C.S.: 541820
Lena Williamson *(Office Mgr)*
Julie Freeman *(Exec VP & Mng Dir)*

MMGY Global - Orlando   (2)
423 S Keller Rd Ste 100, Orlando, FL 32810-6121
Tel.: (407) 875-1111
Web Site: http://www.ypartnership.com
Sales Range: $150-199.9 Million
Emp.: 75
Advertising & Public Relations Agency
N.A.I.C.S.: 541810
Kerry Cannon *(Mng Dir)*
Art Hardie *(Assoc Dir-Creative)*
Nancy Revell *(Grp Dir-Media)*

Subsidiary (Domestic):

Myriad Travel Marketing   (2)
6033 W Century Blvd Ste 900, Los Angeles, CA 90045
Tel.: (310) 649-7700
Web Site: http://www.myriadmarketing.com
Advertising Agencies, Event Marketing, Exhibit/Trade Shows, Public Relations, Sales Promotion, Travel & Tourism
N.A.I.C.S.: 541810
Al Merschen *(Pres-Myriad & Partner)*
Michael Price *(Exec VP)*
Laura Matar *(Dir-Mktg Svcs)*
Julie Cuesta *(Exec VP & Mng Dir)*
Danny Guerrero *(Grp Dir)*
Tricia Carvajal *(Acct Dir)*

Branch (Domestic):

Myriad Travel Marketing   (3)
501 5th Ave Ste 1101, New York, NY 10017
Tel.: (646) 366-8162
Web Site: http://www.myriadmarketing.com
N.A.I.C.S.: 541810

Mackenzie-Childs LLC   (1)
3260 State Route 90, Aurora, NY 13026
Tel.: (315) 364-6118
Web Site: http://www.mackenzie-childs.com
Semivetreous China Tableware, Upholstered & Wood Household Furniture & Home Accessories Designer & Mfr
N.A.I.C.S.: 327110
Rebecca Proctor *(Chief Brand Officer & Creative Dir)*
John Ling *(CEO)*

Subsidiary (Domestic):

Patience Brewster, Inc.   (2)
3872 Jordan Rd, Skaneateles, NY 13152
Tel.: (800) 272-8844
Web Site: http://www.patiencebrewster.com
Holiday Ornaments & Gifts Mfr

EagleTree Capital, LP—(Continued)

N.A.I.C.S.: 459420
Rebecca Dalton (VP-Sls)
Hubbard Stout (VP-Product Dev)
Marietta Gregg (Dir-Mktg)
Holland C. Gregg III (COO)

Moss Inc. (1)
2600 Elmhurst Rd, Elk Grove Village, IL
60007-6312
Tel.: (847) 238-4200
Web Site: http://www.mossinc.com
Emp.: 500
Tension Fabric Structures, Wide Format
Graphics & Specialty Signage Mfr
N.A.I.C.S.: 339950
Mark Ollinger (CFO)
Dan Patterson (Pres & CEO)
Bob Frey (Exec VP-R&D)
Jim Lundberg (Sr VP-Project Admin)
Joe Donley (VP-Production & Logistics)
Sarah Browning (Sr VP-Ops)
Yvonne Illenberg (Dir-Acctg)
Heidi Katherine (VP-Creative Design)
Jim Lovelady (Sr VP-Sls & Enterprise Sls
Ops-North America & Asia)
Dan Scandiff (Exec VP-Sls)
Jason Diesman (Dir-Technical Design)

Northstar Travel Media LLC (1)
100 Lighting Way 2nd Fl, Secaucus, NJ
07094-3619
Tel.: (201) 902-2000
Web Site:
http://www.northstartravelgroup.com
Periodical Publisher; Online Information
Services
N.A.I.C.S.: 513120
Phylis Gebhardt (VP-HR)
Thomas Kemp (Chm & CEO)
Janine Lester Bavoso (Sr VP-HR)
Lori Cioffi (Sr VP & Dir-Editorial-Meetings
Grp)
Beth Koesser (VP-Database Products)
Rich Mastropietro (Sr VP-IT Infrastructure &
Ops)
Roberta Muller (Sr VP-Product Dev)
Sheila Rice (VP-Bus Dev & Licensing)
Robert G. Sullivan (Pres-Travel Grp)
Arnie Weissmann (Sr VP, Editor-In-Chief-
Travel Weekly & Dir-Editorial)
Tim Reid (Publr & VP)
Alan B. Rosenthal (Owner & Partner)
Lisa Cohen (CFO)
David Blansfield (Publr & Exec VP)
Bruce Shulman (Publr-Retail Travel Grp &
VP)
Alicia Evanko (Sr VP-Travel Grp Events)
Matt Yorke (Chief Digital Officer)

Unit (Domestic):

Incentive Magazine (2)
770 Broadway, New York, NY 10003
Tel.: (646) 654-7638
Web Site: http://www.incentivemag.com
Emp.: 50
Incentive Program & Consumer Promotion
Trade Magazine
N.A.I.C.S.: 513120
Lori Cioffi (Sr VP & Dir-Editorial)
Andrea Doyle (Sr Editor)
Josh Lieberman (Editor-Digital)
Jennifer Ruf (Art Dir)
Danielle Cirami-Gillis (VP-Events & Trade-
shows)
Lesley Krautheim (Mng Editor-Custom Me-
dia)
Alison Golub (Sr Editor)
Tessa Sestina (Art Dir)
Joe D'Andrea (Dir-Digital Media Grp)
Shalise DeMott (Media Sls)
David R. Blansfield (Exec VP & Publr)

Subsidiary (Domestic):

Phocuswright Inc. (2)
116 W 32nd St 14th Fl, New York, NY
10001 (100%)
Tel.: (860) 350-4084
Web Site: http://www.phocuswright.com
Emp.: 50
Reservation Technology Services
N.A.I.C.S.: 561599
Cees Bosselaar (VP-Bus Dev)
Kimberly Campetti (Mgr-Events)
Pam Carey (Sr Mgr-Mktg)
Elizabeth Cepeda (Sr Mgr-Res Production
& Accts)

Pete Comeau (Sr VP-Sls & Mktg)
Debra Cortese (Mgr-Events)
Bing Liu (Dir-Surveys & Analytics)
David Juman (Dir-Editorial & Res)
Diane Shuart (Sr Dir-Res Ops)
Monzerrath Gonzalez (Mgr-Product Mktg)
Deepak Jain (Mgr-Data & Analytics)
Catherine Plummer (VP-Events)
Douglas Quinby (Sr VP-Res)
Lorraine Sileo (Sr VP-Res & Bus Ops)
Simon Lehmann (Pres)
Walter Buschta (VP-Mktg)
Trisha Buyer (Exec Dir)
Michael Colleta (Mgr-Res & Innovation)
Alycia Grenesko (Sls Mgr)
Lori Harris (Sr Mgr)
Gillian Huntoon (Sr Mgr-Bus Tech)
Virendra Jain (Dir-Bus Dev-Asia Pacific)
Florence Kaci (Dir-Sls-EMEA)
Eugene Ko (Mgr-Digital Mktg & Comm)
Kirsten Motley (Mgr-Res Sls & Support)
Maggie Rauch (Dir-Res)
Cat Reith (Sr Acct Mgr)
Kimberly Newbury (VP-Sls)

Sterling Valley Systems, Inc. (2)
782 Mtn Blvd, Stowe, VT 05672
Tel.: (802) 253-2905
Web Site: http://corp.inntopia.com
Reservation Technology Services
N.A.I.C.S.: 561599
Trevor Crist (CEO)
Craig DeLuca (Pres)
Corey Ryan (Chief Comml Officer)
John Kitonis (CTO)
Jim Lilly (Sr VP)
Gregg Blanchard (Dir-Mktg)
Katharine Bodan (Sr Mgr-Software Dev)
Anthony Converse (Dir-IT)
Tom Foley (Dir-Bus Intelligence)
Brian Forrest (Dir-Partner Svcs)
Cedar Hannan (Dir-Security & Compliance)
Amy Josef (Dir-Acct Mgmt)
Bill Kushubar (Sr-Sls)
Mike Lawrence (VP-Sls)
Tyler Mumley (VP-Sls)
Andrea Rosamilia (VP-Product Mgmt)
John Spencer (Sr Architect)
Ben Zeeb (Sr VP-Product Dev)
Trisha Buyer (Exec Dir)

Summit Hill Foods, Inc. (1)
100 E 1st Ave, Rome, GA 30161-3212
Tel.: (800) 334-4468
Web Site: http://www.semills.com
Flour & Baked Products Mfr
N.A.I.C.S.: 311999
Chris Wheeler (Dir-Pur)
Jessica Molock (Mgr-Quality Assurance)
Dana Bogardus (Dir-HR)
Peter Hjort (Pres)

Subsidiary (Domestic):

JMH International, LLC (2)
3628 West 1820 S, Salt Lake City, UT
84104
Tel.: (385) 288-1198
Web Site: http://www.jmhpremium.com
Soup & Flavor Base, Gravy, Sauce &
Dressing Mfr & Distr; Recipe Developer &
Publisher
N.A.I.C.S.: 311941
Charles Hayes (Dir-Culinary)
Kevin Dulin (Pres)

The Channel Company LLC (1)
1 Research Dr Ste 400B, Westborough, MA
01581
Tel.: (508) 416-1175
Web Site:
http://www.thechannelcompany.com
IT Channel-Focused Events, Media, Re-
search, Consulting, Sales & Marketing Ser-
vices
N.A.I.C.S.: 541519
Robert Skelley (CEO)
Dan Dignam (Partner & Exec VP)
Lisa MacKenzie (Partner & Sr VP)
Rob Wiseltier (CFO & Partner)
Adelaide J. Reilly (Sr VP-Ops)
Lauren Goldstein (VP & Dir-Strategic Acct)
Bill Jones (Mng Dir-Events & VP)
Rick Bellan (VP-Lead Generation & Analyt-
ics)
Karen Newnam (Sr Dir-Mktg Svcs & Prod-
uct Dev)
Robert DeMarzo (Sr VP-Event Content &
Strategy)

Bob Skelley (Mng Dir-Svcs & Product Dev
& VP)
Erika McGrath (VP-HR)
Kim Sparks (Dir-Mktg)

EAGLEVILLE HOSPITAL
100 Eagleville Rd, Eagleville, PA
19403
Tel.: (610) 635-7605 PA
Web Site:
http://www.eaglevillehospital.org
Year Founded: 1909
Sales Range: $25-49.9 Million
Emp.: 515
Health Care Srvices
N.A.I.C.S.: 622110
Richard Mitchell (Chief Info & Secu-
rity Officer & Dir-IT)
ZoeAnn Yousaitis (Dir-HR)
Maureen King Pollock (CEO)
Sharon A. Harris (Chm)
Eileen Joseph (Treas & Sec)
Alfred Salvitti (CFO)
Anthony J. Scarcelli Jr. (Asst Sec &
Asst Treas)
Eugene J. Ott Jr. (COO)

EAI PARTNERSHIP LP
200 Connecticut Ave Ste 7, Norwalk,
CT 06854
Tel.: (203) 855-2200
Rev.: $21,500,000
Emp.: 125
Investment Counselors
N.A.I.C.S.: 523150

EAI TECHNOLOGIES, LLC
8300 Boone Blvd Ste 300, Vienna,
VA 22182
Tel.: (703) 790-9715
Web Site: http://www.eaiti.com
Year Founded: 2001
Rev.: $2,800,000
Emp.: 25
Computer System Design Services
N.A.I.C.S.: 541512
Velan Thillairajah (Founder & CEO)

EAKES INC.
617 W 3rd St, Grand Island, NE
68801
Tel.: (308) 382-8026
Web Site: http://www.eakes.com
Year Founded: 1945
Computer Services
N.A.I.C.S.: 423430
Doug Gallaway (Mgr-Managed Print
Div)
Nate Schaf (Mgr-Janitorial Div)
Natasha Seacrest (Office Mgr-
Products)
Heather Morrow (Mgr-Furniture Prod-
ucts)
Christian Pohlenz (Mgr-Tech Svcs)
Cindy Jarosz (Coord-Retail)

**EAKIN-YOUNGENTOB ASSO-
CIATES INC.**
4800 Hampden Ln Ste 300,
Bethesda, MD 20814-2932
Tel.: (301) 634-8600 VA
Web Site: http://www.eya.com
Year Founded: 1992
Sales Range: $10-24.9 Million
Emp.: 50
Management Services
N.A.I.C.S.: 561110
Robert Youngentob (Pres)

EARHART PETROLEUM INC.
1494 Lytle Rd, Troy, OH 45373-9401
Tel.: (937) 335-2928
Web Site:
http://www.earhartcompany.com
Year Founded: 1979
Sales Range: $10-24.9 Million
Emp.: 60

Petroleum Product Distr
N.A.I.C.S.: 424720
Mike Rhoades (VP-Trading & Supply)

EARL & BROWN COMPANY
5825 SW Arctic Dr, Beaverton, OR
97005
Tel.: (503) 670-1170
Web Site: https://www.earlbrown.com
Year Founded: 1994
Rev.: $46,300,000
Emp.: 40
Electronic Parts & Equipment Mer-
chant Whslr
N.A.I.C.S.: 423690
Chuck Taylor (CEO)

**EARL DUDLEY ASSOCIATES
INC.**
5352 1st Ave N, Birmingham, AL
35212
Tel.: (205) 595-3796
Web Site:
https://www.earldudley.com
Sales Range: $10-24.9 Million
Emp.: 50
Engineers' Equipment & Supplies,
Nec
N.A.I.C.S.: 423490

EARL ENTERPRISES
4700 Millenia Blvd Ste 400, Orlando,
FL 32839
Tel.: (407) 903-5500
Web Site:
http://www.earlenterprise.com
Entertainment, Leisure, Tourism, Ho-
tel & Restaurant Consultant Services
N.A.I.C.S.: 541618
Robert Ian Leigh (Owner)

Subsidiaries:

Bertucci's Corporation (1)
155 Otis St Ste 2, Northborough, MA 01532
Tel.: (508) 351-2500
Web Site: http://www.bertuccis.com
Italian Restaurant
N.A.I.C.S.: 722511
Steve Clark (Vice Chm & CEO)

EARL G. GRAVES LTD.
130 5th Ave Fl 10, New York, NY
10011-4306
Tel.: (212) 242-8000 NY
Web Site:
http://www.blackenterprise.com
Year Founded: 1970
Sales Range: $25-49.9 Million
Emp.: 55
Communication Service
N.A.I.C.S.: 541611
Earl Gilbert Graves Jr. (Chm)
Natalie Hibbert (VP & Dir-HR & Corp
Ops)
Derek T. Dingle (Editor-in-Chief)
Alfred A. Edmond (Sr VP)
Dirk Caldwell (Sr VP & Dir-Multimedia
Sls-Natl)
Caroline V. Clarke (Dir-Editorial)
Alan Hughes (Dir-Editorial)
Genevieve Michel-Bryan (VP & Dir-
Brdcst)
Terence K. Saulsby (VP & Dir-
Creative)
Sherry Herbert (VP & Dir-Events)
Kyle Allman (VP-Multimedia Sls)
Grace Spellman Castro (VP-
Multimedia Sls)

Subsidiaries:

**Earl G. Graves Publishing Co.,
Inc.** (1)
260 Madison Ave 11th Fl, New York, NY
10016 (100%)
Tel.: (212) 242-8000
Web Site: http://www.blackenterprise.com

Sales Range: $10-24.9 Million
Emp.: 60
Publisher Company
N.A.I.C.S.: 513120
Earl Gilbert Graves Jr. *(Pres & CEO)*

EARL MAY SEED & NURSERY L.C.

208 N Elm St, Shenandoah, IA 51601
Tel.: (712) 246-1020   IA
Web Site: https://www.earlmay.com
Year Founded: 1919
Sales Range: $200-249.9 Million
Emp.: 750
Garden Centers Operator; Seeds,
Gifts, Pet Supplies, Wild Bird Products & Patio Furniture Sales
N.A.I.C.S.: 444240
Bill Shaw *(CEO)*
Angela Shaw *(Dir-Acctg)*
Gordon Sherman *(Dir-Mktg)*
Karen Gutschenritter *(Coord-Payroll & HR)*

EARL R. MARTIN, INC.

1278 E Earl Rd, East Earl, PA 17519
Tel.: (717) 354-4061
Web Site: http://www.earlrmartin.com
Sales Range: $10-24.9 Million
Emp.: 45
Trucking Service
N.A.I.C.S.: 484121
Earl R. Martin *(Pres)*

EARL TINDOL FORD INC.

1901 E Franklin Blvd, Gastonia, NC 28054
Tel.: (704) 867-8341
Web Site:
   http://www.tindolfordonline.com
Year Founded: 1974
Sales Range: $50-74.9 Million
Emp.: 100
Automobile Sales, New & Used
N.A.I.C.S.: 441110
Natalie R. Tindol *(Pres)*

EARL W. COLVARD INC.

816 S Woodland Blvd, Deland, FL 32720-6836
Tel.: (386) 734-6447   FL
Web Site:
   https://www.boulevardtire.com
Year Founded: 1982
Sales Range: $25-49.9 Million
Emp.: 103
Auto & Home Supply Stores
N.A.I.C.S.: 441340
Earl W. Colvard *(Pres & CEO)*

EARLHAM SAVINGS BANK

7300 Lake Dr, West Des Moines, IA 50266
Tel.: (515) 223-4753
Web Site:
   https://www.earlhambank.com
Sales Range: $10-24.9 Million
Emp.: 40
Savings Bank
N.A.I.C.S.: 522110
William W. Hunter *(Chm & Pres)*
Garret Hulse *(VP-Bank Dev)*

EARLY AMERICAN HISTORY AUCTIONS, INC.

PO Box 3507, Rancho Santa Fe, CA 92067
Tel.: (858) 759-3290
Web Site:
   https://www.earlyamerican.com
Sales Range: $1-9.9 Million
Emp.: 10
Antique Dealer
N.A.I.C.S.: 459510
Dana Linett *(Pres)*

EARLY LEARNING COALITION OF ALACHUA COUNTY

4424 NW 13th St Bldg A, Gainesville, FL 32609
Tel.: (352) 375-4110   FL
Web Site: https://www.elcalachua.org
Year Founded: 2000
Sales Range: $10-24.9 Million
Emp.: 43
Child Day Care Services
N.A.I.C.S.: 624410
Remzey Samarrai *(Chm)*
Jacki Jackson *(CEO)*

EARLY LEARNING COALITION OF BREVARD COUNTY, INC.

PO Box 560692, Rockledge, FL 32956-0692
Tel.: (321) 637-1800   FL
Web Site: https://www.elcbrevard.org
Year Founded: 2000
Sales Range: $25-49.9 Million
Emp.: 73
Child Day Care Services
N.A.I.C.S.: 624410
Alan Bergman *(Chm)*

EARLY LEARNING COALITION OF BROWARD COUNTY, INC.

6301 NW 5th Way Ste 3400, Fort Lauderdale, FL 33309
Tel.: (954) 377-2188   FL
Web Site: http://www.elcbroward.org
Year Founded: 2000
Sales Range: $75-99.9 Million
Emp.: 22
Child & Youth Care Services
N.A.I.C.S.: 624110
Laurie Sallarulo *(Chm)*
Christina Klima *(Chief Admin Officer)*
Renee Podolsky *(Treas)*

EARLY LEARNING COALITION OF DUVAL, INC.

8301 Cypress Plaza Dr Ste 201, Jacksonville, FL 32256
Tel.: (904) 208-2044   FL
Web Site:
   http://www.choosequalitychildcare.org
Year Founded: 2000
Sales Range: $50-74.9 Million
Emp.: 91
Educational Support Services
N.A.I.C.S.: 611710
Cathy Parker *(Dir-Provider Svcs)*
Angel Carro *(VP-Fin & Admin)*
Lisa Tyner *(Dir-Child & Family)*

EARLY LEARNING COALITION OF INDIAN RIVER, MARTIN & OKEECHOBEE COUNTIES, INC.

10 SE Central Pkwy Ste 200, Stuart, FL 34994
Tel.: (772) 220-1220   FL
Web Site: https://www.elcirmo.org
Year Founded: 2000
Sales Range: Less than $1 Million
Emp.: 22
Educational Support Services
N.A.I.C.S.: 611710
Migdalia Rosado *(CEO-Interim & Dir-Ops)*
Zack Hackley *(Dir-Fin)*
Pat Houston *(Dir-Provider Svcs)*
Angela Davis-Green *(Dir-Family Svcs)*
Brandon Tucker *(Chm)*
Donna Rivett *(Vice Chm)*
Samantha Reed *(Mgr-Family Svcs)*
Michelle Akins *(Sec)*
William Laughlin *(Treas)*

EARLY LEARNING COALITION

OF LAKE COUNTY

1300 Citizens Blvd Ste 206, Leesburg, FL 34748
Tel.: (352) 435-0566   FL
Web Site: https://www.elclc.org
Year Founded: 2000
Sales Range: $10-24.9 Million
Emp.: 28
Child Educational Support Services
N.A.I.C.S.: 624110
Lesha Buchbinder *(Exec Dir)*
Tameka Mays *(Dir-Quality Ops)*
Aaron Kissler *(Dir-County Health Dept)*
B. E. Thompson *(Chm)*
Eric English *(Vice Chm)*
Hays Ginn *(Vice Chm)*
Bill Giffing *(Vice Chm)*

EARLY LEARNING COALITION OF MANATEE COUNTY, INC.

600 8th Ave W Ste 100, Palmetto, FL 34221
Tel.: (941) 757-2900   FL
Web Site: https://www.elc-manatee.org
Year Founded: 1997
Sales Range: $10-24.9 Million
Emp.: 43
Child Development Services
N.A.I.C.S.: 624110
Paul Sharff *(CEO)*
Pam Parmenter *(Program Mgr-Quality Initiatives & Education)*
Karen Holman *(CFO)*
Cori Perry *(Dir-Provider Rels)*
Howard Veltz *(Chm)*
Sharon Oakes *(COO)*

EARLY LEARNING COALITION OF MIAMI-DADE/MONROE

2555 Ponce de Leon Blvd Ste 500, Coral Gables, FL 33134
Tel.: (305) 646-7220   FL
Web Site: http://www.elcmdm.org
Year Founded: 2005
Sales Range: $10-24.9 Million
Emp.: 233
Child Educational Support Services
N.A.I.C.S.: 624110
Pamela Hollingsworth *(Sr VP-Strategic Initiatives-Program Dev)*

EARLY LEARNING COALITION OF NORTHWEST FLORIDA, INC.

703 W 15th St Ste A, Panama City, FL 32401
Tel.: (850) 747-5400   FL
Web Site:
   http://www.elcofnwflorida.org
Year Founded: 2005
Sales Range: $10-24.9 Million
Child Development Services
N.A.I.C.S.: 624110
Lynne Eldridge *(Exec Dir)*

EARLY LEARNING COALITION OF OSCEOLA COUNTY, INC.

1631 E Vine St Ste E, Kissimmee, FL 34744
Tel.: (407) 933-5353   FL
Web Site: https://www.elcosceola.org
Year Founded: 2000
Sales Range: $10-24.9 Million
Emp.: 5
Child Development Services
N.A.I.C.S.: 624110
Susan Sunka *(Exec Dir)*
Debbie Mookini *(Sec)*
Orine Newton *(Vice Chm)*
Thomas Lang *(Treas)*

EARLY LEARNING COALITION

OF PALM BEACH COUNTY, INC.

2300 High Ridge Rd Ste 115, Boynton Beach, FL 33426
Tel.: (561) 214-8000   FL
Web Site:
   https://www.elcpalmbeach.org
Year Founded: 1999
Sales Range: $75-99.9 Million
Emp.: 26
Child Development Services
N.A.I.C.S.: 624110
Christie Young *(COO)*
Michelle DePalma *(CFO)*
Adam Hasner *(Chm)*
Michael J. Napoleone *(Vice Chm)*
Warren Eldridge *(CEO)*
Diana Kepple *(Mgr-HR)*
Aruna Gilbert *(VP-Program Ops)*

EARLY LEARNING COALITION OF PINELLAS COUNTY, INC.

5735 Rio Vista Dr, Clearwater, FL 33760
Tel.: (727) 548-1439   FL
Web Site: http://www.elcpinellas.net
Year Founded: 2001
Sales Range: $25-49.9 Million
Emp.: 115
Child Care Services
N.A.I.C.S.: 624110

EARLY LEARNING COALITION OF SOUTHWEST FLORIDA, INC.

2675 Winkler Ave Ste 300, Fort Myers, FL 33901
Tel.: (239) 935-6100
Web Site: https://www.elcofswfl.org
Sales Range: $25-49.9 Million
Child Care Services
N.A.I.C.S.: 624110
Joe Paterno *(Sec)*
Gerald Poppe *(Chm)*
Trina Puddefoot *(Vice Chm)*
Peter Seif *(Treas)*
Jennifer Lange *(Owner & Dir-Little People School)*

EARLY LEARNING COALITION OF THE BIG BEND REGION

1940 N Monroe St Ste 70, Tallahassee, FL 32303
Tel.: (850) 385-0504   FL
Web Site: http://www.elcbigbend.org
Year Founded: 2000
Sales Range: $10-24.9 Million
Emp.: 58
Child Day Care Services
N.A.I.C.S.: 624410
Kathy Douglas *(Dir-Distance Learning & Res)*

EARLY LEARNING COALITION OF THE NATURE COAST, INC.

382 N Suncoast Blvd, Crystal River, FL 34429
Tel.: (352) 563-9939   FL
Web Site: http://www.elc-naturecoast.org
Year Founded: 2005
Sales Range: $10-24.9 Million
Emp.: 32
Child Development Services
N.A.I.C.S.: 624110
Sonya Bosanko *(Exec Dir)*
Ingrid Ellis *(Program Mgr)*
Desirae Rickman *(Mgr-Fin)*
Gailen Spinka *(Vice Chm)*
Philip Scarpelli *(Treas)*
Rob Wardlow *(Chm)*
Ryan Hausner *(Sec)*

EARLYBIRDCAPITAL INC.

275 Madison Ave, New York, NY 10016
Tel.: (212) 661-0200   NY

EarlyBirdCapital Inc.—(Continued)

Web Site:
http://www.earlybirdcapital.com
Year Founded: 2000
Sales Range: $1-9.9 Million
Emp.: 30
Private, Equity-Focused Investment
Banking Services
N.A.I.C.S.: 522299
David Nussbaum (Chm)
Steven Levine (Pres & CEO)

EARLYDETECT INC.
2222 Michelson Dr, Irvine, CA 92612-1332
Tel.: (949) 553-1127   NV
Web Site: http://www.earlydetect.com
Sales Range: Less than $1 Million
In Vitro Diagnostic Tests Developer,
Mfr & Marketer
N.A.I.C.S.: 325413
Richard Johnson (CFO)

Subsidiaries:

Pan Probe Biotech, Inc.   (1)
7396 Trade St, San Diego, CA 92121
Tel.: (858) 689-9936
Web Site: http://www.panprobebiotech.com
Biopharmaceutical Researcher & Mfr
N.A.I.C.S.: 325412

EARNEST & ASSOCIATES, LLC
808 Landmark Dr Ste 110, Glen Burnie, MD 21061
Tel.: (410) 766-6076   MD
Web Site:
https://www.earnestassoc.com
Year Founded: 1978
Sales Range: $1-9.9 Million
Emp.: 15,000
Information Technology Consultancy
Services
N.A.I.C.S.: 541690
Tim Earnest (Pres)
Tom Cangelosi (COO)
Thomas F. Fitzgerald (CFO)

EARNEST MACHINE PRODUCTS CO.
1250 Linda St, Rocky River, OH 44116
Tel.: (216) 362-1100
Web Site:
https://www.earnestmachine.com
Sales Range: $10-24.9 Million
Emp.: 48
Fasteners, Industrial: Nuts, Bolts,
Screws & Other Related Items
N.A.I.C.S.: 423840
Kirk Zehnder (Pres)
Chris Levicki (Mgr-Sls)
Tom Knudsen (Mgr-Pur)
Sara Macho Hill (Coord-Mktg)
Kevin Connolly (Engr-Applications)
Stuart Southall (Mgr-Bus Dev)
David Townsend (Mgr-Warehouse)

EARNHARDT TOYOTA SCION
6136 E Auto Loop Ave, Mesa, AZ 85206
Tel.: (480) 807-9700
Web Site:
https://www.earnhardttoyota.com
Year Founded: 2007
Sales Range: $75-99.9 Million
Emp.: 150
New Car Dealers
N.A.I.C.S.: 441110
Gray McDougal (Gen Mgr)
Joe Masiello (Asst Gen Mgr)
Troy Maxwell (Mgr-Sls)

EARNHARDT'S AUTO CENTERS

7300 W Orchid Ln, Chandler, AZ 85226
Tel.: (480) 893-0000   AZ
Web Site: http://www.earnhardt.com
Year Founded: 1951
Sales Range: $600-649.9 Million
Emp.: 1,650
New & Used Automobiles
N.A.I.C.S.: 441120
Hal J. Earnhardt (Pres)

Subsidiaries:

Earnhardt Chrysler-Jeep   (1)
1521 E Drivers Way, Gilbert, AZ
85297-1252   (100%)
Tel.: (480) 497-5995
Web Site: http://www.earnhardt.com
Sales Range: $25-49.9 Million
Emp.: 110
Dealers of New & Used Automobiles, New
& Used Automotive Parts & Automotive Repair Shop
N.A.I.C.S.: 441110
Frank Armani (Gen Mgr)
Hal J. Earnhardt III (Chm & Pres)

Earnhardt Dodge   (1)
1521 E Drivers Way, Gilbert, AZ
85297   (100%)
Tel.: (480) 926-4000
Web Site: http://www.earnhardt.com
Sales Range: $25-49.9 Million
Emp.: 150
New & Used Automobiles; New & Used Automotive Parts; Automotive Repair Shop
N.A.I.C.S.: 441110

Earnhardt Ford   (1)
7300 W Orchard Ln, Chandler, AZ
85226-1205   (100%)
Tel.: (480) 838-6000
Web Site: http://www.earnhardtford.com
Sales Range: $25-49.9 Million
Emp.: 150
Sale of New & Used Automobile & Spare
Services
N.A.I.C.S.: 441110
Windy Devlin (Acct Mgr)

Earnhardt Honda   (1)
10151 W Papago Freeway, Avondale, AZ
85323   (100%)
Tel.: (623) 934-5211
Web Site: http://www.earnhardt.com
Sales Range: $150-199.9 Million
Emp.:
New & Used Automobiles Retailer
N.A.I.C.S.: 441110
Florence Kohler (Controller)
Joe Staples (Gen Mgr)

EARP DISTRIBUTION CENTER
6550 Kansas Ave, Kansas City, KS 66111-2313
Tel.: (913) 287-3311   MO
Web Site:
http://www.earpdistribution.com
Year Founded: 1954
Sales Range: $25-49.9 Million
Emp.: 95
Foods, Beverages & Operating Supplies Distr
N.A.I.C.S.: 424420
Steve Hewlett (CEO & Gen Mgr)
Doug Redman (Dir-Safety)
Mike Hoyle (VP-Ops)
Vince Meighen (Mgr-Transportation)

EARTH CONSULTING GROUP, INC.
1880 W Oak Pkwy Bldg 100 Ste 106,
Marietta, GA 30062
Tel.: (770) 973-2100
Web Site: http://www.earthcon.com
Year Founded: 1998
Sales Range: $25-49.9 Million
Emp.: 135
Environmental & Engineering Consulting Services
N.A.I.C.S.: 541620
Earl H. Scott (Pres & CEO)
Bruce Johnson (Mgr-Hiring)

EARTH CONTACT PRODUCTS, LLC.
15612 S Keeler Ter, Olathe, KS 66062
Tel.: (913) 393-0007
Web Site:
https://www.earthcontactproducts.com
Sales Range: $10-24.9 Million
Emp.: 25
Nonmetallic Mineral Product Mfr
N.A.I.C.S.: 327999
Jeff Tully (Gen Mgr)
Chad Banister (Coord-Engrg)

EARTH FARE INC.
220 Continuum Dr, Fletcher, NC 28732
Tel.: (828) 281-4800
Web Site: http://www.earthfare.com
Year Founded: 1975
Sales Range: $50-74.9 Million
Emp.: 600
Healthy Food Mfr
N.A.I.C.S.: 424490
Frank Scorpiniti (Pres & CEO)
Angela Hind (Chief Medical Officer)

EARTH INC.
1102 N Ellis St, Bensenville, IL 60106
Tel.: (630) 860-7711
Rev.: $12,000,000
Emp.: 30
Local Trucking Services
N.A.I.C.S.: 484110
Thomas Kanzler (Pres)

EARTH MECHANICS, INC.
17800 Newhope St Ste B, Fountain
Valley, CA 92708
Tel.: (714) 751-3826   CA
Web Site:
https://www.earthmech.com
Year Founded: 1989
Sales Range: $10-24.9 Million
Emp.: 29
Soil Preparation, Planting & Cultivating Services
N.A.I.C.S.: 115112
Denise Denise (Mgr-Office & Bus Dev)
Arul K Arulmoli (Principal)
Ignatius Po Lam (Principal)
Lino Cheang (Principal)
Hubert Law (Principal)

EARTH SENSE ENERGY SYSTEMS INC.
W 9715 Highway 96, Dale, WI 54931
Tel.: (920) 779-6647
Web Site: http://www.pellethead.com
Year Founded: 1991
Sales Range: $10-24.9 Million
Emp.: 61
Home Furnishings Services
N.A.I.C.S.: 449129
Jed Martin (Owner)
Chad Curtis (Mgr-Ops)

EARTH SERVICES & ABATEMENT, INC.
116 Gateway Dr, North Sioux City,
SD 57049
Tel.: (605) 232-4554
Web Site: https://www.esasite.com
Year Founded: 1996
Wrecking/Demolition Contractor
Trade Contractor
N.A.I.C.S.: 238910

Subsidiaries:

1 Priority Environmental Services,
LLC   (1)
4028 Daley Ave, Fort Worth, TX 76118
Tel.: (817) 595-0790
Web Site: http://www.go1priority.com

Abatement, Indoor Air Quality & Decontamination Services
N.A.I.C.S.: 238220
Gary Caldwell (CEO)
Heath Watson (VP & Mgr-Company Ops)
Brian Cizek (Project Mgr)
Joe Garcia (Mgr-Acctg & Facility)
Mo Abdalla (Project Mgr)
Fernando Avila (Project Mgr)
Roger Garcia (Project Mgr)
Darryl Moore (Project Mgr)
Dan O'Bryan (Mgr-Houston)
Randy Timms (Project Mgr)

EARTH SUPPLIED PRODUCTS LLC
1060 Collier Center way, Naples, FL 34110
Tel.: (239) 598-5088
Web Site:
https://earthsuppliedproducts.com
Year Founded: 2000
Rev.: $2,800,000
Emp.: 10
Drugs & Druggists Sundries Merchant
Whslr
N.A.I.C.S.: 424210
Peter Boncelet (Pres)
Jeanne Manuri (Mgr-Credit)

EARTHCORE INDUSTRIES LLC.
6899 Phillips Industrial Blvd, Jacksonville, FL 32256
Tel.: (904) 363-3417
Web Site: https://earthcore.com
Rev.: $20,000,000
Emp.: 50
Plumbing & Heating Equipment &
Supplies Merchant Whslr
N.A.I.C.S.: 423720
Carl Spadaro (CEO)

EARTHMOVER CREDIT UNION
2195 Baseline Rd, Oswego, IL 60543
Tel.: (630) 844-4950
Web Site:
https://www.earthmovercu.com
Rev.: $12,800,000
Emp.: 85
Online Banking Services
N.A.I.C.S.: 522130
Todd Westmoreland (VP-Lending & Collections)
Shelley Johnson (Dir-IT)
Richard T. Kish (Sec)
Libby Calderone (Pres & CEO)
Noreen Wilkerson (VP-Fin)
Sheree Coffman (Mgr-Collections)
James Burkiewicz (Vice Chm)
Connie Busby (Chm)
Larry Reddish (Treas)

EARTHQUAKE MEDIA, LLC.
15 E 26th St Ste 802, New York, NY 10010-1505
Tel.: (212) 204-9200
Web Site:
http://www.earthquakemedia.com
Year Founded: 1999
Sales Range: $50-74.9 Million
Emp.: 5
Consulting, Direct Response Marketing, E-Commerce, Event Planning &
Marketing
N.A.I.C.S.: 541810
Robert Davidman (Chm & CEO)
Jeff Giacchetti (VP & Dir-Integrated
Media)
Jon Lumerman (VP & Dir-Integrated
Media)

EARTHTRON LLC
210 W Rd Unit 6, Portsmouth, NH 03801
Tel.: (603) 433-2007
Web Site: http://www.earthtron.com
Year Founded: 2008

Sales Range: $1-9.9 Million
Emp.: 13
Electronic Product Inventory Control
Management Services
N.A.I.C.S.: 541614
John Pallazolaa (CEO)
Janet Call (Mgr-Shipping)
Claudia Pallazola (Controller)

EARTHWORKS PACIFIC INC.
4180 Hoala St, Lihue, HI 96766-2126
Tel.: (808) 246-8808
Web Site:
https://www.earthworkspacific.com
Rev.: $20,800,000
Emp.: 50
Commercial & Institutional Building
Construction Services
N.A.I.C.S.: 236220
Jeffery Fisher (Pres)

EASLEY & RIVERS INC.
207 Townsend Dr, Monroeville, PA
15146-0458
Tel.: (412) 795-4482   PA
Web Site:
https://www.easleyandrivers.com
Year Founded: 1965
Sales Range: $500-549.9 Million
Emp.: 520
Plastering, Drywall & Insulation Ser-
vices
N.A.I.C.S.: 238310
Diane Dumire (Office Mgr)
Glenn Sieber (Pres)
James Cowie (Project Mgr)
Gosia Kolodynski (Mgr-Sls & Mktg)
Neal Rivers (VP)

**EASLEY COMBINED UTILITY
SYSTEM**
110 Peachtree St, Easley, SC 29641
Tel.: (864) 859-4013
Web Site:
https://www.easleyutilities.com
Year Founded: 1911
Sales Range: $25-49.9 Million
Emp.: 85
Water Distr & Electrical Services
N.A.I.C.S.: 221118
Joel D. Ledbetter (Mgr)
Bobby Tinsley (Mgr-Ops)
Alice Simmons (Mgr-Customer Svc)

EAST AIR CORPORATION
337 2nd St, Hackensack, NJ 07601
Tel.: (201) 487-6060
Web Site: https://www.eastair.com
Year Founded: 1950
Sales Range: $10-24.9 Million
Emp.: 30
Aircraft Equipment Mfr & Distr
N.A.I.C.S.: 423860
John Nepola (Pres & CEO)
Gino Nepola (Founder & Chm)
Orlando Camejo (Sr VP-Sales-
Marketing)
Joseph Cosma (VP-Quality
Assurance-Operations)
Patrick Zimmermann (Dir-Marketing-
Sls)
Gary Spada (VP-Accounting & Con-
troller)

**EAST ARKANSAS AREA
AGENCY ON AGING**
2005 E Highland Dr, Jonesboro, AR
72401
Tel.: (870) 972-5980   AR
Web Site: https://www.e4aonline.com
Year Founded: 1978
Sales Range: $10-24.9 Million
Emp.: 653
Elder Care Services
N.A.I.C.S.: 624120

Melissa Prater (Dir-Purchased Svcs)
Jacquelin McDaniel (Fin Dir)

**EAST BALTIMORE DEVELOP-
MENT INC.**
1731 E Chase St, Baltimore, MD
21213
Tel.: (410) 234-0660   MD
Web Site: http://www.ebdi.org
Year Founded: 2002
Sales Range: $25-49.9 Million
Emp.: 95
Community Action Services
N.A.I.C.S.: 624190
Henry Omomah (Dir-HR)
Alphonso Barney (Mgr-Family Advo-
cate Program)
Raymond Skinner (Pres & CEO)

EAST BAY BMW
4350 Rosewood Dr, Pleasanton, CA
94588
Tel.: (925) 463-2555
Web Site:
http://www.eastbaybmw.com
Year Founded: 1995
Sales Range: $10-24.9 Million
Emp.: 175
New Car Retailer
N.A.I.C.S.: 441110
Donna Gebers (Gen Mgr)
James Bingham (Mgr-Pre-Owned
Sls)
Joe Pagano (Mgr-Pre-Owned Sls)
Erwin Henriquez (Mgr-BMW Parts)
Mien Le (Mgr-Sls)
Joshua Presinal (Mgr-BMW Svc)
Mario Valdez (Mgr-Detail)
Phil Wiltz (Mgr-Fin Svcs)
Lena Chi (Mgr-Fin Svcs)
Doug Demasi (Mgr-Fin Svcs)
Ian Higgins (Mgr-Fin Svcs)
Darryl Morris (Mgr-Fin Svcs)
Blair Robinson (Mgr-Sls)
Jim Burke (Mgr-Svc-Columbus)
Danilo Arrienda Jr. (Mgr-Loaner Car)

EAST BAY CLARKLIFT INC.
4701 Oakport St, Oakland, CA 94601
Tel.: (510) 534-6566
Web Site: https://www.cromer.com
Rev.: $21,683,500
Emp.: 65
Materials Handling Machinery, Ser-
vice & Parts
N.A.I.C.S.: 423830
Marshall T. Cromer (Owner & Pres)

**EAST BAY COMMUNITY
FOUNDATION**
200 Frank H Ogawa Plz, Oakland,
CA 94612
Tel.: (510) 836-3223   CA
Web Site: https://www.ebcf.org
Year Founded: 1928
Sales Range: $75-99.9 Million
Emp.: 37
Community Development Services
N.A.I.C.S.: 624190
Alexandra Aquino-Fike (VP-
Development)
Byron Johnson (Officer-Capacity
Building Initiative)
Carlos Velasquez (Mng Dir-
Operations-Facilities)

**EAST BAY FORD TRUCK
SALES, INC.**
70 Hegenberger Loop, Oakland, CA
94621
Tel.: (510) 272-4400
Web Site:
http://www.eastbaytruckcenter.com
Sales Range: $10-24.9 Million
Emp.: 35
New Car Dealers

N.A.I.C.S.: 441110
Ernest Speno (Pres)
Jeff Speno (VP)
Ken Lalanne (Mgr-Sls)
Mike Salata (Mgr-Used Truck)

**EAST BAY INSURANCE
AGENCY INC.**
117 Flamingo Dr, Apollo Beach, FL
33572
Tel.: (813) 645-2502
Web Site: https://www.ebinsure.com
Year Founded: 1972
Sales Range: $10-24.9 Million
Emp.: 12
Insurance Agents
N.A.I.C.S.: 524210
Elizabeth Travis (Pres)

**EAST BAY INTEGRATED
CARE**
3470 Buskirk Ave, Pleasant Hill, CA
94523
Tel.: (925) 887-5678   CA
Web Site:
https://www.hospiceeastbay.org
Year Founded: 1977
Sales Range: $10-24.9 Million
Emp.: 275
Patient Comfort & Caring Services
N.A.I.C.S.: 624190
Daniel Jordan (VP-Fund Dev & Retail
Ops)
Christopher Joyce (VP-HR)
Sally A. Sample (Chief Medical Offi-
cer)
Cindy Hatton (Pres & CEO)
Bob Carlson (Chm)
Frank Martens (Sec)
Ernie Wintter (Treas)
Cindy Silva (Vice Chm)
David Caldwell (CFO)
Missy Ring (VP-Quality Education &
Compliance)

**EAST BAY MUNICIPAL UTIL-
ITY DISTRICT**
375 11th St, Oakland, CA 94607
Tel.: (510) 287-0454
Web Site: https://www.ebmud.com
Sales Range: $250-299.9 Million
Emp.: 1,700
Water Distr & Water Systems Ser-
vices
N.A.I.C.S.: 221310
Doug Linney (Dir-Board)
Frank Mellon (Dir-Board)
Lesa R. McIntosh (Dir-Board)
Andy Katz (Dir-Board)
William B. Patterson (Dir-Board)

EAST BAY RV
4961 Pacheco Blvd, Martinez, CA
94553-4324
Tel.: (925) 335-0900
Sales Range: $10-24.9 Million
Emp.: 22
Recreational Vehicle Whslr
N.A.I.C.S.: 441210
Betina Fox (Mgr)

EAST BAY TIRE CO.
2200 Huntington Dr Unit C, Fairfield,
CA 94533
Tel.: (707) 437-4700
Web Site:
https://www.eastbaytire.com
Rev.: $30,000,000
Emp.: 100
Tires & Tubes Whslr
N.A.I.C.S.: 423130
George M. Pehanick (CEO)
John Hulsey (Gen Mgr-Wholesale
Div)

**EAST BAY ZOOLOGICAL SO-
CIETY**
PO Box 5238, Oakland, CA 94605
Tel.: (510) 632-9525   CA
Year Founded: 1936
Sales Range: $10-24.9 Million
Zoo Operator
N.A.I.C.S.: 712130
Bill Marchant (Sec)
Joel Parrott (Pres & CEO)
Jonathan Harris (Treas)
Kirsten Vital (Chm-Education & Out-
reach)
Lewis Byrd (Chm-Nominating)
Steve Kane (Chm)
Tom Britanik (Vice Chm)

**EAST BOSTON NEIGHBOR-
HOOD HEALTH CENTER
CORP.**
20 Maverick Sq, East Boston, MA
02128
Tel.: (617) 569-5800
Web Site: http://www.ebnhc.org
Year Founded: 1970
Health Care Srvices
N.A.I.C.S.: 622110
Manny Lopes (Pres & CEO)
Jackie S. Fantes (Chief Medical Offi-
cer)
Rita Sorrento (Chm)
Doris Rubio (Vice Chm)

Subsidiaries:

South End Community Health
Center   (1)
1601 Washington St, Boston, MA 02118
Tel.: (617) 425-2000
Web Site: http://www.sechc.org
Sales Range: $10-24.9 Million
Emp.: 257
Health Care Srvices
N.A.I.C.S.: 622110
Bill Walczak (Pres & CEO)
David Goldenheim (Treas)
Erika Wilkinson (Vice Chm)

**EAST CAMBRIDGE SAVINGS
BANK INC.**
292 Cambridge St, Cambridge, MA
02141-1203
Tel.: (617) 354-2700   MA
Web Site: https://www.ecsb.com
Year Founded: 1854
Sales Range: $50-74.9 Million
Emp.: 143
Commericial Banking
N.A.I.C.S.: 522110
Stephen J. DeCesare (Officer-Comml
Loan & VP)
Stephen Ferullo (Officer-Comml Loan
& VP)
Jenison Wallace (Officer-Bus Dev &
Asst VP)
Manuel Rodriguez (Officer-Bus Dev &
Asst VP)
Ernest Chevrette Jr. (Asst VP & Mgr-
Bus Banking)

EAST CENTRAL ENERGY
412 Main Ave N, Braham, MN 55006
Tel.: (320) 396-3351   MN
Web Site:
https://www.eastcentralenergy.com
Year Founded: 1936
Sales Range: $50-74.9 Million
Emp.: 189
Electronic Services
N.A.I.C.S.: 221122
Dave Curtis (Mgr-Ops)
Dennis Korpi (Mgr-HR)

EAST CENTRAL IOWA COOP
602 Washington St, Hudson, IA
50643
Tel.: (319) 988-3257   IA

East Central Iowa Coop—(Continued)

Web Site: http://www.ecicoop.com
Year Founded: 1947
Sales Range: $25-49.9 Million
Emp.: 60
Agricultural Services
N.A.I.C.S.: 424510
Mike Reiter (Pres-Fin)
Bill Hesse (Sec-Fin)
Jason Trumbauer (VP)
Ron Hager (Dir-Fin)

EAST CENTRAL OKLAHOMA ELECTRIC COOPERATIVE, INC.
2001 S Wood Dr, Okmulgee, OK 74447
Tel.: (918) 756-0833   OK
Web Site: https://www.ecoec.com
Year Founded: 1938
Sales Range: $50-74.9 Million
Emp.: 89
Electric Power Distribution Services
N.A.I.C.S.: 221122
Tim Smith (Gen Mgr)

EAST COAST AUTO TRANS-PORT INCORPORATED
2906 Elmhurst Ln, Portsmouth, VA 23701
Tel.: (757) 465-2200
Web Site: http://www.tchss.com
Sales Range: $10-24.9 Million
Emp.: 100
Automobile Transportation Services
N.A.I.C.S.: 484230
Melba Rudiger (Pres)
Barry Rudiger (VP)

EAST COAST AVIATION LLC
5910 Shiloh Rd E Ste 105, Al-pharetta, GA 30005
Tel.: (770) 886-7758
Web Site: http://www.ecaviation.com
Year Founded: 2009
Aviation Products & Supplies Whslr
N.A.I.C.S.: 423860
Koo Kevin Kim (Pres)

EAST COAST DIVERSIFIED CORPORATION
810 Franklin Ct Ste H, Marietta, GA 30067
Tel.: (770) 953-4184   NV
Web Site: http://www.eastcoastdiversified.com
Sales Range: Less than $1 Million
Emp.: 12
Holding Company; GPS & RFID Products Mfr; Mobile Applications
N.A.I.C.S.: 551112
Kayode A. Aladesuyi (Chm, Pres, CEO & Interim CFO)
Meredith Pruden (Sr Mgr-Comm & Media Rels)

Subsidiaries:

Earthsearch Communications, Inc.   (1)
120 Interstate N Pkwy Ste 445, Atlanta, GA 30339
Tel.: (770) 953-4184
Web Site: http://www.earthsearch.us
Radio & Television Broadcasting & Wireless Communications Equipment Mfr
N.A.I.C.S.: 334220
Kayode A. Aladesuyi (Pres & CEO)
Andrea R. Sousa (Controller)
Bill Sengstacken (VP-Mktg)

EAST COAST LUMBER & SUPPLY CO. INC.
308 Ave A, Fort Pierce, FL 34950-4417
Tel.: (772) 466-1700   FL

Web Site: https://www.eastcoastlumber.com
Year Founded: 1902
Sales Range: $25-49.9 Million
Emp.: 125
Lumber & Other Building Materials Distr
N.A.I.C.S.: 423310
William D. Osteen (Pres)
Toni Brown (Mgr-Credit)

EAST COAST LUMBER COM-PANY INC.
9207 Hwy 22 S, Climax, NC 27233
Tel.: (336) 685-5812
Web Site: https://www.eastcoastonline.com
Year Founded: 1973
Sales Range: $25-49.9 Million
Emp.: 25
Lumber Mfr
N.A.I.C.S.: 423310
Johnny Hall (Pres)
Wendy Showalter (CFO)

EAST COAST SPRINKLER SUPPLY
1044 Merrick Rd, Baldwin, NY 11510
Tel.: (516) 223-3660   NY
Web Site: http://www.greenertthome.com
Year Founded: 1981
Rev.: $10,742,428
Emp.: 5
Irrigation Equipment Distr
N.A.I.C.S.: 423820
Lewis Okin (Pres)
Lewis Okin (Pres)

EAST COUNTY PREOWNED SUPERSTORE
327 El Cajon Blvd, El Cajon, CA 92020
Tel.: (619) 588-2278
Year Founded: 2004
Sales Range: $10-24.9 Million
Emp.: 63
Car Whslr
N.A.I.C.S.: 441110
Karl Albright (Mgr-Sls)
Masood Khoroshi (Pres)

EAST COURT PROPERTIES LLC.
1106 East Ct, Dyersburg, TN 38024
Tel.: (731) 286-2772
Sales Range: $10-24.9 Million
Emp.: 30
Electrical Wiring Services
N.A.I.C.S.: 238210
David Wagner (Owner)

EAST HARDWOOD CO. INC.
1308 Lennoxville Rd, Beaufort, NC 28516
Tel.: (252) 728-3843
Web Site: https://www.safrits.com
Sales Range: $10-24.9 Million
Emp.: 60
Lumber & Other Building Materials Mfr
N.A.I.C.S.: 423310
Leonard L. Safrit (Pres & CEO)
Gary Hardesty (Supvr-Yard)
Tawnya Quinn (Mgr-Credit)
Brad Brown (Supvr-Yard)
Buddy Russell (VP-Sales-Marketing)

Subsidiaries:

Jacksonville Builders Supply   (1)
200 Williamsburg Pkwy, Jacksonville, NC 28540
Tel.: (910) 455-3961
Sales Range: $10-24.9 Million
Builders Supply
N.A.I.C.S.: 423310
Dave Leroy (Mgr-Sls)

EAST HARLEM COUNCIL FOR HUMAN SERVICES, INC.
2265 3rd Ave, New York, NY 10035
Tel.: (212) 289-6650   NY
Web Site: https://www.boriken.org
Year Founded: 1965
Sales Range: $10-24.9 Million
Emp.: 200
Health Care Srvices
N.A.I.C.S.: 622110
Arturo Perez (CFO)

EAST HILLS CHEVROLET GEO
1036 Northern Blvd, Roslyn, NY 11576
Tel.: (516) 612-8830
Web Site: http://www.easthillschevrolet roslyn.com
Year Founded: 1989
Sales Range: $10-24.9 Million
Emp.: 40
Car Whslr
N.A.I.C.S.: 441110
Kenneth Brodlieb (Pres)

EAST IDAHO CREDIT UNION
865 S Woodruff Ave, Idaho Falls, ID 83403-1865
Tel.: (208) 523-9068   ID
Web Site: http://www.eastidahocu.org
Year Founded: 1935
Sales Range: $10-24.9 Million
Emp.: 153
Credit Union Operator
N.A.I.C.S.: 522130
Mark Hyndman (Treas)
Nathan Downey (Sec)

EAST JEFFERSON GENERAL HOSPITAL AUXILIARY, INC.
4200 Houma Blvd, Metairie, LA 70006
Tel.: (504) 454-4000   LA
Web Site: http://www.ejgh.org
Year Founded: 1971
Emp.: 3,227
Health Care Srvices
N.A.I.C.S.: 622110
Judy Brown (COO & Exec VP)
Henry Shane (Chm)
Gerald Parton (Pres & CEO)

EAST KENTUCKY POWER CO-OPERATIVE
4775 Lexington Rd, Winchester, KY 40392-0707
Tel.: (859) 744-4812   KY
Web Site: https://www.ekpc.coop
Year Founded: 1941
Sales Range: $350-399.9 Million
Emp.: 653
Electrical Power Generation & Trans-mission
N.A.I.C.S.: 221118
Barry Mayfield (VP-Stategic Plng & External Affairs)
Mike McNalley (CFO & Exec VP)
Tony Campbell (Pres & CEO)
Don Mosier (COO & Exec VP)
David Crews (Sr VP-Power Supply)
Craig Johnson (Sr VP-Power Produc-tion)
Denver York (Sr VP-Power Delivery & Sys Ops)
David Smart (Gen Counsel)
Jerry Purvis (VP-Environmental Af-fairs)
Tom Stachnik (Treas & VP-Fin)

EAST LAKE FOUNDATION
2606 Alston Dr SE, Atlanta, GA 30317
Tel.: (404) 373-4351   GA

Web Site: https://www.eastlakefoundation.org
Year Founded: 1995
Sales Range: $25-49.9 Million
Emp.: 38
Community Support Services
N.A.I.C.S.: 624190
Brittany Glenn Molinaro (Dir-Dev)
Jennifer W. McCrary (Mgr-Resident & Community Support Program)
Rhonda Fischer (COO)
Sharon Hall-Thomas (Mgr-Ops & Special Initiatives)
Catherine Woodling (Dir-Mktg & Comm)
Dwayne Watkins (Mgr-Impact & En-gagement)
Daniel Shoy Jr. (Pres & CEO)

EAST LAKE, LLC
PO Box 39, Tarpon Springs, FL 34688
Tel.: (727) 939-2480
Web Site: http://www.eastlakellc.com
Year Founded: 2000
Sales Range: $10-24.9 Million
Emp.: 10
Property Manager & Owner
N.A.I.C.S.: 531312
Michael Lowe (Pres)

Subsidiaries:

Tarpon Landing Marina   (1)
21 Oscar Hill Rd, Tarpon Springs, FL 34689
Tel.: (727) 937-1100
Web Site: http://www.tarponlandingmarina.com
Emp.: 3
Marinas
N.A.I.C.S.: 713930
Chris Coviello (Gen Mgr)

EAST LOS ANGELES COMMU-NITY UNION
5400 E Olympic Blvd Ste 300, Los Angeles, CA 90022
Tel.: (323) 721-1655
Web Site: http://www.telacu.com
Rev.: $66,932,000
Emp.: 50
Credit Services
N.A.I.C.S.: 522299
David C. Lizarraga (Chm)

EAST MAIN FOODS INC.
100 Gateway Dr, Waupun, WI 53963
Tel.: (920) 324-5526
Sales Range: $10-24.9 Million
Emp.: 35
Grocery Stores
N.A.I.C.S.: 445110
Donald VerHage (Pres)

EAST MISSISSIPPI ELECTRIC POWER ASSOCIATION
2128 Highway 39 N, Meridian, MS 39301
Tel.: (601) 581-8600
Web Site: https://www.emepa.com
Year Founded: 1938
Sales Range: $25-49.9 Million
Emp.: 200
Electronic Services
N.A.I.C.S.: 221122
Wayne Henson (Gen Mgr)
Julie Boles (Mgr-Comm)
Lorie Sloan (Supvr-Acctg)

EAST MOLINE METAL PROD-UCTS COMPANY
1201 7th St, East Moline, IL 61244-1400
Tel.: (309) 752-1350   IL
Web Site: http://www.emmetal.com
Year Founded: 1946
Sales Range: $75-99.9 Million
Emp.: 85

Mfr of Metal Stampings, Fabricated Structural Metal Welding, Hydraulic Hammers, Cement Finishing Equipment & Personnel Lifts
N.A.I.C.S.: 332119
Mike Slonecker (Mgr-Sls)

EAST MUSKEGON ROOFING & SHEET METAL COMPANY
1665 Holton Rd, Muskegon, MI 49445
Tel.: (231) 744-2461
Web Site:
https://www.eastmuskegon.com
Sales Range: $25-49.9 Million
Emp.: 85
Sheet Metal Work Mfg
N.A.I.C.S.: 238390
Gregory R. Kanaar (VP)
Eileen Kanaar (Pres)

EAST OF CHICAGO PIZZA CO.
121 W High St Fl 12, Lima, OH 45801-4349
Tel.: (419) 225-7116
Web Site:
http://www.eastofchicago.com
Year Founded: 1990
Sales Range: $10-24.9 Million
Emp.: 200
Nonfinancial Asset Management Services
N.A.I.C.S.: 533110
Amanda Guerra (Office Mgr)
Anthony Collins (Owner)
Tony Collins (Pres)
Angie Finnerty (Controller)

EAST OF HUDSON WATERSHED CORPORATION
2 Route 164, Patterson, NY 12563
Tel.: (845) 319-6349   NY
Web Site: http://www.eohwc.org
Year Founded: 2011
Rev.: $8,329,780
Assets: $11,458,852
Liabilities: $11,386,810
Net Worth: $72,042
Earnings: $15,730
Emp.: 7
Fiscal Year-end: 12/31/14
Waste Treatment Services
N.A.I.C.S.: 221310
Kevin Fitzpatrick (Project Mgr)

EAST OHIO LUMBER CO. INC.
17535 State Route 644, Salineville, OH 43945
Tel.: (330) 679-2394
Web Site:
https://www.eastohiolumber.com
Sales Range: $10-24.9 Million
Emp.: 10
Lumber: Rough, Dressed & Finished
N.A.I.C.S.: 423310
Donna Smalley (Controller)
George Bach Jr. (Pres)

EAST OLYMPIC POULTRY INC.
1839 E 42nd St, Los Angeles, CA 90058
Tel.: (323) 234-9998
Rev.: $14,700,000
Emp.: 10
Poultry Products
N.A.I.C.S.: 424440
Dennis Mao (Pres)

EAST OREGONIAN PUBLISHING CO.
211 SE Byers Ave, Pendleton, OR 97801
Tel.: (541) 276-2211
Web Site:
https://www.eastoregonian.com
Year Founded: 1875

Sales Range: $10-24.9 Million
Emp.: 200
Commercial Printing & Newspaper Publishing Services
N.A.I.C.S.: 513110
Steve Forrester (Pres & CEO)
Kathryn B. Brown (VP)
Heidi Wright (COO)

Subsidiaries:

East Oregonian   (1)
211 SE Byers Ave, Pendleton, OR 97801
Tel.: (541) 276-2211
Web Site: http://www.eastoregonian.com
Emp.: 10
Newspaper Publishers
N.A.I.C.S.: 513110
Sue Cant (Mgr-Mailroom)
Tammy Malgesini (Editor-Community)
Daniel Wattenburger (Mng Editor)
Matt Entrup (Editor-Sports)
Janna Heimgartner (Mgr-Bus Office)
Kay Karlinsey (Mgr-Production)
Tom Brown (Editor)
Jennine Perkinson (Dir-Adv)
Mike Jensen (Mgr-Production)
Marcy Rosenberg (Mgr-Circulation)
Renee Struthers (Editor-Community Records)
Chris Rush (Dir-Pendleton, Hermiston, John Day & Enterprise & Dir-Revenue)
Wyatt Haupt (Editor-News)

Hermiston Herald   (1)
333 E Main St, Hermiston, OR 97838
Tel.: (541) 567-6457
Web Site: http://www.hermistonherald.com
Sales Range: $10-24.9 Million
Emp.: 12
Newspaper Publishers
N.A.I.C.S.: 513110
Daniel Wattenburger (Editor)

EAST ORLANDO HEALTH & REHAB CENTER INC
250 S Chickasaw Trl, Orlando, FL 32825
Tel.: (407) 380-3466   FL
Web Site:
http://www.eastorlandohealth.com
Year Founded: 2006
Sales Range: $10-24.9 Million
Emp.: 253
Senior Health Care Services
N.A.I.C.S.: 623990
Johnson Kent (CFO)
R. Robert Henderschedt (Chm)
Givens Michelle (Pres)

EAST PALO ALTO TENNIS & TUTORING
625 Campus Dr, Stanford, CA 94305-6201
Tel.: (650) 725-4450   CA
Web Site: http://www.epatt.org
Year Founded: 2008
Sales Range: $1-9.9 Million
Emp.: 50
Tennis Educational Activity Provider
N.A.I.C.S.: 611620
Dave Higaki (Exec Dir & Dir-Tennis)
Kesha Weekes (Dir-Academic-MSG)
Amy Kohrman (Mgr-Dev & Comm)

EAST PENN MANUFACTURING CO., INC.
102 Deka Rd, Lyon Station, PA 19536
Tel.: (610) 682-6361   PA
Web Site: http://www.eastpenn-deka.com
Year Founded: 1946
Storage Batteries, Wires & Cables Mfr
N.A.I.C.S.: 335910
Christopher E. Pruitt (Pres & CEO)
Peter Stanislawczyk (Sr VP-Automotive Sls)

Subsidiaries:

American Battery Company   (1)
2800 SW 4th Ave Unit 20, Fort Lauderdale, FL 33315
Tel.: (954) 583-2470
Web Site: http://www.americanbattery-deka.com
Battery Distr
N.A.I.C.S.: 423610

Ecoult   (1)
Suite 402 Grafton Bond Building 201 Kent Street, Sydney, 2000, NSW, Australia
Tel.: (61) 2 9241 3001
Web Site: http://www.ecoult.com
Emp.: 50
Storage Battery Mfr
N.A.I.C.S.: 335910
John Wood (CEO)
Tze Masters (CFO)

MK Battery   (1)
1631 S Sinclair St, Anaheim, CA 92806
Tel.: (714) 937-1033
Web Site: http://www.mkbattery.com
Emp.: 100
Lead Acid Battery Mfr & Distr
N.A.I.C.S.: 335910
Mark Wels (Co-Founder)
Mark Kettler (Co-Founder)

Subsidiary (Non-US):

MK Battery Asia Pacific Pty Limited   (2)
Unit 16 378 Parramatta Road, Homebush, Sydney, 2140, NSW, Australia
Tel.: (61) 2 9764 5584
Lead Acid Battery Distr
N.A.I.C.S.: 423610

MK Battery International Ltd   (2)
Unit 2 Henson Way Telford Way Industrial Estate, Kettering, NN16 8PX, Northants, United Kingdom
Tel.: (44) 1536 484009
Web Site: http://www.mkbattery.com
Emp.: 10
Lead Acid Battery Distr
N.A.I.C.S.: 423610
Matthew Major (Dir-Sls)

Navitas Systems, LLC   (1)
5451 S State St, Ann Arbor, MI 48108
Tel.: (734) 205-1400
Web Site: http://www.navitassys.com
Renewable Energy Semiconductor Mfr
N.A.I.C.S.: 334413
Nancie Elshafei (CEO)

EAST RIVER ELECTRIC POWER COOPERATIVE
121 SE 1st St, Madison, SD 57042-2924
Tel.: (605) 256-4536   SD
Web Site: http://www.eastriver.coop
Year Founded: 1949
Sales Range: $50-74.9 Million
Emp.: 91
Distr of Electric Energy
N.A.I.C.S.: 221122
Jeffrey L. Nelson (Gen Mgr)
Greg Hollister (CFO)
Scott Parsley (Chief Member & PR Officer)
Jim Edwards (COO)
Bob Sahr (Gen Counsel)
Liz Avery (Mgr-HR & Admin)
Randy Hoffman (Mgr-Budget Svcs)
Barb Strom (Mgr-Fin & Acctg)
Tom Boyko (CEO & Gen Mgr)
Pat Engebretson (CIO)
Jenny Wolff (Coord-Comm)
Josh Bjorklund (Coord-Matls)
Rory Johannsen (Coord-Matls)
Justin Olson (Coord-Matls)
Erica Sperry (Coord-Mktg)
Corey Gunderson (Mgr-Safety & Health)

EAST SHORE RESORT
473 E Shore Dr, Clearwater, FL 33767

Tel.: (727) 442-3636
Web Site:
https://www.eastshoreresort.com
Sales Range: $1-9.9 Million
Hotel Operations
N.A.I.C.S.: 721110
Billy Day (Owner)

EAST SIDE HOUSE, INC.
337 Alexander Ave, Bronx, NY 10454-1108
Tel.: (718) 665-5250   NY
Web Site:
http://www.eastsidehouse.org
Year Founded: 1891
Sales Range: $10-24.9 Million
Emp.: 787
Educational Support Services
N.A.I.C.S.: 611710
Emilia Pena (Dir-HR)
Thomas H. Remien (Pres)
Courtney Booth Christensen (VP)
Dolores O'Brien Miller (VP)
Richard E. Kolman (Treas)
Stephanie B. Clark (Sec)
Daniel Diaz (Exec Dir)
Walter Cortes (Controller)
Miguel Orta (Deputy Dir-Social Svcs)
Laura Daley (Dir-Dev)
Dawn Heyward (Deputy Dir-Early Childhood)
David Boxill (Deputy Dir-Admin)
Philip L. Yang Jr. (Chm)

EAST SIDE LUMBERYARD SUPPLY CO.
1101 W Maple St, Herrin, IL 62948
Tel.: (618) 942-3281
Web Site: http://www.eastsidelbr.com
Sales Range: $25-49.9 Million
Emp.: 40
Lumber, Plywood & Millwork
N.A.I.C.S.: 423310
Ralph F. Reis (Pres)
Don Reis (Sec)

EAST SIDE MARKET PLACE INC.
165 Pitman St, Providence, RI 02906
Tel.: (401) 831-7771
Web Site:
https://www.eastsidemarket.com
Rev.: $26,000,000
Emp.: 100
Independent Supermarket
N.A.I.C.S.: 445110
Steven Deluca (Gen Mgr)

EAST SIDE PLATING INC.
8400 SE 26th Pl, Portland, OR 97202
Tel.: (503) 654-3774
Web Site:
https://www.eastsideplating.com
Sales Range: $10-24.9 Million
Emp.: 200
Electroplating Of Metals Or Formed Products
N.A.I.C.S.: 332813
Gary Rehnberg (Pres)
Tracy Finck (Plant Mgr)
Jared Nissen (Supvr-Production)

EAST TEAK FINE HARDWOODS, INC.
1106 Drake Rd, Donalds, SC 29638
Tel.: (864) 379-2111   DE
Web Site: https://www.eastteak.com
Year Founded: 1972
Hardwood Lumber Distr & Milling Services
N.A.I.C.S.: 423310
Don R. Daseke (Chm)

Subsidiaries:

East Teak Fine Hardwoods, Inc.   (1)
33525 State Rte 2, Sultan, WA 98294

East Teak Fine Hardwoods, Inc.—(Continued)
Tel.: (360) 793-3754
Web Site: http://www.eastteak.com
Sales Range: $75-99.9 Million
Emp.: 16
Hardwood Lumber Distr & Milling Services
N.A.I.C.S.: 423310
Scott R. Hamilton (Sr VP-West Coast)
Rick McKinney (Sr VP)
Marion Hamilton (VP)

EAST TENNESSEE CHIL-DREN'S HOSPITAL
2018 Clinch Ave, Knoxville, TN 37916
Tel.: (865) 541-8000   **TN**
Web Site: https://www.etch.com
Year Founded: 1937
Sales Range: $200-249.9 Million
Emp.: 2,095
Health Care Srvices
N.A.I.C.S.: 622110
Bruce Anderson (Gen Counsel & VP-Legal Svcs)
Sue Wilburn (VP-HR)
Joe Childs (VP-Medical Svcs)
Rudy McKinley (VP-Ops)
Caryn Hawthorne (CFO & VP-Fin)

EAST TENNESSEE FOUNDA-TION
520 W Summit Hill Dr Ste 1101,
Knoxville, TN 37902
Tel.: (865) 524-1223   **TN**
Web Site:
    https://www.easttennesseefoun
    dation.org
Year Founded: 1986
Sales Range: $10-24.9 Million
Emp.: 22
Grantmaking Services
N.A.I.C.S.: 813211
Jan Elston (VP)
Trudy Hughes (Dir-Reg Advance-ment)
Sherri Alley (VP-Advancement)
Michael McClamroch (Pres & CEO)
Carolyn Schwenn (Sec & Exec VP)
Amy Cathey (Exec Dir)
John Johnson (Officer-Fin & Admin)
Jeanette Kelleher (VP-Ops)

EAST TENNESSEE NISSAN MORRISTOWN
5496 W Andrew Johnson Hwy, Mor-ristown, TN 37814
Tel.: (423) 587-2506
Web Site:
    http://www.victoryautomotive
    group.com
Sales Range: $25-49.9 Million
Emp.: 100
New & Used Car Sales
N.A.I.C.S.: 441110
Jeff Cappo (Owner)
Shawne Huff (Gen Mgr)

EAST TEXAS BANCSHARES, INC.
112 W Polk St, Livingston, TX 77351
Tel.: (936) 327-5211
Web Site:
    http://www.fsblivingston.com
Rev.: $13,400,000
Emp.: 5
Bank Holding Company
N.A.I.C.S.: 551111
Robert Sebaugh (Pres)
Ben R. Ogletree Jr. (CEO)
Tony Taylor (Sr VP & Controller)
Eddie Lewis (Sr VP)
Joe K. Puckett (Sr VP)
Kari Parker (VP)
Carol Pixley (Officer-Compliance & VP)
Patti Johnson (VP & Branch Mgr)

Buna Jones (VP & Branch Mgr)
Debra Ward (VP)
Sonia Hidalgo (Officer-Compliance & VP)

Subsidiaries:

First National Bank of Jasper   **(1)**
301 E Houston St, Jasper, TX 75951
Tel.: (409) 384-3486
Web Site: http://www.fnbjasper.com
Rev.: $7,280,000
Assets: $230,538,000
Liabilities: $201,698,000
Net Worth: $28,840,000
Earnings: $1,450,000
Emp.: 55
Fiscal Year-end: 12/31/2013
Retail & Commercial Banking
N.A.I.C.S.: 522180
Stephen Ernest (Pres)

First State Bank of Livingston   **(1)**
112 W Polk St, Livingston, TX 77351
Tel.: (936) 327-5211
Web Site: http://www.fsblivingston.com
Rev.: $6,700,000
Emp.: 50
State Commercial Banks
N.A.I.C.S.: 522110
Robert Sebaugh (Pres)
Ben R. Ogletree Jr. (CEO)
Shellie Mabry (Asst VP)
Margaret Pixley (VP-HR)
Tony Taylor (Sr VP & Controller)

EAST TEXAS COMMUNTIES FOUNDATION, INC.
315 N Broadway Ave Ste 210, Tyler,
TX 75702
Tel.: (903) 533-0208   **TX**
Web Site: https://www.etcf.org
Year Founded: 1989
Sales Range: $10-24.9 Million
Emp.: 4
Philanthropic Services
N.A.I.C.S.: 813211
Kyle Penney (Pres)
Joel Ghris (Fin Dir & Dir-Admin)

EAST TEXAS ELECTRIC CO-OPERATIVE, INC.
2905 Westward Dr, Nacogdoches, TX
75964
Tel.: (936) 560-9532   **TX**
Web Site: https://www.etec.coop
Year Founded: 1987
Sales Range: $250-299.9 Million
Electric Power Distr
N.A.I.C.S.: 221122
M. Ryan Thomas (CFO)

EAST TEXAS FINANCIAL CORPORATION
301 E Main St, Kilgore, TX 75662
Tel.: (903) 984-8671   **TX**
Web Site:
    http://www.citizensbanktx.com
Year Founded: 1990
Sales Range: $50-74.9 Million
Bank Holding Company
N.A.I.C.S.: 551111

Subsidiaries:

Citizens Bank   **(1)**
301 E Main St, Kilgore, TX 75662
Tel.: (903) 984-8671
Web Site: http://www.citizensbanktx.com
Sales Range: $10-24.9 Million
Emp.: 50
Retail & Commercial Banking Services
N.A.I.C.S.: 522110
Larry T. Long (Chm)
Sammy D. York (Pres & CEO)
Frank Connealy (CFO & Sr VP)
Kenneth R. Plunk (Exec VP)
Carmel McElyea (Officer-Loan & Sr VP-Kilgore)
Darla English (VP-Kilgore)
Melvin K. Jordan (Officer-Trust & Exec VP-Kilgore)
Jean Carr (VP-IT Ops-Kilgore)

Alan Clark (VP-Comml Lending-Kilgore)
Maria Sanchez (Asst VP-Kilgore)
Jim Griffin (VP-Oil & Gas-Kilgore)
Margaret Logston (Asst VP-Oil & Gas-Kilgore)
Teri Busby (Asst VP-Kilgore)
Tammy Jackson (VP-Kilgore)
Tobi Newhouser (VP-HR-Kilgore)

EAST TEXAS MACK SALES LLC
2934 Hwy 31 N, Longview, TX 75603
Tel.: (903) 758-9994
Web Site: http://www.east-texas-mack.com
Year Founded: 1976
New & Used Trucks, Tractors & Trail-ers Sales
N.A.I.C.S.: 441227
Drew Bankston (Gen Mgr & Mgr-Used Truck & Mgr-Fin)
David Carroum (Mgr-New Truck Sls)
Dale Manes (Mgr-Parts)
Alan Adams (Mgr-Svc)
James Coates (Mgr-Body Shop)

EAST TEXAS PROFESSIONAL CREDIT UNION
409 E Loop 281, Longview, TX
75605
Tel.: (903) 323-0230   **TX**
Web Site: http://www.etpcu.org
Year Founded: 1953
Rev.: $33,811,490
Assets: $615,308,609
Liabilities: $490,007,479
Net Worth: $125,301,130
Earnings: $11,372,820
Emp.: 253
Fiscal Year-end: 12/31/18
Credit Union Operator
N.A.I.C.S.: 522130
Scot Haines (Sr VP & Mgr-Ops)
Deborah Pearce (Sr VP & Mgr-Acctg Dept)
Greg Jeffery (VP & Branch Mgr-Ops)
William Byron Norton (Pres & CEO)
John Griffin (Sr VP & Mgr-Lending Ops)
Flip Kraus (VP & Mgr-Real Estate)
Doug Martin (VP & Mgr-Indirect Lend-ing Dept)
Kevin Wasson (VP-IT)
Kerri Dalme (VP & Branch Mgr-Ops)
Kelly Evans (VP & Mgr-Acct Resolu-tion)
Kristal Martin (VP-Product Dev & Electronic Svcs)

EAST TEXAS SUPPORT SER-VICES, INC.
109 W Water St, Jasper, TX 75951
Tel.: (409) 384-8751   **TX**
Year Founded: 1985
Sales Range: $10-24.9 Million
Emp.: 100
Community Support Services
N.A.I.C.S.: 624190
Teresa Janeaux (Exec Dir)

EAST WEST CONNECTION, INC.
389 Pittstown Rd, Pittstown, NJ
08867
Tel.: (908) 713-9655
Web Site:
    https://www.eastwestconnec
    tion.com
Sales Range: $10-24.9 Million
Emp.: 24
Gifts & Promotional Merchandise for Large Corporations
N.A.I.C.S.: 561499
Ralph D. Weaver (Founder, Pres & CEO)

EAST WEST COPOLYMER LLC
5955 Scenic Hwy, Baton Rouge, LA
70805-2044
Tel.: (225) 267-3400   **DE**
Web Site:
    http://www.ewcopolymer.com
Year Founded: 1943
Sales Range: $10-24.9 Million
Emp.: 200
Synthetic Rubber Products Mfr
N.A.I.C.S.: 325212
Gregory Nelson (Pres & CEO)
Bobby Rikhoff (VP-Ops)
Dana Coody (VP-HR)
Patrick Bowers (VP-Pur & Sls)
Paula Moreau (CFO & Sr VP)

EAST WEST ENERGY LTD.
5126 Mulberry Gr, Kingwood, TX
77345-1441
Tel.: (281) 361-2028
Web Site: http://www.ewesl.com
Plumbing, Heating & Air-Conditioning Contractors
N.A.I.C.S.: 238220
Howard Chapman (Principal)
Mitchell McGeorge (Chm & CEO)
Christopher Nicholls (Sec)

Subsidiaries:

Rife Energy Operating LLC   **(1)**
3880 Hulen St, Fort Worth, TX 76107-7274
Tel.: (817) 732-8739
Web Site:
    http://www.rifeenergyoperating.com
Oil & Gas Operations
N.A.I.C.S.: 213112
Patty Hill (Mgr)

EAST WEST INDUSTRIAL EN-GINEERING CO. INC.
1099 Highland Dr Ste D, Ann Arbor,
MI 48108-5002
Tel.: (519) 735-3828   **MI**
Web Site: https://www.ewie.com
Year Founded: 1981
Sales Range: $25-49.9 Million
Emp.: 147
Provider of Industrial Supply Services
N.A.I.C.S.: 423840
Brian Peters (COO)
Manoj K. Sachdeva (Co-Founder, Chm, Pres & CEO)
Rick Simmons (Dir-Fin Ops)
Joey Mullick (VP)

EAST WEST MANUFACTUR-ING, LLC
4170 Ashford Dunwoody Rd Ste 560,
Atlanta, GA 30319
Tel.: (404) 252-9441
Web Site: http://www.ewmfg.com
Year Founded: 2001
Fluid Power Pump & Motor Mfr
N.A.I.C.S.: 333996
Scott Ellyson (CEO & Founding Part-ner)
Adam Sanderson (VP-Value Engrg-Corp)
Jeff Sweeney (Founding Partner, CMO & Exec VP)
Mike Picchi (CFO)
Matt Greenfield (VP-Global Ops)
Kathleen Samnik (VP-Admin Ops)
Casey Fagan (Dir-People & Culture)
Adam Agress (VP-Global BUs Dev)
Steven Lustig (VP-Global Supply Chain)
Shawn Mokhtari (VP-Operational Ex-cellence & Integration)

Subsidiaries:

Adcotron EMS Inc.   **(1)**
12 Channel St, Boston, MA 02210
Tel.: (617) 598-3000
Printed Circuit Assembly Mfr
N.A.I.C.S.: 334418

Eastprint, Inc. (1)
350 Willow St S, North Andover, MA 01845
Tel.: (978) 975-5255
Web Site: http://www.eastprint.com
Electronic Components Mfr
N.A.I.C.S.: 334419
Alexander Norton (Reg Mgr-Sls)
Tom Bianchi (Mng Partner & VP)

General Microcircuits, Inc. (1)
1133 N Main St, Mooresville, NC 28115-0748
Tel.: (704) 663-5975
Web Site: http://www.gmimfg.com
Printed Circuit Board Assemblies Mfr
N.A.I.C.S.: 334412
Dave Dalton (Pres & CEO)
Diane Thompson (CFO)

EAST WEST PARTNERS
100 E Thomas Pl 5th Fl, Avon, CO 81620
Tel.: (970) 845-9200
Web Site: http://www.ewpartners.com
Holding Company
N.A.I.C.S.: 523999
Craig Ferraro (Partner-Dev)
Chris Frampton (Mng Partner-EWP)
Mark Smith (Founder & Partner-Dev)
Chuck Madison (Partner-Dev)
Amy Cara (Mng Partner-Denver)
Ryan Stone (Partner-Dev & CFO-Denver)
Peter Goergen (CFO-Snowmass)
Ross Bowker (Partner-Dev)

Subsidiaries:

East West Resort Management (1)
PO Box 8280, Avon, CO 81620
Tel.: (970) 926-5071
Web Site: http://www.eastwestresort.com
Rev.: $40,544,321
Emp.: 50
Real Estate Agent, Commercial
N.A.I.C.S.: 531210
Harry H. Frampton III (Pres)

EAST WEST PARTNERS MAN-AGEMENT CO.
14700 Village Square Pl, Midlothian, VA 23112
Tel.: (804) 739-3800
Web Site:
   https://eastwestcommunities.com
Rev.: $15,634,539
Emp.: 250
Subdividers & Developers, Nec
N.A.I.C.S.: 237210
Gary W. Fenchuk (Pres)

EAST WEST TEA COMPANY, LLC
121 SW Morrison St Ste 925, Portland, OR 97204
Tel.: (541) 461-2160   OR
Web Site:
   https://www.yogiproducts.com
Year Founded: 1972
Sales Range: $25-49.9 Million
Emp.: 350
Tea Distr
N.A.I.C.S.: 424490
Gerry Gegenhuber (VP-Global Pur)

EASTBIZ CORP.
2972 Columbia St, Torrance, CA 90503
Tel.: (310) 212-7143
Web Site: http://www.shipito.com
Year Founded: 2007
Sales Range: $10-24.9 Million
Emp.: 110
Mail Forwarding & Small Package Shipping
N.A.I.C.S.: 561431
David Cap (CIO)

EASTBROOK HOMES INC.
1188 E Paris Ave, Grand Rapids, MI 49546
Tel.: (616) 455-0200   MI
Web Site:
   https://www.eastbrookhomes.com
Year Founded: 1969
Sales Range: $25-49.9 Million
Emp.: 30
Speculative Building & Single-Family Housing
N.A.I.C.S.: 236115
Mick McGraw (Pres & CEO)
Daniele VanDeWege (Coord-Construction)

EASTCO MANAGEMENT COR-PORATION
612 Hwy 152 E, Rockwell, NC 28138
Tel.: (704) 279-5300
Sales Range: $10-24.9 Million
Emp.: 6
Residential Building Lessor Services
N.A.I.C.S.: 531110
Roy B. Staton (Pres)
Geraldine H. Staton (Sec)
Louise R. Ketner (Treas)
Shirley Rogers Ketner (VP)

EASTER ENTERPRISES, INC.
125 W 4th St, Spencer, IA 51301
Tel.: (712) 262-3340   IA
Web Site:
   http://www.farmerstrust.bank
Year Founded: 1959
Sales Range: $10-24.9 Million
Emp.: 43
Bank Holding Company
N.A.I.C.S.: 551111
Mike Bryan (Pres & CEO)

Subsidiaries:

Farmers Trust & Savings Bank (1)
125 W 4th St, Spencer, IA 51301-3815
Tel.: (712) 262-2600
Web Site: http://www.farmerstrust.bank
Savings Bank
N.A.I.C.S.: 522180
Mike Bryan (Pres & CEO)
Bryan Harken (CFO & VP)
Debbie Sundall (Sr VP-HR)
Kent Nelson (Exec VP)

EASTER SEALS CENTRAL TEXAS
8505 Cross Park Dr Ste 120, Austin, TX 78754
Tel.: (512) 478-2581
Web Site:
   http://www.easterseals.com
Year Founded: 1937
Disability Services
N.A.I.C.S.: 624120
Nancy Goguen (Chm)
John Pfeiffer (Vice Chm)
Kathy Daly (Treas)
Diane Deskins Hastert (Sec)
Angela F. Williams (Asst Sec)
Maureen Pusch (CEO-Mahoning, Trumbull & Columbiana)

Subsidiaries:

Vaughn House, Inc. (1)
1701 Evergreen Ave, Austin, TX 78704
Tel.: (512) 444-6081
Web Site: http://www.easterseals.com
Sales Range: $1-9.9 Million
Emp.: 100
Mentoring & Supervising Multi-Disabled Deaf Adults to Re-Enter the Workforce
N.A.I.C.S.: 541612
Denise White (Chief Dev Officer)
Mia Martin (CFO)
Tami Andres (VP-HR)
Tod Marvin (Pres & CEO)

EASTER UNLIMITED INC.
80 Voice Rd, Carle Place, NY 11514
Tel.: (516) 873-9000

Web Site: http://www.fun-world.net
Rev.: $91,625,100
Emp.: 50
Games, Toys & Children's Vehicles
N.A.I.C.S.: 339930
Stanley Geller (Pres)
Alan Geller (VP)
Jenny Li (Mgr-Credit)
Mitchell Schiff (Dir-HR)

EASTERDAY FARMS PRO-DUCE CO.
1427 N 1st Ave, Pasco, WA 99301
Tel.: (509) 544-9595
Web Site:
   https://www.easterdayfarms.com
Year Founded: 1958
Sales Range: $10-24.9 Million
Emp.: 65
Fresh Fruit & Vegetables Whslr
N.A.I.C.S.: 424480
Cody Easterday (Co-Owner)
Jody Easterday (Co-Owner & Supvr-Sls)
Gale Easterday (Co-Owner)
Andrew Wills (Co-Owner & Mgr-Production)
Tammy Heberlein (Office Mgr)
Glenn Waters (Mgr-IT)

EASTERLIN PECAN CO. INC.
PO Box 216, Montezuma, GA 31063-0216
Tel.: (478) 472-7731
Web Site:
   http://www.easterlinpecan.com
Sales Range: $10-24.9 Million
Emp.: 20
Pecan Shellers
N.A.I.C.S.: 424590
Nina Goodman (Dir-HR)
J. B. Easterlin (Pres)

EASTERN AERO MARINE INC.
5502 NW 37th Ave, Miami, FL 33142
Tel.: (305) 871-4050
Web Site: http://www.theraft.com
Rev.: $11,000,000
Emp.: 142
Mfr of Inflatable Safety Gear
N.A.I.C.S.: 326299
Miriam Oroshnik (Pres)
Yvonne Sundberg (Controller)
Steve Kuras (Mgr-Ops)

EASTERN CONTROLS INC.
3866 Providence Rd, Edgemont, PA 19028
Tel.: (610) 325-4600
Web Site:
   https://www.easterncontrols.com
Year Founded: 1969
Sales Range: $25-49.9 Million
Emp.: 85
Controlling Instruments & Accessories
N.A.I.C.S.: 423830
Kyle Devenney (Coord-Svcs)
Denis Hudak (Mgr-IT)
Randy Ruth (Mgr-Sls)

EASTERN DATA, INC.
4386 Park Dr, Norcross, GA 30093
Tel.: (770) 279-8888
Web Site: http://www.ediatlanta.com
Year Founded: 1997
Sales Range: $25-49.9 Million
Emp.: 40
Computer Components Distr; Computing Systems & Services
N.A.I.C.S.: 423430
Joe Chang (Pres)
Cami Parks (Dir-Mktg)
Waylee George (Mgr-Bus Dev)

EASTERN ENGINEERED WOOD PRODUCTS

1245 Easton Rd, Bethlehem, PA 18015
Web Site: https://www.eewp.com
Year Founded: 1997
Sales Range: $25-49.9 Million
Emp.: 60
Whslr of Lumber, Plywood & Millwork
N.A.I.C.S.: 423310
Steve Colson (Owner)

EASTERN ETCHING & MANU-FACTURING CO.
35 Lower Grape St, Chicopee, MA 01013-2693
Tel.: (781) 933-2984   MA
Web Site: https://www.eastern-etching.com
Year Founded: 1935
Name Plates: Engraved, Etched
N.A.I.C.S.: 332812
Michael Cocco (Mgr-Ops)

EASTERN FARMERS COOP-ERATIVE
601 Depot Ave, Garretson, SD 57030
Tel.: (605) 594-3415   SD
Web Site:
   http://www.easternfarmerscoop.com
Year Founded: 1918
Sales Range: $1-9.9 Million
Emp.: 1,000
Grain Elevator & Farm Supplies Whslr
N.A.I.C.S.: 424510
Chuck Miller (Gen Mgr)

EASTERN FEDERAL CORP.
122 Cherokee Rd, Charlotte, NC 28207
Tel.: (704) 377-3495
Web Site:
   http://www.easternfederal.com
Year Founded: 1945
Sales Range: $25-49.9 Million
Emp.: 500
Motion Picture Theater Services
N.A.I.C.S.: 512131
Edward Long (Pres & CEO)
Debbie Craig (CFO)

Subsidiaries:

American Theatre Supply Inc. (1)
901 East Blvd, Charlotte, NC 28203-5203
Tel.: (704) 375-3298
Sales Range: $10-24.9 Million
Emp.: 5
Photographic Equipment & Supplies
N.A.I.C.S.: 423410

EASTERN ILLINI ELECTRIC COOPERATIVE
330 W Ottawa St, Paxton, IL 60957
Tel.: (217) 379-2131
Web Site: https://www.eiec.org
Sales Range: $1-9.9 Million
Emp.: 59
Distribution, Electric Power
N.A.I.C.S.: 221122
Bradley Ludwig (Sec)
Thomas Schlatter (Chm)
Steve Meenen (Treas & Asst Sec)
Bob Hunzinger (Pres & CEO)
Chase Sanders (Mgr-Procurement & Physical Resources)

EASTERN INDUSTRIAL AUTO-MATION
158 Lexington St, Waltham, MA 02454
Tel.: (781) 899-3554
Web Site: http://www.easternia.com
Year Founded: 1963
Sales Range: $50-74.9 Million
Emp.: 145
Machinery Parts Sales & Service

Eastern Industrial Automation—(Continued)

N.A.I.C.S.: 423840
Seymour N. Schwartz (CEO)
Richard Gorsey (Founder & Pres)
Drew Tucci (Dir-Sls & Mktg)
Geoffrey Filker (Principal)

Subsidiaries:

Shanghai Motion Control Technology
Co. Ltd. (1)
Room 507 No 197 ChangShou Road, Fortune Times Building, Shanghai, 200060, China
Tel.: (86) 21 61489770
Web Site: http://www.easternia.cn
Industrial Components Import & Export Services
N.A.I.C.S.: 423830
Haiyun Chen (Mgr)

EASTERN INDUSTRIAL SUPPLIES INC.
247 Interstate Blvd, Greenville, SC 29615
Tel.: (864) 288-8520
Web Site:
  https://www.easternfirst.com
Sales Range: $10-24.9 Million
Emp.: 45
Valves & Fittings
N.A.I.C.S.: 423830
Robby Davis (CFO & VP)
Richy Milligan (Sr VP-Sls & Mktg)
Michael Scaturro (Mgr-Coastal Carolina)

EASTERN INSTRUMENT LABORATORIES, INC.
416 Landmark Dr, Wilmington, NC 28412
Tel.: (910) 392-2490
Web Site:
  http://www.easterninstruments.com
Year Founded: 1984
Electrical Contractor
N.A.I.C.S.: 238210
Mildred R. Brandt (Pres)

EASTERN IOWA LIGHT & POWER COOPERATIVE INC.
600 E 5th St, Wilton, IA 52778
Tel.: (563) 732-2211
Web Site:
  http://www.easterniowa.com
Year Founded: 1935
Sales Range: $50-74.9 Million
Emp.: 90
Providers of Electrical Services
N.A.I.C.S.: 221122
Bob Wiemerslage (Mgr-Acctg Div)
Dennis Hill (Mgr-Engrg Div)
Dave Mohr (Mgr-Bus Dev)
Kirk Trede (CEO)
Joel Carstensen (VP)
Nancy Varner (Pres)
David Timmerman (Sec)
Don Roth (Mgr-Member Svc Div)
Lance Kephart (Mgr-IT)

EASTERN IOWA TIRE CO. INC.
8528 NW Blvd, Davenport, IA 52806
Tel.: (563) 388-0440
Web Site: https://www.eitire.com
Rev.: $12,342,056
Emp.: 90
Tire Repair Shop
N.A.I.C.S.: 811198
Gary Van Blaricom (Pres)
Phil Blaricom (Mgr)

EASTERN KENTUCKY CONCENTRATED EMPLOYMENT PROGRAM, INC.
941 N Main St, Hazard, KY 41701
Tel.: (606) 436-5751
Web Site: http://www.ekcep.org

Year Founded: 1968
Sales Range: $10-24.9 Million
Emp.: 29
Employment Placement Services
N.A.I.C.S.: 561311
Jeff Whitehead (Exec Dir)
Travis Winkler (Mgr-Information Technology)

EASTERN LAND MANAGEMENT (ELM)
142 Hamilton Ave, Stamford, CT 06902
Tel.: (203) 316-5433
Web Site:
  https://www.easternland.com
Year Founded: 1976
Sales Range: $1-9.9 Million
Emp.: 70
Exterior Site Management Services to Commercial Customers
N.A.I.C.S.: 541320

EASTERN LIFT TRUCK CO. INC.
Rte 549 E Linwood Ave, Maple Shade, NJ 08052-0307
Tel.: (856) 779-8880
Web Site:
  http://www.easternlifttruck.com
Year Founded: 1974
Sales Range: $100-124.9 Million
Emp.: 400
Mfr of Industrial Machinery & Equipment
N.A.I.C.S.: 423830
Mike Pruitt (Pres)
Glenda Naylor (Coord-Sls-Used Truck)
Ed Gill (Mgr-Svcs)
Jill Carroll (Mgr-Acct)
Marie Hilton (Coord-Rental)

EASTERN LONG ISLAND HOSPITAL
201 Manor Pl, Greenport, NY 11944
Tel.: (631) 477-1000
Web Site: http://www.elih.org
Year Founded: 1905
Sales Range: $25-49.9 Million
Emp.: 437
Health Care Srvices
N.A.I.C.S.: 622110
Robert T. Goldman (Vice Chm)
Carole G. Donlin (Vice Chm)
Thomas E. Murray Jr. (Chm)
Paul J. Connor III (Pres & CEO)
Frank J. Adipietro Jr. (Vice Chm)

EASTERN MAINE HEALTHCARE SYSTEMS
43 Whiting Hill Rd, Brewer, ME 04412
Tel.: (207) 973-7050
Web Site: http://www.emh.org
Sales Range: $800-899.9 Million
Emp.: 8,000
Hospital Operator & Health Care Services Organization
N.A.I.C.S.: 622110
Michael R. Crowley (Pres-Dev)
Robert A. Thompson (Chief Medical Officer & Sr VP)
Doug Michael (Chief Community Health & Grants Officer)

Subsidiaries:

Affiliated Healthcare Systems, Inc. (1)
931 Union St, Bangor, ME 04401
Tel.: (207) 973-6700
Web Site: http://www.affiliatedahs.com
Sales Range: $100-124.9 Million
Emp.: 560
Medical Supplies Distr & Healthcare Support Services

N.A.I.C.S.: 423450
Scott Oxley (Pres)

Division (Domestic):

Affiliated Laboratory, Inc. (2)
417 State St Ste 240, Bangor, ME 04401
Tel.: (207) 973-6900
Web Site: http://www.affiliatedlab.com
Sales Range: $25-49.9 Million
Emp.: 225
Medical Laboratory Operator & Testing Services
N.A.I.C.S.: 621511

EASTERN MANAGEMENT COMPANY
4 A Cedar Brook Dr, Cranbury, NJ 08512
Tel.: (609) 655-5400
Year Founded: 1975
Sales Range: $25-49.9 Million
Emp.: 20
Single-Family Housing Construction
N.A.I.C.S.: 236115
Joseph Stern (Pres)
Aaron Drillick (CFO)

EASTERN METAL OF ELMIRA INC.
1430 Sullivan St, Elmira, NY 14901
Tel.: (607) 734-2295
Web Site: http://www.usa-sign.com
Sales Range: $25-49.9 Million
Emp.: 90
Signs & Advertising Specialties
N.A.I.C.S.: 339950
Pam Goldsmith (Chm)

EASTERN MUNICIPAL WATER DISTRICT INC.
2270 Trumble Rd, Perris, CA 92570
Tel.: (951) 928-3777
Web Site: https://www.emwd.org
Year Founded: 1950
Sales Range: $150-199.9 Million
Emp.: 621
Provider of Water Supply Services
N.A.I.C.S.: 221310
Charles Bachmann (Asst Gen Mgr-Plng, Engrg & Construction)
Debby Cherney (Deputy Gen Mgr)

EASTERN NATIONAL
470 Maryland Dr, Fort Washington, PA 19034
Tel.: (215) 283-6900
Web Site:
  https://www.easternnational.org
Year Founded: 1948
Sales Range: $10-24.9 Million
Emp.: 50
Provider of Educational Products & Services to America's National Parks & Other Public Trusts
N.A.I.C.S.: 459210
Kevin Kissling (Pres & CEO)
Mark Vineburg (Mgr-Ops Support)
Monta Harrington (Reg Mgr)

EASTERN NATIONAL BANK INC.
9700 S Dixie Hwy Ste 710, Miami, FL 33156
Tel.: (305) 995-5800
Web Site: http://enbdirect.enbfl.com
Year Founded: 1969
Sales Range: $10-24.9 Million
Emp.: 119
Banking Services
N.A.I.C.S.: 522110
Carlos G. Rodriguez (Pres & CEO)

EASTERN NIAGARA HEALTH SERVICES
2600 William St, Newfane, NY 14108
Tel.: (716) 514-5502

Web Site: http://www.enhs.org
Year Founded: 1996
Sales Range: $10-24.9 Million
Emp.: 286
Health Care Srvices
N.A.I.C.S.: 622110

EASTERN OIL COMPANY
590 S Paddock St, Pontiac, MI 48341
Tel.: (248) 333-1333
Web Site: https://www.easternoil.com
Sales Range: $10-24.9 Million
Emp.: 45
Provider of Lubricating Oils & Greases
N.A.I.C.S.: 424720
Mike Skuratovich (Owner)

EASTERN OMNI CONSTRUCTORS INC.
118 Oakmont Dr, Greenville, NC 27858-5936
Tel.: (252) 756-7600
Year Founded: 1980
Sales Range: $25-49.9 Million
Emp.: 500
Building & Construction Services
N.A.I.C.S.: 236210
Harry Sloan (Pres)
Ed Holland (Controller)
Bryan Dixon (Mgr-Safety)

EASTERN ORTHODOX MANAGEMENT CORP.
300 Barber Ave, Worcester, MA 01606
Tel.: (508) 852-1000
Year Founded: 1989
Sales Range: $10-24.9 Million
Emp.: 338
Health Care Srvices
N.A.I.C.S.: 622110
Karen M. Laganelli (Exec Dir)
Dean Messier (Dir-HR)
Claudia Sullivan (Treas)
Evans Tsoules (VP)
Kristina Niedbala (Pres)
Theodore Thamel (Sec)

EASTERN PENN SUPPLY COMPANY (EPSCO)
700 Scott St, Wilkes Barre, PA 18705-3626
Tel.: (570) 823-1181
Web Site:
  https://www.easternpenn.com
Year Founded: 1889
Sales Range: $10-24.9 Million
Emp.: 130
Contracting, Electrical, Industrial & Plumbing Equipment Distr
N.A.I.C.S.: 423720
George H. Conyngham Jr. (Pres)

EASTERN POULTRY DISTRIBUTORS INC.
PO Box 2995, Ponte Vedra Beach, FL 32004-2995
Tel.: (904) 543-9410
Web Site: http://www.epoultry.com
Year Founded: 1956
Sales Range: $250-299.9 Million
Emp.: 35
Mfr of Poultry & Poultry Products
N.A.I.C.S.: 424440
Thomas E. Rueger (CEO)
Thad Eshelman (Sr VP-Eastern Sls)
Henry Buzgon (Sr VP-Eastern Sls)
Ted Rueger (Pres)
Grant M. Conway (COO)
Wesley Cook (Controller)
John Duffy (VP-Eastern Sls)
Jon Poole (VP-Eastern Sls)
Joe Reid (VP-Eastern Sls)

Martin Piffaretti *(VP-Export Sls)*
Kevin Ready *(Mgr-Logistics)*
Richard Hydrick *(Dir-IT)*

EASTERN PROPANE GAS, INC.
28 Industrial Way, Rochester, NH 03866-1800
Tel.: (603) 332-2080
Web Site: https://www.eastern.com
Year Founded: 1932
Sales Range: $10-24.9 Million
Emp.: 100
Liquified Petroleum Gas Sales
N.A.I.C.S.: 457210
Brian B. Boudreau *(VP-HR)*

Subsidiaries:

Eastern Propane Gas, Inc. **(1)**
131 Water St, Danvers, MA 01923
Tel.: (978) 774-1930
Web Site: http://www.eastern.com
Liquefied Petroleum Gas Dealer & Distr
N.A.I.C.S.: 221210
Jim Blake *(Mgr-District)*

EASTERN RESEARCH SERVICES INC.
1001 Baltimore Pke No 208, Springfield, PA 19064
Tel.: (610) 543-0575
Sales Range: $10-24.9 Million
Emp.: 600
Market Analysis Or Research
N.A.I.C.S.: 541910

EASTERN SAVINGS BANK, FSB
Exec Plz 2 11350 McCormick Rd Ste 200, Hunt Valley, MD 21031
Tel.: (410) 785-2200
Web Site:
https://www.easternsavings bank.com
Year Founded: 1905
Sales Range: $25-49.9 Million
Emp.: 114
Federal Savings Bank
N.A.I.C.S.: 522180
Beth H. Goldsmith *(Chm)*
Christopher P. Wooten *(VP)*
Christopher T. Johnson *(Sr VP)*
Michael S. Barrett *(VP)*
Richard C. Zeskind *(Sr VP)*
Linda L. Cashman *(VP)*
William J. Monacelli *(VP)*
Yaakov S. Neuberger *(Pres)*
Joseph J. Slovick *(Chief Credit Officer)*
John C. Kessler *(VP)*
Kirk D. Warner *(Chief Lending Officer & Sr VP)*
Dana L. Coliano *(Asst VP)*
Tracey A. Mandish *(CFO & COO)*
Andrew T. Trainer *(VP)*
R. Anthony Vaccare Jr. *(Asst VP)*

EASTERN SHIPBUILDING GROUP, INC.
2200 Nelson St, Panama City, FL 32401
Tel.: (850) 763-1900
Web Site:
https://www.easternshipbuilding.com
Year Founded: 1976
Sales Range: $200-249.9 Million
Emp.: 400
Ship Building & Repairing
N.A.I.C.S.: 336611
Brian D'Lsernia *(Pres)*
Steve Berthold *(VP-Sls & Mktg)*
Justin C. Smith *(Gen Mgr-Nelson Street Facility)*
Benny C. Bramblette *(Gen Mgr-Allanton Facility)*
Daniel R. Lozier *(Gen Counsel)*

Fernando Malabet *(VP-Engrg)*
Jerry Huff *(Dir-Pur)*
Kenneth R. Munroe *(COO & Exec VP)*
Scott Colemere *(CFO)*

EASTERN SILK MILLS INC.
212 Catherine St, Elizabeth, NJ 07201
Tel.: (908) 355-6700
Web Site: http://www.eastern-silk.com
Sales Range: $10-24.9 Million
Emp.: 30
Silk Goods, Woven
N.A.I.C.S.: 424310
G. Venkatesh *(Pres)*

EASTERN SKATEBOARD SUPPLY INC.
6612 Amsterdam Way, Wilmington, NC 28405
Tel.: (910) 791-8240
Web Site:
https://www.easternskatesupply.com
Rev.: $11,900,000
Emp.: 40
Sporting & Recreation Goods
N.A.I.C.S.: 423910
Reginald Barnes *(Pres)*
Jocelyne Tracy *(Mgr-Sls)*

EASTERN SLEEP PRODUCTS COMPANY INC.
4901 Fitzhugh Ave Ste 300, Richmond, VA 23230-3531
Tel.: (804) 254-1711
Web Site:
https://www.symbolmattress.com
Year Founded: 1983
Sales Range: $10-24.9 Million
Emp.: 300
Mattresses & Box Springs Mfr
N.A.I.C.S.: 337910
Charles Neal *(Pres & CFO)*

Subsidiaries:

Symbol Mattress of New England Inc. **(1)**
312 Lk Rd, Dayville, CT 06241-1537 **(100%)**
Tel.: (860) 779-3112
Web Site: http://www.symbolmattress.com
Sales Range: $10-24.9 Million
Emp.: 46
Supplier Of Mattresses & Bedsprings
N.A.I.C.S.: 337910
Mike McQuiston *(Pres)*
Nicole Slinger *(VP-Specialty Products)*

Subsidiary (Domestic):

White Cross Sleep Products **(2)**
901 E Lycoming St, Philadelphia, PA 19124-5111
Tel.: (215) 289-5556
Rev.: $2,000,000
Emp.: 50
Bedding Mfr
N.A.I.C.S.: 337910
Harvey Freeman *(Pres)*
Mark Freeman *(Owner)*

Symbol Mattress of Wisconsin, Inc. **(1)**
1100 S 12th St, Watertown, WI 53094-7507 **(100%)**
Tel.: (920) 262-7477
Web Site: http://www.symbolmattress.com
Sales Range: $10-24.9 Million
Emp.: 75
Supplier of Mattresses & Bedsprings
N.A.I.C.S.: 337910
Carolyn Henze *(Acct Mgr)*

EASTERN STATES ASSOCIATES INC.
3 Converse Ste 102, Palmer, MA 01069
Tel.: (413) 283-4412

Web Site:
https://www.easternstates.com
Year Founded: 1955
Rev.: $25,000,000
Emp.: 15
Petroleum Industry Machinery
N.A.I.C.S.: 423830
Linda Maxwell *(CFO)*
Edward R. Maxwell Jr. *(Pres)*

EASTERN STATES COMPONENTS, INC.
108 Pratts Junction Rd, Sterling, MA 01564
Tel.: (978) 422-7641
Web Site:
https://www.escomponents.com
Year Founded: 1981
Rev.: $46,000,000
Emp.: 24
Electrical & Electronic Equipment Supplier
N.A.I.C.S.: 423690
Curt Olsen *(Dir-Sls)*
Mehrdad Namin *(VP & Gen Mgr)*
Ike Aubrey *(Pres)*

EASTERN STEEL CORP.
1946 Pitkin Ave, Brooklyn, NY 11207
Tel.: (718) 495-5300
Web Site:
https://www.easternsteel.com
Rev.: $11,053,837
Emp.: 33
Steel
N.A.I.C.S.: 423510
David Laurentz *(Pres)*

EASTERN TECHNOLOGIES, INC.
215 2nd Ave, Ashford, AL 36312
Tel.: (334) 899-4351 **AL**
Web Site: http://www.gri-eti.com
Year Founded: 1987
Sales Range: $1-9.9 Million
Emp.: 50
Protective Clothing & Accessories Mfr & Distr
N.A.I.C.S.: 315990
Mark Fellows *(Treas & VP)*
John B. Steward *(Pres)*
Ashley Johnson *(Controller & Office Mgr)*
Bonnie Jordan *(Mgr-Accts Payable & Payroll)*
Robbie Sharron *(Mgr-Warehouse)*

EASTERNS AUTOMOTIVE GROUP
9950 Washington Blvd, Laurel, MD 20723
Tel.: (301) 776-0001
Web Site: http://www.easterns.com
Sales Range: $10-24.9 Million
Emp.: 300
Used Automobile Dealer
N.A.I.C.S.: 441120
Robert Bassam *(Founder & CEO)*
Alex Galadari *(VP)*
Ali Uddin *(Sr Mgr-Ops)*
Eli Copty *(Gen Mgr)*
Jeffrey Winchester *(Mgr-Sls)*
Jentry Hobson *(Mgr)*
Alicia Thomas *(Mgr-Svc)*
Chester Pinkney *(Sr Mgr-Ops)*
Tim Atkins *(Gen Mgr)*

EASTERS INC.
100 8th St SE Ste G, Altoona, IA 50009
Tel.: (515) 967-0142
Web Site:
http://www.easterseals.com
Rev.: $13,694,142
Emp.: 3
Hardware Stores

N.A.I.C.S.: 444140

EASTERSEALS ARC OF NORTHEAST INDIANA, INC.
4919 Coldwater Rd, Fort Wayne, IN 46825
Tel.: (260) 456-4534
Web Site:
http://www.easterseals.com
Year Founded: 1954
Social Services And Healthcare Services
N.A.I.C.S.: 813319
Donna Elbrecht *(Pres & CEO)*
Karen Bachman *(CFO)*
Danielle Tips *(VP-Health & Residential Supports)*
Thomas Summerville *(COO)*
Kelly Clouse *(Chief Admin Officer)*
Lynn Walker *(Dir-Quality)*
Sheri Ward *(Dir-Dev)*
Janet Schutte *(Dir-Comm & Mktg)*
Joe Cohen *(Chm)*
Eric Whicker *(Vice Chm)*

EASTEX CRUDE COMPANY
10907 State Hwy 11 W, Leesburg, TX 75451
Tel.: (903) 856-2401
Web Site:
http://www.eastexcrude.com
Sales Range: $25-49.9 Million
Emp.: 400
Liquid Petroleum Transport, Non-Local
N.A.I.C.S.: 484230
Zach Rogers *(Engr-Network)*
David Marshall *(Dir-HR)*

EASTEX TELEPHONE COOPERATIVE
3675 US Hwy 79 S, Henderson, TX 75654
Tel.: (903) 854-1000 **TX**
Web Site: https://www.eastex.com
Year Founded: 1950
Sales Range: $25-49.9 Million
Emp.: 70
Provider of Telephone Communication Services
N.A.I.C.S.: 517121
Kenneth Gladden *(Pres)*
M. R. Tiller *(Treas)*
Rusty Dorman *(Office Mgr)*

EASTGATE CHRYSLER JEEP, INC.
500 N Shadeland Ave, Indianapolis, IN 46219
Tel.: (317) 352-9361
Web Site:
http://www.eastgatechryslerjeep.net
Sales Range: $25-49.9 Million
Emp.: 85
Car Whslr
N.A.I.C.S.: 441110
Theresa Kraft *(Pres)*

EASTHAM ENTERPRISES INC.
4710 Bellaire Blvd Ste 350, Bellaire, TX 77401-4505
Tel.: (713) 661-6890
Web Site:
https://www.bigedrilling.com
Year Founded: 1913
Sales Range: $75-99.9 Million
Emp.: 208
Holding Company; Oil Drilling Equipment Mfr & Contracting Services
N.A.I.C.S.: 551112
Lyle Eastham *(Pres)*
Michael Dougherty *(VP)*

Subsidiaries:

Big E Drilling Co. **(1)**

Eastham Enterprises Inc.—(Continued)

4710 Bellaire Blvd Ste 350, Bellaire, TX 77401
Tel.: (713) 661-6890
Web Site: http://www.bigedrilling.com
Sales Range: $10-24.9 Million
Emp.: 35
Oil Well Drilling Services
N.A.I.C.S.: 213111
Lyle Eastham (Pres)

Eastham Forge Inc.   (1)
1050 Neches St, Beaumont, TX 77701-4420
Tel.: (409) 835-4212
Web Site: http://www.easthamforge.com
Sales Range: $10-24.9 Million
Emp.: 100
Mfr of Iron & Steel Forgings
N.A.I.C.S.: 332111
Joe Ryall (VP-Sls)

EASTLAN RESOURCES LLC

16789 Peterson Ridge Rd, Bend, OR 97701
Tel.: (877) 886-3320
Sales Range: $25-49.9 Million
Emp.: 100
Medical Research Services
N.A.I.C.S.: 541910
Mike Gould (Pres & CEO)
David Hastings (Dir-Client Rels)
Bill Shane (Dir-Client Rels)

EASTLAND SHOE CORPORATION

4 Meetinghouse Rd, Freeport, ME 04032
Tel.: (207) 865-6314   ME
Web Site:
    https://www.eastlandshoe.com
Year Founded: 1955
Sales Range: $75-99.9 Million
Emp.: 50
Womens & Mens Casual Shoes Whslr
N.A.I.C.S.: 424340
James B. Klein (Pres)

EASTMAN CREDIT UNION

2021 Meadowview Ln, Kingsport, TN 37660
Tel.: (423) 229-8200   TN
Web Site: https://www.ecu.org
Year Founded: 1934
Sales Range: $100-124.9 Million
Emp.: 618
Credit Union Operator
N.A.I.C.S.: 522130
David W. Atkinson (CFO & Exec VP)
Gary Tucker (Sr VP-Govt & Bus Rels)
Debra Bridwell (Sr VP-Mktg & Facilities)
Darrell Dinsmore (VP-IT)
Kelly Price (VP-Ops)
B. Fielding Rolston (Chm)
E. Wayne Kirk (Vice Chm)
Norris P. Sneed (Treas)
Lisa A. McConnell (Sec)
Cherie S. Monson (Gen Counsel & VP)
Carol S. Cross (VP-HR & Ops Training)
Tammy A. Latture (VP-Member Svcs & Lending)
Olan O. Jones Jr. (Pres & CEO)

EASTMAN INDUSTRIES

70 Ingersoll Dr, Portland, ME 04103
Tel.: (207) 878-5353   ME
Web Site:
    http://www.eastmanind.com
Emp.: 15
Mfr & Distr of Hover Mowers & Eastman Mowers
N.A.I.C.S.: 333112
Nicholas Nikazmerad (Owner)

EASTMAN MACHINE COMPANY

779 Washington St, Buffalo, NY 14203-1308
Tel.: (716) 856-2200   NY
Web Site:
    https://www.eastmancuts.com
Year Founded: 1889
Sales Range: $10-24.9 Million
Emp.: 120
Manual & Automated Cutting Machines, Spreading Equipment & Material Handling Systems Mfr
N.A.I.C.S.: 333248
James Resetar (VP-Fin & Manual Cutting Machine)
Trevor Stevenson (VP-Ops)

EASTMAN PARK MICROGRAPHICS, INC.

100 Latona Rd Bldg 318, Rochester, NY 14652-3621
Tel.: (585) 500-4400   DE
Web Site: http://www.epminc.com
Year Founded: 2011
Micrographic Equipment & Supplies Mfr & Whslr
N.A.I.C.S.: 334118
William D. Oates (Pres & CEO)

Subsidiaries:

Eastman Park Micrographics, Inc. - Dallas   (1)
6300 Cedar Springs Rd, Dallas, TX 75235-5809
Tel.: (214) 580-8390
Web Site: http://www.epminc.com
Micrographics Equipment & Supplies Mfr & Distr
N.A.I.C.S.: 333310
Tim Mortenson (VP-Ops-Global)

EASTON COACH CO.

1200 Conroy Pl, Easton, PA 18040
Tel.: (610) 253-4055
Web Site:
    https://www.eastoncoach.com
Sales Range: $10-24.9 Million
Emp.: 240
Bus & Other Motor Vehicle Transit Systems
N.A.I.C.S.: 485113
Charles Palmeri (VP)
Joe Scott (Pres & CEO)

EASTON SANDERSON & COMPANY

300 E State St Ste G, Jacksonville, FL 32202
Tel.: (904) 356-2228
Web Site: https://www.escresults.com
Rev.: $11,200,000
Emp.: 5
Real Estate Brokers & Agents
N.A.I.C.S.: 531210
Lauri A. Smith (Office Mgr)

EASTPORT HOLDINGS, INC.

813 Ridge Lake Blvd, Memphis, TN 38120
Tel.: (901) 425-9220
Web Site:
    https://www.eastportholdings.com
Year Founded: 2011
Holding Company; Advertising Agencies
N.A.I.C.S.: 551112
Bubba Patton (Chm & CEO)
Jeff Presley (Sec, Treas & Dir)
Matt Wilson (Pres & COO)
Neil Widerschein (Partner-Strategy & Creative)
Carl Saxon (CFO)

Subsidiaries:

BFG Marketing, LLC   (1)
6 Anolyn Ct, Bluffton, SC 29910

Tel.: (843) 837-9115
Web Site: http://www.bfgcom.com
Emp.: 200
Brand Marketing & Promotional Events Marketing
N.A.I.C.S.: 541810
Kevin Meany (Pres & CEO)
Shari Meany (VP-HR & Admin)
Matt Nadler (Creative Dir)
Lisa Ringelstetter (VP-Client Svcs)
Jason Vogt (COO & VP)
Richard Leslie (Chief Strategy Officer)
Rick Fannin (Sr Dir-Technology)
Kate Bradburry (Mng Dir-NYC)
Jesse Bushkar (Sr Dir-Digital & Social)
Holli Hines Easton (Mng Dir-ATL)
Michael Dunn (Creative Dir)
Ryan Kasal (Creative Dir)
Amy-Sakaowan Songsoonthorn (Creative Dir)
Abigail Dudley (Creative Dir)
Riley Easton (Creative Dir)
Jason Ferguson (Creative Dir)
Justin Wolfe (Creative Dir)
Kristofer Gregoire (Creative Dir)
Elliott Allen (Creative Dir)
Jennifer Ingram (Acct Dir)
Scott Seymour (Chief Creative Officer & VP)
Scott Seymour (Chief Creative Officer & VP)

Mindstream Media, LLC   (1)
100 Walnut St, Peoria, IL 61602
Tel.: (307) 677-0400
Web Site: http://mindstreammedia.com
Full-service Media Agency
N.A.I.C.S.: 541810
Terry Tanner (CEO)
Zac Keeney (Pres)

Subsidiary (Domestic):

EdgeCore, LLC   (2)
1025 Technology Pkwy Ste A, Cedar Falls, IA 50613
Tel.: (319) 277-3700
Advetising Agency
N.A.I.C.S.: 541810
Lisa Peterson (Acct Mgr)

Unit (Domestic):

The Cooper Group, Ltd.   (3)
381 Park Ave S Ste 801, New York, NY 10016-8806
Tel.: (212) 696-2512
Advetising Agency
N.A.I.C.S.: 541810
Tom Cooper (Principal)

EASTSIDE FLOOR SERVICES LTD.

129 E 124th St, New York, NY 10035
Tel.: (212) 996-1800   NY
Web Site:
    http://www.eastsidefloors.com
Year Founded: 1986
Sales Range: $10-24.9 Million
Emp.: 11
Flooring Retailer & Installation Services
N.A.I.C.S.: 449121
Gerard Flynn (Owner & CEO)
Kevin O'Donnell (Mgr)
Brian Findleton (Mgr)

Subsidiaries:

Eastside Floor Supplies, Ltd.   (1)
1785 Park Ave, New York, NY 10035
Tel.: (212) 426-8500
Sales Range: $1-9.9 Million
Emp.: 11
Wholesale Retails & Distributes Wood Flooring
N.A.I.C.S.: 423220
Gerard Flynn (CEO)

EASTSIDE FOODS INC.

5900 Southeaster Ave Ste 106, Commerce, CA 90040
Tel.: (323) 685-6820   CA
Year Founded: 1983
Sales Range: $10-24.9 Million
Emp.: 4

Sale of Meats & Meat Products
N.A.I.C.S.: 424470

EASTSIDE RETIREMENT ASSOCIATION

10901 176th Cir NE, Redmond, WA 98052
Tel.: (425) 556-8100   WA
Year Founded: 1992
Sales Range: $10-24.9 Million
Emp.: 377
Lifecare Retirement Community Services
N.A.I.C.S.: 623311
Allan Chambard (CFO & VP-Fin)
Kay Wallin (VP-Mktg & Residential Svcs)
Lisa Hardy (Pres & CEO)
Linda Hussey (Chm)
Jane Walls (Sec)
John Plovie (Vice Chm)

EASTWARD COMPANIES, INC.

155 Crowell Rd, Chatham, MA 02633
Tel.: (508) 945-2300
Web Site:
    https://www.eastwardco.com
Year Founded: 1970
Sales Range: $10-24.9 Million
Emp.: 25
Housing Construction Services
N.A.I.C.S.: 236117
William Marsh (Pres)

EASTWEST MARKETING GROUP, LLC

575 8th Ave 21st Fl, New York, NY 10018
Tel.: (646) 681-4815   DE
Web Site:
    http://www.eastwestmg.com
Advertising Agency
N.A.I.C.S.: 541810
Rod Gonzalez (Creative Dir)
Keith Manzella (VP & Creative Dir)
Lou Ramery (CEO)

EASTWIND MARITIME SA INC.

444 Madison Ave Ste 200, New York, NY 10022
Tel.: (212) 838-1113
Rev.: $118,881,345
Emp.: 50
Chartering Of Commercial Boats
N.A.I.C.S.: 488390
John D. Kousi (Pres)

EASTWOOD HOMES

2857 Westport Rd, Charlotte, NC 28208
Tel.: (704) 399-4663
Web Site:
    https://www.eastwoodhomes.com
Year Founded: 1977
Sales Range: $25-49.9 Million
Emp.: 140
New Construction & Single-Family Housing Developer
N.A.I.C.S.: 236115
Joseph K. Stewart (Founder)
Mike Conley (Pres)
Justin Myers (VP-Ops)
David Nelson (VP-Sls)

EASTWOOD INSURANCE SERVICES

1551 E Ontario Ave Ste 105, Corona, CA 92881
Tel.: (714) 685-8300
Web Site:
    http://www.eastwoodinsurance.com
Sales Range: $50-74.9 Million
Emp.: 600
Insurance Agents, Brokers & Service
N.A.I.C.S.: 524210

Cathy Mave *(Pres)*

EASY BUY PLUS, INC.
7901 Surreywood Pl, Charlotte, NC
28270
Tel.: (980) 245-7496   NV
Year Founded: 2012
Online Merchandise Return Services
N.A.I.C.S.: 513199
John C. Marus *(Pres, CEO, Treas &
Sec)*

EASY DOES IT INC.
1300 Hilltop Rd, Leesport, PA 19533
Tel.: (610) 373-2463   PA
Web Site:
   https://www.easydoesitinc.org
Year Founded: 1989
Sales Range: $1-9.9 Million
Emp.: 20
Drug Addiction Rehabilitation Ser-
vices
N.A.I.C.S.: 621420
Irene Mouchlizis *(Accountant)*
Phillip Frassinelli *(Pres)*
Steve Adams *(Treas)*
Tim McGuirk *(Sec)*
Taniva Wiley *(Mgr-Female Case)*

EASY MONEY GROUP (EMG)
272 Bendix Rd Ste 500, Virginia
Beach, VA 23452
Tel.: (757) 493-0333
Web Site:
   https://www.easymoneynow.com
Rev.: $105,000,000
Emp.: 50
Financial Services
N.A.I.C.S.: 561499

EASY PICKINS INC.
450 7th Ave Ste 701, New York, NY
10123
Tel.: (212) 244-2220
Web Site:
   http://www.easypickins.com
Rev.: $30,175,652
Emp.: 21
Ready-To-Wear Apparel, Women's
N.A.I.C.S.: 458110
Alan Warshak *(Pres)*
Fernando Cacoilo *(Reg Mgr)*
Dimitri Maignan *(Mgr-Sls)*
Matthew Dunlop *(Mgr-IT)*

**EASY WAY FOOD STORES
INC.**
4545 S Mendenhall Rd, Memphis, TN
38141
Tel.: (901) 527-6256
Web Site:
   http://www.easywayproduce.com
Rev.: $22,350,297
Emp.: 300
Supermarkets, Chain
N.A.I.C.S.: 445110
David Carter *(Co-Owner & Treas)*
Barry M. Carter Jr. *(Co-Owner &
Pres)*

EASYSEAT, LLC
140 Whiting St, Plainville, CT 06062
Tel.: (860) 225-6110
Web Site: http://www.easyseat.net
Year Founded: 2005
Sales Range: $1-9.9 Million
Emp.: 5
Online Reseller of Theatre, Sports &
Concert Tickets
N.A.I.C.S.: 517810
David Evans *(Owner & Pres)*

EAT HERE BRANDS, LLC
4500 I-55 N Ste 221, Jackson, MS
39211
Tel.: (601) 956-7419

Web Site: http://www.eathere.com
Full-Service Restaurants
N.A.I.C.S.: 722511
Michael Stack *(Exec Dir)*

EAT WELL INC.
19 North St, Hingham, MA 02043
Tel.: (781) 741-5100
Web Site: http://www.eatwellinc.com
Rev.: $13,000,000
Emp.: 180
Eating Place
N.A.I.C.S.: 722511
Ed King *(Pres)*
Brian Barry *(Mgr-Beverage)*
Erica Chase *(Mgr)*
Karlee Dean-Goffrier *(Mgr-
Restaurant)*

**EAT'N PARK HOSPITALITY
GROUP, INC.**
285 E Waterfront Dr, Homestead, PA
15120
Tel.: (412) 461-2000   PA
Web Site: http://www.eatnpark.com
Year Founded: 1949
Sales Range: $150-199.9 Million
Emp.: 100
Family Restaurants
N.A.I.C.S.: 722511
Jim Broadhurst *(Chm)*
Jeff Broadhurst *(Pres)*
Kevin O. Connell *(Sr VP-Mktg)*

Subsidiaries:

Cura Hospitality Inc.   (1)
2970 Corporate CT Ste 5, Orefield, PA
18069
Tel.: (412) 464-3000
Web Site: http://www.curahospitality.com
Restaurant & Food Services Consultants
N.A.I.C.S.: 541618
Lisa Schairer *(Mng Dir)*
Michael Markey *(Mng Dir-Growth)*

Six Penn Kitchen   (1)
146 6th St, Pittsburgh, PA 15222
Tel.: (412) 566-7366
Web Site: http://www.sixpennkitchen.com
Emp.: 50
Restaurant
N.A.I.C.S.: 722511
David Fortunato *(Gen Mgr)*

EATERIES, INC.
1208 E Broadway Rd Ste 120,
Tempe, AZ 85282
Tel.: (480) 347-3800   OK
Year Founded: 1984
Sales Range: $75-99.9 Million
Emp.: 2,500
Owner, Operator & Franchiser of Ca-
sual Restaurants
N.A.I.C.S.: 722511

**EATHERLY CONSTRUCTORS
INC.**
1010 Boots Rd, Garden City, KS
67846
Tel.: (620) 276-6611
Sales Range: $10-24.9 Million
Emp.: 50
Provider of Pipeline Construction
Services
N.A.I.C.S.: 237110
Robert J. Eatherly *(Pres)*
Laura Eatherly *(Sec)*

EATING RECOVERY CENTER
7351 E Lowry Blvd Ste 200, Denver,
CO 80230
Tel.: (303) 825-8584
Web Site: http://www.eatingrecovery
   center.com
Year Founded: 2008
Sales Range: $25-49.9 Million
Emp.: 375

Health Care Srvices
Kenneth L. Weiner *(Chm & Partner)*
Craig Johnson *(Chief Clinical Officer)*
Len Dryer *(CFO)*
Kathleen Reeves *(COO-Colorado)*
Scott Fisher *(Chief HR Officer)*
Cynthia Eddington *(VP-Revenue
Cycle Mgmt)*
Carolyn Jones *(Sr Mgr-Clinical-San
Antonio)*
Stephen Fahey *(COO)*

**EATON FEDERAL SAVINGS
BANK**
236 S Cochran Ave, Charlotte, MI
48813
Tel.: (517) 543-3880
Web Site: http://www.eatonfed.com
Year Founded: 1936
Sales Range: $10-24.9 Million
Emp.: 92
Federal Savings Bank
N.A.I.C.S.: 522180
Timothy Jewell *(Pres)*

**EATON METAL PRODUCTS
COMPANY**
4800 York St, Denver, CO 80216-
2237
Tel.: (303) 296-4800   CO
Web Site:
   http://www.eatonmetalsales.com
Year Founded: 1919
Sales Range: $100-124.9 Million
Emp.: 210
Steel Fabrication
N.A.I.C.S.: 331110
Timothy J. Travis *(Pres & CEO)*

**EATON OFFICE SUPPLY CO.,
INC.**
180 John Glenn Dr, Amherst, NY
14228
Tel.: (716) 691-6100   NY
Web Site:
   http://www.eatonofficesupply.com
Year Founded: 1915
Sales Range: $100-124.9 Million
Emp.: 100
Commercial Office Supplies Distr
N.A.I.C.S.: 449110
Bruce C. Eaton *(Pres)*
Dan Sundeen *(Controller)*
Andrea Bradley *(Mgr-Mktg)*

EATON STEEL CORPORATION
10221 Capital St, Oak Park, MI
48237-3103
Tel.: (248) 398-3434   MI
Web Site:
   https://www.eatonsteel.com
Year Founded: 1963
Sales Range: $10-24.9 Million
Emp.: 58
Provider of Metal Product Services
N.A.I.C.S.: 423510
Mark Candy *(Sls Mgr)*
Dan McNaughton *(Pur Mgr)*
Marsha Moraschinelli *(Office Mgr)*
Joe Machak *(VP-IT Sys)*
Rod Machak *(VP-Ops)*
Steve White *(Reg Mgr-Sls)*

EATONFORM INC.
2280 Arbor Blvd, Dayton, OH 45439
Tel.: (937) 298-3406
Web Site: https://www.eatonform.com
Sales Range: $10-24.9 Million
Emp.: 21
Business Forms
N.A.I.C.S.: 424120
Richard A. Mullen *(Pres & CEO)*
Pat Westover *(Controller)*
Gene Simone *(VP-Sls)*

**EATZI'S TEXAS BEVERAGE
CORP.**
1435 Dragon St, Dallas, TX 75207
Tel.: (214) 599-8602
Web Site: http://www.eatzis.com
Sales Range: $10-24.9 Million
Emp.: 750
Baked Goods Mfr
N.A.I.C.S.: 311811
Adam Romo Jr. *(CEO)*

EAUKER MINERALS CORP.
1422 Beech Tree Dr, Green Bay, WI
54304
Tel.: (920) 737-0999   NV
Web Site:
   http://www.eaukerminerals.com
Year Founded: 2010
Metal Mining
N.A.I.C.S.: 212290
John Vander Leest *(Pres, CEO,
Treas & Sec)*

EBAA IRON, INC.
30 County Rd 442, Eastland, TX
76448
Tel.: (254) 629-1737   TX
Web Site: http://www.ebaa.com
Year Founded: 1964
Sales Range: $25-49.9 Million
Emp.: 330
Iron Processing Services
N.A.I.C.S.: 331511
Earl Bradley *(Founder)*

EBB AUTO CO. INC.
24999 SE Stark St, Troutdale, OR
97060
Tel.: (503) 667-7077
Web Site: http://www.tonkin.com
Sales Range: $10-24.9 Million
Emp.: 45
New & Used Car Dealers
N.A.I.C.S.: 441110
Ed Tonkin *(VP)*
Brad Tonkin *(VP)*
Scott Fidel *(Gen Mgr)*

EBBTIDE CORPORATION
2545 Jones Creek Rd, White Bluff,
TN 37187
Tel.: (615) 797-3193
Web Site:
   http://www.ebbtideboats.com
Sales Range: $25-49.9 Million
Emp.: 155
Boat Mfr
N.A.I.C.S.: 336612
Richard Anderson *(Pres-North
America)*

**EBC HR & PAYROLL SOLU-
TIONS, INC.**
301 Ohio St Ste 250, Buffalo, NY
14204
Tel.: (716) 674-7900   NY
Web Site: https://www.ebchcm.com
Year Founded: 1964
Human Resource, Payroll & Parking
Facility Equipment Management Ser-
vices
N.A.I.C.S.: 561499
Brian Donovan *(Pres)*

EBC INC.
119 W Allegheny St, Martinsburg, PA
16662
Tel.: (814) 793-4242
Year Founded: 1979
Rev.: $10,700,000
Emp.: 12
Grocery Stores, Independent
N.A.I.C.S.: 445110
Edward F. Barszczowski *(Pres)*

EBC Inc.—(Continued)

EBCO GENERAL CONTRAC- TORS
305 W Gillis St, Cameron, TX 76520
Tel.: (254) 697-8516
Sales Range: $50-74.9 Million
Emp.: 50
Nonresidential Construction Services
N.A.I.C.S.: 236220
Chris Bush *(Project Mgr)*
Ryan Hanel *(Project Mgr)*
Gina Volante *(Project Mgr)*
Patsy Barbo *(Controller)*
Patsy Vitera *(Controller)*

EBCO INC.
4135 E Cotton Ctr Blvd, Phoenix, AZ 85040-8849
Tel.: (602) 426-5292
Web Site: http://www.ebco-inc.com
Year Founded: 1983
Sales Range: $25-49.9 Million
Emp.: 85
Retailer of Furniture
N.A.I.C.S.: 449110

EBEL, SIGNORELLI & WELKE LLC
600 W Fulton St, Chicago, IL 60661
Tel.: (312) 762-7400
Web Site:
http://www.eswpartners.com
Year Founded: 2000
Sales Range: $25-49.9 Million
Emp.: 50
Advetising Agency
N.A.I.C.S.: 541810
James Signorelli *(Founder & CEO)*
Phillip Lanier *(Exec Dir-Creative)*
Pierce Hasler *(Supvr & Dir-Mgmt & Interactive Mktg)*
Lisa Edwards *(VP & Dir-Client Svcs)*
David Sollitt *(Sr VP & Gen Mgr)*

EBEN DESIGN, INC.
7221 5th Ave NE, Seattle, WA 98115
Tel.: (206) 523-9010
Web Site:
http://www.ebendesign.com
Sales Range: $10-24.9 Million
Emp.: 15
Advertising, Brand Development & Integration, Collateral, Content, Corporate Identity, E-Commerce, Email, Environmental, Exhibit/Trade Shows, Internet/Web Design, Package Design, Print
N.A.I.C.S.: 541810
Dan Walker *(Chief Copywriter)*

EBENEZER MEDICAL OUT- REACH, INC.
1448 10th Ave Ste 100, Huntington, WV 25701
Tel.: (304) 529-0753
Web Site: https://www.emohealth.org
Year Founded: 1996
Sales Range: $10-24.9 Million
Emp.: 39
Health Care Srvices
N.A.I.C.S.: 622110
Yvonne Jones *(Exec Dir)*

EBERLESTOCK USA LLC
2900 W Main St, Boise, ID 83702
Tel.: (208) 424-5081
Web Site: https://eberlestock.com
Year Founded: 1985
Hunting Equipment Distr
N.A.I.C.S.: 459110

EBIT INFORMATION SYSTEMS
300 Missouri Ave Ste 100, Jeffersonville, IN 47130
Tel.: (812) 285-8285

Web Site: http://www.ebitinfosys.com
Year Founded: 2005
Sales Range: $1-9.9 Million
Emp.: 45
IT Recruiting & Staffing
N.A.I.C.S.: 541690
Danny Castleman *(Pres)*
Stacy Rogers *(VP-HR & Recruiting)*
Mark Best *(Mgr-Bus Dev)*
Tara Schott *(Mgr- Bus Dev)*
Betsy Lange *(Coord-Client Svs)*

EBIZAUTOS
5584 S Fort Apache Rd, Las Vegas, NV 89148
Tel.: (702) 225-4434
Web Site: http://www.ebizautos.com
Year Founded: 2001
Rev.: $9,600,000
Emp.: 75
Media Representatives
N.A.I.C.S.: 541840
Susan M. Dunn *(Sec)*

EBJ FOODS CORP.
1155 7th St, Oakland, CA 94607-2660
Tel.: (510) 208-6200
Sales Range: $25-49.9 Million
Emp.: 25
Grocery Stores, Chain
N.A.I.C.S.: 445110
Don Chan *(Pres)*
Cecill Chan *(VP)*
Michael Wen *(Gen Mgr)*

EBL PARTNERS LLC
1482 Rail Head Blvd, Naples, FL 34110
Tel.: (239) 431-5003
Web Site:
https://www.eblpartners.com
Year Founded: 2009
Sales Range: $1-9.9 Million
Emp.: 12
Construction & Development Management
N.A.I.C.S.: 236220
Paul A. Benson *(Mng Partner)*
Michael D. Hawkins *(Mng Partner)*
Julio Lopez *(Project Mgr)*

EBMS
2075 Overland Ave, Billings, MT 59102
Tel.: (406) 245-3575
Web Site: https://www.ebms.com
Rev.: $11,740,028
Emp.: 230
Medical Insurance Claim Processing Services
N.A.I.C.S.: 524292
Frederick H. Larson *(CEO)*
Nicki Larson *(Pres)*
Vikki Fosjord *(Dir-Quality Assurance)*
Justin Moser *(Dir-Acct Mgmt)*
James Vertino *(CIO)*
Melissa Lyon *(Exec VP-HR)*

EBONITE INTERNATIONAL IN- CORPORATED
1813 W 7th St, Hopkinsville, KY 42240
Tel.: (270) 881-1200
Web Site: http://www.ebonite.com
Sales Range: $10-24.9 Million
Emp.: 215
Bowling Balls
N.A.I.C.S.: 339920
Robert Reid *(VP-Sls & Mktg)*
Mike Quitter *(VP-Intl)*
Randy Teitloff *(VP-R&D)*
Ed Gallagher *(Brand Mgr)*

EBP SUPPLY SOLUTIONS

200 Research Dr, Milford, CT 06460-8500
Tel.: (203) 878-1814
Web Site: https://www.ebpsupply.com
Year Founded: 1918
Sales Range: $200-249.9 Million
Emp.: 225
Industrial & Personal Services
N.A.I.C.S.: 424130
Meredith Reuben *(CEO)*
William O'Donnell *(CFO)*
Jack Jurkowski *(CIO)*
Dan Colcord *(VP-Healthcare Sls)*
Joseph F. LoPresti *(VP-HR)*
Matthew Sugarman *(VP- Redistribution Sls)*
Eric L. Peabody *(Pres)*
Michael J. Kaplan *(Sr VP-Mktg & Project Strategy)*
Susanne Trotta *(VP-Sls- Massachusetts)*
Brian Reddy *(VP-Sls-New Jersey)*

EBQUICKSTART, LLC
3000 S IH 35 Ste 320, Austin, TX 78704
Tel.: (512) 637-9696
Web Site:
http://www.ebquickstart.com
Year Founded: 2006
Sales Range: $1-9.9 Million
Emp.: 62
Marketing Consulting Services
N.A.I.C.S.: 541613
Timothy Edwards *(Founder & CEO)*
Brenda Bays *(VP-HR)*
Michael Edwards *(VP-Bus Dev)*
Doug Phelps *(VP-Pro Svcs)*
John McLellan *(Chief Revenue Officer)*
Stuart Bontrager *(VP-Sls)*

EBR SYSTEMS, INC.
480 Oakmead Pkwy, Sunnyvale, CA 94085
Tel.: (408) 720-1906
Web Site:
https://www.ebrsystemsinc.com
Year Founded: 2003
Rev.: $1,800,000
Emp.: 16
Polystyrene Foam Product Mfr
N.A.I.C.S.: 326140
Rick Riley *(Founder & COO)*
Allan Will *(Chm)*
Mark Cowan *(VP-Engrg)*
Mark Schwartz *(VP-Clinical & Regulatory Affairs)*
N. Parker Willis *(CTO)*
John McCutcheon *(Pres & CEO)*
Gary W. Doherty *(CFO)*
Michael Hendrickson *(COO)*
Andrew Shute *(Sr VP)*
Spencer H. Kubo *(Chief Medical Officer)*
Erik Strandberg *(Chief Comml Officer)*
Madhuri Bhat *(Chief Regulatory Officer)*

EBRIDGE BUSINESS SOLU- TIONS LLC
7501 New LaGrange Rd Ste 2000, Louisville, KY 40222
Tel.: (502) 491-1980
Web Site:
http://www.ebridgeglobal.com
Year Founded: 2002
Sales Range: $1-9.9 Million
Emp.: 12
Cost Reduction Strategy Services
N.A.I.C.S.: 541618
Jim Headlee *(Chm & CEO)*

EBRIDGE, INC.
1018 N Ward St, Tampa, FL 33607

Tel.: (813) 387-3870
Web Site: https://www.ebridge.com
Year Founded: 2001
Sales Range: $10-24.9 Million
Emp.: 27
Online Document Management Services
N.A.I.C.S.: 541511
Leslie Haywood *(CEO)*
James Hanlon *(CIO)*
Steven Mohr *(Mgr-Natl Acct- Insurance Clients & Prospects)*

EBRYIT INC.
250 Chastain Rd NW Ste 200, Kennesaw, GA 30144
Tel.: (678) 385-0400
Web Site: http://www.ebryit.com
Year Founded: 1990
Computer Peripherals
N.A.I.C.S.: 423430
Sharon Bryant *(CEO)*
Philip Orton *(Mgr-Logistics)*
Debora Harris *(Dir-HR)*

EBSCO INDUSTRIES, INC.
5724 Hwy 280 E, Birmingham, AL 35242-6818
Tel.: (205) 991-6600
Web Site: https://www.ebscoind.com
Year Founded: 1944
Sales Range: Less than $1 Million
Emp.: 4,500
Books Printing
N.A.I.C.S.: 323117
David Walker *(CEO)*
Paul Barber *(Pres-Valent Grp)*
Bryson Stephens *(Chm)*
Ryan Loy *(CIO)*
Eric Essary *(CFO)*
Heather Moore *(VP-Acctg)*
Brian Wilson *(VP-Corp HR)*

Subsidiaries:

Chelsea Teddy Bear Company   **(1)**
400 N Main St, Chelsea, MI 48118
Tel.: (734) 433-5499
Web Site: http://www.chelseateddybear.com
Sales Range: $25-49.9 Million
Emp.: 100
Toy Mfr & Whslr
N.A.I.C.S.: 423920
Neil O'Bryan *(Mgr-HR)*

Crown Products, LLC   **(1)**
3107 Halls Mill Rd, Mobile, AL 36606
Tel.: (251) 665-3600
Web Site: http://www.crownprod.com
Sales Range: $25-49.9 Million
Emp.: 250
Promotional Product Mfr
N.A.I.C.S.: 339999

EBSCO Canada Ltd.   **(1)**
302 10509 81 Ave, Edmonton, T6E 1X7, AB, Canada   **(100%)**
Tel.: (780) 634-2979
Web Site: http://www.ebsco.com
Sales Range: $10-24.9 Million
Emp.: 30
Subscription Agent Services
N.A.I.C.S.: 424920
John Lumsden *(Gen Mgr)*

EBSCO Development Company, Inc   **(1)**
5 Mount Laurel Ave, Birmingham, AL 35242
Tel.: (205) 408-8696
Web Site: http://www.mtlaurel.com
Emp.: 5
Real Estate Brokerage Services
N.A.I.C.S.: 531210
Della Pender *(Mgr-Sls)*

EBSCO Income Properties LLC   **(1)**
5724 Highway 280 E, Birmingham, AL 35242
Tel.: (205) 981-5135
Web Site:
http://www.ebscoincomeproperties.com
Emp.: 3
Investment Management Service
N.A.I.C.S.: 525990

Leslie L. Yeilding (VP & Gen Mgr)

EBSCO Industries Westwood (1)
249 Vanderbilt Ave, Norwood, MA
02062 **(100%)**
Tel.: (781) 501-7000
Rev.: $35,100,000
Emp.: 250
Wholesale Periodical Subscriptions
N.A.I.C.S.: 424920

**EBSCO Industries, Inc. - EBSCO
Creative Concepts Division** (1)
3500 Blue Lake Dr Ste 150, Birmingham,
AL 35243
Tel.: (205) 262-2696
Web Site:
     http://www.ebscocreativeconcepts.com
Sales Range: $10-24.9 Million
Emp.: 16
Promotional Products Distr
N.A.I.C.S.: 339999
Ed Kerr (Acct Exec)
Dusty Snyder (Acct Exec)
Bill Wright (Acct Exec)
Kinsley Foster (Acct Exec)
Christen Thacker (Acct Exec)
John Frank Yother (Mgr-Ops)

**EBSCO Industries, Inc. - EBSCO Me-
dia Division** (1)
801 5th Ave S, Birmingham, AL 35233
Tel.: (205) 323-1508
Web Site: http://www.ebscomedia.com
Commercial Printing Services
N.A.I.C.S.: 323111

**EBSCO Industries, Inc. - EBSCO Re-
ception Room Subscription Services
Division** (1)
5724 Highway 280 E, Birmingham, AL
35242
Tel.: (205) 995-1668
Subscription Management Services
N.A.I.C.S.: 323113

**EBSCO Industries, Inc. - EBSCO Re-
search Division** (1)
1447 Peachtree St Ste 1050, Atlanta, GA
30309
Tel.: (404) 365-9777
Web Site: http://www.bestpickreports.com
Information Services
N.A.I.C.S.: 513199
Greg Robb (VP & Gen Mgr)

**EBSCO Industries, Inc. - Knight &
Hale Division** (1)
715-B Summit Dr, Decatur, AL 35601
Tel.: (256) 260-8900
Web Site: http://www.knightandhale.com
Hunting Device Mfr
N.A.I.C.S.: 339999

**EBSCO Industries, Inc. - NSC Inter-
national Division** (1)
7090 Central Ave, Hot Springs, AR 71913
Tel.: (501) 525-0133
Web Site: http://www.binding.com
Sales Range: $10-24.9 Million
Emp.: 30
Binding & Laminating Equipment Mfr &
Supplier
N.A.I.C.S.: 333248

Division (Domestic):

**NSC International Division - Siegel
Display Products Division** (2)
300 6th Ave N Ste 200, Minneapolis, MN
55401
Tel.: (612) 340-1493
Web Site: http://www.siegeldisplay.com
Display Product Whslr
N.A.I.C.S.: 423440

**EBSCO Industries, Inc. - PRADCO
Fishing Division** (1)
3601 Jenny Lind Rd, Fort Smith, AR 72901-
7301
Tel.: (479) 782-8971
Web Site: http://www.lurenet.com
Sales Range: $25-49.9 Million
Emp.: 150
Fishing Lure Mfr & Whslr
N.A.I.C.S.: 339920
Bruce Stanton (VP & Gen Mgr)

**EBSCO Industries, Inc. - Publisher
Promotion and Fulfillment**

Division (1)
5724 Hwy 280 E, Birmingham, AL 35242
Tel.: (205) 991-1177
Web Site: http://www.ppfebsco.com
Sales Range: $10-24.9 Million
Emp.: 25
Subscription Management Services
N.A.I.C.S.: 541613
Heather Bean (Dir-Client Svcs)
Meg Waites (Dir-Sls & Mktg)
Aryan Billano (Mgr-IT)
Don McClain (Head-Bus Dev)

**EBSCO Industries, Inc. - Stewart
Signs Division** (1)
2201 Cantu Ct Ste 215, Sarasota, FL
34232-6255
Tel.: (941) 378-4242
Web Site: http://www.stewartsigns.com
Sales Range: $10-24.9 Million
Emp.: 100
Sign Board Mfr
N.A.I.C.S.: 339950

**EBSCO Industries, Inc. - Vulcan In-
dustries Division** (1)
300 Display Dr, Moody, AL 35201
Tel.: (205) 640-2400
Web Site: http://www.vulcanind.com
Sales Range: $25-49.9 Million
Emp.: 240
Merchandising Display Solution Provider
N.A.I.C.S.: 337215
William Hutson (VP & Gen Mgr)

EBSCO Information Services (1)
10 Estes St, Ipswich, MA 01938
Tel.: (978) 356-6500
Web Site: http://www.ebsco.com
Sales Range: $50-74.9 Million
Emp.: 900
Information Access & Management Ser-
vices
N.A.I.C.S.: 424920
Ree Sherer (Sr VP-Ops, Fin & Various Intl
Markets)
Elizabeth Jones (Sr VP-Medical Product
Mgmt-Health)
Sam Brooks (Exec VP-Mktg, Sls, Publr Rels
& Strategic Partnerships)
Don Doak (Sr VP-Strategic Partnerships &
Intl Licensing)
Doug Jenkins (CIO)
John Atkins (Sr VP-Corp Plng & Content
Mgmt)
Mark Herrick (Sr VP-Bus Dev)
Mike Laddin (Sr VP-Product Mgmt)
Holley Dumble (VP)
Paul Donovan (Sr VP)
Kathleen McEvoy (Sr VP-Comm)
Allen Powell (Exec VP-Ops & Fin)
Betsy Jones (Sr VP-Medical Product Mgmt)
Cindy DeJesus Northcutt (CFO)
Kheil McIntyre (Chief Revenue Officer)
Kim Stam (Chief Legal Officer & Sr VP)

Division (Domestic):

**EBSCO Industries, Inc. - Subscription
Services Division** (2)
PO Box 1943, Birmingham, AL 35201
Tel.: (205) 991-6600
Web Site: http://www.ebsco.com
Sales Range: $75-99.9 Million
Magazine Publisher
N.A.I.C.S.: 424920
Allen Powell (Exec VP-Ops & Fin)
Cindy DeJesus Northcutt (CFO)
Ree Sherer (Sr VP-Ops, Fin & Markets-Intl)
Beverly St. John (Gen Mgr-Publr Ops)

GOBI Library Soltuions (2)
999 Maple St, Contoocook, NH 03229
Tel.: (603) 746-3102
Web Site: http://www.ybp.com
Library Collection Management & Technical
Services
N.A.I.C.S.: 561499
Mark Kendall (Chief Revenue Officer & Sr
VP)
Kristine S. Baker (VP-Strategic Projects,
Consortia & Admin)
Nathaniel F. Bruning (VP-Content Mgmt)
Jeffrey Pickert (Dir-Ops & Lean Mgmt)
Darby Kopp (COO)
Kate Hartnett (VP-Fin & Acctg)
Michael Zeoli (VP-Content Dev & Partner
Rels)

EBSCO International Inc. (1)

5724 Hwy 280 E, Birmingham, AL
35242-6818 **(100%)**
Tel.: (205) 991-6600
Web Site: http://www.ebsco.com
Emp.: 850
Magazine Publisher
N.A.I.C.S.: 424920
James Stephens (Chm)

EBSCO Signs & Displays (1)
1400 8th St N, Clanton, AL 35045
Tel.: (205) 755-5580
Web Site: http://www.ebscosigns.com
Sales Range: $10-24.9 Million
Emp.: 95
Sign Board Mfr
N.A.I.C.S.: 339950
Tom Sefcik (VP & Gen Mgr)

EBSCO Teleservices (1)
1717 Brittain Rd Ste 107, Akron, OH 44310-
1822
Tel.: (330) 492-5105
Web Site: http://www.ebsco.com
Rev.: $5,000,000
Emp.: 150
Telemarketing Services
N.A.I.C.S.: 561422
Dave Ford (Gen Mgr)

Grand View Media Group (1)
200 Croft St Ste 1, Birmingham, AL 35242
Tel.: (205) 408-3700
Web Site: http://www.gvmg.com
Emp.: 60
Magazine & Custom Publisher
N.A.I.C.S.: 513199
Bob Robb (Editor)
Derrick Nawrocki (Publr)
John Harris (Publr)
Mike Wasson (Publr)
Tracy Aston-Martin (Publr)
Jeff Cross (Editor)
Lori Ditoro (Dir-Editorial-Process Flow Net-
work)

**Green Mountain Rifle Barrel Co.
Inc.** (1)
153 W Main St, Conway, NH 03818
Tel.: (603) 447-1095
Web Site: http://www.gmriflebarrel.com
Rifle Barrel Mfr
N.A.I.C.S.: 332994
Rick Sanborn (VP & Gen Mgr)

H. Wilson Company (1)
2245 Delany Rd, Waukegan, IL
60087 **(100%)**
Tel.: (708) 339-5111
Web Site: http://www.hwilson.com
Sales Range: $10-24.9 Million
Emp.: 30
Audio Visual Equipment & Library Furniture
Mfr
N.A.I.C.S.: 321999

J.M. Stewart Corporation (1)
2201 Cantu Ct Ste 215, Sarasota, FL
34232-6260
Tel.: (941) 378-4242
Web Site: http://www.stewartsigns.com
Sales Range: $25-49.9 Million
Emp.: 60
Hi-Tech Computer Driven Video Displays,
Message Centers, Scoreboards & Business
Identity Signs Designer, Mfr, Installer &
Other Services
N.A.I.C.S.: 339950
Eric Keller (VP-Sls & Mktg)
Mark Deutschle (Reg Mgr)

Knight Rifles, Inc. (1)
715 B Summit Dr, Decatur, AL 35601
Tel.: (256) 260-8950
Web Site: http://www.knightrifles.com
Sales Range: $25-49.9 Million
Emp.: 130
Muzzle Loading Firearms & Accessories Mfr
N.A.I.C.S.: 332994

Luxor Corp. (1)
2245 Delany Rd, Waukegan, IL
60087 **(100%)**
Tel.: (847) 244-1800
Web Site: http://www.luxorfurn.com
Sales Range: $10-24.9 Million
Emp.: 60
Furniture Mfr
N.A.I.C.S.: 337214

Paul Roche (Pres)

MCM GROUP (1)
110 Parkland Plz, Ann Arbor, MI 48103
Tel.: (734) 433-5444
Web Site: http://www.mcmgroup.net
Emp.: 40
Custom Merchandise Mfr & Distr
N.A.I.C.S.: 339999
Bob Turner (VP & Gen Mgr)

**Plastic Research and Development
Corporation** (1)
3601 Jenny Lind Rd, Fort Smith, AR 72901
Tel.: (205) 991-6600
Plastic Fishing Lure Mfr
N.A.I.C.S.: 339920

Division (Domestic):

**Plastic Research and Development
Corporation - Commonwealth Produc-
tions Division** (2)
2602 Main St Ste E2, Benton, KY 42025
Tel.: (270) 527-2786
Web Site:
     http://www.commonwealthproductions.com
Sales Range: $10-24.9 Million
Emp.: 9
Television & Video Production Services
N.A.I.C.S.: 512191
Mike Auten (Gen Mgr)

Publishers Warehouse (1)
2700 Crestwood Blvd, Birmingham, AL
35210-1227 **(100%)**
Tel.: (205) 956-2078
Web Site: http://www.ebscoind.com
Rev.: $3,400,000
Emp.: 21
School Books
N.A.I.C.S.: 459210
William Haver (VP & Gen Mgr)
F.D. Brooke Jr. (VP)

Summit Treestands, LLC (1)
715 Summit Dr SE, Decatur, AL 35601
Tel.: (256) 353-0634
Web Site: http://www.summitstands.com
Sales Range: $10-24.9 Million
Emp.: 100
Treestand Mfr
N.A.I.C.S.: 321999

The H.W. Wilson Co. (1)
950 University Ave, Bronx, NY 10452-4224
Tel.: (718) 588-8400
Sales Range: $25-49.9 Million
Emp.: 350
Indexes, Abstracts, Full-Text & Reference
Works Publisher
N.A.I.C.S.: 513120

Wingscapes, Inc.. (1)
150 Industrial Rd, Alabaster, AL 35007
Tel.: (888) 811-9464
Web Site: http://www.wingscapes.com
Wildlife Camera Mfr
N.A.I.C.S.: 333310

EBSO, INC.
2145 Ford Pkwy Ste 300, Saint Paul,
MN 55116-1912
Tel.: (651) 695-2500   **MN**
Web Site: http://www.somi.com
Year Founded: 1982
Sales Range: $25-49.9 Million
Emp.: 55
Employee Benefit Plans & Services
N.A.I.C.S.: 561499
Cynthia Sheffield (CEO)
Bruce G. Flunker (Pres)

Subsidiaries:

EBSO, Inc. (1)
7020 N Port Washington Rd Ste 206, Glen-
dale, WI 53217-3800
Tel.: (414) 365-4600
Web Site: http://www.ebsobenefits.com
Employee Benefit Plans & Services
N.A.I.C.S.: 561499
Bruce G. Flunker (Pres)
William Edrington (Mng Dir-Mktg & Bus
Dev)
Jeff Farmer (VP-Sls-East)
Rick Lyons (VP-Sls & Distr)
Cynthia Sheffield (CEO)

EBSO, Inc.—(Continued)

EBTH, INC.
6000 Creek Rd, Blue Ash, OH 45242
Tel.: (888) 862-8750
Web Site: http://www.ebth.com
Year Founded: 2008
Emp.: 100
Online Gift Product Distr
N.A.I.C.S.: 513199
Brian Graves *(Founder & Chief Learning Officer)*
Jacquie Denny *(Founder & Chief Dev Officer)*

EBULB, INC.
3500 Review Ave, Long Island City, NY 11101
Tel.: (718) 707-0400
Web Site:
  https://www.bulbamerica.com
Year Founded: 2003
Sales Range: $1-9.9 Million
Emp.: 20
Electrical Apparatus & Equipment, Wiring Supplies & Related Equipment Merchant Whslr
N.A.I.C.S.: 423610
Abraham Cohen *(Pres)*
Corey Frons *(Mgr-PR)*

EBUSINESS STRATEGIS, LLC
18318 Fern Trail Ct, Houston, TX 77084
Tel.: (281) 647-6183
Web Site: https://www.askebiz.com
Year Founded: 2001
Sales Range: $1-9.9 Million
Emp.: 28
Real Estate & Workplace Management Consulting Services
N.A.I.C.S.: 541618
Phil Wales *(CEO)*

EBW ELECTRONICS, INC.
13110 Ransom St, Holland, MI 49424
Tel.: (616) 786-0575
Web Site: https://www.ebw-electronics.com
Year Founded: 1992
Sales Range: $25-49.9 Million
Emp.: 106
Electronic Components Mfr
N.A.I.C.S.: 334419
Cory Steeby *(Pres)*
Dave Pinner *(Supvr-Production)*
Pat LeBlanc *(Chm)*

EBY CORPORATION
2525 E 36th Cir N, Wichita, KS 67219-2303
Tel.: (316) 268-3500   KS
Web Site: https://www.ebycorp.com
Year Founded: 1937
Sales Range: $125-149.9 Million
Emp.: 150
Construction Services
N.A.I.C.S.: 236210
Karman Diehl *(VP-HR)*
R. Adam Dunn *(CFO & VP)*
Linda Walton *(Treas & Sec)*
Mike Grier *(CEO)*
James Grier III *(Chm)*

Subsidiaries:

Martin K. Eby Construction Company, Inc.   (1)
2525 E 36th Cir N, Wichita, KS 67219-2303   (100%)
Tel.: (316) 268-3500
Web Site: http://www.ebycorp.com
Heavy Construction General Contractors Nonresidential & Industrial Buildings & Warehouses, Bridge Tunnel, Elevated Highway, Water Sewer Pipe Line Communication & Power Plant Construction
N.A.I.C.S.: 237210

James R. Grier *(Chm)*
Larry Weis *(Sr VP-Construction Ops)*
R. Adam Dunn *(CFO & VP)*
Kurt T. Grier *(Exec VP)*
Michael A. Grier *(Pres & CEO)*

EC COMPANY INC.
2121 NW Thurman St, Portland, OR 97210-2517
Tel.: (503) 224-3511   OR
Web Site: http://www.e-c-company.com
Year Founded: 1983
Sales Range: $25-49.9 Million
Emp.: 700
Electronic Services
N.A.I.C.S.: 238210
Andrew Beyer *(Pres)*
Kaci Cullen *(Dir-Bus Dev & Mktg)*
Todd Henne *(CFO)*

EC POWER SYSTEMS
3233 Oakland St, Aurora, CO 80010
Tel.: (303) 360-7110
Web Site: http://www.ecpower.com
Rev.: $15,281,699
Emp.: 50
Industrial Machinery & Equipment
N.A.I.C.S.: 423830
Andy Kankula *(Pres)*
Kevin Aldor *(Branch Mgr)*

EC POWER, LLC
341 N Science Park Rd, State College, PA 16803-2417
Tel.: (814) 861-6233
Web Site:
  https://www.ecpowergroup.com
Electrochemical Energy Systems Designer, Developer & Mfr
N.A.I.C.S.: 335910
Puneet Sinha *(VP-Business Development)*

ECAMPUSCASH INC.
4445 Overland Ave, Culver City, CA 90230   NV
Web Site:
  http://www.ecampuscash.com
Year Founded: 2010
Sales Range: $10-24.9 Million
Emp.: 2
College-Oriented, Internet-Based Coupon Service
N.A.I.C.S.: 541890
Kishore Mamillapalli *(Chm, Pres & CEO)*
Douglas K. Haustein *(COO & VP)*

ECAPITAL ADVISORS, LLC.
7700 Xerxes Ave S 370, Bloomington, MN 55431
Tel.: (952) 947-9300   MN
Web Site:
  http://www.ecapitaladvisors.com
Year Founded: 2001
Sales Range: $10-24.9 Million
Emp.: 52
Management Consulting Services
N.A.I.C.S.: 541611
Lisa David *(Partner)*
Matt Frederick *(Partner)*
Steve Whinnery *(Partner)*
Craig Terry *(Mgr-Bus Dev-Dallas & Fort Worth)*
John Bartkowski *(Mgr-Bus Dev-Midwest)*

ECB CORP.
6400 Artesia Blvd, Buena Park, CA 90620
Tel.: (714) 385-8900
Web Site: https://www.omniduct.com
Ducts Sheet Metal
N.A.I.C.S.: 332322

ECCO DOMANI USA INC.
PO Box 1130, Hayward, CA 95448
Tel.: (707) 431-5616
Web Site:
  http://www.eccodomani.com
Sales Range: $400-449.9 Million
Emp.: 999
Wine Mfr
N.A.I.C.S.: 312130
Tracy Long *(CFO)*

ECCO EQUIPMENT CORPORATION
1417 N Susan St, Santa Ana, CA 92703-1415
Tel.: (714) 554-4851   CA
Web Site:
  http://www.eccoequipment.com
Year Founded: 1972
Sales Range: $10-24.9 Million
Emp.: 200
Provider of Heavy Construction Equipment Rental Services
N.A.I.C.S.: 532412
Donald W. Schmid *(Pres)*
Marcia Garcia *(Coord-Payroll)*
Jeff Mancino *(CFO)*
Al Pistritto *(Mgr-Las Vegas)*

ECCO III ENTERPRISES, INC.
201 Saw Mill River Rd, Yonkers, NY 10701
Tel.: (914) 963-3600
Web Site: https://www.eccoiii.com
Sales Range: $10-24.9 Million
Emp.: 75
Highway & Street Construction
N.A.I.C.S.: 237310
Josephine McCaffrey *(Mgr-Risk)*

ECCO SAFETY GROUP
833 W Diamond St, Boise, ID 83705
Web Site:
  https://www.eccosafetygroup.com
Year Founded: 1972
Vehicle Lighting & Warning Systems Mfr & Distr
N.A.I.C.S.: 336390
Doug Phillips *(Pres & CEO)*
Chris Thompson *(VP-Global Sls)*
Todd Mansfield *(VP-Global Engrg)*
Brian Olsen *(VP-Global Ops)*
Brenton Heath *(Mng Dir-ESG Asia Pacific)*
John Ducharme *(Pres-Americas)*
Dan Emmett *(CFO)*

Subsidiaries:

Britax Automotive Equipment Pty   (1)
4 Garret Street, Brendale, 4500, QLD, Australia
Tel.: (61) 7 3000 1900
Web Site: http://www.britaxae.com.au
Emp.: 30
Vehicle Lighting & Warning Systems Distr
N.A.I.C.S.: 423120
Paul Tier *(Sls Mgr-Queensland & New Zealand)*
Gerrard Parkinson *(Sls Mgr-Victoria, Tasmania & South Australia)*
Greg Read *(Sls Mgr-Western Australia & Northern Territory)*
Andrew May *(Acct Mgr)*
Stephen Laughlan *(Acct Mgr)*
Damian Potter *(Sls Mgr-Natl-Australia & New Zealand)*
Allen Zhu *(Mgr-Product Dev)*
Trent Whayman *(Coord-Promotions)*

Britax Autozubehor GmbH   (1)
Riedweg 58-60, 89081, Ulm, Germany
Tel.: (49) 731 935210
Web Site: http://www.britaxauto.com.com
Sales Range: $1-9.9 Million
Emp.: 10
Vehicle Safety Equipment Sales
N.A.I.C.S.: 423120
Lothar Bautsch *(Mng Dir)*

Britax PMG Limited   (1)
Bessingby Industrial Estate, Bridlington,

YO16 4SJ, East Yorkshire, United Kingdom
Tel.: (44) 1262 670161
Web Site: http://www.britax-pmg.com
Vehicle Lighting, Mirrors & Wiper Systems Mfr & Distr
N.A.I.C.S.: 336320
Mike Procter *(Dir-Ops)*

Britax PSV Wypers Ltd.   (1)
Navigation Road, Diglis, Worcester, WR5 3DE, United Kingdom
Tel.: (44) 1905 350500
Web Site: http://www.psv-wypers.com
Emp.: 20
Vehicle Wiper Systems Mfr
N.A.I.C.S.: 336390
Ray Li *(Mgr-Engrg & Quality)*
Paul Curry *(Gen Mgr)*

Britax Signalisation SAS   (1)
38 rue Pierre Mendes, 69120, Vaulx-en-Velin, France
Tel.: (33) 478 796 000
Web Site: http://www.britax-signalisation.fr
Vehicle Lighting & Warning Systems Distr
N.A.I.C.S.: 423120
Javier Gomez de Bonilla *(Acct Mgr)*

Code 3, Inc.   (1)
10986 N Warson Rd, Saint Louis, MO 63114-2029
Tel.: (314) 426-2700
Web Site: http://www.code3esg.com
Sales Range: $25-49.9 Million
Emergency Lighting & Alarm Mfr
N.A.I.C.S.: 334290
Joydip Chakravarty *(Engr-Mfg)*
Dale Tompkins *(Pres & CEO)*
Kelly Kyriakos *(VP-Sls & Mktg)*

Kustom Signals, Inc.   (1)
9652 Loiret Blvd, Lenexa, KS 66219
Tel.: (913) 492-1400
Web Site: http://www.kustomsignals.com
Emp.: 50
Traffic Safety Equipment Designer, Mfr & Marketer
N.A.I.C.S.: 334290
Michael Paulson *(VP-Engrg & Tech)*
Sonya Schoneman *(Acct Mgr)*

Premier Hazard Ltd.   (1)
Bessingby Industrial Estate, Bridlington, YO16 4SJ, East Yorkshire, United Kingdom
Tel.: (44) 113 2391111
Web Site: http://www.premierhazard.co.uk
Emp.: 250
Vehicle Lighting & Warning Systems Mfr & Distr
N.A.I.C.S.: 336390

Public Safety Equipment (Suzhou) Co., Ltd.   (1)
Unit 8C Suchun Industrial Square No 428 Xinlong Road, Suzhou Industrial Park, Suzhou, 215216, Jiangsu, China
Tel.: (86) 512 6295 3962
Web Site: http://www.britax-pmg.com
Vehicle Lighting & Warning Systems Distr
N.A.I.C.S.: 423120

ECDC ENVIRONMENTAL L.C.
675 S Gladiola St, Salt Lake City, UT 84104
Tel.: (801) 952-0500
Rev.: $11,200,000
Emp.: 6
Nonhazardous Waste Disposal Sites
N.A.I.C.S.: 562212

ECHELON REAL ESTATE SERVICES LLC
235 3rd St S Ste 300, Saint Petersburg, FL 33701
Tel.: (727) 803-8222   FL
Web Site:
  http://www.eresproprieties.com
Year Founded: 1996
Sales Range: $50-74.9 Million
Emp.: 16
Real Estate Services, Commercial Real Estate Development & Multi-Family Residential Development
N.A.I.C.S.: 237210

Susan Glatthorn Johnson *(Gen Counsel & Sr VP)*
Michael Talmadge *(Exec VP)*
Lisa Garcia *(Dir-Property Mgmt Svcs)*

ECHO 24, INC.
167 Cypress St SW Ste A, Reynoldsburg, OH 43068
Tel.: (740) 964-7081
Web Site: https://www.echo24.com
Year Founded: 2001
Sales Range: $1-9.9 Million
Emp.: 40
Structured Cabling Telephony & Fiber Optic Services
N.A.I.C.S.: 517121
Debbie Rodriguez *(Office Mgr)*

ECHO AUTOMOTIVE, INC.
16000 N 80th St Ste E, Scottsdale, AZ 85260
Tel.: (480) 682-5445   NV
Web Site:
    http://www.echoautomotive.com
Year Founded: 2008
Sales Range: Less than $1 Million
Emp.: 25
Technologies & Products for Conversion of Existing Vehicles into Fuel Efficient & Plug-In Hybrids
N.A.I.C.S.: 811198
William Daniel Kennedy *(CEO)*
Jason Plotke *(Chm & Pres)*
John E. Waters *(CTO)*
David Crecelius *(VP-Ops & Gen Mgr)*
Amy Dobrikova *(VP-Sls & Bus Dev)*
Jeff Ronning *(VP-Sys Architecture)*
Sean M. Stanley *(VP-Engrg & Chief Engr)*
Bill Barba *(CFO)*

ECHO ENGINEERING & PRODUCTION SUPPLIES, INC.
5406 W 78th St, Indianapolis, IN 46268
Tel.: (317) 876-8848   IN
Web Site: http://www.echosupply.com
Year Founded: 1996
Plastics Material & Resin Mfr
N.A.I.C.S.: 325211
Jeff Darrow *(Mgr-Quality Control)*
Cassie Fagen *(COO)*
Todd Darland *(VP-Mktg)*

Subsidiaries:

Ammex Plastics, LLC   (1)
725 Ternes Dr, Monroe, MI 48162
Tel.: (734) 241-9622
Web Site: http://www.ammexplastics.com
Plastic Products Mfr; Plastic Clips, Automotive Plastics, Fittings, Mounts & Fasteners
N.A.I.C.S.: 326199
David Ayala *(Pres)*

ECHO GROUP, INC.
3426 2nd Ave, Council Bluffs, IA 51501
Tel.: (712) 322-4120
Web Site:
    http://www.echogroupinc.com
Rev.: $4,759,000
Emp.: 20
Electrical Apparatus & Equipment, Wiring Supplies & Related Equipment Merchant Whslr
N.A.I.C.S.: 423610
Greg Johnson *(CFO)*
Mitch Lane *(CEO)*

Subsidiaries:

Echo Systems   (1)
4315 S 120th St, Omaha, NE 68137
Tel.: (402) 334-4900
Web Site: http://echosystemsmidwest.com
Electrical Apparatus & Equipment Whslr
N.A.I.C.S.: 423610
John Palser *(Founder & Principal)*

Subsidiary (Domestic):

Dallas Sight and Sound, Inc.   (2)
14354 Proton Rd, Dallas, TX 75244
Tel.: (972) 392-3202
Web Site:
    http://www.dallassightandsound.com
Sales Range: $1-9.9 Million
Emp.: 28
Audio, Video, Lighting & Electrical Services
N.A.I.C.S.: 238210
David Rogers *(CEO)*
Andrew Ard *(Dir-Mktg)*

ECHO HEALTH, INC
868 Corporate Way, Westlake, OH 44145
Tel.: (440) 835-3511
Web Site:
    http://www.view.echohealthinc.com
Year Founded: 2004
Sales Range: $50-74.9 Million
Emp.: 312
Medical Business Administration & Billing Services
N.A.I.C.S.: 561110
William Davis *(Chm & CEO)*
Ryan Davis *(VP & Gen Mgr)*
Chadwick Davis *(CIO & VP)*
Kris Kern *(CFO & VP)*
Chaz Kirkpatrick *(CTO & VP)*
Roy Mordhorst *(Dir-Sls & Mktg)*
Michael C. Voinovich *(Chief Investment Officer & Exec VP)*

ECHO INTERNATIONAL CO.
5588 N Palm Ave, Fresno, CA 93704
Tel.: (559) 261-0210
Web Site:
    https://www.echointernational.us
Year Founded: 2004
Sales Range: $100-124.9 Million
Emp.: 2
Fruit & Vegetables Distr
N.A.I.C.S.: 424410
Patrick Carroll *(Pres)*
Arturo Velayo *(Mgr-Sls)*

ECHO MAINTENANCE, LLC
6711 N Twin City Hwy, Port Arthur, TX 77642
Tel.: (409) 724-1512
Web Site:
    https://www.echomaintenance.com
Sales Range: $25-49.9 Million
Emp.: 200
Industrial Buildings & Warehouses
N.A.I.C.S.: 236220
Al Dean *(Controller)*
Mike Roebuck *(Pres)*

ECHO ROCK VENTURES INC.
PO Box 3266, Riverside, CA 92507
Tel.: (530) 823-9600
Web Site: http://www.newbasis.com
Sales Range: $10-24.9 Million
Emp.: 20
Mfr of Concrete Products
N.A.I.C.S.: 327390

Subsidiaries:

NewBasis   (1)
2626 Kansas Ave, Riverside, CA 92507   (100%)
Tel.: (951) 787-0600
Web Site: http://www.newbasis.com
Mfr Of Fibreglass Products
N.A.I.C.S.: 327390
Kim Ruiz *(Controller)*

ECHO VALLEY MEATS, INC.
608 W Garfield Ave, Bartonville, IL 61607
Tel.: (309) 697-0083
Web Site:
    https://www.echovalleymeats.com
Year Founded: 1998

Sales Range: $1-9.9 Million
Emp.: 15
Meat Wholesale, Mail Order & E-Commerce
N.A.I.C.S.: 424470
David Alwan *(Founder & Owner)*

ECHO, LLC
PO Box 10093, Dothan, AL 36304
Tel.: (334) 793-7400
Holding Company
N.A.I.C.S.: 551112

Subsidiaries:

Xpress Source   (1)
PO Box 10093, Dothan, AL 36304
Tel.: (334) 793-7400
Sales Range: $10-24.9 Million
Emp.: 20
Outsource Procurement Services
N.A.I.C.S.: 561499

ECHOING HILLS VILLAGE, INC.
36272 County Rd 79, Warsaw, OH 43844
Tel.: (740) 327-2311   OH
Web Site: https://www.ehvi.org
Year Founded: 1966
Sales Range: $25-49.9 Million
Emp.: 1,000
Recreational Outreach Services
N.A.I.C.S.: 624120
Buddy Busch *(Pres & CEO)*
John Swanson *(CFO & Exec VP)*
Ron Hammond *(VP-HR)*
Mark Hutchinson *(Dir-Southeast & Central Ohio)*
Tim Neville *(VP-Ops)*

ECHOLS OIL COMPANY
900 Poinsett Hwy, Greenville, SC 29609
Tel.: (864) 233-6205
Web Site: http://echolsoil.com
Sales Range: $10-24.9 Million
Emp.: 14
Petroleum Products
N.A.I.C.S.: 424720
Earl Riddle *(Mgr)*
Ralph S. Bell Jr. *(Pres)*

ECHOMAIL, INC.
701 Concord Ave Ste 103, Cambridge, MA 02138
Tel.: (617) 354-8585
Web Site: http://www.echomail.com
Sales Range: $1-9.9 Million
Emp.: 35
Email & Social Media Marketing, Monitoring & Management Solutions
N.A.I.C.S.: 541890
V. A. Shiva Ayyadurai *(Founder, Chm & Pres)*
Ramachandran Subramanian *(CMO)*
Ghurhu Ganesh *(Dir-Infrastructure)*

ECK ENTERPRISES LLC
1512-A W Main St, Richmond, VA 23220
Tel.: (804) 381-5604
Web Site: http://eckenterprises.com
Electrical Supplies
N.A.I.C.S.: 423610
Kayla Blair *(Mgr-Property)*

ECK INDUSTRIES, INC.
1602 N 8th St, Manitowoc, WI 54220-1904
Tel.: (920) 682-4618   WI
Web Site:
    https://www.eckindustries.com
Year Founded: 1948
Sales Range: $10-24.9 Million
Emp.: 300
Aluminum Casting Mfr
N.A.I.C.S.: 331523

Philip R. Eck *(Pres)*
Tom Gass *(VP-Matls-Pur)*
David Weiss *(VP-Engrg & R&D)*
Gary Mueller *(Mgr-Production Control)*
Wil Joseph *(Mgr-Quality Control)*
Tyler Eck *(VP-Sls)*
Nicole Robinson *(Mgr-Quality Assurance)*
Kiley Eck Hayon *(VP-HR & Fin)*

ECKARDS HOME IMPROVEMENTS
118 W Main St, Stanberry, MO 64489
Tel.: (660) 783-2611
Web Site:
    https://www.eckardsflooring.com
Sales Range: $10-24.9 Million
Emp.: 30
Floor Covering Stores
N.A.I.C.S.: 449121
Steve Eckard *(Pres & VP)*

ECKARDT ELECTRIC COMPANY, INC.
3690 N Peachtree Rd, Atlanta, GA 30341-2443
Tel.: (770) 458-3155
Web Site:
    http://www.eckardtelectric.com
Sales Range: $10-24.9 Million
Emp.: 115
Electrical Wiring Services
N.A.I.C.S.: 238210
John Riley Stephens *(Pres)*

ECKART COLD STORAGE CO. INC.
905 Clough Rd, Escalon, CA 95320
Tel.: (209) 838-4040
Sales Range: $500-549.9 Million
Emp.: 800
Storage, Frozen Or Refrigerated Goods
N.A.I.C.S.: 493120
Linda Tvedt *(Controller)*
Pete Thompson *(Pres)*

ECKART LLC
426 Quarry Rd NW, Corydon, IN 47112
Tel.: (812) 738-3232
Web Site: http://www.eckart.com
Sales Range: $10-24.9 Million
Emp.: 36
Electrical Plumbing & Heating
N.A.I.C.S.: 423610
Chad Coffman *(CFO)*

ECKEL INDUSTRIES INC.
100 Groton Shirley Rd, Ayer, MA 01432
Tel.: (978) 772-0840
Web Site: https://www.eckelusa.com
Rev.: $10,272,819
Emp.: 35
Acoustical Board & Tile, Mineral Wool
N.A.I.C.S.: 327993
Jeff Morris *(VP)*
Joe Tunnera *(Treas)*

ECKENROD FORD LINCOLN MERCURY OF CULLMAN, INC.
5255 Alabama Hwy 157, Cullman, AL 35058-5931
Tel.: (256) 734-3361
Web Site: https://www.eckenrodford.com
Sales Range: $10-24.9 Million
Emp.: 68
Car Whslr
N.A.I.C.S.: 441110
Mike Eckenrod *(Owner)*

ECKER CENTER FOR BEHAVIORAL HEALTH

Ecker Center For Behavioral Health—(Continued)

1845 Grandstand Pl, Elgin, IL 60123-4983
Tel.: (847) 695-0484   IL
Web Site:
     https://www.eckercenter.org
Year Founded: 1955
Emp.: 100
Behavioral Healthcare Services
N.A.I.C.S.: 621420
Deb Howe *(Dir-Dev)*
Patricia Arroyo *(Sec)*
Meghan Early *(Chm)*
Alan Kirk *(Vice Chm)*
Daphne Sandouka *(CEO)*
Victoria Gesinger *(Chief Clinical Officer)*
Nisha Shah *(Chief Mental Health Officer)*
Steve Lindahl *(CFO)*

ECKER ENTERPRISES INC.
Columbia Centre III 9525 W Bryn
Mawr Ave Ste 900, Rosemont, IL
60018-5264
Tel.: (847) 994-6000   DE
Web Site: http://www.eckerusa.com
Year Founded: 1923
Sales Range: $25-49.9 Million
Emp.: 140
Provider of Plastering, Drywall & Insulation Services
N.A.I.C.S.: 238320
Terry Donovan *(CFO)*
Bob Maramba *(Dir-Mktg)*
Charles E. Vasconez *(Dir-Corp Safety)*
Subsidiaries:

M. Ecker & Co. of Florida, Inc.   **(1)**
1306 E Broward Blvd, Fort Lauderdale, FL
33301-2136   **(100%)**
Tel.: (954) 523-0511
Web Site: http://www.eckerusa.com
Sales Range: $10-24.9 Million
Emp.: 20
Plastering, Drywall & Insulation Services
N.A.I.C.S.: 238310

M. Ecker & Co. of Illinois, Inc.   **(1)**
9525 W Bryn Mawr Ave Ste 900, Rosemont, IL 60018-5264   **(100%)**
Tel.: (847) 994-6000
Web Site: http://www.eckerusa.com
Sales Range: $25-49.9 Million
Emp.: 60
Plastering, Drywall & Insulation Services
N.A.I.C.S.: 238310

ECKER WINDOW CORPORATION
1 Odell Plz, Yonkers, NY 10701
Tel.: (914) 776-0000
Web Site:
     https://www.eckerwindow.com
Year Founded: 1947
Sales Range: $10-24.9 Million
Emp.: 100
Wood Window & Door Mfr
N.A.I.C.S.: 321911
Robert L. Ecker *(Pres-Sls & Mktg)*
Howard J. Ecker *(CEO)*
Ebrahim Miandoabi *(Project Mgr)*
Roberto Criollo *(Mgr-Engrg)*
Deborah Allerdice *(Controller)*
Evadne Bryce *(Mgr-Acctg)*
Bob Funck *(Project Mgr)*
Ann Fitzpatrick *(Mgr-Svc)*

ECKERT COLD STORAGE COMPANY
905 Clough Rd, Escalon, CA 95320-8647
Tel.: (209) 838-4040
Sales Range: $50-74.9 Million
Emp.: 500
Frozen Fruit, Juice & Vegetable Mfr
N.A.I.C.S.: 311411

Pete Thompson *(CEO)*
Mike Cimoli *(Plant Mgr & Mgr-Refrigeration)*
Ed Perez *(Mgr-Environmental & Safety)*
Gary Ford *(CEO)*

ECKERT SEAMANS CHERIN & MELLOTT, LLC
600 Grant St 44th Fl, Pittsburgh, PA 15219-2703
Tel.: (412) 566-6000   PA
Web Site:
     https://www.eckertseamans.com
Year Founded: 1958
Law firm
N.A.I.C.S.: 541110
Timothy Q. Hudak *(CEO)*

ECKERT'S ORCHARDS
951 S Green Mount Rd, Belleville, IL 62220
Tel.: (618) 233-0513
Web Site: https://www.eckerts.com
Year Founded: 1910
Sales Range: $100-124.9 Million
Emp.: 350
Fruit & Vegetable Canning Services
N.A.I.C.S.: 311421
Phil Climaco *(CFO)*
Amanda Morgan *(Mgr-Mktg)*
Larry Eckert *(Chm)*
Chris Eckert *(Pres)*

ECKMAN CONSTRUCTION COMPANY, INC.
84 Palomino Ln, Bedford, NH 03110-6449
Tel.: (603) 623-1713   NH
Web Site:
     https://www.eckmanconstruction.com
Year Founded: 1974
Sales Range: $75-99.9 Million
Emp.: 30
Provider of Construction & Contracting Services
N.A.I.C.S.: 236220
Mark Walsh *(Principal)*
Butch Thornton *(Project Mgr)*

ECLC OF NEW JERSEY
100 Passaic Ave, Chatham, NJ 07928
Tel.: (973) 635-1705   NJ
Web Site: https://www.eclcofnj.org
Year Founded: 1977
Sales Range: $10-24.9 Million
Emp.: 301
Educational Support Services
N.A.I.C.S.: 611710
Bruce Litinger *(Exec Dir)*
Amalia Duarte *(Dir-PR)*
Heather Alonge *(Dir-Dev)*
Jean Earle *(Bus Mgr)*

ECLINICALWORKS, LLC
Westborough Executive Pk 112 Turnpike Rd, Westborough, MA 01581
Tel.: (508) 836-2700
Web Site:
     http://www.eclinicalworks.com
Year Founded: 1999
Sales Range: $25-49.9 Million
Emp.: 315
Software Developer for Medical-Practice Billing & Recordkeeping
N.A.I.C.S.: 513210
Girish Kumar Navani *(CEO)*
Nainil Chheda *(Mgr-Procurement)*
Bonnie Fluet *(Product Mgr)*
Bryan Sequeira *(Product Mgr)*
Sameer Bhat *(VP)*

ECLIPSE AEROSPACE, INC.

2503 Clark Carr Loop SE, Albuquerque, NM 87106
Tel.: (505) 245-7555   DE
Web Site:
     http://www.eclipseaerospace.net
Year Founded: 1998
Sales Range: $25-49.9 Million
Commercial Aircraft Mfr
N.A.I.C.S.: 336411
Edward M. Lundeen *(Sr VP-Bus Ops)*
Michael Press *(Exec VP)*
Kenneth Ross *(Pres-Svc Div)*
Cary A. Winter *(Chief Svc Engr & Sr VP)*
Mason R. Holland Jr. *(Chm & Pres)*

ECM ENERGY SERVICES, INC.
130 Ct St Ste 203, Williamsport, PA 17701
Tel.: (888) 523-9095   DE
Web Site: http://www.ecmenergy.com
On-Shore Oil & Gas Field Equipment
Rental & Water Logistics Services
N.A.I.C.S.: 532412
Harry Wahl *(Owner)*

ECM TRANSPORTATION, INC.
1460 Greensburg Rd, New Kensington, PA 15068-2053
Tel.: (724) 339-8800
Web Site:
     http://www.ecmtransportation.com
Year Founded: 1988
Sales Range: $25-49.9 Million
Emp.: 285
Provider of Trucking Services
N.A.I.C.S.: 484121
Edward Meyer *(Pres)*
Tony Kilcrease *(Mgr-Compliance)*

ECMC FOUNDATION
444 S Flower St Ste 2550, Los Angeles, CA 90071   DE
Web Site:
     https://www.ecmcfoundation.org
Year Founded: 2000
Sales Range: $150-199.9 Million
Emp.: 9
Grantmaking Services
N.A.I.C.S.: 813211
Jennifer Zeisler *(Program Dir-Career Readiness)*
Libby Considine *(Mgr-Grants Admin)*
Sarah Kirschenbaum *(Program Dir-College Readiness & Retention)*
Kyle Miller *(Sr Program Dir-Teacher Dev & Evaluation)*
John F. DePodesta *(Chm)*
Jeremy J. Wheaton *(CEO)*
Lynn Alvarez *(VP-Programs & Strategy)*

ECMD, INC.
2 Grandview St, North Wilkesboro, NC 28659
Tel.: (336) 667-5976   NC
Web Site: https://www.ecmd.com
Year Founded: 1982
Sales Range: $50-74.9 Million
Emp.: 450
Lumber, Plywood & Millwork Services
N.A.I.C.S.: 423310
Allen Dyer *(Founder & Chm)*
Todd Meade *(Pres & CEO)*

ECO CONSTRUCTION & MAINTENANCE MANAGEMENT, LLC
39 Skyline Dr Ste 1017, Lake Mary, FL 32746-7123
Tel.: (407) 478-3258
Year Founded: 2004
Sales Range: $10-24.9 Million
Emp.: 75
Civil Engineering Services
N.A.I.C.S.: 237310

Steve Chamu *(Pres)*
Bobby Jones *(VP-Sls)*
Ken Marsak *(VP)*
Dawn Meiner *(Acct Exec)*
Larry Penkala *(Gen Mgr)*

ECO ENERGY PUMPS, INC.
112 N Curry St, Carson City, NV 89703
Tel.: (775) 284-3713   NV
Year Founded: 2008
Sales Range: $1-9.9 Million
Solar Energy Powered Water Pumps Developer
N.A.I.C.S.: 333996
Matthew J. Zouvas *(Chm, Pres, CEO, Treas & Sec)*

ECO ENGINEERING, INC.
11815 Highway Dr Ste 600, Cincinnati, OH 45241-2065
Tel.: (513) 985-8300
Web Site:
     https://www.ecoengineering.com
Year Founded: 1993
Engineeering Services
N.A.I.C.S.: 541330
Thomas L. Kirkpatrick *(Pres & CEO)*
Brian Roth *(VP-Client Mgmt)*
Emily Gandee *(Dir-HR & Admin)*
Brad Dulle *(Dir-Engrg)*
Jon Prabell *(Mgr-Construction & Installations)*
Bill Brunette *(VP-Sls & Mktg)*
Robert McCoy *(CFO)*
Rhonda Courtney *(Dir-ESCO Mktg Dev)*

ECO FARMS SALES INC.
28790 Las Haciendas St, Temecula, CA 92590-2614
Tel.: (951) 676-4047
Web Site:
     http://www.ecofarmsusa.com
Year Founded: 1989
Sales Range: $10-24.9 Million
Emp.: 50
Producer of Fresh Fruits & Vegetables
N.A.I.C.S.: 424480
Steve Taft *(Pres & CEO)*
Norman Traner *(Partner & Treas)*

ECO SCIENCE SOLUTIONS, INC.
300 S El Camino Real Ste 206, San Clemente, CA 92672   NV
Web Site: https://www.ecossi.com
Year Founded: 2009
ESSI—(OTCIQ)
Assets: $102,106
Liabilities: $15,562,690
Net Worth: ($15,460,584)
Earnings: ($1,242,268)
Emp.: 3
Fiscal Year-end: 01/31/24
Investment Holding Company
N.A.I.C.S.: 551112
Michael Rountree *(CEO & CFO)*

ECO TECH CONTRACTORS INC.
5600 Enterprise Dr, Grimes, IA 50111
Tel.: (515) 225-6677
Rev.: $30,000,000
Emp.: 36
Highway & Street Paving Contractor
N.A.I.C.S.: 237310

ECO-BAGS PRODUCTS, INC.
23-25 Spring St Ste 302, Ossining, NY 10562
Tel.: (914) 944-4556
Web Site: https://www.ecobags.com
Year Founded: 1990
Sales Range: $150-199.9 Million
Emp.: 100
Womens Handbag & Purse Mfr

N.A.I.C.S.: 316990
Lisa Pavlik *(Coord-Production)*
Andrew Dyer *(VP-Ops & Strategic Plng)*

ECOANALYSTS, INC.
1420 S Blaine St Ste 14, Moscow, ID 83843
Tel.: (208) 882-2588
Web Site:
https://www.ecoanalysts.com
Year Founded: 1992
Sales Range: $1-9.9 Million
Emp.: 65
Biotechnology Research & Development
N.A.I.C.S.: 541714
Gary Lester *(Pres & CEO)*
Scott Lindstrom *(CFO)*
Mike Glennon *(Dir-Canadian Bus Dev)*
Dawn Hamilton *(Project Mgr-Natl Aquatic Resources Surveys)*
Rob Bobier *(Mgr-Laboratory)*

ECOAST SALES SOLUTIONS, LTD.
35 E Industrial Way Ste 201, Rochester, NH 03867
Tel.: (603) 516-7450   NH
Web Site:
http://www.ecoastsales.com
Year Founded: 2000
Sales Range: $10-24.9 Million
Emp.: 25
Outsourced Sales & Marketing Services for Technology Companies
N.A.I.C.S.: 561499
Rich Biffon *(CEO)*

ECOEMISSIONS SOLUTIONS, INC.
455 S 48th St Ste 106, Tempe, AZ 85281
Tel.: (480) 968-8900   DE
Web Site: http://www.eco-emissions.com
Diesel Fuel System
N.A.I.C.S.: 213112
Thomas Crom *(CFO & Sec)*
Larry Lorenz *(Pres & CEO)*

ECOGROUP INC.
601 Bayshore Blvd Ste 960, Tampa, FL 33606
Tel.: (813) 251-4868
Web Site:
http://www.ecogroupinc.com
Sales Range: $10-24.9 Million
Emp.: 7
Condominium Developers
N.A.I.C.S.: 236117
Ed Oelschlaeger *(Pres)*

ECOLITE MANUFACTURING CO. INC.
9919 E Montgomery Dr, Spokane, WA 99206
Tel.: (509) 922-8888
Web Site: http://www.ecolite.com
Year Founded: 1970
Sales Range: $10-24.9 Million
Emp.: 125
Aluminum Louvers For Lighting Fixtures
N.A.I.C.S.: 332323
Ron Caferro *(Pres)*

ECOLIVEGREEN CORP.
7076 Spyglass Ave, Parkland, FL 33076
Tel.: (954) 599-3672   FL
Web Site: http://www.carquest.com
Year Founded: 2008

Energy-Saving & Environmentally-Friendly Products Researcher & Developer
N.A.I.C.S.: 541715
Len Bryan *(Pres & Sec)*
Paul L. Culler *(VP)*
Alfred H. Tracy III *(CFO & VP)*

ECOLOGICAL FIBERS INC.
40 Pioneer Dr, Lunenburg, MA 01462
Tel.: (978) 537-0003
Web Site: https://www.ecofibers.com
Year Founded: 1972
Sales Range: $10-24.9 Million
Emp.: 120
Paper Products Mfr
N.A.I.C.S.: 322299
Stephen F. Quill *(Chm)*
Eric Buchholz *(CFO)*
Holly Staples *(Mgr-HR)*
Jennifer Thomas *(Mgr-Mid West Sls)*
Joyce Hardell *(Mgr-Customer Svc)*
John Penatzer *(Plant Mgr)*

ECOLOGY ACTION OF SANTA CRUZ
877 Cedar St Ste 240, Santa Cruz, CA 95060
Tel.: (831) 426-5925   CA
Web Site: https://www.ecoact.org
Year Founded: 1979
Sales Range: $10-24.9 Million
Emp.: 137
Educational Support Services
N.A.I.C.S.: 611710
Jim Murphy *(CEO & Exec Dir)*
Chuck Tremper *(Gen Counsel & VP)*
Joel Kauffman *(VP-Mktg & Customer Engagement)*

ECOLOGY AUTO WRECKING INC.
13780 Imperial Hwy, Santa Fe Springs, CA 90670-4823
Tel.: (562) 921-9974
Web Site: http://www.ecoparts.com
Year Founded: 1966
Sales Range: $50-74.9 Million
Emp.: 350
Provider of Auto & Home Supply Store Services
N.A.I.C.S.: 441330
Paul Mcleath *(Controller & Mgr)*

ECOLOGY CONTROL INDUSTRIES, INC.
15707 S Main St, Gardena, CA 90248
Tel.: (310) 354-9999
Web Site:
https://www.ecologycontrol.com
Year Founded: 1977
Sales Range: $25-49.9 Million
Emp.: 275
Waste Management Services
N.A.I.C.S.: 562998
Ron Flury *(Pres & CEO)*
Steve Smith *(Mgr-Tech)*
Ardena Darnell *(Plant Mgr)*
R. Gilliam *(Plant Mgr)*

Subsidiaries:

Ecology Control Industries, Inc   **(1)**
10680 Silicon Ave, Montclair, CA 91763-3462
Tel.: (909) 625-6645
Web Site:
http://www.consolidatedwaste.com
Sales Range: $10-24.9 Million
Emp.: 58
Hazardous Waste Transport
N.A.I.C.S.: 562211
Jeanne Delperdang *(Mgr-Health & Safety Compliance)*

ECOM ATLANTIC, INC

13760 Noel Rd Ste 500, Dallas, TX 75240
Tel.: (214) 520-1717
Web Site:
http://www.ecomtrading.com
Sales Range: $10-24.9 Million
Emp.: 40
Cotton Merchants
N.A.I.C.S.: 424590
Andrew Halley *(CEO)*
Mark Wildemann *(Dir-HR)*
Lauren Leyendecker *(Coord-HR)*

ECOMARK ENERGY, INC.
4665 Paris St Ste 300-C, Denver, CO 80239
Tel.: (720) 649-4792   CO
Web Site:
https://www.ecomarksolar.com
Sales Range: $1-9.9 Million
Emp.: 120
Solar Panel Electric Systems Designer, Fabricator, Sales & Installation Services
N.A.I.C.S.: 238210
Alex Valdez *(Pres & CEO)*
Jake DiRe *(Co-Founder & VP-Construction)*

ECOMITIZE LLC
PO Box 460849, Papillion, NE 68046
Tel.: (513) 815-5395
Web Site: http://www.ecomitize.com
Year Founded: 2013
Sales Range: $1-9.9 Million
Emp.: 39
Information Technology Services
N.A.I.C.S.: 541512
Jacob North *(Founder & CEO)*
Jean Pierson *(Dir-Projects & Mktg)*
Tami Gilmore *(Mgr-Customer Rels)*
Marko Stevanovic *(Project Mgr)*
Imola Saska *(Project Mgr)*

ECOMMERCE PARTNERS
59 Franklin St Ste 6B, New York, NY 10013
Tel.: (212) 334-3390
Web Site:
https://www.ecommercepartners.net
Year Founded: 1995
Sales Range: $10-24.9 Million
Emp.: 20
Business & Internet Marketing
N.A.I.C.S.: 541613
Gil Levy *(Mng Partner & Co-Founder)*

ECOMNETS, INC.
2553 Dulles View Dr Ste 240, Sterling, VA 20171-5227
Tel.: (703) 481-3035
Web Site: http://www.ecomnets.com
Rev.: $5,043,000
Emp.: 50
IT Systems Management & Compliance Services
N.A.I.C.S.: 541519
Raj Kosuri *(CEO & CTO)*
Shan Naveen *(Mgr-Resource)*

ECOMPANYSTORE, INC.
5945 Cabot Pkwy Bldg 200 Ste 150, Alpharetta, GA 30005
Tel.: (678) 942-3100   GA
Web Site:
http://www.ecompanystore.com
Year Founded: 1998
Sales Range: $10-24.9 Million
Emp.: 88
Internet-Based, Business-to-Enterprise Solutions for the Management & Procurement of Custom Logo Merchandise
N.A.I.C.S.: 339950

Jeff Camp *(CFO)*
Craig Callaway *(CEO)*
Campbell B. Lanier III *(Chm)*

ECOMPEX, INC.
7926 Jones Branch Dr Ste 560, McLean, VA 22102
Tel.: (703) 288-3382
Web Site: http://www.ecompex.com
Sales Range: $10-24.9 Million
Emp.: 120
Information Technology Services & Solutions; Software Development
N.A.I.C.S.: 513210
Hubin Jiang *(Pres & CEO)*
Fanyang Jiang *(CFO)*
Michael Thomas *(VP-Contract Acq & Bus Support)*

ECOMSYSTEMS, INC.
8237 Vicela Dr, Sarasota, FL 34240
Tel.: (941) 342-8811
Web Site:
https://www.ecomsystems.com
Year Founded: 1983
Sales Range: $10-24.9 Million
Emp.: 30
Web-Based Electronic Advertising Systems
N.A.I.C.S.: 541890
Jon Evans *(Owner & CEO)*
Amanda Martinez *(Dir-Art)*
James Stolze *(Dir-Creative Svcs)*
Michael Miller *(Mgr-Tech Svcs)*
David Adams *(Engr-Software)*

ECONO PRODUCTS INC.
132 Humboldt St, Rochester, NY 14610
Tel.: (585) 288-7550
Web Site:
http://www.econoproducts.com
Sales Range: $10-24.9 Million
Emp.: 15
Printing Trades Machinery, Equipment & Supplies
N.A.I.C.S.: 423830
Ronald Pohorence *(Dir-Tech Sls)*
Peter May *(Pres)*
Kathy Cubit *(Coord-Sls)*

ECONO-PRINT INC.
330 Locust Dr, Verona, WI 53593
Tel.: (608) 845-2700
Web Site: http://www.epdigital.com
Year Founded: 1990
Sales Range: $10-24.9 Million
Emp.: 75
Offset Printing
N.A.I.C.S.: 323111
David Genin *(VP-Sls)*

ECONOFFICE PRODUCTS & SUPPLIES, INC.
640 E Douglas Rd Ste A, Oldsmar, FL 34677
Tel.: (813) 854-3469
Year Founded: 2000
Rev.: $5,700,000
Emp.: 8
Supplies Office Products & Supplies to Federal & Corporate Customers
N.A.I.C.S.: 424120
Jean McNally *(Pres)*
Frank Petrino *(VP-Govt Sls)*

ECONOHOMES, LLC.
1905 Kramer Ln Ste B700, Austin, TX 78758
Tel.: (512) 334-1400
Web Site:
http://www.econohomes.com
Year Founded: 2006
Sales Range: $25-49.9 Million
Emp.: 73
Real Estate Investment Services

Econohomes, LLC.—(Continued)
N.A.I.C.S.: 523999
Jeff Ball *(Pres)*
Bill Kerley *(CFO)*
Matt Matza *(VP-Corp Dev)*

ECONOLITE GROUP, INC.
1250 N. Tustin Ave., Anaheim, CA 92807
Tel.: (714) 630-3700
Web Site: https://www.econolite.com
Emp.: 271
Traffic Control Systems
N.A.I.C.S.: 334290
Christian U. Haas *(CEO)*

Subsidiaries:

Econolite Control Products, Inc.   (1)
3360 E La Palma Ave, Anaheim, CA 92806
Tel.: (714) 630-3700
Web Site: http://www.econolite.com
Sales Range: $25-49.9 Million
Emp.: 300
Traffic Control Systems
N.A.I.C.S.: 334290
M. C. Doyle *(CEO)*
G. Duncan *(Sr VP-New Prods & Mktg)*
Jeff Spinazze *(Sr VP-Sls)*
Melvyn Haxby *(Dir-Intl Bus Dev)*

Subsidiary (Non-US):

Econolite Canada, Inc.   (2)
884 Billingham Rd, Pickering, L1W 1Z6, ON, Canada
Tel.: (905) 839-9119
Sales Range: $10-24.9 Million
Emp.: 20
Traffic Control Systems
N.A.I.C.S.: 334511

Western Pacific Signal, LLC   (1)
15890 Foothill Blvd, San Leandro, CA 94578
Tel.: (510) 483-6400
Web Site: http://www.wpsignal.com
Sales Range: $1-9.9 Million
Emp.: 15
Communication Equipment Mfr
N.A.I.C.S.: 334290

ECONOMIC OPPORTUNITY AUTHORITY FOR SAVANNAH-CHATHAM COUNTY, INC.
618 W Anderson St, Savannah, GA 31415
Tel.: (912) 238-2960
Web Site: https://www.eoasga.org
Year Founded: 1965
Sales Range: $10-24.9 Million
Emp.: 263
Community Action Services
N.A.I.C.S.: 624190
Viola E. DeLoach *(Vice Chm)*
Gloria S. Brown *(Sec)*
Elaine Shavers Campbell *(Treas)*

ECONOMIC PACKAGING CORPORATION
48201 Fremont Blvd, Fremont, CA 94538
Tel.: (510) 456-2600
Web Site: http://www.economic.com
Sales Range: $10-24.9 Million
Emp.: 30
Packaging Materials
N.A.I.C.S.: 424990
Mark Dickson *(Pres)*
Maricar Dela Cruz *(Mgr-Pur & Customer Svc)*
Don del Rosario *(Supvr-Warehouse)*

ECONOMICAL SUPER MARKET INCORPORATED
5010 Veterans Memorial Blvd, Metairie, LA 70006
Tel.: (504) 887-1150

Web Site:
https://www.zuppardos.com
Rev.: $19,100,000
Emp.: 135
Supermarket
N.A.I.C.S.: 445110

ECONOMY AUTO OUTLET
4025 Erie Ave SW, Massillon, OH 44646
Tel.: (330) 879-0001
Web Site:
http://www.economyautooutlet.com
Sales Range: $25-49.9 Million
Emp.: 25
Used Car Dealership
N.A.I.C.S.: 441120
Craig Sanders *(Pres)*

ECONOMY CASH & CARRY INC.
1000 E Overland Ave, El Paso, TX 79901-2614
Tel.: (915) 532-2660
Web Site:
http://www.economycashcarry.com
Year Founded: 1958
Sales Range: $10-24.9 Million
Emp.: 70
Provider of Grocery Services
N.A.I.C.S.: 424410
John Sayklay *(VP-Pur)*

ECONOMY LOCKER STORAGE CO. INC.
324 Worthington Ln, Muncy, PA 17756
Tel.: (570) 546-2241
Web Site:
http://www.economylocker.com
Sales Range: $10-24.9 Million
Emp.: 45
Fresh Pork & Processing Services
N.A.I.C.S.: 424470
Susan Scott *(Sec)*

ECONOMY PAVING CO. INC.
1819 New York RR 13, Cortland, NY 13045
Tel.: (607) 756-2819
Sales Range: $10-24.9 Million
Emp.: 300
General Contractor, Highway & Street Construction
N.A.I.C.S.: 237310
Joseph H. Compagni *(Pres)*

ECONOMY PROPANE CORP.
112 Rte 369, Port Crane, NY 13833
Tel.: (607) 648-6030
Rev.: $10,100,000
Emp.: 30
Provider of Home Heating Retailer Services
N.A.I.C.S.: 457210
Pam Peas *(Controller)*
Scott Farr *(Chm & Owner)*

ECONOMY REFRIGERATION HEATING VENTILATION SUPPLY CORP.
13101 Sanford Ave, Flushing, NY 11355
Tel.: (718) 661-2180
Web Site: http://economyref.com
Sales Range: $10-24.9 Million
Emp.: 10
Ventilating Fans & Related Products Mfr
N.A.I.C.S.: 423730

ECONTACTLIVE, INC.
2000 W Briggsmore Ave Ste A, Modesto, CA 95350
Web Site:
http://www.econtactlive.com

Year Founded: 1993
Sales Range: $1-9.9 Million
Emp.: 90
Business Consulting Services
N.A.I.C.S.: 561499
Julie Hutchings *(Pres)*
Jon Worthley *(CEO)*
Chris Peterson *(Mgr-Natl Sls)*

ECORE INTERNATIONAL INC.
715 Fountain Ave, Lancaster, PA 17601
Tel.: (717) 295-3400   PA
Web Site: https://www.ecoreintl.com
Year Founded: 1871
Waste Recycling & Performance Surface Flooring Mfr
N.A.I.C.S.: 321918
Bo Barber *(VP-Mktg & Bus Dev)*
Art Dodge *(CEO)*
John R. Doubman *(COO & Pres-Flooring & Industrial Bus)*
Josh Jensen *(CFO)*
Debra Lechner *(CMO)*
Kal Krishnan *(Pres-Materials Bus)*

Subsidiaries:

Spectraturf Inc.   (1)
555 S Promenade Ave Ste 103, Corona, CA 92879
Tel.: (800) 875-5788
Web Site: http://www.spectraturf.com
Fabricated Rubber Product Mfr
N.A.I.C.S.: 326299
Chris Wolf *(Gen Mgr)*

ECOREXPERIENCE, INC.
17 Square Woods Dr, Lagrangeville, NY 12540
Web Site:
http://www.ecorexperience.com
Year Founded: 2001
Sales Range: $1-9.9 Million
Emp.: 5
Computer System Design Services
N.A.I.C.S.: 541512
Paula Majerowicz *(Founder & Pres)*

ECOSERV LLC
207 Towncenter Pkwy, Lafayette, LA 70506-7524
Tel.: (337) 984-4445   LA
Web Site: http://www.ecoserv.net
Sales Range: $25-49.9 Million
Emp.: 40
Oil Field Environmental Services
N.A.I.C.S.: 562211
Kenny Desormeaux *(Pres)*

ECOSPHERE TECHNOLOGIES, INC.
3515 SE Lionel Ter, Stuart, FL 34997
Tel.: (772) 287-4846   DE
Web Site:
http://www.ecospheretech.com
Year Founded: 1998
ESPH—(OTCBB)
Sales Range: Less than $1 Million
Emp.: 18
Waste Water Treatment Services
N.A.I.C.S.: 562998
Dennis E. McGuire *(Founder, Chm & CEO)*
Jacqueline K. McGuire *(Sec & Sr VP-Admin)*
David D. Brooks *(CFO)*
Michael R. Donn Sr. *(COO)*

ECOTECH MARINE
999 Postal Ave, Allentown, PA 18109
Tel.: (610) 954-8480
Web Site:
http://www.ecotechmarine.com
Year Founded: 2003
Sales Range: $1-9.9 Million
Emp.: 15

Mfr of Water Pumping Products for Aquariums
N.A.I.C.S.: 333914
Stephen Koehler *(Acct Mgr-West Domestic)*
Mark Lindenmoyer *(Engr-Electrical)*
Jordan Inacio *(Engr-Mechanical)*

ECPH MANAGEMENT INC.
2317 Professional Dr, Rocky Mount, NC 27804-2252
Tel.: (252) 443-4028
Year Founded: 1971
Sales Range: $10-24.9 Million
Emp.: 10
Restaurant
N.A.I.C.S.: 561110
Theron Riley *(Pres)*

ECRI
5200 Butler Pike, Plymouth Meeting, PA 19463
Tel.: (610) 825-6000
Web Site: https://www.ecri.org
Year Founded: 1955
Rev.: $20,094,431
Emp.: 300
Product Testing Laboratories
N.A.I.C.S.: 541380
Jeffrey C. Lerner *(Pres & CEO)*
Anthony J. Montagnolo *(COO & Exec VP)*
Ronni P. Solomon *(Gen Counsel & Exec VP)*
Vivian H. Coates *(VP-Info Svcs & Health Tech Assessment)*
Mark E. Bruley *(VP-Accident & Forensic Investigation)*
G. Daniel Downing *(VP-Fin)*
Laurie Menyo *(Dir-PR & Mktg Comm)*
Eric Woo *(Dir-Asia Pacific)*
Bevin O'Neil *(Chief Strategy Officer & VP-Strategy)*

ECRI INSTITUTE
5200 Butler Pike, Plymouth Meeting, PA 19462-1298
Tel.: (610) 825-6000   PA
Web Site: https://www.ecri.org
Year Founded: 1955
Sales Range: $50-74.9 Million
Emp.: 443
Medical Research & Educational Support Services
N.A.I.C.S.: 541715
Marcus Schabacker *(Pres & CEO)*

ECRM IMAGING SYSTEMS, INC.
554 Clark Rd, Tewksbury, MA 01876-1631
Tel.: (978) 851-0207   MA
Web Site: http://www.ecrm.com
Year Founded: 1969
Sales Range: $50-74.9 Million
Emp.: 100
Quality Imaging Technologies for Commercial Graphic Arts & Publishing Businesses
N.A.I.C.S.: 333248
Richard B. Black *(Pres & CEO)*

Subsidiaries:

ECRM Imaging Systems-China   (1)
Rm 1135-1136 Beijing Junefield Plz, 6 Xuan Wu Men Wai Da Jie, Beijing, 100052, China
Tel.: (86) 1063109010
Imaging Systems
N.A.I.C.S.: 541430

ECRM Imaging Systems-Hong Kong   (1)
Unit 710 Tower B South Mark No 11 Yit Hing St, Wong Chuk Hong, Kowloon, China (Hong Kong)
Tel.: (852) 25648989
Web Site: http://www.ecrm.com

Imaging Systems
N.A.I.C.S.: 541430

ECRYPT TECHNOLOGIES, INC.
2028 E Ben White Blvd #240-2835, Austin, TX 78741 **CO**
Web Site: http://www.ecryptinc.com
Year Founded: 2007
Rev.: $190
Assets: $365,831
Liabilities: $2,501,984
Net Worth: ($2,136,153)
Earnings: ($3,323,992)
Fiscal Year-end: 03/31/15
Device-Based Encryption & Security Software & Web-Based Encryption Services
N.A.I.C.S.: 513210
Gabriel Rosu *(CTO)*
Kasia Zukowska *(Gen Mgr)*
Thomas A. Cellucci *(Chm & CEO)*
Urvashi Mehra *(VP-Global Healthcare Solutions)*
Deborah King *(Interim CFO)*

ECS INC.
5665 Tremont Ave, Davenport, IA 52807
Tel.: (563) 322-1525
Web Site: http://www.ecsdav.com
Sales Range: $25-49.9 Million
Emp.: 30
Video Equipment, Electronic
N.A.I.C.S.: 423690
Rex Lawrence *(Pres)*

ECSI
181 Montour Run Rd, Coraopolis, PA 15108
Web Site: http://www.ecsi.net
Year Founded: 1972
Sales Range: $10-24.9 Million
Emp.: 140
Billing, Student Loan Servicing & Collection, Refund Management, Tuition Payment Plans & e-Payment Processing Services
N.A.I.C.S.: 561440
Dan Frazier *(COO)*
Nick Battaglia *(CFO)*
Karri Philipp-Thomas *(Dir-HR)*
Fred Emery *(Dir-Sls-OneCard)*
Melissa Peirano *(Sr Dir-Campus OneCard)*

ECUMEN
3530 Lexington Ave N, Shoreview, MN 55126
Tel.: (651) 766-4300 **MN**
Web Site: https://www.ecumen.org
Year Founded: 1923
Sales Range: $125-149.9 Million
Emp.: 4,016
Elder Care Services
N.A.I.C.S.: 624120
Robin Dunbar Balck *(Chief Strategy Officer & Sr VP-Admin)*
Shelley Kendrick *(CEO)*
Julie Murray *(Chief Bus Dev Officer & Sr VP-Sls & Mktg)*
William McGarry *(CTO & VP-IT)*
Amy Korzenowski *(VP-Ops-Housing & Nursing Home Communities)*
Brett Anderson *(VP-Nursing Svcs)*
Diane Kenney *(VP-Sls & Mktg)*
Cindy Mowan *(VP-Fin)*
Carolyn Perron *(VP-Organizational Dev)*
Morshed Alam *(CFO & Sr VP)*

ECUMENICAL ENTERPRISES INC.
1075 Memorial Hwy, Dallas, PA 18612-1070
Tel.: (570) 675-7336

Web Site: http://www.eeidallaspa.com
Sales Range: $10-24.9 Million
Emp.: 3
Apartment Hotel Operation
N.A.I.C.S.: 531110

ED BELL INVESTMENTS COMPANY INC.
10605 Harry Hines Blvd, Dallas, TX 75220-2634
Tel.: (214) 358-3414 **TX**
Web Site: https://www.edbellconstruction.com
Year Founded: 1973
Sales Range: $25-49.9 Million
Emp.: 250
Highway & Street Construction Services
N.A.I.C.S.: 237310
Edwin S. Bell Jr. *(CEO)*

Subsidiaries:
Construction Equipment Parts Inc. **(1)**
10605 Harry Hines Blvd, Dallas, TX 75220-2634
Tel.: (214) 350-6671
Web Site: http://www.cepimixers.com
Rev.: $18,000,000
Emp.: 40
Industrial Machinery & Equipment Distr
N.A.I.C.S.: 423830

Ed Bell Construction Company Inc. **(1)**
10605 Harry Hines Blvd, Dallas, TX 75220-2634
Tel.: (214) 358-6581
Web Site: http://www.ebcc.com
Rev.: $23,000,000
Emp.: 115
Highway & Street Construction Services
N.A.I.C.S.: 237310
Edwin S. Bell Jr. *(CEO)*

Equipment Storage & Service Inc. **(1)**
3839 E Overton Rd, Dallas, TX 75216-2802
Tel.: (214) 374-3995
Rev.: $5,000,000
Emp.: 24
Equipment Storage Overseas Containers
N.A.I.C.S.: 322219

ED BOZARTH CHEVROLET AND BUICK, INC.
2595 Hwy 6 & 50, Grand Junction, CO 81505
Tel.: (970) 778-4612
Web Site: http://www.edbozarthgrandjunction.com
Year Founded: 1993
Sales Range: $25-49.9 Million
Emp.: 85
New & Used Car Dealer
N.A.I.C.S.: 441110
Mark Miller *(Gen Mgr)*

ED BOZARTH CHEVROLET COMPANY, INC.
2001 S Havana, Aurora, CO 80014
Tel.: (303) 751-7500
Web Site: https://www.edbozarthchevy.com
Sales Range: $25-49.9 Million
Emp.: 500
New & Used Car Dealer
N.A.I.C.S.: 441110
Ed Bozarth *(Owner & Pres)*
Kyle Bell *(Gen Mgr)*
Debbie McGee *(Controller)*

ED FAGAN INC.
769 Susquehanna Ave, Franklin Lakes, NJ 07417
Tel.: (201) 891-4003
Web Site: https://www.edfagan.com
Sales Range: $10-24.9 Million
Emp.: 21

Steel
N.A.I.C.S.: 423510
Pam Russo *(Controller)*
Scott Williams *(Acct Mgr)*
Larry Taylor *(Sr Mgr-Special Accts)*

ED HICKS IMPORTS, LTD.
3102 S Padre Island Dr, Corpus Christi, TX 78415
Tel.: (361) 854-1955
Web Site: http://www.edhicks.com
Year Founded: 1966
Sales Range: $75-99.9 Million
Emp.: 78
Car Whslr
N.A.I.C.S.: 441110
Charles Hicks *(Owner)*

ED KELLUM & SON APPLIANCE CO.
4415 N Central Expy, Dallas, TX 75205
Tel.: (214) 526-1717
Web Site: https://www.edkellum.com
Sales Range: $10-24.9 Million
Emp.: 70
Television Sets
N.A.I.C.S.: 449210
Dan Pidgeon *(Pres)*

ED KENLEY FORD, INC.
1888 N Main St, Layton, UT 84041
Tel.: (801) 776-6401
Web Site: http://www.edkenleyford.com
Sales Range: $10-24.9 Million
Emp.: 100
Car Whslr
N.A.I.C.S.: 441110
Jewe Kenley *(Owner)*
Jewelee Kenley *(Owner)*

ED KIRBY ADVENTURE
1501 Walnut Ave, Dalton, GA 30720
Tel.: (706) 278-1122
Sales Range: $10-24.9 Million
Emp.: 64
New Car Whslr
N.A.I.C.S.: 441110
Glenn Allen *(Sec)*

ED MARTIN ACURA
3800 E 96th St, Indianapolis, IN 46240
Tel.: (317) 588-1989
Web Site: https://www.edmartinacura.com
Sales Range: $10-24.9 Million
Emp.: 68
Car Whslr
N.A.I.C.S.: 441110
Larry Gray *(Gen Mgr)*
Mark Harrison *(Pres)*
Randy Stahl *(Mgr-Internet Sls)*

ED MARTIN CHEVY CADILLAC
5400 S Scatterfield Rd, Anderson, IN 46013-3139
Tel.: (765) 642-8001
Web Site: http://www.edmartinchevycadillac.com
Year Founded: 1978
Sales Range: $10-24.9 Million
Emp.: 80
Car Whslr
N.A.I.C.S.: 441110
Mark Harrison *(Owner)*
Gary Wray *(Mgr-Fixed)*

ED MINIAT, INC.
16250 S Vincennes Ave, South Holland, IL 60473
Tel.: (708) 589-2400 **IL**
Web Site: http://www.miniat.com

Year Founded: 1958
Rev.: $100,000,000
Emp.: 200
Food Processing for Restaurants, Supermarket Chains; Food Service Distributor
N.A.I.C.S.: 424470
David J. Miniat *(CEO)*
Curt Zhyzy *(Controller)*

Subsidiaries:
South Chicago Packing Co. **(1)**
945 W 38th St, Chicago, IL 60609-1442 **(100%)**
Tel.: (708) 589-2400
Web Site: http://www.miniat.com
Sales Range: $25-49.9 Million
Compound Shortenings
N.A.I.C.S.: 311225
David J. Miniat *(CEO)*

ED MITCHELL INC.
670 Post Rd E, Westport, CT 06880
Tel.: (203) 227-5165 **CT**
Web Site: http://www.mitchellstores.com
Year Founded: 1958
Sales Range: $50-74.9 Million
Emp.: 100
Men's Businesswear Stores Owner & Operator
N.A.I.C.S.: 458110
Todd Bonner *(Controller)*
Robert Mitchell *(Co-Pres)*
John Russell Mitchell Jr. *(Co-Pres)*

ED PERRY AUTO PARTS COMPANY, INC.
450 S 580, Inman, SC 29349
Tel.: (864) 472-2166 **SC**
Web Site: https://www.edperryautoparts.com
Sales Range: $10-24.9 Million
Emp.: 26
Provider of Automotive Parts & Supplies
N.A.I.C.S.: 423120
Judy Sims *(Pres)*
Pam Mosley *(VP)*
Merrie Likus *(Controller)*

ED SCHMIDT PONTIAC - GMC TRUCK, INC.
26875 N Dixie Hwy, Perrysburg, OH 43551
Tel.: (419) 874-4331 **OH**
Web Site: http://www.edschmidt.com
Rev.: $132,896,657
Emp.: 100
Automobiles, New & Used
N.A.I.C.S.: 441110
Tom Schmidt *(Owner)*
Richard Cronin *(CFO)*

ED SCHULTS CHEVROLET CADILLAC
300 Fluvanna Ave, Jamestown, NY 14701
Tel.: (716) 664-0101
Web Site: https://www.shultschevy.com
Sales Range: $10-24.9 Million
Emp.: 53
New Car Retailer
N.A.I.C.S.: 441110
Sean Larson *(Gen Mgr-Sls)*
Jesse Milne *(Mgr-Sls)*

ED SEIFRIED CONSTRUCTION, INC.
6985 1st Ave N, Saint Petersburg, FL 33710
Tel.: (727) 347-3333
Web Site: http://www.edseifried.com
Sales Range: $1-9.9 Million
Emp.: 5
Commercial, Institutional & Industrial Construction
N.A.I.C.S.: 236220

Ed Seifried Construction, Inc.—(Continued)

Wayne Seifried (Founder & Owner)
Rick Breeze (VP)
Sean Seifried (VP)
Tina Zeller (Office Mgr)

ED SHULTS OF WARREN, INC.
4060 Market St, Warren, PA 16365
Tel.: (814) 726-3150
Web Site:
 http://www.edshultsofwarren.com
Year Founded: 1984
Sales Range: $10-24.9 Million
Emp.: 70
Car Dealer
N.A.I.C.S.: 441110
Sean Ellsworth (Owner & Gen Mgr)
Lenny Melice (Gen Mgr-Sls)
Art Chamberlin (Asst Mgr-Used Car
Sls & Leasing)

ED SIMAL & ASSOCIATES INC.
1356 Milledge St, East Point, GA
30344
Tel.: (404) 761-7961
Sales Range: $10-24.9 Million
Emp.: 7
Chemicals & Allied Products
N.A.I.C.S.: 424690
Ed Simal (Pres)

ED STAUB & SONS PETRO-LEUM INC.
19828 Stateline Rd, Tulelake, CA
96134
Tel.: (530) 667-2227   CA
Web Site: https://www.edstaub.com
Year Founded: 1959
Sales Range: $50-74.9 Million
Emp.: 10
Petroleum Product Distr
N.A.I.C.S.: 424720
David Staub (Pres)

Subsidiaries:

Ed Staub & Sons   (1)
44015 State Hwy 299 E, Fall River Mills,
CA 96028   (100%)
Tel.: (530) 336-6138
Sales Range: $10-24.9 Million
Emp.: 5
Provider of Petroleum Services
N.A.I.C.S.: 424710
Bill Morris (Plant Mgr)

ED TAYLOR CONSTRUCTION INC.
2713 N Falkenburg Rd Ste A, Tampa,
FL 33619
Tel.: (813) 623-3724
Web Site: https://www.edtaylor.net
Year Founded: 1991
Sales Range: $25-49.9 Million
Emp.: 30
Commercial & Office Building Con-
struction Services
N.A.I.C.S.: 236220
Brian Jackson (Co-Founder)
Mark Weaver (VP)
Bill Wolfe (Sr Project Mgr)
James Walters (Controller)
Mike Profozich (Co-Founder)
Tim Nalls (Project Mgr)
Ben Jackson (Project Mgr)
Matt Jackson (Project Mgr)
Katie Gower (Dir-Bus Dev)

ED TILLMAN AUTO SALES INC.
3207 N Main St, Jacksonville, FL
32206
Tel.: (904) 356-4800
Web Site: http://www.tillmanauto.com
Sales Range: $10-24.9 Million
Emp.: 30
Automobiles, Used Cars Only
N.A.I.C.S.: 441120
Tanya Nye (Office Mgr)

ED VOYLES DEALERSHIPS
2103 Cobb Pkwy, Marietta, GA 30067
Tel.: (770) 951-2211   GA
Web Site: http://www.edvoyles.com
Year Founded: 1975
Sales Range: $200-249.9 Million
Emp.: 500
Automobile Dealership
N.A.I.C.S.: 441110
Pete Richards (Gen Mgr)
Bill Brantley (CEO)

ED WALTON CONSTRUCTION CO.
911 Old Lubbock Hwy, Snyder, TX
79549
Tel.: (325) 573-0146
Rev.: $14,049,433
Emp.: 125
Oil & Gas Pipeline Construction
N.A.I.C.S.: 237120
Dalton D. Walton (CEO)

ED WITTMEIER FORD INC.
2288 Forest Ave, Chico, CA 95928
Tel.: (530) 895-8181
Web Site:
 http://www.wittmeierauto.com
Year Founded: 1978
Rev.: $58,800,000
Emp.: 200
Automobiles, New & Used
N.A.I.C.S.: 441110
Ed Wittmeier (Pres & CEO)
Wayne Wittmeier (VP)

EDAC SYSTEMS INC.
10970 Pierson Dr, Fredericksburg,
VA 22408
Tel.: (540) 361-1580
Web Site:
 https://www.edacsystems.com
Rev.: $15,000,000
Emp.: 10
Computer Peripheral Equipment
N.A.I.C.S.: 423430
David Rawlings (Mgr-Sls)

EDARON INC.
100 Appleton St, Holyoke, MA 01040
Tel.: (413) 533-7159
Sales Range: $10-24.9 Million
Emp.: 19
Puzzles
N.A.I.C.S.: 339930
Louis Moretti (Pres)
Babski Ed (VP-Sls)
Amber Muller (Acct Mgr)

EDC CONSULTING LLC
1600 International Dr Ste 800,
McLean, VA 22102
Tel.: (703) 637-0068
Web Site:
 http://www.edcconsulting.com
Year Founded: 2005
Sales Range: $10-24.9 Million
Emp.: 120
Implementation of ERP Solutions, IT
Services & Business Strategy Sup-
port for the Federal Government
N.A.I.C.S.: 921190
Uli Werner (CEO)
Pete Markakos (Principal)
Ray Boehling (Dir-Program & Dev)

EDCO DISPOSAL CORPORA-TION
6670 Federal Blvd, Lemon Grove, CA
91945
Tel.: (619) 287-7555   CA

Web Site:
 https://www.edcodisposal.com
Year Founded: 1967
Sales Range: $100-124.9 Million
Emp.: 600
Mfr of Refuse Systems
N.A.I.C.S.: 562111
Sandy Burr (VP)
Alan Walsh (CFO)
Bob Hill (Dir-Recycling)
Shelton Stamps (Dir-Ops & Mainte-
nance)

Subsidiaries:

Edco Waste & Recycling Services
Inc.   (1)
224 S Las Posas Rd, San Marcos, CA
92078-2421   (100%)
Tel.: (760) 727-1600
Web Site: http://www.edcodisposal.com
Sales Range: $10-24.9 Million
Emp.: 250
Waste & Recycling Services
N.A.I.C.S.: 812990
Jeff Richie (VP)

EDCO LLC
148 E Ave, Norwalk, CT 06851
Tel.: (203) 855-8088
Rev.: $16,234,385
Emp.: 14
Long Distance Telephone Communi-
cations
N.A.I.C.S.: 517121

EDD INVESTMENT CO.
173 E Freedom Ave, Anaheim, CA
92801-1006
Tel.: (714) 459-0041   CA
Year Founded: 1968
Sales Range: $100-124.9 Million
Emp.: 1,219
Operators of Nonresidential Buildings
N.A.I.C.S.: 531120
Edwin Sheldrake (CEO)
Alen Gray (CFO)

Subsidiaries:

Polly's Inc.   (1)
173 E Freedom Ave, Anaheim, CA 92801-
1006
Tel.: (714) 459-0041
Web Site: http://www.pollyspies.com
Sales Range: $10-24.9 Million
Emp.: 45
Operator of Restaurants
N.A.I.C.S.: 722513
Allan Grey (CEO)

EDDIE BRYANT ENTERPRISES INC.
1555 Goodyear, El Paso, TX 79936
Tel.: (915) 592-8737
Rev.: $11,948,953
Emp.: 11
Grocery Stores
N.A.I.C.S.: 445110
Eddie Bryant (Pres)

EDDIE GILSTRAP MOTORS INCORPORATED
207 S Main St, Salem, IN 47167
Tel.: (812) 883-3481   IN
Web Site:
 https://www.eddiegilstrapmotors.com
Year Founded: 1937
Sales Range: $25-49.9 Million
Emp.: 60
Sales of New & Used Cars
N.A.I.C.S.: 441110
Steven R. Motsinger (Pres)

EDDIES TIRE SERVICE INC.
3077 Valley Rd, Berkeley Springs,
WV 25411
Tel.: (304) 258-1368
Web Site: http://www.eddiestire.net
Rev.: $17,000,000

Emp.: 30
Auto & Home Supply Stores
N.A.I.C.S.: 441330
Louise Stotler (Pres)
Deborah Thayer (CEO)

EDDIES TRUCK SALES IN-CORPORATED
1002 E Omaha St, Rapid City, SD
57701
Tel.: (605) 348-4900
Web Site:
 http://www.eddiestrucksales.com
Sales Range: $10-24.9 Million
Emp.: 48
Trucks, Tractors & Trailers: New &
Used
N.A.I.C.S.: 441110
Craig Uhre (Pres)
Jon Gillam (Gen Mgr)

EDDS SUPPLIES INC.
2665 N 850 W, Shipshewana, IN
46565
Tel.: (260) 768-4513
Web Site:
 https://www.eddssupplies.com
Sales Range: $10-24.9 Million
Emp.: 20
Retails Fertilizer & Other Farm Sup-
plies
N.A.I.C.S.: 424910
Steve Fanning (Pres)

EDDY'S TOYOTA OF WICHITA INC.
7333 E Kellogg Dr, Wichita, KS
67207
Tel.: (316) 652-2222
Web Site:
 https://www.eddystoyota.com
Sales Range: $25-49.9 Million
Emp.: 50
Automobiles, New & Used
N.A.I.C.S.: 441110
Brandon Steven (Owner)

EDELBROCK CORPORATION
2700 California St, Torrance, CA
90503-3907
Tel.: (310) 781-2222   DE
Web Site: http://www.edelbrock.com
Year Founded: 1938
Sales Range: $100-124.9 Million
Emp.: 600
Performance Automotive Equipment,
Manifolds, Carburetor Synchronizers,
Camshafts, Electronic Water Injec-
tion, Chrome Signature Accessories
& Valve Covers Mfr
N.A.I.C.S.: 336390
Wayne P. Murray (COO)
Don Barry (Pres & CEO)
Rob Morse (Acct Mgr-Sls)

Subsidiaries:

Edelbrock Foundry Corp.   (1)
1320 S Buena Vista St, San Jacinto, CA
92583-4665   (100%)
Tel.: (909) 654-6677
Web Site: http://www.edelbrockfoundry.com
Sales Range: $10-24.9 Million
Emp.: 120
Castings Mfr
N.A.I.C.S.: 331523

EDELMANN SCOTT, INC.
3751 Westerre Pkwy Ste A, Rich-
mond, VA 23233
Tel.: (804) 643-1931
Year Founded: 1979
Rev.: $19,864,537
Emp.: 11
Advetising Agency
N.A.I.C.S.: 541810

Robert Judge (CFO & Gen Mgr)
George Fugate (Exec VP & Creative Dir)
Christie Good (Acct Exec)
Dick Scott (Pres-Mktg, Adv & PR)

EDEN & TYE INC.
7483 Candlewood Rd Ste H, Hanover, MD 21076
Tel.: (443) 577-1200
Web Site: http://www.edentye.com
Sales Range: $10-24.9 Million
Emp.: 35
Groceries, General Line
N.A.I.C.S.: 424410
Bill Tye (CEO)
Don Davis (Sr Acct Mgr)
Marcella Larrimore (Dir-Fin)

EDEN CAPITAL MANAGE-MENT LLC
712 5th Ave 27th Fl, New York, NY 10019
Tel.: (212) 588-9000
Web Site: http://www.edencp.com
Year Founded: 2015
Computer & Investment Services
N.A.I.C.S.: 523999
Dina Said (Founder & Mng Partner)
Will Darman (Mng Partner)
Henrik Lund Wibe (VP)
Gregory Bonamour (CFO)
Emilie Hunt (Office Mgr)

Subsidiaries:

White Cup SE, Inc. (1)
129 E 50th St, Garden City, ID 83714
Tel.: (419) 425-4800
Web Site: https://whitecupsolutions.com
Software Development Services
N.A.I.C.S.: 541511
Scottie Girouard (VP-HR)
Brian Friedle (VP-Bus Dev)
Matthew Mullen (CEO)
Allen Pack (CFO)
Pamela Pieper Berchem (CTO & VP-R&D)
Helen Piña (VP-Mktg)
Kristen Thom (Dir-Product Mgmt)
Beth Toland (Dir-Pro Svcs)

EDEN COMPANY, INC.
707 Commercial Ave, Carlstadt, NJ 07072
Tel.: (201) 438-2250
Year Founded: 1940
Sales Range: Less than $1 Million
Emp.: 5
General Merchandise Distr
N.A.I.C.S.: 424210
Robert Schuman (Pres)

EDEN CRYOGENICS LLC
8475 Rausch Dr, Plain City, OH 43064-8067
Tel.: (614) 873-3949
Web Site: https://www.edencryogenics.com
Year Founded: 2006
Sales Range: $25-49.9 Million
Emp.: 15
Cryogenic Product & Equipment Mfr
N.A.I.C.S.: 332420
Steve L. Hensley (Pres)

EDEN FOODS INC.
701 Tecumseh Rd, Clinton, MI 49236-9589
Tel.: (517) 456-7424
Web Site: http://www.edenfoods.com
Year Founded: 1968
Sales Range: $25-49.9 Million
Emp.: 80
Grocery & Related Services
N.A.I.C.S.: 424490
Michael Potter (Pres)

EDEN HOUSING, INC.

409 Jackson St, Hayward, CA 94544
Tel.: (510) 582-1460
Web Site: http://www.edenhousing.org
Year Founded: 1968
Sales Range: $1-9.9 Million
Emp.: 17
Residential Construction
N.A.I.C.S.: 236116
Linda Mandolini (Pres)
Anna Gwyn Simpson (Dir-Resident Svcs)
Janet Lockhart (Sec)
Jim Kennedy (Treas)
John Gaffney (Chm)
Timothy L. Silva Sr. (Vice Chm)

Subsidiaries:

Eden Housing Management, Inc. (1)
22645 Grand St, Hayward, CA 94541
Tel.: (510) 582-1460
Web Site: http://www.edenhousing.org
Real Estate Agents & Brokers
N.A.I.C.S.: 531210

EDEN OIL CO. INC.
2507 Richardson Dr, Reidsville, NC 27320
Tel.: (336) 349-8228
Web Site: http://www.rentz-edenoil.com
Sales Range: $25-49.9 Million
Emp.: 20
Petroleum Bulk Stations & Terminals
N.A.I.C.S.: 424710
Reid Teague (Pres)

EDEN RETIREMENT CENTER INC.
200 S Station Rd, Glen Carbon, IL 62034
Tel.: (618) 288-5014
Web Site: http://www.edenvillage.org
Year Founded: 1979
Sales Range: $10-24.9 Million
Emp.: 354
Elder Care Services
N.A.I.C.S.: 623312
Barb Brown (Dir-Nursing Svcs)

EDEN STONE CO. INC.
W4520 Lime Rd, Eden, WI 53019
Tel.: (920) 477-2521
Web Site: http://www.edenstone.net
Year Founded: 1950
Sales Range: $10-24.9 Million
Emp.: 180
Limestone, Dimension-Quarrying
N.A.I.C.S.: 212311
Barry Gesell (Pres)

EDENS REALTY, INC.
1221 Main St Ste 1000, Columbia, SC 29201
Tel.: (803) 779-4420
Web Site: https://www.edens.com
Year Founded: 1966
Emp.: 256
Commercial Real Estate Investment, Development & Property Management Services
N.A.I.C.S.: 531390
Steven C. Boyle (Mng Dir-Mid-Atlantic Reg)
William C. Caldwell (Mng Dir-Design & Construction)
Lyle Darnall (Mng Dir-Georgia, Florida & South Carolina)
Mark Garside (CFO)
Jami Passer (Chief Investment Officer)
DeAnne Dunn (VP-Tax Strategy & Plng)
Sara Fawcett (VP-HR)
Maria Smith (VP-IR & Treasury)
Elizabeth Furnelli (Mng Dir)
Jessica Bruner (Mng Dir)

Rob Wyant (COO)
Meghann Scherrer (Dir-Comm & Culture)
Brad Dumont (Mng Dir)
David Germakian (Sr VP-Mid-Atlantic)
Gregg Edelstein (Mng Dir)
Herbert Ames (Sr VP-Dev-Southeast)
Jeff Kaufman (Mng Dir)
Norma Morales Perez (Sr VP-Brand & Culture)
Tom Kiler (Mng Dir)
Jodie W. McLean (CEO)

EDENTON MOTORS INC.
1365 N Broad St, Edenton, NC 27932
Tel.: (252) 482-8421
New & Used Automobiles Whslr
N.A.I.C.S.: 441110
Teressa F. Conrad (Controller)
Stewart Deacon (Gen Mgr)

EDER FLAG MANUFACTURING CO.
1000 W Rawson Ave, Oak Creek, WI 53154-0397
Tel.: (414) 764-3522
Web Site: https://www.ederflag.com
Sales Range: $10-24.9 Million
Emp.: 100
Banners, Made From Fabric
N.A.I.C.S.: 314999
Tim Kfoveich (CFO)

EDEREL SPORT INC.
15225 Auton Pkwy Ste 100, Irvine, CA 92618
Tel.: (949) 837-7700
Rev.: $30,600,000
Emp.: 35
Sportswear, Women's & Children's
N.A.I.C.S.: 424350

EDESIA INC.
88 Royal Little Dr, Providence, RI 02904
Tel.: (401) 272-5521
Web Site: http://www.edesiaglobal.org
Year Founded: 2007
Sales Range: $10-24.9 Million
Emp.: 36
Community Food Services
N.A.I.C.S.: 624210
Ronald Yanku (Dir-Plant Ops)
Navyn Salem (Founder, Pres & CEO)
David Duffell (Sec)
John Bucci (CFO)
Paul J. Salem (Treas & Treas)

EDEXPERTS
12977 N 40 Dr Ste 218, Saint Louis, MO 63141
Tel.: (636) 536-3656
Web Site: http://www.edexperts.com
Year Founded: 2004
Rev.: $15,000,000
Emp.: 15
Advertising, Media Buying Services, Web (Banner Ads, Pop-ups, etc.)
N.A.I.C.S.: 541810
Donna Beaird (Coord-Media)
Marlene Todd (Dir-Media)
Sara Stuebgen (Mgr-Media Accts)
Wendy Leavitt (Dir-Acct Svcs)
Christine Palmer (Sr Acct Mgr)

EDG PARTNERS, LLC
2121 Eisenhower Ave Ste 600, Alexandria, VA 22314
Tel.: (703) 562-5120
Web Site: http://www.edgpartners.com
Year Founded: 2004
Privater Equity Firm
N.A.I.C.S.: 523999

Alan C. Dahl (Co-Founder & Mng Dir)
J. Stephen Eaton (Co-Founder & Mng Dir)
Michael P. Gaffney (Co-Founder & Mng Dir)

EDG/SW HOLDINGS LLC
5800 Challenge Dr, Memphis, TN 38115-5014
Tel.: (901) 942-2441
Sales Range: $10-24.9 Million
Emp.: 1
Holding Company
N.A.I.C.S.: 551112
George R. McLaughlin (Chm)

Subsidiaries:

Emess Design Group LLC (1)
10475 Perry Hwy Ste 301, Wexford, PA 15090
Tel.: (724) 758-0707
Web Site: http://www.emessdesign.com
Portable Lamps & Household Lighting Fixtures Mfr
N.A.I.C.S.: 335131
Rich Giron (Pres)

EDGAR BOETTCHER MASON CONTRACTORS
3803 N Euclid Ave, Bay City, MI 48706
Tel.: (231) 941-5802
Web Site: http://www.boettchermasonry.com
Sales Range: $10-24.9 Million
Emp.: 12
Masonry & Other Stonework
N.A.I.C.S.: 238140
Micheal Radofa (Pres)

EDGAR P BENJAMIN HEALTH-CARE CENTER, INC.
120 Fisher Ave, Roxbury, MA 02120
Tel.: (617) 738-1500
Year Founded: 1927
Sales Range: $10-24.9 Million
Emp.: 260
Community Health Care Services
N.A.I.C.S.: 621498
Myrna Wynn (Pres & CEO)

EDGARIZING SOLUTIONS, INC.
10045 Red Run Blvd Ste 140, Owings Mills, MD 21117
Tel.: (855) 545-0251
Year Founded: 2013
Electronic Document Conversion & Filing Solutions
N.A.I.C.S.: 561410
Jerry Gruenbaum (Pres, CEO, CFO, Chief Acctg Officer & Treas)
David Mathias (Sec)

EDGE CAPITAL PARTNERS, LLC
1380 W Paces Ferry Rd Ste 1000, Atlanta, GA 30327
Tel.: (404) 890-7707
Web Site: http://www.edgecappartners.com
Year Founded: 2006
Rev.: $2,500,000,000
Asset Management Services
N.A.I.C.S.: 523999
Barrett Karvis (VP-Bus Admin)
William deButts (Partner)
Bill Maner (Chm)
Peek Garlington (Partner)
Kendrick Mattox (Partner)
Jimmy Patrick (Partner)
Bert Rayle (Partner)
Paul Robertson (Mng Dir)
Whit Davis (Partner-Res)
Dennis Sabo (Mng Dir-Res)

Edge Capital Partners, LLC—(Continued)

Will Skeean *(Mng Partner-Investment)*
Harry Jones *(Mng Partner-Res)*
Jacobi Padgett *(VP-Res)*
William A. Maner IV *(Dir-Advisory)*

EDGE COMMUNICATIONS, INC.
5419 Hollywood Blvd Ste 727, Los Angeles, CA 90027
Tel.: (323) 469-3397   CA
Web Site:
http://www.edgecommunication.com
Year Founded: 1996
Sales Range: $1-9.9 Million
Emp.: 20
Public Relations Agency
N.A.I.C.S.: 541820
Ken Greenberg *(Founder, Pres & CEO)*
Sara Flint *(VP)*

EDGE DEVELOPMENT, INC.
27368 Via Industria Ste 101, Temecula, CA 92590
Tel.: (951) 296-0776
Web Site: http://www.edge-dev.com
Sales Range: $200-249.9 Million
Emp.: 75
Construction, including, Construction Management, General Contracting, Engineering, Prime Trade Work & Design-Build Projects
N.A.I.C.S.: 236210
Jim Richardson *(Project Mgr)*

EDGE ELECTRONICS INC.
75 Orville Dr, Bohemia, NY 11716-2528
Tel.: (631) 471-3343
Web Site:
https://www.edgeelectronics.com
Sales Range: $25-49.9 Million
Emp.: 14
Electronic Parts & Equipment
N.A.I.C.S.: 423690
Adrienne Giannone *(Owner, Pres & CEO-New York)*
Jeffrey Fink *(Mgr-Quality Assurance)*
Michael Fiore *(Product Mgr)*
Robert Tomasino *(Mgr-Sls-Natl)*

EDGE FINANCIAL, INC.
16501 Ventura Blvd Ste 110, Encino, CA 91436
Tel.: (800) 410-8605
Web Site:
http://www.edgefinancial.com
Year Founded: 2001
Sales Range: $1-9.9 Million
Emp.: 200
Financial Support Services
N.A.I.C.S.: 522220
Light Silver *(CEO)*

EDGE NATURAL RESOURCES LLC
5950 Berkshire Ln Ste 1000, Dallas, TX 75225
Tel.: (469) 331-0123   DE
Web Site: https://www.edgenr.com
Emp.: 15
Privater Equity Firm
N.A.I.C.S.: 523999
Stacie Moore *(Co-Founder, CFO & Partner)*
Roy A. Aneed *(Co-Founder & Partner)*
Jesse Bomer *(Co-Founder & Partner)*
Oscar Pate *(Co-Founder & Partner)*
Brian Smiley *(VP)*

Subsidiaries:

Canamax Energy Ltd.   (1)

Suite 610 324 8th Avenue SW, Calgary, T2P 2Z2, AB, Canada
Tel.: (587) 349-5186
Web Site: http://www.canamaxenergy.ca
Sales Range: $1-9.9 Million
Emp.: 14
Oil & Gas Exploration Services
N.A.I.C.S.: 213112
Harry Knutson *(Chm)*
Brad Gabel *(Pres & CEO)*
Bonnie Lamming *(CFO)*
Darrin Krueger *(VP)*
Jessica Metez *(VP)*

EDGE PRODUCTS
1080 S Depot Dr, Ogden, UT 84404
Tel.: (801) 476-3343
Web Site:
https://www.edgeproducts.com
Year Founded: 1999
Sales Range: $25-49.9 Million
Emp.: 120
Diesel Electronic Enhancement Products
N.A.I.C.S.: 336320
Aaron Chapman *(Mgr-Tech Support)*

EDGE SERVICES, INC.
4196 Merchant Plz Ste 714, Woodbridge, VA 22192
Tel.: (703) 492-4955
Web Site:
http://www.edgeservices.com
Year Founded: 1993
Rev.: $15,400,000
Emp.: 93
Information Technology Services
N.A.I.C.S.: 541990
Kevin Utzy *(VP-Mgmt)*
Kevin Clark *(Pres & CEO)*

EDGE SOLUTIONS INC.
7 Old Roswell St, Alpharetta, GA 30009
Tel.: (770) 250-5955
Web Site: http://www.edgewit.com
Year Founded: 2008
Sales Range: $25-49.9 Million
Emp.: 30
IT Solutions Offering Storage, Server & Networking Services
N.A.I.C.S.: 334112
Julie Ison Haley *(CEO)*
Bobby Thomas *(VP-Sls)*
Darin DeHart *(Exec VP)*
Susan Ahmed *(VP-Svcs)*
David Able *(COO)*
Samantha Vince *(VP-Mktg)*

EDGE SYSTEMS, LLC
3S721 W Ave Ste 200, Warrenville, IL 60555
Tel.: (630) 810-9669   IL
Web Site: http://www.edge.com
Year Founded: 1985
Computer Integrated Systems Design Services
N.A.I.C.S.: 541512
Alexander Bishop *(COO)*

EDGE TECH CORP.
1310 N Hill Ctr, Ada, OK 74820
Tel.: (580) 332-6581
Web Site:
http://www.edgetechcorp.com
Rev.: $34,000,000
Emp.: 125
Computer Storage Devices
N.A.I.C.S.: 334112
Matthew Lindhe *(Supvr-Customer Support)*

EDGELINK, LLC
2525 SW 1st Ave, Portland, OR 97201
Tel.: (503) 246-3989
Web Site: http://www.edgelink.com
Sales Range: $1-9.9 Million

Emp.: 30
Techincal Staff Recruiting Services
N.A.I.C.S.: 541612
Patricia Zeman *(Controller)*
Jeff Miller *(Founder & Mng Dir)*
Mike Miadich *(Founder & VP)*
Traci Shields *(Founder)*
Mark Schacter *(Mgr-Direct Hire Svcs)*
Dane Walker *(Mgr-Contract Svcs)*
Carolyn Bentley *(Mgr-HR)*
John Kingdeski *(Mgr-Denver Contract Svcs)*
Aaron Mills *(Mgr-Denver Market)*
Jaimie Mayhew *(Supvr-Acct)*

EDGEMATE, INC.
213 Smith Transport Rd, Roaring Spring, PA 16673
Tel.: (814) 224-5717
Web Site: https://www.edgemate.com
Year Founded: 1968
Sales Range: $10-24.9 Million
Emp.: 150
Hardwood Veneer & Plywood Mfr
N.A.I.C.S.: 321211
Nick Benjamin *(Mgr-Sls-Western US & Canada)*
Jeff Newman *(Mgr-Sls-Eastern US & Canada)*
Harry K. Benjamin *(Owner & Pres)*

EDGERTON HOSPITAL AND HEALTH SERVICES INC.
11101 N Sherman Rd, Edgerton, WI 53534
Tel.: (608) 884-3441   WI
Year Founded: 1968
Sales Range: $10-24.9 Million
Emp.: 215
Health Care Srvices
N.A.I.C.S.: 622110
Caryn Oleston *(Chief Clinical Officer)*
Charles Roeder *(CFO)*
James Schultz *(Chm)*
Jay Peterson *(Vice Chm)*
Melva Sue Larson *(Treas)*
Steve Thompson *(Sec)*

EDGES ELECTRICAL GROUP
1135 Auzerais Ave, San Jose, CA 95126
Tel.: (408) 293-5818   CA
Web Site:
https://www.edgesgroup.com
Year Founded: 1948
Sales Range: $25-49.9 Million
Emp.: 120
Electrical Apparatus & Equipment Distr
N.A.I.C.S.: 423610
Scott Lehmann *(Pres)*

Subsidiaries:

Granite Electrical Supply, Inc.   (1)
801 Striker Ave, Sacramento, CA 95834
Tel.: (916) 648-3900
Web Site: http://www.graniteelectrical.com
Sales Range: $1-9.9 Million
Emp.: 25
Whol Electrical Equipment
N.A.I.C.S.: 423610
Shane Spencer *(Mgr-Warehouse)*

EDGESOURCE CORPORATION
909 N Washington St Ste 200, Alexandria, VA 22314-1555
Tel.: (703) 837-0550
Web Site:
http://www.edgesource.com
Emp.: 100
Custom Computer Programming Services
N.A.I.C.S.: 541511
Chris Lansburgh *(Pres & CEO)*

Subsidiaries:

Newbrook Solutions, Inc.   (1)

8280 Greensboro Dr Ste 620, McLean, VA 22102-3853
Tel.: (571) 723-1523
Web Site:
http://www.newbrooksolutions.com
Computer Related Services
N.A.I.C.S.: 541519
Dustin Smithers *(Pres)*

EDGEWARE COMPUTERS, INC.
1640 Powers Ferry Rd Bldg 3 Ste 300, Marietta, GA 30067
Tel.: (770) 952-4848
Web Site: https://www.edgeware.net
Year Founded: 1983
Sales Range: $1-9.9 Million
Emp.: 34
Cloud-Based Management Software
N.A.I.C.S.: 423430
Derek Jenkins *(Founder & CEO)*

EDGEWATER BEACH RESORT MANAGEMENT, INC.
11212 Front Beach Rd Ste A, Panama City, FL 32407
Tel.: (850) 235-4044
Web Site:
http://www.edgewaterbeach.com
Year Founded: 1982
Sales Range: $150-199.9 Million
Emp.: 400
Developer & Operator of Condominiums
N.A.I.C.S.: 236117
Joe Wheland *(Sec)*
Thomas Sparks *(VP-Ops)*
Wesley Burnham *(Pres)*

EDGEWATER CAPITAL PARTNERS, L.P.
5005 Rockside Rd PH 1300, Cleveland, OH 44131
Tel.: (216) 292-3838
Web Site:
http://www.edgewatercapital.com
Year Founded: 1998
Privater Equity Firm
N.A.I.C.S.: 523999
Christopher Childres *(Founder & Mng Partner)*
Ryan J. Meany *(Mng Partner)*
Richard T. Schwarz *(Partner)*
Chris Springer *(Operating Partner-Engineered Solutions)*
Brian Scanlan *(Operating Partner-Life Science)*

Subsidiaries:

Evantic   (1)
9930 FM 2920, Tomball, TX 77375
Tel.: (855) 686-8600
Web Site: https://evantic.com
Machine & Fabricated Products Mfg.
N.A.I.C.S.: 333998
Tamara Horne *(CEO)*

Subsidiary (Domestic):

Plastic Distributors & Fabricators, Inc.   (2)
419 River St, Haverhill, MA 01832-5114
Tel.: (978) 374-0300
Web Site: http://www.plasticdistributors.com
Machine Shops
N.A.I.C.S.: 332710
Mark A. Abare *(Treas)*

Vertec Polymers, Inc.   (2)
6880 Wynnwood Ln, Houston, TX 77008
Tel.: (832) 618-1500
Web Site: http://www.vertecpolymers.com
Sales Range: $1-9.9 Million
Emp.: 14
Plastics Material & Resin Mfr
N.A.I.C.S.: 325211
Shawn Smith *(Pres)*

Fiber Materials, Inc.   (1)
5 Morin St, Biddeford, ME 04005
Tel.: (207) 282-5911

Web Site: http://www.fibermaterialsinc.com
High Temperature & Composite Materials
Mfr
N.A.I.C.S.: 335991
Michael Lee (CFO)

Unit (Domestic):

Intermat (2)
389 Hill St, Biddeford, ME
04005-4335 (100%)
Tel.: (207) 283-1156
Wrestling Mat Mfr
N.A.I.C.S.: 339999

Haematologic Technologies, LLC (1)
57 River Rd Unit 1021, Essex Junction, VT
05452
Tel.: (802) 878-1777
Web Site: https://www.goprolytix.com
Medical Laboratories
N.A.I.C.S.: 621511
David Sunseri (Pres & CEO)
John Strokis (VP-Quality)
John Moriariyh (VP-Bus Dev)
Matthew Kuhlmeier (Dir-Facilities & IT)

Luxium Solutions, LLC (1)
17900 Great Lakes Pwy, Hiram, OH 44234
Tel.: (440) 834-5600
Web Site: https://luxiumsolutions.com
Radiation Detection, Baggage Scanning &
Other Navigation Instrument Mfr & Distr
N.A.I.C.S.: 334511

Subsidiary (Domestic):

Inrad Optics, Inc. (2)
181 Legrand Ave, Northvale, NJ 07647
Tel.: (201) 767-1910
Web Site: https://www.inradoptics.com
Rev.: $10,631,032
Assets: $9,098,939
Liabilities: $5,431,147
Net Worth: $3,667,792
Earnings: $152,575
Emp.: 59
Fiscal Year-end: 12/31/2022
Optical Components & Laser System De-
vices & Instrumentation
N.A.I.C.S.: 333310
Thomas Caughey (VP-R&D)
Amy Eskilson (Pres & CEO)
George Murray (VP-Sls & Mktg)
Theresa A. Balog (CFO, Treas & Sec)

Division (Domestic):

Inrad Optics, Inc. (3)
6455 Parkland Dr, Sarasota, FL 34243
Tel.: (941) 753-8707
Web Site: http://www.inradoptics.com
Optical Components & Laser System De-
vices & Instrumentation
N.A.I.C.S.: 333310

Subsidiary (Domestic):

Plx, Inc. (2)
40 W Jefryn Blvd, Deer Park, NY 11729
Tel.: (631) 586-4190
Web Site: http://www.plxinc.com
Sales Range: $1-9.9 Million
Emp.: 34
Optical Instruments And Lenses
N.A.I.C.S.: 333310
Jack Lipkins (Pres)
Irina Shats (Engr-Opto Mechanical Design)
Itai Vishnia (CEO)

Naprotek, Inc. (1)
2945 San Ysidro Way, Santa Clara, CA
95051
Tel.: (408) 830-5000
Web Site: http://www.naprotek.com
Sales Range: $1-9.9 Million
Emp.: 65
Mfg Printed Circuit Boards
N.A.I.C.S.: 334418
Najat Badriyeh (CEO)
Fida Shahal Mustafa (Mgr-Matl Control)
Arlis Greco (Mgr-Quality)
Elizabeth Davidson (VP-Sls & Mktg)
Yin Chen (Mgr-Engrg Mfg)
James Lim (Dir-Quality)

Subsidiary (Domestic):

Microfab, Inc. (2)
180 Zachary Rd, Manchester, NH 03109
Tel.: (603) 621-9522

Web Site: http://www.microfabnh.com
Rev.: $1,416,000
Emp.: 6
Radio & Television Broadcasting & Wireless
Communications Equipment Mfr
N.A.I.C.S.: 334220
Wayne M. Stauss (Pres)

PD Holdings, LLC (1)
2629 S Hanley Rd, Saint Louis, MO
63144-2503 (100%)
Tel.: (314) 968-2376
Web Site: http://www.particledynamics.com
Sales Range: $10-24.9 Million
Emp.: 90
Develops & Globally Markets Specialty In-
gredient Product Lines for the Pharmaceuti-
cal Nutritional Personal-Care & Food Indus-
try Mfr
N.A.I.C.S.: 325412
Jeff Dorries (CFO)

EDGEWATER COMMERCIAL CONSTRUCTION, INC.
10200 Clarence St, Panama City, FL
32417
Tel.: (850) 234-7252
Web Site:
http://www.beachcontractors.com
Rev.: $14,100,000
Emp.: 3
New Multifamily Housing Construction
N.A.I.C.S.: 236116
J. David Harris (Pres)
Wesley L. Burnham (Treas & Sec)
J. Wallace Nall Jr. (VP)

EDGEWATER CONSTRUCTION SERVICES,LLC
123 Bruton Ct Ste 100, Chesapeake,
VA 23322
Tel.: (757) 410-3166
Web Site:
https://www.edgewaterconst.com
Year Founded: 2006
Sales Range: $1-9.9 Million
Emp.: 8
Construction Services
N.A.I.C.S.: 236220
James Collins (Pres)
Richard Marano (VP)

EDGEWATER SERVICES, LLC
900 N Michigan Ave Ste 1800, Chi-
cago, IL 60611
Tel.: (312) 649-5666
Web Site:
http://www.edgewaterfunds.com
Privater Equity Firm
N.A.I.C.S.: 523999
James A. Gordon (Founder & Mng
Partner)
Gregory K. Jones (Partner)
David M. Tolmie (Partner)
Jeffrey M. Frient (Partner)
Scott Meadow (Assoc Partner)
Stephen Natali (Partner)
Brian Peiser (Partner)
Gerald Saltarelli (Partner)

Subsidiaries:

Action Products Marketing Corp. (1)
1779 Chessie Ln, Ottawa, IL 61350
Tel.: (515) 276-9610
Web Site: https://www.waterlinerenewal.com
Emp.: 8
Manhole Rehabilitation Services
N.A.I.C.S.: 238990
Keith Walker (Dir-Global Brands)

Apex Parks Group, LLC (1)
27061 Aliso Creek Rd Ste 100, Aliso Viejo,
CA 92656
Tel.: (949) 349-8474
Web Site: http://www.apexparksgroup.com
Amusement Park Operator
N.A.I.C.S.: 713110
Gregg Borman (Sr VP-Ops)
Ken Kobane (VP-Bus Dev)
John Fitzgerald (CEO)
Tyler Zachem (Chm)
Al Weber Jr. (Pres)

Subsidiary (Domestic):

Martin's Fantasy Island (2)
2400 Grand Is Blvd, Grand Island, NY
14072-3198
Tel.: (716) 773-7591
Web Site:
http://www.martinsfantasyisland.com
Amusement & Theme Parks
N.A.I.C.S.: 713110
Martin Dipietro (Pres)

Haystax Technology, Inc. (1)
6475 Camden Ave Ste 203, San Jose, CA
95120
Tel.: (408) 757-5163
Web Site:
http://www.haystaxtechnology.com
Defense, Intelligence & Commercial Tech-
nology Services
N.A.I.C.S.: 518210
Peter Pace (Chm)
Aaron Shilts (Exec VP-Customer Success)
Pete Shah (COO)
Sasi Mudigonda (Sr VP-Product)

Subsidiary (Domestic):

Digital Sandbox, Inc. (2)
8260 Greensboro Dr, McLean, VA 22102
Tel.: (571) 297-3800
Web Site: http://www.dsbox.com
Sales Range: $10-24.9 Million
Emp.: 23
Custom Computer Programming Services
N.A.I.C.S.: 541511

NetCentrics Corp. (2)
205 Van Buren St Ste 420, Herndon, VA
20170
Tel.: (703) 714-7345
Web Site: http://www.haystax.com
Sales Range: $1-9.9 Million
Emp.: 45
Information Technology Support & Software
Development Services
N.A.I.C.S.: 541512
Bob Dougherty (Founder & Vice Chm)
Jeffrey Phillips (VP-Mktg)
Peter Pace (Chm)
John Dillon (Sr VP-Bus Dev)
Kenny Cushing (CEO)
Teena Lavu (Sr VP-Delivery-IT & Cyberse-
curity Svcs)
Alec Newell (VP-Bus Dev)

National Inspection & Consultants,
LLC (1)
9911 Bavaria Rd, Fort Myers, FL 33913
Tel.: (239) 939-4313
Web Site: https://www.nicinc.com
Inspection & Consulting Services for Engi-
neering & Construction Industries
N.A.I.C.S.: 541690
Robert A. Vigne (Pres)
David J. Vigne (VP)
Richard U. Vigne (Mgr-NDE Svcs)
Floyd Bennett (Project Mgr-Field Svcs)
Russel E. Jones (Mgr-Advanced NDT)
Bernard P. Komara (Mgr-Trng & Quality
Svcs)
John C. Shields (Mgr-Recruiting)
Michael Vigne (Project Mgr-Field Svcs)
John W. Buschman Jr. (Project Mgr-Field
Svcs)

Steel & O'Brien Manufacturing,
Inc. (1)
7196 Route 98, Arcade, NY 14009
Tel.: (585) 492-5800
Web Site: http://www.steelobrien.com
Sales Range: $1-9.9 Million
Emp.: 56
Valves And Pipe Fittings, Nec
N.A.I.C.S.: 332919
Bryan Wells (Pres)
Kelly Allard (Treas)
Scott Wells (VP)
Pete Beyette (Gen Mgr)

Subsidiary (Domestic):

Top Line Process Equipment
Company (2)
21 Vly Hunt Dr, Lewis Run, PA 16738
Tel.: (814) 362-4626
Web Site: http://www.toplineonline.com
Sales Range: $10-24.9 Million
Emp.: 33

Supplier of Hygienic Stainless Steel Pro-
cess Equipment
N.A.I.C.S.: 423830
Kevin O'Donald (Pres)

EDGEWATER SYSTEMS FOR BALANCED LIVING
1100 W 6th Ave, Gary, IN 46402-
1711
Tel.: (219) 885-4264   IN
Web Site:
http://www.edgewatersystems.org
Year Founded: 1998
Sales Range: $10-24.9 Million
Emp.: 258
Behavioral Healthcare Services
N.A.I.C.S.: 621420
Danita Johnson Hughes (Pres &
CEO)
Michael LaBroi (CIO)
Arlene Pearson (Chief HR Officer)
Eric Davidson (CFO)

EDGEWEBHOSTING INC.
120 E Baltimore St Ste 1900, Balti-
more, MD 21202
Tel.: (410) 246-8800
Web Site:
http://www.edgewebhosting.net
Year Founded: 1999
Sales Range: $1-9.9 Million
Emp.: 30
Managed Web Hosting Services
N.A.I.C.S.: 541618
Vlad Friedman (CEO & Owner)
Michael Altman (COO)

EDGEWOOD CENTER FOR CHILDREN AND FAMILIES
1801 Vicente St, San Francisco, CA
94116
Tel.: (415) 681-3211   CA
Web Site: https://www.edgewood.org
Year Founded: 1851
Sales Range: $10-24,9 Million
Emp.: 501
Behavioral Healthcare Services
N.A.I.C.S.: 623220
Robin Randall (Dir-Medical)
Lynn Dolce (CEO)

EDGEWOOD COMPANIES
PO Box 2249, Stateline, NV 89449
Tel.: (775) 588-3400   NV
Web Site:
https://edgewoodcompanies.com
Year Founded: 1958
Emp.: 35
Holding Company; Real Estate Prop-
erties
N.A.I.C.S.: 551112
Chuck Scharer (Pres & CEO)
John J. McLaughlin (CFO)
Lynda Ribaudo (Dir-Fin)
Jan Garcia (Mgr-HR)

EDGEWOOD LIFECARE COM-MUNITY
575 Osgood St, North Andover, MA
01845-1975
Tel.: (978) 725-3300   MA
Web Site:
https://www.edgewoodrc.com
Year Founded: 1993
Sales Range: $10-24.9 Million
Emp.: 475
Continuing Care Retirement Commu-
nity Operator
N.A.I.C.S.: 623311
Jane Sullivan (CFO)
Marlene Rotering (Pres & CEO)
Natalie MacBrien (Chief Health Offi-
cer)

EDGEWOOD MOBILE HOMES INC.

Edgewood Mobile Homes Inc.—(Continued)

275 Happy Hollow Rd, Williamsburg, KY 40769
Tel.: (606) 549-5223
Web Site:
https://www.edgewoodhomes.com
Rev.: $10,600,000
Emp.: 15
Mobile Home Dealers
N.A.I.C.S.: 459930
Jason Gambrell *(Mgr)*

EDGEWOOD PROPERTIES INC.
1260 Stelton Rd, Piscataway, NJ 08854
Tel.: (732) 985-1900
Web Site:
https://www.edgewoodproperty.com
Year Founded: 1992
Rev.: $16,500,000
Emp.: 80
Subdividers & Real Estate Developers
N.A.I.C.S.: 237210
Sheryl Weingarten *(VP)*
Jack Morris *(CEO)*
Douglas Flynn *(CFO)*

EDGEWOOD VILLAGE MARKET INC.
2200 Cabot Blvd W Ste 3, Langhorne, PA 19047-1842
Tel.: (215) 752-9440
Web Site: http://www.mccaffreys.com
Rev.: $29,029,652
Emp.: 160
Independent Supermarket
N.A.I.C.S.: 424490
Fred Brohm *(COO)*
James J. McCaffrey III *(Pres & CEO)*
Jim McCaffrey IV *(Exec VP)*

EDI HEALTH GROUP
17701 Cowan Ave Ste 250, Irvine, CA 92614
Tel.: (949) 852-0825
Web Site:
https://www.dentalxchange.com
Sales Range: $10-24.9 Million
Emp.: 48
Internet Host Services
N.A.I.C.S.: 517810
Scott Wellwood *(Pres)*

EDIBLE ARRANGEMENTS INTERNATIONAL, INC.
95 Barnes Rd, Wallingford, CT 06492
Tel.: (203) 774-8000
Web Site:
http://www.ediblearrangements.com
Year Founded: 1999
Sales Range: $100-124.9 Million
Emp.: 100
Fresh Fruit, Specialty Foods & Gifts
N.A.I.C.S.: 459930
Tariq Farid *(Founder & CEO)*
Robert Price *(Pres)*
Anthony Pavese *(Pres-Edible Global, LLC.)*
Kaitlin Reiss *(CMO)*
John Merkin *(COO)*
Cindy Mockler *(VP-Innovation)*

EDIBLES REX
5555 Conner Ave Ste 1058, Detroit, MI 48213
Tel.: (313) 922-3000
Web Site:
https://www.ediblesrex.com
Year Founded: 1993
Sales Range: $1-9.9 Million
Emp.: 80
Full Service Catering & Wholesale Food Services Company
N.A.I.C.S.: 722320

Karen Rachwal *(CFO)*
Liz Bakunovich *(Mgr-Sls & Mktg)*

EDIFECS, INC.
2600 116th Ave NE Ste 200, Bellevue, WA 98004
Tel.: (425) 452-0630   WA
Web Site: http://www.edifecs.com
Year Founded: 1996
Sales Range: $10-24.9 Million
Emp.: 250
Software Devolepment
N.A.I.C.S.: 541511
Sunny Singh *(CEO)*
Kevin Adams *(CTO)*
Gregg Prothero *(Dir-Market Dev)*
Ty Harper *(Gen Counsel)*
Ruby Raley *(Sr Dir-Market Dev)*
Jay Majmudar *(Sr VP)*
Venkat Kavarthapu *(VP-Client Svcs)*
Sumeet Bhatia *(VP-Solutions Consulting)*
Vik Sachdev *(VP-Trading Platform Solutions)*

Subsidiaries:

Health Fidelity, Inc.   (1)
325 Sharon Park Dr Ste 730, Menlo Park, CA 94025-6805
Tel.: (650) 727-3300
Web Site: http://www.healthfidelity.com
Software Publisher
N.A.I.C.S.: 513210
Daniel J. Riskin *(Co-Founder & CEO)*
Steve Whitehurst *(CEO)*

Talix, Inc.   (1)
660 3rd St 3rd Fl, San Francisco, CA 94107
Tel.: (628) 220-3885
Web Site: http://www.talix.com
Sales Range: $1-9.9 Million
Emp.: 200
Software Development Services
N.A.I.C.S.: 541511
Dean Stephens *(CEO)*
Niraj Katwala *(CTO)*
Ashmi Shah *(CFO)*
Jonathan Reese *(VP-Mktg)*
Bob Hetchler *(Sr VP-Sls)*

EDIFICE, INC.
1401 W Morehead St, Charlotte, NC 28208
Tel.: (704) 332-0900
Web Site: http://edificeinc.com
Sales Range: $50-74.9 Million
Emp.: 75
Nonresidential Construction Services
N.A.I.C.S.: 236220
Bryan R. Knupp *(Sr VP)*
Eric Laster *(Pres)*
Jennifer Geis *(Controller)*
Tod Creech *(CFO)*
Gary W. Creed *(COO)*
Vicki Barton *(VP-Marketing-Communications)*

EDIFY MULTIMEDIA GROUP LLC
16 Technology Way, Nashua, NH 03060
Tel.: (603) 943-5308
Web Site:
https://www.edifymultimedia.com
Motion Picture & Video Production
N.A.I.C.S.: 512110
Eric Frank *(Dir-Bus Dev)*
Dale Ouellette *(Dir-Online Media)*
Dave Mackey *(Dir-Creative Svcs)*

Subsidiaries:

Captured Light Studio Inc.   (1)
16 Technology Way, Nashua, NH 03060
Tel.: (603) 355-2010
Web Site: http://www.caplight.com
Rev.: $1,570,000
Emp.: 5
Motion Picture & Video Production
N.A.I.C.S.: 512110

John Snowdon *(Founder)*
Peter Kambol *(Pres)*

EDIMENSIONAL, INC.
2885 Jupiter Park Dr Ste 1200, Jupiter, FL 33458
Tel.: (561) 833-2199   MD
Web Site:
http://www.edimensional.com
Year Founded: 2000
Sales Range: $25-49.9 Million
Emp.: 10
Develops & Sells Virtual Reality
Video Gaming Accessories
N.A.I.C.S.: 423430
Michael Epstein *(Founder & CEO)*

EDIS COMPANY
110 S Poplar St Ste 400, Wilmington, DE 19801-5053
Tel.: (302) 421-5700
Web Site:
http://www.ediscompany.com
Commercial & Institutional Building Construction
N.A.I.C.S.: 236220
Brian Disabatino *(Pres & CEO)*
Melissa Rysak *(Dir-Mktg & Bus Dev Support)*

EDISON BANCSHARES, INC.
13000 S Cleveland Ave, Fort Myers, FL 33907
Tel.: (239) 466-1800
Web Site:
http://www.edisonnationalbank.com
Bank Holding Company
N.A.I.C.S.: 551111
Geoffrey W. Roepstorff *(CEO)*
Robbie B. Roepstorff *(Pres)*

Subsidiaries:

Edison National Bank   (1)
13000 S Cleveland Ave, Fort Myers, FL 33907
Tel.: (239) 466-1800
Web Site:
http://www.edisonnationalbank.com
Rev.: $6,454,000
Assets: $239,583,000
Liabilities: $220,363,000
Net Worth: $19,220,000
Earnings: $1,041,000
Emp.: 41
Fiscal Year-end: 12/31/2013
Banking Services
N.A.I.C.S.: 522110
Geoffrey W. Roepstorff *(Co-Founder & CEO)*
David M. DuVall *(Co-Founder & Chm)*
Daniel E. Dosoretz *(Co-Founder)*
Robbie B. Roepstorff *(Co-Founder & Pres)*
Karen Brazelton *(VP-Loan Ops)*
Patrick Philbin *(CFO & Exec VP)*
Lenor Mason *(Sr VP & Dir-Info Sys)*
Susan Nasworthy *(Sr VP)*

EDISON CHOUEST OFFSHORE, LLC
16201 E Main St, Cut Off, LA 70345-3804
Tel.: (985) 601-4444
Web Site: https://www.chouest.com
Year Founded: 1960
Sales Range: $50-74.9 Million
Emp.: 1,000
Offshore Vessel Services
N.A.I.C.S.: 488320
Roger White *(Mgr-Mktg)*
Rick Fox *(Sr VP & Gen Mgr-Ops-Alaska)*
Charlie Comeaux *(CFO)*
Jonathan Stephenson *(Coord-Logistics)*
Allen Cefalu *(Chief Engr)*
Adrian Danos *(Controller)*
Luke Newman *(Controller)*
Corey Louviere *(Coord-Logistics)*
Jason Gros *(Coord-Ops)*

Danica Braud *(Mgr-HR)*
Corinne Bourg *(Mgr-Insurance)*
Peter Dieter Jansen *(Project Mgr-Special)*
Shane Chiasson *(Coord-QHSE)*

EDISON ELECTRIC INSTITUTE
701 Pennsylvania Ave NW, Washington, DC 20004-2696
Tel.: (202) 508-5000
Web Site: http://www.eei.org
Year Founded: 1933
Sales Range: $75-99.9 Million
Emp.: 200
Electric Utility Association
N.A.I.C.S.: 813910
Brian Farrell *(Dir-Member Rels)*
Lynn J. Good *(Chm)*
Jim Owen *(Exec Dir-Member Rels & Meeting Svcs)*
Quinlan J. Shea *(VP-Environment)*
Brian L. Wolff *(Exec VP-Pub Policy & External Affairs)*
Lawrence E. Jones *(VP-Intl Programs)*
John S. Schlenker *(CFO & Treas)*
Mary D. Miller *(Chief Admin Officer)*
Richard S. Tempchin *(Exec Dir-Retail Energy Svcs)*
Kathryn A. Steckelberg *(VP-Govt Rels)*
Emily Sanford Fisher *(Sec & VP-Legal)*
Scott Aaronson *(VP-Security & Preparedness)*
Stephanie Voyda *(VP-Comm)*
Lisa Wood *(VP-Customer Solutions)*
Philip D. Moeller *(Exec VP-Regulatory Affairs & Bus Ops Grp)*
Gregory E. Abel *(Vice Chm)*
Richard F. McMahon Jr. *(VP-Energy Supply & Fin)*

EDISON LITHOGRAPHING & PRINTING CORP.
3725 Tonnelle Ave, North Bergen, NJ 07047
Tel.: (201) 902-9191
Web Site:
https://www.printingnews.com
Sales Range: $10-24.9 Million
Emp.: 50
Commercial Printing Services
N.A.I.C.S.: 323111
Bill Matzen *(Mgr-Sls-Reg)*
Evan Novick *(Acct Exec)*
Joseph Ostreicher *(COO)*
Karen Nebesky *(Sr Acct Mgr)*
Roger Morel *(Mgr-Production)*
Susan Ostreicher *(Comptroller)*
George Gross *(Pres & CEO)*

Subsidiaries:

Compass Display Group, Inc.   (1)
3130 Moon Station Rd, Kennesaw, GA 30144
Tel.: (404) 367-9100
Web Site: http://www.compassdisplay.com
Sales Range: $1-9.9 Million
Emp.: 20
Point of Sale Display Designer & Mfr
N.A.I.C.S.: 323111
Preston Howard *(Mgr-Production)*
Mark Terry *(VP)*

EDISON MEDIA RESEARCH
6 W Cliff St, Somerville, NJ 08876
Tel.: (908) 707-4707
Web Site:
http://www.edisonresearch.com
Year Founded: 1994
Sales Range: $10-24.9 Million
Emp.: 26
Market Research Services
N.A.I.C.S.: 541910
Larry Rosin *(Co-Founder & Pres)*
Rob Farbman *(Sr VP)*
Melissa DeCesare *(VP)*

Sean Ross *(VP-Music & Program-ming)*
Tom Webster *(VP-Strategy & Mktg)*

EDISON PROPERTIES, LLC

100 Washington St, Newark, NJ 07102-3095
Tel.: (973) 643-7700   NJ
Web Site: https://www.parkfast.com
Year Founded: 1955
Sales Range: $75-99.9 Million
Emp.: 1,500
Parking Company; Mini Storage; Building Management
N.A.I.C.S.: 812930
Jerome Gottesman *(Chm)*
Stephen Nislick *(CEO)*
Antonio Pinto *(Controller)*
Archie Gottesman, *(Exec VP)*

Subsidiaries:

Janeway Properties, Inc.   (1)
100 Washington St, Newark, NJ 07102-3024
Tel.: (973) 643-2884
Web Site: http://www.edisonproperties.com
Real Estate Services
N.A.I.C.S.: 531390

Manhattan Mini Storage   (1)
520 8th Ave 19th Fl, New York, NY 10018-6507
Tel.: (347) 846-2421
Web Site:
    http://www.manhattanministorage.com
Sales Range: $10-24.9 Million
Emp.: 15
Storage Company
N.A.I.C.S.: 493110
Brian Harvey *(Dir-HR)*
Roosevelt Shelby *(Gen Mgr)*

Park Fast of Maryland   (1)
100 West Fayette St, Baltimore, MD 21201-3708
Tel.: (410) 659-7621
Sales Range: $10-24.9 Million
Emp.: 40
Properties Holding Coompany
N.A.I.C.S.: 812930

EDISON VENTURE PARTNERS LLC

281 Witherspoon St, Princeton, NJ 08540
Tel.: (609) 896-1900   DE
Web Site:
    http://www.edisonpartners.com
Year Founded: 1986
Emp.: 20
Equity Invesment & Advisory Firm
N.A.I.C.S.: 523999
Chris Sugden *(Mng Partner)*
Joe Allegra *(Gen Partner)*
Michael Kopelman *(Gen Partner)*
Ryan Ziegler *(Gen Partner)*
Kelly Ford *(COO)*
Lenard Marcus *(Gen Partner)*
Sever Totia *(Partner)*
Tom Vander Schaaff *(Gen Partner)*
John Martinson *(Founder)*
David Nevas *(Principal)*
Chris Sklarin *(VP)*
Joseph D. Giquinto *(CFO)*
Gregg Michaelson *(Gen Partner)*
Kelly Ford Buckley *(CMO & Partner)*
James Hill *(VP)*
Jennifer Lee *(Partner)*
Doba Parushev *(VP)*
Christopher Clark *(Partner)*
Daniel Herscovici *(Partner)*
Jay Naik *(Partner-Operating)*
Gary P. Golding *(Gen Partner)*
Gary P. Golding *(Gen Partner)*

EDISTO ELECTRIC COOPERA-TIVE

896 Calhoun St, Bamberg, SC 29003
Tel.: (803) 245-5141

Web Site:
    http://www.edistoelectric.com
Sales Range: $25-49.9 Million
Emp.: 70
Distribution, Electric Power
N.A.I.C.S.: 221122
David E. Felkel *(Pres & CEO)*

EDITEK, INC.

10907 Middlegate Dr, Fairfax, VA 22032
Tel.: (703) 652-9495
Web Site: https://www.editek.com
Sales Range: $1-9.9 Million
Graphic Arts Software Services
N.A.I.C.S.: 513210

EDLOGICAL GROUP CORP.

111 W Ocean Blvd 4th Fl, Long Beach, CA 90802
Tel.: (424) 247-5530
Web Site: http://www.edlogical.com
Year Founded: 2011
Sales Range: $1-9.9 Million
Emp.: 48
Educational Support Services
N.A.I.C.S.: 611710
Hector Valentin *(Chief Bus Officer)*

EDLONG CORPORATION

225 Scott St, Elk Grove Village, IL 60007-1299
Tel.: (847) 631-6700
Web Site: https://www.edlong.com
Sales Range: $10-24.9 Million
Emp.: 65
Extracts, Flavoring
N.A.I.C.S.: 311942
Rick Schultz *(VP-R&D)*
Laurette Rondenet-Smith *(Pres & CEO)*

EDLUND COMPANY, INC.

159 Industrial Pkwy, Burlington, VT 05401-5437
Tel.: (802) 862-9661   VT
Web Site: http://www.edlundco.com
Year Founded: 1926
Sales Range: $75-99.9 Million
Emp.: 100
Mfr of Can Openers & Can Opening Systems, Scales & Stainless Steel Food Service Equipment
N.A.I.C.S.: 332216
Mary Jennings *(Controller)*
Steve Tallent *(Dir-Sls-Western Reg)*

EDM AMERICAS

301 Fayetteville St Ste 1500, Raleigh, NC 27601   NC
Web Site:
    http://www.edmamericas.com
Year Founded: 1982
Sales Range: $50-74.9 Million
Emp.: 507
Information Technology Consulting Services
N.A.I.C.S.: 541511
Scott A. Byers *(Pres & CEO)*
Arun Singh *(COO & VP-Ops-Global)*
Jimmy Eyerman *(CFO)*
Leo Malsky *(Sr VP-Records Information Mgmt)*
Matthew Schmitt *(Dir-Svc Delivery-Enterprise Solutions)*
Steven C. Krasicky *(Sr Dir-Enterprise Solutions)*
Antoine Acklin *(Dir-Tech Solutions)*
Michael J. Soluri *(Chief Revenue Officer & VP)*

EDMAR CLEANING CORP.

50-05 47th Ave, Woodside, NY 11377
Tel.: (718) 779-7900
Web Site:
    http://www.edmarclean.com

Year Founded: 1972
Sales Range: $10-24.9 Million
Emp.: 60
Janitorial & Sanitary Equipment Distr
N.A.I.C.S.: 423850
Jeff Tokofsky *(VP-Bus Dev)*
Joan Heins *(Office Mgr)*
Al Hart *(Dir-Sls)*

EDMARK GMC PONTIAC BUICK, INC.

15700 Idaho Center Blvd, Nampa, ID 83687
Tel.: (208) 466-6000
Web Site:
    http://www.edmarknampa.com
Sales Range: $10-24.9 Million
Emp.: 100
New Car Dealers
N.A.I.C.S.: 441110
Bill Dougherty *(Gen Mgr)*
Preston Worley *(Mgr-Sls)*
Chris Wolf *(Mgr-Sls)*
Norm Puga *(Mgr-Sls)*
Mike Betts *(Mgr-Sls)*
Craig Harris *(Mgr-Svc Drive)*
Mike Simpson *(Mgr-Fleet)*
Chad Stevens *(Mgr-Svc)*

EDMONTON BANCSHARES INC.

118 S Main St, Edmonton, KY 42129
Tel.: (270) 432-3231
Web Site:
    http://www.edmontonstatebank.com
Year Founded: 1937
Sales Range: $25-49.9 Million
Emp.: 130
State Commercial Banks: Holding Company
N.A.I.C.S.: 522110
John D. Thompson *(Chm & CEO)*
David Thompson *(Pres & CFO)*

Subsidiaries:

Edmonton State Bank   (1)
118 S Main St, Edmonton, KY 42129
Tel.: (270) 432-3231
Web Site:
    http://www.edmontonstatebank.com
Rev.: $6,500,000
Emp.: 45
State Commercial Banks
N.A.I.C.S.: 522110
Andrea Gentry *(Pres-Community-Barren)*
Daniel Johnson *(VP)*
David Thompson *(Pres)*

Subsidiary (Domestic):

Sumner Bank & Trust   (2)
780 Browns Ln, Gallatin, TN 37066
Tel.: (615) 451-4151
Web Site:
    http://www.sumnerbankandtrust.com
Retail & Commercial Banking Services
N.A.I.C.S.: 522110
Ronnie Fox *(Chm)*
Keith Hatley *(Pres & CEO)*
Bonita Spiegl *(CFO & COO)*
Charlie Hooks *(Chief Credit Officer)*
Suk Lowman *(Dir-HR)*

EDMUND INDUSTRIAL OPTICS INC.

101 E Gloucester Pike, Barrington, NJ 08007-1380
Tel.: (856) 547-3488   NJ
Web Site:
    https://www.edmundoptics.com
Year Founded: 1942
Sales Range: $75-99.9 Million
Emp.: 1,000
Mfr & Distr of Industrial Optics & Lens Related Products
N.A.I.C.S.: 333310
Samuel Sadoulet *(Pres & COO)*
Jeremy Chang *(Exec VP-Asian Ops)*

Subsidiaries:

Edmund Optics   (1)
601 Montgomery Ave, Pennsburg, PA 18073-1515   (100%)
Tel.: (215) 679-6272
Web Site: http://www.edmundoptics.com
Precision Optical Components Mfr
N.A.I.C.S.: 333310
Kristen Bjork-Jones *(Dir-Global Mktg & Comm)*
Samuel Sadoulet *(CEO)*
Vincent Thong *(Exec Dir-Global Customer Projects)*
Agnes Huebscher *(Dir-Mktg-Europe)*
Marisa Edmund *(Exec VP-Sls & Mktg)*
Daisuke Arai *(Mgr-Mktg)*
Jeremy Chang *(Exec VP-Asian Ops)*
Johnson Chang *(Mgr-Sls)*
John Cleather *(Mng Dir-UK)*
Gregg Fales *(Sr Mgr-Product Line)*
Gregory Hollows *(Dir-Imaging Bus Unit)*
Jason Mulliner *(CFO)*
Joonho Rhee *(Mgr-Sls)*
Susan Tunney *(Sr Dir-Global HR)*
James Fisher *(Sr VP-Corp Dev)*

Edmund Optics China Co. Ltd.   (1)
5/F Block 3 Luck-King Scientific & Industrial Park Industry East Road, Longhua, Shenzhen, 518109, China
Tel.: (86) 755 2967 5435
Web Site: http://www.edmundoptics.com
Sales Range: $10-24.9 Million
Emp.: 72
Optical Instrument, Lens Mfr & Distr
N.A.I.C.S.: 333310
Jeremy Chang *(Exec VP-Ops-Asian)*

Edmund Optics GmbH   (1)
Zur Giesserei 8, 76227, Karlsruhe, Germany
Tel.: (49) 721 6273730
Optical Instrument & Lens Mfr
N.A.I.C.S.: 333310
Helge Vogt *(Mng Dir)*

Edmund Optics Japan Ltd.   (1)
3 & 4F Hakusan-Asanomi Bldg 5-36-9 Hakusan, Bunkyo-ku, Tokyo, 112-0001, Japan
Tel.: (81) 3 5800 4751
Web Site: http://www.edmundoptics.jp
Optical Instrument & Lens Mfr
N.A.I.C.S.: 333310
Tim Kennedy *(Mgr)*

Edmund Optics Korea Ltd.   (1)
606 Taeyang Bld 22 Yeouidaebang-ro 67-gil, Yeongdeungpo-gu, Seoul, Korea (South)
Tel.: (82) 2 365 9222
Web Site: http://www.edmundoptics.com
Optical Instrument & Lens Mfr
N.A.I.C.S.: 333310

Edmund Optics Ltd.   (1)
Unit 1 Opus Avenue Nether Poppleton, York, YO26 6BL, United Kingdom
Tel.: (44) 1904 788 600
Web Site: http://www.edmundoptics.com
Sales Range: $10-24.9 Million
Emp.: 16
Optical Instrument & Lens Mfr
N.A.I.C.S.: 333310
Marisa Edmund *(Chm)*
Alexis Liagre *(Sls Dir-Europe, Middle East & Africa)*

Edmund Optics Singapore Pte. Ltd.   (1)
18 Woodlands Loop 04-00, Singapore, 738100, Singapore
Tel.: (65) 6273 6644
Web Site: http://www.edmundoptics.com.sg
Emp.: 200
Optical Instrument & Lens Mfr
N.A.I.C.S.: 333310
Samuel Sadoulet *(Pres & COO)*
Robert M. Edmund *(Chm & CEO)*
Marisa Edmund *(CMO)*
Jeremy Chang *(Exec VP-Ops-Asia)*

EDMUND KIM INTERNA-TIONAL INC.

18737 S Reyes Ave, Compton, CA 90221
Tel.: (310) 604-1100   CA
Web Site: http://www.ekii.com

Edmund Kim International Inc.—(Continued)

Year Founded: 1997
Sales Range: $10-24.9 Million
Emp.: 100
Holding Company; Mfr of Apparel &
Textiles
N.A.I.C.S.: 315210
Edmund Kim *(Pres & CEO)*
Lynn Sunjara *(Mgr-Admin)*
Claudia Chavez *(Acct Mgr)*

Subsidiaries:

Edmund Kim Productions Group **(1)**
18737 S Reyes Ave, Rancho Dominguez,
CA 90220 **(100%)**
Tel.: (310) 604-1100
Web Site: http://www.eki.com
Sales Range: $10-24.9 Million
Emp.: 25
Producers of Commercial Lithographic
Printing
N.A.I.C.S.: 315250

Pacific Continental Textile, Inc. **(1)**
18737 S Reyes Ave, Compton, CA 90221-
5609
Tel.: (310) 604-1100
Finishers of Cotton Broadwoven Fabrics
N.A.I.C.S.: 313310
Edmund Kim *(CEO)*

Pacific Continental Textiles, Inc. Ap-
parel Division (PCT-A) **(1)**
18737 S Reyes Ave, Rancho Dominguez,
CA 90221 **(10%)**
Tel.: (310) 886-1989
Web Site: http://www.ekii.com
Sales Range: $10-24.9 Million
Emp.: 20
Mfr of Mens & Boys Clothing & Textiles
N.A.I.C.S.: 315250
Matt Nasab *(Exec Dir-Mktg)*

**EDMUNDS MANUFACTURING
COMPANY**
45 Spring Ln, Farmington, CT 06032
Tel.: (860) 677-2813
Web Site:
    https://www.edmundsgages.com
Sales Range: $10-24.9 Million
Emp.: 53
Measuring & Controlling Devices
N.A.I.C.S.: 334519
Jack Gaughan *(VP-Sls & Mktg)*
Richard Mierzejewski *(Mgr-Engrg-
Applications)*
Robert F. Edmunds Jr. *(Pres)*

EDMUNDS, INC.
2401 Colorado Ave, Santa Monica,
CA 90404
Tel.: (310) 309-6300 **CA**
Web Site: http://www.edmunds.com
Year Founded: 1966
Sales Range: $25-49.9 Million
Emp.: 370
New & Used Car Online Information
Services
N.A.I.C.S.: 513140
Avi Steinlauf *(CEO)*
Bryn MacKinnon *(Mgr)*
Seth Berkowitz *(Pres)*
Mark Rankin *(VP-Dealer Platform
Dev)*
Sven Wood *(VP-Brand & Product
Mktg)*
George Kang *(Sr VP-OEM Bus)*
Kelly Hellwig *(Mng Editor)*
Philip Potloff *(Chief Digital Officer)*
Stephen Felisan *(CTO)*
Laura Perlman *(VP-Corp Strategy)*
Katti Ehoff Fields *(VP-Product Dev &
Dealer Ops)*
Stephen Gandee *(VP-Product & De-
sign)*
Nick Gorton *(VP-Product Innovation)*
Julie Merges *(Chief People Officer)*
Allen Ollis *(CFO)*
Eugene Park *(Chief Product Officer)*

Karim Qazi *(VP-Ad Tech Platform &
Ops)*
Alistair Weaver *(Editor-in-Chief & VP-
Editorial)*
Leah Polk *(Sr Mgr-PR)*

**EDNEY DISTRIBUTING COM-
PANY**
1895 Hwy 14 E, Huron, SD 57350
Web Site: https://www.edneyco.com
Sales Range: $10-24.9 Million
Emp.: 20
Agricultural Machinery & Equipment
N.A.I.C.S.: 423820
W. Douglas Edney *(Pres)*

**EDON CONSTRUCTION COM-
PANY, INC.**
5420 W 122nd St, Alsip, IL 60803-
3149
Tel.: (708) 597-1820
Web Site:
    https://www.edonconstruction.com
Sales Range: $10-24.9 Million
Emp.: 165
Carpentry Services
N.A.I.C.S.: 238350
Kathleen A. Connelly *(Pres)*

**EDON FARMERS COOPERA-
TIVE ASSOCIATION**
205 S Michigan St, Edon, OH 43518
Tel.: (419) 272-2121
Web Site:
    https://www.edonfarmerscoop.com
Emp.: 40
Grain & Agricultural Terminal Opera-
tions
N.A.I.C.S.: 424510
Rick Dunbar *(Pres, Gen Mgr & CEO)*
Bob Walz *(Chm)*
Mark P. Trausch *(Vice Chm)*
Keith Crowl *(Sec)*

EDPA USA, INC.
Empire State Bldg 350 5th Ave Ste
5310, New York, NY 10118
Tel.: (212) 714-0644
Real Estate Development Services
N.A.I.C.S.: 531390

EDPO, LLC
10 S Wacker Dr Ste 3325, Chicago,
IL 60606
Tel.: (312) 254-5965
Web Site: https://www.edplp.net
Propane & Light Fuels Retailer
N.A.I.C.S.: 424720
Thomas E. Knauff *(CEO)*
David R. Stroupe *(VP-Corp Dev)*
Boyd McGathey *(COO)*

Subsidiaries:

Dassels Petroleum Inc. **(1)**
31 Wright Rd, Hollister, CA 95023
Tel.: (831) 636-5100
Web Site: http://www.dassels.com
Oil & Gas Distribution Services
N.A.I.C.S.: 424720
Pete Carpenedo *(Mgr-Safety, Trng & Code
Compliance)*

Van Unen / Miersma Propane,
Inc. **(1)**
20504 S 99 Frontage Rd, Ripon, CA 95366
Tel.: (209) 823-1315
Web Site: http://www.vmpropane.com
Sales Range: $1-9.9 Million
Emp.: 18
Petroleum & Petroleum Products Merchant
Whslr (except Bulk Stations & Terminals)
N.A.I.C.S.: 424720
Richard V. Unen *(Pres)*

EDS MANUFACTURING INC.
765 N Target Range Rd, Nogales, AZ
85621
Tel.: (520) 287-9711

Web Site:
    https://www.edsmanufacturing.com
Sales Range: $10-24.9 Million
Emp.: 7
Harness Assemblies, Mfr
N.A.I.C.S.: 334419
Luis Moreno *(Pres)*
Gracie Ayala *(CFO & VP)*

EDSA
1512 E Broward Blvd Ste 110, Fort
Lauderdale, FL 33301-2126
Tel.: (954) 524-3330 **DE**
Web Site: https://www.edsaplan.com
Year Founded: 1960
Emp.: 200
Landscape Architectural Services
N.A.I.C.S.: 541320
Gregg Sutton *(Principal)*
Jill Martinez *(Exec VP-Mktg)*
Ryan Clifton *(Principal)*
Doug Smith *(Pres & Principal)*

EDSIM LEATHER CO. INC.
131 W 35th St, New York, NY 10001
Tel.: (212) 695-8500
Web Site: https://www.edsim.com
Rev.: $26,000,000
Emp.: 12
Leather Tanning & Finishing
N.A.I.C.S.: 316110
Simone Kamali *(Pres)*

EDSINC.
15300 Commerce Dr N Ste 200,
Dearborn, MI 48120
Tel.: (313) 271-2660
Web Site:
    https://www.edsisolutions.com
Sales Range: $25-49.9 Million
Emp.: 385
Workforce Development & Consulting
Services
N.A.I.C.S.: 611430
Jim Bitterle *(Mng Partner-Consulting)*
Kevin Schnieders *(CEO)*

**EDUCATED DESIGN & DEVEL-
OPMENT, INC.**
901 Sheldon Dr, Cary, NC 27513
Tel.: (919) 469-9434
Web Site:
    https://www.productsafet.com
Year Founded: 1988
Rev.: $4,400,000
Emp.: 31
Instrument Measuring, Testing Elec-
tricity & Electrical Signals Mfr
N.A.I.C.S.: 334515
William S. Bisenius *(Pres)*
Dave Bisenius *(VP)*

EDUCATION CONNECTION
355 Goshen Rd, Litchfield, CT 06759
Tel.: (860) 567-0863 **CT**
Web Site:
    http://www.educationconnection.org
Year Founded: 1972
Sales Range: $10-24.9 Million
Emp.: 1,026
Educational Support Services
N.A.I.C.S.: 611710
JodiLynn Binkley *(Dir-Community
Svcs)*
Danuta Thibodeau *(Exec Dir)*
John Kissko *(VP)*
Melissa Miller *(Treas)*
Deb Bell *(Sec)*
Chris Sanders *(Pres)*
Rob Parenti *(Dir-Bus Ops & Special
Svcs)*
Holli Labarbera *(Dir-Food Svcs)*
Laurene Pesce *(Dir-HR)*
Bert Hughes *(Mgr-Transportation)*
Juleen Flanigan *(Dir-Early Childhood
Svcs)*

Kathi Bleacher *(Dir-Head Start &
Early Head Start)*
Tracey Lay *(Dir-School Age Pro-
grams)*
Jonathan P. Costa Sr. *(Dir-School &
Program Svcs)*

**EDUCATION CORPORATION
OF AMERICA**
3660 Grandview Pkwy Ste 300, Bir-
mingham, AL 35243
Tel.: (205) 329-7900 **DE**
Web Site:
    http://www.ecacolleges.com
Holding Company; Colleges & Voca-
tional Schools Owner & Operator
N.A.I.C.S.: 551112
Avy H. Stein *(Chm)*
Christopher Boehm *(CFO & Exec VP-
Corp Dev)*
Roger L. Swartzwelder *(Chief Compli-
ance Officer, Gen Counsel & Exec
VP)*
Stu Reed *(Pres & CEO)*
Geoffrey Baird *(Pres-Emerging
Brands-Grp)*
Ryan Brewer *(Sr VP-Fin Ops & Con-
troller)*
Paula Frey *(Chief HR Officer & Exec
VP)*
Chris Gorrie *(Pres-Ecotech Institute-
Denver)*
Tom Mikkelson *(CIO & Sr VP)*
Erin Shea *(Chief Student Officer)*
Thomas A. Moore Jr. *(Vice Chm)*

Subsidiaries:

Brightwood Career Institute **(1)**
933 Penn Ave, Pittsburgh, PA 15222
Tel.: (412) 338-4770
Web Site: http://www.brightwoodcareer.edu
Computer & Medical Education
N.A.I.C.S.: 611410

**EDUCATION DEVELOPMENT
CENTER INC.**
43 Foundry Ave, Waltham, MA 02453
Tel.: (617) 969-7100 **DE**
Web Site: https://www.edc.org
Year Founded: 1958
Sales Range: $25-49.9 Million
Emp.: 600
Commercial Nonphysical Research
Services
N.A.I.C.S.: 541720
Vivian Guilfoy *(Sr VP)*
Michael Laflin *(Sr VP)*
Lydia O'Donnell *(Sr VP & Dir-Health
& Human Dev)*
Jerry Reed *(VP-Health & Human
Dev)*
Christine Filosa *(Gen Counsel, VP &
Dir-Office-Legal Affairs)*
Barbara Miller *(VP)*
Cheryl Hoffman-Bray *(CFO & VP)*
Doryn Davis Chervin *(VP)*
Nancy Devine *(Sr VP)*
Robert Spielvogel *(CTO & VP)*
Siobhan Murphy *(Sr VP)*
Stephen Anzalone *(Sr VP)*
Thomas Rielly *(VP & Dir-Ops &
Comm)*

EDUCATION FIRST
2803 Executive Park Dr, Weston, FL
33331
Tel.: (786) 545-7010
Web Site:
    http://www.educationfirstinc.com
Sales Range: $1-9.9 Million
Emp.: 62
Bilingual Early-Childhood Education
Programs
N.A.I.C.S.: 923110

Ana Maria Fernandez *(CEO)*
Alexandra Munera *(Dir-Tour)*

EDUCATION GROWTH LLC

One Landmark Square 21st Fl, Stamford, CT 06901
Tel.: (203) 658-8100
Web Site: http://www.edgrowth.com
Year Founded: 2005
Privater Equity Firm
N.A.I.C.S.: 523999
Andrew E. Kaplan *(Mng Partner)*
Peter J. Campbell *(Mng Partner)*
Brian Nairn *(Partner)*
Jose Wehnes *(Operating Partner)*

EDUCATION PIONEERS

360 22nd St Ste 220, Oakland, CA 94612
Tel.: (510) 893-4374   CA
Web Site:
    http://www.educationpioneers.org
Year Founded: 2003
Sales Range: $10-24.9 Million
Emp.: 229
Educational Support Services
N.A.I.C.S.: 611710
Frances McLaughlin *(Pres)*
Deanna Harnett *(Chief Admin Officer)*
Scott Morgan *(Founder)*
Gale Mondry *(Chm)*
Cantor Fitzgerald *(Vice Pres & Asst Gen Counsel)*
Melissa Wu *(CEO-Boston)*
Gerald Fanion III *(Dir-Tennessee)*

EDUCATION SERVICE CENTER REGION 12

2101 W Loop 340, Waco, TX 76712
Tel.: (254) 297-1212   TX
Web Site: http://www.esc12.net
Year Founded: 1969
Sales Range: $10-24.9 Million
Emp.: 267
Educational Support Services
N.A.I.C.S.: 611710
Jerry Maze *(Exec Dir)*
Angela Matthews *(CTO)*

EDUCATION SERVICE CENTER REGION II

209 N Water St, Corpus Christi, TX 78401
Tel.: (361) 561-8400   TX
Year Founded: 1967
Sales Range: $10-24.9 Million
Emp.: 130
Educational Support Services
N.A.I.C.S.: 611710
Richard Alvarado *(Exec Dir)*
Jeffrey R. Johnston *(CFO)*
Linda Villarreal *(Exec Dir)*
Leo Villarreal *(Vice Chm)*
Naida Soliz *(Sec)*
Ricardo Ramirez *(Chm)*

EDUCATION TECHNOLOGY PARTNERS

17 Maryhill Dr, Saint Louis, MO 63124
Tel.: (314) 432-0222
Web Site:
    http://www.edtechpartners.com
Year Founded: 2003
Sales Range: $1-9.9 Million
Emp.: 15
Technology, Software & Professional Development Services to K-12 Educators
N.A.I.C.S.: 923110
Randy Jennings *(Founder & Pres)*

EDUCATION-PLUS, INC.

6389 Tall Pines Rd, Coeur d'Alene, ID 83814

Tel.: (208) 664-6253   PA
Web Site:
    http://www.educationplushealth.com
Year Founded: 1982
Rev.: $1,308,378
Assets: $582,762
Liabilities: $334,192
Net Worth: $248,570
Earnings: ($71,375)
Emp.: 15
Fiscal Year-end: 12/31/14
Community Health & Educational Support Services
N.A.I.C.S.: 621498
David Castro *(Sec)*
Julie Cousler Emig *(Exec Dir)*
Mary Schuler *(Pres-Idaho)*
Sarah Rosenberg *(Treas)*
Wendy-Anne Roberts-Johnson *(Chm)*

EDUCATIONAL COMMISSION FOR FOREIGN MEDICAL GRADUATES

3624 Market St, Philadelphia, PA 19104-2685
Tel.: (215) 386-5900
Web Site: https://www.ecfmg.org
Rev.: $45,325,539
Emp.: 80
Business Consulting Services
N.A.I.C.S.: 541611
Gerald P. Whelan *(Dir-Acculturation Program)*
Emmanuel Cassimatis *(CEO & Pres)*

EDUCATIONAL COMMUNITY CREDIT UNION

1551 S 9th St, Kalamazoo, MI 49009
Tel.: (269) 375-6702   MI
Web Site: http://www.eccu1.org
Year Founded: 1935
Sales Range: $10-24.9 Million
Emp.: 156
Credit Union
N.A.I.C.S.: 522130
Christine Camp *(VP-Mktg)*
Earle Shelner *(VP-Fin)*
Arthur Parker *(Treas)*
David Aubry *(Chm)*

EDUCATIONAL CREDIT MANAGEMENT CO.

1011 South Washington Ste 1400, Oakdale, MN 55401
Tel.: (651) 221-0566   MN
Web Site: http://www.ecmc.org
Year Founded: 1994
Sales Range: $10-24.9 Million
Emp.: 160
Provider of Credit Services
N.A.I.C.S.: 522299

EDUCATIONAL DATA SYSTEMS, INC.

15300 Commerce Dr N Ste 200, Dearborn, MI 48120
Tel.: (313) 271-2660
Web Site:
    http://www.edsincorporated.com
Year Founded: 1979
Sales Range: $25-49.9 Million
Emp.: 397
Consulting Services
N.A.I.C.S.: 541620

EDUCATIONAL DEVELOPERS, INC.

9801 Westheim Rd Ste 302, Houston, TX 77042
Tel.: (281) 759-6774   TX
Year Founded: 2000
Sales Range: $10-24.9 Million
Educational Support Services
N.A.I.C.S.: 611710
Sylvester Heereman *(Pres)*
Eduardo Vigneaux *(Treas)*

Michael Ryan *(VP)*
Joseph Burtka *(VP)*
Jaime Rodriguez *(Sec)*

EDUCATIONAL EMPLOYEES CREDIT UNION

222 W Shaw Ave, Fresno, CA 93711
Tel.: (559) 437-7700   CA
Web Site: http://www.myeecu.org
Year Founded: 1934
Sales Range: $75-99.9 Million
Emp.: 446
Credit Union Operator
N.A.I.C.S.: 522130
Paul Hokokian *(Sec)*
Frank V. Powell *(Chm)*
Derek F. Scharton *(Vice Chm)*
David A. Roberts *(Treas)*

EDUCATIONAL FUNDING OF THE SOUTH

298 Seven Oakes Dr NW, Knoxville, TN 37922
Tel.: (865) 691-5626
Web Site: http://www.edfinancial.com
Sales Range: $75-99.9 Million
Emp.: 120
Personal Credit Institutions
N.A.I.C.S.: 522291
William Anthony Hollin *(Chm)*

EDUCATIONAL HOUSING SERVICES

55 Clark St, Brooklyn, NY 11201
Tel.: (212) 977-7622   NY
Web Site:
    https://www.studenthousing.org
Year Founded: 1987
Sales Range: $25-49.9 Million
Emp.: 154
Community Housing Services
N.A.I.C.S.: 624229
Faye Bean *(Sr VP-Leasing & Mktg)*
Joseph La Vacca *(Treas)*
Ariel Dybner *(Gen Counsel, Sec & Sr VP)*
Ramalingam Ganesh *(CFO & Sr VP)*
Jeffrey H. Lynford *(Pres & CEO)*

EDUCATIONAL MEDIA FOUNDATION

5700 W Oaks Blvd, Rocklin, CA 95765
Tel.: (916) 251-1600   CA
Web Site:
    http://www.emfbroadcasting.com
Sales Range: $25-49.9 Million
Emp.: 300
Radio Broadcasting Services
N.A.I.C.S.: 516110
David Atkinson *(COO)*
Sam Wallington *(VP-Ops & Engrg)*
Jim Houser *(Chief Content Officer)*
Janet Cherry *(Chief People Officer)*
David Pierce *(Chief Media Officer)*
Christopher Barron *(CIO)*
Shaine Grieshaber *(Gen Counsel)*
Mike McCall *(Chief Engagement Officer)*
Kris Miller *(VP-People & Org Dev)*
Bill Corbin *(VP-Pastoral Care)*
Todd Woods *(CEO)*
Donna Ecton *(Chm)*
Matt Reynolds *(CFO)*
Bethany Davis *(Sr VP-Comm & Mktg Ops)*

EDUCATIONAL OUTFITTERS, LLC

8002 East Brainerd Rd, Chattanooga, TN 37421
Tel.: (423) 499-5052
Web Site:
    http://www.educationaloutfitters.com
Sales Range: $1-9.9 Million

Emp.: 75
School Uniforms & Apparel Retailer
N.A.I.C.S.: 458110
Brian Elrod *(Co-Owner & Pres)*
Jamey Lee Elrod *(Co-Owner & Co-Founder)*

EDUCATIONAL SERVICES OF AMERICA

1321 Murfreesboro Pike Ste 702, Nashville, TN 37217
Tel.: (615) 361-4000
Web Site: http://www.esa-education.com
Year Founded: 2000
Sales Range: $75-99.9 Million
Emp.: 1,500
Elementary & Secondary Schools
N.A.I.C.S.: 611110
Allison O'Neill *(COO-Ombudsman Educational Svcs)*
Gail Debiec *(COO-Spectrum Center Schools & Programs)*
Alan D. Watson *(CIO & Exec VP)*
Karen LeFever *(Chief Dev Officer & Exec VP)*
Donald B. Whitfield *(CFO & Exec VP)*
Cate Lewandowski *(CMO & Exec VP)*
Shirley Hanback *(Exec VP-HR)*
John McLaughlin *(Exec VP & Dir-Res & Analytics)*
Mark Claypool *(Pres & CEO)*
Kevin Mitchell *(Sr VP-Fin)*

EDUCATIONAL TELEVISION ASSOCIATION

1375 Euclid Ave, Cleveland, OH 44115-1835
Tel.: (216) 916-6100
Web Site: https://www.ideastream.org
Year Founded: 1965
Sales Range: $10-24.9 Million
Emp.: 100
Educational Television Broadcasting Stations
N.A.I.C.S.: 516120
Nancy Tatulinski *(Sr Engr)*
David Kanzeg *(Dir-Programming)*
Dan Shellenbarger *(Exec Dir-OGT)*
John Ramicone *(Dir-Distance Learning)*
Kathryn P. Jensen *(COO)*
Linda J. Williams *(Sr Dir-Educational Svcs)*
Kim MacDonald *(Dir-HR)*

EDUCATIONAL TESTING SERVICE INC.

660 Rosedale Rd, Princeton, NJ 08541-0001
Tel.: (609) 921-9000   NJ
Web Site: http://www.ets.org
Year Founded: 1947
Educational Testing & Consulting Services
N.A.I.C.S.: 611710
Jack Hayon *(CFO & Sr VP)*
Ida Lawrence *(Sr VP-R&D)*
David Hunt *(COO & Exec VP)*
Glenn Schroeder *(Sr VP-Strategy, Mktg & Growth)*
Diane Bailey *(Sr VP-Product & Delivery)*
David Hobson *(VP & Sec)*
Andreas Oranje *(VP-Assessment & Learning Tech Dev)*
Wallace Dalrymple *(Chief Security Officer)*
Amit Sevak *(Pres & CEO)*
Michelle Froah *(CMO-Global)*

Subsidiaries:

PSI Services LLC   (1)
611 N Brand Blvd 10 Fl, Glendale, CA 91203
Tel.: (818) 847-6180

Educational Testing Service Inc.—(Continued)

Web Site:
http://www.corporate.psionline.com
Pre-Employment Testing Services
N.A.I.C.S.: 561311
Stephen Tapp (CEO)
Peter Celeste (Pres)

Subsidiary (Domestic):

Caliper Corporation　　　　　　　(2)
500 Alexander Park Ste 200, Princeton, NJ
08540
Tel.: (609) 524-1200
Web Site: http://www.calipercorp.com
Sales Range: $10-24.9 Million
Emp.: 100
Management Consulting Services
N.A.I.C.S.: 541612
James Harmon (CFO)
Amy Yates-Wuelsing (VP-Mktg)
Mark Greenberg (CEO)
Greg Sidler (COO)
John Maketa (Chief Revenue Officer)

Computer Assisted Testing Service,
Inc.　　　　　　　　　　　　　　(2)
1801 Murchison Dr Ste 288, Burlingame,
CA 94010
Tel.: (650) 259-8550
Web Site: http://www.catstest.com
Sales Range: $1-9.9 Million
Emp.: 18
Computer-Based Knowledge Examinations
N.A.I.C.S.: 611710
Mark Dennehy (Pres & CEO)

Software Secure Inc.　　　　　　(2)
90 Oak St, Newton Upper Falls, MA 02464
Tel.: (617) 340-6381
Web Site: http://www.softwaresecure.com
Sales Range: $1-9.9 Million
Emp.: 12
Software Publisher
N.A.I.C.S.: 513210
Allison Sands (Dir-Mktg)
Douglas M. Winneg (Founder & CEO)
Steve Lesser (VP-Sls & Mktg)
Shmuel Cohen (CTO)
Ed Brown (VP-IT & Support)
Michael Malicia (Dir-Svcs)

Prometric LLC　　　　　　　　　(1)
1501 S Clinton St, Baltimore, MD 21224
Tel.: (443) 455-8000
Web Site: http://www.prometric.com
Sales Range: $300-349.9 Million
Emp.: 200
Technology Based Testing & Assessment
Services
N.A.I.C.S.: 611710
Paul Forrester (Sr VP-Test Dev Svcs)
Kewin Gales (Sr VP-HR)
Ramesh Nava (Sr VP & Gen Mgr-Intl)
Michael P. Sawicki (Gen Counsel & Sr VP)
Sean Burke (Chief Client Officer & Sr VP)
Roy Simrell (Pres & CEO)
Brooke Smith (CMO & Sr VP)
Oliver Chang (CTO)

Subsidiary (Domestic):

Schroeder Measurement Technolo-
gies, Inc.　　　　　　　　　　　(2)
25400 US Hwy 19 N, Clearwater, FL 33763
Tel.: (727) 738-8727
Web Site: http://home.smttest.com
Administrative Management & General
Management Consulting Service
N.A.I.C.S.: 541611
Lee Schroeder (Founder & Pres)

Questar Assessment, Inc.　　　　(1)
5550 Upper 147th St W, Apple Valley, MN
55124　　　　　　　　　　　　(100%)
Tel.: (952) 997-0422
Web Site: http://www.questarai.com
Educational Reading Assessment Tests
Publisher
N.A.I.C.S.: 611710
Brad Baumgartner (COO)
Jason Hake (CFO & Exec VP-Fin & Ops)
Cheryl Hilinski (Chief Performance Officer)
Jim McMann (VP-Ops)
Nate Ober (CTO)
Katie McClarty (Chief Assessment Officer)
Stephen Lazer (Pres & CEO)
Brendan Kealey (CIO)
Jenn Dunn (VP-Psychometrics & Research)

Michele Walker (VP-Education Svcs)
Peter Bloomquist (VP-Tech Delivery)
Morgan Henry (Controller)

The Chauncey Group International
Ltd.　　　　　　　　　　　　　(1)
660 Rosedale Rd, Princeton, NJ
08541　　　　　　　　　　　　(100%)
Tel.: (609) 921-3600
Web Site: http://www.chauncey.com
Sales Range: $10-24.9 Million
Emp.: 130
Educational Consulting
N.A.I.C.S.: 611710

EDUCATIONWORKS
684 Whitehead Rd, Lawrenceville, NJ
08648
Tel.: (609) 392-6662　　　　　NJ
Web Site:
http://www.educationworks-
online.org
Year Founded: 2001
Sales Range: $10-24.9 Million
Emp.: 613
Educational Support Services
N.A.I.C.S.: 611710
Kim Alexander (Dir-HR)
Stan Retif (Dir-Mktg & Dev)
Tanya Ruley-Mayo (COO)

EDUCAUSE
282 Century Pl Ste 5000, Louisville,
CO 80027
Tel.: (303) 449-4430
Web Site: http://www.educause.edu
Rev.: $13,638,126
Emp.: 58
Higher Education Information Tech-
nology Services
N.A.I.C.S.: 513130
Gregory Dobbin (Project Mgr)
Nancy Hays (Mgr-Publ)
Stacy Ruwe (CFO)
Bill Hogue (Treas)
John O'Brien (Pres & CEO)
Tracy Schroeder (Vice Chm)
Bruce Maas (Chm)

EDUCERE, LLC
Ambler Plaza 12 E Butler Ave Ste
100, Ambler, PA 19002
Tel.: (215) 283-0380
Web Site: http://www.educere.net
Year Founded: 2002
Sales Range: $1-9.9 Million
Emp.: 20
Online Curriculum & Courses for
Teachers & Students
N.A.I.C.S.: 923110
James Daily (Pres)
Angela Williams (Mgr-Mktg)

EDUCURIOUS PARTNERS
2825 Eastlake Ave E Ste 210, Se-
attle, WA 98102
Tel.: (206) 402-4489　　　　WA
Web Site: http://www.educurious.org
Year Founded: 2010
Rev.: $39,830
Assets: $240,292
Liabilities: $1,205
Net Worth: $239,087
Earnings: ($748,335)
Emp.: 10
Fiscal Year-end: 06/30/14
Learning Resource Provider
N.A.I.C.S.: 519210
Sasha Gourevitch (Program Mgr-
Expert Network)
Leigh Perks (Dir-Project)
Michael Golden (Founder, CEO &
Partner)
Stephen Arnold (Chm)

EDUPOINT EDUCATIONAL
SYSTEMS, LLC

101 Pacifica Ste 240, Irvine, CA
92618-7343
Tel.: (949) 458-0900
Web Site: https://www.edupoint.com
Year Founded: 1997
Sales Range: $10-24.9 Million
Emp.: 200
Educational Software
N.A.I.C.S.: 449210
Robert E. Weathers (Founder &
CEO)
Thomas McGrew (CTO & Exec VP)
Rob Wilson (Pres, COO & Chief In-
novation Officer)
Robert Weathers (Founder & CEO)
Joe Zello (VP-Admin, IT, Technical
Svcs, and Special Education & VP-
Fin & Admin-Special Education Appli-
cations)
Christine Moss (CMO-Sls)
Rob Wilson (Pres & Chief Innovation
Officer)
Tom McGrew (CTO & Exec VP)
Deborah Adolphs (VP-Project Mgmt &
Implementation Svcs)
Joe Zello (VP-Fin & Admin-Special
Education Applications)
Justin Berg (VP)
Mike Lehrack (VP-Instructional Appli-
cations)
Noam Luft (VP-Product Dev)
Christine Moss (CMO-Sls & Chief Sls
& Mktg Officer)

EDUTAINMENTLIVE, LLC
7525 NW 4th Blvd, Gainesville, FL
32607
Tel.: (352) 600-6900
Web Site: http://www.itpro.tv
Year Founded: 2013
Sales Range: $1-9.9 Million
Emp.: 68
Educational Support Services
N.A.I.C.S.: 611710
Tim Broom (Co-Founder & CEO)
Don Pezet (Co-Founder & CIO)
Barry Pruett (Chief Comml Officer)
Denise Broom (CFO)
Phillip Ford (VP-People & Culture)

EDVANTAGES
7416 N Main St Ste A, Dayton, OH
45415
Tel.: (937) 854-6665　　　　OH
Year Founded: 2002
Sales Range: $10-24.9 Million
Emp.: 365
Educational Support Services
N.A.I.C.S.: 611710
Kevin Kirby (Chm)
Clinton Satow (COO)
Robert Pinkerton-Littlejohn (Treas)
Myrrha Pammer-Satow (CEO)

EDVISORS NETWORK, INC.
1250 Hancock St Suite 703N,
Quincy, MA 02169
Tel.: (617) 328-1565
Web Site: http://www.edvisors.com
Year Founded: 1998
Sales Range: $1-9.9 Million
Emp.: 26
Online Education Programs & Direc-
tory Services
N.A.I.C.S.: 923110
Geoffrey Willison (Pres)
Joe Kakaty (CEO)

EDWARD APFFEL CO
12115 Pacific Ave, Santa Fe Springs,
CA 90670-2989
Tel.: (562) 309-0400
Web Site: https://www.apffels.com
Rev.: $20,500,000
Emp.: 50
Coffee, Green Or Roasted

N.A.I.C.S.: 424490
Alvin A. Apffel (Pres)

EDWARD B. HOWLIN INC.
10085 Dunkirk Way, Dunkirk, MD
20754
Tel.: (301) 855-8900
Web Site:
http://www.howlinconcrete.com
Rev.: $14,600,000
Emp.: 43
Ready Mixed Concrete
N.A.I.C.S.: 327320
Edward B. Howlin Jr. (Chm & CEO)

EDWARD B. O'REILLY & AS-
SOCIATES, INC.
30 W Highland Ave, Philadelphia, PA
19118
Tel.: (215) 242-8100
Web Site: https://www.eboreilly.com
Year Founded: 1961
Sales Range: $10-24.9 Million
Emp.: 98
Plumbing, Heating & Air-Conditioning
Services
N.A.I.C.S.: 238220
Richard J. Suffredini (Mgr-Sls)
Lawrence J. Boersig (Head-Engrg
Dept)
Henry F. O'Reilly III (Pres)
Add B. Anderson III (Mgr-Sls & Svcs)

EDWARD C. LEVY CO.
9300 Dix Ave, Dearborn, MI 48120
Tel.: (313) 429-2200　　　　MI
Web Site: https://www.edwclevy.com
Year Founded: 1918
Sales Range: $400-449.9 Million
Emp.: 2,100
Slag Aggregates, Asphalt Mixtures,
Ready-Mix Concrete, Sand & Gravel
& Crushed Stones Mfr; Steel Mill Pro-
cessing Services
N.A.I.C.S.: 327320
Andrew Wilson (CEO)

EDWARD EHRBAR INC.
Ste 155 4 Executive Plz, Yonkers, NY
10701-6803
Tel.: (914) 738-5100
Web Site: http://www.ehrbar.com
Year Founded: 1968
Sales Range: $10-24.9 Million
Emp.: 60
Provider of Construction & Mining
Machinery Supply Services
N.A.I.C.S.: 423810
Patrick Ahern (Pres)
Anthony Olivieri (Branch Mgr)
Edward Ahern (Mgr-IT)
Stephen Schiavetta (Mgr-Sls)
Lawrence McCrann (VP-Sls)
Gina Serratore (Asst Controller)
Vince Altomare (CFO)
Michael Mayo (Mgr-Corp Svc)
Harvey Levine (Mgr-Fin & Credit)
Hank Ruttura (Mgr-Holbrook)
Gerry Dieterich (Mgr-Parts Inventory)
John Barbuto (Mgr-Parts-Columbus)
Deborah Kelly (Mgr-Sls Office)

EDWARD H. WOLF & SONS
INC.
501 Kettle Moraine Dr S, Slinger, WI
53086-9550
Tel.: (262) 644-5030　　　　WI
Web Site: https://www.ehwolf.com
Year Founded: 1976
Sales Range: $10-24.9 Million
Emp.: 41
Petroleum Bulk Stations & Terminals
N.A.I.C.S.: 424710
Steve Kreuser (CFO)

Subsidiaries:

Edward H. Wolf & Sons Inc. (1)
1121 McDonald St, Green Bay, WI 54303
Tel.: (920) 432-7711
Web Site: http://www.ehwolf.com
Emp.: 20
Petroleum Bulk Stations
N.A.I.C.S.: 424710

Zurbuchen Oil, Inc. (1)
309 Bruce St, Verona, WI 53593
Tel.: (608) 845-6989
Sales Range: $1-9.9 Million
Emp.: 12
Petroleum Bulk Stations & Terminals
N.A.I.C.S.: 424710
Barth Zurbuchen (Pres & Treas)

EDWARD HOSPITAL & HEALTH SERVICES

801 S Washington St, Naperville, IL 60540
Tel.: (630) 527-3000
Web Site: https://www.eehealth.org
Year Founded: 1987
Sales Range: $25-49.9 Million
Emp.: 1,500
General Hospital Management & Related Activities
N.A.I.C.S.: 713940

Subsidiaries:

Edward Health Ventures (1)
801 S Washington St, Naperville, IL 60540
Tel.: (630) 355-0450
Web Site: http://www.edward.org
Venture Capital Company
N.A.I.C.S.: 523910
Bill Kottmann (Pres & CEO)

Edward Hospital Inc. (1)
801 S Washington St, Naperville, IL 60540
Tel.: (630) 527-3200
Web Site: http://www.edward.org
General Medical & Surgical Hospital Services
N.A.I.C.S.: 622110
Pamela Davis (Pres & CEO)

EDWARD J. QUIGLEY ASSOCIATES

114 Bradford Ln Ste 100, Lansdale, PA 19446
Tel.: (215) 699-1127 PA
Year Founded: 1980
Sales Range: $10-24.9 Million
Emp.: 5
Advertising Agencies, Full Service
N.A.I.C.S.: 541810
Ed Quigley (Pres)
Judith Kirkland (Dir-Creative)
Kathy Todd (Dir-Art)

EDWARD KRAEMER & SONS INC.

1 Plainview Rd, Plain, WI 53577-0220
Tel.: (608) 546-2311 WI
Web Site: http://www.edkraemer.com
Year Founded: 1911
Sales Range: $125-149.9 Million
Emp.: 500
Provider of Construction Services
N.A.I.C.S.: 237310
Scott W. Peterson (Pres & CEO)
Brenna Mann (Gen Counsel)
Fred Lueck (COO)

EDWARD LESKE CO.

960 Monroe St, Union, NJ 07083
Tel.: (908) 686-7272
Web Site:
  https://www.edwardleske.com
Year Founded: 1950
Sales Range: $10-24.9 Million
Emp.: 100
Industrial Building Construction Services
N.A.I.C.S.: 236210

Frank Del Guercio (Pres & Gen Mgr)

EDWARD LOWE FOUNDATION

58220 Decatur Rd, Cassopolis, MI 49031
Tel.: (269) 445-4200
Web Site:
  https://www.edwardlowe.org
Sales Range: $50-74.9 Million
Emp.: 50
Non Profit Small Business Investments
N.A.I.C.S.: 523999
Susan Zimmer (Controller)

EDWARD M. KENNEDY COMMUNITY HEALTH CENTER, INC.

2000 Century Dr, Worcester, MA 01606
Tel.: (508) 854-2122 MA
Web Site: http://www.kennedychc.org
Year Founded: 1972
Sales Range: $25-49.9 Million
Emp.: 430
Healtcare Services
N.A.I.C.S.: 622110
Valerie Zolezzi-Wyndham (Chm)
Pablo Hernandez (Chief Medical Officer)

EDWARD R. JAMES PARTNERS, LLC

2550 Waukegan Rd Ste 220, Glenview, IL 60025-1777
Tel.: (847) 724-8200 IL
Web Site: https://www.erjames.com
Year Founded: 1949
Sales Range: $75-99.9 Million
Emp.: 10
Real Estate Investment & Development Services
N.A.I.C.S.: 531390
Edward R. James (Chm)
Jerry S. James (Pres)

EDWARD ROSE COMPANY

30057 Orchard Lake Rd Ste 100, Farmington Hills, MI 48334
Tel.: (248) 539-2255 MI
Web Site:
  http://www.roseresidents.com
Year Founded: 1921
Holding Company; Multi-Family Housing Owner, Developer, Construction & Property Management Services
N.A.I.C.S.: 551112
Sheldon Rose (Pres)

Subsidiaries:

Edward Rose & Sons, LLC (1)
30057 Orchard Lake Rd Ste 100, Farmington Hills, MI 48334
Tel.: (248) 539-2255
Web Site: http://www.edwardrose.com
Multi-Family Housing Real Estate Development, Construction & Property Management Services
N.A.I.C.S.: 531110
Sheldon Rose (Pres)

Subsidiary (Domestic):

Edward Rose Building Company (2)
38525 Woodward Ave, Bloomfield Hills, MI 48303-2012
Tel.: (248) 686-5300
Web Site: http://www.edwardrose.com
Sales Range: $25-49.9 Million
Emp.: 70
Apartment Building Operative Builder
N.A.I.C.S.: 236117

EDWARD THOMAS TRADING COMPANY

200 E Briggs Ave Ste A, Fairfield, IA 52556-2925
Tel.: (641) 469-3810

Web Site:
  http://www.edwardthomas.com
Year Founded: 1993
Sales Range: $10-24.9 Million
Emp.: 6
Commodity Contracts Brokerage Services
N.A.I.C.S.: 523160
Tammy Davis (Office Mgr)
Edward Gomes (Owner)

EDWARD W. SCOTT ELECTRIC CO.

1150 25th St, San Francisco, CA 94107
Tel.: (415) 206-7120
Rev.: $45,000,000
Emp.: 12
General Electrical Contractor
N.A.I.C.S.: 238210
Ilene Lynch (VP)
Larry McGill (Project Mgr)

EDWARD'S OIL CO. INC.

820 Hoover Rd N, Virginia, MN 55792-2353
Tel.: (218) 741-9634 MN
Year Founded: 1969
Sales Range: $25-49.9 Million
Emp.: 200
Petroleum Bulk Station Services
N.A.I.C.S.: 424710
Bob Skalko (VP)

EDWARDS BROTHERS, INC.

5949 Jackson Rd, Ann Arbor, MI 48103
Tel.: (734) 769-1000 MI
Web Site:
  http://www.edwardsbrothers.com
Year Founded: 1893
Sales Range: $150-199.9 Million
Emp.: 775
Mfr of Books & Journals
N.A.I.C.S.: 323117
James Mulady (Controller)

Subsidiaries:

Edwards Brothers - Carolina (1)
800 Edwards Dr, Lillington, NC 27546 (100%)
Tel.: (910) 893-2717
Web Site: http://www.edwardbrothers.com
Sales Range: $25-49.9 Million
Emp.: 275
Books & Journals
N.A.I.C.S.: 323117
John Wilton (Mgr-Mfg)

EDWARDS BUSINESS MACHINES INC.

2240 City Line Rd, Bethlehem, PA 18017
Tel.: (610) 266-0200 PA
Web Site:
  https://www.edwardsbusiness.com
Year Founded: 1954
Sales Range: $10-24.9 Million
Emp.: 150
Office Supplies
N.A.I.C.S.: 423420
James B. Edwards (Chm)
Raymond Fuentes (Pres)

EDWARDS CAPITAL, LLC

676 N Michigan Ave Ste 3300, Chicago, IL 60611
Tel.: (312) 327-4520 IL
Web Site:
  http://www.flexpointford.com
Year Founded: 2005
Privater Equity Firm
N.A.I.C.S.: 523999
Stephen H. Haworth (CFO)
Christopher J. Ackerman (Mng Dir)
Perry O. Ballard (Mng Dir)
Ethan A. Budin (Mng Dir)

Charles E. Glew (Mng Dir)
Jonathan T. Oka (Mng Dir)
Donald J. Edwards (CEO)
Steven L. Begleiter (Mng Dir)
Michael S. Fazekas (Principal)
Daniel Edelman (Mng Dir)
Steven Michienzi (Principal)
Missy A. Loudenback (Chief Acctg Officer)
Alex Saporito (Mng Dir)
Dominic A. Hood (Principal)
Mark A. Kelly (Principal)

Subsidiaries:

AFH Financial Group plc (1)
AFH House Buntsford Drive, Stoke Heath, Bromsgrove, B60 4JE, Worcestershire, United Kingdom
Tel.: (44) 1527577775
Web Site: http://www.afhwm.co.uk
Financial Holding Company
N.A.I.C.S.: 551112
Alan Hudson (CEO)
Paul Wright (CFO & Fin Dir)
Austin Broad (Head-Advice)
Barry Willis (Sls Dir)
Becky Hadley (Head-People & Dev)
Chris Handshaw (Head-Adviser Rels)
Dawn Walker-Bennett (Head-Bus Dev)
Jon Sturgess (Controller-Grp Fin)
Khalid Rehman (Mgr-Advice Assurance)
Leonid Nji (Head-Res)
Michael Easton (Head-Investment Ops)
Michelle Lavoipierre (Mgr-Admin Support)
Sascha Kimmel (Head-Mktg)
Simon Goode (Mgr-IT)

Subsidiary (Domestic):

Eunisure Ltd. (2)
99 Fordham Road Snailwell, Newmarket, CB8 7NB, Suffolk, United Kingdom
Tel.: (44) 1638722999
Web Site: http://www.eunisure.co.uk
Insurance Brokerage Services
N.A.I.C.S.: 524210
Ralph Mortlock (Founder & Mng Dir)

Clearstead Advisors, LLC (1)
1100 SUPERIOR Ave E Ste 700, Cleveland, OH 44114
Tel.: (216) 621-1090
Web Site: https://www.clearstead.com
Financial Services
N.A.I.C.S.: 523999

Subsidiary (Domestic):

Wilbanks, Smith & Thomas Asset Management, LLC (2)
150 W Main St Ste 1700, Norfolk, VA 23510
Tel.: (757) 623-3676
Web Site: http://www.wstam.com
Sales Range: $1-9.9 Million
Emp.: 24
Investment Management Service
N.A.I.C.S.: 523940
Wayne F. Wilbanks (CEO-Norfolk & Mid-Atlantic)

GeoVera Holdings, Inc. (1)
1455 Oliver Rd, Fairfield, CA 94534
Tel.: (707) 863-3700
Web Site:
  http://www.geoveraholdingsinc.com
Sales Range: $50-74.9 Million
Emp.: 100
Holding Company
N.A.I.C.S.: 551112
Karen Padovese (COO)
Kevin Nish (CEO)
Sam Oden (Supvr-Ops)
Brian Sheekey (CFO & Sr VP)

Subsidiary (Domestic):

GeoVera Insurance Company Inc. (2)
PO Box 7010, Fairfield, CA 94533
Tel.: (707) 863-3700
Web Site: http://www.geovera.com
Sales Range: $100-124.9 Million
Emp.: 150
Insurance Agents, Brokers & Service
N.A.I.C.S.: 524210

Edwards Capital, LLC—(Continued)

Lereta LLC (1)
1123 Park View Dr, Covina, CA 91724-3748
Web Site: http://www.lereta.com
Accounting Services
N.A.I.C.S.: 541219
John Walsh (Pres & CEO)
John Short (VP-Bus Dev)
Shannon McClaughry (VP-Customer Success)
Jim V. Micali (COO)
P. A. Larkins (Chm)

Propel Insurance Agency, LLC (1)
1201 Pacific Ave Ste 1000, Tacoma, WA 98402
Tel.: (253) 759-2200
Web Site: http://www.propelinsurance.com
Sales Range: $10-24.9 Million
Emp.: 225
Insurance Services
N.A.I.C.S.: 524210
Peter M. Hendrick (CFO)
Kurt Carlson (Pres & CEO)
Anna Reid (Sr Acct Mgr)
Eric Zimmerman (VP-Branch Dev)
Peter Comfort (Sec)

Subsidiary (Domestic):

Propel Insurance-Seattle (2)
925 4th Ave Ste 3200, Seattle, WA 98104
Tel.: (206) 676-4200
Web Site: http://www.propelinsurance.com
Insurance Related Activities
N.A.I.C.S.: 524299
Amy Augustine (Acct Mgr)

South Risk Management LLC (2)
2711 Middleburg Dr Ste 208, Columbia, SC 29204-2486
Tel.: (803) 733-5284
Web Site:
http://www.southriskmanagement.com
Direct Property & Causality Insurance Carriers
N.A.I.C.S.: 524126
Patrick McKain (Partner)

TIS Insurance Services Inc. (2)
3716 Overlook Dr, Macon, GA 31204-1327
Tel.: (478) 897-0407
Web Site: http://www.tisins.com
Insurance Agencies & Brokerages
N.A.I.C.S.: 524210
Monica Thomason (Mgr)

Purchasing Power, LLC (1)
1349 W Peachtree St NW STE 1100, Atlanta, GA 30309-3109
Tel.: (404) 609-5100
Web Site: http://www.purchasingpower.com
Employee Electronic Shopping Services
N.A.I.C.S.: 561499
Racquel Roberts (Chief People Officer)
Melissa Manley (VP-Fin Plng & Analysis)
Timo Kirschner (VP-Supply Chain)
Robert Almeda (Sls Dir-Northwest)
Lisa Lampron (Sls Dir-Southeast)
Bryon Colby (Chief Digital Mktg Officer)
Michael Wilbert (Chief Revenue Officer)
Trey Loughran (CEO)
Ron Oertell (CFO)
Patrick Cleary (Sls Dir-Mid-Central)

WMK, LLC (1)
4199 Kinross Lakes Pkwy Ste 300, Richfield, OH 44286
Tel.: (234) 312-2000
Web Site: http://www.mobilityworks.com
Sales Range: $100-124.9 Million
Emp.: 750
Wheelchair Accessible Vans Retailer & Rental Services
N.A.I.C.S.: 441110
William Koeblitz (Founder & Chm)
Eric H. Mansfield (Pres)
Bryan Everett (CEO)

Subsidiary (Domestic):

Absolute Mobility Center (2)
21704 87th Ave SE, Woodinville, WA 98072
Tel.: (425) 481-6546
Web Site:
http://www.absolutemobilitycenter.com
Rev.: $1,880,000
Emp.: 10
Passenger Car Rental Services

N.A.I.C.S.: 532111

Advanced Mobility Systems of Texas, Inc. (2)
2110 N Beach St, Haltom City, TX 76111-6812 (100%)
Tel.: (817) 429-1273
Web Site: http://www.advancedmobility.net
Emp.: 48
Mobility Solutions Dealer of Wheelchair Accessible Minivans, Full Size Vans & Wheelchair Accessible Trucks
N.A.I.C.S.: 532111
Guy Tucker (Pres)
Jason Brown (Gen Mgr)
Ashley Gomez (Mgr-Sls)

EDWARDS CHEVROLET - 280, INC.
5499 Hwy 280, Birmingham, AL 35242
Tel.: (205) 956-6700
Web Site: http://www.chevyman.com
Sales Range: $10-24.9 Million
Emp.: 60
New & Used Car Dealer
N.A.I.C.S.: 441110
Ted Cook (Principal)

EDWARDS CHEVROLET CO., INC.
1400 3rd Ave N, Birmingham, AL 35203-1827
Tel.: (205) 716-3300
Web Site:
http://downtown.chevyman.com
Year Founded: 1916
Sales Range: $100-124.9 Million
Emp.: 130
New & Used Car Dealer
N.A.I.C.S.: 441110
Leon W. Edwards Jr. (VP & Mgr-Sls)

EDWARDS DEVELOPMENT CORPORATION
3131 Turtle Creek Blvd Ste 1100, Dallas, TX 75219
Tel.: (214) 965-0220
Commercial Banking Services
N.A.I.C.S.: 522110
Spencer Edwards (CEO)

EDWARDS ENGINEERING, INC.
1000 Touhy Ave, Elk Grove Village, IL 60007
Tel.: (847) 364-8100
Web Site:
https://www.edwardsengineering.com
Year Founded: 1979
Mechanical Contracting Service
N.A.I.C.S.: 238220
Randy Felgenhauer (Sr Project Mgr)
Mike Bernauer (Acct Mgr)
Joanne Shedlock (Controller)
Frank Morgan (Dir-Ops)

EDWARDS INDUSTRIES, LLC
7250 Parkway Dr Ste 200, Hanover, MD 21076
Tel.: (443) 561-0180
Web Site: http://www.edwards-ind.com
Year Founded: 1997
Sales Range: $25-49.9 Million
Emp.: 30
Project Management Consulting Services
N.A.I.C.S.: 541618
Steven S. Edwards (Pres & CEO)
Michael R. Thomas (COO & VP)
Sandra H. Ingley (Chief Admin Officer)

EDWARDS JET CENTER
1691 Aviation Pl, Billings, MT 59105
Tel.: (406) 252-0508

Web Site:
https://www.edwardsjetcenter.com
Sales Range: $10-24.9 Million
Emp.: 65
Flying Charter Service
N.A.I.C.S.: 481219
Clifford Edwards (Owner)
Robb Bergeson (Gen Mgr)
Kelly Michaelis (Mgr-Parts)
Alan Lee (Dir-Ops)

EDWARDS PUBLICATIONS INC.
125 Eagles Nest Dr, Seneca, SC 29678-2760
Tel.: (864) 882-3272
Web Site:
http://www.edwgroupinc.com
Year Founded: 1978
Rev.: $18,500,000
Emp.: 325
Newspapers
N.A.I.C.S.: 513110
Jerry L. Edwards (Co-Owner & Pres)
Steve Edwards (Co-Owner & VP)
Joyce Edwards (Treas & Sec)
Sherry Dyer (Comptroller)

Subsidiaries:

Oconee Publishing Inc. (1)
210 W N 1st St, Seneca, SC 29678
Tel.: (864) 882-2375
Web Site: http://www.upstatetoday.com
Rev.: $3,100,000
Emp.: 52
Newspapers, Publishing & Printing
N.A.I.C.S.: 513110
Jerry Edwards (VP)
Hal Welsh (Dir-Adv)

EDWARDS SALES CORPORATION
3700 N Chestnut St, Chaska, MN 55318-3070
Tel.: (952) 929-6794
Web Site:
https://www.edwardssales.com
Sales Range: $10-24.9 Million
Emp.: 15
Adhesives & Sealants
N.A.I.C.S.: 424690
Tom Stauber (Pres)
David Flynn (Mgr-Sls Support)

EDWIN B. STIMPSON COMPANY, INC.
1515 SW 13th Ct, Pompano Beach, FL 33069
Tel.: (954) 946-3500
Web Site: https://www.stimpson.com
Year Founded: 1852
Sales Range: $100-124.9 Million
Emp.: 230
Metal Eyelets, Snap Fasteners, Grommets & Washers, Terminals, Metal Stampings & Attaching Machines Mfr
N.A.I.C.S.: 339993
George A. Fortmuller (CFO)

Subsidiaries:

Wicks Unlimited, Inc. (1)
1515 SW 13th Ct, Pompano Beach, FL 33069
Tel.: (631) 472-2010
Web Site: http://www.wicksunlimited.com
Wick Clip Assembly Mfr
N.A.I.C.S.: 339999
Thomas Rubino (Mgr-Mktg)

EDWIN GOULD SERVICES FOR CHILDREN AND FAMILIES
151 Lawrence St 5th Fl, Brooklyn, NY 11201
Tel.: (212) 437-3500
Web Site: http://www.egscf.org

Year Founded: 1939
Sales Range: $25-49.9 Million
Child & Family Support Services
N.A.I.C.S.: 624190
Sylvia Fety (Dir-Preventive Svcs Div)
Judith Benitez (Co-Sec)
Mary Ann Wall (Co-Sec)
Robert Schanz (Pres)
Sharron Madden (Chief Program Officer)
Lucia Rivieccio (Chief External Affairs Officer)
Ken Semple (CFO)

EDWIN L. HEIM COMPANY INC.
1918 Greenwood St, Harrisburg, PA 17104-2328
Tel.: (717) 233-8711
Web Site: http://www.elheim.com
Year Founded: 1955
Sales Range: $50-74.9 Million
Emp.: 350
Electrical Work Services
N.A.I.C.S.: 238210
Larry D. Bashore (Pres)

Subsidiaries:

GES Automation Technology Inc. (1)
2020 Greenwood St, Harrisburg, PA 17104-2343
Tel.: (717) 236-8733
Web Site: http://www.ges-automation.com
Sales Range: $10-24.9 Million
Emp.: 16
Process Control Instruments Mfr
N.A.I.C.S.: 334513
Gary Slatt (Founder)

EDX INFORMATION SYSTEMS, INC.
46560 Fremont Blvd, Fremont, CA 94538-6491
Tel.: (510) 440-1011
Web Site: https://www.edxinc.com
Rev.: $20,000,000
Emp.: 20
Provider of Computer Related Consulting Services
N.A.I.C.S.: 541512

EDX WIRELESS, INC.
132 E Broadway Ste 590, Eugene, OR 97401
Tel.: (541) 345-0019
Web Site: https://www.edx.com
Year Founded: 1985
Sales Range: $10-24.9 Million
Emp.: 15
Wireless Network Design & Software Developer
N.A.I.C.S.: 513210

EE&G ENVIRONMENTAL SERVICES, LLC
5751 Miami Lakes Dr E, Miami Lakes, FL 33014-2417
Tel.: (305) 374-8300
Web Site: https://www.eeandg.com
Sales Range: $1-9.9 Million
Emp.: 30
Environmental Consulting Services
N.A.I.C.S.: 541620
Carolyn Bailey (VP-Ops)
Susan Galante (VP & Dir-Engrg)
Timothy Gipe (Pres & Dir-Consulting Svcs)
Starr Sutton (VP & Dir-Sls Natl Accts)
Rich Grupenhoff (Sr Project Mgr)
Jay Sall (Dir-Indus Hygiene & Safety Practice)
Mark Skweres (Dir-Project)
Heather Phillips (Mgr-Bus Dev)
Don Schambach (Sr Project Mgr)
Kirk Smith (Sr Project Mgr & Mgr-Ops-Tampa)

EEBOO CORPORATION
170 W 74th St, New York, NY 10023
Tel.: (212) 222-0823
Web Site: https://www.eeboo.com
Year Founded: 1995
Sales Range: $1-9.9 Million
Emp.: 12
Educational Games & Toys
N.A.I.C.S.: 339930
Mia Galison (Dir-Creative & Pres)

EEC, INCORPORATED
303 Hubbard Rd, Landover, MD
20785
Tel.: (301) 341-1000
Web Site: http://www.eecinc.com
Year Founded: 1993
Sales Range: $10-24.9 Million
Emp.: 40
All Other Miscellaneous Waste Management Services
N.A.I.C.S.: 562998
Andre Downey (Pres & CEO)

EECON CONSTRUCTION SERVICES
4584 Mercantile Ave Ste A, Naples,
FL 34104
Tel.: (239) 495-1900
Web Site: http://www.eecon-inc.com
Sales Range: $1-9.9 Million
Emp.: 10
General Contractors
N.A.I.C.S.: 236220
Pete Emidy (Owner & Pres)

EEI GLOBAL, INC.
1400 S Livernois Rd, Rochester Hills,
MI 48307
Tel.: (248) 601-9900
Web Site: http://www.eeiglobal.com
Year Founded: 1981
Sales Range: $10-24.9 Million
Emp.: 150
Experiencial Marketing & Advertising
Services
N.A.I.C.S.: 541890
Derek M. Gentile (Pres & CEO)
Willow Schlachter (CFO)
Kirk A. Brien (VP & Gen Mgr)
Greg Urbanski (VP-Design)
David Varady (CMO)

EEI HOLDING CORPORATION
3009 Singer Ave, Springfield, IL
62703
Tel.: (217) 528-4001   IL
Web Site: http://www.eeiholding.com
Sales Range: $10-24.9 Million
Emp.: 50
Holding Company
N.A.I.C.S.: 238210
Robert W. Egizii (Pres)
Harold Hayes (Dir-Safety)

Subsidiaries:

Egizii Electric, Inc.   (1)
3009 Singer Ave, Springfield, IL 62703
Tel.: (217) 528-4001
Sales Range: $10-24.9 Million
Emp.: 25
Electrical Contractor
N.A.I.C.S.: 238210
Steve Nicholson (Asst VP)
Theresa Pennington (Mgr-HR)

EF HUTTON CORP.
24 Shipyard Dr Ste 102, Hingham,
MA 02043
Tel.: (929) 528-0767   DE
Year Founded: 2021
Investment Services
N.A.I.C.S.: 523999
Benjamin Piggott (CEO & Chm)
Kevin M. Bush (CFO & Treas)
Joseph Rallo (Co-Pres)
David Boral (Co-Pres)

EF INSTITUTE FOR CULTURAL EXCHANGE INC.
2 Education Cr, Cambridge, MA
02141-1805
Tel.: (617) 619-1000   CA
Web Site: http://www.ef.com
Year Founded: 1981
Sales Range: $75-99.9 Million
Emp.: 1,000
Provider of Tour Operation Services
N.A.I.C.S.: 561520
Bill Fisher (Co-Pres)
Monet Uva (Regl Dir)
Pippa Cusimano (Dir)
Anne Demange (Dir)
Jnrgen Oehler (Dir)
Emily Santillo (Co-Pres)

EFACTOR GROUP CORP.
1177 Ave of the Americas Ste 5060,
New York, NY 10036
Tel.: (650) 380-8280   NV
Web Site: http://www.efactor.com
Year Founded: 2001
Sales Range: $1-9.9 Million
Emp.: 55
Social Media Networking Website
Owner & Operator
N.A.I.C.S.: 516520
Thomas Trainer (Chm)
Ruud M. Smeets (Pres-Social Network)
Jeffrey B. Aaronson (CFO)

EFASHIONS SOLUTIONS, LLC
80 Enterprise Ave S, Secaucus, NJ
07094
Tel.: (201) 601-4299
Year Founded: 2001
Rev.: $22,800,000
Emp.: 200
Creates & Manages E-commerce
Sites for Fashion Companies
N.A.I.C.S.: 517810
Jennifer Silano-Foy (Pres & Chief
Creative Officer)
Mike Parise (Sr VP-Sls & Mktg)
Edward Foy Jr. (CEO)

EFC INTERNATIONAL INC.
1940 Craigshire, Saint Louis, MO
63146-4008
Tel.: (314) 434-2888
Web Site: https://www.efc-intl.com
Year Founded: 1983
Sales Range: $10-24.9 Million
Emp.: 100
Fasteners, Industrial: Nuts, Bolts,
Screws, Etc.
N.A.I.C.S.: 423840

EFENDOS GLOBAL, INC.
10301 NW 108th Ave Ste 11, Miami,
FL 33178
Tel.: (954) 580-6677
Web Site:
http://www.berlinmotorslogistics.com
Year Founded: 2011
Sales Range: $10-24.9 Million
Emp.: 6
Vehicle Shipping Services
N.A.I.C.S.: 488490
Robert Fuegert (CEO)

EFFECTIVE ENVIRONMENTAL, INC.
945 E Pleasant Run, Lancaster, TX
75146
Tel.: (972) 329-1200
Web Site: http://www.eff-env.com
Year Founded: 2003
Sales Range: $25-49.9 Million
Emp.: 25
Scientific & Technical Consulting Services
N.A.I.C.S.: 541690

Chris Ewing (Pres)

EFFECTIVE SPEND LLC
210 Barton Springs Rd Ste 400, Austin, TX 78704
Tel.: (512) 553-6875
Web Site:
http://www.effectivespend.com
Year Founded: 2008
Sales Range: $1-9.9 Million
Digital Marketing Services
N.A.I.C.S.: 541810
Brian Wulfe (Founder & CEO)
Natalia Wulfe (Head-Mktg & People
Ops)
Alex Keller (Head-Revenue & Ops)
Kyle Stoldt (Dir-Digital Media)
Paula Thompson (Dir-Digital Media)

EFFICIENCY PRODUCTION INCORPORATED
685 Hull Rd, Mason, MI 48854
Tel.: (517) 676-8800
Web Site:
https://www.efficiencyproduction.com
Year Founded: 1971
Sales Range: $10-24.9 Million
Emp.: 90
Construction Machinery
N.A.I.C.S.: 333120
Mike West (VP-Engrg)
Gary Stephens (VP-Sls)
Greg Ross (Dir-Special Ops Div)
Becky Valdez (Mgr-Shipping)
Billy Padgett (Mgr-Southeast)
Rod Austin (VP-Sls)

EFFICIENT LIGHTING CONSULTANTS, INC.
31 Pecks Lane Unit Ste 2, Newtown,
CT 06470
Tel.: (203) 270-7400
Web Site: https://www.efficientlighting
consultants.com
Year Founded: 2007
Sales Range: $1-9.9 Million
Emp.: 10
Designs & Implements Energy Conservation Projects
N.A.I.C.S.: 541420
Eileen Routhier (Mgr & Consultant)

EFFINGHAM EQUITY INC.
Roadway Ave, Effingham, IL 62401
Tel.: (217) 342-4101   IL
Web Site:
http://www.effinghamequity.com
Year Founded: 1921
Sales Range: $125-149.9 Million
Emp.: 185
Mfr of Farm Supplies
N.A.I.C.S.: 424910
Harry Fehrenbacher (Pres)

EFFINGHAM TRUCK SALES INC.
1701 W Fayette Ave, Effingham, IL
62401
Tel.: (217) 342-9761
Web Site:
http://www.effinghamtrucksales.com
Year Founded: 1968
Sales Range: $25-49.9 Million
Emp.: 160
Sales of Commercial Trucks
N.A.I.C.S.: 423110
Jim Davidson (Mgr-Sls)

EFFORTLESS IT LLC
5121 S Lakeland Dr Ste 1, Lakeland,
FL 33813
Tel.: (863) 226-4079
Web Site: http://www.effortlessit.com
Year Founded: 2009
Sales Range: $1-9.9 Million

IT Services
N.A.I.C.S.: 541519
Bobby Kuzma (Owner)

EFINANCIAL, LLC
13810 SE Eastgate Way Ste 300,
Bellevue, WA 98005-4400
Tel.: (425) 216-1240
Web Site: http://www.efinancial.com
Year Founded: 1999
Sales Range: $10-24.9 Million
Emp.: 150
Insurance Brokerage Services
N.A.I.C.S.: 524210
Kathleen Rowell (Principal)

EFIRD CHRYSLER JEEP DODGE
1711 W Lucas St, Florence, SC
29501
Tel.: (843) 669-1881
Web Site: http://www.efirdcjd.com
Sales Range: $25-49.9 Million
Emp.: 62
New Car Dealers
N.A.I.C.S.: 441110
Howard Efird (Pres)

EFLEETS CORPORATION
7660 Pebble Dr, Fort Worth, TX
76118
Tel.: (817) 616-3161   NV
Web Site: https://www.efleets.com
Year Founded: 2008
Sales Range: Less than $1 Million
Emp.: 15
All Electric Vehicle Mfr
N.A.I.C.S.: 336110
James R. Emmons (Pres, CEO &
CFO)

EFO FINANCIAL GROUP LLC
9180 Galleria Ct Ste 600, Naples, FL
34109
Tel.: (239) 449-1811
Web Site:
http://www.efofinancial.com
Sales Range: $10-24.9 Million
Real Estate Investment Firm
N.A.I.C.S.: 531390
David Goduti (Mng Partner)
Brett Carter (Dir-Project Dev)

Subsidiaries:

Clearwater Development Inc   (1)
4000 Gypsum Creek Rd, Gypsum, CO
81637
Tel.: (970) 777-1700
Sales Range: $10-24.9 Million
Emp.: 25
Real Estate Services
N.A.I.C.S.: 531390

EFOLDER, INC.
707 17th St Ste 3900, Denver, CO
80202
Tel.: (720) 204-4500   DE
Web Site: http://www.efolder.net
Software Publisher
N.A.I.C.S.: 513210
Kevin Hoffman (Founder & CTO)
Robert Leake (Dir-Mktg)
Jason Bystrak (VP-Channels & Distr-
Worldwide)
Angus Robertson (Chief Revenue
Officer)
Tom Atwood (VP-Mktg)
Rick Yates (Mng Dir-Europe, Middle
East, and Africa)
David Bennett (CEO)

EFORCITY CORPORATION
12339 Denholm Dr, El Monte, CA
91732
Tel.: (626) 442-3168
Web Site: http://www.eforcity.com
Year Founded: 1999

Eforcity Corporation—(Continued)

Sales Range: $10-24.9 Million
Emp.: 78
Online Retailer
N.A.I.C.S.: 459999
Alvin Wong (Pres)
Bin Xiao (Engr-Software Application)
Patty Wu (Mgr-Pur)

EFRAME, LLC
16850 Frances St Ste 100, Omaha,
NE 68130
Tel.: (402) 758-0508
Web Site: http://www.geoeframe.com
Rev.: $10,000,000
Emp.: 35
Online Services Technology Consul-
tants
N.A.I.C.S.: 541512
Jessica Schneider (Mgr-HR)

EFULFILLMENT SERVICE, INC.
807 Airport Access Rd Unit D, Tra-
verse City, MI 49686
Tel.: (231) 276-5057   MI
Web Site:
    https://www.efulfillmentservice.com
Year Founded: 2001
Sales Range: $10-24.9 Million
Emp.: 80
Web Based Fulfillment Software
N.A.I.C.S.: 513210
John Lindberg (Pres)
Jordan Lindberg (Exec VP)
Jennifer Robinson (Mgr-Customer
Svc)
Matt Burden (VP-Web Dev)
Jeff Dorsch (VP-Sys Dev)
Linda Sorna (Dir-Client Svcs)
Paula Batzer (Acct Mgr)
Steve Bulger (Mgr-Sls & Mktg)
Jason Dombrowski (Mgr-Ops)

EG CAPITAL GROUP, LLC
39 W 54th S, New York, NY 10019
Tel.: (212) 956-2600
Web Site:
    http://www.egcapitalgroup.com
Privater Equity Firm
N.A.I.C.S.: 523999
Jay Eastman (Mng Dir)

EG SIERRA L.L.C.
108 N Main St, Belton, TX 76513
Tel.: (254) 933-7669
Web Site: http://www.sierra-
venture.com
Sales Range: $10-24.9 Million
Emp.: 25
Commercial & Institutional Building
Construction Services
N.A.I.C.S.: 236220
Erendira Garner (Owner)

EG SYSTEMS LLC
30974 Santana St, Hayward, CA
94544
Tel.: (408) 528-3000
Web Site: http://www.electroglas.com
Sales Range: $10-24,9 Million
Emp.: 15
Mfr of Systems for Quality Testing of
Semiconductor Wafers
N.A.I.C.S.: 334413
Tony Kilaita (Mgr-Engrg)

Subsidiaries:

Nucent Co. Ltd.   (1)
Room 1005 D-Dong Digitalempire Building
980-3 Youngtong-Dong, Youngtong-Gu, Su-
won, 443-813, Kyoungki-Do, Korea (South)
Tel.: (82) 31 303 57304
Web Site: http://www.electroglas.com
Semiconductor Machinery Manufacturing
N.A.I.C.S.: 333242

EGEMIN AUTOMATION INC.
11818 James St, Holland, MI 49424
Tel.: (616) 393-0101
Web Site: http://www.egeminusa.com
Year Founded: 1947
Sales Range: $10-24.9 Million
Emp.: 40
Industrial Machinery Mfr
N.A.I.C.S.: 333922
Nathan Wolf (Project Dir-Mgmt)

Subsidiaries:

Dematic Retrotech   (1)
1275 John St Ste 400, West Henrietta, NY
14586
Tel.: (866) 915-2777
Web Site: http://www.dematic.com
Automated Storage Retrieval Systems Soft-
ware Publisher
N.A.I.C.S.: 513210
Paul Deveikis (Mng Dir)
Geoff Hitchings (Dir-Strategy)
Teri Rhuma (Sr Mgr-HR)

EGENERA, INC.
80 Central St, Foxboro, MA 01719
Tel.: (978) 206-6300
Web Site: http://www.egenera.com
Year Founded: 2000
Sales Range: $25-49.9 Million
Emp.: 325
Software Solutions & Services
N.A.I.C.S.: 513210
Scott Geng (CTO & Exec VP-Engrg)
Kevin Kerrigan (CFO & Sr VP)
Dan Busby (VP-Product Mgmt)
Rick Carbone (VP-Sls-North America)

EGG ELECTRIC INC.
35 W 45th St, New York, NY 10036
Tel.: (212) 633-9551
Web Site:
    http://www.eggelectricinc.com
Sales Range: $10-24.9 Million
Emp.: 130
Electrical Contractor & Engineer
N.A.I.C.S.: 238210
Ellen H. Aschendorf (Pres)

EGGELHOF INCORPORATED
1999 Kolfahl, Houston, TX 77023-
4611
Tel.: (713) 923-2101
Web Site: https://www.eggelhof.com
Year Founded: 1951
Sales Range: $75-99.9 Million
Emp.: 60
Supplier of Industrial Machinery &
Equipment
N.A.I.C.S.: 423830
Robert Robinson (Dir-Sls)

Subsidiaries:

LAM Valves Inc.   (1)
1502 Lombardy St, Houston, TX 77023-
4529
Tel.: (713) 923-7303
Web Site: http://www.lamvalves.com
Sales Range: $10-24.9 Million
Emp.: 6
Provider Of Industrial Supply Services
N.A.I.C.S.: 423830
Maynad Hovland (Gen Mgr)

EGGING CO.
12145 Rd 38, Gurley, NE 69141
Tel.: (308) 884-2233
Web Site: https://www.egging.com
Sales Range: $10-24.9 Million
Emp.: 90
Construction Machinery
N.A.I.C.S.: 333120
Ted F. Egging (Chm)

EGGLAND'S BEST, INC.
70 E Swedesford Rd Ste 150,
Malvern, PA 19355   PA

Web Site:
    http://www.egglandsbest.com
Year Founded: 1988
Chicken Egg Production & Whslr
N.A.I.C.S.: 112310
Kurt A. Misialek (Pres & CEO)
Steve Michella (VP-Sls)
Bart Slaugh (Dir-Quality Assurance)
David Rochon (Sr VP)

**EGIS CAPITAL PARTNERS
LLC**
35 Beechwood Rd Ste 2A, Summit,
NJ 07901
Tel.: (973) 994-0606
Web Site:
    https://www.egiscapitalpartners.com
Offices of Certified Public Accoun-
tants
N.A.I.C.S.: 541211
E. Perot Bissell (Mng Partner)
Robert M. Chefitz (Mng Partner)

Subsidiaries:

ClearObject, Inc.   (1)
8626 E 116th St, Fishers, IN 46038
Tel.: (888) 850-2568
Web Site: http://www.oncloudone.com
Software Development Services
N.A.I.C.S.: 541511
John McDonald (CEO)
John Annakin (Chief Revenue Officer)
Tom Kilcoyne (COO)
Mike Reffeitt (Pres)

**EGLENTOWICZ WRECKING
LLC**
172 Garfield Ave, Kearny, NJ 07032
Tel.: (973) 508-5757
Web Site:
    http://www.eglentowicz.com
Year Founded: 2009
Sales Range: $1-9.9 Million
Emp.: 20
Interior Demolition Services
N.A.I.C.S.: 238910
Gerald Eglentowicz (Pres)

EGLOBAL
854 W 450 N Ste 4, Kaysville, UT
84037
Tel.: (801) 593-6225
Web Site: http://www.eglobal.com
Year Founded: 2003
Sales Range: $10-24.9 Million
Emp.: 57
ATM Services
N.A.I.C.S.: 525990
Jeff Matthews (Pres)

EGNYTE INC.
1890 N Shoreline Blvd, Mountain
View, CA 94043
Tel.: (650) 968-4018
Web Site: http://www.egnyte.com
Year Founded: 2007
Sales Range: $25-49.9 Million
Emp.: 51
Information Technology Consultancy
Services
N.A.I.C.S.: 541512
Vineet Jain (CEO)
Steve Sutter (CFO)
Rajesh Ram (Chief Customer Officer)
Kris Lahiri (Chief Security Officer &
VP-Ops)
Ian McEwan (VP & Gen Mgr-EMEA)
Isabelle Guis (Chief Strategy Officer)
Amrit Jassal (CTO)

EGOLF MOTORS, INC.
1235 Asheville Hwy, Brevard, NC
28712
Web Site: http://www.egolfmotors.net
Year Founded: 1972
Sales Range: $10-24.9 Million
Emp.: 57

Automobile Sales
N.A.I.C.S.: 441110
Jay Egolf (Principal)

**EGON ZEHNDER INTERNA-
TIONAL INC.**
350 Park Ave 8th Fl, New York, NY
10022
Tel.: (212) 519-6000   DE
Web Site:
    http://www.egonzehnder.com
Year Founded: 1964
Sales Range: $350-399.9 Million
Executive Recruitment Firm
N.A.I.C.S.: 541612
Bill Hopkins (Dir-Global IT)
Damien O'Brien (Chm)
Scott Ragusa (Pres)
Joanne Yun (Partner)

Subsidiaries:

Dr Egon Zehnder & Partner AG   (1)
Toblerstrasse 80, 8044, Zurich, Switzerland
Tel.: (41) 442676969
Web Site: http://www.egonzehnder.com
Sales Range: $10-24.9 Million
Emp.: 50
Executive Recruitment Services
N.A.I.C.S.: 541612
Dominik Schaller (Mng Partner)
Jill Ader (Chm)

Egon Zehnder Associes S.A.   (1)
Cours de Rive 10, 1204, Geneva, Switzer-
land
Tel.: (41) 228496868
Web Site: http://www.egonzehnder.com
Sales Range: $10-24.9 Million
Emp.: 15
Executive Recruitment Services
N.A.I.C.S.: 541612
Thomas F. Allgauer (Mng Partner-Zurich &
Geneva)

Egon Zehnder Internacional de
Mexico S.A. de C.V.   (1)
Edificio Torre Optima 1 Despacho 703
Paseo de las Palmas Ste 405, Col Lomas
de Chapultepec, 11000, Mexico, Mexico
Tel.: (52) 5555407635
Sales Range: $10-24.9 Million
Emp.: 10
Executive Recruitment Services
N.A.I.C.S.: 541612
Antonio Puron (Gen Mgr)

Egon Zehnder International (Israel)
Ltd.   (1)
9 Nehardea St, Tel Aviv, 64235, Israel
Tel.: (972) 526018201
Web Site: http://www.egonzehnder.com
Executive Recruitment Services
N.A.I.C.S.: 541612
Lihi Arnon (Gen Mgr)

Egon Zehnder International (M) Sdn
Bhd   (1)
Level 25 Menara 3 PETRONAS Persiaran
KLCC, 50088, Kuala Lumpur, Malaysia
Tel.: (60) 321683333
Web Site: http://www.egonzehnder.com
Sales Range: $10-24.9 Million
Emp.: 9
Executive Recruitment Services
N.A.I.C.S.: 541612
Armin Effendi Abdul Rahman (Office
Leader)

Egon Zehnder International (Shang-
hai) Company Limited   (1)
No 8 Gao An Road, Shanghai, 200030,
China
Tel.: (86) 2124018200
Web Site: http://www.egonzehnder.com
Sales Range: $10-24.9 Million
Emp.: 5
Executive Recruitment Services
N.A.I.C.S.: 541612
Bill Henderson (Partner)

Egon Zehnder International B.V.   (1)
Building 1000 Mahlerlaan 6th Floor, PO Box
75534, Gustav Mahlerlaan, Amsterdam,
1082 MK, Netherlands
Tel.: (31) 203011111
Web Site: http://www.egonzehnder.com

Sales Range: $10-24.9 Million
Emp.: 50
Executive Recruitment Services
N.A.I.C.S.: 541612
Ingrid Van Den Maegdenbergh *(Office Mgr)*

Egon Zehnder International Chile S.A. (1)
Apoquindo 3600 piso, Santiago, Chile
Tel.: (56) 23359988
Web Site: http://www.egonzehnder.com
Sales Range: $10-24.9 Million
Emp.: 10
Executive Recruitment Services
N.A.I.C.S.: 541612

Egon Zehnder International Co., Ltd. (1)
Meiji Yasuda Seimei Bldg 17F 2-1-1, Marunouchi Chiyoda-ku, Tokyo, 100-0005, Japan
Tel.: (81) 352190450
Web Site: http://www.egonzehnder.com
Sales Range: $10-24.9 Million
Emp.: 40
Executive Recruitment Services
N.A.I.C.S.: 541612

Egon Zehnder International Consultores Lda. (1)
Av Duque d'Avila 141-8, 1050-081, Lisbon, Portugal
Tel.: (351) 213138330
Executive Recruitment Services
N.A.I.C.S.: 541612

Egon Zehnder International Ges.m.b.H. (1)
Tuchlauben 7A, Vienna, 1010, Austria
Tel.: (43) 1531720
Web Site: http://www.egonzehnder.com
Sales Range: $10-24.9 Million
Emp.: 20
Executive Recruitment Services
N.A.I.C.S.: 541612

Egon Zehnder International GmbH (1)
Beisheim Center Berliner Freiheit 2, Berlin, 10785, Germany
Tel.: (49) 303279550
Web Site: http://www.egonzehnder.com
Sales Range: $10-24.9 Million
Emp.: 35
Executive Recruitment Services
N.A.I.C.S.: 541612
Christian Rosen *(Gen Mgr)*

Egon Zehnder International GmbH (1)
Ko-Bogen Konigsallee 2A, Dusseldorf, 40212, Germany
Tel.: (49) 211139990
Web Site: http://www.egonzehnder.com
Sales Range: $10-24.9 Million
Emp.: 27
Executive Recruitment Services
N.A.I.C.S.: 541612

Egon Zehnder International GmbH (1)
Guiollettstrasse 48, Frankfurt, 60325, Germany
Tel.: (49) 69633960
Web Site: http://www.egonzehnder.com
Sales Range: $10-24.9 Million
Emp.: 20
Executive Recruitment Services
N.A.I.C.S.: 541612

Egon Zehnder International GmbH (1)
Alsterufer 3, 20354, Hamburg, Germany
Tel.: (49) 403232400
Sales Range: $25-49.9 Million
Emp.: 250
Executive Recruitment Services
N.A.I.C.S.: 541612
Hanns Goeltel *(Office Mgr)*

Egon Zehnder International GmbH (1)
Promenadeplatz 12, 80333, Munich, Germany
Tel.: (49) 892900690
Web Site: http://www.egonzehnder.com
Sales Range: $10-24.9 Million
Emp.: 35
Executive Recruitment Services

N.A.I.C.S.: 541612
Michelle Messer *(Gen Mgr)*

Egon Zehnder International GmbH (1)
Morikestrasse 3, 70178, Stuttgart, Germany
Tel.: (49) 7112730060
Web Site: http://www.egonzehnder.com
Sales Range: $10-24.9 Million
Emp.: 30
Executive Recruitment Services
N.A.I.C.S.: 541612

Egon Zehnder International Kft. (1)
Szabadsag Building 14, Budapest, 1054, Hungary
Tel.: (36) 14749740
Web Site: http://www.egonzehnder.com
Sales Range: $10-24.9 Million
Emp.: 10
Executive Recruitment Services
N.A.I.C.S.: 541612

Egon Zehnder International Ltd. (1)
Level 25 Henley Building 5 Queens Road Central, Hong Kong, China (Hong Kong)
Tel.: (852) 25256340
Web Site: http://www.egonzehnder.com
Sales Range: $10-24.9 Million
Emp.: 25
Executive Recruitment Services
N.A.I.C.S.: 541612

Egon Zehnder International Ltda. (1)
Rua Hungria 1240-8th Floor Jardim Europa, Sao Paulo, 01455-000, SP, Brazil
Tel.: (55) 1130390700
Sales Range: $25-49.9 Million
Emp.: 25
Executive Recruitment Services
N.A.I.C.S.: 541612

Egon Zehnder International Ltda. (1)
Rua Hungria 1240-8th Floor, Sao Paulo, 01455-000, SP, Brazil
Tel.: (55) 1130390700
Web Site: http://www.egonzehnder.com
Sales Range: $10-24.9 Million
Emp.: 40
Executive Recruitment Services
N.A.I.C.S.: 541612

Egon Zehnder International Oy (1)
Mikonkatu 2D, Helsinki, 100, Finland
Tel.: (358) 96840030
Web Site: http://www.egonzehnder.com
Sales Range: $10-24.9 Million
Emp.: 6
Executive Recruitment Services
N.A.I.C.S.: 541612
Richard Lehtola *(Mng Dir)*

Egon Zehnder International Pte Ltd. (1)
6 Battery Road 27-01, Singapore, 049909, Singapore
Tel.: (65) 62250355
Web Site: http://www.egonzehnder.com
Sales Range: $10-24.9 Million
Emp.: 24
Executive Recruitment Services
N.A.I.C.S.: 541612

Egon Zehnder International Pty Ltd. (1)
Level 10 171 Collins Street, Melbourne, 3000, VIC, Australia
Tel.: (61) 396789600
Web Site: http://www.egonzehnder.com
Sales Range: $10-24.9 Million
Emp.: 20
Executive Recruitment Services
N.A.I.C.S.: 541612

Egon Zehnder International Pty Ltd. (1)
Level 49 Governor Phillip Tower 1 Farrer Place, Sydney, 2000, NSW, Australia
Tel.: (61) 292404500
Web Site: http://www.egonzehnder.com
Sales Range: $10-24.9 Million
Emp.: 15
Executive Recruitment Services
N.A.I.C.S.: 541612

Egon Zehnder International Pvt. Ltd. (1)
151-154 Maker Chamber 6 15th Fl 21, Mumbai, 400 021, India
Tel.: (91) 2222846765

Web Site: http://www.egonzehnder.com
Sales Range: $10-24.9 Million
Emp.: 40
Executive Recruitment Services
N.A.I.C.S.: 541612

Egon Zehnder International Pvt. Ltd. (1)
Bldg 9A 11th F, DLF Cyber city, Gurgaon, 122.002, India
Tel.: (91) 1244638000
Web Site: http://www.egonzehnder.com
Sales Range: $10-24.9 Million
Emp.: 31
Executive Recruitment Services
N.A.I.C.S.: 541612
Pallavi Kathuria *(Office Mgr)*

Egon Zehnder International S.A. (1)
Av del Libertador 602 Piso 15 A, Buenos Aires, C1001ABT, Argentina
Tel.: (54) 1148145090
Web Site: http://www.egonzehnder.com
Sales Range: $10-24.9 Million
Emp.: 12
Executive Recruitment Services
N.A.I.C.S.: 541612
Marcelo Grimoldi *(Pres & CEO)*

Egon Zehnder International S.A. (1)
2 Paradissou Street, 151 25, Maroussi, Athens, Greece
Tel.: (30) 2106833333
Web Site: http://www.egonzehnder.com
Sales Range: $10-24.9 Million
Emp.: 11
Executive Recruitment Services
N.A.I.C.S.: 541612

Egon Zehnder International S.A. (1)
Bredgade 70, 1260, Copenhagen, Denmark
Tel.: (45) 33111353
Web Site: http://www.egonzehnder.com
Sales Range: $10-24.9 Million
Emp.: 50
Executive Recruitment Services
N.A.I.C.S.: 541612
Lars Po Goergensen *(Office Mgr)*

Egon Zehnder International S.A. (1)
32 rue de la Republique, 69002, Lyon, France
Tel.: (33) 472411850
Sales Range: $10-24.9 Million
Emp.: 2
Executive Recruitment Services
N.A.I.C.S.: 541612

Egon Zehnder International S.A. (1)
54 Ave Marceau, 75008, Paris, France
Tel.: (33) 144318100
Sales Range: $10-24.9 Million
Emp.: 50
Executive Recruitment Services
N.A.I.C.S.: 541612

Egon Zehnder International S.L. (1)
Avda Diagonal 682 4a planta A2, Barcelona, 08034, Spain
Tel.: (34) 932405135
Web Site: http://www.egonzehnder.com
Sales Range: $10-24.9 Million
Emp.: 15
Executive Recruitment Services
N.A.I.C.S.: 541612

Egon Zehnder International S.L. (1)
Plaza Marques de Salamanca 3-4 4 Pl, 28006, Madrid, Spain
Tel.: (34) 915214115
Web Site: http://www.egonzehnder.com
Sales Range: $10-24.9 Million
Emp.: 20
Executive Recruitment Services
N.A.I.C.S.: 541612
Luis Carvajal *(Office Mgr)*

Egon Zehnder International S.p.A. (1)
Via Santa Margherita 7, 20121, Milan, Italy
Tel.: (39) 02869621
Web Site: http://www.egonzehnder.com
Sales Range: $10-24.9 Million
Emp.: 47
Executive Recruitment Services
N.A.I.C.S.: 541612

Egon Zehnder International Sp. z o.o. (1)
Ul Ksiazeca 4, 00-498, Warsaw, Poland

Tel.: (48) 225377410
Web Site: http://www.egonzehnder.com
Sales Range: $10-24.9 Million
Emp.: 13
Executive Recruitment Services
N.A.I.C.S.: 541612

Egon Zehnder Luxembourg S.A. (1)
Avenue Franklin Roosevelt 14, Brussels, 1000, Belgium
Tel.: (32) 26480083
Web Site: http://www.egonzehnder.com
Sales Range: $10-24.9 Million
Emp.: 30
Executive Recruitment Services
N.A.I.C.S.: 541612
Joost Maes *(Office Mgr)*

PT Egon Zehnder International (1)
One Pacific Place 10th Floor Suite 1001-1002, Sudirman Central Business District Jl Jenderal Sudirman Kav 52-53, Jakarta, 12190, Indonesia
Tel.: (62) 2129355600
Web Site: http://www.egonzehnder.com
Executive Recruitment Services
N.A.I.C.S.: 541612

S.A. Egon Zehnder Associates (International) N.V. (1)
Ave Franklin Roosevelt 14, 1050, Brussels, Belgium
Tel.: (32) 26480083
Web Site: http://www.egonzehnder.net
Sales Range: $10-24.9 Million
Emp.: 30
Executive Recruitment Services
N.A.I.C.S.: 541612
Guy F. Detrilles *(Partner)*

EGP, INC.
1420 W Washington St, Orlando, FL 32805
Tel.: (407) 841-2932
Web Site: http://www.egp.com
Year Founded: 1967
Sales Range: $25-49.9 Million
Emp.: 150
Retailer of Electronic Parts & Equipment
N.A.I.C.S.: 459999
Brian Mollway *(Dir-Sls)*
Jim Stein *(Branch Mgr)*
Judy Patten *(Acct Mgr)*
Tom Toohey *(Mgr-Leasing)*

EGR INTERNATIONAL, INC.
30 Broad St, New York, NY 10004
Tel.: (212) 949-7330
Web Site:
http://www.egrinternational.com
Emp.: 26
Advetising Agency
N.A.I.C.S.: 541810
Jeffrey G. Grisamore *(Pres)*

EGROUP, INC.
482 Wando Park Blvd, Mount Pleasant, SC 29464
Tel.: (843) 284-0146   SC
Web Site: https://www.egroup-us.com
Year Founded: 1999
Sales Range: $10-24.9 Million
Emp.: 31
Custom Computer Programming Services Including Customers' Cost Containment, Revenue Growth & Service Objectives
N.A.I.C.S.: 541511
Mike Carter *(Founder & Principal)*
Catherine Carter *(CFO)*
Brian Corum *(VP-Sls)*

EGS INTERNATIONAL INC.
5534 Olive St, Montclair, CA 91763-1649
Tel.: (909) 946-4610
Web Site: http://www.egsintl.com
Rev.: $10,000,000
Emp.: 10

EGS International Inc.—(Continued)

Design, Manufacture & Sell Spill Containment Systems
N.A.I.C.S.: 562112
Doug Frazier (Pres)

EGS, INC.
333 W Hampden Ave Ste 530, Denver, CO 80110
Tel.: (303) 477-6800
Web Site: https://www.egs-partners.com
Year Founded: 2002
Emp.: 100
Staffing Services
N.A.I.C.S.: 561311
Susan Fenske (Owner)

Subsidiaries:

Aztech Professional Services, Inc.   (1)
60 E Rio Salado Pkwy Ste 900, Tempe, AZ 85281
Tel.: (480) 951-0888
Web Site: http://www.aztechpro.com
Sales Range: $1-9.9 Million
Emp.: 40
Employment Placement Agencies
N.A.I.C.S.: 561311

EGUMBALL, INC.
7525 Irvine Ctr Dr Ste 100, Irvine, CA 92618
Tel.: (949) 597-1000
Web Site: http://www.egumball.com
Year Founded: 2001
Sales Range: $1-9.9 Million
Emp.: 45
Nutritious Food Mfr
N.A.I.C.S.: 541613
John Bauer (Pres & CEO)
Jeffrey Bode (Mgr-Customer Svc)
Toby Tucker (Mgr-Consumer Rels)
Sabrina Barrios (Mgr-Recruiting)
Jennifer Ferraris (Coord-HR)

EGW TEMPORARIES INC.
1700 Clinton St, Buffalo, NY 14206
Tel.: (716) 822-6166
Web Site: http://www.egwpersonnel.com
Rev.: $10,000,000
Emp.: 10
Temporary Help Service
N.A.I.C.S.: 561320
Jeff Wach (Gen Mgr)

EGW UTILITIES, INC.
1406 Hutton Dr, Carrollton, TX 75006
Tel.: (972) 446-1655   TX
Web Site: https://www.egwusa.com
Year Founded: 2001
Sales Range: $10-24.9 Million
Emp.: 30
Utility Distribution Services
N.A.I.C.S.: 221122
Philip Wiegers (Pres)
Herman Chun (Mgr-Procurement & Quality Assurance)
Jeff Burnett (Owner)

EH BAARE CORPORATION
3620 W 73rd St, Anderson, IN 46011
Tel.: (765) 778-7895
Web Site: http://www.ehbaare.com
Year Founded: 1920
Sales Range: $10-24.9 Million
Emp.: 100
Wire Products, Ferrous/Iron: Made In Wiredrawing Plants
N.A.I.C.S.: 331222
Gary Null (Gen Mgr)
Mike Uptmor (Mgr-Sls)
Joel Owens (Mgr-Engrg)
Marla Correll (Pur Mgr)

Rick Wilson (Mgr-Quality Control)
Marcy Lowrance (Sec)
Travis Crumrin (Mgr-Safety)

EH CONSTRUCTION LLC
1188 E Blue Lick Rd, Shepherdsville, KY 40165
Tel.: (502) 957-7471
Web Site: https://www.ehconst.com
Sales Range: $10-24.9 Million
Emp.: 60
Commercial & Office Building, New Construction
N.A.I.C.S.: 236220
James A. Hall (Pres)
Joe Paul Smith (Mgr-Safety & Inventory)
Mike Rippy (Project Mgr)

EH PUBLISHING, INC.
111 Speen St Ste 200, Framingham, MA 01701
Tel.: (508) 663-1500
Web Site: http://www.ehpub.com
Year Founded: 1994
Sales Range: $10-24.9 Million
Emp.: 50
Magazine & Online Publisher; Trade Shows & Events
N.A.I.C.S.: 513120
Kenneth Moyes (CEO)
Elizabeth Crews (VP-Audience Dev)

EHC INC.
1360 Rail Head Blvd, Naples, FL 34110
Tel.: (239) 592-0828
Web Site: http://www.ehcconstruction.com
Year Founded: 1990
Construction Services
N.A.I.C.S.: 236220
Jeffrey A. Hunt (Owner & Pres)
Gregory L. Hunt (Owner & Exec VP)
Anthony P. Hamilton (Owner & VP-Construction Admin)
Shane E. Graves (Owner & Superintendent)

EHLERDING MOTORSPORTS INC.
5525 Hwy 930 E, Fort Wayne, IN 46803
Tel.: (260) 749-9686
Web Site: http://www.ehlerdingmotorsports.com
Year Founded: 1965
Sales Range: $10-24.9 Million
Emp.: 45
Sales of Motorcycles
N.A.I.C.S.: 441227
Donald Ehlerding (Owner)

EHRHARDT, KEEFE, STEINER & HOTTMAN, P.C.
8181 E Tufts Ave Ste 600, Denver, CO 80237-2521
Tel.: (303) 740-9400   CO
Web Site: http://www.eksh.com
Year Founded: 1982
Emp.: 700
Accounting, Tax, Consulting & Wealth Advisory Services
N.A.I.C.S.: 541211
Bob Hottman (Founder, CEO & Partner-Denver Office)
Steve Schenbeck (COO & Partner-Audit-Denver Office)
Lori Nelson (Partner-Denver)
Dave Steiner (Founder, Chm & Partner-Denver)
Chris Stuart (Partner-Intl Tax)
Gaylen Hansen (Partner-Audit & Dir-Quality Assurance)
Joe Adams (Partner-Lead Audit-Denver)

Joseph Bertsch (Partner-Lead Tax-Denver)
Ken Berkeley (Partner-Bus Consulting-Intl)
Doug Ehrhardt (Partner-Denver)
William Keefe (Partner-Tax)
Scott Bemis (Dir-Bus & Community Partnerships)

EHRLICH FOOD COMPANY INC.
581 Austin Pl, Bronx, NY 10455-3890
Tel.: (718) 993-4800
Year Founded: 1947
Sales Range: $10-24.9 Million
Emp.: 3
Food Products Distr
N.A.I.C.S.: 424410
Gloria Ehrlich (Owner)

EHS TECHNOLOGIES CORP.
1221 N Church St Ste 105, Moorestown, NJ 08057
Tel.: (856) 642-7877
Web Site: https://www.ehstech.net
Year Founded: 1996
Sales Range: $10-24.9 Million
Emp.: 100
Scientific & Technical Consulting Services
N.A.I.C.S.: 541690
Denise Eckerle (CEO)
Bill Eckerle (Owner & Pres)
Joseph Bus (CIO)

EI COMPANIES
2570 S Miller Ln, Las Vegas, NV 89117
Tel.: (702) 365-8080
Web Site: http://www.eicompanies.com
Human Resource Consulting Services
N.A.I.C.S.: 541612
Galo Lebron (Pres)

Subsidiaries:

Ei Risk Management Corp.   (1)
2570 S Miller Ln, Las Vegas, NV 89117
Tel.: (702) 365-8080
Engineering Consulting Services
N.A.I.C.S.: 541330
Thomas Cocharan (Pres)

Subsidiary (Domestic):

ABCO Engineering Corp.   (2)
6901 S Yosemite St Ste 205, Englewood, CO 80110
Tel.: (303) 220-8220
Web Site: http://www.abco-corp.com
Engineering Services
N.A.I.C.S.: 541330
Joe Johnson (Pres & CEO)

EICHENBAUM/ASSOCIATES, INC.
219 N Milwaukee St, Milwaukee, WI 53202-5818
Tel.: (414) 225-0011   WI
Year Founded: 1989
Rev.: $18,000,000
Emp.: 13
N.A.I.C.S.: 541810
Neal Bardele (Partner & Client Svcs Dir)

EICO INC.
1054 Yosemite Dr, Milpitas, CA 95035
Tel.: (408) 945-9898
Year Founded: 1984
Rev.: $15,700,000
Emp.: 25
Holding Company: Instruments To Measure Electricity
N.A.I.C.S.: 334515

Arlene Chou (Pres)
Connie Hugh (Controller)

Subsidiaries:

Golden Altos Corporation   (1)
402 S Hillview Dr, Milpitas, CA 95035
Tel.: (408) 956-1010
Web Site: http://www.goldenaltos.com
Integrated Circuit Testers
N.A.I.C.S.: 334515
B. Mendoza (VP-Sls & Mktg & Project Mgmt)

Rucker & Kolls Inc   (1)
1064 Yosemite Dr, Milpitas, CA 95035
Tel.: (408) 934-9875
Web Site: http://www.ruckerkolls.com
Semiconductor Manufacturing Machinery
N.A.I.C.S.: 333242

EID PASSPORT, INC.
5800 NW Pinefarm Pl, Hillsboro, OR 97124
Tel.: (503) 924-5300
Web Site:
   http://www.eidpassport.com
Year Founded: 2001
Sales Range: $10-24.9 Million
Emp.: 100
Sales of Identify Management & Access Control Solutions to Military, Government & Commercial Sectors
N.A.I.C.S.: 561621
James Robell (COO)
Katherine Cowan (Gen Counsel)
Sean Sullivan (VP-Fin & Strategic Initiatives)
Steve Larson (Chm & CEO)
Abrar Ahmed (Grp Pres-Supply Chain, Ops, Sls, IT & Product Dev)
Catherine Sturtevant (VP-HR)
Greg Hendricks (VP-Defense Programs)

EIDE BAILLY LLP
4310 17th Ave SW, Fargo, ND 58108-2545
Tel.: (701) 239-8500   ND
Web Site: https://www.eidebailly.com
Year Founded: 1978
Emp.: 1,200
Accounting, Tax, Auditing & Consulting Services
N.A.I.C.S.: 541211
David L. Stende (CEO & Mng Partner)
Anders Erickson (Dir-Cyber Security)
Janel C. Keenan (Partner)
Ava Archibald (Principal)
Ross Manson (Principal)
Mike Astrup (Chief Admin Officer)
Corey M. Enger (Partner)
Amber Ferrie (Partner)
Lisa Fitzgerald (Dir-HR)
Chad Flanagan (Dir-Valuations)
Mike D. Arvidson (Dir-Infrastructure Svcs)
Jeremy Bendewald (Dir-Forensic Svcs)
Bradley DeJong (Dir-Sr Living)
Shelley Earsley (Dir-Consulting)
David Glennon (Partner)
Renee Gravalin (Partner)
Ramona K. Johnson (Partner & Dir-Wealth Transition Svcs)
Patrick Kautzman (Partner)
Brad Kelley (Dir-Fin Svcs)
Scott Kost (Dir-Tech Consulting)
LaRae Langerud (Dir-Admin)
Jason McKeever (Dir-Trng & Dev)
Mary Jo Richard (Partner)
Ann Rockswold (Principal)
Wade Sandy (Dir-Construction & Real Estate)
Karla R. Wilson (CFO)
Ann Glenz (Partner-Minneapolis)
Pam J. Eggert (Partner)
William Trainor (Partner)

Christopher Gracey (Partner)
Tom Goekeler (Chief Practice Officer-South Central Reg)

Subsidiaries:

Accounting Systems, Inc.   (1)
324 Remington St, Fort Collins, CO 80524
Tel.: (970) 419-3210
Web Site: http://www.asisucceed.com
Sales Range: $1-9.9 Million
Emp.: 13
Accounting Software Developer & Publisher
N.A.I.C.S.: 513210
Bredt P. Eggleston (Founder & Chief Solutions Officer)
Jenny Eggleston (COO)
Katie Jo Cordes (Project Mgr)
Tiffany Hall (Project Mgr)

Secore & Niedzialek P.C.   (1)
2800 N Central Ave Ste 200, Phoenix, AZ 85004-1034
Tel.: (602) 279-9090
Web Site: http://www.sncpa.com
Other Accounting Services
N.A.I.C.S.: 541219

EIG GLOBAL ENERGY PARTNERS, LLC
1700 Pennsylvania Ave NW Ste 800, Washington, DC 20006
Tel.: (202) 600-3300
Web Site: http://www.eigpartners.com
Year Founded: 1982
Emp.: 85
Institutional Investment Services
N.A.I.C.S.: 523999
Terence Bartlett Jupp (Mng Dir)
Robert Blair Thomas (Chm & CEO)
Randall S. Wade (Chief Investment Officer)
Rob Johnson (Mng Dir & Head-Oil & Gas Direct Lending)
Rex Chung (Mng Dir & Head-Asia)
A. J. Washington (Sr VP)
Andrew Ellenbogen (Mng Dir)
Andy Jamison (Sr VP)
Benjamin Vinocour (Chief Corp Dev Officer & Gen Counsel)
Beth Litton (Chief HR Officer & Sr VP)
Brian Boland (Sr VP)
Brian Gilmore (Sr VP)
Carla P. Vogel (Chief Compliance Officer & Sr VP)
Derek Lemke-von Ammon (Mng Dir & Head-Capital Dev)
Eric Long (Mng Dir & Portfolio Mgr-FS Energy & Power Fund)
Marcelia Freeman (Sr VP)
Matthew Fox (Sr VP)
Melanie Levy (Sr VP & Dir-Tax)
Pritpal Aujla (CFO & Sr VP)
Renee Davidovits (Sr VP & Dir-IR)
Rick Caplan (Mng Dir & Head-Capital Markets)
Robert Vitale (Mng Dir & Gen Counsel)
Ruairi Grant (Sr VP)
De la Rey Venter (Mng Dir & CEO-MidOcean Energy)

Subsidiaries:

Harbour Energy Ltd.   (1)
1700 Pennsylvania Ave NW Ste 800, Washington, DC 20006
Tel.: (202) 600-3300
Web Site: http://www.harbourenergy.com
Energy-Focused Investment Holding Company
N.A.I.C.S.: 551112
Eric Long (CFO)
Vahid Farzad (Chief Bus Dev Officer)
Benjamin Vinocour (Gen Counsel)

Prumo Logistica S.A.   (1)
Rua do Russel 804 5th Floor, Gloria, Rio de Janeiro, 22 210-010, Brazil   (100%)
Tel.: (55) 21 3725 8000
Web Site: http://www.prumologistica.com.br

Sales Range: $125-149.9 Million
Port Operation Services
N.A.I.C.S.: 488310
Robert Blair Thomas (Chm)
Eduardo Quartarone (Exec Dir-Legal)
Carlos Tadeu Fraga (CEO)
Luciana Rachid (Dir-Gas Businesses)
Henrique Gonzalez (Exec Officer-HR & Comm)

Southcross Holdings LP   (1)
1717 Main St Ste 5200, Dallas, TX 75201   (33.3%)
Tel.: (214) 979-3700
Web Site: http://www.southcrossholdings.com
Holding Company
N.A.I.C.S.: 551112
John Bonn (Pres)

Holding (Domestic):

Southcross Energy Partners,LLC   (2)
1717 Main St Ste 5200, Dallas, TX 75201
Tel.: (214) 979-3720
Web Site: http://www.southcrossenergy.com
Sales Range: $400-449.9 Million
Oil & Gas Exploration
N.A.I.C.S.: 211120
Patrick Geroir (CEO)
James Lee (CFO & Sr VP)
William C. Boyer (COO & Sr VP)
John Happ (Chief Comml Officer & Sr VP)
Nicole Devore (Dir-HR)
William Waldheim (Chm)

Subsidiary (Domestic):

Southcross Energy GP LLC   (3)
1700 Pacific Ave Ste 2900, Dallas, TX 75201
Tel.: (214) 979-3700
Web Site: http://www.southxenergy.com
Gathering, Processing & Pipeline Transportation of Natural Gas
N.A.I.C.S.: 486210

Southcross Mississippi Industrial Gas Sales, L.P.   (3)
1717 Main St Ste 5200, Dallas, TX 75201-4617
Tel.: (214) 979-3700
Oil & Gas Operation Supporting Services
N.A.I.C.S.: 213112

Southcross Mississippi Pipeline, L.P.   (3)
1700 Pacific Ave Ste 2900, Dallas, TX 75201-4666
Tel.: (214) 979-3760
Sales Range: $10-24.9 Million
Emp.: 12
Natural Gas Pipeline Transportation Services
N.A.I.C.S.: 486210

Southcross NGL Pipeline Ltd.   (3)
1717 Main St Ste 5200, Dallas, TX 75201
Tel.: (214) 979-3767
Web Site: http://www.southcrossenergy.com
Natural Gas Pipeline Transportation Services
N.A.I.C.S.: 486210

EIGHT CROSSINGS
2523 J St Ste 205, Sacramento, CA 95816
Tel.: (916) 444-0002
Web Site: http://www.eightcrossings.com
Year Founded: 2001
Rev.: $2,900,000
Emp.: 85
Document Preparation Services
N.A.I.C.S.: 561410
Patrick Maher (Pres)
Darcy Johnson (Dir-Transcription QA)

EIGHT NORTHERN INDIAN PUEBLOS COUNCIL, INC.
327 Eagle Dr, Ohkay Owingeh, NM 87566
Tel.: (505) 747-1593   NM
Web Site: https://www.enipc.org
Year Founded: 1960
Sales Range: $10-24.9 Million

Emp.: 152
Community Development Services
N.A.I.C.S.: 624190
Diane Gonzales (Mgr-HR)
Gale Yepa (Mgr-Grants)
Moria Robinson (Dir-HR)

EIGHT TO GO LLC.
234 W 44th St Ste 800, New York, NY 10036
Tel.: (212) 510-8564
Year Founded: 2013
Sales Range: $10-24.9 Million
Support Services
N.A.I.C.S.: 561499
Joey Parnes (Exec Dir)
John Pinckard (Exec Dir)

EIGHTEEN SEVENTY CORPORATION
2 Manhattanville Rd, Purchase, NY 10577
Tel.: (914) 694-3999
Sales Range: $10-24.9 Million
Emp.: 9
Investment Advisory Services
N.A.I.C.S.: 523940
Peter M. Kennedy (Chm)
Anna M. Buckley (VP-Fin)
Steve Koch (VP)

Subsidiaries:

DIC Properties Llc   (1)
2 Manhattanville Rd, Purchase, NY 10577
Tel.: (914) 694-3999
Rev.: $280,000
Emp.: 8
Commercial & Industrial Building Operation
N.A.I.C.S.: 531120

Ferguson Copeland LLC   (1)
100 Reep Dr, Morganton, NC 28655
Tel.: (828) 584-0664
Web Site: http://www.fergusoncopeland.com
Upholstered Household Furniture
N.A.I.C.S.: 337121

EIGHTEEN SEVENTY STRAND CORP.
2300 Ships Mechanic Row, Galveston, TX 77550
Tel.: (409) 763-0300
Web Site: http://www.wyndham.com
Sales Range: $50-74.9 Million
Emp.: 285
Hotel
N.A.I.C.S.: 721110
Lori Long (Dir-Sls)
Andrew Jordan (Exec VP-Sls & Mktg & CMO)

EII INC.
530 S Ave E, Cranford, NJ 07016-3208
Tel.: (908) 276-1000   NJ
Web Site: https://www.eiielectric.com
Year Founded: 1984
Sales Range: $25-49.9 Million
Emp.: 300
Providers of Electrical Services
N.A.I.C.S.: 238210
Richard G. Guempel (CEO & Treas)
John T. Guempel (Pres)
Daniel Boublis (Project Mgr-Power T&D)
Mark A. Fiorletti (Project Mgr-Electrical Construction)
Robert Sagendorf (Dir-Safety)

EIKENBERRY CORPORATION
1663 W Sherman Blvd, Muskegon, MI 49441-3564
Tel.: (231) 759-0252   MI
Web Site: http://www.plumbsmarket.com
Year Founded: 1985
Sales Range: $50-74.9 Million
Emp.: 600

Grocery Store Services
N.A.I.C.S.: 551112
Dennis Prey (Controller)

EILEEN FISHER, INC.
2 Bridge St, Irvington, NY 10533-1527
Tel.: (914) 591-5700
Web Site: http://www.eileenfisher.com
Year Founded: 1982
Sales Range: $25-49.9 Million
Emp.: 800
Women's & Misses' Outerwear Mfr
N.A.I.C.S.: 315250
Monique Zhuma (Coord-Wholesale Mktg)
Shaheen Khateeb (Dir-Ops)
Anthony J. Lorusso (Dir-Sls)
Cathy Johnson (Mgr-AP)
Susan Kushnick (Mgr-Product Dev Ops)
Kenneth Pollak (CFO)
Janice Liebson (Dir-Customer Svc)
Loretta Torcicollo (Dir-Production)
Lila Vanagas (Partner-HR)
Shanti Durkee (Dir-Art)

EINHORN YAFFEE & PRESCOTT
NanoFab E 257 Fuller Rd 1st Fl, Albany, NY 12203-2904
Tel.: (518) 795-3800   NY
Web Site: http://www.eypae.com
Year Founded: 1972
Sales Range: $25-49.9 Million
Emp.: 300
Architectural Services
N.A.I.C.S.: 541310

EINSTEIN BROTHERS BAGELS
200 Fillmore St Ste 104, Denver, CO 80206
Tel.: (303) 355-8700
Web Site: http://www.einsteinbros.com
Year Founded: 1996
Rev.: $2,300,000
Emp.: 77
Fiscal Year-end: 12/31/06
Bagels
N.A.I.C.S.: 445291
Robert Hartnett (CEO)

EIQNETWORKS, INC.
31 Nagog Park, Acton, MA 01720
Tel.: (978) 266-9933
Web Site: http://www.eiqnetworks.com
Year Founded: 2001
Sales Range: $10-24.9 Million
Emp.: 100
Security, Risk & Audit Management Software & Services
N.A.I.C.S.: 513210
Vijay Basani (Co-Founder, Pres & CEO)
Jay Reddy (Co-Founder & Gen Mgr)

EISENBERG INTERNATIONAL CORPORATION
948 Griswold Ave, San Fernando, CA 91340
Tel.: (818) 365-8161   CA
Year Founded: 1967
Sales Range: $10-24.9 Million
Emp.: 40
Men's & Boys' Clothing Whslr
N.A.I.C.S.: 424350
Joel Eisenberg (Pres)
Richard Eisenberg (VP)
Betty Winter (Controller)

EISENMAN ASSOCIATES INC.

Eisenman Associates Inc.—(Continued)

401 Broadway 22nd Fl, New York, NY 10013
Tel.: (212) 941-0550　　　**NY**
Web Site: http://www.eisenman.com
Year Founded: 1962
Rev.: $8,000,000
Emp.: 8
Fiscal Year-end: 12/31/04
Fashion/Apparel, Graphic Design, Internet/Web Design, Investor Relations
N.A.I.C.S.: 541810
Nina Eisenman *(Owner & Creative Dir)*
Irene Galperin *(Production Mgr)*

EIT PROFESSIONALS CORP.
44968 Ford Rd Ste L, Canton, MI 48187
Tel.: (734) 416-0059
Web Site:
　　http://www.eitprofessionals.com
Year Founded: 1999
Sales Range: $100-124.9 Million
Emp.: 91
Staffing Services for Information Technology Professionals & Consultants
N.A.I.C.S.: 561311

Subsidiaries:

e-IT Professionals India Pvt. Ltd.　**(1)**
Flat #303 Srinivasa Nagar, Ameerpet, Hyderabad, 500 038, India
Tel.: (91) 40 6625 6649
Information Technology Consulting Services
N.A.I.C.S.: 541690

EIWA INTERNATIONAL INC.
500 E 7th St, Los Angeles, CA 90014-2410
Tel.: (213) 893-6123　　　**CA**
Web Site: http://www.intmarine.com
Year Founded: 1991
Sales Range: $10-24.9 Million
Emp.: 70
Distr of Fish & Seafood
N.A.I.C.S.: 424460

Subsidiaries:

International Marine Products Inc.　**(1)**
500 E 7th St, Los Angeles, CA 90014-2410
Tel.: (213) 893-6123
Web Site: http://www.intmarine.com
Sales Range: $10-24.9 Million
Emp.: 40
Distr of Fish & Seafoods
N.A.I.C.S.: 424460

International Marine Products Nevada Inc.　**(1)**
1741 S Mojave Rd, Las Vegas, NV 89104-4503
Tel.: (702) 431-8896
Sales Range: $10-24.9 Million
Emp.: 3
Provider of Warehousing Sevices
N.A.I.C.S.: 493110

EJ ELECTRIC INSTALLATION CO.
46-41 Vernon Blvd, Long Island City, NY 11101-5308
Tel.: (718) 786-9400　　　**NY**
Web Site: https://www.ej1899.com
Year Founded: 1966
Sales Range: $25-49.9 Million
Emp.: 500
Electrical Work Contractors
N.A.I.C.S.: 238210
Anthony Mann *(Pres)*

Subsidiaries:

Lowy & Donnath, Inc.　**(1)**
1037 49th Ave, Long Island City, NY 11101

Tel.: (718) 392-8222
Web Site: http://www.lowyanddonnath.com
Sales Range: $1-9.9 Million
Emp.: 20
Electrical Contractor
N.A.I.C.S.: 238210
Anthony Scala *(Sec)*

EJ GROUP, INC.
301 Spring St, East Jordan, MI 49727
Web Site: https://www.ejco.com
Gray & Ductile Iron Castings, Brake Drums, Fire Hydrants, Street Castings, Gate Valves & Industrial Castings
N.A.I.C.S.: 331511

EJ'S SHOES INC.
8620 Olive St Rd 334 Sovereign Ct, Ballwin, MO 63011
Tel.: (314) 991-4120
Web Site: http://ejshoes.com
Year Founded: 1972
Sales Range: $10-24.9 Million
Emp.: 100
Sales of Shoes
N.A.I.C.S.: 458210
Edward J. Nusrala *(Pres)*
Robert Brennan *(VP & Controller)*

EJ2 COMMUNICATIONS, INC.
111 E 14th St #284, New York, NY 10003
Tel.: (888) 468-3598
Web Site: http://www.flashpoint-intel.com
Year Founded: 2010
Business Risk Intelligence Services
N.A.I.C.S.: 561621
Josh Lefkowitz *(CEO)*

Subsidiaries:

Risk Based Security, Inc.　**(1)**
3308 W Clay St, Richmond, VA 23230
Web Site: http://www.riskbasedsecurity.com
Scientific & Technical Consulting Services
N.A.I.C.S.: 541690
Barry Kouns *(Pres & CEO)*
Michael Mortensen *(Dir-Security & Risk Intelligence Products & Svcs-Europe)*
Jake Kouns *(CEO)*

EJF CAPITAL LLC
2107 Wilson Blvd Ste 410, Arlington, VA 22201-3042
Tel.: (703) 875-9121
Web Site: https://www.ejfcap.com
Portfolio Management
N.A.I.C.S.: 523940
Frank R. Walker *(Chief Compliance Officer)*
Asheel Shah *(Sr Mng Dir & Head-Real Estate)*

EJM DEVELOPMENT CO.
9061 California State Rte 2, West Hollywood, CA 90069
Tel.: (310) 278-1830
Web Site:
　　http://www.ejmdevelopment.com
Year Founded: 1973
Sales Range: $10-24.9 Million
Real Estate Development & Services
N.A.I.C.S.: 236117
Kim Miller *(Portfolio Mgr)*
Alan Sette *(Dir-Fin & Acq)*
Susan Wincn *(VP)*
Jon Monkarsh *(Partner)*

EJM PIPE SERVICES INC.
7807 Lk Dr, Circle Pines, MN 55014
Tel.: (651) 786-8041
Web Site: http://www.ejmpipe.com
Year Founded: 1976
Sales Range: $10-24.9 Million
Emp.: 47
Underground Utilities Contractor
N.A.I.C.S.: 237110

Allen R. Montgomery *(Pres)*
Vicki J. Lundgren *(VP-Admin)*
Mark A. Montgomery *(VP-Field Ops)*

EK HEALTH SERVICES, INC.
992 S De Anza Blvd Ste 101, San Jose, CA 95129　　　**CA**
Web Site: https://www.ekhealth.com
Year Founded: 1998
Women Healthcare Services
N.A.I.C.S.: 621610
Kerri Wilson *(Pres & COO)*

Subsidiaries:

The Directions Group, LLC　**(1)**
2351 Sunset Blvd Ste 170-893, Rocklin, CA 95765
Tel.: (669) 444-1650
Web Site:
　　http://www.thedirectionsgroup.com
Vocational Rehabilitation Consulting Services
N.A.I.C.S.: 624310

EKAHAU, INC.
1851 Alexander Graham Bell Dr Ste 105, Reston, VA 20191
Web Site: http://www.ekahau.com
Year Founded: 2001
Sales Range: $10-24.9 Million
Wi-Fi Real Time Location System & Optimization Planning Software Developer
N.A.I.C.S.: 541511
Michel Wendell *(Chm & CEO)*
Steven Marinaro *(CFO)*
Mika Hakala *(COO)*
Bill Spahr *(VP-Pro Svcs & Support)*
Jussi Kiviniemi *(VP-Wi-Fi Tools)*
Bob Kennedy *(VP-Sls)*
Franco de Lorenzo *(VP-Engrg)*

EKLUNDS INC.
2860 Market Loop, Southlake, TX 76092
Tel.: (817) 949-2030
Web Site: https://www.eklunds.com
Sales Range: $10-24.9 Million
Emp.: 47
Commercial & Office Buildings, Renovation & Repair
N.A.I.C.S.: 236220
Beth Cunningham *(Pres)*
Susan Flyzik *(Dir-Mktg)*

EKOMI INC.
9107 Wilshire Blvd Ste 450, Beverly Hills, CA 90210
Tel.: (310) 961-4257
Web Site: http://www.ekomi-us.com
Emp.: 250
Internet Consumer Information Management Services
N.A.I.C.S.: 541519
Michael Ambros *(Co-Founder & CEO)*
Gunther Schmidt *(Co-Founder & Mng Dir)*

EKOTROPE INC.
71 Summer St, Boston, MA 02110
Tel.: (617) 453-8047
Web Site: http://www.ekotrope.com
Year Founded: 2010
Sales Range: $1-9.9 Million
Emp.: 9
Energy Efficient Building Design Software
N.A.I.C.S.: 513210
Ziv Rozenblum *(Co-Founder & CEO)*
Cy Kilbourn *(Co-Founder & Dir-Engrg)*
Benjamin DeLillo *(Co-Founder & Engr-Software)*
Nick Sisler *(Co-Founder & Engr)*

EKS GROUP LLC

1341 Providence Rd, Brandon, FL 33511
Tel.: (813) 626-3303
Web Site: https://www.eks-group.com
Year Founded: 2006
Sales Range: $10-24.9 Million
Emp.: 160
Temporary Help Service
N.A.I.C.S.: 561320
Catherine Hunt *(Mgr-Proposal)*

EL CAJON FORD
1595 E Main, El Cajon, CA 92021-5994
Tel.: (619) 579-8888
Web Site:
　　https://www.elcajonford.com
Sales Range: $100-124.9 Million
Emp.: 165
Automobiles, New & Used
N.A.I.C.S.: 532112
Paul F. Leader *(Pres)*
John Blake *(Controller)*
Colleen Manley *(Sec)*
Bobby Morales *(Dir-Internet)*

EL CAMINO RESOURCES LLC
21300 Superior St, Chatsworth, CA 91311-4312
Tel.: (818) 226-6600　　　**CA**
Web Site: http://www.elcaminodr.com
Year Founded: 1979
Emp.: 4
Disaster Recovery Services
N.A.I.C.S.: 561990
David E. Harmon *(Pres & CEO)*

EL CAMINO TRAILWAYS
214 Shaw Rd Ste T, South San Francisco, CA 94080
Tel.: (650) 989-2600　　　**CA**
Year Founded: 1988
Sales Range: $1-9.9 Million
Emp.: 75
Local Bus Charter Service
N.A.I.C.S.: 485510
Kumar Shah *(Chm & CEO)*
Ira Weiss *(Dir-Sls)*
Lynn Markey *(Mgr-Sls & Mktg)*

EL CLASIFICADO
1125 Goodrich Blvd, Los Angeles, CA 90022
Tel.: (323) 278-5310　　　**CA**
Web Site:
　　http://www.elclasificado.com
Year Founded: 1988
Sales Range: $10-24.9 Million
Emp.: 114
Hispanic Newspaper & Online Publisher
N.A.I.C.S.: 513110
Adrian Olmedo *(Mgr-Adv Production)*
Jazmina Vasconez *(Mgr-Sls & Admin)*
Maribel Sauceda *(Mgr-Classifieds Sls)*

EL DORADO BROADCASTERS
51 Zaca Ln Ste 100, San Luis Obispo, CA 93401-7353
Tel.: (805) 545-0101　　　**CA**
Web Site:
　　http://www.edbroadcasters.com
Sales Range: $10-24.9 Million
Emp.: 50
Radio Broadcasting Stations
N.A.I.C.S.: 516110
Ron Roy *(Gen Mgr)*
Kathy Mansell *(Gen Mgr-Sls)*
Niki Kozak *(Dir-Promotions)*
Chris Fleming *(Exec VP)*
Jason Wolff *(Pres)*

Subsidiaries:

El Dorado Broadcasters　**(1)**

12370 Hesperia Rd Ste 17, Victorville, CA 92392
Tel.: (760) 241-1313
Web Site: http://www.edbroadcasters.com
Sales Range: $10-24.9 Million
Emp.: 35
Providing Radio Broadcasting Station Services
N.A.I.C.S.: 516110
Chris Fleming *(Gen Mgr)*

EL DORADO FURNITURE CORP.
4200 NW 167th St, Opa Locka, FL 33054
Tel.: (305) 624-9700
Web Site:
  http://www.eldoradofurniture.com
Year Founded: 1967
Sales Range: $150-199.9 Million
Emp.: 780
Owner & Operator of Furniture Stores
N.A.I.C.S.: 449110
Luis E. Capo *(Pres)*
Pedro Capo *(COO)*

EL DORADO MOBILE HOMES INC.
1724 Jct City Rd, El Dorado, AR 71730
Tel.: (870) 862-9594
Web Site:
  https://www.eldohomes.com
Sales Range: $10-24.9 Million
Emp.: 10
Sales of Mobile Homes
N.A.I.C.S.: 459930
Ricky Davis *(Chm)*

EL DORADO MOTORS INC.
2300 N Central Expy, McKinney, TX 75070
Tel.: (972) 569-0101
Web Site:
  http://www.eldoradomotors.com
Sales Range: $25-49.9 Million
Emp.: 200
New & Used Car Dealers
N.A.I.C.S.: 441110
Stanley V. Graff *(Pres)*
Craig Nedrow *(Mgr-Sls-Used Cars)*
Bryan Northington *(Mgr-Collision Center)*
Patrick Phillips *(Controller)*

EL DORADO SAVINGS BANK, F.S.B.
4040 El Dorado Rd, Placerville, CA 95667
Tel.: (530) 622-1492
Web Site:
  https://www.eldoradosavings
  bank.com
Year Founded: 1956
Sales Range: $50-74.9 Million
Emp.: 304
Federal Savings Bank
N.A.I.C.S.: 522180
Thomas C. Meuser *(Chm)*
George L. Cook Jr. *(Pres & CEO)*

EL ENCANTO INCORPO-RATED
2001 4th St SW, Albuquerque, NM 87102
Tel.: (505) 243-2722
Web Site:
  http://www.buenofoods.com
Year Founded: 1951
Seasonings & Spices
N.A.I.C.S.: 311942
Jacqueline J. Baca *(Pres)*

EL FENIX CORPORATION
2414 N Akard St Ste 500, Dallas, TX 75201
Tel.: (972) 241-2171

Web Site: http://www.elfenix.com
Year Founded: 1918
Sales Range: $10-24.9 Million
Emp.: 850
Owner & Operator of Mexican Restaurants
N.A.I.C.S.: 722511
Lee Villarreal *(Area Mgr)*

EL MILAGRO INCORPORATED
2919 S Western Ave, Chicago, IL 60608
Tel.: (773) 523-5627
Rev.: $50,300,000
Emp.: 300
Tortillas, Fresh Or Refrigerated
N.A.I.C.S.: 311830

EL MOR CHEVROLET
E Main St & Valley Rd, Morgantown, PA 19543
Tel.: (610) 286-5161
Web Site: http://www.el-mor.com
Year Founded: 1948
Sales Range: $10-24.9 Million
Emp.: 30
Car Whslr
N.A.I.C.S.: 441110
Tammy Hartman *(Office Mgr)*

EL PASO COMMUNICATION SYSTEMS, INC.
1630 E Paisano Dr, El Paso, TX 79901
Tel.: (915) 533-5119
Web Site: https://www.epcom.net
Rev.: $10,565,081
Emp.: 25
Communications Equipment
N.A.I.C.S.: 423690
Jorge Saad *(Pres)*
Rudy Jarmillo *(VP)*
Jorge Carreon Mingura *(Dir-Sls)*

EL PASO WATER UTILITIES
1154 Hawkins Blvd, El Paso, TX 79925-6436
Tel.: (915) 594-5500
Web Site: http://www.epwu.org
Year Founded: 1952
Sales Range: $50-74.9 Million
Emp.: 665
Water Supply Services
N.A.I.C.S.: 237110
Terri Garcia *(Treas & Sec)*
Ruth Katherine Brennand *(Vice Chm)*

EL POPOCATAPETL INDUS-TRIES, INC.
1854 W 21st St, Chicago, IL 60608-2715
Tel.: (312) 421-6143
Sales Range: $10-24.9 Million
Emp.: 130
Dried & Dehydrated Food Mfr
N.A.I.C.S.: 311423
Ernesto Avina *(Pres)*
Margaret Avina *(Sec)*
Steve Lineer *(Partner & Mgr-Fin, Sls, Mktg & Mgmt Info Sys)*
Zachariah Peterson *(Mgr-IT)*

EL REY MEXICAN PRODUCTS INC.
1023 S 16th St, Milwaukee, WI 53204
Tel.: (414) 643-1640
Web Site: http://www.elreyfoods.com
Rev.: $15,616,888
Emp.: 105
Grocery Store Operators
N.A.I.C.S.: 445110
Ernesto Villarreal *(Pres & CEO)*

EL RIO SANTA CRUZ NEIGH-

BORHOOD HEALTH CENTER, INC.
839 W Congress St, Tucson, AZ 85745
Tel.: (520) 670-3705   AZ
Web Site: http://www.elrio.org
Year Founded: 1973
Sales Range: $75-99.9 Million
Emp.: 1,023
Health Care Srvices
N.A.I.C.S.: 622110
Enrique Serna *(VP)*
Brian Flagg *(Sec)*
Kathryn Beatty *(Partner)*
Douglas Spegman *(Chief Medical Officer)*
Nancy Johnson *(CFO)*

EL SUPERIOR MEXICAN FOODS LLC.
920 W Fulton Market, Chicago, IL 60607-1309
Tel.: (312) 421-2345
Sales Range: $1-9.9 Million
Emp.: 14
Veal Product Mfr
N.A.I.C.S.: 311612
Veronica Galvez *(Office Mgr)*

EL TAPATIO MARKETS IN-CORPORATED
310 E Florence Ave, Los Angeles, CA 90003
Tel.: (562) 293-4200
Web Site: http://www.eltapatio.com
Rev.: $39,400,000
Emp.: 190
Supermarket
N.A.I.C.S.: 445110
Larry Flores *(Pres)*
Lois Ennis *(VP-Procurement & Adv)*

EL TELAR INC.
Carr 183 Km 21 5, Las Piedras, PR 00771
Tel.: (787) 716-1001
Sales Range: $10-24.9 Million
Emp.: 24
Fabric Stores Piece Goods
N.A.I.C.S.: 459130

EL TORO EXPORT
1469 La Brucherie Rd, El Centro, CA 92243
Tel.: (760) 352-4157
Web Site:
  https://www.eltoroexport.com
Sales Range: $10-24.9 Million
Emp.: 10
Seeds & Bulbs
N.A.I.C.S.: 424910
William Plourd *(Pres)*
Bailey Michael Johnson *(CFO)*

Subsidiaries:

ETX Inc.   (1)
4746 US Hwy 111, Brawley, CA 92227
Tel.: (760) 344-0166
Rev.: $1,800,000
Emp.: 8
Seeds & Bulbs
N.A.I.C.S.: 424910

EL TORO WATER DISTRICT
24251 Los Alisos Blvd, Lake Forest, CA 92630
Tel.: (949) 837-7050
Web Site: https://www.etwd.com
Year Founded: 1960
Sales Range: $25-49.9 Million
Emp.: 50
Water Supply
N.A.I.C.S.: 221310

Robert R. Hill *(Gen Mgr)*
Michael P. Grandy *(CFO & Asst Gen Mgr)*
Ted F. Martin *(Pres)*
M. Scott Goldman *(VP)*

EL-AD GROUP, LTD.
575 Madison Ave 22nd Fl, New York, NY 10022
Tel.: (212) 213-8833
Web Site: https://www.eladgroup.com
Year Founded: 1992
Real Estate Investment Company
N.A.I.C.S.: 551112
Isaac Tshuva *(Chm)*

Subsidiaries:

Agellan Commercial Real Estate Investment Trust   (1)
890 Yonge Street Suite 505, Toronto, M4W 3P4, ON, Canada   (100%)
Tel.: (416) 593-6800
Web Site: http://www.agellanreit.com
Sales Range: $75-99.9 Million
Real Estate Investment Trust
N.A.I.C.S.: 525990
Frank Camenzuli *(CEO)*
Rosalia Lau *(VP-Acctg)*
Terra Attard *(COO & Sec)*
Glen Ladouceur *(Chm)*
Christopher Caswell *(Exec VP)*

ELAINE, INC.
1 Hazel St, Woodland Park, NJ 07424
Tel.: (973) 345-6200
Web Site: https://www.njmeter.com
Sales Range: $10-24.9 Million
Emp.: 5
Compressed Air
N.A.I.C.S.: 333912
Anthony Abbate *(VP)*
Elaine Abbate *(Pres)*

Subsidiaries:

New Jersey Meter Co.   (1)
1 Hazel St, Woodland Park, NJ 07424
Tel.: (973) 345-6200
Web Site: http://www.njmeter.com
Emp.: 25
Moisture Meters Mfr
N.A.I.C.S.: 423730
Anthony Abbate *(Chm & Pres)*

ELAN CHEMICAL COMPANY INC.
268 Doremus Ave, Newark, NJ 07105
Tel.: (973) 344-8014
Web Site: https://www.elan-chemical.com
Year Founded: 1979
Sales Range: $25-49.9 Million
Emp.: 84
Industrial Chemicals & Flavor Extracts Mfr
N.A.I.C.S.: 311942
David Pimentel *(VP-Sls)*

ELAN GROWTH PARTNERS, LLC
1090 Ctr Dr, Park City, UT 84098
Tel.: (760) 309-9436
Web Site: https://elangrowth.com
Year Founded: 2018
Investment Services
N.A.I.C.S.: 523999
Craig Dupper *(Founder & Mng Partner)*

Subsidiaries:

Custom Power, LLC   (1)
10910 Talbert Ave, Fountain Valley, CA 92708
Tel.: (714) 962-7600
Web Site: http://www.houseofbatteries.com
Sales Range: $10-24.9 Million
Battery Assemblies & Energy Solutions
N.A.I.C.S.: 423690
Mel Weis *(CEO)*

Elan Partners—(Continued)

ELAN PARTNERS
15455 Dallas Pkwy Ste 600, Addison, TX 75001
Tel.: (214) 295-2848
Web Site:
　http://www.elanpartners.com
Year Founded: 2006
Sales Range: $1-9.9 Million
Emp.: 41
Staff Augmentation, IT & Engineering Services
N.A.I.C.S.: 561320
Stefanie Nielson (Owner & Mng Dir)
Kim Busker (Sr Acct Mgr)
Colleen Moore (Acct Mgr)

ELAN-POLO INC.
2005 Walton Rd, Saint Louis, MO 63114-5805
Tel.: (314) 655-3300　　　　　MO
Web Site: https://www.elanpolo.com
Year Founded: 1949
Sales Range: $25-49.9 Million
Emp.: 300
Mfr of Footwear
N.A.I.C.S.: 424340
Christina Miller (Acct Mgr-Sls)
Jan Harr (Coord-Ticketing)
Brent Phelps (Product Dir)
Bob Connolly (VP)
Wade Beatty (Mgr-Sourcing)
Lorri Richter (Sr VP)
Rich Demma (VP-Sls)

Subsidiaries:

DVS Footwear International, LLC　(1)
7171 Fenwick Ln, Westminster, CA 92683　　　　　　　　　　(65%)
Tel.: (310) 715-8300
Web Site: http://www.dvsshoes.com
Performance Skate Shoes & Lifestyle Footwear Mfr
N.A.I.C.S.: 316210
Brian Dunlap (VP)
Kerry Getz (Mgr-Global Skate)
Jim Shubin (Dir-Mktg)

ELAND ENERGY INC.
13455 Noel Rd Ste 2000, Dallas, TX 75240
Tel.: (214) 368-6100
Web Site:
　http://www.elandenergy.com
Rev.: $10,100,000
Emp.: 65
Provider of Oil & Gas Exploration Services
N.A.I.C.S.: 213112
Allen Faris (CFO)
Brad Cook (Dir-Fin)
Jane Gordon (Supvr-Joint Interest)
Ralph Butler (Area Mgr-Ops)
Joe Stokes (Mgr-Tax)

ELASTEC/AMERICAN MARINE, INC.
1309 W Main, Carmi, IL 62821
Tel.: (618) 382-2525
Web Site: https://www.elastec.com
Year Founded: 1990
Sales Range: $10-24.9 Million
Emp.: 100
Machine Shops
N.A.I.C.S.: 332710
Jeff Bohleber (Mgr-Fin)
Donald Wilson (CEO)
Joy Scarlett (Mgr-HR)

ELATE GROUP, INC.
305 Broadway Fl 7, New York, NY 10007
Tel.: (212) 920-4450　　　　　DE
Year Founded: 2013
Rev.: $4,979,856
Assets: $1,799,089
Liabilities: $1,462,472

Net Worth: $336,617
Earnings: $1,172,071
Emp.: 27
Fiscal Year-end: 12/31/21
Concierge Services
N.A.I.C.S.: 812990
Kevin Britt (Pres, CEO & Founder)
Garry N. Lowenthal (CFO)
Julia Britt (Chief Acctg Officer)
Mykola Melnyk (Head-Sales)

ELAUWIT LLC
108 Kings Hwy E, Haddonfield, NJ 08033
Tel.: (856) 427-0933
Web Site:
　http://www.elauwitmedia.com
Year Founded: 2004
Sales Range: $1-9.9 Million
Emp.: 42
Newspaper Publishers
N.A.I.C.S.: 513110
Barry Rubens (CEO)
Taylor Jones (CTO)
Bruce Sanders (CMO & Exec VP)
Scott Davis (COO)

ELAYAWAY, INC.
3111 Mahan Dr Ste 20 121, Tallahassee, FL 32308
Tel.: (850) 583-5019　　　　　DE
Web Site: http://www.elayaway.com
Year Founded: 2006
Sales Range: Less than $1 Million
Emp.: 1
Online Payment Services
N.A.I.C.S.: 522320
Jesse Stickle (Dir-Media Rels)

ELBERTA CRATE & BOX CO.
606 Dothan Rd, Bainbridge, GA 31717-3053
Tel.: (229) 246-2266　　　　　GA
Web Site: http://www.elberta.net
Year Founded: 1905
Sales Range: $150-199.9 Million
Emp.: 450
Wood Fruit Crates, Wirebound Boxes & Pallets Mfr
N.A.I.C.S.: 321920
Steve Williams (CEO)
Todd Mills (VP-Sls)

ELBERTON MANUFACTURING COMPANY INCORPORATED
525 7th Ave Rm 1601, New York, NY 10018
Tel.: (212) 840-5700
Rev.: $12,400,000
Emp.: 3
Women's Blouses Mfr
N.A.I.C.S.: 424350
Michael Laufer (Pres)

ELC TECHNOLOGIES
1221 State St Ste 201, Santa Barbara, CA 93101
Tel.: (866) 863-7365
Web Site: http://www.elctech.com
Year Founded: 1999
Sales Range: $1-9.9 Million
Emp.: 28
Developer of Mobile, Cloud & Web Applications
N.A.I.C.S.: 541519
Kamran Pourzanjani (Co-Owner)
Omid Rahmat (Co-Owner)

ELCAR FENCE & SUPPLY CO.
2155 S Valentia St, Denver, CO 80231-3324
Tel.: (303) 755-5211　　　　　CO
Web Site: http://www.elcarfence.com
Year Founded: 1946
Sales Range: $75-99.9 Million
Emp.: 35

Fence Builder
N.A.I.C.S.: 238990
Alfred M. Ellerby (CEO)

ELCAT INC.
163 Washington Vly Rd, Warren, NJ 07059-7180
Tel.: (732) 302-1686
Year Founded: 1995
Sales Range: $10-24.9 Million
Emp.: 60
Mfr of Environmental Controls
N.A.I.C.S.: 334512
John Scansaroli (Pres)

Subsidiaries:

Nedamco North America
Corporation　　　　　　　　　(1)
163 Washington Vly Rd Unit 101, Warren, NJ 07059
Tel.: (732) 302-1686
Sales Range: $10-24.9 Million
Emp.: 2
Chemicals & Allied Products Mfr
N.A.I.C.S.: 424690
John Scansaroli (CEO)

ELCO INC.
4315 Yeager Way, Bakersfield, CA 93313
Tel.: (661) 837-2549
Web Site: http://www.elcoinc.com
Year Founded: 1992
Sales Range: $10-24.9 Million
Emp.: 100
Machine Shop Operator
N.A.I.C.S.: 332710
Greg Dufresne (Mgr-HSE)

ELCO LABORATORIES INC.
2545 Palmer Ave, University Park, IL 60484
Tel.: (708) 534-3000
Web Site: http://www.elcolabs.com
Sales Range: $10-24.9 Million
Emp.: 55
Rug, Upholstery, Or Dry Cleaning Detergents Or Spotters
N.A.I.C.S.: 325612
Norman L. Elliott (Pres)
Bill Elliot (VP)
John Boxell (Controller)
Bob Hettinger (Pres)

ELCOM INC.
470 Providence Main St NW Ste 303, Huntsville, AL 35806
Tel.: (256) 830-4001
Web Site: http://www.elcomsales.com
Rev.: $325,000,000
Emp.: 24
Semiconductor Devices
N.A.I.C.S.: 423690
Kerry Erwin (Pres)

ELCOM INTERNATIONAL, INC.
10 Oceana Way, Norwood, MA 02062
Tel.: (781) 501-4000　　　　　DE
Web Site: http://www.elcom.com
Sales Range: $1-9.9 Million
Emp.: 33
eProcurement & eMarket Solutions
N.A.I.C.S.: 425120
William Lock (Chm)
David Elliott (Exec VP-Fin)
Ian Burford (VP-IT Svcs)

ELCON CORPORATION
1720 75th St SW, Everett, WA 98203-6262
Tel.: (425) 743-5600
Web Site: http://www.elconcorp.com
Sales Range: $10-24.9 Million
Emp.: 100
Water, Sewer & Utility Lines
N.A.I.C.S.: 237110

Peter S. Williams (Pres & CEO)
Joyce McNeil (VP-Fin)
Barnaby Peters (Mgr-Ops)
Jason Decker (Exec VP)
Michael Woeck (Mgr-Bus Dev)

ELCON INC.
600 Twin Rail Dr, Minooka, IL 60447
Tel.: (815) 467-9500
Web Site: http://www.elconinc.net
Sales Range: $10-24.9 Million
Emp.: 50
Control Equipment, Electric
N.A.I.C.S.: 335314
Adam Wilhelmi (Mgr-Electrical Test Dept)
Frank J. Garrone Jr. (Pres)

ELDER AUTOMOTIVE GROUP
777 John R Rd, Troy, MI 48083
Tel.: (248) 585-4000
Web Site: http://www.elderautomotive group.com
Rev.: $46,300,000
Emp.: 137
Holding Company; New & User Car Dealerships Owner & Operator
N.A.I.C.S.: 551112
Irma B. Elder (CEO)

Subsidiaries:

Elder Automotive Group of Tampa Bay, Inc.　　　　　　　　　(1)
320 E Fletcher Ave, Tampa, FL 33612
Tel.: (813) 371-8200
Web Site: http://www.elderautogroup.com
Sales Range: $75-99.9 Million
Emp.: 100
Holding Company; New & Used Car Dealerships
N.A.I.C.S.: 551112
Robert R. Elder (Pres)

Subsidiary (Domestic):

Elder Auto, Inc.　　　　　　　　(2)
11608 N Florida Ave, Tampa, FL 33612
Web Site: http://www.tampamitsubishi.com
New & Used Car Dealer
N.A.I.C.S.: 441110

Elder Ford of Tampa, LLC　　　(2)
9560 N Florida Ave, Tampa, FL 33612
Tel.: (813) 437-2865
Web Site: http://www.elderfordoftampa.com
Emp.: 150
New & Used Car Dealer
N.A.I.C.S.: 441110
Jeff Adelman (Mgr-Inventory)
Joe Kelley (Dir-Parts)
Michelle Santiago (Dir-Fin)
Keith Hodge (Mgr-Used Car Inventory)
Nacer Menouni (Mgr-Fin)

Unit (Domestic):

Jaguar of Tampa　　　　　　　　(2)
320 E Fletcher Ave, Tampa, FL 33612-3409
Tel.: (813) 371-8200
Web Site: http://www.jaguaroftampa.com
Sales Range: $10-24.9 Million
Emp.: 45
New Car Dealers
N.A.I.C.S.: 441110
T. J. Marchand (Dir-Pre-Owned)
Rob Elder (Pres)

Signature Ford of Perry, LLC　(1)
3942 Lansing Rd, Perry, MI 48872
Tel.: (517) 625-5600
Web Site: http://www.sigautogroup.com
Sales Range: $10-24.9 Million
Emp.: 30
New & Used Car Dealer
N.A.I.C.S.: 441110
Joe Falzon (Pres)

Troy Motors, Inc.　　　　　　　　(1)
777 John R Rd, Troy, MI 48083-4302
Tel.: (248) 825-8647
Web Site: http://www.elderford.com
Sales Range: $50-74.9 Million
Emp.: 120
New & Used Car Dealer

N.A.I.C.S.: 441110
Michael Halloran (Sls Mgr-New Vehicle)
Al Murphy (Mgr-Wholesale Parts)

ELDER MANUFACTURING COMPANY, INC.
999 Executive Pkwy Ste 300, Saint Louis, MO 63141
Tel.: (314) 469-1120   MO
Web Site:
   https://www.elderwearwecare.com
Year Founded: 1988
Sales Range: $75-99.9 Million
Emp.: 100
Uniforms Mfr
N.A.I.C.S.: 315250
Gregory Beile (Exec VP)
Richard Pace (Dir-Mktg)
Gregg Hanson (Exec VP)
Robert Branstetter (CFO)

ELDER RESEARCH INC.
300 W Main St Ste 301, Charlottesville, VA 22903
Tel.: (434) 973-7673
Web Site:
   http://www.elderresearch.com
Marketing Research & Public Opinion Polling
N.A.I.C.S.: 541910
Gerhard Pilcher (CEO)
Jeff Deal (VP-Ops)
Peter Bruce (Pres)
Christina Ho (VP-Govt Analytics & Innovation)
John F. Elder IV (Founder & Chm)

Subsidiaries:

Statistics.Com, LLC   (1)
4075 Wilson Blvd 8th, Arlington, VA 22203
Tel.: (571) 281-8817
Web Site: http://www.statistics.com
Professional & Management Development Training
N.A.I.C.S.: 611430
Peter Bruce (Pres)

ELDER SALES & SERVICE INC.
4488 Greenville Sandy Lk Rd, Stoneboro, PA 16153
Tel.: (724) 376-3740
Web Site:
   http://www.eldersalesservice.com
Sales Range: $10-24.9 Million
Emp.: 22
Agricultural Machinery & Equipment
N.A.I.C.S.: 423820
Harry M. Elder Sr. (Pres)

ELDER SERVICES OF CAPE COD & THE ISLANDS, INC.
68 Route 134, South Dennis, MA 02660
Tel.: (508) 394-4630   MA
Web Site: https://www.escci.org
Year Founded: 1972
Sales Range: $10-24.9 Million
Emp.: 167
Elder Care Services
N.A.I.C.S.: 623311
Deborah Tranfaglia (CFO)

ELDER-JONES, INC.
1120 E 80th St Ste 211, Bloomington, MN 55420-1463
Tel.: (952) 345-6069   MN
Web Site:
   https://www.elderjones.com
Year Founded: 1971
General Contractor, Retail Construction & Permit Services
N.A.I.C.S.: 236220
John S. Elder (Owner)
Brian Perkkio (VP-Ops)
Dennis Hill (CFO)
Andrew Hirsch (Project Mgr)

ELDERHOSTEL, INC.
11 Avenue de Lafayette, Boston, MA 02111-1746
Tel.: (978) 323-4141   MA
Web Site:
   https://www.roadscholar.org
Year Founded: 1975
Sales Range: $200-249.9 Million
Emp.: 407
Educational Support Services
N.A.I.C.S.: 611710
Peter Spiers (Sr VP-Strategic Outreach)
JoAnn Bell (VP-Programs)
Lowell Partridge (CFO & Asst Treas)
James Moses (Pres & CEO)

ELDERSERVE, INC.
300 E Market St Ste 190, Louisville, KY 40202
Tel.: (502) 587-8673   KY
Web Site:
   http://www.elderserveinc.org
Year Founded: 1962
Sales Range: $1-9.9 Million
Emp.: 129
Elder Care Services
N.A.I.C.S.: 623312
Julia Meredith (Sec)

ELDERSOURCE
10688 Old St Augustine Rd, Jacksonville, FL 32257
Tel.: (904) 391-6600   FL
Web Site:
   https://www.myeldersource.org
Year Founded: 1974
Sales Range: $10-24.9 Million
Elder Care Services
N.A.I.C.S.: 624120
Linda Levin (Exec Dir)
Susan Alevy (Dir-Programs & Plng)
Renee Knight (Dir-Community Svcs)
Andrea Spencer (Dir-Comm)

ELDON C. STUTSMAN INC.
121 Lassie St, Hills, IA 52235
Tel.: (319) 679-2281   IA
Web Site:
   https://www.stutsmans.com
Year Founded: 1940
Sales Range: $75-99.9 Million
Emp.: 150
Farm Supplies Mfr
N.A.I.C.S.: 424910
Ronald E. Stutsman (Chm)
Scott Szymanek (Pres & CFO)
Mark Stutsman (COO)
Scott Stutsman (CEO)

Subsidiaries:

Bazooka Farmstar Inc.   (1)
800 E 7th St, Washington, IA 52353-2173
Tel.: (319) 653-5080
Web Site: http://www.bazookafarmstar.com
Sales Range: $10-24.9 Million
Emp.: 25
Farm Machinery & Equipment Mfr
N.A.I.C.S.: 333111
Eric Hahn (Mng Partner)
Kevin Wolter (Mgr-Sls & Bus Dev)

ELDORADO ARTESIAN SPRINGS, INC.
1783 Dogwood St, Louisville, CO 80027
Tel.: (303) 499-1316
Web Site:
   http://www.eldoradosprings.com
Year Founded: 1983
Sales Range: $10-24.9 Million
Emp.: 83
Specialty Food Stores
N.A.I.C.S.: 445298
Cathleen M. Shoenfeld (CFO)
Douglas A. Larson (Co-Founder, Pres & Partner)

Jeremy S. Martin (VP-Mktg)
Kate Janssen (VP-Sls)
Kevin M. Sipple (VP-Ops)

ELDRIDGE ELECTRIC CO.
13315 Western Oak, Helotes, TX 78023
Tel.: (210) 695-9113
Web Site: https://www.eldridge-electric.com
Year Founded: 1944
Sales Range: $10-24.9 Million
Emp.: 150
Electronic Services
N.A.I.C.S.: 238210
Pete Cervantes (Pres-HR)
Martin Clemence (Mgr-Parts)
Ernie Ybarra (Project Mgr & Mgr-Project)
Ernie Ybarra (Mgr-Project)
Oscar Eldridge (Founder)

ELDRIDGE INDUSTRIES LLC
600 Stemboat Rd, Greenwich, CT 06830
Tel.: (203) 298-5300
Web Site: http://www.eldridge.com
Privater Equity Firm
N.A.I.C.S.: 523999
Todd L. Boehley (Co-Founder & CEO)
Anthony D. Minella (Co-Founder & Pres)
Duncan Bagshaw (Gen Counsel)
Bill Hagner (Chief Strategy Officer & Head-Human Capital)
John F. Klein (COO & CFO)
Emily Bachman (Principal & Chief Admin Officer)
Todd J. Gilbert (Principal)
Michelei Trogni (Operating Partner)
Dylan Glenn (Sr Dir)

Subsidiaries:

Maranon Capital, L.P.   (1)
303 W Madison St Ste 2500, Chicago, IL 60606
Tel.: (312) 646-1200
Web Site: http://www.maraoncapital.com
Financial Investment Activities
N.A.I.C.S.: 523999
Theresa D. Mozzocci (Principal)
Andrew C. Eshelman (VP)
Tom Gregory (Founder & Mng Dir)

Metropolis Technologies, Inc.   (1)
6278 N Federal Hwy 413, Fort Lauderdale, FL 33308
Tel.: (954) 941-1010
Web Site: http://www.metropolis.com
Sales Range: $1-9.9 Million
Emp.: 21
Computer Software Systems Analysis & Design
N.A.I.C.S.: 541511
Jennifer Locandro (Mgr-Acct-Natl)

Subsidiary (Domestic):

SP Plus Corporation   (2)
200 E Randolph St Ste 7700, Chicago, IL 60601-7702
Tel.: (312) 274-2000
Web Site: https://www.spplus.com
Rev.: $1,553,500,000
Assets: $1,121,400,000
Liabilities: $895,700,000
Net Worth: $225,700,000
Earnings: $45,200,000
Emp.: 12,400
Fiscal Year-end: 12/31/2022
Holding Company; Parking Lot & Garage Management Services
N.A.I.C.S.: 551112
Wenyu Blanchard (Chief Legal Officer & Sec)

Subsidiary (Domestic):

Baggage Airline Guest Services, Inc.   (3)
6751 Forum Dr Ste 200, Orlando, FL 32821
Tel.: (407) 849-0670

Web Site: https://www.bagsinc.com
Baggage Services
N.A.I.C.S.: 488999
Billy Arden (COO)
Amanda Vaughan (VP-Finance)
John Romantic (Sr VP)

City of Oakland Parking Partners   (3)
1250 Martin Luther King Jr Way, Oakland, CA 94612
Tel.: (510) 238-7670
Automobile Parking Services
N.A.I.C.S.: 812930
Bereket Tesfay (Supvr-Acct)

Kinney West 83rd St., Inc.   (3)
2401 21st Ave S 200, Nashville, TN 37212
Tel.: (615) 297-4255
Automobile Parking Services
N.A.I.C.S.: 812930

SP Plus Property Management, Inc.   (3)
15206 Venmtura Blvd Ste214, Sherman Oaks, CA 91403
Tel.: (310) 929-0128
Web Site: https://www.pmgmtservices.com
Emp.: 30
Property Management Services
N.A.I.C.S.: 531390
Charles Hawley (Dir-Asset Mgmt)
Dale Stark (Gen Mgr)
Robert Gottsch (Accountant-Property Mgmt)

SP Plus Security Services, Inc.   (3)
639 Wilshire Blvd, Los Angeles, CA 90017
Tel.: (213) 252-1600
Web Site: https://www.spplussecurity.com
Sales Range: $100-124.9 Million
Security Services
N.A.I.C.S.: 561612

Standard Parking Corporation IL   (3)
900 N Michigan Ave Ste 1600, Chicago, IL 60601
Tel.: (312) 274-2000
Web Site: https://www.standardparking.com
Parking Lot & Garage Management Services
N.A.I.C.S.: 812930

Subsidiary (Non-US):

Standard Parking of Canada Ltd.   (3)
2555 Saint Joseph Blvd, Orleans, K1C 1S6, ON, Canada
Tel.: (613) 830-3328
Parking Lot & Garage Management Services
N.A.I.C.S.: 812930
Bryan L. Wallner (Sr VP & Gen Mgr)

Subsidiary (Domestic):

USA Parking System, Inc.   (3)
1330 SE 4th Ave Ste D, Fort Lauderdale, FL 33316
Tel.: (954) 524-6500
Web Site: https://www.usaparking.net
Parking Management Services
N.A.I.C.S.: 812930

ELDRIDGE SUPPLY COMPANY
1570E Hwy 64, Augusta, AR 72006
Tel.: (870) 362-7082
Web Site:
   https://www.eldridgesupply.com
Sales Range: $10-24.9 Million
Emp.: 75
Farm Implements
N.A.I.C.S.: 423820
Charles P. Eldridge (Owner)
Laura Eldridge (Treas & Sec)

ELECTION SERVICES CORPORATION
1363 Veterans Hwy Ste 32, Hauppauge, NY 11788
Tel.: (516) 248-4200   NY
Web Site:
   http://www.electionservicescorp.com
Year Founded: 1999
Sales Range: $10-24.9 Million
Emp.: 25
N.A.I.C.S.: 561990

Election Services Corporation—(Continued)

Gregg W. McGilvray (CIO)
Frank Fatone (Pres & CEO)
Ingrid Von Holt (VP-Election Svcs)

ELECTRA LINK INC.
21755 IH-45 Bldg 10, Spring, TX 77388
Tel.: (281) 350-6096
Web Site: https://www.electralink.com
Year Founded: 1985
Sales Range: $100-124.9 Million
Emp.: 300
Designer & Installer of Fiber Optic Cables; Cable Laying Construction
N.A.I.C.S.: 237130
Dale Pearson (COO)
Amy Sallee (Controller)

ELECTRI-CORD MANUFAC-TURING CO.
312 E Main St, Westfield, PA 16950-1609
Tel.: (814) 367-2265   PA
Web Site: https://www.electri-cord.com
Year Founded: 1946
Sales Range: $75-99.9 Million
Emp.: 100
lectrical Cord Sets Mfr
N.A.I.C.S.: 335999
Mitch Samuels (Pres & CEO)
Dennis McDonald (Exec VP & Gen Mgr)
Mike Vargeson (Mgr-Estimating & NPI)
Hector Ramon (VP & Gen Mgr-ECMMX)
Lisa Romaneo (CFO)
Subsidiaries:
E.S. Electri-Cord S. de R.L. de C.V.   (1)
Ave Camino Al Iteso 8499 Nave 5, Colonia El Mante, Tlaquepaque, 45080, Jalisco, Mexico   (100%)
Tel.: (52) 3331333681
Web Site: http://www.electri-cord.com.mx
Sales Range: $10-24.9 Million
Emp.: 500
Electrical Cord Sets Mfr & Distr
N.A.I.C.S.: 335999

ELECTRIC ARTISTS, INC.
42 Bond St 3rd Fl, New York, NY 10012
Tel.: (212) 354-2650
Year Founded: 1997
Sales Range: Less than $1 Million
Emp.: 15
N.A.I.C.S.: 541613
Marc Schiller (Founder & CEO)
Howie Kleinberg (Sr VP)
Terry Goldman (Sr Acct Exec)
Claire Hyland (Sr Acct Exec & Brand Strategist)
Maria Elena Diaz (Controller)

ELECTRIC CAR DISTRIBU-TORS INC.
71441 Hwy 111, Rancho Mirage, CA 92270
Tel.: (760) 346-5661
Web Site: http://www.elec-car.com
Rev.: $10,000,000
Emp.: 60
Golf Carts
N.A.I.C.S.: 423860
Robert Thomas Jr. (Founder & Pres)

ELECTRIC CLOUD INC.
676 W Maude Ave, Sunnyvale, CA 94085
Tel.: (408) 419-4300
Web Site: http://www.electric-cloud.com

Year Founded: 2002
Sales Range: $10-24.9 Million
Emp.: 87
Information Technology Solution
N.A.I.C.S.: 513210
Douglas Schrier (Gen Partner)
Steve Brodie (CEO)
Steven Vattuone (CFO)
Jim Ensell (CMO)
Wesley Pullen (VP-Deployment Solutions & Gen Mgr)
Rohit Jainendra (Chief Product Officer)
Jim Ensell (CMO)
Steve Brodie (CEO)
Steven Vattuone (CFO)

ELECTRIC CONDUIT CON-STRUCTION CO.
816 Hicks Dr, Elburn, IL 60119
Tel.: (630) 293-4474
Web Site: https://www.electricconduitconstruction.com
Year Founded: 1958
Sales Range: $25-49.9 Million
Emp.: 150
Provider of Underground Utility Construction Services
N.A.I.C.S.: 237130
James E. Pfleeger (Pres)

ELECTRIC FETUS COMPANY
2000 4th Ave S, Minneapolis, MN 55404
Tel.: (612) 870-9300
Web Site: http://www.efetus.com
Year Founded: 1968
Sales Range: $10-24.9 Million
Emp.: 80
Retailer of Compact Discs, Records & Tapes
N.A.I.C.S.: 459420
Keith Covart (Founder)

ELECTRIC FIXTURE & SUP-PLY COMPANY INC.
1006 N 20th St, Omaha, NE 68102-4314
Tel.: (402) 342-3050
Web Site: http://www.electricfixture.com
Year Founded: 1990
Sales Range: $10-24.9 Million
Emp.: 104
Provider of Electrical Apparatus & Equipment Services
N.A.I.C.S.: 423610
Bobbi Fox (Mgr-Credit-Nebraska)

ELECTRIC MIRROR, INC.
6101 Associative Blvd Ste 101, Everett, WA 98203
Tel.: (425) 776-4946
Web Site: https://www.electricmirror.com
Year Founded: 1992
Sales Range: $10-24.9 Million
Emp.: 100
Enameled Iron & Metal Sanitary Ware Mfr
N.A.I.C.S.: 332999
Christopher Bruce (VP-Sls-Europe)
Jon Johnston (VP-Sls)
Donald J. Jacques (COO)

ELECTRIC MOBILITY CORPO-RATION
1 Mobility Plz, Sewell, NJ 08080-1031
Tel.: (856) 468-0270   NJ
Year Founded: 1974
Sales Range: $25-49.9 Million
Emp.: 450
Wheelchair Mfr
N.A.I.C.S.: 339113

Donna McGehrin (Supvr-Credit)
James Walsh (VP-Mfg & Distr)
John Beetle (VP-Compliance)
Patricia Fischer (Coord-Appeals)
Tammy Swider (VP-Insurance Svcs & Bus Dev)

ELECTRIC MOTION COMPANY INC.
110 Groppo Dr, Winsted, CT 06098
Tel.: (860) 379-8515
Web Site: http://www.electricmotioncompany.com
Rev.: $19,000,000
Emp.: 200
Ground Clamps (Electric Wiring Devices)
N.A.I.C.S.: 335931
Randy Auclair (Pres)

ELECTRIC MOTOR & CON-TRACTING CO., INC.
3703 Cook Blvd, Chesapeake, VA 23323
Tel.: (757) 487-2121
Web Site: https://www.emc-co.com
Rev.: $18,403,433
Emp.: 95
Electric Motor & Generator Parts
N.A.I.C.S.: 335312
James L. King (CEO)
Thad Redmond (Mgr-Acct)
Michael Stone (Acct Mgr)

ELECTRIC MOTOR REPAIR COMPANY
9100 Yellow Brick Rd Ste H, Rosedale, MD 21237
Tel.: (410) 467-8080
Web Site: http://www.emrco.com
Year Founded: 1927
Motor Repair Services
N.A.I.C.S.: 423440
Bruce Peeling (Project Mgr)
Douglas Corbin (CFO)
Jaime Adams (Dir-HR)
Michael George (Dir-IT)
Caroline Kauffman-Kirschnick (Pres)
Emily Martin (Mktg Mgr)

ELECTRIC MOTOR SALES & SUPPLY CO.
1724 Central Ave, Chattanooga, TN 37408
Tel.: (423) 493-8900
Web Site: https://www.emsales.com
Sales Range: $10-24.9 Million
Emp.: 35
Electrical Apparatus & Equipment
N.A.I.C.S.: 423610
Ricky Sanders (Mgr)

ELECTRIC MOTOR SERVICE INC.
4901 Prairie Dock Dr, Madison, WI 53718-3819
Tel.: (608) 241-8866
Web Site: https://www.emsindustrial.com
Rev.: $14,200,000
Emp.: 63
Motors, Electric
N.A.I.C.S.: 423610
William Hinnendael (Pres)
Deva Hinnendael (VP)

ELECTRIC SUPPLY & EQUIP-MENT CO. INC.
1812 E Wendover Ave, Greensboro, NC 27405-6841
Tel.: (336) 272-4123
Web Site: https://www.ese-co.com
Year Founded: 1976
Sales Range: $10-24.9 Million
Emp.: 100

Sales of Electrical Apparatus & Equipment
N.A.I.C.S.: 423610
Brad McCormick (Pres)

ELECTRIC SUPPLY CO.
714 W Johnson St, Raleigh, NC 27603
Tel.: (919) 828-3726
Web Site: https://www.electricsupplycompany.com
Year Founded: 1923
Electrical Supplies Whslr
N.A.I.C.S.: 423610
K. D. Kennedy Jr. (CEO)
Ken Kennedy III (Pres)

ELECTRIC SUPPLY, INC.
4407 N Manhattan Ave, Tampa, FL 33614-7626
Tel.: (813) 872-1894   FL
Web Site: https://www.electricsupplyinc.com
Year Founded: 1970
Sales Range: $75-99.9 Million
Emp.: 125
Electrical Equipment Distr
N.A.I.C.S.: 423610
Frank Burgess (Mgr-Sls-C&I)
Rick Atkinson (Mgr-Unit Sls)
Shaker Brock (VP-Ops)
George M. Adams Jr. (Pres & CEO)

ELECTRIC SUPPLY, INC.
917 W Madison St, Phoenix, AZ 85007
Tel.: (602) 252-2343
Web Site: https://www.electricsupply.com
Year Founded: 1952
Sales Range: $10-24.9 Million
Emp.: 30
Electrical Equipment Whslr
N.A.I.C.S.: 423610
Rich Weber (VP-Fin)
Rey Rodriguez (Mgr-Counter)
Bill Morlan (Pres)
Diane Lowry (Mgr-Pur)
Jim Morlan (CEO)
Donna Holcomb (Mgr-Warehouse)

ELECTRIC TIME CO., INC.
97 W St, Medfield, MA 02052
Tel.: (508) 359-4396
Web Site: https://www.electrictime.com
Year Founded: 1928
Sales Range: $10-24.9 Million
Emp.: 35
Custom Clock Mfr
N.A.I.C.S.: 334519
Thomas Erb (Pres)

ELECTRICAL CONTRACTORS, INC.
2180 Rust Ave, Cape Girardeau, MO 63703
Tel.: (573) 335-4556   MO
Web Site: http://www.eleci.com
Year Founded: 1989
Electrical Contractor
N.A.I.C.S.: 238210
Frank Moreland (Principal)
Jimmy Thele (Pres)

ELECTRICAL CORP. AMERICA INC.
7320 Arlington Ave, Raytown, MO 64133-6567
Tel.: (816) 737-3206
Web Site: https://www.ecahq.com
Sales Range: $50-74.9 Million
Emp.: 250
Electrical Work
N.A.I.C.S.: 238210

Don Laffoon *(Pres & CEO)*
Chris Lacy *(Treas, Sec & VP)*

ELECTRICAL DISTRIBUTING INC.

4600 NW St Helens Rd, Portland, OR 97210
Tel.: (503) 226-4044
Web Site: http://www.edinw.com
Year Founded: 1878
Rev.: $30,000,000
Emp.: 55
Electrical Entertainment Equipment
N.A.I.C.S.: 423620
Marty Cronin *(Pres)*
Nick Nagy *(CFO)*
Ambrose M. Cronin III *(CEO)*

ELECTRICAL DISTRIBUTORS

2301 Century Cir, Irving, TX 75062
Tel.: (469) 533-6250
Web Site: http://www.electrical-distributors.net
Year Founded: 2008
Sales Range: $25-49.9 Million
Emp.: 26
Electrical Products Distr
N.A.I.C.S.: 423610

ELECTRICAL ENGINEERING & EQUIPMENT COMPANY INC.

953 73rd St, Windsor Heights, IA 50324-1031
Tel.: (515) 273-0100   IA
Web Site: https://www.3e-co.com
Year Founded: 1920
Sales Range: $25-49.9 Million
Emp.: 200
Sales of Electrical Apparatus & Equipment
N.A.I.C.S.: 423610
Jeff Stroud *(Pres & CEO)*
Liz Allsup *(VP-HR)*

ELECTRICAL EQUIPMENT COMPANY

1440 Diggs Dr, Raleigh, NC 27603-2755
Tel.: (919) 828-5411   NC
Web Site: http://www.eeco-net.com
Year Founded: 1926
Sales Range: $75-99.9 Million
Emp.: 70
Distribution & Service of Electrical Motors & Equipment
N.A.I.C.S.: 423610
Mike Primm *(Mgr-Pur)*
Jeff Knight *(COO)*
Mark Holmes *(Pres & CEO)*
Zack Lawson *(Pres)*

Subsidiaries:

Electrical Equipment Company   **(1)**
1807 Blvd W, Richmond, VA 23230-4325   **(100%)**
Tel.: (804) 353-7841
Web Site: http://www.eeco-net.com
Sales Range: $25-49.9 Million
Distributes & Services Electrical Motors & Equipment
N.A.I.C.S.: 423610
T. Jackson Lawson *(Pres & CEO)*
Jim Woody *(Mgr-Facility)*
Jeff Knight *(Mgr-Svcs)*
Todd Sprague *(Mgr-Sls)*
Mark Holmes *(Pres)*
Donna Mitchell *(Mgr-Corp Credit)*

ELECTRICAL INSURANCE TRUSTEES

221 N LaSalle St Ste 200, Chicago, IL 60601-1214
Tel.: (312) 782-5442   IL
Web Site: https://www.fundoffice.org
Year Founded: 1930
Sales Range: $150-199.9 Million
Emp.: 24

Employee Medical Benefit Services
N.A.I.C.S.: 525120
Kenneth Bauwens *(Chm)*

ELECTRICAL POWER PRODUCTS INC.

101 Piedmont Park Rd, Greenville, SC 29602
Tel.: (864) 631-1512
Web Site: http://www.elecpwrprod.com
Rev.: $16,000,000
Emp.: 2
Electrical Apparatus & Equipment
N.A.I.C.S.: 423610
Charlie Gossage *(Pres)*

ELECTRICAL REBUILDERS SALES INC.

1559 W 134th St, Gardena, CA 90249
Tel.: (323) 249-7545
Rev.: $15,000,000
Emp.: 40
Rebuilder of Motor Vehicle Parts & Accessories
N.A.I.C.S.: 336390
David Klapper *(Pres)*

ELECTRICAL SUPPLIES INC.

13395 NW 107th Ave, Hialeah Gardens, FL 33018
Tel.: (305) 702-6001
Web Site: https://www.electricalsupplies.com
Year Founded: 1976
Sales Range: $10-24.9 Million
Emp.: 100
Electrical Apparatus & Equipment
N.A.I.C.S.: 423610
Manny Palacios *(Mgr-Wholesale)*

ELECTRICAL SYSTEMS AND INSTRUMENTATION, INC.

6906 Downing Ave Ste B, Bakersfield, CA 93308
Tel.: (661) 587-9322   CA
Web Site: http://www.elect-systems.com
Year Founded: 2004
Sales Range: $10-24.9 Million
Emp.: 160
Electrical Contractor
N.A.I.C.S.: 238210
Robert Riley *(Pres)*
Zach Blackmon *(Project Mgr)*
Ernie Ernest *(Mgr-HSE)*

ELECTRICAL TEST INSTRUMENT, LLC

8430 Spires Way Ste A, Frederick, MD 21701
Tel.: (410) 857-1880
Web Site: https://etiprecision.com
Year Founded: 1994
Consumer Electronics Repair & Maintenance
N.A.I.C.S.: 811210
Ken McComas *(Pres)*

Subsidiaries:

Accuserve Inc.   **(1)**
6600 E Wt Harris Blvd Ste I, Charlotte, NC 28215-5126
Web Site: http://www.accuserve-inc.com
Electronic & Precision Equipment Repair & Maintenance
N.A.I.C.S.: 811210
Michael Griffith *(Pres)*

ELECTRICAL WHOLESALE SUPPLY CO. INC.

1355 Fremont Ave, Idaho Falls, ID 83402
Tel.: (208) 523-2901
Web Site: http://www.ewscoinc.com
Sales Range: $25-49.9 Million

Emp.: 100
Electrical Construction Materials Distr
N.A.I.C.S.: 423610
Grant Richardson *(VP)*
Harold Davis *(CFO)*

ELECTRICAL WHOLESALE SUPPLY CO. UTAH

158 E 4500 S, Salt Lake City, UT 84107
Tel.: (801) 268-2555
Web Site: http://www.ewsutah.com
Sales Range: $25-49.9 Million
Emp.: 125
Electrical Apparatus & Equipment
N.A.I.C.S.: 423610
Reed W. Gardner *(Pres)*
Arwyn Murphy *(Asst Mgr)*
Trent Murphy *(Mgr-Sls & Mktg)*

ELECTRIFICATION COALITION

1111 19th St NW Ste 406, Washington, DC 20036
Tel.: (202) 448-9300   DE
Web Site: https://www.electrificationcoalition.org
Year Founded: 2009
Sales Range: $1-9.9 Million
Electric Vehicle Usage Promotion Services
N.A.I.C.S.: 541614
Raphael Diamond *(Pres & CEO)*

ELECTRO ADAPTER

20640 Nordhoff St, Chatsworth, CA 91311
Tel.: (818) 998-1198
Web Site: https://www.electro-adapter.com
Year Founded: 1969
Rev.: $10,900,000
Emp.: 103
Electric Connectors
N.A.I.C.S.: 335931
Ray F. Fish *(Pres)*
Marylou Martinez-Morgan *(Mgr-HR)*
Jim Alderson *(Dir-Mktg)*

ELECTRO BRAND, INC.

1127 S Mannheim Rd Ste 305, Westchester, IL 60154-2563
Tel.: (708) 338-4400   IL
Web Site: http://www.electrobrandusa.com
Year Founded: 1961
Sales Range: $75-99.9 Million
Emp.: 8
Importer & Wholesaler of Audio Systems
N.A.I.C.S.: 423620
Richard Ettelson *(Chm & Pres)*
Stephen Ettelson *(Sec & Natl Sls Mgr & VP)*
John A. Pionke *(CFO & VP)*

ELECTRO CHEMICAL FINISHING CO.

2610 Remico St SW, Wyoming, MI 49519
Tel.: (616) 531-0670
Web Site: http://www.ecfinc.com
Year Founded: 1977
Sales Range: $10-24.9 Million
Emp.: 150
Plating & Polishing
N.A.I.C.S.: 332813
Terry L. Vollmer *(Pres)*

ELECTRO MANAGEMENT CORPORATION

111 Jackson Ave, Des Moines, IA 50315
Tel.: (515) 288-6774
Web Site: https://www.bakerelectric.com

Sales Range: $50-74.9 Million
Emp.: 100
General Electrical Contractor
N.A.I.C.S.: 238210

Subsidiaries:

Electrical Power Products Inc   **(1)**
1800 Hull Ave, Des Moines, IA 50313
Tel.: (515) 262-8161
Web Site: http://www.ep2.com
Sales Range: $25-49.9 Million
Relay & Control Panel Mfr
N.A.I.C.S.: 335314
Tim O'Donnell *(Pres)*
Randy Dochterman *(Sr Project Mgr)*
Len Shaw *(Mgr-Engrg)*
Wade Anderson *(Mgr-Pur & HR)*
Dawnica King *(Mgr-Estimating)*
Kyle McEwen *(Mgr-Quality Assurance)*
Paul Moon *(Mgr-Production)*

ELECTRO PRIME INC.

4510 Lint Ave Ste B, Toledo, OH 43612
Tel.: (419) 476-0100
Web Site: https://www.electroprime.com
Sales Range: $10-24.9 Million
Emp.: 150
Painting, Coating & Hot Dipping
N.A.I.C.S.: 332813
John Lauffer *(Pres)*

ELECTRO STANDARDS LABORATORIES INC.

36 Western Industrial Dr, Cranston, RI 02921-3403
Tel.: (401) 943-1164   RI
Web Site: https://www.electrostandards.com
Year Founded: 1976
Sales Range: $10-24.9 Million
Emp.: 99
Data Communication Products Mfr & Designer
N.A.I.C.S.: 334210
Brenda Sepe *(Sec)*
Raymond B. Sepe Sr. *(Pres)*
Raymond Sepe Jr. *(VP)*

ELECTRO SWITCH CORPORATION

775 Pleasant St Ste 1, Weymouth, MA 02189-2355
Tel.: (781) 335-1195   DE
Web Site: http://www.electroswitch.com
Year Founded: 1982
Sales Range: $25-49.9 Million
Emp.: 375
Switchgear & Switchboard Apparatus Mfr
N.A.I.C.S.: 335313
Ed McHale *(Dir-New Products)*

Subsidiaries:

Arga Controls, Inc.   **(1)**
128 W Chestnut Ave, Monrovia, CA 91016
Tel.: (626) 799-3314
Web Site: http://www.argacontrols.com
Measuring & Controlling Device Mfr
N.A.I.C.S.: 334513

Digitran   **(1)**
10410 Trademark St, Rancho Cucamonga, CA 91730-5812
Tel.: (909) 581-0855
Web Site: http://www.digitran-switches.com
Sales Range: $100-124.9 Million
Emp.: 50
Data Communications Test & Measurement Equipment Mfr
N.A.I.C.S.: 335313
Rodney Strings *(Engr-Mfg)*
Darrell James *(Mgr-Engrg)*

Electroswitch Electronic Products   **(1)**
2010 Yonkers Rd, Raleigh, NC 27604
Tel.: (919) 833-0707
Web Site: http://www.electro-nc.com

Electro Switch Corporation—(Continued)
Sales Range: $10-24.9 Million
Emp.: 100
Rotary Switch Mfr
N.A.I.C.S.: 335313
Donna Pritchard (Engr-Product Cost)
Andrew Potter (Mgr-HR)
Trey Ayscue (Reg Mgr-Sls)
Kyle Martin (VP & Gen Mgr)

Electroswitch Switches & Relays (1)
180 King Ave, Weymouth, MA 02188
Tel.: (781) 335-5200
Web Site: http://www.electroswitch.com
Sales Range: $10-24.9 Million
Emp.: 300
Switch Relay Mfr
N.A.I.C.S.: 335313
Robert Pineau (Pres)

Fisher Pierce Outdoor Lighting
Controls (1)
54 Commercial St, Raynham, MA 02767
Tel.: (508) 821-1597
Web Site: http://www.fpolc.com
Sales Range: $10-24.9 Million
Emp.: 100
Electronic Lighting Mfr
N.A.I.C.S.: 335139

Sunrise Technologies, Inc. (1)
54 Commercial St, Raynham, MA 02767
Tel.: (508) 821-1597
Web Site: http://www.sun-tech.biz
Sales Range: $25-49.9 Million
Emp.: 30
Street Lighting Photocontrols Mfr
N.A.I.C.S.: 335139
Vance Spillman (VP & Gen Mgr)

ELECTRO TECHNIK INDUS-TRIES
12449 Enterprise Blvd, Largo, FL
33773
Tel.: (727) 536-7861
Web Site:
   http://www.electrotechnik.com
Sales Range: $25-49.9 Million
Emp.: 75
Electrical Harness Assemblies
N.A.I.C.S.: 334416
Mark Ewin (Mgr-Microwave Program)
Gary Zabel (Mgr-Sls-Resistors & Ca-pacitor)
Ken Warner (Mgr-Sls)
Steve Flickinger (Gen Mgr)

Subsidiaries:

Arizona Capacitors, Inc. (1)
1100 S Plumer Ave, Tucson, AZ 85719
Tel.: (520) 573-0221
Web Site: http://www.arizonacapacitors.com
Sales Range: $1-9.9 Million
Emp.: 25
Wound Film Capacitor Mfr
N.A.I.C.S.: 334416
James Hinkle (Mgr-Quality)
Daryl Stahler (Gen Mgr)
Chris Sanders (Mgr-Technical)

Hytronics Corp. (1)
PO Box 18802, Clearwater, FL 33762
Tel.: (727) 535-0413
Web Site: http://www.hytronicscorp.com
Electronic Coil & Transformer Mfr
N.A.I.C.S.: 334416

Inductive Technologies, Inc. (1)
PO Box 18802, Clearwater, FL 33762
Tel.: (727) 532-4459
Web Site: http://www.inductech.com
Electric Equipment Mfr
N.A.I.C.S.: 334416

Nova Microwave, Inc. (1)
380 Tennant Ave Ste 5, Morgan Hill, CA
95037
Tel.: (408) 778-2746
Web Site: http://www.novamicro.com
Microwave Component Mfr
N.A.I.C.S.: 334419

Raycom Electronics, Inc. (1)
1 Raycom Rd, Dover, PA 17315
Tel.: (717) 292-3641
Web Site: http://www.raycomelectronics.com

Transfomer & Inductor Mfr
N.A.I.C.S.: 334416

Star Microwave, Inc. (1)
1310 Tully Rd Ste 115, San Jose, CA
95122
Tel.: (408) 286-6994
Web Site: http://www.starmwi.com
Electric Equipment Mfr
N.A.I.C.S.: 334419
Soukan Darathep (Pres & CEO)
Leo Beas (Mgr-Inside Sls & Customer Svc)

The Winatic Corp. (1)
12449 Enterprise Blvd, Largo, FL 33773
Tel.: (727) 796-1044
Web Site: http://www.electrotechnik.com
Rev.: $2,072,979
Emp.: 60
Coil Windings, Electronic
N.A.I.C.S.: 334416

Wavetronix Corp. (1)
78 E 1700 S, Provo, UT 84606
Tel.: (801) 734-7200
Web Site: http://www.wavetronix.com
Traffic Sensor Mfr
N.A.I.C.S.: 334519
Van Newby (CFO)
Don Christensen (VP-Mfg & Quality)
Bryan Jarrett (VP-Engrg)
Tom Nelson (Dir-Technical Svcs)

ELECTRO-COMMUNICATIONS CO.
6815 216th St SW, Lynnwood, WA
98036-7363
Tel.: (425) 774-6600
Web Site: https://www.electrocom.us
Rev.: $10,400,000
Emp.: 30
Electrical Contractor
N.A.I.C.S.: 238210
David Moore (Pres)
Craig Hess (Treas)

ELECTRO-MATIC VENTURES, INC.
23409 Industrial Park Ct, Farmington
Hills, MI 48335
Tel.: (248) 478-1182
Web Site: https://www.electro-matic.com
Electro Matic Product Mfr
N.A.I.C.S.: 334413
James C. Baker Jr. (CEO)

Subsidiaries:

Electro-Matic Products, Inc. (1)
23409 Industrial Park Ct, Farmington Hills,
MI 48335-2849
Tel.: (248) 478-1182
Web Site: http://www.electro-matic.com
Sales Range: $125-149.9 Million
Emp.: 250
Industrial Automation Components, Sys-tems & Services
N.A.I.C.S.: 423610
James C. Baker (CEO)
Mario Barraco (Pres-EM Integrated)
Richard S. Laramee (Pres & COO)
Jodi Koval (Mgr-Acctg)
Scott Beaver (VP-Strategic Accts)
Dave Scaglione (Pres-EM Visual)

RAF Fluid Power, Inc. (1)
6750 Arnold Miller Pkwy, Solon, OH 44139
Tel.: (440) 498-8465
Web Site: http://www.raffluidpower.com
Sales Range: $1-9.9 Million
Emp.: 39
Automation Components Sales & Services
N.A.I.C.S.: 423690
Thomas Koly (Pres)
Bill Frissell (VP)

ELECTRO-METHODS, INC.
330 Governors Hwy, South Windsor,
CT 06074-2422
Tel.: (860) 289-8661
Web Site: https://www.electro-methods.com
Year Founded: 1965
Sales Range: $75-99.9 Million

Emp.: 160
Mfr of Jet Engine Parts
N.A.I.C.S.: 336412
Stefan Pottinger (Mgr-Sls)
Matthew Panecki (Engr-Mfg)

ELECTRO-METRICS CORPO-RATION
231 Enterprise Rd, Johnstown, NY
12095
Tel.: (518) 762-2600
Web Site: https://www.electro-metrics.com
Year Founded: 1963
Sales Range: $25-49.9 Million
Emp.: 39
Holding Company; Designer, Pro-ducer & Integrator of Systems for
Broadband RF Testing & Communi-cations
N.A.I.C.S.: 334515
Paul Sikora (VP-Engrg)

ELECTRO-OPTIX, INC.
2181 N Powerline Rd, Pompano
Beach, FL 33069
Tel.: (954) 973-2800
Web Site: https://www.electro-optix.com
Year Founded: 1970
Sales Range: $10-24.9 Million
Emp.: 3
Illuminated Magnifiers, Travel Mirrors,
Ball Pens with Flashlights, Reading
Magnifiers & Outdoor Thermometers
Mfr
N.A.I.C.S.: 333310
Chris Schoenjohn (Owner)

ELECTRO-REPS INC.
220 N Rangeline Rd, Carmel, IN
46032
Tel.: (317) 569-7202
Web Site: http://www.electro-reps.com
Year Founded: 1974
Sales Range: $10-24.9 Million
Emp.: 10
Sales of Electronic Parts & Equip-ment
N.A.I.C.S.: 423690
J. R. Infanger (Pres)
Dan Albrecht (Engr-Sls)
Donna Infanger (Mgr-Sls Distr)
Tim Wagner (Engr-Sls)

ELECTROCUBE INCORPO-RATED
3366 Pomona Blvd, Pomona, CA
91768
Tel.: (909) 595-4037
Web Site: https://www.electrocube.com
Year Founded: 1964
Sales Range: $75-99.9 Million
Emp.: 65
Capacitors, Filters & Transformers
Mfr
N.A.I.C.S.: 334419
Clay Parrill (Pres & CEO)

Subsidiaries:

Seacor Capacitors (1)
3366 Pomona Blvd, Pomona, CA 91768
Tel.: (909) 595-4037
Sales Range: $10-24.9 Million
Emp.: 60
Electrical Component Mfr
N.A.I.C.S.: 335999

ELECTRODES, INC.
252 Depot Rd, Milford, CT 06460
Tel.: (203) 878-7408
Web Site: http://www.electrodes-inc.com
Year Founded: 1967

Sales Range: $10-24.9 Million
Emp.: 50
Mfr of Tool & Die Equipment
N.A.I.C.S.: 423830
Steve Dudas (Coord-Sls-Natl)

ELECTROFILM MFG. CO.
25395 Rye Canyon Rd, Valencia, CA
91385-1205
Tel.: (661) 257-2242
Web Site: http://www.ef-heaters.com
Year Founded: 1948
Rev.: $5,000,000
Emp.: 85
Industrial Electrical Heaters, Silinex,
Kapinex & Flex Circuits
N.A.I.C.S.: 335999
Kathy Frick (Mgr-Acctg)
Yolonda Gonzalez (Supvr-Quality Control)

ELECTROIMPACT INC.
4413 Chennault Beach Rd, Mukilteo,
WA 98275
Tel.: (425) 348-8090
Web Site:
   https://www.electroimpact.com
Year Founded: 1986
Sales Range: $25-49.9 Million
Emp.: 600
Machine Tools Mfr
N.A.I.C.S.: 333517
Peter B. Zieve (Founder, Pres & CEO)
John Hartmann (VP)
Paul Rowland (Dir-Support)
Barry Richards (Mng Dir-Engrg-United Kingdom)

ELECTROL SPECIALTIES, INC.
441 Clark St, South Beloit, IL 61080
Tel.: (815) 389-2291
Web Site: https://www.esc4cip.com
Sales Range: $50-74.9 Million
Emp.: 41
Custom Fabricated Stainless Steel
Equipment & Controls Mfr
N.A.I.C.S.: 332313
Frank Bazo (Pres)

ELECTROLOCK INC.
17930 Great Lake Pkwy, Hiram, OH
44234
Tel.: (440) 834-7500
Web Site:
   https://www.electrolock.com
Sales Range: $10-24.9 Million
Emp.: 15
Insulators, Electrical
N.A.I.C.S.: 423610
Wendy Mayes (Controller)
Rob Kessinger (Mgr-IT)
Rich Reed (Mgr-Bus Unit)

ELECTROMET CORPORATION
879 Commonwealth Ave, Hager-stown, MD 21740
Tel.: (301) 797-5900
Web Site:
   https://www.electromet.com
Year Founded: 1974
Sales Range: $25-49.9 Million
Emp.: 300
Sheet Metal Fabrication & Machining
Services
N.A.I.C.S.: 332322
David O. McCain (Pres & CEO)
Todd Estep (Mgr-Machine Shop)

Subsidiaries:

GKI Electronic Enclosures (1)
180 Jim Edward Dr, Johnstown, PA
15904 (100%)
Tel.: (814) 269-2393
Web Site: http://www.gki.com

Sales Range: $25-49.9 Million
Emp.: 75
Electronics Enclosures Mfr
N.A.I.C.S.: 332322

ELECTRON BEAM TECH-NOLOGIES, INC.
1275 Harvard Dr, Kankakee, IL 60901-9471
Tel.: (815) 935-2211   IL
Web Site:
  https://www.electronbeam.com
Year Founded: 1963
Sales Range: $50-74.9 Million
Emp.: 50
OEM Composite Welding Cables & Bulk Electrode Accessories Mfr
N.A.I.C.S.: 333992
Valgene E. Raloff *(Pres & Mgr-Product)*

ELECTRONIC CASH SYS-TEMS, INC.
27422 Portola Pkwy Ste 110, Foothill Ranch, CA 02983
Tel.: (949) 888-8580   CA
Web Site:
  http://www.ecspayments.com
Year Founded: 1997
Sales Range: $125-149.9 Million
Emp.: 30
Credit Card Processing Services
N.A.I.C.S.: 522320
Mark Davis *(VP-Sls)*
Kimberly Cheikha *(VP)*

ELECTRONIC CHECK SER-VICES INC
1615 S Ingram Mill B, Springfield, MO 65804-2261
Web Site:
  http://www.electroniccheckser vices.com
Year Founded: 1997
Sales Range: $75-99.9 Million
Emp.: 13
Credit Cards & Plans Equipment Suppliers
N.A.I.C.S.: 522210
Derron Winfry *(Pres)*
Mark Garner *(VP)*
Peggy Winfrey *(Treas)*

ELECTRONIC COMMERCE INC.
2810 Dexter Dr, Elkhart, IN 46514
Tel.: (574) 970-4400
Web Site: http://www.ecipay.com
Sales Range: $1-9.9 Million
Emp.: 62
Business Management & Consulting Services
N.A.I.C.S.: 541214
Jeffrey Lacy *(Pres & CEO)*
Steve Snead *(CTO & VP)*
Sam Sessenden *(VP-Sls)*

Subsidiaries:

ECI   (1)
2810 Dexter Dr, Elkhart, IN 46514
Tel.: (800) 320-9530
Web Site: http://www.ecipay.com
Rev.: $13,500,000
Human Resource Consulting Services
N.A.I.C.S.: 541612

ELECTRONIC CONTRACTING COMPANY
6501 N 70th St, Lincoln, NE 68507
Tel.: (402) 466-8274
Web Site: https://www.eccoinc.com
Year Founded: 1978
Sales Range: $10-24.9 Million
Emp.: 50
Fire Detection, Burglar Systems & Sound Access Control Security Services

N.A.I.C.S.: 561621
Bruce Peterson *(VP-Fin)*
Karel F. Znamenacek Jr. *(CEO)*

ELECTRONIC CONTROLS DE-SIGN
4287-B SE International Way, Milwaukie, OR 97222-8825
Tel.: (503) 659-6100
Web Site: https://www.ecd.com
Sales Range: $10-24.9 Million
Emp.: 25
Computer Interface Equipment, For Industrial Process Control
N.A.I.C.S.: 334513
Rex L. Breunsbach *(Chm)*
Tara Houle *(Mgr-Acctg)*
Todd L. Clifton *(VP-Sls & Mktg)*
Carson Orud *(Engr-Svcs)*

ELECTRONIC DATA CARRI-ERS INC.
2228 Wirtcrest Ste G, Houston, TX 77055
Tel.: (713) 680-9600
Web Site: https://www.edc-mover.com
Sales Range: $50-74.9 Million
Emp.: 65
Truck Rental With Drivers
N.A.I.C.S.: 484110
George Gilbert *(Pres)*
Gary Hendley *(Mgr)*

ELECTRONIC DATA MAGNET-ICS, INC.
210 Old Thomasville Rd, High Point, NC 27260-8187
Tel.: (336) 882-8115   NC
Web Site:
  http://www.electronicdata.com
Year Founded: 1983
Sales Range: $10-24.9 Million
Emp.: 75
Computer Tab Cards & Forms Mfr
N.A.I.C.S.: 323111
Richard Hallman *(Pres)*
Brian Hallman *(Sr VP-Mktg & Sls)*
Randy Bunnell *(Sr VP-Sls)*

ELECTRONIC DATA PAYMENT SYSTEMS
1013 Front Ave SW, New Philadelphia, OH 44663
Tel.: (866) 578-9740
Web Site:
  http://www.edpaymentsystems.com
Year Founded: 2003
Sales Range: $1-9.9 Million
Emp.: 20
Processes Credit & Debit Card Transactions
N.A.I.C.S.: 522180
Mandy Grimm *(Mgr-Acct)*

ELECTRONIC DRIVES & CON-TROLS
17 Eastmans Rd, Parsippany, NJ 07054-3702
Tel.: (973) 428-0500   NJ
Web Site:
  http://www.electronicdrives.com
Year Founded: 1968
Sales Range: $10-24.9 Million
Emp.: 30
Parts Mfr & Service for Industrial Adjustable Speed Drives
N.A.I.C.S.: 811210
Charles Dillard *(VP-Engrg)*
Naomi Dillard *(Treas)*
Deborah Dillard *(VP)*
Ben Dillard *(VP)*
Henry Dillard III *(Chm & Pres)*

ELECTRONIC ENGINEERING CO.
1015 Keo Way, Des Moines, IA 50309
Tel.: (515) 283-1100
Web Site:
  http://www.connectingyou.com
Sales Range: $25-49.9 Million
Emp.: 60
Paging Services
N.A.I.C.S.: 517112
Mark Clark *(Pres)*
Bill Cronin *(Exec VP)*
Corry Hill *(Mgr-Tech)*
Patty Burkheimer *(Branch Mgr)*

ELECTRONIC ENVIRON-MENTS CORP.
410 Forest St, Marlborough, MA 01752
Tel.: (508) 229-1400
Web Site: http://www.eecnet.com
Sales Range: $10-24.9 Million
Emp.: 75
Provider of Computer Software Development Services
N.A.I.C.S.: 541511
Kenneth A. Rapoport *(Founder & Chm)*
Mike Kingsley *(CEO)*
Jim Lynch *(Mgr-Mechanical Construction)*
James Stark *(Dir-Engrg & Construction)*
Ed Meier *(VP-Strategic)*
John Cummings *(Dir-Facilities)*
Ray Bourque *(Mgr-Enterprise Ops)*
Mark Carroll *(Mgr-Facilities)*
James Lundrigan *(Pres)*

ELECTRONIC HEALTHCARE NETWORK ACCREDITATION COMMISSION
25 Brookshire Ln, Farmington, CT 06032
Tel.: (860) 408-1620   CT
Web Site: http://www.ehnac.org
Year Founded: 1998
Rev.: $1,574,966
Emp.: 2
Fiscal Year-end: 12/31/14
Healtcare Services
N.A.I.C.S.: 622110
Debra Hopkinson *(VP-Ops)*
Barrett Leon *(Exec Dir)*

ELECTRONIC INDUSTRIES ALLIANCE INC.
2500 Wilson Blvd, Arlington, VA 22201-3834
Tel.: (703) 907-7500
Web Site: http://www.eia.org
Year Founded: 1924
Sales Range: $10-24.9 Million
Emp.: 55
Business Association Services
N.A.I.C.S.: 813910
Mike Kennedy *(Chm)*
Paul W. D'Arcy *(Exec VP)*
Brian OConnell *(VP-Sls & Mktg)*
Chris Cleet *(Mgr-Environ Affairs)*
Dan Heinemeier *(Pres-GEIA)*
Danielle Jafari *(Gen Counsel & Sr Dir)*
Storme Street *(VP-Govt Rels)*
Robert Willis *(Pres)*

ELECTRONIC INDUSTRIES CORPORATION
840 Derita Rd, Concord, NC 28027
Tel.: (704) 721-5111
Web Site:
  http://www.racingelectronics.com
Year Founded: 1988
Rev.: $10,000,000

Emp.: 55
Communication Device Retailer
N.A.I.C.S.: 459999
Kevin Hughes *(Mgr-Team Svcs)*

ELECTRONIC INSTRUMENTA-TION & TECHNOLOGY
108 Carpenter Dr, Sterling, VA 20164
Tel.: (703) 478-0700
Web Site: http://www.eitinc.com
Year Founded: 1977
Rev.: $34,573,001
Emp.: 200
Electronic Circuits
N.A.I.C.S.: 334419
Joe T. May *(Chm & CEO)*
Jim Raymont *(Dir-Sls)*
Lou Vannatta *(Gen Mgr-Special Mfg)*
Aaron Brenneman *(Controller)*
Teresa Quigley *(Dir-HR)*

ELECTRONIC KNOWLEDGE INTERCHANGE CO.
33 W Monroe St 17th Fl, Chicago, IL 60603-5300
Tel.: (312) 236-0903
Web Site: http://www.eki-consulting.com
Year Founded: 1996
Sales Range: $10-24.9 Million
Emp.: 48
Computer System Design Services
N.A.I.C.S.: 541512
My-Hien Ngo *(Mng Principal)*
Robert Blackwell Jr. *(Founder & CEO)*

ELECTRONIC MAINTENANCE COMPANY INCORPORATED
8900 S Choctaw Dr, Baton Rouge, LA 70815
Tel.: (225) 925-8900
Web Site:
  http://www.emcotechnologies.com
Sales Range: $10-24.9 Million
Emp.: 400
Antenna Installation Services
N.A.I.C.S.: 811210
Pat Cuntz *(Pres-Comm Div)*
Mike Lee *(CFO)*
Pierre Aguillard *(Mgr-Tech Svcs)*
Todd Bourgeois *(Pres-IT Grp)*

ELECTRONIC PAYMENT SYS-TEMS, LLC
6472 S Quebec St, Englewood, CO 80111
Tel.: (303) 221-2510
Web Site: https://www.eps-na.com
Year Founded: 1994
Sales Range: $10-24.9 Million
Emp.: 50
Electronic Payment Products & Services for Retailers, Small Businesses, Restaurants & Online Sellers
N.A.I.C.S.: 522320
John Dorsey *(Co-Founder & CEO)*
Tom McCann *(Co-Founder & Mng Partner)*
Anthony Maley *(COO)*

ELECTRONIC PAYMENTS, INC.
4062 Grumman Blvd Bldg 81B, Calverton, NY 11933
Tel.: (638) 822-1140
Web Site:
  http://www.electronicpayments.com
Year Founded: 2000
Sales Range: $10-24.9 Million
Emp.: 25
Credit & Debit Card Transaction Services
N.A.I.C.S.: 522320

Electronic Payments, Inc.—(Continued)

Michael Nardy (CEO)
Jim Kimberly (VP)
Megan Best (VP-Client Rels)
Amber Josi (Dir-Mktg)

ELECTRONIC RECYCLERS INTERNATIONAL, INC.
3243 SE Ave Ste 108, Fresno, CA 93725
Tel.: (559) 442-3960
Web Site:
http://www.electronicrecyclers.com
Year Founded: 2002
Sales Range: $25-49.9 Million
Emp.: 400
Electronic Waste Recycler Services
N.A.I.C.S.: 811210
John S. Shegerian (Co-Founder & Chm)
Tammy Shegerian (Co-Founder & COO)
Kevin J. Dillon (Co-Founder & CMO)
Aaron Blum (Co-Founder & Chief Compliance Officer)
Linda Ramos (Dir-Admin)
Carol DeBellis (Dir-HR)
Rich Calzada (CTO)
Tyler Browning (Gen Counsel)

ELECTRONIC SERVICES CORPORATION OF AMERICA
30 Summer St, Winthrop, ME 04364
Tel.: (207) 377-9377
Web Site: http://www.amiems.com
Sales Range: $10-24.9 Million
Emp.: 100
Bare Printed Circuit Board Mfr
N.A.I.C.S.: 334412
Steve Martin (VP-Mfg)
Kim Vandermeulen (CEO)
Greg Boyd (VP-Program & Supply Chain Mgmt)
Scot Story (VP-Sls & Mktg)

ELECTRONIC SYSTEMS PROTECTION, INC.
8001 Knightdale Blvd Ste 121, Knightdale, NC 27545
Tel.: (919) 269-6968
Web Site: http://www.espei.com
Year Founded: 1997
Sales Range: $25-49.9 Million
Emp.: 125
Other Electronic Parts & Equipment Merchant Whslr
N.A.I.C.S.: 423690
David Perrotta (VP-Ops)
Stephen F. Galloway (Pres & CEO)
Rob Wood (CFO)
Shannon Townley (Pres-SurgeX Sls)

ELECTRONIC TECHNOLOGIES INTERNATIONAL, INC.
1100 N Main St, Fort Atkinson, WI 53538
Tel.: (920) 563-0840   WI
Web Site: https://www.etimfg.com
Year Founded: 1990
Sales Range: $1-9.9 Million
Emp.: 40
Electronic Components Mfr
N.A.I.C.S.: 334419
William Brink (Owner & Pres)
Carol Spicuzza (Plant Mgr)
Richard Troon (Dir-Fin)
Barbara Blakely (Mgr-Acctg)
Charles Morgan (Mgr-Customer Svc)
Jeffrey Mortensen (Mgr-Pur & Matls)
Margaret Vogel (Mgr-Customer Svc)
Thomas Olson (Mgr-Production)
Jessica Hillebrand (Mgr-Customer Svc)
Ryan McCullough (Dir-Sls & Mktg)

Subsidiaries:

CMK Enterprises, Inc.   (1)
527 Mitchell Dr, Eagle, WI 53119
Tel.: (262) 594-3045
Web Site: http://www.cmkcalmer.com
Sales Range: $10-24.9 Million
Emp.: 11
Electronic Components
N.A.I.C.S.: 334419

ELECTRONIC THEATRE CONTROLS, INC.
3031 Pleasant View Rd, Middleton, WI 53562-0979
Tel.: (608) 831-4116   WI
Web Site:
https://www.etcconnect.com
Year Founded: 1975
Sales Range: $25-49.9 Million
Lighting Control Systems Mfr
N.A.I.C.S.: 335139
Fred Foster (CEO)
Mark Vassallo (VP-World Sls)
Dick Titus (Pres)
Sarah Danke (VP-Pro Svcs)
Julie Cymbalak (COO)
Bill McGivern (VP-Mfg)
Wynne Cheung (Gen Mgr-ETC Asia)
Philipp Schaeffer (Gen Mgr-ETC Gmbh)
Matthew Brookfield (Gen Mgr-ETC Ltd)
Susanne Krause (Gen Mgr-PENKO)
Jeffrey Welch (VP-Fin)
David Lincecum (VP-Mktg)
Matt Mullen (Mgr-Sls-Rigging-Midwest)
Gary Henley (Mgr-Sls-Rigging-Natl)
Dennis Varian (VP-R&D)
Bob Tollefson (VP-Bus Resources)
Durrell Ramer (VP-ETC Intl Ops)
Jake Dunnum (VP-Comml & Industrial Ops)
Shawn Pedersen (Gen Mgr-Echoflex)

Subsidiaries:

Electronic Theatre Controls Asia   (1)
Room 1801 18/F Phase 1 Tower I Enterprise Square 9 Sheung Yuet Road, Kowloon Bay, Kowloon, China (Hong Kong)
Tel.: (852) 27991220
Web Site: http://www.etcconnect.com
Sales Range: $10-24.9 Million
Emp.: 50
Theatre Lighting Sales & Technical Support
N.A.I.C.S.: 335132
Wynne Cheung (Gen Mgr-Asia)

Electronic Theatre Controls GmbH   (1)
Ohmstrasse 3, 83607, Holzkirchen, Germany
Tel.: (49) 802447000
Web Site: http://www.etcconnect.com
Sales Range: $10-24.9 Million
Emp.: 30
Theatre Lighting Project Management, Research & Development, Marketing, Sales & Service
N.A.I.C.S.: 335132
Philipp Schaeffer (Gen Mgr)

Electronic Theatre Controls Ltd.   (1)
26 28 Victoria Industrial Estate Victoria Road, London, W6 1UU, United Kingdom
Tel.: (44) 2088961000
Web Site: http://www.etcconnect.com
Sales Range: $10-24.9 Million
Emp.: 28
Commercial Lighting & Rigging Mfr
N.A.I.C.S.: 335139
Matthew Brookfield (Gen Mgr)

High End Systems, Inc.   (1)
2105 Gracy Farms Ln, Austin, TX 78758-4031
Tel.: (512) 836-2242
Web Site: http://www.highend.com
Stage Lighting & Control Systems Mfr
N.A.I.C.S.: 335139
Sean Hoey (Natl Mgr-Sls-Latin America Reg)

Betsy Childers (Mgr-Sls & Svc-Ops)
Mark Vassallo (VP-Sls & Sls Mgr-Western Reg,APAC,EMEA)
Bobby Hale (Mgr-Reg Sls-Eastern Reg)
Paul Hancock (Mgr-Reg Sls-Central & Canadian Reg)
Terry Heisler (Mgr-HES-Reg Sls-Western USA)
Clint Wingrome (Reg Sls Mgr-HES-Southeastern USA)
Noel Garcia (Mgr-Reg Sls_Southern & Latin America Reg)

ELECTRONIC TRANSFER, INC.
3107 E Mission Ave, Spokane, WA 99202
Tel.: (509) 924-6730
Web Site:
http://www.electronictransfer.com
Year Founded: 1989
Sales Range: $50-74.9 Million
Emp.: 10
Commercial Financing Services
N.A.I.C.S.: 522320
Michael Knudtson (Pres)
Bob Donegan (Dir-Mktg)

ELECTRONICS MARKETING GROUP
4070 Goldfinch St Ste D, San Diego, CA 92103
Tel.: (619) 231-6907
Year Founded: 1984
Sales Range: Less than $1 Million
Emp.: 5
Advetising Agency
N.A.I.C.S.: 541810
Irene Jernigan (Creative Dir)

ELECTRONICS STAMPING CORP.
19920 S Alameda St, Compton, CA 90221-6210
Tel.: (310) 639-2120   DE
Web Site:
http://electronicstamping.com
Year Founded: 1968
Sales Range: $10-24.9 Million
Emp.: 20
Provider of Metal Stamping
N.A.I.C.S.: 335313
Tom Winningham (Mgr-Quality)

ELECTROREP-ENERGY PRODUCTS
2121 Schuetz Rd, Saint Louis, MO 63146
Tel.: (314) 991-2600
Web Site: https://www.elecrep.com
Year Founded: 1970
Sales Range: $10-24.9 Million
Emp.: 30
Electrical Apparatus & Equipment
N.A.I.C.S.: 423610
Suzanne Mair (Coord-Sls)
Stacey Hart (Pres-Sls)
Cathy Thomas (Office Mgr)
Jill Colombo (Coord-Inside Sls)
Ronda Brown (Coord-Sls)
Barbara Geoffroy (Coord-Stationary Svc)
Mike Cochran (Mgr-Motive Power Svc)
Ray Sitki (VP-Sls-Springfield)

ELECTROSOFT SERVICES INC
11417 Sunset Hills Rd Ste 228, Reston, VA 20190
Tel.: (703) 437-9451
Web Site: http://www.electrosoft-inc.com
Year Founded: 1997
Sales Range: $1-9.9 Million
Emp.: 20
Computer System Design Services
N.A.I.C.S.: 541512

Jose Arias (Facility Security Officer & Dir-Corp Admin)
Sarbari Gupta (Pres & CEO)
J. Greg Hanson (Acting VP-Ops)
Taylor G. Marcum (Dir-Bus Dev)
Mike Tillman (COO)

ELECTROSONIC, INC.
3320 N San Fernando Blvd, Burbank, CA 91504
Tel.: (818) 333-3600
Web Site:
http://www.electrosonic.com
Year Founded: 1964
Sales Range: $50-74.9 Million
Emp.: 400
Motion Picture & Video Production
N.A.I.C.S.: 512110
Chris Conte (VP-Entertainment)
Bryan Hinckley (Pres)
Steve Leyland (Chm)
Sarah Joyce (Mng Dir-EMEA)

ELECTRUM SPECIAL ACQUISITION CORPORATION
700 Madison Ave 5th Fl, New York, NY 10065
Tel.: (646) 365-1600   VG
Year Founded: 2014
Sales Range: Less than $1 Million
Emp.: 2
Investment Services
N.A.I.C.S.: 523999
Thomas S. Kaplan (Chm)
Eric Vincent (CEO)

ELEGANT ILLUSIONS, INC.
542 Lighthouse Ave Ste 5, Pacific Grove, CA 93950-2745
Tel.: (831) 649-1814   DE
Web Site: http://www.tamarag.com
Sales Range: $1-9.9 Million
Emp.: 149
Imitation Jewelry Retailer
N.A.I.C.S.: 458310
Gavin Gear (Co-Founder, Pres & CFO)
James Cardinal (CEO)
Tamara Gear (Co-Founder, Treas & Sec)

ELEGANZA TILES, INC.
3125 E Coronado St, Anaheim, CA 92806
Tel.: (714) 224-1700
Web Site:
https://www.eleganzatiles.com
Year Founded: 2002
Sales Range: $10-24.9 Million
Emp.: 20
Ceramic & Porcelain Tiles Mfr & Distr
N.A.I.C.S.: 327120
Mike Darmawan (CEO)
Tony DeMaggio (Reg Mgr-Sls)
Felix Dominguez (Mgr-Logistics Supply)

ELEISON PHARMACEUTICALS INC.
100 Overlook Ctr 2nd Fl, Princeton, NJ 08540
Tel.: (215) 554-3530   DE
Web Site: https://www.eleison-pharma.com
Year Founded: 2009
Rev.: $1,000,000
Assets: $5,874,444
Liabilities: $4,117,730
Net Worth: $1,756,714
Earnings: ($6,403,032)
Emp.: 2
Fiscal Year-end: 12/31/20
Pharmaceuticals Product Mfr
N.A.I.C.S.: 325412
Edwin J. Thomas (Pres, CEO, Founder & Chm)

Keith Darragh *(CFO & Sec)*
Michael E. Lusty *(VP)*
Patrick J. Maguire *(Chief Medical Officer)*
Matthew Allen Cromie *(VP)*

ELEKTOR INDUSTRIES INC.
304 S Jones Blvd Ste 7356, Las Vegas, NV 89107   WY
Year Founded: 2021
Water Pump Mfr
N.A.I.C.S.: 333996

ELEMENT 78 LLC
2211 York Rd Ste 200, Oak Brook, IL 60523
Tel.: (630) 819-5118   IL
Web Site:
    http://www.e78partners.com
Year Founded: 2016
Accounting, Finance & Technology Solution Services
N.A.I.C.S.: 541219
Gary Modrow *(Mng Dir-Mgmt Consulting)*
Steve Adelstein *(Mng Dir-Tech & Talent Svcs)*
John Signa *(Founder & CEO)*
Brian White *(Pres & COO)*
Seth Deutsch *(Chief Growth Officer)*

Subsidiaries:

9Gauge Partners, LLC   (1)
1717 W 6th St Ste 380, Austin, TX 78703
Tel.: (512) 879-4171
Web Site: http://www.9gauge.com
Sales Range: $1-9.9 Million
Emp.: 22
Financial Services
N.A.I.C.S.: 541611
Brian White *(Founder & Mng Partner)*
Joe Cohen *(Partner-Fin & Bus Intelligence)*
Jonathan Hines *(Partner-Firm Dev)*
Michael Wiggin *(Mng Dir-Transaction Advisory Svcs)*

Trillium Solutions Group, Inc.   (1)
1954 1st St Ste 204, Highland Park, IL 60035
Tel.: (847) 272-2202
Web Site: http://www.trilliumsg.com
Computer Related Services
N.A.I.C.S.: 541519
Donna Lenczycki *(VP-Tech Selection)*

ELEMENT CARE
37 Friend St, Lynn, MA 01902
Tel.: (781) 715-6608   MA
Web Site:
    https://www.elementcare.org
Year Founded: 1994
Sales Range: $75-99.9 Million
Senior Health Care Services
N.A.I.C.S.: 623990
Robert Wakefield *(CEO & Exec Dir)*
John Feehan *(Treas)*
Peter Rossetti *(Pres)*
John Coolong *(CIO)*
Robert Durante *(CFO)*

ELEMENT DATA, INC.
10900 NE 8th St Ste 1170, Bellevue, WA 98004
Tel.: (858) 633-7359
Web Site: http://www.decisioncloud.io
Year Founded: 2016
Web-Platform & Hosting Duties
N.A.I.C.S.: 518210
Cyrus Krohn *(Sr VP-Bus Dev)*
Charles Davis *(Founder & CTO)*

ELEMENT NATIONAL MANAGEMENT COMPANY
1515 S Federal Hwy Ste 302, Boca Raton, FL 33432
Tel.: (561) 314-1444
Web Site:
    https://www.elementmgt.com

Year Founded: 2007
Sales Range: $50-74.9 Million
Emp.: 300
Apartment & Commercial Management
N.A.I.C.S.: 531311
L.V. Lavallii *(Founder)*
Caye Kim *(Asst Controller)*

ELEMENT PARTNERS, LLC
565 E Swedesford Rd Ste 207, Wayne, PA 19087
Tel.: (610) 964-8004
Web Site:
    http://www.elementpartners.com
Private Investment Firm
N.A.I.C.S.: 523999
Patti Szczepaniak *(Office Mgr)*
David F. Lincoln *(Founder & Mng Partner)*
Michael Bevan *(Gen Partner)*
Michael L. DeRosa *(Mng Dir)*
Michael Todd *(CFO)*

Subsidiaries:

Cardello Electric Supply
Company   (1)
401 N Point Dr, Pittsburgh, PA 15233-2141
Tel.: (412) 322-8059
Web Site: http://www.cardello.com
Sales Range: $10-24.9 Million
Emp.: 130
Electrical Apparatus & Lighting Distr
N.A.I.C.S.: 423610
Chris Brennan *(Mgr)*

ELEMENT PAYMENT SERVICES, INC.
14415 S 50th St Ste 200, Phoenix, AZ 85044
Tel.: (480) 993-0700
Web Site: http://www.elementps.com
Rev.: $14,100,000
Emp.: 66
Business Management Services
N.A.I.C.S.: 518210
Sean Kramer *(Pres & CEO)*

ELEMENT RISK MANAGEMENT LLC
310 North High St, West Chester, PA 19380
Tel.: (610) 701-8257
Web Site:
    http://www.elementrisk.com
Independent Insurance Agency
N.A.I.C.S.: 524210
Josh Heebner *(Head-Fin & Ops & Partner)*

Subsidiaries:

Smith's Insurance Agency Inc.   (1)
9444 State Route 209, Williamstown, PA 17098-9452
Tel.: (717) 647-7162
Web Site:
    http://www.smithsinsuranceagency.com
Insurance Agencies & Brokerages
N.A.I.C.S.: 524210
Dawn Carl *(Mgr)*

ELEMENT WHEELS
2125 N Nevada St, Chandler, AZ 85225
Tel.: (480) 966-9044
Web Site:
    http://www.elementwheels.com
Year Founded: 2003
Sales Range: $1-9.9 Million
Emp.: 5
Custom Wheels, Tires & Rims
N.A.I.C.S.: 441340
Robert Chang *(Owner)*
Ryan Zaporteza *(Dir-Sls)*

ELEMENTAL TECHNOLOGIES, INC.

1320 Ave Br Ste 400, Portland, OR 97201
Tel.: (503) 222-3212
Web Site:
    http://www.elementaltechnologies.com
Year Founded: 2006
Sales Range: $10-24.9 Million
Emp.: 49
Television Broadcasting Services
N.A.I.C.S.: 516120
Jesse Rosenzweig *(Co-Founder & CTO)*
Brian Lewis *(Co-Founder)*
Daniel Marshall *(Sr VP-Worldwide Field Ops)*
Keith Wymbs *(CMO)*
Aslam Khader *(Chief Product Officer)*
Greg Zwart *(VP-Global Svcs)*
John Ewert *(CFO)*
John Nemeth *(VP-Field Ops-EMEA)*
Khawaja Shams *(VP-Engrg)*

ELEMENTS BEHAVIORAL HEALTH, INC.
5000 Airport Plaza Dr Ste 100, Long Beach, CA 90815
Tel.: (562) 521-0608
Web Site:
    http://www.elementsbehavioralhealth.com
Sales Range: $10-24.9 Million
Mental Health Treatment Services
N.A.I.C.S.: 621330
Rich Whitney *(Chm)*
Rob Mahan *(COO)*
Vera Appleyard *(Chief Internet & Mktg Officer)*
Elissa Weisberger-Cohen *(Sr VP-HR)*
David Buckley *(VP-Fin)*
Jim Adams *(CFO)*
Jennifer Gallagher *(Chief Dev Officer)*

Subsidiaries:

TRS Behavioral Care, Inc.   (1)
902 W Alabama St, Houston, TX 77006
Tel.: (832) 917-0310
Web Site: http://www.rightstep.com
Sales Range: $10-24.9 Million
Emp.: 200
Outpatient Care Centers
N.A.I.C.S.: 621498

ELEMENTS FOR WOMEN, INC.
701 Lincoln Rd Ste 106, Miami, FL 33139
Tel.: (305) 535-1525   FL
Web Site:
    http://www.elementsforwomen.com
Year Founded: 2004
Sales Range: $1-9.9 Million
Emp.: 18
Fitness Center
N.A.I.C.S.: 713940
Christopher Palumbo *(Founder)*
Bruce Fabel *(CEO)*
Christine Morgenstern *(Dir-Dev)*
Judy Penny *(Dir-Creative)*

ELEMENTS HEALTH INVESTORS, LLC
623 Fifth Ave, 14th Fl., New York, NY 10022
Tel.: (212) 887-2100
Web Site:
    https://www.elementshealthinvestors.com
Emp.: 100
Private Equity
N.A.I.C.S.: 523999
Curtis S. Lane *(Founder & Chm)*

Subsidiaries:

Carisk Partners, Inc.   (1)
10685 N Kendall Dr, Miami, FL 33176
Tel.: (305) 514-5300
Web Site: http://www.cariskpartners.com

Risk Transfer & Care Coordination Company
N.A.I.C.S.: 621399
Kevin Mahoney *(Pres & COO)*
Angel E. Garrido *(Chief Medical Offcer)*
Allen Spokane *(CTO)*
Chrissy Gaul *(VP-Mktg)*
Alana Letourneau *(Chief Clinical Strategy Officer)*
Joseph Berardo Jr. *(CEO)*

Subsidiary (Domestic):

Carisk Specialty Services, Inc.   (2)
25a Hanover Rd Ste 201, Florham Park, NJ 07932
Tel.: (973) 451-9415
Web Site: http://www.cariskpartners.com
Diagnostic Radiology & Testing Network
N.A.I.C.S.: 621512
Stephen P. Ellerman *(Pres)*

ELEMENTS, LLC
600 S Magnolia Ave Ste 150, Tampa, FL 33606
Tel.: (813) 251-0565
Web Site:
    http://www.elementstampa.com
Year Founded: 1990
Sales Range: $1-9.9 Million
Emp.: 10
Interior Design & Architectural Services
N.A.I.C.S.: 541410
Bret Azzarelli *(Co-Founder & VP)*
Debra K. Altenbernd *(Co-Founder & Pres)*
Leesa Nero *(VP-Ops)*
Lourdes Echemendia *(Project Mgr)*

ELEMETAL REFINING, LLC
16064 Beaver Pike, Jackson, OH 45640
Tel.: (740) 286-6457
Web Site: http://www.elemetal.com
Year Founded: 1974
Secondary Precious Metals Refining
N.A.I.C.S.: 331492
Bill Leroy *(Pres)*
Conor Dullaghan *(Exec VP-Sls)*
Mark Wayne *(Exec VP-Ops)*
Alan Stockmeister *(Chm)*

ELENBAAS COMPANY
421 Birch Bay Lynden Rd, Lynden, WA 98264
Tel.: (360) 354-3577
Web Site:
    http://www.elenbaasco.com
Year Founded: 1941
Sales Range: $10-24.9 Million
Feeds & Farm Supplies Mfr & Distr
N.A.I.C.S.: 311119

Subsidiaries:

EPL Feed, LLC   (1)
411 W Front St, Sumas, WA 98295
Tel.: (360) 988-5811
Web Site: http://www.eplfeed.com
Emp.: 55
Dairy Cattle Feed Mfr
N.A.I.C.S.: 311119
Dennis Elenbaas *(Pres)*

ELENCO ELECTRONICS, INC.
150 Carpenter Ave, Wheeling, IL 60090
Tel.: (847) 541-3800
Web Site: https://www.elenco.com
Year Founded: 1972
Sales Range: $25-49.9 Million
Emp.: 40
Electronic Toys & Educational Devices
N.A.I.C.S.: 611710
Arthur F. Seymour *(Pres & CEO)*
Joseph P. Seymour *(CIO & VP)*
Gerald J. Cecchin *(Head-Engrg & VP)*
Jeff Coda *(Mgr-Natl Sls-Elenco Electronics)*

Elenco Electronics, Inc.—(Continued)

ELEPHANT OIL CORP.
700 Milam Ste 1300, Houston, TX
77002
Tel.: (832) 871-5050 **NV**
Web Site: https://www.elephant-
oil.com
Year Founded: 2021
Assets: $2,761,984
Liabilities: $1,817,262
Net Worth: $944,722
Earnings: ($226,518)
Emp.: 3
Fiscal Year-end: 06/30/21
Oil & Gas Exploration Services
N.A.I.C.S.: 213112
Matthew Lofgran (CEO & Founder)
Lanre Oloniniyi (CFO)
Stephen Staley (Chm)

ELEVANCE RENEWABLE SCI-
ENCES, INC.
2501 W Davey Rd, Woodridge, IL
60517 **DE**
Web Site: http://www.elevance.com
Sales Range: $10-24.9 Million
Emp.: 73
Chemical Products Mfr
N.A.I.C.S.: 325998
Kara E. Lawrence (CFO)
Carole Piwnica (Vice Chm)
Del Craig (Exec VP-Special Projects)
Tony Parnell (Chm)
Celene Difrancia (CMO)
Karl Schoene (CEO)

ELEVATE ENTERTAINMENT,
INC.
6300 Wilshire Blvd, Los Angeles, CA
90048
Tel.: (323) 634-0748
Web Site: http://www.elevate-ent.com
Year Founded: 2009
Talent And Literary Management Ser-
vices Provider
N.A.I.C.S.: 541618
Alex Cole (Founder)
Jenny Wood (Partner)
Stephanie Moy (Mgr)
Raquelle David (Mgr)

Subsidiaries:

Cosm, Inc **(1)**
5340 Alla Rd. Ste 140,, Los Angeles, CA
90066
Tel.: (800) 327-5707
Web Site: https://www.cosm.com
Software Publisher
N.A.I.C.S.: 513210

Subsidiary (Domestic):

Evans & Sutherland Computer
Corporation **(2)**
770 Komas Dr, Salt Lake City, UT 84108
Tel.: (801) 588-1000
Web Site: http://www.es.com
Rev.: $27,716,000
Assets: $26,678,000
Liabilities: $19,994,000
Net Worth: $6,684,000
Earnings: ($1,599,000)
Emp.: 95
Fiscal Year-end: 12/31/2019
Simulation, Training & Engineering Hard-
ware & Software Mfr
N.A.I.C.S.: 449210
Paul L. Dailey (CFO & Sec)
Jonathan A. Shaw (CEO)
Kirk D. Johnson (Pres & COO)

Division (Domestic):

Evans & Sutherland Computer Corporation - Digital Theater
Division **(3)**
770 Komas Dr, Salt Lake City, UT 84108-
1229
Tel.: (801) 588-1000
Web Site: http://www.es.com

Sales Range: $75-99.9 Million
Digital Theatre Systems for Planetariums,
Science Centers & Domed Theatres
N.A.I.C.S.: 334111

Evans & Sutherland Computer Cor-
poration - Simulation Division **(3)**
770 Komas Dr, Salt Lake City, UT 84108
Tel.: (801) 588-1000
Web Site: http://www.es.com
Advanced Simulation Technology Mfr
N.A.I.C.S.: 334413

Subsidiary (Domestic):

Spitz Inc. **(3)**
700 Brandywine Dr, Chadds Ford, PA
19317
Tel.: (610) 459-5200
Web Site: http://www.spitzinc.com
Sales Range: $1-9.9 Million
Emp.: 60
Planetarium & Spherical Projection Mfr
N.A.I.C.S.: 333310
Paul Dailey (CFO)
John Fogleman (VP-Ops)
Scott Huggins (Dir-Mktg)
Joyce Towne (Dir-Customer Accounts)
Chris Wright (Dir-Design Engrg)
Chris Seale (Mgr-Mktg)
Michael McConville (Mgr-Acct-Sls)

ELEVATE HOLDINGS, INC.
5 Batchelder Rd, Seabrook, NH
03874
Tel.: (603) 918-9330
Web Site: http://www.ehi.aero
Holding Company
N.A.I.C.S.: 551112
Greg Raiff (Founder & CEO)

Subsidiaries:

Keystone Aviation, LLC **(1)**
303 N 2370 W, Salt Lake City, UT 84116
Tel.: (888) 900-6070
Web Site: http://www.keystoneaviation.com
Oil Transportation Services
N.A.I.C.S.: 481211
Brian Jones (Dir-Sls-Socata)
Charlie Chamberlain (Dir-Managed Aircraft
Sls)
Tad W. Perryman (VP-Mktg)
J. Dan Govatos (Dir-Ops)
Aaron Fish (Pres)

ELEVATE ORAL CARE, LLC
346 Pike Rd Ste 5, West Palm
Beach, FL 33411
Year Founded: 2010
Dental Product Mfr & Distr
N.A.I.C.S.: 339114

ELEVATE STAFFING, INC.
600 N Brand Ste 520, Glendale, CA
91203
Tel.: (424) 250-6156
Web Site: http://www.elevate-
staffing.com
Year Founded: 2014
Sales Range: $1-9.9 Million
Emp.: 32
Staffing & Recruitment Services
N.A.I.C.S.: 541612
Ed Wood (CEO)
Carina Filek (COO)
Kelly Kelley (Dir-Global Mktg)
Zara Hickey (Mng Dir-EMEA)
James Anderson (Pres-NAM)

ELEVATE TECHNOLOGY SO-
LUTIONS
1050 Hingham St Ste 304, Rockland,
MA 02370
Tel.: (508) 591-8230
Web Site: http://www.elevatets.com
Year Founded: 2009
Sales Range: $10-24.9 Million
Emp.: 120
Strategic Consulting Services
N.A.I.C.S.: 541611
Dan Megan (Mng Dir)

ELEVATION
1027 3rd St NW Ste 260, Washing-
ton, DC 20007
Tel.: (202) 380-3230
Web Site: http://www.elevation-
us.com
Year Founded: 2002
Rev.: $20,000,000
Emp.: 18
Advetising Agency
N.A.I.C.S.: 541810
Pablo Izquierdo (Co-Founder & Exec
VP)
James H. Learned (Pres & Mng Dir)
Jessica Reed (Media Dir)
Rodolfo Hernandez (Dir-Creative)
Guayi Fernandez (Sr Dir-Art)
Javier Meijueiro (Copywriter)
Katherine Dodson (Acct Exec)
Alexandria Satar (Coord-Media)
Yanely Tome (Acct Exec)

Subsidiaries:

Elevation **(1)**
1027 W 26th St Ste 260, New York, NY
10001
Tel.: (202) 380-3230
Web Site: http://www.elevation-us.com
Emp.: 13
N.A.I.C.S.: 541810
Jimmy Leonard (CEO)

ELEVATION MARKETING
1955 S Val Vista Dr Ste 101, Mesa,
AZ 85204
Tel.: (480) 775-8880 **AZ**
Web Site:
http://www.elevationb2b.com
Year Founded: 1999
Sales Range: $1-9.9 Million
Emp.: 30
Advetising Agency
N.A.I.C.S.: 541810
Meghan Bas (Acct Dir)
Darren Jones (Dir-Creative)
Jessica Hess (Mgr-Traffic)
Steve Reed (VP-Client Dev)
Greg Setter (VP-Client Svcs)
Michaela Raner (Sr Dir-Client Dev)

ELEVATION PARTNERS
3000 Sand Hill Rd Ste 4-140, Menlo
Park, CA 94025
Tel.: (650) 687-6700
Web Site: http://www.elevation.com
Sales Range: $25-49.9 Million
Emp.: 20
Privater Equity Firm
N.A.I.C.S.: 523999
Roger B. McNamee (Founder & Mng
Dir)
Bret D. Pearlman (Mng Dir)
Adam Hopkins (Mng Dir & Principal)
Avie Tevanian (Mng Dir)
Rami Reyes (Principal)
Steve Vafier (Principal)
Fred D. Anderson Jr. (Mng Dir)
Avadis Tevanian Jr. (Chief Software
Tech Officer)

Subsidiaries:

SDI Media **(1)**
Cambridge House 100 Cambridge Grove,
London, W6 0LE, United Kingdom
Tel.: (44) 2082377956
Web Site: http://www.sdimediagroup.com
Sales Range: $25-49.9 Million
Subtitling & Language Dubbing Services
N.A.I.C.S.: 812990
Nicole Brunnhuber (Mgr-Germany)
Tsuguya Kitade (Chm)

ELEVATION, INC.
12743 Heather Park Dr Ste 106,
Granger, IN 46530
Tel.: (574) 485-2212
Web Site:
http://www.elevationsports.com

Year Founded: 2005
Sales Range: $1-9.9 Million
Emp.: 7
Customizes, Markets, Retails & Dis-
tributes Sports Apparel, Game Uni-
forms & Various Promotional Items
N.A.I.C.S.: 339920
Jeff Robertson (CEO)

ELEVATIONS CREDIT UNION
2960 Diagonal Hwy, Boulder, CO
80301
Tel.: (303) 443-4672
Web Site:
https://www.elevationscu.com
Credit Union
N.A.I.C.S.: 522130
Chris LaVelle (VP-Mktg)

ELEVATOR EQUIPMENT COR-
PORATION
4035 Goodwin Ave, Los Angeles, CA
90039
Tel.: (323) 245-0147
Web Site:
https://www.elevatorequipment.com
Sales Range: $10-24.9 Million
Emp.: 137
Elevators & Equipment
N.A.I.C.S.: 333921
Abe Salehpour (Pres)
Peter Aguirre (Supvr-Sls)

ELEVENTH DAY ENTERTAIN-
MENT INC.
29229 Canwood St Ste 202, Agoura
Hills, CA 91301
Tel.: (818) 784-6403
Web Site:
http://www.eleventhday.com
Year Founded: 1994
Sales Range: $10-24.9 Million
Emp.: 2
Advetising Agency
N.A.I.C.S.: 541870
Frank Martin (Principal)

ELEXA CONSUMER PROD-
UCTS INC.
62 N Hiawatha, Chicago, IL 60646
Tel.: (773) 794-1300
Year Founded: 1993
Sales Range: $25-49.9 Million
Emp.: 17
Mfr of Radio & T.V. Communications
Equipment
N.A.I.C.S.: 334220
Lawrence J. Beger (Pres & CEO)
Vicki Fil (Mgr-Mktg)
Jeff Petras (Sr VP-Sls & Mktg)

ELEY GUILD HARDY ARCHI-
TECTS, PA
1091 Tommy Munro Dr, Biloxi, MS
39532
Tel.: (228) 594-2323
Web Site:
http://www.eleyguildhardy.com
Rev.: $5,052,900
Emp.: 50
Architectural Services
N.A.I.C.S.: 541310
David Hardy (Principal)
Mary Jones (Dir-Fin)

Subsidiaries:

Barlow Eddy Jenkins PA **(1)**
1530 N State St, Jackson, MS 39202
Tel.: (601) 352-8377
Web Site: http://www.bejarch.com
Rev.: $2,416,000
Emp.: 16
Architectural Services
N.A.I.C.S.: 541310
David T. Jenkins (Sec)
Charles C. Barlow Jr. (CEO)
J. Scott Eddy (Pres)

ELF ON THE SHELF, LLC
1174 Hayes Industrial Dr, Marietta,
GA 30062
Tel.: (877) 919-4105   GA
Web Site:
  http://www.elfontheshelf.com
Year Founded: 2005
Sales Range: $1-9.9 Million
Emp.: 70
NoveltyToys & Gifts
N.A.I.C.S.: 513130
Carol V. Aebersold (Co-Founder &
Publr)
Chandra A. Bell (Co-Founder)

ELFA TRADING COMPANY INC.
131 W 35th St Fl 3, New York, NY
10001
Tel.: (212) 947-7779
Year Founded: 1961
Sales Range: $10-24.9 Million
Emp.: 12
Distr of General Merchandise Primar-
ily Home Textiles
N.A.I.C.S.: 424990
Ana Hernandez (Controller)

ELG UTICA ALLOYS, INC.
91 Wurz Ave, Utica, NY 13503
Tel.: (315) 733-0475
Web Site:
  http://www.elguticaalloys.com
Year Founded: 1965
Alloys & Titanium Processing & Recy-
cling
N.A.I.C.S.: 331492
Helen Evans (Mgr-HR)
Dimitrij Orlov (CEO)
Anthony Marino (Pres)
Fredrick Schweizer (VP-Ops)
Nicholas Oliver (VP)
Robert Carbone (Controller)
Heather Dewhurst (Coord-Logistics)
Sandy McGurk (Mgr-Lab)
Ralph Hoffman (Mgr-Solids)
Allan Kashuba (Mgr-Turnings)

Subsidiaries:

ELG Utica Alloys (Hartford), Inc.   (1)
239 W Service Rd, Hartford, CT 06120
Tel.: (860) 522-3123
Web Site: http://www.elguticaalloys.com
Scrap & Recyclable Material Whslr
N.A.I.C.S.: 423930

ELGA CREDIT UNION
2303 S Center Rd, Burton, MI 48519
Tel.: (810) 715-3542   MI
Web Site: https://www.elgacu.com
Year Founded: 1951
Sales Range: $25-49.9 Million
Emp.: 184
Credit Union Operator
N.A.I.C.S.: 522130
Karen Church (CEO)
Frank Wilber (Exec VP)

ELGIA, INC.
1905 Woodstock Rd Ste 5200, Ro-
swell, GA 30075
Tel.: (678) 749-8000
Web Site: http://www.elgia.com
Year Founded: 2001
Sales Range: $1-9.9 Million
Emp.: 20
Telecommunication Servicesb
N.A.I.C.S.: 517810
Stacey Scott (CEO)
Omar Briceno (Mgr-Ops & Svc Deliv-
ery)

ELGIN DAIRY FOODS, INC.
3707 W Harrison St, Chicago, IL
60624-3622
Tel.: (630) 408-9222

Sales Range: $10-24.9 Million
Emp.: 95
Dairy Product Mfr & Distr
N.A.I.C.S.: 311514
Ed Gignac (Pres)
Nicky Oates (Dir-Quality Control)
James Gignac (Exec VP-Sls & Mktg)
John Hartline (VP-Ops & Sec)
Jim Gignac (VP-Sls)
Vanessa Jackson (Dir-Pur)
Ken Forsberg (Dir-Mfg)

ELGIN EQUIPMENT GROUP, LLC
2001 Butterfield Rd, Downers Grove,
IL 60515
Tel.: (630) 434-7200   DE
Web Site:
  http://www.elginindustries.com
Year Founded: 1864
Mining & Mineral, Oil & Gas, Electri-
cal Apparatus & Other Industrial
Equipments Mfr
N.A.I.C.S.: 333131
David Hall (Pres)

Subsidiaries:

Centrifugal & Mechanical Industries,
Inc.   (1)
201 President St, Saint Louis, MO 63118-
4111
Tel.: (314) 776-2848
Sales Range: $25-49.9 Million
Emp.: 50
Centrifuges & Process Equipment Mfr
N.A.I.C.S.: 333131
Alan Lattina (Reg Mgr-Product-West)
John Amos (Mgr-Product)
Bill Cooper (Reg Mgr-Product-East)
Dusty Ward (Sls Mgr-WV Teritory)
Chris Eckenrode (Sls Mgr-OH,PA & MD Ter-
ritory)

ELGIN INDUSTRIES INC.
1100 Jansen Farm Dr, Elgin, IL
60123
Tel.: (847) 742-1720
Web Site: https://www.elginind.com
Rev.: $20,400,000
Emp.: 160
Motor Vehicle Engines & Parts
N.A.I.C.S.: 336390
Bill Skok (Pres)

ELGIN MOLDED PLASTICS INC.
909 Grace St, Elgin, IL 60120-8419
Tel.: (847) 931-2455
Web Site:
  https://www.elginmolded.com
Year Founded: 1949
Sales Range: $10-24.9 Million
Emp.: 100
Injection Molded Finished Plastics
Product Mfr
N.A.I.C.S.: 326199
Clarence Labar (Pres)

Subsidiaries:

EMP of Franklin Inc.   (1)
10155 S 57th St, Franklin, WI 53132
Tel.: (414) 423-9877
Web Site: http://www.empco-lite.com
Rev.: $5,300,000
Emp.: 27
Plastics Materials & Basic Shapes
N.A.I.C.S.: 424610

Empco-Lite Inc.   (1)
1675 Shanahan Dr, South Elgin, IL 60177
Tel.: (847) 931-2455
Web Site: http://www.empco-lite.com
Traffic Light Mfr
N.A.I.C.S.: 335139
LeRoy Goff (Dir-Ops)

ELGIN SWEEPING SERVICES, INC.

1015 W Pershing Rd, Chicago, IL
60609
Tel.: (773) 254-7100
Web Site:
  http://www.elginsweeping.com
Rev.: $12,000,000
Emp.: 110
Industrial Cleaning Services
N.A.I.C.S.: 237310
Christopher P. Cacciatore (Pres)
Joseph Costa (VP-Ops)

ELGIN-BUTLER BRICK COM-PANY
2601 McHale Ct Ste 155, Austin, TX
78758-4428
Tel.: (512) 285-3356   TX
Web Site: http://www.elginbutler.com
Year Founded: 1873
Sales Range: $75-99.9 Million
Emp.: 110
Tile, Face & Fire Brick Mfr
N.A.I.C.S.: 327120
John Russell Butler (Pres)

Subsidiaries:

McIntyre Tile Company Inc.   (1)
55 W Grant St, Healdsburg, CA 95448
Tel.: (707) 433-8866
Web Site: http://www.mcintyre-tile.com
Ceramic Wall And Floor Tile, Nsk
N.A.I.C.S.: 327120

Trikeenan Tilework, Inc.   (1)
40 Shawmut Park Dr, Hornell, NY 14843
Tel.: (607) 281-1120
Web Site: http://www.trikeenan.com
Sales Range: $10-24.9 Million
Emp.: 30
Building Material Dealers
N.A.I.C.S.: 444180
Matt Galvez (Owner)

ELHART MANAGEMENT CORP.
822 Chicago Dr, Holland, MI 49423
Tel.: (616) 392-8517
Web Site: http://www.elhart.com
Sales Range: $25-49.9 Million
Emp.: 150
Automobiles, New & Used
N.A.I.C.S.: 441110
Wayne J. Elhart (Pres)

Subsidiaries:

Elhart Dodge Nissan Hyundai   (1)
870 Chicago Dr, Holland, MI 49423
Tel.: (616) 396-0441
Web Site: http://www.elhart.com
Rev.: $40,000,000
Emp.: 56
Automobiles, New & Used
N.A.I.C.S.: 441110
Jeff Elhart (Pres)
Betty Jones (Controller)

Elhart Pontiac-GMC-Truck Inc.   (1)
822 Chicago Dr, Holland, MI 49423
Tel.: (616) 392-8516
Web Site: http://www.elhart.com
Sales Range: $25-49.9 Million
Emp.: 75
Automobiles, New & Used
N.A.I.C.S.: 441110
Wayne J. Elhart (Pres)

ELI GLOBAL, LLC
2222 Sedwick Rd, Durham, NC
27713
Tel.: (919) 246-4721   DE
Web Site: http://www.eliglobal.com
Year Founded: 1991
Emp.: 4,000
Holding Company
N.A.I.C.S.: 551112
Greg Lindberg (Pres)
Bridgett Hurley (VP-Dev)
Chris E. Herwig (Chief Investment
Officer & Portfolio Mgr)
Matteo Castelvetri (Mng Dir-Global
Bankers Insurance Grp-Europe)

Subsidiaries:

Damovo Deutschland GmbH & Co.
KG   (1)
Heerdter Lohweg 35, 40549, Dusseldorf,
Germany
Tel.: (49) 211 8755 40
Web Site: http://www.damovo.de
Information Communications Technology
Services
N.A.I.C.S.: 541990
Bernhard Bicherl (Head-Svc Analytics-
Global Svc)
Carl Muehlner (Mng Dir)
Mary Bradshaw (Mng Dir-Global Svcs)

Subsidiary (Non-US):

Damovo Belgium N.V/S.A   (2)
Schiphollaan 3 Avenue de Schiphol, 1140,
Brussels, Belgium
Tel.: (32) 27088211
Web Site: http://www.damovo.be
Emp.: 50
Information Communications Technology
Services
N.A.I.C.S.: 541990
Joop Jansen (Mng Dir)
Alain Huys (Mgr-Sls & Solution Architects)
Christel Huybrechts (Mgr-Fin)
Paolo De Luca (Dir-Ops)

Damovo Polska Sp. z o.o.   (2)
Park Postepu ul Postepu 21, 02-676, War-
saw, Poland
Tel.: (48) 22 533 71 00
Web Site: http://www.damovo.pl
Information Communications Technology
Services
N.A.I.C.S.: 541990
Krzysztof Garbacz (Mgr-Bus Dev)
Paulina Waszkiewicz-Socko (Mng Dir)

Damovo Schweiz AG   (2)
Kriesbachstrasse 30, 8600, Dubendorf,
Switzerland
Tel.: (41) 43 255 72 11
Web Site: http://www.damovo.ch
Information Communications Technology
Services
N.A.I.C.S.: 541990
Carl Muehlner (Mng Dir)

Subsidiary (US):

Damovo USA, Inc.   (2)
Atrium 2 221 E 4th St Ste 2500, Cincinnati,
OH 45202
Tel.: (513) 725-4327
Web Site: http://www.damovo.com
Information Communications Technology
Services
N.A.I.C.S.: 541990

Eli Research India Pvt. Ltd.   (1)
SSR Corporate Park 7th Floor 13/6 Sector
27-B NH-2 Delhi-Mathura Road, Faridabad,
121003, Haryana, India
Tel.: (91) 129 4294700
Web Site: http://www.eliindia.com
Business Support Services
N.A.I.C.S.: 561499

Eli Research, LLC   (1)
2222 Sedwick Rd, Durham, NC 27713
Tel.: (919) 281-0474
Web Site: http://www.elijournals.com
Trade Journal & Other Information Products
Publisher
N.A.I.C.S.: 513120
Greg Lindberg (Pres)

Global Bankers Insurance Group,
LLC   (1)
2327 Englert Dr, Durham, NC
27713   (100%)
Tel.: (919) 246-3382
Web Site: http://www.globalbankers.com
Rev.: $3,400,000,000
Holding Company; Life Insurance & Rein-
surance Products & Services
N.A.I.C.S.: 551112
Lou Hensley (Pres & Co-CEO)
Rod Perkins (Head-Govt Rels)
Paul Brown (Exec VP-Fin & Strategy)
Brian Stewart (CFO)
Joe Lurie (CIO)
Chris Herwig (Chief Investment Officer)
Sandy Ball (Exec VP-HR & Talent Dev)
Will Romero (Head-Risk & Strategy)

Eli Global, LLC—(Continued)

Tamre Edwards *(Gen Counsel)*
Ray Martinez *(Head-Regulatory & Strategic Affairs)*
Louis Belo *(Chief Compliance Officer, Chief Audit Officer & Sr VP)*
Dean Fisher *(VP-Corp Fin/Mergers & Acq)*
Matteo Castelvetri *(CEO-Europe)*

Subsidiary (Domestic):

Colorado Bankers Life Insurance Company (2)
5990 Greenwood Plz Blvd Ste 325, Greenwood Village, CO 80111-4704
Tel.: (303) 220-8500
Web Site: http://www.cbllife.com
Sales Range: $50-74.9 Million
Life Insurance Products & Services
N.A.I.C.S.: 524113
Joseph Wieser *(Pres & CEO)*

Pavonia Holdings (US), Inc. (2)
180 Mount Airy Rd Ste 101, Basking Ridge, NJ 07920
Tel.: (908) 203-2620
Holding Company; Life Insurance Products & Services
N.A.I.C.S.: 551112

Southland National Insurance Corporation (2)
2200 Jack Warner Pkwy Ste 150, Tuscaloosa, AL 35401
Tel.: (205) 345-7410
Web Site: http://www.southlandnational.com
Sales Range: $10-24.9 Million
Emp.: 50
Life Insurance Products & Services
N.A.I.C.S.: 524113
James E. Leitner *(VP)*

JHJ Software, Inc. (1)
1967 Oak Tree Rd, Edison, NJ 08820 (100%)
Tel.: (732) 744-2700
Web Site: http://www.mdoffice.com
Sales Range: $1-9.9 Million
Emp.: 500
Electronic Medical Records & Practice Management Systems
N.A.I.C.S.: 513210
Jay P. Lodhia *(CEO & VP)*

ELI'S CHEESECAKE COMPANY
6701 W Forest Preserve Dr, Chicago, IL 60634
Tel.: (773) 736-3417 IL
Web Site: https://www.elicheesecake.com
Year Founded: 1980
Sales Range: $200-249.9 Million
Emp.: 256
Cheesecakes & Desserts Mfr
N.A.I.C.S.: 311813
Marc S. Schulman *(Pres)*
Pete Filippelli *(Sr VP-Sls & Mktg)*
Jolene Worthington *(VP-Ops)*
Debbie Littmann Marchok *(VP-Mktg)*

ELIADA HOMES, INC.
2 Compton Dr, Asheville, NC 28806
Tel.: (828) 254-5356 NC
Web Site: https://www.eliada.org
Year Founded: 1906
Sales Range: $10-24.9 Million
Emp.: 362
Child Care & Development Services
N.A.I.C.S.: 624110
Marie Jensen *(VP-Quality Mgmt)*
Mark C. Upright *(Pres & CEO)*
Tracey A. McCrain *(Dir-Child Dev Svcs)*
Dennis Hawley *(Dir-HR)*
Rebecca Williams *(CFO)*

ELIAS BROTHERS GROUP PAINTING & CONTRACTING, INC.
3570 Enterprise Ave Ste 100, Naples, FL 34104
Tel.: (239) 643-1624 FL
Web Site: http://www.elias-brothers.com
Year Founded: 1989
Emp.: 100
Painting & Wall Covering Contractor
N.A.I.C.S.: 238320
Roni Elias *(Principal)*
Ilan Elias *(Principal)*
Rami Yitzhak *(Principal)*
Maria Elias *(CEO)*

ELIAS WILF CORPORATION
10234 S Dolfield Rd, Owings Mills, MD 21117-3608
Tel.: (410) 363-2400
Web Site: http://www.flooryou.com
Year Founded: 1915
Sales Range: $10-24.9 Million
Emp.: 125
Home Furnishing Whslr
N.A.I.C.S.: 423220
Jeff Striegel *(Pres)*
Sheila Bosworth *(Dir-IT)*
Ginger Chiveral *(Mgr-Credit)*
Linda Depkin *(Controller)*
Sean Gentner *(Supvr-Transportation)*
Gloria Hicks *(Mgr-Inventory)*
Carolyn Wilf *(Office Mgr)*
Tom Gray *(Mgr-Comml Contract Sls)*
Rob Ausfresser *(CFO)*
Marc Faucheux *(VP-Sls-North)*
Ben Brumbaugh *(VP-Sls-South)*

ELICERE INC
400 N Washington St Ste 301, Falls Church, VA 22046
Tel.: (703) 237-0274
Web Site: http://www.elicere.com
Year Founded: 2006
Sales Range: $1-9.9 Million
Emp.: 25
It Consulting
N.A.I.C.S.: 541690
Dennis Ruggeri *(Pres & Chief Mouth Officer)*
Marcial Peredo *(CEO)*

ELIE TAHARI, LTD.
11 W 42nd St 14th Fl, New York, NY 10036
Tel.: (212) 763-2000
Web Site: http://www.elietahari.com
Year Founded: 1974
Sales Range: $75-99.9 Million
Emp.: 700
Women's & Men's Clothing
N.A.I.C.S.: 315250
Elie Tahari *(Chm)*

ELIKO EX-IMPORT INC.
102 Madison Ave FL 4, New York, NY 10016
Tel.: (212) 725-1600
Web Site: http://www.elikorugs.com
Sales Range: $10-24.9 Million
Emp.: 15
Rugs
N.A.I.C.S.: 423220
David Basalely *(Pres)*

ELIM PARK BAPTIST HOME INC.
140 Cook Hill Rd, Cheshire, CT 06410
Tel.: (203) 272-7550 CT
Web Site: http://www.elimpark.org
Year Founded: 1906
Sales Range: $25-49.9 Million
Emp.: 467
Elderly Housing Services
N.A.I.C.S.: 624229
Chris Nelson *(Chm)*
Sam Caligiuri *(Vice Chm)*
Paulette Annon *(Sec)*
Rob Ecker *(Treas)*

ELIMINATOR CUSTOM BOATS INC.
10795 San Sevaine Way, Mira Loma, CA 91752
Tel.: (951) 332-4300
Web Site: https://www.eliminatorboat.com
Sales Range: $10-24.9 Million
Emp.: 14
Custom Fiberglass Boat Building, Sales & Repairing
N.A.I.C.S.: 336612
Bob Leach *(Pres)*

ELIPTICON WOOD PRODUCTS, INC.
600 E Moasis Dr, Little Chute, WI 54140
Tel.: (920) 788-9322 WI
Web Site: https://www.elipticon.com
Year Founded: 1993
Sales Range: $1-9.9 Million
Emp.: 21
Window Moldings & Casings & Other Custom Millwork
N.A.I.C.S.: 337212
John Wiley *(Pres)*
Pat Heckner *(Mgr-Admin)*

ELIS BREAD (ELI ZABAR) INC.
1064 Madison Ave, New York, NY 10028
Tel.: (212) 831-4800
Web Site: http://www.elisbread.com
Rev.: $13,400,000
Emp.: 129
Bread & Bread Type Roll Mixes; From Purchased Flour
N.A.I.C.S.: 311824
Eli Zabar *(Pres)*

ELITE AEROSPACE GROUP, INC.
1641-1645 Reynolds Ave, Irvine, CA 92614
Tel.: (888) 435-4839
Web Site: http://www.eliteaerospacecorp.com
Aircraft Engineering Design & Mfr
N.A.I.C.S.: 334511
Lee Smith *(COO)*
Michael Lanza *(Head-Public Relations)*

ELITE ALUMINUM CORPORATION
4650 Lyons Tech Pkwy, Coconut Creek, FL 33073
Tel.: (954) 949-3200
Web Site: https://www.elitealuminum.com
Year Founded: 1981
Sales Range: $10-24.9 Million
Emp.: 80
Insulated Sandwich Panel Design & Mfr
N.A.I.C.S.: 327390
Peter Zadok *(Co-Pres)*
Bryan Cole *(Gen Mgr-Forts)*

ELITE CME INC
1452 N US Hwy 1 Ste 100, Ormond Beach, FL 32174
Tel.: (386) 615-1812
Web Site: http://www.elitecme.com
Year Founded: 1999
Rev.: $3,100,000
Emp.: 12
Professional Organizations
N.A.I.C.S.: 813920
Lisa Stevens *(Office Mgr)*

ELITE CNC MACHINING, INC.
12395 Belcher Rd S Unit 230, Largo, FL 33773
Tel.: (727) 531-8447

Web Site: http://www.elitecnc.com
Sales Range: $10-24.9 Million
Emp.: 3
Fabricated Metal Products Mfr
N.A.I.C.S.: 332999
Jack Lavery *(Pres & CEO)*

ELITE COLLECTIONS, INC.
1139 Hwy 77 N, Marion, AR 72364-0936
Tel.: (870) 735-1826 AR
Year Founded: 1963
Sales Range: $50-74.9 Million
Emp.: 170
Furniture Whslr
N.A.I.C.S.: 423220
Dan Macintyre *(CFO)*
James O. Pike *(Pres & CEO)*
Todd Sawvelle *(Dir-Mktg)*

ELITE COMPUTER CONSULTANTS LP
10235 Waste Little York Rd Ste 235, Houston, TX 77040
Tel.: (713) 686-9740 TX
Web Site: http://www.ecom-inc.com
Year Founded: 1978
Sales Range: $10-24.9 Million
Emp.: 300
Custom Computer Programming Services
N.A.I.C.S.: 541511
Rodney Holtkamp *(Pres)*

ELITE CORE ENTERPRISES LLC
1191 Sturgis Rd Ste 300, Conway, AR 72034
Web Site: http://www.elitecoreaudio.com
Year Founded: 2014
Sales Range: $1-9.9 Million
Emp.: 42
Lighting Equipment Mfr
N.A.I.C.S.: 335139
Chris Ward *(Pres)*
Trey McClurkin *(VP)*
Grayson Ward *(Mktg Dir)*
Brennan Williams *(Mgr-Product Personalization)*
Tanner Nichols *(Mgr-Metalwork)*

ELITE CRETE SYSTEMS INC.
1061 Transport Dr, Valparaiso, IN 46383
Tel.: (219) 465-7671
Web Site: http://www.elitecrete.com
Sales Range: $10-24.9 Million
Emp.: 19
Concrete Block & Brick
N.A.I.C.S.: 327331
Ken Freestone *(Gen Mgr)*

ELITE CUSTOM BUILDERS LLC
5475 Peoria St Unit 4-106, Denver, CO 80239
Tel.: (303) 296-0361
Web Site: http://www.eliteroofingcolorado.com
Year Founded: 2006
Roofing Contractors
N.A.I.C.S.: 238160
Randy Brothers *(Founder & Pres)*
Brie Reis *(CEO)*

ELITE CUSTOM EXTERIORS, INC.
8585 S Sandy Pkwy, Sandy, UT 84070
Tel.: (801) 733-4000
Web Site: https://www.elitecustomexteriors.com
Year Founded: 1995
Sales Range: $10-24.9 Million
Emp.: 160

Building Exteriors
N.A.I.C.S.: 238190
Cindy Condie *(Mgr-HR)*
Scott Little *(VP)*

ELITE FLOORING & DESIGN INC.

3480 Green Pointe Pkwy, Norcross, GA 30092
Tel.: (770) 409-8228
Web Site:
http://www.eliteflooring.com
Sales Range: $10-24.9 Million
Emp.: 30
Mfr of Floor Coverings
N.A.I.C.S.: 423220
Jim Chapman *(Project Mgr)*

ELITE HUMAN CAPITAL GROUP

155 S Executive Dr Ste 200, Brookfield, WI 53005
Tel.: (262) 785-0900   WI
Web Site:
https://www.elitehumancapital.com
Year Founded: 2003
Sales Range: $1-9.9 Million
Emp.: 20
Human Resource Consulting Services
N.A.I.C.S.: 541612
Nancy La Violette *(VP)*
Carrie McKnight-Saunders *(Program Mgr-Talent Scout)*
Ben Danahar *(VP)*

ELITE INSURANCE PARTNERS, LLC

34125 US Hwy 19 N Unit 200, Palm Harbor, FL 34684
Web Site:
http://www.eliteinsurancepartners.com
Year Founded: 2014
Sales Range: $1-9.9 Million
Emp.: 28
Medical Insurance Services
N.A.I.C.S.: 524114
Jagger Esch *(Co-Founder, Pres & CEO)*
David Haass *(Co-Founder & CTO)*
Scott Valentine *(Dir-Digital Mktg)*
Jamie Webb *(Office Mgr)*
Philip Dalimonte *(COO)*
Anthony Janicki *(CFO)*

ELITE LIMOUSINE PLUS, INC.

32-72 Gale Ave, Long Island City, NY 11101
Tel.: (718) 472-2300   NY
Web Site: https://www.eliteny.com
Year Founded: 1986
Limousine Car Rental
N.A.I.C.S.: 532111
Shafquat Chaudhary *(Pres)*

Subsidiaries:

First Corporate Sedans Inc.   (1)
60 E 42nd St Ste 2424, New York, NY 10165
Tel.: (212) 972-2282
Web Site: http://www.fcsny.com
Passenger Transportation Services
N.A.I.C.S.: 485999

ELITE LOGISTICS, LLC

2751 Commerce Dr, Rock Hill, SC 29730-8930
Tel.: (803) 366-3117   SC
Web Site:
http://www.elitelogisticsllc.com
Third-Party Freight Warehousing & Logistics Services
N.A.I.C.S.: 493110

ELITE MARKET LLC

4050 Hwy 127 N, Crossville, TN 38571
Tel.: (931) 456-4522
Web Site:
http://corporate.exxonmobil.com
Sales Range: $10-24.9 Million
Emp.: 6
Convenience Stores, Independent
N.A.I.C.S.: 445131

ELITE MASONRY, INC.

216 FM 1103, Cibolo, TX 78108
Tel.: (210) 662-7878   TX
Year Founded: 1992
Sales Range: $1-9.9 Million
Emp.: 50
Masonry Contracting Services
N.A.I.C.S.: 238140
Kenneth Reus *(Pres)*

ELITE MEDIA, INC.

145 Brightmoor Ct, Henderson, NV 89074
Tel.: (702) 492-0654
Web Site:
http://www.elitemediainc.com
Year Founded: 2002
Sales Range: $10-24.9 Million
Emp.: 5
Media Buying Services
N.A.I.C.S.: 541830
Chad McCullough *(Pres)*
Jen Grant *(Mgr-Sls)*

ELITE MERCHANT SOLUTIONS

16600 Sherman Way Ste 205, Van Nuys, CA 91406
Web Site:
https://www.elitedatacorp.com
Year Founded: 2002
Sales Range: $1-9.9 Million
Emp.: 23
Merchant Services Company; Authorizing & Settling Credit Transactions
N.A.I.C.S.: 522390
Alicia Menjivar *(Mgr-Acctg)*
Jason Rosales *(Mgr-Sls)*

ELITE MODEL MANAGEMENT CORPORATION

245 5th Ave, New York, NY 10016
Tel.: (212) 529-9700
Web Site: http://www.elitemodel.com
Year Founded: 1971
Sales Range: $25-49.9 Million
Emp.: 81
Modeling Agency
N.A.I.C.S.: 711410
Eddie Trump *(Owner & Pres)*
Aly Wilensky *(Mgr-Model)*

ELITE PACIFIC, LLC

Kahala Mall Office Bldg 4211 Waialae Ave Ste 106, Honolulu, HI 96816
Tel.: (808) 589-2040
Web Site: http://www.elitepacific.com
Year Founded: 2005
Sales Range: $1-9.9 Million
Emp.: 44
Real Estate Management Services
N.A.I.C.S.: 531390
Stephen Cipres *(Founder)*
Margaret Reynolds *(VP-Brokerage)*
Amber Schoneberg *(Mgr-Reservations-Vacation Rentals)*
Munro Murdock *(Gen Mgr-Vacation Rentals)*
Charlotte Sherwood *(Dir-Property Mgmt)*
Riette Jenkins *(Partner)*
Denise Kelly *(Mgr-Property)*
Beth Holiday *(VP-Sls & Dev)*
Lisa Han *(VP-Ops)*
Chuck Garrett *(VP-Bus Dev)*
Anton Steenman *(Pres)*

Paul Mayer *(Mng Partner)*
Alfred Korn *(CTO)*
Joanna Langada *(Dir-Mktg)*

Subsidiaries:

Hawaii Commercial Real Estate, LLC   (1)
733 Bishop St Ste 151, Honolulu, HI 96813-4014
Tel.: (808) 440-2795
Web Site: http://www.hawaiicre.com
Offices of Real Estate Agents & Brokers
N.A.I.C.S.: 531210
Jamie Brown *(Pres)*

ELITE PERFORMANCE HOLDING CORP.

3301 NE 1st Ave Ste M704, Miami, FL 33137   NV
Web Site:
https://www.eliteperformance
holdings.com
Year Founded: 2018
Rev.: $40,210
Assets: $170,738
Liabilities: $3,137,098
Net Worth: ($2,966,360)
Earnings: ($1,447,769)
Fiscal Year-end: 12/31/23
Holding Company
N.A.I.C.S.: 551112
David Sandler *(COO)*
Joey Firestone *(Chm)*

ELITE PIZZA TEXAS, LLC

4519 N Garfield St Ste 4, Midland, TX 79705
Tel.: (432) 570-1990   TX
Franchise Pizza Restaurants Owner & Operator
N.A.I.C.S.: 722513
James C. Gerety *(Owner & Pres)*

ELITE PROPERTIES OF AMERICA, INC.

6385 Corporate Dr Ste 200, Colorado Springs, CO 80919-5912
Tel.: (719) 592-9333   CO
Web Site:
http://www.classichomes.com
Year Founded: 1989
Sales Range: $25-49.9 Million
Emp.: 300
Residential Construction
N.A.I.C.S.: 236115
George Lenz *(Pres)*

ELITE RECRUITING GROUP LLC

6120 Southard Trace, Cumming, GA 30040
Tel.: (678) 513-4297
Web Site:
http://www.eliterecruitinggroup.com
Year Founded: 2003
Sales Range: $1-9.9 Million
Emp.: 135
IT, Logistics, Counter-Intelligence & Counter-Terrorism Staffing
N.A.I.C.S.: 928110
Sandra Dickerson *(Pres)*

ELITE RETAILS SERVICES INC.

465 This Way St, Lake Jackson, TX 77566-5143
Tel.: (979) 285-0712
Web Site: https://www.elite-construction.com
Sales Range: $10-24.9 Million
Emp.: 40
Nonresidential Construction Services
N.A.I.C.S.: 236220
James Spratt *(Pres)*

ELITE ROADS

1101 W Commercial Blvd, Fort Lauderdale, FL 33309
Tel.: (954) 771-4508
Web Site: http://www.eliteroads.com
Sales Range: $10-24.9 Million
Emp.: 21
Retailer of Automotive Tires, Wheels & Accessories
N.A.I.C.S.: 441340
Frank Russ *(Owner)*

ELITE SPICE, INC.

7151 Montevideo Rd, Jessup, MD 20794-9308
Tel.: (410) 796-1900   MD
Web Site: https://www.elitespice.com
Year Founded: 1988
Sales Range: $25-49.9 Million
Emp.: 175
Spice, Seasoning, Capsicum, Oil & Oleoresin Producer for the Commercial Food Industry
N.A.I.C.S.: 311942
Isaac Samuel *(Pres)*
Debbie Ingle *(Controller)*
Paul Kurpe *(VP-Sls)*

ELITE SPORTSWEAR, L.P.

2136 N 13th St, Reading, PA 19612-6400
Tel.: (610) 921-1469
Web Site: https://www.gkelite.com
Year Founded: 1981
Sales Range: $100-124.9 Million
Emp.: 250
Gymnastics & Skating Apparel Mfr
N.A.I.C.S.: 315250
Girisha Chandraraj *(Pres & CEO)*

ELITE STAFFING INC

1400 W Hubbard St Fl 2, Chicago, IL 60642
Tel.: (773) 235-3000
Web Site:
https://www.elitestaffinginc.com
Sales Range: $25-49.9 Million
Emp.: 14,000
Temporary Help Service
N.A.I.C.S.: 561320
Andrew Cole *(COO & Sec)*
Gary Cole *(Pres)*
Ted Rigas *(CFO)*

ELITE TEAM REALTY & PROPERTY MANAGEMENT

756 Tyvola Rd Ste 126, Charlotte, NC 28217-3535
Tel.: (704) 521-2735
Web Site:
http://www.elitecarolinas.net
Year Founded: 2005
Sales Range: $10-24.9 Million
Emp.: 12
Real Estate Brokerage Services
N.A.I.C.S.: 531210
Brian Augustine *(Pres)*

ELITE TECHNOLOGY INC.

330 W 38th St Ste 508, New York, NY 10018
Tel.: (212) 967-5009
Web Site: https://www.etny.com
Year Founded: 1995
Sales Range: $10-24.9 Million
Emp.: 48
Office Equipment Sales & Services
N.A.I.C.S.: 811210
Henry Lu *(CEO)*
Fan Jane *(Mgr)*
William L. Ballhaus *(Exec Chm)*

ELITE TRAVEL MANAGEMENT GROUP

33920 US Hwy 19 N Ste 215, Palm Harbor, FL 34684

Elite Travel Management Group—(Continued)

Tel.: (727) 726-9090
Web Site:
   http://www.elitetravelgroup.net
Year Founded: 2001
Sales Range: $1-9.9 Million
Emp.: 12
Travel Agency
N.A.I.C.S.: 561510
Tammy Levent *(Owner)*
Katie Levent *(Mgr)*

ELITE-WEILER POOLS, INC.
640 Apex Rd, Sarasota, FL 34240
Tel.: (941) 343-9001
Web Site: http://www.eliteweiler.com
Year Founded: 1984
Sales Range: $1-9.9 Million
Residential & Commercial Swimming
Pools & Water Features
N.A.I.C.S.: 238990
Monica Kennedy *(Mng Dir)*

ELITESOFT GLOBAL INC.
18582 N W Holly St Unit 202, Bea-
verton, OR 97006-7014
Tel.: (503) 830-2918   DE
Web Site:
   http://www.elitesoftglobal.com
Year Founded: 2014
Sales Range: Less than $1 Million
Emp.: 3
Information Technology Support Ser-
vices
N.A.I.C.S.: 541512
Mae Ling Khoo *(CFO)*
Cornelius Soon Heng Ee *(Chm, CEO,
Pres & VP-IT)*
Kah Tan *(COO & Sec)*

ELIXIR INDUSTRIES
24800 Chrisanta Dr Ste 210, Mission
Viejo, CA 92691
Tel.: (949) 860-5000   CA
Web Site: http://www.elixirind.com
Year Founded: 1948
Sales Range: $350-399.9 Million
Emp.: 1,200
Mfr & Distributor of Component Parts
for Manufactured Housing, Shelter &
Recreational Vehicle Industries; Alu-
minium Siding; Doors, Roofs & Seal-
ants; Aluminium Extrusions & Plastic
Vacuum Forming
N.A.I.C.S.: 332119
Julie Cameron *(Dir-Intl Sls)*
Christopher Sahm *(CEO)*
Bob Cuthbertson *(CFO)*
John T. Willis *(Dir-Bus Dev)*
Barbara Wright *(Dir-HR)*
Leslie Moreau *(Sec)*
Mary Leonard *(Controller)*

Subsidiaries:

Elixir Door Company - Division
81   (1)
505 Hwy 20 E, Tuscumbia, AL 35674-0309
Tel.: (256) 381-5932
Web Site:
   http://elixirdoorandmetalscompany.com
Metal Siding & Roofing Mfr & Distr
N.A.I.C.S.: 332312

Elixir Industries   (1)
5201 Lincoln Way E, Mishawaka, IN
46544-4204   (100%)
Tel.: (574) 259-7133
Web Site: http://www.elixirind.com
Sales Range: $10-24.9 Million
Emp.: 100
Aluminum Extrusions
N.A.I.C.S.: 331318
Mike O'Bryan *(Acct Mgr)*

Elixir Industries   (1)
2040 Industrial Pkwy, Elkhart, IN
46516-5411   (100%)
Tel.: (574) 294-5685
Web Site: http://www.elixirind.com

Sales Range: $200-249.9 Million
Emp.: 67
Mfr of Mobile Homes Siding & Aluminum
Parts
N.A.I.C.S.: 332312

Elixir Industries   (1)
219 S Mulberry, Mesa, AZ
85202-1123   (100%)
Tel.: (480) 834-1484
Web Site: http://www.elixirind.com
Sales Range: $10-24.9 Million
Emp.: 35
Mfr of Fabricated Aluminum & Galvanized
Materials
N.A.I.C.S.: 332312

Elixir Industries   (1)
1215 Pope Dr, Douglas, GA 31533 (100%)
Tel.: (912) 384-2078
Web Site: http://www.elixirind.com
Sales Range: $25-49.9 Million
Emp.: 160
Metal Siding, Mobile Home Doors & Alumi-
num Extrusions Mfr
N.A.I.C.S.: 332321
Archie Brown *(Gen Mgr-Door Div)*
Philip Smith *(Gen Mgr-Extrusions Div)*
Kayla Douglas *(Mgr-Pur)*

Elixir Industries   (1)
304 E Main St, Leola, PA 17540-1959
Tel.: (717) 656-2831
Web Site: http://www.elixirind.com
Sales Range: $10-24.9 Million
Emp.: 30
Mfr Of Siding For Mobile Homes
N.A.I.C.S.: 332321

Elixir Industries - Division 27   (1)
1300 Pope Dr, Douglas, GA 31533
Tel.: (912) 384-2078
Web Site: http://www.elixirind.com
Sales Range: $50-74.9 Million
Emp.: 350
Aluminum Extrusion Product Mfr
N.A.I.C.S.: 331313
Dwight Knowles *(Pres)*

Elixir Industries, Cargo Trailer
Industry   (1)
243 Washington Ave, Fitzgerald, GA
31750-8218   (100%)
Tel.: (229) 423-4311
Web Site: http://www.elixirdoorcompany.com
Sales Range: $25-49.9 Million
Emp.: 60
Cargo Trailer Component Mfr
N.A.I.C.S.: 332321

Elixir Industries, Waco Div   (1)
5500 Industrial Dr, Waco, TX
76710   (100%)
Tel.: (254) 741-1060
Web Site: http://www.elixirindustries.com
Sales Range: $25-49.9 Million
Emp.: 65
Mfr of Aluminum & Steel Doors
N.A.I.C.S.: 332312
Bob Powers *(Gen Mgr)*

ELIZA BRYANT VILLAGE
7201 Wade Park Ave, Cleveland, OH
44103
Tel.: (216) 361-6141   OH
Web Site: https://www.elizabryant.org
Year Founded: 1896
Sales Range: $10-24.9 Million
Emp.: 385
Elder Care Services
N.A.I.C.S.: 624120
Rufus Heard *(Treas)*
William D. Ginn *(Sec)*
Jean Allen-Jenkins *(Chm)*
Danny R. Williams *(Pres & CEO)*

**ELIZABETH CHRISTIAN PUB-
LIC RELATIONS LLC**
8008 Spicewood Ln, Austin, TX
78759
Tel.: (512) 472-9599   TX
Web Site:
   https://www.echristianpr.com
Year Founded: 1995
Public Relations & Advertising
Agency

N.A.I.C.S.: 541820
Elizabeth Christian *(Founder & CEO)*
Kristin Marcum *(Pres)*
Meg Meo *(Sr VP-Acct Mgmt)*
Kathleen Smith *(Sr VP-Bus Affairs)*
Levente McCrary *(VP-Acct Mgmt)*
Erin Ochoa *(VP-Acct Mgmt)*
Rachel Wyatt *(Creative Dir)*

**ELIZABETH GLASER PEDIAT-
RIC AIDS FOUNDATION**
1140 Connecticut Ave NW Ste 200,
Washington, DC 20036
Tel.: (202) 296-9165   CA
Web Site: https://www.pedaids.org
Year Founded: 1988
Sales Range: $150-199.9 Million
Emp.: 178
Health Care Srvices
N.A.I.C.S.: 813212
Laura Guay *(VP-Res)*
Brad Kiley *(COO)*
Russ Hagey *(Chm)*
Kathleen Cravero-Kristoffersson *(Vice
Chm)*

**ELIZABETH HALL & ASSOCI-
ATES, INC.**
3034 Golden Ave, Cincinnati, OH
45226
Tel.: (513) 871-5127   OH
Web Site: http://www.ehasearch.com
Sales Range: Less than $1 Million
Emp.: 3
Human Resource Consulting Ser-
vices
N.A.I.C.S.: 541612
Elizabeth Hall *(Pres)*

ELIZUR CORP.
9800A McKnight Rd, Pittsburgh, PA
15237
Tel.: (412) 358-4523   PA
Web Site: http://www.elizurcorp.com
Year Founded: 1993
Emp.: 100
Health Equipment Retail Services
N.A.I.C.S.: 456199
James Grant *(Pres)*

Subsidiaries:

ActivAided Orthotics LLC   (1)
700 River Ave Ste 234, Pittsburgh, PA
15212
Tel.: (412) 573-4125
Web Site: http://www.activaided.com
Health Care Equipment Whslr
N.A.I.C.S.: 423490
Kelly Collier *(Founder & Mgr-Product Dev)*

ELJET AVIATION SERVICES
2050 Lincoln Ave, Pasadena, CA
91103
Tel.: (888) 355-3538
Web Site: http://www.e-
aircraftsupply.com
Year Founded: 2006
Sales Range: $1-9.9 Million
Emp.: 9
Charter Flight Services
N.A.I.C.S.: 481211
Ben Schusterman *(VP-Ops)*

**ELK BRAND MANUFACTUR-
ING CO.**
1601 County Hospital Rd, Nashville,
TN 37228-8503
Tel.: (615) 254-4300
Web Site: https://elkbrand.com
Sales Range: $50-74.9 Million
Emp.: 900
Women's Apparel
N.A.I.C.S.: 315250
Walter Marianelli *(Pres)*
Jim Clark *(Controller)*

**ELK GROUP INTERNATIONAL,
INC.**
12 Willow Ln, Nesquehoning, PA
18240
Web Site:
   http://www.elkgroupinternational.com
Holding Company; Lighting & Wood
Furniture Designer, Mfr & Distr
N.A.I.C.S.: 551112
John Haste *(Sr VP-Sls & Mktg)*

Subsidiaries:

Lamp Works   (1)
12 Willow Ln, Nesquehoning, PA 18240
Web Site: http://www.lampworks.com
Used Merchandise Stores
N.A.I.C.S.: 459510
Clay Marsh *(Owner)*

Stein World Operating Co.   (1)
5800 Challenge Dr, Memphis, TN 38115
Tel.: (901) 261-3050
Web Site: http://www.steinworld.com
Furniture Designer, Mfr & Distr
N.A.I.C.S.: 337122
Donnie Lesley *(VP-Mdsg & Mktg)*
Jim Peltier *(VP-Strategic Acct & Direct Im-
ports)*
Adam Firrone *(Mgr-Mdse)*
Natalie Simanovsky *(VP-Intl Ops)*
Rick Stroud *(VP-Sls-Eastern)*

The Pomeroy Collection Ltd.   (1)
4820 Blalock Rd Ste 101, Houston, TX
77041
Tel.: (713) 460-5565
Web Site: http://www.pomeroycollection.com
Decorative Household Goods Designer, Mfr
& Whslr
N.A.I.C.S.: 423220
Sara Scarberry *(VP)*
Todd Pomeroy *(Founder & Dir-Design)*

ELK GROVE PARK DISTRICT
1000 Wellington Ave, Elk Grove Vil-
lage, IL 60007
Tel.: (847) 437-8780
Web Site:
   https://www.elkgroveparks.org
Sales Range: $10-24.9 Million
Emp.: 20
Recreational Services
N.A.I.C.S.: 713990

**ELK REGIONAL HEALTH CEN-
TER**
763 Johnsonburg Rd, Saint Marys,
PA 15857
Tel.: (814) 788-8000   PA
Web Site: http://www.elkregional.org
Year Founded: 1999
Sales Range: $75-99.9 Million
Emp.: 1,200
Health Care Srvices
N.A.I.C.S.: 622110
Mark J. Shulkosky *(Chief Medical Of-
ficer)*
Mary Kaye Halterman *(Chief Nursing
Officer)*
Laurie J. MacDonald *(CFO)*
Frank Scutella *(Chm)*
JoAnne Ryan *(Treas)*
Robert Ordiway *(Vice Chm)*
George Bojalad *(Chief HR Officer)*
Brad Catman *(CEO)*

**ELK RIVER FORD MERCURY,
INC.**
17219 Hwy 10, Elk River, MN 55330-
7009
Tel.: (763) 441-2300
Web Site:
   http://www.cornerstoneauto.com
Sales Range: $10-24.9 Million
Emp.: 90
Car Whslr
N.A.I.C.S.: 441110
Travis Mitchell *(Mgr-IT)*

ELK RIVER PUBLIC UTILITY DISTRICT
217 S Jackson St, Tullahoma, TN 37388
Tel.: (931) 455-9311
Web Site: http://www.erpud.com
Sales Range: $10-24.9 Million
Emp.: 60
Natural Gas Distribution
N.A.I.C.S.: 221210
Eddie Moffitt *(Mgr-Ops)*
Mike Gundersen *(Gen Mgr)*
Rachel McKelvey *(Controller)*

ELK SUPPLY COMPANY
103 Gary Blvd, Clinton, OK 73601
Tel.: (580) 323-1250   OK
Year Founded: 1976
Sales Range: $75-99.9 Million
Emp.: 105
Retailer of Lumber & Building Materials to Construction Contractors
N.A.I.C.S.: 423310
James R. Browning *(Pres)*
George Browning *(Treas, Sec & VP)*

ELKAY PLASTICS COMPANY, INC.
6000 Sheila St, Commerce, CA 90040
Tel.: (323) 722-7073   CA
Web Site:
    http://www.elkayplastics.com
Year Founded: 1968
Sales Range: $100-124.9 Million
Emp.: 150
Plastics Product Mfr
N.A.I.C.S.: 326112
Louis Chertkow *(Pres & CEO)*
Stewart Horwitz *(CFO)*
Bill Lindenmoore *(Dir-Mktg)*

ELKHART GRAIN COMPANY
PO Box 216, Elkhart, IL 62634
Tel.: (217) 792-5433
Web Site:
    http://www.elkhartgrain.com
Sales Range: $10-24.9 Million
Emp.: 5
Grain Elevators Mfr
N.A.I.C.S.: 424510
Janice Funk *(Controller)*
Rick Aylesworth *(Asst Mgr-Grain Mdsg-East & Mgr-Safety)*

ELKHART PLASTICS, INC.
3300 N Kenmore, South Bend, IN 46628
Tel.: (574) 232-8066   DE
Web Site: https://www.epi-roto.com
Year Founded: 1988
Sales Range: $50-74.9 Million
Emp.: 600
Molded Plastic Materials-Handling Container Mfr
N.A.I.C.S.: 326199
Jack Welter *(CEO)*
Jon Wyngarden *(CFO)*

ELKHORN OPERATING CO. INC.
8801 S Yale Ave Ste 420, Tulsa, OK 74137
Tel.: (918) 492-4418
Rev.: $23,200,000
Emp.: 8
Natural Gas Production
N.A.I.C.S.: 211130
Tom Rinehart *(Pres & CEO)*

ELKHORN RURAL PUBLIC POWER DISTRICT
206 N 4th St, Battle Creek, NE 68715
Tel.: (402) 675-2185
Web Site: https://www.erppd.com
Sales Range: $10-24.9 Million

Emp.: 40
Electric Power Distr
N.A.I.C.S.: 221122
Tim D. Means *(VP)*
Thomas Rudloff *(Gen Mgr)*

ELKHORN-LUEPTOW'S INC.
58 W Market St A, Elkhorn, WI 53121-1168
Tel.: (262) 723-2996
Web Site:
    https://www.frankspigglywiggly.com
Year Founded: 1981
Sales Range: $10-24.9 Million
Emp.: 100
Groceries & Supermarkets
N.A.I.C.S.: 445110
Frank Lueptow *(Owner)*
Ray Knutson *(Mgr)*

ELKIN CO.
W 222 N 833 Cheaney Dr, Waukesha, WI 53186-1688
Tel.: (262) 548-0864
Year Founded: 1975
Sales Range: $50-74.9 Million
Emp.: 175
Credit Services
N.A.I.C.S.: 522220
Scott Meinerz *(Pres)*

Subsidiaries:

American Industrial Leasing Company Inc.   (1)
W 222 N 833 Cheaney Dr, Waukesha, WI 53186-1688
Tel.: (262) 549-6640
Web Site: http://www.alco.com
Sales Range: $25-49.9 Million
Emp.: 13
Credit Services
N.A.I.C.S.: 522220

Echo Lake Farm Produce Company Inc.   (1)
316 W Grove St, Burlington, WI 53105-9732
Tel.: (262) 763-9551
Web Site: http://www.echo.com
Sales Range: $25-49.9 Million
Emp.: 150
Provider of Poultry Slaughtering & Processing
N.A.I.C.S.: 311999
Debbie Ahler *(Office Mgr)*

Seiler Tank Truck Service Inc.   (1)
26791 W Michigan Ave PO Box 364, Albion, MI 49224-9503
Tel.: (517) 629-4810
Web Site: http://www.elkin.com
Sales Range: $10-24.9 Million
Emp.: 20
Trucking Service
N.A.I.C.S.: 484220

ELKINS CONSTRUCTORS, INC.
701 W Adams St, Jacksonville, FL 32204
Tel.: (904) 353-6500
Web Site:
    http://www.elkinsconstructors.com
Sales Range: $100-124.9 Million
Emp.: 80
Construction Management & General Contracting Services
N.A.I.C.S.: 236220
Barry L. Allred *(Chm & CEO)*
Matthew D. Welch *(Pres & COO)*
David W. Hamilton *(VP-Comml)*
W. Scott Parker *(VP-Life Care)*

ELKINS FORD LAND
696 Beverly Pike, Elkins, WV 26241
Tel.: (304) 591-1498
Web Site:
    https://www.elkinsfordland.com
Sales Range: $10-24.9 Million
Emp.: 52

Car Whslr
N.A.I.C.S.: 441110
Kent Winn *(Mgr)*
Jim Jackson *(Owner)*

ELLCON-NATIONAL INC.
50 Beechtree Blvd, Greenville, SC 29605-5100
Tel.: (864) 277-5000
Web Site:
    http://www.faiveleytransport.com
Year Founded: 1963
Sales Range: $10-24.9 Million
Emp.: 295
Railroad Equipment Distr
N.A.I.C.S.: 336510
Robert Joyeaux *(Pres)*

ELLENBEE-LEGGETT COMPANY INC.
3765 Port Union Rd, Fairfield, OH 45014-2207
Tel.: (513) 874-3200
Web Site: http://www.pfgc.com
Year Founded: 1954
Sales Range: $10-24.9 Million
Emp.: 100
Foodservice Products Distr
N.A.I.C.S.: 424410
James E. Kite *(Pres)*
Gaylene Smith *(Dir-Mktg)*

Subsidiaries:

Reuss Meats Inc.   (1)
3765 Port Union Rd, Fairfield, OH 45014-2207
Tel.: (513) 874-3200
Sales Range: $10-24.9 Million
Emp.: 8
Meat Packing Services
N.A.I.C.S.: 445240

ELLENDALE ELECTRIC COMPANY, INC.
7722 US Hwy 70, Bartlett, TN 38133-2047
Tel.: (901) 382-0045
Year Founded: 1978
Sales Range: $25-49.9 Million
Emp.: 150
Construction Engineering Services
N.A.I.C.S.: 237310
John F. Anderson *(Pres)*
Cynthia Atkins *(Principal)*
Winston German *(Gen Mgr)*

ELLENTON ICE & SPORTS COMPLEX, LLC
5309 29th St E, Ellenton, FL 34222
Tel.: (941) 723-3663
Web Site: http://www.ellentonice.com
Sales Range: $1-9.9 Million
Sports Complex
N.A.I.C.S.: 713940
Tom Lindemuth *(Gen Mgr)*
Fred Eaton *(Dir-Hockey)*
Lyndon Johnston *(Dir-Figure Skating)*
Marvin Kaplan *(Owner)*

ELLENVILLE REGIONAL HOSPITAL
10 Healthy Way, Ellenville, NY 12428
Tel.: (845) 647-6400   NY
Web Site:
    http://www.ellenvilleregional.org
Year Founded: 2000
Sales Range: $10-24.9 Million
Emp.: 200
Health Care Srvices
N.A.I.C.S.: 622110
Walter Sperling *(Dir-Medical)*
Debbie Briggs *(Community Rels & Volunteer Svcs)*

Ashima Butler *(Compliance & Medical Staff Svcs)*
Ann Marie Gungtlow *(Chief Nursing Officer)*

ELLETT BROTHERS, INC.
267 Columbia Ave, Chapin, SC 29036-8322
Tel.: (803) 345-3751   SC
Web Site:
    http://www.ellettbrothers.com
Year Founded: 1933
Sales Range: $125-149.9 Million
Emp.: 411
Hunting & Shooting Products Mfr & Distr Camping, Archery & Other Related Outdoor Activities
N.A.I.C.S.: 423910
Steven Smith *(Mgr-Purchasing)*

ELLEVATE FINANCIAL, INC.
160 W 24th St Ste 14E, New York, NY 10011
Tel.: (401) 524-2900   DE
Web Site: http://www.ellevest.com
Holding Company; Investment Advisory Services
N.A.I.C.S.: 551112
Sallie L. Krawcheck *(CEO)*
Charles Kroll *(Pres & COO)*

Subsidiaries:

Ellevate Financial LLC   (1)
48 W 25th St 6th Fl, New York, NY 10010
Tel.: (646) 517-1160
Web Site: http://www.ellevatenetwork.com
Emp.: 20
Women's Professional Networking Organization
N.A.I.C.S.: 813920
Sallie L. Krawcheck *(CEO)*
Allyson McDonald *(Pres)*
Kristy Wallace *(COO)*
Mariella Herrera Avila *(Dir-Global Membership)*
Allison Matejczyk *(Dir-Corp Partnerships)*
Tina Pettigrew *(Dir-Communications)*

ELLICOTT DEVELOPMENT CO.
295 Main St Ste 700, Buffalo, NY 14203
Tel.: (716) 854-0060
Web Site:
    https://www.ellicottdevelopment.com
Year Founded: 1972
Sales Range: $50-74.9 Million
Emp.: 250
Land Subdividing Services
N.A.I.C.S.: 237210
Carl P. Paladino *(CEO)*

ELLICOTT PAINT CO. INC.
Art Fulfillment Center 2094 185th Street, Suite G PO Box 1030, Fairfield, IA 52556
Tel.: (641) 472-1495   NY
Web Site:
    http://www.ellicottpaint.artselect.com
Year Founded: 1921
Sales Range: $10-24.9 Million
Emp.: 40
Sales of Paints & Wallpaper
N.A.I.C.S.: 444120
Jack Kedzierski *(VP)*

ELLINGTON HOUSING INC.
53 Forest Ave, Old Greenwich, CT 06870
Tel.: (203) 698-1200   MD
Web Site: https://www.ellington.com
Year Founded: 2012
Real Estate Investment Services
N.A.I.C.S.: 523999

Ellington Housing Inc.—(Continued)

Michael William Vranos (Co-Chief
Investment Officer)
Thomas F. Robards (Chm)
Leo Huang (Pres & CEO)
Howard Barash (CFO)

ELLINGTON MANAGEMENT GROUP, L.L.C.

53 Forest Ave, Old Greenwich, CT
06870
Tel.: (203) 698-1200
Web Site: http://www.ellington.com
Investment Management Services in
Mortgage-Backed Securities & Equities
N.A.I.C.S.: 522310
Michael William Vranos (CEO)
Laurence Eric Penn (COO)
Mark Tecotzky (Mng Dir)
Olivier Cojot-Goldberg (Vice Chm)
Robert Kinderman (Mng Dir)
Nikolay Stoytchev (Mng Dir)

Subsidiaries:

Ellington Financial Inc.   (1)
53 Forest Ave, Old Greenwich, CT 06870
Tel.: (203) 698-1200
Web Site: https://www.ellingtonfinancial.com
Rev.: $140,441,000
Assets: $14,085,886,000
Liabilities: $12,865,000,000
Net Worth: $1,220,886,000
Earnings: ($85,339,000)
Emp.: 150
Fiscal Year-end: 12/31/2022
Real Estate Investment Services
N.A.I.C.S.: 523999
J. R. Herlihy (CFO)
Michael William Vranos (Co-Chief Investment Officer)
Laurence Eric Penn (Pres & CEO)
Vincent Ambrico (Controller)
Jason Frank (Sec & Deputy Gen Counsel)
Mark Ira Tecotzky (Co-Chief Investment Officer)
Christopher Smernoff (Chief Acctg Officer)
Alaael-Deen Shilleh (Sec & Assoc Gen Counsel)
Daniel Reuven Margolis (Gen Counsel)

Subsidiary (Domestic):

Arlington Asset Investment Corp.   (2)
6862 Elm St Ste 320, McLean, VA 22101
Tel.: (703) 373-0200
Web Site: http://www.arlingtonasset.com
Rev.: $43,283,000
Assets: $1,002,318,000
Liabilities: $784,978,000
Net Worth: $217,340,000
Earnings: $5,426,000
Emp.: 9
Fiscal Year-end: 12/31/2022
Investment Banking & Securities Brokerage
Services
N.A.I.C.S.: 523150
Daniel E. Berce (Chm)
Richard E. Konzmann (CFO, Treas & Exec VP)

EF CMO LLC   (2)
53 Forest Ave Ste 301, Old Greenwich, CT
06870-1537
Tel.: (203) 405-3505
Mortgage Loan Brokerage Services
N.A.I.C.S.: 522310

EF Mortgage LLC   (2)
3376 Tamarack Ct NE 204, Grand Rapids,
MI 49525-7204
Tel.: (616) 447-9378
Mortgage Loan Brokerage Services
N.A.I.C.S.: 522310

Ellington Financial Operating Partnership LLC   (2)
53 Forest Ave, Old Greenwich, CT 06870
Tel.: (203) 698-1200
Web Site: http://www.ellington.com
Mortgage Loan Brokerage Services
N.A.I.C.S.: 522310

ELLIO LLC

903 E Oglethorpe Blvd, Albany, GA
31705
Tel.: (229) 432-9700
Web Site:
http://www.albanyhondaonline.net
Year Founded: 1999
Sales Range: $10-24.9 Million
Emp.: 35
New & Used Car Sales
N.A.I.C.S.: 441110
Graham Edwards (Pres)

ELLIOTT & FRANTZ INC.

450 E Church Rd, King of Prussia,
PA 19406-2625
Tel.: (610) 279-5200
Web Site:
https://www.elliottfrantz.com
Year Founded: 1962
Sales Range: $25-49.9 Million
Emp.: 250
Construction & Mining Machinery
N.A.I.C.S.: 423810
James M. Elliott (CEO)
Steve White (VP-Sls & Mktg)
Robert L. Schaeffer (Pres)
Ted Kushner (Mgr-Parts)
William F. McLoughlin (VP)
Peter Schaeffer (Mgr-Sls)
Sally Engelhardt (Gen Mgr-Svc)
Catherine Elliott (COO)

ELLIOTT AVIATION, INC.

6601 74th Ave, Milan, IL 61264
Tel.: (309) 799-3183
Web Site:
https://www.elliottaviation.com
Year Founded: 1936
Rev.: $78,358,305
Emp.: 400
Aviation Services
N.A.I.C.S.: 441227
Wynn Elliott (Chm & CEO)
Mark Wilken (VP-Avionics Programs
& Operational Logistics)
Greg Sahr (Pres)
Becky Meyer (Dir-HR)
Lawrence Harting (VP & Gen Mgr-FCM)
Andrew Evans (Dir-Mktg)
Larry Baker (Project Mgr)
Mike Saathoff (Sr Dir-Technical Sls)
Casey Ritz (Reg Mgr-Sls)
Brian Hahn (VP-Flight Svcs)
Casey Norman (Mgr-Safety & Compliance)
Mindy Zumdome (VP-Talent & Culture)
Mike Mehard (VP-Ops)
Kerry Olson (Dir-Ops-Paint & Interior)

ELLIOTT CHEVROLET, INC.

1100 Greenville Ave, Staunton, VA
24401
Tel.: (540) 885-1584
Web Site: http://www.elliottchevy.com
Year Founded: 1961
Sales Range: $25-49.9 Million
Emp.: 35
New Car Dealers
N.A.I.C.S.: 441110
William J. Elliott IV (Pres)

ELLIOTT COMPANY

375 Hambley Blvd, Pikeville, KY
41501
Tel.: (606) 437-7368
Web Site:
http://www.elliottcompanies.com
Sales Range: $25-49.9 Million
Emp.: 41
General Electrical Contractor
N.A.I.C.S.: 238210
Dick Jarvis (Pres)

ELLIOTT DAVIS DECOSIMO, LLC

200 East Broad St, Greenville, SC
29601
Tel.: (864) 242-3370
Web Site: http://www.elliottdavis.com
Year Founded: 1925
Sales Range: $10-24.9 Million
Emp.: 270
Certified Public Accountants
N.A.I.C.S.: 541211
Rick Davis (CEO)
Denise Bailey (Dir-Acctg Sys Consulting)
Lee Wagner (Sr Mgr)
Russell Quattlebaum (Sr Mgr)
Luanne Runge (COO)

ELLIOTT ELECTRIC SUPPLY

2526 N Stallings Dr, Nacogdoches,
TX 75964-7250
Tel.: (936) 715-4008
Web Site:
https://www.elliottelectric.com
Year Founded: 1972
Sales Range: $50-74.9 Million
Emp.: 350
Electrical Services
N.A.I.C.S.: 423610
Mark Bourgeois (Mgr-Mktg)
Clay Mitchell (Mgr-Ops-Palestine)
Kristy Thompson (Acct Mgr)
Phillip Hale (CIO)

ELLIOTT EQUIPMENT COMPANY INC.

327 N Aurora St, Easton, MD 21601
Tel.: (410) 822-0066
Web Site: http://www.ewtrucks.com
Sales Range: $10-24.9 Million
Emp.: 36
Trucks, Commercial
N.A.I.C.S.: 423110
Tom Vatter (VP-Sls & Mktg)
Jim Glazer (Pres)
Larry Hufford (Owner)

ELLIOTT EQUIPMENT COMPANY INCORPORATED

3100 W 76th St, Davenport, IA 52806
Tel.: (563) 391-4840
Web Site:
http://www.elliottequipco.com
Sales Range: $10-24.9 Million
Emp.: 35
Sales Garbage Trucks & Street
Sweepers
N.A.I.C.S.: 423110
Eugene Elliott (Pres)

ELLIOTT HARDWARE INC.

15340 Watertown Plank Rd, Elm
Grove, WI 53122
Tel.: (262) 782-9000   WI
Web Site: http://www.elliottace.com
Year Founded: 1957
Sales Range: $25-49.9 Million
Emp.: 286
Provider of Hardware Store Services
N.A.I.C.S.: 444140
Doug McConeghy (Mgr)
Stew Elliott (Owner)

ELLIOTT HOMES INC.

340 Palladio Pkwy Ste 521, Folsom,
CA 95630
Tel.: (916) 984-1300   AZ
Web Site:
http://www.elliotthomes.com
Year Founded: 1955
Sales Range: $10-24.9 Million
Emp.: 50
Construction Services
N.A.I.C.S.: 236117

Harry Elliott (Pres)
Steve Hemington (VP)
Mark Regan (Superintendent-Construction)

ELLIOTT MANAGEMENT CORPORATION

40 W 57th St, New York, NY 10019
Tel.: (212) 974-6000   DE
Web Site: http://www.elliottmgmt.com
Year Founded: 1977
Emp.: 100
Mutual Fund Investment Management
Services; Private Equity, Real Estate
& Debt Securities Investment Services
N.A.I.C.S.: 523940
Paul Elliott Singer (Founder, Pres,
CEO & Chief Investment Officer)
David J. Miller (Partner-Equity-Restructuring,US & Sr Portfolio Mgr)
Steven K. Barg (Head-Engagement-Global)
Lisa L. Baldwin (Mng Dir)
Samantha B. Algaze (Portfolio Mgr)

Subsidiaries:

Elliott Advisors (UK) Limited   (1)
Park House 6th Floor 116 Park Street, London, W1K 6AF, United Kingdom
Tel.: (44) 2030091275
Investment Fund
N.A.I.C.S.: 525990
Gordon Matthew Singer (Mng Partner & Partner-Equity)

Holding (US):

Barnes & Noble, Inc.   (2)
122 5th Ave, New York, NY 10011 (82.2%)
Tel.: (212) 633-3300
Web Site: http://www.barnesandnoble.com
Rev.: $3,552,745,000
Assets: $1,705,634,000
Liabilities: $1,261,137,000
Net Worth: $444,497,000
Earnings: $3,769,000
Emp.: 7,000
Fiscal Year-end: 04/27/2019
Holding Company; Books, Magazines &
Newspapers; Digital Reading Technologies
& Software Mfr
N.A.I.C.S.: 551112
Mary Ellen Keating (Sr VP-Corp Comm &
Public Affairs)
Andy Milevoj (VP-IR & Corp Fin)
Allen W. Lindstrom (CFO & Exec VP)
Theresa Thompson (Pres-Sterling Publ)
Peter M. Herpich (Chief Acctg Officer, VP &
Controller)
William Earl Wood (Pres-Digital & Exec VP)
Timothy Mantel (Chief Mdsg Officer & Exec
VP)
Rosa Hakala (VP-Distr & Logistics)
Carlo Pochintesta (CIO)
Joseph Charles Gorman (Exec VP-Ops)
Frank Morabito (VP-Stores)
Michelle Smith (VP-HR)

Subsidiary (Domestic):

Barnes & Noble Booksellers, Inc. (3)
55 Old Orchard Ctr, Skokie, IL 60077
Tel.: (847) 676-2230
Web Site: http://stores.barnesandnoble.com
Book Retailer
N.A.I.C.S.: 459210
Bruce Feagins (Mgr-District)

Subsidiary (Domestic):

NOOK Digital, LLC   (4)
1166 6th Ave, New York, NY
10011-5201   (100%)
Tel.: (212) 414-6000
Web Site: http://www.nookpress.com
Sales Range: $400-449.9 Million
Emp.: 1,000
Books & Related Products Online Retailer &
Marketer
N.A.I.C.S.: 459210
Kevin M. Frain (CFO & VP-Ops)

Subsidiary (Domestic):

SparkNotes, LLC **(3)**
122 5th Ave, New York, NY 10011-5605
Tel.: (212) 633-3300
Web Site: http://www.sparknotes.com
Sales Range: $50-74.9 Million
Emp.: 500
Study Guide Publisher
N.A.I.C.S.: 513199

Sterling Publishing Co., Inc. **(3)**
1166 Ave of the Americas Fl 17, New York,
NY 10036 **(100%)**
Tel.: (212) 532-7160
Web Site: http://www.sterlingpublishing.com
Sales Range: $25-49.9 Million
Emp.: 200
Non-Fiction Books Publishers & Distr
N.A.I.C.S.: 513130

Joint Venture (Non-US):

Thiess Pty. Limited **(2)**
Level 5 179 Grey Street, Southbank, 4101,
QLD, Australia
Tel.: (61) 730029000
Web Site: http://www.thiess.com.au
Emp.: 350
Construction Engineering & Mining
N.A.I.C.S.: 237310
Abdul Jarrah *(Exec Gen Mgr-Strategy, Governance & Transformation)*
Cluny Randell *(Exec Gen Mgr-Ops & Strategy-Indonesia & Mongolia)*
Mark Bartlett *(Gen Mgr-Health, Safety & Security)*
Craig Morton *(CFO)*
Anthony De Domenico *(Exec Gen Mgr-Assets)*
Trish Russell *(Gen Counsel)*

Subsidiary (Domestic):

PYBAR Holdings Pty. Ltd. **(3)**
1668 to 1670 Forest Road, Orange, 2800,
NSW, Australia
Tel.: (61) 263616400
Holding Company; Hard Rock Mining Services Contractor
N.A.I.C.S.: 551112

Subsidiary (Domestic):

PYBAR Mining Services Pty. Ltd. **(4)**
1668-1670 Forest Road, PO Box 2154, Orange, 2800, NSW, Australia
Tel.: (61) 263616400
Hard Rock Mining Services Contractor
N.A.I.C.S.: 213115
Paul Rouse *(Co-Founder & Chm)*
Brendan Rouse *(Co-Founder & CEO)*
Elsie Joubert *(Mgr-HR)*
David Noort *(Mgr-Bus Dev)*

Subsidiary (Domestic):

Quantum Explosives **(3)**
Level 7 371 Queen St, Brisbane, 4001,
QLD, Australia
Tel.: (61) 7 3221 4066
Mining Contractor
N.A.I.C.S.: 213114

Tarong Coal Ltd **(3)**
280 Nibby Smith Way, PO Box 1165, Kingaroy, 4610, QLD, Australia
Tel.: (61) 741607211
Web Site: http://www.thiess.com
Sales Range: $75-99.9 Million
Emp.: 400
Coal Mining
N.A.I.C.S.: 212114
David Waddell *(Project Mgr)*

Holding (Domestic):

Waterstones Booksellers Limited **(2)**
203-206 Piccadilly, London, W1J 9HD,
United Kingdom
Tel.: (44) 8081188787
Web Site: http://www.waterstones.com
Book Store Operator
N.A.I.C.S.: 459210

Subsidiary (Domestic):

Blackwell Ltd. **(3)**
48-51 Broad Street, Oxford, OX1 3BQ,
United Kingdom
Tel.: (44) 1865792792

Web Site: http://www.blackwell.co.uk
Sales Range: $350-399.9 Million
Emp.: 1,500
Holding Company Book Retailer & Publisher
N.A.I.C.S.: 551112
David Prescott *(CEO)*
Kate Stilborn *(Dir-Customer Svc & Ops)*

Subsidiary (US):

Blackwell's North America Inc. **(4)**
2550 W Tyvola Rd Ste 300, Charlotte, NC
28217-4579
Tel.: (503) 684-1140
Web Site: http://www.blackwell.com
Sales Range: $75-99.9 Million
Emp.: 200
Books, Periodicals & Newspapers
N.A.I.C.S.: 424920

Elliott Associates, L.P. **(1)**
40 W 57th St, New York, NY 10019
Tel.: (212) 974-6000
Web Site: http://www.elliottmgmt.com
Emp.: 160
Mutual Fund
N.A.I.C.S.: 525910
Paul Elliott Singer *(Founder & CEO)*

Elliott International, L.P. **(1)**
40 W 57th St, New York, NY 10019
Tel.: (212) 974-6000
Web Site: http://www.elliottmgmg.com
Emp.: 50
Mutual Fund
N.A.I.C.S.: 525910
Paul Elliott Singer *(Founder & CEO)*

**Elliott Investment Management
L.P.** **(1)**
Phillips Point E Tower 777 S Flager Dr Ste
1000, West Palm Beach, FL 33401
Tel.: (212) 974-6000
Web Site: http://www.elliottmgmt.com
Investment Services
N.A.I.C.S.: 523999
David J. Miller *(Partner-Equity & Sr Portfolio Mgr)*
Marc Steinberg *(Partner)*
Jesse A. Cohn *(Mng Partner)*
Steven K. Barg *(Head-Engagement-Global)*
Paul Singer *(Pres, Co-CEO & Co-Chief Investment Officer)*
Jonathan Pollock *(Co-CEO, Partner-Equity & Co-Chief Investment Officer)*
Jason Genrich *(Sr Portfolio Mgr)*

Subsidiary (Domestic):

Ascent Global Logistics, LLC **(2)**
1431 Opus Pl Ste 530, Downers Grove, IL
60515
Web Site: http://www.ascentgl.com
Logistic Services
N.A.I.C.S.: 541614
Christopher W. Jamroz *(Exec Chm & CEO)*
Bill Goodgion *(Pres)*
Chris Cook *(Pres-Domestic Freight Mgmt)*
Micah Holst *(Pres-Intl Freight Forwarding)*
William Vechiarella *(Pres-Retail Consolidation)*

Joint Venture (Domestic):

Syneos Health, Inc. **(2)**
1030 Sync St, Morrisville, NC 27560-5468
Tel.: (919) 876-9300
Web Site: https://www.syneoshealth.com
Rev.: $5,393,082,000
Assets: $8,199,218,000
Liabilities: $4,704,217,000
Net Worth: $3,495,001,000
Earnings: $266,497,000
Emp.: 28,768
Fiscal Year-end: 12/31/2022
Holding Company; Biopharmaceutical & Medical Device Mfr
N.A.I.C.S.: 551112
Colin Shannon *(CEO)*
Michelle Keefe *(CEO)*
Kristen Spensieri *(Head-Corp Comm & Mktg-Global)*
Baba Shetty *(Pres-Tech & Data Solutions)*
Jeanine O'Kane *(Pres-Syneos Heath Comm)*
Hillary Bochniak *(Chief HR Officer)*
Larry A. Pickett Jr. *(CIO)*
Ben Rudnick *(Chief Strategy Officer)*
Michael J. Bonello *(CFO)*

Michael Brooks *(COO)*
Jim Momtazee *(Mng Partner)*
Costa Panagos *(Co-CEO)*
Max Ghez *(Head-Clinical Bus Dev)*
Larry A. Pickett Jr. *(Chief Info & Digital Officer)*
Margaret Alexander *(Founder)*

Subsidiary (Domestic):

INC Research, LLC **(3)**
3201 Beechleaf Ct Ste 600, Raleigh, NC
27604-1547
Tel.: (919) 876-9300
Web Site: http://www.incresearch.com
Pharmaceutical Research & Development Services
N.A.I.C.S.: 541715

Division (Domestic):

INC Research **(4)**
441 Vine St Ste 1200, Cincinnati, OH
45202
Tel.: (513) 381-5550
Web Site: http://www.incresearch.com
Sales Range: $400-449.9 Million
Data Processing of Biopharmaceutical Research
N.A.I.C.S.: 518210
Dana Magly *(Mgr-Facilities)*
Dan Schwartz *(Mgr-IT)*
David Schneider *(Sr Dir-Medical)*

Division (Non-US):

INC Research **(4)**
River View The Meadows Business Park,
Station Approach Blackwater, Camberley,
GU17 9AB, Surrey, United Kingdom
Tel.: (44) 1276481000
Web Site: http://www.incresearch.com
Sales Range: $25-49.9 Million
Contract Biopharmaceutical Research & Development Services
N.A.I.C.S.: 541715
Rosie McKellar *(Sr Dir-Central Monitoring)*
Jane Winter *(Sr VP-Global Consulting Unit)*

INC Research **(4)**
Level 1 20 Atherton Road, Oakleigh, 3166,
VIC, Australia
Tel.: (61) 395677600
Sales Range: $10-24.9 Million
Contract Biopharmaceutical Research & Development Services
N.A.I.C.S.: 541715

INC Research **(4)**
720 King St W, Toronto, M5V 2T3, ON,
Canada
Tel.: (416) 963-9338
Web Site: http://www.incresearch.com
Sales Range: $10-24.9 Million
Early Phase Clinical Development Services
N.A.I.C.S.: 541715
Kerry Schoedel *(Dir-Scientific)*

**INC Research - Global Clinical
Development** **(4)**
Einsteindreef 117-119, 2562 GB, Utrecht,
Netherlands
Tel.: (31) 302584600
Web Site: http://www.incresearch.com
Sales Range: $25-49.9 Million
Contract Clinical Development Services
N.A.I.C.S.: 541715

INC Research - Munich **(4)**
Stefan-George-Ring 6, 81929, Munich, Germany
Tel.: (49) 899939130
Web Site: http://www.incresearch.com
Sales Range: $50-74.9 Million
Contract Biopharmaceutical Research & Development Services
N.A.I.C.S.: 541715

INC Research - Saronno **(4)**
Vicolo del Caldo 36, 21047, Saronno, VA,
Italy
Tel.: (39) 029619921
Sales Range: $25-49.9 Million
Contract Biopharmaceutical Research & Development Services
N.A.I.C.S.: 541715

Subsidiary (Domestic):

Syneos Health, LLC **(3)**
1 Van de Graaff Dr, Burlington, MA 01803

Tel.: (781) 229-8877
Web Site: http://www.syneoshealth.com
Holding Company; Outsourced Clinical Biopharmaceutical Development & Commercialization Services
N.A.I.C.S.: 551112
John M. Dineen *(Chm)*

Subsidiary (Domestic):

Syneos Health US, Inc. **(4)**
1 Van de Graaff Dr, Burlington, MA 01803
Tel.: (781) 229-8877
Web Site: http://www.syneoshealth.com
Outsourced Clinical Biopharmaceutical Development & Commercialization Services
N.A.I.C.S.: 541618

Subsidiary (Domestic):

Syneos Health Clinical, LLC **(5)**
301 College Rd E, Princeton, NJ 08540
Tel.: (609) 951-0005
Web Site: http://www.syneoshealth.com
Holding Company; Clinical Research & Drug Development Services
N.A.I.C.S.: 551112

Branch (Domestic):

Syneos Health Clinical, LLC **(6)**
500 Atrium Dr, Somerset, NJ 08873
Tel.: (800) 416-0555
Web Site: http://www.syneoshealth.com
Clinical Trials Research
N.A.I.C.S.: 541715

Subsidiary (Domestic):

Syneos Health Consulting, Inc. **(6)**
1030 Sync St, Morrisville, NC 27560
Tel.: (919) 876-9300
Web Site: http://www.syneoshealth.com
Pharmaceutical & Biotechnology Management Consulting Services
N.A.I.C.S.: 541618

Subsidiary (Domestic):

Pharmaceutical Institute, LLC **(7)**
1030 Sync St, Morrisville, NC 27560
Tel.: (919) 876-9300
Web Site:
http://www.syneoshealthlearning.com
Training Solutions for Pharmaceutical & Biotech Industry
N.A.I.C.S.: 611430
Celeste Mosby *(VP-Solution Design & Business Dev)*
Yvonne Ash *(VP-Solution Design)*
Freddy Gozum *(Dir-Solutions Design)*
Marissa Liu-Glaister *(Dir-Learning Strategy)*

Subsidiary (Non-US):

Syneos Health IVH UK Limited **(6)**
Farnborough Business Park 1 Pinehurst
Road, Farnborough, GU14 7BF, Hampshire,
United Kingdom
Tel.: (44) 1276 713 000
Web Site: http://www.syneoshealth.com
Phase I-IV Clinical Trials; Data Management & Biostatistics; Regulatory Consulting & Marketing Services
N.A.I.C.S.: 541611

Subsidiary (Non-US):

Syneos Health Germany GmbH **(7)**
Triforum Haus C1, Frankfurter Strasse 233,
63263, Neu-Isenburg, Germany
Tel.: (49) 6102 8130
Web Site: http://www.syneoshealth.com
Phase I-IV Clinical Trials; Data Management & Biostatistics; Regulatory Consulting & Marketing Services
N.A.I.C.S.: 541611

Syneos Health Italy S.R.L. **(7)**
Via Gonzaga 7, 201123, Milan, Italy
Tel.: (39) 02 8905 3715
Web Site: http://www.syneoshealth.com
Phase I-IV Clinical Trials; Data Management & Biostatistics; Regulatory Consulting & Marketing Services
N.A.I.C.S.: 541611

Syneos Health Netherlands B.V. **(7)**
Oval Tower De Entree 99 197 14th floor,
1101 HE, Amsterdam, Netherlands

Elliott Management Corporation—(Continued)
Tel.: (31) 20 3018 500
Web Site: http://www.syneoshealth.com
Phase I-IV Clinical Trials; Data Management & Biostatistics; Regulatory Consulting & Marketing Services
N.A.I.C.S.: 541611

Subsidiary (Domestic):

i3 Pharmaceutical Services, Inc. (6)
5430 Data Ct Ste 200, Ann Arbor, MI 48108
Tel.: (734) 887-0000
Web Site: http://www.syneoshealth.com
Regulatory Consulting, Clinical Research & Clinical Trial Management Services to Biological & Pharmaceutical Firms
N.A.I.C.S.: 541714

Subsidiary (Domestic):

Syneos Health Communications, Inc. (5)
500 Olde Worthington Rd, Westerville, OH 43082
Tel.: (614) 543-6650
Web Site: http://www.syneoshealth.com
Holding Company; Advertising Agencies
N.A.I.C.S.: 551112

Unit (Domestic):

Chamberlain Healthcare Public Relations (6)
200 Vesey St, New York, NY 10281
Tel.: (212) 884-0650
Web Site: http://www.chamberlainpr.com
Health Care, Public Relations
N.A.I.C.S.: 541820

Subsidiary (Domestic):

Gerbig, Snell/Weisheimer Advertising, LLC (6)
500 Olde Worthington Rd, Columbus, OH 43082
Tel.: (614) 848-4848
Web Site: http://www.gsw-w.com
Advetising Agency
N.A.I.C.S.: 541810
Dan Smith (Gen Mgr)
Amanda Joly (Exec VP- Brand & Experience Strategy)
Marc Lineveldt (Exec VP)
Jen Oleski (Mng Dir & Exec VP)
Wendy Rankin (Sr VP & Dir-Agency Ops)

Branch (Domestic):

Gerbig, Snell/Weisheimer Advertising, LLC - New York (7)
200 Vesey St 39th Fl, New York, NY 10281
Tel.: (646) 437-4800
Web Site: http://www.gsw-w.com
Advertising Services
N.A.I.C.S.: 541810
Nick Capanear (Exec VP)
Bryan Roman (Sr VP-Creative Tech)
Michael Austin (Mng Dir-Creative & Tech)

Subsidiary (Domestic):

Palio + Ignite, LLC (6)
450 W 15TH St Ste 600, New York, NY 10011-7082
Tel.: (518) 584-8924
Advetising Agency
N.A.I.C.S.: 541810

inVentiv Medical Communications, LLC (6)
1707 Market Pl Blvd Ste 350, Irving, TX 75063
Tel.: (972) 929-1900
Advetising Agency
N.A.I.C.S.: 541810

Subsidiary (Domestic):

Synteract Corp. (3)
5759 Fleet St Ste 100, Carlsbad, CA 92008
Tel.: (760) 268-8200
Web Site: http://www.synteracthcr.com
Sales Range: $25-49.9 Million
Emp.: 800
Human Clinical Drug Trials Services
N.A.I.C.S.: 621511
Matthew Smith (Sr VP-Comml Ops-Global)
Martine Dehlinger-Kremer (VP-Pediatric Dev-Europe)

Marlo Vasquez (VP-Biometrics-Global)
Heather Davis (Exec Dir-Project Mgmt)
Zia Haque (Exec Dir-Clinical Data Mgmt)
John Whitaker (Exec Dir-Biostatistics)
Steve Powell (CEO)
Frank Santoro (Chief Medical Officer)
Karl Deonanan (CFO)
Jack Shannon (Chief Comml Officer)
Lisa Dilworth (VP-Rare & Orphan Diseases)
Elisabeth Schrader (Exec Dir-Program Strategy, Pediatrics & Rare Diseases)
Mary Mattes (Sr VP-Biometrics)
Cheryl Murphy (Sr VP-Clinical Dev)
Charlotte Oehman (Gen Counsel)
Derek Ansel (Dir-Rare & Orphan Disease Drug Dev)
Hassan Aly (Sr Dir-Medical)

Subsidiary (Non-US):

SynteractHCR Benelux NV (4)
Newsroom Alfons Gossetlaan 30, Sint-Agatha-Berchem, 1702, Groot-Bijgaarden, Belgium
Tel.: (32) 2 4643 900
Web Site: http://www.synteract.com
Clinical Drug Development & Trials
N.A.I.C.S.: 541715
Griet Peeters (Sr Mgr-Clinical Ops)
Steve Powell (CEO)
Frank Santoro (Chief Medical Officer)
Jack Shannon (Chief Comml Officer)
Karl Deonanan (CFO)
Martina Kroner (Sr VP-Corp Dev)
Mary Mattes (Sr VP-Biometrics)
Cheryl Murphy (Sr VP-Clinical Dev)
Charlotte Oehman (Gen Counsel)

SynteractHCR Deutschland GmbH (4)
Albrechtstrasse 14, 80636, Munich, Germany
Tel.: (49) 89 12 66 80 0
Web Site: http://www.synteracthcr.com
Clinical Drug Development & Trials
N.A.I.C.S.: 541715
Martina Kroener (Mng Dir & VP-Europe)

SynteractHCR Eastern Europe Forschungsgesellschaft m.b.H. (4)
Spiegelgasse 2/2/41, 1010, Vienna, Austria
Tel.: (43) 1 504 6591 0
Web Site: http://www.synteracthcr.com
Clinical Drug Development & Trials
N.A.I.C.S.: 541715

SynteractHCR France SAS (4)
16 rue Trezel, 92300, Levallois-Perret, France
Tel.: (33) 1 55 90 57 10
Web Site: http://www.synteracthcr.com
Clinical Drug Development & Trials
N.A.I.C.S.: 541715
Sebastien Duval (VP-Bus Dev-Europe)

SynteractHCR Iberica, SL (4)
Carrer del Princep jordi 21-23 Esc B Entresol 1 B, 08014, Barcelona, Spain
Tel.: (34) 93 226 69 64
Web Site: http://www.synteracthcr.com
Clinical Drug Development & Trials
N.A.I.C.S.: 541715
Steve Powell (CEO)
Charlotte Oehman (Gen Counsel)
Karl Deonanan (CFO)
Frank Santoro (Chief Medical Officer)
Jack Shannon (Chief Comml Officer)

SynteractHCR Limited (4)
Gemini House Bartholomew's Walk, Cambridgeshire Business Park Angel Drove, Ely, CB7 4EA, Cambs, United Kingdom
Tel.: (44) 1353 66 83 39
Web Site: http://www.synteracthcr.com
Emp.: 41
Clinical Drug Trials
N.A.I.C.S.: 541715
Jamie Pearson (Reg Dir-EMEA)
Linda Rawlings (Exec Dir-Strategic Dev)
Pascale Goujard-Paquette (Sr Dir-Clinical Ops-Europe)
Etienne Drouet (VP-Strategic Dev)

SynteractHCR S.r.l. (4)
Via Antonio Vivaldi 13, 00043, Ciampino, Rome, Italy
Tel.: (39) 06 79312131
Web Site: http://www.synteracthcr.com
Clinical Drug Development & Trials
N.A.I.C.S.: 541715

Massimo Ildebrando (Dir-Project Mgmt & Office Mgr)

SynteractHCR Sweden AB (4)
Ringvagen 100 9E, 11860, Stockholm, Sweden
Tel.: (46) 8 751 10 80
Web Site: http://www.synteracthcr.com
Clinical Drug Development & Trials
N.A.I.C.S.: 541715
Ilari Jauro (Dir-Clinical Ops)

Evergreen Coast Capital Corp. (1)
2420 Sand Hill Rd, Menlo Park, CA 94025
Tel.: (650) 233-7500
Privater Equity Firm
N.A.I.C.S.: 523999
Isaac Kim (Mng Dir)
Christian Heim (Mng Dir)

Joint Venture (Domestic):

Citrix Systems, Inc. (2)
851 W Cypress Creek Rd, Fort Lauderdale, FL 33309
Tel.: (954) 267-3000
Web Site: https://www.citrix.com
Rev.: $3,217,170,000
Assets: $6,975,517,000
Liabilities: $6,428,260,000
Net Worth: $547,257,000
Earnings: $307,499,000
Emp.: 9,700
Fiscal Year-end: 12/31/2021
Mfr & Reproducing Magnetic & Optical Media
N.A.I.C.S.: 334610
Tony Gomes (Chief Legal Officer, Sec & Exec VP)
Sridhar Mullapudi (Exec VP-Product Mgmt)
Hector Lima (Exec VP-Customer Experience)
Meerah Rajavel (CIO)
Thomas Berquis (CFO)
Tom Krause (CEO)
Andy Nallappan (COO & CIO)
Ric Chi (VP-Corporate Strategy)
Derek Baden (Gen Mgr-NetScaler eCommerce)
Jacus de Beer (Gen Mgr-XenServer)
Ali Ahmed (Gen Mgr-TIBCO & Enterprise Applications)
Kurt Heusner (Gen Mgr-ShareFile)

Subsidiary (Non-US):

Apere Enterprise Storage Solutions India Pvt. Ltd. (3)
14 3rd Floor Road No 2 Banjara Hills Huda Colony, Hyderabad, 500034, India
Tel.: (91) 9346255332
Software Publishing Services
N.A.I.C.S.: 513210

Subsidiary (Domestic):

App-DNA, Inc. (3)
20 N Martingale Rd Ste 110, Schaumburg, IL 60173
Tel.: (847) 230-0020
Emp.: 12
Software Publishing Services
N.A.I.C.S.: 513210

Subsidiary (Non-US):

Bytemobile European Development Center MEPE (3)
4 Kato - Ano Kastritsiou, Eparchiaki Odos, 26504, Patras, Greece
Tel.: (30) 2610935000
Software Publishing Services
N.A.I.C.S.: 513210

Subsidiary (Domestic):

Cedexis Inc. (3)
421 SW 6th Ave Ste 700, Portland, OR 97204
Web Site: http://www.cedexis.com
Software Development Services
N.A.I.C.S.: 541511

Citrix Online LLC (3)
7414 Hollister Ave, Goleta, CA 93117
Tel.: (805) 690-6400
Web Site: http://www.citrix.com
Sales Range: $100-124.9 Million
Emp.: 1,000
Remote Support & Access Technologies
N.A.I.C.S.: 517810

Brett Caine (Pres)

Subsidiary (Non-US):

Citrix Online AUS Pty Ltd. (4)
1 Julius Avenue Sydney, North Ryde, 2113, NSW, Australia
Tel.: (61) 1800451485
Web Site: http://www.citrixonline.com
Sales Range: $50-74.9 Million
Emp.: 250
Real-Time Application Software Publisher
N.A.I.C.S.: 513210

Subsidiary (Non-US):

Citrix R&D India Private Limited (3)
Prestige Dynasty Phase-2 Ground Floor 33/2 Ulsoor Road, Bengaluru, 560042, Karnataka, India
Tel.: (91) 806 120 2001
Web Site: https://www.citrix.com
Emp.: 1,500
Real-Time Application Software Publisher
N.A.I.C.S.: 513210

Citrix R&D Limited (3)
R&D Chalfont 2-3 Chalfont Park Chalfont St Peter, Gerrards Cross, SL9 0DZ, Buckinghamshire, United Kingdom
Tel.: (44) 1753276200
Software Development Services
N.A.I.C.S.: 541511

Citrix Sistemas de Argentina, S.R.L. (3)
Avenida Ingeniero Huergo 953 Piso 7, Buenos Aires, Argentina
Tel.: (54) 1145156300
Real-Time Application Software Publisher
N.A.I.C.S.: 513210

Citrix Sistemas do Brasil Ltda. (3)
Rua Professor Atilio Innocenti 165 - 13 andar, Itaim Bibi, Sao Paulo, 04538-000, Brazil
Tel.: (55) 113 702 7900
Web Site: https://www.citrix.com
Sales Range: $10-24.9 Million
Emp.: 40
Real-Time Application Software Publisher
N.A.I.C.S.: 513210

Citrix Systems Asia Pacific Pty Ltd. (3)
Level 23 100 Mount Street, North Sydney, 2060, NSW, Australia
Tel.: (61) 28 870 0800
Web Site: https://www.citrix.com
Emp.: 200
Real-Time Application Software Publisher
N.A.I.C.S.: 513210

Citrix Systems Belgium S.P.R.L. (3)
Stockholm Building Leonardo Da Vincilaan 19, 1831, Diegem, Belgium
Tel.: (32) 27882754
Software Services
N.A.I.C.S.: 541511

Citrix Systems Canada, Inc. (3)
125 Commerce Valley Drive West Suite 502, Markham, L3T 7W4, ON, Canada
Tel.: (289) 982-0905
Sales Range: $10-24.9 Million
Emp.: 20
Real-Time Application Software Publisher
N.A.I.C.S.: 513210

Citrix Systems Czech Republic SRO (3)
Na Pankraci 1724/129, 140 00, Prague, Czech Republic
Tel.: (420) 225992200
Software Publishing Services
N.A.I.C.S.: 513210

Citrix Systems Denmark ApS (3)
Kalkbraenderiloebskaj 4, Copenhagen, 2100, Denmark
Tel.: (45) 39193400
Sales Range: $10-24.9 Million
Emp.: 23
Real-Time Application Software Publisher
N.A.I.C.S.: 513210

Citrix Systems Finland Oy (3)
Keilaranta 16, 02150, Espoo, Finland
Tel.: (358) 925107341

Sales Range: $10-24.9 Million
Emp.: 7
Real-Time Application Software Publisher
N.A.I.C.S.: 513210

Citrix Systems France SARL (3)
Coeur Defense - Tour B Etage 31 100 Esplanade du General de Gaulle, La Defense, 92932, Paris, Cedex, France
Tel.: (33) 14 900 3300
Web Site: https://www.citrix.com
Emp.: 87
Real-Time Application Software Publisher
N.A.I.C.S.: 513210

Citrix Systems GmbH (3)
Mariahilferstrasse 123/3, Vienna, 1060, Austria
Tel.: (43) 159999223
Web Site: http://www.citrix.de
Emp.: 8
Real-Time Application Software Publisher
N.A.I.C.S.: 513210

Citrix Systems GmbH (3)
Erika-Mann-Str 67-69, 80636, Munich, Germany
Tel.: (49) 8944 456 4000
Web Site: https://www.citrix.com
Enterprise Mobility Management & Real-Time Application Software Publisher
N.A.I.C.S.: 513210

Citrix Systems Information Technology (Beijing) Ltd (3)
Unit 808-809 Level 8 Tower C Oriental Plaza No 1 East Chang An Street, Dong Cheng District, Beijing, 100738, China
Tel.: (86) 1065216500
Real-Time Application Software Publisher
N.A.I.C.S.: 513210

Citrix Systems International GmbH (3)
Rheinweg 9, 8200, Schaffhausen, Switzerland
Tel.: (41) 526357700
Sales Range: $25-49.9 Million
Emp.: 100
Holding Company
N.A.I.C.S.: 551112

Citrix Systems Netherlands, B.V. (3)
Spaces Zuidas 5th floor Barbara Strozzilaan 201, 1083 HN, Amsterdam, Netherlands
Tel.: (31) 20 301 3400
Web Site: https://www.citrix.com
Sales Range: $25-49.9 Million
Emp.: 40
Real-Time Application Software Publisher
N.A.I.C.S.: 513210

Citrix Systems Norway AS (3)
Nydalsveien 28, 0484, Oslo, Norway
Tel.: (47) 2 152 0150
Web Site: https://www.citrix.com
Real-Time Application Software Publisher
N.A.I.C.S.: 513210
Knut Alnaes (Mgr)

Citrix Systems Poland Sp. z o.o (3)
Sheraton Plaza Building 1st Floor UI Prusa 2, Warsaw, 00-493, Poland
Tel.: (48) 226570171
Software Development Services
N.A.I.C.S.: 541511

Citrix Systems UK Limited (3)
Building 3 Chalfont Park, Chalfont St Peter, Gerrards Cross, SL9 0DZ, Buckinghamshire, United Kingdom
Tel.: (44) 175 327 6200
Web Site: https://www.citrix.com
Emp.: 300
Real-Time Application Software Publisher
N.A.I.C.S.: 513210

Subsidiary (Domestic):

Framehawk, Inc. (3)
177 Post St Ste 650, San Francisco, CA 94108
Tel.: (415) 371-9110
Software Publishing Services
N.A.I.C.S.: 513210

Grasshopper Group, LLC (3)
197 1st Ave Ste 200, Needham, MA 02494
Tel.: (617) 395-5700
Web Site: http://www.grasshopper.com
Emp.: 26

Online Virtual Phone Systems Management & Technical Support Services
N.A.I.C.S.: 517810
Siamak Taghaddos (Co-Founder)
David Hauser (Co-Founder & CTO)

Subsidiary (Non-US):

Peninsula Finance LLC (3)
Studio 5-11, 5 Millbay Road, Plymouth, PL1 3LF, United Kingdom
Tel.: (44) 1752292568
Web Site: http://www.peninsulafinance.com
Financial Management Services
N.A.I.C.S.: 541611
Hugh Michelmore (Chm)
Daniel Palmer (CEO)
Robert Howard (Dir-Risk & Legal Svcs)
Suzanne Deacon (Acct Mgr)
Kelsey Stewart (Mgr-Case)
Matthew Cocking (Accountant)

Podio ApS (3)
Skelbaekgade 2 5th, 1717, Copenhagen, Denmark
Tel.: (45) 31147464
Software Development Services
N.A.I.C.S.: 541511

Ringcube Software Tech Pvt Ltd. (3)
304 Reliance Classic 3rd Floor, Banjara Hills, Hyderabad, 500034, India
Tel.: (91) 4023311125
Software Publishing Services
N.A.I.C.S.: 513210

Subsidiary (Domestic):

Sanbolic, Inc. (3)
309 Waverley Oaks Rd Ste 101, Waltham, MA 02452
Tel.: (617) 833-4242
Web Site: http://www.sanbolic.com
Software Publisher
N.A.I.C.S.: 513210

ShareFile LLC (3)
120 S West St, Raleigh, NC 27603
Tel.: (919) 745-6111
Web Site: http://www.citrix.com
Emp.: 100
File Sharing Software
N.A.I.C.S.: 334610

Solid Instance, Inc. (3)
5255 N Edgewood Dr Ste 300, Provo, UT 84604
Tel.: (801) 805-0300
Software Development Services
N.A.I.C.S.: 541511
Tyrone F. Pike (Co-Founder, Chm, Pres & CEO)
John Rafter (COO & VP-Ops)
Ron C. Steed (Co-Founder & Dir-Ops)
Donald Guarnieri (VP-Mktg)

Subsidiary (Non-US):

Todd Hsu Consultants, Inc. (3)
351 Northland Rd, Sault Sainte Marie, P6C 3N2, ON, Canada
Tel.: (514) 864-5999
Software Publishing Services
N.A.I.C.S.: 513210

Subsidiary (Domestic):

Unidesk Corporation (3)
313 Boston Post Rd W, Marlborough, MA 01752
Tel.: (508) 573-7800
Web Site: http://www.unidesk.com
Software Development Services
N.A.I.C.S.: 513210

Wrike, Inc. (3)
70 N 2nd St, San Jose, CA 95113
Tel.: (650) 318-3551
Web Site: https://www.wrike.com
Emp.: 70
Project Management Software Developer
N.A.I.C.S.: 513210
Andrew Filev (Founder & CEO)
Saranya Babu (Sr VP-Marketing)
Chad Bennett (Chief HR Officer)
Paul Fernandez (Sr Mgr-Corporate Communications)

Joint Venture (Domestic):

Cubic Corporation (2)

9233 Balboa Ave, San Diego, CA 92123
Tel.: (858) 277-6780
Web Site: https://www.cubic.com
Rev.: $1,476,235,000
Assets: $2,324,221,000
Liabilities: $1,336,041,000
Net Worth: $988,180,000
Earnings: ($3,221,000)
Emp.: 6,100
Fiscal Year-end: 09/30/2020
Combat Simulation Training Products; Automatic Fare-Collection Systems Mfr for Public Transit
N.A.I.C.S.: 541519
Michael Knowles (Pres-Mission & Performance Solutions Bus & Gen Mgr)
Min Wei (Chief Customer Officer & Sr VP)
Stevan Slijepcevic (Pres & CEO)
Mac Curtis (Chm)
Peter Torrellas (Pres-Transportation Sys & Sr VP)
Paul Shew (Pres-Defense & Sr VP)
Travis Chester (CFO & Sr VP)
Deborah Cegielski (Chief HR Officer, Chief Diversity Officer & Sr VP)
Matt Luxton (Gen Counsel & Sr VP)

Subsidiary (Non-US):

CUBIC TRANSPORTATION SYSTEMS (ITMS) LIMITED (3)
Cavendish House Clearwater Park, Prince's Wharf, Stockton, TS17 6QY, United Kingdom
Tel.: (44) 1642636700
Web Site: http://www.cubic.com
Emp.: 200
Metal Container Mfr
N.A.I.C.S.: 332439
Chris Bax (VP-Global ITS Strategy)

Subsidiary (Domestic):

Consolidated Converting Co. (3)
879 E Rialto Ave, San Bernardino, CA 92408-1202 (100%)
Tel.: (562) 942-0524
Sales Range: $10-24.9 Million
Paper Products Conversion
N.A.I.C.S.: 322211

Subsidiary (Non-US):

Cubic (UK) Limited (3)
AFC House Honeycrock Lane, Salfords, RH1 5LA, Redhill, United Kingdom (100%)
Tel.: (44) 1737782200
Web Site: http://www.cubic.com
Holding Company
N.A.I.C.S.: 551112

Subsidiary (Domestic):

Cubic Defence UK Ltd (4)
Unit 3 Bridge Court River Lane, Wrecclesham, GU10 4QE, Surrey, United Kingdom
Tel.: (44) 1252725500
Web Site: http://www.cubic.com
Emp.: 30
Defense Systems Mfr
N.A.I.C.S.: 335999

Subsidiary (Non-US):

Cubic Transportation Systems (Deutschland) GmbH (4)
Alter Fischmarkt 11, 20457, Hamburg, Germany
Tel.: (49) 40 300863 690
Web Site: http://www.cubic-cts.de
Sales Range: $25-49.9 Million
Emp.: 40
Fare Collection Systems For Mass Transportation
N.A.I.C.S.: 334519
Stefan Jacobs (Mng Dir)

Subsidiary (Domestic):

Cubic Transportation Systems Limited (4)
AFC House Honeycrock Lane, Salfords, Redhill, RH1 5LA, Surrey, United Kingdom (100%)
Tel.: (44) 1737782200
Web Site: http://www.cts.cubic.com
Emp.: 500
Automatic Ticketing Machines Mfr & Revenue Collections for European Transport
N.A.I.C.S.: 334519

Roger Crow (Mng Dir)

Subsidiary (Non-US):

CTS - Nordic Aktiebolag (5)
S t Knuts vag 19 hus 7A, 211 57, Malmo, Sweden (100%)
Tel.: (46) 40942100
Fare Collection Systems for Mass Transportation
N.A.I.C.S.: 334519

Subsidiary (Domestic):

Cubic Advanced Learning Solutions, Inc. (3)
2001 W Oak Ridge Rd, Orlando, FL 32809
Tel.: (407) 514-1503
Web Site: http://www.atgsites.com
Online Education Services
N.A.I.C.S.: 611710
Tim Mullins (Gen Mgr)

Cubic Applications, Inc. (3)
4550 3rd Ave SE Ste B, Lacey, WA 98503-1033 (100%)
Tel.: (360) 493-6275
Web Site: http://www.cubic.com
Sales Range: $10-24.9 Million
Emp.: 40
Training Systems
N.A.I.C.S.: 541512

Cubic Cyber Solutions, Inc. (3)
205 Van Buren St Ste 310, Herndon, VA 20170 (100%)
Tel.: (703) 821-1516
Web Site: http://www.cubic.com
Sales Range: $10-24.9 Million
Emp.: 20
Security & Networking Services
N.A.I.C.S.: 334290

Cubic Data Systems, Inc. (3)
9333 Balboa Ave, San Diego, CA 92123-1515 (90%)
Tel.: (858) 277-6780
Web Site: http://www.cubic.com
Sales Range: $150-199.9 Million
Emp.: 500
Data Systems
N.A.I.C.S.: 333310

Subsidiary (Non-US):

Cubic Defence Australia Pty. Limited (3)
336 Bayswater Rd, Townsville, 4814, QLD, Australia
Tel.: (61) 747751881
Web Site: http://www.cubic.com
Emp.: 50
Industrial Machinery Mfr
N.A.I.C.S.: 333998
Taiga Aoki (Mng Dir)

Cubic Defence New Zealand Ltd. (3)
Wellesley St, PO Box 6008, 1141, Auckland, New Zealand (100%)
Tel.: (64) 93790360
Web Site: http://www.cdnz.co.nz
Sales Range: $25-49.9 Million
Emp.: 160
Mfr & Developer of Simulation System, Instrumentation & Control Equipment & Defense Training Instruments
N.A.I.C.S.: 334513

Subsidiary (Non-US):

Cubic Technologies Pte. Ltd. (4)
401 Commonwealth Dr 04-02-03, Hawpar Techno Center, Singapore, 149598, Singapore (100%)
Tel.: (65) 62589877
Web Site: http://www.cubic.com
Sales Range: $10-24.9 Million
Emp.: 80
Simulation System, Instrumentation & Control Equipment & Defense Training Instruments Mfr & Developer
N.A.I.C.S.: 334513
Thomas Scott (Mng Dir)

Cubic Technologies Singapore Pte. Ltd. (4)
401 Commonwealth Drive 04-02/03 Haw

Elliott Management Corporation—(Continued)

Par Technocentre, Singapore, 149598, Singapore
Tel.: (65) 65729440
Web Site: http://www.nitorprojects.com
Military Training Facility Design Services
N.A.I.C.S.: 541490

Subsidiary (Domestic):

Cubic Defense Applications, Inc. (3)
9333 Balboa Ave, San Diego, CA
92123-1515 (100%)
Tel.: (858) 277-6780
Web Site: http://www.cubic.com
Sales Range: $150-199.9 Million
Emp.: 500
Engineering, Research & Development of Military Systems
N.A.I.C.S.: 561499

Cubic Foreign Sales, Inc. (3)
9333 Balboa Ave, San Diego, CA
92123-1515 (100%)
Tel.: (858) 277-6780
Web Site: http://www.cubic.com
Sales Range: $125-149.9 Million
Emp.: 300
Distribution Services
N.A.I.C.S.: 333310

Cubic Global Tracking Solutions, Inc. (3)
1919 Gallows Rd Ste 900, Vienna, VA
22182
Tel.: (571) 722-1900
Web Site: http://www.cubic.com
Security System Services
N.A.I.C.S.: 561621

Cubic Land, Inc. (3)
9333 Balboa Ave, San Diego, CA
92123-1515 (100%)
Tel.: (858) 277-6780
Web Site: http://www.cubic.com
Sales Range: $100-124.9 Million
Real Estate Investment Services
N.A.I.C.S.: 531390

Cubic Microchip Development Corporation (3)
9333 Balboa Ave, San Diego, CA
92123-1515 (100%)
Tel.: (858) 277-6780
Sales Range: $100-124.9 Million
Emp.: 500
Developer of Microchips
N.A.I.C.S.: 333310

Cubic Simulation Systems, Inc. (3)
2001 W Oakridge Rd Ste 100, Orlando, FL
32809-3801
Tel.: (407) 859-7410
Web Site: http://www.cubic.com
Sales Range: $25-49.9 Million
Emp.: 140
Computer-Controlled Simulators Distr
N.A.I.C.S.: 541330

Subsidiary (Non-US):

Cubic Transportation Systems (India) Pvt. Limited (3)
4th Floor Block C and D ILabs Technology Centre Plot No 18, Software Units Layout
Sy No 64 Madhapur, Hyderabad, 500081, India
Tel.: (91) 4039605151
Web Site: http://www.cts.cubic.com
Sales Range: $25-49.9 Million
Emp.: 4
Computer Systems Design Mfr
N.A.I.C.S.: 541512
Kishan Kamojjhala (Mng Dir)

Subsidiary (Domestic):

Cubic Transportation Systems, Inc. (3)
5650 Kearny Mesa Rd, San Diego, CA
92111-5587 (100%)
Tel.: (858) 268-3100
Web Site: http://www.cubic.com
Sales Range: $250-299.9 Million
Emp.: 1,500
Fare Collection Systems For Mass Transportation
N.A.I.C.S.: 334519

Ab Jenkins (Gen Counsel, Sec & VP)
Matt Newsome (Gen Mgr-Western Reg-North America)
Tom Walker (Mng Dir/Sr VP-Asia Pacific)
Sushil Rajendran (VP & Gen Mgr-Central Reg-Americas)
Ian Woodroofe (Sr VP-Strategy & Bus Dev)
Laurent Eskenazi (Interim Pres, Mng Dir-Europe, Middle East & Africa & Sr VP)
Kay Maloney (VP/Gen Mgr-East-North America)
Theresa Yousey (Sr VP-Projects & Delivery)
Heather Yazdan (VP-Fin Ops)

Subsidiary (Non-US):

Cubic Transportation Systems (Australia) Pty. Limited (4)
Level 11/10 Eagle Street, Brisbane, 4000, QLD, Australia (50%)
Tel.: (61) 732321000
Web Site: http://www.cts.cubic.com
Sales Range: $10-24.9 Million
Emp.: 100
Automatic Fare Collection Systems
N.A.I.C.S.: 334519
Tom Walker (Mng Dir & Sr VP)

Cubic Transportation Systems Canada, Ltd. (4)
201 Drumlin Circle Unit 4, Concord, L4K 3E7, ON, Canada
Tel.: (905) 738-9505
Web Site: http://www.cubic.com
Industrial Machinery Mfr
N.A.I.C.S.: 333998

Division (Domestic):

Cubic Transportation Systems, Inc.-East (4)
462 7 Ave 14th Fl, New York, NY
10018 (100%)
Tel.: (212) 255-1810
Web Site: http://www.cubic.com
Sales Range: $10-24.9 Million
Emp.: 15
Fare Collection Systems For Mass Transportation
N.A.I.C.S.: 334519

Cubic Transportation Systems, Inc.-Manufacturing Center (4)
1308 S Washington St, Tullahoma, TN
37388-4333 (100%)
Tel.: (931) 455-8524
Web Site: http://www.cts.cubic.com
Sales Range: $25-49.9 Million
Emp.: 180
Mfr of Fare Collection Systems for Mass Transportation
N.A.I.C.S.: 334519

Subsidiary (Domestic):

Cubic Worldwide Technical Services, Inc. (3)
4285 Ponderosa Ave, San Diego, CA
92123 (100%)
Tel.: (858) 505-2489
Web Site: http://www.cubic.com
Sales Range: $1-9.9 Million
Emp.: 20
Provider of Technical & Management Support Services
N.A.I.C.S.: 811210

Subsidiary (Non-US):

Cubic de Mexico (3)
Prolongacion M Juarez 1089-9 Colonia Lindavista, Tijuana, 22129, Mexico
Tel.: (52) 6646215181
Sales Range: $1-4.9 Billion
Military Instrumentation, Training & Application Systems
N.A.I.C.S.: 561499

Subsidiary (Domestic):

DTECH LABS, Inc. (3)
21580 Beaumeade Cir Ste 230, Ashburn, VA 20147
Tel.: (703) 709-5805
Web Site: http://www.dtechlabs.com
Emp.: 30
Communications Systems Mfr
N.A.I.C.S.: 541330
Patrick Higdon (COO)

GATR Technologies Inc. (3)
330 Bob Heath Dr, Huntsville, AL 35806
Tel.: (256) 382-1334
Web Site: http://www.gatr.com
Developer & Marketer of Deployable, Inflatable SatCom Antennas & Systems for High-Bandwidth Communications in Remote Regions
N.A.I.C.S.: 517810
Paul Gierow (Founder)
Roark McDonald (VP & Gen Mgr)

Gridsmart Technologies, Inc. (3)
702 S Illinois Ave, Oak Ridge, TN 37830
Tel.: (865) 482-2112
Rev.: $1,000,000
Emp.: 11
Traffic & Energy Management Technology & Services
N.A.I.C.S.: 541690

INTIFIC, INC (3)
250 Josephine St Commercial Ofc, Peckville, PA 18452
Tel.: (570) 382-3164
Web Site: http://www.intific.com
Software Development Services
N.A.I.C.S.: 541511

MotionDSP, Inc. (3)
21580 Beaumeade Cir, Ashburn, VA 20147
Tel.: (650) 288-1164
Web Site: http://www.motiondsp.com
Custom Computer Programming Services
N.A.I.C.S.: 541511
Sean Varah (Founder)

NEK SERVICES, INC. (3)
2028 Aerotech Dr, Colorado Springs, CO 80916
Tel.: (719) 247-4300
Web Site: http://mss.cubic.com
Emp.: 30
Military Training Services
N.A.I.C.S.: 928110
Bo Todd (Pres & Gen Mgr)
Jeff Keers (VP)

Nuvotronics, Inc. (3)
2305 Presidential Dr, Durham, NC 27703
Tel.: (919) 296-5500
Electronic Components Mfr
N.A.I.C.S.: 334419
Noel Heiks (Founder)

PIXIA Corp. (3)
2350 Corporate Park Dr Ste 400, Herndon, VA 20171 (100%)
Tel.: (571) 203-9665
Web Site: http://www.pixia.com
Software Publisher
N.A.I.C.S.: 513210
Patrick Ernst (Co-Founder & COO)
Ian Heffernan (VP-Tech)
Rudi Ernst (Co-Founder, CEO & CTO)

TeraLogics LLC (3)
21580 Beaumeade Cr Ste 230, Ashburn, VA 20147
Tel.: (571) 258-5020
Web Site: http://www.teralogics.com
Emp.: 50
Software Engineering Services
N.A.I.C.S.: 541511
Mark Snellings (Founder & Dir-Technical)

URBAN INSIGHTS ASSOCIATES, INC. (3)
1225 S Clark St Ste 601, Arlington, VA 22202
Tel.: (914) 482-7621
Web Site: http://www.urban-insights.com
Transportation Consulting Services
N.A.I.C.S.: 488999

XIO Strategies, Inc. (3)
1919 Gallows Rd Ste 900, Vienna, VA 22182-3964
Tel.: (571) 722-1900
Business Consulting Services
N.A.I.C.S.: 541618

eAccess LLC (3)
4285 Ponderosa Ave M/S 2-1, San Diego, CA 92123
Tel.: (858) 565-4760
Web Site: http://www.eaccessid.com
Smartcard Mfr
N.A.I.C.S.: 334519

Holding (Domestic):

Gigamon Inc. (2)

3300 Olcott St, Santa Clara, CA 95054
Tel.: (408) 831-4000
Web Site: http://www.gigamon.com
Sales Range: $300-349.9 Million
Software Publisher
N.A.I.C.S.: 513210
Shehzad T. Merchant (CTO)
Dave Arkley (CFO)
Shane Buckley (Pres & CEO)
Karl Van den Bergh (CMO)
Andrew R. Harding (Chief Product Officer)
Christel Ventura (Chief People Officer)
Ljubo Mandic (Sr VP-Engrg)
Dee Dee Acquista (VP-Alliances & World-wide Channel)
Shane Buckley (Pres & CEO)
Chaim Mazal (Chief Security Officer)
Doug Woodley (Sr VP-Worldwide Sls)

Joint Venture (Domestic):

LogMeIn, Inc. (2)
320 Summer St, Ste 100, Boston, MA 02210
Tel.: (781) 638-9094
Web Site: http://www.LogMeInInc.com
Sales Range: $1-4.9 Billion
Emp.: 3,500
Remote Computer Connectivity Products & Services
N.A.I.C.S.: 541519
Jo Deal (Chief HR Officer)
Scott Romesser (Sr VP-Customer Care & Integration Lead)
Michael J. Donahue (Gen Counsel & Sr VP)
Robin Lawrence (Sr VP-Corp Strategy)
Christopher Manton-Jones (Sr VP-Sls-Worldwide)
Michael J. Donahue (Gen Counsel & Sr VP)
Sharon Gould (Sr VP-Bus Ops)
Richard H. Veldran (CFO)
Jamie Domenici (CMO)
Michael Oberlaender (Chief Info Security Officer)
Mary-Kate Foley (VP-User Experience Design-Global)
Bill Robinson (Chief Revenue Officer)
Nick Caldwell (Co-Founder)

Subsidiary (Non-US):

Jive Communications Mexico, S, de R.L. de C.V. (3)
José Maria Rico 212 Int 306 Officina B Colonia del Valle Centro Juarez, Benito Juarez, Mexico, 03100, Mexico
Tel.: (52) 5541613912
Telecommunication Servicesb
N.A.I.C.S.: 517810

Subsidiary (Domestic):

Jive Communications, Inc. (3)
320 Summer St, Boston, MA 02210
Tel.: (781) 638-9050
Web Site: http://jive.com
Radio, Television & Other Electronics Stores
N.A.I.C.S.: 449210

Subsidiary (Non-US):

Jive Telecomunicacoes do Brasil, Ltda. (3)
Condominio Edificio Glass Tower Av Jandira n 257 Indianopolis, 04080-001, Sao Paulo, Brazil
Tel.: (55) 1131974418
Telecommunication Servicesb
N.A.I.C.S.: 517810

LogMeIn AUS Pty Ltd (3)
Level 19 20 Martin Place, Sydney, 2000, NSW, Australia
Tel.: (61) 280939900
Electronic Wireless Equipment Mfr
N.A.I.C.S.: 334220

LogMeIn Europe B.V. (3)
Jacob Bontius Plaats 9, Amsterdam, 1018 LL, Netherlands
Tel.: (31) 205221800
Sales Range: $10-24.9 Million
Emp.: 1
Remote Access Software & Services
N.A.I.C.S.: 513210

LogMeIn Systems India Private Limited (3)
No 5 Prestige Khoday Tower 1st 2nd And

3rd Floor Raj Bhavan Road, Bengaluru, 560
001, Karnataka, India
Tel.: (91) 8061220001
Software Development Services
N.A.I.C.S.: 541511

Subsidiary (Domestic):

Zamurai Corporation (3)
5205 Prospect Rd Ste 135-159, San Jose,
CA 95129-5034
Tel.: (408) 892-7400
Custom Computer Programming Services
N.A.I.C.S.: 541511

Joint Venture (Domestic):

Nielsen Holdings plc (2)
675 6th Ave, New York, NY 10010
Tel.: (646) 654-5000
Web Site: https://www.nielsen.com
Rev.: $3,500,000,000
Assets: $10,820,000,000
Liabilities: $7,324,000,000
Net Worth: $3,496,000,000
Earnings: $963,000,000
Emp.: 14,000
Fiscal Year-end: 12/31/2021
Holding Company
N.A.I.C.S.: 551112
Karthik Rao (COO)
Henry Iglesias (Principal Acctg Officer &
Controller)
Sara Gubins (Sr VP & Head-IR & Treasury)
George D. Callard (Chief Legal & Corp Af-
fairs Officer)
Sandra Sims-Williams (Chief Diversity Offi-
cer)
Laurie Lovett (Chief HR Officer)
Jamie Moldafsky (Chief Mktg & Comm Offi-
cer)
Sean H. Cohan (Chief Growth Officer &
Pres-Intl)
Isaac Kim (VP)

Subsidiary (Non-US):

The Nielsen Company B.V. (3)
Diemerhof 2, 1112 XL, Diemen,
Netherlands (100%)
Tel.: (31) 20 398 8777
Marketing, Media Rating & Business Infor-
mation Services
N.A.I.C.S.: 541910

Subsidiary (US):

The Nielsen Company (US), LLC (4)
770 Broadway, New York, NY 10003
Tel.: (646) 654-5000
Marketing Information, Media Measurement
Information & Business Information Ser-
vices
N.A.I.C.S.: 541910

Subsidiary (Non-US):

A3 Distrib SAS (5)
2 Rue de la Fleche, PO Box 20726, 49300,
Cholet, Cedex, France
Tel.: (33) 253591240
Web Site: http://www.a3distrib.fr
Customs Consulting Services
N.A.I.C.S.: 541614

Subsidiary (Domestic):

ACNielsen Corporation (5)
85 Broad St, New York, NY 10004
Tel.: (646) 654-5000
Sales Range: $1-4.9 Billion
Emp.: 21,000
Developer of Diagnostic, Market Measure-
ment, Opportunity Identification & Market
Analysis Products & Services
N.A.I.C.S.: 541910

Subsidiary (Domestic):

A.C. Nielsen Company, LLC (6)
150 N Martingale Rd, Schaumburg, IL
60173
Tel.: (847) 605-5000
Emp.: 2
Marketing Research Service
N.A.I.C.S.: 541910

Subsidiary (Domestic):

ACNielsen (US), Inc. (7)

150 N Martingale Rd, Schaumburg, IL
60173-2076
Tel.: (847) 605-5000
Sales Range: $25-49.9 Million
Emp.: 500
Developer of Diagnostic, Market Measure-
ment, Opportunity Identification & Market
Analysis Products & Services
N.A.I.C.S.: 541910

Branch (Domestic):

ACNielsen (8)
600 Hwy 159 Ste 400, Plymouth, MN 55426
Tel.: (763) 593-2000
Sales Range: $10-24.9 Million
Emp.: 80
Developer of Diagnostic, Market Measure-
ment, Opportunity Identification & Market
Analysis Products & Services
N.A.I.C.S.: 541910

ACNielsen (8)
2650 S Ashland Ave, Green Bay, WI 54304-
5361
Tel.: (920) 405-7500
Rev.: $10,200,000
Emp.: 300
Developer of Diagnostic, Market Measure-
ment, Opportunity Identification & Market
Analysis Products & Services
N.A.I.C.S.: 541910

Subsidiary (Non-US):

ACNielsen Company of Canada (7)
160 McNabb Street, Markham, L3R 4B8,
ON, Canada
Tel.: (905) 475-3344
Web Site: https://www.nielsen.com
Sales Range: $25-49.9 Million
Emp.: 500
Developer of Diagnostic, Market Measure-
ment, Opportunity Identification & Market
Analysis Products & Services
N.A.I.C.S.: 541910

Subsidiary (Domestic):

ACNielsen Puerto Rico Inc. (7)
117 Eleanor Roosevelt, Hato Rey, PR
00918
Tel.: (787) 756-0555
Emp.: 50
Developer of Diagnostic, Market Measure-
ment, Opportunity Identification & Market
Analysis Products & Services
N.A.I.C.S.: 541910

Subsidiary (Non-US):

ACNielsen Argentina S.A. (6)
Av del Libertador 6350 piso 6 Ciudad Au-
tonoma de, C1428ART, Buenos Aires, Ar-
gentina
Tel.: (54) 1168415400
Developer of Diagnostic, Market Measure-
ment, Opportunity Identification & Market
Analysis Products & Services
N.A.I.C.S.: 541910

Subsidiary (Non-US):

A.C. Nielsen Chile Limitada (7)
Cerro El Plomo 5680 Piso 13, Las Condes,
8320000, Chile
Tel.: (56) 24632700
Web Site: http://www.nielsen.com
Marketing Management Consulting Services
N.A.I.C.S.: 541613

A.C. Nielsen de Colombia Ltda. (7)
Calle 100 9 A-45 Torre 2 Piso 10, Bogota,
Colombia
Tel.: (57) 6516500
Sales Range: $50-74.9 Million
Emp.: 600
Digital Marketing Services
N.A.I.C.S.: 541810

A.C. Nielsen de Venezuela, S.A. (7)
Av Jose Maria Vargas Torre del Colegio
Apdo 80008, Piso 10 Urb Santa Fe Norte,
Caracas, Venezuela
Tel.: (58) 2129070100
Sales Range: $25-49.9 Million
Emp.: 300
Developer of Diagnostic, Market Measure-
ment, Opportunity Identification & Market
Analysis Products & Services
N.A.I.C.S.: 541910

A.C. Nielsen do Brasil Ltda. (7)
Rua Monte Castelo 55 - Granja Viana, Co-
tia, Sao Paulo, 06710 675, Brazil
Tel.: (55) 1146137000
Web Site: http://www.nielsen.com
Sales Range: $25-49.9 Million
Emp.: 1,000
Marketing Research Service
N.A.I.C.S.: 541910

A.C. Nielsen, S. de RL de C.V. (7)
Blvd Manuel Avila Camacho 191 Piso 8 Col
Polanco, Seccion Del Miguel Hidalgo,
11510, Mexico, DF, Mexico
Tel.: (52) 5553871000
Sales Range: $50-74.9 Million
Emp.: 1,000
Developer of Diagnostic, Market Measure-
ment, Opportunity Identification & Market
Analysis Products & Services
N.A.I.C.S.: 541910

ACNielsen Ecuador S.A. (7)
Kennedy Norte Av Nahim Isalas y Luis Or-
rantia Mz 801 No 28, 090112, Guayaquil,
Ecuador
Tel.: (593) 45005402
Business Research Services
N.A.I.C.S.: 541910

Subsidiary (Non-US):

ACNielsen Cyprus Limited (6)
Makariou 56 Dimofontos 1 6th floor, PO
Box 26758, 1075, Nicosia, Cyprus
Tel.: (357) 22886383
Sales Range: $75-99.9 Million
Emp.: 130
Developer of Diagnostic, Market Measure-
ment, Opportunity Identification & Market
Analysis Products & Services
N.A.I.C.S.: 541910

Subsidiary (Non-US):

AC Nielsen Cote d'Ivoire Limited (7)
Cocody II Plateaux Ste Cecile Rue J106 Lot
2038, PO Box 1258, Abidjan, Cote d'Ivoire
Tel.: (225) 22420044
Management Consulting & Comprehensive
Market Information Solution Provider
N.A.I.C.S.: 541613

ACNielsen (Tanzania) Ltd. (7)
Maktaba/Bibi Titi Mohamed Street Raha
Towers 3rd floor, Dar es Salaam, 76888,
Tanzania
Tel.: (255) 222117628
Web Site: http://tz.nielsen.com
Emp.: 30
Media & Marketing Consulting Services
N.A.I.C.S.: 541910

ACNielsen Cameroon Sarl (7)
Bonadiwoto-Opposite Total Aeroport 4th En-
trance Right, PO Box 11783, Douala, Cam-
eroon
Tel.: (237) 33014407
Emp.: 70
Media & Marketing Research Services
N.A.I.C.S.: 541910
Brian Chung (Mng Dir)

ACNielsen Ghana Limited (7)
4th Floor Gulf House Airport West, Tetteh
Quarshie Roundabout, Accra, Ghana
Tel.: (233) 302503215
Web Site: http://www.gh.nielsen.com
Market Research & Information Solution
Provider
N.A.I.C.S.: 541910

ACNielsen Kazakhstan Ltd. (7)
Auezov Str 60 BC Almaty Residence 10th
Floor, Bussines Center Sarkand, Almaty,
50059, Kazakhstan
Tel.: (7) 87273557750
Web Site: http://kz.nielsen.com
Market Research & Information Solution
Provider
N.A.I.C.S.: 541910

**ACNielsen Limited Liability
Company** (7)
st Tushinskaya 17, 125362, Moscow, Rus-
sia
Tel.: (7) 4956465105
Web Site: http://www.nielsen.com
Sales Range: $25-49.9 Million
Marketing Research Service
N.A.I.C.S.: 541910

ACNielsen Nigeria Limited (7)
1st floor Left Wing 52/54 Isaac John Street,
Ikeja GRA, Lagos, Nigeria
Tel.: (234) 12702085
Sales Range: $10-24.9 Million
Emp.: 100
Marketing Research Service
N.A.I.C.S.: 541910

**ACNielsen Pakistan (Private)
Limited** (7)
Room No 716 Progressive Plaza Beaumont
Rd Civil Lines, Progressive Plaza, Karachi,
75530, Pakistan
Tel.: (92) 21111111226
Web Site: http://www.pk.nielsen.com
Media & Marketing Information Services
N.A.I.C.S.: 541613

ACNielsen S.A. (7)
Louise Riencourt 64, Apollon Tower, 11523,
Athens, Greece
Tel.: (30) 2106999200
Sales Range: $10-24.9 Million
Marketing Research Service
N.A.I.C.S.: 541910

ACNielsen SARL (7)
179 Rue Omar Riffi Imm Al Wahda Entree
B 2eme Etage Appt B6, Casablanca,
20120, Morocco
Tel.: (212) 522441915
Marketing Research Service
N.A.I.C.S.: 541910

UAB ACNielsen Baltics (7)
A Juozapaviciaus g 6/2, Vilnius, LT-09310,
Lithuania
Tel.: (370) 52734145
Emp.: 150
Market Research & Information Solution
Provider
N.A.I.C.S.: 541910

Subsidiary (Non-US):

ACNielsen Europe (6)
Avenue Lavoisier 37, Avenue Einstein 6 -
Bat F, 1300, Wavre, Belgium
Tel.: (32) 10454609
Market Research Services
N.A.I.C.S.: 541910

Subsidiary (Non-US):

A.C. Nielsen Company, S.L. (7)
Orense 34 Torre Norte 8 Planta, 28020,
Madrid, Spain
Tel.: (34) 913777200
Web Site: http://www.nielsen.com
Sales Range: $25-49.9 Million
Emp.: 350
Marketing Research & Monitoring & Docu-
mental Services
N.A.I.C.S.: 541910

A.C. Nielsen Gesellschaft m.b.H. (7)
Big Biz C Dresdner Str 91, 1200, Vienna,
Austria
Tel.: (43) 1981100
Web Site: http://www.nielsen.com
Sales Range: $10-24.9 Million
Emp.: 100
Marketing Research Service
N.A.I.C.S.: 541910

A.C. Nielsen GmbH (7)
Sachsenstrasse 16, 20097, Hamburg, Ger-
many
Tel.: (49) 40236420
Sales Range: $10-24.9 Million
Emp.: 150
Marketing Research Service
N.A.I.C.S.: 541910
Resto Maela (Mng Dir)

A.C. Nielsen Portugal (7)
Rua Dona Filipa De Vilhena 38, 1049, Lis-
bon, Portugal
Tel.: (351) 217811200
Sales Range: $10-24.9 Million
Emp.: 100
Marketing Research Service
N.A.I.C.S.: 541910

A.C. Nielsen of Ireland Limited (7)
14 Riverwalk National Digital Park Citywest
Business Campus, Dublin, 24, Ireland
Tel.: (353) 14690400
Web Site: http://nielsen.com
Emp.: 70

Elliott Management Corporation—(Continued)

Media & Marketing Research Services
N.A.I.C.S.: 541910

ACNielsen (Nederland) B.V. (7)
Radarweg 29B- 9, 1043 NX, Amsterdam,
Netherlands
Tel.: (31) 203988777
Web Site: http://www.nielsen.com
Sales Range: $10-24.9 Million
Emp.: 200
Marketing Research Service
N.A.I.C.S.: 541910

Subsidiary (Non-US):

Nielsen Admosphere, a.s (8)
Ceskobratrska 2778/1, 130 00, Prague,
Czech Republic
Tel.: (420) 22 271 7763
Web Site: https://www.nielsen-
admosphere.eu
Emp.: 190
Media Analysis Services
N.A.I.C.S.: 541910
Michal Jordan *(Deputy Chm)*
Tereza Simeckova *(Chm)*
Tomas Hyncica *(Dir-Bus & Res)*
David Satransky *(Dir-Electronic Res Sec-
tion)*
Magida Sukkari *(Dir-Bus Dev)*
Petr Matyastik *(Dir-Ad Intel)*

**Nielsen Arastirma Hizmetleri Limited
Sirket** (8)
Icerenkoy Mah Umut Sok AND Plaza No
10-12 Kat 1-2, Atasehir, 34752, Istanbul,
Turkiye
Tel.: (90) 2165387000
Marketing Consulting Services
N.A.I.C.S.: 541613

Subsidiary (Non-US):

ACNielsen AB (7)
Gavlegatan 16, Box 6019, 102 31, Stock-
holm, Sweden
Tel.: (46) 2084415
Sales Range: $10-24.9 Million
Emp.: 95
Developer of Diagnostic, Market Measure-
ment, Opportunity Identification & Market
Analysis Products & Services
N.A.I.C.S.: 541910

Subsidiary (Domestic):

Nielsen Services Sweden AB (8)
Gavlegatan 16, Box 6019, 102 31, Stock-
holm, Sweden
Tel.: (46) 2084415
Marketing Research Service
N.A.I.C.S.: 541910

Subsidiary (Non-US):

**The Nielsen Company (Denmark)
Aps** (8)
Tuborg Parkvej 3-1 sal, 2900, Hellerup,
Denmark
Tel.: (45) 39400022
Web Site: http://dk.nielsen.com
Emp.: 80
Media & Marketing Research Services
N.A.I.C.S.: 541613

Subsidiary (Domestic):

**ACNielsen Company (Belgium)
S.A.** (7)
73 Avenue des Pleiades, 1200, Brussels,
Belgium
Tel.: (32) 27787118
Sales Range: $10-24.9 Million
Emp.: 162
Developer of Diagnostic, Market Measure-
ment, Opportunity Identification & Market
Analysis Products & Services
N.A.I.C.S.: 541910

Subsidiary (Non-US):

ACNielsen Company Ltd. (7)
Nielsen House London Rd, Headington,
Oxford, OX3 9RX, Oxfordshire, United King-
dom
Tel.: (44) 1865742742
Web Site: http://www.acnielsen.co.uk

Sales Range: $25-49.9 Million
Emp.: 700
Marketing Research
N.A.I.C.S.: 541910

ACNielsen Norge AS (7)
Harbitzalleen 5, 0275, Oslo, Norway
Tel.: (47) 40614240
Marketing Research Service
N.A.I.C.S.: 541910

ACNielsen S.A. (7)
1 Rue Julius et Ethel Rosenberg, 95870,
Bezons, France
Tel.: (33) 134414444
Sales Range: $25-49.9 Million
Emp.: 500
Marketing Research Service
N.A.I.C.S.: 541910

ACNielsen SA (7)
Via Cassinetta 25, Root, 6900, Lugano,
Switzerland
Tel.: (41) 919609900
Sales Range: $10-24.9 Million
Emp.: 160
Marketing Research Service
N.A.I.C.S.: 541910

**The Nielsen Company (Italy)
S.r.l.** (7)
Centro Direzionale Milanofiori Strada 6 Pa-
lazzo A12, 20090, Assago, MI, Italy
Tel.: (39) 02451671
Web Site: http://www.nielsen.it
Sales Range: $50-74.9 Million
Emp.: 550
Marketing Research Service
N.A.I.C.S.: 541910

Subsidiary (Domestic):

Nielsen Services Italy S.r.l. (8)
Strada 6 Palazzo A12, MilanoFiori, 20090,
Assago, MI, Italy
Tel.: (39) 027491512
Emp.: 1,400
Marketing Research Service
N.A.I.C.S.: 541910
Samantha Rovatti *(Dir-Comm)*
Ombretta Capodaglio *(Mgr-Comm)*

Subsidiary (Non-US):

ACNielsen Group Limited (6)
10/F Dorset House Taikoo Place 979 Kings
Road, Quarry Bay, China (Hong Kong)
Tel.: (852) 2563 9688
Web Site: http://www.hk.nielsen.com
Developer of Diagnostic, Market Measure-
ment, Opportunity Identification & Market
Analysis Products & Services
N.A.I.C.S.: 541910

Subsidiary (Non-US):

ACNielsen (Korea) Ltd. (7)
Korea Fire Marine Insurance Bldg 51-1
Namchang-dong, Jung gu, Seoul, 004-528,
Korea (South)
Tel.: (82) 221227000
Web Site: http://www.acnielsen.co.kr
Sales Range: $25-49.9 Million
Emp.: 300
Marketing Research Service
N.A.I.C.S.: 541910

**The Nielsen Company (Australia) Pty.
Ltd.** (7)
Level 2 Building B 11 Talavera Road, Mac-
quarie Park, Sydney, 2113, NSW, Australia
Tel.: (61) 28 873 7000
Web Site: http://www.nielsen.com
Marketing Research & Media Measurement
Information Services
N.A.I.C.S.: 541910

Subsidiary (Non-US):

ACNielsen (N.Z.) Ltd. (8)
Level 3 Nielsen Centre 129 Hurstmere
Road, Takapuna, Auckland, 0622, New Zea-
land
Tel.: (64) 99704188
Web Site: http://www.nielsen.com
Sales Range: $10-24.9 Million
Emp.: 160
Marketing Research Service
N.A.I.C.S.: 541910

ACNielsen Corporation Japan (8)

Mg Shirokanedai Bldg 5-12-7 Shirokanedai,
Minato-ku, Tokyo, 108-0071, Japan
Tel.: (81) 357989300
Web Site: http://www.nielsen.com
Emp.: 50
Marketing Research Service
N.A.I.C.S.: 541910

Branch (Domestic):

ACNielsen Corporation Japan (9)
Mg Shirokanedai Bldg 5-12-7 Shirokanedai,
Minato-ku, Tokyo, 108-0071, Japan
Tel.: (81) 357989300
Web Site: http://www.acnielsen.co.jp
Sales Range: $10-24.9 Million
Emp.: 223
Marketing Research Service
N.A.I.C.S.: 541910

Subsidiary (Non-US):

**The Nielsen Company Taiwan
Ltd.** (7)
12F No 188 Nanking E Rd Sec 5, Taipei,
105, Taiwan
Tel.: (886) 221715988
Web Site: http://www.nielsen.com
Sales Range: $25-49.9 Million
Emp.: 300
Marketing Research Service
N.A.I.C.S.: 541910

The Nielsen Nepal Pvt. Ltd. (7)
Ravi Bhawan, PO Box 1784, Kathmandu,
Nepal
Tel.: (977) 14273890
Market Research & Information Solution
Services
N.A.I.C.S.: 541910

Subsidiary (Non-US):

**AGB Nielsen Media Research (Thai-
land) Ltd.** (5)
No 323 26th Floor United Center Building
Silom Road, Silom Sub-district Bangrak Dis-
trict, Bangkok, 10500, Thailand
Tel.: (66) 26746000
Television Audience Measurement Services
N.A.I.C.S.: 541613

**AGB Nielsen, medijske raziskave,
d.o.o** (5)
Litijska cesta 259, Crnuce, Ljubljana, 1261,
Slovenia
Tel.: (386) 15809000
Web Site: http://www.agbnielsen.com
Medical Research Services
N.A.I.C.S.: 541910
Mojca Celigoj *(Mng Dir)*
Bostjan Kusnjerek *(Mktg Mgr)*
Marta Ledinek *(Mgr-Panel)*
Jasna Petrovic *(Production Mgr)*

AGB Stat IPSOS sal (5)
Ipsos building, PO Box 55103, Dekwaneh,
Beirut, Lebanon
Tel.: (961) 1494136
Web Site: http://www.ipsos.com
Marketing Research Service
N.A.I.C.S.: 541910

AMER Tunisia Sarl (5)
12 Rue Echabbia Ex Rue 8003 - 4th Floor,
Montplaisir, 1073, Tunis, Tunisia
Tel.: (216) 71903549
Sales Range: $10-24.9 Million
Emp.: 30
Media & Marketing Consulting Services
N.A.I.C.S.: 541613

Admosphere, s.r.o (5)
Ceskobratrska 2778/1, Prague, 130 00,
Czech Republic
Tel.: (420) 222717763
Web Site: http://www.nielsen-
admosphere.cz
Emp.: 100
Business Research Services
N.A.I.C.S.: 541910

Subsidiary (Domestic):

Affinnova, Inc. (5)
265 Winter St Fl 4, Waltham, MA 02451
Tel.: (781) 464-4700
Web Site: http://www.affinnova.com
Software Development Services
N.A.I.C.S.: 513210

Subsidiary (Non-US):

Affinnova France Sarl (6)
9 Avenue des 3 Fontaines CS 20501,
95007, Cergy-Pontoise, Cedex, France
Tel.: (33) 134414444
Business Research Services
N.A.I.C.S.: 541910

Subsidiary (Domestic):

Baseline LLC (5)
3415 S Sepulveda Blvd Ste 200, Los Ange-
les, CA 90034
Tel.: (310) 482-3414
Web Site: http://studiosystem.com
Sales Range: $100-124.9 Million
Emp.: 50
Entertainment Data Analysis Services
N.A.I.C.S.: 541910
Simon Adams *(Chief Product Officer)*

Subsidiary (Non-US):

Brandbank Limited (5)
35B Barnard Road, Norwich, NR5 9JB,
United Kingdom
Tel.: (44) 3305553344
Software Designing Services
N.A.I.C.S.: 513210
Sean Wilkins *(Grp Dir-Comml)*
Ray D'Aprile *(Dir-Comml-North American)*

Subsidiary (Non-US):

Brandbank (Hungary) Kft. (6)
AC Nielsen Piackutato Kft Vaci u 81,
H-1056, Budapest, Hungary
Tel.: (36) 17940184
Web Site: http://www.brandbank.com
Marketing Research Service
N.A.I.C.S.: 541910

Brandbank (Ireland) Limited. (6)
Unit F7 Swords Enterprise Park Feltrim
Road Swords, Dublin, Ireland
Tel.: (353) 15253800
Web Site: http://www.brandbank.com
Marketing Research Service
N.A.I.C.S.: 541910

Brandbank (Netherlands) B .V. (6)
Line vest 4, 3992 DJ, Houten, Netherlands
Tel.: (31) 302040770
Web Site: http://www.brandbank.com
Marketing Research Service
N.A.I.C.S.: 541910

Brandbank (Poland) Sp. z .o.o. (6)
ul Cyfrowa 4, 71-441, Szczecin, Poland
Tel.: (48) 918522648
Web Site: http://www.brandbank.com
Marketing Research Service
N.A.I.C.S.: 541910

Brandbank (Slovakia) s.r.o. (6)
Kutlikova 17, 851 02, Bratislava, Slovakia
Tel.: (421) 1232282902
Marketing Research Service
N.A.I.C.S.: 541910
Slavomila Chovancova *(Acct Mgr-Key
Accts)*

Subsidiary (Domestic):

Gracenote, Inc. (5)
2000 Powell St Ste 1500, Emeryville, CA
94608
Tel.: (510) 428-7200
Web Site: https://www.gracenote.com
Digital Media Identification Products & Ser-
vices
N.A.I.C.S.: 541519
Karthik Rao *(Pres)*
Simon Adams *(Chief Product Officer)*

Subsidiary (Non-US):

Gracenote GmbH (6)
St-Martin-Strasse 61, 81669, Munich, Ger-
many
Tel.: (49) 89 961 1830
Web Site: http://www.gracenote.com
Television Broadcasting Services
N.A.I.C.S.: 516120

Gracenote KK (6)
Shibuya Place 8F 1-10-5 Dogenzaka,
Shibuya-ku, Tokyo, 150-0043, Japan
Tel.: (81) 334647785
Web Site: http://www.gracenote.com

Television Broadcasting Services
N.A.I.C.S.: 516120

Gracenote Korea Ltd. (6)
Seoul City Tower Building 22F 110 Huam
ro, Jung-gu, Seoul, Korea (South)
Tel.: (82) 25985857
Web Site: http://www.gracenote.com
Television Broadcasting Services
N.A.I.C.S.: 516120

Subsidiary (Non-US):

IBOPE eRatings.com Mexico (5)
Calle Bruno Traven 60, Distrito Federal,
Mexico, 03340, Mexico
Tel.: (52) 5556290620
Radio & Television Repair Services
N.A.I.C.S.: 811210

IBOPE eRatings.com do Brasil Ltda. (5)
Al Santos 2101, Sao Paulo, 01419-001,
Brazil
Tel.: (55) 1130610031
Emp.: 22
Business Research Services
N.A.I.C.S.: 541910

Informacion de Medios S.A. (5)
Urdesa Central Balsamos Norte 404,
Guayaquil, Quinta, Ecuador
Tel.: (593) 42885653
Web Site: https://www.infomedia.com.ec
N.A.I.C.S.: 516210

Landsberry & James Marketing Pty Ltd (5)
Suite 1002 Level 10 83 Mount St, North
Sydney, 2060, NSW, Australia
Tel.: (61) 288737600
Web Site: https://www.lj-oz.com
Advertising Services
N.A.I.C.S.: 541810

MEMRB Puls Panel Trgovina DOO (5)
Radnicka Cesta 47, 10000, Zagreb, Croatia
Tel.: (385) 16065500
Environmental Research Services
N.A.I.C.S.: 541715

Subsidiary (Domestic):

Marketing Analytics, Inc (5)
2306 1/2 Orrington Ave, Evanston, IL 60201
Tel.: (847) 733-8459
Web Site:
    http://www.marketinganalytics.com
Sales Range: $25-49.9 Million
Emp.: 5
Marketing Research & Public Opinion Polling
N.A.I.C.S.: 541910

Subsidiary (Non-US):

Media Focus Schweiz GmbH (5)
Stauffacherstrasse 28, 8004, Zurich, Switzerland
Tel.: (41) 433222750
Web Site: https://www.mediafocus.ch
Broadcast Media Rating Services
N.A.I.C.S.: 541910
Tina Fixle (Chief Analytics Officer)
Francis Boillod (COO)
Nicole Brunold (Mgr-Mktg & Comm)
Ueli Weber (CEO)
Michelle Roobol (Coord-Operation)
Stephanie Haas (Sr Mgr-Automation)
Bianca Bosshard (Sr Engr-Bus)

Subsidiary (Domestic):

Media Solutions (5)
770 Broadway, New York, NY 10003-9522
Tel.: (646) 654-5000
Marketing Information Services
N.A.I.C.S.: 541613

Subsidiary (Non-US):

Meterology Data Private Limited (5)
Office No 201-202 2nd Floor C Wing
Godrej Coliseum, Somaiya Hosp Road Sion
E, Mumbai, 400 022, India
Tel.: (91) 2241048800
Web Site: https://www.mdlindia.co.in
Household Meter Panel Mfr
N.A.I.C.S.: 335313

Sumit Singh (Head-Bus)
Sunil Lulla (Chm)

Milenium Espacio Soft, S.A. (5)
C/ Rafael Boti 24, 28023, Madrid, Spain
Tel.: (34) 902500921
Marketing Research Service
N.A.I.C.S.: 541910

Subsidiary (Non-US):

Nexium Portugal - Consultario e Software Lda. (6)
Praca de Alvalade 9 5 S 7, 1700-037, Lisbon, Portugal
Tel.: (351) 218484594
Marketing Research Service
N.A.I.C.S.: 541910

Subsidiary (Domestic):

NM Incite, LLC (5)
770 Bwy, New York, NY 10004
Tel.: (646) 654-5000
Web Site: http://www.nielsensocial.com
Marketing Research Service
N.A.I.C.S.: 541910

NetRatings, LLC (5)
770 Broadway, New York, NY 10003 **(100%)**
Tel.: (212) 703-5900
Web Site: http://www.nielsen-netratings.com
Sales Range: $75-99.9 Million
Emp.: 397
Internet Media & Market Research Services
N.A.I.C.S.: 541910

Division (Domestic):

AdRelevance (6)
964 N 34th St Ste 300, Seattle, WA 98103
Tel.: (206) 632-0300
Web Site: http://www.netratings.com
Tracking & Measurement of Internet Advertising Data
N.A.I.C.S.: 541810

Subsidiary (Non-US):

Netratings France SAS (5)
Le Viking 67 Rue Anatole France, 92309,
Levallois-Perret, France
Tel.: (33) 147595757
Marketing Research Service
N.A.I.C.S.: 541910

Subsidiary (Domestic):

Neurofocus, Inc. (5)
50 Green St, San Francisco, CA 94111
Tel.: (415) 262-2600
Market Research Services
N.A.I.C.S.: 541910

Subsidiary (Domestic):

Innerscope Research, Inc. (6)
98 N Washington St 2nd Fl, Boston, MA 02114
Tel.: (617) 904-0555
Web Site:
    http://www.innerscoperesearch.com
Emp.: 33
Consumer Research Services
N.A.I.C.S.: 541910

Subsidiary (Non-US):

Nexium Software Factory, S.L. (5)
Calle Juan De Quesada Pq Cientifico Y
Tecnologico 30, Las Palmas De Gran Canaria, 35001, Las Palmas, Spain
Tel.: (34) 461625531
Marketing Research Service
N.A.I.C.S.: 541910

Nielsen (India) Private Limited (5)
4B / 4th floor Raheja Platinum Sag Baug
Road off Andheri - Kurla Rd, Marol Andheri
East, Mumbai, 400059, India
Tel.: (91) 2261436400
Marketing Research Service
N.A.I.C.S.: 541910

Subsidiary (Domestic):

Indicus Analytics Private Limited (6)
2nd Floor Nehru House 4 Bahadur Shah
Zafar Marg, New Delhi, 110002, India
Tel.: (91) 1142512400
Web Site: http://www.indicus.net

Marketing Research Service
N.A.I.C.S.: 541910

Subsidiary (Non-US):

The Nielsen Company Nepal Pvt Ltd. (6)
Ravi Bhawan, PO Box 1784, Kathmandu,
Nepal
Tel.: (977) 14273890
Emp.: 52
Marketing Research Services
N.A.I.C.S.: 541910

Subsidiary (Non-US):

Nielsen Admosphere Bulgaria JSC. (5)
Web Site: http://www.nielsen-admosphere.bg
Marketing Research & Data Processing Services
N.A.I.C.S.: 711310
Tereza Simeckova (Chm)
Michal Jordan (Vice Chm)
Petr Matyastik (Dir-Ops)
Julia Grigorova (Mgr-Res)
Elka Petrova (Mgr-Ad Intel)

Nielsen Admosphere Slovakia, s.r.o. (5)
Lazaretska 23, 81109, Bratislava, Slovakia
Tel.: (421) 253410254
N.A.I.C.S.: 541720

Nielsen Audience Measurement (Cyprus) Ltd. (5)
8 Skopa Str 2nd Floor The Nielsen Company Building, 1075, Nicosia, Cyprus
Tel.: (357) 2 288 6600
Sales Range: $25-49.9 Million
Emp.: 140
Media & Marketing Research Services
N.A.I.C.S.: 541910

Nielsen Audience Measurement DOO Beograd (5)
Spanskih boraca 3, 11070, Belgrade, Serbia
Tel.: (381) 114141750
Marketing Research Service
N.A.I.C.S.: 541910

Subsidiary (Domestic):

Nielsen Audio, Inc. (5)
9705 Patuxent Woods Dr, Columbia, MD 21046-1572
Tel.: (410) 312-8000
Web Site: http://www.nielsen.com
Sales Range: $400-449.9 Million
Emp.: 1,292
Media & Marketing Research Services
N.A.I.C.S.: 541810

Subsidiary (Non-US):

Nielsen Consultancy LLC (5)
West Bay Reem Tower 05th Floor, PO Box
14551, Dafna, Doha, Qatar
Tel.: (974) 44121648
Marketing Research Service
N.A.I.C.S.: 541910
AlSharif AbdulAzim (Mgr-Data Aqcuisition)

Subsidiary (Domestic):

Nielsen Consumer Insights, Inc (5)
1 World Trade Ctr Fl 63, New York, NY 10007 **(100%)**
Tel.: (585) 272-8400
Web Site: http://theharrispoll.com
Internet & Traditional Market Research & Polling Services
N.A.I.C.S.: 541910
John Gerzema (Co-CEO)
Will Johnson (Co-CEO)

Subsidiary (Non-US):

Opinion Search Inc. (6)
1800-160 Elgin St, Ottawa, K2P 2P7, ON,
Canada
Tel.: (613) 751-5089
Web Site: http://www.opinionsearch.com
Emp.: 6
Marketing Research & Public Opinion Polling Services
N.A.I.C.S.: 541910

Subsidiary (Non-US):

Nielsen Egypt LLC (5)
8 Abdel Salam Zaki Street, Heliopolis,
Cairo, Egypt
Tel.: (20) 224178207
Marketing Services
N.A.I.C.S.: 541613
Sara Migally (Sr Mgr-Digital Center of Excellence-Global)

Subsidiary (Domestic):

Nielsen Entertainment, LLC (5)
6255 Sunset Blvd 19th Fl Los Angeles, Hollywood, CA 90028
Information, Analytical Tools & Marketing
Services For the Global Entertainment Industry
N.A.I.C.S.: 541910

Subsidiary (Domestic):

Nielsen SoundScan (6)
770 Broadway 8th Fl, New York, NY 10003
Tel.: (813) 366-2144
Web Site: http://www.soundscan.com
Rev.: $120,000
Music Industry Information Services
N.A.I.C.S.: 541910

Subsidiary (Non-US):

Nielsen IBOPE Dominicana, S.R.L. (5)
Pedro Henriquez Urena 138, Santo Domingo, Dominican Republic
Tel.: (809) 3316500
Business Research Services
N.A.I.C.S.: 541910
Vargas Lidia (Mgr-Acctg)

Nielsen Innovate Fund, LP (5)
15 Halamish St Northern Industrial Park,
Caesarea, 30889, Israel
Tel.: (972) 722700790
Web Site: https://nif.vc
N.A.I.C.S.: 523999
Dov Yarkoni (CEO)
Liron Langer (Chief Investment Officer)
Sigal Weidenfeld (CFO)

Nielsen Innovate Ltd. (5)
15 Halamish St, Northern Industrial Park,
Caesarea, 30889, Israel
Tel.: (972) 72 270 0790
Web Site: https://www.nif.vc
Marketing Research Service
N.A.I.C.S.: 541910
Esther Barak Landes (Founder)
Dov Yarkoni (CEO)
Hila Shachar (CFO)
Liron Langer (Chief Investment Officer)

Nielsen Korea Ltd. (5)
50 Central Place 13th to 16th floor,
Seosomun-ro Jung-gu, Seoul, 100-859,
Seosomun, Korea (South)
Tel.: (82) 21227000
Marketing Research Service
N.A.I.C.S.: 541910
Wonseok Choi (Dir-Pub Sector Enterprises
Industry-Consumer Insight)

Nielsen Kozonsegmeres Kft. (5)
Vaci u 81, 1056, Budapest, Hungary
Tel.: (36) 1 461 7050
Web Site: http://www.nielsen.com
Marketing Research Service
N.A.I.C.S.: 541910

Nielsen MMRD (Myanmar) Co., Ltd (5)
3rd Floor Building-18 MICT Park, Hlaing
Township, Yangon, Myanmar
Tel.: (95) 12305367
Marketing Research Service
N.A.I.C.S.: 541910
Khaing Sandar Myint (Mgr-Ops)

Nielsen Media Research AS (5)
Verkstedveien 3, PO Box 514, Skoyen,
Oslo, 0277, Norway
Tel.: (47) 22583400
Web Site: http://no.nielsen.com
Media & Marketing Information Services
N.A.I.C.S.: 541613

Subsidiary (Domestic):

Nielsen Media Research, Inc. (5)

Elliott Management Corporation—(Continued)

85 Broad St, New York, NY 10004
Tel.: (646) 654-8300
Sales Range: $250-299.9 Million
Emp.: 2,100
Television Audience Measurement & Advertising Information Services
N.A.I.C.S.: 541910

Subsidiary (Non-US):

Ebiquity Associates Limited (6)
Citypoint 1 Ropemaker Street, London,
EC2Y 9AW, United Kingdom (100%)
Tel.: (44) 2076509600
Web Site: http://www.ebiquity.com
Technology & Media Monitoring Services
N.A.I.C.S.: 541910

Subsidiary (Non-US):

Nielsen Music Control Nederland B.V. (5)
Catharina van Renneslaan 8, 1217 CX, Hilversum, Netherlands
Tel.: (31) 356254360
Television & Radio Broadcasting & Distr
N.A.I.C.S.: 516110

Division (Domestic):

Nielsen Scarborough (5)
675 6th Ave, New York, NY 10010
Tel.: (800) 753-6043
Web Site: http://www.scarborough.com
Consumer Shopping Pattern Research & Analysis Services
N.A.I.C.S.: 541910

Subsidiary (Non-US):

Nielsen Services Poland Sp. (5)
z.o.o.
Ul Postepu 15b, 02-676, Warsaw, Poland
Tel.: (48) 223387300
Web Site: http://www.nielsen.com
Marketing Research Service
N.A.I.C.S.: 541910

Nielsen Services Spain, S.L. (5)
C/ Practicante Ignacio Rodriguez s/n Edificio Polivalente IV, Tercera Planta Oficinas 307 308 317 Y 318inas, Las Palmas, 35017, Gran Canaria, Spain
Tel.: (34) 928356418
Marketing Research Service
N.A.I.C.S.: 541910

Subsidiary (Domestic):

Nielsen Sports America, LLC. (5)
675 6th Ave, New York, NY 10011
Tel.: (646) 654-5000
N.A.I.C.S.: 518210

Subsidiary (Non-US):

Nielsen Sports Asia Pte. Ltd. (5)
10 Anson Road 36-01A International Plaza, Singapore, 079903, Singapore
Tel.: (65) 62249112
Sports Analytics Services
N.A.I.C.S.: 711320

Nielsen Sports Belgium SA (5)
Avenue des Pleiades 73, 1200, Brussels, Belgium
Tel.: (32) 27787011
Federation & Brand Analytic Services
N.A.I.C.S.: 711310
Jerome Bouchat (Mng Dir)

Nielsen Sports Deutschland GmbH (5)
Scheidtweilerstr 17, 50933, Cologne, Germany
Tel.: (49) 221430730
N.A.I.C.S.: 518210

Nielsen Sports España S.L.U. (5)
Pl Francesc Macia 7 Planta 16, 08029, Barcelona, Spain
Tel.: (34) 933686800
Sports Analytics Services
N.A.I.C.S.: 711320
Pablo Bellido (Co-Mng Dir)
Ramon Amich (Co-Mng Dir)

Nielsen Sports France Sarl (5)
1 rue Julius et Ethel Rosenberg, 95870, Bezons, France

Tel.: (33) 134416262
Marketing Services
N.A.I.C.S.: 541613
Pierre-Emmanuel Davin (Mng Dir)

Nielsen Sports India Private Limited (5)
Prestige Shantiniketan 1st Floor Crescent 4, Whitefield, Bengaluru, 560048, India
Tel.: (91) 8039818000
Marketing Services
N.A.I.C.S.: 541613
R. Pradeep Kumar (Mgr)

Nielsen Sports Italia Srl. (5)
Strada 3 - Palazzo B 4, MilanoFiori, 20090, Assago, MI, Italy
Tel.: (39) 027491512
Sports Analytics Services
N.A.I.C.S.: 711320
Gianluca Mazzardi (Dir-Comml)

Nielsen Sports Japan K.K. (5)
11F Akasaka Tameike Tower 2-17-7, Minato-ku Akasaka, Tokyo, 107-0052, Japan
Tel.: (81) 367219436
Sports Analytics Services
N.A.I.C.S.: 711320

Nielsen Sports Korea LLC (5)
To elect 625 eonju building fifth floor 5F Sunmin Building Eonju-ro, Gangnam-Gu, Seoul, 135-829, Korea (South)
Tel.: (82) 25492675
Sports Analytics Services
N.A.I.C.S.: 711320

Nielsen Sports Nederland B.V. (5)
Repucom Nederland BV Diemerhof 2, 1112 XL, Diemen, Netherlands
Tel.: (31) 203988777
Sports Analytics Services
N.A.I.C.S.: 711320
Sebastiaan Westerhout (Mng Dir)
Cheerkim Keo (Mgr-Client Svcs)
Ronald Nijboer (Mgr-Project)

Nielsen Sports Pty. Ltd. (5)
Level 2 Building B 11 Talavera Road Macquarie Park, Sydney, 2113, NSW, Australia
Tel.: (61) 288737000
N.A.I.C.S.: 518210

Nielsen Sports UK & Ireland Limited (5)
66 Porchester Road, London, W2 6ET, United Kingdom
Tel.: (44) 2072217040
Sports Analytics Services
N.A.I.C.S.: 711320
Andy Milnes (Dir-Grp Acct)
Steve Shaw (Head-Res)
Alastair Pitfield (Head-Client Svcs)
Max Barnett (Head-Digital)

Nielsen TV Audience Measurement S.A. (5)
Via Calloni 1, 6900, Lugano, Switzerland
Tel.: (41) 919609900
Media & Marketing Consulting Services
N.A.I.C.S.: 541613

Nielsen TV Audience Measurement S.r.l. (5)
Viale Angelo Filippetti 37, Milan, 20122, Italy
Tel.: (39) 02582171
Sales Range: $25-49.9 Million
Emp.: 100
Media & Marketing Information Services
N.A.I.C.S.: 541910

Nielsen Tele Medical GmbH (5)
Brenneckestr 20, 39120, Magdeburg, Germany
Tel.: (49) 3916117201
Web Site: http://www.sites.nielsen.com
Medical Device Services
N.A.I.C.S.: 423450

Nielsen Television Audience Measurement Pty. Ltd. (5)
166 Epping Rd, Lane Cove, 2066, NSW, Australia
Tel.: (61) 294906500
Web Site: https://www.nielsentam.com.au
N.A.I.C.S.: 516120

Nielsen Tunisia Sarl (5)

12 Rue Echabbia Montplaisir, 1073, Tunis, Tunisia
Tel.: (216) 71903549
Broadcast Media Rating Services
N.A.I.C.S.: 541910

Nielsen for Consultancies Limited Liability Company (5)
Al Rabia 4 Abdullah Bin Rawaha str Al Rabia Towers 4th floor 2354, Amman, 11181, Jordan
Tel.: (962) 65544683
Marketing Research Service
N.A.I.C.S.: 541910

Nielsen for Market Research LLC (5)
Bldg No 20 Flat No 11 First Floor Street No 1135, PO Box 436, Block No 135 Mutrah Commercial South, 118, Muscat, Oman
Tel.: (968) 24819305
Marketing Services
N.A.I.C.S.: 541613

Nutrino Health Ltd. (5)
94 Yigal Alon Street, Tel Aviv, Israel
Tel.: (972) 722499111
Web Site: http://www.nutrinohealth.com
Nutrition Data Analytic Services
N.A.I.C.S.: 518210

Organotiki S.A. (5)
64 Louise Riencourt Street, 11523, Athens, Greece
Tel.: (30) 2109401088
Web Site: https://organotiki.gr
N.A.I.C.S.: 541511

PT. Nielsen Audience Measurement (5)
Mayapada Tower 15/F Jl Jend Sudirman Kav 28, Jakarta, 12920, Indonesia
Tel.: (62) 2129398100
Emp.: 100
Market Research & Information Solution Provider
N.A.I.C.S.: 541910

PT. The Nielsen Company Indonesia (5)
Millennium Centennial Center 46 Floor Jalan Jendral Sudirman Kav 25, Jakarta, 12920, Indonesia
Tel.: (62) 2129398100
N.A.I.C.S.: 541910

Subsidiary (Domestic):

PointLogic USA Inc. (5)
675 Avenue of the Americas, New York, NY 10011
Tel.: (917) 710-2068
Marketing Budget & Analytic Services
N.A.I.C.S.: 541910
Nathalie Morales (Mgr-Client Relations)
Lee Levitz (VP-Client Solutions)
Melissa Volvovsky (Mgr-Office)
Lisa Antonucci (Dir-Client Solutions)
Jay Wofsy (Mng Dir)

Sorenson Media (5)
703 Palomar Airport Rd Ste 310, Carlsbad, CA 92011-1043
Web Site: http://www.sorensonmedia.com
Publisher
N.A.I.C.S.: 513199
Jim Sorenson (Founder & Chm)

The Cambridge Group, Inc. (5)
222 W Adams Ste 300, Chicago, IL 60606-5058
Tel.: (312) 425-3600
Web Site:
http://www.thecambridgegroup.com
Sales Range: $25-49.9 Million
Emp.: 100
Media & Marketing Consulting Services
N.A.I.C.S.: 541613
Rick Kash (Founder)
Jim Eckels (Mng Partner)
Chris Fosdick (Mng Partner)
Matt Gonwa (Partner)
Jeremy Bartlow (Partner)
Lindsey Leikhim (Assoc Partner)
Christine Wang (Assoc Partner)
Michael Thompson (Assoc Partner)
Kristin Gilbert (Project Mgr)
Lauren Monkiewicz (Project Mgr)
Darren Spicer (Project Mgr)

Austin Vanaria (Project Mgr)
Claire Zhou (Project Mgr)
Eleanor Jacobs (Project Mgr)

Subsidiary (Non-US):

The New Wave Research Ltd. (5)
1 Beser Towers 2 Ben Gurion St, Ramat Gan, 52573, Israel
Tel.: (972) 35766666
Web Site: http://www.nwr.co.il
Marketing Research Service
N.A.I.C.S.: 541910
Offer Levy (Chm-Nielsen Israel Grp)
Reuven Harari (Assoc Mng Dir)
Avi Neeman (Mgr-IT)
Orna Haskor (Mgr-Client Relationship)
Ran Levi (Deputy CEO)
Tzipi Bar (Dir-Quality Control)
Tamar Arnon (Dir-Creative Dept)
Adi Myr (Dir-Client-Grp)
Kobi Levi (Ops Mgr)

Subsidiary (Domestic):

New Sense Research Ltd. (6)
Ramat Hachayal, Tel Aviv, Israel
Tel.: (972) 35766666
Web Site: http://www.newsense.co.il
Sensory Research Services
N.A.I.C.S.: 541715

Subsidiary (Non-US):

The Nielsen Company (Bangladesh) Ltd. (5)
Impetus Center 7th Floor 242/B Tejgaon-Gulshan Link Road Tejgaon I/A, Dhaka, 1208, Bangladesh
Tel.: (880) 9609807060
Sales Range: $25-49.9 Million
Emp.: 150
Media & Marketing Research Services
N.A.I.C.S.: 541910
Anam Mahmud (Mng Dir)

The Nielsen Company (Belgium) SPRL (5)
73 Ave Des Pleiades, 1200, Brussels, Belgium
Tel.: (32) 27787118
Marketing Management Consulting Services
N.A.I.C.S.: 541613

Subsidiary (Non-US):

The Nielsen Company (Philippines), Inc. (6)
25/F Wynsum Corporate Plaza 22 F Ortigas Jr Road, Pasig, 1600, Philippines
Tel.: (63) 27068100
Emp.: 400
Media & Marketing Research Services
N.A.I.C.S.: 541910

Subsidiary (Non-US):

The Nielsen Company (Germany) GmbH (5)
Sachsenstrasse 16, 20097, Hamburg, Germany
Tel.: (49) 40236420
Market Research & Consulting Services
N.A.I.C.S.: 541613
Ludger Wibbelt (CEO-Nielsen Media)

Subsidiary (Domestic):

Nielsen Services Germany GmbH (6)
Insterburger St 16, 60487, Frankfurt, Germany
Tel.: (49) 6979380
Web Site: http://www.nielsen-partner.de
Marketing Consulting Services
N.A.I.C.S.: 541613

Subsidiary (Non-US):

The Nielsen Company (Greece) S.A. (5)
Louise Riencourt 64 Apollon Tower, 11523, Athens, Greece
Tel.: (30) 2106999200
Emp.: 75
Marketing Research Service
N.A.I.C.S.: 541910

The Nielsen Company (Malaysia) Sdn. Bhd. (5)

Level 16 Plaza 33 Tower B No 1 Jln Kema-juan Seksyen 13, 46100, Petaling Jaya, Selangor Darul Ehsan, Malaysia
Tel.: (60) 379409300
Market Research & Information Solution Provider
N.A.I.C.S.: 541910

The Nielsen Company (Shanghai) Ltd. **(5)**
2/F East Ocean Centre Phase II 618 Yanan East Road, Huang Pu District, Shanghai, 200001, China
Tel.: (86) 2123269200
Web Site: http://cn.nielsen.com
Management Consulting & Comprehensive Market Information Solution Provider
N.A.I.C.S.: 541613

The Nielsen Company (Thailand) Limited **(5)**
No 323 26th Floor United Center Building Silom Road, Silom Sub-District Bangrak District, Bangkok, 10500, Thailand
Tel.: (66) 26746000
N.A.I.C.S.: 541720

Division (Domestic):

The Nielsen Company - Advisory Services **(5)**
85 Broad St, New York, NY 10004
Tel.: (646) 654-5000
Web Site: http://www.en-us.nielsen.com
Target Market Research, Analysis & Consulting Services
N.A.I.C.S.: 541910

Subsidiary (Domestic):

BASES **(6)**
50 W River Ctr Blvd Ste 600, Covington, KY 41011
Tel.: (859) 905-4000
Web Site: http://www.bases.com
Sales Range: $400-449.9 Million
Emp.: 650
Pre-Market Consumer Opinion Research, New Product Sales Forecasting, Competitor Analysis & Target Market Research Services
N.A.I.C.S.: 541910

Claritas, Inc. **(6)**
8044 Montgomery Rd Ste 455, Cincinnati, OH 45236
Tel.: (858) 622-0800
Web Site: https://www.claritas.com
Sales Range: $125-149.9 Million
Emp.: 160
Target Market Research, Analysis & Demographic Data Services
N.A.I.C.S.: 541910

Branch (Domestic):

Claritas, Inc. **(7)**
1525 Wilson Blvd Ste 1200, Arlington, VA 22209-2450
Tel.: (703) 812-2700
Web Site: http://www.claritas.com
Sales Range: $10-24.9 Million
Emp.: 100
Marketing Consulting Services
N.A.I.C.S.: 541910

Subsidiary (Domestic):

Spectra Marketing Systems, Inc. **(6)**
200 W Jackson Blvd Ste 2800, Chicago, IL 60606-6910
Tel.: (312) 583-5100
Sales Range: $75-99.9 Million
Emp.: 150
Consumer Segmentation & Targeting Services
N.A.I.C.S.: 541910

Subsidiary (Domestic):

Trade Dimensions International, Inc. **(7)**
40 Danbury Rd, Wilton, CT 06897-4406
Tel.: (203) 222-5750
Sales Range: $10-24.9 Million
Emp.: 105
Publisher of Print & Electronic Retail Site Information Directories
N.A.I.C.S.: 513140

Subsidiary (Non-US):

The Nielsen Company Japan **(5)**
2-17-7 Akasaka Tameike Tower 11F, Akasaka Minato-ku, Tokyo, 107-0052, Japan
Tel.: (81) 368376600
Marketing Research Service
N.A.I.C.S.: 541910

The Nielsen Company Lanka (Private) Limited **(5)**
98 D S Senanayake Mawatha, Colombo, 08, Sri Lanka
Tel.: (94) 1126884468
Media & Marketing Consulting Services
N.A.I.C.S.: 541613

The Nielsen Company Medya Yayincilik ve Tanitim Hizmetleri Anonim Sirketii **(5)**
Nakkastepe Gumusyolu Cad No 22 Altunizade Uskudar, Istanbul, Turkiye
Tel.: (90) 2165537770
Web Site: http://www.nielsen.com
Media & Marketing Consulting Services
N.A.I.C.S.: 541613

Subsidiary (Domestic):

The Perishables Group, Inc. **(5)**
1700 W Irving Park Rd Ste 310, Chicago, IL 60613
Tel.: (847) 426-2665
Web Site: http://www.perishablesgroup.com
Sales Range: $10-24.9 Million
Emp.: 30
Research & Marketing Services
N.A.I.C.S.: 541613

Subsidiary (Non-US):

Toluna Group Limited. **(5)**
Ealing Cross 85 Uxbridge Road, London, W5 5TH, United Kingdom
Tel.: (44) 2088321700
Web Site: http://www.toluna.com
Emp.: 70
Digital Market Research Services
N.A.I.C.S.: 541910

Subsidiary (Domestic):

Visual IQ, Inc. **(5)**
75 2nd Ave Ste 330, Needham, MA 02494
Tel.: (781) 657-9035
Web Site: http://www.visualiq.com
Attribution Management & Marketing Analytics
N.A.I.C.S.: 541613
Manu Mathew (Co-Founder)

Subsidiary (Non-US):

Visual IQ, Inc. **(6)**
25 Sackville Street, London, W1S 3AX, United Kingdom
Tel.: (44) 2037003770
Web Site: http://www.visualiq.com
Attribution Management & Marketing Analytics
N.A.I.C.S.: 541613

Subsidiary (Domestic):

eXelate, Inc. **(5)**
7 W 22nd St 9th Fl, New York, NY 10010
Tel.: (646) 380-4400
Web Site: http://www.exelate.com
Data Management Services
N.A.I.C.S.: 518210

Joint Venture (Non-US):

Travelport Worldwide Limited **(2)**
Axis One Axis Park, Langley, SL3 8AG, Berks, United Kingdom
Tel.: (44) 1753 288000
Web Site: http://www.travelport.com
Rev.: $2,551,064,000
Assets: $2,929,057,000
Liabilities: $3,081,415,000
Net Worth: ($152,358,000)
Earnings: $72,628,000
Emp.: 3,700
Fiscal Year-end: 12/31/2018
Travel Commerce Marketplace
N.A.I.C.S.: 561599
Erika Moore (VP & Gen Mgr-Sls)
Matthew Minetola (CIO & Exec VP)
Stephen Shurrock (Chief Comml Officer & Exec VP)

Bernard L. Bot (CFO)
Mark Meehan (Mng Dir-Asia Pacific, Middle East and Africa)
Simon Ferguson (Pres/Mng Dir-Americas)
Margaret K. Cassidy (Gen Counsel & Exec VP)
Fiona Shanley (Chief Customer & Mktg Officer)
Nick Dagg (Sr VP-Global Agency Sls)
Jason Clarke (Head-Travel Partners)
Damian Hickey (Head-Air Travel Partners-Global)
Antonios Basoukeas (Chief Acctg Officer)
Simon Gros (Interim Chief HR Officer & Grp VP-Industry Affairs)

Subsidiary (Non-US):

Galileo Deutschland GmbH **(3)**
Lyoner Strasse 15, Niederrad, 60528, Frankfurt, Germany
Tel.: (49) 692273670
Online Travel Support Services
N.A.I.C.S.: 561510

Locomote IP Pty. Ltd. **(3)**
42 Barkly Street, Saint Kilda, 3182, VIC, Australia
Tel.: (61) 1300652802
Web Site: http://www.locomote.com
Online Travel Support Services
N.A.I.C.S.: 561510

Locomote Technologies Trading Pty. Ltd. **(3)**
42 Barkly Street, Saint Kilda, 3182, VIC, Australia
Tel.: (61) 412552164
Emp.: 5
Computer Programming Services
N.A.I.C.S.: 541511

Southern Cross Distribution Systems Pty Limited **(3)**
35 Grafton Street Level 6, Bondi Junction, 2022, NSW, Australia
Tel.: (61) 293914000
Software Publisher
N.A.I.C.S.: 513210

Travelport Digital Limited **(3)**
1 Cumberland Place Fenian Street, Dublin, D02 FF20, Ireland
Tel.: (353) 14853452
Web Site: http://digital.travelport.com
Online Travel Support Services
N.A.I.C.S.: 561510

Subsidiary (US):

Travelport Inc. **(3)**
300 Galleria Pkwy, Atlanta, GA 30339
Tel.: (770) 563-7400
Web Site: http://www.travelport.com
Rev.: $2,076,000,000
Assets: $3,088,000,000
Liabilities: $4,399,000,000
Net Worth: ($1,311,000,000)
Earnings: ($189,000,000)
Emp.: 3,500
Fiscal Year-end: 12/31/2013
Online Travel Tools & Services
N.A.I.C.S.: 561599
John A. C. Swainson (Exec Chm)
Ming Foong (Mng Dir-Asia)
Mark Meehan (Mng Dir-Asia Pacific, Middle East & Africa)
Robert Bailey (Chief Strategy Officer)
Greg Webb (CEO)
Nick Bray (CFO)

Subsidiary (Domestic):

Galileo International, LLC **(4)**
400 Interpace Pkwy Bldg A, Parsippany, NJ 07054
Tel.: (973) 939-1000
Web Site: http://www.galileo.com
Sales Range: $550-599.9 Million
Emp.: 3,300
Electronic Global Travel Distribution Services
N.A.I.C.S.: 541512

Subsidiary (Non-US):

Galileo Ireland Ltd. **(5)**
Palmerston House Fenian Street, Dublin, Ireland
Tel.: (353) 6020444

Web Site: http://www.galileo.com
Sales Range: $10-24.9 Million
Emp.: 38
Electronic Global Travel Distribution Services
N.A.I.C.S.: 541512

Subsidiary (Domestic):

Travelport GDS **(4)**
300 Galleria Pkwy, Atlanta, GA 30339
Tel.: (770) 563-7400
Web Site: http://www.travelport.com
Sales Range: $125-149.9 Million
Emp.: 600
Travel Maps & Technologies
N.A.I.C.S.: 561599

Subsidiary (Non-US):

Worldspan Services Ltd. **(5)**
242 Bath Road Axis House, Hayes, UB3 5AY, Middlesex, United Kingdom
Tel.: (44) 2087451900
Web Site: http://www.worldspan.com
Sales Range: $75-99.9 Million
N.A.I.C.S.: 561499

Subsidiary (US):

Travelport, LP **(3)**
300 Galleria Pkwy, Atlanta, GA 30339
Tel.: (770) 563-7400
Online Travel Support Services
N.A.I.C.S.: 561510
Majid Nazir (VP-IR)
David A. Lauderdale (CTO & Sr VP-Technical Ops)
Jeffrey C. Smith (Gen Counsel, Sec & Sr VP-HR)

Subsidiary (Non-US):

travel-IT GmbH & Co. KG **(3)**
Solinger Strasse 16, 45481, Mulheim an der Ruhr, Germany
Tel.: (49) 2083099660
Web Site: http://www.travel-it.de
Online Travel Support Services
N.A.I.C.S.: 561510

Paper Source, Inc. **(1)**
125 S Clark St, Chicago, IL 60603
Tel.: (312) 337-0798
Web Site: http://www.paper-source.com
Emp.: 50
Designer Paper Mfr
N.A.I.C.S.: 424130
James Solon (COO)
Winifred Park (CEO)

ELLIOTT OIL CO. INC.
207 W 2nd St Ste 1, Ottumwa, IA 52501-2748
Tel.: (641) 684-4377   IA
Year Founded: 1963
Sales Range: $25-49.9 Million
Emp.: 200
Gasoline Station Services
N.A.I.C.S.: 457120
Jeff Keep (Mgr-Ops)

Subsidiaries:

Elliott Bulk Services, LLC **(1)**
207 W 2nd St, Ottumwa, IA 52501
Tel.: (641) 684-4377
Petroleum Bulk Stations & Terminals
N.A.I.C.S.: 424710

ELLIOTT TAPE INC.
1882 Pond Run, Auburn Hills, MI 48326-2768
Tel.: (248) 475-5786   MI
Web Site: http://www.egitape.com
Year Founded: 1974
Sales Range: $50-74.9 Million
Emp.: 35
Coated & Laminated Tape Products Mfr
N.A.I.C.S.: 424130

ELLIOTT/WILSON CAPITOL TRUCKS LLC
8300 Ardwick Ardmore Rd, Landover, MD 20785

Elliott/Wilson Capitol Trucks LLC—(Continued)

Tel.: (301) 341-5500
Web Site:
http://www.capitoltrucks.com
Rev.: $24,400,000
Emp.: 50
Sell New & Used Trucks, Tractors &
Trailers
N.A.I.C.S.: 441110
Lynn Tyler *(Mgr-Fin)*
Steve Martin *(Mgr-Svc)*

ELLIS BROTHERS INC.
Roundhouse Ln, Mount Vernon, OH
43050
Tel.: (740) 397-9191
Web Site: http://www.ellisbros.net
Rev.: $15,157,248
Emp.: 20
Ready Mixed Concrete
N.A.I.C.S.: 327320
John P. Ellis *(Pres)*

ELLIS COFFEE COMPANY
2835 Bridge St, Philadelphia, PA
19137
Tel.: (215) 537-9500
Web Site: https://www.elliscoffee.com
Year Founded: 1845
Sales Range: $10-24.9 Million
Emp.: 100
Coffees & Teas
N.A.I.C.S.: 424490
Eugene A. Kestenbaum *(Pres &
CEO)*
Michael Strauss *(Dir-Pur)*

ELLIS CONSTRUCTION SPE-
CIALTIES
12409 Holmboe Ave, Oklahoma City,
OK 73114
Tel.: (405) 751-0880   OK
Web Site: http://www.ellisforms.com
Year Founded: 1976
Sales Range: $10-24.9 Million
Emp.: 20
Concrete Building Products
N.A.I.C.S.: 423320
James A. Holmboe Sr. *(Pres)*

ELLIS HOLDING CO.
2015 High Pt, Brandon, MS 39042
Tel.: (601) 824-7900   MS
Year Founded: 1980
Sales Range: $1-9.9 Million
Emp.: 3
Fast-Food Restaurant Chain Operator
N.A.I.C.S.: 722513
John E. Solomon *(Pres & CEO)*

ELLIS HOSIERY MILLS INC.
1500 13th St Southwest, Hickory, NC
28602
Tel.: (828) 322-1010
Sales Range: $25-49.9 Million
Emp.: 650
Men's, Boys' & Girls' Hosiery
N.A.I.C.S.: 315120

ELLIS MEARES & SON INC.
1143 Main St, Fair Bluff, NC 28439
Tel.: (910) 649-7521
Web Site:
http://ellismearesandsoninc-
northcharleston-
sc.brandsdirect.com
Sales Range: $10-24.9 Million
Emp.: 32
Electrical Appliances, Television &
Radio Distr
N.A.I.C.S.: 423620
Karen Grainger *(Office Mgr)*
Carl W. Meares Jr. *(Pres)*

ELLIS POTTERY INC.

4810 Hazel Jones Rd, Bossier City,
LA 71111
Tel.: (318) 741-3001
Web Site: http://www.ellispottery.com
Rev.: $14,000,000
Emp.: 150
Gift Shop
N.A.I.C.S.: 459420
Allen Ellis *(Pres)*

ELLIS SKINNER COMPANY,
INC.
1500 Plantation, Dallas, TX 75235
Tel.: (214) 638-8044
Web Site: https://www.eskinner.com
Year Founded: 1942
Sales Range: $10-24.9 Million
Emp.: 150
Tile & Terrazzo Contracting Services
N.A.I.C.S.: 238340
Mary Beth Weatherford *(Pres)*
Maria Perez *(Gen Mgr-Ops)*
Marc Alloju *(CFO)*
Ray Torres *(Mgr-Field)*

ELLIS STEEL COMPANY INC.
611 Bugg St, West Point, MS 39773
Tel.: (662) 494-5955
Web Site: http://www.ellissteel.com
Rev.: $45,675,444
Emp.: 145
Fabricated Structural Metal
N.A.I.C.S.: 332312
Frank Hopper *(Pres)*

ELLIS STONE CONSTRUC-
TION COMPANY
3201 Stanley St, Stevens Point, WI
54481
Tel.: (715) 345-5000
Web Site: https://www.elliswi.com
Sales Range: $100-124.9 Million
Emp.: 75
Commercial & Industrial New Con-
struction
N.A.I.C.S.: 236220
James E. Anderson *(Pres)*
Eric Carlson *(Exec VP)*
Patrick Pierce *(Project Mgr)*

ELLIS, MCQUARY, STANLEY &
ASSOCIATES LLC
888 3rd St NW Ste A, Atlanta, GA
30318-5759
Tel.: (678) 904-0555
Web Site:
http://www.ellismcqstanley.com
Year Founded: 2003
Emp.: 3
Holding Company; Private Equity &
Real Estate Investment Firm
N.A.I.C.S.: 551112
Bert Ellis *(Partner)*
Michael McQuary *(Partner)*
Thomas Bahnson Stanley III *(Partner)*

Subsidiaries:

Ellis Capital, LLC   (1)
888 3rd St N, Atlanta, GA 30318
Tel.: (678) 904-0555
Web Site: http://www.elliscapital.net
Venture Capital Investment Firm
N.A.I.C.S.: 523999
Bert Ellis *(Chm & CEO)*
Richard Fraim *(Pres & COO)*
Debra Davis *(VP-Admin)*

Titan Broadcast Management
LLC   (1)
888 3rd St NW Ste A, Atlanta, GA 30318
Tel.: (678) 904-0555
Web Site: http://www.titanbroadcast.com
Sales Range: $10-24.9 Million
Emp.: 100
Television Station Operator
N.A.I.C.S.: 516120
Dan Sullivan *(Chm & CEO)*
Bert Ellis *(Pres)*
Jim Sandry *(CFO)*

Unit (Domestic):

KDBC-TV   (2)
801 N Oregon St, El Paso, TX 79902
Tel.: (915) 496-4444
Web Site: http://www.ktsm.com
Sales Range: $10-24.9 Million
Emp.: 50
Television Broadcasting
N.A.I.C.S.: 516120
Gary Sotir *(Gen Mgr)*
Matt Kaplowitz *(Gen Mgr)*

KMEG-TV   (2)
100 Gold Cir, Dakota Dunes, SD 57049
Tel.: (712) 277-3554
Web Site: http://www.kmeg.com
Sales Range: $10-24.9 Million
Emp.: 2
Television Broadcasting
N.A.I.C.S.: 516120
Steve Scollard *(Gen Mgr)*

KMPH-TV   (2)
5111 E McKinley Ave, Fresno, CA 93727
Tel.: (559) 255-2600
Web Site: http://www.kmph.com
Sales Range: $10-24.9 Million
Television Station
N.A.I.C.S.: 516120
Hull Dave *(Supvr-Master Control)*
Jim Joly *(Dir-Natl Digital Sls)*
Greg Siegel *(VP-Sls-Natl)*

KUBE-TV   (2)
2401 Fountain View Dr Ste 300, Houston,
TX 77057
Tel.: (713) 467-5757
Web Site: http://www.kube57.com
Sales Range: $10-24.9 Million
Emp.: 20
Television Broadcasting
N.A.I.C.S.: 516120
J. D. Huey *(Gen Mgr)*
Veronica Rena *(Dir-HR)*
Geoff Campbell *(Mgr-Gen Sls)*

ELLIS, RICHARD CB & RE-
ICHLE KLEIN
1 Seagate 26th Fl, Toledo, OH 43604
Tel.: (419) 861-1100
Year Founded: 1994
Sales Range: $1-9.9 Million
Emp.: 35
Offices of Real Estate Agents & Bro-
kers
N.A.I.C.S.: 531210
Daniel Klein *(Pres)*

ELLIS-WALKER BUILDERS,
INC.
PO Box 41109, Fayetteville, NC
28309-1109
Tel.: (910) 485-8111
Sales Range: $10-24.9 Million
Emp.: 35
Civil Engineering Services
N.A.I.C.S.: 237310
Joe Walker *(Principal)*

ELLISON MEDIA COMPANY
14804 N Cave Creek Rd, Phoenix,
AZ 85032-4945
Tel.: (602) 404-4000   AZ
Web Site:
http://www.ellisonmedia.com
Year Founded: 1972
Rev.: $22,000,000
Emp.: 40
N.A.I.C.S.: 541810
Michael R. Ellison *(Founder, Pres &
CEO)*
Don Kurtenbach *(CFO & Treas)*
Barbara Griesman *(VP-Media)*
Susan Ellison *(Treas & Sec)*
Jay Griffin *(VP-Mktg)*
Judd Jackson *(VP-Bus Dev)*

ELLISON NURSING GROUP,
LLC
500 Office Center Dr Ste 400, Washington, PA 19034

Tel.: (267) 513-1995
Year Founded: 2003
Sales Range: $1-9.9 Million
Emp.: 150
Women Healthcare Services
N.A.I.C.S.: 621610
Lauren Ellison *(Owner)*

ELLISON TECHNOLOGIES
INC.
9912 Pioneer Blvd, Santa Fe Springs,
CA 90670-3250
Tel.: (562) 949-8311   DE
Web Site:
http://www.ellisontechnologies.com
Year Founded: 1999
Sales Range: $50-74.9 Million
Emp.: 500
Industrial Machinery & Equipment
Engineering, Sales & Services
N.A.I.C.S.: 423830
Tim Kilty *(CEO)*

Subsidiaries:

DMG Mori Ellison Technologies   (1)
4345 Morris Park Dr, Charlotte, NC 28227
Tel.: (704) 545-7362
Web Site:
http://www.ellisontechnologies.com
Sales Range: $25-49.9 Million
Emp.: 60
Metalworking Machinery Whslr
N.A.I.C.S.: 423830

Ellison Technologies, Inc.   (1)
4630 Weaver Pkwy, Warrenville, IL 60555-
3928
Tel.: (630) 393-8900
Sales Range: $50-74.9 Million
Emp.: 60
Metal Cutting Machinery Sales & Service
N.A.I.C.S.: 423830
Don Baskin *(Pres)*

Ellison Technologies, Inc.   (1)
19625 62nd Ave S Ste A109, Kent, WA
98032-1106
Tel.: (253) 872-1661
Web Site: http://www.ellisonmw.com
Sales Range: $10-24.9 Million
Emp.: 10
Metal Cutting Machinery Sales & Service
N.A.I.C.S.: 423830

GNB Corporation   (1)
3200 Dwight Rd Ste 100, Elk Grove, CA
95758-6461   (100%)
Tel.: (916) 395-3003
Web Site: http://www.gnbvalves.com
Sales Range: $10-24.9 Million
Emp.: 75
Metal Cutting Machine Tool Mfr
N.A.I.C.S.: 333517
Ken Harrison *(Pres)*
Mel Sattler *(Mgr-Production)*
Thomas Dobler *(Mgr-Sls-Intl)*

Sierra Concepts Manufacturing Com-
pany Inc.   (1)
9912 Pioneer Blvd, Santa Fe Springs, CA
90670-3250
Tel.: (562) 949-8311
Rev.: $180,000
Emp.: 1
Industrial Machinery & Equipment
N.A.I.C.S.: 423830
Graham Hooper *(CEO)*

ELLO FURNITURE MANUFAC-
TURING CO.
350 N La Salle Dr Ste 1100, Chicago,
IL 60654-5131
Tel.: (815) 964-8601
Year Founded: 1955
Sales Range: $10-24.9 Million
Emp.: 35
Furniture Mfr & Distr
N.A.I.C.S.: 337122
Lothar H. Molton *(Pres)*

ELLSWORTH COOP
100 N Kansas Ave, Ellsworth, KS
67439

Tel.: (785) 472-3261
Web Site:
http://www.ellsworthcoop.com
Sales Range: $10-24.9 Million
Emp.: 30
Grains
N.A.I.C.S.: 424510
Mary Peppiatt *(Office Mgr)*

ELLSWORTH COOPERATIVE CREAMERY
232 N Wallace St, Ellsworth, WI 54011
Tel.: (715) 273-4311
Web Site: http://www.ellsworthcheese curds.com
Year Founded: 1910
Rev.: $145,700,000
Emp.: 150
Cheese Curds Mfr
N.A.I.C.S.: 311513
Paul Bauer *(CEO)*

ELLSWORTH CORPORATION
W 129 N 10825 Washington Dr, Germantown, WI 53022
Tel.: (262) 253-8600   WI
Web Site: https://www.ellsworth.com
Year Founded: 1975
Sales Range: $50-74.9 Million
Emp.: 500
Mfr of Chemicals & Allied Products
N.A.I.C.S.: 424690
Paul Ellsworth *(CEO)*
Mike McCourt *(Pres)*

ELLSWORTH CORPORATION
3636 S I-10 Service Rd Ste 100, Metairie, LA 70001
Tel.: (504) 455-4545   LA
Web Site: https://www.ellsworthcorpo ration.com
Year Founded: 1973
Sales Range: $150-199.9 Million
Emp.: 45
Insurance Agents
N.A.I.C.S.: 524210
Alex Ellsworth *(Pres & CEO)*
Kathryn Moore *(CFO & Exec VP)*

ELLSWORTH FALLS LUMBER CO. INC.
261 State St, Ellsworth, ME 04605
Tel.: (207) 667-7134
Web Site: http://www.ebsbuild.com
Sales Range: $50-74.9 Million
Emp.: 180
Investment Holding Companies,
N.A.I.C.S.: 444110
Dwayne Webber *(Sr VP)*

ELLUMEN INC.
1401 Wilson Blvd Ste 1200, Arlington, VA 22209
Tel.: (703) 253-5555
Web Site: https://www.ellumen.com
Year Founded: 2003
Sales Range: $10-24.9 Million
Emp.: 65
Information Technology Support Services
N.A.I.C.S.: 541512
William J. McCollough *(Founder, CEO & Principal)*
Arthur Carroll *(Pres)*
Dan Wayland *(VP-IT Solutions)*
Mary Vogel *(VP-Client Solutions)*
Michael J. Luby *(Co-Founder & COO)*
R. Russ Rieling III *(VP-Ops)*

ELLWOOD GROUP, INC.
600 Commercial Ave, Ellwood City, PA 16117
Tel.: (724) 752-3680   PA
Web Site:
https://www.ellwoodgroup.com

Year Founded: 1910
Sales Range: $1-4.9 Billion
Emp.: 2,000
Mfr of Iron & Steel Forgings & Ferroalloys Produced in Blast Furnaces
N.A.I.C.S.: 332111
David E. Barensfeld *(Chm, Pres & CEO)*

Subsidiaries:

Ellwood Chrome Crankshaft Company   **(1)**
4166 Mound Rd, Joliet, IL 60436
Tel.: (815) 725-9030
Web Site: http://www.wd.com
Emp.: 20
Metal Equipment Mfr
N.A.I.C.S.: 333248
Tyler Kissick *(Gen Mgr)*

Ellwood City Forge   **(1)**
800 Commercial Ave, Ellwood City, PA 16117-2354   **(100%)**
Tel.: (724) 752-0055
Web Site: http://www.ellwoodgroup.com
Sales Range: $75-99.9 Million
Emp.: 300
Mfr of Open Die Steel Forgings
N.A.I.C.S.: 332111
Daniel P. Hamilton *(Pres-ECF)*
Jay Griffen *(Mgr-Sls)*

Subsidiary (Domestic):

Corry Forge Company   **(2)**
441 E Main St, Corry, PA 16407-2013
Tel.: (814) 664-9664
Web Site: http://www.ellwoodcityforge.com
Sales Range: $25-49.9 Million
Emp.: 100
Steel Producer
N.A.I.C.S.: 332111
David Barensfeld *(Pres)*

Ellwood Mill Products   **(2)**
700 Moravia St, New Castle, PA 16101
Tel.: (724) 658-9632
Forging Product Mfr
N.A.I.C.S.: 331110
Greg Williams *(Engr-Reliability)*

Ellwood Crankshaft & Machine Company, LLC   **(1)**
2727 Freedland Rd, Hermitage, PA 16148-9027   **(100%)**
Tel.: (724) 347-0250
Web Site: http://www.ellwoodgroup.com
Sales Range: $10-24.9 Million
Emp.: 115
Multiple-Throw Crakshaft Mfr
N.A.I.C.S.: 336390
Brian C. Taylor *(Pres)*

Unit (Domestic):

Elwood National Crankshaft Services   **(2)**
1 Front St, Irvine, PA 16329
Tel.: (814) 563-7522
Web Site: http://www.elwd.com
Providing Crankshaft Reconditioning Facility Services
N.A.I.C.S.: 333310

Ellwood Engineered Casting Co   **(1)**
7158 Hubbard Masury Rd, Hubbard, OH 44425
Tel.: (330) 534-8668
Web Site: http://www.ellwoodengineeredcas tings.com
Sales Range: $10-24.9 Million
Emp.: 100
Graphite Product Mfr
N.A.I.C.S.: 335991
Greg Selip *(Gen Mgr)*
Daniel L. Rhoads *(Pres)*

Ellwood National Crankshaft Co   **(1)**
1 Front St, Irvine, PA 16329
Tel.: (814) 563-7522
Crankshaft Mfr & Supplier
N.A.I.C.S.: 423860
Brian C. Taylor *(Pres)*
Joe Spess *(Engr-Maintenance)*

Ellwood National Crankshaft Services   **(1)**
303 Llodio Rd, Hermitage, PA 16148

Tel.: (724) 342-4965
Machine Tools Mfr
N.A.I.C.S.: 333517

Ellwood National Forge Company, LLC   **(1)**
1 Front St, Irvine, PA 16329
Tel.: (814) 563-7522
Web Site: http://www.ellwoodgroup.com
Sales Range: $25-49.9 Million
Emp.: 600
Alloy Steel Ingots & Billets, Rough & Finish Machined Forgings & Assemblies Mfr
N.A.I.C.S.: 332710

Ellwood Quality Steels Company   **(1)**
700 Moravia St, New Castle, PA 16101   **(100%)**
Tel.: (724) 658-6776
Web Site: http://www.ellwoodgroup.com
Sales Range: $25-49.9 Million
Emp.: 198
Carbon & Low-Alloy Steel Ingots Mfr
N.A.I.C.S.: 331110

Ellwood Rose Machine, Inc.   **(1)**
9031 Ley Rd, Houston, TX 77078
Tel.: (713) 670-9007
Web Site: http://www.ellwoodrm.com
Turning & Welding Services
N.A.I.C.S.: 332710
Daniel Ejionye *(Controller)*
Bryan Bruhn *(Mgr-Production)*

Ellwood Specialty Steel Company, LLC   **(1)**
499 Honeybee Ln, New Castle, PA 16105   **(100%)**
Tel.: (724) 657-1160
Web Site: http://www.ess.elwd.com
Sales Range: $10-24.9 Million
Emp.: 30
Custom Forging
N.A.I.C.S.: 332111
Rob Riszk *(Pres)*

Subsidiary (Domestic):

Unisteel, LLC   **(2)**
6155 Sims Dr, Sterling Heights, MI 48313   **(100%)**
Tel.: (586) 826-8040
Web Site: http://www.unisteel.elwd.com
Sales Range: $1-9.9 Million
Emp.: 30
Steel Distr
N.A.I.C.S.: 423510
Matt Snyder *(Gen Mgr)*

Ellwood Texas Forge   **(1)**
12500 Amelia Dr, Houston, TX 77045-4818   **(100%)**
Tel.: (713) 434-5100
Web Site: http://www.ellwoodgroup.com
Sales Range: $25-49.9 Million
Emp.: 140
Mfr Of Forged Products In Carbon Alloy, Stainless Steel & Super Alloys
N.A.I.C.S.: 332111
Oscar Quiroz *(Supvr-HR)*
Jeff Vercher *(Mgr-Mktg & Bus Dev)*

ELM CHEVROLET COMPANY, INC.
301 E Church St, Elmira, NY 14901-2703
Tel.: (607) 215-4556
Web Site:
https://www.elmchevrolet.com
Year Founded: 1939
Sales Range: $50-74.9 Million
Emp.: 65
New Car Dealers
N.A.I.C.S.: 441110
Tim Van Fleet *(Pres)*

ELM CITY SALES INC.
174 Siranton St, New Haven, CT 06511
Tel.: (203) 865-2535
Sales Range: $25-49.9 Million
Emp.: 12
Primary Nonferrous Metals
N.A.I.C.S.: 331410
William Carlson *(Pres)*

ELM CREEK PARTNERS
5949 Sherry Ln Ste 1070, Dallas, TX 75225
Tel.: (214) 871-5651
Web Site:
http://www.elmcreekpartners.com
Year Founded: 2007
Privater Equity Firm
N.A.I.C.S.: 523999
Aaron Handler *(Co-Founder & Partner)*
Zach Wooldridge *(Co-Founder & Partner)*
David Carter *(VP)*
Maria Martin Arena *(Coord-Private Equity)*

Subsidiaries:

Liberty Paper Products LLC   **(1)**
2155 S 75th Ave Ste 115, Phoenix, AZ 85043
Tel.: (602) 269-9797
Web Site: http://www.libertypaper.net
Sales Range: $1-9.9 Million
Emp.: 14
Thermal Paper Products Distr
N.A.I.C.S.: 424110
Mike Rapier *(Founder & CEO)*
Luke Odom *(Acct Exec)*
Sylvia Smith *(Supvr-Acctg)*

TCG Interests, Ltd.   **(1)**
9220 Kirby Dr Ste 1000, Houston, TX 77054
Tel.: (713) 383-2100
Web Site: http://www.caregrp.com
Women Healthcare Services
N.A.I.C.S.: 621610

Subsidiary (Domestic):

Walson, Inc.   **(2)**
50 N 11th St, Beaumont, TX 77702
Tel.: (409) 835-3091
Web Site: http://www.walsoninc.com
Miscellaneous Store Retailers (except Tobacco Stores)
N.A.I.C.S.: 459999

ELM FORD-MERCURY INC.
346 Main St, Woodland, CA 95695
Tel.: (530) 662-2817
Web Site:
http://www.elmfordmercury.com
Rev.: $22,838,687
Emp.: 46
Automobiles, New & Used
N.A.I.C.S.: 441110
Edward B. Landis *(Pres)*
Debbie McClain *(Controller)*

ELM GLOBAL LOGISTICS
50 Emjay Blvd, Brentwood, NY 11717
Tel.: (631) 233-3200
Web Site:
https://www.elmlogistics.com
Rev.: $16,682,827
Emp.: 226
General Warehousing & Storage
N.A.I.C.S.: 493110
Joseph Conboy *(Pres)*
Gale Conboy *(VP)*
Cheryl Lane *(Mgr-Shipping)*
Melissa Carlo *(Office Mgr)*
Marty Pape *(VP)*

ELM GROVE DODGE CHRYSLER JEEP INC.
2538 National Rd, Wheeling, WV 26003
Tel.: (304) 243-1999
Web Site:
https://www.elmgrovechrysler dodgejeep.com
Year Founded: 1988
Sales Range: $10-24.9 Million
Emp.: 40
Car Whslr
N.A.I.C.S.: 441110
Edward M. Constantin *(CEO)*

ELM LLC—(Continued)

ELM LLC
60 State St Ste 201, Peoria, IL 61602
Tel.: (309) 671-4300
Web Site: http://www.elmllc.com
Year Founded: 1997
Cloud-Based Products & Services
N.A.I.C.S.: 518210
Lee C. Graves *(Founder & Chm)*
Josh Hinrichs *(Pres)*

ELM PLATING CO.
1319 S Elm Ave, Jackson, MI 49203
Tel.: (517) 782-8161
Web Site:
    https://www.elmplating.com
Rev.: $11,115,104
Emp.: 70
Plating of Metals or Formed Products
N.A.I.C.S.: 332813
James M. McCluskey *(Pres)*
Ryan Morton *(Mgr-Anodizing)*

**ELM STREET TECHNOLOGY
LLC**
PO Box 10768, Greensboro, NC
27404
Tel.: (336) 389-3201   DE
Web Site:
    http://www.elmstreettechnology.com
Year Founded: 2016
Online Technology & Marketing Services
N.A.I.C.S.: 541613

ELMC HOLDINGS, LLC
260 Madison 15th Fl, New York, NY
10016
Tel.: (212) 455-0322
Web Site: http://www.elmcgroup.com
Year Founded: 2015
Holding Company; Underwriting &
Claims Management
N.A.I.C.S.: 551112
Richard Fleder *(Founder & CEO)*
Kurt Knight *(Exec VP)*

Subsidiaries:

IOA Re, LLC   (1)
190 W Germantown Pke Ste 200, East Norriton, PA 19401-1385
Tel.: (610) 940-9000
Web Site: http://www.ioare.com
Professional Underwriters
N.A.I.C.S.: 524114
John Parker *(Pres & CEO)*
Jeff Circuit *(Exec VP-Sls)*
Chuck Place *(Exec VP-Underwriting)*
Michelle Grasso *(Sr VP)*
Gary Rogers *(Sr VP)*
Bill Reichert *(Sr VP)*
Sheri Barry *(VP)*

ELMDALE PARTNERS, LLC
5301 Dempster St Ste 300, Skokie,
IL 60077
Tel.: (312) 546-6098
Web Site:
    https://www.elmdalepartners.com
Year Founded: 2010
Real Estate Investment Firm
N.A.I.C.S.: 531210
Thomas M. Bretz *(Co-Founder &
Principal)*
Adam Freeman *(Co-Founder & Principal)*
Menash Zadik *(Principal)*
James Sayegh *(Principal)*

Subsidiaries:

Elmdale Management Group,
LLC.   (1)
5301 Dempster St Ste 300, Skokie, IL
60077
Tel.: (312) 546-6098
Web Site: http://elmdalemanagement.com
Property Management Services
N.A.I.C.S.: 531311

Diane Simmons *(Dir-Dev & Leasing)*

ELMEN ENTERPRISES
2901 W 11th St, Sioux Falls, SD
57117-5103
Tel.: (605) 338-1800   SD
Web Site: http://www.af-rentall.com
Year Founded: 1983
Emp.: 100
Furniture & Appliance Reseller &
Rental Services
N.A.I.C.S.: 532210
Rich Elmen *(VP)*

Subsidiaries:

Elmen Enterprises Inc. -
Menominee   (1)
1319 8th Ave, Menominee, MI 49858
Tel.: (906) 864-2600
Web Site: http://www.af-rentall.com
Furniture & Appliance Reseller & Rental
Services
N.A.I.C.S.: 532289

**ELMER BUCHTA TRUCKING,
LLC**
2174 N State Rd 257, Otwell, IN
47564
Tel.: (812) 354-6300
Web Site: https://www.buchta.com
Year Founded: 1976
Sales Range: $10-24.9 Million
Emp.: 170
Trucking Services
N.A.I.C.S.: 484220
Gary Tooley *(Mgr-Svc)*

**ELMER CANDY CORPORA-
TION**
401 N 5th St, Ponchatoula, LA 70454
Tel.: (985) 386-6166
Web Site:
    http://www.elmercandy.com
Year Founded: 1855
Sales Range: $10-24.9 Million
Emp.: 250
Candy Mfr
N.A.I.C.S.: 311352
Diane Blow Bankston *(Mgr-Personnel,
& Payroll)*
Joseph Wiley *(Dir-Mgmt Info Sys)*
Robert Barousse *(CFO)*

ELMER SMITH OIL COMPANY
Hwy 183 S, Clinton, OK 73601
Tel.: (580) 323-2929
Sales Range: $50-74.9 Million
Emp.: 70
Petroleum Bulk Stations
N.A.I.C.S.: 424710
Martin Smith *(Pres)*

ELMER'S RESTAURANTS, INC.
8338 NE Alderwood Rd Ste 175,
Portland, OR 97220
Tel.: (503) 252-1485   OR
Web Site:
    http://www.eatatelmers.com
Year Founded: 1960
Sales Range: $25-49.9 Million
Emp.: 290
Family Oriented Restaurants Franchiser & Operator
N.A.I.C.S.: 722310
Mike Chamberlin *(CFO)*
Travis Caldwell *(Dir-Pur)*

**ELMERS CRANE AND DOZER
INC.**
3600 Rennie School Rd, Traverse
City, MI 49685
Tel.: (231) 943-3443
Web Site:
    https://www.teamelmers.com
Sales Range: $10-24.9 Million
Emp.: 150

Provider of Driveway; Parking Lot &
Blacktop Contractors
N.A.I.C.S.: 238990
Troy Broad *(Pres)*
Eric Ritchie *(Controller)*
Karl Domres *(Mgr-Equipment)*

ELMET TECHNOLOGIES INC.
1560 Lisbon St, Lewiston, ME 04240
Tel.: (207) 333-6100
Web Site:
    https://www.elmettechnologies.com
Year Founded: 1929
Sales Range: $10-24.9 Million
Emp.: 230
Molybdenum & Tungsten Wire, Rod,
Sheet & Machined Products Mfr
N.A.I.C.S.: 332618
Marc Lamare *(Dir-Intl Sls)*
Vinay Desai *(Mgr-Engrg)*
Andrew D. R. Nichols *(Co-Founder &
CEO)*
Peter V. Anania *(Pres)*

ELMHURST AUTO GROUP
440 W Lk St, Elmhurst, IL 60126
Tel.: (800) 266-3000
Web Site:
    http://www.elmhurstautogroup.com
Sales Range: $10-24.9 Million
Car Dealer
N.A.I.C.S.: 441110
Thea Jantamanit *(Mgr-Social Media)*

Subsidiaries:

Elmhurst BMW   (1)
466 W Lake St, Elmhurst, IL 60126-1418
Tel.: (630) 833-7945
Web Site: http://www.elmhurstbmw.com
Sales Range: $50-74.9 Million
Emp.: 50
New & Used Car Whslr
N.A.I.C.S.: 441110
Irv Shenderovsky *(Gen Mgr)*
Nicholas Psaros *(Gen Sls Mgr)*
Tim Baber *(Sls Mgr-Used Car)*
Michal Banach *(Sls Mgr-Internet)*
Eugene Royfe *(Sls Mgr-Internet)*
Jack Metz *(Fin Mgr)*
Korey Bollnow *(Mgr-Svc)*
Bob Saboe *(Dir-Parts)*
Roger Reband *(Mgr-Parts)*

Elmhurst Toyota   (1)
440 W Lk St, Elmhurst, IL 60126
Tel.: (630) 279-2160
Web Site: http://www.elmhursttoyota.com
Car Dealer
N.A.I.C.S.: 441110
Brian Corrigan *(Mgr-Svc)*
Dan Briggs *(Dir-Parts & Svc)*
Jim Magnelli *(Sls Mgr-Pre-Owned)*
Kurt Schiele *(Gen Mgr)*
Mike Hackett *(Mgr-Fin)*
Todd Thiede *(Dir-Sls Ops)*
Tony Gmitrovic *(Dir-Sls Ops)*
Vlad Rikhman *(Mgr-New Car)*
Rob Smithburg *(Sls Mgr-Internet)*
Tim Dion *(Dir-Use Car Sls)*
Thea Jantamanit *(Mgr-Social Media)*

Jaguar Elmhurst   (1)
490 W Lk St, Elmhurst, IL 60126
Tel.: (844) 885-2734
Web Site: http://www.elmhurstjaguar.com
Car Dealer
N.A.I.C.S.: 441110
Kirill Ruditskiy *(Sls Mgr)*
Jack Metz *(Mgr-Fin)*
Tom Sorensen *(Mgr-Svc)*
Irv Shenderovsky *(Gen Mgr)*
Kevin Clifford *(Mgr-Jaguar Pre-Owned)*
Bill Pfeffer *(Mgr-Fin)*
Bob Saboe *(Mgr-Parts)*

ELMHURST DAIRY, INC.
155-25 Styler Rd, Jamaica, NY
11433-1514
Tel.: (718) 526-3442   NY
Web Site:
    http://www.elmhurstdairy.com
Year Founded: 1919

Sales Range: $25-49.9 Million
Emp.: 212
Distr of Fluid Milk
N.A.I.C.S.: 311511
Robert Giurco *(Dir-Quality & Safety)*
Danny Joy *(Mgr-Fleet)*
Ed Sykes *(Mgr-Engrg)*
Jay Valentine *(Gen Mgr)*
Jimmy Sanchez *(Mgr-Payroll)*
Martha Toro *(Supvr-Quality Control)*
Samuel Chadwick *(Supvr-Production)*

ELMHURST GROUP
1 Bigelow Sq Ste 630, Pittsburgh, PA
15219
Tel.: (412) 281-8731
Web Site:
    https://www.elmhurstgroup.com
Investment Services
N.A.I.C.S.: 523999
William Hunt *(Pres & CEO)*
Maria E. Sinclair *(CFO & Treas)*
Eric R. Schindler *(Dir-Leasing)*

**ELMHURST MEMORIAL
HEALTHCARE**
155 E Brush Hill Rd, Elmhurst, IL
60126
Tel.: (331) 221-1000   IL
Web Site: http://www.emhc.org
Year Founded: 1926
Sales Range: $50-74.9 Million
Health Care Srvices
N.A.I.C.S.: 622110
Pamela Dunley *(COO & Chief Nursing Officer)*
Henry Zeisel *(VP-Fin)*
Laura Eslick *(Assoc VP-Hospital Ops)*
Ken Fishbain *(VP-Physician & Ambulatory Network)*
Bobby Burn *(CIO & VP-Info Svcs)*
Vince Pryor *(CFO)*

**ELMHURST-CHICAGO STONE
CO**
400 W 1st St, Elmhurst, IL 60126
Tel.: (630) 832-4000   DE
Web Site:
    http://www.elmhurstchicago
    stoneco.net
Year Founded: 1883
Sales Range: $10-24.9 Million
Emp.: 125
Sand & Gravel Construction Services
N.A.I.C.S.: 212321
Charles Hammersmith *(Pres)*
Ken Lehner *(VP)*

ELMO GREER & SONS INC.
PO Box 730, London, KY 40743
Tel.: (606) 843-6136   KY
Year Founded: 1961
Sales Range: $25-49.9 Million
Emp.: 250
Street & Highway Construction Services
N.A.I.C.S.: 237310
Rex Greer *(Pres)*

ELMORE GROUP LTD.
19 N Grant St FL 2, Hinsdale, IL
60521
Tel.: (630) 325-6228
Rev.: $42,100,000
Emp.: 3
Investment Holding Companies, Except Banks
N.A.I.C.S.: 551112
David G. Elmore *(Pres)*

ELMORE INTEREST INC.
6655 Polk St, Houston, TX 77011
Tel.: (281) 953-3300

Web Site:
http://www.admiralglassand
mirror.com
Rev.: $15,000,000
Emp.: 123
Glass Construction Materials
N.A.I.C.S.: 423390
John Nunlist *(Exec VP)*
Les Craft Jr. *(Pres)*

ELMORE TOYOYA

15300 Beach Blvd, Westminster, CA
92683
Tel.: (714) 894-3322
Web Site:
https://www.elmoretoyota.com
Year Founded: 1966
Sales Range: $25-49.9 Million
Emp.: 85
New Car Retailer
N.A.I.C.S.: 441110
David McHowell *(Grp VP & Gen Mgr-Toyota Div)*

ELSEA INCORPORATED

2015 Stoneridge Dr, Circleville, OH
43113
Tel.: (740) 474-5710   **OH**
Web Site:
http://www.elseahomes.com
Year Founded: 1950
Sales Range: $10-24.9 Million
Emp.: 50
Manufactured Housing Sales
N.A.I.C.S.: 459930
Rodney Hemming *(Mgr-Sls)*
Ron Eitel *(VP)*

ELSER & AUCONE, INC.

521 5th Ave Ste 630, New York, NY
10175
Tel.: (212) 867-3300   **NY**
Web Site:
http://www.elseraucone.com
Year Founded: 1985
Rev.: $10,000,000
Emp.: 25
Financial, Full Service
N.A.I.C.S.: 541810
Arnold J. Elser *(Pres)*
William J. Aucone *(Exec VP)*
Stephen A. Elser *(Sr VP)*
Christopher Elser *(Sr VP)*

Subsidiaries:

Problem Solvers, Inc.   (1)
521 5th Ave Ste 630, New York, NY 10175
Tel.: (212) 687-5590
Web Site: http://www.elseraucone.com
Advertising Specialties,
Publicity/Promotions, Sales Promotion
N.A.I.C.S.: 541810
Arnold J. Elser *(Pres & Dir-Creative)*
William J. Aucone *(Exec VP & Acct Svcs Dir)*
Christopher Elser *(Sr VP & Media Dir)*
Maria DiChiara *(VP)*
Stephen A. Elser *(Sr VP-Mktg & Bus Dev)*

ELSINORE READY MIX CO. INC.

16960 Lakeshore Dr, Lake Elsinore,
CA 92530
Tel.: (909) 674-2127
Rev.: $13,300,000
Emp.: 17
Ready Mixed Concrete
N.A.I.C.S.: 327320

ELSINORE SERVICES, INC.

4201 Connecticut Ave NW Ste 407,
Washington, DC 20008
Tel.: (202) 609-7756   **DE**
Web Site:
http://www.elsinoreservices.com
Year Founded: 2009
Advertising & Marketing Services
N.A.I.C.S.: 541890

Arne Dunhem *(Chm, Pres & CEO)*
Dean V. Schauer *(CFO & Sr VP)*

ELSINORE VALLEY MUNICIPAL WATER DISTRICT

31315 Chaney St, Lake Elsinore, CA
92531
Tel.: (951) 674-3146
Web Site: https://www.evmwd.com
Year Founded: 1950
Rev.: $26,394,708
Emp.: 150
Supplier of Water & Wastewater
N.A.I.C.S.: 221310
John Vega *(Gen Mgr)*
Brian Dickinson *(Dir-Ops)*

ELSNER ENGINEERING WORKS INC.

475 Fame Ave, Hanover, PA 17331
Tel.: (717) 637-5991
Web Site: https://www.elsnereng.com
Year Founded: 1970
Sales Range: $10-24.9 Million
Emp.: 70
Mfr of Paper Industries Machinery
N.A.I.C.S.: 333243
Robert Van Sant *(Controller)*
Alan Sanger *(Mgr-Intl Sls)*
Bertram Elsner II *(Pres, CEO & Treas)*

ELSTON RICHARDS, INC.

3739 Patterson Ave SE, Grand Rapids, MI 49512
Tel.: (616) 698-2698   **MI**
Web Site:
http://www.elstonrichards.com
Year Founded: 1905
Sales Range: $10-24.9 Million
Emp.: 100
General Warehousing & Storage
N.A.I.C.S.: 493110
John E. Holmes *(Pres)*
Rick Greenland *(Gen Mgr)*

ELUM MUSIC COMPANY

280 Federal Ave NW, Massillon, OH
44647
Tel.: (330) 833-4141
Web Site: http://www.elummusic.com
Rev.: $31,779,612
Emp.: 40
Music Systems, Coin-Operated
N.A.I.C.S.: 713990
George E. Elum *(Pres)*

ELUMICOR

8111 Mainland Dr Ste 104 425, San
Antonio, TX 78240
Tel.: (210) 863-9336
Web Site: http://www.Elumicor.com
Year Founded: 2000
Sales Range: $1-9.9 Million
Emp.: 13
Development of e-Discovery Software
Tools in Civil Litigation & Forensics
N.A.I.C.S.: 541512
Lisa McComb *(Pres & COO)*
Melissa Unsell *(Dir-Mktg)*

ELUSYS THERAPEUTICS, INC.

25 Riverside Dr, Pine Brook, NJ
07058
Tel.: (973) 808-0222   **DE**
Web Site: http://www.elusys.com
Biopharmaceutical Developer & Mfr
N.A.I.C.S.: 325414
Elizabeth Posillico *(Pres & CEO)*
Jeremy Middleton *(VP-Corp Dev)*
James Porter *(VP-Dev & Mfg)*
Leslie Casey *(VP-Res)*
Debra Duffy *(Sr Dir-HR & Admin)*
Jeffrey Alan Wolf *(Founder & CEO)*
Lawrence Gyenes *(CFO)*

ELVISRIDGE CAPITAL, LLC

25201 Chagrin Blvd Ste 300, Beachwood, OH 44122
Tel.: (216) 678-9900
Web Site:
https://elvisridgecapital.com
Year Founded: 2019
Holding Company
N.A.I.C.S.: 551112
Jack Miller *(VP-Landscape Products)*

Subsidiaries:

Innovative Concrete Technology
Corp.   (1)
2410 Mcjunkin Rd, Lakeland, FL 33803
Tel.: (863) 665-8787
Web Site:
http://www.innovativeconcrete.com
All Other Miscellaneous Nonmetallic Mineral
Product Mfr
N.A.I.C.S.: 327999

ELWOOD STAFFING SERVICES, INC.

4111 Central Ave, Columbus, IN
47203
Tel.: (812) 372-6200   **IN**
Web Site:
https://www.elwoodstaffing.com
Year Founded: 1980
Sales Range: $900-999.9 Million
Employmentt Placement, Temporary
Staffing, Professional Search & Consulting Services
N.A.I.C.S.: 561311
Michael D. Elwood *(Pres-Pro Div)*
David L. Elwood *(Chm)*
Mark S. Elwood *(Chm & CEO)*
John A. Elwood *(Pres)*
Steven J. Hunnicutt *(CFO)*
Dave Meyercord *(Sr VP)*
Nick Seger *(VP-Ops)*
Lia Elliott *(Gen Counsel)*
John K. Morrison *(Sr VP & Legal Counsel)*
Kevin Hardy *(Sr VP)*
John Niedermeyer *(VP-Strategic Svcs)*
Brett Flora *(VP-Tech)*
Victor Meyer *(VP-Fin)*
Michael Stockard Jr. *(Exec VP)*

Subsidiaries:

Advanced Personnel, Inc.   (1)
902 S Oliver St, Wichita, KS 67218-3216
Tel.: (316) 691-8998
Web Site:
http://www.advancedpersonnel.net
Employment Placement Agencies
N.A.I.C.S.: 561311
Greg Meadows *(Pres)*

BelFlex Staffing Network, LLC   (1)
11591 Goldcoast Dr, Cincinnati, OH 45249
Tel.: (513) 488-8588
Web Site: http://www.belflex.com
Staffing & Recruiting Services
N.A.I.C.S.: 561311
Jason McCaw *(CEO)*

Subsidiary (Domestic):

Premier Staffing, Inc.   (2)
111 Sutter St Ste 550, San Francisco, CA
94104
Tel.: (415) 362-2211
Web Site:
http://www.premiertalentpartners.com
Professional Staffing Services
N.A.I.C.S.: 561320
Sara Menke *(Founder & CEO)*
Matt Ruport *(COO & Partner)*
Krista Tan *(Exec VP & Recruiting)*

Elwood Professional   (1)
4111 Central Ave, Columbus, IN
47202   (100%)
Tel.: (812) 372-6200
Web Site:
http://www.elwoodprofessional.com

Engineering, Information Technology &
Business Management Professional Employment Services
N.A.I.C.S.: 561330
Michael D. Elwood *(Pres)*

Elwood Staffing Services, Inc. -
Grand Rapids   (1)
4595 Broadmoor SE Ste 190, Grand Rapids, MI 49512
Tel.: (616) 698-7979
Web Site: http://www.elwoodstaffing.com
Employment Placement, Temporary Staffing, Professional Search & Consulting Services
N.A.I.C.S.: 561320

ELYRIA MANUFACTURING CORP.

145 Northrup St, Elyria, OH 44036
Tel.: (440) 365-4171
Web Site:
http://www.emcprecision.com
Year Founded: 1925
Sales Range: $10-24.9 Million
Emp.: 82
Precision Turned Product Mfr
N.A.I.C.S.: 332721
Jeffrey B. Ohlemacher *(CEO)*
Brad Ohlemacher *(Pres)*

ELYSIUM CAPITAL MANAGEMENT, LLC

801 Brickell Ave Ste 2260, Miami, FL
33131
Tel.: (786) 693-7850
Web Site:
http://www.elysiumcapitalmgt.com
Wealth management Services
N.A.I.C.S.: 523940
Jose Eduardo Ferreira *(Partner)*

ELZINGA & VOLKERS, INC.

86 E 6th St, Holland, MI 49423-2912
Tel.: (616) 392-2383
Web Site: http://www.elzinga-volkers.com
Year Founded: 1965
Sales Range: $25-49.9 Million
Emp.: 110
Nonresidential Construction
N.A.I.C.S.: 236220
Mike Novakoski *(Pres & CEO)*
Joe Novakoski *(VP-Project Mgmt)*

Subsidiaries:

Elzinga & Volkers Professional Services Inc.   (1)
86 E 6th St, Holland, MI
49423-2912   (100%)
Tel.: (616) 392-2383
Web Site: http://www.elzinga-volkers.com
Sales Range: $10-24.9 Million
Emp.: 135
Provider of Management Consulting Services
N.A.I.C.S.: 236220
Mike Novakoski *(Pres)*

EMA DESIGN AUTOMATION, INC.

225 Tech Park Dr, Rochester, NY
14623
Tel.: (585) 334-6001
Web Site: http://www.ema-eda.com
Year Founded: 1989
Sales Range: $25-49.9 Million
Emp.: 100
Electronic Data Automation Software
N.A.I.C.S.: 541512
Manny Marcano *(Pres & CEO)*

Subsidiaries:

Accelerated Designs, Inc.   (1)
128 Daniel Dr, Huntsville, AL
35811-9620   (100%)
Tel.: (256) 858-8568

EMA Design Automation, Inc.—(Continued)
Web Site: http://www.accelerated-
designs.com
Emp.: 90
Engineering Consultancy Services
N.A.I.C.S.: 541330
Frank E. Frank (Pres)

EMAGINE IT, INC.
3040 Williams Dr Ste 400, Fairfax,
VA 22031
Tel.: (202) 587-5607
Web Site: https://www.eit2.com
Year Founded: 2002
Sales Range: $10-24.9 Million
Emp.: 75
Information Technology Services
N.A.I.C.S.: 541512
Aamir Saleem (Pres)
Song Pak (COO)
Lucas Aimes (Sr VP-Corp Dev)
Rob Holder (Sr VP-Programs)
Priscilla Wang (Dir-HR)
John Weiss (Dir-Program Mgmt)
Andrea Hodges (Dir-Security & Pri-
vacy)
Dana Lacy (Mng Dir)
Jim Henriksen (Controller)
Avani Patel (Mgr-Quality Assurance)

EMAILDIRECT
3101 Zinfandel Dr Ste 300, Rancho
Cordova, CA 95670
Tel.: (916) 378-0323
Web Site: http://www.emaildirect.com
Year Founded: 2005
Sales Range: $1-9.9 Million
Emp.: 20
Enables Online Retailers to Deliver
Marketing e-Mail, Transactional
e-Mail & Related Communication &
Marketing Services Through Hosted
e-Mail Marketing Platforms
N.A.I.C.S.: 518210
Kevin Linden (Co-Founder)
Chris Bryan (Co-Founder)
Brian Linden (Partner)
Richard King (Co-Founder)

EMAK WORLDWIDE, INC.
6330 San Vicente Blvd, Los Angeles,
CA 90048-5425
Tel.: (323) 932-4300
Year Founded: 1983
Sales Range: $150-199.9 Million
Emp.: 309
Communications
N.A.I.C.S.: 541810
Kim H. Thomsen (Co-CEO-Equity
Mktg)
Brian Kristofek (CEO-Upshot)
Tracy L. Tormey (Chief Admin Officer
& Gen Counsel)
Duane Johnson (Sr VP-HR)
Jon Banks (Co-CEO-Equity Mktg)
Simon Wong (Mng Dir)
Jordan H. Rednor (Chm)
Sharon Mord (VP-Bus Dev-Americas)

Subsidiaries:

Logistix   (1)
6330 San Vincente Blvd, Los Angeles, CA
90048
Tel.: (323) 932-4300
N.A.I.C.S.: 541810

EMANCIPET, INC.
7010 Easy Wind Dr Ste 260, Austin,
TX 78752
Tel.: (512) 587-7729
Web Site: http://www.emancipet.org
Year Founded: 1999
Sales Range: $1-9.9 Million
Emp.: 100
Pet Care Services
N.A.I.C.S.: 541940

Myles Chadwick (VP-Consulting &
Trng)
Amy Mills (CEO)
Angela Dorsey (Sec)

Subsidiaries:

Emancipet Central Austin   (1)
5129 Cameron Rd, Austin, TX
78723   (100%)
Tel.: (512) 587-7729
Web Site: http://emancipet.org
Sales Range: $1-9.9 Million
Emp.: 47
Animal Welfare & Veterinary Services
N.A.I.C.S.: 541940
Amy Mills (CEO)
Christy Mallinger (CFO)

EMASON, INC.
11399 16th Ct N Ste 100, Saint Pe-
tersburg, FL 33716
Tel.: (727) 507-3440
Web Site: https://www.eclarifire.com
Year Founded: 2003
Sales Range: $25-49.9 Million
Emp.: 200
Web-Based Process Automation Soft-
ware Products
N.A.I.C.S.: 513210
Jane Mason (Pres & CEO)
Lauren Walling (VP-Sls)

EMATS, INC.
480 Claypool Hill Mall Rd, Cedar
Bluff, VA 24609
Tel.: (276) 963-8888
Web Site: http://www.emats-inc.com
Year Founded: 1998
Design Engineering & Construction
Services
N.A.I.C.S.: 541330
Jon Bowerbank (Owner & Pres)
Larry Mutter (Coord-Safety, Health &
Environmental)

EMBARK CORPORATION
459 Broadway 4F, New York, NY
10013
Tel.: (646) 368-8394
Web Site: http://www.embark.com
Year Founded: 1995
Online Network of Role-Specific Con-
tent, Mission-Critical Functionality &
Advanced Management Tools
N.A.I.C.S.: 513199
Sarita James (CEO)
Michael Turbe (Dir-Engineering)

EMBER INFRASTRUCTURE MANAGEMENT, LP
220 Fifth Ave 18th Fl, New York, NY
10001
Tel.: (646) 374-3942
Web Site: https://ember-infra.com
Private Equity
N.A.I.C.S.: 523940

Subsidiaries:

H2O Innovation Inc.   (1)
330 St-Vallier Est suite 340, Quebec, G1K
9C5, QC, Canada
Tel.: (418) 688-0170
Web Site: https://www.h2oinnovation.com
Rev.: $112,901,779
Assets: $107,252,153
Liabilities: $45,143,032
Net Worth: $62,109,121
Earnings: $2,439,931
Emp.: 600
Fiscal Year-end: 06/30/2021
Membrane Filtration Systems & Alternative
Biological & Physical Water Treatment Pro-
cesess
N.A.I.C.S.: 221310
Frederic Dugre (Founder, Pres & CEO)
Richard Alan Hoel (Vice Chm)
Lisa Henthorne (Chm)
Marc Blanchet (CFO)
Guillaume Clairet (COO)
Gregory Madden (Chief Strategic Officer)

Subsidiary (US):

Environmental Consultants, LLC   (2)
PO Box 3148, Poughkeepsie, NY 12603
Tel.: (845) 486-1030
Web Site: http://www.ecnewyork.com
Sales Range: $1-9.9 Million
Emp.: 33
Water & Sewer Line & Related Structures
Construction
N.A.I.C.S.: 237110

Gulf Utility Service Inc.   (2)
12337 Jones Rd Ste 320, Houston, TX
77070
Tel.: (281) 355-1312
Web Site: http://www.gulfutility.net
Rev.: $5,000,000
Water Supply & Irrigation Systems
N.A.I.C.S.: 221310
Terry Taylor (Pres)

H2O Innovation Inc.   (2)
8900 109th Ave N Ste 1000, Champlin, MN
55316
Tel.: (763) 566-8961
Sales Range: $1-9.9 Million
Emp.: 15
Water Purification System Mfr
N.A.I.C.S.: 333310

H2O Innovation Inc.   (2)
1048 La Mirada Ct, Vista, CA 92081
Tel.: (760) 639-4400
Web Site: https://www.h2oinnovation.com
Sales Range: $75-99.9 Million
Emp.: 15
Water Treatment System Services
N.A.I.C.S.: 221310

H2O Innovation Operation & Mainte-
nance, LLC   (2)
338 Plains Rd, Claremont, NH
03743   (100%)
Tel.: (603) 543-0680
Web Site: http://www.utilitypartnersllc.com
Emp.: 388
Operations, Maintenance & Management of
Public Works, Water, Wastewater & Utility
Billing Systems
N.A.I.C.S.: 221320
Bill Douglass (Mng Dir & Sr VP)

EMBLEM, LLC
7 W 22nd St 10th Fl, New York, NY
10010
Tel.: (212) 979-8200
Web Site: http://www.mblm.com
Sales Range: $1-9.9 Million
Emp.: 70
Advetising Agency
N.A.I.C.S.: 541810
John Diffenbach (Chm)
Claude Salzberger (Pres)
Mario Natarelli (Mng Partner)
Amy Clausi (CFO)
Diego Kolsky (Partner)
Rina Papler (Partner)
Sidney Blank (Partner)
Demetri Mihalakakos (Mng Dir)
Mauricio Carrasco (Mng Dir)
Eduardo Calderon (Mng Partner)
Maria G. Pulido (Mng Partner)
William Shintani (Mng Partner-Dubai)
Jae-yong Hwang (Partner)
David Clover (Assoc Partner-Dubai)
Lyutha Alhabsy (Exec Dir)

EMBLEMHEALTH, INC.
55 Water St, New York, NY 10041
Tel.: (646) 447-5000
Web Site:
https://www.emblemhealth.com
Sales Range: $5-14.9 Billion
Emp.: 5,000
Health Insurance
N.A.I.C.S.: 524114
Stuart H. Altman (Vice Chm)
John D. Feerick (Chm)
Jeffrey D. Chansler (Chief Legal Offi-
cer)
Michael Palmateer (Chief Admin Offi-
cer & Exec VP)

Karen Ignagni (Pres & CEO)
Beth Leonard (CMO & Chief Comm
Officer)
Donna Hughes (Chief HR Officer)
Timothy Nolan (Chief Product Officer
& Exec VP)
Bruce Jarvie (CFO)
Debra M. Lightner (Chief Compliance
Officer)
Thomas MacMillan (CIO)
Jennifer Truscott (Sr VP-Ops & Cus-
tomer Svc)

Subsidiaries:

Group Health Inc.   (1)
PO Box 3000, New York, NY 10116-3000
Tel.: (212) 501-4444
Health Care Srvices
N.A.I.C.S.: 621610

Health Insurance Plan of Greater
New York   (1)
55 Water St, New York, NY 10041
Tel.: (646) 447-5000
Web Site: http://www.emblemhealth.com
Health Management Insurance Services
N.A.I.C.S.: 524114
Patricia Gillespie (Sr Dir-Pur & Corp Svc)

Subsidiary (Domestic):

Connecticare, Inc.   (2)
175 Scott Swamp Rd, Farmington, CT
06032-2579
Tel.: (860) 674-5700
Web Site: http://www.connecticare.com
Sales Range: $100-124.9 Million
Emp.: 500
Health Care Management Insurance Ser-
vices
N.A.I.C.S.: 524114
Kim Kann (Mgr-Mktg)
Mary Bannon (Gen Counsel & Sr VP)
Eric Galvin (Pres & COO)
David Gordon (Sr VP-Strategy & Product
Innovation)
Cheryl Hutchinson (Sr VP-HR)
Stephanie Rich (Sr VP-Health Care Mgmt)
Barbara Vernon (VP-Middle Market, Large
Grp Sls & Acct Mgmt)

EMBRACE HOME LOANS, INC.
25 Enterprise Ctr, Newport, RI 02842
Tel.: (401) 846-3100
Web Site:
http://www.embracehomeloans.com
Year Founded: 1983
Sales Range: $1-4.9 Billion
Emp.: 500
Mortgage Specialists
N.A.I.C.S.: 522310
Dennis F. Hardiman (CEO)
Kurt Noyce (Pres)
Brian Gilpin (VP-Capital Markets)
Tony Hodge (Mgr-Sls)
Jeff McGuiness (Chief Sls Officer)
Anthony Branda (Chief Data Officer)
Benjamin Giumarra (Dir-Regulatory &
Legal Affairs)
Parkes Dibble (Dir-Mortgage Product
Innovation)
Pamela Summers (VP-Market
Growth-Virginia & D.C.)
Tyler Rhea (VP-Market Growth-New
England)
Jason Will (Sr VP-Market Growth)
James Stirling (Reg Sls Mgr-
Southeast)
Steve Adamo (Pres-Natl Retail Pro-
duction)

EMBRY-RIDDLE AERONAUTI-CAL UNIVERSITY
600 S Clyde Morris Blvd, Daytona
Beach, FL 32114-3900
Tel.: (386) 226-6100
Web Site:
http://www.daytonabeach.erau.edu
Year Founded: 1926
Sales Range: $300-349.9 Million

Emp.: 1,300
Colleges & Universities
N.A.I.C.S.: 611310
Christina Frederick-Recascino
(Coord-Program-Human Factors & Sys)
P. Barry Butler *(Pres & CEO)*

Subsidiaries:

ERAU Extended Campus College of
Career Education   (1)
600 S Clyde Morris Blvd, Daytona Beach,
FL 32114-3900
Tel.: (386) 226-6910
Web Site: http://www.erau.edu
Sales Range: $25-49.9 Million
Emp.: 500
Education Services
N.A.I.C.S.: 611310

Embry-Riddle Aeronautical University
- Prescott   (1)
3700 Willow Creek Rd, Prescott, AZ 86301-
3720
Tel.: (928) 777-6600
Web Site: http://www.embryriddle.edu
Aeronautical Educational Institution
N.A.I.C.S.: 611512
Brian Roggow *(Dir-Aviation Safety & Security)*

Embry-Riddle Aeronautical University,
Asia Ltd.   (1)
75 Bukit Timah Road, 02-01/02 Boon Siew
Building, Singapore, 229833, Singapore
Tel.: (65) 6933 9580
Sales Range: $10-24.9 Million
Emp.: 20
Aerospace Education Services
N.A.I.C.S.: 611310
Graham Hunt *(Head-Asia)*

EMC ANALYTICAL SERVICES, LLC
42 Rice Ln, Bedford, NH 03110-4642
Tel.: (603) 203-1942
Web Site:
   http://www.emcanalyticalser
   vices.com
Engineeering Services
N.A.I.C.S.: 541330
Samuel O'Daniel *(Acct Mgr-Federal)*

Subsidiaries:

EMC Management Concepts   (1)
46603 Kingschase Ct, Sterling, VA 20165-
7399
Tel.: (703) 864-7023
Web Site: http://www.emcmanagement.com
Engineeering Services
N.A.I.C.S.: 541330
Brian Farmer *(Pres & Dir-Tech)*

EMC COMPANY
1802 Ellen Rd, Richmond, VA 23230
Tel.: (804) 359-9624
Web Site: http://www.emc-co.com
Sales Range: $25-49.9 Million
Emp.: 180
Mechanical Contractor
N.A.I.C.S.: 238220
Bruce Tibbetts *(Pres)*

Subsidiaries:

American Refrigeration LLC   (1)
11572 Davis Creek Ct, Jacksonville, FL
32256
Tel.: (904) 880-4888
Rev.: $7,000,000
Emp.: 40
Refrigeration Contractor
N.A.I.C.S.: 238220
Sid Anderson *(Pres)*
Curtis Walker *(VP)*

EMC OUTDOOR
5074 W Chester Pike 2nd Fl, Newtown Square, PA 19073-4279
Tel.: (610) 353-9300
Web Site:
   http://www.emcoutdoor.com

Year Founded: 1991
Sales Range: $10-24.9 Million
Emp.: 20
Media Buying Services
N.A.I.C.S.: 541830
S. Thomas Japhe *(Exec VP-OOH Media Strategy)*
Betsy McLarney *(CEO)*
Maryann Ingham *(Exec VP)*
Jerry Buckley *(Dir-Mktg & New Bus)*
Song C. Heo *(COO)*
Rebecca Gamsby *(Coord-Media)*
Laura Scoufield *(Coord-Media)*
Melissa Vassallo *(Coord-Media)*
Jennifer Stuart *(Dir-Events)*
Loren S. Casuto *(Gen Counsel)*
Joyce Luna *(Mgr-Client Svcs)*
Matthew Noll *(Mgr-Mktg Comm)*
Kristen Marino-McCullough *(Mgr-Special Projects)*
Maria Ferrier *(Mgr-Traffic & Production)*
Mary Rush *(Project Coord)*

EMC PUBLISHING, LLC
875 Montreal Way, Saint Paul, MN
55102
Tel.: (651) 290-2800
Web Site:
   http://www.emcponline.com
Year Founded: 1954
Sales Range: $25-49.9 Million
Emp.: 160
Publisher of Textbooks, Teacher Resources, Supplements, Technology & Assessments
N.A.I.C.S.: 513130
Lindsay Ryan *(Coord-Digital Production)*
Dane Lear *(Acct Mgr-Sls)*

EMCO CHEMICAL DISTRIBUTORS INC.
8601-95th St, Pleasant Prairie, WI
53158
Tel.: (847) 689-2200
Web Site: http://www.emcochem.com
Year Founded: 1971
Sales Range: $25-49.9 Million
Emp.: 250
Chemical Services
N.A.I.C.S.: 424690
Bill Bishop *(Mgr-Sls)*

EMCO INC.
2318 Arty Ave, Charlotte, NC 28208
Tel.: (704) 372-8281
Web Site:
   http://www.emcoanswers.com
Sales Range: $10-24.9 Million
Emp.: 29
Power Transmission Equipment & Apparatus
N.A.I.C.S.: 423840
Alan Williams *(Owner)*

EMCO TECH CONSTRUCTION CORP.
19-41 46th St, Astoria, NY 11105
Tel.: (718) 777-1666   NY
Web Site: http://www.emcotech.com
Year Founded: 1987
Sales Range: $10-24.9 Million
Emp.: 100
Commercial & Institutional Building
Construction Services
N.A.I.C.S.: 236220
Nancy Siso *(Pres)*
Emmanuel Michelakis *(Exec VP)*

EMDAY
1526 S Broadway, Los Angeles, CA
90015
Tel.: (213) 748-4444
Web Site: http://www.emday.com
Rev.: $18,700,000

Emp.: 92
Piece Goods & Other Fabrics
N.A.I.C.S.: 424310
Amir Emrani *(VP)*

EMED, LLC
990 Biscayne Blvd Ste 1501, Miami,
FL 33132
Tel.: (866) 955-1173
Web Site: https://www.emed.com
Emp.: 100
Telehealth & Diagnostic Services
N.A.I.C.S.: 621610

Subsidiaries:

Science 37 Holdings, Inc.   (1)
800 Park Offices Dr Ste 3606, Research
Triangle Park, NC 27709
Tel.: (984) 377-3737
Web Site: https://www.science37.com
Rev.: $70,147,000
Assets: $126,448,000
Liabilities: $29,062,000
Net Worth: $97,386,000
Earnings: ($50,988,000)
Emp.: 460
Fiscal Year-end: 12/31/2022
Holding Company
N.A.I.C.S.: 551112
Michael P. Cole *(Dir)*
Jonathan Cotliar *(Chief Medical Officer)*
Jeffrey Schumm *(Dir)*
Christine A. Pellizzari *(Chief Legal Officer)*

EMEDIA GROUP INC
1255 Rio Salado Pkwy Ste 215,
Tempe, AZ 85281
Tel.: (480) 830-2700   NV
Year Founded: 2012
Sales Range: Less than $1 Million
Emp.: 2
Online Business Support Services
N.A.I.C.S.: 541611
Henrik Schaumann Jorgensen *(CEO)*
Christian Hedegaard Pederson *(COO)*

EMENTUM, INC.
6701 Democracy Blvd Ste 300,
Bethesda, MD 20817
Web Site: http://www.ementum.com
Year Founded: 1999
Sales Range: $1-9.9 Million
Emp.: 32
Information Technology Services
N.A.I.C.S.: 541511
Carolyn Merek *(Pres & CEO)*
William Engel *(VP)*

EMERALD AR SYSTEMS
1850 N Central Ave #1010, Phoenix,
AZ 85004
Web Site: http://www.emeraldar.com
Year Founded: 2007
Sales Range: $1-9.9 Million
Emp.: 50
Consulting & Development of Collection Programs for Health Care Companies
N.A.I.C.S.: 561440
Tom Jensen *(Partner)*

EMERALD BIOAGRICULTURE CORP.
4211 Okemos Rd, Okemos, MI
48864-3287
Tel.: (517) 882-7370
Web Site: http://www.emeraldbio.com
Year Founded: 1994
Sales Range: $10-24.9 Million
Emp.: 20
Developer of Agricultural Biochemicals
N.A.I.C.S.: 325320
Frank W. Owen *(Pres & CEO)*

EMERALD COAST UTILITIES AUTHORITY
9255 Sturdevant St, Pensacola, FL
32514
Tel.: (850) 476-5110
Web Site: https://www.ecua.fl.gov
Year Founded: 1981
Sales Range: $75-99.9 Million
Emp.: 509
Sanitation & Water Utility Operations
N.A.I.C.S.: 926130

EMERALD COMPANIES, INC.
400 Travis St Ste 402, Shreveport,
LA 71101
Tel.: (318) 425-7083
Web Site:
   http://www.emeraldcompanies.com
Rev.: $32,100,000
Emp.: 700
Facilities Support Services
N.A.I.C.S.: 561210
Steve Afeman *(COO)*
Paulette Jackson *(Coord-Events)*
Glenn Hebert *(Chm)*
Clay Lee *(CEO)*

EMERALD DATA SOLUTIONS, INC.
519 Johnson Ferry Rd NE Bldg A Ste
100, Marietta, GA 30068
Web Site: http://www.boarddocs.com
Year Founded: 1989
Sales Range: $1-9.9 Million
Emp.: 14
Computer Technology Services
N.A.I.C.S.: 541519
Michael Hanahan *(Chief Mktg & Sls Officer)*

EMERALD FOODS INC.
8181 N Stadium Dr Ste 100, Houston, TX 77054
Tel.: (713) 791-9167
Sales Range: $25-49.9 Million
Emp.: 400
Fast-Food Restaurant, Chain
N.A.I.C.S.: 722513
Mark George *(Pres)*
Brian Harper *(Sr Mgr-Facilities & HR)*

EMERALD HEALTH SERVICES
4640 Admiralty Way Ste 201, Marina
Del Rey, CA 90292-6625
Web Site: http://www.emeraldhs.com
Year Founded: 2002
Sales Range: $50-74.9 Million
Emp.: 50
Healthcare Staffing Services
N.A.I.C.S.: 561311
Mark Stagen *(Founder & CEO)*
Michelle Kane *(Pres)*

EMERALD ISLE EXPLORATIONS LTD.
1218 Purtov St, Kodiak, AK 99615
Tel.: (907) 539-2222
Web Site:
   http://www.emeraldisleexplo
   ration.com
Metal Mining Services
N.A.I.C.S.: 212290
Samuell Eads *(Pres & Sec)*

EMERALD OIL, INC.
200 Columbine St Ste 500, Denver,
CO 80206
Tel.: (303) 595-5600   DE
Web Site: http://www.emeraldoil.com
Sales Range: $100-124.9 Million
Oil & Natural Gas Exploration
N.A.I.C.S.: 211120
McAndrew Rudisill *(Pres & CEO)*
Daniel L. Spears *(Chm)*
Mitch Ayer *(VP-Fin & IR)*

Subsidiaries:

Emerald WB LLC   (1)

Emerald Oil, Inc.—(Continued)

1600 Broadway Ste 1360, Denver, CO
80202
Tel.: (303) 323-0008
Oil Exploration & Production Services
N.A.I.C.S.: 211120

EMERALD PACKAGING, INC.
33050 Western Ave, Union City, CA
94587
Tel.: (510) 429-5700
Web Site: https://www.empack.com
Year Founded: 1963
Sales Range: $10-24.9 Million
Emp.: 125
Plastics Bag Mfr
N.A.I.C.S.: 326111
Kevin Kelly (CEO)
Todd Somers (Dir-Sls)
Francisco Gamez (Dir-Innovation)
Pallavi Joyappa (COO)
Maura Kelly Koberlein (VP)
Jan McGrath (Mgr-Acctg)
James P. Kelly (Founder)

EMERALD SERVICES INC.
7343 E Marginal Way S, Seattle, WA
98108
Tel.: (206) 832-3100
Web Site: http://www.emeraldnw.com
Sales Range: $100-124.9 Million
Emp.: 300
Refuse Collection & Disposal Services
vices
N.A.I.C.S.: 562211
Yvette Deese (Controller)
John Brigham (VP)
Kelly Guiberson (Dir-Bus Dev)
Steve Banchero (Owner)
Jerry Bartlett (VP)
Kevin Schatz (Dir-Safety)

EMERALD TREE FARM
4155 E Mowry Dr, Homestead, FL
33033
Tel.: (305) 257-2323
Web Site:
     http://www.emeraldtree.com
Rev.: $20,000,000
Emp.: 11
Landscape Contractors
N.A.I.C.S.: 561730
Bruce Howard (Pres)
Chris Anderson (CFO)

EMERCHANDISE GROUP LLC
5-B Dutch Ct, Sinking Spring, PA
19608
Web Site:
     http://www.emerchandise.com
Comic Books, Toys, Clothing & Other
Related Merchandise Online Retailer
N.A.I.C.S.: 423940
Jon Belzer (Owner & CEO)

Subsidiaries:

SuperHeroStuff.com   (1)
5-B Dutch Ct, Sinking Spring, PA 19608
Web Site: http://www.superherostuff.com
Comic Books, Toys, Clothing & Other Related Merchandise Online Retailer & Mail
Order
N.A.I.C.S.: 459120
Jon Belzer (Co-Owner & CEO)
Brian Welch (Co-Owner & Head-Ops)
Danielle Deihm (Head-Customer Svc)
Andy Hollinger (Mgr-Catalog)
Eric Frost (Mgr-Wholesale)
Jake Troxell (Dir-Creative)
Ned Butz (Mgr-Warehouse)

**EMERCON CONSTRUCTION
INC.**
2906 E Coronado St, Anaheim, CA
92806
Tel.: (714) 630-9615
Web Site: http://www.emercon.com

Year Founded: 1987
Rev.: $11,000,000
Emp.: 100
Construction of Single-Family Housing
ing
N.A.I.C.S.: 236115
Richard Anderson (Pres)
Saney Wilianf (CFO)
Alan Lavine (Superintendent)
Perry Campbell (Superintendent)
Desiree Martini (Mgr-Bus Dev)

EMERGE 180 INC.
13902 N Dale Mabry Hwy Ste 225,
Tampa, FL 33618
Web Site:
     https://www.emerge180.com
Year Founded: 1993
Sales Range: $10-24.9 Million
Emp.: 25
Financial & Business Consulting Services
vices
N.A.I.C.S.: 541618
Jonathan Field (Pres & CEO)

EMERGE DIGITAL INC.
555 Market St FL 15, San Francisco,
CA 94105
Tel.: (415) 839-5055
Web Site:
     http://www.emergedigital.com
Year Founded: 2009
Sales Range: $10-24.9 Million
Emp.: 75
Advertising Services
N.A.I.C.S.: 541810
Hindol Datta (VP-Fin & Analytics)
Josh Edis (Sr VP-Global Bus Dev)
Chase Norlin (CEO)
Willie Pang (Mng Dir-Emerge Digital
Group APAC)
Alex Rowland (Pres)

EMERGE IT SOLUTIONS, LLC
1895 Airport Exchange Blvd Ste 170,
Erlanger, KY 41018
Tel.: (859) 746-1030
Web Site: https://www.emergeits.com
Year Founded: 2004
Sales Range: $1-9.9 Million
Emp.: 50
Cloud Computing, Network Infrastructure & Messaging Collaboration Services
ture & Messaging Collaboration Services
vices
N.A.I.C.S.: 513210
Richard Brown (Owner & Mng Partner)
ner)
Jesse Kegley (Mng Partner)
Tim Witte (Mng Partner)

EMERGE, INC.
9180 Rumsey Rd Ste D2, Columbia,
MD 21045
Tel.: (410) 884-4420   MD
Web Site: https://www.emergeinc.org
Year Founded: 1976
Sales Range: $25-49.9 Million
Emp.: 697
Developmental Disability Assistance
Services
N.A.I.C.S.: 624120
David Wamsley (Exec Dir)

EMERGENCE CAPITAL PARTNERS
NERS
160 Bovet Rd Ste 300, San Mateo,
CA 94402
Tel.: (650) 573-3100
Web Site: http://www.emcap.com
Year Founded: 2003
Rev.: $575,000,000
Emp.: 16
Venture Capital
N.A.I.C.S.: 523999
Jason Green (Partner)
Kevin Spain (Gen Partner)

Everett Cox (Partner-Venture)
Santiago Subotovsky (Gen Partner)
Cathy Minshall (CFO & Chief Admin
Officer)
Joe Floyd (Partner)
Jake Saper (Gen Partner)
Doug Landis (Partner-Growth)
Viviana Faga (Partner)
Kara Egan (Principal)
Brian Jacobs (Gen Partner)
Carlotta Siniscalco (Principal)
Julie Bell (COO)
Gordon Ritter (Gen Partner)

Subsidiaries:

Zettics, Inc.   (1)
5 Lyberty Way, Westford, MA 01886
Tel.: (978) 254-5329
Data Analytic Services
N.A.I.C.S.: 518210
Sterling Wilson (Pres & CEO)
Asa Kalavade (CTO & Sr VP)
Tal Kedar (CFO)
John Gillespie (Sr VP-Sls)
Ian Herbert-Jones (Sr VP)
Joe Levy (VP-Customer Strategy & Mktg)
Andrew Gibbs (VP-Product Mgmt)
Prasasth Palnati (VP-Engrg)
Stephen Douglas (VP-Tech)
John Thomas (Dir-Res)
Adam Guy (VP-Monetization)

Subsidiary (Domestic):

Velocent Systems, Inc.   (2)
1250 E Diehl Rd, Naperville, IL 60563
Tel.: (630) 799-3800
Web Site: http://www.velocent.com
Emp.: 15
Data Processing Services
N.A.I.C.S.: 423430
Ian Herbert Jones (CEO)
Stephen Douglas (CTO)
Tom Smith (COO)
Jagadeesh Dantuluri (VP-Mktg)
Randy Johnson (VP-Engrg)
Eric Hong (Co-Founder)
Philip Stevens (Sr VP-Sls)
Larry Border (Dir-Fin)

**EMERGENCY ESSENTIALS
INC.**
653 N 1500 W, Orem, UT 84057-
2831
Tel.: (801) 222-9596
Web Site:
     http://www.beprepared.com
Sales Range: $10-24.9 Million
Emp.: 30
Distr of Food Products
N.A.I.C.S.: 339113
David E. Sheets (Pres)
Matt Nettesheim (Exec VP)
Shane Sullivan (Mgr)
Sarah Knight (Supvr-Social Media)
Joel Robertson (Mgr-Online Mktg)
Tyson Wallace (Supvr-Adv)

EMERGENCY FOOD NETWORK
WORK
3318 92nd St S, Lakewood, WA
98499
Tel.: (253) 584-1040   WA
Web Site: https://www.efoodnet.org
Year Founded: 1990
Sales Range: $10-24.9 Million
Community Food Services
N.A.I.C.S.: 624210
Helen McGovern-Pilant (Exec Dir)
Ron Pace (Dir-Fin & Admin)
Paul Stabbert (Dir-Ops)

EMERGENCY MEDICAL FOUNDATION
DATION
112 Carswell Ave, Holly Hill, FL
32117
Tel.: (386) 252-4900
Web Site: http://www.evacamb.org
Sales Range: $10-24.9 Million
Emp.: 250

Ambulance Service
N.A.I.C.S.: 621910
Tracey Riehm (CFO)
Robert Boggess (Dir-Admin)
Mark Davis (Dir)
Terry Sanders (Exec Dir)

EMERGENCY NURSES ASSOCIATION
CIATION
930 E Woodfield Rd, Schaumburg, IL
60173
Tel.: (847) 460-4000
Web Site: http://www.ena.org
Year Founded: 1970
Premier Professional Nursing Association
ciation
N.A.I.C.S.: 813410
Dan Campana (Dir-Comm)
Ron Kraus (Pres)

Subsidiaries:

Triage First Inc.   (1)
594 Old US Hwy 74, Fairview, NC 28730-
8748
Tel.: (828) 628-8029
Web Site: http://www.triagefirst.com
Online Triage Education for Healthcare Professionals
fessionals
N.A.I.C.S.: 611699
Rebecca McNair (Founder & Pres)

**EMERGENCY RESTORATION
EXPERTS, LLC**
7929 Statesville Rd, Charlotte, NC
28269
Tel.: (704) 626-6800   NC
Web Site: http://www.erx247.com
Year Founded: 2013
Sales Range: $10-24.9 Million
Emp.: 90
Building Restoration Services
N.A.I.C.S.: 236118
Amber Monteith (Mng Partner)
Howard Monteith (Mng Partner)
David Stophel (Partner)
Amanda Stophel (Partner)

EMERGENCY VISIONS
739 Trabert Ave Ste F, Atlanta, GA
30318
Tel.: (404) 350-5995
Web Site:
     http://www.emergencyvisions.com
Rev.: $17,100,000
Emp.: 187
Computer Programming & Consulting
Services
N.A.I.C.S.: 541512
Brad McRee (VP-Education)
Randall C. Manaka (VP-R & D)
Matthew Brooks (VP-Client Svcs)
Douglas F. Hale (CFO)
Richard F. Gray (COO)
Shawn D. Smith (Pres & CEO)

EMERGENCY24, INC.
999 E Touhy Ste 500, Des Plaines, IL
60018
Tel.: (773) 777-0707
Web Site:
     https://www.emergency24.com
Sales Range: $1-9.9 Million
Emp.: 100
Monitoring & Security Services
N.A.I.C.S.: 561621
Dante Monteverde (Pres)
Patrick Devereaux (Sr VP)
Kevin Lehan (Mgr-PR)

EMERGENETICS, LLC
2 Inverness Dr E Ste 189, Centennial, CO 80112-5508
nial, CO 80112-5508
Tel.: (303) 660-7920
Web Site:
     http://www.emergenetics.com

Year Founded: 1985
Sales Range: $1-9.9 Million
Emp.: 35
Hiring Processes Utilizing Brain-Based Aptitude Assessments
N.A.I.C.S.: 561311
Geil Browning *(Founder & CEO)*
Morgan Browning *(Pres & COO)*
Karen Hulett *(CFO)*
Harold Suire *(VP-Education & Master Trainer)*
Chris Cox *(VP-Trng & Dev)*

Subsidiaries:

Emergenetics International (1)
Laredo 215 A2 Lomas del Valle San Pedro Garza Garcia, Nuevo Leon, 66256, Mexico
Tel.: (52) 8115436657
Web Site: http://www.emergenetics.com
Distr of Emergenetics Products & Services
N.A.I.C.S.: 561311

Emergenetics International-Asia (EGI-A) (1)
23A Keong Saik Road, Singapore, 089130, Singapore
Tel.: (65) 62256617
Web Site: http://www.emergenetics.com
Global Consultancy & Hiring Services
N.A.I.C.S.: 561311
Terence Quek *(CEO & Head-Strategic Dev & Bus Ops)*

EMERGENT CAPITAL, INC.

5355 Town Ctr Rd Ste 701, Boca Raton, FL 33486
Tel.: (561) 995-4200 FL
Web Site:
http://www.emergentcapital.com
Year Founded: 2006
EMGC—(OTCBB)
Rev.: $41,525,000
Assets: $165,712,000
Liabilities: $123,599,000
Net Worth: $42,113,000
Earnings: $14,496,000
Emp.: 9
Fiscal Year-end: 11/30/19
Holding Company; Insurance Financing Services
N.A.I.C.S.: 551112
Patrick J. Curry *(Chm)*

Subsidiaries:

Imperial Finance & Trading LLC (1)
701 Park Of Commerce Blvd, Boca Raton, FL 33487
Tel.: (561) 995-4200
Web Site: http://www.imprl.com
Management Consulting Services
N.A.I.C.S.: 541611

Imperial Life Settlements, LLC (1)
701 Park of Commerce Blvd, Boca Raton, FL 33487
Tel.: (561) 995-4200
Emp.: 20
International Trade Financing Services
N.A.I.C.S.: 522299

Imperial Premium Finance, LLC (1)
701 Park of Commerce Blvd Ste 301, Boca Raton, FL 33487-3604
Tel.: (561) 373-2475
International Trade Financing Services
N.A.I.C.S.: 522299

PSC Financial, LLC (1)
7900 International Dr Ste 1075, Bloomington, MN 55425
Tel.: (952) 777-3955
Web Site: http://www.pscfinancial.com
Investment Advisory Services
N.A.I.C.S.: 523940
Howard Pakola *(Principal)*
Tracy J. Torland *(Chief Investment Officer)*

EMERGENT MEDICAL ASSOCIATES

898 N Pacific Coast Hwy Ste 600, El Segundo, CA 90245
Tel.: (310) 379-2134

Web Site: https://www.ema.us
Year Founded: 1991
Sales Range: $10-24.9 Million
Emp.: 20
Emergency Care & Episodic Care Management Services
N.A.I.C.S.: 621111
Irv Edwards *(Founder & Pres)*
Mark Bell *(Pres)*
Scott G. Brewster *(Chief Medical Officer)*
Val Warhaft *(Chief Risk Officer)*
Lee R. Weiss *(Chief Clinical Ops Officer)*
Alan Heilpern *(Chief Medical Officer)*
Ari L. Nagler *(CEO)*
Robert Heinemeier *(CFO)*

EMERGENT METHOD, LLC

200 Laurel St Ste 200, Baton Rouge, LA 70801
Tel.: (225) 372-5102
Web Site:
http://www.emergentmethod.com
Year Founded: 2012
Sales Range: $1-9.9 Million
Emp.: 29
Business Management Consulting Services
N.A.I.C.S.: 541611
Nick Speyrer *(Founder & Pres)*
Rachel Carroccio *(Mng Dir)*
Julie Laperouse *(Mng Dir)*
Rachel DiResto *(Mng Dir & VP)*
Anthony Napolitano *(Mng Dir)*

EMERGENT, LLC

8219 Leesburg Pike Ste 300, Vienna, VA 22182
Tel.: (703) 288-4556
Web Site:
http://www.emergent360.com
Sales Range: $25-49.9 Million
Emp.: 50
Information Technology Solution Providers
N.A.I.C.S.: 519290
Greg Christensen *(Pres)*
Paul Kohler *(Exec VP)*
Rick Welborn *(CFO)*
Chris Richards *(VP-Mktg & Customer Satisfaction)*

EMERGING CAPITAL PARTNERS (ECP)

1909 K St NW Ste 340, Washington, DC 20006
Tel.: (202) 280-6200
Web Site:
http://www.ecpinvestments.com
Private Equity Investment Services
N.A.I.C.S.: 523999
Vincent Le Guennou *(CEO-Abidjan, Partner & Mng Dir)*
Bryce Fort *(Partner & Mng Dir-Nairobi)*
Hurley Doddy *(Co-CEO, Partner & Mng Dir)*
Carolyn Campbell *(Founder, Partner & Mng Dir-Washington)*
Brice Lodugnon *(Mng Dir-Abidjan)*
William Nkontchou *(Dir-Paris)*
Nayel-Georges Vidal *(Dir-Tunis)*

Subsidiaries:

ECP-Central Africa (1)
316 Victoria Street 4th Floor Victoria Building, PO Box 753, Douala, Cameroon (100%)
Tel.: (237) 33 42 48 61
Web Site: http://www.ecpinvestments.com
Emp.: 5
Investment Asset Management
N.A.I.C.S.: 523999
Ferdinand Ngon *(Mng Dir)*
Aurore Bahounoui *(VP)*

ECP-Morocco (1)

MIM Registered Office 416 rue Mustapha El Maani 11th floor, 20100, Casablanca, Morocco (100%)
Tel.: (212) 522469911
Web Site: http://www.ecpinvestments.com
Private Equity Investments
N.A.I.C.S.: 523999

ECP-Nigeria (1)
PO Box 56131, Lagos, Ikoyi, Nigeria (100%)
Tel.: (234) 12800940
Web Site: http://www.ecpinvestments.com
Investment Asset Management
N.A.I.C.S.: 523999
Seyi Owodunni *(Mng Dir)*

ECP-North Africa (1)
Immeuble Miniar Bloc B 2 eme Etage Rue du Lac D'Ourmia, Les Berges du Lac, Tunis, 1053, Tunisia (100%)
Tel.: (216) 71962590
Web Site: http://www.ecpinvestments.com
Sales Range: $25-49.9 Million
Emp.: 7
Investment Management Service
N.A.I.C.S.: 523999

ECP-Paris (1)
14 Avenue Franklin Delano Roosevelt 3rd Floor, 75008, Paris, France (100%)
Tel.: (33) 144011684
Web Site: http://www.ecpinvestments.com
Sales Range: $25-49.9 Million
Emp.: 5
Private Equity Investments
N.A.I.C.S.: 523999
William Nkontchou *(Dir)*

ECP-Southern Africa (1)
8th Floor The Forum Building Corner 5th & Maude Streets, Sandton, 2196, Johannesburg, South Africa (100%)
Tel.: (27) 116850830
Web Site: http://www.ecpinvestments.com
Sales Range: $25-49.9 Million
Emp.: 5
Private Equity Investments
N.A.I.C.S.: 523999
Alexhandrah Aime *(Mng Dir)*

ECP-West Africa (1)
Immeuble Crrae Umoa 4th Floor-Aisle C, Avenue Boteau Roussel, Abidjan, 16BP 1450, Plateau, Cote d'Ivoire (100%)
Tel.: (225) 20 31 07 31
Web Site: http://www.ecpinvestments.com
Asset Management Investments
N.A.I.C.S.: 523999

EMERGING OPPORTUNITIES CORP.

1 Gateway Ctr 26th Fl, Newark, NJ 07102
Tel.: (973) 277-4239 DE
Year Founded: 2020
Investment Services
N.A.I.C.S.: 523999
Franklin Ogele *(Pres, CEO, CFO & Sec)*

EMERGING SOVEREIGN GROUP LLC

520 Madison Ave 41st Fl, New York, NY 10022
Tel.: (212) 984-5750 DE
Year Founded: 2002
Investment Management Service
N.A.I.C.S.: 523940
Mete Tuncel *(Co-Founder)*
Jason Kirschner *(Co-Founder)*
J. Kevin Kenny Jr. *(Co-Founder & Mng Partner)*

EMERGING VISION, INC.

520 8th Ave 23 Fl, New York, NY 10018
Tel.: (646) 737-1500 NY
Web Site:
http://www.emergingvision.com
Year Founded: 1992
Sales Range: $50-74.9 Million
Emp.: 150

Optical Retail Stores, Franchisor, Owner & Operator
N.A.I.C.S.: 456130
Brian P. Alessi *(CFO & Treas)*

EMERGING WORLD PHARMA, INC.

10432 Balls Ford Rd Ste 300, Manassas, VA 20109
Tel.: (703) 881-7835
Pharmaceutical Product Mfr & Distr
N.A.I.C.S.: 325411
Brandon Keks *(Pres)*

EMERGTECH BUSINESS SOLUTIONS, INC.

31700 W 13 Mile Rd Ste 210, Farmington Hills, MI 48334
Tel.: (248) 539-3000
Web Site:
http://www.EmergtechInc.com
Year Founded: 2003
Sales Range: $1-9.9 Million
Emp.: 35
Information Technology Services
N.A.I.C.S.: 519290
Meena Raghava *(Owner)*

EMERGYCARE, INC.

1701 Sassafras St, Erie, PA 16502
Tel.: (814) 870-1010
Web Site: http://www.emergycare.org
Rev.: $20,000,000
Emp.: 300
Ambulance Service
N.A.I.C.S.: 621910
David Monroe *(Mgr-Base Site)*
William F. Hagerty IV *(Exec Dir)*

EMERICK CONSTRUCTION CO. INC.

7855 SW Mohawk St, Tualatin, OR 97062
Tel.: (503) 777-5531
Web Site: https://www.emerick.com
Year Founded: 1943
Sales Range: $10-24.9 Million
Emp.: 30
General Contractors of Industrial Buildings & Warehouses
N.A.I.C.S.: 236210
Gretchen Ludwig *(Controller)*
Corey M. Lohman *(Pres)*

Subsidiaries:

McCormack Construction Co. Inc. (1)
422 SW 6th St, Pendleton, OR 97801-2026
Tel.: (541) 276-1353
Web Site:
http://www.mccormackconstruction.com
Sales Range: $10-24.9 Million
Emp.: 18
General Contractors of Nonresidential Construction
N.A.I.C.S.: 236220

EMERLING CHEVROLET INC.

9000 Boston State Rd, Boston, NY 14025
Tel.: (716) 941-5255 NY
Web Site: http://www.emerling.com
Year Founded: 1955
Sales Range: $10-24.9 Million
Emp.: 57
Car Whslr
N.A.I.C.S.: 441110
Russ Belscher *(Mgr-Fleet)*

EMERLING FORD, INC.

150 S Cascade Dr, Springville, NY 14141
Tel.: (716) 794-1966
Web Site:
https://www.emerlingford.com
Year Founded: 1986
Sales Range: $10-24.9 Million

Emerling Ford, Inc.—(Continued)

Emp.: 70
Car Whslr
N.A.I.C.S.: 441110
Carl A. Emerling (Pres)
John Woodruff (Gen Mgr)

EMERSON HARDWOOD COMPANY

2279 NW Front Ave, Portland, OR 97209
Tel.: (503) 227-6414
Web Site:
   https://www.emersonhardwood.com
Rev.: $14,400,000
Emp.: 60
Building Materials, Interior
N.A.I.C.S.: 423310
James T. Price (Pres)
Chris Mongrain (Vice Chm)

EMERSON HOSPITAL

133 Old Rd to Nine Acre Cor, Concord, MA 01742
Tel.: (978) 369-1400
Web Site:
   https://www.emersonhospital.org
Year Founded: 1911
Medical Devices
N.A.I.C.S.: 622110
Christine Schuster (Pres & CEO)
Eric Stastny (COO & Sr VP-Ops)
Barrett Kitch (Chief Medical Officer & Sr VP-Clinical Affairs)
Michael Hachey (CFO & Sr VP)
Christine Gallery (Chief Strategy Officer & Sr VP-Plng)
Joyce Welsh (Chief Nursing Officer & VP-Patient Care Svcs)
Karl Kussin (Chief Philanthropy Officer & VP-Dev)
Patty Ellis (VP-Quality & Patient Safety)
Renee Fosberg (CIO)
Paul Birch (Chm)
Gloria Clough (Vice Chm)
James DiGiovanni (Sec)
Richard Churchill Jr. (Treas)

EMERSON MATTRESS INC.

3675 Industrial Ave, Marion, IA 52302
Tel.: (319) 377-3738
Web Site: http://www.lebeda.com
Rev.: $10,100,000
Emp.: 80
Mattresses
N.A.I.C.S.: 449110
Russell D. Miller (Pres)

EMERSON OIL CO. INC.

352 Sycamore St, Homer, LA 71040
Tel.: (318) 927-2046
Sales Range: $10-24.9 Million
Emp.: 8
Petroleum Bulk Stations
N.A.I.C.S.: 424710
G. Wesley Emerson Jr. (Chm & Pres)

EMERSON REID LLC

630 W Germantown Pike Ste 215, Plymouth Meeting, PA 19462-1069
Tel.: (610) 356-9220
Web Site:
   http://www.emersonreid.com
Year Founded: 1974
Insurance Agencies & Brokerages
N.A.I.C.S.: 524210
George Rosiak (Pres)

Subsidiaries:

JRG Advisors, LLC   (1)
7000 Stonewood Dr Ste 251, Wexford, PA 15090
Tel.: (412) 456-7000
Web Site: http://www.jrgadvisors.net
Insurance Management Services

N.A.I.C.S.: 524298

May Insurance Services, Inc.   (1)
110 Northwoods Blvd Ste C, Columbus, OH 43235-8627
Tel.: (614) 431-1899
Web Site: http://www.mayinsurance.com
Insurance Related Activities
N.A.I.C.S.: 524298
John May (Owner)

EMERSON-SWAN INC.

300 Pond St, Randolph, MA 02368-2661
Tel.: (781) 986-2000   **MA**
Web Site:
   https://www.emersonswan.com
Year Founded: 1967
Sales Range: $10-24.9 Million
Emp.: 130
Mfr of Plumbing Fixtures & Related Equipment
N.A.I.C.S.: 423720
Joseph E. Swan (Chm)
Parker Wheat (CEO)
Bob Oppel (Sr VP-Distr Products Plumbing Sls)
Bruce MacDonald (Mgr-DP Sls)
Mike Fahy (Mgr-Info Svcs)
George Simas (Pres & CEO)
Ken Fagan (Sr VP-Bus Dev)
Joann Newell (Controller)
Al Hanson (Mgr-Sls)
Andrew Stephens (Mgr-Distr Center)
Rick Deforest (Supvr-Warehouse)
Thomas J. Swan Jr. (Chm)

EMERY & ASSOCIATES

4025 Pleasantale Rd Ste 460, Atlanta, GA 30340
Tel.: (770) 414-9099
Web Site:
   https://www.emeryassoc.com
Year Founded: 1996
Sales Range: $1-9.9 Million
Emp.: 10
General Contractors
N.A.I.C.S.: 238190
Haydn W. Fusia (Founder & Pres)

EMERY DISTRIBUTORS INC.

3800 Glover Rd, Easton, PA 18040-9225
Tel.: (610) 258-3651
Web Site:
   https://www.emerydistributors.com
Sales Range: $10-24.9 Million
Emp.: 10
Toy & Hobby Goods Whslr
N.A.I.C.S.: 423920
David Emery (Pres & VP)
Donald L. Emery (Treas & Sec)

EMF CORPORATION

505 Pokagon Trl, Angola, IN 46703
Tel.: (260) 665-9541
Web Site: https://www.emfusa.com
Sales Range: $10-24.9 Million
Emp.: 270
Supplier of Wiring Assemblies & Electrical Components
N.A.I.C.S.: 334419
Tricia Bowerman (Controller)
Howard Sanders (Pres)

EMG - ETHNIC MARKETING GROUP, INC.

26074 Ave Hall Ste 20, Valencia, CA 91355
Tel.: (661) 295-5704
Web Site: http://www.emgad.com
Year Founded: 1991
Sales Range: $10-24.9 Million
Emp.: 17
Advetising Agency
N.A.I.C.S.: 541810

Enrique Gil (Owner)
Mario Echevarria (Mng Dir-Acct Svcs)

EMG, INC.

675 Aviation Blvd Ste B, Santa Rosa, CA 95402
Tel.: (707) 525-9941
Web Site: http://www.emginc.com
Year Founded: 1974
Rev.: $4,000,000
Emp.: 80
Guitar Pick-Ups & Electronic Accessories Mfr
N.A.I.C.S.: 334419
Don Andrews (Mgr-IT)
James Kearney (Mgr-Sls & Admin)

EMI CORP.

PO Box 590, Jackson Center, OH 45334-0590
Tel.: (937) 596-5511
Web Site: http://www.emiplastics.com
Sales Range: $10-24.9 Million
Emp.: 95
Conveyors & Conveying Equipment
N.A.I.C.S.: 333922
Anthony J. Andraitis (Pres)

EMI HEALTH

852 E Arrowhead Ln, Murray, UT 84107-5298
Tel.: (801) 262-7476
Web Site: http://www.emihealth.com
Year Founded: 1935
Sales Range: $25-49.9 Million
Emp.: 135
Health Insurance Carrier
N.A.I.C.S.: 524114
Christie Hawkes (Sr VP-Corp Comm & Provider Rels)
Steven C. Morrison (Pres & CEO)
Ryan Lowther (COO, Exec VP & Sec)
Mike Greenhalgh (CFO, Exec VP & Treas)
Brandon L. Smart (Chief Compliance Officer & Sr VP)
David Wood (Chief Actuary)
Joe Campbell (Exec VP-IT)
Cindy Tovey (Sr VP-Sls & Mktg)
Tiffany B. Bermingham (VP-Enrollment & Customer Svc)

EMI STRATEGIC MARKETING, INC.

15 Broad St, Boston, MA 02109
Tel.: (617) 224-1101
Web Site:
   https://www.emiboston.com
Year Founded: 1989
Sales Range: $50-74.9 Million
Emp.: 40
Brand Development & Integration, Business-To-Business, Direct Response Marketing, Marketing Consulting Services
N.A.I.C.S.: 541613
Campbell Edlund (Pres & Founder)
Ken Lubar (CTO)
Anthony Nygren (Exec VP-Investments Practice)
Charlene Paradise (Dir-Payments Practice)
Mark Malloy (Exec Dir-Creative)

Subsidiaries:

EMI/Dublin   (1)
Crowhill, Inishannon, Dublin, Dublin, Ireland
Tel.: (353) 217432817
Sales Range: $10-24.9 Million
Emp.: 2
N.A.I.C.S.: 541810
Mark Ronan (VP)

EMIDA CORPORATION

27442 Portola Pkwy Ste 150, Foothill Ranch, CA 92610
Tel.: (949) 699-1401
Web Site: https://www.emida.net
Prepayment & Value Transfer Market Solutions & Services
N.A.I.C.S.: 561499
Shane Belovsky (COO)
Aldo Mizrahi (VP & Gen Mgr-Mexico)
Martyn Fricker (VP & Gen Mgr-Intl)

Subsidiaries:

Emida Corporation   (1)
27442 Portola Pkwy Ste 150, Foothill Ranch, CA 92610-2827
Tel.: (949) 699-1401
Sales Range: $25-49.9 Million
Emp.: 50
Prepayment & Value Transfer Market Solutions & Services
N.A.I.C.S.: 561499

EMIGH HARDWARE CO.

3555 El Camino Ave, Sacramento, CA 95821
Tel.: (916) 482-1900
Web Site: https://www.emigh.com
Sales Range: $10-24.9 Million
Emp.: 96
Hardware Stores
N.A.I.C.S.: 444140
Rich Lawrence (Pres)

EMIL VON DUNGEN INC.

553 W Ave, Lockport, NY 14094
Tel.: (716) 433-5901
Sales Range: $10-24.9 Million
Emp.: 12
Fabricated Structural Metal
N.A.I.C.S.: 332312
Jean Smith (Sec)
Emil Von Dungen Jr. (Pres)

EMINENT TECHNOLOGY SOLUTIONS, INC.

5586 Main St Ste 210, Williamsville, NY 14221
Tel.: (716) 650-4133
Web Site:
   https://www.eminenttech.com
Year Founded: 2004
Sales Range: $1-9.9 Million
Emp.: 30
Systems Integration & Software Consulting
N.A.I.C.S.: 541690
Lakshmi Subramaniam (Pres)

EMJ CORPORATION

2034 Hamilton Place Blvd Ste 400, Chattanooga, TN 37421-6000
Tel.: (423) 855-1550   **TN**
Web Site: https://www.emjcorp.com
Year Founded: 1978
Sales Range: $10-24.9 Million
Emp.: 63
Nonresidential Construction Services
N.A.I.C.S.: 236220
Jay Jolley (Chm)
Burt Odom (Pres & CEO)
Rob Eichelroth (Exec VP)
Doug Martin (COO)
Clint Dean (Exec VP)
Chris Hall (VP)
Steve Rice (VP-Construction)
David Henderson (Acct Exec-Natl)
Hal Routh (VP-Bus Dev)
Holly Bischoff (VP-Fin & Acctg)
Jack Bowen (Sr VP-Construction)
Sheri Ginett (Acct Exec-Natl)
Conan Schantz (Dir-Construction-Office & Industrial)
Mike McVey (Dir-Construction-Retail Dev)
James Williams (Dir-Construction)
Jeff Brewer (Acct Exec-Natl)

Colby Cox *(Gen Counsel)*
Ketan Joshi *(VP-Preconstruction)*
Steve Coughran *(CFO)*

EMK CONSULTANTS OF FLORIDA, INC.

7815 N Dale Mabry Hwy, Tampa, FL 33614
Tel.: (813) 931-8900   FL
Web Site: http://www.emkfla.com
Year Founded: 1986
Sales Range: $1-9.9 Million
Emp.: 35
Engineeering Services
N.A.I.C.S.: 541330
Earl Michaels *(Pres)*
Ayse Figanmese *(Project Mgr)*
Robin Kendall *(Sr Project Mgr)*
Trevor Gregory *(Mgr-Construction & Permit)*

EMKAT SOLUTIONS, INC.

2600 Fernbrook Ln N Ste 138, Plymouth, MN 55447
Tel.: (763) 744-1204
Web Site: http://www.emkat.com
Year Founded: 2001
Sales Range: $10-24.9 Million
Emp.: 14
Mobility Solutions Including Mobile Hardware Sales & Service
N.A.I.C.S.: 517112
Brad Kieley *(CEO)*
Chris Kane *(Owner)*

EMKAY, INC.

805 W Thorndale Ave, Itasca, IL 60143-1338
Tel.: (630) 250-7400   IL
Web Site: https://www.emkay.com
Year Founded: 1946
Sales Range: $10-24.9 Million
Emp.: 120
Full-Service Fleet Leasing & Management
N.A.I.C.S.: 522220
Andy Vella *(VP-Fin)*
Dave Nagy *(Sr VP-Sls-North America)*
Gregory Depase *(Pres)*
Greg Tepas *(Pres & CEO)*

EMKEY ENERGY, LLC

2501 Palermo Dr Ste B, Erie, PA 16506
Tel.: (814) 455-5350
Web Site:
    http://www.emkeygathering.com
Emp.: 15
Oil & Natural Gas Distr
N.A.I.C.S.: 213111
Oivind Risberg *(Pres)*

Subsidiaries:

Mid American Natural Resources, LLC   (1)
2501 Palermo Dr Ste A, Erie, PA 16506-7210   (100%)
Tel.: (814) 455-2761
Web Site: http://www.manrenergy.com
Sales Range: $25-49.9 Million
Emp.: 10
Natural Gas Distribution
N.A.I.C.S.: 221210
Nancy Nielsen *(Mgr-Transportation & Exchange)*

EMMA, INC.

2120 8th Ave S, Nashville, TN 37204-2204
Tel.: (615) 292-5888
Web Site: http://www.myemma.com
Year Founded: 2001
Sales Range: $1-9.9 Million
Emp.: 100
Email Marketing Services
N.A.I.C.S.: 541613

Clint Smith *(Founder & CEO)*
Bo Spessard *(COO)*
Simon O'Day *(VP-Global & Partnerships)*
Carrie Gofron *(Dir-Bus Dev)*
Kyle Floyd *(Dir-Customer Support)*
Cynthia Price *(Dir-Mktg)*
Kat Amano *(Product Dir)*
Scott Sears *(VP-Client Svc)*
Patrick Block *(VP-Fin)*
David Wright *(VP-Product)*
Christopher Lester *(VP-Sls)*
Sara McManigal *(VP-Talent)*
Jason Bynum *(VP-Tech)*

EMMER DEVELOPMENT CORP.

2801 SW Archer Rd, Gainesville, FL 32608
Tel.: (352) 376-2444
Web Site:
    https://www.emmergroup.com
Sales Range: $10-24.9 Million
Emp.: 56
Residential Land Subdividers & Developers
N.A.I.C.S.: 237210
Lori McGriff *(Pres)*
Orianna Snook *(CFO)*

EMMERT INDUSTRIAL CORPORATION

11811 SE Hwy 212, Clackamas, OR 97015
Tel.: (503) 655-7191
Web Site:
    https://www.emmertintl.com
Sales Range: $10-24.9 Million
Emp.: 100
Machine Moving & Rigging
N.A.I.C.S.: 238290
Terry W. Emmert *(Pres)*

EMMETSBURG BANK SHARES, INC.

2101 10th St, Emmetsburg, IA 50536
Tel.: (712) 852-3451   IA
Web Site:
    http://www.iowatrustbank.com
Year Founded: 1984
Sales Range: $1-9.9 Million
Bank Holding Company
N.A.I.C.S.: 551111
John F. Spies *(Chm, Pres & CEO)*
Kris M. Ausborn *(Pres & CEO-Iowa Trust & Savings Bank)*
Colleen M. Heldt *(CFO & Treas)*
Cleta Ann Frascht *(Sec & VP-HR-Iowa Trust & Savings Bank)*

Subsidiaries:

Iowa Trust & Savings Bank   (1)
2101 10th St, Emmetsburg, IA 50536
Tel.: (712) 852-3451
Web Site: http://www.iowatrustbank.com
Sales Range: $1-9.9 Million
Commericial Banking
N.A.I.C.S.: 522110
Kris M. Ausborn *(Pres & CEO)*
Lawrence Besch *(VP-Bus Banking)*
John F. Spies *(Chm)*
Rick Brennan *(Exec VP-Bus Dev)*
Colleen M. Heldt *(CFO & Compliance Officer)*
Bradley Sporrer *(Exec VP-Bus Banking)*
Cleta Ann Frascht *(VP-HR & Asst Trust Officer)*
Julie Leners *(VP-Retail Banking)*
Joan Bunda *(VP-Ops & IT)*
Kyle Auten *(Sr VP-Bus Banking)*
Scott Menke *(Chief Credit Officer & Exec VP)*

EMMETSBURG FOOD PRIDE GROCERY & DELI INC.

1307 Broadway St, Emmetsburg, IA 50536
Tel.: (712) 852-2401

Web Site: http://www.pride.net
Sales Range: $10-24.9 Million
Emp.: 40
Owner & Operator of Grocery Stores
N.A.I.C.S.: 445110
Wally Joersz *(Pres)*

EMMIS AUSTIN RADIO BROADCASTING COMPANY, L.P.

8309 N IH 35, Austin, TX 78753
Tel.: (512) 832-4000
Web Site:
    http://www.emmisaustin.com
Radio Communication & Entertainment
N.A.I.C.S.: 516210
Scott Gillmore *(Mgr-Market)*

EMMONS BUSINESS INTERIORS LLC

5225 Joerns Dr, Stevens Point, WI 54481
Tel.: (715) 345-8933
Web Site: http://www.ebiweb.com
Rev.: $10,135,575
Emp.: 580
Office Furniture, Nec
N.A.I.C.S.: 423210
Robert Andersen *(Pres)*
Sherry Lillge *(Coord-Sls & Mktg)*
Barbara Millan *(Mgr-Acct)*
Patti Thompson *(Mgr-Conference Svcs)*
Scott Storey *(Mgr-Pur)*

EMMY BUILDING CO. INC.

3281 Veterans Memorial Hwy Ste E-13, Ronkonkoma, NY 11779
Tel.: (631) 361-6500
Web Site:
    http://www.emmyhomes.com
Year Founded: 1964
Sales Range: $25-49.9 Million
Emp.: 8
Residential Construction
N.A.I.C.S.: 236115
Edward Flax *(Founder & Pres)*

EMO-TRANS INC.

377 Oak St Ste 202, Garden City, NY 11530
Tel.: (516) 867-6800
Web Site: https://www.emotrans-
    global.com
Year Founded: 1965
Sales Range: $10-24.9 Million
Emp.: 400
Foreign Freight Forwarding
N.A.I.C.S.: 488510
Joachim Frigger *(Chm)*
Tom Harlin *(CFO & Exec VP)*
Manuel Espina Ortiz *(Mng Dir)*
Marco Rohrer *(Pres & CEO)*
Rodrigo Navarro Carrasco *(Dir-Sls)*
Stephen Jones *(CFO-Australia)*

Subsidiaries:

EMO Australasia NZ LTD   (1)
18 Triton Drive Unit H, Mairangi Bay, 632, New Zealand
Tel.: (64) 9 415 0084
Web Site: http://www.emotrans.co.nz
Emp.: 10
Logistics Consulting Servies
N.A.I.C.S.: 541614
Rochelle Pattinson *(Mng Dir)*

EMO TRANS (Canada) Freight Ltd.   (1)
7420 Airport Road Suite 108, Mississauga, L4T 4E5, ON, Canada
Tel.: (905) 676-9782
Web Site: http://www.emotrans-global.com
Emp.: 10
Logistics Consulting Servies
N.A.I.C.S.: 541614
Perry C. Northey *(VP)*

EMO TRANS Korea Co Ltd.   (1)
1506 Yongsung Biztel Bldg 109 Hangang-Daero, Yongsan-Gu, Seoul, 140-750, Korea (South)
Tel.: (82) 2 725 9411
Logistics Consulting Servies
N.A.I.C.S.: 541614

EMO TRANS Peru S.A.C.   (1)
AV Pershing 417 Ofic 201, Magdalena del Mar, Lima, Peru
Tel.: (51) 1 261 3400
Logistics Consulting Servies
N.A.I.C.S.: 541614
Oswaldo Melendez Leyton *(Coord-Supply Chain)*

EMO-TRANS GmbH   (1)
Raiffeisenstrasse 9, 70794, Filderstadt, Germany
Tel.: (49) 711 77 00 241
Web Site: http://www.emo.de
Emp.: 20
Air & Sea Freight Transportation Services
N.A.I.C.S.: 481112
Axel Polenz *(Mng Dir-Airfreight)*
Stefan Ritter *(Mng Dir-Oceanfreight)*
Andreas Pfitzner *(Branch Mgr)*
Eckart Moltmann *(Founder)*

Project Logistics International   (1)
10251 Glasgow Pl, Los Angeles, CA 90045-6129
Tel.: (310) 590-1760
Web Site: http://www.emotrans.com
Rev.: $20,000,000
Emp.: 3
Freight Transportation Arrangement
N.A.I.C.S.: 488510

EMONECO, INC.

4901 W 136thÂ St, Leawood, KS 66224
Web Site: http://www.emoneco.com
Year Founded: 2007
Electronic Payment Processing Services
N.A.I.C.S.: 522320
Donald E. Latson *(Pres & CEO)*

EMORY BANCSHARES, INC.

170 E Quitman St, Emory, TX 75440
Tel.: (903) 473-2611   TX
Web Site: http://www.fnbemory.com
Year Founded: 1980
Sales Range: $1-9.9 Million
Emp.: 27
Bank Holding Company
N.A.I.C.S.: 551111
Steve Beaver *(Pres)*

Subsidiaries:

The First National Bank of Emory   (1)
170 E Quitman St, Emory, TX 75440
Tel.: (903) 473-2611
Web Site: http://www.fnbemory.com
Emp.: 14
Retail & Commercial Banking
N.A.I.C.S.: 522110
Steve Beaver *(Pres)*

EMORY ELECTRIC INC.

10 Hillcrest Rd, Asheville, NC 28804
Tel.: (828) 658-8300
Web Site:
    https://www.emoryelectric.com
Sales Range: $10-24.9 Million
Emp.: 125
General Electrical Contractor
N.A.I.C.S.: 238210
Tim Emory *(CEO)*

EMP GLOBAL LLC

1901 Pennsylvania Ave Nw Ste 300, Washington, DC 20006-3405
Tel.: (202) 331-9051
Web Site: http://www.empglobal.com
Rev.: $13,700,000
Emp.: 85
Privater Equity Firm
N.A.I.C.S.: 523999

EMP Global LLC—(Continued)

Moeen A. Qureshi *(Chm & Partner)*
Collins Roth *(Partner)*
A. Shabu Qureshi *(Partner)*

Subsidiaries:

EMP Latin American Management
LLC (1)
900 17th St Nw Ste 910, Washington, DC
20006-2504
Tel.: (202) 331-9051
Financial Investment
N.A.I.C.S.: 523999

EMP MANAGEMENT, LLC
1 Buckhead Plz 3060 Peachtree Rd,
NW, Ste 360, Atlanta, GA 30305
Tel.: (404) 974-2480
Web Site:
  https://www.eaglemerchantpart
  ners.com
Private Equity
N.A.I.C.S.: 523940
Stockton Croft *(Partner)*

Subsidiaries:

Eskola LLC (1)
2418 Morelock Rd, Morristown, TN 37814-
7814
Tel.: (423) 318-2196
Web Site: http://www.eskolaroofing.com
Roofing Contractors
N.A.I.C.S.: 238160
Ty Konkle *(Superintendent & Mgr)*

Subsidiary (Domestic):

Best Environmental Systems Technol-
ogy, Inc. (2)
1108 Nowell Rd, Raleigh, NC 27607
Tel.: (919) 851-3009
Web Site: http://www.bestenvirotech.com
Rev.: $2,700,000
Emp.: 25
Other Building Finishing Contractors
N.A.I.C.S.: 238390
Mary Dudley *(CFO)*
Grey Pardue *(CEO)*

Frontier Roofing, Inc (2)
39950 Business Loop 80, Lyman, WY
82937
Tel.: (307) 786-4101
Rev.: $1,200,000
Emp.: 14
Other Building Finishing Contractors
N.A.I.C.S.: 238390
Robert Wilcock *(Pres)*

Furniture Medic Limited
Partnership (1)
860 Ridge Lake Blvd, Memphis, TN 38120
Tel.: (901) 597-1400
Web Site: http://www.furnituremedic.com
Sales Range: $10-24.9 Million
Commercial & Residential Furniture Repair
Services
N.A.I.C.S.: 811420

EMPACO EQUIPMENT CORP.
2958 Brecksville Rd, Richfield, OH
44286-0535
Tel.: (330) 659-9393
Web Site:
  https://www.empacoequipment.com
Sales Range: $10-24.9 Million
Emp.: 60
Installer of Service Station Equipment
N.A.I.C.S.: 238990
Jim Springston *(Asst Mgr-Property &
Maintenance)*
Paul Backo *(Supvr-Construction)*
Rick Cooper *(Mgr-Svcs)*
Paul Kester *(Controller)*

EMPATH PARTNERS IN CARE
3050 1st Ave S, Saint Petersburg, FL
33712
Tel.: (727) 328-3260
Web Site: https://www.myepic.org
HIV Care & Support Services
N.A.I.C.S.: 813212

Sheryl Hoolsema *(Dir-Pinellas
County)*
Rafael J. Sciullo *(Pres & CEO)*
Craig Bryant *(Treas)*
Lisa E. Cohen *(Vice Chm)*
Charlotte Noble *(Sec)*
Michael Ruppal *(Chm)*
Bridget Narvaez *(Dir-Medical & Edu-
cational Svcs)*
Dave Konnerth *(Dir-Admin Svcs)*
Victoria Fortugno-Oliver *(Dir-
Hillsborough County)*
Joy Winheim *(Exec Dir)*
Janet Roman *(Dir-Cardiac Programs)*

**EMPEIRIA CAPITAL PART-
NERS LLC**
142 W 57th St 12th Fl, New York, NY
10019
Tel.: (212) 887-1126
Web Site: http://www.empeiria.com
Privater Equity Firm
N.A.I.C.S.: 523999
Keith Oster *(Partner)*
Joe Fong *(Partner)*
Alan B. Menkes *(Mng Partner)*

Subsidiaries:

J.L. Bryan Equipment & Lease Ser-
vice, Inc. (1)
902 Southeast 9th Ave, Perryton, TX 79070
Tel.: (806) 435-4511
Web Site: http://www.jlbryan.com
Oil & Gas Equipment Mfr & Distr
N.A.I.C.S.: 333132
Jerry Bryan *(Pres)*
Brent Bryan *(VP)*
Jeff Gillum *(Supvr-Plant)*

EMPEOPLE CREDIT UNION
3950 38th Ave, Moline, IL 61265
Tel.: (800) 338-6739
Web Site: https://empeople.com
Emp.: 100
Credti Union
N.A.I.C.S.: 522130

EMPERIAL AMERICAS, INC.
Sarasota Courthouse Ctr 1990 Main
St Ste 150, Sarasota, FL 33020
Tel.: (941) 309-5408
Web Site:
  http://www.emperialamericas.com
Sales Range: $600-649.9 Million
Emp.: 4
Alcoholic Beverages Importer & Mar-
keter
N.A.I.C.S.: 424820
Alonzo Pierce *(Pres & CEO)*

**EMPEROR PAPER INDUS-
TRIES LTD.**
5050 Quorum Dr Ste 700, Dallas, TX
75254
Tel.: (972) 687-9055
Year Founded: 2017
Emp.: 1
Paper Recycling Services
N.A.I.C.S.: 322299
Rajan Ahluwalia *(Pres, CEO, Treas &
Sec)*

EMPIE, INC.
1682 Langley Ave 2 Fl, Irvine, CA
92614
Tel.: (949) 430-6650
Web Site:
  http://www.empireworks.com
Year Founded: 2002
Sales Range: $50-74.9 Million
Emp.: 500
Exterior Construction & Painting
N.A.I.C.S.: 238320
Jason Reid *(Founder & Chm)*

EMPIRE AIRLINES

11559 N Atlas Rd, Hayden, ID 83835
Tel.: (208) 292-3850
Web Site:
  https://www.empireairlines.com
Year Founded: 1977
Sales Range: $100-124.9 Million
Emp.: 300
Aviation Services; Large Aircraft Con-
tracting
N.A.I.C.S.: 481219
Tim Komberec *(Pres & CEO)*
Vic Walters *(Founder)*
Scott Marikis *(COO & VP)*

Subsidiaries:

Empire Aerospace (1)
11559 N Atlas Rd, Hayden, ID 83835
Tel.: (208) 292-3850
Web Site: http://www.empireaerospace.com
Aviation & Freight Services
N.A.I.C.S.: 481219

**EMPIRE AUTOMATION SYS-
TEMS INC**
20 Vantage Point Dr Ste 4, Roches-
ter, NY 14624-1141
Tel.: (585) 352-3333
Web Site: https://www.maseas.com
Year Founded: 1999
Sales Range: $10-24.9 Million
Emp.: 12
Provider of Heating & Air Condition-
ing Services
N.A.I.C.S.: 423840
Don Davis *(Pres)*
Scott Pask *(Engr-Sls)*
John Flores *(Engr-Application)*

**EMPIRE BUILDING & ENVI-
RONMENTAL SERVICES**
2821 W Vly Blvd, Alhambra, CA
91803
Tel.: (626) 289-8755
Web Site: http://www.empirebuilding-
  es.com
Year Founded: 1976
Sales Range: $10-24.9 Million
Emp.: 200
Janitorial & HVAC Cleaning & Mainte-
nance
N.A.I.C.S.: 561720
Ronnie Garcia *(VP)*

**EMPIRE BUILDING MATERI-
ALS INC.**
608 E Main St, Bozeman, MT 59715-
3768
Tel.: (406) 587-3191
Web Site: http://www.empireinc.com
Year Founded: 1954
Sales Range: $10-24.9 Million
Emp.: 60
Provider of Lumber, Plywood & Mill-
work Services
N.A.I.C.S.: 423310
Tom Simkins *(Pres)*
Susan Hanik *(Controller)*

**EMPIRE CANDLE COMPANY,
LLC**
2925 Fairfax Trwy, Kansas City, KS
66115-1317
Tel.: (913) 621-4555
Web Site:
  https://www.empirecandle.com
Mfr & Marketer of Poured Candles
N.A.I.C.S.: 339999
Rick Langley *(Pres)*

EMPIRE CITY IRON WORKS
1037 46th Rd, Long Island City, NY
11101
Tel.: (718) 361-0100
Rev.: $20,000,000
Emp.: 150
Ornamental Metal Work

N.A.I.C.S.: 332323
Harvey A. Heffner *(Pres)*

**EMPIRE COMMERCIAL & IN-
DUSTRIAL CORPORATION**
2665 Strichen Ave, Henderson, NV
89044
Tel.: (702) 401-6405
Year Founded: 2010
Real Estate Brokerage Services
N.A.I.C.S.: 531210
Steve McFadden *(Pres, CEO, CFO,
Treas & Sec)*

**EMPIRE DIAMOND CORPORA-
TION**
350 5th Ave Ste 3012, New York, NY
10118
Tel.: (212) 564-4777
Web Site:
  http://www.dialadiamond.com
Year Founded: 1931
Sales Range: $75-99.9 Million
Emp.: 100
Whslr of Diamonds & Jewelry
N.A.I.C.S.: 423940
Gregory Herdemian *(CEO & COO)*
Ann Akers *(Dir-Adv)*

**EMPIRE DIE CASTING CO.,
INC.**
635 E Highland Rd, Macedonia, OH
44056-2185
Tel.: (330) 467-0750
Web Site: http://www.empiredie.com
Year Founded: 1948
Sales Range: $25-49.9 Million
Emp.: 200
Aluminum Die-Castings
N.A.I.C.S.: 331523
Bob Boldt *(Dir-Production Control &
Customer Svc)*
Robert Spiegle *(Controller & VP-Fin)*
Amanda Noyes *(Mgr-Pur)*

**EMPIRE ELECTRIC ASSOCIA-
TION, INC.**
801 N Broadway, Cortez, CO 81321-
0676
Tel.: (970) 565-4444
Web Site: https://www.eea.coop
Year Founded: 1939
Sales Range: $150-199.9 Million
Emp.: 62
Distr of Electric Power
N.A.I.C.S.: 221122
William C. Bauer *(Pres)*
Neal Stephens *(Gen Mgr)*

**EMPIRE ENERGY CORPORA-
TION INTERNATIONAL**
4500 College Blvd Ste 240, Leawood,
KS 66211
Tel.: (913) 663-2310
Web Site:
  http://www.empireenergy.com
Year Founded: 1983
Petroleum & Natural Gas Exploration
Services
N.A.I.C.S.: 211120
John C. Garrison *(Pres)*
Malcolm R. Bendall *(CEO & CFO)*

EMPIRE FOOD BROKERS INC.
1837 Harbor Ave PO Box 13098,
Memphis, TN 38113
Tel.: (901) 756-8681
Web Site:
  http://www.empirefoods.com
Sales Range: $25-49.9 Million
Emp.: 35
Bond Brokers
N.A.I.C.S.: 424410

Paula Dickerson *(Controller)*
Todd Jackson *(Bus Mgr)*
Mike Strall *(Acct Exec)*
Danny H. Harris Sr. *(Pres)*

EMPIRE FORD LINCOLN
106 Jonesboro Rd, Abingdon, VA 24210
Tel.: (276) 628-2127
Web Site: https://www.empireford.net
Year Founded: 1992
Sales Range: $10-24.9 Million
Emp.: 41
Car Whslr
N.A.I.C.S.: 441110
Harold J. Crabtree *(Owner)*
Keith Crabtree *(Co-Owner & Gen Mgr)*

EMPIRE GAS COMPANY INC.
PO BOX 353651, San Juan, PR 00936-3651
Tel.: (787) 751-5725
Web Site:
http://www.empiregaspr.com
Year Founded: 1967
Full-service Propane Company
N.A.I.C.S.: 424720
Ramon Gonzalez Jr. *(Vice Chm)*

EMPIRE HYUNDAI, INC.
428 Pleasant St, Fall River, MA 02721
Tel.: (508) 689-4093
Web Site:
https://www.empirehyundai.com
Year Founded: 1999
Sales Range: $10-24.9 Million
Emp.: 51
New Car Dealers
N.A.I.C.S.: 441110
Richard Torres *(Pres)*
Kasey Mathias *(Dir-Internet)*
Debbie Mello *(Comptroller)*

EMPIRE INVESTMENT HOLDINGS, LLC
1000 NW 57th Court Ste 900, Miami, FL 33126
Tel.: (305) 403-1111   DE
Web Site: http://www.empireih.com
Year Founded: 2003
Sales Range: $125-149.9 Million
Emp.: 900
Investment Holding Company
N.A.I.C.S.: 523999
David F. Alfonso *(Founder, Chm & CEO)*
Dennis M. Mahoney *(Partner)*
Robert J. Buhay *(Partner)*

Subsidiaries:

Todd Soundelux   (1)
7080 Hollywood Blvd Ste 1100, Hollywood, CA 90028   **(100%)**
Tel.: (323) 603-3200
Web Site: http://www.toddsoundelux.com
Creative Services to Motion Picture Studios, Independent Producers, Broadcast Networks, Cable Channels, Advertising Agencies & Interactive Producers
N.A.I.C.S.: 512240
David Young *(VP-Engrg & Tech)*
Sara Duran-Singer *(CEO)*

Subsidiary (Domestic):

Soundelux   (2)
7080 Hollywood Blvd 6th Fl, Hollywood, CA 90028-6906
Tel.: (323) 603-3200
Web Site: http://www.soundelux.com
Sales Range: $25-49.9 Million
Emp.: 150
Motion Picture Sound Effects & Music Production Services
N.A.I.C.S.: 512191

The Todd-AO Corporation   (2)

7080 Hollywood Blvd Ste 100, Hollywood, CA 90028
Tel.: (323) 962-4000
Web Site: http://www.todd-ao.com
Sales Range: $10-24.9 Million
Emp.: 30
Post-Production Sound & Video Services
N.A.I.C.S.: 512199

EMPIRE LUMBER COMPANY
14 E Main, Spokane, WA 99202
Tel.: (509) 534-0266
Rev.: $20,000,000
Emp.: 109
Miscellaneous Wood Product Mfr
N.A.I.C.S.: 321999
David A. Klaue *(Chm)*

EMPIRE MANAGEMENT COMPANY
PO Box 467, Concordville, PA 19331
Tel.: (610) 558-1500
Sales Range: $10-24.9 Million
Emp.: 3
Managers of Real Estate
N.A.I.C.S.: 531210

EMPIRE NATURAL GAS CORPORATION
173 Airport Rd, Greene, NY 13778
Tel.: (607) 656-7851
Web Site:
https://www.empirenatgas.com
Year Founded: 1989
Sales Range: $25-49.9 Million
Emp.: 7
Natural Gas Distribution Services
N.A.I.C.S.: 221210
Marcel Barrows *(Pres)*
Seth Barrows *(Exec VP)*
Joanne Young *(Sr Mgr-Accts)*

EMPIRE OFFICE, INC.
105 Madison Ave 15th Fl, New York, NY 10016-4712
Tel.: (212) 607-5500   NY
Web Site:
http://www.empireoffice.com
Year Founded: 1947
Sales Range: $150-199.9 Million
Emp.: 400
Office Furniture Whslr
N.A.I.C.S.: 423210
Lawrence L. Gaslow *(Chm)*
Richard Gulardo *(COO)*
Peter Gaslow *(Pres & CEO)*
Martin Hills *(CFO)*
Jay Binkowski *(Pres-Florida)*
Craig Rothschild *(Dir-Bus Dev)*
Terry Shields *(Sr VP)*
Eran Bendavid *(Sr VP-Fin)*

EMPIRE PACKING COMPANY, L.P.
1837 Harbor Ave, Memphis, TN 38113
Tel.: (901) 948-4788   DE
Web Site:
http://www.ledbetterfoods.com
Year Founded: 1959
Sales Range: $25-49.9 Million
Emp.: 150
Case Ready Meat Products Mfr
N.A.I.C.S.: 424470
John Moore *(Controller)*

EMPIRE PAPER COMPANY
2708 Central Fwy E, Wichita Falls, TX 76301-8050
Tel.: (940) 766-3216
Web Site:
https://www.empirepaper.com
Sales Range: $10-24.9 Million
Emp.: 100
Industrial & Personal Service Paper
N.A.I.C.S.: 424130

John M. Estes *(Pres)*
Dewayne Leath *(Mgr-Sls)*

EMPIRE PIPE & SUPPLY CO., INC.
2301 Alton Rd, Irondale, AL 35210
Tel.: (205) 956-1010
Web Site:
https://www.empirepipe.com
Rev.: $19,000,000
Emp.: 27
Metal Service Centers & Other Metal Merchant Whslr
N.A.I.C.S.: 423510
Mike Campbell *(Pres)*
Michael J. Sawyer *(Treas, Sec & VP-Fin)*

EMPIRE POST MEDIA, INC.
2620 Regatta Dr Ste 102, Las Vegas, NV 89128
Tel.: (832) 256-6714   NV
Year Founded: 2009
Motion Picture & Television Post-Production Services
N.A.I.C.S.: 512110
Ian N. Dixon *(Pres & COO)*
William Sawyer *(CEO)*
Ted Campbell *(Chief Compliance Officer & Sec)*
Tammy Billington *(CFO)*

EMPIRE PROPERTIES
133 Fayetteville St, Raleigh, NC 27601
Tel.: (919) 834-8350
Web Site:
https://www.empire1792.com
Year Founded: 1996
Sales Range: $25-49.9 Million
Emp.: 618
Real Estate Development Services
N.A.I.C.S.: 531390
Barry Overcash *(Head-Maintenance)*
Patricia Wheeley *(Controller)*
Dave Nicolay *(Dir-Construction)*

EMPIRE RECYCLING CORP.
64 N Genesee St, Utica, NY 13502
Tel.: (315) 724-7161
Web Site:
https://www.empirerecycling.com
Sales Range: $10-24.9 Million
Emp.: 67
Scrap Metal Recycling
N.A.I.C.S.: 562920
Steven Kowalsky *(Pres)*
Edward L. Kowalsky *(Exec VP)*
Dave Levitt *(Project Mgr-Ops)*

EMPIRE RESORTS, INC.
c/o Monticello Casino and Raceway
204 State Route 17B, Monticello, NY 12701
Tel.: (845) 807-0001   DE
Web Site:
http://www.empireresorts.com
Year Founded: 1993
Rev.: $194,845,000
Assets: $846,426,000
Liabilities: $634,587,000
Net Worth: $211,839,000
Earnings: ($138,696,000)
Emp.: 1,756
Fiscal Year-end: 12/31/18
Gaming & Hospitality Services
N.A.I.C.S.: 713990
Nanette L. Horner *(Chief Compliance Officer & Exec VP)*
Ryan Eller *(Pres & CEO)*
Robert Alan Berman *(Co-Founder)*
Jamie M. Sanko *(Chief Acctg Officer)*

Subsidiaries:

Alpha Monticello, Inc.   (1)
Monticello Raceway, Monticello, NY 12701

Tel.: (845) 794-4100
Race Track Services
N.A.I.C.S.: 711212

Montreign Operating Company, LLC   (1)
204 State Route 17B, Monticello, NY 12701
Tel.: (845) 807-0001
Web Site: http://www.montreign.com
Hotel Operator
N.A.I.C.S.: 721120

EMPIRE SCREEN PRINTING, INC.
N 5206 Marco Rd, Onalaska, WI 54650
Tel.: (608) 783-3301
Web Site:
https://www.empirescreen.com
Rev.: $25,900,000
Emp.: 350
Commercial Screen Printing
N.A.I.C.S.: 323113
James Brush *(Owner)*
James K. Schwinefus *(VP)*

EMPIRE SOUTHWEST LLC
1725 S Country Club Dr, Mesa, AZ 85210-6003
Tel.: (480) 633-4000   AZ
Web Site: http://www.empire-cat.com
Year Founded: 1984
Sales Range: $450-499.9 Million
Emp.: 1,600
Caterpillar Equipment Dealer
N.A.I.C.S.: 423810
Jeffrey S. Whiteman *(Pres & CEO)*
Chris Zaharis *(CFO & VP)*

Subsidiaries:

Empire Hydraulic Service   (1)
1835 S McDonald, Mesa, AZ 85210-6102
Tel.: (480) 633-4700
Web Site: http://www.empire-cat.com
Sales Range: $25-49.9 Million
Emp.: 28
Hydraulic Equipment Repair
N.A.I.C.S.: 423810

Empire Machinery   (1)
1725 S Country Club Dr, Mesa, AZ 85210-6003   **(100%)**
Tel.: (480) 633-4000
Web Site: http://www.empire-cat.com
Sales Range: $150-199.9 Million
Caterpillar Construction, Paving, Mining & Agriculture Equipment
N.A.I.C.S.: 423810
Jeffrey S. Whiteman *(Chm, Pres & CEO)*
Yolanda Sotelo *(Mgr-Learning & Dev)*

Empire Power Systems   (1)
801 N 44th Ave, Phoenix, AZ 85009-4015
Tel.: (602) 333-5600
Web Site: http://www.empire-cat.com
Sales Range: $100-124.9 Million
Emp.: 1,100
Caterpillar Diesel & Industrial Engines, Electric Generators & Generator Sets
N.A.I.C.S.: 811210
Delores Serrano *(Admin Asst-Pres)*
William Ong *(Mgr-Project-Comml Engine)*

Empire Precision Machining   (1)
41 W Iron Ave, Mesa, AZ 85210-6102
Tel.: (480) 633-4425
Sales Range: $10-24.9 Million
Emp.: 36
Machine Shop, Welding
N.A.I.C.S.: 811210
Jeff Whiteman *(Pres)*

Empire Transport   (1)
40 W Iron Ave, Mesa, AZ 85210-6103
Tel.: (480) 633-4600
Web Site: http://www.empire-cat.com
Sales Range: $25-49.9 Million
Emp.: 60
Trucking- Heavy Haul
N.A.I.C.S.: 484110
Rolland Shill *(Acct Mgr-Credit)*

EMPIRE STAPLE CO.
200 E 55th Ave, Denver, CO 80216

Empire Staple Co.—(Continued)

Tel.: (303) 433-6803
Web Site:
   https://www.empirestaple.com
Sales Range: $10-24.9 Million
Emp.: 60
Industrial Fastener Mfr
N.A.I.C.S.: 423840
Jim Crusius (Controller)
Ed Swinscoe (Mgr-Pur)

EMPIRE STATE RELIEF FUND
53 North Park Ave Ste 302, Rockville
Centre, NY 11570
Tel.: (516) 763-3100   NY
Web Site:
   http://www.empirestaterelief.com
Year Founded: 2012
Sales Range: Less than $1 Million
Individual & Family Support Services
N.A.I.C.S.: 624190
Richard J. Sirota (Treas)

EMPLICITY
9851 Irvine Center Dr, Irvine, CA
92618
Tel.: (714) 230-4740
Web Site: https://www.emplicity.com
Sales Range: $75-99.9 Million
Emp.: 34
Outsourcing Services
N.A.I.C.S.: 541612
Vic Tanon (Founder & Chief Simplicity Officer)
Ari Paredes (Mgr-Benefits)
Nime Ashok (VP-Fin)
Scott Ullmann (Dir-Mktg)

EMPLOY AMERICA, LLC
345 N Canal St Ste 1403, Chicago,
IL 60606
Tel.: (312) 849-2200   IL
Web Site: http://www.workcredit.com
Year Founded: 1985
Sales Range: $150-199.9 Million
Emp.: 10
Risk Managemeng Srvices
N.A.I.C.S.: 524210
Charles Stevenson (Pres)
Peter Scherer (CFO)

EMPLOY-ABILITY UNLIMITED INC.
9901 Linn Station Rd, Louisville, KY
40223
Tel.: (502) 394-2100   OH
Year Founded: 1996
Sales Range: $1-9.9 Million
Emp.: 82
Disabled People Housing & Employment Services
N.A.I.C.S.: 624229
Edward C. MacDonald (Exec Dir)

EMPLOYEE & FAMILY RE-SOURCES INC.
505 5th Ave Ste 600, Des Moines, IA
50309
Tel.: (515) 244-6090   IA
Web Site: http://www.efr.org
Year Founded: 1964
Sales Range: $10-24.9 Million
Emp.: 90
Provider of Individual & Family Services
N.A.I.C.S.: 624190
Fred Buie (Pres)
Louise Crall (Dir-HR)
Rod Warren (VP)

EMPLOYEE BENEFITS INTER-NATIONAL
4700 Rockside Rd Summit One Ste
505, Independence, OH 44131
Tel.: (216) 264-2707

Web Site:
   http://www.employeebenefitsint.com
Year Founded: 2007
Sales Range: $1-9.9 Million
Emp.: 20
Insurance Products & Benefit Program Consulting, Design & Administration Services
N.A.I.C.S.: 524298
James Dustin (Principal)
Brian Hirsch (Principal)
Thomas Caito (Principal)
David Leszcz (Principal)
Brent Tregaskes (Sr Acct Exec)

EMPLOYEE OWNED HOLD-INGS, INC.
5500 N Sam Houston Pkwy W Ste
100, Houston, TX 77086
Tel.: (281) 569-7000
Web Site: http://www.eoh-inc.com
Year Founded: 2007
Holding Company
N.A.I.C.S.: 551112
Richard Neels (Chm, Pres & CEO)
Matthew Weisser (CFO)

Subsidiaries:

Gulf Controls Company, LLC   (1)
5201 Tampa West Blvd, Tampa, FL 33634-2416
Tel.: (813) 884-0471
Web Site: http://www.gulfcontrols.com
Sales Range: $25-49.9 Million
Emp.: 106
Pneumatic, Hydraulic & Electro-Mechanical Motion Control Products Distr
N.A.I.C.S.: 423830
Robert Shafer (Mgr-Customer Svc)
Rod Longnecker (VP-Engrg)
Robert Myers (Product Mgr-Hydraulic)
Ernesto Garcia (Mgr-Sls-Southern Territory)
Scott Gower (Mgr-Sls-Eastern District)
Sid Hendry (Mgr-Mktg & Strategic Pricing)
Bob Yager (Product Mgr-Automation)
Jean Knowles (VP-Sls)
Steve Vance (Mgr-Sls-Central District)
Mark Cima (Mgr-Sls)
John Flieman III (Pres)

Division (Domestic):

Gulf Controls Co. - Action Hydraulics
Division   (2)
7399 NW 74th St, Miami, FL
33166-2409   (100%)
Tel.: (305) 863-8479
Web Site: http://www.gulfcontrols.com
Sales Range: $25-49.9 Million
Emp.: 12
Industrial Hydraulic Services
N.A.I.C.S.: 423830
Chris Sieber (Mgr-Sls)

Hydraquip Custom Systems, Inc.   (1)
12311 Cutten Rd, Houston, TX 77066
Tel.: (281) 822-5000
Web Site: http://www.hydraquip-csi.com
Emp.: 35
Hydraulic Systems Fabrication & Manufacture for Marine & Offshore Industry
N.A.I.C.S.: 333248
Bill Boyle (VP-Sls & Mktg-North America)
Mark Helm (Pres)
Shawn Callow (Mgr-Engrg)
Mel Victory (Exec VP-Intl & Lift Boat Sls)

Hydraquip Distribution, Inc.   (1)
16330 Central Green Blvd Ste 200, Houston, TX 77032
Tel.: (713) 680-1951
Web Site: http://www.hydraquip.com
Emp.: 100
Fluid Power Components & Accessories
Distr
N.A.I.C.S.: 423830
Tim Nichols (Pres)
Scott Nelson (Sls Mgr-Fluid Power)

Supreme Integrated Technology,
Inc.   (1)
915 Distributors Row, Harahan, LA 70123
Tel.: (504) 464-0528
Web Site: http://www.supremeintegratedtech nology.com

Hydraulic, Pneumatic, Automation & Control
Systems Design & Fabrication for Marine &
Offshore Industry
N.A.I.C.S.: 333248
Kevin Hayes (Pres)
Chip Griepenstroph (Exec VP-Ops)

EMPLOYEE SOLUTIONS
6404 International Pkwy Ste 1350,
Plano, TX 75093
Tel.: (214) 420-8367
Web Site:
   http://www.employeesolutions.com
Year Founded: 1997
Sales Range: $50-74.9 Million
Emp.: 60
Specialists in Long-Term Temporary
Staffing, Temp-to-Hire & Payroll Staffing Services
N.A.I.C.S.: 561311
David Bristol (CEO)
Terri Shoate (VP-Ops)
Joey Thomas (Dir-Ops)
Edith Cardenas (Mgr-Ops)
James Garibay (Mgr-Ops)
Jamie Johnson (Controller)
Lauren Truelove (Dir-Admin)
Shelby Park Beshara (Gen Counsel)
Tracy Cutts (Mgr-Ops)

EMPLOYEES LIFE COMPANY MUTUAL
916 Sherwood Dr, Lake Bluff, IL
60044
Tel.: (847) 295-6000
Web Site:
   https://www.elcomutual.com
Year Founded: 1946
Sales Range: $100-124.9 Million
Emp.: 20
Life Insurance Carrier
N.A.I.C.S.: 524113
William D. Bruce (Chm)
Edmund J. Kuplins (Pres)

EMPLOYEES OF MUNICIPAL & OTHER PUBLIC EMPLOYERS
60 Community Dr, Augusta, ME
04330
Tel.: (207) 623-8428   ME
Web Site: http://www.mmeht.org
Year Founded: 1983
Sales Range: $125-149.9 Million
Employee Benefit Services
N.A.I.C.S.: 525120
Anne Charles (Mgr-Health Promotion)
Gregory L'Heureux (Sec)
Linda Mack (Mgr-Eligibility & Data Svcs)
Lisa Rigoulot (Mgr-Member Svcs)

EMPLOYEES ONLY
805 Oakwood Dr Ste 100, Rochester,
MI 48307
Tel.: (248) 276-0950
Web Site:
   http://www.employeesonly.net
Year Founded: 1994
Sales Range: $50-74.9 Million
Emp.: 2,000
Temporary, Contract & Permanent
Staffing Services
N.A.I.C.S.: 561311
Mario D. Apruzzese (CEO)
Janine Gradowski (Pres)
Rob Seale (Gen Mgr)

EMPLOYER FLEXIBLE MAN-AGEMENT, LLC
7850 N Sam Houston Park W Ste
100, Houston, TX 77064
Tel.: (281) 444-0900   TX
Web Site:
   http://www.employerflexible.com
Year Founded: 2003
Sales Range: $75-99.9 Million

Emp.: 55
Human Resource Outsourcing
(HRO), Professional Search & Staff
Recruiters
N.A.I.C.S.: 561320
Michael Hopkins (Co-Founder & VP-HR)
Michael Greathouse (Owner & Co-Founder)
Chris Dollins (Co-Founder & Pres)
Karen Garcia (Dir-Mktg)

Subsidiaries:

Employer Flexible   (1)
6404 International Parkway Ste 1200,
Plano, TX 75093   (100%)
Tel.: (972) 401-3500
Web Site: http://www.employerflexible.com
Professional Staffing Services
N.A.I.C.S.: 561311

Employer Flexible   (1)
8000 IH-10 Ste 240, San Antonio, TX
78230   (100%)
Tel.: (210) 447-6520
Web Site: http://www.employerflexible.com
Sales Range: $10-24.9 Million
Emp.: 4
Professional Staffing Services
N.A.I.C.S.: 561311
Michael Hopkins (CEO)

EMPLOYER MANAGEMENT SOLUTIONS, INC.
5550 W Executive Dr Ste 450,
Tampa, FL 33609-1045
Tel.: (813) 287-2486
Web Site:
   http://www.consultems.com
Year Founded: 1998
Sales Range: $10-24.9 Million
Emp.: 12
Business & Technology Consulting
Services
N.A.I.C.S.: 541511
Richard Torres (Pres & CEO)
Elaine Myrback (Pres & CEO)
Doug Myrback (Sr VP)
Angie May (VP-Admin)

EMPLOYER'S DEPOT INC.
1500 Eastman Ave, Ventura, CA
93003-7759
Tel.: (805) 658-6156   CA
Web Site:
   http://www.employersdepot.com
Year Founded: 1989
Sales Range: $10-24.9 Million
Emp.: 15
Help Supply Services
N.A.I.C.S.: 561330
Cynthia S. Holloway (Pres)

EMPLOYERS MUTUAL CASU-ALTY COMPANY
5826 Executive Dr, Lansing, MI
48911
Tel.: (517) 394-2500
Web Site: http://www.emcins.com
Sales Range: $1-9.9 Million
Emp.: 70
Insurance Agencies & Brokerages
N.A.I.C.S.: 524210
Kathleen Fowler (Mgr)

Subsidiaries:

EMC Insurance Group Inc.   (1)
717 Mulberry St, Des Moines, IA
50309   (100%)
Tel.: (515) 345-2902
Web Site: http://www.emcins.com
Rev: $660,727,000
Assets: $1,685,478,000
Liabilities: $1,119,696,000
Net Worth: $565,782,000
Earnings: ($7,468,000)
Emp.: 2,500
Fiscal Year-end: 12/31/2018
Holding Company; Property & Casualty Insurance & Reinsurance
N.A.I.C.S.: 551112

Lisa A. Simonetta *(Chief Claims Officer & Sr VP)*
Karey S. Anderson *(VP)*
Scott Ronald Jean *(Pres & CEO)*
Elizabeth A. Nigut *(Chief People Officer & Exec VP)*
Kelvin B. Sederburg *(VP)*
Ian C. Asplund *(Chief Strategy Officer & Sr VP)*
Bradley J. Fredericks *(Chief Investment Officer & Sr VP)*
Meyer T. Lehman *(Chief Actuary Officer & Exec VP)*
Todd A. Strother *(Chief Legal Officer, Sec & Exec VP)*
Steven T. Walsh *(VP)*
Daniel C. Crew *(Chief Underwriting Officer & Sr VP)*
Larry G. Hamling *(VP & Controller)*
David J. W. Proctor *(Chm)*
Ann M. Collins *(CFO & Sr VP)*
Sharon R. Cooper *(CMO & Sr VP)*
Phil R. Lucca *(Chief Field Officer & Sr VP)*
Joe R. Riesberg *(CIO & Sr VP)*
Melissa J. Appenzeller *(VP)*
James D. Clough *(VP)*
Robert A. Coon *(VP)*
Derek D. Dunnagan *(VP)*
Jessica J. Hendricks *(VP)*
Ronald D. Herman *(VP)*
Erik J. Keninger *(VP)*
Cindy G. McCauley *(VP)*
Teresa L. Miller *(VP)*
Angela S. Noble *(VP)*
Sean A. Pelletier *(VP)*
Sanja Plynaar *(VP)*
Robert G. Seiler *(VP)*
Lucreia M. Smith *(VP)*
Mondale W. Smith *(VP)*
P. Bryon Snethen *(VP)*
Bruce E. Stanley *(VP)*
Carey R. Verschuure *(Chief Audit Officer & VP)*
Meg M. Weist *(VP)*
Matt G. Wentzel *(VP)*
Deidre N. Williams *(VP)*

Subsidiary (Domestic):

EMC Insurance Companies **(2)**
717 Mulberry St, Des Moines, IA 50309-0712 **(67%)**
Tel.: (515) 280-2511
Web Site: http://www.emcins.com
Sales Range: $750-799.9 Million
Emp.: 1,100
Provides Insurance & Related Services to the Public & the Insurance Industry
N.A.I.C.S.: 524126
Bruce G. Kelley *(Pres, CEO & Treas)*
Eduard Pulkstenis *(Chief Underwriting Officer & Sr VP)*

EMC Underwriters, LLC. **(2)**
717 Mulberry St, Des Moines, IA 50309
Tel.: (515) 345-7650
Web Site: http://www.emcinf.com
Emp.: 3
Property & Casualty Insurance Services
N.A.I.C.S.: 524126
Marcy Boggs *(VP)*

EMCASCO Insurance Company **(2)**
717 Mulberry St, Des Moines, IA 50309
Tel.: (515) 280-2511
Property & Casualty Insurance Services
N.A.I.C.S.: 524126

Hamilton Mutual Insurance Company **(2)**
11311 Cornell Park Dr Ste 500, Blue Ash, OH 45242
Tel.: (513) 221-6010
Web Site: http://www.emcins.com
Property & Casualty Insurance Company
N.A.I.C.S.: 524126
Phil Goedde *(Brand Mgr)*

EMPLOYERS RESOURCE MANAGEMENT INC.
1301 S Bista Ste 200, Boise, ID 83705
Tel.: (208) 376-3000   VA
Web Site:
    http://www.employersresource.com
Year Founded: 1985
Sales Range: $10-24.9 Million

Emp.: 80
Provider of Help Supply Services
N.A.I.C.S.: 561320
George H. Gersema *(Chm & CEO)*
Mary Gersema *(Dir-Ops)*
Ray O'Leary *(Pres)*

EMPLOYERS TEMPORARY SERVICE
30230 John R Rd, Madison Heights, MI 48071
Tel.: (313) 372-7700
Web Site: http://www.etsstaffing.com
Sales Range: $25-49.9 Million
Emp.: 18
Temporary Help Service
N.A.I.C.S.: 561320

EMPLOYERS UNITY INC.
PO Box 173836, Denver, CO 80217
Tel.: (303) 463-3420
Web Site:
    http://www.employersunity.com
Year Founded: 1977
Sales Range: $10-24.9 Million
Emp.: 180
Insurance Agents, Brokers & Service
N.A.I.C.S.: 524210
James L Turner *(CFO & VP)*

EMPLOYMENT CONTROL INC.
414 N Lafayette St, Shelby, NC 28150
Tel.: (704) 484-1812
Web Site: http://www.esieci.com
Sales Range: $10-24.9 Million
Emp.: 50
Temporary Help Service
N.A.I.C.S.: 561320
Bobby Walker *(Pres)*
Shirley Jaynes *(VP-Admin)*

EMPLOYMENT DEVELOPMENT, INC.
8330 County Home Rd, Lisbon, OH 44432
Tel.: (330) 424-7711   OH
Web Site: https://www.employment-development.com
Year Founded: 1969
Rev.: $1,000,000
Emp.: 250
Fiscal Year-end: 12/31/13
Vocational Rehabilitation Services
N.A.I.C.S.: 624310

EMPLOYMENT ENTERPRISES INC.
10550 Linden Lake Plz Ste 200, Manassas, VA 20109
Tel.: (703) 361-2220
Web Site: https://www.eeihr.com
Sales Range: $50-74.9 Million
Emp.: 50
Human Resource Staffing
N.A.I.C.S.: 561320
Jana W. Yeates *(Co-Founder, Owner & CEO)*
Lovey Hammel *(Co-Founder & Pres)*
Tom Hammel *(VP-Employment Enterprises Inc)*
Gala Johnson *(VP-Mktg & Contract Svcs)*
Colleen Clokus *(VP-Workforce Solutions)*
Pauline Tomko *(VP-Bus Dev)*
Verbena Williams *(VP-Acctg)*

Subsidiaries:

Checks and Balances Inc **(1)**
10328 Battleview Pkwy, Manassas, VA 20109
Tel.: (703) 361-2104
Payroll Accounting Service
N.A.I.C.S.: 541214

Temporary Solutions Inc. **(1)**

10550 Linden Lake Plz Ste 200, Manassas, VA 20109
Tel.: (703) 361-2220
Web Site: http://www.eeihr.com
Emp.: 20
Temporary Help Service
N.A.I.C.S.: 561320
Lovey Hammel *(Pres & CEO)*

EMPLOYMENT GROUP HOLDING CORP.
4625 Beckley Rd Bldg 200, Battle Creek, MI 49015
Tel.: (269) 979-9778
Web Site:
    http://www.employmentgroup.com
Year Founded: 1986
Sales Range: $10-24.9 Million
Emp.: 80
Help Supply Services
N.A.I.C.S.: 561320
Mark J. Lancaster *(Pres & CEO)*

Subsidiaries:

Employment Group Inc. **(1)**
4625 Beckley Rd, Battle Creek, MI 49017
Tel.: (269) 660-3500
Web Site: http://www.employmentgroup.com
Employment Services
N.A.I.C.S.: 561311

EMPLOYMENT SOLUTIONS
3600 Mitchell Dr St 50 C, Fort Collins, CO 80525
Tel.: (970) 407-9675
Web Site:
    http://www.employmentsolutions.com
Year Founded: 1994
Sales Range: $10-24.9 Million
Emp.: 30
Employment Services
N.A.I.C.S.: 561311
Rick Wagner *(Pres)*

EMPLOYMENT TECHNOLOGIES CORPORATION
532 S New York Ave, Winter Park, FL 32789
Tel.: (407) 865-6644   FL
Web Site: http://www.etc-easy.com
Year Founded: 1995
Sales Range: $1-9.9 Million
Emp.: 18
Management Consulting Services
N.A.I.C.S.: 541611
Eugenia Sefcik *(Founder)*
Joseph T. Sefcik Jr. *(Pres)*

EMPO CORPORATION
3100 W Lake St Ste 100, Minneapolis, MN 55416-4510
Tel.: (612) 285-8707   MN
Web Site: http://www.empocorp.com
Year Founded: 1999
Sales Range: $10-24.9 Million
Human Resource Outsourcing & Professional Employer Organization
N.A.I.C.S.: 561330
Alan Reid *(Pres & CEO)*

EMPOWER MEDIAMARKETING
15 E 14th St, Cincinnati, OH 45202
Tel.: (513) 871-9454   OH
Web Site:
    https://www.empowermm.com
Year Founded: 1985
Rev.: $325,000,000
Emp.: 165
Advetising Agency
N.A.I.C.S.: 541810
Lynne Veil *(COO & Exec VP)*
Denise Halpin *(Sr VP-Client Leadership)*
Julie Pahutski *(Sr VP-Decision Sciences)*
Joseph Lowry *(CFO-Fin)*

Mitchell Dunn *(Sr VP-Strategic Plng)*
Jason Bender *(VP-Creative)*
Mark Sancrant *(Sr VP-Corp Strategy)*
Kate Rechtsteiner *(Dir-Client Leadership)*
Tim Glover *(VP-Client Leadership)*
Yvonne Starkey-Posey *(Dir-Client Leadership)*
Crystalyn Portwood *(VP)*
Ashley Walters *(Sr VP)*
James W. Price II *(Pres & CEO)*

EMPOWER RF SYSTEMS, INC.
316 W Florence Ave, Inglewood, CA 90301
Tel.: (310) 412-8100
Web Site:
    https://www.empowerrf.com
Year Founded: 2000
Sales Range: $25-49.9 Million
Emp.: 70
Radio Frequency Amplifiers Designer & Mfr
N.A.I.C.S.: 334419
Barry Phelps *(Chm)*
Jon Jacocks *(Pres & CEO)*
Rob Lauria *(VP-Bus Dev & Sls)*
Warren Barry Phelps III *(Exec Chm)*

EMPOWERED PRODUCTS, INC.
3367 W Oquendo Rd, Las Vegas, NV 89118   NV
Web Site:
    https://www.empoweredproducts.com
Year Founded: 2009
EMPO—(OTCBB)
Sales Range: $1-9.9 Million
Emp.: 19
Personal Care & Nutritional Supplement Products Mfr & Distr
N.A.I.C.S.: 424210

Subsidiaries:

Empowered Products Nevada, Inc. **(1)**
3367 W Oquendo Rd, Las Vegas, NV 89118
Tel.: (800) 929-0407
Web Site:
    http://www.empoweredproducts.com
Personal Care & Nutritional Supplement Products Mfr & Distr
N.A.I.C.S.: 424210
Kurt J. Weber *(Controller)*
Scott S. Fraser *(CEO)*

EMPOWERED VENTURES, INC.
401 WCarmel Dr, Carmel, IN 46032
Tel.: (317) 643-2383
Web Site:
    http://www.empowered.ventures
Investment Services
N.A.I.C.S.: 523999
Chris Frederick *(CEO)*

Subsidiaries:

Benoure Plumbing & Heating Inc **(1)**
89 A East Allen Dr, South Burlington, VT 05403
Tel.: (802) 864-7156
Web Site: http://www.benoure.com
Rev.: $4,600,000
Emp.: 33
Site Preparation Contractor
N.A.I.C.S.: 238910
Brad Benoure *(Treas)*
Robin K. Benoure *(Pres)*

Firstar Precision Corp. **(1)**
12340 Plaza Dr, Cleveland, OH 44130
Tel.: (216) 362-7888
Web Site: http://www.firstarcnc.com
Sales Range: $1-9.9 Million
Emp.: 32
Cutting Tool & Machine Tool Accessory Mfr
N.A.I.C.S.: 333515
David Tenny *(Founder)*

Empowered Ventures, Inc.—(Continued)

EMPRESAS BECHARA, INC.
637 Ave Santa Teresa Jornet, May-aguez, PR 00680
Tel.: (787) 834-6666   **PR**
Web Site:
    http://www.empresasbechara.com
Year Founded: 1946
Sales Range: $100-124.9 Million
Emp.: 250
Holding Company; Radio Broadcasting Stations
N.A.I.C.S.: 551112
Dennis Bechara (Owner)

Subsidiaries:

WPRA, Inc.   (1)
637 Ave Santa Teresa Jornet, Mayaguez, PR 00680
Tel.: (787) 834-6666
Web Site: http://www.wpra990.com
Radio Broadcasting Stations
N.A.I.C.S.: 516110
Ada Ramos (Mgr)

EMPRESAS BERRIOS INC.
RR No172 Km Pr 497 Bayamon Berrios Km, Cidra, PR 00739
Tel.: (787) 653-9393
Web Site: http://www.berriospr.com
Sales Range: $150-199.9 Million
Emp.: 800
Furniture Retailer
N.A.I.C.S.: 449110
Florencio Berrios (Pres)
Noel Berrios (VP)

EMPRESAS PUERTORRIQUE-NAS DE DESARROLLO INC.
304 Ave Ponce De Leon St 1100, San Juan, PR 00918
Tel.: (787) 622-8108
Sales Range: $10-24.9 Million
Emp.: 24
Property Management Services
N.A.I.C.S.: 531120
Sara Villamil (Pres)

EMPRESAS SERRALLES INC.
PO Box 198, Mercedita, PR 00715
Tel.: (787) 840-1000
Web Site: http://www.donq.com
Rev.: $123,300,000
Emp.: 300
Rum Distr
N.A.I.C.S.: 312140
Felix Serralles Nevares Jr. (Pres)

EMPRESAS Y-NUINA, INC.
185 Km 0.8 Zona Industrial, Canovanas, PR 00729
Tel.: (787) 876-9191
Web Site: http://www.kikuet.com
Year Founded: 1979
Sales Range: $10-24.9 Million
Emp.: 350
Frozen Food Product Mfr
N.A.I.C.S.: 311412
Enrique Mangual (Pres)
Maximo Figueroa (Gen Mgr)

EMPRESS AMBULANCE SERVICE INC.
722 Nepperhan Ave, Yonkers, NY 10703
Tel.: (914) 965-5040
Web Site:
    https://www.empressems.com
Year Founded: 1985
Sales Range: $10-24.9 Million
Emp.: 220
Ambulance Service
N.A.I.C.S.: 621910

Lenore Minerva (Pres & CEO)
Daryn Baia (Dir-Comm)
Daniel Minerva (VP-Ops)
Michael Minerva (Sr VP)

EMPRISE FINANCIAL CORPO-RATION
257 N Broadway St, Wichita, KS 67202
Tel.: (316) 383-4400
Web Site:
    http://www.emprisebank.com
Sales Range: $100-124.9 Million
Emp.: 380
State Commercial Banks
N.A.I.C.S.: 522110
Thomas A. Page (Pres)
W. A. Michaelis Jr. (Chm)

Subsidiaries:

Emprise Bank   (1)
257 N Broadway, Wichita, KS
67202   (100%)
Tel.: (316) 383-4400
Web Site: http://www.emprisebank.com
Sales Range: $100-124.9 Million
Emp.: 350
Regional Bank
N.A.I.C.S.: 522110
Tom Veatch (CFO)
Galen K. Nelson (Exec VP)
Jim Faith (Exec VP-Comml Banking)
Matt Michaelis (Chm)
Lora A. Barry (Exec VP-Bank Ops)
Bryce K. Carr (Exec VP-Wealth Mgmt)
Teri L. Ginther (Exec VP-Bank Strategy)
Aaron K. Veatch (CFO & Exec VP)
Mark McCaskill (VP-Comml Banking)

EMPYREAN BENEFIT SOLU-TIONS, INC.
3010 Briarpark Dr Ste 8000, Houston, TX 77042
Tel.: (281) 768-2900
Web Site:
    http://www.goempyrean.com
Year Founded: 2006
Sales Range: $25-49.9 Million
Emp.: 253
Human Resource Consulting Services
N.A.I.C.S.: 541612
Richard Wolfe (Founder & CEO)
Colleen Waymel (COO)
Steve Campbell (Chief HR Officer)
Karen Bailey (Officer-Compliance)
Thomas H. Zajac (Chm)
Kelly L. Clark (Chief Info & Tech Officer)

EMPYREAN SERVICES LLC
1108 Ohio River Blvd Ste 805, Sewickley, PA 15143-2049
Tel.: (412) 528-1573
Web Site:
    https://www.empyreanonline.com
Year Founded: 2000
Sales Range: $10-24.9 Million
Emp.: 150
Management Consulting Services
N.A.I.C.S.: 541611
Sushil C. Jain (Pres & CEO)
Patricia G. Tuite (Mng Dir)

EMR TECHNOLOGY SOLU-TIONS, INC.
90 Washington Valley Rd, Bedminster, NJ 07921
Tel.: (908) 997-0617
Rev.: $396,535
Assets: $47,758
Liabilities: $2,569,687
Net Worth: ($2,521,929)
Earnings: ($499,548)
Emp.: 4
Fiscal Year-end: 12/31/20
Medical Records Services
N.A.I.C.S.: 513210

John X. Adiletta (Chm, Pres & CEO)
Lowell Thomas Holden (CFO, Principal Acctg Officer & Sec)

Subsidiaries:

Empower Technologies, Inc.   (1)
90 Washington Vly Rd, Bedminster, NJ 07921
Tel.: (908) 997-0617
Linux-Based Software Publisher
N.A.I.C.S.: 513210

EMRY CAPITAL GROUP, INC.
555 S Australian Ave W, Palm Beach, FL 33401
Tel.: (561) 699-6363   **FL**
Investment Services
N.A.I.C.S.: 523999
Miro Zecevic (Pres, Treas & Sec)

Subsidiaries:

DKG Capital, Inc.   (1)
No 17-2-2 Jalan 3/62D Medan Putra Business Centre, Bandar Menjalara 522C WP, Kuala Lumpur, 52200, Malaysia
Tel.: (60) 7025604373
Sales Range: Less than $1 Million
Investment Services
N.A.I.C.S.: 523999
Tesheb Casimir (Founder & CEO)

EMS CONSULTING - INTELLI-GENT CHAOS
5550 W Executive Dr Ste 450, Tampa, FL 33609
Tel.: (813) 287-2486
Web Site:
    https://www.consultems.com
Year Founded: 1998
Sales Range: $10-24.9 Million
Emp.: 120
Technology Consulting Services
N.A.I.C.S.: 541690
Elaine Myrback (Pres & CEO)
Angie May (VP-Admin)

EMS INDUSTRIAL INC.
4901 Prairie Dock Dr, Madison, WI 53718
Tel.: (608) 241-8866
Web Site:
    https://www.emsindustrial.com
Rev.: $14,200,000
Emp.: 75
Electrical Apparatus & Equipment
Wiring Supplies & Related Equipment Merchant Whslr
N.A.I.C.S.: 423610
William Hinnendael (Pres)

EMS TECHNOLOGY SOLU-TIONS, LLC
3771 Tramore Pointe Pkwy SW, Austell, GA 30106
Web Site: http://www.operativeiq.com
Year Founded: 2007
Sales Range: $1-9.9 Million
Emp.: 15
Software Development Services
N.A.I.C.S.: 541511
E. J. Aufderheide (CEO)

EMSCO INC.
306 Shenango St, Girard, PA 16417
Tel.: (814) 774-3137
Web Site:
    https://www.emscogroup.com
Sales Range: $10-24.9 Million
Emp.: 105
Cleaning Or Polishing Preparations
N.A.I.C.S.: 333310
David B. Oas (Co-Owner)
Steve Oas (Co-Owner & Pres)
Ken Reisenweber (Controller)

EMSCO INC.

22350 Royalton Rd, Strongsville, OH 44149
Tel.: (440) 238-2100
Web Site: http://www.emsco.com
Year Founded: 1970
Sales Range: $10-24.9 Million
Emp.: 55
Swimming Pools, Equipment & Supplies
N.A.I.C.S.: 423910
Mark Stoyanoff (Pres)
Richard Lanvee (VP)

EMSER TILE LLC
8431 Santa Monica Blvd, Los Angeles, CA 90069
Tel.: (323) 650-2000
Web Site: http://www.emser.com
Sales Range: $25-49.9 Million
Emp.: 200
Provider of Ceramic Tile & Natural Stone
N.A.I.C.S.: 423220
Ann Yoen (CIO)
Carl Delia (Gen Mgr)
Alan Brunell (Mgr-Fin Reporting)
Christina Wu (Product Mgr-Sourcing)
Scott Webb (VP-Sls & Branch Ops)
Wes Macauley (Branch Mgr)
Barry Dambrowski (Dir-Credit)
Roger Van House (Mgr-San Diego County)
Patrick Lytle (Reg Mgr-Credit)
Mark Seal (VP-Supply Chain)
Suzanne Zurfluh (Dir-Design & Trend)

EMSIG MANUFACTURING CORP.
263 W 38th St 5th Fl, New York, NY 10018
Tel.: (718) 784-7717
Web Site: https://www.usbutton.com
Rev.: $16,900,000
Emp.: 80
Buttons & Parts
N.A.I.C.S.: 339993
David Kurstedt (VP)

EMSL ANALYTICAL, INC.
200 Route 130 N, Cinnaminson, NJ 08077
Tel.: (856) 858-4800
Web Site: https://www.emsl.com
Year Founded: 1981
Sales Range: $10-24.9 Million
Emp.: 500
Testing Laboratories
N.A.I.C.S.: 541715
Peter Frasca (Pres)
Joe Frasca (Sr VP-Mktg)
Maria Boisclair (Dir-Admin & Customer Svcs)
Patricia Kirkland (Mgr-Natl Quality Assurance)
Josh Trowman (Dir-Product Sls)
Ron Smith (VP-Sls)
Jody Thomason (Dir-Product Dev)
Rob DeMalo (Sr VP-Lab Svcs)
Daniel Kocher (VP-Contract Svcs)
Bruce Faulseit (VP-Engrg)

EMUAMERICAS, LLC.
1799 Pennsylvania St 4th Fl, Denver, CO 80203-3972
Tel.: (303) 733-3385
Web Site:
    http://www.emuamericas.com
Sales Range: $10-24.9 Million
Emp.: 17
Furniture Whslr
N.A.I.C.S.: 423210
Katarina Robinson (Exec Mgr)

EMWOOD LUMBER CO. INC.
155 Railroad Ave, Closter, NJ 07624
Tel.: (201) 327-8737   **NJ**

ENCAP INVESTMENTS L.P.

Year Founded: 1969
Sales Range: $10-24.9 Million
Emp.: 35
Provider of Rough, Dressed & Finished Lumber
N.A.I.C.S.: 423310
Dominick L. Mone (Pres)

EMX CONTROLS INC.
35 Boston St, Uxbridge, MA 01569
Tel.: (508) 876-9700
Web Site:
   http://www.emxcontrols.com
Year Founded: 1963
Sales Range: $25-49.9 Million
Emp.: 40
Electric Controls & Control Accessories, Industrial
N.A.I.C.S.: 335314
Richard Padovano (Pres)

EN-FAB INC.
3905 Jensen Dr, Houston, TX 77026
Tel.: (713) 225-4913
Web Site: https://www.en-fabinc.com
Sales Range: $10-24.9 Million
Emp.: 80
Oil Field Machinery & Equipment
N.A.I.C.S.: 333132
Chandra S. Tripathy (Pres)
Abe Varghese (Project Mgr)

EN-TECH CORP.
91 Ruckman Rd, Closter, NJ 07624
Tel.: (201) 784-1034
Web Site: http://www.en-techcorp.com
Sales Range: $25-49.9 Million
Emp.: 35
Sewer Line Construction
N.A.I.C.S.: 237110
Nada Camali (Pres)
Bob Boost (Controller)

EN-WAY ENTERPRISES INC.
1413 W Randall St, Coopersville, MI 49404
Tel.: (616) 837-9771
Web Site: http://www.foreway.net
Sales Range: $10-24.9 Million
Emp.: 200
Provider of Truckload Services:
Transportation & Related Logistic Services
N.A.I.C.S.: 484121
Pam Hassevoort (CEO)

Subsidiaries:

Ensing Truck Service Inc   (1)
1413 W Randall St, Coopersville, MI 49404
Tel.: (616) 837-9771
Web Site: http://www.foreway.net
Rev.: $250,000
Emp.: 40
General Truck Repair
N.A.I.C.S.: 811111
Pam Hassevoort (Pres)

Foreway Transportation Inc.   (1)
1413 W Randall St, Coopersville, MI 49404
Tel.: (616) 997-9771
Web Site: http://www.foreway.net
Sales Range: $10-24.9 Million
Emp.: 50
Trucking Except Local
N.A.I.C.S.: 484121
Pam Hassevoort (Pres)

ENABLE, INC.
605 Neponset St, Canton, MA 02021
Tel.: (781) 828-4770   MA
Web Site: https://www.enableinc.org
Year Founded: 1981
Sales Range: $10-24.9 Million
Emp.: 243
Therapeutic, Educational & Recreational Services
N.A.I.C.S.: 621340
Peter Brown (Treas)

ENABLEIT, LLC
25 W 36th St 11th Fl, New York, NY 10018
Tel.: (646) 558-3741
Web Site: http://www.enableit.us.com
Year Founded: 2010
Sales Range: $10-24.9 Million
Emp.: 150
Cyber Security Consulting Services
N.A.I.C.S.: 541690
Fabrice Mouret (Founder & Mng Partner)
Sammy Chowdhury (Partner & Head-Svc Delivery)
Michael Stern (Partner & Chief Revenue Officer)
Steve Seideman (Head-Ethical Hacking)

ENABLEWISE, LLC
4014 Gunn Hwy Ste 248, Tampa, FL 33618
Tel.: (813) 490-4260   DE
Web Site: http://www.concertium.com
Year Founded: 1996
Information Technology Consulting Services
N.A.I.C.S.: 541519
Kausik Sarkar (Mng Dir-India)
Rob Weatherford (Controller)
Mark Hegarty (Mgr-NOC)
Soma Bose (Project Mgr-US Projects)
Kaustubh Sarkar (Project Mgr-Managed Svcs)
Amar Nath Singh (Project Mgr-UI & UX)
Sanchari Mukherjee (Mgr-HR)
Sougat Hajra (Assoc Dir-Ops)
Dwayne Leininger (Assoc Dir-Software Dev Svcs)
Seemantini Bose (Mgr-Corp Brand)
Abhishek Bhattacharya (Mgr-Digital Mktg)
Tania Bhattacharya (Mgr-Content)
Anirban Lahiri (Project Mgr-Microsoft Technologies)
Matthew Hall (Sr Mgr-Application Mng Svcs)
Jyoti Sarkar (Sr VP-Dev)
Santiago Casal (Sr VP-Tech Ops)
Charlotte Kibert (Sr VP-Digital Transformation)
Carren Rieger (Pres & CEO)

ENABLX, INC.
100 Enterprise Dr Ste 505, Rockaway, NJ 07866
Tel.: (973) 361-7770
Web Site: https://www.enablx.com
Rev.: $7,000,000
Emp.: 65
Provider of Technology Services & Contact Center Management Solutions
N.A.I.C.S.: 561421
James W. Riff (Pres & CEO)
Ryan Hesterman (Mgr-Ops)
Angela Mancini (Controller)

ENACTUS
3253 E Chestnut Expwy Ste 2, Springfield, MO 65802
Tel.: (417) 831-9505   TX
Web Site: http://www.enactus.org
Year Founded: 1975
Rev.: $11,466,053
Assets: $12,985,356
Liabilities: $5,093,131
Net Worth: $7,892,225
Earnings: ($1,270,550)
Emp.: 78
Fiscal Year-end: 12/31/18
Entrepreneurial Action Services
N.A.I.C.S.: 813910

Mike Moore (Vice Chm)
Kees Kruythoff (Chm)
Jesus Esparza (Pres-Mexico & VP)
Christine Rader (CFO)
Terry Torok (Chief Innovation Officer)
Shmita Ramkumar (Chief Program Officer & VP-India)
Lisa Sepulveda (Chief Client Officer & Sec)
Gonzalve Bich (Vice Chm)
Betsy Liley (Chief Dev Officer)
Rachael A. Jarosh (Pres & CEO)

ENALASYS CORP.
250 Avenida Campillo, Calexico, CA 92231
Tel.: (760) 768-3228   CA
Web Site: http://www.enalasys.com
Year Founded: 1995
Sales Range: $25-49.9 Million
Emp.: 42
Environmental Controls Manufacturing Measuring/Controlling Devices
N.A.I.C.S.: 334512
Eric Taylor (Co-Founder, Pres & CEO)
John Faircloth (Co-Founder)
Kerry Delay McCane (CFO & COO)

ENAMELED STEEL
4568 W Addison St, Chicago, IL 60641
Tel.: (773) 777-5900
Web Site:
   http://www.enameledsteel.com
Electroplating, Plating, Polishing, Anodizing & Coloring
N.A.I.C.S.: 332813
George Davies (Owner)

Subsidiaries:

Arlington Plating Company   (1)
600 S Vermont St, Palatine, IL 60078-0974
Tel.: (847) 359-1490
Web Site: http://www.arlingtonplating.com
Electroplating, Plating, Polishing, Anodizing & Coloring
N.A.I.C.S.: 332813
Jay Ramp (Dir-Sls & Mktg)

ENAP INC.
555 Hudson Vly Ave, New Windsor, NY 12553
Tel.: (845) 564-4900   NY
Web Site: http://www.enap.com
Year Founded: 1967
Sales Range: $10-24.9 Million
Emp.: 49
Provider of Lumber, Plywood & Millwork Services
N.A.I.C.S.: 423310
Stephen J. Sallah (Pres & CEO)
Tom Molloy (VP-Building Matls)
Bob Carson (VP-Bus Dev)
Duncan Facey (VP-Forest Products)

ENCANTO RESTAURANTS, INC
PO Box 11858, San Juan, PR 00922
Tel.: (787) 792-4311   PR
Web Site:
   http://www.empleosencantopr.com
Holding & Acquisition Company
N.A.I.C.S.: 551112
Jorge Berlingeri (COO)

Subsidiaries:

Tricon Restaurant International (PR), Inc.   (1)
D St Lot 22 Amelia Industrial Park, Guaynabo, PR 00969   (100%)
Tel.: (787) 792-4311
Rev.: $173,346,384
Emp.: 110
Fast Food Restaurant Management Offices
N.A.I.C.S.: 722513

Subsidiary (Domestic):

Pizza Hut of Puerto Rico Inc.   (2)
Montehiedra Office Centre 9615 Ave Los Romeros Ste 200, San Juan, PR 00926
Tel.: (787) 792-4311
Emp.: 1,000
Fast Food Services
N.A.I.C.S.: 722513
Humberco Rovira (CEO)

ENCAP INVESTMENTS L.P.
1100 Louisiana Ste 4900, Houston, TX 77002
Tel.: (713) 659-6100   TX
Web Site:
   http://www.encapinvestments.com
Year Founded: 1999
Sales Range: $10-24.9 Million
Emp.: 47
General & Industrial Loan Institutions
N.A.I.C.S.: 541611
Gary R. Petersen (Mng Partner & Principal)
Mitchell Hovendick (Dir-Houston)
Robert Haier (CFO)
Caleb Allen (Mgr-Tax)
Charles W. Bauer (Mng Dir)
D. Martin Phillips (Mng Partner)
Dennis F. Jaggi (Founder & Mng Partner)
Dennis J. McCanless (Partner)
E. Murphy Markham (Mng Partner)
H. Bryan Danmier (VP-Engrg)
James S. Crain (Dir-Dallas)
Jana Jonas (Office Mgr)
Jason Morgan (Dir-Fin Reporting)
Jonathan Patrick (Controller)
Kyle M. Kafka (Mng Dir)
Luke Brandenberg (VP)
M. Sean Smith (Partner)
Matt Crystal (Dir-IR-Houston)
Melissa Standley (Dir-Tax)
Meredith Stieler (Controller)
Morriss L. Hurt (Mng Dir)
Ryan P. Devlin (Dir-Houston)
Scott R. Smetko (Dir-Dallas)
William R. Lemmons (Founder & Mng Partner)
William D. Waldrip (Founder & Mng Partner)
David B. Miller (Mng Partner)
Robert L. Zorich (Mng Partner & Principal)
Brooks Despot (VP)
Bryan Stahl (VP)
George W. Purgason (VP)
J. Zachary Kayem (VP)
Jack Reilly (VP)
Sam Pitts (Mng Dir)
Jerry Smith (Mng Dir-Houston)
Brett Knowles (VP)
Drew Wellsfry (VP)
Jason Hajdik (VP)
Taylor McCay (VP)
Thomas J. Waldrip (VP)
Cole Sanches (VP-Fin Reporting)
James A. Hughes (Mng Partner)
Douglas E. Swanson Jr. (Mng Partner)
Mark E. Burroughs Jr. (Mng Dir)
Mark A. Welsh IV (Mng Dir)
Wynne M. Snoots Jr. (Partner)

Subsidiaries:

EnCap Flatrock Midstream   (1)
1826 N Loop 1604 W Ste 200, San Antonio, TX 78248
Tel.: (210) 494-6777
Web Site: http://www.efmidstream.com
Rev.: $5,600,000,000
Oil & Gas Operations Investment Management Firm
N.A.I.C.S.: 523940
Dennis F. Jaggi (Co-Founder & Mng Partner-Oklahoma City)
William D. Waldrip (Co-Founder & Mng Partner)

EnCap Investments L.P.—(Continued)

Gregory C. King *(Mng Partner)*
Dennis J. McCanless *(Partner)*
Matthew R. Melton *(VP)*
Kyle Stelma *(VP)*
William R. Lemmons Jr. *(Co-Founder & Mng Partner)*

Holding (Domestic):

Lucid Energy Group, LLC   (2)
3100 McKinnon St Ste 800, Dallas, TX 75201
Tel.: (214) 420-4950
Web Site: http://www.lucid-energy.com
Emp.: 40
Oil & Gas Gathering, Compression, Processing & Transportation Services
N.A.I.C.S.: 213112
Jay L. Langham *(Exec VP)*
Michael J. Latchem *(CEO)*
Ryan Moss *(CFO & Exec VP)*
Scott Brown *(Chief Comml Officer & Exec VP)*
Rodney Madden *(Sr VP-Bus Dev & Comml-Crude)*
Robert Suehs *(VP-Ops)*
Stew Fuller *(VP-Fin)*
Jennifer Rost *(VP)*
Brian T. Raber *(COO & Sr VP)*

Rangeland Energy   (2)
2150 Town Sq Pl Ste 700, Sugar Land, TX 77479
Tel.: (281) 566-3000
Web Site: http://www.rangelandenergy.com
Crude Petroleum & Natural Gas Pipeline Operator
N.A.I.C.S.: 486110
Christopher W. Keene *(Pres & CEO)*

Paloma Partners VI Holdings, LLC   (1)
1100 Louisiana Ste 5100, Houston, TX 77002
Tel.: (713) 650-8500
Web Site: http://www.palomaresources.com
Holding Company
N.A.I.C.S.: 551112
Christopher N. O'Sullivan *(Pres)*

Subsidiary (Domestic):

Goodrich Petroleum Corporation   (2)
801 Louisiana Ste 700, Houston, TX 77002
Tel.: (713) 780-9494
Web Site: http://www.goodrichpetroleumcorp.com
Rev.: $93,826,000
Assets: $205,077,000
Liabilities: $163,507,000
Net Worth: $41,570,000
Earnings: ($44,141,000)
Emp.: 43
Fiscal Year-end: 12/31/2020
Holding Company
N.A.I.C.S.: 551112
Gil Goodrich *(CEO)*

ENCAP, LLC
3921 Algoma Rd, Green Bay, WI 54311
Tel.: (920) 406-5050
Web Site: http://www.encap.net
Year Founded: 1999
Sales Range: $25-49.9 Million
Emp.: 26
Lawn Care Products Mfr
N.A.I.C.S.: 115112
Michael Krysiak *(Pres & CEO)*
Chuck Holton *(Mgr-Natl Accts)*
Sarah Vandertie *(Mgr-Acct Svcs)*
Jeff Rindfleisch *(Mgr-Ops)*
Paul Baeten *(Mgr-IT)*
Chris Calawerts *(Mgr-Bus Dev)*
Tomas Roa *(Project Mgr)*

ENCAPSYS LLC
3563839, Appleton, WI 54915
Web Site: http://www.encapsys.com
Coatings & Paint Mfr
N.A.I.C.S.: 325510
Mary Goggans *(Gen Mgr & Exec Dir)*

ENCHOICE, INC.

1400 E Southern Ave Ste 800, Tempe, AZ 85282
Tel.: (480) 477-3838   AZ
Web Site: http://www.enchoice.com
Year Founded: 1993
Computer System Design Services
N.A.I.C.S.: 541512
Brian Curry *(COO)*
Antony White *(Chm)*
Darius DiTallo *(CFO)*
Jim Picardi *(Exec VP-Sls & Mktg)*
John Emerson *(Exec VP-Support Svcs)*
Dave Parks *(CEO)*
Mike Fernandes *(VP-Products)*
Bill Wetzel *(VP-Pro Svcs)*

ENCINO ENVIRONMENTAL SERVICES, LLC
20302 Park Row Dr Ste 1200, Katy, TX 77449
Tel.: (281) 201-3544
Web Site: https://encinoenviron.com
Year Founded: 2010
Environmental Services
N.A.I.C.S.: 541620

ENCO INDUSTRIES, INC.
4 Wilder Dr Ste 7, Plaistow, NH 03865
Tel.: (603) 382-8481
Web Site: http://www.encoind.com
Year Founded: 1994
Sales Range: $1-9.9 Million
Emp.: 8
Environmental Consulting Services
N.A.I.C.S.: 541620
Michael Rosa *(Co-Founder, Pres & CEO)*
George Adyns *(Pres)*

ENCO MANUFACTURING CORP.
43 Baldorioty St, Cidra, PR 00739
Tel.: (787) 739-3751
Web Site: http://www.encomfg.com
Year Founded: 1983
Sales Range: $10-24.9 Million
Emp.: 125
Paint & Coating Mfr
N.A.I.C.S.: 325510
Hiram Diaz *(Gen Mgr)*

ENCOMPASS DIGITAL MEDIA
250 Harbor Dr, Stamford, CT 06902
Tel.: (203) 965-6000
Web Site: https://www.encompass.tv
Year Founded: 2008
Sales Range: $200-249.9 Million
Emp.: 1,131
Media Capture, Management & Distribution Services for Media Companies
N.A.I.C.S.: 541840
Juan Salleras *(Exec VP & Gen Mgr-Latin America)*
Marc Bruce *(Mng Dir-APAC)*
Joe Simon *(COO)*

Subsidiaries:

Encompass Asia   (1)
20 Loyang Crescent, Singapore, 508984, Singapore   (100%)
Tel.: (65) 6548 0388
Web Site: http://www.encompass.tv
Media Center, Media Management & Global Archive Services
N.A.I.C.S.: 541840
Deepakjit Singh *(Mng Dir)*

Encompass Digital Media   (1)
6221 Holly Dr, Lino Lakes, MN 55038   (100%)
Tel.: (612) 330-2771
Web Site: http://www.encompass.tv
Fiber Networks Operations
N.A.I.C.S.: 335921
Scott Baskin *(Exec VP-New York Metro & Minneapolis)*

Encompass Digital Media   (1)
545 Fifth Ave, New York, NY 10017   (100%)
Tel.: (212) 599-1391
Web Site: http://www.encompass.tv
Worldwide Fiber Networks & Northeast Broadcast Operations
N.A.I.C.S.: 516120
Scott Baskin *(Exec VP-New York Metro & Minneapolis)*

Encompass Digital Media, Inc.   (1)
3845 Pleasantdale Rd, Atlanta, GA 30340
Tel.: (678) 421-6600
Web Site: http://www.encompass.tv
Emp.: 500
Digital Media Services
N.A.I.C.S.: 516120
William Tillson *(Exec Chm)*
James Schuster *(Pres & Exec VP)*
Terry Bowen *(Sr VP-Govt Svcs & Bus Ops)*

Encompass Latin America   (1)
Saenz Valiente 2420 Martinez, B1640GNX, Buenos Aires, Argentina   (100%)
Tel.: (54) 11 4106 8400
Web Site: http://www.encompass.tv
Content Management, Channel Origination, Satellite & Fiber Transmission Services
N.A.I.C.S.: 541618
Juan Salleras *(Exec VP & Gen Mgr)*

Encompass London   (1)
1 Stephent Street, London, W1T 1AT, United Kingdom   (100%)
Tel.: (44) 20 7131 6131
Web Site: http://www.encompass.tv
Channel Origination Satellite & Fiber Transmission Engineering & Digital Media Asset Management Service
N.A.I.C.S.: 516120
Brett Belinsky *(Mng Dir-EMEA)*

Encompass Los Angeles   (1)
3030 Andrita St, Los Angeles, CA 90065   (100%)
Tel.: (323) 344-4500
Web Site: http://www.encompass.tv
Network Operations & Broadcast Engineering Services
N.A.I.C.S.: 516120
Ken Fuller *(Sr VP & Gen Mgr)*
Angela J. Pierce *(Sr VP-Administration & Mktg & Chief of Staff)*
Vincent Lyons *(Sr VP-Digital Media)*

ENCOMPASS GROUP LLC
615 Macon St, McDonough, GA 30253
Tel.: (770) 957-3981   GA
Web Site: http://www.encompassgroup.net
Year Founded: 1946
Sales Range: $100-124.9 Million
Emp.: 250
Mfr of Medical Apparel, Sports & Health Products
N.A.I.C.S.: 315250
David Huelsbeck *(VP-Ops)*
Greg Dugger *(VP & Controller)*
Alan Davis *(CFO)*
John J. Wood *(CEO)*

Subsidiaries:

AlbaHealth, LLC   (1)
615 Macon St, McDonough, GA 30253
Tel.: (770) 957-1211
Surgical Dressings & Other Knitted Health Care Products Mfr
N.A.I.C.S.: 339113
Bill Ott *(Pres)*

Encompass Group LLC - Techstyles Division   (1)
615 Macon St, McDonough, GA 30253
Tel.: (800) 284-4540
Pillow Mfr
N.A.I.C.S.: 314120

Encompass Group LLC - The Pillow Factory Division   (1)
955 Campus Dr, Mundelein, IL 60060
Tel.: (847) 680-3388
Pillow Mfr
N.A.I.C.S.: 314120

Encompass Textiles & Interiors   (1)
2609 Territorial Rd, Saint Paul, MN 55114
Tel.: (651) 646-6600
Web Site: http://www.encompassgroup.net
Rev.: $42,000,000
Emp.: 73
Sheets, Textile
N.A.I.C.S.: 423220

Whiteswan/Meta   (1)
13975 Polo Trl, Lake Forest, IL 60045
Tel.: (847) 247-0380
Web Site: http://www.whiteswanbrands.com
Sales Range: $25-49.9 Million
Emp.: 30
Mfr of Healthcare Uniforms
N.A.I.C.S.: 315250
Michael Gann *(Gen Mgr-Sls & Mktg)*

ENCONNEX LLC
4670 Aircirle Cir, Reno, NV 89502
Tel.: (833) 825-5329
Web Site: http://www.enconnex.com
Year Founded: 2012
Computer Product Enginering Mfr & Services
N.A.I.C.S.: 333618
Thane Moore *(Dir-Product Line)*

ENCORE ASSOCIATES INC.
12647 Alcosta Blvd Ste 155, San Ramon, CA 94583
Tel.: (925) 837-6933
Web Site: http://www.encoreassociates.com
Strategic Advisory Firm
N.A.I.C.S.: 541613
Gary Dale Smith *(Mng Partner, Pres & CEO)*
Tom DeMott *(COO, Mng Partner & Exec VP)*
Don Reid *(Mng Dir & Exec VP)*
Lee Merritts *(Sr VP & Sr Partner)*

Subsidiaries:

Encore Consumer Capital LLC   (1)
111 Pine St Ste 1825, San Francisco, CA 94111
Tel.: (415) 296-9850
Web Site: http://www.encoreconsumercapital.com
Sales Range: $25-49.9 Million
Emp.: 10
Privater Equity Firm
N.A.I.C.S.: 523999
Gary Dale Smith *(Partner-Operating)*
Robert Brown *(Mng Dir)*
Scott Sellers *(Mng Dir)*
Kisen Nathu *(Dir-Deal Origination & Execution)*
Raigan Roy *(Office Mgr)*
Bill Shen *(Mng Dir)*
Steve Mintz *(Partner-Operating)*

Joint Venture (Domestic):

Ciao Bella Gelato Company   (2)
745 Boylston St, Boston, MA 02116
Tel.: (973) 373-1200
Web Site: http://www.ciaobellagelato.com
Sales Range: $25-49.9 Million
Ice Cream Mfr; Owned by Sherbrooke Capital LLC & Encore Consumer Capital LLC
N.A.I.C.S.: 424430
Carlos Canals *(CEO)*

Holding (Domestic):

The Lion Brewery, Inc.   (2)
700 N Pennsylvania Ave, Wilkes Barre, PA 18705-2451
Tel.: (570) 823-8801
Web Site: http://www.lionbrewery.com
Brewer & Bottler of Malt Beverages & Specialty Soft Drinks
N.A.I.C.S.: 312120
Leo Orlandini *(Dir-Ops)*
Patrick E. Balardi *(CFO & VP)*
Jay Strausser *(VP-Logistics & Mgmt Inventory)*
Michael Clarke *(CEO)*

ENCORE AVIATION LLC

2210 Palomar Airport Rd, Carlsbad, CA 92011
Tel.: (760) 237-2100   CA
Web Site: https://encoreaviation.aero
Emp.: 100
Aviation & Aerospace Component Mfg
N.A.I.C.S.: 336412

ENCORE BRANDS, INC.
2215-B Renaissance Dr, Las Vegas, NV 89119
Tel.: (310) 699-9937   NV
Web Site:
    http://www.encorebrands.com
Year Founded: 2008
Sales Range: Less than $1 Million
Emp.: 2
Alcoholic Beverages Whslr & Distr
N.A.I.C.S.: 424820
Gareth West *(Chm & CEO)*
Alex G. McKean *(CFO)*

ENCORE FRUIT MARKETING INC.
120 W Bonita Ave Ste 204, San Dimas, CA 91773-3035
Tel.: (909) 394-5640
Web Site:
    https://www.encorefruit.com
Sales Range: $50-74.9 Million
Emp.: 10
Packaged Frozen Goods
N.A.I.C.S.: 424420
Greg Kaiser *(Pres)*
Chris Schubert *(VP-Sls-San Dimas)*
Lisa Coberg *(CEO)*

ENCORE LUXURY COACH LEASING LLC
2491 N Mount Juliet Rd Ste 1123, Mount Juliet, TN 37122-8026
Tel.: (615) 505-3337   DE
Web Site: https://encorecoaches.com
Passenger Transportation
N.A.I.C.S.: 485999

Subsidiaries:

Nitetrain Coach Co Inc.   (1)
7454 Old Hickory Blvd, Whites Creek, TN 37189-9165
Tel.: (615) 242-9696
Web Site: http://www.nitetraincoach.com
Charter Bus Industry
N.A.I.C.S.: 485510

ENCORE MOTORCARS OF SARASOTA, INC.
6000 S Tamiami Trl, Sarasota, FL 34231
Tel.: (941) 922-6337
Web Site:
    https://www.encoreautos.com
Sales Range: $25-49.9 Million
Emp.: 30
New Car Dealers
N.A.I.C.S.: 441110
Guy Lackey *(Gen Mgr)*
Al Pagan *(Gen Mgr-Sls)*
Scott Snyder *(Mgr-Lot)*
George Manooshian Jr. *(Owner)*
George Mannoshian Sr. *(Mgr-Transportation)*

ENCORE NETWORKS INC.
3800 Concorde Pkwy Ste 1500, Chantilly, VA 20151
Tel.: (703) 318-7750   VA
Web Site:
    https://www.encorenetworks.com
Year Founded: 2002
Signaling Conversions & Network Access Products
N.A.I.C.S.: 334118
Peter C. Madsen *(Pres & CEO)*
Mark H. Rafferty *(CFO & VP)*
George Glass *(VP-Engrg)*

ENCORE PARTNERS LLC
PO Box 3624, Williamsburg, VA 23187
Tel.: (757) 564-7226
Web Site:
    http://www.encorepartners.com
Real Estate Agents & Managers
N.A.I.C.S.: 531210
Rob Brown *(CEO)*

ENCRISP, LLC
714 Southview PL NE Ste 100, Leesburg, VA 20176
Tel.: (703) 424-7615
Year Founded: 2004
Rev.: $10,600,000
Emp.: 10
Computer System Design Services
N.A.I.C.S.: 541512
Bhavesh C. Bhagat *(Pres & CEO)*
Jagan Vaman *(VP)*
James Cupps *(Mgr)*

ENCYCLOPAEDIA BRITAN-NICA, INC.
325 N La Salle St Ste 200, Chicago, IL 60654
Tel.: (312) 347-7000   NY
Web Site: http://www.britannica.com
Year Founded: 1768
Sales Range: $400-449.9 Million
Emp.: 200
Encyclopedia Publisher
N.A.I.C.S.: 513130
Jorge Cauz *(Pres)*
Michael Ross *(Sr. VP-Britannica Digital Learning-US & EMEA)*
Leah Mansoor *(Sr VP-Digital Leaning-Intl)*
Chris Mayland *(VP-Consumer Markets)*
Doug Eveleigh *(Gen Counsel)*
Karthik Krishnan *(CEO-Global)*
Jaqui E. Safra *(Chm)*

Subsidiaries:

Merriam-Webster, Inc.   (1)
47 Federal St, Springfield, MA 01105-1127
Tel.: (413) 734-3134
Web Site: http://www.m-w.com
Sales Range: $10-24.9 Million
Emp.: 110
Printer & Publisher of Books
N.A.I.C.S.: 513130
John M. Morse *(Pres & Publr)*
Michael Guzzi *(Dir-Electronic Product Dev)*
Stephen Perrault *(Editor-in-Chief)*

ENDEAVOR ACQUISITION CORP.
477 Madison Ave 6th Fl, New York, NY 10022
Tel.: (212) 287-4092
N.A.I.C.S.:

ENDEAVOR BUSINESS MEDIA LLC
30 Burton Hills Blvd Ste 185, Nashville, TN 37215
Tel.: (800) 547-7377   DE
Web Site:
    https://www.endeavorbusiness
    media.com
Year Founded: 2017
Emp.: 100
Business-To-Business Services
N.A.I.C.S.: 425120
Chris Ferrell *(CEO)*

Subsidiaries:

Construction Business Media, LLC   (1)
579 N 1st Bank Dr Ste 220, Palatine, IL 60067-8126
Tel.: (847) 359-6493
Web Site: http://www.arch-products.com
Rev.: $1,700,000
Emp.: 4

Periodical Publishers
N.A.I.C.S.: 513120
Jim Crockett *(Dir-Editorial)*

ENDEAVOR ENERGY RE-SOURCES LP
110 N Marienfeld St Ste 200, Midland, TX 79701
Tel.: (432) 687-1575
Web Site:
    https://www.endeavorenergylp.com
Rev.: $38,400,000
Emp.: 100
Crude Petroleum Production
N.A.I.C.S.: 211120
Michael Short *(Gen Counsel)*
Kaye Gray *(Dir-HR)*
Brenda R. Schroer *(CFO)*

ENDEAVOR IP, INC.
140 Broadway 46th Fl, New York, NY 10005
Tel.: (212) 585-7514   NV
Web Site: http://www.enip.com
Year Founded: 2009
Sales Range: $1-9.9 Million
Emp.: 1
Intellectual Property Assets Commercialization & Development
N.A.I.C.S.: 561499

ENDEAVOR SCHOOLS, LLC
9350 S Dixie Hwy Ste 950, Miami, FL 33156
Tel.: (305) 677-8670
Web Site:
    http://www.endeavorschools.com
Year Founded: 2012
Sales Range: $75-99.9 Million
Emp.: 1,600
Private School Services
N.A.I.C.S.: 611110
Ricardo E. Campo *(Founder & CEO)*
Danielle Millman *(COO)*
Joe O'Connell *(CFO)*
Paul Diobilda *(CMO)*
Kenneth Kass *(Exec VP-Tech)*

ENDERLE GROUP, INC.
389 Photinia Ln, San Jose, CA 95127
Tel.: (408) 272-8560
Web Site:
    http://www.enderlegroup.com
Sales Range: Less than $1 Million
Emp.: 4
Business Consulting & Advisory Services
N.A.I.C.S.: 541611
Rob Enderle *(Pres)*

ENDGAME SYSTEMS, LLC
2214 Rock Hill Rd 150, Herndon, VA 20170-4231
Tel.: (404) 941-3900
Web Site: http://www.endgame.com
Year Founded: 2008
Sales Range: $10-24.9 Million
Emp.: 100
Cyber Security Solutions
N.A.I.C.S.: 513210
Mark A. Snell *(CFO)*
Rick Hensley *(Sr VP-Svcs)*
Chris Darby *(Chm)*
Jon Brody *(Sr VP-Mktg)*
Jim Tosh *(Sr VP-Engrg)*
Jamie Butler *(CTO)*
Gary Benedetti *(Exec VP-Sls)*
Peter Bloom *(Dir-Advisory)*
Donald Saelinger *(Gen Counsel & Sr VP)*
Thomas E. Noonan *(Co-Founder)*

ENDICOTT CLAY PRODUCTS CO.
57120 707th Rd, Endicott, NE 68350
Tel.: (402) 729-3315

Web Site: https://www.endicott.com
Rev.: $26,000,000
Emp.: 200
Brick & Structural Clay Tile
N.A.I.C.S.: 327120
Ryan Parker *(Pres)*
John Butcher *(Mgr-Specialty Svcs)*
Dean Cerny *(Mgr-Production)*
Shannon Schroeder *(Acct Mgr-Receivable)*
Gary Davis *(VP-Sls)*

ENDICOTT GROUP EQUITY PARTNERS, L.P.
570 Lexington Ave 37th Fl, New York, NY 10022
Tel.: (212) 450-8070
Web Site: http://endicottgp.com
Privater Equity Firm
N.A.I.C.S.: 523940
Wayne Goldstein *(Co-Founder & Partner)*
Rob Usdan *(Co-Founder & Partner)*

Subsidiaries:

SmartProcure, Inc.   (1)
700 W Hillsboro Blvd Ste 4-100, Deerfield Beach, FL 33441-1619
Web Site: http://www.smartprocure.us
Data Processing, Hosting & Related Services
N.A.I.C.S.: 518210
Jeff Rubenstein *(Co-Founder, Chm & CEO)*
Jack Siney *(Co-Founder & Chief Revenue Officer)*
Nate Haskins *(Pres & COO)*

Subsidiary (Domestic):

Fedmine LLC   (2)
13708 Ginkgo Ter, Rockville, MD 20850-5431
Tel.: (301) 279-7575
Web Site: http://www.fedmine.us
Software Publisher
N.A.I.C.S.: 513210
Ashok Mehan *(Founder & CEO)*

ENDICOTT INTERCONNECT TECHNOLOGIES, INC.
1093 Clark St Bldg 258, Endicott, NY 13760
Tel.: (607) 755-1451   NY
Web Site:
    http://www.endicottinterconnect.com
Sales Range: $75-99.9 Million
Emp.: 800
Circuit Board Fabrication & Assembly, Semiconductor Packaging & Precision Equipment Mfr
N.A.I.C.S.: 334418
Rajinder Rai *(CTO)*

ENDLESS CHARGE, INC.
4981 Irwindale Ave Ste 750, Irwindale, CA 91706
Tel.: (818) 649-4738   CA
Web Site:
    http://www.endlesscharge.com
Automobile Battery Mfr & Distr
N.A.I.C.S.: 335910
Garry Mark Mupas *(CEO)*

ENDLESS MOUNTAINS HEALTH SYSTEMS
100 Hospital Dr, Montrose, PA 18801
Tel.: (570) 278-3801   PA
Web Site:
    https://www.endlesscare.org
Year Founded: 1992
Sales Range: $10-24.9 Million
Health Care Srvices
N.A.I.C.S.: 622110

Endless Mountains Health
Systems—(Continued)

Blaine Dibble *(Dir-Ancillary Care
Svcs)*
Loren Stone *(CEO)*

ENDO-THERAPEUTICS, INC.

15251 Roosevelt Blvd Ste 204, Clear-
water, FL 33760-3560
Tel.: (727) 524-4100   FL
Web Site: http://www.bioceps.com
Year Founded: 1992
Emp.: 220
Surgical & Medical Instrument Mfr
N.A.I.C.S.: 339112
Kevin Warren *(Dir-Ops)*
Robert Querido *(Owner)*
Pete Sanchirico *(Pres)*
Todd Adkisson *(Dir-Engrg)*
Sherry Kowallek *(Coord-Document
Control)*
Tania Cefaratti *(CFO)*

ENDOLOGIX, INC.

2 Musick, Irvine, CA 92618
Tel.: (949) 595-7200   DE
Web Site: http://www.endologix.com
Year Founded: 1992
Rev.: $143,370,000
Assets: $307,164,000
Liabilities: $243,308,000
Net Worth: $63,856,000
Earnings: ($64,757,000)
Emp.: 488
Fiscal Year-end: 12/31/19
Developer & Mfr of Treatments for
Vascular Diseases
N.A.I.C.S.: 339112
Michael V. Chobotov *(CTO)*
Daniel T. Lemaitre *(Chm)*
Cindy Pinto *(Interim CFO & VP-Fin
Plng & Analysis)*
Matthew Thompson *(Chief Medical
Officer)*
John Onopchenko *(CEO)*
Jeffry Fecho *(Chief Quality Officer)*
Jeffrey S. Brown *(Chief Ops Officer)*
Reyna Fernandez *(Chief HR Officer)*
Elisa Hebb *(VP-Clinical Res & Regu-
latory Affairs)*
Valerie L. S. Tansley *(VP-Program
Mgmt-Global)*
Brian Chambless *(VP-Sls)*
Tim A. Benner *(Chief Comml Officer)*
Tim Brady *(Principal Acctg Officer,
Sec & Controller)*

Subsidiaries:

Nellix, Inc.   (1)
2465 B Faber Pl, Palo Alto, CA 94303
Tel.: (650) 213-8700
Medical Equipment Whslr
N.A.I.C.S.: 423450

TriVascular Technologies, Inc.   (1)
3910 Brickway Blvd, Santa Rosa, CA 95403
Tel.: (707) 573-8800
Web Site: http://www.trivascular.com
Sales Range: $25-49.9 Million
Holding Company; Medical Appliance Mfr &
Distr
N.A.I.C.S.: 551112

Subsidiary (Non-US):

TriVascular Germany GmbH   (2)
Freiberger Str 39, 01067, Dresden, Ger-
many
Tel.: (49) 35186791454
Medical Instrument Mfr
N.A.I.C.S.: 339112

Subsidiary (Domestic):

TriVascular, Inc.   (2)
3910 Brickway Blvd, Santa Rosa, CA 95403
Tel.: (707) 543-8800
Web Site: http://www.trivascular.com
Medical Appliance Mfr & Distr
N.A.I.C.S.: 339113

ENDOSTIM, INC.

4041 Forest Park Ave Ste 220, Saint
Louis, MO 63108
Tel.: (314) 615-6345   DE
Web Site: http://www.endostim.com
Year Founded: 2009
Sales Range: Less than $1 Million
Emp.: 13
Medical Device Mfr
N.A.I.C.S.: 334510
Bevil J. Hogg *(Co-Founder)*
Shai Policker *(COO)*
Peggy S. Stohr *(CFO)*
Douglas D. French *(Chm)*
Virender K. Sharma *(Co-Founder &
Chief Medical Officer)*
Raul E. Perez *(Co-Founder)*
Rohan Hoare *(Pres & CEO)*

ENDRES MANUFACTURING
CO, INC.

802 S Century Ave, Waunakee, WI
53597
Tel.: (608) 849-4143   WI
Web Site: http://www.endresmfg.com
Year Founded: 1926
Sales Range: $1-9.9 Million
Emp.: 42
Fabricated Structural Metal Mfr
N.A.I.C.S.: 332312
Dan Ballweg *(Treas)*
Diane Endres-Ballweg *(Owner)*
Ken Ballweg *(CEO)*
Sam Ballweg *(Pres)*

Subsidiaries:

Skyline Steel, Inc.   (1)
102 Skyline Dr, Arlington, WI 53911
Tel.: (608) 635-8351
Sales Range: $1-9.9 Million
Emp.: 30
Fabricated Structural Metal Mfr
N.A.I.C.S.: 332312

ENDRES PROCESSING LLC

13420 Courthouse Blvd, Rosemount,
MN 55068
Tel.: (651) 438-3113
Web Site:
    http://www.endresprocessing.com
Rev.: $18,651,690
Emp.: 50
Food Waste Processing & Animal
Feed Mfr
N.A.I.C.S.: 311119
Leon J. Endres *(CEO)*
Shannon Firle *(Coord-Feed Sls)*
Hap Reilly *(Dir-Plng & Analysis)*
Paul Curtis *(COO)*

ENDURA PLASTICS, INC.

7955 Chardon Rd, Kirtland, OH
44094
Tel.: (440) 951-4466
Web Site: http://www.endura.com
Year Founded: 1966
Sales Range: $10-24.9 Million
Emp.: 71
Plastics Product Mfr
N.A.I.C.S.: 326199
Michael R. Sprinzl *(Mgr-Engrg)*
Grant E. Edwards *(Exec VP & Mgr-
Sls)*
Dean R. Williams *(VP-Ops)*
James Stewart *(Pres & CEO)*

ENDURANCE IT SERVICES

4876 Princess Anne Rd Ste 118, Vir-
ginia Beach, VA 23462
Tel.: (757) 216-3671
Web Site: http://www.endurance-
it.com
Year Founded: 2008
Sales Range: $1-9.9 Million
Emp.: 30
IT Services
N.A.I.C.S.: 519290

Blake White *(Pres)*
James Ashmore *(VP)*
Liz Ilagan *(Mgr-Client Svcs)*
Mike Alexander *(Dir-Consulting)*

ENDURIS EXTRUSIONS, INC.

7167 Old Kings Rd N, Jacksonville,
FL 32219
Tel.: (904) 421-3317
Web Site: http://www.enduris.com
Year Founded: 1998
Sales Range: $10-24.9 Million
Emp.: 83
High Quality PVC Deck & Rail Prod-
uct Mfr
N.A.I.C.S.: 325211
John Polidan *(Pres & CEO)*

ENDURO SYSTEMS, INC.

16602 Central Green Blvd, Houston,
TX 77032-2112
Tel.: (713) 358-4000   TX
Web Site:
    https://www.endurocomposites.com
Year Founded: 1975
Fiberglass & Resin Transfer Molded
Product Mfr
N.A.I.C.S.: 326199
Flavio Ortiz *(Sr VP-Sls & Mktg)*

ENE SYSTEMS INC.

480 Neponset Ste 11D, Canton, MA
02021
Tel.: (781) 828-6770   MA
Web Site:
    https://www.enesystems.com
Year Founded: 1987
Sales Range: $10-24.9 Million
Emp.: 128
Energy Management Controls
N.A.I.C.S.: 238210
Lindsay Drisko *(Pres)*
Jay Skinner *(Project Mgr)*
Michael McQuade *(Project Mgr)*
Dennis Tague *(Dir-Ops)*
Jose Fontes *(Sr Acct Exec)*
Vinny Camillo *(Mgr-Sys Support)*

ENER1 GROUP, INC.

1540 Broadway Ste 40, New York,
NY 10036
Tel.: (212) 920-3500   FL
Web Site: http://www.ener1.com
Year Founded: 1985
Sales Range: $75-99.9 Million
Emp.: 769
Holding Company; Lithium Ion Batter-
ies & Fuel Cells Mfr
N.A.I.C.S.: 551112
Thomas J. Snyder *(Chm)*
Ulrik Grape *(Pres-Ener1 Europe)*
Bruce Curtis *(Pres-Grid Energy Stor-
age)*
Alex Sorokin *(Interim CEO)*

Subsidiaries:

Ener1, Inc.   (1)
Web Site: http://www.ener1.com
Rev.: $280,000
Assets: $31,301,000
Liabilities: $38,327,000
Net Worth: ($7,026,000)
Earnings: ($51,710,000)
Emp.: 104
Fiscal Year-end: 12/31/2007
Battery, Fuel Cell & Nanostructured Material
Processing Products Mfr

ENERCO GROUP INCORPO-
RATED

4560 W 160th St, Cleveland, OH
44135
Tel.: (216) 916-3000
Web Site: http://www.enerco.com
Sales Range: $25-49.9 Million
Emp.: 75
Manufactures Portable Heaters

N.A.I.C.S.: 551112
Derek DuRoss *(Mgr-Demand Plng)*
Jeff Haire *(VP)*
Jeffries Daphne *(Dir-IT)*
Joseph Mahan *(Product Mgr)*
Kevin McDonough *(VP-Fin)*

ENERCON ENGINEERING INC.

1 Altorfer Ln, East Peoria, IL 61611
Tel.: (309) 694-1418
Web Site: http://www.enercon-
eng.com
Year Founded: 1975
Sales Range: $25-49.9 Million
Emp.: 200
Control Equipment, Electric
N.A.I.C.S.: 335314
Patsy Geske *(Dir-Corp Supply Chain
Mgmt)*
Dan Hoppe *(Dir-Sls)*
Jeff Crisman *(Mgr-Tech Grp)*
Christian Lee *(Project Mgr)*
Eric Porter *(Reg Mgr-Sls)*
Keith Lozeau *(VP-Sls)*

ENERCON INDUSTRIES COR-
PORATION

W140 N9572 Fountain Blvd, Menom-
onee Falls, WI 53051
Tel.: (262) 255-6070   WI
Web Site:
    https://www.enerconind.com
Year Founded: 1974
Sales Range: $10-24.9 Million
Emp.: 100
Mfr & Designer of Heat Treating Sys-
tems
N.A.I.C.S.: 333994
Dan Nimmer *(VP-Ops)*
Tom Gilbertson *(VP-Application En-
grg)*
Gerry Makovec *(Mgr-Sls-Intl)*
Scott Manning *(VP-Corp Comm)*
Mario Leonardelli *(VP-Engrg & Mgr-
OEM Product)*
Mark Plantier *(VP-Mktg)*
Aaron Hootkin *(Mgr-Reg Sls)*
Jessica Toellner *(Mgr-Sls-Intl)*
Gus Ibarra *(Mgr-Sls-Mexico & Central
America)*
Ryan Schuelke *(VP-Sls)*
Nate Fales *(Mgr-Svc)*
Brian Croke *(Dir-R&D)*

ENERFAB, INC.

4430 Chickering Ave, Cincinnati, OH
45232
Tel.: (513) 641-0500   OH
Web Site: http://www.enerfab.com
Year Founded: 1901
Sales Range: $5-14.9 Billion
Emp.: 2,600
Holding Company; Industrial Equip-
ment Mfr, Maintenance & Contractor
Services
N.A.I.C.S.: 551112
Dave Herche *(Chm)*
Brad Birck *(Gen Mgr-Nashville)*
Trisha Cole *(VP-Fin)*
Daniel Sillies *(CFO)*
Jacob Snyder *(VP-HR, Safety & La-
bor Rels)*
Aaron Landolt *(Pres)*

Subsidiaries:

Aycock, LLC   (1)
8261 Old Derry St, Hummelstown, PA
17036-9308
Tel.: (717) 566-5066
Web Site: http://www.aycockrigging.com
Sales Range: $25-49.9 Million
Emp.: 300
Mechanical Construction Contractor Ser-
vices
N.A.I.C.S.: 238990

Larry Aderholt *(VP-Ops)*
Jeff Budgeon *(Project Mgr)*
Tad Hoffmaster *(Project Mgr)*
Mark Hoover *(Dir-Safety)*
Don Ricker *(Project Mgr)*

Brighton Corporation (1)
1680 Cornell Ct, Lake Forest, IL 60045
Tel.: (309) 828-1916
Web Site:
http://www.brightoncorporation.com
Business Support Services
N.A.I.C.S.: 561499
Michael Wardle *(Dir-Plng)*
Harry G. Sutter *(Pres)*

Brighton Tru-Edge Heads (1)
11861 Mosteller Rd, Cincinnati, OH 45241
Tel.: (513) 771-2300
Web Site: http://www.brightontruedge.com
Sales Range: $10-24.9 Million
Emp.: 50
Mfr of Tank Heads
N.A.I.C.S.: 333248
Steve Hammoor *(VP-Sls & Mktg)*

Enerpipe, Inc (1)
738 Industrial Loop Rd, New London, WI
54961
Tel.: (920) 982-0962
Web Site: http://www.enerfab.com
Emp.: 20
Pipe Fabrication Serviced
N.A.I.C.S.: 332996

ENERFIN RESOURCES LP
3 Riverway Ste 1200, Houston, TX
77056
Tel.: (713) 888-8600
Web Site: http://www.enerfin.com
Sales Range: $25-49.9 Million
Emp.: 13
Natural Gas Pipelines
N.A.I.C.S.: 213112
Patricia A. Abraham *(Mgr-HR)*
Stacey Barclay Richardson *(Mgr-Bus
Optimization & Exec Admin)*
Phil Flato *(Controller)*
Robbie McLearan *(Coord-Gas Acq)*
Jerry Crafton *(Gen Mgr-Midstream
Ops)*
Helen Stacy *(Mgr-Contract Mgmt &
Admin)*
Keith Dudley *(Mgr-Gas Acq)*
M. Peggy Morgan *(Mgr-Land-
Upstream)*

ENERFUND, LLC
1450 S Miami Ave, Miami, FL 33130
Tel.: (305) 507-8797   FL
Web Site: http://www.enerfund.com
Year Founded: 2006
Privater Equity Firm
N.A.I.C.S.: 523999
Mike Zoi *(Owner & CEO)*

Subsidiaries:

T1T Lab, LLC (1)
3363 NE 163rd St Ste 705, North Miami
Beach, FL 33160   (90%)
Tel.: (305) 507-8808
Holding Company; Entertainment Websites
Publisher
N.A.I.C.S.: 551112

Subsidiary (Domestic):

Motorsport.com, Inc. (2)
4100 NE 2nd Ave Ste 302, Miami, FL
33137
Tel.: (305) 877-3097
Web Site: http://www.motorsport.com
Motorsports News Website Publisher
N.A.I.C.S.: 513110
Eric Gilbert *(Chief Product Officer)*
Pablo Elizalde *(Editor-News-Europe)*
Charles Bradley *(Editor-in-Chief)*
Gustavo A. Roche *(Sr VP-Bus Dev)*
Felipe Motta *(Dir-Brazil)*
Khodr Rawi *(Dir-Middle East)*
David Malsher *(Editor)*
Erwin Jaeggi *(Editor-Formula1-Netherlands)*
Jacobo Vega *(Dir-Spain)*
Liam Clogger *(CEO-Motorsportstats.com)*

Alex Rothbert *(Controller)*
Chris Eschenburg *(Pres)*
Filippo Salza *(Pres-European Ops)*
Franco Nugnes *(Dir-Italy)*
Gergely Denes *(Gen Mgr & Editor-in-Chief-
Hungary)*
Guillaume Navarro *(Dir-France)*
Steven Lu *(Dir-China)*
Zak Brown *(Chm)*
Jonathan Noble *(Editor-F1)*
Oriol Puigdemont *(Editor-MotoGP)*
Jim Utter *(Editor-NASCAR)*
Adam Cooper *(Editor-F1)*
Jose L. Mercado Roman *(Dir-Latin America)*
Dmitry Sergeev *(Dir-Russia)*
Andrew van Leeuwen *(Editor-in-Chief-
Austrilia)*
Jamie Klein *(Editor-in-Chief-UK)*
Darshan Chokhani *(Editor-in-Chief-India)*
Tim Biesbrouck *(Editor-in-Chief-
Netherlands)*
Stefan Ehlen *(Mgr-Editorial-Germany)*
Rene Fagnan *(Dir-Canada)*
Cihangir Perperik *(Dir-Turkey)*
Kunihiko Akai *(Editor-in-Chief-Japan)*
Roman Galimon *(Editor-in-Chief-Ukraine)*
Cep Goldia *(Dir-Indonesia)*
Nick DeGroot *(Mgr-News & Community)*
Rainer Ehrhardt *(Mgr-Photo)*
Pavel Surdin *(Mgr-Video)*
Harsh Vardhan Choudhary *(Mgr-Internal
Process)*

Subsidiary (Non-US):

OOO Music1 (2)
Presnenskaya Emb bld 12 office a31,
123317, Moscow, Russia
Tel.: (7) 499 277 1110
Web Site: http://www.music1.ru
Music News & Information Website Pub-
lisher
N.A.I.C.S.: 513110

Subsidiary (Domestic):

Openfilm, LLC (2)
3363 NE 163rd St Ste 705, North Miami
Beach, FL 33160
Tel.: (305) 507-8808
Web Site: http://www.openfilm.com
Motion Picture Industry Business Services
N.A.I.C.S.: 512199
Dmitry Kozko *(Co-Founder & Pres)*

ENERGAS CORP.
1425 N Rockport Rd, Boonville, IN
47601
Tel.: (812) 897-2260
Web Site: https://www.bngas.com
Rev.: $21,000,000
Emp.: 10
Natural Gas Distr
N.A.I.C.S.: 221210
John Lewellyn *(Pres)*

ENERGEN OF VIRGINIA INC.
6305 Hull St Rd, Richmond, VA
23224
Tel.: (804) 745-0066
Web Site:
http://www.richmonddec.com
Year Founded: 1977
Rev.: $14,039,322
Emp.: 49
Carpets
N.A.I.C.S.: 423220
Mark L. Coates *(Pres)*

ENERGETIC PAINTING & DRY-
WALL
2917 Orange Grove Ave, North High-
lands, CA 95660
Tel.: (916) 488-8455
Sales Range: $10-24.9 Million
Emp.: 175
Drywall
N.A.I.C.S.: 238310
Edwin G. Gerber *(Pres)*

ENERGY & EXPLORATION
PARTNERS, INC.
2 City Pl Ste 1700 100 Throckmorton,
Fort Worth, TX 76102
Tel.: (817) 789-6712   DE
Web Site: http://www.enxp.com
Year Founded: 2012
Sales Range: $10-24.9 Million
Emp.: 69
Holding Company; Petroleum & Natu-
ral Gas Exploration & Production
N.A.I.C.S.: 551112
Steven C. Wilson *(Sr VP-Geology)*
Chase Hanna *(VP-Engrg & Ops)*
Patrick O'Bryan *(CEO)*

Subsidiaries:

**Energy & Exploration Partners,
LLC** (1)
2 City Pl Ste 1700 100 Throckmorton, Fort
Worth, TX 76102
Tel.: (817) 789-6712
Web Site: http://www.enxp.com
Petroleum & Natural Gas Exploration &
Production
N.A.I.C.S.: 211120
B. Hunt Pettit *(Founder, Pres & CEO)*
Brian C. Nelson *(CFO & Exec VP)*
John T. Richards *(COO & Exec VP)*
Jamie M. Howe *(Chief Acctg Officer & Exec
VP)*
Tom D. McNutt *(Gen Counsel, Sec & Exec
VP)*
Lawrence B. Van Ingen *(Exec VP-Geology)*
Steven C. Wilson *(Sr VP-Geophysics &
Geological Engrg)*
Chad A. Galloway *(Sr VP-Land & Ops)*
Robert G. Karpman *(Exec VP-Bus Ops &
Dev)*
David L. Patty Jr. *(Exec VP-Land & Bus
Dev)*

ENERGY & POWER SOLU-
TIONS, INC.
150 Paularino Ave Ste A120, Costa
Mesa, CA 92626
Tel.: (714) 586-8002   DE
Web Site: http://www.epsway.com
Year Founded: 2002
Sales Range: $10-24.9 Million
Emp.: 93
Energy Management Software & Ser-
vices
N.A.I.C.S.: 513210
Jay B. Zoellner *(Chm, Pres & CEO)*
Shiva Subramanya *(Exec VP-
Strategic Dev)*
Staffan Akerstrom *(Exec VP-Energy
Solutions)*
Rick Davis *(VP-Sls & Mktg)*
George Botich *(VP-xChange Point)*

ENERGY 1 CORP.
315 SE Mizner Blvd Ste 202, Boca
Raton, FL 33432-6036
Tel.: (561) 347-6462
Web Site:
http://www.e1corporation.com
Motor Vehicle Parts Mfr
N.A.I.C.S.: 336390
Raymond T. Brown *(CEO)*

ENERGY 11, L.P.
120 W 3rd St Ste 220, Fort Worth,
TX 76102
Tel.: (817) 882-9192   DE
Web Site:
http://www.energyeleven.com
Year Founded: 2013
Rev.: $99,792,852
Assets: $351,334,985
Liabilities: $11,345,714
Net Worth: $339,989,271
Earnings: $36,515,080
Emp.: 101
Fiscal Year-end: 12/31/23
Oil & Gas Exploration
N.A.I.C.S.: 211120
Glade M. Knight *(CEO, Gen Partner
& Partner)*

ENERGY ALLIANCE TECH-
NOLOGY CORP.
11 Vista Hermosa Dr, Simi Valley, CA
93065
Tel.: (805) 304-2664   NV
Year Founded: 2014
Fuel Product Distr
N.A.I.C.S.: 424720
J. Daniel Thatcher *(Pres, CEO, CFO,
Treas & Sec)*

ENERGY ALLOYS, LLC
3 Waterway Square Pl Ste 600, The
Woodlands, TX 77380
Tel.: (832) 601-5800   TX
Web Site: http://www.ealloys.com
Year Founded: 1995
Sales Range: $250-299.9 Million
Emp.: 385
High-Performance Metals Used in
Manufacture of Oilfield Equipment Mfr
N.A.I.C.S.: 213112
Dave Warren *(Pres & CEO)*
Mike Williams *(Mgr-Sls)*
Francis Bobb *(COO & Sr VP)*
Paul Patek *(Chief Acctg Officer &
VP-Fin)*

Subsidiaries:

Energy Alloys Services, LLC (1)
9450 W Wingfoot Rd, Houston, TX 77041
Tel.: (713) 690-4340
Web Site: http://www.ealloys.com
Sales Range: $10-24.9 Million
Emp.: 100
Metal Processing Fabrication & Distr
N.A.I.C.S.: 423510

Energy Alloys UK Ltd. (1)
Advantage House Poplar Way, Catcliffe,
Rotherham, S60 5TR, S Yorkshire, United
Kingdom
Tel.: (44) 1709788000
Web Site: http://www.ealloys.com
Sales Range: $10-24.9 Million
Emp.: 35
Hydraulic, Mill & Water Resistant Products
N.A.I.C.S.: 332999
Peter Morris *(Mng Dir)*

ENERGY ANSWERS INTERNA-
TIONAL, INC.
79 N Pearl St FL 4, Albany, NY
12207
Tel.: (518) 434-1227
Web Site:
http://www.energyanswers.com
Sales Range: $25-49.9 Million
Emp.: 7
Recycling, Waste Materials
N.A.I.C.S.: 562920
Patrick F. Mahoney *(Chm, Pres &
CEO)*
Elona Cadman *(Mgr-Mktg & Admin
Svcs)*
Mary Ann Mahoney *(VP)*
Michael W. McNerney *(VP-Engrg)*

Subsidiaries:

**Energy Answers International,
LLC** (1)
1110 Strand St, Christiansted, VI 00820
Tel.: (340) 778-7505
Web Site: http://www.energyanswers.com
Sales Range: $10-24.9 Million
Emp.: 3
Waste Management Solutions
N.A.I.C.S.: 562998

ENERGY CAPITAL PARTNERS
MANAGEMENT, LP
40 Beechwood Rd, Summit, NJ
07901
Tel.: (973) 671-6100   DE
Web Site: http://www.ecpartners.com
Year Founded: 2005
Emp.: 66
Privater Equity Firm
N.A.I.C.S.: 523999

Energy Capital Partners Management,
LP—(Continued)

Douglas W. Kimmelman (*Founder & Sr Partner*)
Pete Labbat (*Mng Partner*)
Murray Karp (*Partner, CFO & COO*)
Tyler Reeder (*Mng Partner*)
Paul Parshley (*Mng Dir*)
Chris Leininger (*Partner & Gen Counsel*)
Michelle Cowell (*Mgr-Acctg*)
Alexandra Termini (*Mng Dir & Controller*)
Kevin Clayton (*Partner*)
Thomas K. Lane (*Vice Chm*)
Schuyler Coppedge (*Partner*)
Matthew DeNichilo (*Partner*)
Andrew Gilbert (*Partner*)
Trent Kososki (*Partner*)
Scott Rogan (*Partner*)
Rahman D'Argenio (*Partner*)
Jennifer Gray (*Mng Dir & Chief Compliance Officer*)

Subsidiaries:

Calpine Corporation **(1)**
717 Texas Ave Ste 1000, Houston, TX
77002 **(100%)**
Tel.: (713) 830-2000
Web Site: https://www.calpine.com
Rev.: $10,072,000,000
Assets: $16,649,000,000
Liabilities: $13,991,000,000
Net Worth: $2,658,000,000
Earnings: $770,000,000
Emp.: 2,300
Fiscal Year-end: 12/31/2019
Other Electric Power Generation
N.A.I.C.S.: 221118
Kevin G. McMahon (*Chief Compliance Officer & Sr VP-Internal Audit*)
Sarah Novosel (*Sr VP-Govt Affairs*)
Zamir Rauf (*CFO & Exec VP*)
Todd Thornton (*Sr VP-Origination & Dev*)
John B. Hill III (*Pres & CEO*)
W. Bryan Kimzey (*Treas & Sr VP-Fin*)
Hether Benjamin Brown (*Chief Admin Officer & Sr VP*)
Shonnie Daniel (*Sr VP, Co-Sec & Deputy Gen Counsel*)
Alex Makler (*Sr VP-West Reg*)
Andrew Novotny (*Exec VP & Co-Head-Comml Ops*)
Steven Schleimer (*Sr VP-Govt & Regulatory Affairs*)
Caleb Stephenson (*Exec VP & Co-Head-Comml Ops*)
Charlie Gates (*Exec VP-Power Ops*)
Rick Colgan (*Sr VP-Svcs*)
Mike Del Casale (*Sr VP-Ops*)
Jeff Koshkin (*Chief Risk Officer, Chief Acctg Officer & Sr VP*)
Tom Long (*Sr VP-Asset Performance Mgmt*)
Rick Pena (*Sr VP-Mergers, Acquisitions & Integration*)
W. Thaddeus Miller (*Vice Chm, Chief Legal Officer, Co-Sec & Exec VP*)
Will Stokes (*Sr VP-Power Trading*)
Thad Hill (*CEO*)

Subsidiary (Domestic):

Calpine Bosque Energy Center,
LLC **(2)**
557 County Rd 3610A, Whitney, TX
76692 **(100%)**
Tel.: (254) 622-4500
Eletric Power Generation Services
N.A.I.C.S.: 221118

Branch (Domestic):

Calpine Corporation - Dublin **(2)**
4160 Dublin Corporate Way Ste 100, Dublin, CA 94568
Tel.: (925) 557-2280
Eletric Power Generation Services
N.A.I.C.S.: 221118

Calpine Corporation -
Middletown **(2)**
10350 Socrates Mine Rd, Middletown, CA
95461
Tel.: (707) 431-6000
Power Generation Services

N.A.I.C.S.: 221122
Dave Jackson (*Mgr-Reg EHS*)

Unit (Domestic):

Calpine Energy Services **(2)**
717 Texas Ave Ste 1000, Houston, TX
77002
Tel.: (713) 830-2000
Electric Power Distribution Services
N.A.I.C.S.: 221122

Subsidiary (Domestic):

Calpine Guadalupe GP, LLC **(2)**
5740 Weil Rd, New Braunfels, TX
78130 **(100%)**
Tel.: (202) 777-7623
Eletric Power Generation Services
N.A.I.C.S.: 221118

Calpine Hidalgo Energy Center,
L.P. **(2)**
4005 N Seminary Rd, Edinburg, TX
78541 **(78.5%)**
Tel.: (956) 318-3800
Power Generation Services
N.A.I.C.S.: 221118

Calpine Merchant Services
Company **(2)**
717 Texas Ave Ste 1000, Houston, TX
77002
Tel.: (713) 830-2000
Electric Power Distr
N.A.I.C.S.: 221122

Unit (Domestic):

Calpine Turbine Maintenance
Group **(2)**
9331 Bay Area Blvd, Pasadena, TX 77507
Tel.: (832) 476-4400
Industrial Maintenance Services
N.A.I.C.S.: 221118

Subsidiary (Domestic):

Champion Energy Services, LLC **(2)**
1500 Rankin Rd Ste 200, Houston, TX
77073
Tel.: (281) 653-5090
Web Site:
http://www.championenergyservices.com
Electric Power Distr
N.A.I.C.S.: 221122
Alon Erlichman (*VP-Customer Ops*)
Zach Deakins (*VP-Fin Ops*)
Michael Sullivan (*Pres & CEO*)

Gilroy Energy Center, LLC **(2)**
717 Texas Ave Ste 1000, Houston, TX
77002 **(100%)**
Tel.: (713) 830-2000
Power Generation Services
N.A.I.C.S.: 221118

Granite Ridge Energy, LLC **(2)**
21 Wentworth Ave, Londonderry, NH
03053 **(100%)**
Tel.: (603) 432-9114
Eletric Power Generation Services
N.A.I.C.S.: 221118

Guadalupe Power Partners, LP **(2)**
5740 Weil Rd, New Braunfels, TX 78130
Tel.: (830) 624-0940
Electric Power Generation Services
N.A.I.C.S.: 221118

Los Medanos Energy Center
LLC **(2)**
750 E 3rd St, Pittsburg, CA 94565 **(100%)**
Tel.: (925) 252-2000
Power Generation Services
N.A.I.C.S.: 221118

Westbrook Energy Center, LLC **(2)**
60 Eisenhower Dr, Westbrook, ME
04092 **(100%)**
Tel.: (207) 854-2216
Electric Power Generation Services
N.A.I.C.S.: 221118

Subsidiary (Non-US):

Whitby Cogeneration Limited
Partnership **(2)**
1550 Wentworth St, Whitby, L1N 7C1, ON,
Canada
Tel.: (905) 665-8390

Power Generation Services
N.A.I.C.S.: 221118

Subsidiary (Domestic):

Zion Energy LLC **(2)**
5701 W 9th St, Zion, IL 60099 **(100%)**
Tel.: (847) 731-6250
Power Generation Services
N.A.I.C.S.: 221118

Dynegy North America, Inc. **(1)**
601 Travis St Ste 1400, Houston, TX 77002
Tel.: (713) 507-6400
Development & Operation of Electricity & Cogeneration Facilities; Distribution of Liquefied Natural Gas
N.A.I.C.S.: 221118
Zin Smati (*Pres & CEO*)
Karim Barbir (*Sr VP-Risk & Portfolio Mgmt*)
Bart Clark (*Gen Counsel & Sr VP*)
Eric Bradley (*Sr VP-Strategy*)

Gopher Resource LLC **(1)**
2900 Lone Oak Pkwy Ste 140A, Eagan,
MN 55121
Tel.: (651) 454-3310
Web Site: http://www.gopherresource.com
Emp.: 600
Environmental Recycling Services
N.A.I.C.S.: 562920
Brian Leen (*Pres & CEO*)
Eric Robinson (*COO & Sr VP*)
Josh Heisick (*Dir-HR*)
Ray Krantz (*Dir-Bus Dev*)
Dan Leach (*Chief Bus Dev Officer & Sr VP*)
Brian Hanley (*VP*)

New Leaf Energy, Inc. **(1)**
55 Technology Dr. Suite 102, Lowell, MA
01851
Tel.: (800) 818-5249
Web Site: https://www.newleafenergy.com
Renewable Electric Energy
N.A.I.C.S.: 221122
Dan Berwick (*CEO*)

North American Power and Gas,
LLC **(1)**
20 Glover Ave, Norwalk, CT 06850
Tel.: (877) 572-0442
Web Site: http://www.napower.com
Natural Gas Distribution Services
N.A.I.C.S.: 221210
Michael O'Brien (*Mgr-Bus Dev*)

STEAG SCR-Tech, Inc. **(1)**
11707 Steele Creek Rd, Charlotte, NC
28273-3718
Tel.: (704) 827-8933
Web Site: http://www.steagscrtech.com
Sales Range: $100-124.9 Million
Emp.: 100
Catalyst Regeneration Technologies & Management Services
N.A.I.C.S.: 334513
Michael F. Mattes (*Co-CEO*)
Thies Hoffman (*Co-CEO*)

ENERGY CENTRAL

2821 S Parker Rd Ste 1105, Aurora,
CO 80014
Tel.: (303) 782-5510
Web Site:
http://www.energycentral.com
Year Founded: 1995
Sales Range: $1-9.9 Million
Emp.: 40
News Website for the Global Power
Industry
N.A.I.C.S.: 517810
Audra Drazga (*VP*)

ENERGY CONTROL CONSULTANTS, INC.

10220 W State Rd 84 Ste 9, Davie,
FL 33324
Tel.: (954) 739-8400
Web Site:
https://www.energycontrol.com
Building Automation Products & Services
N.A.I.C.S.: 238220
R. E. Combs (*Pres*)
Judith L. Combs (*Sec*)

Subsidiaries:

Total Building Environments South,
Inc. **(1)**
1231 Willowick Cir, Safety Harbor, FL
34695
Tel.: (727) 234-0895
Web Site: http://www.tbesouth.com
Energy Saving Solutions
N.A.I.C.S.: 238220
Bruce L. Cramer (*Co-Founder & VP*)
William P. Cheadle III (*Co-Founder & Pres*)

ENERGY CONVERSION SERVICES, INC.

8275 S E Ave Ste 200, Las Vegas,
NV 89123
Tel.: (702) 675-8003 **WY**
Year Founded: 2017
Assets: $19,116
Liabilities: $11,051
Net Worth: $8,065
Earnings: ($181,113)
Fiscal Year-end: 05/31/18
Electric Power Generation
N.A.I.C.S.: 221118
Lisa Averbuch (*Pres, Treas & Sec*)

ENERGY CORPORATION OF AMERICA

4643 S Ulster St, Denver, CO 80237
Tel.: (303) 694-2667 **WV**
Web Site:
http://www.energycorporationof
america.com
Year Founded: 1963
Sales Range: $200-249.9 Million
Oil & Gas Exploration & Production
Services
N.A.I.C.S.: 211120
John Mork (*Founder*)
Dennis L. McGowan (*Sr VP-Bus Dev*)
Donald C. Supcoe (*Gen Counsel & Exec VP*)
J. Michael Forbes (*CFO & Sr VP*)
Kyle M. Mork (*COO*)
Thomas R. Goodwin (*Chm*)
Randall Farkosh (*VP-Mktg*)
Peter A. Sullivan (*VP-Exploration*)

Subsidiaries:

ECA Marcellus Trust I **(1)**
601 Travis, Houston, TX 77002
Tel.: (512) 236-6555
Web Site: https://www.ect.q4web.com
Rev.: $11,622,745
Assets: $17,179,427
Liabilities: $2,187,332
Net Worth: $14,992,095
Earnings: $10,112,359
Fiscal Year-end: 12/31/2022
Investment Services
N.A.I.C.S.: 523999

Eastern Marketing Corporation **(1)**
501 56th St SE, Charleston, WV 25304-2349
Tel.: (304) 926-3100
Web Site: http://www.energycorporationof
america.com
Rev.: $140,000,000
Emp.: 7
Petroleum Products
N.A.I.C.S.: 424720

Eastern Pipeline Corp. **(1)**
500 Corporate Landing, Charleston, WV
25311-1264
Tel.: (304) 925-6100
Web Site: http://www.eca-eaec.com
Sales Range: $1-9.9 Million
Emp.: 110
Oil & Gas Field Services
N.A.I.C.S.: 213112
David E. Jordan (*VP-IT*)
Chad Perkins (*VP-Ops*)
Ryan Deaderick (*VP-Production*)

Energy Corp of America **(1)**
4643 S Ulster St Ste 1100, Denver, CO
80237-4306 **(100%)**
Tel.: (303) 694-6830
Web Site:
http://www.energycorpofamerica.com

Sales Range: $25-49.9 Million
Emp.: 16
Oil & Gas Exploration Services
N.A.I.C.S.: 213112
John Mork *(Pres & CEO)*

Energy Corporation of America   (1)
500 Corporate landing, Charleston, WV
25311
Tel.: (304) 925-6100
Web Site: http://www.eca-eaec.com
Sales Range: $25-49.9 Million
Emp.: 75
Oil & Gas Production & Exploration
N.A.I.C.S.: 211120
John Mork *(CEO)*
Niki Randolph *(VP-Acctg)*
Donald C. Supcoe *(Exec VP)*
J. Michael Forbes *(CFO & Sr VP)*
Thomas R. Goodwin *(Chm)*
Ryan Deaderick *(VP-Production)*
Randall Farkosh *(VP-Mktg)*
David E. Jordan *(VP-IT)*
Julie Ann Kitano *(Sec)*
Eugene J. McCartt *(VP-Tax)*
Dennis L. McGowan *(Sr VP-Bus Dev)*
Chad Perkins *(VP-Ops)*
Peter A. Sullivan *(VP-Exploration)*
Rodney A. Winters *(VP-Bus Dev)*

Subsidiary (Domestic):

Energy Corporation of America   (2)
1380 Rte 286 Hwy E Ste 221, Indiana, PA
15701-1473
Tel.: (724) 463-8400
Web Site: http://www.eaec.com
Sales Range: $50-74.9 Million
Emp.: 33
Oil & Gas Production & Exploration
N.A.I.C.S.: 221210

ENERGY DESIGN SERVICE SYSTEMS
7050 Jomar Dr, Whitmore Lake, MI
48189
Tel.: (810) 227-3377
Web Site:
   https://www.edssenergy.com
Year Founded: 2007
Sales Range: $1-9.9 Million
Emp.: 70
Lighting & Energy Systems
N.A.I.C.S.: 335139
David Ely *(Pres & CEO)*

ENERGY DRILLING COMPANY
413 Liberty Rd, Natchez, MS 39120
Tel.: (601) 446-5259
Web Site:
   https://www.energydrilling.com
Year Founded: 1979
Sales Range: $1-9.9 Million
Emp.: 200
Oil & Gas Services
N.A.I.C.S.: 213111
Jody Helbling *(Gen Mgr)*
Matt Brough *(Engr-Drilling)*
David L. Cothren *(Controller-Fin)*
Pat Burns Jr. *(Pres)*

ENERGY EARTH LLC
501 Cumberland St, Chattanooga, TN
37404
Web Site:
   http://www.energyearth.com
Year Founded: 2011
Sales Range: $10-24.9 Million
Emp.: 42
Household Product Distr
N.A.I.C.S.: 423620
A. Hamid Andalib *(Founder & CEO)*

ENERGY ERECTORS, INC.
31588 Progress Rd, Leesburg, FL
34748
Tel.: (352) 787-3878
Web Site:
   https://www.energyerectors.net
Sales Range: $25-49.9 Million
Emp.: 153

General Electrical Contractor
N.A.I.C.S.: 238210

ENERGY HOLDINGS INTER-NATIONAL, INC.
12012 Wickchester Ln Ste 130,
Houston, TX 77079
Tel.: (281) 752-7314   NV
Web Site: http://www.energyhii.com
Oil & Gas Exploration Services
N.A.I.C.S.: 211120
John W. Adair *(Chm & CEO)*
Jalal Alghani *(CFO)*
Alex Adair *(VP-Oil & Gas)*
Randall Newton *(Controller)*
Mohammad Nasser *(VP)*

ENERGY INTELLIGENCE WORLDWIDE CORP, INC.
100 N Laura St Ste 804, Jacksonville,
FL 32202
Tel.: (904) 398-9004
Web Site: http://www.eiwcorp.com
Sales Range: $1-9.9 Million
Energy Conservation Application Soft-
ware & Consulting Services
N.A.I.C.S.: 513210
Herrald Jonkers *(Pres)*
Thamir Massraf *(CTO)*
Monty Selim *(COO)*
Chris Simpkin *(Chief Data Officer)*
Harri Eloranta *(CFO)*
Ian Taylor *(CIO)*

ENERGY MANAGEMENT COR-PORATION
501 W 700 S, Salt Lake City, UT
84101
Tel.: (801) 366-4100
Web Site:
   http://www.emcsolutions.com
Year Founded: 1979
Sales Range: $10-24.9 Million
Emp.: 65
Motor Controls, Starters & Relays:
Electric
N.A.I.C.S.: 423610
Steve Rossiter *(Pres)*

ENERGY NORTH INCORPO-RATED
2 International Way, Lawrence, MA
01843
Tel.: (978) 640-1100
Web Site: https://energytogo.com
Emp.: 100
Oil & Gas Distr
N.A.I.C.S.: 213111

Subsidiaries:

Haffner's Service Stations, Inc.   (1)
2 International Way, Lawrence, MA 01843
Tel.: (866) 485-4257
Web Site: https://haffners.com
Oil & Gas Distr
N.A.I.C.S.: 457110

Subsidiary (Domestic):

Concord Oil Company Inc.   (2)
147 Lowell Rd, Concord, MA 01742-1712
Tel.: (978) 369-3333
Web Site:
   http://www.concordoilcompany.com
Sales Range: $10-24.9 Million
Emp.: 83
Petroleum Products Mfr
N.A.I.C.S.: 424720
Michael Whaley *(Pres & CEO)*

Subsidiary (Domestic):

Concord Oil of Newport Inc.   (3)
147 Lowell Rd, Concord, MA 01742-1712
Tel.: (978) 692-6248
Web Site:
   http://www.concordoilcompany.com
Sales Range: $10-24.9 Million
Emp.: 7
Producer Of Petroleum Products

N.A.I.C.S.: 424720

ENERGY NORTHWEST
76 N Power Plant Loop, Richland,
WA 99354
Tel.: (509) 372-5000
Web Site: http://www.energy-
   northwest.com
Sales Range: $400-449.9 Million
Emp.: 1,100
Generation, Electric Power
N.A.I.C.S.: 221118
Scott Vance *(Chief Ethics Officer &
Gen Counsel)*
Brad Sawatzke *(CEO)*
Grover Hettel *(Chief Nuclear Officer)*
Bob Schuetz *(Vp-Ops & Gen Mgr-
Columbia Generating Station)*

ENERGY OGRE, LLC
24 Greenway Plz Ste 1100, Houston,
TX 77046
Tel.: (832) 975-1000   TX
Web Site:
   http://www.energyogre.com
Year Founded: 2013
Sales Range: $1-9.9 Million
Emp.: 60
Consumer Electronic Products Distr
N.A.I.C.S.: 423620
Jesson Bradshaw *(CEO)*

ENERGY OPERATORS, L. P.
1431 Graham Dr Ste 203, Tomball,
TX 77375
Tel.: (281) 351-1780
Web Site:
   http://www.energyoperators.com
Year Founded: 1989
Sales Range: $10-24.9 Million
Emp.: 130
Oil & Gas Operating Services
N.A.I.C.S.: 213112
Larry Oliver *(Owner)*

ENERGY OUTREACH COLO-RADO
225 E 16th Ave Ste 200, Denver, CO
80203
Tel.: (303) 825-8750   CO
Web Site:
   http://www.energyoutreach.org
Year Founded: 1989
Sales Range: $10-24.9 Million
Emp.: 19
Energy Management Services
N.A.I.C.S.: 624229
Rose Reed *(Dir-Admin Svcs)*
Andy Caler *(Program Mgr-Utility)*
Ashley Feiertag *(Dir-State Programs)*
Luke Ilderton *(Dir-Energy Efficiency
Programs)*

ENERGY OVERWATCH LLC
5200 DTC Pkwy Ste 530, Greenwood
Village, CO 80111
Tel.: (720) 604-2532   DE
Web Site:
   https://energyoverwatch.com
Scientific & Technical Consulting Ser-
vices
N.A.I.C.S.: 541690

Subsidiaries:

SEMPCheck Services LLC   (1)
17629 El Camino Real 207, Houston, TX
77058
Tel.: (281) 990-0284
Web Site: http://www.sempcheck.com
Sales Range: $1-9.9 Million
Emp.: 19
Custom Computer Programming Services
N.A.I.C.S.: 541511
Robert Albright *(Principal)*
Archie R. Thompson *(CEO)*
Jeffrey W. Scott *(Sr VP)*
Jim Steffler *(VP)*
Tad LeBlanc *(VP-Ops)*

ENERGY PETROLEUM CO. INC.
2130 Kienlen Ave, Saint Louis, MO
63121-5505
Tel.: (314) 383-6828   MO
Web Site:
   http://www.energypetroleum.com
Year Founded: 1931
Sales Range: $10-24.9 Million
Emp.: 60
Fuel Oil Sales
N.A.I.C.S.: 457210
Steve Madras *(Pres)*

ENERGY PROCESS TECH-NOLOGY INC.
3172 North Toledo Ave, Tulsa, OK
74115
Tel.: (918) 835-1011
Web Site:
   http://www.primeenergy.com
Sales Range: $10-24.9 Million
Emp.: 30
Industrial Plant Construction Services
N.A.I.C.S.: 237990
Don Mellott *(Pres)*

Subsidiaries:

Mohawk Field Services Inc   (1)
3171 N Toledo Ave, Tulsa, OK 74115
Tel.: (918) 835-3844
Web Site: http://www.mfsi-tulsa.com
Rev.: $1,900,000
Emp.: 20
Industrial Plant Construction
N.A.I.C.S.: 237990
Jewell Hall *(Pres)*
Randy Light *(CFO)*
Allen Jackson *(VP)*

ENERGY PRODUCTION COR-PORATION
12221 Mary Dr Ste 1200, Dallas, TX
75251
Tel.: (214) 692-8581   TX
Web Site: http://www.epcousa.com
Year Founded: 1968
Sales Range: $25-49.9 Million
Emp.: 20
Crude Petroleum & Natural Gas Ser-
vices
N.A.I.C.S.: 211120
Chet McLain *(Mgr-Exploration)*

ENERGY PRODUCTS INC.
1551 E Lincoln Ave, Madison
Heights, MI 48071
Tel.: (248) 545-7700
Web Site:
   https://www.energyprod.com
Rev.: $24,800,000
Emp.: 60
Electrical Apparatus & Equipment,
Wiring Supplies & Related Equipment
Merchant Whslr
N.A.I.C.S.: 423610
Kurt H. Smith *(Founder & CEO)*
Bill Miller *(Mgr)*

ENERGY PROFESSIONALS, LLC
1315 Cleveland St, Clearwater, FL
33755   FL
Web Site:
   https://www.energyprofessionals.com
Year Founded: 1999
Energy Broker; Virtual Energy Man-
ager
N.A.I.C.S.: 926130
Jim Mathers *(Pres)*
Matt Helland *(VP-New Product Dev)*
Mark Hoover *(VP-Ops)*
Alex Dushaj *(VP-Sls)*

Energy Professionals, LLC—(Continued)

Subsidiaries:

Customer Acquisition Specialists of
America, Inc. (1)
1315 Cleveland St, Clearwater, FL 33755
Tel.: (727) 692-8871
Sales Company
N.A.I.C.S.: 541613
Jim Mathers (Pres)

ENERGY RETAILERS INC.
4 N St, Hingham, MA 02043-2211
Tel.: (781) 749-7676
Web Site:
   http://www.energyretailers.com
Year Founded: 1974
Parking Lot
N.A.I.C.S.: 457120
Robert J Cutler (Chm)

ENERGY SERVICES GROUP INTERNATIONAL INC. (ESG)
3601 La Grange Pkwy, Toano, VA
23168-9348
Tel.: (757) 741-4040
Web Site: https://www.esgi.net
Year Founded: 1983
Sales Range: $25-49.9 Million
Emp.: 600
Staffing & Business Solutions
N.A.I.C.S.: 561320
Thomas Gillman (Pres & CEO)
Michael Warren (VP)
James H. Kuykendall (VP-Bus Dev)

Subsidiaries:

Production Support Services Incorpo-
rated (PSS) (1)
11834 Canon Blvd Ste M, Newport News,
VA 23606 (100%)
Tel.: (757) 599-5959
Web Site: http://www.pssinc.net
Sales Range: $10-24.9 Million
Emp.: 4
Assembly Line & Warehouse Staffing Ser-
vices
N.A.I.C.S.: 561320
Jennifer Christian (Gen Mgr)
Randy Troutman (Mgr-Site)

ENERGY SERVICES GROUP, LLC
141 Longwater Dr Ste 113, Norwell,
MA 02061
Tel.: (781) 347-9000   DE
Web Site: http://esgglobal.com
Year Founded: 1998
Transaction Management & SaaS
based Software Services
N.A.I.C.S.: 518210
Steve Gosling (CFO)
Paul Etherington (CIO & Chief Secu-
rity Officer)

Subsidiaries:

iSIGMA, LLC (1)
1835 Shackleford Ct, Norcross, GA 30093
Tel.: (770) 543-0331
Web-based Customer Care & Billing Ser-
vices
N.A.I.C.S.: 541219

ENERGY SPECTRUM SECURI-TIES CORPORATION
5956 Sherry Ln Ste 900, Dallas, TX
75225
Tel.: (214) 987-6100   TX
Web Site:
   https://www.energyspectrum.com
Year Founded: 1996
Rev.: $2,300,000,000
Emp.: 40
Privater Equity Firm
N.A.I.C.S.: 523999
James W. Spann (Partner)
James P. Benson (Partner)
Leland B. White (Partner)

Alison K. Fischer (CFO)
Terry A. Lowry (Controller)
Chris C. Stewart (Dir-Fin Reporting)
Thomas O. Whitener Jr. (Pres & Part-
ner)

Subsidiaries:

Ceritas Energy, LLC (1)
3 Allen Ctr 333 Clay St Ste 750, Houston,
TX 77002
Tel.: (713) 439-5000
Web Site: http://www.ceritasgroup.com
Natural Gas Pipeline Transportation
N.A.I.C.S.: 486210
John Herbert (VP-Legal & Regulatory Af-
fairs)
David Litchfield (VP)
Len Hesseltine (VP)

West OK Trucking, Inc. (1)
4616 Oil Patch Dr, Woodward, OK 73801
Tel.: (580) 256-1177
Web Site: http://www.westoktrucking.com
Sales Range: $10-24.9 Million
Trucking Service
N.A.I.C.S.: 484110

ENERGY TRUST OF OREGON, INC.
421 SW Oak St Ste 300, Portland,
OR 97204
Tel.: (503) 493-8888   OR
Web Site:
   https://www.energytrust.org
Year Founded: 2002
Sales Range: $200-249.9 Million
Energy Conservation Services
N.A.I.C.S.: 813312
Peter West (Dir-Energy Programs)
Steve Lacey (Dir-Ops)
Amber Cole (Dir-Comm & Customer
Svcs)
Fred Gordon (Dir-Plng & Evaluation)

ENERGY UNITED ELECTRIC MEMBERSHIP CORPORATION
567 Mocksville Hwy, Statesville, NC
28687
Tel.: (704) 873-5241
Web Site:
   https://www.energyunited.com
Year Founded: 1969
Sales Range: $25-49.9 Million
Emp.: 212
Electronic Services
N.A.I.C.S.: 221122
Alec Natt (CFO & VP-Corp Svcs)
Tom Tedrow (VP-HR)
Kathleen Hart (CIO & VP-Customer
Care)
Wayne H. Wilkins (CEO)
Tim Holder (VP-Sls)

ENERGYLOGIC INC
309 Mountain Ave, Berthoud, CO
80513
Web Site: http://www.nrglogic.com
Year Founded: 2006
Sales Range: $1-9.9 Million
Emp.: 32
Home Energy Efficiency & Conserva-
tion Services
N.A.I.C.S.: 541690
Stephen Byers (CEO & Principal)
Janet Howard (CFO)
Will Lorey (COO)
Wynne Maggi (Pres & Chief Culture
Officer)
Robby Schwarz (Principal & Dir-
Builder Rels)
Kathleen Henning (Product Mgr-
Software)
Theron LaFountain (Coord-Mktg)

ENERGYNET.COM, INC.
7201 I-40 W Ste 319, Amarillo, TX
79106
Tel.: (806) 351-2953   TX

Web Site: https://www.energynet.com
Year Founded: 1999
Sales Range: $250-299.9 Million
Oil & Natural Gas Land Auction Ser-
vices
N.A.I.C.S.: 455110
William W. Britian (Co-Founder &
Chm)
Janet K. Cubitt (VP-Land)
Jim J. Brewer (Co-Founder)
Lisa Cox (Mgr-Conveyance)
John S. Munroe (VP-Engrg & Govt
Lease Sls)
Chris Atherton (CEO)
Michael Baker (VP-Bus Dev-Permian
Basin, East Texas & North Louisiana)
Ethan D. House (VP-Bus Dev-Mid
Continent & Texas Panhandle & Dir-
Mktg)
John Klee (VP-Corp Bus Dev)
Cathy Sifuentez (Asst Mgr-Land)
Gus Rivero (Mgr-Govt Lease Sls &
Supvr-Land)
John Laur (CTO)
Lauren Felton (Mgr-Event & Trade
Show)
Lindsay D. Ballard (Mgr-Bus Dev-
Permian Basin)
Lisa Weiss (Mgr-Auction Closing &
Bookkeeper)
Ryan P. Dobbs (VP-Bus Dev-Western
US)
Whitney McEvers (Mgr-Mktg Svcs)
Wildon Woolley (Treas & Sec)
Jim D. Black (Pres-Svcs)

ENERLABS, INC.
800 NE 63rd St, Oklahoma City, OK
73105
Tel.: (405) 879-1752
Web Site:
   http://www.enerlabsinc.com
Testing Laboratories
N.A.I.C.S.: 541380
George Shaw (Pres)

Subsidiaries:

Energy & Environmental Service,
Inc. (1)
241 W Wilshire Blvd, Oklahoma City, OK
73116
Tel.: (405) 843-8996
Web Site: http://www.endurobond.com
Sales Range: $1-9.9 Million
Emp.: 10
Chemicals And Allied Products, Nec
N.A.I.C.S.: 424690
Melvin B. Smith (Founder & CEO)
Todd Jelinek (Dir-Dev)

ENERPHASE INDUSTRIAL SO-LUTIONS, INC.
203 Aero Ct, Greensboro, NC 27409
Tel.: (336) 605-9622
Web Site: http://www.airflowinc.com
Year Founded: 2002
Sales Range: $10-24.9 Million
Emp.: 75
Holding Company; Industrial Equip-
ment & Parts Servicing & Whslr
N.A.I.C.S.: 551112
Stan Shelton (Pres & CEO)

Subsidiaries:

Air Flow (1)
203 Aero Ct, Greensboro, NC 27409
Tel.: (336) 605-9622
Web Site: http://www.airflowinc.com
Whslr & Servicing of Industrial Equipment
for Compressed Air
N.A.I.C.S.: 423830
Jeff Martin (Mgr-Ops)
Stan Shelton (Pres & CEO)
David Vanhoy (Founder & Mgr-Sls)
Jeff Laws (CFO & Gen Mgr)

ENERPIPE LTD

500 S Taylor St Ste 1010, Amarillo,
TX 79101
Tel.: (806) 371-8851
Web Site: http://www.enerpipe.com
Sales Range: $75-99.9 Million
Emp.: 200
Provider of Oil & Gas Pipeline Con-
struction Services
N.A.I.C.S.: 237120
Mike R. Brister (Pres)
Harry Janzen (Treas & Sec)
Eddy Douglass (Dir-Safety)

ENERPULSE TECHNOLOGIES, INC.
2451 Alamo Ave SE, Albuquerque,
NM 87106
Tel.: (505) 842-5201
Web Site: http://www.enerpulse.com
Sales Range: Less than $1 Million
Performance Improvement Technol-
ogy for Spark-Ignited Internal Com-
bustion Engines
N.A.I.C.S.: 336310
Louis S. Camilli (Founder, Pres,
CEO-Interim & CTO)
Bryan C. Templeton (CFO)
Craig Porter (Exec Chm)
Heather Tausch (Dir-Mktg & Comms)
Steve Smith (VPOps)

ENERSYS CORPORATION
12875 Capricorn St, Stafford, TX
77477
Tel.: (281) 598-7100   TX
Web Site:
   http://www.enersyscorp.com
Year Founded: 1994
Sales Range: $1-9.9 Million
Emp.: 21
Management Consulting Services for
Petroleum Companies
N.A.I.C.S.: 541611
Russel W. Treat (Founder & Pres)
Scott Williams (Mgr-IP)
Megan Ikerd (Mgr-Bookkeeping)

ENERVEST, LTD.
1001 Fannin St Ste 800, Houston, TX
77002-6707
Tel.: (713) 659-3500   TX
Web Site: http://www.enervest.net
Year Founded: 1992
Sales Range: $50-74.9 Million
Emp.: 800
Oil & Gas Asset Management Ser-
vices
N.A.I.C.S.: 213112
Ken Mariani (Pres)
John B. Walker (Exec Chm)
James M. Vanderhider (CFO, Exec
VP, Pres/CEO & EnerVest Institu-
tional GP)
Ron Whitmire (Chief Admin Officer &
VP)
Jon Rex Jones (Chm)
Phil C. DeLozier (Exec VP-Bus Dev)
Eric Eaches (VP-IT)
Fabene Welch (Gen Counsel & Sr
VP)
Polly Schott (Sr VP-Fin & Acctg)
Selena Stuchley (VP-HR)
Richard Parrish (VP-Acq & Engrg)
Barry Lay (Sr VP & Gen Mgr)
Dave Kyte (Pres & CEO)
Jim McKinney (Sr VP & Gen Mgr)
Ryan Flory (VP & Controller)
Andy West (VP & Assoc Gen Coun-
sel)
Philip Berry (VP-Bus Dev & Transac-
tions)
Luke Albrecht (VP-Bus Dev)
Michael Cheng (VP-Tax & Structured
Transactions)
Kevin Leonard (Sr VP-Special Proj-
ects & Engrg)
Rhonda Motley (VP)

Subsidiaries:

EnerVest Operating, LLC (1)
1001 Fannin St Ste 800, Houston, TX
77002
Tel.: (713) 659-3500
Web Site: http://www.enervest.net
Sales Range: $25-49.9 Million
Emp.: 180
Crude Petroleum & Natural Gas Production
N.A.I.C.S.: 211120
Jud Walker (COO & Exec VP)
Eric Eaches (VP-IT)
Dave Kyte (Pres & CEO)
Barry Lay (Sr VP)
Levi Maurer (VP)
Steve Millican (VP)
Selena Stuchly (VP-HR)
Karen Taylor (Sr VP-HR)
Fabene Welch (Gen Counsel & Sr VP)
Alex Zazzi (VP)

Harvest Oil & Gas Corp. (1)
1001 Fannin Ste 750, Houston, TX 77002
Tel.: (713) 651-1144
Web Site: https://www.hvstog.com
Rev.: $26,259,000
Assets: $46,859,000
Liabilities: $9,429,000
Net Worth: $37,430,000
Earnings: ($8,875,000)
Fiscal Year-end: 12/31/2020
Holding Company; Oil & Gas Property Acquisition, Development & Operation
N.A.I.C.S.: 551112
Michael E. Mercer (Pres & CEO)
Terry Wagstaff (VP-Acquisitions & Engrg)
Steven J. Pully (Chm)

Subsidiary (Domestic):

EnerVest Monroe Gathering, Ltd. (2)
1001 Fannin Ste 800, Houston, TX 77002
Tel.: (713) 651-1144
Oil & Natural Gas Exploration Services
N.A.I.C.S.: 211130

ENESCO, LLC
225 Windsor Dr, Itasca, IL 60143-
1200
Tel.: (630) 875-5300   IL
Web Site: http://www.enesco.com
Year Founded: 2007
Emp.: 100
Fine Gifts, Collectibles & Home Decor Accessories Mfr
N.A.I.C.S.: 327110
Michael Griffith (Pres)
Emily Brown (CFO)

Subsidiaries:

Enesco (Hong Kong) Ltd. (1)
114 Hsh Kowloon Central, 194 Nathan
Road, Kowloon, China (Hong Kong)
Tel.: (852) 27366161
Web Site: http://www.enesco.com
Sales Range: $25-49.9 Million
Giftware Distr
N.A.I.C.S.: 424990
Ricky Tai Jen Chan (Sr VP-Ops-Asia)

Enesco Canada Corporation (1)
2425 Skymark Ave Unit 3, Mississauga,
L4W 4Y6, ON, Canada
Tel.: (905) 673-9200
Web Site: https://www.enescocanada.com
Sales Range: $25-49.9 Million
Emp.: 50
Import & Export of Giftware
N.A.I.C.S.: 459420

Enesco France S.A.S. (1)
2426 Route Nationale 7, BP 209,
Villeneuve-Loubet, 06270, Cedex, France
Tel.: (33) 493735712
Web Site: http://www.enescofrance.com
Sales Range: $25-49.9 Million
Giftware Distr & Online Retailer
N.A.I.C.S.: 424990
Stephane Puig (Mng Dir)

Enesco Limited (1)
Brunthill Road, Kingstown Industrial Estate,
Carlisle, CA3 0EN, United Kingdom
Tel.: (44) 1228404022
Web Site: http://www.enesco.co.uk

Sales Range: $25-49.9 Million
Giftware & Collectibles
N.A.I.C.S.: 459420
Ken Johnson (Mng Dir)

The Boyds Collection, Ltd. (1)
75 Cunningham Rd, Gettysburg, PA 17325-
7142
Tel.: (717) 633-9898
Web Site: http://www.boydsstuff.com
Sales Range: $75-99.9 Million
Designs, Imports & Distributes Hand
Crafted Collectibles & Other Specialty Products
N.A.I.C.S.: 424990
Peter H. Frost (COO)

ENGAGE
550 Highland St, Frederick, MD
21701
Tel.: (301) 631-1010
Web Site:
  http://www.engagedirectmail.com
Year Founded: 2000
Sales Range: $1-9.9 Million
Emp.: 120
Direct Mail Services for Non-Profit
Organizations
N.A.I.C.S.: 541860
Dennis Hoffman (CEO)
Kathleen Clem (Pres)
Brendan M. Egan (Founder & CMO)

**ENGAGE BEHAVIORAL
HEALTH**
6543 Gunn Hwy, Tampa, FL 33625
Tel.: (813) 374-2070
Web Site:
  http://www.engagebehavioral
  health.com
Year Founded: 2008
Sales Range: $10-24.9 Million
Emp.: 50
Behavior Health Services
N.A.I.C.S.: 621440
Jennifer Phelps (Founder & CEO)
Gianna Fernandez (Dir-Clinical)

ENGAGE HOSPITALITY LLC
2447 Santa Clara Ave, Alameda, CA
94501   CA
Web Site:
  http://www.engagehospitality.com
Year Founded: 2010
Hotel Operator
N.A.I.C.S.: 721110
David Chin (Founder & CEO)

Subsidiaries:

Hotel Union Square (1)
114 Powell St, San Francisco, CA 94102
Tel.: (415) 397-3000
Web Site: http://www.hotelunionsquare.com
Hotel Operator
N.A.I.C.S.: 721110

Kensington Park Hotel (1)
450 Post St, San Francisco, CA 94102
Tel.: (415) 788-6400
Web Site:
  http://www.kensingtonparkhotel.com
Emp.: 130
Hotel Operator
N.A.I.C.S.: 721110

ENGAGE PR
1321 Harbor Bay Pkwy Ste 201,
Alameda, CA 94502
Tel.: (510) 748-8200
Web Site: http://www.engagepr.com
Year Founded: 1996
Sales Range: Less than $1 Million
Emp.: 15
Communications & Digital Media
N.A.I.C.S.: 541820
Jeannette Bitz (CEO)
Chris Nicoll (VP-Strategy)

**ENGAGE TECHNOLOGIES
CORP.**

7041 Boone Ave N, Brooklyn Park,
MN 55428
Tel.: (763) 795-8856
Web Site:
  https://www.engagetechnologies.net
Year Founded: 2004
Holding Company
N.A.I.C.S.: 551112
Dan Pint (VP-Ops)
Chad Carney (VP-Mktg & Corp
Comm)
William T. Hoagland (Pres & CEO)

Subsidiaries:

Cogent Technologies, Inc. (1)
7041 Boone Ave N, Brooklyn Park, MN
55428
Tel.: (952) 941-3300
Web Site: http://www.cogent-tech.com
Ink Drying System Mfr
N.A.I.C.S.: 333248
Chad Carney (VP-Mktg & Corp Comm-
Engage Technologies)

Eastey Enterprises Inc. (1)
7041 Boone Ave, Brooklyn Park, MN 55428
Tel.: (800) 835-9344
Web Site: http://www.eastey.com
Packaging Equipment Mfr
N.A.I.C.S.: 333993

Squid Ink Manufacturing, Inc. (1)
7041 Boone Ave N, Brooklyn Park, MN
55428
Tel.: (763) 795-8856
Web Site: http://www.squidink.com
Ink & Printer& Taping Equipment Mfr
N.A.I.C.S.: 333248

ENGAGE2EXCEL, INC.
149 Crawford Rd, Statesville, NC
28625
Tel.: (704) 872-5231   DE
Web Site:
  http://www.engage2excel.com
Year Founded: 1892
Human Resources & Consulting Services
N.A.I.C.S.: 541612
Joel Kepley (CFO & Sr VP)
Darren E. Findley (Pres)

Subsidiaries:

Engage2Excel Recruitment
Solutions (1)
149 Crawford Rd, Statesville, NC 28625
Tel.: (704) 872-5231
Web Site: http://www.engage2excel.com
Human Resources & Executive Search
Consulting Services
N.A.I.C.S.: 541612
Nicole Cox (Chief Recruitment Officer)

ENGAGEDLY, INC.
911 Washington Ave Ste 660, Saint
Louis, MO 63101
Tel.: (650) 485-1642   DE
Web Site: http://www.engagedly.com
Performance Management & Employee Engagement Software Development Services
N.A.I.C.S.: 541512
Jayashankar Balaraman (CEO &
Founder)

Subsidiaries:

Management Mentors, Inc. (1)
111 Nonantum St, Brighton, MA 02135-2413
Tel.: (650) 487-0860
Web Site: http://www.management-
mentors.com
Software Publisher
N.A.I.C.S.: 513210
Rene D. Petrin (Founder & Pres)

ENGAGEPOINT
6700 N Andrews Ave Ste 210, Fort
Lauderdale, FL 33309
Tel.: (954) 315-0902

Web Site:
  http://www.engagepoint.com
Year Founded: 2007
Sales Range: $10-24.9 Million
Emp.: 170
Healthcare Software Development
Services
N.A.I.C.S.: 541511
Pradeep Goel (CEO)

**ENGEL & VOLKERS AMERI-
CAS, INC.**
300 Altara Ave Ste 1415 Coral
Gables, Miami, FL 33146
Tel.: (305) 443-2424
Web Site: http://miami.evusa.com
Year Founded: 2008
Real Estate Firm
N.A.I.C.S.: 531210
Irving A. Padron (Partner & President)

**ENGELBERTH CONSTRUC-
TION INC.**
463 Mountain View Dr, Colchester,
VT 05446-5966
Tel.: (802) 655-0100   VT
Web Site: http://www.engelberth.com
Year Founded: 1972
Sales Range: $25-49.9 Million
Emp.: 240
Commercial Construction Services
N.A.I.C.S.: 236220
Frank Clark (Controller)
Pierre Leblanc (Pres)

ENGINE COMPANY ONE
451 Pacific Ave, San Francisco, CA
94133
Tel.: (415) 989-2500
Year Founded: 1998
Sales Range: $10-24.9 Million
Emp.: 35
Food Service
N.A.I.C.S.: 541810
Grant Richards (Partner & Dir-
Creative)
Scott Aal (Partner & Dir-Creative)
Wayne Buder (Partner & Mng Dir)
Vince Engel (Principal & Dir-Creative)
Robin Eusebio (Dir-Art)
Nick Fairbairn (Dir-Media)
Jessica Clement (Copywriter)
Von Rohr (Copywriter)
Frank Lewis (Acct Dir & Dir-
Integrated Production)
Karin Knutson (Dir-Acct Plng)
Laura Puccinelli (Dir-Fin-Acctg)
Suosdey Penn (Assoc Dir-Creative)
Gabriel Johnson (Copywriter)

ENGINE MARKETING, LLC
1205 E Central Ave, Fullerton, CA
92831
Tel.: (714) 273-1398   CA
Year Founded: 1998
Sales Range: Less than $1 Million
Emp.: 5
N.A.I.C.S.: 541810
Jeff Moses (Owner & Dir-Creative)
Cynthia Moses (Acct Exec)

ENGINE WAREHOUSE INC.
7415 Empire Central, Houston, TX
77040
Tel.: (713) 937-4000
Web Site:
  http://www.engwarehouse.com
Sales Range: $10-24.9 Million
Emp.: 27
Lawn & Garden Machinery & Equipment
N.A.I.C.S.: 423820
Robert Graham (Pres)
Steve DeWitt (VP-Sls)

Engineered Components Co—(Continued)

ENGINEERED COMPONENTS CO
1100 Davis Rd, Elgin, IL 60123
Tel.: (847) 841-7000
Web Site:
https://www.engcomponents.com
Sales Range: $10-24.9 Million
Emp.: 30
Fasteners, Industrial: Nuts, Bolts,
Screws, Etc.
N.A.I.C.S.: 423840
Diane Coursey (Controller)
Arne Henriksen Jr. (Pres)

ENGINEERED DATA PROD-UCTS, LLC
6800 W 117th Ave, Broomfield, CO
80020
Tel.: (800) 522-3528
Web Site: http://www.edpllc-usa.com
Computer, Storage & Media Furniture
N.A.I.C.S.: 337214
Jeff Symes (Sls Mgr-Products)

Subsidiaries:

EDP Europe   (1)
43 Redhills Rd S Woodham Ferrers,
Chelmsford, CM35UL, Essex, United
Kingdom   (100%)
Tel.: (44) 1245322380
Web Site: http://www.edpeurope.com
Sales Range: $10-24.9 Million
Emp.: 10
Mfr of Computer Storage Devices
N.A.I.C.S.: 334112

ENGINEERED FLOORS, LLC
3510 Corporate Dr, Dalton, GA 30721
Tel.: (706) 625-4334   GA
Web Site:
http://www.engineeredfloors.com
Year Founded: 2009
Sales Range: $10-24.9 Million
Emp.: 50
Carpet & Rug Mfr & Distr
N.A.I.C.S.: 314110
Robert E. Shaw (Chm & CEO)
Louis Fordham (VP-HR)
Brad Root (VP-Sls & Mktg-EF Con-tract)
Susan Curtis (VP-Design & Mktg)

Subsidiaries:

J&J Flooring Group, LLC   (1)
115 W King St, Dalton, GA 30720
Tel.: (706) 529-2100
Web Site: http://www.jjflooringgroup.com
Carpet & Rug Mfr & Distr
N.A.I.C.S.: 314110
Josh Hall (VP-Mfg Ops)

ENGINEERED FLUID INC.
1221 N Elm St, Centralia, IL 62801
Tel.: (618) 533-1351
Web Site:
http://www.engineeredfluid.com
Sales Range: $10-24.9 Million
Emp.: 150
Pumps & Pumping Equipment
N.A.I.C.S.: 333914
William Goodspeed (Pres & CEO)
Chris Byrnes (Mgr-SE Reg)

ENGINEERED GLASS PROD-UCTS LLC
2857 S Halsted St, Chicago, IL
60608
Tel.: (312) 326-4710
Web Site: http://www.egpglass.com
Year Founded: 1947
Products Of Purchased Glass
N.A.I.C.S.: 327215
Mike Hobbs (CEO)

ENGINEERED GLASS WALLS

8130 Lorraine Ave Ste 310, Stockton,
CA 95210
Tel.: (209) 473-7643   CA
Year Founded: 1988
Sales Range: $10-24.9 Million
Emp.: 50
Glass & Glazing Work
N.A.I.C.S.: 238150

Subsidiaries:

Carmel Steel Products Inc   (1)
8130 Lorraine Ave Ste 310, Stockton, CA
95210
Tel.: (209) 473-7610
Web Site:
http://www.CarmelSteelProducts.com
Rev.: $2,200,000
Emp.: 30
Steel Window Wall & Entrance Systems Mfr
N.A.I.C.S.: 332321

ENGINEERED PLASTIC COM-PONENTS INC.
1408 Zimmerman Dr S, Grinnell, IA
50112
Tel.: (641) 236-3100
Web Site: https://www.epcmfg.com
Sales Range: $75-99.9 Million
Emp.: 1,000
Plastics Product Mfr
N.A.I.C.S.: 326199
Reza Kargarzadeh (Pres)
Steve Jacobs (Engr-Quality)
Kim Swanson (Mgr-Quality Assur-ance)
Ronald Brookhart (Acct Mgr-Tech &
Sr Project Engr)
Abbas Razizadeh (Dir-Ops)

Subsidiaries:

EPC, Inc.-East Troy   (1)
2600 Energy Dr, East Troy, WI 53120
Tel.: (262) 642-6500
Web Site: http://www.epcmfg.com
Sales Range: $125-149.9 Million
Emp.: 15
Plastic Injection Molding
N.A.I.C.S.: 326199
Jim Kloster (Gen Mgr)

EPC-Columbia, Inc.   (1)
300 Shellhouse Dr, Rantoul, IL 61866
Tel.: (217) 892-2026
Sales Range: $25-49.9 Million
Emp.: 200
Mfr of Plastic Parts for Vehicles
N.A.I.C.S.: 326199

ENGINEERED PLASTICS INC.
1040 Maple Ave, Lake City, PA
16423
Tel.: (814) 774-2970
Web Site:
https://www.engineeredplastics.com
Sales Range: $10-24.9 Million
Emp.: 135
Plastics Processing
N.A.I.C.S.: 326199
Kurt M. Duska (Pres)
Terry Maloney (VP-Fin)
Ken Szekely (Owner)

ENGINEERED PRODUCTS, INC.
200 Jones St, Verona, PA 15147-1048
Tel.: (412) 423-4000   DE
Web Site: https://www.epimetal.com
Year Founded: 1958
Sales Range: $25-49.9 Million
Emp.: 75
Wholesale Construction Materials;
Manufacture Sheet Metal; Bridge
Repair
N.A.I.C.S.: 423390
Joseph Stein (VP)

Subsidiaries:

EPI/Cleveland   (1)

655 West Wilmus St, Akron, OH 44314
Tel.: (330) 753-7762
Sales Range: $10-24.9 Million
Emp.: 30
Miscellaneous Iron Work
N.A.I.C.S.: 332312

Engineered Products Inc   (1)
200 Jones St, Verona, PA
15147-1048   (100%)
Tel.: (412) 423-4000
Web Site: http://www.epimetal.com
Sales Range: $25-49.9 Million
Emp.: 20
Mfr of Glass & Aluminum Products
N.A.I.C.S.: 238130

ENGINEERED PROTECTION SYSTEMS, INC.
750 Front Ave NW, Grand Rapids, MI
49504
Tel.: (616) 459-0281
Web Site:
https://www.epssecurity.com
Year Founded: 1955
Sales Range: $10-24.9 Million
Emp.: 140
Fire Detection & Burglar Alarm Sys-tems Contracting Services
N.A.I.C.S.: 561621
Terri Ladomersky (Mgr-HR)
John Mueller (Acct Mgr)

ENGINEERED SEAL PROD-UCTS, INC.
5920 Dry Creek Ln NE, Cedar Rap-ids, IA 52402
Tel.: (319) 393-4310   IA
Web Site: https://www.espint.com
Sales Range: $10-24.9 Million
Emp.: 70
Whslr of Industrial Seals
N.A.I.C.S.: 423840
Jeffrey L. Hamilton (Chm & CEO)
Melissa Jones (Exec VP-Global Fin &
Shared Svcs)
Don Grawe (Dir-Sls)
Jeff Albright (Pres-Global Sls & Mktg)

ENGINEERED SPECIALTY PRODUCTS, INC.
3295 Cobb International Blvd NW,
Kennesaw, GA 30152
Tel.: (770) 790-6055
Web Site:
https://www.espgauges.com
Year Founded: 1983
Emp.: 100
Pressure & Temperature Instruments
Mfr & Distr
N.A.I.C.S.: 334512
Ed Millman (CFO)
Brien Whitford (Pres & CEO)

ENGINEERED SPECIALTY TEXTILES LLC
25 E Court St Ste 302, Greenville,
SC 29601
Tel.: (864) 335-4004
Sales Range: $10-24.9 Million
Emp.: 240
Textile Products Mfr
N.A.I.C.S.: 314999
Rodney L. Grandy (Mgr)
William Maness (Mgr-IT)

ENGINEERED TAX SERVICES, INC
303 Evernia St #300, West Palm
Beach, FL 33401
Tel.: (561) 253-6640
Web Site:
http://www.engineeredtaxser
vices.com
N.A.I.C.S.:

Julio Gonzalez (Founder & CEO)
Jeff Pawlow (Mng Dir)
Charles Hylan (Mng Dir)
Jerry Winkelmann (Dir-Bus Dev)

Subsidiaries:

The Growth Partnership   (1)
9338 Olive Blvd Ste 200, Saint Louis, MO
63132
Tel.: (314) 209-0922
Web Site:
http://www.thegrowthpartnership.com
Sales Range: $1-9.9 Million
Emp.: 20
Management Consulting Services
N.A.I.C.S.: 541613
Jeffrey Pawlow (Mng Dir)
Charles Hylan (Mng Dir)

ENGINEERING & COMPUTER SIMULATIONS, INC.
11825 High Tech Ave Ste 250, Or-lando, FL 32817
Tel.: (407) 823-9991   FL
Web Site: https://www.ecsorl.com
Year Founded: 1997
Sales Range: $10-24.9 Million
Emp.: 55
Advanced Learning Technology Solu-tions
N.A.I.C.S.: 513210
Frances Armstrong (CEO)
Larry Kayne (COO & VP)
Joe OConnell (VP-Bus Dev)
Shane Taber (VP-Ops)
Michael Golson (COO)
Paul Cummings (VP-Innovation &
Tech)

ENGINEERING & EQUIPMENT COMPANY INC.
910 N Washington St, Albany, GA
31701-2330
Tel.: (229) 435-5601   GA
Year Founded: 1952
Sales Range: $10-24.9 Million
Emp.: 100
Plumbing Fixtures & Related Equip-ment Mfr
N.A.I.C.S.: 423720

ENGINEERING AND INFORMA-TION TECHNOLOGIES, INC.
11555 Heron Bay Blvd, Coral
Springs, FL 33076
Tel.: (954) 603-0400   FL
Web Site: http://www.eiitinc.net
Technical & Information Technology
Services
N.A.I.C.S.: 541990
Nandita Singh (Pres)

ENGINEERING EXCELLENCE INCORPORATED
10 Knollcrest Dr, Cincinnati, OH
45237
Tel.: (513) 761-6000
Web Site: http://www.engineeringex
cellence.com
Year Founded: 1979
Sales Range: $10-24.9 Million
Emp.: 150
Contractor of Heating & Air Condition-ing; HVAC Facilities Management
Firm
N.A.I.C.S.: 238220
Brandon Studeny (Controller)
Rick Evans (COO & Exec VP)

ENGINEERING RESEARCH & CONSULTING INC.
4901 Corp Dr Ste E, Huntsville, AL
35805
Tel.: (256) 430-3080

Web Site: http://www.erc-incorporated.com
Rev.: $27,437,288
Emp.: 400
Commercial Physical Research
N.A.I.C.S.: 541715
Susan Wu (Chm)
Ernie Wu (Pres & CEO)

ENGINEERING SERVICE, INC.
21556 Telegraph Rd, Southfield, MI
48034-4247
Tel.: (248) 357-3800   MI
Year Founded: 1941
Sales Range: $50-74.9 Million
Emp.: 30
Engineering Services
N.A.I.C.S.: 541330
James Karchon (Pres)
Dennis Karchon (Corp Svcs Dir)

ENGINEERING SERVICES & PRODUCTS COMPANY INC.
1395 John Fitch Blvd, South Windsor,
CT 06074-1029
Tel.: (860) 528-1119   CT
Web Site: http://www.esapco.com
Year Founded: 1981
Sales Range: $25-49.9 Million
Emp.: 300
Farm & Garden Machinery
N.A.I.C.S.: 423820
Barry Goldsher (Pres & CEO)

ENGINEERING SERVICES NETWORK, INC.
2450 Crystal Dr Ste 1015, Arlington,
VA 22202
Tel.: (703) 412-3640   VA
Web Site: https://www.esncc.com
Year Founded: 1995
Sales Range: $25-49.9 Million
Emp.: 175
Engineeering Services
N.A.I.C.S.: 541330
Shelley Smith (Dir-Contracts)
Daniel Shapiro (CFO & Exec VP)
Douglas Lopez (COO)
Wesley Mandler (Controller)
Steve Dutra (Mgr-Ops-Charleston)
Raymond F. Lopez Jr. (Founder, Pres & CEO)

ENGINEERING SYSTEMS SO-LUTIONS INC.
5726 Industry Ln, Frederick, MD
21704-5190
Tel.: (301) 698-1177
Web Site: http://www.essworld.net
Year Founded: 1994
Sales Range: $25-49.9 Million
Emp.: 90
Provider of Computer Integrated Systems Design Services
N.A.I.C.S.: 541512
Tom Goode (Controller)
Jay Nathan (Founder & CEO)
Angela Severino (Exec VP)
Kelli Johnson (Mgr-Bus Dev)

ENGINEERING/REMEDIATION RESOURCES GROUP, INC.
4585 Pacheco Blvd Ste 200, Martinez, CA 94553
Tel.: (925) 969-0750
Web Site: https://www.errg.com
Year Founded: 1997
Sales Range: $50-74.9 Million
Emp.: 148
Business Consulting Services
N.A.I.C.S.: 541690
Doug Bielskis (Mgr-Navy Program)
Caitlin Gorman (Office Mgr-San Francisco)

Brian Wetzsteon (Mgr-Northwest Reg)
Cynthia A. Liu (Pres & CEO)
Dave Williams (Mgr-Ops)

ENGINEERS WITHOUT BORDERS-USA, INC.
1031 33rd St, Denver, CO 80205
Tel.: (303) 772-2723
Web Site: https://ewb-usa.org
Emp.: 100
Non Profit Organization
N.A.I.C.S.: 813990

Subsidiaries:

Engineering World Health   (1)
4819 Emperor Blvd Ste 400, Durham, NC
27703
Tel.: (919) 313-4633
Web Site: http://www.ewh.org
Sales Range: $1-9.9 Million
Health Care Development Services
N.A.I.C.S.: 813212
Mhoire Murphy (Sec)
Michael R. Tracey (Chm)
Jessica Feddersen (Treas)

ENGINETECH INC.
1205 W Crosby Rd, Carrollton, TX
75006
Tel.: (972) 245-0110
Web Site:
    https://www.enginetech.com
Sales Range: $75-99.9 Million
Emp.: 45
Automotive Engines & Engine Parts
N.A.I.C.S.: 423120
Fred Currey (Chm & Pres)
Joe Munoz (Owner & Gen Mgr)
Anne Carroll (CFO & Controller)

ENGINUITY COMMUNICA-TIONS CORPORATION
3545 Stern Ave, Saint Charles, IL
60174
Tel.: (630) 444-0778
Web Site: https://enginuitycom.com
Rev.: $6,500,000
Emp.: 40
All Other Miscellaneous Electrical
Equipment & Component Mfr
N.A.I.C.S.: 335999
Nicholas C. Hindman (CFO)
Steve Todd (Pres)

ENGIS CORPORATION
105 W Hintz Rd, Wheeling, IL 60090
Tel.: (847) 808-9400   DE
Web Site: https://www.engis.com
Sales Range: $10-24.9 Million
Emp.: 145
Diamond Powder
N.A.I.C.S.: 333517
Martin Steindler (CEO)
Stephen Griffin (Pres)
John Smallshaw (VP-Sls)

ENGLAND MOTOR CO. INC.
115 Gamwyn Park Dr, Greenville, MS
38701-6333
Tel.: (662) 332-6341
Web Site:
    http://www.englandmotors.net
Sales Range: $10-24.9 Million
Emp.: 56
New & Used Automobiles
N.A.I.C.S.: 441110
Perry N. England (Pres)
Frank England (VP)
Barbara Bardwell (Office Mgr)
Tim W. Epting (Mgr)
Frank Fyke (Sls Mgr)
Phillip McDade (Sls Mgr)

ENGLANDER ENTERPRISES, INC.

703 Grand Central St, Clearwater, FL
33756
Tel.: (727) 461-4755   FL
Web Site: https://www.eeimfg.com
Year Founded: 1993
Sales Range: $1-9.9 Million
Emp.: 25
Electronic Computer Mfr
N.A.I.C.S.: 334111
Susan C. Englander (Pres)
Kevin McCall (COO)

ENGLANDER KNABE & AL-LEN
801 S Figueroa St Ste 1050, Los Angeles, CA 90017
Tel.: (213) 741-1500
Web Site: https://www.ekapr.com
Year Founded: 2005
Public Relations Services
N.A.I.C.S.: 541820
Matt Knabe (Mng Partner)
Marcus A. Allen (Partner)
Eric Rose (Partner)
Paul A. Haney (Partner-Joint Venture)
Harvey A. Englander (Founding Partner)
Adam Englander (Partner & Gen Counsel)
Alex Cherin (Partner)
Gary Townsend (Partner-Joint Venture)
Jaime de la Vega (Exec VP)
Jeff McConnell (Partner)
Kellie Hawkins (Partner)
Marcia Lewis Smith (Partner-Joint Venture)
Tina Choi (Partner-Joint Venture)

Subsidiaries:

Max Development LLC   (1)
11287 Washington Blvd, Culver City, CA
90230
Tel.: (310) 204-3500
Web Site: http://www.three6ixty.net
Surveying & Mapping Services
N.A.I.C.S.: 541370
Dana Sayles (Principal)
Sara Houghton (VP & Dir-Planning and Land Use)
Courtney Brown (Dir-Permitting)
Carolyn Wispe Burns (Controller)
Fahmida Rashid (Project Mgr-Permitting)
Markie Anderle (Project Mgr-Plng)
Cassandra Menendez (Mgr-Permitting)
Mia Rondone (Project Mgr-Permitting)
Khoa Ho (Associate Permitting Manager)

ENGLE MARTIN & ASSOCI-ATES, LLC
5565 Glenridge Connector Ste 900,
Atlanta, GA 30342
Tel.: (404) 303-7160
Web Site:
    http://www.englemartin.com
Year Founded: 1997
Emp.: 375
Insurance Claim Adjustment Services
N.A.I.C.S.: 524291
W. Todd Evans (Exec VP-Bus Dev)
Stephen Beene (Pres)
Lee Maddox (VP-Specialty Marine & Transportation)
Joseph Slane (Exec VP-Specialty Loss Grp)
Roberto Stewart (COO)
John Ketch (Sr VP-Bus Dev)

Subsidiaries:

EIMC, LLC   (1)
111 Pavonia Ave, Jersey City, NJ 07310
Tel.: (201) 963-3355
Web Site: http://www.eimc.com
Sales Range: $1-9.9 Million
Emp.: 33
Risk Managemeng Srvices
N.A.I.C.S.: 541611
Ruediger Stoer (CEO)
Tiina Ruhlandt-Medel (Mng Dir)

Envista Forensics, LLC   (1)
5565 Glenridge Connector Ste 900, Atlanta,
GA 30342
Tel.: (888) 782-3473
Web Site: http://www.ptclwg.com
Emp.: 20
Forensic Engineering Services
N.A.I.C.S.: 541990
Grover Davis (CEO)
Kevin Dixon (Acct Exec)
John Hicks (Dir-Complex Loss-Canada)
Scott Broad (VP-Ops-Canada)
Gabriel de Carcer (Mng Dir-Mexico & The Caribbean)
Mike Driscoll (Dir-Technical)
Liz Peterson (VP-Forensics-Intl)
Leonel Carrasco (Project Engr-Fire, Electrical & Mechanical)
Miguel Hernandez (Sr Project Engr-Fire, Civil & Structural)
Jennifer Gaster (VP-Mktg)
Lenny Alexander (Chief Experience Officer)
Christina Lucas (Pres)

ENGLE PRINTING & PUBLISH-ING CO., INC.
1425 W Main St, Mount Joy, PA
17552
Tel.: (717) 653-1833
Web Site:
    http://www.engleonline.com
Year Founded: 1966
Sales Range: $25-49.9 Million
Emp.: 425
Printing Services
N.A.I.C.S.: 323111
Charles Engle (Pres)
Tanya Bomberger (Coord-Web Project)
Brad Yost (Mgr-Production)
John Hemperly (Mgr-Sls)
Gregory March (Mgr-Field Sls)

ENGLE-HAMBRIGHT & DA-VIES INC.
1857 William Penn Way, Lancaster,
PA 17601
Tel.: (717) 394-5681
Web Site: http://www.ehd-ins.com
Year Founded: 1970
Sales Range: $10-24.9 Million
Emp.: 110
Insurance Agents
N.A.I.C.S.: 524210
Robert F. McMurtrie (Co-Owner)
Lori Daly (Asst VP & Dir-Trng & Dev)
Laurie Rogers (Mgr-Personal Lines)
Ashley Adams (Dir-Client Svcs)
Amala Abdul (Mgr-Comml Acct)
Amanda Burridge (Mgr-Special Bus Acct)
Erica Fritzeen (Mgr-Comml Acct)
Leanne Gorsuch (CFO)
Marjorie DiBernardo (Supvr-Comml Lines)
Melissa Giljam (Mgr-Comml Acct)
Michael Dietrich (Mgr-Comml Acct)
Morgan Ellis (Mgr-Comml Acct)
Susan Bearinger (Sr VP-Comml Mktg)
Jon K. Miles (Chm, Pres & CEO)
Christine I. Jensen (Sr VP)
Scott Radcliffe (Exec VP-Employee Benefit Svcs)

ENGLEFIELD OIL COMPANY
447 James Pkwy, Heath, OH 43056-1030
Tel.: (740) 928-8215   OH
Web Site:
    http://www.englefieldoil.com
Year Founded: 1961
Sales Range: $500-549.9 Million
Emp.: 1,300
Operator of Gas Stations & Convenience Stores
N.A.I.C.S.: 457120

Englefield Oil Company—(Continued)

F. William Englefield IV *(Founder & Pres)*
Mike Adkins *(VP-Lubricants Div)*

ENGLEKIRK PARTNERS CONSULTING STRUCTURAL ENGINEERS, INC.
888 S Figueroa St Fl 18, Los Angeles, CA 90017
Tel.: (323) 733-6673   CA
Web Site: http://www.englekirk.com
Year Founded: 1969
Sales Range: $75-99.9 Million
Emp.: 75
Structural Engineering
N.A.I.C.S.: 541330
Thomas A. Sabol *(Pres & Principal)*
Tony Ghodsi *(Principal & Dir-Orange County Office)*

Subsidiaries:

Englekirk & Sabol, Inc.   (1)
888 Sigueroa Ste 18 Fl, Los Angeles, CA 90017-1353
Tel.: (323) 733-2640
Web Site: http://www.englekirk.com
Sales Range: $25-49.9 Million
Emp.: 65
Seismic Engineering, Institutional & Wind Studies
N.A.I.C.S.: 541330
Russell Tanouye *(Principal)*

Englekirk Institutional   (1)
888 S Figueroa St 18th Fl, Los Angeles, CA 90017
Tel.: (323) 733-6673
Construction Engineering Services
N.A.I.C.S.: 541330
Kathy Lee-Choi *(Dir-Admin)*
Vladimir A. Volnyy *(Assoc Principal)*
Diana Erickson Nishi *(Assoc Principal)*
Lawrence Y. Ho *(Principal)*
Michael K. Kawaharada *(Principal)*
Christopher R. Rosien *(CFO & Principal)*
Russell Tanouye *(Principal)*

Englekirk Systems Development, Inc.   (1)
2116 Arlington Ave, Los Angeles, CA 90018-1353
Tel.: (323) 733-6673
Web Site: http://www.englekirk.com
Sales Range: $50-74.9 Million
Systems Development & Structural Development
N.A.I.C.S.: 541330
Kimberly Tanouye *(Dir-Mktg)*

ENGLERT INC.
1200 Amboy Ave, Perth Amboy, NJ 08861
Tel.: (732) 826-8614
Web Site: https://www.englertinc.com
Sales Range: $10-24.9 Million
Emp.: 170
Gutters, Sheet Metal
N.A.I.C.S.: 332322
Deborah Harnett *(Pres & CEO)*
Liliana Gomez-Silverio *(Mgr-HR)*
Pat Daniels *(Mgr-South East Reg)*
Adrian Shorb *(Mgr-Field Svcs Center-Denver)*
Michael Munsch *(Mgr-Tolling Sls)*

ENGLEWOOD LAB, LLC
88 W Sheffield Ave, Englewood, NJ 07631
Tel.: (201) 567-2267
Web Site: http://www.englewoodlab.com
Year Founded: 2004
Sales Range: $1-9.9 Million
Emp.: 30
Mfg Toilet Preparations
N.A.I.C.S.: 325620
David C. Chung *(Founder & CEO)*
John Kim *(COO)*

Thomas Drennan *(VP-Ops)*
Patrick Okoye *(VP-Quality)*
Michael Sturman *(Dir-Customer Svc)*

ENGLEWOOD TIRE DISTRIBUTORS, INC.
50 Rte 6 E, Totowa, NJ 07512
Tel.: (201) 935-3444   NJ
Web Site: http://www.englewoodtire.com
Year Founded: 1989
Sales Range: $25-49.9 Million
Emp.: 170
Mfr & Distribution of Tires & Tubes
N.A.I.C.S.: 423130
John Boyle *(Pres)*

ENGLISH + ASSOCIATES ARCHITECTS, INC.
1919 Decatur St, Houston, TX 77007
Tel.: (713) 850-0400   TX
Web Site: http://www.english-architects.com
Year Founded: 1989
Sales Range: $1-9.9 Million
Emp.: 7
Architectural Services
N.A.I.C.S.: 541310
Kathleen English *(Pres)*
Dennis Hopkins *(Mgr-IT & Coord-Production & Documentation)*

ENGLISH COLOR & SUPPLY LLC
810 N Grove Rd, Richardson, TX 75081
Tel.: (972) 235-3104
Web Site: https://www.englishcolor.com
Year Founded: 1946
Rev.: $28,000,000
Emp.: 20
Paints & Coatings Distr
N.A.I.C.S.: 424950
Donna Deets *(Office Mgr)*
Steve Gallob *(CFO)*
Bob English *(Founder)*

ENGLISH LANGUAGE INSTITUTE/CHINA
1629 Blue Spruce Dr, Fort Collins, CO 80524
Tel.: (970) 530-3800   CA
Web Site: https://www.elic.org
Year Founded: 1980
Sales Range: $10-24.9 Million
Emp.: 528
Language Trainer Placement Services
N.A.I.C.S.: 561311
Gary Lausch *(VP-HR)*
Joseph Stowell *(COO, Treas, Sec & Exec VP)*
David Addington *(VP-Mobilization)*
Timothy Davis *(Pres & CEO)*

ENGLUND MARINE SUPPLY CO. INC.
95 Hamburg Ave, Astoria, OR 97103
Tel.: (503) 325-4341
Web Site: https://www.englundmarine.com
Sales Range: $10-24.9 Million
Emp.: 30
Marine Supplies
N.A.I.C.S.: 441222
Jon A. Englund *(Pres)*
Bill Landwehr *(Controller)*

ENHANCED CAPITAL PARTNERS LLC
600 Lexington Ave Ste 1401, New York, NY 10022
Tel.: (212) 207-3385

Web Site: http://www.enhancedcapital.com
Year Founded: 1999
Emp.: 250
Small Business Investment Services
N.A.I.C.S.: 523999
Michael A.G. Korengold *(Pres & CEO)*
Paul Kasper *(Mng Dir)*
Shane McCarthy *(Mng Partner & CFO)*
Richard Montgomery *(Mng Partner)*
Jon Burckin *(Principal)*

ENIGMA-BULWARK, LIMITED
1327 Ocean Ave Ste B, Santa Monica, CA 90401
Tel.: (310) 899-3900
Web Site: http://www.enigma-bulwark.com
Security Management Services
N.A.I.C.S.: 561612
Clive J. Oosthuizen *(Chm, Pres & CEO)*

ENKEI AMERICA INC.
2900 Inwood Dr, Columbus, IN 47201
Tel.: (812) 373-7000
Web Site: http://www.enkeiamerica.com
Sales Range: $100-124.9 Million
Emp.: 800
Dealer of Motor Vehicle Parts
N.A.I.C.S.: 336390
Nikki Lushin Baker *(Asst Gen Mgr-HR)*
Brian Brumley *(Engr-Casting)*
Rick Merkel *(Exec VP)*
Thompson Ron *(Gen Mgr)*
Brent Roberts *(Mgr-Sls)*
Mary Ann McCarty *(Mgr-Employee Dev)*
Matt Wirt *(Mgr-Process Quality)*
Robert Bird *(Supvr-HR)*

ENKO CHEM, INC.
62 Maritime Dr, Mystic, CT 06355
Tel.: (857) 301-7619
Biotechnology Research & Development Services
N.A.I.C.S.: 541714

ENLIGHTENMENT CAPITAL LLC
4445 Willard Ave Ste 950, Chevy Chase, MD 20815
Tel.: (240) 752-9616
Web Site: http://www.enlightenment-cap.com
Privater Equity Firm
N.A.I.C.S.: 523999
Devin Talbott *(Founder & Mng Partner)*
Jason Rigoli *(Partner)*
Jeffrey Guffey *(CFO)*
Pierre Chao *(Operating Partner)*
Robert Dowling *(VP)*
Thomas Young *(Principal)*

Subsidiaries:

Agile Defense, Inc.   (1)
11600 Sunrise Valley Dr Ste 440, Reston, VA 20191
Tel.: (703) 351-9977
Web Site: https://agile-defense.com
Information Technology & Services
N.A.I.C.S.: 513210

Subsidiary (Domestic):

Xor Security LLC   (2)
4511 Rhett Ln, Fairfax, VA 22030-6140
Tel.: (202) 503-9677
Web Site: http://www.xorsecurity.com
Custom Computer Programming Services
N.A.I.C.S.: 541511
Razwan Raja *(Principal)*

Boecore, Inc.   (1)

90 S Cascade Ave Ste 610, Colorado Springs, CO 80903
Tel.: (719) 540-5635
Web Site: http://www.boecore.com
Sales Range: $1-9.9 Million
Emp.: 80
Engineeering Services
N.A.I.C.S.: 541330
Ron Moffat *(Controller)*
Tom Dickson *(Pres)*

Subsidiary (Domestic):

LA Jolla Logic   (2)
444 W C St Ste 220, San Diego, CA 92101
Tel.: (619) 559-6083
Web Site: http://www.lajollalogic.com
Engineeering Services
N.A.I.C.S.: 541330
Daniel Groves *(Sys Engr-Cyber Security)*

Orbit Logic, Inc.   (2)
7500 Greenway Center Dr, Greenbelt, MD 20770
Tel.: (301) 982-6232
Web Site: http://www.orbitlogic.com
Rev.: $2,500,000
Emp.: 9
Software Development Services
N.A.I.C.S.: 513210
Alexander F. Herz *(Pres)*

IntelliBridge, LLC   (1)
1430 Spring Hill Rd Ste 200, McLean, VA 22102
Tel.: (571) 499-4150
Web Site: https://intellibridge.us
Sales Range: $25-49.9 Million
Emp.: 224
Information Technology Services
N.A.I.C.S.: 541512
Thierry Janssens *(VP-Fin & Contracts)*
Cass Panciocco *(Pres & CEO)*

Subsidiary (Non-US):

RevaComm, Inc   (2)
Tel.: (808) 599-8872
Rev.: $2,210,000
Emp.: 10
Computer System Design Services
N.A.I.C.S.: 541512
Brett Kimura *(VP-Ops)*
Caden Morikuni *(Mgr-Software Architect & Dev)*
Kurt Nakamura *(COO)*

Sev1Tech, LLC   (1)
12700 Black Forest Ln Ste 306, Woodbridge, VA 22192
Tel.: (703) 496-3776
Web Site: http://www.Sev1Tech.com
Sales Range: $1-9.9 Million
Emp.: 85
Management Consulting Services
N.A.I.C.S.: 541611
Martin Wright *(CIO & VP-Engrg)*
Joseph Montoya *(COO)*
Kristin Lohfeld *(CFO)*
Tara Berman *(VP-DHS Law Enforcement)*
Valerie Bryce Gauthier *(VP-US Coast Guard Acct)*
Andy Cohen *(VP-Bus Dev)*
Lisa Anderson *(Chief HR Officer)*
Yogesh Khanna *(Chief Tech & Strategy Officer)*
Tim Hays *(VP-Health IT)*
William Zito *(VP-Mission Solutions Grp)*
Zhenia Klevitsky *(Chief Growth Officer)*
Hector Collazo *(CTO)*
Michael Fry *(Deputy CTO)*
Robert E. Lohfeld Jr. *(Founder & CEO)*

Subsidiary (Domestic):

Geocent, LLC   (2)
111 Veterans Memorial Blvd Ste 1600, Metairie, LA 70005
Tel.: (504) 831-1900
Web Site: http://www.geocent.com
Sales Range: $10-24.9 Million
Emp.: 160
Information Technology Services
N.A.I.C.S.: 541512
Robert A. Savoie *(CEO)*
Rick Gremillion *(Pres & COO)*
Jeff Tomeny *(CFO & Exec VP)*
Keith Alphonso *(CTO & VP)*
Torrie Hebert *(Dir-Ops-Federal Bus Unit)*
Brett Camet *(VP-Bus Dev)*

Wayne Eldridge Bourgeois *(VP-Enterprise Tech Solutions)*
Cooper Jumonville *(Coord-Mktg)*
Dax Thibodeaux *(Sr Engr-Software)*
Patrick Scheuermann *(Chief Strategy Officer & Exec VP)*

ENLOE MEDICAL CENTER
1531 Esplanade, Chico, CA 95926
Tel.: (530) 332-7300   CA
Web Site: https://www.enloe.org
Year Founded: 1965
Sales Range: $400-449.9 Million
Emp.: 2,773
Health Care Services Organization
N.A.I.C.S.: 813920
Brady Haynes *(VP-Physician Enterprise)*
Kevin Woodward *(VP-Fin Ops)*
Mike Wiltermood *(CEO)*

ENLOW TRACTOR AUCTION, INC.
9000 New Sapulpa Rd, Tulsa, OK 74131
Tel.: (918) 224-7676
Web Site: http://www.enlow66.com
Sales Range: $10-24.9 Million
Emp.: 30
Farm Machinery Sales
N.A.I.C.S.: 423820
Josh Enlow *(Owner)*

ENMR PLATEAU TELECOM
7111 N Prince St, Clovis, NM 88101-1947
Tel.: (575) 389-5100
Web Site: http://www.enmr.com
Sales Range: $25-49.9 Million
Emp.: 268
Telephone Communication Services
N.A.I.C.S.: 517121
David Robinson *(CEO)*
Tom Phelps *(CEO)*

ENNEN BROTHERS
1305 Old Fairhaven Pkwy, Bellingham, WA 98225-7413
Tel.: (360) 647-2290
Sales Range: $75-99.9 Million
Emp.: 2
Grocery Stores, Chain
N.A.I.C.S.: 445110
David Ennen *(Partner)*

ENNIS FURNITURE CO. INC.
275 S 23rd St, Boise, ID 83702
Tel.: (208) 342-3664
Web Site:
  https://www.ennisfurniture.com
Sales Range: $10-24.9 Million
Emp.: 100
Owner & Operator of Furniture Stores
N.A.I.C.S.: 449110
Richard W. Ennis *(Pres)*
Karl Holzinger *(Controller)*

ENNIS STEEL INDUSTRIES INC.
204 Metro Pk Blvd, Ennis, TX 75119-7031
Tel.: (972) 878-0400
Web Site: http://www.ennissteel.com
Year Founded: 1980
Sales Range: $100-124.9 Million
Emp.: 175
Structural Steel Fabrication
N.A.I.C.S.: 331110
Robert E. Jones *(Pres)*
Paul Tomberlin *(Mgr-Sls)*
Chadd Bentley *(VP)*
Lisa S. Wood *(Treas & Sec)*
Sergio Diaz *(Mgr-Production)*
Melvin Luttrell *(Mgr-QC)*
Hector Godinez *(Mgr-Pur)*

ENNIS, PELLUM & ASSOCIATES, CPAS
5150 Belfort Rd S Bldg 600, Jacksonville, FL 32256
Tel.: (904) 396-5965
Web Site: https://www.jaxcpa.com
Year Founded: 1978
Sales Range: $1-9.9 Million
Emp.: 33
Accounting Services
N.A.I.C.S.: 541211
Ronald R. Pellum *(Pres)*
Robert Ennis *(Founder)*
Dwin Horne *(Dir-Tax Svc)*
Kevin Algee *(Mgr-Audit Svc)*
Russell Meyers *(Mgr-Tax)*
Nicolette Dailey *(Mgr-Tax)*

ENOCH PRATT FREE LIBRARY
400 Cathedral St, Baltimore, MD 21201
Tel.: (410) 396-5430   MD
Web Site: https://www.prattlibrary.org
Year Founded: 1882
Sales Range: $25-49.9 Million
Emp.: 461
Library
N.A.I.C.S.: 519210
Benjamin Rosenberg *(Chm)*
Kate Rawson Powell *(Sec)*
Nancy Dorman *(Vice Chm)*

ENOR CORPORATION
245 Livingston St, Northvale, NJ 07647
Tel.: (201) 750-1680
Web Site: http://www.enor.com
Rev.: $23,000,000
Emp.: 123
Plastics Processing Services
N.A.I.C.S.: 326199
Steven Udwin *(CEO)*
David Tarica *(Pres)*
Peggy Dugan *(Controller)*

ENOVA ILLUMINATION, LLC
1839 Buerkle Rd, Saint Paul, MN 55110
Tel.: (651) 236-8857   MN
Web Site:
  http://www.enovaillumination.com
Year Founded: 1964
Sales Range: $1-9.9 Million
Emp.: 15
Bright Iris LED Surgical Headlights Mfr
N.A.I.C.S.: 339112
Jim Nelson *(Dir-Sls & Mktg)*
Roger Heegaard *(Pres)*

ENOVATION CONTROLS, LLC
5311 S 122nd E Ave, Tulsa, OK 74146
Tel.: (918) 317-4100   DE
Web Site:
  http://www.enovationcontrols.com
Year Founded: 2009
Emp.: 1,004
Natural Gas Engine Control & Fuel Systems Equipment Mfr
N.A.I.C.S.: 336310
Frank W. Murphy III *(Co-Founder, Chm & Co-CEO)*

ENPAC LLC
34355 Melinz Pkwy, Eastlake, OH 44095-4046
Tel.: (440) 975-0070   OH
Web Site: https://www.enpac.com
Year Founded: 1988
Sales Range: $10-24.9 Million
Emp.: 100
Engineered Plastic Vessels & Related Accessory Products Mfr
N.A.I.C.S.: 326199

Scott R. Janda *(Co-Owner & Dir-Bus Dev)*
Howard Debbie *(Coord-Shipping)*

ENPOWER CORP.
2420 Camino Ramon Ste 101, San Ramon, CA 94583
Tel.: (925) 244-1100   CA
Web Site:
  http://www.enpowercorp.com
Year Founded: 2002
Holding Company; Electric Power Generation Business Management & Technical Consulting Services
N.A.I.C.S.: 551112
Edward W. Tomeo *(Pres & CEO)*
Alex A. Sugaoka *(CFO & VP)*
Roland Allred *(Controller)*
Charmaine Bradley *(Mgr-HR)*
Wesley R. Knapp *(Mgr-Oildale Energy Facility)*

Subsidiaries:

Enpower Management Corp.   (1)
2420 Camino Ramon Ste 101, San Ramon, CA 94583
Tel.: (925) 244-1100
Web Site: http://www.enpowercorp.com
Sales Range: $25-49.9 Million
Emp.: 9
Electric Power Generation Business Management & Technical Consulting Services
N.A.I.C.S.: 561110

Subsidiary (Domestic):

Oildale Energy LLC   (2)
1134 Manor St, Bakersfield, CA 93308
Tel.: (661) 393-0290
Web Site: http://www.enpowercorp.com
Sales Range: $1-9.9 Million
Gas Fueled Electric Power Generation
N.A.I.C.S.: 221112
Wesley R. Knapp *(Plant Mgr)*

Wadham Energy Limited Partnership   (2)
6247 Myers Rd, Williams, CA 95987
Tel.: (530) 473-2831
Web Site: http://www.enpowercorp.com
Sales Range: $1-9.9 Million
Biomass Electric Power Generation
N.A.I.C.S.: 221118
Tim St. Cyr *(VP & Plant Mgr)*

Enpower Operations Corp.   (1)
2420 Camino Ramon Ste 101, San Ramon, CA 94583
Tel.: (925) 244-1100
Web Site: http://www.enpowercorp.com
Electric Power Generation Business Management & Technical Consulting Services
N.A.I.C.S.: 561110

Affiliate (Domestic):

EIF KC Landfill Gas, LLC   (2)
17955 Holiday Dr, Shawnee, KS 66217
Tel.: (913) 441-3633
Landfill Gas Electric Power Generation; Owned by Enpower Corp. & by EIF Management, LLC
N.A.I.C.S.: 221118

ENPRO, INC.
121 S Lombard Rd, Addison, IL 60101
Tel.: (630) 629-3504
Web Site: https://www.enproinc.com
Year Founded: 1961
Sales Range: $10-24.9 Million
Emp.: 80
Manufacturer's Representative & Distributor of Instrumentation & Process Control Equipment
N.A.I.C.S.: 423830
Brian L. Cook *(Pres)*

ENROLL AMERICA
1001 G St NW 8th Fl, Washington, DC 20001
Tel.: (202) 737-6340   DC

Web Site:
  http://www.enrollamerica.org
Year Founded: 2010
Sales Range: $25-49.9 Million
Health Insurance Services
N.A.I.C.S.: 524114
Anne Filipic *(Pres)*

ENS GROUP, INC.
8181 W Jefferson Blvd, Fort Wayne, IN 46804
Tel.: (260) 432-1364
Web Site: http://www.ensi.com
Sales Range: $1-9.9 Million
Emp.: 24
Technology Consulting Services
N.A.I.C.S.: 541690
Timothy S. Savage *(Mng Dir & Principal-Infrastructure Practice)*
Matthew Gerber *(Pres & Mng Dir-Data Center Practice)*
Dave Shriner *(Mgr-Learning Solutions)*
Mark Reed *(Mgr-Infrastructure Practice)*
Matt Moran *(Mgr-Data Center Practice)*
Chris Butler *(VP-Consulting Svcs)*

ENSAFE INC.
5724 Summer Trees Dr, Memphis, TN 38134-7309
Tel.: (901) 372-7962
Web Site: https://www.ensafe.com
Year Founded: 1980
Sales Range: $25-49.9 Million
Emp.: 300
Business Consulting Services
N.A.I.C.S.: 541690
Phillip G. Coop *(Chm)*
Craig A. Wise *(VP-Engrg Svcs Grp)*
Michael A. Wood *(CFO & VP)*
Paul V. Stoddard *(VP-Geological Svcs Grp)*
Ginny Gray Davis *(VP-Bus Dev)*
Frank McInturff *(Principal)*
Claire Barnett *(Assoc Principal)*
Michelle Smith *(Assoc Principal)*
Don Bradford *(Pres & CEO)*
Brian Derry *(Principal)*
Bry Roberson *(Principal)*
Jeff James *(Principal)*

ENSAR CORP.
135 E Hintz Rd, Wheeling, IL 60090-6035
Tel.: (847) 520-1001
Web Site: http://www.handi-foil.com
Plastic & Aluminum Products Mfr
N.A.I.C.S.: 331315

ENSCICON CORPORATION
2420 W 26th Ave Ste 500 D, Denver, CO 80211-1011
Tel.: (303) 980-8600
Web Site: https://www.enscicon.com
Year Founded: 1994
Sales Range: $10-24.9 Million
Engineering & Technical Staffing Services
N.A.I.C.S.: 561311
Crystal Anzulewicz *(CFO)*
Jerry Pokorny *(Founder)*
Will Smith *(Founder, Pres & CEO)*
Adam Miller *(VP-Ops)*
Ryan McCabe *(VP-Bus Dev)*

ENSCO INC.
5400 Port Royal Rd, Springfield, VA 22151
Tel.: (703) 321-9000
Web Site: https://www.ensco.com
Year Founded: 1969
Rev.: $81,680,000
Emp.: 600

Ensco Inc.—(Continued)

Commercial Physical Research
N.A.I.C.S.: 541715
Mike Bogdanovic *(Dir-Retirement Plan & Special Projects)*
Joanne McDonald *(Chief Ethics Officer, Sec & VP)*
David Macaluso *(VP-Contracts & Procurement Div)*
Ted Freeman *(VP-Information Sys & Tech Div)*
Neil Fifield *(VP-Ops-Ensco Avionics & Ensco Avionics Canada)*
Boris Nejikovsky *(Pres)*
Kevin Pruett *(VP-Aerospace Sciences & Engrg Div)*
Jeffrey M. Stevens *(VP-Applied Tech & Engrg Div)*
Scott Goldstein *(Chief Strategy & Tech Officer)*
Vernon Joyner *(VP-Security Solutions Div-Natl)*
Julie Hancock *(Dir-Corp Comm)*
Thomas DeFrank *(CFO)*
Julie Ann Phinney *(VP-Bus Dev)*

Subsidiaries:

ENSCO Avionics Canada Inc. (1)
1405 Trans-Canada Hwy Ste 100, Dorval, H9P 2V9, QC, Canada
Tel.: (514) 418-0030
Avionics Engineering
N.A.I.C.S.: 334511

ENSCO Avionics, Inc. (1)
3 Holiday Hill Rd, Endicott, NY 13760
Tel.: (607) 786-9000
Web Site: http://www.enscoavionics.com
Emp.: 60
Avionics Engineering
N.A.I.C.S.: 334511

ENSCO Rail Australia Pty Ltd (1)
Box 7529, Baulkham Hills, NSW, Australia
Tel.: (61) 2 9874 0682
Avionics Engineering
N.A.I.C.S.: 334511

ENSCO Rail, Inc. (1)
5400 Port Royal Rd, Springfield, VA 22151
Tel.: (703) 321-9000
Web Site: http://www.ensco.com
Avionics Engineering
N.A.I.C.S.: 334511

Exostrategies, Inc. (1)
1200 E Hwy 24, Woodland Park, CO 80863-7751
Web Site: http://www.exostrategies.com
Engineeering Services
N.A.I.C.S.: 541330
Daniel Heimerdinger *(Pres & CEO)*

KLD Labs, Inc. (1)
300 Broadway, Huntington Station, NY 11746
Tel.: (631) 493-6000
Web Site: http://www.kldlabs.com
Sales Range: $1-9.9 Million
Emp.: 30
Computer System Design Services
N.A.I.C.S.: 541512
Daniel Magnus *(VP)*
Jim Spalholz *(Engr-Mechanical)*

ENSEMBLE HEALTH PARTNERS, INC.
11511 Reed Hartman Hwy, Cincinnati, OH 45241
Tel.: (704) 765-3715 DE
Year Founded: 2021
Emp.: 6,492
Holding Company
N.A.I.C.S.: 551112
Judson Ivy *(Founder, Pres & CEO)*
Shannon White *(COO)*
Robert Snead *(CFO & Treas)*
Gary S. Bryant *(Chief Acctg Officer, Sr VP & Controller)*

ENSEO INC

1680 Prospect Dr Ste 100, Richardson, TX 75081
Tel.: (972) 234-2513
Web Site: http://www.enseo.com
Year Founded: 2000
Sales Range: $10-24.9 Million
Emp.: 51
Digital Media Player & Signage Distr
N.A.I.C.S.: 423690
Vanessa Ogle *(Founder & CEO)*
Bill Fang *(CTO & VP-Engrg)*
Omar Khan *(Pres)*
Kristin Reichert *(CFO)*
David Simpson *(Chief Product Officer)*

ENSIGHTEN, INC.
226 Airport Pkwy Ste 390, San Jose, CA 95110
Tel.: (650) 249-4712
Web Site: http://www.ensighten.com
Year Founded: 2009
Enterprise Tag Management & Privacy Solutions Developer
N.A.I.C.S.: 513210
Marty Greenlow *(CFO)*

Subsidiaries:

TagMan, Inc. (1)
575 8th Ave Ste 916, New York, NY 10018
Tel.: (646) 569-2000
Web Site: http://www.tagman.com
Computer Software & Services
N.A.I.C.S.: 513210
Dan Dal Degan *(Pres)*

Subsidiary (Non-US):

TagMan Limited (2)
Henry Wood House 2 Riding House, London, W1W 7FA, United Kingdom
Tel.: (44) 203 465 9250
Web Site: http://www.ensighten.com
Emp.: 40
Computer Software & Services
N.A.I.C.S.: 513210
Ian Woolley *(Mng Dir)*

ENSITE, INC.
2401 First St Ste 201, Fort Myers, FL 33901
Tel.: (239) 226-0024
Web Site: http://www.en-site.com
Year Founded: 2005
Sales Range: $1-9.9 Million
Engineering, Landscaping & Architectural Design Services
N.A.I.C.S.: 541330
Jon Romine *(VP)*
Brian Smith *(Pres)*

ENSPIRE LEARNING, INC.
1708 Guadalupe St, Austin, TX 78701
Tel.: (512) 472-8400 TX
Web Site: http://www.enspire.com
Year Founded: 1998
Sales Range: $1-9.9 Million
Emp.: 50
Developer of Sales & Leadership E-Learning Courses
N.A.I.C.S.: 513210
Bjorn Billhardt *(Founder & Chm)*
Mary Maltbie *(CEO)*

ENSTOA, INC.
12 W 31st St Fl 8, New York, NY 10001
Tel.: (212) 913-0870
Web Site: http://www.enstoa.com
Sales Range: $1-9.9 Million
Emp.: 23
Real Estate Business Services
N.A.I.C.S.: 531120
Arnaud Giret *(CFO)*
Kerry Foley *(Sr VP-Sls & Mktg)*
Jordan Cram *(CEO)*
Andrew Kotliar *(Project Mgr)*

ENSTROM CANDIES, INC.
701 Colorado Ave, Grand Junction, CO 81501
Tel.: (970) 242-1655
Web Site: https://www.enstrom.com
Sales Range: $10-24.9 Million
Emp.: 50
Candy Mfr
N.A.I.C.S.: 311352
Douglas Simons *(Pres & CEO)*
Jamee Simons *(Sec & VP)*
Darla Fortner *(Mgr-HR)*

ENSURITYGROUP, L.L.C.
1001 N Hampton Blvd, Dallas, TX 75115
Tel.: (214) 597-4780
Web Site:
http://www.ensuritygroup.com
Year Founded: 1997
Sales Range: $1-9.9 Million
Emp.: 12
Disability & Other Insurance Coverages
N.A.I.C.S.: 524114
Modesto Flores *(Founder, Pres & CEO)*
Yanet Gonzalez *(Mgr)*

ENT PARTNERS LLC
600 Hwy 169 S Ste 650, Saint Louis Park, MN 55426
Tel.: (833) 327-0001
Web Site: https://entpartners.com
Medical Practice Management Services
N.A.I.C.S.: 621111
Jim Feinstein *(CEO)*

Subsidiaries:

Southern Indiana ENT LLC (1)
1655 N Gladstone Ave Ste E, Columbus, IN 47201
Tel.: (812) 376-3071
Web Site:
http://www.southernindianaent.com
Offices of Physicians (except Mental Health Specialists)
N.A.I.C.S.: 621111
Nicholas C. Hollenkamp *(Treas)*
Anthony Sanders *(Partner)*

ENTARA CORPORATION
190 S Lasalle St Ste 3800, Chicago, IL 60603-3432
Tel.: (312) 920-1551
Web Site: http://www.entaracorp.com
Year Founded: 2001
Sales Range: $1-9.9 Million
Emp.: 50
Information Technology Management Services
N.A.I.C.S.: 541618
Linda Maclachlan *(CEO)*
Pam Diaz *(Pres)*
Ryan Ikeler *(VP)*
Daniel Jarzynski *(Fin Dir)*
Mike Brunetti *(Dir-IT Strategy)*

ENTEC SERVICES, INC.
30 Monroe Dr, Pelham, AL 35124
Tel.: (205) 358-1011
Web Site:
http://www.EntecServices.com
Year Founded: 1993
Sales Range: $1-9.9 Million
Emp.: 35
Pollution Testing Services
N.A.I.C.S.: 541620
John Sutton *(Pres)*
D. Lynn Beane *(Dir-Ops)*
Chuck Duncan *(Mgr-Ops)*
Brad Latham *(Mgr-Ops)*
Dan McCombs *(Mgr-Ops)*
Darrin Abernathy *(CFO)*
Rick Owen *(Dir-Bus Dev & Energy Sector Projects)*

ENTECH ENGINEERING INC.
201 Penn St, Reading, PA 19603
Tel.: (610) 373-6667
Web Site:
https://www.entecheng.com
Year Founded: 1981
Sales Range: $10-24.9 Million
Emp.: 132
Water/Wastewater Infrastructure Treatments, Facility Condition Assessments & Architectural Services
N.A.I.C.S.: 562998
Jeffrey C. Euclide *(Pres)*
Matthew S. Lloyd *(Chm & Exec VP)*
Lenette C. Wells *(Principal)*
Bryon A. Killian *(Principal)*
Bryan C. Haag *(Principal)*
Robert J. Weir *(Exec VP)*
Christopher M. Hannum *(Mgr-Engrg)*

Subsidiaries:

Entech Engineering Inc. (1)
500 N Centre StSte101A, Pottsville, PA 17901 (100%)
Tel.: (570) 628-5655
Web Site: http://www.entecheng.com
Emp.: 10
Engineering & Architectural Services
N.A.I.C.S.: 541310
Lenette C. Wells *(Principal)*

Entech Engineering Inc. (1)
315 Clay Rd, Lititz, PA 17543 (100%)
Tel.: (717) 626-6666
Web Site: http://www.entecheng.com
Facilities Management & Engineering Services
N.A.I.C.S.: 561210
Scott J. Compton *(Sr Project Mgr-Facility Condition Assessment)*

Entech Engineering Inc. (1)
685 S Mountain Blvd Ste A, Mountain Top, PA 18707 (100%)
Tel.: (570) 868-0275
Web Site: http://www.entecheng.com
Engineering & Architectural Services
N.A.I.C.S.: 541330
Bryan C. Haag *(Principal & Lead Project Mgr)*

Entech Engineering Inc. (1)
400 Rouser Rd Airport Office Park Bldg 2 Ste 200, Coraopolis, PA 15108 (100%)
Tel.: (412) 264-2800
Web Site: http://www.entecheng.com
Architectural Facility Management & Engineering Services
N.A.I.C.S.: 237990
Tanner A. Sattler *(Principal)*

ENTECH SALES & SERVICE, INC.
3404 Garden Brook Dr, Dallas, TX 75234
Tel.: (469) 522-6000 TX
Web Site:
https://www.entechsales.com
Sales Range: $50-74.9 Million
Emp.: 300
Electronic Controls Installation
N.A.I.C.S.: 238210
Gale Patrick Rucker *(Pres)*
Dan Rice *(Acct Exec)*
Nick Kollasch *(VP)*
Robin Mattes *(VP)*
Scott Perry *(Mgr-Rental Svc)*

ENTECH SOLAR, INC.
641 Industrial Blvd, Grapevine, TX 76051
Tel.: (817) 421-4658 DE
Web Site:
http://www.entechsolar.com
Year Founded: 1984
Sales Range: $200-249.9 Million
Emp.: 18
Solar & Water Power Equipment Mfr
N.A.I.C.S.: 335311
Quentin T. Kelly *(Chm & CEO)*
Chris Sherring *(COO)*
David Hammes *(VP-Sls & Mktg)*

ENTEGRA ROOF TILE CORP-POMPANO
1289 NE 9th Ave, Okeechobee, FL 34972
Tel.: (863) 467-0042
Web Site: http://www.entegra.com
Rev.: $39,900,000
Emp.: 250
Roofing Tiles & Concrete Slabs Mfr
N.A.I.C.S.: 327390
Terry Johnson (Pres)

ENTEK HOLDING LLC
250 Hansard Ave, Lebanon, OR 97355
Tel.: (541) 259-3901
Web Site: http://www.entek.com
Sales Range: $75-99.9 Million
Emp.: 330
Plastics Processing
N.A.I.C.S.: 326199
Brian Looper (Controller)
Jeff Grimm (CFO)

Subsidiaries:

ENTEK International UK Ltd.   **(1)**
Mylord Crescent, Camperdown Industrial Estate, Newcastle upon Tyne, NE12 5XG, United Kingdom
Tel.: (44) 1912685054
Web Site: http://www.entek-international.com
Sales Range: $25-49.9 Million
Emp.: 140
Battery Separator Mfr
N.A.I.C.S.: 334419
Walter Adams (Mng Dir)

ENTEN & ASSOCIATES, INC.
8120 Woodmont Ave Ste 550, Bethesda, MD 20814-2761
Tel.: (301) 913-0010   MD
Web Site: http://www.enten.com
Year Founded: 1988
Rev.: $10,000,000
Emp.: 20
N.A.I.C.S.: 541810
Jon D. Enten (Pres)
Miriam Gorman (Bookkeeper)
Alice Perkoski (Mgr)

ENTERPRISE COMMUNITY PARTNERS, INC.
70 Corporate Ctr 11000 Broken Land Pkwy Ste 700, Columbia, MD 21044
Tel.: (410) 964-1230   MD
Web Site: http://www.enterprisecommunity.com
Year Founded: 1980
Rev.: $258,098,000
Assets: $785,786,000
Liabilities: $221,243,000
Net Worth: $564,543,000
Earnings: $237,151,000
Emp.: 254
Fiscal Year-end: 12/31/18
Community Housing Services
N.A.I.C.S.: 624229
Mary Jo Barranco (VP-Fin)
Jacqueline Waggoner (VP)
Marion Mollegen McFadden (Sr VP-Public Policy)
J. Ronald Terwilliger (Chm)
Sally S. Hebner (CFO)
Allison Knapp Womack (CMO & Sr VP)
Jon Searles (VP-Mktg)
Melinda Clemons (VP)

Subsidiaries:

Bellwether Enterprise Real Estate   **(1)**
1360 E 9th St Ste 300, Cleveland, OH 44114-1730
Tel.: (216) 820-4500
Web Site: http://www.bellwethercap.com
Offices of Real Estate Agents & Brokers
N.A.I.C.S.: 531210

Steve Feldman (Owner)
Todd Johnson (Dir-Equity Products-New Orleans)
Ned Huffman (Pres)
Jeff Chaney (Sr VP)
Dan Baker (Sr VP)
Joe Cortese (Asst VP & Sr Mgr-Transaction)

Subsidiary (Domestic):

Bellwether Enterprise - Charlotte   **(2)**
200 S College St Ste 1520, Charlotte, NC 28202
Tel.: (704) 945-3400
Web Site: http://www.bellwetherenterprise.com
Commercial Real Estate Mortgage Brokers
N.A.I.C.S.: 522310
Cooper Willis (Exec VP & Dir-Southeastern Reg)
Shippen Browne (Exec VP & Dir-Southeastern Reg)
Ridge Stafford (VP)
Alicia Harris (Sr VP)
Mariann Hord (VP-Corp Mgmt)
Mark Ethridge (Asst VP)
Alexis N. Pattison (VP-Loan Closing)

ENTERPRISE COMPUTING SOLUTIONS INC.
26024 Acero, Mission Viejo, CA 92691-2768
Tel.: (949) 609-1980
Web Site: http://www.thinkecs.com
Year Founded: 1995
Sales Range: $10-24.9 Million
Emp.: 15
Provider of Information Technology Infrastructure Solutions
N.A.I.C.S.: 541511
David Butler (Pres & CEO)
Cheryl Butler (CFO)
John Foley (CTO)

ENTERPRISE DISTRIBUTION INC.
3500 Westgate Dr Ste 800, Durham, NC 27707
Tel.: (919) 493-5300
Web Site: http://www.tfxincorprotated.com
Sales Range: $10-24.9 Million
Emp.: 15
Trucking Except Local
N.A.I.C.S.: 484121
John R. Arwood (Pres)
Hardy Butler (Exec VP)

ENTERPRISE ELECTRICAL, INC.
1039 Driessen Dr, Kaukauna, WI 54130
Tel.: (920) 766-1995   WI
Web Site: http://www.enterprise-electric.net
Year Founded: 1995
Electrical Contractor
N.A.I.C.S.: 238210
Pahl Ploetz (Owner)

ENTERPRISE FINANCIAL GROUP, INC.
122 W Carpenter Fwy 6th Fl, Irving, TX 75039
Tel.: (972) 445-8300
Web Site: http://www.efgcompanies.com
Sales Range: $25-49.9 Million
Emp.: 100
Insurance Services
N.A.I.C.S.: 524128
John Pappa (CEO)
Bill Bigley (CFO & VP)

ENTERPRISE FLORIDA, INC.
800 N Magnolia Ave Ste 1100, Orlando, FL 32803
Tel.: (407) 956-5600

Web Site: http://www.enterpriseflorida.com
Year Founded: 1996
Sales Range: $10-24.9 Million
Emp.: 333
Economic Development Promoter
N.A.I.C.S.: 813910
Rick Scott (Chm)
Tim Vanderhoof (Sr VP-Bus Dev)
Angela Adams Suggs (Sr VP-Sports Dev)
Sean Helton (VP-Strategic Comm)
Jamal Sowell (Pres & CEO)
Joe York (Vice Chm)

ENTERPRISE HOLDINGS, INC.
600 Corporate Park Dr, Saint Louis, MO 63105
Tel.: (314) 512-1000   MO
Web Site: https://www.enterprisemobility.com
Year Founded: 1956
Sales Range: $5-14.9 Billion
Emp.: 90,000
Holding Company; Automobile Rental Services
N.A.I.C.S.: 551112
Rose Langhorst (Treas & Sr VP)
Jo Ann Taylor Kindle (Chm-Enterprise Holdings Foundation)
Christine B. Taylor-Broughton (CEO)
Russ Willey (CFO & Sr VP)
Kurt Kohler (Sr VP-Fleet Acquisition & Remarketing-North America)
William Withington (Sr VP-North American Ops)
Randal Narike (Chief Strategy Officer & Exec VP)
David K. Nestor (COO & Exec VP)
Mike Andrew (Chief Legal & Legislative Officer)
Steve Brackney (Chief Admin Officer & Sr VP)
Sara Miller (VP-Corp Comm)
Carolyn Kindle (Pres-Enterprise Holdings Foundation)
Shane Behl (CIO)
Errin Braddock (Chief Diversity Officer & VP)
Shelley Roither (Sr VP-HR)

Subsidiaries:

Enterprise Car Sales   **(1)**
600 Corporate Park Dr, Saint Louis, MO 63105
Tel.: (314) 512-5000
Web Site: http://www.enterprisecarsales.com
Used Motor Vehicles Sales
N.A.I.C.S.: 441227
Andrew C. Taylor (Chm & CEO)
Beth Wheeler (Dir-Bus Dev)
Dave Jung (Mgr-Bus Dev)

Enterprise Fleet Services   **(1)**
600 Corporate Park Dr, Saint Louis, MO 63105
Tel.: (314) 512-5000
Web Site: http://www.enterprise.com
Automobile Acquisition, Delivery, Licensing & Tax Management Services for Businesses
N.A.I.C.S.: 532112
Steve Usselmann (Sr VP)

Enterprise Flex-E-Rent   **(1)**
Flex-E-Rent House Knight Way Battlefield Enterprise Park, Shrewsbury, SY1 3AB, Shropshire, United Kingdom
Tel.: (44) 1743457600
Web Site: http://www.flexerent.co.uk
Emp.: 150
Car Rental Services
N.A.I.C.S.: 532111
Paul Clarke (Mgr-Logistics Engr)

Enterprise International Operations   **(1)**
600 Corporate Pk Dr, Saint Louis, MO 63105
Tel.: (314) 512-5000
Web Site: http://www.eio.com

Sales Range: $800-899.9 Million
Emp.: 7,000
Automobile Rental
N.A.I.C.S.: 532111

Enterprise Leasing Company of Philadelphia, LLC   **(1)**
1226 Chestnut St, Philadelphia, PA 19107
Tel.: (215) 730-0988
Web Site: http://www.enterprisecarshare.com
Sales Range: $25-49.9 Million
Emp.: 60
Passenger Car Rental Services
N.A.I.C.S.: 532111
Andrew C. Taylor (Pres)

Enterprise Rent-A-Car   **(1)**
600 Corporate Park Dr, Saint Louis, MO 63105   **(100%)**
Tel.: (314) 512-1000
Web Site: http://www.enterprise.com
Sales Range: $400-449.9 Million
Emp.: 3,000
Car Rentals & Leasing
N.A.I.C.S.: 532111
Pamela M. Nicholson (Pres & COO)
Tom Mazzurco (Mgr-Rental-Jamestown)
Greyfell Nordic (Partner-Sweden & Norway)
Patrick McGiff (Mgr-Sacramento & Yolo County)
Jenna Cassidy (Mgr-Buffalo, Cheektowaga & Amherst)

Enterprise Rent-A-Car Canada Co.   **(1)**
709 Milner Ave, Scarborough, M1B 6B6, ON, Canada
Tel.: (416) 284-4805
Web Site: http://www.enterprise.ca
Car Rental & Transport Solutions
N.A.I.C.S.: 532120
Andrew C. Taylor (Exec Chm)
Pamela M. Nicholson (CEO)
Christine Taylor (Pres & COO)
Steve Tudela (VP-Canadian Ops)

Subsidiary (Domestic):

Discount Car & Truck Rentals Ltd.   **(2)**
720 Arrow Rd, Toronto, M9M2M1, ON, Canada
Tel.: (416) 744-0123
Web Site: http://www.discountcar.com
Car & Truck Rentals
N.A.I.C.S.: 532111
Herb Singer (Co-Founder)
Rhoda Singer (Co-Founder)

Enterprise Rent-A-Truck   **(1)**
600 Corporate Park Dr, Saint Louis, MO 63105
Tel.: (314) 512-5000
Web Site: http://www.enterprisetrucks.com
Commercial Truck Rentals
N.A.I.C.S.: 532120
Alonzo Byrd (Asst VP-Pub Affairs)

National Car Rentals of Corpus Christi, Inc.   **(1)**
1000 International Blvd, Corpus Christi, TX 78406
Tel.: (361) 289-0515
Web Site: http://www.nationalcar.com
Passenger Car Rental
N.A.I.C.S.: 532111

Vanguard Car Rental USA, LLC   **(1)**
6929 N Lakewood Ave Ste 100, Tulsa, OK 74117
Tel.: (918) 401-6000
Web Site: http://www.vanguardcar.com
Car Rental Services
N.A.I.C.S.: 532111
Greg Stubblefield (Exec VP & Chief Strategy Officer)

Division (Domestic):

Alamo Rent-A-Car   **(2)**
6929 N Lakewood Ave Ste 100, Tulsa, OK 74117
Tel.: (918) 401-6000

Enterprise Holdings, Inc.—(Continued)

Web Site: http://www.alamo.com
Sales Range: $25-49.9 Million
Emp.: 70
Passenger Car Rental
N.A.I.C.S.: 532111

National Car Rental (2)
7777 E Apache St, Tulsa, OK 74115
Tel.: (918) 401-6000
Web Site: http://www.nationalcar.com
Sales Range: $25-49.9 Million
Emp.: 200
Rent-A-Car Service
N.A.I.C.S.: 532111

ENTERPRISE INTEGRATION CORPORATION
2201 Wisconsin Ave NW Ste 300,
Washington, DC 20007
Tel.: (202) 333-7403
Web Site: http://www.eicorp.net
Sales Range: $1-9.9 Million
Emp.: 17
Custom Computer Programming Services
N.A.I.C.S.: 541511
Walter Augustine (Pres & CEO)

ENTERPRISE INTEGRATION, INC.
11737 Central Pkwy, Jacksonville, FL 32224
Tel.: (904) 733-4349
Web Site: http://www.entint.com
Year Founded: 1999
Sales Range: $10-24.9 Million
Emp.: 200
Information Technology Management Services
N.A.I.C.S.: 541519
Tom Kirby (Asst VP-Pro Svcs)
Richard Trayner (Dir-Svc Desk)

ENTERPRISE MASONRY CORPORATION
3010 Bellevue Ave, Wilmington, DE 19802
Tel.: (302) 764-6858
Web Site: https://www.emcbrick.com
Sales Range: $10-24.9 Million
Emp.: 150
Masonry Contracting Services
N.A.I.C.S.: 238140
Rhonda Malatesta (Mgr-Acctg)

ENTERPRISE ONSITE SERVICES CO.
817 N Ware Rd Ste 10, McAllen, TX 78501
Tel.: (956) 534-0296
IT Services to Commercial & Residential Customers
N.A.I.C.S.: 519290
Miguel Sanchez (Owner)

Subsidiaries:

MSL Enterprises, Inc. (1)
817 N Ware Rd Ste 10, McAllen, TX
78501 **(100%)**
Tel.: (956) 534-0296
IT Services to Commercial & Residential Customers
N.A.I.C.S.: 541511
Miguel Sanchez (Owner)

Subsidiary (Domestic):

OnSite Computer Services (2)
2102 Paseo Encan, Mission, TX 78572-6798
Tel.: (956) 534-0296
Web Site: http://www.onsitecss.com
Custom Computer Programming Services
N.A.I.C.S.: 541511
Miguel Sanchez (Owner & Mgr)

ENTERPRISE PRESS, INC.

1 W Forest Ave, Englewood, NJ 07631
Tel.: (201) 894-0444 NY
Web Site: https://www.enterprise-press.com
Year Founded: 1915
Sales Range: $50-74.9 Million
Emp.: 30
Offset Printing Services
N.A.I.C.S.: 323111
Daniel Hort (Pres)

ENTERPRISE PROPERTIES INC.
10220 F St, Omaha, NE 68127-1006
Tel.: (402) 339-3670
Web Site: https://www.enterprise-properties.com
Sales Range: $10-24.9 Million
Emp.: 15
Concrete Products Mfr
N.A.I.C.S.: 327390
Thomas L. Egan (Pres)

ENTERPRISE SECURITY, INC.
1060 N Tustin Ave, Anaheim, CA 92807
Tel.: (714) 630-9100 CA
Web Site: http://www.entersecurity.com
Year Founded: 2000
Sales Range: $1-9.9 Million
Emp.: 25
Security System Services
N.A.I.C.S.: 561621
Daniel Steiner (VP)
Casimir Blonski (Dir-IT & Pro Svcs)
Troy Laughlin (Pres & CEO)

ENTERPRISE SOLUTIONS REALIZED
8820 Columbia 100 Pkwy Ste 310,
Columbia, MD 21045
Tel.: (410) 442-5501
Web Site: http://www.esr-inc.com
Year Founded: 2004
Sales Range: $1-9.9 Million
Emp.: 22
Software Development Solutions
N.A.I.C.S.: 334610
Dennis Christmas (Pres, CEO & CTO)

ENTERPRISE SYSTEMS SOFTWARE LLC
4352 W Sylvania Ave Ste M, Toledo, OH 43623
Tel.: (419) 841-3179
Web Site: http://www.esdontheweb.com
Year Founded: 1990
Sales Range: $25-49.9 Million
Emp.: 45
IT Consulting for the Healthcare Industry
N.A.I.C.S.: 541690
Joe Torti (Pres)

ENTERPRISE TOOL & DIE, INC.
4270 White St SW, Grandville, MI 49418
Tel.: (616) 538-0920
Web Site: https://www.enterprisedie.com
Sales Range: $10-24.9 Million
Emp.: 50
Specialty Tool & Die Mfr
N.A.I.C.S.: 333514
Doug Groom (CEO)
Leslie Larsen (Pres)

ENTERPRISES INTERNATIONAL INC.
200 Blaine and Firman, Hoquiam, WA 98550

Tel.: (360) 533-6222 WA
Year Founded: 1903
Sales Range: $50-74.9 Million
Emp.: 4
Holding Company; Paper Pulp for Printing Industry
N.A.I.C.S.: 333998
Isabelle S. Lamb (Chm)
David E. Lamb (Pres)
Jack Sparks (Sec)

Subsidiaries:

Ovalstrapping Inc. (1)
206 Firman St, Hoquiam, WA
98550-2000 **(100%)**
Tel.: (360) 532-9101
Web Site: http://www.ovalstrapping.com
Sales Range: $10-24.9 Million
Mfr of Machines for Packaging Industries
N.A.I.C.S.: 333248

Plastex Extruders, Inc.USA (1)
120 55th St NE, Fort Payne, AL
35967-8140 **(100%)**
Tel.: (256) 845-8271
Web Site: http://www.plastexmatting.com
Sales Range: $10-24.9 Million
Producer of Plastic Strap for Use in Strapping Machines
N.A.I.C.S.: 325211

ENTERTAINMENT BENEFITS GROUP, LLC
19495 Biscayne Blvd Ste 300, Aventura, FL 33180
Tel.: (305) 907-5020
Web Site: https://www.ebgsolutions.com
Travel & Entertainment Services
N.A.I.C.S.: 561599
Brett D. Reizen (Pres & CEO)
Cheryl Roycroft (Chief People Officer)
Robert Riesenberg (CFO)
Stephanie Baker (CMQ)
Scott Zeiger (Chief Production Officer)
Jason Baker (Sr VP-Ops)
Paul Bausch (Sr VP-Strategic Dev)
Jacqueline Erb Cornell (Gen Counsel)
Bill Marbach (Sr VP-Bus Dev)
David McKee (Sr VP-Tech)
Thomas Murphy (Sr VP-Client Dev & Strategy-Corp Programs)
Ari Strulson (Sr VP-Ticketing Analytics & Dev)
Brandon Warner (Sr VP)

Subsidiaries:

Beneplace, LLC (1)
Echelon III Ste 100 9420 Research Blvd,
Austin, TX 78759-2324
Tel.: (512) 346-3300
Web Site: http://www.beneplace.com
Voluntary Insurance Benefits & Employee Discount Programs
N.A.I.C.S.: 524298
John Pence (CFO)
Rusty Stein (Pres)

Plum Benefits, LLC (1)
19495 Biscayne Blvd Ste 300, Aventura, FL 33180
Tel.: (212) 660-1848
Web Site: http://www.plumbenefits.com
Corporate Entertainment Benefit Services
N.A.I.C.S.: 561499
Lianne Williams (Mgr-Corp Sls & Svc Support)

Tickets & Tours (1)
1421 E Sunset Rd Ste 4, Las Vegas, NV 89119
Tel.: (702) 798-5606
Web Site: http://www.showtickets.com
Sales Range: $25-49.9 Million
Emp.: 185
Entertainment Scheduling Services
N.A.I.C.S.: 561599

ENTERTAINMENT EARTH, INC.

12730 Raymer St Ste 1, North Hollywood, CA 91605
Tel.: (818) 255-0090 CA
Web Site: http://www.entertainmentearth.com
Year Founded: 1996
Sales Range: $10-24.9 Million
Emp.: 26
Online Retailer of Toys, Gifts & Collectibles
N.A.I.C.S.: 423920
Aaron Labowitz (Co-Founder & CEO)
Jason Labowitz (Co-Founder & Pres)
Aaron Lipman (CTO)
Adam Lieber (COO)

ENTERTAINMENT ENGINEERING INC.
6258 E 6th St, Longbeach, CA 90803
Tel.: (818) 954-9100
Year Founded: 1987
Sales Range: $10-24.9 Million
Emp.: 5
Engineering Services
N.A.I.C.S.: 541330
Rich Croson (Dir-Construction)
Jan Croson (VP)

ENTERTAINMENT HOLDINGS, INC.
3625 Cove Point Dr, Salt Lake City, UT 84109
Tel.: (801) 209-0740 OK
Year Founded: 2021
Liabilities: $27,266
Net Worth: ($27,266)
Earnings: ($16,808)
Fiscal Year-end: 06/30/22
Holding Company
N.A.I.C.S.: 551112
Douglas Cole (Pres, Treas & Sec)
G. Reed Petersen (Pres)

ENTERTAINMENT METALS INC.
13351 Saddle Rd Ste 205, Fort Myers, FL 33913
Tel.: (239) 288-4804
Web Site: http://www.entertainmentmetals.com
Sales Range: $1-9.9 Million
Emp.: 12
Entertainment-Related Metal Fabrication
N.A.I.C.S.: 332999
Kevin Kirchner (Co-Owner & CEO)
Ryan Bringardner (Co-Owner & Pres)
John Irvin (CFO)

ENTERTAINMENT PARTNERS GROUP INC.
2835 N Naomi St, Burbank, CA 91504-2024
Tel.: (818) 955-6000
Web Site: http://www.entertainmentpartners.com
Year Founded: 1976
Sales Range: $10-24.9 Million
Emp.: 630
Payroll Services
N.A.I.C.S.: 561311
Markham L. Goldstein (Pres & CEO)
Josephine Gallella (Dir-Product Dev)
Adeel Mansoor (Engr-Lead QA)
Mary McDonnell (VP-Legal)
Mike Reese (Mgr-Software)
Darren Seidel (CFO)
Mike Rose (Chief Strategy Officer)
Patrick Baca (CTO)
Ruben Rodriguez (Exec VP)
Jennifer Bender (Exec VP-Central Casting)
Steve Spiker (Exec VP-Central Casting)
Myfa Cirinna (Exec VP-Mktg)

Davida Lara (Exec VP-Payroll)
Anthony De La Rosa (Exec VP-Residuals)
Michael Wofford (Gen Counsel & Exec VP)
Cheryl Nex (Pres-Canada)
Anita Geller (Sr Exec VP)

ENTERTAINMENT STUDIOS, INC.

1925 Century Park E 10th Fl, Los Angeles, CA 90067
Tel.: (310) 277-3500
Web Site:
  http://www.entertainmentstudio.com
Year Founded: 1993
Produces, Distributes & Sells Advertising for Television Programs
N.A.I.C.S.: 512120
Byron Allen Folks (Founder, Chm & CEO)
Lisa-Renee Ramirez (Exec VP)
Mark DeVitre (Exec VP & Gen Counsel)
Bob Boden (Pres-Production & Dev)
Eric Gould (Chief Investment Officer & Exec VP-Fin)
Peggy Hsieh (Sr VP-Fin)
Janice Arouh (Pres)
Todd Johnson (Chief Content Officer-The Grio-New York)
Mark Eisner (Sr VP-Content Distr, Partnerships & Programming)
Christopher Malone (CFO)
Bill Higgs (CFO-Weather Grp & Exec VP)

Subsidiaries:

Allen Media Broadcasting LLC   (1)
3282 Northside Pkwy Ste 275, Atlanta, GA 30327
Tel.: (470) 355-1944
Web Site:
  http://www.allenmediabroadcasting.com
Television Broadcasting Stations Operator
N.A.I.C.S.: 516120
Byron Allen Folks (Founder & Chm)
Robert S. Prather Jr. (Pres & CEO)
Roseann Cacciola (Exec VP-Ad Sls-AMG Global Syndication)

Subsidiary (Domestic):

Allen Media Broadcasting Evansville, Inc.   (2)
477 Carpenter St, Evansville, IN 47708
Tel.: (812) 465-4567
Web Site: http://www.wevv.com
Television Broadcasting Station
N.A.I.C.S.: 516120
Jeff Fisher (Gen Mgr)
Nicole Neidlinger (Dir-Sls)

Allen Media Broadcasting Lafayette, Inc.   (2)
1500 Eraste Landry Rd, Lafayette, LA 70506
Tel.: (337) 237-1500
Web Site: http://www.kadn.com
Television Broadcasting Station
N.A.I.C.S.: 516120
Nanette Lavergne (Gen Mgr)

Ft. Wayne TV, LLC   (2)
3707 Hillegas Rd, Fort Wayne, IN 46808
Tel.: (260) 471-5555
Web Site: http://www.wfft.com
Television Broadcasting Station
N.A.I.C.S.: 516120
Justin Prince (Dir-Sports)
Fred Brunell (Chief Engr)

KDRV-TV   (2)
1090 Knutson Ave, Medford, OR 97504-4164
Tel.: (541) 773-1212
Web Site: http://www.kdrv.com
Sales Range: $10-24.9 Million
Emp.: 65
Television Broadcasting Station
N.A.I.C.S.: 516120
Scott D. Chambers (Pres)
Mark Hatfield (Dir-News)
Catherine Hatfield (Gen Mgr-Sls)

KEZI-TV   (2)
2975 Chad Dr, Eugene, OR 97408
Tel.: (541) 485-5611
Web Site: http://www.kezi.com
Television Broadcasting Station
N.A.I.C.S.: 516120
Mike Boring (Gen Mgr)
Dan O'Brien (Gen Mgr-Sls)

Lafayette TV, LLC   (2)
2605 Yeager Rd, West Lafayette, IN 47906-1337
Tel.: (765) 463-1800
Web Site: http://www.wlfi.com
Television Broadcasting Station
N.A.I.C.S.: 516120
Robert Marc Elliott (Gen Mgr)

Mississippi TV, LLC   (2)
PO Box 320, Tupelo, MS 38802-0320
Tel.: (662) 842-7620
Web Site: http://www.wtva.com
Sales Range: $10-24.9 Million
Television Broadcasting Station
N.A.I.C.S.: 516120
Jay Richer (Gen Sls Mgr)
Steve Rogers (Dir-News)
Jerry Jones (Gen Mgr)
Gary Savage (Dir-Ops & Tech)
Jason Usry (Asst Dir-Mktg & Promos)

Rochester TV, LLC   (2)
112 N Pennsylvania Ave, Mason City, IA 50401-3404
Tel.: (800) 323-4883
Web Site: http://www.kimt.com
Television Station
N.A.I.C.S.: 516120
Steve Martinson (VP & Gen Mgr)
Mike Fitzgerald (Gen Mgr-Sls & Natl Sls)
Tony Dahle (Mgr-Production & Creative Svcs)
Jerome Risting (Mgr-Programming & Promos)

Terre Haute TV, LLC   (2)
800 Ohio St, Terre Haute, IN 47807
Tel.: (812) 232-9481
Web Site: http://www.wthitv.com
Television Broadcasting Station
N.A.I.C.S.: 516120
Todd Weber (VP & Gen Mgr)
Rod Garvin (Dir-Ops)
Susan Dinkel (Dir-News)
David Shearer (Dir-Promos & Creative Svcs)
Scott Arnold (Dir-Digital & Webmaster)
Jeff Tucker (Chief Engr)
Nick Telezyn (Gen Sls Mgr)
Lauren Cole (Sls Dir-Digital)
Thomas Norton (Mgr-IT)
Michael Delaunois (Mgr-Local Sls)
Mike Latta (Mgr-Assignment)
Christopher Essex (Mgr-Digital Media)

WJRT, Inc.   (2)
2302 Lapeer Rd, Flint, MI 48503-4221
Tel.: (810) 233-3130
Web Site: http://www.abc12.com
Television Broadcasting Station
N.A.I.C.S.: 516120
Brock Rice (Pres & Gen Mgr-ABC12)

Entertainment Studios Motion Pictures, LLC   (1)
1925 Century Park E 10th Fl, Los Angeles, CA 90067
Tel.: (310) 277-3500
Web Site: http://www.esmotionpictures.com
Motion Picture Producer & Distr
N.A.I.C.S.: 512110
Byron Allen Folks (Founder, Chm & CEO)

The Weather Channel, LLC   (1)
300 Interstate N Pkwy SE, Atlanta, GA 30339-2403
Tel.: (770) 226-0000
Web Site: http://www.weather.com
Sales Range: $200-249.9 Million
Live Weather Forecasting Cable Television Network & Website Publisher
N.A.I.C.S.: 516210
Indira K. Venkat (Sr VP-Strategic Res & Consumer Insights)
John Goodwin (Head-Comms)
Tom O'Brien (Pres)

ENTERTAINMENT TECHNOLOGY PARTNERS LLC

2350 Investors Row, Orlando, FL 32837
Tel.: (407) 850-0505
Web Site: https://www.etp.net
Holding Company
N.A.I.C.S.: 551112
Les Goldberg (CEO)

Subsidiaries:

LMG, LLC   (1)
2350 Investors Row, Orlando, FL 32837
Tel.: (407) 850-0505
Web Site: http://www.lmg.net
Rev.: $17,652,612
Emp.: 85
Television Film Production Sale & Rent Audio & Visual Equipment
N.A.I.C.S.: 512110
Les M. Goldberg (CEO)
Kevin McCabe (Sr Dir-Sys Dev)
Neil Morrison (VP-Tech)
Don Mascot (Sr Dir-Client Svcs)
Dan Wilson (Engr-Sls)
Stephen Campbell (VP-Live Events)
Rich Tate (Dir-Show Svcs)
Corey Olson (Dir-Bus Dev)
Ross Hancock (Dir-Sys Integration)
Craig Mitchell (Dir-Touring)
Steven Bodzioch (Dir-Design & Lighting Svcs)
Sean Borowski (Dir-Video Svcs)
Shane Smith (Dir-Audio Svcs)
Larry Andrews (Dir-Engrg)
Stacy Teal (Mgr-Social Media)
Oscar Sturup (Mgr-Audio Svcs)
Daniel Chernault (Mgr-New Media)
Brittany Dansereau (Supvr-Mktg)
David Wagner (Acct Exec-Orange County Convention Center)
Curt Wallen (Dir-Natl Accts-Convention Centers)
Ory Brochet (Acct Exec-Nashville)
Chris Royea (Mgr-Accts-Nashville)

ENTERTAINMENT TRANSPORTATION SPECIALISTS

7620 Airport Business Pkwy Bldg 4, Van Nuys, CA 91406
Tel.: (818) 756-2400
Web Site: http://www.bydeluxe.com
Rev.: $15,000,000
Emp.: 80
Brokers, Shipping
N.A.I.C.S.: 488510
Randy Morgan Farnsworth (Pres)

ENTIA BIOSCIENCES, INC.

13565 SW Tualatin-Sherwood Rd No 800, Sherwood, OR 97140
Tel.: (971) 228-0709   NV
Web Site: https://www.entiabio.com
Year Founded: 2007
ERGO—(OTCBB)
Sales Range: Less than $1 Million
Emp.: 6
Pharmaceutical Researcher & Mfr
N.A.I.C.S.: 325412
Marvin S. Hausman (Chm & Chief Science & Tech Officer)
Timothy A. Timmins (Pres & CEO)
Marvin S. Hausman (Founder, Chm, CTO & Chief Science Officer)

ENTIGO CORPORATION

Ste 206 495 Thomas Jones Way, Exton, PA 19341-2553
Tel.: (484) 359-8362   VA
Web Site: http://www.entigo.com
Year Founded: 1995
Sales Range: $10-24.9 Million
Emp.: 75
Designer of E-Commerce Software Warranty Solutions 7 Mfr
N.A.I.C.S.: 541511
Nick Shelness (CTO)
Joe Cellucci (VP-Pro Svcs)

ENTIRE PRODUCTIONS, INC.

650 California St 7th Fl, San Francisco, CA 94108

Tel.: (415) 291-9191
Web Site:
  https://www.entireproductions.com
Year Founded: 2001
Sales Range: $1-9.9 Million
Emp.: 10
Costume Design Services
N.A.I.C.S.: 541490
Natasha Miller (Pres)
Sarah Bagaman (Dir-Sls)
Rachel Quinlan (Acct Exec)
Elise Munc (Acct Exec)
Kristyn Garcia (Coord-Sls)
Claire O'neill (Acct Exec)
Paul Pimlett (Mgr-Acct)
Michal Swerdlow (Mgr-Acct)
Cheyenne Noell (Coord-Sls)
Karen Waldmann (Mgr-Production Svcs)
Ashe Cleveland (Coord-Sls)
Jillian Ericson (Coord-Event)

ENTISYS SOLUTIONS, INC.

1855 Gateway Blvd Ste 730, Concord, CA 94520
Tel.: (925) 688-8989   CA
Web Site: http://www.entisys360.com
Year Founded: 1994
Sales Range: $10-24.9 Million
Emp.: 105
Local Area Network Systems Integration Services
N.A.I.C.S.: 423430
Mike Strohl (CEO)
Kathy Casdorph (Dir-Mktg)
Doug Kirsten (Sr Acct Exec)

Subsidiaries:

Agile360, Inc.   (1)
47 Discovery Ste 150, Irvine, CA 92618
Tel.: (949) 419-8383
Web Site: http://www.agile360.com
Sales Range: $1-9.9 Million
Data Storage & Disaster Recovery Consulting Services
N.A.I.C.S.: 541690

ENTITLE, INC.

304 Fair Lakes Dr, Wilmington, NC 28405
Tel.: (910) 239-9007
Web Site:
  http://www.entitlebooks.com
Digital Book Subscription Services
N.A.I.C.S.: 459210
Bryan Batten (Founder & CEO)

ENTOLETER LLC

251 Welton St, Hamden, CT 06517-3931
Tel.: (203) 787-3575
Web Site: https://www.entoleter.com
Year Founded: 1940
Industrial Processing Equipment & Air Pollution Control Equipment Mfr
N.A.I.C.S.: 333413

ENTOURAGE YEARBOOKS

39 Everett Dr, Princeton Junction, NJ 08550
Tel.: (609) 452-2665
Web Site:
  https://www.entourageyearbook.com
Year Founded: 2006
Sales Range: $1-9.9 Million
Emp.: 40
Yearbook Publisher
N.A.I.C.S.: 513199
Elias Jo (Pres)

ENTRANCE SOFTWARE

3555 Timmons Ln Ste 1450, Houston, TX 77027
Tel.: (713) 357-4930
Web Site:
  http://www.entrancesoftware.com
Year Founded: 2003

Entrance Software—(Continued)

Sales Range: $1-9.9 Million
Emp.: 30
Software
N.A.I.C.S.: 541511
Nathaniel Richards (Pres & CEO)
Carol Donnelly (Dir-Consulting)
Eric Carlson (Sr Mgr)
Kristen Ortwerth (Dir-Mktg)

ENTRE COMPUTER SERVICES INC.
2000 Winton Rd S Bldg No 1 Ste 300, Rochester, NY 14618
Tel.: (585) 760-1010
Web Site: https://www.entrecs.com
Sales Range: $10-24.9 Million
Emp.: 300
Computer & Software Stores
N.A.I.C.S.: 449210
Andre Godfrey (Pres & CEO)
Deborah Curtis (Supvr-IT Svc & Desk Energy-East Reg)
John Crowley (VP-Application Dev)

ENTREKEN ASSOCIATES, INC.
1100 16th St N, Saint Petersburg, FL 33705
Tel.: (727) 894-1800
Web Site: http://www.fl-valuation.com
Sales Range: $1-9.9 Million
Emp.: 15
Real Estate Appraiser
N.A.I.C.S.: 531320
Jeffrey J. Boyle (Pres)
Michael T. Twitty (VP)
Gayle Schoneman (Mgr)

ENTREPRENEUR MEDIA, INC.
2445 McCabe Way Ste 400, Irvine, CA 92614-4293
Tel.: (949) 261-2325
Web Site:
    http://www.entrepreneur.com
Year Founded: 1987
Sales Range: $25-49.9 Million
Emp.: 80
Information & Services for Small & Mid-Sized Businesses
N.A.I.C.S.: 513120
Ryan Shea (Pres)

Subsidiaries:

Entrepreneur Media SA (Pty) Ltd.   (1)
First Floor Fernglade Fernridge Office Park 5 Hunter Ave, Randburg, South Africa
Tel.: (27) 11 886 6880
Web Site:
    http://www.entrepreneurmag.co.za
Emp.: 38
Magazine Publisher
N.A.I.C.S.: 513120
Andrew Honey (CEO)

ENTREPRENEURIAL EQUITY PARTNERS, LLC
353 N Clark St Ste 1760, Chicago, IL 60654
Tel.: (312) 872-0030
Web Site: http://www.e2pcapital.com
Investment Services
N.A.I.C.S.: 523999
Mark Burgett (Mng Partner)

Subsidiaries:

Daniele International, LLC   (1)
PO Box 106, Pascoag, RI 02859-0106
Tel.: (401) 568-6228
Web Site: http://www.danielefoods.com
All Other Specialty Food Stores
N.A.I.C.S.: 445298
David C. Finch (Exec Chm)
Vlado Dukcevich (CEO)

Subsidiary (Domestic):

Creminelli Fine Meats, LLC   (2)

310 Wright Brothers Dr, Salt Lake City, UT 84116-4116
Tel.: (801) 489-5801
Web Site: http://www.creminelli.com
Meat Processing
N.A.I.C.S.: 311612
Cristiano Creminelli (Partner)

Kronos Foods Corp.   (1)
1 Kronos Dr, Glendale Heights, IL 60139
Tel.: (224) 353-5353
Web Site: http://www.kronosfoodscorp.com
Mediterranean Food Product & Baked Food Mfr
N.A.I.C.S.: 311812
Howard C. Eirinberg (CEO)

Subsidiary (Domestic):

Grecian Delight Foods Inc.   (2)
1201 Tonne Rd, Elk Grove Village, IL 60007-4925
Tel.: (847) 364-1010
Web Site: http://www.greciandelight.com
Mediterranean Foods Including Pita Breads, Gyros Meat & Greek Specialties Mfr
N.A.I.C.S.: 311999
George Georganas (VP-Procurement)
Michael Lerch (CFO)
Peter Parthenis Jr. (Pres & CEO)

ENTRPRIZE CORPORATION
800 Nicollette Mall Ste 2690, Minneapolis, MN 55402
Tel.: (612) 333-0614   DE
Web Site: http://www.metalclad.com
Year Founded: 1947
Sales Range: $10-24.9 Million
Emp.: 14
Insulation Services; Asbestos Abatement & Material Sales
N.A.I.C.S.: 238310
Peter L. Hauser (Pres & CEO)

Subsidiaries:

Metalclad Insulation Corporation   (1)
1818 E Rosslynn Ave, Fullerton, CA 92831-5140
Tel.: (714) 888-2860
Web Site: http://www.metalclad.net
Manufacture & Installation of Metal-Protected Panel & Pipe Insulation Systems
N.A.I.C.S.: 238310
David Trueblood (Pres)
Manuel Pineda (Dir-Safety & Compliance)
Brian Villeneuve (Controller)

ENTRUST, INC.
140 Larrabee Rd, Westbrook, ME 04092
Tel.: (207) 856-6715
Sales Range: $10-24.9 Million
Emp.: 42
New & Used Automobiles
N.A.I.C.S.: 441110
Bill Conner (Pres & CEO)

ENTX GROUP LLC
8100 E Union Ave Ste 807, Denver, CO 80237
Tel.: (303) 459-2441
Web Site: http://www.entxgroup.com
Year Founded: 2005
Oil & Gas Exploration Services
N.A.I.C.S.: 213112
Shumin Liu (Founder, Chm & CEO)

ENVERITY ENGINEERING, LLC.
9229 Delegates Row Ste 150, Indianapolis, IN 46240
Tel.: (317) 706-2075
Web Site: http://www.lacquis.com
Sales Range: $1-9.9 Million
Emp.: 47
Mechanical & Electrical Engineering Services
N.A.I.C.S.: 541330
Ross D. Maue (Pres)

ENVERSA COMPANIES

12404 Park Central Ste 400, Dallas, TX 75251
Tel.: (214) 580-4464
Year Founded: 2005
Rev.: $15,000,000
Emp.: 24
Media Buying Agency
N.A.I.C.S.: 541830

ENVICOR
12900 Firestone Blvd, Santa Fe Springs, CA 90670
Tel.: (562) 921-7715
Web Site: http://www.mhs-ca.com
Rev.: $16,152,902
Emp.: 50
Lumber & Other Building Materials
N.A.I.C.S.: 423310
Alexander Lynn (Pres)

ENVIRATRENDS, INC.
1900 Main St Ste 312, Sarasota, FL 34236
Tel.: (941) 365-8835   WY
Year Founded: 2009
Sales Range: $10-24.9 Million
Emp.: 2
Pet Memorial Glass Products Mfr
N.A.I.C.S.: 327212
Russell Haraburda (Pres, CEO & Principal Acctg Officer)

ENVIRO CLEAN SERVICES LLC
11717 N Morgan Rd, Yukon, OK 73099
Tel.: (405) 373-4545
Web Site:
    http://www.envirocleanps.com
Year Founded: 1994
Sales Range: $10-24.9 Million
Emp.: 150
Transportation & Disposal of Hazardous & Nonhazardous Waste, Soil & Groundwater Remediation, 24-Hour Spill Response & Environmental Products & Consulting
N.A.I.C.S.: 541620
Herschel Roberts (CEO)
Jonathan Behymer (CMO)
Clint Lord (CFO)
John Ausley (Mgr-Sls)
Brandon Griffith (Asst Mgr-Ops & Field Svcs)
Dona Crouch (Mgr-Tech)
Leslie Gwinn (Dir-Ops)
Crystal Schroeder (Dir-HR)

Subsidiaries:

Cardinal Engineering, Inc.   (1)
1015 N Broadway Ste 300, Oklahoma City, OK 73102
Tel.: (405) 842-1066
Web Site: http://www.cardinalengineers.com
Sales Range: $10-24.9 Million
Civil Engineering, Environmental Consulting & Surveying Services
N.A.I.C.S.: 541330
William Swain (Principal)
Kimberly Slingerland (Dir-HR & Contracting)

Enviro Clean Products & Services   (1)
14961 State Highway 412, Mooreland, OK 73852   (100%)
Tel.: (580) 994-2424
Web Site: http://www.envirocleanps.com
Transportation & Disposal of Hazardous & Nonhazardous Waste Materials
N.A.I.C.S.: 562211
Herschel Roberts (CEO)
Jonathan Behymer (CMO)
Jeff Roberts (Atty)

Enviro Clean Products & Services   (1)
110 Airport Dr Ste A, Wappingers Falls, NY 12590   (100%)
Tel.: (845) 463-4571
Web Site: http://www.envirocleanps.com

Transportation & Disposal of Hazardous & Nonhazardous Waste Materials
N.A.I.C.S.: 562211
Jess Hicks (Mgr-Ops)
Marilyn O'Brien (Office Mgr)

Enviro Clean Products & Services   (1)
2405 E Country Rd 123, Midland, TX 79706   (100%)
Tel.: (432) 301-0208
Web Site: http://www.envirocleanps.com
Emp.: 10
Transportation & Disposal of Hazardous & Nonhazardous Waste Materials
N.A.I.C.S.: 562211
Craig McMahon (Gen Mgr)

G-2 International   (1)
PO Box 721090, Oklahoma City, OK 73172-1090   (100%)
Tel.: (405) 373-4315
Web Site: http://www.g-2international.com
Environmental & Geotechnical Applications
N.A.I.C.S.: 562211
Herschel Roberts (CEO)
Randy Molitor (Project Mgr)
Dona Crouch (Mgr-Tech)
David Claytor (Mgr-Ops)
Jonathan Behymer (CMO)
Jeff Roberts (Atty)

ENVIRO TECH CHEMICAL SERVICES, INC.
500 Winmoore Way, Modesto, CA 95358
Tel.: (209) 581-9576
Web Site:
    https://www.envirotech.com
Year Founded: 1991
Sales Range: $10-24.9 Million
Emp.: 74
Basic Inorganic Chemical Mfr
N.A.I.C.S.: 325199
Mike Harvey (CEO)
Jon Howarth (Sr VP-Tech)
Steve Jacobs (Mgr-Sls)
Tom Griffith (Mgr-Sls-Western Reg)
Brent Bankosky (Sr VP-Bus Ops)
Mike Archibald (COO)

ENVIRO-SAFE CONSULTING, LLC
W130 N10500 Washington Dr, Germantown, WI 53022
Tel.: (262) 790-2500
Web Site: https://www.enviro-safe.com
Year Founded: 2002
Environmental, Safety & Resource Recovery Consulting Firm
N.A.I.C.S.: 541690
Deb Hull (Office Mgr)
Jeffrey Vilione (Pres & CEO)
Jim Brahm (Project Mgr)

ENVIROCON TECHNOLOGIES, INC.
PO Box 4444, Midland, TX 79704
Tel.: (432) 687-2582   TX
Web Site:
    http://www.envirocontech.com
Year Founded: 1994
Sales Range: $10-24.9 Million
Emp.: 28
Sustainable Household Cleaning Products Mfr
N.A.I.C.S.: 325611
Dustin Bryson (Dir-Mktg)
James Eggemeyer (Pres)

ENVIROKINETICS INC.
4701 Arrow Hwy Ste B, Montclair, CA 91763
Tel.: (909) 621-7599
Web Site:
    http://www.envirokinetics.com
Rev.: $15,000,000
Emp.: 7
Petroleum Refinery Equipment

N.A.I.C.S.: 333248
Henry Seal *(Pres & CEO)*
Aaron Dyer *(Dir-Projects)*

ENVIROMETRIC PROCESS CONTROLS

12500 West Port Rd, Louisville, KY 40245
Tel.: (502) 495-1511
Web Site: http://www.epc-inc.com
Sales Range: $25-49.9 Million
Emp.: 40
Electric Control Panels Mfr
N.A.I.C.S.: 335313
George Campbell *(Pres)*
Kevin Herbert *(VP)*

ENVIRONAMICS INC.

13935 S Point Blvd, Charlotte, NC 28273
Tel.: (704) 376-3613
Web Site: https://www.environamics-inc.com
Sales Range: $10-24.9 Million
Emp.: 156
Commercial & Office Building Construction Services
N.A.I.C.S.: 236220
Louis Santospago *(Pres)*
Harry Jonhson *(CEO)*
Seth Moody *(Mgr-Warehouse)*
Ed Taylor *(Dir-IT)*

ENVIRONETX, LLC

746 N Industrial Dr, Elmhurst, IL 60126
Tel.: (630) 412-8943   IL
Web Site: http://www.spectrumofficework.com
Year Founded: 1956
Sales Range: $1-9.9 Million
Emp.: 35
Office Furniture Installation Services
N.A.I.C.S.: 238390
Jack Matthews *(Pres & CEO)*

ENVIRONICS COMMUNICATIONS

2000 L St NW Ste 520, Washington, DC 20036
Tel.: (202) 296-2002
Web Site: http://www.environicspr.com
Year Founded: 1994
Sales Range: $10-24.9 Million
Emp.: 68
Brand Stewardship, B2B Communications & Consumer Campaigns
N.A.I.C.S.: 541820
Bruce MacLellan *(CEO)*
David Groobert *(Gen Mgr)*
Paul Lockhard *(Pres)*
Mimi Carter *(Sr VP & Gen Mgr)*
Josh Cobden *(Sr VP-Corp & Fin)*
Steve Acken *(Sr VP-Digital Svcs)*
Vanessa Eaton *(Sr VP-Health Sciences)*
Robin Shimkovitz *(VP-Consumer)*
Andrew Kinnear *(VP-Digital Strategy)*
Greg MacEachern *(VP-Govt Rels)*
Brent Turnbull *(VP & Dir-Creative)*

Subsidiaries:

Capital-Image   (1)
750 Marcel-Laurin Blvd Suite 390, Ville Mont-Royal, Montreal, H4M 2M4, QC, Canada
Tel.: (514) 739-1188
Web Site: http://www.capital-image.com
Emp.: 14
Public Relations & Brand Marketing
N.A.I.C.S.: 541820
Yvon Desautels *(Pres)*

Environics Communications   (1)
33 Bloor St East Suite 900, Toronto, M4W 3H1, ON, Canada
Tel.: (416) 920-9000

Web Site: https://getproof.com
Emp.: 109
Brand Stewardship, Communication Campaigns & Public Relations
N.A.I.C.S.: 541820
Bruce MacLellan *(CEO)*

Environics Communications Inc.   (1)
One Embarcadero Center Suite 500, San Francisco, CA 94111   (100%)
Tel.: (415) 315-7120
Web Site: http://www.environicspr.com
Brand Stewardship & Public Relations
N.A.I.C.S.: 541820

Environics Comunications Inc.   (1)
1 Rideau Street Suite 700, Ottawa, K1N 8S7, ON, Canada
Tel.: (613) 670-5811
Web Site: http://www.getproof.com
Emp.: 4
Brand Stewardship & Public Relation Services
N.A.I.C.S.: 541820
Greg MacEachern *(VP)*

ENVIRONMENTAL ALTERNATIVES

455 W Main St, Quincy, CA 95971
Tel.: (530) 283-3330   CA
Web Site: https://www.ea.org
Year Founded: 1981
Sales Range: $10-24.9 Million
Children Adoption Services
N.A.I.C.S.: 624110
Tim Wilkinson *(Exec Dir)*
Jim Hardee *(Exec Dir)*
Roddy Mac *(Exec Dir)*
Vivian Wilkinson *(Program Dir)*
Jeome Dorris *(Controller)*

ENVIRONMENTAL BIOTECH INTERNATIONAL, LLC

4693 19th St Ct E, Bradenton, FL 34203
Tel.: (941) 757-2591   FL
Web Site: http://www.environmentalbiotech.com
Year Founded: 1991
Sales Range: $1-9.9 Million
Emp.: 28
Environmental Consulting Services
N.A.I.C.S.: 541620
Matt Robinson *(VP-Ops & Product Dev)*
Aziz Tejpar *(CEO)*

ENVIRONMENTAL CHEMICAL CORPORATION

1240 Bayshore Hwy, Burlingame, CA 94010-1805
Tel.: (650) 347-1555   KY
Web Site: https://www.ecc.net
Year Founded: 1985
Sales Range: $10-24.9 Million
Emp.: 200
Refuse System Services
N.A.I.C.S.: 562211
Mangiv Vohra *(Pres)*

ENVIRONMENTAL CONSULTING & TECHNOLOGY, INC.

3701 NW 98th St, Gainesville, FL 32606
Tel.: (352) 332-0444
Web Site: http://www.ectinc.com
Year Founded: 1988
Sales Range: $25-49.9 Million
Emp.: 201
Environmental Consulting Services
N.A.I.C.S.: 541620
Sanjiv Sinha *(VP)*
Lee Smith *(Project Dir)*
Bob Kloepfer *(Pres)*
Dana West *(Mng Dir-Southeast & Sr VP)*

ENVIRONMENTAL CONTAINMENT CORPORATION

2412 Westlake Ave N #4, Seattle, WA 98109
Tel.: (360) 904-0199
Web Site: https://www.envcontainment.com
Year Founded: 1994
Construction Services
N.A.I.C.S.: 236210
Ron Sparks *(CEO)*

Subsidiaries:

Marks Metal Technology Inc.   (1)
10264 SE Jennifer St, Clackamas, OR 97015
Tel.: (503) 656-0901
Web Site: http://www.marksmetal.com
Rev.: $9,855,000
Emp.: 45
Fabricated Structural Metal Mfr
N.A.I.C.S.: 332312
David Marks *(Pres)*
Dan Parker *(CFO)*

ENVIRONMENTAL CONTROLS CORP.

15954 SW 72nd Ave, Tigard, OR 97224
Tel.: (503) 620-4228   OR
Web Site: http://www.eccoregon.com
Year Founded: 1987
Electrical Appliance Installation Services
N.A.I.C.S.: 238210
Dick Schweiger *(Pres)*
Rick Devlin *(VP)*
Kerri Zayas *(VP)*
Bob Elton *(Sls Engr)*
Cliff Neilson *(Sls Engr-Vancouver)*
Mark Hanken *(Sls Engr-Bend)*

ENVIRONMENTAL DESIGN & CONSTRUCTION, LLC

1108 Good Hope Rd SE, Washington, DC 20020
Tel.: (202) 889-6550
Web Site: http://www.envdes.com
Year Founded: 1997
Sales Range: $10-24.9 Million
Emp.: 60
New Multifamily Housing Construction, except Operative Builders
N.A.I.C.S.: 236116
Dennis J. Garbis *(CEO & Principal)*
Korinna Garbis *(VP)*
Ed Fuller *(Dir-Construction)*

ENVIRONMENTAL EARTHSCAPES INCORPORATED

5225 S Swan Rd, Tucson, AZ 85733
Tel.: (520) 318-6760
Web Site: http://www.groundskeeper.com
Year Founded: 1976
Sales Range: $25-49.9 Million
Emp.: 800
Highway Lawn & Garden Maintenance Services
N.A.I.C.S.: 561730
Jonathan Hasbrouck *(CFO)*
Dave Ramsze *(COO)*
Anil I. Hiremath *(CEO)*
Curtis Steinle *(VP-Ops)*

ENVIRONMENTAL ENERGY SERVICES, INC.

5 Turnberry Ln, Sandy Hook, CT 06482
Tel.: (203) 270-0337
Web Site: https://www.eescorp.com
Research & Development in the Physical, Engineering & Life Sciences
N.A.I.C.S.: 541715
Richard Nowak *(Pres & CEO)*

Subsidiaries:

Combustion Technologies Corp.   (1)
1009 Classic Rd, Apex, NC 27539

Tel.: (800) 614-1259
Web Site: http://www.combustiontc.com
Research & Development in the Physical, Engineering & Life Sciences
N.A.I.C.S.: 541715
Dave Earley *(Pres)*

ENVIRONMENTAL ENGINEERING CONSULTANTS, INC.

5119 N Florida Ave, Tampa, FL 33603
Tel.: (813) 237-3781
Web Site: https://www.eec-tampabay.com
Year Founded: 1979
Sales Range: $1-9.9 Million
Emp.: 9
Engineeering Services
N.A.I.C.S.: 541330
Robert E. Wallace *(Pres)*

ENVIRONMENTAL ENGINUITY GROUP LLC

41800 Hayes Rd Ste 552, Clinton, MI 48038
Tel.: (877) 211-9773
Web Site: http://www.eenginuity.com
Holding Company; Environmental Services
N.A.I.C.S.: 551112
W. David Kimbrell *(CEO)*
Richard Hernandez *(COO)*
Richard Goff *(CFO)*
Kyle Wilson *(CMO)*
Gary Boyle *(Gen Counsel)*

Subsidiaries:

Hamer Environmental L.P.   (1)
1510 S 3rd St, Mount Vernon, WA 98273-4908
Tel.: (360) 899-5156
Web Site: http://www.hamerenvironmental.com
Environmental Consulting Services
N.A.I.C.S.: 541620
Tom Hamer *(Mgr & Dir)*
Kristin Murray *(Project Mgr)*

ENVIRONMENTAL ENTERPRISES INC.

10163 Cincinnati Dayton Rd, Cincinnati, OH 45241
Tel.: (513) 772-2818
Web Site: https://www.eeienv.com
Sales Range: $10-24.9 Million
Emp.: 100
Hazardous Waste Transport
N.A.I.C.S.: 562112
Daniel J. McCabe *(Pres)*
Warren Taylor *(Dir-Quality Assurance)*
Gary Brunner *(Mgr-Tech)*

ENVIRONMENTAL EQUIPMENT & SERVICES

27365 Zachary Ave, Elko, MN 55020
Tel.: (952) 461-3650
Web Site: https://www.environmentalequipment.com
Rev.: $25,000,000
Emp.: 200
Chemical Cleaning Services
N.A.I.C.S.: 237310

ENVIRONMENTAL FIRE PROTECTION, INC.

237 Cedar Hill St, Marlborough, MA 01752
Tel.: (508) 485-8183
Web Site: http://www.sprinklers-r-us.com
Year Founded: 1976
Sales Range: $10-24.9 Million
Emp.: 100
Truck Leasing
N.A.I.C.S.: 238220

Environmental Fire Protection, Inc.—(Continued)

Alan Germain *(Chm & CEO)*
Glenn Lyons *(Mgr-Fabrication Logistics)*

ENVIRONMENTAL HEALTH TESTING

5728 Major Blvd Ste 750, Orlando, FL 32819
Tel.: (407) 352-3635
Web Site:
  http://www.envhealthtesting.com
Year Founded: 2000
Rev.: $3,400,000
Emp.: 18
Management Consulting Services
N.A.I.C.S.: 541611
Jeff Belmont *(COO)*

ENVIRONMENTAL HOLDINGS GROUP, LLC.

190 Kitty Hawk Dr, Morrisville, NC 27560
Tel.: (919) 544-6750
Web Site: http://www.ehgllc.com
Year Founded: 2001
Sales Range: $10-24.9 Million
Emp.: 150
Environmental Services
N.A.I.C.S.: 541620
BJ Fungaroli *(Pres & CEO)*
Brian Sanders *(Sr VP)*

ENVIRONMENTAL INFRA-STRUCTURE HOLDINGS CORP.

Four Tower Bridge 200 Barr Harbor Dr Ste 400, West Conshohocken, PA 19428
Tel.: (484) 905-1157
Web Site:
  http://www.environmentalinfra
  structureholdings.com
Sales Range: $1-9.9 Million
Emp.: 12
Holding Company
N.A.I.C.S.: 551112
Kurt M. Given *(CEO-Equisol)*
Donald G. Gibson *(Pres-Equisol LLC)*

Subsidiaries:

Equisol LLC   **(1)**
Four Tower Bridge 200 Barr Harbor Dr Ste 400, West Conshohocken, PA 19428
Tel.: (610) 941-2747
Rev.: $8,300,000
Emp.: 87
Environmental Consulting Services
N.A.I.C.S.: 541620
Dana J. Militello *(VP-Sls & Svc)*

XIOM Corp.   **(1)**
78 Lamar St, West Babylon, NY 11704
Tel.: (631) 643-4400
Web Site: http://www.xiom-corp.com
Plastic Powder Coating Application Technology Developer
N.A.I.C.S.: 325510

ENVIRONMENTAL INKS & COATINGS CORP.

1 Quality Products Rd, Morganton, NC 28655-4759
Tel.: (828) 433-1922
Web Site: http://www.envinks.com
Year Founded: 1978
Sales Range: $50-74.9 Million
Emp.: 200
Printing Ink Mfr & Distr
N.A.I.C.S.: 325910
Ron Zessack *(Dir-Product Dev)*

ENVIRONMENTAL LIGHTING CONCEPTS, INC.

220 W 7th Ave Ste 100, Tampa, FL 33602
Tel.: (813) 621-0058

Web Site: http://www.ott-lite.com
Year Founded: 1989
Rev.: $7,000,000
Emp.: 50
Natural Lighting Products Mfr
N.A.I.C.S.: 335132
Karen Garnes *(Dir-Adv & Creative Svcs)*
Don Barry *(Pres & CEO)*

ENVIRONMENTAL LUBRI-CANTS MANUFACTURING, INC.

311 B Ave, Grundy Center, IA 50638
Tel.: (319) 824-5203
Web Site: http://www.elmusa.com
Year Founded: 2000
Sales Range: $1-9.9 Million
Emp.: 5
Bio-Based Industrial Lubricants Mfr
N.A.I.C.S.: 541615
Lou A. T. Honary *(Founder)*

ENVIRONMENTAL MANAGE-MENT RESOURCES, INC.

3200 Haskell Ave, Lawrence, KS 66046
Tel.: (785) 842-9013
Web Site: http://www.emr-inc.com
Year Founded: 1988
Sales Range: $25-49.9 Million
Emp.: 75
Environmental Consulting, Testing, Engineering & Construction Services
N.A.I.C.S.: 541620
Connie Cook *(CEO)*

ENVIRONMENTAL MANUFAC-TURING SOLUTIONS, LLC

7705 Progress Cir, Melbourne, FL 32904
Tel.: (321) 837-0050
Web Site: https://www.enviromfg.com
Rev.: $28,700,000
Emp.: 67
Chemicals Mfr
N.A.I.C.S.: 325199
John MacDonald *(Pres)*

ENVIRONMENTAL PRODUCTS

99 Great Hill Rd, Naugatuck, CT 06770
Tel.: (203) 720-4059
Web Site: https://www.envipco.com
Year Founded: 1979
Sales Range: $25-49.9 Million
Emp.: 110
Other Accounting Services
N.A.I.C.S.: 541219

ENVIRONMENTAL RECYCLING TECHNOLOGIES

91125 Kaomi Loop, Kapolei, HI 96707
Tel.: (808) 673-3230
Year Founded: 2000
Sales Range: $10-24.9 Million
Emp.: 55
Recylcing Services Holding Company
N.A.I.C.S.: 562920
Blane Yamagata *(Pres)*
Sally Davis *(VP)*

ENVIRONMENTAL SCIENCE ASSOCIATES

550 Kearny St Ste 800, San Francisco, CA 94108
Tel.: (415) 896-5900
Web Site: http://www.esassoc.com
Year Founded: 1969
Sales Range: $10-24.9 Million
Emp.: 300
Environmental Research
N.A.I.C.S.: 541720
Deanna Hansen *(Dir-Community Dev)*

Kelly Dunlap *(Dir-Transportation)*
Margaret Clancy *(Dir-Pacific Northwest)*
Brian Boxer *(Dir-Northern California)*
Leslie Moulton-Post *(Pres & CEO)*
Mike Leech *(Dir-Geospatial Svcs)*
Tom Barnes *(VP & Dir-Water Grp-Southern California)*
Swen Swenson *(Controller)*
John Bartolomi *(Dir-IT)*
Terri Avila *(VP)*
Elizabeth Andrews *(Mgr-Fluvial Program)*
Albert Cuisinot *(CFO)*
Hillary Gitelman *(Dir-Community Dev-Environmental Plng-Bay Area)*
Douglas Skurski *(Dir-Biological Resources-Southeast)*
Eric Haase *(COO)*
John Bourgeois *(Program Mgr-Restoration & Ecology-Bay Area)*
Ruta K. Thomas *(Sr VP & Dir-Southern California)*
Dusty Ramsey *(Dir-IT)*

Subsidiaries:

ESA PWA   **(1)**
550 Kearny St 9th Fl, San Francisco, CA 94108
Tel.: (415) 262-2300
Web Site: http://www.pwa-ltd.com
Sales Range: $10-24.9 Million
Emp.: 40
Engineering & Hydrology Services
N.A.I.C.S.: 541330
Michelle K. Orr *(Dir-Wetlands & Estuaries)*
Ann Borgonovo *(Dir-Ops & Sr VP)*
Philip Williams *(Sr VP & Exec Dir)*
Jeffrey Haltiner *(Principal)*

Janicki Environmental, Inc.   **(1)**
1155 Eden Isle Dr NE, Saint Petersburg, FL 33704
Tel.: (727) 895-7722
Web Site:
  http://www.janickienvironmental.com
Professional, Scientific & Technical Services
N.A.I.C.S.: 541990

ENVIRONMENTAL SERVICE LABORATORIES INC.

1803 Philadelphia St, Indiana, PA 15701
Tel.: (724) 463-8378
Web Site: http://www.envlabs.com
Year Founded: 1988
Sales Range: $10-24.9 Million
Emp.: 54
Environmental Testing Services
N.A.I.C.S.: 541380
Elizabeth Gregg *(Pres & CEO)*
Michael Moyer *(COO)*
Gabriel Taylor *(Dir-Laboratory)*
Laura Rachocki *(Coord-Predrill)*

ENVIRONMENTAL SERVICES OF NORTH AMERICA, INC.

10455 Ford Rd, Dearborn, MI 48126
Tel.: (313) 945-7400
Web Site: https://www.esnainc.com
Year Founded: 2001
Sales Range: $1-9.9 Million
Emp.: 11
Environmental Facilities Management Services
N.A.I.C.S.: 561210
Joe Coelho *(CEO)*

ENVIRONMENTAL SERVICES SPECIALISTS

333 Rose St, Williamsport, PA 17701-6095
Tel.: (570) 326-7000
Web Site:
  http://www.eaglejanitorialsupply.com
Rev.: $26,300,000
Emp.: 75
Janitors' Supplies

N.A.I.C.S.: 423850
Steven Twigg *(Pres)*

ENVIRONMENTAL SYSTEM PRODUCTS HOLDING

7 Kripes Rd, East Granby, CT 06026-9720
Tel.: (860) 392-2100
Web Site: https://www.esp-global.com
Sales Range: $10-24.9 Million
Emp.: 50
Emissions Testing
N.A.I.C.S.: 811198
Mike Kozlowski *(Sr VP-Mktg)*

ENVIRONMENTAL SYSTEMS RESEARCH INSTITUTE INC.

380 New York St, Redlands, CA 92373-8118
Tel.: (909) 793-2853
Web Site: https://www.esri.com
Year Founded: 1969
Sales Range: $300-349.9 Million
Emp.: 3,100
Geographic Information Systems
N.A.I.C.S.: 423430
Jack Dangermond *(Founder & Pres)*

Subsidiaries:

ESRI China (Hong Kong) Ltd.   **(1)**
9th Floor CEO Tower 77 Wing Hong Street, Cheung Sha Wan, Kowloon, China (Hong Kong)
Tel.: (852) 27306883
Web Site: http://www.esrichina-hk.com
Emp.: 100
Geophysical Surveying Software Distr
N.A.I.C.S.: 423430
Winnie Tang *(Chm)*

Esri (Thailand) Co., Ltd.   **(1)**
202 CDG House Nanglinchee Road, Chongnonsee, Yannawa, Bangkok, 10120, Thailand
Tel.: (66) 2 678 0707
Web Site: http://www.esrith.com
Geophysical Surveying Software Distr
N.A.I.C.S.: 423430

Esri (UK) Ltd.   **(1)**
Millennium House 65 Walton Street, Aylesbury, HP21 7QG, Buckinghamshire, United Kingdom
Tel.: (44) 1296 745 500
Web Site: http://www.esriuk.com
Emp.: 250
Geophysical Surveying Software Distr
N.A.I.C.S.: 423430
Pete Delve *(Mgr-Engagement)*
Richard Waite *(Mng Dir)*

Esri BeLux S.A.   **(1)**
Nervierslaan 54, 1780, Wemmel, Belgium
Tel.: (32) 2 460 7480
Web Site: http://www.esribelux.com
Geophysical Surveying Software Distr
N.A.I.C.S.: 423430

Esri Bilgi Sistemleri Muhendislik ve Egitim, Ltd.   **(1)**
2024 Cadde No 14-16 Beysukent, 06800, Ankara, Türkiye
Tel.: (90) 312 233 5050
Web Site: http://www.esriturkey.com.tr
Geophysical Surveying Software Distr
N.A.I.C.S.: 423430

Esri Bulgaria Ltd.   **(1)**
35 Nikola Vaptzarov Blvd floor 4, 1407, Sofia, Bulgaria
Tel.: (359) 2 962 63 66
Web Site: http://www.esribulgaria.com
Geophysical Surveying Software Distr
N.A.I.C.S.: 423430

Esri CIS Limited   **(1)**
52 Bld 6 Smolnaya St, 125445, Moscow, Russia
Tel.: (7) 4959883481
Web Site: http://www.esri-cis.ru
Emp.: 100
Geophysical Surveying Software Distr
N.A.I.C.S.: 423430
Yulia Bystrova *(Gen Dir)*

Esri Canada Limited (1)
12 Concorde Place Suite 900, Toronto,
M3C 3R8, ON, Canada
Tel.: (416) 441-6035
Web Site: http://www.esri.ca
Emp.: 350
Geophysical Surveying Software Distr
N.A.I.C.S.: 423430
Alex Miller (Co-Founder & Pres)
Douglas Bayley (CFO)
Mary-Charlotte Miller (Co-Founder & VP-
Corp Policy)
Lois Boynton (VP)

Esri Chile S.A. (1)
Marchant Pereira 201 piso 9, Santiago,
Chile
Tel.: (56) 2 481 9000
Web Site: http://www.esri.cl
Geophysical Surveying Software Distr
N.A.I.C.S.: 423430

**Esri China Information Technology
Co. Ltd** (1)
19/F Easyhome Tower A3 Dongzhimen
South Street, Dongcheng District, Beijing,
100007, China
Tel.: (86) 10 5763 2288
Web Site: http://www.esrichina.com.cn
Geophysical Surveying Software Distr
N.A.I.C.S.: 423430

Esri Deutschland GmbH (1)
Ringstrasse 7, 85402, Kranzberg, Germany
Tel.: (49) 89 207 005 1200
Web Site: http://www.esri.de
Geophysical Surveying Software Distr
N.A.I.C.S.: 423430

Esri Eastern Africa Ltd. (1)
3rd Floor KUSCCO Centre Kilimanjaro Av-
enue Upper Hill, PO Box 57783, 00200,
Nairobi, Kenya
Tel.: (254) 20 2713630
Web Site: http://www.esriea.co.ke
Geophysical Surveying Software Distr
N.A.I.C.S.: 423430

Esri Finland Oy (1)
Sinikalliontie 3, 02630, Espoo, Finland
Tel.: (358) 207 435 435
Web Site: http://www.esri.fi
Geophysical Surveying Software Distr
N.A.I.C.S.: 423430

Esri Italia S.P.A. (1)
Via Casilina 98, 00182, Rome, Italy
Tel.: (39) 06 406 961
Web Site: http://www.esriitalia.it
Emp.: 100
Geophysical Surveying Software Distr
N.A.I.C.S.: 423430
Bruno Ratti (Gen Mgr)

Esri Japan Corporation (1)
2-7-1 Hirakawa-cho, Chiyoda-ku, Tokyo,
102-0093, Japan
Tel.: (81) 3 3222 3941
Web Site: http://www.esrij.com
Geophysical Surveying Software Distr
N.A.I.C.S.: 423430

Esri Korea, Inc. (1)
36 Teheran-ro 87-gil, Gangnam-gu, 135-
973, Seoul, Korea (South)
Tel.: (82) 2 2086 1900
Web Site: http://www.esri.com
Geophysical Surveying Software Distr
N.A.I.C.S.: 423430

Esri Muscat Co. LLC (1)
4th Floor Al Ofouq Building Shatti Al Qurum,
PO Box 1213, Al Khuwair, 133, Muscat,
Oman
Tel.: (968) 24693723
Web Site: http://www.esrimuscat.com
Geophysical Surveying Software Distr
N.A.I.C.S.: 423430

Esri Nederland B.V. (1)
Weena 695 B2-036 3013AM Rotterdam,
Postbus 29020, 3001GA, Rotterdam, Neth-
erlands
Tel.: (31) 10 217 0700
Web Site: http://www.esri.nl
Geophysical Surveying Software Distr
N.A.I.C.S.: 423430

Esri Polska sp. z o.o. (1)
ul Bonifraterska 17, 00-203, Warsaw, Poland

Tel.: (48) 22 390 4700
Web Site: http://www.esri.pl
Geophysical Surveying Software Distr
N.A.I.C.S.: 423430

Esri Portugal, S.A. (1)
Ruajulieta Ferrao N 10 -10A, 1600-131, Lis-
bon, Portugal
Tel.: (351) 21 781 6640
Web Site: http://www.esriportugal.pt
Geophysical Surveying Software Distr
N.A.I.C.S.: 423430

Esri Romania S.R.L. (1)
Str Roma nr 8 ap 1 Sector 1, 011774, Bu-
charest, Romania
Tel.: (40) 21 231 14 22
Web Site: http://www.esriro.ro
Emp.: 10
Geophysical Surveying Software Distr
N.A.I.C.S.: 423430
Cristian Vasile (Mng Dir)

Esri Rwanda Ltd. (1)
KG 5 Ave Nr 18 Kacyiru, PO Box 6867, Ki-
gali, Rwanda
Tel.: (250) 788 38 19 00
Web Site: http://www.esri.rw
Geophysical Surveying Software Distr
N.A.I.C.S.: 423430
Kaspar Kundert (Mng Dir)
Jean Pierre Gatera (Mng Dir)

Esri Saudi Arabia Ltd. (1)
Olaya, PO Box 62174, Riyadh, 11585,
Saudi Arabia
Tel.: (966) 1 416 2600
Web Site: http://www.esrisaudiarabia.com
Geophysical Surveying Software Distr
N.A.I.C.S.: 423430

Esri Schweiz AG (1)
Josefstrasse 218, 8005, Zurich, Switzerland
Tel.: (41) 58 267 18 00
Web Site: http://www.esri.ch
Geophysical Surveying Software Distr
N.A.I.C.S.: 423430
Adrian Aschwanden (Acct Mgr)
Matthias Schenker (Dir-Implementation
Svcs)

Esri Senegal Sarl (1)
A1 Residence ASDI 4421 SICAP Amitie III,
Dakar, Senegal
Tel.: (221) 33 864 38 34
Geophysical Surveying Software Distr
N.A.I.C.S.: 423430

Esri South Africa (Pty) Ltd. (1)
Block A Whitby Manor 167 14th Road
Noordwyk Extension 61, Midrand, South
Africa
Tel.: (27) 11 238 6300
Web Site: http://www.esri-southafrica.com
Geophysical Surveying Software Distr
N.A.I.C.S.: 423430
Lawrence Modise (Dir-Strategy & Bus Dev)
Nomsa Simelane (Mgr-Sls Liaison)

Esri Suisse SA (1)
route du Cordon 7, 1260, Nyon, Switzerland
Tel.: (41) 58 267 18 60
Web Site: http://fr.esri.ch
Emp.: 12
Geophysical Surveying Software Distr
N.A.I.C.S.: 423430
Imanuele Tennai (Gen Mgr)

Esri Sverige AB (1)
Nobelvagen 2, 802 67, Gavle, Sweden
Tel.: (46) 771 98 48 00
Web Site: http://www.esri.se
Geophysical Surveying Software Distr
N.A.I.C.S.: 423430

Esri Ukraine Ltd. (1)
4 A Petrickogo Str, 03115, Kiev, Ukraine
Tel.: (380) 44 502 4121
Web Site: http://www.esri.ua
Geophysical Surveying Software Distr
N.A.I.C.S.: 423430
Eugene Seragenen (Gen Mgr)

FortiusOne, Inc. (1)
2200 Wilson Blvd, Arlington, VA 22201
Tel.: (703) 247-9280
Web Site: http://www.fortiusone.com
Custom Computer Programming Services
N.A.I.C.S.: 541511

ENVIRONMENTAL TECH-
NIQUES CORP.

2809 Industrial Ln, Garland, TX
75041
Tel.: (972) 278-0301   TX
Web Site: http://www.etcair.com
Year Founded: 2003
Sales Range: $1-9.9 Million
Emp.: 40
Plumbing/Heating/Air Cond Contrac-
tor
N.A.I.C.S.: 238220
Chris Goolsby (Owner & Pres)
Tom Bledsoe (Mgr-Sls Project)
Raymond Miller (Supvr-Field-Comml
Construction)
Ronald L. Keller (Mgr-Sls Project)
Wayne Cronk (Controller)

ENVIRONMENTAL WASTE
MINIMIZATION INC.

14 Brick Kiln Ct, Northampton, PA
18067
Tel.: (484) 275-6900
Web Site: http://www.ewmi-info.com
Sales Range: $25-49.9 Million
Emp.: 57
Environmental Services
N.A.I.C.S.: 541620
Michael F. Acker (Pres)

ENVIRONMENTAL WASTE SO-
LUTIONS LLC

950 S Tamiami Trl Ste 210, Sarasota,
FL 34236-7818
Tel.: (941) 953-2200
Web Site: http://www.environmental-
waste.com
Year Founded: 1994
Sales Range: $25-49.9 Million
Emp.: 30
Environmental Consulting Services
N.A.I.C.S.: 541620
Darwyn Williams (Pres & CEO)
Douglas Maher (Dir-Affiliate Dev)
Diana Shapiro (COO)
Russell Williams (VP)

ENVIRONMENTS INC.

159 Bay Pines Rd, Burton, SC 29906
Tel.: (843) 846-8155
Web Site: http://www.eichild.com
Rev.: $15,000,000
Emp.: 80
School Supplies
N.A.I.C.S.: 423490
Linda Lathrop (Mgr-Production)

ENVIROSOLUTIONS, INC.

11220 Assett Loop Ste 201, Manas-
sas, VA 20109
Tel.: (703) 378-0600
Web Site: http://www.esiwaste.com
Year Founded: 2003
Rev.: $200,000,000
Emp.: 300
Waste Disposal Services
N.A.I.C.S.: 562212
Mike Buchanan (Dir-Maintenance)
Dan Howard (Dir-Safety)
Tim Kyle (CIO & VP)
Marc Shaener (Dir-Market Dev)
Gary Hewes (VP-Ops Support & Pro-
cess Improvement)
Charles Fromm (Gen Counsel & VP)
Bob Gretz (VP-Mid-Atlantic)
Dean Kattler (Pres & CEO)

ENVIROSTRUCT, LLC

26711 Dublin Woods Cir, Bonita
Springs, FL 34135
Tel.: (239) 494-5700
Web Site:
  https://www.envirostruct.net
Sales Range: $1-9.9 Million
Emp.: 20
Commercial, Institutional & Industrial
Construction

N.A.I.C.S.: 236220
Neil W. Simon (Pres)
Stephen McKenna Jr. (VP)

ENVIROTECH ENGINEERING
& CONSULTING, INC.

2500 N 11th St, Enid, OK 73701
Tel.: (580) 234-8780   OK
Web Site:
  https://www.envirotechconsul
  ting.com
Year Founded: 1992
Sales Range: $1-9.9 Million
Emp.: 30
Engineering & Environmental Con-
sulting Services
N.A.I.C.S.: 541620
Jimmy Stallings (Pres)

ENVIROTEK ENVIRONMENTAL
& CONSTRUCTION SERVICES

3007 N 50th St, Tampa, FL 33619
Tel.: (813) 909-0040
Web Site: http://www.envirotek.com
Year Founded: 1992
Sales Range: $10-24.9 Million
Emp.: 24
Environmental & Engineering Ser-
vices
N.A.I.C.S.: 541620
Wyatt Grant (Pres)

ENVIROTRAC LTD.

5 Old Dock Rd, Yaphank, NY 11980
Tel.: (631) 924-3001
Web Site: https://www.envirotrac.com
Year Founded: 1993
Sales Range: $25-49.9 Million
Emp.: 150
Environmental Consulting, Remedial
Engineering & Construction
N.A.I.C.S.: 541620
Joseph Patrick Byrnes (Pres & CEO)
John Buhagiar (CFO)
Theodore F. Masters (VP)
John Ferrill (VP)
Douglas Lessing (VP)
Elizabeth Girsch (Mgr-HR)
Dave Lorthioir (Project Mgr)
Will Heim (Sr Project Mgr)

ENVIROTROL PEST MANAGE-
MENT SYSTEMS INC.

806 N Belt Line Rd, Grand Prairie,
TX 75050
Tel.: (972) 263-2333   TX
Web Site: http://envirotroldfw.com
Year Founded: 2013
Exterminating & Pest Control Ser-
vices
N.A.I.C.S.: 561710
Heather Ritchie (Owner)
Oscar Ortiz (Dir-Ops & Sls Mgr)

ENVIROWASTE SERVICES
GROUP, INC.

4 SE 1st St 2nd Fl, Miami, FL 33131
Tel.: (305) 637-9665   FL
Web Site:
  http://envirowasteservicesgroup.com
Year Founded: 1998
Sales Range: $1-9.9 Million
Emp.: 95
Environmental Consulting
N.A.I.C.S.: 541620
Rafael Edwardo Barba (Pres)

ENVISAGE INFORMATION
SYSTEMS, LLC

31 Dutch Mill Rd, Ithaca, NY 14850
Tel.: (607) 275-5710   NY
Web Site:
  http://www.envisagesystems.com
Sales Range: $10-24.9 Million
Emp.: 250
Software Development Services

Envisage Information Systems, LLC—(Continued)

N.A.I.C.S.: 541511
Christen Marsenison (VP-Client Svc)
Jon Prescott (VP-Institutional Bus Dev)

ENVISAGE TECHNOLOGIES, LLC

101 W Kirkwood Ave Ste 200, Bloomington, IN 47404
Tel.: (812) 330-7101
Web Site:
http://www.envisagenow.com
Rev.: $2,500,000
Emp.: 27
Custom Computer Programming Services
N.A.I.C.S.: 541511
Ari Vidali (CEO)
Brian R. Beckwith (VP-Strategic Rels)

Subsidiaries:

Guardian Tracking, LLC   (1)
2431 Wildwood Ave, Anderson, IN 46011-1389
Tel.: (765) 621-6764
Web Site: http://www.guardiantracking.com
Software Publisher
N.A.I.C.S.: 513210
Leon Wasilewski (Co-Founder)

ENVISION

2301 S Water St, Wichita, KS 67213
Tel.: (316) 440-1500
Web Site:
https://www.envisionus.com
Rev.: $50,526,273
Emp.: 200
Plastic Bags: Made From Purchased Materials
N.A.I.C.S.: 326111
Michael Epp (Mgr-Professional Education-Envision University & Conference)
Michael J. Monteferrante (Pres & CEO)
Deb Wetta (Dir-Vision Rehabilitation Center)
Lisa Capps (Dir-Dev)
Nikki Freeman (Chief HR Officer & VP)
Jay Allen (CFO & VP)
Shamain Bachman (Dir-Mktg & Education)
Bonnie Cochran (Dir-Support Programs)
Heather Hogan (Sr VP-Foundation & Mission Svcs)
Amy Auberger (Dir-Mental Health Svcs)
Douglas C. Hobbs (Vice Chm)
Greg Klenda (Vice Chm)
Randy Summers (Sec)
Sam Williams (Chm)
Mark Eaton (CFO)

ENVISION BUSINESS CONSULTING, LLC.

1512 Larimer St Ste 710, Denver, CO 80202
Tel.: (720) 399-5060
Web Site: http://www.envision-bc.com
Year Founded: 2008
Sales Range: $10-24.9 Million
Emp.: 20
Management Consulting Services
N.A.I.C.S.: 541611
Robert Novick (Founder & Principal)
Kurtiss Wolf (Mng Partner)
Mark Spoor (VP-Talent Solutions)
Kelly Bolin (VP & Partner-Client)
Alain Paolini (VP & Partner-Client)
Nancy Weingarten (VP & Head-Northeast)

Alan Feldmann (Partner-Client & VP)
Colleen Kasch (CFO)
Peter Kahn (VP-Northeast)

ENVISION CAPITAL GROUP LLC

23422 Mill Creek Dr Ste 200, Laguna Hills, CA 92653
Tel.: (949) 553-9420   CA
Web Site: https://www.envisioncapitalgroup.com
Year Founded: 2007
Sales Range: $10-24.9 Million
Emp.: 25
Equipment Leasing, Loans & Vendor Financing
N.A.I.C.S.: 523150
Brett Allen (CEO)
Jeff Edwards (Pres)

ENVISION CREDIT UNION

440 N Monroe St, Tallahassee, FL 32301
Tel.: (850) 942-9000   FL
Web Site:
https://www.envisioncu.com
Year Founded: 1954
Sales Range: $10-24.9 Million
Emp.: 155
Credit Union Operator
N.A.I.C.S.: 522130
Darryl Worrell (Pres & CEO)
Hollie Maddox (Sr VP-Member Svcs)

ENVISION TECHNOLOGY MARKETING GROUP, INC.

1066 Mitchell Ct, San Jose, CA 95128
Tel.: (408) 246-6465   CA
Web Site:
https://www.wedomarketing.com
Year Founded: 1998
Sales Range: $1-9.9 Million
Emp.: 35
Marketing Consulting Services
N.A.I.C.S.: 541613
Michael Grodin (CEO)

ENVISION TELEPHONY INC.

901 5th Ave Ste 3300, Seattle, WA 98164
Tel.: (206) 225-0800
Web Site:
https://www.envisioninc.com
Year Founded: 1994
Sales Range: $10-24.9 Million
Emp.: 100
Software Developer
N.A.I.C.S.: 541511

ENVISION UNLIMITED

8 S Michigan Ave Ste 1700, Chicago, IL 60603
Tel.: (312) 346-6230   IL
Web Site:
http://www.envisionchicago.org
Year Founded: 1964
Sales Range: $25-49.9 Million
Emp.: 506
Developmental Disability Assistance Services
N.A.I.C.S.: 623210
Dan Durbin (Vice Chm)

ENVISIONIT MEDIA, INC.

153 W Ohio St, Chicago, IL 60654
Tel.: (312) 236-2000
Web Site:
http://www.envisionitmedia.com
Year Founded: 2001
Rev.: $2,000,000
Emp.: 28
Graphic Design Services
N.A.I.C.S.: 541430
David Silverstein (COO)
Keith Solomon (Dir-Integrated Mktg)

Todd Brook (Founder & CEO)
Robert Creek (Exec Dir-Creative)
Jason Goldberg (Exec VP)
Adam Kelsven (Dir-Tech)
Amber Davis (Dir-Creative)
Dan Salganik (Mgr-Digital Project)
Kevin Cassman (Mgr-Product Ops)
Laura Rosseter (Mgr-Production)
Marissa Liesenfelt (Dir-Product Mgmt)
Matthew Elliott (Dir-Acct Svcs)
Megan Porter (Dir-Digital Mktg)
Michael Phillips (Dir-Creative Strategy)
Mike Lesniak (Dir-Art)
Sarah Caputo (COO)

ENVISTA, LLC.

11555 N Meridian St Ste 300, Carmel, IN 46032
Tel.: (317) 208-9100
Web Site:
http://www.envistacorp.com
Year Founded: 2008
Sales Range: $25-49.9 Million
Emp.: 180
Business Services
N.A.I.C.S.: 561499
John Stitz (Sr Mng Partner)
David Eckel (Mng Partner-Tech Svcs)
Robert Grace (VP-Ops Dev)
Davison Schopmeyer (Sr Mng Partner-Supply Chain Svcs)
Mike Kasperski (Mng Partner-Facility Design Build Svcs)
Stephen Craig (Mng Partner-Transportation Solutions & Freight Mgmt)
Michael Ingardia (CTO & Mng Partner)
Dominic McGough (Mng Partner-EMEA Ops)
Jim Barnes (CEO)

ENVIZION MEDICAL INC.

762 W Algonquin Rd, Arlington Heights, IL 60005   IL
Web Site:
https://www.envizionmed.com
Medical Equipment Distr
N.A.I.C.S.: 423450

ENVY LABS, LLC

189 S Orange Ave Ste 2010, Orlando, FL 32801
Tel.: (407) 538-1133
Web Site: http://www.envylabs.com
Sales Range: $1-9.9 Million
Emp.: 30
Web Designer & Developer
N.A.I.C.S.: 541511
Jennifer Borders (Project Mgr)

ENXNET, INC.

PO Box 700514, Tulsa, OK 74170
Tel.: (918) 494-6663   OK
Web Site: https://www.enxnet.com
Year Founded: 1999
EXNT—(OTCBB)
Assets: $110,594
Liabilities: $2,090,563
Net Worth: ($1,979,969)
Earnings: ($161,725)
Fiscal Year-end: 03/31/19
Optical Disc Mfr
N.A.I.C.S.: 334610

ENYE MEDIA, LLC

301 1/2 E Main St, Norman, OK 73069
Tel.: (405) 579-3693
Web Site: http://www.enye.com
Year Founded: 2006
Sales Range: Less than $1 Million
Emp.: 3
Advetising Agency
N.A.I.C.S.: 541810

Wilmari Ruiz (Dir-Ops)
Ricardo Sasaki (Partner)
Robert M. Ruiz (Partner)

ENZYME DEVELOPMENT CORPORATION

505 8th Ave Ste 15th Fl, New York, NY 10018-6505
Tel.: (212) 736-1580
Web Site:
https://www.enzymedevelopment.com
Rev.: $19,854,319
Emp.: 10
Industrial Organic Chemicals
N.A.I.C.S.: 325199

ENZYME ENVIRONMENTAL SOLUTIONS, INC.

6020 Huguenard Rd Fort, Waynetown, IN 46818
Tel.: (260) 399-3837
Agricultural Product Mfr
N.A.I.C.S.: 325311
Timothy J. Bredemeyer (CEO)

ENZYMEBIOSYSTEMS

8440 W Lake Mead Ste 214, Las Vegas, NV 89128
Tel.: (702) 907-0615   NV
Web Site:
http://www.enzymebiosystems.com
Year Founded: 2009
Rev.: $15,000
Assets: $44,249
Liabilities: $4,100
Net Worth: $40,149
Earnings: ($95,793)
Emp.: 3
Fiscal Year-end: 06/30/17
Specialty Enzymes & Enzyme Related Products Mfr
N.A.I.C.S.: 325998
John Dean Harper (Chm, Pres, CEO, Treas & Sec)

ENZYMEDICA, INC.

771 Commerce Dr, Venice, FL 34292
Tel.: (941) 505-5565   FL
Web Site:
http://www.enzymedica.com
Year Founded: 1998
Sales Range: $1-9.9 Million
Emp.: 40
Enzyme Supplement Mfr
N.A.I.C.S.: 325998
Tom Bohager (Founder & Chm-Operating)
Maday Labrador (VP-Education)
Gary Trimble (Exec VP)
Julia Craven (VP-Natl Accts)
Scott Sensenbrenner (Pres & CEO)
Dale Bagby (CFO)
Shane McCombs (CIO)
Kevin Tautkus (Exec VP-Mktg)
Michael Murray (Chief Science Officer)
J. Etson Brandenburg (COO)
Paul Davison (Exec VP-Sls)

EO PRODUCTS

90 Windward Way, San Rafael, CA 94901
Tel.: (415) 945-1900
Web Site: http://www.eoproducts.com
Sales Range: $1-9.9 Million
Emp.: 100
Cosmetics Products Mfr
N.A.I.C.S.: 456120
Shannon McDonough (Mgr-Sls)
Brad Black (Co-CEO)
Jeremy Wilson (Asst Controller)
Susan Griffin-Black (Co-CEO)

EOS AIRLINES, INC.

287 Bowman Ave 4th Fl, Purchase, NY 10577

Tel.: (914) 417-2100
Web Site: http://www.eosairlines.com
Business Class Airline Operator
N.A.I.C.S.: 481111
Gil Morgan *(COO)*

EOS INTERNATIONAL, INC.
199 Elm St, New Canaan, CT 06840
Tel.: (203) 652-2525   NY
Web Site: http://www.eosintl
Year Founded: 1999
Sales Range: $10-24.9 Million
Emp.: 45
Holding Company; Consumer Goods
N.A.I.C.S.: 551112

Subsidiaries:

Discovery Toys, LLC   (1)
3037 Independence Dr Ste G, Livermore,
CA 94551
Tel.: (925) 606-2600
Web Site: http://www.discoverytoys.net
Sales Range: $10-24.9 Million
Emp.: 20
Educational Toys, Books & Software Sales
N.A.I.C.S.: 423920
Jerry R. Salerno *(CEO)*
James Myers *(COO)*
Cindy Fredrickson *(Dir-Ops)*

EOS PARTNERS, L.P.
320 Park Ave 9th Fl, New York, NY
10022
Tel.: (212) 832-5800   DE
Web Site:
    http://www.eospartners.com
Year Founded: 1994
Sales Range: $25-49.9 Million
Emp.: 40
Alternative Investment Firm
N.A.I.C.S.: 523999
Steven M. Friedman *(Mng Partner)*
Brian D. Young *(Mng Partner)*
Brendan M. Moore *(Mng Dir)*
Adam S. Gruber *(Principal)*
Beth L. Bernstein *(CFO & Chief Compliance Officer)*
Matthew J. Stern *(Dir-Acctg)*
Frank C. Moy *(Dir-Trading & Ops)*
Marisa A. Wyatt *(Dir-Compliance)*
Brian MacHale *(Mng Dir)*
David Van Steenkiste *(Principal)*
John Lee *(VP)*
Jay Appel *(Dir-Ops)*
Daniel Friedman *(Mgr-Portfolio)*
Michael Schott *(Mgr-Portfolio)*
Mark L. First *(Mng Dir)*

EOS PETRO, INC.
1999 Ave of the Stars Ste 2520, Los
Angeles, CA 90067
Tel.: (310) 552-1555   NV
Web Site: http://www.eos-petro.com
EOPT—(OTCIQ)
Sales Range: Less than $1 Million
Emp.: 1
Oil & Gas Exploration Services
N.A.I.C.S.: 211120
Nikolas Konstant *(Founder & Chm)*
Alan D. Gaines *(CEO)*

EOS PRODUCTS, LLC
19 W 44th St, New York, NY 10036
Tel.: (212) 929-6367   NY
Web Site:
    http://www.evolutionofsmooth.com
Year Founded: 2007
Emp.: 75
Cosmetic Products Mfr & Distr
N.A.I.C.S.: 456120
Jonathan Teller *(Founder & CEO)*
Soyoung Kang *(CMO)*
Carley Caldas *(VP-Brand Mktg & Media)*
Kelsey Newberry *(Sr Mgr-Brand)*

EOS PUBLISHING, LLC

1620 W Fountainhead Pkwy Ste 219,
Tempe, AZ 85282
Tel.: (480) 348-0343   AZ
Web Site:
    http://www.timespublications.com
Year Founded: 2009
Emp.: 60
Newspaper Publishers
N.A.I.C.S.: 513110
Steve Strickbine *(Pres)*

Subsidiaries:

Ahwatukee Foothills News   (1)
1620 W Fountainhead Pkwy Ste 219,
Tempe, AZ 85282
Tel.: (480) 898-7900
Web Site: http://www.ahwatukee.com
Emp.: 50
Newspaper Publishers
N.A.I.C.S.: 513110
Elaine Cota *(Mgr-Classified)*
Paul Maryniak *(Exec Editor)*
Karen Mays *(Acct Exec)*
Laura Meehan *(Acct Exec)*
Steve Strickbine *(Publr)*
Chuck Morales *(Ops Mgr)*
Aaron Kolodny *(Dir-Circulation)*
Courtney Oldham *(Mgr-Advertising Production)*
Ralph Zubiate *(Mng Editor)*
Erica Odello *(Art Dir)*
Robbie Peterson *(Editor in Chief)*

East Valley Tribune   (1)
1620 W Fountainhead Pkwy Ste 219,
Tempe, AZ 85282
Tel.: (480) 898-6500
Web Site: http://www.eastvalleytribune.com
Newspaper Publishers
N.A.I.C.S.: 513110
Steve Strickbine *(Publr)*
Chuck Morales *(Mgr-Ops)*
Aaron Kolodny *(Dir-Circulation)*
Courtney Oldham *(Production Mgr-Adv)*
Elaine Cota *(Mgr-Classified)*
Paul Maryniak *(Exec Editor)*
Ralph Zubiate *(Mng Editor)*

J.Bee NP Publishing, Ltd.   (1)
30423 Canwood St Ste 108, Agoura Hills,
CA 91301
Tel.: (818) 706-0266
Sales Range: $1-9.9 Million
Emp.: 30
Newspaper Publishers
N.A.I.C.S.: 513110
Jim Rule *(Co-Founder)*
John Loesing *(Mng Editor)*
Lisa Rule *(Co-Founder)*
Nadine Johnson *(Dir-Ops)*

EOSCENE CORPORATION
16300 Christensen Rd Ste 211,
Tukwila, WA 98148
Tel.: (206) 577-7033
Web Site: http://www.eoscene.com
Year Founded: 1998
Sales Range: $1-9.9 Million
Emp.: 10
IT & Data Products
N.A.I.C.S.: 518210
Geoffrey A. Griebel *(Pres & CEO)*
Jeof Griebel *(Chm)*

EP TECHNOLOGY CORPORATION
1401 Interstate Dr Ste B, Champaign,
IL 61822
Tel.: (217) 903-5673
Web Site: https://www.eptco.com
Year Founded: 1997
Sales Range: $10-24.9 Million
Emp.: 50
Digital Security Devices Distr
N.A.I.C.S.: 238210
Kevin Wan *(Pres)*

EP WEALTH ADVISORS, LLC
21515 Hawthorne Blvd Ste 1200, Torrance, CA 90503
Tel.: (310) 543-4559   CA
Web Site: http://www.epwealth.com

Year Founded: 2004
Rev.: $1,900,000,000
Investment Advisory & Wealth Management Services
N.A.I.C.S.: 523940
Patrick P. Goshtigian *(CEO)*
Brian E. Parker *(Co-Founder & Mng Dir)*
Derek H. Holman *(Co-Founder & Mng Dir)*
Cristin Harris Rigg *(Partner & VP)*
Brett Anderson *(Partner & Reg Dir)*
Lauren Klein *(VP)*
Jim Mocci *(Head-Mktg & Mktg Dir)*
Ryan Parker *(Pres-Salt Lake)*
Tom Nguyen *(VP)*
Matthew Kuhn *(Partner & Sr VP)*

Subsidiaries:

Ballou Plum Wealth Advisors,
LLC   (1)
250 Lafayette Cir Ste 203, Lafayette, CA
94549-7602
Tel.: (925) 283-2201
Web Site: http://www.ballouplum.com
Sales Range: $1-9.9 Million
Investment Advisory & Wealth Management
Services
N.A.I.C.S.: 523940
Lynn Ballou *(Co-Founder & Mng Partner)*
Marilyn Plum *(Co-Founder & Dir-Portfolio Mgmt)*

Conlon & Dart LLC   (1)
720 Olive Wy Ste 1000, Seattle, WA 98101
Tel.: (206) 728-0222
Financial Investment Activities
N.A.I.C.S.: 523999

International Research & Asset Management, Inc.   (1)
2301 Cedar Springs Ste 150, Dallas, TX
75201
Tel.: (214) 754-0770
Web Site: http://www.intlresearch.com
Financial Planning
N.A.I.C.S.: 523999

Klein Financial Advisors Inc. (1)
4299 MacArthur Blvd Ste 100, Newport
Beach, CA 92660-2019
Tel.: (949) 477-4990
Web Site: http://www.kleinadvisors.com
Investment Advice
N.A.I.C.S.: 523940
Lauren Klein *(Founder & Pres)*

Newfocus Financial Group LLC   (1)
410 W 12th St, Vancouver, WA 98660-2801
Web Site: http://www.newfocusfinancial.com
Financial Investment Activities
N.A.I.C.S.: 523999
Mikki Burton *(Office Mgr)*
Rob Black *(Co-Founder & Partner)*
Chad Burton *(Co-Founder, Partner & Reg Dir)*

EPARTNERS, INC.
1231 Greenway Dr Ste 200, Irving,
TX 75038
Tel.: (972) 819-2700
Web Site:
    http://www.epartnersolutions.com
Sales Range: $25-49.9 Million
Emp.: 360
Business Consulting Services
N.A.I.C.S.: 541512
Dwayne Gunter *(Gen Mgr-Eastern Region)*
Laurie Tomasovsky *(VP-Ops)*
Fred Shepard *(VP-Fin)*

Subsidiaries:

ePartners, Inc.   (1)
12110 Sunset Hills Rd, Reston, VA 20190
Tel.: (703) 817-1400
Sales Range: $25-49.9 Million
Emp.: 100
Business Services
N.A.I.C.S.: 423430

EPAZZ, INC.

205 W Wacker Dr Ste 1320, Chicago,
IL 60606
Tel.: (312) 955-8161   IL
Web Site: http://www.epazz.com
Year Founded: 1999
Sales Range: $1-9.9 Million
Emp.: 8
Web Portal Software & Services
N.A.I.C.S.: 513210
Shaun Passley *(Chm, Pres, CEO & CFO)*
Raymond Kennedy *(Dir-Sls)*

EPB
10 W Mlking Blvd, Chattanooga, TN
37402
Tel.: (423) 648-1372
Web Site: http://www.epb.net
Year Founded: 1939
Sales Range: $350-399.9 Million
Emp.: 400
Electric Power Distr & Phone Services
N.A.I.C.S.: 221122
Greg Eaves *(CFO & Exec VP)*
L. Joe Ferguson *(Chm)*
Danna Bailey *(VP-Crop Comm)*
David Johnson *(CIO & VP-IT)*
Diana Bullock *(VP-Economic Dev & Govt Rels)*
Jim Ingraham *(VP-Strategic Res)*
Kade Abed *(VP-Field Ops)*
Kathy Burns *(VP-Customer Rels)*
Katie Espeseth *(VP-New Products)*
Marie Webb *(VP-HR)*
Ryan Keel *(VP-Technical Ops)*
Steve Clark *(Sr VP-Strategic Sys)*
David Wade *(Pres & CEO)*
Hodgen Mainda *(VP-Community Dev)*
Warren E. Logan Jr. *(Vice Chm)*

EPCSOLUTIONS
10510 Bech Mill Rd, Great Falls, VA
22066
Tel.: (703) 757-4470
Web Site:
    http://www.epcsolutions.com
Year Founded: 2004
Sales Range: $10-24.9 Million
Emp.: 45
RFID (Radio Frequency Identification
Device) Compliance Software Mfr
N.A.I.C.S.: 513210
Kevil J. Kail *(Owner, CEO & Pres)*
Angela Kail *(Dir-Partner Alliances)*
Mark Wildman *(VP & Chief Strategist-Tech)*

EPEAT, INC.
227 SW Pine St Ste 220, Portland,
OR 97204
Tel.: (503) 279-9383
Web Site:
    https://globalelectronicscouncil.org
Sales Range: $1-9.9 Million
Greener Electronics Global Registry
N.A.I.C.S.: 561499
Sarah O'Brien *(Dir-Stakeholder Engagement)*
Wayne Rifer *(Dir-Res & Solutions)*
Jeff Omelchuck *(Exec Dir-Registry Svcs)*
Scott Davis *(CFO)*
Pamela Brody-Heine *(Dir-Standards Dev Projects)*
Christine Ervin *(Sec)*
Susan Herbert *(Mgr-Conformity Assurance-Ottawa)*
Jonas Allen *(Dir-Mktg)*
Miansheng Wang *(Exec Dir-Greater China)*

EPEC ENGINEERED TECHNOLOGIES
176 Samuel Barnet Blvd, New Bedford, MA 02745-1201

Epec Engineered Technologies—(Continued)

Tel.: (508) 995-5171   **MA**
Web Site: https://www.epectec.com
Year Founded: 1952
Sales Range: $10-24.9 Million
Emp.: 100
Printed Circuit Board Mfr
N.A.I.C.S.: 334412
Edward McMahon (CEO)
Kendall Paradise (Pres)
Bryan Nolan (VP-Sls)
Anton Beck (Mgr-Battery Product)
Chris Perry (Mgr-PCB & Flex Heater Supply Chain)
Paul Tome (Product Mgr-Flex & Rigid Flex)
Steve Goodman (Product Mgr-New User Interface)

Subsidiaries:

EC Fans & Drives, LLC   (1)
174 Duchaine Blvd, New Bedford, MA 02745
Tel.: (508) 996-7400
Web Site: http://www.ecdrives.com
Emp.: 75
Motor & Generator Mfr
N.A.I.C.S.: 335312
Dennis Royal (Mgr-Sls-OEM)
Martyn Powell (Dir-Engrg & European Sls)
Simon M. Gidney (Pres)

EPELICAN.COM, INC.
17302 Daimler St, Irvine, CA 92614
Tel.: (949) 398-2620
Web Site: http://www.jemjem.com
Year Founded: 2014
Sales Range: $25-49.9 Million
Emp.: 37
Online Shopping Services
N.A.I.C.S.: 519290
Jay Kim (Pres & CEO)

EPES CARRIERS INC.
3400 Edgefield Ct, Greensboro, NC 27408
Web Site:
   http://www.epestransport.com
Year Founded: 1931
Sales Range: $75-99.9 Million
Emp.: 1,000
Transportation Services
N.A.I.C.S.: 484121
Alvin M. Bodford (Owner)
John Mock (VP-MIS)
Scott Fulton (Sr VP-Sls)
David Leik (VP-Maintenance)
Brian Moser (VP-Pricing)
Tim Long (VP-Safety)
Melissa Nishan (Dir-Recruiting)
Phil Peck (Pres)
Mike Hamiilton (VP-HR)
Alan Oakley (VP-Dedicated Svcs)

Subsidiaries:

EPES Logistics Services, Inc.   (1)
538 N Regional Rd Ste A, Greensboro, NC 27409-9063
Tel.: (336) 665-1553
Web Site: http://www.epeslogistics.com
Sales Range: $10-24.9 Million
Emp.: 50
Provider of Transportation Logistics Services
N.A.I.C.S.: 488510
Tim Langmeyer (VP-Sls)
Berkley Womack (Acct Exec-Logistics)
Brent Horine (Coord-Logistics)
Jason Bodford (Pres)
Samantha Pullium (Coord-Logistics)
David Rodgers (Dir-Sls)

Subsidiary (Domestic):

Epic Logistics, Inc.   (2)
707 N St, Smithfield, NC 27577-4019   (100%)
Tel.: (919) 934-3448
Web Site: http://www.epiclogistics.com
Emp.: 100

Logistics & Supply Chain Services
N.A.I.C.S.: 541614
Jim Davis (VP-Ops)
Don Sherrill (CEO)

Login Logistics LLC   (2)
1300 Baxter St Ste 355, Charlotte, NC 28204
Tel.: (704) 971-0900
Web Site: http://www.loginlogistics.com
Logistic Services
N.A.I.C.S.: 541614
Anthony De Piante (Gen Mgr)

EPES Transport System, Inc.   (1)
3400 Edgefield Ct, Greensboro, NC 27409-9663   (100%)
Tel.: (336) 668-3358
Web Site: http://www.epestransport.com
Sales Range: $25-49.9 Million
Emp.: 500
Provider of Long Distance Trucking Services
N.A.I.C.S.: 484121
Britt Colley (Pres)
Scott Fulton (Sr VP-Sls)
David Leik (VP-Maintenance)

Epes Freight Management   (1)
538-A N Regional Rd, Greensboro, NC 27409
Tel.: (336) 668-9483
Web Site: http://www.epesfms.com
Logistics Consulting Servies
N.A.I.C.S.: 541614
Greg Stimmell (Sr Project Mgr)
Jennifer Comer (Project Mgr)
Kim Shirley (Project Mgr)
Jessica Covey (Mgr-Bus Dev)

Texas Star Express   (1)
2890 S Goliad St, Rockwall, TX 75032-6536
Tel.: (972) 771-5655
Web Site: http://www.tsexpress.com
Sales Range: $25-49.9 Million
Emp.: 161
Provider of Dry Van Truckload Carrying Services
N.A.I.C.S.: 484121
Yessica Vicente (Supvr-Settlements)
Tamara Anthony (Dir-HR)

EPG CONTROLS, INC.
3140 W 84th St Unit Ste 3, Hialeah, FL 33018
Tel.: (305) 828-2299
Web Site:
   https://www.epgcontrols.com
Year Founded: 2001
Sales Range: $1-9.9 Million
Emp.: 10
Mfr & Designer of Power Transfer Switches, Switchgear & Paralleling Controllers
N.A.I.C.S.: 335313
Paulo Guardia (Pres)

EPHIBIAN INC
3180 N Swan Rd, Tucson, AZ 85712
Tel.: (520) 917-4747
Web Site: https://www.ephibian.com
Year Founded: 1996
Rev.: $6,070,965
Emp.: 50
Computer Software Systems Analysis & Design, Custom
N.A.I.C.S.: 541511
Teri Spencer (Co-Founder, Pres & CEO)
Lee Le Clair (Co-Founder & CTO)
Philip Holton (Co-Founder & COO)

EPHOX
2300 Geng Rd Ste 220, Palo Alto, CA 94303
Tel.: (650) 292-9659
Web Site: http://www.ephox.com
Year Founded: 1999
Rev.: $4,100,000
Emp.: 24
Custom Computer Programming Services
N.A.I.C.S.: 541511

Andrew Roberts (Founder & CEO)
William Roberts (Sec)
Damien Fitzpatrick (Sr Dir-Products)
Tim Thatcher (COO)
Amy Chen (CFO)
Michael Fromin (Dir-Client Svcs)
John Hummelstad (Chm)
Jeff Olson (Sr VP-Sls & Bus Dev)

EPHRAIM MCDOWELL HEALTH, INC.
217 S 3rd St, Danville, KY 40422
Tel.: (859) 239-1000
Web Site: https://www.emhealth.org
Emp.: 1,200
Health Care Srvices
N.A.I.C.S.: 621999
Bill Snapp (CFO & Exec VP)
Ina Glass (VP-Patient Care)
Mark Milner (Chief Nursing Officer & VP-EMH & EMRMC)
Allen White (Chm)
Scott Bottoms (Vice Chm)
John D. Trisler (Treas)
Burt Piper (COO & Exec VP)
Julian Gander (Vice Chm)
Daniel E. McKay (Pres & CEO)

Subsidiaries:

McDowell Home Health Agency   (1)
131 Daniel Dr, Danville, KY 40422
Tel.: (859) 236-8946
Web Site:
   http://www.mcdowellhomehealth.com
Rev.: $2,994,034
Assets: $981,073
Liabilities: $455,711
Net Worth: $525,362
Earnings: ($129,811)
Emp.: 46
Fiscal Year-end: 05/31/2012
Women Healthcare Services
N.A.I.C.S.: 621610
Daron Stewart (CEO)

EPHRICON WEB MARKETING LLC
1096 Assembly Dr Ste 210, Fort Mill, SC 29708
Tel.: (803) 578-9960
Web Site: http://www.ephricon.com
Year Founded: 2003
Sales Range: $1-9.9 Million
Emp.: 8
Internet Marketing Services
N.A.I.C.S.: 541890
Jon Payne (Founder & Pres)

EPI-USE AMERICA
2002 Summit Blvd Ste 825, Atlanta, GA 30319
Tel.: (678) 872-0040
Web Site: https://www.epiuse.com
Year Founded: 1998
Rev.: $28,500,000
Emp.: 1,000
Computer Related Consulting Services
N.A.I.C.S.: 541512
Amanda Badenhorst (Acct Mgr)

EPIC BROADBAND SOLUTIONS
751 Maleta Ln Ste 204, Castle Rock, CO 80108
Tel.: (720) 904-5200
Web Site: http://www.epicbbs.com
Year Founded: 2001
Sales Range: $10-24.9 Million
Emp.: 10
Information Technology Solutions
N.A.I.C.S.: 541519
Edward Thompson (CEO)
Emily Wilcox (Acct Mgr-Natl)

EPIC ETAILERS, LLC

6101 Long Prairie Rd Ste 744, Flower Mound, TX 75028
Tel.: (469) 777-6501
Web Site:
   http://www.beautybyearth.com
Year Founded: 2014
Sales Range: $1-9.9 Million
Emp.: 7
Natural Skin Care Product Distr
N.A.I.C.S.: 424210
Prudence Millsap (Mng Partner)
Ryan Greve (CEO)

EPIC GAMES INC.
620 Crossroads Blvd, Cary, NC 27518
Tel.: (919) 854-0070
Web Site: http://www.epicgames.com
Hobby, Toy & Game Stores
N.A.I.C.S.: 459120
Timothy Sweeney (CEO)

Subsidiaries:

RAD Game Tools, Inc.   (1)
550 Kirkland Way Ste 406, Kirkland, WA 98033
Tel.: (425) 893-4300
Web Site: http://www.radgametools.com
Rev.: $1,917,000
Emp.: 12
Software Publisher
N.A.I.C.S.: 513210
Andre LaMothe (CEO)
Michael Legg (Pres)
Ski Park (Mgr)
Yuichiro Kitao (Program Dir)
Blair Fraser (Dir-Ironclad Games)
Mike Pappas (Pres-Media Magic)
Wyeth Ridgway (Pres & Dir-Technical)

EPIC PERSONNEL PARTNERS LLC
5870 Stoneridge Mall Rd Ste 206, Pleasanton, CA 94588
Tel.: (925) 233-2014
Web Site: http://www.epicpp.com
Year Founded: 2013
Sales Range: $10-24.9 Million
Emp.: 1,211
Recruiting Firm Services
N.A.I.C.S.: 561312
Daniel Flores (VP-On-Site Ops)

EPIC RESINS
600 Industrial Blvd, Palmyra, WI 53156
Tel.: (262) 495-3400
Web Site: https://www.epicresins.com
Sales Range: $25-49.9 Million
Emp.: 40
Plastics Material & Resin Mfr
N.A.I.C.S.: 325211
Jeffrey Sodemann (Dir-Tech)
Jon Zarnstorff (Mgr-Sls)

EPIC SEATS, INC.
900 1st Ave S Ste 110, Seattle, WA 98134
Tel.: (206) 281-7060
Web Site: http://www.epicseats.com
Year Founded: 2003
Sales Range: $1-9.9 Million
Emp.: 17
Online Ticket Marketing Services
N.A.I.C.S.: 541890
James Kimmel (Co-Founder & VP-Ops)
Scott Barrows (Co-Founder & VP-Sls)
Edson Gaylord (Mgr-Consignment Program)
Marci James (Mgr-Ops)
Skye Kent (Office Mgr)

EPIC STORES CORP.
20805 N 19th Ave 2, Phoenix, AZ 85027
Tel.: (855) 636-3742   **NV**

Web Site:
http://www.epicthriftstores.com
Year Founded: 2012
Sales Range: $1-9.9 Million
Emp.: 124
Retail Store Operator
N.A.I.C.S.: 459999
Brian Davidson *(Pres, CEO, Sec & Treas)*
Zachary Bradford *(CFO)*
Bob Riggs *(COO)*

EPIC SYSTEMS CORPORATION
1979 Milky Way, Verona, WI 53593
Tel.: (608) 271-9000
Web Site: https://www.epic.com
Year Founded: 1979
Emp.: 10,000
Software Publisher
N.A.I.C.S.: 513210
Daniel S. Bormann *(Chief Security Officer)*
Stephen J. Dickman *(Chief Admin Officer)*
Carl D. Dvorak *(Exec VP)*
Judith R. Faulkner *(CEO)*
Ken Hansen *(Gen Counsel & VP)*

EPIC SYSTEMS, INC.
4142 Meramec Bottom Rd, Saint Louis, MO 63129
Tel.: (314) 845-0077   MO
Web Site:
http://www.epicsystemsinc.net
Year Founded: 1995
Sales Range: $50-74.9 Million
Emp.: 60
Design, Fabrication & Automation of Modular Process Plants & Machine Vision Inspection Systems
N.A.I.C.S.: 541330
John Schott *(Pres & CEO)*
James Owen *(Gen Mgr)*
Ken Sipes *(Mgr-Process & Mechanical Grp)*

EPIC THEATRES, INC.
1798 S Woodland Blvd, Deland, FL 32720
Tel.: (386) 738-2600   FL
Web Site:
https://www.epictheatres.com
Year Founded: 2003
Sales Range: $1-9.9 Million
Emp.: 55
Motion Picture Theater
N.A.I.C.S.: 512131
Chris Morris *(Office Mgr)*

EPIC WINE & SPIRITS
200 Concourse Blvd, Santa Rosa, CA 95403
Tel.: (844) 824-0422
Web Site: http://www.epic-winesandspirits.com
Beverage Distribution
N.A.I.C.S.: 312130
Bill Foley *(CEO)*

Subsidiaries:

Pacific Wine Distributors   (1)
2393 Buena Vista St, Irwindale, CA 91010-1010
Tel.: (626) 471-9997
Web Site: http://www.pwddelivers.com
Wine & Distilled Alcoholic Beverage Merchant Whslr
N.A.I.C.S.: 424820
John Solomon *(Partner)*

EPICENTER NETWORK INC
3500 188th St SW Ste 480, Lynnwood, WA 98037
Tel.: (425) 744-1474
Web Site: http://www.epicenter.net
Year Founded: 2005

Sales Range: $25-49.9 Million
Emp.: 35
Advertising & Marketing
N.A.I.C.S.: 541810
Smokey Burns *(Co-Founder & CEO)*
Dylan McDanniel *(Co-Founder & COO)*
Andy Kahn *(Dir-Epicenter Denver)*

EPICOSITY
1741 S Cleveland Ave Ste 302, Sioux Falls, SD 57103
Tel.: (605) 275-3742
Web Site: http://www.epicosity.com
Year Founded: 2008
Sales Range: $1-9.9 Million
Emp.: 18
Advetising Agency
N.A.I.C.S.: 541810
Eric Siversten *(CEO)*
Scott Ostman *(Dir-Creative)*
Justin Smorawske *(Partner & CMO)*
Cheryl Elbers *(Dir-Client Rels)*
Jeremy Peters *(Dir-Art)*
Chris Kappen *(Dir-Digital)*
Heather Covrig *(Sr Acct Exec)*
Brandon Henderson *(Acct Mgr)*
Sarah Kolbeck *(Office Mgr)*

EPIKA FLEET SERVICES, INC.
8300 Norman Ctr Dr Ste 160, Bloomington, MN 55437
Tel.: (952) 214-4100
Web Site: https://www.epikafleet.com
Year Founded: 2016
Emp.: 100
Truck Transportation
N.A.I.C.S.: 484121
Glenn Sherburne *(Exec Chm)*

Subsidiaries:

Managed Mobile, Inc.   (1)
901 Nancita Circle, Placentia, CA 92870
Tel.: (714) 633-0251
Web Site: http://www.managedmobile.com
Sales Range: $1-9.9 Million
Emp.: 24
General Automotive Repair Shops, Nsk
N.A.I.C.S.: 811111
Paul Rygalski *(Pres & CEO)*

EPILEPSY FOUNDATION OF AMERICA
8301 Professional Pl, Landover, MD 20785-2353
Tel.: (301) 459-3700   DE
Web Site:
http://www.epilepsyfoundation.com
Year Founded: 1967
Sales Range: $10-24.9 Million
Emp.: 85
Grantmaking Services
N.A.I.C.S.: 813211
Brandy Fureman *(VP-Res & New Therapies)*
Bernice Martin Lee *(Pres & CEO)*
Jeff Parent *(Chm)*

EPILOG CORPORATION
16371 Table Mountain Pkwy, Golden, CO 80403
Tel.: (303) 277-1188
Web Site:
https://www.epiloglaser.com
Year Founded: 1988
Sales Range: $1-9.9 Million
Emp.: 200
Laser Systems Designer & Mfr
N.A.I.C.S.: 333310
Steve Garnier *(Pres)*
Vicki Schwarz *(Mgr-Acctg)*
John Doran *(VP-Engrg)*

EPIPHANY DERMATOLOGY PA
6601 Vaught Ranch Rd Ste 200, Austin, TX 78730
Tel.: (512) 628-0465   TX

Web Site:
http://www.epiphanydermatology.com
Dermatology & Skincare Services
N.A.I.C.S.: 621111
Gheorghe Pusta *(CEO)*
Ted Emmert *(Chief Dev Officer)*
Henriikka Penkki *(VP-Ops)*
Jenna Young *(Dir-HR)*
Ashley Rodriguez *(Dir-Compliance)*

Subsidiaries:

J. Michael Maloney, M.D., P.C.   (1)
3773 Cherry Creek N Dr Ste 970, Denver, CO 80209
Tel.: (303) 388-5629
Web Site:
http://www.epiphanydermatology.com
Freestanding Ambulatory Surgical & Emergency Centers
N.A.I.C.S.: 621493
Jacque Crouse *(Mgr)*

EPIRUS BIOPHARMACEUTICALS, INC.
699 Boylston St 8th Fl, Boston, MA 02116
Tel.: (617) 600-3497   DE
Web Site:
http://www.epirusbiopharma.com
Year Founded: 2000
Sales Range: Less than $1 Million
Emp.: 73
Biopharmaceutical Mfr
N.A.I.C.S.: 325412
Thomas A. Shea *(CFO, Treas & Sr VP)*
Scott M. Rocklage *(CEO)*
Michael Wyand *(Pres & COO)*
Robert Ticktin *(Gen Counsel & Sr VP)*
Nicholas Plumeridge *(Sr VP-Bus Dev-Global & Licensing)*
Suman Patel *(VP-Mfg & Quality)*
Cheryl Lassen *(VP-Clinical Dev)*
Alex Waldron *(VP-Comml Ops-Global)*
Jeff Kagy *(VP-HR & Admin)*

Subsidiaries:

EB Sub, Inc.   (1)
699 Boylston St Ste 11, Boston, MA 02116
Tel.: (617) 600-3497
Pharmaceuticals Product Mfr
N.A.I.C.S.: 325412

Epirus Switzerland GmbH   (1)
Gotthardstrasse 3, 6300, Zug, Switzerland
Tel.: (41) 415521282
Pharmaceuticals Product Mfr
N.A.I.C.S.: 325412
Boris Javelle *(Head-Fin Ops)*

EPISCOPAL CHURCH HOME & AFFILIATES LIFE CARE COMMUNITY INC.
705 Renaissance Dr, Williamsville, NY 14221
Tel.: (716) 929-5800   NY
Year Founded: 1995
Sales Range: $10-24.9 Million
Emp.: 275
Continuing Care Retirement Services
N.A.I.C.S.: 623311
James Juliano *(CFO & VP)*
Robert Wallace *(Pres & CEO)*

EPISCOPAL COMMUNITIES & SERVICES
1111 S Arroyo Pkwy Ste 230, Pasadena, CA 91105
Tel.: (626) 403-5880   CA
Web Site:
http://www.ecsforseniors.org
Year Founded: 1920
Sales Range: $25-49.9 Million
Emp.: 480
Community Welfare Services

N.A.I.C.S.: 624190
Terry Quigley *(COO & VP-Ops)*
Tyra Sherman *(CFO & VP-Fin)*

EPISCOPAL HEALTH FOUNDATION
500 Fannin St Ste 300, Houston, TX 77002
Tel.: (713) 225-0900   TX
Web Site:
https://www.episcopalhealth.org
Year Founded: 2013
Sales Range: $100-124.9 Million
Community Health Care Services
N.A.I.C.S.: 621498
Jo Carcedo *(VP-Grantmaking)*
Brian Sasser *(Dir-Comm)*
Susybelle Gosslee *(Chief Admin Officer)*
Shao-Chee Sim *(VP-Applied Res)*

EPISCOPAL RELIEF & DEVELOPMENT
815 2nd Ave, New York, NY 10017
Tel.: (855) 312-4325   NY
Web Site:
http://www.episcopalrelief.org
Year Founded: 2002
Sales Range: $10-24.9 Million
Emp.: 41
Community Welfare Services
N.A.I.C.S.: 624190
Sean McConnell *(Dir-Engagement)*
Imanuel Afful-Yamoah *(Dir-Fin)*
Esther Cohen *(COO)*
Xerxes Eclipse *(Dir-Donor Svcs)*
Lorraine Elshiekh *(Dir-HR)*
Josephine H. Hicks *(VP-Episcopal Church Programs)*
Malaika Kamunanwire *(Sr Dir-Mktg & Comm)*
Patrick B. Jean *(Mgr-IT)*
Robert W. Radtke *(Pres & CEO)*
Betsy Deisroth *(VP-Advancement)*
Hilary Asii Asiah *(Officer-Program-Ghana Health Partnership)*
Ernest Cajuste *(Officer-Program-Haiti)*
Kellie McDaniel *(Officer-Program)*
Vesta Oduro-Kwarteng *(Officer-Admin)*
Michelle Pinedo *(VP-Fin & Ops)*
Daniel McNeel Lane Jr. *(Chm)*

EPITAPH RECORDS
2798 W Sunset Blvd, Los Angeles, CA 90026
Tel.: (213) 413-7353
Web Site: http://www.epitaph.com
Rev.: $22,197,000
Emp.: 30
Personal Service Agents, Brokers & Bureaus
N.A.I.C.S.: 711410
Barry Reynolds *(Controller)*
Richard Myers *(Chm)*
Tonni Maruyama *(Reg Mgr)*

EPITEC GROUP INC.
24800 Denso Dr Ste 150, Southfield, MI 48033-7464
Tel.: (248) 353-6800
Web Site: https://www.epitec.com
Sales Range: $25-49.9 Million
Emp.: 700
Computer Software Systems Analysis & Design
N.A.I.C.S.: 541511
Josie Sheppard *(CEO)*
Mark Ruma *(COO)*
Tony Hollamon *(Exec VP)*
Rebecca Bray *(Pres)*
Alecia Yezback *(Dir-Fin)*
Michelle Rusch *(Mgr-Delivery)*
Sean Rossiter *(Dir-Sls & Delivery)*

EPKO INDUSTRIES INC.

EPKO Industries Inc.—(Continued)

1200 Arthur Ave, Elk Grove Village,
IL 60007-5706
Tel.: (847) 437-4000   IL
Web Site: http://www.epko.com
Year Founded: 1970
Sales Range: $25-49.9 Million
Emp.: 180
Mfr of Paints & Varnishes
N.A.I.C.S.: 424950
Al Rothschild (Pres)
Mike Glynn (Partner)

EPLAN SERVICES, INC.
4949 S Syracuse St Ste 550, Denver,
CO 80237
Tel.: (303) 830-9070
Web Site:
  http://www.eplanservices.com
Year Founded: 2000
Sales Range: $1-9.9 Million
Emp.: 42
Software
N.A.I.C.S.: 513210
Nanda Lankalapalli (VP-Engrg)

EPM SOLUTIONS, INC.
2440 Camino Ramon Ste 275, San
Ramon, CA 94583
Tel.: (415) 818-2600
Web Site:
  https://www.epmsolutions.com
Year Founded: 2003
Sales Range: $1-9.9 Million
Emp.: 28
Management Consulting Services
N.A.I.C.S.: 541611
Sophia Zhou (Pres & CEO)

EPOCH CORPORATION
RR 106, Pembroke, NH 03275
Tel.: (603) 225-3907
Web Site:
  http://www.epochhomes.com
Year Founded: 1983
Rev.: $11,000,000
Emp.: 40
Modular Homes, Prefabricated, Wood
N.A.I.C.S.: 321992
Douglas E. Basnett (COO)

EPOCH PROPERTIES INC.
359 Carolina Ave Ste 200, Winter
Park, FL 32789
Tel.: (407) 644-9055
Web Site:
  http://www.epochproperties.com
Year Founded: 1970
Sales Range: $10-24.9 Million
Emp.: 35
Multi-Family Dwelling Construction
N.A.I.C.S.: 236116
M. Gregory Jacoby (CFO & Exec VP)
Allyson Chiappa (Dir-Asst Mgmt)
Clay Logue (Dir-IT)
Farley Griner (Dir-Mktg Bus Dev)
Shannon Hayden (Dir-Property Mgmt)
Breana Christiana (Asst Controller)
Graig Ludwig (Project Mgr)
Greg Wosaba (VP-Construction)
J. McCarley Davis (Chief Investment
Officer & Exec VP)
Justin Sand (Pres & COO)
Shawn Maes (Project Mgr)
James H. Pugh Jr. (Chm & CEO)

Subsidiaries:

Epoch Management, Inc.   (1)
359 Carolina Ave Ste 100, Winter Park, FL
32789
Tel.: (407) 644-9055
Web Site: http://www.epochresidential.com
Sales Range: $10-24.9 Million
Emp.: 30
Provider of Real Estate Management Ser-
vices
N.A.I.C.S.: 531311

M. Gregory Jacoby (VP)

EPONK GROUP LTD.
220 N Main St, Shawano, WI 54166
Tel.: (715) 526-5555
Rev.: $11,800,000
Emp.: 25
Paints
N.A.I.C.S.: 424950
Douglas Knope (Pres)

Subsidiaries:

Dearco Distributing Inc.   (1)
1495 E Green Bay St, Shawano, WI 54166
Tel.: (715) 526-2126
Paints
N.A.I.C.S.: 424950

Knope Roofing & Furnace Co.   (1)
634 E Division St, Shawano, WI 54166
Tel.: (715) 524-4215
Sales Range: $10-24.9 Million
Emp.: 12
Sheet Metalwork
N.A.I.C.S.: 238390

EPPINGER MANUFACTURING CO.
6340 Schaefer, Dearborn, MI 48126-
2285
Tel.: (313) 582-3205
Web Site: http://www.eppinger.net
Year Founded: 1906
Sales Range: $1-9.9 Million
Emp.: 13
Fishing Lures Mfr
N.A.I.C.S.: 339920
Karen Eppinger (Pres)
John Cleveland (Mgr-Mktg)

EPPSTEIN UHEN ARCHITECTS, INC.
333 E Chicago St, Milwaukee, WI
53202
Tel.: (414) 271-5350   WI
Web Site: https://www.eua.com
Year Founded: 1980
Sales Range: $1-9.9 Million
Emp.: 100
Architectural Services
N.A.I.C.S.: 541310
Bob Norman (Mgr-HR)
Eric Dufek (Dir-Learning Environ-
ments Studio)
John Chapman (Dir-Studio-Madison)
Gillian Hallock Johnson (Principal)
Greg Uhen (CEO & Mng Partner-
Design)
Rich Tennessen (Pres & Principal)
Rick Burkett (Principal)
Rob Beisenstein (Principal)
Scott Uhen (Principal)
T. J. Morley (Principal)
Paul Stefanski (Dir-Healthcare Stu-
dio)

Subsidiaries:

BurkettEUA   (1)
1899 Wynkoop St Ste 300, Denver, CO
80202
Tel.: (303) 595-4500
Web Site: http://www.burketteua.com
Sales Range: $1-9.9 Million
Emp.: 27
Architectural, Planning & Interior Design
Services
N.A.I.C.S.: 541410
Catherine Quintero (Principal)
Kitty Yuen (Principal)

EPROMOS PROMOTIONAL PRODUCTS, INC.
120 Broadway Ste 1360, New York,
NY 10271-1413
Tel.: (212) 286-8008   DE
Web Site: http://www.epromos.com
Year Founded: 1998
Sales Range: $10-24.9 Million
Emp.: 82

Online Promotional Products Distr
N.A.I.C.S.: 541820
Cydney Reuter (Mgr-Sls)

EPROPERTYSITES, LLC
2711 Aliso Creek Rd Ste 155, Aliso
Viejo, CA 92656
Tel.: (949) 328-5000
Web Site:
  http://www.epropertysites.com
Sales Range: $1-9.9 Million
Emp.: 14
Real Estate Management Services
N.A.I.C.S.: 531210
Greg Mazurek (Pres)

EPS CORP.
78 Apple St, Tinton Falls, NJ 07724
Tel.: (732) 747-8277
Web Site: https://www.epscorp.com
Year Founded: 1983
Sales Range: $75-99.9 Million
Emp.: 87
Defense Contractor & Telecommuni-
cations
N.A.I.C.S.: 541690
Francesco A. Musorrafiti (Founder)
Antoinette M. Musorrafiti (Chm, Pres
& CEO)
John E. Gagliano (COO, Gen Coun-
sel & Exec VP)
Susan M. Moran (CFO & Sr VP)
Kelley A. Meritzis (VP-HR)
Lawrence A. Relyea (VP-Strategic
Capture & Proposal Dev Support)
B. Allen Armstrong (CTO & Exec VP)
Pushpa B. Merchant (Sr VP & Gen
Mgr-Info Mgmt Solutions)
Bruce A. Brooke (Sr VP-Bus & Cap-
ture Dev)

Subsidiaries:

EPS Corp   (1)
2111 Thomas Dr Ste 5, Panama City
Beach, FL 32408   (100%)
Tel.: (850) 588-5145
Web Site: http://www.epscorp.com
Maritime Solution Information Technology
Training Fielding & Logistics Services
N.A.I.C.S.: 541690
B. Allen Armstrong (CTO & Exec VP)

EPS SETTLEMENTS GROUP INC.
5613 DTC Pkwy Ste 700, Greenwood
Village, CO 80111
Tel.: (303) 337-0400
Web Site: http://epssg.com
Year Founded: 1973
Emp.: 151
Insurance Claim Adjustment Services
N.A.I.C.S.: 524291
Joseph Costello (CEO)
Tammy Aminian (Mgr-Client Svcs)
Brad Cantwell (Pres)
Ann Taibo (Case Mgr)
Diane Morris (Case Mgr)
Ryan Jandreau (VP-Bus Dev)

EPSILON SYSTEMS SOLUTIONS
9242 Lightwave Ave, San Diego, CA
92123
Tel.: (619) 702-1700
Web Site:
  http://www.epsilonsystems.com
Year Founded: 1998
Sales Range: $10-24.9 Million
Emp.: 100
Marine, Industrial, Energy, Environ-
mental & Applied Technology Ser-
vices
N.A.I.C.S.: 541330
Bryan B. Min (Founder & CEO)
Grady Petty (Sr VP & Gen Mgr-
Nuclear Ops & Environmental Mgmt)
Paul Cassani (Pres-Technical Svcs
Grp)

EPSTEIN BECKER & GREEN, P.C.
250 Park Ave, New York, NY 10177-
1211
Tel.: (212) 351-4500
Web Site: http://www.ebglaw.com
Year Founded: 1973
Sales Range: $125-149.9 Million
Emp.: 501
Legal Advisory Services
N.A.I.C.S.: 541110
Mark E. Lutes (Chm)
William J. Milani (Partner)
Robert G. Chervenak (CFO)
Carmine A. Iannaccone (Mng Dir)
James P. Flynn (Gen Counsel)
Steven Di Fiore (COO)
Amanda L. Schneider (Chief Plng
Officer)
Lance N. Rea (CIO)
Patricia M. Wagner (Chief Privacy
Officer)

EPTING DISTRIBUTORS INC.
300 Industrial Dr, Lexington, SC
29072
Tel.: (803) 356-9899
Web Site:
  http://www.insideairsolutions.com
Sales Range: $10-24.9 Million
Emp.: 88
Warm Air Heating & Air Conditioning
Equipment & Supplies Whslr
N.A.I.C.S.: 423730
Susan Walters (Controller)

EPTURA, INC.
950 E Paces Ferry Road NE Suite
800, Atlanta, GA 30326
Tel.: (617) 227-2508
Web Site: https://eptura.com
Year Founded: 2019
Emp.: 1,000
Integrated Workplace Management
Software Solutions
N.A.I.C.S.: 513210
Brandon Holden (CEO)

Subsidiaries:

Serraview Australia Pty Ltd   (1)
Level 4 419-425 Collins Street, Melbourne,
3000, VIC, Australia
Tel.: (61) 1300885671
Web Site: http://serraview.com
Workplace Management & Optimization
Software
N.A.I.C.S.: 513210

Subsidiary (US):

ARCHIBUS, Inc.   (2)
9350 E 150 Ste 650, Sandy, UT 84070
Tel.: (617) 227-2508
Web Site: http://www.archibus.com
Custom Computer Programming Services
N.A.I.C.S.: 541511

EQ INDIANA AUTO & TRUCK AUCTION INC.
4425 W Washington Center Rd, Fort
Wayne, IN 46818
Tel.: (260) 489-2776
Web Site:
  https://www.indianaautoauction.net
Rev.: $71,400,000
Emp.: 250
Automobile & Other Motor Vehicle
Merchant Whslr
N.A.I.C.S.: 423110
Lisa Autenrieth (Mgr-HR)

EQ1 GIVES, INC.
1762 Technology Dr Ste 106, San
Jose, CA 95110
Tel.: (408) 912-7670
Web Site:
  http://www.eq1realestate.com
Year Founded: 2013

Sales Range: $1-9.9 Million
Real Estate Services
N.A.I.C.S.: 531390
Mike Bui *(Pres & CEO)*
Alvaro Nevarez *(VP-Ops)*
Marlo Ibon *(VP-Bus Dev)*
Naomi Neven *(Mgr-Mktg)*
Carmen Empringham *(Mgr-Admin)*

EQUAL EARTH CORP.

2750 Womble Rd Ste 101, San Diego, CA 92106
Tel.: (800) 791-0981
Web Site:
    http://www.equalearthcorp.com
Year Founded: 2013
Renewable Energy Solutions
N.A.I.C.S.: 221114
Andrew Duggan *(Chm, Pres, CEO & CIO)*
Ben Greet *(Sr VP-Sls & Acq)*
Howie Reed *(Sr VP-Ops)*

Subsidiaries:

Kolona Painting & General Construction, Inc.   (1)
PO Box 4189, Waianae, HI 96792
Tel.: (808) 695-0022
Web Site: http://www.kolonahawaii.com
Painting, Waterproofing & General Construction Services
N.A.I.C.S.: 238320
Blake Kolona *(Pres)*

EQUAL ENTERTAINMENT LLC

934 SE 9th Ave Ste 11, Paloma Beach, FL 33062
Tel.: (323) 828-1946   FL
Emp.: 100
Media Services
N.A.I.C.S.: 541840

Subsidiaries:

Pride Media Inc.   (1)
PO Box 2660, New York, NY 10108
Tel.: (212) 242-8100
Web Site: http://www.pridemedia.com
Emp.: 100
Media Services
N.A.I.C.S.: 541840
Jamie Tredwell *(Mng Dir-Brand Partnerships)*

EQUAL JUSTICE WORKS

1730 M St NW Ste 1010, Washington, DC 20036-4511
Tel.: (202) 466-3686   DC
Web Site:
    http://www.equaljusticeworks.org
Year Founded: 1986
Sales Range: $10-24.9 Million
Emp.: 41
Law firm
N.A.I.C.S.: 541110
Jeanne Van Vlandren *(COO)*
David Stern *(Exec Dir)*
Yvonne Vargas-Santos *(Mgr-Ops)*
Kristen Uhler-McKeown *(Dir-Public Programs)*
Sarah Lackritz *(Dir-Mktg & Comm)*

EQUALIZERCM

5910 Courtyard Dr Ste 350, Austin, TX 78731
Web Site: http://equalizercm.com
Emp.: 900
Revenue Cycle Management Services
N.A.I.C.S.: 541690
Nagi Rao *(Chm)*
Michael Hill *(Pres)*

Subsidiaries:

The MYR Corporation   (1)
2610 W Horizon Rdg Pkwy Ste 205, Henderson, NV 89052-2870
Tel.: (702) 407-8241
Web Site: http://www.themyrcorporation.com

Third Party Administration of Insurance & Pension Funds
N.A.I.C.S.: 524292
Simizas Vuthoori *(Founder)*

EQUALS THREE COMMUNICATIONS

7910 Woodmont Ave Ste 200, Bethesda, MD 20814-3015
Tel.: (301) 656-3100
Year Founded: 1984
Sales Range: $10-24.9 Million
Emp.: 12
N.A.I.C.S.: 541810
Eugene M. Faison *(Chm & CEO)*
Demetrius Goosbey *(Dir-Creative)*

EQUATERRA, INC.

3 Riverway Ste 1290, Houston, TX 77056
Tel.: (713) 470-9812
Rev.: $11,000,000
Emp.: 160
Computer Software Consulting Services
N.A.I.C.S.: 541512
Mark Toon *(CEO)*
Kelly Enos *(CFO)*

EQUIBASE COMPANY LLC

821 Corporate Dr, Lexington, KY 40503-2794
Web Site: http://www.equibase.com
Racetracks
N.A.I.C.S.: 711212
Jack Wilson *(Pres & COO)*
Chris Dawahare *(VP-Data Ops & Dev)*
Stephen Hill *(Mgr-Adv Ops)*
Rhonda Norby *(Dir-Mktg & Comm)*
David Siegel *(CEO)*
Tom Roentz *(Dir-Track & Field)*
Jim Vanderbosch *(VP-Sls & Mktg)*
Greg Robinson *(Mgr-Programming & Bus Support)*
Katja Spencer *(Mgr-Ops)*
Kelley Kraeszig *(VP-Bus Ops & Admin)*

Subsidiaries:

Axcis Information Network Inc.   (1)
821 Corp Dr, Lexington, KY 40503
Tel.: (650) 316-1020
Web Site: http://www.trackmaster.com
Horse Racing Products & Services
N.A.I.C.S.: 711212
Greg Robinson *(Mgr-Acctg)*
Jim Vanderbosch *(VP-Sls & Mktg)*
David Siegel *(Pres & CEO)*
Craig Walker *(Mgr-Customer Svc)*

EQUIFLOR CORPORATION

1500 NW 95 Ave, Miami, FL 33172
Tel.: (305) 594-4445
Web Site: http://www.rioroses.com
Rev.: $22,000,000
Emp.: 39
Flowers, Fresh
N.A.I.C.S.: 424930
Jorge Velarde *(Mgr)*

EQUILAR

1100 Marshall St, Redwood City, CA 94063-2595
Tel.: (650) 241-6600
Web Site: https://www.equilar.com
Year Founded: 2001
Sales Range: $10-24.9 Million
Emp.: 50
Internet Service Providers & Web Search Portals
N.A.I.C.S.: 517810
David Chun *(Founder & CEO)*
Jiunn Lim *(VP-Engrg)*
Ed Kam *(VP-Fin & Admin)*
Jesse MacNish *(VP-Tech)*
Belen Gomez *(Dir-Res & Content)*

Jamie Tassa *(Dir-Strategic Partnerships & Events)*
Song Huang *(VP-Products & Engrg)*

EQUILEASE HOLDING CORP.

50 Washington St Fl 10, Norwalk, CT 06854
Tel.: (203) 354-3654
Web Site: http://northmillef.com
Rev.: $121,500,000
Equipment Rental & Leasing
N.A.I.C.S.: 532490
Gary N. Silverhardt *(Pres & CEO)*
Michael Zwick *(Exec VP)*
Geoff Minsky *(Sr VP)*

Subsidiaries:

Eq Corp.   (1)
50 Washington St Ste 1211, Norwalk, CT 06854
Tel.: (203) 354-3654
Rev.: $55,152,800
Emp.: 1
Consumer Finance Companies
N.A.I.C.S.: 522291

Equilease Financial Services   (1)
50 Washington St Fl 10, Norwalk, CT 06854
Tel.: (203) 354-3654
Web Site: http://www.eqfsdirect.com
Rev.: $3,500,000
Emp.: 5
Personal Credit Institutions
N.A.I.C.S.: 522291
Gary Silverhardt *(Pres)*
Scott Dunn *(Controller)*

EQUILIBRIUM CAPITAL MANAGEMENT LLC

555 Clay St, San Francisco, CA 94111
Tel.: (415) 398-9401
Web Site: http://www.eq-grp.com
Investments & Open-End Investment Funds
N.A.I.C.S.: 523999
Jay Pierrepont *(COO)*
Noel Kullavanijaya *(Head-Distr & Sls)*
David Chen *(CEO)*
Marie Jorajuria *(Head-Fin & Compliance)*
Bill Campbell *(Head-Structuring & Sustainability)*

EQUINOX BUSINESS SOLUTIONS

1293 W 2200 S Ste A, West Valley City, UT 84119
Tel.: (800) 533-4230
Web Site:
    http://www.equinoxbusiness.com
Year Founded: 1998
Sales Range: $75-99.9 Million
Emp.: 145
Tax & Payroll, Fuel Analysis, Bookkeeping & Consulting Services
N.A.I.C.S.: 541213
Colton Lawrence *(Pres)*
Shannon Garlick *(VP-Bus Dev)*
Kathleen Lowther *(VP)*
Scott Christensen *(VP-Tax Svcs)*

EQUIPCO INC.

1889 Mayview Rd, Bridgeville, PA 15017
Tel.: (412) 221-2800   PA
Web Site: http://www.equipco.com
Year Founded: 1982
Rev.: $28,000,000
Emp.: 100
Industrial Machinery & Equipment
N.A.I.C.S.: 423830
Carl Swanson *(Owner)*

EQUIPMENT & CONTROLS, INC.

2 Park Dr, Lawrence, PA 15055-0614
Tel.: (724) 746-3700   PA

Web Site:
    http://www.equipmentandcontrols.com
Year Founded: 1956
Emp.: 275
Industrial Process Controls Whslr & Engineering Repair Services
N.A.I.C.S.: 423830
Dale Robertson *(CFO)*
Don Churchill *(VP-Fisher Valve & Regulator Bus Unit)*
Bob Tracy *(VP-Sls)*
Armando Ocando *(VP-Sys & Reliability)*
Dan Smith *(Pres)*

EQUIPMENT & SYSTEMS FOR THE INDUSTRY

71 S St, Hopkinton, MA 01748
Tel.: (508) 435-9400
Web Site:
    http://www.equipmentsystems.com
Sales Range: $25-49.9 Million
Emp.: 20
Engineer Technology
N.A.I.C.S.: 423830
Les L. Bebchick *(Pres)*

EQUIPMENT INC.

2309 Hwy 80 W, Jackson, MS 39204
Tel.: (601) 948-3272
Web Site:
    http://www.equipmentinc.com
Rev.: $13,842,836
Emp.: 50
Materials Handling Machinery
N.A.I.C.S.: 423830
Chuck Snatka *(Controller)*

EQUIPSYSTEMS, LLC.

117 E 55th St, New York, NY 10022
Tel.: (212) 331-7890
Web Site:
    https://www.equipsystems.com
Sales Range: $1-9.9 Million
Emp.: 30
Industrial Equipment Repair & Maintenance Services
N.A.I.C.S.: 811310
Chris Wilkerson *(Pres)*

EQUIPTO ELECTRONICS CORP.

351 Woodlawn Ave, Aurora, IL 60506-9988
Tel.: (630) 897-4691
Web Site:
    https://www.equiptoelec.com
Rev.: $12,584,000
Emp.: 40
Electronic Enclosures, Stamped Or Pressed Metal
N.A.I.C.S.: 332119
Gary Michelson *(Treas)*
Praveen Pothapragada *(Pres)*

EQUIS STAFFING

27001 Agoura Rd Ste 160, Calabasas, CA 91301
Tel.: (818) 444-0100
Web Site:
    https://www.equisdifference.com
Sales Range: $1-9.9 Million
Emp.: 5
Professional Staffing Services
N.A.I.C.S.: 561320
Carrie Nebens *(Pres)*

EQUISOFT INC.

1835 Market St Ste 2910, Philadelphia, PA 19103
Tel.: (267) 223-6241
Web Site: http://www.equisoft.com
Year Founded: 1994
Business Internet & Software Services
N.A.I.C.S.: 561499

EquiSoft Inc.—(Continued)

Luis Romero (Founder & CEO)
Steeve Michaud (COO & VP)
Nicolas Ledoux (Sr Dir-IT Infrastruc-
ture)
Shawn Gillespie (Mgr-Bus Dev-
Wealth Mgmt Solutions)
Jonathan Georges (VP-Wealth Mgmt
Solutions)
David P. Nicolai (VP-Insurance
Solutions-USA)
Emilio B. Imbriglio (Chm)

Subsidiaries:

Universal Conversion
Technologies   (1)
1701 W Northwest Hwy Ste 100, Grape-
vine, TX 76051
Tel.: (972) 717-5690
Web Site: http://www.uctcorp.com
Sales Range: $1-9.9 Million
Emp.: 35
Software & Total Data Conversion & Migra-
tion Solutions
N.A.I.C.S.: 513210
Dan O'Hara (CEO)
Rae Albertini (Pres)
Christopher Moroz (Dir-Sls)

**EQUISOURCE HOTEL FUND I,
LLP**
2009 E Windmill Ln, Las Vegas, NV
89123
Tel.: (702) 240-0977
Real Estate Investment Services
N.A.I.C.S.: 523999
Andrew Jolley (CEO)

**EQUITABLE FINANCIAL LIFE
INSURANCE COMPANY**
1290 Avenue of the Americas, New
York, NY 10104
Tel.: (212) 554-1234   NY
Web Site: http://equitable.com
Year Founded: 1859
Rev.: $8,126,000,000
Assets: $227,635,000,000
Liabilities: $229,095,000,000
Net Worth: ($1,460,000,000)
Earnings: $1,186,000,000
Emp.: 4,000
Fiscal Year-end: 12/31/22
Financial Investment Services
N.A.I.C.S.: 523940
Mark Pearson (CEO)
Ramon de Oliveira (Chm)
Michael Healy (CIO)
Jeffrey J. Hurd (COO)
Steve M. Joenk (Chief Investment
Officer)
Nick Lane (Pres)
Hillary Menard (Chief Innovation &
Design Officer)
Steve Scanlon (Head-Individual Re-
tirement)
Mark Pearson (CEO)
Jessica Baehr (Head-Grp Retirement)
Darryl W. Gibbs (Chief Diversity Offi-
cer)
Meredith Ratajczak (Chief Actuary)
Gina Tyler (Chief Comm Officer)
Connie Weaver (CMO)
Christy Chandler (Head)
Jose Ramon Gonzalez (Chief Legal
Officer)
Hector Martinez (Head)
Kurt Meyers (Deputy Gen Counsel)
Yun Zhang (Treas)

**EQUITABLE LIFE & CASU-
ALTY INSURANCE COMPANY**
PO Box 2460, Salt Lake City, UT
84110
Tel.: (801) 579-3400
Web Site: http://www.equilife.com
Year Founded: 1935

Sales Range: $10-24.9 Million
Emp.: 140
Direct Life Insurance Services
N.A.I.C.S.: 524113
E. Rod Ross (Chm & CEO)

**EQUITABLE MINERAL & DE-
VELOPMENT INC.**
4440 S Piedras Dr Ste 136, San An-
tonio, TX 78228
Tel.: (210) 468-5356   DE
Year Founded: 2020
Oil & Natural Gas Exploration Ser-
vices
N.A.I.C.S.: 211130
Timothy Austin Gard (Founder, Chm,
Pres, CEO, Treas & Sec)
(1)

**EQUITABLE SAVINGS & LOAN
ASSOCIATION**
221 N 3rd St, Sterling, CO 80751-
1726
Tel.: (970) 522-6522
Web Site: https://www.equitable-
savings.com
Year Founded: 1954
Sales Range: $25-49.9 Million
Emp.: 55
Federal Savings & Loan Association
N.A.I.C.S.: 522180
Donald M. Koenig Jr. (Pres & CEO)

**EQUITY CAPITAL MANAGE-
MENT, LLC**
200 W Madison Ste 3250, Chicago,
IL 60606
Tel.: (312) 827-2270   MD
Web Site: http://www.ecm-funds.com
Sales Range: $25-49.9 Million
Emp.: 20
Real Estate Investment Services
N.A.I.C.S.: 525990
Shelby E.L. Pruett (Chm & CEO)
James G. Koman (Pres)

**EQUITY CONCEPTS REALTY
CORP.**
9894 Rosemont Ave 202, Lone Tree,
CO 80124
Tel.: (303) 721-7070
Sales Range: $10-24.9 Million
Emp.: 2
Real Estate Agents & Managers
N.A.I.C.S.: 531210
Les N. Johnson (Pres)
Ann Johnson (Sec)

**EQUITY COOP LIVESTOCK
SALES ASSOCIATION**
401 Commerce Ave, Baraboo, WI
53913
Tel.: (608) 356-8311
Web Site: http://www.equitycoop.com
Year Founded: 1922
Sales Range: $500-549.9 Million
Emp.: 250
Cattle Sales
N.A.I.C.S.: 424520
Charles Adami (Pres & CEO)
David Johnson (VP-Mktg-Sheep,
Goats & Calves)
Gary Williams (VP-Credit Svcs)
Perry Wolff (Mgr-Market Ops)
Clint Kroening (Mgr-Field Ops)

EQUITY INVESTMENT GROUP
111 E Wayne St Ste 500, Fort
Wayne, IN 46802
Tel.: (260) 426-4704
Web Site:
http://www.equityinvestment
group.com
Sales Range: $100-124.9 Million
Emp.: 20

Provider of Commercial & Industrial
Building Services
N.A.I.C.S.: 531120
George B. Huber (Pres)
Dennis Callison (Dir-Acq)

EQUITY LOANS LLC.
5 Concourse Pkwy Queen Bldg Ste
2250, Atlanta, GA 30328
Tel.: (678) 205-3554
Web Site:
http://www.equityprime.com
Year Founded: 2008
Sales Range: $10-24.9 Million
Emp.: 400
Mortgage Lending Services
N.A.I.C.S.: 522310
K. P. Patel (CEO)
Eddy Perez (Pres)
David Abrahamson (Exec VP-Ops)
Carlos Martinez (Mgr-Rockville)

**EQUITY TRANSPORTATION
CO.**
3685 Dykstra Dr NW, Grand Rapids,
MI 49544
Tel.: (616) 785-3800   MI
Web Site: http://www.equityinc.com
Year Founded: 1981
Sales Range: $10-24.9 Million
Emp.: 136
Provider of Transportation Services
N.A.I.C.S.: 484121
Chad Bishop (VP-Ops)
Lea Picardy (CFO)
Jason Harris (Dir-Ops)
Kevin Ruiter (Mgr-Warehouse)

EQUITY TRUST COMPANY
1 Equity Way, Westlake, OH 44145
Tel.: (440) 366-3756   SD
Web Site: https://www.trustetc.com
Year Founded: 2002
Rev.: $25,000,000,000
Security Brokers
N.A.I.C.S.: 523150
Richard Desich (Co-Founder & Chm)
Jeffrey Desich (Vice Chm)
Richard A. Desich (Co-Founder)
George E. Sullivan (CEO)
Mike Dea (Pres)
Renee Brown (Sr VP-Client Experi-
ence & Analytics)
Matt Gardner (CFO)
Frank Flanagan (CIO)
Casey Roberts (Chief Bus Dev Offi-
cer)

Subsidiaries:

Sterling Trust Company   (1)
7901 Fish Pond Rd, Waco, TX
76710-1013   (100%)
Tel.: (254) 751-1505
Web Site:
http://www.sterlingtrustcompany.com
Trust Company
N.A.I.C.S.: 525920

EQUITY, INC.
4653 Trueman Blvd Ste 100, Hilliard,
OH 43026
Tel.: (614) 802-2900   OH
Web Site: https://www.equity.net
Year Founded: 1989
Sales Range: $1-9.9 Million
Emp.: 100
Development, Construction, Broker-
age & Property Management Ser-
vices
N.A.I.C.S.: 236220
Steve Wathen (CEO)
Hamish Williams (Dir-Brokerage
Svcs-Southeast)
Phil Drake (VP)
Jerry Hall (Sr VP)
Aaron Heath (Dir-Real Estate Svcs-
Brokerage & Retail)

Tom Rocco (Gen Counsel)
Craig Schneider (VP)
Patrick Wathen (Sr VP)

EQUITY38, LLC
75 14th St NE Ste 2700, Atlanta, GA
30309
Tel.: (404) 844-5385
Web Site: http://www.equity38.com
Privater Equity Firm
N.A.I.C.S.: 523999
Brent Leffel (Co-Founder & Mng
Partner)

EQUITYMETRIX
Galleria N Tower II 13727 Noel Rd
Ste 750, Dallas, TX 75240
Tel.: (214) 442-1555
Web Site:
http://www.equitymetrix.com
Year Founded: 2003
Sales Range: $1-9.9 Million
Emp.: 60
Data Management & Revenue Re-
covery Services
N.A.I.C.S.: 518210
Thomas J. Agnew (Co-Founder &
Co-CEO)
F. Del Agnew (Co-Founder & Co-
CEO)
Casey Ragan (Atty)

**EQUUS CAPITAL PARTNERS,
LTD.**
Ellis Preserve at Newtown Sq 3843
W Chester Pike, Newtown Square,
PA 19073
Tel.: (610) 355-3200   PA
Web Site:
https://www.equuspartners.com
Rev.: $4,500,000,000
Private Equity Fund Real Estate Man-
ager
N.A.I.C.S.: 523999
Joseph I. Neverauskas (Sr VP-Acq)
Daniel M. DiLella (Pres & CEO)
Barry Howard (Chief Compliance Offi-
cer & Exec VP)
Arthur P. Pasquarella (COO & Exec
VP)
Robert K. Maloney (CFO)
Stephen M. Spaeder (Sr VP-Acq &
Dev)
Loretta M. Kelly (Gen Counsel)
Roy C. Perry (Sr VP-Acq)
Christopher J. Locatell (Sr VP-
Dispositions)
Joseph G. Nahas Jr. (Sr VP-
Institutional Mktg & IR)

Subsidiaries:

Madison Apartment Group, LP   (1)
1500 Market St, Philadelphia, PA 19102
Tel.: (215) 606-0600
Web Site:
http://www.madisonapartmentgroup.com
Sales Range: $10-24.9 Million
Emp.: 50
Residential Property Lessor & Manager
N.A.I.C.S.: 531110
Joseph Mullen (Pres & CEO)
Dean Holmes (COO)
Megan Hall (Mgr-HR)
Steve Pogarsky (Sr VP-Acq)
Greg Curci (Exec VP)
Allison Strickland (Coord-Trng Div)
Cathy Sanchez (Reg VP)
Kelly Rowley (Dir-Natl Trng)
Maggie Swartz (Coord-Trng Div)
Scott Gilpatrick (Sr VP-Ops)
Stacie Sines (Dir-Mktg Div)
Terri Sherrod (Dir-Natl Mktg)
Carrie Pistone (Mgr-Revenue)

EQUUS GROUP, LLC
1225 Franklin Ave Ste 325, Garden
City, NY 11530
Tel.: (516) 512-8957

Web Site: https://www.equusllc.com
Year Founded: 2006
Sales Range: $25-49.9 Million
Emp.: 30
Supply Chain Advisory Services
N.A.I.C.S.: 561439
John L. Brendle *(Partner)*
Deep R. Parekh *(Partner)*
Steven Laiss *(Partner)*
Tony Verlezza *(Assoc Partner)*
Eduardo Vecchi *(Assoc Partner)*
Martin J. Jarvis *(Partner)*

EQUUS HOLDINGS, INC.
7725 Washington Ave S, Edina, MN 55439
Tel.: (952) 683-7900   MN
Web Site: http://www.eqh.com
Year Founded: 2008
Holding Company
N.A.I.C.S.: 551112
Andy S. Juang *(Founder)*
Rick Green *(CEO)*
Diane Cooke *(Chief HR Officer)*
Jake Pomplun *(CMO)*

Subsidiaries:

Equus Computer Systems, Inc.   **(1)**
7725 Washington Ave S, Edina, MN 55439
Tel.: (612) 617-6200
Web Site: http://www.equuscs.com
Sales Range: $25-49.9 Million
Emp.: 300
Computer Systems Mfr
N.A.I.C.S.: 423430
Andy S. Juang *(Founder & Chm)*
Dave Guzzi *(CEO)*
Lee Abrahamson *(CTO & VP)*

Subsidiary (Domestic):

Servers Direct, LLC   **(2)**
20480 E Business Pkwy, City of Industry, CA 91789
Tel.: (909) 839-6600
Web Site: http://www.serversdirect.com
Emp.: 70
Online Custom Configured Server & Electronic Storage Device Mfr
N.A.I.C.S.: 334112
Samuel Chuang *(VP-Sls & Mktg-Online)*

Rimage Corporation   **(1)**
7725 Washington Ave S, Minneapolis, MN 55439
Tel.: (952) 683-7900
Web Site: http://www.rimage.com
Emp.: 40
Digital Information Disc Publisher
N.A.I.C.S.: 513199
Christopher Rence *(Pres & CEO)*

Subsidiary (Non-US):

Rimage Europe GmbH   **(2)**
Albert Einstein Strasse 26, 63128, Dietzenbach, Germany
Tel.: (49) 6074 8521500
Web Site: http://www.rimage.de
Sales Range: $50-74.9 Million
Emp.: 20
Compact Disc Writer Mfr
N.A.I.C.S.: 512250
Frank Rotermund *(Mng Dir)*

Rimage Japan Co., Ltd.   **(2)**
2F WIND Bldg 7 4 8 Roppongi, Minato ku, Tokyo, 106 0032, Japan
Tel.: (81) 3 5771 7181
Web Site: http://www.rimage.co.jp
Sales Range: $50-74.9 Million
Compact Disc Writer Mfr
N.A.I.C.S.: 334118
Yoshi Oyamada *(VP-Bus Dev)*

EQUUS SOFTWARE, LLC
1331 17th St Ste 515, Denver, CO 80202
Tel.: (303) 292-4200   CO
Web Site: http://www.equusoft.com
Year Founded: 1999
Sales Range: $1-9.9 Million
Emp.: 18
Software Developer

N.A.I.C.S.: 513210
Mark Thomas *(CEO)*
Daniel Turbert *(Dir-Client Svcs)*

ER MARKETING
512 Delaware St, Kansas City, MO 64105-1100
Tel.: (816) 471-1400   MO
Web Site: http://www.ermarketing.net
Year Founded: 2001
Sales Range: $1-9.9 Million
Emp.: 11
Advetising Agency
N.A.I.C.S.: 541810
Renae Gonner *(Co-Founder & Co-Partner)*
Elton Mayfield *(Co-Founder & Co-Partner)*

ER SNELL CONTRACTOR INC.
1785 Oak Rd, Snellville, GA 30078-2233
Tel.: (770) 972-9398
Web Site: https://www.ersnell.com
Rev.: $48,800,000
Emp.: 600
Highway & Street Paving Contractor
N.A.I.C.S.: 237310
Robin J. Snell *(Pres)*

ERA SUNRISE REALTY
157 Reinhardt College Pkwy Ste 100, Canton, GA 30114
Tel.: (770) 720-1515
Web Site: http://www.erasunriserealty.com
Sales Range: $1-9.9 Million
Emp.: 13
Real Estate Consultant
N.A.I.C.S.: 531210
Greg Martin *(Pres)*

ERA VALDIVIA CONTRACTORS, INC.
11909 S Avenue O, Chicago, IL 60617
Tel.: (773) 721-9350
Web Site: https://www.eravaldivia.com
Rev.: $20,500,000
Emp.: 70
Painting & Wall Covering Contractors
N.A.I.C.S.: 238320
Jose Faldivia *(Founder)*

ERASER DUST, INC.
2141 S Lee Travino, El Paso, TX 79932
Tel.: (915) 772-1200
Web Site: http://www.eraserdust.com
Year Founded: 2000
Sales Range: $1-9.9 Million
Emp.: 10
Stationery & Office Supplies Merchant Whslr
N.A.I.C.S.: 424120
Cynthia Huereque *(Pres)*

Subsidiaries:

Manutan Ltd   **(1)**
Black Moor Rd Ebblake Indus Estate, Verwood, BH31 6AT, Dorset, United Kingdom
Tel.: (44) 1202 825 311
Business Equipment Whslr
N.A.I.C.S.: 423420
Jean-Pierre Guichard *(Chm)*
Pierre-Olivier Sec *(Sec)*

ERB ELECTRIC CO.
310 Main St, Bridgeport, OH 43912
Tel.: (740) 633-5055
Web Site: http://www.erbelectric.com
Sales Range: $10-24.9 Million
Emp.: 200
Electrical Wiring Services
N.A.I.C.S.: 238210
Tom Knight *(Gen Mgr)*

ERB EQUIPMENT CO. INC.
200 Erb Industrial Dr, Fenton, MO 63026-4640
Tel.: (636) 349-0200   MO
Web Site: http://www.erbequipment.com
Year Founded: 1943
Sales Range: $25-49.9 Million
Emp.: 80
Construction & Lawn & Garden Equipment Supplier
N.A.I.C.S.: 423810
Carrie Roider *(CEO)*

Subsidiaries:

Erb Equipment   **(1)**
315 Worthington Rd, Owensboro, KY 42301
Tel.: (270) 684-2339
Web Site: http://www.erbequipment.com
Sales Range: $10-24.9 Million
Emp.: 26
Construction & Mining Machinery
N.A.I.C.S.: 423810
Richard Christ *(Branch Mgr)*

ERB INDUSTRIES INC.
1 Safety Way, Woodstock, GA 30188
Tel.: (770) 926-7944
Web Site: https://www.e-erb.com
Sales Range: $10-24.9 Million
Emp.: 130
Safety Products Mfr
N.A.I.C.S.: 314999
Sheila Eads *(Pres & CEO)*
Florrie Erb *(Co-Founder)*
William Erb Sr. *(Co-Founder)*

ERC INCORPORATED
4901 Corporate Dr Ste E, Huntsville, AL 35805
Tel.: (256) 430-3080
Web Site: http://www.erc-incorporated.com
Year Founded: 1988
Rev.: $113,700,000
Emp.: 920
Engineering & Technical Service
N.A.I.C.S.: 541330
Will Perry *(CFO)*
Ken Lyles *(Chief Admin Officer)*
Kenny Frame *(Pres)*
Chris McCain *(Mgr-Saftey)*

ERC PARTS INC.
4001 Cobb International Blvd NW, Kennesaw, GA 30152
Tel.: (770) 984-0276
Web Site: https://www.erconline.com
Year Founded: 1980
Rev.: $18,000,000
Emp.: 85
Sales of Electronic Parts
N.A.I.C.S.: 423690
Ernest Sanchez *(Dir-IT)*
John Cosentino *(Mgr-Tech Svcs)*
Nickie Johnson *(Coord-Svcs)*
Eric Hart *(Dir-Ops)*

ERC PROPERTIES INC.
4107 Massard Rd, Fort Smith, AR 72903
Tel.: (479) 452-9950
Web Site: http://www.erc.com
Sales Range: $25-49.9 Million
Emp.: 25
Multi-Family Dwelling Construction
N.A.I.C.S.: 236116
Ernest R. Coleman *(Chm)*
Lindon Morris *(CFO)*

ERDLE PERFORATING COMPANY
100 Pixley Industrial Pkwy, Rochester, NY 14624-2325
Tel.: (585) 247-4700
Web Site: https://www.erdle.com
Year Founded: 1870

Perforated Metals
N.A.I.C.S.: 332119
Thomas J. Pariso *(Exec VP)*
Bill Johnson *(Sls Mgr)*

ERDMAN HOLDINGS, INC.
6720 Frank Lloyd Wright Ave Ste 200, Middleton, WI 53562
Tel.: (608) 662-2205
Web Site: http://www.erdmanholdings.com
Sales Range: $50-74.9 Million
Emp.: 25
Commercial & Institutional Building Construction Services
N.A.I.C.S.: 236220
Jerry Sholts *(VP)*

ERF WIRELESS, INC.
2911 S Shore Blvd Ste 100, League City, TX 77573
Tel.: (281) 538-2101   NV
Web Site: http://www.erfwireless.com
Year Founded: 2004
Sales Range: Less than $1 Million
Emp.: 59
Wireless Products & Services
N.A.I.C.S.: 334220
John B. Barnett *(Interim Pres, Interim CEO & Interim Sec)*

ERGO SCIENCE CORP.
201 Office Park Dr Ste 150, Birmingham, AL 35223
Tel.: (205) 879-6447
Web Site: http://www.ergoscience.com
Year Founded: 1992
Injury Prevention Services
N.A.I.C.S.: 621111
Deborah Lechner *(Founder & Pres)*

ERGO-FLEX TECHNOLOGIES, LLC
13622 Poplar Cir Ste 403, Conroe, TX 77304
Tel.: (936) 588-5510
Web Site: https://www.ergoflextechnologies.com
Year Founded: 2011
Medical Equipment Mfr
N.A.I.C.S.: 339112

ERGON, INC.
2829 Lakeland Dr, Flowood, MS 39232
Tel.: (601) 933-3000   MS
Web Site: http://www.ergon.com
Year Founded: 1954
Petroleum Refineries
N.A.I.C.S.: 324110
Emmitte Haddox *(Pres & CEO)*
Baxter Burns *(Pres)*

Subsidiaries:

Diversified Technology Inc.   **(1)**
476 Highland Colony Pkwy, Ridgeland, MS 39157-8727
Tel.: (601) 856-4121
Web Site: http://www.dtims.com
Sales Range: $10-24.9 Million
Emp.: 140
Modular Computing Processor Boards, Switching Products & Other Embedded Systems Mfr
N.A.I.C.S.: 334111

Ergon Asphalt & Emulsions, Inc.   **(1)**
2829 Lakeland Dr, Jackson, MS 39232
Tel.: (601) 933-3000
Web Site: http://www.ergonasphalt.com
Asphalt & Asphaltic Paving Mixtures (Not From Refineries)
N.A.I.C.S.: 324121
Gaylon Baumgardner *(Sr VP)*

Ergon, Inc.—(Continued)

Subsidiary (Domestic):

Associated Asphalt Inc. (2)
2677 Roanoke Ave SW, Roanoke, VA
24015
Tel.: (540) 345-8867
Web Site:
https://www.associatedasphalt.com
Rev.: $76,941,190
Emp.: 20
Asphalt Mixture
N.A.I.C.S.: 423320
John W. Kirk III (Pres)

Subsidiary (Domestic):

Seaco, Inc. (3)
2700 William Tuller Dr, Columbia, SC
29205
Tel.: (803) 799-5335
Web Site: http://www.associatedasphalt.com
Asphalt Paving Mixture & Block Mfr
N.A.I.C.S.: 324121

Subsidiary (Domestic):

Blueknight Energy Partners, L.P. (2)
6060 American Plaza Ste 600, Tulsa, OK
74135
Tel.: (918) 237-4000
Web Site: http://www.bkep.com
Rev.: $115,417,000
Assets: $136,898,000
Liabilities: $129,341,000
Net Worth: $7,557,000
Earnings: $110,530,000
Emp.: 130
Fiscal Year-end: 12/31/2021
Oil & Gas Exploration Services
N.A.I.C.S.: 221210
D. Andrew Woodward (CEO)

Subsidiary (Domestic):

BKEP Management, Inc. (3)
6060 American Plz, Tulsa, OK 74135
Tel.: (918) 237-4010
Business Management Consulting Services
N.A.I.C.S.: 541611

BKEP Materials LLC (3)
600 Minton Rd, Saginaw, TX
76131 (100%)
Tel.: (817) 232-4441
Asphalt Mfr
N.A.I.C.S.: 324121

BKEP Materials LLC (3)
600 Minton Rd, Saginaw, TX 76179
Tel.: (817) 232-3658
Web Site: http://www.bkep.com
Sales Range: $25-49.9 Million
Emp.: 13
Brick, Stone & Related Construction Material Merchant Whslr
N.A.I.C.S.: 423320

BKEP Operating, L.L.C. (3)
11501 S Interstate 44 Service Rd, Oklahoma City, OK 73173-8315
Tel.: (918) 237-4005
Crude Oil Terminalling & Pipeline Services
N.A.I.C.S.: 424710

BKEP Services LLC (3)
201 NW 10th St Ste 200, Oklahoma City,
OK 73103
Tel.: (405) 278-6452
Web Site: http://www.bkep.com
Emp.: 100
Crude Oil Terminalling & Pipeline Services
N.A.I.C.S.: 424710

Subsidiary (Domestic):

Crafco, Inc. (3)
6975 W Crafco Way 420 Roosevelt Ave,
Chandler, AZ 85226
Tel.: (602) 276-0476
Web Site: http://www.crafco.com
Sales Range: $10-24.9 Million
Emp.: 50
Mfr of Road Repair Machines & Asphalt
Based Sealant Products
N.A.I.C.S.: 324121
Donald M. Brooks (Sr VP & Gen Mgr)

Subsidiary (Domestic):

Paving Maintenance Supply, Inc. (3)

2400 Rock Rd, Granite City, IL 62040
Tel.: (618) 877-8031
Web Site: http://www.pmsi-usa.net
Emp.: 3
Pavement Maintenance Services
N.A.I.C.S.: 561730
Don Brooks (Pres)

Subsidiary (Non-US):

**Ergon Asfaltos Mexico S. de R.L. de
C.V.** (2)
Privada Universidad No 3 Km 8 5 Carretera
Federal Puebla-Atlixco, Colonia Tlaxcalancingo Cholula, Puebla, CP 72820,
Mexico
Tel.: (52) 222 284 1930
Web Site: http://www.ergonasfaltos.com
Liquid Asphalt Cement Products & Other
Paving Materials Mfr, Distr & Application
Services
N.A.I.C.S.: 324121
Carl Ruiz (Mgr-Sls)
Raul Resendiz Brun (Supvr-Prod)
Jorge Sanchez Guevara (Mgr-HR)
Amida Orozco (Mgr-Fin)

Subsidiary (Domestic):

Paragon Technical Services, Inc. (2)
390 Carrier Blvd, Richland, MS 39218
Tel.: (601) 932-8365
Web Site: http://www.ptsilab.com
Petroleum Refining Research & Development Services
N.A.I.C.S.: 541715
Gaylon Baumgardner (Exec VP)
Codrin Daranga (Dir-Technical Asphalt
Binders, Emulsions & Technical Coatings)
Scott Watson (Sr VP)
Sonia Serna (Mgr-Asphalt Laboratory)
Mike Hemsley Jr. (Dir-Technical Field Svcs,
Mix Design & Performance Testing)

Ergon Energy Partners, LP (1)
PO Box 14476, Monroe, LA 71207
Tel.: (318) 322-1414
Web Site: http://www.ergon.com
Oil Exploration Services
N.A.I.C.S.: 213112

**Ergon Marine & Industrial Supply,
Inc.** (1)
100 Lee St, Vicksburg, MS 39180
Tel.: (601) 636-6552
Marine Equipment Distr
N.A.I.C.S.: 423910

Ergon Properties, Inc. (1)
2829 Lakeland Dr, Jackson, MS 39232
Tel.: (601) 842-1228
Web Site: http://www.ergonproperties.com
Real Estate Management Services
N.A.I.C.S.: 531390
Jim Defoe (VP)

Ergon Refining, Inc. (1)
PO Box 1639, Jackson, MS 39215-1639
Tel.: (601) 933-3000
Web Site: http://ergon.com
Refinery Operator
N.A.I.C.S.: 324110
Kris Patrick (Pres)

Subsidiary (Non-US):

Ergon Europe MEA, Inc. (2)
161 Dreve Richelle Bat C, 1410, Waterloo,
Belgium
Tel.: (32) 2 351 23 75
Web Site: http://www.rgoneurope.com
Emp.: 10
Naphthenic Oil Distr
N.A.I.C.S.: 424720
Veronique Rousseau (Office Mgr)

Subsidiary (Domestic):

Ergon Oil Purchasing, Inc. (2)
390 W Thomas Rd Ste 61, Baton Rouge,
LA 70807
Tel.: (225) 775-0526
Petroleum Product Distr
N.A.I.C.S.: 424720

Ergon-St. James, Inc. (2)
7405 Hwy 18, Saint James, LA 70086
Tel.: (225) 265-8020
Web Site: http://www.ergon.com

Sales Range: $25-49.9 Million
Emp.: 10
Naphthenic Oil Distr
N.A.I.C.S.: 424720
Shane Rougee (Gen Mgr)

Ergon Trucking, Inc. (1)
2829 Lakeland Dr, Jackson, MS 39232
Tel.: (601) 933-3000
Web Site: http://www.ergontrucking.com
Asphalt & Crude Oil Trucking Services
N.A.I.C.S.: 484230
Russ Maroney (Sr VP)
Bobby Barlow (VP-Mktg)
David Purvis (VP-Safety-CDS)
Les Merritt (Mgr-Compliance)
Betty Cole (Mgr-Admin)
Jeff Beam (Supvr-Safety & Trng)
Gary Babb (Supvr-Safety & Trng)

Ergon West Virginia, Inc. (1)
9995 Ohio River Blvd, Newell, WV
26050 (100%)
Tel.: (304) 387-4343
Rev.: $75,100,000
Emp.: 225
Petroleum Refining
N.A.I.C.S.: 324110
H. D. Davis (VP)
Neil Stanton (Plant Mgr)
Kris Patrick (Pres)

ISO Panels, Inc. (1)
630 Industrial Dr, Richland, MS 39218
Tel.: (601) 939-3909
Web Site: http://www.isopanels.com
Emp.: 25
Thermal Insulation Panel System Mfr
N.A.I.C.S.: 326140
Chad Watts (Gen Mgr)
Ed Lewis (Mgr-Contracting)
Paula Welch (Office Mgr)

Lampton-Love, Inc. (1)
380 Carrier Blvd, Jackson, MS 39218-9400
Tel.: (601) 939-8304
Web Site: http://www.lamptonlove.com
Sales Range: $10-24.9 Million
Emp.: 15
Liquefied Petroleum Gas Delivered To Customers Premises
N.A.I.C.S.: 457210

Division (Domestic):

Allgas Inc. of Montgomery (2)
4911 Birmingham Hwy, Montgomery, AL
36018
Tel.: (334) 265-0576
Web Site: http://www.allgasinc.com
Rev.: $550,000
Emp.: 10
Liquefied Petroleum Gas Dealers
N.A.I.C.S.: 457210
Steve Robinson (Mgr)

Lacox, Inc. (2)
1222 Washington St, Franklinton, LA 70438-
1849
Tel.: (985) 839-9808
Web Site: http://www.lamptonlove.com
Rev.: $1,500,000
Emp.: 13
Liquefied Petroleum Gas Delivered To Customer Premises
N.A.I.C.S.: 457210
Jerry McCain (Mgr)

**Lacox Propane Gas Company
Inc.** (2)
108 3rd Ave, Hammond, LA 70403-4958
Tel.: (985) 345-3180
Web Site: http://www.lamptonlove.com
Rev.: $570,000
Emp.: 8
Propane Gas, Bottled
N.A.I.C.S.: 457210

Lampton-Love, Inc. (2)
4150 Hwy 51 S, McComb, MS 39648
Tel.: (601) 684-6391
Web Site: http://www.lamptonlove.com
Rev.: $570,000
Emp.: 9
Liquefied Petroleum Gas Delivered To Customers Premises
N.A.I.C.S.: 457210
Sissy Davenport (Office Mgr)
Lef Lampton (Pres)

Lampton-Love, Inc. (2)

6700 Old Hwy 31 N, Gardendale, AL 35071
Tel.: (205) 631-2232
Web Site: http://www.lamptonlove.com
Rev.: $14,700,000
Emp.: 11
Bottled Propane Gas
N.A.I.C.S.: 424710

Lampton-Love, Inc. (2)
1104 Hwy 80 E, Pelahatchie, MS 39145
Tel.: (601) 854-5256
Web Site: http://www.lamptonlove.com
Rev.: $680,000
Emp.: 8
Liquefied Petroleum Gas Dealers
N.A.I.C.S.: 457210
Rob Love (Owner)
Matt Peters (Branch Mgr)

Lampton-Love, Inc. (2)
1564 B Hwy 49, Magee, MS 39111
Tel.: (601) 849-3496
Rev.: $410,000
Emp.: 5
Liquefied Petroleum Gas Dealers
N.A.I.C.S.: 457210

Magnolia Gas Inc. (1)
4733 Hwy 53, Poplarville, MS 39470
Tel.: (601) 795-4701
Web Site: http://www.lamptonlove.com
Rev.: $470,000
Emp.: 7
Retail Bottled Butane Gas
N.A.I.C.S.: 457210

**Magnolia Marine Transport
Company** (1)
697 Haining Rd, Vicksburg, MS 39181
Tel.: (601) 638-5921
Web Site: http://www.magnoliamarine.com
Sales Range: $10-24.9 Million
Emp.: 40
Asphalt Distr
N.A.I.C.S.: 423320
Stan Humphreys (Sr VP)
Sam Thigpen (VP-Marine Mktg)
Lee Lampton (Pres)
Roger Harris (VP-Ops)
Jim Smith (Mgr-Compliance)
Dino Ross (VP-Engrg-Marine)

Starkville LP Gas Inc. (1)
PO Box 823, Starkville, MS 39759
Tel.: (662) 323-3146
Web Site: http://www.lamptonlove.com
Sales Range: $10-24.9 Million
Emp.: 7
Propane Dealer
N.A.I.C.S.: 457210
Jerry Evans (Mgr)

Tricor Refining, LLC (1)
PO Box 5877, Bakersfield, CA 93388
Tel.: (661) 393-7110
Web Site: http://www.goldenbearoil.com
Sales Range: $25-49.9 Million
Emp.: 30
Mfr of Naphthenic Oils, Extender Oils & Asphalt Products; Owned 50% by Ergon, Inc.
& 50% by San Joaquin Refining Co., Inc.
N.A.I.C.S.: 324110
Jim Brownridge (Mgr-Mktg)
Marilyn Vallembois (Mgr-Svcs)
Joe Frank (Gen Mgr)

ERGONOMIC GROUP INC.
609-3 Cantiague Rock Rd, Westbury,
NY 11590
Tel.: (516) 746-7777
Web Site: http://www.ergogroup.com
Year Founded: 1984
Sales Range: $300-349.9 Million
Emp.: 160
Integrator of Computing Technologies, Systems & Solutions
N.A.I.C.S.: 423430
David Ferguson (Dir-Sls-NY)
Helen Clark (Mgr-Vendor)

ERGOS TECHNOLOGY PARTNERS, INC.
3831 Golf Dr, Houston, TX 77018
Tel.: (713) 621-9220   **TX**
Web Site: http://www.ergos.com
Year Founded: 2002
Sales Range: $10-24.9 Million

Emp.: 52
IT Consulting & Outsourcing Services
N.A.I.C.S.: 541690
Steven Pearce (CTO)
Kevin Tan (Reg Mgr-Quality Assurance)
Francisco Roque Jr. (Mgr-NOC)

ERHARD BMW OF BLOOM-FIELD HILLS
4065 W Maple Rd, Bloomfield, MI 48301
Tel.: (248) 642-6565
Web Site: http://www.erhardbmw.com
Year Founded: 1940
Sales Range: $50-74.9 Million
Emp.: 80
Car Whslr
N.A.I.C.S.: 441110
Erhard Dahm (Pres)

ERI SOLUTIONS, LLC
125 N First St, Colwich, KS 67030
Tel.: (316) 927-4290
Web Site:
    http://www.erisolutions.com
Year Founded: 2007
Environmental Safety Management Services
N.A.I.C.S.: 541620
Nathan Vander Griend (Pres & CEO)

Subsidiaries:

DBI, Inc.   (1)
15440 W 109th St, Lenexa, KS 66219
Tel.: (913) 888-2321
Web Site: http://www.dbindt.com
Professional, Scientific & Technical Services
N.A.I.C.S.: 541990
Jeff Morrow (CEO)
Rick Ruhge (Mgr)
Brad Tesar (Reg Mgr)
Kurt Hoins (Mgr-Ops)
Kurt Sunderman (Mgr-Ops)

ERIC ELECTRONICS, INC.
2220 Lundy Ave, San Jose, CA 95131
Tel.: (408) 432-1111
Web Site: http://www.ericnet.com
Year Founded: 1969
Sales Range: $10-24.9 Million
Emp.: 10
Electronic Parts
N.A.I.C.S.: 423690
Donald Turnquist (Owner)

ERIC MOWER AND ASSOCI-ATES, INC.
211 W Jefferson St, Syracuse, NY 13202
Tel.: (315) 466-1000   NY
Web Site: http://www.mower.com
Year Founded: 1968
Sales Range: $25-49.9 Million
Emp.: 235
Advertising & Public Relations Agency
N.A.I.C.S.: 541810
Eric Mower (Chm & CEO)
James Henderson (Sr VP-Digital Tech)
Kevin Tripodi (Sr VP & Dir-Creative)
John Favalo (Exec VP)
Donna Ricciardi (VP & Acct Dir)
Robin Farewell (VP & Dir-Media)
Cheryl Duggan (CFO)
Brad Rye (Mng Dir & Sr VP)
Ryan Garland (Sr Dir-Digital Media)
Cray Cyphers (Sr VP & Dir-Acct)
Matt Ferguson (Mng Dir & Exec VP)
Lisa V. Huggins (Sr VP-Client Svcs)
Patrick Short (Sr VP & Dir-Creative)
Michael Agoston (Dir-Production)

Christine Dougherty (Mng Dir & Sr VP)
Mary Gendron (Mng Dir & Sr VP)
Geoffrey Thomas (Mng Dir & Sr VP)

Subsidiaries:

EMA Public Relations Services   (1)
211 W Jefferson St, Syracuse, NY 13202-2561
Tel.: (315) 466-1000
Web Site: http://www.mowerpr.com
Sales Range: $25-49.9 Million
Emp.: 100
Public Relations Agency
N.A.I.C.S.: 541820
Greg Loh (Mng Partner-PR & Pub Affairs)
John O'Hara (Partner & Dir-PR)
Chuck Beeler (Dir-Cause Related Mktg)
Laurel S. Case (Acct Supvr-PR/Pub Affairs)
Danielle Gerhart (Acct Exec-PR)
Peter Kapcio (Dir-Reputation Mgmt)
John Lacey (Supvr-Pub Affairs)
Evan Bloom (Supvr-Mgmt & PR)
Patrick Spadafore (Sr Acct Supvr-PR)

Eric Mower and Associates, Inc. -
Albany   (1)
30 S Pearl St Ste 1210, Albany, NY 12207
Tel.: (518) 449-3000
Web Site: http://www.mower.com
Advertising & Public Relations Agency
N.A.I.C.S.: 541810
Sean Casey (Sr VP & Mng Dir)

Eric Mower and Associates, Inc. -
Atlanta   (1)
201 17th St NW Ste 500, Atlanta, GA 30363
Tel.: (678) 587-0301
Web Site: http://www.mower.com
Sales Range: $10-24.9 Million
Emp.: 26
Advertising Agency
N.A.I.C.S.: 541810
Chad Wall (Creative Dir)

Eric Mower and Associates, Inc. -
Boston   (1)
134 Rumford Ave Ste 307, Newton, MA 02466-1378
Tel.: (781) 893-0053
Web Site: http://www.mower.com
Advertising Agency
N.A.I.C.S.: 541810
Kevin Hart (Sr VP & Mng Dir)
Christine Tesseo (Assoc Dir-Creative)
Matthew Gustavsen (Assoc Dir-Creative)

Eric Mower and Associates, Inc. -
Buffalo   (1)
50 Fountain Plz Ste 1300, Buffalo, NY 14202
Tel.: (716) 842-2233
Web Site: http://www.mower.com
Sales Range: $10-24.9 Million
Emp.: 50
Advertising & Public Relations Agency
N.A.I.C.S.: 541810
Douglas C. Bean (COO)
Cheryl Duggan (CFO)
Christine Dougherty (Supvr-Mgmt)
Allison Conte (Dir-PR)
Nicole Lawniczak (Supvr-Acct)
Sara Root (Supvr-Project)
Stephen Bell (Dir-Pub Affairs)
Maura Duggan (Sr Mgr-Activation)
Maggie Kuffner (Mgr-Acct)
Jonathan Brown (Dir-Social Media Strategy)
Amy Durbin (Partner & Exec Dir-Media)
Allie Friedman (Mgr-Content)
Chelsea Carney (Designer-Graphic)
Kevin Rush (Supvr-Project)
Mary Jane Miranda (Supvr-Fin)
Patrick Hornung (Dir-Art)
Patrick Lewis (Sr Dir-Media Svcs)
Samantha DeMart (Sr Project Mgr)
Sarah Neundorfer (Assoc Dir-Creative)
Scott Schuman (Sr Mgr-Production)

Eric Mower and Associates, Inc. -
Charlotte   (1)
1001 Morehead Sq Dr 5th Fl, Charlotte, NC 28203
Tel.: (704) 375-0123
Web Site: http://www.mower.com
Sales Range: $10-24.9 Million
Emp.: 200
Advertising & Public Relations Agency

N.A.I.C.S.: 541810
Gene Hallacy (Partner & Dir-Media)
Patrick Short (Partner & Dir-Creative)
James Wittersheim (Mgr-IT)
Matthew Ferguson (Mng Partner)
Lee Carter (Acct Supvr)
Rick Lyke (Sr Partner-PR)
Peter Smolowitz (Sr Acct Supvr-Pub Rel)
Jennifer Nelson (Mgr-Traffic & Production)
Ann Ittoop (Mgr-Activation)
Katherine Robinson (Supvr-Media)

Eric Mower and Associates, Inc. -
Cincinnati   (1)
830 Main St 10th Fl, Cincinnati, OH 45202
Tel.: (513) 381-8855
Web Site: http://www.mower.com
Emp.: 30
Advertising & Public Relations Agency
N.A.I.C.S.: 541810
Jeff Eberlein (Sr Partner)
Michael Flesch (Assoc Dir-Creative)
Beth Kaiser (Assoc Dir-Creative-Digital)
Tony Magliano (Sr Partner)
Tim Quinlivan (Dir-Creative)
Liz Adkins (Dir-PR)
Chaske Haverkos (Dir-Video & Motion Graphics)
Lauren Niehaus (Sr Mgr-Search Mktg)
Lauren Tate (Mgr-PR Content)

Eric Mower and Associates, Inc. -
Rochester   (1)
1st Federal Plz 28 E Main St Ste 1960, Rochester, NY 14614-1915
Tel.: (585) 385-2000
Web Site: http://www.mower.com
Sales Range: $10-24.9 Million
Emp.: 20
Advertising & Public Relations Agency
N.A.I.C.S.: 541810
John Favalo (Mng Partner-Bus to Bus Svcs)
Brad Rye (Sr Partner & Head-Rochester Office)
John Richelsen (Partner-Res Svcs & Dir-EMA Insight)
David Grome (Acct Supvr)
Keith Hevener (Sr Mgr-Content)
Jenny Lesczinski (Asst Acct Exec-PR Grp)

ERIC SCOTT LEATHERS LTD.
980 Rozier St, Sainte Genevieve, MO 63670
Tel.: (573) 883-7491
Web Site: https://www.ericscott.com
Year Founded: 1985
Sales Range: $10-24.9 Million
Emp.: 100
Personal Leather Goods Mfr
N.A.I.C.S.: 316990
Ronald Coleman (Owner)
Joe Young (Mgr-IT)

ERICA TANOV INC.
1627 San Pablo Ave, Berkeley, CA 94702
Tel.: (510) 524-1762
Web Site: http://www.ericatanov.com
Sales Range: Less than $1 Million
Emp.: 15
Women's & Children's Clothing Designer
N.A.I.C.S.: 458110
Erica Tanov (CEO)
Kristin Nelson (Mgr-Production)
Rebecca Kent (Mgr-Sls)

ERICH HENKEL AUTOMOTIVE GROUP
375 W Dickman Rd, Battle Creek, MI 49037
Tel.: (269) 965-2291
Web Site:
    http://www.henkelautogroup.com
Sales Range: $25-49.9 Million
Emp.: 58
Sales of New & Used Automobiles
N.A.I.C.S.: 441110
Erich Henkel (Pres)

ERICKSEN ADVERTISING & DESIGN, INC.

12 W 37th St 9th Fl, New York, NY 10018-7480
Tel.: (212) 239-3313
Web Site:
    http://www.ericksenadvertising.com
Year Founded: 1979
Sales Range: Less than $1 Million
Emp.: 4
Advetising Agency
N.A.I.C.S.: 541810

ERICKSON ASSOCIATES, INC.
1 Erickson Dr, Savannah, GA 31405
Tel.: (912) 527-9500
Web Site:
    https://www.ericksonassociates.net
Year Founded: 1950
Sales Range: $25-49.9 Million
Emp.: 71
Plumbing, Heating & Air-Conditioning Contractor
N.A.I.C.S.: 238220
Brad Harris (Pres & Owner)
Hogan Pullin (VP)
Steve Cowart (VP)

ERICKSON BUILDERS & CO.
8911 30th St NE, Rogers, MN 55376
Tel.: (763) 497-9209
Web Site: http://www.ericksonbci.com
Year Founded: 1995
Sales Range: $1-9.9 Million
Emp.: 10
Full-Service Residential & Commercial Contractor
N.A.I.C.S.: 236116
Ryan E. Erickson (Pres & Co-Founder)

ERICKSON GMC
890 W Main St, Rexburg, ID 83440
Tel.: (208) 356-4455
Web Site:
    http://www.ypouemcfealor.com
Year Founded: 1967
Sales Range: $10-24.9 Million
Emp.: 40
Car Whslr
N.A.I.C.S.: 441110
Eric Erickson (Co-Owner)

ERICKSON INCORPORATED
3100 Willow Springs Rd, Central Point, OR 97502
Tel.: (541) 664-5544   DE
Web Site:
    https://www.ericksoninc.com
Year Founded: 1971
Heavy Lift Helicopter, Related Components Mfr & Aviation Services
N.A.I.C.S.: 336411
Barry Kohler (CEO)
Kristi Gonzalez (Sr VP-Admin & Admin)
David Merryman (Gen Counsel)
Bernadette McGinn (VP-Accounting & Controller-Corp)

Subsidiaries:

Canadian Air-Crane Ltd   (1)
7293 Wilson Avenue, Delta, V4G 1E5, BC, Canada
Tel.: (604) 940-1715
Emp.: 5
Logging Services
N.A.I.C.S.: 113310
Paul Pakstas (Engr-Aircraft Maintenance)

Evergreen Helicopters Inc.   (1)
3850 Three Mile Lane, McMinnville, OR 97128
Tel.: (503) 472-9361
Web Site: http://www.evergreenaviation.com
Sales Range: $150-199.9 Million
Emp.: 75
Global Aviation Services
N.A.I.C.S.: 481111

Erickson Metals Corporation—(Continued)

ERICKSON METALS CORPORATION
25 Knotter Dr, Cheshire, CT 06410
Tel.: (203) 272-2918
Web Site:
http://www.ericksonmetals.com
Year Founded: 1972
Sales Range: $10-24.9 Million
Emp.: 26
Aluminum Products Mfr
N.A.I.C.S.: 423510
Richard H. Erickson *(Founder)*

ERICKSON TRANSPORT CORPORATION
2255 N Packer Rd, Springfield, MO 65803-5090
Tel.: (417) 862-6741   WI
Year Founded: 1940
Sales Range: $50-74.9 Million
Emp.: 100
Trucking Services
N.A.I.C.S.: 484121
Lisa Todd *(Office Mgr)*
Jim G. Erickson *(Pres)*
Jeff L. Erickson *(VP)*
Harlan Cavin *(Dir-Safety)*

ERICKSONS FLOORING & SUPPLY CO.
1013 Orchard St, Ferndale, MI 48220
Tel.: (248) 543-9663
Web Site:
https://www.ericksonsfloors.com
Year Founded: 1943
Rev.: $10,500,000
Emp.: 60
Wood Flooring
N.A.I.C.S.: 423220
Rick Walters *(Pres & CEO)*

ERICSON MANUFACTURING CO.
4215 Hamann Pkwy, Willoughby, OH 44094
Tel.: (440) 951-8000
Web Site: http://www.ericson.com
Sales Range: $10-24.9 Million
Emp.: 100
Electric Connectors
N.A.I.C.S.: 335931
Katsie Hodar O'Neill *(Mgr-HR)*
John E. Ericson Jr. *(CEO)*

ERIE & NIAGARA INSURANCE ASSOCIATION
8800 Sheridan Dr, Williamsville, NY 14231
Tel.: (716) 632-5433
Web Site: http://www.enia.com
Year Founded: 1875
Sales Range: $25-49.9 Million
Emp.: 60
Cooperative Life Insurance Organizations
N.A.I.C.S.: 524113
Norman J. Orlowski *(Pres)*

ERIE BEARINGS CO. INC.
1432 E 12th St, Erie, PA 16503
Tel.: (814) 453-6871
Web Site:
http://www.eriebearings.com
Rev.: $12,300,000
Emp.: 35
Bearings
N.A.I.C.S.: 423840
Michael Ketchel *(Pres)*
Don Meyer *(Dir-Trng)*
Matt Murphy *(Dir-Sls & Mktg)*

ERIE COMMUNITY FOUNDATION
459 W 6th St, Erie, PA 16507

Tel.: (814) 454-0843   PA
Web Site:
https://www.eriecommunityfoundation.org
Year Founded: 1971
Sales Range: $25-49.9 Million
Emp.: 20
Grantmaking Services
N.A.I.C.S.: 813211
Erin D. Fessler *(VP-Mktg & Community Rels)*
Meghan O'Brien *(Dir-Grants & Scholarships)*
Barbara F. Sambroak *(VP-Fin & Admin)*
Susannah Weis Frigon *(VP-IR & Donor Stewardship)*
Michael L. Batchelor *(Pres)*
Russell S. Warner *(Chm)*
Khristina J. Bowman *(Dir-Mktg & Comm)*
Patrick Herr *(Dir-Community Impact)*
Court Gould *(VP-Community Impact)*

ERIE CONSTRUCTION MIDWEST INC.
4271 Monroe St, Toledo, OH 43606-1943
Tel.: (419) 472-4200
Year Founded: 1982
Sales Range: $25-49.9 Million
Emp.: 300
Supplier & Installer of Home Remodeling Products
N.A.I.C.S.: 238130
Scott Pratt *(Mgr)*
Nick Meyers *(Mgr-Mktg Room)*
Mary Welker *(Mgr-Payroll)*

ERIE COUNTY CARE MANAGEMENT, INC.
1601 Sassafras St, Erie, PA 16502
Tel.: (814) 528-0600   PA
Web Site:
http://www.eriecountycaremanagement.org
Year Founded: 2006
Sales Range: $10-24.9 Million
Developmental Disability Assistance Services
N.A.I.C.S.: 624120
Rebecca Ireson *(Sec)*
Doris Gernovich *(Chm)*

ERIE COUNTY HISTORICAL SOCIETY
419 State St, Erie, PA 16501
Tel.: (814) 454-1813   PA
Year Founded: 1903
Rev.: $2,908,236
Assets: $11,079,164
Liabilities: $290,815
Net Worth: $10,788,349
Earnings: $2,343,982
Emp.: 10
Fiscal Year-end: 06/30/14
Historical Resource Preservation Services
N.A.I.C.S.: 712110
Caleb Pifer *(Exec Dir)*
Jack Watts *(Pres)*
Dick Wachter *(Treas)*
Joe Hilbert *(VP)*
Pam Parker *(Sec)*

ERIE COUNTY INVESTMENT CO.
601 Corp Cir, Golden, CO 80401
Tel.: (303) 384-0200   OH
Web Site: http://www.arbys.com
Year Founded: 1965
Sales Range: $25-49.9 Million
Emp.: 65
Operator of Fast-Food Restaurant Chain
N.A.I.C.S.: 722513

David Bailey *(Pres)*

ERIE COUNTY WATER AUTHORITY
295 Main St Rm 350, Buffalo, NY 14203-2494
Tel.: (716) 849-8484
Web Site: https://www.ecwa.org
Year Founded: 1953
Sales Range: $25-49.9 Million
Emp.: 250
Water Supply
N.A.I.C.S.: 221310
Michael Asklar *(Engr-Traffic Safety)*
Robert Anderson *(Chm)*

ERIE FAMILY HEALTH CENTER
1701 W Superior, Chicago, IL 60622
Tel.: (312) 666-3494   IL
Web Site:
https://www.eriefamilyhealth.org
Year Founded: 1970
Sales Range: $25-49.9 Million
Emp.: 457
Health Care Srvices
N.A.I.C.S.: 621498
Melissa Hilton *(VP-Dev & Comm)*
Lee Francis *(Pres & CEO)*
Matt Aaronson *(Partner & Mng Dir)*
Brian P. Marsella *(Chm)*
Caroline Hoke *(Chief Clinical Officer)*
William G. Kistner *(Treas)*

ERIE FOODS INTERNATIONAL, INC.
401 7th Ave, Erie, IL 61250
Tel.: (309) 659-2233   IL
Web Site: https://www.eriefoods.com
Year Founded: 1938
Protein-based Ingredients & Private Label Products Mfr
N.A.I.C.S.: 311514
David R. Reisenbigler *(CEO)*
Mark Delaney *(CFO)*
Marty Anderson *(Reg Sls Mgr)*
Jim Klein *(COO)*

ERIE HOMES FOR CHILDREN AND ADULTS, INC.
226 E 27th St, Erie, PA 16504
Tel.: (814) 454-1534   PA
Web Site: https://www.ehca.org
Year Founded: 1913
Sales Range: $10-24.9 Million
Emp.: 575
Disability Assistance Services
N.A.I.C.S.: 624120
Peg Smith-Rich *(Dir-Residential & Program Svcs)*
Jonathan Rilling *(Dir-Dev)*

ERIE MATERIALS INC.
4507 Tiffin Ave, Sandusky, OH 44870
Tel.: (419) 625-7374
Web Site:
https://www.erieblacktop.com
Year Founded: 1968
Sales Range: $25-49.9 Million
Emp.: 140
Highway Construction Services
N.A.I.C.S.: 237310

ERIE MATERIALS INC.
500 Factory Ave, Syracuse, NY 13208
Tel.: (315) 455-7434
Web Site:
https://www.eriematerials.com
Sales Range: $75-99.9 Million
Emp.: 75
Roofing & Siding Materials
N.A.I.C.S.: 423330
Bill Ray *(Mgr-Ops)*
Mike Corning *(Mgr-Corp Pur)*
Bob Crandle *(Gen Mgr)*

Kevin Davis *(Gen Mgr)*
Mike Dominikoski *(Gen Mgr)*
Al Frappier *(Gen Mgr)*
Randy Moore *(Gen Mgr)*
Chris Roder *(Gen Mgr)*
Bill Wilsch *(Gen Mgr)*
Scott Baran *(Mgr-Ops)*
Adam Barnhart *(Mgr-Ops)*
Chuck Thorne *(Mgr-Ops)*

ERIE PHILHARMONIC
609 Walnut St, Erie, PA 16502-1852
Tel.: (814) 455-1375
Web Site: http://www.eriephil.org
Sales Range: Less than $1 Million
Emp.: 10
Symphony Orchestra
N.A.I.C.S.: 711130
Daniel Zimmerman *(Pres)*
John Knox *(Co-Pres)*
Amy Denlinger *(VP-Fin & Treas)*
Tom Vicary *(VP-Artistic Affairs)*
Tom New *(VP-Education)*
Linda Wilkinson *(VP-Events)*
Geri Cicchetti *(VP-Mktg)*
Lisa Adams *(Exec VP)*
Thomas Brooks *(Dir-Choir-Erie Philharmonic Chorus)*
Heather Storey *(Principal)*
LeAnne M. Wistrom *(Principal)*
Sean F. Gabriel *(Principal)*

ERIE STEEL, LTD.
5540 Jackman Rd, Toledo, OH 43613
Tel.: (419) 478-3743
Web Site: https://www.erie.com
Year Founded: 1961
Sales Range: $10-24.9 Million
Emp.: 50
Metal Heat Treating Services
N.A.I.C.S.: 332811
Patrick Flynn *(Pres)*
Michael Mouilleseaux *(Gen Mgr)*

ERIE TITLE AGENCY, INC.
29325 Chagrin Blvd Ste 200, Pepper Pike, OH 44122
Tel.: (216) 591-0289
Web Site: https://www.erietitle.com
Year Founded: 1998
Activities Related to Real Estate
N.A.I.C.S.: 531390
Kevin Blum *(Pres)*
Jackie Shear *(Officer-Comml Escrow)*
Libby Martini *(Officer-Comml Escrow)*
Kim Sandler *(Officer-Escrow)*
Michael Gerome *(Officer-Comml Escrow)*
Barb Gehle *(Officer-Escrow)*
Stacie Grmovsek *(Officer-Escrow)*

Subsidiaries:

US Title Agency, Inc.   (1)
1111 Chester Ave Ste 400, Cleveland, OH 44114
Tel.: (216) 621-1424
Web Site: http://www.ustitleagency.com
Sales Range: $1-9.9 Million
Emp.: 35
Title Insurance
N.A.I.C.S.: 524127
Gerald Goldberg *(Pres)*

ERIE-HAVEN INC.
6300 Ardmore Ave, Fort Wayne, IN 46809
Tel.: (260) 478-1674
Web Site: http://www.eriehaven.com
Rev.: $15,000,000
Emp.: 110
Readymix Concrete Mfr
N.A.I.C.S.: 327320
Tim Deal *(Mgr-Credit)*
Larry Gerig *(Pres)*

ERIEVIEW METAL TREATING CO.
4465 Johnston Pkwy, Cleveland, OH 44128
Tel.: (216) 663-1780
Web Site: https://www.erieviewmetal.com
Year Founded: 1961
Sales Range: $10-24.9 Million
Emp.: 100
Electroplating, Plating, Polishing, Anodizing & Coloring Services
N.A.I.C.S.: 332813
Alex Kappos *(Pres)*
Dennis Kappos *(VP-Sls)*
Chris Kappos *(Plant Mgr)*
Bob Kehres *(Mgr-Coatings)*
George Kappos Jr. *(CFO-Accts Payable)*

ERIEZ MANUFACTURING CO. INC.
2200 Asbury Rd, Erie, PA 16506-1402
Tel.: (814) 835-6000 PA
Web Site: http://www.eriez.com
Year Founded: 1942
Sales Range: $150-199.9 Million
Emp.: 600
Magnetic, Vibratory & Metal Detection Equipment Designer, Developer, Mfr & Marketer
N.A.I.C.S.: 333248
Richard A. Merwin *(Chm)*
Charlie Ingram *(Chief Mktg Officer & Exec VP)*
Mike Mankosa *(VP-Global Tech)*
John Blicha *(Dir-Corp Comm)*
Lukas Guenthardt *(Pres & CEO)*
Tim Gland *(VP & Gen Mgr)*
Mark Mandel *(CFO & Treas)*
Dave Heubel *(Sr Sls Dir)*

Subsidiaries:

Eriez Magnetics Europe Ltd (1)
Bedwas House Industrial Estate, Bedwas, Caerphilly, CF83 8YG, United Kingdom
Tel.: (44) 2920868501
Web Site: http://www.eriez.eu
Sales Range: $10-24.9 Million
Emp.: 100
Material Handling Machinery Mfr
N.A.I.C.S.: 333248
Gareth Meese *(Dir-Sls)*

Eriez Magnetics India Private Limited (1)
Door No 1/1 Ambattur-Vangaram Main Road, Anhipet, Chennai, 600 058, India
Tel.: (91) 4426525000
Web Site: http://www.eriez.in
Emp.: 1,000
Mining Machinery & Equipment Mfr
N.A.I.C.S.: 333131
Satish Shenoy *(Mng Dir)*
Ram Mohan *(Asst Gen Mgr)*
Y. Balaji *(Mgr-Natl)*
Kadri Ujwal Ravi *(Gen Mgr-Ops)*

Eriez Manufacturing Co. Inc. - Eriez Flotation Division - Canada (1)
7168 Venture St, Delta, V4G 1H6, BC, Canada
Tel.: (604) 952-2300
Web Site: http://www.en-ca.eriez.com
Sales Range: $10-24.9 Million
Emp.: 25
Mining Machinery & Equipment Mfr
N.A.I.C.S.: 333131

Eriez Manufacturing Co. Inc. - Eriez Flotation Division - Chile (1)
Badajoz 130 Of 1306, Las Condes, 7560908, Santiago, Chile
Tel.: (56) 29523400
Web Site: http://www.eriezflotation.com
Emp.: 4
Mining Machinery & Equipment Mfr
N.A.I.C.S.: 333131
Taigo Valle *(Gen Mgr)*
Javier Barca *(Gen Mgr)*

Eriez Manufacturing Co. Inc. - Eriez Flotation Division - Peru (1)
Av Manuel Olguin 335 Oficina 1008, Surco, Lima, Peru
Tel.: (51) 997508483
Sales Range: $10-24.9 Million
Emp.: 5
Mining Machinery & Equipment Mfr
N.A.I.C.S.: 333131

ERIK'S DELICAFE, INC.
365 Coral St, Santa Cruz, CA 95060
Tel.: (831) 458-1818 CA
Web Site: http://www.eriksdelicafe.com
Sales Range: $10-24.9 Million
Emp.: 270
Cafe
N.A.I.C.S.: 722511
Erik Johnson *(Founder)*

ERIKSEN CHEVROLET-BUICK
325 E 1st Ave, Milan, IL 61264-2507
Tel.: (309) 948-5495
Web Site: https://www.eriksens.com
Year Founded: 1960
Sales Range: $10-24.9 Million
Emp.: 71
New Car Whslr
N.A.I.C.S.: 441110
Bill Minas *(Mgr-Sls)*
Tom Pospisil *(Pres)*

ERIKSEN TRANSLATIONS, INC.
32 Ct St 20th Fl, Brooklyn, NY 11201
Tel.: (718) 802-9010 NY
Web Site: http://www.eriksen.com
Year Founded: 1986
Sales Range: $1-9.9 Million
Emp.: 25
Translation & Interpreting Services
N.A.I.C.S.: 541930
Vigdis Eriksen *(Founder & CEO)*
Kristi L. Gray *(Sr Acct Mgr)*
Peter Deutsch *(Sr Acct Mgr)*
Jennifer Murphy *(Dir-Mktg)*
Loubna Bagnied *(Mgr-Interpreting Svcs)*
Andrea Cabrera *(Mgr-Language Tech)*
Bettiana Quiroga *(Project Mgr)*
Rodrigo Resuche *(Sr Project Mgr)*
Farines Ramos *(Mgr-Acct)*
Courtney Weiner *(Mgr-Acct)*
Nick Mango *(Acct Mgr)*
Kevin Hudson *(Exec VP & Dir-Client Svcs)*

Subsidiaries:

Eriksen Translations S.R.L. (1)
Santa Rosa 320 4 Piso D, X5000ESH, Cordoba, Argentina
Tel.: (54) 3515690205
Translation & Interpreting Services
N.A.I.C.S.: 541930

ERIMAX, INC.
4301 Garden City Dr, Hyattsville, MD 20774
Tel.: (410) 286-8008
Year Founded: 2001
Sales Range: $1-9.9 Million
Emp.: 60
IT Acquisition Planning, Requirements Analysis, Strategic Planning & Program Management for Federal Government Agencies
N.A.I.C.S.: 519290
Eric Franklin *(CEO)*
Dick Richards *(Sr VP)*
Walt Munnikhuysen *(VP-Bus Dev)*
Michelle Graves *(Pres)*

ERLANGER HEALTH SYSTEM
975 E 3rd St, Chattanooga, TN 37403-2103

Tel.: (423) 778-7000
Web Site: http://www.erlanger.org
Year Founded: 1891
Sales Range: $500-549.9 Million
Emp.: 6,500
Healthcare & Medical Services
N.A.I.C.S.: 622110
Greg T. Gentry *(Chief Admin Officer)*
Alana B. Sullivan *(Chief Compliance Officer & Sr VP)*
Robert M. Brooks *(COO & Exec VP)*
Jeffrey Woodard *(Chief Legal Officer)*
Donald J. Mueller *(VP)*
Floyd Chasse *(VP-HR)*
Michael J. Griffin *(Chm)*
Elizabeth Appling *(Chief Diversity Officer)*
J. Britton Tabor *(CFO & Sr VP)*
Joe Winick *(Sr VP-Plng & Bus Dev)*
John J. Loetscher *(VP-Facilities, Engrg & Real Estate)*
Stephen E. Johnson *(VP-Govt & Payer Rels)*
Steven H. Burkett *(Sr VP-Physician Svcs)*
Judy E. Tingley *(CEO/VP-Heart & Lung Institute)*
Jed Mescon *(VP-PR, Mktg & Dev)*
Phil Smartt *(Vice Chm)*
Linda Mines *(Sec)*
Liz Hedges *(Dir-Bus Dev)*
William L. Jackson Jr. *(Pres & CEO)*

Subsidiaries:

Contin-U-Care Home Health Services (1)
1501 Riverside Dr Ste 350, Chattanooga, TN 37406
Tel.: (423) 624-8281
Sales Range: $10-24.9 Million
Emp.: 150
Women Healthcare Services
N.A.I.C.S.: 621610

ERMCO, INC.
1625 W Thompson Rd, Indianapolis, IN 46217-9286
Tel.: (317) 780-2923 IN
Web Site: https://www.ermco.com
Year Founded: 1962
Rev.: $65,000,000
Emp.: 350
Provider of General Electrical Contracting Services
N.A.I.C.S.: 238210
Darrell Gossett *(Pres)*
James R. Tsareff *(VP-Construction Ops)*
Greg Gossett *(VP-Corp Ops)*
Rod Burton *(Controller)*
David Peterson *(Sr VP-Bus Dev & Mktg)*

ERNEST HEALTH, INC.
7770 Jefferson St NE Ste 320, Albuquerque, NM 87109
Tel.: (505) 856-5300 DE
Web Site: https://www.ernesthealth.com
Holding Company; Rehabilitation & Other Post-Acute Healthcare Facilities Owner & Operator
N.A.I.C.S.: 551112
Darby Brockette *(CEO)*
Danny Banks *(Chief Real Estate Officer)*
Keith Longson *(CFO & Exec VP)*
Tony Hernandez *(COO)*
Kristi Duncan *(VP-Fin)*
Denise Kann *(Sr VP)*
Christopher Bergh *(Sr VP-Ops)*
Eudora Cannon *(Sr VP-Bus-Ops)*
Sheryl H. Gentile *(VP-Admin)*
Lynn Fleming *(Sr VP-Ops-Clinical)*
Maureen Fakinos *(Sr VP-Ops)*
Angie Anderson *(Sr VP-Mktg & Dev)*

Subsidiaries:

Weslaco Regional Rehabilitation Hospital, LLC (1)
906 S James, Weslaco, TX 78596
Tel.: (956) 969-2222
Web Site: http://www.weslacorehabhospital.com
Rehabilitation Medicine & Physical, Occupational & Speech Therapy Services
N.A.I.C.S.: 621340
Pedro E. McDougal *(Dir-Medical)*
Rita Mata-Guerrero *(Dir-Nursing)*
Heather Fryar *(Dir-Therapy)*

ERNEST MAIER, INC.
4700 Annapolis Rd, Bladensburg, MD 20710
Tel.: (301) 927-8300
Web Site: http://www.emcoblock.com
Year Founded: 1926
Sales Range: $25-49.9 Million
Emp.: 160
Concrete Block Mfr & Supplier
N.A.I.C.S.: 327331
Brendan Quinn *(CEO)*

Subsidiaries:

Standard Supplies (1)
14 Chestnut St, Gaithersburg, MD 20877-2403
Tel.: (301) 948-2690
Sales Range: $10-24.9 Million
Emp.: 65
Building Supplies & Fabricated Steel Products Whslr
N.A.I.C.S.: 444180
Norm Speth *(Mgr-Sls)*
Kim Collins *(Mgr)*

ERNEST MCCARTY FORD, INC.
1471 Hwy 31 S, Alabaster, AL 35007
Tel.: (205) 663-3831
Web Site: http://www.ernestmccarty.com
Sales Range: $25-49.9 Million
Emp.: 93
Car Whslr
N.A.I.C.S.: 441110
Williamson Chris *(Gen Mgr)*

ERNEST N. MORIAL CONVENTION CTR NEW ORLEANS
900 Convention Center Blvd, New Orleans, LA 70130
Tel.: (504) 582-3001
Web Site: https://www.mccno.com
Sales Range: $75-99.9 Million
Emp.: 350
Auditorium & Hall Operation
N.A.I.C.S.: 531120
Alita Gill *(VP-Fin)*

ERNEST PAPER PRODUCTS, INC.
5777 Smithway St, Commerce, CA 90040
Tel.: (323) 583-6561 CA
Web Site: https://www.ernestpackaging.com
Year Founded: 1946
Sales Range: $75-99.9 Million
Emp.: 100
Industrial Packaging Materials Whslr & Distr
N.A.I.C.S.: 424130
Tim Wilson *(Pres)*
Scott Gardner *(CMO)*

Subsidiaries:

Ernest Paper Products, Inc. - Fresno Facility (1)
2825 S Elm Ave, Fresno, CA 93706
Tel.: (800) 757-4968
Packaging Services
N.A.I.C.S.: 561910

Ernest Paper Products, Inc.—(Continued)

Ernest Paper Products, Inc. - Houston Facility (1)
6387 Windfern Rd, Houston, TX 77040
Tel.: (800) 210-2199
Packaging Services
N.A.I.C.S.: 561910
Brent Walker *(Dir-Client Rels)*

Ernest Paper Products, Inc. - Las Vegas Facility (1)
7440 S Dean Martin Dr Ste 204, Las Vegas, NV 89139
Tel.: (888) 744-7221
Web Site: http://www.ernestpackaging.com
Packaging Services
N.A.I.C.S.: 561910
Bill Evans *(Dir-Client Rels & Gen Mgr)*
Sarah Budz *(Dir-Ops)*

Ernest Paper Products, Inc. - Portland Facility (1)
9255 NE Alderwood Rd, Portland, OR 97220
Web Site: http://www.ernestpackaging.com
Packaging Services
N.A.I.C.S.: 561910
Travis Smith *(VP-Northwest)*

Ernest Paper Products, Inc. - Raleigh-Durham Facility (1)
112 Franklin Park Ave, Youngsville, NC 27596
Tel.: (800) 829-3574
Packaging Services
N.A.I.C.S.: 561910

Ernest Paper Products, Inc. - Reno Facility (1)
360 Lillard Dr, Sparks, NV 89434
Tel.: (775) 829-9700
Web Site: http://www.ernestpackaging.com
Emp.: 30
Packaging Services
N.A.I.C.S.: 561910
Nicole Thackaberry *(Office Mgr)*
Greg Sanguinetti *(Gen Mgr)*

Ernest Paper Products, Inc. - Sacramento Facility (1)
7728 Wilbur Way, Sacramento, CA 95828
Tel.: (800) 486-7222
Web Site: http://www.ernestpkg.com
Emp.: 50
Packaging Services
N.A.I.C.S.: 561910
Clint Howard *(Dir-Client Rels)*
Jamie McCoy *(Office Mgr)*

Ernest Paper Products, Inc. - San Diego Facility (1)
1345 Sycamore Ave, Vista, CA 92081
Tel.: (800) 269-3728
Packaging Services
N.A.I.C.S.: 561910

ERNIE BALL INC.
53973 Polk St, Coachella, CA 92236
Tel.: (760) 775-4222
Web Site: https://www.ernieball.com
Sales Range: $10-24.9 Million
Emp.: 311
Guitars & Musical Instrument Accessories Mfr & Sales
N.A.I.C.S.: 339992
Brian Ball *(Pres)*
Randy Jones *(Plant Mgr)*

ERNIE GREEN INDUSTRIES, INC.
2030 Dividend Dr, Columbus, OH 43228
Tel.: (614) 219-1423   **OH**
Year Founded: 1981
Sales Range: $25-49.9 Million
Emp.: 600
Motor Vehicle Parts & Accessories
N.A.I.C.S.: 336390
Ernie Green *(Chm & CEO)*
Sam Morgan *(Exec VP)*
Larry J. Jutte *(Pres & COO)*
Tim Hopper *(CMO)*

Subsidiaries:

Florida Production Engineering Inc. (1)
2 E Tower Cir, Ormond Beach, FL 32174-8759
Tel.: (386) 677-2566
Web Site: http://www.fpe-inc.com
Sales Range: $25-49.9 Million
Emp.: 400
Provider of Automotive Stampings
N.A.I.C.S.: 336370
Brad Gotts *(Pres & COO)*
Henry Schuster *(Mgr-Facilities)*
Wanda Lawson *(Dir-HR)*

ERNIE PALMER, INC.
1290 Cassat Ave, Jacksonville, FL 32205
Tel.: (904) 389-4561
Web Site:
http://www.erniepalmertoyota.com
Sales Range: $50-74.9 Million
Emp.: 85
Car Whslr
N.A.I.C.S.: 441110
Clay Murphy *(Gen Mgr)*

ERNIE VON SCHLEDORN LTD., INC.
N88W 14167 Main St, Menomonee Falls, WI 53051-2310
Tel.: (262) 255-6000   **WI**
Web Site: http://www.evsauto.com
Year Founded: 1981
Sales Range: $125-149.9 Million
Emp.: 300
New & Used Cars
N.A.I.C.S.: 441110
Ernst Von Schledorn *(Pres)*
Arthur Von Schledorn *(Mgr & Owner)*
Eric Von Schledorn *(VP)*

ERNIE WILLIAMS LTD
2613 US Hwy 18 E, Algona, IA 50511
Tel.: (515) 295-3561
Web Site:
http://www.erniewilliamsltd.com
Year Founded: 1983
Sales Range: $25-49.9 Million
Emp.: 75
Retailer of Farm Implements
N.A.I.C.S.: 423820
Eddie B. Wilcox *(Owner & Pres)*
James Wilcox *(Dir-Ops)*

ERNIE WILLIAMSON, INC.
3100 S Fremont Ave, Springfield, MO 65804
Tel.: (417) 881-1373   **MO**
Web Site: https://erniewilliamson.com
Year Founded: 1986
Sales Range: $1-9.9 Million
Emp.: 24
Ret Musical Instruments Equipment Rental/Leasing
N.A.I.C.S.: 459140
Paul Schmidt *(Mgr-Facilities)*

Subsidiaries:

Flint Hills Music, Inc. (1)
715 Commercial St, Emporia, KS 66801-2912
Tel.: (620) 342-4553
Web Site: http://www.flinthillsmusic.com
Personal & Household Goods Repair & Maintenance
N.A.I.C.S.: 811490

ERNST & YOUNG LLP
5 Times Sq, New York, NY 10036-6530
Tel.: (212) 773-3000   **DE**
Sales Range: $5-14.9 Billion
Accounting, Auditing, Tax Preparation & Advisory Services
N.A.I.C.S.: 541211

Gary Belske *(Deputy Mng Partner-Americas)*
Kate Barton *(Vice Chm-Tax Svcs-Americas)*
Richard M. Jeanneret *(Vice Chm & Mng Partner-Northeast)*
Denise Hummel *(Principal-Human Capital Practice)*
Klaus Woeste *(Partner-Fin Svcs Human Capital Practice)*
Greg Pope *(Partner)*
Jeff Wong *(Global Chief Innovation Officer)*
John Heithaus *(Principal)*
Keith Morice *(Partner)*
Anthony Crandall *(Exec Dir)*
Michael Denove *(Partner)*
Jeffrey Cartisser *(Partner)*
Dominic Verdi *(Partner)*
Joe Huddleston *(Exec Dir-Natl Indirect Tax Grp)*
David Holtze *(Vice Chm-Fin-Global)*
Felice Persico *(Vice Chm-Assurance-Global)*
Jay Nibbe *(Vice Chm-Tax-Global)*
Juliana Pereira *(Partner-Client-serving)*
Lou Pagnutti *(Mng Partner-Bus Enablement-Global)*
Norman Lonergan *(Vice Chm-Advisory-Global)*
Cordry Johns *(Partner-Chicago)*
Dana Douglas *(Exec Dir-Natl Legal-Chicago)*
Kim Letch *(Mng Partner-Orange County)*
Sarah Y. Liang *(Partner-Orange County)*
Tim Rahall *(Partner-Orange County)*
Sam Mukherjee *(Exec Dir-Orange County)*
Kevin Dehner *(Exec Dir)*
Katie A. Johnson *(Partner)*
Brian Harves *(Exec Dir)*
Julie DeDomenic *(Exec Dir)*
Amanda Powell *(Exec Dir)*
William M. Casey *(Vice Chm-Transaction Advisory Svcs-Americas)*
Tiffany Freen *(Partner-Assurance)*
Jim Morton *(Exec Dir-Advisory Supply Chain & Ops Practice)*
Pamela Austin *(Dir-Bus Dev)*
Joshua Axelrod *(Principal-Advisory)*
Kathryn Holland *(Partner-Tax-Indirect Tax Practice)*
Shawn McGrath *(Partner-Fraud Investigation & Dispute Svcs Practice)*
Mike Schank *(Exec Dir-Fin Svcs Advisory)*
Sean O'Connell *(Principal-Fin Svcs Advisory Practice)*
Kelly Guterl *(Principal-Tax)*
Scott Nelson *(Partner-Transaction Advisory Svcs)*
Ashley P. Scott *(Partner-Tax)*
Udanda Clark *(Partner-Assurance-Atlanta)*
Justin Gentry *(Partner-Assurance Svcs Practice)*
Brent Papek *(Partner-Assurance Svcs Practice-Phoenix)*
Tracy Benedict *(Partner-Austin)*
Ashley McCloud *(Exec Dir-Indirect Tax Svcs Practice)*
Walter Kress *(Chief Investment Officer-Defined Benefit & Defined Contribution &)*
Debra Aerne *(Partner-St. Louis)*
Brian Kennedy *(Partner-Milwaukee)*
Brian Sinclair *(Exec Dir-People Advisory Svcs Practice-Chicago)*
Steve Starzynski *(Partner-Transaction Tax-TAS Practice-Chicago)*
John Gillardi *(Exec Dir-Advisory Practice-St. Louis)*

Beverly DeWitt *(Mgr-Assurance-Wichita)*
Shekima Smith *(Mgr-Assurance-Wichita)*
Christopher J. Girod *(Exec Dir-Tax Practice)*
Stefanie Cavanaugh *(Auditor)*
Tim Devetski *(Principal)*
Joe Muscat *(Mng Partner-Redwood Shores)*
Ibi Krukrubo *(Mng Partner-San Jose)*
Paul Reading *(Exec Dir-Operational Transactions Svcs)*
Fredrik Burger *(Partner)*
David Brown *(Sr Partner-Bermuda)*
Dan Scott *(Reg Mng Partner)*
Daphne Snedegar *(Exec Dir)*
Steve Varley *(Chm & Mng Partner-UK & Ireland)*
Simon O'Neill *(Mng Partner-Birmingham & Midlands)*
Sara Fowler *(Partner-Fraud Investigation & Dispute Svcs Practice)*
Mark Chambers *(Principal-Tax)*
Brad McLamb *(Partner-Assurance)*
Jimmy Palik *(Partner-Assurance)*
J. David Thompson *(Exec Dir-Indirect Tax)*
Lucy Hamilton *(Dir-Fin-Southeast)*
Emily Garrett *(Partner-Assurance)*
Josh Trusley *(Partner-Assurance)*
Doug Gottschalk *(Partner-TAS Practice-Chicago)*
Patricia Morris *(Exec Dir-Las Vegas)*
Ryan Cupersmith *(Partner-Las Vegas)*
Dale Fedun *(Principal-Redwood Shores)*
Neeraj Gupta *(Exec Dir-Redwood Shores)*
Tracy Fisher *(Exec Dir-Portland)*
Peter Doubleday *(Mng Partner-Portland)*
Katherine Hammack *(Exec Dir-Govt & Pub Sector)*
Mike Herrinton *(Partner)*
Mark Godson *(Partner-Actuarial)*
Brendan McCorryM *(Mng Partner-Providence)*
Steven Napier *(Exec Dir-Transaction Advisory Svcs Practice-Bermuda)*
Julie Boland *(Vice Chm & Mng Partner-Central)*
Angie Kelly *(Mng Partner-Detroit)*
George Lenyo *(Partner-Coordinating-Global)*
Dan Allyn *(Exec Dir-Govt & Pub Sector Advisory Practice)*
Mark Freedman *(Partner)*
Eileen Garvey *(Mng Partner)*
Carl Ghattas *(Exec Dir-Govt & Public Sector Advisory Practice)*
Linda Marston-Weston *(Head-Tax-Midlands)*
Chris Marjoram *(Assoc Partner-Transaction Tax Team-Midlands)*
Eric Laughlin *(Mng Dir-Legal Managed Svcs)*
Jocelyn Murta *(Partner)*
Michael Hayek *(Mng Dir)*
Scott Stoll *(Founder-Asset Liability Mgmt advisory Practice)*
James C. Bly Jr. *(Exec Dir-Private Client Svcs)*

Subsidiaries:

Pangea3, LLC (1)
530 Fifth Ave 7th Fl, New York, NY 10036
Tel.: (212) 689-3819
Web Site: http://www.pangea3.com
Legal Process Outsourcing Solutions
N.A.I.C.S.: 541199
Greg McPolin *(Mng Dir)*
Kim Culpepper *(Sr Mgr-Mktg & Comm)*
Suneese Eagleton *(Dir-Litigation Solutions)*
Umair Muhajir *(VP-Global Litigation Solutions)*

Christine Langstieh *(Mgr)*
Janaki Dighe *(Asst Mgr)*
Scott Augustin *(Sr Dir-Comm)*

Society Consulting, LLC (1)
901 104th Ave NE, Bellevue, WA 98004
Tel.: (206) 420-3500
Web Site: http://www.ey-society.com
Business Management Consulting Services
N.A.I.C.S.: 541618
Chad Richeson *(Partner & Principal)*
John Bergen *(Partner & Principal)*
Josiah Johnson *(Principal-Advisory Svcs)*
P. J. Ohashi *(Principal-Advisory Svcs-Data & Analytics)*
Steve Newman *(Exec Dir-Analytics, Data, Innovation & Product Dev)*
Tanja Wisskirchen-Curtis *(Dir-Digital Analytics & Sr Mgr)*
Mandy Emel *(Asst Dir)*
Buddy Wilson *(Dir-Bus Dev)*
Barry Ota *(Asst Dir-Bus Dev)*
Franklin Huynh *(Exec Dir-Advisory Svcs)*
Charley Shoemaker *(Mng Dir-Analytics & Experience & Exec Dir-Natl Advisory-Analytics)*
Felix Chen *(Exec Dir-Data & Analytics)*
Dan Glavin *(Asst Dir)*

ERNST AUTO CENTER INCORPORATED
615 E 23rd St, Columbus, NE 68601
Tel.: (402) 564-2736
Web Site: http://www.ernstauto.com
New & Used Automobiles
N.A.I.C.S.: 441110
Brent Bond *(Gen Mgr)*
Rick Kerkman *(Mgr-Sls)*
Brendon Findley *(Mgr-Fin)*

ERNST ENTERPRISES, INC.
3361 Successful Way, Dayton, OH 45414
Tel.: (937) 233-5555
Web Site: https://www.ernstconcrete.com
Year Founded: 1946
Sales Range: $100-124.9 Million
Emp.: 320
Supplier of Ready-Mixed Concrete Products
N.A.I.C.S.: 327320
Mark Van de Grift *(VP-Ops)*
Kevin Heaney *(Gen Mgr)*
Dave Ernst *(VP)*
John C. Ernst Jr. *(Pres)*

ERNST VON SCHLEDORN INC.
N88W14167 Main St, Menomonee Falls, WI 53051
Tel.: (262) 255-6000
Sales Range: $25-49.9 Million
Emp.: 130
Car Whslr
N.A.I.C.S.: 441110
April Liberski *(Mgr-Customer Rels)*
Ernie von Schledorn *(Pres)*

ERO MEAT COMPANY
680 Washington Ave Ste 1, Holland, MI 49423-4965
Tel.: (616) 394-5102
Web Site: http://erogroup.net
Rev.: $10,200,000
Meats & Meat Products
N.A.I.C.S.: 424470
Kenneth E. Boire *(Pres)*

EROOMSYSTEM TECHNOLOGIES, INC.
150 Airport Rd Ste 1200, Lakewood, NJ 08701
Tel.: (732) 730-0116   NV
Develops In Room Computer Platform & Communications Networks For The Lodging Industry
N.A.I.C.S.: 334118

David A. Gestetner *(Chm, Pres, CEO & Sec)*
Subsidiaries:

eRoomSystem SPE, Inc. (1)
1072 Madison Ave, Lakewood, NJ 08701
Tel.: (732) 730-0116
Web Site: http://www.eroomsystem.com
Sales Range: $125-149.9 Million
Emp.: 5
Computer Peripheral Equipment Mfr
N.A.I.C.S.: 334118

ERP ANALYSTS, INC.
425 Metro Pl N Ste 510, Dublin, OH 43017
Tel.: (614) 718-9222   OH
Web Site: http://www.erpanalysts.com
Year Founded: 1999
Sales Range: $10-24.9 Million
Emp.: 200
Business Consulting Services
N.A.I.C.S.: 541618
Srikanth Gaddam *(Pres)*
Harsha Roddam *(Exec VP-Consulting Svcs)*
Sabrina Stover *(CFO)*
Kiran Beeravelli *(Chief Innovation Officer)*
Peter Koutroubis *(Sr VP-BI & Analytics)*
Louis Leclerc *(VP-Delivery)*

ERP INTERNATIONAL, LLC.
603 7th St Ste 203, Laurel, MD 20707
Tel.: (301) 490-0080
Web Site: https://www.erpinternational.com
Year Founded: 2006
Sales Range: $10-24.9 Million
Emp.: 170
Human Resource Consulting Services
N.A.I.C.S.: 541612
Melvin Petty *(CEO & Mng Partner)*
John Ely *(Pres-Clinical Svcs & COO)*
Jenny Jin *(Dir-Fin & Acctg)*
Prad Coomaraswamy *(CTO)*

ERP IRON ORE, LLC
28754 Co Rd 61, Grand Rapids, MN 55744
Tel.: (218) 969-9349   VA
Web Site: http://www.erpironore.com
Iron Ore Concentrate & Iron Ore Pellet Plant Operator
N.A.I.C.S.: 212210
Todd Roth *(CEO)*
Subsidiaries:

Magnetation, Inc. (1)
102 NE 3rd S Ste 120, Grand Rapids, MN 55744
Tel.: (218) 999-5165
Web Site: http://www.magnetation.com
Iron Ore Mining Company
N.A.I.C.S.: 212210
Joe Broking *(CFO)*

ERRAND SOLUTIONS, LLC
118 S Clinton St Ste 760, Chicago, IL 60661
Tel.: (312) 475-3800
Web Site: http://www.errandsolutions.com
Year Founded: 2000
Rev.: $11,900,000
Emp.: 92
Business Products & Services
N.A.I.C.S.: 561439
Marsha Mcvicker *(Founder & CEO)*

ERRANDS PLUS, INC.
12270 Wilkins Ave, Rockville, MD 20852

Web Site: https://www.rmalimo.com
Emp.: 550
Transportation Services
N.A.I.C.S.: 485999
Robert Alexander *(CEO)*
Subsidiaries:

International Limousine Service, Inc. (1)
2300 T St NE, Washington, DC 20002
Tel.: (202) 388-6800
Web Site: http://www.internationallimo.com
Emp.: 200
Limousine Service
N.A.I.C.S.: 485320
John Schmidt *(COO & Exec VP)*
Teresa Stivers *(Dir-Sls)*
Richard P. Kane *(Pres & CEO)*

ERS INDUSTRIES INC.
1005 Indian Church Rd, West Seneca, NY 14224
Tel.: (716) 675-2040
Web Site: http://www.ersindustries.com
Year Founded: 1936
Railroad Equipment & Supplies
N.A.I.C.S.: 423860
David E. Egner *(Gen Mgr)*
Craig Goodenough *(Mgr-Sls)*
Robert Lauber *(Mgr-Engrg)*
Bob Wingles *(VP)*
Subsidiaries:

American & Ohio Locomotive Crane Co. (1)
811 Hopley Ave, Bucyrus, OH 44820
Tel.: (419) 562-6010
Web Site: http://www.aolcrane.com
Sales Range: $10-24.9 Million
Emp.: 21
Engineers & Manufactures Locomotive Cranes
N.A.I.C.S.: 336510
Robert Goodenough *(Mgr-Sls)*
Chuck Billman *(Mgr-Parts)*
Lisa K. Butler *(Mgr-Acctg)*
Lonnie Stayman *(Plant Mgr)*

Ebenezer Railcar Services (1)
1005 Indian Church Rd, West Seneca, NY 14224
Tel.: (716) 674-5650
Sales Range: $10-24.9 Million
Emp.: 50
Repairs, Refurbishes & Remanufactures Railcars & Components
N.A.I.C.S.: 336510

Liberty Railway Services, Inc. (1)
598 N States Ave, Pueblo West, CO 81007
Tel.: (719) 544-6867
Web Site: http://www.lrsx.com
Freight Car Repair Services
N.A.I.C.S.: 811198

North American Equipment Sales (Canada) Ltd. (1)
8 Riverside Court, Binbrook, Hamilton, L0R 1C0, ON, Canada
Tel.: (905) 624-3006
Web Site: http://www.naescanada.com
Emp.: 2
New & Used Crane Parts Distr
N.A.I.C.S.: 423120
David Wylie *(VP)*
Paul O'Shell *(Pres & CEO)*

ERT SALES OF HAWAII INC.
98-1005 Moanalua Rd Spc 866, Honolulu, HI 96701-4728
Tel.: (808) 484-2500
Web Site: http://www.pricebustershawaii.com
Rev.: $10,400,000
Emp.: 200
Discount Retail Store Chain Operator
N.A.I.C.S.: 455219
Elizabeth Tom *(Pres)*
Dave Kimler *(Exec VP)*
Dan Marshall *(Dir-Sls)*

ERVIN EQUIPMENT, INC.

608 N Ohio St, Toledo, IL 62468
Tel.: (217) 238-3125
Web Site: https://www.ervinusa.com
Year Founded: 1981
Sales Range: $100-124.9 Million
Emp.: 40
Logistics & Transportation Services
N.A.I.C.S.: 541614
Cole Ervin *(CEO)*
Jeff Weber *(VP-Sls & Mktg)*
Chad Strader *(Pres)*
Tim Jones *(VP-Pur & Bus Dev)*
Tracy Cope *(Sr Mgr-Sls)*
Erick Albarran *(Mgr-Mexico Sls)*
Mitchell Shaw *(VP-Leasing Memphis Branch)*
Preston Owen *(CFO & Gen Counsel)*
Christina Bland *(VP-Ops)*
Jeff Thomas *(Mgr-Sls & Fin)*

ERVIN INDUSTRIES, INC.
3893 Research Park Dr, Ann Arbor, MI 48108-2217
Tel.: (734) 769-4600   MI
Web Site: https://www.ervinindustries.com
Year Founded: 1920
Sales Range: $75-99.9 Million
Emp.: 350
Metal Abrasives & Related Products Mfr
N.A.I.C.S.: 327910
Gene Brown *(Mgr-Sls)*
Subsidiaries:

Ervin Amasteel Division of Ervin Industries Inc. (1)
915 Tabor St, Adrian, MI 49221-3966   (100%)
Tel.: (517) 265-6118
Sales Range: $25-49.9 Million
Emp.: 100
Mfr Of Abrasives
N.A.I.C.S.: 327910
Jan Gramm *(Plant Mgr)*

Branch (Domestic):

Ervin Amasteel Div. (2)
681 E Butler Rd, Butler, PA 16002-9127
Tel.: (724) 282-1060
Web Site: http://www.ervinindustries.com
Sales Range: $25-49.9 Million
Emp.: 100
Abrasives Mfr
N.A.I.C.S.: 327910
Mike Fleger *(Gen Mgr)*

Subsidiary (Non-US):

Ervin Amasteel UK LP (2)
George Henry Rd, Great Bridge, Tipton, DY4 7BZ, West Midlands, United Kingdom   (100%)
Tel.: (44) 1215222777
Web Site: http://www.ervinamasteel.eu
Sales Range: $25-49.9 Million
Emp.: 60
Mfr of Metal Abrasives Made of Steel & Cast Iron
N.A.I.C.S.: 327910
Norman Wallace *(Dir-Mfg)*

Ervin Germany GmbH (1)
Auf dem Bruch 11, 45549, Sprockhovel, Germany
Tel.: (49) 23249022244
Web Site: http://www.ervin-germany.com
Sales Range: $10-24.9 Million
Emp.: 25
Steel Abrasive Mfr
N.A.I.C.S.: 327910
Wolfgang Assmann *(Mng Dir)*
John E. Pearson *(Mng Dir)*

Ervin Industries, Inc. - Ervin Technologies Division (1)
200 Industrial Dr, Tecumseh, MI 49286
Tel.: (517) 423-5477
Metal Alloy Mfr
N.A.I.C.S.: 332111
Gary Gillen *(Gen Mgr)*

Ervin Industries, Inc.—(Continued)

Ervin Leasing Company (1)
3893 Research Park Dr, Ann Arbor, MI
48108
Tel.: (734) 332-5400
Web Site: http://www.ervinleasing.com
Emp.: 20
Equipment Leasing Services
N.A.I.C.S.: 522220
R. J. Grimshaw (Pres)

ERVIN MARKETING CREATIVE COMMUNICATIONS
5615 Pershing Ave Ste 27, Saint
Louis, MO 63112
Tel.: (314) 454-1143 MO
Web Site: http://www.ervin-marketing.com
Year Founded: 1988
Sales Range: Less than $1 Million
Emp.: 8
Advetising Agency
N.A.I.C.S.: 541810
Sallie Ervin (CEO & Chief Creative
Officer)
Erica Schwan (VP & Dir-Creative)
Brigid Doherty (Acct Exec)
Jean Corea (Sr Dir-Art)
Ted Kneidl (Dir-Comm Strategy)

ERVING INDUSTRIES, INC.
97 E Main St, Erving, MA 01344-
9756
Tel.: (413) 422-2700 MA
Web Site:
https://www.ervingpaper.com
Year Founded: 1905
Sales Range: $75-99.9 Million
Emp.: 125
Napkins & Consumer Paper Products
Mfr
N.A.I.C.S.: 322120
Charles B. Housen (Chm)
Kathy Gibbs (Coord-Benefits Dept)

Subsidiaries:

Erseco, Inc. (1)
97 E Main St, Erving, MA 01344-9717
Tel.: (413) 422-2700
Water Treatment & Landfill Operation
N.A.I.C.S.: 562119
Charles B. Housen (Dir)
Morris Housen (Pres)
Denis L. Emmett (Treas & Sec)

Erving Paper Products, Inc. (1)
2954 Holmgren Way, Green Bay, WI
54304-5716 (100%)
Tel.: (920) 337-2500
Sales Range: $25-49.9 Million
Paper Converter-Napkins & Placemats for
Food Service & Mass Market
N.A.I.C.S.: 322299

Flamingo Products, Inc. (1)
3095 E 11th Ave, Hialeah, FL
33013-3511 (100%)
Tel.: (305) 691-4641
Sales Range: $1-9.9 Million
Emp.: 25
Napkins & Placemats Mfr
N.A.I.C.S.: 322120

ERWIN PEARL INC.
389 5th Ave FL 9, New York, NY
10016
Tel.: (212) 889-7410
Web Site: http://www.erwinpearl.com
Rev.: $13,000,000
Emp.: 30
Costume Jewelry
N.A.I.C.S.: 339910

ES ADVERTISING
6222 Wilshire Blvd Ste 302, Los Angeles, CA 90048
Tel.: (323) 964-9001
Web Site:
http://www.esadvertising.net

Year Founded: 1999
Rev.: $10,000,000
Emp.: 25
Advetising Agency
N.A.I.C.S.: 541810
Sandra Lee (Pres & CEO)
Lillian Chang (Acct Exec)

ES ORIGINALS INC.
440 9th Ave 7th Fl, New York, NY
10001
Tel.: (212) 736-8124
Web Site:
https://www.esoriginals.com
Sales Range: $25-49.9 Million
Emp.: 50
Shoes
N.A.I.C.S.: 424340
Patrick Donohue (Mgr-Children
Brands Ops)
Kevin Lynch (Brand Mgr)
Maria Fiorentino (Coord-Production)
Mari Chamberlin (Pres)
Stephen Bombara (Dir-Nautical Foot-
wear Design)
Gwen Murphy (Sr Dir-Design)
Penny Perillo (Dir-Payroll & HR)

ES ROBBINS CORPORATION
2802 E Avalon Ave, Muscle Shoals,
AL 35661
Tel.: (256) 248-2400
Web Site: https://www.esrobbins.com
Year Founded: 1967
Sales Range: $10-24.9 Million
Emp.: 150
Plastics Film & Sheet Mfr
N.A.I.C.S.: 326113
Ed Robbins (Pres & CEO)
Stan Denton (VP-Sls-Aleco Div)
Bony Pardu (Coord-Mktg)

ES-O-EN CORP
PO Box 607, Meridian, ID 83680
Tel.: (208) 888-6428
Sales Range: $25-49.9 Million
Emp.: 10
Fast-Food Restaurant, Chain
N.A.I.C.S.: 722513
Timothy W. Nicolaysen (VP)
Dennis Miester (COO)

ESA ENVIRONMENTAL SPE-CIALISTS, INC.
1332 Vexter St, Charlotte, NC 28204
Tel.: (704) 598-4407
Sales Range: $10-24.9 Million
Emp.: 75
Environmental Consulting Services
N.A.I.C.S.: 541620
Charles J. Cole (Pres & CEO)
Nathan Bender (Pres-Opers)
Dave Eppling (Sr VP)
Jake Cole (Dir-Construction & Envi-
ron Svcs)
Joe Bednarczyk (Gen Mgr-
Construction)

ESAC, INC.
11 N Washington St Ste 540, Rock-
ville, MD 20850-0389
Tel.: (301) 458-7386
Web Site: http://www.esacinc.com
Year Founded: 2000
Sales Range: $1-9.9 Million
Emp.: 25
Research Data Management, Bioin-
formatics & Health Care IT Services
N.A.I.C.S.: 541715
Pat Clark (Specialist-HR)

ESALEN INSTITUTE
55000 Hwy 1, Big Sur, CA 93920
Tel.: (831) 667-3000 CA
Web Site: https://www.esalen.org
Year Founded: 1963

Sales Range: $10-24.9 Million
Educational Support Services
N.A.I.C.S.: 611710
Cheryl Fraenzl (Dir-Programs)
Elizabeth Stacey (Dir-Advancement)
Patrick Sheridan (Dir-Ops)

ESCALADE SPORTS INC
817 Maxwell Ave, Evansville, IN
47711-3870
Tel.: (812) 467-1200
Web Site:
http://www.escaladesports.com
Rev.: $13,000,000
Emp.: 350
Provider of Archery Equipment
N.A.I.C.S.: 459110
Jack Bowman (Dir-Bear Archery)

ESCALANTE GOLF, INC.
2930 Bledsoe Ste 124, Fort Worth,
TX 76107
Tel.: (817) 386-9721
Web Site:
https://www.escalantegolf.com
Year Founded: 1991
Golf Course Owner, Operator & Man-
agement Consulting
N.A.I.C.S.: 713910
David McDonald (Pres)
Elcio Silva (VP-Ops)
Robert Silva (VP-Bus Dev)
David Matheson (VP-Corp Comm &
Mktg)

Subsidiaries:

Black Diamond Ranch (1)
3125 W Black Diamond Cir, Lecanto, FL
34461
Tel.: (352) 746-3440
Web Site:
http://www.blackdiamondranch.com
Golf Course & Club
N.A.I.C.S.: 713910
Kerry Rosselet (Dir-Membership)
Matt DiMase (Dir-Golf Course Maintenance)
John Hilker (Mgr-Club)

Country Club of the North (1)
1 Club North Dr, Beavercreek, OH 45385
Tel.: (937) 374-5000
Web Site:
http://www.countryclubofthenorth.com
Golf Course & Country Club
N.A.I.C.S.: 713910
Brian Corry (Dir-Community & Residential
Svcs)

Gray Plantation Golf Club and the
Sport Club at Graywood (1)
6150 Graywood Pkwy, Lake Charles, LA
70605
Tel.: (337) 562-1663
Web Site: http://www.graywoodllc.com
Golf Course & Club
N.A.I.C.S.: 713910
Devin Thomas (Gen Mgr)

Pine Creek Golf Club (1)
9850 Divot Trl, Colorado Springs, CO
80920
Tel.: (719) 594-9999
Web Site: http://www.pinecreekgc.com
Golf Course & Club
N.A.I.C.S.: 713910
Al Sellers (Gen Mgr)

Spanish Wells Country Club (1)
9801 Treasure Cay Ln, Bonita Springs, FL
34135
Tel.: (239) 992-5100
Web Site:
http://www.spanishwellscountryclub.com
Golf Course & Country Club
N.A.I.C.S.: 713910
Cara Corr (Dir-Wellness & Fitness)
Debbie Volk (Office Mgr)

Tarpon Cove Yacht and Racquet
Club (1)
471 Bay Club Dr, Naples, FL 34110
Tel.: (239) 592-9808
Web Site: http://www.tarponcoveclub.com
Yacht & Racquet Club

N.A.I.C.S.: 713910
Mark Nicklas (Gen Mgr-Club)
Mycke Loomis (Dir-Ops-Tennis)
Phil Landauer (Dir-Ops-Tennis)
Cara Corr (Dir-Wellness & Fitness)
Debbie Volk (Dir-Member Svcs)
Joni Platt (Dir-Food & Beverage Ops)

The Club at Grand Haven (1)
500 Riverfront Dr, Palm Coast, FL 32137
Tel.: (386) 445-2327
Web Site: http://www.grandhavengc.com
Golf Course & Club
N.A.I.C.S.: 713910
Jeri Harper (Dir-Sls)

The Crosby Club (1)
17102 Bing Crosby Blvd, San Diego, CA
92127
Tel.: (858) 756-6310
Web Site: http://www.thecrosbyclub.com
Emp.: 25
Golf Course & Club
N.A.I.C.S.: 713910
Ed Sanabria (Gen Mgr)

The Golf Club at Dove Mountain (1)
6501 Boulder Bridge Pass, Marana, AZ
85658
Tel.: (520) 572-3500
Web Site:
http://www.thegolfclubatdovemoun
tain.com
Golf Course & Club
N.A.I.C.S.: 713910
Matt Nuechterlein (Gen Mgr)

The Raven at Three Peaks (1)
2929 N Golden Eagle Rd, Silverthorne, CO
80498
Tel.: (970) 262-3636
Web Site:
http://www.ravenatthreepeaks.com
Emp.: 30
Golf Course & Club
N.A.I.C.S.: 713910
Reese McCall (Gen Mgr)

ESCALON SERVICES INC.
2345 Yale St Fl 1, Palo Alto, CA
94306
Tel.: (800) 956-8019
Web Site: http://escalon.services
Year Founded: 2006
Sales Range: $1-9.9 Million
Emp.: 192
Payroll Processing Services
N.A.I.C.S.: 541214
Anurag Pal (CEO)
Ruby Sahiwal (Chm)
Sarah Lerche (Pres & CFO-Svcs)
Gina Garcia (Dir-Controller Svcs)
Benjamin Samson (Dir-HR Svcs)
Amod Dandge (Head-Delivery-Global)

Subsidiaries:

Early Growth Financial Services,
LLC (1)
2033 Gateway Pl 5th Fl, San Jose, CA
95110
Tel.: (415) 234-3437
Web Site: http://www.earlygrowthfinancialser
vices.com
Scientific & Technical Consulting Services
N.A.I.C.S.: 541690
Steven Olson (CFO & Partner)
Gadiel Morantes (Pres)
David Ehrenberg (Founder & CEO)

ESCAMBIA COUNTY SCHOOL READINESS COALITION, INC.
3300 N Pace Blvd Ste 210, Pensa-
cola, FL 32505
Tel.: (850) 595-5400 FL
Web Site:
http://www.elcescambia.org
Year Founded: 2000
Sales Range: $10-24.9 Million
Emp.: 40
Child & Family Support Services
N.A.I.C.S.: 624190
Mona Jackson (Treas)

ESCANABA & LAKE SUPE-

RIOR RAILROAD CO.
6366 S 1St St, Wells, MI 49894
Tel.: (906) 786-0693   MI
Web Site: http://www.elsrr.com
Year Founded: 1991
Sales Range: $10-24.9 Million
Emp.: 60
Provider of Full-Service Railcar Repair & Paint Facility
N.A.I.C.S.: 482111
John Larkin *(Pres)*
Tom Klimek *(VP)*

ESCAPE MEDIA GROUP, INC.
201 SE 2nd Ave Ste 209, Gainesville, FL 32601
Web Site:
   http://www.grooveshark.com
Year Founded: 2006
Sales Range: $10-24.9 Million
Emp.: 130
Music Downloading
N.A.I.C.S.: 516210
Samuel Tarantino III *(Pres)*

ESCAPE POD
750 N Orleans Ste 403, Chicago, IL 60610
Tel.: (312) 274-1180
Web Site:
   http://www.theescapepod.com
Sales Range: $10-24.9 Million
Emp.: 12
N.A.I.C.S.: 541810
Vinny Warren *(Co-Founder & Exec Dir-Creative)*
Greg Nations *(Dir-Creative)*
Norm Bilow *(Co-Founder & Grp Mng Dir)*
Matthew Johnson *(Sr VP & Dir-Accts)*
Heather Hayden *(Dir-Talent)*
Jared Creason *(Dir-Creative)*
Leah Hattendorf *(Sr VP)*
Celia Jones *(CEO)*
Dan Funk *(Dir-Strategy)*
Blagica Bottigliero *(Dir-Social Strategy)*

ESCAPOLOGY LLC
11951 International Dr Unit 2A1, Orlando, FL 32821
Tel.: (407) 287-1515
Web Site: http://www.escapology.com
Year Founded: 2014
Sales Range: $1-9.9 Million
Emp.: 65
Travel Agency Services
N.A.I.C.S.: 561510
Simon Davison *(CEO)*

ESCENDENT, LLC
47 W Polk St Ste 232, Chicago, IL 60605-2085
Tel.: (312) 445-4500
Web Site:
   https://www.escendent.com
Year Founded: 2003
Rev.: $2,400,000
Emp.: 22
Computer Facilities Management Services
N.A.I.C.S.: 541513
Travis Powers *(Partner)*
James T. Whitelow *(Owner)*

ESCHER GROUP LIMITED
133 Federal St, Boston, MA 02110
Tel.: (857) 366-9500
Web Site:
   http://www.eschergroup.com
Year Founded: 1989
Sales Range: $10-24.9 Million
Emp.: 140
Messaging & Data Management Solutions & Services
N.A.I.C.S.: 513210

Liam Church *(Pres)*
Fionnuala Higgins *(Mng Dir-Postal Retail Div)*
Peter Dreifus *(COO)*
Jeremy Folkes *(CTO)*
Jacob Skowronek *(VP-Svcs-Americas)*
Pauline Kenna *(VP-Svcs-EMEA)*
Nick Manolis *(CEO)*
Monica Bruni *(CFO)*
Wayne Haubner *(CTO)*
Amy Harvey *(COO)*
Rodrigo Medgenberg *(Chief Sls Officer)*
Alan Kilduff *(VP-Product Dev)*
Mike Sackton *(Chief Architect)*

Subsidiaries:

Escher Asia Pacific Private
Limited   (1)
13-03 Singapore Post Centre, 10 Eunos Road 8, Singapore, 408600, Singapore
Tel.: (65) 6745 7745
Web Site: http://www.eschergroup.com
Emp.: 45
Information Technology Services
N.A.I.C.S.: 541519
Mauro Rivas *(Mng Dir)*
Jasjit Nehal *(Mng Dir-Asia Pacific)*

Escher Europe Limited   (1)
111 St Stephen's Green, Dublin, 2, Ireland
Tel.: (353) 12545400
Web Site: http://www.eschergroup.com
Information Technology Services
N.A.I.C.S.: 541519
Jasjit Nehal *(Mng Dir)*

Escher UK Limited   (1)
Chancery Court Business Centre, Lincolns Inn Lincoln Road, High Wycombe, HP12 3RE, Bucks, United Kingdom
Tel.: (44) 1494 429352
Web Site: http://www.escher.com
Emp.: 4
Information Technology Services
N.A.I.C.S.: 541519
Jeremy Folkes *(Gen Mgr)*

ESCO GROUP
3450 3rd St, Marion, IA 52302
Tel.: (319) 377-6655
Web Site:
   https://www.theescogroup.com
Sales Range: $25-49.9 Million
Emp.: 250
Electrical Work
N.A.I.C.S.: 238210
Ray Brown *(CFO)*
Hill Swayze *(Acct Mgr)*
Jamie Parman *(Controller)*
Stacy Postier *(Dir-Mktg)*

ESCO INDUSTRIES INCORPORATED
185 Sink Hole Rd, Douglas, GA 31533
Tel.: (912) 384-1417
Web Site:
   https://www.escoindustries.com
Year Founded: 1981
Sales Range: $10-24.9 Million
Emp.: 30
Gypsum Board
N.A.I.C.S.: 327420
Faith Haulk *(Controller)*
William C. Ellis Jr. *(Pres)*

ESCO INDUSTRIES, INC.
115 4th St, Waite Park, MN 56387
Tel.: (320) 259-9470   MN
Web Site:
   http://www.performanceseed.com
Year Founded: 1991
Sales Range: $10-24.9 Million
Emp.: 45
Prepared Bird Food
N.A.I.C.S.: 311119
Sheldon Sturgis *(Pres)*

ESCO LTD.
1800 Woodlawn Dr, Baltimore, MD 21207
Tel.: (410) 944-1666
Web Site:
   http://www.shoecityonline.com
Year Founded: 1949
Sales Range: $25-49.9 Million
Emp.: 45
Mfr of Footwear & Athletic Clothing
N.A.I.C.S.: 458210
Israel Freedman *(Chm)*
Don Heasley *(VP)*
Michael Fortwengler *(Controller)*
Karen Mishler *(Office Mgr)*

ESCROW OPTIONS GROUP INC.
9901 Irvine Ctr Dr, Irvine, CA 92618-4308
Tel.: (949) 753-7888
Web Site: http://www.evrlending.com
Trust, Fiduciary & Custody Activities
N.A.I.C.S.: 523991
Tina Rector *(Owner)*

Subsidiaries:

Everest Escrow, Inc.   (1)
4040 Barranca Pkwy Ste 220, Irvine, CA 92604
Tel.: (949) 783-2430
Web Site: http://www.everestescrow.com
Escrow Services
N.A.I.C.S.: 531390
Erin Drago *(Dir-Ops)*
Fabienne Eskandar *(Mgr-Banking)*
Soo Moon *(Officer-Escrow & Branch Mgr)*
Tara Johnson *(VP-Ops)*
Tom Blank *(Reg Mgr-Sls)*

ESET, LLC
610 W Ash St Ste 1700, San Diego, CA 92101
Tel.: (619) 876-5400
Web Site: http://www.eset.com
Year Founded: 1992
Sales Range: $100-124.9 Million
Emp.: 250
Security Software Development & Sales
N.A.I.C.S.: 513210
Lukas Raska *(COO-Asia Pacific)*
Richard Marko *(CEO)*
Andres Tamburi *(Dir-Corp Comm)*
Gimena Pauletti *(Mgr-Press Rels)*
Ryan Grant *(VP-Sls)*
Brent McCarty *(Pres-North America)*

Subsidiaries:

ESET, spol. s.r.o.   (1)
Aupark Tower 16th Floor, Einsteinova 24, Bratislava, 851 01, Slovakia
Tel.: (421) 232244111
Web Site: http://www.eset.sk
Computer Security Software Developer
N.A.I.C.S.: 513210
Richard Marko *(CEO)*

ESG CONSULTING INC.
2880 Lakeside Dr Ste 343, Santa Clara, CA 95054-2826
Tel.: (408) 970-8595   CA
Web Site: http://www.esginc.com
Year Founded: 1987
Sales Range: $25-49.9 Million
Emp.: 110
Provider of Computer Related Services
N.A.I.C.S.: 541512
Sal Shafi *(Pres)*

ESG REPUBLIC
2811 Fruitvale Ave Ste B 4029 Coffee Rd, Bakersfield, CA 93308
Tel.: (661) 588-8118
Web Site:
   http://www.esgrepublic.com
Sales Range: $25-49.9 Million

Emp.: 16
Payroll, Benefits & Worker's Compensation
N.A.I.C.S.: 541214
Jeff Thorn *(Owner)*
Greg Knittel *(Dir-Ops)*
Jason Thomasy *(Area Mgr)*
Zohaib Qazi *(Engr-Software)*

ESHARES, INC.
333 Bush St Fl 23 Ste 2300, San Francisco, CA 94104
Tel.: (650) 669-8381
Web Site: http://www.carta.com
Year Founded: 2012
Sales Range: $1-9.9 Million
Emp.: 1,000
Software Development Services
N.A.I.C.S.: 541511
Henry Ward *(Founder & CEO)*

ESHELMAN COMPANY INC.
1131 Greenwood Crossing Ct, Bessemer, AL 35022
Tel.: (205) 424-7570
Web Site:
   http://www.eshelmancompany.com
Sales Range: $25-49.9 Million
Emp.: 9
Mfr of Pollution Control Equipment
N.A.I.C.S.: 423830

ESHENBAUGH LAND COMPANY
2502 N Rocky Point Dr Ste 675, Tampa, FL 33607
Tel.: (813) 287-8787
Web Site: http://www.thedirtdog.com
Sales Range: $25-49.9 Million
Real Estate Broker
N.A.I.C.S.: 531210
Bill Eshenbaugh *(Pres)*
Lynda Keever *(Exec VP)*
Ryan Sampson *(Principal)*

ESI ACQUISITION, INC.
823 Broad St, Augusta, GA 30901
Tel.: (706) 823-0911   GA
Web Site: http://www.esi911.com
Year Founded: 1996
Crisis Information Management Technology Design, Installation, Integration & Support Services
N.A.I.C.S.: 513210
Nadia D. Butler *(Pres & CEO)*
Chuck Dolejs *(Mgr-Intl)*
Francis P. Butler *(CFO)*
Curtis R. MacDonald *(COO)*

ESI CONTRACTING, CORP.
3001 E 83rd St, Kansas City, MO 64132
Tel.: (816) 523-5081   MO
Web Site:
   https://www.esicontractingcorp.com
Year Founded: 2005
Sales Range: $10-24.9 Million
Emp.: 300
Excavation Services
N.A.I.C.S.: 238910
Alan E. Wolfe *(Gen Mgr)*
Anthony Fields *(Dir-Payroll & Union Contracts)*
Bob Wilson *(Superintendent)*

Subsidiaries:

Environmental Specialists, Inc.   (1)
3001 E 83rd St, Kansas City, MO 64132-2547
Tel.: (816) 523-5081
Web Site:
   http://www.esicontractingcorp.com
Sales Range: $10-24.9 Million
Emp.: 40
Environmental Remediation Services
N.A.I.C.S.: 562211
Allan Walse *(Gen Mgr)*

ESI Group USA—(Continued)

ESI GROUP USA
950 Walnut Ridge Dr, Hartland, WI
53029-9388
Tel.: (262) 369-3535
Web Site:
  https://www.esigroupusa.com
Year Founded: 1995
Sales Range: $10-24.9 Million
Emp.: 25
Nonresidential Construction Services
N.A.I.C.S.: 236220
Michelle Draghicchio (Mgr-Admin)
Luke Waite (Reg Mgr)
Timothy Nguyen (Sr VP)

ESI VENTURES LLC
9777 Wilshire Blvd, Beverly Hills, CA
90212
Tel.: (818) 887-0700
Web Site:
  http://www.esiventures.com
Investment Firm
N.A.I.C.S.: 523999
Brandon Wolsic (Exec VP)

Subsidiaries:

The Georgian Hotel   (1)
1415 Ocean Ave, Santa Monica, CA 90401
Tel.: (310) 395-9945
Web Site: http://www.georgianhotel.com
Hotels (except Casino Hotels) & Motels
N.A.I.C.S.: 721110
Everardo Choza (Chief Engr)

ESIR1, INC.
433 N Camden Dr 6th Fl, Beverly
Hills, CA 90210
Tel.: (323) 866-1803   CA
Web Site: http://esir1inc.com
Year Founded: 2005
Sales Range: $25-49.9 Million
Oil & Gas Operations
N.A.I.C.S.: 213112
Martinez Rise Walden (Pres)
Alan Chamberlain (Treas)
Nelia Teodoro (VP)
Reggie Walden (Sec)

ESKATON
5105 Manzanita Ave, Carmichael, CA
95608
Tel.: (916) 334-0810
Web Site: https://www.eskaton.org
Sales Range: $25-49.9 Million
Emp.: 1,200
Continuing Care Retirement Commu-
nities Operator
N.A.I.C.S.: 623311
William Pace (CFO)
Betsy Donovan (COO & Sr VP)
Charles Garcia (CIO)
Lola Rain (Dir-Social Media)
Sheri Peifer (Pres)

**ESKENAZI HEALTH FOUNDA-
TION**
720 Eskenazi Ave 5th 3rd Bank Bldg,
Indianapolis, IN 46202
Tel.: (317) 880-4900   IN
Web Site:
  http://www.eskenazihealthfoun
  dation.org
Year Founded: 1985
Sales Range: $1-9.9 Million
Philanthropic Support Services
N.A.I.C.S.: 813211
Julie L. Rowlas (COO)
Trey V. Everly (Dir-Fin & Gift Admin)
Mark Gargula (Treas)
Kevin Hipskind (Chm)
Tom Grande (Sec)
Cherri D. Hobgood (Vice Chm)
William Farkas (VP-Major Gifts)

Kimberly McElroy-Jones (Dir-
Community Partnerships-Community
Health)
Ernest Vargo II (Pres & CEO)

ESKYE SOLUTIONS, INC.
250 E 96th St, Indianapolis, IN 46240
Tel.: (317) 574-6400
Web Site: http://www.eskye.com
Sales Range: $25-49.9 Million
Emp.: 40
Wine & Spirits Software & Web-
Based Solutions
N.A.I.C.S.: 424810
J. Smoke Wallin (Founder, Chm &
CEO)
Thomas Vanneman (CFO)

ESMARK INC.
100 Hazel Ln Ste 300, Sewickley, PA
15143
Tel.: (412) 259-8868
Web Site: http://www.esmark.com
Sales Range: $10-24.9 Million
Emp.: 350
Oil & Gas Exploration Services
N.A.I.C.S.: 213112
James P. Bouchard (Founder, Chm &
CEO)
Stephen W. Powers (Exec VP-
Strategic Dev)
Michael P. DiClemente (Treas & Exec
VP)
Katie Regan (Dir-Comm)

ESMARK INCORPORATED
2500 Euclid Ave, Chicago Heights, IL
60411
Tel.: (708) 756-0400
Web Site: http://www.esmark.com
Holding Company
N.A.I.C.S.: 551112
James P. Bouchard (Founder, Chm &
CEO)
J. Gregory Pilewicz (Pres)
Michael J. Bush (VP-Comml Sls)

Subsidiaries:

Esmark Steel Group, LLC   (1)
2500 Euclid Ave, Chicago Heights, IL 60411
Tel.: (708) 756-0400
Web Site: http://www.esmarksteelgroup.com
Sales Range: $25-49.9 Million
Emp.: 100
Holding Company; Steel Products Distr
N.A.I.C.S.: 551112
John Krupinski (CFO)
Michael Ogrizovich (Vice Chm-Mill Ops &
Pres)
Roberto M. Alvarez (CEO)

Subsidiary (Domestic):

Century Steel   (2)
2500 Euclid Ave, Chicago Heights, IL
60411-1289
Tel.: (708) 758-3839
Sales Range: $25-49.9 Million
Emp.: 28
Flat-Rolled Steel Distr
N.A.I.C.S.: 423510

Chicago Steel & Iron   (2)
700 Central Ave, University Park, IL 60484
Tel.: (782) 672-2000
Flat-Rolled Steel Products Distr
N.A.I.C.S.: 423510

Independent Steel   (2)
615 Liverpool Dr, Valley City, OH 44280
Tel.: (330) 225-7741
Web Site: http://www.independentsteel.com
Sales Range: $25-49.9 Million
Emp.: 45
Flat-Rolled Steel Processing & Distribution
N.A.I.C.S.: 423510

RG Steel Wheeling, LLC   (2)
1134 Market St, Wheeling, WV 26003
Tel.: (304) 234-2400
Steel Mfrs
N.A.I.C.S.: 331110

Melvin E. Baggett (VP-HR)

Sun Steel Co.   (2)
2500 Euclid Ave, Chicago Heights, IL 60411
Tel.: (708) 756-0400
Web Site: http://www.sunsteelco.com
Sales Range: $25-49.9 Million
Emp.: 20
Flat-Rolled Steel Distr
N.A.I.C.S.: 423510
Bernie Hincks (Mgr)

ESO SOLUTIONS, INC.
11500 Alterra Pkwy Ste 100, Austin,
TX 78758
Tel.: (512) 593-6376
Web Site:
  http://www.esosolutions.com
Year Founded: 2004
Sales Range: $1-9.9 Million
Emp.: 41
Healthcare & Public Safety Market
Interoperability Software Developer
N.A.I.C.S.: 513210
Chris Dillie (Chm)
Allen Johnson (Chief Strategy Officer)
Brent Myers (Chief Medical Officer)
Erica Holland (VP-Corp Dev)
Robert Munden (Chief Legal Officer &
Chief Compliance Officer)
Bill Gardner (Sr Dir-Fire Products)
Garrett D. Hall (Sr Dir-Hospital Pro-
grams)
Reinhard Ekl (Sr VP-Product)
Brent LaBathe (Chief Revenue Offi-
cer)
Eric Beck (Pres & CEO)

Subsidiaries:

Lancet Technology Inc   (1)
123 South St, Boston, MA 02111
Tel.: (617) 728-7272
Web Site: http://www.lancettechnology.com
Rev.: $1,050,000
Emp.: 12
Custom Computer Programming Services
N.A.I.C.S.: 541511
Leon Bowman (Pres)

**ESOLUTION ARCHITECTS,
INC.**
3325 Kessinger Dr, Montgomery, AL
36116
Tel.: (334) 324-1262
Web Site: http://www.e-sainc.com
Year Founded: 2005
Sales Range: $1-9.9 Million
Emp.: 70
Technology Consulting, Network Se-
curity & Infrastructure & Customized
Application Development to Govern-
ment & Commercial Operations
N.A.I.C.S.: 541690
William Woodhouse (Pres & CEO)
Tim Castro (VP-Network Solutions &
Chief Sec Officer)
Stacy Waldrep (VP & CTO)

**ESP COMPUTER SERVICES,
INC.**
12444 Victory Blvd 4th Fl, North Hol-
lywood, CA 91606
Tel.: (818) 487-4500
Web Site: http://www.espcomp.com
Year Founded: 1971
Sales Range: $10-24.9 Million
Emp.: 100
Subscription Fulfillment & Marketing
N.A.I.C.S.: 518210
Jack Miller (Chm)
Stefan Beeli (CTO)
Michael Jordan (COO)

ESP TECHONOLOGIES CORP.
140 Broadway 21st Fl, New York, NY
10005
Tel.: (212) 485-5120

Web Site:
  http://www.esptechnologies.com
Financial Software Developer
N.A.I.C.S.: 513210
Joshua S. Levine (CEO)
Michael L. Charland (CFO)
Scott Kurland (Head-Product Dev)

ESPANOLA MERCANTILE CO.
1302 N Riverside Dr, Espanola, NM
87532
Tel.: (505) 753-2176
Web Site:
  http://www.espanolatransit.com
Sales Range: $25-49.9 Million
Emp.: 200
Ready Mixed Concrete
N.A.I.C.S.: 327320
Richard P. Cook (Pres)

ESPARZA ADVERTISING
423 Cooper Ave NW, Albuquerque,
NM 87102
Tel.: (505) 765-1505
Web Site:
  http://www.esparzaadvertising.com
Rev.: $13,000,000
Emp.: 16
Advertising, Bilingual Marketing,
Graphic Design, Hispanic Marketing,
Logo & Package Design, Media Buy-
ing Services, Merchandising, Out-
door, Pharmaceutical, Print, T.V.
N.A.I.C.S.: 541810
Del Esparza (Pres)
Adam Greenhood (VP & Dir-Creative)
Tiffany Hobson (Exec VP)
Vicki Lee Newsom (Sr Acct Exec)
Jeremy Spencer (Assoc Dir-Creative)
Thatcher Dorn (Dir-Art)
Dustin Simon (Assoc Acct Exec)
Erin Riley (Dir-Media)

**ESPEE BIOPHARMA & FINE-
CHEM, LLC**
1701 E Woodfield Rd Ste 636,
Schaumburg, IL 60173
Web Site: http://www.espeeusa.com
Year Founded: 2009
Sales Range: $25-49.9 Million
Emp.: 10
Pharmaceuticals Product Mfr
N.A.I.C.S.: 325412
Anar Modi (Dir-Bus Dev)

**ESPERANZA HEALTH CEN-
TER**
4417 N 6th St, Philadelphia, PA
19140-2319
Tel.: (215) 302-3600   PA
Web Site:
  https://www.esperanzahealth.com
Year Founded: 1987
Sales Range: $10-24.9 Million
Emp.: 145
Health Care Srvices
N.A.I.C.S.: 622110
Cassandra Jackson (Dir-HR)
Ted Voboril (Dir-Dev)
Andrea Daft (Dir-Nursing)
Erik Davis (Dir-Fin)
Barbara Bradford (Sec)
David Crosscombe (Pres)
Ken MacBain (Treas)
Roberto Vargas (VP)

ESPERO BIOPHARMA, INC.
14286-19 Beach Blvd #270, Jackson-
ville, FL 32250
Tel.: (904) 834-2665   DE
Web Site: http://esperobio.com
Pharmaceutical Company
N.A.I.C.S.: 325412
Jeffrey Cole (Co-Founder)
Quang Pham (Chm & CEO)

Subsidiaries:

Espero Pharmaceuticals, Inc.　(1)
14286-19 Beach Blvd Ste 270, Jacksonville, FL 32250
Tel.: (904) 834-2665
Pharmaceuticals Mfr
N.A.I.C.S.: 325412

ESPIRE DENTAL PRACTICE, LLC
6825 E Tennessee Ave Ste 621, Denver, CO 80224
Tel.: (720) 966-2436
Web Site:
　http://www.levinfamilydental.com
Year Founded: 2018
Offices of Dentists
N.A.I.C.S.: 621210
Liz Prothro (Office Mgr)

Subsidiaries:

La Costa Dental Group　(1)
501 N El Camino Real Ste 200, Encinitas, CA 92024-1335
Tel.: (760) 350-3496
Web Site:
　http://www.lacostadentalgroup.com
Offices of Dentists
N.A.I.C.S.: 621210
Omer Anisso (Partner)

ESPORTIA INTERNATIONAL INC.
2397 Bateman Ave, Duarte, CA 91010
Tel.: (626) 301-0280
Web Site:
　http://www.espgroupltd.com
Year Founded: 1981
Sales Range: $10-24.9 Million
Emp.: 48
Mens & Boys Clothing Mfr
N.A.I.C.S.: 424350
William Yau (Pres)

ESPRIX TECHNOLOGIES, LP
7680 Matoaka Rd, Sarasota, FL 34243
Tel.: (941) 355-5100
Web Site:
　https://www.esprixtech.com
Year Founded: 1982
Sales Range: $10-24.9 Million
Emp.: 14
Specialty Chemicals Distr
N.A.I.C.S.: 424690
Ken Jennings (VP-Mktg-MST Aluminum Brazing Flux & Solder Flux Activators)
Brian Roberts (Sr VP-Microelectronics/Microparticles/Silk Screen Imaging)
Tonya Pless (VP-Electrostatic Imaging Materials)
Cary A. Veith (Pres & CEO)
Philip W. Nace Jr. (Founder & Chm)

ESQUIRE RADIO & ELECTRONICS INC.
140 Se 5th Ave Ph 49, Boca Raton, FL 33432-5055
Tel.: (718) 499-0020　NY
Year Founded: 1946
Sales Range: $75-99.9 Million
Emp.: 20
Importer & Distributor of Private Label Telecommunications & Consumer Electronic Products
N.A.I.C.S.: 423690
Harvey Lieberman (Chm & Pres)

Subsidiaries:

Tangent Industries Ltd.　(1)
140 Se 5th Ave Ph 49, Boca Raton, FL 33432-5055　(100%)
Tel.: (860) 738-7449
Web Site: http://www.tangentindinc.com

Sales Range: $25-49.9 Million
Emp.: 19
Radio Sales
N.A.I.C.S.: 811210

ESROCK PARTNERS
14550 S 94th Ave, Orland Park, IL 60462-2652
Tel.: (708) 349-8400　IL
Web Site: http://www.esrock.com
Year Founded: 1978
Sales Range: $10-24.9 Million
Emp.: 30
N.A.I.C.S.: 541810
Jack Coughlin (Pres)
Don Peterson (Partner-Pub Rel & Res)
Kevin Wilson (Partner)
Tracy O'Malley (Mgr-Bus)
Jackie Krupko (Mgr-Ops)

ESSCHEM INC.
4000 Columbia Ave, Linwood, PA 19061-1139
Tel.: (610) 497-9000
Web Site: https://www.esschem.com
Sales Range: $10-24.9 Million
Emp.: 50
Plastics Materials & Resins
N.A.I.C.S.: 325211
Edward Sobolewski (VP)
Gary Shaw (Mng Dir-Europe)
Sue Sheariss (VP)
Claire Rogers (Mgr-Accts Receivable)
Henry M. Justi (Founder, Pres & CEO)

ESSENCE COMMUNICATIONS INC.
241 37th St 4th Fl, Brooklyn, NY 11232
Tel.: (800) 938-4660
Web Site: http://www.essence.com
Year Founded: 1968
Magazines & Books, Marketer of Eyewear Products & Organizer of Annual Music Festival
N.A.I.C.S.: 513120
Staci Hallmon-Bazzani (VP & Dir-Brand Sls)
Caroline Wanga (Interim CEO)

Subsidiaries:

Essence Magazine　(1)
135 W 50th St 4th Fl, New York, NY 10020
Tel.: (800) 274-9398
Magazine Publisher
N.A.I.C.S.: 513120

ESSENTIA HEALTH
502 E 2nd St, Duluth, MN 55805
Tel.: (218) 786-8376　MN
Web Site:
　http://www.essentiahealth.org
Year Founded: 2003
Sales Range: $75-99.9 Million
Health Care Srvices
N.A.I.C.S.: 622110
Teresa O'Toole (Chief Legal Officer & Sec)
Michael J. Mahoney (VP-Pub Policy)
Timothy P. Sayler (COO-West)
Greg Glasner (Pres-Eastern North Dakota & Western Minnesota)
James Anderson (Vice Chm)
David Gaddie (Chm)
Walter Leino (Dir-Medicare Beneficiary)
James Seitz (Dir-Medicare Beneficiary)
Bert Norman (CFO & Treas)
David C. Herman (CEO)
Shawn Christianson (Chief Quality Officer)
Daniel Collins (Officer-Improvement & Quality Assurance)
Dennis Dassenko (CIO)

Diane Davidson (Chief HR Officer)
Bruce Hein (Treas)
Peter Henry (Chief Medical Officer)
Scott Johnson (Chief Medical Officer-West)
Jeff Korsmo (Exec VP-Ops & Admin)
Michael C. Metcalf (Exec VP-Clinic Ops)
Dan Nikcevich (Co-Pres)
Rajesh Prabhu (Officer-Improvement & Quality Assurance)
Adam Rees (Co-Pres)
Kristi Schmidt (Chief Mktg & Comm Officer)
Anne Stephen (Chief Medical Officer-East)
Timothy D. Zager (Co-Pres)
Brad Beard (COO-Northeastern Minnesota & Northwestern Wisconsin)

ESSENTIA INSTITUTE OF RURAL HEALTH
502 E 2nd St, Duluth, MN 55805
Tel.: (218) 786-3940　MN
Web Site:
　http://www.essentiainstitute.org
Year Founded: 2009
Sales Range: $10-24.9 Million
Emp.: 92
Health & Human Welfare Support Services
N.A.I.C.S.: 813311
Kevin Galazen (Dir-Ops)
Kate Dean (Exec Dir-Interim)
Nancy Dold (Mgr-Res Grants)

ESSENTIAL DATA CORPORATION
4 Research Dr Ste 402, Shelton, CT 06484
Tel.: (203) 359-1400
Web Site:
　https://www.essentialdata.com
Sales Range: $10-24.9 Million
Emp.: 12
Data Processing & Preparation
N.A.I.C.S.: 518210
Antoinette Allocca (Founder & Pres)
Thomas Walsh (VP)
Lisa Benne (Mng Dir)
Michelle Brown (Mgr-Engagement)

ESSENTIAL FREIGHT SYSTEMS INC.
3500 Sunrise Hwy Bldg 200 Ste 200, Great River, NY 11739
Tel.: (631) 321-1222
Web Site:
　http://www.essentialfreight.com
Rev.: $16,647,069
Emp.: 7
Freight Forwarding
N.A.I.C.S.: 484121

ESSENTIAL HOUSING INVESTMENT
915 W 4th St, Winston Salem, NC 27101
Tel.: (336) 724-1000
Rev.: $33,600,000
Emp.: 7
Real Estate, Entertainment & Equipment Sales
N.A.I.C.S.: 523999

ESSENTIAL PERSONNEL, INC.
3415 W State St Ste B, Grand Island, NE 68803
Tel.: (308) 381-4400
Web Site:
　http://www.essentialpersonnel.com
Staffing Services
N.A.I.C.S.: 561311
Travis R. Powell (Pres)

Subsidiaries:

Cecor Staffing Inc.　(1)
5460 S Quebec St Ste 315, Greenwood Village, CO 80111
Tel.: (303) 873-9855
Web Site: http://www.cecor.com
Human Resources & Executive Search Consulting Services
N.A.I.C.S.: 541612
Travis Powell (Owner)

ESSENTIAL PHARMACEUTICAL CORP.
1906 W Holt Ave, Pomona, CA 91768
Tel.: (909) 623-4565
Web Site:
　https://www.essentialpharma.com
Year Founded: 1986
Sales Range: $10-24.9 Million
Emp.: 15
Pharmaceutical Preparation Mfr
N.A.I.C.S.: 325412
Bruce Lin (Co-Founder)
Rebecca Lin (Co-Founder)

ESSENTIAL SECURITY, INC.
50 Cragwood Rd Ste 318, South Plainfield, NJ 07080
Tel.: (908) 222-0850
Web Site:
　http://www.essentialsecurityinc.com
Year Founded: 2002
Sales Range: $10-24.9 Million
Emp.: 70
Security Guards & Patrol Services
N.A.I.C.S.: 561612
Loretta Tamzoke (Sec)

ESSENTIAL WHOLESALE
2211 NW Nicolai St, Portland, OR 97210
Tel.: (503) 893-1100
Web Site:
　https://www.essentialwholesale.com
Year Founded: 2003
Sales Range: $10-24.9 Million
Emp.: 26
Toilet Preparation Mfr
N.A.I.C.S.: 325620
Kathy Steinbock (Acct Exec)
Shane Burns (Mgr-Distr Center)
Joseph Carmody (Mgr-HR)
Diane Humke (Pres)

ESSEX BUILDERS CORP.
275 Tpke St Ste 310, Canton, MA 02021
Tel.: (781) 326-3466
Web Site:
　http://www.essexbuilderscorp.com
Sales Range: $10-24.9 Million
Emp.: 15
Housing Construction Services
N.A.I.C.S.: 236117
David O'Neil (Pres)

ESSEX CORPORATION
11606 Nicholas St Ste 100, Omaha, NE 68154
Tel.: (402) 431-0500
Web Site:
　http://www.essexcommunities.com
Year Founded: 1976
Sales Range: $25-49.9 Million
Emp.: 75
Land Subdividers & Developers Commercial
N.A.I.C.S.: 237210
Kent Braasch (Pres)
Michael McGillick (Co-Pres)
Phil Warren (CFO)

ESSEX COUNTY COMMUNITY FOUNDATION
175 Andover St Ste 101, Danvers, MA 01923

Essex County Community Foundation—(Continued)

Tel.: (978) 777-8876   MA
Web Site: https://www.eccf.org
Year Founded: 1998
Sales Range: $10-24.9 Million
Emp.: 9
Charitable Fundraising Services
N.A.I.C.S.: 813211
Michelle Xiarhos Curran (Mgr-Comm)
Joan Henkels (Office Mgr)
Jonathan Payson (Chm)

**ESSEX EQUITY MANAGE-
MENT, LLC**
70 S Orange Ave Ste 105, Livingston,
NJ 07039
Tel.: (908) 988-1090   DE
Web Site:
    http://www.essexequity.com
Investment Management Service
N.A.I.C.S.: 523940
John D. Liu (CEO)

Subsidiaries:

Richmond Hill Investments, LLC   (1)
375 Hudson St 12th Fl, New York, NY
10014
Tel.: (212) 989-2700
Web Site: http://www.essexequity.com
Emp.: 12
Investment Advisory & Asset Management
Services
N.A.I.C.S.: 523940
John D. Liu (Mng Partner)

**ESSEX GRAIN PRODUCTS,
INC.**
9 Lee Blvd, Frazer, PA 19355-1234
Tel.: (610) 647-3800   PA
Web Site: http://www.essexgrain.com
Year Founded: 1972
Sales Range: $50-74.9 Million
Emp.: 38
Distr of Wholesale Food Ingredients
N.A.I.C.S.: 424490
Luke Palante (Pres)
Jeff Keener (Controller)
Meehan Keith (Reg Mgr-Sls)
Candy Jumbo (VP-Customer Svc)
Kim Mellilo (Office Mgr)

ESSEX INDUSTRIES, INC.
7700 Gravois Rd, Saint Louis, MO
63123
Tel.: (314) 832-4500   MO
Web Site: http://www.essexind.com
Year Founded: 1947
Sales Range: $200-249.9 Million
Emp.: 300
Cryogenic Machinery, Industrial
N.A.I.C.S.: 333248
Mickey Waldman (Pres)
Sidney H. Guller (Chm)
Evan Waldman (CEO)

Subsidiaries:

Stevens Manufacturing Company
Incorporated   (1)
220 Rock Ln, Milford, CT 06460-3803
Tel.: (203) 878-2328
Web Site: http://www.stevensmfgco.com
Rev.: $4,510,000
Emp.: 22
Aircraft Parts & Auxiliary Equipment Mfr
N.A.I.C.S.: 336413
Stephen Fogler (Pres)

**ESSEX INVESTMENT MAN-
AGEMENT COMPANY, LLC**
125 High St 18th Fl, Boston, MA
02110-2702
Tel.: (617) 342-3200   DE
Web Site:
    https://www.essexinvest.com
Year Founded: 1976
Sales Range: $1-4.9 Billion
Emp.: 25

Investment Management Service
N.A.I.C.S.: 523940
Stephen D. Cutler (Pres & Sr Portfo-
lio Mgr)
Michael S. McCarthy (COO, Chief
Compliance Officer & Sr VP)
Nancy B. Prial (Co-CEO & Sr Portfo-
lio Mgr)
Martin B. Cournan (Sr VP)
Elizabeth F. Giroux (Sr VP)
Saralyn Sacks (Sr VP & Portfolio
Mgr)
Marcy R. Carlin (Sr VP)
Joseph Claudius McNay (Chm, Chief
Investment Officer & Sr Portfolio Mgr)
Alexander A. Forse (VP & Portfolio
Mgr)
Anne Marie McMichael (VP)
William H. Page (Sr VP & Sr Portfolio
Mgr)
Robert J. Uek (Co-CEO & Sr Portfolio
Mgr)

ESSEX MANUFACTURING INC.
309A Spring St, Washington, GA
30673-1668
Tel.: (706) 678-2141
Year Founded: 1978
Sales Range: $10-24.9 Million
Emp.: 10
Mfr of Waterproof Outerwear
N.A.I.C.S.: 315250
Charles Baum (Pres)
Peter J. Baum (CFO & COO)

**ESSEX WOODLANDS MAN-
AGEMENT, INC.**
335 Bryant St 3rd Fl, Palo Alto, CA
94301
Tel.: (650) 543-1555   DE
Web Site:
    http://www.essexwoodlands.com
Year Founded: 1985
Sales Range: $1-4.9 Billion
Emp.: 30
Privater Equity Firm
N.A.I.C.S.: 523999
Petri Vainio (Mng Dir)
Steve Wiggins (Mng Dir)
Jeffrey Himawan (Mng Dir)
Ronald W. Eastman (Mng Dir)
Brooks Andrews (Principal)
Bryan Morton (Partner-Operating)
Evis Hursever (Partner)
Mike Warmuth (Partner-Operating)
Richard Kolodziejcyk (CFO & Chief
Compliance Officer)
Scott Barry (Mng Dir)
Shaunak Parikh (Principal)
Immanuel Thangaraj (Mng Dir)
Martin P. Sutter (Mng Dir)
Guido J. Neels (Mng Dir)
Guido J. Neels (Operating Partner &
Mng Dir)

Subsidiaries:

EUSA Pharma (UK) Limited   (1)
Ground Floor Suite GE Breakspear Park
Breakspear Way, Hemel Hempstead, HP2
4TZ, United Kingdom
Tel.: (44) 330 500 1140
Web Site: http://www.eusapharma.com
Specialty Biopharmaceutical Developer, Mfr
& Whslr
N.A.I.C.S.: 325412
Lee Morley (CEO)
Emma Johnson (CFO)
Paul Davisson (Head-Technical Ops)
Claire Harding (Dir-HR)
Jonathan Morgan (Dir-Medical)
Ben Owens (Dir-Bus Dev)
Bryan Morton (Chm)

Subsidiary (US):

EUSA Pharma (US) LLC   (2)
100 Horizon Ctr Blvd, Hamilton, NJ 08691
Tel.: (609) 528-5620
Specialty Biopharmaceutical Whslr

N.A.I.C.S.: 424210
Paul Davisson (Grp Head-Technical Ops)

ESSEX, LLC
21805 W Field Pkwy Ste 250, Deer
Park, IL 60010
Tel.: (847) 777-7800   IL
Web Site: https://www.essexllc.com
Money Management Services
N.A.I.C.S.: 523940
Arthur A. Freedman (COO)
James Hartwell (Pres)
Robert Tutela (Chief Compliance Offi-
cer & Mgr-Portfolio)

ESSMUELLER COMPANY
334 Ave 'A' AirBase, Laurel, MS
39441
Tel.: (601) 649-2400
Web Site:
    https://www.essmueller.com
Rev.: $14,000,000
Emp.: 120
Bulk Handling Conveyor Systems
N.A.I.C.S.: 333922
William L. McLean (Pres & CEO)

ESTABROOK CORPORATION
700 W Bagley Rd, Berea, OH 44017
Tel.: (440) 234-8566
Web Site:
    https://www.estabrookcorp.com
Rev.: $11,715,106
Emp.: 30
Pumps & Pumping Equipment Sales
N.A.I.C.S.: 333914
Kelly Sutula (Treas)
Dave Purvis (Engr-Inside Sls)

**ESTABROOK FORD LINCOLN
MERCURY INC.**
3689 14th St, Pascagoula, MS 39567
Tel.: (228) 762-2641
Web Site:
    http://www.estabrookford.dealer
    connection.com
Rev.: $26,100,000
Emp.: 100
Automobile Dealers
N.A.I.C.S.: 441110
Chris Doebler (Mgr-Bus)
Phillip Everett (Mgr-Fleet)
James B. Estabrook Jr. (Pres)

ESTACADO ENERGY LLC
2600 K Ave, Plano, TX 75074
Tel.: (972) 633-8886
Emp.: 100
Oil & Gas Operations
N.A.I.C.S.: 213112
Dennis Eubanks (Pres)

**ESTAD STAMPING & MANU-
FACTURING COMPANY**
1005 Griggs St, Danville, IL 61832
Tel.: (217) 442-4600   DE
Web Site:
    http://www.estadstamping.com
Year Founded: 1996
Rev.: $3,000,000
Emp.: 17
Metal Stamping Mfr
N.A.I.C.S.: 332618
Robert Rew (Pres)
Eva Cotton (Treas)

**ESTANCIA CAPITAL MANAGE-
MENT, LLC**
20865 N 90th Pl Ste 200, Scottsdale,
AZ 85255
Tel.: (480) 998-7000   AZ
Web Site:
    http://www.estanciapartners.com
Sales Range: $1-9.9 Million
Emp.: 5
Privater Equity Firm
N.A.I.C.S.: 523999

Takashi Moriuchi (Partner)
Michael Mendez (Partner)
Danny Kang (Partner)
Darrin C. Jeffries (COO, Chief Com-
pliance Officer & Gen Counsel)
Dana Alan Kurttila (Sr VP)

Subsidiaries:

North Square Investments, LLC   (1)
10 S LaSalle St Ste 1925, Chicago, IL
60603
Tel.: (312) 857-2160
Web Site: http://www.northsquareinvest.com
Investment Services
N.A.I.C.S.: 523999
Mark D. Goodwin (Founder & CEO)
Martin Gawne (Head-Mktg)
Phil Callahan (Head-Distr)
Dan Ellenwood (Chief Compliance Officer)
Alan Molotsky (CFO & Gen Counsel)
Brendan Kinnarney (VP-Distr)
Joe Michelotti (VP-Distr)
Steve Schneider (VP-Distr)

Holding (Domestic):

C.S. McKee LP   (2)
420 Ft Duquesne Blvd 8th Fl CS Mckee,
Pittsburgh, PA 15222-1435
Tel.: (412) 566-1234
Web Site: http://www.csmckee.com
Sales Range: $50-74.9 Million
Emp.: 30
Investment Management Service
N.A.I.C.S.: 523940
Eugene M. Natali (CEO)
Boyd M. Hanson (Sr VP & Mgr-Client Svc)
Brian S. Allen (Sr VP & Portfolio Mgr-Fixed
Income)
Bryan R. Johanson (Sr VP & Portfolio Mgr-
Fixed Income)
Jack P. White (Sr VP & Portfolio Mgr-Fixed
Income)
Robert A. McGee (Sr VP & Portfolio Mgr-
Equity)
Gregory M. Melvin (Chief Investment Officer
& Exec VP)
Mark R. Gensheimer (Pres)
Harish Aiyar (VP)
Jeffrey R. Davidek (Sr VP & Mgr-Client Svc)
Len Boss (VP & Mgr-Ops)
Michael J. Donnelly (VP)
Nancy Y. Banker (Sr VP & Mgr-Client Svc)
Shane M. Nickolich (Mgr-Mktg & Client Svc)
Shawna Aufman (VP)
Andrew Faderewski (Sr VP & Portfolio Mgr-
Fixed Income)
Robert M. Rossi (Sr VP & Mgr-Client Svc)
Ulf Skreppen (Chief Compliance Officer, Sr
VP & Dir-Ops)
Mark Hutter (Sr VP)

Subsidiary (Domestic):

The Patterson Capital
Corporation   (3)
2029 Century Park E, Los Angeles, CA
90067
Tel.: (310) 556-2496
Sales Range: $1-9.9 Million
Emp.: 15
Investment Advice
N.A.I.C.S.: 523940
Jean Clark (Sr VP)

ESTATES WINDOWS LTD.
950 N Shore Dr, Lake Bluff, IL
60044-2202
Tel.: (847) 234-3302
Web Site:
    http://www.estateswindows.com
Sales Range: $10-24.9 Million
Emp.: 25
Windows
N.A.I.C.S.: 423310
Dennis Valentini (Pres)

ESTAUGH
RR 70 1 Medford Leas Way, Med-
ford, NJ 08055
Tel.: (609) 654-3000
Web Site:
    http://www.medfordleas.org
Sales Range: $10-24.9 Million

Emp.: 400
Retirement Hotel Operation
N.A.I.C.S.: 623110
Jeremy Vickers *(Pres)*

ESTEEM BROADCASTING, LLC
101 Lee St, Bristol, VA 24201-4355
Tel.: (276) 645-1555
Television Broadcasting
N.A.I.C.S.: 516120
Jack Dempsey *(Gen Mgr)*

ESTEIN & ASSOCIATES USA LTD.
4705 S Apopka Vineland Rd, Orlando, FL 32819
Tel.: (407) 354-3307
Real Estate Development & Management Services
N.A.I.C.S.: 531120
Lance Fair *(COO)*

ESTERLE MOLD & MACHINE CO. INC.
1539 Commerce Dr, Stow, OH 44224
Tel.: (330) 686-1685
Web Site: https://www.esterle.com
Year Founded: 1976
Sales Range: $10-24.9 Million
Emp.: 55
Mfr of Industrial Molds
N.A.I.C.S.: 333511
Adam Esterle *(Founder & Chm)*
Richard Esterle *(Pres)*

ESTES CONSTRUCTION
131 W 2nd St Ste 400, Davenport, IA 52801
Tel.: (563) 322-7301
Web Site:
  https://www.estesconstruction.com
Year Founded: 1970
Sales Range: $10-24.9 Million
Emp.: 75
Civil Engineering Services
N.A.I.C.S.: 237310
Laura Andersen *(Coord-Mktg)*
Kent Pilcher *(Pres)*
Amy Follis *(Project Coord)*
Blake Burns *(Mgr-Pre-Construction)*
Brian Wicklund *(Project Mgr)*
Michelle Breneman *(VP-Acctg & Admin)*

ESTES EXPRESS LINES, INC.
3901 W Broad St, Richmond, VA 23230-3962
Tel.: (804) 353-1900   VA
Web Site: https://www.estes-
  express.com
Year Founded: 1936
Sales Range: $1-4.9 Billion
Emp.: 21,700
General Freight Trucking, Long-Distance, Less than Truckload
N.A.I.C.S.: 484122
Paul J. Dugent *(VP-Pricing)*
Webb Estes *(Pres & COO)*
Rob Estes *(Bd of Dirs, Chm, Chm, Pres, CEO, CEO & CEO)*
Billy Hupp *(Vice Chm & Exec VP)*

Subsidiaries:

Big E Transportation LLC   (1)
3901 W Broad St, Richmond, VA 23230
Tel.: (866) 491-9255
Freight Shipping & Trucking Services
N.A.I.C.S.: 484121

Estes   (1)
14727 Alondra Blvd, La Mirada, CA 90638-5617
Tel.: (714) 523-1122
Web Site: http://www.estes-express.com
Sales Range: $150-199.9 Million
Emp.: 2,000
Trucking Distr

N.A.I.C.S.: 484121
Robert Waller *(Gen Mgr)*

Estes Express Lines, Inc. - Estes
Level2 Logistics Division   (1)
3901 W Broad St, Richmond, VA 23230
Tel.: (855) 693-7878
Web Site: http://www.level2logistics.com
Logistics Management Consulting Services
N.A.I.C.S.: 541614

Estes Express Lines, Inc. - Estes
Specialized Truckload and Delivery
Services Division   (1)
2920 Grandview Dr, Simpsonville, SC 29680
Tel.: (877) 795-1505
Logistics Management Consulting Services
N.A.I.C.S.: 541614

Estes Express Lines, Inc. - Estes
SureMove Division   (1)
3901 W Broad St, Richmond, VA 23230
Web Site: http://www.estessuremove.com
Household Goods Transportation Services
N.A.I.C.S.: 484210

Estes Forwarding Worldwide
LLC   (1)
1100 Commerce Rd, Richmond, VA 23224
Tel.: (804) 205-5907
Web Site: http://www.efwnow.com
Sales Range: $75-99.9 Million
Emp.: 190
Domestic & International Shipping & Logistics
N.A.I.C.S.: 488510
Scott Fisher *(Pres & CEO)*

ESTES HEATING & AIR CONDITIONING, INC.
3981 Tradeport Blvd, Atlanta, GA 30354-3730
Tel.: (470) 594-5053
Web Site: https://www.estesair.com
Year Founded: 1949
Sales Range: $10-24.9 Million
Emp.: 150
Plumbing Services
N.A.I.C.S.: 238220
Tommy Estes *(Owner)*

ESTEX MANUFACTURING COMPANY
402 E Broad St, Fairburn, GA 30213
Tel.: (770) 964-3322
Web Site: https://www.estexmfg.com
Year Founded: 1900
Sales Range: $10-24.9 Million
Emp.: 120
Canvas & Vinyl Related Products Mfr
N.A.I.C.S.: 314910
Brent Wilkes *(Pres & CEO)*
Michael Scott *(VP-Sls)*

ESTEY-HOOVER INC. ADVERTISING-PUBLIC RELATIONS
20201 SW Birch St Ste 150, Newport Beach, CA 92660
Tel.: (949) 756-8501
Year Founded: 1975
Rev.: $12,750,000
Emp.: 18
Advetising Agency
N.A.I.C.S.: 541810
Daniel W. Hoover *(Pres, CEO & Founder)*
John Cooper *(VP-Creative & Co-Creative Dir)*
Joan Carol *(VP-Ops)*
Dave Gyurina *(VP-Acct Svcs)*
Bill Maloney *(Supvr-Automotive)*
Myrna Horn *(Dir-Media)*
Don Allen *(Pub Rel Asso-Tech, Fin)*
Bob Wittenburg *(VP-Corp & Mktg Comm)*
Christine Sudut *(Specialist-Digital Media Acct)*

ESTILL MEDICAL TECHNOLOGIES, INC.
4144 N Central Expy Ste 260, Dallas, TX 75204-3100
Tel.: (214) 561-6001
Web Site:
  http://www.thermalangel.com
Emp.: 100
Thermal Angel Blood & IV Fluid Infusion Warmer Mfr
N.A.I.C.S.: 339112
Jay Lopez *(Pres & CEO)*

ESTLICK-GIRVIN & LEFEVER INC.
102 W Van Buren St, Columbia City, IN 46725
Tel.: (260) 248-6088
Web Site:
  http://www.starfinancial.com
Sales Range: $10-24.9 Million
Emp.: 54
Insurance Agents, Brokers & Service
N.A.I.C.S.: 524210
John W. Lefever *(Pres)*

ESTUARY INVESTMENT CORP.
3711 Cortez Rd West, Bradenton, FL 34210-3108
Tel.: (941) 756-0677
Year Founded: 1970
Sales Range: $25-49.9 Million
Emp.: 60
Manager of Real Estate Investment Trusts
N.A.I.C.S.: 525990

Subsidiaries:

Neal Communities Inc.   (1)
5800 Lakewood Ranch Blvd, Sarasota, FL 34240
Tel.: (941) 328-1111
Web Site: http://www.nealcommunities.com
Sales Range: $125-149.9 Million
Emp.: 125
Real Estate Developers
N.A.I.C.S.: 237210
Jim Schier *(Sr VP-Fin)*
Patrick Neal *(CEO)*
Leisa Weintraub *(VP-Mktg & Dir-Creative)*
Kathy Forinash *(VP-Design)*
Eddie Gaudette *(Mgr-Warranty)*
Cathy Engels *(VP-Pur)*
Sandy Foster *(Mgr-Pur)*
Charlene Neal *(Pres-PureStyle & VP-Design)*
Michael Storey *(Pres)*
Randy Olson *(Mgr-Land Dev)*
Jodi McConnell *(Mgr-Acctg)*
Christopher Clark *(VP-Ops)*
Nancy Reynolds *(CFO)*
Michael R. Greenberg *(Pres-Southwest Florida)*
Tammy Kramer *(Mgr-Architectural Plans)*
Mark Evans *(VP-Land Dev)*
Nicole Brooks *(VP-Sls-North)*
Diane Kerper *(VP-Sls & Mktg-South)*
Tashara Cronshaw *(VP-HR)*
Debbie Gericke *(Mgr-Area Sls)*
Jason Frost *(VP-Land Acq)*
Michael Agins *(VP-Sls & Mktg-South)*
Carlos Puente *(VP-Sls-North)*
Christine McKelvey *(Mktg Mgr)*
Lara Bommersheim *(Coord-Mktg)*

Subsidiary (Domestic):

John Neal Homes, Inc.   (2)
8141 Lakewood Main St Ste 210, Lakewood Ranch, FL 34202
Tel.: (941) 328-1202
Web Site: http://www.homesbyjohnneal.com
Sales Range: $25-49.9 Million
Emp.: 20
New Housing Construction
N.A.I.C.S.: 236115
Mark Sochar *(VP-Special Projects)*
Tony Campano *(Mgr-Pur)*
Randy Craig *(Mgr-Building)*

ESW CAPITAL, LLC

401 Congress Ave Ste 2650, Austin, TX 78701
Tel.: (512) 524-6149   DE
Year Founded: 1988
Software-Focused Private Equity & Investment Management Firm
N.A.I.C.S.: 523999
Andrew Price *(CFO)*

Subsidiaries:

Aurea Software, Inc.   (1)
401 Congress Ave Ste 2650, Austin, TX 78701
Tel.: (512) 201-8287
Web Site: http://www.aurea.com
Commercial Customer Experience Software & Services
N.A.I.C.S.: 513210
Keith Green *(Sr VP-HR-Global)*
Scott F. Brighton *(Pres & CEO)*
Hub Vandervoort *(CTO)*
Eric Levine *(CMO)*
Curt Richtermeyer *(Sr VP-Sls-Global)*
Pat McClain *(CFO)*
Jonathan Berkowitz *(Chief Product Officer)*
Ben Cohen *(Chief Revenue Officer)*
Andy Montgomery *(Sr VP-Engrg)*
Mark Hall *(VP-Channels)*
Bernd Recker *(Head-EMEA)*

Subsidiary (Domestic):

Aurea Energy Solutions, Inc.   (2)
401 Congress Ave Ste 2650, Austin, TX 78701   (100%)
Tel.: (512) 201-8287
Energy & Water Metering Equipment Mfr
N.A.I.C.S.: 334515
Ruediger Neubauer *(Sr VP-Electronic Data Interchange & Customer Info Sys)*
Rachel Collins *(VP-Customer Success)*

Subsidiary (Non-US):

Aurea Software GmbH   (2)
Operngasse 17-21, 1040, Vienna, Austria   (81.5%)
Tel.: (43) 1878550
Web Site: http://www.update.com
Sales Range: $25-49.9 Million
Emp.: 291
Customer Relationship Management Software Publisher
N.A.I.C.S.: 513210
Todd Brooks *(CEO & Member-Mgmt Bd)*

Subsidiary (US):

update CRM Inc.   (3)
1200 Route 22 E, Bridgewater, NJ 08807   (100%)
Tel.: (908) 253-3597
Web Site: http://www.update.com
Customer Relationship Management Software Publisher
N.A.I.C.S.: 513210

Subsidiary (Domestic):

BroadVision, Inc.   (2)
460 Seaport Ct Ste 102, Redwood City, CA 94063
Tel.: (650) 331-1000
Web Site: http://www.broadvision.com
Large-Scale, Personalized Business on the Global Internet, Intranets & Extranets Application Solution Supplier
N.A.I.C.S.: 334610
Pehong Chen *(Chm, Pres, CEO & Interim CFO)*
Stefano Gargioli *(VP & Gen Mgr-BroadVision Global Svcs)*
Fadi Micaelian *(VP-Sls)*
Toshi Sakayori *(Gen Mgr-Japan)*
Yuk Chan *(VP-Engrg)*
Yun-Ping Hsu *(Gen Mgr-Asia Pacific)*

Holding (Non-US):

BroadVision Deutschland GmbH   (3)
Feringastrasse 6 Unterfohring, 85774, Munich, Germany
Tel.: (49) 8999216418
Web Site: http://www.broadvision.com
Content Management, Online Merchandising, e-Business Solutions, e-Commerce & Portal
N.A.I.C.S.: 541511

ESW Capital, LLC—(Continued)

BroadVision France, S.A. (3)
27 Ave de l Opera, Paris, 75001,
France (100%)
Tel.: (33) 970445858
Sales Range: $10-24.9 Million
Emp.: 5
Sales & Marketing of Software
N.A.I.C.S.: 449210
Pehong Chen (Chm, Pres & CEO)

BroadVision Japan K.K. (3)
1006 Renai Partire Shiodome 2-18-3 Hi-
gashi, Shinbashi Minato-ku, Tokyo, 105
0021, Japan (100%)
Tel.: (81) 57777040
Web Site: http://www.broadvision.com
Sales Range: $100-124.9 Million
Emp.: 5
Document Information Software
N.A.I.C.S.: 449210
Toshi Sakayori (Gen Mgr)

Subsidiary (Non-US):

BroadVision System PVT LTD, (3)
Incubex-Indiranagar 728 Grace Platina 4th
Floor CMH Road, Bengaluru, 560 038, India
Tel.: (91) 8032477357
Sales Range: $10-24.9 Million
Emp.: 6
Enterprise Portal Software Publisher
N.A.I.C.S.: 513210

Holding (Non-US):

BroadVision UK, Ltd. (3)
Copthall Bridge House Station Bridge, Har-
rogate, HG1 1SP, Berkshire, United
Kingdom (100%)
Tel.: (44) 1423790118
Web Site: http://www.broadvision.com
Software Sales & Marketing
N.A.I.C.S.: 513210

Subsidiary (Domestic):

BroadVision, Inc. (3)
400 5th Ave, Waltham, MA 02451-8733
Tel.: (781) 290-0710
Web Site: http://www.broadvision.com
Sales Range: $75-99.9 Million
Supplier of Internet Application for One to
One Management
N.A.I.C.S.: 541511

Subsidiary (Non-US):

Interleaf GmbH (3)
Feringastrasse 6, Munchen, Unterfohring,
85774, Bavaria, Germany
Tel.: (49) 8999216418
Emp.: 20
Enterprise Portal & Business Management
Software Publisher
N.A.I.C.S.: 513210

Subsidiary (Domestic):

Jive Software, Inc. (2)
300 Orchard City Dr 100, Campbell, CA
95008-2945
Tel.: (669) 282-4000
Web Site: http://www.jivesoftware.com
Social Business Software Developer
N.A.I.C.S.: 513210
Scott F. Brighton (CEO)

Subsidiary (Non-US):

Jive Software Australia Pty Ltd. (3)
Level 27 101 Collins Street, Melbourne,
3000, VIC, Australia
Tel.: (61) 392216190
Web Site: http://www.jivesoftware.com
Software Development Services
N.A.I.C.S.: 541511

DNN Corp. (1)
401 Congress Ave Ste 2650, Austin, TX
78701
Tel.: (650) 288-3150
Web Site: http://www.dnnsoftware.com
Website Content Management & Web Appli-
cation Development Services
N.A.I.C.S.: 513210
Andy Tryba (CEO)

Ignite Technologies, Inc. (1)

401 Congress Ave Ste 2650, Austin, TX
78701
Tel.: (512) 861-2859
Web Site: http://www.ignitetech.com
Holding Company; Enterprise Software &
Services
N.A.I.C.S.: 551112
Eric Vaughan (CEO)
Andrew Price (CFO)
Davin W. Cushman (CEO)
Greg Coyle (VP-Product Mgmt)

Subsidiary (Domestic):

FirstRain, Inc. (2)
1500 Fashion Is Blvd Ste 200, San Mateo,
CA 94404
Tel.: (650) 356-9040
Web Site: http://www.firstrain.com
Business Analytics Data Services
N.A.I.C.S.: 518210
Rajiv Arora (Mgr-Data Science Engrg)

Ignite RMSA Retail Solutions,
LLC (2)
401 Congress Ave, Austin, TX 78701
Tel.: (800) 248-0027
Web Site: http://www.ignitetech.com
Retail Proprietary Planning & Forecasting
Inventory Software Solutions
N.A.I.C.S.: 513210

Ignite ScaleArc Solutions, Inc. (2)
401 Congress Ave Ste 2650, Austin, TX
78701
Tel.: (800) 248-0027
Web Site: http://www.ignitetech.com
Database Traffic Management Services
N.A.I.C.S.: 513210

Subsidiary (Domestic):

ScaleBase, Inc. (3)
85 Wells Ave Ste 300, Newton, MA 02459
Tel.: (617) 630-2800
Web Site: http://www.scalebase.com
Database Management Systems
N.A.I.C.S.: 541511

Subsidiary (Domestic):

Knowledge Marketing, LLC (2)
3650 Annapolis Ln N Ste 190, Plymouth,
MN 55447
Tel.: (763) 746-2780
Software Services; Integrated Audience Da-
tabase, Analytics & Reporting
N.A.I.C.S.: 513210

Kayako Limited (1)
4th Floor 34 Bridge Street, Reading, RG1
2LU, United Kingdom
Tel.: (44) 20 3769 0237
Web Site: http://www.kayako.com
Customer Service Software Publisher
N.A.I.C.S.: 513210

Olive Software, Inc. (1)
2101 S Blackhawk St Ste 240, Aurora, CO
80014
Tel.: (720) 747-1220
Software Publisher
N.A.I.C.S.: 513210
Emil Shteinvil (CTO)
Susan Davis (CFO)
Dewayn Davis (CEO)
Yoni Stern (Founder & Pres-Tech)
Shmil Levy (Chm)
Drew Bartlett (Dir-Product Mgmt & Product
Mktg)
Joe Wikert (Dir-Strategy & Bus Dev)
Chandler Gray (Partner-Programs & Sr Dir-
World Wide Channels)
Randal Meske (VP-Sls & Mktg-Global)
Mark Sanner (VP-Technical Svcs)

SLI Systems, Inc. (1)
78 106 Manchester Street, Christchurch,
8011, New Zealand
Tel.: (64) 3 5208029
Web Site: http://www.sli-systems.com
Emp.: 50
Software Publisher
N.A.I.C.S.: 513210
Wayne Munro (Mgr-Engg)

Trilogy Enterprises, Inc. (1)
401 Congress Ave Ste 2650, Austin, TX
78701
Tel.: (512) 874-3100
Web Site: http://www.trilogy.com

Holding Company; Specialty Software Pub-
lisher & Services
N.A.I.C.S.: 551112
Greg Gunwall (VP-Product Mgmt)
Kim Irwin (VP-Customer Success)
Michael Richards (Pres-Automotive Bus-
Global)

Vasona Networks, Inc. (1)
2025 Gateway Place Ste 285, San Jose,
CA 95110
Tel.: (408) 492-1301
Web Site: http://www.vasonanetworks.com
Computer Software Publisher
N.A.I.C.S.: 513210
Biren Sood (CEO)
Rui Frazao (CTO)
John Reister (Sr VP-Mktg & Product)
Uri Bechar (VP-Engrg)

Versata, Inc. (1)
401 Congress Ave Ste 2650, Austin, TX
78701-4411
Tel.: (512) 377-9700
Web Site: http://www.versata.com
Holding Company; Software Publisher &
Whslr
N.A.I.C.S.: 551112

Subsidiary (Domestic):

Artemis International Solutions
Corporation (2)
6011 W Courtyard Dr, Austin, TX 78730
Tel.: (572) 874-3100
Web Site: http://www.aisc.com
Sales Range: $25-49.9 Million
Enterprise Software Solutions
N.A.I.C.S.: 541512

Subsidiary (Non-US):

Artemis Finland Oy (3)
Takojankatu 15B, FIN 33540, Tampere,
Finland
Tel.: (358) 103094250
Web Site: http://fi.aisc.com
Sales Range: $10-24.9 Million
Emp.: 50
Enterprise Software Solutions
N.A.I.C.S.: 541512

Artemis International France (3)
NCI Boulogne-Morizet 67 Avenue Morizet,
92100, Boulogne-Billancourt, Cedex,
France
Tel.: (33) 146106500
Web Site: http://www.aisc.com
Sales Range: $10-24.9 Million
Emp.: 1
Enterprise Software Solutions
N.A.I.C.S.: 541512

Artemis International Gmbh (3)
Ridlerstrasse 31A, Munich, 80339, Ger-
many
Tel.: (49) 87812029830
Web Site: http://www.de.aisc.com
Sales Range: $1-9.9 Million
Emp.: 30
Enterprise Software Solutions
N.A.I.C.S.: 541512
Jacques-Henry Pinhas (Mng Dir)

Artemis International Srl (3)
via Carducci 125, Sesto San Giovanni,
20099, Milan, Italy
Tel.: (39) 0227004779
Web Site: http://www.aisc.com
Sales Range: $1-9.9 Million
Emp.: 35
Enterprise Software Mfr
N.A.I.C.S.: 541512

Subsidiary (Domestic):

Compressus, Inc. (2)
101 Constitution Ave NW Ste 800, Wash-
ington, DC 20001-2133
Tel.: (202) 742-4307
Web Site: http://www.compressus.com
Health Care Services Management Soft-
ware Publisher & Whslr
N.A.I.C.S.: 513210
Leela Kaza (CEO)
Gregg Cohen (Sr VP-Product Line Mgmt-
MEDxConnect)
Jim Way (VP-Ops)
Tom Hohman (Controller)

Ecora Software Corporation (2)

6011 W Courtyard Dr Ste 300, Austin, TX
78730
Tel.: (512) 524-6149
Web Site: http://www.ecora.com
Sales Range: $10-24.9 Million
Emp.: 80
Software Publisher
N.A.I.C.S.: 541511
Andrew Price (CFO)
Frank Kopas (Sr VP-Sls)

Everest Software Inc. (2)
6011 W Courtyard Dr Ste 300, Austin, TX
78730
Tel.: (703) 234-6600
Web Site:
http://www.everestsoftwareinc.com
Computer Software Development Services
N.A.I.C.S.: 513210
Robert Johnson (Controller)

Evolutionary Technologies Interna-
tional, Inc. (2)
6011 W Courtyard Dr Ste 300, Austin, TX
78730
Tel.: (512) 377-9700
Web Site: http://www.eti.com
Sales Range: $1-9.9 Million
Emp.: 75
Software Products for Data Integration Man-
agement
N.A.I.C.S.: 513210

Gensym Corporation (2)
52 26011 West Courtyard Drive, Austin, TX
78730
Tel.: (512) 377-9700
Web Site: http://www.gensym.com
Sales Range: $10-24.9 Million
Emp.: 65
E-Infrastructure Software Products
N.A.I.C.S.: 334610

Subsidiary (Non-US):

Gensym B.V. (3)
Rapebburg 16, 2311EW, Leiden, Nether-
lands
Tel.: (31) 715682600
Web Site: http://www.gensym.com
Sales Range: $10-24.9 Million
Emp.: 6
E-Infrastructure Software Products
N.A.I.C.S.: 334610

Subsidiary (Domestic):

Nextance, Inc. (2)
6011 W Courtyard Dr Ste 300, Austin, TX
78730-5113
Tel.: (650) 716-2400
Web Site: http://www.nextance.com
Sales Range: $10-24.9 Million
Emp.: 79
Management Software & Services
N.A.I.C.S.: 541511
Scott Buoy (CEO)

Versata Software, Inc. (2)
401 Congress Ave Ste 2650, Austin, TX
78701-3708
Tel.: (512) 377-9700
Web Site: http://www.ignitetech.com
Prepackaged Software
N.A.I.C.S.: 513210

ZephyrTel, Inc. (1)
401 Congress Ave Ste 2650, Austin, TX
78701
Tel.: (920) 490-7327
Web Site: http://www.zephyrtel.com
Telecommunication Servicesb
N.A.I.C.S.: 517810
Mike Shinya (CEO)
Mooly Beeri (COO)
Martyn Lambert (CMO)

Subsidiary (Non-US):

Accuris Networks Limited (2)
7th & 8th Floor OConnell Bridge House DO-
lier St, Dublin, 2, Ireland
Tel.: (353) 1 8818700
Web Site: http://www.accuris-networks.com
Mobile Data Communication Solutions
N.A.I.C.S.: 334220
Malachy McGuinness (VP-Ops & Customer
Mgmt)
David Guilmartin (CFO & COO)
Ian Smith (VP-Engrg)

Finbarr Coghlan *(CTO)*
David Reeder *(VP-Sls & Bus Dev-Americas)*
Larry Quinn *(Chm & CEO)*

Subsidiary (Non-US):

Accuris Networks Limited (3)
Takanawa Sky 601 4-8-6 Takanawa,
Minato-Ku, Tokyo, 108-0074, Japan
Tel.: (81) 9098469023
Communication Equipment Distr
N.A.I.C.S.: 423690

**Accuris Networks Malaysia Sdn.
Bhd.** (3)
14th Floor Suite 14-3 Wisma UOA II 21
Jalan, Kuala Lumpur, 50450, Penang, Malaysia
Tel.: (60) 321616232
Communication Equipment Distr
N.A.I.C.S.: 423690
Simon Gooi *(Mgr-Global Ops)*

Subsidiary (Domestic):

Volt Delta Resources, Inc. (2)
3750 Monroe Ave Ste 4B, Pittsford, NY
14534
Holding Company; Multi-Channel Contact
Center Software & Services
N.A.I.C.S.: 551112

Subsidiary (Non-US):

Volt Delta International B.V. (3)
Nobelstraat 14A, Heerlen, 6411 EM, Netherlands
Tel.: (31) 45 571 3242
Software Services for Telecommunications
Companies
N.A.I.C.S.: 541511

Volt Delta International GmbH (3)
Landsberger Str 110, 80339, Munich, Germany
Tel.: (49) 89455660
Software Development Services
N.A.I.C.S.: 541511

Subsidiary (Domestic):

Volt Delta Resources, LLC (3)
3750 Monroe Ave Ste 4B, Pittsford, NY
10018
Sales Range: $75-99.9 Million
Emp.: 300
Telephone Communications Services; Computer Programming Services
N.A.I.C.S.: 541512

ESW, INC.
670 N Madison St, Crown Point, IN
46307
Tel.: (219) 226-1766
Web Site: http://www.eswinc.com
Year Founded: 1987
Rev.: $4,200,000
Emp.: 83
Human Resource Consulting Services
N.A.I.C.S.: 541612
Lawrence M. Caldwell *(Pres)*
Dave Bartlett *(Gen Mgr)*
Jerry Trump *(Mgr-Sls)*
Cindy Kielbasa *(Mgr-HR)*

ET INTERNATIONAL LTD
13540 Airline Hwy, Baton Rouge, LA
70817-5919
Tel.: (225) 273-2861
Web Site:
   http://www.acuraofbatonrouge.com
Rev.: $14,700,000
Emp.: 52
Automobiles, New & Used
N.A.I.C.S.: 441110
John Fabre *(Pres)*

ETACTICS INC.
4835 Darrow Rd, Stow, OH 44224
Tel.: (330) 342-0568
Web Site: http://www.etacticsinc.com
Sales Range: $10-24.9 Million
Emp.: 32

Online Document Generation Services
N.A.I.C.S.: 513199
Carl Trownson *(VP-Sls & Mktg)*
Mathew Cantor *(Dir-EDI Solutions)*
Ray Dalessandro *(Dir-Sls & Mktg)*

ETAN INDUSTRIES INC.
13355 Noel Rd Ste 2100, Dallas, TX
75240
Tel.: (972) 233-9614
Web Site:
   http://www.creditprotect.com
Rev.: $89,914,053
Emp.: 800
Collection Agency
N.A.I.C.S.: 561440
Susanne Grande *(Dir-HR)*
Bob Stewart *(Dir-Payroll & Taxation)*

ETC INC. INTERNATIONAL LOGISTICS
874 Bud Cleary Rd, Stantonville, TN
38379
Tel.: (731) 632-3880
Sales Range: $10-24.9 Million
Emp.: 12
Transportation Services
N.A.I.C.S.: 488510
Danny Elam *(Pres)*
David Dierks *(Controller)*

ETCO DEVELOPMENT INC.
9952 Santa Monica Blvd, Beverly
Hills, CA 90212
Tel.: (951) 479-3000
Web Site: http://www.etcohomes.com
Sales Range: $10-24.9 Million
Emp.: 14
Cemetery Subdividers & Developers
N.A.I.C.S.: 523999
Afshin Etebar *(Co-Founder & Pres)*
Bob Etebar *(VP)*

ETCO INCORPORATED
25 Bellows St, Warwick, RI 02888
Tel.: (401) 467-2400
Web Site: https://www.etco.com
Rev.: $19,400,000
Emp.: 80
Stamping Metal For The Trade
N.A.I.C.S.: 332119
David Dunn *(Chm)*
John Stiness *(VP-Sls)*
John J. Macaluso *(Pres)*
Vinod Reddy *(Acct Mgr-Technical-India)*

ETCON INC.
439 EE Butler Pkwy, Gainesville, GA
30501
Tel.: (770) 532-8449   GA
Web Site: https://www.etcon.net
Year Founded: 1985
Sales Range: $10-24.9 Million
Emp.: 50
Employment Agency
N.A.I.C.S.: 561320
Bonnie Wood *(Owner & Pres)*

ETECH, INC.
1903 Berry Dr, Nacogdoches, TX
75964
Tel.: (936) 559-2200
Web Site: https://www.etechgs.com
Year Founded: 1997
Sales Range: $75-99.9 Million
Emp.: 2,300
Customer Acquisition & Service Solutions
N.A.I.C.S.: 561499
Dilip Barot *(Founder & Chm)*
Matthew Rocco *(Pres)*
Veronica Ellison *(VP-HR)*
Gurudatt Medtia *(Asst VP-IT & Operational Excellence)*

Jim Iyoob *(Chief Customer Officer)*
Ronnie Mize *(Chief Security Officer)*
Kaylene Eckels *(COO)*

**ETERNAL WORD TELEVISION
NETWORK INC.**
5817 Old Leeds Rd, Irondale, AL
35210-2164
Tel.: (205) 271-2900
Web Site: https://www.ewtn.com
Year Founded: 1981
Sales Range: $25-49.9 Million
Emp.: 300
Television Broadcasting Station Services
N.A.I.C.S.: 516120
Michael P. Warsaw *(Chm & CEO)*
Montse Alvarado *(Pres/COO-EWTN
News Inc)*

ETEX TELEPHONE COOPERATIVE
1013 State Highway 155 N, Gilmer,
TX 75644
Tel.: (903) 797-2711
Web Site: http://www.etex.net
Year Founded: 1978
Sales Range: $10-24.9 Million
Emp.: 103
Local Telephone Communications
N.A.I.C.S.: 517121
Charlie Cano *(Gen Mgr)*

ETFS ASIAN GOLD TRUST
c/o ETF Securities USA LLC 48 Wall
St 11th Fl, New York, NY 10005
Tel.: (212) 918-4954   NY
Web Site:
   http://www.etfsecurities.com
Investment Services
N.A.I.C.S.: 523999
Graham Tuckwell *(Chm)*
Thomas Quigley *(CFO, Treas, Sec &
VP)*

ETG INTERNATIONAL LLC
654 Madison Ave, New York, NY
10065
Tel.: (212) 813-9360
Web Site: http://www.etgglobal.com
Sales Range: $125-149.9 Million
Emp.: 5
Deep Sea Foreign Transportation Of
Freigh
N.A.I.C.S.: 813910
Kimball Chen *(Chm & CEO)*
Alexander W. Evans *(Pres & COO)*

ETHAN ALLEN DESIGN CENTER
1541 Route 22 W, Watchung, NJ
07069
Tel.: (908) 754-7200
Web Site: http://www.ethanallen.com
Sales Range: $25-49.9 Million
Emp.: 30
Furniture Retailer
N.A.I.C.S.: 449110
Corey Whitely *(Interim CFO, Treas &
Exec VP-Ops)*
Pamela A. Banks *(VP)*
Farooq Kathwari *(CEO)*

ETHERIDGE OIL COMPANY
502 N Gardner Ave, Kenly, NC 27542
Tel.: (919) 284-2074
Sales Range: $25-49.9 Million
Emp.: 20
Fuel Oil Dealers
N.A.I.C.S.: 457210
Ken Etheridge *(Chm)*
Michael Body *(COO)*

ETHICAL SOLUTIONS, LLC
177 Governors Hwy, South Windsor,
CT 06074

Tel.: (860) 640-0074
Web Site:
   https://www.ethicalchem.com
Plant-based Chemical Solutions
N.A.I.C.S.: 541620
Geeta Dahal *(Sys Engr-Environmental)*
Jen Holcomb *(Mgr-Technology-Lab)*

Subsidiaries:

EthicalChem (1)
65 W Dudley Town Rd Ste 100, Bloomfield,
CT 06002
Tel.: (860) 640-0074
Web Site: http://www.verutek.com
Plant-based Chemical Solutions
N.A.I.C.S.: 541620
Dan Socci *(CEO)*
Geeta Dahal *(Environmental Engr)*
Jen Holcomb *(Mgr-Tech & Lab)*

ETHIKA INVESTMENTS LLC
1880 Century Park E Ste 1016, Los
Angeles, CA 90067
Tel.: (310) 954-2009   DE
Web Site:
   http://www.ethikainvestments.com
Year Founded: 2009
Emp.: 15
Real Estate Investment, Development
& Portfolio Management Services
N.A.I.C.S.: 531390
Andres Szita *(Chm)*
Jean-Paul Szita *(Co-Founder & Pres)*
Rafael Marcos *(Co-Founder)*
Philip W. Cyburt *(CEO)*
Austin Khan *(Chief Investment Officer)*
B. J. Turner *(VP-Capital Markets)*
Gabriel Daniel Kabbaz *(VP-Capital
Markets-Latin America)*
John Harounian *(VP-Bus Dev)*
Thuong Luong *(VP-Portfolio Mgmt)*
Konstantin Daskalov *(VP-Dev)*
Frederique Calluaud *(Mgr-Mktg)*
Dasha Holubec *(Mgr-IR)*
Ameya Shinde *(Mgr-Asset)*
Betty Jones *(Mgr-Asset)*
Doug Kiel *(CFO)*
Marisa Lizak *(Dir-Capital Markets)*

Subsidiaries:

Laurus Corp. (1)
1880 Century Park E Ste 1016, Los Angeles, CA 90067
Tel.: (310) 277-8600
Web Site: http://www.lauruscorporation.com
Real Estate Investment, Development &
Portfolio Management Services
N.A.I.C.S.: 531390
Frederique Calluaud *(VP-Corp Comm)*
Simran Bindra *(Gen Counsel & Dir-Corp
Affairs)*
Sam Bakhshandehpour *(Mng Dir)*

ETHIOPIAN COMMUNITY DEVELOPMENT COUNCIL, INC.
901 S Highland St, Arlington, VA
22204
Tel.: (703) 685-0510   VA
Web Site: https://www.ecdcus.org
Year Founded: 1983
Sales Range: $10-24.9 Million
Emp.: 112
Refugee & Immigrant Care Services
N.A.I.C.S.: 624230
Azeb Tadesse *(Dir-Fin)*
Allene Wright *(Sr VP)*
Tsehaye Teferra *(Pres)*
Redda G. Mehari *(Mng Dir-African
Community Center-Las Vegas)*
Sarah Zullo *(Mng Dir-African Community Center-Washington)*
Anam Gnaho *(Assoc Dir-Self-Sufficiency Programs)*

Ethiopian Community Development Council,
Inc.—(Continued)

Emily Nesheim Bullock (Assoc Dir-
Refugee Resettlement Program)
Wossenseged Hailu (Mgr-IT)
Benaiah Duku (Program Officer)
Melissa Theesen (Dir-ACC-Denver)
Reza Yawari (Program Officer)
Steven Gallo (Program Officer-R&P)
Vanessa Reintertson (Program
Officer-R&P)

ETHOS CAPITAL, LLC
716 Beacon St, Newton, MA 02459
Tel.: (929) 300-3400
Web Site:
    http://www.ethoscapital.com
Privater Equity Firm
N.A.I.C.S.: 523999
Erik Brooks (Co-CEO)
Fadi Chehade (Co-CEO)
Marie Wieck (Partner)

Subsidiaries:

Donuts Inc.   (1)
10500 NE 8th St Ste 750, Bellevue, WA
98004
Tel.: (425) 298-2200
Web Site: http://www.donuts.domains
Domain Names Registry
N.A.I.C.S.: 513199
Alvaro Alvarez (Gen Counsel, Sec & Sr VP)
Serina Ness (VP-Fin & Acctg)
Matt Overman (Sr VP-Sls)
Ben Levac (VP-Engrg)
Dave McBreen (VP-Registrar)
Akram J. Atallah (CEO)
Randy Haas (CFO & EVP)
Mina Neuberg (CMO)

Subsidiary (Domestic):

Afilias, Inc.   (2)
300 Welsh Rd Bldg 3 Ste 105, Horsham,
PA 19044
Tel.: (215) 706-5700
Web Site: http://www.afilias.info
Sales Range: $1-9.9 Million
Data Processing, Hosting & Related Ser-
vices
N.A.I.C.S.: 518210
Henry Lubsen (Co-Founder)
Roland LaPlante (CMO & Sr VP)
Philipp Grabensee (Co-Founder)
Ram Mohan (COO)
Steve Heflin (VP-Sls)

Rightside Group, Ltd.   (2)
5808 Lk Washington Blvd NE Ste 300, Kirk-
land, WA 98033
Tel.: (425) 298-2200
Sales Range: $50-74.9 Million
Domain Name Services
N.A.I.C.S.: 518210

Newforma, Inc.   (1)
225 Franklin St 27th Floor, Boston, MA
02110
Tel.: (877) 875-8252
Web Site: http://www.newforma.com
Computer Software Product Mfr
N.A.I.C.S.: 513210
Scott R. Stevens (Principal)
Gregg Monastiero (Partner)
Brock Philp (CEO)
Carl Veillette (Chief Product Officer)
Mike Lewis (CMO)
Kevin Murray (Sr VP-Fin)
Rick Saladino (Sr VP-Strategic Sls)
Ken Weeks (Exec VP-Global Customer
Care)
Tammy Fuller (Sr VP-Software Delivery)
Marge Hart (Sr VP-Product Mgmt)
Rob Stephen (VP-Sls & Ops-EMEA)
Tara Anderson (VP-Customer Success)
Victoria Salvador (Sr Dir-Performance Mktg,
Brands, and Buzz)
Stacey Vigna (Sr Dir-HR)

ETHOS RISK SERVICES LLC
PO Box 55246, Saint Petersburg, FL
33732
Tel.: (866) 783-0525
Web Site: http://www.ethosrisk.com

Year Founded: 2006
Risk Mitigation Services Provider
N.A.I.C.S.: 561621
Bethany Thomas (Dir-National Ac-
counts)

Subsidiaries:

Combined Investigators, Inc   (1)
300 1st Ave S St. 300, St. Petersburg, FL
33701
Tel.: (800) 772-2428
Web Site:
    https://www.combinedinvestigators.com
Investigation Services
N.A.I.C.S.: 561611

ETICA ENTERTAINMENT INC.
PO Box 2064, Escondido, CA 92033
Tel.: (760) 480-8791
Web Site: http://www.truepath.com
Year Founded: 1997
Sales Range: $25-49.9 Million
Emp.: 4
Holding Company
N.A.I.C.S.: 551112
Gil Vidals (CEO)

Subsidiaries:

Position Research   (1)
312 W 3rd St, Escondido, CA 92925
Tel.: (760) 480-8791
Web Site: http://www.positionresearch.com
Sales Range: $10-24.9 Million
Emp.: 25
Search Engine Marketing & Optimization
Consulting Services
N.A.I.C.S.: 541890

Truepath.com   (1)
PO Box 2064, Escondido, CA 92033
Tel.: (760) 480-8791
Web Site: http://www.truepath.com
Sales Range: $10-24.9 Million
Internet Hosting Services
N.A.I.C.S.: 517810
Gil Vidals (Pres & CEO)

ETISON LLC
3443 W Bavaria St, Eagle, ID 83616
Tel.: (208) 323-9451
Web Site:
    http://www.clickfunnels.com
Year Founded: 2014
Sales Range: $75-99.9 Million
Emp.: 96
Software Development Services
N.A.I.C.S.: 541511
Russell Brunson (Co-Founder, CEO
& Head-Mktg)
Todd Dickerson (Co-Founder & Head-
Tech)
John Parkes (Head-Adv)
Dave Woodward (Head-Bus Dev)
Ryan Montgomery (Chief Technical
Officer)

ETKIN EQUITIES
200 Franklin Ct 29100 Northwestern
Hwy, Southfield, MI 48034
Tel.: (248) 358-0800
Web Site: http://www.etkinllc.com
Year Founded: 1982
Sales Range: $10-24.9 Million
Emp.: 50
Operator of Franchised Hotels
N.A.I.C.S.: 531210
Douglas M. Etkin (Principal)
Curtis Burstein (Pres)

ETM MANUFACTURING
24 Porter Rd, Littleton, MA 01460
Tel.: (978) 486-9050
Web Site: https://www.etmmfg.com
Sales Range: $1-9.9 Million
Emp.: 26
Sheet Metal Mfr
N.A.I.C.S.: 332322

Rob Olney (Pres)
Mike Jancosko (VP-Customer Dev)
Harold Long (VP-Ops)

ETM-ELECTROMATIC INC.
35451 Dumbarton Ct, Newark, CA
94560
Tel.: (510) 797-1100
Web Site: https://www.etm-inc.com
Year Founded: 1973
Sales Range: $25-49.9 Million
Emp.: 94
Microwave Communication Equip-
ment
N.A.I.C.S.: 334220
Tom Hayse (Pres & CEO)
Ryan Pollace (Product Dir)
John Capovilla (Vice Chm)

ETNA PRODUCTS CO. INC.
99 Madison Ave Fl 11, New York, NY
10016-7419
Tel.: (212) 989-7591
Sales Range: $25-49.9 Million
Emp.: 10
Gifts & Novelties
N.A.I.C.S.: 424990
Jeffrey Snyder (Pres)
Raymond Trinh (Controller)

ETNA SHARED SERVICES
529 32nd St SE, Grand Rapids, MI
49548
Tel.: (616) 241-5414
Web Site: http://www.etnasupply.com
Year Founded: 1972
Sales Range: $100-124.9 Million
Emp.: 300
Provider of Services to Contractors,
Engineers, Architects & Homeowners
N.A.I.C.S.: 423720
Russ Bisner (CEO)

ETNYRE INTERNATIONAL
LTD. INC.
1333 S Daysville Rd, Oregon, IL
61061-9783
Tel.: (815) 732-2116
Web Site: https://www.etnyre.com
Year Founded: 1898
Sales Range: $25-49.9 Million
Emp.: 422
Construction Machinery Mfr
N.A.I.C.S.: 333120
Tom Brown (Pres)
Mark Zeigler (Controller)

Subsidiaries:

ED Etnyre & Co. Inc.   (1)
1333 S Daysville Rd, Oregon, IL 61061-
9783
Tel.: (815) 732-2116
Web Site: http://www.etnyre.com
Sales Range: $25-49.9 Million
Emp.: 400
Construction Machinery Mfr
N.A.I.C.S.: 333120

ETR
4 Carbonero Way, Scotts Valley, CA
95066
Tel.: (831) 438-4060
Web Site: http://www.etr.org
Year Founded: 1981
Sales Range: $10-24.9 Million
Science Research & Education Ser-
vices
N.A.I.C.S.: 541715
Coleen Cantwell (Dir-Bus Dev &
Plng)
Talita Sanders (Dir-Human Re-
sources)
Matt McDowell (Dir-Mktg)
Eric Blanke (CIO)
Vignetta Charles (CEO)

ETRANSERVICES, LLC

707 Westwood Ofc Park, Fredericks-
burg, VA 22401-5115
Tel.: (571) 405-5560
Web Site:
    http://www.etranservices.com
Computer System Design Services
N.A.I.C.S.: 541512
Chris Beckford (Pres)

Subsidiaries:

Innovation Network, Inc.   (1)
1625 K St Nw, Washington, DC 20006
Tel.: (202) 728-0727
Web Site: http://www.innonet.org
Rev.: $1,500,000
Emp.: 15
Administrative Management & General
Management Consulting Service
N.A.I.C.S.: 541611
Allison H. Fine (Dir)
Brian Smith (Controller)

ETRE REIT, LLC
44 Wall St, New York, NY 10005
Tel.: (212) 596-7225
Real Estate Investment Services
N.A.I.C.S.: 523999
Paul Frischer (Pres & CEO)
Jesse Stein (COO, Interim Chief
Acctg Officer & Sec)

ETRIGUE CORPORATION
6399 San Ignacio Ave 2 Fl, San
Jose, CA 95119
Tel.: (408) 490-2900
Web Site: https://www.etrigue.com
Sales Range: $25-49.9 Million
Marketing Automation Software
N.A.I.C.S.: 513210
Jim Meyer (VP & Gen Mgr)
Jeff Holmes (CEO)

ETS INTERNATIONAL
57 Teed Dr, Randolph, MA 02368
Tel.: (617) 472-9900
Web Site: https://www.etsintl.net
Year Founded: 2006
Sales Range: $1-9.9 Million
Emp.: 60
Airport Ground Handling Services
N.A.I.C.S.: 488119
Peter Greene (VP & Gen Mgr)
Norren Murphy (Mgr-Reservation)
Ed Forestall (Mgr-Dispatch)

ETTLESON CADILLAC-BUICK-GMC, INC.
6201 LaGrange Rd, Hodgkins, IL
60525-4140
Tel.: (708) 579-5000
Web Site:
    https://www.ettlesoncadillac.com
Year Founded: 1986
Sales Range: $10-24.9 Million
Emp.: 75
Car Whslr
N.A.I.C.S.: 441110
Larry Smolinski (Gen Mgr)
Brian Kuehl (Mgr-Sls-New Car)
Darren Dandre (Dir-Fixed Ops)
Dave Rodriguez (Asst Mgr-Parts)
Ed Komenda (Mgr-Parts)
Frank Amadeo (Gen Mgr-Sls)
Ken Bacigalupo (Mgr-Used Car)
Kristin Fritz (Mgr-Internet Sls)
Peter Engel (Mgr-Svc)
Rob Scumaci (Mgr-Bus)

EUCLID INDUSTRIES INC.
1655 Tech Dr, Bay City, MI 48706-
9792
Tel.: (989) 686-8920
Web Site:
    https://www.euclidindustries.com
Year Founded: 1978
Sales Range: $10-24.9 Million

Emp.: 275
Provider of Industrial Machinery Services
N.A.I.C.S.: 332710
Ron Deedee (Pres)

EUCLID INSURANCE SERVICES, INC.
234 Spring Lk Dr, Itasca, IL 60143
Tel.: (630) 694-2320
Web Site:
   http://www.euclidprograms.com
Year Founded: 1952
Insurance Services
N.A.I.C.S.: 524298
John Colis (Pres & CEO)
John N. Colis (Pres & CEO)
David N. Bailey (VP-Underwriting-Euclid Life Science Specialty, LLC)
Ryann Elliott (Mng Principal-Euclid Life Science Specialty, LLC)

EUCON CORPORATION
4201 Snake River Ave, Lewiston, ID 83501
Tel.: (208) 743-6356
Web Site:
   https://www.euconcorp.com
Year Founded: 1932
Concrete, Crushed Aggregate, Portable Rock Crushing, Mining & Customer Relations
N.A.I.C.S.: 212319
A. Neil DeAtley (Chm & CEO)
Mark DeAtley (Dir)
Marty Zacha (Dir)
Ken Schumacher (Pres & CFO)
Angela Cromer (Treas, Sec & Dir-Acctg)

EUE/SCREEN GEMS LTD.
1223 23rd St N, Wilmington, NC 28405
Tel.: (910) 343-3500   NC
Web Site:
   https://www.euescreengems.com
Year Founded: 1948
Television & Film Production
N.A.I.C.S.: 512199
Bill Vassar (Exec VP)
Chris Cooney (COO)
Kris Bagwell (Exec VP)
Christian Lovschal (Gen Mgr)

EUGENE B. SMITH & CO. INC.
4514 Cole Ave Ste 706, Dallas, TX 75205
Tel.: (214) 528-9800
Web Site: http://www.ebsmithco.com
Sales Range: $10-24.9 Million
Emp.: 5
Farm Product Warehousing & Storage
N.A.I.C.S.: 493130
Ed Farow (CFO)

EUGENE BIRO CORP.
581 5th Ave 3rd Fl, New York, NY 10017
Tel.: (212) 997-0146
Web Site: http://www.eugenebiro.com
Year Founded: 1974
Sales Range: $10-24.9 Million
Emp.: 45
Diamond & Jewelry Mfr
N.A.I.C.S.: 423940
Eugene Biro (CEO)
Anne Jones-Fox (VP-Sls-Diamond Jewelry)

EUGENE BURGER MANAGEMENT CORP.
6600 Hunter Dr, Rohnert Park, CA 94928-2418
Tel.: (707) 584-5123
Web Site: https://www.ebmc.com

Year Founded: 1969
Sales Range: $10-24.9 Million
Emp.: 400
Residential Property Management Services
N.A.I.C.S.: 531311
Stephen Burger (Pres)

EUGENE FREEZING & STORAGE CO.
310 S South Seneca Rd, Eugene, OR 97402
Tel.: (541) 343-1694
Web Site: https://snotemp.com
Sales Range: $10-24.9 Million
Emp.: 45
Refrigerated Warehousing & Storage Services
N.A.I.C.S.: 493120
Jason Lafferty (Gen Mgr)

EUGENE RACANELLI INC.
45 Mall Dr Ste 5, Commack, NY 11725-5700
Tel.: (631) 543-6700
Web Site:
   https://www.eugeneracanelli.com
Sales Range: $10-24.9 Million
Emp.: 25
General Construction & Construction Managment Services
N.A.I.C.S.: 237990
Eugene Racanelli (Pres)
Andrew Enrique (Controller)

EUPEN CABLE USA INC.
5181 110th Ave N Unit D, Clearwater, FL 33760
Tel.: (727) 527-7955
Web Site: https://www.eupen.us
Rev.: $10,600,000
Emp.: 45
Electrical Apparatus & Equipment, Wiring Supplies & Related Equipment Merchant Whslr
N.A.I.C.S.: 423610
Bill Holland (Pres)

EURAMEX MANAGEMENT GROUP, LLC
1010 Huntcliff Ste 2315, Atlanta, GA 30350
Tel.: (770) 518-7705
Web Site: http://www.euramex.com
Year Founded: 1981
Emp.: 271
Real Estate Development Services
N.A.I.C.S.: 925120
Ignacio Diego (Principal)
Pablo Diego (Principal)
Jaime Diego (Principal)

EUREKA CHEMICAL COMPANY
234 Lawrence Ave, South San Francisco, CA 94080-6817
Tel.: (650) 761-3536   CA
Web Site: http://www.fluid-film.com
Year Founded: 1940
Sales Range: $1-9.9 Million
Emp.: 14
Chemical Corrosion Control Systems & Fluid Film Mfr
N.A.I.C.S.: 325998
Genevieve E. Hess (Chm & Pres)
Jeff Wilson (Dir-Sls)
Dan Williams (Product Mgr)

EUREKA EQUITY PARTNERS, L.P.
1717 Arch St 34th Fl, Philadelphia, PA 19103
Tel.: (267) 238-4200
Web Site:
   http://www.eurekaequity.com
Year Founded: 2000

Emp.: 12
Investment Management Firm
N.A.I.C.S.: 523940
Christopher G. Hanssens (Mng Partner)
Michael J. Foran (CFO & Chief Compliance Officer)
Jonathan R. Zimbalist (Partner)
Christian T. Miller (Partner)
Jonathan Y. Chou (Partner)
Alexandra Oswald (VP)
Chris Parton (Co-CEO)
Lisa Harris Millhauser (VP)
Nathan Milikowsky (Co-CEO)
T. J. Haas (Dir-Bus Dev)
Ed Warchol (Pres)

Subsidiaries:

MedForce LLC   (1)
20 Ave at the Common, Shrewsbury, NJ 07702
Tel.: (732) 450-8400
Web Site: http://www.medforce.net
Pharmaceutical & Health Care Marketing & Educational Consulting Services
N.A.I.C.S.: 541613

Merit Service Solutions   (1)
52 E Swedesford Rd, Malvern, PA 19355
Web Site:
   http://www.meritservicesolutions.com
Landscape & Snow Removal Contractors
N.A.I.C.S.: 561730

EUREKA SAVINGS BANK
250 Marquette St, La Salle, IL 61301
Tel.: (815) 223-0700
Web Site:
   https://www.eurekasavings.com
Year Founded: 1885
Sales Range: $10-24.9 Million
Emp.: 45
State Savings Bank
N.A.I.C.S.: 522180
Mark A. Van De Wyngaerde (Exec VP)
Kathryn J. Stokvis (Treas & Sec)
Michael S. Porter (VP-LaSalle)
William G. Quesse (Dir-Computer Svcs)
Laura Anke (Asst VP)
Anna Arteaga (Asst VP-Mendota)
Lisa M. Scholle (Asst Branch Mgr)
Doris A. Forgy (Asst VP)
Nancy M. Hybki (VP-LaSalle)
Gina M. Keeney (Asst VP)
Saralyn K. Shetterly (VP)
John F. McCormick III (Pres)

EUREKA STONE QUARRY INC.
800 Lowr State Rd, Chalfont, PA 18914
Tel.: (215) 822-0593   PA
Web Site: http://www.jdm-inc.com
Year Founded: 1955
Sales Range: $10-24.9 Million
Emp.: 100
Provider of Asphalt Paving Mixture Services
N.A.I.C.S.: 324121
John Schenken (Office Mgr)

EUREKA WATER PROBES
2113 Wells Branch Pkwy Ste 4400, Austin, TX 78758
Tel.: (512) 302-4333
Web Site:
   https://www.waterprobes.com
Year Founded: 2002
Water Quality Sensors, Instruments & Systems Mfr
N.A.I.C.S.: 334516
Stuart Garner (Mng Partner)

EURO PACIFIC CAPITAL, INC.
88 Post Rd W 3rd Fl, Westport, CT 06880

Tel.: (203) 662-9700   CA
Web Site: http://www.europac.net
Year Founded: 1997
Sales Range: $1-9.9 Million
Emp.: 60
Investment Banking & Securities Dealing
N.A.I.C.S.: 523150
Peter Schiff (CEO)
Eric Steingruebner (Mgr-Natl Sls)
Andrew Schiff (Dir-Comm & Mktg)
John Calicchio (COO)
Marlon Varsace (VP-Investments)

EURO PERFORMANCE CARS, INC.
800 S Colony Rd Rte 5, Wallingford, CT 06492
Tel.: (203) 294-9000
Web Site:
   https://www.audiofwallingford.com
Year Founded: 1971
Sales Range: $10-24.9 Million
Emp.: 30
Car Whslr
N.A.I.C.S.: 441110
Fred M. Valenti (Pres)

EURO SOLUTIONS GROUP INC.
88 Trap Falls Rd, Shelton, CT 06484
Tel.: (212) 230-1155
Web Site:
   http://www.esolutionsgroup.com
Rev.: $10,000,000
Emp.: 75
Computer System Design Services
N.A.I.C.S.: 541512
Marc J. Downes (Pres)

EURO-AMERICAN FOODS GROUP CO., INC.
425 Route 3, Secaucus, NJ 07096-2427
Tel.: (201) 583-1101
Web Site:
   http://www.fasolinofoods.com
Sales Range: $125-149.9 Million
Emp.: 325
Pasta Product Mfr
N.A.I.C.S.: 311991
Joseph T. Gianasio (CFO)
Antonio R. Fasolino (Pres & CEO)

EUROFIX
140 Royal Oaks Blvd, Franklin, TN 37067
Tel.: (615) 591-2475
Web Site:
   https://www.eurofixonline.com
Year Founded: 1999
Sales Range: $1-9.9 Million
Emp.: 60
Car Repair & Maintenance Services
N.A.I.C.S.: 811111
Aaron Stokes (Founder)

EUROMOTORS INC.
500 8th St, San Francisco, CA 94103
Tel.: (415) 673-2000
Web Site: http://www.sfbenz.com
Sales Range: $75-99.9 Million
Emp.: 200
Automobiles, New & Used
N.A.I.C.S.: 441110
Eddy Sung (Mgr-Sales)

EUROPA SPORTS PRODUCTS, INC.
11401 Granite St, Charlotte, NC 28273
Tel.: (704) 525-0792
Web Site:
   https://www.europasports.com
Year Founded: 1990
Sales Range: $200-249.9 Million

Europa Sports Products, Inc.—(Continued)

Emp.: 346
Sport Equipment Distr
N.A.I.C.S.: 459110
Eric Hillman (Co-Founder & CEO)
Jeff Compton (Co-Founder)
Tim Williams (Mgr)
David Swaim (CFO)
Marcus Hermens (Dir-Creative)
Stephen Morris (Project Mgr)
Ryan Coggins (Reg Mgr-Sls)
Robbie Duncan (VP)

EUROPEAN AMERICAN ASSOCIATION

2827 W Division St, Chicago, IL
60622
Tel.: (773) 342-5868
Web Site:
    https://www.eaachicago.org
Year Founded: 1991
Sales Range: $10-24.9 Million
Emp.: 811
Community Welfare Services
N.A.I.C.S.: 624190
John Herman (Founder & Exec Dir)

EUROPEAN AUTO SERVICE LTD.

21425 Woodward Ave, Ferndale, MI
48220
Tel.: (248) 548-0444
Rev.: $12,500,000
Emp.: 50
Automobiles; New & Used
N.A.I.C.S.: 441110
Josef L. Nunner (Pres)
Charlie Pernick (Owner)
Rene Nunner (Mgr-Fin)

EUROPEAN MOTORCARS

9997 Hickman Rd, Urbandale, IA
50322
Tel.: (515) 278-4808
Web Site:
    http://www.europeanmotorcars.com
Sales Range: $10-24.9 Million
Emp.: 70
New & Used Car Dealers
N.A.I.C.S.: 441110
Ed Collinet (Gen Mgr)
Jamie Arend (Office Mgr)

EUROPLAY CAPITAL ADVISORS, LLC

15260 Ventura Blvd 20th Fl, Sherman
Oaks, CA 91403
Tel.: (818) 444-4400
Web Site:
    https://www.europlaycapital.com
Technology Industry Venture Capital
Investment Firm
N.A.I.C.S.: 523999
Mark Dyne (Chm, CEO & Mng Dir)
Joseph Miller (Mng Dir)

EUROPRINT, INC.

14271 Jeffrey Rd #305, Irvine, CA
92620
Tel.: (714) 962-3771
Year Founded: 2001
Sales Range: $1-9.9 Million
Emp.: 3
Newspapers
N.A.I.C.S.: 541810
Tim Garth (Pres)

EURPAC SERVICE CO

1421 Diamond Springs Rd, Virginia
Beach, VA 23455
Tel.: (757) 460-1060
Web Site: http://www.eurpac.com
Rev.: $178,000,000
Emp.: 500
Retailer of Groceries
N.A.I.C.S.: 424490

John T. Becker (Pres)

EURPAC SERVICE INCORPORATED

101 Merrtt 7 Corporate Park, Norwalk, CT 06851
Tel.: (203) 847-0800
Web Site: http://www.eurpac.com
Sales Range: $25-49.9 Million
Emp.: 700
Groceries Distr
N.A.I.C.S.: 424410
Michael Stewart (Pres)
Mike Skinner (VP)

EUS COMMUNICATION INC.

55 Main St, Trenton, NJ 08620
Tel.: (609) 585-0577
Web Site: http://www.euscom.com
Sales Range: $10-24.9 Million
Emp.: 90
Telephone & Communication Line
Construction
N.A.I.C.S.: 238210
Kenneth Samu (Pres)

EUSTIS MORTGAGE CORP.

1100 Poydras St, New Orleans, LA
70163
Tel.: (504) 586-0075
Web Site:
    http://www.eustismortgage.com
Rev.: $7,960,000
Emp.: 40
Real Estate Credit
N.A.I.C.S.: 522292
Robert Eustis (Chm)
Alan Novotny (CEO)
Brett Mativi Sr. (Sr VP)
Kate DeKay Sr. (Sr VP)

Subsidiaries:

Signature Mortgage Corporation   (1)
4790 Douglas Cir NW, Canton, OH 44718
Tel.: (330) 305-1996
Web Site: http://www.smcinc500.com
Sales Range: $1-9.9 Million
Emp.: 16
Real Estate Financial Services
N.A.I.C.S.: 522292
Bob Catlin (Sr VP)

EUTAW CONSTRUCTION COMPANY INC.

109 1/2 W Commerce St, Aberdeen,
MS 39730
Tel.: (662) 369-8868
Web Site:
    http://www.eutawconstruction.com
Year Founded: 1980
Sales Range: $10-24.9 Million
Emp.: 300
General Contractor, Highway & Street
Construction
N.A.I.C.S.: 237310
Thomas S. Elmore (Founder)
Christie B. Kirkpatrick (Sec)
William E. Cox (Exec VP)
Jonathan Hust (Mgr-Private)
Matt McQueen (Mgr-Tennessee)
Lane Williams (Mgr-Utility)

EUTHYMICS BIOSCIENCE, INC.

43 Thorndike St Ste S1 3, Cambridge, MA 02141
Tel.: (617) 758-0300
Web Site: http://www.euthymics.com
Emp.: 6
Biopharmaceutical Research & Development Services
N.A.I.C.S.: 541715
Walter Piskorski (VP-Tech Ops)
William T. Pappafotopoulos (VP-Fin &
Admin)
Campbell Murray (Chm)

EV CHARGING USA, INC.

180 N LaSalle St 37th Fl, Chicago, IL
60601
Tel.: (312) 216-5106
Electrical Vehicle Charging Station
Services
N.A.I.C.S.: 457120
Brian Howe (Pres, CEO & CFO)

EV MARTIN CORPORATION

780 E Main St, New Holland, PA
17557
Tel.: (717) 354-4241
Web Site:
    http://www.powerproequipment.com
Sales Range: $10-24.9 Million
Emp.: 19
Provider of Building & Construction
Services
N.A.I.C.S.: 423810
Earl S. Martin (Pres & CEO)
Sherrie Weaver (Controller)
Paul Irvin (VP-Svcs)
Jim Martinson (VP-Ops)

EVA-DRY

12157 W Linebaugh Ave, Tampa, FL
33626
Web Site: http://www.eva-dry.com
Sales Range: $1-9.9 Million
Dehumidifier Mfr
N.A.I.C.S.: 334512
James Wetzel (Pres)

EVAN THOMAS GLOBAL LLC

111 S Albany Ave, Tampa, FL 33606-
1710
Tel.: (813) 251-1600
Web Site:
    http://www.evanthomas.com
Year Founded: 1989
Sales Range: $1-9.9 Million
Emp.: 10
Human Resources & Executive
Search Consulting Services
N.A.I.C.S.: 541612
Thomas L. Ratchford (CEO)
Donald W. Schmeling (CFO)
Kelly Conlon (Dir-Mktg & Recruiting
Svcs)

EVANGELICAL CHILDREN'S HOME

8240 St Charles Rock Rd, Saint
Louis, MO 63114
Tel.: (314) 427-3755   MO
Web Site:
    https://www.everychildshope.org
Year Founded: 1858
Sales Range: $10-24.9 Million
Emp.: 226
Child Care & Development Services
N.A.I.C.S.: 624110
Michael P. Brennan (CEO)
Valorie Holden (Dir-Early Education
Center)
Sharon Fenoglio (Chief Advancement
Officer)
Shari Smith (Pres)
E. David Viehmann (VP)
Paul G. Flynn (Treas)
Stephen R. Schroeder (Asst Treas)
Dennis B. Mertz (Sec)
Lisa Rees (Dir-Mktg & Contractual
Svcs)
David Juedemann (Dir-Performance
Improvement)
Eve Dyson (Dir-Family Connections)
Sharon Veit (Dir-Ops-St Louis)
Brandi Behne (CFO)
Wade Thurmon (Dir-Info Sys)

EVANGELICAL HOMES OF MICHIGAN

14900 Shoreline Dr, Sterling Heights,
MI 48313

Tel.: (586) 247-4700   MI
Web Site:
    http://www.evangelicalhomes.org
Year Founded: 1879
Sales Range: $50-74.9 Million
Emp.: 945
Elderly People Assistance Services
N.A.I.C.S.: 624120
Denise Rabidoux (Pres & CEO)
Dennis Purdy (VP-Philanthropy)
Peter Kovalszki (Dir-Medical Affairs)
Diane White (Chm)
Hakim Berry (Vice Chm)
Lynda Olinski (CFO & COO)
Paul Stavros (VP-Mktg & Bus Dev)
Allison Demarais (Chief HR Officer)
Thomas Hosinski (Sr VP-Housing &
Healthcare Svcs)
Robert K. Livingston (Sec)
James Polson (Treas)
Nancy Swierz (VP-Success Strategies & Process Improvement)

EVANGELICAL LUTHERAN CHURCH IN AMERICA

8765 W Higgins Rd, Chicago, IL
60631
Tel.: (773) 380-2700
Web Site: https://www.elca.org
Year Founded: 1988
Educational Support Services
N.A.I.C.S.: 611710

EVANS & ASSOCIATES ENTERPRISES

3320 N 14th St, Ponca City, OK
74601
Tel.: (580) 765-6693
Web Site: https://www.evans-
    assoc.com
Rev.: $37,700,000
Emp.: 125
Highway & Street Paving Contractor
N.A.I.C.S.: 237310
Linda I. Brown (Pres & CEO)
Lee Evans (VP)
Glen Nickles (VP)
Sherry Smith (Mgr-HR)

EVANS & SONS CONSTRUCTION

25812 Springbrook Ave, Santa
Clarita, CA 91350-2565
Tel.: (661) 254-8787
Web Site: https://evansandson.com
Year Founded: 1960
Sales Range: $10-24.9 Million
Emp.: 69
Civil Engineering Services
N.A.I.C.S.: 237310
Julie Evans (VP)

EVANS BROTHERS INC.

7589 National Dr, Livermore, CA
94550
Tel.: (925) 443-0225
Web Site:
    http://www.evansbrothers.com
Year Founded: 1976
Sales Range: $10-24.9 Million
Demolition Contractor
N.A.I.C.S.: 238190
Dan L. Evans (Pres)

EVANS CONCRETE LLC

100 Strickland Ln, Claxton, GA 30417
Tel.: (912) 739-3733
Web Site:
    http://www.evansconcrete.com
Rev.: $25,000,000
Emp.: 30
Ready Mixed Concrete
N.A.I.C.S.: 327320
Terri McCloud (Controller)
Bo Strickland (Pres)

Elmer Berry *(Mgr-Area)*
Leo Rogers *(Dir-EHS)*
Ricky Cleland *(Mgr-Area)*

EVANS DEDICATED SYSTEMS, INC.

6001 E Washington Blvd 2nd Fl, Commerce, CA 90040
Tel.: (323) 725-2928   CA
Web Site: http://www.evansdedicated.com
Year Founded: 1906
Sales Range: $10-24.9 Million
Emp.: 170
Liquid Petroleum Transport
N.A.I.C.S.: 484230
Bill Culbertson *(COO)*
Blanca Kelley *(Dir-Safety)*
Hugo Rodriguez *(Dir-Ops)*
Tom Forrest *(CFO)*

EVANS ENTERPRISES, INC.

1536 SW Ave, Oklahoma City, OK 73109-1422
Tel.: (405) 631-1344   OK
Web Site: http://www.goevans.com
Year Founded: 1954
Sales Range: $10-24.9 Million
Emp.: 130
Sales & Services of Electric Motors
N.A.I.C.S.: 335314
Steve Campbell *(Pres)*
David Woodman *(CFO)*

EVANS ENVIRONMENTAL & GEOLOGICAL SCIENCE AND MANAGEMENT INC.

5751 Miami Lakes Dr, Miami Lakes, FL 33014-1525
Tel.: (305) 374-8300   FL
Web Site: http://www.eeandg.com
Year Founded: 1986
Sales Range: $1-9.9 Million
Emp.: 58
Testing & Analytical Services; Engineering, Environmental, Construction, Demolition & Electrical Services
N.A.I.C.S.: 541690
Ximena Suarez *(Mgr-Business Development)*

EVANS FRUIT COMPANY

200 Cowiche City Rd, Cowiche, WA 98923
Tel.: (509) 678-4127
Web Site: https://www.evansfruitco.com
Rev.: $50,000,000
Emp.: 600
Apple Orchards
N.A.I.C.S.: 111331
Jeanette Evans *(Treas & Sec)*

EVANS GRADING CO.

3225 Alabama Hwy, Rome, GA 30164
Tel.: (706) 235-1117
Sales Range: $10-24.9 Million
Emp.: 120
Paper/Pulp Mill Construction
N.A.I.C.S.: 236220
Donald Lynn Evans *(CEO)*
Kevin Evans *(Pres)*

EVANS GRAIN & ELEVATOR CO. INC.

PO Box 3765, Ogden, UT 84405-4506
Tel.: (801) 476-0277   UT
Web Site: http://www.evansgrain.com
Year Founded: 1964
Sales Range: $10-24.9 Million
Emp.: 45
Grain & Field Beans
N.A.I.C.S.: 424510

Subsidiaries:

Western Seeds   (1)
1531 S Hwy 30, Heyburn, ID 83336-8642
Tel.: (208) 678-2268
Web Site: http://www.westernseeds.com
Sales Range: $10-24.9 Million
Emp.: 15
Distr of Seeds
N.A.I.C.S.: 424910

EVANS HOTELS CORPORATION

998 W Mission Bay Dr, San Diego, CA 92109
Tel.: (858) 488-0551
Web Site: https://www.evanshotels.com
Rev.: $14,300,000
Emp.: 55
Resort Hotel
N.A.I.C.S.: 721110
Anne L. Evans *(Owner & Chm)*
Grace Evans Cherashore *(Chm)*
C. Scott Ward *(Treas & VP-Fin)*
Robert H. Gleason *(Pres & CEO)*
Dan Ferbal *(VP-HR)*
Julia De Beers *(Chief Admin Officer & Gen Counsel)*
Jayne Aston *(Gen Mgr-Bahia Resort)*
Will Cherashore *(CFO)*

EVANS INCORPORATED

3110 Fairview Park Dr Ste 1100, Falls Church, VA 22042
Tel.: (703) 663-2480
Web Site: http://www.evansincorporated.com
Year Founded: 1994
Management Consulting Services
N.A.I.C.S.: 541611
Sue Evans *(Founder & Chm)*
Jack Moore *(Mng Partner)*
Richard Hudson *(Sr Dir-Ops)*
Jim Wright *(Dir-Bus Dev)*
Bob Etris *(Mng Partner)*
Stephanie Perlick *(Sr Dir-Client Delivery)*
Kristi Ausberry *(Dir-Fin)*
Iliana Alvarado *(Dir-Innovation)*
Lee Plumb *(Dir-Federal Bus Dev)*

EVANS LANDSCAPING INC.

3700 Round Bottom Rd, Cincinnati, OH 45244
Tel.: (513) 271-1119
Web Site: http://www.evanslandscaping.com
Year Founded: 1975
Rev.: $13,000,000
Emp.: 50
Farm Supplies
N.A.I.C.S.: 424910
Douglas Evans *(Pres)*
Heather Henry *(Mgr-Payroll & HR)*
Debbie Couch *(Mgr-Acctg)*

EVANS MACTAVISH AGRICRAFT INC.

5123 Ivy Ct, Wilson, NC 27893-7572
Tel.: (252) 243-4006   NC
Web Site: http://www.evansmachinery.com
Year Founded: 1979
Sales Range: $50-74.9 Million
Emp.: 40
Mfr of Tobacco Processing Machinery
N.A.I.C.S.: 333111
Donald Evans *(Pres & CEO)*
Amanda Barnes *(Sec)*
Beverly Lanham *(Mgr-Intl Sls Admin)*

Subsidiaries:

Evans MacTavish Agricraft   (1)
7429 Whitepine Rd, Richmond, VA 23237
Tel.: (252) 243-4006
Web Site: http://www.mactavish.com

Sales Range: $10-24.9 Million
Emp.: 3
Tobacco Products Machinery Mfr
N.A.I.C.S.: 333248
Sam Levy *(VP-Sls & Mktg)*
Francis Smith *(Controller)*

EVANS MANUFACTURING INC.

7422 Chapman Ave, Garden Grove, CA 92841
Tel.: (714) 379-6100
Web Site: http://www.evans-mfg.com
Sales Range: $10-24.9 Million
Emp.: 245
Plastic Molding Mfr
N.A.I.C.S.: 326199
Alan Vaught *(Owner)*
Greg Kahn *(CFO)*
Jim Schneiderman *(Dir-HR)*
David Goldfarb *(Mgr-Mktg)*

EVANS MEATS, INCORPORATED

617 21st Ave W, Birmingham, AL 35204
Tel.: (205) 324-6666
Web Site: https://www.evansmeats.com
Year Founded: 1998
Sales Range: $10-24.9 Million
Emp.: 52
Meat & Meat Product Whslr
N.A.I.C.S.: 424470
Addam Evans *(VP)*
John Kennemer *(Mgr-Production)*

EVANS PROPERTIES INC.

660 Beachland Blvd Ste 301, Vero Beach, FL 32963
Tel.: (772) 234-2410
Web Site: http://www.evansprop.com
Year Founded: 1951
Sales Range: $10-24.9 Million
Emp.: 75
Grower of Citrus Fruits
N.A.I.C.S.: 111320
Lionel Lowry *(Vice Chm)*
Ronald L. Edwards *(Pres & CEO)*
Jimmy Evans Jr. *(Chm)*
Emmett Evans III *(VP)*

EVANS SERVICE COMPANY INC.

1421 College Ave, Elmira, NY 14901
Tel.: (607) 734-8838
Web Site: https://www.evansroofingcompany.com
Rev.: $17,100,000
Emp.: 23
Roofing Contractors
N.A.I.C.S.: 238160
Kevin Kennedy *(Exec VP)*

EVANS TIRE & SERVICE CENTERS, INC.

2520 Pioneer Ave, Vista, CA 92081
Tel.: (760) 579-4470   CA
Web Site: http://www.evanstire.com
Year Founded: 2001
Sales Range: $25-49.9 Million
Automotive Tire Dealership & Service Centers Owner & Operator
N.A.I.C.S.: 441340
John K. Andonian *(Pres & CEO)*

EVANSHARDY & YOUNG, INC.

829 De La Vina St Ste 100, Santa Barbara, CA 93101-3238
Tel.: (805) 963-5841   DE
Web Site: http://www.ehy.com
Year Founded: 1986
Rev.: $45,000,000
Emp.: 40
N.A.I.C.S.: 541810
Jim Evans *(Founder)*
Sue Andrews *(CFO & Sr VP)*

Dennis Hardy *(Pres & CEO)*
Suzan Sonna *(Mgr-Production)*
Lily Katz-Smolenske *(Sr VP & Media Dir)*
Pamela Landis *(VP & Dir-Brdcst)*
Lisa Tumminello *(Pres-PR)*
Keith Butler *(VP-Interactive)*
K. T. Thayer *(Chief Creative Officer)*
Jaime Eschette *(Dir-Mktg)*

EVANSTON PARTNERS, LLC

1563 Sherman Ave Ste 200, Evanston, IL 60201
Tel.: (847) 868-3902
Web Site: http://www.evanstonpartners.com
Privater Equity Firm
N.A.I.C.S.: 523999
Jeffrey D. Ellis *(Principal)*
Sylvia Anguelov *(CFO)*

Subsidiaries:

Auto Driveaway Franchise Systems, LLC   (1)
1 E 22nd St Ste 107, Lombard, IL 60148
Tel.: (312) 341-1900
Web Site: http://www.autodriveaway.com
Sales Range: $10-24.9 Million
Emp.: 100
Delivery Services for Automobiles, Trucks & Other Vehicles
N.A.I.C.S.: 561990
Rodney Ruth *(Pres & CEO)*
Grant Waddell *(Dir-Sls & Mktg-Natl)*
Marianne Stewart *(Mgr-Bus & Product Dev-Client Svcs)*
Matthew Salm *(COO)*
Jeffrey Ellis *(CFO)*

Subsidiary (Domestic):

J&J Drive Away Systems, LLC   (2)
16011 College Blvd Ste 200, Lenexa, KS 66219
Tel.: (913) 851-4010
Web Site: http://www.jjdriveaway.com
General Freight Services
N.A.I.C.S.: 484121
Rodney Ruth *(Pres & CEO)*
Jeff Moe *(Pres)*

EVANSTON SUBARU IN SKOKIE

3340 Oakton St, Skokie, IL 60076-2953
Tel.: (847) 869-5700
Web Site: https://www.evanstonsubaru.com
Year Founded: 1996
Sales Range: $10-24.9 Million
Emp.: 50
New Car Whslr
N.A.I.C.S.: 441110
Ray Eichenlaub *(Dir-Svc)*
Robert E. Paddor *(Pres)*
Sabrina Sigel *(Office Mgr)*

EVANSVILLE TEACHERS FEDERAL CREDIT UNION

4401 Theater Dr, Evansville, IN 47715
Tel.: (812) 477-9271
Web Site: https://www.etfcu.org
Year Founded: 1936
Credit Union
N.A.I.C.S.: 522130
Ken Wempe *(Chm)*
Andrew Guarino *(Vice Chm)*
Jane Magary *(Treas)*
Harold Smith *(Sec)*

Subsidiaries:

Liberty Financial   (1)
4220 Shelbyville Rd, Louisville, KY 40207
Web Site: http://www.liberty.financial
Commercial Banking & Lending Services
N.A.I.C.S.: 522110

EVCI CAREER COLLEGES HOLDING CORP.

EVCI Career Colleges Holding Corp.—(Continued)

320 W 31st St, New York, NY 10001
Tel.: (914) 623-0700 DE
Web Site: http://www.evcinc.com
Year Founded: 1997
Sales Range: $50-74.9 Million
Emp.: 465
Holding Company; Technical & Pro-
fessional Schools Owner & Operator
N.A.I.C.S.: 551112
John J. McGrath *(Pres & CEO)*

Subsidiaries:

Pennsylvania School of Business,
Inc. (1)
265 Lehigh St, Allentown, PA 18102
Tel.: (610) 841-3333
Web Site: http://www.psb.edu
Education Services Focused on Business
N.A.I.C.S.: 611410
Michael O'Brien *(Pres)*

Technical Career Institutes, Inc. (1)
320 W 31st St, New York, NY 10001
Tel.: (212) 594-4000
Web Site: http://www.tcicollege.edu
Education Services Focusing on Technology
N.A.I.C.S.: 611519

EVCO PLASTICS INC.
100 W N St, De Forest, WI 53532
Tel.: (608) 846-6000
Web Site:
   https://www.evcoplastics.com
Rev.: $29,400,000
Emp.: 400
Plastics Product Mfr
N.A.I.C.S.: 326199
Dale Evans *(Pres)*
Chris Evans *(Treas)*
Steven Evans *(Sec & VP)*

EVCO WHOLESALE FOODS
309 Merchant St, Emporia, KS 66801
Tel.: (620) 343-7000
Web Site:
   https://www.evcofoods.com
Rev.: $19,700,000
Emp.: 75
Groceries, General Line
N.A.I.C.S.: 561499
Charles Evans *(Pres)*

EVED, LLC
350 W Ontario St, Chicago, IL 60654
Tel.: (312) 902-3833
Web Site: http://www.eved.com
Year Founded: 2004
Sales Range: $1-9.9 Million
Emp.: 26
Online Business To Business Ser-
vices
N.A.I.C.S.: 425120
Talia Mashiach *(Founder & CEO)*
Sue Buckles *(VP-Dev)*
Christi Zeck *(CTO)*
Remus Hociota *(VP-IT)*
Trista Hannan *(Sr VP-Client Solu-
tions)*
Christopher Yoo *(VP-Fin & Ops)*
Tevi Hirschhorn *(Dir-Design)*
Josh Gray *(Pres & COO)*

EVELAND'S INC.
Hwy 371 N, Backus, MN 56435
Tel.: (218) 947-4932
Web Site:
   http://www.scamptrailers.com
Year Founded: 1971
Sales Range: $10-24.9 Million
Emp.: 45
Trailers Mfr
N.A.I.C.S.: 336214
Kent Eveland *(Pres)*

EVELYN & ARTHUR INC.
1912 Corporate Dr, Boynton Beach,
FL 33426

Tel.: (561) 572-0900
Web Site:
   http://www.evelynandarthur.com
Sales Range: $10-24.9 Million
Emp.: 75
Women's Apparel Retailer
N.A.I.C.S.: 458110
Fred Weissman *(CFO)*

EVENING POST PUBLISHING CO.
134 Columbus St, Charleston, SC
29403-4809
Tel.: (843) 577-7111 SC
Web Site:
   http://www.postandcourier.com
Year Founded: 1894
Sales Range: $1-4.9 Billion
Emp.: 1,800
Holding Company; Newspaper &
Magazine Publisher & Television
Broadcasting
N.A.I.C.S.: 551112
Pierre Manigault *(Chm)*
Arthur M. Wilcox *(Sec)*
Mark Mulholland *(VP-Mktg-
Newspaper Div)*
Lynn McLamb *(VP-Ops-Ccommunity
Newspapers)*
P. J. Browning *(CEO)*

Subsidiaries:

Aiken Standard (1)
326 Rutland Dr NW PO Box 456, Aiken, SC
29801
Tel.: (803) 648-2311
Web Site: http://www.aikenstandard.com
Sales Range: $10-24.9 Million
Emp.: 100
Newspaper Publishers
N.A.I.C.S.: 513110
Letitia Jefferson *(Mgr-Customer Svc)*
Larry Taylor *(Editor-Night)*
Michael Smith *(Exec Dir)*
Haley Culp *(Acct Exec)*
Diane Daniell *(Mgr-Adv Sls)*
Holly Ellington *(Editor-News)*
Joe Harty *(Acct Exec)*
Lauren Molony *(Acct Exec)*
Scott Rodgers *(Editor-News)*
Mary Watson *(Designer-Graphic)*
Sharye Whisenant *(Acct Exec)*
R. J. Benner *(Publr & Dir-Adv)*
John Boyette *(Exec Editor)*

Clear Night Group (1)
325 Cedar St Ste 1001, Saint Paul, MN
55101
Tel.: (651) 379-0050
Web Site: http://www.clearnightgroup.com
Marketing Services
N.A.I.C.S.: 541613
John Hyduke *(Pres & CEO)*

Subsidiary (Domestic):

Gabriel deGrood Bendt LLC (2)
515 N Washington Ave, Minneapolis, MN
55401
Tel.: (612) 547-5000
Web Site: http://www.gdbagenncy.com
Emp.: 23
Advertising Agencies
N.A.I.C.S.: 541810
Tom Gabriel *(CEO & Dir-Creative)*
Doug de Grood *(Partner & Dir-Creative)*
Kris Fitzpatrick *(Acct Supvr)*
Maggie Dalrymple *(Assoc Dir-Media)*
Teresa McFarland *(Pres)*

Davie County Enterprise-Record (1)
171 S Main St, Mocksville, NC 27028
Tel.: (336) 751-2120
Web Site: http://www.ourdavie.com
Sales Range: $10-24.9 Million
Emp.: 4
Newspaper Publishers
N.A.I.C.S.: 513110
Robin Snow *(Gen Mgr)*

Evening Post Digital (1)
134 Columbus St, Charleston, SC 29403
Tel.: (843) 577-7111
Web Site: http://www.postandcourier.com

Sales Range: $25-49.9 Million
Emp.: 400
Online Newspaper Publishing
N.A.I.C.S.: 513110

Garden & Gun (1)
409 King St 2nd Fl, Charleston, SC 29403
Tel.: (843) 795-1195
Web Site: http://www.gardenandgun.com
Sales Range: $10-24.9 Million
Emp.: 40
Magazine Publisher
N.A.I.C.S.: 513120
Rebecca Wesson Darwin *(Founder & CEO)*
David Dibenedetto *(Sr VP & Editor-in-Chief)*
Christian Bryant *(Publr & VP)*

Georgetown Communications,
Inc. (1)
615 Front St, Georgetown, SC 29440
Tel.: (843) 546-4148
Web Site: http://www.southstrandnews.com
Sales Range: $10-24.9 Million
Emp.: 20
Newspaper Publishers
N.A.I.C.S.: 513110
Dale Lambert *(Mgr-Sls)*
John Cioni *(Gen Mgr & Dir-Adv)*
Vicky Boyd *(Publr)*

Unit (Domestic):

The News (2)
511 N Longstreet St, Kingstree, SC 29556
Tel.: (843) 355-6397
Web Site: http://www.kingstreenews.com
Sales Range: $10-24.9 Million
Emp.: 7
Newspaper Publishers
N.A.I.C.S.: 513110
Patricia McCrea *(Mgr-Classified)*

KATC Communications, Inc. (1)
1103 Eraste Landry Rd, Lafayette, LA
70506
Tel.: (337) 235-3333
Web Site: http://www.katc.com
Sales Range: $10-24.9 Million
Emp.: 75
Television Broadcasting Station
N.A.I.C.S.: 516120
Andrew Shenkan *(Pres & Gen Mgr)*
Cathy Schexnayder *(Mgr-Bus)*
Letitia Walker *(Dir-News)*
Arte Richard *(Dir-Mktg)*
Travis Webb *(Dir-Sports)*
Mike Zikmund *(Dir-Sls)*

KRIS Communications Inc. (1)
301 Artesian St, Corpus Christi, TX 78401-
3330
Tel.: (361) 886-6100
Web Site: http://www.kristv.com
Sales Range: $10-24.9 Million
Emp.: 60
Television Broadcasting Station
N.A.I.C.S.: 516120
Greg McAlister *(Gen Mgr)*
Kristen Darden *(Sls Mgr-Local)*
Paul Alexander *(Dir-News)*

KSBY Communications, Inc. (1)
1772 Calle Joaquin, San Luis Obispo, CA
93405
Tel.: (805) 541-6666
Web Site: http://www.ksby.com
Sales Range: $10-24.9 Million
Emp.: 70
Television Broadcasting Station
N.A.I.C.S.: 516120
Evan Pappas *(Pres & Gen Mgr)*
Brandon Downing *(Dir-Creative)*
Matt SantaMaria *(Dir-Sports)*

Post Publishing Company (1)
131 W Innes St, Salisbury, NC 28144-4338
Tel.: (704) 633-8950
Web Site: http://www.salisburypost.com
Sales Range: $10-24.9 Million
Emp.: 73
Newspaper Publishers
N.A.I.C.S.: 513110
Elizabeth Cook *(Editor)*
Brian Tant *(Bus Mgr)*
Elisha Hubbard *(District Mgr)*
Mike Bostian *(Mgr-Single Copy)*
Michael LeRoy *(Coord-Press)*
Sharon Jackson *(Mgr-Pre-Press)*

Sangre de Cristo Communications,
Inc. (1)

2200 7th Ave, Pueblo, CO 81003
Tel.: (719) 544-5781
Web Site: http://www.koaa.com
Television Broadcasting Station
N.A.I.C.S.: 516120
Evie Hudson *(Dir-HR)*
Quentin Henry *(Chief Engr)*

Summerville Communications,
Inc. (1)
104 E Doty Ave, Summerville, SC
29483 (100%)
Tel.: (843) 873-9424
Web Site: http://www.journalscene.com
Sales Range: $10-24.9 Million
Emp.: 20
Newspaper Publishers
N.A.I.C.S.: 513110
Judy Watts *(Exec Editor)*
Nick Daniels *(Mgr-Adv)*
David Kennard *(Mgr-Bus)*

The Post & Courier, LLC (1)
134 Columbus St, Charleston, SC 29403
Tel.: (843) 577-7111
Web Site: http://www.postandcourier.com
Sales Range: $25-49.9 Million
Emp.: 500
Newspaper Publishers
N.A.I.C.S.: 513110
Charles R. Rowe *(Editor-Editorial & Opinion
Pages)*
William E. N. Hawkins *(Publr & Editor)*
Frank Wooten *(Editor)*
Alan Seim *(Editor-Charlestonnet)*
Jamie Drolet *(Mgr-Retail Adv)*
Steve Wagenlander *(Dir-Audience Dev)*

Unit (Domestic):

The Charleston Mercury (2)
180 E Bay St 310, Charleston, SC
29401
Tel.: (843) 793-3723
Web Site:
   http://www.charlestonmercury.com
Sales Range: $10-24.9 Million
Emp.: 50
Newspaper Publishers
N.A.I.C.S.: 513110
Charles W. Waring III *(Publr)*

WLEX Communications, LLC (1)
1065A Russell Cave Rd, Lexington, KY
40505
Tel.: (859) 259-1818
Web Site: http://www.lex18.com
Sales Range: $10-24.9 Million
Emp.: 100
Television Broadcasting Station
N.A.I.C.S.: 516120
Pat Dalbey *(Pres & Gen Mgr)*

EVENT MANAGEMENT SER-VICES, INC.
3748 Turman Loop Ste 101, Wesley
Chapel, FL 33544
Tel.: (727) 443-7115 FL
Web Site:
   http://www.emsincorporated.com
Year Founded: 1990
Sales Range: $1-9.9 Million
Emp.: 16
Public Relations
N.A.I.C.S.: 541820
Marsha Friedman *(Founder & CEO)*
Steve Friedman *(Partner)*
Damon Friedman *(VP-Bus Dev)*
Alex Hinojosa *(VP-Media Ops &
Strategy)*
Rich Ghazarian *(Mgr-Radio Cam-
paigns)*
Ginny Grimsley *(Mgr-Print Cam-
paigns)*
Russ Handler *(Mgr-Television Cam-
paigns)*
Penny Carnathan *(Dir-Creative)*
Will Candler *(Dir-Mktg)*
Marti Carlson *(Office Mgr)*
Rachel Friedman *(Dir-Bus Dev)*
Ronnie Blair *(Sr Dir-Creative)*

EVENT NETWORK, INC.

1010 Turquoise St Ste 325, San Diego, CA 92109
Tel.: (858) 488-7507
Web Site:
    http://www.eventnetwork.com
Sales Range: $25-49.9 Million
Emp.: 50
Retail Shop Operator for Museums, Zoos, Aquariums & Botanical Gardens
N.A.I.C.S.: 459999
Jerry Gilbert *(Principal & VP-Mktg)*
Larry Gilbert *(Pres & CEO)*
Helen Sherman *(Exec VP-Product)*
Lorna Davis *(Exec VP-Stores & Store Plng)*
Andrea Froehle *(Dir-Partnership Dev)*
Annie Evans *(Dir-Community & Culture)*
Lorena Bubel *(Exec VP-Pur)*
Philippe Vanier *(COO)*
Ryan Close *(Exec VP-Tech)*
Jane Casanta *(VP-Partnership Dev)*

EVENT SALES INC.
3359 Central Ave NE, Minneapolis, MN 55413
Tel.: (612) 781-1502
Web Site: https://www.eventsale.com
Sales Range: $10-24.9 Million
Emp.: 25
Merchandise Liquidators
N.A.I.C.S.: 561900
Anthony Hofstede *(Co-Founder)*
Val Vavere *(Co-Founder)*

EVENT SOLUTIONS LLC
1253 Martin St, Nashville, TN 37203
Tel.: (615) 788-2251   TN
Web Site:
    http://www.evolutioneventsolu
    tions.com
Year Founded: 2012
Sales Range: $1-9.9 Million
Emp.: 8
Travel Agency Services
N.A.I.C.S.: 561510
Falon Veit Scott *(Founder & CEO)*

EVENT TECHNOLOGY, LLC
1629 Prime Ct Ste 100, Orlando, FL 32809-7410
Tel.: (407) 251-1400
Web Site: http://www.etechav.com
Year Founded: 1996
Sales Range: $1-9.9 Million
Emp.: 26
Rental & Installation of Audio Visual Equipment
N.A.I.C.S.: 532420
Tom Brandt *(Pres & CEO)*
Cliff Ferris *(Dir-Ops)*

EVENTEQ, LLC
9520 Gerwig Ln Ste T, Columbia, MD 21046
Tel.: (410) 242-5050
Web Site: http://www.eventeq.com
Year Founded: 2005
Sales Range: $10-24.9 Million
Emp.: 11
Sound Recording Industries
N.A.I.C.S.: 512290
Jag Singh *(Supvr-Production)*

EVENTIDE SENIOR LIVING COMMUNITIES
2405 8th St S Ste A, Moorhead, MN 56560
Tel.: (218) 291-2230   MN
Web Site: http://www.eventide.org
Year Founded: 1951
Sales Range: $25-49.9 Million
Emp.: 1,314
Community Care Services
N.A.I.C.S.: 624229

Peter Seljevold *(Treas)*

EVENTPRO STRATEGIES, INC.
7373 N Scottsdale Rd Ste B 120, Scottsdale, AZ 85253
Tel.: (480) 449-4100   NC
Web Site:
    http://www.eventprostrategies.com
Year Founded: 2005
Sales Range: $10-24.9 Million
Emp.: 35
Marketing Event Staffing, Execution & Project Management Solutions
N.A.I.C.S.: 561320
Jessica Browder-Stackpoole *(Founder & CEO)*
Meggan Ballard-Gomez *(Mgr-Sls Team)*

EVENTPRO STRATEGIES, LLC.
7373 N Scottsdale Rd Ste B-120, Scottsdale, AZ 85253
Tel.: (480) 449-4100
Web Site:
    http://www.eventprostrategies.com
Year Founded: 1999
Sales Range: $10-24.9 Million
Emp.: 5,637
Event Staffing Consulting Services
N.A.I.C.S.: 541618
Jessica Stackpoole *(Founder & CEO)*
John Anderson *(CFO)*
Teresa Puschnig *(Dir-Ops)*
Kelly Springs Kelley *(Dir-Mktg)*
Lisa Major *(Mgr-Social Media & Talent Rels)*
Tanya Groff *(Mgr-Ops Team)*
Traci Danek *(VP-Ops)*

EVENTS.COM, INC.
4660 La Jolla Village Dr Ste 600, La Jolla, CA 92122
Tel.: (858) 652-4747
Web Site: http://www.events.com
Emp.: 25
Online Event Management Services
N.A.I.C.S.: 541519
Mitch Thrower *(Founder & Chm)*

Subsidiaries:

Brown Paper Tickets LLC   (1)
220 Nickerson St, Seattle, WA 98109-1622
Tel.: (317) 207-0171
Web Site:
    http://www.brownpapertickets.com
Travel Arrangement & Reservation Services
N.A.I.C.S.: 561599

Pixelpushers, Inc.   (1)
20101 Birch St Ste 250, Newport Beach, CA 92660
Tel.: (949) 851-1600
Web Site: http://www.pixelpushers.com
Sales Range: $1-9.9 Million
Emp.: 13
Custom Computer Programming Services
N.A.I.C.S.: 541511
Jeanne Gregg *(VP-Ops)*

EVENTWORKS INC.
340 W 131st St, Los Angeles, CA 90061
Tel.: (323) 321-1793
Web Site:
    http://www.eventworks.com
Sales Range: $1-9.9 Million
Emp.: 20
Event Production Services
N.A.I.C.S.: 337215
Janet Elkins *(Pres)*
Ted Bowers *(Exec VP)*
Selena Akaose *(Dir-Admin Svcs)*
Carolyn Vasi *(Mgr-Production)*

EVERBERG CAPITAL, LLC
589 5th Ave Ste 1602, New York, NY 10017

Tel.: (212) 390-9768
Web Site:
    https://www.everbergcapital.com
Year Founded: 2019
Privater Equity Firm
N.A.I.C.S.: 523940
Scott Siegel *(Founder & Mng Partner)*

EVERBRITE, LLC
4949 S 110th St, Greenfield, WI 53228-3100
Tel.: (414) 529-3500   WI
Web Site: http://www.everbrite.com
Year Founded: 1928
Sales Range: $350-399.9 Million
Emp.: 1,500
Provider of Outdoor & Indoor Point-of-Purchase Signs
N.A.I.C.S.: 339950
Jim Flanigan *(Mgr-Mktg)*
Jay Jensen *(Dir-Sls)*
Brian Kuhnau *(Pres)*

Subsidiaries:

Everbrite Electronics, Inc   (1)
720 West Cherry St, Chanute, KS 66720
Tel.: (620) 431-7383
Sales Range: $10-24.9 Million
Emp.: 40
Electronic Components Mfr
N.A.I.C.S.: 334419

Everbrite LaCrosse   (1)
3145 Airport Rd, La Crosse, WI 54603-1257
Tel.: (608) 781-8700
Sales Range: $10-24.9 Million
Emp.: 50
Mfr Custom-Made Signs
N.A.I.C.S.: 339950

Fluoresco Services LLC   (1)
5505 S Nogales Hwy, Tucson, AZ 85706
Tel.: (520) 623-7953
Web Site: http://www.fluoresco.com
Sales Range: $25-49.9 Million
Emp.: 150
Outdoor Lighting & Electric Sign Maintenance Services
N.A.I.C.S.: 339950
Ladd M. Kleiman *(Pres)*
Ira A. Kleiman *(Exec VP)*
Andy Kleiman *(Exec VP)*
Michael Martinez *(Mgr-Production)*
Mary Kidder *(VP-Corp Ops)*

GHN   (1)
7472 Chapman Ave, Garden Grove, CA 92841-2106   (100%)
Tel.: (714) 620-7440
Web Site: http://www.neoncentral.com
Sales Range: $10-24.9 Million
Emp.: 60
Mfr of Neon Signs
N.A.I.C.S.: 339950

Mount Vernon Neon   (1)
1 Neon Dr, Mount Vernon, IL 62864-6723
Tel.: (618) 242-0645
Sales Range: $25-49.9 Million
Emp.: 140
Mfr of Neon Signs
N.A.I.C.S.: 339950

EVERCEL, INC.
382 NE 191st St Ste 90959, Miami, FL 33179
Tel.: (646) 666-3400   DE
Web Site: http://www.evercel.com
EVRC—(OTCIQ)
Rev.: $57,609,000
Assets: $92,853,000
Liabilities: $12,679,000
Net Worth: $80,174,000
Earnings: $8,743,000
Fiscal Year-end: 03/29/19
Printing Equipment Mfr
N.A.I.C.S.: 333248

Subsidiaries:

Zagg Incorporated   (1)
910 W Legacy Ctr Way Ste 500, Midvale, UT 84047
Tel.: (801) 263-0699

Web Site: http://www.zagg.com
Rev.: $521,922,000
Assets: $469,231,000
Liabilities: $277,752,000
Net Worth: $191,479,000
Earnings: $13,920,000
Emp.: 628
Fiscal Year-end: 12/31/2019
Protective Coverings, Audio Accessories & Power Solutions for Consumer Electronic & Hand-Held Devices Designer, Mfr & Distr
N.A.I.C.S.: 334310
Abby Barraclough *(Gen Counsel)*
Jim Kearns *(COO)*

Subsidiary (Domestic):

HzO, Inc.   (2)
5151 McCrimmon Pkwy, Morrisville, NC 27560
Tel.: (919) 439-0505
Web Site: http://www.hzo.com
Waterproof Electronic Product Mfr
N.A.I.C.S.: 334419
Richard D. Holder *(Pres & CEO)*
Stephen Gold *(Chief Comml Officer)*
Bill McCombe *(CFO)*
Dirk Cartus *(Exec VP)*
David Gilbert *(Exec VP)*
Richard D. Holder *(Pres & CEO)*

Mophie Inc.   (2)
15495 Sand Canyon 4th Fl, Irvine, CA 92618
Tel.: (269) 746-1340
Web Site: http://www.mophie.com
Cellular Accessories
N.A.I.C.S.: 334220

EVERENCE
1110 N Main St, Goshen, IN 46527-0483
Tel.: (574) 533-9511
Web Site: https://www.everence.com
Sales Range: $50-74.9 Million
Emp.: 250
Accident & Health Insurance
N.A.I.C.S.: 524114
Vyron Schmidt *(Sr VP)*
Kenneth Dean Hochstetler *(Pres & CEO)*
Madalyn Metzger *(Sr VP-Mktg)*
Jim Alvarez *(CEO)*

EVEREST CONSULTANTS INC.
15100 SW Koll Pkwy Ste K, Beaverton, OR 97006
Tel.: (503) 643-3990
Web Site: http://www.everestinc.com
Sales Range: $1-9.9 Million
Emp.: 75
Software Consultining
N.A.I.C.S.: 518210
Sriram Edupuganti *(Founder & CEO)*
Rania Edupuganti *(Pres)*
Dan Glass *(Dir-Bus Dev-Project Svcs)*
Ron Minter *(Dir-Bus Dev)*

EVEREST CONSULTING GROUP
3840 Park Ave Ste 203, Edison, NJ 08820
Tel.: (732) 548-2700
Web Site:
    https://www.everestconsulting.net
Rev.: $18,888,618
Emp.: 55
Computer Software Development
N.A.I.C.S.: 541511
P. Vijay *(VP-Business Development)*

EVEREST CONSULTING GROUP LP
9840 Old Perry Hwy, Wexford, PA 15090
Tel.: (412) 548-1550
Sales Range: $10-24.9 Million
Emp.: 20
Real Estate Brokers & Agents
N.A.I.C.S.: 531210

Everest Consulting Group LP—(Continued)

Wendy West *(Pres)*

Subsidiaries:

Northwood Realty Services **(1)**
9840 Old Perry Hwy, Pittsburgh, PA 15090
Tel.: (800) 715-3695
Web Site:
  http://www.northwoodrealtyservices.com
Real Estate Services
N.A.I.C.S.: 531210

Subsidiary (Domestic):

PPR Realty Inc. **(2)**
9840 Old Perry Hwy, Wexford, PA 15090
Tel.: (412) 367-8028
Web Site: http://www.thepreferredrealty.com
Real Estate Brokers & Agents
N.A.I.C.S.: 531210
Ronald F. Croushore *(Owner)*

EVERETT BUICK PONTIAC GMC
21115 Interstate 30, Bryant, AR 72022-6239
Tel.: (501) 315-7100
Web Site:
  http://www.everettbgmc.com
Year Founded: 2006
Sales Range: $50-74.9 Million
Emp.: 150
Car Whslr
N.A.I.C.S.: 441110
Chad Hendrix *(Gen Mgr)*
Jerry Odon *(Gen Mgr)*

EVERETT CASH MUTUAL INSURANCE CO.
10591 Lincoln Hwy, Everett, PA 15537-7047
Tel.: (814) 652-6111
Web Site:
  http://www.everettcash.com
Insurance Agencies & Brokerages
N.A.I.C.S.: 524210
Randy Shaw *(Pres)*

EVERETT CHEVROLET INC.
7300 Evergreen Way, Everett, WA 98203-5662
Tel.: (425) 355-6690
Web Site:
  http://www.everettchevrolet.com
Rev.: $40,000,000
Emp.: 85
New Car Dealers
N.A.I.C.S.: 441110
Brian Brighella *(Mgr-Sls)*
Isaac Wages *(Mgr-Svc)*
Katrina Kuenzi *(Office Mgr)*
Michelle Adamek *(Mgr-Fin)*
Mila Bill *(Mgr-Internet Sls)*
Paul Grey *(Mgr-Parts)*
Terry Parris *(Mgr-Sls)*
Ward Fleishmann *(Gen Mgr-Sls)*

EVERETT DYKE'S GRASSING CO., INC.
1339 Georgia Hwy 112, Cochran, GA 31014
Tel.: (478) 934-2707
Year Founded: 1968
Sales Range: $10-24.9 Million
Emp.: 50
Provider of Highway & Street Construction Services
N.A.I.C.S.: 237310
Jerry Van Dykes *(Pres)*
Kailey Taylor *(Mgr-Payroll & HR)*

EVERETT FINANCIAL, INC.
14801 Quorum Dr Ste 300, Dallas, TX 75254
Tel.: (214) 340-5225
Web Site:
  https://www.supremelending.com

Year Founded: 1997
Sales Range: $50-74.9 Million
Emp.: 459
Mortgage & Nonmortgage Loan Brokers
N.A.I.C.S.: 522310
Scott Everett *(Pres)*
Barry Logan *(Mgr-Producing-Birmingham)*
Robert Wills *(Sls Mgr-South Florida)*
James J. Flood *(Mgr-Bus Dev-South Florida)*

EVERETT FOODLINER INC.
250 W Main St, Everett, PA 15537
Tel.: (814) 652-2211
Web Site:
  https://www.everettfoodliner.com
Rev.: $13,595,279
Emp.: 105
Independent Supermarket
N.A.I.C.S.: 445110
Joe Appleby *(Pres)*
Vickie Owens *(Office Mgr)*
Bob Appleby *(Treas)*

EVERETT HOLDING COMPANY
11030 Hickman Mills Dr, Kansas City, MO 64134
Tel.: (816) 765-0733
Rev.: $20,000,000
Emp.: 2
Asphalt & Asphaltic Paving Mixtures
N.A.I.C.S.: 324121

EVERETT J. PRESCOTT INC.
32 Prescott St Libby Hill Business Park, Gardiner, ME 04345-2321
Tel.: (207) 582-1851
Web Site: https://www.ejprescott.com
Year Founded: 1955
Sales Range: $75-99.9 Million
Emp.: 200
Plumbing Fixtures, Equipment & Supplies
N.A.I.C.S.: 423720
Peter E. Prescott *(CEO)*
Edward H. Boudreau *(Treas & VP-Financial)*
Steven E. Prescott *(Pres)*

EVERFAST INC.
203 Gale Ln, Kennett Square, PA 19348
Tel.: (610) 444-9700
Web Site:
  http://www.calicocorners.com
Year Founded: 1948
Retailer of Decorative Fabrics & Furniture
N.A.I.C.S.: 459130
Scott Berman *(Controller)*

Subsidiaries:

Calico Corners **(1)**
203 Gale Ln, Kennett Square, PA 19348-1735
Tel.: (610) 444-9700
Web Site: http://www.calicocorners.com
Rev.: $1,500,000
Emp.: 100
Retailer of Decorative Fabric Distr
N.A.I.C.S.: 459130

EVERFI, INC.
3299 K St NW 4th Fl, Washington, DC 20007
Tel.: (202) 625-0011
Web Site: http://www.everfi.com
Year Founded: 2008
Educational Technology Products & Services
N.A.I.C.S.: 513210
Jon Chapman *(Co-Founder & Pres-Natl Partnerships)*

Ramon M. Martinez *(Co-Founder & Pres-Fin Svcs)*
Ellen Patterson *(COO)*
Walter Leach *(Gen Counsel)*
Tom Davidson *(Co-Founder & Pres)*

Subsidiaries:

LawRoom **(1)**
1255 Treat Blvd Ste 530, Walnut Creek, CA 94597-7990
Tel.: (925) 937-1506
Web Site: https://www.lawroom.com
Online Compliance Education Products & Training
N.A.I.C.S.: 513210

Unit (Domestic):

CampusClarity **(2)**
1255 Treat Blvd Ste 530, Walnut Creek, CA 94597
Tel.: (800) 652-9546
Web Site: http://home.campusclarity.com
Compliance & Prevention Education Software for Higher Education Students, Staff & Faculty
N.A.I.C.S.: 513210
Tom Davidson *(CEO)*

EVERFLOW EASTERN PARTNERS L.P.
585 W Main St, Canfield, OH 44406
Tel.: (330) 533-2692   DE
Rev.: $14,318,317
Assets: $49,204,347
Liabilities: $22,378,828
Net Worth: $26,825,519
Earnings: $9,092,584
Emp.: 17
Fiscal Year-end: 12/31/22
Oil & Gas Exploration Services
N.A.I.C.S.: 211120
William A. Siskovic *(VP)*

EVERGLADES TECHNOLOGIES
1 Union Sq W Ste 302, New York, NY 10003
Tel.: (212) 741-0000
Web Site: http://www.etny.net
Year Founded: 2000
Rev.: $4,700,000
Emp.: 25
Business Consulting Services
N.A.I.C.S.: 541618
Rhonda Riedel *(Dir-Bus)*
Jose Cordero *(Sr Project Mgr)*
Fernando Zorrilla *(CEO)*
Ben Jones *(Dir-Sls)*
Ruddy Melendez *(Mgr-IT)*
Erika Espinal *(Asst Project Mgr)*
Craig Bray *(Coord-Acctg)*
Rob Francke *(Supvr-Pur)*
Greg Fils-Aime *(Coord-Sls)*
Noah Siber-Sanderowitz *(Coord-Sls)*
Miguel Cruz *(Coord-Svc)*
Marcus Ulrich *(Project Mgr)*
Peter Capalbo *(Engr-Sys)*
Sean Cooney *(Acct Exec)*
Chris Smith *(VP-Bus Dev)*

EVERGREEN
1130 N Westfield St, Oshkosh, WI 54902
Tel.: (920) 233-2340   WI
Web Site:
  https://www.evergreenoshkosh.com
Year Founded: 1965
Sales Range: $10-24.9 Million
Continuing Care Retirement Community Services
N.A.I.C.S.: 623311
Peggy Bellin *(VP-Health & Support Svcs)*
John Krueger *(VP-Fin & Info Svcs)*
Ken Arneson *(Pres & CEO)*
Erin Sanders *(VP-HR)*

Carol C. Staszkiewicz *(VP-Foundation Advancement)*
Mary Hansen *(Vice Chm)*
Rick Picard *(Chm)*

EVERGREEN ADVISORS, LLC
9256 Bendix Rd Ste 300, Columbia, MD 21045
Tel.: (410) 997-6000
Web Site:
  http://evergreenadvisorsllc.com
Year Founded: 2000
Portfolio Management
N.A.I.C.S.: 523940
Rick Kohr *(CEO)*
Mike Gill *(Chm)*
William Egge *(Dir-Bus Valuations Practice)*
Greg Huff *(Mng Principal)*
Eric Clarke *(VP)*
Jessica Stoehr *(Coord-Mktg)*
Joseph T. Bradley *(Mng Dir-Investment Banking)*
Harris Charalambous *(VP)*
Paul Klick *(Mng Dir-Investment Banking)*
James Webb *(Dir-Bus Valuation)*
Shawn Moxley *(Dir-Bus Valuation)*

Subsidiaries:

The Baker-Meekins Company Inc. **(1)**
1404 Frnt Ave, Lutherville, MD 21093
Tel.: (410) 823-2600
Web Site: http://www.bakermeekins.com
Professional, Scientific & Technical Services
N.A.I.C.S.: 541990
Ross Adams *(Pres)*

EVERGREEN CAPITAL L.P.
551 5th Ave 21st Fl, New York, NY 10176
Tel.: (914) 400-4277   NY
Web Site:
  http://www.evergreencap.net
Year Founded: 2003
Investment Management Service
N.A.I.C.S.: 523940
Gavin H. Wolfe *(Mng Partner-Wolfe Holdings)*

Subsidiaries:

Evergreen International NZ, LLC **(1)**
5 Kellow Place, Wiri, 2104, Auckland, New Zealand **(100%)**
Tel.: (64) 958080000
Web Site: http://www.armourguard.co.nz
Security Services
N.A.I.C.S.: 561612
Ian Anderson *(Pres & Gen Mgr-New Zealand & Fiji)*
Mark O'Brien *(Mgr-Manned Svcs-Provincial)*
Shane O'Halloran *(COO-New Zealand)*
Tim Lawrence *(Mgr-Manned Svcs-Metropolitan)*
Chris Whiting *(Gen Mgr-Sls)*
Stuart Morgan *(Natl Mgr-Risk & Compliance-New Zealand)*
Ashley Burkhart *(Natl Mgr-Logisitcs Ops)*
Denise Dabinette *(Natl Mgr-Cash Ops-New Zealand)*

Wormald Australia Pty. Ltd. **(1)**
38 South Street, Rydalmere, 2116, NSW, Australia
Tel.: (61) 2 9638 8500
Web Site: http://www.wormald.com.au
Electronic Security & Fire Protection Systems & Services
N.A.I.C.S.: 561621
Andrew Lee *(CEO)*

Subsidiary (Domestic):

National Fire Holdings Pty. Limited **(2)**
2-8 South Street, Rydalmere, 2116, NSW, Australia
Tel.: (61) 261016997
Web Site: http://www.natfire.com.au
Holding Company, Fire Protection Services
N.A.I.C.S.: 551112

Subsidiary (Domestic):

National Fire Solutions (QLD) Pty
Ltd   **(3)**
151/157 Wayne Goss Drive, Berrinba, Bris-
bane, 4117, QLD, Australia
Tel.: (61) 1300791586
Web Site: http://www.natfire.com.au
Fire Protection Services
N.A.I.C.S.: 922160

National Fire Solutions (WA) Pty
Ltd   **(3)**
1 Eyre Street, Rivervale, Perth, 6103, WA,
Australia
Tel.: (61) 1300791586
Web Site: http://www.natfire.com.au
Fire Protection Services
N.A.I.C.S.: 922160

EVERGREEN CREDIT UNION
225 Riverside St, Portland, ME 04103
Tel.: (207) 221-5000   ME
Web Site: https://www.egcu.org
Year Founded: 1951
Sales Range: $10-24.9 Million
Emp.: 66
Credit Union
N.A.I.C.S.: 522130
H. Tucker Cole *(Pres & CEO)*
Kathleen Archambault *(CFO & Sr VP-
Info Tech)*
Timothy Verreault *(Sr VP-Retail
Banking)*

EVERGREEN DEVCO INC.
200 N Maryland Ave Ste 201, Glen-
dale, CA 91206-4262
Tel.: (818) 240-8727   CA
Web Site: http://www.evgre.com
Year Founded: 1975
Sales Range: $10-24.9 Million
Emp.: 100
Commercial Real Estate Developer
N.A.I.C.S.: 237210
Andy Skipper *(CEO)*
Bruce Pomeroy *(Chm & Mng Princi-
pal)*
Christine McRight *(Sr Mgr-Dev)*
Bryan Lamond *(Dir-Leasing)*
Kaycee Roberts *(Asst Mgr-Property)*
Rogg Collins *(Principal)*
Reuben Garbett *(CFO & Principal)*
Doug Leventhal *(COO & Principal)*

EVERGREEN ENERGY INC.
1225 17th St Ste 1300, Denver, CO
80202-5506
Tel.: (303) 293-2992   DE
Web Site: http://www.evgenergy.com
Year Founded: 1988
Sales Range: Less than $1 Million
Emp.: 23
Energy Production
N.A.I.C.S.: 221118
Mike Carducci *(VP-Partner Dev &
Prof Svcs)*

**EVERGREEN ENTERPRISES,
INC.**
5915 Midlothian Tpke, Richmond, VA
23225
Tel.: (804) 231-1800
Web Site:
    http://www.myevergreen.com
Year Founded: 1993
Sales Range: $25-49.9 Million
Emp.: 70
Home & Garden Decor Mfr & Whslr
N.A.I.C.S.: 423220
Ting Xu *(Founder & Chm)*
Frank Qiu *(Co-Founder & CEO)*
Melissa Barton *(Mgr-Sls-South East
District)*
Terri Shiffer *(Mgr-HR)*
Brittany Toler *(Sr VP)*
Lisa Kluthe *(VP-Art & Licensing)*
Leslie Newton *(CFO)*

Subsidiaries:

Cape Craftsmen, Inc.   **(1)**
5915 Midlothian Tpke, Richmond, VA 23225
Tel.: (804) 545-8018
Sales Range: $10-24.9 Million
Gifts & Novelties
N.A.I.C.S.: 424990
Brittany Toler *(Gen Mgr)*

Plow & Hearth, LLC   **(1)**
7021 Wolftown-Hood Rd, Madison, VA
22727
Tel.: (540) 948-2272
Web Site: http://www.plowhearth.com
Sales Range: $100-124.9 Million
National Mail Order Specializing in Fire-
place & Hearth Accessories, Yard & Garden
Furniture & Accessories, Shoes & Apparel
N.A.I.C.S.: 423220
Ting Xu *(Owner-Plow & Hearth & Chm)*
Dana Pappas *(CFO)*

Division (Domestic):

HearthSong, Inc.   **(2)**
7021 Wolftown Hood Rd, Madison, VA
22727
Tel.: (540) 948-2272
Web Site: http://www.hearthsong.com
Sales Range: $50-74.9 Million
Toys Whslr
N.A.I.C.S.: 459120
John Haydock *(Gen Mgr)*

Magic Cabin   **(2)**
7021 Wolftown-Hood Rd, Madison, VA
22727
Tel.: (540) 948-2272
Web Site: http://www.magiccabin.com
Sales Range: $75-99.9 Million
Children Game Toy Craft Doll & Doll House
Mfr
N.A.I.C.S.: 339930

**EVERGREEN FEDERAL SAV-
INGS & LOAN ASSOCIATION**
969 SE 6th St, Grants Pass, OR
97526
Tel.: (541) 479-3351
Web Site:
    http://www.evergreenbanking.com
Year Founded: 1934
Sales Range: $10-24.9 Million
Emp.: 90
Federal Savings & Loan Associations
N.A.I.C.S.: 522180
Jeffrey Hyde *(Pres)*

**EVERGREEN FIRE ALARMS,
LLC**
2720 S J St, Tacoma, WA 98409
Tel.: (253) 627-3794   WA
Web Site:
    http://www.evergreenfire.com
Year Founded: 2000
Sales Range: $10-24.9 Million
Emp.: 80
Fire & Security Systems & Services
N.A.I.C.S.: 561621
John Burgess *(Pres)*

Subsidiaries:

Monitor Dynamics LLC   **(1)**
12500 Network Blvd Ste 303, San Antonio,
TX 78249
Tel.: (210) 477-5400
Web Site: http://www.mdisecure.com
Sales Range: $1-9.9 Million
Emp.: 20
Security System Management Equipment
Mfr
N.A.I.C.S.: 335999

EVERGREEN FORD
1500 18th Ave NW, Issaquah, WA
98027
Tel.: (425) 315-7141
Web Site:
    https://www.evergreenford.com
Sales Range: $25-49.9 Million
Emp.: 110
New Car Retailer

N.A.I.C.S.: 441110
Michael Fulmer *(Mgr-Sls)*
Jonathan Ling *(Mgr-Fin)*
Chet Kono *(Mgr-Sls)*
Daniel Rowe *(Owner)*
Robert Whalley *(Mgr-Fin)*
Tom Noe *(Gen Mgr)*

EVERGREEN FS INC.
402 N Hershey Rd, Bloomington, IL
61702-1367
Tel.: (309) 663-2392
Web Site: https://www.evergreen-
fs.com
Sales Range: $75-99.9 Million
Emp.: 250
Grains
N.A.I.C.S.: 424510
Kendall Miller *(Gen Mgr)*
Jon Thomas *(Mgr-FS Farmtown)*
Tutti Davis *(Office Mgr)*

EVERGREEN HOLDINGS INC.
2415 Campus Dr Ste 225, Irvine, CA
92612
Tel.: (949) 757-7770   OR
Web Site:
    http://www.evergreenoil.com
Year Founded: 1984
Sales Range: $50-74.9 Million
Emp.: 200
Re-Refining Lubricating Oils &
Greases
N.A.I.C.S.: 324191
Jake Voogd *(Chm & CEO)*
Jesus Romero *(CFO & VP-Admin)*

EVERGREEN IMPLEMENT CO.
605 S Main St, Warren, MN 56762
Tel.: (218) 745-4516
Web Site:
    http://www.evergreenimplement.com
Sales Range: $25-49.9 Million
Emp.: 60
Agricultural Machinery & Equipment
N.A.I.C.S.: 423820
Harvey Sedlacek *(Pres)*
Jean Walker *(Office Mgr)*

EVERGREEN IMPLEMENT INC.
1415 S 1st Ave, Othello, WA 99344
Tel.: (509) 488-5222
Web Site: http://www.eiijd.com
Sales Range: $10-24.9 Million
Emp.: 35
Farm Tractors
N.A.I.C.S.: 459999
Roger Thieme *(Pres)*
Gayle Lathim *(Gen Mgr-Sls)*
Joe Kurkowski *(Gen Mgr-Sls)*
Rich Mollotte *(CEO)*

**EVERGREEN INDUSTRIES
INC.**
4921 Babcock Trl Ste 1, Inver Grove
Heights, MN 55077
Tel.: (651) 457-4441
Web Site:
    http://www.evergreenindustries.net
Rev.: $22,800,000
Emp.: 400
Novelties, Bric-A-Brac & Hobby Kits
N.A.I.C.S.: 339999
Joseph E. Ahern *(Co-Pres)*

EVERGREEN LABS, INC.
4 W Rees Ave, Walla Walla, WA
99362
Tel.: (509) 527-0607
Web Site: http://www.wineaway.com
Sales Range: Less than $1 Million
Emp.: 20
Cleaning & Sanitation Supplies Whslr
N.A.I.C.S.: 424690
Staci Wanichek *(CEO & Mgr-Sls-Natl)*
Cheryl Corn *(Dir-Intl Sls & Mktg)*

EVERGREEN LIFE SERVICES
2101 Hwy 80, Haughton, LA 71037
Tel.: (318) 949-5500   LA
Web Site:
    https://www.evergreenls.org
Year Founded: 1959
Sales Range: $25-49.9 Million
Emp.: 2,407
Disability Assistance Services
N.A.I.C.S.: 624120
Kent Craft *(CFO & Exec VP)*
Sue Buchholtz *(Pres & CEO)*
Beth Ann Holmes *(VP-Admin)*
Corey Shadd *(VP-External Rels)*
Sousan Kayhani *(VP-Western Reg)*
Claire Brooks *(Chm)*
Robert Breedlove *(CIO)*
Sharon Gomez *(VP-Central Reg)*
Debbie Orand *(Dir-Data Strategy &
Dev)*
Nancy Giles *(Dir-Social Enterprise)*
Peggy Johnson *(Dir-Dev)*
Yvone Mackey *(Officer-Strategic Ops)*
Luke Queen *(VP-Eastern Reg)*

**EVERGREEN LIVING INNOVA-
TIONS, INC.**
11875 S Sunset Dr Ste 100, Olathe,
KS 66061
Tel.: (913) 477-8227   KS
Web Site: http://www.eliinc.org
Year Founded: 1997
Sales Range: $10-24.9 Million
Emp.: 189
Disability Assistance Services
N.A.I.C.S.: 624120
Chris Osborn *(Chief Bus Dev Officer)*

**EVERGREEN MEDICAL SER-
VICES, INC**
824 Locust St, Hendersonville, NC
28792
Tel.: (828) 693-0466
Web Site:
    http://www.evergreenmedical.com
Rev.: $1,100,000
Emp.: 9
Industrial Building Construction
N.A.I.C.S.: 236210
Elmo Strickland *(Project Mgr)*
Steve Bradshaw *(Pres)*

**EVERGREEN MONEYSOURCE
MORTGAGE CO.**
2265 1st Ave, Seattle, WA 98134
Tel.: (425) 974-8500
Web Site:
    http://www.emoneysource.com
Year Founded: 1987
Rev.: $11,200,000
Emp.: 100
Mortgage Banker
N.A.I.C.S.: 522310
Donald M. Burton *(CEO)*

**EVERGREEN OAK ELECTRIC
SUPPLY & SALES CO. INC.**
1000 Davey Rd, Crestwood, IL
60445-1430
Tel.: (708) 597-4220   IL
Web Site:
    http://www.evergreenoak.com
Year Founded: 1964
Sales Range: $25-49.9 Million
Emp.: 180
Electrical Apparatus & Equipment Mfr
N.A.I.C.S.: 423610
Howard Shellberg *(Exec VP)*
Jim Power *(Branch Mgr-Chicago)*
Sheila Kottler *(Exec VP-Crest)*

**EVERGREEN OIL COMPANY
INC.**
1202 Bergen Pkwy Ste 303, Evergreen, CO 80439-9559

Evergreen Oil Company Inc.—(Continued)

Tel.: (303) 674-7497   CO
Year Founded: 1973
Sales Range: $10-24.9 Million
Emp.: 25
Gasoline Sales
N.A.I.C.S.: 457120
Andrew Smith *(Pres)*

EVERGREEN PACIFIC MORTGAGE

1500 Vly River Dr Ste 270, Eugene, OR 97401
Tel.: (541) 342-2535
Rev.: $93,000,000
Emp.: 9
Mortgage Brokers Arranging for Loans
N.A.I.C.S.: 522310
Jennifer Nunley *(Gen Mgr)*

EVERGREEN PACIFIC PARTNERS MANAGEMENT CO., INC.

1700 7th Ave Ste 2300, Seattle, WA 98101
Tel.: (206) 262-4709
Web Site: http://www.eppcapital.com
Rev.: $700,000,000
Privater Equity Firm
N.A.I.C.S.: 523999
Timothy D. Bernardez *(Co-Founder & Mng Partner)*
Thomas J. McGill *(Co-Founder & Mng Partner)*
Michael A. Nibarger *(Co-Founder & Mng Partner)*
Timothy J. Brillon *(CFO)*
Dave Dandel *(Sr VP)*
Ed Whatley *(Sr VP)*
Sheri Hughes *(Office Mgr)*
Chris Brenes *(Sr VP)*
Scott Jensen *(VP)*

Subsidiaries:

Haney Truck Line LLC   (1)
3710 Gun Club Rd, Yakima, WA 98901-9531
Tel.: (509) 248-2996
Web Site: http://www.gohaney.com
Sales Range: $75-99.9 Million
Emp.: 500
Freight Trucking Services
N.A.I.C.S.: 484110
Shane Adams *(VP-Sls & Mktg)*
Peter Carlander *(Pres)*

Branch (Domestic):

Haney Truck Line LLC - Portland   (2)
10505 NE 2nd Ave, Portland, OR 97211
Tel.: (503) 289-0755
Web Site: http://www.gohaney.com
Sales Range: $50-74.9 Million
Emp.: 150
Freight Trucking Services
N.A.I.C.S.: 484110

Western Broadband, LLC   (1)
9666 E Riggs Rd Ste 108, Sun Lakes, AZ 85248
Tel.: (480) 895-8010
Web Site: http://www.westernbroadband.net
Sales Range: $1-9.9 Million
Emp.: 25
Cable Television & Broadband Internet Services
N.A.I.C.S.: 517121

EVERGREEN PRINTING COMPANY

101 Haag Ave, Bellmawr, NJ 08031
Tel.: (856) 933-0222
Web Site: https://www.egpp.com
Sales Range: $10-24.9 Million
Emp.: 140
Printing, Subscription Fulfillment & Mail List Management Services
N.A.I.C.S.: 323111

Carmen Pinto *(Pres)*
John Dreisbach *(VP-Sls & Mktg)*
Christine DiTullio *(Controller)*
Stephanie Truitt *(Mgr-HR)*
Dan Wegmann *(Mgr-Press Room)*
Jim Privito *(Mgr-Evening Production)*
Alan Morse *(Mgr-Shipping)*
Jim Halferty *(Mgr-PIC Technical Svcs)*
Jim Lamb *(Coord-Sls & Mktg)*
Tanya Erickson *(Dir-Client Svcs)*
Chris Geimer *(Mgr-Production)*

EVERGREEN RECREATIONAL VEHICLES, LLC

10758 County Rd 2, Middlebury, IN 46540
Tel.: (574) 825-4298   IN
Web Site: http://www.goevergreenrv.com
Year Founded: 2008
Sales Range: $10-24.9 Million
Travel Trailers & Campers Mfr
N.A.I.C.S.: 336214
Kelly L. Rose *(Chm)*
Michael H. Schoeffler *(CEO)*
Don Emahiser *(Pres)*

EVERGREEN RV CENTER, INC.

1710 IH 35 N, New Braunfels, TX 78130
Tel.: (830) 625-5500   TX
Web Site: https://www.evergreenrv.com
Sales Range: $25-49.9 Million
Emp.: 50
Recreational Vehicle Dealers
N.A.I.C.S.: 441210
John Eastty *(Owner, Pres & CEO)*

EVERGREEN SC, LLC

4732 Moorefield St PO Box 297, Hodges, SC 29653
Tel.: (864) 374-7200   SC
Year Founded: 2001
Sales Range: $1-9.9 Million
Emp.: 40
Plant Propagation Technology
N.A.I.C.S.: 111421
Robert K. Pollock *(Chief Engr)*
Gianpaolo Bonaca *(Tech Ops Mgr)*
Eric D. Johnson *(Head-Farm Ops)*
Beto Avila *(Farm Mgr)*

Subsidiaries:

Jackson & Perkins Company   (1)
2 Floral Ave, Hodges, SC 29653
Web Site:
   http://www.jacksonandperkins.com
Sales Range: $75-99.9 Million
Grower & Mail Order Retailer of Roses & Various Plants
N.A.I.C.S.: 424930
James Ferguson *(Dir-IT)*
Diane Reeder *(Mgr-Mdse)*
Karen Park Jennings *(Owner)*

EVERGREEN SWEETENERS, INC.

600 Silks Run Ste 2290, Hallandale Beach, FL 33009
Tel.: (305) 931-1321
Web Site:
   http://www.esweeteners.com
Year Founded: 1925
Sales Range: $100-124.9 Million
Emp.: 100
Sweetener Mfr
N.A.I.C.S.: 311930
Arthur Green *(Pres)*
Carole Green *(Treas)*
Mark Gilden *(VP-Ops)*

EVERGREEN TRANSPORT, LLC

PO Box 727, Evergreen, AL 36401
Tel.: (251) 578-5000
Web Site:
   http://www.evergreentrans.com
Year Founded: 1988
Sales Range: $25-49.9 Million
Emp.: 300
Trucking Service
N.A.I.C.S.: 484121

EVERGREENE ARCHITECTURAL ARTS, INC.

253 36th St Ste 5C, Brooklyn, NY 11232
Tel.: (212) 244-2800
Web Site:
   https://www.evergreene.com
Sales Range: $10-24.9 Million
Emp.: 130
Painting & Paper Hanging Services
N.A.I.C.S.: 238320
Jeff Greene *(Chm)*

EVERLY BANCORPORATION

301 N Main St, Everly, IA 51338
Tel.: (712) 834-2221
Web Site: http://www.statebank-spencer.com
Year Founded: 1980
Bank Holding Company
N.A.I.C.S.: 551111
Wayne Johnson *(Founder)*

Subsidiaries:

State Bank   (1)
728 Grand Ave, Spencer, IA 51301-3644
Tel.: (712) 262-6580
Web Site: http://www.statebankspencer.com
Sales Range: $1-9.9 Million
Emp.: 17
Nondepository Credit Intermediation
N.A.I.C.S.: 522299
Michael Gathman *(Dir)*

EVERLYWELL, INC.

800 W Cesar Chavez St, Austin, TX 78701
Tel.: (512) 309-5588
Web Site: http://www.everlywell.com
Year Founded: 2015
Medical Testing Products Mfr
N.A.I.C.S.: 621511
Julia Cheek *(CEO)*

Subsidiaries:

Home Access Health
Corporation   (1)
2401 Hassell Rd Ste 1510, Hoffman Estates, IL 60169-7241
Tel.: (847) 781-2500
Web Site: http://www.homeaccess.com
Rev.: $1,200,000
Emp.: 25
Agents & Managers for Artists, Athletes, Entertainers & Other Public Figures
N.A.I.C.S.: 711410
Mary E. Vogt *(Mng Dir)*

EVERNOTE CORPORATION

2400 Broadway Ste 210, Redwood City, CA 94063
Tel.: (408) 746-9900   DE
Web Site: https://www.evernote.com
Year Founded: 2006
Sales Range: $1-9.9 Million
Emp.: 36
Note & Digital Imaging Software Publisher
N.A.I.C.S.: 513210
Stepan Pachikov *(Founder)*
Troy Malone *(Gen Mgr-Asia Pacific)*
Amy Gu *(Gen Mgr-China)*
Ken Inoue *(Gen Mgr-Japan)*
Cristina Riesen *(Gen Mgr-Europe)*
Jeff Shotts *(CFO)*

Ira Soshinsky *(Gen Mgr-Russia)*
Greg Chiemingo *(Sr Dir-Comm)*
Anirban Kundu *(CTO)*
Ian Small *(CEO)*

EVERS HEILIG, INC.

5640 Feltl Rd, Minnetonka, MN 55343
Tel.: (952) 938-7494   MN
Web Site: http://www.eversheilig.com
Year Founded: 1972
Emp.: 28
Independent Food Brokerage Services
N.A.I.C.S.: 424410
Thomas E. Rendahl *(Owner & Pres)*

Subsidiaries:

Evers Heilig, Inc. - Waukesha   (1)
2236 W Bluemound Rd F, Waukesha, WI 53186
Tel.: (262) 798-9696
Sales Range: $1-9.9 Million
Emp.: 10
Independent Food Brokerage Services
N.A.I.C.S.: 424410
Andy O'Brien *(VP & Gen Mgr)*

EVERSEAL GASKET, INC.

8309 Cole Pkwy, Shawnee Mission, KS 66227
Tel.: (913) 441-9232
Web Site:
   https://www.eversealgasket.com
Year Founded: 1960
Rev.: $10,000,000
Emp.: 35
Gaskets Mfr
N.A.I.C.S.: 339991
Ken Lane *(CEO)*

EVERSHORE FINANCIAL GROUP, INC.

7284 W Palmetto Park Rd Ste 106, Boca Raton, FL 33433
Tel.: (561) 910-2566
Web Site: https://www.evershore.com
Sales Range: $25-49.9 Million
Emp.: 50
Investment Advisory & Banking Services
N.A.I.C.S.: 523940
Robert D. Barboni *(Pres & Mng Partner)*
Daniel C. Zagata *(Mng Dir)*
Steven Zborowski *(Mng Dir)*

Subsidiaries:

Evershore Financial Group, Inc.   (1)
1900 Summit Tower Blvd Ste 450, Orlando, FL 32810
Tel.: (321) 304-4000
Investment Advisory & Banking Services
N.A.I.C.S.: 523940

EVERSTAFF

6500 Rockside Rd Suite 385, Cleveland, OH 44131
Web Site: http://www.everstaff.com
Year Founded: 2001
Sales Range: $10-24.9 Million
Emp.: 40
Recruiting & Staffing Specialists
N.A.I.C.S.: 561311
George Thomas *(VP-Sls & Ops)*

EVERWATCH CAPITAL

8 Sound Shore Dr Ste 200, Greenwich, CT 06830
Tel.: (203) 629-7950
Web Site:
   http://www.everwatchcapital.com
Privater Equity Firm
N.A.I.C.S.: 523999
Matt Womble *(Co-Founder & Mng Dir-Private Investments)*

Frohman Anderson (Co-Founder)
Joe Monaco (CFO)
Stacey Tarantino (Office Mgr)
Subsidiaries:

EWC-HH&B Holdings, LLC   (1)
1661 Murfreesboro Pike, Nashville, TN
37217
Tel.: (615) 221-4200
Investment Holding Company
N.A.I.C.S.: 551112
Leonard Higgins (Mng Partner)

Subsidiary (Domestic):

The Nexus Group, Inc.   (2)
1661 Murfreesboro Pike, Nashville, TN
37217
Tel.: (615) 221-4200
Web Site: http://www.nxs.net
Sales Range: $10-24.9 Million
Information Technology Infrastructure Services
N.A.I.C.S.: 541519
Leonard Higgins (Pres & CEO)
James Higgins (Exec VP-Bus Dev)
Stephen Baird (CTO & Exec VP)
Andy Bass (Mng Dir-Engrg)
Andy Hayes (VP-Sls)

EVERYDAYFAMILY, INC.
2406 Cypress Glen Dr Ste 101, Wesley Chapel, FL 33544
Tel.: (949) 608-0524
Web Site:
  http://www.everydayfamily.com
Year Founded: 2005
Sales Range: $1-9.9 Million
Emp.: 18
Assists Advertisers in Initiating & Cultivating Customer Relationships with Families & New Parents
N.A.I.C.S.: 541613
Elijah Klay (Engr-Software)

EVERYSPORT.NET, INC.
100 Chesterfield Business Parkway Ste 200, Chesterfield, MO 63005
Web Site: http://www.everysport.net
Year Founded: 1997
Sales Range: $1-9.9 Million
Emp.: 4
Total Online Organization Management Systems
N.A.I.C.S.: 541618
Brandon Haynes (CEO)

EVERYTHING ICE, INC.
115 School St, Salix, PA 15952
Tel.: (814) 487-6056
Web Site: http://www.everything-ice.com
Rev.: $1,300,000
Emp.: 15
Industrial Valve Mfr
N.A.I.C.S.: 332911
John Burley (Owner)

Subsidiaries:

Magic Ice Usa, Inc.   (1)
1350 Sheeler Ave, Apopka, FL 32703-6542
Tel.: (407) 886-1110
Web Site: http://www.magiciceusa.com
All Other Miscellaneous Store Retailers (except Tobacco Stores)
N.A.I.C.S.: 459999
Brad Holland (VP)

EVERYTHING2GO COM, LLC
250 E Wisconsin Ave, Milwaukee, WI 53202
Tel.: (414) 765-1100   WI
Web Site:
  http://www.everything2go.com
Year Founded: 2005
Sales Range: $10-24.9 Million
Emp.: 14
Online Retailer of Furniture
N.A.I.C.S.: 449110
David Wierdsma (Co-Founder)

EVERYTICKET.COM
1874 West Ave, Miami Beach, FL 33139
Tel.: (305) 534-5773
Web Site: http://www.everyticket.com
Sales Range: $1-9.9 Million
Emp.: 8
Online Ticket Retailer
N.A.I.C.S.: 713990
Sharon Deveney (Mgr)

EVERYWARE GLOBAL, INC.
519 N Pierce Ave, Lancaster, OH 43130
Tel.: (740) 687-2500
Web Site:
  http://www.everywareglobal.com
Year Founded: 1848
Sales Range: $350-399.9 Million
Emp.: 1,707
Tabletop & Food Preparation Products Mfr
N.A.I.C.S.: 333241
Colin Walker (Sr VP-Fin)
Anthony Reisig (Sr VP-Ops & Supply Chain)
Robert M. Ginnan (CFO)
Erika Schoenberger (Gen Counsel)
Jeff Jarrett (CMO)
Samantha Nahra (VP-Comm)
David N. Weinstein (Chm)

Subsidiaries:

Anchor Hocking, Canada, Inc.   (1)
391B Matheson Blvd, Mississauga, L4Z2H2, ON, Canada
Tel.: (740) 681-6900
Glass Products Mfr
N.A.I.C.S.: 327212

Anchor Hocking, LLC   (1)
519 N Pierce Ave, Lancaster, OH 43130
Tel.: (740) 687-2111
Web Site: http://www.anchorhocking.com
Sales Range: $200-249.9 Million
Glassware Products Mfr
N.A.I.C.S.: 327212
Barbara Wolf (Mgr-Comm & Mktg)

Subsidiary (Domestic):

Bartlett-Collins Co., Inc.   (2)
PO Box 1288, Sapulpa, OK 74067-1288
Tel.: (918) 224-1860
Sales Range: $50-74.9 Million
Mfr of Glass Tableware
N.A.I.C.S.: 327212

Delco International, Ltd.   (1)
200 Broad Hollow Rd Ste 400, Melville, NY 11747
Tel.: (631) 427-9000
Kitchenware Distr
N.A.I.C.S.: 423220

Oneida Ltd.   (1)
163-181 Kenwood Ave, Oneida, NY 13421
Tel.: (315) 361-3000
Web Site: http://www.oneida.com
Sales Range: $350-399.9 Million
Flatware, Crystal Giftware & Stemware, Cutlery & China Dinnerware Mfr & Distr
N.A.I.C.S.: 332215
Foster Sullivan (Pres-Foodservice Div)
Norman S. Matthews (Chm)

Subsidiary (Domestic):

Buffalo China, Inc.   (2)
3040 S Park Ave, Buffalo, NY 14218-2643   (90%)
Tel.: (716) 824-8515
Sales Range: $25-49.9 Million
Vitrified Hotel China Ware Mfr
N.A.I.C.S.: 327110

Subsidiary (Non-US):

Oneida (Guangzhou) Foodservice Co. Ltd.   (2)
2909-2910 Goldlion Digital Network Center 138 Tiyu Rd East, Tianhe, Guangzhou, 510620, China
Tel.: (86) 2038780612
Kitchenware Distr

N.A.I.C.S.: 423220
Gregory L. Woodhall (Mng Dir-Asia Pacific)
Tony Feng (Mgr-Sls-South China)
Frank Fan (Mgr-Sls-East China)
Nick Sui (Mgr-Sls-North China)
Minnie Zheng (Coord-Mktg)
Gary Wei (Mgr-Customer Svc & Logistics)

Oneida Canada Ltd.   (2)
8699 Stanley Ave, Niagara Falls, L2E 6X1, ON, Canada   (100%)
Tel.: (905) 356-1591
Web Site: http://www.oneida.com
Sales Range: $10-24.9 Million
Mfr of Silverplated Flatware, Stainless Flatware & Silverplated Holloware
N.A.I.C.S.: 332215

Division (Domestic):

Oneida Consumer Products Division   (2)
163-181 Kenwood Ave, Oneida, NY 13421
Tel.: (315) 361-3000
Web Site: http://www.onieda.com
Sales Range: $25-49.9 Million
Consumer Retail Fine China, Flatware & Holloware Products Whslr
N.A.I.C.S.: 423220

Subsidiary (Domestic):

Oneida Food Service, Inc.   (2)
163 Kenwood Ave, Oneida, NY 13421
Tel.: (315) 361-3000
Web Site: http://foodservice.oneida.com
Sales Range: $25-49.9 Million
Commercial Fine China, Flatware & Holloware Products Whslr
N.A.I.C.S.: 423220
Foster Sullivan (Pres)

Oneida Silversmiths Inc.   (2)
163-181 Kenwood Ave, Oneida, NY 13421
Tel.: (315) 361-3000
Web Site: http://www.oneida.com
Sales Range: $10-24.9 Million
Silverplated Flatware Mfr
N.A.I.C.S.: 332215

Subsidiary (Non-US):

Oneida, S.A. de C.V.   (2)
Edificio World Trade Center Montecito 38 Piso 37 Oficina 37, Col Napoles, Mexico, 03810, Mexico   (100%)
Tel.: (52) 55 9000 4171
Sales Range: $10-24.9 Million
Emp.: 10
Silverplated Flatware & Stainless Flatware Mfr & Distr
N.A.I.C.S.: 332215
Sergio Franco (Gen Mgr)

Samuel Groves Limited   (1)
Station Road Langley Green, Oldbury, B69 4LY, W Midlands, United Kingdom   (100%)
Tel.: (44) 121 569 7900
Web Site: http://www.samuelgroves.co.uk
Emp.: 30
Consumer & Commercial Bakeware Mfr & Distr
N.A.I.C.S.: 332215
Julian Williams (Mng Dir)

Universal TableTop, Inc.   (1)
519 N Pierce Ave, Lancaster, OH 43130-2927
Tel.: (740) 687-2500
Holding Company
N.A.I.C.S.: 551114

EVESHAM MUNICIPAL UTILITIES AUTHORITY
984 Tuckerton Rd, Marlton, NJ 08053
Tel.: (856) 983-1878
Web Site:
  http://www.eveshammua.com
Year Founded: 1959
Sales Range: $10-24.9 Million
Emp.: 60
Water Supply
N.A.I.C.S.: 221310

EVIDENT SOFTWARE, INC.
603 Mattison Ave 5th Fl, Asbury Park, NJ 07712

Tel.: (973) 622-5656
Web Site:
  http://www.evidentsoftware.com
Year Founded: 1997
Sales Range: $10-24.9 Million
Emp.: 50
Prepackaged Software
N.A.I.C.S.: 513210
Frank Cicio (VP-Ops)
Brian Nicholas (VP-IBM Strategic Alliance)
Scott Barnett (Pres & CEO)

EVIDENT THERMOELECTRICS
65 First St, Troy, NY 12180
Tel.: (518) 273-6266
Web Site:
  http://www.evidenttech.com
Year Founded: 2000
Emp.: 25
Commercial Physical Research
N.A.I.C.S.: 541720
Clint Ballinger (Pres & CEO)

Subsidiaries:

GMZ Energy, Inc.   (1)
11 Wall St, Waltham, MA 02453
Tel.: (781) 996-3036
Web Site: http://www.gmzenergy.com
Professional, Scientific & Technical Services
N.A.I.C.S.: 541990
Cheryl A. Diuguid (Pres, Treas & Sec)

EVIEW 360
39255 Country Club Dr Ste B-1, Farmington Hills, MI 48331
Tel.: (248) 306-5191   MI
Web Site: http://www.eview360.com
Year Founded: 1999
Sales Range: $1-9.9 Million
Emp.: 26
Brand Design & Marketing Including Print, Digital & Physical Environments
N.A.I.C.S.: 541613
Lindsay Poczik (Designer-Interiors)
Lamberto Smigliani (Dir-Program & Production)
KLee Loskill (Project Mgr)

Subsidiaries:

Eview 360   (1)
11F Jin Niu Building 77 E'Shan Rd, Shanghai, 200127, China   (100%)
Tel.: (86) 21 5010 5052
Web Site: http://www.eview360.com
Brand & Design Marketing
N.A.I.C.S.: 541613
Lamberto Emigliani (VP & Dir-Program & Production)

EVIGILANT SECURITY
8253 Backlick Rd Ste M, Lorton, VA 22079
Tel.: (703) 294-4117
Web Site: http://www.evigilant.com
Year Founded: 1999
Sales Range: $1-9.9 Million
Emp.: 25
Security System Services
N.A.I.C.S.: 561621

EVINS COMMUNICATIONS, LTD.
635 Madison Ave, New York, NY 10022-1009
Tel.: (212) 688-8200   NY
Web Site: http://www.evins.com
Year Founded: 1988
Emp.: 45
Advertising & Public Relations Agency
N.A.I.C.S.: 541810
Mathew L. Evins (Chm)
Louise Evins (Pres & CEO)
Glen Johnson (VP-Lifestyle)
Drew Tybus (VP-Food, Spirits & Wine Grp)
Robert Schaltenbrand (Sr VP)

5553

Evins Communications, Ltd.—(Continued)

Kara Terek *(Sr VP-Travel & Hospitality Grp)*
David Harrison *(VP-Digital Content & Brand Integration Grp)*
Matthew Berritt *(Dir-Lifestyle Grp)*
Ethan Nguyen *(VP-Fin)*
Michelle Kelly *(VP-Travel & Lifestyle)*

Subsidiaries:

Teuwen One Image, Inc.   (1)
133 W 25th St 4W, New York, NY 10001
Tel.: (212) 244-0622
Web Site: http://www.teuwen.com
Chemicals Mfr
N.A.I.C.S.: 325992
Marisa Jetter *(Sr Acct Exec)*
Stephanie Teuwen *(Co-Founder & Pres)*

EVINS PERSONNEL CONSULTANTS, INC.
2013 W Anderson Ln, Austin, TX 78757
Tel.: (512) 454-9561
Web Site: http://www.hrnetconnection.com
Year Founded: 1967
Sales Range: $10-24.9 Million
Emp.: 31
Employment Services
N.A.I.C.S.: 561311
Mary E. Evins *(Founder)*

EVIVE HEALTH, LLC
600 W Van Buren Ave Ste 603, Chicago, IL 60607
Tel.: (312) 824-6653
Web Site: http://www.evivehealth.com
Year Founded: 2007
Software Publisher
N.A.I.C.S.: 513210
Jeff Lietz *(Exec VP-Bus Dev)*
Shashidhar Akkihebbal *(VP-Product-India)*
Pia Opulencia *(VP-Product)*
Prashant Srivastava *(Founder & CEO)*

Subsidiaries:

WiserTogether, Inc.   (1)
51 Melcher St 1st Fl, Boston, MA 02210
Tel.: (202) 503-3700
Web Site: http://www.wisertogether.com
Custom Computer Programming Services
N.A.I.C.S.: 541511
Max Khan *(CEO)*
Scott Leisher *(Sr VP-Growth)*
Karen Gardner *(Sr VP-Client Services)*

EVO ENTERTAINMENT GROUP, LLC
800 Brazos St. Ste 220, Austin, TX 78701-2547
Tel.: (512) 353-7077
Web Site: https://www.evo.co
Year Founded: 2014
Entertainment Providers
N.A.I.C.S.: 711410

EVO PAYMENTS INTERNATIONAL, LLC
515 Broadhollow Rd, Melville, NY 11747
Tel.: (516) 479-9000   DE
Web Site: http://www.evopayments.com
Year Founded: 1989
Payment Processing Products & Services
N.A.I.C.S.: 522320
Ray Sidhom *(Founder & Chm)*
Jim Kelly *(CEO)*
Jeff Rosenblatt *(Vice Chm-Merchant Svcs)*

Michael L. Reidenbach *(CIO-Worldwide)*
Brendan F. Tansill *(Pres-North America)*
Steven J. de Groot *(Gen Counsel-Worldwide & Exec VP)*
Darren Wilson *(Pres-Intl)*
Kevin Lambrix *(Chief Credit & Risk Officer)*

Subsidiaries:

EVO Payments International GmbH   (1)
Elsa-Brandstrom-Strasse 10-12, 50668, Cologne, Germany
Tel.: (49) 221995770
Payment Processing Products & Services
N.A.I.C.S.: 522320

EVO Payments International, LLC - Canada   (1)
505 de Maisonneuve Blvd West Suite 150, Montreal, H3A 3C2, QC, Canada
Tel.: (877) 355-2082
Web Site: http://www.evopayments.ca
Payment Processing Products & Services
N.A.I.C.S.: 522320

EVO Payments International, LLC - USA   (1)
515 Broadhollow Rd, Melville, NY 11747
Tel.: (516) 479-9000
Web Site: http://www.evopayments.us
Payment Processing Products & Services
N.A.I.C.S.: 522320
Jeff Rosenblatt *(Pres)*
Peter S. Cohen *(Gen Counsel-North America & Sr VP)*
Mark Harrelson *(Chief Sls & Mktg Officer-US & Canada)*
Jim Kelly *(CEO)*
Alon Kindler *(Chief Acctg Officer)*
Jim Raftice *(Pres-US & Canada)*
Greg Robertson *(COO-US & Canada)*

Sterling Payment Technologies, Inc.   (1)
1111 N Westshore Blvd Ste 500, Tampa, FL 33607
Tel.: (813) 637-9696
Web Site: http://www.sterlingpayment.com
Payment Processing Services
N.A.I.C.S.: 522320
Paul L. Hunter *(Pres & CEO)*

EVOCATIVE, INC.
600 W 7th St Ste 510, Los Angeles, CA 90017   CA
Web Site: http://www.evocative.com
Year Founded: 1998
Emp.: 100
Prepackaged Software Services
N.A.I.C.S.: 513210
Derek Garnier *(CEO)*
Robert Doherty *(CFO)*
David Glettner *(COO)*
John Semmens *(VP-Sls)*
Renee Lawrence *(VP-Global Mktg & Product)*
Tony Hansel *(Gen Counsel)*

Subsidiaries:

Cyberverse, Inc.   (1)
600 W 7th St Ste 510, Los Angeles, CA 90017-3864
Web Site: http://www.cyberverse.com
Data Processing, Hosting & Related Services
N.A.I.C.S.: 518210
Greg Domeno *(Pres)*

VPLS Inc.   (1)
600 W 7th St Ste 510, Los Angeles, CA 90017
Tel.: (888) 365-2656
Web Site: https://www.vpls.com
Wired Telecommunications Carriers
N.A.I.C.S.: 517111

Subsidiary (Domestic):

ZR Systems Group LLC   (2)
98-810 Moanalua Rd H-4, Aiea, HI 96701
Tel.: (808) 369-1000

Web Site: http://www.zrsystems.com
Computer Related Services
N.A.I.C.S.: 541519
Ricky Zheng *(Founder)*

EVOK ADVERTISING
1485 International Pkwy, Heathrow, FL 32746
Tel.: (407) 302-4416
Web Site: http://www.evokad.com
Year Founded: 2001
Sales Range: $10-24.9 Million
Emp.: 35
Advertising Agencies
N.A.I.C.S.: 541810
Larry Meador *(CEO & Chief Strategy Officer)*
Terry Mooney *(COO, Partner & Officer-New Bus)*
Christopher LeBlanc *(VP & Exec Dir-Creative)*

EVOKE RESEARCH & CONSULTING LLC
1000 Wilson Blvd Ste 2500, Arlington, VA 22209
Tel.: (703) 415-1008
Web Site: http://www.evokeconsulting.com
Year Founded: 2005
Sales Range: $1-9.9 Million
Emp.: 50
Federal Management Consulting
N.A.I.C.S.: 541618
Greg Blaisdell *(Mng Partner)*
Jim Loreto *(Mng Partner)*
David Dastvar *(VP-Bus Dev)*
Joshua Rubin *(Chief Growth Officer)*

EVOL FOODS
100 Arapahoe Ste 10, Boulder, CO 80302
Tel.: (303) 815-1491
Web Site: http://www.evolfoods.com
Year Founded: 2002
Sales Range: $1-9.9 Million
Emp.: 70
Mfr of Frozen Burritos, Wraps, Snacks, Entrees, Flatbreads & Pizzas Using Antibiotic-Free Meat & Cage-Free Eggs
N.A.I.C.S.: 311412
Tom Spier *(Chm)*
Philip Anson *(COO)*
Andrew Jaffe *(VP-Mktg)*
Alyssa Ferenz *(CFO)*
Jon Jennings *(VP-Comm)*

EVOLA MUSIC CENTER INC.
2184 S Telegraph Rd, Bloomfield Hills, MI 48302
Tel.: (248) 334-0566
Web Site: https://www.evola.com
Sales Range: $10-24.9 Million
Emp.: 15
Musical Instrument Sales
N.A.I.C.S.: 459140
Jim Evola *(Pres)*
Tony Trupiano *(Asst Mgr)*

EVOLUCIA INC.
7040 Professional Pkwy E, Sarasota, FL 34240
Tel.: (941) 751-6800   NV
Web Site: http://www.evolucialighting.com
Year Founded: 2005
Sales Range: $1-9.9 Million
Emp.: 2
Light Emitting Diode (LED) Lighting, Solar Energy & Infrared Solutions
N.A.I.C.S.: 334413
Richard Craig Hall *(Founder)*
Thomas Seifert *(Interim CEO & Interim CFO)*

EVOLUCION INNOVATIONS, INC.
3500 1st Ave NW, Seattle, WA 98107
Tel.: (206) 973-4470   WA
Web Site: http://www.evo.com
Year Founded: 2001
Sales Range: $1-9.9 Million
Emp.: 150
Sports Equipment & Apparel Retailer
N.A.I.C.S.: 459110
Bryce Phillips *(Founder & CEO)*
Jerry Chezassus *(Mgr-Retail Ops)*

EVOLUTION BUREAU
1596 Howard St, San Francisco, CA 94105
Tel.: (415) 281-3950
Web Site: http://www.evb.com
Year Founded: 2000
Rev.: $1,500,000
Emp.: 12
Fiscal Year-end: 12/31/06
Commercial Art And Graphic Design
N.A.I.C.S.: 541430
Cary Savas *(Client Svcs Dir)*
Gary Brown *(VP-Fin & Ops)*
Aaron Mcguire *(Dir-Tech)*
Geno Burmester *(Dir-Art)*
Aaron Feiger *(Dir-Art)*
Max Stein *(Editor)*
James Gassel *(Pres)*
Michael Chamberlin *(Dir-Strategy & Innovation)*
Steve Babcock *(Exec Dir-Creative)*
Scott Potter *(VP & Dir-Production)*

EVOLUTION CAPITAL MANAGEMENT LLC
11390 W Olympic Blvd Ste 100, Los Angeles, CA 90064
Tel.: (310) 315-8888   DE
Web Site: http://www.evofg.com
Year Founded: 2002
Debt Servicing, Private Equity, Venture Capital, Investment Management & Securities Brokerage
N.A.I.C.S.: 523940
Michael L. Lerch *(Founder, Pres & Chief Investment Officer)*
Richard G. Chisholm *(CEO & Partner)*
Adrian J. Brindle *(CFO, COO & Partner)*
Jason Sausto *(Mng Dir)*

Subsidiaries:

Evolution Capital Investments LLC   (1)
11390 W Olympic Blvd Ste 100, Los Angeles, CA 90064
Tel.: (310) 315-8888
Web Site: http://www.evofg.com
Private Equity & Venture Capital Firm
N.A.I.C.S.: 523999
Richard G. Chisholm *(CEO & Partner)*
Michael L. Lerch *(Founder, Pres & Chief Investment Officer)*

Subsidiary (Domestic):

Global Acoustic Partners LLC   (2)
11390 W Olympic Blvd Ste 100, Los Angeles, CA 90064
Tel.: (310) 315-8888
Private Equity Firm
N.A.I.C.S.: 523999
Richard Chisholm *(Dir)*

Holding (Non-US):

TEAC Corporation   (3)
1-47 Ochiai, Tama, 206-8530, Tokyo, Japan   (54.6%)
Tel.: (81) 423569178
Web Site: https://www.teac.co.jp
Rev.: $103,591,920
Assets: $78,467,310
Liabilities: $54,843,170
Net Worth: $23,624,140
Earnings: ($350,330)
Emp.: 571

Fiscal Year-end: 03/31/2024
Computer Peripherals, Measurement, Communication, Video & Mass Storage Products & Professional & Consumer Audio Products Mfr
N.A.I.C.S.: 334118
Yuji Hanabusa *(Pres & CEO)*
Nobuo Wada *(Exec Officer)*
Koichiro Nakamura *(Exec Officer)*
Shinya Yoshino *(Exec Officer)*
Kenji Hayashi *(Exec Officer)*
Hiroshi Tokushige *(Exec Officer)*
Yoshihiro Kurahara *(CFO)*
Yosuke Matsuno *(Exec Officer)*
Odawara Road *(Exec Officer)*

Subsidiary (Non-US):

DONGGUAN TEAC ELECTRONICS Co., LTD. (4)
Shang-Sha, Chang-An District, Dongguan, Guang Dong, China
Tel.: (86) 769 8554 8848
Web Site: http://www.teac.com.cn
Electronic Components Mfr
N.A.I.C.S.: 334419

Dongguan Dongfa TEAC Audio Co., Ltd. (4)
Shang Sha Chang An District, Dongguan, Guang Dong, China (100%)
Tel.: (86) 7695548848
Web Site: http://www.teac.com.cn
Sales Range: $10-24.9 Million
Emp.: 25
Audio & Visual Products Mfr
N.A.I.C.S.: 334310

Subsidiary (Domestic):

ESOTERIC COMPANY (4)
47 Ochiai 1-chome, Tama, 206-8530, Tokyo, Japan
Tel.: (81) 42 356 9230
Web Site: http://www.esoteric.jp
Audio Compact Disk Player Mfr
N.A.I.C.S.: 334310

Subsidiary (Non-US):

P.T. TEAC Electronics Indonesia (4)
Batam Industrial Pk Block 10, Jalan Beringin Muka Kuning, Batam, 29432, Indonesia (60%)
Tel.: (62) 770611088
Web Site: http://www.teac.com
Sales Range: $50-74.9 Million
Emp.: 800
Data Storage Products Mfr
N.A.I.C.S.: 334112

Subsidiary (US):

TEAC America, Inc. (4)
1834 Gage Rd, Montebello, CA 90640
Tel.: (323) 726-0303
Web Site: http://www.teac.com
Sales Range: $300-349.9 Million
Emp.: 30
Electronic Audio & Video Equipment Systems, Recorders & Workstations Distr
N.A.I.C.S.: 423620
Tanja M. Pino *(Mgr-HR)*
Koichiro Nakamura *(Pres)*
Derek Davis *(COO & Exec VP)*
Joe Stopka *(VP-Sls & Bus Dev-TASCAM-Chicago)*

Subsidiary (Non-US):

TEAC Audio (China) Co., Ltd. (4)
1709 1710 17 Fl Shatin Galleria, 18 24 Wo Shui St, Sha Tin, China (Hong Kong) (100%)
Tel.: (852) 26901333
Web Site: http://www.teac.com
Sales Range: $10-24.9 Million
Emp.: 10
Audio & Visual Products Mfr
N.A.I.C.S.: 334310
Morino Takao *(Pres)*

TEAC Canada Ltd. (4)
5939 Wallace St, Mississauga, L4Z 1Z8, ON, Canada (100%)
Tel.: (905) 890-8008
Web Site: http://www.teac.com
Sales Range: $25-49.9 Million
Emp.: 10
Audio & Visual Products Mfr

N.A.I.C.S.: 449210

TEAC Deutschland GmbH (4)
Bahnstrasse 12, 62005, Wiesbaden, Erbenheim, Germany (100%)
Tel.: (49) 6117158417
Web Site: http://www.teac.de
Sales Range: $25-49.9 Million
Emp.: 50
Computer Component Measurement Data Recorder & Audio Equipment Distr
N.A.I.C.S.: 423430

TEAC EUROPE GmbH. (4)
Bahnstrasse 12, Erbenheim, 65205, Wiesbaden, Germany
Tel.: (49) 611 71 58 0
Web Site: http://www.teac.eu
Audio & Video Equipment Mfr
N.A.I.C.S.: 334310

TEAC Electronics (M) Sdn. Bhd. (4)
Lot 22 Batu Berendam, Free Trade Zone Phase III, 75350, Melaka, Malaysia (100%)
Tel.: (60) 62843402
Web Site: http://www.teac.com.my
Sales Range: $25-49.9 Million
Emp.: 500
Data Storage Products Mfr
N.A.I.C.S.: 334112

Subsidiary (Domestic):

TEAC Manufacturing Solutions Corporation (4)
22-17 Higashi-Icchome Shimo Yoshida Fuji, Yoshida-shi, Yamanashi, 403-0008, Japan (100%)
Tel.: (81) 555241222
Web Site: http://www.teac.co.jp
Sales Range: $25-49.9 Million
Emp.: 75
Computer Components, Measurement Data Recorders & Audio Equipment
N.A.I.C.S.: 334310

TEAC Manufacturing Solutions Corporation (4)
8-10-12 Shinmachi, Ome, 198-0024, Tokyo, Japan
Tel.: (81) 428 32 1521
Web Site: http://www.tms.teac.co.jp
Audio Equipment Mfr
N.A.I.C.S.: 334310

Subsidiary (Non-US):

TEAC Mexico S.A. de C.V. (4)
Av Rio Churubusco No 364 Colonia Del Carmen Delegacion Coyoacan, CP 04100, Mexico, DF, Mexico (100%)
Tel.: (52) 55 5010 6000
Web Site: http://www.teacmexico.net
Sales Range: $25-49.9 Million
Emp.: 25
Computer Components, Measurement Data Recorders & Audio Equipment Mfr
N.A.I.C.S.: 423430

TEAC Nederland B.V. (4)
Oeverkruid 15, 4941 VV, Raamsdonksveer, Netherlands
Tel.: (31) 162 510210
Computer Components, Measurement Data Recorders & Audio Equipment Mfr
N.A.I.C.S.: 334310

Subsidiary (Domestic):

TEAC System Create Corporation (4)
47 Ochiai 1-chome, Tama-shi, Tokyo, 206-8530, Japan
Tel.: (81) 42569100
Web Site: http://www.tsc.teac.co.jp
Sales Range: $25-49.9 Million
Emp.: 100
Provider of Computers & Peripherals
N.A.I.C.S.: 423430

Subsidiary (Non-US):

TEAC UK Ltd. (4)
I2 Office Meridien House 69-71 Clarendon Road Croxley Business Pk, Watford, WD17 1DS, Herts, United Kingdom
Tel.: (44) 8451302511
Web Site: http://www.teac.co.uk

Sales Range: $25-49.9 Million
Emp.: 6
Computer Components, Measurement Data Recorders & Audio Equipment Sales
N.A.I.C.S.: 423430

Taiwan TEAC Corporation (4)
3Fl No 45 Sec 1 Min Chuan E Rd, 104, Taipei, Taiwan (100%)
Tel.: (886) 225978608
Web Site: http://www.teac.com.tw
Sales Range: $10-24.9 Million
Emp.: 6
Audio & Visual Products Mfr
N.A.I.C.S.: 334310
Tetsuo Oikawa *(Chm)*

Evolution Japan Co., Ltd. (1)
New Otani Garden Court 12F 4-1 Kioicho, Chiyoda-ku, Tokyo, 102-0094, Japan
Tel.: (81) 345103300
Web Site: http://www.evofg.com
Holding Company; Debt Servicing, Private Equity, Venture Capital, Investment Management & Securities Brokerage
N.A.I.C.S.: 551112
Shaun M. Lawson *(Dir)*

Red Planet Japan, Inc. (1)
7-1 Akasaka 1-chome, Minato-ku, Tokyo, 107-0052, Japan (70.5%)
Tel.: (81) 5058350966
Web Site: http://www.redplanetjapan.com
Rev.: $2,624,220
Assets: $38,409,690
Liabilities: $33,985,800
Net Worth: $4,423,890
Earnings: $7,005,090
Fiscal Year-end: 12/31/2022
Compact Disk Distribution Services
N.A.I.C.S.: 334610
Simon Gerovich *(Chm)*
Yoshihisa Ikurumi *(CFO)*
Yoshimi Abe *(COO)*
Shiho Boda *(Auditor)*
Toshiaki Ohashi *(Auditor)*
Masaya Takakuwa *(Auditor)*

EVOLUTION CAPITAL PARTNERS, LLC
3333 Richmond Rd Ste 480, Beachwood, OH 44122
Tel.: (216) 593-0402
Web Site:
http://www.evolutioncp.com
Year Founded: 2005
Sales Range: $25-49.9 Million
Emp.: 6
Privater Equity Firm
N.A.I.C.S.: 523999
Brendan D. Anderson *(Co-Founder & Mng Partner)*
Jeffrey D. Kadlic *(Co-Founder & Partner)*
Denea Jackson *(Office Mgr)*
Jeffrey Mihalek *(CFO)*
Kim Lapcewich *(Partner)*

EVOLUTION FINANCIAL TECHNOLOGIES, LLC
67 Wall St, New York, NY 10005
Tel.: (212) 905-7600
Web Site: http://www.evoft.com
Rev.: $11,000,000
Emp.: 40
Computer Software Development
N.A.I.C.S.: 541511
Daryl Denson *(COO)*

EVOLV SOLUTIONS, LLC
9401 Indian Creek Pkwy Ste 250, Overland Park, KS 66210
Tel.: (913) 469-8900
Web Site:
http://www.evolvsolutions.com
Year Founded: 2001
Sales Range: $10-24.9 Million
Emp.: 15
Sells, Leases & Services Copiers, Printers, Fax Machines & Digital Image Programs
N.A.I.C.S.: 532420

Eric Harland *(VP-Tech)*
Damon Washington *(CFO & Controller)*
Krystal Harrison *(Asst Controller)*
Ronald Harland Jr. *(VP)*

EVOLVE BANK & TRUST
Triad Centre III 6070 Poplar Ave Ste 100, Memphis, TN 38119
Tel.: (901) 624-2555
Web Site: http://www.getevolved.com
Year Founded: 1925
Sales Range: $75-99.9 Million
Emp.: 600
Banking & Financial Services
N.A.I.C.S.: 522110
W. Scott Stafford *(Pres & CEO)*
B. Scot Lenoir *(Chm)*
Donald B. Clanton *(Pres-Small Bus Lending)*
Dan Springfield *(Chief Credit Officer & Exec VP)*
Ramona Martin *(VP & Dir-HR)*
Rob Lance *(VP-Comml Lending-Banking Div-Arkansas)*
George Andreaus *(Mgr-Sls-Small Bus Lending-Natl)*
Craig Dodds *(Exec VP & COO)*
Donna L. Embry *(Sr VP-Payment Strategies-Payment Processing Div-Global)*
Thomas E. Holmes Jr. *(Sr VP & Dir-Mktg & Comm)*

EVOLVE MANUFACTURING TECHNOLOGIES
960 Linda Vista, Mountain View, CA 94043
Tel.: (650) 968-9292
Web Site: http://www.evolvemfg.com
Year Founded: 1999
Sales Range: $25-49.9 Million
Emp.: 60
Contract Mfr for Semiconductor & Medical Equipment Companies
N.A.I.C.S.: 334413
Noreen King *(CEO)*
Juliea Chu *(Mgr-Pur)*
Trang Tran *(Mgr-Production)*

EVOLVE MEDIA, LLC
5140 Goldleaf Cir Ste 100C, Los Angeles, CA 90056
Tel.: (310) 449-1890   CA
Web Site:
http://www.evolvemediallc.com
Year Founded: 1999
Sales Range: $75-99.9 Million
Emp.: 215
Online Marketing Services
N.A.I.C.S.: 541890
Brian Fitzgerald *(Founder & Pres)*
Josh Ellingwood *(Gen Counsel)*
Geoff Schiller *(Chief Revenue Officer)*
Aaron Broder *(Founder & CEO)*
Vincent Krsulich *(Sr VP-Sls, Crave & Martini Media)*
David Denton *(Chief Product Officer)*
Walder Amaya *(Exec VP-Sls & Ops-Intl)*
Maria Cadbury *(Mng Dir)*

Subsidiaries:

DogTime Media, Inc. (1)
PO Box 576, San Francisco, CA 94104-0576
Tel.: (415) 830-9300
Web Site: http://dogtime.com
Online Advertising & Pet Publications Services
N.A.I.C.S.: 541890

Martini Media Network, Inc. (1)
415 Brannan St, San Francisco, CA 94107
Tel.: (415) 913-7445
Web Site: http://www.martinimediainc.com
Emp.: 1
Digital Media & Content Platforms

Evolve Media, LLC—(Continued)
N.A.I.C.S.: 541519
Erik Pavelka (CEO)
John Southard (VP-Fin)
Peter Nanjo (VP-Engrg)
Paul Hsu (Sr VP-Ops)

Total Beauty Media, Inc. (1)
1158 26th St Ste 535, Santa Monica, CA 90403
Tel.: (310) 295-9593
Web Site: http://www.totalbeautymedia.com
Online Beauty Health Publisher
N.A.I.C.S.: 513199
Ivan Ivankovich (CFO)
Ann Marie MacDougall (VP-Sls)
Emrah Kovacoglu (Founder & CEO)
Beth Mayall (Exec VP-Programming & Engagement & Editor-in-Chief)
Geoffrey Hale (Gen Counsel)
Ethelbert Williams (Head-Mktg)
John Atkinson (Dir-Product Dev)

EVOLVE TALENT AGENCY
8831 Venice Blvd, Los Angeles, CA 90034
Tel.: (561) 843-1402
Year Founded: 1999
Sales Range: Less than $1 Million
Emp.: 3
Advetising Agency
N.A.I.C.S.: 541810
Jonathan Elliottt (Owner)

EVOLVED INDUSTRIES, INC.
2261 Morganza Hwy, New Roads, LA 70760-4519
Tel.: (225) 638-4016
Sales Range: $10-24.9 Million
Emp.: 80
Animal Feed Mfr
N.A.I.C.S.: 311119

EVOLVENT TECHNOLOGIES INC.
5111 Leesburg Pike Ste 506, Falls Church, VA 22041
Tel.: (703) 824-6000
Web Site: http://www.evolvent.com
Sales Range: $50-74.9 Million
Emp.: 219
Healthcare Information Technology Services
N.A.I.C.S.: 456199
Bill W. Oldham (Chm & CEO)
Paul A. Ramsaroop (Founder)
Geoff Howard (CTO & Exec VP)
Guy Sherburne (Sr VP-Security Programs)
Monty Nanton (Exec VP-Military Health)

EVRARD-STRANG CONSTRUCTION, INC.
1703 E DeYoung St, Marion, IL 62959
Tel.: (618) 997-8997
Web Site: http://www.evrardstrangconstruction.com
Year Founded: 2001
Commercial Building Construction Services
N.A.I.C.S.: 236220
Rodney K. Evrard (Pres)

EVY OF CALIFORNIA, INC.
1875 E 22nd St, Los Angeles, CA 90058
Tel.: (213) 746-4647
Web Site: http://www.evy.com
Year Founded: 1986
Sales Range: $25-49.9 Million
Emp.: 520
Mfr of Girls' Dresses & Sportswear
N.A.I.C.S.: 315250

Lauren Schnell-Higgins (VP-Sls)
Lydia Badr (VP-Design & Mdsg)
Roberto Yrigoyen (Mgr)
Saul Avitia (Mgr-Shipping)

EWALD AUTOMOTIVE GROUP, LLC
6319 S 108th St, Franklin, WI 53132
Tel.: (414) 376-7933
Web Site: https://www.ewaldauto.com
Year Founded: 1964
Sales Range: $200-249.9 Million
Emp.: 400
New & Used Automobiles Retailer
N.A.I.C.S.: 441110
Craig A. Ewald (Co-Owner)
Tom Ewald (Co-Owner)

Subsidiaries:

Ewald Chevrolet Buick, LLC (1)
36833 E Wisconsin Ave, Oconomowoc, WI 53066
Tel.: (262) 567-5555
Web Site: http://www.ewaldchevroletbuick.com
Sales Range: $25-49.9 Million
Emp.: 100
Automobile Dealers
N.A.I.C.S.: 441110
Scott Kussow (Mgr-Fleet)
Brett Ewald (Gen Mgr)
Charles Ericson (Mgr-Bus)
Kenneth Hirn (Mgr-Acct)
Chuck Akers (Mgr-Svc)
Brian Ewald (Gen Mgr)
Randy Wermager (Mgr-Parts)
Jim Hansen (Mgr-Comml Truck)
Jennifer Seelig (Mgr-Bus)
Mike Finn (Mgr-Used Cars)

Ewald Chrysler Jeep Dodge, LLC (1)
6319 S 108th St, Franklin, WI 53132
Tel.: (414) 427-2000
Web Site: http://www.ewaldchryslerjeepdodge.com
Sales Range: $25-49.9 Million
Emp.: 25
Automobile Dealers
N.A.I.C.S.: 441120

Ewald Chrysler, LLC (1)
36833 E Wisconsin Ave, Oconomowoc, WI 53066
Tel.: (262) 567-3400
Web Site: http://www.ewaldchrysler.com
Sales Range: $25-49.9 Million
Emp.: 130
Automobile Dealers
N.A.I.C.S.: 441110
Eric Ewald (Gen Mgr)

Ewald's Hartford Ford-Lincoln-Mercury, LLC (1)
2570 E Sumner St, Hartford, WI 53027
Tel.: (262) 673-9400
Web Site: http://www.ewaldshartfordfordlincolnmercury.com
Sales Range: $25-49.9 Million
Emp.: 30
Automobile Dealers
N.A.I.C.S.: 441110
J. E. Walt (Gen Mgr)

Mayfair Rent-A-Car, LLC - Waukesha (1)
1720 Paramount Dr Hwy 18, Waukesha, WI 53186
Tel.: (262) 513-3300
Web Site: http://www.mayfairleasing.com
Car Lending Services
N.A.I.C.S.: 532112
Steve Farnam (Mgr)

EWALD'S VENUS FORD, LLC.
2727 E Layton Ave, Cudahy, WI 53110
Tel.: (414) 914-2811
Web Site: https://www.ewaldsvenusford.com
Year Founded: 2004
Sales Range: $25-49.9 Million

Emp.: 95
Car Whslr
N.A.I.C.S.: 441110
Brian Ewald (Gen Mgr)
Eric Ewald (Gen Mgr)

EWI CONSTRUCTION, LLC
1228 E 7th Ave, Tampa, FL 33605
Tel.: (813) 964-3885
Web Site: http://www.ewiconstruction.com
Sales Range: $1-9.9 Million
Construction Services
N.A.I.C.S.: 236220
Casey Ellison (Co-Founder)
Sam Ellison (Chm)

EWING CONSTRUCTION CO., INC.
615 Oliver Ct, Corpus Christi, TX 78408-3241
Tel.: (361) 882-6525
Web Site: http://www.ewingcc.com
Sales Range: $25-49.9 Million
Emp.: 50
Commercial & Office Building Contractors
N.A.I.C.S.: 236220
Roddy Black (Sr VP & Dir-Safety)
William Ewing Jr. (Pres)

EWING IRRIGATION PRODUCTS INC.
3441 E Harbour Dr, Phoenix, AZ 85034-7229
Tel.: (602) 437-9546
Web Site: http://www.ewingirrigation.com
Year Founded: 1922
Sales Range: $75-99.9 Million
Emp.: 800
Plumbing Fixtures, Equipment & Supplies Mfr
N.A.I.C.S.: 423720
Doug York (Pres)
Richard York (Exec VP)

EWING-LEAVITT INSURANCE AGENCY, INC.
4025 St Cloud Dr, Loveland, CO 94558-7586
Tel.: (970) 067-7333
Web Site: http://www.markheroldwines.com
Emp.: 100
Insurance Agencies & Brokerages
N.A.I.C.S.: 524210
Steve Ewing (Mgr)

Subsidiaries:

Stolte Insurance Agency, Inc. (1)
7707 Ralston Rd, Arvada, CO 80002-2431
Tel.: (303) 420-4766
Web Site: http://www.stolteins.com
Emp.: 200
Insurance Agencies & Brokerages
N.A.I.C.S.: 524210
Rodger Bailey (Owner)

EWINGCOLE, INC.
100 N 6th St, Philadelphia, PA 19106
Tel.: (215) 923-2020
Web Site: https://www.ewingcole.com
Year Founded: 1961
Full-Service Firm of Architects, Engineers, Interior Designers & Planners
N.A.I.C.S.: 541310
Joseph T. Kelly (CFO)
James M. Wilson (Mng Principal)
Donald Dissinger (Sr VP)
Pradeep R. Patel (Principal)
Jared Loos (Exec VP)
J. Andrew Jarvis (Mng Principal)
William McCullough (Principal)
Craig Schmitt (Principal)
Mark Hebden (Pres)
Michael Rantilla (Dir-Raleigh)

Subsidiaries:

BBH Design (1)
8208 Brownleigh Dr, Raleigh, NC 27617
Tel.: (919) 460-6700
Web Site: http://www.ewingcole.com
Architectural Services
N.A.I.C.S.: 541310
Richard Beale (Mng Principal)

Gaudreau, Inc. (1)
810 Light St, Baltimore, MD 21230
Tel.: (410) 837-5040
Architectural Services
N.A.I.C.S.: 541310
Randal Gaskins (VP)
Stephen A. Leonhardt (Assoc Principal)

EWINWIN, INC.
5334 Primrose Lake Cir, Tampa, FL 33647
Tel.: (813) 579-1399
Web Site: http://www.ewinwin.com
Year Founded: 2000
Sales Range: $1-9.9 Million
Emp.: 20
Software Publisher
N.A.I.C.S.: 513210
Greg Mesaros (Founder & CEO)

EWR WEATHER RADAR SYSTEMS
336 Leffingwell Ave, Saint Louis, MO 63122
Tel.: (314) 821-1022
Web Site: https://www.ewradar.com
Year Founded: 1982
Sales Range: $10-24.9 Million
Emp.: 15
Portable Weather Radar Designer & Mfr
N.A.I.C.S.: 334511
Don LaPoint (Pres)

EX-CELL HOME FASHIONS INC.
1333 Broadway 8th Fl, New York, NY 10018-7103
Tel.: (212) 213-8000
Web Site: http://www.croscill-living.com
Year Founded: 1950
Sales Range: $25-49.9 Million
Emp.: 400
Curtains, Draperies & Home Fashions
N.A.I.C.S.: 314120
Lillian Soto (Mgr-Fashion Bath Product)
Toni Panarese (Coord-Design Studio)
Holly Slavin (Mgr-CAD)

EXACT CARE PHARMACY, LLC
8333 Rockside Rd, Valley View, OH 44125
Tel.: (216) 369-2200
Web Site: https://www.exactcarepharmacy.com
Year Founded: 2009
Sales Range: $25-49.9 Million
Emp.: 132
Specialty Pharmacy Operator
N.A.I.C.S.: 456110
Dale Wollschleger (Pres & CEO)
Larry DeCaria (VP-Bus Dev)
Marty Butler (CFO)
Tony Casanova (CIO)
Aaron Link (VP-Ops)
Douglas Present (Chm)
Terry Rogers (Chief Growth Officer)

EXACT COLOR SYSTEMS, LLC
1323 W Walnut Ave Ste 2-195, Dalton, GA 30720
Web Site: https://www.exactcolorsystems.com

Dyes & Chemicals Distr
N.A.I.C.S.: 424690
John Good *(Pres)*

Subsidiaries:

Dixie Dye & Chemical Inc. (1)
1721 S Hwy 27, La Fayette, GA 30728
Tel.: (706) 638-5751
Web Site: http://www.dixiedye.com
Sales Range: $10-24.9 Million
Emp.: 20
Chemicals & Dye Products Whslr
N.A.I.C.S.: 424690
Kay L. Dendy *(CEO & CFO)*

EXACT DATA, LLC
33 N Dearborn St 200, Chicago, IL
60602-3100
Tel.: (847) 866-9600   NY
Web Site: http://www.exactdata.com
Year Founded: 2001
Sales Range: $10-24.9 Million
Information Technology Applications
Testing Services
N.A.I.C.S.: 541512
Larry Organ *(CEO)*

Subsidiaries:

Exact Data ConsumerBase LLC (1)
33 N Dearborn St Ste 200, Chicago, IL
60602-3100   **(100%)**
Tel.: (312) 600-8000
Web Site: http://www.exactdata.com
Sales Range: $1-9.9 Million
Emp.: 150
Internet & Business Marketing & Consulting
Services
N.A.I.C.S.: 541613
Jeff Tindell *(CTO)*
Larry Organ *(CEO)*
Zora Senat *(CMO)*
Colm Ronan *(CFO & COO)*
Hannah Wasilowski *(VP-Client Svcs)*

EXACT STAFF, INC.
21031 Ventura Blvd Ste 501, Woodland Hills, CA 91364
Tel.: (818) 348-1100   CA
Web Site: http://www.exactstaff.com
Year Founded: 1996
Sales Range: $25-49.9 Million
Emp.: 6,200
Employment Agencies
N.A.I.C.S.: 561311
Karenjo Goodwin *(Founder & Pres)*
Farrah Walker *(Mgr-Bus Dev)*
Gina Sarracino *(Reg Mgr)*

EXACTA CORP.
16595 W Bluemound Rd, Brookfield,
WI 53005
Tel.: (262) 796-0000
Web Site: http://www.exactacorp.net
Rev.: $12,088,142
Emp.: 110
Custom Computer Programming Services
N.A.I.C.S.: 541511
Wolfhart K. Schubach *(Owner)*
Royce Bacon *(Mgr-IS)*
Brian Dziwulski *(Sr Acct Mgr)*

EXACTA PACKAGING DESIGNS, INC.
1223 Crowley Dr, Carrollton, TX
75006-3703
Tel.: (972) 323-1063
Web Site:
https://www.exactapak.com
Year Founded: 1996
Die-Cut Paper & Board Mfr
N.A.I.C.S.: 322130
Tom Spitz *(Mng Partner)*
Jose Cruz *(Mgr-Maintenance)*
Judith Gutierrez *(Mgr-Admin)*

EXAKTIME, INC.

27001 Agoura Rd Ste 280, Calabasas, CA 91301
Tel.: (877) 435-6411
Web Site: http://www.exaktime.com
Year Founded: 2000
Sales Range: $1-9.9 Million
Emp.: 70
Time Clock Mfr for Construction Sites
N.A.I.C.S.: 334519
Tony Papas *(CEO)*
Scott Prewett *(CTO)*
John O'Hara *(Pres)*
Casey Powers *(VP-Mktg)*

EXALT INTEGRATED TECHNOLOGIES
401 Bombay Ln, Roswell, GA 30076
Tel.: (770) 217-4688
Web Site: http://www.exaltit.com
Year Founded: 2004
Sales Range: $1-9.9 Million
Emp.: 15
Information Technology Consulting
Services
N.A.I.C.S.: 541512
Dwayne Hayes *(Founder & Pres)*
P. Lawson *(Co-Founder)*

EXASERV, INC.
30000 Mill Creek Ave Ste 350, Alpharetta, GA 30022
Tel.: (678) 808-0400
Web Site: http://www.exaserv.com
Year Founded: 2004
Rev.: $6,900,000
Emp.: 36
Professional Scientific Technical Services
N.A.I.C.S.: 541990
Wim De Smet *(CEO)*

EXCALIBUR EXHIBITS
7120 Brittmoore Rd Ste 430, Houston, TX 77041
Tel.: (713) 856-8853   TX
Web Site:
http://www.excaliburexhibits.com
Year Founded: 1997
Sales Range: $1-9.9 Million
Emp.: 24
Trade Show Exhibit Designs
N.A.I.C.S.: 541850
Peggy Swords *(Owner & Pres)*
Camie Barber *(Controller)*
Becky Thiredill *(Office Mgr)*
Daniel Ruiz *(Acct Mgr)*

EXCALIBUR PIZZA LLC
1830 Vernon St Ste 1, Roseville, CA
95678-6309
Tel.: (916) 781-3365
Rev.: $11,900,000
Emp.: 12
Pizzeria Chain
N.A.I.C.S.: 722513

EXCALIBUR TECHNOLOGY CORP.
700 Fox Glen Lowr Level, Barrington,
IL 60010
Tel.: (847) 842-9570
Web Site: http://www.excaltech.com
Year Founded: 1994
Rev.: $3,600,000
Emp.: 28
Information Technology Services
N.A.I.C.S.: 541512
Scott Cummings *(CEO)*
Cole Markee *(COO)*
Amanda Regan *(Mgr-Ops)*

EXCEED CORPORATION
8100 Professional Pl Ste 211, Lanham, MD 20785
Tel.: (301) 731-3790

Web Site:
http://www.exceedcorporation.com
Year Founded: 1998
Sales Range: $10-24.9 Million
Emp.: 250
Program & Records Management &
Purchasing & Acquisition Support to
the Federal Government & Private
Industry
N.A.I.C.S.: 561499
Al Edwards *(Pres & CEO)*
Sharna Graham *(VP-Contracts & Admin)*

EXCEL GROUP, INC.
17747 Airline Hwy, Prairieville, LA
70769
Tel.: (225) 408-1300   LA
Web Site: https://www.excelusa.com
Sales Range: $50-74.9 Million
Emp.: 5,000
Holding Company; Industrial Construction, Maintenance, Fabrication &
Engineering Services
N.A.I.C.S.: 551112
Lisa Oubre *(Dir-HR)*
Danny A. Oubre *(Dir-Corp Safety)*
Paul Friloux *(Pres-Maintenance Ops)*
Kim Roccaforte Wigley *(Dir-Mktg)*

Subsidiaries:

EXCEL Engineering,
Incorporated (1)
1227 Highway 30, Gonzales, LA 70737
Tel.: (225) 647-1209
Web Site: http://www.excelengineering.com
Industrial Engineering Services
N.A.I.C.S.: 541330
Wade Whittington *(Sr Project Mgr)*

EXCEL Midstream Solutions,
Incorporated (1)
1250 Wood Branch Park Dr Ste 500, Houston, TX 77079-1226
Tel.: (713) 579-7710
Web Site: http://www.excelmidstream.com
Emp.: 85
Construction Engineering Services
N.A.I.C.S.: 541330
Greg Rudichuk *(Pres)*

Excel Fabrication & Construction,
Inc. (1)
39222 Highway 621, Gonzales, LA 70737
Tel.: (225) 647-6600
Web Site: http://www.excelusa.com
Sales Range: $50-74.9 Million
Industrial Construction & Metal Pipe Fabrication Services
N.A.I.C.S.: 237990

EXCEL STAFFING COMPANIES
1700 Louisiana Blvd NE Ste 210, Albuquerque, NM 87110
Tel.: (505) 262-1871
Web Site: http://www.excelstaff.com
Sales Range: $10-24.9 Million
Emp.: 25
Executive Placement
N.A.I.C.S.: 541612
Barbara Trythall *(Pres)*
Marcie Porter *(Sr Mgr-Staffing)*
Jodi Butler *(Mgr-Quality)*
Rhonda Maio *(Mgr-Staffing)*
Shunnae Love *(VP-Reg)*

EXCELDA MANUFACTURING COMPANY
12785 Emerson Dr, Brighton, MI
48116
Tel.: (248) 486-3800
Web Site: http://www.excelda.com
Sales Range: $50-74.9 Million
Emp.: 160
Lubricating Oils & Greases; Chemicals
N.A.I.C.S.: 324191

Mike Lamarra *(Pres)*
Cheryl Ferguson *(Mgr-Logistics)*

EXCELHIGH INC.
120 Secatogue Ave, Farmingdale, NY
11735
Tel.: (516) 293-8850
Web Site: http://www.excelhigh.com
Sales Range: $10-24.9 Million
Emp.: 10
Apparel Mfr & Distr
N.A.I.C.S.: 315250
Gurdev Singh *(Pres & CEO)*

EXCELL AGENT SERVICES LLC
2625 S Plz Dr, Tempe, AZ 85282
Tel.: (602) 808-1511   AZ
Web Site:
http://www.excellagent.com
Year Founded: 1994
Sales Range: $75-99.9 Million
Emp.: 2,000
Business Services
N.A.I.C.S.: 561499
Greg Sorenson *(CFO)*

EXCELLA CONSULTING
2300 Wilson Blvd Ste 600, Arlington,
VA 22201
Tel.: (703) 840-8600
Web Site: http://www.excella.com
Year Founded: 2002
Sales Range: $10-24.9 Million
Emp.: 273
Computer System Design Services
N.A.I.C.S.: 541512
Steve G. Cooper *(Co-Founder, CFO, Partner & VP)*
Jeff D. Gallimore *(Partner & Sec)*
Burton White *(Co-Founder & CEO)*
Mark Wainwright *(Partner)*
Zak Mahshie *(Gen Counsel & Partner)*
Erin Grace *(Mktg Dir-Comm)*
Matt Pincombe *(Partner)*
Mahreen Rashid *(Sr VP-People Svcs)*
Sandy Gillespie *(COO)*
Christina Seiden *(VP-Strategic Growth & FedHealthIT)*
Nadina Kezel *(Exec VP-Fin)*
Eddie Morris *(VP-Strategic Pricing & Profitability)*

EXCELLED SHEEPSKIN & LEATHER COAT CORPORATION
1400 Broadway-31st Fl, New York,
NY 10018-5300
Tel.: (212) 594-5843
Web Site: https://www.excelled.com
Sales Range: $25-49.9 Million
Emp.: 25
Leather Clothing Mfr
N.A.I.C.S.: 315250
Myron Goldman *(Chm)*
Michael Holzberg *(VP-Production)*
Ken Walton *(CFO)*

Subsidiaries:

Excelled Sheepskin & Leather Coat
Corporation (1)
1400 Broadway 31st Fl, New York, NY
10018-5300
Tel.: (212) 594-5843
Web Site: http://www.excelled.com
Sales Range: $25-49.9 Million
Emp.: 35
Mfr of Leather Clothing
N.A.I.C.S.: 315250

Excelled Sheepskin & Leather Coat
Corporation (1)
1700 Burlington Ave, Kewanee, IL
61443-3200   **(100%)**
Tel.: (309) 852-3341
Web Site: http://www.leathercoatsetc.com

Excelled Sheepskin & Leather Coat
Corporation—(Continued)

Sales Range: $25-49.9 Million
Mfr of Leather Clothing
N.A.I.C.S.: 458320

EXCELLENT COFFEE CO. INC.
259 East Ave, Pawtucket, RI 02860
Tel.: (401) 724-6393   RI
Web Site:
   http://www.excellentcoffee.com
Year Founded: 1960
Sales Range: $10-24.9 Million
Emp.: 65
Provider of Coffee & Related Products
N.A.I.C.S.: 311920
William Kapos *(Pres & CEO)*

EXCELLENT PACKAGING & SUPPLY
3220 Blume Dr Ste 111, Richmond,
CA 94806
Tel.: (510) 243-9501
Web Site:
   http://www.excellentpackaging.com
Year Founded: 2003
Rev.: $12,900,000
Emp.: 10
Industrial & Personal Service Paper
Merchant Whslr
N.A.I.C.S.: 424130
Allen F. King *(Pres)*
Greg Stevens *(VP)*
Esther Wagner *(CFO)*

EXCELLERE CAPITAL MANAGEMENT LLC
100 Fillmore Pl Ste 300, Denver, CO
80206
Tel.: (303) 765-2400   DE
Web Site:
   http://www.excellerepartners.com
Year Founded: 2006
Privater Equity Firm
N.A.I.C.S.: 523999
David L. Kessenich *(Co-Founder & Mng Partner)*
Matthew C. Hicks *(Partner)*
Patrick J. O'Keefe *(Partner)*
Brenda Goscha *(Dir-Acctg & Admin)*
Ryan Glaws *(Partner)*
Brad Cornell *(Partner)*
Justin Unertl *(Principal)*
Michael Geldart *(Partner)*
Ross Gundry *(VP)*
Eric Mattson *(Principal)*
Mike Vieth *(Prinicipal)*
Nick Coleman *(VP)*
Matt Halverson *(VP)*

Subsidiaries:

Flavours, Inc.   (1)
24855 Corbit Pl, Yorba Linda, CA 92887
Tel.: (714) 692-2950
Sales Range: $10-24.9 Million
Spice & Extract Mfr
N.A.I.C.S.: 311942

Personable General Insurance
Agency, Inc.   (1)
350 10th Ave Ste 1450, San Diego, CA
92101
Tel.: (619) 702-7022
Web Site:
   http://www.personableinsurance.com
Insurance Agency & Claims Services
N.A.I.C.S.: 524210
Kieran A. Sweeney *(Pres & CEO)*
Rick Becker *(Sr VP-Ops)*
Brian Jewell *(VP)*
Rick Lavite *(Chm)*
Christal LaVite *(VP)*
Ken Perilli *(Sr VP-Fin)*

Subsidiary (Domestic):

Network Holdings Inc.   (2)
2889 Elmwood Dr SE, Smyrna, GA 30080
Tel.: (770) 436-7575

Web Site: http://www.finusa.com
Sales Range: $10-24.9 Million,
Emp.: 40
Insurance Agents
N.A.I.C.S.: 524210

Subsidiary (Domestic):

First Insurance Network Inc.   (3)
2889 Elmwood Dr SE, Smyrna, GA 30080
Tel.: (770) 436-7575
Web Site: http://www.finusa.com
Rev.: $10,000,000
Insurance Agents
N.A.I.C.S.: 524210

Peaches Insurance Agency Inc   (3)
2899 Elmwood Dr SE, Smyrna, GA 30080
Tel.: (770) 436-7575
Web Site: http://www.finusa.com
Sales Range: Less than $1 Million
Insurance Agents, Brokers & Service
N.A.I.C.S.: 524210

Peachtree Casualty Insurance
Company   (3)
350 10th Ave Ste 1400, San Diego, CA
92101-8701
Tel.: (770) 436-7575
Property & Casualty Insurance Agent
N.A.I.C.S.: 524210
Ricardo J. Lavite *(CEO)*

SCA Pharmaceuticals, LLC   (1)
8821 Knoedl Ct, Little Rock, AR 72205-
4600
Tel.: (501) 312-2800
Web Site:
   http://www.sterilecompoundingusa.com
Drugs & Druggists' Sundries Merchant
Whslr
N.A.I.C.S.: 424210
Heather L. Mason *(Chm)*
Matt Graves *(Exec VP)*
Gene Graves *(Founder)*
Matt White *(Dir-Pharmacy Ops)*
Rich Colucciello *(VP-Fin & HR)*
Heather L. Mason *(Chm)*
Scott Luce *(CEO)*

EXCELLINE FOOD PRODUCTS, LLC
20232 Sunburst St, Chatsworth, CA
91311-6218
Tel.: (818) 701-7710
Web Site:
   http://www.excellinefoods.com
Year Founded: 1979
Sales Range: $25-49.9 Million
Emp.: 150
Frozen Specialties
N.A.I.C.S.: 311412
Silvia Donohue *(Pres & Gen Mgr)*
Gerry Staub *(CFO)*
Katie Horvath *(Mgr-Sls Ops)*
Ouenda Baaissa *(Controller)*

EXCELSA ACQUISITION CORP.
450 Park Ave Ste 2703, New York,
NY 10022
Tel.: (212) 321-4200   Ky
Year Founded: 2021
Investment Services
N.A.I.C.S.: 523999
Mark Rosen *(CEO)*
Juan Goicochea *(CFO)*
Carlos Tomas Rodriguez-Pastor
(Chm)

EXCELSIOR DEFENSE, INC.
2660 5th Ave N, Saint Petersburg, FL
33713
Tel.: (727) 527-9600
Web Site:
   https://www.excelsiordefense.com
Year Founded: 1994
Sales Range: $1-9.9 Million
Emp.: 420
Security Guards
N.A.I.C.S.: 561612

Evangelia Halverson *(Sec)*
Kris Halverson *(Mng Dir)*
John Ortiz *(Branch Mgr)*

Subsidiaries:

Defense Academics   (1)
2232 Central Ave, Saint Petersburg, FL
33712
Tel.: (727) 362-0007
Web Site:
   http://www.defenseacademics.com
Security Guard Training Services
N.A.I.C.S.: 561612

EXCELSIOR ELECTRIC MEMBERSHIP CORPORATION
986 SE Broad St, Metter, GA 30439
Tel.: (912) 685-2115
Web Site:
   https://www.excelsioremc.com
Sales Range: $10-24.9 Million
Emp.: 52
Distribution, Electric Power
N.A.I.C.S.: 221122
Gary Drake *(Gen Mgr)*
W. D. Johnson *(Pres)*

EXCELSIOR PRINTING COMPANY
123 Massmoca way, North Adams,
MA 01247-3235
Tel.: (413) 663-3771   MA
Web Site:
   http://www.excelsiorprinting.com
Year Founded: 1892
Sales Range: $10-24.9 Million
Emp.: 60
Commercial Printing Services
N.A.I.C.S.: 323111
Gebbie Mark *(Supvr-Press Room)*
Kimberly Mulcahy *(Mgr-Sls & Support)*
Paula LaBonte *(Acct Exec)*
Sheila Gibeau *(Controller)*
Stephanie Melito *(Acct Mgr)*

Subsidiaries:

Excelsior Integrated, LLC.   (1)
10 Valley St Docks 8 & 9, Lee, MA 01238
Tel.: (413) 637-0600
Web Site:
   http://www.excelsiorintegrated.com
Marketing Consulting Services
N.A.I.C.S.: 541613
David Crane *(Chm & CEO)*
Shawn Ouillette *(VP-Fulfillment)*

Excelsior Printing Company - Oatmeal Studios Division   (1)
60 Roberts Dr, North Adams, MA 01247
Tel.: (413) 663-3771
Web Site: http://www.oatmealstudios.com
Greeting Card Publishers
N.A.I.C.S.: 513191

Seed Print   (1)
60 Roberts Dr, North Adams, MA 01240
Tel.: (413) 663-3771
Web Site: http://www.seedprint.com
Printing Services
N.A.I.C.S.: 323120
David Crane *(Pres)*

EXCELSYS TECHNOLOGIES
156 Liberty Ln, Rockwall, TX 75032-
8463
Tel.: (972) 771-4544
Web Site: http://www.excelsys.com
Medical, Dental & Hospital Equipment
& Supplies Merchant Whslr
N.A.I.C.S.: 423450
Jim Oursler *(VP)*

EXCEPTIONAL CHILDREN'S FOUNDATION
8740 Washington Blvd, Culver City,
CA 90232
Tel.: (310) 204-3300   CA
Web Site: http://www.ecf.net

Year Founded: 1946
Sales Range: $10-24.9 Million
Emp.: 703
Developmental Disability Assistance
Services
N.A.I.C.S.: 623210
Gene Siciliano *(Sec)*
Shelley I. Smith *(Chm)*

EXCEPTIONAL RISK ADVISORS, LLC
1 International Blvd Ste 625,
Mahwah, NJ 07495
Tel.: (201) 512-0110
Web Site:
   https://www.exceptionalriskad
   visors.com
Year Founded: 2006
Sales Range: $1-9.9 Million
Emp.: 12
Developing, Underwriting & Processing Insurance Products
N.A.I.C.S.: 524113
Edward A. Tafaro *(CEO)*
Frank Zuccarello *(Exec VP)*
Henry A. Tafaro *(Exec VP)*
Laura Muka *(Sr VP)*

EXCET, INC.
8001 Braddock Rd Ste 303, Springfield, VA 22151
Tel.: (703) 635-7089
Web Site: http://www.excetinc.com
Year Founded: 2005
Sales Range: $25-49.9 Million
Emp.: 50
IT, Engineering & Research & Development Services
N.A.I.C.S.: 519290
Richard Matuszko *(Pres)*
James Fye *(Mgr-Program)*
Rob Hallsworth *(Dir-Contracts & Pur)*
Patrick Nolan *(VP)*

EXCHANGE BANK & TRUST
600 Commercial St, Atchison, KS
66002
Tel.: (913) 367-6000
Web Site:
   http://www.myexchangebank.com
Year Founded: 1856
Rev.: $11,200,000
Emp.: 116
Commercial Banking Services
N.A.I.C.S.: 522110
Lora Weishaar *(VP)*
Becky Hawk *(VP)*
Todd Gigstad *(Sr VP)*
Mark Windsor *(Pres)*
Russ McCort *(Sr VP)*
Paul H. Adair *(Chm)*
Bill Cassity *(VP)*
Christy Brull *(Asst VP)*
Colby Gwartney *(Officer-Loan)*
Douglass J. Adair *(VP)*
Joe Penning *(Officer-Loan)*
Sandra Becker *(VP)*
Tom Hall *(VP)*
Rich Dickason Sr. *(CEO)*

EXCHANGE BANKSHARES, INC.
250 W Hancock St, Milledgeville, GA
31061
Tel.: (478) 452-4531
Web Site:
   http://www.exchangebankshare.com
Rev.: $13,110,000
Emp.: 74
Commercial Banking Services
N.A.I.C.S.: 522110
Melvin T. Couey *(Sr VP)*
Lisa Beall *(VP)*
Henry J. Pope Jr. *(Pres & CEO)*

EXCLUSIVE CONCEPTS, INC

30 Corporate Dr Ste 350, Burlington, MA 01803
Tel.: (781) 362-5300
Web Site:
    http://www.exclusiveconcepts.com
Year Founded: 1997
Sales Range: $1-9.9 Million
Emp.: 23
Online Business Marketing & Development Services
N.A.I.C.S.: 541519
Scott Smigler *(Founder & Pres)*
Sheila McAneney *(VP-Ops)*
Nikhil Rajpal *(VP-Mktg Science)*
Frank Kjaersgaard *(VP-Product Dev)*

EXCOLERE ACQUISITION CORP.

2029 Century Park E Ste 400N, Los Angeles, CA 90067
Tel.: (310) 867-2758   DE
Year Founded: 2021
Investment Services
N.A.I.C.S.: 523999
Anthony Miller *(Chm & CEO)*
Peter Davis *(Pres, COO & Sec)*
Jeffrey M. Glick *(CFO)*

EXECUJET CHARTER SERVICE, INC.

4751 Jim Walter Blvd, Tampa, FL 33607
Tel.: (813) 490-0208   FL
Web Site:
    https://www.execujetcharter.com
Year Founded: 1994
Sales Range: $1-9.9 Million
Emp.: 25
Chartered Passenger Air Transportation
N.A.I.C.S.: 481211
Peter Cunzolo *(Pres & CEO)*
Michael Marconi *(Dir-Ops)*
Thomas May *(Dir-Charter Sls)*

EXECUTECH UTAH, LLC

10813 S Riverfront Pkwy Ste 410, South Jordan, UT 84095
Tel.: (801) 253-4541
Web Site: http://www.executech.com
Year Founded: 1999
Information Technology Services
N.A.I.C.S.: 541512
Eric Montague *(Pres)*
Lex Watterson *(VP-Bus Dev)*
DJ Dorff *(CEO)*

Subsidiaries:

DSA Technologies Inc.   (1)
105 Dexter Cir, Madison, AL 35757-8005
Web Site: http://www.dsatechnologies.com
Information Services
N.A.I.C.S.: 519290
Darrell Brown *(Owner)*

Pact-One Solutions, Inc.   (1)
8215 S Eastern Ave Ste 101, Las Vegas, NV 89123
Tel.: (702) 492-6105
Web Site: http://www.pact-one.com
Computer & Computer Peripheral Equipment & Software Merchant Whslr
N.A.I.C.S.: 423430
Dan Edwards *(CEO)*

EXECUTIVE AFFILIATES INC.

47W210 Rte 30, Big Rock, IL 60511
Tel.: (630) 556-3731
Year Founded: 1967
Sales Range: $10-24.9 Million
Emp.: 90
Property Management
N.A.I.C.S.: 531210
Alan J. Feldman *(Exec VP)*

EXECUTIVE AIR TAXI CORP

2301 University Dr, Bismarck, ND 58504

Tel.: (701) 258-5024
Web Site: https://www.executive-air.com
Year Founded: 1973
Chartered Air Transportation
N.A.I.C.S.: 481211
Paul Vetter *(COO)*

EXECUTIVE BUSINESS CENTERS

11330 Lakefield Dr Bldg 2 Ste 200, Duluth, GA 30097
Tel.: (770) 814-4300
Web Site: http://www.ebcnet.com
Year Founded: 1984
Sales Range: $10-24.9 Million
Emp.: 20
Provider of Office Facilities & Secretarial Services
N.A.I.C.S.: 561599
Thomas N. Dye *(Pres & CEO)*

EXECUTIVE CABINETRY,LLC

2838 Grandview Dr, Simpsonville, SC 29680
Tel.: (864) 963-7011   DE
Web Site:
    https://www.executivecabinetry.com
Emp.: 202
Wood Kitchen Cabinet & Countertop Mfr
N.A.I.C.S.: 337110
David Romeo *(CEO)*

Subsidiaries:

Tedd Wood, Inc.   (1)
758 Johnstown Rd, Thompsontown, PA 17094
Tel.: (717) 463-3615
Web Site: http://www.teddwood.com
Rev.: $7,200,000
Emp.: 80
Wood Kitchen Cabinet & Countertop Mfr
N.A.I.C.S.: 337110

EXECUTIVE CAPITAL CORP.

47 W 210 Rte 30, Big Rock, IL 60511
Tel.: (630) 556-3731   IL
Year Founded: 1968
Sales Range: $75-99.9 Million
Emp.: 75
Real Estate Investment Services
N.A.I.C.S.: 531210
Jeff Ratzer *(VP)*

EXECUTIVE CAR LEASING CO.

7807 Santa Monica Blvd, Los Angeles, CA 90046-5302
Tel.: (323) 654-5000   NJ
Web Site:
    http://www.executivecarleasing.com
Year Founded: 1955
Sales Range: $125-149.9 Million
Emp.: 150
Passenger Car Leasing Services
N.A.I.C.S.: 532112
Richard Schrieken *(VP-HR & Controller)*
Mary Nalbandyan *(Controller)*
Jim Keller *(VP-DP)*

EXECUTIVE CATERERS INC.

6111 Landerhaven Dr, Mayfield Heights, OH 44124
Tel.: (440) 449-0700   OH
Web Site:
    https://www.landerhaven.com
Year Founded: 1971
Sales Range: $25-49.9 Million
Emp.: 150
Catering Services
N.A.I.C.S.: 551111
Jeannie F. Vassanelli *(Dir-Sls)*
Melissa Marik *(Dir-Bus Dev)*

EXECUTIVE COACH BUILDERS INC.

4400 W Production St, Springfield, MO 65803
Tel.: (417) 831-3535
Web Site: http://www.ecblimo.com
Sales Range: $10-24.9 Million
Emp.: 100
Automobile Assembly, Including Specialty Automobiles
N.A.I.C.S.: 336110
David Bakare *(Owner)*
Nick Koehl *(Mgr-Reg Sls)*

EXECUTIVE COFFEE SERVICE INC

3105 E Reno Ave, Oklahoma City, OK 73117-6615
Tel.: (405) 236-3932
Web Site:
    http://www.neighborscoffee.com
Sales Range: $10-24.9 Million
Emp.: 80
Roasted Coffee
N.A.I.C.S.: 311920
Steve Neighbors *(Founder & Pres)*
Fred Neighbors *(Pres)*

EXECUTIVE COMMUNICATIONS, INC.

10300 Linn Station Rd Ste 100, Louisville, KY 40223
Tel.: (502) 412-5450
Web Site: http://www.executive-com.com
Year Founded: 1997
Rev.: $4,800,000
Emp.: 17
Management Consulting Services
N.A.I.C.S.: 541613
Lisa Cates *(Co-Founder & Dir-Community Impact)*
Amy S. Broadhurst *(Pres)*
Rachel Butler *(Founder & Partner)*

EXECUTIVE DIRECTION INC.

847 Sansome St 4th Fl, San Francisco, CA 94111
Tel.: (415) 394-5500
Web Site: https://www.exdir.com
Year Founded: 1979
Sales Range: $10-24.9 Million
Emp.: 17
Executive Placement Services
N.A.I.C.S.: 541612
Fred Naderi *(CEO)*
Marie Domeny *(Mgr-Natl Acct-San Francisco)*
Ellette Durlacher *(VP-Sls & Ops)*
Nariman Naderi *(CEO-San Francisco)*
Nancy Upton *(Area Mgr-Bus Dev)*
Nariman Kazeminejad *(Pres)*

EXECUTIVE DODGE, INC.

406 S Orchard St, Wallingford, CT 06492
Tel.: (475) 253-5932
Web Site:
    https://www.executivedodge.com
Year Founded: 1989
Sales Range: $10-24.9 Million
Emp.: 33
New Car Dealers
N.A.I.C.S.: 441110
John Orsini *(Owner)*

EXECUTIVE EXPRESS, INC.

3105 County Rd, Waite Park, MN 56387
Tel.: (320) 253-2226
Web Site:
    http://www.executiveexpress.biz
Year Founded: 1979
Airport Shuttle Services
N.A.I.C.S.: 492210
Larry Logeman *(Owner)*

EXECUTIVE IMAGE SOLUTIONS INC.

840 State St, Lemoyne, PA 17043
Tel.: (717) 441-5969
Web Site: https://www.eximage.com
Year Founded: 1989
Office Equipment Sales & Service
N.A.I.C.S.: 423420
Frank Mandalino *(Owner)*
Troy Price *(VP-Svc)*
Matt Lipsett *(Pres)*
Rob Walters *(Dir-IT Svcs)*

EXECUTIVE INFORMATION SYSTEMS, LLC

6901 Rockledge Dr Ste 600, Bethesda, MD 20817-7836
Tel.: (301) 581-8594
Web Site:
    http://www.execinfosys.com
Software Publisher
N.A.I.C.S.: 513210
Charles Mathews *(Pres)*

Subsidiaries:

Zencos Consulting LLC   (1)
1400 Crescent Green Ste 210, Cary, NC 27518
Tel.: (919) 459-4600
Web Site: http://www.zencos.com
Sales Range: $1-9.9 Million
Emp.: 15
Data Analysis & Consulting Services
N.A.I.C.S.: 541618
David Septoff *(Co-Founder & CEO)*
Benjamin Zenick *(Co-Founder & CTO)*

EXECUTIVE JEEP NISSAN

900 Universal Dr N, North Haven, CT 06473
Tel.: (203) 239-5371
Web Site:
    http://www.executivejeepnissan.net
Year Founded: 1996
Sales Range: $10-24.9 Million
Emp.: 40
Car Whslr
N.A.I.C.S.: 441110
Mark Altieri *(Dir-Ops)*
Scott Orsini *(Gen Mgr)*

EXECUTIVE MANAGEMENT ASSOCIATES, INC.

14800 Seneca Rd, Darnestown, MD 20874
Tel.: (301) 330-2531
Web Site: http://www.execman.com
Year Founded: 1993
Sales Range: $1-9.9 Million
Emp.: 25
Financial Management, Procurement, Training, IT & Strategic Planning Consulting for Government Agencies & Nonprofit Organizations
N.A.I.C.S.: 541618
Nancy J. Slomowitz *(Pres)*

EXECUTIVE MANAGEMENT SERVICES INC.

8071 Knue Rd, Indianapolis, IN 46250
Tel.: (317) 594-6000
Web Site: http://www.emsinc.com
Rev.: $17,000,000
Emp.: 80
Commercial Cleaning, Security, Maintenance & Exterior Services
N.A.I.C.S.: 561720
David Bego *(Pres)*
Barb Bego *(VP)*
Steve Evans *(VP-Sls)*

Subsidiaries:

Moorfeed Corporation   (1)
1445 Brookville Way Ste R, Indianapolis, IN 46239
Tel.: (317) 545-7171

Executive Management Services
Inc.—(Continued)

Web Site: http://www.moorfeed.com
Sales Range: $10-24.9 Million
Emp.: 20
Electronic Component Machinery
N.A.I.C.S.: 333248

EXECUTIVE NATIONAL BANK
9600 N Kendall Dr, Miami, FL 33176
Tel.: (305) 274-8382
Web Site:
http://www.executivebank.com
Year Founded: 1972
Sales Range: $10-24.9 Million
Emp.: 90
National Commercial Banks
N.A.I.C.S.: 522110
Isabel Marin (Sr VP)

EXECUTIVE PERILS INSUR-ANCE SERVICES
11845 W Olympic Blvd Ste 750, Los
Angeles, CA 90064
Tel.: (310) 444-9333
Web Site: http://www.eperils.com
Year Founded: 2000
Sales Range: $10-24.9 Million
Emp.: 10
Disability Insurance Services
N.A.I.C.S.: 524298
Peter R. Taffae (Mng Dir)
Damien Magnuson (Sr VP-Broker
Svcs)

EXECUTIVE PLACEMENTS, LLC
7110 Forest Ave Ste 200, Richmond,
VA 23226
Tel.: (804) 441-8336
Web Site:
http://www.executiveplacement.com
Year Founded: 2014
Sales Range: $1-9.9 Million
Emp.: 11
Human Resource Consulting Ser-
vices
N.A.I.C.S.: 541612
Alex Weedon (Co-Owner)
Dheryld Houston (Co-Owner)

EXECUTIVE PROTECTION SYSTEMS LLC
161 Commonwealth Ct, Winchester,
VA 22602
Tel.: (540) 662-4640
Web Site: http://www.epssafety.com
Year Founded: 2001
Sales Range: $10-24.9 Million
Emp.: 25
Emergency Preparedness Products &
Training
N.A.I.C.S.: 624230

EXECUTIVE REPORTING SER-VICE
Ulmerton Business Center 13555 Au-
tomobile Blvd Ste 130, Clearwater,
FL 33762
Tel.: (727) 823-4155
Web Site:
https://www.executivereporting.com
Year Founded: 1981
Sales Range: $1-9.9 Million
Emp.: 15
Court Reporting Service
N.A.I.C.S.: 561492
Diane T. Emery (Pres)

EXECUTIVE SERVICES, INC.
2828 5th Ave, Des Moines, IA 50313-
4202
Tel.: (515) 244-1656   IA
Web Site:
https://www.printuniversal.com
Year Founded: 1966

Commercial Printing Services
N.A.I.C.S.: 323111
Bruce Hoium (Sr Acct Mgr)
Sara Springer (Pres)
Brian D. Springer (VP)
Mark Hansen (Acct Mgr)
Chuck Carpenter (Acct Mgr)
George H. Springer III (CEO)

EXECUTONE TELECOMMUNI-CATIONS, LLC
32450 Dequindre, Warren, MI 48092
Tel.: (248) 649-9100
Web Site: http://www.executone.biz
Sales Range: $10-24.9 Million
Emp.: 50
Integrated Solution Services
N.A.I.C.S.: 423690
Stuart Novick (Owner & Pres)

EXELCO INC.
5201 Desoro Plz, Laredo, TX 78041
Tel.: (956) 722-8921
Sales Range: $10-24.9 Million
Emp.: 600
Fast-Food Restaurant, Chain
N.A.I.C.S.: 722513
Hugo Chaparro (Pres)
Griselda Garza (Office Mgr)
Ron Eichorst (VP)

EXELED HOLDINGS, INC.
4885 Ward Rd Ste 300, Wheat
Ridge, CO 80033
Tel.: (720) 361-2056   DE
Web Site: https://exeledholdings.com
Year Founded: 1982
ELED—(OTCIQ)
Sales Range: Less than $1 Million
Emp.: 5
Commercial, Industrial & Institutional
Electric Lighting Fixture Manufactur-
ing
N.A.I.C.S.: 335132
Harold Hansen (Pres & CEO)
Richard Cole Dennard (CFO)
Thomas H. Rockers (Sec)

Subsidiaries:

Energie LLC   (1)
4885 Ward Rd Ste 300, Wheat Ridge, CO
80033
Tel.: (720) 963-8055
Web Site: http://www.energielighting.com
Sales Range: $1-9.9 Million
Emp.:
LED Lighting Equipment Mfr
N.A.I.C.S.: 335139
Joe Durzo (Exec VP)
Kristin Rapp (Mgr-Admin)
Rick Ayers (Mgr-Production)

EXEMPLIS LLC
6415 Katella Ave, Cypress, CA
90630-5245
Tel.: (714) 995-4800   CA
Web Site: https://www.exemplis.com
Year Founded: 1996
Office Furniture Mfr
N.A.I.C.S.: 337214
Mike Phelan (CFO & Exec VP)

Subsidiaries:

Timbuk2 Designs, Inc.   (1)
583 Shotwell St, San Francisco, CA 94110
Tel.: (415) 252-4300
Web Site: http://www.timbuk2.com
Sales Range: $25-49.9 Million
Emp.: 70
Custom Messenger Bags
N.A.I.C.S.: 316990
Patti M. Cazzato (CEO)

EXENCIAL WEALTH ADVI-SORS, LLC
9108 N Kelley Ave, Oklahoma City,
OK 73131
Tel.: (405) 478-1971   OK

Web Site:
http://www.exencialwealth.com
Wealth Management Services
N.A.I.C.S.: 523940
John Burns (CEO)
Jerry P. Georgopoulos (Founder)
Tim Courtney (Chief Investment Offi-
cer)
Derek Northup (CFO & Dir-Tax)
Matt Ventura (Mng Dir)
Caleb Dillard (COO & Chief Compli-
ance Officer)

Subsidiaries:

Shoreline Financial Advisors,
LLC   (1)
246 Goose Ln Ste 201, Guilford, CT 06437-
2186
Tel.: (203) 458-6800
Web Site: http://www.sfadvisors.com
Investment Advice
N.A.I.C.S.: 523940
Brendan Smith (Partner)

EXERGEN CORPORATION
400 Pleasant St, Watertown, MA
02472
Tel.: (617) 926-1217
Web Site: https://www.exergen.com
Sales Range: $10-24.9 Million
Emp.: 50
Non-Invasive Thermometry Systems:
Infrared Scanners, Thermometers,
Sensors & Controls Mfr
N.A.I.C.S.: 334516
Marybeth Pompei (Chief Clinical Sci-
entist & Sr VP)
Bob Harris (Mgr-Indus Sls)
Stan Orluk (Mgr-Customer Svc)

EXHEDRA SOLUTIONS, INC.
3005 Taragrove Dr, Tampa, FL 33618
Tel.: (813) 833-2290
Web Site: http://www.exhedra.com
Software Publisher
N.A.I.C.S.: 513210
Ian Ippolito (Founder & CEO)

EXHIBIT SYSTEMS, INC.
12600 W Burleigh Rd, Brookfield, WI
53005
Tel.: (262) 432-8410
Web Site:
http://www.exhibitsystems.com
Portfolio Management Services
N.A.I.C.S.: 523940
Richard Magliocco (Pres & Partner-
Principal)
David Jentz (Partner & Exec VP)

Subsidiaries:

Kmk Industries, Inc.   (1)
4005 W Green Tree Rd, Milwaukee, WI
53209
Tel.: (414) 351-1330
Web Site: http://www.kmkexhibits.com
Sign Mfr
N.A.I.C.S.: 339950
Patti Malliet (Sr Mgr-Acct)

EXHIBIT WORKS INC.
13211 Merriman Rd, Livonia, MI
48150
Tel.: (734) 525-9010
Web Site:
http://www.ewiworldwide.com
Sales Range: $100-124.9 Million
Emp.: 450
Displays & Exhibits Work
N.A.I.C.S.: 541890
Alan LaFreniere (Pres-Retail)
Janis Healy (VP-Retail Strategy)
Jorja Rapelje (VP-Events)

EXHIBITOR SOURCE BY SKY-LINE

144 Bain Dr Ste 100, La Vergne, TN
37086
Tel.: (615) 287-9800
Web Site: https://www.esourcetn.com
Year Founded: 1999
Sales Range: $10-24.9 Million
Emp.: 34
Sign Mfr
N.A.I.C.S.: 339950
John A. Hamari (Pres)
Lori McCarrall (Controller)
Marc Quinn (Project Mgr)

EXHIBITS USA, INC.
3510 Himalaya Rd, Aurora, CO
80011
Tel.: (303) 722-6565
Web Site: https://www.pgexhibits.com
Year Founded: 1999
Sales Range: $10-24.9 Million
Emp.: 50
Trade Show Exhibit Design & Pro-
duction
N.A.I.C.S.: 561920
Dave Walker (Mgr)
James P. McGrath (Owner)

EXIDA.COM LLC
64 N Main St, Sellersville, PA 18960
Tel.: (215) 453-1720
Web Site: http://www.exida.com
Year Founded: 2000
Rev.: $10,300,000
Emp.: 70
Engineeering Services
N.A.I.C.S.: 541330
Rainer Faller (CEO & Partner)
William M. Goble (Partner)

EXIDE TECHNOLOGIES, LLC
13000 Deerfield Pkwy Bldg 200, Mil-
ton, GA 30004-6118
Tel.: (678) 566-9000   DE
Web Site: http://www.exide.com
Year Founded: 1888
Sales Range: $1-4.9 Billion
Lead Acid Batteries Mfr & Supplier
N.A.I.C.S.: 335910
Lou Martinez (CFO & Exec VP)
Brad S. Kalter (Gen Counsel & Exec
VP)
Timothy Vargo (Chm, Pres & CEO)
Daniel Royer (Sr VP-Mfg & Supply
Chain Plng)
Tim Rehg (Sr VP-Product & Process
Engrg)
Wendy Henderson (Chief HR Officer
& Sr VP)
Joseph R. Hinrichs (Chm)

Subsidiaries:

EXIDE HOLDING NETHERLANDS
B.V.   (1)
Produktiestraat 25, Vlaardingen, 3133 ES,
Zuid-Holland, Netherlands
Tel.: (31) 104455666
Sales Range: $25-49.9 Million
Emp.: 30
Investment Management Service
N.A.I.C.S.: 523940

EXIDE SINGAPORE PTE
LIMITED   (1)
48A Changi S St 1, Singapore, 486114,
Singapore
Tel.: (65) 65434767
Storage Battery Mfr
N.A.I.C.S.: 335910

EXIDE SLOVAKIA S.R.O.   (1)
Jiskrova 4, Kosice, 040 01, Slovakia
Tel.: (421) 552383534
Storage Battery Mfr
N.A.I.C.S.: 335910

EXIDE TECHNOLOGIES GMBH   (1)
Im Thiergarten, 63654, Budingen, Germany
Tel.: (49) 604281154
Web Site: http://www.exide.com

Sales Range: $150-199.9 Million
Emp.: 800
Storage Battery Mfr
N.A.I.C.S.: 335910
Stefan Gries *(Mgr-Export)*

EXIDE TECHNOLOGIES OY **(1)**
Takkatie 21, Helsinki, 00370, Nayta kartalla, Finland
Tel.: (358) 941545500
Web Site: http://www.exide.fi
Sales Range: $25-49.9 Million
Emp.: 28
Storage Battery Mfr
N.A.I.C.S.: 335910
Almo Hekkeinei *(Mng Dir)*

EXIDE TECHNOLOGIES RECY-CLING S.L. **(1)**
Ronda De Dalt, 17164, Gerona, Spain
Tel.: (34) 972421017
Storage Battery Mfr
N.A.I.C.S.: 335910

EXIDE TECHNOLOGIES SAS **(1)**
5 allee des Pierres, Mayettes, 92636, Gennevilliers, France
Tel.: (33) 141212300
Web Site: http://www.exide.fr
Emp.: 15
Storage Battery Mfr
N.A.I.C.S.: 335910
Sean Burke *(Chief Info & Digital Officer)*

Exide Technologies (Shanghai) Company Limited **(1)**
Room 1806-1811, Hua Xu International Tower, No 336 Xizang Zhong Road, Shanghai, 200001, China
Tel.: (86) 21 2322 3800
Web Site: http://www.exideworld.com.cn
Sales Range: $100-124.9 Million
Battery Mfr
N.A.I.C.S.: 335910

Exide Technologies AB **(1)**
Bultgatan 40 A, 442 40, Kungalv, Vaestra Goetaland, Sweden
Tel.: (46) 303331000
Web Site: http://www.exide.com
Sales Range: $25-49.9 Million
Emp.: 80
Storage Battery Mfr
N.A.I.C.S.: 335910
Christina Jahn *(Office Mgr)*

Subsidiary (Non-US):

EXIDE TECHNOLOGIES AS **(2)**
Moloveien 3, Horten, 3191, Norway
Tel.: (47) 33020666
Web Site: http://www.exide.com
Storage Battery Mfr
N.A.I.C.S.: 335910

EXIGEN INC.
505 Montgomery St # 2300 345 CAl St 10th FL, San Francisco, CA 94104
Tel.: (415) 402-2600
Web Site:
    http://www.exigengroup.com
Rev.: $42,900,000
Emp.: 120
Computer Software Development & Applications
N.A.I.C.S.: 541511
Greg Shenkman *(Mng Partner)*

EXIGENT TECHNOLOGIES, LLC
400 Vly Rd Ste 203, Mount Arlington, NJ 07856
Tel.: (973) 770-0500
Web Site: http://www.exigent.net
Year Founded: 1997
Sales Range: $1-9.9 Million
Emp.: 18
Information Technology Consulting Services
N.A.I.C.S.: 541690
Daniel J. Haurey *(Founder & Pres)*
Chris Jastrzebski *(Supvr-Tech Svcs)*
Gerald R. Busardo *(Sr VP-Ops)*
Eric Burke *(VP-Tech)*

Frank Vizzuso *(VP-Bus Dev)*
Paul Bender *(VP-Application Dev)*
Dan Roth *(VP-Bus Dev)*

EXIGER LLC
1095 Ave of the Americas 5th Fl, New York, NY 10036
Tel.: (212) 455-9400
Web Site: http://www.exiger.com
Year Founded: 2013
Financial Crime, Risk & Compliance Company
N.A.I.C.S.: 541611
Michael Beber *(Co-Founder & Chm)*
Michael Cherkasky *(Co-Founder)*
Renee Michael *(Assoc Mng Dir-Washington)*
Brandon Daniels *(CEO)*

Subsidiaries:

Supply Dynamics LLC **(1)**
6279 Tri Ridge Blvd Ste 310, Loveland, OH 45140
Tel.: (513) 965-2000
Web Site: http://www.supplydynamics.com
Supplier & Consultant for High-Performance/High-Temperature Metals
N.A.I.C.S.: 423510
Trevor Stansbury *(Founder & CEO)*
Rich Caserta *(CFO)*

EXISS ALUMINUM TRAILERS INC.
900 E Trl Blvd, El Reno, OK 73036
Tel.: (405) 262-6471
Web Site: https://www.exiss.com
Rev.: $15,900,000
Emp.: 200
Truck Trailers
N.A.I.C.S.: 336212
Rodney Norvell *(Mgr-Custom Trailer)*

EXIT
2024 Arkansas Valley Dr Ste 605, Little Rock, AR 72212
Tel.: (501) 907-7337
Web Site: http://www.exitideas.com
Year Founded: 2004
Sales Range: Less than $1 Million
Emp.: 6
N.A.I.C.S.: 541810
Shawn Solloway *(Pres)*
Katie Rice *(Acct Dir)*

EXIUM PARTNERS, LLC
144 Village Lndg Ste 276, Fairport, NY 14450   NY
Web Site:
    https://www.exiumpartners.com
Year Founded: 2013
Private Equity & Management Consulting Firm
N.A.I.C.S.: 523999
Jeff Valentine *(Co-Founder & Partner)*

EXLINE INC.
3256 E Country Club Rd, Salina, KS 67402-1487
Tel.: (785) 825-4683
Web Site: https://www.exline-inc.com
Year Founded: 1872
Sales Range: $25-49.9 Million
Emp.: 160
Pipeline Construction
N.A.I.C.S.: 237110
Howard Terrell *(VP)*
Jon Ramsey *(CFO & Exec VP)*
Robert Exline Jr. *(Pres & CEO)*

EXMOVERE HOLDINGS, INC.
1600 Tysons Blvd 8th Fl, McLean, VA 22102
Tel.: (703) 245-8513   DE
Web Site: http://www.exmovere.com
Year Founded: 2006
Sales Range: Less than $1 Million
Emp.: 2

Biosensor & Emotion Detection Technologies Developer & Marketer
N.A.I.C.S.: 541715
David Bychkov *(Chm, Pres, CEO, CFO & Principal Acctg Officer)*

EXODYNE INC.
8433 N Black Canyon Hwy Ste 200, Phoenix, AZ 85021
Tel.: (602) 995-3700
Web Site: https://www.exodyne.com
Rev.: $68,000,000
Emp.: 950
Product Testing Laboratory
N.A.I.C.S.: 541330
Ralph A. Rockow *(Chm)*

EXOTIC AUTOMATION & SUP-PLY, INC.
34700 Grand River Ave, Farmington Hills, MI 48335-3375
Tel.: (248) 477-2122   MI
Web Site:
    http://www.exoticautomation.com
Year Founded: 1963
Fluid Connector Motion Controlled Products & Rubber Plastic Products Mfr
N.A.I.C.S.: 424610
Tom Marino *(Pres & CEO)*

Subsidiaries:

Bond Fluidaire Inc. **(1)**
5506 36th St SE, Grand Rapids, MI 49512
Tel.: (616) 942-1060
Web Site: https://www.bondfluidaire.com
Sales Range: $10-24.9 Million
Emp.: 50
Industrial Machinery & Equipment
N.A.I.C.S.: 423830
Bob Bond *(Pres)*

Branch (Domestic):

Bond Fluidaire Inc. **(2)**
1656 Hilltop Rd, Saint Joseph, MI 49085
Tel.: (269) 983-2501
Web Site: http://www.bondfluidaire.com
Industrial Machinery & Equipment
N.A.I.C.S.: 423830

Bond Fluidaire Inc. **(2)**
1422 Trade Ctr Dr, Traverse City, MI 49696
Tel.: (231) 933-1107
Web Site: http://www.bondfluidaire.com
Emp.: 4
Industrial Machinery & Equipment
N.A.I.C.S.: 423840

Bond Fluidaire, Inc. - Westside **(2)**
600 Scribner NW, Grand Rapids, MI 49504
Tel.: (616) 776-0008
Web Site: http://www.bondfluidaire.com
Sales Range: $10-24.9 Million
Emp.: 6
Industrial Machinery & Equipment Mfr
N.A.I.C.S.: 332912

Sidener Engineering Company, Inc. **(1)**
17450 Bataan Ct, Noblesville, IN 46062
Tel.: (317) 773-8119
Web Site: http://www.exoticautomation.com
Industrial Equipment Mfr
N.A.I.C.S.: 423830
Doug Webster *(Mgr-Foundry & Safety Products)*

EXOTIC METALS FORMING COMPANY LLC.
5411 S 226th St, Kent, WA 98032
Tel.: (253) 395-3710
Web Site: http://www.emfcowa.com
Rev.: $24,900,000
Emp.: 300
Aircraft Parts & Auxiliary Equipment Mfr
N.A.I.C.S.: 336413
Chris Capuano *(Engr-Mktg Staff)*
Debby Yaconetti *(Controller)*

EXPANSION CAPITAL GROUP, LLC
5801 S Corporate Pl, Sioux Falls, SD 57108
Web Site: http://www.ecg.com
Year Founded: 2013
Sales Range: $25-49.9 Million
Emp.: 70
Financial Investment Services
N.A.I.C.S.: 523940
Vincent Ney *(CEO)*
Tim Mages *(Chief Strategy Officer)*
Herk Christie *(COO)*
Brittney Newell *(CFO)*
Marc Helman *(VP-Bus Dev)*

EXPANSION STRATEGIES INC.
17 Rollingwood Dr, New Hartford, NY 13413-2707
Tel.: (315) 793-3137
Web Site:
    http://www.expansionstrategiesinc.com
Year Founded: 1986
Sales Range: Less than $1 Million
Emp.: 639
Provider of Management Consulting Services
N.A.I.C.S.: 541611
Neville Barnett *(Pres)*

EXPEDIEN, INC.
Phoenix Tower 3200 SW Freeway Ste 3300, Houston, TX 77027
Tel.: (713) 840-6090
Web Site: http://www.expedien.net
Year Founded: 2003
Sales Range: $10-24.9 Million
Emp.: 100
Specialized Business Intelligence, Data Warehousing, Data Integration & Application Integration Services
N.A.I.C.S.: 518210
Shibajee Dutta Gupta *(Dir-EIM Practice)*
Jiten Kumar Agarwal *(Founder & CEO)*
Richard Lucas *(Mgr-HR)*

EXPEDITION CAPITAL PART-NERS LLC
2918 N Sheffield Ste 1S, Chicago, IL 60657
Tel.: (773) 857-0210   DE
Web Site: http://www.expedition-partners.com
Privater Equity Firm
N.A.I.C.S.: 523999
Michael Hendrie *(Mng Dir)*

EXPERIENCE WORKS, INC.
4401 Wilson Blvd Ste 1100, Arlington, VA 22203
Tel.: (703) 522-7272   VA
Web Site:
    http://www.experienceworks.org
Year Founded: 1965
Older Worker Training, Employment & Community Services
N.A.I.C.S.: 624310
Andrea Bridgewater *(Dir-Program Ops)*
William Miller *(Chm)*
Cynthia Metzler *(Vice Chm)*
Mary Ann Wyrsch *(Sec)*
Sally A. Boofer *(Pres & CEO)*
Rosemary Schmidt *(Controller)*
Cristal Kurtz *(Dir-HR)*
Marianne Ferguson *(Dir-IT)*
Adela Rexhepaj *(Dir-Budget, Procurement & Compliance)*
Marvin Jones *(Dir-Training & Quality Assurance)*

EXPERIMENTAL AIRCRAFT ASSOCIATION

Experimental Aircraft Association—(Continued)

3000 Poberezny Rd, Oshkosh, WI
54903
Tel.: (920) 426-4800
Web Site: https://www.eaa.org
Rev.: $19,800,410
Emp.: 200
Aviation Club, Membership
N.A.I.C.S.: 713990
Jack Pelton (Chm)
Bob Campbell (Dir-Museum & Museum Education)
Rebecca A. Fischer (Mgr-Bus Relationship)
Charlie Becker (Mgr-Homebuilt Community & Dir-Chapters)

EXPERITEC INC.
504 Trade Center Blvd, Chesterfield,
MO 63005
Tel.: (636) 681-1500
Web Site: https://www.experitec.com
Sales Range: $25-49.9 Million
Emp.: 50
Industrial Supplies
N.A.I.C.S.: 423840
Tom Stachowski (VP-Oil & Gas & Dir-Engrg Svcs)
Don Schafer (Mgr-Engrg)

EXPERT COMPUTER INTERNATIONAL
17800 S Main St Ste 409, Gardena,
CA 90248-3553
Tel.: (310) 965-0101
Web Site: http://www.expertcom.com
Sales Range: $10-24.9 Million
Emp.: 8
Electronic Computers
N.A.I.C.S.: 334111
Ruby Chu (Mgr)

EXPERT CONSTRUCTION INC.
3222 Lakeside Ave, Cleveland, OH
44114
Tel.: (216) 335-9555
Web Site:
    https://www.expertconstruction.com
Year Founded: 1999
Sales Range: $1-9.9 Million
Emp.: 20
Commercial Carpentry Subcontractor
Services
N.A.I.C.S.: 238350
Kyle Kazak (Pres & CEO)

EXPERT SEMICONDUCTOR TECH
10 Victor Sq Ste 100, Scotts Valley,
CA 95066
Tel.: (831) 439-9300
Web Site: https://www.expert-tech.com
Sales Range: $10-24.9 Million
Emp.: 35
Semiconductor Manufacturing Machinery
N.A.I.C.S.: 333242
Jonathan George (Pres)

EXPERT WIRELESS SOLUTIONS, INC.
8221 Old Courthouse Rd Ste 104,
Vienna, VA 22182-3839
Tel.: (703) 760-9180
Sales Range: $10-24.9 Million
Emp.: 15
Radio Frequency Engineering & Network Design Services
N.A.I.C.S.: 517810
Shawn Ziglari (Pres)

Subsidiaries:

eXpert Wireless Solutions, Inc.   (1)
2050 Ctr Ave Polygon Plz Ste 320, Fort
Lee, NJ 07024

Tel.: (201) 944-7780
Web Site: http://www.expertwireless.com
Sales Range: $10-24.9 Million
Emp.: 10
Radio Frequency Engineering & Network
Design Services
N.A.I.C.S.: 517810

EXPERTICITY, INC.
9 Exchange Pl Ste 1000, Salt Lake
City, UT 84111
Tel.: (801) 869-6167
Web Site: http://www.experticity.com
Software Publisher
N.A.I.C.S.: 513210
Jeremy Knudsen (Dir-Tech)
Kevin Knight (CMO)
Tom Stockham (CEO)

EXPLORE COMMUNICATIONS
3213 Zuni St, Denver, CO 80211
Tel.: (303) 393-0567
Web Site: https://www.explorehq.com
Year Founded: 1996
Sales Range: $10-24.9 Million
Emp.: 12
Media Buying Services
N.A.I.C.S.: 541810
Brin Schwartz (Media Planner & Buyer)
Megan Miller (Media Planner & Buyer)
Mindy Gantner (Media Dir)
Becky Swepston (Coord-Media)

EXPLORE CONSULTING
10900 NE 8th St Ste 200, Bellevue,
WA 98004
Tel.: (425) 462-0100
Web Site:
    http://www.exploreconsulting.com
Year Founded: 2001
Sales Range: $1-9.9 Million
Emp.: 44
Computer Related Services
N.A.I.C.S.: 541512
Steve Jones (CEO)
Kathryn Wunnicke (Acct Mgr)
Paul Witten (Sr Acct Exec-NetSuite)
Rick Audette (Sr Acct Mgr)

EXPLORER PIPELINE COMPANY
PO Box 2650, Tulsa, OK 74101
Tel.: (918) 493-5100   DE
Web Site: https://www.expl.com
Refined Petroleum Products Pipeline
Operator
N.A.I.C.S.: 486910
Terry Biehl (CFO)
Tom Jensen (Pres & CEO)
Dolin Argo (VP-Ops & Bus Dev)
Todd Golla (Dir-IT)
Jim Sieck (Dir-Engrg, Health, Safety, Security & Environmental)
Angel Stacy (Dir-HR)
Celeste Johnson (Gen Counsel)

EXPLORER VAN COMPANY
2749 N Fox Farm Rd, Warsaw, IN
46580
Tel.: (574) 267-7666
Web Site:
    https://www.explorervan.com
Sales Range: $50-74.9 Million
Emp.: 200
Sales of Recreational & Customized
Explorer Vans
N.A.I.C.S.: 336213
Rose Wilcox (CEO)

EXPLORING.COM, INC.
3655 Atlanta Industrial Dr Bldg 100,
Atlanta, GA 30331
Tel.: (770) 933-9030
Web Site: http://www.exploring.com
Sales Range: $10-24.9 Million

Emp.: 50
Flooring Solutions
N.A.I.C.S.: 238330
Stacy Barnes (Mgr-Natl Sls)
James Zacharias (Sr Acct Mgr)
Leslie Schemanske (Sr Acct Mgr)
Rick Pierson (Sr Acct Mgr)
Jennie Chastain (Acct Mgr)
Earl Cooper (Mgr-Logistics)
Vivek Ruparel (VP-Fin & Ops)
Dave Walens (Pres)

EXPLORNATION ENERGY, INC.
14511 Falling Creek Dr Ste 105,
Houston, TX 77014
Tel.: (281) 782-5332   TX
Web Site:
    https://www.explornation.com
Year Founded: 2010
Holding Company; Oil & Gas Fund
Investment & Asset Management
Services
N.A.I.C.S.: 551112
Rodney D. Giles (Pres & CEO)

Subsidiaries:

ExplorNation Management LLC   (1)
14511 Falling Creek Dr Ste 105, Houston,
TX 77014
Tel.: (281) 782-5332
Web Site: http://www.explornation.com
Oil & Gas Asset Investment Management
N.A.I.C.S.: 523940
Rodney D. Giles (Pres & CEO)

EXPO INDUSTRIES, INC.
7455 Carroll Rd, San Diego, CA
92121-2303
Tel.: (858) 566-3110
Web Site:
    http://www.expoindustries.com
Sales Range: $10-24.9 Million
Emp.: 65
Exterior Building Materials Mfr
N.A.I.C.S.: 423310
Melissa Walker (Mgr-HR)

EXPO LOGIC
553 Foundry Rd, East Norriton, PA
19403
Tel.: (484) 751-5100
Web Site: http://ww2.expologic.com
Year Founded: 1979
Sales Range: $10-24.9 Million
Event Planning Services
N.A.I.C.S.: 711320
Jeff Cooper (Pres)
Dave Bradfield (VP-Client Success)
Scott Jennings (Mgr-Registration Svcs)
Jarred Singer (Mgr-Lead Retrieval & IT Infrastructure)
Mike Bridges (Mgr-Logistics)
Sandhya Chennuru (Dir-Software Dev)
Russ Chinoy (VP-IT)
Cathy Dalton (Sr Mgr-Acct)
Alan Johnston (VP-Bus Dev)
Kimberly Muenzel (Mgr-Customer Svc)
Mark Tarquinio (Asst Mgr-Logistics)
Brandee Waters (Sr Mgr-Acct)
Kathleen Wong (Sr Mgr-Acct)
Lauren Zirkelbach (Mgr-Acct)

EXPONENTIAL INTERACTIVE, INC.
2200 Powell St Ste 600, Emeryville,
CA 94608
Tel.: (510) 250-5500   DE
Web Site:
    http://www.exponential.com
Year Founded: 2000
Sales Range: $150-199.9 Million
Emp.: 639

Digital Advertising Agency
N.A.I.C.S.: 541810
Dilip DaSilva (Founder & CEO)
Jason Tsang (Mgr-China)
John McKoy (Chief Revenue Officer)
Danielle Cravatt (VP-Sls)
Jason Wolf (VP-Sls-Central)
Evan Kramer (VP-Sls-East)
Doug Conely (Chief Product & Strategy Officer)
Jessica Batt (Dir-Mktg-Global)
Ittai Shiu (VP-Creative Strategy Mgmt)
Fabrice Leclerc (Mng Dir-France)
Federico Carrera (Mng Dir-Latam)
Maija Gwynn (Dir-Sls Ops)
Penelope Lima (Dir-Publ Ops-EU)
Roland Tanaka (Exec Dir-Bus Dev)
Ruslan Melnikov (Dir-Product Mgmt)
Sahil Zafar (Dir-Publ Dev)
Celine Liew (Mgr-Malaysia)
Alex Locker-LeMersier (Sls Dir-Singapore)
Steffen Crouwel (Comml Dir-Asia Pacific)

EXPONENTIAL PROPERTY CONSTRUCTION, LLC
1701 W Northwest Hwy Ste 100,
Grapevine, TX 76051
Tel.: (817) 305-0610   TX
Web Site:
    http://www.exponentialproperty.
    group.com
Year Founded: 2011
Sales Range: $25-49.9 Million
Emp.: 200
Real Estate Investment Services
N.A.I.C.S.: 531390
Kim Radaker Bays (Founder & Principal)
Matthew Bays (Chief Dev Officer & Principal)
Natasha Austin (Dir-Property Mgmt)
Carl Pankratz (VP-Dev)
Marc Swank (CMO)

EXPORT OIL FIELD SUPPLY COMPANY INTERNATIONAL
3350 Bingle Rd, Houston, TX 77255
Tel.: (713) 939-1200
Web Site: https://www.exoilsup.com
Year Founded: 1929
Sales Range: $10-24.9 Million
Emp.: 15
Oil Well Machinery
N.A.I.C.S.: 423830
Edward J. Carney (CEO)

EXPORT PACKAGING CO. INC.
525 E 10th Ave, Milan, IL 61264-3117
Tel.: (309) 787-0440   IL
Web Site: https://www.xpac.com
Year Founded: 1996
Sales Range: $75-99.9 Million
Emp.: 1,000
Packing & Crating
N.A.I.C.S.: 488991
Donald L. Ruggles (CEO)
Greg Ruggles (Pres)

EXPORT-IMPORT BANK OF THE UNITED STATES
811 Vermont Ave NW, Washington,
DC 20571-0001
Tel.: (202) 565-3946
Web Site: https://www.exim.gov
Year Founded: 1934
Sales Range: $100-124.9 Million
Emp.: 406
Federal Export & Import Banking
Services
N.A.I.C.S.: 522299
Michael Cushing (Sr VP-Resource Mgmt)

Michele A. Kuester *(Sr VP)*
Robert Morin *(Sr VP-Bus & Product Dev)*
William Marsteller *(VP-Country Risk & Economic Analysis)*
Angela Mariana Freyre *(Gen Counsel & Sr VP)*
Charles J. Hall *(Chm, Pres-Acting, COO & Exec VP)*
Annette B. Maresh *(VP-Trade Fin Insurance)*
Catrell Brown *(VP-Pub Affairs & Comm)*
Scott Schloegel *(Vice Chm & First VP-Acting)*
Michael S. Whalen *(VP-Structured Fin Div)*
Andrew Falk *(VP-Transportation Portfolio Mgmt Div)*
David W. Carter *(VP-Credit Policy Div)*
David M. Sena *(CFO)*
Nathalie Herman *(Treas & VP)*
Pamela S. Bowers *(VP-Bus Credit Div)*
George Garcia *(Chief Human Capital Officer)*
Michael Howard *(Mng Dir-Central Reg)*
Sharyn H. Koenig *(Mng Dir-Eastern Reg)*
David Josephson *(Mng Dir-Western Reg)*
Jesse Law *(Sr VP)*
Patricia Wolf *(VP & Controller)*
Maria A. Fleetwood *(VP-Acquisition & Bus Svcs Div)*
Rebecca M. Rose *(VP-Comm)*
Rochele Barham *(VP-Customer & Bus Solutions)*
Nicole M. B. Valtos *(VP-Ops & Data Quality Div)*
Helene Walsh *(VP-Policy Analysis)*

EXPORTS OF WASHINGTON INCORPORATED

435 Martin St Ste 4000, Blaine, WA 98230
Tel.: (360) 332-5239
Sales Range: $10-24.9 Million
Emp.: 40
Investor Relations
N.A.I.C.S.: 523999
Kenneth L. Kellar *(Pres)*

EXPOS2 INC.

33 N First St, Ashland, OR 97520
Tel.: (541) 201-8141
Web Site: http://www.expos2.com
Sales Range: $10-24.9 Million
Emp.: 10
Physical & Virtual Trade Shows & Conventions
N.A.I.C.S.: 561920
Steve Strickland *(Founder, Pres & CEO)*
Nobuko Nakamura *(Dir-Sls-Asia)*
Naomi Forkash *(Mgr-Customer Svc)*

EXPRESS A BUTTON, INC.

38791 County Rd 104, Dakota, MN 55925
Tel.: (507) 643-6933   MN
Web Site:
    http://www.expressabutton.com
Year Founded: 1987
Sales Range: $1-9.9 Million
Emp.: 32
Signs & Advertising Specialty Services
N.A.I.C.S.: 339950
Cindy Bergler *(Pres)*

EXPRESS AIR FREIGHT UN-LIMITED, INC.

147 20 184th St, Jamaica, NY 11413
Tel.: (718) 995-2900
Web Site:
    https://www.expressairfreight.com
Year Founded: 1990
Sales Range: $25-49.9 Million
Emp.: 18
Freight Transportation Services
N.A.I.C.S.: 488510
David Marx *(Pres)*
Julio Valdivia *(Mgr-Sls)*
Ronald Marx *(VP)*
Russell Howitt *(Mgr-Station)*
Nancy Medina *(Mgr-HR)*
Mike Alger *(Mgr-Station)*
Brian Piorkowski *(Mgr-Station)*
Dan Lacy *(Mgr-Ops)*
Yolanda Gonzalez *(Mgr-Acctg-HR)*
Brian Carroll *(Reg Mgr)*
Robert Ortiz *(Mgr-Station)*
Candy Yuen *(Mgr)*
Louis Chan *(Project Mgr)*
John Bright *(Reg Mgr)*
Jeremy Smollen *(Mgr-Station Ops)*
Michael Livingston *(Mgr-Station)*
Roberto Sanchez *(Mgr-Station)*

EXPRESS CHECK ADVANCE LLC

2034 Hamilton Pl Blvd Ste 100, Chattanooga, TN 37421-6098
Tel.: (423) 899-4088
Web Site:
    http://www.expresscheckadvance.com
Year Founded: 1998
Sales Range: $10-24.9 Million
Emp.: 20
Personal Financial Services
N.A.I.C.S.: 522291
Randel McCoy *(Pres)*

EXPRESS CREDIT AUTO, INC.

9014 SE 29th St, Oklahoma City, OK 73150
Tel.: (405) 792-2280
Web Site:
    http://www.expresscreditauto.com
Sales Range: $50-74.9 Million
Emp.: 100
Used Car Whslr
N.A.I.C.S.: 441120
Doug Swift *(Dir-Ops-Oklahoma)*

EXPRESS EMPLOYMENT PROFESSIONALS

1590 N McMullen Booth Rd Ste K2, Clearwater, FL 33759
Tel.: (727) 712-0607
Web Site:
    http://clearwaterfl.expresspros.com
Year Founded: 1996
Sales Range: $10-24.9 Million
Emp.: 8
Staffing Services
N.A.I.C.S.: 561311
Raina Baker *(Coord-Front Office)*
Tiffany Iacuone *(Mgr-Acct)*
Phill Powell *(Mng Partner-Indianapolis & Columbus-Franchises)*

EXPRESS EMPLOYMENT PROFESSIONALS, INC.

8516 NW Expy, Oklahoma City, OK 73162
Tel.: (405) 840-5000   OK
Web Site:
    http://www.expresspros.com
Year Founded: 1983
Sales Range: $1-4.9 Billion
Emp.: 200
Staffing Services
N.A.I.C.S.: 561320
William H. Stoller *(Chm & CEO)*
Jamie Allison *(VP-Fin Analysis)*
Linda Marie Arredondo *(CIO)*

Brandon Rogers *(Branch Mgr-Rogersville)*
Steve Scully *(Chief Sls & Mktg Officer)*
Keith McFall *(COO)*
Erin Ricke *(Dir-Specialized Recruiting-Specialized Recruiting Grp)*
Robert A. Funk Sr. *(Founder, Vice Chm & Pres)*

EXPRESS KCS INC.

120 Fifth Ave Ste 2700, Pittsburgh, PA 15222
Tel.: (412) 961-8160
Web Site: http://www.expresskcs.com
Sales Range: $25-49.9 Million
Emp.: 650
Media Related Outsourcing Services
N.A.I.C.S.: 561499
Robert Berkeley *(Pres)*
Tariq Husain *(CEO)*

EXPRESS KITCHENS

231 Weston St., Hartford, CT 06120
Tel.: (860) 247-1000
Web Site:
    https://expresskitchens.com
Wood Kitchen Cabinet & Counter Top Mfr
N.A.I.C.S.: 337110
Max Kothari *(CEO)*

Subsidiaries:

Direct Cabinet Sales Inc.   (1)
180 Herrod Blvd, Dayton, NJ 08810
Tel.: (908) 587-9577
Web Site: http://www.directcabinetsales.com
Rev.: $10,764,412
Emp.: 68
Fiscal Year-end: 12/31/2014
Full Line Cabinet Whslr & Distr to New Construction
N.A.I.C.S.: 337110
Joseph DeMussi *(Pres)*
Janet Camacho *(Dir-HR)*
Bill Sutter *(Mgr-Sls-Philadelphia North & East Metro Markets)*

EXPRESS LAINE CONVE-NIENCE STORES INC.

22208 Timberlake Rd, Lynchburg, VA 24502
Tel.: (434) 239-4242
Sales Range: $10-24.9 Million
Emp.: 50
Independent Convenience Store
N.A.I.C.S.: 445131
Warren K. Crist *(Pres)*
Diane Reagan *(Office Mgr)*
Ken Shaw *(Gen Mgr)*

EXPRESS LANE INC.

600 Ohio Ave Ste A, Lynn Haven, FL 32444-1777
Tel.: (850) 769-8977   FL
Web Site: http://www.expressln.com
Year Founded: 1984
Sales Range: $50-74.9 Million
Emp.: 400
Convenience Store Operators
N.A.I.C.S.: 445131
James E. Lewis *(CEO)*
Nikki Loveless *(Mgr-Mktg)*

EXPRESS LEASING INC.

1322 Washington Ave, Bay City, MI 48708
Tel.: (989) 893-3330
Web Site: http://www.transport.com
Sales Range: $25-49.9 Million
Emp.: 85
Long Haul Trucking
N.A.I.C.S.: 484121
Allison Short *(Pres)*
Phil Reagh *(Mgr-HR)*
Gary Short *(VP)*

EXPRESS PIPE & SUPPLY CO. INC.

2644 30th St Ste 102, Santa Monica, CA 90405-3062
Tel.: (310) 204-7238
Web Site:
    http://www.expresspipe.com
Rev.: $36,220,000
Emp.: 12
Plumbing & Hydronic Heating Supplies
N.A.I.C.S.: 423720
Mark Jones *(Mgr)*
Jeff Smith *(Coord-Safety)*

EXPRESS TIRE AUTO SERVICE CENTERS

1148 Industrial Ave, Escondido, CA 92029
Tel.: (760) 741-4044
Web Site: http://www.expresstire.com
Rev.: $15,300,000
Emp.: 360
Automotive Tire Sales & Preventative Maintenance Services
N.A.I.C.S.: 441340
John Marchioni *(Pres)*
Greta Waggoner *(CFO & VP)*

EXPRESSION NETWORKS, LLC

1140 3rd St NE Ste 310, Washington, DC 20002
Web Site: http://www.expr.net
Year Founded: 1997
Sales Range: $1-9.9 Million
Information Technology Consulting Services
N.A.I.C.S.: 541512
Abir Ray *(CEO)*
Gavin Greene *(Chief Growth Officer)*
Tom Meccia *(COO)*
Kenneth Lecky *(Dir-Tech)*
Wu Wu *(Dir-Fin)*

EXPRESSJET AIRLINES INC.

990 Toffie Ter, Atlanta, GA 30354
Tel.: (404) 856-1000   GA
Web Site: http://www.expressjet.com
Year Founded: 1979
Sales Range: $5-14.9 Billion
Emp.: 9,000
Regional Air Carrier
N.A.I.C.S.: 481111
Kevin Wade *(VP-Fin & Controller)*
Brandee Reynolds *(VP-In-Flight Svcs)*
John Varley *(Chief Admin Officer, Gen Counsel & Sr VP)*
Subodh Karnik *(Chm & CEO)*
John Greenlee *(Pres)*
Bruce Jones *(VP-Maintenance & Engrg)*
Captain Scott Hall *(VP-Flight Ops)*
Larry Snyder *(Mng Dir-Ops Support Center)*
Kevin Langford *(VP-HR)*
Neville Randeria *(CFO)*
Bobby Looney *(Dir-Safety)*

Subsidiaries:

ExpressJet Airlines, Inc.   (1)
700 N Sam Houston Pkwy W Ste 200, Houston, TX 77067
Tel.: (832) 353-1000
Web Site: http://www.expressjet.com
Sales Range: $1-4.9 Billion
Regional & Chartered Air Transportation Services
N.A.I.C.S.: 481111

ExpressJet Services, LLC   (1)
4750 World Houston Pkwy Ste 100, Houston, TX 77067
Tel.: (832) 353-3400
Sales Range: $1-4.9 Billion
Airline Maintenance, Repair & Overhaul Services

ExpressJet Airlines Inc.—(Continued)
N.A.I.C.S.: 488190

EXPRESSPOINT TECHNOL-OGY SERVICES, INC.
1109 Zane Ave N, Minneapolis, MN
55422-4605
Tel.: (763) 543-6000   DE
Web Site:
    http://www.expresspoint.com
Year Founded: 1997
Sales Range: $50-74.9 Million
Emp.: 250
Mfr of Computers, Peripherals & Software
N.A.I.C.S.: 423430
David A. Anderson *(Chm & CEO)*
Kelly Dudek *(Sr VP-Ops)*
Traci Kreun *(Mgr-Delivery)*

EXPRESSWAY DODGE INC.
5531 E Indiana St, Evansville, IN
47715
Tel.: (812) 471-2000
Web Site:
    http://www.expresswaydodge.com
Sales Range: $25-49.9 Million
Emp.: 125
New & Used Car Dealers
N.A.I.C.S.: 441110
Robert J. Bulkley *(Pres)*
Ed Goebel *(Mgr-Sls)*
Jim Hale *(Mgr-Sls)*

EXQUISITA TORTILLAS INC.
700 W Chapin St, Edinburg, TX
78541
Tel.: (956) 383-6712   TX
Web Site:
    https://www.exquisitatortillas.com
Year Founded: 1982
Tortilla Mfr
N.A.I.C.S.: 311830
Bill Guerra *(COO)*

EXQUISITE TIMEPIECES, INC.
4380 Gulfshore Blvd N Ste 800,
Naples, FL 34103
Tel.: (239) 262-4545
Web Site:
    http://www.exquisitetimepieces.com
Sales Range: $10-24.9 Million
Watch Retailer
N.A.I.C.S.: 423940
Timothy Richardson *(Pres)*

EXTECH INDUSTRIES INC.
87 Bowne St, Brooklyn, NY 11231
Tel.: (718) 786-2288
Web Site:
    https://www.extechbuilding.com
Rev.: $35,000,000
Emp.: 110
Sales of Trim & Sheet Metal
N.A.I.C.S.: 423310
Gautam Bhayana *(Mgr-IT)*

EXTENSIONENGINE LLC
196 Broadway, Cambridge, MA
02142
Tel.: (978) 475-9199
Web Site:
    http://www.extensionengine.com
Year Founded: 2000
Sales Range: $1-9.9 Million
Software Services
N.A.I.C.S.: 334610
Stjepan Radovic *(Partner)*
Bob Allard *(Co-Founder & Mng Partner)*
Niksa Radovic *(Partner)*
Furqan Nazeeri *(Partner)*
Shlomi Dinoor *(COO)*
Evan Brown *(Dir-Product Mgmt)*

Subsidiaries:

extensionEngine   (1)
Tijardoviceva 20, Split, Croatia   **(100%)**
Tel.: (385) 91 504 5403
Web Site: http://www.extensionengine.com
Emp.: 2
Software Engineering Solutions
N.A.I.C.S.: 334610
Stjepan Radovic *(COO)*

EXTENSYS, INC.
253 Pine Ave N Bldg B, Oldsmar, FL
34677
Tel.: (813) 855-3909   FL
Web Site:
    http://www.extensysinc.com
Year Founded: 2002
Sales Range: $1-9.9 Million
Emp.: 40
Scientific & Technical Consulting Services
N.A.I.C.S.: 541690
Christopher Jordan *(VP-Architecture)*
Brian Hamm *(Pres)*
Greg Renner *(VP-Svcs)*
Stephen Gorham *(VP-Cloud & Managed Svcs)*

EXTERNETWORKS, INC.
10 Corporate Pl S Ste 1-05, Piscataway, NJ 08854
Tel.: (732) 465-0001
Web Site:
    http://www.externetworks.com
Year Founded: 2001
Sales Range: $10-24.9 Million
Emp.: 180
Information Technology Consulting
Services
N.A.I.C.S.: 541512
Malik Zakaria *(Mng Dir)*

EXTOLE INC.
625 2nd St Ste 101, San Francisco,
CA 94107
Tel.: (415) 625-0500
Web Site: http://www.extole.com
Year Founded: 2009
Sales Range: $25-49.9 Million
Emp.: 90
Social Media Marketing
N.A.I.C.S.: 541613
Matthew J. Roche *(CEO)*
Mark Cyster *(CTO)*
Chris Duskin *(VP-Mktg)*
Erik Zech *(CFO)*
Lee Bierman *(VP-Tech)*

EXTRA INNINGS FRANCHISE COMPANY
264 S Main St, Middleton, MA 01949
Tel.: (978) 762-0448
Web Site:
    https://www.eifranchise.com
Year Founded: 1996
Baseball & Softball Training Facility
Services
N.A.I.C.S.: 711211
Rob Nash *(Founder)*
Robert Warren *(Mgr)*

EXTRA MILE TRANSPORTA-TION LLC
4295 Harris Hill Rd, Buffalo, NY
14221
Tel.: (716) 276-2045
Web Site:
    http://www.extramileonline.com
Year Founded: 1995
Sales Range: $1-9.9 Million
Emp.: 10
National Trucking, Without Storage
N.A.I.C.S.: 484110

Kevin M. Large *(Coord-Dispatch)*
Maureen Barth *(Mgr-Reg Sls)*
Shasha T. Moose *(Acct Mgr)*
Keith Acquard *(Comptroller)*

EXTRA SPORTS WEAR INC.
115 Kennedy Dr, Sayreville, NJ
08872-1459
Tel.: (732) 721-0022
Year Founded: 1979
Sales Range: $10-24.9 Million
Emp.: 30
Clothing Distr
N.A.I.C.S.: 424350
Joe Sutton *(Pres)*

EXTRACO CORPORATION
1700 N Valley Mills Dr, Waco, TX
76710
Tel.: (254) 776-0330
Web Site:
    http://www.extracobanks.com
Year Founded: 1902
Rev.: $33,900,000
Emp.: 90
Bank Holding Company
N.A.I.C.S.: 551111
S. Spencer Brown *(Chm)*

Subsidiaries:

Extraco Banks   (1)
1700 N Valley Mills Dr, Waco, TX 76710
Tel.: (254) 776-0160
Web Site: http://www.extracobanks.com
Rev.: $7,744,000
Emp.: 50
National Commercial Banks
N.A.I.C.S.: 522110
Gail Bartay *(Sr VP)*
Mark Reynolds *(Pres-North Reg)*
Tammy Richards *(Exec VP)*
Jarrett Warren *(Officer-Bank)*

Extraco Mortgage Corp.   (1)
1704 N Valley Mill Dr, Waco, TX 76710
Tel.: (254) 761-2300
Web Site: http://www.extraconet.com
Rev.: $9,744,725
Emp.: 25
Mortgage Bankers & Loan Correspondents
N.A.I.C.S.: 522310
James Geeslin *(VP)*

EXTRACTABLE, INC.
612 Howard St Ste 400, San Francisco, CA 94105
Tel.: (415) 227-4300
Web Site: http://www.extractable.com
Year Founded: 1999
Sales Range: $1-9.9 Million
Emp.: 35
Internet Related Advertising Services
N.A.I.C.S.: 541890
Craig McLaughlin *(Founder, Pres & CEO)*
Joel Oxman *(VP-Bus Dev)*
Simon Mathews *(Chief Strategy Officer)*
Mark Ryan *(Chief Analytics Officer)*
Sean Brown *(CTO)*
Esther Scanlan *(CFO)*
Anne Sophie Hurst *(COO)*
Wolfgang Strack *(Chief Creative Officer)*

EXTRAKARE LLC
3230 Peachtree Corners Cir, Norcross, GA 30092-3655
Tel.: (770) 449-6898
Web Site: http://www.extrakare.com
Year Founded: 2004
Sales Range: $1-9.9 Million
Emp.: 40
All Other Miscellaneous Store Retailers, except Tobacco Stores
N.A.I.C.S.: 459999
Laura Toops *(Coord-Patient Care)*
Lou Melfi *(Mgr-Ops)*

Rita Harris *(Coord-Patient Intake)*
Chyrel Neal *(Coord-Compliance)*
Danielle Roberts-Obeng *(Coord-Patient Care)*

EXTREME ENGINEERING SO-LUTIONS, INC.
3225 Deming Way Ste 120, Middleton, WI 53562
Tel.: (608) 833-1155
Web Site: http://www.xes-inc.com
Year Founded: 2002
Rev.: $19,900,000
Emp.: 42
Engineeering Services
N.A.I.C.S.: 541330
Brad Bilse *(Mgr-Ops)*
Bret Farnum *(VP-Sls & Mktg)*
Anthony Gionta *(Mgr)*
Ben Klam *(VP-Engrg)*
Zachary Krohn *(Sr Engr)*
Aaron Lindner *(Mgr-Engrg)*
Dave Scidmore *(COO)*
Rob Scidmore *(Pres & CEO)*

EXTREME HOLDINGS, INC.
3111 Farmtrail Rd, York, PA 17406
Tel.: (717) 717-9580
Web Site:
    http://www.extremeholdings.com
Holding Company Services
N.A.I.C.S.: 551112
David Pridgen *(Co-Pres & CEO)*
Regis Maher *(Founder & Co-Pres)*
Roger Monson *(CFO)*

Subsidiaries:

Mervin Manufacturing, Inc.   (1)
701 N 34th St Ste 100, Seattle, WA 98103
Tel.: (206) 204-7800
Web Site: http://www.mervin.com
Sales Range: $25-49.9 Million
Snowboard & Skateboard Products Mfr
N.A.I.C.S.: 339920
Peter Saari *(Co-Founder)*
Mike Olson *(Co-Founder)*

EXTREME REACH, INC.
75 2nd Ave Ste 720, Needham, MA
02494
Tel.: (781) 577-2016
Web Site:
    https://www.extremereach.com
Year Founded: 2008
Sales Range: $25-49.9 Million
Emp.: 8
Video Advertising Services
N.A.I.C.S.: 541890
Tim Conley *(Co-Founder, Pres & COO)*
Dan Brackett *(Co-Founder & CTO)*
Patrick Hanavan *(Co-Founder & Chief Client Officer)*
John Roland *(Co-Founder)*
Tim Hale *(Chief Talent Officer)*
Sandy Drayton *(VP-Corp Comm)*
Melinda McLaughlin *(CMO)*
Matt Timothy *(Chief Revenue Officer)*
Jennifer Wambold *(Chief HR Officer)*

EXTREME STEEL, INC
480 Shady Elm Rd, Winchester, VA
22602
Tel.: (540) 868-9150   VA
Year Founded: 2000
Rev.: $8,000,000
Emp.: 58
Fabricated Structural Metal Mfr
N.A.I.C.S.: 332312
Robert Pilham *(Pres & CEO)*

EXTRON LOGISTICS, LLC
496 S Abbott Ave, Milpitas, CA 95035
Tel.: (510) 353-0177
Web Site: http://www.extroninc.com
Emp.: 50

Supply Chain Solutions for Technology Industry
N.A.I.C.S.: 541614
Sandeep Duggal *(CEO)*
Kien Nguyen *(VP-Customer Integration)*
Dinesh Chatkara *(VP-Quality & Ops)*

EXTRUSIONS INC.
2401 S Main St, Fort Scott, KS 66701
Tel.: (620) 223-1111
Web Site:
https://www.aluminumextrusion.com
Rev.: $14,178,789
Emp.: 100
Aluminum Extruded Products
N.A.I.C.S.: 331318
Matthew Ida *(Pres)*
Brian McGowen *(Gen Mgr)*

EXUBRIO GROUP LLC
1321 Millersport Hwy Ste 204, Williamsville, NY 14221
Tel.: (716) 830-5219
Year Founded: 2002
Sales Range: Less than $1 Million
Emp.: 6
Advertising, Consulting, Direct Response Marketing, Public Relations, Strategic Planning/Research
N.A.I.C.S.: 541810
Grace Lazzara *(Partner)*

EXUDE BENEFITS GROUP, INC.
2218 Race St, Philadelphia, PA 19103
Tel.: (215) 875-8730
Web Site:
http://www.exudebenefits.com
Sales Range: $1-9.9 Million
Emp.: 27
Insurance Services
N.A.I.C.S.: 524298
Marcos R. Lopez *(CEO)*
Alison DiFlorio *(Pres-HR)*
Cori Green *(Mng Partner-Benefits Div)*
Lauren Urbanski *(Acct Mgr)*
Chrissy DiGiacoma-Denston *(Mgr-Acctg & Ops)*
Jessica Mulholland *(CFO)*
David DiStefano *(Pres & COO)*
Eric Halpern *(Dir-Risk Mgmt & Client Rels)*
Morgan Festa *(Mgr-Mktg)*
Caesar D. Williams *(Pres)*

EXX INC.
1350 E Flamingo Rd Ste 689, Las Vegas, NV 89119-5263
Tel.: (702) 598-3223   NV
Sales Range: $100-124.9 Million
Emp.: 675
Holding Company; Designer, Mfr & Distr of Toys & Electromechanical Products
N.A.I.C.S.: 339930

Subsidiaries:

Henry Gordy International Inc.   (1)
108 S Franklin Ave Ste 7, Valley Stream, NY 11580-6105   (100%)
Tel.: (573) 486-3270
Sales Range: $10-24.9 Million
Emp.: 10
Mfr Toys & Watches
N.A.I.C.S.: 339930

Steven Toys   (1)
809A Market St, Hermann, MO 65041-1318   (100%)
Tel.: (573) 486-3270
Sales Range: $10-24.9 Million
Emp.: 25
Mfr Toys
N.A.I.C.S.: 339930

TX Technology Corp.   (1)
7 Emery Ave, Randolph, NJ 07869-1308   (100%)
Tel.: (973) 442-7500
Web Site: http://www.txtechnology.com
Rev.: $29,514,000
Emp.: 25
Mfr Cable Pressurization & Monitoring Equipment for Telecommunications Industry
N.A.I.C.S.: 334513
Donald Black *(Gen Mgr)*

EXXACT EXPRESS INC.
621 N Lk Parker Ave, Lakeland, FL 33801
Tel.: (863) 682-4101
Web Site: http://www.exxact.net
Year Founded: 1986
Sales Range: $10-24.9 Million
Emp.: 25
Trucking Services
N.A.I.C.S.: 484121
Debbie Kedzuf *(VP)*
Brandon Bodine *(Mgr-Logistics)*

EXXEL OUTDOORS, INC.
6235 Lookout Rd Ste B, Boulder, CO 80301
Tel.: (205) 486-5258   DE
Web Site: http://www.exxel.com
Year Founded: 1997
Sales Range: $25-49.9 Million
Emp.: 73
Recreational Apparel & Gear Mfr
N.A.I.C.S.: 314999
Harry Kazazian *(Co-Founder & CEO)*
Armen Kouleyan *(Co-Founder & Chm)*
Scott Magardichian *(VP-Intl Sls)*
Eric Greene *(VP)*
Mike Wagner *(COO)*
Jim Hesse *(CMO)*

Subsidiaries:

Insta-bed, Inc.   (1)
6235 Lookout Rd Ste B, Boulder, CO 80301
Tel.: (800) 325-4121
Web Site: http://instabed.com
Air Mattress Whslr
N.A.I.C.S.: 423210

Kelty, Inc.   (1)
6235 Lookout Rd, Boulder, CO 80301
Web Site: http://www.kelty.com
Camping Equipment Whslr
N.A.I.C.S.: 423910
Andrew Day *(Product Mgr)*

Sierra Designs, Inc.   (1)
6235 Lookout Rd Ste C, Boulder, CO 80301
Tel.: (800) 736-8592
Web Site: http://www.sierradesigns.com
Recreational Goods Whslr
N.A.I.C.S.: 423910
Bill Conradt *(Head-Global Sls)*
Stephen Barnes *(Sr Mgr-Product)*
Eric Greene *(Div VP & Gen Mgr-Exxel Outdoors Performance Grp)*

Slumberjack Inc.   (1)
6235 Lookout Rd Ste G, Boulder, CO 80301
Tel.: (800) 233-6283
Web Site: http://www.slumberjack.com
Emp.: 50
Recreational Goods Whslr
N.A.I.C.S.: 423910
Russell Rowell *(VP)*

Ultimate Direction, Inc.   (1)
6235 Lookout Rd Ste B, Boulder, CO 80301
Tel.: (800) 426-7229
Web Site: http://www.ultimatedirection.com
Sporting Goods Store Operator
N.A.I.C.S.: 459110

EXXEL PACIFIC, INC.
323 Telegraph Rd, Bellingham, WA 98226
Tel.: (360) 734-2872

Web Site:
https://www.exxelpacific.com
Sales Range: $10-24.9 Million
Emp.: 78
Nonresidential Construction Services
N.A.I.C.S.: 236220
Kevin R. DeVries *(Principal)*

EYE CARE ASSOCIATES
7100 Six Forks Rd, Raleigh, NC 27615
Tel.: (919) 863-2020
Web Site:
http://www.eyecareassociates.com
Year Founded: 1978
Sales Range: $25-49.9 Million
Emp.: 204
Optometry Services
N.A.I.C.S.: 621320
Stephen Bolick *(Founder & CEO)*
Jim Speight *(CFO)*
Wes Hinson *(Dir-Regional Ops)*
Robert H. Brodney *(Pres)*
Norah Goldman *(Dir-Mktg)*
Jason Niebauer *(Dir-Regional Ops)*
Angela McCoy *(Dir-Bus Sys)*
Joe Cochran *(Mgr-IT & IS Systems)*
Ken Graham *(Mgr-Lab)*
Laura Lewis *(Dir-HR)*
Laura Brandt *(Mgr-Bus Dev)*

EYE LOVE LLC
1805 Clemson Rd Ste 291827, Columbia, SC 29229
Web Site:
http://www.eyelovethesun.com
Year Founded: 2015
Health Care Srvices
N.A.I.C.S.: 621610
Jenna Zigler *(Co-Founder)*
Travis Zigler *(Co-Founder)*
Bryan MacDonald *(Mktg Dir)*

EYE SPECIALIST OF MID FLORIDA P.A.
407 Ave K SE, Winter Haven, FL 33880
Tel.: (863) 294-3504
Web Site: https://www.eyesfl.com
Rev.: $10,000,000
Emp.: 150
Office of Physicians
N.A.I.C.S.: 621111
Jane Dempsey *(Supvr)*
Mary Perry *(Mgr)*
Daniel Welch *(Pres)*
David Loewy *(Treas)*

EYE SURGEONS
13300 Hargrave Rd Ste 300, Houston, TX 77070-4374
Tel.: (281) 890-1784
Web Site:
http://www.1960eyesurgeons.com
Investment Banking & Securities Dealing
N.A.I.C.S.: 523150
Deann Fry *(Office Mgr)*

EYE-MART EXPRESS LTD.
13800 Senlac Dr Ste 200, Dallas, TX 75234-8823
Tel.: (972) 488-2002
Web Site:
http://www.eyemartexpress.com
Sales Range: $10-24.9 Million
Emp.: 30
Optical Goods Stores
N.A.I.C.S.: 456130
H Doug Barnes *(Pres)*
Kathy Mahdak *(Controller)*
Bob Dyke *(Dir-Equipment Svcs)*

EYECON MARKETING GROUP
6738 Jamestown Dr, Alpharetta, GA 30005

Tel.: (770) 752-0043
Web Site:
https://www.eyeconmktg.com
Year Founded: 2000
Sales Range: $1-9.9 Million
Emp.: 2
Fiscal Year-end: 12/31/14
Advetising Agency
N.A.I.C.S.: 541810
Scott Lederer *(Pres)*

EYEEGO, LLC
331 Valley Mall Pkwy #258, East Wenatchee, WA 98802
Tel.: (509) 470-6270
Web Site:
http://www.snapitscrew.com
Sales Range: $1-9.9 Million
Optical Lens Screw Mfr
N.A.I.C.S.: 332722
Nancy Tedeschi *(Owner)*

EYEGLASS SERVICE INDUSTRIES
481 Sunrise Hwy, Lynbrook, NY 11563
Tel.: (516) 599-1135   NY
Year Founded: 1958
Sales Range: $10-24.9 Million
Emp.: 6
Optical Goods Stores
N.A.I.C.S.: 456130
Bruce Topol *(Pres)*

EYES ON THE GO, INC.
40 Fulton St 24th Fl, New York, NY 10389
Tel.: (908) 229-4933   DE
Web Site:
http://www.eyesonthego.com
Sales Range: Less than $1 Million
Security System Mfr
N.A.I.C.S.: 561621
Christopher J. Carey *(CEO)*
Mary Weaver Carey *(VP-Ops)*

EYEVIEW, INC.
29 E 19th St Fl 4, New York, NY 10003
Tel.: (646) 430-3777
Web Site:
http://www.eyeviewdigital.com
Emp.: 100
Video Advertising Software Publishers
N.A.I.C.S.: 513210
Oren Harnevo *(Co-Founder & CEO)*
Brian Pozesky *(Chief Product Officer)*
Gabi Peles *(COO)*
Dave Donnelly *(Sr VP-Sls)*
Erik Schear *(VP-Sls, Auto, Travel & New Markets)*
West Naze *(VP-Sls-CPG & Shopper Mktg)*
Amy Dolan *(Sr VP-HR & Office Ops)*
Caitlin Mooney *(VP-Sls-Midwest)*
Brian Katz *(VP-Advanced TV Insights & Strategy)*
Utpal Kalita *(CTO)*
Tom St. John *(Sr VP-Media)*
Mick Suh *(VP-CPG Sls)*
Yvonne Nikas *(VP-Decision Sciences)*
Rami Klein-Shemesh *(VP-Engrg)*
Chevan Nanayakkara *(VP-Media)*
Debby Hannigan *(VP-Midwest)*
Nick Tarant *(VP-Retail & Central Sls)*
Fiona McIndoe *(VP-Sls)*
Matt Leingang *(VP-Sls-West)*
Melanie Pereira *(CFO)*

EYEWEAR DESIGNS, LTD.
136 Oak Dr, Syosset, NY 11791
Tel.: (516) 364-3664
Web Site:
http://www.eyeweardesigns.com

Eyewear Designs, Ltd.—(Continued)
Year Founded: 1972
Sales Range: $10-24.9 Million
Emp.: 62
Ophthalmic Goods Whslr
N.A.I.C.S.: 423460
Dean Warner (CEO)

EYKON WALL SOURCES INC.
5675 E Shelby Dr, Memphis, TN
38141
Tel.: (901) 365-1903
Web Site: http://www.eykon.net
Year Founded: 1972
Rev.: $12,000,000
Emp.: 100
Wallcoverings
N.A.I.C.S.: 424950
Gary Morris (Pres)

EYNON PONTIAC BUICK INC.
150 Scranton Carbondale Hwy, Eynon, PA 18403
Tel.: (570) 876-2474
Year Founded: 1996
Sales Range: $25-49.9 Million
Emp.: 20
Car Whslr
N.A.I.C.S.: 441110
Larry Benson (Pres)

EYP, INC.
201 Fuller Rd 5th Fl, Albany, NY
12203
Tel.: (518) 795-3800   MA
Web Site: https://www.eypae.com
Year Founded: 1972
Holding Company; Architectural &
Engineering Services
N.A.I.C.S.: 551112
Richard Clarke (Dir-Integrated Design)
Mary Cregut (Chief HR Officer)
Kefalari Mason (CFO)

Subsidiaries:

EYP Architecture & Engineering,
P.C.   (1)
201 Fuller Rd 5th Fl, Albany, NY 12203
Tel.: (518) 795-3800
Web Site: http://www.eypaedesign.com
Sales Range: $50-74.9 Million
Emp.: 300
Architectural & Engineering Services
N.A.I.C.S.: 541310
Tom Birdsey (Pres)
Leila Kamal (VP-Design & Expertise)
Peter Ottavio (Dir-Engrg)
John Tobin (VP-Ops)
John Kempf (CFO)
Susan Radzyminski (Dir-Mktg)
Robert Eichelman (Engr-Electrical)
Gregory Bordynowski (Sr Dir-Project)
Richard Clarke (Dir-Integrated Design)
Mary Cregut (Chief HR Officer)
Greg Foster (Sr Project Mgr-Dallas)
Jeremy Oberc (Mng Principal-Boston)
Guillermo Andrade (Dir-Technical-Houston)
Stephen Feige (Sr Dir-Project-Boston)
Charles Field (Sr Project Mgr-Denver)
Scott Butler (CEO)
Terence McCabe (Mng Principal-Raleigh)
Teresa Rainey (Dir-Engrg)
Kelly Donahue (Principal & Mgr-PR)
Chris Baylow (Mng Principal-Boston)
Kelly Bliss (Exec Dir-Bus Dev & Strategy-Boston)
Eric Kern (Sr Project Dir-Behavioral Health)

WHR Architects, Inc.   (1)
1111 Louisiana Fl 26, Houston, TX 77002
Tel.: (713) 665-5665
Web Site: http://www.whrarchitects.com
Healthcare Industry Architectural Design &
Engineering Services
N.A.I.C.S.: 541310
David H. Watkins (Founder, Pres & Grp
Head-Healthcare Practice)
Jill Hope (Mktg Mgr-Healthcare Practice)

Jennifer Conrad (Dir-Bus Dev-Healthcare
Practice)
Laurie Winchester (Dir-Admin Ops)

EZ ELECTRIC
1250 Birchwood Dr, Sunnyvale, CA
94089-2205
Tel.: (408) 734-4282
Web Site: https://www.ez-electric.com
Year Founded: 1986
Sales Range: $25-49.9 Million
Emp.: 200
Provider of General Electrical Contractor Services
N.A.I.C.S.: 238210
Terry Shouse (Acct Mgr)
Scott Reynolds (Mgr-Pur)

EZ FUEL & TANK SOLUTIONS
3883 Rogers Bridge Rd Ste 205-A,
Duluth, GA 30097
Tel.: (770) 232-9090
Web Site: http://www.ezfuel.com
Year Founded: 1998
Sales Range: $1-9.9 Million
Emp.: 15
Petroleum Products Merchant Whslr
N.A.I.C.S.: 424720
Dave Polak (Pres)
Adam Polak (Gen Mgr)
Curtis Mitchell (Mgr-Pur)

**EZ GROUT CORPORATION,
INC.**
405 Watertown Rd, Waterford, OH
45786
Tel.: (740) 749-0602
Web Site: http://www.ezgrout.com
Year Founded: 1998
Rev.: $8,100,000
Emp.: 28
Labor Saving Masonry & Fencing
Equipment Mfr
N.A.I.C.S.: 327390
Doug Taylor (CFO)
Mark Dille (Dir-Info Sys)

**EZ LOADER BOAT TRAILERS,
INC.**
717 N Hamilton St, Spokane, WA
99202-2044
Tel.: (509) 489-0181   WA
Web Site: https://www.ezloader.com
Year Founded: 1948
Sales Range: $150-199.9 Million
Emp.: 400
Boat & Utility Trailers
N.A.I.C.S.: 336214
Randy D. Johnson (Pres)
Doug MacCallum (Reg Mgr-Sls)
Christina Johnson (Sec)

Subsidiaries:

EZ Loader Adjustable Sales Corporation, Inc.   (1)
1462 Commerce Center Dr, Port Saint Lucie, FL 34986
Tel.: (800) 323-8190
Boat Transporter Trailer Whslr
N.A.I.C.S.: 423830

EZ Loader Custom Boat Trailers,
Inc.   (1)
PO Box 270, Midway, AR 72651-0270
Tel.: (870) 481-5138
Trailer & Transportation Equipment Mfr
N.A.I.C.S.: 336214

**EZ PAY PAYMENT CENTERS
INC.**
1460 7th St Ste A, Oakland, CA
94607-1983
Tel.: (510) 834-6300   CA
Web Site: http://www.ezpaydmv.com
Year Founded: 2009
Automobile Registration Services
N.A.I.C.S.: 488999

Ebtesam Ayesh (Pres)

EZANGA.COM, INC.
222 Carter Dr Ste 201, Middletown,
DE 19709
Tel.: (302) 279-1020
Web Site: https://www.ezanga.com
Year Founded: 2003
Sales Range: $1-9.9 Million
Emp.: 35
Pay-Per-Click Advertising Services
N.A.I.C.S.: 541890
Richard K. Kahn (Founder & CEO)
Beth Kahn (CFO)

EZLO, INC.
1255 Broad St, Clifton, NJ 07013
Tel.: (860) 502-0899
Web Site: http://www.ezlo.com
Year Founded: 2014
Software Engineering Services
N.A.I.C.S.: 541330
Bilgehan Evren (Founder & COO)
Mark Samuel (CEO)

Subsidiaries:

Centralite Systems, Inc.   (1)
1701 Industrial Park Dr, Mobile, AL 36693
Tel.: (251) 607-9119
Web Site: http://www.centralite.com
Home Automation & Security Products Design, Mfr & Distr
N.A.I.C.S.: 335139
James L. Busby (Founder)
Sean Bryant (Pres & CEO)
Philip Cahoon (CFO & Exec VP)
Jeffery Nigh (Chm)

**EZRAS CHOILIM HEALTH
CENTER INC.**
49 Forest Rd, Monroe, NY 10950
Tel.: (845) 782-3242   NY
Web Site: https://www.echckj.org
Year Founded: 1996
Sales Range: $10-24.9 Million
Emp.: 143
Health Care Srvices
N.A.I.C.S.: 622110
Joel Mittelman (Exec Dir)
Jeffery Kaminetzky (Dir-Internal Medicine)
Adam Polinger (Dir-Pediatrics)

EZZELL TRUCKING INC.
11535 Taylors Br Hwy, Harrells, NC
28444
Tel.: (910) 532-4101
Web Site:
https://www.ezzelltrucking.com
Year Founded: 1970
Sales Range: $25-49.9 Million
Emp.: 300
Local Trucking Services
N.A.I.C.S.: 484121
Al Ganey (Pres)
Mitch Baird (Dir-Sls)
Walt Hairr (Mgr-Acctg)

EZZIES WHOLESALE INC.
Hwy 2 E, Malta, MT 59538
Tel.: (406) 654-2331   MT
Web Site: http://www.ezzies.com
Year Founded: 1979
Sales Range: $25-49.9 Million
Emp.: 50
Provider of Oil Services
N.A.I.C.S.: 424710
Mark Kunze (Mgr)

F & M, INC.
2201 Hamlin Rd, Utica, MI 48317
Tel.: (586) 731-6440
Web Site: http://www.fm-companies.com
Sales Range: $10-24.9 Million
Emp.: 80
Concrete Finishing Services

N.A.I.C.S.: 238140

F&A FOOD SALES CO. INC.
2221 Lincoln St, Concordia, KS
66901
Tel.: (785) 243-2301
Web Site:
https://www.fafoodsales.com
Sales Range: $25-49.9 Million
Emp.: 85
Bond Brokers
N.A.I.C.S.: 424410
Dan R. Farha (Pres)
Michelle Gallagher (Controller)

F&D HUEBNER LLC
52 Glen Rd Ste 101, Garner, NC
27529
Tel.: (919) 772-1677
Web Site: http://www.mcdonalds.com
Sales Range: $10-24.9 Million
Emp.: 1,100
Fast Food Restaurants
N.A.I.C.S.: 722513
Gloria Santona (Gen Counsel, Sec &
Exec VP)
Dave Hoffmann (Pres-High Growth
Markets)
Doug Goare (Pres-Intl Lead Markets)

**F&E AIRCRAFT MAINTE-
NANCE**
1720 E Holly Ave, El Segundo, CA
90245
Tel.: (310) 338-0068
Web Site:
http://www.feairmaintenance.com
Rev.: $24,600,000
Emp.: 50
Aircraft & Heavy Equipment Repair
Services
N.A.I.C.S.: 811310
Chandel Young (Office Mgr)

F&H CONSTRUCTION
1115 E Locksord St, Lodi, CA 95240
Tel.: (209) 931-3738
Web Site: http://www.f-hconst.com
Year Founded: 1963
Sales Range: $10-24.9 Million
Emp.: 200
Commercial & Office Building Construction Services
N.A.I.C.S.: 236220
Harold Jones (Pres)
Jane Murphy (Office Mgr)

**F&H ELECTRICAL CONTRAC-
TORS, INC.**
3684 N Citrus Ave, Crystal River, FL
34428
Tel.: (352) 795-0525
Web Site:
http://www.fandhcontractors.com
Year Founded: 1997
Sales Range: $10-24.9 Million
Emp.: 150
Electrical Contractor
N.A.I.C.S.: 238210
David Finley (Pres)
Daniel Williams (Exec VP)
Edward Gerrits (CFO)
Thomas Guida (COO)

F&H FOOD EQUIPMENT CO
1526 S Enterprise Ave, Springfield,
MO 65804
Tel.: (417) 881-6114
Web Site:
http://www.fhfoodequipment.com
Sales Range: $10-24.9 Million
Emp.: 30
Food Product Manufacturing Machinery
N.A.I.C.S.: 423830
Jeff Aft (CEO)

F&H SUPPLY CO. INC.
4014 24th St, Long Island City, NY 11101
Tel.: (718) 392-7788
Web Site:
http://www.sunsetofficesupply.com
Rev.: $12,386,097
Emp.: 52
Office Supplies; Computer & Furniture
N.A.I.C.S.: 424120
Henry Haber *(Pres)*

F&I SENTINEL, LLC
3500 Financial Plz, Ste 350, Tallahassee, FL 32312
Tel.: (850) 425-4040
Web Site: https://fandisentinel.com
Insurance Agents Brokers & Service
N.A.I.C.S.: 524210
Stephen McDaniel *(CEO)*

F&M BANK
911 E Robert Toombs Ave, Washington, GA 30673
Tel.: (706) 678-2187
Web Site:
http://www.fmbanknow.com
Year Founded: 1950
Sales Range: $10-24.9 Million
Emp.: 54
Provider of Banking Services
N.A.I.C.S.: 522110
Edward Pope III *(Pres & CEO)*

Subsidiaries:

F&M Bank-South Sioux City   (1)
2024 Dakota Ave, South Sioux City, NE 68776
Tel.: (402) 494-4215
Web Site: http://www.fmbankne.bank
Banking Services
N.A.I.C.S.: 522110

F&M BANK & TRUST COMPANY
505 Broadway, Hannibal, MO 63401
Tel.: (573) 221-6424   MO
Web Site: https://www.bankfm.com
Year Founded: 1870
Emp.: 35
Commercial Banking Services
N.A.I.C.S.: 522110
Donald M. Bastian *(Chm)*
Carl C. Watson *(Pres & CEO)*
April Baldwin *(Chief Lending Officer & Exec VP)*
Bret Gosney *(Pres-Market-Monroe)*

F&M CONSTRUCTION CO.
215 Keys Rd, Yakima, WA 98901
Tel.: (509) 248-0444
Web Site:
http://www.fandmconstruction.com
Sales Range: $10-24.9 Million
Emp.: 4
Commercial & Office Building Contractors
N.A.I.C.S.: 236220
Ron Zerr Jr. *(Project Mgr)*

F&M EXPRESSIONS UNLIMITED
2011 Is Rd, Mahwah, NJ 07430
Tel.: (201) 512-3338
Web Site:
http://www.fmexpressions.com
Sales Range: $10-24.9 Million
Emp.: 94
Fashion Plates: Printing
N.A.I.C.S.: 323111
Frank Flanagan *(Pres & CEO)*

F&M FINANCIAL CORP.
221 N Main St, Salisbury, NC 28144
Tel.: (704) 633-1772
Web Site: http://www.fmbnc.com

Sales Range: $10-24.9 Million
Emp.: 160
Banking Services
N.A.I.C.S.: 522110
Paul E. Fisher *(Chm)*
Steven Fisher *(Pres)*
Guy Hoskins *(CFO)*

F&M FINANCIAL CORPORATION
50 Franklin St, Clarksville, TN 37040-3436
Tel.: (931) 245-4274   TN
Web Site: http://www.myfmbank.com
Year Founded: 1985
Sales Range: $25-49.9 Million
Emp.: 236
Bank Holding Company
N.A.I.C.S.: 551111

Subsidiaries:

F&M Bank   (1)
50 Franklin St, Clarksville, TN 37040-3436
Tel.: (931) 645-2400
Web Site: http://www.myfmbank.com
Sales Range: $25-49.9 Million
Emp.: 142
Commericial Banking
N.A.I.C.S.: 522110
John R. Wallace *(Chm)*
William Samuel Stuard *(Pres & CEO)*
Joe Snyder *(CIO & Sr VP)*
Jo Hughes *(Sr VP & Dir-Security)*
Shela Williams *(Sr VP)*
Sue Palmore *(Sr VP-Loan Admin)*
Sally Lee *(VP & Sr Comml Loan Processor)*
Amanda Dean *(VP-Mortgage)*
Steve Jackson *(Sr VP & Mgr-Comml Sls)*
C. DeWayne Olive *(CFO & Exec VP)*
Renata Wallace *(Sr VP & Controller)*
Lynn Olive *(Sr VP & Dir-HR)*
JoRene Jezwinski *(Sr VP-Bank Ops)*
Donna Lancaster *(Sr VP & Dir-Internal Audit & Compliance)*
Denise Alexander *(Sr VP & Ops Mgr-Mortgage)*
Bill Wyatt *(Exec VP-Comml Lending)*
Fred Landiss *(Sr VP-Mktg & PR)*
Brian Jones *(VP)*
Billy Winfree *(VP)*
Chad Winn *(VP)*
Suzanne Woods *(VP)*
Mike Smalling *(VP)*
Craig Sanders *(VP)*
Tina Reed *(VP-HR)*
Sarah Schneider *(VP)*
Rhonda McKinney *(VP-Collateral Svcs)*
Rose McCroy *(VP)*
Rod Hawkins *(VP)*
Jason Hass *(VP)*
Kathy Harris *(VP)*
Pamela Settle-Kelley *(Sr VP & Mgr-Ops)*
Khandra Smalley *(Sr VP-Mktg Res)*
Kristin Fleming *(Asst VP & Branch Mgr-Lebanon)*

F&P ENTERPRISES INC.
402 Davis Mill, Blackstone, VA 23824
Tel.: (434) 292-7511
Sales Range: $10-24.9 Million
Emp.: 15
Logging
N.A.I.C.S.: 113310
Christopher L. Pembelton *(Owner)*
Ray Pembelton *(Owner)*
Brian Pembelton *(Owner)*

F&W FORESTRY SERVICES INC.
PO Box 3610, Albany, GA 31706
Tel.: (229) 883-0505
Web Site: http://www.fwforestry.com
Emp.: 100
Timber Tract Operations
N.A.I.C.S.: 113310
Marshall D. Thomas *(Pres)*

Subsidiaries:

Inland Forest Management, Inc.   (1)
123 S 3rd St Ste 10, Sandpoint, ID 83864-1358

Tel.: (208) 263-9420
Web Site: http://www.inlandforest.com
Forestry Services
N.A.I.C.S.: 115310
Mike Wolcott *(Pres)*

F. GAVINA & SONS, INC.
2700 Fruitland Ave, Vernon, CA 90058
Tel.: (323) 582-0671
Web Site: https://www.gavina.com
Year Founded: 1870
Sales Range: $50-74.9 Million
Emp.: 295
Roasted Coffee Mfr
N.A.I.C.S.: 311920
Leonor Gavina *(VP-Mktg)*

F. J. O'HARA & SONS INC.
7 Kennedy Ave, Boston, MA 02210
Tel.: (617) 790-0722   MA
Web Site: http://www.fjohara.com
Year Founded: 1980
Sales Range: $10-24.9 Million
Emp.: 30
Seafoods Whslr
N.A.I.C.S.: 424460
Charles O'Brien *(Pres)*
Charles Di Pesa *(VP)*

F. KORBEL BROS. INC.
13250 River Rd, Guerneville, CA 95446-9593
Tel.: (707) 824-7000   CA
Web Site: https://www.korbel.com
Year Founded: 1882
Sales Range: $150-199.9 Million
Emp.: 537
Champagne Mfr
N.A.I.C.S.: 111332
Matt Healey *(VP-Fin)*

Subsidiaries:

Heck Estates   (1)
15401 Bear Mtn Winery Rd, Di Giorgio, CA 93203-9743
Tel.: (661) 854-6120
Sales Range: $10-24.9 Million
Emp.: 50
Brandy, Bulk Wines, Juices & Brandy Concentrate Mfr
N.A.I.C.S.: 312130

F. RAY MOORE OIL CO. INC.
189 Cherry Ln Rd, Washington, NC 27889-8653
Tel.: (252) 946-9061   NC
Year Founded: 1968
Sales Range: $10-24.9 Million
Emp.: 40
Petroleum Products Whslr
N.A.I.C.S.: 424710
Gray Deans *(CFO)*
Theresa Moore *(Sec)*
Frances Ray Moore Jr. *(Pres)*

F. RUGGIERO & SONS INC.
726 Morris Park Ave, Bronx, NY 10462
Tel.: (718) 828-1800
Web Site:
http://www.josephluccesefu
neralhome.com
Rev.: $13,000,000
Emp.: 5
Director of Funeral Services
N.A.I.C.S.: 812220
Joseph Lucchese *(Owner)*

F. SCHUMACHER & CO.
D&D Bldg 979 3rd Ave Ste 832, New York, NY 10022
Tel.: (212) 415-3900   NY
Web Site:
https://www.fschumacher.com
Year Founded: 1889
Sales Range: $350-399.9 Million
Emp.: 1,300

Home Decorative Fabrics, Wallpaper & Soft Goods Marketer & Mfr
N.A.I.C.S.: 424310
Paul Arasi *(Dir-Procurement)*

F. W. OWENS COMPANY, INC.
4800 Poplar Place Dr, Louisville, KY 40213
Tel.: (502) 637-4225
Web Site: http://www.fwowens.com
Sales Range: $1-9.9 Million
Emp.: 20
Commercial & Institutional Building Construction Services
N.A.I.C.S.: 236220
Mark Heckman *(Pres)*

F.A. DAVIS PUBLISHING COMPANY
1915 Arch St, Philadelphia, PA 19103
Tel.: (215) 568-2270
Web Site: http://www.fadavis.com
Year Founded: 1879
Sales Range: $25-49.9 Million
Emp.: 150
Textbook Publisher
N.A.I.C.S.: 513130
George Lang *(Mgr-Content Dev, Health Professions & Medicine)*
Phyllis Love *(Mgr-Customer Svc)*
Robert H. Craven Jr. *(Pres)*

F.A. WILHELM CONSTRUCTION CO., INC.
3914 Prospect St, Indianapolis, IN 46203-2344
Tel.: (317) 359-5411   IN
Web Site: https://www.fawilhelm.com
Year Founded: 1923
Sales Range: $200-249.9 Million
Emp.: 400
Provider of Contracting & Construction Management Services
N.A.I.C.S.: 236210
Joseph D. Cathcart *(CFO)*
Philip G. Kenney *(Pres)*
Jay R. Watson *(VP-Construction)*
Doug Curts *(Mgr-Ops)*

F.B. WASHBURN CANDY CORP.
137 Perkins Ave, Brockton, MA 02302-3850
Tel.: (508) 588-0820
Web Site:
https://www.fbwashburncandy.com
Year Founded: 1856
Sales Range: $10-24.9 Million
Emp.: 40
Hard Candies Mfr
N.A.I.C.S.: 311340
James R. Gilson *(Pres)*
Douglas B. Gilson *(VP)*

F.B. WRIGHT CO.
9999 Mercier Ave, Dearborn, MI 48121
Tel.: (313) 843-8250   MI
Web Site: https://www.fbwright.com
Year Founded: 1938
Sales Range: $75-99.9 Million
Emp.: 100
Rubber & Plastic Industrial Supplies Whslr
N.A.I.C.S.: 423840
Jeff Chard *(Mgr-Sls)*
Dave Bova *(CFO & Treas)*
Chuck Mozdzen *(Mgr-Ops)*
Rich Dauer *(Pres & Gen Mgr)*

F.C. INDUSTRIES INC.
4900 Webster St, Dayton, OH 45414
Tel.: (937) 275-8700
Web Site: https://www.fcindinc.com
Year Founded: 1989
Sales Range: $50-74.9 Million

F.C. Industries Inc.—(Continued)

Emp.: 225
Holding Company; Industrial Machinery Mfr
N.A.I.C.S.: 333514
Subsidiaries:

A.F.C. Tool Company Inc.   (1)
4900 Webster St, Dayton, OH 45414
Tel.: (937) 275-8700
Web Site: http://www.afctool.com
Sales Range: $25-49.9 Million
Special Dies, Tools, Jigs & Fixtures
N.A.I.C.S.: 333514
Mike Casella *(Pres & CEO)*

AFC Stamping & Production Inc.   (1)
4900 Webster St, Dayton, OH 45414
Tel.: (937) 275-8700
Web Site: http://www.afcstamping.com
Sales Range: $50-74.9 Million
Emp.: 200
Metal Stamping Mfr
N.A.I.C.S.: 332119
Joe Weigandt *(CFO)*

BarSplice Products, Inc.   (1)
4900 Webster St, Dayton, OH 45414
Tel.: (937) 275-8700
Web Site: http://www.barsplice.com
Splicing Mfr
N.A.I.C.S.: 238210
Lui Santacaterina *(VP-Intl)*
Phil Mink *(Mgr-Customer Svc)*
David Cridlin *(Mgr-Pur)*
Michael Isenbarger *(Reg Mgr-Sls)*
Mike Monnier *(Supvr-Svc Field)*

Dayton Precision Punch Inc.   (1)
4900 Webster St, Dayton, OH 45414
Tel.: (937) 275-8700
Web Site: http://www.daytonaero.com
Sales Range: $10-24.9 Million
Emp.: 25
Mfg. of Special Dies, Tools, Jigs & Fixtures
N.A.I.C.S.: 333514
Mike Casella *(Pres)*
Kurt Aucoin *(Mgr-Sls)*
Lui Santacaterina *(VP-Intl)*
Leslie Henry *(Mgr-Bus Dev)*
Mike Henson *(Mgr-Corp Contracts & Procurement)*

F.C. KERBECK & SONS
100 Route 73 N, Palmyra, NJ 08065
Tel.: (856) 829-8200
Web Site: http://www.fckerbeck.com
Rev.: $35,300,000
Emp.: 100
Automobiles, New & Used
N.A.I.C.S.: 441110
Joe Innaurato *(Gen Mgr)*
Eric Bloom *(Mgr-Sls)*

F.C.L. GRAPHICS
4600 N Olcott Ave, Harwood Heights, IL 60706-4604
Tel.: (708) 867-5500
Web Site:
    https://www.fclgraphics.com
Year Founded: 1973
Sales Range: $100-124.9 Million
Emp.: 200
Provider of Printing Services
N.A.I.C.S.: 323111
Dino DeVivo *(VP-Production)*
Gary Skoczynski *(VP-Sls)*
Stephen Flood *(Pres & CEO)*
Lou Tazioli *(Pres & CEO)*

F.D. HAYES ELECTRIC COMPANY
2301 Beal Ave, Lansing, MI 48910
Tel.: (517) 482-0608
Web Site: https://www.fdhayes.com
Rev.: $12,781,437
Emp.: 12
General Electrical Contractor
N.A.I.C.S.: 238210
Victor Biegaj *(Sr Project Mgr)*
Tammy Silvey *(Dir-Admin)*

F.D. STERRITT LUMBER CO.
110 Arlington St, Watertown, MA 02472
Tel.: (617) 547-0040
Web Site:
    https://www.sterrittlumber.com
Sales Range: $10-24.9 Million
Emp.: 45
Retailer of Lumber & Other Building Materials
N.A.I.C.S.: 423310
Gary Mackin *(Pres)*

F.E. HALE MANUFACTURING COMPANY
120 Benson Pl, Frankfort, NY 13340
Tel.: (315) 894-5490   NY
Web Site:
    http://www.halesince1907.com
Year Founded: 1907
Sales Range: $1-9.9 Million
Emp.: 40
Wooden Bookcases Mfr
N.A.I.C.S.: 337211
Jim Benson *(Pres)*
Lee Maley *(Plant Mgr)*
Penny Clark *(Mgr-Traffic)*

F.F. PHILLIPS INC.
945 Hwy 27, New Brunswick, NJ 08903
Tel.: (732) 247-4124
Web Site: http://www.phillips.com
Rev.: $14,100,000
Emp.: 60
Ready Mixed Concrete
N.A.I.C.S.: 327320
Cohen Phillips *(Pres)*

F.H. BONN COMPANY
338 W Columbus Rd, South Charleston, OH 45368
Tel.: (937) 323-7024   OH
Web Site: https://www.fhbonn.com
Year Founded: 1947
Sales Range: $75-99.9 Million
Emp.: 35
Pad & Cover for Laundry & Dry Cleaning Pressing Equipment Mfr
N.A.I.C.S.: 313210
Darrin Bonn *(VP-Mfg)*
Subsidiaries:

International Steel Wool
Corporation   (1)
PO Box 1888, Springfield, OH 45501-1888
Tel.: (956) 583-7998
Web Site: http://www.steelwool.com
Sales Range: $10-24.9 Million
Emp.: 4
Steel Wool & Special Metal Wools Mfr
N.A.I.C.S.: 327910

F.H. CHASE, INC.
50 Constitution Dr, Taunton, MA 02780-1070
Tel.: (508) 339-3309   MA
Web Site:
    https://www.fhchaseinc.com
Year Founded: 1973
Sales Range: $75-99.9 Million
Emp.: 50
Sales & Installer of Interior Building Systems
N.A.I.C.S.: 236220
Domenic Russo *(Pres & CEO)*
Eric Gray *(VP-Sls)*
Joseph T. Kearns *(CFO)*

F.H. PASCHEN, S.N. NIELSEN, INC.
5515 NE River Rd, Chicago, IL 60656
Tel.: (773) 444-3474
Web Site:
    https://www.fhpaschen.com

Year Founded: 1975
Rev.: $190,000,000
Emp.: 150
Renovation & Repair of Commercial & Office Buildings
N.A.I.C.S.: 236220
James Blair *(Pres & CEO)*
Chuck Freiheit *(COO)*
Joseph Scarpelli *(Exec VP)*
Doug Pelletier *(VP)*
Timothy Stone *(Sr VP)*
Mark Barkowski *(VP)*
Robert Zitek *(Sr VP)*
Jim Habschmidt *(CFO)*
Leo Wright *(Sr VP)*
Frank H. Paschen Jr. *(Founder)*

F.H. STOLTZE LAND & LUMBER COMPANY
600 Half Moon Rd, Columbia Falls, MT 59912
Tel.: (406) 892-7000   MT
Web Site:
    https://www.stoltzelumber.com
Year Founded: 1912
Sales Range: $75-99.9 Million
Emp.: 120
Lumber Distr
N.A.I.C.S.: 321113
Greg A. Johnson *(Pres)*

F.J. KROB & CO., INC.
1705 Dows St, Ely, IA 52227
Tel.: (319) 848-4161   IA
Web Site: http://www.fjkrob.com
Year Founded: 1907
Sales Range: $25-49.9 Million
Emp.: 40
Supplier of Farm Supplies
N.A.I.C.S.: 424510
David Krob *(Pres)*

F.J. SCIAME CONSTRUCTION CO. INC.
14 Wall St, New York, NY 10005
Tel.: (212) 232-2200   NY
Web Site: http://www.fjsciame.com
Year Founded: 1975
Sales Range: Less than $1 Million
Emp.: 70
Construction Managers & General Contractors
N.A.I.C.S.: 236220
Ralph Thompson *(Exec VP)*
Joseph Mizzi *(Pres)*
Michael Porcelli *(Exec VP)*
Subsidiaries:

Sciame Construction, LLC   (1)
14 Wall St, New York, NY 10005
Tel.: (212) 232-2200
Web Site: http://www.sciame.com
Commercial Building Construction Services
N.A.I.C.S.: 236220
Frank J. Sciame Jr. *(Chm & CEO)*

Sciame Development, Inc.   (1)
14 Wall St, New York, NY 10005
Tel.: (212) 232-2200
Web Site:
    http://www.sciamedevelopment.com
Emp.: 50
Administration Building Construction Services
N.A.I.C.S.: 236220
Frank J. Sciame Jr. *(Pres)*
John T. Randolph II *(Exec VP)*

F.L. CRANE & SONS INC.
508 S Spring St, Fulton, MS 38843-1710
Tel.: (662) 862-2172   MS
Web Site: https://www.flcrane.com
Year Founded: 1952
Sales Range: $50-74.9 Million
Emp.: 500
Provider of Building Services
N.A.I.C.S.: 238310

Chip Crane *(CEO)*
Kevin Payne *(Exec VP)*

F.L. CRANE & SONS, INC.
508 S Spring St, Fulton, MS 38843
Tel.: (662) 862-2172
Web Site: https://www.flcrane.com
Sales Range: $100-124.9 Million
Emp.: 700
Plastering Services
N.A.I.C.S.: 238310
Johnny Lee Crane II *(Pres)*

F.L. MOTHERAL CO. INC.
4251 Empire Rd, Fort Worth, TX 76155
Tel.: (817) 868-2249   TX
Web Site: http://www.motheral.com
Year Founded: 1934
Sales Range: $25-49.9 Million
Emp.: 260
Commercial Printing & Lithographic Services
N.A.I.C.S.: 323111
Jim Motheral *(Pres)*

F.L. ROBERTS & CO., INC.
93 W Broad St, Springfield, MA 01105-2525
Tel.: (413) 781-7444   MA
Web Site: https://www.flroberts.com
Year Founded: 1920
Sales Range: $50-74.9 Million
Emp.: 600
Owner & Operator of Automotive Service Facilities
N.A.I.C.S.: 457120
Stephen M. Roberts *(Pres & CEO)*

F.M. BROWN'S SONS INC.
205 Woodrow Ave, Sinking Spring, PA 19608
Tel.: (610) 678-4567   PA
Web Site: https://www.fmbrown.com
Year Founded: 1843
Sales Range: $25-49.9 Million
Emp.: 157
Mfr of Small Animal Foods
N.A.I.C.S.: 424910
Daryl Harris *(Controller)*
Carl Brown *(Treas)*
Steve Deysher *(Mgr-Sls)*
Cecil Campbell *(VP-Sls & Mktg)*

F.M. HOWELL & CO. INC.
79 Pennsylvania Ave, Elmira, NY 14904-1455
Tel.: (607) 734-6291   NY
Web Site: http://www.howellpkg.com
Year Founded: 1883
Packaging Materials Mfr
N.A.I.C.S.: 322212
Katherine Roehlke *(Owner)*
John Marczyk *(Mgr-Printing)*

F.N. SHEPPARD & CO.
1261 Jamike Ave, Erlanger, KY 41018
Tel.: (859) 525-2358
Web Site:
    https://www.fnsheppard.com
Rev.: $11,392,168
Emp.: 75
Rubber Belting
N.A.I.C.S.: 333922
James E. Reilly *(CEO)*
Kelly Reilly *(Comptroller)*
Wayne Siemer *(VP-Sls & Mktg)*

F.N.B.C. OF LA GRANGE, INC.
620 W Burlington Ave, La Grange, IL 60525
Tel.: (708) 482-7700   IL
Web Site: https://www.fnbcbt.com
Sales Range: $10-24.9 Million
Emp.: 112

Bank Holding Company
N.A.I.C.S.: 551111
John J. Madden *(Pres & CEO)*

Subsidiaries:

FNBC Bank & Trust **(1)**
620 W Burlington Ave, La Grange, IL 60525
Tel.: (708) 482-7700
Web Site: http://www.mysbi.com
Sales Range: $10-24.9 Million
Commercial Banking
N.A.I.C.S.: 522110
John J. Madden *(Chm & CEO)*
Brian Beerman *(VP)*
Thomas Manfre III *(CFO, COO & Exec VP)*

F.P. HORAK COMPANY
401 Saginaw St, Bay City, MI 48708
Tel.: (989) 892-6505 MI
Web Site: http://www.fphorak.com
Year Founded: 1946
Sales Range: $10-24.9 Million
Emp.: 180
Distr of Continuous Forms, Office &
Business
N.A.I.C.S.: 323111
Frederick W. Horak *(CEO)*
Timothy Dust *(Pres)*

F.R.F. SYSTEMS INC.
5030 Base Line Rd, Montgomery, IL
60538-1125
Tel.: (630) 896-1991 IL
Web Site:
http://www.foxriverfoods.com
Year Founded: 1948
Sales Range: $25-49.9 Million
Emp.: 500
Fresh Fruits & Vegetables
N.A.I.C.S.: 484110
Kenneth M. Nagel *(Pres)*
Frank Karabetsos *(Exec VP)*
MaryKay Pilmer *(Controller)*
Jennifer Karabetsos *(Dir-Mktg)*
Ed Peot *(VP-Sls)*

Subsidiaries:

Fox River Foods Transport Inc. **(1)**
5030 Base Line Rd, Montgomery, IL 60538-
1125
Tel.: (630) 896-1991
Web Site: http://www.frf.com
Sales Range: $10-24.9 Million
Emp.: 3
Local Trucking without Storage
N.A.I.C.S.: 424420

F.S. BANCORP
220 S Detroit St, LaGrange, IN 46761
Tel.: (260) 463-7111 IN
Web Site:
http://www.farmersstatebank.com
Sales Range: $25-49.9 Million
Emp.: 250
Bank Holding Company
N.A.I.C.S.: 551111
Joseph Urbanski *(Pres & CEO)*
Roger A. Bird *(Chm)*

Subsidiaries:

Farmers State Bank **(1)**
220 S Detroit St, LaGrange, IN 46761
Tel.: (260) 463-7111
Web Site: http://www.farmersstatebank.com
Sales Range: $25-49.9 Million
Commercial Banking Services
N.A.I.C.S.: 522110
Kerry Sprunger *(Chief Loan Officer & Exec VP)*
Lori White *(COO & Exec VP)*
Joseph Urbanski *(Pres & CEO)*

F.S. LOPKE CONTRACTING INC.
3430 State Route 434, Apalachin, NY
13732
Tel.: (607) 687-1114
Web Site: https://www.lopke.net
Year Founded: 1986

Sales Range: $10-24.9 Million
Emp.: 100
Construction Materials Sales
N.A.I.C.S.: 423320
Frank S. Lopke *(Pres)*

F.S. SPERRY CO. INC.
1907 Vanderhorn Dr, Memphis, TN
38134
Tel.: (901) 373-9000
Web Site: https://www.fssperry.com
Sales Range: $10-24.9 Million
Emp.: 50
Industrial Plant Construction
N.A.I.C.S.: 237990
Richard A. Sperry *(Chm)*
R. Barry Cox *(Pres)*
Kenny Moore *(Mgr-Columbia)*

F.S. VANHOOSE & COMPANY INC.
625 Depot Rd, Paintsville, KY 41240
Tel.: (606) 789-4075
Web Site:
https://www.fsvanhooselumber.com
Rev.: $11,057,968
Emp.: 30
Lumber & Other Building Materials
N.A.I.C.S.: 423310
Joe Vanhoose *(Pres)*

F.T. REYNOLDS COMPANY
1014 W Bell St, Glendive, MT 59330-
1531
Tel.: (406) 377-4923 MT
Web Site:
https://www.reynoldsmarket.com
Year Founded: 1925
Sales Range: $25-49.9 Million
Emp.: 180
Groceries Whslr
N.A.I.C.S.: 445110
John K. Reynolds *(Pres)*
Kevin McGovern *(Mgr-Meat)*
Greg McGovern *(Treas & Sec)*

F.W. BRYCE, INC.
8 Pond Rd, Gloucester, MA 01930-
1833
Tel.: (978) 283-7080 MA
Web Site: https://www.fwbryce.com
Year Founded: 1947
Sales Range: $10-24.9 Million
Emp.: 25
Frozen Seafood Distr
N.A.I.C.S.: 424420
Keith Moores *(Pres)*
Ian W. Moores *(Gen Counsel)*

Subsidiaries:

Atlantic Reefer Terminals Inc. **(1)**
8 Pond Rd, Gloucester, MA
01930-1833 **(100%)**
Tel.: (978) 281-4251
Sales Range: Less than $1 Million
Emp.: 3
Refrigerated Warehousing & Storage
N.A.I.C.S.: 493120
Frank Souza *(Mgr-Logistics)*

F.W. DAVISON & COMPANY, INC.
225 Tpke Rd, Southborough, MA
01748
Tel.: (508) 747-7261 DE
Web Site: http://www.prismhr.com
Year Founded: 1985
Human Resource Management Soft-
ware Developer & Publisher
N.A.I.C.S.: 513210
Frederick W. Davison *(Founder & Chm)*
Gary Noke *(Pres & CEO)*
Craig Babigian *(Exec VP)*
Adam Van Beek *(CTO)*
Scott Hastings *(Sr VP)*
Ray Ruddy *(VP-Fin)*

David Wolverton *(VP-Strategic Solu-
tions)*
Keith Knowles *(VP-Product Mgmt & Mktg)*
Michael DeLessio *(VP-Pro & Support Svcs)*
Brian Unruh *(CFO)*

Subsidiaries:

Summit Software, Inc. **(1)**
7307 River Pointe Dr, North Little Rock, AR 72113
Tel.: (501) 771-2600
Web Site: http://www.summit-sw.com
Staffing Software Developer & Cloud-Based
Hosting Services
N.A.I.C.S.: 541511
Kraig Sanders *(Dir-Mktg & Sls)*

F.W. KIBLER MILLING INC.
4663 Tri County Hwy, Mount Orab,
OH 45154
Tel.: (937) 444-2555
Web Site:
http://www.kiblerlumber.com
Rev.: $21,787,878
Emp.: 69
Lumber & Other Building Materials
N.A.I.C.S.: 423310

F.W. VAN ZILE POPULAR TOURS INC.
3540 Winton Pl, Rochester, NY
14623
Tel.: (585) 244-1100
Web Site: https://www.vanzile.com
Year Founded: 1911
Sales Range: $25-49.9 Million
Emp.: 50
Travel Agencies
N.A.I.C.S.: 561510
Katharine Van Zile *(Pres, Treas & Sec)*

F.W. WALTON ROOFING, INC.
8350 Mosley Rd, Houston, TX 77075
Tel.: (713) 674-9777
Web Site:
https://www.waltonroofing.com
Sales Range: $10-24.9 Million
Emp.: 85
Roofing Installation Services
N.A.I.C.S.: 238390
Jean Walton *(Treas & Sec)*

F.W. WEBB COMPANY
160 Middlesex Tpke, Bedford, MA
01730
Tel.: (781) 272-6600 MA
Web Site: https://www.fwwebb.com
Year Founded: 1866
Sales Range: $350-399.9 Million
Emp.: 950
Plumbing Fixtures, Equipment & Sup-
plies
N.A.I.C.S.: 423720
John D. Pope *(Owner)*
Tom Blades *(Gen Mgr)*
Jim O'Connor *(Office Mgr)*
Ernie Coutermarsh *(Sr VP-Industrial Bus Dev)*
Jeff Pope *(Pres)*
Robert Mucciarone *(COO)*

Subsidiaries:

Dowal Plumbing Supply Co Inc **(1)**
184 Church St, Poughkeepsie, NY 12601
Tel.: (845) 452-3200
Rev.: $5,000,000
Emp.: 18
Plumbing & Heating Equipment & Supplies,
Hydronics, Merchant Whslr
N.A.I.C.S.: 423720

F.W. Webb Company - Victor Manufacturing Division **(1)**
150 Locust St, Hartford, CT 06114
Tel.: (860) 722-2433
Web Site: http://www.victormfg.com

Plumbing & Heating Equipment Whslr
N.A.I.C.S.: 423720
Darren Juan *(Mgr-Ops)*

F.W. Webb Company - Webb Bio-
Pharm Division **(1)**
3 Slater Rd, Cranston, RI 02920
Tel.: (401) 463-4176
Web Site: http://www.webbbiopharm.com
Bio Processing Component Mfr
N.A.I.C.S.: 335999
Ruth Martin *(Sr VP-HR)*
Michael Michaud *(Sr VP-IT)*
Brendan Monaghan *(Sr VP-Ops)*

F.W. Webb Company - Webb Water
Systems Division **(1)**
3 Slater Rd, Cranston, RI 02920-4458
Tel.: (401) 463-8300
Web Site:
http://www.webbwatersystems.com
Water Treatment Equipment Mfr
N.A.I.C.S.: 333310
James Paulus *(Dir)*

Kentrol/Sevco, Inc. **(1)**
37 Heywood Rd, Winslow, ME 04901
Tel.: (800) 452-1928
Web Site: http://www.kentrol.com
Emp.: 50
Pressure Control Valve Mfr
N.A.I.C.S.: 332911
Daryl Schoellkopf *(Gen Mgr)*

Utilities Supply Company **(1)**
98 Lindbergh Ave, Methuen, MA 01844
Tel.: (781) 395-9023
Web Site: http://www.uscosupply.com
Emp.: 80
Plastic Pipe & Pipe Fitting Distr
N.A.I.C.S.: 326122
John Pope *(CEO)*

Webb Pump **(1)**
3 Slater Rd, Cranston, RI 02920
Tel.: (401) 463-4108
Web Site: http://www.webbpump.com
Sales Range: $10-24.9 Million
Emp.: 16
Commercial & Industrial Pump Mfr
N.A.I.C.S.: 333914
Brian Clark *(Mgr-Ops)*

F1 COMPUTER SOLUTIONS, INC.
28 Blackwell Park Ln 102, Warrenton,
VA 20186
Tel.: (540) 349-5370
Web Site:
http://www.f1computersolutions.com
Year Founded: 2000
Rev.: $2,600,000
Emp.: 22
Computer System Design Services
N.A.I.C.S.: 541512
Lanny Cornwell *(CTO)*
Mary Lieb *(Pres & CEO)*
Don Spady *(Engr-Network)*

F45 TRAINING HOLDINGS INC.
3601 S Congress Ave Bldg R, Austin,
TX 78704
Tel.: (737) 787-1955 DE
Web Site:
https://www.f45training.com
Year Founded: 2019
FXLV—(NYSE)
Rev.: $104,423,000
Assets: $142,706,000
Liabilities: $185,618,000
Net Worth: ($42,912,000)
Earnings: ($178,799,000)
Emp.: 113
Fiscal Year-end: 12/31/22
Holding Company
N.A.I.C.S.: 551112
Adam Gilchrist *(Founder)*
Luke Armstrong *(Chief Revenue Offi-
cer)*
John Minty *(CMO)*
Elliot Capner *(Chief Comml Officer)*
Patrick Grosso *(Chief Legal Officer)*
Dorian Workman *(CTO)*

F45 Training Holdings Inc.—(Continued)

Heather Christie (COO)
Mark Wahlberg (Chief Brand Officer)
Ruth Zukerman (Gen Mgr-Avalon House & Malibu Crew)
Tom Dowd (Pres & CEO)

F5 FINISHES, INC.
6571 Las Positas Rd, Livermore, CA 94551
Tel.: (415) 298-1243   DE
Web Site: http://www.f5finishes.com
Year Founded: 2007
Emp.: 110
Commercial Building Architectural Services
N.A.I.C.S.: 541310
Michael Patton (Pres & CEO)
Mark H. Wilson (CFO)

FAA CREDIT UNION
PO Box 26406, Oklahoma City, OK 73126-0406
Tel.: (405) 682-1990   OK
Web Site: http://www.faaecu.org
Year Founded: 1946
Sales Range: $10-24.9 Million
Emp.: 160
Credit Union
N.A.I.C.S.: 522130
Steve Rasmussen (Pres & CEO)

FAB FOURS, INC.
2213 Industrial Park Rd, Lancaster, SC 29720
Tel.: (803) 416-1100
Web Site: https://www.fabfours.com
Year Founded: 2004
Sales Range: $1-9.9 Million
Emp.: 30
Replacement Bumpers for Automobiles Mfr
N.A.I.C.S.: 423120
Gregory Higgs (Owner)
Matthew McShane (Pres)
Tim Gunnels (Dir-Engrg)

FAB INDUSTRIES CORP.
98 Cutter Mill Rd Ste 412, Great Neck, NY 11021
Tel.: (516) 498-3200   DE
Web Site: http://www.fab-industries.com
Year Founded: 1966
Sales Range: $25-49.9 Million
Emp.: 475
Warp Knit & Laminated Fabrics Mfr
N.A.I.C.S.: 313240
Sam Hiatt (VP)
Steven S. Myers (Pres & COO)
Jim Sitterly (VP-Ops)

Subsidiaries:

Circular Knit Division   (1)
98 Catter Mill Rd Ste 412 N, Great Neck, NY 11021
Tel.: (516) 498-3200
Sales Range: $50-74.9 Million
Emp.: 10
Textile Goods
N.A.I.C.S.: 313310
Tom Haglund (Mgr)

Mohican Mills, Inc.   (1)
1419 Gaston St, Lincolnton, NC 28093   (100%)
Tel.: (704) 735-2573
Web Site: http://www.fab-industries.com
Sales Range: $50-74.9 Million
Emp.: 350
Finished Consumer Products; Cut & Sew Operations & Over-the-Counter Retail
N.A.I.C.S.: 314120
Jerry Deese (VP)

Raval Lace Division   (1)
200 Madison Ave, New York, NY 10016-3903
Tel.: (212) 592-2700

Sales Range: $10-24.9 Million
Emp.: 7
Lace Products Mfr
N.A.I.C.S.: 313240

FAB TECH INC.
114 Rosemont Ln, Imler, PA 16655
Tel.: (814) 276-9611
Web Site: http://www.corle.com
Sales Range: $10-24.9 Million
Emp.: 100
Metal Fabrications Mfr
N.A.I.C.S.: 331110
Johnny J. Corle (Pres & CEO)

FAB UNIVERSAL CORP.
5001 Baum Blvd Ste 770, Pittsburgh, PA 15213
Tel.: (412) 621-0902   CO
Web Site: https://www.fabuniversal.com
Year Founded: 1995
Sales Range: $150-199.9 Million
Emp.: 188
Speech Recognition & Text-To-Speech Software & Hardware Products & Services
N.A.I.C.S.: 334118
John L. Busshaus (CFO)

FABCO ENTERPRISES INC.
5255 74th St, Elmhurst, NY 11373
Tel.: (718) 898-4200
Web Site: http://www.fabshoes.com
Sales Range: $25-49.9 Million
Emp.: 270
Women's Shoes
N.A.I.C.S.: 458210
David Weinman (Pres)
Terri Dio (Office Mgr)
Geraldine Cahill (Mgr-Payroll)

FABCO-AIR, INC.
3716 NE 49th Ave, Gainesville, FL 32609-1699
Tel.: (352) 373-3578
Web Site: https://www.fabco-air.com
Year Founded: 1958
Sales Range: $75-99.9 Million
Emp.: 120
Pneumatic Cylinders & Valves Mfr
N.A.I.C.S.: 332911
William R. Schmidt (Pres)
Scot Lamar (VP)

FABER BROS. BROADLOOM CO.
350 W Clinton St, Haledon, NJ 07508
Tel.: (973) 595-7523
Web Site: https://www.faberbro.com
Rev.: $10,000,000
Emp.: 50
Owner & Operator of Floor Covering Stores
N.A.I.C.S.: 449121
Jacob Faber Jr. (Owner)

FABER ENTERPRISES, INC.
14800 S Figueroa St, Gardena, CA 90248
Tel.: (818) 999-1300   CA
Web Site: http://www.faberent.com
Year Founded: 1947
Sales Range: $75-99.9 Million
Emp.: 135
Mfr of Hydraulic Fittings
N.A.I.C.S.: 336413
Esther Faber (Chm)
Ronald E. Spencer (Pres)
Marilyn Spencer (Treas & Sec)
Gloria Semer (Controller)

FABER, COE & GREGG, INC.
550 Meadowlands Pkwy, Secaucus, NJ 07094-1815
Tel.: (201) 330-1515   NY
Web Site: https://www.faber-intl.com

Year Founded: 1848
Sales Range: $150-199.9 Million
Emp.: 600
Operator of Retail Gift Shops & Newsstands
N.A.I.C.S.: 459210
Charles D. Finkelstein (Pres)
Nancy Ortiz (Mgr-HR)
Roberta Rubin (Sr VP)

FABIANO BROS INC.
1885 Bevanda Ct, Bay City, MI 48706
Tel.: (989) 509-0200
Web Site: https://www.fabianobrothers.com
Year Founded: 1969
Sales Range: $25-49.9 Million
Emp.: 250
Brewers of Beer & Ale
N.A.I.C.S.: 424810
James C. Fabiano (Chm, Pres & CEO)

FABIANO COMMUNICATIONS, INC.
7819 E Greenway Rd Ste 5, Scottsdale, AZ 85260
Tel.: (480) 478-8500
Year Founded: 1992
Sales Range: $25-49.9 Million
Emp.: 25
Advertising Services
N.A.I.C.S.: 541810
Mark Weber (CFO & Controller)

FABICK CAT
101 Fabick Dr, Fenton, MO 63026
Tel.: (636) 349-5500   MO
Web Site: https://www.fabickcat.com
Year Founded: 1917
Emp.: 1,200
Heavy Construction Machinery Whslr
N.A.I.C.S.: 423810

Subsidiaries:

Fabick CAT - Springfield   (1)
2222 E Kearney St, Springfield, MO 65803-4944
Tel.: (417) 866-6651
Web Site: http://www.fabickcat.com
Construction & Mining Machinery Rental Services & Whslr
N.A.I.C.S.: 423810

Fabick CAT - Wisconsin   (1)
11200 W Silver Spring Rd, Milwaukee, WI 53225-3118
Tel.: (414) 461-9100
Web Site: http://www.fabickcat.com
Construction & Mining Machinery Whslr
N.A.I.C.S.: 423810

Plant (Domestic):

Fabco   (2)
1111 Applegate Rd, Madison, WI 53713-3218
Tel.: (608) 271-6200
Web Site: http://www.fabco.com
Rev.: $420,000
Emp.: 7
Specialty Trade Contractors
N.A.I.C.S.: 423430

FABRI-QUILT, INC.
901 E 14th Ave, Kansas City, MO 64116-3703
Tel.: (816) 421-2000
Web Site: https://www.fabri-quilt.com
Year Founded: 1962
Sales Range: $25-49.9 Million
Emp.: 250
Supplier of Pleating & Stitching Items
N.A.I.C.S.: 313310
Barry Olstrk (VP)
Adlai Kunst (Owner)
Scott Summers (Plant Mgr)
Deena White (Dir-Art)

FABRIC RESOURCES INTERNATIONAL LTD.
9 Park Pl, Great Neck, NY 11021-5030
Tel.: (516) 829-4550   NY
Year Founded: 1978
Sales Range: $25-49.9 Million
Emp.: 225
Broadwoven Fabric Mill Services
N.A.I.C.S.: 313210
Steven Richman (Pres & CEO)
Mike Rosenberg (Mgr-Acctg)
Michael Rosenberg (Mgr-Acctg)

FABRICATED COMPONENTS CORPORATION
130 W Bristol Ln, Orange, CA 92865
Tel.: (714) 974-8590
Web Site: https://www.summitinterconnect.com
Sales Range: $10-24.9 Million
Emp.: 150
Printed Circuit Boards
N.A.I.C.S.: 334412
Ed Aghaian (Controller)

FABRICATED GLASS SPECIALTIES
101 E Rapp Rd, Talent, OR 97540
Tel.: (541) 535-1581
Web Site: http://www.fabglass.com
Rev.: $23,700,000
Emp.: 100
Glass Construction Materials
N.A.I.C.S.: 423390
J. R. Holtz (Pres)

FABRICATED METALS LLC
6300 Kenjoy Dr, Louisville, KY 40214
Tel.: (502) 363-2625
Web Site: http://www.fabricatedmetals.com
Year Founded: 1955
Sales Range: $10-24.9 Million
Emp.: 100
Metal Housings, Enclosures, Casings & Other Containers
N.A.I.C.S.: 332322
Thomas C. Diebold (Chm)
Vic Judd (Supvr-Shop)
Shirley Jaggers (VP-HR)

FABRICATED PIPE, INC.
15881 Airline Hwy, Baton Rouge, LA 70817
Tel.: (225) 293-9375
Web Site: https://www.fabricatedpipe.com
Sales Range: $10-24.9 Million
Emp.: 112
Pipe & Pipe Fitting Mfr
N.A.I.C.S.: 332996
Ronnie Polito (Pres)
Charlie Gibson (Mgr-Engrg)
John Cassagne (Dir-Safety)
Clint Tetrick (Plant Mgr)
Brian Hanson (Supvr-Quality Assurance & Quality Control)

FABRICATED STEEL PRODUCTS, INC.
2487 N Flannery Rd, Baton Rouge, LA 70815
Tel.: (225) 272-8990
Web Site: http://www.fabricatedsteel.net
Year Founded: 1986
Sales Range: $10-24.9 Million
Emp.: 55
Fabricated Structural Metal Mfr
N.A.I.C.S.: 332312
Kevin B. Tabor (CEO)
Blake Tabor (VP)

George Billy Powers *(Plant Mgr-Choctaw)*
Geri Brackin *(Office Mgr)*
Lavester Wyre *(Controller-Quality)*
James Watson Jr. *(Mgr-Fabrication)*

FABRICATION & CONSTRUCTION SERVICES, LP.
4665 FM 1960, Dayton, TX 77535-9803
Tel.: (936) 257-0466
Web Site:
http://www.fandcservices.com
Year Founded: 1998
Sales Range: $10-24.9 Million
Emp.: 10
Petroleum Refinery Services
N.A.I.C.S.: 324110
Daniel Walsh *(Co-Owner)*
Ellie Thibodeaux *(Office Mgr)*
Wayne Wood *(Co-Owner)*

FABRICATORS SUPPLY COMPANY
50 National Rd, Edison, NJ 08837
Web Site:
http://www.fabricatorssupply.com
Rev.: $16,800,000
Emp.: 45
Building Materials, Interior
N.A.I.C.S.: 423310

FABRICLEAN SUPPLY, INC.
8301 Ambassdor Rd, Dallas, TX 75247
Tel.: (214) 826-4161
Web Site:
https://www.fabricleansupply.com
Sales Range: $25-49.9 Million
Emp.: 83
Dry Cleaning, Laundry & Janitorial Supplies Distr
N.A.I.C.S.: 423850
Jim Hericks *(Pres)*
Trevor Hericks *(Mgr-Ops)*

FABRICON PRODUCTS INC.
1721 W Pleasant St, River Rouge, MI 48218-0358
Tel.: (313) 841-8200   MI
Web Site:
https://www.fabriconproducts.com
Year Founded: 1919
Sales Range: $10-24.9 Million
Emp.: 50
Mfr of Waxed Paper, Cellophane & Poly-ethylene Wrappers & Bags, Decorative Plastic Sheets
N.A.I.C.S.: 326111
Roland David *(VP & Controller)*

FABRICUT INC.
9303 E 46th St, Tulsa, OK 74145-4829
Tel.: (918) 622-7700   OK
Web Site: https://www.fabricut.com
Year Founded: 1954
Sales Range: $25-49.9 Million
Emp.: 400
Finishing of Cotton Broadwoven Fabrics
N.A.I.C.S.: 313310
Carol Alexander *(Mgr-MRO)*
Darin Guyer *(Mgr-Comml Credit)*
Elizabeth Ramsey *(Supvr-Contract Dept)*
Rebecca Pohlest *(VP)*
Michael Guterman *(COO)*
David Finer *(CEO)*

Subsidiaries:

Clarence House, Inc.   (1)
979 3rd Ave Ste 205, New York, NY 10022
Tel.: (212) 752-2890
Web Site: http://www.clarencehouse.com
Draperies

N.A.I.C.S.: 423220
Bob Appelbaum *(Pres)*
Nina Butkin *(Principal)*

FABRIK INDUSTRIES INC.
5213 Prime Pkwy, McHenry, IL 60050
Tel.: (815) 385-9480
Web Site: https://www.fabrikind.com
Year Founded: 1980
Sales Range: $25-49.9 Million
Emp.: 300
Plastic Moldings Mfr
N.A.I.C.S.: 326199

FABRIZI TRUCKING & PAVING CO.
20389 First Ave, Middleburg Heights, OH 44130
Tel.: (330) 273-2784
Rev.: $25,431,952
Emp.: 20
Highway & Street Paving Contractor
N.A.I.C.S.: 237110
Nio Fabrizi *(Pres)*
Maria Fearer *(CFO & VP)*
Emil Fabrizi *(Pres)*

FABRY INDUSTRIES SARANAC WORLD OF GLOVES
999 Lombardi Ave, Green Bay, WI 54304
Tel.: (920) 435-3737
Web Site:
https://www.saranacglove.com
Sales Range: $10-24.9 Million
Emp.: 50
Gloves, Sport & Athletic: Boxing, Handball
N.A.I.C.S.: 339920
John Fabry *(Pres)*
Dan Small *(CEO)*
Tina Rooks *(Controller)*

FAC PROPERTYS LLC
1329 Needham Ave, Bronx, NY 10469
Tel.: (718) 798-3983
Real Estate Investment Services
N.A.I.C.S.: 523999
Ferris Christian *(CEO)*

FACCHIANO, MICHAEL CONTRACTING INC.
801 McNeilly Rd, Pittsburgh, PA 15226
Tel.: (412) 344-5503
Web Site:
http://www.mafacchianocontracting.com
Year Founded: 1956
Sales Range: $10-24.9 Million
Emp.: 80
Highway & Street Construction Services
N.A.I.C.S.: 237310
Michael Facchiano *(Owner)*

FACCHINA GLOBAL SERVICES LLC
102 Centennial St Ste 100, La Plata, MD 20646
Tel.: (301) 539-4425
Web Site: http://www.fgs-llc.com
Year Founded: 2005
Sales Range: $25-49.9 Million
Emp.: 150
Network Security, Video Teleconferencing, Information Assurance, Intelligence Collections Planning & Management & Counterintelligence Services
N.A.I.C.S.: 921190
Paul Facchina *(Founder & Pres)*
Tom McDonough *(VP & Mgr-Programs)*

Michelle Coleman *(Sr Mgr-Contracts)*
Douglas Dick *(CFO)*
Gina DeMatteo *(Dir-HR)*
Carol Fullerton *(Dir-HR)*
Frank Kippenbrock *(VP-Intelligence Ops-Natl)*

FACEMIRE FOODS INC.
81 Wv Forest Products Rd, Gassaway, WV 26624
Tel.: (304) 364-8307   WV
Web Site: http://www.wvdsl.net
Year Founded: 1961
Sales Range: $10-24.9 Million
Emp.: 450
Operates Grocery Stores
N.A.I.C.S.: 445110
Douglas Facemire *(Pres)*
Karen Linger *(Sec)*

FACES MAGAZINE INC.
210 E State Rte 4 Ste 211, Paramus, NJ 07652-5103
Tel.: (201) 843-4004
Year Founded: 1983
Sales Range: $25-49.9 Million
Emp.: 200
Publisher of Magazines
N.A.I.C.S.: 513120
Scott Figman *(Pres)*
Fred Rott *(CEO)*

FACETIME STRATEGY
4201 Connecticut Ave NW Ste 407, Washington, DC 20008
Tel.: (202) 386-6159
Advertising Services
N.A.I.C.S.: 541810
Todd Mason *(Chm & CEO)*
Scott Dinsmore *(Pres-Direct Mktg Practice Group)*
Drew Caracciolo *(Sr Acct Exec)*
Brian Shedd *(CMO)*
Chris Cantele *(Exec VP-Chicago Client Portal)*

Subsidiaries:

FaceTime Strategy   (1)
430 W Roosevelt Rd, Wheaton, IL 60187-5056
Tel.: (312) 324-3198
Sales Range: $10-24.9 Million
Emp.: 10
Advetising Agency
N.A.I.C.S.: 541810

FaceTime Strategy   (1)
325 N Saint Paul St Ste 600, Dallas, TX 75201
Tel.: (214) 827-8888
Sales Range: $10-24.9 Million
Emp.: 25
N.A.I.C.S.: 541810

FACETS MULTI-MEDIA, INC.
1517 W Fullerton Ave, Chicago, IL 60614-2096
Tel.: (773) 281-9075
Web Site: http://www.facetsdbd.com
Year Founded: 1975
Sales Range: Less than $1 Million
Emp.: 50
Artistic Film Screener & Video Retailer
N.A.I.C.S.: 449210
Eric Holst *(Mgr-Ops)*
Jenny Grist *(Mgr-Customer Svc)*
Mary Hayes *(Coord-Dev)*
Nancy Goldenberg *(Dir-Children's Programs & Dev)*

FACILITEC, INC.
4501 E McDowell Rd, Phoenix, AZ 85008
Tel.: (602) 275-0101
Rev.: $35,000,000
Emp.: 75
Whslr of Office Furniture

N.A.I.C.S.: 423210
Edward J. Cain *(Owner)*
Arica Hingtgen *(Mgr-Design)*
Kasey McBroom *(Project Mgr)*

FACILITECH INC.
1111 Valley View Ln, Irving, TX 75061
Tel.: (817) 858-2000
Web Site:
https://www.businessinteriors.com
Rev.: $85,000,000
Emp.: 135
Office Furniture
N.A.I.C.S.: 423210
Kathy White *(Pres & CEO)*
Mary Arnett *(CFO)*

FACILITIES CONNECTION, INC.
240 E Sunset Rd, El Paso, TX 79922
Tel.: (915) 833-8303
Web Site:
http://www.facilitiesconnection.com
Sales Range: $10-24.9 Million
Emp.: 23
Office Interior Design Services
N.A.I.C.S.: 541410
Patricia Holland *(CEO)*
Andrea Ross *(Mgr-Design)*

FACILITIES RESOURCE GROUP INC.
100 Dodd Ct, Napa, CA 94581
Tel.: (707) 647-3700
Web Site: http://www.frgwaste.com
Year Founded: 1982
Sales Range: $10-24.9 Million
Emp.: 10
Furniture Mfr
N.A.I.C.S.: 562920
Rhonda Fillion *(CFO & VP)*
Tim Shea *(Founder, Pres & CEO)*

FACILITY CONCEPTS INC.
7676 Zionsville Rd, Indianapolis, IN 46268
Web Site: http://www.facility-concepts.com
Emp.: 100
Trade Agents & Brokers Whslr
N.A.I.C.S.: 425120
Elizabeth Parker *(VP)*
Ken Weaver *(CEO)*

Subsidiaries:

Surface Technologies, Inc.   (1)
7106 E Truman Rd, Kansas City, MO 64126
Tel.: (816) 241-2982
Web Site: http://www.surfacetech.com
Sales Range: $1-9.9 Million
Emp.: 100
Wood Kitchen Cabinet & Countertop Mfr
N.A.I.C.S.: 337110
Larry Silver *(CEO)*

FACILITY GATEWAY CORPORATION
4916 E Broadway, Madison, WI 53716-4139
Tel.: (608) 838-6060
Web Site:
https://www.facilitygateway.com
Year Founded: 2008
Sales Range: $10-24.9 Million
Emp.: 50
Data Site Design, Implementation & Data Recovery Services
N.A.I.C.S.: 541512
Tyler Marks *(CEO)*
Brian Gilbertson *(Mgr-Ops)*
Frank Horner *(Acct Mgr)*
Kurt Hanusa *(Acct Mgr-Natl)*
Jason Perry *(Mng Partner)*
Danielle Heiman *(Project Coord)*

FACILITY INTERIORS INC.

Facility Interiors Inc.—(Continued)

1433 W Frankford Rd Ste 130, Carrollton, TX 75007
Tel.: (972) 392-1852   TX
Web Site:
   http://www.facilityinteriors.com
Year Founded: 1994
Sales Range: $10-24.9 Million
Emp.: 65
Office Furniture Whslr
N.A.I.C.S.: 423210
Charles H. Griggsby *(Pres & CEO)*

FACILITY MATRIX GROUP INC.

555 Friendly Dr, Pontiac, MI 48341
Tel.: (248) 334-8000   MI
Web Site:
   http://www.facilitymatrix.com
Year Founded: 1985
Sales Range: $10-24.9 Million
Emp.: 20
Supplier of Furniture
N.A.I.C.S.: 423210
Chris Sowers *(CEO)*
David Daugherty *(Pres)*
Karly L. Webb *(Acct Exec)*

FACILITY MERCHANDISING, INC.

5959 Topanga Canyon Blvd Ste 125, Woodland Hills, CA 91367
Tel.: (818) 703-6690
Web Site: http://www.facilitymerchandising.com
Year Founded: 1981
Sales Range: $10-24.9 Million
Emp.: 15
Concession Operator
N.A.I.C.S.: 713990
Milton A. Arenson *(Pres & CEO)*
Robert Arenson *(Exec VP)*

FACILITY SOLUTIONS GROUP, INC.

4401 Westgate Blvd Ste 310, Austin, TX 78745-1494
Tel.: (703) 234-6555
Web Site: https://fsg.com
Engineering Services
N.A.I.C.S.: 541330
Bill Graham *(Pres & CEO)*
John Ancona *(COO-Facility Svcs)*

Subsidiaries:

Capital Architectural Signs, Inc.   (1)
10712 N Lamar Blvd Ste B, Austin, TX 78753
Tel.: (512) 490-0049
Web Site: http://www.casaustin.com
Sales Range: $1-9.9 Million
Emp.: 12
Sign Mfr
N.A.I.C.S.: 339950
Michael Soheili *(Founder & Gen Mgr)*

West-Lite Supply Co., Inc.   (1)
12951 166th St, Cerritos, CA 90703
Tel.: (562) 802-0224
Web Site: http://www.west-lite.com
Sales Range: $10-24.9 Million
Emp.: 24
Lighting Fixtures
N.A.I.C.S.: 423610
Garry J. Haverland *(Pres)*
Louis Montes *(Mgr-Customer Svc)*

FACTION MEDIA

1730 Blake St Ste 200, Denver, CO 80202
Tel.: (303) 339-0206
Web Site:
   http://www.factionmedia.com
Sales Range: $10-24.9 Million
Emp.: 25
Advertising Agencies
N.A.I.C.S.: 541810
Aaron Batte *(Founder & Pres)*
Kurt Greves *(Partner)*

Dave Greves *(Founder & CEO)*
Sarah Swartzendruber *(Sr Dir-Art)*
Melaina Daniel *(Acct Mgr)*
Geoff Eakin *(Dir-Creative)*
Jim Maroney *(CFO)*
Matt Smolenski *(Dir-Client Svcs)*
John Gilbert *(Dir-Integrated Svcs)*

FACTOR 89 PARTNERS, LLC

900 W Jackson Blvd Ste 2W, Chicago, IL 60607
Tel.: (630) 841-7552   DE
Web Site: https://factor89.com
Year Founded: 2023
Investment Management Service
N.A.I.C.S.: 523999
Barrett Carlson *(Mng Partner)*

Subsidiaries:

Master Magnetics Inc.   (1)
747 S Gilbert St, Castle Rock, CO 80104
Tel.: (303) 688-3966
Web Site: http://www.magnetsource.com
Sales Range: $50-74.9 Million
Emp.: 73
Magnetic Products Mfr & Distr
N.A.I.C.S.: 423990
John E. Nellessen *(Pres)*
Jim Madsen *(Mgr-Sls)*
Debbie Markham *(Mgr-HR)*
Jennifer Brown *(CEO)*

FACTOR SALES, INC.

676 N Archibald St, San Luis, AZ 85349
Tel.: (928) 627-8033
Year Founded: 1982
Sales Range: $50-74.9 Million
Independent Grocery Store
N.A.I.C.S.: 445110
Victor M. Salcido *(Pres & CEO)*
Andres A. Salcido *(Sec)*
Lucia Valencia *(Treas)*
Alicia Mendoza *(VP)*

FACTORY 360

120 5 Ave 8th Fl, New York, NY 10011
Tel.: (212) 242-2417
Web Site: http://www.factory-360.com
Year Founded: 2003
Sales Range: $1-9.9 Million
Emp.: 2,000
Event Production & Experiential Marketing Specialists
N.A.I.C.S.: 541613
Michael Fernandez *(Pres & CEO)*
Jason Coughlin *(VP-Client Activations)*
Gabriela Neves *(Partner)*
Hugo Burton *(Creative Dir)*

FACTORY BUILDER STORES INC.

8700 Fallbrook Dr, Houston, TX 77064
Tel.: (281) 477-6464
Web Site:
   https://www.factorybuilderstore.com
Sales Range: $25-49.9 Million
Emp.: 32
Major Electrical Appliances
N.A.I.C.S.: 423620
Steve Gause *(Exec VP)*

FACTORY CONNECTION, LLC

2300 Hwy 79 S, Guntersville, AL 35976-2220
Tel.: (256) 264-9400   AL
Web Site: https://www.factory-connection.com
Year Founded: 1976
Emp.: 1,300
Women's Clothing Store
N.A.I.C.S.: 458110
Mike Reaves *(Pres & CEO)*
Steve Williams *(CFO)*

FACTORY DESIGN LABS, INC.

158 Fillmore St, Denver, CO 80206
Tel.: (303) 573-9100   CO
Year Founded: 1997
Sales Range: $25-49.9 Million
Emp.: 95
Advertising Services
N.A.I.C.S.: 541810
Michael Bennett *(CFO)*
Andee Conner Foutch *(Exec VP-Media Svcs)*
Jonas Tempel *(CEO)*
Kelvin Leong *(Dir-Creative)*
Andreas Schmid *(Dir-Digital)*
Nat Potter *(Exec Dir-Creative)*
Chris Pan *(Mng Dir)*
George Karalexis *(Mng Dir-LA)*
Ryan Dadd *(Mng Dir-NYC)*
Leslie Harris *(Sr Mgr-HR)*
Kris Fry *(VP & Dir-Creative)*

FACTORY DIRECT APPLIANCE INC.

14105 Marshall Dr, Lenexa, KS 66215
Tel.: (913) 888-8028
Web Site: https://www.kcfda.com
Year Founded: 1993
Sales Range: $25-49.9 Million
Emp.: 100
Supplier of Kitchen Appliances
N.A.I.C.S.: 423620
Dennis Birkestrand *(Owner)*
Steve Johnson *(VP)*
Phil Hattaway *(Controller)*

FACTORY MUTUAL INSURANCE COMPANY

270 Central Ave, Johnston, RI 02919-4949
Tel.: (401) 275-3000   RI
Web Site: https://www.fm.com
Year Founded: 1835
Rev.: $7,308,800,000
Assets: $34,479,000,000
Liabilities: $12,000,100,000
Net Worth: $22,478,900,000
Earnings: $3,748,500,000
Fiscal Year-end: 12/31/23
Commercial & Industrial Property Insurance Services
N.A.I.C.S.: 524126
Malcolm C. Roberts *(Exec VP)*
Sanjay Chawla *(Chief Investment Officer & Sr VP)*
Deanna Fidler *(Chief HR Officer & Sr VP)*
James Thompson *(Sr VP & Mgr-Asia-Pacific)*
Alex S. Tadmoury *(Sr VP & Mgr-Middle Market Bus-AFM)*
Lyndon D. Broad *(Chief Underwriting Officer & Sr VP)*
Omar Hameed *(Co-Chief Legal Officer & Sr VP)*
Andrew J. Bryson *(Sr VP-Engineering & Res)*
Christopher M. Dempsey *(Sr VP & Mgr-EMEA Division)*
Johnell R. Holly *(Sr VP-Global Client Svc, Sales, and Marketing)*
David M. Johnson *(Chief Client Experience Officer & Sr VP)*
Laurel J. Rudnick *(Sr VP & Mgr-FM Affiliated Division)*
Nicholas W. Stepina *(Sr VP & Mgr-Central Division)*
Jeremy Gallant *(Sr VP-Claims)*
Bradley Parrish *(Sr VP & Mgr-Western Division)*
Steven J. Wrinkle *(Sr VP-Strategy & Bus Transformation)*
Srinivasan Krishnamurthy *(CIO, Chief Strategy Officer & Sr VP)*

Subsidiaries:

Affiliated FM Insurance
Company   (1)
270 Central Ave, Johnston, RI 02919
Tel.: (401) 275-3000
Web Site: http://www.affiliatedfm.com
Engineering-Driven Property Insurance Services
N.A.I.C.S.: 524126

FM Approvals, LLC   (1)
1151 Boston-Providence Tpke, Norwood, MA 02062
Tel.: (781) 762-4300
Web Site: http://www.fmglobal.com
Third Party Property Loss Prevention Products & Services
N.A.I.C.S.: 524292
Richard Ferron *(VP & Mgr-Testing & Certification Ops)*
Charles Mahall *(Mgr-Technical Team-Fire Protection)*
Robert Azimi *(Mgr-New Bus Dev-Americas)*
Cynthia Frank *(Asst VP & Mgr-Building Matls)*
David Fuller *(Asst VP & Mgr-Fire Protection)*
Robert Lovell *(Mgr-Quality Assurance & Auditing)*
James Marquedant *(Mgr-Electrical Sys)*
Teresa Pellegrino *(Asst VP & Mgr-Bus Ops)*
Jean-Philippe Roisin *(Asst VP & Mgr-New Bus Dev-EMEA)*
Abby So *(Mgr-New Bus Dev-Asia Pacific)*
Paris Stavrianidis *(Gen Mgr)*

FM Engineering Consulting (Shanghai) Co. Ltd   (1)
Unit 03-09 3rd Floor Buildine One Corporate Avenue 222 Hubin Road, Luwan District, Shanghai, 200021, China
Tel.: (86) 21 2329 8008
Web Site: http://www.fmglobal.com.cn
Management Consulting Services
N.A.I.C.S.: 541618

FM Engineering Internation Ltd   (1)
28/F Tower 2 The Enterprise Center 6766 Ayala Ave cor Paseo De Roxas, Makati, 1226, Philippines
Tel.: (63) 2 849 3879
General Insurance Services
N.A.I.C.S.: 524210

FM Engineering International
Limited   (1)
Centro Empresarial Parque Norte Calle Serrano Galvache, 56 Edificio Encina 2a Planta, 28033, Madrid, 28033, Spain
Tel.: (34) 917664433
Web Site: http://www.fmglobal.com
Property Insurance Services
N.A.I.C.S.: 524126

FM Engineering International Ltd   (1)
Suite 2A-19-1 Level 19 Block 2A Plaza Sentral Jalan Station Sentral 5, Kuala Lumpur, 50470, Malaysia
Tel.: (60) 3 2723 1313
Web Site: http://www.fmglobal.com
Sales Range: $25-49.9 Million
Emp.: 14
General Insurance Services
N.A.I.C.S.: 524210
Nanthakumaran Marimuthu *(Plant Mgr)*

FM Engineering International Ltd   (1)
Unit 902 9th Floor The Millenia Tower B No 1 & 2 Murphy Road Ulsoor, Bengaluru, 560008, India
Tel.: (91) 80 6694 0200
Sales Range: $25-49.9 Million
Emp.: 22
General Insurance Services
N.A.I.C.S.: 524210
Sanjeev Misra *(VP)*

FM Engineering International Ltd   (1)
1 Jongno CEO Suite 15th Floor Kyobo Building, Jongno-gu, Seoul, 03154, Korea (South)
Tel.: (82) 2 2010 8910
General Insurance Services
N.A.I.C.S.: 524210

FM Global de Mexico   (1)
Ave Pedro Ramirez Vazquez 200-11 Piso 6, Col Valle Oriente, Garza Garcia, 66269, Nuevo Leon, Mexico

Tel.: (52) 81 8262 4700
Web Site: http://www.fmglobal.mx
General Insurance Services
N.A.I.C.S.: 524210

FM Insurance Company Limited (1)
Eschersheimer Landstrasse 55, 60322,
Frankfurt, Germany
Tel.: (49) 69154060
Sales Range: $50-74.9 Million
Emp.: 150
Property Insurance Services
N.A.I.C.S.: 524126
Achim Hillgraf (CEO)

FM Insurance Company Limited (1)
8 Cours Du Triangle, Defense 4, 92937,
Paris, France
Tel.: (33) 146939700
Sales Range: $25-49.9 Million
Emp.: 16
Property Insurance Services
N.A.I.C.S.: 524126

FM Insurance Company Limited (1)
600 Bourke Street Level 36, Melbourne,
3000, VIC, Australia
Tel.: (61) 396091300
Web Site: http://www.fmglobal.com
Sales Range: $50-74.9 Million
Emp.: 75
Property Insurance Services
N.A.I.C.S.: 524126
Ian Berg (VP-Ops)

FM Insurance Company Limited (1)
Via Mike Bongiorno 13, 20124, Milan, Italy
Tel.: (39) 024351731
Web Site: http://www.fmglobal.com
Property Insurance Services
N.A.I.C.S.: 524126

FM Insurance Company Limited (1)
Guscez Mahlerlaan 36, 1082 MC, Amster-
dam, Netherlands
Tel.: (31) 0205045500
Web Site: http://www.fmglobal.com
Sales Range: $25-49.9 Million
Emp.: 30
Property Insurance Services
N.A.I.C.S.: 524126
Henk Fleurke (Office Mgr)

FM Insurance Company Limited (1)
Birger Jarlsgatan 27 2nd Floor, Stockholm,
11145, Sweden
Tel.: (46) 84539200
Web Site: http://www.fmglobal.com
Sales Range: $25-49.9 Million
Emp.: 30
Property Insurance Services
N.A.I.C.S.: 524126
Tom Fehrleng (Gen Mgr)
Sofia Telgevik (Gen Mgr)

FM Insurance Company Limited (1)
1 Windsor Dials Arthur Road, Windsor, SL4
1RS, Berkshire, United Kingdom
Tel.: (44) 1753750000
Web Site: http://www.fmglobal.com
Sales Range: $50-74.9 Million
Emp.: 300
Property Insurance Services
N.A.I.C.S.: 524126
Angela Kelly (VP-Diversity & Intl HR)

FM Insurance Company Limited (1)
Unit 1601 Level 16 Tower One Grand Cen-
tury Place 193 Prince Edward Rd, West
Mongkok, Kowloon, China (Hong Kong)
Tel.: (852) 2622 6588
Sales Range: $25-49.9 Million
Emp.: 50
General Insurance Services
N.A.I.C.S.: 524210

FM Insurance Company Limited (1)
18-08 Novena Square Tower A 238A Thom-
son Rd, 307684, Singapore, Singapore
Tel.: (65) 6216 0066
Web Site: http://www.fmglobal.com
Sales Range: $25-49.9 Million
Emp.: 50
General Insurance Services
N.A.I.C.S.: 524210

FM Insurance Company Limited (1)
Rue des Colonies 11 Regus Brussel Central
Station, Brussels, 1000, Belgium
Tel.: (32) 2 661 32 00

Sales Range: $25-49.9 Million
Emp.: 13
General Insurance Services
N.A.I.C.S.: 524210

FM do Brasil Servicos de Prevencao
de Perdas Ltda (1)
Rua Joaquim Floriano 100-12 Andar, Sao
Paulo, 04534-000, SP, Brazil
Tel.: (55) 01131671005
Property Insurance Services
N.A.I.C.S.: 524126

Factory Mutual Insurance Company -
Canada (1)
165 Commerce Valley Dr W Ste 500,
Thornhill, L3T 7V8, ON, Canada
Tel.: (905) 763-5555
Web Site: http://www.fmglobal.com
Sales Range: $50-74.9 Million
Emp.: 125
Property Insurance Services
N.A.I.C.S.: 524126
David M. Thompson (Sr VP-Ops-Toronto)
Kenneth V. Lavigne (Sr VP)

Branch (Domestic):

Factory Mutual Insurance Company -
Canada (2)
600 rue de la Gauchetiere West, 14th Floor,
Montreal, H3B 4LB, QC, Canada
Tel.: (514) 876-7400
Sales Range: $125-149.9 Million
Property Insurance Services
N.A.I.C.S.: 524126

Mutual Boiler Re (1)
1200 Atwater Dr Ste 250, Malvern, PA
19355
Tel.: (610) 407-7800
Web Site: http://www.mutualboilerre.com
Sales Range: $50-74.9 Million
Emp.: 60
Boiler & Machinery Insurance Services
N.A.I.C.S.: 524126
Becky Davis (Mgr-Processing)
Michael J. Devlin (VP-Ops & Mgr-Corp Re-
insurance)
Richard M. Gillen (VP & Mgr-Ops)
Stephen M. Konopelski (VP-Ops & Mgr-IT)
Mary E. Menkins (VP-Ops & Mgr-
Underwriting)
Mark Smith (Asst VP & Asst Mgr-
Reinsurance)
Brian Olshefski (Asst VP & Asst Mgr-
Claims)
Dirk P. Smith (VP & Mgr-Engrg)
Jonathan A. Brislin (VP-Ops & Mgr-New
Bus Dev)
Bryan Kalisch (Mgr-Reinsurance-
Minneapolis-Midwest)
David Ritzinger (Mgr-Reinsurance-Los
Angeles-Western)
Greg Poorvin (Mgr-Reinsurance-Charlotte-
Southeast)
Gregory Fontana (Sr Mgr-Reinsurance-
Orlando-Southeast)
Heather Shaughnessy (Sr Mgr-
Reinsurance-Malvern-Northeast)
Jennifer Strawn (Mgr-Reinsurance-Wichita-
Midwest)
Justin McAleer (Mgr-Reinsurance-Omaha-
Midwest)
Kirk Fritz (Sr Mgr-Reinsurance-Sacramento-
Western)
Michael Pironti (Mgr-Reinsurance-Malvern-
Northeast)
James J. Callahan III (VP-Ops & Mgr-
Claims)

TSB Loss Control Consultants,
Inc. (1)
3940 Morton Bend Rd, Rome, GA 30161
Tel.: (706) 291-1222
Web Site: http://www.tsblosscontrol.com
Sales Range: $25-49.9 Million
Emp.: 6
Insurance Loss Consulting Services
N.A.I.C.S.: 524298
Curtis Doyle (Pres & CEO)

FADO PUBS INC.
2964 Peachtree Rd Ste 600, Atlanta,
GA 30305
Tel.: (404) 848-8433   GA
Web Site:
https://www.fadoirishpub.com

Year Founded: 1996
Emp.: 200
Resturant & Irish Pub
N.A.I.C.S.: 722410
Kieran McGill (Pres, Owner & CEO)
John Piccirillo (Partner & Dir-Mktg &
Dev)
Ellen Peacock (Mgr-Natl Mktg)

FAEGRE DRINKER BIDDLE &
REATH LLP
1 Logan Sq Ste 2000, Philadelphia,
PA 19103
Tel.: (215) 988-2700   DE
Web Site:
http://www.faegredrinker.com
Year Founded: 1849
Law Firm
N.A.I.C.S.: 541110
Edward A. Gramigna Jr. (Partner &
Member-Mgmt Bd)
Andrew C. Kassner (Co-Chm)
Lora Brzezynski (Partner-
Washington)
Thomas Froehle (Co-Chm)
David Barrett (Partner)
Gina Kastel (Partner)
Jack Sperber (Partner)
Bill Connolly (Partner)
Judy Reich (Partner)
Jane Koehl (COO)
Lindsay Gotwald (Chief Client Dev &
Mktg Officer)

FAGEN INC.
501 Hwy 212 W, Granite Falls, MN
56241-1308
Tel.: (320) 564-3324   MN
Web Site: https://www.fageninc.com
Year Founded: 1988
Sales Range: $50-74.9 Million
Emp.: 400
Contracting Services
N.A.I.C.S.: 236220
Jennifer A. Johnson (CFO)
Aaron Fagen (CEO)
Matt Luukkonen (Project Mgr)
Reid Jurgenson (Project Mgr)
Chris Howard (Project Mgr)

FAGER COMPANY
2058 State Rd, Camp Hill, PA 17011
Tel.: (717) 632-0560
Web Site: https://www.rffager.com
Rev.: $23,000,000
Emp.: 94
Plumbing Fittings & Supplies
N.A.I.C.S.: 423720
Bryce F. Fager (VP)
Richard F. Fager Jr. (Pres)

FAGER-MCGEE COMMERCIAL
CONSTRUCTION INC.
347 S Williams St, Murphysboro, IL
62966
Tel.: (618) 687-3900
Web Site: https://www.fager-
mcgee.com
Rev.: $12,000,000
Emp.: 25
Commercial & Institutional Building
Construction
N.A.I.C.S.: 236220
Bruce E. Fager (Co-Founder & Pres)
Steven L. McGee (Co-Founder & Sr
VP)
Darin P. Fager (VP-Ops)
Aurelio Granados (VP-Construction)
Chad L. Hanson (Project Mgr)
Matthew R. Rongey (Project Mgr)
Neil A. Pettijohn (Project Mgr)

FAH MAI HOLDINGS GROUP
INC.
3651 Lindell Rd St D891, Las Vegas,
NV 89103

Tel.: (702) 479-3012   NV
TRHF—(OTCBB)
Liabilities: $10,000
Net Worth: ($10,000)
Earnings: ($7,000)
Emp.: 75
Fiscal Year-end: 12/31/19
Teeth Whitening Product Distr
N.A.I.C.S.: 423450

FAHNESTOCK PLUMBING,
HVAC & ELECTRIC
3532 N Comotara St, Wichita, KS
67226-1303
Tel.: (316) 943-4328
Web Site:
https://www.fahnestockhvac.com
Sales Range: $10-24.9 Million
Emp.: 120
Electrical Wiring Services
N.A.I.C.S.: 238210
Scot Pennington (Pres)

FAHRNER ASPHALT SEAL-
ERS, L.L.C.
2800 Mecca Dr, Plover, WI 54467
Tel.: (715) 341-2868
Web Site:
https://www.fahrnerasphalt.com
Year Founded: 1995
Sales Range: $10-24.9 Million
Emp.: 200
Highway & Street Construction Ser-
vices
N.A.I.C.S.: 237310
Pat Peterson (Pres)

FAHRNEY-KEEDY HOME &
VILLAGE
8507 Mapleville Rd, Boonsboro, MD
21713
Tel.: (301) 733-6284   MD
Web Site: https://www.fkhv.org
Year Founded: 1905
Sales Range: $10-24.9 Million
Emp.: 231
Lifecare Retirement Community Op-
erator
N.A.I.C.S.: 623311
Deborah Haviland (Dir-Community
Dev)
Cassandra Weaver (Dir-Assisted Liv-
ing)
Mary Rosborough (Sec)
Sara Wolfe (Pres)
Stephen Coetzee (CEO)
Joseph Bachtell (Treas)
Diane Giffin (VP)
Katrina Graham (Sec)
John Miller (Vice Chm)

FAI CAPITAL MANAGEMENT
INC.
109 S MacDill Ave, Tampa, FL 33609
Tel.: (813) 874-6621
Rev.: $230,000,000
Investment Firm
N.A.I.C.S.: 523999
Jerry Ford (Pres)

FAIL TELECOMMUNICATIONS
CORP.
12 S 3rd St, Bay Springs, MS 39422
Tel.: (601) 764-3463
Web Site: https://www.failcorp.com
Sales Range: $10-24.9 Million
Emp.: 25
Local Telephone Communications
N.A.I.C.S.: 517121
Dorothea C. Fail (Pres)
Donna F. Alexander (Exec VP)
S. Wesley Ellis (CFO)

Subsidiaries:

Chickamauga Telephone
Company   (1)

Fail Telecommunications Corp.—(Continued)

300 Thomas Ave, Chickamauga, GA 30707
Tel.: (706) 375-3195
Web Site: http://www.chickamauga.com
Rev.: $2,000,000
Emp.: 13
Local & Long Distance Telephone Communications
N.A.I.C.S.: 517121
Mark Mcdonald *(Gen Mgr)*

FAIR HAVEN COMMUNITY HEALTH CENTER

374 Grand Ave, New Haven, CT 06513
Tel.: (203) 777-7411   **CT**
Web Site: https://www.fhchc.org
Year Founded: 1971
Sales Range: $10-24.9 Million
Emp.: 236
Health Care Srvices
N.A.I.C.S.: 622110
Abigail Paine *(Dir-Grants & Quality Mgmt)*
Suzanne Lagarde *(CEO)*
Sharon Anderson *(Dir-Medical)*
Evelyn Cumberbatch *(Dir-Behavioral Health Dept)*
Ronald Birmingham *(Dir-Dental)*
Francisca Melina Tibo *(Sec)*
Nitza M. Diaz *(Pres)*
Thomas Candrick *(Treas)*
Camila Molina-Rubino *(VP-Ops)*
Douglas Olson *(VP-Clinical Affairs)*
Jeannette de Jesus *(Sr VP)*
Patricia Moro *(VP-Fin)*
Robyn Hoffmann *(Officer-Compliance)*

FAIR HEALTH, INC.

530 5th Ave 18th Fl, New York, NY 10036
Tel.: (212) 370-0704   **NY**
Web Site: http://www.fairhealth.org
Year Founded: 2009
Sales Range: $10-24.9 Million
Emp.: 45
Health Insurance Services
N.A.I.C.S.: 524114
Ashley Smyth *(Exec Dir-Policy & Comm)*
Ben Casado Garcia *(CTO)*
Bart Bronfman *(COO)*
Donna Smith *(Exec Dir-Bus Dev)*
Michelle Scott *(Gen Counsel)*
Robin Gelburd *(Pres)*
Sara Rosenbaum *(Chm)*
Ali Russo *(CIO)*
Jim Wilson *(Chief Information Security Officer)*
Roger Adler *(CFO)*
Dean Sicoli *(Exec Dir-Comm & Govt Rels)*
Rachel Kent *(Sr Dir-Mktg, Outreach & Comm)*

FAIR OAKS FARMS INC.

7600 95th St, Pleasant Prairie, WI 53158-2713
Tel.: (262) 947-0320
Web Site:
    http://www.fairoaksfarms.com
Year Founded: 1995
Sales Range: $25-49.9 Million
Emp.: 285
Sausages & Other Prepared Meats
N.A.I.C.S.: 311612
Gary Corbett *(CEO)*
Julie Basich *(Gen Mgr)*
Michael L. Thompson *(Pres & CEO)*

FAIR-RITE PRODUCTS CORP.

1 Commercial Row, Wallkill, NY 12589
Tel.: (845) 895-2055   **NY**
Web Site: http://www.fair-rite.com

Year Founded: 1952
Sales Range: $10-24.9 Million
Emp.: 110
Provider of Electronic Components
N.A.I.C.S.: 334419
Carole Parker *(Pres)*

FAIRBANKS DAILY NEWS-MINER INC.

200 N Cushman St, Fairbanks, AK 99707
Tel.: (907) 456-6661
Web Site:
    https://www.newsminer.com
Rev.: $17,000,000
Emp.: 185
Newspaper Publishers
N.A.I.C.S.: 513110
Rod Boyce *(Mng Editor)*
Monica Hoffman *(Dir-Sls & Mktg)*
Alan Hoover *(Dir-Reader Dev)*
Richard Harris *(Publr)*

Subsidiaries:

Kodiak Daily Mirror   (1)
1419 Selig St, Kodiak, AK 99615
Tel.: (907) 459-7532
Web Site: http://www.kodiakdailymirror.com
Sales Range: $10-24.9 Million
Emp.: 10
Newspaper Publishers
N.A.I.C.S.: 513110
Derek Clarkston *(Mng Editor)*

FAIRBANKS SCALES INC.

821 Locust St, Kansas City, MO 64106-1908
Tel.: (816) 471-0231   **KS**
Web Site: http://www.fairbanks.com
Year Founded: 1830
Industrial Weighing Equipment Distr
N.A.I.C.S.: 333998
F. A. Norden *(Chm)*
Rick Norden *(CEO)*

FAIRBANKS SYMPHONY ASSOCIATION

234 Fine Arts Complex 312 Tanana Dr, Fairbanks, AK 99775
Tel.: (907) 474-5733
Web Site:
    http://www.fairbankssymphony.org
Year Founded: 1958
Sales Range: $50-74.9 Million
Emp.: 4
Symphony Orchestra
N.A.I.C.S.: 711130
Laura Bergh *(Exec Dir)*
Chuck Lemke *(Pres)*
George Rydlinski *(Dir-Mktg)*

FAIRBORN USA, INC.

205 Broadview St, Upper Sandusky, OH 43351
Tel.: (419) 294-4987
Web Site:
    https://www.fairbornusa.com
Year Founded: 1975
Rev.: $18,000,000
Emp.: 100
Dock Seals & Dock Enclosures Mfr
N.A.I.C.S.: 332311
Mark E. Dillon *(Pres & CEO)*

FAIRBRIDGE PARTNERS LLC

30 Vreeland Dr Unit 2-3, Skillman, NJ 08558
Tel.: (609) 580-1831
Web Site:
    http://www.fairbridgeusa.com
Year Founded: 2013
Sales Range: $25-49.9 Million
Emp.: 7
Real Estate Management Services
N.A.I.C.S.: 531210
Dmitry Gordeev *(Founder & Mng Partner)*

FAIRBROTHER & COMPANY LLC

22 Park Row, Chatham, NY 12037
Tel.: (518) 392-7700   **NY**
Web Site: http://www.fairbrother.com
Year Founded: 1988
Sales Range: $10-24.9 Million
Emp.: 11
Advertising Agencies
N.A.I.C.S.: 541810
Wendy Kahn *(Acct Exec)*

FAIRBURN READY-MIX, INC.

1127 Senoia Rd, Tyrone, GA 30290
Tel.: (770) 964-4588   **GA**
Web Site:
    http://www.fairburnreadymix.com
Sales Range: $10-24.9 Million
Emp.: 60
Readymix Concrete Mfr
N.A.I.C.S.: 327320
Greg M. Harrell *(Pres)*
Merrell Moore *(VP)*
Lang Thompson *(VP-Sls)*
Deborah Strozier *(Office Mgr)*
Brian Moore *(Gen Mgr)*
Johnnie Thompson *(Mgr-Credit)*

FAIRCHILD CAPITAL PARTNERS, LLC

PO Box 197, Elma, NY 14059
Tel.: (716) 225-4032
Web Site:
    http://www.fairchildcapitalpartners.com
Investment Services
N.A.I.C.S.: 523999
Ryan Martin *(Founder & Mng Partner)*

Subsidiaries:

Weco Manufacturing Group   (1)
6364 Dean Pkwy, Ontario, NY 14519
Tel.: (585) 265-3000
Web Site: http://www.wecomfg.com
Precision Sheet Metal Fabrication
N.A.I.C.S.: 332999
Mike Faulkner *(CEO)*

Subsidiary (Domestic):

FTT Manufacturing, Inc.   (2)
112 Riverside Dr, Geneseo, NY 14454
Tel.: (585) 243-0300
Web Site: http://fttmfg.com
Sales Range: $1-9.9 Million
Emp.: 55
Iron & Steel Product Mfr
N.A.I.C.S.: 331110
Pam Hill *(Office Mgr-Accts Receivable)*

FAIRCHILD EQUIPMENT, INC.

2140 Hutson Rd, Green Bay, WI 54303
Tel.: (920) 494-8726
Web Site:
    https://www.fairchildequipment.com
Material Handling Services
N.A.I.C.S.: 562920
Gary Fairchild *(Pres)*

Subsidiaries:

Lift Truck Specialists, Inc.   (1)
N50W13824 Overview Dr, Menomonee Falls, WI 53051
Tel.: (262) 783-7870
Web Site: http://www.lifttruckspecialists.net
Sales Range: $1-9.9 Million
Emp.: 28
Repair Shops & Related Services
N.A.I.C.S.: 811490

FAIRCOM CORPORATION

6300 W Sugar Creek Dr, Columbia, MO 65203-9052
Tel.: (573) 445-6833   **MO**
Web Site: https://www.faircom.com
Year Founded: 1979
Emp.: 40

Database Software Publisher, Sales & Support
N.A.I.C.S.: 513210
Raymond Brown *(Pres)*
Cindy Mantle *(Controller)*
Jon Klaas *(Engr-Software)*
Randal Hoff *(VP-Engrg)*
Jay Trinidad *(Chief Product Officer)*
John E. Pierantoni *(Sr VP-Fin & Risk)*
Pat Wilkison *(Gen Mgr-Uber Program)*
Scott Painter *(Founder & CEO)*

Subsidiaries:

FairCom Brazil, Inc.   (1)
Avenida Professor Alfonso Bovero 1057 cj 38, 05019 011, Sao Paulo, Brazil
Tel.: (55) 11 3872 9802
Web Site: http://www.faircom.com
Database Software Sales & Support
N.A.I.C.S.: 423430

FairCom Europe S.r.l.   (1)
Via Caduti di Superga n 1, Gazzaniga, 24025, BG, Italy
Tel.: (39) 035 721 321
Web Site: http://www.faircom.com
Emp.: 6
Database Software Sales & Support
N.A.I.C.S.: 423430
Francesco Cortinovis *(Mng Dir)*

FAIRDINKUM CONSULTING, LLC

1150 Avenue of the Americas Ste 703, New York, NY 10036
Tel.: (212) 624-3219   **NY**
Year Founded: 2002
Sales Range: $10-24.9 Million
Emp.: 17
Custom Computer Programming Services
N.A.I.C.S.: 541511
Thomas Hall *(Principal-Admin)*

Subsidiaries:

Warren Systems Group, Inc.   (1)
584 Broadway Rm 409, New York, NY 10012
Tel.: (212) 219-9060
Web Site: http://www.wsginc.net
Custom Computer Programming Services
N.A.I.C.S.: 541511
Bruce Leibstone *(Founder)*

FAIREY CHEVROLET CADILLAC

2885 Saint Matthews Rd, Orangeburg, SC 29118
Tel.: (803) 536-1600
Web Site:
    http://www.faireymotors.com
Rev.: $21,570,309
Emp.: 25
New & Used Automobiles
N.A.I.C.S.: 441110
Joe K. Fairey III *(Pres)*

FAIRFAX COUNTY WATER AUTHORITY INC.

8570 Executive Park Ave, Fairfax, VA 22031-2218
Tel.: (703) 698-5600   **VA**
Web Site: http://www.fcwa.org
Year Founded: 1957
Emp.: 475
Water Utility Services
N.A.I.C.S.: 221310
Steven T. Edgemon *(Deputy Gen Mgr)*
Michele L. Moore *(Dir-Fin)*
Charles M. Murray *(Gen Mgr)*

FAIRFAX DATA SYSTEMS, INC.

30 Bridge St, New Milford, CT 06776
Tel.: (860) 354-4472

Web Site:
http://www.fairfaxdatasystems.com
Rev.: $1,100,000
Emp.: 10
Custom Computer Programming Services
N.A.I.C.S.: 541511
David L. Suess *(Founder)*

FAIRFAX HOLDING COMPANY INC.
14504 Greenview Dr Ste 210, Laurel, MD 20708
Tel.: (301) 953-7650
Sales Range: $10-24.9 Million
Emp.: 12
Ready Mixed Concrete
N.A.I.C.S.: 327320
Caleb Gould *(Sec)*

Subsidiaries:

Fairfax Materials Inc. (1)
8490 Garrett Hwy, Oakland, MD 21550
Tel.: (301) 334-8101
Readymix Concrete Mfr
N.A.I.C.S.: 212311
Pat Adams *(Gen Mgr)*

FAIRFAX IMPORTS INC.
11050 Main St, Fairfax, VA 22030
Tel.: (703) 273-6700
Web Site:
http://www.fairfaxvolvo.com
Rev.: $69,900,000
Emp.: 100
New & Used Automobiles
N.A.I.C.S.: 441110
Carey Schwab *(Pres)*
Jim Burns *(Gen Mgr)*
Fawad Osmani *(Dir-Fin)*
David Perrin *(Dir-Sls-Used Car)*

FAIRFIELD AUTO GROUP INC.
5071 Lycoming Mall Dr, Montoursville, PA 17754
Tel.: (570) 368-8121 PA
Web Site:
https://www.fairfieldautogroup.com
Year Founded: 1963
Sales Range: $25-49.9 Million
Emp.: 110
Sales of New & Used Automobiles
N.A.I.C.S.: 441110
William P. Manos *(Owner)*
Kimberly Vuocolo *(Comptroller)*
Rick Quigley *(Gen Mgr)*
Robert Houston *(Mgr-Sls)*

FAIRFIELD BANCSHARES INC.
220 E Main St, Fairfield, IL 62837
Tel.: (618) 842-2107
Web Site: http://www.fairfieldnb.com
Year Founded: 1903
Sales Range: $1-9.9 Million
Emp.: 47
Bank Holding Company
N.A.I.C.S.: 551111

Subsidiaries:

Fairfield National Bank (1)
PO Box 429, Fairfield, IL 62837
Tel.: (618) 842-2107
Web Site: http://www.fairfieldnb.com
Emp.: 50
National Commercial Banks
N.A.I.C.S.: 551111

FAIRFIELD CHAIR COMPANY
1331 Harper Ave SW, Lenoir, NC 28645
Tel.: (828) 758-5571
Web Site:
http://www.fairfieldchair.com
Sales Range: $75-99.9 Million
Emp.: 500
Furniture Mfr

N.A.I.C.S.: 337121
Dixon Mitchell *(Pres & COO)*
Phil Cooper *(Dir-Motion Seating Div)*

FAIRFIELD COUNTY BANK, MHC
150 Danbury Rd, Ridgefield, CT 06877
Tel.: (203) 438-6518
Web Site:
http://www.fairfieldcountybank.com
Year Founded: 1871
Mutual Holding Company
N.A.I.C.S.: 551112
David Schneider *(CEO)*
Dan Berta *(Pres)*
Stephen Wooters *(Exec VP-Mktg, Digital Banking & Payments)*

Subsidiaries:

Fairfield County Bank Corp. (1)
150 Danbury Rd, Ridgefield, CT 06877
Tel.: (203) 438-6518
Web Site:
http://www.fairfieldcountybank.com
Bank Holding Company
N.A.I.C.S.: 551111
David A. Schneider *(CEO)*

Division (Domestic):

Fairfield County Bank (2)
150 Danbury Rd, Ridgefield, CT 06877
Tel.: (203) 857-5560
Web Site:
http://www.fairfieldcountybank.com
Provider of Savings Institutions
N.A.I.C.S.: 522180
Kevin D. McMahon *(VP & Mgr-Mortgage Sls)*
Renuka Kumar *(Sr VP-Credit Admin)*
Chuck Balocca *(Exec VP)*

FAIRFIELD ELECTRIC COOPERATIVE
3129 US Highway 321 N, Winnsboro, SC 29180
Tel.: (803) 635-4621 SC
Web Site: http://www.fairelec.com
Year Founded: 1939
Sales Range: $150-199.9 Million
Emp.: 57
Distr of Electric Power
N.A.I.C.S.: 221122
William L. Hart *(CEO)*
Peggy B. Jeffcoat *(Sec)*
Doug Payne *(VP-Member & Strategic Svcs)*
Beth Mason *(Mgr-Admin Svcs & Personnel)*
Thomas Black *(VP-Engrg)*
D. Mark Connor *(VP-Fin)*
W. C. Good *(Treas)*
Bruce Bacon *(VP-Ops)*

FAIRFIELD FEDERAL SAVINGS & LOAN ASSOCIATION
111 E Main St, Lancaster, OH 43130
Tel.: (740) 653-3863
Web Site:
https://www.fairfieldfederal.com
Sales Range: $10-24.9 Million
Emp.: 63
Federal Savings & Loan Associations
N.A.I.C.S.: 522180
Bruce Baughman *(VP & Dir-Info Sys)*
Mary Snider *(Exec VP)*
Sharon Drumm *(VP)*
Judy Root *(Pres)*
Diane Hall *(VP-Acctg)*
Linda Johnson *(VP)*
Robin Ball *(Asst VP)*
Kristy Fosnaugh *(VP-Personnel)*
Janetta Hussey *(Asst VP & Branch Mgr)*
Heidi Withem *(Sec)*
Matt Wideman *(VP)*

Tracy Embrey *(VP-Personal Checking Accounts)*
Susan Fernow *(Officer-Loan & VP)*

FAIRFIELD GLADE COMMUNITY CLUB
7827 Peavine Rd, Fairfield Glade, TN 38558
Tel.: (931) 484-3780 TN
Web Site:
https://www.fairfieldglade.cc
Year Founded: 1973
Sales Range: $10-24.9 Million
Emp.: 494
Social Club
N.A.I.C.S.: 813410
Bob Diller *(Pres)*
Barbara Storer *(Dir-Timeshare)*
Bob Stackhouse *(Treas)*
Jack Sixkiller *(Head-Golf Pro)*
Jeff Houston *(Head-Pro Stonehenge Golf Club & Dir-Golf)*
Rag Jones *(Head-Golf Pro)*
Sean VanHoose *(Superintendent-Golf Course)*

FAIRFIELD GOURMET FOOD CORP.
12 Commerce Rd, Fairfield, NJ 07004
Tel.: (973) 227-2800
Sales Range: $10-24.9 Million
Emp.: 95
Cookie & Cracker Mfr
N.A.I.C.S.: 311821
Yossi Ostreicher *(VP)*
Tanveer Ahmad *(Mgr-Quality Assurance & R&D)*
Ken Schiliro *(VP-Sls)*
Ari Margulies *(CFO)*
Gene Bazzarelli *(Mgr-Ecommerce)*
Marc Benichou *(Mgr-Pur)*
Barbara Faggioli *(Reg Mgr-Sls)*
John Griner *(Mgr-Mfg)*
Christopher Mennella *(Reg Mgr-Sls)*
Oliver Tress *(Mgr)*

FAIRFIELD LINE INC.
605 W Stone Ave, Fairfield, IA 52556
Tel.: (641) 472-3191
Web Site: http://www.fairfieldline.com
Sales Range: $10-24.9 Million
Emp.: 20
Glove Mfr
N.A.I.C.S.: 315990
Nicole Hunt *(Pres)*

FAIRFIELD MAXWELL LTD.
Chrysler Bldg 405 Lexington Ave Fl 55, New York, NY 10174
Tel.: (212) 297-9030 NY
Web Site: http://fairfieldmaxwell.com
Year Founded: 1957
Sales Range: $50-74.9 Million
Emp.: 10
Management Services; Shipping Agents; Fuel Oil; Deep Sea Foreign Transportation of Freight
N.A.I.C.S.: 541611
Kaytaro G. Sugahara *(Pres)*
Vincent Yax *(Treas & Sr VP)*
Karita Hannon *(Controller)*

Subsidiaries:

Fairfield Industries Inc. (1)
1111 Gillinghan Ln, Sugar Land, TX 77478 (100%)
Tel.: (281) 275-7500
Web Site: http://www.fairfield.com
Sales Range: $50-74.9 Million
Geophysical Exploration
N.A.I.C.S.: 213112
Kevin Crosby *(CFO)*
Chuck Davidson *(Pres & CEO)*

FAIRFIELD MEDICAL CENTER

401 N Ewing St, Lancaster, OH 43130
Tel.: (740) 687-8000 OH
Web Site: https://www.fmchealth.org
Year Founded: 1982
Sales Range: $200-249.9 Million
Emp.: 2,356
General Medical Services
N.A.I.C.S.: 622110
Ron Burris *(Chm)*
John R. Janoso Jr. *(Pres & CEO)*

FAIRFIELD PROCESSING CORP.
88 Rose Hill Ave, Danbury, CT 06813-1157
Tel.: (203) 744-2090
Web Site: http://www.poly-fil.com
Year Founded: 1950
Sales Range: $10-24.9 Million
Emp.: 250
Mfr of Cotton & Polyester Products
N.A.I.C.S.: 325220
Roy Young *(CEO)*

FAIRFIELD PROPERTIES L.P.
7301 N State Hwy Ste 260, Irving, TX 75039
Tel.: (817) 816-9400
Web Site: http://www.fairfield-properties.com
Sales Range: $10-24.9 Million
Emp.: 550
Apartment Complex Construction
N.A.I.C.S.: 531210
Liz Culibrk *(Sr VP-Western Reg)*
Kim Bender *(Exec VP & Head-Property Mgmt)*
Shant Koumriqian *(CFO & Exec VP)*
Greg Pinkalla *(Chm & CEO)*
Jon A. MacDonald *(Gen Counsel & Exec VP)*
Richard Boynton *(Sr VP-Acquisition)*
Brent Ball *(Sr VP-Asset Mgmt-Dev)*
Christopher Ruffolo *(Sr VP-Asset Mgmt-Redevelopment East)*
Tony Duplisse *(Sr VP-Asset Mgmt-Redevelopment West)*
Tommy Brunson *(Sr VP-Dev Mgmt-Eastern Reg)*
Brendan Hayes *(Sr VP-Dev Mgmt-Northern California & San Diego)*
Larry Scott *(Sr VP-Dev Mgmt-Southern California)*
Zach Johnston *(VP-Dev Mgmt-Central, Southwest & Student Housing)*
Andrew McGeorge *(VP-Dev Mgmt-Mid-Atlantic Reg)*
Robb Hewitt *(VP-Dev Mgmt-Northeast Reg)*
Jason Martin *(VP-Dev Mgmt-Pacific Northwest & Colorado Reg)*
Marc Brambrut *(VP-Dev Mgmt-Southeast Reg)*
Paulette Green *(VP-Property Mgmt-California Reg)*
Claire Michael *(VP-Property Mgmt-Florida, Georgia & North Carolina Reg)*
Christy White *(VP-Property Mgmt-IN, MI, OH & Southern Virginia Reg)*
Brett Stevens *(VP-Property Mgmt-Southern California & Washington Reg)*
Cathy Stiles *(VP-Property Mgmt-Texas Reg)*

FAIRFIELD TECHNOLOGIES INC.
14139 Robert Paris Court, Chantilly, VA 20151
Tel.: (703) 968-7800
Web Site:
http://www.fairfieldtech.com
Year Founded: 1990

Fairfield Technologies Inc.—(Continued)

Sales Range: $1-9.9 Million
Emp.: 35
IT Consulting & Professional Services for Federal Organizations
N.A.I.C.S.: 541690
Ken Fried (Pres)

FAIRGREEN CAPITAL L.P.
6065 Roswell Rd NE Ste 900, Atlanta, GA 30328-4019
Tel.: (404) 255-1936 **GA**
Year Founded: 1991
Sales Range: $75-99.9 Million
Emp.: 300
Nonresidential Building Operators
N.A.I.C.S.: 531120

FAIRHAVEN CAPITAL MANAGEMENT, LLC
1 Hampshire St 7th Fl, Cambridge, MA 02139
Tel.: (617) 452-0800
Web Site:
  http://www.fairhavencapital.com
Year Founded: 2007
Privater Equity Firm
N.A.I.C.S.: 523999
Jim Goldinger (Partner)
Paul Ciriello (Partner)
Rick Grinnell (Partner)
Wan Li Zhu (Partner)
Bob Schnibbe (COO)

Subsidiaries:

Digital Guardian, Inc. **(1)**
860 Winter St Ste 3, Waltham, MA 02451
Tel.: (781) 788-8180
Web Site: http://www.digitalguardian.com
Data Protection Services
N.A.I.C.S.: 541519
Ed Durkin (CFO)
Douglas Bailey (Chief Strategy Officer)
Constance Stack (CMO)
Peter Tyrrell (COO)
David McKeough (Exec VP-Global Field Ops)
Mark Stevens (Sr VP-Global Svcs)
David Karp (Sr VP-Global Field Engrg & Tech Enablement)
Luke Brown (VP & Gen Mgr-EMEA, India & LATAM)
Brian Mullins (VP-Content & Programs Strategy)
Craig Hansen (VP-Sls-Federal)
Peter Rooney (Sr VP-Technical Ops)
David Stienes (Chm)
Jan van Vliet (VP/Gen Mgr-EMEA)
Mordecai Rosen (CEO)

Subsidiary (Domestic):

Code Green Networks, Inc. **(2)**
385 E Moffett Park Dr Ste 105, Sunnyvale, CA 94089
Tel.: (408) 716-4200
Web Site:
  http://www.codegreennetworks.com
Computer Data Loss Prevention & Content Security Solutions
N.A.I.C.S.: 513210
Rhett Ohlson (VP-Fin & Admin)
John O'Leary (VP-Sls & Mktg)
Douglas Bailey (Gen Mgr)
Emanoel Daryoush (VP-Engrg)

FAIRHAVEN CHRISTIAN RETIREMENT CENTER
3470 N Alpine Rd, Rockford, IL 61114
Tel.: (815) 877-1441 **IL**
Web Site: https://www.fairhaven.cc
Year Founded: 1965
Sales Range: $10-24.9 Million
Emp.: 295
Senior Living Services
N.A.I.C.S.: 623311
Christine Hintzsche (Dir-Mktg & Resident Svcs)
Tom Bleed (Exec Dir)

FAIRLAND MARKET INC.
43251 Rescue Ln RR 235, Hollywood, MD 20636
Tel.: (301) 373-5848
Web Site:
  http://www.mckayssupermarket.com
Rev.: $31,383,050
Emp.: 240
Grocery Stores, Independent
N.A.I.C.S.: 445110
David McKay (CEO)
Tommy McKay (Pres)

FAIRLANE FINANCIAL CORPORATION
1200 S Pine Island Rd Ste 100, Fort Lauderdale, FL 33324-4469
Tel.: (954) 476-2505
Web Site: http://www.888fairlane.com
Year Founded: 1955
Sales Range: $75-99.9 Million
Emp.: 20
Annuity Distr
N.A.I.C.S.: 524298
Samuel R. Lane (Chm)

FAIRLANE FORD SALES INC.
14585 Michigan Ave, Dearborn, MI 48126
Tel.: (313) 846-5000 **MI**
Web Site: http://www.fairlaneford.com
Year Founded: 1923
Sales Range: $25-49.9 Million
Emp.: 92
Sales & Service of New & Used Automobiles
N.A.I.C.S.: 441110
Lorraine Neuman (Mgr-Fin Svcs)
John Markovski (Mgr-Gen Sls)

FAIRLY PAINLESS ADVERTISING
44 E 8th St Ste 300, Holland, MI 49423
Tel.: (616) 394-5900
Web Site:
  https://www.fairlypainless.com
Year Founded: 1992
Sales Range: $10-24.9 Million
Emp.: 18
Advertising Agencies
N.A.I.C.S.: 541810
Chris Cook (CEO)
Steve Groenink (Pres)

FAIRMONT FOODS OF MINNESOTA INC.
905 E 4th St, Fairmont, MN 56031-4014
Tel.: (507) 238-9001 **MN**
Web Site:
  http://www.fairmontfoods.com
Year Founded: 1987
Sales Range: $25-49.9 Million
Emp.: 250
Producers of Frozen Specialties
N.A.I.C.S.: 311412
Tom Kyne (Supvr-QA)

FAIRMONT PRESS, INC.
700 Indian Trail Lilburn Rd NW, Lilburn, GA 30047-3724
Tel.: (770) 925-9388 **GA**
Web Site:
  http://www.fairmontpress.com
Year Founded: 1973
Sales Range: $10-24.9 Million
Emp.: 13
Advertising Agencies
N.A.I.C.S.: 541810
Brian Douglas (Pres)
Linda Hutchings (Mgr)

FAIRMONT SIGN COMPANY
3750 E Outer Dr, Detroit, MI 48234
Tel.: (313) 368-4000

Web Site:
  https://www.fairmontsign.com
Sales Range: $10-24.9 Million
Emp.: 100
Custom Sign Mfr
N.A.I.C.S.: 339950
Nick Hanna (VP-Mfg)

FAIRN & SWANSON INC.
400 Lancaster St, Oakland, CA 94601
Tel.: (510) 533-8260
Web Site: http://www.fairn.com
Sales Range: $25-49.9 Million
Emp.: 250
Duty Free Distributor of Alcohol, Tobacco & Other Items
N.A.I.C.S.: 424210
Ireen Rojas (Dir-Mktg)
Joel Sjostrom (CEO)
Nicole Uhlig (Pres)

FAIRPLAY
5260 Carillon Pt, Kirkland, WA 98033
Tel.: (425) 242-4646
Web Site: http://www.fairplay.com
Sales Range: $1-9.9 Million
Emp.: 73
Real Estate Services
N.A.I.C.S.: 531390
William J. Thale (CFO)
Todd Hager (Chief Credit Officer)

FAIRPLAY INC.
4640 S Halsted St, Chicago, IL 60609
Tel.: (773) 247-3077
Web Site:
  https://www.fairplayfoods.com
Year Founded: 1975
Sales Range: $50-74.9 Million
Emp.: 400
Grocery Stores, Chain
N.A.I.C.S.: 445110
Richard Goodrich (Pres)

FAIRVALUE SUPERMARKET INC.
128 Fairway Shopping Center Ste 2, Hudson, NC 28638
Tel.: (828) 728-4771
Web Site: http://www.fairvalue.com
Sales Range: $10-24.9 Million
Emp.: 35
Grocery Stores
N.A.I.C.S.: 445110
Mark Yambor (Pres)

FAIRVIEW ADVERTISING
112 Bauer Dr, Oakland, NJ 07436-3105
Tel.: (201) 651-9784
Year Founded: 1982
Sales Range: $10-24.9 Million
Emp.: 13
Advertising Agencies
N.A.I.C.S.: 541810
Christine Silvestri (Dir-Print Media)

FAIRVIEW CAPITAL PARTNERS, INC.
75 Isham Rd, West Hartford, CT 06107
Tel.: (860) 674-8066
Web Site:
  http://www.fairviewcapital.com
Rev.: $10,000,000
Emp.: 22
Commodity Contracts Dealing
N.A.I.C.S.: 523160
Laurence C. Morse (Co-Founder & Mng Partner)
Joann H. Price (Co-Founder & Mng Partner)
Kola Olofinboba (Mng Partner)
Michael Friedman (Mgr-Acctg)

Michele A. Chow-Tai (Head-Bus Dev)
Peter Ruchwa (Asst Controller-Ops)
Laurence C. Morse (Co-Founder & Mng Partner)
Kwesi Quaye (Partner)

FAIRVIEW HEALTH SERVICES
2450 Riverside Ave, Minneapolis, MN 55454
Tel.: (612) 672-7272
Web Site: https://www.fairview.org
Sales Range: $1-4.9 Billion
Emp.: 22,000
Medical Health Network
N.A.I.C.S.: 622110
Daniel Fromm (CFO)
Ann Hengel (Chm)
Mark F. Thomas (Pres-Sr Svcs)
Carolyn Jacobson (Chief HR Officer)
Alistair Jacques (CIO)
James Hereford (CEO)
Mark Welton (Chief Medical Officer)
Laura Reed (COO & Pres-Acute Care Hospitals)

Subsidiaries:

Grand Itasca Clinic & Hospital **(1)**
1601 Golf Course Rd, Grand Rapids, MN 55744
Tel.: (218) 326-3401
Web Site: http://www.granditasca.org
Health Care Srvices
N.A.I.C.S.: 622110
Jean MacDonell (Pres & CEO)
Sandra Lenarz (VP-Hospital Svcs)
Dan Soular (VP-Medical Affairs)
Melissa Walters (Sr Dir-Ancilliary Svcs)
Todd Christensen (Dir-Fin)
Katherine Burns-Christenson (Dir-HR)
Christy Gustafson (Dir-Quality)

HealthEast Care System **(1)**
559 Capitol Blvd, Saint Paul, MN 55103-2101
Tel.: (651) 232-2300
Web Site: http://www.fairview.org
Health Care Srvices
N.A.I.C.S.: 622110
James Hereford (Pres)

Subsidiary (Domestic):

Bethesda Hospital **(2)**
559 Capitol Blvd, Saint Paul, MN 55103
Tel.: (651) 232-2000
Web Site: http://www.fairview.org
Specialty & Long-Term Medical Services
N.A.I.C.S.: 622110

HealthEast St. John's Hospital **(2)**
1575 Beam Ave, Maplewood, MN 55109
Tel.: (651) 232-7000
Web Site: http://www.fairview.org
Hospital Services
N.A.I.C.S.: 622110

FAIRVIEW INSURANCE AGENCY ASSOCIATES INC
25 Fairview Ave, Verona, NJ 07044
Tel.: (973) 857-0870
Web Site:
  https://www.fairviewinsurance.com
Rev.: $17,000,000
Emp.: 22
Insurance Agents, Nec
N.A.I.C.S.: 524210
John F. X. Graham (Founder)
Glenn Jacobs (Exec VP)
Zachary W. Edelman (Dir-Bus Dev)

FAIRVIEW MILLS INC.
32 S 6th St, Seneca, KS 66538
Tel.: (785) 336-2149
Web Site:
  http://www.fairviewmills.com
Sales Range: $10-24.9 Million
Emp.: 6
Pet Food Mfr
N.A.I.C.S.: 311119

FAIRVIEW MILLWORK INCOR-PORATED

100 Pearl St, Bridgewater, MA 02324
Tel.: (508) 697-6128
Web Site: https://www.fairvu.com
Rev.: $17,000,000
Emp.: 55
Retailer of Lumber & Building Products
N.A.I.C.S.: 444110
John T. Mahoney (Pres)
Jack Wallace (Controller)

FAIRWAY FORD HENDERSON, INC.

301 US Highway 79 S, Henderson, TX 75654-3607
Tel.: (903) 657-2566
Web Site:
   http://www.fairwayfordtexas.com
Rev.: $10,400,000
Emp.: 40
New Car Dealers
N.A.I.C.S.: 441110
Dennis Smith (Mng Partner)
Barney Rubin (Owner & Pres)

FAIRWAY FORD OF AUGUSTA, INC.

4333 Washington Rd, Evans, GA 30809
Tel.: (706) 854-9200
Web Site:
   http://www.fairwayfordevans.com
Sales Range: $50-74.9 Million
Emp.: 120
New Car Dealers
N.A.I.C.S.: 441110
Mike Combs (Gen Mgr)

FAIRWAY FORD, INC.

2323 Laurens Rd, Greenville, SC 29607-3246
Tel.: (864) 242-5060   SC
Web Site:
   https://www.fairwayford.com
Year Founded: 1961
Sales Range: $25-49.9 Million
Emp.: 100
New & Used Automobile Dealer
N.A.I.C.S.: 441110
A. Foster McKissick (Pres)
Gary McAlister (Gen Mgr)
Charlie Eassy (Mgr-Parts)
Fred Sizemore (Mgr-Svc)

Subsidiaries:

Fairway Auto Body Repair   (1)
723 Keith Dr, Greenville, SC
29607   (100%)
Tel.: (864) 242-2887
Web Site:
   http://www.fairwayautobodyrepair.com
Sales Range: $10-24.9 Million
Emp.: 10
Automotive Body Repair Services
N.A.I.C.S.: 811121

FAIRWAY INDEPENDENT MORTGAGE CORPORATION

781 Lois Dr, Sun Prairie, WI 53590
Tel.: (608) 837-4800
Web Site:
   http://www.fairwayindependent.com
Sales Range: $1-4.9 Billion
Emp.: 3,000
Real Estate Credit
N.A.I.C.S.: 522292
Steve Jacobson (Founder & CEO)
Len Krupinski (COO)
Joe Theison (Branch Mgr-Sun Prairie)
Paul Walnick (Pres-Mortgage Ops)
Brian Moore (Mgr-Holden)
Justin Tulman (VP)
Sarah Pichardo (Mgr-Fairfax)
Bob Orkis (CIO)

Elizabeth T. Steinhaus (Chief Legal Officer)
Sarah Middleton (Exec VP)
Ted Jeschke (Mgr-Florida)
Ashley Hickmon (Branch Mgr)
Randy Allen (Co-CIO)
Eric Brown (Exec VP-Bus Dev)
Scott Fletcher (Pres-Risk & Compliance)
Julie Fry (Exec VP-HR)
Todd Gavinski (CFO)
John Hotchkiss (Chief Risk Officer)
Trista Mayer (Chief Compliance Officer)
Tim Valentyn (Chief Legal Officer & Gen Counsel)
Joe Theisen (Mgr)
Juan Barraza (Sls Mgr-Greater Los Angeles)
David Lazowski (Pres-Retail Sls-East)
Michael Romano (Sls Mgr)

FAIRWAY INVESTMENTS, LLC

2830 Cahaba Rd, Birmingham, AL 35223
Tel.: (205) 802-7202
Web Site:
   https://www.fairwayinvestments.com
Sales Range: $1-9.9 Million
Emp.: 7
Real Estate Investment, Management & Development
N.A.I.C.S.: 531390
Michael D. Thompson (Pres)
Joe Clifton (Exec VP)
Sims Garrison (CFO)
Greg Cherry (Dir-Asset Mgmt)
Curt Stokes (Dir-Fin & Acctg)
Paul Darden (Mgr-Dev & Construction)

FAIRWAY LAWNS, LLC

1848 N 105th E Ave, Tulsa, OK 74116
Web Site:
   http://www.fairwaylawns.com
Emp.: 100
Landscaping Services
N.A.I.C.S.: 561730
Lisa Szurgot (VP-Admin Svcs)
Greg Harbison (CEO)

Subsidiaries:

LK Estate Services, Inc.   (1)
1900 Sheena Dr, Pittsburgh, PA 15239-1782
Tel.: (412) 795-6125
Web Site: https://kappslawn.com
Emp.: 100
Landscaping Services
N.A.I.C.S.: 561730
Marty Ferguson (Mgr)

FAIRWAY MOTORS INC.

Rte 309 N, Hazleton, PA 18201
Tel.: (570) 455-7701   PA
Web Site:
   http://www.fairwaymotors.com
Year Founded: 1960
Sales Range: $50-74.9 Million
Emp.: 75
Sales of New & Used Automobiles
N.A.I.C.S.: 441110
Laura Corazza (Pres)
Rosslyn Stimpel (Gen Mgr-Accessories Parts & Coord-SFE)

FAIRWAY STORES INC.

11270 Mary St Ste C, Castroville, CA 95012
Tel.: (831) 633-4639
Sales Range: $25-49.9 Million
Emp.: 5
Grocery Stores, Chain
N.A.I.C.S.: 445110
Jon Torres (Gen Mgr)

FAIRWAY SUPPLY INC.

6621 N Belt Line Rd Ste 130, Irving, TX 75063
Tel.: (214) 350-0021
Web Site:
   https://www.fairwaysupply.com
Year Founded: 1980
Rev.: $14,000,000
Emp.: 125
Provider of Security Devices
N.A.I.C.S.: 423710
Don Bradford (Owner & CEO)
Robert Carter (Pres)
Tony Eyler (Dir-Pur)
Steven Brooks (Mgr-Sls)
Shelia Moss (Mgr-Credit)
Glen Millican (VP)
Gwen Cardwell (Office Mgr)

FAIRWINDS CREDIT UNION

3087 N Alafaya Trl, Orlando, FL 32826
Tel.: (407) 277-5045   FL
Web Site: http://www.fairwinds.org
Emp.: 465
Credit Union
N.A.I.C.S.: 522130
Larry F. Tobin (Pres & CEO)
Kathy A. Chonody (Co-CFO & Sr Exec VP)
Phillip C. Tischer (CFO & Sr Exec VP)
James D. Adamczyk (Chief Lending Officer & Exec VP)
Mathy M. Hogan (Exec VP-e-Bus)
Charles S. Lai (CIO & Exec VP)
Dianne K. Owen (Exec VP-Mktg)
Jason Albu (Chm)
Truth Wilmot (Reg VP)
Andrew T. Dixon (Gen Counsel & Sr VP)

Subsidiaries:

Friends Bank   (1)
2222 State Road 44, New Smyrna Beach, FL 32168
Tel.: (386) 428-2299
Web Site: http://www.friendsbank.com
Banking Services
N.A.I.C.S.: 522110
Pete Klironomos (Pres & CEO)
Marsha Matlack (Officer-Compliance & Sr VP)
Sandra Kellogg (VP & Sr Officer-Credit)
Cathy Leclair (Mgr-Customer Svc)
Patti Kennedy (VP-Info & Bank Security)
Breece E. Bennett III (Exec VP & Mgr-Special Assets)

FAIRWINDS INTERNATIONAL

128 Northpark Blvd, Covington, LA 70433
Tel.: (985) 809-3808
Web Site:
   https://www.fairwindsintl.com
Year Founded: 1994
Rev.: $5,600,000
Emp.: 25
Engineering & Management Services
N.A.I.C.S.: 541330
William J. Napier Jr. (Pres)
Darrel Kempf (Engr)
Bill Shaffer (Engr)
Christine D. Napier (Treas)

FAIRWINDS PARTNERS, LLC

1000 Potomac St NW Ste 350, Washington, DC 20007
Tel.: (202) 223-9726
Web Site:
   https://www.fairwindspartners.com
Sales Range: $1-9.9 Million
Emp.: 25
Domain Name Strategy Consulting Services
N.A.I.C.S.: 541611
Josh Bourne (Mng Partner)
Nao Matsukata (Pres & CEO)

Taylor Frank (VP-Strategy & Dev)
Yvette Miller (VP-Strategic Comm & Media Rels)
Samantha Demetriou (VP-Consulting & Strategy)
Brenda Forrester (Mgr-Domain Name Admin)
Wendy Zimmerhanzel-Gitlitz (Mgr-Domain Name Admin)
Jennifer Goldberg (Dir-Consulting & Strategy)
Lillian Fosteris (Dir-Consulting & Strategy)

FAISON & ASSOCIATES LLC

121 W Trade St 27th Fl, Charlotte, NC 28202
Tel.: (704) 972-2500
Web Site: http://www.faison.com
Emp.: 125
Real Estate Developer, Investment & Property Management Services
N.A.I.C.S.: 237210
Cynthia T. Myers (Dir-HR)
Shawn Nelson (Controller)
David B. Chandler (Mng Dir-Fin)
Michael S. Jones (Mng Dir-Tax)
David C. Lampke (Mng Dir-Investments)
Susan Bracken (Dir-Corp Compliance & Risk Mgmt)
Christopher J. Branch (Sr Mng Dir)
Thomas W. Brasse (Mng Dir-Residential Construction & Dev)
Kris Fetter (Mng Dir-Residential Construction & Dev)
Kenneth D. McCoy (Sr Mng Dir-Asset Mgmt)
Jane McIntyre (Dir-Charitable Giving)
William S. Barnett (Mng Dir-Investments)
Chris M. Poplin (CFO, COO & Treas)
H. Thomas Webb III (Pres & CEO)

FAISS FOLEY WARREN

919 E Bonneville Ave, Las Vegas, NV 89101
Tel.: (702) 933-7777
Year Founded: 1990
Sales Range: $10-24.9 Million
Emp.: 11
Public Relations Agency
N.A.I.C.S.: 541820
Linda Faiss (Partner)
Helen Foley (Partner)
Melissa Warren (Mng Partner)
Cherryl Kaopua (Acct Exec)

FAITH & LEARNING INTERNA-TIONAL

209 E Liberty Dr, Wheaton, IL 60187
Tel.: (630) 221-0648   IL
Web Site:
   https://www.faithandlearning.org
Year Founded: 2004
Sales Range: $1-9.9 Million
Christian Ministry Services
N.A.I.C.S.: 813110

FAITH DIRECT INC.

601 S Washington St, Alexandria, VA 22314-3004
Tel.: (703) 519-5710
Web Site: http://www.faithdirect.net
Year Founded: 2004
Sales Range: $1-9.9 Million
Emp.: 13
Electronic Church Donations Processing
N.A.I.C.S.: 522320
W. Brian Walsh (Pres & Founder)

FAITH REGIONAL HEALTH SERVICES

2700 W Norfolk Ave, Norfolk, NE 68701

Faith Regional Health Services—(Continued)

Tel.: (402) 371-4880 NE
Web Site: https://www.frhs.org
Year Founded: 1996
Emp.: 1,326
Health Care Srvices
N.A.I.C.S.: 621610
Janet Pinkelman (VP-Human Resources-Mission Svcs)
Tom Lee (VP-Support-Ancillary)
Kelly Driscoll (Interim Pres & Interim CEO)
Linda Miller (Vice Chm)
Brett Jackson (Treas)
Brandon Morfeld (VP-Performance Improvement)

FAITHBRIDGE GROUP LLC.
2655 Northwinds Pkwy Ste 500, Alpharetta, GA 30009
Tel.: (678) 690-7100 GA
Web Site:
  https://www.faithbridgefostercare.org
Year Founded: 2006
Sales Range: $1-9.9 Million
Emp.: 21
Child Adoption & Foster Care Services
N.A.I.C.S.: 624110
Kelvin Stewart (Controller)
Kris Isom (Mng Dir-Area)
Richard L. Jackson (Chm)
Wayne Stolz (Co-Founder)

FAITHWAY FEED CO. INC.
4201 Lk Guntersville Pkwy, Guntersville, AL 35976
Tel.: (256) 582-5646
Web Site: http://faithwayfeedco.com
Sales Range: $10-24.9 Million
Emp.: 47
Farm Supplies
N.A.I.C.S.: 424910
Jerry Lynn Daniel (Owner)

FALCON ACQUISITION CORP.
1230 Avenue of the Americas 2nd Fl, New York, NY 10020
Tel.: (310) 464-2733 Ky
Year Founded: 2020
Investment Services
N.A.I.C.S.: 523999
Ziad Ghandour (CEO)
Jordan Plemmons (CFO)
Matthew Grimes (Pres)
Thomas Joseph Barrack Jr. (Chm)

FALCON AFFILIATES, LLC
919 E. Main St Suite 1050, Richmond, VA 23219
Tel.: (804) 716-1785
Web Site:
  http://www.falconaffiliates.com
Emp.: 100
Equity Investment Firm
N.A.I.C.S.: 523999
Will Krusen (Pres)

Subsidiaries:

Tidewater Fleet Supply (1)
3666 Progress Rd, Norfolk, VA 23502
Tel.: (757) 436-7679
Web Site:
  http://www.tidewaterfleetsupply.com
Sales Range: $10-24.9 Million
Emp.: 90
Automotive & Truck Parts Distr
N.A.I.C.S.: 423120
Crystal Gray (Coord-Mktg)
Allan Parrott (Pres)

Subsidiary (Domestic):

TNT Parts Inc. (2)
3000 S Corporate Pkwy Ste 400, Forest Park, GA 30297 (100%)
Tel.: (404) 675-9361

Web Site: http://www.tntpartsinc.com
Rev.: $3,584,000
Emp.: 80
Furniture Merchant Whslr
N.A.I.C.S.: 423210
Greg Woods (Pres)
Dale Adams (Branch Mgr)

FALCON AIR EXPRESS INC.
2601 Nw 105th Ave, Doral, FL 33172-2176
Tel.: (305) 592-5672
Web Site: http://www.flyfalconair.com
Rev.: $35,200,000
Emp.: 315
Scheduled Passenger Air Transportation
N.A.I.C.S.: 481111
Sandi Magder (VP)
Emilio Dirube (Pres)
Jose Lazaga (Exec VP)

FALCON ASPHALT REPAIR EQUIPMENT
2000 Austin St, Midland, MI 48642
Tel.: (989) 495-9332
Web Site: http://www.falconrme.com
Year Founded: 2004
Sales Range: $1-9.9 Million
Emp.: 40
Mfr of Portable, Affordable Asphalt Recyclers for Routine Pavement Repairs
N.A.I.C.S.: 333998
Clayton Carroll (VP-Sls & Dealer Support)

FALCON COMMUNICATIONS INC.
1708 N Douglass St, Malden, MO 63863
Tel.: (573) 276-5169
Web Site:
  http://www.falconcommunications.com
Year Founded: 1967
Sales Range: $10-24.9 Million
Emp.: 60
Provider of Telephone & Telephone Equipment Installation
N.A.I.C.S.: 238210
Donald J. Cook (Pres & CEO)
Keith A. Brown (Exec VP)
Sonda Brown (Office Mgr)

FALCON CONTAINERS
7717 Gilbert Ln, Manor, TX 78653
Tel.: (512) 231-9603
Web Site:
  http://www.falconcontainers.com
Year Founded: 2002
Sales Range: $1-9.9 Million
Emp.: 23
Container Boxes Mfr
N.A.I.C.S.: 321920
Stephen Shang (Founder & CEO)
Bill Allen (CFO)
Amy Sandlin (Dir-Sls)
John McAlonan (Pres & COO)

FALCON CONTRACTING CO., INC.
1500 Moss St, Columbus, MS 39701
Tel.: (662) 327-2053
Web Site:
  https://www.falconcontracting.com
Rev.: $14,600,000
Emp.: 40
Highway & Street Construction
N.A.I.C.S.: 237310
Robert Neal Coker (Pres)
Doug Phillips (Treas & Sec)

FALCON EXECUTIVE AVIATION, INC.
4766 E Falcon Dr, Mesa, AZ 85215-2542

Tel.: (480) 832-0704
Web Site:
  http://www.falconaviation.com
Sales Range: $10-24.9 Million
Emp.: 55
Industrial Machinery & Equipment Whslr
N.A.I.C.S.: 423830
Nancy Severt (VP)

FALCON FOUNDRY COMPANY
96 6th St, Lowellville, OH 44436
Tel.: (330) 536-6221
Web Site:
  http://www.falconfoundry.com
Year Founded: 1953
Sales Range: $10-24.9 Million
Emp.: 90
Copper Foundry Services
N.A.I.C.S.: 331529
Gary Slaven (Pres)
Lisa Mendozzi (Treas & Sec)

FALCON HOLDINGS, LLC
7 Village Cir Ste 300, Westlake, TX 76262-5906
Tel.: (817) 693-5151
Web Site:
  http://www.falconholdings.com
Sales Range: $10-24.9 Million
Emp.: 40
Franchisee Owner & Operator of Church's Chicken Restaurants
N.A.I.C.S.: 722513
Aslam Khan (CEO)
Khaled Habash (Pres)
Giovanna Koning (Co-CFO)
Mahmood Ahmed (Controller)
Patty Groves (Mgr-AP)
Vicki Blancett (Dir-HR)
Sarmad Zaheer (Mgr-Ops)

FALCON INTERNATIONAL BANK
7718 McPherson Rd, Laredo, TX 78045
Tel.: (956) 723-2265
Web Site:
  https://www.falconbank.com
Sales Range: $50-74.9 Million
Emp.: 300
Banking, Insurance & Investment Services
N.A.I.C.S.: 522110
Gilbert Narvaez Jr. (Pres & CEO)

FALCON NATIONAL BANK
183 Cedar Dr, Foley, MN 56329
Tel.: (320) 968-6300
Web Site:
  https://www.falconnational.com
Year Founded: 2003
Sales Range: $1-9.9 Million
Emp.: 38
Commericial Banking
N.A.I.C.S.: 522110
John Herges (CEO)
Kendra Berger (VP & Mgr-Retail Lending)
Dan Kvas (VP-Leasing)
Troy Cameron (Sr VP-Bus Banking)
Jessica Bitz (Pres-Foley)
Anita Reichert (Exec VP-Richmond)

Subsidiaries:

Falcon Leasing, LLC (1)
28 11th Ave S Ste 103, Saint Cloud, MN 56301
Web Site: http://www.falconnational.com
Rev.: $10,000,000
Emp.: 6
Equipment Sales & Franchise Financing Services
N.A.I.C.S.: 522299
Dan Kvas (Gen Mgr)

FALCON PACKAGING, INC.

2000 Mote Dr, Covington, OH 45318 OH
Tel.: (937) 473-3252
Web Site: http://www.falconpac.com
Year Founded: 1994
Sales Range: $1-9.9 Million
Emp.: 30
General Warehousing & Storage
N.A.I.C.S.: 493110
Clifton R. Perryman (Controller)
Jason Gibson (Gen Mgr)
Jerry Thompson (Mgr-Ops Sls)
Joe Fritscher (Dir-Pur)
Lenny Mayer (Pres)

FALCON PLASTICS INC.
1313 Western Ave, Brookings, SD 57006
Tel.: (605) 696-2500
Web Site:
  https://www.falconplastics.com
Year Founded: 1975
Rev.: $17,621,398
Emp.: 185
Injection Molding Of Plastics
N.A.I.C.S.: 326199
Jay Bender (Pres)
Lars Perry (Mgr-Maintenance)
Sarah Perry (VP)
Kathy Ritter (Supvr-QA)
Kenn Skluzacek (Coord-Automation)
Lyle Steenson (Mgr-Quality)

FALCON SEABOARD HOLD-INGS LP
109 N Post Oak Ln Ste 540, Houston, TX 77024
Tel.: (713) 622-0055 DE
Web Site:
  http://www.falconseaboard.com
Year Founded: 1996
Sales Range: $25-49.9 Million
Emp.: 7
Electronic Services
N.A.I.C.S.: 221118
E. H. Dewhurst (Treas & VP-Fin)
David H. Dewhurst (Co-Founder, Chm & CEO)
Gene Dewhurst (Partner, Treas & VP-Fin)
Humberto Sirvent (Mng Dir-Mergers & Acquisitions)

Subsidiaries:

Falcon Seaboard Oil & Gas Company (1)
109 N Post Oak Ln Ste 540, Houston, TX 77024-7752
Tel.: (713) 622-0055
Web Site: http://www.falconseaboard.com
Sales Range: $25-49.9 Million
Drilling Oil & Gas Wells
N.A.I.C.S.: 213111

FALCON STAMPING INC.
1125 Grand Oaks Dr, Howell, MI 48843
Tel.: (517) 540-6197
Web Site:
  http://www.falconstampinginc.com
Year Founded: 2000
Sales Range: $1-9.9 Million
Emp.: 8
Metal Stamping
N.A.I.C.S.: 332119
Mark Mobley (Pres)
Cheryl Swaim (Sec)

FALCON STEEL CO.
4201 Old Denton Rd, Haltom City, TX 76117
Tel.: (817) 581-9500
Web Site:
  http://www.falconsteelco.com
Rev.: $24,000,000
Emp.: 100
Fabricated Structural Metal
N.A.I.C.S.: 332312

Matt Towns *(Dir-Acctg & Fin)*
Dirk Tillery *(Natl Acct Mgr)*
Jim Taylor *(CEO)*

FALCON STEEL INC.
2610 N Eastgate Ave, Springfield, MO 65803
Tel.: (417) 866-6000
Web Site: https://www.falcon-steel.com
Year Founded: 1999
Rev.: $10,000,000
Emp.: 25
Steel
N.A.I.C.S.: 423510
Terry Heinz *(Pres)*

FALCON TRANSPORT CO.
4944 Belmont Ave, Youngstown, OH 44505
Tel.: (330) 793-1345
Web Site:
http://www.falcontransport.com
Sales Range: $200-249.9 Million
Emp.: 2,500
Fiscal Year-end: 12/31/14
Trucking Services
N.A.I.C.S.: 484121
Don Constantini *(Pres)*
Mark Constantini *(Exec VP)*
Brad Constantini *(Exec VP)*

FALCONHEAD CAPITAL, LLC
75 Rockefeller Plz Ste 1600B, 10019, New York, NY
Tel.: (212) 634-3304
Web Site:
http://www.falconheadcapital.com
Privater Equity Firm
N.A.I.C.S.: 523999
David Moross *(Founder, Chm & CEO)*
David Gubbay *(Gen Partner)*
Robert J. Fioretti *(Mng Dir)*
Colbey Arden *(Principal)*
Linda Marr *(Dir-Admin & HR)*

Subsidiaries:

Kwik Tek Inc. **(1)**
12000 E 45th Ave Unit 104, Denver, CO 80239
Tel.: (303) 733-3722
Web Site: http://www.airhead.com
Snow & Water Sporting Goods Mfr & Online Retailer
N.A.I.C.S.: 339920
Aaron Kramer *(Owner)*

Multi Flow Industries, LLC **(1)**
1434 County Line Rd, Huntingdon Valley, PA 19006
Tel.: (215) 322-1800
Web Site: https://www.multiflow.net
Beverage Products & Equipment Mfr
N.A.I.C.S.: 722515

Subsidiary (Domestic):

Draft Beer Services of Atlanta, Inc. **(2)**
133 Bethea Rd #801, 30214, Fayetteville, GA
Tel.: (770) 716-0441
Web Site: http://draftbeerservices.com
Craft Beer Breweries
N.A.I.C.S.: 312120
Neil Williamson *(Pres)*

NYDJ Apparel, LLC **(1)**
5401 S Soto St, Vernon, CA 90058
Tel.: (323) 581-9040
Web Site: http://www.nydj.com
Sales Range: $50-74.9 Million
Emp.: 200
Women's Designer Jeans & Other Apparel Mfr & Distr
N.A.I.C.S.: 315250
Mackey J. McDonald *(Chm)*

FALFURRIAS CAPITAL PART-NERS, LP
100 N Tryon St Ste 4100, Charlotte, NC 28202
Tel.: (704) 371-3220
Web Site:
http://www.falfurriascapital.com
Year Founded: 2006
Privater Equity Firm
N.A.I.C.S.: 523999
Marc D. Oken *(Chm)*
Ed McMahan *(Mng Partner)*
Ken Walker *(Partner)*

Subsidiaries:

Industry Dive, LLC **(1)**
1255 23rd St, NW Ste 550, Washington, DC 20037
Tel.: (202) 331-2480
Web Site: http://www.industrydive.com
Software Publisher
N.A.I.C.S.: 513210
Eli Dickinson *(Co-Founder & CTO)*
Sean Griffey *(Co-Founder & CEO)*
Ryan Willumson *(Co-Founder & Chief Revenue Officer)*
Meg Hargreaves *(COO)*
Noelle Knox *(Mng Editor)*
Robin Robinson *(Editor-PharmaVoice)*
Meagan Parrish *(Sr Editor-PharmaVoice)*
Taren Grom *(Co-Founder & Editor-in-Chief-PharmaVoice)*
Roberto Torres *(Editor-CIO Dive)*
Delilah Alvarado *(Assoc Editor)*
Edwin Lopez *(Mng Editor)*

Marquis Software Solutions, Inc. **(1)**
5208 Tennyson Pkwy Ste 120, Plano, TX 75024
Tel.: (800) 365-4274
Web Site: http://www.gomarquis.com
Custom Computer Programming Services
N.A.I.C.S.: 541511
Susan R. Faulkner *(CEO)*
Chip Irek *(CTO)*
Tony Rizzo *(CMO & Chief Creative Officer)*
Leslie Watson-Stracener *(Chief Compliance & Client Experience Officer)*
Curtis Hill *(Sr VP-Product Mgmt)*
Robin Sullivan *(Chief HR Officer)*

North American Transmission & Distribution Group **(1)**
c/o ITEC PO Box 23088, Charlotte, NC 28227-0272
Tel.: (704) 282-4331
Web Site: http://www.natdg.com
Holding Company
N.A.I.C.S.: 551112
Chip Johnson *(CFO)*
David Pacyna *(CEO)*

Subsidiary (Domestic):

Instrument Transformer Equipment Corporation **(2)**
2402 Walkup Ave, Monroe, NC 28110
Tel.: (704) 282-4331
Web Site: http://www.itec-ctvt.com
Revenue Metering & Protective Relaying Electrical Products Mfr & Whslr
N.A.I.C.S.: 334515
Clinton Gehimann *(Pres)*

Sauer Brands, Inc. **(1)**
2000 W Broad St, Richmond, VA 23220-2006
Tel.: (804) 359-5676
Web Site: http://www.cfsauer.com
Mayonnaise, Salad Products, Spices & Extracts Mfr
N.A.I.C.S.: 311942

Subsidiary (Domestic):

Metrolina Plastics, Inc. **(2)**
1800 W Marshall St, Richmond, VA 23220
Tel.: (804) 353-8990
Web Site: http://www.metrolinaplastics.com
Sales Range: $10-24.9 Million
Emp.: 23
Mfr of Plastic Jugs
N.A.I.C.S.: 326199
Richard Brisson *(Mgr-Ops)*

The Spice Hunter **(2)**
184 Suburban Rd, San Luis Obispo, CA 93401 **(100%)**
Tel.: (805) 544-4466
Web Site: http://www.spicehunter.com

Sales Range: $10-24.9 Million
Emp.: 101
Mfr of Spices & Extracts
N.A.I.C.S.: 311942
Pat Winkle *(Mgr-Production)*
Eric Stever *(Mgr-Quality Assurance)*
Daniela Massey *(Product Mgr-Dev)*

Synergy ECP, LLC **(1)**
6996 Columbia Gateway Dr Ste 101, Columbia, MD 21046-3302
Tel.: (443) 956-7055
Web Site: http://www.synergyecp.com
Custom Computer Programming Services
N.A.I.C.S.: 541511
Dave Wisniewski *(Co-Founder & CEO)*

Subsidiary (Domestic):

Softtech Solutions, Inc. **(2)**
8907 Sumner Grove Dr, Laurel, MD 20708-3535
Tel.: (410) 730-7445
Web Site: http://www.softtech-solutions.com
Custom Computer Programming Services
N.A.I.C.S.: 541511
Jane Lee *(Pres)*

FALK INDUSTRIES INC.
477 Madison Ave, New York, NY 10022
Tel.: (212) 966-2800
Sales Range: $10-24.9 Million
Emp.: 7
Piece Goods & Other Fabrics
N.A.I.C.S.: 424310
Maurice Falk *(Pres)*

FALK INTEGRATED TECH-NOLOGIES
2316 Golden Gate Dr Apt B, Greensboro, NC 27405-4341
Tel.: (336) 852-0455
Web Site:
http://www.falkcompanies.com
Year Founded: 1986
Sales Range: $10-24.9 Million
Emp.: 70
Computer Related Consulting Services
N.A.I.C.S.: 541512
Harry S. Falk *(Pres & CEO)*

Subsidiaries:

iWork Software LLC **(1)**
2316 Golden Gate Dr Apt B, Greensboro, NC 27405-4341
Tel.: (336) 852-0455
Web Site: http://www.falkcompanies.com
Rev.: $10,000,000
Emp.: 35
Computer Software Development
N.A.I.C.S.: 541511

FALL ADVERTISING
10960 Wheatlands Ave Ste 106, Santee, CA 92071-5617
Tel.: (619) 258-6225
Web Site: http://www.fallads.com
Year Founded: 1965
Sales Range: $10-24.9 Million
Emp.: 5
Advertising Agency
N.A.I.C.S.: 541810
Donald R. Fall *(Owner)*
Russ Turner *(Sr VP, Creative Dir & Acct Supvr)*
Dan Fall *(Media Buyer)*

FALL RIVER FIVE CENTS SAVINGS BANK
79 N Main St, Fall River, MA 02720
Tel.: (774) 888-6100   MA
Web Site: http://www.bankfive.com
Year Founded: 1855
Sales Range: $10-24.9 Million
Emp.: 160
Financial Services
N.A.I.C.S.: 522180
Michael Berriby *(CFO & Sr VP-Tres)*
Robert Collins *(VP-Credit)*

FALL RIVER HEALTH SYSTEM
1201 Highway 71 S, Hot Springs, SD 57747
Tel.: (605) 745-3159   SD
Web Site: https://www.frhssd.org
Year Founded: 1998
Sales Range: $10-24.9 Million
Emp.: 148
Health Care Srvices
N.A.I.C.S.: 622110
Paul Schoenfelder *(Dir-Nursing)*
Steven Larson *(CIO)*
Tricia Uhlir *(CEO)*
Jesse Naze *(CFO)*

FALL RIVER NEWS CO. INC.
144 Robeson St, Fall River, MA 02720
Tel.: (508) 679-5266   MA
Year Founded: 1964
Sales Range: $10-24.9 Million
Emp.: 135
Delivery of Newspapers & Magazines
N.A.I.C.S.: 424920
David W. Boland *(Pres & Controller)*
David Boland III *(VP)*

FALL RIVER RURAL ELECTRIC COOPERATIVE, INC.
1150 N 3400 E, Ashton, ID 83420
Tel.: (208) 652-7431
Web Site:
https://www.fallriverelectric.com
Sales Range: $10-24.9 Million
Emp.: 53
Electric Power Distr
N.A.I.C.S.: 221122
Bryan Case *(CEO & Gen Mgr)*

FALLBROOK PUBLIC UTILITY DISTRICT
990 E Mission Rd, Fallbrook, CA 92028
Tel.: (760) 728-1125
Web Site: https://www.fpud.com
Year Founded: 1922
Sales Range: $10-24.9 Million
Emp.: 67
Water Supply & Irrigation System Services
N.A.I.C.S.: 221310
Mike Page *(Mgr-Engrg & Construction)*

FALLBROOK TECHNOLOGIES INC.
505 Cypress Creek Rd Ste L, Cedar Park, TX 78613
Tel.: (512) 519-5300
Web Site:
http://www.fallbrooktech.com
Year Founded: 2000
Sales Range: $1-9.9 Million
Emp.: 47
Transmission Mfr
N.A.I.C.S.: 333613
Paul A. DeHart *(COO)*
Jeffrey A. Birchak *(Gen Counsel, Sec & VP-Intellectual Property)*
Robin Grey *(CFO)*

Subsidiaries:

Hodyon L.P. **(1)**
120 E Old Settlers Blvd, Round Rock, TX 78664
Tel.: (512) 225-0165
Web Site: http://www.hodyon.com
Energy Efficient Products & Systems Mfr & Distr
N.A.I.C.S.: 336390

Fallbrook Technologies Inc.—(Continued)

FALLER, DAVIS & ASSOCIATES, INC.

5525 W Cypress St Ste 300, Tampa, FL 33607
Tel.: (813) 261-5136
Web Site: http://www.fallerdavis.com
Year Founded: 1985
Sales Range: $1-9.9 Million
Emp.: 30
Engineering & Environmental Consulting Services
N.A.I.C.S.: 541330
Nancy Faller Brown *(Pres)*
Bruce G. Hasbrouck *(VP & Dir-Environ Svc)*
Douglas E. Williams *(VP & Mgr-Traffic Svcs)*
Kenneth R. Muzyk Jr. *(Exec VP)*

FALLON HEALTH

10 Chestnut St, Worcester, MA 01608
Tel.: (508) 799-2100   MA
Web Site: http://www.fallonhealth.org
Year Founded: 1975
Sales Range: $1-4.9 Billion
Health Care Srvices
N.A.I.C.S.: 622110
R. Scott Walker *(Exec VP)*
David Przesiek *(Chief Sls Officer & Sr VP)*
Christine Cassidy *(Chief Comm Officer & Sr VP)*
Richard P. Burke *(Pres & CEO)*
Kevin Grozio *(CFO & Sr VP)*
Ann K. Tripp *(Treas)*
B. John Dill *(Vice Chm)*
Mary Ritter *(Sr VP-Strategy & Bus Dev)*
Carolyn Langer *(Chief Medical Officer)*
Frederick M. Misilo Jr. *(Chm)*

FALLON LUMINOUS PRODUCTS CORPORATION

1412 Deleglise St, Antigo, WI 54409-1569
Tel.: (864) 576-6366   SC
Web Site: http://www.fallonneon.com
Year Founded: 1987
Sales Range: $25-49.9 Million
Emp.: 325
Provider of Signs & Advertising Specialties
N.A.I.C.S.: 339950

Subsidiaries:

FALLON Visual Products Corp.   (1)
1412 Deleglise St, Antigo, WI 54409-1569
Tel.: (715) 627-4373
Web Site: http://www.fallonneon.com
Rev.: $8,500,000
Emp.: 80
Signs & Advertising Specialties
N.A.I.C.S.: 339950

FALLON MEDICA LLC

620 Shrewsbury Ave, Tinton Falls, NJ 07701
Tel.: (732) 345-3500
Web Site: http://www.clinedavis.com
Year Founded: 2002
Sales Range: $10-24.9 Million
Emp.: 30
N.A.I.C.S.: 541810
Timothy Fallon *(Pres)*
Bina O'Brien *(VP-Ops)*

FALLS COMMUNICATIONS, INC

Terminal Tower 50 Public Sq Fl 25, Cleveland, OH 44113
Tel.: (216) 696-0229   OH
Web Site: https://fallsandco.com
Year Founded: 1989

Public Relations & Marketing Services
N.A.I.C.S.: 541820
Tom Bernot *(Pres & COO)*
Robert Falls *(Chm & CEO)*

Subsidiaries:

Wyse Advertising, Inc.   (1)
668 Euclid Ave, Cleveland, OH 44114
Tel.: (216) 696-2424
Advertising Agencies
N.A.I.C.S.: 541810

FALLS COMMUNITY HOSPITAL & CLINIC

322 Coleman St, Marlin, TX 76661
Tel.: (254) 803-3561   TX
Web Site: https://www.fallshospital.com
Year Founded: 1960
Sales Range: $10-24.9 Million
Emp.: 234
Health Care Srvices
N.A.I.C.S.: 622110
Jeff Johnson *(Dir-Radiology)*
Jan Stimmel *(Dir-Clinic Ops)*
Dileep Bhateley *(Dir-Laboratory)*
Donna Ryan *(Mgr-Laboratory)*

FALLS SIDING, INC.

3844 Oak Ridge Ct, Colgate, WI 53017
Tel.: (262) 628-0808   WI
Web Site: http://www.fallssiding.com
Year Founded: 1982
Sales Range: $1-9.9 Million
Emp.: 10
Siding Contractors
N.A.I.C.S.: 238170
James A. Johnson *(Pres)*

FALLSWAY EQUIPMENT CO., INC.

PO Box 4537, Akron, OH 44310-0537
Tel.: (330) 633-6000   OH
Web Site: http://www.fallsway.com
Year Founded: 1959
Sales Range: $25-49.9 Million
Emp.: 135
Service & Rental of Industrial Machinery & Equipment
N.A.I.C.S.: 423830
Jeff McDiffitt *(Mgr-Svc)*

FALMOUTH TOYOTA, INC.

290 MacArthur Blvd, Bourne, MA 02532
Tel.: (508) 759-1900
Web Site: https://www.falmouthtoyota.com
Year Founded: 1980
Sales Range: $10-24.9 Million
Emp.: 40
Car Whslr
N.A.I.C.S.: 441110
Bob Andrews *(Mgr-Parts & Svc)*

FALVEY LINEN SUPPLY INC.

50 Burnham Ave, Cranston, RI 02910-1410
Tel.: (401) 942-8900
Web Site: https://www.falveylinen.com
Sales Range: $10-24.9 Million
Emp.: 110
Linen Supply
N.A.I.C.S.: 812331
Jim O'Hara *(Pres)*
Donald Maida *(VP-Ops)*
Mike Fabiano *(Branch Mgr)*
Kaitlin Ohara *(Mgr)*

FALVEY'S MOTORS, INC.

395 W Thames St, Norwich, CT 06360-6751
Tel.: (860) 300-2239

Web Site: https://www.falveys.com
Year Founded: 1983
Sales Range: $10-24.9 Million
Emp.: 75
Car Whslr
N.A.I.C.S.: 441110
Richard Falvey Jr. *(Pres)*

FAMA PR, INC.

Liberty Wharf 250 Northern Ave Ste 300, Boston, MA 02210
Tel.: (617) 986-5002
Web Site: http://www.famapr.com
Year Founded: 2002
Sales Range: $1-9.9 Million
Public Relations
N.A.I.C.S.: 541820
Matt Flanagan *(Founding Partner)*
Ed Harrison *(Mng Partner)*
Keith Watson *(Founding Partner)*

FAMC CORPORATION

501 Corporate Ctr Dr Ste 400, Franklin, TN 37067
Tel.: (615) 778-1000
Web Site: http://www.franklinamerican.com
Sales Range: $1-9.9 Million
Emp.: 150
Full Service Mortgage Banker
N.A.I.C.S.: 522292
Daniel G. Crockett *(Pres & CEO)*
Andrew R. Taylor *(Exec VP & Dir-Natl Sls)*
Robert C. Frank *(Exec VP & Dir-Wholesale Ops)*
Dutch Schorgl *(VP-Production)*
Michael George *(VP-Wholesale Ops)*
Thomas H. Williams *(Sr VP & Mgr-Ops)*
Holly Sedgwick *(Acct Exec)*

Subsidiaries:

Franklin American Mortgage Company (FAMC)   (1)
470 Forest Ave, Portland, ME 04101   (100%)
Tel.: (207) 879-4393
Web Site: http://www.franklinamerican.com
Emp.: 4
Retail Mortgage Brokers
N.A.I.C.S.: 522310
Garrett Ryan *(Branch Mgr)*

Franklin American Mortgage Company (FAMC)   (1)
6100 Tower Cir Ste 600, Franklin, TN 37067   (100%)
Tel.: (615) 778-1000
Web Site: http://www.franklinamerican.com
Retail Mortgage Brokers
N.A.I.C.S.: 522310

FAMILIES FORWARD PHILADELPHIA

111 N 49th St, Philadelphia, PA 19139
Tel.: (215) 240-4800   PA
Web Site: https://www.familiesforwardphilly.org
Year Founded: 1915
Sales Range: $1-9.9 Million
Emp.: 100
Homeless Family Assistance Services
N.A.I.C.S.: 624221
Jennifer L. Bellot *(Pres)*
David Michelson *(CFO)*

FAMILY & CHILDREN'S ASSOCIATION

100 E Old Country Rd, Mineola, NY 11501
Tel.: (516) 746-0350   NY
Web Site: http://www.familyandchildrens.org
Year Founded: 1998
Sales Range: $10-24.9 Million
Emp.: 465

Community Action Services
N.A.I.C.S.: 624190
H. Richard Grafer *(Vice Chm)*
Judy Sanford Guise *(Sec)*
Drew Crowley *(Chm)*
Thurston O'Neal *(Asst VP-Prevention & Community Engagement)*
Jeffrey L. Reynolds *(Pres & CEO)*

FAMILY & CHILDREN'S CENTER

1707 Main St, La Crosse, WI 54601
Tel.: (608) 785-0001   WI
Web Site: https://www.fcconline.org
Year Founded: 1881
Sales Range: $10-24.9 Million
Emp.: 382
Family Support Services
N.A.I.C.S.: 624190
Vanessa Southworth *(Dir-Svcs)*
Diane Weigel *(CFO)*
Rich Petro *(Dir-HR)*
Tita Yutuc *(Pres & CEO)*

FAMILY & CHILDRENS SERVICES

650 S Peoria Ave, Tulsa, OK 74120
Tel.: (918) 587-9471   OK
Web Site: https://www.fcsok.org
Year Founded: 1944
Sales Range: $10-24.9 Million
Emp.: 617
Individual & Family Support Services
N.A.I.C.S.: 623220
Jan Dietrich *(CFO)*
Alan Bingham *(Dir-HR)*
Trent A. Gudgel *(VP-Programs & Quality)*
Chris Murphy *(VP-Fin)*
Gail Lapidus *(CEO)*
Steve Wyett *(Pres)*

FAMILY & COMMUNITY SERVICES, INC.

705 Oakwood St Ste 221, Ravenna, OH 44266
Tel.: (330) 297-7027   OH
Web Site: http://www.fcsohio.org
Year Founded: 1941
Sales Range: $10-24.9 Million
Emp.: 528
Individual & Family Support Services
N.A.I.C.S.: 624190
Greg Musci *(Dir-Fin)*
Paul Huchok *(Treas)*
Alice Hurd *(Sec)*
Jackie Parsons *(Pres)*
Todd Goodwin *(Exec Dir)*

FAMILY ALLERGY & ASTHMA

9800 Shelbyville Rd Ste 220, Louisville, KY 40223
Tel.: (502) 429-8585
Web Site: https://www.familyallergy.com
Year Founded: 1979
Rev.: $12,900,000
Emp.: 85
Medical Devices
N.A.I.C.S.: 621111
Stephen Pollard *(Co-Founder)*
Timothy Feger *(Sr Partner)*
Kay Tyler *(Office Mgr)*

FAMILY CENTER OF HARRISONVILLE INC.

2601 Cantrell Rd, Harrisonville, MO 64701
Tel.: (816) 884-6100
Web Site: http://www.familycenter.us.com
Sales Range: $10-24.9 Million
Emp.: 93
Hardware Stores
N.A.I.C.S.: 444140
Bill Manion *(Mgr)*

FAMILY CENTERS, INC.
40 Arch St, Greenwich, CT 06830
Tel.: (203) 869-4848   CT
Web Site:
https://www.familycenters.org
Year Founded: 1995
Sales Range: $10-24.9 Million
Emp.: 215
Individual & Family Support Services
N.A.I.C.S.: 624190
Bill Brucker *(Dir-Comm)*
Marion Beale *(Dir-Fin)*
Laurie Grauer *(Vice Chm)*
Mike McKeever *(Treas)*
Bob Arnold *(Pres & CEO)*
Laurie Host *(Chm)*
Nancy Casserley *(Vice Chm)*
Kate Clark *(Sec)*
Jennifer Flatow *(Dir-Community Engagement)*
Aleksa Lazarewicz-Anstey *(Mgr-Special Events)*
Kate McCallum *(Mgr-Site)*
Donna Spellman *(Dir-Self Sufficiency & Independent Living)*
Megan Sweeney *(Dir-ECE & Head Start Preschools/School Readiness)*
Alex Fichter *(Mgr-Site Warburg Center)*
Helma Gregorich *(Sr Mgr-Nurturing Families Network)*
Dena Mastrangelo *(Dir-HR)*
Leslie Sexer *(Dir-Clinical Outreach Svcs & WorkLife Solutions)*
Dennis Torres *(Dir-Healthcare Svcs)*
Stephanie Johnson *(CFO)*

FAMILY CENTRAL INC.
840 SW 81st Ave, North Lauderdale, FL 33068
Tel.: (561) 514-3300
Web Site:
http://www.familycentral.org
Rev.: $162,000,000
Emp.: 500
Child & Youth Services
N.A.I.C.S.: 624110
Barbara-Ann Weinstein *(Pres & CEO)*
Richard G. Schagrin *(Treas)*
Allan A. Joseph *(Chm)*
Jennifer Coleman *(VP-HR)*
Wendy Salomon *(Chief Program Officer)*
Ana M. Barranco *(Mgr)*
Claudia Lear *(Mgr)*
Mark Gross *(VP-Program Res & Dev)*
Norma Bonet *(Mgr)*
Lisa K. Aronson *(Dir-Dev)*
Joseph Pannullo *(CFO)*

FAMILY CHEVROLET CADILLAC
4050 Mother Lode Dr, Shingle Springs, CA 95682-8494
Tel.: (530) 677-2999
Year Founded: 1982
Sales Range: $10-24.9 Million
Emp.: 36
New Car Whslr
N.A.I.C.S.: 441110
Tony Montalbano *(Owner & Pres)*

FAMILY CHRISTIAN STORES INC.
5300 Patterson Ave SE, Grand Rapids, MI 49530
Tel.: (616) 554-8700
Web Site:
http://www.familychristian.com
Sales Range: $300-349.9 Million
Emp.: 4,500
Book Stores
N.A.I.C.S.: 459210
Dennis Tyson *(Dir-Store Dev)*
Lindsay Weiskittel *(Mgr-Content)*
Darryl Tawney *(Mgr-Customer Svc)*

Nate Elston *(Mgr-E-Commerce)*
Holly Sofia *(Mgr-Mdsg)*
Bill Tucker *(Mgr-Mdsg)*
Craig Klamer *(Sr VP-Supply Chain)*
Jessica Bowers *(Supvr-Benefits)*
Mike Bowles *(Asst VP-Ministry Initiatives)*
Lisa Fulton *(Coord-Mdse Admin Dept)*
Kimberly Griffin *(Mgr-Digital Adv)*
Sue Boylan *(Mgr-E-Commerce Mdse)*
Linda Petersen *(Mgr-Mdse & Gift Dept)*
Tim Way *(Mgr-Mdse Div)*
Todd Headen *(Mgr-Mdsg)*
Laurel Book *(Sr Mgr-Mdse)*
Olivia Marx *(Sr VP-Mdse)*
Michael Jardina *(VP-Stores)*
Charles Bengochea *(Pres & CEO)*
Rick Jackson *(Chm)*
Mark Haase Jr. *(Mgr-Mdse Sys)*

Subsidiaries:

Gathering Place Books & Coffee Inc.   (1)
101 W Broad St, Falls Church, VA 22046
Web Site: http://www.familychristian.com
Rev.: $510,000
Emp.: 10
Book Stores
N.A.I.C.S.: 459210

FAMILY CHRYSLER DODGE JEEP RAM
6735-39 Essington Ave, Philadelphia, PA 19153
Tel.: (215) 883-8451
Web Site:
https://www.familyautos.com
Year Founded: 1956
Sales Range: $25-49.9 Million
Emp.: 48
New Car Dealers
N.A.I.C.S.: 441110
Frank Ingargiola *(Gen Mgr-Sls)*
Bryan Boice *(Asst Mgr-Sls)*
German Konig *(Mgr-Fin & Insurance)*
Amanda Gentile *(Coord-Internet Sls & Mktg)*

FAMILY DAIRIES USA
4001 Nakoosa Trl Ste 100, Madison, WI 53714-1381
Tel.: (608) 244-3373   WI
Web Site:
http://www.formfirstdairycoop.com
Year Founded: 1971
Sales Range: $10-24.9 Million
Emp.: 8
Producer of Dairy Products
N.A.I.C.S.: 424430
Peter Kleiman *(Pres)*
Tina Larson *(Controller)*

FAMILY EMPOWERMENT COUNCIL, INC.
225 Dolson Ave Ste 403, Middletown, NY 10940
Tel.: (845) 343-8100   NY
Web Site:
http://www.familyempowerment.org
Year Founded: 1993
Sales Range: $10-24.9 Million
Emp.: 630
Disability Assistance Services
N.A.I.C.S.: 624120
Lori Lentini *(VP-HR & Quality Assurance)*
Ronald J. Colavito *(VP-Indus Ops & Program Svcs)*
Amy Anderson-Winchell *(CEO)*
Katariina Hoaas *(VP-Clinical & Program Svcs)*
Maude A. Rosado *(CFO)*

FAMILY ER + URGENT CARE

1415 Legacy Dr Ste 250, Frisco, TX 75034
Tel.: (214) 447-0381
Web Site: http://www.familyer.com
Medical Emergency & Urgent Care Centers
N.A.I.C.S.: 621493
Scott Pickett *(CEO)*

Subsidiaries:

Texas Emergency Care Centers, LLC   (1)
25202 NW Frwy Ste H, Cypress, TX 77429-1106
Tel.: (832) 220-1290
Web Site: http://www.txercare.com
Emergency Medical Care Centers
N.A.I.C.S.: 621493
Rhonda Sandel *(CEO)*

FAMILY FEDERATION FOR WORLD PEACE & UNIFICATION
3224 16th St NW, Washington, DC 20010
Tel.: (202) 319-3200
Web Site: http://www.familyfed.org
Year Founded: 1977
Sales Range: $10-24.9 Million
Emp.: 30
Publishing Services
N.A.I.C.S.: 813990
Thomas Walsh *(Pres)*

Subsidiaries:

Atlantic Video Inc.   (1)
1133 19th St Nw Ste 800, Washington, DC 20036-3655
Tel.: (202) 408-0900
Web Site: http://www.atlanticvideo.com
Provider of Motion Picture & Video Production Services
N.A.I.C.S.: 512110

ILHWA American Corporation   (1)
24 Link Dr, Rockleigh, NJ 07647-2504
Tel.: (973) 759-1996
Sales Range: Less than $1 Million
Emp.: 1
Provider of Grocery Services
N.A.I.C.S.: 424490

Manhattan Center Studios Inc.   (1)
311 W 34th St 5th Fl, New York, NY 10001-2402
Tel.: (212) 279-7740
Web Site: http://www.mcstudios.com
Sales Range: $10-24.9 Million
Provider of Business Services
N.A.I.C.S.: 512240
Jessica Rothstein Berman *(VP-Sls)*
Markus Karr *(Pres)*

News World Communications, Inc.   (1)
3600 New York Ave NE, Washington, DC 20002-1947
Tel.: (202) 636-3000
Web Site: http://www.washingtontimes.com
Publisher of Daily Newspapers
N.A.I.C.S.: 541840

Subsidiary (Domestic):
The Washington Times, LLC   (2)
3600 New York Ave NE, Washington, DC 20002-1947
Tel.: (202) 636-3000
Web Site: http://www.washingtontimes.com
News Print Organization
N.A.I.C.S.: 513199
David Dadisman *(Gen Mgr)*
Christopher Dolan *(Pres & Exec Editor)*
Adam Vercammen *(Dir-Digital & Mktg)*
Ian Bishop *(Editor-Digital)*
Greg Groesch *(Editor-Graphics)*
Victor Morton *(Editor-News-Natl)*

United Press International, Inc.   (2)
1133 19th St NW Ste 800, Washington, DC 20036
Tel.: (202) 898-8000
Web Site: http://www.upi.com
News & Information Services
N.A.I.C.S.: 516210

One Up Enterprises Inc.   (1)
7777 Leesburg Pke Ste 406N, Falls Church, VA 22043-2403
Tel.: (703) 448-7333
Sales Range: $10-24.9 Million
Emp.: 4
Provider of Publishing Services
N.A.I.C.S.: 513130

Subsidiary (Domestic):
True World Group, Inc.   (2)
24 Link Dr, Rockleigh, NJ 07647
Tel.: (201) 750-0024
Web Site: http://www.trueworldgroup.com
Wholesale Seafood
N.A.I.C.S.: 311710

Subsidiary (Domestic):
True World Foods Chicago LLC   (3)
950 Chase Ave, Elk Grove Village, IL 60007-4828
Tel.: (201) 750-0024
Web Site: http://www.trueworldfoods.com
Provider of Grocery Services
N.A.I.C.S.: 424460

True World Foods International, Inc.   (3)
1515 Puyallup St, Sumner, WA 98390
Tel.: (253) 826-3700
Web Site: http://www.kanimi.com
Emp.: 160
Imitation Crab Meat Mfr
N.A.I.C.S.: 311710

Subsidiary (Domestic):
New Hope Marine Inc.   (4)
2620 W Commodore Way, Seattle, WA 98199
Tel.: (206) 286-6683
Boat Repair Services
N.A.I.C.S.: 713930

Subsidiary (Domestic):
True World Foods Miami LLC   (3)
11205 NW 36th Ave, Miami, FL 33167-3306
Tel.: (305) 687-4303
Web Site: http://www.trueworldfoods.com
Supplier of Fish & Seafoods
N.A.I.C.S.: 424460
Tomio Goto *(Mgr-Facility)*
Mark Takagi *(Pres)*

True World Foods New York LLC   (3)
32 34 Papetti Plz, Elizabeth, NJ 07206-1421
Tel.: (908) 351-1400
Web Site: http://www.trueworldfoods.com
Supplier of Fish & Seafoods
N.A.I.C.S.: 424460
Sangsu Choe *(Gen Mgr)*

True World Foods San Francisco LLC   (3)
1815 Williams Sta, San Leandro, CA 94577-2301
Tel.: (510) 352-8081
Web Site: http://www.trueworldfoods.com
Supplier of Fish & Seafoods
N.A.I.C.S.: 424460

True World Foods Seattle LLC   (3)
1501 S 92nd Pl Ste D, Seattle, WA 98108-5103
Tel.: (206) 766-8006
Web Site: http://www.trueworldfoods.com
Supplier of Fish & Seafoods
N.A.I.C.S.: 424460

True World Foods, Inc. of Hawaii   (3)
2696 Waiwai Loop, Honolulu, HI 96819-1938
Tel.: (808) 836-3222
Web Site: http://www.trueworldfoods.com
Supplier of Fish & Seafoods
N.A.I.C.S.: 424460

True World Foods-Alaska   (3)
517 Shelikof St, Kodiak, AK 99615-6049
Tel.: (907) 486-5741
Sales Range: $10-24.9 Million
Emp.: 300
Provider of Fresh & Frozen Packaged Fish Services
N.A.I.C.S.: 722511
Sune Forsman *(Gen Mgr)*

Family Federation for World Peace &
Unification—(Continued)

Stellar Printing Inc.   **(1)**
3838 Ninth St, Long Island City, NY 11101-
6110
Tel.: (718) 361-1600
Sales Range: $10-24.9 Million
Provider of Commercial Printing Services
N.A.I.C.S.: 323111
Jessica Morales Velez (Dir-Personnel)
Bill Ednie (Mgr-Ops)
Dirk Anthonis (Pres)
Richard Summers (MgrPost Press & Acct
Exec)

FAMILY FOCUS, INC.
310 S Peoria St Ste 301, Chicago, IL
60607
Tel.: (312) 421-5200   **IL**
Web Site: http://www.family-focus.org
Year Founded: 1975
Sales Range: $10-24.9 Million
Emp.: 640
Individual & Family Support Services
N.A.I.C.S.: 624190
Sarah Holliday (Asst Dir-Grants)
Gail Waters (Controller)
Carolyn Nopar (Dir-Dev)
Caterina Varvaro (SR VP-Admin &
Fin)
Andrea Tobias (Office Mgr)
Alisha Flores (Dir-Community
Schools & Youth)
Charles Johnson (Dir-Facilities &
Tech)
Rosaura Realegeno (Dir-Sr Center)
Steve Majsak (Sr VP-External Rels)
Mariana Osoria (VP-Centers)
Colette Allen (Dir-Evanston Center)
Darren Harris (Dir-Family Svcs)
Merri Ex (Pres & CEO)
Loretta Barriffe (VP-Centers)
Sherneron Hilliard (VP-Early Child-
hood Education & Programs)

FAMILY FOODS OF GATES-
VILLE
104 Ct St, Gatesville, NC 27938
Tel.: (252) 357-0241
Web Site:
  http://www.familyfoodssuper
  markets.com
Rev.: $16,000,000
Emp.: 3
Independent Supermarket
N.A.I.C.S.: 445110

FAMILY FORD INC.
30 Rte New Jersey 183, Netcong, NJ
07857
Tel.: (973) 347-3000   **NJ**
Web Site:
  http://www.familyfordnj.com
Year Founded: 1978
Rev.: $25,000,000
Emp.: 45
Car Dealership
N.A.I.C.S.: 441110
Bob Taiber (Dir-Svcs)
Tom Maino (Dir-Fixed Ops)

FAMILY FORD LINCOLN
831 Straits Tpke, Watertown, CT
06795
Tel.: (860) 880-1206
Web Site: https://www.familyford.com
Sales Range: $10-24.9 Million
Emp.: 62
Car Whslr
N.A.I.C.S.: 441110
Corey Shaker (Pres)

FAMILY FORD OF EINFIELD
65 Hazard Ave, Enfield, CT 06082-
3813
Tel.: (860) 745-1111

Web Site:
  http://familyfordofenfield.com
Sales Range: $10-24.9 Million
New & Used Automobiles Retailer
N.A.I.C.S.: 441110
Greg Larouche (Mgr-Internet Sls)

FAMILY FURNITURE CENTERS
INC.
7870 Central Ave, Landover, MD
20785
Tel.: (301) 499-4300
Web Site:
  http://www.familyfurniture.com
Sales Range: $1-9.9 Million
Emp.: 50
Furniture Retailer
N.A.I.C.S.: 449110
Norman Guilden (Co-Pres)

FAMILY GUIDANCE CENTERS,
INC.
310 W Chicago Ave, Chicago, IL
60654
Tel.: (312) 943-6545   **IL**
Web Site: https://www.fgcinc.org
Year Founded: 1968
Sales Range: $10-24.9 Million
Emp.: 283
Behavioral Healthcare Services
N.A.I.C.S.: 623220
Allison Alexander (VP)

FAMILY HEALTH & HOUSING
FOUNDATION INC.
15760 Ventura Blvd Ste 920, Encino,
CA 91436
Tel.: (818) 905-8000   **CA**
Year Founded: 2000
Sales Range: $10-24.9 Million
Emp.: 462
Continuing Care Retirement Commu-
nity Operator
N.A.I.C.S.: 623311
Cordero Emmanuel Maralit (Dir-
Nursing)
Moore Corona (Asst Dir-Nursing)

FAMILY HEALTH CENTER
1600 Providence Dr, Waco, TX
76707
Tel.: (254) 313-4200   **TX**
Web Site: http://www.wacofhc.org
Year Founded: 1998
Sales Range: $25-49.9 Million
Emp.: 550
Community Health Care Services
N.A.I.C.S.: 621498
D. Michael Hardin (Dir-Residency
Program)
Kelley Reynolds (Chief Medical Offi-
cer)
Roland Goertz (CEO)
John Shultz (Chief Dev Officer)
Antonio Falcon (Dir-Medical-Rio
Grande City)

FAMILY HEALTH CENTER INC.
117 W Paterson St, Kalamazoo, MI
49007
Tel.: (269) 349-4257   **MI**
Web Site: http://www.fhckzoo.com
Year Founded: 1971
Sales Range: $10-24.9 Million
Emp.: 241
Health Care Srvices
N.A.I.C.S.: 622110

FAMILY HEALTH CENTERS OF
SOUTHWEST FLORIDA INC.
2232 Grand Ave, Fort Myers, FL
33901
Tel.: (239) 278-3600
Web Site: https://www.fhcswf.org
Sales Range: $25-49.9 Million
Emp.: 440

Medical & Dental Services
N.A.I.C.S.: 621498
Jorge M. Quinonez (Chief Medical
Officer & Exec VP)
Marie Andress (CFO & Sr VP)
Trri Buchanan (VP-Admin Svcs)
Frank Mazzeo Jr. (Pres & CEO)

FAMILY HEALTH CENTERS,
INC.
3310 Magnolia St, Orangeburg, SC
29115
Tel.: (803) 531-6900   **SC**
Web Site: https://www.myfhc.org
Year Founded: 1970
Sales Range: $10-24.9 Million
Emp.: 176
Health Care Srvices
N.A.I.C.S.: 622110
Doris Haigler (COO)
Kevan Coffey (Dir-Medical)
Jesus Hernandez (CEO)

FAMILY HEALTH SERVICES
CORPORATION
794 Eastland Dr, Twin Falls, ID
83301
Tel.: (208) 734-3312   **ID**
Web Site: https://www.fhsid.org
Year Founded: 1982
Sales Range: $10-24.9 Million
Emp.: 246
Community Health Care Services
N.A.I.C.S.: 621498
Cindy Lohmann (Dir-Ops)
Adam Hodges (Dir-Dental)
Camille Smith (Dir-Medical)
Chris Wingfield (CIO)
Aaron Houston (CFO)
John Varin (VP)
Lynn Hudgens (CEO)
Marta Hernandez (Treas & Sec)
Melody Lefler (Pres)
Patty Kleinkopf (COO)
Tori Torgrimson (Dir-Behavioral
Health)
Yolanda Cabello (Dir-Nursing)
Cheryl Phillips (Dir-HR)

FAMILY HEALTHCARE
301 NP Ave, Fargo, ND 58102
Tel.: (701) 271-3344   **ND**
Web Site:
  http://www.famhealthcarefargo.org
Year Founded: 1993
Sales Range: $10-24.9 Million
Emp.: 137
Health Care Srvices
N.A.I.C.S.: 622110
Andrea Wilson (Dir-Dental)
Al Frisinger (Mgr-Facilities)
Pat Gulbranson (COO)
Patricia Patron (CEO)
Sam Kundinger (Chief Bus Dev Offi-
cer)

FAMILY HOME HEALTH SER-
VICES LLC
801 W Ann Arbor Trl Ste 200, Plym-
outh, MI 48170
Tel.: (734) 414-9990
Web Site:
  http://www.familycaresforyou.com
Sales Range: $10-24.9 Million
Emp.: 2,000
Blood & Organ Banks
N.A.I.C.S.: 621991
Kevin R. Ruark (Pres & CEO)
James H. Pilkington (Chief Dev Offi-
cer)
James M. Mitchell (CFO)
Vicki L. Welty (Exec Dir-Home Health
Ops)
Tina M. Griffith (Dir-IT)

FAMILY HOME HEALTH SER-
VICES, INC.
2171 Executive Dr Ste 450, Addison,
IL 60101
Tel.: (630) 317-3300   **NV**
Web Site: http://www.familyhhs.com
Sales Range: $10-24.9 Million
Emp.: 350
Women Healthcare Services
N.A.I.C.S.: 621610
Deb Muffoletto (COO)

FAMILY INNS OF AMERICA,
INC.
3124 Tammy King Rd, Pigeon Forge,
TN 37863-3335
Tel.: (865) 453-4988   **TN**
Year Founded: 1972
Sales Range: $25-49.9 Million
Emp.: 750
Motels, Restaurants & Lounges
Owner & Operator
N.A.I.C.S.: 533110
Harold Foshie (Controller)
Jeffrey Stewart (Mgr-Desk)

Subsidiaries:

Group Sales Divison   **(1)**
PO Box 10, Pigeon Forge, TN
37868-0010   **(100%)**
Tel.: (865) 453-4988
Web Site: http://www.grandresorthotel.com
Sales Range: $10-24.9 Million
Emp.: 5
Real Estate Development Firm
N.A.I.C.S.: 541910

Innco Management Corp.   **(1)**
8167 Kingston Pike, Knoxville, TN
37919-5446   **(33.33%)**
Tel.: (865) 453-4988
Sales Range: $25-49.9 Million
Emp.: 74
Motel, Restaurant & Lounge
N.A.I.C.S.: 541611

Kenneth M. Seaton Enterprises   **(1)**
3124 Tammy King Rd, Pigeon Forge, TN
37863   **(100%)**
Tel.: (865) 453-4988
Sales Range: $10-24.9 Million
Emp.: 125
Motel & Real Estate Development Firm
N.A.I.C.S.: 721110

Profit Management Corp.   **(1)**
3124 Tammy King Rd, Kingston, TN
37763   **(51%)**
Tel.: (865) 453-4988
Sales Range: $10-24.9 Million
Emp.: 70
Motel, Restaurant & Lounge
N.A.I.C.S.: 721110

FAMILY LEAGUE OF BALTI-
MORE CITY, INC.
2305 N Charles St Ste 200, Balti-
more, MD 21218
Tel.: (410) 662-5500   **MD**
Web Site: http://www.flbcinc.org
Year Founded: 1991
Sales Range: $10-24.9 Million
Emp.: 41
Child Care & Development Services
N.A.I.C.S.: 624410
Demaune A. Millard (COO)
Jeff Walley (CFO)
Julia Baez (Chief Strategy Officer)
Amy L. Bernstein (Dir-External Rels)
Amanda Moderson-Kox (Dir-Res &
Evaluation)
Bruce Nelson (Dir-High School Initia-
tives)
Glenn Love (Dir-Equity & Opportu-
nity)
Kim Eisenreich (Dir-School Support
Program)
Karen Janssen (Sr Dir-Funded Part-
nerships)
Keianna Thompson (Dir-Fin)

Laura Latta *(Dir-Early Childhood Initiatives)*
Yasmin Viera *(Dir-Partnership Mgmt)*
Jonathon Rondeau *(Pres & CEO)*

FAMILY LEGACY MISSIONS INTERNATIONAL

5005 W Royal Ln Ste 252, Irving, TX 75063
Tel.: (972) 620-2020   TX
Web Site:
    http://www.familylegacy.com
Year Founded: 2000
Sales Range: $10-24.9 Million
Emp.: 50
Orphan Relief Services
N.A.I.C.S.: 624410
Doug Harrison *(CFO & COO)*
Andrew Knight *(Dir-Sponsorship Ministries)*
Anne Ferguson *(Chief Program Officer)*
Holly Scurry *(Chief Dev Officer & Sr VP)*
Susan Kendall *(Dir-Short Term Missions)*
Sommer Clayman *(CFO)*
Classie Pierre *(VP-HR)*

FAMILY MANAGEMENT CORPORATION

3420 S Post Rd, Indianapolis, IN 46239
Tel.: (317) 862-9100
Rev.: $38,000,000
Emp.: 100
Automobiles & Other Motor Vehicles
N.A.I.C.S.: 423110
Tom Schuler *(CFO)*

FAMILY MARKETS LLC

1611 N Reynolds Rd, Bryant, AR 72022
Tel.: (501) 847-7964
Web Site:
    http://www.summerwoodpartners.com
Rev.: $10,700,000
Emp.: 10
Grocery Stores, Chain
N.A.I.C.S.: 445110
David Hendrix *(Pres)*
Bobby Gather *(Controller)*

FAMILY MORTGAGE INC.

4600 Military Trl Ste 201, Jupiter, FL 33458
Tel.: (561) 625-2660
Web Site:
    http://www.familymortgage.com
Sales Range: $25-49.9 Million
Emp.: 10
Mortgage Services
N.A.I.C.S.: 522292
Evan McDonough *(Gen Mgr)*
R. F. McDonough Jr. *(Pres)*

FAMILY MOTORS GROUP

6000 Wible Rd, Bakersfield, CA 93313
Tel.: (661) 617-6200
Web Site:
    http://www.familymotorsgroup.com
Sales Range: $50-74.9 Million
Emp.: 85
Automobiles, New & Used
N.A.I.C.S.: 441110
Jose Arredondo *(Pres)*

FAMILY RESEARCH COUNCIL

801 G St NW, Washington, DC 20001
Tel.: (800) 225-4008   DC
Web Site: http://www.frc.org
Year Founded: 1992
Sales Range: $10-24.9 Million

Emp.: 97
Family Support Services
N.A.I.C.S.: 624190
J. P. Duffy *(Sr VP-Comm)*
William G. Boykin *(Exec VP)*
David Christensen *(VP-Govt Affairs)*
Robert Schwarzwalder *(Sr VP)*
Paul Tripodi *(VP-Admin)*
Doug Gillquist *(VP-Dev)*
Tony Perkins *(Pres)*
Travis Weber *(Dir-Policy & Govt Affairs)*
Gil Mertz *(Dir-Foundations)*
Quena Gonzalez *(Dir-State & Local Affairs)*
Chrysta Johnson *(Mgr-Events)*
Jared Bridges *(VP-Brand Advancement)*
Kenyn Cureton *(VP-Church Ministries)*
J. Christopher Curry *(Dir-Charitable Gift Plng)*
Mary Szoch *(Dir-Human Dignity)*

FAMILY RESIDENCES AND ESSENTIAL ENTERPRISES INC.

191 Bethpage-Sweet Hollow Rd, Old Bethpage, NY 11804-1314
Tel.: (516) 870-1600   NY
Web Site: http://www.familyres.org
Year Founded: 1977
Sales Range: $75-99.9 Million
Emp.: 2,034
Intellectual & Developmental Disability Assistance Services
N.A.I.C.S.: 623210
Robert S. Budd *(Pres & CEO)*

FAMILY RESTAURANTS INC.

2706 W Colfax Ave, Denver, CO 80204
Tel.: (303) 534-3773
Sales Range: $10-24.9 Million
Emp.: 400
Family Restaurants
N.A.I.C.S.: 722511
David Lidvall *(Pres)*
Michael Scott *(CEO)*

FAMILY SAVINGS CREDIT UNION

711 E Meighan Blvd, Gadsden, AL 35903
Tel.: (256) 543-9530   AL
Web Site:
    https://www.familysavingscu.com
Year Founded: 1951
Sales Range: $10-24.9 Million
Emp.: 203
Credit Union
N.A.I.C.S.: 522130
Monte J. Hill *(CEO)*
Robert Rayburn *(Chief Lending Officer)*
Deborah Huff *(CFO)*
Danny Varnon *(Exec VP)*

FAMILY SECURITY CREDIT UNION

2204 Family Security Pl SW, Decatur, AL 35603
Tel.: (256) 340-2000   AL
Web Site: https://www.myfscu.com
Year Founded: 1953
Sales Range: $25-49.9 Million
Emp.: 235
Financial Support Services
N.A.I.C.S.: 523999
Zachary Howell *(VP-Mktg & Admin)*
Debra McCaghren *(VP-Fin & Office Ops)*
J. Cole Sharp *(VP-Lending & Branch Ops)*
M. Shane Nobbley *(Pres & CEO)*

FAMILY SERVICE ASSOCIATION

21250 Box Springs Rd, Moreno Valley, CA 92557
Tel.: (951) 686-1096   CA
Web Site: https://www.fsaca.org
Year Founded: 1953
Sales Range: $10-24.9 Million
Emp.: 580
Family Support Services
N.A.I.C.S.: 624190
Veronica Dover *(Co-COO)*
Judith Wood *(COO-Child Dev)*
Dominick Betro *(CEO)*
Ellie Bennett *(Sec)*
David Demers *(Treas)*
Lugena Wahlquist *(Vice Chm)*
Jane Adams *(Chm)*
Richard Teichert *(CFO)*

FAMILY SERVICE OF RHODE ISLAND, INC.

134 Thurbers Ave, Providence, RI 02905
Tel.: (401) 331-1350   RI
Web Site:
    http://www.familyserviceri.org
Year Founded: 1892
Sales Range: $10-24.9 Million
Emp.: 506
Community Care Services
N.A.I.C.S.: 624190
Margaret Holland McDuff *(CEO)*
Johnnie Chace *(Dir-Philanthropy)*
John C. Simmons *(Pres)*

FAMILY SERVICES OF WESTCHESTER

1 Gateway Plz 4th Fl, Port Chester, NY 10573
Tel.: (914) 937-2320   NY
Web Site: https://www.fsw.org
Year Founded: 1954
Sales Range: $10-24.9 Million
Emp.: 574
Individual & Family Support Services
N.A.I.C.S.: 624190
Dierdra Gray Clark *(Vice Chm)*
Douglas McClintock *(Asst Treas)*
Nick Wolff *(Chm)*
Edward M. Foley Jr. *(Treas)*
Gary Zahakos Sr. *(Sec)*

FAMILY SPORTS CONCEPTS, INC.

5660 W Cypress St Ste A, Tampa, FL 33607
Tel.: (813) 226-2333
Web Site:
    https://www.beefobradys.com
Year Founded: 1985
Operator of Franchised Chain of Family-Style Eateries
N.A.I.C.S.: 722511

FAMILY STATIONS INC.

1350 S Loop Rd Ste 130, Alameda, CA 94502
Tel.: (510) 568-6200
Web Site: http://www.familyradio.org
Sales Range: $10-24.9 Million
Emp.: 270
Christian Radio Broadcasting Stations
N.A.I.C.S.: 516110
Marcus Vincent *(Supvr-Printing & Maintenance)*
Michael Wood *(Mgr-DP)*

FAMILY TREE PRODUCE

5510 E La Palma Ave, Anaheim, CA 92807
Tel.: (714) 696-3037
Web Site:
    https://www.familytreeproduce.com
Sales Range: $25-49.9 Million
Emp.: 115

Fresh Fruit & Vegetable Merchant Whslr
N.A.I.C.S.: 424480
William Grigsby *(Mgr-IT)*
Fidel Guzman *(Pres)*
Edie Smith *(VP-HR)*
David Figueroa *(VP-Sls & Procurement)*
Patricia Jimenez *(Mgr-Pur)*
Frank Guzman *(Controller)*

FAMILYCARE HEALTH PLANS, INC.

825 NE Multnomah St Ste 300, Portland, OR 97232
Tel.: (503) 471-2149   OR
Web Site: http://www.familycareinc.org
Year Founded: 1997
Sales Range: $25-49.9 Million
Emp.: 16
Health Care Srvices
N.A.I.C.S.: 621491
Resa Bradeen *(Dir-Medical)*
Bill Guest *(VP-Provider Network Svcs)*
Roger Muller *(Chief Medical Officer)*
Raghu Valluri *(VP-IT)*

FAMILYLINKS

2644 Banksville Rd, Pittsburgh, PA 15216
Tel.: (412) 343-7166   PA
Web Site: http://www.familylinks.org
Year Founded: 1970
Sales Range: $10-24.9 Million
Emp.: 413
Individual & Family Support Services
N.A.I.C.S.: 624190
John Amato *(Dir-Trng-Consultation Svcs)*

FAMOUS BRANDS INTERNATIONAL

8001 Arista Pl Ste 600, Broomfield, CO 80021-4135
Tel.: (720) 599-3350
Web Site:
    http://www.famousbrandsintl.com
Food Service Contractors
N.A.I.C.S.: 722310
Dustin Lyman *(CEO)*

FAMOUS ENTERPRISES INC.

109 N Union St, Akron, OH 44304-1350
Tel.: (330) 762-9621   OH
Web Site: http://www.famous-supply.com
Year Founded: 1992
Sales Range: $50-74.9 Million
Emp.: 450
Warm Air Heating & Air Conditioning Equipment & Products Distr
N.A.I.C.S.: 423730
Jay Blaushild *(Chm)*

Subsidiaries:

Famous Distribution Inc.   **(1)**
109 N Union St, Akron, OH 44304-1350
Tel.: (330) 762-9621
Web Site: http://www.famous-supply.com
Rev.: $114,200,000
Emp.: 54
Providers of Warm Air Heating & Air Conditioning Services
N.A.I.C.S.: 423730
Jay Blaushild *(Chm)*

Famous Industries Inc.   **(1)**
109 N Union St, Akron, OH 44304-1350
Tel.: (330) 762-9621
Web Site: http://www.famous-supply.com
Sales Range: $10-24.9 Million
Emp.: 55
Plumbing Fixtures, Equipment & Supplies
N.A.I.C.S.: 423720

Famous Supply Co   **(1)**
109 N Union St, Akron, OH 44304
Tel.: (330) 762-9621

Famous Enterprises Inc.—(Continued)

Web Site: http://www.famous-supply.com
Sales Range: $1-9.9 Million
Industrial Equipment Distr
N.A.I.C.S.: 423840
Elio Andreatta (Dir-HVAC Products)
Jeff Rosenblum (Mgr-Technical Support)
Tanja Kozul (Dir-Multi-Family Housing &
Property Mgmt)

J F Good Company Inc (1)
166 N Union St, Akron, OH 44304
Tel.: (330) 535-1811
Web Site: http://www.jfgood.com
Industrial Supplies Whslr
N.A.I.C.S.: 423840
Brian Blaushild (Mgr-Customer Support
Center)

Pittsburgh Plumbing & Heating
Corp. (1)
434 Melwood Ave, Pittsburgh, PA 15213-
1134
Tel.: (412) 622-8100
Web Site: http://www.famous-supply.com
Rev.: $16,300,000
Emp.: 50
Plumbing Fixtures, Equipment & Supplies
N.A.I.C.S.: 459999

FAMOUS HORSE INC.
164-01 Jamaica Ave, Jamaica, NY
11432
Tel.: (718) 387-3777
Web Site: https://www.vim.com
Sales Range: $250-299.9 Million
Emp.: 2,500
Family Clothing Stores
N.A.I.C.S.: 458110

FAMOUS MARKS, INC.
4105 Ridgebrook Bluffs Dr, Raleigh,
NC 27603
Tel.: (919) 779-5968
Web Site:
    http://www.famousmarks.com
Year Founded: 1994
Sales Range: $1-9.9 Million
Emp.: 3
Sales Promotion
N.A.I.C.S.: 541810
Joyce A. Shevelev-Putzer (Pres)

FAMOUS RAMONA WATER,
INC.
250 Aqua Ln, Ramona, CA 92065
Tel.: (760) 789-0174
Web Site: https://www.famousramona
    water.com
Sales Range: $10-24.9 Million
Emp.: 80
Bottled Water Mfr
N.A.I.C.S.: 312112
Julian C. Filer (CEO)
Mark Filer (VP)
Javier Cervantes (Mgr-IT)
Debbie Bruni (Mgr)
Carlos Bustamante (Plant Mgr)

FAMOUS TATE ELECTRIC CO.,
INC.
8317 N Armenia Ave, Tampa, FL
33604-2733
Tel.: (813) 935-3151 FL
Web Site:
    https://www.famoustate.com
Year Founded: 1954
Sales Range: $50-74.9 Million
Emp.: 190
Household Appliance & Bedding Re-
tailer
N.A.I.C.S.: 449210
John Horst (Pres)
Claude Ward (Gen Mgr)

FAMOUS TOASTERY OF CON-
CORD, LLC
101 N Main St, Davidson, NC 28036
Tel.: (704) 655-2778

Web Site:
    http://www.famoustoastery.com
Year Founded: 2005
Sales Range: $25-49.9 Million
Emp.: 1,190
Food & Beverage Restaurant Ser-
vices
N.A.I.C.S.: 722513
Robert Maynard (Co-Founder &
CEO)
Brian Burchill (Co-Founder)
Mike Sebazco (Pres)
Rob Sterioti (VP-Ops)

FAMOUS-AMOS RESTAU-
RANTS INC.
9310 Old Kings Rd S Ste 1101, Jack-
sonville, FL 32257-6196
Tel.: (904) 731-3396
Web Site: http://www.famousamos.bz
Sales Range: $10-24.9 Million
Emp.: 550
Family Restaurant Operator
N.A.I.C.S.: 722511
Edna J. Moise (Chm)
Kenny Ridgos (CFO)

FANCHER INDUSTRIES INC.
PO Box 8, Falconer, NY 14733
Tel.: (716) 665-4313
Web Site:
    http://www.fancherchair.com
Year Founded: 1807
Sales Range: $10-24.9 Million
Emp.: 125
Chair Mfr
N.A.I.C.S.: 337122
L. Bruce Erickson (Pres)
Pete Scheira (VP)

Subsidiaries:

Fancher Chair Co. Inc. (1)
121 S Work St, Falconer, NY 14733
Tel.: (716) 665-4313
Web Site: http://www.fancherchair.com
Sales Range: $10-24.9 Million
Dining Room Furniture: Wood
N.A.I.C.S.: 337122

FANCHEST, INC.
155 Water St, Brooklyn, NY 11201
Web Site: http://www.fanchest.com
Year Founded: 2014
Sales Range: $1-9.9 Million
Emp.: 13
Sports Product Distr
N.A.I.C.S.: 459110
Jeffrey Lin (Founder)

FANCORT INDUSTRIES, INC.
31 Fairfield Pl, West Caldwell, NJ
07006-6206
Tel.: (973) 575-0610
Web Site: https://www.fancort.com
Year Founded: 1970
Sales Range: $1-9.9 Million
Emp.: 23
Assembly & Handling Equipment Mfr
N.A.I.C.S.: 333514
Robert Antonelli (VP-Sls)
Diane Buchanan (Controller)
Ronald J. Corey (CEO)

FANCY FOODS INC.
Bldg B12 Huntspoint Co-op Market,
Bronx, NY 10474
Tel.: (718) 617-3000 NY
Web Site: http://www.fancyfoods.com
Year Founded: 1981
Sales Range: $10-24.9 Million
Emp.: 55
Producer of Meats & Meat Products
N.A.I.C.S.: 424470
Stephen Nerone (Sr VP)

FANCY PUBLICATIONS INC.

2401 Beverly Blvd, Los Angeles, CA
90057-1001
Tel.: (213) 385-2222
Web Site: http://www.bowtieinc.com
Sales Range: $25-49.9 Million
Emp.: 350
Magazine Publishing
N.A.I.C.S.: 513120
Norman Ridker (Pres)
Patrick Trowbridge (Publr)
Craig Wisda (Controller)
Nikki Dutra (Mgr-List)
Nicole Fabian (Sr Controller)
Jeff Scharf (Sr VP-Sls)

Subsidiaries:

Bowtie Press (1)
3 Burroughs, Irvine, CA
92618-2804 (100%)
Tel.: (949) 855-8822
Web Site: http://www.bowtiepress.com
Sales Range: $25-49.9 Million
Emp.: 150
Publisher of Magazines
N.A.I.C.S.: 513120
Norman Ridker (Pres)
Thoroughbred Times Company
Inc. (1)
2008 Mercer Rd, Lexington, KY
40511 (100%)
Tel.: (859) 260-9800
Web Site:
    http://www.thoroughbredtimes.com
Rev.: $2,400,000
Emp.: 70
Commercial Printing
N.A.I.C.S.: 323111

FANG CLOTHING INC.
18455 S Figueroa St, Gardena, CA
90248
Tel.: (810) 768-3377
Web Site: http://www.fang-
    fashion.com
Rev.: $12,192,827
Emp.: 111
Men's & Boys' Sportswear & Athletic
Clothing
N.A.I.C.S.: 315250
Tony Kim (Pres)

FANNIN BANK
230 E 3rd St, Bonham, TX 75418
Tel.: (903) 583-5522 TX
Web Site:
    https://www.fanninbank.com
Year Founded: 1925
Sales Range: $25-49.9 Million
Emp.: 20
Provider of Financial Services
N.A.I.C.S.: 522180
Felicia Mollenkopf (VP)
Dorothy Spiller (VP)
Laura Hartnett (VP)

FANNIN INDUSTRIES INCOR-
PORATED
4889 Sinclair Rd Ste 103, Columbus,
OH 43229-5433
Tel.: (614) 885-4936
Sales Range: $10-24.9 Million
Emp.: 4
Men's & Boy's Clothing
N.A.I.C.S.: 424350
Larry Fannin (Pres)

FANNON PETROLEUM SER-
VICES INC.
7755 Progress Ct, Gainesville, VA
20155
Tel.: (703) 468-2060 VA
Web Site:
    http://www.fannonpetroleum.com
Year Founded: 1962
Sales Range: $10-24.9 Million
Emp.: 25
Provider of Petroleum Services
N.A.I.C.S.: 424720

John Fannon (VP)
Chester Fannon (Pres & CEO)

FANSTEEL, INC.
1739 Commerce Rd, Creston, IA
50801 DE
Tel.: (641) 782-8521
Web Site: http://www.fansteel.com
Year Founded: 1907
Sales Range: $75-99.9 Million
Emp.: 685
Holding Company; Steel & Specialty
Metal Castings & Powdered Metal
Components Mfr
N.A.I.C.S.: 551112
Jim Mahoney (CEO)

Subsidiaries:

American Sintered Technologies,
Inc. (1)
513 E 2nd St, Emporium, PA 15834
Tel.: (814) 486-0400
Web Site: http://www.fansteel.com
Sales Range: $50-74.9 Million
Emp.: 60
Powdered Metal Components Mfr
N.A.I.C.S.: 332117

FANT'S FOODLAND
201 Main St, Crossville, AL 35962
Tel.: (256) 528-7155
Web Site:
    http://fantsfoodland.bzfs.com
Rev.: $10,000,000
Emp.: 20
Grocery Stores
N.A.I.C.S.: 445110
Billy Fant (Pres)

FANTAGRAPHICS BOOKS,
INC.
7563 Lake City Way NE, Seattle, WA
98115
Tel.: (206) 524-1967
Web Site:
    https://www.fantagraphics.com
Sales Range: $1-9.9 Million
Emp.: 20
Comics & Graphic Novels Publisher
N.A.I.C.S.: 513130
Kim Thompson (Owner)

FANTAS EYES INC.
385 5th Ave Fl 9, New York, NY
10016
Tel.: (212) 997-4433
Web Site: http://www.fantas-
    eyes.com
Sales Range: $10-24.9 Million
Emp.: 21
Sunglasses
N.A.I.C.S.: 423990
Larry Kalina (Pres)
Sam Terzi (Pres)
Orly Sultan (Acct Mgr-Sls)
Tom Goldstein (Acct Exec)

FANTASIA ACCESSORIES
LTD.
31 W 34th St Fl 5, New York, NY
10001-3015
Tel.: (212) 391-1080
Web Site: http://www.fantasia.com
Year Founded: 1980
Sales Range: $25-49.9 Million
Emp.: 75
Mfr of Women's Fashion Accessories
N.A.I.C.S.: 339999
Edward Azar (CEO)

FANTASY FLIGHT GAMES
1995 W County Rd B2, Roseville, MN
55113
Tel.: (651) 639-1905 MN
Web Site:
    https://www.fantasyflightgames.com
Year Founded: 1995

Sales Range: $10-24.9 Million
Emp.: 64
Online Fantasy Games & Software
N.A.I.C.S.: 339930
Christian Petersen (CEO)
Brian Schomburg (Mgr-Graphic Design)
Zoe Robinson (Dir-Art)

FANTEX, INC.
660 4th St Ste 691, San Francisco,
CA 94107
Tel.: (415) 592-5950   DE
Web Site: https://fantex.com
Year Founded: 2012
Brand Marketing & Development
N.A.I.C.S.: 541613

FANTINI & GORGA LLC
155 Federal St Ste 1402, Boston, MA
02110
Tel.: (617) 951-2600   MA
Web Site:
    http://www.fantinigorga.com
Sales Range: $25-49.9 Million
Emp.: 13
Real Estate Financial Services
N.A.I.C.S.: 522310
Wayne Clough (Mng Dir)
John R. Gorga (Pres & Principal)
Casimir Groblewski (Sr Mng Dir)
Tim O'Donnell (Exec Mng Dir & Principal)
Derek L. Coulombe (Sr Mng Dir)
Keith Wentzel (Mng Dir)
Heather Baldassari (Sr VP)
George J. Fantini Jr. (Founder & Chm)

FAPCO INC.
216 Post Rd, Buchanan, MI 49107
Tel.: (269) 695-6889
Web Site: https://www.fapcoinc.com
Year Founded: 1970
Rev.: $12,500,000
Emp.: 350
Crating Goods For Shipping
N.A.I.C.S.: 488991
Larry Gardiner (Founder & Pres)
Ken Douglas (Controller)

FAPS INC.
371 Craneway St, Newark, NJ 07114-3114
Tel.: (973) 589-5656
Web Site: https://www.fapsinc.com
Year Founded: 1956
Sales Range: $25-49.9 Million
Emp.: 392
Provider of Marine Cargo Handling
Services
N.A.I.C.S.: 488320
August Lobue (VP)

FAR NORTHERN COORDINATING COUNCIL ON DEVELOPMENTAL DISABILITIES, INC.
1900 Churn Creek Rd Ste 319, Redding, CA 96002-0277
Tel.: (530) 222-4791   CA
Web Site:
    https://www.farnorthernrc.org
Year Founded: 1967
Sales Range: $100-124.9 Million
Emp.: 192
Developmental Disability Assistance
Services
N.A.I.C.S.: 624120
Laura Larson (Exec Dir)

FAR REACH TECHNOLOGIES CORPORATION
123 N Charles St, Daytona Beach,
FL 32114-3115
Tel.: (386) 673-5116
Rev.: $15,600,000

Emp.: 75
Internet Service Provider
N.A.I.C.S.: 517810
Okey Rawson (Pres)

FAR SIGHTED MEDIA INC.
5306 Sandy Shell Dr, Apollo Beach,
FL 33572
Tel.: (859) 285-6350   FL
Year Founded: 2014
Software Development Services
N.A.I.C.S.: 541511
Eric Haskins (CEO)
Randy Tobia (Sec)

FAR WEST FIBERS INC.
12820 NE Marx St, Portland, OR
97230
Tel.: (503) 255-2299
Web Site:
    http://www.farwestfibers.com
Sales Range: $10-24.9 Million
Emp.: 40
Waste Paper
N.A.I.C.S.: 423930
Mike McCracken (CFO & VP)
Stanley Girard (COO)
Jeff Steinfeld (Mgr-Ops)
Joe Brewer (Mgr-Operations)
Steven Peery (Mgr-Operations)
Vinod Singh (Mgr-Outreach)

FAR WEST RICE
3455 Nelson Rd, Durham, CA 95938
Tel.: (530) 891-1339
Web Site:
    https://www.farwestrice.com
Year Founded: 1985
Sales Range: $10-24.9 Million
Emp.: 50
Rice Milling Services
N.A.I.C.S.: 311212
William C. Johnson (Founder)
Greg Johnson (Exec VP)

FARAGO+PARTNERS
71 Broadway, New York, NY 10006
Tel.: (212) 344-9472
Web Site: http://www.farago.com
Year Founded: 1988
Sales Range: $25-49.9 Million
Emp.: 25
Collateral, Direct Marketing, Full Service
N.A.I.C.S.: 541810
Peter Farago (Principal)
Greg Ylagan (Creative Dir)
Bob Steiler (Coord-Traffic & Production)

FARALLON CAPITAL MANAGEMENT, L.L.C.
1 Maritime Plz Ste 2100, San Francisco, CA 94111-3528
Tel.: (415) 421-2132
Web Site:
    https://www.faralloncapital.com
Sales Range: $50-74.9 Million
Emp.: 120
Investment Management & Private
Equity Firm
N.A.I.C.S.: 523999
Thomas F. Steyer (Mng Partner)
Stephen L. Millham (Mng Partner)
Richard Bollini (Mng Dir)
Stephen P. Heath (Mng Dir)
Jacquelyn R. Suen (Mng Dir)
Daniel Meade (Mng Dir)
Andrew J. M. Spokes (Mng Partner)
Ashish Gupta (Partner)
Caroline Chang (Mng Dir-London)
Charles Gunawan (Mng Dir-Singapore)
Hong Kong (Partner)
Matthew Trentini (Mng Dir & CTO-San Francisco)

Nancy B. Y. Wu (Partner)
William S. Seybold (Mng Dir-San Francisco)
Wissam Charbel (Mng Dir-London)
Richard Brachman Fried (Co-Head-Real Estate Grp)
G. Raymond Zage III (Partner)

FARALLON CONSULTING, LLC
975 5th Ave NW Ste 100, Issaquah,
WA 98027
Tel.: (425) 427-0061   WA
Web Site:
    http://www.farallonconsulting.com
Year Founded: 1998
Sales Range: $1-9.9 Million
Emp.: 32
Scientific & Technical Consulting Services
N.A.I.C.S.: 541690
Clifford T. Schmitt (Co-Founder)
Tim Zier (CFO)
Gerald J. Portele (Principal)
Peter D. Jewett (Co-Founder)

Subsidiaries:

Grette Associates, LLC   (1)
151 S Worthen St Ste 101, Wenatchee, WA
98801
Tel.: (509) 663-6300
Web Site: http://www.gretteassociates.com
Sales Range: $1-9.9 Million
Emp.: 11
Scientific & Technical Consulting Services
N.A.I.C.S.: 541690
Glenn Grette (Principal)
Matthew Boyle (Principal)
Colleen Kimble (Accountant)

FARBEST FOODS, INC.
4689 S 400 W, Huntingburg, IN
47542
Tel.: (812) 683-4200
Web Site:
    https://www.farbestfoods.com
Rev.: $41,900,000
Emp.: 420
Poultry Processing
N.A.I.C.S.: 311615
Thomas W. Seger (Owner)
Shawn Archie (Dir-QA)
Brian Hawkins (VP-Ops)
Dana McKinney (Sec)
Shannon Opel (Supvr-Food Safety)
Sherman Wolf (Asst Mgr-Food Safety)
Marilyn Smith (Coord-Traffic)
Judy Jochem-Nino (Mgr-HR)
Kevin Meyer (Mgr-Traffic)

FARBEST-TALLMAN FOODS CORP.
1 Maynard Dr Ste 3101, Park Ridge,
NJ 07656
Tel.: (201) 573-4900
Web Site: https://www.farbest.com
Year Founded: 1955
Sales Range: $10-24.9 Million
Emp.: 65
Dry, Condensed & Evaporated Products Mfr
N.A.I.C.S.: 311514
Daniel M. Meloro (Pres)
Stacey Kroposki (Mgr-Acctg & Credit)

FARCO PLASTICS SUPPLY INC.
11701 US Hwy 19 N, Clearwater, FL
33764-7492
Tel.: (727) 572-7722
Web Site:
    https://www.farcoplastics.com
Sales Range: $10-24.9 Million
Emp.: 50
Plastics Sheets & Rods
N.A.I.C.S.: 424610
Paul Aucremann (Office Mgr)

FAREWAY STORES, INC.
2300 Industrial Park Rd E 8th St,
Boone, IA 50036
Tel.: (515) 432-2623   IA
Web Site: http://www.fareway.com
Year Founded: 1938
Sales Range: $750-799.9 Million
Emp.: 7,000
Grocery Store Operator
N.A.I.C.S.: 445110
Fred R. Griner (Pres)
Craig A. Shepley (CFO)
Mike Mazour (Dir-HR)
Reynolds W. Cramer (CEO)
Richard P. Beckwith (Chm)
Andrea Chase (Asst VP-Category Mgmt)
B. J. Van Der Linden (Reg VP)
Chris Boothe (VP-Produce Pur)
Wes Bass (VP-Warehouse & Trucking Ops)
Tom Laven (VP-Direct Store Delivery)
Matt Sherwood (VP-Engrg)
Mike McCormick (Sr VP-Mdsg)
Aaron Irlbeck (Sr VP-Procurement)

FARGO GLASS & PAINT COMPANY
1801 7th Ave N, Fargo, ND 58102-3203
Tel.: (701) 235-4441   ND
Web Site:
    https://www.fargoglass.com
Year Founded: 1917
Sales Range: $125-149.9 Million
Emp.: 180
Glass Products Mfr
N.A.I.C.S.: 423310
Dan Martinson (Pres)
Duane Voit (Mgr-Info Sys)
Wade Bakke (Mgr-Fin)

FARGO TRUSS SYSTEMS INC.
1208 Main Ave W, West Fargo, ND
58078
Tel.: (701) 281-0871
Web Site: https://www.fargotruss.com
Rev.: $12,000,000
Emp.: 18
Trusses, Wooden Roof
N.A.I.C.S.: 321215
Gene Gallager (Pres)
Kim Wolfe (Gen Mgr)

FARGO-MOORHEAD SYMPHONY
808 3rd Ave S Ste 300, Fargo, ND
58103
Tel.: (218) 233-8397
Web Site:
    https://www.fmsymphony.org
Sales Range: Less than $1 Million
Emp.: 4
Symphony Orchestra
N.A.I.C.S.: 711130
Charles Peterson (Chm)
Bethany Eighmy (Vice Chm)
Todd Hase (Treas)
Linda Boyd (Exec Dir)
Sara Granger (Dir-Dev)
Joan Covington (Mgr-Librarian/Personnel)

FARHEAP SOLUTIONS, INC.
7582 Las Vegas Blvd Ste 487, Las
Vegas, NV 89123
Tel.: (949) 417-1500
Web Site: http://www.farheap.com
Year Founded: 1998
Printing, Software Development &
Graphic Design Services
N.A.I.C.S.: 541430
Brett Heap (Founder)

Faria Beede Instruments, Inc.—(Continued)

FARIA BEEDE INSTRUMENTS, INC.
385 Norwich New London Turnpike,
Uncasville, CT 06382
Tel.: (860) 848-9271   **CT**
Web Site: http://www.fariabeede.com
Year Founded: 1956
Engine Instrumentation Mfr; Tachometer, Speedometer, Control Instruments
N.A.I.C.S.: 334514
Kevin Terry (VP-Engrg)

FARIA BEEDE INSTRUMENTS, INC.
385 Norwich New London Tpke, Uncasville, CT 06382
Tel.: (860) 848-9271
Web Site: http://www.faria-instruments.com
Year Founded: 1956
Engine Monitoring Instruments Mfr
N.A.I.C.S.: 334519
Jason Blackburn (VP-Sls & Mktg)
Bill Randall (VP-Ops)
Kevin Terry (VP-Engrg)

Subsidiaries:

Beede Electrical Instrument Co,
Inc.   (1)
88 Village St, Penacook, NH 03303
Tel.: (603) 753-6362
Web Site: http://www.faria-instruments.com
Sales Range: $1-9.9 Million
Emp.: 110
Engine Monitoring Instruments & Gauges Mfr
N.A.I.C.S.: 334519
Bruce Holso (Dir-Engrg)
Ken LaPage (Mgr-Sls Engrg)

FARIA CORPORATION
385 Norwich New London Tpke, Uncasville, CT 06382
Tel.: (860) 848-9271
Web Site: http://www.bgmfg.com
Sales Range: $25-49.9 Million
Emp.: 265
Mfr of Toothpaste, Beauty Aids & Metal Collapsible Tubes
N.A.I.C.S.: 325611
Dave Hickey (Pres)

Subsidiaries:

Sheffield Laboratories   (1)
170 Broad St, New London, CT 06320-5313
Tel.: (860) 442-4451
Sales Range: $25-49.9 Million
Emp.: 125
Toilet & Pharmaceutical Preparation Mfr
N.A.I.C.S.: 325620
Christine Lacoursiere (Mgr-HR)
Anita delaCruz (Mgr-R&D)
Jeffrey Davis (COO)
Luke Zinsky (Mgr-Bus Dev)
Bill Mencer (Controller)

FARIBAULT FOODS INC.
222 S 9th St Ste 3380, Minneapolis,
MN 55402
Tel.: (612) 333-6461   **MN**
Web Site:
  https://www.faribaultfoods.com
Year Founded: 1895
Sales Range: $200-249.9 Million
Emp.: 600
Mfr of Canned Vegetables, Dry Packed Beans, Pasta & Soups
N.A.I.C.S.: 311421
Frank Lynch (Exec VP-New Bus Dev)
James Nelson (Exec VP-Innovation & Tech)
Gary Kindseth (Exec VP)
Jim Noonan (VP-Branded Sls)

Subsidiaries:

Faribault Foods, Inc.   (1)
128 NW 15th St, Faribault, MN 55021-3037
Tel.: (507) 331-1400
Web Site: http://www.faribaultfoods.com
Sales Range: $25-49.9 Million
Emp.: 300
Mfr of Canned Vegetables
N.A.I.C.S.: 311421
Frank Lynch (Exec VP-Sls & Mktg)

FARIBAULT MILLS, INC.
1500 NW 2nd Ave, Faribault, MN
55021-3018
Tel.: (507) 412-5510   **MN**
Web Site:
  http://www.faribaultmill.com
Year Founded: 1865
Blankets, Throws & Accessories Mfr
N.A.I.C.S.: 313210
Paul Mooty (Partner)

FARIS MACHINERY COMPANY
5770 E 77th Ave, Commerce City,
CO 80022
Tel.: (303) 289-5743
Web Site:
  https://www.farismachinery.com
Year Founded: 1953
Sales Range: $10-24.9 Million
Emp.: 55
Distr of Construction & Mining Machinery & Equipment
N.A.I.C.S.: 423810
Ray Webb (VP-Parts)
Mark Shelton (VP-Operations)

FARLIE, TURNER & CO., LLC
401 E Las Olas Blvd Ste 2360, Fort
Lauderdale, FL 33301
Tel.: (954) 358-3800
Web Site: http://www.farlieturner.com
Sales Range: $1-9.9 Million
Emp.: 17
Investment Banking
N.A.I.C.S.: 523150
Craig L. Farlie (Mng Dir)
Michael F. Turner (Founder & Mng Dir)
Erik H. Rudolph (Mng Dir)
Steven B. Zuckerman (Mng Dir)
Chris Calton (Mng Dir & Head-Healthcare)
Scott J. Saunders (Mng Dir)
Andy Burke (Mng Dir)
Daniel G. Vetrano (VP)
Kyle Jones (VP)

FARM & FLEET OF DE KALB INC.
4014 E Racine St, Janesville, WI
53546-2320
Tel.: (815) 899-1716
Web Site:
  http://www.farmandfleet.com
Year Founded: 1958
Sales Range: $25-49.9 Million
Emp.: 400
Variety Stores
N.A.I.C.S.: 455219
Robert S. Blain (Owner & Pres)

FARM & RANCH AUTO SALES, INC.
4328 Louisburg Rd, Raleigh, NC
27604-4398
Tel.: (919) 876-7286
Web Site:
  http://www.farmandranchauto.com
Year Founded: 1980
Sales Range: $10-24.9 Million
Emp.: 12
Used Car Whslr
N.A.I.C.S.: 441120
David Burns (Mgr-Sls)
George R. Bell Sr. (Pres)

FARM BUREAU MUTUAL INSURANCE COMPANY OF IDAHO, INC.
275 Tierra Vista Dr, Pocatello, ID
83205
Tel.: (208) 232-7914
Web Site: http://www.idfbins.com
Year Founded: 1947
Sales Range: $50-74.9 Million
Emp.: 150
Fire, Marine & Casualty Insurance
N.A.I.C.S.: 524126
Phillip Joslin (CEO)
Frank S. Priestley (Pres)

Subsidiaries:

Farm Bureau Finance Company
Inc.   (1)
275 Tierra Vista Dr, Pocatello, ID 83205
Tel.: (208) 232-7914
Web Site: http://www.idfbfs.com
Provider of Personal Credit Services
N.A.I.C.S.: 524126

FARM BUREAU MUTUAL INSURANCE COMPANY OF MICHIGAN INC.
7373 W Saginaw Hwy, Lansing, MI
48917-1124
Tel.: (517) 323-7000
Web Site:
  https://www.farmbureauinsurance-mi.com
Year Founded: 1949
Sales Range: $200-249.9 Million
Emp.: 500
Fire, Marine & Casualty Insurance
N.A.I.C.S.: 524126
Jim Robinson (Exec VP)
Carl Begnarski (Pres)

Subsidiaries:

Community Service Acceptance
Company   (1)
7373 W Saginaw Hwy, Lansing, MI
48909   (100%)
Tel.: (517) 323-7000
Sales Range: $100-124.9 Million
Emp.: 6
Insurance Agents, Brokers & Service
N.A.I.C.S.: 524210

FARM CHEMICALS INC.
2274 Saint Pauls Dr, Raeford, NC
28376
Tel.: (910) 875-4277
Web Site: https://www.fciag.com
Sales Range: $50-74.9 Million
Emp.: 14
Ferilizer & Lime Seed
N.A.I.C.S.: 424510
Mike Anderson (Plant Mgr)
Keith Hedgpeth (Plant Mgr)
Duncan Malloy (Mgr-Warehouse)
Alfred K. Leach Jr. (Pres)

FARM CITY ELEVATOR INC.
PO Box 628, Darien, WI 53114-0628
Tel.: (262) 724-5757   **WI**
Web Site:
  http://www.farmcityelevator.com
Year Founded: 1965
Sales Range: $25-49.9 Million
Emp.: 6
Grain & Field Beans
N.A.I.C.S.: 424510
Roger G. Wuttke (Pres & Treas)

FARM COUNTRY CO-OP
417 North Main St, Pine Island, MN
55963
Tel.: (507) 356-8313
Web Site:
  http://www.farmcountrycoop.com
Sales Range: $25-49.9 Million
Emp.: 120
Provider of Farm Supplies

N.A.I.C.S.: 424910

FARM CREDIT EAST
240 S Rd, Enfield, CT 06082-4451
Tel.: (860) 741-4380
Web Site:
  http://www.farmcrediteast.com
Year Founded: 1916
Rev.: $416,921,000
Assets: $7,264,520,000
Liabilities: $5,810,579,000
Net Worth: $1,453,941,000
Earnings: $177,921,000
Fiscal Year-end: 12/31/18
Credit & Financial Services
N.A.I.C.S.: 522390
John P. Knopf (Vice Chm)
Laurie K. Griffen (Chm)

FARM CREDIT MID-AMERICA
1601 UPS Dr, Louisville, KY 40223
Tel.: (800) 444-3276
Web Site: http://www.e-farmcredit.com
Year Founded: 1916
Sales Range: $750-799.9 Million
Emp.: 1,100
Agricultural Lending Services
N.A.I.C.S.: 561499
Brandon Robbins (Vice Chm)
Andrew Wilson (Chm)
Dan Wagner (COO & Exec VP)
Heather Vidourek (Sr VP)
Art Whaley (Sr VP-Consumer Lending)
Steve Zagar (CFO)
John Kuegel Jr. (Sec)

FARM CREDIT OF CENTRAL FLORIDA ACA
115 S Missouri Ave Ste 400, Lakeland, FL 33815-4601
Tel.: (863) 682-4117
Web Site:
  https://www.farmcreditcfl.com
Sales Range: $25-49.9 Million
Emp.: 30
Credit Services
N.A.I.C.S.: 522299
Reginald T. Holt (Pres & CEO)
Scarlet Detjen (Chief Credit Officer)

FARM CREDIT OF FLORIDA
11903 Southern Blvd Ste 200, West
Palm Beach, FL 33411
Tel.: (561) 965-9001   **FL**
Web Site: http://www.farmcreditfl.com
Year Founded: 1916
Rev.: $90,615,000
Assets: $1,448,601,000
Liabilities: $1,128,794,000
Net Worth: $319,807,000
Earnings: $39,904,000
Fiscal Year-end: 12/31/21
Credit Services
N.A.I.C.S.: 522291
Laura Craker (CFO & Sr VP)
Robert Teston (CEO)
Marcus Boone (Chief Lending Officer & Sr VP)
Ashley Layson (CMO & Sr VP)
Roland Kampf (Chief Risk Officer & Sr VP)
Dawn Goodspeed (Chief Ops & IT Officer & Sr VP)
Deborah Caldeira (Chief HR Officer & Sr VP)

FARM CREDIT OF NORTH FLORIDA ACA
12300 NW US Highway 441, Alachua, FL 32615
Tel.: (386) 462-4201
Web Site: http://www.fcnf.com
Sales Range: $10-24.9 Million

Emp.: 35
Credit Services
N.A.I.C.S.: 522299
Roger Scarborough (CFO)
Laura Craker (Controller)

FARM CREDIT OF NORTH-WEST FLORIDA ACA
5052 Hwy 90 E, Marianna, FL 32446
Tel.: (850) 526-4910
Web Site: http://www.farmcredit-fl.com
Rev.: $19,060,000
Assets: $296,140,000
Liabilities: $212,334,000
Net Worth: $83,806,000
Earnings: $6,853,000
Fiscal Year-end: 12/31/18
Credit Services
N.A.I.C.S.: 522291
DeAndrea Barber (COO)
Ricky K. Bitner (Pres & CEO)
Cindy Eade (Chm)
John P. Mottice (CFO)
Chuck Thiele (Chief Credit Officer)
Dorislynn White-Padgett (Mgr-Human Capital)
Jesse Dumas (Reg Mgr-Lending)
Michael Digmon (Reg Mgr-Lending)

FARM CREDIT OF WESTERN NEW YORK ACA INC.
4363 Federal Dr, Batavia, NY 14020-9107
Tel.: (585) 815-1900
Web Site: http://www.farmcreditwny.com
Year Founded: 1988
Sales Range: $25-49.9 Million
Emp.: 80
Credit Services
N.A.I.C.S.: 522299
Henry Adams (Vice Chm)

FARM CREDIT SERVICE OF CENTRAL ARKANSAS INC.
3809 McCain Park Dr, North Little Rock, AR 72116-7803
Year Founded: 1989
Sales Range: $25-49.9 Million
Emp.: 100
Credit Services
N.A.I.C.S.: 522299
Charles Conklen (CEO)

FARM CREDIT SERVICES MANDAN
1600 Old Red Trl, Mandan, ND 58554
Tel.: (701) 663-6487
Web Site: https://www.farmcreditmandan.com
Rev.: $16,500,000
Emp.: 50
Credit Services
N.A.I.C.S.: 522299
Mike O'Keeffe (CEO)
Robert Wingenbach (Asst VP-Ops)
Michael J. Schaaf (Vice Chm)
James Vander Vorst (Chm)

FARM CREDIT SERVICES MISSOURI
1930 E Miller Hwy 50 E, Jefferson City, MO 65102
Tel.: (573) 636-7131
Web Site: https://www.myfcsfinancial.com
Year Founded: 1917
Sales Range: $50-74.9 Million
Emp.: 160
Credit Services
N.A.I.C.S.: 522130
Curtis Fischer (Asst VP)

FARM CREDIT SERVICES OF

AMERICA PCA/FLCA
5015 S 118 St, Omaha, NE 68137
Tel.: (402) 348-3333
Web Site: https://www.fcsamerica.com
Year Founded: 1933
Sales Range: $200-249.9 Million
Emp.: 1,030
Credit Services
N.A.I.C.S.: 522299
Craig Kinnison (CFO & Sr VP)

FARM CREDIT SERVICES OF NORTH DAKOTA
3100 10th St SW, Minot, ND 58701
Tel.: (701) 852-1265
Web Site: http://www.farmcreditnd.com
Sales Range: $10-24.9 Million
Emp.: 90
Lending Service To Farmers
N.A.I.C.S.: 561450
Claude Sem (CEO)
Rollin Tonneson (Chm)
Ross Johnson (VP-Fin)
Teresa Kjellberg (Dir-Mktg & Credit Svcs)

FARM CREDIT SERVICES SOUTHWEST
3003 S Fair Ln, Tempe, AZ 85282
Tel.: (602) 438-2515   AZ
Web Site: http://www.fcssw.com
Year Founded: 1916
Sales Range: $25-49.9 Million
Emp.: 50
Credit Services
N.A.I.C.S.: 522299

FARM EQUIPMENT COMPANY
406 Hwy 165 N, Portland, AR 71663
Tel.: (870) 474-4303
Web Site: https://agup.com
Sales Range: $10-24.9 Million
Emp.: 30
Farm Implements
N.A.I.C.S.: 423820

FARM JOURNAL, INC.
1 Penn Sq W 30 S 15 St Ste 900, Philadelphia, PA 19102
Tel.: (215) 557-8900   DE
Web Site: http://www.farmjournalmedia.com
Year Founded: 1877
Sales Range: $25-49.9 Million
Agricultural Magazine Publisher; Television Broadcasting
N.A.I.C.S.: 513120
Andrew J. Weber (CEO)
Stephen J. Custer (Pres & CEO)
Will Murphy (Sr VP-Sls)
Jeff Pence (Pres-Television, Newletter & Database Bus)
Mitch Rouda (Pres-eMedia)
Charlene Finck (Chief Content Officer & Exec VP)
Brian Conrady (VP & Gen Mgr-Farm Journal Television)
Joseph Matthews (CFO & Sr VP)
Ron Wall (Pres-Magazines, Branded Events & Database Solutions)

FARM KING SUPPLY INC.
730 Bower Rd, Macomb, IL 61455-2512
Tel.: (309) 837-9929   IL
Web Site: http://www.farmking.com
Year Founded: 1959
Sales Range: $1-9.9 Million
Emp.: 450
Miscellaneous General Merchandise Distr
N.A.I.C.S.: 455219
Richard Severs (Pres)
Brad Severs (VP)

FARM PUMP AND IRRIGATION CO.
535 N Shafter Ave, Shafter, CA 93263
Tel.: (661) 589-6901
Web Site: http://www.fpi-co.com
Rev.: $11,690,954
Emp.: 50
Pumps & Pumping Equipment
N.A.I.C.S.: 423830
John Gargan (CEO)

FARM SERVICE COMPANY
4040 S Expy St, Council Bluffs, IA 51501
Tel.: (712) 323-7167
Web Site: http://www.farmservicecompany.com
Year Founded: 1931
Sales Range: $10-24.9 Million
Emp.: 85
Provider of Farm Supplies
N.A.I.C.S.: 424910
Ben Torell (CFO)
Randy Behrens (Gen Mgr)

FARM SERVICE COOPERATIVE INC.
2308 Pine St, Harlan, IA 51537-0429
Tel.: (712) 755-3185   IA
Web Site: https://www.fscoop.com
Year Founded: 1930
Sales Range: $100-124.9 Million
Emp.: 150
Provider Of Agricultural Services
N.A.I.C.S.: 424510

FARM SERVICE INCORPORATED
1050 SW Front St, Walnut Ridge, AR 72476
Tel.: (870) 886-7779
Rev.: $32,349,792
Emp.: 27
Farm Co-Op Supplies
N.A.I.C.S.: 424910
Larry Singleton (Gen Mgr)

FARM STAND FOODS
1301 Carlisle Pike, Hanover, PA 17331
Tel.: (717) 637-2251
Web Site: http://www.farmstandfoods.com
Frozen Food Products
N.A.I.C.S.: 424420

Subsidiaries:

John Cope's Food Products, Inc.   (1)
156 W Harrisburg Ave, Rheems, PA 17570
Tel.: (717) 367-5142
Web Site: http://www.copefoods.com
Sales Range: $10-24.9 Million
Emp.: 130
Mfr Dried & Frozen Vegetables & Fruits
N.A.I.C.S.: 311411

FARM STORES
18001 Old Cutler Rd Ste 370, Palmetto, FL 33157
Tel.: (305) 677-0616   FL
Web Site: http://www.farmstores.com
Year Founded: 1937
Sales Range: $200-249.9 Million
Emp.: 900
Convenience Food Stores; Gasoline Stations
N.A.I.C.S.: 445131
Carlos Bared (CEO)
Maurice Bared (COO)

FARMCHEM CORPORATION
616 Madison St, Floyd, IA 50435
Tel.: (641) 398-2893
Web Site: http://www.farmchem.com
Sales Range: $10-24.9 Million
Emp.: 80

Agricultural Machinery & Equipment
N.A.I.C.S.: 423820
Deon Buhman (Pres)
Justin Peterson (VP)
Bruce Carr (Mgr-Mfg & Distr)

FARMER BOY AGRICULTURAL SYSTEMS INC.
50 W Stoever Ave, Myerstown, PA 17067
Tel.: (717) 866-7565   PA
Web Site: https://www.farmerboyag.com
Year Founded: 1995
Sales Range: $10-24.9 Million
Emp.: 65
Provider of Farm & Garden Machinery
N.A.I.C.S.: 423820
Dale W. Martin (Pres)
Dean Weaver (VP)
Leonard Martin (VP)

FARMER'S SUPPLY COOPERATIVE INC.
514 SW 4th Ave, Ontario, OR 97914-2623
Tel.: (541) 889-5365   OR
Year Founded: 1935
Sales Range: $50-74.9 Million
Emp.: 100
Lawn & Garden Supplies Retail
N.A.I.C.S.: 459999
Steve Mendiola (Gen Mgr)
Jackie Tolman (Mgr-Store)

Subsidiaries:

Farmers' Aerial Applicators Inc.   (1)
514 SW 4th Ave, Ontario, OR 97914-2623
Tel.: (541) 889-5365
Sales Range: Less than $1 Million
Emp.: 25
Crop Planting & Protection
N.A.I.C.S.: 115112

FARMERS & MERCHANTS BANK
111 W Clayton St, Baldwyn, MS 38824
Tel.: (662) 365-1200
Web Site: https://www.frnbms.com
Year Founded: 1941
Sales Range: $10-24.9 Million
Emp.: 64
Retail & Commercial Banking
N.A.I.C.S.: 522111
John Haynes (Pres & CEO)
Kathy Reed (Sr VP & Mgr-Relationship-Newport Beach & Corona del Mar)
Barton E. Black (Pres)
Aubrey Michael Wilkerson (CEO)

FARMERS & MERCHANTS INVESTMENT INC.
3643 S 48th St, Lincoln, NE 68506
Tel.: (402) 323-1828   NE
Web Site: http://www.ubt.com
Year Founded: 1965
Sales Range: $125-149.9 Million
Emp.: 1,520
Bank Holding Company
N.A.I.C.S.: 551111
Michael S. Dunlap (Chm)
Angie Muhleisen (CEO)
Brad Crain (CFO)

Subsidiaries:

Union Bank & Trust Company   (1)
3643 S 48th St, Lincoln, NE 68506-6426
Tel.: (402) 323-1828
Web Site: http://www.ubt.com
Sales Range: $50-74.9 Million
Emp.: 120
Retail & Commercial Banking
N.A.I.C.S.: 522110

Farmers & Merchants Investment Inc.—(Continued)

Brad Crain *(CFO)*
Stacy Brass *(VP-Bus Loan-Lincoln)*
Todd Furasek *(VP-Bus Loan-Lincoln)*
Jake Muhleisen *(VP-Bus Loan-Lincoln)*
Russ Ripa *(VP-Bus Loan-Lincoln)*
L. G. Searcey *(Sr VP-Bus Loan-Lincoln)*
Bryan Shank *(VP-Bus Loan-Lincoln)*
Jan Sheridan *(VP-Treasury Mgmt)*
Jim Smith *(VP-Treasury Mgmt)*
Chris Wagner *(VP-Bus Loan-Lincoln)*
Carrie Weiler *(Asst VP-Treasury Mgmt)*

Affiliate (Domestic):

Infovisa Inc.   (2)
11120 Trynorth Dr, Cornelius, NC 28031
Tel.: (704) 892-3270
Web Site: http://www.infovisa.com
Rev.: $31,200,000
Emp.: 13
Software Devolement
N.A.I.C.S.: 522291
Michael Dinges *(Pres)*

Subsidiary (Domestic):

Union Agency, Inc.   (2)
4719 Prescott Ave, Lincoln, NE 68506
Tel.: (402) 483-4527
Web Site: http://www.unionagency.com
Sales Range: $1-9.9 Million
Insurance Brokerage Services
N.A.I.C.S.: 524210
Chris Smith *(Pres)*
Dawn Hanson *(Mgr-Acct)*
Ellie Whiting *(Mgr-Acct)*
Marcia Spieker *(Sr Mgr-Acct)*
Tony Rasmussen *(VP-Comml Lines Producer)*
Vera Schneider *(Sr VP)*
Kathy Hurlbut *(Mgr-Acct)*
Amy Rose *(Mgr-Employee Benefits Acct)*
Libby Szwanek *(Office Mgr)*
Randy Trost *(VP-Fin Svcs)*

Union Title Company, LLC   (2)
3800 Normal Blvd, Lincoln, NE 68506
Tel.: (877) 456-1066
Web Site: http://www.uniontitle.com
Emp.: 15
Insurance Management Services
N.A.I.C.S.: 524298
Duane Want *(Pres)*
Christine Luu *(Officer-Escrow)*
Rocky Bouma *(Officer-Escrow)*

FARMERS ALLIANCE MUTUAL INSURANCE CO., INC.
1122 N Main, McPherson, KS 67460-1401
Tel.: (620) 241-2200
Web Site: https://www.fami.com
Year Founded: 1888
Sales Range: $100-124.9 Million
Emp.: 800
Provider of Fire, Marine & Casualty
Insurance Products
N.A.I.C.S.: 524126
Jack M. Rader *(CMO & VP)*
Paul Taliaferro *(CFO & Treas)*
Brian D. Lopata *(Pres & CEO)*
Andy Edwardson *(CIO & VP-IT)*

Subsidiaries:

Alliance Indemnity Company Inc. (1)
1122 N Main St, McPherson, KS 67460-2846
Tel.: (620) 241-2200
Web Site: http://www.sami.com
Sales Range: $25-49.9 Million
Emp.: 3
Provider of Insurance Products & Services
N.A.I.C.S.: 524210

Sanilac Mutual Insurance Co,
Inc.   (1)
PO Box 186, Croswell, MI 48422
Tel.: (810) 657-9500
Sales Range: $1-9.9 Million
Emp.: 15
Insurance Agencies & Brokerages
N.A.I.C.S.: 524210
Lynn Morell *(Pres)*

FARMERS AUTOMOBILE INSURANCE ASSOCIATION
2505 Court St, Pekin, IL 61558
Tel.: (309) 346-1161
Web Site:
    http://www.evangelpress.com
Rev.: $193,912,287
Emp.: 560
Life Insurance Carrier
N.A.I.C.S.: 524113
Daniel Connell *(Treas & VP)*
Gordon Walker *(Chm & CEO)*

FARMERS BANCORPORATION, INC.
914 Main St, Buhl, ID 83316   **ID**
Tel.: (208) 543-4351
Web Site:
    http://www.farmersbankidaho.com
Year Founded: 1993
Sales Range: $10-24.9 Million
Emp.: 86
Bank Holding Company
N.A.I.C.S.: 551111
J. Michael Hamilton *(Pres & CEO)*

Subsidiaries:

Farmers Bank   (1)
914 Main St, Buhl, ID 83316
Tel.: (208) 543-4351
Web Site: http://www.farmersnatlbank.com
Sales Range: $10-24.9 Million
Emp.: 84
National Commercial Banks
N.A.I.C.S.: 522110
Mike Hamilton *(Chm & Pres)*
Kevin J. Helmick *(Exec VP-Retail & Wealth Management)*
Coni Bolton *(Officer-Credit & VP)*
Darcie Upton *(CFO)*
Pat Hamilton Jr. *(CIO & VP)*

FARMERS BANCSHARES INC.
115 Shelbyville St, Center, TX 75935
Tel.: (936) 598-3311
Web Site:
    http://www.farmersbankcenter.com
Sales Range: $10-24.9 Million
Emp.: 80
Bank Holding Company
N.A.I.C.S.: 551111
David Chadwick *(Sr VP-Ops)*
Nelson Davis *(Sr VP-Lending)*
Paul M. Reed *(Chm, Pres & CEO)*

Subsidiaries:

Farmers State Bank   (1)
115 Shelbyville St, Center, TX 75935
Tel.: (936) 598-3311
Rev.: $1,900,000
Emp.: 50
State Commercial Banks
N.A.I.C.S.: 551111

FARMERS BANK & TRUST
1017 Harrison, Great Bend, KS 67530
Tel.: (620) 792-2411
Web Site:
    http://www.farmersbankks.com
Banking Services
N.A.I.C.S.: 522110
W.R. Robbins *(Pres & CEO)*

FARMERS BANK AND TRUST
400 W Main St, Blytheville, AR 72315
Tel.: (870) 763-8101
Web Site:
    http://www.farmersbankbly.com
Year Founded: 1908
Sales Range: $10-24.9 Million
Emp.: 50
State Commercial Banks
N.A.I.C.S.: 522110
Randy Scott *(Pres)*
Licey McClish *(Asst VP-Ops)*

Shelly Crosskno *(CFO)*
Carroll Valentino *(VP)*
Greg Clapp *(Asst VP-Frankfort)*

FARMERS CO-OP ELEVATOR CO. HUDSONVILLE
3300 Prospect St, Hudsonville, MI 49426
Tel.: (616) 669-9596
Web Site: http://www.fcelevator.com
Year Founded: 1917
Sales Range: $25-49.9 Million
Emp.: 28
Agricultural Services
N.A.I.C.S.: 424510
Dan Vander Schuur *(Gen Mgr)*

FARMERS CO-OP INC
705 Packwaukee St, Ames, IA 50010
Tel.: (319) 983-2259
Web Site: http://www.fccoop.com
Sales Range: $10-24.9 Million
Emp.: 30
Grains
N.A.I.C.S.: 424510
Jim Chism *(Gen Mgr)*

FARMERS CO-OP OF HANSKA INC.
103 E 1st St, Hanska, MN 56041
Tel.: (507) 439-6244
Web Site: https://www.hanskaco.com
Year Founded: 1929
Sales Range: $10-24.9 Million
Emp.: 70
Whslr of Grain & Field Beans
N.A.I.C.S.: 424510
Gerald Grathwohl *(Pres)*
John Schmidt *(Mgr-Feed Dept)*

FARMERS CO-OP SUPPLY & SHIPPING ASSOCIATION
570 Commerce St, West Salem, WI 54669
Tel.: (608) 786-1100
Sales Range: $10-24.9 Million
Emp.: 36
Feed
N.A.I.C.S.: 424910

FARMERS CO-OPERATIVE OIL CO.
461 2nd Ave W, Echo, MN 56237
Tel.: (507) 925-4114
Sales Range: $10-24.9 Million
Emp.: 20
Farm Supplies
N.A.I.C.S.: 457120
David Forkrud *(Gen Mgr)*

FARMERS COOP ASSOCIATION
406 E K St, Forest City, IA 50436
Tel.: (641) 585-2814
Web Site: https://www.farmersca.com
Year Founded: 1916
Sales Range: $10-24.9 Million
Emp.: 27
Agricultural Services
N.A.I.C.S.: 424510
Randy Broesder *(Gen Mgr)*

FARMERS COOP ELEVATOR OTTOSEN
71 Brady Ave, Ottosen, IA 50570
Tel.: (515) 379-1065
Web Site:
    https://www.ottosenelevator.com
Year Founded: 1952
Sales Range: $10-24.9 Million
Emp.: 15
Marketer of Grains
N.A.I.C.S.: 424510
Kevin Walker *(Gen Mgr)*
Jeff Wiuff *(Pres)*
Joel Schmidt *(VP)*

Jess Welter *(Sec)*
Keith Thilges *(Mgr-Agronomy & Petroleum)*
Cal Haug *(Mgr-Feed & Grain)*

FARMERS COOP MILL & ELEVATOR ASSOCIATION
106 S Broadway Ave, Carnegie, OK 73015
Tel.: (580) 654-1016
Web Site:
    https://www.carnegiecoop.com
Sales Range: $10-24.9 Million
Emp.: 60
Grain Elevators
N.A.I.C.S.: 424510
Mike Sawyer *(Gen Mgr)*

FARMERS COOPERATIVE
325 W 1st St, Pilger, NE 68768   **NE**
Tel.: (402) 396-3414
Year Founded: 1918
Sales Range: $10-24.9 Million
Emp.: 30
Farm Supplies
N.A.I.C.S.: 424910
Joan Liebermann *(Pres)*

FARMERS COOPERATIVE
208 W Depot St, Dorchester, NE 68343   **NE**
Tel.: (402) 946-2211
Web Site: https://www.farmersco-operative.com
Year Founded: 1903
Sales Range: $10-24.9 Million
Emp.: 100
Grain & Field Beans Distr
N.A.I.C.S.: 424510
Stan Mitchell *(CFO)*
Brian Bohling *(Controller)*

Subsidiaries:

Farmers Cooperative   (1)
501 E Main St, Plymouth, NE 68424
Tel.: (402) 656-3615
Web Site: http://www.fcecply.com
Grain Elevators
N.A.I.C.S.: 424510
Ron Velder *(CEO)*

FARMERS COOPERATIVE ASSOCIATION
428 4th St, Alva, OK 73717
Tel.: (580) 327-3854
Web Site: http://www.alvacoop.com
Sales Range: $10-24.9 Million
Emp.: 40
Grain Elevators
N.A.I.C.S.: 424510
Randy Sweatfenger *(Pres)*

FARMERS COOPERATIVE ASSOCIATION
3522 S Ranch Dr, Tonkawa, OK 74653
Tel.: (580) 765-5736
Web Site: http://www.gocoopok.com
Sales Range: $10-24.9 Million
Emp.: 25
Grains
N.A.I.C.S.: 424510
Bob Mulligan *(Gen Mgr)*

FARMERS COOPERATIVE ASSOCIATION
110 S Keokuk Washington Rd, Keota, IA 52248
Tel.: (641) 636-3748
Web Site:
    https://www.keotafarmerscoop.com
Year Founded: 1916
Sales Range: $50-74.9 Million
Emp.: 25
Fertilizer & Fertilizer Materials Whslr

N.A.I.C.S.: 424910
Tom Edwards *(Gen Mgr)*
Brian Wood *(Mgr-Ainsworth)*
Tony Bos *(Mgr-Batavia)*
Dick Reed *(Mgr-Hedrick)*
Randy Bombei *(Mgr-Richland)*
Terry King *(Mgr-Stockport)*
Brent Ness *(Mgr-Sigourney)*

FARMERS COOPERATIVE AS-SOCIATION
402 E County Rd, Columbus, KS 66725
Tel.: (620) 429-2296
Web Site: http://www.farmersco-op.coop
Sales Range: $10-24.9 Million
Emp.: 25
Provider of Grain Elevators
N.A.I.C.S.: 424510
Machelle Shouse *(Gen Mgr)*

FARMERS COOPERATIVE AS-SOCIATION INC.
1206 S Douglas Hwy, Gillette, WY 82716
Tel.: (307) 682-4468
Sales Range: $25-49.9 Million
Emp.: 48
Grain Merchant Whslr
N.A.I.C.S.: 424510
Annie Brimmer *(Sec)*
Philip Habeck *(VP)*
Debra Dawkins *(Controller-Debbie Clements & Acct)*
Dave Shippy *(Pres)*

FARMERS COOPERATIVE AS-SOCIATION OF RAVENNA
35885 Ravenna Rd, Ravenna, NE 68869
Tel.: (308) 452-3257
Web Site: https://www.farmerscooperative.net
Sales Range: $10-24.9 Million
Emp.: 40
Soil Preparation, Planting & Cultivating
N.A.I.C.S.: 115112
Phil Zeller *(Mgr-Agronomy)*
Pam Treffer *(Office Mgr)*
Lonnie Bohn *(VP)*
Greg Hervert *(Treas & Sec)*
Jason Jakob *(VP)*
Brenda Schroeder *(CFO & Office Mgr)*

FARMERS COOPERATIVE CO.
196 E RailRd, Afton, IA 50830
Tel.: (641) 347-8428   IA
Web Site: http://www.farmerscoopco.com
Year Founded: 1920
Sales Range: $25-49.9 Million
Emp.: 130
Retailer of Fertilizer & Feeds
N.A.I.C.S.: 115112
Larry Weis *(Pres)*
James Schendt *(Gen Mgr)*

FARMERS COOPERATIVE CO.
304 Ellsworth St, Dows, IA 50071
Tel.: (515) 852-4136
Web Site: http://www.fccdows.com
Sales Range: $10-24.9 Million
Emp.: 25
Grains
N.A.I.C.S.: 424510
Vic Vandehaar *(Gen Mgr)*

FARMERS COOPERATIVE CO.
223 E 1st St, Readlyn, IA 50668
Tel.: (319) 279-3396   IA
Sales Range: $10-24.9 Million
Emp.: 15
Whslr of Feed & Agronomy

N.A.I.C.S.: 424910
Jeff Brunscheon *(Mgr)*

FARMERS COOPERATIVE CO. INC.
105 E Main St, Hinton, IA 51024
Tel.: (712) 947-4212   IN
Web Site: http://www.my-coop.com
Year Founded: 1925
Sales Range: $10-24.9 Million
Emp.: 100
Provider of Grain Elevators & Agronomy Services
N.A.I.C.S.: 424510

FARMERS COOPERATIVE COMPANY
Hwy 54 & Main St, Haviland, KS 67059
Tel.: (620) 862-5225
Web Site: http://www.havilandcoop.com
Rev.: $14,007,849
Emp.: 22
Grain Elevators
N.A.I.C.S.: 424510
Rob Paxson *(Mgr)*

FARMERS COOPERATIVE COMPANY
10741 N 142nd St PO Box 70, Waverly, NE 68462
Tel.: (402) 786-2665
Web Site: http://www.waverlyc.com
Sales Range: Less than $1 Million
Emp.: 100
Disrtributions Of Grains
N.A.I.C.S.: 424510
Harold Hummel *(CEO)*
Norma Jones *(Controller)*
James Rodney *(Mgr-Ops)*
Dave Snyder *(Mgr)*

FARMERS COOPERATIVE COMPRESS INC.
3800 Southeast Dr, Lubbock, TX 79404
Tel.: (806) 763-9431
Web Site: http://www.farmerscompress.com
Year Founded: 1948
Sales Range: $10-24.9 Million
Emp.: 145
Farm Product Warehousing & Storage Services
N.A.I.C.S.: 493130
Ron Harkey *(Pres & CEO)*
Don Harper *(VP)*

FARMERS COOPERATIVE EL-EVATOR CO.
401 N Main St, Garden Plain, KS 67050
Tel.: (316) 535-2221
Web Site: https://www.gardenplaincoop.com
Emp.: 45
Grains
N.A.I.C.S.: 424510

FARMERS COOPERATIVE EL-EVATOR CO.
317 Ausborne St, Hemingford, NE 69348
Tel.: (308) 487-3317
Web Site: http://www.farmcoop.com
Sales Range: $25-49.9 Million
Emp.: 25
Grains
N.A.I.C.S.: 424510
Dale Anderson *(CFO)*

FARMERS COOPERATIVE EL-EVATOR CO.

90 Railway, Cottonwood, MN 56229
Tel.: (507) 423-5412
Web Site: http://www.farmerscoopelevator.com
Sales Range: $50-74.9 Million
Emp.: 30
Grain Elevators
N.A.I.C.S.: 424510
Scott Dubbelde *(Gen Mgr)*

FARMERS COOPERATIVE EL-EVATOR COMPANY
109 Isabella St, Radcliffe, IA 50230
Tel.: (515) 899-2101
Web Site: http://www.radcliffecoop.com
Sales Range: $10-24.9 Million
Emp.: 18
Grain Elevators
N.A.I.C.S.: 424510
Dave Hinderaker *(Pres)*

FARMERS COOPERATIVE EL-EVATOR COMPANY
18 W 1st St, Kingsley, IA 51028
Tel.: (712) 378-2888
Web Site: http://www.kingsleycoop.com
Year Founded: 1912
Sales Range: $10-24.9 Million,
Emp.: 35
Provider of Grain Elevators
N.A.I.C.S.: 424510
Chris Pedersen *(Gen Mgr)*

FARMERS COOPERATIVE EL-EVATOR COMPANY
1972 510th St, Hanley Falls, MN 56245-0059
Tel.: (507) 768-3448
Web Site: https://www.farmerscoopelevator.com
Year Founded: 1972
Sales Range: $25-49.9 Million
Emp.: 35
Animal Feed Mfr
N.A.I.C.S.: 311119
Scott Dubbelde *(Gen Mgr)*

FARMERS COOPERATIVE EL-EVATOR OF SISSETON & NEW EFFINGTON
101 Oak St W, Sisseton, SD 57262
Tel.: (605) 698-3251
Web Site: http://www.sissetonelevator.com
Sales Range: $10-24.9 Million
Emp.: 13
Grain Elevators
N.A.I.C.S.: 424510

FARMERS COOPERATIVE EQUITY CO.
300 N Burr St, Isabel, KS 67065
Tel.: (620) 739-4335
Web Site: http://www.fceisabel.com
Sales Range: $10-24.9 Million
Emp.: 15
Grains
N.A.I.C.S.: 424510
Charles Swayze *(Gen Mgr)*

FARMERS COOPERATIVE GRAIN ASSOCIATION
9011 N A St, Wellington, KS 67152
Tel.: (620) 326-7496
Web Site: http://www.wellingtoncoop.com
Sales Range: $10-24.9 Million
Emp.: 24
Grains
N.A.I.C.S.: 424510
Curt Guinn *(Pres)*

FARMERS COOPERATIVE INC.
2105 Industrial Park Rd, Van Buren, AR 72956
Tel.: (479) 474-6622   AR
Web Site: https://www.farmercoop.com
Year Founded: 1944
Sales Range: $50-74.9 Million
Emp.: 120
Farm Supplies
N.A.I.C.S.: 424910
Jay Carter *(Gen Mgr)*

Subsidiaries:

Galloway Tire Company Inc.   (1)
7200 S 11th St, Fort Smith, AR 72901-4526   (100%)
Tel.: (479) 782-6051
Rev.: $6,100,000
Emp.: 17
Tires & Tubes
N.A.I.C.S.: 423130
Gene Bruick *(Pres)*

FARMERS COOPERATIVE SO-CIETY
317 3rd St NW, Sioux Center, IA 51250
Tel.: (712) 722-2671
Web Site: https://www.farmerscoopsociety.com
Rev.: $81,870,999
Emp.: 100
Grain Elevators
N.A.I.C.S.: 424510
Ken Ehrp *(Gen Mgr)*
Marvin Wynia *(Pres)*
Brian Billick *(Mgr-Boyden Elevator)*

FARMERS COOPERATIVE, INC.
1841 Howard St W, Live Oak, FL 32064
Tel.: (386) 362-1459
Web Site: http://www.farmandhomedepot.com
Year Founded: 1947
Rev.: $10,200,000
Emp.: 45
Fertilizer Mfr
N.A.I.C.S.: 325314
Tim Steichen *(Pres)*
Pauline Cogdill *(Mgr-Credit)*
Todd Lawrence *(Treas & Sec)*

FARMERS ELECTRIC CO-OPERATIVE
2000 Interstate Hwy 30, Greenville, TX 75402
Tel.: (903) 455-1715
Web Site: https://www.farmerselectric.coop
Sales Range: $25-49.9 Million
Emp.: 80
Electric Services
N.A.I.C.S.: 221118
Mark Stubbs *(Gen Mgr)*

FARMERS ELECTRIC COOP-ERATIVE CORPORATION
300 Hwy 367 N, Newport, AR 72112-0708
Tel.: (870) 523-3691   AR
Web Site: https://www.farmersecc.com
Year Founded: 1937
Sales Range: $10-24.9 Million
Emp.: 26
Electric Power Distr
N.A.I.C.S.: 221122
Larry Bright *(Gen Mgr)*
Bill Fortune *(VP)*
Jim DuPree *(Pres)*
Sam Houston *(Treas & Sec)*

FARMERS ELEVATOR CO-OP
1219 Main St, Rock Valley, IA 51247
Tel.: (712) 476-5321

Farmers Elevator Co-Op—(Continued)

Web Site:
http://www.farmerselevator.com
Sales Range: $25-49.9 Million
Emp.: 50
Grain Elevators, Grain Seed &
Agronomy
N.A.I.C.S.: 424510
Dave Van Holland *(Pres)*
Leon Vanden Bosch *(Sec)*
Mike Ter Wee *(Treas)*
Gerald Brands *(VP)*
Mark Finck *(Gen Mgr)*
Don Harberts *(Mgr-Agronomy Div)*
Kristy Kammrad *(Mgr-Alvord)*
Deric Kruse *(Mgr-Doon & Ops)*
Denny Kelderman *(Mgr-Feed Div)*
Wayne Kollis *(Mgr-Grain)*
Randy Schouten *(Mgr-Hawarden)*
Justin Teunissen *(Mgr-Hudson)*
Chad Rus *(Mgr-Inwood)*
Jim Jensen *(Mgr-Larchwood)*
Lonn Kellenberger *(Mgr-Lester)*
Wes Koedam *(Mgr-Rock Rapids)*
Jim Faber *(Mgr-Sys)*
Kristi Habben *(Office Mgr-Doon)*
Bill Hinkhouse *(Controller)*
Terry Lively *(Dir-Safety & Risk)*

FARMERS ELEVATOR COMPANY
Hwy 1, Alvarado, MN 56710
Tel.: (218) 965-4812
Web Site:
http://www.farmerselevator.com
Sales Range: $10-24.9 Million
Emp.: 13
Grains
N.A.I.C.S.: 424510
Bruce Chwialkowski *(Gen Mgr)*
Mike Ginter *(Mgr)*
Kelly Kotowicz *(Mgr-Seed)*

FARMERS ELEVATOR COMPANY OF MANTENO
51 W 4th St, Manteno, IL 60950
Tel.: (815) 468-3461
Web Site:
https://www.fecmanteno.com
Year Founded: 1913
Sales Range: $10-24.9 Million
Emp.: 5
Grain & Bean Whslr
N.A.I.C.S.: 424510
Jerry Heisner *(Treas & Sec)*
Ron Reiter *(VP)*
Harold McQueen *(Pres)*

FARMERS ELEVATOR GRAIN & SUPPLY
16-917 RD B, New Bavaria, OH
43548-0249
Tel.: (419) 653-4132
Web Site:
https://www.thefarmerselevator.com
Sales Range: $10-24.9 Million
Emp.: 20
Grain Elevators
N.A.I.C.S.: 424510
Tim Hockman *(Gen Mgr)*
Kelly Verhoff *(Office Mgr)*

FARMERS ELEVATOR OF LAKEFIELD
105 Main St, Lakefield, MN 56150
Tel.: (507) 662-5271
Web Site:
http://www.farmerselevator.com
Sales Range: $25-49.9 Million
Emp.: 10
Grains
N.A.I.C.S.: 424510

FARMERS EQUIPMENT COMPANY
410 19th St, Lynden, WA 98264
Tel.: (360) 354-4451
Web Site:
http://www.farmersequip.com
Sales Range: $10-24.9 Million
Emp.: 55
Farm Implements
N.A.I.C.S.: 532412
Kenneth D. Stremler *(Pres)*
Kevin Pawlowsky *(Pres)*
Dave Snyder *(Gen Mgr)*

FARMERS FEED & GRAIN COMPANY
306 Birch St, Riceville, IA 50466
Tel.: (641) 985-2147   IA
Web Site: https://www.ffgcoinc.com
Sales Range: $10-24.9 Million
Emp.: 25
Marketer of Grains
N.A.I.C.S.: 424510
Steve Eastman *(Pres)*

FARMERS FEED MILL INC.
251 W Loudon Ave, Lexington, KY
40508
Tel.: (859) 255-7602
Web Site:
https://www.hallwayfeeds.com
Sales Range: $10-24.9 Million
Emp.: 30
Livestock Feeds
N.A.I.C.S.: 424510
Betsy Satterfield *(Office Mgr-Acctg)*
Lee Hall *(VP)*
Jeff Pendleton *(Gen Mgr)*
Robert Hall Jr. *(Pres)*

FARMERS FOODS CHASE CITY INCORPORATED
428 Dodd St, Chase City, VA 23924
Tel.: (434) 372-0423
Web Site:
http://www.farmersfoods.com
Sales Range: $50-74.9 Million
Emp.: 350
Grocery Stores
N.A.I.C.S.: 445110

FARMERS GRAIN & COAL CO. INC.
PO Box 189, Mason City, IL 62664-
0189
Tel.: (217) 482-3238
Web Site:
http://www.farmersgraincoal.com
Sales Range: $10-24.9 Million
Emp.: 10
Grain Elevators
N.A.I.C.S.: 424510

FARMERS GRAIN COMPANY
302 W Broadway St, Pond Creek, OK
73766
Tel.: (580) 532-4273
Web Site:
http://www.farmersgrainco.com
Sales Range: $250-299.9 Million
Emp.: 10
Grains
N.A.I.C.S.: 424510
Kent Prickett *(Gen Mgr)*
Rusty Pearman *(Mgr)*

FARMERS GRAIN OF LATHAM INC.
111 N Main St, Latham, IL 62543
Tel.: (217) 674-3413
Web Site:
http://farmersgrainlatham.com
Sales Range: $10-24.9 Million
Emp.: 5
Grain Elevators
N.A.I.C.S.: 424510
Terry Cundall *(Mgr)*

FARMERS GRAIN TERMINAL INC.
1977 Harbor Front Industrial Pk,
Greenville, MS 38702
Tel.: (662) 332-0987
Web Site: https://www.fgtcoop.com
Year Founded: 1968
Sales Range: $125-149.9 Million
Emp.: 65
Farm Product Warehousing & Storage
N.A.I.C.S.: 493130
Harvey Parrish *(Sr VP)*

FARMERS INC.
525 Railroad St, Allenton, WI 53002
Tel.: (262) 629-4104
Web Site: http://www.farmersinc.com
Sales Range: $10-24.9 Million
Emp.: 40
Agricultural Machinery & Equipment
Retailer & Distr
N.A.I.C.S.: 423820
Dan Drohman *(Gen Mgr)*

FARMERS MERCHANTS COOP OIL CO.
45316 S Dakota Hwy 34, Madison,
SD 57042
Tel.: (605) 256-4516
Sales Range: $10-24.9 Million
Emp.: 39
Petroleum Products
N.A.I.C.S.: 424720
Paul Schultz *(Gen Mgr)*

FARMERS MILL & ELEVATOR CO.
203 Main Ave S, Hankinson, ND
58041
Tel.: (701) 242-7501
Sales Range: $10-24.9 Million
Emp.: 6
Grain Elevators
N.A.I.C.S.: 424510

FARMERS MUTUAL FIRE INSURANCE
125 W Broadway, Salem, NJ 08079
Tel.: (856) 935-1851
Web Site:
https://www.farmersofsalem.com
Year Founded: 1851
Sales Range: $25-49.9 Million
Emp.: 40
Fire, Marine & Casualty Insurance
N.A.I.C.S.: 524126
James Doherty *(Pres & CEO)*

FARMERS MUTUAL HAIL INSURANCE COMPANY OF IOWA
6785 Westown Pkwy, West Des
Moines, IA 50266-7727
Tel.: (515) 282-9104
Web Site: https://www.fmh.com
Crop Insurance
N.A.I.C.S.: 524126
Kevin A. Johnson *(Mgr-Sls)*
Patrick Faga *(Exec VP)*

Subsidiaries:

Global Ag Insurance Services,
LLC   **(1)**
45 E River Park Pl W Ste 601, Fresno, CA
93720
Tel.: (559) 530-2767
Web Site: https://www.globalag.com
General Insurance Services
N.A.I.C.S.: 524210

FARMERS MUTUAL INSURANCE COMPANY OF NEBRASKA INC.
501 S 13th St, Lincoln, NE 68508
               NE
Tel.: (402) 434-8300

Web Site: http://www.fmne.com
Year Founded: 1891
Sales Range: $50-74.9 Million
Emp.: 100
Insurance Services
N.A.I.C.S.: 524126
Byron Boslau *(Chm & CEO)*
Mark T. Walz *(CFO & Sr VP)*
James B. Dobler *(Exec VP)*
Gregory Allen *(Sr VP)*

FARMERS MUTUAL PROTECTIVE ASSOCIATION TEXAS
2301 S 37th St, Temple, TX 76504
Tel.: (254) 773-2181
Web Site: https://www.rvos.com
Rev.: $31,388,202
Emp.: 80
Property Damage Insurance
N.A.I.C.S.: 524126
Richard Hykel *(Dir-Facility)*

FARMERS NATIONAL COMPANY
11516 Nicholas St Ste 100, Omaha,
NE 68154-8016
Tel.: (402) 496-3276   NE
Web Site:
http://www.farmersnational.com
Year Founded: 1929
Sales Range: $25-49.9 Million
Emp.: 260
Farm & Ranch Management Services
& Real Estate Sales
N.A.I.C.S.: 115116
David Knutson *(CFO, Treas & Sr
Exec VP)*
Terri Piccolo *(Sr VP-Fin)*
David Smith *(Sr VP-Oil & Gas Mgmt)*
Susan Christensen *(VP-Mktg)*
David Englund *(Sr VP-Farm & Ranch
Mgmt)*
Michael Pfantz *(Sr VP-Risk Mgmt)*
Wes Turiano *(VP-Oil & Gas Mgmt)*
Scott Porterfield *(Mgr-Bus Dev-
Northeast)*
Nathan Elting *(Asst Mgr-Farm & Sls-
Real Estate)*
Matt Joynt *(Asst Mgr-Farm & Sls-
Real Estate)*
Richard Hickman *(Asst VP-Real Estate)*
Max Hendrickson *(Mgr-Farm)*
Scott Huether *(Mgr-Farm)*
Huether Scott *(Mgr-Farm)*
Stephen Wright *(VP-Eastern Area)*
Chase Sullivan *(Mgr-Pro Farm)*
Paul Schadegg *(Sr VP-Real Estate
Ops)*
Clayton Becker *(Pres)*

FARMERS PRODUCE EXCHANGE
225 S Jefferson Ave, Lebanon, MO
65536
Tel.: (417) 532-3174
Rev.: $11,861,317
Emp.: 28
Farm Supplies
N.A.I.C.S.: 424910
John Percival *(Mgr)*

FARMERS RANCHERS COOP ASSOC.
224 S Main St, Ainsworth, NE 69210
Tel.: (402) 387-2811
Web Site:
http://www.farmersrancherscoop.com
Sales Range: $10-24.9 Million
Emp.: 60
Livestock Feeds
N.A.I.C.S.: 311119
Linda Schumacher *(Controller)*

FARMERS RICE COOPERATIVE

2566 River Plz Dr, Sacramento, CA 95833
Tel.: (916) 923-5100
Web Site: http://www.farmersrice.com
Year Founded: 1944
Sales Range: $200-249.9 Million
Rice Milling & Marketing Services
N.A.I.C.S.: 311212
Herbert R. Holzapfel *(Chm)*
Kenneth Collins *(Vice Chm)*
Bill Tanimoto *(Chief Fin & Operating Officer, Sec & Sr VP)*
Steven Michel *(VP-Mktg)*
Rick Rhody *(Pres & CEO)*
Charley Mathews Jr. *(Vice Chm)*

FARMERS RURAL ELECTRIC COOP CORP.
504 S Broadway St, Glasgow, KY 42141
Tel.: (270) 651-2191
Web Site:
https://www.farmersrecc.com
Sales Range: $10-24.9 Million
Emp.: 69
Distribution of Electric Power
N.A.I.C.S.: 221122
Paul C. Hawkins *(Chm)*
William T. Prather *(Pres & CEO)*

FARMERS SAVINGS BANK INC.
305 Doty St, Mineral Point, WI 53565
Tel.: (608) 987-3321
Web Site:
https://www.farmerssavings.com
Rev.: $10,900,000
Emp.: 50
Commericial Banking
N.A.I.C.S.: 522110
Mary Jo Ceniti *(Chm)*
Suzanne Nechkash *(Officer-Loan & VP)*
Patrick W. Forsyth *(Officer-Loan & Sr VP)*
Joseph L. Witmer *(Pres)*
Cherie L. Davis *(Asst VP & Officer-Loan)*
Ross A. Smith *(Officer-Investment)*
Kimberly Phillips *(Officer-IT)*
Ashley Tibbits *(Officer-Loan)*
L. Dale Hatfield *(Officer-Loan & Sr VP)*
Matthew J. Staver *(Officer-Loan & VP)*
Andrew Baber *(Officer-Mortgage Loan)*

FARMERS SEAFOOD CO. INC.
1192 Hawn Ave, Shreveport, LA 71107
Tel.: (318) 222-9504
Web Site:
https://www.farmersseafood.com
Sales Range: $10-24.9 Million
Emp.: 30
Fish & Seafoods
N.A.I.C.S.: 424460
Alex S. Mijalis *(Chm)*

FARMERS STATE BANK
103 Main St, Victor, MT 59875
Tel.: (406) 642-3431
Web Site:
https://www.farmersebank.com
Year Founded: 1907
Sales Range: $10-24.9 Million
Emp.: 97
Provider of Banking Services
N.A.I.C.S.: 522110
Mark Anderson *(Officer-Consumer Loan & VP)*

Subsidiaries:

State Bank of Fox Lake   (1)
314 W State St, Fox Lake, WI 53933

Tel.: (920) 928-3161
Web Site: http://www.ergobank.com
Savings Institutions
N.A.I.C.S.: 522180

FARMERS SUPPLY ASSOCIA-TION
16240 Hwy 14 E, Harrisburg, AR 72432
Tel.: (870) 578-2468
Sales Range: Less than $1 Million
Emp.: 32
Farm Supplies
N.A.I.C.S.: 424910
Roger Pohlner *(Pres)*
Butch Hunter *(Dir-Safety)*

FARMERS SUPPLY SALES INC.
1409 E Ave, Kalona, IA 52247
Tel.: (319) 656-2291   IA
Web Site:
http://www.jddealer.deere.com
Year Founded: 1953
Sales Range: $10-24.9 Million
Emp.: 30
Wholesalers of Farm Implements
N.A.I.C.S.: 423820
Anthony Bentley *(Pres & Gen Mgr)*

FARMERS TELECOMMUNICA-TIONS COOPERATIVE, INC.
144 McCurdy Ave N, Rainsville, AL 35986
Tel.: (256) 638-2144
Web Site: https://www.farmerstel.com
Sales Range: $10-24.9 Million
Emp.: 97
Provider of Telephone Communications
N.A.I.C.S.: 517121
Brandi Lyles *(Dir-Mktg)*

FARMERS TELEPHONE CO. INC.
404 4th St, Batavia, IA 52533
Tel.: (641) 662-2373
Web Site:
http://www.bataviatelephone.com
Rev.: $13,000,000
Emp.: 6
Telephone Communications
N.A.I.C.S.: 517121
Steve Dallner *(Pres)*

FARMERS TELEPHONE CO-OPERATIVE
1101 E Main St, Kingstree, SC 29556-4105
Tel.: (843) 382-2333   SC
Web Site: http://www.ftc-i.net
Year Founded: 1951
Sales Range: $150-199.9 Million
Emp.: 500
Telephone Communication Services
N.A.I.C.S.: 517121
Brad Erwin *(CEO)*
Jamie Mouzon *(Coord-Tech Svc)*
Curt Gowdy *(Mgr-Safety & Security)*
Diane M. Banar *(Sec)*
Kenny Clark *(Chief HR Officer)*
Tyler Gibbs *(Supvr-Sls)*
Gene Failmezger *(Engr-IP Video)*
Jeff Williamson *(Mgr-Credit)*

FARMERS UNION COOP
101 N Main St, Friend, NE 68359
Tel.: (402) 947-4291   NE
Web Site:
http://www.farmersunioncoop.com
Year Founded: 1919
Sales Range: $10-24.9 Million
Emp.: 18
Agricultural Services
N.A.I.C.S.: 424510

Ed Menke *(Gen Mgr)*
Brian Brahmstedt *(Mgr-Agronomy Dept)*
Ed Menke *(Gen Mgr)*

FARMERS UNION COOP SUP-PLY COMPANY
214 E 1st St, Clarkson, NE 68629
Tel.: (402) 892-3422
Rev.: $10,000,000
Emp.: 30
Grain Elevator, Storage Only
N.A.I.C.S.: 457120
Keith Dostalo *(Gen Mgr)*

FARMERS UNION COOPERA-TIVE
1913 County Rd B32, Ossian, IA 52161
Tel.: (563) 532-9381   IA
Web Site:
https://www.farmerunion.net
Year Founded: 1916
Sales Range: $10-24.9 Million
Emp.: 50
Grains Mfr
N.A.I.C.S.: 424510
Dave Hemesath *(Gen Mgr)*
Linus Kuhn *(Pres)*
Dan Dietzenbach *(Sec)*
Keith Steinlage *(Mgr-Agronomy)*
Roy Hageman *(Treas)*

FARMERS UNION COOPERA-TIVE ASSOCIATION
131 N Nebraska St, Salem, SD 57058
Tel.: (605) 425-2691
Sales Range: $10-24.9 Million
Emp.: 45
Grain Elevators
N.A.I.C.S.: 424510
Lon Zeller *(Gen Mgr)*

FARMERS UNION HOSPITAL ASSOCIATION
1801 W 3rd St, Elk City, OK 73644
Tel.: (580) 225-2511   OK
Web Site: https://www.gprmc-ok.com
Year Founded: 1929
Sales Range: $25-49.9 Million
Emp.: 519
Healtcare Services
N.A.I.C.S.: 622110
Corey Lively *(CEO)*

FARMERS UNION MARKETING & PROCESSING ASSOCIA-TION
590 W Park Rd, Redwood Falls, MN 56283
Tel.: (507) 637-2938
Web Site: http://www.fumpa.com
Sales Range: $25-49.9 Million
Emp.: 237
Rendering Company
N.A.I.C.S.: 311119
Don W. Davis *(Pres)*

FARMERS UNION MUTUAL INSURANCE CO.
1415 12th Ave SE, Jamestown, ND 58401
Tel.: (701) 252-2341
Web Site: https://www.ndfu.org
Year Founded: 1944
Sales Range: $25-49.9 Million
Emp.: 50
Fire, Marine & Casualty Insurance
N.A.I.C.S.: 524126
Woody Barth *(Pres)*
Terry Borstad *(Treas)*
Mark Anderson *(Gen Mgr)*

Ellen Linderman *(Sec)*
Bob Kuylen *(VP)*
Carla Edinger *(Supvr-Education Dev)*

FARMERS UNION OIL BISMARCK/MANDAN
2006 E Broadway Ave, Bismarck, ND 58501
Tel.: (701) 223-8707
Web Site:
http://wwwbismarckmandan.com
Sales Range: $25-49.9 Million
Emp.: 120
Diesel Fuel
N.A.I.C.S.: 424720
Cyril Fix *(CEO)*

FARMERS UNION OIL CO.
105 4th Ave Sw, Rugby, ND 58368
Tel.: (701) 776-5221
Web Site: http://rugbyfarmers.com
Sales Range: $10-24.9 Million
Emp.: 20
Fertilizer & Fertilizer Materials
N.A.I.C.S.: 424910
Steve Dockter *(Gen Mgr)*
Thomas Powell *(Mgr)*
Tim Cornett *(Asst Mgr-Energy)*

FARMERS UNION OIL COM-PANY
108 2nd Ave W, Oslo, MN 56744
Tel.: (218) 695-2511
Sales Range: $10-24.9 Million
Emp.: 18
Fertilizer & Fertilizer Materials
N.A.I.C.S.: 424910
Robert Hjeldness *(Gen Mgr)*

FARMERS UNION OIL COM-PANY OF KENMARE
Hwy 52 S, Kenmare, ND 58746
Tel.: (701) 385-4277
Web Site:
http://farmersunionkenmare.com
Sales Range: $25-49.9 Million
Emp.: 70
Farm Products & Diesel Fuel Distr
N.A.I.C.S.: 424720
Don Boos *(Gen Mgr)*

FARMERS UNION OIL MOHALL/SHERWOOD
102 Industrial Ave, Mohall, ND 58761
Tel.: (701) 756-6814
Web Site: http://www.srt.com
Sales Range: $50-74.9 Million
Emp.: 35
Petroleum Terminal
N.A.I.C.S.: 424710
Travis Halvorson *(Gen Mgr)*

FARMERS UNION OIL MOOR-HEAD
1772 W Main Ave, West Fargo, ND 58078
Tel.: (218) 233-2497
Web Site:
http://www.petroserveusa.com
Sales Range: $75-99.9 Million
Emp.: 300
Petroleum Products
N.A.I.C.S.: 424720
Kent Satrang *(CEO)*

FARMERS UNION OIL OF SOUTHERN VALLEY
204 S Front St, Fairmount, ND 58030
Tel.: (701) 474-5440
Web Site: https://www.fuosv.com
Sales Range: $25-49.9 Million
Emp.: 50
Petroleum Bulk Stations
N.A.I.C.S.: 424710

Farmers Union Oil of Southern
Valley—(Continued)

Lynn Nelson *(Gen Mgr)*
Brenda Muehler *(Controller)*
Brad Kubela *(Pres)*

FARMERS WEST

5300 Foothill Rd, Carpinteria, CA
93013
Tel.: (805) 684-5531
Web Site:
http://www.farmerswest.com
Sales Range: $10-24.9 Million
Emp.: 200
Flowers, Fresh
N.A.I.C.S.: 424930
Wilja Happe *(CEO)*
John Thomas *(E-commerce & Product Mgr & Dir-Community Outreach)*
Maximino Santillan *(Pres)*

FARMERS' ELECTRIC COOPERATIVE INC. OF NEW MEXICO

3701 N Thornton St, Clovis, NM
88101
Tel.: (575) 762-4466
Web Site: http://www.fecnm.org
Sales Range: $25-49.9 Million
Emp.: 48
Provider of Electric Services
N.A.I.C.S.: 221118
Lance Adkins *(Gen Mgr)*
Michael B. West *(Pres)*
Pat Woods *(Treas & Sec)*
Thom Moore *(Dir-Svcs)*

FARMGIRL FLOWERS INC.

901 16th St, San Francisco, CA
94107　　　　　　　　　　　　CA
Web Site:
http://www.farmgirlflowers.com
Year Founded: 2010
Sales Range: $10-24.9 Million
Emp.: 106
Flower Bouquet & Plant Distr
N.A.I.C.S.: 424930
Christina Stembel *(Founder & CEO)*

FARMINGTON BANCORP, INC.

16 N Main St, Farmington, IL 61531
Tel.: (309) 245-2441　　　　IL
Web Site:
http://www.bankoffarmington.com
Bank Holding Company
N.A.I.C.S.: 551111
Joseph L. Higgs *(Pres & CEO)*

Subsidiaries:

Bank of Farmington　　　　　(1)
16 N Main St, Farmington, IL 61531
Tel.: (309) 245-2441
Web Site: http://www.bankoffarmington.com
Sales Range: $1-9.9 Million
Commericial Banking
N.A.I.C.S.: 522110
Joseph L. Higgs *(Pres & CEO)*

FARMINGTON COUNTRY CLUB

1625 Country Club Cir, Charlottesville, VA 22901
Tel.: (434) 296-5661　　　　VA
Web Site:
https://www.farmingtoncc.com
Year Founded: 1951
Sales Range: $10-24.9 Million
Emp.: 545
Country Club
N.A.I.C.S.: 713910
Joseph Krenn *(COO & Gen Mgr)*
Allyn Gutauskas *(Mgr-HR)*
Tom Zimmermann *(Dir-Membership)*
Tyler Pickens *(Mgr-Club)*
Christy Cormons *(Dir-Catering)*
Robyn Evans *(Dir-Fin)*

Ronnie Hass *(Dir-Racquet Sports)*
Brandon Johnson *(Mgr-Club)*
Monica LaRue Camfield *(Mgr-Member Svcs)*
Julie Brown *(CFO)*
Russell Napper *(Dir-Housekeeping)*
Darryl Lawson *(Dir-Maintence)*
Michael Goolsby *(Mgr-Clubhouse Ops)*
Janet Rogers *(Mgr-Grounds)*

FARMINGTON HILLS HOLDING COMPANY

35200 Grand River Ave, Farmington,
MI 48335-3212
Tel.: (248) 478-0500　　　　DE
Sales Range: $125-149.9 Million
Emp.: 170
Automobile Dealership
N.A.I.C.S.: 441110
Sara Rader *(VP-Sls & Design)*
Michael Fitzgerald *(VP-Construction)*
Robert Mechigian Sr. *(Pres)*

Subsidiaries:

Bob Saks Buick　　　　　　　(1)
35080 Grand River Ave, Farmington Hills,
MI 48335-3269　　　　　　(100%)
Tel.: (248) 478-0500
Web Site: http://www.bobsaks.com
Sales Range: $10-24.9 Million
Emp.: 50
Car Dealership Owner & Operator
N.A.I.C.S.: 441110

FARMLAND CO-OP, INC.

405 E Edison St, Brush, CO 80723
Tel.: (970) 842-5059
Year Founded: 1931
Sales Range: $1-9.9 Million
Emp.: 23
Petroleum Bulk Stations & Terminals
N.A.I.C.S.: 424710

FARMWAY

803 3rd St, Clay Center, KS 67432
Tel.: (785) 632-5632
Web Site:
http://www.farmwaycoop.com
Sales Range: $10-24.9 Million
Emp.: 8
Grains
N.A.I.C.S.: 424510
Matthew File *(Assoc Dir-Beloit-Kansas)*
Tim Porter *(Chm)*
Jacob Porter *(Sec-Mankato-Kansas)*
Alan Aufdemberge *(Vice Chm)*
Monte Broeckelman *(CFO)*
Jeff Jensby *(VP-Agronomy)*
Wes O'Bannon *(Exec VP-Grain)*
Mallory Wittstruck *(VP-Comm & Member Svcs)*
Julie Harrison *(VP-HR)*

FARMWAY CO-OP INC.

204 E Ct St, Beloit, KS 67420-3242
Tel.: (785) 738-2241　　　　KS
Web Site:
http://www.farmwaycoop.com
Year Founded: 1911
Sales Range: $25-49.9 Million
Emp.: 150
Provider of Agricultural Products & Services
N.A.I.C.S.: 424510
Mike Jordan *(Chm)*
John Keller *(Vice Chm)*
Doug Rominger *(Mgr-Info Sys)*
Jeff Bechard *(Mgr-AgMark)*
Art Duerksen *(CEO)*
Jerry Brown *(VP-Agronomy)*

Subsidiaries:

Farmway Co-Op Inc. - Beloit Fertilizer
Plant　　　　　　　　　　　(1)
1101 Cottonwood St, Beloit, KS 67420

Tel.: (785) 738-2228
Emp.: 10
Fertilizer Mfr
N.A.I.C.S.: 325314
Clay Henningsen *(Mgr)*

Farmway Co-Op Inc. - NorKan
Plant　　　　　　　　　　　(1)
1301 Rust Rd, Beloit, KS 67420
Tel.: (785) 738-2241
Fertilizer Mfr
N.A.I.C.S.: 325314
Francis Williams *(Mgr)*

FARNHAM & PFILE CONSTRUCTION, INC.

1200 Maronda Way, Monessen, PA
15062
Tel.: (724) 653-1010
Web Site: https://www.farnham-pfile.com
Year Founded: 1985
Rev.: $10,910,933
Emp.: 66
Industrial Plant Construction Services
N.A.I.C.S.: 423810
Douglas B. Farnham *(Pres)*
Robert F. McMahon *(Founder, Treas & Sec)*

FARNSWORTH DEVELOPMENT COMPANIES

460 S Greenfield Rd, Mesa, AZ
85206-2062
Tel.: (480) 830-7784　　　　AZ
Web Site:
http://www.farnsworthcompanies.com
Year Founded: 1958
Sales Range: $75-99.9 Million
Emp.: 165
Holding Company; Subsidiaries Involved in Construction & Real Estate
N.A.I.C.S.: 237210
Jim Nichols *(Controller)*
David Palmer *(Sec & VP-Treasury)*
Craig Ahlostron *(Pres)*
Ross Farnsworth *(Chm & CEO)*

Subsidiaries:

Farnsworth Realty and Management
Co.　　　　　　　　　　　(1)
460 S Greenfield Rd Ste 5, Mesa, AZ
85206
Tel.: (480) 830-9945
Web Site: http://www.farnsworthrealty.com
Real Estate & Property Management Services
N.A.I.C.S.: 531190
Joe Farnsworth *(Pres)*
Steve Vaughn *(VP)*
Stephenie Edge *(Mgr-Property)*
Laura Lanhart *(Coord-Maintenance)*

R&K Building Supplies　　　(1)
25 W Baseline Rd, Gilbert, AZ 85233
Tel.: (480) 892-0025
Web Site: http://www.randk.com
Emp.: 250
Building Supplies Distr
N.A.I.C.S.: 444180
Chad Coons *(Pres)*

FARNSWORTH WHOLESALE COMPANY

27 W Baseline Rd, Gilbert, AZ 85233
Tel.: (480) 497-2222
Web Site: http://www.fwcaz.com
Sales Range: $10-24.9 Million
Emp.: 85
Plumbing Fittings & Supplies
N.A.I.C.S.: 423720
Ross Farnsworth *(Chm)*
Mike Wood *(Controller)*
Jack Stapley *(Founder & VP)*

Subsidiaries:

FWC　　　　　　　　　　　(1)
8051 Olive Ave, Peoria, AZ 85345
Tel.: (623) 412-2333

Web Site: http://www.fwcaz.com
Sales Range: $10-24.9 Million
Emp.: 15
Plumbing Fittings & Supplies
N.A.I.C.S.: 423720

FAROL ASSET MANAGEMENT LP

540 Madison Ave 21st Fl, New York,
NY 10022
Tel.: (646) 507-5927
Web Site: https://www.farolam.com
Year Founded: 2011
Privater Equity Firm
N.A.I.C.S.: 523999
Robert Azeke *(Mng Partner)*

FARRAR & FARRAR

45 W 45th St, New York, NY 10036
Tel.: (212) 201-0600
Year Founded: 1986
Sales Range: Less than $1 Million
Emp.: 9
Advertising Agencies
N.A.I.C.S.: 541810
Carol Estrich *(Founding Partner & Principal)*

FARRAR CORPORATION

142 W Burns Ave, Norwich, KS
67118
Tel.: (620) 478-2212
Web Site: https://www.farrarusa.com
Sales Range: $10-24.9 Million
Emp.: 80
Gray & Ductile Iron Foundries
N.A.I.C.S.: 331511

FARRATECH, INC.

2791 Peterson Pl, Norcross, GA
30071
Tel.: (770) 582-1188
Web Site: http://www.farratech.com
Year Founded: 1990
Sales Range: $1-9.9 Million
Emp.: 26
Toner Supplies, Printers & Service
N.A.I.C.S.: 424120
Maria Mendillo *(Pres & CEO)*
Geri Williams *(Dir-Ops)*
Philip Harvin *(Mgr-Production & Logistics)*
Tim Moore *(Mgr-Svc)*

FARREL CORPORATION

1 Farrel Blvd, Ansonia, CT 06401-
1256
Tel.: (203) 736-5500　　　　DE
Web Site: http://www.farrel-pomini.com
Year Founded: 1986
Sales Range: $50-74.9 Million
Emp.: 90
Machinery Mfr for Rubber & Plastics
Industries
N.A.I.C.S.: 333248
James Burns *(Gen Counsel)*
Paul Zepp *(Mgr-Flight)*

Subsidiaries:

Farrel Ltd.　　　　　　　　(1)
Queensway Castleton, PO Box 27,
Rochdale, OL11 2PF, Lancashire, United
Kingdom　　　　　　　　(100%)
Tel.: (44) 706647434
Web Site: http://www.farrel.com
Sales Range: $25-49.9 Million
Mfr of Special Industrial Machinery
N.A.I.C.S.: 333310

FARRELL DISTRIBUTING CORP.

5 Holmes Rd, South Burlington, VT
05403-7706
Tel.: (802) 864-4422
Web Site:
https://www.farrelldistributing.com
Year Founded: 1928

Sales Range: $25-49.9 Million
Emp.: 236
Brewers of Beer & Ale
N.A.I.C.S.: 424810
David J. Farrell *(Pres & CEO)*
Peter Blandy *(Mgr-Sls-Rutland)*
Cathy Campbell *(Controller)*
Chris Vance *(Dir-Sls)*
Kim Campagna *(Mgr-Acctg)*
Ryan Chaffin *(Dir-Mktg)*
Todd Bouton *(Gen Mgr)*
Jason Leduc *(Mgr-Fine Wine)*
Cindy Bessery *(Mgr-Graphic Arts)*
Graig Cummings *(Mgr-Sls Support)*

FARRELL EQUIPMENT & SUP-PLY CO., INC.
1510 N Hastings Way, Eau Claire, WI 54703
Tel.: (715) 835-4334
Web Site:
    https://www.farrellequipment.com
Rev.: $14,200,000
Emp.: 32
Construction & Mining Equipment
N.A.I.C.S.: 423810
John D. Saxe *(Pres)*
Glenn Saxe *(Treas & Sec)*

FARRELL FORWARDING CO. INC.
15030 132nd Ave Ste 201, Jamaica, NY 11434
Tel.: (800) 327-7355
Web Site: http://www.farrellintl.com
Rev.: $23,981,714
Emp.: 13
Customhouse Brokers
N.A.I.C.S.: 488510
James F. Farrell *(Pres)*
Joe Conte *(VP)*

FARRELL-CALHOUN INC.
221 E Carolina Ave, Memphis, TN 38126
Tel.: (901) 526-2211
Web Site: http://www.farrell-calhoun.com
Year Founded: 1905
Sales Range: $25-49.9 Million
Emp.: 140
Paints Mfr
N.A.I.C.S.: 325510
Anthony Ward *(VP-Sls)*
Tony Suey *(Mgr-Store)*
Craig Ferguson *(Mgr-Sls)*
John A. Ward Jr. *(Pres)*

FARREY'S WHOLESALE HARDWARE CO., INC.
1850 NE 146th St, Miami, FL 33181
Tel.: (305) 947-5451   FL
Web Site: https://www.farreys.com
Year Founded: 1924
Sales Range: $25-49.9 Million
Emp.: 100
Lighting, Kitchen & Bath Fixtures, Ceiling Fans & Other Hardware Retailer & Whslr
N.A.I.C.S.: 449129
John F. Farrey *(Founder)*
Paige Farrey *(Dir-Mktg)*
Luis Costa *(VP-Sls)*

FARRIS FASHIONS INC.
82 Johnson Loop, Greenbrier, AR 72058-9752
Tel.: (870) 734-1470
Web Site:
    http://www.redoakranch.com
Rev.: $12,000,000
Emp.: 139
Men's & Boys' Sportswear & Athletic Clothing
N.A.I.C.S.: 315250
Farris Burroughs Sr. *(Pres)*

FARRISH OF FAIRFAX INC.
9610 Lee Hwy, Fairfax, VA 22031
Tel.: (703) 352-4050
Sales Range: $25-49.9 Million
Emp.: 137
Car Whslr
N.A.I.C.S.: 441110
Kevin Farrish *(Pres & Gen Mgr)*

FARWEST CORROSION CONTROL CO.
12029 Regentview Ave, Downey, CA 90241-5517
Tel.: (310) 532-9524
Web Site:
    https://www.farwestcorrosion.com
Sales Range: $10-24.9 Million
Emp.: 100
Industrial Machinery & Equipment
N.A.I.C.S.: 423830
Troy Gordon Rankin *(Pres)*

FARWEST FREIGHT SYSTEMS INC.
4504 E Vly Hwy E, Sumner, WA 98390
Tel.: (253) 804-0500
Web Site:
    http://www.farwestfreight.com
Rev.: $12,400,000
Emp.: 135
Freight Transportation Arrangement
N.A.I.C.S.: 488510
Becki Wolford *(COO)*
Robert A. Geddes *(Owner & Pres)*
Lenny Glenn *(VP-Trucking Ops)*

FARWEST STEEL CORPORATION
2000 Henderson Ave, Eugene, OR 97403-2224
Tel.: (541) 686-2000   OR
Web Site:
    https://www.farweststeel.com
Year Founded: 1991
Sales Range: $25-49.9 Million
Emp.: 750
Provider of Metal Maintenance Services
N.A.I.C.S.: 423510
Pat Eagen *(Pres)*
Steve Brockamp *(Mgr-Traffic)*
C. J. Lewis *(Mgr-Contract)*
Stewart McCondochie *(Mgr-Pur)*
Bret Parzuchowski *(Mgr-Acctg)*
Kevin Burnette *(Project Mgr)*
Randy Leonard *(Mgr-Vancouver Reg)*
Brett Rankin *(Branch Mgr-Sls)*

FARYLROBIN FOOTWEAR
200 Park Ave S Ste 1610, New York, NY 10003
Tel.: (212) 219-1211
Web Site: http://www.farylrobin.com
Year Founded: 2002
Sales Range: $1-9.9 Million
Emp.: 10
Shoe Stores
N.A.I.C.S.: 458210
Robin Faryl *(Principal)*

FASHION AVENUE KNITS, INC.
525 7th Ave Fl 4, New York, NY 10018-6713
Tel.: (718) 456-9000   NY
Web Site:
    http://www.fashionavenueknits.com
Year Founded: 1985
Sales Range: $10-24.9 Million
Emp.: 125
Knit Outerwear Mfr
N.A.I.C.S.: 315120
Ron Hollenberg *(Gen Mgr)*
Dianne Patterson *(Sr Mgr-Production)*

FASHION CARPETS INC.

4500 Havana St, Denver, CO 80239
Tel.: (303) 307-9700
Web Site:
    http://www.onsaleonline.com
Rev.: $15,147,840
Emp.: 10
Floor Covering Stores
N.A.I.C.S.: 449121
Jim Jensen *(VP)*

FASHION GLASS & MIRROR INC.
585 Interstate 35 E, Desoto, TX 75115
Tel.: (972) 223-8936
Web Site:
    https://www.fashionglass.com
Rev.: $31,400,000
Emp.: 300
Glass Construction Materials
N.A.I.C.S.: 423390
Larry Jaynes *(Owner, Chm & CEO)*
Greg Jaynes *(CFO)*

FASHION SHOP OF KENTUCKY INC.
11008 Decimal Dr, Louisville, KY 40299-2420
Tel.: (502) 267-5415   KY
Year Founded: 1961
Sales Range: $125-149.9 Million
Emp.: 300
Sales of Women's Apparel
N.A.I.C.S.: 458110

FASHION WORLD INC.
420 N Rodeo Dr, Beverly Hills, CA 90210
Tel.: (310) 273-6544
Web Site: http://www.bijan.com
Sales Range: $10-24.9 Million
Emp.: 15
Men's Clothing Stores
N.A.I.C.S.: 458310
Daryoush Mahboubi *(VP)*

FASHIONCRAFT FLOORS INC.
1630 Faraday Ave, Carlsbad, CA 92008-7313
Tel.: (714) 637-6900
Web Site:
    http://www.fashioncraftfloors.com
Sales Range: $10-24.9 Million
Emp.: 50
Resilient Floor Laying
N.A.I.C.S.: 238330
Ken Hoffman *(VP)*

FASHIONPHILE
9551 Wilshire Blvd, Beverly Hills, CA 90212
Tel.: (310) 279-1136
Web Site:
    http://www.fashionphile.com
Year Founded: 2004
Sales Range: $1-9.9 Million
Emp.: 11
Reseller of Second Hand Luxury Handbags
N.A.I.C.S.: 459999
Sarah Davis *(Founder)*

FASHIONTECH INC.
2010 SE Eighth Ave, Portland, OR 97214-4652
Tel.: (503) 238-0666   OR
Web Site:
    http://www.fashiontech.com
Year Founded: 1978
Sales Range: $10-24.9 Million
Emp.: 110
Provider of Home Furnishing Services
N.A.I.C.S.: 423220
Chuck Lauberth *(Gen Mgr)*

FASIG-TIPTON CO. INC.
2400 Newtown Pike, Lexington, KY 40511-8469
Tel.: (859) 255-1555   KY
Web Site:
    https://www.fasigtipton.com
Year Founded: 1898
Sales Range: $150-199.9 Million
Emp.: 100
Thoroughbred Horses Auction Sales
N.A.I.C.S.: 424590
Boyd T. Browning *(Pres)*
Max Hodge *(VP-Client Svcs)*
Donald Butte *(Controller)*
Dennis Lynch *(Acct Exec)*
William E. Graves *(VP-Recruiting & Selections)*
Evan Ferraro *(Mgr-Recruiting & Mktg)*
Anna Seitz Ciannello *(Mgr-Client Dev & PR)*
Bayne Welker *(Exec VP)*

Subsidiaries:

Fasig-Tipton Kentucky, Inc.   **(1)**
2400 Newtown Pke, Lexington, KY 40511-8469
Tel.: (859) 255-1555
Web Site: http://www.fasigtipton.com
Sales Range: $10-24.9 Million
Emp.: 20
Sales of Horses
N.A.I.C.S.: 424590
Boyd T. Browning *(COO & Exec VP)*
Terence Collier *(Dir-Mktg)*
William E. Graves *(VP-Recruiting & Selections)*
William Meissner *(Plant Mgr-Saratoga)*
Dennis Lynch *(Acct Exec)*
Bayne Welker *(VP-Sls)*
Evan Ferraro *(Mgr-Recruiting & Acct Exec)*
Linda Diehl *(Office Mgr)*
Paul Barlow *(Mgr-IT)*

FASONE & PARTNERS
4003 Pennsylvania Ave, Kansas City, MO 64111
Tel.: (816) 753-7272   MO
Web Site:
    http://www.fasonepartners.com
Year Founded: 1975
Sales Range: $10-24.9 Million
Emp.: 20
Advetising Agency
N.A.I.C.S.: 541810
Janette Boehm *(Exec VP)*
Michael Fasone *(CEO)*
Julie Records *(Sr VP-Media)*
Darren Roubinek *(Creative Dir)*
Alyson Harper *(Production Mgr)*
Toni Kerr *(Bus Mgr)*
Karol Albert *(VP & Acct Exec)*
Heather Silliman *(VP & Acct Exec)*

FASSFORWARD CONSULTING GROUP
629 5th Ave, Pelham, NY 10803
Tel.: (914) 738-7200
Web Site:
    https://www.fassforward.com
Sales Range: $1-9.9 Million
Emp.: 8
Business Management Consulting Services
N.A.I.C.S.: 541611
Rose Fass *(CEO)*
Gavin McMahon *(Co-Founder & Sr Partner)*

FAST ENTERPRISES, LLC
7229 S Alton Way, Centennial, CO 80112
Tel.: (303) 770-3700
Web Site: http://www.gentax.com
Year Founded: 1997
Rev.: $15,800,000
Emp.: 350
Software Services for Revenue Agencies

Fast Enterprises, LLC—(Continued)
N.A.I.C.S.: 513210
Dave Pearson *(Partner)*
Dennis Manalo *(Partner)*

FAST FOOD ENTERPRISES
144 Vista Royale Sq, Vero Beach, FL 32962
Tel.: (772) 569-3420
Web Site:
　https://www.fastfoodent.com
Sales Range: $10-24.9 Million
Emp.: 1
Fast-Food Restaurant, Chain
N.A.I.C.S.: 722513
Mark Holm *(Pres)*

FAST FUSION LLC
PO Box 158, Palisade, CO 81526
Tel.: (970) 640-7223
Web Site: http://www.fast-fusion.com
Year Founded: 2003
Sales Range: $1-9.9 Million
Emp.: 25
Vermeer/Ditchwitch Type Utility Equipment Mfr
N.A.I.C.S.: 335999
Dick McKinley *(CEO & Principal)*

FAST HEAT INC.
776 Oaklawn Ave, Elmhurst, IL 60126
Tel.: (630) 359-6300
Web Site: http://www.fastheat.com
Rev.: $22,800,000
Emp.: 9
Heating Units & Devices, Industrial; Electric
N.A.I.C.S.: 333994
Tim Stojka *(CEO)*
Deb Dynako *(Coord-Mktg)*

FAST LANE ACQUISITION, INC.
5130 S Fort Apache Rd Ste 215-258, Las Vegas, NV 89148
Tel.: (561) 215-4276
Year Founded: 2014
Investment Services
N.A.I.C.S.: 523999
Holden K. Richbell *(Pres, CEO, CFO, Chief Acctg Officer, Treas & Sec)*

FAST LANE CLOTHING COMPANY, INC.
5112 N 22nd St, Tampa, FL 33610
Tel.: (813) 879-3298
Web Site:
　http://www.fastlaneclothing.com
Sales Range: $10-24.9 Million
Emp.: 23
Apparels Mfr
N.A.I.C.S.: 315250
Lori J. Davis *(Pres)*
Juan Davis *(CEO)*

FAST PETROLEUM, INC.
711 1/2 Morrison St, McMinnville, TN 37110
Tel.: (931) 473-6521
Web Site:
　http://www.fastpetroleum.com
Sales Range: $10-24.9 Million
Emp.: 3
Petroleum & Gas Station Services
N.A.I.C.S.: 457120
Jim White *(Mgr)*

FAST POINT FOOD STORES INC.
2811 Reidville Rd Ste 11, Spartanburg, SC 29301-5650
Tel.: (864) 587-1009
Year Founded: 1979
Sales Range: $25-49.9 Million
Emp.: 160

Convenience Store
N.A.I.C.S.: 445131

FAST SWITCH, LTD.
4900 Blazer Pkwy, Dublin, OH 43017
Tel.: (614) 336-1122
Web Site: https://www.fastswitch.com
Year Founded: 1996
Rev.: $16,700,000
Emp.: 500
Computer Related Services
N.A.I.C.S.: 541512
Mark Pukita *(Mng Dir)*

FAST TRACK COMPUTER SOLUTIONS, INC.
4241 Anaconda Dr, New Port Richey, FL 34655
Tel.: (727) 942-2066
Web Site:
　https://fasttrackcomputer.com
Year Founded: 2001
Sales Range: $1-9.9 Million
Information Technology Services
N.A.I.C.S.: 541512
Scott T. Neal *(CEO)*

FAST UNDERCAR INC.
4277 Transfort St, Ventura, CA 93003
Tel.: (805) 676-3410
Web Site:
　https://www.fastundercar.com
Sales Range: $10-24.9 Million
Emp.: 25
Supplier of Motor Vehicle Supplies & New Parts
N.A.I.C.S.: 423120
Victor Davis *(Pres & CEO)*

Subsidiaries:
3 D&V　　　　　　　　　　(1)
3701 Old Conejo Rd, Newbury Park, CA 91320-1001
Tel.: (805) 495-3410
Web Site: http://www.fastundercar.com
Rev.: $150,000
Emp.: 15
Automotive Parts
N.A.I.C.S.: 441330

Fast Pro Inc.　　　　　　　(1)
2555 Lafayette St Ste 103, Santa Clara, CA 95050
Tel.: (408) 566-0200
Web Site: http://www.fastundercar.com
Rev.: $2,300,000
Emp.: 20
Motor Vehicle Supplies & New Parts
N.A.I.C.S.: 423120
Brian Smith *(Owner)*

FASTBUCKS HOLDING CORPORATION
7920 Beltline Rd Ste 600, Dallas, TX 75254-8132
Tel.: (972) 490-3330
Web Site: http://www.fastbucks.com
Sales Range: $25-49.9 Million
Holding Company; Consumer Lending & Check Cashing Stores Owner & Operator
N.A.I.C.S.: 551112
Charles Horton *(Pres & CEO)*
Rene Beasley *(Gen Counsel)*
John Bloss *(Asst Controller)*

FASTENER INDUSTRIES INC.
1 Berea Commons, Berea, OH 44017-2534
Tel.: (440) 243-0034
Web Site: http://www.on-b.com
Year Founded: 1980
Sales Range: $10-24.9 Million
Emp.: 200
Bolts, Nuts, Rivets & Washers
N.A.I.C.S.: 339993
Pat Finnegan *(Pres & CEO)*
Linda Kerekes *(Controller)*

Subsidiaries:
Brainard Rivet Company　　　(1)
222 Harry St, Girard, OH 44420-1759
Tel.: (330) 545-4931
Web Site: http://www.brainardrivet.com
Sales Range: Less than $1 Million
Emp.: 33
Rivet Mfr
N.A.I.C.S.: 332722
Judy Volpe *(Gen Mgr)*
Bob Byers *(Mgr-Sls)*

Buckeye Fasteners Inc.　　　(1)
5250 W 164th St, Cleveland, OH 44142-1506　　　　　　　　(100%)
Tel.: (216) 267-2240
Web Site: http://www.buckeyefasteners.com
Rev.: $13,030,170
Emp.: 25
Distr of Hardware
N.A.I.C.S.: 423710
Larry Kelly *(Mgr-Bus Dev)*
Dough Campbell *(Mgr-Sls)*

Joseph Industries Inc.　　　(1)
10039 Aurora Hudson Rd, Streetsboro, OH 44241-1622
Tel.: (330) 528-0091
Web Site: http://www.joseph.com
Rev.: $9,039,187
Emp.: 52
Industrial Machinery & Equipment
N.A.I.C.S.: 423830

Ohio Nut & Bolt Co　　　　(1)
33 Lou Groza Blvd, Berea, OH 44017-1237　　　　　　　　(100%)
Tel.: (440) 243-0200
Web Site: http://www.on-b.com
Sales Range: $10-24.9 Million
Emp.: 60
Mfr Bolts, Nuts, Rivets & Washers
N.A.I.C.S.: 339993
Larry Kelly *(Mgr-Sls)*

Ohio Nut & Bolt of Canada, Ltd.　(1)
5582 Tomken Road, Mississauga, L4W 1P4, ON, Canada　　　　(100%)
Tel.: (905) 624-2828
Web Site: http://www.onb-canada.com
Sales Range: $10-24.9 Million
Emp.: 2
Mfr of Fasteners
N.A.I.C.S.: 332722

FASTENER TOOL & SUPPLY INC.
30350 Bruce Industrial Pkwy, Solon, OH 44139-3938
Tel.: (440) 248-2710
Web Site: http://www.ibegin.com
Rev.: $13,324,313
Emp.: 60
Miscellaneous Fasteners
N.A.I.C.S.: 423710
Mark Dively *(VP)*
Chris Massopust *(Mgr-Military & Aerospace Dept)*
Henry Tuttle *(Project Coord)*
Michael Virant *(Acct Mgr)*

FASTENERS INC.
640 44th St SE, Grand Rapids, MI 49548
Tel.: (616) 241-3448
Web Site:
　http://www.fastenersincmi.com
Sales Range: $25-49.9 Million
Emp.: 50
Power Tools & Accessories
N.A.I.C.S.: 423710
John Szlenkier *(Pres)*
Scott Battershell *(VP-Ops)*
Tom Rickers *(Treas, Sec & VP)*

FASTENING SOLUTION INC
3075 Selma Hwy, Montgomery, AL 36108
Tel.: (334) 284-8300
Web Site: http://www.ssiusa.com
Sales Range: $10-24.9 Million
Emp.: 150
Distr of Staplers & Tackers

N.A.I.C.S.: 423840
Mike Winsted *(Controller)*

FASTEXPERT, INC.
2275 Huntington Dr Ste 101, San Marino, CA 91108
Web Site: http://www.fastexpert.com
Year Founded: 2014
Sales Range: $1-9.9 Million
Real Estate Services
N.A.I.C.S.: 531390
Kevin Tran *(Acct Mgr)*

FASTLANE
55 Mountain Ave, Caldwell, NJ 07006
Tel.: (973) 226-4379
Year Founded: 2006
Sales Range: $10-24.9 Million
Emp.: 18
Advertising, Brand Development & Integration, Communications, Corporate Communications, E-Commerce, High Technology, Multimedia, Nonprofit/Social Marketing, Public Relations
N.A.I.C.S.: 541810
Christopher Faust *(Founder & CEO)*
Emilio Dabul *(Dir-Pub Rels)*
Ersin Eser *(Dir-Interactive Svcs)*
Alex Pires *(Partner & VP-Client Rels & Project Mgmt)*
Patty Buchanana *(Dir-Comm)*
Eduardo Pires *(Partner & Dir-Creative)*
Rick Anderson *(Strategic Advisor & Dir-Fin Comm)*
Laura Squier *(Dir-Fin)*
Marina Lauand *(Assoc Project Mgr)*
Jeremy Van Eyk *(Sr Project Mgr)*

FASTLINE PUBLICATIONS INC.
4900 Fox Run Rd, Buckner, KY 40010
Tel.: (502) 222-0146
Web Site: https://www.fastline.com
Year Founded: 1978
Rev.: $20,000,000
Emp.: 200
Magazine Publisher
N.A.I.C.S.: 513120
Jim Hughey *(VP-Production)*
Susan Arterburn *(Mgr-Mktg)*
Lauri Rush *(Mgr-Natl Acct)*
Johnny Carraro *(Mgr-Natl Sls)*

FASTPENCIL, INC.
1608 W Campbell Ave Ste 239, Campbell, CA 95008
Tel.: (408) 540-7571
Web Site: http://www.fastpencil.com
Year Founded: 2008
Online Book Publishing Services
N.A.I.C.S.: 513130
Steve Wilson *(Pres & CEO)*

FASTRAC MARKETS LLC
6500 Newventure Year Dr Ste 100, East Syracuse, NY 13057
Tel.: (315) 552-6800
Web Site:
　http://www.fastracmarkets.com
Sales Range: $500-549.9 Million
Emp.: 575
Fiscal Year-end: 12/31/14
Operator of Convenience Stores
N.A.I.C.S.: 445131
Tom Wright *(VP-Ops)*

FASTRACK COMPLETE CAR CARE
801 Lancaster Ave, Reading, PA 19607
Tel.: (610) 777-6521
Web Site: http://www.fastrackccc.com
Sales Range: $25-49.9 Million

Emp.: 100
New Car Retailer
N.A.I.C.S.: 441110
Kate Goodman *(Pres)*

FASTRON CO.
11800 Franklin Ave, Franklin Park, IL 60131
Tel.: (630) 766-5000
Web Site: http://www.fastron.com
Rev.: $12,700,000
Emp.: 25
Screws & Fasteners
N.A.I.C.S.: 332722
Tracy Martin *(Pres)*

FASTTRAC TRANSPORTA-TION, INC.
16220 Air Center Blvd, Houston, TX 77032
Tel.: (281) 869-5660
Web Site:
  https://www.fasttractrans.com
Year Founded: 1996
Sales Range: $10-24.9 Million
Emp.: 42
Transportation Services
N.A.I.C.S.: 488999
Eloy Garcia *(Mgr-Air Cartage)*
Jeff Steele *(Gen Mgr)*
Robyn Payne *(VP-Fin)*

FASTVUE INC.
548 Market St Ste 71453, San Francisco, CA 94104
Web Site: https://www.fastvue.co
Network Monitoring & Reporting Software Developer
N.A.I.C.S.: 513210
Scott Glew *(Founder)*

Subsidiaries:

WebSpy US Inc.   (1)
5701 Lonetree Blvd Ste 220/221 J, Rocklin, CA 95765
Tel.: (888) 885-6711
Web Site: http://www.webspy.com
Sales Range: $10-24.9 Million
Emp.: 2
Monitoring, Analysis & Reporting Software for Internet, Email & Network Usage
N.A.I.C.S.: 513210

FATH MANAGEMENT COM-PANY
255 E 5th St Ste 2300, Cincinnati, OH 45202
Tel.: (513) 721-4070
Web Site:
  http://www.fathproperties.com
Year Founded: 1970
Rev.: $52,000,000
Emp.: 180
Real Estate Management
N.A.I.C.S.: 531210
Becky Alejandrino *(COO)*
Bob Winkler *(VP-HR)*
Donna Renner *(Reg Mgr)*
Bob Williams *(CFO)*
Brent Neiger *(Dir-Maintenance)*
Jen Johnson *(Dir-Mktg & Trng)*
Harry J. Fath Jr. *(Owner)*

FATHER BILL'S & MAIN-SPRING
430 Belmont St, Brockton, MA 02301
Tel.: (508) 427-6448   MA
Web Site: https://www.helpfbms.org
Year Founded: 1985
Sales Range: $10-24.9 Million
Emp.: 258
Housing Assistance Services
N.A.I.C.S.: 624229
John Yazwinski *(Pres & CEO)*
Nicole Fitzgerald *(VP-Asset Mgmt)*
Kristyn Lahiff *(CFO)*
Lucille Cassis *(Mng Editor)*

Terri MacNayr *(Dir-HR)*
April Connolly *(COO)*
Stephen Muzrall *(Chief Dev Officer)*

FATHER TIME, INC.
3700 Massachusetts Ave NW Ste 110, Washington, DC 20016
Tel.: (571) 277-3506   DE
Year Founded: 2016
Assets: $30
Liabilities: $7,531
Net Worth: ($7,501)
Fiscal Year-end: 12/31/18
Software Development Services
N.A.I.C.S.: 541511
Robert Waligunda *(Chm, Pres, CEO, CFO, Treas & Sec)*

FATHERS AND SONS INC.
214 New Bridge St, West Springfield, MA 10894-4224
Tel.: (413) 785-1631
Web Site: http://www.fathers-sonsvw.com
Rev.: $46,706,914
Emp.: 82
Automobiles, New & Used
N.A.I.C.S.: 441110
Kimberlynn Cartelli *(Dir-Mktg)*

FATHOM, LLC
8200 Sweet Valley Dr Ste 100, Valley View, OH 44125
Tel.: (216) 369-2220   OH
Web Site:
  http://www.fathomdelivers.com
Year Founded: 2005
Sales Range: $25-49.9 Million
Emp.: 130
Computer Related Marketing Services
N.A.I.C.S.: 541519
Scot Lowry *(Pres & CEO)*
Kevin Shaw *(Chm)*
Kevin Herendeen *(CFO)*
Steve Kessen *(Pres-Enterprise Solutions)*
Efi Golan *(VP-Analytics & Tech)*
Stephen Lehner *(Dir-Nurture Solutions Consulting)*
Sean Wenger *(Exec VP-Client Svcs)*
Jessica Baker *(VP-People)*

FATPIPE NETWORKS INC.
4455 S 700 E, Salt Lake City, UT 84107
Tel.: (801) 281-3434
Web Site: http://www.fatpipeinc.com
Year Founded: 1989
Sales Range: $25-49.9 Million
Emp.: 125
Computer Peripheral Equipment Mfr
N.A.I.C.S.: 334118
Sanchaita Bhaskar *(CTO)*
Ragula Bhaskar *(Pres & CEO)*
Sanchaita Datta *(VP-Engrg)*
Matt Gwyther *(Dir-Comm & PR)*
Phil Hinson *(Sr VP-Strategic Bus)*

FAULCONER CONSTRUCTION CO. INC.
2496 Old Ivy Rd, Charlottesville, VA 22903
Tel.: (434) 295-0033
Web Site:
  https://www.faulconerconstruction.com
Rev.: $28,123,229
Emp.: 173
Dams, Waterways, Docks & Other Marine Construction
N.A.I.C.S.: 236210
Ed Stelter *(Dir-Partnerships & Innovative Pursuits)*
Bruce Kohn *(VP)*

David Galloway *(VP)*
Jack Sanford Jr. *(CEO)*
F. A. Burke III *(Exec VP)*

FAULK & FOSTER REAL ES-TATE
1811 Auburn Ave, Monroe, LA 71201
Tel.: (318) 325-4666
Web Site:
  https://www.faulkandfoster.com
Rev.: $12,000,000
Emp.: 55
Real Estate Agents & Managers
N.A.I.C.S.: 531210
Mike Ardoin *(Project Mgr)*
Joe Derry *(Pres)*
Ralph Thomas *(Sr VP)*
John W. Perry Jr. *(Owner, Chm & CEO)*

FAULK & MEEK GENERAL CONTRACTORS, LLC.
3595 I 10 Frontage Rd, Port Allen, LA 70767
Tel.: (225) 383-4505
Web Site:
  https://www.faulkandmeek.com
Sales Range: $10-24.9 Million
Emp.: 20
Commercial & Building Construction Services
N.A.I.C.S.: 236220
David Faulk *(Co-Owner)*
John Meek *(Co-Owner)*
Andi Chatelain *(Office Mgr)*

FAULKNER BUICK, GMC TRUCK INC.
705 Autopark Blvd, West Chester, PA 19382
Tel.: (610) 674-0610
Web Site:
  https://www.faulknerauto.com
Year Founded: 1932
Rev.: $52,000,000
Emp.: 65
Owner & Operator of Car Dealerships
N.A.I.C.S.: 441110
William Morrison *(Pres & Gen Mgr)*
Mary Brodoway *(Controller)*

FAULKNER CADILLAC INC.
4447 E St, Trevose, PA 19053
Tel.: (215) 639-9700   PA
Web Site:
  http://www.faulknercadillac.com
Year Founded: 1981
Sales Range: $100-124.9 Million
Emp.: 80
Automobile Dealership
N.A.I.C.S.: 441110
Tim Galen *(Mgr)*

FAULKNER CHEVROLET INC.
2000 Bennett Ave, Lancaster, PA 17601-0000
Tel.: (717) 299-0961
Web Site:
  http://www.faulknercars.com
Year Founded: 1932
Sales Range: $10-24.9 Million
Emp.: 55
Car Dealership
N.A.I.C.S.: 441110
Ed Buckman *(Controller)*

FAULKNER CIOCCA FORD OF SOUDERTON
3470 Bethlehem Pike, Souderton, PA 18964
Tel.: (215) 721-9100
Web Site:
  http://www.fcfordsouderton.com
Sales Range: $10-24.9 Million
Emp.: 45
New Car Retailer

N.A.I.C.S.: 441110
Ag Antonios *(Gen Mgr)*
Don Kistier *(Mgr-Parts Dept)*
Ed Simpson *(Dir-Internet Dept)*
Eric Baldwin *(Mgr-Special Fin)*
Jason Patterson *(Mgr-Fin)*
Kyle Eggy *(Dir-Fin Dept)*
Mike Giambattista *(Mgr-Pre-Owned Sls)*

FAULKNER FORD MERCURY INC.
321 South West End Blvd, Quakertown, PA 18951
Tel.: (215) 536-8600
Web Site:
  http://www.faulknerfordmercury.com
Sales Range: $10-24.9 Million
Emp.: 170
Sales of New & Used Automobiles
N.A.I.C.S.: 441110
Joseph Faulkner *(Chm)*
Gregg Ciocca *(CEO & Principal)*
Joe Mayer *(Gen Mgr)*
Don Kistler *(Mgr-Parts)*

FAULKNER HARRISBURG INC.
2060 Paxton St, Harrisburg, PA 17111-1033
Tel.: (717) 238-7324
Web Site:
  http://www.faulknerharrisburg.com
Rev.: $35,400,000
Emp.: 80
Automobiles New & Used Service Department & Body Shop
N.A.I.C.S.: 441110
Chad Berger *(Pres)*

FAULKNER/HAYNES & ASSO-CIATES, INC.
7240 ACC Blvd, Raleigh, NC 27617
Tel.: (919) 781-8840
Web Site: http://www.fha-hvac.com
Rev.: $18,630,736
Emp.: 25
Warm Air Heating & Air Conditioning Services
N.A.I.C.S.: 423730
Jim Haynes *(VP)*
Suzanna Williamson *(Coord-Tech Sls)*
Ryan Short *(Branch Mgr)*

FAULKNERUSA
8303 N Mo Pac Expy Ste 110a, Austin, TX 78759-8393
Tel.: (512) 652-4000
Year Founded: 1978
Sales Range: $25-49.9 Million
Emp.: 100
Commercial & Office Building, New Construction
N.A.I.C.S.: 236220
Mark Schultz *(Pres)*

FAULTLESS LAUNDRY COM-PANY
330 W 19th Ter, Kansas City, MO 64108
Tel.: (816) 421-2373
Web Site:
  http://www.faultlesslinen.com
Rev.: $10,200,000
Emp.: 570
Textile Maintenance & Management Services to Health Care & Hospitality Clients
N.A.I.C.S.: 812320
Mark Spence *(COO)*
Susan Witcher *(Pres & CEO)*

FAULTLESS STARCH/BON AMI COMPANY

Faultless Starch/Bon Ami Company—(Continued)

1025 W 8th St, Kansas City, MO
64101-1207
Tel.: (816) 842-1230   **MO**
Web Site: http://www.faultless.com
Year Founded: 1887
Sales Range: $150-199.9 Million
Emp.: 400
Laundry & Household Cleaning Products Mfr
N.A.I.C.S.: 825612
Benjamin Stark (VP-Mktg)
Robert B. Beaham (Vice Chm, Co-
CEO & Treas)
Shannan Habiger (VP-Fin)
Gordon T. Beaham III (Chm & Co-
CEO)

Subsidiaries:

Faultless Starch/Bon Ami Company -
Garden Weasel Division   (1)
1025 W 8th St, Kansas City, MO 64101-
1200
Tel.: (816) 842-1230
Web Site: http://www.gardenweasel.com
Sales Range: $10-24.9 Million
Emp.: 100
Gardening Tool Mfr
N.A.I.C.S.: 333112

**FAULTLINE BREWING CO.
INC.**
1235 Oakmead Pkwy, Sunnyvale, CA
94085
Web Site:
    https://www.faultlinebrewing.com
Year Founded: 1994
Sales Range: $1-9.9 Million
Emp.: 50
Resturant & Brewery (Alcoholic Beverage)
N.A.I.C.S.: 312120
Steven C. Geiszler (Pres)

**FAUSER OIL COMPANY IN-
CORPORATED**
106 Center St, Elgin, IA 52141
Tel.: (563) 426-5811   **IA**
Web Site:
    http://www.fauserenergy.com
Year Founded: 1969
Sales Range: $150-199.9 Million
Emp.: 17
Petroleum Bulk Stations
N.A.I.C.S.: 424710
Don L. Fauser (Pres)

**FAUST DISTRIBUTING CO.,
INC.**
PO Box 24728, Houston, TX 77229-
4728
Tel.: (713) 673-5111
Web Site:
    http://www.faustdistributing.com
Year Founded: 1957
Sales Range: $25-49.9 Million
Emp.: 175
Beer & Ale Products Mfr
N.A.I.C.S.: 424810
Tysen Faust (Pres)
Don Faust Sr (Owner)
Scott Murray (VP-Sls)

FAVI ENTERTAINMENT
5680 18 Mile Rd, Sterling Heights, MI
48314
Tel.: (248) 805-1080
Web Site:
    http://www.favientertainment.com
Year Founded: 2006
Sales Range: $1-9.9 Million
Emp.: 8
Consumer Electronics
N.A.I.C.S.: 423620
Jeremy Yakel (Pres & CEO)

FAVO REALTY, INC.
1461 Franklin Ave 1st Fl S, Garden
City, NY 11530
Year Founded: 1999
Real Estate Services
N.A.I.C.S.: 531390
Vincent Napolitano (CEO)

FAVORITE FOODS, INC.
29 Interstate Dr, Somersworth, NH
03878
Tel.: (603) 692-4990   **NH**
Web Site:
    https://www.favoritefoods.com
Year Founded: 1987
Sales Range: $25-49.9 Million
Emp.: 50
Commercial Equipment Merchant
Whslr
N.A.I.C.S.: 423440
Chris Barstow (Pres)
Dave Myers (COO)
Jeff Sargent (Mgr-Pur)
John Langella (Mgr-Pur)
Steve Gerasimchik (Mgr-Pur)
Joe Hanson (Mgr-Ops)
Petra Barstow (Mgr-Credit)
Chris Langella (VP-Sls)
John Libby (COO)
Kelly Barstow (VP-Bus Ops)

**FAVORITE HEALTHCARE
STAFFING, INC.**
7255 W 98th Ter Bldg 5 Ste 150,
Overland Park, KS 66212
Tel.: (913) 383-9733   **KS**
Web Site:
    http://www.favoritestaffing.com
Year Founded: 1981
Sales Range: $10-24.9 Million
Emp.: 300
Healthcare Staffing Services
N.A.I.C.S.: 561320
Nicole Olson (Dir-Favorite Manages
Svcs)

**FAWCETT MARINE SUPPLIES
LLC**
919 Bay Ridge Rd, Annapolis, MD
21403
Tel.: (410) 267-8681
Web Site:
    http://www.fawcettboat.com
Year Founded: 1948
Boat Dealers
N.A.I.C.S.: 441222
Tom Ripley (Co-Owner)
Bernard Jammet (Co-Owner)

Subsidiaries:

Annapolis Inflatables   (1)
603 Chinquapin Round Rd, Annapolis, MD
21401-4009
Tel.: (410) 080-4443
Web Site:
    http://www.annapolisinflatables.net
Boat Building
N.A.I.C.S.: 336612

**FAWLEY BRYANT ARCHI-
TECTS, INC.**
5391 Lakewood Ranch Blvd N Ste
300, Sarasota, FL 34240
Tel.: (941) 343-4070   **FL**
Web Site: http://www.fawley-
    bryant.com
Year Founded: 1994
Sales Range: $1-9.9 Million
Emp.: 17
Architectural Services
N.A.I.C.S.: 541310
Rick Fawley (Pres)
Steve Padgett (VP)

FAWN INDUSTRIES, INC.

1920 Greenspring Dr Ste 140, Timo-
nium, MD 21093-4112
Tel.: (410) 308-9200   **MD**
Web Site: http://www.fawn-ind.com
Year Founded: 1950
Sales Range: $150-199.9 Million
Emp.: 512
Plastic Products Mfr
N.A.I.C.S.: 326199
John B. Franzone (Pres & CEO)
Barbara Mathewson (Supvr-Accts
Receivable & Customer Svc)
Michael Brady (Dir-IT)
Sheryl L. Conley (Coord-Proposal)

FAXONGILLIS HOMES INC.
825 Timber Creek Dr, Cordova, TN
38018
Tel.: (901) 759-7000
Web Site: http://www.faxongillis.com
Year Founded: 1899
Sales Range: $25-49.9 Million
Emp.: 10
New Construction, Single-Family
Houses
N.A.I.C.S.: 236115
Jerry Gillis (Chm & CEO)
Bobbi Gillis (Exec VP)

**FAY, SPOFFORD &
THORNDIKE, INC.**
5 Burlington Woods, Burlington, MA
01803-4542
Tel.: (781) 221-1000   **MA**
Web Site: http://www.fstinc.com
Year Founded: 1914
Sales Range: $25-49.9 Million
Emp.: 285
Engineering Consulting Services
N.A.I.C.S.: 541330
Michael A. Roache (Mgr-Facilities
Div)
Peter J. Howe (Pres & CEO)
Jerome Guerra (Mgr-Mktg & Strategic
Bus Dev)
Brian E. Shea (Deputy Mgr-
Environmental Div)
William R. Moore (Deputy Mgr-
Transportation Div)
Leonard V. Dzengelewski (Mgr-
Structural Div)

Subsidiaries:

FST Engineers, Inc.   (1)
534 Broadhollow Rd Ste 305, Melville, NY
11747
Tel.: (631) 756-5999
Web Site: http://www.fstinc.com
Sales Range: $10-24.9 Million
Emp.: 10
Engineeering Services
N.A.I.C.S.: 541330
James Branch (Principal & VP)

**FAYE BUSINESS SYSTEMS
GROUP INC.**
5950 Canoga Ave Ste 615, Woodland
Hills, CA 91367
Tel.: (818) 280-4820
Web Site: http://www.fayebsg.com
Year Founded: 2009
Sales Range: $1-9.9 Million
Business Software Development Ser-
vices
N.A.I.C.S.: 541511
David Faye (Founder & CEO)

Subsidiaries:

Atcore Systems, LLC   (1)
1405 Alcovy Rdg Crossing, Loganville, GA
30052
Tel.: (404) 323-8988
Business Software Solutions & Consulting
Services
N.A.I.C.S.: 423430

FAYETTE MEMORIAL HOSPI-

TAL ASSOCIATION INC
1941 Virginia Ave, Connersville, IN
47331
Tel.: (765) 825-5131   **IN**
Web Site:
    http://www.fayetteregional.org
Year Founded: 1913
Sales Range: $50-74.9 Million
Emp.: 550
Fiscal Year-end: 12/12/14
Health Care Srvices
N.A.I.C.S.: 622110
Rhonda McPherson (VP-HR)
Beth A. Wampler (VP-Patient Care)
Dennis Lockard (CFO)

**FAYETTEVILLE ELECTRIC
SYSTEM, INC.**
408 W College St, Fayetteville, TN
37334
Tel.: (931) 433-1522
Web Site: https://www.fpu-tn.com
Sales Range: $25-49.9 Million
Emp.: 108
Electric Power Distr
N.A.I.C.S.: 221122
Britt Dye (CEO & Gen Mgr)

FAYEZ SAROFIM & CO.
909 Fannin St Ste 2907, Houston, TX
77010
Tel.: (713) 654-4484
Web Site: https://www.sarofim.com
Year Founded: 1958
Sales Range: $50-74.9 Million
Emp.: 140
Investment Advisory & Portfolio Man-
agement Services
N.A.I.C.S.: 523940
Fayez Shalaby Sarofim (Chm, Pres &
Chief Investment Officer)
Christopher Binyon Sarofim (Chm &
Pres)
Raye G. White (Exec VP)
William Lee (CEO & Co-Chief Invest-
ment Officer)
Ralph B. Thomas (Sr VP)
Charles E. Sheedy (Sr VP)
Reynaldo Reza (VP)
Douglas K. Alder (VP)
Catherine P. Crain (VP & Portfolio
Mgr)
Brian W. Lemasters (VP)
Kenneth M. Burke Jr. (VP)
David T. Searls III (VP)

FAZ RESTAURANT INC.
5121 Hopyard Rd, Pleasanton, CA
94588
Tel.: (925) 469-1600
Web Site:
    http://www.fazrestaurants.com
Sales Range: $10-24.9 Million
Emp.: 9
Eating Place
N.A.I.C.S.: 722511
Faz Poursohi (Pres)

FB BANCORP
17300 Henderson Pass, San Antonio,
TX 78232
Tel.: (210) 637-4810
Web Site:
    http://www.farmbureaubank.com
Sales Range: $50-74.9 Million
Emp.: 140
Bank Holding Company
N.A.I.C.S.: 522180
Thomas Jaeger (CFO)
William Hileman (Pres & CEO)
David Winkles (Chm)

Subsidiaries:

Farm Bureau Bank FSB   (1)
17300 Henderson Pass, San Antonio, TX
78232-1568

Tel.: (210) 637-4800
Web Site: http://www.farmbureaubank.com
Sales Range: $50-74.9 Million
Emp.: 87
Banking Services
N.A.I.C.S.: 522180
Mark Cromer (Sr VP)
William Hileman (Pres & CEO)
Noel Luna (Mgr-Mktg & Sls)
Gary Armstrong (Chief Comml Banking Officer)

FB CAPITAL PARTNERS, L.P.

Cira Centre 2929 Arch St Ste 675, Philadelphia, PA 19104-2867
Tel.: (215) 495-1150
Web Site: http://tranklinsquare.com
Year Founded: 2005
Sales Range: $25-49.9 Million
Emp.: 50
Privater Equity Firm
N.A.I.C.S.: 523999
Stephanie Peterson (Controller)
Michael C. Forman (Mng Gen Partner)

Subsidiaries:

Seagrave Fire Apparatus, LLC   (1)
105 E 12th St, Clintonville, WI 54929-1518
Tel.: (715) 823-2141
Web Site: http://www.seagrave.com
Sales Range: $50-74.9 Million
Heavy-Duty Specialized On-Off Highway Trucks & Fire Apparatus Mfr
N.A.I.C.S.: 336120
Therese Sell (Controller)
Bradley Krueger (Dir-Customer Svc)
Daryl George (Mgr-Facilities Engrg)
Daniel Hohn (Dir-Product Improvement & Quality Assurance)
Dennis Warren (Dir-Natl Sls)

FBA II, INC.

601 Biscayne Blvd, Miami, FL 33132
Tel.: (786) 777-4328   DE
Year Founded: 1997
Holding Company; Professional Basketball Team
N.A.I.C.S.: 551112
Nick Arison (Partner)
Julio Iglesias (Partner)
Raanan Katz (Partner)
Sidney Kimmel (Partner)
Robert Sturges (Partner)
John Vidalin (Chief Revenue Officer & Exec VP)

Subsidiaries:

Miami Heat Limited Partnership   (1)
601 Biscayne Blvd, Miami, FL 33132-1801
Tel.: (786) 777-1000
Web Site: http://www.nba.com
Professional Basketball Team
N.A.I.C.S.: 711211
Micky M. Arison (Gen Partner)
Pat Riley (Pres)
Michael McCullough (CMO & Exec VP)
Eric Woolworth (Pres-Bus Ops)
Raquel Libman (Gen Counsel & Exec VP)
Andy Elisburg (Sr VP-Basketball Ops & Gen Mgr)
Jeff Craney (VP-Mktg Div)
Jarred Diamond (Exec VP-Heat Group Enterprises)
Kim Stone (Exec VP & Gen Mgr-American Airlines Arena)
Nick Arison (CEO)
Sonia Harty (VP-HR)
Chet Kammerer (VP-Player Personnel)
Jennifer Mallery (VP-Ticket Ops & Strategic Plng)
Chris Maragno (VP-Corp Partnerships Sls & Svc)
Jeff Morris (VP-Fin)
Alonzo Mourning (VP-Player Programs)
John Vidalin (Chief Revenue Officer & Exec VP)
Adam Simon (Asst Gen Mgr)

FBC MORTGAGE, LLC

189 S Orange Ave Ste 970, Orlando, FL 32801

Tel.: (407) 872-3383   FL
Web Site: https://www.fbchomeloans.com
Year Founded: 2005
Emp.: 800
Mortgage Loan Brokers
N.A.I.C.S.: 522310
Joe Nunziata (Co-CEO)
Rob Nunziata (Co-CEO)
Daniel Herbon (CIO & Chief Information Security & Privacy Officer)
Dyron Watford (CFO)
Irene Gonzalez (Sr VP-HR)
Michael Dunn (Gen Counsel)
Todd Boss (Sls Mgr-Natl)
Vinay Miglani (Sr VP-Capital Markets)
Jim Girard (Chief Credit Officer, Officer-Dev-Natl & Sr VP)
Kelley Hailstone (COO)
Rick Norris (Dir-Builder Div)
Stephanie Simmons (Dir-Mktg & Corp Culture)
Salvatore Nunziata (Vice Chm)

FBG SERVICE CORPORATION

407 S 27th Ave, Omaha, NE 68131-3609
Tel.: (402) 346-4422
Web Site: https://www.fbgservices.com
Year Founded: 1968
Sales Range: $75-99.9 Million
Emp.: 1,700
Building Maintenance Services
N.A.I.C.S.: 561720
Terri Gogetap (Pres)
Kathy Clark (CFO)
Jim Simmonds (COO & VP)
Barbara Luna (Dir-Mktg)

FBI BUILDINGS, INC.

3823 W 1800 S, Remington, IN 47977
Tel.: (219) 261-2157
Web Site: https://www.fbibuildings.com
Year Founded: 1958
Sales Range: $25-49.9 Million
Emp.: 230
Commercial & Building Construction Services
N.A.I.C.S.: 236220
Edwin A. Bahler (Founder)
Miles Ridgway (Pres)
John Lehman (Mgr-Mfg & Logistics)

FBMC BENEFITS MANAGEMENT, INC.

3101 Sessions Rd, Tallahassee, FL 32303
Tel.: (850) 425-6200
Web Site: https://www.fbmc.com
Sales Range: $25-49.9 Million
Emp.: 350
Benefits Administration
N.A.I.C.S.: 541611
Michael H. Sheridan (Chm)
Jerome Osteryoung (Treas)
Agnes McMurray (Sec)
David Faulkenberry (Pres)
John R. Marks III (Vice Chm & Gen Counsel)

FBS FIRST COAST INC.

5143 Longleaf St, Jacksonville, FL 32209
Tel.: (904) 924-0033
Web Site: http://www.foglemanbuilders supply.com
Sales Range: $25-49.9 Million
Emp.: 30
Builders' Hardware Materials Supplier
N.A.I.C.S.: 423710
William D. Fogleman (CEO)
Chris Fogleman (Pres)

FC CONSTRUCTION SERVICES

8350 N Central Expy 300, Dallas, TX 75206
Tel.: (800) 388-8827
Web Site: http://www.fc-cs.com
Year Founded: 1989
Sales Range: $10-24.9 Million
Emp.: 120
Construction Management Services
N.A.I.C.S.: 236116
I. D. Walker (CEO)

FC CRESTONE LLC

5555 DTC Pkwy Ste 277, Greenwood Village, CO 80111
Tel.: (720) 407-4401   CO
Web Site: http://www.fccrestone.com
Year Founded: 2007
Privater Equity Firm
N.A.I.C.S.: 523999
Rich Horrigan (Co-Founder & Partner)
Stephen Schmeltekopf (Co-Founder & Partner)
Michael Houy (Partner)

FCA COOP

105 Jackson St, Jackson, MN 56143
Tel.: (507) 847-4160
Web Site: http://www.fcajackson.com
Sales Range: $25-49.9 Million
Emp.: 70
Grain Elevators
N.A.I.C.S.: 457120
Mark Eggiman (Pres)
Gene Michelson (Treas)
Matt Benson (Mgr-Dept)
David Faber (Mgr-Dept)
Jerry Svoboda (Gen Mgr)

FCB FINANCIAL CORP.

111 Barnard St, Savannah, GA 31401
Tel.: (912) 629-2900   GA
Web Site: https://www.firstchatham.com
Year Founded: 2001
Sales Range: $25-49.9 Million
Bank Holding Company
N.A.I.C.S.: 551111
Stephen S. Green (Chm)
Lawrence M. Austin (CFO)
Ken Farrell (Interim Pres & Interim CEO)
William M. Austin Jr. (COO)

Subsidiaries:

First Chatham Bank   (1)
111 Barnard St, Savannah, GA 31401
Tel.: (912) 629-2900
Web Site: http://www.firstchatham.com
Emp.: 96
Retail & Commercial Banking
N.A.I.C.S.: 522110
Lawrence M. Austin (CFO)
Kenneth R. Farrell (CEO & Officer-Credit)
Sharon Spradley (Mgr-Retail Banking)
Benny H. Curl (Chm)
Stephen S. Green (Vice Chm)

FCCI MUTUAL INSURANCE HOLDING COMPANY

6300 University Pkwy, Sarasota, FL 34240-8424
Tel.: (941) 907-3224   FL
Web Site: http://www.fcci-group.com
Year Founded: 1959
Sales Range: $500-549.9 Million
Emp.: 773
Holding Company; Insurance
N.A.I.C.S.: 551112
Thomas Koval (Chief Legal Officer & Exec VP)
Lisa Krouse (Chief HR Officer & Exec VP)
Joe Keene (Exec VP-Claims)
John T. Stafford (Chm)

Chris Shoucair (CFO, Exec VP & Treas)
Lisa Weiland (COO & Exec VP)

Subsidiaries:

FCCI Insurance Group Inc.   (1)
6300 University Pkwy, Sarasota, FL 34240-8424
Tel.: (941) 907-3224
Web Site: http://www.fcci-group.com
Accident & Health Insurance Services
N.A.I.C.S.: 524210
Paul Ayoub (CIO & Sr VP)
Lisa Krouse (Chief HR Officer & Exec VP)
Mike Noble (Asst VP-Gulf Coast Reg)
John Cox (Chm)
Ann Driscoll (VP-HR)
Michael Janicki (Dir-Risk Control & Risk Mgmt)
Joe Keene (Exec VP-Corp Claims)
Ian Massay (Dir-Underwriting, Risk Control & Agribus)
John Wilks (Treas & Dir-Ops)
Frank Zayas (Dir-Underwriting & Agribus)
Christina Welch (Pres & CEO)

Monroe Guaranty Companies Inc.   (1)
9025 River Rd Ste 300, Indianapolis, IN 46240
Tel.: (317) 571-3000
Web Site: http://www.fcci-group.com
Rev.: $133,341,656
Emp.: 100
Holding Companies
N.A.I.C.S.: 551112
Tracy Pfab (VP)

FCF PARTNERS, LP

250 W Coventry Ct Ste 201, Milwaukee, WI 53217
Tel.: (414) 967-7008   DE
Web Site: http://www.fcffunds.com
Sales Range: $50-74.9 Million
Emp.: 5
Privater Equity Firm
N.A.I.C.S.: 523999
Scott Roeper (Mng Partner)
Paul J. Raab (Mng Partner)
G. Woodrow Adkins (Mng Partner)
Susan Chipman (Office Mgr)

Subsidiaries:

Oshkosh Floor Designs, Inc.   (1)
911 E Main St, Winneconne, WI 54986
Tel.: (920) 582-9977
Web Site: http://www.oshkoshdesigns.com
Sales Range: $1-9.9 Million
Flooring Inlay Mfr
N.A.I.C.S.: 321918
Brenda Kubasta (Pres)
Lee Bettes (Pres)

Riverside Engineering, Inc.   (1)
121 Interpark Blvd Ste 604, San Antonio, TX 78216-1847
Tel.: (210) 227-9090
Web Site: http://www.rsengr.com
Sales Range: $10-24.9 Million
Metal Shredders & Recycling Equipment Mfr
N.A.I.C.S.: 333248
Martin Rios (Supvr-Warehouse)

FCH ENTERPRISES INC.

1765 S King St, Honolulu, HI 96826
Tel.: (808) 973-0880
Web Site: http://fchenterprises.com
Sales Range: $25-49.9 Million
Emp.: 2,000
Limited-Service Restaurants
N.A.I.C.S.: 722513
Maryline Ancheta (Mgr-Restaurant)
Nelson Miyasato (Mgr-Store)
Sarah Keener (Mgr)
Jeanine Mamiya-Kalahiki (Mgr-Mktg)
Wesley Leong (Controller)
James Kim (Dir-Trng)
Laurie Sapalasan (Mgr)
Nathan Higashionna (Mgr)
Peter Gois (Mgr-IS)
Janette Makaena (Mgr-Store)

FCH Enterprises Inc.—(Continued)

Veronica Claveran *(Mgr-Store)*
Paul Yokota *(Pres)*
Edna Ladines *(Supvr-Acctg)*

FCI CONSTRUCTORS INC.
3070 I 70 B Build A, Grand Junction, CO 81504
Tel.: (970) 434-9093   CO
Web Site: http://www.fciol.com
Year Founded: 1978
Sales Range: $200-249.9 Million
Emp.: 230
Provider of Nonresidential Construction Services
N.A.I.C.S.: 236220
Ed Forsman *(Pres)*

FCL BUILDERS INC.
1150 Spring Lake Dr, Itasca, IL 60143
Tel.: (630) 773-0050
Web Site: https://www.fclbuilders.com
Year Founded: 1977
Sales Range: $10-24.9 Million
Emp.: 87
Provider of Industrial Building & New Construction Services
N.A.I.C.S.: 236210
Michael Boro *(Pres)*
Carmen G. Dodaro *(Exec VP)*
Christopher P. Linn *(VP-Construction)*
Dean O'Brien *(Treas & VP-Fin)*

FCM BANNOCKBURN
2101 Waukegan Rd, Ste 300, Bannockburn, IL 60015
Tel.: (800) 227-1908
Web Site: http://www.us.fcm.travel
Rev.: $17,500,000
Emp.: 65
Travel Agencies
N.A.I.C.S.: 561510
John Beauvais *(Pres)*

FCN BANK
501 Main St, Brookville, IN 47012
Tel.: (765) 647-4116   IN
Web Site: https://www.fcnbank.com
FBVI—(OTCIQ)
Rev.: $18,216,000
Assets: $474,066,000
Liabilities: $417,745,000
Net Worth: $56,321,000
Earnings: $5,720,000
Fiscal Year-end: 12/31/19
Commercial Banking Services
N.A.I.C.S.: 522110
Thomas D. Horninger *(Pres & CEO)*
Tony Windle *(VP-Mortgage)*
Kris Lacy *(VP-Mortgage Lender & Product Mgr)*
Roger R. Potraffke *(Chief Lending Officer)*

FCP GROTON LLC
155 Hill St, Milford, CT 06475
Tel.: (860) 388-9001
Web Site: http://www.fcpgroton.com
Year Founded: 1986
Sales Range: $10-24.9 Million
Emp.: 50
Automotive Parts & Accessories Stores
N.A.I.C.S.: 441330
Nick Bauer *(Pres)*
Scott Drozd *(CEO)*

FCS FINANCIAL
1934 E Miller St, Jefferson City, MO 65101
Tel.: (573) 636-7809
Web Site:
    https://www.myfcsfinancial.com
Rev.: $49,500,000
Emp.: 180

Financial Services
N.A.I.C.S.: 522299
Steve Harrington *(Exec VP-Fin)*
Mark Pierce *(Vice Chm)*
Jeff Houts *(Exec VP-Ops)*
Robert Bock *(Chief Credit Officer)*
Steve Iversen *(Exec VP-Risk Mgmt)*
Dennis Hunsberger *(CIO & Exec VP)*
Rob Guinn *(CEO)*

FD2S
500 Chicon, Austin, TX 78702
Tel.: (512) 476-7733
Web Site: http://www.fd2s.com
Year Founded: 1985
Sales Range: Less than $1 Million
Emp.: 11
Advetising Agency
N.A.I.C.S.: 541810
Larry Paul Fuller *(Co-Founder)*
Curtis Roberts *(Principal)*
Steven L. Stamper *(Co-Founder)*

FDC MANAGEMENT INC.
PO Box 29890, Anaheim, CA 92809
Tel.: (714) 685-7000
Web Site:
    https://www.fdcmanagement.com
Rev.: $15,000,000
Emp.: 100
Real Estate Managers
N.A.I.C.S.: 531210
Patrick M. Kelly *(Chm)*
Diane Summo *(Controller)*
Claudiu Polizu *(Mgr-Property)*
James Wohrman *(Pres)*
Michelle Villegas *(Mgr-Resident)*

FDG ASSOCIATES LP
485 Lexington Ave 23rd Fl, New York, NY 10017
Tel.: (212) 940-6864
Web Site:
    http://www.fdgassociates.com
Privater Equity Firm
N.A.I.C.S.: 523999
S. Matthew Katz *(Mng Dir)*
David S. Gellman *(Mng Dir)*

FDL CORPORATION
1020 W 31st St, Downers Grove, IL 60515-5591
Web Site: http://www.fdl-life.com
Year Founded: 1968
Sales Range: $10-24.9 Million
Emp.: 150
Insurance And Financial Services
N.A.I.C.S.: 524210

FDS MANUFACTURING COMPANY INCORPORATED
2200 S Reservoir St, Pomona, CA 91769
Tel.: (909) 591-1733
Web Site: https://www.fdsmfg.com
Rev.: $22,000,000
Emp.: 145
Corrugated Paper Mfr
N.A.I.C.S.: 322299
Robert Stevenson *(Chm, Pres & CEO)*

FE-MA ENTERPRISES INC.
6503 S Cage St, Pharr, TX 78577
Tel.: (956) 781-4207
Year Founded: 1981
Rev.: $14,700,000
Emp.: 300
Grocery Store Operators
N.A.I.C.S.: 445110

FEATHER PUBLISHING CO., INC.
287 Lawrence St, Quincy, CA 95971
Tel.: (530) 283-0800

Web Site:
    https://www.plumasnews.com
Sales Range: $10-24.9 Million
Emp.: 85
Publisher of Newspapers
N.A.I.C.S.: 513110
Michael C. Taborski *(Pres)*

Subsidiaries:

Chester Progressive   (1)
135 Main St, Chester, CA 96020
Tel.: (530) 258-3115
Web Site: http://www.plumasnews.com
Sales Range: $10-24.9 Million
Emp.: 50
Newspapers
N.A.I.C.S.: 513110

Feather River Bulletin   (1)
287 Lawrence St, Quincy, CA 95971
Tel.: (530) 283-0800
Web Site: http://www.plumasnews.com
Sales Range: $10-24.9 Million
Emp.: 30
Newspapers
N.A.I.C.S.: 513110
Michael C. Taborski *(Pres & Publr)*

Indian Valley Record   (1)
PO Box 469, Greenville, CA 95947
Tel.: (530) 284-7800
Web Site: http://www.plumasnews.com
Sales Range: $10-24.9 Million
Emp.: 2
Newspapers
N.A.I.C.S.: 459999
Eva Small *(Mgr-Composing)*
Tom Forney *(Mgr-Production)*
Cobey Brown *(Mgr-Print Shop)*

Portola Reporter   (1)
133 W Sierra Ave, Portola, CA 96122
Tel.: (530) 832-4646
Web Site: http://www.plumasnews.com
Newspapers
N.A.I.C.S.: 323111

FEATHERINGILL CAPITAL, LLC
2317 3rd Ave N Ste 101, 35203, Birmingham, AL
Tel.: (205) 879-2722
Web Site:
    https://www.featheringillcapital.com
Privater Equity Firm
N.A.I.C.S.: 523999
Bill Fox *(Mng Partner)*
Liz Pharo *(Mng Partner)*
Conner McCabe *(Dir-M&A)*

Subsidiaries:

Experlogix Inc.   (1)
10808 S River Front Pkwy Ste 650, 84095, South Jordan, UT
Tel.: (805) 504-9729
Web Site: http://www.experlogix.com
Business to Business Electronic Markets
N.A.I.C.S.: 425120
Bill Fox *(CEO)*
Mark Conway *(VP-Sls-Europe, Middle East & Africa)*
Angie Cox *(VP-Sls-North America)*
Beth Thornton *(Chief Revenue Officer)*

Investedge, Inc.   (1)
1151 Freeport Rd 396, Pittsburgh, PA 15238
Tel.: (412) 600-1643
Web Site: http://www.investedge.com
Rev.: $2,700,000
Emp.: 19
Computer & Computer Peripheral Equipment & Software Merchant Whslr
N.A.I.C.S.: 423430
Robert S. Stewart *(CEO)*
Lisa Binotto *(Mgr-HR)*
Brian Burns *(CEO)*

FEATURE FILMS FOR FAMILIES INC.
5286 Commerce Dr, Salt Lake City, UT 84117
Tel.: (855) 326-4599   UT
Web Site: http://www.familytv.com

Year Founded: 1988
Provider of Record & Prerecorded Tape Store Services
N.A.I.C.S.: 449210
Brian Inman *(Mgr-Ops)*

FECHTEL BEVERAGE & SALES INC.
425 W Elm St, Jefferson City, MO 65101
Tel.: (573) 636-5161
Rev.: $13,300,000
Emp.: 50
Beer & Ale Merchant Whslr
N.A.I.C.S.: 424810
Bernard J. Fechtel *(Pres)*

FEDCAP PARTNERS, LLC
1760 Old Meadow Rd Ste 150, McLean, VA 22102
Tel.: (703) 291-0350
Web Site:
    http://www.fedcappartners.com
Sales Range: $10-24.9 Million
Emp.: 5
Privater Equity Firm
N.A.I.C.S.: 523999
William Doroh *(Principal)*
Clark Knop *(Principal)*

Subsidiaries:

Point One, LLC   (1)
1215 S Clark St Ste 1102, Arlington, VA 22202
Tel.: (703) 414-5440
Web Site: http://www.pointoneinc.com
Technical Consulting Services
N.A.I.C.S.: 541690

Subsidiary (Domestic):

Summit Solutions, Inc.   (2)
1362 Mellon Rd Ste 140, Hanover, MD 21076
Tel.: (410) 782-2081
Web Site: http://www.summitsolve.com
Sales Range: $10-24.9 Million
Computer System Design Services
N.A.I.C.S.: 541512

FEDCAP REHABILITATION SERVICES, INC.
633 Third Ave 6th Fl, New York, NY 10017
Tel.: (212) 727-4200   NY
Web Site: http://www.fedcap.org
Year Founded: 1935
Sales Range: $75-99.9 Million
Emp.: 1,855
Employment Placement Services
N.A.I.C.S.: 561311
Joseph Giannetto *(COO)*
Christine McMahon *(Pres & CEO)*
Lorrie Lutz *(Chief Strategy Officer)*
Martha Sproule *(Treas)*
Mark O'Donoghue *(Chm)*
Judy Bergtraum *(Sec)*
Laurence Ach *(Vice Chm)*
Karen Wegmann *(CFO)*
Kenneth Brezenoff *(Gen Counsel & VP-Strategic Initiatives)*
Donald Harreld *(Sr VP-Education)*
Craig Stenning *(Sr VP-Occupational Health)*
Grant E. Collins *(Sr VP-Workforce Dev)*
Steven Coons *(VP-Facilities Mgmt)*
Aisha Lucas *(VP-Home Care)*
Frank Maness *(VP-Human Capital, Org Dev, Strategy & Ops)*
Lyell Ritchie *(VP-Strategic Bus Dev)*

FEDCO ELECTRONICS, INC.
1363 Capital Dr, Fond Du Lac, WI 54937
Tel.: (920) 922-6490

Web Site:
http://www.fedcoelectronics.com
Year Founded: 1975
Rev.: $11,500,000
Emp.: 48
Storage Battery Mfr
N.A.I.C.S.: 335910
Peter Victor (Pres)
Stephen P. Victor Jr. (CEO)

FEDER'S SUBARU
243 Dolson Ave, Middletown, NY
10940
Tel.: (845) 344-3100
Year Founded: 1989
Sales Range: $10-24.9 Million
Emp.: 24
Car Whslr
N.A.I.C.S.: 441110
Joseph Feder (Owner & Gen Mgr)

FEDERACION DE ASC PEC-UARIAS PR
333 Zona Portaria Malecon Ward,
Mayaguez, PR 00680
Tel.: (787) 834-9191
Rev.: $25,000,000
Emp.: 100
Livestock Feeds
N.A.I.C.S.: 311119
Antonio Sisco (Pres)
Raphael Acevego (Controller)
Jose Millian (VP)

FEDERAL BUILDING SER-VICES, INC.
1641 Barclay Blvd, Buffalo Grove, IL
60089-4544
Tel.: (847) 279-7360
Web Site:
http://www.federalbuildingser
vice.com
Year Founded: 1963
Sales Range: $10-24.9 Million
Emp.: 1,500
Provider of Janitorial Services
N.A.I.C.S.: 561720
Stephen E. Kulp (Chm & CEO)
William Hoffman (Exec VP-Midwest)
Robert Kulp (Exec VP-South)
Peter Kulp (Pres)
Ken Raffensberger (Exec VP-East)

FEDERAL BUSINESS PROD-UCTS, INC.
150 Clove Rd 5th Fl, Little Falls, NJ
07424
Tel.: (973) 667-9800   NJ
Web Site: https://www.feddirect.com
Year Founded: 1926
Sales Range: $150-199.9 Million
Emp.: 350
Printer of Continuous, Snapout &
Other Business Forms; Direct Mail
Services
N.A.I.C.S.: 323111
Bill Evans (COO)
Angela Stubbs (Pres)

FEDERAL CAPITAL PART-NERS
5425 Wisconsin Ave Ste 202, Chevy
Chase, MD 20815
Tel.: (240) 395-2000
Web Site: http://www.fcpdc.com
Sales Range: $25-49.9 Million
Emp.: 18
Real Estate Investment & Develop-
ment Services
N.A.I.C.S.: 531110
Lacy I. Rice III (Co-Founder & Mng
Partner)
Esko I. Korhonen (Mng Partner)
Alex J. Marshall (Mng Partner)
Thomas A. Carr (Mng Partner)
Garland E. Faist (CFO & Sr VP)

Edward Corwin (Sr VP-Structured
Investments)
Summer Kassir Haltli (VP-Asset
Mgmt)
Chris LoSapio (Dir-Asset Mgmt)
Jason Bonderenko (Sr VP-Residential
Acquisition)
Nikita Rao (Sr VP)
Wade Casstevens (Sr VP)
James M. Rensen (Controller & VP)
Steve Walsh (Sr VP-Capital Markets)
Doug Rigler (VP-Construction)
Jason L. Ward (VP-Structured Invest-
ments)
Sarah Hubbard (VP-Comml Asset
Mgmt)
Matt Valentini (VP-Dev)
Bruce Gago (VP-Acq)
Erik Weinberg (Sr VP-Comml Invest-
ments)
Liz Koteles (VP-Comml Investments-
Atlanta)

Subsidiaries:

American Community Properties
Trust   (1)
222 Smallwood Village Ctr, Saint Charles,
MD 20602
Tel.: (301) 843-8600
Web Site: http://www.acptrust.com
Sales Range: $75-99.9 Million
Real Estate Owner & Developer
N.A.I.C.S.: 237210
Lacy I. Rice III (Chm)
Matthew M. Martin (CFO)
Mark L. Macfarland (VP-Land Dev)
Craig J. Renner (VP-Pub Affairs & Commu-
nity Rels)

Subsidiary (Domestic):

American Rental Management
Company   (2)
222 Smallwood Village Ctr, Saint Charles,
MD 20602
Tel.: (301) 843-8600
Sales Range: $75-99.9 Million
Nonresidential Building Operators
N.A.I.C.S.: 531312

FEDERAL CASTERS CORPO-RATION
785 Harrison Ave, Harrison, NJ
07029
Tel.: (973) 483-6700   NY
Web Site:
https://www.fedcosteel.com
Sales Range: $10-24.9 Million
Emp.: 50
Mfr of Industrial Casters
N.A.I.C.S.: 423510
Charles Cumella (Pres)

FEDERAL COMPRESS & WAREHOUSE COMPANY, INC.
6060 Primacy Pkwy Ste 400, Mem-
phis, TN 38119-5745
Tel.: (901) 524-4000   DE
Web Site:
http://www.federalcompress.com
Year Founded: 1977
Sales Range: $150-199.9 Million
Emp.: 500
Cotton Warehousing & Services
N.A.I.C.S.: 493130
Robert B. Cohen (Treas & VP)
Vicky L. Cortise (VP-Personnel &
Risk Mgmt)
Charlie Jackson (Pres)

FEDERAL CONTRACTING INC
7025 Campus Dr, Colorado Springs,
CO 80920
Tel.: (719) 632-5355
Web Site:
http://www.bryanconstruction.com
Emp.: 100
Civil Infrastructure Services
N.A.I.C.S.: 541330

Scott Bryan (CEO & Founder)

Subsidiaries:

Drahota Construction Co   (1)
4700 Innovation Dr Bldg C, Fort Collins, CO
80525
Tel.: (970) 204-0100
Web Site: http://www.drahota.com
Emp.: 15
Construction Services
N.A.I.C.S.: 236118
Terry Drahota (Pres, CEO & Founder)

FEDERAL DEPOSIT INSUR-ANCE CORPORATION
550 17th St NW, Washington, DC
20429
Web Site: http://www.fdic.gov
Year Founded: 1933
Sales Range: $5-14.9 Billion
Emp.: 8,150
Financial Deposit Insurance Services
N.A.I.C.S.: 524128
Barbara A Ryan (COO)
Steven O. App (CFO)
Arleas Upton Kea (Dir-Admin Div)
Arthur J. Murton (Dir-Complex Finan-
cial Institutions-Office)
Thomas J. Curry (Comptroller-
Currency)
Mark Pearce (Dir-Depositor & Con-
sumer Protection Div)
Bret D. Edwards (Dir-Resolutions &
Receiverships Div)
Fred S. Carns (Dir-Intl Affairs)
Diane Ellis (Dir-Insurance & Res Div)
John Vogel (Deputy Dir-Ops)
Barbara Hagenbaugh (Deputy Chm-
Comm)
Jelena McWilliams (Chm)
Maureen Sweeney (Dir-Resolutions &
Receiverships)
Frank R. Hughes (Dir-New York)

Subsidiaries:

Silicon Valley Bank   (1)
3003 Tasman Dr, Santa Clara, CA 95054
Tel.: (408) 654-7400
Web Site: https://www.svb.com
Emp.: 1,457
Commercial Bank & Savings Institution
N.A.I.C.S.: 522110
Marc Cadieux (Pres-Comml Banking)
Michelle A. Draper (CMO)
Gagan Kanjlia (Chief Product Officer)
Jennifer Friel Goldstein (Head-Bus Dev,
Tech & Healthcare)
Patrick Flynn (COO-UK & Europe, Middle
East & Africa)
Erin Platts (Pres-UK & Head-Europe,
Middle East & Africa)
Kevin O'Flanagan (Mng Dir-Private Banking
& Wealth Advisory Div)
Yvette S. Butler (Pres-Private Banking &
Wealth Mgmt)
Christopher Hollins (Head-Product Sls)
Jeffrey Leerink (CEO-Leerink)
Roger F. Dunbar (Chm)
Tosh Ernest (Head-Access Innovation)
Jesse Hurley (Head-Global Fund Banking)
Joan Parsons (Head-Tech & life Science
Banking)
Michael Tramack (Head-Loan Admin)
Peter Bristow (Pres)
Richard D. Daniels (Sr VP)

Subsidiary (Domestic):

SVB Asset Management   (2)
3003 Tasman Dr, Santa Clara, CA 95054
Tel.: (408) 654-7400
Web Site:
http://www.svbassetmanagement.com
Sales Range: $650-699.9 Million
Asset & Wealth Management Services
N.A.I.C.S.: 523940

Subsidiary (Non-US):

Silicon Valley Bank UK Limited   (2)
Alphabeta 14-18 Finsbury Square, London,
EC2A 1BR, United Kingdom
Tel.: (44) 2073677800

Financial Investment Services
N.A.I.C.S.: 523999

FEDERAL DISTRIBUTORS, INC.
2075 Lisbon Rd, Lewiston, ME 04241
Tel.: (207) 783-1777
Web Site:
http://www.federaldistributors.com
Wine & Distilled Alcoholic Beverage
Merchant Whslr
N.A.I.C.S.: 424820
Dennis Belanger (VP-Sls & Mktg)

FEDERAL FARM CREDIT BANKS FUNDING CORPORA-TION
10 Exchange Pl Ste 1401, Jersey
City, NJ 07302
Tel.: (201) 200-8000   NJ
Web Site:
http://www.farmcreditfunding.com
Year Founded: 1983
Sales Range: $1-9.9 Million
Emp.: 50
Agricultural & Rural Credit Financial
Services
N.A.I.C.S.: 522390
J. Less Guthrie (Chm)
Glenn Doran (Mng Dir)

Subsidiaries:

AgFirst Farm Credit Bank   (1)
1901 Main St, Columbia, SC 29201
Tel.: (803) 799-5000
Web Site: http://www.agfirst.com
Agricultural Lending Institution
N.A.I.C.S.: 522299
Charl L. Butler (COO & Exec VP)
Benjamin F. Blakewood (CIO)
Christopher L. Jones (Chief Credit Officer)
Tim Amerson (CFO)
Stephen Gilbert (CFO & Sr VP)
Frances Griggs (Gen Counsel & Sr VP)
Curtis Hancock (Chm)
Sam Esfahani (CIO & Sr VP)
Will Brown (Chief Credit Officer & Sr VP)

AgriBank, FCB   (1)
30 E 7th St Ste 1600, Saint Paul, MN
55101
Tel.: (651) 282-8800
Web Site: http://www.info.agribank.com
Emp.: 13,000
Agricultural Lending Institution
N.A.I.C.S.: 522299
Jeffery R. Swanhorst (Chief Credit Officer &
Exec VP-Credit)
Matthew Walther (Chm)
William J. Thone (CEO)
John Grace (Chief Risk Officer)
Jim Jones (Chief Credit Officer)
Jeffrey Moore (CFO)
Barbara Stille (Chief Admin Officer & Gen
Counsel)

Farm Credit Bank of Texas   (1)
Tel.: (512) 465-0400
Web Site: https://www.farmcreditbank.com
Emp.: 288
Agricultural Lending Institution
N.A.I.C.S.: 522299
Larry R. Doyle (CEO)
Stan Ray (Chief Admin Officer)
James F. Dodson (Chm)
Lester Little (Vice Chm)
Michael Elliott (CIO)
Amie Pala (CFO)
John Sloan (Chief Credit Officer)
Nanci Tucker (Gen Counsel)

Farm Credit Leasing Services
Corporation   (1)
1600 Colonnade 5500 Wayzata Blvd, Min-
neapolis, MN 55416-1252
Tel.: (952) 417-7800
Web Site: http://www.fcleasing.com
Agricultural Leasing Institution
N.A.I.C.S.: 532490
Paul Rolvaag (Mgr-Asset)

Federal Fruit & Produce Co., Inc.—(Continued)

FEDERAL FRUIT & PRODUCE CO., INC.
1890 E 58th Ave, Denver, CO 80216
Tel.: (303) 292-1303   CO
Web Site: http://www.fedfruit.com
Year Founded: 1987
Sales Range: $10-24.9 Million
Emp.: 100
Growers of Fresh Fruits & Vegetables
N.A.I.C.S.: 424480
Stanley Kouba (Pres)

FEDERAL HOME LOAN BANK OF ATLANTA
1475 Peachtree St NE, Atlanta, GA 30309
Tel.: (404) 888-8000
Web Site: https://www.fhlbatl.com
Year Founded: 1932
Rev.: $2,527,000,000
Assets: $151,622,000,000
Liabilities: $143,976,000,000
Net Worth: $7,646,000,000
Earnings: $184,000,000
Emp.: 316
Fiscal Year-end: 12/31/22
Mortgage & Loan Banking Services
N.A.I.C.S.: 522310
Kirk R. Malmberg (Pres & CEO)
Reginald T. O'Shields (Chief Compliance & Ethics Officer, Gen Counsel & Exec VP)
Scott M. Brennan (Sr VP & Dir-Sls)
William T. Shaw (Sr VP & Controller)
Sharon B. Cook (CMO & Sr VP)
Brian E. Argrett (Vice Chm)
Alp E. Can (Chief Risk Officer & Exec VP)
Joel Badger (Chief Audit Officer & Sr VP)
Haig H. Kazazian III (CFO)
Annette Hunter (Exec VP)
Jeff Afonso (CIO)
Dawn Gehring (Chief HR Officer)
R. Thornwell Dunlap III (Chm)

FEDERAL HOME LOAN BANK OF BOSTON
800 Boylston St, Boston, MA 02199
Tel.: (617) 292-9600
Web Site:
   https://www.fhlbboston.com
Rev.: $1,226,964,000
Assets: $62,897,549,000
Liabilities: $59,482,228,000
Net Worth: $3,415,321,000
Earnings: $184,211,000
Emp.: 188
Fiscal Year-end: 12/31/22
Mortgage & Loan Banking Services
N.A.I.C.S.: 522310
Frank Nitkiewicz (CFO, COO & Exec VP)
Brian G. Donahue (Chief Acctg Officer, Sr VP & Controller)
Timothy J. Barrett (Pres & CEO)
Donna L. Boulanger (Vice Chm)
Martin J. Geitz (Chm)
Sean R. McRae (CIO & Sr VP)
Edward A. Schultze (Chief Risk Officer & Sr VP)
Keith Walsh (Gen Counsel)

FEDERAL HOME LOAN BANK OF CHICAGO
200 E Randolph Dr, Chicago, IL 60601
Tel.: (312) 565-5700
Web Site: http://www.fhlbc.com
Rev.: $816,000,000
Assets: $96,954,000,000
Liabilities: $90,202,000,000
Net Worth: $6,752,000,000
Earnings: $275,000,000

Emp.: 458
Fiscal Year-end: 12/31/21
Mortgage & Loan Banking Services
N.A.I.C.S.: 522310
David Feldhaus (Dir-External Affairs)
Thomas H. W. Harper (Exec VP)
Michael A. Ericson (Pres & CEO)
John K. Reinke (Chm)
Michelle Jonson (Chief Risk Officer, Exec VP & Head-Risk Mgmt-Grp)
James T. Ashworth (Vice Chm)
Samuel J. Nicita (CIO, Exec VP & Head-IT-Grp)
Carolyn Jaw (Exec VP & Head-Sls, Strategy & Solutions-Grp)
Chris Milne (Mng Dir-Institutional Sls)
Jaronda Hall (Dir-Institutional Sls)
Jeff Long (Dir-Institutional Sls)
Kimberly Cullotta (Exec VP & Head-People, Culture & Comm-Grp)
Virxhini Gjonzeneli (CFO, Exec VP & Grp Head-Markets & Fin Acctg)
Laura M. Turnquest (Gen Counsel, Sec & Exec VP)
Roger Platt (Mng Dir-Institutional Sls)
Erin Kopecky (Dir-Comm)
Cedric D. Thurman (Chief Diversity Officer & Exec VP)
Raj Misra (Dir-Institutional Sls)
Sean Harper (Assoc Dir-Institutional Sls)
Travis Schroll (Dir-Institutional Sls)
Steve Sikora (Assoc Dir-Institutional Sls)

FEDERAL HOME LOAN BANK OF CINCINNATI
600 Atrium Two, Cincinnati, OH 45201-0598
Tel.: (513) 852-7500
Web Site: https://www.fhlbcin.com
Year Founded: 1932
Rev.: $2,116,952,000
Assets: $108,609,504,000
Liabilities: $102,107,273,000
Net Worth: $6,502,231,000
Earnings: $251,996,000
Emp.: 240
Fiscal Year-end: 12/31/22
Home Loan Banking Services
N.A.I.C.S.: 522310
Andrew S. Howell (Pres & CEO)
Stephen J. Sponaugle (CFO & Exec VP)
Donald J. Mullineaux (Chm)
Daniel A. Tully (Chief Risk & Compliance Officer & Sr VP)
James A. England (Vice Chm)
John Christopher Bates (Chief Acctg Officer & Sr VP)
Tami L. Hendrickson (Sr VP)
Roger B. Batsel (COO & Exec VP)
Bridget C. Hoffman (Gen Counsel & Sr VP)
Amy L. Konow (Sr VP)
Karla M. Russo (Chief HR Officer)

FEDERAL HOME LOAN BANK OF DALLAS
8500 Freeport Pkwy S Ste 600, Irving, TX 75063-2547
Tel.: (214) 441-8500
Web Site: https://www.fhlb.com
Year Founded: 1932
Rev.: $1,864,745,000
Assets: $114,348,556,000
Liabilities: $108,347,479,000
Net Worth: $6,001,077,000
Earnings: $317,245,000
Emp.: 200
Fiscal Year-end: 12/31/22
Mortgage Banking Services
N.A.I.C.S.: 522299
Sanjay K. Bhasin (Pres & CEO)
Tom Lewis (CFO & Exec VP)
Margo S. Scholin (Vice Chm)

Jibo Pan (Exec VP & Head-Capital Markets)
Kalyan Madhavan (Chief Bus Officer & Exec VP)
Robert M. Rigby (Chm)

FEDERAL HOME LOAN BANK OF DES MOINES
909 Locust St, Des Moines, IA 50309
Tel.: (515) 412-2100
Web Site: https://www.fhlbdm.com
Year Founded: 1932
Rev.: $2,774,000,000
Assets: $164,169,000,000
Liabilities: $155,418,000,000
Net Worth: $8,751,000,000
Earnings: $430,000,000
Emp.: 354
Fiscal Year-end: 12/31/22
Mortgage Banking Services
N.A.I.C.S.: 522292
Kristina K. Williams (Pres & CEO)
Joelyn R. Jensen-Marren (Chief Risk & Compliance Officer & Exec VP)
Deborah G. Baldwin (Chief Diversity & Inclusion Officer & Sr VP)
Cherie Schuler (Sr Dir)
Katie Steinke (Chief HR Officer)
Rob Dixon (Gen Counsel)
Ellen Z. Lamale (Vice Chm)

FEDERAL HOME LOAN BANK OF INDIANAPOLIS
8250 Woodfield Crossing Blvd, Indianapolis, IN 46240
Tel.: (317) 465-0200
Web Site: https://www.fhlbi.com
Year Founded: 1932
Rev.: $1,390,636,000
Assets: $72,283,780,000
Liabilities: $68,900,082,000
Net Worth: $3,383,698,000
Earnings: $176,746,000
Emp.: 257
Fiscal Year-end: 12/31/22
Mortgage & Loan Banking Services
N.A.I.C.S.: 522310
Gregory L. Teare (CFO & Exec VP)
Gregory J. McKee (Chief Internal Audit Officer & Sr VP)
Karen F. Gregerson (Vice Chm)
Dan L. Moore (Chm)
Deron J. Streitenberger (Chief Bus Ops Officer & Exec VP)
Jonathan W. Griffin (Chief Bus Dev Officer & Sr VP)
Chad A. Brandt (Treas & Sr VP)
Kania D. Lottie (Chief HR, Diversity & Inclusion Officer & Sr VP)
Christopher Dawson (CIO & Sr VP)
Brendan McGrath (Chief Risk Officer & Exec VP)
Shaun Healy Clifford (Chief Compliance Officer, Officer-Ethics, Gen Counsel & Sr VP)
Kristina Cunningham (Sr VP & Sr Dir-Compliance & Operational Risk Analysis)
K. Lowell Short Jr. (Chief Acctg Officer & Sr VP)

FEDERAL HOME LOAN BANK OF NEW YORK
101 Park Ave, New York, NY 10178
Tel.: (212) 681-6000
Web Site: https://www.fhlbny.com
Year Founded: 1932
Rev.: $2,758,182,000
Assets: $157,391,489,000
Liabilities: $149,044,106,000
Net Worth: $8,347,383,000
Earnings: $417,376,000
Emp.: 327
Fiscal Year-end: 12/31/22
Mortgage & Loan Banking Services
N.A.I.C.S.: 522310

Jose Ramon Gonzalez (Pres & CEO)
Adam Goldstein (Chief Bus Officer & Sr VP)
Kevin M. Neylan (CFO & Sr VP)
Larry E. Thompson (Vice Chm)
Stephen C. Angelo (Chief Audit Officer & Sr VP)
Jonathan R. West (Chief Legal Officer & Sr VP)
Michael L. Radziemski (CIO & Sr VP)
John R. Buran (Chm)

FEDERAL HOME LOAN BANK OF PITTSBURGH
601 Grant St, Pittsburgh, PA 15219
Tel.: (412) 288-3400
Web Site: https://www.fhlb-pgh.com
Rev.: $1,621,300,000
Assets: $96,141,167,000
Liabilities: $91,243,052,000
Net Worth: $4,898,115,000
Earnings: $227,068,000
Emp.: 224
Fiscal Year-end: 12/31/22
Home Loan Banking Services
N.A.I.C.S.: 522292
Edward V. Weller (CFO & Chief Acctg Officer)
Bradford E. Ritchie (Chm)
John P. Cassidy (Chief Tech & Ops Officer)
Carolyn M. McKinney (Chief HR Officer)
Mark Evanco (Chief Bus Dev & Strategy Officer)
Pritha Madhavan (Deputy CEO)
Winthrop Watson (Pres & CEO)
David G. Paulson (COO)

FEDERAL HOME LOAN BANK OF SAN FRANCISCO
333 Bush St Ste 2700, San Francisco, CA 94104
Tel.: (415) 616-1000
Web Site: https://www.fhlbsf.com
Rev.: $2,122,000,000
Assets: $121,056,000,000
Liabilities: $113,333,000,000
Net Worth: $7,723,000,000
Earnings: $323,000,000
Emp.: 297
Fiscal Year-end: 12/31/22
Mortgage & Loan Banking Services
N.A.I.C.S.: 522310
Kevin A. Gong (Sr VP)
Jeremy Empol (Sr VP-Pub Affairs & Industry Outreach)
F. Daniel Siciliano (Chm)
Gregory A. Ward (COO & Exec VP)
Simone F. Lagomarsino (Vice Chm)
Mary Long (Sr Dir-Mktg Comm)
Arlene Coyle (Sr VP)
Tony Wong (Chief Banking Officer & Exec VP)
Maxine Moir (Chief HR Officer & Sr VP)
Kevin Blackburn (Mng Dir-Pub Affairs)
Anne Segrest McCulloch (Chief Legal Officer & Exec VP)
Mani Massoomi (Chief Risk Officer & Exec VP)
Kelly Gear (Sr VP)

FEDERAL HOME LOAN BANK OF TOPEKA
500 SW Wanamaker Rd, Topeka, KS 66606
Tel.: (785) 233-0507
Web Site:
   https://www.fhlbtopeka.com
Year Founded: 1932
Rev.: $1,381,275,000

Assets: $71,992,842,000
Liabilities: $68,316,298,000
Net Worth: $3,676,544,000
Earnings: $240,736,000
Emp.: 243
Fiscal Year-end: 12/31/22
Mortgage & Loan Banking Services
N.A.I.C.S.: 522310
Jeffrey B. Kuzbel *(Pres & CEO)*
Dan J. Hess *(Chief Bus Officer & Sr VP)*
G. Bridger Cox *(Chm)*
Thomas E. Millburn *(Sr VP)*
Amy Crouch *(Chief Acctg Officer, Interim Principal Fin Officer & VP)*
Amanda Kiefer *(Chief HR Officer)*
Matt Koupal *(Chief Compliance Officer)*
Robert E. Caldwell II *(Vice Chm)*
Martin L. Schlossman Jr. *(Chief Risk Officer & Sr VP)*

FEDERAL INTERNATIONAL INC.

7935 Clayton Rd, Clayton, MO 63117
Tel.: (314) 721-3377
Web Site:
https://www.federalinternational.com
Year Founded: 1914
Sales Range: $25-49.9 Million
Emp.: 15
Plastics Foam Products
N.A.I.C.S.: 326150
Melvyn Lefkowitz *(Pres)*
Michelle Keller *(Mgr-Customer Svc)*

Subsidiaries:

Federal Foam Technologies Inc.   **(1)**
600 Wisconsin Dr, New Richmond, WI 54017-2608
Tel.: (715) 246-9500
Web Site: http://www.federalfoam.com
Sales Range: $25-49.9 Million
Flexible Cellular & Plastic Materials Mfr
N.A.I.C.S.: 326150
Wyman Smith *(Pres)*
Todd Kidder *(Mgr-Natl Sls)*
Greg Windsperge *(Mgr-Sls)*
Dale Kautz *(Mgr-Ops)*
Jon Seeger *(Mgr-Environmental)*

Subsidiary (Domestic):

Federal Foam Technologies, Inc. -
Cokato Division   **(2)**
150 Industrial Blvd, Cokato, MN 55321
Tel.: (320) 286-2696
Web Site: http://www.federalfoam.com
Flexible Cellular & Plastic Materials Mfr
N.A.I.C.S.: 326150

FEDERAL LAND BANK ASSOCIATION YOSEMITE

800 W Monte Vista Ave, Turlock, CA 95382
Tel.: (209) 667-2366
Web Site:
http://www.yosmitefederal.com
Rev.: $50,222,000
Emp.: 100
Federal Land Banks
N.A.I.C.S.: 522299
Leonard Van Elderen *(CEO)*

FEDERAL LIFE INSURANCE COMPANY

3750 W Deerfield Rd, Riverwoods, IL 60015
Tel.: (847) 520-1900
Web Site: https://www.federallife.com
Year Founded: 1899
Life Insurance & Annuities
N.A.I.C.S.: 524113
Joseph D. Austin *(Chm)*
William S. Austin *(Pres & CEO)*
Michael Austin *(CMO & Exec VP)*
Anders Raaum *(CFO)*

FEDERAL MARINE TRANSMISSIONS, INC.

5310 E Ave, Countryside, IL 60525-3134
Tel.: (708) 352-2200
Web Site:
https://www.federalmarinetransmissions.com
Year Founded: 1994
Sales Range: $10-24.9 Million
Emp.: 4
Transportation Equipment & Supply Whslr
N.A.I.C.S.: 423860
James Aspel *(Pres)*

FEDERAL MARKET CO. INC.

3366 Genesee St, Buffalo, NY 14225
Tel.: (716) 633-1390   **NY**
Web Site:
https://www.federalmeats.com
Year Founded: 1975
Sales Range: $10-24.9 Million
Emp.: 200
Food Distr
N.A.I.C.S.: 445240
William P. Dowdall Jr. *(Pres)*

FEDERAL PRISON INDUSTRIES INC.

400 1st St NW, Washington, DC 20534
Tel.: (800) 827-3168   **DC**
Web Site: http://www.unicor.gov
Year Founded: 1934
Sales Range: $450-499.9 Million
Inmate Training & Staffing Services
N.A.I.C.S.: 561311
David D. Spears *(Chm)*

FEDERAL PROCESS CORPORATION

4520 Richmond Rd, Cleveland, OH 44128-5757
Tel.: (216) 464-6440   **OH**
Web Site:
http://www.federalprocess.com
Year Founded: 1915
Sales Range: $25-49.9 Million
Emp.: 50
Chemicals Mfr
N.A.I.C.S.: 325520
Jon H. Outcalt *(Pres)*
Richard Schmidt *(Sr VP-Sls & Mktg)*
Dave Johnson *(Reg Mgr)*
Natalie Guillaume *(Mgr-Retail Channel)*
Brian Sedlock *(VP-Fin & Admin Svcs)*
Tom Hoinski *(Reg Mgr-Sls)*

Subsidiaries:

Fedchem LLC   **(1)**
4520 Richmond Rd, Cleveland, OH 44128
Tel.: (216) 464-6440
Web Site: http://www.fedchemproducts.com
Aluminium Products Mfr
N.A.I.C.S.: 331315

J&B Products, Inc.   **(1)**
6851 Enterprise Dr, South Bend, IN 46628   **(100%)**
Tel.: (574) 288-0607
Web Site: http://www.jb-products.com
Sales Range: $10-24.9 Million
Emp.: 30
Mfr of Plastic Tubular Products Sold Primarily to the Conventional Housing Industry
N.A.I.C.S.: 326191
Rita Rupp *(CFO & Controller)*

The Noble Company   **(1)**
7300 Enterprise Dr, Spring Lake, MI 49456
Tel.: (231) 799-8000
Web Site: http://www.noblecompany.com
Sales Range: $1-9.9 Million
Emp.: 18
Mfr of Membranes & Shower Elements
N.A.I.C.S.: 339999
Lynnette Bloomberg *(COO)*

FEDERAL RESERVE BANK KANSAS CITY

1 Memorial Dr, Kansas City, MO 64198
Tel.: (816) 881-2000
Web Site: http://www.kc.frb.org
Sales Range: $1-4.9 Billion
Emp.: 960
Provider of Banking Services
N.A.I.C.S.: 521110
Barbara S. Pacheco *(Sr VP-Payments Sys Res & Strategies Div)*
Alan D. Barkema *(VP)*
Kelly J. Dubbert *(COO & First VP)*
Stephen E. McBride *(Sr VP-Admin Svcs Div)*
Karen A. Pennell *(Sr VP-IT & Fin Svcs Div)*
Diane M. Raley *(Sec & Sr VP)*
Josias A. Aleman *(Sr VP)*
Veronica M. Sellers *(Gen Counsel & Sr VP)*

FEDERAL RESERVE BANK OF ATLANTA

1000 Peachtree St NE, Atlanta, GA 30309
Tel.: (404) 498-8500
Web Site: http://www.frbatlanta.org
Year Founded: 1914
Sales Range: $5-14.9 Billion
Federal Reserve Banking Services
N.A.I.C.S.: 521110
Princeton Rose *(Asst VP-Large Bank Grp)*
John Kolb *(VP-Risk & Resiliency Grp)*
Cynthia C. Goodwin *(VP-Large Bank Grp)*
Richard A. Jones *(Gen Counsel & Sr VP-Legal)*
Leah Davenport *(Sr VP-District Ops & Admin Svcs)*
Christopher Alexander *(VP-Central Admin-Retail Payments Office)*
Carolyn C. Healy *(Asst VP-Community & Reg Bank Grp)*
Andre T. Anderson *(Sr VP)*
Juan Sanchez *(VP-Credit, Compliance, Intl & Supervisory Support)*
Allen Stanley *(Asst VP-Community & Reg Bank Grp)*
Suzanna J. Costello *(VP-Admin Support)*
Chapelle D. Davis *(Asst VP-Credit, Compliance, Intl & Supervisory Support)*
Mary Kepler *(Sr VP-Compliance & Enterprise Risk Mgmt)*
Marie Gooding *(COO & First VP)*
Maria Smith *(Asst VP-Risk & Resiliency Grp)*
Angela Dirr *(VP & Assoc Gen Counsel)*
Gregory Fuller *(Asst VP-Fin Statistics & Structure Analysis)*
Doris Quiros *(VP-Credit, Compliance, Intl & Supervisory Support)*
Jeff Thomas *(Asst VP-Auditing)*
Kim Blythe *(Asst VP-HR)*
Elaine Phifer *(Asst VP-Compliance & Enterprise Risk Mgmt)*
Richard M. Fraher *(VP-Legal)*
Dwight Blackwood *(VP-Legal)*
Stephen Levy *(Asst VP-Fin Mgmt & Plng)*
Torion Kent *(Asst VP-Tech Solutions Svcs)*
Ken Wilcox *(Asst VP-Bus Continuity Office)*
Amy S. Goodman *(VP-Cash Ops & Cash Function Office & Dir-Cash Function)*
Evette Jones *(Asst VP-Cash Ops-Atlanta Office)*
Christina Wilson *(VP-Cash Ops-Jacksonville Branch)*
Paul Graham *(VP-Cash Ops-Miami Branch)*
Adrienne C. Slack *(VP-Res-New Orleans)*
Jeff Devine *(VP-Facilities Mgmt, Law Enforcement & Product Dev)*
Blake Lyons *(VP-HR)*
David E. Altig *(Exec VP & Dir-Res)*
Michael Johnson *(Exec VP-Supervision & Regulation)*
Cheryl Venable *(Sr VP-Retail Payments Office & Product Mgr-RPO)*
Karen Clayton *(Officer-EEO, Deputy Diversity Officer & Asst VP)*
Todd Greene *(VP-Community & Economic Dev)*
Paige Harris *(Asst VP-Credit, Compliance, Intl & Supervisory Support)*
Brian Bowling *(Sr VP-Auditing & Auditor)*
Robin Ratliff *(Asst VP-Pub Affairs)*
Trey Wheeler *(Asst VP-Community & Reg Bank Grp)*
Mark Gibson *(Asst VP-Credit & Risk Mgmt Function-Atlanta Fed's Supervision & R)*
Mike Chriszt *(VP-Pub Affairs)*
Anita Brown *(VP-Fin Mgmt & Plng)*
Michael Bryan *(VP-Res)*
Paula Tkac *(VP-Res)*
Brian Egan *(Sr VP-Ops & Admin)*
Becky Gunn *(Sec & Asst VP-Corp Engagement)*
Tony Stallings *(Asst VP-Facilities Mgmt & Law Enforcement)*
Karen Gilmore *(VP-Res-Miami)*
Mike Williams *(Asst VP-Law Enforcement, Ops & Admin)*
Charlie Weems *(VP-Ops & Admin)*
Richard Squires *(Asst VP-Cash Ops-New Orleans)*
Karl Lamb *(Asst VP-Law Enforcement)*
Paige Dennard *(Asst VP-Res)*
Lesley McClure *(VP-Res-Birmingham)*
Christopher L. Oakley *(VP-Res-Jacksonville)*
Jennifer Gibilterra *(Asst VP-Admin Support)*
Lani Mauriello *(Asst VP-Admin Support)*
Steve Wise *(VP-Community & Reg Bank Grp)*
Molly Willison *(Asst VP-Credit, Compliance, Intl & Supervisory Support)*
Jeff Schiele *(Asst VP-Ops & Admin)*
Paul Roberts *(Asst VP-Large Bank Grp)*
Russell Eubanks *(VP-Tech Solutions Svcs)*
Gregory Johnston *(VP-Tech Solutions Svcs)*
Jon Burns *(Asst VP-Risk & Resiliency Grp)*
Patrick Dierberger *(Asst VP-Fin Mgmt & Plng)*
Dan Baum *(Asst VP-Product Dev)*
Patrick Dyer *(VP-Facilities Mgmt & Law Enforcement)*
Joan Redwing *(Asst VP)*
Tonya Bird-Sorrells *(Asst VP-HR)*
Lisa Lee-Fogarty *(Asst VP-Pub Affairs)*
V. Srinivas Nori *(Asst VP-Tech Solutions Svcs)*
Karen Leone de Nie *(Asst VP-Community & Economic Dev)*
Beverly Ferrell *(Asst VP-Res-Miami)*
Kathryn Hinton *(Asst VP-Community & Reg Bank Grp)*
John Pelick *(Asst VP-Large Bank Grp)*
Kelly Bernard *(VP-FRB Minneapolis)*

Federal Reserve Bank of Atlanta—(Continued)

Darlene Martin *(Asst VP-Ops & Admin)*
Nell Campbell-Drake *(VP-Product Dev)*
Denise Connor *(Sr VP-FRB Kansas City-Tech Svcs)*
Scott Dake *(Sr VP-FRB Minneapolis-Tech Svcs)*
Kevin Jansen *(VP-FRB Minneapolis-Tech Svcs)*
Renu Mehra *(VP-FRB-Kansas City-Tech Svcs)*
Brosie Strada *(VP-FRB Kansas City-Tech Svcs)*
Cindy Rasche *(VP-FRB-Chicago-Tech Svcs)*
Keith Melton *(Chief Strategy Officer & Sr VP-Retail Payments Office)*
Dana Keeley *(Asst VP-Retail Payments Office)*
Travis Fix *(Asst VP-Enterprise Risk Mgmt)*
Charles Prime *(Asst VP-Facilities Mgmt)*
Raphael W. Bostic *(Pres & CEO)*
Laurel Graefe *(VP)*
Jennifer Cowart *(Chief Diversity Officer, Sr VP & Dir-Office of Diversity, Equity & Inclusion)*
Elizabeth A. Smith *(Chm)*

Subsidiaries:

Central Reserve Bank Of Atlanta **(1)**
1000 Peachtree St NE, Atlanta, GA 30309-3904
Tel.: (404) 498-8500
Rev.: $10,000
Emp.: 1,100
Real Estate Agents & Managers
N.A.I.C.S.: 521110
Dennis Lockhart *(Pres)*

FEDERAL RESERVE BANK OF BOSTON

600 Atlantic Ave Ste 100, Boston, MA 02210
Tel.: (617) 973-3000
Web Site: http://www.bos.frb.org
Year Founded: 1914
Sales Range: $1-4.9 Billion
Emp.: 1,200
Federal Reserve Bank
N.A.I.C.S.: 522180
Robert K. Triest *(VP)*
Jacqueline Palladino *(Chief Admin Officer & Exec VP)*
Gary L. Gottlieb *(Chm)*
Christopher J. Haley *(Sr VP)*
Anna Afshar Steiger *(Officer-Admin Dept & Community Outreach & VP)*
Ashley O'Connor *(VP)*
Mike Rodehorst *(Chief Info Security Officer & VP)*
Steffanie A. Brady *(VP)*
Patricia Geagan *(VP)*
Jeanne MacNevin *(Sec & VP)*
Carol McDermott *(VP)*
Scott Strah *(Asst VP)*
Joel Werkema *(VP)*
Lucy Warsh *(Asst VP)*
Maureen B. Savage *(VP)*
Michael D. Watson *(VP)*
Lynn Carroll *(Asst VP)*
Manoj Pothvath *(Asst VP)*
Tamar Kotelchuck *(Asst VP-Regional & Community Outreach Dept)*
Phillip L. Clay *(Deputy Chm)*
Kenneth C. Montgomery *(COO & First VP)*
Astier Sium *(Officer-Acctg & VP)*
Alan W. Bloom *(Sr VP)*
Carl S. Madsen *(VP)*
Christopher H. Ritchie *(VP)*
Elizabeth Ching *(VP)*
Jeannine Delano *(VP)*

John T. Foley *(VP)*
John J. Kroen *(VP)*
Judith S. Quenzel *(VP)*
Leah A. Maurer *(VP)*
Marianne D. Crowe *(VP)*
Paul W. Brassil *(VP)*
Theresa J. Barry *(VP)*
Brianna DeGennaro *(Asst VP-Fin Support Office)*
Heidi Furse *(Asst VP-Corp Comm Dept)*
Randy Balducci *(Sr VP)*
Adrian Hodor *(Asst VP-FedNow Svc)*
Bernadette Ksepka *(VP-FedNow Program & Deputy Head-Product Mgmt-FedNow Program)*
Miriam Sheril *(Asst VP-Core Product Mgmt-FedNow)*
Nick Stanescu *(Sr VP-FedNow)*
Dana E. Warren Jr. *(VP)*

FEDERAL RESERVE BANK OF CHICAGO

230 S La Salle St, Chicago, IL 60604
Tel.: (312) 322-5322
Web Site: http://www.chicagofed.org
Sales Range: $5-14.9 Billion
Emp.: 1,289
Banking Services
N.A.I.C.S.: 521110
Ellen Bromagen *(COO & First VP)*
Steve Durfey *(Sr VP-Supervision & Regulation)*
Spencer Krane *(Sr VP)*
Sean Rodriguez *(Sr VP)*
Jorge Ramirez *(Pres)*
Anna Paulson *(Sr VP, Dir--Economic Res Dept & Assoc Dir)*
Katherine Hilton Schrepfer *(Gen Counsel, Sec & Sr VP)*
Jeremiah P. Boyle *(Mng Dir-Community & Economic Dev)*
Pamela Rieger *(Sr VP-Supervision & Regulation)*
Julie Williams *(Sr VP-Supervision & Regulation Dept)*
Jonas D. M. Fisher *(VP & Dir-Macroeconomic Res)*
Daniel Aaronson *(VP & Dir-Microeconomic Res)*
Hesna Genay *(VP & Dir-Policy & Comm)*
Robert Cox *(VP-Fin Markets)*
Douglas Tillett *(VP-Pub Affairs)*
Mark H. Kawa *(VP-Supervision & Regulation)*
Rebecca Chmielewski *(VP-Supervision & Regulation)*
Kathryn Medina *(Chief HR Officer & Sr VP-People & Culture)*

FEDERAL RESERVE BANK OF CLEVELAND

1455 E 6th St, Cleveland, OH 44114
Tel.: (216) 579-2000
Web Site:
  http://www.clevelandfed.org
Sales Range: $1-4.9 Billion
Federal Reserve Bank
N.A.I.C.S.: 522110
Gregory L. Stefani *(COO & First VP)*
Guhan Venkatu *(VP-Pittsburgh)*
Loretta J. Mester *(Pres & CEO)*
Valarie L. Sheppard *(Chm-Cincinnati)*
Doris Carson Williams *(Chm-Pittsburgh)*
William D. Fosnight *(Gen Counsel & Sr VP)*
Ellis Tallman *(Exec VP & Dir-Res)*
Thomas J. Fitzpatrick IV *(Asst VP)*

FEDERAL RESERVE BANK OF DALLAS

2200 N Pearl St, Dallas, TX 75201-2216

Tel.: (214) 922-6000
Web Site: http://www.dallasfed.org
Year Founded: 1913
Sales Range: $1-4.9 Billion
Emp.: 1,000
Federal Reserve Bank
N.A.I.C.S.: 521110
Claude E. Davis *(Asst VP)*
Robert G. Feil *(Assoc Sec & VP)*
Donald N. Bowers *(VP-Houston)*
Javier R. Jimenez *(Asst VP)*
Kathy K. Johnsrud *(VP)*
Harvey R. Mitchell *(Sr VP)*
Sharon A. Sweeney *(Gen Counsel, Corp Sec & Sr VP)*
Thomas F. Siems *(Asst VP)*
Paul T. Elzner *(VP)*
Matthew K. Rose *(Vice Chm)*
Robert S. Kaplan *(Pres & CEO)*
Alfreda B. Norman *(Sr VP)*
Dana S. Merritt *(VP & Dir-OMWI)*
Shareef Shaik *(Asst VP)*
Tommy E. Alsbrooks *(VP)*
Vincent G. Pacheco *(Asst VP)*
Jill Cetina *(VP-Banking Supervision)*
Mike Eliason *(Asst VP-Engrg, Plng & Bus Ops)*
Missy Luton *(Asst VP & Assoc Gen Counsel)*
Robert L. Triplett III *(Sr VP)*
Bobby E. Coberly Jr. *(VP)*

Subsidiaries:

Federal Reserve **(1)**
301 E Main Dr, El Paso, TX 79901-1326
Tel.: (915) 544-4730
Web Site: http://www.dallasfed.org
Sales Range: $50-74.9 Million
Emp.: 80
Bank
N.A.I.C.S.: 522110
Javier R. Jimenez *(Asst VP)*

Federal Reserve Bank of Dallas, Houston Branch **(1)**
1801 Allen Pkwy, Houston, TX 77019-2504 **(100%)**
Tel.: (713) 483-3000
Web Site: http://www.dallasfed.org
Sales Range: $100-124.9 Million
Emp.: 200
Banking
N.A.I.C.S.: 522110
Daron D. Peschel *(Sr VP-In Charge)*
Hazel W. Adams *(Asst VP)*
Stephan D. Booker *(Asst VP)*
Mario Hernandez *(Asst VP)*
Helen E. Holcomb *(COO & First VP)*
Javier R. Jimenez *(Asst VP)*
Rita Riley *(Asst VP)*
Shareef Shaik *(Asst VP)*
Michelle D. Trevino *(Asst VP)*
Paul Wheeler *(Asst VP)*
Donald N. Bowers II *(VP)*
William W. Shaffer Jr. *(Asst VP)*

Federal Reserve Bank-San Antonio **(1)**
402 Dwyer Ave, San Antonio, TX 78204-1221
Tel.: (210) 978-1200
Web Site: http://www.dallsfed.org
Rev.: $79,000,000
Emp.: 85
Full Service Federal Reserve Bank
N.A.I.C.S.: 531110
Blake Hastings *(Sr VP)*
Keith R. Phillips *(Asst VP)*
James Conrad Weaver *(Chm-Pro Tem, San Antonio Branch)*

FEDERAL RESERVE BANK OF MINNEAPOLIS

90 Hennepin Ave, Minneapolis, MN 55401-1804
Tel.: (612) 204-5000
Web Site:
  http://www.minneapolisfed.org
Year Founded: 1914
Sales Range: $900-999.9 Million
Federal Savings Institutions
N.A.I.C.S.: 522180

Ron J. Feldman *(Exec VP)*
Duane A. Carter *(Sr VP & Dir-OMWI)*
Linda M. Gilligan *(Sr VP)*
Michael Garrett *(VP)*
Paul D. Rimmereid *(CFO & First VP)*
John E. Yanish *(VP & Deputy Gen Counsel)*
Richard M. Todd *(VP)*
Jacqueline G. King *(VP)*
Sheryl L. Britsch *(VP)*
Michelle Brunn *(VP)*
Mark A. Rauzi *(VP)*
Diann Townsend *(VP)*
Terry Fitzgerald *(VP)*
Peter Baatrup *(VP & Asst Gen Counsel)*
Karin Bearss *(VP)*
Kenneth R. Beauchemin *(Asst VP)*
Bradley Beytien *(Asst VP)*
Jacquelyn K. Brunmeier *(Asst VP)*
Mesude Cingilli *(Asst VP)*
Gregory Cutshall *(Asst VP)*
Timothy L. Devaney *(VP)*
Joseph Fahnhorst *(VP)*
Scott Thomas-Forss *(Asst VP)*
Michael Grover *(Asst VP)*
Ken Heinecke *(VP)*
Elizabeth W. Kittelson *(Asst VP)*
Debra L. Knilans *(VP)*
Amy Kytonen *(Asst VP)*
Todd A. Maki *(Asst VP)*
Frederick L. Miller *(Asst VP)*
Barbara J. Pfeffer *(VP)*
Sharon Sylvester *(VP)*
Thomas Tallarini *(Asst VP)*
Darian Vietzke *(Asst VP)*
Mark Vukelich *(Asst VP)*
Chris Wangen *(Asst VP)*
MayKao Y. Hang *(Chm)*
Kendall J. Powell *(Deputy Chm)*
Samuel Schulhofer-Wohl *(Sr VP & Dir-Res)*
Matthew Diette *(Asst VP)*
Susan Woodrow *(Helena Branch Officer & Asst VP)*
Neel Kashkari *(Pres & CEO)*
Karl Riem *(Sr VP)*
Niel Williardson *(Gen Counsel, Sec & Sr VP)*
Christine Gaffney *(VP)*
Richard Wargin *(VP & Dir-Pub Affairs)*
James West *(VP)*
Alan Weintraub *(VP)*
Ramon Flores *(Asst VP)*
Pamela Hasenberg *(Asst VP)*
Christopher Johnson *(Asst VP)*
Patrice Kunesh *(Asst VP)*
Chad Lauber *(Asst VP)*
Helene Mann *(Asst VP)*
Danita Ng *(Asst VP)*
Jean Hinz *(Asst VP)*
Daniel Maynard *(Asst VP)*
Brendan Murrin *(Asst VP)*
Jeff Peal *(Officer-Info Security & Asst VP)*
Sridevi Srivatsan *(Asst VP)*
Aaron Zabler *(Asst VP)*
LuAnne Pederson *(Asst VP)*

FEDERAL RESERVE BANK OF NEW YORK

33 Liberty St, New York, NY 10045-1003
Tel.: (212) 720-6130
Web Site: http://www.newyorkfed.org
Sales Range: $5-14.9 Billion
Emp.: 3,400
Federal Reserve Bank
N.A.I.C.S.: 522180
Linda S. Goldberg *(Sr VP-Integrated Policy Analysis Grp)*
Sara Horowitz *(Chm)*
Joshua Rosenberg *(Chief Risk Officer, Exec VP & Head-Risk Grp)*

Antoine Martin (Sr VP-Res & Statistics Grp)
Sarah Bell (VP)
Adrian Franco (Dir-Economic Education Program)
John C. Williams (Pres & CEO)
Laurie S. Goodman (Portfolio Mgr-Mortgage & Sr Analyst-Fixed Income)

FEDERAL RESERVE BANK OF PHILADELPHIA

10 Independence Mall, Philadelphia, PA 19106-1574
Tel.: (215) 574-6000
Web Site: http://www.phil.frb.org
Year Founded: 1913
Sales Range: $1-4.9 Billion
Emp.: 900
Federal Reserve Bank
N.A.I.C.S.: 522110
Charles Kirkland (VP-Fin Statistics)
Robin P. Myers (Asst VP-Supervision, Regulation & Credit)
Gail Todd (Officer-Credit & Asst VP-Supervision, Regulation & Credit)
Vish P. Viswanathan (Officer-Discount & VP-Supervision, Regulation & Credit)
James K. Welch (VP-Law Enforcement & Facilities Mgmt)
Gregory Fanelli (VP-IT Svcs)
Brian Calderwood (Asst VP-Groupware Leadership Center)
Patrick F. Turner (VP-Groupware Leadership Center)
Mary Ann Hood (Officer-EEO, Sr VP & Dir-HR)
John D. Ackley (VP-Cash Svcs)
Keith Sill (VP & Dir-Real Time Data Res Center)
Jeanne R. Rentezelas (Gen Counsel & Sr VP-Legal)
D. Blake Prichard (COO & First VP)
Arun K. Jain (Sr VP-Treasury & Fin Svcs)
Terry E. Harris (CIO & Sr VP-IT Svcs)
Donna L. Franco (CFO & Sr VP)
Herbert E. Taylor (Asst VP-HR)
Patrick T. Harker (Pres & CEO)
Donna L. Brenner (VP-Enterprise Risk Mgmt)
Jennifer E. Cardy (VP-Fin Mgmt Svcs)
Paul Calem (Asst VP-Supervision, Regulation & Credit)
Heather Derbyshire (Officer-Fin Statistics)
Julia Cheney (Asst VP-Payment Cards Center)
Christopher Ivanoski (Asst VP-Facilities-Plant Ops)
Keith Morales (VP-Info Tech Svcs & Officer-Info Security)
Stanley Sienkiewicz (VP-Res Support)
Jeffrey Willis (Coord-Fin & Regulatory Reporting)
William T. Wisser (Asst VP-Supervision, Regulation & Credit)
Joanne M. Branigan (Asst VP-Supervision, Regulation & Credit)
Christopher Henderson (Asst VP-Supervision, Regulation & Credit)
Larry Kenneth Cordell (VP-Supervision, Regulation & Credit)
Wanda Preston (Asst VP-Supervision, Regulation & Credit)
Michael Dotsey (Sr VP & Dir-Res)
Brian M. McNeill (Deputy Chm)
Roc Armenter (VP)
Michelle M. Scipione (VP & Auditor)
Michael Costello (Asst VP-Supervision, Regulation & Credit)
Mitchell Berlin (VP)
James D. Narron (COO & First VP)
Michelle Reardon (VP-Pub Affairs)

Deborah L. Hayes (Sr VP-Corp Affairs)
William G. Spaniel (Officer-Lending & Sr VP-Supervision, Regulation & Credit)
Michael T. Doyle (VP-Treasury Payments)
Stephen G. Hart (VP-HR)
Robert Hunt (VP & Dir-Payment Cards Center)
Robert F. Mucerino (VP-Collateral Mgmt & Admin Svcs)
Leonard Nakamura (VP)
Patrick M. Regan (VP-Info Tech Svcs)
Theresa Y. Singleton (Officer-Community Affairs & VP-Supervision, Regulation & Credit)
Patricia A. Wilson (Sec & VP)
Kori Ann Connelly (Asst VP)
Maryann T. Connelly (Asst VP)
Suzanne W. Furr (Asst VP)
John P. Kelly (Asst VP-Enterprise Risk Mgmt)
Andrew Kish (Asst VP-Supervision, Regulation & Credit)
Chellappan Ramasamy (Asst VP-Supervision, Regulation & Credit)
Gregory A. Ramick (Asst VP-Cash Svcs)
Stephen J. Smith (Asst VP)
H. Robert Tillman (Asst VP-Supervision, Regulation & Credit)
Jill Hettinger (Officer-Enterprise Risk Mgmt)
James Lofton (Officer-Cash Svcs)
Linda Van Valkenburg (Officer-IT Svcs)
Anthony T. Scafide Jr. (Asst VP-Fin Institutions Rels)
A. Reed Raymond III (Chief Admin Officer & VP-Supervision, Regulation & Credit)
John J. Munera III (Asst VP-Supervision, Regulation & Credit)

FEDERAL RESERVE BANK OF RICHMOND

701 E Byrd St, Richmond, VA 23219
Tel.: (804) 697-8000
Web Site: http://www.rich.frb.org
Sales Range: $5-14.9 Billion
Emp.: 1,700
Federal Reserve Banking Services
N.A.I.C.S.: 813910
Michelle H. Gluck (Chief Risk Officer, Gen Counsel & Exec VP)
Janice E. Clatterbuck (CIO & Sr VP)
Jennifer J. Burns (Exec VP)
David E. Beck (Sr VP)
Matthew A. Martin (Sr VP)
Becky C. Bareford (Sr VP)
Thomas Barkin (Pres & CEO)
Kartik B. Athreya (Exec VP & Dir-Res)

FEDERAL RESERVE BANK OF ST. LOUIS

One Federal Reserve Bank Pl, Saint Louis, MO 63102
Tel.: (314) 444-8444
Web Site: http://www.stls.frb.org
Year Founded: 1914
Rev.: $1,161,000,000
Emp.: 814
National Commercial Banks
N.A.I.C.S.: 521110
Alberto G. Musalem (Pres & CEO)
Suzanne Sitherwood (Deputy Chm)
Karl W. Ashman (Exec VP)
David Sapenaro (COO, First VP & Dir-Payments Strategy)
Timothy A. Bosch (Grp VP)
Marilyn K. Corona (VP)
James Bullard (Pres & CEO)
Suzanne Sitherwood (Deputy Chm)

Christopher J. Waller (Exec VP & Dir-Res)
Karen L. Branding (Sr VP)
Matthew W. Torbett (Sr VP)
Adam L. Brown (VP)
Carl D. White (VP)
Carlos Garriga (VP)
Debra E. Johnson (VP)
Donny J. Trankler (VP)
James L. Warren (VP)
Kent T. Eckert (VP)
Roy A. Hendin (VP)
Scott M. Trilling (VP)
Stephen D. Williamson (VP)
Timothy C. Brown (VP)
Timothy R. Heckler (VP)

FEDERAL STAFFING RESOURCES, LLC

2200 Somerville Rd Ste 300, Annapolis, MD 21401
Tel.: (410) 990-0795
Web Site: http://www.fsrpeople.com
Year Founded: 2002
Sales Range: $25-49.9 Million
Emp.: 273
Professional & Healthcare Staffing Services
N.A.I.C.S.: 561311
Candice Keane (Mgr-Program)
Tracy Balazs (Pres & CEO)

FEDERAL WAREHOUSE COMPANY

200 National St, East Peoria, IL 61611
Tel.: (309) 271-1243
Web Site:
https://www.federalcos.com
Sales Range: $25-49.9 Million
Emp.: 300
General Warehousing Services
N.A.I.C.S.: 493110
William Cirone (Pres)

FEDERALCONFERENCE.COM

3912 Lansing Court, Dumfries, VA 22026
Tel.: (571) 494-5733
Web Site:
http://www.federalconference.com
Year Founded: 2006
Sales Range: $10-24.9 Million
Emp.: 20
Event Planning & Conference Services to the Federal Government
N.A.I.C.S.: 711310
Paul Trapp (Co-Founder & CEO)

Subsidiaries:

DavisTrapp LLC   (1)
3912 Lansing Ct, Dumfries, VA
22026   (100%)
Tel.: (571) 494-5733
Web Site: http://www.davistrapp.com
Full Service Event Planning Supporting Federal & State Clients
N.A.I.C.S.: 921190
Corey Holeman (CFO & Co-Owner)
Stephen Davis (Co-Founder, Owner, Pres & COO)
Paul Trapp (CEO & Co-Founding Owner)
Jessica Davis (Dir-Fin)
Denise Radcliff (Sr Acct Exec)
Kelly McWhinney (Dir-Event Ops)
Femi Shodeinde (Dir-IT)
Tina Mincks (Mgr-Registration)

FEDERATED HEALTHCARE SUPPLY HOLDINGS, INC.

1016 S Broadway, Lexington, KY 40504
Tel.: (484) 845-3200   DE
Web Site: http://www.fedhs.com
Year Founded: 2018
Holding Company
N.A.I.C.S.: 551112

Gregg Rivkind (CEO)

Subsidiaries:

Ecologically Sound Medical
Services   (1)
1865 N MacArthur Dr, Tracy, CA 95376-2820
Tel.: (209) 835-6868
Web Site: http://www.e-ecosound.com
Healthcare Product & Medical Supply Distr
N.A.I.C.S.: 423450
Don Huhn (Co-Founder)
Mark Hineser (Co-Founder)
Patrick Meadows (COO)

Federated Healthcare Supply,
Inc.   (1)
25 Creek Circle, Boothwyne, PA 19061
Tel.: (484) 845-3200
Computer Software Development Services; Business-to-business Sales Solution Services
N.A.I.C.S.: 425120

T-Plex Industries, Inc.   (1)
255 Wolfner Dr, Fenton, MO 63026
Tel.: (636) 349-5858
Medical, Dental & Hospital Equipment & Supplies Merchant Whslr & Distr
N.A.I.C.S.: 423450
Paul Telker (Pres)

FEDERATED IT, INC.

1200 G St NW Ste Ste 800, Washington, DC 20005
Tel.: (202) 434-8959
Web Site: http://www.federatedit.com
Year Founded: 2002
Rev.: $9,700,000
Emp.: 35
Computer System Design Services
N.A.I.C.S.: 541512
Matthew Bucholz (Pres)
Kyle von Bucholz (CEO)
Bethany Rose (Dir-HR)
Carlos Rivera (Exec VP-Bus Dev)

FEDERATED LINEN & UNIFORM SERVICES

11620 Wilshire Blvd, Los Angeles, CA 90025
Tel.: (310) 473-4833
Sales Range: $25-49.9 Million
Emp.: 900
Linen Supply Services
N.A.I.C.S.: 812331
Jill T. Werner (Pres & CEO)
Bruce Moskowitz (Treas)

Subsidiaries:

Martin Linen Supply Company   (1)
11620 Wilshire Blvd, Los Angeles, CA 90025
Tel.: (310) 473-4833
Rev.: $20,000,000
Emp.: 10
Linen Supply Services
N.A.I.C.S.: 812331

FEDERATED MEDIA INC.

245 Edison Rd Ste 250, Mishawaka, IN 46545
Tel.: (574) 295-2500   DE
Web Site:
http://www.federatedmedia.com
Holding Company; Radio Broadcasting Stations Operator, Newspaper Publisher & Outdoor Advertising Services
N.A.I.C.S.: 551112
Jim Allgeier (Mgr-Market)

Subsidiaries:

Federated Interactive LLC   (1)
245 W Edison Rd Ste 250, Mishawaka, IN 46545
Tel.: (574) 295-2500
Web Site: http://www.federatedmedia.com

Federated Media Inc.—(Continued)

Interactive Media Development & Support Services
N.A.I.C.S.: 541990
James Derby *(Dir-Interactive Media)*

OnDisplay Advertising LLC   (1)
1800 Blankenship Rd Ste 200, West Linn, OR 97068
Tel.: (503) 650-7132
Web Site: http://www.ondisplayads.com
Outdoor Advertising Services
N.A.I.C.S.: 541850

Pathfinder Communications Corporation   (1)
245 W Edison Rd Ste 250, Mishawaka, IN 46545
Tel.: (574) 295-2500
Web Site: http://www.federatedmedia.com
Sales Range: $50-74.9 Million
Emp.: 200
Holding Company; Radio Broadcasting Stations Operator
N.A.I.C.S.: 551112
John F. Dille III *(Pres & CEO)*

Subsidiary (Domestic):

Jam Communications, Inc.   (2)
2915 Maples Rd, Fort Wayne, IN 46816
Tel.: (260) 447-5511
Web Site: http://www.989thebear.com
Radio Broadcasting Stations
N.A.I.C.S.: 516110
Jim Allgeier *(Mgr-Market)*
Matt Talluto *(Dir-Program)*
Paige Franse *(Dir-Promotions)*

Talking Stick Communications, LLC   (2)
245 W Edison Rd Ste 250, Mishawaka, IN 46545
Tel.: (574) 258-5483
Online Radio Broadcasting Stations
N.A.I.C.S.: 516110

Truth Publishing Company Inc.   (1)
421 S 2nd St, Elkhart, IN 46516
Tel.: (574) 294-1661
Web Site: http://www.elkharttruth.com
Rev.: $11,000,000
Emp.: 185
Newspaper Publishers
N.A.I.C.S.: 513110
John F. Dille III *(Pres & CEO)*

FEDERATED MUTUAL INSURANCE COMPANY
121 E Park Sq, Owatonna, MN 55060-3046
Tel.: (507) 455-5200   MN
Web Site: http://www.federatedinsurance.com
Year Founded: 1904
Fire, Casualty, Accident & Health Insurance Provider
N.A.I.C.S.: 524126
Jeffrey E. Fetters *(Chm & CEO)*
Michael G. Kerr *(Pres & COO)*
Michael N. Keller *(CFO, Sec, Treas & Exec VP)*
Jonathan R. Hanson *(Gen Counsel & Sr VP)*
Mark D. Heyne *(Exec VP & Dir-Insurance Ops)*
Elizabeth A. Hyland *(Sr VP & Dir-HR)*
Nicholas R. Lower *(Sr VP & Dir-Insurance Ops)*
Sean G. Pick *(Exec VP & Dir-Insurance Ops)*
Ryker J. Richardson *(CIO & Sr VP)*
James A. Thou *(Exec VP & Dir-Insurance Ops)*

Subsidiaries:

Granite RE, Inc.   (1)
14001 Quailbrook Dr, Oklahoma City, OK 73134-1757
Tel.: (405) 752-2600
Web Site: http://www.granitere.com
Reinsurance Carriers
N.A.I.C.S.: 524130

FEDERATION OF AMERICAN SOCIETIES FOR EXPERIMENTAL BIOLOGY
9650 Rockville Pike, Bethesda, MD 20814
Tel.: (301) 634-7000   DC
Web Site: http://www.faseb.org
Year Founded: 1912
Sales Range: $10-24.9 Million
Emp.: 363
Biological Research Services
N.A.I.C.S.: 541715

FEDERATION OF ORGANIZATIONS
1 Farmingdale Rd, West Babylon, NY 11704
Tel.: (631) 669-5355   NY
Web Site: https://www.fedoforg.org
Year Founded: 1972
Sales Range: $25-49.9 Million
Emp.: 673
Community Care Services
N.A.I.C.S.: 624190
Barbara Faron *(CEO)*
Philip Matcovsky *(COO)*
Anthony J. Angelo *(Chief Medical Officer)*
Stephen McCarthy *(CFO)*

FEDERATION OF RESPONSIBLE CITIZENS, INC.
210 N Patrick St Ste 100, Alexandria, VA 22314
Tel.: (703) 259-6470   DE
Web Site: http://www.frcitizens.org
Year Founded: 1989
Sales Range: $10-24.9 Million
Emp.: 6
Political Consulting Services
N.A.I.C.S.: 541820
Sharon Hockenbury *(Sec)*
Denise Singleton *(Pres)*

FEDERATION OF STATE BOARDS OF PHYSICAL THERAPY
124 W St S 3rd Fl, Alexandria, VA 22314
Tel.: (703) 299-3100   AL
Web Site: https://www.fsbpt.org
Year Founded: 1987
Sales Range: $10-24.9 Million
Emp.: 63
Physical Therapy Services
N.A.I.C.S.: 621999
Susan C. Layton *(COO)*
Nancy R. Kirsch *(Pres & Pres)*

FEDSTORE CORPORATION
1 Preserve Pkwy Ste 620, Rockville, MD 20852
Tel.: (240) 715-4320
Web Site: https://www.FedStore.com
Year Founded: 2001
Sales Range: $25-49.9 Million
Emp.: 15
Government Services & Technology Solutions
N.A.I.C.S.: 921190

FEDTECH SERVICES, INC.
5300 W Cypress St Ste150, Tampa, FL 33607
Web Site: http://www.fedtechservices.com
Year Founded: 2008
Sales Range: $10-24.9 Million
Emp.: 20
It Consulting
N.A.I.C.S.: 541690
Jocelyn Noble *(Pres)*

FEDVAR CORP.

1025 Connecticut Ave NW Ste 1000, Washington, DC 20036
Tel.: (202) 857-9770
Web Site: http://www.fedvar.com
Rev.: $1,000,000
Emp.: 10
Computer System Design Services
N.A.I.C.S.: 541512
Anthony Brown *(Pres)*

FEDWAY ASSOCIATES INC.
505 Martinsville Rd, Basking Ridge, NJ 07920
Tel.: (973) 624-6444   NJ
Web Site: https://www.fedway.com
Year Founded: 1978
Sales Range: $650-699.9 Million
Emp.: 750
Exclusive Wines & Distilled Beverage Distr
N.A.I.C.S.: 424820
Kevin Krapels *(VP & Gen Mgr)*
Sean Weinerman *(VP & Sr Dir-Wine)*
Chris Kelly *(CFO)*
Peter McDonagh *(Sr VP & Dir-Mktg-Spirits)*
Rob Felton *(Mgr-Sls)*
Danielle Barber *(Coord-Mktg Svcs)*
Bill Swenarton *(Dir-Sls)*

Subsidiaries:

Federal Wine & Liquor Company Inc.   (1)
56 Hackensack Ave, Kearny, NJ 07032
Tel.: (973) 624-6444
Web Site: http://www.fedway.com
Rev.: $71,600,000
Emp.: 100
Wine And Distilled Beverages
N.A.I.C.S.: 424820

Gateway Distributors Inc.   (1)
195 Campus Dr, Kearny, NJ 07032
Tel.: (973) 624-6444
Web Site: http://www.fedway.com
Sales Range: $10-24.9 Million
Emp.: 80
Distr of Wine & Distilled Beverages
N.A.I.C.S.: 424820
Neil Barnett *(Pres)*

Jersey National Captial   (1)
56 Hackensack Ave, Kearny, NJ 07032
Tel.: (973) 624-6444
Web Site: http://www.wine-and-liquor-depot.com
Sales Range: $10-24.9 Million
Emp.: 80
Distr of Wine & Distilled Beverages
N.A.I.C.S.: 424820

FEECE OIL COMPANY
1700 Hubbard Dr, Batavia, IL 60510
Tel.: (630) 879-1911
Web Site: http://www.feeceoil.com
Rev.: $25,000,000
Emp.: 25
Gasoline Whslr & Retailer
N.A.I.C.S.: 424720
Jill Feece *(Pres)*
Mike Feece *(VP)*

FEECO INTERNATIONAL INC.
3913 Algoma Rd, Green Bay, WI 54311-9707
Tel.: (920) 469-5100
Web Site: https://www.feeco.com
Sales Range: $10-24.9 Million
Emp.: 100
Fabricated Plate Work (Boiler Shop)
N.A.I.C.S.: 333131
Daniel P. Madigan *(Pres)*
Shane Le Capitaine *(Sys Engr-Process Sls)*
Craig Peppin *(Mgr-Customer Service-Lab)*

FEECORP CORPORATION
7995 Allen Rd, Canal Winchester, OH 43110

Tel.: (614) 837-3010
Web Site: http://feecorpinc.com
Sales Range: $10-24.9 Million
Emp.: 135
Specialty Trade Contractors
N.A.I.C.S.: 238910
Karen S. Fee *(CEO)*

FEED AMERICA FIRST
1105 Blue Springs Rd, Franklin, TN 37069
Tel.: (615) 512-5915   TN
Web Site: http://www.feedamericafirst.com
Year Founded: 2000
Sales Range: $10-24.9 Million
Emp.: 8
Hunger Relief Services
N.A.I.C.S.: 624210
Mike Womack *(Mgr-Ops)*

FEED INGREDIENT TRADING CORP.
316 Delaware Ave Ste 12, Delmar, NY 12054-1932
Tel.: (518) 478-7850
Web Site: https://www.feedcorp.com
Sales Range: $25-49.9 Million
Emp.: 12
Wholesale & Retail Grains
N.A.I.C.S.: 424510
Richard Casler *(CEO)*
Michael O'Meara *(Mgr-Logistics)*

FEED PRODUCTS SOUTH INC.
11406 Gravois Rd, Saint Louis, MO 63126-3610
Tel.: (314) 843-7300
Web Site: http://www.feedproducts.net
Sales Range: $10-24.9 Million
Emp.: 300
Producer of Animal Feeds
N.A.I.C.S.: 424910
Greg E. Fallin *(Pres & CEO)*

FEED THE CHILDREN, INC.
333 N Meridian Ave, Oklahoma City, OK 73107
Tel.: (405) 942-0228
Web Site: https://www.feedthechildren.org
Year Founded: 1979
Sales Range: $10-24.9 Million
Emp.: 650
Emergency Relief Organization
N.A.I.C.S.: 624230
Travis Arnold *(Pres & CEO)*
C. E. Crouse *(Treas)*
Becky Graninger *(CMO & Chief Dev Officer)*
Bob Thomas *(Chief Admin Officer)*
Christy Tharp *(CFO)*
Diane Moss *(Sr VP-HR)*
Kathy Doyle Thomas *(Sec)*
Mike Panas *(CIO)*
Rick England *(Chm)*
Scott Killough *(Sr VP-Intl Ops)*

Subsidiaries:

World Neighbors, Inc.   (1)
4127 NW 122nd St, Oklahoma City, OK 73120
Tel.: (405) 752-9700
Web Site: http://www.wn.org
Sales Range: $10-24.9 Million
Emp.: 147
International Development Services
N.A.I.C.S.: 925120
Kate Schecter *(Pres & CEO)*

FEEDING SOUTH FLORIDA
2501 SW 32 Ter, Pembroke Park, FL 33023
Tel.: (954) 518-1818   FL
Web Site: https://www.feedingsouthflorida.org

Year Founded: 1981
Rev.: $28,720,202
Emp.: 50
Not-for-Profit Food Bank
N.A.I.C.S.: 624210
Jeffrey Jones *(VP-Ops)*
Eddie Rivera *(Sec)*
Benny Gonzalez *(Treas)*
Delmer Swab *(Asst Mgr-Distr)*
Jennifer Millon *(Coord-Comm)*
Arelis Ferro *(Coord-Special Events)*
Rochelle Nolan *(Dir-Dev)*
Charles Bandy *(Mgr-Food Indus)*
Cagney Kobrin *(Mgr-Food Indus)*
Camille Jorge *(Mgr-HR)*
Peter Dunne *(Mgr-Inventory)*
Sari Vatske *(VP-Community Rels)*
Wells Fargo *(Co-Treas)*

FEEDSTUFFS PROCESSING CO. INC.
337 E 4th St, Ripon, CA 95366-0478
Tel.: (209) 599-1048   CA
Year Founded: 1942
Sales Range: $1-9.9 Million
Emp.: 12
Prepared Feeds
N.A.I.C.S.: 311119

FEELGOODZ, LLC
5435 Raynor Rd, Garner, NC 27529
Tel.: (888) 670-7950   NC
Web Site: http://feelgoodz.com
Year Founded: 2007
Casual Footwear Brands
N.A.I.C.S.: 316210
Kyle Berner *(Founder)*

FEENEY BROTHERS EXCAVATION LLC
103 Clayton St, Dorchester, MA 02122
Tel.: (617) 287-1004
Web Site:
   http://www.feeneybrothers.com
Year Founded: 1988
Emp.: 700
Site Preparation Contractor
N.A.I.C.S.: 238910
Bill Egan *(Dir-Support Svcs-Trng, Safety & Compliance)*
Paul Guerin *(Dir-Comml)*
Ed Healy *(Dir-Ops)*
Brendan Feeney *(Co-Founder & Pres)*
Greg Feeney *(Co-Founer & VP)*
Phil O'Flaherty *(CFO)*
Sean Devlin *(Sec & Gen Counsel)*

Subsidiaries:

The DDS Companies   (1)
45 Hendrix Rd, West Henrietta, NY 14586
Tel.: (585) 359-7540
Web Site: http://www.ddscompanies.com
Emp.: 500
Designs, Engineers & Constructs Commercial & Residential Properties
N.A.I.C.S.: 236220
Sean Donohoe *(Founder & Pres)*
Brian J. Sorochty *(VP-Engrg)*
Earl Knapp *(VP-Utilities)*
Mike Jenson *(Gen Mgr-Telecom)*
Justin Cerqua *(Gen Mgr-Civil)*
John Kupiec *(Gen Mgr-Energy Svcs)*

FEHR BROS INDUSTRIES INC.
895 Kings Hwy, Saugerties, NY 12477
Tel.: (845) 246-9525
Web Site: http://www.fehr.com
Sales Range: $1-9.9 Million
Emp.: 55
Chain Cable & Rope & Wire
N.A.I.C.S.: 423510
Bob Miller *(VP)*
Lenny Iannizzotto *(Controller)*
Fred Couse *(Pres)*

FEI, INC
913 14th St SW, Valley City, ND 50782
Web Site: http://www.feiinc.com
Year Founded: 1978
Fertilizer & Chemical Application Equipment Sales
N.A.I.C.S.: 423820
Shelly Rodriguez *(Dir-HR)*
Jim Reddington *(VP-Energy)*
Christy Fliflet *(Pres & CEO)*

Subsidiaries:

Midwest Meter Inc.   (1)
1605 170th St, Hampton, IA 50441
Tel.: (641) 456-3444
Web Site: http://www.midwestmeter.com
Sales Range: $10-24.9 Million
Emp.: 23
Distribution & Repair of Liquid Meters
N.A.I.C.S.: 334514
Rick Salbesan *(Pres)*

Subsidiary (Domestic):

Midwest Computer Register Corp.   (2)
1605 170th St, Hampton, IA 50441
Tel.: (641) 456-5205
Web Site: http://www.midcomcorp.com
Rev.: $6,720,000
Emp.: 30
Radio & Television Broadcasting & Wireless Communications Equipment Mfr
N.A.I.C.S.: 334220

FEIGHNER INSURANCE INC.
959 E 4th St, Marion, IN 46952
Tel.: (765) 664-2333
Web Site: http://www.insmgt.com
Year Founded: 1954
Rev.: $11,500,000
Emp.: 50
Insurance Agencies & Brokerages
N.A.I.C.S.: 524210
Robert Lada *(Mgr-DP)*
Robert Stone *(Treas & Sec)*
Trent Dailey *(Mgr)*

FEIT MANAGEMENT COMPANY
2870 Stirling Rd Ste 2A, Hollywood, FL 33020
Tel.: (954) 921-4321
Real Estate Services
N.A.I.C.S.: 531210

Subsidiaries:

Creekside Associates Limited   (1)
2500 Knights Rd Creek Side Apt, Bensalem, PA 19020-3410
Tel.: (215) 638-2240
Web Site:
   http://www.creeksideapartments.net
Rev.: $1,200,000
Emp.: 30
Apartment Building Operator
N.A.I.C.S.: 531110
Edwin Nieves *(Mgr-Property)*
Mildred Morales *(Asst Mgr-Property)*

FEIZY IMPORT & EXPORT COMPANY INC.
1949 N Stemmons Fwy, Dallas, TX 75207-3102
Tel.: (214) 747-6000   TX
Web Site: http://www.feizy.com
Year Founded: 1975
Sales Range: $25-49.9 Million
Emp.: 110
Homefurnishings
N.A.I.C.S.: 423220

FELD ENTERTAINMENT, INC.
8607 Westwood Center Dr, Vienna, VA 22182-7506
Tel.: (703) 448-4000   VA
Web Site:
   http://www.feldentertainment.com
Year Founded: 1967

Sales Range: $1-4.9 Billion
Emp.: 2,500
Circus, Ice Show & Motor Sports Producer & Promoter
N.A.I.C.S.: 711190
Kenneth Feld *(Chm & CEO)*
Juliette Feld *(COO)*

Subsidiaries:

Feld Motor Sports, Inc.   (1)
4255 Meridian Pkwy, Aurora, IL 60504-7901
Tel.: (630) 566-6100
Web Site: http://www.feldentertainment.com
Sales Range: $150-199.9 Million
Emp.: 160
Producer & Promoter of Motor Sports Events
N.A.I.C.S.: 711320
Charlie Mancuso *(Pres)*
Ryan McSpadden *(VP-Sls)*

Division (Domestic):

International Hot Rod Association   (2)
9 1/2 E Main St, Norwalk, OH 44857
Tel.: (419) 663-6666
Web Site: http://www.ihra.com
Sales Range: $25-49.9 Million
Emp.: 20
Producer & Promoter of Motor Sports Events
N.A.I.C.S.: 711320
Aaron Polburn *(Pres)*
Mike Baker *(Sr Dir-Race Ops)*
Donna Harper *(Mgr-Points)*
Jim Marchyshyn *(VP-Mktg)*
Skooter Peaco *(VP)*
Sherrie Barbour *(Mgr-Special Programs)*
Sharon Ramlow *(Dir-Ops)*
Robert Kinton *(Dir-Reg Tech)*
Russell Prater *(Dir-Field Ops)*
Amanda Crum *(Coord-Acctg)*

Ringling Bros., Barnum & Bailey Combined Shows, Inc.   (1)
8607 Westwood Centre Dr, Vienna, VA 22182-7506   (100%)
Tel.: (703) 448-4000
Web Site: http://www.ringling.com
Sales Range: $25-49.9 Million
Emp.: 300
Circus
N.A.I.C.S.: 711190

FELDER COMMUNICATIONS GROUP
6886 Cascade Rd SE Ste E, Grand Rapids, MI 49546
Tel.: (616) 732-8000   MI
Web Site: https://www.felder.com
Year Founded: 1994
Sales Range: Less than $1 Million
Emp.: 4
Advertising Agencies
N.A.I.C.S.: 541810
Stan Felder *(Pres & CEO)*
Sue McIntire *(Mgr-Fin)*

FELDERS CONSTRUCTION, LLC
PO BOX 7096, Florence, SC 29502
Tel.: (803) 738-8882
Web Site:
   http://feldersconstructionllc.com
Year Founded: 1996
Sales Range: $1-9.9 Million
Emp.: 9
General Contractors
N.A.I.C.S.: 238910
Thomas Felders *(Pres)*

FELDMAN WOOD PRODUCTS CO. INC.
1 Herricks Rd, Garden City Park, NY 11040
Tel.: (516) 248-4700
Web Site:
   http://www.feldmanwoodproducts.com
Sales Range: $10-24.9 Million

Emp.: 25
Millwork
N.A.I.C.S.: 423310
Frederic Z. Konigsberg *(Pres)*

FELDMANN IMPORTS MERCEDES-BENZ
4901 American Blvd W, Bloomington, MN 55437-1100
Tel.: (952) 837-6300
Web Site:
   https://www.feldmannimports.com
Sales Range: $25-49.9 Million
Emp.: 125
Car Whslr
N.A.I.C.S.: 441110
Joe Feldmann *(Principal)*
Kathy LaMere *(Treas & VP)*

FELDMEIER EQUIPMENT, INC.
6800 Townline Rd, Syracuse, NY 13211-1325
Tel.: (315) 454-8608   NY
Web Site: https://www.feldmeier.com
Year Founded: 1952
Sales Range: $25-49.9 Million
Emp.: 350
Stainless Steel Food Processing Equipment & Storage Tanks Mfr
N.A.I.C.S.: 333241
Jeanne Jackson *(VP)*

FELIX CHEVROLET-CADILLAC
3330 S Figueroa St, Los Angeles, CA 90007-3795
Tel.: (213) 748-6141
Web Site: http://www.felixautos.com
Sales Range: $50-74.9 Million
Emp.: 113
Automobiles, New & Used
N.A.I.C.S.: 441110
Jeanette Shammas *(Pres)*

FELIX MEDIA SOLUTIONS, INC.
3601 S Congress Ave H200, Austin, TX 78704
Tel.: (512) 572-1777   TX
Web Site:
   http://www.felixmediasolutions.com
Year Founded: 2010
Sales Range: $1-9.9 Million
Emp.: 19
Media Advertising Services
N.A.I.C.S.: 541840
Lionel Felix *(CEO)*
Mike Watts *(VP-Design)*
Lindsey Rima *(CFO & COO)*

FELKER BROTHERS CORPORATION
22 N Chestnut Ave, Marshfield, WI 54449-2056
Tel.: (715) 384-3121   WI
Web Site:
   https://www.felkerbrothers.com
Year Founded: 1908
Sales Range: $10-24.9 Million
Emp.: 300
Steel Pipe & Tubes & Fitting & Prefabricated Piping Systems
N.A.I.C.S.: 331210
Thomas Umhoefer *(Owner)*
Lois Umhoefer *(Owner & Controller)*
Randy Krogman *(Mgr-Sls)*
David Hendrickson *(Pres)*

Subsidiaries:

Felker Brothers Corporation - Glasgow Manufacturing Facility   (1)
125 Beaver Trl, Glasgow, KY 42141
Tel.: (270) 678-4143
Stainless Steel Wire Mfr
N.A.I.C.S.: 332996

Felker Brothers Corporation - Marshfield Manufacturing Facility   (1)
1707 E 4th St, Marshfield, WI 54449

Felker Brothers Corporation—(Continued)

Tel.: (715) 384-3121
Stainless Steel Wire Mfr
N.A.I.C.S.: 332996

FELLERS, INC.

6566 E Skelly Dr, Tulsa, OK 74145
Tel.: (918) 621-4400
Web Site: http://www.fellers.com
Year Founded: 1986
Sales Range: $25-49.9 Million
Emp.: 225
Vinyl Sign Supply Services
N.A.I.C.S.: 339950
Frank Fellers (Owner)
Phil LaFata (Pres)
Tom Brophy (CEO)

FELLING TRAILERS, INC.

1525 Main St S, Sauk Centre, MN
56378-2600
Web Site: http://www.felling.com
Truck Trailer Mfr
N.A.I.C.S.: 336212
Brenda Jennissen (Pres & CEO)
Merle J. Felling (Founder)
Pat Jennissen (VP-Sls & Mktg)
Nathan Uphus (Mgr-Sls)

Subsidiaries:

Larson Cable Trailers, Inc.   (1)
601 Lincoln Ave NW, Huron, SD 57350
Web Site: http://www.larsonct.com
Truck Trailer Mfr
N.A.I.C.S.: 336212
Greg Owens Kramer (VP)

FELLOW HEALTH PARTNERS, INC.

3500 Sunrise Hwy Bldg 100 Ste 200,
Great River, NY 11739   NY
Web Site:
  http://fellowhealthpartners.com
Medical Business Solution Services
N.A.I.C.S.: 541219
Michael Brown (CEO)
Alexandra Stephens (Dir-Billing Ops)
Fran Sharkey (CMO)

Subsidiaries:

Billing Services, Inc.   (1)
87 Newtown E, Hampton, NY 11937
Tel.: (212) 249-5411
Web Site: http://www.billingservicesinc.com
Sales Range: $1-9.9 Million
Emp.: 20
Accounting Services
N.A.I.C.S.: 541219
Jack Emptage (Pres)

FELLOWES, INC.

1789 Norwood Ave, Itasca, IL 60143-
1059
Tel.: (630) 893-1600   IL
Web Site: https://www.fellowes.com
Year Founded: 1917
Sales Range: $500-549.9 Million
Emp.: 1,500
Computer & Office Accessories Mfr
N.A.I.C.S.: 333310
James Lewis (COO)
Peter Fellowes (Vice Chm)
Kathleen Noe (Chief Corp Dev Officer)
Steve Carson (Gen Counsel, Sec & VP)

Subsidiaries:

Fellowes (Australia) Pty Ltd   (1)
79-81 South Centre Road Melbourne Airport
Business Park, Tullamarine, 3045, VIC,
Australia
Tel.: (61) 3 8336 9700
Web Site: http://www.fellowes.com
Sales Range: $10-24.9 Million
Emp.: 35
Office Machinery Mfr
N.A.I.C.S.: 333310

Michael Ryan (Mng Dir)

Fellowes Benelux B.V.   (1)
Gesworenhoekseqeg 3a, 5047 TM, Tilburg,
Netherlands
Tel.: (31) 13 4580 580
Web Site: http://www.fellowes.com
Office Accessory Mfr & Distr
N.A.I.C.S.: 424120
Hazel Goesaert (Mgr-Trade Mktg)

Fellowes Canada Ltd.   (1)
1200 Rodick Rd, Markham, L3R 8C3, ON,
Canada
Tel.: (905) 475-6320
Web Site: http://www.fellowes.com
Emp.: 50
Office Equipment Distr
N.A.I.C.S.: 423420

Fellowes Germany GmbH   (1)
Dieselstrasse 27, 30827, Garbsen, Germany
Tel.: (49) 5131 49770
Web Site: http://www.fellowes.com
Sales Range: $10-24.9 Million
Emp.: 12
Office Machinery Mfr
N.A.I.C.S.: 333310
Bernd Mazzurana (Gen Mgr)

Fellowes Hi-Q Malaysia Sdn
Bhd.   (1)
27 Jalan Salung 33/26 Seksyen 33 Shah
Alam Technology Park, Shah Alam, 40400,
Selangor, Malaysia
Tel.: (60) 3 5122 1231
Web Site: http://www.fellowes.com.my
Sales Range: $10-24.9 Million
Emp.: 8
Office Accessory Mfr & Supplier
N.A.I.C.S.: 424120
Daniel Lee (Mgr)

Fellowes Hi-Q Singapore Pte
Ltd.   (1)
37 Keppel Road 04-10 Tanjong Pagar Dis-
triPark, Singapore, 89064, Singapore
Tel.: (65) 6221 3811
Web Site: http://www.fellowes.com
Sales Range: $10-24.9 Million
Emp.: 11
Office Accessory Mfr & Distr
N.A.I.C.S.: 424120
Eleanor Ng (Mng Dir)

Fellowes Iberica S.L.   (1)
P de las Flores 23 Nave 3 y 4, Coslada,
28820, Madrid, Spain
Tel.: (34) 902 33 55 69
Web Site: http://www.fellowes.com
Office Accessory Mfr & Supplier
N.A.I.C.S.: 337214
Carla Piedade (Mgr-PR & Comm)

Fellowes Japan K.K.   (1)
7F Tokyo Nissan Nishi-Gotanda Bldg
4-32-1, Nishi-Gotanda Shinagawa-ku, To-
kyo, 141-0031, Japan   (100%)
Tel.: (81) 3 5496 2401
Web Site: http://www.fellowes.co.jp
Sales Range: $1-9.9 Million
Office Accessory Whslr
N.A.I.C.S.: 424120
Yamawaki Takashi (Pres)

Fellowes Leonardi S.p.A   (1)
Via Direttissima del Conero 27, Camerano,
60021, Ancona, Italy
Tel.: (39) 071 730041
Web Site: http://www.fellowes.com
Emp.: 20
Office Accessory Mfr & Supplier
N.A.I.C.S.: 339940
Paolo Leonardi (Gen Mgr)

Fellowes Ru Ltd   (1)
Volokolamskoe Shosse 1, 125080, Moscow,
Russia
Tel.: (7) 4952807180
Web Site: http://www.fellowes.ru
Office Accessory Mfr & Distr
N.A.I.C.S.: 424120

Fellowes United Kingdom Ltd.   (1)
Yorkshire Way West Moor Park, Doncaster,
DN3 3FB, South Yorkshire, United Kingdom
Tel.: (44) 1302 836836
Web Site: http://www.fellowes.com
Emp.: 100

Office Accessory Mfr & Supplier
N.A.I.C.S.: 424120
Tania Cheesmond (Mgr-Trade Mktg)

Trendway Corporation   (1)
13467 Quincy St, Holland, MI 49424
Tel.: (616) 399-3900
Web Site: http://www.trendway.com
Mfr of Open Office Furniture Systems, Floor
to Ceiling Moveable Partitions & Seating
N.A.I.C.S.: 337214
Don Heeringa (Chm)
Bill Bundy (Pres & CEO)
Barbara Witt (Dir-HR)

FELLOWSHIP FOUNDATION

2145 N 24th St, Arlington, VA 22207
Tel.: (703) 536-6591   IL
Web Site:
  http://www.thefellowshipfoun
  dation.org
Year Founded: 1942
Sales Range: $10-24.9 Million
Emp.: 144
Christian Ministry Services
N.A.I.C.S.: 813110
William D. Cavin (Pres)
Christy Atkinson (Treas)
Kent Ford (Sec)
Michael Foster (VP)

FELLOWSHIP SENIOR LIVING

8000 Fellowship Rd, Basking Ridge,
NJ 07920
Tel.: (908) 580-3800   NJ
Web Site:
  https://www.fellowshipsenior
  living.org
Year Founded: 1992
Sales Range: $25-49.9 Million
Emp.: 421
Elder Care Services
N.A.I.C.S.: 624120
Jack Ellias (VP-Health Svcs)
Phylis Tranotti (Exec VP-Hospitality &
Dev)
Mark Aguilar (CFO)
Brian G. Lawrence (Pres & CEO)
Tim Ghales (VP-Chaplaincy)

FELMLEY-DICKERSON CO.

401 E Lafayette St, Bloomington, IL
61701
Tel.: (309) 828-4317
Web Site: http://www.fdco.com
Sales Range: $50-74.9 Million
Emp.: 25
Commercial & Office Building, New
Construction
N.A.I.C.S.: 236220
John Meek (Owner & Pres)

FELTON INC.

7 Burton Dr, Londonderry, NH 03053-
7435
Tel.: (603) 425-0200   NH
Web Site: https://www.feltoninc.com
Year Founded: 1852
Sales Range: $75-99.9 Million
Emp.: 97
Engineered Assemblies for Industrial
Applications
N.A.I.C.S.: 339999
Dick Currier (Mgr-Ops)
Dan Boehm (Pres & CEO)

FEM ELECTRIC ASSOCIA-TION, INC.

800 5th Ave, Ipswich, SD 57451
Tel.: (605) 426-6891   SD
Web Site:
  https://www.femelectric.coop
Year Founded: 1949
Sales Range: $10-24.9 Million
Emp.: 23
Electric Power Distr
N.A.I.C.S.: 221122

Rhonda Tuscherer (Dir-Fin & Benefits)
Scott Moore (CEO & Gen Mgr)
Gary Bachman (VP)
Tom Thorpe (Treas & Sec)

FEMCO HOLDINGS, LLC

754 S Main St, Punxsutawney, PA
15767
Tel.: (814) 938-9763   DE
Web Site:
  https://www.femcomachine.com
Heavy Machinery Repair Services
N.A.I.C.S.: 811310
Daniel J. Rondeau (Pres & CEO)
Scott Walker (VP-Sls & Mktg)

Subsidiaries:

Spencer-Harris Machine & Tool
Co.   (1)
520 E Broadway Ave, Gladewater, TX
75647
Tel.: (903) 845-2117
Web Site:
  http://spencerharris.femcomachine.com
Sales Range: $1-9.9 Million
Emp.: 41
Machine Shop, Jobbing & Repair
N.A.I.C.S.: 332710

FEMTEC HEALTH, INC.

3614 University B, Houston, TX
77005-3360
Tel.: (832) 699-0401
Web Site:
  http://www.femtechealth.com
Healthcare Services
N.A.I.C.S.: 621610
Kim Capone (Chief Scientific Officer)

Subsidiaries:

Birchbox, Inc.   (1)
230 Park Ave S 12th Fl, New York, NY,
10003
Web Site: http://www.birchbox.com
Sales Range: $10-24.9 Million
Online Health & Beauty Products Retailer
N.A.I.C.S.: 456120
Hayley Barna (Co-Founder)
Katia Beauchamp (Co-Founder & CEO)
Mollie Chen (Dir-Editorial)
Terre Layton (Global VP-Product Mgmt &
User Experience)
Fran Gaitanaros (VP-Creative)

Subsidiary (Non-US):

Beautycom SAS   (2)
1 rue Ambroise Thomas, 75009, Paris,
France
Tel.: (33) 966 860 880
Web Site: http://www.birchbox.com
Emp.: 3
Online Health & Beauty Products Retailer
N.A.I.C.S.: 541613
Quentin Vacher (CEO)

FENDRICH INDUSTRIES INC.

7025 Augusta Rd, Greenville, SC
29605
Tel.: (864) 299-0600
Web Site:
  http://www.carolinamfg.com
Rev.: $33,198,424
Emp.: 75
Dyed Fabrics & Textiles Mfr
N.A.I.C.S.: 313310
Shiron McCarthy (Chm)

FENDT BUILDERS SUPPLY INC.

22005 Gill Rd, Farmington Hills, MI
48335
Tel.: (248) 474-3211
Web Site:
  https://www.fendtproducts.com
Sales Range: Less than $1 Million
Emp.: 20
Cinder & Concrete Block Mfr
N.A.I.C.S.: 327331
Bob Schuessler (Mgr-Sls)

FENIX CONSTRUCTORS INC.
215 Drew St SW, Ardmore, OK 73401
Tel.: (580) 223-4313
Web Site: https://www.fenixci.com
Rev.: $13,635,088
Emp.: 25
Commercial & Office Building, New Construction
N.A.I.C.S.: 236220
William Owen (Pres)

FENIX MANUFACTURING SOLUTIONS, LLC
2063 University Pkwy, Aiken, SC 29801-6343
Tel.: (803) 649-1381   SC
Web Site: http://www.fenix-mfg.com
Year Founded: 1947
Sales Range: $50-74.9 Million
Emp.: 490
Electronic Components Mfr
N.A.I.C.S.: 334419
David Mosier (Owner, Pres & CEO)
Steve Johnson (Dir-Quality)
Kathy Sapp (CFO & Exec VP)
Doug Azbell (VP-Engineered Products Div)
Chris Wood (VP-Specialty Mfg Div)

FENNEMORE CRAIG, P.C.
2394 E Camelback Rd Ste 600, Phoenix, AZ 85016
Tel.: (602) 916-5000
Web Site:
   http://www.fennemorecraig.com
Year Founded: 1885
Emp.: 181
Law firm
N.A.I.C.S.: 541110
Scott L. Altes (Chm-Health Care Litigation & Regulation Practice Grp)
Amy Abdo (Atty)
Alexander Arpad (Atty)
Robert D. Anderson (Atty)
David Haga (Atty)
Kendis Muscheid (Atty)
Marc Lamber (Atty)
Kathy Hancock (Exec Dir)
Sarah Strunk (Chm)
Alexis Glascock (Atty)
Dave Bassuk (CFO)
Marlene Humbert (Dir-HR)
Whitney Murray (Dir-Mktg)
Dean Seiveno (CIO)
Laura Lo Bianco (Chm-Nonprofit & Tax Exempt Org Practice)
Ryan Curtis (Atty)
John Kaites (Atty)
William Ridenour (Atty)
Brenoch Wirthlin (Dir-Las Vegas)
Lori Albert (Dir-Denver)
Troy Rackham (Mng Partner-Denver)
Dawn Meidinger (Chm-Natural Resources, Energy & Environmental Law Practice Grp)
Steve Good (Mng Partner)
Richard Aaron (Chm-California Reg)
James Goodnow (CEO)
John J. Balitis Jr. (Atty)

Subsidiaries:

Dowling Aaron Incorporated   (1)
8080 N Palm Ave 3rd Fl, Fresno, CA 93711-5730
Tel.: (559) 432-4500
Web Site: http://www.dowlingaaron.com
Emp.: 44
Law firm
N.A.I.C.S.: 541110
Michael D. Dowling (Atty)
Christopher A. Brown (Atty)
David J. Weiland (Atty)
Richard M. Aaron (Atty)
Michael J. Hogan (Atty)
Shelley Corkins (Acctg Supvr & Coord-HR)

Paul Bauer (Atty)
Leigh Burnside (Pres)
James D. Burnside III (Atty)

Wendel, Rosen, Black & Dean LLP   (1)
1111 Broadway, Oakland, CA 94607
Tel.: (510) 834-6600
Web Site: http://www.wendel.com
Emp.: 100
Law firm
N.A.I.C.S.: 541110
C. Gregg Ankenman (Atty)
Greggory C. Brandt (Atty)
Elizabeth Berke-Dreyfuss (Partner)
Mark S. Bostick (Atty)
William C. Acevedo (Atty)
Tammy France (Mgr-HR)
Jeffery Levi (Atty)
Brooke Wilson (Atty)
Quinlan Tom (Atty)
Allan Moore (Partner-Land Use Practice)
Amara Morrison (Partner-Land Use Practice)
Katie Ferrier (Atty-Real Estate Practice)
Monica Dell'Osso (Partner-Trusts & Estates Practice Grp)

FENNICK/MCCREDIE ARCHITECTURE LTD.
70 Franklin St, Boston, MA 02110
Tel.: (617) 350-7900
Web Site:
   https://www.fmarchitecture.com
Year Founded: 2003
Sales Range: $1-9.9 Million
Emp.: 35
Designs Architectural Sustainable Buildings
N.A.I.C.S.: 236220
Deborah Fennick (Co-Founder & Principal)
Jonathan McCredie (Co-Founder & Mng Principal)

FENTELL CORPORATION
2301 Evesham Rd Ste 702, Voorhees, NJ 08043
Tel.: (856) 772-1212
Web Site: https://www.fentell.com
Rev.: $20,000,000
Emp.: 7
Subdividers & Developers
N.A.I.C.S.: 237210
James S. Feigenbaum (Pres)

FENTON RIGGING & CONTRACTING, INC.
2150 Langdon Farm Rd, Cincinnati, OH 45237
Tel.: (513) 631-5500
Web Site:
   https://www.fenton1898.com
Year Founded: 1898
Rigging & Concrete & Railroad Restoration Services
N.A.I.C.S.: 238990
Tim Besl (CEO)
Bill Besl (COO)
Chris Besl (Project Mgr-Rigging)
Dottie Reinhold (Controller)
Chris Hartle (CFO)
David Williams (Mgr-CCM)
Mark Hoffman (Mgr-Pur & Shop)
Doug Hollstegge (Project Mgr)
Dave Metzcar (Project Mgr)
Garry Miller (Project Mgr)
Jack Stowers (Project Mgr)
Bryan Erickson (Project Mgr-Contracting)

FENTRESS ARCHITECTS
421 Broadway, Denver, CO 80203
Tel.: (303) 722-5000
Web Site:
   https://www.fentressarchitects.com
Year Founded: 1980
Sales Range: $100-124.9 Million
Emp.: 155

Architectural Svcs
N.A.I.C.S.: 541310
Bob Louden (Principal)
Brian H. Chaffe (Principal)
Jeff Olson (Principal)
Michael O. Winters (Principal & Dir-Design & Interiors)
Ned Kirschbaum (Principal & Dir-Tech Design)
Thomas J. Walsh (Dir-Aviation Plng)
Tom Theobald (Principal)
Curtis Fentress (Pres & CEO)
Steven White (Principal & Dir-Washington)
Jack Cook (Principal)
Mark A. Outman (Principal)
Patrick McCue (COO)
John Kudrycki (Principal)

FENWAY HEALTH
1340 Boylston St, Boston, MA 02115
Tel.: (617) 267-0900   MA
Web Site:
   https://www.fenwayhealth.org
Year Founded: 1973
Sales Range: $100-124.9 Million
Emp.: 528
Health Care Srvices
N.A.I.C.S.: 622110
Alex Gonzalez (Dir-Medical)
Henia Handler (Dir-Govt Affairs)
John R. Stewart (Treas)
Jane Powers (Interim CEO)

FENWAY PARTNERS, LLC
152 W 57th St 59th Fl, New York, NY 10019-3310
Tel.: (212) 698-9400   DE
Web Site:
   https://www.fenwaypartners.com
Year Founded: 1994
Rev.: $2,100,000,000
Emp.: 20
Privater Equity Firm
N.A.I.C.S.: 523999
Peter Lamm (Co-Founder & Mng Partner)
Richard Dresdale (Co-Founder & Mng Dir)
Gregg Smart (Mng Dir)
Walter Wiacek (CFO & VP)

Subsidiaries:

AAC Group Holding Corp.   (1)
7211 Cir S Rd, Austin, TX 78745   (82%)
Tel.: (512) 444-0571
Sales Range: $250-299.9 Million
Holding Company; Class Rings & Yearbooks Mfr
N.A.I.C.S.: 551112
Steven Parr (Pres & CEO)

Subsidiary (Domestic):

American Achievement Corporation   (2)
7211 Cir S Rd, Austin, TX 78745
Tel.: (512) 444-0571
Web Site:
   http://www.americanachievementcorp.com
Yearbooks & Class Rings Mfr & Sales
N.A.I.C.S.: 339999
Steven Parr (Chm)
Robert Myers (Pres & CEO)

Subsidiary (Domestic):

Commemorative Brands, Inc.   (3)
7211 Cir S Rd, Austin, TX 78745-6603
Tel.: (512) 444-0571
Web Site: http://www.balfour.com
Class Rings & Yearbooks Mfr & Retailer
N.A.I.C.S.: 339910
Steven Parr (Pres & CEO)

Taylor Publishing Co.   (3)
1550 W Mockingbird Ln, Dallas, TX 75235-5007
Tel.: (214) 637-2800
Web Site: http://www.taylorpub.com
High School & College Yearbooks Publisher

N.A.I.C.S.: 513130
Steven Parr (Pres & CEO)

BRG Sports, Inc.   (1)
9801 W Higgins Rd Ste 800, Rosemont, IL 60018   (54.3%)
Tel.: (224) 585-5200
Web Site: http://www.brgsports.com
Rev.: $780,432,000
Assets: $957,943,000
Liabilities: $601,440,000
Net Worth: $356,503,000
Earnings: ($15,141,000)
Emp.: 2,397
Fiscal Year-end: 12/28/2013
Holding Company; Sporting Goods Mfr & Whslr
N.A.I.C.S.: 551112
Allison M. Boersma (CFO & COO)
Terry G. Lee (Chm)
Daniel J. Arment (Pres & CEO)

Subsidiary (Non-US):

BG Sports EUROPE Sarl   (2)
Z A La Piece 4 Building 4 Route De l Etraz, 1180, Rolle, Switzerland
Tel.: (41) 79935 8438
Sports Equipment Whslr
N.A.I.C.S.: 423910

BRG Sports Mexico, S.A. de C.V.   (2)
Aguila Americana No 5981, Tijuana, 22684, Baja California, Mexico
Tel.: (52) 664 454 3942
Sporting & Athletic Goods Mfr
N.A.I.C.S.: 339920
Jorge Gonzalez (Dir-Fin & Ops)

Subsidiary (Domestic):

Riddell Sports Group, Inc.   (2)
1700 W Higgins Rd Ste 500, Des Plaines, IL 60018
Tel.: (773) 794-1994
Web Site: http://www.riddell.com
Provider & Reconditioner of Athletic Equipment Uniform & Practice Gear Mfr
N.A.I.C.S.: 339920
Daniel J. Arment (Pres)

Subsidiary (Domestic):

Gunther's Athletic Service, Inc.   (3)
1021 E Orangethorpe Ave, Anaheim, CA 92801
Tel.: (714) 992-1420
Web Site: http://www.gunthersathletic.net
Sales Range: $10-24.9 Million
Sporting & Recreational Goods & Supplies Merchant Whslr
N.A.I.C.S.: 423910

Riddell, Inc.   (3)
669 Sugar Ln, Elyria, OH 44035
Tel.: (440) 366-8225
Web Site: http://www.riddell.com
Emp.: 400
Sports Equipment Whslr
N.A.I.C.S.: 423910
Allison M. Boersma (CFO & COO)
Daniel J. Arment (Pres & CEO)

Subsidiary (Domestic):

All American Sports Corporation   (4)
669 Sugar Ln, Elyria, OH 44035
Tel.: (440) 366-8225
Web Site: http://www.riddell.com
Emp.: 1,000
Sports Equipment Reconditioning Services
N.A.I.C.S.: 811490
Ray Cromwell (VP-Ops)

Simbex LLC   (4)
10 Water St Ste 410, Lebanon, NH 03766
Tel.: (603) 448-2367
Web Site: http://www.simbex.com
Sales Range: $1-9.9 Million
Emp.: 18
Engineeering Services
N.A.I.C.S.: 541330
Jeffrey J. Chu (VP-Engrg)
Jonathan G. Beckwith (Dir-Res)
Theresa Hays (Bus Mgr)

Fastfrate Holdings Inc.   (1)
9701 Hwy 50, Woodbridge, L4H 2G4, ON, Canada
Tel.: (905) 893-2600

Fenway Partners, LLC—(Continued)

Web Site: http://www.fastfrate.com
Transportation & Logistics Services
N.A.I.C.S.: 541614
Manny Calandrino (Pres)
Frank Figliomeni (Chief Comml Officer)
Richard Rose (Exec VP)
John King (VP)
Sylvie Lalanne (VP)
Kim Wonfor (VP)
Mark Knott (VP)
Alfonso Triolo (VP)
Sebastian Carta (VP)
Jay Lee (VP)

Division (Domestic):

Fastfrate Holdings Inc. - Calgary Division (2)
11440-54th Street SE, Calgary, T2C4Y6, AB, Canada
Tel.: (403) 264-1687
Web Site: http://www.fastfrate.com
Emp.: 350
Freight Transportation Services
N.A.I.C.S.: 488510

Fastfrate Holdings Inc. - Montreal Division (2)
4415 Rue Fairway, Lachine, H8T 1B5, QC, Canada
Tel.: (514) 639-7747
Web Site: http://www.fastfrate.com
Transportation & Logistics Services
N.A.I.C.S.: 541614

Fastfrate Holdings Inc. - Toronto Division (2)
9701 Highway 50, Woodbridge, L4H 2G4, ON, Canada
Tel.: (905) 856-4522
Transportation & Logistics Services
N.A.I.C.S.: 541614

Fastfrate Holdings Inc. - Vancouver Division (2)
1375 Kingsway Ave, Port Coquitlam, V3C 4W1, BC, Canada
Tel.: (604) 941-0691
Logistics Management & Consulting Services
N.A.I.C.S.: 541614

FENWAY SPORTS GROUP HOLDINGS, LLC
4 Yawkey Way Fenway Park, Boston, MA 02215
Tel.: (617) 267-9440　　DE
Year Founded: 2001
Sales Range: $25-49.9 Million
Emp.: 300
Investment Holding Company
N.A.I.C.S.: 551112
Thomas C. Werner (Chm)

Subsidiaries:

Boston Red Sox Baseball Club Limited Partnership (1)
4 Yawkey Way Fenway Park, Boston, MA 02215
Tel.: (617) 226-6000
Web Site: http://boston.redsox.mlb.com
Sales Range: $10-24.9 Million
Emp.: 120
Professional Baseball Club
N.A.I.C.S.: 711211
Thomas C. Werner (Chm)
Samuel H. Kennedy (Pres)
Lawrence Cancro (Sr VP-Fenway Concerts & Entertainment)
John W. Henry (Owner)
J. Joseph Cochran (Mgr-Visiting Clubhouse)
Raquel S. Ferreira (Sr VP-Major & Minor League Ops)
Elaine Steward (VP-Club Counsel)
Sean P. Carragher (Mgr-Ticket Acctg & Ops)
Phillip H. Morse (Vice Chm)
Troup Parkinson (SR VP-Partnerships)
Jonathan Gilula (Exec VP-Bus Affairs)
Ron Bumgarner (Sr VP-Ticketing, Fenway Events & Concerts)
Brian O'Halloran (Exec VP & Asst Gen Mgr)
Zack Scott (Sr VP & Asst Gen Mgr)

Ethan Faggett (Asst Dir-Florida Baseball Ops)
Amiel Sawdaye (VP-Amateur & Intl Scouting)
Cathy Fahy (Sr Mgr-Payroll & Admin)
Sarah McKenna (VP-Fan Svcs & Entertainment)
Brian Abraham (Dir-Minor League Ops)
Richard Ginsburg (Dir-Behavioral Health Program)
Mike Rikard (Dir-Amateur Scouting)
Steve Sanders (Asst Dir-Amateur Scouting)
Gus Quattlebaum (Dir-Pro Scouting)
Allard Baird (Sr VP-Player Personnel)
Mike Regan (Dir-Baseball Admin & Special Projects)
Amy Waryas (Sr VP-HR)
Frank Wren (Sr VP-Baseball Ops)
Dave Dombrowski (Pres-Baseball Ops)
Eddie Romero (Exec VP & Asst Gen Mgr)
Joe McDonald (Dir-Baseball Analytics)
Marcus Cuellar (Coord-Player Personnel)
Alex Gimenez (Coord-Major League Ops)
Patrick McLaughlin (Coord-Baseball Ops-Florida)
Chaim Bloom (Head-Baseball Ops)

Liverpool Football Club & Athletic Grounds Ltd. (1)
Anfield Road, Liverpool, L4 0TH, United Kingdom
Tel.: (44) 1512632361
Web Site: http://www.liverpoolfc.tv
Sales Range: $10-24.9 Million
Emp.: 200
Professional Soccer Team
N.A.I.C.S.: 711211
John Henry (Owner)
Tom Werner (Chm)
Mike Gordon (Pres)
Peter Moore (CEO)

New England Sports Enterprises, LLC (1)
82 Brookline Ave, Boston, MA 02215　　(100%)
Tel.: (617) 226-6300
Web Site: http://www.fenwaysportsgroup.com
Sales Range: $50-74.9 Million
Emp.: 25
Sports Marketing & Investment Firm
N.A.I.C.S.: 523999
Samuel H. Kennedy (Pres)
Mark Lev (Mng Dir)
Billy Hogan (Mng Dir)
Frank Huckabone (Exec VP-Sls)
Tim Zue (VP-Ventures)
Jon Chin (VP-Integrated Sls)
Matt Murrey (VP-Boston College Mktg)
Kelly Kaufman (Controller)

Joint Venture (Domestic):

Roush Corporation (2)
4600 Roush Pl NW, Concord, NC 28027　　(50%)
Tel.: (704) 720-4600
Web Site: http://www.roushfenway.com
Sales Range: $25-49.9 Million
Professional Motorsports Organization
N.A.I.C.S.: 711211
Steve Newmark (Pres)

FENWICK & WEST LLP
801 California St, Mountain View, CA 94041
Tel.: (650) 988-8500
Web Site: https://www.fenwick.com
Year Founded: 1972
Sales Range: $200-249.9 Million
Emp.: 248
Legal Advisory Services
N.A.I.C.S.: 541199
Sally M. Abel (Chm-Trademark & Partner-Intellectual Property)
Samuel B. Angus (Partner)
Stephen D. Gillespie (Partner-Tech Transactions)
David A. Bell (Partner)
Brad Bonnington (Dir-Practice Support)
Darren E. Donnelly (Partner-Litigation)
Gordon K. Davidson (Partner)

Virginia K. DeMarchi (Partner-Litigation)
Daniel Dorosin (Partner)
Richard L. Dickson (Partner)
Michael T. Esquivel (Partner)
James D. Evans (Partner)
Connie L. Ellerbach (Partner-Intellectual Property)
David L. Forst (Partner)
Michael W. Farn (Partner-Intellectual Property)
Robert A. Freedman (Chm-Securities & Corp Fin & Partner)
Kathryn J. Fritz (Partner-Litigation)
Michael S. Dicke (Chm-Securities Enforcement & Partner-Securities Litigation)
Daniel M. Becker (Partner-Intellectual Property Practice)
Karen Yan (Corp Partner)
J. David Hadden (Partner-Litigation)
Eric Ball (Partner-Litigation)
Gerald Audant (Partner)
Kenneth B. Clark (Chm & Partner-Tax-Litigation)
Kristine M. Di Bacco (Partner)
Jeffrey Greene (Partner-Trademark-New York)
James Koenig (Co-Chm-Privacy & Cybersecurity Practice & Partner-New York)
Tyler G. Newby (Co-Chm-Privacy & Cybersecurity Practice)
Idan Netser (Partner-Tax)
Adam S. Halpern (Chm-Tax)
Cindy Clarfield Hess (Chm-Startups & Venture Capital Grp)
Pat Lyden (Chief HR Officer)
Robert A. Kahn (CMO)
Cheri A. Vaillancour (Chief Professional Dev Officer)
Kevin K. Moore (Chief Security Officer)
Jim McKenna (CIO)
Stephen M. Graham (Partner)

FERCHE MILLWORK, INC.
400 Division St N, Rice, MN 56367-8773
Tel.: (320) 393-5700　　MN
Web Site: https://www.ferche.com
Year Founded: 1958
Sales Range: $25-49.9 Million
Emp.: 200
Millwork
N.A.I.C.S.: 321211
Ken Ludvingson (Controller)
Gerald Grider (Pres)
Joel Ferche (Mgr-Pur)

FERCO MOTORS, CORP.
1740 SW 1st St, Miami, FL 33135
Tel.: (305) 541-3386
Web Site: https://www.fercomotors.com
Year Founded: 1995
Sales Range: $10-24.9 Million
Emp.: 5
Used Car Retailer
N.A.I.C.S.: 441120
Luis Hernandez Jr. (Gen Mgr-Sls)

FERDINAND BUILDING DEVELOPMENT CORPORATION
1 City Hall Sq Ste 813, Boston, MA 02201
Tel.: (617) 635-4532　　MA
Year Founded: 2011
Sales Range: Less than $1 Million
Economic Development Services
N.A.I.C.S.: 541720
David Sweeney (Pres)
John Barros (Treas)

FERGUSON BROS INC.

1300 E Chester St, Jackson, TN 38301
Tel.: (731) 424-7194
Year Founded: 1972
Sales Range: $10-24.9 Million
Emp.: 9
Distr of Petroleum Products
N.A.I.C.S.: 424710
Bobby Ferguson (VP)
Tom Ferguson (VP)

FERGUSON BUICK GMC
950 S Academy Blvd, Colorado Springs, CO 80910-3965
Tel.: (719) 896-2773　　CO
Web Site: http://www.peakbuickgmc.com
Sales Range: $50-74.9 Million
Emp.: 100
Automobiles Retailer & General Auto Repair Services
N.A.I.C.S.: 441120
Dave Stock (Owner)
Mike Bartko (Mgr-Sls-New Cars)

FERGUSON CONSTRUCTION
13810 SE Eastgate Way Ste 110, Bellevue, WA 98005
Tel.: (425) 974-8400
Web Site: https://www.fergusonconstruction.com
Sales Range: $50-74.9 Million
Emp.: 75
Commercial & Institutional Building Construction
N.A.I.C.S.: 236220
Jay Clark (Project Mgr)
Tom Whiteman (Dir-Bus Dev)

FERGUSON CONSTRUCTION COMPANY INC.
PO Box 726, Sidney, OH 45365-0726
Tel.: (937) 498-2381　　OH
Web Site: http://www.fergusonconstruction.com
Year Founded: 1983
Sales Range: $25-49.9 Million
Emp.: 200
Industrial Buildings & Warehouses
N.A.I.C.S.: 236210
Martin L. Mick (Pres)
Jason Stiver (VP & Ops Mgr)
Benjamin J. Lindsay (Gen Mgr-Columbus)
Douglas Fortkamp (Pres)

FERGUSON ELECTRIC COMPANY INC.
112 Northwest Dr, Plainville, CT 06062
Tel.: (860) 747-4566
Web Site: http://www.fergusonelectric.com
Sales Range: $10-24.9 Million
Emp.: 50
General Electrical Contractor
N.A.I.C.S.: 238210
Lee Ferguson (Pres & CEO)
Joanne Erdman (Exec VP)
Charles Zettergren (CFO)

FERGUSON ELECTRIC HOLDINGS CORP.
333 Ellicott St, Buffalo, NY 14203
Tel.: (716) 852-2010　　DE
Web Site: https://www.fergusonelectric.com
Year Founded: 2000
Holding Company; Electrical Contractor
N.A.I.C.S.: 551112
Paul C. Reilly (Co-Pres & Head-Svc Div)
Angelo A. Veanes (Co-Pres & Head-Construction Div)
Jeffrey H. Lattimer (CFO)

Kevin M. Mislin *(VP-Estimating & Mktg-Construction Div)*
Ronald H. Markowski *(VP-Project Ops-Construction Div)*

Subsidiaries:

Ferguson Electric Construction Co., Inc. (1)
333 Ellicott St, Buffalo, NY 14203-1618
Tel.: (716) 852-2010
Web Site: http://www.fergusonelectric.com
Sales Range: $50-74.9 Million
Electrical Contractor
N.A.I.C.S.: 238210
Angelo Veanes *(Pres)*
Mike Schmitz *(Mgr-Product Safety)*
Kevin M. Mislin *(VP-Mktg)*
Ronald H. Markowski *(VP-Project Ops)*
Jeffrey H. Lattimer *(CFO)*
James Schneider *(VP-Engrg & Design)*

Ferguson Electric Service Co., Inc. (1)
333 Ellicott St, Buffalo, NY 14203-1618
Tel.: (716) 853-3321
Web Site: http://www.fergusonelectric.com
Sales Range: $25-49.9 Million
Electrical Contractor
N.A.I.C.S.: 238210
Paul C. Reilly *(Pres)*
Dale R. Peters *(VP & Gen Mgr)*
Kevin Roland *(VP & Dir-Engrg)*

FERGUSON ENTERPRISES INC
751 Lkfrnt Commons, Newport News, VA 23606-3322
Tel.: (414) 327-8400
Web Site: https://www.ferguson.com
Year Founded: 1953
Rev.: $1,500,000
Emp.: 10
Plumbing & Heating Equipment & Supplies, Hydronics, Merchant Whslr
N.A.I.C.S.: 423720
Bryan Dombrowicki *(Gen Mgr)*

FERGUSON MANUFACTURING & EQUIPMENT COMPANY, INC.
4900 Singleton Blvd, Dallas, TX 75212-3337
Tel.: (214) 631-3000   TX
Web Site: http://www.ferguson.com
Year Founded: 1933
Sales Range: $50-74.9 Million
Emp.: 25
Compaction Equipment Mfr
N.A.I.C.S.: 333120
Dan Sheehan *(Pres)*
Evelyn Wilson *(Office Mgr)*

FERGUSON PONTIAC-GMC INC.
1015 Interstate Dr, Norman, OK 73069-6354
Tel.: (405) 253-0923
Web Site: https://www.fergusonchallenge.com
Sales Range: $50-74.9 Million
Emp.: 83
Automobiles, New & Used
N.A.I.C.S.: 441110
Gary Burton *(Gen Mgr)*

FERGUSON SUPPLY & BOX MANUFACTURING CO
10820 Quality Dr, Charlotte, NC 28278-0205
Tel.: (704) 597-0310
Web Site: http://www.fergusonbox.com
Sales Range: $10-24.9 Million
Emp.: 110
Boxes Materials & Supplies
N.A.I.C.S.: 322211
Paige Ferguson Burgess *(Pres)*

FERGUSON SUPPLY CO.

345 Pleasant St SW, Grand Rapids, MI 49503
Tel.: (616) 456-1688
Web Site: https://www.fergusonsupplycompany.com
Sales Range: $10-24.9 Million
Emp.: 25
Provider of Plumbing & Hydronic Heating Supplies
N.A.I.C.S.: 423720
Craig Hecker *(Chm & CEO)*
Richard Kutschinski *(Controller)*

FERLAND INDUSTRIES INC.
99 Jersey Ave, New Brunswick, NJ 08901
Tel.: (732) 246-3200
Web Site: http://www.ferlandindustries.com
Sales Range: $10-24.9 Million
Emp.: 2
Coated Fabrics, Not Rubberized
N.A.I.C.S.: 313320
Jesus Ferro *(Pres)*

FERMA CORP.
1265 Montecito Ave # 200, Mountain View, CA 94043
Tel.: (650) 961-2742   CA
Web Site: http://www.fermacorp.com
Year Founded: 1963
Sales Range: $25-49.9 Million
Emp.: 200
Site Preparation Contractor
N.A.I.C.S.: 238910
Robert Verga *(Mgr)*
Marc Ferrari *(Pres)*

FERMAN AUTOMOTIVE MANAGEMENT SERVICES, INC.
1306 W Kennedy Blvd, Tampa, FL 33606-1849
Tel.: (813) 251-2765   FL
Web Site: http://www.fermanauto.com
Year Founded: 1895
Sales Range: $500-549.9 Million
Emp.: 1,000
New & Used Automobiles Motorcycle & Truck Distr
N.A.I.C.S.: 423110
James Laurens Ferman Jr. *(Pres)*
Nick Boichess *(Controller)*

Subsidiaries:

Ferman Chevrolet (1)
43520 United States Hwy 19 N, Tarpon Springs, FL 34689
Tel.: (727) 934-5789
Rev.: $70,700,000
Emp.: 85
Automobiles, New & Used
N.A.I.C.S.: 441110
Sarah Smith *(Mgr-Internet)*

Ferman Motor Car Co., Inc. (1)
1306 W Kennedy Blvd, Tampa, FL 33606-1849   (100%)
Tel.: (813) 251-2765
Web Site: http://www.fermanauto.com
Sales Range: $10-24.9 Million
Emp.: 900
Dealer of New & Used Automobiles
N.A.I.C.S.: 441110
James Laurens Ferman Jr. *(Pres)*
Preston Farrior *(VP-Automobile Ops)*
Stephen Straske *(VP-Legal Counsel)*
Nick Boicheff *(Controller & Dir-Info Sys)*

FERNANDEZ ENTERTAINMENT
91-246 Oihana St, Kapolei, HI 96707
Tel.: (808) 682-5767
Web Site: http://www.ekfernandez.com
Sales Range: $25-49.9 Million
Emp.: 70
Amusement Arcade

N.A.I.C.S.: 713120
Kane S. Fernandez *(Pres-EK Fernandez)*
Linda Fernandez *(Pres)*
Steven Lau *(CFO & Controller)*

Subsidiaries:

Fun Factory Inc. (1)
91-246 Oihana St, Kapolei, HI 96707
Tel.: (808) 682-5767
Web Site: http://www.funfactorygames.com
Rev.: $20,000,000
Emp.: 40
Amusement Arcade
N.A.I.C.S.: 713120
Warren Asing *(Mgr-Ops)*

FERNANDEZ HOLDINGS, INC.
901 Bringham Ave, Los Angeles, CA 90049
Tel.: (310) 593-0798   CA
Web Site: http://www.fernandezholdings.com
Investment Services
N.A.I.C.S.: 523999
Kirk Fernandez *(Founder, Chm & CEO)*
Jeremy Johnson *(Pres)*

Subsidiaries:

Solutionz, Inc. (1)
901 Bringham Ave, Los Angeles, CA 90049
Tel.: (310) 571-1207
Web Site: http://www.solutionzinc.com
Sales Range: $1-9.9 Million
Emp.: 18
Wired Telecommunications Carriers
N.A.I.C.S.: 517111
Kirk Fernandez *(Pres)*
Barry Green *(VP-Sls)*
Deborah Jefferies *(Dir)*
Bill Warnick *(CEO)*

Subsidiary (Domestic):

Total Video Products, Inc. (2)
414 Southgate Ct, Mickleton, NJ 08056
Tel.: (856) 423-7400
Web Site: http://www.totalvideoproducts.com
Audio Visual & Video Solution Services
N.A.I.C.S.: 334310
Jim Hokesema *(Dir-Sls)*
Leo Hughes *(Dir-Fin)*
Joe Blanch *(Mgr-Ops)*
Joe Reale *(Mgr-Svc)*
Larry Gallner *(Pres)*
Adam Strashinsky *(Project Mgr)*
Earl Smith *(Mgr-Pro Svcs)*
Kevin Corson *(Mgr-Installation)*
Mark Brasch *(Project Mgr)*
Rusty Lynch *(Mgr-Quality Assurance)*

United Construction & Forestry, LLC (1)
396 County Rd, Westbrook, ME 04092
Tel.: (207) 544-4396
Web Site: https://www.unitedcf.com
Construction & Forestry Vehicle Dealerships Owner & Operator
N.A.I.C.S.: 423810

FERNBANK MUSEUM OF NATURAL HISTORY
767 Clifton Rd NE, Atlanta, GA 30307
Tel.: (404) 929-6300   GA
Year Founded: 1939
Sales Range: $10-24.9 Million
Emp.: 164
Museums
N.A.I.C.S.: 712110
Susan E. Neugent *(Pres & CEO)*
Jennifer Grant Warner *(Chief Programming Officer)*
Leslie K. Rutkowski *(VP-Dev)*
Dana L. Harvey *(CTO)*
Catherine Nowell *(CFO)*
Nicole Holman *(Coord-Mktg & PR)*

FERNCO INCORPORATED
300 S Dayton St, Davison, MI 48423
Tel.: (810) 653-9626

Web Site: https://www.fernco.com
Rev.: $14,000,000
Emp.: 140
Plastic Plumbing Fixture Fittings, Assembly
N.A.I.C.S.: 332913
Mark Cooper *(Pres)*
Bill Shorey *(VP-Engrg & Mfg)*

FERNDALE ELECTRIC COMPANY INC.
915 E Drayton St, Ferndale, MI 48220-1409
Tel.: (248) 545-4404   MI
Web Site: http://www.ferndale-electric.com
Year Founded: 1959
Sales Range: $25-49.9 Million
Emp.: 200
Electrical Work
N.A.I.C.S.: 238210

FERNDALE LABORATORIES INC.
780 W 8 Mile Rd, Ferndale, MI 48220-2422
Tel.: (248) 548-0900   MA
Web Site: http://www.ferndalelabs.com
Year Founded: 1897
Sales Range: $25-49.9 Million
Emp.: 210
Pharmaceutical Services
N.A.I.C.S.: 325412
Carey Cribbs *(Supvr-Incoming Quality Control)*
Suzanne Cooper *(Dir-Quality Assurance)*
Leon Dupuis *(VP-Quality Control & Validation)*
Lori Sloane *(VP-Mfg)*

FERNDALE READY MIX & GRAVEL
144 River Rd, Lynden, WA 98264
Tel.: (360) 384-5393
Web Site: http://www.ferndalereadymix.net
Rev.: $10,000,000
Emp.: 25
Ready Mixed Concrete
N.A.I.C.S.: 327320
Brad BeHaan *(Mgr)*
Jeremiah Harlan *(Mgr)*

FERNO-WASHINGTON INC.
70 Weil Way, Wilmington, OH 45177-9371
Tel.: (937) 382-1451
Web Site: https://www.ferno.com
Year Founded: 1955
Sales Range: $25-49.9 Million
Emp.: 475
Mfr & Distributor of Mortuary Products
N.A.I.C.S.: 339113
Elroy Bourgraf *(Chm & CEO)*
Nancy Keeton *(Mgr-Intl Customer Svc)*
Karen Horn-McKenzie *(Dir-IT)*
Kris Turner *(Dir-Bus Dev)*
Jim Smalley *(Mgr-Network)*
Garland Brock *(Engr-Design)*
Robert Fissel *(Controller)*
Bob Ginter *(VP-HR)*
Larry Newberry *(Mgr-Engrg Plant)*
Vickie Giannetti *(Asst Mgr-Sls & Mktg)*

FEROLIE CORPORATION
2 Van Riper Rd, Montvale, NJ 07645
Tel.: (201) 307-9100   NJ
Web Site: http://www.feroliegroup.com
Year Founded: 1945
Sales Range: $450-499.9 Million

Ferolie Corporation—(Continued)

Emp.: 1,000
Bond Brokers
N.A.I.C.S.: 424410
Larry Ferolie (CEO)
Al Nagy (Chief Admin Officer)
James Ferolie (CIO)
Julie Shasteen (VP-HR)
Daryl Fox (Gen Counsel)
Craig Chapin (Dir-Retail Grocery)
Tony Scudieri (Pres & COO)
Chris Darley (VP-Fin)

FEROLITO, VULTAGGIO & SONS
60 Crossways Park Dr W, Woodbury, NY 11797
Tel.: (516) 812-0300
Web Site:
http://www.drinkarizona.com
Sales Range: $50-74.9 Million
Emp.: 200
Soft Drink Distr
N.A.I.C.S.: 312111
Don Vultaggio (Chm)

Subsidiaries:

Hornell Brewing Co., Inc.   (1)
60 Crossways Park Dr W Ste 400, Woodbury, NY 11797
Tel.: (516) 812-0300
Sales Range: $25-49.9 Million
Mfr of Alcoholic Beverages
N.A.I.C.S.: 424810
John Posicillo (Mng Dir)

FERRAGON CORPORATION
11103 Memphis Ave, Cleveland, OH 44144
Tel.: (216) 671-6161
Web Site: https://www.ferragon.com
Rev.: $17,500,000
Emp.: 160
Steel
N.A.I.C.S.: 423510
Eduardo Gonzalez (Pres)

Subsidiaries:

Autolum Processing Co.   (1)
27800 W Jefferson Ave, Gibraltar, MI 48173
Tel.: (734) 727-0500
Web Site:
http://www.autolumprocessing.com
Emp.: 25
Aluminum Sheet Mfr
N.A.I.C.S.: 331315
Eduardo Gonzalez (Pres)
Mark Nester (Gen Mgr)
Terry Kirkland (Plant Mgr)
Tom Stackpole (Mgr-Ops)
Sonia A. Cobos (Office Mgr)
Dave Rickus (Dir-Safety)

Ferrolux Metals Co. LLC   (1)
36263 Michigan Ave, Wayne, MI 48184
Tel.: (734) 727-6161
Web Site: http://www.ferrolux.com
Sales Range: $150-199.9 Million
Steel Processing; Joint Venture Between Ferragon (51%) & Steel Technologies (49%)
N.A.I.C.S.: 331221
Eduardo Gonzalez (Pres)
Mark Nester (Gen Mgr)
Terry Kirkland (Plant Mgr)
Sonia A. Cobos (Dir-Safety)
Dave Rickus (Dir-Safety)

FerrouSouth   (1)
38 County Road 370, Iuka, MS 38852
Tel.: (662) 424-0115
Web Site: http://www.ferrousouth.com
Steel Products Mfr
N.A.I.C.S.: 331110
Eduardo Gonzalez (Pres)
Dave Rickus (Dir-Safety)

Ferrous85" Co.   (1)
PO Box 429, Newport, KY 41072-0429
Tel.: (859) 261-6161
Web Site: http://www.ferrous85.com
Steel Products Mfr
N.A.I.C.S.: 331110

Eduardo Gonzalez (Pres)
Luis Gonzalez (VP-Ops)

FERRAN SERVICES & CONTRACTING
530 Grand St, Orlando, FL 32805-4795
Tel.: (407) 422-3551
Web Site: https://www.ferran-services.com
Rev.: $10,971,675
Emp.: 97
Warm Air Heating & Air Conditioning Contractor
N.A.I.C.S.: 238220
Adolph Marmetschke (Pres)
David Hase (VP-Construction)
James J. Flaherty (Mgr-Construction)
Pam Stone (Mgr-HR)
Cathy Zellner (VP & Mgr-Electrical)

FERRAR-CARANO VINEYARDS WINERY
8761 Dry Creek Rd, Healdsburg, CA 95448
Tel.: (707) 433-6700
Web Site: http://www.ferrar-carano.com
Rev.: $12,100,000
Emp.: 65
Winery
N.A.I.C.S.: 312130

FERRARA BROS. BUILDING MATERIALS CORP.
120 05 31st Ave, Flushing, NY 11354
Tel.: (718) 939-3030   NY
Web Site: http://www.ferrarabros.com
Year Founded: 1969
Sales Range: $10-24.9 Million
Emp.: 85
Producer of Ready Mixed Concrete
N.A.I.C.S.: 327320
Joseph A. Ferrara (Pres & CEO)
Leonard Ferrara (VP)
Mark Capone (Dir-Sls)

FERRARA WINERY
1120 W 15th Ave, Escondido, CA 92025-5548
Tel.: (760) 745-7632
Web Site:
http://www.ferrarawinery.com
Year Founded: 1932
Sales Range: $25-49.9 Million
Emp.: 100
Vineyard & Wine Mfr
N.A.I.C.S.: 111332
Gaspar Ferrara (Owner)

FERRARI PARTNERS LP
357 Riverside Dr Ste 230, Franklin, TN 37064
Tel.: (615) 591-2727
Web Site:
http://www.ferraripartners.com
Year Founded: 1997
Sales Range: $1-9.9 Million
Emp.: 6
Commercial, Multi-Family, Residential & Developmental Real Estate Properties Owner & Manager
N.A.I.C.S.: 531312
Keith Ferrari (Mng Partner)
Chad Ferrari (Partner)

FERREIRA CONSTRUCTION COMPANY, INC.
31 Tannery Rd, Branchburg, NJ 08876
Tel.: (908) 534-8655
Web Site:
https://www.ferreiraconstruction.com
Year Founded: 1988
Sales Range: $125-149.9 Million
Emp.: 254

Full-Service Heavy Construction Services
N.A.I.C.S.: 237310
Brian Delpome (VP-Field Ops)
Nancy Vliet (VP)
Dictino Garcia (Exec VP)
Nelson Ferreira (Pres & CEO)

FERRELS CARD SHOP INC.
1041B Sam Walton Ln, Lees Summit, MO 64086
Tel.: (816) 524-0700
Web Site: http://www.ferrels.com
Sales Range: $10-24.9 Million
Emp.: 9
Greeting Cards
N.A.I.C.S.: 459420
Wynn Ferrel (Pres)

FERRER FREEMAN & COMPANY, LLC
10 Glenville St, Greenwich, CT 06831
Tel.: (203) 532-8011   CT
Web Site: http://www.ffandco.com
Year Founded: 1995
Emp.: 7
Privater Equity Firm
N.A.I.C.S.: 523999
David A. Freeman (Co-Founder & Partner)
Nicole Sansone (CFO)
Theodore B. Lundberg (Partner)

Subsidiaries:

Arcadia Solutions, LLC   (1)
20 Blanchard Rd Ste 10, Burlington, MA 01803
Tel.: (781) 202-3600
Web Site: http://www.arcadiasolutions.com
Sales Range: $10-24.9 Million
Health Care Consulting Services
N.A.I.C.S.: 541618
Sean Carroll (CEO)
Michael Gleeson (Chief Innovation Officer & Chief Strategy Officer)
Richard Parker (Chief Medical Officer)
Jonathan F. Cook (CTO)
Alyssa Drew (Dir-Strategic Mktg)
Loretta D. Keane (CFO)
Brian Croegaert (Sr VP-Value Based Care Svcs)
Michael Meucci (Sr VP-Growth)
Nick Stepro (Sr VP-Product Mgmt)
Jim Crook (Chm)

Subsidiary (Domestic):

Sage Technologies Co.   (2)
630 E Jefferson St, Rockford, IL 61107-4026
Tel.: (815) 966-0192
Web Site: http://www.usesage.com
Sales Range: $1-9.9 Million
Managed Care Solutions & Services
N.A.I.C.S.: 541519
Brian Croegaert (CEO)

FERRERI SEARCH LLC
500 N Westshore Blvd Ste 960, Tampa, FL 33609
Tel.: (813) 490-0004
Web Site:
http://www.ferrerisearch.com
Year Founded: 2007
Sales Range: $1-9.9 Million
Emp.: 23
Employment Services
N.A.I.C.S.: 561311
Frank Ferreri (Founder & Mng Partner)
Damien Munnings (Acct Mgr-Fin & Acctg)
Peter Grabowski (CFO)

FERRETERIA TESORO DEL EBANISTA
251 Calle Guayama, San Juan, PR 00917
Tel.: (787) 758-6520

Web Site: http://www.tesoropr.com
Rev.: $10,741,534
Emp.: 60
Lumber: Rough, Dressed & Finished
N.A.I.C.S.: 423310
Jesus Morales (Pres)

FERRI SUPERMARKETS INC.
3913 Old William Penn Hwy, Murrysville, PA 15668
Tel.: (724) 327-0921
Sales Range: $10-24.9 Million
Emp.: 40
Operator of Independent Supermarket
N.A.I.C.S.: 445110
John Ferri (Pres)

FERRINI USA INC.
1810 Surveyor Blvd, Carrollton, TX 75006-5108
Tel.: (972) 478-7878
Web Site: http://www.ferriniusa.com
Rev.: $19,000,000
Emp.: 10
Sell Leather & Leather Products
N.A.I.C.S.: 316990
Vino Ferrini (Pres)

FERRIOT, INC.
1000 Arlington Cir, Akron, OH 44306-3973
Tel.: (330) 786-3000
Web Site: https://www.ferriot.com
Year Founded: 1860
Sales Range: $10-24.9 Million
Emp.: 165
Plastics Product Mfr
N.A.I.C.S.: 326199
Gene Ferriot (Pres & CEO)
Roger Peck (Dir-Sls & Mktg)
David Murphy (Dir-HR)
Denver Bortz (VP)

FERRITE INTERNATIONAL COMPANY
39105 Magnetics Blvd, Wadsworth, IL 60083
Tel.: (847) 249-4900
Web Site:
https://www.tscinternational.com
Sales Range: $10-24.9 Million
Emp.: 50
Ferrite & Ferrite Parts
N.A.I.C.S.: 327110
Bob Grubiak (Mgr-Customer Svc-Web Design)
Andy Petrancosta (Mgr-Lamination Production)
Tempel Smith Jr. (Pres)

FERRY INDUSTRIES INC.
4445 Allen Rd, Stow, OH 44224-1093
Tel.: (330) 920-9200
Web Site:
https://www.ferryindustries.com
Rev.: $25,000,000
Emp.: 95
Custom Machinery
N.A.I.C.S.: 333998
Ann Rowland (Mgr-Sales-Intl)

FERTIG CABINET COMPANY INC.
137 Beans Ln, Moorefield, WV 26836
Tel.: (304) 538-6215
Web Site:
https://www.fertigcabinet.com
Rev.: $13,000,000
Emp.: 80
Mfr & Distributor of Cabinets, Countertops, Vanity Tops, Kitchen & Bath Fixtures & Hardware
N.A.I.C.S.: 444180
Sue Williams (Treas & Sec)
Robert Fertig Sr. (CEO)
Robert Fertig Jr. (Pres)

FERTILIZER COMPANY OF ARIZONA
2850 S Peart Rd, Casa Grande, AZ 85193
Tel.: (520) 836-7477
Web Site: https://www.fertizona.com
Sales Range: $25-49.9 Million
Emp.: 50
Provider of Fertilizers
N.A.I.C.S.: 325314
James R. Compton Jr. *(Pres)*

FERTILIZER DEALER SUPPLY INC.
106 W Monroe St, Philo, IL 61864
Tel.: (217) 684-2080
Web Site:
https://www.fertilizerdealer.com
Rev.: $14,572,793
Emp.: 200
Agricultural Machinery & Equipment
N.A.I.C.S.: 423820
Lukas Meharry *(Mgr-Svc)*
Cathy Evans *(Dir-HR)*

FERTILIZER EQUIPMENT INC.
913 14th St SW, Valley City, ND 58072-4202
Tel.: (701) 845-1113
Web Site: https://www.feiinc.com
Year Founded: 1996
Sales Range: $10-24.9 Million
Emp.: 30
Holding Company
N.A.I.C.S.: 423820
Clay Adams *(Mgr-Customer Svcs)*

FERTITTA ENTERTAINMENT, INC.
1510 W Loop S, Houston, TX 77027
Tel.: (713) 850-1010   **TX**
Web Site:
https://www.tilmanfertitta.com
Year Founded: 2010
Sales Range: Less than $1 Million
Emp.: 46,500
Offices of Other Holding Companies
N.A.I.C.S.: 551112
Subsidiaries:

Landry's, Inc.   **(1)**
1510 W Loop S, Houston, TX 77027
Tel.: (713) 850-1010
Web Site: http://www.landrysinc.com
Sales Range: $1-4.9 Billion
Emp.: 26,000
Holding Company; Restaurants Owner, Franchisor & Operator; Casino Hotels Owner & Operator
N.A.I.C.S.: 551112
Tilman J. Fertitta *(Chm, Pres & CEO)*

Subsidiary (Domestic):

Bubba Gump Shrimp Co. Restaurants, Inc.   **(2)**
1510 W Loop S, Houston, TX 77027
Tel.: (713) 850-1010
Web Site: http://www.bubbagump.com
Sales Range: $200-249.9 Million
Seafood Restaurants Franchisor & Operator
N.A.I.C.S.: 722511
Tilman J. Fertitta *(Pres & CEO)*

C.A. Muer Corporation   **(2)**
1510 W Loop S, Houston, TX 77027-9505
Tel.: (713) 850-1010
Web Site: http://www.muer.com
Sales Range: $500-549.9 Million
Emp.: 20,000
Restaurants Franchisor & Operator
N.A.I.C.S.: 722511
Tilman J. Fertitta *(Pres & CEO)*

Del Frisco's Double Eagle Steak House   **(2)**
2323 Olive St, Dallas, TX 75201
Tel.: (972) 490-9000
Steakhouse
N.A.I.C.S.: 722511
Gina Cook *(Gen Mgr)*

Unit (Domestic):

Golden Nugget Hotel & Casino - Atlantic City   **(2)**
Huron Ave & Brigantine Blvd, Atlantic City, NJ 08401
Tel.: (609) 441-2000
Web Site: http://www.goldennugget.com
Casino Hotels
N.A.I.C.S.: 721120
Adrian Ford *(Sr Exec Dir-Player Dev)*
Alan Korman *(Sr Exec Dir-Player Dev)*
Anthony Speziale *(Exec Dir-Player Dev)*
Alisa Weiss *(Exec Dir-Player Dev)*
Chris Merlino *(Sr Exec Dir-Player Dev)*
Dianna Odonnell *(Exec Dir-Player Dev)*
Marixsa Pagan *(Exec Dir-Player Dev)*
Ralph Dambrosio *(VP-Mktg-Natl)*
Sonny Ianoale *(Sr Exec Dir-Player Dev)*

Golden Nugget Hotel & Casino - Las Vegas   **(2)**
129 E Fremont St, Las Vegas, NV 89101-5603
Tel.: (702) 385-7111
Web Site: http://www.goldennugget.com
Sales Range: $50-74.9 Million
Emp.: 3,000
Hotel & Casino Operator
N.A.I.C.S.: 721120
William Sylvester *(CFO & VP)*
Amy Chasey *(VP-Mktg)*
Gerry Del Prete *(Sr VP & Gen Mgr)*

Golden Nugget Hotel & Casino - Laughlin   **(2)**
2300 S Casino Dr, Laughlin, NV 89028-7111
Tel.: (702) 298-1111
Sales Range: $1-9.9 Million
Emp.: 60
Hotel & Casino Operator
N.A.I.C.S.: 721120

Subsidiary (Domestic):

Houlihan's Restaurants, Inc.   **(2)**
8700 State Line Rd Ste 100, Leawood, KS 66206
Tel.: (913) 901-2500
Web Site: http://www.houlihans.com
Casual Dining Restaurants
N.A.I.C.S.: 722511
Robert Ellis *(Chief Dev Officer)*
Jennifer Gulvik *(VP-Mktg)*
Michael Slavin *(VP-Culinary & Menu Innovation)*
Bill Leibengood *(CMO)*

MFM Winter Park, LLC   **(2)**
1030 W Canton Ave Ste 100, Winter Park, FL 32789
Tel.: (407) 333-7440
Web Site:
http://www.mitchellsfishmarket.com
Sales Range: $50-74.9 Million
Seafood Restaurants Operator & Franchisor
N.A.I.C.S.: 722511
Matthew Barber *(Gen Mgr)*

McCormick & Schmick's Seafood Restaurants, Inc.   **(2)**
1510 W Loop S, Houston, TX 77027
Tel.: (713) 850-1010
Web Site:
http://www.mccormickandschmicks.com
Sales Range: $300-349.9 Million
Emp.: 6,582
Seafood Restaurant Chain
N.A.I.C.S.: 722511
Steven L. Scheinthal *(Sec & VP)*

Subsidiary (Non-US):

The Boathouse Restaurants of Canada, Inc.   **(3)**
1305 Arbutus Street, Vancouver, V6J 5N2, BC, Canada
Tel.: (604) 738-5487
Web Site:
http://www.boathouserestaurants.ca
Sales Range: $25-49.9 Million
Emp.: 120
Seafood Restaurant Operator
N.A.I.C.S.: 722511

Subsidiary (Domestic):

Rainforest Cafe, Inc.   **(2)**

1510 W Loop S, Houston, TX 77027-9505
Tel.: (713) 850-1010
Web Site: http://www.rainforestcafe.com
Sales Range: $400-449.9 Million
Emp.: 7,000
Restaurant
N.A.I.C.S.: 722511
Tilman J. Fertitta *(CEO)*
Steven L. Scheinthal *(Gen Counsel & VP-Admin)*
Richard H. Liem *(VP-Fin)*

Saltgrass Inc.   **(2)**
1510 W Loop S, Houston, TX 77027
Tel.: (713) 436-0799
Web Site: http://www.saltgrass.com
Sales Range: $75-99.9 Million
Emp.: 1,000
Restaurant Operators
N.A.I.C.S.: 722511
Terry Turney *(VP-Ops)*

The Events Company   **(2)**
1237 N Post Oak Rd, Houston, TX 77055
Tel.: (713) 426-5800
Sales Range: $25-49.9 Million
Emp.: 40
Event Planning
N.A.I.C.S.: 561920
Richard W. Flowers *(COO)*
Daisy Sloan White *(Dir-Bus Dev & Mgr-Event)*

Unit (Domestic):

The San Luis Resort, Spa & Conference Center   **(2)**
5222 Seawall Blvd, Galveston, TX 77551
Tel.: (409) 744-1500
Web Site: http://www.sanluisresort.com
Rev.: $16,800,000
Emp.: 300
Hotel Resort
N.A.I.C.S.: 721110
Beverly Burns *(Asst Controller)*
David Townsend *(Dir-Conference Plng)*
Jody Jones *(Dir-HR)*
Philett Carter *(Dir-Guest Rels)*
Mike Regli *(Reg Dir-Sls)*
Elizabeth Himes *(Brand Mgr)*
Michael Hammes *(Dir-Food & Beverage)*
Rex Kilgo *(Dir-Engrg)*
Dana Loukanis *(Sr Mgr-Sls-Natl)*
Carly Rowland *(Mgr-Resort Sls)*
Melonee Scurlock *(Mgr-Conference Plng)*
Kristin Shirley *(Mgr-Mktg)*
Nancy Van Bramer *(Mgr-Resort Sls)*
Allison Vasquez *(Mgr-Resort Sls)*
Lauraleigh Vogel *(Mgr-Resort Sls)*

FESCO SYSTEMS LLC
Ste F 3985 Steve Reynolds Blvd, Norcross, GA 30093-3094
Tel.: (770) 825-0955
Web Site:
http://www.fescosystems.com
Rev.: $11,204,909
Emp.: 40
Machinery Installation
N.A.I.C.S.: 333515
Billy McGee *(Mgr-Sls)*

FESLER AUTO MALL
1922 Hwy 34 W, Fairfield, IA 52556-8630
Tel.: (641) 843-7147
Web Site:
https://www.feslerautomall.com
Year Founded: 2006
Sales Range: $10-24.9 Million
Emp.: 40
Car Whslr
N.A.I.C.S.: 441110
Monte Humble *(Owner)*

FESSENDEN CO-OP ASSOCIATION INC.
900 Railway St S, Fessenden, ND 58438-0126
Tel.: (701) 547-3291   **ND**
Web Site: https://www.fesscoop.com
Year Founded: 1943
Sales Range: $10-24.9 Million
Emp.: 40

Grain & Field Beans
N.A.I.C.S.: 424510
Mark Hovland *(Gen Mgr)*

FESSENDEN HALL INCORPORATED
1050 Sherman Ave, Pennsauken, NJ 08110
Tel.: (856) 665-2210
Web Site:
https://www.fessendenhall.com
Rev.: $50,750,000
Emp.: 95
Plywood
N.A.I.C.S.: 423310
Ray Jungclaus *(Treas)*
Roeby Birdsall *(Gen Mgr)*
Tom Boland *(Mgr-IT)*
Rosemary Leister *(Mgr-Specification)*
Jack Parks *(Product Mgr-Surfaces)*
Robert Schaefer *(Product Mgr)*
Jack Conroy *(Mgr-Resource)*

FESTIVA RESORTS LLC
1 Vance Gap Rd, Asheville, NC 28805
Tel.: (828) 254-3378
Web Site:
http://www.festivaresorts.com
Year Founded: 2000
Sales Range: $10-24.9 Million
Emp.: 550
Hotel & Resort Operation Services
N.A.I.C.S.: 721120
Butch Patrick *(Pres)*
Dessie Laster *(CFO)*
Don McQuade *(Sr VP-Sls)*
J. Lance Croft *(Sr VP-Mktg)*
Scott Sonnone *(COO & Sr VP)*

FESTIVAL FUNPARKS LLC
4590 MacArthur Blvd Ste 400, Newport Beach, CA 92660
Tel.: (949) 261-0404
Web Site:
http://www.palaceentertainment.com
Sales Range: $50-74.9 Million
Emp.: 45
Miniature Golf Course Operation
N.A.I.C.S.: 713940
Fernando Eiroa *(Pres)*

FESTIVAL ICE CREAM CORP.
91 18th Ave, Paterson, NJ 07513
Tel.: (973) 684-8935
Web Site:
http://www.festivalicecream.net
Rev.: $16,100,000
Emp.: 55
Ice Cream & Ices
N.A.I.C.S.: 424430
Mario C. Calbi *(Pres)*

FESTIVE FOODS, LLC.
7811 County Rd D, Waupaca, WI 54981
Tel.: (715) 258-7740
Web Site:
https://www.festivefoodsllc.com
Sales Range: $10-24.9 Million
Emp.: 150
Frozen Pizza Mfr & Distr
N.A.I.C.S.: 311412
Michael Holmgren *(Pres)*
Julie Compton *(Plant Mgr-Quality Control)*

FETCH LOGISTICS, INC.
25 Northpointe Pkwy Ste 200, Amherst, NY 14228
Tel.: (716) 689-4556
Web Site:
http://www.fetchlogistics.com
Year Founded: 1997
Sales Range: $10-24.9 Million
Emp.: 30

Fetch Logistics, Inc.—(Continued)
Freight Transportation Management
Services
N.A.I.C.S.: 488510
William Wilcox *(Founder)*
Dave Bryk *(Partner)*
Robert Atwater *(Partner)*
Robert R. Closs II *(Founder)*

FETCHS ENTERPRISES INC.
180 Wyoming Ave, Wyoming, PA
18644-1723
Tel.: (570) 779-9864
Rev.: $20,000,000
Emp.: 60
Independent Supermarket
N.A.I.C.S.: 445110
David R. Fetch Jr. *(Pres)*

FETCO HOME DECOR INC.
84 Teed Dr, Randolph, MA 02368-
4202
Tel.: (781) 963-3636 **MA**
Web Site:
http://www.fetcohomedecor.com
Year Founded: 1972
Sales Range: $25-49.9 Million
Emp.: 111
Homefurnishings
N.A.I.C.S.: 423220
Nancy Babine Kucinski *(Pres & CEO)*

FETTER PRINTING COMPANY
700 Locust Ln, Louisville, KY 40217-
2997
Tel.: (502) 634-4771 **KY**
Web Site: http://www.fettergroup.com
Year Founded: 1888
Sales Range: $10-24.9 Million
Emp.: 120
Lithographic Commercial Printing
N.A.I.C.S.: 323111
John Roos *(CFO)*
Terance W. Gill Jr. *(Pres & CEO)*

FEUTZ CONTRACTORS, INC.
1120 N Main St, Paris, IL 61944
Tel.: (217) 465-8402
Web Site:
https://www.feutzcontractors.com
Sales Range: $10-24.9 Million
Emp.: 25
Highway, Street & Bridge Construc-
tion Services
N.A.I.C.S.: 237310
J. Steve Blair *(Chm & CEO)*

FEV NORTH AMERICA, INC.
4554 Glenmeade Ln, Auburn Hills, MI
48326-1766
Tel.: (248) 373-6000 **CA**
Web Site: https://www.fev.com
Year Founded: 1985
Emp.: 4,000
Engineeering Services
N.A.I.C.S.: 541330
Patrick Hupperich *(Pres & CEO)*

FEY INDUSTRIES, INC.
200 4th Ave N, Edgerton, MN 56128
Tel.: (507) 442-4311 **MN**
Web Site: http://www.fey-line.com
Year Founded: 1965
Sales Range: $25-49.9 Million
Emp.: 175
Novelties & Plastics Mfr
N.A.I.C.S.: 326199
Don Spencer *(Mgr-Northeast)*
Dan Musielewicz *(Controller)*

Subsidiaries:

Molenaar, LLC (1)
601 West Highway 40, Willmar, MN 56201
Tel.: (320) 231-2610
Web Site: http://www.miline.com

Sales Range: $10-24.9 Million
Emp.: 120
Other Commercial Printing
N.A.I.C.S.: 323111
Kevin Gilbertson *(Dir-Inside Sls)*

**FEYEN ZYLSTRA ELECTRIC
INC.**
210 Frnt Ave SW, Grand Rapids, MI
49504
Tel.: (616) 224-7707 **MI**
Web Site: http://www.feyen-
zylstra.com
Year Founded: 1993
Sales Range: $25-49.9 Million
Emp.: 240
Electrical Contracting Services
N.A.I.C.S.: 238210
Roger Tjoelker *(CFO)*
Nate Koetje *(COO)*

FEZELL ENTERPRISES INC.
200 Commons Dr, Du Bois, PA
15801
Tel.: (814) 375-9300
Year Founded: 2000
Operator of Supermarkets
N.A.I.C.S.: 445110
Donald R. Fezell *(Owner)*

Subsidiaries:

Fezell Enterprises II Inc. (1)
201 Hampton Ave, Punxsutawney, PA
15767
Tel.: (814) 938-2820
Web Site: http://www.fezellshopnsave.com
Sales Range: $25-49.9 Million
Emp.: 115
Operator of Supermarkets
N.A.I.C.S.: 445110
Donald Fezell *(Pres)*

FF SYSTEMS INC.
4841 Waycross Rd, Fort Myers, FL
33905
Tel.: (239) 288-4255
Web Site:
http://www.ffsystemsinc.com
Sales Range: $10-24.9 Million
Access Panels Mfr
N.A.I.C.S.: 334419
Thomas K. Trieloff *(Pres & CEO)*
Manuela Lyons *(Gen Mgr)*
Debbie Lloyd *(Office Mgr)*
Chuck Kreitner *(Mgr-Sls)*

FFC LIMITED PARTNERSHIP
166 S Gate Dr Ste 10, Boone, NC
28607-4906
Tel.: (828) 262-1811 **NC**
Web Site:
http://www.tarheelcapital.com
Year Founded: 1993
Sales Range: $150-199.9 Million
Emp.: 3,000
Eating Place
N.A.I.C.S.: 722513
Jim Furman *(CEO)*

FFF ENTERPRISES INC.
41093 County Ctr Dr, Temecula, CA
92591-6025
Tel.: (951) 296-2500
Web Site:
http://www.fffenterprises.com
Year Founded: 1988
Sales Range: $25-49.9 Million
Emp.: 370
Sales of Drugs, Proprietaries & Sun-
dries
N.A.I.C.S.: 424210
Patrick M. Schmidt *(Founder, Pres &
CEO)*
Jeff Primovic *(Sr VP-Strategic Rela-
tionships)*
Jonathan Hahn *(VP-Info Sys)*

FFI CONTRACTING SERVICES
12437 Brantley Commons Ct, Fort
Myers, FL 33907
Tel.: (239) 333-1777
Web Site: http://www.ffi1.com
Sales Range: $1-9.9 Million
Emp.: 12
Preservation & Renovation of Dis-
tressed Properties
N.A.I.C.S.: 236118
Annalisa Xioutas *(Pres & CEO)*

FFL PARTNERS, LLC
1 Maritime Plz 22nd Fl, San Fran-
cisco, CA 94111
Tel.: (415) 402-2100 **DE**
Web Site: http://www.fflpartners.com
Year Founded: 1998
Private Equity Investment Firm
N.A.I.C.S.: 523999
David L. Lowe *(Co-Founder)*
Tully Michael Friedman *(Mng Partner)*
Robert A. Eckert *(Operating Partner)*
Chris Harris *(Partner)*
Spencer C. Fleischer *(Co-Founder &
Chm)*
Christopher A. Masto *(Co-Founder)*
Karen Winterhof *(VP)*
Catherine Chen *(VP-IR)*

Subsidiaries:

ALKU, LLC (1)
200 Brickstone Sq Ste 503, Andover, MA
01810
Tel.: (978) 296-6900
Web Site: http://www.alku.com
Contract Staffing Services
N.A.I.C.S.: 561320
Mark Eldridge *(CEO)*
Matt Ovanes *(Pres-Expansion & Dev)*
Kathie Boles *(VP-Fin & Strategy)*
David Bruner *(VP-Bus Dev)*
Jon Kujala *(VP-Ops)*
Kate Lelievre *(VP-HR)*
Nathan O'Keeffe *(VP)*
David Tuell *(Dir-Healthcare IT Recruiting)*
Michael O'Brien *(Dir-HCIT & Security Sls)*
Marc Cirrone *(VP)*
Andrew Bull *(VP)*
Kyle Ketcham *(Dir-Bus Tech)*
Emily Collins *(Project Mgr)*
Aleksia Qirjazi *(Ops Mgr)*
Jonathan Martell *(Controller)*

Bacharach, Inc. (1)
621 Hunt Vly Cir, New Kensington, PA
15068
Tel.: (724) 334-5000
Web Site: http://www.mybacharach.com
Handheld Gas Detection Instrument Mfr
N.A.I.C.S.: 334519
Jim Mowery *(Dir-Sls)*
John Anuskiewicz *(Engr)*
James Burke *(Mgr-OEM Accts-Sls Ops)*
Chuck Hayden *(Mgr-Sls-Texas)*
Clint Daniel *(Mgr-Sls-Southeast USA &
Puerto Rico)*
Scott Franklin *(Mgr-Sls-Western USA,
Alaska & Hawaii)*

Subsidiary (Domestic):

Neutronics Inc. (2)
456 Creamery Wy, Exton, PA 19341
Tel.: (610) 524-8800
Automotive Parts & Accessories Stores
N.A.I.C.S.: 441330
David Halpern *(COO)*
Gary Halpern *(Pres)*
Jim Connor *(Mgr-Mfg)*

New Look Vision Group, Inc. (1)
1 Place Ville Marie Suite 3670, Montreal,
H3B 3P2, QC, Canada
Tel.: (514) 877-4119
Web Site: http://www.newlookvision.ca
Rev.: $227,938,213
Assets: $295,615,273
Liabilities: $174,060,725
Net Worth: $121,554,548
Earnings: $14,844,126
Emp.: 2,599
Fiscal Year-end: 12/28/2019
Eye Wear Accessories Distr

N.A.I.C.S.: 423460
Antoine Amiel *(Pres & CEO)*
Tania M. Clarke *(CFO & Sr VP)*
France Reimnitz *(VP-Mktg & Mdsg)*
Caroline Rouleau *(VP-Professional Svcs &
HR Optician Networks)*
Jean-Michel Maltais *(Sr VP-Omni-Channel)*
Stephane Seguin *(VP-IT)*
Michael Tovey *(VP-Frames & Product Dev)*
Jason Schonfeld *(Sr VP-Bus Dev)*
Jean-Francois Lacasse *(VP-Bus Dev)*

Subsidiary (Domestic):

IRIS The Visual Group Inc. (2)
3030 Boul Le Carrefour Suite 1200, Laval,
H7T 2P5, QC, Canada
Tel.: (450) 688-9060
Web Site: http://www.iris.ca
Eye Care Product Distr
N.A.I.C.S.: 423450

Summit Healthcare Management,
LLC (1)
389 Nichol Mill Ln Ste 100 & 160, Franklin,
TN 37067
Tel.: (615) 435-3725
Web Site: http://www.summitbhc.com
Behavioral Health Centers Management
N.A.I.C.S.: 621420
William Brent Turner *(CEO)*
Trey Carter *(Co-Founder)*
Chuck Edwards *(Co-Founder & CFO)*
Jeff Barnett *(COO)*
Karen Prince *(Co-Founder)*
Danny Carpenter *(Exec VP-Fin Ops)*
Jill Shrader *(VP-Quality & Compliance)*
Lisa Smith *(VP-HR)*
Christina Hawkins *(VP-Strategic Dev & PR)*
K. Anderson *(VP-Admission Center Ops)*
Jon O'Shaughnessy *(Pres)*
Brent Turner *(CEO)*

Subsidiary (Domestic):

Summit BHC Sevierville, LLC (2)
1096 Alpine Dr, Sevierville, TN 37876
Tel.: (877) 309-9963
Web Site: http://englishmountain.com
Drug & Alcohol Addiction Rehabilitation Ser-
vices
N.A.I.C.S.: 624190
William Brent Turner *(CEO)*
Clay Phillips *(VP-Strategy & Managed
Care)*
Brent Turner *(CEO)*
Chuck Steiner *(Chief Strategy Officer)*

The Ranch at Dove Tree LLC (2)
1406 Quinlan St, Lubbock, TX 79403
Tel.: (806) 746-6777
Web Site: http://www.ranchatdovetree.com
Outpatient Mental Health & Substance
Abuse Centers
N.A.I.C.S.: 621420
Curt G. Maddon *(CEO)*
Jeanette Franks *(Dir-Quality & Risk Mgmt)*
Katie Trungale *(Dir-Bus Dev)*

U.S. Orthopaedic Partners (1)
2520 Northwinds Pkwy Ste 100, Alpharetta,
GA 30009
Tel.: (404) 445-4480
Web Site: https://www.us-orthopartners.com
Orthopaedic Services
N.A.I.C.S.: 621111
Glen Silverman *(CEO)*

Subsidiary (Domestic):

Midstate Orthopaedic and Sports
Medicine Center, Inc. (2)
3351 Masonic Dr, Alexandria, LA 71301
Tel.: (318) 473-9556
Web Site: http://www.midstateortho.com
Health Practitioners
N.A.I.C.S.: 621399
Spencer Michael *(CEO)*

**FFVA MUTUAL INSURANCE
CO.**
800 Trafalgar Ct Ste 200, Maitland,
FL 32751
Tel.: (321) 214-5300
Web Site:
https://www.ffvamutual.com
Year Founded: 1956
Sales Range: $100-124.9 Million

Emp.: 200
Insurance Carrier
N.A.I.C.S.: 524128
Craig Menzl (Pres & CEO)
Alan Hair (CFO, Treas & Sec)
Donna Grier (VP-Underwriting Ops)
Jose Ramos (VP-Safety & Loss Control)
Sandra Riding (VP-Claims)
Glenn R. Rogers (Vice Chm)
Fred Allen (VP-IT)
Bruce Clement (VP-Investments)
Melissa Hide (VP-Mktg & Brand Dev)
Ronald Kifer (Asst VP-Claims)
Les W. Dunson III (Chm)

FG HAGGERTY COMPANY, INC.
1318 Hatton Rd, Wichita Falls, TX 76302-3008
Tel.: (940) 761-1161
Web Site:
    https://www.fghaggerty.com
Sales Range: $10-24.9 Million
Emp.: 50
Plumbing Services
N.A.I.C.S.: 238220
Mike Haggerty (Pres)

FGI GROUP INC.
3901 S Lamar Blvd Ste 100, Austin, TX 78704-7989
Tel.: (512) 448-9898
Year Founded: 1984
Sales Range: $400-449.9 Million
Emp.: 25
Commercial Construction Services
N.A.I.C.S.: 236220
Royce Faulkner (Pres)

Subsidiaries:

Dynamic Systems Inc.   (1)
3901 S Lamar Blvd Ste 300, Austin, TX 78704-8718
Tel.: (512) 443-4848
Sales Range: $50-74.9 Million
Provider of Plumbing, Heating & Air-Conditioning Services
N.A.I.C.S.: 238220
Mark Ridley (CFO, Treas & Sr VP)
Randy Rehmann (Pres & CEO)
Peyton Henderson (CFO, Treas & Sr VP)

FGP INTERNATIONAL, INC.
15 Brendan Way, Greenville, SC 29615
Tel.: (864) 297-0000
Web Site:
    http://www.findgreatpeople.com
Year Founded: 1982
Sales Range: $10-24.9 Million
Emp.: 50
Temporary & Permanent Staffing Services
N.A.I.C.S.: 561311
Steve Hall (VP-Bus Dev)
John Uprichard (Pres)
Beth Mcnamara (Dir-Bus Dev)
Vicki Peek (VP-Ops)
Tecumseh Hooper Jr. (Chm)

FH COMPANIES, INC.
5003 E 61st St N, Kechi, KS 67067-0250
Tel.: (316) 264-2208
Web Site: https://www.f-hcompanies.com
Year Founded: 1979
Sales Range: $10-24.9 Million
Emp.: 130
Industrial Insulation & Scaffolding Contractor
N.A.I.C.S.: 238310
John Pfister (Owner, Pres & CEO)
Richard Yust (CFO)
Randy Wheeler (Dir-Safety & Trng)
Mark Rossillon (VP)

FHC CONTRACTING, INC.
400 E Centre Park Blvd Ste 103, Desoto, TX 75115-8802
Tel.: (972) 224-3093
Web Site:
    http://www.fhccontracting.com
Sales Range: $10-24.9 Million
Emp.: 27
Nonresidential Construction Services
N.A.I.C.S.: 236220
Paul Fehmel (Owner)

FHC HEALTH SYSTEMS INC.
240 Corporate Blvd, Norfolk, VA 23502
Tel.: (757) 459-5100
Web Site:
    http://www.fhchealthsystems.com
Year Founded: 1983
Sales Range: $1-4.9 Billion
Emp.: 8,100
Behavorial Health Care Services
N.A.I.C.S.: 621330
Ronald I. Dozoretz (Founder, Chm & CEO)
Bob Esposito (CIO & Exec VP)
E. Paul Dunn Jr. (CFO)

FHC HOLDING COMPANY
2509 29th St SW, Wyoming, MI 49519
Tel.: (616) 538-3231   MI
Web Site:
    https://www.franklinholwerda.com
Sales Range: $10-24.9 Million
Emp.: 101
Holding Company; Plumbing, Heating, Ventilation & Air Conditioning Contracting Services
N.A.I.C.S.: 551112
Darrell Boerema (Pres)
Micah Holt (Treas & Sec)
Douglas Holt (VP)

Subsidiaries:

Franklin Holwerda Company   (1)
2509 29th St SW, Wyoming, MI 49519   (100%)
Tel.: (616) 538-3231
Web Site: http://www.franklinholwerda.com
Plumbing, Heating, Ventilation & Air Conditioning Contracting Services
N.A.I.C.S.: 238220
Raymond Holt (Controller)
Douglas Holt (VP)
Brent Appleyard (Project Mgr)
Micah Holt (Treas & Sec)
Greg Johnson (Supvr-Fire Protection)
Eric Kiliszewski (Mgr-Shop)
David Reynhout (Project Mgr)

FHC MARKETING
4711 N Lamon Ave, Chicago, IL 60630
Tel.: (773) 777-6100
Web Site:
    http://www.fhcmarketing.com
Year Founded: 1920
Sales Range: $10-24.9 Million
Emp.: 60
Brand Development, Merchandising, Point of Purchase, Point of Sale, Retail, Sales Promotion
N.A.I.C.S.: 541810
Michelle Lopez (Controller)
Todd Carmichael (Principal)
Robert Anderson (Project Mgr)
Jim Sarnowski (Project Mgr)
Cindy Obos (Supvr-Customer Svc)

FHI 360
359 Blackwell St Ste 200, Durham, NC 27701
Tel.: (919) 544-7040   NC
Web Site: http://www.fhi360.org
Year Founded: 1973
Sales Range: $650-699.9 Million
Emp.: 4,500

Non Profit Medical Research & Technical Assistance Center
N.A.I.C.S.: 541720
Pamela Myers (Chief HR Officer)
Sean Temeemi (Chief Compliance Officer)

FI CONSULTING
1101 Wilson Blvd Ste 1810, Arlington, VA 22209
Tel.: (571) 255-6900
Web Site:
    https://www.ficonsulting.com
Year Founded: 2003
Rev.: $4,100,000
Emp.: 30
Management Consulting Services
N.A.I.C.S.: 541611
Roman Iwachiw (Co-Founder & CEO)
Allison Kirsch (COO)
Krzysztof Fizyta (Mgr)
Michelle Valinote (Office Mgr)
Susan Streich (Sr Mgr)
Robert Silverman (Mng Dir-Solutions)

FI-MED MANAGEMENT, INC.
2200 N Mayfair Rd Ste 200, Wauwatosa, WI 53226
Tel.: (414) 258-9511   WI
Web Site: http://www.fimed.com
Year Founded: 1993
Sales Range: $1-9.9 Million
Emp.: 76
Management Services to Healthcare Facilities
N.A.I.C.S.: 561110
Adrian Velasquez (Pres)
Christine Krause (VP)

FIAT INCORPORATED
5135 E ingram St, Mesa, AZ 85205-6953
Tel.: (480) 807-0255   AZ
Web Site: http://www.fiatinc.com
Year Founded: 2003
Heating & Air Conditioning Services
N.A.I.C.S.: 238220
John M. Hooper (Founder, Pres & CEO)

Subsidiaries:

Burt-Burnett, Inc.   (1)
1920 E Third St Ste 1, Tempe, AZ 85281
Tel.: (480) 557-8593
Web Site: http://www.burt-burnett.com
Sales Range: $1-9.9 Million
Emp.: 17
Commercial Heating & Air Conditioning Services
N.A.I.C.S.: 238220
Mark Winder (Mgr-Svc)
John M. Hooper (CEO)
Randall A. Gleave (COO)
James Strassels (CFO)

FIBA TECHNOLOGIES INC.
1535 Grafton Rd, Millbury, MA 01527
Tel.: (508) 887-7100
Web Site: http://www.fibatech.com
Year Founded: 1971
Sales Range: $10-24.9 Million
Emp.: 200
Industrial Machinery & Equipment Testing & Repair Services
N.A.I.C.S.: 423830
Chris Adams (Dir-Mktg)
Joe Sandello (Exec VP)
Bill O'Brien (VP-Ops)

Subsidiaries:

Amko Service Company   (1)
3211 Brightwood Rd, Midvale, OH 44653
Tel.: (330) 602-7300
Web Site: http://www.amkotech.com
Cryogenic Equipment Repair
N.A.I.C.S.: 811310

FIBER & YARN PRODUCTS INC.
585 11th St NW, Hickory, NC 28601
Tel.: (828) 324-9133
Web Site:
    http://www.fiberandyarn.com
Year Founded: 1980
Sales Range: $10-24.9 Million
Emp.: 60
Mfr of Yarns, Nylon & Polyester
N.A.I.C.S.: 424990
David Poole (Pres)

FIBER COMPOSITES, LLC
181 Random Dr, New London, NC 28127
Tel.: (704) 463-7120
Web Site:
    https://www.fiberondecking.com
Sales Range: $25-49.9 Million
Emp.: 300
Composite Decking Materials Mfr & Distr
N.A.I.C.S.: 423390
Doug Mancosh (Pres)
Anne-Marie Davis (Controller)
Rick Lappin (Product Mgr-Design & Compliance)
Tammy Sanders (Coord-Warranty & Consumer Svcs)

FIBER FIX, LLC
1021 S 1680 W Orem, Pleasant Grove, UT 84508
Tel.: (801) 701-0096
Web Site: http://www.fiberfix.com
Sales Range: $1-9.9 Million
Adhesive Mfr
N.A.I.C.S.: 325520
Eric Child (Co-Founder)
Spencer Quinn (Co-Founder)

FIBER FUELS INC.
755 W Armory Rd, Jefferson, SC 29718
Tel.: (843) 658-3960
Web Site: https://www.fiber-fuels.com
Rev.: $20,000,000
Emp.: 25
Lumber: Rough, Dressed & Finished
N.A.I.C.S.: 423310

FIBER GLASS HAWAII INC.
1377 Colburn St, Honolulu, HI 96817
Tel.: (808) 847-3951
Web Site:
    http://www.fiberglasshawaii.com
Sales Range: $10-24.9 Million
Emp.: 32
Resins, Synthetic
N.A.I.C.S.: 424610
Edward Wilson (Pres)

FIBER GLASS INDUSTRIES INC.
69 Edson St, Amsterdam, NY 12010
Tel.: (518) 842-4000
Web Site:
    http://www.fiberglassindustries.com
Sales Range: $10-24.9 Million
Emp.: 130
Fiberglass Fabrics
N.A.I.C.S.: 313210
John Menzel (Chm)
James Farnan (Controller)
Lora Mosher (Mgr-Pur)
Georgie Constantino (Coord-Sls)

FIBERCON INTERNATIONAL INC.
100 S 3rd St, Evans City, PA 16033
Tel.: (724) 538-5006
Web Site:
    https://www.fiberconfiber.com
Year Founded: 1981
Sales Range: $300-349.9 Million

Fibercon International Inc.—(Continued)

Emp.: 70
Iron & Steel Mill Services
N.A.I.C.S.: 331110
Keith Foley *(VP-Sls & Mktg)*
Cliff Armstrong *(Mgr-Logistics)*

FIBERDYNE LABS INC.
127 Bus Park Dr, Frankfort, NY
13340
Tel.: (315) 895-8470
Web Site: https://www.fiberdyne.com
Rev.: $12,000,000
Emp.: 110
Fiber Optic Cable (Insulated)
N.A.I.C.S.: 335921
Jim Hains *(Sr VP-Bus Dev-United States)*
Michael Polidori *(Project Mgr)*
Justin Welyczko *(Reg Dir)*

FIBERESIN INDUSTRIES, INC.
37031 E Wisconsin Ave, Oconomowoc, WI 53066-3146
Tel.: (262) 567-4427   WI
Web Site: https://www.fiberesin.com
Laminated Particle Board & Wood
Composites Mfr
N.A.I.C.S.: 321219
Mike Macdougal *(Pres & CEO)*

FIBERLAY INC
24 S Idaho St, Seattle, WA 98134
Tel.: (206) 782-0660   WA
Web Site: http://www.fiberlay.com
Year Founded: 1950
Sales Range: $10-24.9 Million
Emp.: 32
Roofing & Siding Merchant Whslr
N.A.I.C.S.: 423330
Scott Macindoe *(Pres)*
Christina MacIndoe *(Mgr-Fin & Admin)*

FIBERNET CORP
1155 S 800 E, Orem, UT 84097
Tel.: (801) 223-9939
Web Site: http://www.fiber.net
Sales Range: $1-9.9 Million
Emp.: 33
Data Processing, Hosting & Related
Services
N.A.I.C.S.: 518210
Lane Livingston *(CEO)*
Lee Livingston *(CFO)*
Adam Bayless *(CTO)*
Wendy Knouse *(Coord-Sls)*
Ashton Herrmann *(Dir-Acct Mgmt)*
Adam Sorensen *(Dir-Mktg)*
Cathi Spence *(Mgr-HR)*

FIBEROPTICS TECHNOLOGY INC.
1 Quassett Rd, Pomfret, CT 06258
Tel.: (860) 928-0443
Web Site: http://www.fiberoptix.com
Year Founded: 1977
Sales Range: $10-24.9 Million
Emp.: 100
Textile Glass Fibers
N.A.I.C.S.: 334419
Keith Knowlton *(Founder & Pres)*
Tim Beeman *(Mgr-Sls)*
Steven Giamundo *(Mgr-Mktg)*

FIBERWAVE CORP.
140 58 St, Brooklyn, NY 11220
Tel.: (718) 802-9011
Web Site: http://www.fiberwave.com
Rev.: $48,500,000
Emp.: 50
Fiber Optics Communications Equipment
N.A.I.C.S.: 334210
John V. Romeo *(Pres)*

FIBRE FEDERAL CREDIT UNION
822 Commerce Ave, Longview, WA
98632
Tel.: (360) 423-8750
Web Site: https://www.fibrecu.com
Rev.: $25,500,000
Emp.: 155
Credit Union
N.A.I.C.S.: 522130
John Barker *(Chm)*
Christopher Bradberry *(CEO)*

FIBREBOND CORPORATION
1300 Davenport Dr, Minden, LA
71055
Tel.: (318) 377-1030   LA
Web Site: https://www.fibrebond.com
Year Founded: 1982
Sales Range: $150-199.9 Million
Emp.: 650
Mfr of Concrete Products
N.A.I.C.S.: 327390
Claud Walker *(Founder)*
Nelwyn Warren *(Dir-Telecom & Bus)*
Ritchie Reid *(Mgr-Tech)*
Mike Pedroza *(Mgr-Integration Center)*
Penny Brents *(Asst Project Mgr)*
David Risher *(Project Mgr)*
Keith Bucher *(CFO & VP)*
Stacey Colvin *(Project Mgr)*

FIBRES INTERNATIONAL, INC.
2600 94th St SW, Everett, WA 98204
Tel.: (425) 405-1700   DE
Web Site: http://www.fibres.net
Year Founded: 1974
Sales Range: $300-349.9 Million
Emp.: 50
Recycling
N.A.I.C.S.: 562211

Subsidiaries:

Fibres International, Inc.   (1)
2600 94th St SW Ste 100, Everett, WA
98204   (100%)
Tel.: (425) 455-9811
Web Site: http://www.fibres.net
Sales Range: $10-24.9 Million
Emp.: 30
Recycling of Fibers
N.A.I.C.S.: 562211
Tonny Rounds *(VP-Ops)*

FIBREWORKS CORPORATION
2417 Data Dr, Louisville, KY 40299
Tel.: (502) 499-9944
Web Site: http://www.fibreworks.com
Sales Range: $10-24.9 Million
Emp.: 75
Resilient Floor Covering Mfr
N.A.I.C.S.: 321918
Teri Bennett *(Mgr-Credit)*

FIBRWRAP CONSTRUCTION, INC.
4255 E Airport Dr, Ontario, CA 91761
Tel.: (909) 390-4363
Web Site:
http://www.fibrwrapconstruction.com
Year Founded: 1988
Rev.: $11,378,477
Emp.: 200
Structural Renovation Services
N.A.I.C.S.: 236118
Julie Mizzi *(Reg Mgr)*

FICKLER OIL COMPANY INC.
725 Maverick Ln, Deer Lodge, MT
59722
Tel.: (406) 846-3970
Sales Range: $10-24.9 Million
Emp.: 50
Petroleum Bulk Stations
N.A.I.C.S.: 424710

Lawrence Fickler *(Pres)*
Joe Grey *(Controller)*

FICKLING & COMPANY IN-CORPORATED
577 Mulberry St, Macon, GA 31201
Tel.: (478) 746-9421
Web Site: http://www.fickling.com
Year Founded: 1939
Sales Range: $10-24.9 Million
Emp.: 30
Real Estate Services
N.A.I.C.S.: 237210
Elaine Lee *(Sr VP)*

FIDELIS CAPITAL LLC
820 Shades Creek Pkwy St 1200,
Birmingham, AL 35209
Tel.: (205) 588-6022
Web Site: http://www.fideliscapital.net
Privater Equity Firm
N.A.I.C.S.: 523999
Steve Dauphin *(Co-Founder)*
William Reiser *(Co-Founder)*
John Stein *(Co-Founder)*
Stephen Sistrunk *(VP)*

Subsidiaries:

Time Domain Corp.   (1)
Cummings Research Park 4955 Corporate
Dr Ste 101, Huntsville, AL 35805
Tel.: (256) 922-9229
Web Site: http://www.timedomain.com
Ultra Wideband Ranging Radio & Radar
Sensors Mfr
N.A.I.C.S.: 334220
Anthony Buszka *(Treas & Controller)*
Rachel Reinhardt *(CEO)*
Brandon Dewberry *(CTO)*
Kevin E. Davis *(Dir-Strategic Bus Dev)*
John Stein *(Chm)*

FIDELITONE, INC.
1260 Karl Ct, Wauconda, IL 60084-1081
Tel.: (847) 487-3300
Web Site: https://www.fidelitone.com
Year Founded: 1929
Full Service Inventory Management
Distribution & Logistics Services
N.A.I.C.S.: 423690
Craig Hudson *(Mgr-Corp Asset & Doc)*

Subsidiaries:

Purnell Furniture Services, Inc.   (1)
7900 Notes Dr, Manassas, VA 20109
Tel.: (703) 366-1300
Web Site: http://www.purnellusa.com
Sales Range: $10-24.9 Million
Emp.: 90
Furniture Delivery Services
N.A.I.C.S.: 484220

Remar, Inc.   (1)
6200 E Division St, Lebanon, TN 37090
Tel.: (615) 449-0231
Web Site: http://www.remarinc.com
Packaging Solutions, Print Management,
Direct Mail, Signage, Product Fulfillment,
Distribution & Logistics
N.A.I.C.S.: 561910
Greg Myers *(VP-Ops)*
Tracy Batts *(VP-Sls & Mktg)*
Nelson Remus *(Pres & CEO)*

FIDELITY ASSURANCE, INC.
5051 66th St N, Saint Petersburg, FL
33709-3119
Tel.: (727) 545-9891
Year Founded: 1969
Sales Range: $10-24.9 Million
Emp.: 13
General Insurance Services
N.A.I.C.S.: 524210
Mel Gross *(Pres)*
Laurie Plumlee *(Mgr)*
Robert Gross *(VP)*
Marc Sinton *(Dir-Mktg)*

FIDELITY BANK OF FLORIDA, N.A.
1380 N Courtenay Pkwy, Merritt Island, FL 32953
Tel.: (321) 452-0011
Web Site:
http://www.fidelitybankofflorida.com
Rev.: $24,700,000
Emp.: 40
Commericial Banking
N.A.I.C.S.: 522110
Biggs Knauer *(Sr VP)*

FIDELITY CHARITABLE GIFT FUND
PO Box 770001, Cincinnati, OH
45277-0053
Tel.: (617) 563-5800   MA
Web Site:
http://www.fidelitycharitable.org
Year Founded: 1990
Sales Range: $1-4.9 Billion
Grantmaking Services
N.A.I.C.S.: 813211
Jill Weiner *(Sec)*
Deborah Segal *(Chief Compliance Officer)*
Sarah Libbey *(Pres)*

FIDELITY ENGINEERING LLC
25 Loveton Cir, Sparks, MD 21152
Tel.: (410) 771-9400
Web Site:
http://www.fidelityengineering.com
Year Founded: 1945
Sales Range: $10-24.9 Million
Emp.: 250
Engineeering Services
N.A.I.C.S.: 541330
Keith Klann *(VP-New Company Integration & Technologies)*
Jay Stephan *(Mgr-Corp Safety)*
Carmine Mistichelli *(Partner & COO)*
Jim Slechta *(Pres & Partner-Power Sys)*
Bernadette Scarborough *(VP-Svc Ops)*

Subsidiaries:

Environmental Systems   (1)
Corporation
18 Jansen Ct, West Hartford, CT 06110-1913
Tel.: (860) 953-8800
Web Site: http://www.esccontrols.com
Computer System Design Services
N.A.I.C.S.: 541512
Donald McCurdy *(Pres)*

Fidelity Engineering Corp.   (1)
Ashburn
19955 Highland Vista Dr, Ashburn, VA
20147
Tel.: (703) 726-9900
Sales Range: $10-24.9 Million
Emp.: 50
Engineeering Services
N.A.I.C.S.: 541330

Power of Clean Energy LLC   (1)
810 Dominican Dr, Nashville, TN 37228
Tel.: (615) 238-9484
Web Site:
http://www.powerofcleanenergy.com
Sales Range: $1-9.9 Million
Emp.: 50
Electrical Contractor Services
N.A.I.C.S.: 238210
Kevin Johnson *(CEO)*
Lewis Dunn *(VP-Construction)*
Chris Klein *(VP-Project Dev)*
Brent Alexander *(Pres & COO)*

FIDELITY FINANCIAL CORPORATION
100 E English St, Wichita, KS 67202
Tel.: (316) 265-2261   KS
Web Site: http://www.fidelitybank.com
Year Founded: 1985
Bank Holding Company

N.A.I.C.S.: 551111
H. Clay Bastian (Chm, Pres & CEO)
M. Clark Bastian (VP)

Subsidiaries:

Fidelity Bank (1)
100 E English St, Wichita, KS 67202
Tel.: (316) 265-2261
Web Site: http://www.fidelitybank.com
Sales Range: $100-124.9 Million
Emp.: 400
Commericial Banking
N.A.I.C.S.: 522110
M. Clark Bastian (CEO)
Brian Cain (Sr VP-IT)
Aaron Bastian (Pres)
Nikki Epley (Mgr-Culture & Talent Project)
Brian Bueche (Chief Credit Officer & Sr VP)
Todd Williams (Exec VP)
Mustafa Chike-Obi (Chm)

Subsidiary (Domestic):

Fidelity Development, Inc. (2)
100 E English St, Wichita, KS 67202
Tel.: (316) 265-2261
Rev.: $71,000
Emp.: 1
Apartment Building Operator
N.A.I.C.S.: 531110

Fidelity Insurance Agency, Inc. (2)
100 E English St, Wichita, KS 67202
Tel.: (316) 268-7273
Web Site: http://www.fidelityinsagency.com
Rev.: $210,000
Emp.: 3
Insurance Agents
N.A.I.C.S.: 524210
Dale Bing (Pres)

Fidelity Management Corporation (2)
100 E English St Ste 500, Wichita, KS 67202
Tel.: (316) 265-2261
Rev.: $1,200,000
Emp.: 54
Apartment Building Operator
N.A.I.C.S.: 531110

Division (Domestic):

Oklahoma Fidelity Bank (2)
2225 W Hefner Rd, Oklahoma City, OK 73156
Tel.: (405) 755-5330
Web Site: http://www.fidelitybank.com
Emp.: 35
Commericial Banking
N.A.I.C.S.: 522110
Bert Collingbourne (VP)
Doug Sanders (Sr VP & Mgr-Comml Bus Lending)
Christian Lehr (Sls Mgr-Treasury Mgmt)

Subsidiary (Domestic):

The Fidelity Investment
Company (2)
100 E English St, Wichita, KS 67202
Tel.: (316) 265-2261
Rev.: $370,592
Emp.: 400
Investment Holding Companies, Except Banks
N.A.I.C.S.: 551112

Glenwood Properties, Inc. (1)
526 Pine St, Glenwood Springs, CO 81601
Tel.: (970) 945-6511
Web Site: http://www.hotelcolorado.com
Emp.: 110
Hotel
N.A.I.C.S.: 721110
Larry Welch (Gen Mgr)
Jon Seiring (Gen Mgr)

FIDELITY FOUNDATION
11 Keewaydin Dr Ste 100, Salem, NH 03079
Tel.: (603) 681-4375 DE
Web Site:
   http://www.fidelityfoundation.org
Year Founded: 1992
Sales Range: $200-249.9 Million
Grantmaking Services
N.A.I.C.S.: 813211

Daniel Ardito (Controller)
Kathleen Ward (Dir-Grants Mgmt)
Paul Kuenstner (VP)

FIDELITY HOMESTEAD SAVINGS BANK
5643 Corporate Blvd, Baton Rouge, LA 70808
Tel.: (504) 529-5011
Web Site:
   http://www.fidelityhomestead.com
Year Founded: 1908
Sales Range: $50-74.9 Million
Emp.: 92
Savings & Loan Associations, Not Federally Chartered
N.A.I.C.S.: 522180
Patrick Griggs (Chief Credit & Risk Officer & Exec VP)
Katherine Andry Crosby (Chm)

FIDELITY INDUSTRIES INC.
559 State Route 23, Wayne, NJ 07470
Tel.: (973) 696-9120
Web Site:
   https://www.fidelitywall.com
Sales Range: $10-24.9 Million
Emp.: 40
Wallcovering Mfr
N.A.I.C.S.: 326299
Mordecai Rivkin (Pres)

FIDELITY PAPER & SUPPLY CORP.
901 Murray Rd, East Hanover, NJ 07936
Tel.: (973) 599-0222
Web Site:
   https://www.fidelitypaper.com
Rev.: $18,000,000
Emp.: 32
Paperboard & Products
N.A.I.C.S.: 424130

FIDELITY PRIVATE CREDIT COMPANY LLC
245 Summer St, Boston, MA 02210
Tel.: (617) 563-7000 DE
Web Site: https://www.fidelity.com
Year Founded: 2021
Rev.: $146,978,099
Assets: $1,442,422,467
Liabilities: $767,330,699
Net Worth: $675,091,768
Earnings: $95,279,402
Fiscal Year-end: 12/31/23
Investment Management Service
N.A.I.C.S.: 523999

FIDELITY SECURITY LIFE INSURANCE COMPANY
3130 Broadway, Kansas City, MO 64111
Tel.: (816) 756-1060
Web Site: http://www.fslins.com
Year Founded: 1969
Sales Range: $10-24.9 Million
Emp.: 115
Direct Life Insurance Services
N.A.I.C.S.: 524113
Leroy McCarty (VP)
Martha E. Madden (Gen Counsel & VP)
Bryce L. Jones (VP)
Dana L. Hamilton (Asst VP)
Michael E. Hall (Sr VP)
Brenda S. Gordanier (Asst VP)
Bradford R. Jones (VP)
Peter Lindquist (VP)
Tim Knott (VP-Mktg)
Richard F. Jones Sr. (Pres)
Richard F. Jones Jr. (VP)

FIDELITY TECHNOLOGIES CORP.
2501 Kutztown Rd, Reading, PA 19605
Tel.: (610) 929-3330
Web Site:
   https://www.fidelitytech.com
Year Founded: 1987
Sales Range: $10-24.9 Million
Emp.: 110
Global Supplier of Defense & Aerospace Products & Services to U.S. & International Customers
N.A.I.C.S.: 334511
David Gulati (Pres & Co-Owner)
Joseph Russell (Gen Mgr)
Michael Gulati (Controller & Co-Owner)

FIDELITY VOICE AND DATA
23250 Chagrin Blvd, Beachwood, OH 44122
Tel.: (216) 595-9050
Web Site:
   http://www.fidelityvoice.com
Year Founded: 1999
Sales Range: $10-24.9 Million
Emp.: 50
Full Service Data & Voice Services
N.A.I.C.S.: 334112
Robert Marks (Co-Founder & Pres)
Mitchell Marks (VP & Co-Founder)
Nick Brown (VP-Sls & Mktg)
Jason Valore (VP-Ops)

FIDUCIARY COMPANY INCORPORATED
600 5th Ave, New York, NY 10020
Tel.: (212) 632-3000 MA
Web Site:
   http://www.fiduciarytrust.com
Year Founded: 1885
Rev.: $29,307,215
Emp.: 140
Management of Financial Assets
N.A.I.C.S.: 522110

Subsidiaries:

Fiduciary Trust Co. Inc. (1)
175 Federal St, Boston, MA 02110-2210
Tel.: (617) 482-5270
Web Site: http://www.fiduciary-trust.com
Rev.: $32,973,504
Emp.: 130
State Commercial Banks
N.A.I.C.S.: 522110
Sidney F. Queler (Head-Wealth Mgmt)
Austin V. Shapard (Pres & CEO)
Stacy K. Mullaney (Chief Fiduciary Officer)
Anne K. Trinque (Gen Counsel & Sec)
Todd H. Eckler (CMO & Exec Dir-Charitable)
Joel Mittelman (VP)
Scott Sumner (VP & Head-Custody)
Peter Andersen (Chief Investment Officer)
Grenville Anderson (VP)
W. Douglas Burden (VP)
Michael N. Costa (VP)
Paul G. Curtis (VP)
Christopher T. Doyle (VP)
Jody R. King (VP & Dir-Fin Plng)
Alan L. Newton (VP)
Charles C. J. Platt (VP & Dir-Client Svcs)
J. Brian Potts (VP)
Richard Olney (VP)
Peter Whitlock (VP)
Robert Jeffers (COO)
James Cosentino (VP)
Neal Hegge (VP)
Kelly Guarino (VP)
Patricia Schatzlein Smock (VP)
Hans F. Olsen (Chief Investment Officer)
Rick Tyson (VP)
John P. Morey (Head-Client Svc & Bus Dev)
Priya Amar (VP)
Emily D. Griset (VP)
Sidney Queler (Head-Wealth Mgmt)
Thomas Nonnweiler (VP)
Thomas A. DeMarco III (VP)

Subsidiary (Domestic):

Pennsylvania Trust Co. (2)

5 Radnor Corporate Ctr Ste 450, Radnor, PA 19087-4526
Tel.: (610) 526-9069
Web Site: http://www.penntrust.com
Investment Advice
N.A.I.C.S.: 523940
Richardson Merriman (CEO)
Nan M. Lansinger (Dir-Mktg & Client Dev)
George C. McFarland (Pres & Chief Investment Officer)
Diane A. Ferrie (VP)
Francis X. Mehaffey (Sr VP & Dir-Tax Svcs)
Douglas H. DeLong (Sr VP & Dir-Portfolio Mgmt)
Ryan J. McDonald (VP-Fixed Income Portfolio Mgmt)
William C. Madeira (VP-investment Dept & Portfolio Mgr)
Jeffrey L. Biberman (VP-Tax Svcs Dept)
Charles L. Sheppard II (Sr VP & Dir-Equity Res & Strategy)

FIDUCIARY MANAGEMENT ASSOCIATES, LLC
55 W Monroe St Ste 2550, Chicago, IL 60603-5021
Tel.: (312) 930-6850 DE
Web Site: http://www.fmausa.com
Year Founded: 1980
Investment Management Service
N.A.I.C.S.: 523940
Lloyd J. Spicer (Mng Dir)
Kathryn A. Vorisek (Sr Mng Dir & Chief Investment Officer)
Daniel J. Dutile (Dir-Res)
Leo Harmon (Mng Dir)
Candice L. Melcher (Chief Compliance Officer & Mng Dir)
Nancy Fisher (Sr Dir-Trading)
John M. Odum (Dir-Client Svc & Ops)
Eric Welt (Mng Dir)

FIEDLER GROUP
2322 W 3rd St, Los Angeles, CA 90057-1906
Tel.: (213) 381-1517
Web Site:
   http://www.fiedlergroup.com
Year Founded: 1957
Building Equipment Contractors
N.A.I.C.S.: 238290
Patrick Fiedler (Pres)
John Dzwonczyk (Principal-Ohio)

Subsidiaries:

JGD Associates Inc. (1)
92 Moore Rd, Avon Lake, OH 44012-1110
Tel.: (440) 933-6825
Web Site: http://www.jgdpe.com
Engineeering Services
N.A.I.C.S.: 541330

FIELD HOTEL ASSOCIATES
251 W Dekalb Pike, King of Prussia, PA 19406
Tel.: (610) 265-5333
Year Founded: 1973
Sales Range: $10-24.9 Million
Emp.: 10
Manager of Franchise-Affiliated Hotels
N.A.I.C.S.: 721110
Martin W. Field (Partner)
Elaine LaRosa (Dir-Sls & Mktg)
Michael Lamond (Dir-HR)

FIELD INDUSTRIES LLC
6620 Dixie Rd, Houston, TX 77087
Tel.: (832) 736-1839
Web Site:
   http://www.fieldindustries.com
Year Founded: 2011
Sales Range: $1-9.9 Million
Steel & Alloy Piping Distr
N.A.I.C.S.: 423510
Jared Field (Pres & Gen Mgr)
Zach Kitchens (VP-Sls)
Virginia Saenz (VP-Ops)

Field Industries LLC—(Continued)

FIELD LINING SYSTEMS, INC.
439 S 3rd Ave, Avondale, AZ 85323
Tel.: (623) 842-1255
Web Site:
    http://www.fieldliningsystems.com
Sales Range: $10-24.9 Million
Emp.: 50
Specialty Lining Systems
N.A.I.C.S.: 238990
Phil Ramos (Pres)
Kristy Lagunas (Pres)

FIELD NATION, LLC
310 4th Ave S Suite 8100, Minneapolis, MN 55415
Tel.: (877) 573-4353
Web Site: http://www.fieldnation.com
Year Founded: 2008
Sales Range: $25-49.9 Million
Emp.: 15
Online Work Platform Connecting
Businesses & Workers
N.A.I.C.S.: 561499
Mynul Khan (CEO)
Teri Calderon (Exec VP-HR)
Mike Nigai (CEO)
Wael Mohammed (VP-Product Mgmt)

FIELD PAPER CO. INC.
3950 D St, Omaha, NE 68107-1101
Tel.: (402) 733-3600   **NJ**
Web Site: https://www.fieldpaper.com
Year Founded: 1988
Sales Range: $25-49.9 Million
Emp.: 62
Distr of Printing & Writing Paper
N.A.I.C.S.: 424110
Mike Freeland (Pres)

FIELD PROS DIRECT LLC
107 Technology Pkwy #206,
Peachtree Corners, GA 30092
Tel.: (844) 973-4732
Web Site:
    http://www.fieldprosdirect.com
Insurance Claims Adjusting & Related
Services
N.A.I.C.S.: 524291
Matthew Anderson (CEO)

Subsidiaries:

Bridgewater Group, LLC   (1)
3 Northridge, 400 8383 Dunwoody Pl, Atlanta, GA 30350
Tel.: (770) 392-1440
Web Site: http://www.bridgewatergroup.net
Rev.: $3,200,000
Emp.: 28
Insurance Claims Adjusting & Related Services
N.A.I.C.S.: 524291
Barry Kriegel (Founder)
Cindy Custard (Pres)

FIELDALE FARMS CORPORATION
PO Box 558, Baldwin, GA 30511-0558
Tel.: (706) 778-5100   **GA**
Web Site: http://www.fieldale.com
Year Founded: 1972
Sales Range: $450-499.9 Million
Emp.: 4,590
Poultry Mfr
N.A.I.C.S.: 311615
Jon Allen (Dir-HR)
Walter Burrell (Dir-Engrg Fabrication)
Sammy Franklin (Dir-Sls)
Lynda King (Coord-Corp Labeling)
Kenneth Martin (Supvr-Production)
Jim McGahee (Mgr-Commodity Sls)
Kirby Phillips (Mgr-Feed Delivery)
Melissa Raybon (Plant Mgr)
Barb Shubert (Asst Mgr-Hatchery)
Janet Smith (Mgr-Laboratory)

Gabe Southards (Mgr-Enterprise Solutions Dev)
Marie Wells (Dir-Quality Assurance)
Craig West (Mgr-New Tech & Telecom)
David L. Wicker (VP-Live Ops)
John Wright (VP-Ops)
Ben Cash (Mgr-Personnel Svcs)
Denise Ivester (Mgr-Health & Wellness Grp)
Eric Dean (Supvr-Flock)
Tony Maturo (Controller-Ops)

Subsidiaries:

Best Aviation   (1)
555 Broiler Blvd, Baldwin, GA 30511-0558
Tel.: (706) 778-5100
Sales Range: $25-49.9 Million
Emp.: 150
Raise & Sell Poultry
N.A.I.C.S.: 481219
Eddie Eilrod (Mgr-Corp Credit)

FIELDBROOK VALLEY WINERY INC.
4241 Fieldbrook Rd, McKinleyville, CA 95519
Tel.: (707) 839-4140
Web Site:
    https://www.fieldbrookwinery.com
Year Founded: 1976
Sales Range: $10-24.9 Million
Emp.: 1
Wine Mfr
N.A.I.C.S.: 312130
Robert Hodgson (Owner)

FIELDHOME
2300 Catherine St, Cortlandt Manor, NY 10567
Tel.: (914) 739-2244   **NY**
Web Site: http://www.fieldhome.com
Year Founded: 1985
Sales Range: $10-24.9 Million
Emp.: 336
Community Care Services
N.A.I.C.S.: 624120
Richard Scheibe (Dir-Recreation &
Volunteers)
Molly Greece (Dir-Recreation & Volunteers)
John R. Ahearn (CEO)
Ian D. Smith (Treas & VP)

FIELDPOINT PRIVATE BANK & TRUST
100 Field Point Rd, Greenwich, CT 06830
Tel.: (203) 413-9300
Web Site:
    https://www.fieldpointprivate.com
Year Founded: 2008
Sales Range: $10-24.9 Million
Emp.: 54
Private Banking Services
N.A.I.C.S.: 522110
Michael White (CMO)
Daniel J. Donahue (Founder)
Kevin O'Hanlon (Chief Credit Officer & Exec VP)
Timothy J. Tully (Chm)
Scott Noah (Chief Compliance Officer)
Christopher DeLaura (Chief Admin Officer-Wealth Advisory)
Brian Smith (Mng Dir-Florida)
David Komansky (Founder)
Daniel Tully (Founder)
William Schreyer (Founder)
Joseph Moglia (Founder)
Paine Webber (Founder)
Joseph Grano (Founder)
Bernard Marcus (Founder)
Kenneth Langone (Founder)
Ian McMahon (CFO)

Marianne Morelli (Mng Dir-HR & Corp Rels)
Brent Yamaato (COO)
Russ Holland (Pres & CEO)

FIELDS BMW
963 N Wymore Rd, Winter Park, FL 32789
Tel.: (407) 478-3935
Web Site: https://www.fieldsauto.com
Year Founded: 1989
Sales Range: $10-24.9 Million
Emp.: 200
New Car Whslr
N.A.I.C.S.: 441110
Joe Allegra (Mgr-Svc)
John Fields (Owner)
John Mantione (Gen Mgr)
Richard Dupuis (Mgr-Svc)

FIELDS BMW OF DAYTONA
1220 N Tomoka Farms Rd, Daytona Beach, FL 32124-1050
Tel.: (386) 274-1200
Web Site:
    http://www.fieldsbmwofdaytona.com
Year Founded: 2006
Sales Range: $10-24.9 Million
Emp.: 65
New Car Retailer
N.A.I.C.S.: 441110
Steve McDonald (Gen Mgr)
Robert Dunn (Mgr-New Car Sls)
Chris Fellows (Mgr-Used Car)
Chris Decarlo (Mgr-Svc)
Michelle Lewis (Mgr-Parts)

FIELDS EQUIPMENT CO. INC.
3203 Havendale Blvd NW, Winter Haven, FL 33881
Tel.: (863) 967-0602
Web Site:
    https://www.fieldsequip.com
Sales Range: $10-24.9 Million
Emp.: 55
Farm Equipment & Supplies
N.A.I.C.S.: 459999
Chuck Fields (Pres)

FIELDS, INC.
3760 Sixes Rd Ste 126-331, Canton, GA 30114
Tel.: (678) 710-8585
Web Site: http://www.fields-inc.com
Year Founded: 2005
Sales Range: $10-24.9 Million
Emp.: 60
Sports Field Construction Services
N.A.I.C.S.: 237990
Brian F. Storm (Co-Founder, Pres & CEO)
Mark Stalnaker (Co-Founder & VP)
Pete Fox Jr. (Co-Founder & Sr Dir-Ops)

FIELDSTONE LANDSCAPE SERVICES LLC
4801 122nd Ave, Clearwater, FL 33762
Tel.: (727) 822-7866
Web Site:
    https://www.fieldstonels.com
Sales Range: $1-9.9 Million
Emp.: 75
Landscaping Services
N.A.I.C.S.: 561730
Chris Eastman (CFO)
Michael Thackrey (VP)
Adam McKown (Acct Mgr & Mgr-Horticulture)
Jessie Wert (Office Mgr)
Tave Close (Mgr-Irrigation & Enhancement)
John Ziegler (Mgr-Maintenance)
Dorian Matthews (Mgr-Acctg)
Adam Parrott (Mgr-Enhancement)

Chris Beckner (Mgr-Field Production-Pinellas)
Joe Pichardo (Supvr-Acct)
Scott LeRoy (VP)
George Lara (VP-Ops)

FIELDTECH AVIONICS & INSTRUMENTS, INC.
4151 N Main St, Fort Worth, TX 76106
Tel.: (817) 625-2719
Web Site: https://www.ftav.com
Sales Range: $10-24.9 Million
Emp.: 61
Aircraft/Aerospace Flight Instruments & Guidance Systems
N.A.I.C.S.: 334511
Kevin Nelms (Pres)
Todd McDonough (Mgr-Instrument Shop)

FIELDWARE, LLC
549 W Randolph St Ste 701, Chicago, IL 60661-2316
Tel.: (312) 258-1000
Web Site: http://www.fieldware.com
Automatic Environmental Control Mfr for Residential, Commercial & Appliance Use
N.A.I.C.S.: 334512
Peter Miley (Engr-.NET)

Subsidiaries:

Orion Communications, Inc.   (1)
8235 Douglas Ave, Dallas, TX 75225
Tel.: (214) 361-1203
Web Site: http://www.orioncom.com
Sales Range: $1-9.9 Million
Emp.: 22
Information Technology Services And Products
N.A.I.C.S.: 541512
Leslie Delatte (Pres & CEO)
William Bagwell (Dir-Tech)
Heather E. Kocks (Dir-Ops)
Jackie Belasky (Dir-Sls & Mktg)
Steven Jones (Mgr-Ops)

FIELDWORK BREWING COMPANY
1160 6th St, Berkeley, CA 94710
Tel.: (510) 898-1203
Web Site:
    http://www.fieldworkbrewing.com
Year Founded: 2014
Sales Range: $10-24.9 Million
Emp.: 102
Beer Mfr
N.A.I.C.S.: 312120
Stuart Self (VP-Fin & Ops)

FIERCE INC.
101 Yesler Way Ste 200, Seattle, WA 98104
Tel.: (206) 787-1100
Web Site: http://www.fierceinc.com
Year Founded: 1999
Sales Range: $1-9.9 Million
Emp.: 37
Leadership Development & Communication Training
N.A.I.C.S.: 611430
Susan Scott (Founder)
Stacey Engle (Exec VP-Mktg)
Christine Douglas (Exec VP-Trng)
Ed Beltran (CEO)

FIESTA AUTO INSURANCE CENTER
16162 Beach Blvd Ste 100, Huntington Beach, CA 92647
Tel.: (714) 842-5420
Web Site:
    http://www.fiestainsurance.com
Year Founded: 1999
Sales Range: $1-9.9 Million
Emp.: 15

Insurance Services
N.A.I.C.S.: 524210
John Rost (*Pres*)
Deane Silke (*VP*)

FIESTA CANNING CO., INC.
1480 E Bethany Home Ste 110,
Phoenix, AZ 85014
Tel.: (602) 212-2424
Web Site: http://www.fiestacan.com
Sales Range: $10-24.9 Million
Emp.: 75
Canned Food Mfr
N.A.I.C.S.: 311422
Woodrow Johnson (*Pres*)
Edmond Haddad (*VP & Treas*)
Troy Johnson (*Dir-Sls*)
Bob Neckes (*Mgr-HR*)

FIESTA FORD LINCOLN MERCURY
78990 Varner Rd, Indio, CA 92203-9710
Tel.: (760) 772-8020
Web Site:
http://www.fiestafordinc.com
Year Founded: 1966
Sales Range: $25-49.9 Million
Emp.: 126
Car Whslr
N.A.I.C.S.: 441110
Gary Boldizar (*Mgr-Sls*)

FIESTA MEXICANA MARKET LTD. PARTNER
8141 E Kaiser Blvd Ste 203, Anaheim, CA 92808-2241
Tel.: (714) 518-5490
Year Founded: 1996
Sales Range: $10-24.9 Million
Emp.: 110
Grocery Stores
N.A.I.C.S.: 445110

FIFIELD LAND CO.
4307 Fifield Rd, Brawley, CA 92227-9507
Tel.: (760) 344-6391
Web Site: https://www.kfseeds.com
Rev.: $16,700,000
Emp.: 20
Agricultural Seed Producer & Distr
N.A.I.C.S.: 424910
George Neek (*Gen Mgr*)

FIFO WIRELESS
10900 NW 21 St Ste 210, Miami, FL 33172
Web Site: https://www.fifousa.com
Year Founded: 2000
Sales Range: $10-24.9 Million
Emp.: 25
Mfr & Distr of Cell Phone Accessories
N.A.I.C.S.: 334210
Abraham Mekki (*Pres*)
Hamid Mekki (*VP*)
Yvette Blanco (*Mgr-Ops*)

FIFTH DISTRICT SAVINGS BANK
4000 General Degaulle Dr, New Orleans, LA 70114
Tel.: (504) 362-7544
Web Site: https://www.fifthdistrict.com
Sales Range: $10-24.9 Million
Emp.: 70
Banking Services
N.A.I.C.S.: 522180
David A. Nolan (*Sr VP-Ops & Admin*)
Lisa L. Chartier (*Asst VP*)

FIFTH GEAR LLC
9100 Purdue Rd Ste 400, Indianapolis, IN 46268
Tel.: (317) 631-0907
Web Site: http://www.infifthgear.com

Year Founded: 1982
Sales Range: $50-74.9 Million
Emp.: 400
Systems & Software Mfr
N.A.I.C.S.: 541512
Matthew L. Konkle (*Pres*)
Jeffrey S. Dahltorp (*VP-Plng & Assessment*)
Donald J.B. Van der Wiel (*CFO*)

FIFTH GROUP RESTAURANTS
229 Peachtree St NE Peachtree Ctr International Tower Ste 600, Atlanta, GA 30303
Tel.: (404) 815-4700
Web Site: https://www.fifthgroup.com
Year Founded: 1993
Sales Range: $25-49.9 Million
Emp.: 556
Restaurant Operators
N.A.I.C.S.: 722511
Robby Kukler (*Co-Partner*)
Steve Simon (*Co-Partner*)
Kris Reinhard (*Co-Partner & Gen Mgr*)
Vajra Stratigos (*Dir-Food & Beverage Standards*)
Jason Pristash (*Controller*)
Leah Sonson (*Mgr-Hiring*)
Mark Wilson (*Dir-Ops*)
Deborah Daoudi (*Mgr-Dining Sls Team*)
Jim Robertson (*Dir-Mktg*)
Lissa Bowen (*Dir-Recruiting & Talent Mgmt*)

FIFTH STREET ASSET MANAGEMENT INC.
777 W Putnam Ave 3rd Fl, Greenwich, CT 06830
Tel.: (203) 681-3600   DE
Web Site:
http://www.fifthstreetfinance.com
Year Founded: 2014
Holding Company; Asset Management
N.A.I.C.S.: 551112
Leonard Mark Tannenbaum (*Founder & Chm*)
Robyn E. Friedman (*Exec Dir & Head-IR*)
Brian T. Walter (*Mktg Dir & Head-Institutional Products*)

FIFTH STREET CAPITAL LLC
10 Bank St 12th Fl, White Plains, NY 10606
Tel.: (914) 286-6800   NY
Web Site:
http://www.fifthstreetfinance.com
Emp.: 70
Privater Equity Firm
N.A.I.C.S.: 523999
Leonard Mark Tannenbaum (*Chm & CEO*)

Subsidiaries:

Fifth Street Management LLC   (1)
1819 Peachtree Rd NE Ste 575, Atlanta, GA 30309
Tel.: (404) 419-9600
Web Site: http://www.gofifthstreet.com
Investment Advisory & Portfolio Management Services
N.A.I.C.S.: 523940
David H. Harrison (*Chief Compliance Officer*)
Leonard Mark Tannenbaum (*Mng Partner*)
Alexander Charles Frank (*CFO & COO*)
Bernard D. Berman (*Mng Partner*)

Affiliate (Domestic):

Oaktree Specialty Lending
Corporation   (2)
333 S Grand Ave 28th Fl, Los Angeles, CA 90071
Tel.: (213) 830-6300

Web Site:
https://www.oaktreespecialtylending.com
Rev.: $381,665,000
Assets: $3,198,341,000
Liabilities: $1,710,530,000
Net Worth: $1,487,811,000
Earnings: $175,052,000
Fiscal Year-end: 09/30/2024
Holding Company; Private Equity Investment Funds
N.A.I.C.S.: 551112
Mathew M. Pendo (*Pres & COO*)
Armen Panossian (*CEO & Chief Investment Officer*)
Raghav Khanna (*Mng Dir & Asst Portfolio Mgr*)
Aman Kumar (*Mng Dir*)
Christine Pope (*Mng Dir*)
Lindsay Berz (*Mng Dir*)
Nilay Mehta (*Mng Dir*)
Michael Shannon (*Mng Dir*)
Christopher McKown (*CFO & Treas*)
Mary Gallegly (*Mng Dir & Sr VP*)
Matthew Wong (*Mng Dir & Sr VP*)
Rahul Anand (*Sr VP & VP*)
Lucia Kim (*Sr VP & VP*)
Kevin Ng (*Sr VP & VP*)
Evelyn You (*Sr VP & VP*)
Kent Bailey (*Mng Dir*)
Steve DeNelsky (*Mng Dir*)
John B. Frank (*Vice Chm*)

FIG LEAF SOFTWARE INC
1400 16th St NW, Washington, DC 20036
Tel.: (202) 797-7711
Web Site: http://www.figleaf.com
Year Founded: 1992
Sales Range: $10-24.9 Million
Emp.: 50
Computer System Design Services
N.A.I.C.S.: 541512
Steven Drucker (*Pres & Partner*)
Bret Peters (*Partner & VP-Sls & Mktg*)
Dave Watts (*Co-Founder, Partner & CTO*)
Dave Gallerizzo (*Partner & CEO*)

FIKE CHEVROLET COMPANY
213 N Main St, Masontown, PA 15461
Tel.: (724) 583-7738
Web Site:
http://www.fikechevrolet.com
Year Founded: 1927
Sales Range: $10-24.9 Million
Emp.: 20
Sales of New & Used Automobiles
N.A.I.C.S.: 441110
Frank E. Martin (*Pres & CEO*)
Nevin Bryan (*Co-Owner & Gen Mgr*)

FIKE CORPORATION
704 SW 10th St, Blue Springs, MO 64015
Tel.: (816) 229-3405   MO
Web Site: https://www.fike.com
Year Founded: 1945
Sales Range: $150-199.9 Million
Emp.: 350
Rupture Discs, Flanges, Pressure Relief Devices, Explosive Vents, Fire Extinguishing Systems & Components & Metal Fabrication Explosion Suppression Systems Mfr
N.A.I.C.S.: 332919
Brad Batz (*Pres & CEO*)
Dave Peirano (*Exec VP-Ops*)
Josh Batz (*CTO*)
Justin Iske (*Exec VP-Fin*)

Subsidiaries:

Fike Canada, Inc.   (1)
4400 Mainway, Burlington, L7L 5Y5, ON, Canada   (100%)
Tel.: (905) 681-3100
Web Site: http://www.fike.com
Sales Range: $25-49.9 Million
Emp.: 28
N.A.I.C.S.: 332911

Fike Europe   (1)
Toekomstlaan 52, 2200, Herentals, Antwerp, Belgium   (100%)
Tel.: (32) 14210031
Web Site: http://www.fike.be
Sales Range: $1-9.9 Million
Emp.: 80
Fire Fighting Equipment Mfr
N.A.I.C.S.: 332919
Roger Bours (*Mgr-Pressure Release*)

Fike Japan Corporation   (1)
Toranomon Bldg 1F 1-19-9 Toranomon, Minato Ku, Tokyo, 105001, Japan   (50%)
Tel.: (81) 335951291
Web Site: http://www.fike.co.jp
Sales Range: $25-49.9 Million
Emp.: 7
N.A.I.C.S.: 332911
Yoshi Shimura (*Gen Mgr*)

Intelligent Technologies & Services, Inc.   (1)
1031 Serpentine Ln Ste 101, Pleasanton, CA 94566
Tel.: (925) 484-3701
Web Site: http://www.intellitechservices.com
Sales Range: $10-24.9 Million
Emp.: 30
Provider of Fire Management Services
N.A.I.C.S.: 561990
Debbie Johnston (*Gen Mgr*)

FIKES CHEVROLET BUICK INCORPORATED
771 Military St N, Hamilton, AL 35570
Tel.: (205) 921-2199
Web Site:
http://www.fikesautomotive.com
Year Founded: 1978
Sales Range: $10-24.9 Million
Emp.: 40
Automobiles, New & Used
N.A.I.C.S.: 441110
Jeffrey Fikes (*Pres*)

FIKES TRUCK LINE INC.
2600 E 3rd St, Hope, AR 71801
Tel.: (870) 777-6540
Web Site: http://www.fikes.com
Year Founded: 1981
Sales Range: $10-24.9 Million
Emp.: 32
Trucking Services
N.A.I.C.S.: 484121
Max Campbell (*Dir-Recruiting & Contractor Svcs*)

FILCO, INC.
1415 Fulton Ave, Sacramento, CA 95825-3612
Tel.: (916) 483-4526   CA
Web Site:
https://www.filcosuperstore.com
Year Founded: 1972
Sales Range: $75-99.9 Million
Emp.: 25
Retail Sales of Televisions, Stereo Equipment, Cameras, Photographic Equipment & Major Household Appliances
N.A.I.C.S.: 449210
Tony Saca (*Chm*)
David Saca (*Pres*)
Freddy Saca (*Gen Mgr*)

FILIAGGI HOLDING COMPANY INC.
RR 21, Masontown, PA 15461
Tel.: (724) 277-8282
Sales Range: $10-24.9 Million
Emp.: 6
New & Used Car Dealers
N.A.I.C.S.: 441110

FILISTER ENTERPRISES
5750 E River Rd, Minneapolis, MN 55432
Tel.: (763) 571-3300
Web Site: http://www.filister.com

Filister Enterprises—(Continued)

Sales Range: $10-24.9 Million
Emp.: 100
Apartment Hotel Operation
N.A.I.C.S.: 531110
Harvey Filister (Owner)
Kay Lusk (Mgr-Property)
Ray Goettl (Dir-Property Mgmt)

FILLMORE CAPITAL PART-NERS, LLC
4 Embarcadero Ctr Ste 710, San Francisco, CA 94111
Tel.: (415) 834-1477
Web Site: http://www.fillmorecap.com
Year Founded: 2003
Sales Range: $25-49.9 Million
Emp.: 12
Private Real Estate Equity Firm
N.A.I.C.S.: 525990
Ronald E. Silva (Pres & CEO)
Timothy C. Getz (Exec VP)
Michael O. Reinardy (Sr VP-Investments)
Diane Olmstead (Mng Dir)

Subsidiaries:

Golden Living (1)
1000 Fianna Way, Fort Smith, AR 72919
Tel.: (317) 791-4280
Web Site:
  http://www.goldenlivingcenters.com
Sales Range: Less than $1 Million
Nursing Rehabilitation Facility Institutional & Mail Order Pharmaceutical Assisted Acute Long-Term Transitional Hospital Living Project & Home Health Center Operator Services
N.A.I.C.S.: 623311

Subsidiary (Domestic):

Aegis Therapies (2)
1000 Franna Way, Fort Smith, AR 72919
Tel.: (479) 201-2000
Web Site: http://www.goldenliving.com
Sales Range: $25-49.9 Million
Geriatric Rehabilitation Services
N.A.I.C.S.: 624190
Martha Schram (Pres)
Jeffrey M. Kreger (CFO)

FILM SCORE MONTHLY
4470 W Sunset Blvd Ste 705, Los Angeles, CA 90027
Tel.: (323) 461-2240
Web Site:
  http://www.filmscoremonthly.com
Year Founded: 1990
Sales Range: Less than $1 Million
Emp.: 1
CD Producer; Movie & Television Music Appreciation Newsletter Publisher
N.A.I.C.S.: 513199
Lukas Kendall (Founder & Publr)
Tim Curran (Editor)
Kristen Romanelli (Mng Editor)

FILM SOCIETY OF LINCOLN CENTER, INC.
70 Lincoln Center Plz, New York, NY 10023-6595
Tel.: (212) 875-5610   NY
Web Site: http://www.filmlinc.com
Year Founded: 1969
Sales Range: $10-24.9 Million
Emp.: 107
Film Promotion Services
N.A.I.C.S.: 711310
Ira S. Rimerman (Vice Chm)
Wendy Keys (Sec)
Abigail Hirschhorn Beroutsos (VP)
Ann Tenenbaum (Chm)
Bennett Goodman (Treas)

FILMET COLOR LABORATO-RIES INC.

1051 Russellton Rd 202 Falcon Ln, Cheswick, PA 15024
Tel.: (724) 265-5500   PA
Web Site: http://www.filmet.com
Year Founded: 1901
Sales Range: $10-24.9 Million
Emp.: 60
Provider of Photographic Services
N.A.I.C.S.: 812921
Rick Bachelder (Pres)

FILMFAX, INC.
1320 Oakton St, Evanston, IL 60202
Tel.: (847) 866-7155
Year Founded: 1986
Sales Range: $50-74.9 Million
Emp.: 1
Movie & Television Magazines Publisher
N.A.I.C.S.: 513120
Michael Stein (Editor & Publr)

FILMTOOLS
1400 W Burbank Blvd, Burbank, CA 91506
Tel.: (818) 845-8066
Web Site: https://www.filmtools.com
Year Founded: 2000
Rev.: $4,700,000
Emp.: 30
Photographic & Photocopying Equipment Mfr
N.A.I.C.S.: 333310
Stan McClain (CEO)
Kim McClain (Controller)
Joseph Bevans (Mgr-Rental Ops)

FILMTRACK INC.
12001 Ventura Pl Ste 500, Studio City, CA 91604
Tel.: (818) 766-2607
Web Site: https://www.filmtrack.com
Sales Range: $1-9.9 Million
Emp.: 75
Entertainment Content & Rights Management Technology Developer
N.A.I.C.S.: 513210
Mike Zinsmeister (Head-Global Sls)
Jason Kassin (Co-Founder & CEO)
Stephen Kassin (Co-Founder & Pres)
Thomas Coleman (CTO)
Gary Davis (Exec VP-Ops)
Michael McGuire (COO)
Sam Sippl (CFO)
Sam Straub (Sr VP)

Subsidiaries:

Dashbox Inc. (1)
2001 Wilshire Blvd Ste 501, Santa Monica, CA 90403
Tel.: (424) 238-7318
Web Site: http://www.dashbox.com
Web Based Software Publishing Services
N.A.I.C.S.: 513210
Bob Roback (CEO)
Brian Boys (COO)
Jon Steingold (VP-Bus Dev)
Steve Skrzyniarz (CTO)
Nina Ristani (VP-User Experience)

Jaguar Consulting, Inc. (1)
117 E Colorado Blvd Ste 225, Pasadena, CA 91105
Tel.: (626) 796-1955
Web Site: http://www.jaguartc.com
Rights & Royalty Management Software Services
N.A.I.C.S.: 513210
Randolph Johnson (Co-Founder)
Don Rothenberg (CEO)
Carol Guillebeaux (Mgr-Quality Assurance)

FILTER SALES & SERVICE INC.
15 Adams St, Burlington, MA 01803
Tel.: (781) 272-0060   MA
Web Site: http://www.filtersales.com
Year Founded: 1983
Sales Range: $10-24.9 Million

Emp.: 27
Distr of Filtration For Air & Water
N.A.I.C.S.: 423330
Alan Ouellet (Exec VP)
Tom Ouellet (Exec VP)

FIN-WEST GROUP
1131 W 6th St Ste 300, Ontario, CA 91762
Tel.: (909) 595-1996
Web Site:
  http://www.firstmortgage.com
Year Founded: 1975
Sales Range: $100-124.9 Million
Emp.: 500
Mortgage Banker
N.A.I.C.S.: 522292
Clement Ziroli (Chm & CEO)
Pac Dong (CFO, Exec VP & Controller)
Ronald T. Vargas (Sr VP-Secondary Mktg)
Scott Lehrer (Sr VP-Loan Servicing)

FINALE DESSERTERIE & BAKERY
9 Travis St, Allston, MA 02134
Tel.: (617) 206-9105
Web Site:
  http://www.finaledesserts.com
Year Founded: 1997
Rev.: $5,800,000
Emp.: 130
Food & Beverage Services
N.A.I.C.S.: 445298
Paul Conforti (Co-Founder & Pres)
Chris Kane (VP-Ops)

FINANCE FACTORS, LIM-ITED1952
1164 Bishop St Ste 300, Honolulu, HI 96813-2810
Tel.: (808) 522-2000
Web Site:
  http://www.financefactors.com
Year Founded: 1952
Sales Range: $100-124.9 Million
Emp.: 200
Mortgage & Loan Services
N.A.I.C.S.: 522299
Craig Camello (VP & Mgr-Bus Dev)
Dirk Apao (VP & Mgr-Bus Dev)
Keenan Eto (VP & Mgr-Bus Dev)
Jaimee Manago (VP & Mgr-Bus Dev)
Kei Kido (Sr VP & Mgr-Comml Real Estate)
Rory Matsumoto (VP & Mgr-Bus Dev)
Steven J. Teruya (Pres & COO)
Ron Cole (Mgr-Bus Dev)
Paula Kobayashi (Mgr-Bus Dev)
Romeo Anacan (VP & Mgr-Bus Dev)
Bill Grant (VP & Mgr-Bus Dev)
Gigi Infante-Delos Santos (Asst VP & Branch Mgr)
Paul Vella (Chief Credit Officer)
Kristi Maynard (CFO)

Subsidiaries:

Finance Insurance Ltd. (1)
1164 Bishop St Ste 400, Honolulu, HI 96813
Tel.: (808) 522-2040
Web Site: http://www.financeinsurance.com
Rev.: $27,800,000
Emp.: 60
Insurance Agents
N.A.I.C.S.: 524210
Melvin Young (Pres & COO)

Finance Realty Company Ltd. (1)
1164 Bishop St 1089, Honolulu, HI 96813
Tel.: (808) 548-3347
Web Site:
  http://www.financeenterprises.com
Sales Range: $10-24.9 Million
Emp.: 6
Land Subdividers & Developers, Commercial
N.A.I.C.S.: 237210

FINANCIAL ACCOUNTING FOUNDATION
401 Merritt 7, Norwalk, CT 06856-5116
Tel.: (203) 847-0700   DE
Web Site:
  http://www.accountingfoundation.org
Year Founded: 1972
Rev.: $55,731,000
Assets: $89,055,000
Liabilities: $18,926,000
Net Worth: $70,129,000
Earnings: $4,252,000
Emp.: 202
Fiscal Year-end: 12/31/18
Accounting Services
N.A.I.C.S.: 541219
Mary P. Crotty (COO)
John W. Auchincloss (Exec Dir)
Matthew J. Broder (VP-Pub Affairs)
Kathleen L. Casey (Chm)
Elizabeth Ann Garti (VP-HR)
Steven Hobbs (Gen Counsel & VP)

FINANCIAL ADVANTAGE INC.
10211 Wincopin Cir Ste 220, Columbia, MD 21044
Tel.: (410) 715-9200
Web Site: http://www.investfai.com
Year Founded: 1987
Sales Range: $1-9.9 Million
Emp.: 15
Financial Planning & Investment Management Services
N.A.I.C.S.: 523940
J. Michael Martin (Chief Investment Officer & Principal)
Lyn A. Dippel (Principal)
Curtis R. Gross (Principal)

FINANCIAL CENTER CREDIT UNION
18 S Center St, Stockton, CA 95202-2803
Tel.: (209) 948-6024   CA
Web Site: http://www.fccuburt.org
Year Founded: 1954
Sales Range: $10-24.9 Million
Emp.: 100
Credit Union
N.A.I.C.S.: 522130
Steve Leiga (VP-Acct & Fin)
Nora Stroh (COO & Exec VP)
Michael Duffy (Pres & CEO)

FINANCIAL CORPORATION OF LOUISIANA
128 N Parkerson Ave, Crowley, LA 70526
Tel.: (337) 783-4014   LA
Web Site: http://www.fnb-la.com
Year Founded: 2002
Bank Holding Company
N.A.I.C.S.: 551111
Richard Seale (Chm)

Subsidiaries:

First National Bank of Louisiana (1)
128 N Parkerson Ave, Crowley, LA 70526
Tel.: (337) 783-4014
Web Site: http://www.fnb-la.com
Sales Range: $25-49.9 Million
Emp.: 35
Commericial Banking
N.A.I.C.S.: 522110
J. Randall Prather (Chm, Pres & CEO)
Jim Lyons (COO)

Rayne State Bank & Trust Company (1)
200 S Adams Ave, Rayne, LA 70578
Tel.: (337) 334-3191
Web Site: http://www.bankonnet.com
Commericial Banking
N.A.I.C.S.: 522110
Steve Hollier (Pres & CEO)
Larry Prevost (CFO)
Yvonne D. Menard (COO, Sec & Sr VP)

FINANCIAL DESIGNS LTD.
7979 E Tufts Ave Ste 1550, Denver, CO 80237
Tel.: (303) 832-6100
Web Site: http://fdltd.com
Year Founded: 1970
Wealth Management & Executive Benefits Planning Services
N.A.I.C.S.: 523991
J. Dave Hunter *(Founder & Chm)*
Adam L. Truitt *(Pres)*
Karen M. Cecile *(COO)*

FINANCIAL FEDCORP, INC.
1715 Aaron Brenner Dr Ste 100, Memphis, TN 38120
Tel.: (901) 756-2848   TN
Web Site:
https://www.finfedmem.com
Year Founded: 1985
Sales Range: $10-24.9 Million
Emp.: 56
Bank Holding Company
N.A.I.C.S.: 551111
Kent Wunderlich *(Chm, CEO & Gen Counsel)*
Leigh Harwell *(Sr VP)*
Gideon L. Scoggin *(Sr VP)*
Steve A. Sutton *(Chief Credit Officer & Exec VP)*
Jon Van Hoozer *(Sr VP)*
Susan C. Yount *(CFO & Exec VP)*
John Loebel *(Exec VP)*
Mary H. Floyd *(Exec VP)*
Cynthia Burton *(Sr VP)*
Ruth Carr *(Sr VP)*
Ean D. Colley *(Sr VP)*
Stephen B. Curnutte *(Sr VP)*
Sam Hubbard *(Sr VP)*
Alex Neale *(Sr VP)*
John Summers *(Sr VP)*
Ben Sutton *(Sr VP)*
Dan Wiggins *(Sr VP)*
Judson Williford *(Sr VP)*
Richard T. Wood III *(Exec VP)*

Subsidiaries:

Financial Federal Bank   **(1)**
6305 Humphreys Blvd Ste 100, Memphis, TN 38120
Tel.: (901) 756-2848
Web Site: http://www.finfedmem.com
Sales Range: $10-24.9 Million
Commericial Banking
N.A.I.C.S.: 522110
Kent Wunderlich *(Chm, CEO & Gen Counsel)*
William R. Tayloe *(Pres)*
Susan Yount *(CFO & Exec VP)*
Steve Sutton *(Chief Credit Officer & Exec VP)*
Mary H. Floyd *(Exec VP)*
Sam Hubbard *(Sr VP)*
Carolyn Sobral *(VP)*
John Loebel *(Sr VP & Mgr-Residential Lending)*
Amy Betts *(VP)*
Eric Beaty *(VP-Comml Banking)*
Battle Williford *(VP)*
Gideon Scoggin *(Sr VP-Comml Banking)*
Ruth Carr *(Sr VP)*
Ginny Johnson *(VP)*
Ethan Minderman *(VP & Mgr-IT)*
John Summers *(Sr VP)*
Ben Sutton *(Sr VP)*
Cindy Perry *(VP-Deposit Svcs-Memphis)*
Cynthia Burton *(Sr VP)*
Ean D. Colley *(Sr VP)*
Alex Neale *(Sr VP)*
Judson Williford *(Sr VP)*
Richard T. Wood III *(Exec VP)*

FINANCIAL GUARANTY INSURANCE COMPANY
463 7th Ave, New York, NY 10018
Tel.: (212) 312-3000
Web Site: https://www.fgic.com
Sales Range: $200-249.9 Million
Insurance Holding Company
N.A.I.C.S.: 551112

A. Edward Turi *(Gen Counsel & Exec VP)*
Kenneth L. Degen *(Mng Dir)*
Jamie B. Stewart Jr. *(Chm)*

Subsidiaries:

FGIC UK Limited   **(1)**
c/o Mazars LLP Tower Bridge House, Saint Katharine's Way, London, E1W 1DD, United Kingdom   **(100%)**
Tel.: (44) 2077963900
Web Site: http://www.fgic.com
Sales Range: $25-49.9 Million
Emp.: 20
Financial Guaranty Insurance
N.A.I.C.S.: 524126
Glenn Fox *(Mng Dir)*

FINANCIAL HOLDING CORP.
300 W 11th St, Kansas City, MO 64105-1618
Tel.: (816) 391-2000   MO
Web Site: http://www.americo.com
Sales Range: $50-74.9 Million
Emp.: 971
Insurance Holding Company
N.A.I.C.S.: 551112
Mark Fallon *(CFO)*
Wang Dongzhi *(Chm)*
Zheng Li *(Interim CEO)*

Subsidiaries:

Americo Life, Inc.   **(1)**
300 W 11th St, Kansas City, MO 64105-1575   **(100%)**
Tel.: (816) 391-2000
Web Site: http://www.americo.com
Life Insurance & Annuities
N.A.I.C.S.: 524113
John Joplin *(Asst VP)*
Kern Baker *(Sr Acct Exec)*

Subsidiary (Domestic):

Americo Financial Life & Annuity Insurance Company   **(2)**
300 W 11th St Fl 3, Kansas City, MO 64105
Tel.: (816) 474-9330
Web Site: http://www.americo.com
Insurance Agents
N.A.I.C.S.: 524113
Melanie Neighbor *(Supvr-Policy Support)*

Financial Assurance Life Insurance Company   **(2)**
300 W 11th St, Kansas City, MO 64141
Fire Insurance Services
N.A.I.C.S.: 524113

Great Southern Life Insurance Company   **(2)**
300 W 11th St, Kansas City, MO 64105
Tel.: (816) 391-2000
Web Site: http://www.greatsouthern.com
Emp.: 400
Fire Insurance Services
N.A.I.C.S.: 524113

Investors Life Insurance Company of North America   **(2)**
6500 River Place Blvd Bldg 1, Austin, TX 78730
Tel.: (512) 404-5000
Fire Insurance Services
N.A.I.C.S.: 524113

National Farmers Union Life Insurance Company   **(2)**
300 W 11th St, Kansas City, MO 64141
Tel.: (800) 366-6100
Fire Insurance Services
N.A.I.C.S.: 524113

The Ohio State Life Insurance Company   **(2)**
500 N Akard St Ste 500, Dallas, TX 75201-3320
Tel.: (214) 954-8100
Web Site: http://www.ohiostatelife.com
Life Insurance Products & Services
N.A.I.C.S.: 524113

United Fidelity Life Insurance Company   **(2)**
300 W 11th St, Kansas City, MO 64141

Tel.: (800) 366-6100
Fire Insurance Services
N.A.I.C.S.: 524113

FINANCIAL INDUSTRY REGULATORY AUTHORITY, INC.
1735 K St NW, Washington, DC 20006-1506
Tel.: (202) 728-8000
Web Site: http://www.finra.org
Year Founded: 1939
Sales Range: $1-4.9 Billion
Emp.: 3,440
Self-Regulating Organization of the Securities Industry
N.A.I.C.S.: 523210
Todd T. Diganci *(CFO, Chief Admin Officer & Exec VP)*
Cameron K. Funkhouser *(Exec VP-Fraud Detection & Market Intelligence)*
Marcia E. Asquith *(Exec VP)*
Tracy Johnson *(Sr VP-HR)*
Thomas M. Selman *(Exec VP-Regulatory Policy)*
Robert L. D. Colby *(Chief Legal Officer)*
Steven J. Randich *(CIO & Exec VP)*
Michael Rufino *(Exec VP & Head-Member Regulation-Sls Practice)*
Jonathan S. Sokobin *(Sr VP)*
Richard W. Berry *(Exec VP & Dir-Dispute Resolution)*
Thomas Gira *(Exec VP-Market Regulation)*
Robert W. Cook *(Pres & CEO)*
Gregory J. Dean *(Sr VP-Office of Govt Affairs)*
Josh Drobnyk *(Sr VP-Corp Comm)*
Jennifer Piorko Mitchell *(VP-Corp Governance)*
Susan Schroeder *(Exec VP & Head-Enforcement)*
Feral Talib *(Exec VP & Head-Surveillance & Market Intelligence)*
Stephanie Dumont *(Exec VP & Head-Market Regulation & Transparency Svcs)*

Subsidiaries:

FINRA Dispute Resolution, Inc.   **(1)**
1 Liberty Plz 165 Broadway 27th Fl, New York, NY 10006
Tel.: (212) 858-4200
Financial Management Services
N.A.I.C.S.: 523940
Richard W. Berry *(Exec VP)*

FINRA Regulation   **(1)**
9509 Key W Ave Decoverly Bldg, Rockville, MD 20850-4302
Tel.: (301) 590-6500
Sales Range: $100-124.9 Million
Emp.: 600
Regulate Broker Dealers
N.A.I.C.S.: 523210

FINANCIAL INFORMATION TECHNOLOGIES, INC.
7702 Woodland Center Blvd Ste 50, Tampa, FL 33614
Tel.: (813) 288-1980   FL
Web Site: http://www.fintech.net
Year Founded: 1991
Sales Range: $10-24.9 Million
Emp.: 50
Electronic Funds Transfer & Invoice Settlement Solutions
N.A.I.C.S.: 522320
Scott P. Riley *(CEO)*
Joe Kwo *(CIO & Exec VP)*
Buck Jones *(CFO)*
Ron Floto *(Dir-Strategic Dev)*
Richard Verrecchia *(VP-Analytics)*
Brooke Cote *(VP-Client Svcs)*
Chad Hardwick *(Sr VP-Sls)*
Benjamin Boehm *(VP-Fin)*
Tad Phelps *(Pres)*

Brooke Belcher *(VP-Client Svcs)*
Trey Williams *(COO)*
Walter E. Pickel Jr. *(VP-Product Dev)*

FINANCIAL INNOVATIONS CENTER INC
20 N Clark Ste 1950, Chicago, IL 60602
Tel.: (312) 881-5856   IL
Web Site:
http://www.cfsinnovation.com
Year Founded: 2005
Sales Range: $10-24.9 Million
Emp.: 42
Financial Management Services
N.A.I.C.S.: 523999
Jeanne Hogarth *(VP-Policy)*
Sarah E. Gordon *(Sr VP)*
Laura Barger *(Chief Mktg Officer)*
Carole Brite *(CFO)*

FINANCIAL INVESTMENTS CORPORATION
50 E Washington St Ste 400, Chicago, IL 60602
Tel.: (312) 494-4513   IL
Web Site: http://www.fic-sff.com
Year Founded: 1967
Rev.: $650,000,000
Asset Management & Private Equity Firm
N.A.I.C.S.: 523940
Kenneth D. Hooten *(Mng Dir)*
Ian G. Ross *(Partner)*
Nicholas W. Sayers *(Principal)*
David M. Gervase *(CFO)*
Harrison I. Steans *(Chm)*
Frank A. Reppenhagen *(Partner)*
Jack H. Dickens *(VP)*
Marion C. Zehner *(Mgr-IR)*
Alicia Hernandez *(Mgr-Acct Mgr)*
Jennifer W. Steans *(Pres & CEO)*

Subsidiaries:

Concentric Equity Partners   **(1)**
50 E Washington St Ste 400, Chicago, IL 60602
Tel.: (312) 494-4513
Web Site: http://www.ficcep.com
Privater Equity Firm
N.A.I.C.S.: 523999
Kenneth D. Hooten *(Partner)*
Jennifer W. Steans *(Partner)*
Ian G. Ross *(Principal)*
David M. Gervase *(CFO)*
Harrison I. Steans *(Chm)*
Frank A. Reppenhagen *(Partner)*

Holding (Domestic):

Rapid Fire Safety & Security LLC   **(2)**
2 CityPlace Dr Ste 200, Saint Louis, MO 63141
Tel.: (314) 252-0788
Web Site: https://www.rapidfiress.com
Emp.: 100
Fire Alarms, Test & Inspections & Security Services
N.A.I.C.S.: 922160
Mike McLeod *(CEO)*
Colin Harrold *(Pres)*

Subsidiary (Domestic):

Pacific Auxiliary Fire Alarm Company   **(3)**
95 Boutwell St, San Francisco, CA 94124-1903
Tel.: (415) 467-9393
Web Site: http://www.pafa.com
Emp.: 100
Security System Services
N.A.I.C.S.: 561621
Douglas Shackley *(Pres & CEO)*

Security & Access Systems   **(3)**
3811 Rutledge Rd NE, Albuquerque, NM 87109-5564
Tel.: (505) 823-1561
Web Site:
http://www.securityandaccess.com

Financial Investments Corporation—(Continued)

Emp.: 100
Electrical Apparatus & Equipment, Wiring Supplies & Related Equipment Merchant Whslr
N.A.I.C.S.: 423610
Chris Ipitios (Pres)

FINANCIAL INVESTMENTS INC
462 Herndon Pkwy Ste 205, Herndon, VA 20170
Tel.: (703) 435-2777
Web Site: https://www.financialii.com
Year Founded: 1995
Sales Range: $1-9.9 Million
Emp.: 2
Investment Management Service
N.A.I.C.S.: 523940
Craig B. Kendall (Owner & Mgr)
Melanie Martin (Mgr-Admin)

FINANCIAL MARKETS, INC.
1540A Samco Rd Ste A, Rapid City, SD 57702
Tel.: (605) 342-2438
Web Site: http://www.fm-inc.com
Year Founded: 1990
Sales Range: $10-24.9 Million
Emp.: 12
Insurance Services
N.A.I.C.S.: 524210
Edward D. Bartling (COO)
R. Neil Sperling (VP)
Robert L. Sperling (Pres)
Stephanie Owens (Office Mgr)

FINANCIAL MORTGAGE GROUP LTD.
21 Linden Dr, Broomall, PA 19008
Tel.: (610) 353-2209
Sales Range: $10-24.9 Million
Emp.: 3
Mortgage Bankers & Loan Correspondents
N.A.I.C.S.: 522310
Jay Finkel (CEO)

FINANCIAL PARTNERS CREDIT UNION
7800 E Imperial Hwy, Downey, CA 91030
Tel.: (562) 904-4208
Web Site: https://www.fpcu.org
Year Founded: 1937
Sales Range: $25-49.9 Million
Emp.: 210
Fiscal Year-end: 12/31/15
Credit Union
N.A.I.C.S.: 522130
Nader Moghaddam (Pres & CEO)
Laurie Tyler (VP-Sls & Member Svc)
Wanda Williams (Sr VP-Plng, Tech & Risk Mgmt)
Lori Reeves (Sr VP-Ops & Electronic Svcs)
Michael Patterson (Chief Lending Officer & Sr VP)
Mary Torsney (CFO)

FINANCIAL PLANNING ASSOCIATION
7535 E Hampden Ave Ste 600, Denver, CO 80231
Tel.: (303) 759-4900
Web Site: http://www.fpanet.org
Year Founded: 2000
Sales Range: $10-24.9 Million
Emp.: 78
Financial Management Services
N.A.I.C.S.: 813910
George Bradley (Dir-Pro Dev)
Mark A. Badami (Pres)

FINANCIAL PLUS CREDIT UNION
800 Chestnut St, Ottawa, IL 61350

Web Site: https://www.financialplus.org
Year Founded: 1951
Sales Range: $10-24.9 Million
Emp.: 72
Financial Support Services
N.A.I.C.S.: 523999

FINANCIAL RECOVERY SERVICES, INC.
4510 W 77th St Ste 200, Edina, MN 55435
Tel.: (952) 831-4800
Web Site: http://www.fin-rec.com
Year Founded: 1996
Sales Range: $10-24.9 Million
Emp.: 228
Collection Services
N.A.I.C.S.: 561440
Brian C. Bowers (Pres & CEO)
Mark Pearson (VP-New Bus Dev)
Brad Bowers (Sr Support Mgr-Admin Svcs)
Mark Patin (CIO)

FINANCIAL SERVICES CORP.
2024 Center Ave, Fort Lee, NJ 07024
Tel.: (201) 592-7474
Web Site: http://www.bnbbank.com
Rev.: $10,951,747
Emp.: 3
National Commercial Banks
N.A.I.C.S.: 522110
Sam C. Chung (CEO)

Subsidiaries:

BNB Bank　　　　　　　　　(1)
2024 Center Ave, Fort Lee, NJ 07024
Tel.: (201) 592-7474
Web Site: http://www.bnbbank.com
Sales Range: $25-49.9 Million
Emp.: 41
National Commercial Banks
N.A.I.C.S.: 522110
Angela Torres (Mgr-SBA)

FINANCIAL STATEMENT SERVICES
3300 S Fairview St, Santa Ana, CA 92704
Tel.: (714) 436-3300
Web Site: https://www.fssi-ca.com
Year Founded: 1980
Rev.: $16,014,915
Emp.: 200
Business Communications Services
N.A.I.C.S.: 323111
Jon Dietz (Founder)
Jennifer P. W. Dietz (Pres)
Dick O'Neil (Sr VP-Mktg)

FINANCIAL TECHNOLOGY VENTURES MANAGEMENT CO. LLC
555 California St Ste 2850, San Francisco, CA 94104
Tel.: (415) 229-3000
Web Site: http://www.ftvcapital.com
Year Founded: 1998
Privater Equity Firm
N.A.I.C.S.: 523999
Robert Anderson (Partner)
Brad Bernstein (Mng Partner)
Dylan Bishop (Dir-Res)
Brent Fierro (VP)
Richard Garman (Partner)

Subsidiaries:

Docupace Technologies LLC　　(1)
11766 Wilshire Blvd Ste 1120, Los Angeles, CA 90025
Tel.: (310) 445-7722
Web Site: http://www.docupace.com
Financial Industry Electronic Processing Software Developer & Publisher
N.A.I.C.S.: 513210

Ron Wallis (CTO)
Joel Friedman (Exec VP-Client Delivery & Support Svcs)
Michael Pinsker (Founder & Pres)
John DeVincent (Exec VP-Mktg)
David Donell (CFO)
Alan Giancaterino (Exec VP-Sls)
James Caulkins (Chief Revenue Officer)
Rickey Bijlani (Dir-Mktg)
David Knoch (CEO)

Tango Card, Inc.　　　　　　(1)
4700 42nd Ave S W Ste 430a, Seattle, WA 98116
Tel.: (877) 558-2646
Web Site: http://www.tangocard.com
Digital Gift Card Distr
N.A.I.C.S.: 459420
David Leeds (Founder & CEO)
Chek Lim (CTO)
Carrie Casanas (CFO)
Nat Salvione (Chief Comml Officer)
Mary Shelley (Chief People Officer)

Subsidiary (Domestic):

GiftCertificates.com Corporation　(2)
11510 Blondo St, Omaha, NE 68164-3846
Web Site: http://www.gcincentives.com
Online Gift Certificates Retailer
N.A.I.C.S.: 513199
Rob Gregersen (VP-Fin & Admin)
Paul Hubert (VP-Ops & Merchnat Svcs)
Cindy Mielke (Dir-Mktg & Sls Ops)

FINANCIAL WEST INVESTMENT GROUP INC.
4510 E 1000 Oaks Blvd Ste 100, Westlake Village, CA 91362-3875
Tel.: (805) 497-9222
Web Site: http://www.fwg.com
Year Founded: 1985
Sales Range: $25-49.9 Million
Emp.: 28
Security Brokers & Dealers
N.A.I.C.S.: 523150
Gene C. Valentine (Chm & CEO)

FINANCIALOGIC, INC.
1333 W Mcdermott Dr Ste 200, Allen, TX 75013-3089
Tel.: (972) 480-0464
Web Site: http://www.financeknight.com
Year Founded: 1992
Sales Range: $10-24.9 Million
Emp.: 2
Financial & Management Services
N.A.I.C.S.: 561110
Cliff McKenzie (Pres & CEO)

FINCH TRANSPORTATION, LLC
323 Lynn Dr, Santa Rosa Beach, FL 32459
Tel.: (850) 650-6333
Web Site: https://www.sunshineshuttle.com
Year Founded: 2004
Sales Range: $1-9.9 Million
Emp.: 50
Shuttle & Limousine Services
N.A.I.C.S.: 485320
John Finch (Owner)

FINCH TURF EQUIPMENT INCORPORATED
1127 Littlestown Pke, Westminster, MD 21157
Tel.: (410) 848-7211
Web Site: http://www.finchinc.com
Sales Range: $10-24.9 Million
Emp.: 220
Golf Goods & Equipment
N.A.I.C.S.: 459110
Justin O'Connor (Mgr-Svc-Turf)
Keith Gorsuch (Mgr-Svc-Agricultural)
Brad Finch (VP)
Dann Finch (VP)

FINCHEY CORPORATION OF CA
800 S Brand Blvd, Glendale, CA 91204
Tel.: (818) 246-5600
Web Site: https://www.pacificbmw.com
Rev.: $39,400,000
Emp.: 200
Automobiles, New & Used
N.A.I.C.S.: 441110
Steve Lindstrom (Gen Mgr)

FINCK CIGAR CO.
414 Vera Cruz, San Antonio, TX 78207-5642
Tel.: (210) 226-4191
Web Site: http://www.finckcigarcompany.com
Year Founded: 1893
Sales Range: $75-99.9 Million
Emp.: 100
Pipe, Tobacco & Cigar Retailer & Mfr
N.A.I.C.S.: 312230
Bill Finck Sr. (Pres)
Bill Finck Jr. (VP-Adv)

FINDLAY AUTOMOTIVE INC.
310 N Gibson Rd, Henderson, NV 89014
Tel.: (702) 558-8888
Web Site: http://www.findlayautomotive.com
Rev.: $73,900,000
Emp.: 100
Automobiles, New & Used
N.A.I.C.S.: 441110
Clifford J. Findlay (Pres)

FINDLAY IMPLEMENT CO.
1640 Northridge Rd, Findlay, OH 45840
Tel.: (419) 424-0471
Web Site: http://www.findlay-imp.com
Year Founded: 1972
Sales Range: $10-24.9 Million
Emp.: 30
Agricultural Machinery & Equipment
N.A.I.C.S.: 423820
Tom Marquart (Owner)

FINDLAY LINCOLN
310 N Gibson Rd, Henderson, NV 89014-6702
Tel.: (702) 457-0321
Web Site: https://www.findlaylincolnofhenderson.com
Sales Range: $10-24.9 Million
Emp.: 49
New Car Whslr
N.A.I.C.S.: 441110
Nathan Findlay (Gen Mgr)
Kelli McConaughy (Dir-Mktg)

FINDLAY TOYOTA GROUP
5030 E Marketplace Dr, Flagstaff, AZ 86004
Tel.: (928) 852-4414
Web Site: https://www.findlaytoyotaflagstaff.net
Year Founded: 2008
Sales Range: $10-24.9 Million
Emp.: 75
Car Whslr
N.A.I.C.S.: 441110
Sheila Duffy (Mgr-Customer Rels)
Robby Findlay (Gen Mgr)

FINDLAY VOLKSWAGEN
983 Auto Show Dr, Henderson, NV 89014-6714
Tel.: (702) 710-5990
Web Site: https://www.findlayvw.com
Sales Range: $10-24.9 Million
Emp.: 75
Car Whslr

N.A.I.C.S.: 441110
D. J. Burman *(Mgr-Internet Sls)*
Russell Garceau *(Dir-Fixed Ops)*
Roger Gosher *(Dir-Fixed Ops)*

FINDMYCOMPANY.COM LLC
611 S Congress Ave Ste 130, Austin, TX 78704
Web Site:
https://www.findmycompany.com
Year Founded: 2007
Sales Range: $1-9.9 Million
Emp.: 30
Website Marketing
N.A.I.C.S.: 541613
Heidi Buckner *(Dir-Operations)*

FINDTAPE.COM LLC
1330 Rt 206 Ste 103-149, Skillman, NJ 08558
Tel.: (908) 248-0427
Web Site: http://www.findtape.com
Year Founded: 2003
Sales Range: $1-9.9 Million
Emp.: 2
Online Source for Pressure-Sensitive Adhesive Tape & Accessories
N.A.I.C.S.: 325520
Kevin Mahoney *(Owner)*

FINE ARTS ENTERPRISES, INC.
645 Summer St, Boston, MA 02210
Tel.: (617) 268-7200
Web Site: http://www.faeboston.com
Sales Range: $10-24.9 Million
Emp.: 10
Fine Art Transportation & Storage
N.A.I.C.S.: 484121
Larry Doherty *(Pres)*
John Kane *(VP & Gen Mgr)*
Marielle Sinclair *(Mgr-Warehouse)*
Craig Prest *(Mgr-Ops)*
Andrew Larue *(Mgr-Safety)*

FINE ARTS MUSEUMS OF SAN FRANCISCO
50 Hagiwara Tea Garden Dr, San Francisco, CA 94118
Tel.: (415) 750-3600   CA
Web Site: https://www.famsf.org
Year Founded: 1895
Sales Range: $25-49.9 Million
Emp.: 455
Art Museum Operator
N.A.I.C.S.: 712110
Michele Gutierrez-Canepa *(CFO)*
Michael Webb *(Dir-IT)*
Linda Butler *(Dir-Mktg, Comm & Visitor Experience)*
Thomas P. Campbell *(CEO)*
Dede Wilsey *(Chm)*

FINE DESIGNS STORE
705 S Sherman St Ste 705K, Richardson, TX 75081
Tel.: (214) 796-4569
Web Site:
http://www.finedesigns.com
Year Founded: 1990
Sales Range: $10-24.9 Million
Emp.: 527
On-Site Complete Custom Apparel Printing Services
N.A.I.C.S.: 323113
Victor Kostroub *(Pres)*

FINE ENTERTAINMENT CO.
3355 S Las Vegas Blvd, Las Vegas, NV 89109
Tel.: (702) 731-9683
Web Site:
http://www.therockhousebar.com
Year Founded: 2006
Sales Range: $1-9.9 Million
Emp.: 80

Restaurant & Entertainment Management
N.A.I.C.S.: 722410
Jeremiah Wilke *(Gen Mgr)*
Mark Fine *(Co-Owner)*
Jeffrey Fine *(Co-Owner)*
Avi Kopelman *(Gen Mgr)*

FINE LIGHT, INC.
1801 S Liberty Dr Ste 300, Bloomington, IN 47403
Tel.: (812) 339-6700
Year Founded: 1984
Emp.: 150
N.A.I.C.S.: 541810
Sherman Rogers *(Owner & CEO)*
Alan Pope *(Pres)*
Lindsay Resnick *(CMO)*
Jeannene Manning *(Sr VP & Acct Supvr)*
Greg Henderson *(Sr VP & Grp Acct Dir)*
Mike Hawkins *(Dir-Creative Grp)*
Anne Goetz *(Dir-Creative Grp)*
Marybeth Peters *(Sr VP & Dir-Media)*
Scott Thielen *(Assoc Dir-Creative)*
Holly Laugle *(VP-Client Svcs)*
Terry Followell *(Assoc Dir-Creative)*
Elizabeth Blevins *(Acct Supvr)*
Charlie Rohlfing *(Assoc Dir-Creative)*
Steve Stockbauer *(Acct Supvr)*
Ashleigh Bills *(Assoc Dir-Creative)*
Erika Evans *(Assoc Acct Exec)*
April Moore *(Dir-HR)*
Susan Arterburn *(Sr Acct Exec)*
Chris Kolehmainen *(VP-Digital Svcs)*

Subsidiaries:

Fine Light, Inc.   (1)
123 E Main St Ste 201, Louisville, KY 40202
Tel.: (502) 589-5896
Emp.: 15
N.A.I.C.S.: 541810
Christy Keese *(Media Planner/Buyer)*
Patty Anderson *(Sr VP & Dir-Media)*

FINE LINE GRAPHICS CORP.
1481 Goodale Blvd, Columbus, OH 43212
Tel.: (614) 486-0276
Web Site:
http://www.finelinegraphics.com
Sales Range: $10-24.9 Million
Emp.: 43
Offset Printing Services
N.A.I.C.S.: 323111
Jim Basch *(Pres)*
Greg Davis *(VP-Sls)*

FINE ORGANICS CORPORATION
420 Kuller Rd, Clifton, NJ 07015-2277
Tel.: (973) 478-1000   DE
Web Site:
https://www.fineorganicscorp.com
Year Founded: 1939
Sales Range: $50-74.9 Million
Emp.: 9
Specialty Industrial Cleaning Compounds Mfr
N.A.I.C.S.: 325998
William J. Reidy *(Chm & CEO)*
Gary F. Straub *(Pres & COO)*
Lewis Goldberg *(Mgr-Sls)*

FINE PROMOTIONS, INC.
8156 Zionsville Rd, Indianapolis, IN 46268
Tel.: (317) 298-3100
Web Site:
https://www.finepromotions.com
Year Founded: 1977
Rev.: $2,100,000
Emp.: 10
Services Related to Advertising

N.A.I.C.S.: 541890
Robb Fine *(CEO)*
Victoria Randle-Fine *(Pres)*
Jo Weiker *(Acct Exec)*
Vanessa Kestler *(Office Mgr)*

FINE SHEER INDUSTRIES INC.
350 5th Ave Ste 5001, New York, NY 10118
Tel.: (212) 594-4224
Web Site: http://www.finesheer.com
Sales Range: $25-49.9 Million
Emp.: 10
Socks
N.A.I.C.S.: 315120

FINELINE INDUSTRIES INC.
2047 Grogan Ave, Merced, CA 95341
Tel.: (209) 384-0255
Web Site:
https://www.centurionboats.com
Boatbuilding & Repairing
N.A.I.C.S.: 336612
Les Clark *(VP-Mfg)*

FINELINENS.COM
1193 Lexington Ave, New York, NY 10028
Tel.: (212) 737-2123
Web Site: https://www.finelinens.com
Year Founded: 1975
Sales Range: $1-9.9 Million
Emp.: 4
Luxury Online Linen Retailer
N.A.I.C.S.: 812331
Steven Hirsch *(Co-Owner)*
David Hirsch *(Co-Owner)*

FINELITE INC.
30500 Whipple Rd, Union City, CA 94587-1530
Tel.: (510) 441-1100
Web Site: https://www.finelite.com
Year Founded: 1991
Sales Range: $10-24.9 Million
Emp.: 100
Commercial Lighting Fixtures
N.A.I.C.S.: 335132
Terry Clark *(Founder, Chm & CTO)*
Jerry Mix *(CEO)*
Dean Mayes *(Plant Mgr)*
Vickie Lauck *(Dir-Applications)*
Brian Blackhart *(Dir-Info Svcs)*
Manisha Hiralal *(Sr Acct Mgr)*
Trish Dortch *(Acct Exec-Inside Sls)*

FINELLI CONSULTING ENGINEERS, INC.
2605 Nazareth Rd, Easton, PA 18045
Tel.: (610) 559-1000
Web Site:
https://www.finelliconsulting.com
Year Founded: 2006
Sales Range: $1-9.9 Million
Emp.: 17
Civil Engineering Consulting Services
N.A.I.C.S.: 541330
Leila Finelli *(CFO)*
Michael S. Finelli *(Pres)*
Dawson Bloom *(COO)*
Eugene N. Weber *(Branch Mgr & Sr Engr)*
John S. Sims *(Mgr-IT)*

Subsidiaries:

Finelli Consulting Engineers, Inc. (1)
205 Route 31 N, Washington, NJ 07882   (100%)
Tel.: (908) 835-9500
Web Site: http://www.finelliconsulting.com
Civil Engineering Consulting & Municipal Engineering Services
N.A.I.C.S.: 237990
Michael S. Finelli *(Pres)*

FINEOUT ENTERPRISES INC.

1780 S Buckner Tarsney Rd, Grain Valley, MO 64029
Tel.: (816) 228-7455
Web Site: https://www.meravic.com
Year Founded: 1980
Sales Range: $10-24.9 Million
Emp.: 40
Artificial Flowers
N.A.I.C.S.: 424930
Vicki Sue Digby *(Owner & CEO)*

FINER FOODS INC.
3100 W 36th St, Chicago, IL 60632
Tel.: (312) 733-5566
Web Site: http://www.finerfoods.com
Rev.: $10,600,000
Emp.: 65
Fresh Fruit & Vegetable Merchant Whslr
N.A.I.C.S.: 424480
Mary A. Fitzgerald *(Pres)*

FINERGY DEVELOPMENT, LLC
2170 Main St Ste #401, Sarasota, FL 34237
Tel.: (941) 917-0494
Web Site:
http://www.finergygroup.com
Commercial & Residential Real Estate Developer
N.A.I.C.S.: 237210
Enzo Gagliardi *(Founder & CEO)*

FINFROCK
2400 Apopka Blvd, Apopka, FL 32703
Tel.: (407) 293-4000
Web Site: https://www.finfrock.com
Year Founded: 1945
Sales Range: $50-74.9 Million
Emp.: 215
Construction Engineering Services
N.A.I.C.S.: 541330
Vic Iacone *(Mgr-Pur)*
Ronald Heinkel *(Dir-Preconstruction)*

FINGER COMPANIES INC.
99 Detering St Ste 200, Houston, TX 77007
Tel.: (713) 864-3313
Web Site:
http://www.fingercompanies.com
Rev.: $10,000,000
Emp.: 50
Apartment Hotel Operation
N.A.I.C.S.: 531110
Marvy A. Finger *(Pres & CEO)*
Gordon Pilmer *(CFO & Exec VP)*

FINGER FURNITURE COMPANY, INC.
9002 G Chimney Rock Rd, Houston, TX 77096-2509
Tel.: (713) 221-4441   TX
Web Site:
http://www.fingerfurniture.com
Year Founded: 1927
Sales Range: $200-249.9 Million
Emp.: 600
Home Furniture Retailer
N.A.I.C.S.: 449110
Rodney Finger *(Pres & CEO)*

FINGER LAKES BUSINESS SERVICES
42 Westlake Ave, Auburn, NY 13021
Web Site: http://www.callflas.com
Year Founded: 2002
Sales Range: $1-9.9 Million
Emp.: 64
Telephone Answering Services
N.A.I.C.S.: 561421
Gardner McLean *(Pres)*
Lisa Richardson *(Dir-HR)*

FINGER LAKES CHEMICALS INC.

Finger Lakes Chemicals Inc—(Continued)

418-440 Saint Paul St, Rochester, NY 14605
Tel.: (585) 454-4760
Web Site:
https://www.castlepackspower.com
Mfr of Cleaning Compounds
N.A.I.C.S.: 424690
Hans Blatter (Pres)

FINGER LAKES CONSTRUCTION COMPANY
10269 Old Rte 31 W, Clyde, NY 14433
Tel.: (315) 923-7777
Web Site:
http://www.fingerlakesconstruction.com
Year Founded: 1969
Rev.: $15,896,007
Emp.: 30
Commercial & Office Building, New Construction
N.A.I.C.S.: 236220

FINGERLE LUMBER CO.
617 S 5th Ave, Ann Arbor, MI 48104-2905
Tel.: (734) 663-0581 MI
Web Site:
http://www.fingerlelumber.com
Year Founded: 1931
Sales Range: $100-124.9 Million
Emp.: 80
Lumber & Building Supplies Distr
N.A.I.C.S.: 444110
John B. Fingerle (Pres)
Mark M. Fingerle (VP)
Lawrence J. Fingerle (Co-Owner)
Robert Pieknik (VP)

FINISH THOMPSON, INC.
921 Greengarden Rd, Erie, PA 16501
Tel.: (814) 455-4478
Web Site:
http://www.finishthompson.com
Rev.: $4,700,000
Emp.: 50
Pump & Pumping Equipment Mfr
N.A.I.C.S.: 333914
Peter Scantlebury (VP-Dev)
Todd Bennett (Mgr-Info Sys)

Subsidiaries:

Penguin Pumps, Inc. (1)
7932 Ajay Dr, Sun Valley, CA 91352
Tel.: (818) 504-2391
Web Site: https://www.filterpump.com
Sales Range: $1-9.9 Million
Emp.: 50
Pump & Pumping Equipment Mfr
N.A.I.C.S.: 333914
Jerome Hollander (Pres)
Brandon Vise (Pres & CEO)

FINK'S JEWELERS INC.
3545 Electric Rd, Roanoke, VA 24018-2004
Tel.: (540) 344-8697 VA
Web Site: https://www.finks.com
Year Founded: 1960
Sales Range: $25-49.9 Million
Emp.: 200
Jewelry Stores
N.A.I.C.S.: 458310
Marc S. Fink (Pres & CEO)

FINLAY MANAGEMENT, INC.
1102 A1A N Ste 206, Ponte Vedra Beach, FL 32082
Tel.: (904) 280-1000
Web Site: http://www.finlayllc.com
Year Founded: 1980
Sales Range: $1-9.9 Million
Emp.: 40
Property & Asset Management
N.A.I.C.S.: 531390

Christopher C. Finlay (Chm & CEO)
Kathy Hensley (VP-Florida)
Jim Eddings (CFO & Co-COO)
Stacey Hess (Controller)
T. J. Jenkins (Mgr-Property-Orlando & Jacksonville)
Alice Viego (Dir-Talent Mgmt)
Jerry Haley (Dir-Facilities)
Shyla Shepard (Sr VP-Texas)
Holly Costello (Pres & Co-COO)
Susan Truesdale (VP-East Coast)
Michael Dickerson (VP-Texas)

FINLAYSON BANCSHARES, INC.
2203 Finland Ave, Finlayson, MN 55735
Tel.: (320) 233-7575 MN
Web Site:
https://www.northviewbank.com
Year Founded: 1980
Sales Range: $25-49.9 Million
Emp.: 142
Bank Holding Company
N.A.I.C.S.: 551111
Bruce Pogatchnik (CEO)

Subsidiaries:

First Independent Bank (1)
300 Front St, Russell, MN 56169
Tel.: (507) 823-4391
Web Site: http://www.fibmn.com
Sales Range: $10-24.9 Million
Emp.: 65
Commericial Banking
N.A.I.C.S.: 522110
Duke Pogatchnik (Pres & CEO)
Kathy Neels (COO & Exec VP)
David Smith (Chief Credit Officer & Exec VP)
Karolyn Barron (Officer-Compliance & Sec)

Northview Bank (1)
2203 Finland Ave, Finlayson, MN 55735
Tel.: (320) 233-7575
Web Site: http://www.northviewbank.com
Sales Range: $10-24.9 Million
Emp.: 77
Commericial Banking
N.A.I.C.S.: 522110
Jeremy Byers (Officer-Loan, VP & Branch Mgr)
Paula Pogatchnik Diaz (Pres & CEO)
Bill Loew (Exec VP)
Wayne Nelson (Chief Credit Officer & Pres-Market)
Ron Carlson (Sr VP)

FINLEY FARMERS GRAIN & ELEVATOR COMPANY
Burlington Northern Right Of Way PO Box 477, Finley, ND 58230
Tel.: (701) 524-1500 ND
Web Site:
http://www.finleyfarmerselevator.com
Year Founded: 1911
Sales Range: $100-124.9 Million
Emp.: 20
Grain Elevators; Petroleum Products; Fertilizer & Fertilizer Materials
N.A.I.C.S.: 424510

FINLEY FIRE EQUIPMENT CO.
5255 N State Rt 60 NW, McConnelsville, OH 43756
Tel.: (740) 962-4328
Web Site: http://www.finleyfire.com
Year Founded: 1972
Sales Range: $10-24.9 Million
Emp.: 75
Firefighting Equipment
N.A.I.C.S.: 423850
Norm Mansfield (VP-Equipment Sls)
Rick Ebersole (VP)
Rita Murphy (Controller)

FINLEY INDUSTRIES INC.
174 Avenue Glendao, Sparks, NV 89491

Tel.: (775) 353-0404
Web Site:
http://www.napaautoparts.com
Sales Range: $10-24.9 Million
Emp.: 80
Automotive Supplies & Parts
N.A.I.C.S.: 423120
David Finley (Pres)

FINN CORPORATION
9281 Le Saint Dr, Fairfield, OH 45014-5464
Tel.: (513) 874-2818
Web Site: https://www.finncorp.com
Year Founded: 1989
Sales Range: $10-24.9 Million
Emp.: 75
Suppliers of Lawn & Garden Equipment
N.A.I.C.S.: 333112
Ron Ciolfi (Reg Mgr-Sls)

Subsidiaries:

DHG Inc. (1)
9281 Le Saint Dr, Fairfield, OH 45014-5464
Tel.: (513) 874-2818
Web Site: http://www.fincorp.com
Sales Range: $10-24.9 Million
Emp.: 30
Supplier of Lawn & Garden Equipment
N.A.I.C.S.: 333112

FiNN All Seasons (1)
4125 Port Union Rd, Fairfield, OH 45014
Tel.: (513) 881-4580
Web Site: http://www.finnallseasons.com
Emp.: 10
Farm Supplies Whslr; Industrial Machinery & Equipment Rental Services
N.A.I.C.S.: 424910
Brent Cox (Gen Mgr)
Dwayne Clark (Ops Mgr)
Brad Dawson (Mgr-Territory)

FINN PARTNERS, INC.
301 E 57th St, New York, NY 10022
Tel.: (212) 715-1600 CA
Web Site:
http://www.finnpartners.com
Year Founded: 1993
Emp.: 100
Management Consulting Services
N.A.I.C.S.: 541611
Maria De Varenne (Sr Partner)
Elizabeth Seigenthaler Courtney (Mng Partner-Southeast)
Peter Finn (CEO & Mng Partner)
Fern Lazar (Mng Partner)
Gil Bashe (Mng Partner-Health)
Ryan Barr (Mng Partner-Fin Svcs)
John Acunto (Sr Partner)
Dan Pooley (Founder & Mng Partner-Midwest Reg)
Victoria Petrock (VP)
Mark Day (Sr Partner-Southeast)
Philip McGowan (Sr Partner-Southeast)
Brianne O'Donnell (Partner-Higher Education)
Margaret S. Dunning (Mng Partner-Higher Education Practice)
Laura Shuey-Kostelac (Partner-Global Pub Affairs)

Subsidiaries:

Lazar Partners Ltd. (1)
420 Lexington Ave Ste 830, New York, NY 10170
Tel.: (212) 867-1762
Web Site: http://www.lazarpartners.com
Public Relations & Communications Services
N.A.I.C.S.: 541820
Fern Lazar (Pres & CEO)
Chantal Beaudry (Mng Dir)
David Carey (Mng Dir)
Tom Vickery (Mng Dir)

Missy Farren & Associates Ltd. (1)
301 E 57th St, New York, NY 10022

Tel.: (212) 593-6428
Web Site: http://www.mfaltd.com
Public Relations Agencies
N.A.I.C.S.: 541820
Missy Farren (Founder, CEO & Mng Partner)

Rachel Kay Public Relations LLC (1)
243 N Hwy 101 Ste 18, Solana Beach, CA 92075
Tel.: (619) 867-7353
Web Site: http://www.rkpr.net
Marketing Research & Public Opinion Polling
N.A.I.C.S.: 541910
Natalie Terashima (Mng Partner)
Rachel Kay (Founder & CEO)

FINN POWER ENERGY CORP
48 Wall St Ste 1100, New York, NY 10005
Tel.: (212) 203-7229 DE
Year Founded: 2016
Emp.: 2
Power Plant Maintenance Services
N.A.I.C.S.: 237990
Franky Yason (Pres, Treas & Sec)

FINNEGAN, HENDERSON, FARABOW, GARRETT & DUNNER, L.L.P.
901 New York Ave NW, Washington, DC 20001-4413
Tel.: (202) 408-4000
Web Site: https://www.finnegan.com
Year Founded: 1965
Sales Range: $300-349.9 Million
Emp.: 501
Legal Advisory Services
N.A.I.C.S.: 541110
Erika Harmon Arner (Partner)
Danny M. Awdeh (Partner)
Cortney S. Alexander (Partner)
M. Paul Barker (Partner)
James R. Barney (Partner)
Jeffrey A. Berkowitz (Partner)
Christopher T. Blackford (Partner)
Michele C. Bosch (Partner)
Paul W. Browning (Partner)
Richard V. Burgujian (Partner)
Adriana L. Burgy (Partner)
Robert L. Burns (Partner)
L. Scott Burwell (Partner)
Virginia L. Carron (Partner)
Patrick J. Coyne (Partner)
Kathleen A. Daley (Partner)
Aaron Capron (Partner)
Aaron Parker (Partner)
Elizabeth Ferrill (Partner)
Anthony Del Monaco (Partner)
Minjae Kang (Partner)
Mareesa Frederick (Partner)
Krista Bianco (Partner)
C. Brandon Rash (Partner)
Timothy McAnulty (Partner)
Naresh Kilaru (Partner)
B. Brett Heavner (Partner)
Doris Johnson Hines (Partner)
Eric J. Fues (Partner)
Kenie Ho (Partner)
Leslie A. McDonell (Partner)
Thomas L. Irving (Partner)
Thomas H. Jenkins (Partner)
Vincent P. Kovalick (Partner)
York M. Faulkner (Partner)
Susan Tull (Partner)
Erin Sommers (Partner)
David Mroz (Partner)
Luke McCammon (Partner)
Scott B. Felrice (CFO)
Dawn M. Ibbott (Chief HR Officer)
Terra M. Liddell (Chief Mktg Officer)
Timothy M. Henderson (Chief Recruitment & Pro Dev Officer)
James B. Monroe (Chm & Partner)
John M. Kuttler (CIO)
Michael B. Sikora (COO)
Smith R. Brittingham IV (Partner)

FINROCK GROWTH PART-NERS, LLC

2025 Guadalupe St Ste 260, Austin, TX 78705
Tel.: (512) 861-8788
Web Site: http://www.finrock-growth.com
Privater Equity Firm
N.A.I.C.S.: 523999
Girish Pashilkar *(Mng Partner)*

Subsidiaries:

BP Logix, Inc. (1)
1470 Encinitas Blvd, Ste 232, Encinitas, CA 92024
Tel.: (760) 643-4121
Web Site: http://www.bplogix.com
Custom Computer Programming Services
N.A.I.C.S.: 541511
Jay O'Brien *(CEO)*

FINS, FURS, FEATHERS, INC.

14271 Corporate Dr, Garden Grove, CA 92843
Tel.: (714) 385-0080
Web Site: http://www.marinedepot.com
Year Founded: 2001
Sales Range: $10-24.9 Million
Emp.: 45
General Merchandise Whslr
N.A.I.C.S.: 455219
Ben Ros *(Dir-Ops)*
Ken Wong *(CEO)*
Jose Fontao *(Mgr-Tech)*
Randolth Yuson *(Supvr-Design)*

FIONDELLA, MILONE & LA-SARACINA LLP

300 Winding Brook Dr, Glastonbury, CT 06033
Tel.: (860) 657-3651
Web Site: https://www.fmlcpas.com
Year Founded: 2002
Advisory Services
N.A.I.C.S.: 541199

Subsidiaries:

Bregman & Company, PC (1)
350 Bedford St, Stamford, CT 06901
Tel.: (203) 325-4155
Web Site: http://www.bregman-cpa.com
Offices of Certified Public Accountants
N.A.I.C.S.: 541211
Owen W. Bregman *(Mng Partner)*

FIORE ASSOCIATES, INC.

7 E Frederick Pl Ste 400, Cedar Knolls, NJ 07927-1813
Tel.: (973) 359-4444   NJ
Year Founded: 1983
Sales Range: $10-24.9 Million
Emp.: 17
New Product Development, Public Relations, Strategic Planning/Research
N.A.I.C.S.: 541810

FIORE BUICK GMC

808 Logan Blvd, Altoona, PA 16602
Tel.: (814) 943-6181
Web Site: http://www.fiorebpgaltoona.com
Year Founded: 1970
Sales Range: $10-24.9 Million
Emp.: 46
New Car Retailer
N.A.I.C.S.: 441110
Jerry Hutchison *(Mgr-Sls)*

FIORE MOTORS INC.

445 Winding Rd, Old Bethpage, NY 11804
Tel.: (516) 586-6536
Web Site: https://www.fioremotorclassics.com
Sales Range: $10-24.9 Million

Emp.: 25
Automobiles, New & Used
N.A.I.C.S.: 441110
Michael R. Fiore *(Owner)*

FIORE STONE, INC.

19930 Jolora Ave, Corona, CA 92881
Tel.: (909) 424-0221
Web Site: http://www.fiorestone.com
Sales Range: $25-49.9 Million
Emp.: 50
Garden Statuary & Cast-Stone Fountains Mfr
N.A.I.C.S.: 327999
Reindert Nefkens *(Mgr-Mktg)*

FIRE & FLAVOR GRILLING CO.

1160 S Milledge Ave Ste 230, Athens, GA 30605
Tel.: (706) 369-9466
Web Site: https://www.fireandflavor.com
Year Founded: 2003
Sales Range: $10-24.9 Million
Emp.: 14
Grocery & Related Products Merchant Whslr
N.A.I.C.S.: 424490
Genevieve Knox *(Founder & CEO)*
Brandon King *(Controller)*

FIRE KING SECURITY GROUP

101 Security Pkwy, New Albany, IN 47150-9366
Tel.: (812) 822-5574   KY
Web Site: https://www.fireking.com
Year Founded: 1951
Sales Range: $10-24.9 Million
Emp.: 500
Fire Resistant Insulated Filing Cabinet & Safe & Digital Video Recorders Mfr
N.A.I.C.S.: 337214
Van G. Carlisle *(Pres & CEO)*
David Goffinet *(CIO)*
Mike Smith *(VP-R&D)*
Mark Essig *(CEO)*
Ed Carpenter *(COO)*
Peter Berens *(CTO)*
Gary Weisman *(Pres-Office Products)*
James Currey *(Sr VP-Bus Dev-Intl)*
John Rhoads *(Sr VP-Product & Channel Dev-Safes)*
Greg Gillham *(Sr VP-Sls-Office Products)*
Mike McGunn *(VP-Comml Svc)*
Brenda Lee Lally *(VP-HR & Continuous Improvement)*

FIRE PROTECTION SERVICES CORP.

3293 Harrison Blvd, Ogden, UT 84403
Tel.: (801) 594-8700
Web Site: http://www.mountainalarm.com
Rev.: $2,900,000
Emp.: 250
Fire & Security Solutions
N.A.I.C.S.: 561621
Michael Bailey *(CFO)*

Subsidiaries:

Burgarello Alarm Inc. (1)
50 Snider Way, Sparks, NV 89431
Tel.: (775) 588-6251
Web Site: http://www.burgarelloalarm.com
Rev.: $3,400,000
Emp.: 40
Security Systems Services, except Locksmiths
N.A.I.C.S.: 561621
Louie Burgarello *(Founder)*
Eric Dahl *(Mgr-Ops)*
Paul Bryant *(Gen Mgr)*
Steven Saari *(Controller)*

FIRE SPRINKLER SYSTEMS INC.

705 E Harrison St Ste 200, Corona, CA 92879
Tel.: (951) 272-2662
Web Site: https://www.fireinc.net
Rev.: $17,134,968
Emp.: 25
Fire Sprinkler System Installation
N.A.I.C.S.: 238220
Amy Descoteaux *(Mgr-Engrg)*
Edie Abbott *(Coord-Construction)*
Jessica Quintanilla *(Coord-CRM)*
Juan Nieto *(Mgr-Field Ops)*
Ralph Tolomei *(Controller)*
Rene Leyva *(Mgr-Warehouse)*

FIRE SYSTEMS WEST INC.

206 Frontage Rd N Ste C, Pacific, WA 98047
Tel.: (253) 833-1248
Web Site: https://www.firesystemswest.com
Sales Range: $25-49.9 Million
Emp.: 100
Design, Commercial & Industrial
N.A.I.C.S.: 541420
Jay Blackburn *(Pres)*
Jim Turk *(Mgr-Fire Sprinkler Svc)*
Phi Le *(Mgr-Electrical Accts)*

FIRE-DEX, LLC

780 S Progress Dr, Medina, OH 44256
Tel.: (330) 723-0000
Web Site: https://www.firedex.com
Year Founded: 1983
Fire Fighter Clothing Mfr
N.A.I.C.S.: 922160
Steve Allison *(Pres)*
Bill Burke *(Owner & CEO)*
Jenny McPherson *(Mgr-Mktg)*
Dave Liana *(CFO)*
John Karban *(VP-Ops)*
Todd Herring *(Dir-Mktg)*
Jeff Koledo *(Mgr-Sls-Natl)*

Subsidiaries:

Gear Wash LLC (1)
657 S 72nd St, Milwaukee, WI 53214-1558
Tel.: (870) 686-5386
Web Site: http://www.gearwash.com
Industrial Launderers
N.A.I.C.S.: 812332
Andrew R. Oliver *(Owner & Pres)*

FIREBIRD MANAGEMENT LLC

152 W 57th St 24th Fl, New York, NY 10019
Tel.: (212) 698-9260
Web Site: https://www.fbird.com
Year Founded: 1994
Sales Range: $25-49.9 Million
Emp.: 15
Privater Equity Firm
N.A.I.C.S.: 523999
Ian Christopher Hague *(Principal & Mgr-Fund)*
Natalya Zhirova *(Office Mgr)*
Harvey Sawikin *(Co-Founder & Principal)*
James Passin *(Principal)*
Joanne Tuckman *(CFO & COO)*
Blake Horowitz *(Chief Compliance Officer)*

FIREFLY ENERGY, INC.

5407 N University St Arbor Hall 2nd Fl, Peoria, IL 61614
Tel.: (309) 690-7500
Web Site: http://www.fireflyenergy.com
Year Founded: 2003
Sales Range: $1-9.9 Million
Emp.: 36
Battery Mfr
N.A.I.C.S.: 335910

Chen Jun *(Mgr-Logistics)*
Rajen Patel *(COO)*
Mukesh Bhandari *(Founder & Chm)*

FIREFLY TECHNOLOGIES

20827 NW Cornell Rd Ste 400, Hillsboro, OR 97124
Tel.: (503) 614-0808
Web Site: http://www.fireflypos.com
Year Founded: 2001
Rev.: $3,400,000
Emp.: 24
Computer Software Services
N.A.I.C.S.: 423420
Sandy Howell *(Mgr)*
Ben Albright *(Mgr-Sls)*
Brad Lough *(Mgr)*

FIREGUARD, INC.

4404 S 76th Cir, Omaha, NE 68127
Tel.: (402) 592-1999
Web Site: http://www.fireguardusa.com
Fire Protection Equipment Supplier
N.A.I.C.S.: 423850
Robert Sorensen *(Pres)*

FIREHOST INC.

2360 Campbell Creek Blvd Ste 525, Richardson, TX 75082
Tel.: (877) 262-3473
Web Site: http://www.firehost.com
Sales Range: $25-49.9 Million
Emp.: 180
Cloud Hosting Security Software Developer
N.A.I.C.S.: 513210
Chris Drake *(Founder & CEO)*
Kurt Hagerman *(Chief Info Security Officer)*
Ben McCormack *(VP-Svc Delivery)*
Noah Knippa *(CFO)*
Diana Massaro *(CMO)*
Nikhil Eapen *(Chief Strategy & Investment Officer & Sr Exec VP-ST Telemedia)*
Josh Bosquez *(Sr VP-Engrg)*

FIREHOUSE BREWING COMPANY, INC.

865 E University Blvd, Tucson, AZ 85745
Tel.: (520) 624-4177
Sales Range: $25-49.9 Million
Emp.: 100
Brewery Mfr
N.A.I.C.S.: 312120
Tauna Arnold *(COO & Partner)*

FIREHOUSE, INC.

14860 Landmark Blvd No 247, Dallas, TX 75254
Tel.: (972) 692-0911   TX
Web Site: http://www.firehouseagency.com
Year Founded: 1997
Sales Range: $25-49.9 Million
Emp.: 29
Brand Strategy & Identity & Public Relations
N.A.I.C.S.: 541810
Doug Miller *(CFO & Partner)*
Steve Smith *(Partner-Acct Plng)*
Mark Hall *(Founder & Pres)*
Tripp Westbrook *(Chief Mktg Officer & Partner)*
Greg Hunter *(Principal & Grp Dir-Creative)*
Trae Watlington *(Dir-Strategic Plng)*
Amanda Driggers *(Acct Dir)*
Evan Henderson *(Acct Dir)*
Blair Torres *(Acct Dir)*
Megan Brueggemann *(Dir-Project Mgmt)*
Everett Wilder *(Principal & Dir-Grp Creative)*

Firelake Capital Management, LLC—(Continued)

FIRELAKE CAPITAL MANAGE-MENT, LLC
575 High St Ste 330, Palo Alto, CA 94301-1648
Tel.: (650) 321-0880
Web Site:
　http://www.firelakecapital.com
Venture Capital Firm
N.A.I.C.S.: 523999
Candice Eggerss *(Mng Dir)*
Fred Kittler *(Mng Dir)*
Martin Lagod *(Mng Dir)*
Peter Shannon *(Mng Dir)*
Lisa Lee *(CFO)*

FIRELANDS ELECTRIC COOPERATIVE, INC.
1 Energy Pl, New London, OH 44851
Tel.: (419) 929-1571
Web Site:
　https://www.firelandsec.com
Year Founded: 1936
Sales Range: $10-24.9 Million
Emp.: 33
Electric Energy Distribution Services
N.A.I.C.S.: 221122
April Bordas *(Gen Mgr)*
Kolleen Patton *(Accountant)*
Tabi Shepherd *(Dir-Fin & Acctg)*
Andrea Gravenhorst *(Dir-Member Svcs)*
Denny Marugg *(Dir-Electric Ops)*
Don Englet *(Dir-Ops)*

FIRELIGHT CAPITAL PARTNERS LLC
1700 E. Las Olas Blvd, Ste 302,, Fort Lauderdale, FL 33301
Tel.: (917) 331-1925
Web Site:
　https://www.firelightcapital.com
Year Founded: 2016
Privater Equity Firm
N.A.I.C.S.: 523999
Rick Perkal *(CEO & Mng Partner)*

Subsidiaries:

Fromm International, Inc.　　　　**(1)**
603 Dempster St, Mount Prospect, IL 60056
Tel.: (847) 498-8200
Web Site: http://www.frommbeauty.com
Durable Goods Merchant Whslr
N.A.I.C.S.: 423990
Kevin Barrett *(Pres)*
Martin L. Okner *(CEO)*

FIRELINE CORPORATION
4506 Hollins Ferry Rd, Baltimore, MD 21217
Tel.: (410) 247-1422
Web Site: https://www.fireline.com
Sales Range: $10-24.9 Million
Emp.: 150
Fire Extinguishers
N.A.I.C.S.: 459999
Phil Bowers *(Mgr-Portables Dept)*
Anna W. Gavin *(Pres)*

FIRELINE SPRINKLER CORPORATION
5036 Clairemont Dr, Appleton, WI 54913
Tel.: (920) 757-9590
Web Site:
　https://www.firelinesprinkler.com
Rev.: $23,000,000
Emp.: 130
Plumbing Heating & Air-Conditioning Contractors
N.A.I.C.S.: 238220
Daniel G. Romenesko *(Sec & VP)*
Edward J. Esselman Jr. *(Pres)*

FIRELINE, INC.

300 Andrews Ave, Youngstown, OH 44505-3061
Tel.: (330) 743-1164
Year Founded: 1967
Rev.: $13,600,000
Emp.: 80
Fire Prevention Equipments Distr
N.A.I.C.S.: 922160
Chris Vrabel *(Mgr-Sls)*
Mike DeCore *(Mgr-Sls)*
William Stadler *(Product Mgr-Engrg)*
Dave Hofmann *(Mgr-Market Dev)*

FIREMAN CAPITAL PARTNERS LLC
800 South St Ste 600, Waltham, MA 02453
Tel.: (617) 671-0555
Web Site:
　http://www.firemancapital.com
Year Founded: 2008
Emp.: 10
Privater Equity Firm
N.A.I.C.S.: 523999
Paul Fireman *(Chm)*
Dan Fireman *(Mng Partner)*
Chris Akelman *(Principal)*
Russell Kazorek *(VP & Controller)*
Ekta Sharma *(VP)*
Devon Howard *(VP)*

Subsidiaries:

Cigar City Brewing LLC　　　　**(1)**
3924 W Spruce St Ste A, Tampa, FL 33607
Tel.: (813) 348-6363
Web Site: http://www.cigarcitybrewing.com
Brewery
N.A.I.C.S.: 312120
Joseph Redner *(CEO)*

FIRESIDE HEARTH & HOME
2540 S Hastings Way, Eau Claire, WI 54701
Tel.: (715) 832-5232
Web Site:
　https://www.wisconsinfireplace.com
Sales Range: $10-24.9 Million
Emp.: 10
Prefabricated Fireplace Mfr
N.A.I.C.S.: 449129
Randy Nickerson *(Owner)*
Robert Bennett *(Reg Mgr-Sls)*

FIRESIDE OFFICE PRODUCTS INC.
1713 E Bismarck Expy, Bismarck, ND 58504
Tel.: (701) 258-8586
Web Site: https://www.firesideops.com
Sales Range: $10-24.9 Million
Emp.: 45
Office Furniture
N.A.I.C.S.: 423210
Chris Whalen *(Pres)*

FIRESPRING
1201 Infinity Ct, Lincoln, NE 68512
Tel.: (402) 437-0000
Web Site: https://www.firespring.com
Year Founded: 1992
Sales Range: $1-9.9 Million
Emp.: 100
Advertising & Marketing
N.A.I.C.S.: 541810
Dustin Behrens *(VP-Ops)*

FIRESTREAM WORLDWIDE, INC.
18336 Edison Ave, Chesterfield, MO 63005
Tel.: (636) 778-2800
Web Site: http://www.firestream.com
Year Founded: 2001
Sales Range: Less than $1 Million
Emp.: 81
Software Developer
N.A.I.C.S.: 541512

Glenn Turner *(Pres & CEO)*
Curt Hummel *(Controller)*
Steve Lange *(Dir-Corp Dev)*
Jr Massie *(VP-Product Dev)*
Matthew Mossotti *(Dir-Mktg)*
Jason Blom *(VP-Sls & Mktg)*
J. P. McNeiland *(VP-Product Mgmt)*

FIRETREE, LTD.
800 W 4th St, Williamsport, PA 17701
Tel.: (570) 601-0877
Web Site: https://www.firetree.com
Year Founded: 1990
Sales Range: $10-24.9 Million
Emp.: 119
Community Center Operator
N.A.I.C.S.: 624190
Scott Snyder *(Dir-Administration)*

FIREWATCH CONTRACTING OF FLORIDA LLC
5815 S MacDill Ave, Tampa, FL 33611-4450
Tel.: (813) 839-3000
Web Site:
　http://www.fwcontracting.com
Sales Range: $1-9.9 Million
Emp.: 15
General Building Contractors
N.A.I.C.S.: 236116
Melvin E. Lowe *(Pres)*
Shawn Tedesco *(Mgr-Contract)*
Charolette Darnell *(Office Mgr)*

FIRKINS CHRYSLER JEEP DODGE RAM
2700 1st St, Bradenton, FL 34208
Tel.: (941) 909-3762
Web Site: https://www.firkinscj.com
Year Founded: 1951
Sales Range: $25-49.9 Million
Emp.: 110
New Car Retailer
N.A.I.C.S.: 441110
Jason Crowley *(Mgr)*
Royce Oliver *(Mgr-Sls-Used Car)*
Ron Cliburn *(Mgr-Sls-Used Car)*

FIRST & PEOPLES BANK & TRUST CO.
1001 Diederich Blvd, Russell, KY 41169
Tel.: (606) 836-0211
Web Site:
　https://www.firstandpeoples bank.com
Sales Range: $200-249.9 Million
Emp.: 70
State Commercial Banks
N.A.I.C.S.: 522110
Robert Sorrell *(VP)*

FIRST ALARM SECURITY & PATROL, INC.
1111 Estates Dr, Aptos, CA 95003
Tel.: (831) 476-1111
Web Site: https://www.firstalarm.com
Sales Range: $10-24.9 Million
Emp.: 600
Security System Maintenance & Monitoring Services; Security Guard & Patrol Services
N.A.I.C.S.: 561621
Jarl E. Saal *(Founder & Chm)*
Cal Horton *(Pres)*
Dave Hood *(Pres-First Alarm)*
Teresa Huerta Larkin *(Dir-Legal Affairs)*

Subsidiaries:

First Alarm　　　　**(1)**
1111 Estates Dr, Aptos, CA 95003
Tel.: (831) 476-1111
Web Site: http://www.firstalarm.com
Security System Services
N.A.I.C.S.: 561621

Jarl E. Saal *(Founder & Chm)*

First Security Services　　　　**(1)**
1731 Technology Dr 800, San Jose, CA 95110
Tel.: (800) 778-3017
Web Site:
　http://www.firstsecurityservices.com
Emp.: 25
Security Guards & Patrol Services
N.A.I.C.S.: 561612
Cal Horton *(Pres & CEO)*

FIRST AMERICAN BANCSHARES, INC.
1251 First American Dr, Iuka, MS 38852
Tel.: (662) 423-3656
Web Site: https://www.fanb.bank
Bank Holding Company
N.A.I.C.S.: 551111

Subsidiaries:

First American National Bank　**(1)**
51 1st Amercian Dr, Iuka, MS 38852
Tel.: (662) 423-3656
Web Site: http://www.fanb.net
Sales Range: $10-24.9 Million
Emp.: 67
National Commercial Banks
N.A.I.C.S.: 522110
Deborah Bowling *(VP)*
Rhonda Brown *(VP-Ops)*
Lisa Phelps *(Controller & Asst VP)*

FIRST AMERICAN BANK & TRUST CO.
300 College Ave, Athens, GA 30601
Tel.: (706) 354-5000
Web Site:
　http://www.firstamericanishere.com
Sales Range: $25-49.9 Million
Emp.: 100
State Commercial Banks
N.A.I.C.S.: 522110
Joseph Nemetz *(Chief Credit Officer & Exec VP)*
John D. McLanahan *(Chm)*
C. Rhodes McLanahan *(Pres & CEO)*
Craig Meeks *(Chief Lending Officer & Exec VP)*
John Loftis *(Sr VP-Comml Banking)*
Johnny Barnard *(Sr VP-Comml Div)*
Paul Rice *(Officer-Comml Lending & Sr VP)*
Tommy Carraway *(Sr VP-Comml Div)*

FIRST AMERICAN BANK CORPORATION
700 Busse Rd, Elk Grove Village, IL 60007
Tel.: (847) 228-9300
Web Site:
　http://www.firstambank.com
Year Founded: 1972
Sales Range: $125-149.9 Million
Emp.: 580
Commercial Banking Services
N.A.I.C.S.: 551111
Thomas E. Wells IV *(Chm)*
Adelbert Spaan *(Exec VP-Retail Branches)*
James M. Lynch *(Vice Chm-Comml Loans)*
Jane Nagel *(Exec VP-Wealth Mgmt)*
John B. Ward *(Pres-Retail Loans)*
John Olsen *(Exec VP)*
Martin J. Carmody *(Sr Exec VP)*
Sarah A. Herbst *(Sr VP)*
Nathan Webb *(Exec VP)*
Brian T. Hagan *(Exec VP)*
Steve J. Eikenberry *(Sr VP)*
Mark E. Kroencke *(Sr VP)*

Subsidiaries:

Continental National Bank of Miami　　　　**(1)**
1801 SW 1st St, Miami, FL 33135
Tel.: (305) 642-2440
Web Site: http://www.continentalbank.com

Sales Range: $200-249.9 Million
Emp.: 108
Banking Services
N.A.I.C.S.: 522110
Guillermo Diaz-Rousselot (Pres & CEO)
Jeannette Blanch (Chief Lending Officer)
Jose M. Touzet (Sr VP)
Sonia Canessa-Gonzalez (CFO & Sr VP)
Jacqueline Dascal Chariff (Chm)
Rodolfo Lleonart (COO & Exec VP)

First American Bank   (1)
700 Busse Rd, Elk Grove Village, IL 60007-
2137
Tel.: (847) 228-9300
Web Site: http://www.firstambank.com
Sales Range: $125-149.9 Million
Commericial Banking
N.A.I.C.S.: 522110
Thomas E. Wells IV (Chm-Mgmt Bd)
Adelbert Spaan (Exec VP-Retail Branches)
James M. Lynch (Vice Chm-Comml Loans)
Jane Nagel (Exec VP-Wealth Mgmt)
John B. Ward (Pres-Retail Loans)

FIRST AMERICAN COMMUNI-CATIONS ENTERPRISE INC.

15283 Hwy 56, Sherman, TX 75092
Tel.: (903) 893-8500
Sales Range: $10-24.9 Million
Emp.: 5
Telephone Cable Service, Land Or
Submarine
N.A.I.C.S.: 517111
Tom Johnson (Pres)

Subsidiaries:

Comanche County Telecom   (1)
6100 Hwy 16, De Leon, TX 76444
Tel.: (254) 893-7000
Web Site: http://www.cctc.net
Sales Range: $1-9.9 Million
Cellular Telephone Services
N.A.I.C.S.: 517111

FIRST ANTLERS BANCORPO-RATION, INC.

100 N High St, Antlers, OK 74523
Tel.: (580) 298-3368
Year Founded: 1985
Sales Range: $25-49.9 Million
Emp.: 127
Bank Holding Company
N.A.I.C.S.: 551111
Mark Burrage (CEO)

Subsidiaries:

FirstBank   (1)
100 N High St, Antlers, OK 74523
Tel.: (580) 298-3368
Sales Range: $25-49.9 Million
Commericial Banking
N.A.I.C.S.: 522110
Jonathan W. Pennington (Chief Acctg Offi-
cer)
Mark Burrage (CEO)

FIRST ARKANSAS BANCSHARES, INC.

600 W Main St, Jacksonville, AR
72076
Tel.: (501) 982-4511
Web Site:
http://www.firstarkansasbank.com
Year Founded: 1949
Rev.: $15,000,000
Emp.: 150
Holding Company: State Commercial
Banks
N.A.I.C.S.: 551111

Subsidiaries:

First Arkansas Bank & Trust   (1)
600 W Main St, Jacksonville, AR 72076
Tel.: (501) 982-4511
Web Site: http://www.firstarkansasbank.com
Rev.: $19,000,000
Emp.: 50
State Commercial Banks
N.A.I.C.S.: 522110

Larry T. Wilson (Pres)
Mark Wilson (Chief Credit Officer & Sr VP)
Tammy Tompkins (Mgr-Mortgage Dept)

First Arkansas Mortgage Co.   (1)
112 N Bailey St, Jacksonville, AR 72076
Tel.: (501) 985-4050
Web Site: http://www.firstarkansasbank.com
Rev.: $941,947
Emp.: 15
Mortgage Bankers & Loan Correspondents
N.A.I.C.S.: 522310

FIRST ARTESIA BANCSHARES, INC.

303 W Main St, Artesia, NM 88210
Tel.: (575) 746-8000   NM
Web Site: http://www.firstamb.net
Year Founded: 1903
Sales Range: $25-49.9 Million
Emp.: 275
Bank Holding Company
N.A.I.C.S.: 551111
William F. Mershon (Chm)
Greg Marrs (Chm-First American
Bank)

Subsidiaries:

First American Bank   (1)
303 W Main St, Artesia, NM 88210
Tel.: (575) 746-8000
Web Site: http://www.firstamb.net
Sales Range: $50-74.9 Million
Emp.: 250
Banking Services
N.A.I.C.S.: 522110
John Attwood (Officer-Trust & VP)
Marianne Gillespie (Officer-Trust & VP)
Sue McGee-Chiodini (Officer-Trust & VP)

FIRST ASSIST INC

7201 Wisconsin Ave Ste 705,
Bethesda, MD 20814
Tel.: (301) 718-2210
Web Site: http://www.firstassist.com
Year Founded: 1986
Sales Range: $10-24.9 Million
Emp.: 12
Medical Staffing Services
N.A.I.C.S.: 561311
Mary Richardson (Pres)

FIRST ATLANTIC CAPITAL LTD.

477 Madison Ave Ste 330, New York,
NY 10022
Tel.: (212) 207-0300
Web Site:
http://www.firstatlanticcapital.com
Year Founded: 1989
Private Equity Investment Services
N.A.I.C.S.: 523999
Roberto Buaron (Chm & CEO)
Emilio S. Pedroni (Mng Dir)
Peter M. Patricola (CFO & Chief
Compliance Officer)
Brinda Cherian (Principal)
Thomas A. Berglund (Mng Dir)

Subsidiaries:

C-P Converters, Inc.   (1)
15 Grumbacher Rd, York, PA 17406
Tel.: (717) 764-1193
Web Site: http://www.cpflexpack.com
Sales Range: $10-24.9 Million
Emp.: 150
Flexible Packaging Products Mfr
N.A.I.C.S.: 322220
Greg Collins (VP-Mfg)
Mark Coffman (Pres & CEO)

Subsidiary (Domestic):

Flexo Transparent, LLC   (2)
28 Wasson St, Buffalo, NY 14210
Tel.: (716) 825-7710
Web Site: http://www.flexotransparent.com
Commercial Flexographic Printing
N.A.I.C.S.: 323111

Ronald D. Mabry (Pres)
Thomas Neuman (Mgr-Engrg & Mainte-
nance Plant)
Brian Mabry (VP-Sls & Mktg)
Sharon Mabry (Owner)
Dan Steger (Dir-Sls & Strategic Projects)

Genpak LLC   (2)
10601 Westlake Dr, Charlotte, NC 28273
Web Site: http://www.genpak.com
Sales Range: $50-74.9 Million
Emp.: 80
Disposable Drinking Cup, Tray & Food Con-
tainer Mfr
N.A.I.C.S.: 322219
James J. Reilly (Pres)
Stephanie Kelly (Mgr-Benefits & Wellness)
Tanya Smith (Mgr-Cost Mgmt)
Paul Haviland (Asst Mgr-Logistics)
Kevin Smith (Dir-Info Sys & Tech)
Joseph Kovach (VP-Ops)

Plant (Non-US):

Genpak   (3)
3185 Pepper Mill Court, Mississauga, L5L
4X3, ON, Canada
Tel.: (905) 569-3660
Web Site: http://www.genpak.com
Sales Range: $50-74.9 Million
Disposable Food Containers Paper Cup &
Paper Plate Mfr
N.A.I.C.S.: 322219

Subsidiary (Domestic):

MRI Flexible Packaging
Company   (2)
122 Penns Trl, Newtown, PA 18940-1815
Tel.: (215) 860-7676
Web Site: http://www.mriflex.com
Label Products Design, Printing & Mfr
N.A.I.C.S.: 323111
Rich Speeney (VP & Gen Mgr)
Jennifer Hegarty (Coord-Production)
Jim Mallon (Dir-Sls & Mktg)

FIRST BANCORPORATION INC.

401 Main St, La Crosse, WI 54601
Tel.: (608) 784-4600
Web Site:
http://www.statebankfinancial.com
Year Founded: 1879
Sales Range: $25-49.9 Million
Emp.: 65
Bank Holding Company
N.A.I.C.S.: 551111
Steve McConaghy (VP)

Subsidiaries:

State Bank Financial   (1)
401 Main St, La Crosse, WI 54601
Tel.: (608) 784-4600
Web Site: http://www.statebankfinancial.com
Rev.: $20,000,000
Emp.: 85
Commercial Banking Services
N.A.I.C.S.: 522110
Colin Fleming (VP-Bus Banking)
Dale Pertzborn (VP-Bus Banking)
Tim Willenbring (VP-Bus Banking)
Tim Kotnour (Pres & CEO)
Mark Carpenter (Exec VP)

FIRST BANCSHARES CORPO-RATION

1400 Delta Ave, Gladstone, MI 49837
Tel.: (906) 428-3535   MI
Bank Holding Company
N.A.I.C.S.: 551111
Todd D. Maki (Pres/CEO-First Bank,
Upper Michigan)
Jeanine Dagenais (Chm, Pres &
CEO)

Subsidiaries:

First Bank, Upper Michigan   (1)
1400 Delta Ave, Gladstone, MI 49837
Tel.: (906) 428-3535
Web Site: http://www.first-bank.com
Commericial Banking
N.A.I.C.S.: 522110
Jeanine K. Dagenais (Chm)

FIRST BANCSHARES INC.

600 E 84th Ave, Merrillville, IN 46410
Tel.: (219) 755-4660
Web Site: http://www.centier.com
Year Founded: 1895
Emp.: 465
Bank Holding Company; Commercial
Banking
N.A.I.C.S.: 551111
Michael E. Schrage (Pres)

Subsidiaries:

Centier Bank Inc.   (1)
600 E 84th Ave, Merrillville, IN
46410   (100%)
Tel.: (219) 755-4660
Web Site: http://www.centier.com
Sales Range: $50-74.9 Million
Banking Services
N.A.I.C.S.: 522110
Michael E. Schrage (Chm & CEO)
Thomas J. Wilk (Chief Lending Officer-Bus
Banking & Sr VP)
Christopher Campbell (Sr VP)
Deborah Robinson (Sr VP-Community Rels
& Bus Dev)
LaKetra N. Williams (Mgr-Miller)
Beverly Strickland (Asst VP)
Brian Thurman (Mgr-Fin Intelligence Unit-
Corp Centre)
Dan Gibson (Dir-Talent Dev)
Ryan Glassman (Mgr-Ops & Performance
Analyst)
Amanda McCord (Mgr-Downtown South
Bend)
Todd Hentschel (Mktg Mgr-Bus Line)
Angela Mendez (Mktg Dir)
Sabrina Kiser (Asst VP)
Amy Bowman (Asst VP)
Jason Taege (VP-Bus Banking)
Dermot O'Doherty (Chief Digital Officer & Sr
VP)
Yolanda Davis (VP)
Timothy Woloszyn (Asst VP-Bus Banking-
Downtown Valparaiso)
Teresa Quezad (Branch Mgr-Munster)

FIRST BANCSHARES, INC.

650 Kansas Ave, Kansas City, KS
66105
Tel.: (913) 371-1242
Rev.: $4,654,000
Emp.: 20
Commericial Banking
N.A.I.C.S.: 522110
David Herndon (Pres)

Subsidiaries:

Community First Bank   (1)
650 Kansas Ave, Kansas City, KS 66105
Tel.: (913) 371-1242
Banking Services
N.A.I.C.S.: 522110
David Spehar (Pres & CEO)

FIRST BANK & TRUST CO.

923 W Main St, Duncan, OK 73533
Tel.: (580) 255-1810
Web Site: http://www.fb247.com
Year Founded: 1988
Retail & Commercial Banking
N.A.I.C.S.: 522110
Hal Pennington (Exec VP)
Craig Heaton (Sr VP & Mgr-Trust
Dept)
Jason Groves (Pres-OKC South
Metro-Norman 36th Banking Center)
Michael Caldwell (VP-Norman 36th
Banking Center)
Mindy Thomas (Mgr-OKC South
Metro-Norman 36th & Norman
Alameda Banking Centers)

FIRST BANK & TRUST EAST TEXAS

104 N Temple Dr, Diboll, TX 75941
Tel.: (936) 829-4721
Web Site: http://www.fbtet.com

First Bank & Trust East Texas—(Continued)

Year Founded: 1953
Rev.: $35,705,252
Emp.: 79
State Commercial Banks
N.A.I.C.S.: 522110
Brad Browder (Branch Mgr)
Codie Jenkins (VP)

FIRST BANK CORP.

602 Garrison Ave, Fort Smith, AR 72901-2542
Tel.: (479) 788-4600
Web Site: https://www.fnbfs.com
Year Founded: 1989
Sales Range: $200-249.9 Million
Emp.: 665
Banking Services
N.A.I.C.S.: 522110
Albert Snider (Sr VP-Acctg)
Charles Cook (Sr VP-Special Assets)
Charles Girard (VP-Compliance)
Jim Fourmy (Sr VP-Loans)
Drew Linder (Sr VP)
Samuel T. Sicard (Pres & CEO-First Natl Bank Fort Smith)
Barbara Bethell (VP)
Mont S. Echols Jr. (Chm)

Subsidiaries:

The First National Bank of Fort
Smith   (1)
602 Garrison Ave, Fort Smith, AR 72901-2542
Tel.: (479) 782-2041
Web Site: http://www.fnbfs.com
Sales Range: $1-9.9 Million
Emp.: 270
Banking Services
N.A.I.C.S.: 522110
Samuel T. Sicard (Pres & CEO)
Mont S. Echols Jr. (Chm)

Division (Domestic):

First National Bank of Rogers   (2)
801 N Dixieland Rd, Rogers, AR 72756
Tel.: (479) 621-6800
Web Site: http://www.fnbrogers.com
Commercial Banking Services
N.A.I.C.S.: 522110
Mitzi Bird (VP)
Sharon Grounds (VP-Ops)
Ron Wey (VP-Bus Dev)
Samuel T. Sicard (Pres & CEO)
Clinton Ryan (VP-Comml Lending)

National Bank of Sallisaw   (2)
1000 S Kerr Blvd, Sallisaw, OK 74955
Tel.: (918) 775-5501
Web Site: http://www.banknbs.com
Sales Range: $1-9.9 Million
Commercial Banking Services
N.A.I.C.S.: 522110
Debbie Fleetwood (VP)
Glenda Callahan (Branch Mgr)
Leasa Steiner (Officer-Loan Ops)
Matt Caldwell (Pres & CEO)
Stacy Day (Branch Mgr)
Susan M. Chandler (VP)

FIRST BANK OF HIGHLAND PARK

1835 1st St, Highland Park, IL 60035
Tel.: (847) 432-7800
Web Site: http://www.firstbankhp.com
Sales Range: $25-49.9 Million
Emp.: 75
Bank Holding Company
N.A.I.C.S.: 516210
Denise Bryant (Dir-Mktg)
Ia Backstrom (Sr VP)
David Giangiorgi (Sr VP-Retail Lending)
Michael Trimble (VP)
Vicki Peloquin (VP)
Randy L. Green (CEO)
Barbara Winter (Sr VP)
Eric Ephraim (Pres & COO)
Patricia Widmar (VP)
Norman Weinandy (VP-Cash Mgmt)

Marc Zisook (VP-Comml Real Estate)
Jessica Brown (VP-Ops)
Erin Reardon Cohn (Exec VP & Dir-Treasury Mgmt)
Todd G. Roth (VP-Bus Lending)
David Evely (Exec VP-Comml Banking)
Thomas Walsh (VP-Treasury Mgmt)
Brian Parshall (Asst VP-Personal Banking)
Deanna Levin (Sr VP & Dir-Credit Underwriting & Portfolio Mgmt)
Sara DeKuiper (Sr VP-Comml Lending)
Stacy Theodorakakis (VP-Private Client Relationships)
Victor P. Stasica (Exec VP)
Patrick Tatarek (Sr VP-Lease Fin & Comml Banking)
Tom Ishikawa (VP-Treasury Mgmt)
Courtney Olson (VP-Bus Banking)
Zachary Goldman (Asst VP-Comml Real Estate)
Magdalena Wrobel (VP-Treasury Mgmt)
Laurie Brown (Sr VP)
Emma Montagu (Sr VP)
Amy Kahhat (VP-Personal Banking)
Dean Jukovich (Exec VP-Fin)
Brien Leahy (Exec VP-Retail Banking)
Nicole DiVito (Mgr-Talent)
Jodi Sugar (Sr VP-Comml Banking)
Vanessa Lundgren (Asst VP-Large Corp & Lease Fin)
Louise Gordon (Mgr-Teller)
Monika Martynkova (Mgr-Teller)
Joseph M. Haugh (Mng Dir/Sr VP-Comml Banking)
Andy Kocur (Asst VP-Comml Banking)
Debra Hutchinson-Dettwiller (Asst VP-Treasury Mgmt)
Charles Gitles (Sr VP-Comml Banking)
Nathan Bowker (VP-Comml Real Estate)
Tricia Poisson (VP-Sys & Applications Support)
Anne O'Connor (Sr VP-Comml Real Estate & Portfolio Mgr)
Kerry Bell (Asst VP)
Luke Krzesaj (VP & Controller)
Jacqueline Flick (VP & Branch Mgr)
Jean K. Choi (VP-Comml Banking)
Farhan Khan (Asst VP)
Stacy Raven (Mgr-Mktg & Event)

FIRST BANK OF OWASSO

8601 N Garnett, Owasso, OK 74055
Tel.: (918) 272-5301
Web Site: http://www.firstbank.net
Year Founded: 1962
Sales Range: $1-9.9 Million
Emp.: 60
Banking Services
N.A.I.C.S.: 522110
Dominic M. Sokolosky (Pres, CEO & Officer-Loan)
Dennis Phillips (Chief Lending Officer & Sr VP)
Cindy Scott (Sr VP & Cashier)

FIRST BANKCORP INC.

18528 Lee Hwy, Abingdon, VA 24210
Tel.: (276) 623-2323
Web Site: http://www.firstbank.com
Rev.: $20,990,785
Emp.: 3
State Commercial Banks
N.A.I.C.S.: 522110
Bill Hayter (Pres & CEO)
Keith Phillips (Sr VP-Agriculture Lending)

Subsidiaries:

First Bank and Trust   (1)

18528 Lee Hwy, Abingdon, VA 24210
Tel.: (276) 623-2323
Rev.: $19,500,000
Emp.: 60
State Commercial Banks
N.A.I.C.S.: 522110
Austin Phipps (VP-Agriculture & Comml Lending)

FIRST BANKS, INC.

600 James S McDonnell Blvd, Saint Louis, MO 63042
Tel.: (314) 854-4600
Web Site: http://www.firstbanks.com
Year Founded: 1978
Sales Range: $200-249.9 Million
Emp.: 1,200
Bank Holding Company
N.A.I.C.S.: 551111
Peter D. Wimmer (Gen Counsel)
Rick Sems (Pres-Comml-Midwest)
Joe Ambrose (Vice Chm)
Jim Babbage (Sr VP & Dir-Ministry Dev)
Deb Bostic (Chief HR Officer)
Therese Degroot (Mng Dir)
Ed Furman (Chief Investment Officer)
Andrew Johnston (Officer-Comml Loan)
Bala Nibhanupudi (CIO)
Peter Ostapko (VP & Mgr-Relationship)
Gene Todd (Mng Dir)
Shelley J. Seifert (Chm & CEO)

Subsidiaries:

First Bank   (1)
11901 Olive Blvd, Creve Coeur, MO 63141
Tel.: (314) 995-8700
Web Site: http://www.firstbanks.com
Sales Range: $125-149.9 Million
Banking Services
N.A.I.C.S.: 522180
Julie Hardy (VP-Comml Banking)
Kory Kunze (VP & Mgr-Product & Client Segment-Product Mgmt Dept)

FIRST BELLS BANKSHARES, INC.

615 E Bells Blvd, Bells, TX 75414
Tel.: (903) 965-7755
Web Site:
    https://www.cenderabank.com
Year Founded: 1980
Sales Range: $1-9.9 Million
Emp.: 20
Bank Holding Company
N.A.I.C.S.: 551111
C. Alan Renfroe (Pres & CEO)

Subsidiaries:

The First National Bank of
Bells/Savoy   (1)
615 E Bells Blvd, Bells, TX 75414
Tel.: (903) 965-7755
Web Site: http://www.fnbbells.com
Emp.: 60
Retail & Commercial Banking
N.A.I.C.S.: 522110
Russell Clapp (VP)
Samie Campbell (VP-Mortgage Div)
Daniel Gutierrez (Branch Mgr)

FIRST BERNE FINANCIAL CORPORATION

222 Heritage Trl, Berne, IN 46711-6711
Tel.: (260) 589-2151
Web Site:
    https://www.firstbankofberne.com
Bank Holding Company
N.A.I.C.S.: 551111
Kent Liechty (Pres & CEO)

Subsidiaries:

First Bank of Berne   (1)
222 Heritage Trl, Berne, IN 46711
Tel.: (260) 589-2426
Web Site: http://www.firstbankofberne.com

Federal Saving Bank Services
N.A.I.C.S.: 522180
Kent Liechty (Pres & CEO)
Sharon Neuenschwander (Dir-HR)
Kevin Gould (CFO)
Deon Shoaf (COO)

FIRST BOOK

1319 F St NW Ste 1000, Washington, DC 20004
Tel.: (202) 393-1222
Web Site: https://www.firstbook.org
Year Founded: 1992
Sales Range: $100-124.9 Million
Emp.: 91
Literary Support Services
N.A.I.C.S.: 611691
Becki Last (Sr VP-Engagement)
Kyle Zimmer (Pres & CEO)

FIRST BRECKENRIDGE BANCSHARES

240 N 1st St, Irvington, KY 40146
Tel.: (270) 547-2271
Web Site:
    http://www.firststatebankky.com
Sales Range: $10-24.9 Million
Emp.: 25
State Commercial Banks
N.A.I.C.S.: 522110
Roberta Anthony (Mgr-HR)

Subsidiaries:

Bank of Clarkson   (1)
101 E Main St, Clarkson, KY 42726
Tel.: (270) 242-2111
Web Site: http://www.bankofclarkson.com
Rev.: $3,415,000
Emp.: 21
State Commercial Banks
N.A.I.C.S.: 522110

West Point Bank   (1)
601 Main St, West Bend, KY 41077
Tel.: (502) 922-4755
Rev.: $1,100,000
Emp.: 9
State Commercial Banks
N.A.I.C.S.: 522110

FIRST BROKEN ARROW CORPORATION

121 S Main St, Broken Arrow, OK 74012
Tel.: (918) 251-5371
Web Site: https://www.fnbba.com
Rev.: $11,996,895
Emp.: 17
Bank Holding Company
N.A.I.C.S.: 551111
Audra Alvord (VP)
Carmen Medina (VP)
Donnie Cox (Chief Lending Officer & Exec VP)
Derek Steeley (Sr VP)
Gina McFadden (VP-Fin & Admin Dept)
Kathryn Srader (VP)
Mark A. Poole (Pres & COO)
Phillip Stephens (VP)
Greg Graham (Chm & CEO)
Paige Miller (CFO)
Ryan Herron (VP)

Subsidiaries:

The First National Bank & Trust Company of Broken Arrow   (1)
121 S Main St, Broken Arrow, OK 74012
Tel.: (918) 251-5371
Web Site: http://www.fnbba.com
Rev.: $13,010,000
Emp.: 40
National Trust Companies with Deposits; Commercial
N.A.I.C.S.: 551111
Gregory S. Graham (Chm)
Mark A. Poole (Pres)
Paige Miller (CFO)
Andrew Marshall (VP-Comml Lender)

FIRST BUSINESS BANCORP CO.

525 W Roosevelt Rd, Chicago, IL 60607
Tel.: (312) 491-7000   IL
Web Site:
http://www.banksouthcentral.com
Year Founded: 1991
Sales Range: $10-24.9 Million
Bank Holding Company
N.A.I.C.S.: 551111
Marc Grayson (Chm & CEO)
Charles Rudy (CFO)

FIRST CALL TEMPORARY SERVICES

7202 E 87th St Ste 110, Indianapolis, IN 46256
Tel.: (317) 596-3280
Web Site: http://www.firstcallinc.com
Rev.: $15,117,855
Emp.: 16
Temporary Help Service
N.A.I.C.S.: 561320
Rita Zoller (Pres)

FIRST CALL TRADING CORPORATION

2374 Seipstown Rd, Fogelsville, PA 18051
Tel.: (610) 366-1166
Web Site: https://www.profruit.com
Rev.: $11,251,535
Emp.: 7
Baking Supplies
N.A.I.C.S.: 424490
Paul S. Wagner (Pres)

FIRST CAPITAL REAL ESTATE TRUST INCORPORATED

60 Broad St 34th Fl, New York, NY 10004
Tel.: (212) 388-6800   MD
Web Site: http://fcretrust.com
Sales Range: $1-9.9 Million
Real Estate Investment Services
N.A.I.C.S.: 525990
Stephen M. Johnson (CFO)

FIRST CARE MEDICAL SERVICES

955 Redna Ter, Cincinnati, OH 45215
Tel.: (513) 563-8811
Web Site: https://www.firstcare.us
Sales Range: $1-9.9 Million
Emp.: 88
Medical Transportation Services
N.A.I.C.S.: 622110
Dennis Young (Pres)
Jennifer Naylor (VP-Bus Dev)
Michelle Dobrosky (VP-Bus Dev-Toledo)

FIRST CAROLINA FINANCIAL SERVICES, INC.

171 N Winstead Ave, Rocky Mount, NC 27804
Tel.: (252) 937-2152   NC
Web Site:
http://www.firstcarolinastate bank.com
Bank Holding Company
N.A.I.C.S.: 551111
Ronald A. Day (Pres & CEO)
John A. Williams (Chm)

Subsidiaries:

First Carolina State Bank   (1)
171 N Winstead Ave, Rocky Mount, NC 27804   **(89%)**
Tel.: (252) 937-2152
Web Site: http://www.fcsbank.com
Sales Range: $1-9.9 Million
Retail & Commercial Banking
N.A.I.C.S.: 522110
Ronald A. Day (Pres & CEO)

FIRST CATHOLIC SLOVAK UNION US

6611 Rockside Rd Ste 300, Cleveland, OH 44131
Tel.: (216) 642-9406
Web Site: http://www.fcsu.com
Sales Range: $10-24.9 Million
Emp.: 15
Life Insurance Agency
N.A.I.C.S.: 524210
Andrew M. Rajec (Pres)
Kenneth A. Arendt (Sec)
Gary J. Matta (Gen Counsel)
Rudolf Ondrejco (Dir-Fraternal Activities)
George F. Matta II (Treas)
Andrew Harcar Sr. (VP)

FIRST CECILIAN BANCORP, INC.

104 E Main St, Cecilia, KY 42724
Tel.: (270) 862-3294   KY
Web Site:
http://www.cecilianbank.com
Year Founded: 1991
Emp.: 100
Bank Holding Company
N.A.I.C.S.: 551111
Bob G. Owsley (Chm, Pres & CEO)
Greg Pawley (Pres/CEO-Cecilian Bank & Sec)

Subsidiaries:

The Cecilian Bank   (1)
104 E Main St, Cecilia, KY 42724
Tel.: (270) 862-3294
Web Site: http://www.thececilianbank.com
Sales Range: $25-49.9 Million
Emp.: 224
Commericial Banking
N.A.I.C.S.: 522110
Greg Pawley (Pres & CEO)
Bob G. Owsley (Chm)

The Lincoln National Bank of Hodgenville   (1)
41 Lincoln Sq, Hodgenville, KY 42748
Tel.: (270) 358-4116
Web Site: http://www.mylnb.com
Sales Range: $10-24.9 Million
Commercial Banking Services
N.A.I.C.S.: 522110
Paula Gearon (CFO & Sr VP)
Doc Meredith (Pres)
Arthur Hawkins (CIO & Sr VP)
Sheila Bloyd (COO & Sr VP)
Tiffany Perry (Sr VP & Mgr-Enterprise Risk)
John Downs (Officer-Loan, VP & Branch Mgr)
Leon Kessinger (Officer-Loan, Sr VP & Branch Mgr)
Rebecca Eads (VP & Mgr-HR)
Charles Cravens (Chm)
Judy Wells (Sr VP)

FIRST CENTURY BANCORP

807 Dorsey St, Gainesville, GA 30501-6619
Tel.: (678) 450-8000
Web Site:
http://www.myfirstcenturybank.com
Year Founded: 2002
Offices of Bank Holding Companies
N.A.I.C.S.: 551111
William R. Blanton (Chm & CEO)

Subsidiaries:

First Century Bank, National Association   (1)
807 Dorsey St, Gainesville, GA 30501
Tel.: (770) 297-8060
Web Site: http://www.firstcenturybank.com
Rev.: $2,500,000
Emp.: 14
Banking Services
N.A.I.C.S.: 522110
Gary H. Anderson (Pres)

FIRST CENTURY BANK

1780 N Broad St, Tazewell, TN 37879
Tel.: (423) 626-7261
Web Site: http://www.fcbtn.com
Sales Range: $10-24.9 Million
Emp.: 100
Provider of Banking Services
N.A.I.C.S.: 522110
Eleanor Yoakum (Chm)
Rob Barger (Pres & CEO)

FIRST CHOICE COMMUNITY HEALTHCARE, INC.

2001 N Centro Familiar SW, Albuquerque, NM 87105
Tel.: (505) 873-7401   NM
Web Site: https://www.fcch.com
Year Founded: 1973
Sales Range: $25-49.9 Million
Emp.: 457
Community Health Care Services
N.A.I.C.S.: 621498
Jeremiah Dye (Dir-Dental)

FIRST CHOICE PACKAGING INC.

1501 W State St, Fremont, OH 43420
Tel.: (419) 333-4100
Web Site: https://www.firstchoicepackaging.com
Rev.: $11,000,000
Emp.: 100
Packaging
N.A.I.C.S.: 561910
Paul Tomick (Owner)
Dick Braddick (Mgr-Sls-Midwest)
Steve Thomas (Bus Mgr)

FIRST CHOICE PROPERTIES, INC.

1600 Dave Ward Dr, Conway, AR 72034
Tel.: (501) 327-6731   AR
Web Site: http://www.tracytidwell.com
Sales Range: $1-9.9 Million
Real Estate Agency
N.A.I.C.S.: 531210
Mark Tidwell (Co-Owner)
Tracy Tidwell (Co-Owner & Principal Broker)

FIRST CHOICE SEAFOOD, INC.

1712 S Field Ter, Indianapolis, IN 46241
Tel.: (317) 381-9060
Sales Range: $10-24.9 Million
Emp.: 10
Fish & Seafood Markets
N.A.I.C.S.: 445250
Kam Cheung (Pres)
Pedro Jimenez (Mgr-Sls)

FIRST CITIZENS FINANCIAL CORP.

2601 4th St SW, Mason City, IA 50401
Tel.: (641) 423-1600   IA
Web Site: http://www.myfcb.bank
Year Founded: 1973
Sales Range: $50-74.9 Million
Emp.: 203
Bank Holding Company
N.A.I.C.S.: 551111
Marti T. Rodamaker (Pres & CEO)

Subsidiaries:

First Citizens Bank   (1)
2601 4th St SW, Mason City, IA 50401
Tel.: (641) 423-1600
Web Site: https://www.myfcb.bank
Sales Range: $50-74.9 Million
Commericial Banking
N.A.I.C.S.: 522110
Sarah N. Nielsen (CFO)
Joleen M. Fleming (COO & Chief Retail Officer)

Dan McGuire (Chief HR Officer)
Bob J. Klocke (Chief Credit Officer)
Jeff Gribben (Chief Strategy Officer & Exec VP)
Nicole R. Olson (Chief Wealth Mgmt Officer)
Marti T. Rodamaker (Chm & CEO)

FIRST CITRUS BANCORPORATION, INC.

10824 N Dale Mabry Hwy, Tampa, FL 33618
Tel.: (813) 792-7177
Web Site: https://www.firstcitrus.com
Emp.: 50
Bank Holding Company
N.A.I.C.S.: 551111
Michael Adcock (Chm)

Subsidiaries:

First Citrus Bank   (1)
10824 N Dale Mabry Hwy, Tampa, FL 33618
Tel.: (813) 792-7177
Web Site: http://www.firstcitrus.com
Rev.: $9,516,000
Assets: $231,007,000
Liabilities: $207,630,000
Net Worth: $23,377,000
Earnings: $371,000
Emp.: 53
Fiscal Year-end: 12/31/2013
Commercial Banking
N.A.I.C.S.: 522110
John M. Barrett (Pres & CEO)
John Linton (CFO)
Lisa Millman-Nodal (Sr VP)
Nancy Gordon (Sr VP-Bus Banking)
Thomas Menendez (VP)
Sarah Perez (Mgr-Mktg)
Jessica Kendall Hornof (Exec VP-Retail Banking)
Lisa Pitts (Mgr-Brandon)
Matthew Coughlin (VP & Controller)
Madison Jones (VP)
JoEllen Henderson (Chief Credit Officer)
Cheryl Holly (Asst VP & Mgr-Bus Relationship)
Larry Whiting (VP-Bus Banking)
Keyur Patel (VP)
Leslie Bridges (Sr VP-Bus Banker)

FIRST CITY CREDIT UNION

717 W Temple St, Los Angeles, CA 90012
Tel.: (213) 482-3477   CA
Web Site: http://www.firstcitycu.org
Year Founded: 1937
Sales Range: $10-24.9 Million
Emp.: 128
Financial Support Services
N.A.I.C.S.: 523999

FIRST CLASS MOVING SYSTEMS, INC.

8110 Anderson Rd Ste 100, Tampa, FL 33634
Tel.: (813) 280-5130   FL
Web Site:
https://www.movewithclass.com
Year Founded: 2001
Sales Range: $1-9.9 Million
Emp.: 20
Moving & Storage Services
N.A.I.C.S.: 484210
William Fallon (Pres)
Chris J. Hunt (CEO)
Ken Hover (Mgr-Fleet)
John Pardee (Mgr-Sls)
Gina Eck (Mgr-Ops)
Wayne Hill (Mgr-Logistics)
Brendan O'Connell (Mgr-Sls)

FIRST CLASS SERVICES INC.

9355 US Hwy 60 W, Lewisport, KY 42351-0478
Tel.: (270) 295-3746
Web Site:
https://www.firstclassservices.com
Year Founded: 1989

First Class Services Inc.—(Continued)

Sales Range: $10-24.9 Million
Emp.: 100
Local Trucking without Storage
N.A.I.C.S.: 484110
Randy Stroup *(Pres & CEO)*

FIRST CLASS, INC.
5410 W Roosevelt Rd Ste 222, Chicago, IL 60644-1490
Tel.: (773) 378-1009
Web Site:
　　https://www.firstclassinc.com
Year Founded: 1992
Sales Range: $1-9.9 Million
Emp.: 10
Media Buying Services
N.A.I.C.S.: 541830
Lonna Schulz *(Pres)*
Bailey Hughes *(Project Mgr)*

FIRST COAST AUCTION & RE-ALTY, INC.
5562-2 Timuquana Rd, Jacksonville, FL 32254
Tel.: (904) 384-4556
Web Site:
　　http://www.firstcoastauction.com
Sales Range: $10-24.9 Million
Emp.: 3
Fee Basis Auctioneers
N.A.I.C.S.: 531210
Tom Garner *(Owner)*
Robert Garner *(VP)*

FIRST COAST LOGISTICS SERVICES
1133 Baisden, Jacksonville, FL 32218
Tel.: (904) 757-6008
Web Site: http://www.firstcoast.net
Sales Range: $25-49.9 Million
Emp.: 200
Transportation Services
N.A.I.C.S.: 551112
Deborah Cannon *(Controller)*
Dell Gordy *(Mgr-Admin, Bill & PR)*
Jeff Burch *(Mgr-IT)*
Steven Forrand *(VP-Bus Dev)*
Mack Brown *(VP-Ops)*
H. R. Bowser Jr. *(Pres & CEO)*

FIRST COAST SUPPLY INC.
6860 Phillips Industrial Blvd, Jacksonville, FL 32256-3028
Tel.: (904) 872-1535
Web Site: https://www.fcsjax.com
Sales Range: $10-24.9 Million
Emp.: 25
Refrigerators & Freezers
N.A.I.C.S.: 423620
Stanley Kantor *(Pres)*
Tim Deck *(Owner)*

FIRST COAST WORKFORCE DEVELOPMENT, INC.
1845 Town Center Blvd Ste 250, Fleming Island, FL 32003
Tel.: (904) 356-5627　　　　　FL
Web Site:
　　http://www.careersourcenefl.com
Year Founded: 1996
Sales Range: $10-24.9 Million
Employment & Placement Services
N.A.I.C.S.: 561311
Lynda Phinney *(VP-HR)*
Bruce Ferguson *(Pres & CEO)*
Dianna Davis *(VP-Compliance)*
Joel Hickox *(Chief Admin Officer)*

FIRST COLLINSVILLE BANK INC.
800 Belt Line Rd, Collinsville, IL 62234
Tel.: (618) 346-9000
Web Site: https://www.fcbbanks.com

Sales Range: $10-24.9 Million
Emp.: 300
Financial Institution
N.A.I.C.S.: 522110
Ward Billhartz *(CEO)*
Jodie Gibbs *(VP-Ops)*
Jim Carlson *(Exec VP)*
Diana Walter *(Dir-Mktg & Adv)*

FIRST COLOMBIA GOLD CORP.
6000 Poplar Ave Ste 250, Memphis, TN 34119
Year Founded: 1997
Metal Ore Mining Services
N.A.I.C.S.: 212290
Jason Castenir *(CEO)*

FIRST COLONY COFFEE & TEA COMPANY
204-222 W 22nd St, Norfolk, VA 23517-0005
Tel.: (757) 622-3658
Year Founded: 1902
Sales Range: $75-99.9 Million
Emp.: 85
Mfr of Gourmet Tea & Coffee
N.A.I.C.S.: 311920

FIRST COLONY COMMUNITY ASSOCIATION
4350 Austin Pkwy, Sugar Land, TX 77479
Tel.: (281) 634-9500　　　　　TX
Web Site: https://www.firstcolony.org
Year Founded: 1987
Sales Range: $10-24.9 Million
Community Housing Services
N.A.I.C.S.: 624229
Doug Pepping *(Mgr-Fin)*
Noel Mascarenhas *(Treas)*
Rick Conley *(Pres)*
Hillary Goldstein *(Sec)*

FIRST COMMERCE CREDIT UNION
2073 Summit Lake Dr Ste 100, Tallahassee, FL 32317
Tel.: (850) 488-0035　　　　　FL
Web Site:
　　https://www.firstcommercecu.org
Year Founded: 1940
Sales Range: $25-49.9 Million
Emp.: 146
Financial Support Services
N.A.I.C.S.: 525120
Mary Estes *(Exec VP)*
Greg Adams *(CFO & Sr VP)*
Cecilia Homison *(CEO)*
Kim Howes *(VP-Mktg)*

FIRST COMMUNITY BANCSHARES, INC.
1325 Harrison St, Batesville, AR 72501
Tel.: (870) 612-3400　　　　　AR
Web Site:
　　https://www.firstcommunity.net
Year Founded: 1997
Sales Range: $25-49.9 Million
Emp.: 194
Bank Holding Company
N.A.I.C.S.: 551111
Dale E. Cole *(Chm, Pres & CEO)*
Josh Matthews *(Asst VP & Branch Mgr)*
Amanda McClish *(Asst VP-Acct Svcs-Race)*
Latricia Davis *(Asst VP-New Accts)*
Rita King *(Asst VP-New Accts)*
Lindsey Ashlock *(Mgr-Bridgeport)*
Carla Martin *(Mgr-Eagle Mountain)*
Heather Fulbright *(VP & Dir-HR-Batesville)*

Subsidiaries:

First Community Bank　　　　　(1)
1325 Harrison St, Batesville, AR 72501　　　　　　　　　　　(100%)
Tel.: (870) 612-3400
Web Site: http://www.firstcommunity.net
Emp.: 100
Retail & Commercial Banking
N.A.I.C.S.: 522110
Boris Dover *(Pres & COO)*
Dale E. Cole *(Chm & CEO)*
David Wood *(Pres-Market & Exec VP)*
Hank Pearce *(Sr VP-Comml Lending)*
Jason Taylor *(CFO & Exec VP)*
Michelle Reesor *(Exec VP & Dir-Risk Mgmt)*
Troy Henley *(Sr VP-Ops)*
Judy Swaim *(Sr VP & Mgr-Ops)*
Laura Cornett *(Sr VP & Dir-Mktg)*
Randy Rewis *(Sr VP-Comml Lending)*
Jennifer Scarbrough *(Sr VP & Mgr-Secondary Mortgage Dept)*
Dewey Shanks *(Sr VP-Comml Lending)*
Alan Bufford *(Sr VP-Comml Lending & Special Projects)*
Paul Hindman *(Officer-Credit & Sr VP)*
Heather Fulbright *(VP & Dir-HR-Batesville)*
Laura Brissey *(Gen Counsel & Exec VP)*
Ron Carter *(Sr VP-Comml Lending)*
Mike Chesnut *(Sr VP-Comml Lending)*
Kenny Gerhardt *(Sr VP-Teller Ops)*
Charles Green *(Sr VP-Comml Lending)*
Austin Brightop *(Sr VP-Comml Lending)*
Matt House *(Sr VP-Comml Lending)*
Karl Kemp *(Sr VP & Dir-IT)*
Tom Massey *(Sr VP-Bus Resources)*
Keith Melson *(Sr VP & Mgr-Loan Review)*
Stuart Puckett *(Officer-Credit & Sr VP)*
Robb Roberts *(Sr VP-Comml Lending & Special Projects)*
Leann Siler *(Sr VP-Comml Lending)*
Chris Treat *(Officer-Trust, Sr VP & Mgr)*
Josh Tate *(CMO & Sr VP)*

FIRST COMMUNITY BANCSHARES, INC.
507 N Gray St, Killeen, TX 76541
Tel.: (254) 554-4252　　　　　TX
Year Founded: 1983
Sales Range: $50-74.9 Million
Emp.: 375
Bank Holding Company
N.A.I.C.S.: 551111
Bobby Hoxworth *(Exec VP)*
George Waggoner *(Exec VP)*
Jerold B. Katz *(Chm & CEO)*
James W. Meredith *(CFO)*

Subsidiaries:

First National Bank Texas　　　　(1)
507 N Gray St, Killeen, TX 76541
Tel.: (254) 554-6699
Web Site: http://www.1stnb.com
Retail & Commercial Banking
N.A.I.C.S.: 522110
Bobby Hoxworth *(Pres)*
Chris Baughman *(Sr VP)*
Dan Yancey *(Sr VP)*
Larry Linder *(Sr VP)*
Joe Burnett *(Sr VP)*

Division (Domestic):

First Convenience Bank　　　　(2)
507 N Gray St, Killeen, TX 76541
Tel.: (254) 554-6699
Web Site: http://www.1stcb.com
Retail & Commercial Banking
N.A.I.C.S.: 522110

Fort Hood National Bank　　　　(1)
TJ Mills Blvd Bldg 109, Fort Hood, TX 76544
Tel.: (254) 532-2161
Web Site: http://www.fhnb.com
Sales Range: $50-74.9 Million
Emp.: 95
Banking Services
N.A.I.C.S.: 522110
George Waggoner *(Pres)*
Chris Baughman *(Sr VP)*
Tommy J. Wallace *(Sr VP)*
Dan Yancey *(Sr VP)*
Larry Linder *(Sr VP)*

FIRST CONSTRUCTION GROUP

3729 West Ave, Burlington, IA 52601
Tel.: (319) 752-4400
Sales Range: $10-24.9 Million
Emp.: 35
Commercial & Office Building Contractors
N.A.I.C.S.: 236220
Steve Freese *(Pres)*

FIRST COOPERATIVE ASSOCIATION
960 Riverview Dr, Cherokee, IA 51012
Tel.: (712) 225-5400　　　　　IN
Web Site: http://www.firstcoop.com
Year Founded: 1926
Sales Range: $300-349.9 Million
Emp.: 100
Mfr of Farm Supplies
N.A.I.C.S.: 444240

FIRST COUNTY BANK
117 Prospect St, Stamford, CT 06901
Tel.: (203) 462-4400
Web Site:
　　https://www.firstcountybank.com
Sales Range: $50-74.9 Million
Emp.: 200
Mutual Savings Bank
N.A.I.C.S.: 522180
Paul J. Bubniak *(VP & Officer-Trust)*
David M. Metzgar *(Officer-Trust & Sr VP)*
Wendy Macedo *(Asst VP)*
Steven G. Ferguson *(Asst VP)*

FIRST CREDIT BANK
9255 W Sunset Blvd, Los Angeles, CA 90069-3309
Tel.: (310) 273-3120　　　　　CA
Year Founded: 1983
Sales Range: $10-24.9 Million
Emp.: 30
Commericial Banking
N.A.I.C.S.: 522110
Farhad Ghassemieh *(Chm & CEO)*
Hoffein Eslami *(Sr VP)*

FIRST CREDIT UNION
25 S Arizona Pl Ste 111, Chandler, AZ 85225
Tel.: (480) 756-5500　　　　　AZ
Web Site: https://www.firstcu.net
Year Founded: 1929
Sales Range: $10-24.9 Million
Emp.: 213
Credit Union
N.A.I.C.S.: 522130
Kenneth Mullins *(Sec)*
Caryn Horvitz-Strauss *(Chm)*
Mickey Kinder *(VP-Ops)*
David Morgan *(Chief Lending Officer-Michigan)*
Sven Leander *(COO)*

FIRST DAKOTA ENTERPRISES INCORPORATED
1223 Sale Barn Rd, Fort Pierre, SD 57532
Tel.: (605) 223-9600
Web Site:
　　https://www.firstdakotaenterprises.com
Rev.: $22,000,000
Emp.: 76
New Construction, Single-Family Houses
N.A.I.C.S.: 236115
Archie Baumann *(Owner)*

FIRST DAKOTA FINANCIAL CORP.
225 Cedar St, Yankton, SD 57078
Tel.: (605) 665-7432
Web Site:
　　https://www.firstdakota.com
Sales Range: $10-24.9 Million

Emp.: 250
Banking Services
N.A.I.C.S.: 522110
Larry F. Ness *(Chm & CEO)*

Subsidiaries:

First Dakota National Bank   **(1)**
225 Cedar St, Yankton, SD 57078
Tel.: (605) 665-7432
Web Site: http://www.firstdakota.com
Rev.: $24,545,000
Emp.: 85
National Commercial Banks
N.A.I.C.S.: 522110
Larry F. Ness *(Chm & CEO)*
Rob Ness *(CFO)*
Rob Stephenson *(Pres & COO)*
Matt Tereshinski *(VP-Ag Banking)*
Nate Franzen *(Pres-Agri Bus Div)*
Michael Ness *(Pres-Sioux Falls)*
Aaron Ness *(Exec VP-Market & Mgr-Yankton)*
Marc Mooney *(Dir-Branch Admin)*
Larry Gehle *(Chief Risk Officer)*
Gailen Meyerink *(Chief Lending Officer & Mgr-Market)*
Mary Pfeiffer *(VP-Residential Real Estate)*

FIRST DATA CORPORATION

5565 Glenridge Connectoer NE Ste 2000, Atlanta, GA 30342
Tel.: (404) 890-2000
Web Site: http://www.firstdata.com
Commerce- Enabling Techonology Services
N.A.I.C.S.: 523999

Subsidiaries:

Payzone Ireland Limited   **(1)**
Payzone House 4 Heather Rd, Sandyford
Indus Estate, Dublin, 18, Ireland
Tel.: (353) 12076000
Web Site: http://www.payzone.ie
Sales Range: $1-4.9 Billion
Automatic Teller Machine & Payment Networks
N.A.I.C.S.: 522320
Jim Deignan *(Mng Dir)*
Eric O'Connor *(Controller-Fin)*
Olivia Noonan *(Head-Bus Dev & Mktg)*
Gary Dent *(Head-Ops)*
Barry Keegan *(Head-Sls)*

FIRST DENTAL HEALTH

5771 Copley Dr Ste 101, San Diego, CA 92111
Web Site:
https://www.firstdentalhealth.com
Year Founded: 1995
Sales Range: $1-9.9 Million
Emp.: 41
Dental Network Management Services
N.A.I.C.S.: 339116
Michael S. Grossman *(Pres & CEO)*
Jeannie Kemper *(COO)*
Stephen Johnson *(Coord-Ops)*
Susan Lawson *(Dir-Client Svcs & Sls)*
Sandie Pruett *(Acct Mgr-NDC)*
Gustavo Tonella *(Acct Mgr)*
Leslie Christofferson *(Acct Mgr)*

FIRST DISTRICT ASSOCIATION

101 S Swift Ave, Litchfield, MN 55355-2834
Tel.: (320) 693-3236   MN
Web Site: https://www.firstdistrict.com
Year Founded: 1921
Sales Range: $75-99.9 Million
Emp.: 140
Provider of Cooperative Services for Dairy Products
N.A.I.C.S.: 311513
Clint Fall *(Pres)*
Allen Rothstein *(Controller-Fin)*
Doug Anderson *(Plant Mgr)*

FIRST EAGLE MANAGEMENT CORP.

5 Railroad Pl, Athol, MA 01331
Tel.: (978) 249-3581
Rev.: $22,318,303
Emp.: 20
Beer & Ale
N.A.I.C.S.: 541618
Irene Perkins *(Office Mgr)*
George Girardi Jr. *(Pres)*

FIRST EDGE SOLUTIONS, INC.

544 South 1st St, Milwaukee, WI 53204
Tel.: (414) 289-8300   WI
Web Site:
http://www.firstedgesolutions.com
Year Founded: 2003
Sales Range: $1-9.9 Million
Emp.: 85
Communication Software Development Services
N.A.I.C.S.: 541511
Robert M. Kraft *(Pres & CEO)*
Robert R. King *(CTO)*
Robert A. Irvin *(Sr VP-SE)*
Michael P. Herald *(Dir-Mfg)*
John Smilanich *(Dir-Natl Sls)*

FIRST ELECTRIC COOPERATIVE CORP.

1000 S JP Wright Loop Rd, Jacksonville, AR 72076-3201
Tel.: (501) 982-4545   AR
Web Site:
https://www.firstelectric.coop
Year Founded: 1937
Sales Range: $200-249.9 Million
Emp.: 178
Electric Power Distr
N.A.I.C.S.: 221122
Bruce Andrews *(CFO)*
Brad Ford *(COO)*
Don Crabbe *(Pres & CEO)*

FIRST EMPIRE SECURITIES INC.

2 Fl 100 Motor Pkwy, Hauppauge, NY 11788
Tel.: (631) 979-0097
Web Site: http://www. 1empire.com
Rev.: $14,600,000
Emp.: 110
Brokers Security
N.A.I.C.S.: 523150
George Fulton *(Sr VP-Investments)*
Andrew Okolski *(Mng Dir-Fin Strategies Grp)*
Stephanie Rella *(VP)*
Richard Stark *(Sr VP)*
Stasie Tillman *(Asst Mgr-Analytics)*
Christopher O'Connor *(Pres)*
Bonnie Moser *(Dir-Mktg)*

FIRST ENTERPRISE BANK INC.

1000 W Britton Rd, Oklahoma City, OK 73114
Tel.: (405) 848-6611
Web Site: https://www.febokc.com
Year Founded: 1907
Sales Range: $1-9.9 Million
Emp.: 61
Provider of Banking Services
N.A.I.C.S.: 522110
Darryl Klimeck *(Pres)*
Clayton Beach *(CFO)*
Joan Stephenson *(Sr VP)*

FIRST EQUIPMENT CO.

4851 Keller Springs Rd Ste 100, Addison, TX 75001
Tel.: (972) 380-2300
Web Site:
https://www.firstequipment.com
Sales Range: $10-24.9 Million
Emp.: 45
Computer Rental & Leasing

N.A.I.C.S.: 532420

FIRST EQUITY GROUP, INC.

15 Riverside Ave 1st Fl, Westport, CT 06880-4214
Tel.: (203) 291-7700   CT
Web Site: http://www.firstequity.com
Year Founded: 1985
Investment Holding Company
N.A.I.C.S.: 551112
Aaron Hollander *(Chm, Pres & CEO)*
Joshua Krotec *(Sr VP)*
Paul Bolton *(COO)*
Eva Geier *(Sec & Controller)*
Josh Krotec *(Sr VP)*

Subsidiaries:

First Aviation Services Inc.   **(1)**
15 Riverside Ave, Westport, CT 06880-4214
Tel.: (203) 291-3300
Web Site: http://www.firstaviation.com
Aircraft Parts & Components Supplier & Distr
N.A.I.C.S.: 336413
Aaron Hollander *(Chm & CEO)*
Larissa A. Strautman *(Sec & Controller)*
Joshua T. Krotec *(Sr VP)*
Janelle Miller *(Chief Admin Officer)*

Subsidiary (Domestic):

Aviation Blade Services, Inc.   **(2)**
3969 Merlin Dr, Kissimmee, FL 34741
Tel.: (407) 846-6780
Web Site: http://www.absblade.com
Air Traffic Control
N.A.I.C.S.: 488111
Leonard Peterson *(Pres)*

First Equity Development
Incorporated   **(1)**
15 Riverside Ave, Westport, CT 06880-4214
Tel.: (203) 291-7700
Web Site: http://www.firstequity.com
Emp.: 4
Investment Banking
N.A.I.C.S.: 523150
Aaron Hollander *(Chm, Pres & Ceo)*

FIRST EQUITY MORTGAGE BANKERS, INC.

9300 S Dadeland Blvd Ste 500, Miami, FL 33156
Tel.: (305) 666-3333   FL
Web Site: https://www.fembi.com
Year Founded: 1997
Sales Range: $300-349.9 Million
Emp.: 150
Mortgage Banking
N.A.I.C.S.: 522310
Daniel Rodriguez *(Pres)*
Agustin Rojo *(Exec VP)*
Michael Acevedo *(VP-Ops)*
Hector Martinez *(CFO)*
Sonja Rodriguez *(Comptroller)*

FIRST FARMERS BANCSHARES INC.

120 Village Dr, Portland, TN 37148
Tel.: (615) 325-2265
Web Site:
http://www.thefarmersbank.net
Year Founded: 1984
Sales Range: $10-24.9 Million
Emp.: 120
Commercial banking Services
N.A.I.C.S.: 522110

Subsidiaries:

The Farmers Bank   **(1)**
120 Village Dr, Portland, TN 37148
Tel.: (615) 325-2265
Web Site: http://www.thefarmersbank.net
Sales Range: $10-24.9 Million
Emp.: 111
Provider of Banking Services
N.A.I.C.S.: 522110
Mickie E. Hodge *(COO, Chief Acctg Officer & Exec VP)*
Tommy Whittaker *(Pres & CEO)*
John C. Wilkinson *(Chm)*

Kimberly J. Monday *(CFO & Exec VP)*
Andy Nash *(Exec VP)*
Bryon Dispennett *(Mgr-Merchant Svcs)*
Brandi Dunn *(Mgr-Talent Acq)*

FIRST FARMERS FINANCIAL CORPORATION

123 N Jefferson St, Converse, IN 46919
Tel.: (765) 395-7746   IN
Web Site: http://www.ffbt.com
Year Founded: 1995
Sales Range: $50-74.9 Million
Emp.: 400
Bank Holding Company
N.A.I.C.S.: 551111
Gene Miles *(Pres & CEO)*

Subsidiaries:

First Farmers Bank & Trust
Company   **(1)**
123 N Jefferson St, Converse, IN 46919
Tel.: (765) 395-3316
Web Site: http://www.ffbt.com
Sales Range: $50-74.9 Million
Retail & Commercial Banking
N.A.I.C.S.: 522110
David L. Eikenberry *(Sr VP & Dir-Ops)*
Norman Lavengood *(Sr VP & Dir-Comml & Agriculture Lending)*
Joe Lenon *(Sr VP & Dir-Mortgage & Consumer Lending)*
Keith Hill *(CFO)*
Craig Langley *(Sr VP)*
Tade J. Powell *(VP-Mktg & PR)*
Mark Jones *(Sr VP & Dir-Loan Review & Special Assets)*
Tom Dolezal *(VP-Comml Lending)*
Mark Wolf *(Sr VP-Comml & Ag Lending)*
Brian Renbarger *(Chm)*
Cherie Planalp *(Chief Retail Officer & Sr VP)*
Mark A. Holt *(Pres & CEO)*

FIRST FEDERAL BANCORP, INC.

4705 W US Hwy 90, Lake City, FL 32055
Tel.: (386) 755-0600
Web Site: http://www.ffbf.com
Year Founded: 2007
Sales Range: $125-149.9 Million
Emp.: 817
Bank Holding Company
N.A.I.C.S.: 551111
Keith C. Leibfried *(Chm)*
Pamela K. Hitt *(COO & Sr Exec VP)*
John A. Medina *(Pres & CEO)*
James G. Moses *(Chief Risk Officer & Sr Exec VP)*
David Brewer *(CFO & Exec VP)*

Subsidiaries:

First Federal Bank   **(1)**
4705 US Hwy 90 W, Lake City, FL 32055
Tel.: (386) 755-0600
Web Site: http://www.ffbf.com
Sales Range: $125-149.9 Million
Savings Bank
N.A.I.C.S.: 522180
Keith C. Leibfried *(Chm)*
James G. Moses *(Chief Risk Officer & Sr Exec VP)*
Pamela K. Hitt *(COO & Sr Exec VP)*
David Brewer *(CFO & Exec VP)*
William Beardsley *(Chief Compliance Officer & Exec VP)*
Georgia C. Jones *(Chief Credit Officer & Exec VP)*
Robert Turbeville *(Chief Lending Officer & Exec VP)*
John A. Medina *(Pres & CEO)*
Wayne Cochran *(CIO & Exec VP)*

FIRST FEDERAL BANK OF KANSAS CITY

6900 Executive Dr, Kansas City, MO 64120
Tel.: (816) 241-7800
Web Site: https://www.ffbkc.com
Year Founded: 1934

First Federal Bank of Kansas City—(Continued)

Sales Range: $10-24.9 Million
Emp.: 160
Federal Savings & Loan Associations
N.A.I.C.S.: 522180
Donald P. Hileman *(CFO)*
Clarence Zugelter *(Chm)*
Alex Zimmerman *(Controller)*
Brenda Butrum *(VP)*
J.R. Buckner *(Pres & CEO)*

FIRST FEDERAL BANK OF LOUISIANA

1135 Lakeshore Dr, Lake Charles, LA 70601
Tel.: (337) 433-3611
Web Site: http://www.ffbla.com
Year Founded: 1949
Sales Range: $25-49.9 Million
Banking Services
N.A.I.C.S.: 522180
Charles V. Timpa *(Pres & CEO)*
Darryl G. Drewett *(CFO & Treas)*
Samuel V. Wilkinson *(Chief Risk Officer & Dir-HR)*
Jeffrey M. Lee *(Chief Lending Officer)*
Pam Whiteard *(Sr VP)*
Eric J. Mire *(VP)*
Robert A. Leavines *(Pres-Cenla Market)*
Jeffrey A. Marien *(Reg Mgr-Cenla)*
Robert Hollingsworth *(Sr VP & Mgr-Retail Banking)*
Ricky Hanks *(Sr Acct Mgr)*
Pam Thompson *(Mgr-Agency)*
Michael Clifton *(VP)*
Trey Hays *(VP)*
Ross Abraham *(Acct Mgr)*
Kyle Duplantis *(VP)*
James M. Fazende III *(COO)*

FIRST FEDERAL BANK OF OHIO

140 N Columbus St, Galion, OH 44833
Tel.: (419) 468-1518
Web Site:
　https://www.firstfederalbankof
　ohio.com
Rev.: $10,300,000
Emp.: 80
Federal Savings & Loan Associations
N.A.I.C.S.: 522180
Dave Beach *(Pres)*

FIRST FEDERAL COMMUNITY BANK

630 Clarksville St, Paris, TX 75460
Tel.: (903) 784-0881
Web Site: http://www.1st-fed.com
Rev.: $15,727,000
Emp.: 100
Federal Savings & Loan Associations
N.A.I.C.S.: 522180
Richard M. Amis *(Pres & CEO)*
John Brockman *(Chief Lending Officer & Exec VP-Downtown)*
Howard Corriston *(Officer-Comml Loan & Asst VP-Downtown)*
Carolyn Drake *(Officer-Collection & Asst VP-Downtown)*
Robert Slider *(Officer-IT & Sr VP-Downtown)*
Jason Schoggins *(Assistant VP)*
Teena McDowra *(Assistant VP)*
Lori Benson *(Assistant VP)*

FIRST FEDERAL MHC

479 Main St, Hazard, KY 41701
Tel.: (606) 436-3860
Year Founded: 2005
Mutual Holding Company
N.A.I.C.S.: 551111

Subsidiaries:

Kentucky First Federal Bancorp　**(1)**
655 Main St, Hazard, KY 41702　**(55.5%)**
Tel.: (502) 223-1638
Rev.: $16,528,000
Assets: $374,968,000
Liabilities: $326,971,000
Net Worth: $47,997,000
Earnings: ($1,721,000)
Emp.: 56
Fiscal Year-end: 06/30/2024
Bank Holding Company
N.A.I.C.S.: 551111
Don D. Jennings *(CEO)*

Subsidiary (Domestic):

First Federal Savings & Loan Association　**(2)**
479 Main St, Hazard, KY 41702　**(100%)**
Tel.: (502) 223-1638
Sales Range: $1-9.9 Million
Emp.: 13
Federal Savings Bank
N.A.I.C.S.: 522180
Lou Ella Farler *(Pres & CEO)*

Frankfort First Bancorp, Inc.　**(2)**
216 W Main St, Frankfort, KY 40602　**(100%)**
Tel.: (502) 223-1638
Web Site: http://www.ffsbfrankfort.com
Sales Range: $25-49.9 Million
Emp.: 27
Bank Holding Company
N.A.I.C.S.: 551111
Don D. Jennings *(Vice Chm & CEO)*
Teresa Kuhl *(Exec VP)*

Subsidiary (Domestic):

First Federal Savings Bank of Frankfort　**(3)**
216 W Main St, Frankfort, KY 40601　**(100%)**
Tel.: (502) 223-1638
Web Site: http://www.ffsbfrankfort.com
Sales Range: $1-9.9 Million
Emp.: 25
Federal Savings Bank
N.A.I.C.S.: 522180
Don D. Jennings *(Pres & CEO)*
Wick Asbury *(VP)*
Stan Betsworth *(VP)*
Stacey Greenawalt *(VP)*
Teresa Hulette *(Exec VP)*
Kim Moore *(VP)*

FIRST FEDERAL SAVINGS & LOAN

118 NE 3rd St, McMinnville, OR 97128
Tel.: (503) 472-6171
Web Site:
　http://www.firstfedmcm.com
Year Founded: 1922
Sales Range: $25-49.9 Million
Emp.: 50
Federal Savings Institutions
N.A.I.C.S.: 522180
Kathy Sticka *(Officer-Loan Compliance & VP-Residential Underwriter)*
Caroll Riley *(VP)*
Aimee Belliard *(Branch Mgr)*
Tyler Birman *(Mgr-Comml Relationship)*
Jim Schlotfeldt *(Pres & CEO)*
Cindy De Las Heras *(Officer-Residential Mortgage)*
Donald L. Brown *(VP & Mgr-Amity Branch)*
Jill Faughender *(Sr VP & Dir-HR)*
Lisa McKinney *(Officer-Residential Mortgage & VP)*
Matt Baker *(CFO & Sr VP)*
Matt Zoch *(CIO & Sr VP)*
Michele Pitta *(COO & Sr VP)*
Robert Luettjohann *(Chief Credit Officer & Sr VP)*
Sandra Schultz *(VP & Mgr-Carlton Branch)*

Tara L. Quincy *(VP & Mgr-Baker Creek Branch)*
Angel A. Aguiar Jr. *(VP & Mgr-Newberg Branch)*

FIRST FEDERAL SAVINGS & LOAN ASSOCIATION OF GREENE COUNTY

25 E High St, Waynesburg, PA 15370
Tel.: (724) 627-6116
Web Site:
　http://www.firstfederalofgreene.com
Sales Range: $25-49.9 Million
Emp.: 112
Federal Savings & Loan Associations
N.A.I.C.S.: 522180
Chad M. Moore *(Treas & VP)*
Miles M. Baker *(Sec & VP)*
Judi Tanner *(Pres & CEO)*

FIRST FEDERAL SAVINGS & LOAN ASSOCIATION OF LAKEWOOD

14806 Detroit Ave, Lakewood, OH 44107
Tel.: (216) 221-7300
Web Site: http://www.ffl.net
Year Founded: 1935
Sales Range: $100-124.9 Million
Emp.: 400
Banking Services
N.A.I.C.S.: 522180
David T. Shaw *(Sec & Sr VP)*
James D. Lechko *(Asst VP & Mgr-Investment Svcs)*

FIRST FEDERAL SAVINGS & LOAN ASSOCIATION OF LORAIN

3721 Oberlin Ave, Lorain, OH 44053
Tel.: (440) 282-6188
Web Site:
　http://www.firstfedlorain.com
Rev.: $23,401,000
Emp.: 75
Federal Savings & Loan Associations
N.A.I.C.S.: 522180
John Malanowski *(Pres)*

FIRST FEDERAL SAVINGS & LOAN ASSOCIATION OF PASCAGOULA-MOSS POINT

903 Jackson Ave, Pascagoula, MS 39568-0640
Tel.: (228) 762-4034
Web Site: https://www.firstwithus.com
Year Founded: 1955
Sales Range: $25-49.9 Million
Emp.: 60
Federal Savings & Loan Associations
N.A.I.C.S.: 522180

FIRST FEDERAL SAVINGS BANK

200 E Divine St, Dunn, NC 28334-5306
Tel.: (910) 892-7187
Web Site:
　https://www.firstfederalbanknc.com
Sales Range: $25-49.9 Million
Emp.: 95
Federal Savings & Loan Associations
N.A.I.C.S.: 522180
Clement E. Medley *(Pres & CEO)*

FIRST FEDERAL SAVINGS BANK

301 E 9th St, Rochester, IN 46975
Tel.: (574) 223-2128
Web Site:
　http://www.firstfederalbanking.com
Year Founded: 1966
Sales Range: $10-24.9 Million
Emp.: 150
Bank Holding Company

N.A.I.C.S.: 522180
Dennis Bilinski *(Pres-Bremen Div)*
Juli Eckel *(VP-Comml Lending-Warsaw)*

FIRST FEDERAL SAVINGS BANK

633 La Salle St, Ottawa, IL 61350
Tel.: (815) 434-3500
Web Site: https://www.ffsbweb.com
Year Founded: 1889
Rev.: $20,932,000
Emp.: 130
Federal Savings & Loan Association
N.A.I.C.S.: 522180
Laurence Bartman *(CFO)*
Lori Burke *(Branch Mgr)*

FIRST FEDERAL SAVINGS BANK TWIN FALLS

383 Shoshone St N, Twin Falls, ID 83301
Tel.: (208) 733-4222
Web Site: http://www.firstfd.com
Rev.: $12,566,000
Emp.: 200
Banking Services
N.A.I.C.S.: 522180
Michael D. Traveller *(CFO & Sr VP)*
Jay P. Dodds *(COO, Treas, Sec & Exec VP)*
Joan L. Howard *(Asst VP-Payroll & Benefits Admin)*
Jason A. Meyerhoeffer *(Pres & CEO)*
James N. Thompson *(VP)*
Norman D. Wright *(VP)*
Kevin G. Welch *(Officer-Bus Banking & VP)*
Brenda K. Hughes *(Sr VP & Dir-Mortgage & Retail Lending)*
Jeff C. Jardine *(CIO & Sr VP)*
Rebecca L. Nelson *(Sr VP & Dir-HR)*
Seth E. Collins *(VP & Mgr-Loan Ops)*
Gary W. Karnes *(Officer-Bus Banking & Asst VP)*
M. Kai Mathews *(Officer-Bus Banking & Asst VP)*
Shawn W. Broadbent *(Officer-Bus Banking & VP)*
Cindy Morgado *(Officer-Loan)*
Esteban O. Martinez *(Officer-Loan & Asst VP)*
Jessica Meade *(Officer-Loan-Blue Lakes)*
Kiley M. Mathews *(Officer-Loan-Blue Lakes)*
Pansy Pettit *(Officer-Loan-Buhl Branch)*
Gina Ables *(Officer-Loan-Eastland Branch)*
Doug Cook *(Officer-Loan-Meridian Lending)*
Susan Taylor *(Officer-Loan-Meridian Lending)*
Taren Hutchison *(Officer-Loan-Rupert Branch)*
Deanne M. Bailey *(VP & Branch Mgr-Lending-Falls)*
Gregory A. Fluckiger *(VP & Mgr-IT)*

FIRST FIDELITY BANCORP, INC.

5100 N Classen Blvd Ste 500, Oklahoma City, OK 73118-4433
Tel.: (405) 416-2223　　OK
Web Site: http://www.first-fidelity.com
Year Founded: 1981
Sales Range: $50-74.9 Million
Emp.: 278
Bank Holding Company
N.A.I.C.S.: 551111
Lee R. Symcox *(Pres & CEO)*
William M. Cameron *(Chm)*
Suzanne M. Symcox *(Exec VP & Chief Comm officer)*
Don R. Symcox *(Vice Chm)*

Subsidiaries:

First Fidelity Bank (1)
5100 N Classen Blvd Ste 500, Oklahoma
City, OK 73118
Tel.: (405) 416-2222
Web Site: http://www.ffb.com
Commercial Banking
N.A.I.C.S.: 522110
Lee R. Symcox *(Pres & CEO)*
Kristi Tenbusch *(VP)*
Don R. Symcox *(Vice Chm)*
James W. Finch *(Exec VP)*
William E. Goodwin *(Exec VP)*
James R. Karcher *(Exec VP)*
Tim Cook *(VP & Mgr-Pro & Executive Relationship)*
David Lorenz *(Sr VP)*
Thomas Rossiter *(VP & Mgr-Comml Relationship)*
James P. Boggs *(Pres-Edmond & Exec VP)*
Herman Lewkowitz *(Sr VP)*
Dawnetta Moore *(Mgr-Mustang)*
Cynthia Nenni *(Mgr-Rose Creek)*
Daniel Avery *(VP & Reg Mgr-Retail)*
Ana Guerrero *(Mgr-West Moore)*
Thomas V. Graham Jr. *(Exec VP)*

FIRST FINANCIAL BANC COR-PORATION

214 N Washington, El Dorado, AR
71730
Tel.: (870) 863-7000
Web Site: https://www.ffb1.com
Year Founded: 1934
Sales Range: $50-74.9 Million
Emp.: 276
Bank Holding Company
N.A.I.C.S.: 522180

Subsidiaries:

First Financial Bank (1)
214 N Washington, El Dorado, AR 71730
Tel.: (870) 863-7000
Web Site: http://www.ffb1.com
Sales Range: $50-74.9 Million
Emp.: 180
Provider of Banking Services
N.A.I.C.S.: 522180
Debby Davis *(VP-HR)*
Craig Mobley *(COO)*
Chris Johnson *(Pres-Arkansas)*

FIRST FINANCIAL CREDIT UNION

601 Tijeras Ave NW, Albuquerque,
NM 87102
Tel.: (505) 766-5600 NM
Web Site: https://www.ffnm.org
Year Founded: 1937
Sales Range: $25-49.9 Million
Emp.: 231
Credit Union
N.A.I.C.S.: 522130
Ronald Moorehead *(CEO)*
Dawn J. Dal Porto *(VP-Branch Ops)*
Andrew T. Schol *(VP-IT)*
Karen Broten *(COO)*

FIRST FINANCIAL CREDIT UNION

PO Box 90, West Covina, CA 91793
Tel.: (626) 814-4611 CA
Web Site: https://www.ffcu.org
Year Founded: 1933
Sales Range: $25-49.9 Million
Emp.: 144
Credit Union
N.A.I.C.S.: 522130
Carlton Musmann *(Pres & CEO)*
Larry Raspberry *(Sr VP)*
Torri Scott *(VP)*
Sandra Sarabia *(VP)*
Vivian Vega Dominguez *(VP)*
Asa Bert *(Treas)*
Gary Skraba *(Chief Admin Officer & Sr VP)*
Knowelle Decker *(Vice Chm)*
Ron Trotter *(Chm)*
Valerie Wilkins *(VP)*

FIRST FINANCIAL EMPLOYEE LEASING, INC.

201 W Marion Ave Ste 1209, Punta
Gorda, FL 33950
Tel.: (941) 625-7141
Year Founded: 1996
Sales Range: $450-499.9 Million
Emp.: 170
Human Resources, Employee Benefits, Payroll & Workers' Compensation Services
N.A.I.C.S.: 561499
Bruce T. Smith *(CEO)*
Tom Hughes *(Mgr-Safety)*

FIRST FINANCIAL HOLDINGS INC.

25 Rockwood Pl, Englewood, NJ
07631
Tel.: (201) 567-3311
Web Site:
http://www.firstfinancial.com
Rev.: $13,148,357
Emp.: 60
Mortgage Services
N.A.I.C.S.: 522310
David Sadek *(CEO)*

FIRST FINANCIAL OF TEN-NESSEE

913 Congress Pkwy N Ste 100, Athens, TN 37303
Tel.: (423) 745-9789 TN
Web Site: http://www.ffoftn.com
Year Founded: 1994
Sales Range: $25-49.9 Million
Emp.: 15
Mortgage Services
N.A.I.C.S.: 522310
Stanley Womac *(CEO)*

FIRST FINANCIAL RE-SOURCES INC.

611 Kimberly Dr, Denton, TX 76208
Tel.: (940) 382-4599
Rev.: $75,000,000
Emp.: 705
Railroad Maintenance & Repair Services
N.A.I.C.S.: 488210
Glenn L. Hulcher *(Owner)*

FIRST FINANCIAL SERVICES, INC.

6230 Fairview Rd Ste 450, Charlotte,
NC 28210
Tel.: (704) 365-3097 NC
Web Site:
http://www.ffsmortgage.com
Year Founded: 1991
Sales Range: $25-49.9 Million
Emp.: 188
Financial Services
N.A.I.C.S.: 523999
Kyle Kilpatrick *(Exec VP)*

FIRST FITNESS INTERNA-TIONAL

1430 Bradley Ln Ste 196, Carrollton,
TX 75007
Tel.: (972) 820-2100
Web Site: http://www.firstfitness.com
Rev.: $20,000,000
Emp.: 30
Nutritional Supplements
N.A.I.C.S.: 493110
David Lee Causey *(Chm)*

FIRST FLORIDA BUILDING CORP.

1533 Sunset Dr Ste 150, Miami, FL
33143
Tel.: (305) 665-1146
Web Site: http://www.firstflorida.com
Year Founded: 1963
Sales Range: $1-9.9 Million

Emp.: 20
Multi-Family Housing Contractor
N.A.I.C.S.: 236116
Gregory Wyka *(Pres)*

FIRST FLORIDA CREDIT UNION

500 W 1st St, Jacksonville, FL 32202
Tel.: (904) 359-6800 FL
Web Site: http://www.firstflorida.org
Year Founded: 1950
Emp.: 155
Credit Union
N.A.I.C.S.: 522130
Bradley A. Long *(CFO & Sr VP)*
Tim Brown *(CTO & VP)*
Brent E. Lister *(Pres & CEO)*
Libby Polk *(Sr VP-Administration)*
Dean Willis *(Chm)*
Jonathan R. Lyon *(Vice Chm)*
Ken Jones *(Treas)*
Nancy H. Meier *(Sec)*
Andrea Hurley *(Sr VP-Risk Management)*
Joey Carpenter *(Exec VP-Operations)*
Michelle Troha *(Sr VP-Marketing-Community Relations)*

FIRST FLORIDA INSURANCE NETWORK

1 Florida Pk Dr S Ste 1, Palm Coast,
FL 32137
Tel.: (386) 447-8950
Web Site:
http://www.firstfloridainsurance.com
Year Founded: 1995
Automotive, Homeowners & Life Insurance Services
N.A.I.C.S.: 524210
Norman Sapp *(Pres)*

FIRST GENERATION

410 Allentown Dr, Allentown, PA
18109
Tel.: (610) 437-4300
Web Site:
https://www.firstgencom.com
Year Founded: 1987
Sales Range: $1-9.9 Million
Emp.: 31
Integrated Marketing Communications
N.A.I.C.S.: 541613
William E. Carmody *(CEO)*
Alexandra Shade *(Pres)*
Chris Allen *(VP-Bus Dev)*
Steve White *(VP-Bus Dev)*

Subsidiaries:

First Generation (1)
1775 I St NW, Washington, DC
20006 (100%)
Tel.: (202) 587-5633
Web Site: http://firstgensdvosb.com
Full Service Integrated Marketing Communications
N.A.I.C.S.: 541613
William E. Carmody *(Founder & CEO)*

First Generation (1)
Contra San Tomaso 24, 36100, Vicenza,
Italy (100%)
Tel.: (39) 03421456370
Web Site: http://www.firstgencom.com
Integrated Marketing Communications &
Audio/Visual Services
N.A.I.C.S.: 541613

FIRST GILMER BANKSHARES, INC.

206 US Hwy 271 N, Gilmer, TX
75644
Tel.: (903) 843-4100 TX
Web Site: https://www.fnbgilmer.com
Bank Holding Company
N.A.I.C.S.: 551111
Kelly D. Stretcher *(Pres & CEO)*

Subsidiaries:

First National Bank of Gilmer (1)
206 US Hwy 271 N, Gilmer, TX 75644
Tel.: (903) 843-4100
Web Site: http://www.fnbgilmer.com
Sales Range: $10-24.9 Million
Emp.: 97
Commercial Banking
N.A.I.C.S.: 522110
Danny W. Weems *(Pres & CEO)*

FIRST GROESBECK HOLDING COMPANY

409 S Ellis, Groesbeck, TX 76642
Tel.: (254) 729-3054 TX
Web Site:
http://www.fnbgroesbeck.com
Year Founded: 1984
Sales Range: $1-9.9 Million
Bank Holding Company
N.A.I.C.S.: 551111
Bobby L. Reed *(Chm)*
Wanda S. Fewell *(Pres)*
Carl B. Sadler III *(Treas)*
Alton Sims *(Sec)*
Benjie Reed *(VP)*

Subsidiaries:

First National Bank (1)
409 S Ellis St, Groesbeck, TX 76642
Tel.: (254) 729-3054
Web Site: http://www.fnbgroesbeck.com
Sales Range: $1-9.9 Million
Emp.: 16
Retail & Commercial Banking
N.A.I.C.S.: 522110
Wanda S. Fewell *(CEO)*

FIRST GUARANTY MORT-GAGE CORP.

1900 Gallows Rd Ste 800, Tysons
Corner, VA 22182
Tel.: (703) 556-3333
Web Site: http://www.fgmc.com
Rev.: $11,312,769
Emp.: 150
Mortgage Bankers & Loan Correspondents
N.A.I.C.S.: 522310
Andrew S. Peters *(CEO)*
Dea O'Hopp *(COO)*
Robert B. Eastep *(CFO)*
Mark Mayhook *(Mng Dir-TPO Production)*
Michael J. McElroy *(Gen Counsel)*
Richard S. Donine *(Sr VP & Dir-Mktg-Natl)*
Jeff Mack *(Dir-Capital Markets)*
Ben Sizemore Jr. *(CIO)*

Subsidiaries:

GoodMortgage.com (1)
3325 S Tryon St, Charlotte, NC 28217
Tel.: (704) 523-3886
Web Site: http://www.goodmortgage.com
Sales Range: $10-24.9 Million
Emp.: 92
Internet Based Mortgage Brokers
N.A.I.C.S.: 522310
Keith A. Luedeman *(CEO)*
Brad Cooke *(Mgr-Ops)*
Ellen Bleau *(Dir-Recruiting)*
James E. Cappello *(Mgr-Secondary Pricing)*
Jeff Van Deusen *(Mgr-Sls-Charlotte)*

FIRST HELP FINANCIAL, LLC

199 Wells Ave Ste 211, Newton, MA
02459 MA
Web Site:
http://www.firsthelpfinancial.com
Year Founded: 2006
Sales Range: $25-49.9 Million
Emp.: 100
Financial Consulting Services
N.A.I.C.S.: 523940
Pushan Sen Gupta *(CEO)*

First Home Builders of Florida—(Continued)

FIRST HOME BUILDERS OF FLORIDA
1870 Colonial Blvd, Fort Myers, FL 33907
Tel.: (239) 458-8000
Web Site:
http://www.firsthomebuilders.com
Year Founded: 1996
Sales Range: $50-74.9 Million
Emp.: 4
New Construction, Single-Family Houses
N.A.I.C.S.: 236115
Tim Graney (Pres)

FIRST HOSPITALITY GROUP, INC.
10275 W Higgins Rd Ste 300, Rosemont, IL 60018
Tel.: (847) 299-9040
Web Site: http://www.fhginc.com
Year Founded: 1984
Sales Range: $150-199.9 Million
Emp.: 1,500
Property Management Services
N.A.I.C.S.: 531190
Steven L. Schwartz (Founder & Chm)
Wendy Stevens (Exec VP)
Carolyn Murphy (Gen Mgr-Hilton Garden Inn-Minneapolis)
Paul Hitselberger (Exec VP-Ops)
Mary Pat Knight (Sr VP-People Svcs)
Kelly Mascari (Sr VP-Sls & Mktg)
Daniel Smith (Exec VP)
Stacey J. Brown (Chief HR Officer)
David Duncan (Pres & CEO)

FIRST HOUSING DEVELOPMENT CORPORATION OF FLORIDA
107 S Willow Ave, Tampa, FL 33606-1945
Tel.: (813) 289-9410
Web Site:
https://www.firsthousingfl.com
Year Founded: 1979
Sales Range: $1-9.9 Million
Emp.: 50
Mortgage Services
N.A.I.C.S.: 522310
Randall J. Enders (CFO & Treas)
Edward A. Busansky (Sr VP-Credit Underwriting & Loan Analysis)
Candyce Jones (Sr VP-Internal Audit & Quality Control)
Scott Moreman (Sr VP-HUD Programs)
Tricia L. Gallagher (VP-Loan Admin)
Anne Gehlsen (Sec & Office Mgr)
Douglas I. McCree (Pres & CEO)

FIRST ILLINOIS BANCORP, INC.
6900 Clayton Ave, Saint Louis, MO 63139
Tel.: (314) 645-7700   DE
Year Founded: 1978
Sales Range: $25-49.9 Million
Bank Holding Company
N.A.I.C.S.: 551111
Melvin Leon Hall (Chm, Pres & CEO)

Subsidiaries:

First Illinois Bank   (1)
327 Missouri Ave, East Saint Louis, IL 62201-3085
Tel.: (618) 271-8700
Web Site: http://www.firstillinoisbank.com
Sales Range: $1-9.9 Million
Emp.: 12
Commericial Banking
N.A.I.C.S.: 522110
Melvin Leon Hall (Chm, Pres & CEO)

Lindell Bank & Trust Company   (1)

6900 Clayton Ave, Saint Louis, MO 63139-3739
Tel.: (314) 646-7700
Web Site: http://www.lindellbank.com
Sales Range: $10-24.9 Million
Emp.: 108
Savings Bank
N.A.I.C.S.: 522180
Melvin Leon Hall (Chm, Pres & CEO)
James C. Seitz (Sec)

FIRST IMPRESSION INTERACTIVE, LLC
1658 N Milwaukee Ave Ste 372, Chicago, IL 60647
Tel.: (844) 764-3477
Web Site: http://www.fii-inc.com
Year Founded: 2006
Sales Range: $10-24.9 Million
Emp.: 4
Online Interactive Marketing Services
N.A.I.C.S.: 541613
Dale Brown (COO)

FIRST INDEPENDENCE CORPORATION
7310 Woodward Ave Ste 101, Detroit, MI 48202
Tel.: (313) 256-8400   MI
Web Site:
http://www.firstindependence.com
Year Founded: 1984
Sales Range: $25-49.9 Million
Emp.: 83
Bank Holding Company
N.A.I.C.S.: 551111
Elizabeth Zuchelkowski (CFO & VP)

Subsidiaries:

First Independence Bank   (1)
7310 Woodward Ave Ste 101, Detroit, MI 48202
Tel.: (313) 256-8400
Web Site: http://www.firstindependence.com
Sales Range: $25-49.9 Million
Commericial Banking
N.A.I.C.S.: 522110
Kenneth Kelly (Chm & CEO)
Elizabeth Zuchelkowski (CFO & VP)
James Dunn (COO & Exec VP)
Dimitrius Hutcherson (CTO, Chief Admin Officer & Exec VP)
Alberta Pearson (Sr VP-Admin)
Rosalind McNorton (VP-Treasury Mgmt)
Catherine Ballard (VP-IT & Ops Mgr-Bank)

FIRST INSURANCE PARTNERS LLC
110 Mathis Dr Ste 105, Dickson, TN 37056
Tel.: (615) 446-2814
Web Site:
http://www.firstinsurancepartners.com
Year Founded: 2004
Insurance Agencies & Brokerages
N.A.I.C.S.: 524210
Kyle Ruf (Owner)

FIRST KANSAS BANCSHARES, INC.
1 N Main St, Hutchinson, KS 67501
Tel.: (620) 663-1521   KS
Web Site: http://www.fnbhutch.com
Year Founded: 1876
Bank Holding Company
N.A.I.C.S.: 551111
R. A. Edwards III (Chm)
Keith Hughes (CEO)
Greg Binns (Pres)

Subsidiaries:

The First National Bank of Hutchinson   (1)
1 N Main St, Hutchinson, KS 67501
Tel.: (620) 663-1521
Web Site: http://www.fnbhutch.com
Rev.: $21,053,000
Emp.: 101

Retail & Commercial Banking
N.A.I.C.S.: 522180
R. A. Edwards III (Chm)
Greg Binns (Pres)
Keith Hughes (CEO)
Troy Hutton (Chief Lending Officer)
Kris Doswell (Sr VP & Mgr-Mktg & Trng)
Rod Jones (Sr VP & Mgr-Bus Dev)
Mike Pritchett (Exec VP & Mgr-Correspondent Bank Svcs)
Dustin Stull (VP-Investments)

FIRST KENTUCKY BANK, INC.
223 S 6th St, Mayfield, KY 42066
Tel.: (270) 247-1403   KY
Web Site:
https://www.firstkentucky.com
Year Founded: 1899
Sales Range: $10-24.9 Million
Emp.: 112
Banking Services
N.A.I.C.S.: 522110
Jean G. Crawford (Chm)
David A. Long (Pres & CEO)
Spencer K. Hawkins (CFO)
Gary L. Cardin (Chief Credit Officer)
Nicole Sullivan (Officer-HR)
Kenny Brown (Sr VP-Pennyrile)
Danny Cornette (Sr Credit Officer & Sr VP)
Dana Frensley (VP & Mgr-Loans Svcs)
Nicki Short (Officer-Compliance)
Marianne Rentfro (Sec)
Stacy Overby (VP-Comml Lending)
Jimmie Prince (Controller)
Mike Russell (Mgr-IT)
Richard Scoggins (Sr Risk Officer)
Laura Stinson (Dir-Mktg)
Kristie Stamper (Mgr-Mayfield 6th St)
Haley Diel (Mgr-Mayfield South Office)
Rachel Spraggs (Mgr-Cunningham)
Jamie Walker (Mgr-Bardwell)
Krystal Brindley (Mgr-Benton)
Michele Defew (Mgr-Draffenville)
Bruce Akin (Mgr-Grand Rivers)
Jeanie Isbell (Mgr-Central City)
Carol Wininger (Mgr-Greenville)
Kristina Jones (Mgr-Ohio County)

FIRST KEYES BANCSHARES, INC.
301 S Polk, Keyes, OK 73947
Tel.: (580) 546-7511
Bank Holding Company
N.A.I.C.S.: 551111
Cindy Conner (Exec VP)

Subsidiaries:

High Plains Bank   (1)
301 S Polk, Keyes, OK 73947
Tel.: (580) 546-7511
Web Site: http://www.hpbank.us
Sales Range: $1-9.9 Million
Emp.: 17
Commericial Banking
N.A.I.C.S.: 522110
Dirk Bagenstos (CEO)

S G Bancshares Inc.   (1)
202 N Main, Okeene, OK 73763
Tel.: (580) 822-4466
Bank Holding Company; Commercial Banking
N.A.I.C.S.: 551111
James Sublett (Pres)

Subsidiary (Domestic):

State Guaranty Bank   (2)
202 N Main St, Okeene, OK 73763
Tel.: (580) 822-4466
Web Site: http://www.sgbok.com
Banking Services
N.A.I.C.S.: 522110

FIRST LENDERS MORTGAGE CORP.
909 Holland Ave, Albertville, AL 35951
Tel.: (256) 891-0681
Web Site: http://www.firstlenders.com
Sales Range: $10-24.9 Million
Emp.: 10
Mortgage Bankers & Loan Correspondents
N.A.I.C.S.: 522310
Joel Brant (Pres)

FIRST LEVEL ENTERTAINMENT GROUP, INC.
305 S Andrew Ave 203, Fort Lauderdale, FL 33301
Tel.: (954) 599-3672   FL
Year Founded: 2008
Children's Music, Videos & Discs Distr
N.A.I.C.S.: 512250
Alfred Fernandez (CFO)
Steven Berman (COO)
Steve Adelstein (Chm & CEO)
Robert Hussey (Pres)

FIRST LEXINGTON CORP.
200 Crescent Ct Ste 1375, Dallas, TX 75201
Tel.: (214) 756-6300   DE
Web Site: http://www.firstlex.com
Year Founded: 1970
Sales Range: $1-9.9 Million
Emp.: 84
Bolt, Nut, Screw, Rivet & Washer Mfr
N.A.I.C.S.: 332722
Robert Bennett (CEO)

FIRST LIBERTY CAPITAL CORPORATION
321 4th St, Hugo, CO 80821
Tel.: (719) 743-2415   CO
Web Site: https://www.fnbhugo.com
Year Founded: 1979
Sales Range: $1-9.9 Million
Emp.: 22
Bank Holding Company
N.A.I.C.S.: 551111
Randy C. Younger (Pres & CEO)

Subsidiaries:

The First National Bank of Hugo   (1)
321 4th St, Hugo, CO 80821
Tel.: (719) 743-2415
Web Site: http://www.fnbhugo.com
Sales Range: $1-9.9 Million
Federal Savings Bank
N.A.I.C.S.: 522180
Randy C. Younger (Pres)
Shelly V. Lofdahl (Pres-Hugo)
Justin D. Fisher (Sr VP)
Mark A. Ward (Sr VP)
Stacy J. Vick (VP)
Jane A. Thompson (VP)

FIRST LINDEN BANCSHARES, INC.
PO Box 481119, Linden, AL 36748
Tel.: (334) 295-8741
Web Site:
http://www.firstbanklinden.com
Bank Holding Company
N.A.I.C.S.: 551111
Ann Yelverton (Pres & CEO)

Subsidiaries:

First Bank of Linden   (1)
116 E Coats Ave, Linden, AL 36748
Tel.: (334) 295-8741
Web Site: http://www.firstbanklinden.com
Emp.: 13
Commercial Bank
N.A.I.C.S.: 522110
Anne Scott Yelverton (Pres)

FIRST LINE TECHNOLOGY, LLC
3656 Centerview Dr Ste 4, Chantilly, VA 20151
Tel.: (703) 995-7510

Web Site:
https://www.firstlinetech.com
Year Founded: 2003
Sales Range: $1-9.9 Million
Emp.: 8
Emergency Response Equipment Mfr & Distr
N.A.I.C.S.: 335132
Amit Kapoor *(Pres)*
Randy Sakowitz *(VP)*
Jason Croson *(Mgr-Natl Sls)*
Jackie Simpson *(Mgr-Acctg)*
Jennie Tal Williams *(Mgr-Mktg & Coord-HR)*
Emily Crawford *(Mgr-Mktg)*
Mike Kuykendall *(Mgr-Sls-Natl)*
Luis Mascolo *(Mgr-Warehouse)*
Ashley Timmel *(Office Mgr)*

FIRST MANHATTAN CO.
399 Park Ave, New York, NY 10022
Tel.: (212) 756-3300
Web Site:
https://www.firstmanhattan.com
Sales Range: $50-74.9 Billion
Emp.: 110
Investment Services
N.A.I.C.S.: 523150
Edward I. Lefferman *(Sr Mng Dir & Portfolio Mgr)*
Simon E. Porter *(Mng Dir & Portfolio Mgr)*
Charles Rosenthal *(Sr Mng Dir)*
Allan H. Glick *(Sr Mng Dir & Portfolio Mgr)*
Robert J. Aylward *(Mng Dir & Portfolio Mgr)*
Jay Vodofsky *(Sr Mng Dir & Mgr-Relationship)*
Paul E. Patrick *(Mng Dir & Portfolio Mgr)*
Michael J. Kelter *(Mng Dir & Portfolio Mgr)*

FIRST MANUFACTURING COMPANY
3800 W Oceanside Rd, Oceanside, NY 11572
Tel.: (516) 763-0400
Web Site:
http://www.firstmanufacturing.com
Rev.: $15,126,497
Emp.: 30
Mfr of Leather Goods
N.A.I.C.S.: 424990
Mohamed Cheema *(CEO)*

FIRST MARKET RESEARCH CORP.
84 Eastbourne Rd, Newton Center, MA 02459-1206
Tel.: (617) 734-7080
Web Site: http://www.firstmarket.com
Sales Range: $25-49.9 Million
Emp.: 2
Market Analysis & Research
N.A.I.C.S.: 541910
Jack Reynolds *(Pres)*

FIRST MEDIA GROUP INC.
120 E Washington St Ste 721, Syracuse, NY 13202
Tel.: (315) 471-7800 NY
Year Founded: 1980
Sales Range: $25-49.9 Million
Emp.: 8
N.A.I.C.S.: 541810
Michael Hamidi *(Pres)*
Gail Hamidi *(VP)*

FIRST MEDIA SERVICES, LLC
494 Blue Prince Rd, Bluefield, WV 24701
Tel.: (304) 327-9266 WV
Year Founded: 2005

Radio Broadcasting Stations Owner & Operator
N.A.I.C.S.: 516110
Charles Robert Spencer *(Mng Partner)*

Subsidiaries:

WAMN-FM (1)
494 Blue Prince Rd, Bluefield, WV 24701
Tel.: (304) 327-9266
Web Site: http://www.mywillie.com
Radio Broadcasting Stations
N.A.I.C.S.: 516110

WHAJ-FM (1)
900 Bluefield Ave, Bluefield, WV 24701
Tel.: (304) 327-7114
Web Site: http://www.j1045.com
Radio Broadcasting Stations
N.A.I.C.S.: 516110
Brock Mathews *(Program Dir)*

WHKX-FM (1)
900 Bluefield Ave, Bluefield, WV 24701
Tel.: (304) 327-7114
Web Site: http://www.kickscountry.com
Radio Broadcasting Stations
N.A.I.C.S.: 516110
Danny Clemons *(Gen Mgr)*
Joey Jarvis *(Program Dir)*

WKQR-FM (1)
494 Blue Prince Rd, Bluefield, WV 24701
Tel.: (304) 327-9266
Web Site: http://www.kissplaysthehits.com
Radio Broadcasting Stations
N.A.I.C.S.: 516110

FIRST MIAMI BANCSHARES, INC.
2 N Main St, Miami, OK 74354
Tel.: (918) 542-3371 OK
Sales Range: $1-9.9 Million
Bank Holding Company
N.A.I.C.S.: 551111
Charles C. Neal *(Chm)*

Subsidiaries:

Bank of Billings (1)
104 NE Elm St, Billings, MO 65610
Tel.: (417) 744-2567
Web Site: http://www.thebankofbillings.com
Sales Range: $1-9.9 Million
Commericial Banking
N.A.I.C.S.: 522110
Mark Jenkins *(Pres & CEO)*
Karri Stanton *(Exec VP)*
Aaron Allen *(Officer-Loan & VP)*
Bradley Roam *(Officer-Loan-Marionville & VP)*
Andrew Buckler *(Officer-Loan & Asst VP)*

The First National Bank & Trust Company of Miami (1)
2 N Main St, Miami, OK 74354
Tel.: (918) 542-3371
Web Site: http://www.fnbmiami.com
Sales Range: $1-9.9 Million
Emp.: 38
Commericial Banking
N.A.I.C.S.: 522110
Charles C. Neal *(Chm)*
Ann L. Neal *(Vice Chm & Sr VP)*
Robert Kimbrough *(Pres & CFO)*
Steve Cline *(Sr VP-Consumer Lending)*
Tammy Bro *(Sr VP)*
Jared Lamb *(Sr VP)*

FIRST MIDWEST ACQUISITION CORP.
2911 S Air Depot Blvd, Midwest City, OK 73110
Tel.: (405) 732-4571
Web Site: https://www.fnbmwc.com
Year Founded: 2003
Sales Range: $10-24.9 Million
Emp.: 115
Bank Holding Company
N.A.I.C.S.: 551111

Subsidiaries:

FNB Community Bank (1)

2911 S Air Depot Blvd, Oklahoma City, OK 73110
Tel.: (405) 732-4571
Web Site: http://www.fnbmwc.com
Rev.: $17,053,000
Assets: $436,209,000
Liabilities: $388,557,000
Net Worth: $47,652,000
Earnings: $2,905,000
Emp.: 113
Fiscal Year-end: 12/31/2013
Retail & Commercial Banking
N.A.I.C.S.: 522110
Robert H. Croak *(Chm)*
Timothy T. Ballard *(CFO, Exec VP & Mgr-Ops Div)*
John R. Croak *(Vice Chm, Exec VP & Mgr-Sls Div)*
William H. Croak *(Vice Chm, Pres & CEO)*
Dan Maloy *(VP & Dir-HR)*
Cheryl Rittterskamp *(VP)*
Camille Phillips *(Asst VP-Mktg & Sls)*
Jeff Arvin *(Officer-Comml Banking & VP)*
Sandy Breed *(VP & Mgr-Harrah)*
Tracy Burton *(Asst VP & Asst Mgr-Choctaw)*
Angie Dowdy *(Asst VP-Personal Banking & Asst Mgr-Douglas)*
Mistie Gibson-Kennedy *(VP & Mgr-Choctaw)*
Alex Lancaster *(Officer-Comml Banking & VP)*
Niki Latschar *(Officer-Personal Banking, VP & Mgr-Douglas)*

FIRST MIDWEST BANK OF POPLAR BLUFF
704 N Westwood Blvd, Poplar Bluff, MO 63901
Tel.: (573) 785-8461
Web Site: http://www.1midwest.com
Sales Range: $1-9.9 Million
Emp.: 80
Banking Services
N.A.I.C.S.: 522110
Joseph McLane *(Pres)*

FIRST MUTUAL OF RICHMOND, INC.
20 N 9th St, Richmond, IN 47375
Tel.: (765) 962-2581 DE
Web Site:
https://www.firstbankrichmond.com
Year Founded: 1997
Sales Range: $25-49.9 Million
Emp.: 173
Bank Holding Company
N.A.I.C.S.: 551111
Garry D. Kleer *(Pres & CEO)*
Beth A. Brittenham *(Sec, Sr VP & Dir-HR)*
Donald A. Benziger *(CFO & Exec VP)*

Subsidiaries:

First Bank Richmond (1)
20 N 9th St, Richmond, IN 47374
Tel.: (765) 962-2581
Web Site: http://www.firstbankrichmond.com
Sales Range: $25-49.9 Million
Commericial Banking
N.A.I.C.S.: 522110
Garry D. Kleer *(Chm & CEO)*
Donald A. Benziger *(CFO & Exec VP)*
Scott A. George *(CTO & VP)*
Beth A. Brittenham *(Sr VP & Dir-HR)*
Brett Baumeister *(Pres-Market-Western Ohio)*
Jackie Davis *(COO-Mutual Federal)*
Dean Weinert *(Pres-Mutual Federal)*
Albert E. Fullerton Jr. *(CIO, Chief Info Security Officer & Sr VP)*

Division (Domestic):

Mutual Federal, a division of First Bank Richmond (2)
121 S Ohio Ave, Sidney, OH 45365
Tel.: (937) 498-1195
Web Site: http://www.mutualbancorp.com
Commericial Banking
N.A.I.C.S.: 522110

Dean Weinert *(Pres)*
Jackie Davis *(Sr VP-Retail Banking)*
David Sassenger *(Sr VP-Comml Banking)*
Nate Counts *(VP)*

FIRST NATION GROUP LLC
4566 Hwy 20 E Courtyard Plz Ste 208, Niceville, FL 32578-8839
Tel.: (850) 389-8448
Web Site:
https://www.firstnationgroup.com
Community Resources, Including Job Training, Education Programs & Health Services
N.A.I.C.S.: 923130
Cheryl Nilsson *(CEO)*
Steve Baugh *(Pres)*
Mike Jarosz *(CFO & Exec VP)*
Chris Maier *(CIO, Chief Risk Officer & VP)*
Wendy Tommelleo *(Exec VP)*
Glenn Munroe *(VP-Sls)*
Ellen Carpenter *(Dir-Order Processing & Customer Svc)*
Marian Olson *(Dir-Contracts)*
Stacey Mansfield *(Sr Mgr-Facilities)*
Lillian Ebersole *(Mgr-Transaction Processing)*

Subsidiaries:

Jordan Reses Supply Company (1)
148 S Industrial Dr, Saline, MI 48176
Tel.: (734) 944-3640
Web Site: http://firstnationgroup.com
Medical Equipment & Supplies Distr
N.A.I.C.S.: 423450
Steve Baugh *(Pres)*
Michael Jarosz *(CFO & Exec VP)*
Wendy Tommelleo *(Exec VP)*
Chris Maier *(CIO & Chief Risk Officer & VP)*
Glenn Munroe *(VP-Sls)*
Ellen Carpenter *(Dir-Order Processing & Customer Svc)*
Kendra Smith *(Reg Sls Mgr-Southern)*
Cheryl Nilsson *(CEO)*
Marian Olson *(Dir-Contracts)*
Stacey Mansfield *(Sr Mgr-Facilities)*
Lillian Ebersole *(Mgr-Transaction Processing)*

FIRST NATIONAL BANCORP, INC.
100 First National Ave, Green Forest, AR 72638
Tel.: (870) 438-5214 AR
Web Site:
http://www.anstaffbank.com
Year Founded: 1997
Sales Range: $10-24.9 Million
Emp.: 130
Bank Holding Company
N.A.I.C.S.: 551111
Stephen E. Stafford *(Chm, Pres & CEO)*

Subsidiaries:

Anstaff Bank (1)
100 First National Ave, Green Forest, AR 72638
Tel.: (870) 438-5214
Web Site: http://www.anstaffbank.com
Sales Range: $10-24.9 Million
Emp.: 94
Commericial Banking
N.A.I.C.S.: 522110
Stephen E. Stafford *(Chm & CEO)*
Spencer Adams *(Asst VP)*

Twin Lakes Community Bank (1)
301 S 1st St, Flippin, AR 72634
Tel.: (870) 453-8522
Web Site: http://www.tlcbank.net
Sales Range: $1-9.9 Million
Emp.: 35
Commericial Banking
N.A.I.C.S.: 522110
Jerry Cunningham *(Pres & CEO)*
Brent Conklin *(CFO)*

FIRST NATIONAL BANK

First National Bank—(Continued)

1500 N Fabens Rd, Fabens, TX 79838
Tel.: (915) 764-2214
Web Site: http://www.fnbelpaso.com
Sales Range: $1-9.9 Million
Emp.: 65
Provider of Banking Services
N.A.I.C.S.: 522110
Jimmy Onick (Sr VP-Loans)

FIRST NATIONAL BANK
202 E 11th St, Goodland, KS 67735
Tel.: (785) 899-5611
Web Site: http://www.fnb.com
Sales Range: $10-24.9 Million
Emp.: 110
National Commercial Banks
N.A.I.C.S.: 522110
Dwane Timm (Pres)

FIRST NATIONAL BANK
125 W Sioux Ave, Pierre, SD 57501
Tel.: (605) 945-3900
Web Site:
http://www.firstnationalbanks.com
Sales Range: $10-24.9 Million
Emp.: 200
National Commercial Banks
N.A.I.C.S.: 522110
Craig Davis (CEO)
Bill Fuchs (CFO)

FIRST NATIONAL BANK
341 Military St S, Hamilton, AL 35570
Tel.: (205) 921-7435
Web Site:
http://www.firstnationalathome.com
Year Founded: 1976
Sales Range: $25-49.9 Million
Emp.: 35
National Commercial Banks
N.A.I.C.S.: 522110
Pat R. Duke (COO)
Jill W. Cox (Sr VP)
Shannon Lollar (Officer-Loan)

FIRST NATIONAL BANK & CO.
235 E Choctaw Ave, McAlester, OK 74501
Tel.: (918) 426-0211
Web Site:
http://www.fnbmcalester.com
Year Founded: 1896
Sales Range: $50-74.9 Million
Emp.: 100
National Commercial Banks
N.A.I.C.S.: 522110
Carlton Bass (Chm)
Boyd C. Bass (Vice Chm)
E. Jane Auld (CFO & Exec VP)

Subsidiaries:

First National Bank & Trust Company of McAlester (1)
235 E Choctaw Ave, McAlester, OK 74501
Tel.: (918) 426-0211
Web Site: http://www.fnbmcalester.com
Rev.: $28,629,000
National Commercial Banks
N.A.I.C.S.: 522110
Vic Wheeler (Sr VP)

FIRST NATIONAL BANK & TRUST CO.
130 E MacArthur St, Shawnee, OK 74804
Tel.: (405) 275-8830
Web Site: https://www.fnbokla.bank
Year Founded: 1984
Sales Range: $25-49.9 Million
Emp.: 29
Commericial Banking
N.A.I.C.S.: 522110
Larry E. Briggs (Pres & CEO)
Annette Stuckey (CFO & Exec VP)

Jeff Scroggins (VP-Mortgage Lending)
Diane Hinton (VP-Credit Risk)
Randy Waters (Chief Lending Officer & Exec VP)
Kathey Birch (Sr VP & Ops Mgr-Retail)
Drew Adams (Pres-Market, VP & Mgr-Holdenville)
Greg Arbuckle (Officer-Compliance & VP)
Darci Williams (Officer-Banking & Mgr-HR)
Renah Coffman (Officer-Banking)
Misty Crisel (Officer-Banking & Mgr-Lawton)

FIRST NATIONAL BANK IN ALAMOGORDO
414 10th St, Alamogordo, NM 88310
Tel.: (575) 437-4880
Web Site: https://www.fnb4u.com
Rev.: $12,803,000
Emp.: 106
National Commercial Banks
N.A.I.C.S.: 522110
Bill Mayton (CFO)
S. W. Atkins (Chm)
Phil Stevens (VP-Comml Loans)

FIRST NATIONAL BANK IN NEW BREMEN
435 S Washington St, New Bremen, OH 45869
Tel.: (419) 629-2761
Web Site: http://www.firstnbank.com
Year Founded: 1934
Sales Range: $25-49.9 Million
Emp.: 50
Banking Services
N.A.I.C.S.: 522110
William Wente (Pres)
Jerry S. Lehman (Officer-Loan & VP)

FIRST NATIONAL BANK IN OLNEY
101 E Main St, Olney, IL 62450
Tel.: (618) 395-8541
Web Site: https://www.fnbolney.com
Sales Range: $10-24.9 Million
Emp.: 90
National Commercial Banks
N.A.I.C.S.: 522110
Bruce A. Peters (Pres & CEO)
Randy Kistler (Chm)

FIRST NATIONAL BANK IN STAUNTON
115 S Elm St, Staunton, IL 62088
Tel.: (618) 635-2234
Web Site:
http://www.fnbstaunton.com
Rev.: $17,600,000
Emp.: 200
Savings Institutions
N.A.I.C.S.: 522180
Larry J. Ziglar (Pres)

FIRST NATIONAL BANK OF AMERICA INC.
241 E Saginaw St, East Lansing, MI 48823
Tel.: (517) 351-2660
Web Site: http://www.fnba.com
Year Founded: 1955
Sales Range: $50-74.9 Million
Emp.: 150
Provider of Banking Services
N.A.I.C.S.: 522110
Sandy Eastwood (Mng Dir)
Joanne Lose (Asst VP-Ops & Security)
David Secord (Supvr-Mgmt Records)
Frederick Foote (Sr VP)

Paul Dankert (Asst VP)
Jason Fitnich (Mgr-Credit)
Martin E. Adams (Chm)

FIRST NATIONAL BANK OF ARENZVILLE
110 S Charles St, Arenzville, IL 62611
Tel.: (217) 997-5585
Web Site:
https://www.fnbarenzville.com
Year Founded: 1882
Sales Range: $25-49.9 Million
Emp.: 20
Banking Services
N.A.I.C.S.: 522110
Barbara Lovekamp (CFO & VP)

FIRST NATIONAL BANK OF BASTROP
489 Hwy 71 W, Bastrop, TX 78602
Tel.: (512) 321-2561
Web Site: http://www.fnbbastrop.com
Year Founded: 1889
Sales Range: $10-24.9 Million
Emp.: 105
Provider of Banking Services
N.A.I.C.S.: 522110
Reid Sharp (Pres & CEO)
David Lewis (Sr VP-Lending)
Fil Valderrama (Exec VP-Lending)
Deleigh Brooks (Chief Risk Officer)
Clay Ingram (Sr VP-Lending)
Brad Hurta (Pres-Lending-Smithville)
Keisha Tischler (Asst VP-Acctg)
Jose Gonzales (VP-Lending)
Amanda Wickliffe (CFO)
Michael Hancock (Chief Credit Officer)
Sam Blanton (CTO)
Cody Mauck (Sr VP-Customer Rels)
Madonna Abarca (Officer-Loan)
Pam Buerger (Officer-Bank-Financial)
Essie Espinoza (Officer-Bank-BSA)
Jenna Fohn Thomas (Officer-HR)
Jorge Gonzalez (Officer-Loan-CRA)
Nicole Herring (Officer-Security)
Connie Juarez (Officer-Mktg)
Kyle Mogonye (Officer-Loan)
Angelica Padron (Officer-Customer Svc)
Kris Slay (Officer-Bank)
Vicki Tate (Officer-Loan)
Stacy Tiner (Officer-Loan & Asst Branch Mgr)

FIRST NATIONAL BANK OF BEMIDJI
PO Box 670, Bemidji, MN 56619
Tel.: (218) 751-2430
Web Site: http://www.fnbbemidji.com
Year Founded: 1897
Sales Range: $10-24.9 Million
Emp.: 108
Bank Holding Company
N.A.I.C.S.: 551111
Tom Welle (Pres)
Hugh Welle (VP & Officer-Comml Loan)
Susan S. Engel (Dir-Sls & Mktg)
Jan Loisel (Mgr-South & Officer-Retail Loan)
Karen Oftelie (Mgr-Personal Banking)
Russ Moen (Officer-Loan)
Jodi Schroeder (Officer-Loan)
Liz Smyithe (Sec)
Nikki Brink (Mgr-HR)
Randy Frisk (Officer-Loan)

FIRST NATIONAL BANK OF DRYDEN
7 W Main St, Dryden, NY 13053
Tel.: (607) 844-8141
Web Site:
https://www.drydenbank.com

Year Founded: 1902
Rev.: $5,500,000
Emp.: 34
Commercial Banking Services
N.A.I.C.S.: 522110
Leland B. Taylor (Vice Chm)
William J. Pomeroy (Vice Chm)
Ronald C. Denniston (Chm)
Sharon L. Keech (Sr VP)
Sandra L. Prugh (Exec VP)
Robert B. Porteus (Exec VP)
Donna M. Jackson (VP)
Michael W. Shattuck (Sr VP)
Michelle Browngardt (VP)
Clinton S. Brooks (VP)

FIRST NATIONAL BANK OF GRANBURY
101 E Bridge St, Granbury, TX 76048
Tel.: (817) 573-2655
Web Site:
https://www.fnbgranbury.com
Year Founded: 1887
Sales Range: $10-24.9 Million
Emp.: 120
Provider of Banking Services
N.A.I.C.S.: 522110
John Henry Luton (Chm)
Greg Warren (Chief Risk Officer & VP)
Mark Webb (Chief Lending Officer & Sr VP)
Ron Hampton (Officer-Mortgage Lending & VP)
Larry Wilkins (VP)
Kelly Staley (VP-Consumer Lending)
Corey Tucker (VP-Comml Lending)

FIRST NATIONAL BANK OF HUNTSVILLE
1300 11th St, Huntsville, TX 77340
Tel.: (936) 295-5701
Web Site:
http://www.fnbhuntsvilletx.com
Year Founded: 1841
Sales Range: $10-24.9 Million
Emp.: 580
Banking Services
N.A.I.C.S.: 522110
Laura Lehman (VP)
Sam H. Burris Jr. (Chm)

FIRST NATIONAL BANK OF MONTEREY
6222 E Main St, Monterey, IN 46960
Tel.: (574) 542-2121
Web Site: http://www.pwrtc.com
Year Founded: 1935
Sales Range: $10-24.9 Million
Emp.: 50
Banking Services
N.A.I.C.S.: 522110
Claiborn M. Wamsley (Pres)

FIRST NATIONAL BANK OF ONEIDA
18418 Alberta St, Oneida, TN 37841
Tel.: (423) 569-8586
Web Site: https://www.fnboneida.com
Sales Range: $50-74.9 Million
Emp.: 65
Provider of Banking Services
N.A.I.C.S.: 522110
Michael B. Swain (Chm)
Mona Queen (Chief Admin Officer)
Vickie Daniels (VP & Dir-Compliance)

FIRST NATIONAL BANK OF OXFORD
101 Courthouse Sq, Oxford, MS 38655
Tel.: (662) 234-2821
Web Site: http://www.fnboxford.com
Year Founded: 1910
Sales Range: $10-24.9 Million
Emp.: 60

Provider of Banking Services
N.A.I.C.S.: 522110
John L. Barrett *(Pres & CEO)*
Jane Shaw *(Exec VP)*
Jennifer Kuhn *(VP & Mgr-HR)*
Linda White *(Mgr-DP)*
Ragan Hayward *(Chief Credit Officer & Sr VP)*

FIRST NATIONAL BANK OF PALMERTON

4th St & Lafayette Ave, Palmerton, PA 18071
Tel.: (610) 826-2239
Web Site:
http://www.fnbpalmerton.com
Year Founded: 1972
Sales Range: $50-74.9 Million
Emp.: 70
Banking Services
N.A.I.C.S.: 522110
Salvatore Checho *(Chm, Pres & CEO)*
Michael R. Harleman *(Exec VP)*
Michael O. DePaulo *(COO & Sr VP)*
Albert Yesu *(CFO & VP)*
Bonnie L. Paules *(Sr VP & Asst Sec)*
Bradley Browne *(VP)*
Brenda Kowalsky *(VP)*
Christopher Checho *(Asst Sec & Co-VP)*
Richard Snyder *(Sr VP-Consumer Lending)*
Denise Krupa *(VP & Branch Mgr)*
Janene Smith *(VP)*
Anna Marie Checho *(Sec)*
Susan Choy *(VP-Residential Mortgage Lending)*
Marlene Coffman *(VP & Branch Mgr)*
Anne Davis-Shupp *(VP & Dir-Mktg)*
Anthony Rosencrance *(Sr VP-Comml Lending)*
Lisa Wentz *(VP & Branch Mgr)*
Mary Williams *(VP & Branch Mgr)*
Kevin Reiner *(VP-Comml Lending)*
Lori Solt *(VP & Branch Mgr)*
Barry Wolfe *(VP-Compliance)*
David Semmel *(VP)*
Donna Snyder *(VP)*
Jason Geake *(Chief Admin Officer & VP)*
Frank Checho *(Sr Exec VP)*

FIRST NATIONAL BANK OF PONTOTOC

19 S Main St, Pontotoc, MS 38863
Tel.: (662) 489-1631
Web Site:
http://www.1stnbpontotoc.com
Sales Range: $10-24.9 Million
Emp.: 70
National Commercial Banks
N.A.I.C.S.: 522110
Larry Russell *(Sec)*
Buddy R. Montgomery *(Pres & CEO)*
Julie Henry *(Exec VP)*
Greg Baker *(VP)*
Michelle Rodgers *(Asst VP)*

FIRST NATIONAL BANK OF RIVER FALLS

104 E Locust St, River Falls, WI 54022
Tel.: (715) 425-2401
Web Site: https://www.fnbrf.com
Year Founded: 1904
Sales Range: $25-49.9 Million
Emp.: 100
Provider of Banking Services
N.A.I.C.S.: 522110
Connie Ruppert *(VP-Comml Loans)*
Jack Cullen *(VP-Comml Loans)*
Thomas Pechacek *(VP-IT & Security)*
Lois Jenkins *(VP & Controller)*

Pam Deal *(VP-Compliance & Officer-Loan Review)*
Matt Russell *(Chief Credit Officer & Exec VP)*

FIRST NATIONAL BANK OF SCOTIA

201 Mohawk Ave, Scotia, NY 12302
Tel.: (518) 370-7200
Web Site: https://www.firstscotia.com
Year Founded: 1923
Sales Range: $10-24.9 Million
Emp.: 136
National Commercial Banks
N.A.I.C.S.: 522110
Louis H. Buhrmaster *(Chm)*
John H. Buhrmaster *(Pres & CEO)*
Laura M. Dieterich *(Sec & Sr VP)*
Andrew T. Trainor *(Sr VP)*
Kevin R. Buhrmaster *(Officer-Ops & VP)*
David Teta *(Officer-Ops & Asst VP-Schenectady)*
Debra A. Lindsay *(Officer-Ops & Asst VP-Colonie)*
Donna M. Anscombe *(Officer-Ops & Asst VP-Glenville)*
Jessica R. Petraccione *(VP & Mgr-Clifton Park)*
Kelly A. Gibbons *(VP & Area Mgr)*
Nancy R. Harrigan *(Officer-Ops & Asst VP)*
Patricia J. Crowley *(Officer-Ops-Clifton Park)*
Teresa A. Freeman *(VP & Mgr-Schenectady)*

FIRST NATIONAL BANK OF SHARP COUNTY

636 Ash Flat Dr, Ash Flat, AR 72513
Tel.: (870) 994-2311
Web Site: https://www.fnbc.us
Year Founded: 1912
Sales Range: $10-24.9 Million
Emp.: 120
National Commercial Banks
N.A.I.C.S.: 522110

FIRST NATIONAL BANK, ALBANY/BRECKENRIDGE

100 S Main St, Albany, TX 76430
Tel.: (325) 762-2222   TX
Web Site: http://www.fnbab.com
Year Founded: 1883
National Commercial Banks
N.A.I.C.S.: 522110
Randall Palmore *(Pres)*
Lance McWhorter *(VP)*
Dan A Neff *(CEO)*
Harold G. Cox *(Lending Officer)*
DeVonna Davis *(Exec VP & CFO)*
Brent Clegg *(VP)*
Robert Dacus *(VP)*
Justin Winters *(Asst VP)*

FIRST NATIONAL BANKERS BANKSHARES, INC.

7813 Office Park Blvd, Baton Rouge, LA 70809
Tel.: (225) 924-8015   DE
Web Site: https://www.bankers-bank.com
Year Founded: 1984
Sales Range: $50-74.9 Million
Bank Holding Company
N.A.I.C.S.: 551111
Jay Wisener *(Pres-Arkansas)*
Joseph F. Quinlan Jr. *(Chm)*

Subsidiaries:

First National Banker's Bank   (1)
7813 Ofc Park Blvd, Baton Rouge, LA 70809
Tel.: (225) 924-8015
Web Site: http://www.bankers-bank.com
Federal Savings Bank

N.A.I.C.S.: 522180
Carolyn C. Dyer *(CFO & Exec VP)*
Christopher L. Rolfsen *(Chief Credit Risk Officer & Exec VP)*
Lori Anderson *(Sr VP-Compliance Svcs)*
Laura J. Boudreaux *(Compliance Officer & Sr VP)*
Jeanie Cassano *(Sr VP-HR)*
Cheryl Kennedy *(Sr VP-Mktg)*
Jason Hebert *(Sr VP-IT)*
Jimmy Devane *(Sr VP-Loan Review)*
James M. Hudson *(Pres & CEO)*
Herbert Thomas *(Sr VP & Mgr-Relationship-Little Rock)*
Joseph F. Quinlan Jr. *(Chm)*

FIRST NATIONAL CORPORATION OF ARDMORE, INC.

405 W Main St, Ardmore, OK 73401
Tel.: (580) 223-1111   OK
Web Site: https://www.1nb.com
Sales Range: $10-24.9 Million
Bank Holding Company
N.A.I.C.S.: 551111
Curtis Davidson *(CEO)*
Keith King *(CFO)*

Subsidiaries:

First National Bank & Trust Company
of Ardmore   (1)
405 W Main St, Ardmore, OK 73401
Tel.: (580) 223-1111
Web Site: http://www.1nb.com
Sales Range: $10-24.9 Million
Commercial Banking Services
N.A.I.C.S.: 522110
Curtis Davidson *(CEO)*
Becky Crawford *(COO & Sr VP)*
Blake Hollingsworth *(Chief Lending Officer & Sr VP)*
Brent James Wade *(Sr VP & Mgr-Lone Grove)*
Clayton Lodes *(Pres)*
Cynthia Bryant *(VP & Controller)*
Robert P. Bates *(Sr VP)*
Vicky Tyler *(Officer-Trust & Sr VP)*
Deanna Oldham *(Officer-Collection & Sr VP)*
Dana Williams *(Officer-Trust Ops & VP)*
Sheila Bell *(Officer-Mktg & Sr VP)*
Laura Kidd *(Officer-Compliance & Sr VP)*
Jean Roberts *(Sr VP)*
Keith King *(CFO & Exec VP)*
Fred Resz *(CTO & Sr VP)*
Matt Farve *(Sr VP)*
Sandy Holybee *(VP)*
John Veazey *(Officer-Trust & Sr VP)*
Charles Hollingsworth *(Pres-Market & Sr VP)*
Dorothy Roberts *(Sr VP)*
Jacob Howard Charnock *(Chief Credit Officer & Sr VP)*
Shirley Gayle Word *(Sr VP & Branch Mgr)*
Ryan Youderian *(Sr VP & Dir-Mktg Res)*
Cara Stubbs *(VP)*
Kim McLaughlin *(VP)*
Lisa Armstrong *(VP)*
Gerri Sue Kelly *(VP & Branch Mgr-Marietta)*
F. Lovell McMillin *(Chm)*
Sam Huffman *(Pres-Madill Market & Sr VP)*
Glen Payne III *(Chief Acctg Officer & VP)*

FIRST NATIONAL CORPORATION OF WYNNE

528 Merriman Ave E, Wynne, AR 72396
Tel.: (870) 238-2361   AR
Year Founded: 1984
Sales Range: $10-24.9 Million
Bank Holding Company
N.A.I.C.S.: 551111
Sean H. Williams *(Pres)*

Subsidiaries:

The First National Bank of
Wynne   (1)
528 E Merriman Ave, Wynne, AR 72396
Tel.: (870) 238-2361
Web Site: http://www.fnbwynneonline.com
Commericial Banking
N.A.I.C.S.: 522110
Sean H. Williams *(Pres)*

FIRST NATIONAL FINANCIAL SERVICES, INC.

812 Main St, Elk River, MN 55330-1575
Tel.: (763) 241-3637   MN
Web Site: http://www.elkriver.bank
Year Founded: 1979
Sales Range: $10-24.9 Million
Emp.: 55
Bank Holding Company
N.A.I.C.S.: 551111
John K. Houlton *(Chm, Pres & CEO)*
Becky Wiehoff *(Pres/CEO-First Bank Elk River)*

Subsidiaries:

First Bank Elk River   (1)
812 Main St NW, Elk River, MN 55330
Tel.: (763) 241-3637
Web Site: http://www.elkriver.bank
Sales Range: $10-24.9 Million
Commericial Banking
N.A.I.C.S.: 522110
Scott Fritz *(Chief Credit Officer & Sr VP)*
John K. Houlton *(Chm)*
Debra Koehler *(Mgr-Compliance)*
Pam Hayes *(Mgr-Loan Review)*
Becky Wiehoff *(Pres & CEO)*
Christy Langer *(Sr VP & Dir-HR)*
Roger Hebeisen *(VP)*
Sandy Langer *(VP)*
Leonard Kirscht *(VP-Bus Banking)*
Amanda Reinert *(Controller)*

FIRST NATIONAL OF NE-BRASKA, INC.

1620 Dodge St, Omaha, NE 68197
Tel.: (402) 602-3777   NE
Web Site: https://www.fnni.com
Year Founded: 1968
Sales Range: $900-999.9 Million
Emp.: 5,000
Bank Holding Company
N.A.I.C.S.: 551111
Clark D. Lauritzen *(Pres)*
Bruce R. Lauritzen *(Chm)*
Michael S. Foutch *(Exec VP-Customer & Employee Experience)*
Mihaela Kobjerowski *(Chief Credit Officer & Exec VP)*
Jerry J. O'Flanagan *(Exec VP)*

Subsidiaries:

Castle Bank N.A.   (1)
121 W Lincoln Hwy, Dekalb, IL 60115-3609   (100%)
Tel.: (815) 758-7007
Web Site: http://www.castlebank.com
Sales Range: $50-74.9 Million
Emp.: 300
Bank Holding Companies
N.A.I.C.S.: 522110
Timothy A. Struthers *(Pres)*
Bruce R. Lauritzen *(Chm)*

First National Bank Fremont   (1)
152 E 6th St, Fremont, NE 68025
Tel.: (402) 753-2272
Web Site: http://www.www.fnbo.com
Sales Range: $25-49.9 Million
Emp.: 20
Banking Services
N.A.I.C.S.: 522110
Jennifer Benson *(VP-Bus Dev & Private Banking)*
Jack Weeks *(Pres-Market-Lincoln)*

First National Bank South
Dakota   (1)
1800 N Main St, Mitchell, SD 57301
Tel.: (605) 996-1005
Web Site: http://www.fnbsd.com
Sales Range: $25-49.9 Million
Emp.: 6
Banking Services
N.A.I.C.S.: 522110

First National Bank of Omaha   (1)
1620 Dodge St, Omaha, NE 68197
Tel.: (402) 341-7283
Web Site: http://www.fnbomaha.com
Commercial & State Bank
N.A.I.C.S.: 522110

First National of Nebraska, Inc.—(Continued)

Daniel K. O'Neill *(Pres)*
Anna Castner Wightman *(Sr Dir-Government Relations)*

First National Investment
Banking   (1)
1620 Dodge St, Omaha, NE 68197
Tel.: (402) 633-3553
Sales Range: $50-74.9 Million
Emp.: 90
Investment Banking
N.A.I.C.S.: 523150

Subsidiary (Domestic):

Cybus Capital Markets   (2)
215 10th St Ste 1110, Des Moines, IA
50309
Tel.: (515) 246-8558
Investment Banking & Private Equity Fund
Management
N.A.I.C.S.: 523999

FIRST NATIONAL TRADING CO. INC.

503 Chancellor Ave, Irvington, NJ
07111
Tel.: (973) 351-7711
Rev.: $35,000,000
Emp.: 4
Textile Mfr
N.A.I.C.S.: 424990
Mike Ong *(Mgr)*

FIRST NEBRASKA BANK

330 N Spruce St, Valley, NE 68064
Tel.: (402) 359-2281
Web Site:
http://www.firstnebraskabank.com
Sales Range: $1-9.9 Million
Emp.: 60
Provider of Banking Services
N.A.I.C.S.: 522110
Clark Lehr *(Pres)*
Brian Lundy *(Sr VP)*
Daniel D. Huss *(VP)*
Jeanne Quinn *(Asst VP-Loan Admin)*
Jerry Sukup *(VP)*
Kristin Stracke *(Asst VP)*

FIRST NEW YORK SECURITIES LLC

90 Park Ave, New York, NY 10016
Tel.: (212) 848-0600
Web Site: http://www.fnysllc.com
Year Founded: 1985
Sales Range: $10-24.9 Million
Emp.: 300
Investment Services
N.A.I.C.S.: 523150
Roger Egbert *(Partner)*
Christine Nastro *(Mgr)*
Charles Peterson *(Controller)*
Brandt Mandia *(Mng Dir-Electronic Trading & Direct Market Access)*
Keith Yanowitz *(Portfolio Mgr)*
Sandro Polverino *(CTO)*

FIRST NORTHERN CREDIT UNION

230 W Monroe St Ste 2850, Chicago,
IL 60606
Tel.: (312) 394-8500
Web Site: https://www.fncu.org
Rev.: $10,700,000
Emp.: 75
Credit Union
N.A.I.C.S.: 522130
Alex Malone *(VP)*

FIRST OHIO HOME FINANCE, INC

385 County Line Rd W Ste 200,
Westerville, OH 43082
Tel.: (614) 818-1850   OH
Web Site:
https://www.firstohiohome.com

Year Founded: 1996
Sales Range: $1-9.9 Million
Emp.: 70
Mortgage Lending Services
N.A.I.C.S.: 522310
Donna Ford *(Mgr-Mktg)*

FIRST OKMULGEE CORPORATION

610 E 8th St, Okmulgee, OK 74447
Tel.: (918) 756-8440   OK
Web Site: http://www.mybankfnb.com
Year Founded: 1976
Sales Range: $10-24.9 Million
Bank Holding Company
N.A.I.C.S.: 551111
Terry Bemis *(Exec VP)*
Kyle Powell *(Pres & CEO)*

Subsidiaries:

The First National Bank & Trust Company of Okmulgee   (1)
610 E 8th St, Okmulgee, OK 74447
Tel.: (918) 756-8440
Web Site: http://www.mybankfnb.com
Sales Range: $10-24.9 Million
Emp.: 67
Commericial Banking
N.A.I.C.S.: 522110
Kathy Kennedy *(Sr VP)*
Shawna Thomas *(Sr VP)*
Kyle Powell *(Pres & CEO)*
Gayle Machetta *(VP)*
Judy Stidman *(VP)*
Terry Bemis *(Exec VP)*
Page H. Hayden *(Sr VP)*
Debbie Moudy *(VP)*
Matt Harris *(VP)*

FIRST PACIFIC ADVISORS, LLC

11601 Wilshire Blvd Ste 1200, Los
Angeles, CA 90025
Tel.: (310) 473-0225   DE
Web Site: http://www.fpafunds.com
Year Founded: 1954
Sales Range: $25-49.9 Billion
Emp.: 77
Investment Advisory & Asset Management Services
N.A.I.C.S.: 523940
Robert L. Rodriguez *(Mng Partner)*
Eric S. Ende *(Partner)*
Steven T. Romick *(Mng Partner)*
Thomas H. Atteberry *(Partner)*
Dennis M. Bryan *(Partner)*
Steven R. Geist *(Partner)*
Christopher H. Thomas *(Chief Compliance Officer & VP)*
J. Richard Atwood *(Mng Partner)*
Rikard B. Ekstrand *(Partner)*
Julian W. H. Mann *(VP)*
Ann M. Shigemura-Hildebrand *(VP)*
J. Mark Hancock *(Partner)*
Brande L. Winget *(Sr VP-Client Svc)*
E. Lake Setzler III *(VP & Controller)*

FIRST PALMETTO FINANCIAL CORP.

407 Dekalb St, Camden, SC 29020
Tel.: (803) 432-2265
Web Site:
http://www.firstpalmetto.com
Bank Holding Company
N.A.I.C.S.: 551111

FIRST PARAGOULD BANKSHARES, INC.

200 W Court St, Paragould, AR
72450
Tel.: (870) 239-8521   AR
Web Site: http://www.fnbank.net
Year Founded: 1983
Sales Range: $25-49.9 Million
Emp.: 200
Bank Holding Company
N.A.I.C.S.: 551111

William E. Brewer *(Chm, Pres & CEO)*

Subsidiaries:

First National Bank   (1)
200 W Court St, Paragould, AR 72450
Tel.: (870) 215-4000
Web Site: http://www.fnbank.net
Sales Range: $25-49.9 Million
Commericial Banking
N.A.I.C.S.: 522110
William E. Brewer *(Chm, Pres & CEO)*

FIRST PEOPLES BANKSHARES, INC.

105 Chipley St, Pine Mountain, GA
31822
Tel.: (706) 663-2700   GA
Web Site:
https://www.firstpeoplesbank.com
Year Founded: 1995
Sales Range: $1-9.9 Million
Emp.: 30
Bank Holding Company
N.A.I.C.S.: 551111

Subsidiaries:

First Peoples Bank   (1)
105 Chipley St, Pine Mountain, GA 31822
Tel.: (706) 663-2700
Web Site: http://www.firstpeoplesbank.com
Sales Range: $1-9.9 Million
Commericial Banking
N.A.I.C.S.: 522110
Charles E. Sweat *(Pres & CEO)*
J. Randal McKoon *(CFO & Sr VP)*
Jane J. Lawson *(COO & Sr VP)*
Doug Etheridge *(Chief Lending Officer & Sr VP)*
April Scott *(Asst VP-Loans & Mgr-Ops)*

FIRST PIEDMONT FEDERAL SAVINGS & LOAN ASSOCIATION OF GAFFNEY

1229 W Floyd Baker Blvd, Gaffney,
SC 29341
Tel.: (864) 489-6046   SC
Web Site:
https://www.firstpiedmont.com
Year Founded: 1933
Federal Savings & Loan Bank
N.A.I.C.S.: 522180
Mark Hood *(VP)*

FIRST PIONEER BANK CORP.

145 W 4th St, Wray, CO 80758-1701
Tel.: (970) 332-4824
Web Site: http://www.efpnb.com
Bank Holding Company
N.A.I.C.S.: 551111
Keith E. Waggoner *(Pres & CEO)*

Subsidiaries:

Farmers State Bank of Brush   (1)
200 Clayton St, Brush, CO 80723
Tel.: (970) 842-5101
Web Site: http://www.fsbbrushakron.com
Sales Range: $1-9.9 Million
Emp.: 20
Commericial Banking
N.A.I.C.S.: 522110
Susan V. Coronado *(Officer-Trust)*
Spencer Farnik *(VP)*
Wesley E. Sailsbery *(VP)*
Jaime Stafford *(VP)*
Susan Nelson *(Officer-Loan)*

First Pioneer National Bank   (1)
145 W 4th St, Wray, CO 80758
Tel.: (970) 332-4824
Web Site: http://www.fpnb.bank
Commericial Banking
N.A.I.C.S.: 522110
Keith E. Waggoner *(Pres & CEO)*
Mark A. Valko *(Chief Credit Officer & Exec VP)*

FIRST PULASKI NATIONAL CORPORATION

206 S 1st St, Pulaski, TN 38478

Tel.: (931) 363-2585   TN
Web Site: http://www.fnbforyou.com
Year Founded: 1981
Sales Range: $25-49.9 Million
Emp.: 174
Bank Holding Company
N.A.I.C.S.: 551111
Mark A. Hayes *(Chm & CEO)*
Tracy Porterfield *(CFO)*
Milton Nesbitt *(Officer-Credit)*
Rebecca Graves *(Sr VP & Mgr-Deposit Ops)*

Subsidiaries:

First National Bank of Pulaski   (1)
206 S 1st St, Pulaski, TN 38478
Tel.: (931) 363-2585
Web Site: http://www.fnbforyou.com
Sales Range: $25-49.9 Million
National Commercial Banks
N.A.I.C.S.: 522110
Mark A. Hayes *(Chm & CEO)*
Donald A. Haney *(Pres & COO)*
Tracy Porterfield *(CFO)*
Rebecca Graves *(Sr VP & Mgr-Deposit Ops)*
Lyman Cox *(Officer-Loan & Exec VP)*
Amy Woodard *(Dir-Mkty)*
Cecelia Hargrove *(Dir-Mortgage Loan)*

FIRST QUALITY ENTERPRISES, INC.

80 Cuttermill Rd Ste 500, Great
Neck, NY 11021
Tel.: (516) 829-3030   PA
Web Site: https://www.firstquality.com
Year Founded: 1990
Emp.: 4,000
Holding Company; Adult Incontinence
Products, Disposable Washcloths &
Feminine Hygiene Paper Products
Mfr & Distr
N.A.I.C.S.: 551112
Nader Damaghi *(Chm)*
Aryeh Ciment *(Atty)*

Subsidiaries:

Fempro Inc.   (1)
1330 Rue Michaud, Drummondville, J2C
2Z5, QC, Canada
Tel.: (819) 475-8900
Web Site: https://www.firstquality.com
Feminine Hygiene Products Mfr
N.A.I.C.S.: 322291

First Quality Fibers, LLC   (1)
60 Flexnet Dr, Reedsville, PA 17084
Tel.: (570) 769-6900
Web Site: http://www.firstquality.com
Adult Incontinence Products, Disposable
Washcloths & Feminine Hygiene Paper
Products Mfr
N.A.I.C.S.: 322291

First Quality Products, Inc.   (1)
80 Cuttermill Rd, Great Neck, NY 11021
Tel.: (516) 829-3030
Web Site: http://www.firstquality.com
Sales Range: $350-399.9 Million
Emp.: 5,000
Sanitary Paper Products Distr
N.A.I.C.S.: 424130
Nader Damaghi *(Pres)*

FIRST RATE STAFFING CORPORATION

12150 Bloomfield Ave Unit B, Santa
Fe Springs, CA 90670
Tel.: (562) 863-9564   DE
Web Site: https://www.first-ratestaffing.com
Year Founded: 2010
Sales Range: $25-49.9 Million
Staffing & Recruiting Services
N.A.I.C.S.: 561311
Cliff Blake *(CEO)*
Devon Galpin *(COO)*

FIRST RATE, INC.

1903 Ascension Blvd, Arlington, TX
76006

Tel.: (817) 525-1900   TX
Web Site: http://www.firstrate.com
Year Founded: 1991
Sales Range: $10-24.9 Million
Emp.: 90
Software Developer; Computer Systems Design Services
N.A.I.C.S.: 541512
David A. Stone *(Founder & CEO)*
Craig Wietz *(Pres)*
Terry Gaines *(Mng Dir & Mgr-Bus Dev)*
Curt Graham *(Dir-Products)*
Deborah Repak *(Dir-Products)*
John Watkins *(Dir-Products & Mgr)*
Trina Stone *(CFO)*
Marshall Smith *(COO)*

Subsidiaries:

Vantage Software   (1)
3 Allied Dr Ste 303, Dedham, MA 02026
Tel.: (212) 750-2256
Web Site: http://www.vantage-software.com
Wired Telecommunications Carriers
N.A.I.C.S.: 517111
Daniel Sundin *(CEO)*
Karthik Thanikachalam *(Head-Ops)*

FIRST RESERVE MANAGEMENT, L.P.

290 Harbor Dr, Stamford, CT 06902
Tel.: (203) 661-6601   Ky
Web Site: http://www.firstreserve.com
Year Founded: 1984
Privater Equity Firm
N.A.I.C.S.: 523999
John A. Hill *(Mng Dir)*
Alex Townsend Krueger *(Pres & CEO)*
Jeffrey Quake *(Mng Dir)*
John William Gervase Honeybourne *(Partner & Mng Dir)*
Edward Bialas *(Mng Dir)*
William R. Brown *(Mng Dir & Dir-Houston)*
Gary D. Reaves *(Mng Dir)*
Carolina Sierra *(Dir-Technical)*
Ryan Nicholson *(VP)*
Nick Lednicky *(VP)*
Neil A. Wizel *(Mng Dir)*

Subsidiaries:

9REN Group   (1)
C/ Maria de Molina, 39, Madrid, Spain
Tel.: (34) 915168310
Web Site: http://www.9ren.org
Sales Range: $50-74.9 Million
Emp.: 80
Photovoltaic & Alternative Energy Systems
N.A.I.C.S.: 221118

AFGlobal Corporation   (1)
945 Bunker Hill Rd, Houston, TX 77024
Tel.: (713) 393-4200
Web Site: http://www.afglobalcorp.com
Holding Company; Industrial Hardware & Metal Components Mfr
N.A.I.C.S.: 551112
Curtis Samford *(Pres & CEO)*

Division (Domestic):

AF Gloenco Inc.   (2)
452 Sunapee St, Newport, NH 03773
Tel.: (603) 863-1270
Web Site: http://www.gloenco.com
Emp.: 50
Forged Components & Assemblies Mfr
N.A.I.C.S.: 332999
Rick Thomas *(Pres)*

Unit (Domestic):

AF Gloenco Inc. - Greenville   (3)
299 C Garlington Rd, Greenville, SC 29615
Tel.: (864) 672-1500
Web Site: http://www.gloenco.com
Sales Range: $1-9.9 Million
Emp.: 15
Forged Components & Assemblies Mfr
N.A.I.C.S.: 332999

Subsidiary (Non-US):

Advanced Measurements Inc.   (2)
7110 Fisher Road SE, Calgary, T2H 0W3, AB, Canada
Tel.: (403) 571-7273
Software Development Services
N.A.I.C.S.: 541511

Division (Domestic):

Century Corrosion Technologies, Inc.   (2)
9710 Telge Rd, Houston, TX 77095
Tel.: (281) 858-1000
Web Site: http://www.centurycorrosion.com
Sales Range: $1-9.9 Million
Emp.: 25
Corrosion Control Coating Application Services
N.A.I.C.S.: 332812

Cuming Corporation   (2)
264 Bodwell St, Avon, MA 02322
Tel.: (508) 521-6700
Web Site: http://www.cumingcorp.com
Sales Range: $125-149.9 Million
Foam Buoyancy & Insulation Product Mfr
N.A.I.C.S.: 326150

Subsidiary (Domestic):

Cuming Insulation Corp.   (3)
4401 Curtis Ln, New Iberia, LA 70560
Tel.: (337) 367-8383
Web Site: http://www.cumingcorp.com
Sales Range: $1-9.9 Million
Emp.: 15
Foam Buoyancy & Insulation Product Mfr
N.A.I.C.S.: 326150

Division (Domestic):

NRG Manufacturing, Inc.   (2)
11311 Holderrieth Rd Ste 100, Tomball, TX 77375
Tel.: (281) 320-2525
Web Site: http://www.nrgm.com
Sales Range: $1-9.9 Million
Emp.: 20
Drilling Equipment Mfr
N.A.I.C.S.: 333132
Tom Gable *(Dir-Well Stimulation Engrg)*

Taper-Lok Corp.   (2)
945 Bunker Hill, Houston, TX 77024
Tel.: (713) 467-3333
Web Site: http://www.taper-lok.com
Emp.: 20
Assembly & Connector Mfr
N.A.I.C.S.: 332722
Curtis Samford *(Pres)*

Texas Metal Works   (2)
13770 Industrial Rd, Houston, TX 77015-6821
Tel.: (713) 222-0139
Web Site: http://www.texmet.com
Sales Range: $25-49.9 Million
Emp.: 85
Forged Flange Mfr
N.A.I.C.S.: 332111
Paul Stevens *(Mgr)*

CHC Group Ltd.   (1)
190 Elgin Avenue, Georgetown, KY1-9005, Grand Cayman, Cayman Islands (59.3%)
Web Site: http://www.chc.ca
Helicopter Operator
N.A.I.C.S.: 488190
Paul King *(CIO)*
Duncan Trapp *(VP-Safety & Quality)*
David Balevic *(Interim CEO)*
David Lisabeth *(Sr VP-HR)*
Barry Parsons *(Sr VP-Global Sls)*
Vincent D'Rozario *(Dir-Asia Pacific)*
Brian Bianco *(Sr Mgr-Comm)*
John Gremp *(Chm)*

Subsidiary (Non-US):

CHC Helicopter Corporation   (2)
4740 Agar Drive, Richmond, V7B 1A3, BC, Canada
Tel.: (604) 276-7500
Web Site: https://www.chcheli.com
Sales Range: $1-4.9 Billion
Helicopter Services
N.A.I.C.S.: 481212

Harry F. Quarls *(Chm)*
Scott Thanisch *(CFO & Sr VP)*

Subsidiary (Non-US):

CHC Europe (UK)   (3)
CHC House Howe Moss Drive, Kirkhill Industrial Estate, Aberdeen, AB21 0GL, Scotland, United Kingdom
Tel.: (44) 1224846000
Web Site: http://www.chc.ca
Sales Range: $25-49.9 Million
Helicopter Transportation Provider
N.A.I.C.S.: 481212

CHC Helicopters (Australia)   (3)
45 Greenhill Road, 5034, Wayville, Australia
Tel.: (61) 883727700
Web Site: http://www.chcaustralia.com
Sales Range: $25-49.9 Million
Emp.: 28
Helicopter Transportation Provider
N.A.I.C.S.: 481212

CHC Helicopters, Inc.   (3)
PO Box 2546, 8000, Cape Town, South Africa
Tel.: (27) 219340560
Web Site: http://www.chc.ca
Sales Range: $25-49.9 Million
Emp.: 93
Helicopter Transportation Provider
N.A.I.C.S.: 481212

Division (Domestic):

Heli-One   (3)
4800 80th Street, Delta, V4K 3N3, BC, Canada
Tel.: (604) 952-7700
Web Site: http://www.heli-one.ca
Helicopter Support Services, Including Sales, Leasing, Maintenance & Repair Services
N.A.I.C.S.: 488190
Michael Bell *(Dir-Sls-North America)*

Division (US):

Heli-One Colorado   (4)
655 N State Hwy 161, Irving, TX 75039
Tel.: (970) 492-1000
Web Site: http://www.heli-one.com
Sales Range: $25-49.9 Million
Emp.: 100
Helicopter Service, Repair & Overhaul
N.A.I.C.S.: 488190

Division (Non-US):

Heli-One Europe   (4)
PO Box 204, 4097, Sola, Norway
Tel.: (47) 51941400
Web Site: http://www.heli-one.com
Sales Range: $50-74.9 Million
Helicopter Transportation Provider
N.A.I.C.S.: 481212

Dixie Electric LLC   (1)
6413 N State Hwy 349 Bldg I Ste B, Midland, TX 79705
Tel.: (432) 580-7095
Web Site: http://www.dixielectric.com
Emp.: 750
Oil Field Electrical Infrastructure Construction & Maintenance Services
N.A.I.C.S.: 237130
Jeff Johnson *(CEO)*
Brooke Martin *(Controller)*
David Czarnecki *(COO)*
Chuck Lowrey *(CFO)*

First Reserve International Limited   (1)
25 Victoria St, London, SW1H 0EX, United Kingdom   (100%)
Tel.: (44) 2079302120
Web Site: http://www.firstreserve.com
Sales Range: $25-49.9 Million
Emp.: 15
Privater Equity Firm
N.A.I.C.S.: 523999
Neil J. Hartley *(Mng Dir)*
Claudi Santiago *(Mng Dir)*

First Reserve Management, L.P. - Houston   (1)
600 Travis St Ste 6000, Houston, TX 77002
Tel.: (713) 227-7890
Web Site: http://www.firstreserve.com

Sales Range: $50-74.9 Million
Emp.: 25
Privater Equity Firm
N.A.I.C.S.: 523999
Gary D. Reaves *(Mng Dir)*
Neil A. Wizel *(Mng Dir)*
Jesse Krynak *(Dir-Houston)*
Paul J. Steen *(Mng Dir)*

Hearthstone Utilities, Inc.   (1)
1375 E 9th St Ste 3100, Cleveland, OH 44114
Tel.: (800) 570-5688
Web Site: http://www.huinc.net
Holding Company; Natural Gas Production, Pipeline Transportation & Distribution
N.A.I.C.S.: 551112
Morgan K. O'Brien *(Pres & CEO)*
Curtis Richardson *(Dir-Tech Ops)*
Annmarie Vincent *(Mgr-HR)*

Subsidiary (Domestic):

Bangor Natural Gas Company   (2)
498 Main Ave, Bangor, ME 04401
Tel.: (207) 941-9595
Web Site: http://www.bangorgas.com
Holding Company; Natural Gas Distr
N.A.I.C.S.: 551112

Subsidiary (Domestic):

Bangor Gas Company   (3)
498 Maine Ave, Bangor, ME 04401
Tel.: (207) 941-9595
Web Site: http://www.bangorgas.com
Natural Gas Distr
N.A.I.C.S.: 221210
Jerry E. Livengood *(Pres & Gen Mgr)*
Andrew Barrowman *(Mgr-Mktg & Sls)*

Subsidiary (Domestic):

Energy West Montana, Inc.   (2)
1 1st Ave S, Great Falls, MT 59401
Tel.: (406) 791-7500
Web Site: http://www.ewst.com
Natural Gas Distribution Services
N.A.I.C.S.: 221210
Jed D. Henthorne *(Pres)*
Cheryl A. Johnson *(Coord-Cope Svcs)*
Evan C. Mathews *(Superintendent)*
Mary L. Stanich *(Coord-Contract)*

Subsidiary (Domestic):

Cut Bank Gas Company   (3)
403 E Main St, Cut Bank, MT 59427
Tel.: (406) 873-5531
Natural Gas Distribution Services
N.A.I.C.S.: 221210

Energy West Resources, Inc.   (3)
1 1st Ave S, Great Falls, MT 59401-3633
Tel.: (406) 791-7500
Natural Gas Well Development, Production & Marketing Services
N.A.I.C.S.: 213111

Subsidiary (Domestic):

Frontier Natural Gas Company   (2)
110 PGW Dr, Elkin, NC 28621
Tel.: (336) 526-2690
Web Site: http://www.frontiernaturalgas.com
Holding Company; Natural Gas Distr
N.A.I.C.S.: 551112
Fred Steele *(Gen Mgr)*
John Gosh *(Controller)*
Josh Wagoner *(Ops Mgr)*
Ted Gambill *(Engr)*

Northeast Ohio Natural Gas Corp.   (2)
5640 Lancaster-Newark Rd, Pleasantville, OH 43148
Tel.: (740) 862-3300
Web Site: http://www.neogas.com
Natural Gas Distribution Services
N.A.I.C.S.: 221210

Hoover Ferguson Group, Inc.   (1)
2135 Highway 6 S, Houston, TX 77077-4319   (100%)
Tel.: (770) 664-4047
Web Site: http://www.hooverferguson.com
Holding Company; Industrial Containers Mfr, Sales, Rental & Support Services
N.A.I.C.S.: 551112
Donald W. Young *(Chm & CEO)*
Arash Hassanian *(Sr VP-Sls & Mktg-Global)*

First Reserve Management, L.P.—(Continued)

Chad Vidrine *(VP-Major Accts)*
Jake Rippstein *(VP-Tech)*
Johan Wramsby *(COO)*
Paul Lewis *(Pres)*
Rodney L. Branch *(VP-HR, Health, Safety & Environment)*
Scott T. Meints *(VP-Ops)*
Troy L. Carson *(CFO)*

Unit (Domestic):

Catalyst & Chemical Containers (2)
4935 Timber Creek Dr, Houston, TX 77017
Tel.: (713) 926-3330
Web Site: http://www.ccc-hooverferguson.com
Industrial Chemical Container Mfr & Whslr
N.A.I.C.S.: 332420
John Tribou *(VP & Gen Mgr-USA)*
William Stacy *(Dir-Bus Dev-Global)*

Subsidiary (Non-US):

Ferguson Group Ltd (2)
Ferguson House Midmill Business Park, Aberdeen, AB51 0QG, United Kingdom
Tel.: (44) 1467 626500
Web Site: http://www.hooverferguson.com
Emp.: 60
Offshore Container Whslr
N.A.I.C.S.: 423840
David Mair *(Dir-Sls & Bus Dev)*
Emile Bado *(Reg Mgr-Middle East & North Africa)*
David Mitchell *(Dir-Dir)*

Subsidiary (Non-US):

Ferguson Group Australia Pty Ltd (3)
16 Alacrity Place, Henderson, 6166, WA, Australia
Tel.: (61) 894948200
Web Site: http://www.ferguson-group.com
Emp.: 20
Offshore Container Whslr
N.A.I.C.S.: 423840
Paul Edwards *(Mgr-Ops-Australia)*

Ferguson Group Singapore Pte Ltd (3)
25 Loyang Crescent Loyang Offshore Supply Base Block 103 04-04, Tops Avenue 1, Singapore, 508988, Singapore
Tel.: (65) 6589 0440
Web Site: http://www.ferguson-group.com
Offshore Container Whslr
N.A.I.C.S.: 423840
Simon de Koning *(Gen Mgr)*
Alex Yip *(Mgr-Bus Dev)*
Sam Yap *(Asst Mgr-Ops)*

Ferguson Middle East FZE (3)
JAFZA Views - LOB 18 14th Floor Office 1401, PO Box 17898, Dubai, POE17898, United Arab Emirates
Tel.: (971) 4 899 7300
Web Site: http://www.ferguson-group.com
Emp.: 5
Offshore Container Whslr
N.A.I.C.S.: 423840
Mike Neville *(Gen Mgr)*

Ferguson Norge AS (3)
Platformveien 9, 4056, Tananger, Norway
Tel.: (47) 51 64 79 00
Offshore Container Whslr
N.A.I.C.S.: 423840
Christian Harestad *(Mgr-Bus Dev)*
Helge Qverneland *(Mgr-Bus Dev)*

Subsidiary (Domestic):

Hoover Materials Handling Group, Inc. (2)
2135 Hwy 6 S, Houston, TX 77077-4319
Tel.: (281) 870-8402
Web Site: http://www.hoversolutions.com
Industrial Containers Mfr, Sales, Rental & Support Services
N.A.I.C.S.: 332420
Donald W. Young *(Chm & CEO)*
Paul Lewis *(Pres)*
Joseph S. Levy *(CFO & Sr VP)*
Johan Wramsby *(COO & Sr VP)*
Arash Hassanian *(Sr VP-Sls & Mktg-Global)*
Scott T. Meints *(VP-Ops)*
Rodney L. Branch *(Safety & Environment)*

Jake Rippstein *(VP-Tech)*
Brandon Mack *(VP-Bulk Transportation)*
Jan Sekse *(VP-Procurement-Global)*
Adolpho Aguilera *(VP-Mfg)*

Subsidiary (Non-US):

Container Company (Aberdeen) Ltd. (3)
Lomond House Wellington Circle, Redmoss, Aberdeen, AB12 3JG, United Kingdom
Tel.: (44) 1224 894222
Web Site: http://www.cca-ltd.com
Industrial Container Mfr & Distr
N.A.I.C.S.: 332439
Andy Drummond *(Mng Dir)*
John Dickie *(Ops Mgr)*
Ben Drummond *(Mktg Mgr-UK)*
Mike Beattie *(Mgr-Bus Dev)*
Lynsey Melvin *(Mgr-Health, Safety & Environment)*

Hoover Container Solutions Norway AS (3)
Plattformvegen 9, 4056, Tananger, Norway
Tel.: (47) 51 71 58 80
Web Site: http://www.hoversolutions.no
Industrial Container Sales & Rental Services
N.A.I.C.S.: 423840
Eivind Rosnes *(Mgr-Quality, Health, Safety & Environment)*
Kjetil Skaaren *(Gen Mgr)*
Thomas Sekse *(Sls Mgr)*
Martin Tyldum *(Fin Mgr)*

Hoover Container Solutions Pty. Ltd. (3)
70 Endeavor Way, Sunshine, 3020, VIC, Australia
Tel.: (61) 3 9325 1135
Web Site: http://www.hoversolutions.com
Industrial Container Distr
N.A.I.C.S.: 423840

LineStar Integrity Services LLC (1)
4203 Montrose Blvd, Houston, TX 77006
Tel.: (832) 830-8531
Web Site: http://www.linestar.com
Emp.: 741
Holding Company
N.A.I.C.S.: 551112

Subsidiary (Domestic):

LineStar Services, Inc. (2)
4203 Montrose Blvd, Houston, TX 77006
Tel.: (713) 338-3433
Oil & Gas Infrastructure Integrity, Maintenance & Construction Services
N.A.I.C.S.: 237120

Subsidiary (Domestic):

Tucker Construction Co. (3)
915 SE 4th St, Lindsay, OK 73052
Tel.: (405) 756-3958
Web Site:
http://www.tuckerconstructionco.com
Oil & Gas Pipeline Construction Services
N.A.I.C.S.: 237120

Tucker Midstream, Inc. (3)
11108 W County Rd 46, Midland, TX 79707
Tel.: (432) 683-7074
Web Site:
http://www.tuckerconstructionco.com
Oil & Gas Pipeline & Related Structures Construction
N.A.I.C.S.: 237120

Subsidiary (Domestic):

The Compliance Group, Inc. (2)
14884 Hwy 105 W Ste 100, Montgomery, TX 77356-5248
Tel.: (936) 447-6100
Oil & Gas Regulatory & Environmental Consulting Services
N.A.I.C.S.: 926130

Refuel Operating Company, LLC (1)
1181 Venning Rd, Mount Pleasant, SC 29464
Tel.: (843) 388-4966
Web Site: http://www.refuelmarket.com
Gasoline Stations with Convenience Stores
N.A.I.C.S.: 457110
Mark Jordan *(Pres & CEO)*
Travis Smith *(Chief Admin Officer)*
Jon Rier *(CFO)*

Subsidiary (Domestic):

Refuel, LLC (2)
1181 Vennig Rd, Mount Pleasant, SC 29464
Tel.: (843) 388-4966
Fuel Dealer; Gasoline Stations with Convenience Stores
N.A.I.C.S.: 457110
Mark Jordan *(Pres & CEO)*

Subsidiary (Domestic):

Double Quick Inc. (3)
415 Pershing Ave, Indianola, MS 38751-3150
Tel.: (662) 884-5000
Web Site:
http://www.greshampetroleum.com
Sales Range: $50-74.9 Million
Emp.: 600
Provider of Grocery Store Services
N.A.I.C.S.: 445131
Thomas Gresham *(CEO & Mng Partner)*
Bill McPherson *(Mng Partner)*
Scott Shaffer *(Dir-Ops)*
Alvin Taylor *(Mgr-Bus Intelligence)*

TNT Crane & Rigging, Inc. (1)
925 S Loop W, Houston, TX 77054-4606
Tel.: (713) 644-6113
Web Site: http://www.tntcrane.com
Cranes & Aerial Lift Equipment Rental & Leasing
N.A.I.C.S.: 532412
Deana Haygood *(CFO)*
Alex Murray *(Mgr-Houston)*
Kregg Lunsford *(Pres)*
Jenni Barcenas *(Controller)*
Mark H. Irion *(CEO)*
David E. Fanta *(Chm)*

Subsidiary (Domestic):

RMS Cranes Inc. (2)
1961 E 64th Ave, Denver, CO 80229
Tel.: (303) 794-7095
Web Site: http://www.rmscranes.com
Crane & Rigging Services
N.A.I.C.S.: 333120

Rocky Mountain Structures Inc. (2)
1961 E 64th Ave, Denver, CO 80229
Tel.: (303) 794-7095
Web Site: http://www.rmscranes.com
Emp.: 15
Crane Rental & Leasing
N.A.I.C.S.: 532412
Cody Gilliland *(CEO)*

Branch (Domestic):

TNT Crane & Rigging, Inc. (2)
578 Good Hope St, Norco, LA 70079
Tel.: (985) 764-6551
Web Site: http://www.tntcrane.com
Crane Rental Services
N.A.I.C.S.: 532412
Ken Wenning *(Gen Mgr)*

TNT Crane & Rigging, Inc. - Oklahoma City (2)
8020 SW 74th St, Oklahoma City, OK 73169
Tel.: (405) 745-2318
Web Site: http://www.tntcrane.com
Cranes, Aerial Lift & Forestry Machinery Equipment Rental & Leasing
N.A.I.C.S.: 532412
Nathan Huffman *(Branch Mgr)*

TPC Group Inc. (1)
500 Dallas St Ste 1000, Houston, TX 77002
Tel.: (713) 627-7474
Web Site: http://www.tpcgrp.com
Emp.: 525
Petrochemical Mfr
N.A.I.C.S.: 325110
Charles W. Graham *(Sr VP-Comml)*
Ed Dineen *(Chm & CEO)*
Courtney Ruth *(VP-Reliability & Capital Project Mgmt)*
Peter Dumoulin *(Sr VP-HR)*
Dan Valenzuela *(CFO & VP)*
Patrick Hurt *(Gen Counsel & VP)*
Adrian Jacobsen *(VP-Corp Dev-Fuels & Strategic Raw Materials)*
Dona Burke *(VP-Supply Chain)*

Subsidiary (Domestic):

Port Neches Fuels, LLC (2)

2102 Spur 136, Port Neches, TX 77651
Tel.: (713) 627-7474
Web Site: http://www.tpcgrp.com
Petrochemical Mfr
N.A.I.C.S.: 325110
Ed Dineen *(CEO)*

Texas Butylene Chemical Corporation (2)
3524 Cities Service Highway, Westlake, LA 70669
Tel.: (337) 882-1380
Web Site: http://www.tbcgroup.com
Emp.: 3
Petrochemical Mfr
N.A.I.C.S.: 325110

Tri-Point Oil & Gas Production Systems, LLC (1)
1800 Augusta Dr Ste 220, Houston, TX 77057-3164
Tel.: (713) 600-9400
Web Site: http://www.tri-pointllc.com
Holding Company; Oil & Gas Products & Services
N.A.I.C.S.: 551112
Britt O. Schmidt *(Co-Founder & CEO)*
J. David Lucke *(Co-Founder & CFO)*
Steve Russom *(VP-Integration)*

Subsidiary (Domestic):

Leed Fabrication Services, LLC (2)
12505 County Rd 2, Brighton, CO 80603
Tel.: (303) 659-6801
Web Site: http://www.leedfab.com
Well Head Production & Ancillary Equipment Mfr
N.A.I.C.S.: 332999

Streamline Production Systems, Inc. (2)
13604 Hwy 69, Village Mills, TX 77663
Tel.: (409) 834-6096
Web Site: http://www.streamlinetexas.com
Oil & Gas Operating Services
N.A.I.C.S.: 213112

Superior Fabrication, Inc. (2)
801 S Eastern Ave, Elk City, OK 73644
Tel.: (580) 243-5693
Web Site: http://www.superiorfab.com
Oil & Natural Gas Production Equipment Mfr
N.A.I.C.S.: 333132
Terry Morse *(Founder, Pres & CEO)*
Randy Morse *(COO & Ops Mgr)*
Jimmie Don Newberry *(Plant Mgr-Elk City South)*
Tony Landreth *(Shop Mgr-Elk City South)*
Debbie Thomas *(Supvr-Warehouse-Elk City South)*

Subsidiary (Domestic):

Casinjac, Inc. (3)
1703 S Main St, Elk City, OK 73644
Tel.: (580) 821-2369
Web Site: http://www.casinjac.com
Oil & Gas Industry Casing Jack Mfr, Refurbishment & Maintenance Services
N.A.I.C.S.: 333132
Joe Cansler *(Gen Mgr)*

Unit (Domestic):

SFI Energy (3)
PO Box 790, Sentinel, OK 73664
Tel.: (580) 393-4314
Web Site: http://www.supres.net
Emp.: 15
Oil & Natural Gas Real Estate Brokerage Services
N.A.I.C.S.: 531210
Kelly Smith *(Mgr)*
Amanda Hamblin *(Office Mgr)*

SFI Superior Implements (3)
1920 A St, Ada, OK 74820
Tel.: (580) 332-9300
Web Site: http://www.sfiimplements.com
Scrapers, Blades & Other Industrial Machinery Attachments Mfr
N.A.I.C.S.: 333112
Dan Marshall *(Plant Mgr)*
Bruce Andrews *(Project Mgr)*

Subsidiary (Domestic):

Superior Trucking Services (3)

2019 US Hwy 283, Sayre, OK 73662
Tel.: (580) 928-5693
Web Site:
      http://www.superiortruckingservice.com
Oil & Gas Industry Trucking & Lifting Ser-
vices
N.A.I.C.S.: 484230
Chuck Parham (Ops Mgr)
April Howell (Office Mgr)
Sam Moore (Mgr-Safety & Sls)

West Oil Company Inc.   (1)
712 N 5th St, Hartsville, SC 29550
Tel.: (843) 332-2201
Web Site: http://www.westoilco.com
Sales Range: $25-49.9 Million
Emp.: 300
Provider of Petroleum Products
N.A.I.C.S.: 424720
Alexander West (Owner)

FIRST RESIDENTIAL MORT-
GAGE SERVICES CORP.

570 Sylvan Ave, Englewood Cliffs, NJ
07632-3101
Tel.: (201) 861-0531
Web Site:
      http://www.firstresmortgage.com
Rev.: $11,385,451
Emp.: 45
Mortgage Bankers & Loan Corre-
spondents
N.A.I.C.S.: 522310
Arelis Olivieri-Collado (VP-Sls)
Matt Schofield (Mgr-Sls)

FIRST RESOURCE BANK

Tel.: (610) 363-9400   PA
Web Site:
      https://www.firstresourcebank.com
Year Founded: 2005
FRSB—(OTCIQ)
Rev.: $15,402,479
Assets: $336,418,925
Liabilities: $308,441,568
Net Worth: $27,977,357
Earnings: $2,321,768
Emp.: 50
Fiscal Year-end: 12/31/19
Banking Services
N.A.I.C.S.: 522110
Pamela Finkbiner (Asst VP)
James B. Griffin (Chm & Pres)
Lauren C. Ranalli (Pres, Pres, CFO &
CFO)
Glenn B. Marshall (Vice Chm & CEO)
Natalie M. Carrozza (COO, Chief
Risk Officer & Exec VP)
Lisa A. Donnon (Chief Lending Offi-
cer, Chief Credit Officer & Exec VP)
Bridget M. Moran (COO, Exec VP &
Sr VP-Retail Banking)
Lee Herzer (Chief Lending Officer,
Exec VP & VP-Comml Lending)
Joe DiTommaso (VP, Branch Mgr &
Mgr-Customer Svc)
Kristen Fries (CFO & Exec VP)
Brian S. Jackson (CIO & Exec VP)
Jennifer MacMullen (Chief Retail
Banking Officer & Exec VP)
Kenneth R. Kramer (Chief Credit Offi-
cer & Exec VP)
John A. Durso Jr. (Sr VP-Deposit
Strategies)

FIRST RUSHMORE BANCOR-
PORATION, INC.

1433 Oxford St, Worthington, MN
56187
Tel.: (507) 376-9747
Web Site:
      https://www.firststatebanksw.com
Year Founded: 1993
Sales Range: $10-24.9 Million
Emp.: 87
Bank Holding Company
N.A.I.C.S.: 551111

Subsidiaries:

First State Bank Southwest   (1)
1433 Oxford St, Worthington, MN 56187
Tel.: (507) 376-9747
Commercial Banking
N.A.I.C.S.: 522110
Greg Raymo (Chm, Pres & CEO)

FIRST SAVINGS BANK

201 N 3rd St, Beresford, SD 57004-
0431
Tel.: (605) 763-2009
Web Site:
      https://www.firstsavingsbanks.bank
Year Founded: 1913
Sales Range: $25-49.9 Million
Emp.: 25
Banking Services
N.A.I.C.S.: 522180
Robin Graf (VP-Compliance)

Subsidiaries:

First Savings Bank FSB   (1)
201 N 3rd St, Beresford, SD 57004
Tel.: (605) 763-2009
Web Site: http://www.firstsavingsbank.com
Rev.: $5,298,000
Emp.: 20
National Commercial Banks
N.A.I.C.S.: 522110
Morgan Larson (CEO)

FIRST SAVINGS BANK OF
HEGEWISCH

13220 S Baltimore Ave, Chicago, IL
60633
Tel.: (773) 646-4200   IL
Web Site:
      https://www.fsbhegewisch.com
Year Founded: 1914
Federal Savings Bank
N.A.I.C.S.: 522110
Therese Gorny (VP & CFO)
Thomas Backofen (Pres & CEO)

FIRST SAVINGS BANK
PERKASIE

219 S 9th St, Perkasie, PA 18944
Tel.: (215) 257-5035
Web Site:
      http://www.firstSavingsOnline.com
Sales Range: $25-49.9 Million
Emp.: 16
Federal Savings & Loan Associations
N.A.I.C.S.: 522180
Eric Brunner (VP & Dir-Mktg)

FIRST SAVINGS MORTGAGE
CORP.

8444 Westpark Dr 4th Fl, McLean,
VA 22102
Tel.: (703) 883-9010
Web Site:
      https://www.firstsavingsmort
      gage.com
Sales Range: $10-24.9 Million
Emp.: 140
Mortgage Banker
N.A.I.C.S.: 522310
Larry F. Pratt (CEO)
John Petraglia (Sr VP-Secondary
Mktg)
David Alden (COO & Sr VP)

FIRST SECURITY BANCORP

314 N Spring St, Searcy, AR 72143
Tel.: (501) 279-3400   AR
Web Site: http://www.fsbancorp.com
Year Founded: 1980
Emp.: 900
Bank Holding Company
N.A.I.C.S.: 551111

Subsidiaries:

Crews & Associates Incorporated   (1)
521 President Clinton Ave Ste 800, Little
Rock, AR 72201

Tel.: (501) 907-2000
Web Site: http://www.crewsfs.com
Rev.: $21,715,436
Emp.: 100
Investment Services
N.A.I.C.S.: 523150
D. Henry Blevins (Mng Dir)
Allen McKay (Sr VP)

First Security Bank   (1)
314 N Spring St, Searcy, AR 72143-7703
Tel.: (501) 279-3400
Web Site: http://www.fsbank.com
Sales Range: $50-74.9 Million
Emp.: 85
Commercial Banking Services
N.A.I.C.S.: 522110
Frank Faust (Pres-Trust & Wealth Mgmt)
John McPike (Sr VP-Jonesboro)

FIRST SECURITY BANK-
SHARES INC.

12461 Augusta Rd, Lavonia, GA
30553
Tel.: (706) 356-4444
Web Site:
      https://www.northeastgabank.com
Year Founded: 1906
Sales Range: $10-24.9 Million
Emp.: 32
Bank Holding Company
N.A.I.C.S.: 551111
Richard A. Basinger (Pres)

Subsidiaries:

Northeast Georgia Bank   (1)
12461 Augusta Rd, Lavonia, GA 30553
Tel.: (706) 356-4444
Web Site: http://www.northeastgabank.com
Sales Range: $10-24.9 Million
Emp.: 30
State Commercial Banks
N.A.I.C.S.: 522110
John C. Seay (Pres & CEO)
Richard A. Basinger (Exec VP)

FIRST SEED FARMS INC.

5950 Berkshire Ln #1460, Dallas, TX
75225
Tel.: (214) 679-5115
Web Site:
      http://www.firstseedfarms.com
Hemp Genetics Mfr
N.A.I.C.S.: 424590
Trey Weidner (Pres)

Subsidiaries:

OrgHarvest, Inc.   (1)
774 Mays Blvd 10-536, Incline Village, NV
89451
Tel.: (310) 460-8426
Web Site: http://www.orgharvest.us
Biotechnology Research & Development
Services
N.A.I.C.S.: 541714
Carlos Calixto (COO)
J. Larry Cantrell (Pres & CEO)

FIRST SERVE HOSPITALITY
GROUP

326 Rte 1, Kittery, ME 03904
Tel.: (207) 439-0300
Hospitality Management Services
N.A.I.C.S.: 721110
Shiva Natarajan (Dir)

FIRST SERVICE CREDIT
UNION

9621 W Sam Houston Pkwy N, Hous-
ton, TX 77064
Tel.: (713) 676-7777   TX
Web Site: http://www.fscu.com
Year Founded: 1977
Sales Range: $25-49.9 Million
Emp.: 176
Credit Union
N.A.I.C.S.: 522130
J. David Bleazard (Pres & CEO)
Jana Heaton (CFO)

Frank Halstead (CIO)
Kourtney Calhoun (Treas)
Janet Hill (Vice Chm)

FIRST SERVICE NETWORKS,
INC.

12002 E Shea Blvd Ste 2, Scottsdale,
AZ 85259
Tel.: (480) 614-4552
Web Site:
      http://www.firstservicenetworks.com
Sales Range: $10-24.9 Million
Emp.: 100
Facilities Maintenance & Repair Ser-
vices
N.A.I.C.S.: 561210
Michael Ferreira (Pres)
Mark McEneaney (CFO)
Russell Joyner (VP-IT)
Rick Watts (VP-Ops)
Georgette Proestakis (VP-HR)

FIRST SERVICE REALTY INC.

13155 SW 42nd St Ste 200, Miami,
FL 33175-3440
Tel.: (305) 551-9400
Web Site: http://www.fsr-gmac.com
Year Founded: 1994
Sales Range: $750-799.9 Million
Emp.: 350
Real Estate Services
N.A.I.C.S.: 531210
Raul Gonzalez (VP)
Renate Smith (Gen Mgr)
Suzy Corona (Mgr-Miami Lakes)
Robin Payan (Dir-Pro Dev)
Michael Ruane (Mgr)

FIRST SHORE FEDERAL SAV-
INGS & LOAN ASSOCIATION

106 S Division St, Salisbury, MD
21801
Tel.: (410) 546-1101
Web Site:
      http://www.firstshorefederal.com
Sales Range: $25-49.9 Million
Emp.: 75
Federal Savings & Loan Associations
N.A.I.C.S.: 522180
Catherine A. M. Tyson (Chm)
Martin T. Neat (Pres & CEO)
W. Thomas Hershey (Vice Chm)

FIRST SLEEPY EYE BANCOR-
PORATION, INC.

625 S Minnesota Ave Ste 202, Sioux
Falls, SD 57101
Tel.: (605) 335-1508   MN
Web Site:
      http://www.firstsecuritybanks.com
Year Founded: 1974
Bank Holding Company
N.A.I.C.S.: 551111
Lloyd Amundson (Owner, Pres &
CEO)

Subsidiaries:

First Security Bank - Canby   (1)
102 Saint Olaf Ave N, Canby, MN 56220
Tel.: (507) 223-7231
Web Site: http://www.firstsecuritybanks.com
Sales Range: $1-9.9 Million
Emp.: 14
Commercial Banking Services
N.A.I.C.S.: 522110
Mark Greenway (Pres)
Lenae Deslauriers (VP)

First Security Bank - Sleepy Eye   (1)
100 E Main St, Sleepy Eye, MN 56085
Tel.: (507) 794-3911
Web Site: http://www.firstsecuritybanks.com
Emp.: 11
Commercial Banking
N.A.I.C.S.: 522110
Thomas Goetz (Pres)

FIRST SONORA

FIRST SONORA —(CONTINUED)

BANCSHARES, INC.
102 E Main St, Sonora, TX 76950
Tel.: (325) 387-3861
Web Site:
http://www.sonorabank.com
Sales Range: $10-24.9 Million
Emp.: 83
Bank Holding Company
N.A.I.C.S.: 551111
Robert A. Malone (Exec Chm, Pres & CEO)
Kyle Barton (CFO)
Patrick Holt (COO & Exec VP)
Mike Schultz (COO-Bank & Exec VP)
Laura Whitley (Sr VP-Admin)

Subsidiaries:

The First National Bank of
Sonora   (1)
102 N Main St, Sonora, TX 76950
Tel.: (325) 387-3861
Web Site: http://www.sonorabank.com
Sales Range: $10-24.9 Million
Commericial Banking
N.A.I.C.S.: 522110
Robert A. Malone (Exec Chm, Pres & CEO)
Kyle Barton (CFO)
Mike Schultz (COO & Exec VP)

FIRST SOUTH FARM CREDIT
Three Paragon Ctr Ste 100 574 Highland Colony Pkwy, Ridgeland, MS 39157
Tel.: (601) 977-8381
Web Site:
http://www.firstsouthfarmcredit.com
Sales Range: $25-49.9 Million
Emp.: 225
Agricultural Credit Services
N.A.I.C.S.: 522299

FIRST SOUTH FINANCIAL CREDIT UNION
6471 Stage Rd, Bartlett, TN 38134
Tel.: (901) 380-7400   **TN**
Web Site: https://www.firstsouth.com
Year Founded: 1957
Sales Range: $25-49.9 Million
Emp.: 126
Financial Services
N.A.I.C.S.: 522320
George Lumm (CFO)
Tammy Craig (CIO)
Diane Williamson (COO & Exec VP)
W. Craig Esrael (Pres & CEO)
Summers Townsend (Sr VP-Branch Ops)

FIRST SOUTHERN BANCORP, INC.
102 W Main St, Stanford, KY 40484
Tel.: (606) 365-2137   **KY**
Web Site: https://www.fsnb.net
Year Founded: 1987
Sales Range: $25-49.9 Million
Emp.: 300
Bank Holding Company
N.A.I.C.S.: 551111
Jesse Thomas Correll (Chm & Pres)

Subsidiaries:

First Southern National Bank   (1)
102 W Main St, Stanford, KY 40484
Tel.: (606) 365-2137
Web Site: http://www.fsnb.net
Sales Range: $25-49.9 Million
Emp.: 43
Retail & Commercial Banking Services
N.A.I.C.S.: 522110
Jesse Thomas Correll (Chm, Pres & CEO)

FIRST SOUTHWEST CORPORATION
100 S Broadway St, McComb, MS 39648
Tel.: (601) 684-2231   **MS**

Web Site:
http://www.firstbankms.com
Year Founded: 1895
Sales Range: $10-24.9 Million
Emp.: 35
Bank Holding Company
N.A.I.C.S.: 551111

Subsidiaries:

First Bank   (1)
100 S Broadway St, McComb, MS 39648
Tel.: (601) 684-2231
Web Site: http://www.firstbankms.com
State Commercial Banks
N.A.I.C.S.: 522110
James W. Covington (Chm, Pres & CEO)
Casey Graham (CFO)
Jonathan Taylor (Chief Credit Officer & Exec VP)
Richard C. Dodd (Sr VP)
Brenda Marsalis (Sr VP)
Vickie M. Webb (Sr VP)
Curtis Butler (Sr VP)
Brad Whitaker (Sr VP)
Daniel Stewart (Sr VP)
John M. Shappley (Pres & COO)

FIRST STATE BANCORP, INC.
100 W 3rd St, Caruthersville, MO 63830
Tel.: (573) 333-1700   **MO**
Web Site: http://www.fsbtrust.com
Year Founded: 1982
Sales Range: $10-24.9 Million
Emp.: 112
Bank Holding Company
N.A.I.C.S.: 551111
Duane S. Michie (Chm)

Subsidiaries:

First State Bank & Trust Company, Inc.   (1)
100 W 3rd St, Caruthersville, MO 63830
Tel.: (573) 333-1700
Web Site: http://www.fsbtrust.com
Rev.: $14,947,000
Assets: $341,809,000
Liabilities: $305,542,000
Net Worth: $36,267,000
Earnings: $3,161,000
Fiscal Year-end: 12/31/2012
Commericial Banking
N.A.I.C.S.: 522110
Duane S. Michie (Chm)
Lance Crawford (COO & Exec VP)
Matthew Drake (Pres & CEO)
Sara Patterson (CFO, Officer-Trust & Exec VP)
Zachary Fayette (Pres-North Market)

FIRST STATE BANCORPORATION, INC.
9000 N Knoxville Ave, Peoria, IL 61615
Tel.: (309) 966-4850   **IL**
Web Site:
http://www.bankfortress.com
Sales Range: $10-24.9 Million
Emp.: 91
Bank Holding Company
N.A.I.C.S.: 551111
Andrew J. Bastert (Pres-Illinois)
Mike Bavery (Sr VP-Lending-Illinois)
Dean A. Heinzmann (Exec VP)
Lee H. Garlach (Chm)
Barbara Duryea (CFO & COO)
Troy Mccrery (Sr VP-Retail Banking Div-First State Bank of Illinois)
Blair Callaway (Officer-Investment & VP)
Keith Worner (Asst VP & Mgr-Relationship)

Subsidiaries:

Fortress Bank   (1)
9000 N Knoxville Ave, Peoria, IL 61615
Tel.: (309) 966-4850
Web Site: http://www.bankfortress.com

Sales Range: $10-24.9 Million
Savings Bank
N.A.I.C.S.: 522180
Andrew J. Bastert (Pres-Western Illinois Reg)
Michael T. Bavery (Sr VP-Lending)
Barbara Duryea (CFO & COO)
Lee H. Garlach (Chm)
John Bradley (Sr VP)
Troy McCrery (Sr VP & Dir-Sls & Dev)
Tracy McDowell (Controller)

FIRST STATE BANCSHARES INC.
113 W N Water St, New London, WI 54961
Tel.: (920) 982-3300
Web Site:
http://www.bankfirststate.com
Sales Range: $10-24.9 Million
Emp.: 100
Bank Holding Company
N.A.I.C.S.: 551111
Robert Van Asten (Pres & CEO)

Subsidiaries:

First State Bank   (1)
113 W N Water St, New London, WI 54961
Tel.: (920) 982-3300
Web Site: http://www.bankfirststate.com
Rev.: $10,000,000
State Commercial Banks
N.A.I.C.S.: 522110
Harry Radix (CEO)

FIRST STATE BANCSHARES INC.
201 E Columbia St, Farmington, MO 63640
Tel.: (573) 756-4547
Web Site: http://www.fscb.com
Sales Range: $75-99.9 Million
Emp.: 350
Bank Holding Company
N.A.I.C.S.: 551111
Carol Rigdon (VP)
Greg Allen (Pres & CEO)
Keith Wade (CFO)

Subsidiaries:

First State Community Bank   (1)
201 E Columbia St, Farmington, MO 63640
Tel.: (573) 756-4547
Web Site: http://www.fscb.com
Sales Range: $50-74.9 Million
Emp.: 60
State Commercial Banks
N.A.I.C.S.: 522110
Matt Sebastian (Pres)
Andy Buchanan (VP)

FIRST STATE BANCSHARES, INC.
2002 Broadway, Scottsbluff, NE 69361
Tel.: (308) 632-4158   **NE**
Year Founded: 1978
Sales Range: $10-24.9 Million
Emp.: 74
Bank Holding Company
N.A.I.C.S.: 551111
Ron Van Voast (Pres/CEO-Security First Bank)
Michael W. Downey (Pres-First State Bank)
Marvin Hefti (Chm, Pres & CEO)

Subsidiaries:

First State Bank   (1)
2002 Broadway, Scottsbluff, NE 69361
Tel.: (308) 632-4158
Web Site: http://www.fsbcentral.com
Sales Range: $10-24.9 Million
Emp.: 51
Commericial Banking
N.A.I.C.S.: 522110
Michael W. Downey (Pres)
Marvin Hefti (Chm & CEO)
Crystal Nielsen (CFO & VP)
Richard L. Tuggle (COO & Exec VP)

Brad Bode (VP-Bus Dev)
Ernest Charles (Mgr-IT)
Donna Clifton (Asst VP)
Kathy Herron (Asst VP-Loan Admin)
Cheryl Hinojosa (Asst VP & Mgr-Data Processing)
Martin Mickey (Asst VP-Loans)
Randall A. Olson (Sr VP-Loans)
Paula Schlaepfer (Asst VP-Ops)

Security First Bank   (1)
500 W 18th St, Cheyenne, WY 82001
Tel.: (307) 775-6500
Web Site: http://www.sec1stbank.com
Sales Range: $1-9.9 Million
Emp.: 23
Commericial Banking
N.A.I.C.S.: 522110

FIRST STATE BANK INC.
302 N Main St, Stratford, TX 79084
Tel.: (806) 396-5521
Web Site:
https://www.firstclassbanking.com
Year Founded: 1948
State Commercial Banks
N.A.I.C.S.: 522110
Suzanne Ashley (VP-Bank Svc Mgr)
Adam Bell (Asst VP & Mgr-IT)
Cindy Larance (VP-New Accts & Mortgage Originator)

FIRST STATE BANK OF BLOOMINGTON
204 N Prospect Rd, Bloomington, IL 61704
Tel.: (309) 662-0411
Web Site: http://www.fsbblm.com
Rev.: $4,313,000
Emp.: 16
Savings Institutions
N.A.I.C.S.: 522180
Michael Atwood (CFO)
Randy W. Bruenger (VP)
Jennifer Doran (Officer-Trust & VP)
Laura Kinney (VP-Compliance & Risk Mgmt)
Matt Lauritzen (VP)
Heather Mariotti (VP-Retail Banking)
Anne Matalonis (VP-Mktg & Dev)

Subsidiaries:

First State Bank of Bloomington - Heyworth   (1)
117 E Main St, Heyworth, IL 61745-7647
Tel.: (309) 473-2828
Web Site: http://www.fsbblm.com
Commercial Banking Services
N.A.I.C.S.: 522110

FIRST STATE BANK OF THE FLORIDA KEYS
1201 Simonton St, Key West, FL 33040
Tel.: (305) 296-8535
Web Site: https://www.keysbank.com
Sales Range: $10-24.9 Million
Emp.: 130
State Commercial Banks
N.A.I.C.S.: 522110
Karen Sharp (Pres)
Rose G. Johnson (Coord-Credit)
William Estenoz (VP)

FIRST STATE BANK OF UVALDE
200 E Nopal St, Uvalde, TX 78801-5336
Tel.: (830) 278-6231   **TX**
Web Site: http://www.fsbuvalde.com
Year Founded: 1907
Sales Range: $25-49.9 Million
Emp.: 78
Commericial Banking
N.A.I.C.S.: 522110
Dickie Geries (CEO)
Daniel L. Dietert (VP)
Greg A. Visel (Exec VP)

FIRST STATE CHEVROLET, INC.
300 S Dupont Hwy, Georgetown, DE 19947
Tel.: (302) 856-2521
Web Site:
http://www.firststatechevy.com
Sales Range: $10-24.9 Million
Emp.: 32
Automobiles, New & Used
N.A.I.C.S.: 441110
Bob Hansen (Co-Owner)
Richard Paugh (Mgr-Collision Center)
Bill Hansen (Gen Mgr)
Penuel Barrett (Mgr-Used Car)

FIRST STATE CORP.
708 Azalea Dr, Waynesboro, MS 39367
Tel.: (601) 735-3124
Web Site:
http://www.firststatebnk.com
Sales Range: $10-24.9 Million
Emp.: 130
State Commercial Banks
N.A.I.C.S.: 522110
Joel C. Clements (Chm/Pres/CEO-First State Bank)
Alan Hodoe (CFO)
Jeffrey B. Lacey (COO-First State Bank)

FIRST STATE FINANCIAL CORP.
24300 Little Mack St, Saint Clair Shores, MI 48080
Tel.: (586) 775-5000   MI
Web Site: http://www.thefsb.com
Year Founded: 1979
Sales Range: $50-74.9 Million
Emp.: 185
State Commercial Banks
N.A.I.C.S.: 522110
Eugene Lovell (Chm & Pres)

Subsidiaries:

First State Bank of East Detroit Inc.   (1)
24300 Little Mack Ave, Saint Clair Shores, MI 48080-3249
Tel.: (586) 775-5000
Web Site: http://www.thefsb.com
Rev.: $34,020,000
Emp.: 95
Banking Services
N.A.I.C.S.: 522110

FIRST STATE HOLDING CO.
5617 Thompson Creek Blvd Ste 1, Lincoln, NE 68516
Tel.: (402) 421-3535   NE
Web Site: http://www.1fsb.com
Year Founded: 1976
Sales Range: $10-24.9 Million
Emp.: 112
Bank Holding Company
N.A.I.C.S.: 551111
Thomas G. Damkroger (Pres & CEO)

Subsidiaries:

First State Bank Nebraska   (1)
4915 Old Cheney Rd, Lincoln, NE 68516
Tel.: (402) 420-5200
Web Site: http://www.1fsb.com
Sales Range: $10-24.9 Million
Emp.: 14
Commercial Banking
N.A.I.C.S.: 522110
Tom Oerter (CFO)
Thomas G. Damkroger (Chm)
Jerry L. Lentfer (Pres & CEO)
Jeff Kanger (Exec VP)

FIRST STEP, INC.
407 Carson St, Hot Springs, AR 71901
Tel.: (501) 624-6468   AR

Web Site:
https://www.firststeparkansas.com
Year Founded: 1985
Sales Range: $25-49.9 Million
Emp.: 1,380
Disability Assistance Services
N.A.I.C.S.: 624120
Pamela Bland (Exec Dir)

FIRST STERLING CORPORATION
1650 Broadway Ste 1212, New York, NY 10019-6833
Tel.: (212) 759-6620
Rev.: $15,000,000
Emp.: 5
Commercial Real Estate
N.A.I.C.S.: 531120
Faith Golding (Chm)
Ira Krauss (Pres)
Terry Havel (VP)

FIRST SUN MANAGEMENT CORPORATION
977 Tiger Blvd, Clemson, SC 29631-1419
Tel.: (864) 654-7493   SC
Web Site:
http://www.wendysfsmc.com
Year Founded: 1989
Sales Range: $50-74.9 Million
Emp.: 2,000
Fast-Food Restaurant Franchise Owner
N.A.I.C.S.: 722513
Kelly Durham (Pres)
Rob McGinn (VP-Ops)
Joseph J. Turner Jr. (Chm & CEO)

FIRST SUPPLY LLC
PO Box 1028, La Crosse, WI 54602-1028
Tel.: (608) 784-3839   WI
Web Site: http://www.1supply.com
Year Founded: 1897
Sales Range: $25-49.9 Million
Emp.: 750
Plumbing Fixtures, Equipment & Supplies
N.A.I.C.S.: 423720
Mike Hickok (Exec VP)
Joe Poehling (CEO)
James Poehling (Dir-Engrg)
Stefana Pretasky (Mgr-Showroom)
Dan Mansfield (Mgr-Sls & Mktg-Fluid Handling)
Judy Kimble (Mgr-Product & Mktg-Kitchen & Bath Stores)
Linda Maremont (Dir-HR)
Paul Kennedy (Pres)
Diane Pankonin (Dir-Fin)
Kathryn Poehling Seymour (COO-Kitchen & Bath Stores)

Subsidiaries:

First Supply   (1)
2100 W College Ave, Appleton, WI 54914-4607   (100%)
Tel.: (920) 739-3136
Web Site: http://www.1supply.com
Sales Range: $10-24.9 Million
Emp.: 40
Whslr of Plumbing Fixtures, Equipment & Supplies
N.A.I.C.S.: 423720
Todd Restel (CFO)

First Supply Group Inc.   (1)
6800 Gisholt Dr, Madison, WI 53713-4803
Tel.: (608) 222-7799
Web Site: http://www.1supply.com
Rev.: $26,600,000
Emp.: 125
Metals Service Centers & Offices
N.A.I.C.S.: 423720
Mike Hickok (VP & COO)

First Supply LLC - Eau Claire   (1)

596 Cameron St, Eau Claire, WI 54703-4723
Tel.: (715) 832-6638
Web Site: http://www.1supply.com
Sales Range: $10-24.9 Million
Emp.: 65
Warm Air Heating & Air Conditioning Distr
N.A.I.C.S.: 423720
Brian Heidtke (Gen Mgr)

First Supply Milwaukee Inc.   (1)
7550 S 6th St, Oak Creek, WI 53154-2018
Tel.: (414) 764-6900
Web Site: http://www.1supply.com
Rev.: $12,800,000
Emp.: 45
Plumbing Fixtures, Equipment & Supplies
N.A.I.C.S.: 423720
Tom Bruce (Branch Mgr)

La Crosse Plumbing Supply Co. Inc.   (1)
106 Cameron Ave, La Crosse, WI 54601-4420   (100%)
Tel.: (608) 784-3839
Web Site: http://www.1supply.com
Sales Range: $25-49.9 Million
Emp.: 75
Plumbing Fixtures, Equipment & Supplies
N.A.I.C.S.: 423720

Rochester Supply Corporation   (1)
3815 Hwy 14 W, Rochester, MN 55901-5911   (100%)
Tel.: (507) 287-0202
Rev.: $12,700,000
Emp.: 50
Warm Air Heating & Air Conditioning
N.A.I.C.S.: 423730

FIRST SURGICAL PARTNERS INC.
411 1st St, Bellaire, TX 77401
Tel.: (713) 665-1111   DE
Web Site:
http://www.firstsurgical.com
Year Founded: 1998
Sales Range: $50-74.9 Million
Emp.: 150
Holding Company; Ambulatory Surgery Centers Owner & Operator
N.A.I.C.S.: 551112
Jacob Varon (Chm)
Anthony F. Rotondo (Pres & CEO)
Don Knight (CFO, Principal Acctg Officer & VP-Fin)

FIRST TEAM REAL ESTATE-ORANGE COUNTY INC.
108 Pacifica Ave, Ste 300, Irvine, CA 92618
Tel.: (949) 539-0824
Web Site: http://www.firstteam.com
Year Founded: 1976
Sales Range: $10-24.9 Million
Emp.: 300
Real Estate Agents & Managers
N.A.I.C.S.: 531210
Cameron Merage (Founder & CEO)

Subsidiaries:

Coast Cities Escrow Inc.   (1)
108 Pacifica Ste 250, Irvine, CA 92618
Tel.: (949) 988-3050
Web Site: http://www.coastcitiesescrow.com
Sales Range: Less than $1 Million
Emp.: 4
Real Estate Agents & Managers
N.A.I.C.S.: 531210
Debi Peters (Mgr-Applications)
Lori Lane (Asst Gen Mgr)

First Team Real Estate-Orange County Inc. - First Team Commercial Division   (1)
25212 Marguerite Pkwy Ste 200, Mission Viejo, CA 92692-2929
Tel.: (949) 458-1033
Web Site: http://www.firstteam.com
Emp.: 150
Real Estate Management Services
N.A.I.C.S.: 531390
Dutch Kleindienst (Mgr)

Hallmark Escrow Co., Inc.   (1)
108 Pacifica Ste 250, Irvine, CA 92618
Tel.: (949) 988-3050
Web Site: http://www.HallmarkEscrow.com
Escrow Services
N.A.I.C.S.: 531390
Dee Anna Pope (Sr VP & Gen Mgr)
Lori Lane (Asst Gen Mgr)
Debi Peters (Mgr-Escrow Applications)

Western Resources Title Co   (1)
625 The City Dr Ste 150, Orange, CA 92868
Tel.: (714) 748-7000
Web Site:
http://www.WesternResourcesTitle.com
Escrow Services
N.A.I.C.S.: 531390
Craig Beukelman (VP & Mgr-Territory Dev)
Damon Parker (VP & Mgr-Sls-San Diego)
Ed Lorette (CEO)
Janik Hopkins (Acct Exec)
Jared Rau (Acct Exec)
Martha Flores (VP & Mgr-State Escrow Ops)
Nancy Fletcher (Officer-Operating & Exec VP)

FIRST TECHNOLOGY CAPITAL, INC.
3080 Troy Pike, Versailles, KY 40383
Tel.: (859) 873-9905
Web Site: http://www.ftc-us.com
Year Founded: 1990
Retailer of Refurbished Banking Equipment; Business Continuity Services
N.A.I.C.S.: 532420
James L. Bates (Founder & Owner)
Rita Carpenter (Coord-Ops)

FIRST TEK, INC.
1551 S Washington Ave Ste 402 A, Piscataway, NJ 08854
Tel.: (732) 745-0700
Web Site: http://www.first-tek.com
Year Founded: 2001
Sales Range: $10-24.9 Million
Emp.: 250
Information Technology & Communications Solutions & Services
N.A.I.C.S.: 561499
Satyakumar Bhavanasi (CEO)

Subsidiaries:

Cenergy International Services, LLC   (1)
12650 Crossroads Park Dr, Houston, TX 77065
Tel.: (713) 965-6200
Web Site: http://www.cenergyintl.com
Sales Range: $150-199.9 Million
Emp.: 913
Staffing & Consulting Services
N.A.I.C.S.: 561320
June Ressler (Founder & CEO)
Jim Picou (Pres)
Michael A. Ferrier (Gen Counsel)

FIRST TENNESSEE HUMAN RESOURCE AGENCY
704 Rolling Hills Dr, Johnson City, TN 37604
Tel.: (423) 461-8200   TN
Web Site: https://www.fthra.org
Year Founded: 1974
Sales Range: $10-24.9 Million
Emp.: 333
Human Resource Consulting Services
N.A.I.C.S.: 541612

FIRST TEXAS BANCORP, INC.
900 S Austin Ave, Georgetown, TX 78626
Tel.: (512) 863-2594
Year Founded: 1971
Sales Range: $25-49.9 Million
Emp.: 250
Bank Holding Company

First Texas Bancorp, Inc.—(Continued)

N.A.I.C.S.: 551111
Barry J. Haag *(Pres-Bank)*
John A. Kirkpatrick *(Pres)*
Gary L. Nelon *(Chm)*
John Patrick *(Pres)*

Subsidiaries:

First Texas Bank　　　　　　　(1)
900 S Austin Ave, Georgetown, TX
78626-0649　　　　　　　　(100%)
Tel.: (512) 863-2567
Web Site: http://www.firsttexasbank.net
Sales Range: $50-74.9 Million
Emp.: 100
Commercial Banking Services
N.A.I.C.S.: 522110
Van P. Swift *(Pres & CEO)*
Sandy Arnold *(Sr VP-Lending)*
Janice Heath *(Sr VP-Lending)*
Kelly Long *(Sr VP-HR)*
Janelle McNeill *(Sr VP-Compliance)*
Karen Domel *(Officer-Banking)*
David Edgar *(Officer-Banking)*
Sara Edwards *(Officer-Banking)*
Melissa Lindemann *(Officer-Banking)*
Gilbert Moreno *(Officer-Banking)*

FIRST TEXAS HOMES INC.

500 Crescent Ct Ste 350, Dallas, TX
75201
Tel.: (214) 613-3400　　　TX
Web Site:
　https://www.firsttexashomes.com
Year Founded: 1985
Sales Range: $10-24.9 Million
Emp.: 50
Provider of Housing Construction
Services
N.A.I.C.S.: 236115
Randall Van Wolfwinkel *(Pres)*
Keith Hardesty *(VP-Construction)*
Christy Murday *(Controller)*

FIRST TITLE ABSTRACT & SERVICES, LLC

7666 E 61st St Ste 230, Tulsa, OK
74133
Tel.: (918) 250-1641　　　OK
Web Site: http://www.firstitle.com
Year Founded: 1984
Sales Range: $1-9.9 Million
Emp.: 48
Title Insurance
N.A.I.C.S.: 524210
Thomas Kivell *(CEO)*

Subsidiaries:

Allegiance Title Company　　　(1)
6030 Sherry Ln, Dallas, TX 75225-6401
Tel.: (214) 373-3500
Web Site: http://www.allegiancetitle.com
Insurance Related Activities
N.A.I.C.S.: 524298
Smith Devoss *(Atty)*
Diana Lansing *(Sr VP)*

FIRST TRINITY FINANCIAL CORPORATION

7633 E 63rd Pl Ste 230, Tulsa, OK
74133-1246
Tel.: (918) 249-2438　　　OK
Web Site:
　https://www.firsttrinityfinancial.com
Rev.: $65,559,099
Assets: $665,864,037
Liabilities: $614,211,525
Net Worth: $51,652,512
Earnings: $6,184,703
Emp.: 18
Fiscal Year-end: 12/31/22
Financial Holding Company
N.A.I.C.S.: 551112
Gregg E. Zahn *(Founder, Chm, Pres & CEO)*
Jeffrey J. Wood *(CFO)*
Alvin Begnoche *(VP-Mktg)*

Porter Horgan *(VP & Dir-Mortgage Ops)*
Michael McArthur *(VP & Controller)*

Subsidiaries:

Family Benefit Life Insurance
Company　　　　　　　　(1)
7633 E 63rd Pl Ste 230, Tulsa, OK 74133
Tel.: (918) 249-2438
Web Site: https://familybenefitlife.com
Direct Life Insurance Services
N.A.I.C.S.: 524113
Gregg E. Zahn *(Chm, Pres & CEO)*
Alvin Begnoche *(VP-Mktg)*

FIRST TRUST PORTFOLIOS L.P.

120 E Liberty Dr Ste 400, Wheaton,
IL 60187
Tel.: (630) 765-8000　　　IL
Web Site:
　https://www.ftportfolios.com
Year Founded: 1991
Investment Fund Management & Advisory Services
N.A.I.C.S.: 523940
Mark R. Bradley *(CFO & COO)*

Subsidiaries:

First Trust Advisors L.P.　　　(1)
120 E Liberty Dr Ste 400, Wheaton, IL 60187
Tel.: (630) 765-8000
Web Site: http://www.ftportfolios.com
Investment Advisory Services
N.A.I.C.S.: 523940
Jim Dykas *(CFO & COO)*

First Trust Energy Infrastructure
Fund　　　　　　　　　(1)
120 E Liberty Dr Ste 400, Wheaton, IL 60187
Tel.: (630) 765-8798
Web Site: http://www.ftportfolios.com
Sales Range: $10-24.9 Million
Closed-End Investment Fund
N.A.I.C.S.: 525990
James Allen Bowen *(Chm)*

First Trust MLP and Energy Income
Fund　　　　　　　　　(1)
120 E Liberty, Lisle, IL 60532
Tel.: (630) 765-8000
Web Site: http://www.ftportfolios.com
Sales Range: $10-24.9 Million
Closed-End Investment Fund
N.A.I.C.S.: 525990
Daniel J. Lindquist *(VP)*

FIRST UNION FINANCIAL CORP.

102 W McCloy St, Monticello, AR
71655
Tel.: (870) 367-3453
Sales Range: $10-24.9 Million
Emp.: 12
State Commercial Banks
N.A.I.C.S.: 522110
Dave Dickson *(Pres)*

Subsidiaries:

Union Bank & Trust Company　(1)
102 W McCloy St, Monticello, AR 71655
Tel.: (870) 367-3453
Web Site: http://www.unionbnk.com
Rev.: $10,972,705
Emp.: 43
State Commercial Banks
N.A.I.C.S.: 522110
Sandra Wright *(VP)*
Mark Tiner *(VP)*
Dave Dickson *(Pres)*

FIRST VANDALIA CORP.

432 W Gallatin St, Vandalia, IL 62471
Tel.: (618) 283-1141　　　DE
Web Site: http://www.thefnb.com
Year Founded: 1984
Sales Range: $10-24.9 Million
Bank Holding Company
N.A.I.C.S.: 551111

Michael R. Radliff *(Pres)*

Subsidiaries:

The FNB Community Bank　　(1)
432 W Gallatin St, Vandalia, IL 62471
Tel.: (618) 283-1141
Web Site: http://www.thefnb.com
Sales Range: $10-24.9 Million
Emp.: 83
National Commercial Banks
N.A.I.C.S.: 522110
Steve Henna *(Chief Lending Officer)*
Chris Barth *(Officer-Loan)*
Dusty Bauer *(Officer-Residential & Comml Loan)*
Jennifer Lay *(Officer-Consumer & Residential Loan)*
Joe Schaal *(Officer-Comml Loan)*
Steve Hickerson *(Officer-Residential & Comml Loan)*
Sarah Phelps *(Officer-Consumer & Residential Loan)*
Steve Lay *(Officer-Comml Loan)*
Ty McNary *(Officer-Comml Loan)*

FIRST VOLUNTEER CORPORATION

728 Broad St, Chattanooga, TN
37402
Tel.: (423) 266-7000　　　TN
Web Site:
　http://www.firstvolunteer.com
Sales Range: $10-24.9 Million
Emp.: 315
Bank Holding Company
N.A.I.C.S.: 551111
Robert R. Anderson *(Chm)*
Patti W. Steele *(Pres & CEO)*
Frank Perez *(CFO)*

Subsidiaries:

First Volunteer Bank　　　　(1)
728 Broad St, Chattanooga, TN 37402
Tel.: (423) 668-4600
Web Site: http://www.firstvolunteerbank.com
Emp.: 220
Short-Term Business Credit Institutions, Except Agricultural
N.A.I.C.S.: 522299
Patti W. Steele *(Pres & CEO)*

FIRST WASHINGTON REALTY INC.

7200 Wisconsin Ave Ste 600,
Bethesda, MD 20814
Tel.: (301) 907-7800
Web Site: https://www.firstwash.com
Emp.: 100
Financial Services
N.A.I.C.S.: 523999
Daniel J. Radek *(Pres)*

Subsidiaries:

Donahue Schriber Realty Group,
Inc.　　　　　　　　　(1)
200 E Baker St Ste 100, Costa Mesa, CA 92626
Tel.: (714) 545-1400
Web Site: http://www.donahueschriber.com
Sales Range: $75-99.9 Million
Emp.: 110
Real Estate Investment Trust Services
N.A.I.C.S.: 531120
Mark L. Whitfield *(Exec VP-Investments)*
Lisa L. Hirose *(Chief Admin Officer & Exec VP)*
Suzanne Douglass *(Chief People Officer & VP)*
Michael Glimcher *(Chm, Pres & CEO)*
Kevin Halleran *(CFO & Exec VP)*
Doreen Woods *(Dir-Corp Svcs, Branding & Community Outreach)*

FIRST WATERLOO BANCSHARES, INC.

228 S Main, Waterloo, IL 62298
Tel.: (618) 939-6194
Web Site:
　http://www.fnbwaterloo.com
Bank Holding Company
N.A.I.C.S.: 551111

Gary D. Hemmen *(Pres & CEO)*

Subsidiaries:

First National Bank Waterloo　(1)
228 S Main St, Waterloo, IL 62298
Tel.: (618) 939-6194
Web Site: http://www.fnbwaterloo.com
Sales Range: $25-49.9 Million
Emp.: 75
Fiscal Year-end: 12/30/2014
Provider of Banking Services
N.A.I.C.S.: 522110
Gary D. Hemmen *(Pres & CEO)*
Glen E. Lutz *(Sr VP-Loan Lending & Mgr-North Banking)*
Wilbur J. Meyer *(VP)*
Dan Spickard *(VP)*
Russ Thomas *(VP)*

FIRST WAVE MARINE INC.

2102 Broadway St, Houston, TX
77012
Tel.: (713) 847-4600
Rev.: $80,000,000
Emp.: 18
Shipbuilding & Repairing
N.A.I.C.S.: 336611
Grady Walker *(Pres)*

FIRST WESTERN BANCSHARES INC.

80 W Main St, Booneville, AR 72927
Tel.: (479) 675-3000
Web Site: http://www.fwbank.com
Year Founded: 1910
State Commercial Banks
N.A.I.C.S.: 522110

FIRST WESTERN BANK & TRUST

900 S Broadway, Minot, ND 58701
Tel.: (701) 852-3711
Web Site:
　http://www.bankfirstwestern.com
Sales Range: $50-74.9 Million
Emp.: 75
Bank & Lending Institution
N.A.I.C.S.: 522110
J. H. Hoeven *(Chm)*
Bob Mongeon *(VP-Comml Lending)*
Brenda Foster *(Pres & CEO)*
Chris Lamoureux *(Exec VP)*
Tom Larson *(VP-Agricultural Lending)*
JoAnn Holtz *(Sr VP)*
Kevin Bohl *(VP-Comml Lending)*
Chad Johnson *(Pres-Loan Production Office-Bismarck)*
Becky Dolley *(Officer-Credit Review)*
Becky Elder *(Officer-Ops Support)*
Fred Beuchler *(Chief Lending Officer & Sr VP)*
Jersey Benson *(VP-Comml Lending)*
Pam Degele *(VP-Mortgage Lending)*
Tim Mihalick *(Sr VP-Bus Dev & Facilities)*
Kristi Bertsch *(VP-Insurance Placement & Bonds)*
Jim Paszek *(Chief Risk Officer, Sr VP & Mgr-Trust Dept)*
Brent Matts *(Sr VP-First Western Insurance)*

Subsidiaries:

Advance Acceptance
Corporation　　　　　　(1)
100 Prairie Ctr Dr, Eden Prairie, MN 55344
Tel.: (952) 516-7320
Web Site: http://www.advacc.com
Sales Range: $25-49.9 Million
Emp.: 35
Machinery & Equipment Finance Leasing
N.A.I.C.S.: 522299
Fred Kuhnen *(CEO)*

State Bank of Lismore　　　　(1)
190 S 3rd St, Lismore, MN 56155
Tel.: (507) 472-8221
Web Site:
　http://www.statebankoflismore.com

Sales Range: $1-9.9 Million
Emp.: 8
Commericial Banking
N.A.I.C.S.: 522110
Gary Loosbrock (VP)
Mark Loosbrock (Pres)
Troy Loosbrock (VP)

FIRST WORLD IMPORTS, INC.
4100 N Powerline Rd Ste J1, Pompano Beach, FL 33073
Tel.: (954) 972-5864
Web Site:
https://firstworldimports.com
Sales Range: $10-24.9 Million
Emp.: 17
Grocery Product Whslr
N.A.I.C.S.: 424490
Wayne Barrios (Pres)

FIRST YORK BAN CORP.
529 Lincoln Ave, York, NE 68467
Tel.: (402) 363-7411   NE
Web Site:
https://www.cornerstonecon
nect.com
Year Founded: 1973
Sales Range: $50-74.9 Million
Emp.: 408
Bank Holding Company
N.A.I.C.S.: 551111
C. G. Kelly Holthus (Chm & CEO)

Subsidiaries:

Cornerstone Bank   (1)
529 Lincoln Ave, York, NE 68467
Tel.: (402) 363-7411
Web Site:
http://www.cornerstoneconnect.com
Sales Range: $50-74.9 Million
Commericial Banking
N.A.I.C.S.: 522110
Kristie Holthus Holoch (Pres & CEO)
Russ A. Henning (VP & Branch Mgr-Murray)

FIRST-CHOICE HOME CARE, INC.
11 Middle Neck Rd Ste 212, Great Neck, NY 11021
Tel.: (516) 487-8484   NY
Web Site:
http://www.firstchoicehomecare.com
Year Founded: 1992
Sales Range: $1-9.9 Million
Emp.: 150
Women Healthcare Services
N.A.I.C.S.: 621610
Violette Copelman (Pres)

FIRSTBANC OF ALABAMA, INC.
120 N St E, Talladega, AL 35160
Tel.: (256) 362-2334
Web Site: http://www.firstbankal.com
Bank Holding Company
N.A.I.C.S.: 551111
Chad Jones (Pres & CEO)

Subsidiaries:

First Bank of Alabama   (1)
120 N St E, Talladega, AL 35160
Tel.: (256) 362-2334
Web Site: http://www.firstbankal.com
Commericial Banking Services
N.A.I.C.S.: 522110
Chad Jones (Pres & CEO)

Subsidiary (Domestic):

SouthFirst Bank   (2)
126 N Norton Ave, Sylacauga, AL 35150
Tel.: (256) 245-4365
Web Site: http://www.southfirst.com
Sales Range: $100-124.9 Million
Emp.: 30
Banking Services
N.A.I.C.S.: 522180
Randall L. Fields (Pres & CEO)
Allen Gray McMillan III (Chm)
H. David Foote Jr. (Vice Chm)

Subsidiary (Domestic):

SouthFirst Mortgage, Inc.   (3)
2159 Rocky Rdg Rd, Birmingham, AL 35216
Tel.: (205) 979-8776
Web Site: http://www.southfirst.com
Mortgage Services
N.A.I.C.S.: 522310
Linda Taylor (Pres)

FIRSTBANK HOLDING COMPANY OF COLORADO, INC.
12345 W Colfax Ave, Lakewood, CO 80215
Tel.: (303) 232-3000
Web Site: http://www.efirstbank.com
Year Founded: 1963
Sales Range: $200-249.9 Million
Emp.: 2,000
Holding Company
N.A.I.C.S.: 522180
Brian Jensen (Sr VP-Mktg)
John Ikard (CEO)
Dawn Davis (Pres-North)
Nicole Staudinger (Pres-Northern Colorado)
Brian Ballard (Pres-West)
Cleve Wortham (Pres-Denver)
Jeffrey Miller (VP-Phoenix)
R. J. Gildea (Sr VP-West Valley)
Aimee Hamilton (Chief Risk Officer)
Calvin Dunning (Sr VP & Dir-Community Dev)

Subsidiaries:

First Bank of Arapahoe County   (1)
8600 E Arapahoe Rd, Englewood, CO 80112-1403
Tel.: (303) 347-9000
Rev.: $3,100,000
Emp.: 7
Provider of Banking Services
N.A.I.C.S.: 522110
Theresa Smith (Gen Mgr)

First Bank of Cherry Creek   (1)
100 St Paul St Ste 100, Denver, CO 80206-5107
Tel.: (303) 333-1000
Web Site: http://www.efirstbank.com
Sales Range: $25-49.9 Million
Emp.: 22
Non-Federally Chartered Savings Institution
N.A.I.C.S.: 522180

First Bank of Littleton, Inc.   (1)
101 W County Line Rd, Littleton, CO 80129-1900
Tel.: (303) 798-3000
Web Site: http://www.efirstbank.com
Sales Range: $25-49.9 Million
Emp.: 30
Non-Federally Chartered Savings Institution
N.A.I.C.S.: 522180
Andrew Hancock (Pres)

Firstbank Data Corporation   (1)
12345 W Colfax Ave, Lakewood, CO 80215-3742
Tel.: (303) 232-3000
Web Site: http://www.efirstbank.com
Sales Range: $25-49.9 Million
Emp.: 900
Data Processing & Preparation
N.A.I.C.S.: 518210
John Ikard (Pres & CEO)

Firstbank North   (1)
8800 Wadsworth Blvd, Westminster, CO 80021
Tel.: (303) 467-1000
Web Site: http://www.efirstbank.com
Sales Range: $25-49.9 Million
Emp.: 30
Banking Institute
N.A.I.C.S.: 522180
Dawn Davis (Pres)

Firstbank at Wadsworth/Cole Mine, Inc.   (1)
6701 S Wadsworth Blvd, Littleton, CO 80123
Tel.: (303) 973-7000
Web Site: http://www.firstbank.com

Sales Range: $25-49.9 Million
Emp.: 15
Non-Federally Chartered Savings Institution
N.A.I.C.S.: 522180

Firstbank of Arvada, Inc.   (1)
6355 Ward Rd, Arvada, CO 80004-3821
Tel.: (303) 422-3000
Web Site: http://www.efirstbank.com
Sales Range: $25-49.9 Million
Emp.: 36
Non-Federally Chartered Savings Institution
N.A.I.C.S.: 522180
Jodi Thomas (Pres)
Frankie Cole (Sr VP)

Firstbank of Aurora, Inc.   (1)
2300 S Havana St, Aurora, CO 80014-1610
Tel.: (303) 337-2000
Web Site: http://www.efirstbank.com
Sales Range: $25-49.9 Million
Emp.: 35
Non-Federally Chartered Savings Institution
N.A.I.C.S.: 522180
David Mittan (Pres)

Firstbank of Avon, Inc.   (1)
0011 W Beaver Creek Blvd, Avon, CO 81620
Tel.: (970) 949-0100
Web Site: http://www.efirstbank.com
Sales Range: $25-49.9 Million
Emp.: 40
State Commercial Banks
N.A.I.C.S.: 522110
Ellen Moritz (Pres)

Firstbank of Boulder, Inc.   (1)
6500 Lookout Rd, Boulder, CO 80301-3383
Tel.: (303) 530-1000
Web Site: http://www.efirstbank.com
Sales Range: $25-49.9 Million
Emp.: 10
Chain of Savings Institutions Without Federal Charters
N.A.I.C.S.: 522180
Brian Larson (Reg Pres)
Kevin Coasson (Pres)

Firstbank of Colorado, Inc.   (1)
10403 W Colfax Ave, Denver, CO   (100%)
80215-3811
Tel.: (303) 232-2000
Web Site: http://www.efirstbank.com
Sales Range: $50-74.9 Million
Emp.: 91
Chain of National Commercial Banks
N.A.I.C.S.: 522110
Koger Propst (Pres)
Kevin Classen (Pres)
Brian Jensen (VP-Mktg)

Firstbank of Douglas County   (1)
2 Plum Creek Pkwy, Castle Rock, CO 80104-2667
Tel.: (303) 688-5000
Web Site: http://www.efirstbank.com
Sales Range: $25-49.9 Million
Emp.: 25
Chain of Savings Institutions Without Federal Charters
N.A.I.C.S.: 522180
Wes King (Pres)

Firstbank of Erie, Inc.   (1)
512 Briggs St, Erie, CO 80516
Tel.: (303) 828-3393
Web Site: http://www.efirstbank.com
Sales Range: $25-49.9 Million
Emp.: 4
Chain of State Commercial Banks
N.A.I.C.S.: 522110
Bruce Robins (Pres)

Firstbank of Lakewood, Inc.   (1)
1940 S Kipling Pkwy, Lakewood, CO 80227-2079
Tel.: (303) 987-1000
Web Site: http://www.efirstbank.com
Sales Range: $25-49.9 Million
Emp.: 20
Non-Federally Chartered Savings Institution
N.A.I.C.S.: 522180
Tony Oum (Mgr)

Firstbank of Longmont, Inc.   (1)
1707 N Main St, Longmont, CO 80501-7407
Tel.: (303) 772-5500
Web Site: http://www.efirstbank.com

Sales Range: $25-49.9 Million
Emp.: 51
Non-Federally Chartered Savings Institution
N.A.I.C.S.: 522180

Firstbank of Northern Colorado, Inc.   (1)
1013 E Harmony Rd, Fort Collins, CO 80525-3354
Tel.: (970) 223-4000
Web Site: http://www.efirstbank.com
Sales Range: $25-49.9 Million
Emp.: 200
Provider of Banking Services
N.A.I.C.S.: 522180
Nicole Staudinger (Pres)

Firstbank of South Jeffco, Inc.   (1)
5125 S Kipling St, Littleton, CO 80127-1711
Tel.: (303) 988-2000
Web Site: http://www.efirstbank.com
Sales Range: $25-49.9 Million
Emp.: 35
State Commercial Banks
N.A.I.C.S.: 522110
Tony Antista (Pres)

Firstbank of Summit County   (1)
160 US Hwy 6, Silverthorne, CO 80498
Tel.: (970) 468-8000
Web Site: http://www.efirstbank.com
Sales Range: $25-49.9 Million
Emp.: 34
Non-Federally Chartered Savings Institution
N.A.I.C.S.: 522180
Jeff Campeau (Pres)

Firstbank of Tech Center, Inc.   (1)
5105 S Denver Tech Ctr Pkwy, Greenwood Village, CO 80111-2610
Tel.: (303) 694-1000
Web Site: http://www.efirstbank.com
Sales Range: $25-49.9 Million
Emp.: 35
Non-Federally Chartered Savings Institution
N.A.I.C.S.: 522180
Dave Fisher (Pres)

Firstbank of Vail, Inc.   (1)
17 Vail Rd, Vail, CO 81657-5708
Tel.: (970) 476-5686
Web Site: http://www.efirstbank.com
Sales Range: $25-49.9 Million
Emp.: 30
Chain of State Commercial Banks
N.A.I.C.S.: 522110
Taul Wible (CFO)

Firstbank of Wheat Ridge, Inc.   (1)
4350 Wadsworth Blvd, Wheat Ridge, CO 80033-4641   (100%)
Tel.: (303) 423-1400
Web Site: http://www.efirstbank.com
Sales Range: $25-49.9 Million
Emp.: 55
Chain of Non-Federally Chartered Savings Institutions
N.A.I.C.S.: 522180

Firstbank, Hampden & Yosemite   (1)
8901 E Hampden Ave, Denver, CO 80231-4932
Tel.: (303) 337-5400
Web Site: http://www.efirstbank.com
Sales Range: $50-74.9 Million
Emp.: 20
Non-Federally Chartered Savings Institution
N.A.I.C.S.: 522110
Dave Baker (COO)

Firstbank, Republic Plaza Branch   (1)
370 17th St, Denver, CO 80202
Tel.: (303) 623-2000
Web Site: http://www.efirstbank.com
Non-Federally Chartered Savings Institution
N.A.I.C.S.: 522180
Ron Tilton (Pres)

FIRSTEXPRESS
1135 Freightliner Dr, Nashville, TN 37210-2213
Tel.: (615) 244-1425
Web Site:
http://www.firstexpress.com
Sales Range: $25-49.9 Million
Emp.: 226

FirstExpress—(Continued)

Long-Distance & Truckload Freight
Trucking Services
N.A.I.C.S.: 484121
William Keith (Chm)
Bo Keith (Pres)
Jeff Lillard (Dir-Ops)
Sonny Petty (Dir-Safety)
Kitty Demant (Dir-Maintenance)
Adam Dillon (Mgr-Dispatch)

FIRSTFED BANCORP, INC.
1630 4th Ave N, Bessemer, AL 35020
Tel.: (205) 428-8472   DE
Web Site:
https://www.ffbalabama.com
Year Founded: 1936
Sales Range: $10-24.9 Million
Bank Holding Company
N.A.I.C.S.: 551111
Kyle Goodwin (CFO & Exec VP)
Neil Walker (Sr VP)

Subsidiaries:

First Financial Bank   (1)
1630 4th Ave N, Bessemer, AL 35020
Tel.: (205) 428-8472
Sales Range: $50-74.9 Million
Emp.: 95
Banking Services
N.A.I.C.S.: 521110
B. K. Goodwin III (Pres, CEO & Chm)
Jamie Anderson (CFO)
John Gavigan (Chief Admin Officer)
Bill Harrod (Chief Credit Officer)
Anthony M. Stollings (Chief Banking Officer)
Karen Woods (Gen Counsel)
Archie M. Brown Jr. (Pres & CEO)

FIRSTFLEET INC.
202 Heritage Park Dr, Murfreesboro,
TN 37129-1556
Tel.: (615) 890-9229
Web Site:
https://www.firstfleetinc.com
Year Founded: 1986
Sales Range: $25-49.9 Million
Emp.: 850
Trucking Service
N.A.I.C.S.: 484121
Gary Wilson (Pres)
Adam Bond (Mgr-Sys)
Mike Francis (Mgr-Recruiting)
Bronson Laney (Mgr)
Jim Skaare (Mgr-Safety)
Jill Speight (Mgr-Customer Svc)
Shellie Williams (Mgr-Compliance)
Dave Sivils (Dir-IT)
Mark McKnight (Controller)
Mike Murphy (Dir-Maintenance)

FIRSTHAND CAPITAL MANAGEMENT, INC.
150 Almaden Blvd Ste 1250, San
Jose, CA 95113
Tel.: (408) 886-7096   CA
Web Site:
https://www.firsthandcapital.com
Year Founded: 1998
Investment Advisory & Asset Management Services
N.A.I.C.S.: 523940
Kevin Michael Landis (Founder, Pres
& Chief Investment Officer)

Subsidiaries:

Firsthand Technology Value Fund,
Inc.   (1)
150 Almaden Blvd Ste 1250, San Jose, CA
95113
Tel.: (408) 886-7096
Web Site: https://www.firsthandtvf.com
Rev.: $122,631
Assets: $8,808,354
Liabilities: $7,547,983
Net Worth: $1,260,371
Earnings: ($29,349,220)
Emp.: 1

Fiscal Year-end: 12/31/2023
Closed-End Venture Capital Investment
Fund
N.A.I.C.S.: 525990
Kevin Michael Landis (Chm, Pres, CEO,
CFO & Chief Investment Officer)
Kelvin Karfun Leung (Gen Counsel)
Phil Mosakowski (VP-Bus Dev)
Greg Sheppard (Dir-Res)

Holding (Domestic):

IntraOp Medical Corp.   (2)
570 Del Rey Ave, Sunnyvale, CA 94085
Tel.: (408) 636-1020
Web Site: http://www.intraop.com
Sales Range: $1-9.9 Million
Emp.: 21
Electromedical & Electrotherapeutic Apparatus Mfr
N.A.I.C.S.: 334510
Kevin Michael Landis (CEO)
Donald Goer (Pres & CEO)
Oliver Janssen (CFO)
Richard Belford (VP-Regulatory Affairs)

Wrightspeed, Inc.   (2)
650 W Tower Ave, Alameda, CA 94501
Web Site: http://www.wrightspeed.com
Electric Automotive Power Train Systems
Developer, Mfr & Whslr
N.A.I.C.S.: 336350
Kevin Michael Landis (CEO)
Ian Wright (Founder)
Tim Dummer (Chief Bus Officer)
Kevin Landis (Chm)
Suzy Taherian (CFO)
Chris Gross (VP-Mfg)
Ann Lee-Blythe (VP-Supply Chain)
Derek Richards (Dir-Testing & Validation)
Gilbert Passin (CEO & COO)

FIRSTHEALTH OF THE CAROLINAS, INC.
155 Memorial Dr, Pinehurst, NC
28374
Tel.: (910) 715-1000   NC
Web Site: https://www.firsthealth.org
Year Founded: 1995
Health Care Srvices
N.A.I.C.S.: 813910
Lynn S. DeJaco (CFO)
Brian T. Canfield (COO-Moore Reg
Hospital)
Mickey W. Foster (CEO)
John F. Krahnert Jr. (Chief Medical
Officer)

Subsidiaries:

FirstHealth Moore Regional
Hospital   (1)
155 Memorial Dr, Pinehurst, NC 28374
Tel.: (910) 715-1000
Web Site: http://www.firsthealth.org
Hospital Operator
N.A.I.C.S.: 622110
Brian T. Canfield (COO)

FIRSTMARK CREDIT UNION
PO Box 701650, San Antonio, TX
78270-1650
Tel.: (210) 342-8484   TX
Web Site: http://www.firstmarkcu.org
Year Founded: 1932
Rev.: $59,524,335
Assets: $1,025,180,631
Liabilities: $924,471,915
Net Worth: $100,708,716
Earnings: $7,214,245
Emp.: 391
Fiscal Year-end: 12/31/18
Credit Union
N.A.I.C.S.: 522130
Donald Pinson (Chm)
Rudy Pena (Vice Chm)
Nathanael Tarwasokono (Pres &
CEO)
Ignacio Orozco (Sec)
Matthew Ralph (Treas)
Marisa Perez-Diaz (Exec Dir-
Firstmark Foundation)

FIRSTPERRYTON BANCORP, INC.
201 S Main St, Perryton, TX 79070
Tel.: (806) 435-3676   TX
Web Site: http://www.fbsw.com
Year Founded: 1983
Bank Holding Company
N.A.I.C.S.: 551111
Andy Marshall (Pres/CEO-FirstBank
Southwest)

Subsidiaries:

FirstBank Southwest   (1)
2401 S Georgia St, Amarillo, TX 79109
Tel.: (806) 355-9661
Web Site: http://www.fbsw.com
Sales Range: $50-74.9 Million
Emp.: 197
Commericial Banking
N.A.I.C.S.: 522110
Jerry D. Williams (CFO, COO & Exec VP)
Debora K. Cowan (Exec VP & Controller)
Dennis W. Falk (Sr VP)
Brady R. Yeary (Pres-Perryton Market)
Marty R. Murry (Exec VP)
Kevin L. Kuehler (Sr VP & Mgr-Retail Banking)
Nicole Staumper (Pres-Northern)
Wendy L. Curry (Chief Compliance Officer
& Exec VP)
Annette Asencio (Sr VP, BSA Officer & Ops
Mgr-Bank)
Andy Marshall (Pres & CEO)
Will C. Miller (Chief Lending Officer & Pres-
Amarillo Market)
Lance E. Purcell (Gen Counsel, Exec VP &
Sr Trust Officer)
Mike D. Schueler (Pres-Hereford Market)
Kelly McDonald (Sr VP & Dir-HR)

FIRSTRADE SECURITIES, INC.
30-50 Whitestone Expwy Ste A301,
Flushing, NY 11354
Tel.: (718) 961-6600   NY
Web Site: http://www.firstrade.com
Year Founded: 1985
Sales Range: $1-9.9 Million
Emp.: 50
Online Stocks, Options, Mutual Funds
& Exchange Traded Funds (EFTs)
N.A.I.C.S.: 523150
John Liu (Chm)
Andy Yeung (Pres & CEO)

FIRSTRUST BANK
15 E Ridge Pike, Conshohocken, PA
19428
Tel.: (610) 238-5000   PA
Web Site: https://www.firstrust.com
Year Founded: 1934
Sales Range: $100-124.9 Million
Emp.: 350
Financial Institution; Banking Services
N.A.I.C.S.: 522180
Richard J. Green (Chm & CEO)
Timothy J. Abell (Pres)
Richard Preskenis (VP-Comml Lending)
Thomas Hayes (Mng Dir)

FIRSTRUST CORPORATION
909 Poydras St, New Orleans, LA
70112
Tel.: (504) 584-5900
Web Site: https://www.fbtonline.com
Sales Range: $100-124.9 Million
Emp.: 350
Bank Holding Company
N.A.I.C.S.: 522110
Joe Canizaro (Chm)
Summer Woodburn (Branch Mgr)

Subsidiaries:

First Bank & Trust   (1)
909 Poydras St Ste 100, New Orleans, LA
70112
Tel.: (504) 584-5900
Web Site: http://www.sbtonline.com
Rev.: $20,788,000
Emp.: 50
State Commercial Banks

N.A.I.C.S.: 522110
Paul Queyrouze (Mgr-Acctg)
Joseph Canivaro (Chm)
Gary Blossman (Pres)

FIRSTSOURCEHR, INC.
2727 Ulmerton Rd Ste 325, Saint Petersburg, FL 33701
Tel.: (727) 954-8801
Web Site:
http://www.firstsourcehr.com
Sales Range: $1-9.9 Million
Emp.: 6
Payroll & Human Resource Outsourcing Services
N.A.I.C.S.: 561330
Peter VanSon (Pres)

FISCHBACH & DOUGHERTY, INC.
1215 Ashford Creek Park Ne, Atlanta,
GA 30319-5057
Tel.: (404) 250-1300   GA
Year Founded: 1978
Sales Range: $75-99.9 Million
Emp.: 5
Real Estate Investment Firm
N.A.I.C.S.: 531110

Subsidiaries:

Metro Atlanta Properties   (1)
792 Jolly Ave S, Clarkston, GA 30021-2130
Tel.: (404) 250-1400
Web Site: http://www.metroatlantaprop.com
Sales Range: $25-49.9 Million
Real Estate
N.A.I.C.S.: 531210

FISCHER & WIESER SPECIALTY FOODS, INC.
411 S Lincoln St, Fredericksburg, TX
78624
Tel.: (830) 997-7194   TX
Web Site: http://fischer-wieser.com
Year Founded: 1969
Sales Range: $1-9.9 Million
Emp.: 47
Fruit & Vegetable Canning
N.A.I.C.S.: 311421
Case D. Fischer (CEO)
Patricia Evans (Acct Mgr-Inside Sls)

Subsidiaries:

Fredericksburg Fudge Co.   (1)
218 E Main St, Fredericksburg, TX 78624-
4116
Tel.: (830) 997-0533
Web Site: http://www.fbgfudge.com
Confectionery & Nut Stores
N.A.I.C.S.: 445292

FISCHER CHEVROLET & NISSAN
1128 S Hopkins Ave, Titusville, FL
32780
Tel.: (321) 269-3311
Web Site: http://www.fischercars.com
Sales Range: $10-24.9 Million
Emp.: 30
Sales of New & Used Automobiles
N.A.I.C.S.: 441110
Patrick Fischer (Pres)

FISCHER HEIGHTS GIANT EAGLE
1300 Country Club Rd, Monongahela,
PA 15063
Tel.: (724) 258-5011
Web Site: http://www.gianteagle.com
Rev.: $26,900,000
Emp.: 125
Supermarket Operator
N.A.I.C.S.: 445110
Aldo Bartolotta (Pres)

FISCHER INTERNATIONAL SYSTEMS CORPORATION

5801 Pelican Bay Blvd Ste 300,
Naples, FL 34108
Tel.: (239) 643-1500
Web Site:
   http://www.fischerinternational.com
Sales Range: $10-24.9 Million
Emp.: 60
Identity Management Software
N.A.I.C.S.: 513210
Harold McCabe (CFO)
Addison M. Fischer (Founder & Chm)
Andrew Sroka (Pres & CEO)
Dennis McDermott (CMO & VP-Sls & Mktg)
Ajith Dominic (CTO)

FISCHER LUMBER CO. INC.
210 N Shamrock St, East Alton, IL
62024
Tel.: (618) 259-7434
Web Site:
   https://www.fischerlumber.com
Sales Range: $10-24.9 Million
Emp.: 65
Lumber & Other Building Materials
N.A.I.C.S.: 423310
David Fischer (Pres)
Jim Fischer (Sec)

FISEN CORP.
6871 Dutton Industrial Dr, Dutton, MI
49316
Tel.: (616) 698-7279   MI
Web Site: https://www.fisenusa.com
Year Founded: 2004
Sales Range: $1-9.9 Million
Emp.: 30
Customization & Manufacture of
Commercial & Industrial HVAC Equipment
N.A.I.C.S.: 333415
Chris Beggs (Owner)
Andrew Smith (Mgr-Ops)
Loren Hickman (Mgr-Ops)

**FISH & GAME FRONTIERS,
INC.**
305 Logan Rd, Wexford, PA 15090
Tel.: (724) 935-1577
Web Site:
   http://www.frontierstravel.com
Year Founded: 1969
Sales Range: $50-74.9 Million
Emp.: 70
Travel Agency
N.A.I.C.S.: 561510
Mollie Fitzgerald (Dir-Elegant Journeys Dept)

FISH & RICHARDSON PC
1 Marina Park Dr, Boston, MA 02210
Tel.: (617) 542-5070
Web Site: http://www.fr.com
Year Founded: 1878
Sales Range: $350-399.9 Million
Emp.: 360
Law firm
N.A.I.C.S.: 541110
Thad C. Kodish (Mng Principal)
John Farrell (Principal)
Paul E. Franz (Principal-Atlanta)
Tim French (Principal-Boston)
Christian Chu (Principal)
Joseph V. Colaianni (Principal-Washington)
Lauren A. Degnan (Principal-Washington)
Gwilym J. Attwell (Principal)
Anita L. Meiklejohn (Principal)
Beau Mersereau (Dir-Legal Tech Solutions)
Janis K. Fraser (Principal-Boston)
Bret T. Winterle (Principal)
Jonathan A. Solomon (Principal)
Jeremy J. Monaldo (Principal-Washington)

Matthew K. Wernli (Principal-Austin)
Adam J. Kessel (Principal)
Frank E. Scherkenbach (Principal-Boston & Silicon Valley)
Mark S. Puzella (Principal-Boston)
Roger D. Feldman (Sr Principal-Boston)
Todd E. Garcia (Principal)
Rob Courtney (Principal-Twin Cities)
John F. T. Conroy (Principal)
Gus P. Coldebella (Principal)
Kurt L. Glitzenstein (Principal)
Benjamin Thompson (Principal)
Ajit Singh Dang (Principal)
Caroline K. Simons (Principal)
Frank L. Gerratana (Principal)
Peter R. Poulin (Principal)
Adam R. Shartzer (Principal)
Michael Headley (Principal-Silicon Valley)
Jeremy D. Anderson (Principal-Delaware)
James W. Babineau (Principal)
John C. Adkisson (Pres & CEO)
Michael A. Amon (Principal-Southern California)
Kristine McKinney (COO)
Andy Schwentker (Principal-Intellectual Property Litigation Grp-Washington)
Kia Scipio (Mgr-Diversity & Inclusion-Washington)
Christopher C. Bowley (Principal)
Brian P. Boyd (Principal)
Carl Bruce (Principal)
Betty H. Chen (Principal)
Craig Countryman (Principal)
Ahmed J. Davis (Principal)
Peter J. Devlin (Principal-Admin)
Christopher Dillon (Principal)
Corrin N. Drakulich (Principal)
Benjamin C. Elacqua (Principal)
Mark S. Ellinger (Sr Principal)
Christine A. Goddard (Principal)
Christopher O. Green (Principal)
Brian J. Gustafson (Principal)
David J. Healey (Sr Principal)
Charles Hieken (Sr Principal)
Aamir A. Kazi (Principal)
Andrew R. Kopsidas (Principal)
S. Peter Ludwig (Sr Principal)
Christopher Marchese (Principal)
Christina V. McDonough (Principal)
John B. Pegram (Sr Principal)
Frank Porcelli (Principal)
Russell N. Rippamonti (Sr Principal)
Hans R. Troesch (Sr Principal)
Esha Bandyopadhyay (Principal)
John Hinrichs (CIO-Twin Cities)
Melanie Green (Chief Mktg & Bus Dev Officer)
Katie Creedon (Chief Legal Talent & Inclusion Officer)
Joshua A. Griswold (Mng Principal-Dallas)
Liz McCarthy (Mgr-PR)

**FISH & STILL EQUIPMENT CO.
INC.**
3927 NW Stallings Dr, Nacogdoches,
TX 75964
Tel.: (936) 564-7303
Web Site: http://www.fishandstillequipment.com
Sales Range: $25-49.9 Million
Emp.: 75
Retail Farm Equipment & Supplies
N.A.I.C.S.: 459999
C. Hawkens (Partner)
Chris James (Gen Mgr)

FISH CONSTRUCTION COMPANY
905 S Fair Oaks Ave, Pasadena, CA
91105

Tel.: (626) 773-8800
Web Site: http://www.regencypk.com
Sales Range: $50-74.9 Million
Emp.: 12
Single-Family Housing Construction
N.A.I.C.S.: 236115
Emil Fish (Pres)

Subsidiaries:

Regency Park Senior Living, Inc.   **(1)**
905 S Fair Oaks Ave, Pasadena, CA
91105   **(100%)**
Tel.: (626) 773-8800
Web Site: http://www.regencypk.com
Assisted Senior Living Services
N.A.I.C.S.: 623312
Emil Fish (Pres)

FISH FURNITURE SHOP INC.
1443 SOM Center Rd, Mayfield
Heights, OH 44124
Tel.: (440) 461-1050   OH
Web Site:
   https://www.fishfurniture.com
Year Founded: 1925
Sales Range: $10-24.9 Million
Emp.: 120
Retailer of Home Furnishings
N.A.I.C.S.: 449110
Albert I. Geller (Chm)
Dan Geller (Pres)

FISH MARKETING
107 SE Washington St Ste 620, Portland, OR 97214
Tel.: (503) 972-8977   OR
Web Site: https://www.fish-marketing.com
Year Founded: 2011
Sales Range: $1-9.9 Million
Emp.: 25
Advetising Agency
N.A.I.C.S.: 541810
Douglas Fish (Pres)
Michael Griffin (Dir-Inbound Mktg)
Karen Tolvstad (Dir-Pub Affairs & PR)
Don Skramovsky (Dir-Media)
Nate Parr (Partner & VP-Brand Leadership)
Alex Brauer (Brand Dir)
Holly Landaker (Office Mgr)
Lacey Hinkle (Brand Dir)
Billy Holiday (VP-Furcasting)
Melissa Jaacks (VP-Ops)

**FISH WINDOW CLEANING
SERVICES INC.**
200 Enchanted Pkwy, Saint Louis,
MO 63021
Tel.: (636) 530-7334   MO
Web Site:
   https://www.fishwindowcleaning.com
Year Founded: 1978
Sales Range: $1-9.9 Million
Emp.: 24
Janitorial Services
N.A.I.C.S.: 561720
Mike Merrick (CEO)
Linda Merrick (Exec VP)
Angie Masters (Dir-HR)
Chip Hotze (Dir-Distr & Special Projects)
Doug Apt (District Mgr)
John English (Mgr-Franchise Dev)
Mark Sweetnam (Mgr-Branding & Tech)
Mike Carnahan (Mgr-Franchise Dev)
Nathan Merrick (VP-Franchise & Dev)
Randy Cross (Owner & Pres)
Luke Schulte (Mgr-Dev-Franchise)
Alan Hibbler (Mgr-District)
Joe Merrell (Mgr-District)

FISHBACK FINANCIAL CORPORATION
520 6th St, Brookings, SD 57006

Tel.: (605) 696-2265   SD
Web Site: http://www.bankeasy.com
Year Founded: 1880
Bank Holding Company
N.A.I.C.S.: 551111
Van D. Fishback (Chm)
Kevin D. Tetzlaff (Pres & CEO)

FISHBELT FEEDS INC.
PO Box 609, Moorhead, MS 38761
Tel.: (662) 246-5065
Sales Range: $25-49.9 Million
Emp.: 40
Animal Feed Mfr
N.A.I.C.S.: 311119
Alvin Simpson (Plant Mgr)

FISHBOWL INVENTORY
580 E Technology Ave Bldg C Ste
1100, Orem, UT 84097
Tel.: (801) 932-1100
Web Site:
   https://www.fishbowlinventory.com
Year Founded: 2001
Rev.: $5,900,000
Emp.: 88
Business Services
N.A.I.C.S.: 512290
Grant Kimball (VP)
David Williams (Chm & CEO)
Mary Scott (Pres)

FISHBOWL MARKETING
44 Canal Ctr Plz Ste 500, Alexandria,
VA 22314
Tel.: (703) 836-3421
Web Site: http://www.fishbowl.com
Sales Range: $1-9.9 Million
Emp.: 90
Marketing Consulting Services
N.A.I.C.S.: 541613
Scott Shaw (Founder)
Daniel Dreymann (Chief Product Officer)
Prem Kiran (Chief Strategy Officer)
Mike Lukianoff (Chief Analytics Officer)
Jim Soss (CEO)

FISHER & ASSOCIATES, LLC
2315 Bellair Rd, Clearwater, FL
33764
Tel.: (727) 443-4436
Web Site:
   https://www.fisherarchitects.com
Sales Range: $1-9.9 Million
Emp.: 15
Architectural Services
N.A.I.C.S.: 541310
Bryan C. Fisher (Dir-Design)
William J. Fisher Jr. (Pres)

FISHER & COMPANY INCORPORATED
33300 Fisher Dr, Saint Clair Shores,
MI 48082
Tel.: (586) 296-1770
Web Site: http://www.fisherco.com
Rev.: $190,000,000
Emp.: 300
Motor Vehicle Parts & Accessories
N.A.I.C.S.: 336390
John A. Fisher (Mng Dir)
Mike Gabriel (Engr-Electrical Control)
Alfred J. Fisher Jr. (Chm)

FISHER & PHILLIPS LLP
1230 Peachtree St NE Ste 3300, Atlanta, GA 30309
Tel.: (404) 231-1400
Web Site:
   https://www.fisherphillips.com
Year Founded: 1943
Sales Range: $150-199.9 Million
Law firm
N.A.I.C.S.: 541110

Fisher & Phillips LLP—(Continued)

D. Albert Brannen *(Mng Partner-Atlanta)*
Michael V. Abcarian *(Mng Partner-Dallas)*
Christine Baran *(Partner)*
David A. Young *(Partner)*
Michael R. Greco *(Mng Partner-Denver & Partner-Philadelphia)*
David S. Jones *(Partner)*
Myra K. Creighton *(Co-Partner)*
Robert C. Christenson *(Co-Partner)*
Tillman Y. Coffey *(Co-Partner)*
Burton F. Dodd *(Co-Partner & Gen Counsel)*
Jennifer B. Sandberg *(Mng Partner-Regional & Partner)*
Ted Boehm *(Partner)*
Jessica T. Cook *(Partner)*
Edwin G. Foulke *(Partner)*
Corey J. Goerdt *(Dir-Pro Bono & Community Engagement)*
Ree Harper *(Partner)*
Marty Heller *(Partner)*
Dave Lentz *(COO)*
Lorie Maring *(Partner)*
Howard A. Mavity *(Partner)*
Tracy L. Moon Jr. *(Partner)*
Roger K. Quillen *(Partner)*
Andria Lure Ryan *(Partner)*
Matthew R. Simpson *(Partner)*
John W. Stapleton *(Partner)*
Shanon R. Stevenson *(Partner)*
Terri R. Stewart *(Mng Partner-Regional)*
Douglas R. Sullenberger *(Partner)*
Joshua H. Viau *(Mng Partner-Regional)*
C. R. Wright *(Partner)*
Cynthia J. Yarbrough *(Partner)*

FISHER AUCTION COMPANY, INC.
2112 E Atlantic Blvd, Pompano Beach, FL 33062
Tel.: (954) 942-0917
Web Site:
http://www.fisherauction.com
Year Founded: 1967
Sales Range: $1-9.9 Million
Emp.: 20
Real Estate Auctioneers
N.A.I.C.S.: 531390
Andre LaBauve *(CFO)*
Francis D. Santos *(COO & Exec VP)*
Lamar P. Fisher *(Pres & CEO)*
Midge Navarro *(Dir-Mktg)*
Ruben Socarras *(Gen Counsel)*
Neil Saffer *(Head-Bus Dev)*
Louis B. Fisher Jr. *(Founder & Chm)*

FISHER AUTO PARTS INC.
512 Greenville Ave, Staunton, VA 24401
Tel.: (540) 885-8901
Web Site:
https://www.fisherautoparts.com
Rev.: $242,700,000
Emp.: 300
Automotive Supplies & Parts
N.A.I.C.S.: 423120
Joe Rader *(Dir-Risk Svcs)*
Herb Godschalk *(Co-Pres)*
Tom Jones *(Reg Mgr-Sls)*
Gray Turner *(VP-Sls)*

FISHER CHEVROLET INC.
775 E 32nd St, Yuma, AZ 85365-4204
Tel.: (928) 726-5500
Web Site: http://www.fisherchev.com
Sales Range: $50-74.9 Million
Emp.: 80
Owner & Operator of Car Dealerships
N.A.I.C.S.: 441110

Patty Ellsworth *(Controller)*
Joseph Fisher II *(Pres)*
Joseph Fisher Sr. *(VP)*

FISHER DEVELOPMENT INC.
201 Spear St Ste 220, San Francisco, CA 94105-1632
Tel.: (415) 468-1717
Web Site: http://www.fisherinc.com
Sales Range: $100-124.9 Million
Emp.: 175
Commercial & Office Building, New Construction
N.A.I.C.S.: 236220
Sydney Bernier *(VP-Mktg)*
Spencer Reiner *(VP-Construction Ops)*

FISHER ENTERPRISES, LLC
322 Central Park W, New York, NY 10025
Tel.: (212) 223-1044
Web Site:
https://www.fisherenterprisesllc.com
Year Founded: 2001
Sales Range: $1-9.9 Million
Emp.: 20
Securities Brokerage
N.A.I.C.S.: 523150
David Franklin *(Mng Partner)*

Subsidiaries:

Crumbs Bake Shop, Inc. **(1)**
5101 Charter Oak Dr, Paducah, KY 42001
Tel.: (855) 727-8627
Web Site: http://www.crumbs.com
Holding Company; Retail Bakeries Owner & Operator
N.A.I.C.S.: 551112

Subsidiary (Domestic):

Crumbs Broadway LLC **(2)**
1675 Broadway, New York, NY 10019
Tel.: (212) 399-3100
Web Site: http://www.crumbs.com
Bakery Products Retailer
N.A.I.C.S.: 311813

Crumbs Columbus LLC **(2)**
775 Columbus Ave, New York, NY 10025
Tel.: (917) 410-5896
Web Site: http://www.crumbs.com
Emp.: 8
Bakery Products Retailer
N.A.I.C.S.: 311813
Michele Burgos *(Gen Mgr)*

Crumbs Federal Street, LLC **(2)**
176 Federal St, Boston, MA 02110
Tel.: (617) 918-7352
Web Site: http://www.crumbs.com
Bakery Products Retailer
N.A.I.C.S.: 311813

Crumbs Garment Center LLC **(2)**
1385 Broadway, New York, NY 10018
Tel.: (646) 780-0454
Web Site: http://www.crumbs.com
Emp.: 8
Bakery Products Retailer
N.A.I.C.S.: 311813
Melissa Pilotin *(Gen Mgr)*

Crumbs Grand Central LLC **(2)**
420 Lexington Ave, New York, NY 10170
Tel.: (212) 297-0500
Web Site: http://www.crumbs.com
Bakery Products Retailer
N.A.I.C.S.: 311813

Crumbs Lexington LLC **(2)**
1418 Lexington Ave 93rd, New York, NY 10128
Tel.: (917) 410-5776
Web Site: http://www.crumbs.com
Bakery Products Retailer
N.A.I.C.S.: 311813

Crumbs Times Square LLC **(2)**
261 W 42nd St, New York, NY 10036
Tel.: (212) 938-0400
Web Site: http://www.crumbs.com
Bakery Products Retailer
N.A.I.C.S.: 311813

Crumbs Union Square LLC **(2)**
124 University Pl, New York, NY 10003
Tel.: (212) 206-8011
Web Site: http://www.crumbs.com
Emp.: 5
Bakery Products Retailer
N.A.I.C.S.: 311813

Crumbs Union Station LLC **(2)**
40 Massachusetts Ave NW, Washington, DC 20002
Tel.: (202) 408-1001
Web Site: http://www.crumbs.com
Emp.: 8
Bakery Products Retailer
N.A.I.C.S.: 311813

FISHER FOODS MARKETING INC.
4855 Frank Rd NW, Canton, OH 44720
Tel.: (330) 497-3000
Web Site: http://www.fisherfoods.com
Rev.: $39,900,000
Emp.: 200
Independent Supermarket
N.A.I.C.S.: 445110
John Halkias *(VP-HR)*
Jeffrey A. Fisher *(Pres)*

FISHER INDUSTRIES
3020 Energy Dr, Dickinson, ND 58601
Tel.: (701) 456-9184
Web Site: https://www.fisherind.com
Year Founded: 1945
Sales Range: $50-74.9 Million
Emp.: 350
Construction & Mining
N.A.I.C.S.: 212321
Tommy Fisher *(Pres & CEO)*

Subsidiaries:

Fisher Sand & Gravel Co. Inc. **(1)**
PO Box 1034, Dickinson, ND 58601
Tel.: (701) 456-6184
Web Site: http://www.fisherind.com
Sales Range: $75-99.9 Million
Producer of Construction Sand & Gravel
N.A.I.C.S.: 212321
Tommy Fisher *(Pres)*

General Steel & Supply Co., Inc. **(1)**
3020 Energy Dr, Dickinson, ND 58601-7184
Tel.: (701) 456-9184
Web Site: http://www.fisherind.com
Sales Range: $10-24.9 Million
Emp.: 75
Mfr of Mining Machinery
N.A.I.C.S.: 333131
Florian Friedt *(Gen Mgr)*

FISHER ISLAND CLUB, INC.
1 Fisher Island Dr, Miami, FL 33109
Tel.: (305) 535-6000
Web Site:
http://www.fisherislandclub.com
Sales Range: $10-24.9 Million
Emp.: 500
Resort Club & Hotel
N.A.I.C.S.: 713990
Scott Barter *(CFO)*
Kay Fisher *(Dir-Membership Sls)*
Bernard Lackner *(CEO)*

FISHER LYNCH CAPITAL, LLC
2929 Campus Dr Ste 420, San Mateo, CA 94403
Tel.: (650) 287-2700
Web Site:
https://www.fisherlynch.com
Sales Range: $25-49.9 Million
Emp.: 22
Privater Equity Firm
N.A.I.C.S.: 523999
Brett Fisher *(Co-Founder & Mng Dir)*
Leon Kuan *(Mng Dir)*

Subsidiaries:

Fisher Lynch Capital, LLC - East Coast Office **(1)**

500 Boylston St Ste 1640, Boston, MA 02116
Tel.: (617) 406-3120
Web Site: http://www.fisherlynch.com
Privater Equity Firm
N.A.I.C.S.: 523999
Linda Lynch *(Mng Dir)*
Marshall Bartlett *(Mng Dir)*
Anthony Limberis *(Mng Dir)*
Anne Hannan *(Office Mgr)*
Ben Cluff *(VP)*
Brett Fisher *(Mng Dir)*
Chris Alfert *(VP)*
Chris Montclare *(CFO)*
Leon Kuan *(Mng Dir)*
Marcus Wood *(Mng Dir)*
Marina Hegstrom *(Controller)*
Michelle Bautista *(Office Mgr)*
Teresa Gorrebeeck *(Mgr-Ops)*

FISHER MANUFACTURING COMPANY
1900 S O St, Tulare, CA 93274
Tel.: (559) 685-5200
Web Site: https://www.fisher-mfg.com
Year Founded: 1936
Commercial Plumbing Systems Mfr
N.A.I.C.S.: 332913
Jeff Westley *(VP-Sls)*
Melissa Hulsey *(Coord-Mktg)*
Ray Fisher Jr. *(Pres & Owner)*

FISHER PRINTING INC.
2257 N Pacific St, Orange, CA 92865
Tel.: (714) 998-9200
Web Site:
http://www.fisherprinting.com
Rev.: $15,900,000
Emp.: 140
Offset Printing
N.A.I.C.S.: 323111
Tom Scarpati *(COO-Midwest)*
Maria Dolberg *(Dir-HR West Coast)*
Byron Holeman *(Mgr-West Coast)*

FISHER PROPERTY GROUP, INC.
50 Cocoanut Row Ste 211, Palm Beach, FL 33480
Tel.: (561) 802-4477
Web Site:
http://www.fisherpropertygroup.com
Emp.: 10
Real Estate Investment
N.A.I.C.S.: 531390
Jeffrey H. Fisher *(Pres & CEO)*

FISHER STORES INC.
110 Riverdale Rd, New Bern, NC 28562-9445
Tel.: (252) 633-6300   NC
Web Site: https://fisherstores.com
Year Founded: 1975
Sales Range: $25-49.9 Million
Emp.: 75
Retail Fuel Markets
N.A.I.C.S.: 445131
Windey Fisher *(Pres)*

FISHER TANK COMPANY
3131 W 4th St, Chester, PA 19013
Tel.: (610) 494-7200
Web Site: https://www.fishertank.com
Sales Range: $50-74.9 Million
Emp.: 160
Tanks, Standard Or Custom Fabricated: Metal Plate
N.A.I.C.S.: 332420
Michael Szelak *(CEO)*

FISHER'S DOCUMENT SYSTEMS, INC.
575 E 42nd St, Boise, ID 83714
Tel.: (208) 947-3606
Web Site: http://www.fisherstech.com
Year Founded: 1936
Sales Range: $10-24.9 Million
Emp.: 90

Office Machinery & Equipment Distr
N.A.I.C.S.: 423420
Chris Taylor (CEO)
Eric Strand (VP-Bus Dev)
J. T. Jones (CFO)
Jahn Deim (Mgr-Ops)
Zack White (Dir-IT)

Subsidiaries:

Terrell's Office Machines, Inc. (1)
215 Haggerty Ln, Bozeman, MT 59715
Tel.: (406) 587-4455
Web Site: http://www.terrellsoffice.com
Sales Range: $1-9.9 Million
Emp.: 13
Miscellaneous Store Retailers (except Tobacco Stores)
N.A.I.C.S.: 459999
Aaron Noreen (Mgr)

FISHER-BARTON INCORPORATED

201 Frederick St, Watertown, WI 53094
Tel.: (920) 261-0131
Web Site:
    http://www.fisherbartonsp.com
Year Founded: 1972
Sales Range: $25-49.9 Million
Emp.: 300
Metal Products Mfr
N.A.I.C.S.: 333112
Shawn Williams (Mgr-Pur)
Troy Benkert (Mgr-Matls)
Meg Blankschein (Mgr-HR)
Yan Glanz (Mgr-Sls-European)
Andrea Loppnow (Mgr-Engrg)
Darrel Turner (VP-Engrg)
Anand Kulkarni (VP-Sls & North-South America)

FISHER-TITUS MEDICAL CENTER

272 Benedict Ave, Norwalk, OH 44857
Tel.: (419) 668-8101   OH
Web Site: http://www.fisher-titus.org
Year Founded: 1911
Sales Range: $100-124.9 Million
Emp.: 1,108
Health Care Srvices
N.A.I.C.S.: 621610
Duane Woods (CFO & VP-Fin)
Phillip J. Annarino (Sr VP-HR)
John Britton (VP-Info Svcs)
Fred Wiechers (Sec)
John D. Payne (Treas)
Kraig Korbas (Dir-Pharmacy)
Katie L. Chieda (Sr VP-Clinical Svcs)
Matthew Mattner (COO)

FISHERIES SUPPLY COMPANY

1900 N Northlake Way, Seattle, WA 98103-9051
Tel.: (206) 632-4462   WA
Web Site:
    https://www.fisheriessupply.com
Year Founded: 1928
Sales Range: $75-99.9 Million
Emp.: 80
Marine Supplies; Automotive Supplies & Parts
N.A.I.C.S.: 423860
John Rothermel (VP-Sls)
Carl F. Sutter Jr. (Pres)

FISHERMANS MARINE SUPPLY INC.

901 N Columbia Blvd, Portland, OR 97217
Tel.: (503) 283-8310
Web Site: http://www.fishermans-marine.com
Rev.: $13,000,000
Emp.: 150
Bait & Tackle
N.A.I.C.S.: 459110

Dan Grogan (Pres)
Steve Wills (Controller)

FISHERS BAKERY & SANDWICH CO., INC.

1519 Brookside Dr, Raleigh, NC 27604-2002
Tel.: (919) 901-0739
Sales Range: $10-24.9 Million
Emp.: 99
Dried & Dehydrated Food Mfr
N.A.I.C.S.: 311423
T. Winfield (Pres)
Arlene Fisher (Sec)

FISHMAN & ASSOCIATES, INC.

143 E Miami Ave, Venice, FL 34285
Tel.: (941) 484-8800
Web Site:
    https://www.fishmaninc.com
Year Founded: 1986
Sales Range: $1-9.9 Million
Emp.: 10
Restaurant Design & Equipment Mfr & Distr
N.A.I.C.S.: 541490
C.J. Fishman (Pres)
Marisa Mangani (Project Mgr)

FISHMAN & TOBIN, INC.

4000 Chemical Rd Ste 500, Plymouth Meeting, PA 19462-1708
Tel.: (610) 828-8400
Web Site:
    http://www.fishmantobin.com
Year Founded: 1914
Boys' & Men's Trousers & Clothing Distr
N.A.I.C.S.: 315250
Marvin Walker (VP-Western Hemisphere Sourcing & Distr)
Nicholas Vetere (CFO)

FISHMAN PUBLIC RELATIONS

3400 Dundee Rd Ste 300, Northbrook, IL 60062
Tel.: (847) 945-1300
Web Site: https://www.fishmanpr.com
Year Founded: 1991
Emp.: 50
Public Relations & Communications
N.A.I.C.S.: 541820
Sherri Fishman (Pres & Owner)
Debra Vilchis (COO)
Sara Faiwell (VP)
Daniel O'Donnell (Mgr-Content Mktg)

FISHMAN SUPPLY INC.

1345 Industrial Ave, Petaluma, CA 94952
Tel.: (707) 763-8161
Web Site:
    https://www.fishmansupply.com
Sales Range: $10-24.9 Million
Emp.: 35
Service Establishment Equipment Supply Whslr
N.A.I.C.S.: 423850
John Tully (Mgr-Sls)

FISKE BROTHERS REFINING COMPANY

129 Lockwood St, Newark, NJ 07105
Tel.: (973) 589-9150   NY
Web Site: https://www.lubriplate.com
Year Founded: 1871
Sales Range: $75-99.9 Million
Emp.: 110
Cutting Oil Drawing Compound & Other Metal Working Lubricant Mfr
N.A.I.C.S.: 324191
Richard T. McCluskey (Pres & CEO)
Jim Girard (CMO & Exec VP)
Steve Morrow (VP-Sls)

Subsidiaries:

Fiske Brothers Refining Company - Toledo Division (1)
1500 Oakdale Ave, Toledo, OH 43605-3843   (100%)
Tel.: (419) 691-2491
Web Site: http://www.lubriplate.com
Sales Range: $10-24.9 Million
Emp.: 47
Lubricating Oils And Grease
N.A.I.C.S.: 324191
Richard T. McCluskey (Pres & CEO)

Lubriplate Lubricants (1)
129 Lockwood St, Newark, NJ 07105
Tel.: (973) 465-5700
Web Site: http://www.lubriplate.com
Sales Range: $10-24.9 Million
Emp.: 20
Lubricant Product Mfr
N.A.I.C.S.: 324191
James Girard (VP)

FISTER INCORPORATED

2305 Palumbo Dr, Lexington, KY 40509
Tel.: (859) 266-2153
Web Site:
    http://www.vincentfister.com
Rev.: $14,717,831
Emp.: 80
Trucking Service
N.A.I.C.S.: 484110

Subsidiaries:

Fister Distribution Inc. (1)
2305 Palumbo Dr, Lexington, KY 40509
Tel.: (859) 266-2153
Web Site: http://www.fisterdistribution.com
Rev.: $1,803,860
Emp.: 30
Agents, Shipping
N.A.I.C.S.: 488510
David Downs (VP-Sls)

Fister Moving & Storage (1)
2305 Palumbo Dr, Lexington, KY 40509
Tel.: (859) 266-2153
Web Site: http://www.vincentfister.com
Rev.: $4,433,568
Emp.: 15
Household Goods Transport
N.A.I.C.S.: 484110
Dennis Toulson (Pres)

Safeway Moving & Storage Inc (1)
772 Winchester Rd, Lexington, KY 40505
Tel.: (859) 253-0891
Web Site: http://www.unigroupinc.net
Rev.: $1,144,370
Emp.: 20
Household Goods Transport
N.A.I.C.S.: 484210
Philip McMillan (Gen Mgr)

Vincent Fister Inc. (1)
2305 Palumbo Dr, Lexington, KY 40509
Tel.: (859) 266-2153
Web Site: http://www.vincentfister.com
Rev.: $6,920,868
Emp.: 50
Trucking Except Local
N.A.I.C.S.: 484121
Dennis Tollson (CEO)

FIT AFTER FIFTY, INC.

206 Laguna Ct Saint, Saint Augustine, FL 32086
Year Founded: 1998
Fitness Services
N.A.I.C.S.: 713940
Gerald Williams (CEO)

FIT AMERICA INC.

3315 NE 15th St, Fort Lauderdale, FL 33304
Tel.: (954) 566-8244
Web Site: http://www.fitamerica.com
Sales Range: $10-24.9 Million
Emp.: 10
Weight Loss Program
N.A.I.C.S.: 812191
Debi Davis (Founder & CEO)

FIT MY FEET ORTHOTIC LAB & SHOES, INC.

2621 S Minnesota Ave, Sioux Falls, SD 57105
Tel.: (605) 274-0138
Web Site: http://www.fitmyfeet.com
Year Founded: 2013
Sales Range: $1-9.9 Million
Emp.: 22
Prosthetic Product Distr
N.A.I.C.S.: 456199
Nick Kolterman (Owner)
J. Bob (Mgr-Inventory)
L. Christine (Specialist-Insurance & Billing)
T. Justin (Mgr-Store)
H. Nate (Dir-Corp Rels)

FIT/NHNH, INC.

122 Market St, Manchester, NH 03101
Tel.: (603) 641-9441   NH
Web Site: http://www.fitnh.org
Year Founded: 1991
Community Housing Services
N.A.I.C.S.: 624229
Stephanie Allain Savard (COO)
Michele Talwani (VP-Comm & Mktg)
Lisa Allard (CFO)
Cathy Kuhn (Chief Strategy Officer)
Pamela Hawkes (VP-Resource Dev)
Meghan Shea (VP-Clinical & Supportive Svcs)
Patrick D. Bergeron (Dir-HR & Info)
Kristen McGuigan (Dir-Family Svcs)
Rebecca Pichardo (Dir-Shelter Ops)
Chris Wellington (Dir-Housing Dev & Ops)
Scott W. Ellison (Chm)
Roy Tilsley (Vice Chm)
Robert Bartley (Treas)
Frank Saglio (Asst Treas)
Kristi Scarpone (Sec)

Subsidiaries:

New Horizons for New Hampshire (1)
199 Manchester St, Manchester, NH 03103
Tel.: (603) 668-1877
Web Site: http://www.newhorizonsfornh.org
Homeless Shelter Provider
N.A.I.C.S.: 624221
Mary K. Silva (Mgr-Volunteer & In-Kind Program)
Frank Saglio (Asst Treas)
Michelle Casale (Mgr-Events)
Lisa Allard (CFO)
Cathy Kuhn (Chief Strategy Officer)
Stephanie Savard (COO)
Rebecca Pichardo (Dir-Shelter Ops)
Pamela Hawkes (VP-Resource Dev)
Michele Talwani (VP-Mktg)
Scott W. Ellison (Chm)
Roy Tilsley (Vice Chm)
Robert Bartley (Treas)
Kristi Scarpone (Sec)

FITE BUILDING COMPANY, INC.

3116 Sexton Rd SE Ste A, Decatur, AL 35603-1453
Tel.: (256) 353-5759
Web Site:
    https://www.fitebuilding.com
Sales Range: $25-49.9 Million
Emp.: 100
Nonresidential Construction Services
N.A.I.C.S.: 236220
Jack Fite (Pres)
Chuck Reep (Mgr-Bus Dev)

FITEK, LLC

333 Thornall St 2nd Fl, Edison, NJ 08837
Tel.: (732) 767-5437
Web Site: https://www.fi-tek.com
Year Founded: 2001
Sales Range: $1-9.9 Million

Fitek, LLC—(Continued)
Emp.: 110
Custom Computer Programming Services
N.A.I.C.S.: 541511
Joan Wagner (*Sr Mng Dir-Trust Portal Ops*)
Richard Gelinas (*CFO*)
Subir Chatterjee (*Founder, Pres & CEO*)
Ramsey El-Fakir (*CIO & Sr Mng Dir-Tech & Infrastructure*)
Surajit Banerjee (*Mng Dir-Offshore Ops & HedgeTek*)
Frank Judisch (*Mng Dir-Wealth Mgmt*)
R. Darcy Lee (*Mgr-Opsourcing Bus*)
Mary Heckelman (*Sr Mgr-Wealth Mgmt Solutions*)
Anthony N. Mitchell (*Mng Dir*)
Ranjan Roy (*CTO-Offshore Ops*)
James Okamura (*Pres-First State Trust Company*)
Kelly Brockstedt (*Sr VP & Mgr-Relationship-First State Trust Company*)

Subsidiaries:

Rockit Solutions, LLC   (1)
201 Tresser Blvd Ste 200, Stamford, CT 06901
Tel.: (866) 497-9111
Web Site: http://www.rockitco.com
Sales Range: $1-9.9 Million
Emp.: 13
Computer System Design Services
N.A.I.C.S.: 541512
Susan McDermott (*COO*)
David R. Bauman (*Sr VP-Res & Dev*)
Daniel Berg (*CTO*)
Patricia Carroll (*Sr VP-Partnership Acctg & Tax Svc*)
Melissa Zwickel (*Dir-Ops*)
Alan Perl (*Dir-Client Svc & Implementations*)
Stephen Dreyer (*Mgr-Partnership Acctg*)

FITLIFE FOODS
1902 S Dale Mabry Hwy, Tampa, FL 33629
Tel.: (813) 644-6868
Web Site:
    https://www.eatfitlifefoods.com
Sales Range: $25-49.9 Million
Health Food Stores
N.A.I.C.S.: 456191
David Osterweil (*Founder & Owner*)
Paul Farr (*Mgr-Kitchen*)
Tammy Myers (*VP-Retail Ops*)

FITNESS ANYWHERE LLC
1660 Pacific Ave, San Francisco, CA 94109
Tel.: (415) 655-4740
Web Site: http://www.trxtraining.com
Year Founded: 2003
Sales Range: $50-74.9 Million
Emp.: 100
Fiscal Year-end: 12/31/15
Fitness Training & Exercise Program Sales
N.A.I.C.S.: 713940
Randy Hetrick (*Founder*)

FITNESS CONSULTING GROUP
PO Box 1539, Elizabethtown, KY 42702
Web Site:
    http://www.fitnessconsulting
    group.com
Year Founded: 2005
Sales Range: $1-9.9 Million
Emp.: 20
Tools & Resources for Fitness Professionals to Build Their Businesses
N.A.I.C.S.: 713940

Pat Rigsby (*Co-Founder*)
Nick Berry (*Co-Founder & Co-CEO*)
Ryan Ketchum (*Exec Dir-Fitness Revolution Sls & Mktg*)
Craig Myers (*Coord-Coaching*)
Natalie Walkley (*Dir-Mktg*)
Julie Hatfield (*Exec Dir-IYCA*)
Miles Noland (*Mgr-Paid Mktg*)
Amy Busse (*VP-Fin*)

FITNESS CUBED INC.
350 W Ontario St, Chicago, IL 60654
Web Site: http://www.cubii.com
Year Founded: 2014
Sales Range: $10-24.9 Million
Emp.: 13
Home Health & Fitness Product Mfr
N.A.I.C.S.: 339920
Arnav Dalmia (*CEO*)

FITNESS GALLERY INC.
216 N Center St, Mesa, AZ 85201-6629
Tel.: (480) 705-1901
Web Site: http://www.fitgallery.com
Year Founded: 1997
Rev.: $14,527,453
Emp.: 20
Sales of Exercise Equipment
N.A.I.C.S.: 459110

FITNESS ONBOARD
600 S Barracks St Ste 202, Pensacola, FL 32502
Tel.: (850) 912-8089
Web Site:
    http://www.fitnessonboard.com
Sales Range: $1-9.9 Million
Fitness Center
N.A.I.C.S.: 713940
Cindi Bonner (*Founder*)

FITNESS PLUS EQUIPMENT SERVICES INC.
108 Hamilton Industrial Ct, Wentzville, MO 63385
Tel.: (636) 634-2202
Web Site:
    http://www.fitnessrepairparts.com
Year Founded: 1995
Sales Range: $1-9.9 Million
Emp.: 16
Replacement Parts for Fitness Equipment
N.A.I.C.S.: 333998
John Jacobs (*Founder*)
Jeremy Jacobs (*VP-E-Commerce*)

FITNESS TOGETHER
9092 Ridgeline Blvd Ste A, Highlands Ranch, CO 80129
Web Site:
    http://www.fitnesstogether.com
Year Founded: 1999
Rev.: $12,500,000
Emp.: 22
Health Services
N.A.I.C.S.: 621111
Kristine Fisher (*Exec VP-Ops Svcs*)
Dan Colbourne (*CFO*)
Jeffrey L. Jervik (*Pres & CEO*)
Rick Sikorski (*Founder*)
Jessica Gammans (*Coord-Mktg & Comm*)
Abby Lee (*CMO & Exec VP*)
John Kutac (*COO & Exec VP*)
Scott Wendrych (*Exec VP-Dev*)

FITWEISER HOLDINGS, INC.
5348 Vegas Dr, Las Vegas, NV 89108
Tel.: (702) 373-8615   NV
Year Founded: 2010
Investment Services
N.A.I.C.S.: 523999

Rudy Campidonica (*Chm & CEO*)
Harry L. Langdon (*CFO, Sec & Treas*)
G. S. Tuthill (*CTQ*)
Michael A. Soriano (*COO*)

FITWORKS HOLDING LLC
26391 Curtiss Wright Pkwy Ste 104, Richmond Heights, OH 44143
Tel.: (216) 289-3100
Web Site: http://www.fitworks.com
Sales Range: $10-24.9 Million
Emp.: 100
Health Club
N.A.I.C.S.: 713940
Patrick D. Petrecca (*Pres*)
Tony Salvo (*Controller*)

FITZ DESIGN
3853 Acline Rd Ste 119, Punta Gorda, FL 33950
Tel.: (941) 505-1801
Web Site:
    http://www.creationsbyfitzdesign.com
Year Founded: 2007
Sales Range: $1-9.9 Million
Emp.: 12
Jewellery Distr
N.A.I.C.S.: 423940
Dan Fisher (*Owner*)

FITZGERALD & MASTROI-ANNI, INC.
32 Hampden St, Springfield, MA 01103
Tel.: (413) 737-8757   MA
Year Founded: 2005
Sales Range: Less than $1 Million
Emp.: 2
N.A.I.C.S.: 541810
Gerry Fitzgerald (*Owner*)
Susan Mastroianni (*Partner*)

FITZGERALD AUTO MALLS
11411 Rockville Pike, Rockville, MD 20852
Tel.: (301) 881-4000
Web Site: https://www.fitzmall.com
Year Founded: 1966
Sales Range: $25-49.9 Million
Emp.: 180
Owner & Operator of Car Dealerships
N.A.I.C.S.: 441110
Suzy Noble (*Mgr-Corp Accts Receivable*)

FITZGERALD BROTHERS BEVERAGES
152160 Dix Ave, Glens Falls, NY 12801
Tel.: (518) 793-3431
Web Site:
    https://www.fitzgeraldbros.com
Rev.: $19,356,689
Emp.: 75
Soft Drinks
N.A.I.C.S.: 424490
William E. Fitzgerald (*Chm*)

FITZGERALD EQUIPMENT COMPANY INCORPORATED
4650 Boeing Dr, Rockford, IL 61109
Tel.: (815) 397-7050
Web Site: http://www.fitzequip.com
Year Founded: 1962
Sales Range: $10-24.9 Million
Emp.: 45
Industrial Machinery & Equipment Repair
N.A.I.C.S.: 811210
Kevin Fitzgerald (*Pres*)

FITZMARTIN INC.
2917 Central Ave Ste 211, Homewood, AL 35209
Tel.: (205) 322-1010

Web Site: https://www.fitzmartin.com
Year Founded: 1992
Sales Range: $1-9.9 Million
Emp.: 6
Business-To-Business Marketing & Sales Communication
N.A.I.C.S.: 541890
Sean Doyle (*Co-Founder, Principal & Dir-Strategy*)
Mac Logue (*Dir-Creative*)

FITZPATRICK & HUNT, PAGANO, AUBERT, LLP
Twr 49 12 E 49th St 31st Fl, New York, NY 10017
Tel.: (212) 937-4000   NY
Web Site: https://www.fitzhunt.com
Emp.: 19
Law firm
N.A.I.C.S.: 541110
Ralph V. Pagano (*Partner*)
Garrett J. Fitzpatrick (*Mng Partner*)
Garth W. Aubert (*Partner*)
James W. Hunt (*Partner*)

FITZPATRICK & WELLER, INC.
PO Box 490, Ellicottville, NY 14731-0490
Tel.: (716) 699-2393   NY
Web Site: http://www.fitzweller.com
Year Founded: 1892
Sales Range: $75-99.9 Million
Emp.: 90
Lumber & Wood Products Mfr
N.A.I.C.S.: 321918
Dana G. Fitzpatrick (*Chm*)
Gregory J. Fitzpatrick (*Pres*)
Cheryl A. Schmidt (*Controller*)

FITZPATRICK AUTO CENTER INC.
1301 N Lk Ave, Storm Lake, IA 50588
Tel.: (712) 732-2474
Web Site:
    http://www.fitzpatrickauto.com
Rev.: $21,000,000
Emp.: 51
New Car Dealers
N.A.I.C.S.: 441110
Bob Baschke (*Comptroller*)
William L. Fitzpatrick (*Treas & Sec*)

FITZPATRICK COMPANIES INC.
705 Present St, Lee, MA 01238
Tel.: (413) 243-1474
Web Site:
    http://www.countrycurtains.com
Sales Range: $100-124.9 Million
Emp.: 195
Mail-Order Houses
N.A.I.C.S.: 449129
Jane P. Fitzpatrick (*Founder*)
Laura Connor (*Sec*)
Nancy Fitzpatrick (*Vice Chm*)
Paula Beck (*VP-Fin*)
Sandra Dignard (*VP-Ops*)
Rebecca Riordan (*VP-HR*)
Leo Kavanaugh (*VP-Mdsg*)

Subsidiaries:

Country Curtains Retail Inc.   (1)
705 Pleasant St, Lee, MA 01238
Tel.: (413) 243-1474
Web Site: http://www.countrycurtains.com
Rev.: $7,400,000
Emp.: 185
Drapery & Upholstery Stores
N.A.I.C.S.: 449129
John Fitzpatrick (*Founder*)
Celia Clancy (*Pres & CEO*)
Bob Kliewe (*CFO & COO*)
Steve Donnelly (*Controller*)

Roaring Llc   (1)
30 Main St, Stockbridge, MA 01262

Tel.: (413) 298-5545
Rev.: $9,000,000
Emp.: 100
Inns
N.A.I.C.S.: 721191

**FITZPATRICK MANUFACTUR-
ING CO.**
33637 Sterling Ponds Blvd, Sterling
Heights, MI 48312
Tel.: (586) 825-0066
Web Site:
  http://www.fitzpatrickmfgco.com
Sales Range: $10-24.9 Million
Emp.: 82
Machine & Other Job Shop Work
N.A.I.C.S.: 332710
Michael M. Fitzpatrick (Pres)

**FITZPATRICK'S GMC TRUCKS,
INC.**
27 Sears Ln, Burlington, VT 05401
Tel.: (802) 864-5754
Year Founded: 1908
Sales Range: $10-24.9 Million
Emp.: 30
New Car Dealers
N.A.I.C.S.: 441110
Martin Fitzpatrick (Pres)

**FIVE ACRES - THE BOYS'
AND GIRLS' AID SOCIETY OF
LOS ANGELES COUNTY**
760 W Mountain View St, Altadena,
CA 91001
Tel.: (626) 798-6793   CA
Web Site: http://www.fiveacres.org
Year Founded: 1888
Sales Range: $25-49.9 Million
Emp.: 550
Child & Family Support Services
N.A.I.C.S.: 624190
Daniel Braun (CFO)
Karen Evans (COO)
Carmen Benitez (Chief Admin Officer)

**FIVE AREA TELEPHONE
COOP INC.**
302 Uvalde St, Muleshoe, TX 79347
Tel.: (806) 272-5533
Web Site: https://www.fivearea.com
Sales Range: $10-24.9 Million
Emp.: 40
Telecommunication Servicesb
N.A.I.C.S.: 517121
Sandy Vandezender (CEO)

FIVE ARROWS INC.
910 E 127th Ave, Tampa, FL 33612
Tel.: (813) 972-1400
Web Site:
  http://www.servicepainting.com
Sales Range: $10-24.9 Million
Emp.: 180
Commercial Painting & Waterproofing
N.A.I.C.S.: 238320
Kathleen Frazier (Mgr-Acctg-Tampa)
Melissa Williams (Office Mgr-Tampa)
Ed Dolan (Project Mgr-Orlando)
Jeff Heim (Project Mgr-Tampa)
Randy Jaskiewicz (Project Mgr-
Tampa)
Robert Pope (Project Mgr-Tampa)
Todd Monroe (VP-Orlando)

Subsidiaries:

Service Painting Corporation   (1)
1423 Long St, Orlando, FL 32805
Tel.: (407) 872-7555
Web Site: http://www.servicepainting.com
Rev.: $80,000
Emp.: 70
Painting & Paper Hanging
N.A.I.C.S.: 238320
Todd Monroe (VP)
Ed Dolan (Mgr-Project)
Kathleen Frazier (Mgr-Acct)
Jeff Heim (Mgr-Project)

Randy Jaskiewicz (Mgr-Project)
Robert Pope (Mgr-Project)
Steve Tyer (Treas)
Scott Wesolowski (Mgr-Project)
Melissa Williams (Office Mgr)

FIVE COUNTY CREDIT UNION
765 Washington St, Bath, ME 04530
Tel.: (207) 443-3528   ME
Web Site: https://www.fivecounty.com
Year Founded: 1956
Sales Range: $10-24.9 Million
Emp.: 154
Credit Union
N.A.I.C.S.: 522130
Merlin Suggs (Vice Chm)
Robert E. Brewer Jr. (Chm)

FIVE CROWNS CAPITAL, LLC
2729 West Coast Hwy, Newport
Beach, CA 92663
Tel.: (949) 340-3808
Web Site:
  http://www.fivecrownscapital.com
Investment Services
N.A.I.C.S.: 523999

**FIVE ELMS CAPITAL MAN-
AGEMENT LLC**
4801 Main St Ste 700, Kansas City,
MO 64112
Tel.: (913) 953-8960
Web Site: http://www.fiveelms.com
Privater Equity Firm
N.A.I.C.S.: 523999
Chris Barton (VP)
Lauren Janek (VP-Ops)
Brooke Longtin (VP)
Fred Coulson (Founder & Mng Part-
ner)

**FIVE GUYS ENTERPRISES,
LLC**
10718 Richmond Hwy, Lorton, VA
22079-2079
Tel.: (703) 339-9500
Web Site: http://www.fiveguys.com
Year Founded: 1986
Sales Range: $1-4.9 Billion
Fast Food Restaurants Owner, Fran-
chisor & Operator
N.A.I.C.S.: 722513
Jerry Murrell (Founder & CEO)

**FIVE MILE CAPITAL PART-
NERS LLC**
Three Stamford Plz 301 Tresser Blvd
12th Fl, Stamford, CT 06901
Tel.: (203) 905-0950
Web Site:
  http://www.fivemilecapital.com
Sales Range: $1-9.9 Million
Emp.: 30
Investment & Asset Management
Services
N.A.I.C.S.: 523999
Steven P. Baum (Co-Founder & Prin-
cipal)
Thomas A. Kendall (Co-Founder &
Principal)
Konrad R. Kruger (Co-Founder &
Principal)

**FIVE NINES TECHNOLOGY
GROUP**
5000 Central Park Dr Ste 101, Lin-
coln, NE 68504
Tel.: (402) 817-2630
Web Site: http://www.gonines.com
Year Founded: 2006
Sales Range: $1-9.9 Million
Emp.: 40
Personalized IT Consulting & Support
Services
N.A.I.C.S.: 541618

Nick Bock (Co-Founder & CEO)
James Bowen (Co-Founder & CIO)
Blaine Kahle (Dir-Engrg)
Joel Friesen (Dir-Sls & Mktg)
Jennie Scheel (CFO)

FIVE POINT CAPITAL, INC.
13280 Evening Creek Dr S 200, San
Diego, CA 92128
Web Site:
  http://www.fivepointcapital.com
Year Founded: 1999
Sales Range: $10-24.9 Million
Emp.: 65
Equipment Leasing Financial Ser-
vices
N.A.I.C.S.: 522220
David Gilbert (Co-Founder & CEO)

FIVE POINT ENERGY LLC
825 Town and Country Ln Ste 700,
Houston, TX 77024
Tel.: (713) 351-0700
Web Site:
  http://www.fivepointenergy.com
Energy Investment Firm
N.A.I.C.S.: 523999
David N. Capobianco (CEO & Mng-
Partner)

Subsidiaries:

TERM Holdings, LLC   (1)
8847 W Sam Houston Pkwy N, Houston,
TX 77040   (50%)
Tel.: (713) 341-7300
Web Site: http://www.twineagle.com
Emp.: 500
Holding Company
N.A.I.C.S.: 551112
Griff Jones (Pres/CEO-Twin Eagle Re-
source Mgmt)
Chuck Watson (Chm)

Subsidiary (Domestic):

Twin Eagle Resource Management,
LLC   (2)
1700 City Plaza Dr Ste 500, Spring, TX
77389
Tel.: (713) 341-7300
Web Site: http://www.twineagle.com
Petroleum & Natural Gas Transportation &
Distribution Services
N.A.I.C.S.: 213112
Griff Jones (Pres & CEO)
Charles L. Watson (Chm)
Larry B. Leverett (Exec VP)
James F. Thomas (Exec VP-Midstream
Ops)
Tom Godbold (Gen Counsel & Exec VP)
Larry Leverett (CFO)
Jimmy Thomas (Chief Admin Officer)
Jeremy Davis (Chief Comml Officer)

WaterBridge Resources LLC   (1)
3 Memorial City Plz 840 Ste 100, Houston,
TX 77024
Tel.: (713) 230-8864
Web Site: http://h2obridge.com
Waste Management Services
N.A.I.C.S.: 221310
Stephen M. Johnson (CEO)

**FIVE POINTS TECHNOLOGY
GROUP, INC.**
5971 Cattleridge Blvd, Sarasota, FL
34232
Tel.: (941) 751-1901
Web Site: https://www.fiveptg.com
Year Founded: 1999
Sales Range: $1-9.9 Million
Emp.: 40
Software Publisher
N.A.I.C.S.: 513210
Anne Folsom (Pres)

**FIVE RIVERS MEDICAL CEN-
TER INC**
2801 Medical Center Dr, Pocahontas,
AR 72455
Tel.: (870) 892-6000   AR

Web Site:
  http://www.fiveriversmc.com
Year Founded: 2010
Sales Range: $10-24.9 Million
Emp.: 254
Healtcare Services
N.A.I.C.S.: 622110
Joey Radcliff (CFO)

**FIVE STAR AIRPORT ALLI-
ANCE, INC.**
1630 S 4800 W Ste D, Salt Lake
City, UT 84104
Tel.: (801) 401-5500
Web Site: https://www.fivestaraa.com
Year Founded: 2012
Baggage Conveyor Contractor
N.A.I.C.S.: 238210
George Saffo (Owner)
Paul Shaffer (Pres & CEO)
Tim Berndt (COO)
Shawna Wichtoski (VP-Fin)
Dan Bell (VP-Ops)

FIVE STAR COOPERATIVE
1949 N Linn Ave, New Hampton, IA
50659
Tel.: (641) 394-3052
Web Site:
  http://www.fivestarcoop.com
Year Founded: 1946
Sales Range: $50-74.9 Million
Emp.: 130
Marketer of Grains
N.A.I.C.S.: 424510
Robert Lynch (Controller & Asst Mgr)
ken Smith (CEO & Gen Mgr)

FIVE STAR CREDIT UNION
411 N Foster St, Dothan, AL 36303-
4623
Tel.: (334) 793-7714
Web Site: http://www.fivestarcu.com
Year Founded: 1964
Rev.: $9,800,000
Emp.: 57
Fiscal Year-end: 12/31/07
Federal Credit Unions
N.A.I.C.S.: 522130

**FIVE STAR DEVELOPMENT,
INC.**
1501 Preble Ave, Pittsburgh, PA
15233
Tel.: (412) 802-2500
Web Site:
  https://www.fivestardev.com
Year Founded: 1997
Sales Range: $1-9.9 Million
Emp.: 40
Corporate Consulting & Training Ser-
vices
N.A.I.C.S.: 541611
Lou Camerlengo (Co-Founder &
Pres)
David N. Colaizzi (Co-Founder, CEO
& CTO)
Angel Lehrian (Dir-HR)
Cory Seaman (Dir-Res & IT Svcs)
Nathan Smith (Dir-New Bus Dev)

FIVE STAR DODGE INC.
3068 Riverside Dr, Macon, GA 31210
Tel.: (478) 474-3700
Web Site:
  http://www.fivestaronline.net
Rev.: $53,000,000
Emp.: 125
Sales of New & Used Automobiles
N.A.I.C.S.: 441110
Charlie Cantrell Jr. (Owner)

**FIVE STAR ELECTRIC MO-
TORS**
4729 Shavano Oak, San Antonio, TX
78249

Five Star Electric Motors—(Continued)

Tel.: (210) 492-4200
Web Site:
http://www.fivestarelectric.com
Sales Range: $25-49.9 Million
Emp.: 30
Motor Controls, Starters & Relays:
Electric
N.A.I.C.S.: 423610
Aron Sekula (Mgr-Engrg)
Reagan Wiseman (Engr-Design)
Christopher Pitts (Engr-Automation)
James Cullinan (Owner & Gen Mgr)

FIVE STAR EQUIPMENT INC.
1300 Dunham Dr, Dunmore, PA
18512
Tel.: (570) 346-1701   PA
Web Site:
http://www.fivestarequipment.com
Year Founded: 1984
Sales Range: $10-24.9 Million
Emp.: 110
Sales of Industrial Machinery &
Equipment
N.A.I.C.S.: 423830
Mike Kozlowski (Controller)
Steve Nebzydoski (Mgr-Sls)
Jeffery Beggin (Mgr-Terminal)

FIVE STAR FORD
1635 S I 35 E, Carrollton, TX 75006
Tel.: (972) 242-6415
Web Site:
http://www.sampacksfivestar
ford.com
Rev.: $130,000,000
Emp.: 212
Automobiles, New & Used
N.A.I.C.S.: 441110
Sam Pack (Pres & CEO)
Bobby Richardson (Mgr-Used Car
Sls)
Brian Huth (Gen Mgr)
Alan J. Rosner (Dir-Comml Fleet
Bus)
Trey Russell (Gen Mgr-Sls)

**FIVE STAR INTERNATIONAL
LLC**
1810 S 19th St, Harrisburg, PA 17104
Tel.: (717) 986-1500
Web Site: http://www.fivestarintl.com
Year Founded: 1997
Sales Range: $10-24.9 Million
Emp.: 300
Trucks, Tractors & Trailers: New &
Used
N.A.I.C.S.: 441110
Peter F. Scheler (Co-Owner)
Frederick Scheler (Pres)
John A. Scheler (Co-Owner)

FIVE STAR MOTORS
711 E Wishkah St, Aberdeen, WA
98520
Tel.: (360) 533-3673
Web Site:
http://www.fivestargr8deals.com
Rev.: $50,900,000
Emp.: 60
Automobiles, New & Used
N.A.I.C.S.: 441110
Debbie Gleeson (Office Mgr)

**FIVE STAR OF COLORADO
INC.**
1540 Auto Mall Loop, Colorado
Springs, CO 80920
Tel.: (719) 867-6400
Rev.: $92,000,000
Emp.: 80
Automobiles, New & Used
N.A.I.C.S.: 441110
Gerald Cimino (Pres)

FIVE STAR OF KNOX INC.
1209 S Heaton St, Knox, IN 46534
Tel.: (574) 772-4184
Rev.: $10,000,000
Emp.: 35
Grocery Stores, Independent
N.A.I.C.S.: 445110
Randall Weiss (Pres)

FIVE STAR PARKING
600 S Spring St Ste 1750, Los Ange-
les, CA 90014
Tel.: (213) 627-8211
Web Site: http://tlrgc.com
Rev.: $14,800,000
Emp.: 10
Parking Garage
N.A.I.C.S.: 812930
Joseph Lumer (Pres)

FIVE STAR RESTAURANT LLC
1856 Pama Ln Ste A, Las Vegas, NV
89119
Tel.: (702) 914-0441
Web Site:
http://www.zeffirinolasvegas.com
Sales Range: $10-24.9 Million
Emp.: 200
Eating Place
N.A.I.C.S.: 722511
David Williamson (Pres)

**FIVE-O MARKETING SER-
VICES INC.**
115 Mokauea St, Honolulu, HI 96819
Tel.: (808) 842-6111
Rev.: $13,200,000
Emp.: 50
General Line Grocery Merchant
Whslr
N.A.I.C.S.: 424410
Richard M. Kunimoto (VP)
William F. Francis (Pres)
Glenn Sakuda (Treas & Sec)

FIVEABLE, INC.
2550 N Lake Dr Ste 2, Milwaukee,
WI 53211
Web Site: http://hi.fiveable.me
Primary/Secondary Education Pro-
gram Services
N.A.I.C.S.: 923110
Amanda DoAmaral (Co-Founder &
CEO)

FIXATION MARKETING
4340 E-W Hwy Ste 200, Bethesda,
MD 20814
Tel.: (240) 207-2009   DC
Web Site: http://www.fixation.com
Year Founded: 1963
Sales Range: $50-74.9 Million
Emp.: 17
N.A.I.C.S.: 541810
Jean Whiddon (Pres & CEO)
Sharyn G. Collinson (Mng Dir)
Elizabeth Ellen (Sr Graphic Designer)
John Frantz (Sr Art Dir)
Randy Guseman (Sr Dir-Art)
Alexis De La Rosa (Acct Mgr)
Amelia Whiddon (Acct Exec)
Megan Campbell (Acct Dir)
Leo Salazar (Acct Exec-Interactive)

**FIZZANO BROTHERS CON-
CRETE PRODUCTS**
1776 Chester Pike, Crum Lynne, PA
19022
Tel.: (610) 833-1100
Web Site: https://www.fizzano.com
Sales Range: $10-24.9 Million
Emp.: 11
Concrete & Cinder Block Mfr & Distr
N.A.I.C.S.: 423320
Vince Tocci (Controller)
Anthony Fizzano III (Owner)

FJ CAPITAL MANAGEMENT
1313 Dolley Madison Blvd Ste 306,
McLean, VA 22101
Tel.: (703) 331-5500
Web Site: http://www.fjcapital.com
Investment Advisor
N.A.I.C.S.: 523940
Martin Friedman (Founder & CEO)

Subsidiaries:

Georgia Banking Company   (1)
6190 Powers Ferry Rd NW 150, Sandy
Springs, GA 30339
Tel.: (770) 690-9100
Web Site: http://www.geobanking.com
Banking Services
N.A.I.C.S.: 522110
S. Trezevant Moore Jr. (Mng Dir)
Elliott Miller (Pres)
Thomas Rockwood (VP-Comml Lending)
Joy Beam-Burns (VP-Bus Dev & Ware-
house Lending)
Bartow Morgan Jr. (CEO)
James R. Lientz Jr. (Chm)

FJ MANAGEMENT, INC.
185 S State St Ste 1300, Salt Lake
City, UT 84111-1561
Tel.: (801) 624-1000   UT
Web Site: http://www.fjmgt.com
Year Founded: 1968
Sales Range: $15-24.9 Billion
Emp.: 15,000
Offices of Other Holding Companies
N.A.I.C.S.: 551112
Brett Bailey (Gen Counsel)
Amanda Poitra (Chief HR Officer)

Subsidiaries:

Big West Oil, LLC   (1)
1104 Country Hills Dr Ste 500, Ogden, UT
84403   (100%)
Tel.: (801) 624-1000
Web Site: http://www.bigwestoil.com
Sales Range: $1-4.9 Billion
Emp.: 410
Petroleum Refining Services
N.A.I.C.S.: 324110

Fleet Sales LLC   (1)
1980 S 1250 W, Ogden, UT 84401
Tel.: (801) 619-2812
Web Site: http://www.ftsales.com
Sales Range: $10-24.9 Million
Emp.: 7
Used Heavy-Duty Truck & Equipment
Dealer
N.A.I.C.S.: 441227

Subsidiary (Domestic):

Flying J Insurance   (2)
1104 Country Hill Dr, Ogden, UT 84403
Tel.: (801) 624-4500
Insurance Services
N.A.I.C.S.: 524126

Flying J Transportation (Fuel
Distribution)   (1)
1104 Country Hills Dr, Ogden, UT 84403
Tel.: (801) 624-1000
Bulk Fuel Carrier
N.A.I.C.S.: 484230

Flying J, Inc-Real Estate Division (1)
3707 N Canyon Rd Ste 1B, Provo, UT
84604
Tel.: (801) 363-2444
Travel Facility Real Estate
N.A.I.C.S.: 531390

Transportation Alliance Bank   (1)
4185 Harrison Blvd Ste 200, Ogden, UT
84403
Tel.: (801) 624-4800
Web Site: http://www.tabbank.com
Sales Range: $50-74.9 Million
Emp.: 200
Financial Services
N.A.I.C.S.: 522320
Bill Bahls (VP-Bus Dev-Northeast)
Justin Hatch (Sr VP-East)

**FKQ ADVERTISING + MAR-
KETING INC.**

15351 Roosevelt Blvd, Clearwater,
FL 33760-3534
Tel.: (727) 539-8800   FL
Web Site: https://www.fkq.com
Year Founded: 1961
Sales Range: $10-24.9 Million
Emp.: 80
Advetising Agency
N.A.I.C.S.: 541810
Robert O. Faller (Founder)
Lisa M. Faller (Pres)
Karen L. Gorenflo (Exec VP)
George Ferris (Exec VP)
Stacy Howell (Sr VP)
Christine Karner-Johnson (Dir-Media)
Ahjah Robert (Acct Coord)
Amanda Hebbeler (Mgr-Traffic)
Michele Davella (Grp Acct Mgr)

FLACK STEEL LLC
425 W Lakeside Ave Ste 200, Cleve-
land, OH 44113
Tel.: (480) 575-3221   DE
Web Site:
https://flackglobalmetals.com
Year Founded: 2010
Metals Mfr
N.A.I.C.S.: 332312
Jeremy Flack (Founder & CEO)

Subsidiaries:

Fabral, Inc.   (1)
3449 Hempland Rd, Lancaster, PA 17601
Tel.: (717) 397-2741
Web Site: http://www.fabral.com
Sales Range: $25-49.9 Million
Emp.: 220
Metal Work Mfr
N.A.I.C.S.: 332322
Adam Coffinberger (Mgr-Production)

Pacesetter Steel Service, Inc.   (1)
1045 Big Shanty Rd NW, Kennesaw, GA
30144
Tel.: (770) 919-8000
Web Site: http://www.teampacesetter.com
Sales Range: $125-149.9 Million
Emp.: 200
Provider of Steel Services
N.A.I.C.S.: 423510
Steven Leebow (COO)
Jessica Clare (Mgr-Credit)
Aviva Leebow (CEO)

FLACKS HOMES LLC
1450 Brickell Ave Ste 1900, Miami,
FL 33131
Tel.: (305) 647-2655   FL
Web Site: http://flacksgroup.com
Year Founded: 1985
Emp.: 7,000
Holding Company
N.A.I.C.S.: 551112
Michael Flacks (Chm & CEO)
Patricia Christensen (CFO)
Russell Goldman (VP)
Charles Gassenheimer (Mng Dir)
James Desnick (Mng Dir)

Subsidiaries:

Corizon Health, Inc.   (1)
103 Powell Ct, Brentwood, TN 37027
Tel.: (615) 373-3100
Web Site: http://www.corizonhealth.com
Correctional Facility Healthcare Services
N.A.I.C.S.: 622110
J. Scott King (Chief Legal Officer & Exec
VP)
Frank Fletcher (Chief Growth Officer & Sr
VP)
Martha Harbin (Dir-External Affairs)
Douglas Thompson (Exec VP)
Scot Ward (Chief Admin Officer & Exec VP)
Jim Donovan (COO)
Levin Jones (Sr VP-Community Correc-
tions)
Rolly Maldonado (Sr VP-State Corrections)
Sally Powers (Chief HR Officer)
Shalin Shah (CFO)

Gregory A. Ladele *(Chief Medical Officer)*
Steven C. Tomlin *(Sr VP-Bus Dev)*
James E. Hyman *(CEO)*

Subsidiary (Domestic):

Corizon Health, Inc. **(2)**
12647 Olive Blvd, Saint Louis, MO 63141
Tel.: (314) 919-8501
Web Site: http://www.corizonhealth.com
Sales Range: $650-699.9 Million
Correctional Facility Healthcare Services
N.A.I.C.S.: 622110
Michael Miller *(VP-Client Partnerships)*

FLAD ARCHITECTS

644 Science Dr, Madison, WI 53711-1072
Tel.: (608) 238-2661
Web Site: https://www.flad.com
Year Founded: 1985
Sales Range: $25-49.9 Million
Emp.: 270
Architectural Services
N.A.I.C.S.: 541310
William J. Bula *(Principal)*
Chuck Mummert *(Principal)*
Mark Corey *(Principal)*
Javier Garay *(Principal)*
Paul Hansen *(Principal)*
Jeffrey Charles Raasch *(Principal)*
David Black *(Principal)*
Jim Gazvoda *(Principal)*
John Mickow *(Principal)*
Laura Serebin *(Principal)*
Rachel Nelan *(Principal)*

FLAG PUBLICATION, INC

11934 Ocean Gateway, Ste 6, Ocean City, MD 21842
Tel.: (410) 723-6397
Web Site:
https://www.oceancitytoday.com
Publications
N.A.I.C.S.: 513199

FLAG SHIP CORPORATION

260 Madison Ave 8th Fl, New York, NY 10016
Tel.: (917) 267-4567   Ky
Year Founded: 2021
Emp.: 2
Investment Services
N.A.I.C.S.: 523999
Matthew Chen *(CEO & Chm)*
Luhuan Zhong *(CFO)*

FLAGG RV CENTER

66 W Boylston St, West Boylston, MA 01583
Tel.: (508) 835-3190
Web Site: http://www.flaggrv.com
Year Founded: 1981
Sales Range: $10-24.9 Million
Emp.: 40
Recreational Vehicle Whslr
N.A.I.C.S.: 441210
Brigitte Flagg *(Mgr-Fin & Insurance)*
Maro P. Flagg Jr. *(Pres)*

FLAGGER FORCE

1411 Stoneridge Dr, Middletown, PA 17057
Tel.: (717) 944-8440
Web Site:
https://www.flaggerforce.com
Year Founded: 2002
Sales Range: $25-49.9 Million
Emp.: 766
Flagging & Traffic Control Services
N.A.I.C.S.: 561990
Mike Doner *(Co-Founder, Pres & CEO)*
Corey Gauker *(Coord-Warehouse)*
Michael Henry *(Mgr-Traffic Safety)*
Edd J. Gall *(VP-Risk Mgmt)*
Jen Strobel *(VP-HR)*

FLAGHOUSE INC.

601 Flaghouse Dr, Hasbrouck Heights, NJ 07604-3116
Tel.: (201) 288-7600   NJ
Web Site: https://www.flaghouse.com
Year Founded: 1986
Sales Range: $10-24.9 Million
Emp.: 105
Sporting & Recreation Goods
N.A.I.C.S.: 423910
George Carmel *(Pres)*
John Ruggiero *(Mgr-Sls)*
Fred Packard *(Mgr-Pur)*
Toni Ferrante *(Mgr-Acctg)*
Ileana Ferrandiz *(Mgr-Sls)*

FLAGLER BANCSHARES CORPORATION

555 Northlake Blvd, North Palm Beach, FL 33408
Tel.: (561) 841-3868
Emp.: 100
Bank Holding Company
N.A.I.C.S.: 551111

FLAGLER SYSTEM INC.

1 S County Rd, Palm Beach, FL 33480
Tel.: (561) 655-6611
Web Site:
http://www.thebreakers.com
Year Founded: 1989
Sales Range: $350-399.9 Million
Emp.: 2,000
Hotels (except Casino Hotels) & Motels
N.A.I.C.S.: 721110
Bruce Leet *(Mgr-Natl Sls)*
Cara Pregadio *(Sls Mgr-Natl)*
Jessica Walters *(Sls Mgr-Natl)*
Dan Jenkins *(Sls Mgr-Natl)*
Jim Mostad *(Sr VP-Sls)*
Lauren Abriola *(Sls Mgr-Natl)*
Marguerite Beau *(Dir-Sls)*
Shannon Favole *(Sls Mgr-Natl)*

Subsidiaries:

Breakers Palm Beach Inc. **(1)**
1 S County Rd, Palm Beach, FL 33480-4023
Tel.: (561) 655-6611
Web Site: http://www.thebreakers.com
Sales Range: $200-249.9 Million
Emp.: 1,800
Hotel Services
N.A.I.C.S.: 721110
Paul Leone *(Pres)*
Lauren Abriola *(Mgr-Sls-Natl)*
Marguerite Beau *(Dir-Sls)*
Shannon Favole *(Mgr-Sls-Natl)*
Loren Glenn *(Mgr-Sls-Natl)*
Bruce Leet *(Mgr-Sls-Natl)*
Cara Pregadio *(Mgr-Sls-Natl)*
Caitlin Schilkie *(Mgr-Bus Dev Sls)*
Tricia Taylor *(Exec VP & Gen Mgr)*
Denise Bober *(Sr VP-HR)*

Breakers West Development Corp. **(1)**
1 S County Rd, Palm Beach, FL 33480
Tel.: (561) 655-6611
Web Site: http://www.breakers.com
Condominium & Rental Property Management Services
N.A.I.C.S.: 531311
Paul N. Leone *(Pres)*

FLAGSHIP AUTO CENTER

908 W Lima St, Kenton, OH 43326
Tel.: (419) 673-7216
Web Site:
http://www.flagshipautocenter.com
Sales Range: $10-24.9 Million
Emp.: 35
Sales of New & Used Automobiles
N.A.I.C.S.: 441110
Rose Droesch *(Controller)*
Danny Faulder *(Gen Mgr)*

FLAGSHIP BIOSCIENCES, INC.

11800 Ridge Pkwy Ste 450, 80021, Broomfield, CO
Tel.: (303) 325-5894
Web Site:
https://www.flagshipbio.com
Year Founded: 2009
Emp.: 100
Spatial Biology & Biomarker Services Company
N.A.I.C.S.: 541714
Gina M. Wallar *(Chief Comml Officer)*
Trevor Johnson *(CEO)*

Subsidiaries:

Interpace BioPharma, LLC **(1)**
300 Interpace Pkwy, Parsippany, NJ 07054
Tel.: (862) 207-7800
Digital Communication Services
N.A.I.C.S.: 519290
Donna McConeghey *(Mgr-Specialty Territory)*

FLAGSHIP CREDIT CORPORATION

3 Christy Dr Ste 201, Chadds Ford, PA 19317
Tel.: (610) 717-1900   DE
Web Site: http://www.flagshipacc.com
Year Founded: 2014
Emp.: 595
Holding Company; Automobile Sales Financing & Lending Services
N.A.I.C.S.: 551112
Michael C. Ritter *(Pres & CEO)*
Jeffrey Butcher *(Interim Co-CFO)*
Kenneth J. Sicinski *(Interim Co-CFO)*
David Bertoncini *(Chief Risk Officer & Chief Strategy Officer)*
Dennis Morris *(COO)*
Debra Glasser *(Gen Counsel & Sec)*
Christopher Keiser *(Chief Compliance Officer & Regulatory Counsel)*

Subsidiaries:

CarFinance Capital LLC **(1)**
7525 Irvine Ctr Dr Ste 250, Irvine, CA 92618
Tel.: (317) 717-1665
Web Site: http://www.carfinancecapital.com
Automobile Sales Financing & Lending Services
N.A.I.C.S.: 522291
Debra Glasser *(Gen Counsel)*
Dennis Morris *(COO)*

Flagship Credit Acceptance LLC **(1)**
3 Christy Dr Ste 201, Chadds Ford, PA 19317
Tel.: (610) 717-1900
Web Site: http://www.flagshipacc.com
Automobile Sales Financing & Lending Services
N.A.I.C.S.: 522220
Michael C. Ritter *(Chm)*
Robert A. Hurzeler *(CEO)*
Kenneth J. Sicinski *(CFO & Sr VP)*
David Bertoncini *(Sr VP-Strategic Dev & Risk)*
Bob Hurzeler *(CEO)*
Jeffrey Haymore *(Pres & COO)*

FLAGSHIP FACILITY SERVICES, INC.

405 S Kimball Ave, Southlake, TX 76092
Tel.: (844) 649-8884
Web Site: https://flagshipinc.com
Year Founded: 1988
Emp.: 6,000
Facilities Services
N.A.I.C.S.: 561210
David Pasek *(CEO & Founder)*

Subsidiaries:

Managed Lab Services Inc. **(1)**
16855 W Bernardo Dr Ste 320, San Diego, CA 92127-1667
Tel.: (858) 771-3622
Web Site: http://www.managedlab.com

Medical Laboratories
N.A.I.C.S.: 621511
Taylor Moyer *(Pres, CEO & Acct Mgr)*

FLAGSHIP FINANCIAL GROUP, INC.

445 E Lake St Ste 110, Wayzata, MN 55391-1670
Tel.: (952) 473-1959
Web Site:
http://www.flagshipbanks.com
Sales Range: $1-9.9 Million
Emp.: 19
Bank Holding Company
N.A.I.C.S.: 551111
Roy Terwilliger *(Chm, Pres & CEO)*
Jackie Herman *(CFO)*

Subsidiaries:

Flagship Bank Minnesota **(1)**
445 E Lake St Ste 110, Wayzata, MN 55391-1670
Tel.: (952) 473-1959
Web Site: http://www.flagshipbanks.com
Rev.: $4,282,000
Assets: $90,032,000
Liabilities: $81,865,000
Net Worth: $8,167,000
Earnings: $201,000
Fiscal Year-end: 12/31/2012
Commericial Banking
N.A.I.C.S.: 522110
Roy Terwilliger *(Chm)*
Steve Droen *(Pres & CEO)*
Jackie Herman *(CFO, Sr VP & Dir-Ops)*
Erin Steckler *(Sr VP & Comml Credit Officer)*
Pat Layde *(VP & Compliance Officer)*
Don Kleinschmidt *(VP-Bus Banking)*
Suzette Onstad *(VP-Bank Admin)*
Andy Schornack *(Pres & CEO)*
Julie Schornstein *(Mgr-Ops)*
Brian Wagner *(Sr VP-Bus Banking)*

FLAGSHIP FOOD GROUP, LLC

2205 E Riverside Dr Ste 200, Eagle, ID 83616
Tel.: (208) 383-9600
Web Site:
https://flagshipfoodgroup.com
Diversified Food Company
N.A.I.C.S.: 311999

Subsidiaries:

Yucatan Foods, LLC **(1)**
9841 Airport Blvd Ste 578, Los Angeles, CA 90045
Tel.: (310) 342-5363
Web Site: http://www.avocado.com
Canning Services
N.A.I.C.S.: 311422

FLAGSHIP RESORT DEVELOPMENT

4272 Harbor Beach Blvd, Brigantine, NJ 08203
Tel.: (609) 266-7400
Web Site:
http://www.fantasearesort.com
Rev.: $33,232,265
Emp.: 500
Time-Sharing Real Estate Sales, Leasing & Rentals
N.A.I.C.S.: 531390
Tracy Good *(Dir-HR)*

FLAGSHIP TRADING CORP.

734 Alpha Dr, Cleveland, OH 44143-2125
Tel.: (440) 605-0022
Web Site: http://www.lumberone.com
Sales Range: $10-24.9 Million
Emp.: 16
Structural Lumber & Timber, Treated Wood
N.A.I.C.S.: 321114
Steven A. Belman *(Pres)*

FLAGSHIP VENTURES

Flagship Ventures—(Continued)

1 Memorial Dr 7th Fl, Cambridge, MA 02142
Tel.: (617) 868-1888
Web Site:
　http://www.flagshipventures.com
Year Founded: 1999
Sales Range: $10-24.9 Million
Emp.: 45
Venture Capital & Investments
N.A.I.C.S.: 523999
Noubar B. Afeyan (Founder)
Jim Matheson (Partner)
David Berry (Gen Partner)
Roger James Pomerantz (Sr Partner)
Robert Berendes (Partner-Venture)
Chuck Carelli (CFO)
Dessi Jablenski (Controller)
Lauren Digange (Mgr-Mktg)
Brian Baynes (Partner)
Ignacio Martinez (Partner)
Stacie Rader (Partner-Talent Mgmt)
Jeffrey Krasner (Sr Dir-Comm)
Miguel Ilzarbe (VP-Exec Ops)
Daniel McIntyre (Partner-Strategic Comm)
Jim Gilbert (Sr Partner)
Michael Rosenblatt (Chief Medical Officer)
Stephen A. Berenson (Partner)
Christine Heenan (Sr Partner & Chief Comm Officer)
Edwin M. Kania Jr. (Co-Founder & Mng Partner)
David R. Epstein (Partner)

FLAMBEAU RIVER PAPERS LLC

200 1st Ave N, Park Falls, WI 54552
Tel.: (715) 762-3231
Web Site:
　http://www.flambeauriverpapers.com
Year Founded: 2006
Sales Range: $10-24.9 Million
Emp.: 300
Paper Mill Services
N.A.I.C.S.: 322120
John Pettit (Pres)
Tammy Carrano (VP-Ops-CellMark Paper)

FLAME ENTERPRISES INCORPORATED

21500 Glenhill St, Chatsworth, CA 91311
Tel.: (818) 700-2905
Web Site: https://www.flamecorp.com
Sales Range: $10-24.9 Million
Emp.: 40
Electronic Parts
N.A.I.C.S.: 423690
Mike Epstein (Pres)

FLAME FURNACE CO.

2200 E 11 Mile Rd, Warren, MI 48091
Tel.: (586) 582-1700
Web Site:
　https://www.flamefurnace.com
Sales Range: $10-24.9 Million
Emp.: 110
Heating Systems Repair & Maintenance
N.A.I.C.S.: 238220
Gary Marowske (Pres)

FLAMINGO OIL COMPANY

205 NE 179th St, Miami, FL 33162
Tel.: (305) 652-2944
Web Site: http://www.pinkbird.com
Rev.: $20,000,000
Emp.: 60
Petroleum & Petroleum Products Merchant Whslr
N.A.I.C.S.: 424720

Dale U. Moseley Jr. (Pres, Treas, Sec & VP)

FLANDERS ELECTRIC MOTOR SERVICE INC.

8101 Baumgart Rd, Evansville, IN 47725-1509
Tel.: (812) 867-7421　　　**IN**
Web Site:
　http://www.flanderselectric.com
Year Founded: 1964
Sales Range: $25-49.9 Million
Emp.: 600
Armature Rewinding Shops
N.A.I.C.S.: 811310
Mary Wiener (Coord-HR)
Zack Bristow (Engr-Power Electronics)

FLANDERS INDUSTRIES, INC.

1901 Wheeler Ave, Fort Smith, AR 72901-5425
Tel.: (479) 785-2351　　　**AR**
Web Site:
　http://www.lloydflanders.com
Year Founded: 1970
Sales Range: $150-199.9 Million
Emp.: 400
Wooden Furniture Mfr
N.A.I.C.S.: 337126
Don H. Flanders (Chm)
Dudley K. Flanders (Pres)
Jeffrey Starks (Sec & Treas)

Subsidiaries:

Lloyd/Flanders Industries, Inc.　　(1)
3010 10th St, Menominee, MI 49858-1704
Tel.: (906) 863-4491
Web Site: http://www.loydflanders.com
Sales Range: $50-74.9 Million
Emp.: 100
Mfr of Wicker & Aluminum Furniture
N.A.I.C.S.: 337126
Dudley K. Flanders (Pres)
Jeff Starks (Controller)

FLANNER & BUCHANAN, INC.

600 E Ohio St, Indianapolis, IN 46202
Tel.: (317) 387-7000
Web Site:
　http://www.flannerbuchanan.com
Funeral Home Operator
N.A.I.C.S.: 812210
Bruce W. Buchanan (CEO)
Tony Lloyd (Pres & COO)
Carlos Figueroa (CFO & Sr VP)
Ted Mau (Chief Admin Officer & Sr VP)

Subsidiaries:

Lavenia Smith & Summers Home for Funerals　　(1)
5811 E 38th St, Indianapolis, IN 46218
Tel.: (317) 547-5814
Web Site: http://www.laveniasummers.com
Funeral Homes & Funeral Services
N.A.I.C.S.: 812210
Natalie Summers-Henson (Dir-Funeral)
George Brown (Dir-Funeral)
Emanuel C. Smith Jr. (Mng Dir)

FLANNERS AUDIO & VIDEO INC.

16271 W Lincoln Ave, West Allis, WI 53214
Tel.: (262) 860-6220
Web Site: http://www.flanners.com
Sales Range: $10-24.9 Million
Emp.: 25
High Fidelity Stereo Equipment Sales
N.A.I.C.S.: 449210
John Flanner (Pres)

FLASH EXTERMINATING, INC.

310 Montgomery St, Brooklyn, NY 11225-2722

Tel.: (347) 748-8023
Web Site:
　http://www.nycwildliferemoval.com
Exterminating & Pest Control Services
N.A.I.C.S.: 561710
Aaron M. Dominguez (Owner)

Subsidiaries:

Cook's Pest Control, Inc.　　(1)
1741 5th Ave SE, Decatur, AL 35601-5923
Tel.: (256) 355-3285
Web Site: http://www.cookspest.com
Sales Range: $10-24.9 Million
Emp.: 100
Provider of Disinfecting & Pest Control Services
N.A.I.C.S.: 561710
Jim Aycock (Pres & CEO)
Faye Golden (Mgr-Govt Affairs)
Ricky McCollister (Mgr-Property Mgmt)
Scott Pearman (Mgr-Wdo Claims)
Jeremy Bradley (Mgr-Nashville District)
Robin Jackson (Mgr-HR)
Johnny Fargason (Acct Exec)

FLASH LOGISTICS SERVICES INC.

10 Old Bloomfield Ave, Pine Brook, NJ 07058
Tel.: (973) 808-3366
Web Site:
　http://www.flashlogistics.com
Rev.: $20,000,000
Emp.: 46
Supply Chain Solutions
N.A.I.C.S.: 493110
Jim van Leenan (Pres & CEO)

FLASH MARKETS INC.

105 W Harrison Ave, West Memphis, AR 72301-4230
Tel.: (870) 732-2242　　　**AR**
Web Site:
　http://www.flashmarketinc.com
Year Founded: 1986
Sales Range: $10-24.9 Million
Emp.: 25
Grocery Store & Gasoline Station Operator
N.A.I.C.S.: 445131
Jamie Patterson (Controller)
Shane Patterson (Pres)
Harold Patterson (Owner)

FLASH, INC.

630 Commercial Ave, Green Lake, WI 54941
Tel.: (920) 294-0430
Web Site:
　https://www.flashtrucking.com
Rev.: $13,600,000
Emp.: 125
Trucking Services
N.A.I.C.S.: 484110
Lynn M. Connell (Pres)
Patrick M. Connell (CEO)

FLASHCO MANUFACTURING, INC.

1452 Industrial Ave, Sebastopol, CA 95472
Tel.: (707) 824-4448
Web Site: https://www.flashco.com
Rev.: $7,329,000
Emp.: 7
Metal Service Centers & Other Metal Merchant Whslr
N.A.I.C.S.: 423510
Greg Morrow (CEO)

Subsidiaries:

Metkote Laminated Products Inc.　　(1)
1151 Union St, Taylor, PA 18517-8517
Web Site: http://www.metkote.com
Electroplating, Plating, Polishing, Anodizing & Coloring
N.A.I.C.S.: 332813
Elaine Rusnak (Office Mgr)

FLASHFUNDERS, INC.

6 Venture Ste 295, Irvine, CA 92618
Tel.: (310) 504-3706
Web Site:
　https://www.flashfunders.com
Investment Banking
N.A.I.C.S.: 523150
Brian Park (Founder)

Subsidiaries:

Sutter Securities, Inc.　　(1)
12 Geary St Ste 402, San Francisco, CA 94108
Tel.: (415) 352-6300
Web Site: http://www.suttersecurities.com
Security Brokers And Dealers
N.A.I.C.S.: 523150
Ander de Jounge (Mng Dir)
Berit Muh (Mng Dir)
Bert Moerings (Sr Mng Dir)
Gilbert E. Matthews (Chm & Sr Mng Dir)
Charles W. Dunn (Sr Mng Dir)
Frank Sorbara (Sr VP-Investments)
Lincoln Joe Smith (Chief Compliance Officer)
John Hong (Dir-Ops)

FLASHPARKING, INC.

3801 S Capital of Texas Hwy Ste 250, Austin, TX 78704
Web Site:
　https://www.flashparking.com
Emp.: 508
IT Consulting & Services
N.A.I.C.S.: 541690
Juan Rodriguez (Co-Founder & CEO)

Subsidiaries:

Ticketech, Inc.　　(1)
2704 41st Ave, Long Island City, NY 11101
Tel.: (718) 786-6988
Web Site: http://www.ticketech.com
Sales Range: $1-9.9 Million
Emp.: 25
Accounting Services
N.A.I.C.S.: 541219
Mauricio Cotto (COO)
Giselle Seychett (CFO)
Enrique Wauters (Chief Admin Officer)

FLASPOHLER RESEARCH GROUP, INC

1100 Main St, Kansas City, MO 64105
Tel.: (816) 421-5504
Web Site: http://www.frsurveys.com
Rev.: $1,500,000
Emp.: 10
Marketing Research & Public Opinion Polling
N.A.I.C.S.: 541910
Carol Seitz (Project Dir)
Curt Watkins (Sr VP)
James Flaspohler (Pres)
Rick Flaspohler (Pres)

FLASTER CORP.

3422 Old Capitol Trl, Wilmington, DE 19808
Tel.: (302) 442-7409　　　**DE**
Year Founded: 2011
Dry Goods Distr
N.A.I.C.S.: 424310
Ludmila Dijokene (CEO & CFO)
Jelena Gecevicha (Sec)

FLAT AUDIO TECHNOLOGIES, LLC

17802 134th Ave NE Bldg 4 Ste 20, Woodinville, WA 98072-8806
Tel.: (425) 686-7640
Web Site:
　http://www.tectonicaudiolabs.com
Year Founded: 2011
Emp.: 12
Audio Equipment Mfr
N.A.I.C.S.: 334310
David Stokes (COO)
Craig Hubbell (Chm & CEO)

Subsidiaries:

Tectonic Elements Ltd. (1)
Oakpark Business Centre, Alington Road,
Saint Neots, PE19 6WA, Cambridgeshire,
United Kingdom
Tel.: (44) 1480 216 214
Web Site: http://www.tectonicelements.com
Sales Range: $1-9.9 Million
Emp.: 19
Audio Speaker System Technology Developer
N.A.I.C.S.: 334310
Caroline O'Brien (Mng Dir)
Neil Robb (Sls Mgr-Europe)

Subsidiary (Non-US):

HiWave (Hong Kong) Limited (2)
Unit 212 Core Bldg 1, Hong Kong Science
Park, Sha Tin, NT, China (Hong Kong)
Tel.: (852) 2358 9932
Audio Equipment Mfr
N.A.I.C.S.: 334310

FLAT BRANCH HOME LOANS
101 S 5th St Ste 200, Columbia, MO
65201
Tel.: (573) 442-3850
Web Site:
https://www.flatbranchhome
loans.com
Year Founded: 2006
Sales Range: $1-9.9 Million
Emp.: 40
Mortgage Loan Brokers
N.A.I.C.S.: 522310
Jim Yankee (Pres)
Stephanie Turner (Mgr-Sls)

FLAT ENTERPRISES INC.
11058 W Addison St, Franklin Park,
IL 60131
Tel.: (847) 349-1500
Web Site: http://www.allpfs.com
Sales Range: $10-24.9 Million
Emp.: 32
Sanitary Food Containers Mfr & Distr
N.A.I.C.S.: 424130
Brian Flynn (Pres)
Greg Mejak (CFO)
Paul Flynn (Mgr-Sls)
Kurt Miller (Mgr-Pur)
Steve Schweikert (Mgr-Mktg)

FLAT RATE MOVING NEW YORK
27 Bruckner Blvd, New York, NY
10454
Tel.: (718) 475-5787
Web Site: http://www.flatrate.com
Sales Range: $10-24.9 Million
Emp.: 250
Trucking Service
N.A.I.C.S.: 484110
Sharone Ben-Harosh (Founder)
Israel Carmel (CFO)
Matt Brown (VP-Sls)

FLAT ROCK CAPITAL CORP.
1350 6th Ave 18th Fl, New York, NY
10019
Tel.: (212) 596-3413   MD
Web Site:
http://www.flatrockglobal.com
Year Founded: 2017
Rev.: $6,695,755
Assets: $105,629,206
Liabilities: $49,659,336
Net Worth: $55,969,870
Earnings: $3,219,153
Fiscal Year-end: 12/31/19
Financial Investment Services
N.A.I.C.S.: 523940
Robert K. Grunewald (Pres & CEO)
Richard A. Petrocelli (CFO & COO)

**FLATHEAD ELECTRIC COOP-
ERATIVE, INC.**

2510 US Hwy 2 E, Kalispell, MT
59901-2312
Tel.: (406) 751-4483
Web Site:
https://www.flatheadelectric.com
Sales Range: $400-449.9 Million
Emp.: 160
Electric Power Distribution Services
N.A.I.C.S.: 221122
Chris Byrd (VP)
Duane Braaten (Sec)
Mark Johnson (Gen Mgr)
George R. Taylor (Pres)

**FLATWORK TECHNOLOGIES
LLC**
3130 S 1030 W Ste 1, Salt Lake City,
UT 84119
Web Site:
http://www.powerblanket.com
Year Founded: 2005
Sales Range: $10-24.9 Million
Emp.: 200
Heated Wrap Mfr
N.A.I.C.S.: 333414
Brent Reddekopp (Pres)
Nate Evans (VP-Mktg)
Brad Mecham (Plant Mgr)
Shelby Thompson (Sls Mgr)
Jordan Olson (Controller)

**FLAVINE NORTH AMERICA,
INC.**
10 Reuten Dr, Closter, NJ 07624
Tel.: (201) 768-4190
Web Site: http://www.flavine.com
Year Founded: 1995
Sales Range: $25-49.9 Million
Emp.: 50
Chemical Products Distr
N.A.I.C.S.: 424690
Sunyog Chauhan (Pres & CEO)

**FLAVOR & FRAGRANCE SPE-
CIALTIES**
3 Industrial Ave, Mahwah, NJ 07430
Tel.: (201) 825-2025   NJ
Web Site: http://www.ffs.com
Year Founded: 1983
Flavoring & Fragrance Additives Mfr
N.A.I.C.S.: 311930
Michael Bloom (Pres)
Dianne Sansone (Dir-Technical Svcs)
Ed Duderich (Mgr-Pur)
Jorge Castrillon (Gen Mgr)

FLAVORS15, LLC
4201 Lyons Rd, Miamisburg, OH
45432
Web Site:
http://www.flavorsunited.com
Year Founded: 2015
Sales Range: $1-9.9 Million
Emp.: 13
Electronic Cigarette Mfr
N.A.I.C.S.: 339999
Emma May (Mgr-Customer Svc)

FLAX ARTIST'S MATERIALS
1501 Martin Luther King Jr Way,
Oakland, CA 94612
Tel.: (415) 552-2355
Web Site: http://www.flaxart.com
Year Founded: 1938
Sales Range: $10-24.9 Million
Emp.: 40
Art Supplies Retailer
N.A.I.C.S.: 459999

FLAX DESIGNS
303 Gunderman Rd, Spencer, NY
14883-9623
Tel.: (607) 273-0283   NY
Web Site: http://www.flaxdesigns.com
Year Founded: 1986
Sales Range: $10-24.9 Million

Emp.: 48
Mfr of Women's & Misses Outerwear
N.A.I.C.S.: 315250
Mary Johanson (Mgr-Sls)

FLAYCO PRODUCTS, INC.
4821 N Hale Ave, Tampa, FL 33684
Tel.: (813) 879-1356   FL
Web Site: https://www.flayco.com
Year Founded: 1976
Sales Range: $1-9.9 Million
Flavor Extracts, Food Colorings,
Juices, Sauces & Seasonings
N.A.I.C.S.: 311930
Jorge Astorquiza (Pres)

FLEENOR
2225 Harbor Bay Pkwy, Alameda, CA
94502
Tel.: (510) 633-2531
Web Site:
https://www.fleenorpaper.com
Rev.: $13,800,000
Emp.: 1,000
Paper Products Mfr
N.A.I.C.S.: 322299
Rebecca Fleenor (Pres & CEO)
John Rochex (Pres-Sls & Mktg)

**FLEENOR SECURITY SYS-
TEMS, INC.**
3 Morgan Ct, Johnson City, TN
37604
Tel.: (423) 282-3755
Web Site:
https://www.fleenorsecurity.com
Year Founded: 1972
Security System Services
N.A.I.C.S.: 561621
Norman D. Fleenor (Pres & Owner)
Debbie Bingham (Gen Mgr)
Will Fleenor (VP)
Roy Wagner (Sls Mgr)
Nick Mathes (Svc Mgr)
Angela Jackson (Mgr-Installation)
Andrew Foister (Mgr-Central Station)
Andre Duhime (Branch Mgr-Knoxville)

FLEET ACQUISITIONS LLC
6510 Golden Groves Ln, Tampa, FL
33610
Tel.: (813) 621-1734
Web Site:
http://www.fleetproductsfl.com
Sales Range: $10-24.9 Million
Emp.: 120
Truck Parts & Accessories
N.A.I.C.S.: 423120
Michael O'Brien (Controller)
Robert Langly (Mgr-Pur)

FLEET ADVANTAGE, LLC.
401 E Las Olas Blvd Ste 1720, Fort
Lauderdale, FL 33301
Tel.: (954) 615-4400
Web Site:
http://www.fleetadvantage.net
Year Founded: 2008
Sales Range: $100-124.9 Million
Emp.: 27
Software Product Development Ser-
vices
N.A.I.C.S.: 541511
John J. Flynn (CEO)
Michael D. Spence (Sr VP-Fleet
Svcs)
Peter Flynn (Sr VP-Portfolio Mgmt &
Remarketing)
Brian Holland (Pres & CFO)
Sandra Rosenfeld (Mgr-Ops)
Marc Gingold (VP-Syndication)
Fran Flynn (VP-Sustainability, Mktg &
Community Rels)
Jeff Morris (VP-Fin & Controller)
Trip O'Neil (Sr VP-Bus Dev)
Al Barner (VP-Bus Dev)

Terry Clouser (VP-Fleet Svcs)
Jon Keller (Sr VP-Sls)
Matt Hendrix (Sr Dir-Fleet Svcs)
James C. Griffin Jr. (CTO)

FLEET CAR LEASE INC.
7563 Dahlia St, Commerce City, CO
80022-1463
Tel.: (303) 288-4600   CO
Web Site: http://www.fleetcar.com
Year Founded: 1984
Sales Range: $25-49.9 Million
Emp.: 39
Auto Leasing Services
N.A.I.C.S.: 484230
Raymond J. Bonanno (Pres & CEO)
Ronald Jordan (CFO)

FLEET CARD FUELS INC.
4200 Buck Owens Blvd, Bakersfield,
CA 93308-4935
Tel.: (661) 321-9961   CA
Web Site:
http://www.fleetcardfuels.com
Year Founded: 1987
Sales Range: $25-49.9 Million
Emp.: 150
Petroleum Products
N.A.I.C.S.: 424720
William P. Davies (Owner)
Tom Dwelle (Pres)

FLEET ENGINEERS, INC.
1800 E Keating Ave, Muskegon, MI
49442-6121
Tel.: (231) 777-2537   MI
Web Site:
https://www.fleetengineers.com
Year Founded: 1963
Sales Range: $75-99.9 Million
Emp.: 100
Motor Vehicle Parts & Accessories
Mfr
N.A.I.C.S.: 336390
Wes Eklund (Owner, Pres & CEO)
Steve Antekeier (VP-Mfg)
Mark DeWitt (Mgr-HR)
Mike Thorsby (Dir-Supply Chain
Mgmt)

Subsidiaries:

Save-A-Load, Inc. (1)
327-A W Tremont Ave, Charlotte, NC
28203
Tel.: (704) 334-9062
Web Site: http://www.saveaload.com
Sales Range: $1-9.9 Million
Emp.: 20
Mfr of Cargo Bars for Tractor Trailers &
Pick-Up Trucks
N.A.I.C.S.: 336390
Cathy Littlejohn (VP & Gen Mgr)
Larry H. Sweet (Pres & CEO)

The Access Works, Inc. (1)
1800 E Keating Ave, Muskegon, MI
49442-6121   (100%)
Tel.: (231) 777-7291
Sales Range: Less than $1 Million
Emp.: 99
Mfr of Roll-Up Doors
N.A.I.C.S.: 336390

FLEET FEET, INC.
406 E Main St, Carrboro, NC 27510
Tel.: (919) 942-3102
Web Site:
http://www.fleetfeetsports.com
Year Founded: 1976
Sales Range: $1-9.9 Million
Emp.: 14
Shoe Stores
N.A.I.C.S.: 458210
Tom Raynor (Chm & CEO)
Jeff Phillips (Pres)

FLEET LEASE DISPOSAL INC.

Fleet Lease Disposal Inc.—(Continued)

272 SE 5th Ave, Delray Beach, FL 33483
Tel.: (561) 272-1300
Web Site: http://www.fleetlease.com
Sales Range: $10-24.9 Million
Emp.: 20
Automobiles
N.A.I.C.S.: 423110
Richard Tepper (Gen Mgr)
Gary A. Mott (Pres)
Ron Breslow (COO)
Carol Fowler (Dir-Bus Dev)
Chris Martelli (Dir-Bus Dev)
Holly Hill (Dir-Bus Dev)
Mike Agnew (Dir-Heavy Duty Sls-Natl)
Rita Miller (CFO)

FLEET MORRIS PETROLEUM INC.

108 Solleftea Dr, Madison, MS 39110
Tel.: (601) 898-3830
Rev.: $10,800,000
Emp.: 7
Convenience Store Operator
N.A.I.C.S.: 445131
Bradley Morris (Pres)
Brian Lee (Mng Dir)
Pamela Rutland (Mgr)

FLEET STREET LTD.

512 7th Ave, New York, NY 10018
Tel.: (212) 354-8990
Web Site:
    http://www.fleetstreetouterwear.com
Rev.: $22,200,000
Emp.: 55
Women's & Children's Outerwear
N.A.I.C.S.: 424350
Manny Haber (Founder, Pres & CEO)
Steve Haber (VP)
Howard Gutterman (Controller)

FLEET TEAM, INC.

6155 Rockside Rd, Ste 200, Independence, OH 44131
Tel.: (614) 699-2500
Web Site: https://fleetteam.com
Year Founded: 2012
Business Consulting Company
N.A.I.C.S.: 541618
Doug Riddle (Pres)

Subsidiaries:

Forklift Training Systems, Inc   (1)
1911 W High St, Newark, OH 43055-8127
Tel.: (614) 583-5749
Scientific & Technical Consulting Services
N.A.I.C.S.: 541690
David Hoover (Pres)

FLEET TIRE INCORPORATED

3730 N Wilson Way, Stockton, CA 95205
Tel.: (209) 466-1881
Web Site:
    https://www.brannontire.com
Rev.: $15,785,621
Emp.: 60
Automotive Tires
N.A.I.C.S.: 441340
Carey L. Cumberlege (Pres)

FLEETCO INC.

3003 Brick Church Pike, Nashville, TN 37207
Tel.: (615) 256-0600
Web Site: https://www.fleetco.net
Sales Range: $25-49.9 Million
Emp.: 30
Trailers For Trucks, New & Used
N.A.I.C.S.: 423110
Dale Broadrick (Founder & Pres)
Ricky Crague (Mgr-Svc)
Wayne Raymond (Mgr-Parts)

FLEETMASTER EXPRESS INC.

1814 Hollins Rd NE, Roanoke, VA 24012
Tel.: (540) 344-8834
Web Site:
    https://www.fleetmasterexpress.com
Rev.: $20,931,873
Emp.: 75
Trucking Service
N.A.I.C.S.: 484121
Steve Worman (CFO)
Gary Kasza (Dir-Safety & Risk Mgmt)

FLEETWING CORPORATION

742 S Combee Rd, Lakeland, FL 33801-6314
Tel.: (863) 665-7557   FL
Web Site: http://www.fleetwingoil.com
Year Founded: 1956
Sales Range: $150-199.9 Million
Emp.: 60
Petroleum Products
N.A.I.C.S.: 424720
Debbie Tate (Dir-Mktg)
Les Smith (Controller)

FLEETWOOD TRANSPORTA-TION SERVICES INC.

7642 S US Hwy 59, Diboll, TX 75941
Tel.: (936) 829-4735   TX
Web Site: http://www.ftwd.net
Year Founded: 1989
Sales Range: $25-49.9 Million
Emp.: 300
Trucking
N.A.I.C.S.: 488510
Dennis Berryhill (Pres & COO)
Wendy Bryan (Controller)
Ronny King (Treas)
Gary Powell (VP)

FLEETWOOD-FIBRE PACKAG-ING & GRAPHICS, INC.

15250 Don Julian Rd, City of Industry, CA 91745-1001
Tel.: (626) 968-8503   CA
Web Site: https://www.fleetwood-fibre.com
Year Founded: 1952
Sales Range: $25-49.9 Million
Emp.: 300
Corrugated & Solid Fiber Boxes
N.A.I.C.S.: 322211
Brad Jordan (Pres)
Debbie Manz-Slaman (Dir-HR)

FLEGELS HOME FURNISH-INGS

870 Santa Cruz Ave, Menlo Park, CA 94025
Tel.: (650) 326-9661
Web Site: http://www.flegels.com
Sales Range: $10-24.9 Million
Emp.: 30
Furniture Retailer
N.A.I.C.S.: 449110
Mark A. Flegel (Pres)
Ron Lohr (Mgr-Ops)

FLEGLER INVESTMENT COM-PANY

2021 S Lewis Ave Ste 400, Tulsa, OK 74104
Tel.: (918) 743-9100
Web Site:
    https://www.amscosupply.net
Sales Range: $10-24.9 Million
Emp.: 7
Heating & Air Conditioning Equipment & Supplies Whslr
N.A.I.C.S.: 423730
John Flegler (Pres)
Dick Fleglar (CEO)

FLEMING & VAN METRE

630 W Germantown Pke Ste 400, Plymouth Meeting, PA 19462
Tel.: (610) 941-0395   PA
Web Site: http://www.thinkfvm.com
Year Founded: 1987
Sales Range: $10-24.9 Million
Emp.: 25
Advertising Agencies
N.A.I.C.S.: 541810
Karen Murphy (Dir-Media-Campaigns)

FLEMING BROTHERS OIL COMPANY INC

6912 109th Ave, South Haven, MI 49090
Tel.: (269) 637-5255
Sales Range: $25-49.9 Million
Emp.: 81
Heating Oil Sales
N.A.I.C.S.: 457210
Thomas Fleming (Pres)
Cymbre Peterson (CFO)

FLEMING FEED & GRAIN INC.

309 N Main St, Leon, KS 67074
Tel.: (316) 742-3411
Web Site: https://www.flemingag.com
Rev.: $15,274,541
Emp.: 10
Grains
N.A.I.C.S.: 424510
Dick Fleming (Pres)
Debbie Fleming (Owner)

FLEMING PHARMACEUTI-CALS

1733 Gilsinn Ln, Fenton, MO 63026-2000
Tel.: (636) 343-5306   MO
Year Founded: 1960
Sales Range: $75-99.9 Million
Emp.: 125
Ethical Pharmaceuticals Mfr
N.A.I.C.S.: 325412
Phillip Dritsas (Pres)
Deborah Fleming Wurdack (Chief Ad-min Officer)

FLEMINGTON AUDI PORSCHE VOLKSWAGEN

213 Hwy 202, Flemington, NJ 08822
Tel.: (908) 782-2400
Web Site:
    https://www.flemingtonaudi.com
Car Whslr
N.A.I.C.S.: 441110
Steve Opdyke (Gen Mgr)
Peter Costigan (Gen Mgr-Sls)
Doug Mathewson (Sls Mgr)
Rob Barcellona (Mgr-Pre-Owned)
Zaneta Graf (Mgr-Internet Sls)
Corey Evans (Mgr-Fin)
Jon Budd (Mgr-Fin)

FLEMINGTON INSTRUMENT CO. INC.

55 Sandra Rd, Ringoes, NJ 08551
Tel.: (908) 782-4229
Web Site:
    https://www.flemingtoninstru-ment.com
Year Founded: 1977
Sales Range: $10-24.9 Million
Emp.: 80
Electronic Controls Installation
N.A.I.C.S.: 238210
Ralph Migliaccio (Pres)
James Pokriots (Project Mgr)

FLETCH'S INC.

825 Charlevoix Ave, Petoskey, MI 49770
Tel.: (231) 347-9651
Web Site: http://www.fletchs.com
Sales Range: $25-49.9 Million

Emp.: 40
New & Used Car Dealership
N.A.I.C.S.: 441110
John B. Johnson (Pres & Gen Mgr)
Bob Johnson (Co-Owner & Mgr-Fast Track, Collision Center & Svc)
Dana Burnett (Mgr-Parts)
Sarah Sobleski (Office Mgr)

FLETCHER ALLEN HEALTH CARE, INC.

111 Colchester Ave, Burlington, VT 05401-1473
Tel.: (802) 847-0000   VT
Web Site: http://www.fahc.org
Year Founded: 1983
Sales Range: $550-599.9 Million
Emp.: 4,836
Hospital Management Services
N.A.I.C.S.: 622110
Dawn LeBaron (VP-Hospital Svcs)
Laurie Gunn (VP-HR)
John Brumsted (CEO)
Eileen Whalen (Pres & COO)

FLETCHER INDUSTRIES INC.

1548 The Greens Way Ste 4, Jack-sonville Beach, FL 32250
Tel.: (904) 285-6921
Sales Range: $10-24.9 Million
Emp.: 10
Land Subdividers & Developers
N.A.I.C.S.: 237210
Jerome S. Fletcher (Pres)

FLETCHER INDUSTRIES-INTERNATIONAL, INC.

1485 Central Dr, Southern Pines, NC 28387-2105
Tel.: (910) 692-7133
Web Site:
    https://www.fletcherindustries.com
Yarn Processing, Winding/Weaving Machinery & Accessories Worldwide Mfr & Distr
N.A.I.C.S.: 333248
John H. Taws (Pres)

FLETCHER JONES MANAGE-MENT GROUP, INC.

7300 W Sahara Ave, Las Vegas, NV 89117
Tel.: (702) 739-9800
Web Site:
    http://www.fletcherjones.com
Sales Range: $25-49.9 Million
Emp.: 1,500
Buying & Selling of New & Used Cars
N.A.I.C.S.: 541611
Shawn Dettrey (CFO)
Rhonda Brees (Controller)
Fletcher Jones III (COO)
Fletcher Jones Jr. (Chm)

Subsidiaries:

Carson Toyota   (1)
1333 E 223rd St, Carson, CA 90745-4314
Tel.: (220) 220-2250
Web Site: http://www.carsontoyota.com
New Car Dealers
N.A.I.C.S.: 441110
Albert Skinner (Pres)

FLETCHER MUSIC CENTERS INC.

3966 Airway Cir, Clearwater, FL 33762
Tel.: (727) 571-1088
Web Site:
    http://www.fletchermusic.com
Year Founded: 1905
Sales Range: $100-124.9 Million
Emp.: 130
Musical Instrument & Supplies Sales
N.A.I.C.S.: 459140

John Riley *(Owner)*
Rick Dorn *(Pres & COO)*
Eric Garson *(Mgr)*
Tom Davison *(Mgr)*

FLETCHER VAN GILDER LLP

436 E Wayne St, Fort Wayne, IN 46802
Tel.: (260) 425-9777
Web Site: https://www.fvglaw.com
Year Founded: 2004
Law Firm; Legal Services
N.A.I.C.S.: 541110
David E. Bailey *(Atty)*

FLETCHER'S TIRE AND AUTO SERVICE

2228 W Northern Ave B101, Phoenix, AZ 85021
Tel.: (602) 246-4670
Web Site:
http://www.fletcherstireandauto.net
Sales Range: $10-24.9 Million
Emp.: 164
Automotive & Tire Repair
N.A.I.C.S.: 811198
Jerry Fletcher *(Mgr-Comml Sls)*
Ryan Miller *(Mgr)*

FLETCHER-REINHARDT COMPANY

3105 Corporate Exchange Ct, Bridgeton, MO 63044
Tel.: (314) 506-0700
Web Site: https://www.fr-electric.com
Rev.: $30,389,372
Emp.: 25
Electrical Apparatus & Equipment
N.A.I.C.S.: 423610
James G. Reinhardt *(Pres)*

FLEX HR, INC.

10700 Medlock Bridge Rd Ste 206, Johns Creek, GA 30097
Tel.: (770) 814-4225
Web Site: http://www.flexhr.com
Year Founded: 2001
Sales Range: $1-9.9 Million
Emp.: 25
Human Resource Consulting Services
N.A.I.C.S.: 541612
Jim Cichanski *(Pres & CEO)*
Philip A. Davis *(Sr VP)*
Joseph Dickens *(Sr VP)*
John Cascone *(Sr VP)*
Richard G. Woods *(Sr VP)*
Gene Caudle *(Sr VP)*
Paul Sundberg *(Sr VP)*
Heleen Grossman *(Sr VP)*
Michael G. Miller *(Sr VP)*
Doris Coleman *(Sr VP)*
Diana Farmer *(VP)*
Lauren W. Hawkins *(Sr VP)*
Teresa Monday *(Dir-Recruiting)*
Barry E. Flink *(Partner & Exec VP)*
George Hamilton *(Sr VP)*
Mike Zagrodny *(Sr VP)*
Cherie Pritchard *(Sr VP-HR Ops)*
Scears Lee III *(Sr VP)*

FLEX TECHNOLOGIES INC.

5479 Gundy Dr, Midvale, OH 44653
Tel.: (740) 922-5992   OH
Web Site:
https://www.flextechnologies.com
Year Founded: 1975
Sales Range: $25-49.9 Million
Emp.: 300
Mfr of Plastic Products
N.A.I.C.S.: 326199
Steve Kosla *(Acct Mgr)*

Subsidiaries:

Flex Technologies Inc. - Polyflex
Division   (1)

State Route 93, Baltic, OH 43804
Tel.: (330) 897-6311
Web Site:
http://www.polyflexcompounding.com
Emp.: 150
Lab Equipment Mfr & Distr
N.A.I.C.S.: 334516
Glen Burkett *(CEO)*

FLEX-A-LITE CONSOLIDATED INC.

7009 45th St Ct E, Fife, WA 98424
Tel.: (253) 922-2700
Web Site: http://www.flex-a-lite.com
Rev.: $11,000,000
Emp.: 75
Urethane & Other Foam Product Mfr
N.A.I.C.S.: 326150
Connie Rosi *(Controller)*
Lisa Chissus *(Owner & Pres)*

FLEX-N-GATE CORPORATION

1306 E University Ave, Urbana, IL 61802-2013
Web Site: https://www.flex-n-gate.com
Year Founded: 1956
Sales Range: $1-4.9 Billion
Emp.: 27,000
Other Motor Vehicle Parts Manufacturing
N.A.I.C.S.: 336390
Chris Evangelisti *(Dir-Security)*

Subsidiaries:

Flex-N-Gate Canada Company   (1)
538 Blanchard Park, Tecumseh, N8N 2L9, ON, Canada   **(100%)**
Tel.: (519) 727-3931
Web Site: http://www.flexngate.com
Sales Range: $25-49.9 Million
Emp.: 150
Mfr of Automotive Stampings
N.A.I.C.S.: 332119
Shahid Khan *(Owner & Pres)*

Plant (Domestic):

Ventra Plastics - Peterborough   (2)
775 Technology Dr, PO Box 660, Peterborough, K9J 6Z8, ON, Canada   **(100%)**
Tel.: (705) 742-3534
Web Site: http://www.ventraplastics.com
Sales Range: $100-124.9 Million
Plastic Auto Parts
N.A.I.C.S.: 326199

Ventra Angola, LLC   (1)
3000 Woodhull Dr, Angola, IN 46703-9318
Tel.: (260) 624-2397
Motor Vehicle Bumper & Structural Components Mfr
N.A.I.C.S.: 336370

Ventra Evart, LLC   (1)
601 W 7th St, Evart, MI 49631
Tel.: (239) 679-4270
Sales Range: $75-99.9 Million
Emp.: 450
Mfr of Plastic Parts for Vehicles
N.A.I.C.S.: 326199
Joseph Kasperlik *(Controller)*
Fred McCrory *(Supvr-Assembly)*
Don Duncan *(Supvr-Production)*

Ventra Ionia Main, LLC   (1)
14 N Beardsley Rd, Ionia, MI 48846-9734
Tel.: (616) 597-3220
Web Site: http://www.flex-n-gate.com
Sales Range: $125-149.9 Million
Emp.: 960
Motor Vehicle Bumpers, Trailer Hitches & Chrome Plated Plastic Components Mfr
N.A.I.C.S.: 336370
Ted Nelson *(Mgr-Pur)*
Brian Sparks *(Engr-Controls)*

Ventra LLC Grand Rapids Plant 5   (1)
3075 Breton St, Grand Rapids, MI 49512-1753
Tel.: (616) 949-1250
Web Site: http://www.ventra.com
Sales Range: $25-49.9 Million
Emp.: 200

Motor Vehicle Plastic & Trim Components Mfr
N.A.I.C.S.: 336390

FLEX-O-GLASS, INC.

1100 N Cicero Ave, Chicago, IL 60651
Tel.: (773) 379-7878   IL
Web Site: https://www.flexoglass.com
Year Founded: 1924
Sales Range: $100-124.9 Million
Emp.: 180
Plastic Film & Plastic Products Mfr
N.A.I.C.S.: 326113
Harold G. Warp *(Mgr-HR)*

Subsidiaries:

Flex-O-Film Plastic Div.   (1)
1100 N Cicero Ave, Chicago, IL 60651-3214
Tel.: (773) 379-7878
Web Site: http://www.flexoglass.com
Sales Range: $10-24.9 Million
Emp.: 8
Mfr of Plastics
N.A.I.C.S.: 326113

Warp Brothers   (1)
4647 W Augusta Blvd, Chicago, IL 60651-3310
Tel.: (773) 261-5200
Web Site: http://www.warps.com
Plastic Window Materials; Plastic Film & Sheeting; Other Plastic Products Mfr
N.A.I.C.S.: 326113
Harold G. Warp *(Pres & COO)*
David K. Roadruck *(Mgr-Adv & Mktg)*

FLEX-PAC

6075 Lakeside Blvd, Indianapolis, IN 46278
Tel.: (317) 872-0097
Web Site: https://www.flexp.com
Sales Range: $10-24.9 Million
Emp.: 62
Other Miscellaneous Nondurable Goods Whslr
N.A.I.C.S.: 424990
Mark Dinwiddie *(Owner & Pres)*
Eric W. Toth *(VP)*
Brad Anderson *(Mgr-Svc)*
Dawn Mayfield *(VP-First Response)*
Amie Roche *(Mgr-Pur)*

FLEX-PAC, INC.

6075 Lakeside Blvd, Indianapolis, IN 46278
Tel.: (317) 872-0097
Web Site: https://www.flexp.com
Year Founded: 1985
Sales Range: $10-24.9 Million
Emp.: 50
Piece Goods, Notions & Other Dry Goods Merchant Whslr
N.A.I.C.S.: 424310
Mark Dinwiddie *(Founder)*

FLEX-POWER INC.

823 Gilman St, Berkeley, CA 94710
Tel.: (510) 898-1359   CA
Web Site: http://www.flexpower.com
Pain Relief Cream Developer & Distr
N.A.I.C.S.: 325412
Rasheen Smith *(Pres)*

FLEXASEAL ENGINEERED SEALS AND SYSTEMS, LLC

291 Hurricane Ln, Williston, VT 05495
Tel.: (802) 878-8307   DE
Web Site: http://www.flexaseal.com
Year Founded: 2020
Industrial Supplies Merchant Whslr
N.A.I.C.S.: 423840
Hank Slauson *(Chm)*
Alex Slauson *(Pres)*
Trey Maxwell *(CEO)*
Jon Watzka *(Mgr-Svc & Ops-Pacific Northwest Seal Svc & Repair Ctr)*

Subsidiaries:

Flex-A-Seal, Inc.   (1)
1 Jackson St, Essex Junction, VT 05452
Tel.: (802) 878-8307
Web Site: http://www.flexaseal.com
Rev.: $8,800,000
Emp.: 50
Industrial Supplies Merchant Whslr
N.A.I.C.S.: 423840
Steve Pontbriand *(VP & Gen Mgr)*
Bruce Hale *(Mgr-Pur)*
Kimball Simmons *(VP)*

Momentum Engineered Systems, Inc.   (1)
7545 E Orem Dr, Houston, TX 77075
Tel.: (832) 804-7424
Web Site: http://www.momentumsys.com
Mechanical Seal Products Mfr
N.A.I.C.S.: 333996
Trey Maxwell *(CEO)*

Sound Seal & Packing Co.   (1)
7729 212th St SW, Edmonds, WA 98026
Tel.: (425) 771-0866
Sales Range: $1-9.9 Million
Emp.: 7
Industrial Supplies Whslr
N.A.I.C.S.: 423840
Ward Forrest *(Pres)*

FLEXBAR MACHINE CORP.

250 Gibbs Rd, Islandia, NY 11749-2612
Tel.: (631) 582-8440
Web Site: https://www.flexbar.com
Year Founded: 1965
Sales Range: $50-74.9 Million
Emp.: 30
Mfr of Machine Tools & Gauging Specialties
N.A.I.C.S.: 333515
Jonathan Adler *(Pres)*
Lou Valenti *(Dir-Sls)*
Larry Derrig *(Gen Mgr)*
Julia Mullen *(Mgr-Ops)*
John Faraci *(Product Mgr)*
Keith Donaldson *(Mgr-Pur)*

FLEXCON CORPORATION

1 Flexcon Indus Pk, Spencer, MA 01562-2642
Tel.: (508) 885-8200   MA
Web Site: http://www.flexcon.com
Year Founded: 1955
Sales Range: $600-649.9 Million
Emp.: 800
Holding Company; Film & Adhesive Products Mfr
N.A.I.C.S.: 551112
Don Ryel *(VP-Global Sourcing)*
Karen Petronis *(Coord-Bus Dev-Intl)*
David Vonderwalde *(Mgr-Sls-Mexico)*
Lavon Winkler *(Pres-North America)*
Harrison Chien *(VP-Sls-North America)*
Kara Weiner *(COO-North America)*

Subsidiaries:

Arlon Graphics, LLC   (1)
200 Boysenberry Ln, Placentia, CA 92870
Tel.: (714) 985-6300
Web Site: http://www.arlon.com
Sales Range: $50-74.9 Million
Emp.: 160
Tape & Pressure Sensitive Material Mfr
N.A.I.C.S.: 326199
Andrew McNeill *(Pres & CEO)*

Flexcon Glenrothes Ltd   (1)
Whitworth Road Southfield Industrial Estate, Glenrothes, KY6 2TF, Fife, United Kingdom
Tel.: (44) 1592 663 200
Adhesive Mfr
N.A.I.C.S.: 325520

FLEXCON INDUSTRIES, INC.

300 Pond St, Randolph, MA 02368
Tel.: (781) 986-2424   MA
Web Site: https://www.flexconind.com
Year Founded: 1987

Flexcon Industries, Inc.—(Continued)

Sales Range: $10-24.9 Million
Emp.: 123
Diaphragm Expansion Tank Mfr
N.A.I.C.S.: 332420
Michael Kennedy (VP-Fin & Ops)
Matt Kearney (Engr-Mfg)
John Birtz (Project Mgr)

FLEXFAB HORIZONS INTER-NATIONAL, LLC

1699 W M 43 Hwy, Hastings, MI
49058-9629
Tel.: (269) 945-3533　　　　　MI
Web Site: https://www.flexfab.com
Year Founded: 1961
Sales Range: $150-199.9 Million
Emp.: 400
Flexible Non-Metallic Hoses & Ducting Mfr
N.A.I.C.S.: 333998
Dave Anderson (Dir-Pur)

Subsidiaries:

Flexfab Europe Ltd.　　　　　(1)
Unit D Willow Drive Sherwood Park, Nottingham, NG15 0DP, United
Kingdom　　　　　　　　　　(100%)
Tel.: (44) 1623688100
Web Site: http://www.flexfabeurope.co.uk
Sales Range: $10-24.9 Million
Emp.: 15
Designer & Mfr of Hose, Ducts, Flexible
Connectors, Boots, Bellows & Special
Shapes
N.A.I.C.S.: 326220

Flexfab LLC　　　　　　　　(1)
1699 W M 43 Hwy, Hastings, MI
49058-8377　　　　　　　　(100%)
Tel.: (269) 945-2433
Web Site: http://www.flexfab.com
Sales Range: $25-49.9 Million
Mfr of High Performance Hose & Other
Products for Use in Extreme Environments
N.A.I.C.S.: 333998
Matt Decamp (Pres & CEO)
Kerry Boulter (Coord-Trng)
Bill Haywood (Dir-Global Program-Aerospace)
Robert Snow (Dir-Quality Sys)

Flexfab South America Ltda.　(1)
Rua Andre Rosa Copini 160 Jardim Calux,
Sao Bernardo do Campo, 09895-300, Sao
Paulo, Brazil
Tel.: (55) 11 43930274
Polymer Product Mfr
N.A.I.C.S.: 325211

FLEXFIT, LLC

350 Karin Ln, Hicksville, NY 11801
Tel.: (516) 932-8800
Web Site: https://www.flexfit.com
Year Founded: 1976
Sales Range: $75-99.9 Million
Emp.: 100
Patented Hats & Headwear Developer, Designer & Mfr
N.A.I.C.S.: 458110
Mark Stern (VP-Sls)
Andy Lew (Dir-Mktg)

FLEXFUNDS ETP LLC

1221 Brickell Ave Ste 1500, Miami,
FL 33131
Tel.: (646) 820-8001
Web Site: http://www.flexfunds.com
Year Founded: 2011
Sales Range: $1-9.9 Million
Emp.: 50
Real Estate Manangement Services
N.A.I.C.S.: 531390
Jose Carlos Gonzalez (CEO)
Emilio Veiga Gil (CMO & Exec VP)
Amy Hernandez (Chief Compliance Officer)
Daris Hechevarria (COO)
Alex Contreras (Dir-Global Sls)

FLEXIBILITY & CO., LLC

2124 Jefferson Davis Hwy Ste 301,
Stafford, VA 22554
Tel.: (866) 781-0726
Web Site: http://flexrn.com
Year Founded: 2001
Nursing Facilities
N.A.I.C.S.: 623110
Ogden Cummings (Pres & Treas)
Diana Wylie (Exec Dir)
Tiffany Washington (COO)

Subsidiaries:

Progressive Nursing Staffers Inc. (1)
5531 B Hempstead Way, Springfield, VA
22151
Tel.: (703) 750-1010
Web Site:
　http://www.progressivenursing.com
Rev.: $45,800,000
Emp.: 102
Temporary Nursing Staffing Services
N.A.I.C.S.: 561320
Gary Hughes (Pres)
Jim Narron (CFO)
Diana Upchurch (Dir-Mktg)
Patti Jones (Dir-Natl)

FLEXIBLE BENEFIT ADMINISTRATORS INC.

509 Viking Dr Ste F, Virginia Beach,
VA 23450
Tel.: (757) 340-4567
Web Site: http://www.flex-admin.com
Year Founded: 1985
Sales Range: $1-9.9 Million
Emp.: 50
Third-Party Administrator of Employee Benefit Programs
N.A.I.C.S.: 524292
Landon Browning (Pres)
Brandi Alverson (Mgr-Ops)
Ava Elkins (Mgr-COBRA Div)

FLEXIBLE BUSINESS SYSTEMS

85 Corporate Dr, Hauppauge, NY
11788
Tel.: (631) 756-0404
Web Site:
　http://www.flexiblesystems.com
Sales Range: $1-9.9 Million
Emp.: 26
Information Technology Services
N.A.I.C.S.: 541512
Marty Schmitt (Partner)
Seth Belous (Pres)
Steven Santiago (Office Mgr)

FLEXIBLE METAL HOSE & RUBBER PRODUCTS

2467 Mtn Industrial St, Tucker, GA
30084
Tel.: (770) 493-1100
Web Site:
　http://www.flexiblemetal.com
Sales Range: $10-24.9 Million
Emp.: 50
Flexible Metallic Hose Mfr
N.A.I.C.S.: 332999
Don Heye (Chm)

FLEXIBLE PACKAGING & CO. INC.

PO Box 4321 Bayamon Garden Sta,
Bayamon, PR 00959-1321
Tel.: (787) 622-7225
Web Site: http://www.flepak.com
Year Founded: 1976
Rev.: $14,100,000
Emp.: 115
Packaging Materials Mfr
N.A.I.C.S.: 326113
Carlos A. Casellas (Founder & CEO)
Olga Badillo (Pres)
Juan Carlos Martinez (Mgr-Matls)
Maritza Torres (Mgr-Ops)

FLEXIBLE PLAN INVESTMENTS LTD.

3883 Telegraph Rd Ste 100, Bloomfield Hills, MI 48302
Tel.: (248) 642-6640　　　MI
Web Site:
　https://www.flexibleplan.com
Year Founded: 1981
Sales Range: $25-49.9 Million
Emp.: 65
Investment Advisory Services
N.A.I.C.S.: 523940
Michelle Higgins (Mgr-Ops)
Jerry Wagner (Founder, Pres & CEO)
Leonard Durso (VP-Natl Sls)

FLEXIBLE STAFFING OF GEORGIA, INC.

3315 Sugarloaf Pkwy Ste 3, Lawrenceville, GA 30044
Tel.: (770) 545-6399　　　GA
Web Site: http://www.flxstaffing.com
Year Founded: 2013
Sales Range: $1-9.9 Million
Emp.: 11
Human Resource Consulting Services
N.A.I.C.S.: 541612
Thomas Navarro (Pres)

FLEXIBLE STEEL LACING COMPANY

2525 Wisconsin Ave, Downers Grove,
IL 60515-4241
Tel.: (630) 971-0150　　　IL
Web Site: https://www.flexco.com
Year Founded: 1907
Sales Range: $150-199.9 Million
Emp.: 725
Fastener Mfr
N.A.I.C.S.: 332510
Krista Howland (Head-HR)
Thomas S. Wujek (COO & Exec VP)
Glen Paradise (CFO)

Subsidiaries:

Clipper Belt Lacer Company　(1)
1995 Oak Industrial Dr NE, Grand Rapids,
MI 49505-6009　　　　　　(100%)
Tel.: (616) 459-3196
Web Site: http://www.flexco.com
Sales Range: $10-24.9 Million
Emp.: 92
Light, Medium & Heavy Duty Conveyor Belt
Fasteners; Beltline Maintenance Accessories & Belt Cleaners
N.A.I.C.S.: 332618
Jayne Dore (Mgr-Adv)
Beth Miller (Mgr-Market-Flexco Light Duty)

Flexco (Aust) Pty. Ltd.　　(1)
10 Solent Circuit, PO Box 6365, Baulkham
Hills, 2153, NSW, Australia
Tel.: (61) 2 8818 2000
Web Site: http://www.flexco.com
Emp.: 70
Cleaning Conveyor Belt Mfr
N.A.I.C.S.: 333922
Mark Colbourn (Mng Dir)

Flexco Conveying Equipment Trading
(Shanghai) Co., Ltd.　　　(1)
C-7 No 3 of Lane 180 Jin Xi Road, Song
Jiang District, Shanghai, 201613, China
Tel.: (86) 21 33528388
Conveyor Belt & Tool Mfr
N.A.I.C.S.: 333922

Flexco Pte Ltd　　　　　　(1)
Quartz Industrial Building 5 Upper Aljunied
Link, Singapore, 367903, Singapore
Tel.: (65) 6281 7278
Sales Range: $10-24.9 Million
Emp.: 7
Conveying Equipment Distr
N.A.I.C.S.: 423830

FLEXICON INC.

165 Chicago St, Cary, IL 60013
Tel.: (847) 639-3530
Web Site: http://www.ampac.com

Sales Range: $10-24.9 Million
Emp.: 65
Plastic Packaging Products Mfr
N.A.I.C.S.: 326112
Brian Scampini (CFO, VP-Ops & Controller)

FLEXICORE OF TEXAS, L.P.

8634 McHard Rd, Houston, TX 77053
Tel.: (281) 437-5700
Web Site:
　http://www.flexicoreoftexas.com
Year Founded: 1953
Sales Range: $10-24.9 Million
Emp.: 200
Mfr of Prestressed, Precast Concrete Products
N.A.I.C.S.: 327390
Don Epsel (Mgr-Sls)
Ben Carson (Pres)

FLEXON INDUSTRIES INC.

366 Frelinghuysen Ave, Newark, NJ
07114-1418
Tel.: (973) 824-5530　　　NJ
Web Site:
　https://www.flexonhose.com
Year Founded: 1971
Sales Range: $25-49.9 Million
Emp.: 120
Industrial Supplies
N.A.I.C.S.: 423840
David Rauch (Pres)
Henry Rosenbaum (Controller)

FLEXPORT INC.

760 Market St 8th Fl, San Francisco,
CA 94102
Tel.: (415) 231-5252
Web Site: https://www.flexport.com
Emp.: 2,500
Freight Transportation Arrangement
N.A.I.C.S.: 488510
Ryan Petersen (Founder & Co-CEO)
Sanne Manders (COO)
Ben Braverman (Chief Customer Officer)
James Chen (CTO)
Will Urban (Chief Revenue Officer)
Chris Ferro (Chief Legal Officer)
Philippe Lyko (Head-Fin)
Neil Davies (Head-People)
Neel Jones Shah (Exec VP & Head-Airfreight)
Nerijus Poskus (VP-Ocean)
Kevin Paige (Chief Info Security Officer)

FLICK FUSION LLC

7733 Douglas Ave, Urbandale, IA
50322
Tel.: (515) 333-4337
Web Site: https://www.flickfusion.com
Automotive Dealership Marketing Services
N.A.I.C.S.: 541890
Tim James (COO)
Lehel Reeves (Dir-Partnerships & Bus Dev)

Subsidiaries:

Dealer Fusion, Inc.　　　　(1)
440 North Wolfe Rd, Sunnyvale, CA 94085
Tel.: (925) 969-8300
Web Site: http://www.dealerfusion.com
Sales Range: $1-9.9 Million
Emp.: 32
Automotive Dealership Marketing Services
N.A.I.C.S.: 541890
Keith Kester (Mgr-Ops)

FLICK'S IGA LTD.

1786 Burlington Pike, Burlington, KY
41005
Tel.: (859) 586-7655
Year Founded: 1982
Sales Range: $10-24.9 Million

Emp.: 120
Owner & Operator of Independent
Supermarket
N.A.I.C.S.: 445110
Robert A. Flick (Owner)

FLIGG HOLDING COMPANY
5525 NE 22Nd St, Des Moines, IA
50313
Tel.: (515) 246-2070
Web Site: http://www.llinsulation.com
Sales Range: $10-24.9 Million
Emp.: 50
Insulation Materials
N.A.I.C.S.: 423330
Gary Marker (Bus Mgr)

FLIGHT DIRECTOR INC.
4707 Commercial Park Dr, Austin, TX
78728
Tel.: (512) 834-2000
Web Site:
 http://www.flightdirector.com
Year Founded: 1984
Sales Range: $10-24.9 Million
Emp.: 35
Aircraft Equipment & Supplies
N.A.I.C.S.: 423860
Michael W. Hanrahan (CEO)
Donald J. Hanrahan (Pres)
Eleanor L. Smith (CFO)
James Kyle (Mgr-Quality Assurance)

FLIGHT ENVIRONMENTS INC.
570 Linne Rd Ste 100, Paso Robles,
CA 93446-9460
Tel.: (805) 239-2222
Web Site:
 http://www.flightenvironments.com
Sales Range: $10-24.9 Million
Emp.: 15
Aircraft Insulation
N.A.I.C.S.: 327993
Evelyn Reichel (Controller)
Bobby Martinez (Dir-Flight Interiors)
Ken Archambault (Dir-Engrg)

FLIGHT SYSTEMS, INC.
207 Hempt Rd, Mechanicsburg, PA
17050
Tel.: (717) 590-7330   PA
Web Site:
 https://www.flightsystems.com
Year Founded: 1968
Sales Range: $50-74.9 Million
Emp.: 18
Electronic Controls & Engine Moni-
tors Rebuilder & Repair Services
N.A.I.C.S.: 811210
Robert A. York (Pres & CEO)
John D. Weaver (Mgr-Generator Con-
trols Sls)
Anthony Misiti (COO)

Subsidiaries:

Flight Systems Detroit   (1)
1040 E Maple Rd, Troy, MI 48083-2813
Tel.: (248) 577-2610
Sales Range: $10-24.9 Million
Emp.: 3
Mfr & Rebuilder of Solid-State Controls &
Accessories Used on Standby Generator
Sets, Automotive Electronics, Local Cable
TV Outlet
N.A.I.C.S.: 336320

FLIMP MEDIA INC.
2 Hayden Rowe St, Hopkinton, MA
01748
Tel.: (508) 686-2807
Web Site: https://www.flimp.net
Sales Range: $1-9.9 Million
Emp.: 25
Media Software & Marketing
N.A.I.C.S.: 513210

Wayne Wall (CEO)
Richard DiBona (CTO)
Chip Arndt (Exec VP)

FLINN SCIENTIFIC, INC.
770 N Raddant, Batavia, IL 60510
Tel.: (630) 879-6900
Web Site: https://www.flinnsci.com
Year Founded: 1977
Sales Range: $10-24.9 Million
Emp.: 185
Other Professional Equipment & Sup-
ply Whslr
N.A.I.C.S.: 423490
Mike Lavelle (Pres)

FLINT CO. INC.
1120 S Utica Ave, Tulsa, OK 74104
Tel.: (918) 587-8451
Web Site: http://www.flintco.com
Year Founded: 1908
Sales Range: $450-499.9 Million
Emp.: 720
Civil Engineering Services
N.A.I.C.S.: 237310
C. W. Wienecke (Mgr)

**FLINT COMMUNICATIONS,
INC. & ADFARM**
101 N 10th St Ste 300, Fargo, ND
58107
Tel.: (701) 237-4850   ND
Web Site: http://www.flintcom.com
Year Founded: 1946
Rev.: $29,816,000
Emp.: 78
N.A.I.C.S.: 541810
Roger Reierson (Pres & CEO)
Kim Kemmer (Dir-Customer Insight)
Donna Dodge (Media Dir)
Colin Clarke (Dir-Client Svcs)
Jodi Duncan (VP-Client Svcs)
Chris Hagen (Dir-PR)
Lisa Vining (Coord-Multimedia)
Jim Bolluyt (Dir-Art)
Sarah Lee (Acct Mgr)

Subsidiaries:

Flint Interactive   (1)
11 E Superior St Ste 514, Duluth, MN
55802
Tel.: (218) 740-3516
Web Site: http://www.flintinteractive.com
Emp.: 2
N.A.I.C.S.: 541810
Nicole Senmen (Mgr)

Hatling Flint   (1)
330 Hwy 10 S, Saint Cloud, MN 56304
Tel.: (320) 259-7976
Emp.: 4
N.A.I.C.S.: 541810
Bill Hatling (Pres)
Jessica Koskela (Acct Mgr)

Simmons Flint   (1)
33 S Third St Ste D, Grand Forks, ND
58201
Tel.: (701) 746-4573
Sales Range: $10-24.9 Million
Emp.: 10
N.A.I.C.S.: 541810
Linda Muus (Acct Mgr)
Susan Mickelson (Acct Mgr & Dir-Client
Svcs)

WestmorelandFlint   (1)
11 E Superior St Ste 514, Duluth, MN
55802
Tel.: (218) 727-1552
Web Site: http://www.westmorelandflint.com
Rev.: $2,000,000
Emp.: 20
Advertising Agencies, Full Service,
Internet/Web Design, Public Relations
N.A.I.C.S.: 541810
John Hyduke (Pres)
Ed Koch (Sr Acct Mgr)
Joan Henrik (Art Dir)
Jessica Stauber (Dir-PR)
Laura Sieger (VP)
Amanda Rolfe (Acct Coord)

**FLINT ELECTRIC MEMBER-
SHIP CORPORATION**
103 S Macon St, Reynolds, GA
31076-3001
Tel.: (478) 847-3415
Web Site:
 http://www.flintenergies.com
Year Founded: 1937
Sales Range: $100-124.9 Million
Emp.: 230
Electronic Services
N.A.I.C.S.: 221122
William L. Brown (Chm)
Jimmy Autry (VP-Member Rels)
Bob Ray (CEO)
Robert L. Dickey III (Chm-Board)

**FLINT ENERGY CONSTRUC-
TION SERVICES INC.**
7633 E 63rd Pl Ste 500, Tulsa, OK
74133-1218
Tel.: (918) 294-3030   DE
Web Site: http://www.flintenergy.com
Year Founded: 1998
Sales Range: $50-74.9 Million
Emp.: 900
Water, Sewer & Utility Lines
N.A.I.C.S.: 237120

**FLINT EQUIPMENT HOLD-
INGS, INC.**
1206 Blaylock St, Albany, GA 31705-
1342
Tel.: (229) 888-1212   GA
Web Site:
 http://www.flintequipco.com
Sales Range: $150-199.9 Million
Emp.: 400
Holding Company; Construction, Min-
ing, Farming & Industrial Equipment
Dealerships Owner & Operator
N.A.I.C.S.: 551112
Chris Cannon (Pres & CEO)

Subsidiaries:

Albany Tractor Co.   (1)
1709 S Slappey Blvd, Albany, GA 31701-
2636
Tel.: (229) 432-7468
Web Site: http://www.flintequipco.com
Sales Range: $10-24.9 Million
Emp.: 80
Tractor & Other Farm Equipment Dealer
N.A.I.C.S.: 423820
John Salter (Gen Mgr)
Chad Scarbor (Mgr-Product Support)
Doug Wishum (Mgr-Credit)
Don Bowman (Mgr-Parts)

Division (Domestic):

Albany Tractor Co. - Lawn & Garden
Division   (2)
741 Hwy 82 W, Leesburg, GA 31763
Tel.: (229) 432-7468
Web Site: http://www.flintequipco.com
Emp.: 50
Lawn & Garden Equipment Dealer
N.A.I.C.S.: 423820
Chad Scarbor (Mgr-Product Support)

Flint Equipment Co.   (1)
1206 Blaylock St, Albany, GA 31705-1342
Tel.: (229) 888-1212
Web Site: http://www.flintequipco.com
Sales Range: $25-49.9 Million
Emp.: 280
Construction & Mining Equipment Dealer-
ships Operator
N.A.I.C.S.: 423810
Keith Hutchins (Controller)
Chris Cannon (Pres & CEO)
Tony Byron Sammons (CFO)

Branch (Domestic):

Flint Equipment Co. - Atlanta   (2)
4500 Wendell Dr SW, Atlanta, GA 30336-
1627
Tel.: (404) 691-9445
Web Site: http://www.flintequipco.com
Construction & Mining Equipment Distr

N.A.I.C.S.: 423810
Todd Smith (Mgr-Inventory & Ops)

Flint Equipment Co. - West
Columbia   (2)
3464 Sunset Blvd, West Columbia, SC
29169-3042
Tel.: (803) 794-9340
Web Site: http://www.flintequipco.com
Sales Range: $25-49.9 Million
Emp.: 100
Construction & Mining Machinery
N.A.I.C.S.: 423810
Chris Cannon (CEO)

Flint Power Systems   (1)
1204 Blalock St, Albany, GA 31705
Tel.: (229) 888-1900
Web Site: http://www.flintpower.com
Sales Range: $10-24.9 Million
Emp.: 60
Provider of Industrial Machinery & Equip-
ment
N.A.I.C.S.: 423830
Keith Hutchins (Controller)
Teresa Pollard (Coord-Parts)
Carla Montgomery (Mgr-Quality & Shipping)
Tracey Paul Boyd (Supvr-Parts Depth)

**FLINT HILLS RURAL ELEC-
TRIC COOP**
1564 S 1000 Rd, Council Grove, KS
66846-0610
Tel.: (620) 767-5144   KS
Web Site:
 https://www.flinthillsrec.com
Year Founded: 1938
Sales Range: $10-24.9 Million
Emp.: 35
Electric Power Distribution Services
N.A.I.C.S.: 221122
Damien Hebert (Mgr-Ops)
Diann Diehl (Mgr-Member Svcs)
Robert Reece (Gen Mgr)
Roger W. Zimmerman (Pres)
Duane E. Carlson (Treas & Sec)
Duane Kaiser (VP)

FLINT INDUSTRIES, INC.
1624 W 21st St, Tulsa, OK 74107-
2708
Tel.: (918) 587-8451   OK
Web Site: http://www.flintco.com
Year Founded: 1908
Sales Range: $700-749.9 Million
Emp.: 785
General Contracting, Design, Con-
struction & Project Management Ser-
vices
N.A.I.C.S.: 236220

FLINT RIVER MILLS
1100 Dothan Rd, Bainbridge, GA
39818-0280
Tel.: (229) 246-2232   GA
Web Site: https://www.frmfeeds.com
Year Founded: 1934
Sales Range: $75-99.9 Million
Emp.: 125
Poultry & Livestock Feeds Mfr
N.A.I.C.S.: 311119
June Gainous (Mgr-Credit)

**FLINT WARM AIR SUPPLY CO.
(FWA)**
4187 Somers Dr, Burton, MI 48529
Tel.: (810) 743-9000   MI
Web Site: http://www.fwagrp.com
Year Founded: 1931
Sales Range: $10-24.9 Million
Emp.: 16
HVAC Systems Whslr & Distr
N.A.I.C.S.: 423730
Jeff Slater (VP)

FLIP FLOP SHOPS
2885 Hilton Cir NW, Kennesaw, GA
30152
Tel.: (949) 385-3547

Flip Flop Shops—(Continued)

Web Site:
http://www.flipflopshops.com
Year Founded: 2007
Sales Range: $10-24.9 Million
Emp.: 10
Retail Flip Flop Chain
N.A.I.C.S.: 458210
Darin Kraetsch (Principal)

FLIPPO CONSTRUCTION CO. INC.
3820 Penn Belt Pl, Forestville, MD 20747
Tel.: (301) 967-6800
Web Site: https://www.flippo.com
Rev.: $50,809,798
Emp.: 75
Underground Utilities Contractor
N.A.I.C.S.: 237110
Brian Flippo (Exec VP)
Jeff Flippo (Exec VP)
Greg Mehallick (Pres & COO)
John Morgan (VP)

FLIPSIDE, INC.
15260 Ventura Blvd. Suite 2000, Manhattan Beach, CA 91403
Tel.: (310) 647-6000
Web Site: http://www.flipside.com
Year Founded: 1996
Sales Range: $10-24.9 Million
Emp.: 125
Online Games Store
N.A.I.C.S.: 518210

Subsidiaries:

iWin, Inc.   (1)
150 Spear St Ste 1400, San Francisco, CA 94105-1540
Tel.: (310) 647-6000
Web Site: http://www.iwin.com
Publisher & Developer of Online Games & Entertainment With Prizes
N.A.I.C.S.: 513199
C. J. Wolf (CEO)
Curtis Ng (VP-Fin & Admin)
Joe Cain (Dir-Game Design)
Michael Ewins (VP-Engrg)
Brian Frederick (Dir-Product)

Subsidiary (Domestic):

Gamezebo, Inc.   (2)
2443 Fillmore St Ste 502, San Francisco, CA 94115
Tel.: (415) 692-4798
Web Site: http://www.gamezebo.com
Online Mobile Game Publishers
N.A.I.C.S.: 513210
Joel Brodie (Founder & CEO)

FLIXENTERTAINMENT LLC
2000 S IH 35 Ste Q11, Round Rock, TX 78681
Tel.: (512) 238-0938
Web Site:
http://www.flixentertainment group.com
Year Founded: 2011
Sales Range: $25-49.9 Million
Emp.: 1,300
Full Restaurant Services
N.A.I.C.S.: 722511
Matthew Baizer (COO)

FLM GRAPHICS CORPORATION
123 Lehigh Dr, Fairfield, NJ 07004
Tel.: (973) 575-9450
Web Site:
http://www.flmgraphics.com
Year Founded: 1972
Sales Range: $10-24.9 Million
Emp.: 80
Offset Printing
N.A.I.C.S.: 323111
Frank L. Misischia (Chm, Pres & CEO)

Peter Desbets (Dir-Mktg)
Vincent Gagliardi (Exec VP)
Tony Gagliardi (Exec VP)

FLO CONTROL, INC.
80 Center Road, Cartersville, GA 30121
Tel.: (770) 382-0006
Web Site: http://www.flo-control.com
Year Founded: 1967
Mfr of Full range & Actuated Valves
N.A.I.C.S.: 332911

FLO-TEC, INC.
13033 Fairlane, Livonia, MI 48150
Tel.: (734) 455-7655
Web Site: http://www.flotecinc.com
Sales Range: $10-24.9 Million
Emp.: 10
Industrial Filters Mfr
N.A.I.C.S.: 423840
Timothy Yarnell (Pres)
Wes Yarnell (Mgr-Customer Svc)

FLOATOGRAPH TECHNOLOGIES, LLC
125 E Victoria St Ste B, Santa Barbara, CA 93101
Tel.: (301) 563-3082
Web Site: http://www.floatograph.com
Year Founded: 1989
Sales Range: $1-9.9 Million
Emp.: 27
Aerostat Manufacturer
N.A.I.C.S.: 334419
Kurt Liestenfeltz (Pres)

FLOCO UNLIMITED INC.
521 Shirley Ave, Douglas, GA 31533-2003
Tel.: (912) 384-1246
Year Founded: 1997
Sales Range: $50-74.9 Million
Emp.: 100
Provider of Petroleum Services
N.A.I.C.S.: 424710
Normalynn Hand (Pres)
Jeri Tanner (VP)

Subsidiaries:

Fletcher Oil Co. Inc.   (1)
1406 Baker Hwy W, Douglas, GA 31533-2003
Tel.: (912) 384-1246
Web Site: http://www.fletcheroil.com
Sales Range: $10-24.9 Million
Emp.: 25
Petroleum Services
N.A.I.C.S.: 424710
Norma Hand (Pres)

Subsidiary (Domestic):

Quick Change Inc.   (2)
521 Shirley Ave, Douglas, GA 31533-2003
Tel.: (912) 383-7262
Sales Range: $10-24.9 Million
Emp.: 30
Convenience Store
N.A.I.C.S.: 445131
Norman Fletcher (Chm)
Bobby Carver (Controller)

FLODYNE INC.
1000 Muirfield Dr, Hanover Park, IL 60133
Tel.: (630) 563-3600
Web Site: https://www.cmafh.com
Year Founded: 1974
Sales Range: $10-24.9 Million
Emp.: 85
Pneumatic Tools & Equipment
N.A.I.C.S.: 423830
Frank J. Machac (Pres)
Rob Shepherd (CEO)

FLOE INTERNATIONAL, INC.
48473 State Highway 65, McGregor, MN 55760

Tel.: (218) 426-3563   MN
Web Site: https://www.floeintl.com
Year Founded: 1983
Sales Range: $10-24.9 Million
Emp.: 70
Trailers & Trailer Equipment
N.A.I.C.S.: 336214
Wayne Floe (CEO)

FLOLO CORPORATION
1061 E Green St, Bensenville, IL 60106
Tel.: (630) 595-1010
Web Site: http://www.flolo.com
Sales Range: $10-24.9 Million
Emp.: 25
Motors, Electric
N.A.I.C.S.: 423610
George Flolo (VP)

FLOOD COMMUNICATIONS, LLC
11128 John Galt Blvd Ste 25, Omaha, NE 68137
Tel.: (402) 884-0968
Web Site: https://floodcomm.com
Year Founded: 2000
Media Operations; News, Radio, TV Channels
N.A.I.C.S.: 516120
Andy Ruback (CEO)
Mike Flood (Founder)

FLOOR ASSOCIATES INCORPORATED
410 W St Rd, Feasterville Trevose, PA 19053
Tel.: (267) 536-5485
Web Site:
https://www.feastervillefloor.com
Rev.: $10,000,000
Emp.: 30
Installer of Flooring & Carpets
N.A.I.C.S.: 449121
John Menarde (Pres)

FLOOR DECOR CENTER INC
1433 Murray St, Kansas City, MO 64116
Tel.: (816) 741-9612
Web Site: http://www.fdccontract.com
Sales Range: $10-24.9 Million
Emp.: 22
Floor Covering Stores
N.A.I.C.S.: 449121
Todd Saunders (Gen Mgr)

FLOOR KING INC.
10961 Research Blvd, Austin, TX 78759
Tel.: (512) 346-7034
Web Site: https://www.floorking.net
Year Founded: 1986
Sales Range: $25-49.9 Million
Emp.: 50
Floor Coverings
N.A.I.C.S.: 423220
Kurt Wade (CEO)
John Surko (Pres)
Roy Whittaker (Mgr-Sls)

FLOORCRAFT INC.
15810 Bear Creek Pkwy, Redmond, WA 98052
Tel.: (425) 885-4161
Sales Range: $10-24.9 Million
Emp.: 12
Floor Covering Stores
N.A.I.C.S.: 449121
Curtis Reed (CEO)

FLOORING GALLERY LLC
2208 Plantside Dr, Louisville, KY 40299-1926
Tel.: (502) 964-3301

Web Site: http://www.theflooringgallery-in.com
Emp.: 35
Floor Covering Stores
N.A.I.C.S.: 449121
Nicholas Freadreacea (Pres)
Carey Henegar (Mgr-Ops)

FLOORSHOP.COM, INC.
18375 Olympic Ave S, Tukwila, WA 98188
Tel.: (805) 339-3784   CA
Sales Range: $10-24.9 Million
Emp.: 20
Retailer of Floor Coverings
N.A.I.C.S.: 449121

FLORACRAFT CORPORATION
1 Longfellow Pl, Ludington, MI 49431-1591
Tel.: (231) 845-5127   MI
Web Site: https://www.floracraft.com
Year Founded: 1946
Sales Range: $25-49.9 Million
Emp.: 150
Sales of Plastic Foam Products
N.A.I.C.S.: 326150
R. Lee Schoenherr (Owner, Chm & CEO)
Eric J. Erwin (Pres & CMO)

Subsidiaries:

Floracraft of Philadelphia Inc.   (1)
2341 N Seventh St, Philadelphia, PA 19133-2103
Tel.: (215) 763-1000
Sales Range: $10-24.9 Million
Emp.: 11
Mfr Styrafoam Film
N.A.I.C.S.: 326113

FLORAL SUPPLY SYNDICATE
3800 Via Pescador, Camarillo, CA 93012
Tel.: (805) 389-1141
Web Site: https://www.fss.com
Rev.: $50,000,000
Emp.: 30
Florists' Supplies
N.A.I.C.S.: 424930
Hassan Sedghi (Mgr-Floor)

FLORAS DISTRIBUTORS INC.
11927 W Sample Rd, Coral Springs, FL 33065
Tel.: (954) 785-3100
Web Site: http://www.florafoods.com
Sales Range: $10-24.9 Million
Emp.: 37
Dairy Products Distr
N.A.I.C.S.: 424430
John Flora (Pres)

FLORENCE & WHITE FORD DEALERSHIP
710 W Broad St, Smithville, TN 37166-1008
Tel.: (615) 597-2300
Web Site:
http://www.florenceandwhiteford.com
Year Founded: 1996
Sales Range: $10-24.9 Million
Emp.: 50
New Car Whslr
N.A.I.C.S.: 441110
Jim Florence (Pres)

FLORENCE CEMENT COMPANY
12585 23 Mile Rd, Shelby, MI 48315
Tel.: (586) 997-2666
Web Site:
http://www.florencecement.com
Sales Range: $10-24.9 Million
Emp.: 150

Concrete Construction Services
N.A.I.C.S.: 237310
Antonio Melaragni *(Pres & Dir-Paving Ops)*
Orfeo Guerrieri *(Treas, Sec & Dir-Excavation & Underground Ops)*
Angelo S. Lanni *(Exec VP & Dir-Admin)*
Michael Pittiglio *(VP)*
Steven J. Pantaleo *(Project Mgr & Engr)*
Steven M. Lampton *(Sr Project Mgr & Engr)*

FLORENCE CONCRETE PRODUCTS CO. INC

1517 N Cashua Dr, Florence, SC 29502-5506
Tel.: (843) 662-2549
Web Site:
https://www.florenceconcretepro ducts.com
Rev.: $15,360,245
Emp.: 180
Prestressed Concrete Products
N.A.I.C.S.: 327390
Fred H. Cross *(Treas & Sec)*
Sherry Millerjones *(Pres)*

FLORENCE CORPORATION

1647 E Jericho Tpke, Huntington, NY 11743-5711
Tel.: (631) 499-6220   NY
Web Site:
http://www.florencecorp.com
Year Founded: 1946
Sales Range: $125-149.9 Million
Emp.: 160
Whslr of Wood Framed Windows & Doors; Roofing & Siding Materials; Manufacturer of Metal Doors & Metal Framed Windows
N.A.I.C.S.: 423330
Greg Barnych *(VP)*
Rob Holden *(Pres)*

FLORENCE ELECTRIC LLC

290 Pine St, Canton, MA 02021
Tel.: (781) 769-7110
Web Site: https://www.teamfloco.com
Year Founded: 1994
Sales Range: $10-24.9 Million
Emp.: 200
Electrical Contractor
N.A.I.C.S.: 238210
Gerry Amirault *(Project Mgr)*
Walter Nunes *(Project Mgr)*
Laura Caron *(Project Mgr)*

FLORENCE SAVINGS BANK INC.

85 Main St, Florence, MA 01062-1400
Tel.: (413) 586-1300   MA
Web Site:
http://www.florencebank.com
Year Founded: 1873
Sales Range: $25-49.9 Million
Emp.: 200
Federal Savings Institutions
N.A.I.C.S.: 522180
Tony Sanches *(Asst VP)*
Susan Pepin-Phillips *(Asst VP & Mgr-Mktg)*
Michael Davey *(VP)*
Cynthia Malinowski *(VP & Mgr-Northampton office)*
John F. Heaps Jr. *(Pres & CEO)*

FLORESTONE PRODUCTS CO.

2851 Falcon Dr, Madera, CA 93637
Tel.: (559) 661-4171
Web Site: http://www.florestone.com
Sales Range: $10-24.9 Million
Emp.: 40
Shower Stalls, Fiberglass & Plastics

N.A.I.C.S.: 326191
Ron Flores *(Pres & CEO)*
Bill White *(Controller)*
Carol Flores Deaver *(Owner)*

FLORIDA AGENCY NETWORK, LLC

1503 S Alexander St Ste 103, Plant City, FL 33563
Tel.: (866) 259-4440   FL
Web Site: http://www.flagency.net
Year Founded: 2014
Real Estate Title Insurance & Development Services
N.A.I.C.S.: 524127
Aaron M. Davis *(CEO)*
Amy Gregory *(Chief Admin Officer & Pres-Title Ops)*
Mike LaRosa *(COO)*
Wayne Harrell *(CFO)*
Chris LaChance *(Sls Mgr)*
Jay Roberts *(CTO)*

Subsidiaries:

Total Title Solutions, LLC   **(1)**
2911 SR 590 Ste 22, Clearwater, FL 33759
Tel.: (727) 796-7600
Web Site: http://www.mytotaltitle.com
Title Insurance Services
N.A.I.C.S.: 524127

FLORIDA ARF

2475 Apalachee Pkwy Ste 205, Tallahassee, FL 32301-4946
Tel.: (850) 877-4816   FL
Web Site: http://www.floridaarf.org
Year Founded: 1976
Sales Range: $25-49.9 Million
Emp.: 25
Disabled People Assistance Services
N.A.I.C.S.: 624120
Courtney Swilley *(Dir-Member Services)*

FLORIDA BANCSHARES, INC.

13315 US Hwy 301, Dade City, FL 33525
Tel.: (352) 521-0141
Web Site: http://www.fnbpasco.com
Emp.: 50
Bank Holding Company
N.A.I.C.S.: 551111
Steven D. Hickman *(Pres & CEO)*

Subsidiaries:

First National Bank of Pasco   **(1)**
13315 US Hwy 301, Dade City, FL 33525
Tel.: (352) 521-0141
Web Site: http://www.fnbpasco.com
Rev.: $6,107,000
Assets: $144,932,000
Liabilities: $130,975,000
Net Worth: $13,957,000
Earnings: $606,000
Emp.: 35
Fiscal Year-end: 12/31/2013
Banking Services
N.A.I.C.S.: 522110
Steven D. Hickman *(Pres & CEO)*
Kerry M. Westbrook *(CFO & Exec VP)*
A. P. Gibbs *(Chm)*
Paul Midili *(Vice Chm)*
Jody Grenville *(Sec)*
Mike Mashke *(Chief Lending Officer & Exec VP)*
Suzie Swailes *(Officer-Compliance & Asst VP)*
Mike Briggs *(Officer-Comml Loan & Sr VP)*
Tammi Cartwright *(Sr VP & Mgr-Loan Ops)*
Tracy Mahon *(Sr VP-Branch Ops)*
Nancy Pepper *(Sr VP & Mgr-Credit Dept)*
Tod Pukas *(Officer-Comml Loan & Sr VP)*
Robert Shoemaker *(Officer-Comml Loan & Sr VP)*

FLORIDA BULK SALES INC.

1126 Kyle Wood Ln, Brandon, FL 33511
Tel.: (863) 668-9000

Web Site:
https://www.floridabulksales.com
Sales Range: $10-24.9 Million
Emp.: 7
Juices
N.A.I.C.S.: 424490
Suzy Nolan *(Gen Mgr)*

FLORIDA BUSINESS DEVELOPMENT CORPORATION

6801 Lake Worth Rd Ste 209, Lake Worth, FL 33467
Tel.: (561) 433-0233   FL
Web Site: http://www.fbdc.net
Year Founded: 1989
Sales Range: $1-9.9 Million
Emp.: 30
Mortgage & Nonmortgage Loan Brokers
N.A.I.C.S.: 522310
Emmanuel Manos *(Pres)*
Greg Bossow *(Sr VP)*
Angie Winter *(VP)*
Bill Habermeyer *(VP)*
Mark Hoeller *(Mgr-Market-West Florida)*
Curry Workman *(VP-North Florida & Jacksonville)*
Daniel F. Martinez III *(VP)*

FLORIDA CANCER SPECIALISTS, P.L.

4371 Veronica S Shoemaker Blvd, Fort Myers, FL 33916
Tel.: (239) 274-8200
Web Site: http://www.flcancer.com
Year Founded: 1984
Sales Range: $75-99.9 Million
Emp.: 1,500
Oncology Physicians' Offices & Research Services
N.A.I.C.S.: 621111
Brad Prechtl *(CEO)*
Todd Schonherz *(CIO)*
Shelly Glenn *(Chief Mktg & Sls Officer)*
Denice Veatch *(Dir-Fin Reporting & Analysis)*
Jeff Esham *(VP-Radiation Oncology)*
William N. Harwin *(Founder)*
Tom P. Clark *(Chief Legal Officer & Gen Counsel)*
Inga Gonzalez *(VP-Practice Ops)*
Jeffrey Rubin *(VP-Practice Ops)*

FLORIDA CAPITAL PARTNERS, INC.

500 N Westshore Blvd Ste 605, Tampa, FL 33609
Tel.: (813) 222-8000   FL
Web Site:
http://www.fcpinvestors.com
Year Founded: 1988
Sales Range: $250-299.9 Million
Emp.: 5
Privater Equity Firm
N.A.I.C.S.: 523999
Peter B. Franz *(Mng Dir)*
Felix J. Wong *(Mng Dir)*
Nancy Wall *(Office Mgr)*

Subsidiaries:

Standard Tools & Equipment Co. Inc.   **(1)**
4810 Clover Rd, Greensboro, NC 27405-9607
Tel.: (336) 697-7177
Web Site: http://www.toolsusa.com
Sales Range: $10-24.9 Million
Mfr Special Industry Machineries
N.A.I.C.S.: 333248
Michael Kestler *(Pres)*

FLORIDA CITIZENS BANK

3919 W Newberry Rd, Gainesville, FL 32607

Tel.: (352) 332-4727
Web Site:
http://www.floridacitizensbank.com
Rev.: $70,000,000
Emp.: 90
National Commercial Banks
N.A.I.C.S.: 522110
Carl Walls *(Pres & CEO)*
J. T. Varn *(VP)*
Kathy Rowe *(VP-Lending)*
Lynn Reid *(Mgr-Ops)*
Sheri Higginbotham *(CFO)*
Tom Word *(Sr VP)*
Bob Page *(Exec VP)*

FLORIDA CITRUS MUTUAL, INC.

PO Box 1576, Bartow, FL 33801
Tel.: (863) 682-1111
Web Site:
http://www.flcitrusmutual.com
Year Founded: 1948
Sales Range: $1-9.9 Million
Emp.: 6
Orange Groves
N.A.I.C.S.: 111310
Michael W. Sparks *(CEO & Exec VP)*
Kevin Metheny *(Controller)*
Andrew Meadows *(Dir-PR)*
Drew Love *(Dir-State Legislative Affairs)*
Melanie Burns *(Dir-Market Info)*
Rusty Wiygul *(Dir-Grower Affairs)*

FLORIDA COMMERCIAL LAUNDRY SYSTEMS, INC.

6100 Powerline Rd, Fort Lauderdale, FL 33309
Tel.: (954) 772-7100
Web Site: https://www.aaxon.com
Year Founded: 1989
Sales Range: $1-9.9 Million
Emp.: 20
Laundry Equipment & Supplies
N.A.I.C.S.: 423850
Frank D'Annunzio *(Pres)*

FLORIDA CREDIT UNION

2831 NW 43rd St, Gainesville, FL 32606
Tel.: (352) 377-4141   FL
Web Site: http://www.flcu.org
Year Founded: 1954
Rev.: $86,539,062
Assets: $1,266,313,568
Liabilities: $1,131,972,744
Net Worth: $134,340,824
Earnings: $19,582,485
Emp.: 248
Fiscal Year-end: 12/31/19
Credit Union Operator
N.A.I.C.S.: 522130
Mark Starr *(Pres, CEO & Mgr-Credit)*
Jacquelyn D. Hart *(Sec)*
William Hopgood *(Vice Chm)*
Andrew Sutherland *(Treas)*
Thom Beck *(CIO & Sr VP-Information Svcs)*
Evan Pitts *(Sr VP-Comml Svcs)*
Jane Harris *(VP & Mgr-Bus Relationship)*
Beatrice Cherry *(VP-Mktg)*
Matthew Teoli *(VP-Delivery Channels)*
Marlena Wesh *(VP-HR)*
Wes Colson *(VP-Member-Solutions)*
Sarah King *(VP-Project Admin & Trng)*
Greg Purvis *(VP-Lending)*
Chris Logan *(VP & Mgr-Bus Relationship)*
Pam Bolin *(VP-Acctg)*
Daniel Arreola *(VP-Risk Mgmt)*
Heather Gilliam *(VP-Branch Ops)*
Lynn Jones Sr. *(Chm)*

FLORIDA CROWN DEVELOPMENT CORP.

Florida Crown Development Corp.—(Continued)

3600 Vineland Rd Ste 101, Orlando, FL 32811
Tel.: (407) 841-1414   FL
Year Founded: 1977
Sales Range: $25-49.9 Million
Emp.: 124
Real Estate Development & Ownership
N.A.I.C.S.: 531390
Daniel Webb (Pres)

FLORIDA CRYSTALS CORPORATION

1 N Clematis St Ste 200, West Palm Beach, FL 33401-5551
Tel.: (561) 366-5100   FL
Web Site:
   http://www.floridacrystals.com
Year Founded: 1987
Sales Range: $5-14.9 Billion
Emp.: 5,500
Sugar Cane & Sugar Beets Mfr
N.A.I.C.S.: 111930
Jose F. Fonjul (Vice Chm, Pres & COO)
Alfonso Fanjul (Chm & CEO)

Subsidiaries:

American Sugar Refining, Inc.   (1)
1 N Clematis St Ste 200, West Palm Beach, FL 33401
Tel.: (561) 366-5100
Web Site: http://www.asr-group.com
Cane Sugar Refining Services
N.A.I.C.S.: 311314
Greg Smith (CFO)
Jim O'Mealy (Controller-Pkg-MRP)
Jose Prieto (Dir-Dev, M&A & Strategy)
Kimberly Castillo (Mgr-HR Compensation)
Celso Maldonado (Mgr-Raw Sugar Ops)
Michael Mahoney (Mgr-Safety)
Andy Pollard (Supvr-Boiler & Powerhouse)
Frank Hoch (Supvr-Engrg-Power Plant Ops)
Daniel Macone (VP-Risk Mgmt)

Subsidiary (Domestic):

C&H Sugar Company, Inc.   (2)
830 Loring Ave, Crockett, CA 94525
Tel.: (510) 787-2121
Web Site: http://www.chsugar.com
Sales Range: $400-449.9 Million
Emp.: 550
Sugars
N.A.I.C.S.: 311314

Plant (Domestic):

Domino Foods - Arabi Sugar Refinery   (2)
7417 N Peters St, Arabi, LA 70032-1543
Tel.: (504) 271-5331
Web Site: http://www.asr-group.com
Sales Range: $50-74.9 Million
Emp.: 400
Sugar Refining
N.A.I.C.S.: 311314
Alan Reichert (Controller)
Michael Rymas (Controller)

Domino Foods - Baltimore Sugar Refinery   (2)
1100 E Key Hwy, Baltimore, MD 21230-5123
Tel.: (410) 752-6150
Web Site: http://www.dominosugar.com
Sales Range: $50-74.9 Million
Emp.: 300
Sugar Refining Services
N.A.I.C.S.: 311314
Denis Powers (VP-Supply Chain)

Subsidiary (Non-US):

Redpath Sugar Ltd.   (2)
95 Queens Quay E, Toronto, M5E 1A3, ON, Canada   (100%)
Tel.: (416) 366-3561
Web Site: http://www.redpathsugars.com
Sales Range: $25-49.9 Million
Emp.: 300
Refined Cane & Beet Sugar Mfr
N.A.I.C.S.: 311314

Phil Guglielmi (Plant Mgr)

Subsidiary (Domestic):

Tate & Lyle North American Sugars Inc.   (2)
2200 E Eldorado St, Decatur, IL 62521-1578
Tel.: (217) 423-4411
Cane Sugar Refining
N.A.I.C.S.: 561110

Florida Sugar Distributors Inc.   (1)
1 N Clematis St Ste 200, West Palm Beach, FL 33401
Tel.: (561) 366-5100
Sales Range: $10-24.9 Million
Emp.: 20
Sugar Distribution Services
N.A.I.C.S.: 311314

New Hope South Inc.   (1)
Hwy 27, South Bay, FL 33493
Tel.: (561) 992-8901
Web Site: http://www.floridacrystals.com
Sales Range: $10-24.9 Million
Emp.: 70
Producer of Sugarcane & Sugar Beets
N.A.I.C.S.: 111930
Louis Antiago (Mgr-Div)

Okeelanta Corporation   (1)
1 N Clematis St Ste 200, West Palm Beach, FL 33401-5551
Tel.: (561) 366-5100
Web Site: http://www.floridacrystals.com
Sales Range: $100-124.9 Million
Emp.: 2,000
Raw Cane Sugar Producer
N.A.I.C.S.: 311314

Osceola Farms Co. Inc.   (1)
1 N Clematis St Ste 200, West Palm Beach, FL 33401-5551
Tel.: (561) 924-7156
Sales Range: $25-49.9 Million
Emp.: 300
Provider of Food Services
N.A.I.C.S.: 311340

Sugar Farms Inc.   (1)
1 N Clematis St Ste 200, West Palm Beach, FL 33401-5551
Tel.: (561) 655-6303
Web Site: http://www.floridacrystals.com
Sales Range: $10-24.9 Million
Emp.: 15
Producer of Sugarcane & Sugar Beets
N.A.I.C.S.: 541618

FLORIDA DESIGN CONSULTANTS, INC.

707 N Franklin St 6th Fl, Tampa, FL 33602
Tel.: (813) 414-5661   FL
Web Site: http://www.fldesign.com
Year Founded: 1996
Sales Range: $1-9.9 Million
Emp.: 85
Engineeering Services
N.A.I.C.S.: 541330
Keith Mazur (COO)
Cyndi Tarapani (VP-Plng)
Alfonso Belluccia (Sr VP)

FLORIDA DIGITAL NETWORK INC.

2301 Lucien Way Ste 200, Maitland, FL 32751
Tel.: (407) 835-0300
Sales Range: $10-24.9 Million
Emp.: 560
Long Distance Telephone Communications
N.A.I.C.S.: 517111

FLORIDA EVERBLADES

11000 Everblades Pkwy, Estero, FL 33928
Tel.: (239) 948-7825
Web Site:
   https://www.floridaeverblades.com
Hockey Teams
N.A.I.C.S.: 711211

Craig Brush (Pres & Gen Mgr)
Chris Palin (VP-Sls & Mktg)
Trent Ferguson (Dir-Sls)
Alex Reed (VP-Sls & Mktg)
Peter Karmanos Jr. (Chm)

FLORIDA EXECUTIVE REALTY

15802 Amberly Dr, Tampa, FL 33647
Tel.: (813) 972-3430
Web Site:
   https://www.floridaexecutiverealty.com
Sales Range: $150-199.9 Million
Emp.: 100
Real Estate Broker
N.A.I.C.S.: 531210
Doug Loyd (Owner)
Michelle Weinhold (Gen Mgr)
Patricia Cafferty (Dir-Re-Location)

FLORIDA EYE SPECIALISTS, P.A.

11512 Lake Mead Ave Ste 534, Jacksonville, FL 32256
Tel.: (904) 642-2222
Web Site:
   https://www.floridaeyespecialists.com
Emp.: 15
Offices of Eye Physicians
N.A.I.C.S.: 621111
Rajesh Shetty (Founder)

FLORIDA FAMILY INSURANCE COMPANY

27599 Riverview Center Blvd Ste 100, Bonita Springs, FL 34134-4323
Tel.: (239) 495-4700   FL
Web Site: http://www.flfamily.com
Year Founded: 1996
Sales Range: $100-124.9 Million
Emp.: 60
Property & Casualty Insurance Services
N.A.I.C.S.: 524126
Rick Hardy (Chm)
Brent Brummer (Sr VP-Claims & Legislative Affairs)
Bill Wiggs (CEO)

FLORIDA FIRST CAPITAL FINANCE CORPORATION

1351 N Gadsden St, Tallahassee, FL 32303
Tel.: (850) 681-3601
Web Site: https://www.ffcfc.com
Sales Range: $1-9.9 Million
Emp.: 30
Mortgage & Nonmortgage Loan Brokers
N.A.I.C.S.: 522310
Todd G. Kocourek (Pres & CEO)
Debra E. Petrell (Sr VP)
Gail Lagace (Sr VP & Mgr-Credit)
Lynn McDaniel (Sr VP, Dir-Loan Admin & Mgr-Closing)
Barbra Boutin (Dir-Corp Admin)

FLORIDA GIFT FRUIT SHIPPERS ASSOCIATION INC.

5500 W Concord Ave, Orlando, FL 32808-7700
Tel.: (407) 295-1491   FL
Web Site: http://www.fgfsa.com
Year Founded: 1946
Sales Range: $10-24.9 Million
Emp.: 9
Shipping Consolidator
N.A.I.C.S.: 484110
Donna Garren (Exec VP)

FLORIDA GROUNDWATER SERVICES, INC.

120 E Dr Martin Luther King Jr Blvd, Tampa, FL 33603

Tel.: (813) 623-1557   FL
Web Site:
   http://www.thefgsgroup.com
Year Founded: 1989
Sales Range: $10-24.9 Million
Emp.: 50
Scientific & Technical Consulting Services
N.A.I.C.S.: 541690
Robert D. Tolbert Jr. (Pres)

FLORIDA GULF CONTRACTING, INC.

4863 Gum Rd, Tallahassee, FL 32304
Tel.: (850) 575-0930
Year Founded: 2006
Sales Range: $10-24.9 Million
Emp.: 30
Construction Management Services
N.A.I.C.S.: 237110
Steven Law (Sec)

FLORIDA GULFSHORE CAPITAL LLC

2640 Golden Gate Pkwy Ste 105, Naples, FL 34105
Tel.: (239) 659-0288
Web Site: https://gulfshorecap.com
Emp.: 100
Investment Services
N.A.I.C.S.: 523999
Richard Molloy (Founder & Mng Partner)

FLORIDA HARDWARE LLC

436 Cassat Ave, Jacksonville, FL 32254-3720
Tel.: (904) 783-1650   FL
Web Site:
   https://www.floridahardware.com
Year Founded: 1827
Sales Range: $1-4.9 Billion
Emp.: 120
Hardware, Tools, Plumbing & Ventilation Components, Electrical Components, Paint, Housewares, Motor Vehicle Supplies, Industrial Supplies, Lawn & Garden Supplies Distr
N.A.I.C.S.: 423710
Don Thieman (Owner & Pres)

FLORIDA HEALTH CARE NEWS, INC.

215 Bullard Pkwy, Temple Terrace, FL 33617
Tel.: (813) 989-1330
Web Site:
   https://www.flhealthcarenews.com
Year Founded: 1987
Sales Range: $1-9.9 Million
Emp.: 20
Newspaper Publishers
N.A.I.C.S.: 513110
Barry P. Levine (Pres)

Subsidiaries:

Pinellas Health Care News   (1)
215 Bullard Pkwy, Temple Terrace, FL 33617
Tel.: (813) 989-1330
Web Site: http://www.ifoundmydoctor.com
Emp.: 12
Newspaper Publishers
N.A.I.C.S.: 513110
Barry P. Levin (Publr)

FLORIDA HEALTHY KIDS CORPORATION

661 E Jefferson St 2nd Fl, Tallahassee, FL 32301
Tel.: (850) 224-5437   FL
Web Site: http://www.healthykids.org
Year Founded: 1990
Sales Range: $350-399.9 Million
Emp.: 40
Health Care Srvices
N.A.I.C.S.: 622110

Stephanie Haridopolos *(Chm)*

FLORIDA HOME BUILDERS ASSOCIATION, INC.
201 E Park Ave, Tallahassee, FL 32301
Tel.: (850) 224-4316   FL
Web Site: http://www.fhba.com
Year Founded: 1946
Sales Range: $1-9.9 Million
Emp.: 25
Business Associations
N.A.I.C.S.: 813910
Kimberly S. Scott *(CFO & COO)*
Douglas Buck *(Dir-Govt Affairs)*

FLORIDA HOME IMPROVE-MENT ASSOCIATES INC.
3044 SW 42nd St, Fort Lauderdale, FL 33312
Tel.: (954) 792-4415
Web Site:
   http://www.fhaproducts.com
Year Founded: 2007
Sales Range: $50-74.9 Million
Emp.: 500
Window & Door Mfr & Distr
N.A.I.C.S.: 321911
Austin Weiss *(Mgr-Sls)*
Mel Feinberg *(Founder & CEO)*

Subsidiaries:

Mad City Windows & Baths, LLC   (1)
5020 Voges Rd, Madison, WI 53718
Tel.: (608) 208-6908
Web Site: http://www.madcitywindows.com
Rev.: $1,240,000
Emp.: 10
Other Building Finishing Contractors
N.A.I.C.S.: 238390
Nathan Richmond *(Pres & CEO)*

Statewide Remodeling, Inc.   (1)
2450 Esters Blvd Ste 200, Grapevine, TX 75261
Tel.: (214) 891-7559
Web Site:
   http://www.statewideremodeling.com
Sales Range: $25-49.9 Million
Emp.: 125
Home Improvement & Remodeling Services Including Roofing, Siding & Window Replacement
N.A.I.C.S.: 236118
Rob Levin *(Pres)*

FLORIDA HOME PARTNER-SHIP, INC.
201 14th Ave SE Ste H, Ruskin, FL 33570
Tel.: (813) 672-7860   FL
Web Site: http://www.flhome.org
Year Founded: 1993
Sales Range: $1-9.9 Million
Emp.: 23
New Single-Family Housing Construction
N.A.I.C.S.: 236115
Earl Pfeiffer *(Exec Dir)*
Vanessa Ortiz *(Bus Mgr)*
Joey Henderson *(Mgr-Community Dev)*
Hope Martinez *(Mgr-Home Loan)*
David Snyder *(Mgr-Fin)*
Eric Isenbergh *(Pres)*
Paul Cliff *(VP)*
Sandy Council *(Sec)*
Tom Ludwig *(Treas)*

FLORIDA HOUSING FINANCE CORPORATION
227 N Bronough St Ste 5000, Tallahassee, FL 32301-1329
Tel.: (850) 488-4197
Web Site:
   https://www.floridahousing.org
Year Founded: 1980
Rev.: $250,000,000

Emp.: 110
Mortgage Assistance Services
N.A.I.C.S.: 522292
Barbara Goltz *(CFO)*
Susan Parks *(Mgr-Data Reporting)*
Ken Reecy *(Interim Exec Dir)*

FLORIDA INDUSTRIAL PROD-UCTS INC.
1602 N 39th St, Tampa, FL 33605-5853
Tel.: (813) 247-5356
Web Site: https://www.fiponline.com
Rev.: $16,500,000
Emp.: 35
Pipes & Fittings, Plastic
N.A.I.C.S.: 423720
David Ingram *(Pres & CEO)*
Thomas Mahfood *(Controller)*
Brad Atkinson *(VP-Sls & Mktg)*
Clyde Deese *(VP-Branch Ops)*

FLORIDA INSURANCE GUAR-ANTY ASSOCIATION, INC.
PO Box 14249, Tallahassee, FL 32317
Tel.: (850) 386-9200   FL
Web Site: https://www.figafacts.com
Year Founded: 1970
Sales Range: $50-74.9 Million
Emp.: 33
General Insurance Services
N.A.I.C.S.: 525190
Lenox Godfrey *(Dir-Claims)*

FLORIDA KEYS AQUEDUCT AUTHORITY
1100 Kennedy Dr, Key West, FL 33040
Tel.: (305) 296-2454
Web Site: http://www.fkaa.com
Year Founded: 1937
Sales Range: $50-74.9 Million
Emp.: 257
Water Utility Services
N.A.I.C.S.: 221310
Robert Feldman *(Gen Counsel)*
Timothy Esquinaldo *(Auditor-Internal Compliance)*
Kathryn A. Ovide *(Mgr-Customer Svc)*
Kerry Shelby *(Deputy Exec Dir)*
James Robert Dean *(Chm)*
Kirk C. Zuelch *(Exec Dir)*
Richard Kellough *(Mgr-Technical Svcs)*
Karen M. Rodriguez *(Mgr-HR)*
Thomas G. Walker *(Deputy Exec Dir)*

FLORIDA KEYS ELECTRIC COOPERATIVE ASSOCIATION, INC.
91630 Overseas Hwy, Tavernier, FL 33070
Tel.: (305) 852-2431
Web Site: https://www.fkec.com
Sales Range: $75-99.9 Million
Emp.: 120
Electric Power Distr
N.A.I.C.S.: 221122
Scott Newberry *(CEO)*
Jim Boilini *(Pres)*
Mike Puto *(Sec)*
Frank Hawkins *(Treas)*
Gretchen Holland *(VP)*
Chris Beaty *(CFO)*
John Stuart *(COO)*
Sara Hamilton *(Mgr-Environmental)*
Keith Kropf *(Dir-Engrg)*
Dennis Minton *(Dir-Power Supply & Delivery)*
Harry Holmbraker *(Mgr-Info Sys)*
Nicole Kraus *(Dir-HR)*

FLORIDA KNIFE CO.
1735 Apex Rd, Sarasota, FL 34240

Tel.: (941) 371-2104   OH
Web Site: https://www.florida-knife.com
Year Founded: 1978
Sales Range: $1-9.9 Million
Emp.: 12
Knives, Cutting Tools & Other Related Products Mfr
N.A.I.C.S.: 333515
Thomas Johanning *(Pres)*

FLORIDA LANDSCAPE CON-SULTANTS INC.
8501 Sunstate St, Tampa, FL 33634
Tel.: (813) 886-7755
Web Site:
   http://www.floridalandscapeconsultants.com
Sales Range: $1-9.9 Million
Emp.: 60
Landscaping Services
N.A.I.C.S.: 561730
Mike Lancaster *(Pres)*

FLORIDA LANDSCAPE DOC-TOR, INC.
144 Lake Edge Trl, Interlachen, FL 32148
Tel.: (386) 684-2042
Web Site:
   http://www.floridalandscapedoctor.com
Sales Range: $1-9.9 Million
Emp.: 30
Landscaping Services
N.A.I.C.S.: 561730
Keith C. Valentine *(Pres)*

FLORIDA LEMARK CORPORA-TION
2040 NW 94th Ave, Doral, FL 33172
Tel.: (305) 593-1442
Web Site:
   https://www.floridalemark.com
Rev.: $18,000,000
Emp.: 110
Poured Concrete Foundation & Structure Contractors
N.A.I.C.S.: 238110
Emilio Rodriguez *(VP)*
Linda Rodriguez *(Pres)*
Andres Rodriguez *(VP)*

FLORIDA LIFESTYLE HOMES OF FORT MYERS, INC.
14440 Metropolis Ave Ste 103, Fort Myers, FL 33912
Tel.: (239) 454-9154
Web Site: http://www.flhfl.com
Year Founded: 1993
Sales Range: $1-9.9 Million
Emp.: 20
New Housing Construction
N.A.I.C.S.: 236115
Jimmy Gustafson *(Project Mgr)*
Leeann James *(Controller)*
John Blackman *(Mgr-Pur)*
Andrew Olmstead *(Mgr-Construction)*

FLORIDA LIFT SYSTEMS, INC.
115 S 78th St, Tampa, FL 33619
Tel.: (813) 734-7940   FL
Web Site: https://www.sstlift.com
Year Founded: 1952
Sales Range: $25-49.9 Million
Emp.: 300
Lift & Material Handling Equipment Sales & Rental Services
N.A.I.C.S.: 423830
Jeff Fischer *(Co-Owner & Pres)*
Chris Stephenson *(Mgr-Ops)*
Todd Bartley *(Acct Mgr-Major)*
Tony Caro *(Supvr-Parts)*
Kristine Coyer *(Mgr-HR)*
Rob Budd *(Branch Mgr)*
Michael Weathers *(Branch Mgr-Ops)*

Mike Shenefield *(CFO)*
Joseph Watson *(Mgr-Territory)*
Patricia Hemingway *(VP-IT)*
Jennifer Zondor *(Mgr-HR)*
Michael McClelland *(Mgr-IT Ops)*
Mark Asadorian *(Mgr-Sarasota)*
Paul Stephens *(Mgr-Sls-Georgia)*
Kerry Reese *(Mgr-Corp Svc Admin)*

Subsidiaries:

Southern States TOYOTAlift   (1)
560 Cynthia St, Jacksonville, FL 32254-3580
Tel.: (904) 764-7662
Web Site: http://www.sstlift.com
Sales Range: $25-49.9 Million
Emp.: 75
Lift & Material Handling Equipment Sales & Rental Services
N.A.I.C.S.: 423830
Jeff Fischer *(Pres)*
Kevin Dean *(Mgr-Svc)*
Scott Lamothe *(Branch Mgr-Ops)*
Christian Glisson *(Mgr-Territory)*
Patricia Hemingway *(VP-Info Sys)*
Jennifer Zondor *(Mgr-HR)*
Michael McClelland *(Mgr-IT Ops)*
Paul Stephens *(Mgr-Sls-Georgia)*

FLORIDA LIVING NURSING CENTER
3355 E Semoran Blvd, Apopka, FL 32703
Tel.: (407) 862-6263   FL
Web Site:
   http://www.floridalivingnursing.com
Year Founded: 2006
Sales Range: $10-24.9 Million
Emp.: 372
Nursing Care Services
N.A.I.C.S.: 623110
Kent Johnson *(CFO)*
Robert R. Henderschedt *(Chm)*
Michelle Givens *(Pres)*

FLORIDA LIVING OPTIONS INC
851 W Lumsden Rd, Brandon, FL 33511
Tel.: (309) 343-1550   FL
Year Founded: 2001
Sales Range: $25-49.9 Million
Emp.: 761
Lifecare Retirement Community Operator
N.A.I.C.S.: 623311
Ron Wilson *(CFO)*

FLORIDA MARINE TANKS, INC.
120 Peter Gill Rd, Henderson, NC 27537
Tel.: (305) 620-9030   FL
Web Site:
   https://www.floridamarinetanks.com
Year Founded: 1974
Sales Range: $10-24.9 Million
Emp.: 10
Marine Tank Mfr
N.A.I.C.S.: 332420
Freeman Metcalf *(Gen Mgr)*

FLORIDA MARLINS, L.P.
501 Marlins Way, Miami, FL 33125
Tel.: (305) 480-1300   DE
Web Site:
   http://www.miami.marlins.mlb.com
Year Founded: 1993
Sales Range: $75-99.9 Million
Emp.: 135
Professional Baseball Club
N.A.I.C.S.: 711211
David P. Samson *(Pres)*
Jeffrey H. Loria *(Owner & CEO)*
Joel A. Mael *(Vice Chm)*
Michel Bussiere *(CFO & Exec VP)*
David Kuan *(Mgr-Database & Applications)*
Dan Jennings *(VP & Gen Mgr)*

Florida Marlins, L.P.—(Continued)

P. J. Loyello (Sr VP-Comm & Brdcst)
Sean Flynn (Sr VP-Mktg & Event Booking)
Angela Smith (Dir-Community Outreach)
Dale Hendricks (VP-Bus Dev)
Brendan Cunningham (Sr VP-Corporate Partnerships)
Susan Jaison (Sr VP-Fin)
Ana Hernandez (VP-HR)
Alfred Hernandez (Dir-Creative Svcs)
Albert Gonzalez (Asst Dir-Scouting)
Gregg Leonard (Dir-Intl Ops)
Matthew Roebuck (Dir-Media Rels)
Derek Jackson (Gen Counsel & VP)
Stan Meek (VP-Scouting)
Brian Chattin (Dir-Player Dev)
John Silverman (Mgr-Equipment)
Marty Sewell (Mgr-Media Rels)
Spencer Linden (Dir-Ticket Ops)
Robert Vigon (Mgr-Creative Svcs)
Larry Blocker (Dir-Game Presentation & Events)
Alina Trigo (Controller)
Claude Delorme (Exec VP-Ops & Events)
Marty Scott (VP-Player Dev)
Dan Noffsinger (Dir-Baseball Ops)
Carolina Perrina de Diego (Dir-Bus Comm)
Emmanuel Munoz (Dir-Brdcst)
Darling Jarquin (Mgr-Multicultural Mktg)
Alexander Buznego (Mgr-Digital & Social Media)
Ralph Capdevila (Supvr-Promo)
Randy Cousar (Dir-Engrg-Game Presentation/Events)
Eric Ramirez (Mgr-Game Presentation/Video Production)
Luis Dones (Mgr-Game Presentation & Events)
Andrew Silverman (Sr VP-Sls & Svcs)
Amy Chwick (Dir-Premium Svcs)
Fred Espinoza (Dir-Risk Mgmt)
Michael Hurt (Dir-Ballpark Ops)
Greg Terp (Dir-Security)
John Tavarez (Mgr-Security)
Chad Mulholland (Dir-Grounds)
Jared Olson (Mgr-Grounds)

FLORIDA MEDICAL CLINIC P.A.
38135 Market Sq, Zephyrhills, FL 33542
Tel.: (813) 780-8440
Web Site:
　https://www.floridamedicalclinic.com
Year Founded: 1993
Sales Range: $150-199.9 Million
Emp.: 950
Multi-Specialty Physicians Offices
N.A.I.C.S.: 621111
Joe Delatorre (CEO)
Chandresh Saraiya (Treas)
Mark Eisner (Sec)
Barry Frank (VP)
Emilio Dominguez (Chief Medical Officer)

FLORIDA METAL PRODUCTS INC.
6940 Stuart Ave, Jacksonville, FL 32254
Tel.: (904) 783-8400
Web Site: https://www.flamco.com
Sales Range: $10-24.9 Million
Emp.: 50
Metal Roofing & Roof Drainage Equipment
N.A.I.C.S.: 332322
John Klarfeld (CFO)
Pete Alderman (Gen Mgr)
Lee B. Jones IV (Pres)

FLORIDA MUNICIPAL POWER AGENCY
8553 Commodity Cir, Orlando, FL 32819
Tel.: (407) 355-7767
Web Site: http://www.fmpa.com
Year Founded: 1978
Sales Range: $650-699.9 Million
Emp.: 67
Eletric Power Generation Services
N.A.I.C.S.: 221118
Mark J. Larson (Asst Gen Mgr-Fin & IT)
Jacob A. Williams (CEO & Gen Mgr)
Frank Gaffney (COO)
Jody Lamar Finklea (Chief Legal Officer & Gen Counsel)
Linda Howard (CFO)

FLORIDA ORGANIC AQUA-CULTURE, LLC
930 W Indiantown Rd Ste 204, Jupiter, FL 33458
Tel.: (561) 741-3000
Web Site:
　http://www.flaquaculture.com
Sales Range: $1-9.9 Million
Emp.: 50
Aquaculture Farming
N.A.I.C.S.: 112512
Clifford Morris (Founder & Pres)
Pieter Jansen (CFO)

FLORIDA PAINTS & COAT-INGS LLC
3521 All-American Blvd, Orlando, FL 32801
Tel.: (407) 293-4175
Web Site: http://www.paintflorida.com
Year Founded: 2012
Paints Mfr
N.A.I.C.S.: 325510
Rick Strube (Co-Founder)
Jeff Grasty (Pres)
Mike Davis (Exec VP)
Tom Neron (Mgr-Production)
Randy Stephens (Dir-R&D)
Angela Giattino (VP-Fin)
Kevin Adkins (Mgr-Pur)
Don Strube Jr. (Co-Founder)

FLORIDA PENINSULA INSUR-ANCE COMPANY
903 NW 65th St Ste 200, Boca Raton, FL 33487
Tel.: (561) 994-8366
Web Site:
　http://www.floridapeninsula.com
Sales Range: $200-249.9 Million
Emp.: 50
Homeowners Insurance
N.A.I.C.S.: 524126
Paul M. Adkins (Chm)
Roger L. Desjadon (CEO)
Francis L. Lattanzio (Co-Founder)
Gary A. Cantor (Co-Founder & CFO)
Clint B. Strauch (Pres)
Stacey Giulianti (Chief Legal Officer)
Eric Love (Dir-Sls)
Mindy King (Dir-Customer Experience)
Joe Fagan (VP-Underwriting)

FLORIDA PRESS ASSOCIA-TION INC.
1025 Greenwood Blvd Ste 191, Lake Mary, FL 32746-5410
Tel.: (321) 283-5255
Web Site: http://www.flpress.com
Year Founded: 1879
Emp.: 40
Press Association Operator
N.A.I.C.S.: 813910
Dean Ridings (Pres & CEO)
Jim Gouvellis (Chm)

Tim Burke (Vice Chm-The Palm Beach Post)
Dawn Willis (Treas)
Jodi Bell (Vice Chm & Sec)
Andy Blizzard (Chm)

Subsidiaries:

Intersect Media Solutions　　　　**(1)**
1025 Greenwood Blvd Ste 191, Lake Mary, FL 32746-5410
Web Site:
　http://www.intersectmediasolutions.com
Sales Range: $50-74.9 Million
Emp.: 30
Marketing & Media Services
N.A.I.C.S.: 541830
Dean Ridings (Pres & CEO)
Jessica Pitts (VP-Ops)
Mark Burger (CFO & VP-Fin)

FLORIDA RADIOLOGY IMAG-ING
875 Concourse Pkwy S Ste 150, Maitland, FL 32751
Tel.: (407) 949-6439
Year Founded: 2002
Rev.: $11,900,000
Emp.: 130
Analytical Laboratory Instrument Mfr
N.A.I.C.S.: 334516
Bryan Stiltz (Chm & CEO)
Elsy Draitor (Mgr)
Eric Ostarly (CFO & Mgr)

FLORIDA RESTORATION OF TAMPA BAY LLC
7163 123rd Cir, Largo, FL 33773
Tel.: (727) 224-3122
Web Site:
　http://www.floridarestorations.com
Sales Range: $1-9.9 Million
Restoration & Remodeling Services
N.A.I.C.S.: 236118
Joe Mazzara (Owner)

FLORIDA SILICA SAND CO. INC.
181 S Bryan Rd, Dania, FL 33004
Tel.: (954) 923-8323
Web Site:
　http://www.floridasilicasand.com
Year Founded: 1948
Sales Range: $10-24.9 Million
Emp.: 50
Sand Processor & Distr
N.A.I.C.S.: 423320

FLORIDA SOUTHERN ROOF-ING & SHEET METAL, INC.
6653 19th St E, Sarasota, FL 34243
Tel.: (941) 954-8811
Web Site:
　https://www.floridaroofing.com
Year Founded: 1992
Sales Range: $1-9.9 Million
Emp.: 70
Roofing Contractors
N.A.I.C.S.: 238160
Brian T. Wallace (Pres & CEO)
Tim Wallace (VP)
Cindi Bass (Dir-Bus Dev)
Raymond Palfy (CFO)

FLORIDA STATE ELKS ASSO-CIATION, INC.
24175 SE Hwy 450, Umatilla, FL 32784
Tel.: (352) 669-2241
Web Site: http://www.floridaelks.org
Year Founded: 1973
Sales Range: $10-24.9 Million
Emp.: 9
Civic & Social Organization
N.A.I.C.S.: 813410
Steve Harmon (Dir-IT)
Carl T. Seibert (COO)
Krys Ragland (Asst Dir-Camp)

Nick Miller (Dir-Youth Camp)
Greg Weis (Dir-Mktg)
Jenny Chatham (Dir-HR & Accountant)
Brian T. Burns (Pres)
Joseph B. Bryant (Treas)
Dan E. Tabor (VP)
Vincent P. Como (Chm)

FLORIDA STATE SECURITY, INC.
6221 Pembroke Rd, Hollywood, FL 33023
Tel.: (954) 987-4483
Web Site: http://www.fssecurity.com
Year Founded: 1988
Home & Business Alarm Monitoring Equipment, Electronic Security, Fire & Integrated Systems
N.A.I.C.S.: 561621
Justin Falzetti (Project Mgr)

FLORIDA TOURISM INDUSTRY MARKETING CORPORATION
2540 W Executive Center Cir Ste 200, Tallahassee, FL 32301
Tel.: (850) 205-3865
Web Site: https://www.visitflorida.org
Sales Range: $125-149.9 Million
Emp.: 101
Tourism Marketing Services
N.A.I.C.S.: 561591
Damien Raimondi (Mgr-Creative Svcs)
Kimberly Faulk (VP-Sls)
Meredith M. DaSilva (VP-Exec Ops & Admin)
David Dodd (VP-Visitor Svcs)
Vicki Allen (Sr Mgr-Res)
Brenna Dacks (Mgr-Partnership-North Reg)
Dorothy Thames (Brand Mgr)
Staci Mellman (VP-Interim-Global Brand)
Tim Declaire (Dir-PR-Global)
John Tomlin (Chm)
Ken Lawson (Pres & CEO)
Cynthia Hefren (CFO)
Daniel Olson (COO)
John Tupps (VP-Govt Rels)
Alfredo Gonzalez (VP-Meetings-Global & Travel Trade)

FLORIDA TRAILS, INC.
130 Madrid Dr, Sebring, FL 33876
Tel.: (863) 655-5547
Web Site:
　https://www.annettbuslines.com
Year Founded: 1976
Sales Range: $1-9.9 Million
Emp.: 85
Bus Charter Services
N.A.I.C.S.: 485510
Brian Annett (Pres)
David Annett (VP)
Tamra Annett (Dir-Sls & Mktg)
Joe Schirk III (Dir-Safety & Trng)

FLORIDA TRUCK GROUP
2455 S Orange Blossom Trl, Apopka, FL 32703
Tel.: (407) 295-3846
Web Site:
　https://www.floridatruckgroup.com
Rev.: $50,700,000
Emp.: 125
New & Used Truck Inventory Sales
N.A.I.C.S.: 336120
John Taggart (Pres)
Jason Taggert (VP)

Subsidiaries:

Ocala Freightliner, Inc.　　　　**(1)**
3950 W Highway 326, Ocala, FL 34482
Tel.: (352) 840-0070
Web Site: http://www.ocalafreightliner.com

Truck Dealer
N.A.I.C.S.: 441110
Scott Pauley (Mgr-Svc)

Orlando Freightliner Inc. (1)
2455 South Orange Blossom Trl, Apopka,
FL 32703
Tel.: (407) 295-3846
Web Site: http://www.floridatruckgroup.com
Trucks, Tractors & Trailers: New & Used
N.A.I.C.S.: 441110
John Taggart (Pres)

FLORIDA UNITED METHODIST CHILDREN'S HOME
51 Children's Way, Enterprise, FL
32725
Tel.: (386) 668-4774   FL
Web Site:
    http://www.allchildrenfirst.org
Year Founded: 1908
Sales Range: $10-24.9 Million
Emp.: 350
Child Care Services
N.A.I.C.S.: 624110
Diahann Suchan (VP-Residential
Care)
Elisabeth Gadd (Chief Dev Officer)
Scott Davidson (Chm)

FLORIDA UTILITY TRAILERS INC.
1101 S Orange Blossom Trl, Apopka,
FL 32703
Tel.: (407) 880-2211
Web Site: https://www.flutility.com
Sales Range: $10-24.9 Million
Emp.: 100
Utility Trailers
N.A.I.C.S.: 441227
Jeff Chambers (Mgr-Svcs)
Todd Richards (Mgr-Parts)
Jack Beville (Gen Mgr)

FLORIDA WEST COAST CRUISES, INC.
25 Causeway Blvd Slip Ste 58, Clear-
water, FL 33767
Tel.: (727) 462-2628
Web Site:
    https://www.starlitecruises.com
Sales Range: $10-24.9 Million
Dinner Cruises Operator
N.A.I.C.S.: 722511
Phil M. Henderson Jr. (Pres & CEO)

FLORIDA WEST COAST PUB-LIC BROADCASTING, INC.
1300 N Blvd, Tampa, FL 33607-5699
Tel.: (813) 254-9338
Web Site: https://www.wedu.org
Year Founded: 1958
Emp.: 40
Public Television Station
N.A.I.C.S.: 516120
Larry Jopek (VP-Mktg & Community
Partnerships)
Claire O'Connor-Solomon (VP-Dev)

FLORIDA WORKERS' COM-PENSATION INSURANCE GUARANTY ASSOCIATION, INC.
1400 Village Square Blvd Ste 3-008,
Tallahassee, FL 32312
Tel.: (850) 386-9200   FL
Web Site: https://www.fwciga.org
Year Founded: 1998
Sales Range: $10-24.9 Million
Emp.: 18
Employee Benefit Services
N.A.I.C.S.: 524292
Charlie Greene (Mgr-Claims)
Mike Hoey (Dir-Claims)

FLORIDIAN PARTNERS, LLC

108 S Monroe St, Tallahassee, FL
32301
Tel.: (850) 681-0024
Web Site:
    https://www.flapartners.com
Sales Range: $1-9.9 Million
Emp.: 10
Corporate & Public Affairs Consulting
N.A.I.C.S.: 541820
Charles F. Dudley (Mng Partner)
Jorge Chamizo (Partner)

FLORIKAN ESA LLC
1579 Barber Rd, Sarasota, FL 34240
Tel.: (941) 379-4048
Web Site: http://www.florikan.com
Year Founded: 1981
Sales Range: $10-24.9 Million
Emp.: 40
Agricultural Products Mfr & Distr
N.A.I.C.S.: 325320
Eric Rosenthal (Pres)

Subsidiaries:

Dynamite Plant Food (1)
PO Box 190, Oxford, FL 34484
Tel.: (800) 447-3304
Agricultural Products Mfr & Distr
N.A.I.C.S.: 325320

FLORSTAR SALES, INC.
1075 Taylor Rd, Romeoville, IL
60446-4265
Tel.: (815) 836-2800   IL
Web Site: https://www.florstar.com
Year Founded: 1988
Sales Range: $100-124.9 Million
Emp.: 300
Distr of Flooring Materials
N.A.I.C.S.: 423220
F. Wade Cassidy (Owner & CEO)
Scott Rozmus (Pres)
Gregory Stirrett (CFO)

FLORY INDUSTRIES, INC.
4737 Toomes Rd, Salida, CA 95368
Tel.: (209) 545-1167   CA
Web Site:
    http://www.floryindustries.com
Year Founded: 1939
Sales Range: $1-9.9 Million
Emp.: 75
Farm Machinery And Equipment, Nsk
N.A.I.C.S.: 333111
Howard Flory (Owner)

Subsidiaries:

Coe Orchard Equipment, Inc. (1)
3453 Riviera Rd, Live Oak, CA 95953
Tel.: (530) 695-5121
Web Site: http://www.coeshakers.com
Rev.: $5,350,000
Emp.: 25
Hand & Edge Tool Mfr
N.A.I.C.S.: 332216
Lyman Coe (Co-Founder)
Lois Coe (Co-Founder)

FLOTEC CORPORATION
1820 Shiloh Rd Ste 1105, Tyler, TX
75703-2458
Tel.: (972) 554-6199   TX
Year Founded: 1998
Sales Range: $75-99.9 Million
Emp.: 3
Valves, Pumps & Other Industrial
Equipment Distr
N.A.I.C.S.: 423830
Harold Dupree (Pres)
Jim Sayles (Head-Sls)

FLOTURN INC.
4236 Thunderbird Ln, Fairfield, OH
45014-5482
Tel.: (513) 860-8040
Web Site: https://www.floturn.com
Year Founded: 1988
Sales Range: $10-24.9 Million

Emp.: 175
Provider of Industrial Machinery &
Equipment
N.A.I.C.S.: 332710
M. North (Pres)
Robert Glutting (CEO)
Denise Fornshell (Controller)
Michael Finn (Mgr-Metal Form)
Scott Matthews (Mgr-Pur)
Linda Dietz (Mgr-HR)

Subsidiaries:

Advanced Interconnect Manufactur-
ing, Inc. (1)
780 Canning Pkwy, Victor, NY 14564
Tel.: (585) 288-2220
Web Site: http://www.aim-mfg.com
Sales Range: $1-9.9 Million
Computer Cable Mfr
N.A.I.C.S.: 334419
John Durst (Pres)
Steve Yost (Mgr-Technical & Engrg Sls)
Diane Pepe (Mgr-Sls & Matls)
David Elliott (Mgr-Ops)
Gretchen Dunfey (Mgr-HR)
Mike Simone (Supvr-Production Control)
Jon Martin (Engr-Procurement)
Matthew Myers (Supvr-Quality)

Floturn Photoreceptor (Kunshan) Co.,
Ltd. (1)
526 Nanbang Road, Kunshan, 215334, Ji-
angsu, China
Tel.: (86) 512 5790 0800
Printer Component Mfr
N.A.I.C.S.: 334419

Magnus Precision Manufacturing
Inc. (1)
1912 State Rte 96, Phelps, NY
14532-9705 (100%)
Tel.: (315) 548-8032
Web Site: http://www.magnusprecision.com
Sales Range: $10-24.9 Million
Emp.: 70
Provider of Industrial Machinery & Equip-
ment
N.A.I.C.S.: 335314
Grant Overdorf (Pres)

Printer Components Inc. (1)
100 Photikon Dr Ste 2, Fairport, NY 14450
Tel.: (585) 924-5190
Web Site: http://www.pcivictor.com
Sales Range: $10-24.9 Million
Emp.: 60
Provider of Photographic Equipment & Sup-
plies
N.A.I.C.S.: 333310

FLOURISH INC.
1001 Huron Rd E Ste 102, Cleve-
land, OH 44115-1755
Tel.: (216) 696-9116
Web Site:
    http://www.flourishagency.com
Year Founded: 1998
Sales Range: Less than $1 Million
Emp.: 10
Full Service Agency
N.A.I.C.S.: 541810
Christopher Ferranti (Owner)

FLOURNOY DEVELOPMENT CO. LLC
900 Brookstone Ctr Pkwy, Columbus,
GA 31904
Tel.: (706) 324-4000
Web Site: http://www.flournoydevelop
    ment.com
Year Founded: 1967
Sales Range: $50-74.9 Million
Emp.: 447
Subdividers & Developers
N.A.I.C.S.: 237210
Thomas H. Flournoy (Pres & COO)
Brady T. Blair (Sr VP)
Rodney S. Dawson (Chief Acctg Offi-
cer)
Ryan M. Foster (Sr VP)
Jeremy W. Brewer (Gen Counsel &
Sec)

Paul L. Wieczorek (Pres & COO)
Joel A. Mies (Sr Project Mgr)
J. Blake Breimann (VP)
John R. Akin Jr. (CFO & Chief Invest-
ment Officer)

FLOW AUTOMOTIVE CENTER OF WINSTON-SALEM, LLC
1400 S Stratford Rd, Winston Salem,
NC 27103
Tel.: (336) 760-7000   NC
Web Site: http://www.flowauto.com
Sales Range: $25-49.9 Million
Emp.: 190
New & Used Car Dealer
N.A.I.C.S.: 441110
Donald Flow (Pres)

FLOW BMW
2565 Peters Creek Pkwy, Winston
Salem, NC 27127
Tel.: (336) 788-3333
Web Site: https://www.flowbmw.com
Sales Range: $10-24.9 Million
Emp.: 55
Car Whslr
N.A.I.C.S.: 441110
Donald Flow (Pres)
Doug Weaver (Gen Mgr)
Robin Agee (Mgr-Fin Svcs)

FLOW BUICK GMC OF WINSTON-SALEM
1400 S Stratford Rd, Winston Salem,
NC 27103-2902
Tel.: (336) 701-6612
Web Site: https://flowgmauto.com
Rev.: $26,100,000
Emp.: 55
New & Used Automobile Dealership
N.A.I.C.S.: 441110
Don Flow (CEO)

FLOW MANAGEMENT TECH-NOLOGIES, INC.
112 S Broadway Ste 1, Saratoga
Springs, NY 12866-4560
Tel.: (518) 580-9844
Web Site: http://www.flowmgt.com
Year Founded: 1996
Sales Range: $10-24.9 Million
Emp.: 20
Software, Technology & Services for
Health Care Industry
N.A.I.C.S.: 541511
Scott Person (Supvr-Call Center)

FLOW MOTORS, INC.
425 Silas Creek Pkwy, Winston-
Salem, NC 27127
Tel.: (336) 723-3524
Web Site: http://www.flowauto.com
Sales Range: $25-49.9 Million
Emp.: 170
Auto Dealer
N.A.I.C.S.: 441110
Don Flow (Owner)

FLOWER CITY PRINTING INC.
1725 Mount Read Blvd, Rochester,
NY 14606-2827
Tel.: (585) 663-9000
Web Site: http://www.fcp.biz
Year Founded: 1970
Sales Range: $25-49.9 Million
Emp.: 400
Point of Purchase Displays Mfr
N.A.I.C.S.: 322212

FLOWER FACTORY INC.
5655 Whipple Ave NW, Canton, OH
44720
Tel.: (330) 494-7978
Web Site:
    http://www.flowerfactoryinc.com
Rev.: $33,000,000

Flower Factory Inc.—(Continued)
Emp.: 500
Gifts & Novelties
N.A.I.C.S.: 424990
Gary Jackson (Mgr-Software Dev)

FLOWERBUD.COM
PO Box 761, Lake Oswego, OR
97034-0076
Tel.: (503) 697-1790
Web Site: http://www.flowerbud.com
Year Founded: 1999
Sales Range: $10-24.9 Million
Emp.: 9
Flowers Distr
N.A.I.C.S.: 459310
Marcy Lepine (Gen Mgr)

**FLOWERS BAKING CO. OF
BARDSTOWN, LLC.**
1755 Pkwy Dr, Bardstown, KY
40004-3253
Tel.: (502) 350-4700
Sales Range: $25-49.9 Million
Emp.: 160
Baked Goods Mfr
N.A.I.C.S.: 311811
Marlene Mejia (Asst Dir-HR)
Amos Carey (Supvr-Production)
Glen Pickette (Dir-Sls)

FLOWMASTER INC.
100 Stony Point Rd Ste 125, Santa
Rosa, CA 95401
Tel.: (707) 544-4761
Web Site:
http://www.flowmastermufflers.com
Year Founded: 1983
Sales Range: $25-49.9 Million
Emp.: 275
Motor Vehicle Mufflers Mfr
N.A.I.C.S.: 336390
Ray T. Flugger (Founder)
Joe von Dohlen (Supvr-Machine
Shop)

**FLOYD & BEASLEY TRANS-
FER CO. INC.**
18060 Alabam Hwy 21, Sycamore,
AL 35149
Tel.: (256) 245-4386
Web Site: http://www.fbtcinc.com
Sales Range: $10-24.9 Million
Emp.: 300
Trucking Service
N.A.I.C.S.: 484121
Cassie Burton (Chm & Exec VP)
Mike Miller (Mgr)
Toney Cooksey (Mgr-Safety)
Jeff Floyd (Pres)

FLOYD ENERGY INC.
36310 Lakeford Hwy, Belle Haven,
VA 23306
Tel.: (757) 442-2444
Web Site: http://www.floyd-
energy.com
Sales Range: $10-24.9 Million
Emp.: 10
Petroleum Products Sales
N.A.I.C.S.: 424720
H. Allen Floyd Jr. (Pres)

**FLOYD'S TRUCK CENTER,
INC.**
322 S Beltline Hwy E, Scottsbluff, NE
69361
Tel.: (308) 632-2911
Web Site:
https://www.floydstrucks.com
Sales Range: $10-24.9 Million
Emp.: 90
Automobile & Motor Vehicle Merchant
Whslr
N.A.I.C.S.: 423110

Mark Gillam (Pres)

FLOYDS STORES INC.
3650 Chester Ave, Bakersfield, CA
93301
Tel.: (661) 410-4602
Web Site: https://www.floyds.com
Rev.: $10,086,054
Emp.: 15
Army-Navy Goods Sales
N.A.I.C.S.: 455219
Thomas Chan (CEO)

FLP HOLDINGS INC.
8801 Frost Ave, Saint Louis, MO
63134
Tel.: (314) 522-1112
Rev.: $25,200,000
Lubricating Oils & Greases
N.A.I.C.S.: 424720
Frank L. Palazzo (Pres)

**FLUENTSTREAM TECHNOLO-
GIES, LLC**
2260 N Broadway, Denver, CO
80205
Tel.: (303) 462-5683
Web Site:
http://www.fluentstream.com
Year Founded: 2010
Sales Range: $1-9.9 Million
Emp.: 41
Telecommunication Servicesb
N.A.I.C.S.: 517810
Cass Gilmore (CEO)
Theo Zourzouvillys (CTO)
Pedro Noyola (Pres)
Nicole Kennedy (CFO)
Lacy Russell (COO)
Amber Tobias (Head-Corp Dev)
Kevin Beede (Dir-Channel Success &
Enablement)
Tracy Pullman (VP-Mktg)

FLUID END SALES, INC.
8009 S I 35 Service Rd, Oklahoma
City, OK 73149
Tel.: (405) 631-7728
Web Site: http://www.fivestarrig.com
Year Founded: 1983
Construction & Mining, except Oil
Well, Machinery & Equipment Mer-
chant Whslr
N.A.I.C.S.: 423810
Jason Clayton (Pres)

**FLUID ENERGY PROCESSING
& EQUIPMENT CO.**
2629 Penn Ave, Hatfield, PA 19440
Tel.: (215) 368-2510
Web Site:
http://www.fluidenergype.com
Sales Range: $10-24.9 Million
Emp.: 60
Grinding Castings For The Trade
N.A.I.C.S.: 325180
Ilean Barndt (Mgr-Accts)
Monang Panchal (Engr-Solidworks
Design)

**FLUID EQUIPMENT DEVELOP-
MENT COMPANY LLC**
800 Ternes Dr, Monroe, MI 48162
Tel.: (734) 241-3935
Web Site: http://www.fedco-usa.com
Year Founded: 1997
Sales Range: $10-24.9 Million
Emp.: 38
High-Pressure Pumps & Engine Re-
covery Turbines
N.A.I.C.S.: 333914
Eli Oklejas (Chm & CEO)
Thomas Clinton (Exec VP-Comml
Dev)

FLUID FLOW PRODUCTS INC.

2108 Crown View Dr, Charlotte, NC
28227
Tel.: (704) 847-4464
Web Site: http://www.fluidflow.com
Sales Range: $10-24.9 Million
Emp.: 65
Industrial Supplies
N.A.I.C.S.: 423840
Drew Schwartc (Pres)

**FLUID MANAGEMENT COM-
PANY, LLC**
3761 E Raines Rd, Memphis, TN
38118
Tel.: (901) 266-1030
Web Site: http://www.fluidmngt.com
Year Founded: 1998
Industrial Machinery & Equipment
Distr
N.A.I.C.S.: 423830
Shannon Haynes (Chief Admin Offi-
cer)

**FLUID POWER PRODUCTS
INC.**
1251 Georgetown Rd Ste F, Lexing-
ton, KY 40511
Tel.: (859) 231-8882
Web Site: http://www.bwrogers.com
Sales Range: $10-24.9 Million
Emp.: 200
Hydraulic Systems, Equipment &
Supplies Whslr
N.A.I.C.S.: 423830
Rick Rogers (Pres)

**FLUID PROCESS EQUIPMENT,
INC.**
4797 Campus Dr, Kalamazoo, MI
49008
Tel.: (269) 345-1923
Web Site: https://www.fpepumps.com
Year Founded: 1985
Sales Range: $10-24.9 Million
Emp.: 30
Industrial Machinery & Equipment
Whslr
N.A.I.C.S.: 423830
Peter Clark (Engr-Sls & Application)
Ross Draper (Engr-Sls & Application)
Scott Lyke (Engr-Sls & Application)
Tim Ostergren (Engr-Sls & Applica-
tion)
Cristina Pye (Engr-Sls & Application)

**FLUID SYSTEM COMPO-
NENTS INC.**
2315 S 170th St, New Berlin, WI
53151
Tel.: (262) 827-2700
Rev.: $6,270,000
Emp.: 100
Industrial Supplies Merchant Whslr
N.A.I.C.S.: 423840
Randy Thostenson (Mgr)

Subsidiaries:

Hydrotech Inc. (1)
10052 Commerce Park Dr, Cincinnati, OH
45246
Tel.: (513) 881-7000
Web Site: https://www.hydrotech.com
Sales Range: $50-74.9 Million
Emp.: 40
Distr & Manufacturers' Representative of
Industrial Machinery & Equipment
N.A.I.C.S.: 423830
Mike Tonyan (Reg VP-Sls)
Tamara Jones Andersson (Pres)
Rex Wetherill (CEO)
John Campbell (Pres)

Subsidiary (Domestic):

The Isaacs Company (2)
6091 Commerce Ct, Mason, OH 45040
Tel.: (513) 336-8500
Web Site: http://www.isaccsfluidpower.com

Sales Range: $10-24.9 Million
Emp.: 37
Fluid Power Equipment Distr
N.A.I.C.S.: 423830
Bruce Becknell (VP)
Beverley Massey (Treas)

FLUIDMASTER, INC.
30800 Rancho Viejo Rd, San Juan
Capistrano, CA 92675-1564
Tel.: (949) 728-2000
Web Site:
https://www.fluidmaster.com
Year Founded: 1957
Sales Range: $25-49.9 Million
Emp.: 385
Plumbing Fixture Fittings & Trim Ser-
vices
N.A.I.C.S.: 332913

Subsidiaries:

Kolektor LIV d.o.o. (1)
Industrijska c 2, 6230, Postojna, Slovenia
Tel.: (386) 57283700
Web Site: http://www.kolektor.com
Sales Range: $50-74.9 Million
Household Appliances, Machinery & Equip-
ment Mfr
N.A.I.C.S.: 335220
Barbara Zuzek (Mgr-Mktg)

Opella Limited (1)
Rotherwas Industrial Estate, Twyford Road,
Hereford, HR2 6JR, United Kingdom
Tel.: (44) 1432357331
Web Site: http://www.opella.co.uk
Sales Range: $25-49.9 Million
Emp.: 200
Tap & Valve Mfr
N.A.I.C.S.: 332911
Paul Watton (Dir-Fin)

FLUIDMESH NETWORKS LLC
81 Prospect St, Brooklyn, NY 11201
Tel.: (617) 209-6080
Web Site: http://www.fluidmesh.com
Year Founded: 2005
Sales Range: $10-24.9 Million
Communication Service
N.A.I.C.S.: 517312
Umberto Malesci (Co-Founder &
CEO)
Cosimo Malesci (Co-Founder & VP-
Sls & Mktg)

**FLUITEC INTERNATIONAL
LLC**
333 Washington St Ste 201, Jersey
City, NJ 07302
Tel.: (201) 946-4584
Web Site: http://www.fluitec.com
Sales Range: $150-199.9 Million
Lubricant Related Software Publisher;
Lubricant Related Technology
N.A.I.C.S.: 513010
Greg Livingstone (Chief Innovation
Officer)
Pierre Vanderkelen (CEO)
Cristian Soto (COO)

Subsidiaries:

Fluitec International China (1)
Room 2611 Hongyun Dihao Building, 151
Wusi Road, Fuzhou, 350003, Fujian, China
Tel.: (86) 591 8801 1021
Lubricant Related Software Publisher; Lubri-
cant Related Technology
N.A.I.C.S.: 213112

Fluitec International Europe (1)
Friendship Building Rijnkaai 37, 2000, Ant-
werp, Belgium
Tel.: (32) 3 205 71 40
Lubricant Related Software Publisher; Lubri-
cant Related Technology
N.A.I.C.S.: 513010
Jo Ameye (Gen Mgr)

FLURIDA GROUP, INC.
11220 Rojas Ste C-3, El Paso, TX
79935

Tel.: (915) 599-8866   NV
Web Site: http://www.flurida.com
Year Founded: 2006
Sales Range: $25-49.9 Million
Appliance Parts Marketer & Distr
N.A.I.C.S.: 423620
Jianfeng Ding *(Chm, Pres & CEO)*
Yaru Huang *(CFO)*

**FLUSHING HOSPITAL MEDI-
CAL CENTER**
4500 Parsons Blvd, Flushing, NY
11355
Tel.: (718) 670-5000   NY
Web Site:
   https://www.flushinghospital.org
Year Founded: 1884
Sales Range: $200-249.9 Million
Emp.: 2,078
Health Care Srvices
N.A.I.C.S.: 622110
Bruce J. Flanz *(Pres & CEO)*
Mounir F. Doss *(CFO & Exec VP)*
Robert V. Levine *(COO & Exec VP)*

FLY TIMBER CO. INC.
2178 Hwy 7 N, Grenada, MS 38901
Tel.: (662) 226-2276
Rev.: $20,333,169
Emp.: 50
Lumber: Rough, Dressed & Finished
N.A.I.C.S.: 423310
Ricky Fly *(Pres)*
Dotty Fly *(Treas & Sec)*

FLYERS ENERGY, LLC
2360 Lindbergh St, Auburn, CA
95602-9562
Tel.: (530) 885-0401   CA
Web Site:
   http://www.flyersenergy.com
Year Founded: 1979
Gasoline & Other Petroleum Products
Distr; Gasoline Station Franchisor
N.A.I.C.S.: 424720
Tom Dwelle *(Founder)*
Steve Dwelle *(Founder)*
Walt Dwelle *(Founder & Mng Partner)*
David Dwelle *(Founder)*

FLYING A
35 N Arroyo Pkwy Ste 230, Pasa-
dena, CA 91103
Tel.: (626) 376-4770
Web Site:
   https://www.flyingamedia.com
Year Founded: 1978
Sales Range: $10-24.9 Million
Emp.: 7
Media Buying Services
N.A.I.C.S.: 541810
Michael G. Amsbry *(Founder)*
Sharon Reid *(Dir-Media)*
Liz Amsbry *(Mgr-Pub Rels)*
Paula Zigant *(Controller)*
Patrick Amsbry *(Pres)*

FLYING FOOD GROUP, LLC
212 N Sangamon St Ste 1-A, Chi-
cago, IL 60607-1722
Tel.: (312) 243-2882   IL
Web Site: http://www.flyingfood.com
Year Founded: 1983
Sales Range: $150-199.9 Million
Emp.: 2,100
Airline & Industrial Catering Services
N.A.I.C.S.: 722320
David Cotton *(CFO)*
Nicolas Rondeau *(Exec VP-Sls &
Mktg)*

Subsidiaries:

Flying Food Fare, Inc.   (1)
3533 S Lemaire Ave, Chicago, IL 60638-
3000
Tel.: (312) 243-2122
Web Site: http://www.flyingfoodfare.com

Sales Range: $10-24.9 Million
Emp.: 100
Contract Food Services & Retail of Frozen
Dinners
N.A.I.C.S.: 722320

FLYING PIE PIZZARIA, INC.
6508 Fairview Ave, Boise, ID 83704
Tel.: (208) 376-3454   ID
Web Site: http://www.flyingpie.org
Year Founded: 1979
Sales Range: $1-9.9 Million
Emp.: 75
Pizzeria
N.A.I.C.S.: 722513
Florian Penalva *(Owner)*

FLYING POINT MEDIA, INC.
494 8th Ave 20th Fl, New York, NY
10001
Tel.: (212) 629-4960
Web Site:
   http://www.flyingpointmedia.com
Year Founded: 2002
Sales Range: $10-24.9 Million
Emp.: 20
Advetising Agency
N.A.I.C.S.: 541810
Vlada Briks *(Acct Dir)*
Matt Strietelmeier *(Dir-Paid Search)*
Mike Levin *(Dir-SEO)*
Jenna Manula *(Dir-Social Media
Mktg)*

FLYING W PLASTICS INC.
487 Vanhorn Dr, Glenville, WV 26351
Tel.: (304) 462-5779
Web Site: https://flyingwplastics.com
Year Founded: 1984
Emp.: 150
Polyethylene Pipe Products Mfr
N.A.I.C.S.: 326122
Shelly Demarino *(Owner)*
Fred Lowther *(Mgr-Shipping)*
Wesley Smith *(Plant Mgr)*
Frank Montgomery *(Mgr-
Maintenance)*
Rick Nolan *(Sls Mgr)*
Jim Harper *(Mgr-Polyethylene Pro-
duction)*
Nick Dent *(Dir-Safety & HR)*

FLYNN & FRIENDS
437 Franklin St, Buffalo, NY 14202
Tel.: (716) 881-2697
Web Site:
   http://www.flynnandfriends.com
Year Founded: 1986
Sales Range: Less than $1 Million
Emp.: 8
Full Service
N.A.I.C.S.: 541810
Mitch Flynn *(Owner)*
Marc Adler *(VP-Client Svcs)*
Kristin Taylor *(Designer)*
Linda Leman *(Bookkeeper)*
Laura Elia *(Copywriter)*

**FLYNN & O'HARA UNIFORMS
INC.**
10905 Dutton Rd, Philadelphia, PA
19154
Tel.: (215) 637-4600
Web Site:
   https://www.flynnohara.com
Year Founded: 1972
Sales Range: $25-49.9 Million
Emp.: 200
Uniforms Mfr
N.A.I.C.S.: 458110
Sean Flynn *(Pres & CEO)*
Jim Natale *(VP-Sls)*
Eireann Flynn *(VP-Mktg)*
Paul Toomey *(CFO)*

**FLYNN & REYNOLDS AGENCY
INC.**
220 Howard St Ste 200, Lowell, MA
01851-2653
Tel.: (978) 454-1098
Web Site: http://www.flynn-
   reynolds.com
Electrical Supplies & Engineered
Products Mfr
N.A.I.C.S.: 335999
Ed Scannapieco *(VP-Ops)*
Bryan Lally *(Pres)*

Subsidiaries:

Mills Talbot Company   (1)
100 Thompson St, Fayetteville, NY 13066
Tel.: (315) 637-0511
Web Site: http://www.millstalbot.com
Rev.: $4,720,000
Emp.: 5
Miscellaneous Durable Goods Merchant
Whslr
N.A.I.C.S.: 423990
Tom Talbot *(Partner)*
Dan Sciulli *(VP-Sls)*

**FLYNN BROTHERS CON-
TRACTING INC.**
1213 Outer Loop, Louisville, KY
40219-3417
Tel.: (502) 364-9100   KY
Web Site:
   http://www.flynnbrothers.com
Year Founded: 1974
Sales Range: $25-49.9 Million
Emp.: 200
General Utility Contractor Services
N.A.I.C.S.: 237110
William Reed *(Pres)*
Peter Rastocny *(Controller)*
Jason Rice *(Project Mgr)*

Subsidiaries:

Flynn Brothers Contracting Inc. - As-
  phalt Material Plant   (1)
4620 Robards Ln, Louisville, KY 40218
Tel.: (502) 451-4830
Asphalt Product Mfr
N.A.I.C.S.: 324122

Flynn Trucking LLC   (1)
129 Pine Hill Rd, Bridgewater, VT 05035
Tel.: (802) 672-4321
Utility Construction Services
N.A.I.C.S.: 237110

FLYNN ENTERPRISES, LLC
2203 S Walnut St, Hopkinsville, KY
42240
Tel.: (270) 886-0223   KY
Rev.: $65,000,000
Emp.: 80
Men's & Boys' Dungarees Mfr
N.A.I.C.S.: 315250
Bill R. Flynn *(Pres)*

**FLYNN'S TIRE & AUTO SER-
VICE**
2908 Mercer W Middlesex Rd, West
Middlesex, PA 16159
Tel.: (724) 906-8091
Web Site:
   https://www.FlynnsTire.com
Year Founded: 1964
Sales Range: $10-24.9 Million
Emp.: 123
Home Supply Whslr
N.A.I.C.S.: 441330
Joseph L. Durkoske *(Principal)*
Joe Flynn *(Pres)*

FLYPRIVATE
80 Research Rd, Hingham, MA
02043
Tel.: (781) 740-9700
Web Site: http://www.flyprivate.com
Year Founded: 2002
Rev.: $9,700,000

Emp.: 15
Nonscheduled Air Transportation
N.A.I.C.S.: 481212
Greg Goodwin *(COO & VP-Mktg)*
Don Smith *(CEO)*
Steve Schofield *(Dir-Client Svcs)*

**FM FACILITY MAINTENANCE,
LLC**
10 Columbus Blvd 4th Fl, Hartford,
CT 06106
Tel.: (860) 466-7400
Web Site: http://www.fmfacilitymainte
   nance.com
Year Founded: 1993
Sales Range: $100-124.9 Million
Emp.: 359
Facility Maintenance for Multi Site
Restaurant & Retail Locations
N.A.I.C.S.: 541990
Suellen Aldina *(Sr VP-Vendor Mgmt)*
Bryan Hartnett *(COO & Exec VP)*

Subsidiaries:

US Signs, Inc.   (1)
5225 Katy Freeway Ste 350, Houston, TX
77007
Tel.: (713) 977-7900
Web Site: http://www.ussigns.com
Sales Range: $10-24.9 Million
Emp.: 25
Sign Mfr
N.A.I.C.S.: 339950

**FM STRUCTURAL PLASTIC
TECHNOLOGY INC.**
3535 W Hudson Rd, Rogers, AR
72756
Tel.: (479) 636-3540   AR
Web Site: https://www.fmcorp.com
Year Founded: 1987
Sales Range: $25-49.9 Million
Emp.: 200
Molded Plastic Products Mfr
N.A.I.C.S.: 326199
Marc Campbell *(CFO)*

FMA ALLIANCE LTD.
12339 Cutten Rd, Houston, TX
77066-1807
Tel.: (281) 931-5050
Web Site:
   https://www.fmaalliance.com
Sales Range: $10-24.9 Million
Emp.: 150
Collection Agency
N.A.I.C.S.: 561440
Jeffery L. Spiegelhauer *(Chm)*
Doyle Burkett *(CEO)*
Karen Hollingsworth *(Dir-HR & Acctg)*
Mike Janakes *(Pres)*

FMA COMMUNICATIONS, INC.
833 Featherstone Rd, Rockford, IL
61107
Tel.: (815) 399-8700
Web Site: http://www.fma-
   communications.com
Sales Range: $1-9.9 Million
Emp.: 85
Other Commercial Printing
N.A.I.C.S.: 323111
Dan Davis *(Editor-in-Chief)*
Dave Brambert *(Publr)*
Kim Clothier *(Mgr-Circulation)*
Vicki Bell *(Mgr-IT)*

**FMB OF S.C. BANCSHARES,
INCORPORATED**
8624 Old State Rd, Holly Hill, SC
29059
Tel.: (803) 496-3430   SC
Web Site: https://www.fmbsc.com
Sales Range: $10-24.9 Million
Emp.: 85
Bank Holding Company
N.A.I.C.S.: 551111

FMB of S.C. Bancshares,
Incorporated—(Continued)

John L. Hutto *(Pres)*

Subsidiaries:

Farmers & Merchants Bank of South
Carolina   **(1)**
8624 Old State Rd, Holly Hill, SC 29059
Tel.: (803) 496-3430
Web Site: http://www.fmbsc.com
State Commercial Banks
N.A.I.C.S.: 522110
Jennifer Myers *(Asst VP & MgrCameron
Branch)*
Stacy D. Weathers *(Asst VP & MgrEutaw-
ville Branch)*
E. Matt Stokes *(VP & Mgr-Bowman Branch)*
Steven M. Sabback *(VP & Mgr-Cames
Crossroads Branch)*
Thierry P. Longueville *(VP & Mgr-Moncks
Corner Branch)*
Brian P. West *(VP & Mgr-Saint Stephen
Branch)*
Thomas E. Jennings Jr. *(Asst VP & Mgr-
Branchville Branch)*
Charles D. Paramore Jr. *(VP & Mgr-Holly
Hill Branch)*

FMC GLOBALSAT HOLDINGS, INC.

3301 SE 14th Ave, Fort Lauderdale,
FL 33316
Tel.: (954) 678-0697   **DE**
Year Founded: 2017
Rev.: $305,403
Assets: $733,818
Liabilities: $195,715
Net Worth: $538,103
Earnings: ($1,943,182)
Emp.: 4
Fiscal Year-end: 12/31/18
Holding Company
N.A.I.C.S.: 551112
Emmanuel Cotrel *(Chm, CEO, CFO
& Chief Acctg Officer)*
Ian Thompson *(Gen Counsel & Sec)*

FMC INC.

4145 Wagon Trl Ave, Las Vegas, NV
89118-3803
Tel.: (702) 263-7164
Year Founded: 1997
Sales Range: $10-24.9 Million
Emp.: 45
Supplier of Drugs, Proprietaries &
Sundries
N.A.I.C.S.: 424210

Subsidiaries:

Drogueria De La Villa Inc.   **(1)**
17 Ave De Diego, Arecibo, PR 00612-4546
Tel.: (787) 878-2105
Sales Range: $10-24.9 Million
Emp.: 11
Supplier of Drugs, Proprietaries & Sundries
N.A.I.C.S.: 424210

FMG SUITE, LLC

2783 NW Lolo Dr Ste 120, Bend, OR
97703
Web Site:
https://www.agencyrevolution.com
Emp.: 100
Insurance Marketing Platform Devel-
oper
N.A.I.C.S.: 524298
Scott White *(CEO)*

Subsidiaries:

Forge3, Limited   **(1)**
116 Research Dr, Bethlehem, PA 18015
Tel.: (484) 734-0005
Web Site: http://www.forge3.com
Sales Range: $1-9.9 Million
Emp.: 10
Customer Acquisition & Workflow Automa-
tion Through Web & Mobile Technology,
Strategic Planning & Social Media
N.A.I.C.S.: 541820
Jeff Teschke *(Founder)*

FMI CORPORATION

5171 Glenwood Ave Ste 200, Ra-
leigh, NC 27612
Tel.: (919) 787-8400   **NC**
Web Site: http://www.fminet.com
Year Founded: 1979
Sales Range: $10-24.9 Million
Emp.: 200
Management Consulting Services
N.A.I.C.S.: 541618
Denise L. Proctor *(CFO, Treas &
Sec)*
George H. Reddin *(Mng Dir-
Investment Banking)*
Stephen P. Darnell *(Mng Dir)*
Brian A. Moore *(Principal)*
Terry D. Gray *(Mng Dir-Risk Mgmt
Consulting Practice)*
W. Christopher Daum *(Pres & CEO)*
Rebecca Esler *(Mgr-Mktg)*
Tom Alafat *(Principal)*
Jason Baumgarten *(Principal)*
Sal DiFonzo *(Mng Dir)*
Andy Patron *(Principal)*
William Spragins *(Principal)*

Subsidiaries:

Kiley Advisors LLC   **(1)**
5220 Weslayan Ste C112, Houston, TX
77005
Tel.: (713) 840-1775
Web Site: http://www.kileyadvisors.com
Consulting Services for Engieering & Con-
struction Industries
N.A.I.C.S.: 541611
Pat Kiley *(Founder)*

FMI EXPRESS CORP.

800 Federal Blvd, Carteret, NJ 07008
Tel.: (732) 750-9000
Web Site: http://www.fmiint.com
Sales Range: $10-24.9 Million
Emp.: 70
Freight Transportation Arrangement
N.A.I.C.S.: 488510
Greg DeSaye *(Chm)*
Joseph DeSaye *(COO)*
Neil Devine *(CFO)*
Paul Gaidis *(Sr VP-IT)*
Debbie Giuliano *(VP-Bus Dev)*
Juan Rocio *(Sr VP-Client Svcs)*
Owen Kelly *(Sr VP-Supply Chain Sls)*
Joseph M. Milstein *(Asst VP-Bus
Dev)*
Rich Nazzaro *(Sr VP-Transportation)*
Thomas Wyville *(Dir-Sls & Mktg)*

FMI HANSA MEDICAL PROD-UCTS, LLC

505 Production Ave, Madison, AL
35758
Tel.: (256) 461-0900
Web Site: http://www.fmihansa.com
Sales Range: $1-9.9 Million
Emp.: 110
Medicinal Product Mfr
N.A.I.C.S.: 339112
Elizabeth Vickers *(Mgr-HR)*

FMI TRUCK SALES & SER-VICE

8305 NE M L King Blvd, Portland,
OR 97211-1343
Tel.: (503) 286-2800
Web Site: https://www.fmitrucks.com
Year Founded: 1985
Sales Range: $10-24.9 Million
Emp.: 54
New Car Whslr
N.A.I.C.S.: 441110
Don Emerson *(Pres)*
Greg Mcginley *(Mgr-Body & Equip-
ment)*
Nancy Sotta *(Mgr-HR & Risk)*

FMR LLC

245 Summer St, Boston, MA 02210
Tel.: (617) 563-9840   **DE**
Web Site: https://www.fidelity.com
Year Founded: 1946
Sales Range: $5-14.9 Billion
Emp.: 68,000
Miscellaneous Financial Investment
Activities
N.A.I.C.S.: 523999
Abigail P. Johnson *(Chm, Chm, Chm,
Pres, Pres, CEO, CEO & CEO)*
Vadim Zlotnikov *(Head-Fidelity Institu-
tional)*
Jonathan Chiel *(Exec VP & Gen
Counsel)*

Subsidiaries:

Colt Group S.A.   **(1)**
K2 Building Forte 1 2a rue Albert Bor-
schette, L-1246, Luxembourg, Luxembourg
Tel.: (352) 24514833
Web Site: http://www.colt.net
Rev.: $1,732,746,120
Assets: $2,464,890,736
Liabilities: $703,873,800
Net Worth: $1,761,016,936
Earnings: ($32,673,648)
Emp.: 5,438
Fiscal Year-end: 12/31/2014
Holding Company; Commercial Telecommu-
nications & Information Technology Services
N.A.I.C.S.: 551112
Caroline Griffin Pain *(Sec)*
Detlef Spang *(CEO-Colt Data Center Svcs)*
Rakesh Bhasin *(CEO)*
Francois Eloy *(Exec VP-Network Svcs)*
Jurgen Hernichel *(Exec VP-Colt Enterprise
Svcs)*
Mark Leonard *(Exec VP-Tech Svcs)*
Richard Oosterom *(Exec VP-Voice Svcs)*
Paul Musson *(Exec VP-HR)*
Michael Wilens *(Chm)*
Sohail Qadri *(Exec VP-Strategy & Bus Dev)*
Falk Weinrich *(Exec VP-Colt Integrated So-
lutions & Partner Svcs)*
Hugo Eales *(CFO)*
Sujeet Deshpande *(Head-India-Colt Data
Centre Svcs)*

Subsidiary (Non-US):

Colt Technology Services GmbH   **(2)**
Gervinusstr 18-22, 60322, Frankfurt am
Main, Germany   **(100%)**
Tel.: (49) 69566060
Web Site: http://www.colt.net
Telecommunication Servicesb
N.A.I.C.S.: 517111
Christian Klaesener *(Dir-Sls-Major Enter-
prise Div)*
Tim Passingham *(VP-Wholesale Sls-
Europe)*
Ashish Surti *(Chief Info Security Officer)*
Rajiv Datta *(COO)*
Randy Nicklas *(VP-Network Engrg)*
Andrew Edison *(VP-Wholesale)*
Keri Gilder *(CEO)*
Mark Gilmour *(Head-Mobile Connectivity
Solutions)*
Kenji Hioki *(Vice Chm)*
Masato Hoshino *(Pres-Japan, Head-Asia &
Dir-Rep)*
Nola Pocock *(Head-PR)*
Mirko Voltolini *(Head-Network-Global)*
Tessa Raum *(Exec VP-HR)*

Colt Technology Services S.p.A.   **(2)**
Viale E Jenner 56, 20159, Milan,
Italy   **(100%)**
Tel.: (39) 02303331
Web Site: http://www.colt.net
Sales Range: $25-49.9 Million
Emp.: 100
Telecommunication Servicesb
N.A.I.C.S.: 517111

Colt Telecom A/S   **(2)**
Borgmester Christiansens Gade 55, Copen-
hagen, 2450, Denmark   **(100%)**
Tel.: (45) 70212330
Web Site: http://www.colt.net
Sales Range: $25-49.9 Million
Emp.: 38
Telecommunication Servicesb
N.A.I.C.S.: 517111
John Jacobsen *(Mng Dir)*

Colt Telecom AB   **(2)**
Luntmakargatan 18, PO Box 3458, 103 69,
Stockholm, Sweden   **(100%)**
Tel.: (46) 87818000
Emp.: 29
Telecommunication Servicesb
N.A.I.C.S.: 517111
Victoria Karlsson *(Mng Dir)*

Colt Telecom AG   **(2)**
Murtschenstrasse 27, 8048, Zurich,
Switzerland   **(100%)**
Tel.: (41) 585601600
Web Site: http://www.colt.ch
Sales Range: $50-74.9 Million
Emp.: 120
Telecommunication Servicesb
N.A.I.C.S.: 517111
Joerg Dannheim *(Mgr-Fin)*
Vinoo Mehera *(Gen Mgr)*

Colt Telecom Austria GmbH   **(2)**
Karntner Ring 10-12, Vienna, 1010,
Austria   **(100%)**
Tel.: (43) 1205000
Web Site: http://www.colt.net
Sales Range: $25-49.9 Million
Emp.: 55
Telecommunication Servicesb
N.A.I.C.S.: 517111
Semih Calaskan *(Mng Dir)*

Colt Telecom B.V.   **(2)**
Van der Madeweg 12-14a, PO Box 94014,
1090 GA, Amsterdam, Netherlands **(100%)**
Tel.: (31) 208882020
Web Site: http://www.colt.net
Sales Range: $50-74.9 Million
Emp.: 120
Telecommunication Servicesb
N.A.I.C.S.: 517111
Lars Van Gelder *(Dir-Sls)*

Colt Telecom Espana SA   **(2)**
Calle Telemaco 5, Madrid, 28027,
Spain   **(100%)**
Tel.: (34) 917899000
Web Site: http://www.colt.net
Sales Range: $25-49.9 Million
Emp.: 60
Telecommunication Servicesb
N.A.I.C.S.: 517111

Colt Telecom Ireland Limited   **(2)**
1st Fl 1 Gate Way E Wall Rd, Dublin, 3,
Ireland   **(100%)**
Tel.: (353) 14365900
Web Site: http://www.colt.net
Sales Range: $25-49.9 Million
Emp.: 25
Telecommunication Servicesb
N.A.I.C.S.: 517111
Andrew Finnigan *(Gen Mgr)*

Colt Telecom NV/SA   **(2)**
Culliganlaan 2H, Rue du Planeur, 1130,
Brussels, Belgium   **(100%)**
Tel.: (32) 27901616
Telecommunication Servicesb
N.A.I.C.S.: 517111

Colt Telecom Portugal   **(2)**
Estrada da Outurela 118, Edificio B, Car-
naxide, 2790-114, Portugal   **(100%)**
Tel.: (351) 211200000
Web Site: http://www.colt.net
Sales Range: $25-49.9 Million
Emp.: 50
Telecommunication Servicesb
N.A.I.C.S.: 517111
Catarina Pessanha *(Dir-Fin)*

Colt Telecommunications France   **(2)**
23-27 Rue Pierre Valette, 92240, Malakoff,
Cedex, France   **(100%)**
Tel.: (33) 170995500
Emp.: 500
Telecommunication Servicesb
N.A.I.C.S.: 517111

Devonshire Investors, Inc.   **(1)**
82 Devonshire St R7B, Boston, MA 02109
Tel.: (617) 563-9106
Sales Range: $25-49.9 Million
Emp.: 50
Equity Investment Firm
N.A.I.C.S.: 523999

Eight Roads Ventures   **(1)**
25 Cannon Street, London, EC4M 5TA,
United Kingdom

Tel.: (44) 2070745610
Web Site:
　　http://www.fidelitygrowthpartners.eu
Venture Capital Investment Firm
N.A.I.C.S.: 523999
Chris Barchak (Principal)
Davor Hebel (Partner)
Yong Ben (Venture Partner)
Yong Ben (Venture Partner)

Emoney Advisor, LLC (1)
4 Radnor Corporate Center 100 Matsonford
Rd Ste 300, Radnor, PA 19087
Tel.: (610) 684-1100
Web Site: http://www.emoneyadvisor.com
Emp.: 328
Wealth Management & Financial Industry
Services
N.A.I.C.S.: 513210
Drew DiMarino (Exec VP-Sls)
Frank Tropiano (Head-Client Svcs)
Matthew J. Schulte (Head-Financial Plng)
Edward O'Brien (CEO)
Nicholas J. Dilisi Jr. (Head-Tech)

**FIL (Luxembourg) S.A., Sverige
filial** (1)
Jakobsbergsgatan 17, Box 3488, 103 69,
Stockholm, Sweden
Tel.: (46) 8 505 257 00
Web Site: http://www.fidelity.se
Investment Management Service
N.A.I.C.S.: 523940

FIL Limited (1)
Oakhill House 130 Tonbridge Rd, Ton-
bridge, TN11 9DZ, Kent, United Kingdom
Tel.: (44) 17 323 61144
Web Site: http://www.fidelity.co.uk
Investment Management Service
N.A.I.C.S.: 523940

Fidelity Brokerage Services LLC (1)
82 Devonshire St, Boston, MA 02109
Tel.: (617) 563-7000
Web Site: http://www.fidelity.com
Sales Range: $25-49.9 Million
Emp.: 21
Brokerage Products, Solutions & Services
N.A.I.C.S.: 522320
Stephen Gresham (Sr VP-Investment Prod-
uct Mgmt)
James Burton (Pres)
Kathy Murphy (Pres-Personal Investing)

**Fidelity Employer Services Company
LLC** (1)
82 Devonshire St, Boston, MA 02109-3605
Tel.: (617) 563-7000
Retirement & Human Resources Services
to Corporate Clients
N.A.I.C.S.: 923130

Fidelity Investments Canada Ltd. (1)
483 Bay Street Suite 300, Toronto, M5G
2N7, ON, Canada (100%)
Tel.: (416) 307-5200
Web Site: https://www.fidelity.ca
Sales Range: $100-124.9 Million
Emp.: 700
Mutual Fund Investment Services
N.A.I.C.S.: 525910
David Wolf (Portfolio Mgr-Asset Allocation)

**Fidelity Investments Institutional Ser-
vices Company** (1)
82 Devonshire St, Boston, MA 02110
Tel.: (617) 563-7000
Web Site: http://advisor.fidelity.com
Investment Management Service
N.A.I.C.S.: 523999

**Fidelity Investments Japan
Limited** (1)
7 7 7 Roppongi Minato-ku, Tokyo, 1056019,
Japan
Tel.: (81) 345606000
Investment Management Service
N.A.I.C.S.: 523940

**Fidelity Investments Life Insurance
Company** (1)
175 E 400 South 8th Fl, Salt Lake City, UT
84111 (100%)
Tel.: (801) 537-2364
Web Site: http://www.fidelity.com
Life & Health Insurance Services
N.A.I.C.S.: 524113

Subsidiary (Domestic):

**Empire Fidelity Investments Life In-
surance Company** (2)

200 Liberty St 1 World Financial Ctr, New
York, NY 10281 (100%)
Tel.: (212) 335-5082
Life Insurance
N.A.I.C.S.: 524113

**Fidelity Investments Management
(H.K.) Limited** (1)
Level 21 Two Pacific Place 88 Queensway
Admiralty, Hong Kong, China (Hong Kong)
Tel.: (852) 2629 2629
Web Site: http://www.fidelity.com.hk
Investment Management Service
N.A.I.C.S.: 523940

**Fidelity Personal Trust Company,
FSB** (1)
82 Devonshire St Ste 73G, Boston, MA
02109 (100%)
Tel.: (617) 563-1419
Savings Bank
N.A.I.C.S.: 522180

HR Access Solutions S.L. (1)
Calle Anabel segura 16 Arroyo de la Vega,
Alcobendas, 28108, Madrid, Spain
Tel.: (34) 91 790 4300
Web Site: http://www.hraccess.com
Sales Range: $75-99.9 Million
Emp.: 900
Corporate Human Resource Support Ser-
vices & Software
N.A.I.C.S.: 561499

Subsidiary (Non-US):

HR Access Solutions SAS (2)
Le Triangle de l'Arche 8 cours du Triangle,
La Defense 12, Paris, 92937, France
Tel.: (33) 1 7038 3100
Web Site: http://www.hraccess.com
Corporate Human Resource Support Ser-
vices & Software Mfr
N.A.I.C.S.: 561499
Xavier Daguzan (Gen Mgr-France & West-
ern Europe)

National Financial Services LLC (1)
200 Liberty St NY4F, New York, NY
10281 (100%)
Tel.: (212) 335-5000
Web Site: http://www.nationalfinancial.com
Brokerage Services
N.A.I.C.S.: 523150
Sanjiv Mirchandani (Pres)
Patrick H. McEvoy (VP-Broker Dealer Ops)

Pyramis Global Advisors, LLC (1)
82 Devonshire St, Boston, MA 02109
Tel.: (617) 563-5800
Web Site: http://www.pyramis.com
Investment Management Service
N.A.I.C.S.: 523999
James Carroll (Sr VP-Client Svc)
Nancy D. Prior (Vice Chm)
Michael Palermo (Head-Institutional Rela-
tionship Mgmt)

**FMS MACHINE TOOL DIS-
TRIBUTORS**
6886 Pearl Rd Ste 206, Cleveland,
OH 44130
Tel.: (440) 886-3232
Web Site:
　　http://www.fmsmachinery.com
Rev.: $10,000,000
Emp.: 6
Machine Tools & Accessories
N.A.I.C.S.: 423830
A David Saiko (Pres)

**FMS PURCHASING & SER-
VICES, INC.**
711 S Belcher Rd, Clearwater, FL
33764
Tel.: (727) 725-2090
Web Site:
　　http://www.fmspurchasing.com
Sales Range: $1-9.9 Million
Emp.: 12
Group Purchasing
N.A.I.C.S.: 561499
Timothy E. Gregson (CEO)
Ronald F. Peabody (VP-Ops)
Vicki L. Kerley (VP-Sls)
Debra Frisch (Mgr-Computer Ops)

FMSBONDS, INC.
4775 Technology Way, Boca Raton,
FL 33431-4918
Tel.: (305) 937-0660
Web Site: https://www.fmsbonds.com
Rev.: $35,800,000
Emp.: 104
Securities Brokerage
N.A.I.C.S.: 523150
James A. Klotz (Co-Founder)
Paul Feinsilver (Co-Founder)

FNA GROUP, INC.
1825 Greenleaf Ave, Elk Grove Vil-
lage, IL 60007
Tel.: (847) 348-1500
Web Site: http://www.fna-group.com
Emp.: 200
Electric & Gas Pressure Washers,
Pumps & Hoses Mfr
N.A.I.C.S.: 333912
Bill Fischer (VP-Sales-Indus)

FNB BANCORP, INC.
40 S State St, Newtown, PA 18940
Tel.: (215) 860-9100
Web Site: https://www.fnbn.com
National Commercial Banks
N.A.I.C.S.: 522110

Subsidiaries:

**First National Bank & Trust Co of
Newtown** (1)
40 S State St, Newtown, PA 18940-0158
Tel.: (215) 860-9100
Web Site: http://www.fnbn.com
Rev.: $36,235,000
Emp.: 100
National Commercial Banks
N.A.I.C.S.: 522110
Missy Lenaham (Mgr-Ops)
Lindsay DeOre Lambert (VP-Comml Mort-
gages & Construction Lending)
Margaret Young (VP-Comml & Retail Lend-
ing)
Daniel J. Schaffer (Pres & CEO)
Donna Dunham-Smith (Sr VP-Deposit Ops)
Barry L. Pflueger Jr. (Exec VP-Trust &
Wealth Mgmt)

FNB BANCSHARES INC.
233 S Stephenson Ave, Iron Moun-
tain, MI 49801
Tel.: (906) 774-2200
Web Site: http://www.fnbimk.com
Sales Range: $10-24.9 Million
Emp.: 77
Bank Holding Company
N.A.I.C.S.: 551111
David Cashin (Pres)

Subsidiaries:

**The First National Bank & Trust Com-
pany of Iron Mountain** (1)
233 S Stephenson Ave, Iron Mountain, MI
49801
Tel.: (906) 774-2200
Web Site: http://www.fnbimk.com
Sales Range: $10-24.9 Million
National Commercial Banks
N.A.I.C.S.: 522110
Dave Kashian (Pres & CEO)
James Moln (COO & Sr VP)
Matthew Lutz (CFO & VP)
Nathan Goudreau (Chief Risk Officer & Sr
VP)
Russell Kassin (Chief Lending Officer & Sr
VP)

FNBH BANCORP, INC.
101 E Grand River Ave, Howell, MI
48843
Tel.: (517) 546-3150 MI
Web Site: http://www.fnbh.com
Year Founded: 1989
Rev.: $19,701,000
Assets: $554,508,000
Liabilities: $490,809,000
Net Worth: $63,699,000
Earnings: $6,795,000

Fiscal Year-end: 12/31/20
Bank Holding Company
N.A.I.C.S.: 551111
Ronald Long (Pres & CEO)
Mark J. Huber (CFO & Sr VP)
Patricia Griffith (VP & Dir-Ops & Info)
Leslie Brown (Chief Credit Officer &
Sr VP)
Rick James (Chief Risk Officer & Sr
VP)
Martin Smith (Sr VP)

Subsidiaries:

First National Bank in Howell (1)
101 E Grand River Ave, Howell, MI
48843 (100%)
Tel.: (517) 546-3150
Web Site: http://www.fnbh.com
Sales Range: $25-49.9 Million
Emp.: 35
Savings, Loans, Commercial & Investment
Banking Services
N.A.I.C.S.: 522110
Ronald Long (Pres & CEO)
Mark J. Huber (CFO & Sr VP)

FNBK HOLDINGS, INC.
100 S State Hwy 274, Kemp, TX
75143
Tel.: (903) 498-8541 TX
Web Site: https://www.fnbkemp.com
Year Founded: 2014
Bank Holding Company
N.A.I.C.S.: 551111
John J. Carona (Founder & CEO)

Subsidiaries:

The First National Bank of Kemp (1)
100 S State Hwy 274, Kemp, TX 75143
Tel.: (903) 498-8541
Web Site: http://www.fnbkemp.com
Sales Range: $1-9.9 Million
Emp.: 22
Commericial Banking
N.A.I.C.S.: 522110
Vidal Jones (Pres & CEO)

**FNBT BANCSHARES, PERRY,
OK, INC.**
401 N 7th St, Perry, OK 73077
Tel.: (580) 336-5562 OK
Web Site: http://www.bankfbt.com
Year Founded: 1985
Sales Range: $1-9.9 Million
Emp.: 43
Bank Holding Company
N.A.I.C.S.: 551111
Jon Q. Alexander (Co-Pres & Chief
Lending Officer)
Shirley Scott (Co-Pres & CFO)

Subsidiaries:

First Bank & Trust Company (1)
401 N 7th St, Perry, OK 73077
Tel.: (580) 336-5562
Web Site: http://www.bankfbt.com
Sales Range: $1-9.9 Million
Commercial Banking Services
N.A.I.C.S.: 522110
Jon Q. Alexander (Co-Pres & Chief Lending
Officer)
Shirley Scott (Co-Pres & CFO)
Marvin D. Dement (Officer-Loan)
Lori J. Pierce (Officer-Loan)
K. Michelle Woods (Officer-Loan)
Mason Bolay (Officer-Loan)

FNL TECHNOLOGIES, INC.
22 Boston Wharf Rd, Boston, MA
02210
Tel.: (508) 479-2873
Web Site: http://www.my.hoo.be
Social Media Platform Owner & Op-
erator
N.A.I.C.S.: 541840
Jordan Greenfield (CEO)

Subsidiaries:

Grapevine Logic, Inc. (1)

FNL Technologies, Inc.—(Continued)

9 Newbury St, Boston, MA 02116
Tel.: (855) 638-7427
Web Site: http://www.grapevinelogic.com
Social Media Marketing Platform
N.A.I.C.S.: 541519
Grant Deken (Co-Founder & CEO)
Kimberley Bond (Co-Founder & Dir-Ops)
Alex Riina (Dir-Engrg)
Kristen Standish (Sr VP & Gen Mgr)
Jibran Malek (Mktg Dir)
Laura Picard (Sr Mgr-Acct)
Daniel Shields (Sr Mgr-Strategic)
Casey Nulph (Sr Mgr-Acct)
Erica Riordan (Sr Mgr-Acct)
Emily Fletcher (Controller)

FNP, INC.

1313 Broadwater Ave, Billings, MT
59102
Tel.: (406) 245-7022   **MT**
Web Site:
    http://www.firstnationalpawn.com
Sales Range: $10-24.9 Million
Pawnshops Owner & Operator
N.A.I.C.S.: 522299
Benjamin L. Brown Sr. (Founder &
Owner)

FNS, INC.

1545 Francisco St, Torrance, CA
90501
Tel.: (661) 615-2300
Web Site: http://www.fnsusa.com
Year Founded: 1977
Emp.: 3,500
Freight Forwarding
N.A.I.C.S.: 488510
Wook Jin Choi (Mng Dir)

FOA & SON CORPORATION

122 E 42nd St 46 Fl, New York, NY
10168
Tel.: (212) 432-1234
Web Site: https://www.foason.com
Sales Range: $75-99.9 Million
Emp.: 80
Insurance Services
N.A.I.C.S.: 524210
Conrad Foa (Chm)
Justin Foa (Pres)
Bradley Hamburger (Sr VP)

FOAM DESIGN INCORPO-
RATED

444 Transport Ct, Lexington, KY
40511
Tel.: (859) 231-7006
Web Site:
    https://www.foamdesign.com
Sales Range: $10-24.9 Million
Emp.: 100
Packaging & Shipping Materials,
Foamed Plastics
N.A.I.C.S.: 326150
Tom Keck (VP-Natl Accts & Military
Products)
John Boggs (VP-New Product Dev)
Doug Gradek (Pres)

FOAM MOLDERS AND SPE-
CIALTIES

20004 State Rd, Cerritos, CA 90703
Tel.: (562) 924-7757
Web Site:
    https://www.foammolders.com
Rev.: $19,839,139
Emp.: 120
Plastics Foam Products
N.A.I.C.S.: 326150
Daniel M. Doke Sr. (Pres)

FOAM RUBBER PRODUCTS
COMPANY

2000 Troy Ave, New Castle, IN 47362
Tel.: (765) 521-2000

Web Site:
    http://www.foamseating.com
Rev.: $22,500,000
Emp.: 120
Plastics Foam Products
N.A.I.C.S.: 326150
Frank P. Nold (CEO)
Jamie Rust (Controller)
Terry Warrum (CFO)
Norman Smith (Pres)

FOAMCRAFT INC.

9230 Harrison Park Ct, Indianapolis,
IN 46216
Tel.: (317) 545-3626
Web Site:
    https://www.foamcraftinc.com
Rev.: $23,000,000
Emp.: 30
Foam Rubber
N.A.I.C.S.: 326299
Robert W. Elliott (Founder & Pres)
Mike Weldon (Plant Mgr)
Nathan Elliott (Mgr-Mktg)

FOAMPRO MANUFACTURING,
INC.

1781 Langley Ave, Irvine, CA 92614
Tel.: (949) 252-0112
Web Site:
    https://www.foampromfg.com
Year Founded: 1952
Foam Paint Applicators, Brooms &
Waxers Mfr
N.A.I.C.S.: 339994
Gregory Isaac (Pres)
Fanny Hellwig (Controller)

FOCUS BUSINESS SOLU-
TIONS, INC.

6995 Monroe Blvd, Taylor, MI 48180
Tel.: (313) 292-7000
Web Site: https://www.focus-
    solutions.net
Year Founded: 1999
Sales Range: $1-9.9 Million
Emp.: 43
International Trade Consulting Includ-
ing Customs Laws, Regulations &
Trade Treaties
N.A.I.C.S.: 522299
Steven D. Haywood (Pres)
Andrew Astor (CFO & VP)
Kathy Vollmerhausen (Co-Dir-Ops)
Bill Vollmerhausen (Co-Dir-Ops)
David Allan (Dir-Quality & Trng)

FOCUS ENTERPRISES INC.

1626 Ringling Blvd Ste 400, Sara-
sota, FL 34236-6815
Tel.: (219) 464-4600
Web Site:
    http://www.focushotels.com
Rev.: $27,800,000
Emp.: 35
Hotel Owner & Operator
N.A.I.C.S.: 237210
Jerald J. Good (Pres)

Subsidiaries:

Focus Hospitality Services, LLC   **(1)**
1626 Ringling Blvd Ste 400, Sarasota, FL
34236
Tel.: (941) 907-9155
Web Site: http://www.focushotels.com
Hotel Development & Management
N.A.I.C.S.: 721110
Jerald J. Good (Pres & CEO)
Pat Good (VP-Admin Svcs & Design)
Rob Evans (VP-Ops)
Anthony Homer (VP-Real Estate)

FOCUS FORWARD LLC

950 W Valley Rd Ste 2700, Wayne,
PA 19087
Tel.: (215) 367-4000
Web Site: https://www.focusfwd.com

Year Founded: 2003
Sales Range: $1-9.9 Million
Emp.: 50
Qualitative Recruiting for the Market
Research Industry
N.A.I.C.S.: 561311
Kim Harrison (CEO)
Liz Granahan (Pres)
Chris Goering (Dir-Application Dev)
Meghan Surdenas (Dir-Bus Dev)
Chris Beebie (Dir-Online Project)
Mark Mundy (Dir-Recruiting)
Rohina Iqbal (Dir-Transcription Svcs)
David Pataki (Exec VP)
Danica Burns (Mgr-Client Svcs)
Dawn Roth (Mgr-HR)
Marissa Incitti (Project Mgr-
Qualitative)
Monica Montes (Project Mgr-
Qualitative)
Kathrina Ramroop (Project Mgr-
Qualitative)
Krystina Brindley (Sr Project Mgr)
Matt Devine (Sr Project Mgr)
Lisa Diamond (Sr Project Mgr)
Thomas Galaznik (Sr Project Mgr)
Andrew Postell (VP-Sls & Mktg)

FOCUS IN CHINUCH INC.

48 Baker Town Rd Ste 512, Monroe,
NY 10950
Tel.: (845) 781-2100   **NY**
Year Founded: 2006
Sales Range: $1-9.9 Million
Emp.: 39
Jewish Community Services
N.A.I.C.S.: 624190
Samuel Landau (Pres)

FOCUS MANAGEMENT
GROUP USA, INC.

5001 W Lemon St, Tampa, FL 33609
Tel.: (813) 281-0062   **FL**
Web Site: http://www.focusmg.com
Year Founded: 1998
Sales Range: $25-49.9 Million
Emp.: 150
Management Consulting & Financial
Advisory Services
N.A.I.C.S.: 541611
J. Tim Pruban (Founder & CEO)
Daniel McMurray (Sr Mng Dir)
Juanita Schwartzkopf (Mng Dir)
Alan L. Weiner (Mng Dir)
Michael Doland (COO)
Barrey Davis (Sr Mng Dir)
Robert O. Riiska (Sr Mng Dir)
Michael P. Grau (Mng Dir)
Joe Karel (Mng Dir)
Robert Wanat (Mng Dir)
Samuel M. Williams (Mng Dir)
Katrina Secrest (Mgr-Mktg)
Aarti Mehta (Controller)
Stephen Weber (Mng Dir)
Perry Kalajian (Sr Mng Dir)
Tom Thompson (Sr Mng Dir)

FOCUS RECEIVABLES MAN-
AGEMENT, LLC

1130 Northchase Pkwy Ste 150,
Marietta, GA 30067
Tel.: (678) 228-0000   **GA**
Web Site: http://www.focusrm.com
Sales Range: $10-24.9 Million
Debt Collection Agency
N.A.I.C.S.: 561440
Gregory E. Schubert (Co-Founder,
Mng Partner, Pres & CEO)
Peter Hendricks (Co-Founder & Part-
ner)
William J. Strang (Co-Founder &
Partner)

FOCUS TECHNOLOGY SOLU-
TIONS, INC.

93 Ledge Rd, Seabrook, NH 03874
Tel.: (603) 766-0000
Web Site: http://www.focustsi.com
Year Founded: 1998
Sales Range: $10-24.9 Million
Emp.: 35
IT Services
N.A.I.C.S.: 541512
Bruce Crochetiere (CEO)
Bill Smeltzer (CTO)

FOCUS VENTURE PARTNERS,
INC.

969 Postal Rd Ste 100, Allentown, PA
18109   **NV**
Web Site:
    http://www.focusventurepart
    ners.com
Sales Range: $25-49.9 Million
Emp.: 105
Holding Company
N.A.I.C.S.: 551112
Theresa Carlise (CFO)
Michael Palleschi (CEO & COO)
Christopher B. Ferguson (Chm &
Pres)

FOCUSED IMAGE

2941 Fairview Park Dr Ste 650, Falls
Church, VA 22042
Tel.: (703) 739-8803
Web Site:
    https://www.focusedimage.com
Sales Range: $10-24.9 Million
Emp.: 15
Advertising Agencies
N.A.I.C.S.: 541810
Toby Eckhardt (CEO & Chief Creative
Officer)
Dave Scanlon (Exec VP-Strategic
Plng)
Kristina Messner (VP-PR)
Christine Pittman (VP & Dir-Creative
& Print Comm)
Greg German (VP & Dir-Creative,
Web & Interactive Comm)
Matt Marsden (VP-Bus Dev)

FOELGNER, RONZ & STRAW,
P.A.

1301 66th St N, Saint Petersburg, FL
33710
Tel.: (727) 347-1120
Web Site: https://www.frscpa.com
Year Founded: 1984
Sales Range: $1-9.9 Million
Emp.: 37
Accounting & Tax Services
N.A.I.C.S.: 541211
Claudia A. Straw (Mng Partner)
Paul Horowitz (Partner)
Ana Herron (Partner)

FOG CUTTER CAPITAL
GROUP INC.

5 Centerpointe Dr Ste 400, Lake
Oswego, OR 97035
Tel.: (503) 721-6500   **MD**
Web Site: http://www.fccgi.com
Year Founded: 1997
Investment Holding Company; Real
Estate Investment Trusts & Debt Refi-
nancing Services
N.A.I.C.S.: 551112

Subsidiaries:

Buffalo's Franchise Concepts,
Inc.   **(1)**
785 Seaboard Dr Ste 105, Dallas, GA
30132
Tel.: (770) 420-1800
Web Site: http://www.buffaloscafe.com
Sales Range: $50-74.9 Million
Restaurant Franchise
N.A.I.C.S.: 533110

FAT Brands Inc.   **(1)**

9720 Wilshire Blvd Ste 500, Beverly Hills, CA 90212 **(81.2%)**
Tel.: (310) 319-1850
Web Site: https://www.fatbrands.com
Rev.: $407,224,000
Assets: $1,213,303,000
Liabilities: $1,372,481,000
Net Worth: ($159,178,000)
Earnings: ($126,188,000)
Emp.: 1,100
Fiscal Year-end: 12/31/2022
Restaurant Services
N.A.I.C.S.: 722511
Donald J. Berchtold *(Bd of Dirs & Chief Concept Officer)*
Andrew A. Wiederhorn *(Chm)*
Thayer D. Wiederhorn *(COO)*
Taylor A. Wiederhorn *(Chief Dev Officer)*
Mason A. Wiederhorn *(Bd of Dirs & Chief Brand Officer)*
Kenneth J. Kuick *(Co-CEO & CFO)*
Jake Berchtold *(COO-Fast Casual Div)*
Robert Rosen *(Co-CEO & Exec VP-Capital Markets)*
Allen Sussman *(Gen Counsel & Exec VP)*
Jenn Johnston *(CMO)*
Michael Chachula *(CIO)*
Gregg Nettleton *(Pres & COO-Casual Dining Div)*
Allison Lauenstein *(Pres & Pres-Quick-Service Div)*
Joe Hummel *(Pres-Polished Casual Div)*
David Pea *(Pres-Round Table Pizza)*

Subsidiary (Domestic):

Fatburger North America, Inc. **(2)**
9720 Wilshire Blvd Ste 500, Beverly Hills, CA 90212
Tel.: (310) 319-1850
Fast Food Restaurant Operator
N.A.I.C.S.: 722513

Global Franchise Group, LLC **(2)**
5555 Glenridge Con #850, Norcross, GA 30342
Tel.: (770) 514-4500
Web Site: http://www.globalfranchise.com
Brand Management Services
N.A.I.C.S.: 523940
Jenn Johnston *(Chief Brand Officer & Pres-Franchise Ops)*
Jim Parrish *(COO)*
Allison Lauenstein *(Chief Innovation Officer-Innovation Center)*
David Kaiser *(Exec VP-Brand Integration & Corp Svcs)*
Chris Cheek *(Chief Dev Officer)*
Annica Conrad *(CMO)*
Pam Maxwell *(VP-France)*
Lisa Cheatham *(VP-Growth Mktg)*
Paul Damico *(CEO)*
Sam Patterson *(CFO)*
Jason Dowd *(VP-Culinary Innovation)*
Jon Gordon *(VP-Creative Svcs)*

Subsidiary (Domestic):

GAC Franchising, LLC **(3)**
1346 Oakbrook Dr Ste 170, Norcross, GA 30093
Tel.: (770) 514-4500
Web Site: http://www.greatamericancookies.com
Sales Range: $250-299.9 Million
Cookie & Confection Quick-Services Restaurant Franchisor
N.A.I.C.S.: 533110

Plant (Domestic):

GAC Supply, LLC **(4)**
4685 Frederick Dr SW, Atlanta, GA 30336-1807
Tel.: (404) 696-1700
Web Site:
    http://www.greatamericancookies.com
Sales Range: $50-74.9 Million
Emp.: 35
Cookie Dough & Other Franchise Supplies Mfr & Distr
N.A.I.C.S.: 311824
Chris Dull *(Pres)*

Subsidiary (Domestic):

HDOS Enterprises **(3)**
5942 Priestoy Dr, Carlsbad, CA 92008
Tel.: (323) 480-2386
Web Site: http://www.hotdogonastick.com

Snack Food Stores Operator & Franchisor
N.A.I.C.S.: 722515
Melissa Diaz *(Dir-Ops)*
Lisa Merrell *(VP)*
Daniel Bylund *(CFO)*

MaggieMoo's Franchising, LLC **(3)**
5555 Glenridge Connector Ste 850, Atlanta, GA 30342
Tel.: (770) 514-4500
Web Site: http://www.maggiemoos.com
Ice Cream Quick-Service Restaurant Franchisor
N.A.I.C.S.: 533110

Marble Slab Franchising, LLC **(3)**
1346 Oakbrook Ste 170, Norcross, GA 30093
Tel.: (770) 514-4500
Web Site: http://www.marbleslab.com
Sales Range: $250-299.9 Million
Ice Cream Quick-Service Restaurant Franchisor
N.A.I.C.S.: 533110
M. Christopher Dull *(Pres)*

PM Franchising, LLC **(3)**
1346 Oakbrook Dr Ste 170, Norcross, GA 30093
Tel.: (770) 514-4500
Web Site: http://www.pretzelmaker.com
Sales Range: $250-299.9 Million
Pretzel Quick-Service Restaurant Franchisor
N.A.I.C.S.: 533110
M. Christopher Dull *(Pres)*

Round Table Pizza **(3)**
1390 Willow Pass Rd Ste 300, Concord, CA 94520
Tel.: (925) 969-3900
Web Site: http://www.roundtablepizza.com
Pizzerias Owner & Operator
N.A.I.C.S.: 722513
Christopher Isbell *(Sr Mgr)*

Subsidiary (Domestic):

Hurricane AMT, LLC **(2)**
9720 Wilshire Blvd Ste 500, Beverly Hills, CA 90212
Tel.: (310) 319-1850
Web Site: http://www.hurricanewings.com
Restaurant Operators
N.A.I.C.S.: 722511

Ponderosa Steakhouse **(2)**
7598 W Irlo Bronson Memorial Hwy, Kissimmee, FL 34747
Tel.: (407) 396-7721
Web Site: http://www.pon-bon.com
Full-Service Restaurants
N.A.I.C.S.: 722511

Smokey Bones, LLC **(2)**
8427 S Park Cir Ste 250, Orlando, FL 32819
Tel.: (407) 355-5800
Web Site: http://www.smokeybones.com
Sales Range: $125-149.9 Million
Restaurant Operators
N.A.I.C.S.: 722511
Roger J. Drake *(Sr VP-Mktg)*
Tom Porfiris *(Sr Dir-Ops)*
James O'Reilly *(CEO)*
Javier Retamar *(CFO)*
Hal Lawlor *(Pres & COO)*

The Johnny Rockets Group, Inc. **(2)**
2 S Pointe Dr Ste 200, Lake Forest, CA 92630
Tel.: (949) 643-6100
Web Site: http://www.johnnyrockets.com
Diner Style Hamburger Restaurant Chain Operator & Franchisor
N.A.I.C.S.: 722513
Cozette Phifer *(Dir-Comm)*
Christopher J. Ainley *(Chm)*
Cozette Phifer Koerber *(VP-Brand Mktg & Corp Comm)*
James Walker *(Pres-Ops & Dev)*
Marc Abénoja *(Dir-Ops-Intl)*
Alan Hinson *(Exec Dir-Legal Svcs)*
Jim Hicks *(Sr VP-Domestic Ops)*
Chris Ferguson *(Dir-Ops-East Coast)*
Dillon McFarland *(Mgr-Intl Franchise Support-Middle East & Asia)*
Naresh Vinod Worlikar *(VP-Intl)*
Calvin Harris *(Dir-Culinary Innovation)*
Harry Yu *(Sr Dir-IT)*

Crystal Wells *(Dir-Franchise Sls)*
Susanne Marie Stover *(CFO)*
Rumbani Mchawe *(Dir-Mature Markets)*
Ray Masters *(Sr VP-Pur)*

Yalla Mediterranean Franchising Company, LLC **(2)**
1781 N Victory Pl, Burbank, CA 91502
Tel.: (818) 565-0426
Web Site: http://www.yallamedi.com
Restaurant Services
N.A.I.C.S.: 722511

Fatburger Corporation **(1)**
9606 Santa Monica Blvd, Beverly Hills, CA 90210
Tel.: (310) 319-1850
Web Site: http://www.fatburger.com
Sales Range: $25-49.9 Million
Emp.: 30
Fast-Food Restaurant Franchisor & Operator
N.A.I.C.S.: 722513
Andrew A. Wiederhorn *(CEO)*
Don Berchtold *(Pres & COO)*
Lovie Yancey *(Founder)*

Homestyle Dining, LLC **(1)**
2929 Custer Rd #302D, Plano, TX 75075
Tel.: (972) 244-8900
Restaurants Management & Franchising
N.A.I.C.S.: 722511
Fred Schmelling *(Mgr-Accts Receivable)*
Kim Jackson *(Mgr-Asset)*

Division (Domestic):

Bonanza Restaurants **(2)**
3701 W Plano Pkwy Ste 200, Plano, TX 75075
Tel.: (972) 244-8900
Web Site:
    http://www.bonanzasteakhouses.com
Sales Range: $250-299.9 Million
Emp.: 127
Family Restaurants
N.A.I.C.S.: 722511
Jill Laird *(VP-Mktg)*

Ponderosa Steakhouse **(2)**
3701 W Plano Pkwy Ste 200, Plano, TX 75075
Tel.: (972) 244-8900
Web Site:
    http://www.ponderosasteakhouses.com
Sales Range: $125-149.9 Million
Emp.: 1,800
Full-Service Restaurants
N.A.I.C.S.: 722511
Brian Cable *(Gen Mgr)*

FOGEL ANDERSON CONSTRUCTION
1212 E 8th St, Kansas City, MO 64106
Tel.: (816) 842-6914
Web Site: https://www.fogel-anderson.com
Sales Range: $25-49.9 Million
Emp.: 60
Civil Engineering Services
N.A.I.C.S.: 237310
Ted A. Anderson *(CEO)*
Roger Summers *(Partner)*

FOGELMAN PROPERTIES, LLC
6060 Poplar Ave, Memphis, TN 38119
Tel.: (901) 767-6500
Rev.: $6,250,400
Emp.: 42
Commodity Contracts Dealing
N.A.I.C.S.: 523160
Rick Fogelman *(CEO)*
Mike Aiken *(Sr VP-Investments)*
Mark Fogelman *(Pres)*
Melissa Smith *(Chief Admin Officer)*
Lori Marada *(Sr VP-Shared Svcs)*
Melissa Brady *(VP-Strategic Mktg)*
Thomas Henry *(VP-Acq)*
Will Drummond *(CFO)*

Subsidiaries:

Lake Cameron, LLC **(1)**

1000 Cameron Woods Dr, Apex, NC 27523
Tel.: (984) 246-2641
Web Site: https://www.lakecameron.com
Residential Building & Dwelling Leasing Services
N.A.I.C.S.: 531110

FOGGS ACE HARDWARE BUILDING SUPPLIES
Lake Morey Rd Exit 15, Fairlee, VT 05045
Tel.: (802) 333-4248
Web Site:
    http://www.foggshardware.com
Rev.: $10,000,000
Emp.: 18
Lumber Products
N.A.I.C.S.: 444110
Alan Fogg *(CEO)*
Gary Miller *(Controller)*

FOGLES INC.
5500 Neeses Hwy, Neeses, SC 29107
Tel.: (803) 247-3015
Year Founded: 1986
Sales Range: $25-49.9 Million
Emp.: 250
Grocery Store Operator
N.A.I.C.S.: 445110
Chuck Fogle *(Controller)*

FOGO HOSPITALITY, INC.
5908 Headquarters Dr Ste K200, Plano, TX 75024
Tel.: (972) 960-9533   DE
Year Founded: 2018
Rev.: $204,824,000
Assets: $749,161,000
Liabilities: $564,574,000
Net Worth: $184,587,000
Earnings: ($57,044,000)
Emp.: 4,769
Fiscal Year-end: 01/03/21
Holding Company
N.A.I.C.S.: 551112
G. Barry McGowan *(CEO)*
Anthony D. Laday *(CFO)*
Rick A. Lenderman *(COO)*
Janet Gieselman *(CMO)*
Eytan Tigay *(Chm)*

FOLCARELLI SHEET METAL INC.
4141 6th Ave, Altoona, PA 16602
Tel.: (814) 943-0287   PA
Web Site:
    http://www.folcarellisupply.com
Year Founded: 1951
Sales Range: $10-24.9 Million
Emp.: 145
Plumbing & Heating Technologies Distr
N.A.I.C.S.: 238160
James D. Folcarelli *(Pres)*

FOLCOMER EQUIPMENT CORPORATION
629 S Philadelphia Blvd, Aberdeen, MD 21001
Tel.: (410) 575-6580
Web Site: http://www.folcomer.com
Year Founded: 1994
Sales Range: $25-49.9 Million
Emp.: 40
Industrial Machinery & Equipment
N.A.I.C.S.: 423830
Mike Youse *(Branch Mgr)*
Butch Nicholson *(Gen Mgr)*

FOLDCRAFT COMPANY
615 Centennial Dr, Kenyon, MN 55946
Tel.: (507) 789-5111
Web Site: http://www.foldcraft.com
Year Founded: 1967
Rev.: $37,000,000

Foldcraft Company—(Continued)

Emp.: 250
Bar, Restaurant & Cafeteria Furniture
N.A.I.C.S.: 337127
Dale Quam (CEO)

FOLDER FACTORY, INC.

5421 Main St 300, Mount Jackson,
VA 22842
Tel.: (540) 477-3852
Web Site: http://www.folder-factory.com
Rev.: $2,600,000
Emp.: 16
Commercial Lithographic Printing
N.A.I.C.S.: 323111
Mark Gentile (Pres)
Dwight McKelvey (Mgr-IT)

FOLEY & LARDNER LLP

777 E Wisconsin Ave, Milwaukee, WI
53202-5306
Tel.: (414) 271-2400
Web Site: http://www.foley.com
Year Founded: 1842
Legal Advisory Services
N.A.I.C.S.: 541110
Douglas Heffer (Partner)
Jason Hille (Partner)
Frank Pasquesi (Partner)
Jon Israel (Partner)
Fred S. Ridley (Partner)
Liane Peterson (Partner)
Katharine Beattie (Partner)
Eric Pearson (Partner)
Rebecca Hays (Partner)
Ruben Rodrigues (Partner)
Kyle Faget (Partner)
Nick Welle (Partner)
Morgan Tilleman (Partner)
Stephen Meli (Partner-Boston)
Kathleen Dreyfus Bardunias (Partner)
Garrett F. Bishop (Partner)
Amy A. Ciepluch (Partner)
David W. Clark (Partner)

Subsidiaries:

Gardere Wynne Sewell LLP   (1)
2021 Mckiney Ave St Ste 1600, Dallas, TX
75201
Tel.: (214) 999-3000
Legal Advisory Services
N.A.I.C.S.: 541110
Evan Stone (Partner)
Paul Storm (Partner)

FOLEY CUSTOM POOLS INC.

6065 Sports Village Rd, Plano, TX
75034
Tel.: (972) 423-7178
Web Site: http://www.foleypools.com
Year Founded: 1990
Sales Range: $10-24.9 Million
Emp.: 30
Swimming Pool Construction
N.A.I.C.S.: 238990
Sandy Foley (Treas & Sec)
John J. Foley III (Owner)

FOLEY FAMILY WINES HOLD-INGS INC

10300 Chalk Hill Rd, Healdsburg, CA
95448
Tel.: (855) 883-8688   DE
Sales Range: $1-9.9 Million
Emp.: 100
Holding Company; Wine Mfr
N.A.I.C.S.: 551112
William P. Foley II (Founder & CEO)

Subsidiaries:

Foley Family Wines, Inc.   (1)
200 Concourse Blvd, Santa Rosa, CA
95403
Tel.: (707) 708-7600
Web Site: http://foleyfamilywines.com

Sales Range: $10-24.9 Million
Wine Mfr
N.A.I.C.S.: 312130
William P. Foley II (Founder & Owner)

Subsidiary (Domestic):

Firestone Vineyard   (2)
5017 Zaca Station Rd, Los Olivos, CA
93441
Tel.: (805) 688-3940
Web Site: http://www.firestonewine.com
Sales Range: $10-24.9 Million
Emp.: 100
Vineyards & Winery
N.A.I.C.S.: 312130

Subsidiary (Non-US):

Foley Wines Limited   (2)
13 Waihopai Valley Road, RD6 Blenheim,
Marlborough, 7276, New Zealand
Tel.: (64) 35728200
Web Site: https://www.foleywines.co.nz
Rev.: $39,851,675
Assets: $148,373,206
Liabilities: $60,150,718
Net Worth: $88,222,488
Earnings: $3,793,062
Emp.: 11
Fiscal Year-end: 06/30/2023
Grapes & Wine Production & Sales
N.A.I.C.S.: 312130
Paul Robert Brock (Deputy Chm)
Antony Mark Turnbull (CEO & Exec Dir)

Subsidiary (Domestic):

Sebastiani Vineyards, Inc.   (2)
389 Fourth St E, Sonoma, CA 95476
Tel.: (707) 933-3230
Web Site: http://www.sebastiani.com
Sales Range: $10-24.9 Million
Emp.: 100
Winery
N.A.I.C.S.: 312130

Silverado Vineyards Inc.   (2)
6121 Silverado Trl, Napa, CA 94558
Tel.: (707) 257-1770
Web Site:
   http://www.silveradovineyards.com
Sales Range: $1-9.9 Million
Emp.: 35
Wine Mfr
N.A.I.C.S.: 312130
Diane Miller (Co-Owner)
Russell Weis (Gen Mgr)
Ron Miller (Co-Owner)
Jon Emmerich (Asst Gen Mgr)
Pamela Ford (Dir-Sls-East)
Kimberli Rogers (Dir-Sls-West)

Stryker Sonoma   (2)
5110 Hwy 128, Geyserville, CA 95441-9422
Web Site: http://www.strykersonoma.com
Wineries
N.A.I.C.S.: 312130
Craig MacDonald (Owner)

FOLEY HOAG LLP

Seaport W 155 Seaport Blvd, Boston,
MA 02210-2600
Tel.: (617) 832-1000
Web Site: https://www.foleyhoag.com
Year Founded: 1943
Sales Range: $150-199.9 Million
Emp.: 201
Legal Advisory Services
N.A.I.C.S.: 541110
Gil Arie (Partner)
Alexander J. Aber (Chm-Mergers &
Acquisition Practice Grp & Partner)
Adam P. Kahn (Partner)
William R. Kolb (Mng Partner & Co-Partner-Boston)
Tom Block (COO)
Neil Austin (Partner-Boston)
Matthew C. Baltay (Partner-Boston)
Mark A. Barnett (Partner-Boston)
Joseph J. Basile (Chm-Bus Dev &
Partner)
Eric D. Belsley (Partner-Boston)
Arlene L. Bender (Partner-Boston)
Robert L. Birnbaum (Partner-Boston)
Paul Bork (Partner-Boston)

Christopher R. K. Cawley (Partner)
Joshua Jarvis (Partner)
Stacie Aarestad (Partner)
Audra K. Callanan (Dir-Bus Dev-Boston)
Cindy Lewiton Jackson (Dir-Pro Dev)
Dina Wreede (Dir-Legal Recruiting-Boston)
Eugene Stein (Dir-IT-Boston)
Holly Evers (Dir-Ops-Boston)
Julie A. Hackett (Dir-HR-Boston)
Kenneth S. Leonetti (Partner)
Peter M. Rosenblum (Partner)
Heather Miles (Partner)
Tafadzwa Pasipanodya (Partner)
Thomas Draper (Partner-Bus Dept &
Chm-Debt Fin Practice)
Areta Kupchyk (Co-Chm-FDA Law
Practice grp)

FOLEY INCORPORATED

855 Centennial Ave, Piscataway, NJ
08854-3912
Tel.: (732) 885-5555
Web Site: http://www.foleyinc.com
Year Founded: 1957
Sales Range: $50-74.9 Million
Emp.: 350
Construction & Portable Power Sys-
tems Sales, Rental & Support Ser-
vices
N.A.I.C.S.: 532412
Tom Wagenblast (VP-Product)
Ryan Foley (Pres)
Jamie Foley (CEO)
Mike Pohndorf (Mgr-Product Support
Sls-Construction Div)
Fran Cocco (Mgr-Environmental,
Health & Safety)
Kim Foley (Chm)
Scott Yappen (Dir-Bus Dev)

FOLEY INDUSTRIES, INC.

1550 SW St, Wichita, KS 67213-1638
Tel.: (316) 943-4211   KS
Web Site: https://www.foleyeq.com
Year Founded: 1987
Sales Range: $125-149.9 Million
Emp.: 200
Industrial Machinery Distr
N.A.I.C.S.: 423810
Ann Konecny (Pres)
Lewis Erickson (CFO & VP)

Subsidiaries:

Foley Equipment Company   (1)
1550 SW St, Wichita, KS 67213-1638
Tel.: (316) 943-4211
Web Site: http://www.foleyeq.com
Sales Range: $50-74.9 Million
Wholesale Distribution of General Construc-
tion Machinery & Equipment; Industrial Ma-
chinery & Equipment
N.A.I.C.S.: 423830
Charlotte Kerner (CFO)

FOLEY PRODUCTS COMPANY, LLC

1030 1st Ave, Columbus, GA 31901
Tel.: (706) 256-2534
Web Site:
   http://www.foleyproducts.com
Emp.: 100
Concrete Pipe Mfr
N.A.I.C.S.: 327332
Chris Davidson (VP-Ops)

Subsidiaries:

Coastal Precast of Florida, Inc.   (1)
7100 Pennsylvania St, Fort Myers, FL
33912
Tel.: (239) 482-7468
Web Site: http://www.coastalprecast.com
Sales Range: $1-9.9 Million
Emp.: 35
Concrete Products Mfr
N.A.I.C.S.: 327390
Craig Kovacs (Pres)

FOLEY TIMBER & LAND COM-PANY, LP

1700 Foley Ln, Perry, FL 32347
Tel.: (850) 838-2200
Year Founded: 1994
Sales Range: $1-9.9 Million
Emp.: 24
Management Consulting Services
N.A.I.C.S.: 541618
Howard H. Leach (Pres, Gen Partner
& Principal)
Bo Taff (Sr VP)

FOLEY-BELSAW COMPANY

1173 Benson St, River Falls, WI
54022
Tel.: (952) 856-7500   MN
Web Site:
   http://www.foleybelsaw.com
Year Founded: 1926
Sales Range: $75-99.9 Million
Emp.: 100
Holding Company
N.A.I.C.S.: 611519
Jim Letourneau (Pres)
Walter M. Ringer Jr. (Chm)
Walter M. Ringer III (Vice Chm &
CEO)

Subsidiaries:

Foley-Belsaw Institute   (1)
PO Box 419593, Kansas City, MO
64141   (100%)
Tel.: (816) 483-2700
Web Site: http://www.foley-belsaw.com
Sales Range: $10-24.9 Million
Emp.: 8
Selling of Knife Sharpeners & Blades
N.A.I.C.S.: 541860
Tim Compton (Dir)

Foley-United/Neary Division   (1)
393 Troy St, River Falls, WI
54022-1581   (100%)
Tel.: (715) 426-5151
Web Site: http://www.foleyunited.com
Sales Range: $10-24.9 Million
Emp.: 30
Mfr & Distributor of Fiber-United & Neary
Grand Industrial Sharpening Equipment
N.A.I.C.S.: 333517
James Letourneau (Pres)

FOLEYS INC.

4015 Cheyenne Dr, Archdale, NC
27263
Tel.: (336) 883-6131
Web Site: http://www.foleysinc.com
Sales Range: $10-24.9 Million
Emp.: 25
Drugs, Proprietaries & Sundries
N.A.I.C.S.: 424210
Joseph L. Foley III (Pres)

FOLGER NOLAN FLEMING DOUGLAS INCORPORATED

725 15th St NW, Washington, DC
20005
Tel.: (202) 783-5252   DE
Web Site: https://www.fnfd.com
Year Founded: 1889
Sales Range: $200-249.9 Million
Emp.: 59
Provider of Investment Services
N.A.I.C.S.: 523150
Lee M. Folger (Chm)
Richard S. Foster (Pres & CEO)
David M. Brown (Sr VP)
Richard S. Foster (Pres & CEO)
Neil C. Folger (Sr VP)
Christopher Durchanek (Exec VP)
David M. Brown (Sr VP)

Subsidiaries:

Folger Nolan Fleming Douglas Capital Management, Inc.   (1)
725 15th St NW Ste 1, Washington, DC
20005
Tel.: (202) 626-5220

Investment Management Service
N.A.I.C.S.: 523940
George Hill (VP)

FOLGER SUBARU OF CHAR-LOTTE
5701 E Independence Blvd, Charlotte, NC 28212
Tel.: (704) 536-9635
Web Site:
http://www.folgersubaru.com
Year Founded: 1937
Sales Range: $25-49.9 Million
Emp.: 80
New Car Retailer
N.A.I.C.S.: 441110
J. P. Christy (Gen Mgr)

FOLICA, INC.
90 Stults Rd, Dayton, NJ 08810
Tel.: (609) 860-8430
Web Site: http://www.folica.com
Sales Range: $1-9.9 Million
Emp.: 55
Online Hair Care Products Retailer
N.A.I.C.S.: 456199
Katharine Chen (Dir-Mdse)
Matthew Ohlmeyer (Dir-Infrastructure Tech)
Theresa Falcone (Controller)

FOLIENCE, INC.
230 2nd St SE Ste 100, Cedar Rapids, IA 52401
Tel.: (319) 200-2800   IA
Web Site: https://www.folience.com
Year Founded: 2017
Investment Management Service
N.A.I.C.S.: 523940
Daniel Goldstein (Pres & CEO)
Tom Pientok (Chm)
Cathy Terukina (Exec VP)
Paul Nus (CTO)
Kelly O'Hara (CFO)
Ashley Gansen (Dir-HR)
Denise Lewis (Dir-Acctg)

Subsidiaries:

Cimarron Trailers, Inc.   (1)
1442 Highway 62, Chickasha, OK 73018
Tel.: (405) 222-4800
Web Site: http://www.cimarrontrailers.com
Travel Trailer & Camper Mfr
N.A.I.C.S.: 336214

FOLIOFN, INC.
8180 Greensboro Dr Ste 800, McLean, VA 22102-3865
Tel.: (703) 245-4000   VA
Web Site:
http://www.folioinvesting.com
Year Founded: 1998
Sales Range: $1-9.9 Million
Emp.: 68
Online Brokerage Services, Portfolio Management & Trading Technology
N.A.I.C.S.: 517810
Steve M.H. Wallman (Founder & CEO)

Subsidiaries:

First Affirmative Financial Network LLC   (1)
5475 Mark Dabling Blvd Ste 108, Colorado Springs, CO 80918   (100%)
Tel.: (719) 636-1045
Web Site: http://www.firstaffirmative.com
Financial Investment Activities
N.A.I.C.S.: 523999
George R. Gay (CEO)
Steven J. Schueth (Pres & CMO)
Kathleen J. Lewis (VP, Chief Compliance Officer & Dir-Ops)
R. Kevin O'Keefe (Chief Investment Officer)

FOLK OIL CO. INC.
203 W Main St, Homer, MI 49245-1045

Tel.: (517) 568-4114   MI
Web Site: http://www.folkoil.com
Year Founded: 1973
Sales Range: $25-49.9 Million
Emp.: 125
Gasoline Service Stations
N.A.I.C.S.: 457120
Richard Folk (Pres & Treas)
Ed Heath (VP-Operations)

FOLKS RESTAURANTS, LTD.
508 Harmon Ave, Panama City, FL 32401
Tel.: (850) 763-0501
Web Site: http://www.pofolks.com
Sales Range: $1-9.9 Million
Emp.: 1,100
Family Restaurants
N.A.I.C.S.: 722511
Peter Sostheim (Pres)

FOLLETT CORPORATION
3 Westbrook Corporate Ctr Ste 200, Westchester, IL 60154
Tel.: (708) 884-0230   IL
Web Site: https://www.follett.com
Year Founded: 1873
Emp.: 4,000
Offices of Other Holding Companies
N.A.I.C.S.: 551112
Emmanuel Kolady (CEO)

Subsidiaries:

Baker & Taylor, LLC   (1)
2550 W Tyvola Rd Ste 300, Charlotte, NC 28217
Tel.: (704) 998-3100
Web Site: http://www.btol.com
Wholesale Distr of Books & Value-Added Services to Libraries & Bookstores; DVDs, Videocassettes & Audio CDs & Cassettes; Computer Software
N.A.I.C.S.: 424920
George F. Coe (COO)
David Cully (Pres)
Gary Dayton (Exec VP-Ops)
Amandeep Kochar (Exec VP-Digital Content, Software Products Svcs & Sls)
Raynier Picard (Mng Dir-Mexico)
Gareth Powell (Mng Dir-UK)

Follett Higher Education Group, Inc.   (1)
3 Westbrook Corporate Ctr Ste 200, Westchester, IL 60154   (100%)
Tel.: (708) 884-0000
Web Site: http://www.follett.com
Sales Range: $25-49.9 Million
Emp.: 300
College Bookstores Contract Management
N.A.I.C.S.: 459210
Clay Wahl (Exec VP-Sls Ops)
Joe Miller (Sr VP-Course Matls)
Patrick Usher (Sr VP-Sls & Mktg)
Roe J. McFarlane (Chief Digital Officer)
Emmanuel Kolady (CEO)
Ryan Petersen (Pres)
Samantha M. Swick (VP-PR)

Subsidiary (Domestic):

Advanced Graphic Products Inc.   (2)
750 Gateway Blvd, Coppell, TX 75019
Tel.: (972) 471-5400
Web Site: http://www.advanced-online.com
Sales Range: $1-9.9 Million
Emp.: 80
Ecommerce Branded Merchandise Store Programs for Education & Corporate Customers
N.A.I.C.S.: 541519
Brendan Thornton (Pres)

allCanes Corp.   (2)
5831 Ponce de Leon Blvd, Coral Gables, FL 33146   (100%)
Tel.: (305) 661-9011
Web Site: http://www.allcanes.com
Sales Range: $1-9.9 Million
Emp.: 10
University Merchandise & Apparel Retailer
N.A.I.C.S.: 459420
Christian Bello (VP & Mgr-Mktg)

Follett Software Company   (1)
1391 Corporate Dr, McHenry, IL 60050-7041
Tel.: (815) 344-8700
Web Site: http://www.fsc.follett.com
Sales Range: $50-74.9 Million
Emp.: 350
Sale of Software to Schools & Libraries
N.A.I.C.S.: 449210
Simona Rollinson (Pres)

Subsidiary (Domestic):

X2 Development Corporation   (2)
350 Lincoln St Ste 1103, Hingham, MA 02043
Tel.: (781) 740-2679
School Administration Software Development Services
N.A.I.C.S.: 541511
Gillian Riggs (Engr-Software)

Follett of Canada Inc.   (1)
1193 North Service Rd West Unit C-6327, Oakville, L6M 2V8, ON, Canada
Tel.: (800) 323-4506
Web Site: http://www.follettofcanada.ca
Book Retailer
N.A.I.C.S.: 459210
Bob Scholl (Sr VP-Retail Ops)

Valore Inc.   (1)
268 Summer St 5th Fl, Boston, MA 02210
Tel.: (617) 630-6100
Web Site: http://www.valore.com
Online Textbook Rental Services
N.A.I.C.S.: 518210

Valore Inc.   (1)
5 Bedford St, Burlington, MA 01803
Tel.: (716) 672-7099
Web Site: http://www.valorebooks.com
Book Stores
N.A.I.C.S.: 459210

FOLMAR & ASSOCIATES LLP
3472 Spring Hill Ave, Mobile, AL 36608
Tel.: (251) 343-3777
Year Founded: 1970
Sales Range: $75-99.9 Million
Emp.: 6
Real Estate Development Services
N.A.I.C.S.: 237210
Curt Wilson (Dir-Real Estate)
Pat Eagan (Sec)

FOLSOM BUICK GMC
12640 Auto Mall Cir, Folsom, CA 95630-8099
Tel.: (916) 358-8963
Web Site: http://www.folsombpg.com
Sales Range: $50-74.9 Million
Emp.: 55
New Car Dealers
N.A.I.C.S.: 441110
Denise Dewey (Controller)
Steve Rector (Mgr-Internet Ops)

FOLSOM CHEVROLET
12655 Auto Mall Cir, Folsom, CA 95630-8099
Tel.: (916) 985-5600
Web Site:
https://www.folsomchevy.com
Sales Range: $25-49.9 Million
Emp.: 130
New Car Retailer
N.A.I.C.S.: 441110
Marshal Crossan (Pres)
Bruce Carroll (Mgr-Used Car)
Richard Downey (Mgr-Digital Bus Dev)

FOLSOM CORPORATION
43 McKee Dr Ste 1, Mahwah, NJ 07430
Tel.: (201) 529-3550
Web Site: http://www.folsomcorp.com
Sales Range: $25-49.9 Million
Emp.: 40
Fishing Tackle

N.A.I.C.S.: 423910
Lou Sedsott (Pres)
Dave Dowling (Mgr-Warehouse)
Ed Feldsott (VP)

FOLSOM INVESTMENTS INC.
16475 Dallas Pkwy Ste 800, Addison, TX 75001
Tel.: (972) 931-7400
Web Site:
http://www.folsomcompanies.com
Sales Range: $10-24.9 Million
Emp.: 28
Real Estate Development Services
N.A.I.C.S.: 237210
Kathy Timmons (Mgr-HR)
Danny Holman (Chm)

FOLSOM LAKE FORD
12755 Folsom Blvd, Folsom, CA 95630
Tel.: (916) 353-2000   CA
Web Site:
https://www.folsomlakeford.com
Year Founded: 1990
Sales Range: $100-124.9 Million
Emp.: 300
Automobile Dealership
N.A.I.C.S.: 441110
Chuck Peterson (Pres)
John Sears (VP-Ops)
Sherry Hart (Controller)

FONALITY, INC.
6900 Dallas Pkwy Ste 250, Plano, TX 75024
Tel.: (877) 366-2549
Web Site: http://www.fonality.com
Year Founded: 2005
Sales Range: $10-24.9 Million
Emp.: 70
Communications Solutions
N.A.I.C.S.: 517810
David Scult (CEO)
Raul Vera (CTO)
Jeff Valentine (CMO)
David Beagle (VP-Channel Dev)
John Young (Sr VP-Global Sls)

FONG BROTHERS PRINTING INC.
320 Valley Dr, Brisbane, CA 94005
Tel.: (415) 467-1050
Web Site: https://www.fbp.com
Rev.: $20,900,000
Emp.: 170
Offset Printing
N.A.I.C.S.: 323111
Tina Vu (Acct Mgr)

FONON CORPORATION
1101 N Keller Rd Ste G, Orlando, FL 32810
Tel.: (407) 477-5618   DE
Web Site: http://www.fonon.us
Year Founded: 2003
Sales Range: Less than $1 Million
Fiber & CO2 Laser Material Processing Equipment for Marking, Cutting & Engraving Applications Mfr
N.A.I.C.S.: 339999
Demitri Nikitin (CEO)

FONTAINEBLEAU HOTEL
4441 Collins Ave, Miami Beach, FL 33140
Tel.: (305) 538-2000
Web Site:
http://www.fontainebleu.com
Sales Range: $25-49.9 Million
Emp.: 2,500
Hotel Operations
N.A.I.C.S.: 721110

Fontainebleau Hotel—(Continued)

Scott Flexman (*VP-Sls & Mktg*)
David Chin (*Dir-IT*)
Kevin Bryant (*Exec Dir-Sls-Property*)

FONTANA WATER COMPANY
15966 Arrow Rd, Fontana, CA 92335
Tel.: (909) 822-2201
Web Site:
   https://www.fontanawater.com
Sales Range: $25-49.9 Million
Emp.: 50
Water Supply Services
N.A.I.C.S.: 221310
Robert H. Nicholson (*Pres*)

Subsidiaries:

Arizona Water Company (1)
3805 N Black Canyon Hwy, Phoenix, AZ 85015
Tel.: (602) 240-6860
Web Site: http://www.azwater.com
Sales Range: $25-49.9 Million
Water Supply
N.A.I.C.S.: 221310
Bill Garfield (*Pres*)
Linda Nogalo (*Dir-HR*)
Ted Millspaugh (*VP-Ops*)
Fred Schneider (*VP-Engrg*)
Joseph D. Harris Jr. (*Treas & VP*)

San Gabriel Valley Water Co (1)
11142 Garvey Ave, El Monte, CA 91733
Tel.: (626) 448-6183
Web Site: http://www.sgvwater.com
Water Supply
N.A.I.C.S.: 221310
R. W. Nicholson (*Pres*)

FONTANA WOOD PRODUCTS INC.
10712 Live Oak Ave, Fontana, CA 92337-7258
Tel.: (909) 823-9950
Web Site: http://fontanawp.com
Year Founded: 1987
Sales Range: $10-24.9 Million
Emp.: 90
Sawmill & Planing Mill Services
N.A.I.C.S.: 321912
Natalie Gravitt (*Mgr*)

FONTANESI AND KANN COMPANY
13380 Capital St, Oak Park, MI 48237
Tel.: (248) 543-0095
Web Site: http://www.ezhvac.com
Year Founded: 1991
Rev.: $11,000,000
Emp.: 24
General Construction Machinery & Equipment
N.A.I.C.S.: 423810
Joseph Fontanesi (*Pres*)
Jill LaFountain (*Office Mgr*)

FOOD & GAS, INC.
3970 Rogers Br Rd, Duluth, GA 30097
Tel.: (678) 436-0150
Web Site:
   http://www.foodandgasinc.com
Sales Range: $75-99.9 Million
Emp.: 20
Petroleum Whslr & Distr
N.A.I.C.S.: 445110

FOOD & WATER WATCH
1616 P St NW Ste 300, Washington, DC 20036
Tel.: (202) 683-2500
Web Site:
   http://www.foodandwaterwatch.org
Year Founded: 2005
Sales Range: $10-24.9 Million
Emp.: 145

Food & Water Resource Conservation Services
N.A.I.C.S.: 813312

FOOD ALLERGY RESEARCH & EDUCATION, INC.
7925 Jones Branch Dr Ste 1100, McLean, VA 22102
Tel.: (703) 691-3179
Web Site: http://www.foodallergy.org
Year Founded: 1998
Sales Range: $10-24.9 Million
Emp.: 72
Food Research & Education Services
N.A.I.C.S.: 541715
Sandeep Dhar (*CFO & Sr VP*)
Mary Jane Marchisotto (*Sr VP-Res & Ops-Intl*)
Denise A. Bunning (*Sec*)
Janet Atwater (*Chm*)
Michael Lade (*Treas*)
Robert Nichols (*Vice Chm*)
Lois A. Witkop (*Chief Advancement Officer*)
Steve Danon (*Sr VP-External Affairs*)
Lisa Gable (*CEO*)
Bruce Roberts (*Chief Res, Science & Innovation Officer*)

FOOD AUTOMATION - SERVICE TECHNIQUES, INC.
905 Honeyspot Rd, Stratford, CT 06615
Tel.: (203) 377-4414
Web Site: http://www.fastinc.com
Year Founded: 1970
Sales Range: $10-24.9 Million
Emp.: 120
Time Cycle & Program Controllers Mfr
N.A.I.C.S.: 334513
Bernard G. Koether (*Chm*)
George F. Koether (*Pres & CEO*)
Patricia M. Balkonis (*Dir-HR*)
Edward Musial (*Sr Dir-New Product Introduction*)
Mike Pardoe (*Mng Dir-Europe*)
William Flynn (*VP-Engrg*)

FOOD BANK OF CONTRA COSTA AND SOLANO
4010 Nelson Ave, Concord, CA 94520
Tel.: (925) 676-7543
Web Site:
   https://www.foodbankccs.org
Year Founded: 1975
Sales Range: $50-74.9 Million
Emp.: 62
Community Food Services
N.A.I.C.S.: 624210
Hisham Hamdy (*Dir-Ops*)
Hulynne Besharatpour (*Dir-Fin*)
Caitlin Sly (*Program Dir*)
Lisa Sherrill (*Dir-Comm*)
Veronica Wimer (*Mgr-Pur*)
Paul Gabbard (*Chm*)
Larry Sly (*Exec Dir*)

FOOD BANK OF SAN LUIS OBISPO COUNTY
2212 Golden Hill Rd, Paso Robles, CA 93446
Tel.: (805) 238-4664
Web Site: http://www.slofoodbank.org
Year Founded: 1988
Sales Range: $10-24.9 Million
Emp.: 49
Community Food Services
N.A.I.C.S.: 624210

FOOD BANK OF THE ROCKIES
10700 E 45th Ave, Denver, CO 80239

Tel.: (303) 371-9250 CO
Web Site:
   http://www.foodbankrockies.org
Year Founded: 1978
Sales Range: $100-124.9 Million
Emp.: 593,239
Hunger Relief Services
N.A.I.C.S.: 624210
Cindy Mitchell (*Dir-Programs*)
Lee Boteler (*Chief Programs Officer*)
Marshall Aster (*CFO*)
Kim Ruotsala (*Chief Dev Officer*)
Patrick Fairfield (*Treas*)
Bob Deuschle (*Sec*)
Kevin Seggelke (*Pres & CEO*)
Tony Alexis (*COO*)
Janie Gianotsos (*Dir-Mktg & Community Rels*)
Mitch Jelniker (*Mgr-Corp Rels*)
Lorena Toland (*Dir-HR*)

FOOD CIRCUS SUPERMARKETS INC.
853 Hwy 35, Middletown, NJ 07748-4205
Tel.: (732) 671-2220
Web Site: http://www.foodcircus.com
Year Founded: 1955
Sales Range: $150-199.9 Million
Emp.: 1,200
Supermarket Operations
N.A.I.C.S.: 445110
John Azzolina (*Co-Owner*)
Philip Scaduto (*VP-Mktg & Admin & Co-Owner*)
Alice White (*Asst Mgr*)
Barry Elliott (*Dir-Loss Prevention & Safety*)
Patty Rispoli (*Supvr-Deli*)
Louis J. Scaduto Jr. (*Pres*)

FOOD CONCEPTS INTERNATIONAL
2575 S Loop 289, Lubbock, TX 79423
Tel.: (806) 785-8686
Web Site: http://www.abuelos.com
Year Founded: 1975
Chain Restaurant
N.A.I.C.S.: 722511

FOOD COUNTRY USA INC.
566 E Main St, Abingdon, VA 24210
Tel.: (276) 628-4412
Web Site:
   http://www.foodcountryusainc.com
Sales Range: $50-74.9 Million
Emp.: 17
Independent Grocery Store Operator
N.A.I.C.S.: 445110
Charles W. Henderson (*Pres & CEO*)
Don Henderson (*COO*)
Todd Creasy (*Controller*)

FOOD EQUIPMENT REPRESENTATIVES, INC.
3716 SW 30th Ave, Hollywood, FL 33312
Tel.: (954) 587-9347 FL
Web Site: http://www.ferinc.net
Year Founded: 1990
Sales Range: $25-49.9 Million
Emp.: 15
Restaurant Equipment & Supplies
N.A.I.C.S.: 423440
J. Gabriel Puerto (*Mng Partner*)
Gabriel Puerto (*Mng Partner*)
Gregory R. Olsen (*Partner-Tampa*)
Martha Lozano (*Office Mgr & Coord-Sls*)
Thomas E. Dickie (*Partner-Hollywood*)
Craig Hodges (*Partner-Orlando*)
Thomas E. Dickie (*Partner & Partner-Hollywood*)

Martha Lozano (*Office Mgr & Coord-Sls*)
Craig Hodges (*Partner & Partner-Orlando*)

FOOD EXPORT ASSOCIATION OF THE MIDWEST USA
309 W Washington St Ste 600, Chicago, IL 60606
Tel.: (312) 334-9200 IL
Web Site: https://www.foodexport.org
Year Founded: 1969
Sales Range: $10-24.9 Million
Emp.: 18
Hunger Relief Services
N.A.I.C.S.: 624210
John Belmont (*Mgr-Comm*)
Tim Hamilton (*Exec Dir*)
Robert Lowe (*Mgr-Fin*)
Teresa Miller (*Mgr-Intl Mktg Program*)

FOOD EXPRESS INC.
521 N 1st Ave, Arcadia, CA 91006
Tel.: (626) 574-9094
Web Site: http://www.foodexp.com
Year Founded: 1983
Sales Range: $10-24.9 Million
Emp.: 250
Food Transport Services
N.A.I.C.S.: 484110
Kevin Keeney (*VP*)
Joanna Keeney (*Treas & Sec*)

FOOD FAST CORPORATION
4703 DC Dr Ste 100, Tyler, TX 75701-0405
Tel.: (903) 534-0028
Web Site:
   http://www.foodfastcorp.com
Year Founded: 1997
Sales Range: $25-49.9 Million
Emp.: 300
Grocery Stores
N.A.I.C.S.: 445131
Mike Skidmore (*Mgr-Mktg*)

FOOD FOR LANE COUNTY
770 Bailey Hill Rd, Eugene, OR 97402
Tel.: (541) 343-2822 OR
Web Site:
   https://www.foodforlanecounty.org
Year Founded: 1986
Sales Range: $10-24.9 Million
Emp.: 195
Hunger Relief Services
N.A.I.C.S.: 624210
Beverlee Hughes (*Exec Dir*)
Ron Detwiler (*Dir-Ops*)
Blake Arnold (*Dir-IT*)
Tauna Stephens (*Dir-Fin*)

FOOD FOR THE POOR, INC.
6401 Lyons Rd, Coconut Creek, FL 33073
Tel.: (954) 427-2222 FL
Web Site:
   https://www.foodforthepoor.org
Year Founded: 1982
Sales Range: $900-999.9 Million
Emp.: 406
Hunger Relief Services
N.A.I.C.S.: 624210
Angel Aloma (*Exec Dir*)
Alvaro J. Pereira (*Exec VP*)
Dennis North (*CFO*)
Frederick Khouri (*COO*)
David T. Price (*Gen Counsel & Sec*)
Burchell McPherson (*Treas*)
P. Todd Kennedy (*Chm*)
William G. Benson (*Vice Chm*)

FOOD KING INC.

1350 Galloping Hill Rd Ste A, Union, NJ 07083-8902
Tel.: (908) 686-5155
Sales Range: $10-24.9 Million
Emp.: 120
Supermarket Operator
N.A.I.C.S.: 445110
Ron Ginsberg (Pres)

FOOD KING, INC.
5708 Wabash Ave, Baltimore, MD 21215
Tel.: (410) 764-3900   MD
Sales Range: $25-49.9 Million
Emp.: 180
Supermarket Operator
N.A.I.C.S.: 445110
Bernard Meizlish (Pres)
Herb Beckenheimer (CEO)

FOOD MANAGEMENT PART-NERS, INC.
120 Chula Vista Dr, San Antonio, TX 78232
Tel.: (210) 403-3725   TX
Web Site: http://www.foodmps.com
Year Founded: 1999
Holding Company; Full-Service Restaurants Owner & Operator; Fresh & Frozen Prepared Food Mfr & Whslr
N.A.I.C.S.: 551112
Brian Bailey (VP-Ops)
Larry F. Harris (Co-Founder & Chm)
Allen J. Jones (Co-Founder, Pres & CEO)
Jason R. Kemp (Co-Founder & CFO)
Brian Padilla (Partner-Ops)
Robert Amaro (VP-Fin)
Mike Griffith (Dir-Mktg)
Peter Donbavand (VP-Real Estate & Bus Dev)
Tracy Amass (Dir-HR)
Hugo Gonzalez (Dir-IT)

Subsidiaries:

Dynamic Foods   (1)
1001 E 33rd St, Lubbock, TX 79404
Tel.: (806) 723-5600
Web Site: http://www.dynamicfoods.com
Emp.: 200
Fresh & Frozen Prepared Foods Mfr
N.A.I.C.S.: 311991
Gabriel Olivarez (Mgr-Indus Maintenance)

FMP Restaurant Management, LLC   (1)
120 Chula Vista Dr, San Antonio, TX 78232
Tel.: (210) 403-3725
Web Site: http://www.foodmps.com
Restaurant Operators
N.A.I.C.S.: 561110
Brian Bailey (VP-Ops)
Larry F. Harris (Co-Founder & Chm)
Allen J. Jones (Co-Founder, Pres & CEO)
Jason R. Kemp (Co-Founder & CFO)
Robert Amaro (VP-Fin)
Tracey Amass (Dir-HR)
Mike Griffith (Dir-Mktg)
Hugo Gonzalez (Dir-IT)

Subsidiary (Domestic):

Buffet Partners Holding Company, LLC   (2)
120 Chula Vista Dr, San Antonio, TX 78232
Tel.: (210) 403-3725
Web Site: http://www.furrs.net
Holding Company; Full-Service Family Restaurants Operator
N.A.I.C.S.: 551112
Brian Bailey (VP-Ops)

Catalina Restaurant Group Inc.   (2)
120 Chula Vista Dr, San Antonio, TX 78232
Tel.: (210) 403-3725
Holding Company; Full-Service Restaurants Operator
N.A.I.C.S.: 551112
Brian Bailey (VP-Ops)

Rita Restaurant Corp.   (2)
120 Chula Vista Dr, San Antonio, TX 78232

Tel.: (210) 403-3725
Web Site: http://www.donpablos.com
Holding Company; Full-Service Restaurants Operator
N.A.I.C.S.: 551112
Brian Bailey (VP-Ops)

Ovation Brands, Inc.   (1)
11923 NE Sumner St Ste 727044, Portland, OR 97204
Tel.: (702) 333-2228
Web Site: http://www.ovationbrands.com
Emp.: 10,000
Buffet Restaurant Owner & Operator
N.A.I.C.S.: 722511
Marc Albert (Reg Mgr)
Roe Hatlen (Co-Founder)
C. Dennis Scott (Co-Founder)

Subsidiary (Domestic):

Tahoe Joe's Famous Steakhouse, Inc.   (2)
120 Chula Vista Hollywood Park, San Antonio, TX 78232
Tel.: (210) 403-3725
Web Site: http://www.tahoejoes.com
Restaurant Operators
N.A.I.C.S.: 722511

FOOD MARKET MANAGE-MENT, INC.
215 Reindollar Ave, Marina, CA 93933
Tel.: (831) 582-2494
Web Site:
https://www.gingerpeople.com
Year Founded: 1984
Sales Range: $25-49.9 Million
Emp.: 100
Organic Ginger Product Mfr
N.A.I.C.S.: 111419
Abbie Leeson (Exec VP)

FOOD MARKETING SER-VICES, INC.
1001 N Ellsworth Ave, Villa Park, IL 60181
Tel.: (630) 833-3000
Web Site: http://www.fmservil.com
Rev.: $14,500,000
Emp.: 25
General Line Grocery Merchant Whslr
N.A.I.C.S.: 424410
Doug Applequist (Owner)

FOOD MASTERS INC.
5017 Memory Rd, Raleigh, NC 27609
Tel.: (919) 876-0957
Web Site:
http://www.foodmastersinc.com
Sales Range: $10-24.9 Million
Emp.: 250
Eating Place
N.A.I.C.S.: 722511
Charles Casteen (Office Mgr)
Bill Casteen (Treas & Sec)
Matt Moore (VP)

FOOD OPPORTUNITIES OR-GANIZATION &. DISTRIBU-TION INC.
3403 E Central Ave, Fresno, CA 93725
Tel.: (559) 237-3663   CA
Web Site:
http://www.communityfoodbank.net
Year Founded: 1992
Sales Range: $50-74.9 Million
Emp.: 38
Community Food Services
N.A.I.C.S.: 624210
Andrew Souza (Pres & CEO)
Denise O'Canto (Mgr-Corp Rels & Community Engagement)
Renee Nuanes (Mgr-Comm & Events)

Natalie Caples (Dir-Programs)
Kym Dildine (Dir-Dev)
Maria Ramirez (Coord-Agency Rels)

FOOD PANTRY LTD. INC.
3536 Harding Ave Ste 500, Honolulu, HI 96816-2453
Tel.: (808) 732-5515   HI
Web Site:
http://www.sullivanfamilyco.com
Year Founded: 1960
Sales Range: $50-74.9 Million
Emp.: 500
Grocery Stores
N.A.I.C.S.: 445110
Jenai Sullivan Wall (Chm & CEO)
Andy Kawano (Pres)

FOOD SCIENCES CORPORA-TION
821 E Gate Dr, Mount Laurel, NJ 08054
Tel.: (856) 778-8080
Web Site:
https://www.foodsciences.com
Rev.: $11,200,000
Emp.: 80
Vitamins, Natural or Synthetic
N.A.I.C.S.: 325411
Valerie Dowers (Coord-Sales)

FOOD SERVICE INSURANCE MANAGERS
3260 Penryn Rd, Loomis, CA 95650-8858
Tel.: (916) 660-0267
Web Site: http://www.fsimonline.com
Year Founded: 1987
Sales Range: $10-24.9 Million
Emp.: 35
Employee Compensation Insurance Services
N.A.I.C.S.: 524126
John A. Stassi (COO)
Demetri Alvero (Dir-Medical Mgmt)
Alonso Bayardo (VP-Acctg & Fin)
Matthew J. Costa (Mgr-Underwriting)

FOOD SERVICE OF TALLA-HASSEE
PO Box 4089, Tallahassee, FL 32303
Tel.: (850) 224-7080
Sales Range: $10-24.9 Million
Emp.: 10
Steak Restaurant
N.A.I.C.S.: 722511
James H. Hill Jr. (Pres)

FOOD SERVICE REFRIGERA-TION INC.
1440 Sw 31st Ave, Pompano Beach, FL 33069
Tel.: (954) 917-9765
Web Site:
http://www.fsrrefrigeration.com
Rev.: $11,400,000
Emp.: 125
Plumbing, Heating & Air-Conditioning Contractors
N.A.I.C.S.: 238220
Maureen Haynes (Office Mgr)

FOOD SHOULD TASTE GOOD, INC.
PO Box 776, Needham Heights, MA 02494
Tel.: (877) 588-3784
Web Site: http://www.foodshouldtaste good.com
Year Founded: 2006
Sales Range: $25-49.9 Million
Emp.: 34
Mfr of All-natural Corn Tortilla Chips in Unusual Flavors
N.A.I.C.S.: 311919

FOOD SPECIALISTS INC.
255 3rd St Ste 102, Oakland, CA 94607
Tel.: (510) 302-0999
Web Site:
http://www.scottseastbay.com
Sales Range: $10-24.9 Million
Emp.: 10
Family Restaurant Operator
N.A.I.C.S.: 722511
Raymond Gallagher (Pres)
Steve Fagalae (CFO)

FOOD SYSTEMS UNLIMITED, INC.
750 Florida Central Pkwy, Longwood, FL 32750
Tel.: (407) 830-5338
Web Site:
https://www.foodsystemsunlimi ted.com
Year Founded: 1991
Sales Range: $10-24.9 Million
Emp.: 625
Food Court Operator
N.A.I.C.S.: 722513
Biagio Schiano (Pres)
Kim Thieman (Controller)

FOOD WAREHOUSE CORPO-RATION
7350 L State Bovoni Unit C 121, Charlotte Amalie, VI 00802
Tel.: (340) 777-7787
Rev.: $15,000,000
Emp.: 54
Groceries, General Line
N.A.I.C.S.: 424410
Robert Cimino (Pres)

FOOD-N-FUN, INC.
603 Jefferson Ter, New Iberia, LA 70560
Tel.: (337) 365-7280   LA
Web Site: http://www.foodnfun.com
Sales Range: $25-49.9 Million
Emp.: 200
Operator of Convenience Stores
N.A.I.C.S.: 445131
Todd W. Street (Pres & CEO)
Tony Ridge (Controller)
Melissa Robicheaux (Mgr-HR)

FOODBANK OF SOUTHEAST-ERN VIRGINIA AND THE EASTERN SHORE
800 Tidewater Dr, Norfolk, VA 23504
Tel.: (757) 627-6599   VA
Web Site:
https://www.foodbankonline.org
Year Founded: 1981
Sales Range: $25-49.9 Million
Emp.: 70
Community Food Services
N.A.I.C.S.: 624210
Renee Figurelle (COO)
William Jesse Owens (Treas & Sec)
Tom Dykes (Mgr-HR)
Debra Kleeger (Mgr-Child Nutrition)
Lisa Cuba (VP)
Paul G. Finch (Pres)
Charmin Horton (Mgr-Eastern Shore Branch)
Robert Galewski (Mgr-Warehouse & Facilities)
Dan Barger (CFO)
Ruth Jones Nichols (CEO)
Tom Weiglein (Chief Strategy Officer)

FOODGUYS
30470 SW Pkwy Ave Ste A, Wilsonville, OR 97070
Tel.: (503) 570-2871
Web Site: http://www.foodguys.com
Year Founded: 1991
Sales Range: $10-24.9 Million
Emp.: 26

foodguys—(Continued)

Food Products Mfr Including Management, Quality Assurance & Logistics Services
N.A.I.C.S.: 722310
Mark Nyman (Owner, Pres & CEO)
Slade Crooks (Mgr-Sls)
John Eld (Supvr-Acctg)
Debbie Nelson (Mgr-HR)

FOODLAND SUPER MARKET LIMITED
3536 Harding Ave, Honolulu, HI 96816
Tel.: (808) 732-0791
Web Site: https://www.foodland.com
Sales Range: $200-249.9 Million
Emp.: 67
Supermarkets, Chain
N.A.I.C.S.: 445110
Jenai Sullivan Wall (Chm & CEO)
Andy Kawano (CFO)

FOODLAND WAREHOUSE FOODS INC.
5401 Collinsville Rd, Fairmount, IL 62201
Tel.: (618) 874-8431
Rev.: $13,000,000
Emp.: 20
Owns & Operates Independent Grocery Stores
N.A.I.C.S.: 445110
Barney Miller (Pres)

FOODMASTER SUPER MARKETS INC.
100 Everett Ave Ste 12, Chelsea, MA 02150-2374
Tel.: (617) 660-1300
Web Site:
http://www.foodmasterinc.com
Year Founded: 1947
Sales Range: $100-124.9 Million
Emp.: 1,300
Grocery Stores
N.A.I.C.S.: 445110
John A. Dejesus (Chm, Pres & Treas)
Richard Hinds (CFO)

FOODMAVEN CORPORATION
3610 N Stone Ave, Colorado Springs, CO 80907
Tel.: (719) 472-3113
Web Site: http://www.foodmaven.com
Year Founded: 2015
Online Marketplace Owner & Operator
N.A.I.C.S.: 513199
Patrick Bultema (Founder & Chm)
Ben Deda (CEO)
Jason Rembert (CTO)
Brad Larue (Dir-Sls)
Megan Cornish (VP-Govt & Indus Affairs)

Subsidiaries:

Anderson Boneless Beef, Inc. (1)
909 E 75th Ave, Denver, CO 80229
Tel.: (303) 289-5551
Sales Range: $10-24.9 Million
Emp.: 35
Meat & Meat Product Whslr
N.A.I.C.S.: 424470
Charlie Tan (Founder & CEO)

FOODMIX MARKETING COMMUNICATIONS
103 W Arthur St, Elmhurst, IL 60126
Tel.: (630) 366-7500
Web Site: http://www.foodmix.net
Year Founded: 2000
Rev.: $25,000,000
Emp.: 20
N.A.I.C.S.: 541810

Dan O'Connell (Founder & CEO)
Sloan Salah (Dir-Market Research)
John Schuller (VP-Strategy)
Steve Megel (COO)
Eric Olson (Sr VP & Exec Dir-Creative)
Pat Taflinger (Dir-Media)
Sara Hagen (Pres)
Peter Baughman (Dir-Comm)
Tim O'Brien (Dir-Creative)

FOODPRO
321 E 5th St, Frederick, MD 21701
Tel.: (301) 663-3171
Web Site: http://www.myfoodpro.com
Sales Range: $25-49.9 Million
Emp.: 106
Produce, Meats, Poultry & Seafood Whslr
N.A.I.C.S.: 424480
Ed Furbee (Pres)
Kevin McAteer (VP-Sls)
Rocky Rinehart (VP-Mktg)
Grayson Ramsburg (Mgr-Customer Svcs)
Will Donnell (Mgr-Bus Dev)

FOODS NORTH LLC
7013 Danyeur Rd, Redding, CA 96001
Tel.: (530) 226-1130
Sales Range: $10-24.9 Million
Emp.: 300
Eating Place
N.A.I.C.S.: 722511
Michael Mills (Pres)

FOODSWING, INC.
904 Woods Rd, Cambridge, MD 21613
Tel.: (410) 228-1644
Web Site: http://www.foodswing.com
Year Founded: 1999
Sales Range: $10-24.9 Million
Emp.: 88
Fruit & Vegetable Canning Mfr
N.A.I.C.S.: 311421
Roger Hoffman (Pres & CEO)
Michael K. Ballard (Exec VP & CFO)
Charles J. Crawford (Dir-Ops)
Stephen J. Connolley (Dir-Comm)
Fred Jewett (Dir-Food Tech)
Howard Covenko (VP)
Grey Cole (Mgr-Pur)

FOODTEAM INC.
1007 N Main St, Columbia, IL 62236
Tel.: (618) 281-3100
Web Site: http://www.rifood.com
Sales Range: $10-24.9 Million
Emp.: 13
Temporary Help Service
N.A.I.C.S.: 561320
William Timmons (Pres)
Kit Timmons (VP)
Michelle Timmons (Controller)

FOODTOWN, INC.
485 Rte 1 South Bldg E Ste 170, Iselin, NJ 08830
Tel.: (732) 596-6000
Web Site:
http://www.shopfoodtown.com
Year Founded: 1975
Sales Range: $10-24.9 Million
Emp.: 50
Grocery Stores
N.A.I.C.S.: 445110
Bob Gee (Mgr-Pricing)
Dean Holmquist (Dir-Produce & Floral)
Ellen Henkin (Mgr-Programming)
Rose Johnson (Dir-Risk Mgmt)

Subsidiaries:

Foodtown Supermarket Inc. (1)

444 S Fulton Ave, Mount Vernon, NY 10553-1718 (100%)
Tel.: (914) 667-6400
Grocery Stores
N.A.I.C.S.: 445110
Sidney Katz (Pres)
Daniel Katz (VP)

FOOTE PARTNERS LLC
445 N A1A Ste 224, Vero Beach, FL 32963
Tel.: (772) 234-2787
Web Site:
http://www.footepartners.com
Sales Range: $1-9.9 Million
Management Consulting & IT Research Services
N.A.I.C.S.: 541611
David Foote (Co-Founder, CEO & Chief Research Officer)
George Foote (Co-Founder)

FOOTHILL RIDGE APARTMENTS
1334 W Foothill Blvd, Upland, CA 91786-8012
Web Site:
http://www.foothillridge.com
Lessors of Residential Buildings & Dwellings
N.A.I.C.S.: 531110
Jackie Logan (Mgr)

FOOTHILLS FARMERS COOPERATIVE
1514 W Broadway Ave, Maryville, TN 37801
Tel.: (865) 982-2761
Web Site:
http://foothillsfarmerscoop.com
Year Founded: 1945
Rev.: $13,742,412
Emp.: 50
Feed & Farm Supply
N.A.I.C.S.: 459999
James I. Messler (Pres)

FOOTHILLS LAND CONSERVANCY
373 Ellis Ave, Maryville, TN 37804
Tel.: (865) 681-8326
Web Site: http://www.foothillsland.org
Year Founded: 1985
Sales Range: $200-249.9 Million
Emp.: 4
Land Conservation Services
N.A.I.C.S.: 813312
Bill Clabough (Exec Dir)
Elise Eustace (Dir-Development-Communications)

FOOTHILLS RURAL TELEPHONE COOPERATIVE CORPORATION INC.
1621 Kentucky Route 40 W, Staffordsville, KY 41256
Tel.: (606) 297-3501
Web Site: https://www.foothills.net
Year Founded: 1951
Sales Range: $25-49.9 Million
Emp.: 67
Telecommunication Services
N.A.I.C.S.: 517810
Ruth Conley (CEO & Gen Mgr)

FOOTPRINT RETAIL SERVICES
2200 Western Ct Ste 150, Lisle, IL 60532
Tel.: (630) 324-3400
Web Site: https://www.fprs.com
Emp.: 2,800
Support Services for Retailers
N.A.I.C.S.: 561499
William J. McKenna (Chm)
Kevin Lee (VP)

Joann Kohout (Coord-Client Svc)
Lyra Long (Dir-Acq Integrations & Processes)
John Prapuolenis (Dir-Client Svc)
Erin Scarpelli (Dir-Client Svcs)
Marc Richardson (Mgr-Call Center)
Joe Honn (Mgr-Client Svc)
Bryant Love (Sr Mgr-Network Infrastructure)
Mark Gilbert (VP-Bus Dev)
Tom Crepeau (Mgr-Bus Dev)

FOOTWEAR UNLIMITED INC.
99 Larkin Williams Industrial Ct, Fenton, MO 63026
Tel.: (636) 343-9914
Web Site:
http://www.footwearunlimited.com
Sales Range: $25-49.9 Million
Emp.: 45
Footwear
N.A.I.C.S.: 424340
Nicholas Licaboli (CFO)
Andrew Smith (VP & Gen Mgr)
Bill Downey (VP)
Steve Mullen (VP & Mgr-Sls-Natl)
Jon Hanson (Exec VP/Gen Mgr-Spyder)
Pat Mooney (CEO)

FOR THE BRIDE BY DEMETRIOS
222 W 37th St, New York, NY 10018-6606
Tel.: (212) 967-5222
Web Site:
http://www.demetriosbride.com
Year Founded: 1980
Sales Range: $75-99.9 Million
Emp.: 100
Bridal Gown Designer & Bridal Magazine Publisher
N.A.I.C.S.: 315250
John Vlahoyiannis (Pres)

FORAM GROUP, INC.
600 Brickell Ave Ste 1400, Miami, FL 33131
Tel.: (305) 358-9807
Web Site:
http://www.foramgroup.com
Year Founded: 1978
Sales Range: $1-9.9 Million
Emp.: 15
Real Estate Asset Management, Development & Brokerage Services
N.A.I.C.S.: 541611
Loretta H. Cockrum (Chm & CEO)
Tracy Story (Pres-Mgmt & Leasing)
William Urban II (CFO)

FORAN SPICE COMPANY
7616 S 6th St, Oak Creek, WI 53154
Tel.: (414) 764-1220
Web Site: http://www.foranspice.com
Rev.: $34,000,000
Emp.: 130
Spice & Extract Mfr
N.A.I.C.S.: 311942
John Goetz (CTO)

FORBES HAMILTON MANAGEMENT COMPANY
123 S Clyde Ave, Kissimmee, FL 34741
Tel.: (407) 847-2111
Web Site: http://www.fhhotels.com
Year Founded: 1986
Emp.: 4
Hotel Management
N.A.I.C.S.: 721110
Thomas M. Johnsen (Pres)
Katie Saumell (VP-Admin)

Subsidiaries:

Santa Maria Suites Resort (1)

1401 Simonton St, Key West, FL 33040
Tel.: (305) 296-5678
Web Site: http://www.santamariasuites.com
Hotel
N.A.I.C.S.: 721110

FORBES MEDIA LLC
499 Washington Blvd, Jersey City, NJ 07310
Tel.: (212) 620-2200   DE
Web Site: https://www.forbes.com
Year Founded: 2006
Emp.: 500
Holding Company; Business & Investment Information Publisher
N.A.I.C.S.: 551112
Jessica Sibley (Chief Revenue Officer)
William Adamopoulos (CEO-Asia)
Michael Federle (CEO)
Abbey Smith (VP-Acct Mgmt)
Sherry Phillips (CMO)
Maria Rosa Cartolano (Gen Counsel)
Nina Gould (Chief Product Officer)
Vadim Supitskiy (CTO)
Ali Intres (Sr VP-HR & Talent Mgmt)
Taha Ahmed (VP-Dev & Strategy)
Peter Hung (Pres-Licensing & Branded Ventures)
Randall Lane (Chief Content Officer)
Lynn Schlesinger (Chief Customer Experience Officer)
Michael York (CFO)
Joyce Bautista Ferrari (Mng Editor)
C. W. Benston (VP-Social & Emerging Media)
Laura Brusca (VP-Comm)
Erika Burho (VP-ForbesWomen)
Jessica Charles (VP-Programming-ForbesLive)
Brooke Dunmore (VP-Benefits & HRIS)
Janett Haas (Sr VP-Sls)
Alica Hallett-Chan (Dir-Design)
Merryl Holland (Grp VP-Sls Dev)
Emily Jackson (Sr VP-E-Commerce)
David Johnson (Sr VP-Bus Intelligence)
Doug Lopenzina (VP-Content Licensing & Syndication)
Sade Muhammad (VP-Representation & Inclusion Practice)
Josh Robinson (Sr VP-Content & Design Svcs)
Rebeca Solorzano (Sr VP-Programmatic Ops & Strategy)
Christina Vega Magrini (VP-Comm)
Alyson Williams (Sr VP-Digital Ops & Strategy)
Jay Webster (Grp VP-Mktg, Strategy & Communites)
Alex Wood (Mng Dir-Europe)
Moira Forbes (Pres-ForbesWomen & Exec VP)
Adam Wallitt (Sr VP-Data Strategy & Sales & Grp VP-Data Strategy & Sls)
Leann Bonanno (Sr VP-ForbesLive & Marketing & Grp VP-ForbesLive)
Paul Reiss (Sr VP-Accolades & Strategic Partnerships & Grp VP-Strategic Partnerships & Licensing)
Kyle Vinansky (Sr VP-Global Sls & VP-Sls-East,Midwest)
Seth Cohen (Chief Impact Officer)
Seth Boyarsky (VP-Compensation)
Jennifer Bruno (VP-Bus Strategy)
Sara Colodner (VP-Business Development & Partnerships-Newsletters)
Katie Delgado (VP-Engineering)
Katie Doyle (Sr VP-Content & Forbes Marketplace)
Samantha Evans (VP-Demand Gen & Community Mktg)
Kristine Francisco (VP-Content Design)
Lauren Gurnee (VP-Programmatic Partnerships)

Matt Herrmann (VP-Creative & Design)
Jonathon Jones (Sr VP-Strategy & Forbes Marketplace)
Susan Kessler (VP-ForbesLive)
Nikki Koval (VP & Asst Gen Counsel)
Luisa Kroll (Exec Editor)
Kerry Lauerman (Exec Editor)
Seth Matlins (Mng Dir-Forbes CMO Network)
John Paczkowski (Exec Editor)

Subsidiaries:

Forbes China   (1)
1000 Lujiazui Ring Road, Pudong, Shanghai, 200120, China
Tel.: (86) 2168412939
Web Site: http://www.forbeschina.com
Sales Range: $25-49.9 Million
Emp.: 200
Financial Magazine Publisher
N.A.I.C.S.: 513120

Forbes India   (1)
Web18 New Era Mills Compound N Magnet Mall Moghul Lane Matunga, Mumbai, 400016, India
Tel.: (91) 22 66184400
Magazine Publisher
N.A.I.C.S.: 513130

Forbes Investors Advisory Institute Inc.   (1)
60 5th Ave, New York, NY 10011-8802
Tel.: (212) 620-2200
Web Site:
   http://www.newsletters.forbes.com
Investing Research Services & Information Publisher
N.A.I.C.S.: 513120
Wallace Forbes (Pres)

Forbes Israel   (1)
Brothers Slavuta 15, Tel Aviv, Israel
Tel.: (972) 3 6272030
Web Site: http://www.forbes.co.il
Sales Range: $10-24.9 Million
Emp.: 8
Magazine Publisher
N.A.I.C.S.: 513130

Forbes Magazine   (1)
60 5th Ave, New York, NY 10011-8802
Tel.: (212) 620-2200
Web Site: http://www.forbes.com
Sales Range: $50-74.9 Million
Emp.: 400
Magazine Publishing
N.A.I.C.S.: 513120
Malcolm Stevenson Forbes Jr. (Chm)
Rich Karlgaard (Publr)
Tim W. Ferguson (Exec Editor)
Avik Roy (Editor-Opinion Page)
Nikolai Mazurin (Acting Editor-in-Chief)

Forbes Romania   (1)
Queen Elizabeth Avenue No 44 sc 1 4th floor apartment 45, Bucharest, Romania
Tel.: (40) 372 919 777
Web Site: http://www.forbes.ro
Magazine Publisher
N.A.I.C.S.: 513130

Forbes Russia   (1)
ul Dokukina Ste 16 building 1 floor 6, Moscow, 129226, Russia
Tel.: (7) 495 980 52 52
Web Site: http://www.forbes.ru
Sales Range: $10-24.9 Million
Emp.: 200
Magazine Publisher
N.A.I.C.S.: 513130
Regina von Flemming (Mng Dir)

Forbes Ukraine   (1)
104A Frunze St, 04080, Kiev, Ukraine
Tel.: (380) 442054304
Web Site: http://www.umh.com.ua
Magazine Publisher
N.A.I.C.S.: 513130

Forbes.com LLC   (1)
E 60 5th Ave, New York, NY 10011-5204   (100%)
Tel.: (212) 620-2200
Web Site: http://www.forbes.com
Sales Range: $25-49.9 Million
Emp.: 200
Online Business Information Services

N.A.I.C.S.: 519290
William J. Flatley (VP & Chief Adv Officer)

FORCE AMERICA INC.
501 E Cliff Rd, Burnsville, MN 55337
Tel.: (952) 894-7711   MN
Web Site:
   https://www.forceamerica.com
Sales Range: $50-74.9 Million
Emp.: 250
Hydraulic Systems Equipment & Supplies
N.A.I.C.S.: 423830
John L. Stenz (Chm & CEO)
Ryan Pobuda (VP-Sls)
Robert Pokrzywa (VP-Distr)
Eric Holland (VP-Mfg)
Matthew Loeffler (VP-Products & Engrg)

Subsidiaries:

Atlanta Powertrain & Hydraulics, Inc.   (1)
640 Airport S Pkwy Ste 600, College Park, GA 30349
Tel.: (404) 361-2818
Web Site: http://www.atlantapowertrain.com
Rev.: $1,600,000
Emp.: 15
Motor Vehicle Supplies & New Parts Merchant Whslr
N.A.I.C.S.: 423120
Dennis Hartley (Mgr-Sls)

FORCE BY DESIGN, INC.
50 Fremont St Ste 1650, San Francisco, CA 94105
Tel.: (415) 323-3008
Web Site:
   http://www.forcebydesign.com
Year Founded: 2008
Sales Range: $1-9.9 Million
Emp.: 20
Software Development Services
N.A.I.C.S.: 541511
Dave Stanton (CEO)
Dan Becker (Co-Founder & Chm)

FORCE CONTROL INDUSTRIES, INC.
3660 Dixie Hwy, Fairfield, OH 45014
Tel.: (513) 868-0900
Web Site:
   https://www.forcecontrol.com
Year Founded: 1959
Sales Range: $10-24.9 Million
Emp.: 45
Oil Shear Clutch & Brake Systems for Industrial Applications Mfr
N.A.I.C.S.: 333613
Eric Ferry (CFO)
Bill Ashley (Supvr-Machine Shop)
John Sunderhaus (Coord-Mfg)
Jerry Boyd (Mgr-Pur)

FORCE MARKETING LLC
3098 Piedmont Rd NE 4th Fl, Atlanta, GA 30305
Tel.: (678) 208-0667
Web Site: https://www.forcemktg.com
Year Founded: 2004
Sales Range: $1-9.9 Million
Emp.: 47
Advertising & Marketing
N.A.I.C.S.: 541810
John Fitzpatrick (Pres & CEO)
Cody Tomczyk (VP-Sls)
Jessica Sims (Mgr-Client Success)
Kate Andra (VP-Strategy)
Randy Sieger (CTO)
Maria Trigo (Mgr-Client Success)
Lauren Benton (Dir-Logistics)
Amy Farley (Dir-Mktg & Media)
Eric Mercado (VP-Sls)
Jason Scherr (CFO)
Jonathan Thompson (VP-Sls)
Heather Troline (COO)

Erin Mueller (Dir-Mktg & Media)
Wesley Miller (Dir-Client Success)
Jeff Brown (Chief Revenue Officer)

FORCE MINERALS CORP.
6302 Mesedge Dr, Colorado Springs, CO 80919
Tel.: (970) 660-8197   NV
Year Founded: 2005
Emp.: 1
Natural Gas & Oil Exploration & Mining Services
N.A.I.C.S.: 211120

FORCE REALTY
12507 Bel Red Rd, Bellevue, WA 98005
Tel.: (206) 261-2440
Web Site:
   http://www.theforcerealty.com
Year Founded: 2004
Sales Range: $1-9.9 Million
Emp.: 275
Real Estate Brokerage
N.A.I.C.S.: 531210
Gerhard Swiderski (Principal)
Eddie Quintero (Mgr-The Force Realty)

FORCEFIELD ENERGY INC.
4443 Lyons Rd Ste 212, Coconut Creek, FL 33073
Tel.: (786) 412-6085   NV
Web Site:
   http://www.forcefieldenergy.com
Sales Range: $1-9.9 Million
Alternative Energy Products & Technologies Mfr & Distr
N.A.I.C.S.: 221122
David Natan (Chm & CEO)

Subsidiaries:

17th Street ALD Management Corp.   (1)
6861 Nancy Rdg Dr Ste C, San Diego, CA 92121
Tel.: (858) 549-2324
Electrical Equipment Distr
N.A.I.C.S.: 423440

American Lighting Supply Inc.   (1)
800 Indian Trail Rd Ste C 109, Lilburn, GA 30047
Tel.: (770) 923-5426
Sales Range: $1-9.9 Million
Emp.: 8
Lighting Equipment Whslr
N.A.I.C.S.: 423610
William Milligan (Owner)

FORCEWORKS LLC
401 S Florida Ave Ste 200, Tampa, FL 33602
Tel.: (866) 580-4075
Web Site: http://www.forceworks.com
Sales Range: $1-9.9 Million
Software Developer
N.A.I.C.S.: 513210
Chris Bianco (Founder)

FORCHT GROUP OF KENTUCKY, INC.
200 S Kentucky St, Corbin, KY 40701
Tel.: (606) 528-9600   KY
Web Site:
   https://www.forchtgroup.com
Year Founded: 2011
Emp.: 2,200
Investment Holding Company
N.A.I.C.S.: 551112
Terry E. Forcht (Chm & CEO)
Debbie Reynolds (Pres)
Jackie L. Willis (Sec)
Rodney Shockley (Gen Counsel)

Subsidiaries:

Forcht Bancorp, Inc.   (1)
2404 Sir Barton Way, Lexington, KY 40509

Forcht Group of Kentucky, Inc.—(Continued)

Tel.: (859) 264-0030
Web Site: http://www.forchtgroup.com
Bank Holding Company; Commercial Banking Services
N.A.I.C.S.: 551111
Terry E. Forcht (Chm & CEO)
Tucker Ballinger (Pres)

Subsidiary (Domestic):

Forcht Bank, N.A. (2)
2404 Slr Barton Way, Lexington, KY 40509
Tel.: (859) 264-2265
Web Site: http://www.forchtbank.com
Savings Bank
N.A.I.C.S.: 522180
Tucker Ballinger (Pres)

Forcht Broadcasting, Inc. (1)
625 Monticello St Ste 1, Somerset, KY 42501
Tel.: (606) 485-4444
Web Site:
http://www.forchtbroadcasting.com
Radio Broadcasting Stations Operator
N.A.I.C.S.: 516110
Mike Tarter (Pres & CEO)
Amy Stroud (Sr VP)
Gary Hansford (Dir-IT)
Paula McKinney (Dir-Traffic & Billing)
Larry Jones (Dir-Telesales)

Unit (Domestic):

WSIP-FM (2)
121 Main St, Paintsville, KY 41240
Tel.: (606) 789-5311
Web Site: http://www.wsipfm.com
Radio Broadcasting Stations
N.A.I.C.S.: 516110
Spike Berkhimer (Gen Mgr)

Kentucky National Insurance Group, LLC (1)
2709 Old Rosebud Rd, Lexington, KY 40509
Tel.: (859) 367-5200
Web Site: http://www.kynatins.com
Holding Company; Insurance Products & Services
N.A.I.C.S.: 551112
David McMullen (Pres)

Subsidiary (Domestic):

Kentucky Home Life Insurance Company (2)
2416 Sir Barton Way, Lexington, KY 40509
Tel.: (859) 264-0332
Web Site: http://www.kyhomelife.com
Life Insurance Products & Services
N.A.I.C.S.: 524113
Jeffrey E. Breeze (Pres)

Kentucky National Insurance Company (2)
2416 Sir Barton Way, Lexington, KY 40509
Tel.: (859) 367-5200
Rev.: $20,800,000
Emp.: 12
Fire, Marine & Casualty Insurance
N.A.I.C.S.: 524126
John R. Miner (Pres)
Rodney Shockley (CEO)

Mountain Life Insurance Company (2)
2416 Sir Barton Way, Lexington, KY 40509
Web Site: http://www.mountainlife.com
Life Insurance Products & Services
N.A.I.C.S.: 524113
Rodney Shockley (Pres)

My Favorite Things, LLC (1)
2721 Old Rosebud Rd, Lexington, KY 40509
Tel.: (859) 264-0923
Web Site: http://www.mftky.com
Furniture & Home Furnishings Retailer
N.A.I.C.S.: 449110
Terry E. Forcht (Chm & CEO)

FORD ALBERIC AUTO SALES
PO Box 70320, San Juan, PR 00936
Tel.: (787) 474-2222
Sales Range: $10-24.9 Million
Emp.: 120

Car Whslr
N.A.I.C.S.: 441110
Alberic Colon (Pres)

FORD AUDIO-VIDEO SYSTEMS INC.
4800 W I 40 Service Rd, Oklahoma City, OK 73128
Tel.: (405) 946-9966
Web Site: https://www.fordav.com
Sales Range: $10-24.9 Million
Emp.: 200
Safety & Security Specialization
N.A.I.C.S.: 561621
Jim Ford (Pres)
Rhianna Beckham (Coord-Sls Center)
Dan Berg (Sr Acct Mgr)

FORD AUTO BODY, INC.
7857 Sepulveda Blvd, Van Nuys, CA 91405
Tel.: (818) 988-7200
Web Site:
https://www.fordautobody.com
Sales Range: $10-24.9 Million
Emp.: 49
Car Whslr
N.A.I.C.S.: 441110
Patrick Moore (Mgr-Fin & Sls)

FORD BUSINESS MACHINES, INC.
29 Ladys Ln, Uniontown, PA 15401
Tel.: (724) 437-4050
Web Site: http://www.buyfbm.com
Rev.: $1,100,000
Emp.: 12
Office Equipment Merchant Whslr
N.A.I.C.S.: 423420
Johnathan Garlow (Pres & CEO)
Carol King (Office Mgr)
Michael Kenney (Gen Mgr)
Tracey Richardson (Dir-Ops)

Subsidiaries:

Ford Business Machines (1)
10475 Perry Hwy Ste 102G, Wexford, PA 15090-9213
Tel.: (724) 628-9050
Web Site: http://www.buyfbm.com
Furniture Merchant Whslr
N.A.I.C.S.: 423210
John M. Garlow (CEO)

Stefano's Printing, Inc. (1)
266 Furnace Hill Rd, Dunbar, PA 15431
Tel.: (724) 277-8374
Web Site: http://www.stefanosprinting.com
Rev.: $1,064,000
Emp.: 7
Commercial Lithographic Printing Services
N.A.I.C.S.: 323111

FORD CONSTRUCTION COMPANY
1311 E Court St, Dyersburg, TN 38024
Tel.: (731) 285-5185
Web Site: https://www.bid-best.com
Year Founded: 1955
Sales Range: $25-49.9 Million
Emp.: 450
Highway, Street & Bridge Construction Services
N.A.I.C.S.: 237310
John H. Ford (Pres)
Jean Moore (VP)
Sam Baggett (VP & Mgr-Bridge)
Tim Glidewell (Sec)
Calvin Lambert (Mgr-Asphalt)
Collie Berry (Mgr-Safety & HR)
Mike Harrison (Mgr-Union City)
Blaine Stanley (Mgr-Jackson)

FORD CONSTRUCTION COMPANY INC.
639 E Lockeford St, Lodi, CA 95240
Tel.: (209) 333-1116

Web Site: http://www.ford-construction.com
Rev.: $27,600,000
Emp.: 100
Earth Moving Contractor
N.A.I.C.S.: 236210
Bob Jones (Pres)

FORD DEVELOPMENT CORPORATION
11148 Woodward Ln, Sharonville, OH 45241-1857
Tel.: (513) 772-1521
Web Site:
https://www.forddevelopment.com
Year Founded: 1971
Sales Range: $10-24.9 Million
Emp.: 70
Excavation Work, Commercial & Industrial Concrete Work & Utility Work
N.A.I.C.S.: 236220
Barbara Gorman (Controller)
Robert F. Henderson (Pres)
Andrew Kloene (Exec VP)
Robert J. Henderson Sr. (Chm & CEO)

FORD FINANCIAL FUND II, L.P.
200 Crescent Ct Ste 1350, Dallas, TX 75201
Tel.: (214) 871-5151
Web Site: http://www.fordfundlp.com
Privater Equity Firm
N.A.I.C.S.: 523999
Gerald J. Ford (Co-Mng Partner)
Kenneth D. Russell (Partner)
Jonathan S. Sobel (Partner)
Coleman J. Johnson (Partner)

Subsidiaries:

Mechanics Bank (1)
1350 N Main St, Walnut Creek, CA 94596 (79%)
Tel.: (925) 210-8170
Web Site: https://www.mechanicsbank.com
Rev.: $467,475,055
Assets: $17,207,238,203
Liabilities: $14,909,277,893
Net Worth: $2,297,960,310
Earnings: $57,726,323
Emp.: 2,218
Fiscal Year-end: 12/31/2019
Commericial Banking
N.A.I.C.S.: 522110
Carl B. Webb (Chm)
Raulin J. Butler (Exec VP & Dir-Retail Banking)
Deberah B. Kelley (Exec VP & Dir-Wealth Mgmt)
Nathan Duda (CFO & Exec VP)
Randal W. Stoller (Sr VP & Head-Mortgage Lending)
John W. DeCero (Pres & CEO)
Scott Givans (Chief Credit Officer & Exec VP)
Doug Lutz (Chief Comml Banking Officer & Exec VP)
Glenn Shrader (Gen Counsel & Exec VP)
William Katafias (CEO-CRB Auto)
Kristie Shields (Chief Compliance Counsel & Exec VP)
Christopher D. Pierce (COO & Exec VP)
Saqib A. Kheiri (Chief Risk Officer & Exec VP)
Brett Reid (Chief HR Officer & Exec VP)

FORD FINANCIAL SERVICES, INC.
101 Leucadia Blvd Ste 100, Encinitas, CA 92024-1713
Tel.: (760) 944-9758
Web Site: https://www.ffsiusa.com
Year Founded: 1991
Equipment Leasing Services
N.A.I.C.S.: 532490

FORD GROVES
PO Box 778, Cape Girardeau, MO 63701
Tel.: (573) 335-5572

Web Site: http://fordgroves2.com
Sales Range: $10-24.9 Million
Emp.: 78
New Car Whslr
N.A.I.C.S.: 441110
Bob Neff (Pres)
Heath Lucas (Mgr-Sls)

FORD GUM & MACHINE COMPANY, INC.
18 Newton Ave, Akron, NY 14001
Tel.: (716) 542-4561
Web Site: http://www.fordgum.com
Year Founded: 1913
Sales Range: $10-24.9 Million
Emp.: 100
Candy, Gum & Gumball Dispenser Mfr
N.A.I.C.S.: 311340
George Stege (Pres)
John Kennelly (CFO)
Mike Crandell (Reg Mgr-Sls)

FORD HOLDING COMPANY INC.
12466 US Hwy 400, Ford, KS 67842
Tel.: (620) 369-2252
Year Founded: 1979
Sales Range: $125-149.9 Million
Emp.: 60
Holding Company; Beef Cattle Feedlot Services
N.A.I.C.S.: 551112
Ronnie Herman (CEO & CFO)

Subsidiaries:

Ford County Feed Yard Inc. (1)
12466 US Hwy 400, Ford, KS 67842 (100%)
Tel.: (620) 369-2252
Sales Range: $10-24.9 Million
Emp.: 50
Cattle Feedlot Services
N.A.I.C.S.: 112112
Danny Herrmann (Gen Mgr)

FORD MODELS INC.
11 E 26th St 14th Fl, New York, NY 10010
Tel.: (212) 219-6500
Web Site:
https://www.fordmodels.com
Sales Range: $25-49.9 Million
Emp.: 140
Modeling Agency
N.A.I.C.S.: 711410
Andrea Pagliughi (CFO)
Patty Sicular (VP)

FORD OF MONTEBELLO, INC.
2747 Via Campo, Montebello, CA 90640
Tel.: (323) 838-6920
Web Site:
https://www.fordofmontebello.com
Year Founded: 1999
Sales Range: $25-49.9 Million
Emp.: 50
New Car Dealers
N.A.I.C.S.: 441110
Jim Ross (Pres & Gen Mgr)
Javier Sandoval (Asst Mgr-Sls)

FORD OF OCALA INC.
2816 NW Pine Ave, Ocala, FL 34475
Tel.: (352) 732-4800
Web Site: http://www.fordofocala.com
Sales Range: $10-24.9 Million
Emp.: 117
Sales of New & Used Cars
N.A.I.C.S.: 441110
Steve Hollosi (Gen Mgr)
Melanie Waite (Controller)
Tom Males (Dir-MKtg)
Pat Candelora (Mgr-New Cars Sls)
Rich Stager (Mgr-Pre-Owned Sls)

Hester Hester Hill *(Mgr-Inventory)*
Blane Greer *(Gen Mgr-Sls)*
Lance Abshier *(Mgr-Fin)*
Juliana Angus *(Mgr-Fin)*
Donna Vezina *(Dir-Parts & Svc)*
Hob Rardin *(Dir-Svc)*
Wes Mccubbin *(Mgr-Parts)*
Ted Winter *(Mgr-Reconditioning & Facility)*
Philnetra Kingcade *(Asst Mgr-Reconditioning)*

FORD OF TULSA LLC

2555 Telegraph Rd, Bloomfield Hills, MI 48302
Tel.: (248) 648-2517
Year Founded: 1927
Rev.: $198,900,000
Emp.: 600
New & Used Car Sales
N.A.I.C.S.: 441110
David Martin *(CFO)*

FORD TOWN OF ALBANY INC.

2926 N Slappey Blvd, Albany, GA 31701
Tel.: (229) 883-3100
Web Site:
http://www.fordtownofalbany.com
Sales Range: $25-49.9 Million
Emp.: 60
Car Dealership
N.A.I.C.S.: 441110
Wall Coward *(Owner)*
Pete Pines *(Gen Mgr)*

FORD WHOLESALE CO., INC. OF SAN BERNARDINO

4429 N Baldwin Ave, El Monte, CA 91731-1177
Tel.: (626) 443-8969   CA
Web Site:
http://www.fordwholesaleroo fing.com
Year Founded: 1954
Sales Range: $10-24.9 Million
Roofing, Siding & Insulation Whslr
N.A.I.C.S.: 423330
William Thomas *(Pres)*

FORD'S PRODUCE CO., INC.

1109 Agriculture St Ste 1, Raleigh, NC 27603-2371
Tel.: (919) 833-7559
Web Site:
https://www.fordsproduce.com
Year Founded: 1946
Sales Range: $10-24.9 Million
Emp.: 60
Fruit & Vegetable Whslr & Distr
N.A.I.C.S.: 115114
Vaughn Ford *(VP)*

FORD-GELATT & ASSOCIATES, INC.

18359 Petroleum Dr, Baton Rouge, LA 70809
Tel.: (225) 753-3887
Web Site: https://www.ford-gelatt.com
Year Founded: 1984
Sales Range: $10-24.9 Million
Emp.: 20
Industrial Machinery & Equipment Whslr
N.A.I.C.S.: 423830
Michael Ford *(Pres)*

FORDE JOHNSON OIL COMPANY

2695 S Blvd, Idaho Falls, ID 83404
Tel.: (208) 522-4190
Sales Range: Less than $1 Million
Emp.: 9
Convenience Store
N.A.I.C.S.: 445131
Kenlon P. Johnson *(Pres)*

FORDHAM & DOMINION BREWING CO.

1284 McD Dr, Dover, DE 19901
Tel.: (302) 678-4810
Web Site:
http://www.fordhamdominion.com
Year Founded: 2007
Craft Beer Brewery
N.A.I.C.S.: 312120
Bill Muehlhauser *(Co-Owner)*

FORDHAM AUTO SALES INC.

236 W Fordham Rd, Bronx, NY 10468
Tel.: (718) 367-0400
Web Site:
https://www.fordhamtoyota.com
Rev.: $27,000,000
Emp.: 40
Automobiles, New & Used
N.A.I.C.S.: 441110
Carmelo Giufre *(Pres)*

FORDS INC.

1701 Scottsville Rd, Bowling Green, KY 42104
Tel.: (270) 842-0188
Web Site:
https://www.fordsfurniture.com
Sales Range: $10-24.9 Million
Emp.: 48
Owner & Operator of Furniture Stores
N.A.I.C.S.: 449110
Andy Ford *(Pres)*

FORE GOLF SERVICES, LP

10688 Crestwood Dr, Manassas, VA 20109-3464
Tel.: (703) 367-7237
Web Site:
http://www.foregolfservices.com
Sales Range: $10-24.9 Million
Emp.: 168
Golf Course Management; Sporting Goods Retail
N.A.I.C.S.: 713910
Charlie Staples *(Partner)*
Michael Moralia *(VP)*

Subsidiaries:

Bayou Golf Club   (1)
7979 Bayou Club Blvd, Largo, FL 33777-3040
Tel.: (727) 399-1000
Web Site: http://www.bayouclubgolf.com
Emp.: 30
Golf Club Operations
N.A.I.C.S.: 713910
Jim King *(Head-Teaching Pro)*

Lpga International Girls Golf Club, Inc.   (1)
1000 Champions Dr, Daytona Beach, FL 32124
Tel.: (386) 274-5742
Web Site: http://www.lpgainternational.com
Sales Range: $1-9.9 Million
Emp.: 65
Golf Courses & Country Clubs
N.A.I.C.S.: 713910

FORE SUPPLY CO.

1205 Capitol Dr, Addison, IL 60101
Tel.: (630) 543-4422
Web Site: http://www.foresupply.com
Year Founded: 1945
Emp.: 25
Sporting Goods Retailer
N.A.I.C.S.: 459110
George Thein *(Pres)*

Subsidiaries:

Country Club Supply, Inc.   (1)
722 W Algonquin Rd, Arlington Heights, IL 60005
Tel.: (847) 734-6555
Web Site: http://www.countryclubsupply.com
Sporting Goods Retailer
N.A.I.C.S.: 459110

FORE!KIDS FOUNDATION

11005 Lapalco Blvd, Avondale, LA 70094
Tel.: (504) 342-3000   LA
Web Site:
http://www.forekidsfoundation.com
Year Founded: 1958
Sales Range: $10-24.9 Million
Emp.: 7
Fundraising Services
N.A.I.C.S.: 813211
Steve Worthy *(CEO)*

FORE-PAR GROUP INC.

7650 Stage Rd, Buena Park, CA 90621
Tel.: (714) 736-9190
Web Site: http://www.fore-par.com
Rev.: $15,000,000
Emp.: 72
Sporting & Recreational Goods & Supplies Merchant Whslr
N.A.I.C.S.: 423910
Andy Kielawa *(Mgr-Ops)*
Howard Moore *(Gen Mgr)*
Sheri Laudenslayer *(Mgr-Mktg)*
Kenton Nicholson *(Dir-Tech)*
Rita Chadwick *(Controller)*
Scott Mallory *(Pres)*
Urson Russell *(Mgr-Bus Dev)*
Craig Price *(CEO)*

FORECAST INTERNATIONAL INC.

22 Commerce Rd, Newtown, CT 06470
Tel.: (203) 426-0800   CT
Web Site: http://www.forecast1.com
Year Founded: 1973
Sales Range: $10-24.9 Million
Emp.: 50
Books Mfr
N.A.I.C.S.: 513120
Ed Nebinger *(Founder & CEO)*
Ray Peterson *(VP-Res & Editorial Svcs & Mng Dir)*
John Edwards *(Dir-Mktg)*
Stuart Slade *(Dir-Consulting Ops)*

FORECASTER OF BOSTON INC.

74 Fall River Ave, Rehoboth, MA 02769-1010
Tel.: (774) 901-5490
Web Site:
http://www.forecasterofboston.com
Rev.: $10,800,000
Emp.: 215
Raincoat Mfr
N.A.I.C.S.: 315250
Greg Davis *(Pres)*
Gail Lisi *(Gen Mgr)*

FORECLOSURE VENTURE CAPITAL, INC.

2104 Grier Ave, Linden, NJ 07036
Tel.: (908) 447-2522   NJ
Year Founded: 2010
Real Estate Investment Services
N.A.I.C.S.: 531390
Esther Jimenez *(CEO)*
Natavarbhai Patel *(Pres)*

FOREGROUND SECURITY

801 International Pkwy 5th Fl, Orlando, FL 32746
Tel.: (407) 562-1925
Web Site:
http://www.foregroundsecurity.com
Year Founded: 1999
Rev.: $2,100,000
Emp.: 12
IT Services
N.A.I.C.S.: 449210
David Amsler *(Pres & CIO)*
Alison Kidd *(Exec VP-Sls & Mktg)*

Jeffrey Mauro *(Dir-Ops)*
Christopher Randle *(Mng Principal)*
Adam Cresswell *(Dir-Fin & HR)*
George Baker *(Dir-Pro Svcs)*
Mark Orlando *(Dir-Cyber Ops)*
Ryan Shaw *(Dir-Res & Dev)*

FOREIGN TIRE SALES INC.

2204 Morris Ave, Union, NJ 07083
Tel.: (908) 687-0559
Web Site: http://www.foreigntire.com
Year Founded: 1972
Sales Range: $10-24.9 Million
Emp.: 12
Whslr & Importer of Tires
N.A.I.C.S.: 423130
Richard Kuskin *(Pres)*
Ron Smith *(VP)*
Maureen Gardner *(Mgr)*

FOREIGN TRADERS, INC.

2873 Cox Rd, Santa Fe, NM 87507
Tel.: (505) 983-6441
Web Site:
http://www.foreigntraders.com
Year Founded: 1927
Sales Range: $10-24.9 Million
Emp.: 3
Household Wares, Furnishings, Rugs, Gifts & Artwares Retailer
N.A.I.C.S.: 337212
Alex Tschursin *(Owner)*

FOREMANS INC.

301 N Hughes Blvd, Elizabeth City, NC 27909
Tel.: (252) 335-5454
Sales Range: $10-24.9 Million
Emp.: 10
Retailer of Lumber & Other Building Materials
N.A.I.C.S.: 423310
Paul Foreman *(VP)*
Clay B. Foreman Jr. *(Pres)*

FOREMOST FARMS USA COOPERATIVE

E 10889 A Penny Ln, Baraboo, WI 53913-8115
Tel.: (608) 355-8700   WI
Web Site:
http://www.foremostfarms.com
Year Founded: 1995
Dairy Cooperative Mfr
N.A.I.C.S.: 112120
Jim Hamm *(VP-Strategy & Bus Dev)*
Rick Burkhamer *(Sec)*
James Dague *(Asst Sec & Treas)*
Ralph Briggs *(COO)*
John Robison *(VP-Gen Counsel)*
Virginia Hendricks *(Chief HR Officer)*
Declan Roche *(VP-Dairy Ingredients)*
Greg Schlafer *(Pres & CEO)*

FOREMOST GROUPS, INC.

906 Murray Rd, East Hanover, NJ 07936
Tel.: (973) 428-0400
Web Site:
https://www.foremostgroups.com
Year Founded: 1988
Sales Range: $150-199.9 Million
Emp.: 150
Bathroom Furnishings & Fixtures, Commercial Food-Service Equipment & Indoor/Outdoor Furniture
N.A.I.C.S.: 337121
Scott Kensey *(Sr VP)*

Subsidiaries:

Foremost Groups, Inc.   (1)
906 Murray Rd, East Hanover, NJ 07936
Tel.: (973) 428-0400
Web Site: http://www.foremostgroups.com
Foodservice Products Mfr/Distr
N.A.I.C.S.: 311999

Foremost Groups, Inc.—(Continued)

Bruce Henderson (VP-Sls & Mktg)
Scott Kensey (Sr VP)

Foremost International Ltd. (1)
5970 Chedworth Way Unit A, Mississauga,
L5R 3V5, ON, Canada (100%)
Tel.: (905) 507-2005
Web Site: http://www.foremostcanada.com
Emp.: 35
Bathroom Furnishings & Furniture &
Indoor/Outdoor Furniture Distr
N.A.I.C.S.: 337121
Jay K.J. Yeh (Pres)

FOREMOST INDUSTRIES INC.
2375 Buchanan Trl W, Greencastle,
PA 17225
Tel.: (717) 597-7166
Web Site:
http://www.foremosthomes.com
Sales Range: $10-24.9 Million
Emp.: 200
Modular Houses Mfr
N.A.I.C.S.: 321992
Ralph S. Michael (Pres)
Jack Harbaugh (Mgr-Pur)

FOREMOSTCO INC.
8457 NW 66th St, Miami, FL 33166
Tel.: (305) 592-8986
Web Site:
https://www.foremostco.com
Year Founded: 1987
Sales Range: $10-24.9 Million
Emp.: 95
Marketer of Plant Cuttings
N.A.I.C.S.: 424930
Joseph C. Roberts (CEO)
Randy L. Goff (Gen Mgr)
Ana Cortes (Mgr-Ops)
Andrew Zohn (Controller)

FORENSIC FLUIDS LABORA-TORIES, INC.
225 Parsons St, Kalamazoo, MI
49007
Tel.: (269) 492-7700
Web Site:
https://www.forensicfluids.com
Year Founded: 2005
Sales Range: $10-24.9 Million
Emp.: 90
Drug Tests & Testing Facilities
N.A.I.C.S.: 621511
Bridget Lorenz Lemberg (Founder)

FORENSICS CONSULTING SO-LUTIONS, LLC
2600 N Central Ave Ste 700, Phoe-nix, AZ 85004
Tel.: (602) 992-3600   AZ
Web Site:
http://www.forensicsconsulting.com
Year Founded: 2001
Sales Range: $10-24.9 Million
Emp.: 35
Forensics Consulting Firm
N.A.I.C.S.: 541512
Kelly J. Kuchta (Founder & CEO)
Nancy Kuchta (Mng Dir)
Paul B. Rajski (CIO)
Linda Joy Hood (VP-Client Dev & Mktg)
Ray Moralez (VP-Bus Optimization)
D. Shawn Edwards (VP-Pro Svcs)

FORENTA L.P.
185 Cold Creek Dr, Morristown, TN
37814
Tel.: (423) 586-5370
Web Site:
https://www.forentausa.com
Year Founded: 1961
Pressing & Finishing Equipment for
the Dry Cleaning & Shirt Laundering
Industries Mfr

N.A.I.C.S.: 333310

FORESIGHT SOFTWARE, LLC
1906 Quail Run, Lawrenceville, GA
30044
Tel.: (770) 206-1000
Web Site: https://www.foresight-esp.com
Year Founded: 1995
Software Mfr
N.A.I.C.S.: 513210
Mark Tyndall (Pres, CEO & Owner)

FORESITE CAPITAL MANAGE-MENT, LLC
900 Larkspur Landing Cir Ste 150,
Larkspur, CA 94939
Tel.: (415) 877-4887
Web Site:
https://www.foresitecapital.com
Venture Capital & Growth Equity Firm
N.A.I.C.S.: 523999

Subsidiaries:

Pardes Biosciences, Inc. (1)
2173 Salk Ave Ste 250 PMB 052, Carlsbad,
CA 92008
Tel.: (415) 649-8758
Web Site: https://www.pardesbio.com
Assets: $275,259,000
Liabilities: $8,965,000
Net Worth: $266,294,000
Earnings: ($38,518,000)
Emp.: 30
Fiscal Year-end: 12/31/2021
Biotechnology Research & Development
Services
N.A.I.C.S.: 541714
Brian P. Kearney (Chief Dev Officer)
Heidi Henson (CFO)
Tom G. Wiggans (Chm)
Lee D. Arnold (Chief Scientific Officer)

FORESITE GROUP, INC.
5185 Peachtree Pkwy Ste 240, Nor-cross, GA 30092
Tel.: (770) 368-1399
Web Site:
http://www.foresitegroupinc.com
Year Founded: 2003
Sales Range: $1-9.9 Million
Emp.: 40
Engineeering Services
N.A.I.C.S.: 541330
William Brant Aden (Founder, Partner
& VP)
Erik S. Johnston (Founder, Pres,
COO & Principal)
Brett C. Basquin (Co-Founder &
Chief Engr)

FORESITE LIFE SCIENCES CORP.
600 Montgomery St Ste 4500, San
Francisco, CA 94111
Tel.: (415) 877-4887   DE
Year Founded: 2021
Investment Services
N.A.I.C.S.: 523999
Jim Tananbaum (Pres & CEO)
Dennis Ryan (CFO)
Michael Rome (VP)

FORESITE TECHNOLOGIES, INC
99 E River Dr 7th Fl, East Hartford,
CT 06108
Tel.: (860) 528-1100
Web Site:
http://www.foresitetech.com
Sales Range: $1-9.9 Million
Emp.: 20
Webiste Development & Network
Services
N.A.I.C.S.: 541511
Michael Giuffrida (CEO)
Bonnie Leroux (Dir-Mktg)
Mary Blair (Dir-Production)

Michael Dumlao (Dir-Art)
Tracy Fox (Dir-Sls)
Scott Serencha (Mgr-Team Dev)
Peter Wilson (Project Mgr)
Jen Lemke (Acct Mgr)
Janaura Bishop (Mgr-Bus Dev)
Marc Brungardt (Pres)
Jana Pinkerton (VP-Sls)

FOREST AUSTELL PROD-UCTS INC.
1916 Hwy 159 N, Gordo, AL 35466
Tel.: (205) 364-8256
Web Site:
https://www.austellforest.com
Sales Range: $10-24.9 Million
Emp.: 25
Sawmill Services
N.A.I.C.S.: 321113
Robert Montgomery (Plant Mgr)

FOREST CITY TECHNOLO-GIES INC.
299 Clay St, Wellington, OH 44090
Tel.: (440) 647-2115
Web Site:
http://www.forestcitytech.com
Sales Range: $25-49.9 Million
Emp.: 580
Gaskets & Sealing Devices
N.A.I.C.S.: 339991
Andy Landis (Engr-IT Sys)
Jack Nunney (Mgr-Pur)
Mike Deeks (Mgr-Quality)
Rick Frame (Mgr-Ops)
Scott Shays (Plant Mgr)
Neica Davies (Asst Controller)
Keith Merry (Engr-Quality)

FOREST CITY TRADING GROUP, LLC
10250 SW Greenburg Rd Ste 300,
Portland, OR 97223-5461
Tel.: (503) 246-8500   OR
Web Site: https://www.fctg.com
Year Founded: 1964
Sales Range: $1-4.9 Billion
Emp.: 500
Forest Product Distribution & Market-ing Services
N.A.I.C.S.: 423310
Derrick Coder (VP-Fin)
Craig Johnson (CEO)
Dirk Koetter (VP-Fin)

Subsidiaries:

Affiliated Resources, Inc. (1)
4380 SW Macadam Ave Ste 200, Portland,
OR 97239
Tel.: (503) 228-3802
Web Site: http://www.affiliatedresources.net
Sales Range: $1-9.9 Million
Emp.: 15
Wood Products Mfr
N.A.I.C.S.: 321999
Mike Wilkins (Pres)
Debbie Dietz (VP-Fin & Admin)
Kelly Rykken (Dir-Acctg)

**Birmingham International Forest
Products, LLC** (1)
300 Riverhills Business Park Ste 320, Bir-mingham, AL 35242
Tel.: (205) 972-1500
Web Site: http://www.bifp.com
Sales Range: $10-24.9 Million
Emp.: 30
Lumber Whslr
N.A.I.C.S.: 423310
Wylene Perot (Office Mgr)
Shane Naish (Pres)

Buckeye Pacific, LLC (1)
4386 SW Macadam Ave Ste 200, Portland,
OR 97239-0001
Tel.: (503) 228-3330
Web Site: http://www.buckeyepacific.com
Lumber Whslr
N.A.I.C.S.: 423310
Jeff Dill (Pres)

Olympic Industries, Inc. (1)
Suite 402 221 West Esplanade North, North
Vancouver, V7M 3J3, BC, Canada
Tel.: (604) 985-2115
Web Site: https://www.olympicind.com
Emp.: 35
Lumber Mfr & Distr
N.A.I.C.S.: 423310
Carla Hubbert (Controller)
Gerry Pankratz (Pres)

Plateau Forest Products, LLC (1)
320 SW Upper Terrace Dr Ste 104, Bend,
OR 97701
Tel.: (541) 385-7675
Web Site: http://www.plateaufp.com
Sales Range: $10-24.9 Million
Emp.: 15
Lumber Brokerage Services
N.A.I.C.S.: 423310
Cindy Merwin (Mgr-Ops)
Terry Atkins (Gen Mgr)
John Strickland (Mgr-Logistics)

Richmond International Forest Prod-ucts, LLC (1)
4050 Innslake Dr Ste 100, Glen Allen, VA
23060-3327
Tel.: (804) 747-0111
Web Site: http://www.rifp.com
Sales Range: $10-24.9 Million
Emp.: 40
Lumber Brokerage Services
N.A.I.C.S.: 423310
Casey Mickelson (Pres)
Laurence Balagot (Mgr-Traffic)
Cory Scott (Controller)

Seaboard International Forest Prod-ucts LLC (1)
22F Cotton Rd, Nashua, NH 03063
Tel.: (603) 881-3700
Web Site: http://www.sifp.com
Sales Range: $550-599.9 Million
Emp.: 35
Lumber Distr
N.A.I.C.S.: 423310
Jim Dermody (Pres)

**Tampa International Forest Products,
LLC** (1)
4630 Woodland Corporate Blvd Ste 155,
Tampa, FL 33614
Tel.: (813) 880-7300
Web Site: http://www.tifp.com
Sales Range: $10-24.9 Million
Emp.: 43
Lumber Distr
N.A.I.C.S.: 423310

Viking Forest Products, LLC (1)
7615 Smetana Ln Ste 140, Eden Prairie,
MN 55344-4700
Tel.: (952) 941-6512
Web Site: http://www.vikingforest.com
Sales Range: $10-24.9 Million
Emp.: 50
Lumber Brokerage Services
N.A.I.C.S.: 423310
Bruce Johnson (Pres)
Ty Whitney (Controller)

Western International Forest Prod-ucts, LLC (1)
14795 SW Murray Scholls Dr Ste 210, Bea-verton, OR 97007
Tel.: (503) 521-5500
Sales Range: $10-24.9 Million
Emp.: 30
Timber Products Distr
N.A.I.C.S.: 423310
Mark Donovan (Pres)

FOREST CONSTRUCTION COMPANY
3302 E Thousand Oaks Blvd, West-lake Village, CA 91362
Tel.: (805) 386-8000
Web Site:
https://www.forestconstruction.com
Sales Range: $10-24.9 Million
Emp.: 15
New Construction, Single-Family
Houses
N.A.I.C.S.: 236115
James A. Rice (Pres & Principal)

FOREST CORP.

1665 Enterprise Pkwy, Twinsburg, OH 44087
Tel.: (330) 425-3805
Web Site:
  http://www.forestcorporation.com
Rev.: $13,700,000
Emp.: 90
Screen Printing
N.A.I.C.S.: 323113
Forest Bookman *(Pres & CEO)*
John Hammond *(VP)*

FOREST FORD, INC.

1126 Hwy 35 N, Forest, MS 39074
Tel.: (601) 748-7098
Web Site:
  https://www.forestfordinc.com
Sales Range: $10-24.9 Million
Emp.: 30
New Car Distr & Repair Services
N.A.I.C.S.: 441110
Richard Smith *(Owner)*

FOREST INVESTMENTS, INC.

800 S St Ste 230, Waltham, MA 02453
Tel.: (617) 735-3006   DE
Web Site:
  http://www.greatelmcap.com
Year Founded: 1994
GEC—(NASDAQ)
Rev.: $64,098,000
Assets: $195,445,000
Liabilities: $130,765,000
Net Worth: $64,680,000
Earnings: ($12,975,000)
Emp.: 349
Fiscal Year-end: 06/30/20
Holding Company; Investment Activities
N.A.I.C.S.: 523999
Peter A. Reed *(CEO)*
Jeffrey S. Serota *(Co-Chm)*
Adam M. Kleinman *(Pres)*
Brent J. Pearson *(CFO)*
Jason W. Reese *(Co-Chm)*

Subsidiaries:

Great Elm Capital Corp.   (1)
800 S St Ste 230, Waltham, MA 02453
Tel.: (617) 375-3006
Web Site: https://www.greatelmcc.com
Rev.: $24,429,000
Assets: $310,112,000
Liabilities: $225,303,000
Net Worth: $84,809,000
Earnings: $10,461,000
Fiscal Year-end: 12/31/2022
Financial Investment Management Services
N.A.I.C.S.: 523940
Adam M. Kleinman *(Chief Compliance Officer)*
Matt Kaplan *(Pres & CEO)*
Keri A. Davis *(CFO & Treas)*

Subsidiary (Domestic):

Prestige Capital Corp.   (2)
400 Kelby St 10th Fl, Fort Lee, NJ 07024
Tel.: (201) 944-4455
Web Site: http://www.prestigecapital.com
Nondepository Credit Intermediation
N.A.I.C.S.: 522299
Stuart Rosenthal *(Pres)*
Alan Eliasof *(CEO)*
Christopher Foss *(Mgr-Direct Sls)*

Openwave Systems Brasil Ltda   (1)
Ave Brigadeiro Faria Lima 3729 5 Andar, Sao Paulo, 04538 905, SP, Brazil   **(100%)**
Tel.: (55) 1134436333
Sales Range: $100-124.9 Million
Mfr of Infrastructure Software & Applications
N.A.I.C.S.: 334610

Openwave Systems Japan KK   (1)
Shinjuku Square Tower 17 Floor 6-22-1 Nishishinjuku Shinjuku, Tokyo, 163-1030, Japan   **(100%)**
Tel.: (81) 359096100
Web Site: http://www.openwave.com

Sales Range: $100-124.9 Million
Mfr of Infrastructure Software & Applications
N.A.I.C.S.: 334610

FOREST LAKE CHRYSLER DODGE JEEP & RAM

321 19th St SW, Forest Lake, MN 55025
Tel.: (651) 236-6377
Web Site:
  https://www.forestlakechrysler.com
Year Founded: 2010
Car Whslr
N.A.I.C.S.: 441110
Tamir Khalil *(Gen Mgr)*

FOREST PARK FOREVER

5595 Grand Dr, Saint Louis, MO 63112
Tel.: (314) 367-7275   MO
Web Site:
  https://www.forestparkforever.org
Year Founded: 1986
Sales Range: $10-24.9 Million
Emp.: 55
Forest Park Conservation Services
N.A.I.C.S.: 712190
John O'Gorman *(Sr VP-Dev)*
Tamara Sheffield *(Sr VP-Finance-Operations)*
Lesley S. Hoffarth *(Pres)*
Faith Maddy *(VP-Development-Campaigns)*
Lawrence E. Thomas *(Chm)*
Benjamin Akande *(Sec)*

FOREST PLYWOOD SALES INC.

14711 Artesia Blvd, La Mirada, CA 90638
Tel.: (714) 523-1721
Web Site:
  https://www.forestplywood.com
Rev.: $18,100,000
Emp.: 60
Distr of Plywood
N.A.I.C.S.: 423310
Joseph Bolton *(Pres)*
Russell Hullinger *(VP)*
Rick Feliciano *(Gen Mgr)*

FOREST PRODUCTS DISTRIBUTORS, INC.

4200 Beach Dr Ste 2, Rapid City, SD 57702
Tel.: (605) 341-6500
Web Site: https://www.forpd.com
Sales Range: $25-49.9 Million
Emp.: 25
Lumber; Rough, Dressed & Finished
N.A.I.C.S.: 423310
Carroll Korb *(Pres)*
Jim Sorenson *(Sec)*
Tim Dannely *(VP)*

FOREST REALTY MANAGEMENT INC.

67A Forest Dr, Springfield, NJ 07081
Tel.: (973) 379-4500
Web Site:
  http://www.forestrealtyinc.com
Year Founded: 1991
Sales Range: $10-24.9 Million
Emp.: 15
Apartment Building Operator
N.A.I.C.S.: 531110
Ferdinand G. Weisbrod *(Founder & Pres)*

FOREST ROAD SECURITIES, LLC

2120 Colorado Ave Ste 150, Santa Monica, CA 90404
Tel.: (917) 740-2841
Web Site: https://www.frs.xyz
Investment Management Service

N.A.I.C.S.: 523999

FOREST SALES CORPORATION

2913 Mixon CT, Augusta, GA 30904
Tel.: (706) 738-7786
Web Site:
  http://www.forestsalescorp.com
Year Founded: 1968
Sales Range: $10-24.9 Million
Emp.: 8
Lumber & Lumber Products Whslr
N.A.I.C.S.: 423310
Don A. Grantham *(Pres)*

FORESTON TRENDS, INC.

1483 W Via Plata St, Long Beach, CA 90810
Tel.: (310) 952-8500   CA
Web Site:
  http://www.forestontrends.com
Rev.: $19,000,000
Emp.: 95
Table & Bath Linens Sales
N.A.I.C.S.: 423220
David Alden *(Pres)*
Siony Potenciano *(Supvr-AR)*

FORESTRY RESOURCES, INC.

4353 Michigan Link, Fort Myers, FL 33916
Tel.: (239) 334-7343   FL
Web Site:
  https://www.themulchsoilco.com
Year Founded: 1983
Sales Range: $10-24.9 Million
Emp.: 100
Miscellaneous Wood Product Mfr
N.A.I.C.S.: 321999
John Cauthen *(Pres)*

FORETRAVEL INC.

1221 NW Stallings Dr, Nacogdoches, TX 75964
Tel.: (936) 564-8367
Web Site: https://www.foretravel.com
Year Founded: 1976
Rev.: $90,000,000
Emp.: 150
Motor Home Mfr
N.A.I.C.S.: 336213
David King *(Dir-HR)*
Mark Harvey *(Mgr-Svc)*
Drew Pierce *(Mgr-Sls)*

FOREVER CHANGED INTERNATIONAL

19215 SE 34th St Ste 106-387, Camas, WA 98607
Tel.: (360) 836-7626   WA
Web Site:
  https://www.foreverchangedinternational.org
Year Founded: 1990
Sales Range: $1-9.9 Million
Emp.: 2
Child Welfare Services
N.A.I.C.S.: 624110
Heather Radu *(Founder)*

FOREVER LIVING PRODUCTS INTERNATIONAL, INC.

7501 E McCormick Pkwy Ste 135, Scottsdale, AZ 85258-3495
Tel.: (480) 998-8888   NV
Web Site:
  http://www.foreverliving.com
Year Founded: 1978
Sales Range: $500-549.9 Million
Emp.: 1,000
Direct Sales of Diet, Nutritional & Skincare Products
N.A.I.C.S.: 456120
Navaz Ghaswala *(Exec VP)*
Dave Hall *(VP)*

Subsidiaries:

ForeverLiving.Com LLC   (1)
7501 E McCormick Pkwy Ste 135, Scottsdale, AZ 85258-3495
Tel.: (480) 998-8888
Web Site: http://www.foreverliving.com
Sales Range: $25-49.9 Million
Emp.: 150
Internet Marketing Of Diet, Nutritional & Skin Care Products
N.A.I.C.S.: 424210
Rex Maughan *(Chm & CEO)*
Adaine O'Hare *(VP-Mktg)*
R. J. Lloyd *(CFO)*

FOREVER MEDIA, INC.

1 Forever Dr, Hollidaysburg, PA 16648
Tel.: (814) 941-9800
Web Site:
  https://www.forevermediainc.com
Radio Stations Owner & Operator
N.A.I.C.S.: 516110

Subsidiaries:

Forever Media, Inc. - Franklin   (1)
484 Allegheny Blvd Ste A, Franklin, PA 16323
Tel.: (814) 432-2188
Web Site: http://www.foreverradio.com
Sales Range: $1-9.9 Million
Emp.: 20
Radio Broadcasting Stations Operator
N.A.I.C.S.: 516110
Jim Shields *(Gen Mgr & Sls Mgr)*

FOREVER RESORTS, LLC

7501 E McCormick Pkwy, Scottsdale, AZ 85258-3495
Tel.: (480) 998-9977   AZ
Web Site:
  https://www.foreverresorts.com
Year Founded: 1981
Sales Range: $10-24.9 Million
Emp.: 250
Houseboat Marinas, Resorts & Hotels
N.A.I.C.S.: 712190
Rex G. Maughan *(CEO)*
Dave Hall *(VP-Fin)*
Karie Stupek *(Dir-Trng)*

FORGE CAPITAL PARTNERS LLC

102 W Whiting St Ste 600, Tampa, FL 33602
Tel.: (813) 574-6770
Web Site:
  http://www.forgecapitalpartners.com
Rev.: $400,000,000
Real Estate Investment, Management, Development & Brokerage Services
N.A.I.C.S.: 523999
Robert Moreyra *(Founder & Mng Principal)*
Peter H. Collins *(Founder & Mng Principal)*
Deborah Moreyra *(Dir-Asset Mgmt)*
Caetie Berger *(Dir-Acq)*
Catherine Hill *(Controller-Fund)*
David Padilla *(Mgr-Leasing)*
Anthony Littlejohn *(Controller)*
Ashley Sayers *(Mgr-Asset)*

FORGE COMPANY INC.

1050 Thomas Jefferson St NW Ste 100, Washington, DC 20007-3837
Tel.: (202) 295-8100   DQ
Year Founded: 1977
Sales Range: $75-99.9 Million
Emp.: 800
Holding Company
N.A.I.C.S.: 551112
Russell C. Lindner *(Chm & CEO)*
Ezra Becker *(Mgr-Ops)*

Forge Company Inc.—(Continued)

Subsidiaries:

Colonial Parking, Inc. (1)
1050 Thomas Jefferson St NW Ste 100,
Washington, DC 20007
Tel.: (202) 295-8100
Web Site: http://www.ecolonial.com
Sales Range: $10-24.9 Million
Emp.: 100
Automobile Parking Services
N.A.I.C.S.: 812930
Russell C. Lindner (Chm)
Andrew C. Blair (Pres & CEO)
Bereket Woldu (Exec VP)
Abu Woldeamanuel (VP & Dir-Facility Care)
William Cook (COO & Exec VP)
Lori Gagnon (VP & Dir-Customer Care)
Ronald E. Peck (CFO & Exec VP)
Rich Rosenberger (VP & Gen Mgr)
Byron Wills (VP & Gen Mgr)
Mark E. Terrenzi (Sr VP-Ops)

FORGE INDUSTRIES, INC.
4450 Market St, Youngstown, OH
44512-1512
Tel.: (330) 782-8301
Year Founded: 1942
Sales Range: $450-499.9 Million
Emp.: 8
Provider of Industrial Supplies
N.A.I.C.S.: 423840
Carl James (Mng Dir)

Subsidiaries:

Akron Gear & Engineering Inc. (1)
501 Morgan Ave, Akron, OH 44311-2431
Tel.: (330) 773-6608
Web Site: http://www.akrongear.com
Sales Range: $10-24.9 Million
Mfr Of Industrial Gears
N.A.I.C.S.: 332710
Joe Stohovitch (Mgr-Engrg & Ops)
Mike Stohovitch (Pres)

BDI Canada, Inc. (1)
6235 Tomken Rd, Mississauga, L5T 1K2,
ON, Canada (100%)
Tel.: (905) 238-3392
Web Site: http://www.bdi-canada.com
Sales Range: $10-24.9 Million
Emp.: 1,500
Mfr of Industrial Products
N.A.I.C.S.: 334513

**FORGE MARKETING COMMU-
NICATIONS**
4283 Chestnut St 1st Fl, Emmaus,
PA 18049
Tel.: (610) 928-3333 DE
Web Site: http://www.forgemc.com
Year Founded: 1954
Sales Range: $10-24.9 Million
Emp.: 10
Advertising Agencies
N.A.I.C.S.: 541810
Dan Ross (Owner)
Bill Childs (Dir-Creative)

**FORGE SPONSORSHIP CON-
SULTING, LLC**
25 Terrace Ave Ste 104, San
Anselmo, CA 94960
Tel.: (415) 456-8588
Web Site:
http://www.forgesponsorship.com
Year Founded: 2004
Sales Range: $1-9.9 Million
Emp.: 3
Sports Sponsorship & Event Market-
ing
N.A.I.C.S.: 541820
Marla Murphy (Partner)

FORGE STAFFING INC.
5011 28th St, Grand Rapids, MI
49512
Tel.: (616) 285-6860
Web Site: http://www.forgestaff.com

Year Founded: 1995
Rev.: $50,000,000
Emp.: 10
Temp Staffing Agency
N.A.I.C.S.: 561320
Richard Detamble (Owner)

FORGE WORLDWIDE
142 Berkeley St, Boston, MA 02116-
5143
Tel.: (617) 262-4800
Web Site:
https://www.forgeworldwide.com
Year Founded: 2005
Sales Range: $10-24.9 Million
Emp.: 15
Advertising Agencies
N.A.I.C.S.: 541810
Harry G. Chapin (CEO & Partner)
Rob Stewart (Chief Creative Officer &
Partner)
Jim Bell (Assoc Dir-Creative)
Andrew Clayton (Dir-Mktg)
Melissa Koehler (Dir-Mktg)
Laura Mortenson (Acct Mgr)
Andrew Riley (Assoc Dir-Creative)
Mike Gustafson (Sr Dir-Art)
Tara Kearney (Assoc Dir-Art)

FORGELIGHT, LLC
5 Bryant Park, New York, NY 10018
Tel.: (516) 507-7162
Web Site: http://forgelight.com
Year Founded: 2019
Investment Services
N.A.I.C.S.: 523999
Wade Davis (Founder & CEO)
Michael Weissman (Partner)

Subsidiaries:

Univision Holdings, Inc. (1)
605 3rd Ave 33rd Fl, New York, NY 10158
Tel.: (212) 455-5200
Web Site: http://www.univision.com
Sales Range: $1-4.9 Billion
Holding Company; Television & Radio
Broadcasting
N.A.I.C.S.: 551112
Henry G. Cisneros (Chm)
Sameer Dean (Chief Digital Officer)
Wade Davis (CEO)
Rafael Urbina (Exec VP & Gen Mgr-AVOD
Streaming)

Holding (Domestic):

Univision Communications Inc. (2)
8551 NW 30th Ter, Miami, FL 33122
Tel.: (212) 455-5200
Web Site: http://corporate.univision.com
Sales Range: $1-4.9 Billion
Spanish-Language Media Holding Company
N.A.I.C.S.: 551112
Jose Valle (Pres-Political & Advocacy Sls)
Jorge Daboub (Exec VP-Local Media Sls)
Peter H. Lori (CFO)
Carlos Deschapelles (Exec VP)
Trisha Pray (Exec VP-Sls & Client Dev)
Roberto Ruiz (Exec VP-Strategy & Insights)
Jason E. Newman (VP-Sports Sls)
Rachel Gross (Sr VP-Event Mktg)
Rosemary Mercedes Beepat (VP-Corp &
Digital Comm)
Alberto Ciurana (Pres-Programming & Con-
tent)
Jonathan D. Schwartz (Chief Legal & Corp
Affairs Officer)
Hilary Dubin (VP-Bus Dev)
Diana Terry (VP-Brand Dev & Corp Mktg)
Derek Bond (Sr VP-Production Strategy)
David Rabinowitz (Exec VP-Brdcst Ops &
Tech)
Rosemary Mercedes (Chief Comm Officer &
Exec VP)
Jorge Dominguez (Sr VP-Art & Design)
Alejandro Nieto Molina (Sr VP & Gen Mgr-
Radio)
Jed Meyer (Exec VP-Corp Res)
Mark Collazo (Mgr-Sls)
Diego Rodriguez (Chief Global Security Of-
ficer)
Annie Fong (Dir-Programmatic Ad Ops)

Dayana Hoffman (Dir-Sls Programmatic
Revenue & Platform)
David Katz (VP-Programmatic Revenue
Platforms & Ops & Gen Mgr)
Silvia Garcia (Sr VP-Media Plng & Multiplat-
form Strategy-Miami)
Lourdes Diaz (Pres-Entertainment-Los An-
geles)
Adrian Santucho (Exec VP-Univision
Studios-Miami)
Stephen J. McGowan (Sr VP-Corp Res)
Danny Lowry (VP-Radio Natl Sls)
Christine Escobar (VP, Gen Mgr & Dir-Sls-
Austin)
Rosemary Ravinal (VP-Entertainment &
Consumer PR-Miami)
Steve Mandala (Pres-Adv Sls & Mktg)
Jack Randall (Exec VP-Bus Dev)
John Kozack (Sr VP-New York Network &
Digital Sls)
Ronald Estrada (Sr VP-Corp Social Re-
sponsibility & Community Empowerment)
Stephen Keppel (VP-Social Impact/Gen
Mgr-Rise Up-Miami)
Jessica Herrera-Flanigan (Exec VP-Govt &
Corp Affairs)
Adam Shippee (Sr VP-Corp Bus Dev &
Head-IR)
Roberto Yanez (Sr VP/Gen Mgr-New York)
Michael S. Mueller (Sr VP-Bus Dev)
Liz Blacker (Sr VP-Branded Content Rev-
enue)
Lisa Valentino (Exec VP-Revenue Innova-
tion)
Michael Schwimmer (Pres-Platform Strategy
& Revenue-Global)
Wade Davis (CEO)
Ignacio Meyer (Pres-Networks-US)

Subsidiary (Domestic):

Galavision, Inc. (3)
605 3rd Ave 12th Fl, New York, NY 10158-
1299
Tel.: (212) 455-5200
Web Site: http://www.univision.com
Sales Range: $50-74.9 Million
Emp.: 320
International Network & Basic Cable Ser-
vice
N.A.I.C.S.: 516210
Elidieth Stern (Office Mgr)
Carlos Deschapelles (Sr VP-Sports Sls)

Division (Domestic):

Univision Radio (3)
3102 Oak Lawn Ave Ste 215, Dallas, TX
75219-4259
Tel.: (214) 525-7700
Sales Range: $350-399.9 Million
Emp.: 55
Spanish Language Radio Broadcasting
Services
N.A.I.C.S.: 516110

Unit (Domestic):

KSCA-FM (4)
655 N Central Ave Ste 2500, Glendale, CA
91203
Tel.: (818) 500-4500
Web Site: http://www.univision.com
Sales Range: $25-49.9 Million
Spanish Language Radio Programming
N.A.I.C.S.: 516110

KTNQ-AM (4)
655 N Central Ave Ste 2500, Glendale, CA
91203-1422
Tel.: (818) 500-4500
Spanish-Language Radio Broadcasting
Station
N.A.I.C.S.: 516110

WADO-AM (4)
485 Madison Ave Fl 3, New York, NY 10022
Tel.: (212) 310-6000
Web Site: http://wado1280am.univision.com
Sales Range: $10-24.9 Million
Spanish Radio Broadcasting Stations
N.A.I.C.S.: 516110

Subsidiary (Domestic):

Vix, Inc. (3)
2121 Ponce de Leon Blvd Ste 800, Coral
Gables, FL 33134
Tel.: (305) 476-2974
Web Site: http://www.vix.com

Publishing Services
N.A.I.C.S.: 513199
Rafael Urbina (CEO)

Subsidiary (Domestic):

Womensforum.com, Inc. (4)
444 N Michigan Ave Ste 3550, Chicago, IL
60611
Tel.: (312) 396-1800
Web Site: http://www.womensforum.com
Website Publisher
N.A.I.C.S.: 513120
Mark Kaufman (Co-Founder & CEO)
Jodi Luber (Co-Founder & Pres)

FORGEN, LLC
6025 S Quebec St Ste 300, Centen-
nial, CO 80111
Tel.: (720) 266-6030
Web Site: http://www.forgen.com
Year Founded: 2009
Construction Services
N.A.I.C.S.: 237990
Chris Shea (Pres & CEO)

Subsidiaries:

Inquip Associates Incorporated (1)
1340 Old Chain Bridge Rd Ste 400,
McLean, VA 22101
Tel.: (703) 442-0143
Web Site: http://www.inquip.com
Sales Range: $10-24.9 Million
Emp.: 5
Flurry Wall Construction Services
N.A.I.C.S.: 237110
Dominique Nammy (Pres)

Subsidiary (Domestic):

Inquip Associates (2)
PO Box 2182, Santa Barbara, CA 93120
Tel.: (805) 687-2007
Web Site: http://www.inquip.com
Sales Range: $1-9.9 Million
Emp.: 3
Water & Sewer Line Construction
N.A.I.C.S.: 237110
James Edwards (VP)

**FORGIVEN BOTTLING GROUP,
INC.**
7024 Bluebird Wing St, North Las
Vegas, NV 89084
Tel.: (702) 591-1534 NV
Web Site:
http://www.takeforgiven.com
Year Founded: 2010
Sales Range: Less than $1 Million
Alcohol Metabolizing Product Mfr
N.A.I.C.S.: 325412
Thomas J. Lavin (Sec)
Paul Grady (COO)
Charles Aday III (Chm, Pres, CEO,
CFO, Chief Acctg Officer & Treas)

FORGOTTEN HARVEST, INC.
21800 Greenfield Rd, Oak Park, MI
48237
Tel.: (248) 967-1500 MI
Web Site:
http://www.forgottenharvest.org
Year Founded: 1990
Sales Range: $75-99.9 Million
Emp.: 100
Emergency Food Services
N.A.I.C.S.: 624210
Hollie Bartoni (Controller)
Kristen Yandora (CFO)
Anna Wallbillich (Sr Dir-Dev)
Colleen Peters (Sr Dir-Strategic &
Planned Gifts)
Peter Oleksiak (Treas)
Chris Nemeth (Sr Dir-Social Enter-
prise)
Lori L. Wingerter (Sec)
Susan Ellis Goodell (Pres & CEO)
Tim Hudson (Chief Dev Officer)
Kirk Mayes (CEO)
Mike Szymanski (Dir-Food Safety &
Mfg)

John Owens *(Dir-Mktg & PR)*
Ashleigh Dunham *(Dir-Corp Dev)*
Lisa Kravitz *(Dir-HR)*
Marc Berke *(Sr Dir-Major Gifts)*

FORIA INTERNATIONAL INC.
18689 Arenth Ave, City of Industry, CA 91748
Tel.: (626) 912-6100
Web Site: http://www.foria.com
Sales Range: $10-24.9 Million
Emp.: 80
Men's & Boy's Clothing
N.A.I.C.S.: 424350
Joe Wang *(Controller)*

FORINO CO., L.P.
555 Mountain Home Rd, Sinking Spring, PA 19608
Tel.: (610) 670-2200
Web Site: https://www.forino.com
Year Founded: 1975
Sales Range: $25-49.9 Million
Emp.: 82
Construction Management, General Contracting, Design Survey & Site Analysis
N.A.I.C.S.: 236220
Anthony Forino *(Pres)*
John Smith *(VP)*
Eileen Hauptly *(CFO)*
Nathan Pletscher *(Dir-Business Development)*

FORINO DEVELOPERS COMPANY
555 Mountain Home Rd, Reading, PA 19608
Tel.: (610) 670-2200
Web Site: http://www.forino.com
Sales Range: $25-49.9 Million
Emp.: 70
Land Subdividing Services
N.A.I.C.S.: 237210
Anthony Forino *(Pres)*

FORISH CONSTRUCTION COMPANY, INC.
Mainline Dr, Westfield, MA 01086
Tel.: (413) 568-8624
Web Site:
   https://www.forishconstruction.com
Year Founded: 1946
Sales Range: $10-24.9 Million
Emp.: 30
Commercial & Building Construction Services
N.A.I.C.S.: 236220
Eric Forish *(Pres)*
Linda Day *(Gen Mgr)*
Al Delude *(Project Mgr)*
Dan Ryan *(Project Mgr)*

FORK-CO USA SALES LLC
19113 Amoco Dr S, Alvin, TX 77511
Tel.: (281) 692-1667
Web Site: http://www.fork-co.com
Year Founded: 2001
Custom Forklift Attachments Solutions
N.A.I.C.S.: 333924
Jamie Todd *(Pres & CEO)*

FORKLIFT OF ST. LOUIS INC.
4720 LaGuardia Dr, Saint Louis, MO 63134-3116
Tel.: (314) 426-4040
Web Site: http://www.flstl.com
Year Founded: 1947
Sales Range: $25-49.9 Million
Emp.: 145
Sales & Repairs of Material Handling Equipment
N.A.I.C.S.: 423830
Robert Whittingham Sr. *(Pres)*

Subsidiaries:

Forklift of Cape Girardeau   (1)
4430 Nash Rd, Cape Girardeau, MO
63701   (100%)
Tel.: (573) 335-2244
Sales Range: $10-24.9 Million
Emp.: 18
Construction Equipment Distr
N.A.I.C.S.: 423830
Tammy Piel *(Gen Mgr)*

Forklifts of Central Missouri   (1)
4502 Hwy 50 W, Jefferson City, MO 65102
Tel.: (314) 426-4040
Web Site: http://www.forklift.com
Sales Range: $10-24.9 Million
Emp.: 15
Mfr of Industrial Machinery & Equipment
N.A.I.C.S.: 423830
Carl Hammond *(Gen Mgr)*

Forklifts of Quincy, Inc.   (1)
2426 W Schneidman Dr, Quincy, IL
62305-1294   (100%)
Tel.: (217) 224-6600
Sales Range: $10-24.9 Million
Emp.: 10
Industrial Machinery & Equipment Sales & Service
N.A.I.C.S.: 423830
Jerry Edmond *(Gen Mgr)*

FORKLIFT SYSTEMS INC.
884 Elm Hill Pike, Nashville, TN
37210-2851
Tel.: (615) 255-6321   TN
Web Site:
   https://www.forkliftsystems.com
Year Founded: 1978
Industrial Machinery & Equipment
N.A.I.C.S.: 423830
Duane T. Hardy *(Pres)*
Kathy Henry *(CFO)*
Mike Mosley *(VP)*
Gary Schield *(Sr Acct Mgr)*
Jim Wilson *(Sr Acct Mgr)*

FORKLIFTS OF MINNESOTA, INC.
2201 W 94th St, Bloomington, MN
55431-2313
Tel.: (952) 887-5400   MN
Web Site:
   https://www.forkliftsofmn.com
Year Founded: 1949
Sales Range: $25-49.9 Million
Emp.: 160
Forklift Rental, Sales & Services
N.A.I.C.S.: 423830
Clayton Schubert *(Co-Owner)*
Larry Carpenter *(Mgr-Sls)*
Sid Lemcke *(Mgr-Parts)*
Jeff Schubert *(Co-Owner)*
Kevin Uecker *(Mgr-Svc)*

Subsidiaries:

Forklifts of Minnesota, Inc. - FORK-
LIFTS OF WISCONSIN Division   (1)
2201 W 94th St, Bloomington, MN 55431
Tel.: (952) 887-5400
Web Site: http://www.forkliftsofmn.com
Forklift Repair & Maintenance Services
N.A.I.C.S.: 811310
Clayton Schubert *(Pres)*

Forklifts of North Dakota, Inc.   (1)
1808 E Main Ave, West Fargo, ND
58078-2204   (100%)
Tel.: (701) 282-2334
Web Site: http://www.forkliftsofmn.com
Sales Range: $25-49.9 Million
Emp.: 34
Forklift Sales & Services
N.A.I.C.S.: 423830
Jeff Schubert *(VP)*

FORM SERVICES INC.
717 Wedeman Ave, Linthicum, MD
21090
Tel.: (410) 247-9500

Web Site:
   https://www.formservices.com
Rev.: $23,000,000
Emp.: 90
General Construction Machinery & Equipment
N.A.I.C.S.: 423810
Bob Stumps *(Controller)*
Brian Hargett *(Mgr-IT)*

FORM-A-FEED, INC.
PO Box 9, Stewart, MN 55350
Tel.: (320) 562-2413
Web Site: http://www.formafeed.com
Sales Range: $10-24.9 Million
Emp.: 125
Animal Feed Mfr
N.A.I.C.S.: 311119
Steve Nelson *(Pres)*
Brant Groen *(Dir-Dairy Wellness)*
Gary Asche *(Dir-Nutrition)*
Jim Schwiderski *(Mgr-Acctg)*
Rick Mages *(Mgr-Field Sls)*

FORMAGGIO CHEESE
250 Hilldale Rd, Hurleyville, NY
12747
Tel.: (845) 436-4200
Web Site:
   http://www.formaggiocheese.com
Year Founded: 1925
Sales Range: $10-24.9 Million
Emp.: 93
Cheese Mfr
N.A.I.C.S.: 311513
Demetrious Georgio *(Mgr-HR)*

FORMAN INC.
2036 Lord Baltimore Dr, Baltimore,
MD 21244-2501
Tel.: (410) 298-7500
Web Site: http://www.formaninc.com
Year Founded: 1978
Sales Range: $10-24.9 Million
Emp.: 75
Industrial & Personal Service Paper Distr
N.A.I.C.S.: 424130
Wayne Littlefield *(Pres & CEO)*

Subsidiaries:

Forman Equipment, Inc.   (1)
2036 Lord Baltimore Dr, Baltimore, MD
21244-2501   (100%)
Tel.: (410) 298-7500
Web Site: http://www.foremaninc.com
Sales Range: $10-24.9 Million
Emp.: 35
Industrial & Personal Service Paper Distr
N.A.I.C.S.: 424130
Wayne Littlefield *(Pres)*

FORMATION CAPITAL, LLC
3500 Lenox Rd Ste 510, Atlanta, GA
30326
Tel.: (770) 754-9660   GA
Web Site:
   http://www.formationcapital.com
Year Founded: 1999
Privater Equity Firm
N.A.I.C.S.: 523999
Arnold M. Whitman *(Founder & Chm)*

Subsidiaries:

Genesis Healthcare, Inc.   (1)
101 E State St, Kennett Square, PA
19348   (53.8%)
Tel.: (610) 444-6350
Web Site: https://www.genesishcc.com
Rev.: $3,906,223,000
Assets: $4,062,246,000
Liabilities: $5,224,493,000
Net Worth: ($1,162,247,000)
Earnings: ($58,963,000)
Emp.: 44,000
Fiscal Year-end: 12/31/2020
Holding Company; Nursing Homes & Assisted Living Facilities Operator
N.A.I.C.S.: 551112

Paul D. Bach *(COO & Exec VP)*
Thomas DiVittorio *(CFO & Sr VP)*
Jason H. Feuerman *(Sr VP-Strategic Dev & Managed Care)*
James W. Tabak *(Sr VP-Admin & Govt Affairs)*
Stephen S. Young *(Chief Acctg Officer & Treas)*
Michael Scott Sherman *(Gen Counsel, Sec & Sr VP)*
JoAnne Susan Reifsnyder *(Chief Nursing Officer & Exec VP-Clinical Ops)*
David Harrington *(Chm)*
Harry Wilson *(CEO)*
Joseph C. Montgomery *(CIO & Sr VP)*
Larry Baider *(Sr VP-People Strategy & HR)*

Subsidiary (Domestic):

Genesis HealthCare Corporation   (2)
101 E State St, Kennett Square, PA 19348-
3109
Tel.: (610) 444-6350
Web Site: http://www.genesishcc.com
Sales Range: $1-4.9 Billion
Emp.: 35,500
Skilled & Intermediate Nursing Care & Operator of Eldercare Facilities
N.A.I.C.S.: 623110
David C. Almquist *(Pres-West Div & Exec VP)*

Unit (Domestic):

Barkley Center   (3)
4747 Alben Barkley Dr, Paducah, KY 42001
Tel.: (270) 444-9661
Web Site: http://www.genesishcc.com
Nursing Care Facilities Services
N.A.I.C.S.: 623110
Michele Burgess *(Dir-Nursing)*
Tracy Summers *(Dir-Rehabilitation)*
Candice Neckel *(Dir-Admissions)*
Christy Tygett *(Exec Dir)*

Bay Tree Center   (3)
2600 Highlands Blvd N, Palm Harbor, FL
34684-2114
Tel.: (727) 785-5671
Web Site: http://www.genesishcc.com
Sales Range: $25-49.9 Million
Short-Term Rehabilitation, VA Approved & Long-Term Skilled Nursing Services
N.A.I.C.S.: 623110
Suzie Prince *(Dir-Admissions)*
Candee Higgins *(Program Dir-Rehabilitation)*

Subsidiary (Domestic):

Bradford Square Nursing, LLC   (3)
1040 US Highway 127 S, Frankfort, KY
40601-4326
Tel.: (502) 875-5600
Web Site: http://www.genesishcc.com
Emp.: 12
Skilled Nursing & Rehabilitation Services
N.A.I.C.S.: 623110
Beth Collins-Young *(Dir-Nursing)*
Staci Dennis *(Dir-Admissions)*
Janie Cunningham *(Exec Dir)*

Unit (Domestic):

Brakeley Park Center   (3)
290 Red School Ln, Phillipsburg, NJ 08865
Tel.: (908) 859-2800
Web Site: http://www.genesishcc.com
Sales Range: $1-9.9 Million
Emp.: 170
Nursing Care & Rehabilitation Facility Operator
N.A.I.C.S.: 623110
Nicole Diomedo *(Dir-Mktg & Admissions)*
Erica Gruber *(Dir-Rehabilitation)*
Valentina Krizel *(Dir-Nursing)*

Brandywine Hall Care Center   (3)
800 W Miner St, West Chester, PA 19382-
2149
Tel.: (610) 696-3120
Web Site: http://www.genesishcc.com
Sales Range: $25-49.9 Million
Short Stay Rehabilitation Unit, Wound & Complex Medical Care, Respite, Dementia & Long-Term Care Services
N.A.I.C.S.: 623110

Formation Capital, LLC—(Continued)
Sharon McDermond *(Exec Dir)*
Chanel Dale *(Dir-Nursing)*
Debbie Henderson *(Dir-Admissions)*

Burlington Woods Care Center (3)
115 Sunset Rd, Burlington, NJ 08016-4153
Tel.: (609) 387-3620
Web Site: http://www.genesishcc.com
Sales Range: $25-49.9 Million
Emp.: 225
Clinical, Skilled & Rehabilitation Services for
Short Stay & Long Term Patients, ALso In-
patient & Outpatient Dialysis
N.A.I.C.S.: 623110
Joanna Pastore *(Exec Dir)*
Suprena Sabella *(Mgr-Admin)*
Maria Leah Lopez *(Dir-Nursing)*

Clipper Harbor Center (3)
188 Jones Ave, Portsmouth, NH 03801-
5516
Tel.: (603) 431-2530
Web Site: http://www.genesishcc.com
Sales Range: $25-49.9 Million
Senior Adult Residential Housing & Person-
alized Services, Nursing & Rehabilitation
Therapies
N.A.I.C.S.: 623110
Michelle Spriggs *(Dir-Nursing)*
Catherine Maynard *(Exec Dir)*
Melissa Kivela *(Dir-Admissions)*

Colonial Hill Center (3)
62 Rochester Hill Rd, Rochester, NH
03867-3216
Tel.: (603) 335-3955
Web Site: http://www.genesishcc.com
Nursing Care Facilities Services
N.A.I.C.S.: 623110
Christopher Caverretta *(Exec Dir)*
Dannielle Libby *(Exec Nurse)*
Nicole Faucher *(Dir-Rehabilitation)*
Kara Couture *(Dir-Admissions)*

Cooper River West (3)
5101 North Park Dr, Pennsauken, NJ
08109-4643
Tel.: (856) 665-8844
Web Site: http://www.genesishcc.com
Sales Range: $25-49.9 Million
Convalescent & Hospice Facility
N.A.I.C.S.: 623110
Terry Gagliano *(Exec Dir)*
Kelly Grimaldi *(Dir-Nursing)*
Bob Pulverenti *(Program Dir-Rehabilitation)*

Crestview Center (3)
262 Toll Gate Rd, Langhorne, PA 19047-
1377
Tel.: (215) 968-4650
Web Site: http://www.genesishcc.com
Sales Range: $10-24.9 Million
Short Stay Rehabilitation, Long Term &
Transitional Care & Cardiac Management &
Holistic Services
N.A.I.C.S.: 623110
Erin Dalhausser *(Dir-Nursing)*

**Fairview Care Center of Bethlehem
Pike** (3)
184 Bethlehem Pike, Philadelphia, PA
19118-2815
Tel.: (215) 247-5311
Web Site: http://www.genesishcc.com
Sales Range: $25-49.9 Million
Skilled & Intermediate Care Facility
N.A.I.C.S.: 623110
Patty Edwards *(Dir-Nursing)*
Patty Ludwig *(Dir-Nursing)*
Kerri Avery-Natale *(Program Dir-
Rehabilitation)*
Melanie Molnar *(Dir-Admissions)*
Rosemarie Cockill *(Exec Dir)*

**Fairview Care Center of Paper Mill
Road** (3)
850 Paper Mill Rd, Glenside, PA 19038-
7833
Tel.: (215) 233-0920
Web Site: http://www.genesishcc.com
Skilled Nursing, Short Stay Rehabilitation,
Long-Term & Respite Care Services
N.A.I.C.S.: 623110
June Hudak *(Exec Dir)*
Patricia Fritz *(Dir-Nursing)*
Daly Simpson *(Dir-Admissions)*

Division (Domestic):

**Genesis HealthCare Corporation -
Western Division** (3)

101 Sun Ave NE, Albuquerque, NM
87109-5264 **(100%)**
Tel.: (505) 821-3355
Web Site: http://www.genesishcc.com
Sales Range: $75-99.9 Million
Long-Term & Subacute Care Facilities,
Nursing Homes & Acute Rehab
N.A.I.C.S.: 623110
Raymond L. Thivierge *(Exec VP-Western
Div)*
Greg Sanchez *(VP & Controller)*
Michelle Taylor *(Dir-Fin)*

Subsidiary (Domestic):

**Great Falls Health Care - Butte
Center** (4)
2400 Continental Dr, Butte, MT
59701-6563 **(100%)**
Tel.: (406) 723-6556
Web Site: http://www.genesishcc.com
Rehabilitation Therapy, Hospice & Short
Stay Health Services
N.A.I.C.S.: 621610
William Powell *(Exec Dir)*
Jamie LeProwse *(Dir-Admissions)*
Tammy O'Mara *(Mgr-Rehabilitation Pro-
gram)*
Geri Shea *(Dir-Nursing)*

**Great Falls Health Care - Deer
Lodge** (4)
1100 Texas Ave, Deer Lodge, MT
59722-1829 **(100%)**
Tel.: (406) 846-1655
Web Site: http://www.genesishcc.com
Nursing Facility Offering Hospice Care, Pri-
vate & Semi-Private Rooms &Health Ser-
vices
N.A.I.C.S.: 621610
Travis Johnson *(Exec Dir)*
Gale Hood *(Dir-Nursing)*

**Great Falls Health Care - Missouri
River Center** (4)
1130 17th Ave S, Great Falls, MT
59405-4523 **(100%)**
Tel.: (406) 771-4500
Web Site: http://www.genesishcc.com
Rehabilitation Recovery & Hospice Services
N.A.I.C.S.: 621610
Michael Taylor *(Dir-Rehabilitation)*

**Great Falls Health Care Company,
L.L.C.** (4)
1801 9th St S, Great Falls, MT 59405-5608
Tel.: (406) 771-7440
Web Site: http://www.genesishcc.com
Emp.: 40
Assisted Living Facilities
N.A.I.C.S.: 623312
Frances O'Neil *(Dir-Nursing)*
Nicole Jemming *(Exec Dir)*

**Harbor View Behavioral Health
Center** (4)
490 W 14th St, Long Beach, CA 90813
Tel.: (562) 591-8701
Web Site: http://www.genesishcc.com
Nursing Care Facilities Services
N.A.I.C.S.: 623110
Michael Meyer *(Exec Dir)*
Saham Plong *(Dir-Nursing)*
Leslie Evans *(Dir-Clinical)*

**Olive Vista Behavioral Health
Center** (4)
2335 S Towne Ave, Pomona, CA 91766-
6227
Tel.: (909) 628-6024
Web Site: http://www.genesishcc.com
Nursing Care Facilities Services
N.A.I.C.S.: 623110
Mariela Pizzatti *(Program Dir)*

**Peak Medical - Bear Creek
Center** (4)
150 Spring St, Morrison, CO 80465-0117
Tel.: (303) 697-8181
Web Site: http://www.genesishcc.com
Physical, Occupational & Speech Therapy
Services
N.A.I.C.S.: 621340
Kathleen Mitchell *(Dir-Nursing)*
Kelley Liebel *(Dir-Rehab/Specialty Pro-
grams)*

Peak Medical - McKinley Center (4)
306 E Nizhoni Blvd, Gallup, NM 87301-
5794

Tel.: (505) 863-9551
Web Site: http://www.genesishcc.com
Emp.: 65
Nursing Care & Long-Term Facilities Ser-
vices
N.A.I.C.S.: 623110
Greta Rucker *(Dir-Rehabilitation Programs)*
Loretta Begay *(Dir-Social Services)*
Kelly Anderson *(Exec Dir)*

**Peak Medical - Pikes Peak
Center** (4)
2719 N Union Blvd, Colorado Springs, CO
80909-1145
Tel.: (719) 636-1676
Web Site: http://www.genesishcc.com
Nursing Care Rehabilitation Services
N.A.I.C.S.: 623110
Debra Welker *(Exec Dir)*

**Peak Medical Idaho Operations,
Inc.** (4)
660 S 2nd W, Rexburg, ID 83440-2300
Tel.: (208) 356-0220
Web Site: http://www.genesishcc.com
Nursing Care Facilities Services
N.A.I.C.S.: 623110
Monte Jones *(Exec Dir)*
Jodie Hinshaw *(Dir-Nursing)*

Peak Medical of Idaho, Inc. (4)
674 Eastland Dr, Twin Falls, ID 83301-6846
Tel.: (208) 734-4264
Web Site: http://www.genesishcc.com
Short-Term Rehabilitation & Long-Term
Care & Outpatient Therapy
N.A.I.C.S.: 623110
Lori Bentzler *(Exec Dir)*
Rachel Krieger *(Dir-Nursing)*

**SunBridge Brittany Rehabilitation
Center, Inc.** (4)
3900 Garfield Ave, Carmichael, CA 95608-
6647
Tel.: (916) 481-6455
Web Site: http://www.genesishcc.com
Medicare & Medicaid Approved Nursing
Care Facilities
N.A.I.C.S.: 623110
Ana Ramirez *(Dir-Admissions)*
Barbara Oulrey *(Dir-Rehab/Specialty Pro-
gram)*
Eric VanWalleghem *(Exec Dir)*

**SunBridge Care Enterprises West,
Inc.** (4)
1101 Stroud Ave, Kingsburg, CA 93631-
1016
Tel.: (559) 897-5881
Web Site: http://www.genesishcc.com
Medicare & Medicaid Approved Nursing
Facility
N.A.I.C.S.: 623110
Stephane Russo *(Exec Dir)*
Angelie Limlingan *(Dir-Nursing)*
Jana Kohnert *(Dir-Rehabilitation)*
Rosie Muneton *(Dir-Admissions)*

**SunBridge Carmichael Rehabilitation
Center, Inc.** (4)
8336 Fair Oaks Blvd, Carmichael, CA
95608-1906
Tel.: (916) 944-3100
Web Site: http://www.genesishcc.com
Sales Range: $10-24.9 Million
Medicare & Medicaid Approved Nursing
Care Facilities
N.A.I.C.S.: 623110
Bianca Haskell *(Dir-Admissions)*
Tina Debotarri *(Dir-Rehabilitation)*
Harumi Hurrianko *(Exec Dir)*

**SunBridge Hallmark Health Services,
Inc.** (4)
7716 W Manchester Ave, Playa Del Rey,
CA 90293-8408
Tel.: (310) 823-4694
Web Site: http://www.genesishcc.com
Medicare & Medicaid Approved Nursing
Care Facilities
N.A.I.C.S.: 623110
Cecil Reynolds *(Dir-Nursing)*
Rahim Kanji *(Dir-Rehab/Specialty Program)*
Amparo Vaca *(Dir-Admissions)*
Brian Bellantuoni *(Exec Dir)*

Sundance Services Corporation (4)
1919 112th St SW, Everett, WA 98204-3784
Tel.: (425) 513-1600

Web Site: http://www.genesishcc.com
Rehabilitation & Nursing Care Facilities
Services
N.A.I.C.S.: 623110
Jim Rush *(Exec Dir)*
Melissa Jenquin *(Dir-Admissions)*
Alaina Torzillo *(Dir-Nursing)*
Fiona Smith *(Mgr-Rehabilitation Program)*

Unit (Domestic):

**Genesis HealthCare-Phillipsburg
Center** (3)
843 Wilbur Ave, Phillipsburg, NJ 08865-
3453
Tel.: (908) 454-2627
Web Site: http://www.genesishcc.com
Convalescent Center
N.A.I.C.S.: 623110
Nicole Diomedo *(Dir-Mktg & Admissions)*

**Genesis Healthcare Lopatcong
Center** (3)
390 Red School Lane, Phillipsburg, NJ
08865-2230
Tel.: (908) 859-0200
Web Site: http://www.genesishcc.com
Sales Range: $25-49.9 Million
Convalescent Center
N.A.I.C.S.: 623312
Lynn Sysook *(Dir-Nursing)*
Nicole Diomedo *(Dir-Mktg & Admissions)*

Genesis Magnolia Ridge (3)
420 Dean Dr, Gardendale, AL 35071-2763
Tel.: (205) 631-8709
Web Site: http://www.genesishcc.com
Nursing Care Facilities & Short-Term Reha-
bilitation Services
N.A.I.C.S.: 623110
Ashley Hicks *(Dir-Nursing)*
Gregory Hill *(Dir-Medical)*
Cindy Johnson *(Program Dir-Rehabilitation)*

Hamilton Arms Center (3)
336 SW End Ave, Lancaster, PA 17603-
5043
Tel.: (717) 393-0419
Web Site: http://www.genesishcc.com
Sales Range: $10-24.9 Million
Emp.: 100
Skilled Nursing & Rehabilitation Facility
N.A.I.C.S.: 623110
Linda Sullivan *(Exec Dir)*
Mike Mangini *(Dir-Admissions)*
Urszula Altdoerffer *(Program Dir-
Rehabilitation)*

Heartland Villa Center (3)
8005 US Hwy 60 W, Lewisport, KY 42351-
7079
Tel.: (270) 295-6756
Web Site: http://www.genesishcc.com
Emp.: 55
Nursing Care & Rehabilitation Facility Ser-
vices
N.A.I.C.S.: 623110
Kathryn Tardif *(Dir-Admissions)*
Apryl Goatee *(Dir-Nursing)*
Tracey Bulter *(Exec Dir)*

Hillcrest Center (3)
1245 Church Rd, Wyncote, PA 19095-1800
Tel.: (215) 884-9990
Web Site: http://www.genesishcc.com
Sales Range: $25-49.9 Million
Convalescent & Rehabilitation Facility
N.A.I.C.S.: 623110
Susan Pagliaro *(Exec Dir)*
Catherine Levitsky *(Dir-Nursing)*
Ray Ebner *(Program Dir-Rehabilitation)*
Gemma Frankhouser *(Sr Dir-Admissions)*

Homestead Center (3)
1900 E Main St, Lancaster, OH 43130-9302
Tel.: (740) 653-8630
Web Site: http://www.genesishcc.com
Rehabilitation Hospitals Services
N.A.I.C.S.: 623990
Melody Veyon *(Dir-Nursing)*
Sue Call *(Dir-Rehab/Specialty Program)*
Alisa Bond *(Dir-Admissions)*
Brian Dutiel *(Exec Dir)*

Hopkins Center (3)
460 S College St, Woodburn, KY 42170-
9638
Tel.: (270) 529-2853
Web Site: http://www.genesishcc.com
Nursing Care Facility Services

N.A.I.C.S.: 623110
Jennifer Hammons *(Dir-Rehabilitation)*
Jennifer Soldevilla *(Exec Dir)*
Eddie Wagoner *(Dir-Admissions)*

Subsidiary (Domestic):

**Huntington Place Limited
Partnership** (3)
1775 Huntington Lane, Rockledge, FL
32955-3136
Tel.: (321) 632-7341
Web Site: http://www.genesishcc.com
Rehabilitation for Medicare Approved Patients
N.A.I.C.S.: 623110
Luis Garcia *(Dir-Admissions)*

Unit (Domestic):

Kresson View Center (3)
2601 Evesham Rd, Voorhees, NJ 08043
Tel.: (856) 596-1113
Web Site: http://www.genesishcc.com
Sales Range: $25-49.9 Million
Short Stay Rehabilitation & Long Term
Care, Respiratory Therapy Programs &
Sub-Acute Rehabilitation Services
N.A.I.C.S.: 623110
Rita DeGore *(Exec Dir & Mgr-Admin)*
Rita Sutton *(Dir-Nursing)*

Larkin Chase Center (3)
15005 Health Center Dr, Bowie, MD 20716-1017
Tel.: (301) 805-6070
Web Site: http://www.genesishcc.com
Sales Range: $10-24.9 Million
Emp.: 3
Rehabilitation & Nursing Care Facilities
N.A.I.C.S.: 623110
Millie Fefegula *(Dir-Nursing)*
Natalie Adams *(Dir-Admissions)*

Magnolia Village (3)
1381 Campbell LN, Bowling Green, KY
42104-1049
Tel.: (270) 843-0587
Web Site: http://www.genesishcc.com
Sales Range: $10-24.9 Million
Medicare & Nursing Care Facility Services
N.A.I.C.S.: 623110
Ruth Neal *(Dir-Rehabilitation)*

Marietta Center (3)
117 Bartlett St, Marietta, OH 45750-2683
Tel.: (740) 373-1867
Web Site: http://www.genesishcc.com
Specialized Rehabilitation, Long-Term Care
& Activity-Based Dementia Services
N.A.I.C.S.: 623110
Kelli Love *(Exec Dir)*
Jennifer Childress *(Exec Nurse)*
Beth Ann Kendall *(Program Dir-Rehab/Specialty)*
Amy Bortell *(Dir-Admissions)*

Mineral Springs Center (3)
1251 White Mountain Hwy, North Conway,
NH 03860
Tel.: (603) 356-7294
Web Site: http://www.genesishcc.com
Nursing Care, Rehabilitation, Assisted Living, Dementia & Long-Term Care & Hospice
Services
N.A.I.C.S.: 623110
Barbara White *(Exec Dir)*
Christina Voight *(Dir-Nursing)*
Alan Dunn *(Program Mgr-Rehabilitation)*
Jane Galloway *(Dir-Admissions)*

New Haven Center (3)
1201 Daly Dr, New Haven, IN 46774-1891
Tel.: (260) 749-0413
Web Site: http://www.genesishcc.com
Nursing Care Facilities Services
N.A.I.C.S.: 623110
Andrea Kever *(Program Mgr)*

New Martinsville Center (3)
225 Russell Ave, New Martinsville, WV
26155-1572
Tel.: (304) 455-2600
Web Site: http://www.genesishcc.com
Nursing Care Facility Services
N.A.I.C.S.: 623110
Camissa McCurdy *(Dir-Admissions)*

**Orchard Ridge Care & Rehabilitation
Center** (3)

4927 Voorhees Rd, New Port Richey, FL
34653-5542
Tel.: (727) 848-3578
Web Site: http://www.genesishcc.com
Rehabilitation & Skilled Nursing Care Facilities Services
N.A.I.C.S.: 623110
Chasmin Snyder *(Dir-Admissions)*
Kim Bedoya *(Program Dir-Rehab & Specialty)*
Beth Wills *(Exec Nurse)*
Scott Ratliff *(Exec Dir)*

Owenton Center (3)
905 Hwy 127 N, Owenton, KY 40359-9302
Tel.: (502) 484-5721
Web Site: http://www.genesishcc.com
Nursing Care Facilities Services
N.A.I.C.S.: 623110
Alan Wade *(Exec Dir)*
Pamela Smoot *(Dir-Admissions)*
Jen Rylen *(Mgr-Specialty Program)*

**Pinebrook Care & Rehabilitation
Center** (3)
1240 Pinebrook Rd, Venice, FL 34285-6421
Tel.: (941) 488-6733
Web Site: http://www.genesishcc.com
Medicare & Medicaid Approved Nursing
Care Facilities & Short-Term Rehabilitation
Services
N.A.I.C.S.: 623110
Regan Pruett *(Dir-Admissions)*
Leneigh Sharkey *(Program Mgr)*
Dana Bedford *(Exec Dir)*

Point Place Center (3)
6101 N Summit, Toledo, OH 43611-1242
Tel.: (419) 727-7870
Web Site: http://www.genesishcc.com
Medicare & Medicaid Approved Nursing
Care & Rehabilitation Services
N.A.I.C.S.: 623110
Christine M. Smith *(Exec Dir)*
Shawn McCauley *(Dir-Rehabilitation)*
Betsy York *(Dir-Admissions)*

Presidential Center (3)
524 James Way, Marion, OH 43302-7801
Tel.: (740) 389-6306
Web Site: http://www.genesishcc.com
Sales Range: $50-74.9 Million
Emp.: 140
Skilled Nursing, Medical & Rehabilitative
Care Specializing in Cardiac Recovery Services
N.A.I.C.S.: 623110
Shannon Kellogg *(Exec Dir)*
Terri Meade *(Dir-Admissions & Mktg)*

**Renaissance Terrace Care & Reha-
bilitation Center** (3)
257 Patton Lane, Harriman, TN 37748-8618
Tel.: (865) 354-3941
Web Site: http://www.genesishcc.com
Nursing Care & Special Needs
Dementia/Alzheimer's Unit & Therapy Gym
N.A.I.C.S.: 623110
Roger Parker *(Exec Dir)*
Brenda Higgins *(Dir-Nursing)*
Connie Hendrickson *(Dir-Admissions)*

**Riverdale Place Care & Rehabilitation
Center** (3)
315 Uppr Riverdale Rd, Riverdale, GA
30274-2500
Tel.: (770) 991-1050
Web Site: http://www.genesishcc.com
Long-Term Care, Rehabilitation, Nursing &
Supportive Care Facilities
N.A.I.C.S.: 623110
Margaret J.H. Bowden *(Exec Dir)*

**Salem Care & Rehabilitation
Center** (3)
255 Sunbridge Dr, Salem, WV 26426-8400
Tel.: (304) 782-3000
Web Site: http://www.genesishcc.com
Skilled Nursing & Short-Term Rehabilitation
Facility
N.A.I.C.S.: 623110
Sheilla Jones *(Gen Mgr)*
Jody Mohr *(Exec Dir)*
Michele Lamp *(Exec Nurse)*
Anna Meckley *(Dir-Rehabilitation)*
Pamela Tenney *(Dir-Admissions)*

Silver Stream Center (3)
905 Penllyn Pike, Spring House, PA 19477

Tel.: (215) 646-1500
Web Site: http://www.genesishcc.com
Nursing & Patient Rehabilitation Services
N.A.I.C.S.: 623110
George E. Miller *(Exec Dir)*
Joseph O'Brien *(Dir-Nursing)*
Dawn Hojnacki *(Program Dir-Rehabilitation)*
Bonnie Gaul *(Dir-Admissions)*

Somerton Center (3)
650 Edison Ave, Philadelphia, PA 19116-1237
Tel.: (215) 673-5700
Web Site: http://www.genesishcc.com
Sales Range: $25-49.9 Million
Nursing & Convalescent Center to Multi
Language Pulmonary Patients
N.A.I.C.S.: 623110
Marie Gallagher *(Dir-Nursing)*
Alyse McCusker *(Program Mgr-Rehabilitation)*

St. Camillus Center (3)
494 Elm St, Stamford, CT 06902-5115
Tel.: (203) 325-0200
Web Site: http://www.genesishcc.com
Clinical & Rehabilitation Care Services
N.A.I.C.S.: 623110
Helen Byron *(Exec Dir)*
Jennifer Almonte *(Dir-Rehabilitation Svcs)*

St. Joseph's Center (3)
6448 Main St, Trumbull, CT 06611
Tel.: (203) 268-6204
Web Site: http://www.genesishcc.com
Independent Living, Adult Day, Short-Term
Rehabilitation, Long-Term Care & Hospice
Services
N.A.I.C.S.: 623110
Marian Gaudioso *(Exec Dir)*
Shelley O'Brien *(Dir-Nursing)*
Tracey Samela *(Program Dir-Rehabilitation)*
Melissa Hripak *(Dir-Admissions)*

**Sunset Point Care & Rehabilitation
Center - Clearwater** (3)
1980 Sunset Point Rd, Clearwater, FL
33765-1132
Tel.: (727) 443-1588
Web Site: http://www.genesishcc.com
Medicare & Medicaid Approved Nursing
Care Facilities & Services
N.A.I.C.S.: 623110
Alicen Tutsch *(Dir-Rehabilitation)*

Twin Rivers Center (3)
395 Harding St, Defiance, OH 43512-1315
Tel.: (419) 784-1450
Web Site: http://www.genesishcc.com
Sales Range: $10-24.9 Million
Medicare & Medicaid Approved Nursing
Care Facilities Services
N.A.I.C.S.: 623110
Mike Adams *(Exec Dir)*
Dawn Ludwig *(Dir-Admissions)*
Amber Ryan *(Dir-Rehabilitation Svcs)*
Amy Quigley *(Dir-Nursing)*

West Bay of Tampa (3)
3865 Tampa Rd, Oldsmar, FL 34677-3008
Tel.: (813) 855-4661
Web Site: http://www.genesishcc.com
Medicare & Medicaid Approved Skilled
Nursing & Rehabilitation Center
N.A.I.C.S.: 623110
Maya Perez *(Exec Dir)*
Rebecca Gorski *(Dir-Admissions)*
Frederick Coburn *(Dir-Social Svcs)*

Willow Ridge Center (3)
215 Richardson Way, Maynardville, TN
37807-3803
Tel.: (865) 992-5816
Web Site: http://www.genesishcc.com
Sales Range: $10-24.9 Million
Nursing Care Facilities Services
N.A.I.C.S.: 623110
Rebecca Mills *(Exec Dir)*
Sharon Overholt *(Dir-Nursing)*
Kathy Chesney *(Dir-Admissions)*

Wolfeboro Bay Center (3)
39 Clipper Dr, Wolfeboro, NH 03894-4222
Tel.: (603) 569-3950
Web Site: http://www.genesishcc.com
Skilled Nursing, Rehabilitation Therapy,
Long-Term Care & an Alzheimer's Program
N.A.I.C.S.: 623312
Lisa Peacock *(Exec Dir)*
Mary Wakefield *(Dir-Nursing)*
Valerie Murray *(Program Mgr-Therapy)*
Donah Brookes *(Dir-Admissions)*

**Millenium Home Health Care,
Inc.** (1)
370 Reed Rd Ste 319, Broomall, PA 19008-4018
Tel.: (610) 543-4126
Web Site: http://www.mhomehealth.com
Emp.: 200
Medicare-Certified Home Health Care Services
N.A.I.C.S.: 621610
Anthony P. Angelo *(Pres & CEO)*
Sanford K. Pearl *(CFO)*

Subsidiary (Domestic):

Angel's Touch Home Care, Inc. (2)
341 Wyoming Ave Suite 2, West Pittston,
PA 18643 (100%)
Tel.: (570) 655-3581
Web Site: http://www.mhomehealth.com
Medicare-Certified Home Care Services
N.A.I.C.S.: 621610
Kathleen Sokoloski *(Exec Dir)*
Eileen Martin *(Mgr-Administration)*

FORMATION8 PARTNERS LLC
501 2nd St Ste 300, San Francisco,
CA 94107
Tel.: (415) 366-8393
Web Site: http://www.formation8.com
Year Founded: 2011
Venture Capital Investment Firm
N.A.I.C.S.: 523999
Joe Lonsdale *(Co-Founder)*
Brian Bonwoong Koo *(Co-Founder)*
Jim Kim *(Co-Founder)*

FORMETCO, INC.
2963 Pleasant Hill Rd, Duluth, GA
30096
Tel.: (770) 476-7000
Web Site: https://www.formetco.com
Year Founded: 1969
Sales Range: $25-49.9 Million
Emp.: 130
Signs & Advertising Specialties Mfr
N.A.I.C.S.: 339950
John Gibb *(Exec VP-Bus-Intl)*
Matt Xander *(Pres & CEO)*
Matt Leech *(Mgr-Digital Billboard Sls)*
Blake Bearden *(Mgr-Sports & Video
Sys Sls-Sports)*
Todd Heller *(VP-Digital Products-
Sports)*
Jim Leisge *(Mgr-Pur)*

FORMIC MEDIA, INC.
300 NE Failing St, Portland, OR
97212
Tel.: (503) 595-6050
Web Site:
http://www.formicmedia.com
Year Founded: 2009
Sales Range: Less than $1 Million
Emp.: 12
N.A.I.C.S.: 541810
Kent Lewis *(Founder & Pres)*
Anna Hutson *(Sr Acct Exec)*
John McPhee *(VP)*
Alex Peerenboom *(Acct Exec)*

**FORMOST GRAPHIC COMMU-
NICATIONS, INC.**
19209-A Chennault Way, Gaithers-
burg, MD 20879
Tel.: (301) 424-4242
Web Site: https://www.formostgc.com
Sales Range: $10-24.9 Million
Emp.: 20
Business Forms
N.A.I.C.S.: 424120
Jeff Richards *(Founder & VP-Bus
Dev)*
John Hendershot *(Founder & Pres)*
Charlie Ryan *(VP)*
Mary Szita *(Office Mgr)*

FORMS & SUPPLY, INC.
6410 Orr Rd, Charlotte, NC 28213

Forms & Supply, Inc.—(Continued)

Tel.: (704) 598-8971   NC
Web Site: http://www.fsioffice.com
Year Founded: 1962
Sales Range: $75-99.9 Million
Emp.: 325
Office Supplies & Furniture Distr
N.A.I.C.S.: 424120
Jimmy D. Godwin (CEO)
Diane Godwin (Pres)
Doug Whetstone (Mgr-Pur)
Larry Abrams (Sr Acct Mgr)
John Cassady (Mgr-Adv)

FORMS & SURFACES, INC.
30 Pine St, Pittsburgh, PA 15223
Tel.: (412) 781-9003
Web Site: https://www.forms-
surfaces.com
Sales Range: $10-24.9 Million
Emp.: 325
Architectural Surfaces & Lighting
Product Design & Mfr
N.A.I.C.S.: 327991
George Hickmann (CFO)
Jason Norris (VP-Resource)
Keith Lewis (Mgr-IT)
Jeffrey Stork (Owner)

FORMS DISTRIBUTION CORP.
10670 Gateway Blvd, Saint Louis,
MO 63132
Tel.: (314) 997-1102
Web Site:
http://www.materialogic.com
Sales Range: $10-24.9 Million
Emp.: 125
Provider of Storage, Distribution &
General Warehousing Services
N.A.I.C.S.: 493110
Milton Cornwell (COO)

FORMTECH ENTERPRISES, INC.
1616 Commerce Dr, Stow, OH 44224
Tel.: (330) 688-2171   OH
Web Site: http://www.formtech.com
Year Founded: 1970
Rev.: $18,943,784
Emp.: 38
Fabricated Extrusion Products
N.A.I.C.S.: 326199
David Turk (Pres & CEO)
Dana Gomolekoff (Mgr-Tool & Die &
Engr-Dev)

FORMULA
1215 Cushman Ave, San Diego, CA
92110
Tel.: (619) 234-0345
Web Site:
https://www.havasformula.com
Sales Range: $1-9.9 Million
Emp.: 75
Public Relation Agency Services
N.A.I.C.S.: 541820
Michael A. Olguin (Founder & Pres)
Emily Porter (Sr VP-Bus & Tech)
Adrienne Cadena (VP-Havas Street)
David Heimlich (VP-Bus Dev)
Donovan Roche (VP-Strategic Svcs)
Alexis McCance (Sr VP-Ops)
Ditas Mauricio (Sr VP-Consumer)
Tara Reid (VP-Consumer Tech)
Taryn Unruh (VP-Sports & Entertain-
ment)
Maria Amor (VP-Havas FORMULA-
TIN)

FORMULA 1 FEEDS INC.
RR 2 Box 230, New Albany, PA
18833
Tel.: (570) 363-2225   PA
Year Founded: 1979
Sales Range: $10-24.9 Million
Emp.: 5

Animal Feed Mfr
N.A.I.C.S.: 311119
Pat Newton (VP)
Walter E. Newton III (Pres)

FORMULA BREWING, LLC
1875 NW Poplar Wy, Issaquah, WA
98027
Tel.: (425) 961-0854
Web Site:
https://www.formulabrewing.com
Food & Beverages
N.A.I.C.S.: 722511

Subsidiaries:

Revitalization Partners, LLC   (1)
WRF Venture Ctr Ste 300 2815 Eastlake
Ave E, Seattle, WA 98102
Tel.: (206) 903-1855
Web Site:
http://www.revitalizationpartners.com
Emp.: 10
Turnaround Management & Investment
Services
N.A.I.C.S.: 541611
Alan M. Davis (Principal)

FORMULATED SOLUTIONS, LLC.
11775 Starkey Rd, Largo, FL 33773-
4727
Tel.: (727) 373-3970
Web Site:
https://www.formulatedsolutions.com
Year Founded: 1999
Sales Range: $10-24.9 Million
Emp.: 90
Cosmetic & Drug Product Mfr
N.A.I.C.S.: 325620
Mark Pacelli (Dir-Bus Dev)
Diane Burmeister (VP-Sls & Mktg)
Eric Dann (Founder & CEO)
Scott Carpenter (Partner-Innovation &
VP-Mktg)
Ricardo Garcia (VP-Operational Ex-
cellence)
Daron Riebe (VP-Procurement)
Dan Tummillo (VP-Quality & Regula-
tory)

FORNACA INC.
2400 National City Blvd, National
City, CA 91950-6628
Tel.: (619) 474-5573   CA
Web Site:
https://www.franktoyota.com
Year Founded: 1961
Sales Range: $150-199.9 Million
Emp.: 190
Holding Company; New Car Dealers
N.A.I.C.S.: 551112

Subsidiaries:

Frank Motors, Inc.   (1)
2400 National City Blvd, National City, CA
91950
Tel.: (619) 474-5573
Web Site: http://www.frankmotors.com
Sales Range: $25-49.9 Million
Emp.: 50
New & Used Car Dealer
N.A.I.C.S.: 441110
Gary Fenelli (Pres)

Unit (Domestic):

Frank Hyundai   (2)
3150 National City Blvd, National City, CA
91950-7232   (100%)
Tel.: (619) 474-5502
Web Site: http://www.frankhyundai.com
New & Used Car Dealership
N.A.I.C.S.: 441110
Jeff Ward (Mgr-Parts)

FORNAZOR INTERNATIONAL INC.
455 Hillsdale Ave, Hillsdale, NJ
07642

Tel.: (201) 664-4000
Web Site: https://www.fornazor.com
Sales Range: $25-49.9 Million
Emp.: 35
Animal Feeds Mfr & Distr
N.A.I.C.S.: 424910
John Fornazor (Pres)

FORNEY INDUSTRIES INC.
2057 Vermont Dr, Fort Collins, CO
80525
Tel.: (970) 482-7271
Web Site: http://www.forneyind.com
Sales Range: $25-49.9 Million
Emp.: 264
Welding Machinery & Equipment
N.A.I.C.S.: 423830
Jack D. Forney (Chm)
Steve Anderson (Pres & CEO)
Kyle Pettine (COO)
Ron Ferguson (VP-Sls & Mktg)

FORRER STRATEGIC BUSI-NESS INTERIORS INC.
555 W Estabrook Blvd, Milwaukee,
WI 53212
Tel.: (414) 906-3200
Web Site: http://www.forrersbi.com
Sales Range: $25-49.9 Million
Emp.: 70
Furniture Merchant Whslr
N.A.I.C.S.: 423210
Scott Grade (Mgr-Installation)
Cammy Harvey (Acct Mgr)
Jane Haven (Acct Mgr)
Randal S. Howard (Pres)
Jon Kaml (Acct Mgr)
David J. Schlapman (VP-Sls & Mktg)

FORRER SUPPLY COMPANY INC.
W 194 North 11811 McCormick Dr,
Germantown, WI 53022
Tel.: (262) 255-3030   WI
Web Site:
http://www.forrersupply.com
Year Founded: 1982
Sales Range: $10-24.9 Million
Emp.: 40
Supplier of Materials Serving the
Construction, OEM, Maintenance,
Environmental & Industrial Markets
N.A.I.C.S.: 423720
Stephen R. Forrer (Pres)
Kathy Kelser (Mgr-Admin)
Melissa Staller (Mgr-Supply Chain)

FORREST & BLAKE INC.
1139 Spruce Dr 2nd Fl, Mountain-
side, NJ 07092
Tel.: (908) 789-6800
Web Site:
http://www.forrestandblake.com
Year Founded: 1994
Sales Range: $10-24.9 Million
Emp.: 10
Advetising Agency
N.A.I.C.S.: 541810
Joe Arbadji (Sr Acct Exec-Client Dev)
Ann Shallcross (Pres)
Wayne A. Freitag (VP & Dir-Creative)

FORREST PAINT CO.
1011 McKinley St, Eugene, OR
97402
Tel.: (541) 342-1821
Web Site:
https://www.forrestpaint.com
Sales Range: $10-24.9 Million
Emp.: 100
Paints Mfr
N.A.I.C.S.: 325510
Londa Odell (Mgr-Export)
Scott Forrest (Pres)
Jeanne Savage (VP-Fin)

FORREST SOLUTIONS GROUP
19 W 44th St 9th Fl, New York, NY
10036
Tel.: (212) 986-3600
Web Site: http://www.thinkfsg.com
Year Founded: 1976
Sales Range: $25-49.9 Million
Emp.: 1,300
Staffing & Outsourcing Services
N.A.I.C.S.: 561330
David Reiss (Mgr-Experience)
Gail Bloom (Mgr-Staffing)
Greg Boudreau (Mgr-Talent)
Olga Jackson (Sr Mgr-Staffing)
Steve Forrest (Owner)
Jim Caton (Co-Owner & Pres)

FORREST T. JONES & COM-PANY, INC.
3130 Broadway St, Kansas City, MO
64111-2406
Tel.: (816) 756-1060   MO
Web Site: https://www.ftj.com
Year Founded: 1953
Sales Range: $50-74.9 Million
Emp.: 250
Insurance Agents, Brokers & Service
N.A.I.C.S.: 524210
Bill Hobbs (Controller)
Leroy McCarty (VP-Ops)
Gary Brownsberger (Mgr-IT Team)

FORRESTER LINCOLN-MERCURY INC.
832 Lincoln Way E, Chambersburg,
PA 17201
Tel.: (717) 263-9525
Web Site:
http://www.forrestersonline.com
Year Founded: 1965
Sales Range: $10-24.9 Million
Emp.: 40
Owner & Operator of Car Dealerships
N.A.I.C.S.: 441110
Toby Forrester (Principal)
Toni Forrester (Gen Mgr)

FORRISTALL ENTERPRISES, INC.
3404 17th St E, Palmetto, FL 34221
Tel.: (941) 729-8150   FL
Web Site: http://www.forristall.com
Year Founded: 1990
Sales Range: $1-9.9 Million
Emp.: 35
Wrecking & Demolition
N.A.I.C.S.: 238910
Mary C. Forristall (Pres)
Stephen P. Forristall (VP)
Deborah Fries (Controller)
Lynn Tomczak (Project Coord)
Michael Forristall (Dir-Ops)
Jessica Forristall (Dir-HR & Bus Dev)

FORS MARSH GROUP LLC.
1010 N Glebe Rd Ste 510, Arlington,
VA 22201
Tel.: (571) 858-3800
Web Site:
http://www.forsmarshgroup.com
Year Founded: 2002
Sales Range: $10-24.9 Million
Emp.: 80
Research & Consulting Services
N.A.I.C.S.: 541910
Brian Griepentrog (Sr VP-Res)
Ben Garthwaite (CEO)
Jennifer L. Gibson (Dir-Scientific
Techniques & Analysis)
Megan Fischer (Mgr-Mktg)

Kimberly Wyborski *(Supvr-Survey Admin)*
Katherine Ely *(Dir-Military Recruiting Res)*
John Low *(Dir-Learning Technologies)*
Ronne Ostby *(VP-Comm Res)*

Subsidiaries:

Brunet-Garcia Advertising, Inc.　**(1)**
1510 Hendricks Ave, Jacksonville, FL 32207
Tel.: (904) 346-1977
Web Site: http://www.brunetgarcia.com
Sales Range: $1-9.9 Million
Emp.: 20
Advetising Agency
N.A.I.C.S.: 541810
Diane Brunet-Garcia *(Dir-Creative)*
Jorge Brunet-Garcia *(Pres & CEO)*
Aerien Mull *(Sr Dir-Art)*
Molly Walker *(VP)*
Chad Villarroel *(Mgr-Acct)*
Kate Jolley *(Sr Mgr-Acct)*
Bianca Borghi *(Dir-Art)*
Christy Schell *(Mgr-Compliance)*
Katy Garrison *(Dir-Art)*

FORSBERG CONSTRUCTION, INC.
6475 Golf Course Blvd, Punta Gorda, FL 33982
Tel.: (941) 637-8500
Web Site:
　http://www.forsbergconstruction.com
Sales Range: $10-24.9 Million
Emp.: 80
Underground Utility & Road Construction
N.A.I.C.S.: 237110
Bruce Wendorf *(Pres)*
Gregg Marsh *(VP)*

FORSHAW INC.
650 State St, Charlotte, NC 28208
Tel.: (704) 372-6790　　　　**NC**
Web Site: https://www.forshaw.com
Year Founded: 1961
Pesticides Distr
N.A.I.C.S.: 424910
Mark DeGeare *(Dir-Sls & Bus Dev)*
Warren Huneycutt *(CFO)*
Marinn Bengel *(Head-HR)*
Shane Dooley *(Dir-Warehouse & Ops)*
Thomas Gray *(Mgr-Facilities)*
Mark Tew *(Mgr-Collections)*
Dave Araujo *(Mgr-Sls Ops)*
Chris Miller *(Mgr-NC Core Account)*
Brian Wardwell *(Mgr-Key Account)*
Suzanne Staton *(Mgr-NC/SC Core Account)*
David Whitaker *(Mgr-Warehouse)*
Thomas Forshaw IV *(Pres)*

FORSTER & HOWELL INCORPORATED
2572 Fortner St Ste 1, Dothan, AL 36305
Tel.: (334) 793-1916
Web Site: http://www.grocery-
　outlet.com
Rev.: $10,300,000
Emp.: 3
Grocery Stores, Independent
N.A.I.C.S.: 445110
Kent Forster *(Pres)*

FORSTMANN LITTLE & CO.
767 5th Ave 45th Fl, New York, NY 10153
Tel.: (212) 355-5656　　　　**NY**
Year Founded: 1978
Sales Range: $5-14.9 Billion
Emp.: 17,034
Privater Equity Firm
N.A.I.C.S.: 523999
Winston Hutchins *(CFO)*

FORSYTH CAPITAL INVESTORS LLC
8040 Forsyth Blvd, Saint Louis, MO 63105-1707
Tel.: (314) 726-2152
Web Site:
　http://www.forsythcapital.com
Private Investment Firm
N.A.I.C.S.: 523999
Chet Walker *(Sr Mng Dir)*
Ryan Gable *(Mng Dir)*
Kyle Chapman *(Mng Dir)*

Subsidiaries:

Baldwin Technology Company, Inc.　**(1)**
8040 Forsyth Blvd, Saint Louis, MO 63105
Tel.: (314) 726-2152
Web Site: http://www.baldwintech.com
Sales Range: $150-199.9 Million
Emp.: 590
Printing Press Equipment Mfr
N.A.I.C.S.: 333248

Division (Domestic):

AMS Spectral UV　**(2)**
674 Highland Dr, River Falls, WI 54022
Tel.: (715) 425-5600
Web Site: http://www.amsspectraluv.com
IR drying, UV & LED UV Curing Equipment & Other Printing Machinery Mfr
N.A.I.C.S.: 333248
Stephen J. Metcalf *(Pres)*

Subsidiary (Domestic):

Baldwin Americas Corporation　**(2)**
14600 W 106th St, Lenexa, KS 66215
Tel.: (913) 888-9800
Web Site: http://www.baldwintech.com
Sales Range: $10-24.9 Million
Emp.: 15
Printing Controls & Accessories Mfr
N.A.I.C.S.: 333248

Subsidiary (Non-US):

Baldwin Americas do Brasil Ltada　**(3)**
Ave Agami 359, SP 04522 001, Sao Paulo, Brazil
Tel.: (55) 1150522030
Web Site: http://www.baldwintech.com
Sales Range: $10-24.9 Million
Emp.: 2
Printing Controls & Accessories Mfr
N.A.I.C.S.: 423430

Subsidiary (Domestic):

Baldwin Graphic Systems, Inc.　**(3)**
14600 W 106th St, Lenexa, KS 66215
Tel.: (913) 888-9800
Web Site: http://www.baldwintech.com
Emp.: 45
Printing & Graphics Equipment Sales
N.A.I.C.S.: 333248
Kyle Chapman *(Pres)*

Division (Domestic):

Baldwin Graphic Systems　**(4)**
14600 W 106th St, Lenexa, KS 66215　**(100%)**
Tel.: (913) 888-9800
Web Site: http://www.baldwintech.com
Rev.: $4,000,000
Emp.: 28
Consumer Products Mfr
N.A.I.C.S.: 333248
Shaun Kilfoyle *(Pres-Latin America)*
Rich Bennett *(Pres-Latin America)*

Subsidiary (Domestic):

Baldwin Oxy-Dry Americas　**(3)**
3041 Woodcreek Dr Ste 102, Downers Grove, IL 60515
Tel.: (630) 595-3651
Emp.: 8
Printing Accessories & Controls
N.A.I.C.S.: 333248
Donald Gustafson *(Pres)*

Horizon Lamps, Inc.　**(3)**
2 Danforth Dr, Easton, PA 18045-7820　**(100%)**
Tel.: (610) 829-4240

Emp.: 100
UV Drying & Curing Application Equipment Mfr
N.A.I.C.S.: 333310
Jeffrey Bade *(Mgr-Mktg & Sls)*

Subsidiary (Domestic):

Baldwin Asia Pacific Corporation　**(2)**
2 Trap Falls Rd Ste 402, Shelton, CT 06484-4616
Tel.: (203) 402-1000
Web Site: http://www.baldwintech.com
Sales Range: $25-49.9 Million
Emp.: 20
Printing Controls & Accessories Mfr
N.A.I.C.S.: 333248

Subsidiary (Non-US):

Baldwin Graphic Equipment Pty.　**(3)**
Level 1 27 Crescent St, Rozelle, 2039, NSW, Australia　**(100%)**
Tel.: (61) 295559975
Web Site: http://www.baldwintech.com
Sales Range: $10-24.9 Million
Emp.: 4
Printing & Graphics Equipment Distr
N.A.I.C.S.: 423830
Peter Tkachuk *(Mng Dir)*

Baldwin Printing Control Equipment (Beijing) Company, Ltd.　**(3)**
Room 726 Building A Golden Peacock Mansion No 13 Dong Tu Cheng Road, No. 2 South Guan Dong Dian Str, Chao Yang District, Beijing, 100013, China
Tel.: (86) 51319022
Web Site: http://www.baldwintech.com
Sales Range: $125-149.9 Million
Printing Machinery & Equipment Mfr
N.A.I.C.S.: 333248

Baldwin Printing Controls Ltd.　**(3)**
Unit 8 7/F K Wah Centre 191 Java Road North Point, Hong Kong, China (Hong Kong)
Tel.: (852) 28112987
Web Site: http://www.baldwintech.com
Sales Range: $25-49.9 Million
Emp.: 10
Printing Equipment Mfr
N.A.I.C.S.: 333248
Peter Pkachuk *(CEO-China)*

Baldwin-Japan Ltd.　**(3)**
2 4 34 Toyo 2, Kohtoh-ku, Tokyo, 135 8384, Japan　**(100%)**
Tel.: (81) 356062771
Web Site: http://www.baldwin.co.jp
Mfr & Whslr of Pre-Press Equipment
N.A.I.C.S.: 333248

Subsidiary (Domestic):

Baldwin Europe Consolidated Inc.　**(2)**
2 Trap Falls Rd Ste 402, Shelton, CT 06484
Tel.: (203) 402-1000
Sales Range: $25-49.9 Million
Emp.: 20
Printing Controls & Accessories Mfr
N.A.I.C.S.: 333248

Subsidiary (Non-US):

Baldwin France S.A.R.L.　**(3)**
30 Ave De Bergoide, 60550, Verneuil-en-Halatte, France　**(100%)**
Tel.: (33) 344250681
Web Site: http://www.baldwintech.com
Sales Range: $10-24.9 Million
Emp.: 12
Printing Equipment
N.A.I.C.S.: 423830

Baldwin Germany GmbH　**(3)**
Joseph Baur Strabe 2, Friedberg, 86316, Germany
Tel.: (49) 82179420
Web Site: http://www.baldwintech.com
Sales Range: $75-99.9 Million
Emp.: 150
Printing Controls & Accessories Mfr
N.A.I.C.S.: 423430
Detar Wressler *(Mng Dir)*

Baldwin Sweden Holding AB　**(3)**
Testvagen 16, Arlov, 23237, Sweden
Tel.: (46) 40439800
Web Site: http://www.baldwin.com

Sales Range: $50-74.9 Million
Holding Company
N.A.I.C.S.: 551112
Peter Hultbere *(Mng Dir)*

Subsidiary (Domestic):

Baldwin IVT AB　**(4)**
Stoerydsvagen 13, PO Box 6, 573 21, Tranas, Sweden　**(100%)**
Tel.: (46) 140385180
Web Site: http://www.ivtg.se
Sales Range: $25-49.9 Million
Emp.: 30
Mfr of IR & UV Printing Press
N.A.I.C.S.: 333248
Magnus Sijurtsson *(Mgr-Svc)*

Baldwin Jimek AB　**(4)**
Testvagen 16, PO Box 14, Arlov, 232 21, Sweden　**(100%)**
Tel.: (46) 40439800
Web Site: http://www.jimek.com
Sales Range: $25-49.9 Million
Emp.: 80
Spray Dampening & Cleaning Systems for Printing Presses
N.A.I.C.S.: 333248
Peter Hultberg *(Mng Dir)*
Bosse Horqvist *(Mgr-Tech Svc)*
Joacim Wellander *(Dir-Sls & Svc)*
Per Schroder *(Mng Dir)*

Subsidiary (Non-US):

Baldwin U.K. Holding Limited　**(3)**
552 Faillee Rd, Slough, SL1 4PY, Berkshire, United Kingdom
Tel.: (44) 1753558060
Sales Range: $1-9.9 Million
Holding Company
N.A.I.C.S.: 551112

Subsidiary (Domestic):

Baldwin (UK) Ltd.　**(4)**
816 Leigh Rd, Slough, SL1 4BD, Berkshire, United Kingdom　**(100%)**
Tel.: (44) 202739030
Printing Machines Mfr & Distr
N.A.I.C.S.: 333248

Subsidiary (Domestic):

Acrotec UK Ltd.　**(5)**
Unit 13 Apex Business Center Boscombe Road, Dunstable, LU5 4SB, Beds, United Kingdom
Tel.: (44) 1582 477499
Printing Controls & Accessories Mfr
N.A.I.C.S.: 333248

Baldwin Globaltec Ltd.　**(5)**
22 Wessex Trade Centre, Poole, BH12 3PQ, Dorset, United Kingdom　**(100%)**
Tel.: (44) 1202739030
Sales Range: $10-24.9 Million
Emp.: 50
Consumer Products Distr
N.A.I.C.S.: 532289

Baldwin UV Ltd.　**(5)**
552 Fairlie Road, Slough, SL1 4PY, Berkshire, United Kingdom　**(100%)**
Tel.: (44) 1753558000
Accelerated Drying & Curing Equipment Mfr
N.A.I.C.S.: 333310
Leon Forest *(Dir-Ops)*

Subsidiary (Domestic):

Western Quartz Products, Inc.　**(2)**
2432 Spring St, Paso Robles, CA 93446-6208
Tel.: (805) 238-3524
Web Site: http://www.westernquartz.com
Medical, Dental & Hospital Equipment & Supplies Merchant Whslr
N.A.I.C.S.: 423450
Jon A. Dallons Jr. *(Pres & CEO)*

Machine Solutions, Inc.　**(1)**
2951 W Shamrell Blvd Ste 107, Flagstaff, AZ 86005
Tel.: (928) 556-3109
Web Site: http://www.machinesolutions.com
Sales Range: $10-24.9 Million
Emp.: 100
Machine Tools Mfr
N.A.I.C.S.: 333517

Forsyth Capital Investors LLC—(Continued)

Brian Strini *(Pres & CEO)*
Danny Bogen *(Dir-Sls-Global)*

Subsidiary (Domestic):

PlasticWeld Systems Inc. (2)
3600 Coomer Rd, Newfane, NY 14108
Tel.: (716) 778-7691
Web Site:
http://www.plasticweldsystems.com
Sales Range: $1-9.9 Million
Emp.: 10
Surgical & Medical Instrument Mfr
N.A.I.C.S.: 339112
Norman Strobel *(Pres)*
Scott Dewitt *(Gen Mgr)*
John Strobel *(Mgr-Technical)*
Pete Strobel *(Mgr-Shop)*

Steeger USA, LLC (2)
2230 Highway 292, Inman, SC 29349
Tel.: (864) 472-7000
Web Site: http://www.steegerusa.com
Sales Range: $1-9.9 Million
Emp.: 22
Industrial Braiding Equipment Machinery
Mfr
N.A.I.C.S.: 333248
Sean Hargett *(Pres)*

FORT ASHFORD HOLDINGS, LLC
107 2, Aliso Viejo, CA 92663
Tel.: (949) 333-3133
Web Site: http://www.fortashford.com
Year Founded: 1996
Private Equity
N.A.I.C.S.: 523999
Francis P. Kavanaugh *(Co-Founder-Fort Ashford Funds, LLC & Mng Dir-Fort Ashford Funds, LLC)*

FORT BELKNAP ELECTRIC COOP
1302 W Main St, Olney, TX 76374
Tel.: (940) 564-3526
Web Site:
https://www.fortbelknapec.com
Sales Range: $10-24.9 Million
Emp.: 23
Electric Power Distr
N.A.I.C.S.: 221122
Kendall Montgomery *(CFO & Gen Mgr)*
Rick Ickert *(Pres)*

FORT BEND SERVICES INC.
13303 Redfish Ln, Stafford, TX 77477
Tel.: (281) 261-5199
Web Site:
https://www.fortbendservices.com
Rev.: $10,174,419
Emp.: 26
Alkalines & Chlorine Sales
N.A.I.C.S.: 424690
Tammy Faber *(VP-Ops)*
Lanasa Moyer *(Pres)*

FORT BOISE PRODUCE
28519 Hwy 20/26, Parma, ID 83660
Tel.: (208) 674-3200
Web Site: https://www.fortboise.com
Year Founded: 1982
Rev.: $10,900,000
Emp.: 50
Vegetables Whslr
N.A.I.C.S.: 445230
Jim Farmer *(Pres)*
Dave Larsen *(Mgr-Pkg Facility)*
Norma Burbank *(Office Mgr)*
Ashley Robertson *(Mgr-Sls)*

FORT DAVIS STATE BANK
100 S State St, Fort Davis, TX 79734
Tel.: (432) 426-3211   TX
Web Site: https://www.fdsb.com
Year Founded: 1911
Commericial Banking

N.A.I.C.S.: 522110
Elizabeth Villanueva *(VP & Loan Officer)*
Jo Ann Buchanan *(Exec VP)*
Zach Dean *(Pres & CEO)*
Christine Shackelford *(Sr VP & CFO)*
Brenda Sanchez *(VP & COO)*
Carolina Fierro *(VP & Banking Officer)*
Bonnie Hamilton *(VP & Compliance Officer)*
Hannah Gray *(VP & Loan Officer)*
Laura Cardona *(Asst VP & Asst Cashier)*
Mary James *(VP & Banking Officer)*
Yolanda Natera *(VP & Mgr-Alpine Branch)*
Nereida Marquez *(VP & Pres-Presidio Branch)*
Blanca Lorena Tavarez *(VP & Asst Branch Mgr-Presidio)*

FORT FRANKLIN
46 Plymton St 3rd Fl, Boston, MA 02118
Tel.: (617) 728-0037
Web Site: http://www.fortfranklin.com
Year Founded: 1999
Sales Range: Less than $1 Million
Emp.: 15
N.A.I.C.S.: 541810

FORT HILL CONSTRUCTION INC.
8118 Hollywood Blvd, Los Angeles, CA 90069-1610
Tel.: (323) 656-7425   CA
Web Site: http://www.forthill.com
Year Founded: 1981
Sales Range: $25-49.9 Million
Emp.: 80
Single-Family Housing Construction
N.A.I.C.S.: 236115
George L. Peper *(Pres)*

FORT HILL NATURAL GAS AUTHORITY INC.
311 S Pendleton St, Easley, SC 29640-3049
Tel.: (864) 859-6375   SC
Web Site: https://www.fhnga.com
Year Founded: 1952
Sales Range: $25-49.9 Million
Emp.: 80
Natural Gas Distr
N.A.I.C.S.: 221210
Robyn Moore *(Dir-Mktg)*
Ken Porter *(Pres)*

FORT HOOD FAMILY HOUSING LP.
18010 T J Mills Blvd Ste B209, Fort Hood, TX 76544
Tel.: (254) 220-4799   TX
Web Site: https://www.forthoodfh.com
Year Founded: 2000
Sales Range: $10-24.9 Million
Emp.: 215
Real Estate Brokerage Services
N.A.I.C.S.: 531210
Victoria Floyd *(Mgr-Comm)*
Jeffery Simon *(Pres)*
Vanessa Szezepanski *(Mgr)*

FORT INC.
903 Central Ave, Nebraska City, NE 68410
Tel.: (402) 873-7388
Web Site: http://www.the-fort.com
Rev.: $14,858,209
Emp.: 30
Clothing Retailer
N.A.I.C.S.: 458110
Carl C. Wohlfarth *(VP & Gen Mgr)*

FORT LOUDOUN ELECTRIC COOPERATIVE
116 Tellico Port Rd, Vonore, TN 37885
Tel.: (423) 884-2049
Web Site: https://www.flec.org
Year Founded: 1938
Sales Range: $25-49.9 Million
Emp.: 75
Electric Power Distr
N.A.I.C.S.: 221122
Jarrod Brackett *(Gen Mgr)*
Chad Kirkpatrick *(VP-Ops & Engrg)*
Jerry Raper *(Supvr-Fleet & Facilities)*

FORT MCDOWELL YAVAPAI MATERIALS
17100 E Shea Blvd, Fountain Hills, AZ 85268
Tel.: (480) 789-8900
Web Site:
https://www.fmyavapaimaterials.com
Year Founded: 1980
Sales Range: $10-24.9 Million
Emp.: 150
Readymix Concrete Mfr
N.A.I.C.S.: 327320
Ellen Wodiuk *(Mgr-Credit)*
Nina Scott *(Mgr-Credit)*

FORT MOJAVE TRIBAL COUNCIL
500 Merriman Ave, Needles, CA 92363
Tel.: (760) 629-4591
Web Site: http://www.fotmojave.com
Sales Range: $10-24.9 Million
Emp.: 300
Casino Operator
N.A.I.C.S.: 721120
Timothy Williams *(Chm)*

FORT NORFOLK RETIREMENT COMMUNITY INC.
1 Colley Ave, Norfolk, VA 23510
Tel.: (757) 616-7900   VA
Web Site:
https://www.harborsedgenorfolk.com
Year Founded: 2002
Sales Range: $10-24.9 Million
Emp.: 233
Healtcure Services
N.A.I.C.S.: 622110
Cathy L'Heureux *(CFO)*
George C. Crawley *(Chm)*

FORT PIERCE UTILITIES AUTHORITY
206 S 6th St, Fort Pierce, FL 34950
Tel.: (772) 466-1600
Web Site: http://www.fpua.com
Year Founded: 1972
Sales Range: $100-124.9 Million
Emp.: 278
Electric & Other Services Combined
N.A.I.C.S.: 221118
Evelyn I. Walker *(Dir-Shared Svcs)*
Timothy E. Perkins *(Dir-Water & Wasterwater Sys)*
Nina B. Hurtubise *(Dir-Fin Svcs)*
Daniel M. Delulio *(Vice Chm)*
Darryl Thomas-Bey *(Deputy Sec)*
Glynda Cavalcanti *(Chm)*
Clayton W. Lindstrom *(Dir-Utilities)*
Paul A. Jakubczak *(Dir-Electric & Gas Sys)*

FORT PITT CONSOLIDATORS INC.
200 Jones St, Verona, PA 15147-1048
Tel.: (412) 826-1111
Year Founded: 1965
Sales Range: $25-49.9 Million
Emp.: 34

Provider of Freight Transportation Arrangement Services
N.A.I.C.S.: 488510
Barry I. Sheer *(Pres & CEO)*
Robert DiNardo *(Exec VP & Dir-Mktg)*
Ken Asztalos *(VP-Natl Accts)*

FORT POINT CAPITAL, LLC
185 Dartmouth St 6th Fl, Boston, MA 02116
Tel.: (617) 303-2444
Web Site:
http://www.fortpointcapital.com
N.A.I.C.S.:
Brooke Ablon *(Partner)*

Subsidiaries:

Advantage Media Services, Inc. (1)
29120 Commerce Center Dr, Valencia, CA 91355
Tel.: (661) 775-0611
Web Site: http://www.amsfulfillment.com
Packing & Crating
N.A.I.C.S.: 488991
Jay Catlin *(CEO)*

Subsidiary (Domestic):

Echo Data Group Inc. (2)
121 N Shirk Rd, New Holland, PA 17557
Tel.: (717) 351-4200
Web Site: http://www.echodata.com
Full Service Order Fulfillment Services
N.A.I.C.S.: 541511
Lee Brown *(Mgr-Acctg)*
Stephen Reed *(Mgr-Ops)*

Jones Fish Hatcheries & Distributors, LLC (1)
3433 Church St, Cincinnati, OH 45244
Tel.: (513) 561-2615
Web Site: http://www.jonesfish.com
Sales Range: $1-9.9 Million
Emp.: 20
Finfish Farming & Fish Hatcheries
N.A.I.C.S.: 112511
Laura Jones *(CFO)*
Robert P. Jones *(Pres)*
Kelly Veatch *(CEO)*

Subsidiary (Domestic):

Aqua Services, Inc. (2)
23360 US Hwy 431, Guntersville, AL 35976-8992
Tel.: (256) 582-9101
Web Site: http://www.aquaservicesinc.com
Sales Range: $1-9.9 Million
Emp.: 13
Environmental Consulting Services
N.A.I.C.S.: 541620
Terry Goldsby *(Pres)*
Bryan Goldsby *(VP)*

NewBold LLC (1)
450 Weaver St, Rocky Mount, VA 24151-2200
Tel.: (540) 489-4400
Web Site: http://www.addressograph.com
Sales Range: $50-74.9 Million
Emp.: 95
Imprinter Models, AFIS Products & the Security Imprinter Line, Bank Plastic Cards, Point of Sale Cash Registers, Metal Plate & Plastic Card Embossers Mfr & Distr
N.A.I.C.S.: 333310
Mark Hathaway *(Mgr-Mktg)*
Robert Scott *(Pres)*

Division (Domestic):

NewBold Corporation - Addressograph Division (2)
450 Weaver St, Rocky Mount, VA 24151-2200
Tel.: (540) 489-4401
Plastic Card Mfr
N.A.I.C.S.: 326199

FORT RECOVERY INDUSTRIES INC.
2440 State Route 49, Fort Recovery, OH 45846
Tel.: (419) 375-4121

Web Site:
https://www.fortrecoveryindus
tries.com
Year Founded: 1945
Sales Range: $25-49.9 Million
Emp.: 400
Die Cast Hardware & Components
Supplier
N.A.I.C.S.: 423710
Wesley M. Jetter *(CEO)*
Larry Holmes *(VP-Fin)*

FORT ROHR MOTORS INC.
5900 Illinois Rd, Fort Wayne, IN
46804
Tel.: (260) 436-4567
Web Site:
http://www.fortwaynelexus.com
Sales Range: $10-24.9 Million
Emp.: 100
New & Used Car Dealers
N.A.I.C.S.: 441110
Robert Rohrman *(CEO)*
Dan Schroeder *(Controller)*

FORT SANDERS REGIONAL MEDICAL CENTER
1901 Clinch Ave, Knoxville, TN 37916
Tel.: (865) 331-1111
Web Site: https://www.fsregional.com
Year Founded: 1954
Sales Range: $300-349.9 Million
Emp.: 2,054
Health Care Srvices
N.A.I.C.S.: 622110
Kelly Miles *(Chief Nursing Officer & VP)*
Ronnie S. Beeler *(CFO & VP)*
Leslie Irwin *(VP)*
Keith N. Altshuler *(Co-Pres & Chief Admin Officer)*

FORT SILL APACHE TRIBE OF OKLAHOMA
43187 US Hwy 281, Apache, OK
73006
Tel.: (580) 588-2298
Web Site: https://www.fortsillapache-
nsn.gov
Native American Tribal Government
Organization
N.A.I.C.S.: 921150
Lori Gooday Ware *(Vice Chm)*
Leland Michael Darrow *(Treas & Sec)*

Subsidiaries:

Apache Casino Hotel (1)
2315 E Gore Blvd, Lawton, OK 73501
Tel.: (580) 248-5905
Web Site:
http://www.apachecasinohotel.com
Casino Hotel Operator
N.A.I.C.S.: 721120
Daran Gard *(Dir-Mktg)*
Benne Brewer *(Mktg Mgr)*
Barrett DeFay *(Mktg Dir)*

FSA Industries, LLC (1)
1201 Arlington Ste D, Ada, OK 74821
Tel.: (580) 279-0587
Web Site: http://www.fortsillapache.com
Emp.: 12
Holding Company; Civil Engineering & Con-
struction Services; Information Technology
Services
N.A.I.C.S.: 551112
Deryl W. Wright *(Pres & CEO)*
Dee Youn *(VP-Ops)*
Kriss Ethridge *(COO)*

Subsidiary (Domestic):

FSA Construction, LLC (2)
1201 Arlington Ste D1, Ada, OK 74821
Tel.: (580) 421-6467
Civil Engineering & Construction Services
N.A.I.C.S.: 237990
Deryl W. Wright *(Pres & CEO)*

FSA Technology, LLC (2)
1201 Arlington Ste D2, Ada, OK 74821

Tel.: (580) 421-6469
Information Technology Services
N.A.I.C.S.: 541513
Deryl W. Wright *(Pres & CEO)*
Dee Youn *(VP-Ops)*
Jason Kinsey *(Mgr)*

FORT SILL FEDERAL CREDIT UNION
4116 Thomas St, Fort Sill, OK 73503
Tel.: (580) 353-2124
Web Site: http://www.fsfcu.com
Year Founded: 1955
Emp.: 75
Credit Union
N.A.I.C.S.: 522130
Denise Floyd *(Pres & CEO)*
Cindy Collins *(VP-Lending)*
Sonya Forbes *(Chm)*
Dennis Porter *(Vice Chm)*
James Apriesnig *(Treas)*
Nita Russell *(Sec)*

FORT WAYNE METALS RE-SEARCH PRODUCTS CORP.
9609 Ardmore Ave, Fort Wayne, IN
46809-9625
Tel.: (260) 747-4154
Web Site: https://www.fwmetals.com
Year Founded: 1971
Sales Range: $25-49.9 Million
Emp.: 500
Steel Wire & Related Products
N.A.I.C.S.: 331222
Mark Michael *(Pres & COO)*
Troy Linder *(CFO)*

Subsidiaries:

Fort Wayne Metals Ireland Ltd (1)
Castlebar Technology Park Moneen Road,
Co Mayo, Castlebar, F23 CK27, Ireland
Tel.: (353) 94 904 3500
Web Site: http://www.fwmetals.com
Emp.: 65
Wire Mfr & Distr
N.A.I.C.S.: 331222
Michael O'Donnell *(Mng Dir)*

FORT WAYNE WIRE DIE INC.
2424 American Way, Fort Wayne, IN
46809-3098
Tel.: (260) 747-1681
Web Site: https://www.fwwd.com
Sales Range: $10-24.9 Million
Emp.: 200
Wire Dies Mfr
N.A.I.C.S.: 333514
Darin McIntosh *(Mgr-Quality Assur-
ance)*
John Dabbelt *(Reg Mgr-Sls)*
Maureen Watson *(Supvr-Gen Acctg)*
Paul Gammons *(Engr-Mfg)*
Tino Corral *(Reg Mgr-Sls)*
Jamie Johnson *(Supvr-Production)*

FORT WORTH BOLT & TOOL CO.
2804 Bledsoe St, Fort Worth, TX
76107
Tel.: (817) 335-3361
Web Site: http://www.boltandtool.com
Sales Range: $10-24.9 Million
Emp.: 50
Industrial Tools Distr
N.A.I.C.S.: 423840
James H. Russell *(Pres)*

FORT WORTH CARRIER COR-PORATION
4501 N Beach St, Fort Worth, TX
76137
Tel.: (817) 831-5248
Sales Range: $10-24.9 Million
Emp.: 250
Contract Haulers
N.A.I.C.S.: 484121

Robert R. Durden *(Pres)*
Tom Leftwich *(Gen Mgr)*
Louis Johnson *(Dir-Safety)*

FORT WORTH COMMUNITY CREDIT UNION
1905 Forest Ridge Dr, Bedford, TX
76021-5724
Tel.: (817) 835-5000
Web Site: http://www.ftwccu.org
Year Founded: 1940
Rev.: $41,696,397
Assets: $936,300,964
Liabilities: $852,137,168
Net Worth: $84,163,796
Earnings: $3,720,722
Emp.: 200
Fiscal Year-end: 12/31/18
Credit Union
N.A.I.C.S.: 522130
Richard Howdeshell *(Pres & CEO)*
Kyle Koke *(Sr VP-Lending)*
Diane Dorsey *(Exec VP)*
Michael Franko *(Sr VP-Fin)*
Carl Auzenne *(VP-IT)*
Henry Christiansen *(Treas & Sec)*
Tammy Trudelle *(VP-HR)*
Tomas Tijerina *(Chm)*
Tunisia Sadruddin *(Vice Chm)*
Valerie Grosskurth *(VP-Payment Sys
& Risk Mgmt)*
Karen Martinez *(VP-Ops)*
Brandy Scarlett *(VP-Mktg)*
Neil Spencer *(VP-Support Svcs)*

FORT WORTH F & D HEAD COMPANY
3040 Peden Rd, Fort Worth, TX
76179
Tel.: (817) 236-8773
Web Site: https://www.fwfdhead.com
Sales Range: $10-24.9 Million
Emp.: 70
Metal Tank Mfr
N.A.I.C.S.: 332420
Chris Wagner *(Mgr-Sls)*
Jeff Bryant *(Mgr-Sls)*

FORT WORTH LUMBER COM-PANY
9101 S Fwy, Fort Worth, TX 76140
Tel.: (817) 293-5211
Web Site:
https://www.fortworthlumber.com
Year Founded: 1956
Sales Range: $75-99.9 Million
Emp.: 60
Rough, Dressed & Finished Lumber
Distr
N.A.I.C.S.: 423310
Emily Fiesler *(Pres)*

Subsidiaries:

Fort Worth Sash and Door Co. (1)
9125 S Freeway, Fort Worth, TX 76140
Tel.: (817) 615-8933
Web Site: http://www.fwsd.biz
Emp.: 20
Door & Window Whslr
N.A.I.C.S.: 423310

FORT WORTH MUSEUM OF SCIENCE AND HISTORY
1600 Gendy St, Fort Worth, TX
76107
Tel.: (817) 255-9300
Web Site: https://www.fwmuseum.org
Year Founded: 1941
Sales Range: $10-24.9 Million
Emp.: 330
Science & Historical Museum Opera-
tor
N.A.I.C.S.: 712110
Lynny Sankary *(Sec)*
Dwight Horton *(Treas)*
Richard A. Russack *(Vice Chm)*
Alston Roberts *(Chm)*

FORT WORTH ZOOLOGICAL ASSOCIATION INC.
1989 Colonial Pkwy, Fort Worth, TX
76110
Tel.: (817) 759-7555
Web Site:
https://www.fortworthzoo.org
Year Founded: 1950
Sales Range: $10-24.9 Million
Wildlife Conservation Services
N.A.I.C.S.: 813312
Michael Fouraker *(Exec Dir)*
Ardon Moore *(Pres)*
Breck Ray *(Sec)*
Kit Moncrief *(Co-Chm)*
Michael Hyatt *(Treas)*
Ramona Bass *(Co-Chm)*

FORTE CAPITAL ADVISORS, LLC
170 Varick St 2nd Fl, New York, NY
10013
Tel.: (212) 509-8907
Web Site: http://www.fortenyc.com
Privater Equity Firm
N.A.I.C.S.: 523999
Jason DeYonker *(Mng Partner)*
Aaron Kanter *(Gen Counsel & Chief
Compliance Officer)*

FORTE RESEARCH SYSTEMS, INC.
1200 John Q Hammons DR Ste 300,
Madison, WI 53717
Tel.: (608) 826-6000
Web Site:
http://www.forteresearch.com
Year Founded: 2000
Sales Range: $1-9.9 Million
Emp.: 44
Custom Computer Programming Ser-
vices
N.A.I.C.S.: 541511
Colleen M. Krattiger *(VP-Product
Mgmt, Quality Assurance & Regula-
tory Affairs)*
Orla Mester *(VP-Implementation,
Trng & Support Svcs)*

FORTE TRANSPORTATION LOGISTICS
301 54th Ave E Ste 200, Fife, WA
98424
Tel.: (253) 926-5456
Web Site: https://www.fortetlc.com
Rev.: $14,700,000
Emp.: 15
Freight Forwarding
N.A.I.C.S.: 488510

FORTECH PRODUCTS, INC.
7600 Kensington Ct, Brighton, MI
48116
Tel.: (248) 446-9500
Web Site:
https://www.fortechproducts.com
Year Founded: 1994
Sales Range: $10-24.9 Million
Emp.: 30
Paint & Coating Mfr
N.A.I.C.S.: 325510
Creighton E. Forester *(Pres & CEO)*

FORTH'S FOODS, INC.
3090 Woodville Dr, Huntington, WV
25701
Tel.: (304) 525-3293
Web Site:
http://www.foodfairmarkets.com
Year Founded: 1988
Sales Range: $50-74.9 Million
Emp.: 500
Grocery Wholesale Trade Agency &
Distr; Supermarket Owner & Operator
N.A.I.C.S.: 425120
Charles T. Forth *(Owner & Pres)*

Fortier Inc.—(Continued)

FORTIER INC.
551 Equity Ave, Conway, AR 72032
Tel.: (501) 329-6309
Web Site: https://www.fortierinc.com
Rev.: $27,000,000
Emp.: 68
Store Equipment Supplier to Convenience Stores
N.A.I.C.S.: 423440

FORTIFIBER CORPORATION
300 Industrial Blvd, Fernley, NV 89451-9309
Tel.: (775) 833-6161
Year Founded: 1939
Sales Range: $50-74.9 Million
Emp.: 75
Building Paper, Waterproof & Reinforced Wrapping Paper, Chemically Coated & Treated Industrial Paper, Extrusion Coated Paper & Foil
N.A.I.C.S.: 322220
Christopher Yount (Pres & COO)
Jim Rossner (VP-Sls & Mktg)
Vicky Ness (Office Mgr)
William Rieger (VP-Mfg)

Subsidiaries:

Fortifiber Building Systems Group (1)
300 Industrial Dr, Fernley, NV 89408
Tel.: (775) 333-6400
Sales Range: $10-24.9 Million
Emp.: 55
Housewrap Stucco Paper & Underslab Vapor Barrier Building Product Mfr
N.A.I.C.S.: 322299

FORTILINE WATERWORKS, INC.
7025 Northwinds Dr NW, Concord, NC 28027
Tel.: (704) 788-9800
Web Site: http://www.fortiline.com
Year Founded: 1997
Emp.: 100
Underground Utility Supplierc
N.A.I.C.S.: 423390
Frank Seymour (Pres)
Keith Young (Reg Mgr-Sls)
Trey Peterson (Mgr-Sls-Florida)

Subsidiaries:

Construction Site Services LLC (1)
Pkwy & Hwy 69 Exit 50 552 SR 69 N, Hartford, KY 42327
Tel.: (270) 298-4545
Web Site: http://www.csspipe.com
Underground Water Utility Supplies
N.A.I.C.S.: 423390
Kathy Wemhoener (Pres & GM)

FORTIS ADVISORS, LLC
1045 1st Ave Ste 120, King of Prussia, PA 19406
Tel.: (858) 200-8688
Web Site: http://www.fortisrep.com
Corporate Shareholder Representation & Advisory Services
N.A.I.C.S.: 561499
Rick Fink (Co-Founder & CEO)
Adam Lezack (Co-Founder & Mng Dir)
Ryan Simkin (Co-Founder & Mng Dir)
Tori Geft (Sr Dir-Mergers & Acq)
Melissa Mackin (Sr Dir-Sys & Infrastructure)
Kim Ocampo (Sr Dir-M&A Acctg)

FORTIS CONSTRUCTION, INC.
1705 SW Taylor St Ste 200, Portland, OR 97205
Tel.: (503) 459-4477
Web Site:
http://www.fortisconstruct.com
Year Founded: 2003

Sales Range: $125-149.9 Million
Emp.: 70
Construction Management Services
N.A.I.C.S.: 236220
Jim Kilpatrick (Pres)
Marcus Klein (Project Mgr)
Jim Gunther (Coord-MEP)
Morgan Jeanes (Coord-Field Office)
Kristin Doherty (Mgr-Talent Acq)
Lori Van Orden (Coord-Field Office)

FORTIS ENERGY SERVICES, INC.
36700 Woodward Ave Ste 107, Bloomfield Hills, MI 48304
Tel.: (248) 283-7100
Web Site:
http://www.fortisenergyservices.com
Year Founded: 2004
Sales Range: $10-24.9 Million
Emp.: 90
Oil & Gas Field Operating Services
N.A.I.C.S.: 213112
Nathan Conway (CEO)
Meghan Berg (VP-Human Resources)

FORTIS FIRE & SAFETY, INC.
1515 Woodfield Rd Ste 630, Schaumburg, IL 60173
Web Site: https://fortisfire.com
Year Founded: 2021
Fire Protection Services
N.A.I.C.S.: 922160
Rich Ennis (CEO)

Subsidiaries:

CJ Suppression, Inc. (1)
205 Lewis Ct, Corona, CA 92882
Tel.: (951) 735-5560
Web Site: http://www.cjsuppression.com
Rev.: $3,460,000
Emp.: 10
Fire Protection Services
N.A.I.C.S.: 922160

Golden State Fire Protection, Inc. (1)
15535 Arrow Blvd, Fontana, CA 92335
Tel.: (909) 356-5644
Web Site: http://www.goldenstate-fire.com
Rev.: $1,000,000
Emp.: 100
Site Preparation Contractor
N.A.I.C.S.: 238910
Brenda Harrelson (Treas)
Walter Sarratt (Pres)

Piper Fire Protection, Inc. (1)
521 S Commerce Dr, Largo, FL 33770
Tel.: (727) 581-9339
Web Site: http://www.piperfire.com
Fire Protection Services
N.A.I.C.S.: 922160
Chris Johnson (Pres)
Terry Johnson (Founder)
Edward McGaffagan (Mgr-Fire Sprinkler Svc & Inspection Div)
Mark Stoefen (VP-Ops)
Ben Ward (Mgr-Fire Suppression & Extinguisher Div)
Duane Tankersley (Mgr-Fire Sprinkler Construction Div)
Ellen Poole (Gen Counsel)
Ron Carter (Mgr-Customer Svc)
Kristen Hesse (Mgr-HR)

FORTIS LIFE SCIENCES
1440 Main St Ste 300, Waltham, MA 02451
Tel.: (936) 597-6111
Web Site: http://www.fortislife.com
Year Founded: 2020
Life Sciences Research & Development Services
N.A.I.C.S.: 541715
Brian S. Kim (CEO)
Grace A. Johnston (Chief Comml Officer)
Shawn Lynch (CFO)

Ken Yoon (COO)
Andy Wolf (CTO)
Debra Thompson (Chief People & Integration Officer)

Subsidiaries:

Bethyl Laboratories, Inc. (1)
25043 W Farm to Market 1097, Montgomery, TX 77356
Tel.: (936) 597-6111
Antibody Products & Services for Clinical & Research Applications
N.A.I.C.S.: 541714
John Carwile (CEO)

FORTIS MINERALS, LLC
1111 Bagby St Ste 2150, Houston, TX 77002
Web Site:
http://www.fortisminerals.com
Year Founded: 2019
Mineral Exploration Services
N.A.I.C.S.: 213115
Christopher H. Transier (Pres & CEO)
Brad D. Wright (CFO & Exec VP)
W. Scott Dole (Chief Acctg Officer & Exec VP)
Ashley A. Yates (Gen Counsel, Sec & Exec VP)
Skye A. Callantine (Chm)
Bart Borej (VP-Engrg)
Patrick J. Hesseler (VP-Corp Dev & Strategy)
Michelle Massaro (VP-Fin)
Michael D. Ostrow (VP-Acctg)
Freddie Barela Jr. (Exec VP-Bus Dev & Land)

FORTIS PAYMENT SYSTEMS LLC
43155 Main St Ste 2310C, Novi, MI 48375
Tel.: (855) 465-9999
Web Site:
http://www.fortispayments.com
Year Founded: 2009
Financial Services
N.A.I.C.S.: 522320
Greg Cohen (CEO)

Subsidiaries:

Blue Dog Business Services, LLC (1)
2205 14th Ave, Vero Beach, FL 32960
Tel.: (772) 360-4646
Web Site: http://www.yourbluedog.com
Financial Transactions Processing, Reserve & Clearinghouse Activities
N.A.I.C.S.: 522320
Ron Dichter (CEO)

GotoBilling, Inc. (1)
218 E Bearss Ave Ste 368, Tampa, FL 33613
Web Site: http://www.omnifund.com
Sales Range: $1-9.9 Million
Emp.: 50
Financial Services
N.A.I.C.S.: 523999
Stacy Roderick (CEO)

FORTIS RIDERS
200 N Main St Ste 303, Greenville, SC 29601
Tel.: (864) 272-3400
Web Site: http://www.fortisnet.com
Year Founded: 2000
Sales Range: $1-9.9 Million
Emp.: 28
Chauffeured Management & Global Transportation Services
N.A.I.C.S.: 485320
Matt Lawrence (COO & Dir-Bus Dev)
Joel Mangin (Sr Acct Exec)

FORTISTAR LLC
1 N Lexington Ave, White Plains, NY 10601
Tel.: (914) 421-4900

Web Site: http://www.fortistar.com
Year Founded: 1974
Emp.: 42
Energy Generation Services
N.A.I.C.S.: 221117
David Unger (Head-Renewable Natural Gas Dev Strategy)
Charles D. Bryceland (Mng Dir)
Mark S. Comora (Pres)

Subsidiaries:

Fortistar North Tonawanda, Inc. (1)
1070 Erie Ave, North Tonawanda, NY 14120
Tel.: (716) 694-9874
Electric Power Generation
N.A.I.C.S.: 221118

TruStar Energy LLC (1)
10225 Philadelphia Ct, Rancho Cucamonga, CA 91730
Tel.: (909) 793-3700
Web Site: http://www.trustarenergy.com
Fueling Station Solutions
N.A.I.C.S.: 213112
Adam Comora (Pres)
Scott Edelbach (Gen Mgr-Ops)
Steve Phillips (Sr VP-Sls & Mktg)
John Snell (CFO)
Juan Reina (Dir-Biogas)
Dave Unger (Sr VP)

FORTNEY & WEYGANDT INC.
31269 Bradley Rd, North Olmsted, OH 44070
Tel.: (440) 716-4000
Web Site:
https://fortneyweygandt.com
Year Founded: 1978
Sales Range: $75-99.9 Million
Emp.: 175
Nonresidential Construction Services
N.A.I.C.S.: 236220
Greg Freeh (Pres)
Kris Martin (Treas)
Mitch Lapin (CEO)
John Krisanda (Dir-Rollout)
Chris Hagen (Dir-Field Ops)
Bard Fulton (VP)

FORTRESS ITX LLC
100 Delawanna Ave Ste 200, Clifton, NJ 07014
Tel.: (888) 500-0774
Web Site: http://www.fortressitx.com
Year Founded: 1997
Sales Range: $1-9.9 Million
Emp.: 19
IT Services
N.A.I.C.S.: 541519
Jason Silverglate (Pres & CEO)
Ross Brouse (COO)
Lori Greaves Navalny (Dir-Fin & HR)
Brandon Hale (Dir-Sls)
Josh Ewin (Dir-Mktg)
Lou Ardolino (Dir-Managed Svcs)
Salvatore Poliandro III (Dir-IT)

FORTRESS PARTNERS CAPITAL MANAGEMENT, LTD.
700 Walnut Rdg Dr Ste 200, Hartland, WI 53029
Tel.: (262) 369-1095
Web Site:
http://www.fortresspartners.com
Year Founded: 1991
Sales Range: Less than $1 Million
Emp.: 2
Investment & Portfolio Management Services
N.A.I.C.S.: 523940
Jon C. Bruss (CEO & Mng Principal)

Subsidiaries:

Fortress Partners Strategic Capital Advisors (1)
700 Walnut Ridge Dr Ste 200, Hartland, WI 53029
Tel.: (262) 369-1095

Investment Advisory Services
N.A.I.C.S.: 523940
Jon C. Bruss (CEO)

FORTRON/SOURCE CORP.
23181 Antonio Pkwy, Rancho Santa
Margarita, CA 92688
Tel.: (949) 766-9240   CA
Web Site:
   http://www.fortronsource.com
Year Founded: 1983
Sales Range: $10-24.9 Million
Emp.: 21
Electronic Components Mfr
N.A.I.C.S.: 334419
Jackson Wang (Pres & CEO)

FORTUNA MOTORS, INC.
195 Fortuna Blvd, Fortuna, CA 95540
Tel.: (707) 725-6921
Web Site:
   http://www.fortunamotors.com
Sales Range: $10-24.9 Million
Emp.: 55
New Car Retailer
N.A.I.C.S.: 441110
David Annesley Somerville (Mgr)

FORTUNE
1271 Avenue of the Americas, New
York, NY 10020
Tel.: (212) 522-1212
Web Site: http://www.fortune.com
Sales Range: $100-124.9 Million
Emp.: 70
Business Magazine Publisher
N.A.I.C.S.: 513120
Geoffrey Colvin (Sr Editor)
Franklin L. Terkelsen (Treas)
Andrew Nusca (Sr Editor)
Jaclyn LoRaso (Editor-Photo)
Neil Harris (Assoc Editor-photo)
Alan Murray (Pres & CEO)
Adam Lashinsky (Editor)
Patricia Sellers (Exec Dir-MPW Sum-
mits & Live Content)
Jonathan Rivers (CTO)
Brian O'Keefe (Acting Editor-in-Chief)

FORTUNE CAPITAL PART-
NERS, INC.
2600 Douglas Rd PH-1, Coral
Gables, FL 33134
Tel.: (305) 225-7522
Web Site: https://www.fcpmiami.com
Year Founded: 1998
Emp.: 20
Holding Company; Real Estate Ser-
vices
N.A.I.C.S.: 551112
Miguel Poyastro (Pres)
Seth Heller (Mng Dir)
Barbara Perez (CFO)

Subsidiaries:

GREC Conversions   (1)
2600 Douglas Rd Ph 1, Coral Gables, FL
33134
Tel.: (305) 225-7522
Web Site: http://www.fcpmiami.com
Rev.: $89,800,000
Emp.: 5
Real Estate Management & Residential
Construction
N.A.I.C.S.: 531210
Miguel Poyastro (Pres)

FORTUNE CASUALS, LLC
10119 Jefferson Blvd, Culver City, CA
90232-3519
Tel.: (310) 733-2100   CA
Year Founded: 1999
Sales Range: $50-74.9 Million
Emp.: 100
Sportswear Mfr & Importer
N.A.I.C.S.: 315250
Walter Lachter (CFO & Controller)

FORTUNE FINANCIAL INC.
PO Box 296, New Brighton, PA
15066-0296
Tel.: (724) 846-2488   FL
Web Site:
   http://www.fortunefinancialser
vices.com
Sales Range: $25-49.9 Million
Emp.: 200
Automobile Insurance
N.A.I.C.S.: 522310
Greg Bentley (Pres)

FORTUNE FOOTWEAR INC.
174 Hudson St 3rd Fl, New York, NY
10013
Tel.: (212) 431-8400
Web Site:
   https://www.fortunefootwear.com
Rev.: $31,000,000
Emp.: 60
Footwear Merchant Whslr
N.A.I.C.S.: 424340
Joey Barraclough (Acct Mgr)
Michael Silverberg (VP-First Cost
Div)
Thomas Paccione (CFO)
Gertrudis Martinez (Mgr-Billing-LC)

FORTUNE HOMES OF TALLA-
HASSEE INC.
2417 Millcreek Ct Ste 2, Tallahassee,
FL 32308
Tel.: (850) 894-9696
Sales Range: $10-24.9 Million
Emp.: 3
Housing Construction Services
N.A.I.C.S.: 236117
Mike Askri (Pres)

FORTUNE INTERNATIONAL
REALTY, INC.
2666 Brickell Ave 3rd Fl, Miami, FL
33129
Tel.: (305) 856-2600
Web Site:
   http://www.fortuneinternational
realty.com
Year Founded: 1983
Sales Range: $1-4.9 Billion
Emp.: 1,430
Real Estate Broker
N.A.I.C.S.: 531210
Walter DeFortuna (Chm)
Amparo Fontanet (Dir-Mktg)
Fabio Fernando Faerman (Dir-Comml
Div)
Genesis Abascal (Mgr-Acctg)
Jasmin Aydagul (Sr Mgr-Mktg &
Comm)
Juanita Santana-Devia (Mgr-Acctg)
Monica DeFortuna (VP)
Ruth Palma (VP)
Terri Alvarez (Dir-Sls)

FORTUNE INTERNATIONAL,
INC.
56 Veronica Ave, Somerset, NJ
08873
Tel.: (732) 214-0700   NJ
Web Site: https://www.fortune-
cnc.com
Year Founded: 1989
Sales Range: $1-9.9 Million
Emp.: 14
Industrial Machinery & Equipment Mfr
N.A.I.C.S.: 423830

FORTUNEBUILDERS INC.
4655 Cass St Ste 214, San Diego,
CA 92109
Tel.: (203) 624-0444
Web Site:
   http://www.fortunebuilders.com
Year Founded: 1972
Sales Range: $10-24.9 Million

Emp.: 25
Real Estate Investment Services
N.A.I.C.S.: 525990
Than Merrill (Co-Founder & Pres)
Paul Esajian (Co-Founder)
Konrad Sopielnikow (Co-Founder)
Michelle Kruse (Dir-Learning & Trng
Dev)

FORTUS GROUP INC.
181 Genesee St Ste 600, Utica, NY
13501
Tel.: (315) 768-3322
Web Site:
   http://www.fortusgroup.com
Year Founded: 1993
Sales Range: $1-9.9 Million
Emp.: 70
Recruitment & Placement of Dialysis
& Transplantation Professionals
N.A.I.C.S.: 561311
Michael H. Maurizio (CEO)

FORTY FORT EYE ASSOCI-
ATES
1600 Wyoming Ave, Forty Fort, PA
18704-4220
Tel.: (570) 287-4955   PA
Web Site: http://www.ffeahec.com
Year Founded: 1952
Sales Range: $50-74.9 Million
Emp.: 27
Contact Lenses Mfr
N.A.I.C.S.: 621320
Joseph J. Smith (Co-Pres)
Jason R. Smith (Co-Pres)

FORUM COMMUNICATIONS
COMPANY
101 5th St N, Fargo, ND 58102-4826
Tel.: (701) 235-7311   ND
Web Site:
   http://www.forumcomm.com
Year Founded: 1917
Newspaper Publishing & Broadcast
Media Services
N.A.I.C.S.: 513110
William C. Marcil (Chm)
Dennis Hall (VP-Comml Printing)
John Hajostek (COO & Exec VP)
Aaron Becher (VP-Newspaper Ops)
Mari Ossenfort (VP-Brdcst)
Mary Jo Hotzler (VP-Content)
Katie Pinke (Gen Mgr-Agweek-Grand
Forks)
Steve Wagner (Dir-Forum News Svc)
Josh Rohrer (Gen Mgr-Broadcast)
Mark Von Bank (Dir-Adv)
Stephanie Schroeder (Chief Digital
Mktg Officer)
William Marcil Jr. (Pres, CEO &
Publr)

Subsidiaries:

Brainerd Dispatch   (1)
506 James St, Brainerd, MN 56401
Tel.: (218) 829-4705
Web Site: http://www.brainerddispatch.com
Newspaper Publishers
N.A.I.C.S.: 513110
Kari Lake (Controller & Dir-HR)
Rennee Richardson (Mng Editor)
Jason Allord (Mgr-Ops)
Susie Alters (Dir-Adv)
Dianna Blanck (Mgr-Circulation)
Leo Miller (Coord-Mktg)
Pete Mohs (Publr)
Jamie Olson (Mgr-Production)
Matt Erickson (Editor)

Duluth News Tribune   (1)
424 W 1st St, Duluth, MN 55802-1596
Tel.: (218) 723-5281
Web Site: http://www.duluthsuperior.com
Sales Range: $10-24.9 Million
Emp.: 250
Newspaper Publishers
N.A.I.C.S.: 513110

Ken Browall (Gen Mgr)
JoLissa Kowalik (Mgr-Circulation)
Dave Ojala (Editor-Copy)
Deb Williams (Coord-HR)
Neal Ronquist (Publr)
Megan Wedel (Dir-Adv)

Grand Forks Herald   (1)
375 2nd Ave N, Grand Forks, ND 58203-
3707
Tel.: (701) 780-1100
Web Site: http://www.gfherald.com
Sales Range: $10-24.9 Million
Emp.: 140
Newspaper Publishers
N.A.I.C.S.: 513110
Korrie Wenzel (Publr & Editor)
Kirsten Stromsodt (Editor)

Post Bulletin Company LLC   (1)
18 1st Ave SE, Rochester, MN 55904-3722
Tel.: (507) 285-7600
Web Site: http://www.postbulletin.com
Provider of Newspaper Services
N.A.I.C.S.: 513110

RedWing Republican Eagle   (1)
2760 N Service Dr, Red Wing, MN 55066
Tel.: (651) 388-8235
Web Site: http://www.republican-eagle.com
Sales Range: $10-24.9 Million
Emp.: 80
Newspapers
N.A.I.C.S.: 513110
Steve Engelhart (Dir-Adv)
Steve Gall (Publr)
Sally Shepherd (Dir-Digital Media)

The Daily Telegram   (1)
1410 Tower Ave, Superior, WI 54880
Tel.: (715) 395-5000
Web Site: http://www.superiortelegram.com
Rev.: $55,500,000
Emp.: 10
Newspaper Distr
N.A.I.C.S.: 513110
Vince Bodiford (Publr)

The Jamestown Sun   (1)
121 3rd St NW, Jamestown, ND 58401
Tel.: (701) 252-3120
Web Site: http://www.jamestownsun.com
Emp.: 50
Newspaper Publishers
N.A.I.C.S.: 513110
Rob Keller (Publr)
Kathy Steiner (Mng Editor)

FORUM PERSONNEL INC.
260 Madison Ave Rm 200, New York,
NY 10016
Tel.: (212) 687-4050
Web Site: http://www.forumgrp.com
Rev.: $100,000,000
Emp.: 50
Employment Agencies
N.A.I.C.S.: 561311
Frank Fusaro (Pres)

FORWARD CORPORATION
219 N Front St, Standish, MI 48658-
9428
Tel.: (989) 846-4501
Web Site:
   https://www.forwardcorp.com
Year Founded: 1955
Sales Range: $50-74.9 Million
Emp.: 600
Grocery & Gasoline Services
N.A.I.C.S.: 445110

Subsidiaries:

Forward Lodging   (1)
2980 Cook Rd, West Branch, MI 48661
Tel.: (989) 345-3503
Sales Range: $10-24.9 Million
Emp.: 30
Operator of Hotels
N.A.I.C.S.: 721110

Forward Transport   (1)
219 N Front St, Standish, MI 48658-9428
Tel.: (989) 846-4501
Web Site: http://www.forwardcorp.com
Sales Range: $25-49.9 Million
Emp.: 30
Trucking Services
N.A.I.C.S.: 213112

Forward Corporation—(Continued)

Dave Gould (VP)

T.R. McTaggart   (1)
219 N Front St, Standish, MI 48658-9428
Tel.: (989) 846-4501
Web Site: http://www.trmctaggart.com
Screen Printing & Embroidery
N.A.I.C.S.: 445110
Tina Debolt (Gen Mgr)

FORWARD HEALTH
30 W St Ste 4A, New York, NY
10004
Tel.: (877) 766-0525
Web Site:
http://www.forwardhealth.com
Year Founded: 2003
Sales Range: $1-9.9 Million
Emp.: 6
Website Management Operations
Covering Health Services
N.A.I.C.S.: 519290
Arthur Meyerovich (Mng Partner)
Alina Kaganovsky (Mng Partner)
Robert Scott (Gen Counsel)

FORWARD MEDIA INC.
245 8th Ave Ste 129, New York, NY
10011
Tel.: (646) 290-7535
Web Site: http://www.forward-
media.com
Year Founded: 2007
Sales Range: $1-9.9 Million
Emp.: 20
Media Buying Services
N.A.I.C.S.: 541810
Sherif Abdel Moneim (Owner)
Ashraf Sedky (VP-Bus Dev)
Naglaa Seifeldin (Exec VP-Ops)

FORWARD SOLUTIONS
73 Cedar Ave, Hershey, PA 17033
Tel.: (678) 389-7126
Web Site: https://forward-
solutions.com
Facilities Services
N.A.I.C.S.: 561210
Joe Orednick (CEO)

Subsidiaries:

Electrorep, Inc.   (1)
2015 Bridgeway Ste 201, Sausalito, CA
94965
Tel.: (415) 332-4100
Web Site: http://www.electrorep.com
Sales Range: $1-9.9 Million
Emp.: 25
Whol Electrical Equipment
N.A.I.C.S.: 423610
Ronald Haedt (CEO)
Kelly Boyd (Pres)
Damiko Dickson (VP-Ops)

Jackson and Associates, Inc.   (1)
15460 Herriman Blvd, Noblesville, IN 46060
Tel.: (317) 773-6660
Web Site: http://www.jackson-assoc.us
Direct Selling Establishments
N.A.I.C.S.: 541611
Barry Kavich (Partner & VP)

Lund-Iorio, Inc.   (1)
29122 Rancho Viejo Rd Ste 115, San Juan
Capistrano, CA 92675
Tel.: (949) 443-4855
Web Site: http://www.lund-iorio.com
Food Service Equipment Distr
N.A.I.C.S.: 423830
Greg Iorio (Principal)
Scott Lund (Principal)
Mark Micallef (Principal)
Joel Dishno (Principal)
Jason Dunahee (Coord-Inside Sls)

FORZA MIGLIOZZI, LLC
5419 Hollywood Blvd Ste C313, Hollywood, CA 90027
Tel.: (213) 973-4001

Web Site:
http://www.forzamigliozzi.com
Year Founded: 2007
Rev.: $24,000,000
Emp.: 24
Advetising Agency
N.A.I.C.S.: 541810
Michael Migliozzi (Mng Partner &
Dir-Creative)

**FOSS MANUFACTURING
COMPANY LLC**
11 Merrill Industrial Dr, Hampton, NH
03842
Tel.: (603) 929-6000   **NH**
Web Site: http://www.fossmfg.com
Year Founded: 1954
Sales Range: $150-199.9 Million
Emp.: 500
Mfr of Engineered Non-Woven Tex-
tiles
N.A.I.C.S.: 313230
Stephen W. Foss (Pres)
David Rowell (Exec VP)
Kevin Sexton (Sr VP-Fin)
A. J. Nassar (CEO)

Subsidiaries:

Foss Manufacturing Company LLC -
The Kunin Group Division   (1)
11 Merrill Industrial Dr, Hampton, NH
03843-5000
Tel.: (603) 929-6000
Web Site: http://www.kuningroup.com
Nonwoven Fabric Mfr
N.A.I.C.S.: 313230

FOSS MOTORS, INC.
133 Portsmouth Ave, Exeter, NH
03833-2105
Tel.: (603) 772-3702
Web Site: https://www.fosscars.com
Year Founded: 1961
Sales Range: $10-24.9 Million
Emp.: 40
New Car Whslr
N.A.I.C.S.: 441110
Lawrence Foss (Pres)

**FOSTER & FOSTER CONSULT-
ING ACTUARIES INC.**
1342 Parker Commons Blvd Ste 104,
Fort Myers, FL 33912
Tel.: (239) 433-5500
Web Site: http://www.foster-
foster.com
Sales Range: $1-9.9 Million
Emp.: 30
Actuarial Consulting Services
N.A.I.C.S.: 541219
Brad Heinrichs (Pres)

FOSTER ASSOCIATES, INC.
1 Church St Ste 101, Rockville, MD
20850
Tel.: (301) 664-7800
Web Site: http://www.foster-fa.com
Rev.: $42,400,000
Emp.: 49
Marketing Research & Consulting
Services
N.A.I.C.S.: 541910
Kathleen C. McShane (Pres)
Nancy R. Kay (VP)
Kimbugwe A. Kateregga (VP)
Edgar D. Boshart (VP)

FOSTER AUTO PARTS INC.
16393 NE Cameron Blvd, Portland,
OR 97230
Tel.: (503) 777-4531
Web Site: http://www.fosterauto.com
Sales Range: $10-24.9 Million
Emp.: 75
Auto & Home Supply Stores
N.A.I.C.S.: 441330
Fred J. Hopp (Pres)

**FOSTER BLUE WATER OIL,
LLC**
36065 Water St, Richmond, MI 48062
Tel.: (586) 727-3996   **MI**
Web Site: http://www.fosteroil.com
Rev.: $137,134,347
Emp.: 16
Gasoline Distr
N.A.I.C.S.: 424720
Tom McCartney (Dir-Sls & Mktg)

Subsidiaries:

Blue Flame Propane, Inc.   (1)
36065 Water St, Richmond, MI 48062
Tel.: (586) 727-3996
Web Site:
http://www.blueflamepropaneinc.com
Propane Supplier
N.A.I.C.S.: 457210
John Foster (Pres & CEO)

Sunrise Stores, LLC   (1)
36065 Water St, Richmond, MI 48062-0430
Tel.: (586) 727-3996
Web Site: http://www.fosteroil.com
Rev.: $78,701,765
Emp.: 14
Convenience Store Operator
N.A.I.C.S.: 445131

FOSTER CARE TO SUCCESS
21351 Gentry Dr Ste 130, Sterling,
VA 20166
Tel.: (571) 203-0270   **VA**
Web Site: http://www.fc2success.org
Year Founded: 1981
Sales Range: $10-24.9 Million
Emp.: 34
Grantmaking Services
N.A.I.C.S.: 813211
Lynn Davis (Dir-Partnership Dev)
Tina Raheem (Dir-Scholarships &
Grants)

**FOSTER CHEVROLET-
CADILLAC, INC.**
2504 Hayes Ave, Sandusky, OH
44870-5358
Tel.: (419) 625-1313   **OH**
Web Site:
http://www.fostersandusky.com
Year Founded: 1955
Sales Range: $10-24.9 Million
Emp.: 70
Car Whslr
N.A.I.C.S.: 441110
Douglas Foster (Pres)
Dawson Foster (VP)

FOSTER CORPORATION
45 Ridge Rd, Putnam, CT 06260-
Tel.: (860) 928-4102   **CT**
Web Site:
http://www.fostercorporation.com
Year Founded: 1989
Medical Pharmaceutical & Biotechnol-
ogy Polymer Product Mfr
N.A.I.C.S.: 326199
Lawrence A. Acquarulo Jr. (Founder,
Owner, Pres & CEO)

Subsidiaries:

Putnam Plastics Company, LLC   (1)
130 Louisa Viens Dr, Dayville, CT 06241
Tel.: (860) 774-1559
Web Site: http://www.putnamplastics.com
Sales Range: $10-24.9 Million
Emp.: 150
Medical Polymer Tubing Mfr
N.A.I.C.S.: 326199
James V. Dandeneau (Owner & CEO)

**FOSTER DEVELOPMENT
COMPANY**
146 Spring St, Macon, GA 31201
Tel.: (478) 742-5376
Year Founded: 1965
Sales Range: $10-24.9 Million
Emp.: 6

Real Estate Development Services
N.A.I.C.S.: 237210
William M. Foster (Pres)

**FOSTER DOLAN ENTER-
PRISES INC.**
5635 W Las Positas Blvd 406, Hay-
ward, CA 94588
Tel.: (510) 887-7260   **CA**
Year Founded: 1968
Sales Range: $50-74.9 Million
Emp.: 1,200
Restaurant Services
N.A.I.C.S.: 722513
Randy Rodriguez (Pres & CEO)
Lorna Evans (VP-Acctg)

FOSTER FINANCIAL GROUP
17300 Preston Rd Ste 260, Dallas,
TX 75252
Tel.: (972) 661-0101
Web Site:
https://www.fosterfinancialgroup.com
Year Founded: 1969
Sales Range: $10-24.9 Million
Emp.: 8
Financial Services
N.A.I.C.S.: 525990
Christi Barnes (Mgr-Client)
Larry J. Foster (Founder & Chm)
Joe Foster (Pres-Wealth Mgmt Div)

FOSTER FUELS INC.
16720 Brookneal Hwy, Brookneal, VA
24528
Tel.: (434) 376-2322
Web Site:
https://www.fosterfuels.com
Rev.: $40,673,409
Emp.: 30
Petroleum Products
N.A.I.C.S.: 424720
Watt R. Foster Jr. (Pres & CEO)
John George (Dir-Safety)
Mary Neighbors (Mgr-Propane Sls &
Svcs)
Darrell St. John (Mgr-IT)
W. Robert Foster Sr. (Pres)

FOSTER GARVEY PC
1111 Third Ave Ste 3000, Seattle, WA
98101
Tel.: (206) 447-4400
Web Site: http://www.foster.com
Year Founded: 2019
Law firm
N.A.I.C.S.: 541199
Joseph Arellano (Principal & Mng Dir-
Office)
Jen Castleberry (CMO & Chief Bus
Dev Officer)

**FOSTER HOLDING GROUP
INC.**
313 Winter St, Superior, WI 54880
Tel.: (715) 394-6099   **WI**
Web Site:
https://www.jefffostertrucking.com
Year Founded: 1991
Sales Range: $10-24.9 Million
Emp.: 275
Holding Company
N.A.I.C.S.: 551112
Jeff Foster (CEO)
Leo Norman (COO)
Jim Manion (CFO)
Dean M. Brickson (Exec VP)
Karen Gucinski (Mgr-Payroll)
Joe Wischnewski (Mgr-IT & A/R
Collections)

FOSTER LUMBER YARD INC.
3280 Sonoma Blvd, Vallejo, CA
94590
Tel.: (707) 557-3000

Web Site:
https://www.fosterlumber.com
Rev.: $13,119,472
Emp.: 25
Builders' Hardware
N.A.I.C.S.: 444140
David Jones *(Owner)*

Subsidiaries:

Foster Lumber Yard Inc. -
Fairfield (1)
1601 W Texas St, Fairfield, CA 94533
Tel.: (707) 425-3400
Web Site: http://www.fosterlumber.com
Sales Range: $10-24.9 Million
Emp.: 5
Home Center Operator
N.A.I.C.S.: 444110

FOSTER MARKETING COMMUNICATIONS
3909-F Ambassador Caffrey, Lafayette, LA 70503
Tel.: (337) 235-1848
Web Site:
http://www.fostermarketing.com
Year Founded: 1980
Advetising Agency
N.A.I.C.S.: 541810
George Foster *(CEO)*
Tiffany Harris *(Pres)*
Vicki Wyatt *(Mgr-Production & Traffic)*
Bob Wallace *(Exec VP-Houston)*
Megan Hebert *(Coord-Trade Show & Acct Assoc)*
Jamie Efurd *(VP-Mktg)*
Gary Meeks *(Controller)*
Kristy Bonner *(Strategist-Digital & Acct Exec)*
Erica Bille *(Mgr-Office)*
Chelsea Troxler *(Dir-Mktg)*

Subsidiaries:

Foster Marketing
Communications (1)
650 N Sam Houston Pkwy E Ste 220,
Houston, TX 77060
Tel.: (281) 448-3435
Web Site: http://www.fostermarketing.com
Advetising Agency
N.A.I.C.S.: 541810

FOSTER PRINTING SERVICE, INC.
4295 Ohio St, Michigan City, IN 46360
Tel.: (219) 879-8366
Web Site:
http://www.fosterprinting.com
Year Founded: 1923
Sales Range: $10-24.9 Million
Emp.: 80
Commercial Printing
N.A.I.C.S.: 323111
Matthew Griswold *(Co-Owner)*
Mike Herbert *(VP-Sls)*
Nicholas Griswold *(Owner)*

FOSTER WAYLAND INCORPORATED
17 Ontario Way, Trenton, NJ 08648
Tel.: (609) 771-6861
Sales Range: $25-49.9 Million
Emp.: 24
Consulting Businesses; Metal Equipment; Construction
N.A.I.C.S.: 459999

FOSTERS FREEZE, LLC
8360 Red Oak Ave Ste 202, Rancho Cucamonga, CA 91730-3880
Tel.: (909) 944-0815   CA
Web Site:
http://www.fostersfreeze.com
Year Founded: 1946
Sales Range: $25-49.9 Million
Emp.: 5

Restaurants & Ice Cream Parlors
Owner & Franchisor
N.A.I.C.S.: 722513
Edward Yoon *(Owner & Mgr)*

FOSTERS INC.
1235 Peters Dr, Waterloo, IA 50704
Tel.: (319) 235-6548
Web Site: https://www.fostersinc.com
Sales Range: $10-24.9 Million
Emp.: 30
Fertilizer & Fertilizer Materials
N.A.I.C.S.: 424910
John Leman *(Pres)*

FOTH & VAN DYKE & ASSOCIATES INC.
2737 S Rdg Rd PO Box 19012,
Green Bay, WI 54304-5513
Tel.: (920) 497-2500   WI
Web Site: http://www.foth.com
Year Founded: 1938
Sales Range: $100-124.9 Million
Emp.: 550
Engineeering Services
N.A.I.C.S.: 541330
Tim Weyenberg *(Pres & CEO)*

Subsidiaries:

Foth Production Solutions, LLC (1)
2121 Innovation Ct, De Pere, WI 54115
Tel.: (920) 497-2500
Web Site: http://www.foth.com
Sales Range: $25-49.9 Million
Emp.: 400
Custom Machine Development & Mfr
N.A.I.C.S.: 541330
John Leonardi *(Pres)*

FOTO ELECTRIC SUPPLY CO., INC.
1 Rewe St, Brooklyn, NY 11211
Tel.: (212) 260-0666   NY
Web Site: http://www.fescony.com
Year Founded: 1962
Sales Range: $50-74.9 Million
Emp.: 25
Holding Company
N.A.I.C.S.: 551112
Emerich Goldstein *(Chm)*

Subsidiaries:

Etronics, Inc. (1)
216 Maspeth Ave, Brooklyn, NY 11211
Tel.: (212) 475-2450
Web Site: http://www.etronics.com
Sales Range: $75-99.9 Million
Consumer Electronics & Related Items Retailer
N.A.I.C.S.: 449210
Emerich Goldstein *(Chm)*
Mayer Balser *(COO)*
Leo Landau *(VP-Sls & Mktg)*

FOTO-WEAR INC.
473D Easton Tpke, Lake Ariel, PA 18436-4796
Tel.: (570) 307-3600
Web Site: http://www.fotowear.com
Rev.: $11,000,000
Emp.: 11
Stationery Products
N.A.I.C.S.: 322230

FOTV MEDIA NETWORKS INC.
338 N Canon Dr Fl 3, Beverly Hills, CA 90210   DE
Web Site: http://www.fotvmedia.com
Year Founded: 2007
Sales Range: $10-24.9 Million
Emp.: 156
Medical Management Services
N.A.I.C.S.: 518210
Alkiviades A. David *(Chm & CEO)*
Sanjay Reddy *(Exec VP-FOTV)*
Nick Kutovyy *(CTO)*
Kim Hurwitz *(Chief Content Officer)*

Donna Kay Smith *(Pres-CinemaNow)*
Carl Dawson *(CMO)*
Peter Van Pruissen *(CFO, Treas & Sec)*

FOUGHT & COMPANY INC.
14255 SW 72nd Ave, Tigard, OR 97224
Tel.: (503) 639-3141
Web Site:
https://www.foughtsteel.com
Sales Range: $10-24.9 Million
Emp.: 140
Structural Steel Erection
N.A.I.C.S.: 238120
Rex Smith *(Pres)*

FOULGER-PRATT CONTRACTING LLC
12435 Park Potomac Ave Ste 200, Potomac, MD 20854
Tel.: (240) 499-9600
Web Site:
https://www.foulgerpratt.com
Sales Range: $25-49.9 Million
Emp.: 120
Commercial & Office Building, New Construction
N.A.I.C.S.: 236220
Lisa Wood *(Mgr-Mktg & Bus Dev)*

FOUNDATION 9 ENTERTAINMENT, INC.
9 Pasteur Ste 100, Irvine, CA 92618
Tel.: (949) 698-1500
Web Site: http://www.f9e.com
Emp.: 200
Interactive Entertainment Products Developer
N.A.I.C.S.: 513210
James North-Hearn *(CEO)*
Steve Sardegna *(CFO & Exec VP)*
Chauncey Gammage *(VP-HR)*
Michael Dean *(VP-Ops)*
Lindsay Gupton *(VP-Studios)*
Patrick Gilmore *(VP-Studios)*
Stuart Knowles *(Gen Counsel & VP)*

Subsidiaries:

Backbone Entertainment (1)
1375 55th St, Emeryville, CA 94608
Tel.: (510) 547-6101
Web Site:
http://www.backboneentertainment.com
Sales Range: $25-49.9 Million
Emp.: 100
Interactive Entertainment Products Developer
N.A.I.C.S.: 513210

ImagineEngine (1)
1881 Worcester Rd, Framingham, MA 01702
Tel.: (508) 739-0120
Web Site: http://www.imaginengine.com
Sales Range: $10-24.9 Million
Emp.: 30
Online Educational Games
N.A.I.C.S.: 513130

FOUNDATION AUTOMOTIVE CORP
211 Highland Cross Dr Ste #260, Houston, TX 77073
Tel.: (832) 400-9400
Web Site:
http://www.foundationauto.com
New Car Dealers
N.A.I.C.S.: 441110
Kevin Kutchinski *(Pres & CEO)*

Subsidiaries:

Patterson
Oldsmobile-Gmc-Toyota (1)
315 Central Fwy E, Wichita Falls, TX 76301
Tel.: (940) 766-0293
Web Site: http://www.pattersonauto.com
Rev.: $86,465,507
Emp.: 250

Car Dealership Of Automobiles, New & Used
N.A.I.C.S.: 441110
Harry E. Patterson Jr. *(Owner)*

FOUNDATION CAPITAL, LLC
550 High St 3rd Fl, Palo Alto, CA 94301
Tel.: (650) 614-0500
Web Site:
http://www.foundationcapital.com
Year Founded: 1996
Sales Range: $25-49.9 Million
Emp.: 25
Privater Equity Firm
N.A.I.C.S.: 523999
Ashu Garg *(Gen Partner)*
Skip Glass *(Operating Partner)*
Paul Holland *(Gen Partner)*
Paul G. Koontz *(Gen Partner)*
Steven Vassallo *(Gen Partner)*
Warren M. Weiss *(Gen Partner)*
Adit Singh *(Partner)*
Jonathan Ehrlich *(Partner)*
Meg Sloan *(Partner-Mktg)*
Dave Singer *(CFO)*
Joanne Chen *(Partner)*
Rodolfo Gonzalez *(Partner)*
Zach Noorani *(Partner)*
Charles Moldow *(Gen Partner)*

FOUNDATION CENTER
32 Old Slip Fl 24, New York, NY 10005
Tel.: (212) 620-4230
Web Site:
http://www.foundationcenter.org
Sales Range: $10-24.9 Million
Emp.: 129
Directory Publisher
N.A.I.C.S.: 513140
Bradford Smith *(Pres)*

FOUNDATION COMMUNITIES
3036 S 1st St, Austin, TX 78704
Tel.: (512) 447-2026   TX
Web Site: http://www.foundcom.org
Year Founded: 1990
Sales Range: $10-24.9 Million
Emp.: 424
Community Housing Assistance Services
N.A.I.C.S.: 624229
Karen Lyons Serna *(Dir-Asset Building Programs)*

FOUNDATION CONSTRUCTORS INC.
81 Big Break Rd, Oakley, CA 94561
Tel.: (925) 754-6633
Web Site:
https://www.foundationpiledriving.com
Rev.: $38,845,371
Emp.: 150
Pile Driving Contractor
N.A.I.C.S.: 236210
Dermot Fallon *(Pres)*

FOUNDATION FINANCIAL HOLDINGS, INC.
225 Water St Ste 1290, Jacksonville, FL 32202
Tel.: (904) 356-4481
Web Site:
http://www.nsurance.ffg.com
Sales Range: $10-24.9 Million
Emp.: 253
Financial Management Services
N.A.I.C.S.: 523999
Mark W. Boyer *(Pres & CEO)*
Kris S. Williams *(Co-Founder & Pres)*
Paul V. Scott *(Co-Founder & Chm)*
William A. Gordon *(Sr VP-Ops)*

Foundation Financial Holdings, Inc.—(Continued)

Roy E. Kelly *(Exec VP)*
Marc Chillion *(Exec VP-Sls-Atlanta)*
James Brodsky *(Chief HR Officer)*

FOUNDATION FOR EDUCATIONAL SERVICES
1300 O St, Lincoln, NE 68508
Tel.: (402) 479-6933   NE
Web Site: http://www.fes.org
Year Founded: 1986
Sales Range: $10-24.9 Million
Emp.: 207
Educational Support Services
N.A.I.C.S.: 611710
Irene Williams *(CFO & VP-HR)*
Dan Kunzman *(VP-Educational Svcs)*
Dan Delzell *(VP-IT Svcs)*

FOUNDATION FOR EMBRYONIC COMPETENCE
140 Allen Rd Ste 300, Basking Ridge, NJ 07920
Tel.: (908) 580-1200   NJ
Web Site: https://www.feclabs.org
Year Founded: 2013
Sales Range: $75-99.9 Million
Emp.: 25
Medical Assistance Services
N.A.I.C.S.: 622110
Lyn Jacobson *(Sec)*
Rebekah Zimmerman *(Dir-Clinical Genetics)*
Richard T. Scott *(Pres)*
William Chow *(Treas)*

FOUNDATION FOR EXCELLENCE IN EDUCATION
215 S Monroe St Ste 420, Tallahassee, FL 32301
Tel.: (850) 391-4090   FL
Web Site: https://www.excelined.org
Year Founded: 2007
Sales Range: $10-24.9 Million
Emp.: 53
Child Educational Support Services
N.A.I.C.S.: 611710
Patricia Levesque *(CEO)*
Jeb Bush *(Chm & Pres)*

FOUNDATION FOR FOOD & AGRICULTURE RESEARCH
401 9th St NW Ste 630, Washington, DC 20004
Tel.: (202) 624-0700   DC
Web Site:
    http://www.foundationfar.org
Year Founded: 2014
Rev.: $69,647,073
Assets: $254,494,599
Liabilities: $248,507,550
Net Worth: $5,987,049
Earnings: $614,265
Emp.: 1
Fiscal Year-end: 12/31/18
Research & Advocacy Services
N.A.I.C.S.: 813319
Sally Rockey *(Exec Dir)*
Doug Cameron *(Mng Dir)*
Mark E. Keenum *(Chm)*
Chris Mallett *(Treas)*
Alton Thompson *(Exec Dir)*
Kathryn J. Boor *(VP)*

FOUNDATION FOR JEWISH PHILANTHROPIES
2640 N Forest Rd Ste 200, Getzville, NY 14068-1573
Tel.: (716) 204-1133   NY
Web Site:
    https://www.jewishphilanthropy.org
Year Founded: 1911
Sales Range: $10-24.9 Million
Emp.: 11
Philanthropic Services

N.A.I.C.S.: 813211
Lisa J. Collins *(Dir-Admin)*
Peter Fleischmann *(CEO)*
Teresa C. K. David *(Dir-Fin)*
Janine M. Allen *(Dir-IT)*

FOUNDATION FOR NEWARK'S FUTURE
60 Park Pl Ste 604, Newark, NJ 07102
Tel.: (973) 639-1600   NJ
Web Site:
    http://www.foundationfornewarks future.org
Year Founded: 2010
Sales Range: $10-24.9 Million
Emp.: 9
Educational Support Services
N.A.I.C.S.: 611710
Shannon Boehmer *(Project Dir-My Very Own Library)*
Kimberly Baxter McLain *(Pres & CEO)*
Cody Evans *(Office Mgr)*

FOUNDATION FOR SURGICAL FELLOWSHIP
11300 W Olympic Blvd Ste 600, Los Angeles, CA 90064
Tel.: (310) 424-3332   CA
Web Site:
    https://www.surgicalfellowships.org
Year Founded: 2010
Sales Range: $1-9.9 Million
Health & Welfare Fund Services
N.A.I.C.S.: 525120
Linda Schultz *(Exec Dir)*
Colleen Elkins *(Dir-Dev)*
Dennis Fowler *(Pres)*
Bruce Wolff *(VP)*
Patrick O'Leary *(Sec)*
Ravi S. Chari *(Treas)*

FOUNDATION FOR THE CAROLINAS
220 N Tryon St, Charlotte, NC 28202
Tel.: (704) 973-4500   NC
Web Site: https://www.fftc.org
Year Founded: 1958
Sales Range: $300-349.9 Million
Emp.: 65
Community Foundation
N.A.I.C.S.: 813211
Brian Collier *(Exec VP)*
Michael Marsicano *(Pres & CEO)*
Laura Smith *(Exec VP)*
Greg Beuris *(Dir-Investment Reporting & VP)*
Debra S. Watt *(Chief HR Officer)*
Devire Robinson *(VP-Center for Nonprofit Sustainability)*
Rebecca Rodriguez *(Controller)*
Marla Neely *(VP-Special Events)*
Alyssa R. Federico *(VP & Dir-Fin)*
Paul Fisher *(Dir-Information Technology & VP)*
Tara Keener *(VP & Dir-Mktg & Comm)*
Andrea C. Phelps *(VP-Donor Rels)*
Nikhil Sawant *(CIO & Exec VP-Bus Svcs)*

FOUNDATION FOR THE ELDERLY
145 Beach St, Far Rockaway, NY 11691
Tel.: (718) 327-6300   NY
Year Founded: 1992
Sales Range: $1-9.9 Million
Emp.: 369
Health Care Srvices
N.A.I.C.S.: 621111
Norman Neiger *(VP)*
Maurice D. Meisels *(Treas & Sec)*
Naftali Reiner *(Pres)*

FOUNDATION FOR THE GLOBAL COMPACT
685 3rd Ave 12th Fl, New York, NY 10017
Tel.: (212) 907-1301   NY
Web Site:
    https://www.globalcompactfoun dation.org
Year Founded: 2006
Sales Range: $10-24.9 Million
Emp.: 85
Fundraising Services
N.A.I.C.S.: 813211

FOUNDATION HEALTHCARE, INC.
13900 N Portland Ave Ste 200, Oklahoma City, OK 73134
Tel.: (405) 608-1700   OK
Web Site: http://www.fdnh.com
Year Founded: 2003
FDNHD—(OTCQB)
Holding Company; Hospitals, Ambulatory Surgery Centers & Sleep Centers
N.A.I.C.S.: 551112
Stanton M. Nelson *(CEO)*
Thomas A. Michaud *(Chm)*
Marcelo Puiggari *(Gen Counsel & VP-Legal Affairs)*
Hubert King *(CFO & Chief Acctg Officer)*

Subsidiaries:

Foundation Bariatric Hospital of San Antonio, LLC   (1)
9522 Huebner Rd, San Antonio, TX 78240
Tel.: (210) 478-5400
Web Site: http://www.fshsanantonio.com
Health Care Srvices
N.A.I.C.S.: 622110
Blake W. Hubbard *(CEO)*

Foundation Surgical Hospital Management, LLC   (1)
13919 N May Ave Ste B, Oklahoma City, OK 73134-5004
Tel.: (405) 608-1759
Health Care Srvices
N.A.I.C.S.: 622110
Judy Beech *(Controller)*

Nocturna Sleep Center, LLC   (1)
9077 S Pecos Rd Ste 3700, Henderson, NV 89074
Tel.: (702) 896-7378
Web Site: http://www.nocturnasleep.com
Diversified Health Care Services
N.A.I.C.S.: 621999

Nocturna Sleep Therapy, LP   (1)
3120 W Southlake Blvd Ste 120, Southlake, TX 76092
Tel.: (817) 741-8860
Sales Range: $10-24.9 Million
Emp.: 3
Health Care Srvices
N.A.I.C.S.: 621999
Brennen Johnson *(Gen Mgr)*

somniCare, Inc.   (1)
10203 Metcalf Ave Ste 100, Overland Park, KS 66212
Tel.: (913) 498-1331
Sales Range: $10-24.9 Million
Emp.: 6
Health Care Srvices
N.A.I.C.S.: 621999
Linda Summer *(Mgr)*

FOUNDATION INVESTMENT PARTNERS, LLC
7160 Chagrin Rr Ste 100, Chagrin Falls, OH 44023
Tel.: (440) 903-1791
Web Site:
    http://www.foundationpartners.net
Privater Equity Firm
N.A.I.C.S.: 523999
David Wood *(Mng Partner)*
Amy Forsythe *(Principal)*
Laura Redinger *(Principal)*

Subsidiaries:

Spartan Tool Supply Company, Inc.   (1)
1660 Alum Creek Dr, Columbus, OH 43209
Tel.: (614) 443-7607
Web Site:
    https://www.spartantoolcolumbus.com
Rev.: $5,700,000
Emp.: 10
Industrial Supplies Merchant Whslr
N.A.I.C.S.: 423840
Dick Bateman *(Pres)*
Derek Elbaor *(CEO)*

FOUNDATION TECHNOLOGIES, INC.
1400 Progress Industrial Blvd, Lawrenceville, GA 30043
Tel.: (678) 407-4640   GA
Web Site:
    http://www.foundationtechnology.com
Year Founded: 1986
Sales Range: $25-49.9 Million
Emp.: 20
Specialty Foundation Construction Products Distr
N.A.I.C.S.: 423390
Frank Queen *(Pres & CEO)*
Paul McCrea *(Mgr-Ops)*

FOUNDATION TITLE, LLC
601 Route 73 N Ste 201 4 Greentree Ctr, Marlton, NJ 08053
Tel.: (856) 834-2600   NJ
Web Site: https://www.ftnj.com
Year Founded: 2005
Sales Range: $10-24.9 Million
Emp.: 130
Title Insurance Agency
N.A.I.C.S.: 524210
Edward Rickenbach *(Founder)*

Subsidiaries:

Red Bank Title Agency Inc.   (1)
25 Sycamore Ave, Little Silver, NJ 07739
Tel.: (732) 747-8444
Web Site: http://www.redbanktitle.com
Sales Range: $1-9.9 Million
Title Insurance Agency
N.A.I.C.S.: 524210
Richard E. Marshall *(Founder & Pres)*

FOUNDERS 3 REAL ESTATE SERVICES
252 E Highland Ave, Milwaukee, WI 53202
Tel.: (414) 271-1111
Web Site: https://founders3.com
Year Founded: 2017
Emp.: 250
Real Estate Brokerage & Management Firm
N.A.I.C.S.: 531210
LeeAnn Abrams *(Mgr)*

FOUNDERS BREWING CO.
235 Grandville Ave SW, Grand Rapids, MI 49503
Tel.: (616) 776-2182
Web Site:
    https://www.foundersbrewing.com
Year Founded: 1997
Emp.: 262
Brewery Operator
N.A.I.C.S.: 312120
Mike Stevens *(Co-Founder & CEO)*

FOUNDERS EQUITY, INC.
545 5th Ave Ste 401, New York, NY 10017
Tel.: (212) 829-0900
Web Site: https://www.fequity.com
Year Founded: 1969
Sales Range: $10-24.9 Million
Emp.: 5
Privater Equity Firm
N.A.I.C.S.: 523999

Warren H. Haber *(Founder & Partner)*
John L. Teeger *(Partner)*
J. Ryan Kelley *(Partner)*
John D. White Jr. *(Partner)*

Subsidiaries:

Richardson Brands Company **(1)**
101 Erie Blvd, Canajoharie, NY 13317
Tel.: (518) 673-3553
Web Site: http://www.richardsonbrands.com
Sales Range: $25-49.9 Million
Candy & Other Food Product Mfr
N.A.I.C.S.: 311340

Subsidiary (Domestic):

Dryden & Palmer Company **(2)**
101 Erie Blvd, Canajoharie, NY
13317 **(100%)**
Tel.: (203) 481-3725
Web Site: http://www.richardsonbrands.com
Sales Range: $25-49.9 Million
Rock Candy Mfr
N.A.I.C.S.: 311340
Don Butte *(CEO)*

Gravymaster Inc. **(2)**
101 Erie Blvd, Canajoharie, NY 13317-1148
Tel.: (203) 481-2276
Sales Range: $25-49.9 Million
Mfr of Seasoning & Browning Sauces
N.A.I.C.S.: 311941

The Colibri Group, Inc. **(1)**
25 Fairmount Ave, East Providence, RI
02914
Tel.: (401) 943-2100
Web Site: http://www.colibri.com
Sales Range: $100-124.9 Million
Mfr & Distr of Jewelry, Lighters, Accessories
& Clocks; Owned by Founders Equity Inc.,
Main Street Resources & CITIC Group
N.A.I.C.S.: 423940
Yazir Phelps *(CMO)*
Jim Fox *(CFO)*

Subsidiary (Domestic):

Western Schools, Inc. **(2)**
PO Box 1930, Brockton, MA 02303-1930
Tel.: (508) 638-7000
Web Site: http://www.westernschools.com
Home Study Continuing Education (for
Nurses)
N.A.I.C.S.: 611710

The Pay-O-Matic Corp. **(1)**
160 Oak Dr, Syosset, NY 11791
Tel.: (516) 496-4900
Web Site: http://www.payomatic.com
Sales Range: $75-99.9 Million
Check Cashing & Financial Services
N.A.I.C.S.: 522390

Subsidiary (Domestic):

Freeman Management Corp. **(2)**
254 Kingston Ave, Brooklyn, NY 11213
Tel.: (615) 383-3111
Sales Range: $100-124.9 Million
Provider of Financial & Security Services
N.A.I.C.S.: 522390

Pay-O-Matic Check Cashing
Corp. **(2)**
254 Kingston Ave, Brooklyn, NY 11213
Tel.: (718) 778-4300
Sales Range: $50-74.9 Million
Emp.: 4
Check Cashing Services
N.A.I.C.S.: 522390

Rapid Armored Corporation **(2)**
254 Scholes St, Brooklyn, NY 11206
Tel.: (718) 366-8103
Web Site: http://www.rapidarmored.com
Sales Range: $25-49.9 Million
Provider of Armored Car Services
N.A.I.C.S.: 561613
Ron Vasquez *(Dir-Security)*

The Pay-O-Matic Corp. **(2)**
254 Kingston Ave, Brooklyn, NY 11213
Tel.: (718) 778-4300
Web Site: http://www.payomatic.com
Check Cashing & Money Transmitter Ser-
vices
N.A.I.C.S.: 522390
Richard Gaccione *(CEO)*

FOUNDERS FUND INC.
One Letterman Dr Bldg C Ste 420,
San Francisco, CA 94129
Tel.: (415) 230-5800
Web Site:
    http://www.foundersfund.com
Year Founded: 2005
Venture Capital Investment Services
N.A.I.C.S.: 523999
Luke Nosek *(Mng Partner)*
Peter A. Thiel *(Co-Founder & Part-
ner)*
Ken Howery *(Co-Founder & Partner)*
Brian Singerman *(Mng Partner)*
Cyan Banister *(Partner-Investing)*
Trae Stephens *(Principal)*
Napolean Ta *(Principal)*
Geoff Lewis *(Partner)*
Scott Nolan *(Partner)*
Lauren Gross *(COO & Partner)*
Neil Pai *(Gen Counsel)*
Keith Rabois *(Gen Partner)*

FOUNDRY COMMERCIAL LLC
420 S Orange Ave Ste 950, Orlando,
FL 32801
Tel.: (407) 540-7700
Web Site:
    http://www.foundrycommercial.com
Year Founded: 2007
Emp.: 258
Commercial Real Estate Services
N.A.I.C.S.: 531210
Paul Ellis *(CEO)*
Pryse Elam *(Pres-Dev & Investment
& Principal)*
Moses Salcido *(Principal-Dev & In-
vestment)*
Andy Hawkins *(Sr VP-Brokerage
Svcs)*
Greg Main-Baillie *(Mng Dir-
Construction & Dev Svcs)*
Ankoor J. Jivan *(Partner & VP-Dev &
Investments)*
Rick Wilson *(Dir-Project Mgmt-
Orlando & Tampa)*
Adna Rubio *(Mgr-Real Estate-
Raleigh)*
Alex Rosario *(Principal-Brokerage
Svcs)*
Chris Mauth *(VP-Healthcare Svcs)*
Daniel Matovich *(Sr Mgr-Real Estate-
Religious, Education & Not-for-Profit
Grp)*
Edward Young *(Mgr-Real Estate)*
Gregg Ickes *(Mng Dir-Svcs & Princi-
pal)*
J. Paul Reynolds *(Principal-
Brokerage Svcs)*
Scott Ghent *(Sr Chief Engr)*
Scott Renaud *(COO & Principal)*
Stephen Ball *(Sr Project Mgr)*
Stephen Hess *(Mgr-Facilities)*
Tim Castino *(Mgr-Real Estate)*
Zac Brown *(Sr Project Mgr)*
Joey Blakley *(VP-Religious, Educa-
tion & Not-for-Profit Grp)*
Jonathan Balthrop *(VP-Dev & Invest-
ment)*
Justin Ruby *(Sr VP-Brokerage Svcs)*
Mark Meara *(Sr Chief Engr)*
Mark Meyer *(Project Dir-Project
Mgmt)*
Nancy Hanson *(Sr Mgr-Real Estate)*
Nick McKinney *(Officer-Strategy &
Principal)*
PJ Behr *(VP-Brokerage Svcs)*
Jeff Patterson *(Sr VP)*
John Ball *(Partner)*
Kevin Maddron *(CFO)*
Alexis Lambeth *(Sr VP-Industrial Bro-
kerage Svcs)*
Andrew Maxwell *(Sr VP)*
Bill Simerville *(Mng Dir & Principal)*
Brad Chrischilles *(Principal-Brokerage
Svcs)*

Brandy Garnero *(Mng Dir-Human
Capital)*
Brian Brtalik *(Mng Dir & Principal)*
Brian Craver *(Sr VP)*
Charles Jonas *(Partner & Sr Mng Dir)*
Chris Bury *(Partner & Sr VP-
Religious, Education & Not-For-Profit
Grp)*
Chris Hurd *(Mng Dir)*
Vince Dunavant *(Sr VP-Advisory &
Transaction Svcs)*
Jim Traynor *(Mng Dir-Dev & Invest-
ments)*
Zach Strunk *(VP-Ops-Seniors Hous-
ing)*

FOUNDRY GROUP LLC
1050 Walnut St Ste 210, Boulder, CO
80302
Tel.: (303) 642-4050
Web Site:
    http://www.foundrygroup.com
Rev.: $225,000,000
Venture Capital Firm
N.A.I.C.S.: 523150
Bradley A. Feld *(Partner)*
Seth Levine *(Partner)*
Ryan McIntyre *(Partner)*
Jason Mendelson *(Partner)*

FOUNDSTONE
27201 Puerta Real #400, Mission
Viejo, CA 92691
Tel.: (949) 297-5600
Web Site: http://www.foundstone.com
Year Founded: 1999
Sales Range: $10-24.9 Million
Emp.: 125
Software Security Systems
N.A.I.C.S.: 561621
Stuart McClure *(Co-Founder & CTO)*

FOUNTAIN CONSTRUCTION COMPANY, INC.
5655 Hwy 18 W, Jackson, MS 39209
Tel.: (601) 373-4162 MS
Web Site:
    https://www.fountainconstruction.com
Year Founded: 1959
Sales Range: $50-74.9 Million
Emp.: 550
Industrial Buildings & Warehouses
N.A.I.C.S.: 236210
Brad Fountain *(Pres)*
Chris Fountain *(VP)*

FOUNTAIN HOUSE, INC.
425 W 47th St, New York, NY 10036
Tel.: (212) 582-0340 NY
Web Site:
    https://www.fountainhouse.org
Year Founded: 1948
Sales Range: Less than $1 Million
Mental Health Services
N.A.I.C.S.: 621420
Guy L. de Chazal *(Co-Chm)*
Nancy T. Farrell *(Co-Chm)*
William B. Brannan *(Co-Vice Chm)*
Elizabeth Seidman *(Sec)*
Lorna Hyde Graev *(Co-Vice Chm)*
Henry P. van Ameringen *(Second
Vice Chm)*
Kenneth J. Dudek *(Pres)*
Jennifer Rivera *(Dir-HR)*
Lisa Tai *(Comptroller)*
Jeffrey Aron *(Dir-External Affairs)*
Alan Doyle *(Dir-Colleague Trng)*
Andrew D. Schonebaum *(CFO)*
Charles J. Marsden *(Treas)*

FOUNTAIN ROCK MANAGE-MENT CORPORATION
124 N Market St, Frederick, MD
21701-5422
Tel.: (301) 631-0089
Sales Range: $25-49.9 Million

Emp.: 200
Brewery Mfr
N.A.I.C.S.: 312120
Charles Bowers *(VP)*
Philip Bowers *(Mgr-Consumer In-
sights)*

FOUNTAINHEAD CAPITAL MANAGEMENT, LLC
10 Independence Blvd Ste 120, War-
ren, NJ 07059
Tel.: (732) 346-1900
Year Founded: 2011
Sales Range: $1-9.9 Million
Financial Planning & Services
N.A.I.C.S.: 523999
Marc Rock *(Mng Partner)*

FOUNTAINHEAD DEVELOP-MENT INC.
1501 Queens Way, Fairbanks, AK
99701
Tel.: (907) 456-7143 AK
Web Site:
    http://www.fountainheadhotels.com
Sales Range: $10-24.9 Million
Emp.: 18
Hotel Owner & Operator
N.A.I.C.S.: 721110
Timothy Cerny *(Chm)*
John Nelson *(Controller)*

FOUNTAINHEAD DEVELOP-MENT, LLC
1394 Broadway Ave, Braselton, GA
30517
Tel.: (770) 867-0903 GA
Year Founded: 1982
Sales Range: $25-49.9 Million
Emp.: 600
Hotel Owner & Operator
N.A.I.C.S.: 721110
Don Panoz *(Pres)*

Subsidiaries:

Chateau Elan Ltd. **(1)**
100 Tour De France Dr, Braselton, GA
30517-2419
Tel.: (678) 425-0900
Web Site: http://www.chateauelan.com
Sales Range: $25-49.9 Million
Producer of Alcoholic Beverages
N.A.I.C.S.: 721110
Henk Evers *(Pres)*

Chateau Elan Winery & Resort **(1)**
100 Rue Charlemagne Dr, Braselton, GA
30517-2435 **(100%)**
Tel.: (678) 425-0900
Web Site:
    http://www.chateauelanatlanta.com
Sales Range: $50-74.9 Million
Emp.: 400
Lodging Services
N.A.I.C.S.: 721110
Clarissa Danna *(Mgr-Sls-Natl)*
Kevin Rosa *(Dir-Sls & Mktg)*
Ed Walls *(Gen Mgr)*

FOUNTAINS COUNTRY CLUB
4476 Fountains Dr, Lake Worth, FL
33467
Tel.: (561) 642-2700 FL
Web Site:
    http://www.fountainscc.com
Year Founded: 1979
Sales Range: $10-24.9 Million
Emp.: 100
Country Club
N.A.I.C.S.: 713910
Janet Kresge *(First VP)*
Sean Lutman *(CEO & Gen Mgr)*

FOUR CORNERS COMMUNITY BANK
500 W Main St, Farmington, NM
87401
Tel.: (505) 327-3222

Four Corners Community Bank—(Continued)

Web Site:
http://www.thebankforme.com
Year Founded: 2000
Sales Range: $10-24.9 Million
Emp.: 45
Commercial Bank
N.A.I.C.S.: 522110
Sheila I. Mathews *(Pres & CEO)*
Frank A. Macaluso *(Chm)*
M. Greg Anesi *(Vice Chm)*
Felix Briones Jr. *(Sec)*

FOUR COUNTY ELECTRIC MEMBERSHIP CORPORATION
1822 Hwy 53 W, Burgaw, NC 28425
Tel.: (910) 259-2171
Web Site: https://www.fourcty.org
Year Founded: 1937
Sales Range: $25-49.9 Million
Emp.: 98
Electronic Services
N.A.I.C.S.: 221122
Dan Allen *(VP-Cust Svcs)*
Gary Chitwood *(VP-Fin & Acctg)*
Mitchell Keel *(CEO)*
Franklin Williams *(Pres)*
Bertice Lanier *(VP)*
Gregg Cohn *(VP-Engrg)*
Doug Krynicki *(VP-IT)*
Billy McGavock *(VP-Ops)*

FOUR COUNTY ELECTRIC POWER ASSOCIATION
5265 S Frontage Rd, Columbus, MS 39703
Tel.: (662) 327-8900
Web Site: http://www.4county.org
Sales Range: $50-74.9 Million
Emp.: 170
Electric Power Distr
N.A.I.C.S.: 221122
Joe Cate *(CEO)*

FOUR CROWN INC.
434 Hale Ave N Ste 160, Oakdale, MN 55128-6146
Tel.: (651) 714-0030
Web Site:
http://www.wendysfourcrown.com
Rev.: $20,000,000
Emp.: 2,000
Fast Food Restaurant Operator
N.A.I.C.S.: 722513
Don Jensen *(Controller)*
Paul Peterson *(Gen Mgr)*
Dan Opitz *(VP)*

FOUR FOODS GROUP HOLDINGS
871 S Automall Dr, American Fork, UT 84003
Tel.: (801) 642-3800
Web Site:
http://www.fourfoodsgroup.com
Year Founded: 2008
Sales Range: $10-24.9 Million
Emp.: 460
Restaurants, Bakery & Cafe Management
N.A.I.C.S.: 722511
Andrew Smith *(Co-Founder & CEO)*
Shauna Smith *(Co-Founder & Chief Mdsg Officer)*
Tyler Nelson *(CFO)*
Josh Boshard *(COO)*
Nate Duvall *(VP-Restaurant Dev)*

FOUR HANDS, LLC
2090 Woodward St, Austin, TX 78744
Tel.: (512) 371-7575
Web Site: https://www.fourhands.com
Year Founded: 1991
Sales Range: $50-74.9 Million
Emp.: 88

Furniture Designer, Mfr & Distr
N.A.I.C.S.: 423210
Matthew Briggs *(Pres & CEO)*
Curt Welch *(CFO)*
Jackie Fitzgerald *(Sr Acct Exec-Special Projects)*
Chris Miller *(Mgr-Sls-Natl)*
Michael Bullock *(Chief Mktg Officer)*
Jerome Kearns *(COO & Exec VP)*
Matthew Evans *(Chief Sourcing Officer)*
Adam Dunn *(Creative Dir)*
Cindy Hammes *(VP-Supply Chain)*
Rick Lovegrove *(VP-Upholstery)*
Matt Briggs *(Chm)*

FOUR LANE AUTO SALES
3130 Rock Mart Rd SE, Rome, GA 30161
Tel.: (770) 382-3399
Web Site:
http://www.fourlaneauto.com
Motor Vehicle Parts Merchant Whslr
N.A.I.C.S.: 423140
Asad Ali *(Mgr)*

Subsidiaries:

Salvage Hunter Auto Parts   (1)
4029 Anderson Farm Rd, Austell, GA 30106-1003
Tel.: (770) 943-9979
Web Site: http://www.salvagehunter.net
Machine & Automobile Parts Distr
N.A.I.C.S.: 423140
Cathy Williamson *(Owner)*

FOUR M HOLDINGS LLC
111 Brook St, Scarsdale, NY 10583
Tel.: (914) 747-0015
Holding Company
N.A.I.C.S.: 551112
Dennis Mehiel *(Chm & CEO)*

Subsidiaries:

Mannkraft Corporation   (1)
100 Frontage Rd, Newark, NJ 07114
Tel.: (973) 589-7400
Web Site: http://www.mannkraft.com
Corrugated Retail Display, Die-Cut Packaging, Shipping Container & Sheet Mfr
N.A.I.C.S.: 322211
Jackie Simmons *(Dir-HR)*

U.S. Display Group, Inc.   (1)
810 S Washington St, Tullahoma, TN 37388
Tel.: (931) 455-9585
Web Site: http://www.usdisplaygroup.com
Sales Range: $10-24.9 Million
Emp.: 72
Retail Display Packaging Mfr
N.A.I.C.S.: 322219
Dennis D. Mehiel *(Owner & CEO)*

Unit (Domestic):

U.S. Display Group   (2)
100 Electric Ave, Secaucus, NJ 07094
Tel.: (973) 589-2155
Web Site: http://www.usdisplaygroup.com
Sales Range: $10-24.9 Million
Emp.: 6
Retail Display Packaging Mfr
N.A.I.C.S.: 322219
Greg Moore *(Pres)*

FOUR OAKS FAMILY & CHILDREN'S SERVICES
5400 Kirkwood Blvd SW, Cedar Rapids, IA 52404
Tel.: (319) 364-0259
Web Site: http://www.fouroaks.org
Year Founded: 1971
Sales Range: $25-49.9 Million
Emp.: 893
Child Care Services
N.A.I.C.S.: 624110
Liz Mathis *(Chief Community Officer)*
Dean Bliss *(Chief Quality Officer)*
Tami Gillmore *(Chief Fin & Admin Officer)*

Jason Glass *(Chief People Officer)*
Mary Beth O'Neill *(Pres & CEO)*
Lydia Brown *(Chm)*

FOUR SALES, LTD.
6405 10th St, Alexandria, VA 22307
Tel.: (703) 256-8300
Web Site: https://www.foursales.com
Sales Range: $1-9.9 Million
Emp.: 38
Real Estate Distribution Services
N.A.I.C.S.: 531390
Daniel Sanders *(Pres & CEO)*

FOUR SEASON EQUIPMENT
8111 Mills Rd, Houston, TX 77064
Tel.: (281) 807-9777
Web Site: http://www.fourseason-equip.com
Year Founded: 2001
Rev.: $33,400,000
Emp.: 80
General Construction Machinery & Equipment
N.A.I.C.S.: 532412
Dave Keim *(Pres)*
Mitch Nevins *(CEO)*
Sandie Sluder *(Mgr-Ops)*
Brad Brousseau *(VP-Ops)*
Brian Emr *(VP-Customer Svc)*
Dale DuBord *(VP)*
Darrell Plant *(Mgr-Parts)*
Darren McFarlain *(CFO)*
Dave Keim *(Pres)*
George Nevins *(Chm)*
Jess Dennis *(Mgr-Svc)*
Jim Liggett *(Exec VP)*
Kevin Jones *(Mgr-Sls)*
Mitch Nevins *(Chm & CEO)*

FOUR SEASONS ELECTRICAL SERVICES
116 4th St SE Unit B, Fort Walton Beach, FL 32548-5438
Tel.: (850) 244-0705
Year Founded: 1992
Sales Range: $10-24.9 Million
Emp.: 20
New Car Whslr
N.A.I.C.S.: 441110
James B. Harrington *(Pres)*

FOUR SEASONS FORD
601 Duncan Hill Rd, Hendersonville, NC 28793
Tel.: (828) 693-4281
Web Site:
http://www.fourseasonsford.com
Year Founded: 1959
Sales Range: $10-24.9 Million
Emp.: 55
Car Whslr
N.A.I.C.S.: 441110
Roger Gregg *(Pres)*
Armando Love *(Mgr-Fin)*
David Reyes *(Dir-BDC)*
John Sutterfield *(Gen Mgr)*
Rebecca Weekley *(Controller)*

FOUR SEASONS PRODUCE, INC.
400 Wabash Rd, Ephrata, PA 17522-0788
Tel.: (717) 721-2800
Web Site: https://www.fsproduce.com
Year Founded: 1976
Rev.: $16,800,000
Emp.: 600
Fruits & Vegetables Whslr
N.A.I.C.S.: 115116
David L. Hollinger *(Chm)*

FOUR SEASONS TRIANGLE STOP
751 Ash St, Hendersonville, NC 28792

Tel.: (828) 692-0246
Web Site:
http://www.trianglestop.com
Sales Range: $10-24.9 Million
Emp.: 75
Convenience Store Operator
N.A.I.C.S.: 457120
Hall Waddell *(Pres)*
Scott Doggett *(Controller)*

FOUR SPRINGS CAPITAL TRUST
1901 Main St, Lake Como, NJ 07MD
Web Site: http://www.fsctrust.com
Year Founded: 2012
Sales Range: $10-24.9 Million
Emp.: 16
Real Estate Investment Services
N.A.I.C.S.: 531110
Coby R. Johnson *(COO & Sec)*
John E. Warch *(CFO & Treas)*
Jared W. Morgan *(Sr VP & Head-Acq)*
Cynthia M. Daly *(VP-Underwriting)*
William P. Dioguardi *(Chm & CEO)*
Gregory Kammerer *(Sr VP-Capital Markets)*
Bill Auble *(Sr VP-Sls)*
Eric Paul *(Pres)*
Hall Jones *(Sr VP-Bus Dev)*

FOUR STAR HOLDINGS, INC.
100 Four Star Ln, Odenville, AL 35120
Tel.: (205) 640-3726
Web Site:
http://www.4starholdings.com
Sales Range: $10-24.9 Million
Emp.: 12
Land Developer, Home Builder & Real Estate Brokerage Services
N.A.I.C.S.: 237210
Al Rhoney *(CFO)*

FOUR STAR SALON SERVICES INC.
385 Oser Ave, Hauppauge, NY 11788
Tel.: (631) 951-4444
Web Site:
http://www.fourstarsalonservice.com
Year Founded: 1989
Sales Range: $10-24.9 Million
Emp.: 74
Beauty Parlor Equipment & Supplies
N.A.I.C.S.: 423850
Jeff Cohen *(Founder & Pres)*
Herb Frey *(CFO & COO)*

FOUR STAR TRANSPORTATION CO.
2947 Greenfield, Melvindale, MI 48122
Tel.: (313) 386-0100
Web Site:
https://www.fourstartrans.com
Year Founded: 1994
Sales Range: $10-24.9 Million
Emp.: 2
Trucking & Transport Service
N.A.I.C.S.: 484121
Michael C. Leoni *(Pres)*
Tom A. Hayes *(Gen Mgr)*
Chris Kondakor *(Mgr-Ops)*

FOUR WINDS INTERACTIVE LLC
1859 York St, Denver, CO 80206
Tel.: (720) 259-5000
Web Site:
http://www.fourwindsinteractive.com
Year Founded: 2005
Sales Range: $25-49.9 Million
Emp.: 190
Digital Display Software
N.A.I.C.S.: 513210

David Levin *(Pres & CEO)*
Janet Eden-Harris *(CMO)*
Jenny Brook *(Gen Counsel)*
Nigel Alexander *(CFO)*
Lane Brannan *(Chief Revenue Officer)*
Margot Moellenberg *(Chief People & Fin Officer)*

FOUR WINDS INVESTMENT CORP.
1908 Strand St, Galveston, TX 77553
Tel.: (409) 765-6361
Web Site:
http://www.farmersmarine.com
Rev.: $54,000,000
Emp.: 150
Holding Company
N.A.I.C.S.: 423510
Bruce J. Farmer Jr. *(Pres)*

Subsidiaries:

Farmers Copper & Industrial
Supply   (1)
202 37th St, Galveston, TX 77550
Tel.: (409) 765-9003
Web Site: http://www.farmerscopper.com
Sales Range: $25-49.9 Million
Emp.: 100
Metal Distr
N.A.I.C.S.: 423510
Robert Farmer *(Pres)*

Farmers Marine Copper Works   (1)
1908 Strand St Ste B, Galveston, TX
77550-1629   (100%)
Tel.: (409) 765-6361
Web Site: http://www.farmersmarine.com
Sales Range: $25-49.9 Million
Emp.: 50
Pipe Fabrication; General Metal Fabrication;
Code Pressure Vessels;Machining, Sheet
Metal - All Alloys
N.A.I.C.S.: 332710
Thomas E. Farmer *(Co-Pres)*

Great Western Metals Inc.   (1)
14121 Gulf Fwy, Houston, TX
77034-5320   (100%)
Tel.: (281) 484-1150
Web Site:
http://www.greatwesternmetals.com
Sales Range: $25-49.9 Million
Emp.: 22
Stainless Steel, Aluminum & Nickel Alloys,
Water Jet & Laser Cutting Machine Tool Mfr
N.A.I.C.S.: 332322

FOUR WINDS TRUCK BRO-KERS, INC.
1160 SW 9th Ave, Ontario, OR 97914
Tel.: (541) 889-8844
Sales Range: $10-24.9 Million
Emp.: 21
Air Cargo Services
N.A.I.C.S.: 488510
Robert J. Bolyard *(Pres & Sec)*

FOURJAY LLC
42 Parkstone Cir, North Little Rock,
AR 72116
Tel.: (501) 372-2000
Web Site: https://www.fourjayllc.com
Sales Range: $25-49.9 Million
Emp.: 1,400
Franchise Owner of Fast-Food Res-taurants
N.A.I.C.S.: 722513

FOURSHORE CAPITAL LLC
901 Ponce de Leon Blvd Ste 402,
Coral Gables, FL 33134
Tel.: (786) 535-4617   FL
Web Site:
http://www.fourshorecapital.com
Holding Company
N.A.I.C.S.: 551112
Jose Costa *(Principal)*

Subsidiaries:

Buske Lines, Inc.   (1)
7 Gtwy Commerce Ctr Dr PO Box 929, Ed-wardsville, IL 62025
Tel.: (618) 931-6091
Web Site: http://www.buske.com
Sales Range: $25-49.9 Million
Emp.: 550
Trucking Except Local
N.A.I.C.S.: 484121
Jack McDaniel *(VP-Safety)*
John Babington *(Pres)*
Nick Heinz *(CEO)*

North State Acceptance, LLC   (1)
2305 E Millbrook Rd, Raleigh, NC 27604
Tel.: (919) 878-0034
Web Site:
http://www.northstateacceptance.com
All Other Business Support Services
N.A.I.C.S.: 561499

FOURSOME FINER FOODS INC.
4640 S Halsted St, Chicago, IL
60609
Tel.: (773) 247-3077
Web Site:
http://www.fairplayfoods.com
Sales Range: $50-74.9 Million
Emp.: 150
Grocery Store Operator
N.A.I.C.S.: 445110
Richard Goodrich *(Pres)*

FOURSQUARE LABS, INC.
50 W 23rd St 8th Fl, New York, NY
10010
Tel.: (646) 380-4813   DE
Web Site: http://www.foursquare.com
Custom Computer Programming Ser-vices
N.A.I.C.S.: 541511
Dennis Crowley *(Founder & Chm)*
Gary Little *(Pres & CEO)*
Oren Teich *(Sr VP-Product)*

Subsidiaries:

Factual Inc.   (1)
1999 Ave of the Stars 4th Fl, Los Angeles,
CA 90067
Tel.: (310) 286-9400
Web Site: http://www.factual.com
Software Publisher
N.A.I.C.S.: 513210
Bill Michels *(VP-Product Mgmt & Partner-ships)*
Brian Czarny *(Sr VP-Mktg)*
Gil Elbaz *(CEO)*
Ross Webster *(Mng Dir-Europe)*
Rob Jonas *(Chief Revenue Officer)*

FOURSTAR WEALTH ADVI-SORS LLC
351 W Hubbard Ste 420, Chicago, IL
60654
Web Site:
https://www.fourstarwealth.com
Year Founded: 2014
Financial Servcies
N.A.I.C.S.: 523999
Brian Lance Kasal *(CEO & Founder)*
Christopher Reardon *(Dir-Dev)*

FOURTH POINT WEALTH
4590 MacArthur Blvd Ste 500, New-port Beach, CA 92660
Tel.: (949) 662-8090
Web Site:
https://fourthpointwealth.com
Financial Securities & Advisory Ser-vices
N.A.I.C.S.: 522320
Chris Janeway *(Owner & President)*

FOURTH TECHNOLOGIES INC.
1816 Springdale Rd, Cherry Hill, NJ
08003
Tel.: (856) 751-4848

Web Site: https://www.fortek.com
Sales Range: $10-24.9 Million
Emp.: 120
Custom Computer Programming Ser-vices
N.A.I.C.S.: 541511
Ravi Shankar *(Pres)*
Mike Samy *(VP)*
Gene Krishnasami *(Dir-HR & Control-ler)*

FOUSHEE & ASSOCIATES CO., INC.
3260 118th Ave SE Ste 1000, Belle-vue, WA 98005
Tel.: (425) 746-1000
Web Site: https://www.foushee.com
Year Founded: 1977
Sales Range: $10-24.9 Million
Emp.: 80
Commercial & Institutional Building
Construction Services
N.A.I.C.S.: 236220
Eric Jones *(Pres & CEO)*
Robert Guymer *(COO)*
Mark Stillwell *(Principal)*
Britt Slone *(Principal)*
Lisa Koch *(CFO)*

FOUTZ & BURSUM CON-STRUCTION CO.
3201 N 1st St, Bloomfield, NM 87413
Tel.: (505) 634-4000
Web Site:
http://www.constructco.com
Sales Range: $10-24.9 Million
Emp.: 65
Pipeline Construction Services
N.A.I.C.S.: 237110
Steve Foutz *(Pres)*
Steven Steele *(Project Mgr)*

FOWLER BUICK-GMC INC.
5801 Hwy 80 E, Pearl, MS 39208-8932
Tel.: (601) 354-5200
Web Site:
http://www.fowlerbuickpontiac.com
Sales Range: $50-74.9 Million
Emp.: 50
New & Used Car Dealers
N.A.I.C.S.: 441110
Frann Monk *(Bus Mgr)*
Bob Jones *(Mgr-Fleet)*
Tony McEwen *(Mgr-Parts)*
Robb Colson *(Mgr-Sls)*
Tom Hudson *(Pres)*
Tommy Nance *(Asst Mgr-Svc)*

FOWLER CONSTRUCTION & DEVELOPMENT, INC.
10491 6 Mile Cypress Pkwy Ste 280,
Fort Myers, FL 33966
Tel.: (239) 275-7000   FL
Web Site:
https://www.fowlercompany.com
Year Founded: 1968
Sales Range: $1-9.9 Million
Emp.: 10
Residential & Commercial Construc-tion
N.A.I.C.S.: 236115
Robert B. Fowler *(Chm, Pres & CEO)*

FOWLER CUSTOM HOMES
3800 Old Cheney Rd Ste A, Lincoln,
NE 68516
Tel.: (402) 420-5566
Web Site:
http://www.fowlercustomhomes.com
Sales Range: $10-24.9 Million
Emp.: 30
New Construction, Single-Family
Houses
N.A.I.C.S.: 236116
Barry Fowler *(Pres)*

FOWLER ELEVATOR INC.
120 S 4th St, Seymour, IA 52590
Tel.: (641) 898-7711
Sales Range: $10-24.9 Million
Emp.: 23
Grain Elevators
N.A.I.C.S.: 424510
Tom T. Fowler *(Pres)*
John Flood *(Treas & Sec)*

FOWLER FOODS INC.
139 SW Dr, Jonesboro, AR 72401
Tel.: (870) 935-6032
Sales Range: $10-24.9 Million
Emp.: 15
Fast Food Restaurant Operator
N.A.I.C.S.: 722513
Peter Meyers *(Asst Mgr)*
Richard Blount *(Partner & Area Mgr)*
Wallace W. Fowler Sr. *(Chm)*

FOWLER GENERAL CON-STRUCTION, INC.
2161 Henderson Loop, Richland, WA
99354
Tel.: (509) 375-3331
Web Site: https://www.fowlergc.com
Year Founded: 2004
Sales Range: $10-24.9 Million
Emp.: 45
Commercial & Building Construction
Services
N.A.I.C.S.: 236220
John Payne *(Pres)*
Jeff Durfee *(VP)*
Monte Dunn *(Project Dir)*
Brooks Payne *(Project Mgr)*
Cameron Boffey *(Project Mgr)*
Dave Creech *(Mgr-Safety)*

FOWLER-FLEMISTER CON-CRETE INC.
711 N Wilkinson St, Milledgeville, GA
31061
Tel.: (478) 452-0541
Web Site:
https://www.fowlerflemister.com
Rev.: $10,000,000
Emp.: 85
Ready Mixed Concrete
N.A.I.C.S.: 327320
Linda Hammett *(Treas & Sec)*

FOWLERS INC.
9630 Kingston Pike, Knoxville, TN
37933
Tel.: (865) 539-0036
Web Site:
http://www.fowlersfurnitureinc.com
Sales Range: $10-24.9 Million
Emp.: 100
Owner & Operator of Furniture Stores
N.A.I.C.S.: 449110
Donald P. Fowler *(Owner)*

FOWNES BROTHERS & CO., INC.
16 E 34th St 5th Fl, New York, NY
10016-2203
Tel.: (212) 683-0150   NY
Year Founded: 1777
Sales Range: $10-24.9 Million
Emp.: 250
Gloves, Scarves & Hats Mfr
N.A.I.C.S.: 424350
Chris Giattino *(Exec VP-Sls)*
Tom Faivre *(CFO)*
Andrew Gluckman *(VP)*

FOX & JAMES INC.
216 Marsh Ln, Latrobe, PA 15650
Tel.: (724) 537-6630   PA
Web Site:
http://www.foxandjames.com
Year Founded: 1949
Sales Range: $25-49.9 Million

Fox & James Inc.—(Continued)

Emp.: 30
Sales of Commercial Trucks
N.A.I.C.S.: 423110
Linda James (Controller)

FOX ASSOCIATES INC.

116 W Kinzie St, Chicago, IL 60654-4655
Tel.: (312) 644-3888   IL
Web Site: https://www.foxrep.com
Year Founded: 1968
Sales Range: $25-49.9 Million
Emp.: 75
Provider of Advertising Sales Services for Newspapers, Magazines & Other Publications
N.A.I.C.S.: 541840
Marlys Fox (Founder, Pres & CEO)
Steve Schwanz (Exec VP)
Vince Backley (Chm)

FOX BROS PIGGLY WIGGLY INC.

505 Cottonwood Ave, Hartland, WI 53029
Tel.: (262) 367-2922
Web Site:
    https://www.foxbrospigglywiggly.com
Sales Range: $10-24.9 Million
Emp.: 300
Grocery Store Operator
N.A.I.C.S.: 445110
Patrick Fox (Pres)

FOX CHRYSLER DODGE JEEP

346 Grant Avenue Rd, Auburn, NY 13021-8201
Tel.: (315) 704-5696
Web Site:
    https://www.foxchryslerdodgejeep.com
Year Founded: 1975
Sales Range: $10-24.9 Million
Emp.: 48
Car Dealer
N.A.I.C.S.: 441110
David Donlick (Mgr-Sls)
Jason Baldwin (Mgr-Sls)
Rick Samson (Bus Mgr)
Frank Pinckney (Mgr-Parts)

FOX COMPANIES

2 Riverbend Ct, Hamilton, MT 59840
Tel.: (406) 363-5140
Web Site: https://www.foxlumber.com
Sales Range: $50-74.9 Million
Emp.: 45
Lumber: Rough, Dressed & Finished
N.A.I.C.S.: 423310
Thomas L. Fox (Pres)

FOX CONTRACTORS CORP.

5430 W Ferguson Rd, Fort Wayne, IN 46809-9612
Tel.: (260) 747-7461   IN
Web Site:
    http://www.foxcontractors.com
Year Founded: 1974
Sales Range: $10-24.9 Million
Emp.: 50
Highway & Street Excavation
N.A.I.C.S.: 237310
Dallas Day (Pres)

FOX CONVERTING INC.

1250 Cornell Rd, Green Bay, WI 54313
Tel.: (920) 434-5272
Web Site:
    https://www.foxconverting.com
Rev.: $17,000,000
Emp.: 120
Sanitary Paper Product Mfr.
N.A.I.C.S.: 322291
Matthew Skaletski (Coord-IS)

FOX ELECTRIC LTD.

1104 Colorado Ln, Arlington, TX 76015-1503
Tel.: (817) 461-2571   TX
Web Site: https://www.foxelectric.com
Year Founded: 1996
Sales Range: $25-49.9 Million
Emp.: 275
Electrical Work
N.A.I.C.S.: 238210
Wes Shahan (Pres & CEO)

FOX HOME CENTER INC.

11150 S Cicero Ave, Alsip, IL 60803
Tel.: (708) 636-3500
Web Site:
    https://www.foxhomecenter.com
Rev.: $12,000,000
Emp.: 60
Millwork & Lumber
N.A.I.C.S.: 444110

FOX PERFORMING ARTS CHARITABLE FOUNDATION

462 N Taylor Ave Ste 203, Saint Louis, MO 63108
Tel.: (314) 367-1573   MO
Web Site: http://www.foxpacf.org
Year Founded: 2002
Sales Range: $10-24.9 Million
Emp.: 5
Performing Art Promotion Services
N.A.I.C.S.: 711310
Mary Strauss (Pres)
Marlene Birkman (VP)

FOX PETROLEUM INC.

545 8th Ave Ste 401, New York, NY 10018
Tel.: (212) 560-5195   NV
Web Site: http://www.fox-petroleum.com
Sales Range: Less than $1 Million
Emp.: 2
Oil & Gas Exploration Services
N.A.I.C.S.: 211120
James R. Renfro (CEO & Interim CFO)

FOX POWERSPORTS LLC

5637 State Route 5, Herkimer, NY 13350-3516
Tel.: (616) 453-5467
Web Site:
    http://www.foxpowersports.com
Emp.: 100
Motorcycle, ATV & All Other Motor Vehicle Dealers
N.A.I.C.S.: 441227
Terry Fox (Owner)

Subsidiaries:

Peacock, Ltd.   (1)
276 S M 37, Baldwin, MI 49304
Tel.: (231) 745-4606
Web Site: http://www.peacockltd.com
Sales Range: $1-9.9 Million
Emp.: 100
Ret Misc Vehicles Ret Boats
N.A.I.C.S.: 441227

FOX RIVER WATER RECLA-MATION DISTRICT

1957 N LaFox Rte 31, Elgin, IL 60177
Tel.: (847) 742-2068
Web Site: https://www.frwrd.com
Year Founded: 1922
Sales Range: $25-49.9 Million
Emp.: 50
Waste Water Treatment Company
N.A.I.C.S.: 221320
Bruce Corn (Pres)
Bob Trueblood (Exec Dir)

FOX ROTHSCHILD LLP

2000 Market St 20th Fl, Philadelphia, PA 19103-3222
Tel.: (215) 299-2000   PA
Web Site:
    https://www.foxrothschild.com
Year Founded: 1907
Sales Range: $200-249.9 Million
Emp.: 900
Law firm
N.A.I.C.S.: 541110
Mark L. Morris (Mng Partner-Firmwide)
Carrie B. Nase-Poust (Partner-Warrington)
Michael J. Maransky (Partner-Blue Bell)
Jean A. Durling (Chief Talent Officer)
John J. Stubbs (CIO & Chief Compliance Officer)
Alka Bahal (Partner-Morristown)
Christina A. Stoneburner (Partner-Morristown)
Scott L. Vernick (Partner-Philadelphia)
Thomas D. Paradise (Gen Counsel)
Nevena Simidjiyska (Partner)
E. Badway (Partner-New York)
Ian D. Meklinsky (Partner)
Jacqueline M. Carolan (Partner-Philadelphia)
Jeffrey H. Nicholas (Partner)
Mitchell Berns (Partner-New York)
Stephen A. Ploscowe (Partner-Morristown)
Elaine Calcote Britt (Partner-Princeton)
Rhonda E. Ores (Partner-New York)
Michael G. Menkowitz (Partner)
William L. Stang (Partner-Pittsburgh)
Linda Rhone Enion (Partner)
William A. Rudy (Partner-Denver)
Beth L. Weisser (Partner-Philadelphia)
James C. Clark (Partner-Warrington)
David J. Garraux (Partner-Pittsburgh)
Seth I. Corbin (Partner-Pittsburgh)
Jennifer E. Benda (Partner-Denver)
Stanley Barsky (Partner)
Mark G. McCreary (Partner & Chief Privacy Officer)
Phillip H. Wang (Partner-New York)
Robert C. Castle (Partner-Labor & Employment)
C. Robert Beattie (Partner-Minneapolis)
Jessica Forbes Olson (Partner-Minneapolis)
Patrick M. Fenlon (Partner-Litigation-Minneapolis)
Gary Hansen (Partner-Minneapolis)
Barbara J. Grahn (Partner-Intellectual Property)
D. William Kaufman (Partner-Minneapolis)
Ranelle Leier (Partner-Minneapolis)
Archana Nath (Partner-Minneapolis)
Joseph A. DeMaria (Partner-Miami)
Jonathan H. Stechmann (Partner-Minneapolis)
Gregory A. Nelson (Partner-West Palm Beach)
Michael A. Hyett (Partner-Taxation & Atty-Wealth Plng)
David I. Greenbaum (Partner & Atty-Intellectual Property)
Robert C. Nagle (Partner-Blue Bell)
Hilary B. Bloom (Partner-Denver)
Eleanor Vaida Gerhards (Partner-Warrington)
Stephanie B. Fineman (Partner)
Christian Moffitt (Partner-Blue Bell)
Andy Nikolopoulos (Partner-Dallas)
Christopher P. Beall (Partner-New York)
Craig R. Tractenberg (Partner-Philadelphia & New York)

Marc Simon (Partner-New York)
Christopher Hines (Partner-Chicago)
Rick L. Etter (Partner-Lbor & Employment Practice)
Ashley L. Beach (Partner-Litigation)
Brian A. Berkley (Partner-Litigation)
Bruce Ashley (Partner-Litigation)
Catherine T. Barbieri (Partner-Labor & Employment)
Charles Bender (Partner-Taxation & Wealth Plng)
D. Erik Albright (Partner-Entertainment)
Daniel T. Berkley (Partner-Labor & Employment)
David Aronoff (Partner-Entertainment)
Eliana Baer (Partner-Litigation)
Gerald E. Arth (Partner-Litigation)
Jonathan D. Ash (Partner-Labor & Employment)
Karen Binder (Partner-Real Estate)
Kathleen M. Aiello (Partner-Fin Restructuring & Bankruptcy)
Kenneth J. Abdo (Partner-Entertainment)
Larina Alton (Partner-Intellectual Property)
Lincoln Bandlow (Partner-Entertainment)
Matthew S. Adams (Partner-Litigation)
Michael Barabander (Partner-Labor & Employment)
Patrick L. Abramowich (Partner-Litigation)
Robert N. Amkraut (Partner-Fin Restructuring & Bankruptcy)
Ryan T. Becker (Partner-Litigation)
Sarah B. Biser (Partner-Litigation)
Scott M. Badami (Partner-Litigation)
Terence G. Banich (Partner-Fin Restructuring & Bankruptcy)
Robert W. Gundlach Jr. (Partner-Warrington)
Sylvia L. Magid (Partner)

Subsidiaries:

Fox Rothschild LLP - San Francisco, CA-Front Street   (1)
345 California St Ste 2200, San Francisco, CA 94104
Tel.: (415) 781-4400
Web Site: http://www.foxrothschild.com
Emp.: 13
Law firm
N.A.I.C.S.: 541110
Dwight C. Donovan (Partner)
Laura Terry Howard (Partner)
Bill Mandel (Partner)
Jonathan S. O'Donnell (Partner)
Peter S. Myers (Partner-Estate Plng & Trust & Atty-Probate Law)
Sean R. Kenney (Partner-Taxation & Trusts & Atty-Estates)
Matthew R. Mraule (Partner-Litigation)
Gregory Nelson (Partner)
Thomas D. Paradise (Gen Counsel)
Jean A. Durling (Chief Talent Officer)
Edward Gillespie (CFO)
Tricia M. Lilley (CMO)
Catherine M. Monte (Chief Knowledge Officer)
Michael Rinehart (CIO)
Paul Straub (COO)
John J. Stubbs (Chief Info Mgmt & Compliance Officer)

FOX RUN CRAFTSMEN

1907 Stout Dr, Warminster, PA 18974
Tel.: (215) 675-7700
Sales Range: $10-24.9 Million
Emp.: 45
Kitchenware
N.A.I.C.S.: 423220
Allison Hansen (Mgr-Trade Show)
Missy Rieser (Mgr-Credit & Collection)

FOX SALES

4494 36th St SE, Grand Rapids, MI
49512
Tel.: (616) 949-1210
Web Site: http://www.fox-sales.com
Sales Range: $10-24.9 Million
Emp.: 100
Sales of Wine & Related Products
N.A.I.C.S.: 424820
Henry A. Fox Jr. *(Chm)*

FOX SERVICE CO.
4300 S Congress Ave, Austin, TX
78745
Tel.: (512) 442-6782
Web Site: http://www.foxservice.com
Sales Range: $25-49.9 Million
Emp.: 200
Air Heating & Air Conditioning Con-
tractor
N.A.I.C.S.: 238220
Robert Nagel *(Pres)*

FOX THREE PARTNERS LLC
1072 Laskin Rd Ste 201, Virginia
Beach, VA 23451
Tel.: (757) 296-3454
Web Site:
   http://www.fox3partners.com
Privater Equity Firm
N.A.I.C.S.: 523999
Taylor Grant *(Founder & Mng Part-
ner)*

Subsidiaries:

Burlington Medical LLC   (1)
3 Elmhurst St, Newport News, VA 23603
Tel.: (757) 888-8994
Web Site: http://www.burmed.com
Sales Range: $1-9.9 Million
Emp.: 125
Protective Medical Supplies Mfr & Distr
N.A.I.C.S.: 339113
John Williams *(CEO)*

FOX TOYOTA SCION, INC.
228 Fox Family Ln, Clinton, TN
37716
Tel.: (865) 457-1773
Year Founded: 1966
Sales Range: $10-24.9 Million
Emp.: 70
New Car Whslr
N.A.I.C.S.: 441110
Ronnie Fox *(Pres)*

FOX TRANSPORT CO.
100 Hunt St, Paxton, IL 60957
Tel.: (217) 379-2521
Sales Range: $10-24.9 Million
Emp.: 6
Trucking Service
N.A.I.C.S.: 484121

FOX VALLEY FIRE & SAFETY
COMPANY, INC.
2730 Pinnacle Dr, Elgin, IL 60124
Tel.: (847) 695-5990
Web Site:
   https://www.foxvalleyfire.com
Year Founded: 1960
Sales Range: $25-49.9 Million
Emp.: 260
Electronic Services
N.A.I.C.S.: 238210
Scott Volkening *(VP)*

FOX VALLEY STEEL & WIRE
CO.
111 N Douglas St, Hortonville, WI
54944-9408
Tel.: (920) 779-4544   WI
Sales Range: $50-74.9 Million
Emp.: 100
Steel & Wire Products Mfr
N.A.I.C.S.: 332618
James J. Monroe *(Pres)*

FOX VALLEY SYSTEMS, INC.
640 Indus Dr, Cary, IL 60013-1944
Tel.: (847) 639-5744   IL
Web Site: http://www.foxpaint.com
Year Founded: 1988
Sales Range: $75-99.9 Million
Emp.: 20
Striping & Marking Equipment &
Paints Mfr
N.A.I.C.S.: 325510
Thomas J. Smart *(Pres)*

FOX VALLEY TOOL & DIE,
INC.
2310 E Main St, Kaukauna, WI
54130
Tel.: (920) 766-9455
Web Site: https://www.fvtd.com
Year Founded: 1966
Sales Range: $10-24.9 Million
Emp.: 150
Special Die & Tool Die Set Jig & Fix-
ture Mfr
N.A.I.C.S.: 333514
Mark Dennis *(Sec)*

FOX VALLEY TRUCK SERVICE
INC.
5668 Neubert Rd, Appleton, WI
54913-7972
Tel.: (920) 757-9400
Web Site:
   https://www.foxvalleytruck.com
Sales Range: $50-74.9 Million
Emp.: 74
Truck Sales & Service
N.A.I.C.S.: 441110
Dan Toppins *(Pres)*

FOX WORLD TRAVEL
8685 N Port Washington Rd, Milwau-
kee, WI 53217
Tel.: (414) 352-4212
Web Site: http://www.gofox.com
Year Founded: 1960
Sales Range: $10-24.9 Million
Emp.: 168
Travel Agencies
N.A.I.C.S.: 561510
Lesley Vroman *(Acct Mgr-Svcs)*
Rebecca Kollmann *(Dir-Mktg-
Vacation Travel)*
Jim Hodges *(Mgr-Bus Dev-Grp Vaca-
tions)*
Nahren Youkhana *(Sls Dir-Global)*
Michael Heck *(Dir-Supplier Solutions)*
Andrea Pradarelli *(Dir-Vacation Travel
Sls & Ops)*
Brianne Bloom *(VP-Vacation Travel)*
Tifani Jones *(Dir-Global Dev & Sls
Ops)*
Tina Husemoller *(VP-Meetings & In-
centives)*
Beth Marino *(COO)*

FOX-ROWDEN-MCBRAYER
INC.
1458 Beaver Run Rd, Norcross, GA
30093
Tel.: (770) 923-3520
Rev.: $14,000,000
Emp.: 40
Electrical Supplies
N.A.I.C.S.: 423610
Robin Vold *(CFO & Controller)*

FOXDALE VILLAGE CORPO-
RATION
500 E Marylyn Ave, State College,
PA 16801
Tel.: (814) 272-2146   PA
Web Site:
   https://www.foxdalevillage.org
Year Founded: 1986
Sales Range: $10-24.9 Million
Emp.: 286

Retirement Community Operator
N.A.I.C.S.: 623311
Sophie Penney *(Dir-Dev & Commu-
nity Outreach)*
Bill Kehler *(Dir-Dining Svcs)*
Corey Hamilton *(Dir-Fin)*
Adam Day *(Dir-Environmental Svcs)*
Meg Clouser *(Dir-Health Svcs)*
Julie Hartley *(Dir-HR)*
Rich Lysle *(Exec Dir)*
Libby Mortensen *(Dir-Residency Plng
& Mktg)*

FOXFIRE PRINTING & PACK-
AGING
750 Dawson Dr, Newark, DE 19713
Tel.: (302) 368-9466
Web Site:
   http://www.foxfireprinting.com
Sales Range: $10-24.9 Million
Emp.: 100
Provider of Commercial Printing &
Lithographic Services
N.A.I.C.S.: 323111
John Ferretti *(CEO)*

FOXIT SOFTWARE INC.
41841 Albrae St, Fremont, CA 94538
Tel.: (510) 438-9090   CA
Web Site:
   http://www.foxitsoftware.com
Year Founded: 2001
Software Publishing Services
N.A.I.C.S.: 513210
Eugene Xiong *(Founder, Chm &
Pres)*
Frank Kettenstock *(CMO)*
Phil Lee *(Chief Revenue Officer)*
Jenny Li *(Sr VP-Product Strategy)*
George Z. Gao *(CEO)*
Carsten Heiermann *(CEO-Foxit Eu-
rope)*
Shinichi Mori *(CEO-Foxit Japan)*
Max Jhuang *(Gen Mgr-Taiwan Ops)*
Karl De Abrew *(CIO)*
Susana De Abrew *(Pres-Foxit SDK
BU)*
Rowan Hanna *(Sr VP-Foxit SDK BU)*
Steven Li *(CTO)*

Subsidiaries:

CVISION Technologies, Inc.   (1)
118-35 Queens Blvd Ste 910, Forest Hills,
NY 11375
Tel.: (718) 793-5200
Web Site: http://www.cvisiontech.com
Document Imaging Software
N.A.I.C.S.: 513210
Tim Jefferies *(Mgr-Natl Acct)*

FOXLAND HARVESTORE INC.
1400 Rosehill Rd, Little Chute, WI
54140
Tel.: (920) 766-3783
Web Site:
   http://www.foxlandharvestore.com
Sales Range: $10-24.9 Million
Emp.: 60
Agricultural Machinery & Equipment
N.A.I.C.S.: 423820
Mike Gries *(Project Mgr)*

FOXTRONICS EMS
3448 W Mockingbird Ln, Dallas, TX
75235
Tel.: (214) 358-4425   TX
Web Site:
   https://www.foxtronicsems.com
Year Founded: 2000
Sales Range: $1-9.9 Million
Emp.: 10
Search, Detection, Navigation, Guid-
ance, Aeronautical & Nautical System
& Instrument Mfr
N.A.I.C.S.: 551112
Robert Underwood *(Sec)*
Wayne Ostrander *(CEO)*

Subsidiaries:

Accutron, Inc.   (1)
1733 W Parkside Ln, Phoenix, AZ 85027-
1382
Tel.: (623) 780-2020
Web Site: http://www.accutron-inc.com
Medical Sedation Equipment & Accessories
Mfr
N.A.I.C.S.: 339113

OSDA, Inc.   (1)
291 Pepe''s Farm Road, Milford, CT 06460
Tel.: (203) 878-2155
Web Site: http://www.osda.com
Rev.: $2,333,333
Emp.: 20
Bare Printed Circuit Board Mfr
N.A.I.C.S.: 334412
Bill DeProfio *(Mgr-Engrg)*

FOXWORTH-GALBRAITH
LUMBER COMPANY
4965 Preston Park Blvd Ste 400,
Plano, TX 75093
Tel.: (972) 665-2400   DE
Web Site: https://www.foxgal.com
Year Founded: 1901
Sales Range: $500-549.9 Million
Emp.: 2,500
Lumber & Building Material Retailer
Distr
N.A.I.C.S.: 423310
Mack Good *(Mgr)*

Subsidiaries:

Foxworth-Galbraith Lumber
Company   (1)
3105 N Stone Ave, Colorado Springs, CO
80907-5305
Tel.: (719) 471-4500
Web Site: http://www.foxgal.com
Rev.: $78,777,184
Emp.: 20
Processing & Distribution of Lumber
N.A.I.C.S.: 423310

Subsidiary (Domestic):

Foxworth Galbraith Truss Co.   (2)
4005 Interpark Dr Bldg B, Colorado
Springs, CO 80907-4214
Tel.: (719) 598-4500
Web Site: http://www.foxgal.com
Sales Range: $25-49.9 Million
Emp.: 12
Structural Wood Member Mfr
N.A.I.C.S.: 321215
Jimmy Galbraith III *(Pres)*

FOXX LIFE SCIENCES, LLC
6 Delaware Dr, Salem, NH 03079
Tel.: (603) 890-3699   NH
Web Site:
   http://www.foxxlifesciences.com
Year Founded: 2013
Life Sciences Products Developer,
Mfr & Whslr
N.A.I.C.S.: 334516
Thomas Foxx Taylor *(Pres & CEO)*
Greg Bousquet *(COO)*
Stephanie Aznoian *(CFO)*
Mark Robillard *(Sr VP-Global Sls &
Bus dev)*

FP INTERNATIONAL, INC.
1090 Mills Way, Redwood City, CA
94063
Tel.: (650) 261-5300
Web Site: http://www.fpintl.com
Year Founded: 1967
Sales Range: $100-124.9 Million
Emp.: 500
Fiscal Year-end: 12/26/15
Protective Packaging Products &
Packaging Systems Mfr
N.A.I.C.S.: 326150
Joe Nezwek *(Pres)*
Steven A. Jackson *(CFO)*

FP PROPERTY RESTORATION

FP PROPERTY RESTORATION —(CONTINUED)

OF NORTH FLORIDA, LLC
204 Center Rd, Fort Myers, FL 33907
Tel.: (239) 319-4637   FL
Web Site:
http://www.fprestoration.com
Year Founded: 2011
Sales Range: $10-24.9 Million
Emp.: 59
Building Restoration Services
N.A.I.C.S.: 236118
Steve Glozik (Pres)

FPC CORPORATION
355 Hollow Hill Rd, Wauconda, IL
60084
Tel.: (847) 487-4583
Web Site:
https://www.surebonder.com
Rev.: $19,000,000
Emp.: 50
Chemical & Allied Products Merchant
Whslr
N.A.I.C.S.: 424690
Patrick Kamins (VP)
Michael Kamins (Pres & CEO)
Rick Warner (Mgr-Sls-Indus Adhesive)

FPI MANAGEMENT, INC.
800 Iron Point Rd, Folsom, CA 95630
Tel.: (916) 357-5300   CA
Web Site: https://www.fpimgt.com
Sales Range: $1-9.9 Million
Emp.: 3,000
Multifamily Residential Property Manager
N.A.I.C.S.: 531311
Dennis Treadaway (Pres & CEO)
David Divine (Sr VP-Ops)
Kristin Wood (Dir-IT)
Michelle Fisher (Sr VP-Southern California)
June Valle (VP-Southern California-Affordable)
Carrie Briggs (VP)
Bonnie Darrah (Sr VP)
Vanessa Siebern (VP)
Mike Watembach (CFO)
Christina Treadaway (Sr VP-Northern California)
Subsidiaries:
Pinnacle Galleria LLC   (1)
1100 Roseville Pkwy, Roseville, CA 95678
Tel.: (916) 788-4141
Web Site: http://www.pinnaclegalleria.com
Multifamily Residential Property Manager
N.A.I.C.S.: 531311

FPO, LLC
8035 Broadway, San Antonio, TX
78209
Tel.: (210) 829-8855
Sales Range: Less than $1 Million
Emp.: 4
Below-the-Line, Retail, Strategic
Planning/Research, Viral/Buzz/Word
of Mouth
N.A.I.C.S.: 541810
Manuel Hernandez (CEO)

FPX, LLC
8300 Norman Ctr Dr Ste 1275, Minneapolis, MN 55437   TX
Web Site: http://www.fpx.com
Year Founded: 1983
Sales Range: $1-9.9 Million
Emp.: 40
Software Publisher, Sales Proposal
Generation
N.A.I.C.S.: 513210
Dave Batt (CEO)
Vince Evers (Pres-Sls)
Stephen Peary (VP & Gen Counsel)
James Scheper (VP-Bus Dev)

Scott Lastine (CFO-Bloomington)
Adam Hatch (CMO)
Richard Hearn (CEO)
Subsidiaries:
Intelliquip, Inc.   (1)
3 W Broad St Ste 4, Bethlehem, PA 18018
Tel.: (484) 821-0350
Web Site: http://www.intelliquip.com
Industrial Sales Software & Data Services
N.A.I.C.S.: 541511
Trygve Dahl (Sr VP-Bus Dev & Tech)
Dave Brockway (Pres)
David L. Tress (VP-Ops)

FRACTAL ANALYTICS INC.
1840 Gateway Dr, San Mateo, CA
94404
Tel.: (650) 378-1284
Web Site:
http://www.fractalanalytics.com
Year Founded: 2000
Sales Range: $25-49.9 Million
Emp.: 143
Data Analytic Services
N.A.I.C.S.: 518210
Srikanth Velamakanni (Co-Founder,
Vice Chm & Grp CEO)
Pranay Agrawal (Co-Founder)
Careen Foster (CMO & Sr VP)
Natwar Mall (Sr VP-Fractal Sciences)
Rasesh Shah (CIO & Sr VP)
Ajoy Singh (Sr VP & Head-Analytics
Capabilities & Solutions)
Saurabh Mittal (Sr VP-Strategic Client
Partnerships)
Amit Johari (Sr VP-People Analytics)
Rajeswari Aradhyula (Chief People
Officer)
Sameer Dhanrajani (Chief Strategy
Officer)
Fran Slavich (Chief Sls Officer-New
Jersey)
Ashwath Bhat (CFO)

FRAEN MACHINING CORPORATION
324 New Boston St, Woburn, MA
01801
Tel.: (781) 205-5400
Web Site: https://www.fraen.com
Year Founded: 1968
Sales Range: $50-74.9 Million
Emp.: 75
Precision-Turned Metal Components
N.A.I.C.S.: 332721
Philip Scarfo (Gen Mgr)

FRAENKEL COMPANY, INC.
8560 Jefferson Hwy Ste B, Baton
Rouge, LA 70809-1826
Tel.: (225) 275-4242   LA
Web Site: http://www.fraenkel.com
Year Founded: 1959
Sales Range: $125-149.9 Million
Emp.: 150
Furniture Mfr & Sales
N.A.I.C.S.: 423210
Susan Pourciau (Treas, Sec & VP)

FRAGOMEN, DEL REY, BERNSEN & LOEWY, LLP
7 Hanover Sq, New York, NY 10004-
2756
Tel.: (212) 688-8555
Web Site: http://www.fragomen.com
Sales Range: $250-299.9 Million
Emp.: 300
Legal Advisory & Assistance Services
N.A.I.C.S.: 541199
Austin T. Fragomen (Partner)
Bo Cooper (Partner)
Alexandra LaCombe (Partner)
Daniel Schwarz (Partner)
Isha Atassi (Partner)
Alison Swenton Arjoon (Chief Mktg &
Bus Dev Officer)

Andreas Rothe (CFO)
Scott M. Angelo (CIO)
Hugh W. Thistlethwaite III (Partner)

FRAGRANCE OUTLET INC.
508 NE 190th St, Miami, FL 33179
Tel.: (305) 654-8015
Rev.: $17,300,000
Emp.: 15
Perfumes & Colognes
N.A.I.C.S.: 456120

FRAGRANCEX.COM
5 Plant Ave, Hauppauge, NY 11788-
3817
Tel.: (718) 482-6970
Web Site:
https://www.fragrancex.com
Year Founded: 2002
Rev.: $31,300,000
Emp.: 20
Drugs & Sundries Merchant Whslr
N.A.I.C.S.: 424210
Ron Yakuel (Pres)
Annmarie Ramkeesoon (Mgr)

FRALIN AND WALDRON, INC.
90 Towncenter St, Daleville, VA
24083
Tel.: (540) 774-4415
Web Site: http://www.fwinc.com
Year Founded: 1962
Sales Range: $10-24.9 Million
Emp.: 40
Provider of Single Family House Construction Services
N.A.I.C.S.: 236115
Karen H. WaldRon (CEO)
Andrew Kelderhouse (Pres)
Dave Cotton (Treas & Exec VP)

FRAMED PICTURES ENTERPRISE INC.
483 Hwy 6 W, Batesville, MS 38606-
2561
Tel.: (662) 563-5608   MS
Year Founded: 1983
Sales Range: $25-49.9 Million
Emp.: 440
Wood Products Mfr
N.A.I.C.S.: 339999
S. Sally (CFO)

FRAMERICA CORPORATION
2 Todd Ct, Yaphank, NY 11980
Tel.: (631) 650-1000
Web Site: http://www.framerica.com
Year Founded: 1969
Sales Range: $50-74.9 Million
Emp.: 350
Materials Molding Services
N.A.I.C.S.: 423310
Gordon Van Vechten (Co-Chm)
Gene Eichner (Co-Chm)
Dave Rosner (Sr VP-Mktg)
Jay Van Vechten (VP-Production)
Catherine Michel (Mgr-Credit)
Scott Auj (Dir-Pur)

FRAMEWORK CAPITAL PARTNERS
1700 Post Oak Blvd 1BLVD Place
Ste 600, Houston, TX 77056
Tel.: (713) 826-9351
Web Site: http://www.framework-
capital.com
Year Founded: 2013
Private Equity Firm
N.A.I.C.S.: 523999
Jerry G. McGee (Mng Dir)
Molly Risak (Dir)
Subsidiaries:
Gibraltar Cable Barrier Systems,
LP   (1)
1208 Houston Clinton Dr, Burnet, TX 78611

Tel.: (833) 715-0810
Web Site: http://www.gibraltarglobal.com
Fabricated Metal Cable Barrier Product Mfr
N.A.I.C.S.: 332999
Bryan Hoefling (Reg Sls Mgr-US)
Jay Winn (Reg Sls Mgr-US)
Ron Faulkenberry (Pres)
Clay Amuny (Controller)
Julie Ray (Dir-Ops)

FRAN'S WICKER AND RATTAN INC.
295 Rte 10 E, Succasunna, NJ
07876
Tel.: (973) 584-2230
Web Site: https://www.franswicker.com
Rev.: $4,000,000
Emp.: 25
Home Furnishings Retailer
N.A.I.C.S.: 449129
David Gruber (Pres)

FRANA & ASSOCIATES INC.
1945 3rd Ave SE, Rochester, MN
55904
Tel.: (507) 285-1884
Web Site:
http://www.andersonsformal
wear.com
Rev.: $125,000,000
Emp.: 50
Tuxedo Rental
N.A.I.C.S.: 532281
David G. Frana (Pres)
Randy Crawford (CFO)
Rick Caulson (VP)
Subsidiaries:
Anderson's Formal Wear Inc.   (1)
1945 3rd Ave SE PO Box 1145, Rochester,
MN 55903
Tel.: (507) 285-1884
Web Site:
http://www.andersonsformalwear.com
Rev.: $3,638,208
Emp.: 30
Tuxedo & Formal Wear Rentals
N.A.I.C.S.: 532281

FRANCES MAHON DEACONESS HOSPITAL
621 3rd St S, Glasgow, MT 59230
Tel.: (406) 228-3500   MT
Web Site: https://www.fmdh.org
Year Founded: 1914
Sales Range: $10-24.9 Million
Emp.: 273
Health Care Srvices
N.A.I.C.S.: 622110
Randall G. Holom (CEO)
Shelly VanBuren (Dir-HR)
Brenda Koessl (Dir-Nursing Svcs)
Ellen Guttenberg (COO)
Bev Falcon (Dir-Cardiac Rehabilitation)

FRANCES MARY ACCESSORIES, INC.
3732 Mt Diablo Blvd, Lafayette, CA
94549-3632
Tel.: (925) 962-2111
Web Site:
http://www.maryfrances.com
Sales Range: $1-9.9 Million
Emp.: 1,020
Women's Handbag & Purse Mfr
N.A.I.C.S.: 316990
Mary Shaffer (Pres)

FRANCESCHI ADVERTISING & PUBLIC RELATIONS, INC.
PO Box 1773, Tallahassee, FL 32302
Tel.: (850) 385-2900   FL
Web Site:
http://www.franadvertising.com
Year Founded: 1968
Sales Range: $10-24.9 Million
Emp.: 7

Advertising Agencies, Automotive, Brand Development, Business-To-Business, Financial, Government/Political/Public Affairs, Media Buying Services, Public Relations, Real Estate
N.A.I.C.S.: 541810
Duane Franceschi *(Owner)*
Lee Ann Franceschi *(Pres)*
Tracy Viggiani *(Media Coord)*
Jarvis Addison *(Dir-Art)*
John Hanlon *(Copy Chief)*

FRANCHI MANAGEMENT COMPANY
182 W Central St Ste 303, Natick, MA 01760
Tel.: (508) 650-4900
Web Site:
    https://www.franchimanagement.com
Year Founded: 1963
Sales Range: $1-9.9 Million
Emp.: 40
Real Estate Management & Investment Services
N.A.I.C.S.: 531311
Louis Franchi *(VP-Ops)*
Pasquale Franchi *(Founder)*

FRANCHINO MOLD & ENGINEERING CO.
5867 W Grand River Ave, Lansing, MI 48906
Tel.: (517) 321-5609
Web Site: http://www.franchino.com
Sales Range: $10-24.9 Million
Emp.: 55
Industrial Molds
N.A.I.C.S.: 333511
Mike Hetherington *(Mgr-Ops)*
Wayne Shirey *(Mgr-Quality & Engrg)*
Brad Rusthoven *(Mgr-Personnel)*
Robert Franchino *(Pres)*

FRANCHISE CONCEPTS, INC.
221 First Executive Ave, Saint Peters, MO 63376-1697
Tel.: (281) 775-5200   DE
Web Site:
    http://www.franchiseconcepts.com
Year Founded: 1979
Sales Range: $75-99.9 Million
Emp.: 20
Print, Poster & Custom Framing Retailer
N.A.I.C.S.: 459999
Joe Lynch *(CFO)*
Dave Dahl *(VP-Dev)*
Subsidiaries:

Ashley Avery's Collectibles   (1)
Ste 330 12707 North Fwy, Houston, TX 77060-1236
Tel.: (713) 820-0789
Web Site: http://www.ashleyaverys.com
Sales Range: $25-49.9 Million
Emp.: 15
Gifts & Collectible Items Made of Glass, Porcelain & Other Materials
N.A.I.C.S.: 459420

Deck the Walls   (1)
221 First Executive Ave, Saint Peters, MO 63376
Tel.: (866) 719-8200
Web Site: http://www.deckthewalls.com
Framed & Specialty Printing Services
N.A.I.C.S.: 323111

Framing Art Centre   (1)
3524 Mainway, Burlington, L7M 1A8, ON, Canada
Tel.: (800) 563-7263
Web Site: http://www.framingartcentre.com
Emp.: 1
Custom Picture Frame Shop Distr
N.A.I.C.S.: 449129

The Great Frame Up   (1)

221 First Executive Ave, Saint Peters, MO 63376
Tel.: (866) 719-8200
Web Site: http://www.thegreatframeup.com
Emp.: 13
Framed & Specialty Printing Services
N.A.I.C.S.: 323111
Joe Lynch *(CFO)*

FRANCHISE DEVELOPMENT, L.P.
1622 Deerfield Ct, Richmond, TX 77406-6507
Tel.: (281) 342-7474   TX
Web Site:
    https://franchisedevelopment.com
Year Founded: 2003
Franchise Brokerage Services
N.A.I.C.S.: 425120
Freddy O'Pry *(Pres)*

FRANCHISE OPERATIONS INC.
14105 Lorain Ave, Cleveland, OH 44111
Tel.: (216) 252-0023   DE
Sales Range: $25-49.9 Million
Emp.: 650
Franchise Owner of Fast-Food Restaurants
N.A.I.C.S.: 722513
Michael Showalter *(Pres)*
Randall Showalter *(VP)*
Jan Lawlor *(Controller)*

FRANCHISE SERVICES OF NORTH AMERICA INC.
1052 Highland Colony Parkway Suite 204, Ridgeland, MS 39157
Tel.: (601) 713-4333   Ca
Web Site: http://www.fsna-inc.com
Year Founded: 1998
Car Rental Franchisor
N.A.I.C.S.: 532111
O. Kendall Moore *(Gen Counsel, Sec & VP)*
Ashley M. Chambliss *(Interim CFO)*
Thomas P. McDonnell III *(CEO)*
Subsidiaries:

Rent-A-Wreck Systems Inc   (1)
204 7710 5th Street SE, Calgary, T2H 2L9, AB, Canada
Tel.: (800) 668-8591
Web Site: http://www.rentawreck.ca
Car Rental & Sales Services
N.A.I.C.S.: 561613

Sonoran National Insurance
Group   (1)
7502 E Pinnacle Peak Rd Ste B 210, Scottsdale, AZ 85255
Tel.: (866) 998-1001
Web Site: http://www.sonorannational.com
General Insurance Services
N.A.I.C.S.: 524210
Teresa K. Quale *(Mgr-Agency)*

U-Save Auto Rental of America, Inc.   (1)
1052 Highland Colony Pkwy Ste 204, Ridgeland, MS 39157
Tel.: (601) 713-4333
Web Site: http://www.usave.com
Car Rental Services
N.A.I.C.S.: 532111

FRANCIS DRILLING FLUIDS LTD.
240 Jasmine Rd, Crowley, LA 70526
Tel.: (337) 783-8685
Web Site: http://www.fdfltd.com
Rev.: $31,561,405
Emp.: 85
Drilling Fluid Distr
N.A.I.C.S.: 424690
Alex Dore *(Mgr)*
Barry Charpentier *(CEO)*

FRANCIS FORD COPPOLA WINERY
300 Via Archimedes, Geyserville, CA 95441
Tel.: (707) 857-1471
Web Site:
    https://www.francisfordcoppola
    winery.com
Winery
N.A.I.C.S.: 312130
Subsidiaries:

Geyser Peak Winery   (1)
2306 Magnolia Dr, Healdsburg, CA 95448
Tel.: (707) 857-2500
Web Site: http://www.geyserpeakwinery.com
Sales Range: $10-24.9 Million
Emp.: 80
Wine Producer & Distr
N.A.I.C.S.: 312130

FRANCIS MANUFACTURING CO.
500 E Main St, Russia, OH 45363-0400
Tel.: (937) 526-4551
Web Site:
    https://www.francismanufac
    turing.com
Year Founded: 1946
Sales Range: $10-24.9 Million
Emp.: 125
Nonferrous Foundry Services
N.A.I.C.S.: 331523
David J. Francis *(VP)*
William T. Francis *(Pres)*

FRANCIS O. DAY CO., INC.
850 E Gude Dr Ste A, Rockville, MD 20850-1387
Tel.: (301) 652-2400
Web Site: http://www.foday.com
Year Founded: 1948
Sales Range: $25-49.9 Million
Emp.: 500
Provider of Highway & Street Paving Contracting Services
N.A.I.C.S.: 324121
Peter Hitchen *(Treas & VP)*
Mike Moore *(Controller)*

FRANCIS SCOTT KEY AUDI
6001 Urbana Pike, Frederick, MD 21704
Tel.: (301) 662-7600
Web Site: http://www.fskautos.com
Sales Range: $10-24.9 Million
Emp.: 32
Automobiles, New & Used
N.A.I.C.S.: 441110
Marvin J. Adcock *(Pres)*
Lauren Church *(Controller)*

FRANCISCAN ALLIANCE, INC.
1515 W Dragoon Trl, Mishawaka, IN 46546
Tel.: (574) 256-3935
Web Site:
    http://www.franciscanalliance.org
Sales Range: $1-4.9 Billion
Emp.: 9,000
Hospital Services
N.A.I.C.S.: 622110
Kevin Leahy *(Pres & CEO)*
Randall Moore *(COO/Sr VP-Franciscan Health & Care Solutions)*
Agnes Therady *(Chief Nursing Officer & Sr VP)*

FRANCISCAN HEALTH SYSTEM
1717 S J St, Tacoma, WA 98405
Tel.: (253) 426-6156   WA
Web Site:
    http://www.chifranciscan.org
Year Founded: 1891

Health Care Services Organization
N.A.I.C.S.: 813910
Laurie Brown *(Chief Experience Officer)*
Mike Fitzgerald *(CFO)*
Sharon Royne *(Sr VP-HR)*
Ian G. Worden *(COO)*
Tony McLean *(Pres-South King County)*
Thomas Kruse *(Sr VP & Chief Strategy Officer)*
Michael Marshall *(Pres & Chief Medical Officer)*
Terri Rambosek *(VP-Regional General Counsel)*
Holly Stroud *(VP-Corp Responsibility)*
Gregory Unruh *(Pres)*
Ketul J. Patel *(CEO)*
Subsidiaries:

Harrison Medical Center   (1)
2520 Cherry Ave, Bremerton, WA 98310
Tel.: (360) 377-3911
Web Site: http://www.harrisonmedical.org
Hospital & Other Health Care Facilities Operator
N.A.I.C.S.: 622110
Steve Dixon *(Engr-Sys)*
David W. Schultz *(Pres)*
Jeanell Rasmussen *(Chief Nursing Officer & Sr VP)*
Laurie Brown *(Chief Nursing Officer)*
Mike Fitzgerald *(CFO)*
Dianna Kielian *(Sr VP-Mission)*
Ketul J. Patel *(CEO)*
Sharon Royne *(Sr VP-HR)*
Ian Worden *(COO)*

Subsidiary (Domestic):

Advanced Medical Imaging, LLC   (2)
1780 NW Myhre Rd Ste 1220, Silverdale, WA 98383
Tel.: (360) 337-6500
Web Site: http://www.amiradiology.com
Sales Range: $10-24.9 Million
Diagnostic Imaging Centers
N.A.I.C.S.: 621512
J. Wesley Solze *(Dir-Medical)*

Virginia Mason Health System   (1)
1100 9th Ave, Seattle, WA 98101
Tel.: (206) 583-6083
Web Site: http://www.virginiamason.org
Sales Range: $10-24.9 Million
Health Care Srvices
N.A.I.C.S.: 621610
Robert Lemon *(Treas)*
James Orlikoff *(Vice Chm)*
Gary S. Kaplan *(Co-Chm & CEO)*
Craig Goodrich *(CFO)*
Lynne Chafetz *(Sr VP)*

FRANCISCAN HOSPITAL FOR CHILDREN
30 Warren St, Brighton, MA 02135
Tel.: (617) 254-3800   MA
Web Site:
    http://www.franciscanhospital.org
Year Founded: 1945
Sales Range: $50-74.9 Million
Emp.: 895
Children Healthcare Services
N.A.I.C.S.: 622110
Aimee Carew-Lyons *(Chief Nursing Officer)*
Gloria Carpinello *(VP-Mission Effectiveness)*
James Mandel *(Vice Chm)*
Jane OBrien *(Chief Medical Officer)*

FRANCISCO PARTNERS MANAGEMENT, LP
1 Letterman Dr Bldg C Ste 410, San Francisco, CA 94129
Tel.: (415) 418-2900   DE
Web Site:
    http://www.franciscopartners.com
Year Founded: 1999
Privater Equity Firm
N.A.I.C.S.: 523999
Neil Garfinkel *(Co-Founder & Partner)*
Keith B. Geeslin *(Partner)*

Francisco Partners Management, LP—(Continued)

Ezra Perlman (Co-Pres)
David Golob (Chief Investment Officer)
Tom Ludwig (COO)
Deep Shah (Co-Pres & Co-Head-European Investing)
Chris Adams (Partner-Deal)
Petri Oksanen (Partner-Deal)
Matt Spetzler (Partner-Deal)
Peter Christodoulo (Partner-Deal)
Brian Decker (Partner-Deal)
Andrew J. Kowal (Partner-Deal)
Adam Solomon (Principal)
Christine Wang (Principal)
Evan Daar (Principal)
Jonathan Murphy (Principal)
Mario Razzini (Principal)
Jason Brein (Partner-Deal)
Quentin Lathuille (VP)
Mike Kohlsdorf (Pres-Consulting)
Ali Evans (VP)
Fouad G. Tamer (Operating)
Ford Tamer (Senior Operating Partner)
Dipanjan Deb (CEO)
Dipanjan Deb (CEO)

Subsidiaries:

Avangate B.V. (1)
Prins Hendriklaan 26 II, 1075 BD, Amsterdam, Netherlands
Tel.: (31) 20 8908080
Web Site: http://www.avangate.com
Sales Range: $10-24.9 Million
E-Commerce Software
N.A.I.C.S.: 513210
Carmen Sebe (COO)
Joseph G. Brown (Sr VP-Worldwide Sls)
Cristian Badea (CIO)
Laurentiu Ghenciu (VP-Sls-EMEA)
Andy Tung (VP-Sls-APAC)
Jeff Hodges (CFO)
Brian Stewart (VP-Sls-America)
Matthijs Koorn (VP-Sls-Western Europe)

Subsidiary (US):

Avangate Inc. (2)
555 Twin Dolphin Dr Ste 155, Redwood City, CA 94065
Tel.: (650) 249-5280
Web Site: http://www.avangate.com
E-Commerce Software
N.A.I.C.S.: 513210
Brian Stewart (VP-Sls-North America)
Carl Theobald (Pres)
John Keating (Sr VP-Svc & Support)
Len Eschweiler (Sr VP-Worldwide Sls)
Alex Hart (CEO)
Gregor Morela (CFO)

BARBRI, Inc. (1)
12222 Merit Dr Ste 1340, Dallas, TX 75251
Tel.: (877) 385-6238
Web Site: http://www.barbri.com
Legal Education Services
N.A.I.C.S.: 541199
Steve Fredette (CEO)
Dan Wilson (CFO & Operating Officer)

Subsidiary (Domestic):

GLK Enterprises, Inc. (2)
12222 Merit Dr Ste 1340, Dallas, TX 75251
Tel.: (800) 522-7737
Web Site: http://www.legalstudies.com
Professional & Management Development Training
N.A.I.C.S.: 611430

Strafford Publications, Inc. (2)
590 Dutch Valley Road NE, Atlanta, GA 30324
Tel.: (404) 881-1141
Web Site: http://www.straffordpub.com
Rev.: $3,028,048
Emp.: 15
Prepress Services
N.A.I.C.S.: 323120

Bitglass, Inc. (1)
655 Campbell Technology Pkwy Ste 225, Campbell, CA 95008
Tel.: (408) 337-0190

Web Site: http://www.bitglass.com
Data Security & Cloud Computing Services
N.A.I.C.S.: 518210
Anurag Kahol (CTO)
Nat Kausik (Founder)
Mike Leigh (VP-Sls)
Andrew Urushima (VP-Fin)
Chris Chan (VP-Engrg)
Dean Hickman-Smith (Sr VP-Worldwide Field Ops)
Rich Campagna (CEO)
Steven Armstrong (Dir-Sls-UK, Ireland & Sub Saharan Africa)
Eduard Meelhuysen (VP-Sls-EMEA)

Blancco Technology Group Plc (1)
Chapel House Tremhall Park Start Hill, Bishops Stortford, London, CM22 7WE, Hertfordshire, United Kingdom
Tel.: (44) 3300521546
Web Site: https://www.blancco.com
Sales Range: $125-149.9 Million
Emp.: 350
Holding Company; Consumer Electronics Diagnostics, Repair & Data Erasure Services
N.A.I.C.S.: 551112
Russ Ernst (CTO)
Sarah Smith (Sr VP-Human Resources)
Jon Mellon (Pres & Pres-Sales, Marketing, and Field Ops)
Satoru Ogawa (CFO)
Matt Jones (CEO)

Subsidiary (Non-US):

ANOVO Nordic AB (2)
PO Box 53, 68122, Kristinehamn, Sweden (100%)
Tel.: (46) 55085500
Web Site: http://www.anovo.se
Sales Range: $25-49.9 Million
Emp.: 60
Computer Facilities Management Services
N.A.I.C.S.: 541513

Blancco Japan Inc. (2)
Gaien Bldg 5F 2-23-8 Minami-Aoyama, Minato-ku, Tokyo, 107-0062, Japan
Tel.: (81) 357727491
Web Site: http://www.blancco.jp
IT Devices & Data Erasure Software
N.A.I.C.S.: 541511
Masayuki Morita (Pres)

Subsidiary (US):

Blancco LLC (2)
11675 Rainwater Dr Bldg 600 Ste 100, Alpharetta, GA 30009
Tel.: (770) 971-9770
Software Development Services
N.A.I.C.S.: 541511
Nina Willgren (Mgr-Fin)
Richard Stiennon (Chief Strategy Officer)
Ragini Bhalla (Sr Dir-Global Comm)
Steve Holton (Pres & Chief Revenue Officer)
Rob Woodward (Chm)
Matt Jones (CEO)
Adam Moloney (CFO)

Subsidiary (Non-US):

Blancco Australasia Pty Ltd (3)
Level 19 10 Eagle Street, Brisbane, 4000, QLD, Australia
Tel.: (61) 730673602
Software Development Services
N.A.I.C.S.: 541511
Karl Gaines (Mng Dir)

Blancco Central Europe GmbH (2)
Monreposstrasse 53, 71634, Ludwigsburg, Germany
Tel.: (49) 71419566025
Software Development Services
N.A.I.C.S.: 541511
Torsten Lay (Mgr-Sls)

Blancco France SAS (3)
29/31 Rue du Chemin de Fer, 59100, Roubaix, France
Tel.: (33) 320271932
Software Development Services
N.A.I.C.S.: 541511

Blancco Oy Ltd (3)
Lansikatu 15, 80110, Joensuu, Finland
Tel.: (358) 207433850

Software Development Services
N.A.I.C.S.: 541511
Laura Kupari (Head-Reg Sls)

Blancco SEA Sdn Bhd (3)
Suite B-10-2 Level 10 Tower B Plaza Pantai Off Jalan Pantai Baru, 59200, Kuala Lumpur, Malaysia
Tel.: (60) 322011920
Software Development Services
N.A.I.C.S.: 541511
Shin Lim (Mgr-Mktg)

Blancco Sweden SFO (3)
Engelbrektsgatan 7, 11432, Stockholm, Sweden
Tel.: (46) 86786900
Software Development Services
N.A.I.C.S.: 541511
Sebastian Rosendahl (Mgr-Sls)

Blancco UK Ltd (3)
Stansted Business Centre Parsonage Road, Takeley, CM22 6PU, Essex, United Kingdom
Tel.: (44) 1279874200
Software Development Services
N.A.I.C.S.: 541511
Glyn Parry (Mgr-Grp Fin)

Subsidiary (Non-US):

Regenersis (Bucharest) SRL (2)
Bulevardul Timisoara 92 Sector 6, Bucharest, Romania
Tel.: (40) 214041440
Web Site: http://www.regenersis.ro
Electronic Component Repair Service
N.A.I.C.S.: 811210
Alexandru Capatina (Mng Dir)
Ana Neagu (Mgr-Quality & Environmental)
Anca Marginean (Mgr-HR)
Carmina Popa (Mgr-Fin)
Ioan Brezeanu (Project Mgr)

Regenersis (Czech) s.r.o (2)
CT Park Pod Dolni Drahou 105, Krupka, 417 42, Czech Republic
Tel.: (420) 417568302
Electronic Component Repair Service
N.A.I.C.S.: 811210
Pavel Patek (Officer-IT)

Regenersis (Deutschland) GmbH (2)
Bahndamm 39, Schloss Holte-Stukenbrock, 33758, Germany (100%)
Tel.: (49) 52079290102
Web Site: http://www.regenersis.com
Sales Range: $25-49.9 Million
Emp.: 160
Logistics, Repair & Fully Managed Solutions
N.A.I.C.S.: 541614
Alfons Krauthausen (Mng Dir-Tech Svcs)

Subsidiary (Domestic):

Regenersis (Glenrothes) Ltd. (2)
1 James Watt Avenue, Westwood Park, Glenrothes, KY7 4UA, Fife, United Kingdom (100%)
Tel.: (44) 1592774704
Web Site: http://www.regenersis.com
Computer Logistics, Repair, Testing, Refurbishing & Customer Services
N.A.I.C.S.: 811210
Cameron Radford (Mng Dir)

Regenersis (Huntingdon) Ltd. (2)
Kingfisher Way, Hinchingbrooke Bus Park, Huntingdon, PE29 6FN, Cambs, United Kingdom (100%)
Tel.: (44) 1480431431
Web Site: http://www.regenersis.com
Sales Range: $25-49.9 Million
Emp.: 150
Logistics, Managed Services, Parts & Inventory Management, Call Center & Training Solutions
N.A.I.C.S.: 541614
Wayne Hellewell (Gen Mgr)

Subsidiary (Non-US):

Regenersis (Nederland) BV (2)
Schiphol Boulevard 127, 1118 BG, Amsterdam, Netherlands
Tel.: (31) 207005585
Holding Company
N.A.I.C.S.: 551112

Regenersis (Portugal) Ltd (2)

Avenida Severiano Falcao N 6 6 Prior Velho, Lisbon, 2685-378, Portugal
Tel.: (351) 215947444
Electronic Component Repair Service
N.A.I.C.S.: 811210
Rodrigo Correia (Engr-Quality)

Regenersis (Sommerda) GmbH (2)
Erfurter Hohe 10a, 99610, Sommerda, Germany
Tel.: (49) 36343199888
Web Site: http://www.regenersis.de
Electronic Component Repair Service
N.A.I.C.S.: 811210
Alfons Krauthausen (Mng Dir)
Eduard Falkenreck (Dir-Sls-Industrial & Healthcare)
Thomas Skorzewski (Dir-Sls-Cash & Retail Payment)

Regenersis (South Africa) (PTY) Ltd (2)
Unit C Alphen Square West 338 George Street, Randjespark, Midrand, 1685, Gauteng, South Africa
Tel.: (27) 112377800
Electronic Component Repair Service
N.A.I.C.S.: 811210
Shajil Thottungal (Engr-Quality)

Regenersis (Spain) Comanditaria Simple (2)
Av Leonardo Da Vinci 13, Getafe, 28906, Madrid, Spain
Tel.: (34) 916240500
Holding Company
N.A.I.C.S.: 551112

Regenersis (Warsaw) Sp.z.o.o, (2)
Janki Ul Falencka 1B, 05-090, Raszyn, Poland
Tel.: (48) 227201020
Web Site: http://www.regenersis.pl
Electronic Component Repair Service
N.A.I.C.S.: 811210

Regenersis Digital Care AB (2)
Smedjegatan 6 3tr, 131 54, Nacka, Sweden
Tel.: (46) 842003880
General Insurance Services
N.A.I.C.S.: 524210
Asa Hjelm (Mgr-Ops)

Subsidiary (US):

Regenersis Inc. (2)
3919 Hickory Hill Rd, Memphis, TN 38115
Tel.: (901) 201-5635
Electronic Component Repair Service
N.A.I.C.S.: 811210

Subsidiary (Non-US):

Regenersis Istanbul Teknoloji Danismanligi Limited Sirketi (2)
Tatlisu Mahallesi Senol Gunes Bulvari Mira Tower Sitesi No 2 Zemin Kat, Umraniye, 34775, Istanbul, Turkiye
Tel.: (90) 2165945680
Electronic Component Repair Service
N.A.I.C.S.: 811210

Regenersis Mexico S.A.de C.V. (2)
Tres Anegas 425 Bodega 7 Col Nueva Industrial Vallejo, Delegacion Gustavo A Madero, 07700, Mexico, Mexico
Tel.: (52) 5551195929
Electronic Component Repair Service
N.A.I.C.S.: 811210
Aitor Echevarria Trivino (Mgr-Client Delivery-Sony)

Regenersis Rus O.o.o (2)
Lavochkina st19, Moscow, Russia
Tel.: (7) 4952680135
Web Site: http://www.regenersis.ru
Electronic Component Repair Service
N.A.I.C.S.: 811210

SafeIT Security Sweden AB (2)
Engelbrektsgatan 7, 114 32, Stockholm, Sweden
Tel.: (46) 86657958
Web Site: http://www.safeit.se
Software Development Services
N.A.I.C.S.: 541511

Subsidiary (US):

Tabernus LLC (2)

11130 Jollyville Rd Ste 203, Austin, TX 78759
Tel.: (512) 372-9823
Web Site: http://www.tabernus.com
Software Development Services
N.A.I.C.S.: 541511

Subsidiary (Non-US):

Tabernus Europe Limited   **(3)**
Unit 8 Waterside Court Albany Street, Newport, NP20 5NT, South Wales, United Kingdom
Tel.: (44) 1639505731
Software Development Services
N.A.I.C.S.: 541511
Daniel Dyer *(VP-Global Ops)*

Subsidiary (US):

WhiteCanyon Software, Inc.   **(2)**
947 S 500 E Ste 300, American Fork, UT 84003
Tel.: (801) 224-8900
Web Site: http://www.whitecanyon.com
Software Publisher
N.A.I.C.S.: 513210
Bill Glynn *(CEO)*

BluJay Solutions Ltd.   **(1)**
Blue Tower 14th Floor MediaCityUK, Salford Quays, Manchester, M50 2ST, United Kingdom
Tel.: (44) 1619054600
Web Site: http://www.blujaysolutions.com
Supply Chain Management Software Mfr
N.A.I.C.S.: 334610
Mohit Paul *(Sr VP-EMEA)*
Sam Addeo *(CTO)*
Andrew Kirkwood *(CEO)*
Doug Surrett *(Chief Strategy Officer)*

Branch (Non-US):

Kewill   **(2)**
5Q1A3 Cyber Towers HITEC City Madhapur, Hyderabad, 500081, Andhra Pradesh, India
Tel.: (91) 4023100600
Web Site: http://www.four-soft.com
Sales Range: $25-49.9 Million
Software Development Services
N.A.I.C.S.: 541511
Biju S. Nair *(Exec VP & Head-Ops)*

Subsidiary (Non-US):

Kewill Belgium NV   **(2)**
Abtsdreef 10b, Stabroek, 2950, Belgium
Tel.: (32) 35683131
Web Site: http://www.kewill.com
Sales Range: $10-24.9 Million
Emp.: 8
Supply Chain Management Software Mfr
N.A.I.C.S.: 334610
Ben De Vos *(COO-Europe)*

Kewill Co., Ltd.   **(2)**
Room D 9F Baoding Bldg 550 Xu Jia Hui Road, Luwan District, Shanghai, 200023, China
Tel.: (86) 21 6466 3030
Supply Chain Management Software Mfr
N.A.I.C.S.: 334610

Kewill GmbH   **(2)**
Norsk-Data-Strasse 1, 61352, Bad Homburg, Germany
Tel.: (49) 6172 9268 0
Web Site: http://www.kewill.com
Supply Chain Management Software Mfr
N.A.I.C.S.: 334610
Andreas O. Heil *(Mng Dir-Germany, Austria & Switzerland)*

Kewill Holding B.V   **(2)**
Laan van Londen 100, Dordrecht, 3317, South Holland, Netherlands
Tel.: (31) 786202200
Web Site: http://www.kewill.com
Sales Range: $50-74.9 Million
Holding Company
N.A.I.C.S.: 551112
Ben De Vos *(Gen Mgr)*

Subsidiary (Domestic):

Kewill BV   **(3)**
Laan van Londen 100, Dordrecht, 3317 DA, Netherlands
Tel.: (31) 786123744

Web Site: http://www.kewill.com
Sales Range: $10-24.9 Million
Emp.: 100
Supply Chain Management Software Mfr
N.A.I.C.S.: 334610
Douglas Brown *(CEO)*

Kewill Service Logistics B.V.   **(3)**
Randstad 22-179, 1316 BM, Almere, Netherlands
Tel.: (31) 365345565
Web Site: http://www.kewill.com
Sales Range: $10-24.9 Million
Emp.: 13
Logistics Consulting Servies
N.A.I.C.S.: 541614

Subsidiary (US):

Kewill Inc.   **(2)**
1 Executive Dr, Chelmsford, MA 01824
Tel.: (978) 482-2500
Web Site: http://www.kewill.com
Sales Range: $25-49.9 Million
Trade & Logistics Software Publisher & Distr
N.A.I.C.S.: 513210

Subsidiary (Domestic):

Four Soft USA, Inc.   **(3)**
150 Motor Pkwy Ste 302, Hauppauge, NY 11788
Tel.: (631) 752-7700
Sales Range: $1-9.9 Million
Emp.: 29
Computer System Design Services
N.A.I.C.S.: 541512

Subsidiary (Non-US):

Kewill Limited   **(2)**
Unit 987 9th Floor Kowloonbay Intl Trade & Exhibition Centre, 1 Trademart Drive, Kowloon, China (Hong Kong)
Tel.: (852) 28824321
Web Site: http://www.kewill.com
Sales Range: $10-24.9 Million
Emp.: 8
Supply Chain Management Software Mfr
N.A.I.C.S.: 334610

Kewill Pte Ltd   **(2)**
73 Science Park Drive No B1-16/19 CIN-TECH I, Singapore Science Park I, Singapore, 118254, Singapore
Tel.: (65) 64913939
Web Site: http://www.kewill-ipacs.com
Sales Range: $25-49.9 Million
Supply Chain Management Software Mfr & Whslr
N.A.I.C.S.: 334610

Bomgar Corporation   **(1)**
578 Highland Colony Pkwy Paragon Ctr Ste 200, Ridgeland, MS 39157
Tel.: (601) 519-0123
Web Site: http://www.beyondtrust.com
Enterprise Remote Support Services
N.A.I.C.S.: 513210
Matt Dircks *(CEO)*
Martin Willoughby *(Chief Privacy Officer & Gen Counsel)*
Janine K. Seebeck *(CFO)*
Dan Derosa *(Chief Product Officer)*
Liz Shulof *(CMO)*
David Giles *(Chief Customer Success Officer)*
Carl Helle *(Chief Revenue Officer)*
Mark Rankin *(Chief HR Officer)*
Morey J. Haber *(CTO & Chief Info Security Officer)*
Raj Cherukuri *(Exec VP-Tech & Engrg)*

Subsidiary (Non-US):

Avecto Limited   **(2)**
Building One Trident Business Park Styal Road, Manchester, M22 5XB, United Kingdom
Tel.: (44) 1628480210
Web Site: http://www.beyondtrust.com
Security Software Development Services
N.A.I.C.S.: 541511

Subsidiary (Domestic):

BeyondTrust Software, Inc.   **(2)**
5090 N 40th St Ste 400, Phoenix, AZ 85018
Tel.: (877) 826-6427

Web Site: http://www.beyondtrust.com
Cyber Security Solutions
N.A.I.C.S.: 513210
Carl Helle *(Chief Revenue Officer)*

Capsule Technologies, Inc.   **(1)**
300 Brickstone Sq Ste 203, Andover, MA 01810
Tel.: (978) 482-2300
Web Site: http://www.capsuletech.com
Device Connectivity & Data Management Services
N.A.I.C.S.: 561499
John Trzeciak *(Interim CEO)*
Kevin Phillips *(VP-Product Mgmt)*
Frederic Darguesse *(VP-Engrg)*

Subsidiary (Domestic):

Bernoulli Enterprise, Inc.   **(2)**
200 Cascade Blvd, Milford, CT 06460
Tel.: (203) 877-1999
Web Site: http://www.bernoullihealth.com
Sales Range: $1-9.9 Million
Emp.: 30
Medical Device Monitoring Software Solutions
N.A.I.C.S.: 513210
Jay McGuire *(CTO)*
Sam Larson *(VP-Mktg)*
John Zaleski *(CIO & Exec VP)*
Paul Blodgett *(VP-Ops)*
William Noble *(VP-Sls)*
Jeanne J. Venella *(Chief Nursing Officer)*

Subsidiary (Domestic):

Nuvon, Inc.   **(3)**
4801 S Broad St Ste 120, Philadelphia, PA 19112
Tel.: (215) 600-2627
Web Site: http://www.nuvon.com
Sales Range: $1-9.9 Million
Emp.: 15
Medical Device Connectivity & Clinical Informatics Technologies Devloper
N.A.I.C.S.: 334118
Christopher Gatti *(CEO)*
Vedran Jukic *(Founder & CTO)*
John Zaleski *(Chief Informatics Officer)*
Jeanne J. Venella *(Chief Nursing Officer)*
Mike Portnoy *(VP-Engrg)*
Bill Zeruld *(VP-Sls & Bus Dev)*

Connecture, Inc.   **(1)**
18500 W Corporate Dr Ste 250, Brookfield, WI 53045
Tel.: (262) 432-8282
Web Site: http://www.connecture.com
Rev.: $76,746,000
Assets: $83,078,000
Liabilities: $160,303,000
Net Worth: ($77,225,000)
Earnings: ($15,544,000)
Emp.: 320
Fiscal Year-end: 12/31/2017
Web-Based Sales, Services & Process Automation Solutions for the Healthcare Industry
N.A.I.C.S.: 513199
Mark E. Granville *(Chief Delivery Officer)*
David A. Sockel *(Exec VP-Corp & Product Strategy)*
Lea DeVillers *(Gen Counsel)*
Jeffrey A. Surges *(Pres & CEO)*
Stephanie Meyer *(Chief Mktg Officer)*
Peter Urbain *(Sr VP-Provider Segment)*
Jean Landsverk *(Sr VP-Sls)*
Brian D. Lindstrom *(CFO & Sec)*
Jeff Hyman *(Dir-Channel Mktg)*
Joe Donlan *(Sr VP-Broker Segment & Sls)*
Robert Bates *(Sr VP-Engrg)*
Scottie Girouard *(Sr Dir-Human Capital)*
Vincent E. Estrada *(Exec VP-Corp Dev)*

EG A/S   **(1)**
Lautrupvang 24, 2750, Ballerup, Denmark
Tel.: (45) 7013 2211
Web Site: http://www.eg.dk
Emp.: 1,000
Information Technology Consultancy & Technical Services
N.A.I.C.S.: 541690
Allan Buhl Moller *(CTO)*
Mikkel Bardram *(CEO)*
Henrik Hansen *(CFO)*

Subsidiary (Domestic):

EG Kommuneinformation A/S   **(2)**

Amaliegate 3-5, 1060, Copenhagen, Denmark
Tel.: (45) 33280300
Web Site: http://global.eg.dk
IT Administrative Solutions
N.A.I.C.S.: 541519
Martin Holngard *(Gen Mgr)*

Subsidiary (Non-US):

EG Norge AS   **(2)**
Jerikoveien 10B, 1067, Oslo, Norway
Tel.: (47) 51 96 37 80
Web Site: http://www.egnorge.no
IT Consulting Services
N.A.I.C.S.: 541690
Morten Saelemyr *(Dir-Admin)*

Division (Domestic):

EG Retail & Medie   **(2)**
Taekkemandsvej 1, 4300, Holbaek, Denmark
Tel.: (45) 7015 3003
Web Site: http://www.global.eg.dk
Sales Range: $50-74.9 Million
Retail & Media Business Information Technology Services
N.A.I.C.S.: 541519
Henrik R. Moller *(Dir-Retail & Media)*

Subsidiary (Non-US):

EG Sverige AB   **(2)**
Kistagangen 20 B, 164 40, Kista, Sweden   **(100%)**
Tel.: (46) 8 631 78 00
Web Site: http://www.egsverige.se
IT Consulting Services
N.A.I.C.S.: 541690
Ole Fritze *(Mng Dir)*
Edward Bjurstrom *(Mgr-Retail Bus Unit)*
Jesper Rosleff *(Interim Country Mgr-Utility)*

Subsidiary (Domestic):

EG Utility A/S   **(2)**
Industrivej Syd 13 C, 7400, Herning, Denmark
Tel.: (45) 7013 2211
Web Site: http://www.global.eg.dk
Sales Range: $25-49.9 Million
Emp.: 150
IT Solutions for Utility Companies
N.A.I.C.S.: 541519
Bo Haaber *(Dir-Utility)*

Silkeborg Data A/S   **(2)**
Dusager 25, 8200, Silkeborg, Denmark
Tel.: (45) 70132211
Web Site: http://www.silkeborgdata.dk
Sales Range: $25-49.9 Million
IT-based Payroll & HR Solution Services
N.A.I.C.S.: 541512

Florida MicroElectronics, LLC   **(1)**
1601 Hill Ave, West Palm Beach, FL 33407-2234
Tel.: (561) 845-8455
Web Site: http://www.flmicroelec.com
Sales Range: $25-49.9 Million
Electronic Components Mfr
N.A.I.C.S.: 334210
Amy Ferreira *(Mgr-Production)*

Follett School Solutions, Inc.   **(1)**
1340 Ridgeview Dr, McHenry, IL 60050
Tel.: (815) 759-1700
Web Site: http://www.follett.com
PreK-12 Textbooks & Other Eduational Materials Whslr
N.A.I.C.S.: 424920
Nader Qaimari *(Pres)*
Britten Follett *(Exec VP)*
Paul Isle *(CEO)*

Forcepoint LLC   **(1)**
10240 Sorrento Valley Rd, San Diego, CA 92121
Tel.: (858) 320-8000
Web Site: http://www.forcepoint.com
Sales Range: $350-399.9 Million
Emp.: 1,609
Web Filtering & Security, Data Loss Prevention, Email Anti-Spam & Security Solutions
N.A.I.C.S.: 513210
Thomas A. Kennedy *(Chm)*
Matthew T. Santangelo *(CFO)*
John D. Holmes *(Chief Legal Officer)*
Brian J. Miller *(Sr VP-Customer Success & Ops)*

Francisco Partners Management, LP—(Continued)

Sean D. Berg *(Sr VP & Gen Mgr-Governments & Critical Infra-Global)*
Kevin Isaac *(Chief Revenue Officer)*
Matt Preschern *(Chief Mktg Officer)*
David Coffey *(Sr VP-Engrg)*
Laurie O'Brien *(Chief HR Officer)*
Lisa Schreiber *(Chief Customer Success Officer)*
Rees Johnson *(Chief Product Officer)*
Manny Rivelo *(CEO)*
Joseph Bell *(Chief Info Security Officer-Global Governments & Critical Infrastructure)*
Karen Clark *(Chief HR Officer-Global Governments & Critical Infrastructure)*
James Wallace *(Chief Legal Officer-Global Governments & Critical Infrastructure)*
Jason Facer *(Interim CFO-Global Governments & Critical Infrastructure)*
Greg Higham *(Interim CIO-Global Governments & Critical Infrastructure)*

Subsidiary (Non-US):

Forcepoint Deutschland GmbH   **(2)**
Feringastrasse 4, Munchen Unterfohring, Munich, 85774, Germany
Tel.: (49) 89 244 1058 00
Web Site: http://www.forcepoint.com
Internet Security Software
N.A.I.C.S.: 513210

Forcepoint France   **(2)**
Arches des Dolines 7 rue Soutrane, 6560, Valbonne, France
Tel.: (33) 497234300
Web Site: http://www.forcepoint.com
Internet Security Software
N.A.I.C.S.: 513210

Forcepoint International Limited   **(2)**
Custom House Plaza Block 6, International Financial Services Centre, Dublin, Ireland
Tel.: (353) 8007231166
Web Site: http://www.forcepoint.com
Emp.: 50
Holding Company
N.A.I.C.S.: 551112

Subsidiary (Domestic):

Forcepoint International Technology Limited   **(3)**
Minerva House Simmonscourt Rd, Dublin, Ireland
Tel.: (353) 1 536 0000
Web Site: http://www.forcepoint.com
Emp.: 50
Web Filtering & Security, Data Loss Prevention, Email Anti-Spam & Security Solutions
N.A.I.C.S.: 513210

Subsidiary (Non-US):

Forcepoint Italy S.r.l.   **(2)**
Bastioni Di Porta Nuova 21, 20121, Milan, Italy
Tel.: (39) 0289041000
Web Site: http://www.forcepoint.com
Internet Security Software
N.A.I.C.S.: 513210

Forcepoint Japan KK   **(2)**
2nd Floor Shinbashi Tokyu Bldg 4-21-3 Shinbashi, Minato-ku, Tokyo, 105-0004, Japan
Tel.: (81) 3 6895 7474
Web Site: http://www.forcepoint.com
Internet Security Software
N.A.I.C.S.: 513210

Forcepoint S.C. Pty Ltd   **(2)**
Level 6 111 Pacific Highway, North Sydney, 2060, NSW, Australia
Tel.: (61) 2 9414 0000
Web Site: http://www.forcepoint.com
Emp.: 30
Content Security Software
N.A.I.C.S.: 334610

Forcepoint UK Limited   **(2)**
420 Thames Valley Park, Reading, RG6 1PT, Berkshire, United Kingdom
Tel.: (44) 118 938 8600
Web Site: http://www.forcepoint.com
Emp.: 150
Internet Security Software
N.A.I.C.S.: 513210
Kevin Isaac *(Chief Revenue Officer)*

Hal Leonard Corporation   **(1)**
7777 W Bluemound Rd, Milwaukee, WI 53213
Tel.: (414) 774-3630
Web Site: http://www.halleonard.com
Emp.: 500
Music Print Publisher; Music Related Products Distr
N.A.I.C.S.: 512230
Larry Morton *(Pres)*
Keith Mardak *(Chm & CEO)*
Doug Lady *(Sr VP)*
Jeff Schroedl *(Exec VP)*
Linda Nelson *(Creative Dir)*

Hover-Davis, Inc.   **(1)**
100 Paragon Dr, Rochester, NY 14624
Tel.: (585) 352-9590
Web Site: http://www.hoverdavis.com
Component Feeding Solutions
N.A.I.C.S.: 333519

Ichor Holdings, Ltd.   **(1)**
3185 Laurelview Ct, Fremont, CA 94538
Tel.: (510) 897-5200
Web Site: https://www.ichorsystems.com
Rev.: $1,280,069,000
Assets: $1,083,742,000
Liabilities: $496,246,000
Net Worth: $587,496,000
Earnings: $72,804,000
Emp.: 2,280
Fiscal Year-end: 12/30/2022
Semiconductor Components Mfr
N.A.I.C.S.: 334413
Jeffrey S. Andreson *(CEO)*
Thomas M. Rohrs *(Chm)*
Greg F. Swyt *(CFO)*

Subsidiary (Domestic):

Ajax-United Patterns & Molds, Inc.   **(2)**
34585 7th St, Union City, CA 94587-3673
Tel.: (510) 476-8000
Plastic & Metal Products Assembly & Mfr
N.A.I.C.S.: 326199

Ichor Systems, Inc.   **(2)**
9660 SW Herman Rd, Tualatin, OR 97062
Tel.: (503) 625-2251
Web Site: http://www.ichorsystems.com
Sales Range: $450-499.9 Million
Emp.: 540
Industrial Product Mfr & Distr
N.A.I.C.S.: 332912
Jeffrey S. Andreson *(Pres)*
Thomas M. Rohrs *(Chm & CEO)*
Philip R. Barros *(CTO)*
Maurice Carson *(CFO)*
Kevin Canty *(COO)*
Iain McGregor *(Sls Dir)*

Subsidiary (Domestic):

IMG Companies, LLC   **(3)**
225 Mountain Vista Pkwy, Livermore, CA 94551
Tel.: (925) 273-1100
Web Site: http://www.imgprecision.com
Industrial & Commercial Machinery & Equipment Mfr
N.A.I.C.S.: 333924
Kam Pasha *(CEO)*
Mahesh Kumar *(COO)*
Brian Magann *(Mng Dir-Engrg)*
Kiran Mukkamala *(Mng Dir-Fin & Planning)*
Suleiman Aboutaam *(Mng Dir-Human Capital & Admin)*

Subsidiary (Domestic):

Applied Fusion Inc.   **(4)**
1915 Republic Ave, San Leandro, CA 94577
Tel.: (510) 351-8314
Web Site: http://www.appliedfusioninc.com
All Other Miscellaneous Fabricated Metal Product Mfr
N.A.I.C.S.: 332999

INTA Technologies Corporation   **(4)**
2281 Calle De Luna, Santa Clara, CA 95054
Tel.: (408) 748-9955
Web Site: http://www.intatech.com
Sales Range: $1-9.9 Million
Emp.: 30
Machine Tooling Equipment Mfr
N.A.I.C.S.: 333517

Don Ankrom *(Mgr-Sls)*

Subsidiary (Domestic):

Precision Flow Technologies, Inc.   **(3)**
1600 Enterprise Dr Bldg 64, Kingston, NY 12401
Tel.: (845) 383-1964
Web Site: http://www.precisionflow.com
Sales Range: $25-49.9 Million
Industrial Machinery Mfr
N.A.I.C.S.: 333248

LogMeIn, Inc.   **(1)**
320 Summer St, Ste 100, Boston, MA 02210
Tel.: (781) 638-9094
Web Site: http://www.LogMeInInc.com
Sales Range: $1-4.9 Billion
Emp.: 3,500
Remote Computer Connectivity Products & Services
N.A.I.C.S.: 541519
Michael J. Donahue *(Gen Counsel & Sr VP)*
Jo Deal *(Chief HR Officer)*
Robin Lawrence *(Sr VP-Corp Strategy)*
Christopher Manton-Jones *(Sr VP-Sls-Worldwide)*
Scott Romesser *(Sr VP-Customer Care & Integration Lead)*
Michael J. Donahue *(Gen Counsel & Sr VP)*
Sharon Gould *(Sr VP-Bus Ops)*
Richard H. Veldran *(CFO)*
Jamie Domenici *(CMO)*
Michael Oberlaender *(Chief Info Security Officer)*
Mary-Kate Foley *(VP-User Experience Design-Global)*
Bill Robinson *(Chief Revenue Officer)*
Nick Caldwell *(Co-Founder)*

Subsidiary (Non-US):

Jive Communications Mexico, S. de R.L. de C.V.   **(2)**
Jose Maria Rico 212 Int 306 Officina B Colonia del Valle Centro Juárez, Benito Juarez, Mexico, 03100, Mexico
Tel.: (52) 5541613912
Telecommunication Servicesb
N.A.I.C.S.: 517810

Subsidiary (Domestic):

Jive Communications, Inc.   **(2)**
320 Summer St, Boston, MA 02210
Tel.: (781) 638-9050
Web Site: http://jive.com
Radio, Television & Other Electronics Stores
N.A.I.C.S.: 449210

Subsidiary (Non-US):

Jive Telecomunicacoes do Brasil, Ltda.   **(2)**
Condominio Edificio Glass Tower Av Jandira n 257 Indianopolis, 04080-001, Sao Paulo, Brazil
Tel.: (55) 1131974418
Telecommunication Servicesb
N.A.I.C.S.: 517810

LogMeIn AUS Pty Ltd   **(2)**
Level 19 20 Martin Place, Sydney, 2000, NSW, Australia
Tel.: (61) 280939900
Electronic Wireless Equipment Mfr
N.A.I.C.S.: 334220

LogMeIn Europe B.V.   **(2)**
Jacob Bontius Plaats 9, Amsterdam, 1018 LL, Netherlands
Tel.: (31) 205221800
Sales Range: $10-24.9 Million
Emp.: 1
Remote Access Software & Services
N.A.I.C.S.: 513210

LogMeIn Systems India Private Limited   **(2)**
No 5 Prestige Khoday Tower 1st 2nd And 3rd Floor Raj Bhavan Road, Bengaluru, 560 001, Karnataka, India
Tel.: (91) 8061220001
Software Development Services
N.A.I.C.S.: 541511

Subsidiary (Domestic):

Zamurai Corporation   **(2)**

5205 Prospect Rd Ste 135-159, San Jose, CA 95129-5034
Tel.: (408) 892-7400
Custom Computer Programming Services
N.A.I.C.S.: 541511

Lumata Holdings Limited   **(1)**
57-63 Scrutton Street, London, EC2A 4PF, United Kingdom
Tel.: (44) 20 7613 8900
Holding Company
N.A.I.C.S.: 551112
Steve Callaghan *(Chm)*

Holding (Non-US):

Lumata Australasia Pty. Ltd.   **(2)**
Level 4 2 Elizabeth Plaza, North Sydney, 2060, NSW, Australia
Tel.: (61) 294099600
Mobile Software Development & Marketing Services
N.A.I.C.S.: 541613

Lumata Italia S.r.l.   **(2)**
c/o Centro Leoni Edificio B Via Spadolini 7, 20141, Milan, MI, Italy
Tel.: (39) 02 58 21 31
Mobile Software Development & Marketing Services
N.A.I.C.S.: 541613
Maria De Matteo *(Mgr-Sls)*

Lumata Netherlands B.V.   **(2)**
Van Heuven Goedhartlaan 935, 1181 LD, Amstelveen, Netherlands
Tel.: (31) 205308760
Marketing Services Via Internet, Mobile Phones & Other Media
N.A.I.C.S.: 541613

Network Merchants, LLC   **(1)**
1450 American Ln Ste 1200, Schaumburg, IL 60173
Tel.: (847) 352-4850
Web Site: http://www.nmi.com
Financial Services
N.A.I.C.S.: 522320
Vijay Sondhi *(CEO)*
Scott Hart *(CFO)*
Phillip Goericke *(Sr VP-Engrg)*
Robert Hoblit *(Chief Revenue Officer)*
Roy Banks *(CEO)*

Subsidiary (Domestic):

USAePay, Inc.   **(2)**
1833 Victory Blvd, Glendale, CA 91201
Tel.: (323) 931-2233
Web Site: http://www.usaepay.info
Financial Transactions Processing, Reserve & Clearinghouse Activities
N.A.I.C.S.: 522320
Natalie Goretsky *(Principal)*
Ben Goretsky *(CEO)*

New Relic, Inc.   **(1)**
188 Spear St Ste 1000, San Francisco, CA 94105
Tel.: (650) 777-7600
Web Site: https://www.newrelic.com
Rev.: $785,521,000
Assets: $1,427,666,000
Liabilities: $1,083,276,000
Net Worth: $344,390,000
Earnings: ($250,402,000)
Emp.: 2,217
Fiscal Year-end: 03/31/2022
Software Analytics
N.A.I.C.S.: 513210
Kristy Friedrichs *(COO)*
David Barter *(CFO & Exec VP)*
Hope F. Cochran *(Bd of Dirs, Executives)*
Gregory Quillon *(CTO-Europe, Middle East & Africa)*
Bonney Pelley *(Sr VP-Strategy & Ops)*
John Siebert *(Exec VP-Sls-Americas)*
Jay Snyder *(Chief Customer Officer & Exec VP)*
David Barter *(CFO)*
Siva Padisetty *(Sr VP-Telemetry Data Platform & Global Infrastructure & Gen Mgr-Telemetry Data Platform & Global Infrastructure)*
Mark Dodds *(Chief Revenue Officer)*

PayScale, Inc.   **(1)**
542 1st Ave S Ste 400, Seattle, WA 98104
Tel.: (206) 223-7590
Web Site: http://www.payscale.com

Online Compensation Data for Employees & Employers
N.A.I.C.S.: 513199
Dave Smith *(Chief Product Officer)*
Barnaby Dorfman *(Chief Engrg Officer)*
Stacey Klimek *(VP-People)*
Melody Brown *(Sr VP-Sls)*
Ronni Bernhard *(Controller)*
Preston Heffernan *(VP-Bus Dev)*
Emily Jensen *(VP-Customer Success)*
Carl Oliveri *(VP-Enterprise Sls)*
Lydia Frank *(VP-Content Strategy)*
Melissa McCann-Tilton *(Chief Sls Officer)*
James Redfern *(CFO)*
Scott Torrey *(CEO)*
Shelly Holt *(Chief People Officer)*
Adrianna Burrows *(CMO)*

Perforce Software, Inc. (1)
400 N 1st Ave Ste 200, Minneapolis, MN 55401
Tel.: (615) 517-2100
Web Site: http://www.perforce.com
Computer Software Publisher
N.A.I.C.S.: 513210
Tim Russell *(Chief Product Officer)*
Mark Ties *(Pres & CEO)*
Mike Goergen *(CFO)*
Wes Fredenburg *(Chief Legal Officer)*

Subsidiary (Domestic):

Delphix Corp. (2)
275 Middlefield Rd Ste 50, Menlo Park, CA 94025-4008
Tel.: (703) 629-8989
Web Site: http://www.delphix.com
Software Solutions
N.A.I.C.S.: 541519
Rick Hopfer *(CIO)*
Marc Aronson *(Sr VP-Engrg)*
Tony Orlando *(Sr VP-Field Ops-Global)*
Monika Saha *(CMO)*
Eric Schrock *(CTO)*
Orlando de Bruce *(VP-Corp Mktg & Brand)*
Tammi Warfield *(Sr VP-Customer Success)*
Alex Hesterberg *(Chief Customer Officer)*
Steve Barrett *(Sr VP-Intl Ops)*

Subsidiary (Domestic):

Axis Technology, LLC (3)
70 Federal St, Boston, MA 02110
Tel.: (857) 445-0110
Web Site: http://www.axistechnologyllc.com
IT Consulting Services
N.A.I.C.S.: 541519
Ron Sherwood *(VP-Sls)*
John E. David *(Co-Founder & Pres)*
Michael Logan *(Co-Founder & Pres)*
Randy Barron *(VP-Ops & HR)*
George Barroso *(Mng Dir-Data Svcs)*
Michael Stiglianese *(Sr Mng Dir)*

Subsidiary (Non-US):

Perforce Software Pty. Ltd. (2)
Level 13 Suite 5 56 Berry Street, North Sydney, 2060, NSW, Australia
Tel.: (61) 290543712
Web Site: http://www.perforce.com
Computer Software Publisher
N.A.I.C.S.: 513210

Perforce Software UK Ltd. (2)
West Forest Gate Wellington Road, Wokingham, RG40 2AT, Berks, United Kingdom
Tel.: (44) 1189 771020
Web Site: http://www.perforce.com
Computer Software Publisher
N.A.I.C.S.: 513210

Subsidiary (Domestic):

Perforce Software, Inc.-Ohio (2)
6960 Cintas Blvd, Mason, OH 45040
Tel.: (513) 754-1655
Web Site: http://www.perforce.com
Application Lifecycle Management Software Developer & Publisher
N.A.I.C.S.: 513210

Rogue Wave Software, Inc. (2)
1315 W Century Dr Ste 150, Louisville, CO 80027
Tel.: (303) 473-9118
Web Site: http://www.roguewave.com
Sales Range: $25-49.9 Million
Cross-Platform Application Software Developer & Publisher

N.A.I.C.S.: 541511
Brian Pierce *(CEO)*
Ted Smith *(CIO & VP-Engrg)*
Christine Bottagaro *(CMO)*
Rod Cope *(CTO)*
Ian McLeod *(Chief Product Officer)*

Subsidiary (Non-US):

Rogue Wave Software Japan K.K. (3)
Bancho Fifth Building 5-5 Nibancho, Chiyoda-ku, Tokyo, 102-0084, Japan
Tel.: (81) 3 5211 7760
Web Site: http://www.roguewave.jp
Sales Range: $50-74.9 Million
Cross-Platform Application Software Developer & Publisher
N.A.I.C.S.: 513210
Toshitomo Kobayashi *(Pres)*

Subsidiary (Domestic):

Zend Technologies, Inc. (3)
10080 N Wolfe Rd Ste SW3 301, Cupertino, CA 95014
Tel.: (408) 253-8800
Web Site: http://www.zend.com
Custom Computer Programming & Consulting Services
N.A.I.C.S.: 541511
Zeev Suraski *(Founder & CTO)*

Plex Systems, Inc. (1)
1731 Harmon Rd, Auburn Hills, MI 48326
Tel.: (248) 391-8001
Web Site: http://www.plex.com
Sales Range: $25-49.9 Million
Online Development Services
N.A.I.C.S.: 541511
Jerry Foster *(CTO)*
Jason Prater *(VP-Dev)*
Jim Shepherd *(VP-Strategy)*
Chris Bishop *(VP-Global Svcs & Support)*
Karl Ederle *(VP-Product Mgmt)*
Elisa Lee *(Chief Legal Officer, Gen Counsel & Sec)*
Todd Weeks *(VP-Cloud Ops)*
Richard Murray *(Grp VP-Engrg)*
Fred Hehl *(Chief Sls Officer)*

Subsidiary (Domestic):

Kors Engineering Company, Inc. (2)
2805 Pontiac Lk Rd Ste 2B, Waterford, MI 48328
Tel.: (248) 706-1540
Web Site: http://www.korsengineering.com
Sales Range: $1-9.9 Million
Emp.: 10
Scientific & Technical Consulting Services
N.A.I.C.S.: 541511
Sally Delvecchio *(Principal)*
Tony Kaczmarek *(CEO)*
Brian Gillespie *(Chief Sls Officer)*

Procera Networks, Inc. (1)
47448 Fremont Blvd, Fremont, CA 94538
Tel.: (510) 230-2777
Web Site: http://www.proceranetworks.com
Sales Range: $75-99.9 Million
Network Traffic Identification, Management & Control Solutions For Broadband Service Networks
N.A.I.C.S.: 541511
Alexander Havang *(CTO)*
Cam Cullen *(VP-Global Mktg)*
Mike Kay *(VP-Bus Dev)*
Debra Machado *(VP-Global HR)*
Lyndon Cantor *(CEO)*
Mark Driedger *(COO)*
Richard Deggs *(CFO)*
Tom Carter *(Sr VP-Global Sls & Svcs)*

Subsidiary (Non-US):

Procera Networks AB (2)
Birger Svenssons Vag 28 D, 432 40, Varberg, Sweden
Tel.: (46) 340483800
Web Site: http://www.proceranetworks.com
Network Traffic Identification, Management & Control Solutions For Broadband Service Networks
N.A.I.C.S.: 541511

Quest Software Inc. (1)
4 Polaris Way, Aliso Viejo, CA 92656
Tel.: (949) 754-8000
Web Site: http://www.quest.com

Prepackaged Software
N.A.I.C.S.: 513210
John Milburn *(Pres-Identity & Security Mgmt)*
Michael Tweddle *(Pres-Platform Mgmt)*
Ronnie Wilson *(Pres-Data Protection & Endpoint Mgmt)*
Brad Haque *(Gen Counsel)*
Carolyn McCarthy *(CFO)*
Katherine Tate *(Chief Bus Ops Officer)*
LuAnn Johnson *(Chief HR Officer)*
Patrick Nichols *(CEO)*
Colleen Langevin *(CMO)*
Chris DeBiase *(COO)*

Subsidiary (Domestic):

ApexSQL, LLC (2)
11312 US 15-501 N Ste 107-212, Chapel Hill, NC 27517-6375
Tel.: (919) 968-8444
Web Site: http://www.apexsql.com
Software Publisher
N.A.I.C.S.: 513210
John Ducatte *(Mgr-Sls)*

BakBone Software Incorporated (2)
4 Polaris Way, Aliso Viejo, CA 92656
Tel.: (949) 754-8000
Web Site: http://www.quest.com
Data Protection & Storage Management Software to Open Systems Market Developer & Distr
N.A.I.C.S.: 541511
Andrew Unsworth *(Mng Dir-EMEA)*

Renaissance Learning, Inc. (1)
2911 Peach St, Wisconsin Rapids, WI 54494-1905
Tel.: (715) 424-3636
Web Site: http://www.renaissance.com
K-12 School Assessment & Progress-Monitoring Technology
N.A.I.C.S.: 513210
Samir Joglekar *(Exec VP-Sls)*
Gene M. Kerns *(Chief Academic Officer & VP)*
Paula O'Gorman *(Sr VP-Corp Affairs)*
Kim Mitchell *(Chief People Officer)*
Chris Bauleke *(CEO)*
Dan Conrad *(Gen Counsel)*
Erez Tocker *(Mng Dir-Intl)*
John Roselli *(Chief Strategy Officer)*
Lynn Danko *(CFO)*
Sarah Difrancesco *(CMO)*
Todd Brekhus *(Chief Product Officer)*

Subsidiary (Non-US):

Renaissance Learning UK Limited (2)
14th Floor South Quay Building 189 Marsh Wall, London, E14 9SH, United Kingdom (100%)
Tel.: (44) 20 7184 4000
Web Site: http://www.renlearn.co.uk
Educational Software Development Services
N.A.I.C.S.: 513210
Sarah Haythornthwaite *(Mktg Dir)*

Sandvine Corporation (1)
410 Albert St Suite 201, Waterloo, N2L 3V3, ON, Canada
Tel.: (519) 880-2600
Web Site: https://www.sandvine.com
Sales Range: Less than $1 Million
Intelligent Broadband Network Solutions
N.A.I.C.S.: 334118
Lyndon Cantor *(CEO)*
Samir Marwaha *(Chief Strategy Officer)*
Mark Driedger *(COO)*
Alexander Havang *(Chief Technical Officer)*
Jeff Kupp *(CFO)*
Tim Swango *(Chief Admin Officer)*
Pam Dullaghan *(Sr VP-Customer Success)*
Ambuj Mittal *(Chief Dev Officer)*
Hashem Eid *(Chief Comml Officer)*

Subsidiary (Domestic):

Sandvine Incorporated ULC (2)
408 Albert St, Waterloo, ON, Canada
Tel.: (519) 880-2600
Web Site: http://www.sandvine.com
Communication Equipment Technology Services
N.A.I.C.S.: 541512

Sectigo Limited (1)

5 Becker Farm Rd, Roseland, NJ 07068
Tel.: (888) 266-6361
Web Site: http://www.sectigo.com
Web Security Products Mfr
N.A.I.C.S.: 561621
Christopher Bray *(Sr VP-Partner-eCommerce Sls)*
Jason Soroki *(CTO)*
David Mahdi *(Chief Strategy Officer)*
Elliot Harrison *(Dir-Comm-Global)*
Kevin Weiss *(CEO)*

Subsidiary (Domestic):

Icon Laboratories, Inc. (2)
3636 Westown Pkwy Ste 203, West Des Moines, IA 50266-6713
Tel.: (515) 226-0565
Web Site: http://www.icon-labs.com
Embedded OEMs & IoT Device Mfr
N.A.I.C.S.: 423430
Alan Grau *(Founder)*

SintecMedia, Inc. (1)
21 Nahum Hafzadi St, PO Box 34406, Jerusalem, 9134302, Israel
Tel.: (972) 2 651 5122
Web Site: http://www.operative.com
Emp.: 1,300
Business Management Software Solution Services
N.A.I.C.S.: 513210
Jason Witt *(COO)*
Lorne Brown *(CEO)*
Paul Wheeler *(CFO)*
Glen Ceniza *(CTO)*
Lance Roncalli *(Chief Revenue Officer)*
Brenda Salce-Garcia *(Sr VP-Customer Success)*
Devlin Jefferson *(Sr VP-Product Mgmt)*
Seth Metsch *(Gen Counsel)*

Subsidiary (US):

Operative Media, Inc. (2)
6 E 32nd St 3rd Fl, New York, NY 10016
Tel.: (212) 994-8930
Web Site: http://www.operative.com
Emp.: 250
Advertising Resource Management Solutions
N.A.I.C.S.: 513210
Lorne Brown *(Founder, Pres & CEO)*
John Briar *(Chief Svcs Officer)*
Eli Curi *(Chief Legal Officer & Chief Bus Affairs Officer)*
Jason Witt *(Chief Product Officer)*
Rick Glickman *(CFO)*
Don Amboyer *(Gen Mgr)*
David Villano *(CTO)*
Dawn Tavoletti *(VP-Product Strategy-Local Brdcst Market)*
Andrew Sullivan *(Sr VP-Product Strategy)*

Subsidiary (Non-US):

SintecMedia Global Ltd. (2)
1st Floor Artemis Odyssey Business Park, West End Road South Ruislip, London, HA4 6QE, Mddx, United Kingdom
Tel.: (44) 2087820700
Web Site: http://www.sintecmedia.com
Software Development & Broadcasting Services
N.A.I.C.S.: 541511
Sandy Cusick *(VP-Project Delivery)*
Maurizio Uzzielli *(VP-Project Delivery-EMEA)*
Tanya Yankelevich *(VP-Ops)*
Fabrice Beer-Gabel *(Exec VP-Sls-EMEA & APAC)*

Subsidiary (Non-US):

SintecMedia AMS B.V. (3)
Haarlemmerweg 317A, 1051 LG, Amsterdam, Netherlands
Tel.: (31) 206205687
Web Site: http://www.sintecmedia.com
Software Development Services
N.A.I.C.S.: 541511
Herman Maat *(Mng Dir-MediaPro Div)*

Subsidiary (US):

SintecMedia DV Inc. (3)
1580 Lincoln St Ste 560, Denver, CO 80203
Tel.: (303) 830-0600
Web Site: http://www.sintecmedia.com

Francisco Partners Management,
LP—(Continued)

Broadcast Management Software Retailer
N.A.I.C.S.: 423430

Subsidiary (Non-US):

SintecMedia Syd Pty Ltd (3)
233 Castlereagh St Level 5 Suite 502, Sydney, 2000, NSW, Australia
Tel.: (61) 2 9285 0000
Web Site: http://www.sintecmedia.com
Broadcast Management Software Retailer
N.A.I.C.S.: 423430

Subsidiary (Domestic):

SintecMedia Wem Ltd (3)
1st Floor Artemis Odyssey Business Park,
West End Road South Ruislip, London,
HA4 6QE, Mddx, United Kingdom
Tel.: (44) 2087820700
Web Site: http://www.sintecmedia.com
Software Development Services
N.A.I.C.S.: 513210

Sumo Logic, Inc. (1)
855 Main St Ste 100, Redwood City, CA
94063
Tel.: (650) 810-8700
Web Site: https://www.sumologic.com
Rev.: $300,668,000
Assets: $579,098,000
Liabilities: $203,988,000
Net Worth: $375,110,000
Earnings: ($124,815,000)
Emp.: 983
Fiscal Year-end: 01/31/2023
Data Analytic Services
N.A.I.C.S.: 541512
Stewart Grierson (CFO)
Joe Kim (Pres)
Sophie Kitson (Chief HR Officer)
Tej Redkar (Chief Product Officer)
Paris Georgallis (Chief Customer Officer)
Todd Hanna (Chief Legal Officer)
Russell Rosa (Chief Revenue Officer)
Liz Shulof (CMO)

Universal Instruments
Corporation (1)
33 Broome Corporate Park, Conklin, NY
13748
Tel.: (607) 727-2230
Web Site: http://www.uic.com
Sales Range: $150-199.9 Million
Automated Electronic Assembly Equipment
Mfr
N.A.I.C.S.: 333248
Jeff Zopff (Mgr-Mktg Comm-Global)
Brad Bennett (VP-Global Customer Ops)
David Cooke (Gen Mgr-Western Americas)
Ulyses Wolfskill (Country Mgr-Mexico)
Patrick Chan (Gen Mgr-Southeast Asia)
Jean-Luc Pelissier (CEO)

Vendavo, Inc. (1)
401 E Middlefield Rd, Mountain View, CA
94043
Tel.: (650) 960-4300
Web Site: http://www.vendavo.com
Sales Range: $1-9.9 Million
Emp.: 32
Price Management & Optimization Software
Solutions
N.A.I.C.S.: 513210
Michael Hoffman (Chief Comml Officer)
Bruno Slosse (Pres & CEO)
Mark Horner (Chief Svcs Officer)
John Oosterhouse (CFO)
Maarten de Bruijn (VP & Gen Mgr-Sls &
Svc-EMEA)
David Edwards (CTO)
C. Edward Brice (CMO)
Joe Marcin (Chief Revenue Officer)
Gina Bates (Chief Revenue Officer)

Subsidiary (Domestic):

Endeavor Commerce, Inc. (2)
13140 Coit Rd, Dallas, TX 75240
Tel.: (214) 736-7178
Custom Computer Programming Services
N.A.I.C.S.: 541511
Jamie Riell (VP-Product Enrng)
Jose Fontanez (Sr Dir-Customer Ops)

VeriFone Systems, Inc. (1)
88 W Plumeria Dr, San Jose, CA 95134
Tel.: (408) 232-7800

Web Site: http://www.verifone.com
Sales Range: $1-4.9 Billion
Emp.: 5,600
Holding Company; Point-of-Sale Software &
Technologies Mfr & Distr
N.A.I.C.S.: 551112
Bulent Ozayaz (Pres-EMEA)
Michael Pulli (CEO)
Vikram Varma (Gen Counsel)
Bruce Gureck (Exec VP-Engrg & Product)
Peyton O'Connor (Exec VP-HR)
Tom Weikart (Exec VP-Ops)
Tim O'Loughlin (Pres-Americas)

Subsidiary (Domestic):

2Checkout.com, Inc. (2)
Versa Grandview 1201 Dublin Rd, Columbus, OH 43215
Tel.: (678) 666-2660
Web Site: http://www.2checkout.com
Emp.: 300
Payment Processing Services
N.A.I.C.S.: 459999
Alex Hart (Co-CEO)
Erich Litch (Pres & Co-CEO)
Christopher Wassenaar (Chief Risk Officer,
Gen Counsel & Sec)

Subsidiary (Non-US):

EFTPOS New Zealand Limited (2)
Level 14 80 Boulcott Street, Wellington,
6011, New Zealand
Tel.: (64) 43857055
Web Site: http://eftpos.co.nz
Electronic Financial Payment Services
N.A.I.C.S.: 522320
Paul Galant (CEO)

Subsidiary (Domestic):

Hypercom Corporation (2)
8888 E Raintree Dr Ste 300, Scottsdale, AZ
85260
Tel.: (480) 642-5000
Electronic Payment Services
N.A.I.C.S.: 522320

Subsidiary (Non-US):

Point International AS (2)
Eastern Aker vei 24, 0581, Oslo, Norway
Tel.: (47) 81502200
Web Site: http://www.point.no
Secure Electronic Payment Provider
N.A.I.C.S.: 522320

VeriFone Denmark A/S (2)
Knapholm 7, 2730, Herlev, Denmark
Tel.: (45) 44 53 16 10
Web Site: http://www.verifone.com
Electronic Payment Solutions
N.A.I.C.S.: 541519
Chris Lund-Hansen (Mng Dir)

VeriFone Finland Oy (2)
Vantaankoskentie 14 C, 01670, Vantaa,
Finland
Tel.: (358) 9 477 4330
Web Site: http://www.verifone.fi
Electronic Payment Solutions
N.A.I.C.S.: 541519

VeriFone New Zealand (2)
Unit A 525 Great South Rd Penrose, Auckland, 1061, New Zealand
Tel.: (64) 95820550
Web Site: http://www.verifone.co.nz
Computer Peripheral Equipment Mfr
N.A.I.C.S.: 334118

VeriFone Norway AS (2)
Ostre Aker vei 24, 0581, Oslo, Norway
Tel.: (47) 23247400
Web Site: http://www.verifone.com
Electronic Payment Transaction Handling
Services
N.A.I.C.S.: 522320

VeriFone Services UK & Ireland
Ltd. (2)
100 Eureka Park, Ashford, TN25 4AZ, Kent,
United Kingdom
Tel.: (44) 3333236667
Web Site: http://www.verifone.co.uk
Sales Range: $100-124.9 Million
Emp.: 200
Secure Electronic Payment Provider
N.A.I.C.S.: 522320

Douglas Adams (Acct Mgr-New Bus)
Matt Cross (Mgr-Bus Dev-UK Existing Accounts)
Steve Metcalfe (Head-UK & Eire Corp Sls)
Brendan McGrath (Acct Mgr-UK Corp Sls)

VeriFone Sweden AB (2)
Ljusslingan 4, Box 92031, 120 31, Stockholm, Sweden
Tel.: (46) 8 566 287 00
Web Site: http://www.verifone.com
Electronic Payment Transaction Handling
Services
N.A.I.C.S.: 522320
Morgan Georg Sellen (CEO)

Subsidiary (Domestic):

Babs Paylink AB (3)
Sankt Eriksgatan 117, 113 43, Stockholm,
Sweden
Tel.: (46) 8 6916900
Web Site: http://www.babspaylink.se
Payment Clearance & Settlement Services
for Card Purchases; Operator of Wireless
Payment Card Terminals
N.A.I.C.S.: 522320

Electronic Transaction Group Nordic
Holding AB (3)
Karlavagen 58, 114 49, Stockholm, Sweden
Tel.: (46) 8 56628700
Sales Range: $25-49.9 Million
Emp.: 9
Holding Company
N.A.I.C.S.: 551112

Subsidiary (Domestic):

VeriFone, Inc. (2)
88 W Plumeria Dr, San Jose, CA 95134
Tel.: (408) 232-7800
Web Site: http://www.verifone.com
Sales Range: $1-4.9 Billion
Point-of-Sale Software & Technologies Mfr
& Distr
N.A.I.C.S.: 334118
Christophe Job (CTO)

Subsidiary (Non-US):

Hypercom Financial Terminals
AB (3)
Drottninggatan 21 4TR, 582 25, Linkoping,
Sweden
Tel.: (46) 13367200
Computer Hardware & Related Equipments
Mfr & Distr
N.A.I.C.S.: 423430

VeriFone (U.K.) Limited (3)
Symphony House 7 Cowley Business Park,
High Street Cowley, Uxbridge, UB9 2AD,
United Kingdom
Tel.: (44) 1895 275275
Web Site: http://www.verifone.co.uk
Sales Range: $25-49.9 Million
Emp.: 300
Supplier of Electronic Equipment Software
& Terminal
N.A.I.C.S.: 423430

VeriFone Africa (Pty) Ltd (3)
1st Floor Block B Knightsbridge 33 Sloane
Str, Bryanston, Sandton, 2191, South Africa
Tel.: (27) 11 521 9000
Web Site: http://www.verifone.co.za
Supplies & Supports Payment Systems
N.A.I.C.S.: 541519
Jeffrey C. Dumbrell (Exec VP-EMEA)

VeriFone Asia Pacific (3)
Room 2508 Ccwuo Bulding 3022308
Tenese Rd, Wan Chai, Hong Kong, China
(Hong Kong)
Tel.: (852) 28272101
Sales Range: $100-124.9 Million
Emp.: 4
Electronic Equipment, Software & Terminals
N.A.I.C.S.: 449210
Steve Aliferis (Pres)

VeriFone Australia (HAPL) Pty
Ltd (3)
Level 7 213 Miller Street, North Sydney,
2060, NSW, Australia
Tel.: (61) 294640000
Web Site: http://www.verifone.com
Sales Range: $125-149.9 Million
Emp.: 80

End-to-End Electronic Payment Solutions,
Including Card Payment Systems, Peripherals, Network Products, Ascendent Software
& E-Commerce Payment Solutions
N.A.I.C.S.: 334118

VeriFone GmbH (3)
Konrad Zuse Str 19 21, 36251, Bad Hersfeld, Germany
Tel.: (49) 662184500
Sales Range: $50-74.9 Million
Emp.: 170
Credit & Debit Card Payment Processing
Systems
N.A.I.C.S.: 522320
Markus Hovekamp (Gen Mgr)

VeriFone Israel Ltd. (3)
Labor 11 Park Afek, Rosh Ha'Ayin, 48092,
Israel
Tel.: (972) 39029740
Web Site: http://www.verifone.co.il
Sales Range: $200-249.9 Million
Emp.: 985
Engineering Services
N.A.I.C.S.: 541330

VeriFone Italia S.r.l. (3)
Piazza Don Mapelli 1, 20099, Sesto San
Giovanni, Italy
Tel.: (39) 0291757623
Web Site: http://www.verifone.it
Electronic Payment Equipment Mfr
N.A.I.C.S.: 541519

Unit (Domestic):

VeriFone Latin America & the
Caribbean (3)
501 Brickell Key Dri, Miami, FL 33131
Tel.: (305) 670-1820
Web Site: http://www.verifone.com
Supplier of Electronic Equipment Software
& Terminals
N.A.I.C.S.: 334118
Gennie Acosta (Office Mgr)

Subsidiary (Domestic):

VeriFone Media, LLC (3)
1400 Broadway 32nd Fl, New York, NY
10018
Tel.: (800) 498-5759
Web Site: http://www.verifonemedia.com
Taxicab Advertising Services
N.A.I.C.S.: 541810

Subsidiary (Non-US):

VeriFone Singapore Pte. Ltd. (3)
11 Keppel Road #11-02 ABI Plaza, Singapore, 089057, Singapore
Tel.: (65) 6390 6200
Electronic Payment Solutions Mfr & Marketer
N.A.I.C.S.: 541519

VeriFone Sp. z o.o (3)
Domaniewska 44 A, 02-672, Warsaw, Poland
Tel.: (48) 223801700
Sales Range: $10-24.9 Million
Emp.: 7
Supplier of Electronic Equipment, Software
& Terminals
N.A.I.C.S.: 449210
Adam Biedrzycki (Gen Mgr-Europe)

VeriFone Systems (China), Inc. (3)
97 Balizhuangxili, Zhubang 2000 Business
Center Bldg 4 Room 2001, Chaoyang District, Beijing, China
Tel.: (86) 10 83913700
Web Site: http://www.verifone.cn
Electronic Payment Solutions Equipment
Mfr
N.A.I.C.S.: 334118
Arthur Jiang (Sr VP & Gen Mgr)

VeriFone Systems Australia Pty.
Ltd. (3)
Level 7 213 Miller Street, North Sydney,
2060, NSW, Australia
Tel.: (61) 294640000
Computer Programming Services
N.A.I.C.S.: 541511
Michael Ward (Dir-Ops-Asia Pacific)

VeriFone Systems France SAS (3)
10-12 rue Paul Dautier, 78140, Velizy-
Villacoublay, France

Tel.: (33) 139451210
Web Site: http://www.verifone.com
Sales Range: $10-24.9 Million
Emp.: 8
Supplier of Electronic Equipment, Software & Terminals
N.A.I.C.S.: 423430

VeriFone Systems Spain SLU (3)
Calle Via de los Poblados 1, PE Alvento Edificio C 2 B y D, 28033, Madrid, Spain
Tel.: (34) 91 598 21 40
Web Site: http://www.verifone.es
Designs, Markets & Services Electronic Payment Solutions
N.A.I.C.S.: 541519

VeriFone Uruguay (3)
Technology & Business Park Zonamerica Ruta 8 Km 17 500, Edificio Synergia Oficina 005, 91 600, Montevideo, Uruguay
Tel.: (598) 25182250
Web Site: http://www.verifone.com
Sales Range: $25-49.9 Million
Emp.: 100
Transaction Reconciliation & Payment Infra-structure Software & Solutions
N.A.I.C.S.: 541511

VeriFone do Brasil Ltda. (3)
Rua Gomes de Carvalho 1507 10 Andar, Villa Olimpia, Sao Paulo, 04547-005, SP, Brazil
Tel.: (55) 1120789710
Web Site: http://www.verifone.com
Sales Range: $100-124.9 Million
Emp.: 500
Supplier of Electronic Equipment, Software & Terminals
N.A.I.C.S.: 449210

VeriFone, S.A. de C.V. (3)
Boulevard Manuel Avila Camacho 40 Piso 15 Torre Esmeralda 1, Col Lomas de Chapultepec, Mexico, 11000, DF, Mexico
Tel.: (52) 5559803300
Supplier of Electronic Equipment, Software & Terminals
N.A.I.C.S.: 423430

WatchGuard Technologies, Inc. (1)
505 5th Ave S Ste 500, Seattle, WA 98104-3892
Tel.: (206) 613-6600
Web Site: http://www.watchguard.com
Sales Range: $75-99.9 Million
Emp.: 600
Specialized Internet Security Services
N.A.I.C.S.: 513210
Shari McLaren (Sr VP-Customer Svcs & Support)
Prakash Panjwani (CEO)
Andrew Young (Sr VP-Product Mgmt)
Wayson Vannatta (CIO)
Sean Price (Sr VP-Worldwide Sls)
Paul Sadler (Mgr-Mktg-Asia Pacific)
Corey Nachreiner (CTO)
Michelle Welch (Sr VP-Mktg)
Jack Waters (Sr VP-Engrg)
HoJin Kim (Chief Revenue Officer & Sr VP)
Chris Warfield (Dir-Comm)

Subsidiary (Non-US):

Panda Security S.L. (2)
Gran Via Don Diego Lopez de Haro 4, Bil-bao, 48001, Spain
Tel.: (34) 94 425 11 00
Web Site: http://www.pandasecurity.com
Cloud-Based Security Solutions
N.A.I.C.S.: 513210
Santiago Mayoralas (CFO)
Jose Sancho (Pres)
Juan Santamaria (CEO)
Maria Campos (VP-Sls, Key Acct, Managed Security Svc Provider & Telecom)

Subsidiary (US):

Panda Security, Inc. (3)
2600 Lake Lucien Dr Ste 115, Maitland, FL 32751
Tel.: (407) 215-3026
Web Site: http://www.pandasecurity.com
Emp.: 20
Security Software Developer
N.A.I.C.S.: 513210
Joao Caires (Mng Dir-Subsidiaries)

Subsidiary (Non-US):

WatchGuard Technologies Canada, Inc. (2)

90 Burnhamthorpe Road West Suite 1400, Mississauga, L5B 3C3, ON, Canada
Tel.: (905) 804-1855
Sales Range: $25-49.9 Million
Internet Security Solution
N.A.I.C.S.: 513210

bswift LLC (1)
10 S Riverside Plz Ste 1100, Chicago, IL 60606
Tel.: (877) 927-9438
Web Site: https://www.bswift.com
Software Development Services
N.A.I.C.S.: 541511
Ted Bloomberg (CEO)

FRANCISCO TAVARES INC.
69 Old Meeting House Rd, East Falmouth, MA 02536
Tel.: (508) 548-0911   MA
Web Site:
  https://www.franciscotavares.com
Year Founded: 1975
Sales Range: $10-24.9 Million
Emp.: 70
Landscape Construction, Site Devel-opment & Excavation Services
N.A.I.C.S.: 541320
Gary Tavares (Pres)

FRANCO MANUFACTURING CO. INC.
555 Prospect St, Metuchen, NJ 08840-2271
Tel.: (732) 494-0500   NJ
Web Site: http://www.francomfg.com
Year Founded: 1952
Sales Range: $25-49.9 Million
Emp.: 500
Mfr of Licensed Home-made Textiles
N.A.I.C.S.: 313310
David Franco (VP)
Susan Megill (Treas)
Morris Franco (Owner)
Mike Kaplin (CEO)

FRANCO PUBLIC RELATIONS GROUP
400 Renaissance Ctr Ste 1000, De-troit, MI 48243
Tel.: (313) 567-2300
Web Site: https://www.franco.com
Year Founded: 1964
Sales Range: $1-9.9 Million
Emp.: 13
Public Relations Agency
N.A.I.C.S.: 541820
Tina Kozak (CEO)
Joe Ferlito (Acct Mgr)
Stephanie Casola (Acct Mgr)
Andrea Kenski (Supvr-Acct)
Patricia Adanti-Joy (VP)
Tina Benvenuti Sullivan (Pres & COO)
Erica Swoish (Acct Exec)
Dan Horn (Sr Acct Exec)
John C. Mozena (Acct Dir)
Daniel Stocking (Acct Exec)
Ann Barnette (Exec Dir)
Lori Cook (Office Mgr)
Ann Marie Fortunate (Supvr-Acct)
Elizabeth Robbins-Sabourin (Supvr-Acct)
Brent Snavely (VP-Media Rels)

FRANCO'S ATHLETIC CLUB
100 Bon Temps Roule, Mandeville, LA 70471
Tel.: (985) 792-0200
Web Site: http://www.myfrancos.com
Year Founded: 1986
Sales Range: $10-24.9 Million
Emp.: 250
Food Supplement Retailer
N.A.I.C.S.: 456191
Ron Franco (Co-Owner, Pres & CEO)
Sandy Franco (Co-Owner)
Wayne Morris (Gen Mgr)

FRANCOIS OIL COMPANY INC.
128 W Main St, Belleville, WI 53508
Tel.: (608) 424-3375
Web Site:
  http://www.thestationstores.com
Year Founded: 1939
Sales Range: $75-99.9 Million
Emp.: 115
Petroleum Bulk Stations
N.A.I.C.S.: 457120
Richard Francois (Pres)

FRANCONIA INTERNATIONAL INC.
38 Green St, Souderton, PA 18964
Tel.: (215) 723-8121
Rev.: $10,800,000
Emp.: 12
Piece Goods & Notions
N.A.I.C.S.: 424310
Kerry E. Gingrith (Pres)

FRANCORP, INC.
2521 St Andrews Dr, Olympia Fields, IL 60461
Tel.: (708) 481-2900
Web Site: http://www.francorp.com
Rev.: $5,600,000
Emp.: 28
Franchise Consulting Services
N.A.I.C.S.: 541611

FRANDSEN CORPORATION
5481 Saint Croix Trl Ste 200, North Branch, MN 55056
Tel.: (651) 407-5700   MN
Web Site: https://www.frandsencorporation.com
Year Founded: 1997
Assets: $1,500,000,000
Emp.: 1,000
Investment Holding Company
N.A.I.C.S.: 551112
Dennis Frandsen (Chm & CEO)
Melanie Knutson (Dir-Acctg)

Subsidiaries:

Frandsen Financial Corporation (1)
4388 Round Lake Rd W, Arden Hills, MN 55112
Tel.: (651) 242-5700
Web Site:
  http://www.frandsencorporation.com
Emp.: 45
Bank Holding Company
N.A.I.C.S.: 551111
Dennis Frandsen (Pres & Co-CEO)
Rich Hoban (Co-CEO)
Anthony C. Johnson (Sr VP)

Subsidiary (Domestic):

Frandsen Bank & Trust (2)
116 Central St W, Lonsdale, MN 55046
Tel.: (507) 744-2361
Web Site: http://www.frandsenbank.com
Emp.: 8
Commericial Banking
N.A.I.C.S.: 522110
Dennis Frandsen (Founder & Chm)
Dennis Welch (Mgr-SBA)
Tim Swanson (Sr VP-Comml Banking Team)
Jim Kraft (Pres-Baxter)
Karen Brekke (Chm, Chief Admin Officer & Exec VP)
Randy Morehart (Vice Chm & Exec VP)

Industrial Netting, Inc. (1)
7681 Setzler Pkwy N, Minneapolis, MN 55445
Tel.: (763) 496-6355
Web Site: http://www.industrialnetting.net
Rev.: $5,135,000
Emp.: 30
Fabricator, Converter & Marketer of Plastic Netting, Mesh & Tubes
N.A.I.C.S.: 326199
Karen Slater (Mgr-Sls)
Mike Rog (Plant Mgr)
Sheryl Hopkins (Office Mgr)

Miller Manufacturing Company (1)
2910 Waters Rd Ste 150, Eagan, MN 55121
Tel.: (651) 982-5100
Web Site: http://www.miller-mfg.com
Sales Range: $10-24.9 Million
Emp.: 100
Mfr of Farm, Ranch & Pet Products
N.A.I.C.S.: 333111
Dennis Frandsen (Chm & CEO)

Subsidiary (Domestic):

Springer Magrath Company (2)
1400 W 13th St, Glencoe, MN 55336
Tel.: (651) 982-5121
Web Site: http://www.springermagrath.com
Sales Range: $1-9.9 Million
Emp.: 24
Mfr & Distr of Stock Prods & Veterinary Supplies
N.A.I.C.S.: 335999

Plastech Corporation (1)
920 S Frandsen Ave, Rush City, MN 55069
Tel.: (651) 407-5700
Web Site:
  http://www.plastechcorporation.com
Sales Range: $50-74.9 Million
Emp.: 300
Mfr of Injection Molded Components & As-sembled Products
N.A.I.C.S.: 333511
Dennis Frandsen (Chm & CEO)
Joel Kruger (Controller)

FRANGER GAS CO. INC.
27795 County Rd 10, Elkhart, IN 46514
Tel.: (574) 264-2118
Web Site:
  https://www.frangergas.com
Rev.: $20,000,000
Emp.: 35
Whslr & Retailer of Propane Gas
N.A.I.C.S.: 424720
Michael Franger (Pres)

FRANK AMBROSE INC.
2300 Meijer Dr, Troy, MI 48084
Tel.: (248) 655-2300
Web Site: http://www.ambroseinternational.com
Rev.: $21,000,000
Emp.: 40
Fine Paper
N.A.I.C.S.: 424110
Robert D. Ambrose (Pres & CEO)

FRANK B. ROSS CO. INC.
970 New Brunswick Ave Ste H, Rah-way, NJ 07065
Tel.: (732) 669-0810   NJ
Web Site: http://www.frankbross.com
Year Founded: 1902
Sales Range: $50-74.9 Million
Emp.: 8
Industrial Wax Products Mfr
N.A.I.C.S.: 325612
Larry Powell (Pres)
Don Ayerlee (VP)
Carmen Mangan (VP)
Mary Ann Willemson (VP)

FRANK BRUNCKHORST CO., LLC
Ste 800 1819 Main St, Sarasota, FL 34236-5926
Tel.: (941) 955-0994
Sales Range: $100-124.9 Million
Emp.: 2,000
Prepared Meat Products Mfr & Distr
N.A.I.C.S.: 424470
Robert S. Martin (CEO)

Subsidiaries:

Boar's Head Provisions Co., Inc. (1)
1819 Main St Ste 800, Sarasota, FL 34236-5926
Tel.: (941) 955-0994

Frank Brunckhorst Co., LLC—(Continued)

Web Site: http://www.boarshead.com
Sales Range: $1-4.9 Billion
Emp.: 2,100
Meats & Meat Products Mfr & Distr
N.A.I.C.S.: 424470
Elizabeth Ward *(Sr Mgr-Comm)*
RuthAnn LaMore *(Dir-Comm & Retail Mktg)*

FRANK BRYAN INC.
1263 Chartiers Ave, McKees Rocks,
PA 15136
Tel.: (412) 331-1630
Web Site:
    http://www.bryanmaterialsgroup.com
Sales Range: $10-24.9 Million
Emp.: 6
Construction Services
N.A.I.C.S.: 327320
James P. Bryan Jr. *(VP)*

**FRANK C. ALEGRE TRUCK-
ING INC.**
5100 W Hwy 12, Lodi, CA 95242
Tel.: (209) 334-2112
Web Site:
    https://www.alegretrucking.com
Year Founded: 1963
Sales Range: $25-49.9 Million
Emp.: 380
Provider of Trucking Services
N.A.I.C.S.: 484220
Anthony Alegre *(Pres)*
Robert Fowler *(VP)*
Dan Ruoff *(Supvr-Maintenance)*
Imelda Itliong *(Controller)*
Rocio Escoto *(Mgr-Credit)*
Micki Schultz *(Gen Mgr)*
Justin Serpa *(Coord-Bid)*
Nallely Gomez *(Supvr-Personnel)*

FRANK CALANDRA, INC.
258 Kappa Dr, Pittsburgh, PA 15238-
2818
Tel.: (412) 963-9071
Web Site: http://www.jennmar.com
Year Founded: 1922
Sales Range: $25-49.9 Million
Emp.: 400
Supplier of Mining Machinery
N.A.I.C.S.: 333131
John M. Calandra *(Pres)*
James McEvoy *(VP-IT)*

Subsidiaries:

JM Steel Corp.   **(1)**
1050 N Steel Cir, Huger, SC
29450   **(100%)**
Tel.: (843) 336-4929
Sales Range: $10-24.9 Million
Emp.: 71
Steel Product Mfr & Distr
N.A.I.C.S.: 331221
Shelly George *(VP-Sls)*
Dexter Skidmore *(Plant Mgr)*

Jennmar Corporation   **(1)**
258 Kappa Dr, Pittsburgh, PA 15238-2818
Tel.: (412) 963-9071
Web Site: http://www.jennmar.com
Supplier of Mining Machinery
N.A.I.C.S.: 333131
John Stankus *(Pres-Keystone Mining Svcs)*
Karl Anthony Calandra *(Pres)*
Paul Calandra *(VP)*
Art Craven *(Mgr-Wire Mesh)*
Rodney Poland *(VP-Sls & Technical Re-
sources)*
Jared Schofield *(Plant Mgr)*
Thomas Squashic *(Plant Mgr-Pennsylvania)*
Ray Wilson *(Sls Mgr-Midwest)*
Robert Wise *(COO)*
Frank Calandra Jr. *(Chm)*

Subsidiary (Domestic):

Jennmar Corporation of West Virginia
Inc.   **(2)**
Rte 92 S, Reedsville, WV 26547
Tel.: (304) 864-3601
Web Site: http://www.jannmar.com

Sales Range: $25-49.9 Million
Emp.: 100
Producer of Bolts, Nuts, Rivets & Washers
N.A.I.C.S.: 332722
Frank Calandra *(Pres)*

Jennmar of Kentucky Inc.   **(2)**
PO Box 501, Winchester, KY 40391
Tel.: (859) 744-9600
Web Site: http://www.jennmar.com
Sales Range: $25-49.9 Million
Emp.: 80
Ground Control Product Mfr
N.A.I.C.S.: 332722

Subsidiary (Domestic):

DSI Tunneling LLC   **(3)**
1032 E Chestnut St, Louisville, KY 40204
Tel.: (502) 473-1010
Web Site: https://www.dsituneling.com
Construction Engineering Services
N.A.I.C.S.: 541330

Subsidiary (Domestic):

SanShell Products, Inc.   **(2)**
256 Industrial Dr, Oak Hill, WV 25901-9714
Tel.: (304) 465-0651
Web Site:
    http://www.sanshellproductsinc.com
Emp.: 13
Mining Machinery & Equipment Mfr
N.A.I.C.S.: 333131
Sam Jasper *(VP)*
Bruce Johnson *(Gen Mgr)*

Marjenn Trucking Company Inc.   **(1)**
134 Easter Ave, Cresson, PA 16630-1702
Tel.: (814) 886-4121
Sales Range: $10-24.9 Million
Emp.: 3
Provider of Long Distance Trucking Ser-
vices
N.A.I.C.S.: 484121

FRANK CHERVAN INC.
2005 Greenbrier Ave Se, Roanoke,
VA 24013-2628
Tel.: (540) 586-5600
Web Site: https://www.chervan.com
Sales Range: $10-24.9 Million
Emp.: 160
Wood Office Furniture
N.A.I.C.S.: 337211
Gregory M. Terrill *(Pres)*
Richard Terrill *(Owner)*

**FRANK COLUCCIO CON-
STRUCTION CO.**
9600 ML King Way S, Seattle, WA
98118
Tel.: (206) 722-5306
Web Site: http://www.coluccio.com
Rev.: $70,000,000
Emp.: 240
Water & Sewer Line Construction
Services
N.A.I.C.S.: 237110
Larry Mayo *(CFO)*

**FRANK CONSOLIDATED EN-
TERPRISES**
666 Garland Pl, Des Plaines, IL
60016
Tel.: (847) 699-7000
Web Site: http://www.wheels.com
Year Founded: 1939
Sales Range: $1-4.9 Billion
Emp.: 600
Holding Company; Fleet Management
Services
N.A.I.C.S.: 551112
James Frank *(Pres & CEO)*
Steve Loos *(VP-IT & CIO)*

Subsidiaries:

Wheels Inc.   **(1)**
666 Garland Pl, Des Plaines, IL 60016-
4725
Tel.: (847) 699-7000
Web Site: http://www.wheels.com
Automobiles & Trucks Leasing Services

N.A.I.C.S.: 532112
James Frank *(Chm)*
Scott Pattullo *(Sr VP-Sls & Mktg)*
Shlomo Crandus *(VP-Fin)*
Norman Din *(VP-Sls)*
Daniel Z. Frank *(Pres & CEO)*
Christine Steinberg *(VP-Customer Svc Ops)*
John Round *(Asst VP-Sls)*
Laura Jozwiak *(Sr VP-Sls & Client Rels)*
Sandra Wilson *(COO)*
Tim O'Hara *(CIO)*
Mary Formosa *(VP-HR)*
Zollie Frank *(Founder)*
Armund Schoen *(Founder)*

FRANK DONIO, INC.
692 N Egg Harbor Rd, Hammonton,
NJ 08037-2636
Tel.: (609) 561-2466
Web Site: https://www.donio.com
Year Founded: 1998
Sales Range: $10-24.9 Million
Emp.: 20
Producer of Fresh Fruits & Veg-
etables
N.A.I.C.S.: 424480
Dave Arena *(Pres)*

FRANK EDWARDS CO. INC.
1565 Adrian Rd, Burlingame, CA
94010
Web Site: http://www.feco.net
Rev.: $89,500,000
Emp.: 5
Engines, Gasoline
N.A.I.C.S.: 423830

**FRANK FLETCHER COMPA-
NIES, LTD.**
6301 Frobing Rd, Little Rock, AR
72209
Tel.: (501) 562-1000
Web Site:
    http://www.frankfletcher.com
Holding Company
N.A.I.C.S.: 551112
Frank Fletcher *(Pres)*
Thomas W. Roy *(CFO)*
Shapoor Karimi *(Mgr)*

Subsidiaries:

Frank Fletcher Auto Group, LLC   **(1)**
6301 Forbing Rd, Little Rock, AR 72209
Tel.: (501) 562-1000
Web Site: http://www.fletcherauto.com
New & Used Car Dealerships Operator
N.A.I.C.S.: 441110

Unit (Domestic):

Frank Fletcher Honda
Bentonville   **(2)**
2921 Moberly Ln, Bentonville, AR 72712
Tel.: (479) 273-3000
Web Site: http://www.fletcherhonda.com
Emp.: 100
New & Used Car Dealer
N.A.I.C.S.: 441110
Ryan Blake *(Gen Mgr)*

Frank Fletcher Kia Bentonville   **(2)**
2901 Moberly Ln, Bentonville, AR 72712-
3749
Tel.: (479) 273-3000
Web Site: http://www.fletcherkia.com
Sales Range: $10-24.9 Million
Emp.: 64
New & Used Car Dealer
N.A.I.C.S.: 441110
David Guarno *(Gen Mgr)*

Frank Fletcher Nissan   **(2)**
2327 S Range Line Rd, Joplin, MO 64804
Tel.: (417) 781-1177
Web Site:
    http://www.fletchernissanstore.com
New & Used Car Dealer
N.A.I.C.S.: 441110
Greg Martin *(Mgr-F&I)*
Jeremy Elick *(Gen Mgr)*

**FRANK G. LOVE ENVELOPES
INC.**

10733 E Ute St, Tulsa, OK 74116
Tel.: (918) 836-3535
Web Site:
    https://www.loveenvelopes.com
Rev.: $11,300,000
Emp.: 110
Envelope Mfr
N.A.I.C.S.: 322230
Michael Edward Love *(Chm)*

FRANK G. SULLIVAN JR. INC.
9313 S Choctaw Dr, Baton Rouge,
LA 70815
Tel.: (225) 927-8476
Web Site: http://www.fgsullivan.com
Sales Range: $25-49.9 Million
Emp.: 150
General Contractor, Highway & Street
Construction
N.A.I.C.S.: 237310
Frank G. Sullivan Jr. *(Pres)*

FRANK H. REIS INC.
475 Washington Ave, Kingston, NY
12401
Tel.: (845) 338-4656
Web Site:
    https://www.reisinsurance.com
Year Founded: 1966
Sales Range: $10-24.9 Million
Emp.: 45
Insurance Services
N.A.I.C.S.: 524210
Frank L. Casciaro *(CFO & Mgr-IT)*
Paul G. Casciaro *(Chm & CEO)*
Steven A. Thornton *(COO)*

FRANK HILL ASSOCIATES
630 5th Ave Ste 2401, New York, NY
10111-0100
Tel.: (212) 218-2811
Year Founded: 1966
Sales Range: $25-49.9 Million
Emp.: 2
Private Investing Services
N.A.I.C.S.: 332812
Andrew Frankel *(CEO)*
Mary Lou Holcombe *(Pres)*

FRANK I. ROUNDS COMPANY
65 York Ave, Randolph, MA 02368
Tel.: (781) 963-6440
Web Site:
    https://www.frankirounds.com
Year Founded: 1936
Rev.: $18,000,000
Emp.: 65
Boilers & Oil & Fuel Burner Distr
N.A.I.C.S.: 423720
Lee Ehrenzeller *(Pres)*

FRANK INVESTMENT INC.
6733 Black Horse Pike, Egg Harbor
Township, NJ 08234
Tel.: (561) 776-4747
Rev.: $15,000,000
Emp.: 200
Theater Building, Ownership & Op-
eration
N.A.I.C.S.: 531120
Alvin Frank *(Chm)*

**FRANK KASMIR & ASSOCI-
ATES INC.**
3191 Commonwealth Dr, Dallas, TX
75247
Tel.: (214) 631-8040
Web Site:
    https://www.kasmirfabrics.com
Year Founded: 1962
Sales Range: $25-49.9 Million
Emp.: 177
Mfr of Piece Goods
N.A.I.C.S.: 424310
Dale Jones *(VP)*

Subsidiaries:

Draperycrafters Inc. (1)
3191 Commonwealth Dr, Dallas, TX
75247 (100%)
Tel.: (214) 631-8040
Web Site: http://www.kasmirfabrics.com
Sales Range: $25-49.9 Million
Emp.: 150
Drapery Products Sales
N.A.I.C.S.: 424310
Fred Johnston (Comptroller)
Linda Kasmir (Pres)

FRANK L. BEIER RADIO INC.

1150 N Causeway Blvd, Mandeville,
LA 70471
Tel.: (504) 341-0123
Web Site: http://www.beierradio.com
Sales Range: $10-24.9 Million
Emp.: 50
Marine Supplies & Equipment
N.A.I.C.S.: 441222
Karl Beier (Owner)

FRANK L. BLUM CONSTRUC-TION COMPANY

830 E 25th St, Winston Salem, NC
27105
Tel.: (336) 724-5528
Web Site: https://www.flblum.com
Year Founded: 1923
Sales Range: $10-24.9 Million
Emp.: 75
Commercial & Institutional Building
Construction Services
N.A.I.C.S.: 236220
J. Andrews Hancock (CEO)
Michael E. Lancaster (Pres)
Mark R. Dunnagan (VP-Project Dev)
Chris White (VP-Preconstruction
Svcs)
William L. Ball III (CFO)

FRANK LILL & SON INC.

656 Basket Rd, Webster, NY 14580
Tel.: (585) 265-0490 **NY**
Web Site:
http://www.franklillandson.com
Year Founded: 1922
Sales Range: $25-49.9 Million
Emp.: 50
Power Plant Construction Services
N.A.I.C.S.: 237990
Charles G. Lill (Pres & CEO)
Tim Moon (Controller)
Greg Andrews (Project Mgr)
William Cole Jr. (Project Mgr)

FRANK LIQUOR COMPANY INCORPORATED

2115 Pleasant View Rd, Middleton,
WI 53562
Tel.: (608) 836-6000
Web Site: http://www.frankbeer.com
Rev.: $35,000,000
Emp.: 60
Bottling Wines & Liquors
N.A.I.C.S.: 424820
Steve Frank (Pres & CEO)
Tim Geier (Mgr-Sls)
Jim Abderholden (Mgr-Sls-Wine Div)
Mike Kicmol (Supvr-Sls)

FRANK M. BOOTH INC.

222 3rd St, Marysville, CA 95901
Tel.: (530) 742-7134
Web Site: http://www.frankbooth.com
Sales Range: $10-24.9 Million
Emp.: 300
Commercial & Institutional Building
Construction
N.A.I.C.S.: 236220
Frank Martin Booth (CEO)
Richard Gabel (CFO)
Larry R. Booth (Pres)

Subsidiaries:

Frank M. Booth Design Build Co. (1)
4220 Douglas Blvd Ste 5, Granite Bay, CA
95746
Tel.: (916) 784-0777
Web Site: http://www.frankbooth.com
Mechanical Engineering & Design/Build
Services
N.A.I.C.S.: 541330
Larry R. Booth (Pres)
F. Martin Booth (Chm)
Richard W. Gabel (CFO)
Clint Studebaker (Chief Contracting Officer)

Valley Sheet Metal Company (1)
391 Forbes Blvd, South San Francisco, CA
94080
Tel.: (650) 871-8292
Web Site: http://www.frankbooth.com
Designs, Fabricates & Installs Architectural
Sheet Metal Systems for Commercial & In-
stitutional Facilities
N.A.I.C.S.: 332322

FRANK MARTZ COACH COM-PANY INC.

239 Old River Rd, Wilkes Barre, PA
18702-1616
Tel.: (570) 821-3838
Web Site:
http://www.martztrailways.com
Year Founded: 1963
Rev.: $32,938,331
Emp.: 517
Charter Bus Distr
N.A.I.C.S.: 485510

Subsidiaries:

Gold Line Inc. (1)
5500 Tuxedo Rd, Hyattsville, MD 20781-
1314
Tel.: (570) 821-3838
Web Site: http://www.graylinedc.com
Rev.: $10,473,496
Emp.: 200
Charter Bus Services
N.A.I.C.S.: 485210

FRANK MAYBORN ENTER-PRISES

10 S 3rd St, Temple, TX 76501
Tel.: (254) 778-4444
Web Site: https://www.tdtnews.com
Sales Range: $25-49.9 Million
Emp.: 150
Newspapers
N.A.I.C.S.: 513110
Jerry Prickett (Mng Editor)

FRANK MAYER & ASSOCI-ATES INC.

1975 Wisconsin Ave, Grafton, WI
53024
Tel.: (262) 377-4700
Web Site: http://www.frankmayer.com
Sales Range: $25-49.9 Million
Emp.: 100
Signs & Advertising Specialties
N.A.I.C.S.: 339950
Michael S. Mayer (Pres)
Ryan Lepianka (Dir-Creative)
Steve Champagne (Acct Exec)
Scott Wigton (Acct Exec-West Coast)

FRANK MERCEDE & SONS INC.

700 Canal St, Stamford, CT 06902
Tel.: (203) 967-2000
Web Site:
http://www.frankmercede.com
Year Founded: 1923
Sales Range: $10-24.9 Million
Emp.: 4
Construction Services
N.A.I.C.S.: 236210
Dennis R. Orgera (Sec & VP)

FRANK MILLARD CO. INC.

107 Valley St, Burlington, IA 52601

Tel.: (319) 752-4571 **IA**
Web Site:
https://www.frankmillard.com
Year Founded: 1870
Sales Range: $10-24.9 Million
Emp.: 100
Heating & Air-Conditioning Contract-
ing Services
N.A.I.C.S.: 238220
Steve Coffin (VP)
Lyle Gibson (Dir-Safety & HR)
Diana McCannon (Mgr-Payroll)
Scott Smith (Dir-Bus Dev)

FRANK MYERS AUTO MAXX

4200 N Patterson Ave, Winston Sa-
lem, NC 27105
Tel.: (336) 276-0065
Web Site:
https://www.frankmyersauto.com
Year Founded: 1925
Sales Range: $1-9.9 Million
Emp.: 33
Used Car Distr
N.A.I.C.S.: 441120
Tracy E. Myers (Owner)
Denise Ireland (Controller)
Bryan Hawks (Dir-Quality Control)

FRANK N. MAGID ASSOCI-ATES, INC.

1 Research Ctr, Marion, IA 52302
Tel.: (319) 377-7345
Web Site: http://www.magid.com
Sales Range: $10-24.9 Million
Emp.: 115
Market Analysis & Research
N.A.I.C.S.: 541910
Steve Ridge (COO)
Michael Vorhaus (Pres-Magid Advi-
sors)

FRANK NOVAK & SONS, INC.

23940 Miles Rd, Cleveland, OH
44128
Tel.: (216) 475-5440
Web Site:
https://www.franknovak.com
Year Founded: 1912
Sales Range: $10-24.9 Million
Emp.: 100
Painting & Wall Covering Contracting
Services
N.A.I.C.S.: 238320
Allen J. Pinchot (Pres)
James B. Carr (Mgr-Div)

FRANK PAXTON LUMBER COMPANY

7455 Dawson Rd, Cincinnati, OH
45243
Tel.: (513) 984-8200
Web Site:
https://www.paxtonwood.com
Year Founded: 1914
Lumber Whslr
N.A.I.C.S.: 423310
Tom Varley (Gen Mgr)

FRANK REWOLD & SON, INC.

303 E 3rd St Ste 300, Rochester, MI
48307
Tel.: (248) 651-7242
Web Site:
https://www.frankrewold.com
Year Founded: 1918
Sales Range: $10-24.9 Million
Emp.: 65
Nonresidential Construction Services
N.A.I.C.S.: 236220
Craig Wolanin (Mgr)

FRANK SHIREY CADILLAC INC.

10125 S Cicero, Oak Lawn, IL 60453-
4083

Tel.: (708) 636-6600
Web Site:
http://www.shireycadillac.com
Rev.: $40,000,000
Emp.: 60
New & Used Automobiles
N.A.I.C.S.: 441110
Thomas F. Shirey (Pres)
Keith Sanders (Mgr-Internet)

FRANK SHIREY CADILLAC, INC.

10125 S Cicero Ave, Oak Lawn, IL
60453-4083
Tel.: (708) 636-6600
Web Site:
http://www.shireycadillac.com
Year Founded: 1964
Sales Range: $10-24.9 Million
Emp.: 60
Car Whslr
N.A.I.C.S.: 441110
Sue Jucius (Office Mgr)
Olga Pawlenko (CFO)
Tina Sills (Principal)
Joseph Garcia (Dir-Svc)

FRANK SHOOP, INC.

1470 Cherry Blossom Way, George-
town, KY 40324
Tel.: (502) 863-3727
Web Site: http://www.frankshoop.com
Sales Range: $10-24.9 Million
Emp.: 38
Car Whslr
N.A.I.C.S.: 441110
Kevin May (Gen Mgr-Sls)
Stacey Mulligan (Acct Mgr)
Ann Ritchie (Controller)
Langdon Shoop (Pres)
Frank Shoop (VP)

FRANK TAYLOR LUMBER & DEVELOPMENT CO.

360 S Meridian St, Cedarville, MI
49719
Tel.: (906) 484-2204
Web Site:
http://www.tricountybuilding
centers.com
Sales Range: $10-24.9 Million
Emp.: 45
Wholesale Lumber Products
N.A.I.C.S.: 444110
Mike Patrick (Mgr-Taylor Lumber)
Brian Hanna (Pres)

FRANK THEATRES, LLC

1003 W Indiantown Rd Ste 210, Jupi-
ter, FL 33458-7169
Tel.: (561) 776-4747
Web Site:
http://www.franktheatres.com
Year Founded: 1921
Sales Range: $250-299.9 Million
Emp.: 3,000
Movie Theater Owner & Operator
N.A.I.C.S.: 512131
Bruce Frank (Pres)
Joyce Frank (Sr VP)
Joey Duhon (Gen Mgr)

FRANK W. CAWOOD & ASSO-CIATES

103 Clover Grain, Peachtree City, GA
30269
Tel.: (770) 487-6307
Web Site: http://www.fca.com
Sales Range: $25-49.9 Million
Emp.: 100
Book Publishing
N.A.I.C.S.: 513130
Tim Anders (CEO)
Anne Kaufmann (Mgr-Creative Svcs)
Shane Wright (Mgr-Customer Svc)

FRANK W. DIVER INC.

Frank W. Diver Inc.—(Continued)

2101 Pennsylvania Ave, Wilmington, DE 19806-2494
Tel.: (302) 575-0161
Web Site: https://www.diverchev.com
Sales Range: $50-74.9 Million
Emp.: 90
Automobiles, New & Used
N.A.I.C.S.: 441110
Rich Diver (Pres)

FRANK W. WHITCOMB CONSTRUCTION CORP.

187 Whitcomb Rd, Walpole, NH 03608
Tel.: (603) 445-5555
Sales Range: $25-49.9 Million
Emp.: 100
Resurfacing Contractor
N.A.I.C.S.: 237310
Frank L. Whitcomb (Pres)
Allison Lewis (VP-Fin)

FRANK W. WINNE & SON, INC.

521 Fellowship Rd Ste 115, Mount Laurel, NJ 08054
Tel.: (215) 627-8080   **PA**
Web Site: http://www.frankwinne.com
Sales Range: $125-149.9 Million
Emp.: 140
Rope Twine Safety Supply Rubber Product Agricultural Product & Packaging Product Distr
N.A.I.C.S.: 423840
J. Douglas Coath Jr. (Pres & CEO)

Subsidiaries:

Tubbs Cordage Inc.   (1)
521 Fellowship Rd Ste 115, Mount Laurel, NJ 08054-3413
Tel.: (520) 798-3752
Sales Range: $1-9.9 Million
Emp.: 24
Cordage & Twine Mfr
N.A.I.C.S.: 314994

FRANK'S CASING CREW & RENTAL TOOLS, INC.

700 E Verot School Rd, Lafayette, LA 70508-2502
Tel.: (337) 233-0303   **LA**
Web Site:
    http://www.frankscasing.com
Year Founded: 1938
Sales Range: $150-199.9 Million
Emp.: 2,000
Provider of Oil & Gas Field Services
N.A.I.C.S.: 213112
Leonard Castille (VP-Sls)
Blake Hebert (Coord-Production)
Cliff Roberts (Dir-HSE)
Dustin Romero (Supvr-Casing)
Johnnie Stinson (Mgr-Production)
Joshua Simon (Coord-Ops)
Jude Patin (Mgr-Mfg)
Phillip Champagne (Mgr-FCC Asset)
Reese Comeaux (Mgr-Engrg)
Thomasine Hollier (Mgr-Insurance Dept)
Russel Foti (Supvr-Trng)
Ben Talley (Coord-Production)

Subsidiaries:

Frank's Tong Service Inc.   (1)
2701 Haindl Dr, Oklahoma City, OK 73129-6447
Tel.: (405) 672-8064
Sales Range: $25-49.9 Million
Emp.: 35
Provider of Oil & Gas Field Services
N.A.I.C.S.: 213112

FRANK'S SUPPLY COMPANY INC.

3311 Stanford Dr NE, Albuquerque, NM 87107
Tel.: (505) 884-0000

Web Site: https://www.franks-supply.com
Sales Range: $10-24.9 Million
Emp.: 100
General Construction Machinery & Equipment
N.A.I.C.S.: 423810
Melissa Deaver Rivera (Pres)

FRANKCRUM

100 S Missouri Ave, Clearwater, FL 33756
Tel.: (727) 726-2786   **FL**
Web Site: http://www.frankcrum.com
Year Founded: 1981
Sales Range: $1-4.9 Billion
Emp.: 190
Professional Employer Organization; Staffing & Insurance Services
N.A.I.C.S.: 561330
Rich Gibaldi (Mgr-Pricing)
David Peasall (Dir-HR)
Angie Garcia (VP-Mktg)
Sarah Tupper (VP-Direct Sls)
Anne Lanning (Branch Mgr)
Debbie Moran (VP-Payroll Ops)
Matthew C. Crum (Pres-Frank Winston Crum Insurance)
Steve Gober (VP-Underwriting)
Farid Nagji (Exec VP-Ops & Tech)
T. Mike Oddo II (VP-Broker Sls)

FRANKEL CADILLAC CO.

10400 York Rd, Cockeysville, MD 21030-2502
Tel.: (410) 666-5000
Sales Range: $10-24.9 Million
Emp.: 85
Car Whslr
N.A.I.C.S.: 441110
Olivia Bahr (Comptroller)
Guy Christopher (Exec VP)
Robert E. Frankel (Pres)
Richard Giroux (Exec VP)

FRANKEL MANAGEMENT INC.

1845 Walnut St Ste 2345, Philadelphia, PA 19103
Tel.: (215) 751-0900
Web Site:
    https://www.frankelenterprises.com
Sales Range: $10-24.9 Million
Emp.: 65
Real Estate Managers
N.A.I.C.S.: 531210
William Frankel (Pres)

FRANKEL STAFFING PARTNERS

3700 National Dr Ste 109, Raleigh, NC 27612
Tel.: (919) 783-6300
Web Site:
    http://www.frankelstaffing.com
Year Founded: 1994
Recruitment Services
N.A.I.C.S.: 561320
Lee Frankel (Co-Founder & VP-Recruitment & Ops)
Rod Frankel (Co-Founder & Pres)
Will Barfield (Sr Dir-Bus Dev)

FRANKENMUTH BAVARIAN INN, INC.

713 S Main St, Frankenmuth, MI 48734
Web Site:
    https://www.bavarianinn.com
Year Founded: 1950
Sales Range: $10-24.9 Million
Motel & Restaurant Owner & Operator
N.A.I.C.S.: 722511
Amy Zehnder (Gen Mgr)
Kati Zehnder (Mgr-Frankenmuth River Place Shops)

Judy Zehnder Keller (Pres-Bavarian Inn Lodge)
Michael Zehnder (Gen Mgr)
Don Keller (Treas)
Martha Zehnder Keller (VP-Sls & Mktg)
Willam Zehnder Keller (Mgr-Frankenmuth River Place Shops)
William A. (Pres)

FRANKENMUTH MUTUAL INSURANCE CO.

1 Mutual Ave, Frankenmuth, MI 48787-0001
Tel.: (989) 652-6121
Web Site: https://www.fmins.com
Sales Range: $150-199.9 Million
Emp.: 500
Fire, Marine & Casualty Insurance: Mutual
N.A.I.C.S.: 524126
Brian McLeod (Treas, Sec & VP-Fin)
Bryan L. Gilleland (Sr VP)
Philip J. McCain (VP)
Andrew H. Knudsen (VP)
Jami M. Kelly (VP)
John S. Benson (Chm & CEO)
Frederick A. Edmond Jr. (Pres & COO)

FRANKFORD CANDY & CHOCOLATE CO.

9300 Ashton Rd, Philadelphia, PA 19114
Tel.: (215) 735-5200
Web Site:
    http://www.frankfordcandy.com
Rev.: $13,800,000
Emp.: 225
Chocolate
N.A.I.C.S.: 311351
Studerd Stlick (CEO)
Aseem Kherg (CFO)

FRANKLIN BANCORP INC.

317 N Main St, Franklin, KY 42134
Tel.: (270) 586-7121
Web Site: http://www.fbtco.com
Sales Range: $10-24.9 Million
Emp.: 45
Bank Holding Company
N.A.I.C.S.: 551111
Gary Broady (Pres & CEO)
Jill Gregory (CFO & Sr VP)
Fay Neal Jr. (COO, CIO & Sr VP)

Subsidiaries:

Franklin Bank & Trust Company   (1)
317 N Main St, Franklin, KY 42134
Tel.: (270) 586-7121
Web Site: http://www.fbtco.com
Personal & Commercial Banking Services
N.A.I.C.S.: 522110
Jill Gregory (CFO)
John Bowen (Chm)
Alex Downing (Pres & CEO)

FRANKLIN BOWLES GALLERIES

765 Beach St, San Francisco, CA 94109
Tel.: (415) 441-8008   **CA**
Web Site: https://www.franklinbowles
    gallery.com
Year Founded: 1969
Rev.: $12,050,101
Emp.: 40
Art Dealers
N.A.I.C.S.: 459920
Robert Grannen (Controller)
Stacey Bellis (Gen Mgr & Dir-Mktg)

FRANKLIN BRONZE & ALLOY CO.

655 Grant St, Franklin, PA 16323
Tel.: (814) 437-6891

Web Site:
    https://www.franklinbronze.com
Year Founded: 1978
Sales Range: $10-24.9 Million
Emp.: 80
Bronze Foundry
N.A.I.C.S.: 331529
Robert E. Barber (Pres)

Subsidiaries:

Franklin Bronze & Alloy Co., Sand Casting Division   (1)
Rte 322 W, Franklin, PA 16323
Tel.: (814) 432-2230
Web Site: http://www.franklinbronze.com
Sales Range: $10-24.9 Million
Emp.: 20
Provider of Castings in Brass, Bronze, Aluminum & Stainless Steel Alloys
N.A.I.C.S.: 331529
Robert Barber (Pres)

Franklin Bronze & Alloy Company, Investment Casting Division   (1)
655 Grant St, Franklin, PA 16323
Tel.: (814) 437-6891
Web Site: http://www.franklinbronze.com
Sales Range: $1-9.9 Million
Emp.: 75
Tools; Provider of Precision Investment Castings in Brass & Bronze, Aluminum, Stainless Steel & Nickel-base Alloy Mfr
N.A.I.C.S.: 331529

FRANKLIN BSP CAPITAL CORPORATION

9 W 57th St Ste 4920, New York, NY 10019
Tel.: (212) 588-6770   **DE**
Web Site: https://www.fbccbdc.com
Year Founded: 2020
Rev.: $56,744,000
Assets: $816,183,000
Liabilities: $443,762,000
Net Worth: $372,421,000
Earnings: $31,470,000
Emp.: 359
Fiscal Year-end: 12/31/22
Financial Services
N.A.I.C.S.: 523940
Richard J. Byrne (Chm, Pres & CEO)

FRANKLIN BUILDING SUPPLY CO. INC.

11700 W Franklin Rd, Boise, ID 83709-0139
Tel.: (208) 322-4567   **ID**
Web Site: https://www.franklinbuilding
    supply.com
Year Founded: 1976
Sales Range: $25-49.9 Million
Emp.: 250
Lumber & Other Building Materials
N.A.I.C.S.: 423310
Rick Lierz (Owner)
Rhonda Millick (CFO)
Stan Buscher (Gen Mgr)

FRANKLIN COLLECTION SERVICE, INC.

2978 W Jackson St, Tupelo, MS 38801
Tel.: (662) 844-7776
Web Site:
    https://www.franklinservice.com
Year Founded: 1980
Sales Range: $10-24.9 Million
Emp.: 275
Collection Agency Services
N.A.I.C.S.: 561440
Dan Franklin (Owner, Pres & CEO)
Christy Stewart (Mgr-Client Svcs)

FRANKLIN CORPORATION

601 Franklin Dr, Houston, MS 38851

Tel.: (662) 456-4286   MS
Web Site:
  http://www.franklincorp.com
Year Founded: 1970
Sales Range: $75-99.9 Million
Emp.: 1,200
Upholstered Reclining Household
Furniture
N.A.I.C.S.: 337121
Hassell H. Franklin *(CEO)*

FRANKLIN COUNTY PUD INC.
PO Box 2407, Pasco, WA 99302-
2407
Tel.: (509) 547-5591   WA
Web Site: http://www.franklinpud.com
Year Founded: 1947
Sales Range: $25-49.9 Million
Emp.: 87
Electronic Services
N.A.I.C.S.: 221122
Debbie Boneharris *(Dir-Public Rela-
tions)*

FRANKLIN COUNTY RESIDEN-
TIAL SERVICES, INC.
1021 Checkrein Ave, Columbus, OH
43229-1106
Tel.: (614) 844-3800   OH
Web Site: http://www.fcres.com
Year Founded: 1980
Sales Range: $10-24.9 Million
Emp.: 431
Developmental Disability Assistance
Services
N.A.I.C.S.: 623210
Matt Hobbs *(Dir-HR)*
Susie Burke *(Dir-Community Living
Svcs)*

FRANKLIN DISPLAY GROUP,
INC.
910 E Lincoln Ave, Belvidere, IL
61008
Tel.: (815) 544-6676
Web Site:
  https://www.franklindisplay.com
Year Founded: 1978
Sales Range: $10-24.9 Million
Emp.: 110
Miscellaneous Fabricated Wire Prod-
ucts
N.A.I.C.S.: 332618
Don Mutert *(VP)*

FRANKLIN ELECTRONIC PUB-
LISHERS, INC.
8 Terri Ln, Burlington, NJ 08016-4901
Tel.: (609) 386-2500   PA
Web Site: http://www.franklin.com
Year Founded: 1981
Sales Range: $25-49.9 Million
Emp.: 80
Hand-Held Electronic Information De-
vice Designer, Developer, Retailer &
Publisher
N.A.I.C.S.: 333310
Barry J. Lipsky *(Pres & CEO)*
Gregory J. Winsky *(Exec VP)*
Howard Lee Morgan *(Chm)*
Bradley Tennant *(CFO)*

Subsidiaries:

Franklin Electronic Publishers (Aust)
Pty. Ltd.   (1)
Unit 3 277 Lane Cove Road, North Ryde,
2113, NSW, Australia   (100%)
Tel.: (61) 0298826110
Web Site:
  http://www.franklinelectronics.com.au
Sales Range: $1-9.9 Million
Emp.: 4
Whslr of Handheld Electronics & Software
Products
N.A.I.C.S.: 513210

Franklin Electronic Publishers
Deutschland GmbH   (1)
Kapellenstr 13, D 85622, Feldkirchen,
Germany   (100%)
Tel.: (49) 89908990
Web Site: http://www.franklin-de.com
Sales Range: $100-124.9 Million
Electronic & Software Publisher
N.A.I.C.S.: 513210

Franklin Electronic Publishers
France   (1)
66 rue des Vanesses, PO Box 54 394, 95
943, Roissy-en-France, Cedex, CDG,
France   (100%)
Tel.: (33) 0148639940
Web Site: http://www.franklin.com
Sales Range: $1-9.9 Million
Emp.: 2
Electronic & Software Publishers
N.A.I.C.S.: 513210

Franklin Electronic Publishers,
Ltd.   (1)
220 Bayview Drive Unit 3, Barrie, L4N 4Y8,
ON, Canada
Tel.: (705) 721-1582
Web Site: http://www.franklin.com
Sales Range: $1-9.9 Million
Emp.: 3
Electronic Publisher & Distr
N.A.I.C.S.: 513210
Barry Lipsky *(Pres)*

Franklin Publishers De Mexico   (1)
Callejon Tlatetilpan No 17-F Col Barrio San
Lucas, Coyoacan, 04030, Mexico
Tel.: (52) 55 56 58 12 16
Web Site: http://www.franklin.com.mx
Sales Range: $10-24.9 Million
Emp.: 6
Software Development Services
N.A.I.C.S.: 513210

Franklin U.K.   (1)
SC House Vanwall Road, Maidenhead, SL6
4UW, Berkshire, United Kingdom   (100%)
Tel.: (44) 8707000988
Sales Range: $100-124.9 Million
Electronic Publisher & Distr
N.A.I.C.S.: 513210

Yorter International Limited   (1)
Unit 1807 18/F Thriving Ind Centre 26-38
Sha Tsui Rd Tsuen Wan, NT, Hong Kong,
China (Hong Kong)   (100%)
Tel.: (852) 24166636
Web Site: http://www.yorter.com
Sales Range: $100-124.9 Million
Electronic Product Distr
N.A.I.C.S.: 423990

FRANKLIN FORD
175 E Central St, Franklin, MA 02038
Tel.: (508) 528-0040
Web Site: https://franklinford.com
Year Founded: 1975
Sales Range: $10-24.9 Million
Emp.: 40
Car Whslr
N.A.I.C.S.: 441110
Barry Madden *(Gen Mgr)*
John Madden *(Pres)*

FRANKLIN HILL ACQUISITION
CORPORATION
9454 Wilshire Blvd 610, Beverly Hills,
CA 90212
Tel.: (601) 929-5689   CA
Year Founded: 2015
Emp.: 1
Holding Company
N.A.I.C.S.: 551112
Lay Wah Khoo *(Pres, CEO, CFO,
Treas & Sec)*

FRANKLIN INTERIORS INC.
2740 Smallman St Ste 600, Pitts-
burgh, PA 15222
Tel.: (412) 261-2525   PA
Web Site:
  https://www.franklininteriors.com
Year Founded: 1945
Sales Range: $25-49.9 Million

Emp.: 45
Provider of Residential Interior De-
sign
N.A.I.C.S.: 423210
Todd Irwin *(VP-Sls)*
Stacey Dixon *(Acct Exec)*

FRANKLIN INTERNATIONAL
INC.
2020 Bruck St, Columbus, OH
43207-2329
Tel.: (614) 443-0241
Web Site: http://www.titebond.com
Year Founded: 1935
Sales Range: $25-49.9 Million
Emp.: 350
Provider of Plastics Materials, Adhe-
sives & Sealants
N.A.I.C.S.: 325520
Evan Williams *(CEO)*
Craig Stones *(Mgr-Mktg)*
Don McCloskey *(VP-Intl)*
Scott Bowen *(VP-Sls-North America
& China)*
Glen Steinke *(Dir-Logistics)*
Forest Driggs *(VP-Fin & Dev)*

FRANKLIN L. HANEY COM-
PANY
1250 Maryland Ave SW Ste 503,
Washington, DC 20024
Tel.: (202) 479-1101
Web Site:
  http://www.flhcompany.com
Real Estate Development Services
N.A.I.C.S.: 531390
Franklin L. Haney Sr. *(Founder &
CEO)*
Frank Haney Jr. *(Pres)*

Subsidiaries:

Premium Brands of Northwest Arkan-
sas, Inc.   (1)
1601 E Pump Sta Rd, Fayetteville, AR
72701
Tel.: (479) 442-9971
Web Site:
  http://www.premiumbrandsnwa.com
Rev.: $7,000,000
Emp.: 24
Beer, Malt Beverage & Non-Alcoholic Bev-
erage Distr
N.A.I.C.S.: 424810
Franklin L. Haney Sr. *(Owner)*
Heath Sutherland *(Gen Mgr)*

FRANKLIN MINING, INC.
777 N Rainbow Blvd Ste 250, Las
Vegas, NV 89107
Tel.: (702) 944-9208
Web Site:
  http://www.franklinmining.com
Iron Ore Mining
N.A.I.C.S.: 212210
William A. Petty *(Chm & CEO)*
Kurt V. Spenkoch *(Treas & Sec)*

FRANKLIN MOUNTAIN EN-
ERGY, LLC
44 Cook St Ste 1000, Denver, CO
80206
Tel.: (720) 640-7517
Web Site: http://www.fmellc.com
Oil & Gas Field Exploration Services
N.A.I.C.S.: 213112
Paul Foster *(Chm)*
Jeff Stevens *(CEO)*
Shelly Albrecht *(Dir-Land)*
Mark Hinaman *(Dir-Engrg)*
Travis Hutchinson *(Dir-Facilities En-
grg)*
Ben Kessel *(Dir-Geology)*
Ryan Lake *(Mgr-Acctg)*
Rachael Overbey *(Dir-Ops, Plng &
Regulatory)*
Blake Pickett *(Gen Counsel & VP)*

Audrey Robertson *(Co-Founder &
Exec VP-Fin)*
Vladimir Roudakov *(Dir-Drilling Op-
erations)*
Craig Walters *(COO)*
Brandon White *(VP-Corp Dev)*

FRANKLIN PARK ASSOCI-
ATES, LLC
251 St Asaphs Rd 3 Bala Plz Ste 500
W, Bala Cynwyd, PA 19004
Tel.: (610) 822-0500
Web Site:
  https://www.franklinparkllc.com
Year Founded: 2003
Sales Range: $1-9.9 Million
Emp.: 23
Investment Advice
N.A.I.C.S.: 523940
Karl J. Hartmann *(Co-Founder, Mng
Dir, COO & Chief Compliance Officer)*
Bradley T. Atkins *(Co-Founder, CEO
& Mng Dir)*
Michael D. Bacine *(Co-Founder &
Mng Dir)*
Laure A. Brasch *(Mng Dir)*
R. Narayan Chowdhury *(Co-Founder
& Mng Dir)*
James B. McGovern *(Co-Founder &
Mng Dir)*
Neil K. Mowery *(Co-Founder & Mng
Dir)*
Kristine A. O'Connor *(Mng Dir &
CFO)*

FRANKLIN PONTIAC BUICK
GMC
1413 Murfreesboro Rd, Franklin, TN
37067
Tel.: (615) 794-2572
Web Site: http://www.franklinpbg.com
Rev.: $31,000,000
Emp.: 30
Automobiles, New & Used
N.A.I.C.S.: 441110

FRANKLIN PRIMARY HEALTH
CENTER, INC.
1303 Dr Martin Luther King Jr Ave,
Mobile, AL 36603
Tel.: (251) 432-4117   AL
Web Site:
  https://www.franklinprimary.org
Year Founded: 1975
Sales Range: $10-24.9 Million
Emp.: 260
Community Health Care Services
N.A.I.C.S.: 621498
Chris McGadney *(Chm)*
Stan Chavis *(Vice Chm)*
Henry Caddell *(Sec)*
Ronald Martin Sr. *(Treas)*

FRANKLIN PROPERTY & DE-
VELOPMENT GROUP LLC
10109 Lake Ave, Tampa, FL 33619
Tel.: (813) 630-9280
Sales Range: $75-99.9 Million
Emp.: 11
Real Estate Investment, Development
& Management
N.A.I.C.S.: 523999
David Franklin *(Pres)*

FRANKLIN SAVINGS BANK
387 Central St, Franklin, NH 03235-
0339
Tel.: (603) 934-4445
Web Site: https://www.fsbnh.bank
Rev.: $15,524,000
Emp.: 67
Banking Services
N.A.I.C.S.: 522180
Jeffery B. Savage *(CEO & Sec)*
Cheri M. Caruso *(Officer-Tech & Sr
VP)*

Franklin Savings Bank—(Continued)

Deborah Tessier *(Officer-Loan & VP)*
Ronald L. Magoon *(Pres & CEO)*
Martha K. Lefebvre *(Controller)*
Melissa Mansfield *(VP-Retail Loan Ops)*
Sarah E. M. Stanley *(Officer-Community Rels)*
Joseph A. Thornton *(VP & Officer-HR)*
Dawn M. Beers *(Officer-Mktg & Asst VP)*
Dorothy J. Savery *(Asst Sec)*
Jim T. DuBois *(Sr VP & Officer-Loan)*
Brian Bozak *(CFO)*
Heather Jewell *(Asst Mgr-Tilton)*
Brian Lamontagne *(Asst Mgr-Gilford)*
Heather Capraro *(VP)*

FRANKLIN SAVINGS BANK

197 Main St, Farmington, ME 04938
Tel.: (207) 778-3339
Web Site: http://www.fsbme.com
Rev.: $21,663,278
Emp.: 70
Federal Savings Bank
N.A.I.C.S.: 522180
Lorna Niedner *(Sr VP & Dir-Residential & Consumer Lending)*
Shelley W. Deane *(Exec VP-Admin & HR)*
Chrissy St. Laurent *(Asst VP)*
Brad Martin *(VP & Dir-IT)*
Timothy J. Thompson *(Pres & CEO)*
Derek Hayes *(Sr VP & Dir-Comml Lending)*
Patrick Dore *(Mgr-Skowhegan)*
RaeAnn Pike *(VP)*
Morgan Allarie *(VP & Dir-Branch Administration & Deposit Svcs)*
Amanda Lee *(Branch Mgr)*

FRANKLIN SPORTS, INC.

17 Campanelli Pkwy, Stoughton, MA
02072-0508
Tel.: (781) 344-1111   DE
Web Site:
   https://www.franklinsports.com
Year Founded: 1946
Sales Range: $75-99.9 Million
Emp.: 225
Athletic & Sporting Goods Whslr
N.A.I.C.S.: 339920
Larry J. Franklin *(Pres & CEO)*
Michael Kirby *(VP-Info Sys)*
Richard Hayes *(Controller)*

Subsidiaries:

Franklin Sports, Inc. - Uniforce Tactical Division   (1)
17 Campanelli Pkwy, Stoughton, MA 02072-4904
Tel.: (781) 344-1111
Web Site: http://www.uniforcetactical.com
Sporting Goods Mfr
N.A.I.C.S.: 339920

FRANKLIN SQUARE HOLDINGS, L.P.

201 Rouse Blvd, Philadelphia, PA
19112
Tel.: (215) 495-1150   PA
Web Site:
   https://www.fsinvestments.com
Year Founded: 2007
Alternative Asset Investment & Fund Management Services
N.A.I.C.S.: 523999
Michael C. Forman *(Chm & CEO)*
Michael Gerber *(Exec VP-Corp Affairs)*
Michael Kelly *(Pres & Chief Investment Officer)*
Zachary Klehr *(Exec VP-Fund Mgmt)*
Gerald F. Stahlecker *(Pres-FS Investment Corp & Exec VP-Legal & Fin)*

Phil Browne *(Mng Dir-Fin & Admin)*
Stephen Sypherd *(Gen Counsel & Mng Dir-Legal)*
Steve Landau *(Sr VP-Product Dev)*
John R. Shain *(Co-Founder)*
Greg Bassuk *(Head-Liquid Alternatives Strategies)*
Ania Mikson *(Chief HR Officer & Sr VP)*
Steve DeAngelis *(Exec VP & Head-Distr)*
Mike Carter *(Exec VP & Head-Strategy)*
David J. Adelman *(Vice Chm)*
Robert Stark *(Sr Mng Dir-Corp Dev)*

Subsidiaries:

FS Energy & Power Fund   (1)
201 Rouse Blvd, Philadelphia, PA 19112
Tel.: (215) 495-1150
Web Site: https://www.fsinvestments.com
Rev.: $184,967,000
Assets: $2,558,781,000
Liabilities: $805,033,000
Net Worth: $1,753,748,000
Earnings: $69,769,000
Emp.: 400
Fiscal Year-end: 12/31/2022
Energy & Power Industry Debt & Equity Securities Investment Fund
N.A.I.C.S.: 525990
Michael C. Forman *(Chm & CEO)*
Edward T. Gallivan Jr. *(CFO)*

FS KKR Capital Corp.   (1)
201 Rouse Blvd, Philadelphia, PA 19112
Tel.: (215) 495-1150
Web Site: https://www.fskkradvisor.com
Rev.: $1,635,000,000
Assets: $16,124,000,000
Liabilities: $9,112,000,000
Net Worth: $7,012,000,000
Earnings: $865,000,000
Fiscal Year-end: 12/31/2022
Debt Securities Investment Fund
N.A.I.C.S.: 525990
Michael C. Forman *(Chm & CEO)*
Ryan L. G. Wilson *(Co-COO)*
Stephen S. Sypherd *(Gen Counsel & Sec)*
Steven C. Lilly *(CFO)*
Drew O'Toole *(Co-COO)*
James F. Volk *(Chief Compliance Officer)*
Rony Ma *(VP)*
Daniel Pietrzak *(Co-Pres & Chief Investment Officer)*

Subsidiary (Domestic):

Corporate Capital Trust, Inc.   (2)
450 S Orange Ave, Orlando, FL 32801
Web Site:
   http://www.corporatecapitaltrust.com
Rev.: $386,468,000
Assets: $4,430,696,000
Liabilities: $1,671,364,000
Net Worth: $2,759,332,000
Earnings: $210,096,000
Fiscal Year-end: 12/31/2016
Closed-End Investment Fund
N.A.I.C.S.: 525990
Kirk Montgomery *(Chief Compliance Officer, Gen Counsel & Sec)*
William Goebel *(CFO)*

FRANKLIN STREET

600 NW Shore Ste 600, Tampa, FL
33609
Tel.: (813) 839-7300
Web Site: http://www.franklinstreetfinancial.com
Year Founded: 2006
Sales Range: $10-24.9 Million
Emp.: 190
Real Estate Investment & Management Services
N.A.I.C.S.: 531210
Andrew Wright *(Chm & CEO)*
Darron Kattan *(Mng Dir)*
Robert Goldfinger *(Mng Dir)*
William Sadlowski *(CFO)*
Monetha Cobb *(CMO)*
Patrick McGucken *(VP-Comml)*
Carrie Schramek *(Controller)*

Chad Rupp *(Mng Dir-Office & Indus)*
Chris Butler *(Mng Dir-Office & Indus)*
Valentina Mandarin *(Asst Mgr-Comml Property)*
Eric Smith *(Dir-Risk Mgmt & Claims)*
Lisa Jesmer *(Sr VP-Investor Client Accts)*
Robert Granda *(Dir-Retail Investment Sls-South)*
Kurt Keaton *(Pres-Real Estate Svcs & Mgmt Svcs)*
Tom Farmer *(Dir-Agency Leasing)*
Tom Kersting *(Pres-Insurance Svcs)*
Westcott Toole *(Reg Mgr)*
Eual Tyler Cathey *(COO & Gen Counsel)*
Nancy Sheinberg *(VP)*
Greg Matus *(Sr VP-Investment Sls)*
Ted Holler *(Dir-Insurance Svcs)*
Ryan Dagenais *(Asst Controller-Institutional Property Mgmt)*
Todd Simon *(Dir-Ops-Multifamily Properties)*
Jerry Shafer *(Mgr-Property-Multifamily-Atlanta)*
Claire Bayles *(Mgr-Atlanta)*
Laura Roy *(Mgr-Property-Morrison)*
Melissa Hazlewood *(VP-Office & Indus)*
Julie Palmer-Nicholson *(VP-Office & Indus)*
Chris Shaeffer *(VP-Bus Ops)*
Danielle Oliva *(Dir-HR)*
Greg Eisenman *(Sr Dir-Retail Tenant Svcs)*
Joe Rubin *(Dir-Multifamily Investment Sls Div)*
Chad DeFoor *(Sr Dir-Multifamily Investment Sls-Atlanta)*
Mike Battey *(Dir-Retail Leasing-Orlando)*

FRANKLIN STREET MARKETING

9700 Farrar Ct, Richmond, VA 23236
Tel.: (804) 320-3838   VA
Web Site:
   http://www.franklinstreet.com
Year Founded: 1986
Sales Range: $10-24.9 Million
Emp.: 19
Advetising Agency
N.A.I.C.S.: 541810
William B. Flynn *(Founder & Pres)*
Kelly Jackson *(Mgr-Opers)*
Tim Roberts *(VP & Dir-Creative)*
Dean Ruth *(Dir-Production)*
Kenya Gibson *(Acct Supvr)*
Allison Luck *(Acct Mgr)*

FRANKLIN-JEFFERSON STRATEGIES, LLC

977 David Dr, Red Lion, PA 17356
Tel.: (717) 417-8499   PA
Year Founded: 2011
Sales Range: Less than $1 Million
Emp.: 2
Investment Advisory Services
N.A.I.C.S.: 523940
Al Bowman *(Owner)*

FRANKLIN/GLENBURN HOME, INC.

618 Glenburn Rd, Linton, IN 47441
Tel.: (812) 847-2221   IN
Year Founded: 1993
Sales Range: $10-24.9 Million
Emp.: 321
Individual & Family Support Services
N.A.I.C.S.: 624190
Sue Sowders *(CEO)*

FRANKS FOREIGN CAR SERVICE INC.

509 S El Camino Real, San Clemente, CA 92672
Tel.: (949) 492-6515
Web Site:
   https://www.franksmotorcars.com
Sales Range: $10-24.9 Million
Emp.: 35
Automobiles, Used Cars Only
N.A.I.C.S.: 441120
Francisco Sanchez *(Pres)*
Mabel Sanchez *(VP)*

FRANNET LLC

10302 Brookridge Village Blvd Ste 201, Louisville, KY 40291
Tel.: (502) 753-2380   NJ
Web Site: http://www.frannet.com
Year Founded: 1987
Sales Range: $1-9.9 Million
Emp.: 8
Franchised Business Consulting
N.A.I.C.S.: 541618
Jania Bailey *(CEO)*
Jack Armstrong *(Chm)*
Parker Staten *(Coord-Social Media & Content)*
Steven Gray *(Coord-Data)*
Cat Hyle *(Coord-Mktg Brand)*
Drew Hayden *(Mgr-Conference & Events)*
Megan Allen *(Pres-Denver)*

FRANPOS, INC.

4699 Old Ironsides Dr Ste 100, Santa Clara, CA 95054
Tel.: (408) 898-3217
Web Site: http://www.franpos.com
Year Founded: 2012
Sales Range: $1-9.9 Million
Software Development Services
N.A.I.C.S.: 541511
Subodh Gupta *(Founder & CEO)*
Yulia Rivas *(Dir-Engrg)*
Pavel Malinnikov *(Dir-Android Tech)*
Viacheslav Galanov *(Mng Dir)*
Vitaly Druzhko *(Project Mgr)*

FRANTZ MANUFACTURING COMPANY INC.

PO Box 497, Sterling, IL 61081-0497
Tel.: (815) 625-3333   IL
Web Site: http://www.frantz-mfg.com
Year Founded: 1909
Sales Range: $10-24.9 Million
Emp.: 250
Ball & Roller Bearings Mfr
N.A.I.C.S.: 332991
Doug Sandberg *(VP-Mktg)*

FRANTZ MEDICAL GROUP

7740 Metric Dr, Mentor, OH 44060
Tel.: (440) 255-1155
Web Site:
   http://www.frantzgroup.com
Sales Range: $10-24.9 Million
Emp.: 20
Surgical & Medical Instruments
N.A.I.C.S.: 339112
Mark G. Frantz *(Pres & Mng Partner)*
Tom Pavsek *(Product Mgr)*

FRANZ FOODS INC.

504 W Main St, West Plains, MO
65775
Tel.: (417) 256-0838
Rev.: $30,000,000
Emp.: 11
Poultry & Poultry Product Merchant Whslr
N.A.I.C.S.: 424440
Phillip Franz *(Pres & Treas)*

FRANZELLA PRODUCE INC.

125 Terminal Ct 5556, South San Francisco, CA 94080
Tel.: (650) 588-0760

Web Site:
http://www.franzellaproduce.com
Rev.: $20,768,757
Emp.: 34
Bond Brokers
N.A.I.C.S.: 424410
Phillip S. Franzella *(Owner & Pres)*

FRANZIA/SANGER WINERY
17000 E Hwy 120, Ripon, CA 95366-9412
Tel.: (209) 599-4111
Sales Range: $25-49.9 Million
Emp.: 200
Wine Mfr
N.A.I.C.S.: 312130
Arthur Ciocca *(Partner)*
F. L. Bates *(Partner)*

FRANZISKA RACKER CENTERS
3226 Wilkins Rd, Ithaca, NY 14850
Tel.: (607) 272-5891   NY
Web Site:
http://www.rackercenters.org
Year Founded: 1948
Sales Range: $25-49.9 Million
Emp.: 986
Disability Assistance Services
N.A.I.C.S.: 624120
Pat Montanez *(Dir-Residential Svcs)*
Cris Donovan *(Dir-Community Svcs)*
Cecilia Campbell *(Fin Dir)*
Dan Brown *(Exec Dir)*
Jody Scriber *(Dir-Clinical & Educational Svcs)*

FRASCA INTERNATIONAL INC.
906 Airport Rd, Urbana, IL 61802-7407
Tel.: (217) 344-9200
Web Site: https://www.frasca.com
Year Founded: 1958
Sales Range: $10-24.9 Million
Emp.: 150
Flight Training Equipment Mfr
N.A.I.C.S.: 336413
Rudolf Frasca *(Founder)*
John Frasca *(CEO)*

Subsidiaries:

Era Training Center, LLC   (1)
960 W Lincoln Rd, Lake Charles, LA
70607   **(50%)**
Tel.: (337) 656-4200
Web Site: http://www.eratrainingcenter.com
Helicopter Pilot Training
N.A.I.C.S.: 611512

FRASCO, INC.
215 W Alameda Ave Ste 203, Burbank, CA 91502
Tel.: (818) 848-3888   CA
Web Site: http://www.frasco.com
Year Founded: 1964
Investigation Services
N.A.I.C.S.: 561611
John C. Simmers *(CEO)*
Adam McMahan *(VP-Claims Ops)*
Ken Carll *(Reg Mgr)*
Noelle Harling *(VP)*
Richard F. Smith *(VP-Major Accts & Program Mgmt)*
Steven Schulmeister *(Reg Mgr)*
Timothy W. Harper *(VP-Special Investigations Unit)*
Jason J. Simmers *(Pres)*
Jeffrey L. Davis *(VP-Bus Dev)*
Laura S. Pfaffman *(CFO)*
Mary K. Elterman *(Dir-Corp Ops)*
Todd Savar *(Dir-IT)*

Subsidiaries:

JSSF, Inc.   (1)
175 W Broadway, Oviedo, FL 32762-1330
Tel.: (407) 977-6877
Investigation Services

N.A.I.C.S.: 561611

FRASCONA BUICK, INC.
13000 W Capital Dr, Brookfield, WI 53005
Tel.: (414) 258-9960
Year Founded: 1957
Sales Range: $10-24.9 Million
Emp.: 53
New Car Dealers
N.A.I.C.S.: 441110
Anthony J. Frascona *(Pres)*
Andy Cobb *(Mgr-Sls)*

FRASER ADVANCED INFORMATION SYSTEMS
320 Penn Ave, Reading, PA 19611
Tel.: (610) 378-0101
Web Site: https://www.fraser-ais.com
Year Founded: 1971
Rev.: $17,000,000
Emp.: 110
Automation & Documentation Management Solutions
N.A.I.C.S.: 561410
Glen Gallant *(Controller)*
Danelle Wagner *(Mgr-Credit & Collections)*
Eric Pelko *(Mgr-Reading Branch Svc)*

FRASER COMMUNICATIONS
1631 Pontius Ave, Los Angeles, CA 90025
Tel.: (310) 319-3737
Web Site:
http://www.frasercommunications.com
Year Founded: 1992
Rev.: $40,000,000
Emp.: 32
N.A.I.C.S.: 541810
Renee White Fraser *(Pres & CEO)*
Ilene Prince *(Sr VP & Dir-Client Svcs)*
Leah Mitchell *(Sr VP & Dir-Media)*
Marcie Langenthal *(Assoc Dir-Media)*
Bruce Dundore *(Dir-Creative)*
Sergio Belletini *(Assoc Dir-Creative)*
Dyan Ullman *(Office Mgr-HR)*
Jennie Crandall *(Controller)*
Vivian Silverman *(Dir-Spot Brdcst)*
Malina Brown *(VP-Pub Rel)*

FRASIER TIRE SERVICE INC.
310 E Liberty St, Sumter, SC 29150
Tel.: (803) 773-1423
Web Site: https://www.frasiertire.com
Sales Range: $10-24.9 Million
Emp.: 53
Automotive Tires
N.A.I.C.S.: 441340
Kruno Cerovecki *(CFO & Exec VP)*
Cathy Springs *(Mgr-Accts Payable)*
Tripp Lee *(Mgr-Ops & Sls)*
Wendy Hinkley *(Mgr-Payroll, HR & AR)*
Julian G. Frasier III *(Owner & Pres)*

FRATTALONE COMPANIES, INC.
3205 Spruce St, Little Canada, MN 55117-1045
Tel.: (651) 484-0448
Web Site:
http://www.frattalonecompanies.com
Year Founded: 1970
Sales Range: $25-49.9 Million
Emp.: 225
Excavation Services
N.A.I.C.S.: 238910
Nick Frattalone *(Pres)*
Tony Frattalone *(CEO)*
Chris Niemand *(Project Mgr)*
Dylan Larson *(VP-Ops)*
Frank Frattalone *(Founder)*
Jeff Viner *(Dir-Safety)*
Nate Adams *(Project Mgr)*

Paul Pearson *(Project Mgr)*
Scott Spisak *(Mgr-Bus Dev)*
Shelly Boss *(Dir-Comm)*
Thomas Kinmouth *(Project Mgr)*
Todd Olund *(Mgr-Ops)*

FRATTALONE'S HARDWARE
3527 Lexington Ave N, Saint Paul, MN 55126-8017
Tel.: (651) 484-3327
Sales Range: $10-24.9 Million
Emp.: 250
Hardware Whslr
N.A.I.C.S.: 423710
Michelle Brunell *(Mgr)*
Larry Frattalone *(Owner & Principal)*
Jim Solin *(Partner & Gen Mgr)*

FRAZEE INC.
4351 35th St, Orlando, FL 32811
Tel.: (770) 948-5555
Web Site: http://www.frazeeinc.com
Year Founded: 1976
Sales Range: $25-49.9 Million
Emp.: 30
Hotel Renovations
N.A.I.C.S.: 236220
Clark W. Frazee *(Exec VP)*
Jan Hulsey *(Sec)*
Daniel G. Ward *(Pres)*

FRAZER FROST, PLC
425 W Capitol Ste 3300, Little Rock, AR 72201
Tel.: (501) 376-9241
Web Site: https://www.frostpllc.com
Sales Range: $10-24.9 Million
Emp.: 90
Accounting Services
N.A.I.C.S.: 541211
Dan Peregrin *(Mng Partner)*
Doug Richardson *(CEO)*

FRAZIER & COMPANY, INC.
2 Union Sq 601 Union St Ste 3200, Seattle, WA 98101
Tel.: (206) 621-7200   WA
Web Site:
http://www.frazierhealthcare.com
Year Founded: 1991
Rev.: $2,900,000,000
Healthcare-Focused Private Equity Firm
N.A.I.C.S.: 523999
Alan J. Levy *(Venture Partner)*
Alan D. Frazier *(Founder & Chm)*
Nathan Every *(Gen Partner)*
Nader Naini *(Mng Partner)*
Steve Bailey *(Partner & CFO)*
Brian Morfitt *(Gen Partner)*
Ben Magnano *(Mng Partner)*
Daniel J. Estes *(Partner)*
Brett Moraski *(Operating Partner)*
James N. Topper *(Mng Gen Partner)*
Jennifer Martin *(Controller)*
Carol Eckert *(Dir-IR)*
Elizabeth Park *(Mgr-Mktg & IR)*
Jim Brady *(Operating Partner-Growth Buyout Practice)*
Glen Moller *(Operating Partner)*
Phil Zaorski *(Principal)*
Christina Miller *(Principal)*
Danica Elliott *(Dir-Human Capital-Life Sciences)*
Robert M. Hershberg *(Venture Partner)*

Subsidiaries:

CCHN Group Holdings, Inc.   (1)
9201 E Mountain View Ste 220, Scottsdale, AZ 85258   **(53.2%)**
Web Site: http://www.matrixforme.com
Holding Company; In-Home Health Assessment & Care Management Services
N.A.I.C.S.: 551112
Walter W. Cooper *(CEO)*

Subsidiary (Domestic):

Community Care Health Network,
Inc.   (2)
9201 E Mountain View Ste 220, Scottsdale,
AZ 85258
Web Site:
https://www.matrixmedicalnetwork.com
Sales Range: $50-74.9 Million
Emp.: 650
In-Home Health Assessment & Care Management Services
N.A.I.C.S.: 621610
Catherine Tabaka *(CEO)*
Joseph Buchanan *(Sr VP)*
Sophia Kim *(Chief Comml Officer)*
Kevin O'Kelly-Lynch *(CFO)*
Thor Treadwell *(COO)*

Subsidiary (Domestic):

Matrix Medical Network of Arizona,
L.L.C.   (3)
9201 E Mountain View Ste 220, Scottsdale,
AZ 85258
Tel.: (480) 862-1887
Web Site: http://www.matrixforme.com
In-Home Health Assessment & Care Management Services
N.A.I.C.S.: 621610
Brian Morfitt *(Chm)*

EPTAM Precision Solutions   (1)
2 Riverside Business Pk, Northfield, NH
03276-4407
Tel.: (603) 286-8009
Web Site: http://www.eptam.com
Medical Device Mfr
N.A.I.C.S.: 339112
Mark Kemp *(CEO)*

Subsidiary (Domestic):

Mendell Machine and Manufacturing,
LLC   (2)
21463 Grenada Ave, Lakeville, MN 55044
Tel.: (952) 469-5500
Web Site: http://www.mendell.com
Precision Parts Manufacturer
N.A.I.C.S.: 332710
Bryan K. Bartz *(CEO)*

Micro Molding, Inc.   (2)
65 Howard St, Phillipsburg, NJ 08865
Tel.: (908) 454-1225
Web Site: http://www.micromoldinginc.com
All Other Miscellaneous Fabricated Metal
Product Mfr
N.A.I.C.S.: 332999

FRAZIER & DEETER, LLC
1230 Peachtree St NE Ste 1500, Atlanta, GA 30309
Tel.: (404) 253-7500   GA
Web Site:
http://www.frazierdeeter.com
Year Founded: 1981
Emp.: 300
Accounting, Tax Preparation & Consultancy Services
N.A.I.C.S.: 541211
Seth McDaniel *(CEO & Mng Partner-Natl)*
Mike Hendricks *(Partner-Tax)*
Donna Beatty *(Partner)*
Beth Garrett *(Partner)*
Kelly Garrison *(Partner)*
Angie Wellford *(Sr Mgr)*
Brian Holloway *(Principal-Tax)*
Patrick Crouch *(Partner-Audit Practice)*
Joann Gotschall *(Sr Mgr-Audit)*
Jessica Weissinger *(Sr Mgr)*
Barnabas Kane *(Mgr)*
Andrew Case *(Partner-Tax)*
John Bush *(Mgr)*
Abbie McBurnette *(Sr Mgr)*
Jason Nelson *(Sr Mgr-Tax)*
Lauren Hicks *(Sr Mgr)*
Andrew Moore *(Sr Mgr)*
Tracey Webb *(Principal-Audit)*
Clint Mock *(Partner-Audit)*
Jason Sammons *(Head-Natl Process, Risk & Governance Practice)*

Frazier & Deeter, LLC—(Continued)

Bryce Nations (Partner)
Monique Quindsland (Partner)
Heather Mullins (Partner)
Kristen Oliver (Mgr)
Matthew Foster (Partner-Tax)
Matt Beacham (Mgr-Pass Through Tax Grp)
Eddie Bradford (Sr Mgr)
Michael Whitacre (Partner-Tax Practice)
Bill Godshall (Partner)
Ronny Greer (Partner)
Gina Gondron (Partner-Process, Risk & Governance Practice)
Jennifer Gruner (Sr Mgr)
Clay Huffman (Sr Mgr)
Keith Longacre (Partner-Process, Risk & Governance Practice)
Paul Dubsky (Principal)
Patricia Lee (Sr Mgr)
Mindy Regen (Sr Mgr)
Steven Massey (Sr Mgr-Audit)
Scott Melton (Sr Mgr-Assurance & Advisory Svcs)
Ashley Babinchak (Partner-Audit Practice)
Robert Soares (Partner-Audit Practice)
Sasan Zamani (Mng Partner-Nashville)
Ross Burden (Sr Mgr-Audit)
Tim Koch (Mng Partner-Charlotte)
Devin Wayne (Mgr-PRG-Nashville)
Sumit Anand (Mgr-Tax-Nashville)
Michael Truscott (Principal-Tax Dept)
James Dawson (Partner-Tax)
Brian Dermott (Principal-Transaction Advisory Svcs Grp-Charlotte)
Chase Gund (Mgr-Transaction Advisory Svcs Grp-Charlotte)
Rasheedah Luqman (Mgr-Diversity, Equity & Inclusion)
Dave Kim (Partner-Intl Tax)
John Hightower (Chief Strategy Officer)
Shawn Fowler (CFO)
Jeremy Sperring (COO)
Sheila R. Anderson (Principal-Credits & Incentives Tax-Tax Practice)
Josh Haxel (Partner-Process, Risk & Governance Practice)
Biju Samuel (CIO)
Chris Etheridge (Mng Partner-Alpharetta)

Subsidiaries:

Frazier & Deeter, LLC - Tampa Office   (1)
2801 W Busch Blvd Ste 200, Tampa, FL 33618
Tel.: (813) 874-1280
Web Site: http://www.frazierdeeter.com
Emp.: 18
Accounting, Tax Preparation & Consultancy Services
N.A.I.C.S.: 541211
Robert Soares (Sr Mgr-Acctg & Auditing Svcs)
Jeffrey Bauman (Sr Mgr-Acctg & Auditing Svcs)
Loribel Jacobs (Sr Mgr-Tax)
Heather L. Brown (Mgr-Acctg & Auditing Svcs)
Neil R. Winter (Partner)
Jackie Ramirez (Mgr-Tax)
Mike Hendricks (Mng Partner)
Patrick Crouch (Sr Mgr-Audit)
Jerry Johnson (Principal-Audit Practice)

FRAZIER & FRAZIER INDUSTRIES
817 S 1st St, Coolidge, TX 76635
Tel.: (254) 786-2293
Web Site: https://www.ffcastings.com
Rev.: $11,800,000
Emp.: 300

Iron Foundry
N.A.I.C.S.: 331511
Charles W. Frazier Jr. (Pres)

FRAZIER INDUSTRIAL COMPANY INC.
91 Fairview Ave, Long Valley, NJ 07853-3176
Tel.: (908) 876-3001
Web Site: https://www.frazier.com
Year Founded: 1949
Sales Range: $10-24.9 Million
Emp.: 100
Office & Store Partitions & Fixtures
N.A.I.C.S.: 337126
Carlos Oliver (Pres)

FRAZIER MANAGEMENT, LLC
2 Union Square 601 Union St Ste 3200, Seattle, WA 98101
Tel.: (206) 621-7200
Web Site: http://www.frazierhealthcare.com
Year Founded: 1991
Private Equity Firm
N.A.I.C.S.: 523940
Alan Frazier (Chm)
Nader Naini (Mng Partner)

Subsidiaries:

BioMatrix Specialty Pharmacy, LLC   (1)
855 SW 78th Ave Ste C200, Plantation, FL 33324
Web Site: http://www.biomatrixsprx.com
Sales Range: $1-9.9 Million
Emp.: 500
Specialty Pharmacy Services
N.A.I.C.S.: 456110
Ted Kramm (CEO)
Kathee Kramm (Pres)
Nick Karalis (Chm)
Tara Marchese (Sr Dir-Mktg)

FRC HOLDING CORP.
129 Rawls Rd, Des Plaines, IL 60018
Tel.: (847) 390-6200
Web Site: http://www.finzerroller.com
Year Founded: 1968
Sales Range: $25-49.9 Million
Emp.: 100
Holding Company; Fabricated Rubber Products
N.A.I.C.S.: 326299

FRCH DESIGN WORLDWIDE
311 Elm St Ste 600, Cincinnati, OH 45202
Tel.: (513) 241-3000
Web Site: http://www.frch.com
Emp.: 250
Brand Strategy, Graphic Design, Interior Design & Architectural Services
N.A.I.C.S.: 541810
James R. Tippmann (CEO & Partner)
Paul Lechleiter (Chief Creative Officer & Partner)
Thomas Horwitz (Partner & Exec VP)
James Stapleton (Principal & Sr VP)
Jim Harkin (Principal & Sr VP)
Randy Ng (Principal & Sr VP)
Monica Gerhardt (Principal & Sr VP)
Rob Depp (Principal & Sr VP)
Shane Kavanagh (Principal & Sr VP)
Jonathan Schaefer (Coord-Project)
Luke Munz (Project Coord-Dept Stores Studio)
Donna Szarwark (Sr VP-HR)
Kristi Ward (Sr VP-Fin)

FRED A. MORETON & COMPANY
709 E S Temple, Salt Lake City, UT 84102
Tel.: (801) 531-1234
Web Site: http://www.moreton.com
Rev.: $12,500,000

Emp.: 100
Insurance Agents
N.A.I.C.S.: 524210
William R. Moreton (Pres)

FRED ALLEN ENTERPRISES INC.
5855 Carson St, Lakewood, CA 90713
Tel.: (562) 497-0370
Rev.: $28,100,000
Emp.: 20
Tires & Tubes
N.A.I.C.S.: 423130
Fred Allen (Pres)
Patrick Tucker (District Mgr)
Keith Gurnard (CFO)

FRED B. JOHNSTON COMPANY, INC.
300 E Boundary St, Chapin, SC 29036-9416
Tel.: (803) 345-5481
Year Founded: 1928
Rev.: $24,000,000
Emp.: 100
Commercial Graphics & Industrial Printing Services
N.A.I.C.S.: 323111
Phil Farchione (CEO & VP)
Jeff Cain (CFO & VP-Fin)

Subsidiaries:

F.B. Johnston Graphics   (1)
300 E Boundary St, Chapin, SC 29036-9416   (100%)
Tel.: (803) 345-5481
Web Site: http://www.fbjohnston.com
Sales Range: $25-49.9 Million
Nameplates, Overlays & Labels For OEMs
N.A.I.C.S.: 323111

FRED BEANS CHEVROLET, INCORPORATED
845 N Easton Rd, Doylestown, PA 18902
Tel.: (215) 348-3586
Web Site: https://www.fredbeanschevrolet.com
Sales Range: $10-24.9 Million
Emp.: 55
Car Whslr
N.A.I.C.S.: 441110
Steve Mihalik (Mgr-Svc)

FRED BEANS FORD OF BOYERTOWN
Rte 100 N, Boyertown, PA 19512
Tel.: (610) 367-2081
Web Site: http://www.fredbeans.com
Sales Range: $25-49.9 Million
Emp.: 80
Automobiles, New & Used
N.A.I.C.S.: 441110
Dennis B. Malloy (Pres)
Christine Halterman (Controller)
Chad Baker (Mgr-Sls)
Ian Kreiner (Mgr-Used Car)

FRED BEANS LINCOLN MERCURY
876 N Easton Rd, Doylestown, PA 18902
Tel.: (215) 348-2900
Web Site: http://www.fredbeans.com
Sales Range: $75-99.9 Million
Emp.: 100
Automobiles, New & Used
N.A.I.C.S.: 441110
Fred W. Beans (Pres)
Beth Beans Gilbert (VP)

FRED BERGLUND & SONS INC.
8410 S Chicago Ave, Chicago, IL 60617

Tel.: (773) 374-1000
Web Site: https://www.berglundco.com
Sales Range: $100-124.9 Million
Emp.: 375
Commercial & Office Building, New Construction
N.A.I.C.S.: 236220
Fred Berglund (Pres)

FRED BORMAN ENTERPRISES, INC.
3130 S Horner Blvd, Sanford, NC 27332
Tel.: (919) 774-8864
Web Site: http://www.sanfordhonda.com
New & Used Car Dealers
N.A.I.C.S.: 441110
David Marsh (Owner)
Stacey Cheek (Gen Mgr)

FRED C. CHURCH INC.
41 Wellman St, Lowell, MA 01851
Tel.: (978) 458-1865
Web Site: https://www.fredcchurch.com
Year Founded: 1865
Sales Range: $10-24.9 Million
Emp.: 100
Insurance Services
N.A.I.C.S.: 524210
Patricia E. MacKay (Mgr-Comml Lines & VP)
Chris Duble (CEO & Acct Exec-Comml)
Peter F. Quinlan (Sr VP & Acct Exec-Comml)
Michael S. Reilly (Exec VP, Mgr-Employee Benefits & Acct Exec)
John C. Reilly (Exec VP, Mgr-Employee Benefits & Acct Exec)

FRED C. HOLMES LUMBER COMPANY
211 W Elm St, Fort Bragg, CA 95437
Tel.: (707) 964-6377
Sales Range: $10-24.9 Million
Emp.: 8
Wholesale Lumber
N.A.I.C.S.: 423310
Steven Holmes (VP)
Vicki Johnson (Controller)

FRED CARL'S NEW SALEM SAAB
2017 Central Ave, Albany, NY 12205
Tel.: (518) 862-2795
Web Site: http://www.newsalemsaab.com
Sales Range: $10-24.9 Million
Emp.: 45
Automobiles, New & Used
N.A.I.C.S.: 441110
Darryl Carl (Owner & Pres)

FRED CHRISTEN & SONS COMPANY
714 George St, Toledo, OH 43608
Tel.: (419) 243-4161
Year Founded: 1897
Sales Range: $10-24.9 Million
Emp.: 350
Roofing Contractors
N.A.I.C.S.: 238160
M. P. Christen (Treas & Sec)
Fredrick R. Christen (Pres & CEO)

FRED FINCH YOUTH CENTER
3800 Coolidge Ave, Oakland, CA 94602-3311
Tel.: (510) 482-2244
Web Site: https://www.fredfinch.org
Year Founded: 1891
Sales Range: $25-49.9 Million
Emp.: 481

Youth & Family Support Services
N.A.I.C.S.: 624190
Thomas N. Alexander *(Pres & CEO)*
Leah Jones *(Dir-Dev & Comm)*
Ed Hsu *(CFO)*
Timothy Trickett-Robles *(Sr Dir-Admin)*

FRED FORD MARTIN INC.
4701 Mahoning Ave, Youngstown, OH 44515
Tel.: (330) 793-2444
Web Site:
   http://www.fredmartinonline.com
Sales Range: $10-24.9 Million
Emp.: 55
Car Whslr
N.A.I.C.S.: 441110
Fred Martin *(Pres)*

FRED FREDERICKS CHRYSLER
39 Washington Blvd S, Laurel, MD 20707
Tel.: (301) 776-7373
Web Site:
   http://www.fredfrederick.com
Sales Range: $25-49.9 Million
Emp.: 32
Sell New & Used Cars
N.A.I.C.S.: 441110
Cindy Fredrick *(Controller)*
Sylvester G. Fredericks Jr. *(Pres)*

FRED GARRISON OIL COMPANY
1107 Walter Griffin St, Plainview, TX 79072-5401
Tel.: (806) 296-6353
Web Site: http://www.allstarfuel.com
Year Founded: 1954
Sales Range: $10-24.9 Million
Emp.: 48
Provider of Petroleum Products
N.A.I.C.S.: 424720
Gary Garrison *(Pres)*
Lorry Phoebe *(Controller)*

FRED GELLER ELECTRICAL, INC.
3732 55th St, Woodside, NY 11377-2436
Tel.: (718) 350-3900
Sales Range: $25-49.9 Million
Emp.: 300
General Electrical Contractor
N.A.I.C.S.: 238210
Oleg J. Samilenko *(Pres)*
Stanley Kleinberg *(Controller)*
Alex Samilenko *(Pres)*

FRED JONES ENTERPRISES
900 W Main St, Oklahoma City, OK 73106
Tel.: (405) 272-9261
Web Site: http://www.fred-jones.com
Rev.: $120,000,000
Emp.: 50
Motor Vehicle Parts & Accessories
N.A.I.C.S.: 336390
Scott Weaver *(Pres & CEO)*
Gerald Barnett *(Gen Mgr)*
Brent Worcester *(Mgr-Sls)*

FRED JONES ENTERPRISES, INC.
123 S Hudson St, Oklahoma City, OK 73102
Tel.: (405) 232-2400
Web Site: http://www.fred-jones.com
Sales Range: $10-24.9 Million
Emp.: 50
New Car Whslr
N.A.I.C.S.: 441110
Carrie Kniffing *(Dir-HR)*

FRED LOYA INSURANCE AGENCY
1800 Lee Trevino 101, El Paso, TX 79936
Tel.: (915) 590-5692
Web Site: http://www.fredloya.com
Year Founded: 1974
Rev.: $17,500,000
Emp.: 50
Insurance Agents, Brokers & Service
N.A.I.C.S.: 524210
Jeff Curl *(Mgr-Fin & Acctg)*
Sivi Contreras *(Mgr-HR)*

FRED M. STARLING, INC.
5969 Cattleridge Blvd Ste 200, Sarasota, FL 34232
Tel.: (941) 378-3811   FL
Web Site: https://www.starling-group.com
Year Founded: 1981
Sales Range: $1-9.9 Million
Emp.: 12
Commercial & Institutional Building Construction
N.A.I.C.S.: 236220
Fred M. Starling *(Owner)*

FRED MARTIN NISSAN LLC.
3388 S Arlington Rd, Akron, OH 44312-5257
Tel.: (330) 644-8888
Web Site:
   http://www.fredmartinnissan.com
Sales Range: $10-24.9 Million
Emp.: 45
Car Whslr
N.A.I.C.S.: 441110
Jess Pennell *(Gen Mgr)*

FRED MARTIN SUPERSTORE
3195 Barber Rd, Norton, OH 44203
Tel.: (330) 877-7777
Web Site:
   http://www.fredmartinsuperstore.com
Sales Range: $25-49.9 Million
Emp.: 40
New Car Retailer
N.A.I.C.S.: 441110
Adam Huff *(Pres)*
Tom Dunn *(Gen Mgr)*
William Huff *(Treas)*

FRED MCGILVRAY INC.
8690 NW 58th St, Miami, FL 33166
Tel.: (561) 471-3349
Web Site:
   http://www.fredmcgilvrayinc-wpb.com
Rev.: $40,715,870
Emp.: 133
Plumbing, Heating & Air-Conditioning Services
N.A.I.C.S.: 238220
Fred McGilvray *(CEO)*

FRED MUELLER AUTOMOTIVE, INC.
448 Grand Ave, Schofield, WI 54476
Tel.: (715) 359-5544
Web Site:
   http://www.fredmuelleauto.com
Year Founded: 1981
Sales Range: $10-24.9 Million
Emp.: 45
Car Whslr
N.A.I.C.S.: 441110
Fred Mueller *(Pres)*

FRED NACKARD WHOLESALE LIQUOR CO.
5660 E Penstock Ave, Flagstaff, AZ 86004
Tel.: (928) 526-2229
Web Site:
   http://www.nackardcompanies.com

Sales Range: $25-49.9 Million
Emp.: 39
Liquor Distr
N.A.I.C.S.: 424820
Patrick M. Nackard *(Pres)*

FRED OLIVIERI CONSTRUCTION CO.
6315 Promway Ave NW, North Canton, OH 44720
Tel.: (330) 494-1007
Web Site:
   https://www.fredolivieri.com
Year Founded: 1959
Sales Range: $10-24.9 Million
Emp.: 160
Commercial & Institutional Building Construction Services
N.A.I.C.S.: 236220
Dean L. Olivieri *(Pres)*
Alfred A. Olivieri *(CEO)*

FRED SMITH COMPANY
400 Riverwood Dr, Clayton, NC 27527-5500
Tel.: (919) 550-8086
Web Site:
   https://www.fredsmithcompany.com
Year Founded: 1986
Sales Range: $25-49.9 Million
Emp.: 150
Civil Engineering Services
N.A.I.C.S.: 237310
Fred J. Smith Jr. *(Pres)*

FRED TAYLOR COMPANY INC.
2700 Palmyra Rd, Albany, GA 31706
Tel.: (229) 883-5200
Web Site:
   https://www.fredtaylorcompany.com
Sales Range: $75-99.9 Million
Emp.: 3
Trucking Service
N.A.I.C.S.: 532120
James F. Taylor *(Chm)*

FRED TEITELBAUM CONSTRUCTION CO. INC.
5526 N Kedzie Ave, Chicago, IL 60625-3924
Tel.: (773) 267-7676   IL
Year Founded: 1953
Sales Range: $10-24.9 Million
Emp.: 27
Provider of Construction Services
N.A.I.C.S.: 236117
Harvey Teitelbaum *(Pres & Treas)*
Edgar Gettleman *(Exec VP)*
Joel Gettleman *(VP)*

Subsidiaries:

Teitelbaum Concrete   (1)
1721 NW 22nd Ct, Pompano Beach, FL
33069-1323   (100%)
Tel.: (954) 971-1700
Provider of Construction Services
N.A.I.C.S.: 236117

FRED USINGER, INC.
1030 N Dr Martin Luther King Jr Dr, Milwaukee, WI 53203-1302
Tel.: (414) 276-9100   WI
Web Site: https://www.usinger.com
Year Founded: 1880
Sales Range: $100-124.9 Million
Emp.: 200
Sausages Mfr
N.A.I.C.S.: 311612
Jon Gabe *(VP-Sls)*
Kathy Troc *(Controller)*
Fritz Usinger IV *(Pres)*

FRED V. FOWLER COMPANY, INC.
66 Rowe St, Newton, MA 02466-1530
Tel.: (617) 332-7004   MA

Web Site:
   http://www.fowlerprecision.com
Year Founded: 1946
Sales Range: $10-24.9 Million
Emp.: 50
Mechanical & Electronic Precision Measuring Tools for the Metal Working Industry Whslr & Distr
N.A.I.C.S.: 423830
David Francis *(Pres & CEO)*

FRED WEBER, INC.
2320 Creve Coeur Mill Rd, Maryland Heights, MO 63043-8501
Tel.: (314) 344-0070   DE
Web Site:
   http://www.fredweberinc.com
Year Founded: 1928
Sales Range: $200-249.9 Million
Emp.: 700
Construction Products & Services
N.A.I.C.S.: 237990
Wendy C. Alexander *(Sr VP-Fin Mgmt)*
Douglas K. Weible *(Chm & CEO)*
Dale C. Hoette *(Pres & CFO)*
Phillip C. Hagemann *(CIO)*
Deborah A. Puyear *(Treas & VP-Corp Svcs)*
Julie L. Shields *(Sec & Sr VP-HR)*
Paul E. Robinson *(VP-Ops)*
Roger L. Gagliano *(COO & Pres-Ops)*
Konn E. Wilson *(Pres-Bus Dev)*
Dale Lickenbrock *(VP-Safety & Health)*
Tom Bindbeutel *(VP-Asphalt Ops)*

Subsidiaries:

Millstone Weber, LLC   (1)
601 Fountain Lakes Blvd, Saint Charles, MO 63301-4347
Tel.: (636) 949-0038
Web Site: http://www.millstoneweber.com
Sales Range: $25-49.9 Million
Emp.: 200
Highway & Street Construction Services
N.A.I.C.S.: 237310
Thomas Kuhn *(Pres)*
Chris Gottman *(Sr VP-Construction)*

FREDDIE MAC INC
8200 Jones Branch Dr, McLean, VA 22102-3110
Tel.: (703) 903-2000
Web Site:
   https://www.freddiemac.com
Year Founded: 1970
Financial Services
N.A.I.C.S.: 522310

FREDE, NORMAN CHEVROLET
16801 Feathercraft, Houston, TX 77058-2693
Tel.: (281) 486-2206
Web Site:
   https://www.fredechevrolet.com
Year Founded: 1968
Sales Range: $25-49.9 Million
Emp.: 95
Car Whslr
N.A.I.C.S.: 441110
Joan McKinney *(Gen Mgr)*

FREDERICK CHEVROLET INC.
275 N Walnut St, Slatington, PA 18080
Tel.: (610) 767-1181
Sales Range: $10-24.9 Million
Emp.: 30
Automobiles; New & Used
N.A.I.C.S.: 441110
Richard Rentschler *(Pres)*

FREDERICK COOPER LLC
516 Paul St, Rocky Mount, NC 27803

Frederick Cooper LLC—(Continued)
Tel.: (252) 446-2192
Web Site:
   https://www.frederickcooper.com
Year Founded: 1923
Sales Range: $10-24.9 Million
Emp.: 20
Mfr of Table Lamps
N.A.I.C.S.: 335131

**FREDERICK DERR & COM-
PANY INCORPORATED**
3801 N Orange Ave, Sarasota, FL
34234
Tel.: (941) 355-8575
Web Site:
   http://www.frederickderrcom
   pany.com
Year Founded: 1961
Sales Range: $10-24.9 Million
Emp.: 110
Highway Construction, Site Develop-
ment & Utility Installation
N.A.I.C.S.: 237310
Frederick M. Derr (Chm & CEO)
Keith A. Ravazzoli (Pres & COO)
Roland Carter (Project Mgr)
Raymond L. Rogers (Project Mgr)
Tom Ruth (Controller)
Gemma Fulton (Asst Controller)
Rex Jensen (Pres)

**FREDERICK FELL PUBLISH-
ERS, INC.**
2131 Hollywood Blvd Ste 305, Holly-
wood, FL 33020
Tel.: (954) 925-5242
Web Site: http://www.fellpub.com
Year Founded: 1943
Sales Range: $1-9.9 Million
Emp.: 42
Book Publishers
N.A.I.C.S.: 513130
Donald L. Lessne (Publr)

FREDERICK GOLDMAN INC.
154 W 14th St, New York, NY 10011-
7307
Tel.: (212) 924-6767
Web Site: http://b2b.fgoldman.com
Sales Range: $10-24.9 Million
Emp.: 150
Fine & Bridal Jewelry Mfr
N.A.I.C.S.: 339910

FREDERICK LIVING
2849 Big Rd, Zieglerville, PA 19492
Tel.: (610) 754-7878
Web Site:
   https://www.frederickliving.org
Year Founded: 1896
Sales Range: $10-24.9 Million
Emp.: 393
Continuing Care Retirement Commu-
nity Operator
N.A.I.C.S.: 623311
Brian Fallon (VP-Fin Svcs)
Brad Mellon (Dir-Advancement &
Pastoral Care)
Marlon Back (Dir-Plant Ops)
Vicki Kriczky (Dir-Mktg)
Susan Reitsma (Mgr-Community
Rels)
Robert Bricker (Chm)
John Hendrickson (CEO)
Matthew Giannini (VP-Ops)

**FREDERICK MEISWINKEL,
INC.**
850 S Van Ness Ave # 18, San Fran-
cisco, CA 94110-1911
Tel.: (415) 550-0400
Year Founded: 1945
Sales Range: $10-24.9 Million
Emp.: 183

Plastering, Drywall & Insulation Services
N.A.I.C.S.: 238310

**FREDERICK MEMORIAL HOS-
PITAL, INC.**
400 W 7th St, Frederick, MD 21701
Tel.: (240) 566-3300
Web Site: http://www.fmh.org
Year Founded: 1897
Emp.: 3,300
Health Care Srvices
N.A.I.C.S.: 622110
Anne-Herbert Rollins (Chm)

FREDERICK MOTOR CO.
1 Waverley Dr, Frederick, MD 21702
Tel.: (301) 663-6111
Web Site:
   http://www.frederickmotor.com
Sales Range: $25-49.9 Million
Emp.: 100
Automobiles, New & Used
N.A.I.C.S.: 441110
John C. Warfield (CEO)
Quick Lane (Mgr-Quicklane)

FREDERICK P. WINNER, LTD.
10000 Franklin Square Dr, Notting-
ham, MD 21236
Tel.: (410) 646-5500
Web Site:
   http://www.indigowinegroup.com
Year Founded: 1960
Sales Range: $25-49.9 Million
Emp.: 300
Beer, Wine & Spirits Distr
N.A.I.C.S.: 424810
Ron Ward (CFO)
G. L. Fronk (Mgr-Pershing Div)

**FREDERICK SUPERMARKET
OF CARS**
1505 Quentin Rd, Lebanon, PA
17042
Tel.: (717) 274-1461
Web Site:
   http://www.fredericktoyota.com
Sales Range: $50-74.9 Million
Emp.: 300
Sales of New & Used Automobiles
N.A.I.C.S.: 441110
Frederick Laurenzo (Pres)

FREDERICK-THOMPSON CO.
26600 Van Born Rd, Detroit, MI
48210
Tel.: (313) 295-0502
Web Site: http://www.loadfti.com
Rev.: $37,500,000
Emp.: 75
Trucking Service
N.A.I.C.S.: 484121

**FREDERICKS FUEL & HEAT-
ING SERVICE**
225 Oak Rdg Rd, Oak Ridge, NJ
07438
Tel.: (973) 697-4774
Web Site:
   http://www.fredericksfuel.com
Sales Range: $10-24.9 Million
Emp.: 45
Fuel Oil Dealers
N.A.I.C.S.: 457210
Mark J. Fredericks (Pres & CEO)

**FREDERICKSBURG FARMERS
COOP**
110 N Jefferson St, Fredericksburg,
IA 50630
Tel.: (563) 237-5324
Web Site: http://www.fburgcoop.com
Year Founded: 1919
Sales Range: $25-49.9 Million
Emp.: 40

Mfr of Grains
N.A.I.C.S.: 424510
Jim Erickson (Gen Mgr)
Pam Williams (Controller)
Chris Hagedorn (Pres)
Ron Cruise (Mgr-Agronomy)
Roger DeSloover (VP)

**FREDMAN BROS. FURNITURE
COMPANY INC.**
8226 Lackland Rd, Saint Louis, MO
63114-4509
Tel.: (314) 426-3999
Year Founded: 1915
Sales Range: $50-74.9 Million
Emp.: 342
Mfr & Sales of Metal Household Fur-
niture
N.A.I.C.S.: 337126
Yos Fredman (Chm)
Zev Fredman (CFO)

FREDRIC'S CORPORATION
7664 Voice of America Centre Dr,
West Chester, OH 45069
Tel.: (513) 874-2226
Sales Range: $25-49.9 Million
Emp.: 154
Toilet Product Mfr
N.A.I.C.S.: 325620
Frederic J. Holzberger (Pres)

**FREDRICK RAMOND INCOR-
PORATED**
12600 Berea Rd, Cleveland, OH
44111
Web Site:
   http://www.fredrickramond.com
Sales Range: $10-24.9 Million
Emp.: 148
Residential Lighting Fixtures
N.A.I.C.S.: 335131
Fredrick Ramond Glassman (Pres)

FREE ENTERPRISES INC.
241 S State Rd, Medina, OH 44256-
2430
Tel.: (330) 722-2031
Web Site:
   https://www.freeenterprisesinc.com
Rev.: $25,200,000
Emp.: 74
Distributes Petroleum Products
N.A.I.C.S.: 424720
Tonia Fisher (Owner)
Paula Hudak (Dir-Retail Ops)
James H. Patneau Jr. (VP)

FREE FOR ALL, INC.
921 Pleasant Vly Ave Ste 100, Mount
Laurel, NJ 08054
Tel.: (856) 652-2249
Web Site:
   http://www.freeforallinc.com
Year Founded: 2009
Sales Range: $1-9.9 Million
Emp.: 20
Prescription Discount Services
N.A.I.C.S.: 524114
Eric Shugarts (Co-Founder & CIO)

**FREE SERVICE TIRE COM-
PANY, INC.**
183 Lynn Rd, Johnson City, TN
37604
Tel.: (423) 979-2250
Web Site:
   http://www.freeservicetire.com
Year Founded: 1919
Sales Range: $75-99.9 Million
Emp.: 195
Tires & Automotive Services
N.A.I.C.S.: 811198
Harrison Wexler (Owner)
Ron Jones (VP-Comml)

Matthew Wilhjelm (VP-Fin & Corp
Admin)
Lewis P. Wexler Jr. (Pres)

FREEBAIRN & CO.
3475 Lenox Rd Ste 900, Atlanta, GA
30326
Tel.: (404) 237-9945
Web Site: http://www.freebairn.com
Year Founded: 1980
Rev.: $17,000,000
Emp.: 17
Advertising Agency
N.A.I.C.S.: 541810
John C. Freebairn (Pres)
Toni Cooper (CFO & Sr VP)
Sandy Chapman (Dir-Media)
Jean G. Cobb (Mgmt Supvr)
Don Patton (Sr Dir-Art)
Mack Kirkpatrick (Dir-Creative)
Jay Hatfield (Sr Dir-Art)
Milo Ippolito (Mgr-Pub Rel)

Subsidiaries:

Freebairn & Company Public
Relations   (1)
3475 Lenox Rd Ste 900, Atlanta, GA 30326
Tel.: (404) 237-9945
Web Site: http://www.freebairn.com
Public Relations Agency
N.A.I.C.S.: 541820
John C. Freebairn (Pres)
Jean G. Cobb (Mgmt Supvr)
Jay Tillinghast (Acct Exec-PR)
Mack Kirkpatrick (Dir-Creative)
Sandy Chapman (Dir-Media)
Milo Ippolito (Mgr-PR)
Don Patton (Sr Dir-Art)

**FREEBORN COUNTY CO-OP
OIL CO.**
1840 Margaretha Ave, Albert Lea, MN
56007
Tel.: (507) 373-3991
Sales Range: $10-24.9 Million
Emp.: 20
Petroleum Bulk Stations & Terminals
N.A.I.C.S.: 424710
Kevin Kiser (Gen Mgr)
Amanda Huper (Office Mgr)

FREECAST, INC.
6901 TPC Dr Ste 100, Orlando, FL
32822
Tel.: (407) 374-1607
Web Site: https://www.freecast.com
Year Founded: 2011
Rev.: $269,791
Assets: $85,584
Liabilities: $3,470,463
Net Worth: ($3,384,879)
Earnings: ($1,085,834)
Emp.: 9
Fiscal Year-end: 12/31/19
Media Streaming Services
N.A.I.C.S.: 512120
Christopher M. Savine (CFO)
Tracy J. West (Exec VP-Digital Con-
tent & Channel Distribution)
Irwin Podhajser (Exec VP-Media &
Network Partnerships)
Gary Engel (CMO)
Erik Genrich (Chief Revenue Officer)
Jonathan Morris (CFO)
William A. Mobley Jr. (Founder, Chm
& CEO)

FREED ADVERTISING
1650 Hwy 6 Ste 400, Sugar Land, TX
77478
Tel.: (281) 240-4949
Web Site:
   http://www.freedadvertising.com
Year Founded: 1984
Rev.: $21,000,000
Emp.: 30
Advertising Agency
N.A.I.C.S.: 541810

Gerald Freed (Founder & CEO)
Dallas Baker (VP & Exec Dir-Creative)

FREED, TELLER & FREED'S
436 N Canal St Ste 2, South San Francisco, CA 94080-4668
Tel.: (650) 589-8500
Web Site:
http://www.freedscoffeetea.com
Year Founded: 1899
Sales Range: $10-24.9 Million
Emp.: 25
Coffee & Tea Mfr
N.A.I.C.S.: 311920
August Techeira (CEO)

FREEDMAN OFFICE FURNITURE, LLC
5035 W Hillsborough Ave, Tampa, FL 33634
Tel.: (813) 875-7775
Web Site:
http://www.freedmansonline.com
Year Founded: 1980
Sales Range: $1-9.9 Million
Emp.: 37
Office Furniture Retailer & Mfr; Office Supplies
N.A.I.C.S.: 449110
Steven D. Freedman (Owner & CEO)
Harold Freedman (VP-Pur)
Mel Keller (Mgr-Ops)
Chuck Kretchman (Controller)

FREEDMAN, GIBSON & WHITE INC.
100 E Business Way Ste 300, Cincinnati, OH 45241
Tel.: (513) 241-3900   OH
Year Founded: 1959
Rev.: $50,000,000
Emp.: 40
Advetising Agency
N.A.I.C.S.: 541810
Adam Powell (Founder)
Irene Warner (Founder & CEO)
Steve Driskill (Founder)

Subsidiaries:

Focus FGW   (1)
100 E-Business Way Ste 300, Cincinnati, OH 45241
Tel.: (513) 241-3900
Emp.: 5
Fiscal Year-end: 12/31/2004
N.A.I.C.S.: 541810
Harold Mann (Sr VP & Customer Relationship Mktg Mgr)
Katie Dickens (Acct Exec)
John Beard (Sr VP)

FREEDOM + PARTNERS
20 Jay St Ste 830, Brooklyn, NY 11201
Tel.: (646) 915-4293
Sales Range: $100-124.9 Million
Emp.: 15
Advetising Agency
N.A.I.C.S.: 541810
Mark Ferdman (Founder & CEO)

FREEDOM 3 CAPITAL, LLC
12 E 49th St 27th Floor Tower 49, New York, NY 10017
Tel.: (212) 235-2160   DE
Web Site: http://freedom3.com
Privater Equity Firm
N.A.I.C.S.: 523999
Jason Block (Partenr & CIO)
Daniel Tamkin (Partner & COO)
Erik Glover (Partner)
Fred Buffone (Partner)

Subsidiaries:

Alaska Communications Systems Group, Inc.   (1)

600 E 36th Ave, Anchorage, AK 99503-6091
Tel.: (907) 297-3000
Web Site:
http://www.alaskacommunications.com
Rev.: $240,569,000
Assets: $569,432,000
Liabilities: $403,513,000
Net Worth: $165,919,000
Earnings: ($1,073,000)
Emp.: 564
Fiscal Year-end: 12/31/2020
Telecommunications & Internet Services
N.A.I.C.S.: 517121
Leonard A. Steinberg (Sr VP-Legal, Regulatory & Govt Affairs)
Laurie Butcher (CFO)
William H. Bishop (Pres & CEO)
Diedre Williams (Sr VP-Ops)
Tiffany Hoogerhyde (VP-Fin & Controller)
Sandy Knechtel (COO)
Heather Marron (Mgr-Corp Comm)
Matthew McConnell (CEO)
Michael Prior (Chm)

Subsidiary (Domestic):

ACS Internet, Inc.   (2)
600 Telephone Ave, Anchorage, AK 99503
Tel.: (907) 565-2200
Sales Range: $100-124.9 Million
Provider of Computer Communications: Internet
N.A.I.C.S.: 517810

ACS Long Distance License Sub, Inc.   (2)
600 Telephone Ave, Anchorage, AK 99503
Tel.: (907) 297-3000
Sales Range: $400-449.9 Million
Telephone Communications
N.A.I.C.S.: 517121
Anand Vadapalli (Pres & CEO)
Anand Vadapalli (Pres & CEO)

Alaska Communications Systems Holdings, Inc.   (2)
600 Telephone Ave, Anchorage, AK 99503
Tel.: (907) 297-3000
Telecommunication Services Provider
N.A.I.C.S.: 517121

TekMate, LLC   (2)
600 E 36th Ave, Anchorage, AK 99503
Tel.: (907) 297-3000
Web Site:
https://www.alaskacommunications.com
Sales Range: $1-9.9 Million
Emp.: 60
Information Technology Services
N.A.I.C.S.: 541512
Shawn Fuller (Pres & VP-Bus Dev)

FREEDOM BANK OF AMERICA
1200 4th St N, Saint Petersburg, FL 33701
Tel.: (727) 820-8600
Web Site:
http://www.freedombank.com
Year Founded: 2005
Sales Range: $1-9.9 Million
Emp.: 30
Banking Services
N.A.I.C.S.: 522110
G. Andrew Williams (Vice Chm)
Cathy Swanson (CEO)
Susan L. Blackburn (Pres & COO)
William B. McQueen (Vice Chm)
Neil W. Savage (Chm)
Adam M. Curtis (Exec VP)
Corey E. McLaughlin (VP)
Tim D. Stark (Mgr-Credit Admin)
M. Catherine Schrader (Asst VP & Mgr-Retail)
Debra L. Coleman (Sr VP & Mgr-Treasury Svcs)

FREEDOM CONSULTING GROUP LLC
9881 Broken Land Pkwy Ste 300, Columbia, MD 21046
Tel.: (410) 290-9035

Web Site:
http://www.freedomconsultinggroup.com
Year Founded: 2004
Sales Range: $1-9.9 Million
Emp.: 92
Information Technology Support Services
N.A.I.C.S.: 541511
Norm Walters (COO)
Scott Beall (CTO)
Vernon Saunders (CEO)
Roger Alan Nichols (Chief Growth Officer)
Grady Lincalis (CFO)

FREEDOM CREDIT UNION
626 Jacksonville Rd Ste 250, Warminster, PA 18974
Tel.: (215) 612-5900
Web Site: http://www.freedomcu.org
Year Founded: 1934
Rev.: $21,075,873
Emp.: 78
Federal Credit Unions
N.A.I.C.S.: 522130
Gina Noblit (Dir-HR)
Charlene Smolkowicz (Mgr-Comml Credit)
Andrew Sullivan (Asst VP-Member Bus Lending)
Glenn Welch (Pres)

FREEDOM FOREVER LLC
43445 Business Park Dr Ste 110, Temecula, CA 92590
Tel.: (951) 727-7800
Web Site:
http://www.freedomforever.com
Year Founded: 2013
Sales Range: $100-124.9 Million
Emp.: 358
Solar Electric Power Generation Services
N.A.I.C.S.: 221114
Brett Bouchy (CEO)
Greg Albright (Pres)
Jessica Mae Sumikawa (Chief Legal Officer & Exec VP)
Lynette Wilkerson (CFO)
Valentina Rozas (VP-Ops)

FREEDOM GRAPHIC SYSTEMS INC.
1101 S Janesville St, Milton, WI 53563-1838
Tel.: (608) 373-6500
Web Site: https://www.fgs.com
Year Founded: 1986
Rev.: $27,000,000
Emp.: 125
Offset Printing Services
N.A.I.C.S.: 323111
Terry Brady (CFO)
Eric Blohm (Pres)
Scott Liebert (Sr VP-Sls & Mktg)

Subsidiaries:

Freedom Imaging Systems Inc.   (1)
780 McClure Rd, Aurora, IL 60502
Tel.: (630) 838-1070
Web Site: http://www.fgs.com
Rev.: $12,000,000
Emp.: 70
Printing & Direct Mail Services
N.A.I.C.S.: 323111

FREEDOM HEALTH INC.
5403 N Church Ave, Tampa, FL 33614
Tel.: (813) 506-6000
Web Site:
http://www.freedomhealth.com
Year Founded: 2004
Sales Range: $150-199.9 Million
Emp.: 231

Insurance Benefits & Medicare Assistance Supplier
N.A.I.C.S.: 524292
Rupesh R. Shah (CEO)
Lucy O'Connor (VP-Ops)
Patel Nikhil (Mgr-Ancillary Contracting)
Dee Avalos (Mgr-Utilization)
Alphons Immanuel (Dir-Info)
Kevin Adhia (VP-Info Sys)
Jigar Desai (CFO)

FREEDOM HOUSE, INC.
1850 M St NW 11th Fl, Washington, DC 20036
Tel.: (202) 296-5101   NY
Web Site:
https://www.freedomhouse.org
Year Founded: 1941
Rev.: $40,180,012
Assets: $9,253,493
Liabilities: $4,543,013
Net Worth: $4,710,480
Emp.: 174
Fiscal Year-end: 06/30/18
Human Rights Organizations
N.A.I.C.S.: 813311
Jane L. Harman (Chm)
Peter Bass (Treas)
Michael J. Abramowitz (Pres)

FREEDOM INFORMATION SYSTEMS, INC.
8331 Madison Blvd Ste 400, Madison, AL 35758
Tel.: (256) 721-6399   AL
Web Site: http://www.freedomis.com
Year Founded: 2003
Sales Range: $25-49.9 Million
Emp.: 41
Information Technology Support & Consulting Services
N.A.I.C.S.: 541690
Mark Ogles (Pres)
Larry Miles (CFO)

FREEDOM INTERNET GROUP, INC.
151 Calle San Francisco Ste 200, San Juan, PR 00901
Tel.: (628) 237-7300   PR
Web Site: https://www.figiroyalty.com
Year Founded: 2018
Rev.: $51,331
Assets: $1,069,170
Liabilities: $14,277
Net Worth: $1,054,893
Earnings: ($409,160)
Fiscal Year-end: 12/31/22
Investment Services
N.A.I.C.S.: 523940
Noah B. Rosenfarb (Chm & CFO)
Ronald G. Rosenfarb (COO & Sec)
Alton Chapman Jr. (Founder & CEO)

FREEDOM LEXINGTON
1560 E New Cir Rd, Lexington, KY 40509-1022
Tel.: (859) 268-3000   KY
Web Site: http://www.freedomlex.com
Year Founded: 1989
Sales Range: $10-24.9 Million
Emp.: 130
New & Used Cars
N.A.I.C.S.: 441110

FREEDOM MANAGEMENT
27122 B Paseo Espada Ste 1024, San Juan Capistrano, CA 92675
Tel.: (949) 489-0430
Sales Range: Less than $1 Million
Emp.: 3
Retirement Hotel Operation
N.A.I.C.S.: 531110
Gresham Roskamp (Partner)
Tom Stringer (Mng Partner)

FREEDOM METALS INC.

Freedom Metals Inc.—(Continued)

1225 S 15th St, Louisville, KY 40210
Tel.: (502) 637-7657
Web Site:
 http://www.freedommetals.com
Year Founded: 1983
Rev.: $58,100,000
Emp.: 130
Scrap & Waste Material Whslr
N.A.I.C.S.: 423930
Bud Webster (Mgr-Buyer)
David Atherton (Gen Mgr)
Spencer Blue (Pres)

FREEDOM MORTGAGE CORPORATION
907 Pleasant Vly Ave Ste 3, Mount Laurel, NJ 08054
Tel.: (856) 231-9800
Web Site:
 http://www.freedommortgage.com
Year Founded: 1990
Sales Range: $350-399.9 Million
Emp.: 1,829
Real Estate Financial Services
N.A.I.C.S.: 522292
Stanley C. Middleman (Chm, Pres & CEO)

Subsidiaries:

J.G. Wentworth Home Lending, LLC   (1)
3350 Commission Ct, Woodbridge, VA 22192   (100%)
Tel.: (703) 643-1002
Web Site: http://www.jgwentworth.com
Mortgage Banker
N.A.I.C.S.: 522310
Phil Buscemi (Pres)
Brandon Nott (Sr VP-Ops)
Van Richardson (VP-Direct Lending)

FREEDOM OIL COMPANY
814 W Chestnut St, Bloomington, IL 61701-2816
Tel.: (309) 828-7750 IL
Web Site:
 https://www.freedomoil.com
Year Founded: 1958
Sales Range: $125-149.9 Million
Emp.: 300
Gasoline Station Services
N.A.I.C.S.: 457120
Judy Melcher (VP)

FREEDOM PARTNERS
2200 Wilson Blvd SE 102-533, Arlington, VA 22201
Tel.: (703) 888-2527 DE
Web Site:
 http://www.freedompartners.org
Year Founded: 2011
Sales Range: $50-74.9 Million
Emp.: 8
Business Associations
N.A.I.C.S.: 813910
Marc Short (Pres)

FREEDOM PLAZA LTD.
13373 N Plaza Del Rio Blvd, Peoria, AZ 85381
Tel.: (623) 972-1776
Web Site:
 http://www.brookdaleliving.com
Year Founded: 1987
Sales Range: $10-24.9 Million
Emp.: 175
Apartment Building Operator
N.A.I.C.S.: 531110
Jai Larman (Exec Dir)

FREEDOM SCIENTIFIC INC.
11800 31st Ct N, Saint Petersburg, FL 33716
Tel.: (727) 803-8000
Web Site:
 http://www.freedomscientific.com

Custom Computer Programming Services
N.A.I.C.S.: 541511
Tom Tiernan (Pres & CEO)

Subsidiaries:

Algorithmic Implementations, Inc. (1)
130 Taconic Business Park, Manchester Center, VT 05255
Tel.: (802) 362-3612
Web Site: http://www.aisquared.net
Rev.: $2,800,000
Emp.: 18
Computer & Software Stores
N.A.I.C.S.: 449210
David Wu (CEO)

Freedom Scientific GmbH (1)
Hi-Tech-Center 2, Taegerwilen, 8274, Switzerland
Tel.: (41) 71 666 77 10
Web Site: http://www.freedomscientific.ch
Custom Computer Programming Services
N.A.I.C.S.: 541511

The Paciello Group, LLC (1)
5 Pine Street Extension #6 Annex Unit 2-F, Nashua, Nashua, NH 03060
Tel.: (603) 882-4122
Web Site: http://www.paciellogroup.com
Management Consulting Services
N.A.I.C.S.: 541618
Matt Ater (VP & Gen Mgr)
Travis Brown (VP-Bus Dev & Professional Svcs)
Steve Faulkner (Dir-Technical)
Leonie Watson (Dir-Comm)

FREEDOM SOLUTIONS GROUP, L.L.C.
550 W Jackson Blvd 200, Chicago, IL 60661
Tel.: (630) 598-1100
Web Site: http://www.litera.com
Rev.: $8,100,000
Emp.: 50
Custom Computer Programming Services
N.A.I.C.S.: 541511
Deepak Massand (CEO)
Norm Thomas (Sr VP-Corp Dev)
Chuck Henrich (Dir-Product Mgmt)
Rich Powers (Partner-Reseller Channel Mgmt & Dir-Sls-Western Reg)
Dawn Hudgins (Dir-Mktg)
Donovan Alexander (Dir-Sls Engrg)
Jeremy Leonard (Gen Counsel & Dir-Bus Affairs)
Jill Goldstein (Dir-Bus Dev)
Joy Heathrush (VP-Client Dev)
Ken Manford (Sr Dir-Sls Engrg)
Nicholas Maviano (Dir-Project Mgmt)
Pradeep Bhaskar Menon (Dir-Bus Dev-India)
Raina Massand (VP-Bus Dev)
Richard Ward (Dir-Client Dev-EMEA)
Simon Dandy (VP-R&D)
Sheryl Hoskins (CEO)

Subsidiaries:

Concep Group Limited (1)
3rd Floor 201 Borough High Street, London, SE1 1JA, United Kingdom
Tel.: (44) 20 7952 5570
Web Site: http://www.concep.com
Email Marketing Software
N.A.I.C.S.: 513210
Daniel Morgan (CEO)

Subsidiary (US):

Concep Inc. (2)
25 Broadway 94, New York, NY 10004
Tel.: (212) 925-0380
Web Site: http://www.concep.com
Emp.: 100
Email Software Publisher
N.A.I.C.S.: 513210
Mark Power (CEO)

Subsidiary (Non-US):

Concep Pty Ltd (2)

Suite 6 02 37 Pitt St, Surry Hills, Sydney, 2000, NSW, Australia
Tel.: (61) 2 8030 8810
Web Site: http://www.concep.com
Emp.: 7
Email Software Publisher
N.A.I.C.S.: 513210
Ralph Koschek (Mng Dir)

DocsCorp Pty. Limited (1)
Level 5 66 Clarence Street, Sydney, 2000, NSW, Australia
Tel.: (61) 1300559451
Web Site: http://www.docscorp.com
Software Development Services
N.A.I.C.S.: 541511

FREEDOM STORES INC.
700 Godwin Ave Ste 210, Midland Park, NJ 07432
Tel.: (201) 447-3723
Web Site:
 http://www.freedom4credit.com
Sales Range: $25-49.9 Million
Emp.: 130
Radio, Television & Electronic Stores
N.A.I.C.S.: 449210
John F. Melley (COO)
Leonard B. Melley Jr. (Pres & CEO)

FREEDOM TECHNOLOGIES, INC.
1100 Wilson Blvd Ste 1200, Arlington, VA 22209
Tel.: (202) 371-2220
Web Site:
 http://www.freedomtechnologies inc.com
Year Founded: 1992
Strategic Consulting Services
N.A.I.C.S.: 541611
Janice I. Obuchowski (Pres)
Fred Wentland (Sr VP)
John Alden (VP)
Mary Greczyn (VP)
Cathy Slesinger (VP)
Albert Halprin (VP)

FREEDOM TRUCK CENTERS INC.
10310 W Westbow Blvd, Spokane, WA 99224
Tel.: (509) 744-0390
Web Site:
 http://www.freedomtruckcenters.com
Sales Range: $25-49.9 Million
Emp.: 80
Truck Parts & Accessories
N.A.I.C.S.: 423120
Jerrad Avery (Gen Mgr)

FREEHOLD CARTAGE INC.
825 Highway 33, Freehold, NJ 07728-8431
Tel.: (732) 462-1001 NJ
Web Site:
 https://www.freeholdcartage.com
Year Founded: 1962
Sales Range: $25-49.9 Million
Emp.: 300
Recycling of Materials
N.A.I.C.S.: 484121
Michelle Fareri (Controller)

FREEHOLD CHRYSLER JEEP
4304 Rte 9 S, Freehold, NJ 07728-8361
Tel.: (732) 410-7404
Web Site:
 https://www.freeholdchryslerjeep.net
Sales Range: $50-74.9 Million
Emp.: 150
Car Dealership
N.A.I.C.S.: 441110
Carmello Giuffre (Co-Owner)
Wally Darwish (Gen Mgr)
Greg Gilley (Gen Mgr-Sls)
Pat Tapke (Mgr-Sls)

Keith Horton (Mgr-Sls)
Sal Hernandez (Mgr-Svc)
Paul Johnson (Mgr-Parts)
Ignazio Giuffre (Co-Owner)

FREEHOLD FORD INC.
3572 Route 9 S, Freehold, NJ 07728
Tel.: (732) 702-0262
Web Site:
 http://www.freeholdford.com
Year Founded: 1986
Sales Range: $10-24.9 Million
Emp.: 70
Car Whslr
N.A.I.C.S.: 441110
John Morotta Sr. (Owner)

FREEHOLD PONTIAC BUICK GMC
4404 Rte 9 & Craig Rd, Freehold, NJ 07728
Tel.: (732) 462-0847
Web Site:
 http://www.freeholdautos.com
Sales Range: $10-24.9 Million
Emp.: 58
Car Whslr
N.A.I.C.S.: 441110
Grace Tonks (Controller-Fin)

FREEHOLD SAVINGS BANK
68 W Main St, Freehold, NJ 07728
Tel.: (732) 462-6700
Web Site: http://www.freeholdsavings bank.com
Year Founded: 1853
Sales Range: $10-24.9 Million
Emp.: 21
Commercial Banking Services
N.A.I.C.S.: 522180
David J. Hage (Pres & CEO)
Maryanne P. Barth (VP-Mortgages)
Thomas Zarycki (COO & Sr VP)
Lawrence J. Metz (Chm)
James H. Wainwright (Pres)
Dwight W. Pittenger (VP)
Michael T. Stocko (CFO, Treas & Sr VP)
Barbara E. Arcoleo (Sec & Asst VP)

FREEHOLD SUBARU-DODGE
299 South St, Freehold, NJ 07728
Tel.: (732) 462-1600
Web Site:
 http://www.freehold dodge.net
Sales Range: $10-24.9 Million
Emp.: 38
Car Whslr
N.A.I.C.S.: 441110
David Butkus (Owner)

FREEHOLD TOYOTA
4268 Route 9 S, Freehold, NJ 07728
Tel.: (732) 431-1300
Web Site:
 https://www.dchfreeholdtoyota.com
Year Founded: 1984
Sales Range: $10-24.9 Million
Emp.: 107
Car Whslr
N.A.I.C.S.: 441110
William Liang (Gen Mgr)

FREEIT DATA SOLUTIONS, INC.,
PO Box 1572, Austin, TX 78767
Web Site: http://www.freeitdata.com
Year Founded: 2009
Sales Range: $1-9.9 Million
Emp.: 10
Data Storage & Management Solutions
N.A.I.C.S.: 334112
Leslie Spinks (Dir-Marketing)

FREELANCE TECHNICAL ASSOCIATES, INC.

207 Fairmont Ave, Fairmont, WV
26554
Tel.: (304) 366-6288   WV
Web Site: https://ftassociatesinc.com
Year Founded: 1995
Rev.: $1,580,000
Emp.: 10
Engineeering Services
N.A.I.C.S.: 541330
Danny L. Bainbridge (Owner & VP)

FREELANCERS CONSUMER OPERATED & ORIENTED PROGRAM OF NEW JERSEY, INC.

570 Broad St Ste 1100, Newark, NJ
07102
Tel.: (732) 887-8269   NJ
Web Site:
  http://www.newjersey.healthre
  public.us
Year Founded: 2011
Sales Range: $10-24.9 Million
Emp.: 41
Health Insurance Services
N.A.I.C.S.: 524114
Arleen Tyndorf (Chief Compliance
Officer)
Catherine Ann Sauner (COO)
Cynthia Jay (CMO)
Ed Remsen (Chm)
Gregory Muller (CIO)

FREELAND MOORE, INC.

4336 Tamiami Trl, Port Charlotte, FL
33980
Tel.: (941) 629-1171
Web Site:
  http://www.harbornissan.com
Sales Range: $10-24.9 Million
Emp.: 50
Car Dealership
N.A.I.C.S.: 441110
Chris Freeland (Owner)
Scott Blomquist (Mgr-Brand)
Bill Smith (Mgr-Parts)
Debbie Clark (Comptroller)
Virginia Freeland-Byrd (Dir-Mktg)
Cody Hansen (Mgr-Fin)
Sonja Worst (Mgr-Fin)
Tom Bishop (Mgr-Gen Sls)
Jeff Cox (Mgr-New Car Sls)
Russell Knox (Mgr-New Car Sls)
Eddie Sharfenaker (Mgr-Pre Owned
Sls)
James Gardner (Mgr-Used Car)
Harold Shead (Mgr-Pre-Owned Sls)
Joe Moore (Mgr-Svc-Columbus)

FREEMAN AUTOMOTIVE COMPANY LLC

39680 Hwy 20, Dallas, TX 75237
Tel.: (214) 800-6500
Web Site:
  https://www.freemanhonda.net
Rev.: $37,200,000
Emp.: 55
Automobiles, New & Used
N.A.I.C.S.: 441110
Gerry Freeman (Owner & Pres)
Dane Minor (Gen Mgr)

FREEMAN CORPORATION

415 Magnolia St, Winchester, KY
40391
Tel.: (859) 744-4311
Web Site:
  http://www.freemancorp.com
Sales Range: $25-49.9 Million
Emp.: 250
Hardwood Veneer Manufacturing
N.A.I.C.S.: 321211
George W. Freeman (CEO)
Reid Freeman (Pres)
Scott Hisle (CFO)

FREEMAN DECORATING CO.

14221 Dallas Pkwy Ste 200, Dallas,
TX 75254
Tel.: (214) 445-1000   IA
Web Site: http://www.freeman.com
Year Founded: 1927
Sales Range: $800-899.9 Million
Emp.: 3,300
Convention & Trade Show Organizing
Services
N.A.I.C.S.: 561920
Bob Priest-Heck (CEO)
Carrie Freeman Parsons (Chm)
Bob Priest-Heck (CEO)
Janet Dell (Pres)
Alan Grottle (CFO)
Martin Moggre (Chief Client Officer)
Dawnn Repp (Chief Legal Officer &
Chief Admin Officer)

Subsidiaries:

Encore Productions, Inc.   (1)
5150 S Decatur Blvd, Las Vegas, NV
89118-4972
Tel.: (702) 739-8803
Web Site: http://www.encoreproductions.net
Sales Range: $25-49.9 Million
Emp.: 180
Audio & Video Production Services
N.A.I.C.S.: 561920

Exhibit Surveys, Inc.   (1)
7 Hendrickson Ave, Red Bank, NJ 07701
Tel.: (732) 741-3170
Web Site: http://www.exhibitsurveys.com
Marketing Research & Consulting Services
N.A.I.C.S.: 541910
Jonathan Cox (Pres & CEO)
Ian K. Sequeira (Exec VP)
Alissa M. Algarin (Dir-Project)
Jan H. Goldsmith (Exec Dir-Res)
Jeff Stanley (Exec Dir-Strategic Res Dev)
Darren Leib (Dir-Res Sys)
Nancy Flora (Dir-Res)
Kurt Marttila (Dir-Mktg & Bus Dev)

Freeman Audio Visual, Inc.   (1)
4545 W Davis St, Dallas, TX
75211   (100%)
Tel.: (214) 623-1300
Web Site: http://www.freemanco.com
Emp.: 200
Rental & Sale of Audio-Visual Equipment;
Production of Multimedia Presentations
N.A.I.C.S.: 532210
Ken Sanders (Pres)
Doak Collins (Acct Mgr-Natl)
Larry Luteran (Chief Sls Officer)

Subsidiary (Non-US):

Staging Connections Group
Limited   (2)
Locked Bag 21 68-72 Lilyfield Road, Sydney, 2039, NSW, Australia
Tel.: (61) 295568880
Web Site: http://www.scgl.com.au
Event Production & Staging Services
N.A.I.C.S.: 561920
Tony Chamberlain (CEO & Mng Dir)
Malcolm Craig (CFO & Sec)
Gary Daly (Mng Dir-Exhibition & Trade
Fairs)
Ian Terry (Mng Dir-The Event Company)

Subsidiary (Domestic):

Exhibitions and Trade Fairs Pty
Limited   (3)
Unit 5 21 South Street, Rydalmere, 2116,
NSW, Australia
Tel.: (61) 295567999
Web Site: http://www.etf.com.au
Trade & Consumer Exhibition Services
N.A.I.C.S.: 711310
Gary Daly (Mng Dir)
Nigel Southern (Officer-Fin)
Paul Grimble (Gen Counsel)

Freeman Exhibit Fabrication &
Graphics   (1)
2940 114th St, Grand Prairie, TX
75050   (100%)
Tel.: (817) 607-2600
Web Site: http://www.totalshow.com
Sales Range: $10-24.9 Million
Emp.: 40
Provides Exhibits for Trade Shows

N.A.I.C.S.: 541420
FreemanXP   (1)
350 Rhode Island St Ste 220N, San Francisco, CA 94103
Tel.: (415) 655-2200
Web Site: http://www.freemanxp.com
Marketing & Advertising Services
N.A.I.C.S.: 541890
Lisa VanRosendale (Sr VP)
Daniel Hoffend Jr. (Pres)

Sparks Marketing Group LLC   (1)
2828 Charter Rd, Philadelphia, PA 19154-
2111
Tel.: (215) 676-1100
Web Site: https://www.wearesparks.com
Sales Range: $100-124.9 Million
Emp.: 400
Exhibits, Displays & Store Fixtures Designer
& Mgr
N.A.I.C.S.: 561920
David Sudjian (Pres)

Subsidiary (Domestic):

3D Exhibits, Inc.   (2)
800 Albion Ave, Schaumburg, IL 60193
Tel.: (847) 250-9000
Web Site: http://www.3dexhibits.com
Sales Range: $10-24.9 Million
Emp.: 110
Trade Show & Other Exhibit Services
N.A.I.C.S.: 541890
Bob Prihoda (Exec VP)
Nicole Genarella (Exec VP-Sls & Mktg)
Jeff Bartle (Chief Creative Officer)
Dara Lamere (Dir-Programs-Intl)
Evan Plotkin (Mgr-Interactive Tech)
Gene Faut (Pres)
Kelly Collins (Mgr-Bus Dev)

Sparks Custom Retail, LLC   (2)
2828 Charter Rd, Philadelphia, PA 19154-
2111
Tel.: (215) 602-8100
Web Site: http://www.sparksretail.com
Sales Range: $10-24.9 Million
Emp.: 50
Custom-Made Fixtures & Displays for Retailers
N.A.I.C.S.: 541850
Matt Wood (Pres)

Sparks Exhibits & Environments
Corp.   (2)
2828 Charter Rd, Philadelphia, PA 19154-
2111
Tel.: (215) 676-1100
Web Site: http://www.sparksonline.com
Sales Range: $25-49.9 Million
Emp.: 200
Themed Interior Exhibits Designer & Marketer
N.A.I.C.S.: 561920
David Sudjian (Pres)
Robin Lickliter (Sr VP-Events)
Mike Ellery (Chief Creative Officer)
Jane Hawley (Sr VP)
Sally Maturana (VP-Events)
Ben Nazario (Sr VP)
David Smiertka (VP-Creative)

mdg   (1)
2445 5th Ave Ste 450, San Diego, CA
92101-1670
Tel.: (619) 298-1445
Web Site: http://www.mdg.agency
Graphic Design Services
N.A.I.C.S.: 541430
Kimberly Hardcastle-Geddes (Pres)
Jacquelyn Wells (VP)
Erin Lee (VP-Digital Mktg Stategy)

FREEMAN MANUFACTURING & SUPPLY COMPANY

1101 Moore Rd, Avon, OH 44011-
1011
Tel.: (440) 934-1902   OH
Web Site:
  https://www.freemansupply.com
Year Founded: 1902
Sales Range: $75-99.9 Million
Emp.: 90
Supplies & Equipment for the Pattern,
Mold & Model Shop & Foundry Industries Distr

N.A.I.C.S.: 325991
Lou Turco (Pres)

FREEMAN MARINE EQUIPMENT, INC.

28336 Hunter Creek Rd, Gold Beach,
OR 97444
Tel.: (541) 247-7078
Web Site:
  http://www.freemanmarine.com
Year Founded: 1975
Rev.: $18,100,000
Emp.: 130
Nonferrous Foundries
N.A.I.C.S.: 331529
Dana Smith (CFO)
Franz A. Shindler (Sec)
Bo Shindler (Gen Mgr)

FREEMAN MATHIS & GARY, LLP

100 Galleria Pkwy Ste 1600, Atlanta,
GA 30339-5948
Tel.: (770) 818-0000
Web Site: http://www.fmglaw.com
Year Founded: 1997
Law firm
N.A.I.C.S.: 541110
Bradley T. Adler (Gen Counsel-
Admin)
Ben Mathis (Mng Partner)
Chris Echols (CEO)
Paul Bigley (Mng Partner-California)
Dana Maine (Gen Counsel-Risk
Mgmt)
Phil Savrin (Chm-Insurance Coverage)
Chad Weaver (Chm-Fin Svcs)
Jack Hancock (Sr Partner & Mng
Partner-Forest Park)
Jen Ward (Mng Partner-Pennsylvania
& New Jersey)
Claudia Lee (Mgr-Accts)
Stephanie Magdaleno (Mgr-California
Office)
Allison Asher (Mgr-HR)
Lucia Martin (Mgr-Mktg)
Kim Washington (Mgr-Billing)
Patrick McCormick (Dir-IT)
Alicia Santocki (Partner-New York
City & Mng Dir-Assurance)
Jessica Farrelly (Partner-Tampa)

FREEMAN OIL COMPANY INC.

Hwy 270 E, Sheridan, AR 72150
Tel.: (870) 942-3431
Sales Range: $10-24.9 Million
Emp.: 4
Petroleum Bulk Stations
N.A.I.C.S.: 424710
Robert Freeman (VP)

FREEMAN PUBLIC RELATIONS

16 Furler St, Totowa, NJ 07512
Tel.: (973) 470-0400   NJ
Web Site: http://www.freemanpr.com
Year Founded: 1955
Sales Range: $1-9.9 Million
Emp.: 30
Public Relations Agency
N.A.I.C.S.: 541820
Bruce Maguire (CEO)

FREEMAN SPOGLI & CO. INCORPORATED

11100 Santa Monica Blvd Ste 1900,
Los Angeles, CA 90025
Tel.: (310) 444-1822   CA
Web Site:
  http://www.freemanspogli.com
Year Founded: 1983
Investment Firm
N.A.I.C.S.: 523999
Bradford M. Freeman (Co-Chm)
Lou A. Losorelli (CFO)

Freeman Spogli & Co. Incorporated—(Continued)

Ronald P. Spogli (Co-Founder & Co-Chm)
John M. Roth (CEO)
Jon D. Ralph (Pres & COO)
William M. Wardlaw (Chief Compliance Officer)

Subsidiaries:

Batteries Plus, LLC **(1)**
1325 Walnut Rdg Dr, Hartland, WI 53029
Tel.: (262) 912-3199
Web Site: http://www.batteriesplus.com
Sales Range: $150-199.9 Million
Batteries Retailer & Store Franchisor
N.A.I.C.S.: 455219
Michael J. Lehman (CIO)
Scott K. Williams (CEO)
Scott Williams (CEO)
Joe Malmuth (VP-Franchise Dev & Rels)
Jon Sica (Chief Strategy & Dev Officer)
Scott K. Williams (CEO)

Easy Ice, LLC **(1)**
925 W Washington St Ste 100, Marquette, MI 49855
Tel.: (866) 327-9423
Web Site: https://www.easyice.com
Commercial Ice Machines, Service, Cleaning & Repairs
N.A.I.C.S.: 811310

Subsidiary (Domestic):

Credential Leasing Corp. **(2)**
880 Old Hwy 92, Dandridge, TN 37725-4611
Tel.: (865) 484-1594
Web Site: http://www.credentialleasing.com
Consumer Lending
N.A.I.C.S.: 522291
Charles Lutz (Pres)

Cube Aire **(2)**
9933 Channel Rd, Lakeside, CA 92040-3003
Tel.: (619) 561-5514
Web Site: http://www.cube-aire.com
Commercial & Industrial Machinery & Equipment Repair & Maintenance
N.A.I.C.S.: 811310

Hutto Refrigeration Sales & Service, LLC. **(2)**
3103 Meeting St, North Charleston, SC 29405-7965
Tel.: (843) 747-7331
Web Site: http://www.huttorefrigeration.com
Refrigeration Equipment & Supply Whslr
N.A.I.C.S.: 423740
Francis C. Hutto (Owner)

Thrifty Air Conditioning & Refrigeration, Inc.
3340 Royalston Ave, Fort Myers, FL 33916 **(2)**
Tel.: (239) 337-5859
Rev.: $1,460,000
Emp.: 10
Heating & Air-Conditioning Services
N.A.I.C.S.: 238220

Tri City Supply, Inc. **(2)**
1101 N Main St, Baytown, TX 77520
Tel.: (281) 422-0222
Sales Range: $1-9.9 Million
Emp.: 11
Whol Electrical Supplies
N.A.I.C.S.: 423610
James Haarmeyer (Pres)
Connie Files (Sec)

Wholesale Supply Inc. **(2)**
2232 S Green St, Longview, TX 75602-3454
Tel.: (903) 753-7621
Web Site:
    http://www.wholesalesupplyinc.com
Wholesale Trade Agents & Brokers
N.A.I.C.S.: 425120
Rod Bullard Jr. (VP)

FASTSIGNS International, Inc. **(1)**
2542 Highlander Way, Carrollton, TX 75006-2366
Tel.: (214) 346-5600
Web Site: http://www.fastsigns.com
Sign Production & Print Shops Franchisor
N.A.I.C.S.: 533110

Catherine Monson (CEO)
Drue Townsend (Sr VP-Mktg)
Mark Jameson (Exec VP-Franchise Support & Dev)
Chris Becraft (VP-Accts-Natl)
Jennifer Herskind (CMO)

Five Star Food Service Inc. **(1)**
6005 Century Oaks Dr Ste 100, Chattanooga, TN 37416
Tel.: (423) 643-2600
Web Site: http://www.fivestar-food.com
Holding Company; Vending Machine Operators & Catering Services
N.A.I.C.S.: 445132
Alan Recher (Chm)
Richard Kennedy (Pres & CEO)
Mike Hand (Mng Partner)
Mike McLean (CFO)
Charly Caldwell (VP-Dining Svcs)
Rob Spence (VP-IT)
Scott Hale (VP-South)
C. J. Recher (VP-Mktg)

Subsidiary (Domestic):

Canteen Service Co. of Owensboro, Inc. **(2)**
712 Industrial Dr, Owensboro, KY 42301
Tel.: (270) 683-2471
Web Site: http://www.canteenatservices.com
Rev.: $22,000,000
Emp.: 350
Vending Machine & Catering Services
N.A.I.C.S.: 445132
Gary Schroader (Pres)
Eric Roberts (Coord-Warehouse)
Lacey Harville (Mgr-HR)
Jack Wells (CEO)

Branch (Domestic):

Five Star Food Service - Chattanooga **(2)**
6011 Century Oaks Dr, Chattanooga, TN 37416-3658
Tel.: (423) 490-4428
Web Site: http://www.fivestar.com
Sales Range: $25-49.9 Million
Vending Machine Operators & Catering Services
N.A.I.C.S.: 445132
Richard Bowden (Branch Mgr)
Kent Freeman (Dir-Dining Svcs)
Orlando Lomascolo (Dir-Sls)

Five Star Food Service - Cookeville **(2)**
1409 Interstate Dr, Cookeville, TN 38501-4153
Tel.: (931) 526-4011
Web Site:
    http://www.fivestarfoodservice.com
Sales Range: $25-49.9 Million
Vending Maching Operators & Catering Services
N.A.I.C.S.: 445132
Allen Mathney (Branch Mgr)

Five Star Food Service - Knoxville **(2)**
3225 Regal Dr, Alcoa, TN 37701-3234
Tel.: (865) 977-7332
Web Site: http://www.fivestar-food.com
Sales Range: $25-49.9 Million
Vending Machine Operators & Catering Services
N.A.I.C.S.: 445132
Michael Phillips (Mgr-Ops)
Gary Biggs (Mgr-Ops)
Orlando Lomascolo (Dir-Sls)
Tim Seaton (Gen Mgr)

Five Star Food Service - LaGrange **(2)**
1001 Longley Pl, Lagrange, GA 30240-5734
Tel.: (706) 882-7703
Sales Range: $25-49.9 Million
Vending Machine Operators & Catering Services
N.A.I.C.S.: 445132
Bob Robert (District Mgr)
Scott Hale (Dir-Sls)

Five Star Food Service - Martinsville **(2)**
221 College St, Martinsville, VA 24112-3633
Tel.: (540) 632-3400
Web Site: http://www.fivestar-food.com

Food Service
N.A.I.C.S.: 445132

Five Star Food Service - Nashville **(2)**
440 Allied Dr, Nashville, TN 37211
Tel.: (615) 833-7983
Web Site: http://www.fivestar-food.com
Vending Machine Operators & Catering Services
N.A.I.C.S.: 445132
Mark Stephanos (Sr VP-Micro-Markets)
Pat Barger (VP-Sls)
Beth Conyer (VP-Central)
Buddy Duke (VP-North)
Landon Martin (Dir-Risk Mgmt)
Gregory McCall (Chief Revenue Officer)
Alan Recher (Pres & CEO)
Peggy Russell (VP-HR)

Subsidiary (Domestic):

Franks Vending Service, Inc. **(2)**
1185 W College St, Pulaski, TN 38478
Web Site:
    http://www.franksvendingservice.com
Vending Machine Operators
N.A.I.C.S.: 445132

Merchandise Vending Company, Inc. **(2)**
703 Hamric Dr W, Oxford, AL 36203-2338
Tel.: (256) 831-9310
Sales Range: $25-49.9 Million
Vending Machine Operators
N.A.I.C.S.: 445132

Freeman Spogli Management Co., LLC **(1)**
11100 Santa Monica Blvd, Los Angeles, CA 90025
Tel.: (310) 444-1822
Web Site: http://www.freemanspogli.com
Emp.: 20
Private Equity Investment Management Services
N.A.I.C.S.: 523940
Bradford Freeman (Principal)

Galco Industrial Electronics, Inc. **(1)**
26010 Pinehurst Dr, Madison Heights, MI 48071
Tel.: (248) 542-9090
Web Site: http://www.galco.com
Sales Range: $10-24.9 Million
Electronic Parts Distr
N.A.I.C.S.: 423690
Bault Lori (Supvr-Pur)
Douglas Bauman (Mgr-Acct)
Randy Barbret (Mgr-Repair Svcs & Drives Product Sls)
Ray Cadrette (Dir-Tech Ops)
Dave Anderson (Mgr-Product)
Karen Mandarino (VP-Ops)

Integrated Supply Network, LLC **(1)**
2727 Interstate Dr, Lakeland, FL 33805-2304
Tel.: (800) 966-8478
Web Site: http://www.isnweb.com
Emp.: 1,000
Automotive Tools & Equipment Whslr & Distr
N.A.I.C.S.: 423120
Bruce Weber (CEO)
John Snowden (Pres/COO-USA)
Tracy Veillette (CFO)

Kamps, Inc. **(1)**
2900 Peach Ridge Ave NW, Grand Rapids, MI 49544
Tel.: (616) 453-9676
Web Site: http://www.kampspallets.com
Mfr of Wood Pallets
N.A.I.C.S.: 321920
Bill Zeilstra (Controller)
Pat Carey (Mgr-IT)
Tony Sokoloski (Reg Mgr)
Dan DeVries (Dir-Sls-Natl)
Bernie Kamps (CEO)
Mitchell Kamps (Pres)

Subsidiary (Domestic):

John Rock, Inc. **(2)**
500 Independence Way, Coatesville, PA 19320
Tel.: (610) 857-8080
Web Site: http://www.johnrock.com
Wood Container & Pallet Mfr

N.A.I.C.S.: 321920
Bill MacCauley (Pres)

L & R Pallet Service, Inc. **(1)**
3855 Lima St, Denver, CO 80239
Tel.: (303) 355-5083
Web Site: http://www.lrpallet.com
Rev.: $1-9.9 Million
Emp.: 110
Electronic & Precision Equipment Repair & Maintenance
N.A.I.C.S.: 811210
Doris Ruder (Sec)

MicroStar Keg Management LLC **(1)**
5299 DTC Blvd Ste 510, Greenwood Village, CO 80111
Tel.: (800) 245-2200
Web Site: http://www.microstarkegs.com
Emp.: 17
General Management Consulting Services
N.A.I.C.S.: 541611

U.S. Med-Equip, Inc. **(1)**
7028 Gessner Rd, Houston, TX 77040
Tel.: (713) 983-8860
Web Site: http://www.usmedequip.com
Sales Range: $10-24.9 Million
Emp.: 65
Biomedical Equipment Sales & Rental Services
N.A.I.C.S.: 423450
Gurmit Bhatia (Pres)
Mike Pandher (Dir-IT)
Rabindra Shrestha (Mgr-Pur)
Tim Heck (VP-Strategic Alliances)

Subsidiary (Domestic):

Freedom Medical, Inc. **(2)**
219 Welsh Pool Rd, Exton, PA 19341
Tel.: (610) 903-0200
Web Site: http://www.freedommedical.com
Sales Range: $10-24.9 Million
Emp.: 120
Provider of Medical Equipment Rentals & Services
N.A.I.C.S.: 532283
Frank Gwynn (Co-Founder)
Eric Tyler (Dir-IT)
Art Savage (Mgr-Collection)
James McDevitt (Mgr-Ops)

totes Isotoner Corporation **(1)**
9655 International Blvd, Cincinnati, OH 45246
Tel.: (513) 682-8200
Web Site: http://www.totes-isotoner.com
Sales Range: $150-199.9 Million
Emp.: 1,200
Weather-Resistant Products & Apparel Accessories Mfr & Distr
N.A.I.C.S.: 315990
Douglas P. Gernert (Pres & CEO)
Doug Baker (VP-Ops)
Donna Deye (CFO & Exec VP)
Kristin Vrsansky (VP-Outdoor Products)
Paul Grone (CIO & VP)
Aaron Sullivan (Dir-Mktg-Digital & eCommerce)

Holding (Non-US):

totes Isotoner (UK) Limited **(2)**
Eastman House Radford Crescent, Billericay, CM12 0DN, Essex, United Kingdom
Tel.: (44) 1277630277
Web Site: http://www.totes.co.uk
Sales Range: $50-74.9 Million
Emp.: 80
Rainwear, Gloves & Umbrellas Distr
N.A.I.C.S.: 424350
Mike Bate (Chm)

totes Isotoner Canada Ltd. **(2)**
426 Watline Avenue, Mississauga, L4Z 1X2, ON, Canada
Tel.: (905) 564-4817
Web Site: https://www.totes-isotoner.ca
Sales Range: $50-74.9 Million
Emp.: 25
Rainwear, Gloves & Umbrellas Distr
N.A.I.C.S.: 424350
Robin Perry (VP & Gen Mgr)

FREEPORT PRESS INC.
121 W Main St, Freeport, OH 43973
Tel.: (740) 658-4000

Web Site:
https://www.freeportpress.com
Sales Range: $10-24.9 Million
Emp.: 140
Commercial Printing Services
N.A.I.C.S.: 323111
James Pilcher *(VP-Mfg)*
David P. Pilcher *(VP-Sls & Mktg)*

FREEPORT TRANSPORT IN-DUSTRIES, INC.
1200 Butler Rd, Freeport, PA 16229
Tel.: (724) 295-2181
Sales Range: $10-24.9 Million
Emp.: 110
Trucking Service
N.A.I.C.S.: 484121
Donald L. Smetanick *(Pres)*

FREEPORT WELDING & FAB-RICATION INC
200 N Navigation Blvd, Freeport, TX 77541
Tel.: (979) 233-0121
Web Site: http://www.freeweld.com
Rev.: $10,006,071
Emp.: 150
Metal Welding & Fabrication Services
N.A.I.C.S.: 332313
Roy E. Yates *(Owner)*

FREESE & NICHOLS INC.
4055 Intl Plz Ste 200, Fort Worth, TX 76109-4814
Tel.: (817) 735-7300   TX
Web Site: http://www.freese.com
Year Founded: 1924
Sales Range: $25-49.9 Million
Emp.: 500
Provider of Civil Engineering Services
N.A.I.C.S.: 541330
Cindy Milrany *(CFO)*
Robert Pence *(Chm)*

FREESE JOHNSON, LLC
1355 Terrell Mill Rd Bldg 1470 Ste 100, Marietta, GA 30067
Tel.: (770) 850-9393
Web Site:
https://www.freesejohnson.com
Sales Range: $25-49.9 Million
Emp.: 50
Construction Services
N.A.I.C.S.: 236220
Patrick A. Freese *(CEO)*
Henry D. Johnson *(Chief Strategy Officer)*
Rodger Foresman *(Pres)*

FREESTONE COMPANIES
6820 20th SE Ste A, Fife, WA 98424
Tel.: (253) 896-1300
Web Site:
http://www.freestonecompanies.com
Year Founded: 2004
Sales Range: $25-49.9 Million
Emp.: 25
New Homes Building Construction
N.A.I.C.S.: 236115

FREESTONE RESOURCES, INC.
101 W Ave D, Ennis, TX 75201
Tel.: (214) 880-4870   NV
Web Site:
http://www.freestoneresources.com
Rev.: $1,163,860
Assets: $1,600,166
Liabilities: $3,731,926
Net Worth: ($2,131,760)
Earnings: ($1,138,132)
Emp.: 16
Fiscal Year-end: 06/30/18
Oil & Gas Production Services
N.A.I.C.S.: 213112
Michael J. McGhan *(Pres & CEO)*

FREEUS, LLC
4699 Harrison Blvd, Ogden, UT 84403
Tel.: (385) 240-3920
Web Site: http://www.freeus.com
Year Founded: 2008
Sales Range: $25-49.9 Million
Emp.: 30
Security System Services
N.A.I.C.S.: 561621
Josh Garner *(CEO)*

FREEWAY CORPORATION
9301 Allen Dr, Cleveland, OH 44125-4632
Tel.: (216) 524-9700   OH
Web Site:
https://www.freewaycorp.com
Year Founded: 1944
Sales Range: $75-99.9 Million
Emp.: 250
Metal Stampings, Assemblies & Screw Machine Products
N.A.I.C.S.: 332722
Don Lagoni *(VP-Mfg)*
Randy Scherler *(VP)*
Robb Scherler *(Pres & CEO)*

Subsidiaries:

Freeway Rockford   (1)
4701 Boeing Dr, Rockford, IL
61109-2903   (100%)
Tel.: (815) 397-6425
Web Site:
http://www.freewaycorporation.com
Sales Range: $1-9.9 Million
Emp.: 15
Metal Washers
N.A.I.C.S.: 332722
Mike Rosegger *(Controller)*
Scott Summers *(VP-Rockford Subsidiary & Gen Mgr)*
Rob Scherler *(Pres & CFO)*

Freeway Washer, Ltd.   (1)
1820 Meyerside Drive, Mississauga, L5T 1B4, ON, Canada   (100%)
Tel.: (905) 564-2288
Web Site: http://www.freewaywasher.com
Sales Range: $10-24.9 Million
Emp.: 20
Mfr of Various Washer Parts
N.A.I.C.S.: 332722
Roger Alfred *(VP)*
Jason Hawksworth *(Pres)*

Triangle Machine Product Co.   (1)
6055 Hillcrest Dr, Valley View, OH
44125-4619   (100%)
Tel.: (216) 524-5872
Web Site: http://www.trianglemachprod.com
Sales Range: $10-24.9 Million
Emp.: 30
Mfg Screw Machine Products
N.A.I.C.S.: 332721
Roy Scherler *(VP)*

FREEWAY FOODS INC.
4533 W Market St, Greensboro, NC 27407
Tel.: (336) 855-0251
Year Founded: 1955
Sales Range: $25-49.9 Million
Emp.: 700
Family Restaurants Franchise Services
N.A.I.C.S.: 722511
Gary Fly *(Pres)*
Chris Patane *(VP-Ops)*

FREEWAY FORD TRUCK SALES, INC.
8445 W 45th St, Lyons, IL 60534
Tel.: (708) 442-9000
Web Site:
http://www.freewaytruck.com
Sales Range: $25-49.9 Million
Emp.: 30
New Car Dealers
N.A.I.C.S.: 441110

Mary Dolan *(Pres)*
Thomas Dolan *(VP & Gen Mgr)*
Patricia Hensley *(Mgr-F & I)*
Pete Kilduff *(Mgr-Used Truck Sls)*

FREEWAY MOTORS INC.
4724 Roosevelt Way NE, Seattle, WA 98105
Tel.: (206) 633-4630
Sales Range: $100-124.9 Million
Emp.: 230
New Car Dealers
N.A.I.C.S.: 441110
Tim Anderson *(Controller)*
Robert Will Jr. *(Owner)*

FREIGHT ALL KINDS INC.
10885 E 51st Ave, Denver, CO 80239-2507
Tel.: (303) 289-5433   CO
Web Site: http://www.fakinc.com
Year Founded: 1983
Sales Range: $10-24.9 Million
Emp.: 50
Brokerage for Trucking Services
N.A.I.C.S.: 484121
Sam Marcove *(CEO)*
Ron Harms *(Gen Mgr)*
Debra Ogden *(VP-Credit)*
James Collins *(Dir-Safety & Compliance)*

FREIGHT HANDLERS INC.
310 N Judd Pkwy NE, Fuquay Varina, NC 27526
Tel.: (919) 552-3157
Web Site:
http://www.freighthandlers.com
Rev.: $14,000,000
Emp.: 900
Labor Resource Services
N.A.I.C.S.: 561320
Chuck Wall *(Co-Founder & Co-Chm)*
Jeff Newton *(Sr VP-Retail Svc)*
Richard Johnson *(VP-Ops)*
Rick Wiggins *(Sr VP-Logistics)*
Ryan Wall *(Pres & CEO)*
Dave Gray *(Sr VP-Ops)*
Robert Hull *(VP-IT)*
Reid Durst *(COO)*
Will Seel *(Dir-Bus Dev)*

FREIGHT MANAGEMENT TEAM INC.
15644 Madison Ave, Cleveland, OH 44107
Tel.: (216) 862-0187
Web Site:
http://www.freightmanagement
team.com
Year Founded: 2012
Sales Range: $1-9.9 Million
Emp.: 9
Freight Transportation Services
N.A.I.C.S.: 488510
Chuck Lombardy *(Pres)*
Gregg Arrendale *(Sr Acct Exec)*
Stephanie Kotema *(Sr Acct Exec)*
Steve Langdon *(Sr Acct Exec)*
Mike Zimmer *(Sr Acct Exec)*

FREIGHT MANAGEMENT, INC
739 N Ave, Glendale Heights, IL 60139
Tel.: (630) 627-6560
Web Site: https://www.gofmi.com
Year Founded: 2000
Sales Range: $10-24.9 Million
Emp.: 55
Logistic Services
N.A.I.C.S.: 481219
Joseph M. Mayo *(Pres & CEO)*
Joseph A. Mayo *(VP-Fin)*
Robert Mayo *(COO)*

FREIGHT SALES INC.

15490 N 83rd Way, Scottsdale, AZ 85260
Tel.: (480) 966-3100   AZ
Web Site:
http://www.audioexpressusa.com
Year Founded: 1975
Sales Range: $25-49.9 Million
Emp.: 350
Automotive Sound Equipment Mfr & Distr
N.A.I.C.S.: 441330
Darlene Lester *(Dir-HR)*
Marlon Buchholtz *(CFO)*

FREIGHT SOLUTION PROVIDERS
2851 Gold Tailings Ct, Rancho Cordova, CA 95670
Tel.: (916) 373-3353
Web Site: http://www.shipfsp.com
Rev.: $24,700,000
Emp.: 200
Freight Transportation Arrangement
N.A.I.C.S.: 488510
Lielanie Steers *(CEO)*
Ken Steers *(Pres)*
Jeff Adams *(Exec VP & Acct Mgr)*

FREIGHT-BASE SERVICES INC.
605 Country Club Dr Ste M, Bensenville, IL 60106-1330
Tel.: (630) 766-7000   IL
Web Site: http://www.freightbase.com
Year Founded: 1984
Sales Range: $10-24.9 Million
Emp.: 25
Freight Transportation Arrangement Services
N.A.I.C.S.: 488510
Jack Groit *(Owner)*

Subsidiaries:

Freight-Base Customs Brokers
Inc.   (1)
605 Country Club Dr Ste M, Bensenville, IL 60106-1330   (100%)
Tel.: (630) 766-7000
Sales Range: $10-24.9 Million
Emp.: 11
Freight Transportation Arrangement Services
N.A.I.C.S.: 488510

FREIGHTCENTER INC.
34125 US 19 N Ste 300, Palm Harbor, FL 34684
Tel.: (727) 450-7800
Web Site:
https://www.freightcenter.com
Year Founded: 1998
Sales Range: $25-49.9 Million
Emp.: 100
Logistics & Transportation
N.A.I.C.S.: 485999
Matthew J. Brosious *(CEO)*
Jim Brosious *(CFO)*
Therese Kerrigan *(Sr Mgr-Mktg)*
Justin Langley *(Product Dir)*
Tiffany Brown *(Mgr-HR)*
Ali Choiniere *(COO)*
Terrence O'Toole *(Dir-Brokerage & Enterprise Sls)*
Natalie Lane *(Dir-Mktg)*
Robin Kelly *(Mgr-Acctg)*
Stan Grayzyk *(Mgr-Software Dev)*
Jason Katzwinkel *(Sr Mgr-Creative Svcs)*
Amy Van Ness *(Controller)*
Justin Raynor *(Mgr-Quality Assurance)*

FREIGHTLINER OF AUSTIN
1701 Smith Rd, Austin, TX 78721
Tel.: (512) 389-0000
Web Site:
http://www.freightlinerofaustin.com

Freightliner of Austin—(Continued)

Sales Range: $10-24.9 Million
Emp.: 51
Trucks, Tractors & Trailers: New &
Used
N.A.I.C.S.: 441110
David Rehak *(Mgr-Parts)*
Jay Hendrix *(Pres)*
Carlton Hempel *(VP)*
Sonya Sowerby *(Mgr-Warranty)*
Scott Miller *(Bus Mgr)*

FREIGHTLINER OF DES MOINES
3601 Adventureland Dr, Altoona, IA
50707
Tel.: (515) 967-3500
Web Site: http://www.freightlinerdes
moines.com
Sales Range: $10-24.9 Million
Emp.: 50
Sales of Trucks & Tractors
N.A.I.C.S.: 441110
Carl T. Schwab *(Pres)*
C. Bingaman *(Sec)*
David Nelsen *(Mgr-Sls)*

FREIGHTLINER OF HART-FORD, INC.
199 Roberts St, East Hartford, CT
06108
Tel.: (860) 290-0201
Web Site:
https://www.freightlinerofhart
ford.com
Sales Range: $10-24.9 Million
Emp.: 74
New Car Dealers
N.A.I.C.S.: 441110
Dave Bosio *(Mgr)*
Lindy Bigliazzi *(Mgr)*

FREIGHTLINER OF NEW HAMPSHIRE
8 Horizon Dr, Londonderry, NH
03053
Tel.: (603) 421-9000
Web Site: http://www.fnh.com
Year Founded: 1977
Sales Range: $25-49.9 Million
Emp.: 75
Sales of New & Used Trucks Tractors
& Trailers
N.A.I.C.S.: 488510
Carol Brewin *(Controller)*
Scott Stebbins *(VP)*
Joseph R. Alosa Jr. *(Pres)*

Subsidiaries:

Freightliner of New Hampshire -
Lebanon   **(1)**
165 Heater Rd, Lebanon, NH 03766
Tel.: (603) 443-9955
Web Site: http://www.fnh.com
Sales Range: $1-9.9 Million
Emp.: 15
New Car Dealers
N.A.I.C.S.: 441110
Bill Wiley *(Mgr-Sls)*

FREIGHTLINER OF UTAH, LLC
2240 S 5370 W, Salt Lake City, UT
84120
Tel.: (801) 978-8000
Web Site: http://www.warnertc.com
Year Founded: 1983
Truck Sales & Service
N.A.I.C.S.: 423110
Jerry Zmyslo *(CFO)*

FREMAR FARMERS COOP-ERATIVE INC.
PO Box 357, Marion, SD 57043-2109
Tel.: (605) 648-3941
Year Founded: 1991
Sales Range: $10-24.9 Million

Emp.: 115
Provider Of Agricultural Services
N.A.I.C.S.: 424510
Matt Ashton *(Gen Mgr)*

Subsidiaries:

Freeman Feed Service Inc.   **(1)**
PO Box 459, Freeman, SD 57029
Tel.: (605) 925-4501
Web Site: http://www.fremarcoop.com
Sales Range: $10-24.9 Million
Emp.: 3
Provider of Farm Supplies
N.A.I.C.S.: 423840

FREMONT AREA COMMUNITY FOUNDATION
4424 W 48th St, Fremont, MI 49412
Tel.: (231) 924-5350
Web Site: http://www.tfacf.org
Year Founded: 1951
Sales Range: $10-24.9 Million
Emp.: 18
Grantmaking Services
N.A.I.C.S.: 813211
Kathy Pope *(VP-Fin)*
Robin Cowles *(Mgr-Philanthropic
Svs)*
Carla Roberts *(Pres & CEO)*
Robert Jordan *(VP-Philanthropic
Svcs)*
Todd Jacobs *(VP-Community Invest-
ment)*
Mark Petz *(Coord-Special Projects)*
Mary Crisman *(Dir-Admin Svcs)*
Jessica Folkema *(Dir-Mktg & Comm)*
Maria Gonzalez *(Mgr-Foundation)*
Vonda Carr *(Mgr-Grants)*

FREMONT AUTO CENTER INC.
1401 N Federal Blvd, Riverton, WY
82501
Tel.: (307) 332-4083
Web Site:
http://www.fremontmotorchevy.com
Sales Range: $10-24.9 Million
Emp.: 40
Automobiles Dealership
N.A.I.C.S.: 441110
Charles Guschewsky *(Owner)*
Betty Baker *(Office Mgr-Fremont
Toyota)*

FREMONT BANCORPORATION
39150 Fremont Blvd, Fremont, CA
94538-5101
Tel.: (510) 792-2300
Web Site:
http://www.fremontbank.com
Year Founded: 1964
Sales Range: $25-49.9 Million
Emp.: 500
Personal & Commercial Banking
N.A.I.C.S.: 551111
Alan L. Hyman *(Vice Chm)*
Howard L. Hyman *(Exec VP)*
Bradford L. Anderson *(Vice Chm)*
Michael J. Wallace *(Chm)*
Hattie Hyman Hughes *(Pres & Exec
VP-Nonprofit Grp)*
Andrew Mastorakis *(CEO)*

Subsidiaries:

Fremont Bank   **(1)**
39150 Fremont Blvd, Fremont, CA
94538   **(100%)**
Tel.: (510) 792-2300
Web Site: http://www.fremontbank.com
Sales Range: $25-49.9 Million
Emp.: 12
Private & Commercial Banking
N.A.I.C.S.: 522110
Howard L. Hyman *(Exec VP)*
Bradford L. Anderson *(Vice Chm)*
Morris Hyman *(Chm)*
Michael W. Wallace *(Chm)*
Andy Mastorakis *(Pres & CEO)*
Dipak Roy *(VP-Comml Banking)*

Oscar Harrison *(VP-Wealth Mgmt)*
Don Marek *(Sr VP)*
Aileen Chao *(Mgr-Comml Relationship-
SBA)*
Alexis Kleinhans *(VP & Mgr-Comml Rela-
tionship)*

FREMONT BEVERAGES INC.
821 Pulliam Ave, Worland, WY 82401
Tel.: (307) 347-4231
Web Site:
http://www.admiralbeverage.com
Sales Range: $10-24.9 Million
Emp.: 48
Soft Drink Distr
N.A.I.C.S.: 312111
Kelly Clay *(Pres)*

FREMONT GROUP, LLC
199 Fremont St Ste 1900, San Fran-
cisco, CA 94105-2261
Tel.: (415) 284-8500
Web Site:
http://www.fremontgroup.com
Year Founded: 1898
Sales Range: $150-199.9 Million
Emp.: 80
Equity Investment Firm
N.A.I.C.S.: 523999
Matthew J. Reidy *(Partner-Fremont
Realty Capital)*
Alan M. Dachs *(Pres & CEO)*
Bob Peck *(Mng Dir-Pub Opportuni-
ties)*
Andrew Raab *(Mng Dir-Pub Opportu-
nities)*
Lori A. Menachof *(Gen Counsel)*
Keiri T. Custodio *(Principal-Fremont
Realty Capital)*
David R. Covin *(CFO, COO & Treas)*
Timothy Sheehy *(Partner)*
Scott R. Earthy *(Mng Partner)*
Ashminder Singh *(Principal)*
Helen Chen *(Principal)*
Frances Cordova *(Principal)*
Tanya Cota *(Sr VP-Taxes & Acquisi-
tion Svcs)*
Alexander S. Ramsay *(Principal)*
Susan Webster *(Gen Counsel)*
Claude J. Zinngrabe Jr. *(Mng Part-
ner)*

Subsidiaries:

FPR Partners LLC   **(1)**
199 Fremont St 25th Fl, San Francisco, CA
94105-2261
Tel.: (415) 284-8888
Web Site: http://www.fprpartners.com
Investment Advisory Services
N.A.I.C.S.: 523940
Bob Peck *(Mng Dir)*
Andy Raab *(Mng Dir)*
Siu Chiang *(CFO)*
Cam Anderson *(Dir-Ops)*
Alyssa Fantelli *(Office Mgr)*
Ted Johann *(COO)*

Fremont Investment Advisors   **(1)**
90 New Montgomery St, San Francisco, CA
94105-3468
Tel.: (415) 284-8989
Web Site:
http://www.fremontinvestmentadvisor.com
Rev.: $90,000,000
Emp.: 200
N.A.I.C.S.: 523910

Fremont Private Holdings, LLC   **(1)**
444 Madison Ave 31st Fl, New York, NY
10022
Tel.: (212) 771-1801
Web Site:
http://www.fremontprivateholdings.com
Private Equity Firm
N.A.I.C.S.: 523999
Scott Earthy *(Mng Partner)*
Timothy N. Sheehy *(Mng Dir)*

Fremont Realty Capital   **(1)**
199 Fremont St Ste 2200, San Francisco,
CA 94105-2261
Tel.: (415) 284-8194

Web Site: http://www.fremontgroup.com
Sales Range: $50-74.9 Million
Investment Management Service
N.A.I.C.S.: 523940
Matthew J. Reidy *(Partner)*
Keiri T. Custodio *(Mng Dir)*
Lori A. Menachof *(Gen Counsel)*
Ashminder Singh *(Mng Dir)*
Claude Joseph Zinngrabe Jr. *(Mng Partner)*

Fremont Realty Capital (New
York)   **(1)**
375 Park Ave Ste 2706, New York, NY
10152-3102
Tel.: (212) 771-1800
Web Site:
http://www.fremontrealtycapital.com
Sales Range: $10-24.9 Million
Emp.: 8
Investment Banking
N.A.I.C.S.: 531210

FREMONT MOTOR COMPANY
555 E Main St, Lander, WY 82520
Tel.: (307) 332-4355
Web Site:
http://www.fremontfordlander.com
Rev.: $11,900,000
Emp.: 43
New Car Dealers
N.A.I.C.S.: 441110
Charles Guschewsky *(Pres)*

FREMONT-RIDEOUT HEALTH GROUP
989 Plumas St, Yuba City, CA 95991
Tel.: (530) 751-4010
Web Site: http://www.frhg.org
Year Founded: 1984
Sales Range: $25-49.9 Million
Emp.: 153
Health Care Srvices
N.A.I.C.S.: 622110
Robert Chason *(CEO)*

FRENCH BROAD ELECTRIC MEMBERSHIP CORPORATION
3043 Hwy 213, Marshall, NC 28754
Tel.: (828) 649-2051
Web Site:
https://www.frenchbroademc.com
Year Founded: 1939
Sales Range: $50-74.9 Million
Emp.: 112
Electric Power Distr
N.A.I.C.S.: 221118
Phyllis Holt *(Office Mgr)*
Bobby Suttles *(Coord-DP)*

FRENCH GERLEMAN ELEC-TRIC CO., INC.
2023 Westport Center Dr, Saint
Louis, MO 63146-3564
Tel.: (314) 569-3122
Web Site:
http://www.frenchgerleman.com
Year Founded: 1923
Sales Range: $25-49.9 Million
Emp.: 281
Electrical Apparatus & Equipment Mfr
N.A.I.C.S.: 423610
William B. French *(CEO)*
Mike Stanfill *(Pres)*
Steve French *(VP-Ops)*
Adam Ruebsam *(VP-Comml & Indus-
trial Sls)*
Mike Kelsch *(VP-Supply)*
Jim Wojkovich *(VP-Construction Sls)*
Craig Reynolds *(VP-Western Reg)*

Subsidiaries:

Applied Technologies Inc.   **(1)**
12125 Bridgeton Sq Dr, Bridgeton, MO
63044   **(100%)**
Tel.: (636) 728-5995
Sales Range: $10-24.9 Million
Emp.: 20

Computer Systems & Electrical Integration Services
N.A.I.C.S.: 541512
Steve Grimm (Gen Mgr)

FRENCH-AMERICAN FOUNDATION

28 W 44th St Ste 1420, New York, NY 10036
Tel.: (212) 829-8800　　　　DE
Web Site:
http://www.frenchamerican.org
Year Founded: 1976
Sales Range: $1-9.9 Million
Emp.: 17
National Relationship Development Services
N.A.I.C.S.: 541820
Charles Kolb (Pres)
Dana Arifi (COO & VP)
Nathalie Bastin (Dir-Global Comm & Media Programs)
Irene Savvas (Chief Leadership Dev Officer)
Walter J. P. Curley (Chm)

FRENCH-ELLISON TRUCK CENTER INC.

4300 N Cage Blvd, Pharr, TX 78577-7518
Tel.: (956) 781-2401
Web Site:
http://www.frenchellison.com
Year Founded: 1968
Sales Range: $25-49.9 Million
Emp.: 206
Provider of Motor Vehicle Supplies & New Part Services
N.A.I.C.S.: 423120
Jay Ellison (Pres & CEO)

FRENCH/BLITZER/SCOTT LLC

275 Madison Ave 4th Fl, New York, NY 10016
Tel.: (212) 255-2650　　　　DE
Year Founded: 1985
Sales Range: Less than $1 Million
Emp.: 5
Aviation, Business-To-Business, Financial, Print
N.A.I.C.S.: 541810
Robert Scott (Pres)
Ray Gaulke (Exec VP)

FRENCH/WEST/VAUGHAN, LLC

112 E Hargett St, Raleigh, NC 27601
Tel.: (919) 832-6300
Web Site: https://www.fwv-us.com
Year Founded: 2001
Sales Range: $50-74.9 Million
Emp.: 70
Advertising & Public Relations Agencies
N.A.I.C.S.: 541810
Richard French (Chm & CEO)
David Gwyn (Pres)
Barrie Hancock (Sr VP)
Natalie Best (Exec VP & Dir-Client Svcs)
Jack Glasure (Pres-Sports & Entertainment Practice)
Scott Palmer (VP-Digital & Social Media)
Rich Griffis (Sr Dir-Art)
Jenny Pilewski (Sr VP)
Leah Knepper (VP)
Angela DeRusha (VP-Adv Svcs)
Dean Logan (Dir-Creative)
Brad Grantham (VP)
Melissa Timney (VP)

Subsidiaries:

Fetching Communications　　　(1)
PO Box 222, Tarpon Springs, FL 34688
Tel.: (727) 480-8030

Web Site:
http://www.fetchingcommunications.com
Pet & Veterinary Public Relations & Marketing Services
N.A.I.C.S.: 541820
Kristen Levin (Sr VP-Pet & Veterinary Practice)

French/West/Vaughan, LLC　　　(1)
185 Madison Ave Ste 401, New York, NY 10016
Tel.: (212) 213-8562
Web Site: http://www.fwv-us.com
Full Service
N.A.I.C.S.: 541810

French/West/Vaughan, LLC　　　(1)
2211 E 7th Ave, Tampa, FL 33605
Tel.: (727) 647-0770
Web Site: http://www.fwv-us.com
Sales Range: $10-24.9 Million
Advertising Agencies
N.A.I.C.S.: 541810

The Millerschin Group, Inc.　　　(1)
3250 University Dr Ste 115, Auburn Hills, MI 48326
Tel.: (248) 276-1970
Web Site: http://www.millerschingroup.com
Sales Range: Less than $1 Million
Emp.: 8
Advertising Agencies
N.A.I.C.S.: 541820
Erin Millerschin (Pres & CEO)
John Millerschin (COO)
Byron Pope (Acct Dir & Dir-Editorial)
Jeanne Sommerfield (Mgr-Acctg)

FRENCHIES CHEVROLET

255 E Orvis St, Massena, NY 13662-2255
Tel.: (315) 764-1760
Web Site:
http://www.frenchieschevrolet.com
Sales Range: $10-24.9 Million
Emp.: 45
Automobiles, New & Used
N.A.I.C.S.: 441110
Real Frenchie Coupal (Owner)
Dennis Binan (Mgr-Svc)
Todd Goolden (Mgr-Collision Center)
Sue Stiles (Mgr-Parts)
Ernie Miller (Gen Mgr-Sls)
Thelma Coupal (VP)
Michael J. Foote (Mgr-F&I & Compliance)

FRENCHMAN VALLEY FARMERS COOP. INC.

202 Broadway St, Imperial, NE 69033
Tel.: (308) 882-3200
Web Site: http://www.fvcoop.com
Year Founded: 1912
Sales Range: $75-99.9 Million
Emp.: 160
Grain & Feed Mfr
N.A.I.C.S.: 424510
Jim Haarberg (Chm)
Max Kaiser (Treas & Sec)
Rick Taylor (Vice Chm)
Cliff Church (CFO)
M. John Bender (CEO)

Subsidiaries:

Frenchman Valley Coop.　　　(1)
E Hwy 61 & 23, Grant, NE 69140
Tel.: (308) 352-4524
Web Site: http://www.fvcoop.com
Provider of Grain & Feed Services
N.A.I.C.S.: 424510
Cliff Church (Mgr-Acctg)

FRES-CO SYSTEM USA INCORPORATED

3005 State Rd, Telford, PA 18969-1033
Tel.: (215) 721-4600
Web Site: https://www.fresco.com
Year Founded: 1978
Sales Range: $50-74.9 Million
Emp.: 300

Packaging Machinery & Equipment
N.A.I.C.S.: 423830
Tullio Vigano (Pres & CEO)
Mark Stinson (CFO)
Jeffrey Beer (Dir-Tech)
John Keefe (Mgr-Production)
Chris Burger (Mgr-Coffee Market)
Colleen Hearn (Supvr-QA)
Dave Morrell (Supvr-Production)
Craig Rybitski (Dir-IT)
Albert Schoenberger (Engr-Pkg Sys)
Bob Lutz (Coord-Graphics)
Paul Laub (Supvr-Graphics Dept)
Trish Goffredo (Coord-Graphic)
Troy Adams (Mgr-Bus Dev)
Terry Baker (VP-Sls & Mktg)
William Livelsberger (Mgr-Customer Svc)
Jennifer Flexer (Mgr-Fin & Acctg)
Joan Tschepikiewski (Sec-Tech)
Raul Hauser (Dir-Liquid Pkg)
Larry Ashton (Exec VP)
Michele Langston (Mgr-Bus Dev)
Patti Bendik (Mgr-Logistics)
Peter Scheer (Mgr-Plastics)
Jennifer Marshall (Mgr-Quality)
John Thomas (Mgr-Tech)
Travis Blose (Plant Mgr)
Stephen Latshaw (Supvr-Finish)
Chuck Loh (Bus Mgr)
R. Jefferson Babbitt (Mgr-Analytical Svcs)
Rodrigo Sosa (Plant Mgr)

FRESH AS A DAISY, INC.

3601 Huntingridge Dr, High Point, NC 27265
Tel.: (336) 869-3002
Year Founded: 1999
Sales Range: $10-24.9 Million
Emp.: 150
Polish & Other Sanitation Good Mfr
N.A.I.C.S.: 325612
Cookie Golden (Pres)
Patrick Golden (VP)

FRESH CONSULTING LLC

914 140th Ave NE Ste 201, Bellevue, WA 98005
Web Site:
http://www.freshconsulting.com
Year Founded: 2007
Sales Range: $1-9.9 Million
Emp.: 26
Marketing, Website & Social Media Consulting
N.A.I.C.S.: 541613
Jeff Dance (CEO)
Steve Hulet (CTO)
Richard Rose (CFO)
Jeff Alexander (Chief Science Officer)

FRESH ENCOUNTER INC.

317 W Main Cross St, Findlay, OH 45840-3314
Tel.: (419) 422-8090　　　　OH
Web Site:
https://www.freshencounter.com
Sales Range: $450-499.9 Million
Emp.: 1,500
Supermarket Chain & Wholesaler of Groceries
N.A.I.C.S.: 423440
Michael S. Needler (Pres & CEO)

Subsidiaries:

Chief Super Market, Inc.　　　(1)
750 Deatrick St, Defiance, OH 43512
Tel.: (419) 782-9156
Web Site: http://www.chiefmarkets.com
Sales Range: $50-74.9 Million
Emp.: 1,200
Grocery Stores Owner & Operator
N.A.I.C.S.: 445110
Stacey Butler (Dir-Store)
Doug Brown (Asst Mgr)

Remke Markets Incorporated　　　(1)
1299 Cox Ave, Erlanger, KY 41018
Tel.: (859) 594-3400
Web Site: http://www.remkes.com
Independent Supermarket
N.A.I.C.S.: 445110
Jim Wood (Dir-Store)

FRESH ENTERPRISES, LLC

320 Commerce Ste 100, Irvine, CA 92602
Tel.: (805) 495-4704　　　　CA
Web Site: http://www.bajafresh.com
Year Founded: 1990
Sales Range: $10-24.9 Million
Emp.: 40
Mexican Food Restaurant Operator
N.A.I.C.S.: 722513
Jerry de Lucia (Dir-Mktg)
Chuck Rink (Pres & CEO)
Christina Paniagua (Coord-Mktg & Social Media)
Yvonne Durkan (Coord-HR)
Bob Gonda (CFO)
Roberto Lopez (Dir-Product Dev)

Subsidiaries:

La Salsa, Inc.　　　(1)
5900 Ketella Ave Ste A101, Cypress, CA 90630
Tel.: (805) 495-4704
Web Site: http://www.lasalsa.com
Sales Range: $75-99.9 Million
Emp.: 22
Fast Food Franchise
N.A.I.C.S.: 722513

FRESH EXPRESS FOODS CORPORATION, INC.

706 S Central Ave, Medford, OR 97501-7818
Tel.: (541) 773-4431
Web Site:
http://www.freshexpress.com
Year Founded: 1984
Sales Range: $10-24.9 Million
Emp.: 68
Fresh Produce Distr
N.A.I.C.S.: 424480
John Quicker (Pres)

FRESH INC.

25 Drydock Ave, Boston, MA 02210
Tel.: (617) 482-9411
Web Site: http://www.fresh.com
Year Founded: 1991
Sales Range: $10-24.9 Million
Emp.: 75
Cosmetics Mfr
N.A.I.C.S.: 424210

FRESH ISLAND FISH CO. INC.

312 Alamaha St Ste G, Kahului, HI 96732
Tel.: (808) 871-1111
Web Site:
http://www.freshislandfish.com
Rev.: $13,875,852
Emp.: 70
Fish, Fresh
N.A.I.C.S.: 424460
Bruce Johnson (Owner & CEO)

FRESH MARK, INC.

1888 Southway St SW, Massillon, OH 44646
Tel.: (330) 832-7491　　　　OH
Web Site: https://www.freshmark.com
Year Founded: 1920
Sales Range: $450-499.9 Million
Emp.: 1,400
Full Line Meat Processor Mfr
N.A.I.C.S.: 311612
Neil Genshaft (Chm & CEO)
Dave Cochenour (CFO, Treas & VP)
Alicia Pucky (Mgr-Pur)

Fresh Mark, Inc.—(Continued)

Subsidiaries:

Fresh Mark, Inc   **(1)**
1735 S Lincoln Ave, Salem, OH
44460-4250   **(100%)**
Tel.: (330) 332-8508
Sales Range: $50-74.9 Million
Emp.: 800
Processing & Packaging of Meat
N.A.I.C.S.: 311611
Rick Foster *(VP-Ops)*
Keith Kiewall *(Mgr)*

Sugardale Food Service   **(1)**
1011 Fox Run Rd, Findlay, OH 45840
Tel.: (419) 423-0122
Web Site:
   http://www.sugardalefoodservice.com
Emp.: 1
Smoked & Processed Meat Distr
N.A.I.C.S.: 424470
Brian Berry *(Reg Mgr-Sls)*

Sugardale Foods Inc.   **(1)**
1600 Harmont Ave NE, Canton, OH
44705-3302   **(100%)**
Tel.: (330) 455-5253
Web Site: http://www.freshmark.com
Sales Range: $50-74.9 Million
Emp.: 1,000
Meat Packing Company
N.A.I.C.S.: 311612
Tom Fee *(Dir-HR)*
Tim Cranor *(Pres)*

Superior's Brand Meats   **(1)**
1888 Southway SE, Massillon, OH
44646   **(100%)**
Tel.: (330) 832-7491
Web Site: http://www.superiorsbrand.com
Sales Range: $25-49.9 Million
Emp.: 700
Mfr Meat Products
N.A.I.C.S.: 311612
Ron Gaydosh *(Mgr-Sls)*
Dave Coconaer *(CFO)*
Neil Genshaft *(CEO)*

**FRESH MEADOW COUNTRY
CLUB**
255 Lakeville Rd, Lake Success, NY
11020
Tel.: (516) 482-7300   **NY**
Web Site:
   https://www.freshmeadow.org
Year Founded: 1921
Sales Range: $10-24.9 Million
Emp.: 210
Private Club
N.A.I.C.S.: 713910
Martel Meyer *(Gen Mgr)*

**FRESH PRODUCE SPORTS-
WEAR INC.**
2865 Wilderness Pl Ste B, Boulder,
CO 80301-2248
Tel.: (303) 444-7573
Web Site:
   http://www.freshproduceclothes.com
Year Founded: 1984
Sales Range: $25-49.9 Million
Emp.: 400
Family Apparel Retailer
N.A.I.C.S.: 424350
Thomas C. Vernon *(Co-Founder)*
Mary Ellen Vernon *(Co-Founder &
Chief Brand Officer)*
Jo Stone *(Pres)*
Dorothy Sadd *(COO)*

FRESH QUEST INC.
1580 Sawgrass Corporate Pkwy,
Sunrise, FL 33323
Tel.: (954) 316-5365
Web Site: http://www.freshquest.net
Year Founded: 1993
Sales Range: $10-24.9 Million
Emp.: 25
Distr of Fresh Fruits And Vegetables
N.A.I.C.S.: 424480

Sharon Imm *(Mgr-Acctg)*
Brad Palmer *(Mgr-Sls)*

**FRESHBREW GROUP USA,
L.P.**
11600 Big John St, Houston, TX
77038-3302
Tel.: (281) 847-2222   **TX**
Web Site:
   http://www.freshbrewgroup.com
Year Founded: 1995
Sales Range: $1-9.9 Million
Emp.: 45
Coffee, Tea & Coffee Bags Mfr; Vend-
ing Operations
N.A.I.C.S.: 311920
Dari Ansari *(CEO)*
Thomas Duffy *(VP-Sls-Vending Svcs
Div)*
Ali Ansari *(Pres)*
Fenton Allen *(Exec VP-Ops & Food
Svc Div)*
Steven Weyel *(COO-Vending Svcs
Div)*

Subsidiaries:

FreshBrew Vending   **(1)**
11600 Big John Blvd, Houston, TX 77038
Tel.: (409) 842-5577
Web Site: http://www.freshbrewvending.com
Vending Machine Mfr
N.A.I.C.S.: 333310

**FRESKA PRODUCE INTERNA-
TIONAL, LLC**
511 Mountain View Ave, Oxnard, CA
93030
Tel.: (805) 650-1040   **CA**
Web Site:
   https://www.freskaproduce.com
Year Founded: 2004
Produce Distr
N.A.I.C.S.: 424480
Tom Hall *(Mgr-Sls)*

FRESNO CHAFFEE ZOO
894 W Belmont Ave, Fresno, CA
93728
Tel.: (559) 498-5910   **CA**
Web Site:
   https://www.fresnochaffeezoo.org
Year Founded: 2005
Sales Range: $10-24.9 Million
Emp.: 181
Zoo
N.A.I.C.S.: 712130
Sharon Levy *(Sec)*
Tom Richards *(Vice Chm)*
Craig Saladino *(Treas)*
John Valentino *(Chm)*

**FRESNO ECONOMIC OPPOR-
TUNITIES COMMISSION**
1920 Mariposa Mall Ste 330, Fresno,
CA 93721
Tel.: (559) 263-1000   **CA**
Web Site: https://www.fresnoeoc.org
Year Founded: 1965
Sales Range: $100-124.9 Million
Emp.: 1,739
Community Action Services
N.A.I.C.S.: 624190
Naomi Quiring-Mizumoto *(Chief Pro-
grams Officer)*
Salam Nalia *(CFO)*
Paul McLain-Lugowski *(Chief Innova-
tion Officer)*
Gary Joseph *(Dir-Food Svcs & Tran-
sit Sys)*
Brian Angus *(CEO)*

FRESNO OXYGEN
2825 S Elm Ave Ste 101, Fresno, CA
93706
Tel.: (559) 233-6684

Web Site:
   http://www.fresnooxygen.com
Year Founded: 1949
Sales Range: $10-24.9 Million
Emp.: 30
Industrial Machinery & Equipment
N.A.I.C.S.: 423830
Michael Barnes *(Pres)*
Todd Rayburn *(CFO)*
David Barnes *(Sr VP-Branch Ops)*
Lawrence T. Barnes Jr. *(CEO)*

**FRESNO PLUMBING & HEAT-
ING INC.**
2585 N Larkin Ave, Fresno, CA
93727
Tel.: (559) 292-4065
Web Site:
   https://www.fresnoplumbinginc.com
Sales Range: $10-24.9 Million
Emp.: 140
Plumbing Products & Services
N.A.I.C.S.: 238220
Patty Kumpe *(Sec)*

FRESNO TRUCK CENTER
2727 E Central Ave, Fresno, CA
93725
Tel.: (559) 486-4310
Web Site:
   http://www.californiatruckcenter.com
Sales Range: $150-199.9 Million
Emp.: 200
Heavy Duty Trucks
N.A.I.C.S.: 441110
Doug Howard *(Owner)*
Brian Nicholson *(VP)*

**FRESNO VALVES & CAST-
INGS INC.**
7736 E Springfield Ave, Selma, CA
93662-0040
Tel.: (559) 834-2511   **CA**
Web Site:
   https://www.fresnovalves.com
Year Founded: 1952
Sales Range: $25-49.9 Million
Emp.: 365
Fabricated Structural Metal Mfr
N.A.I.C.S.: 331529
Denise Cano *(Mgr-HR)*

Subsidiaries:

Pierce Fittings   **(1)**
10 N Garfield St, Eugene, OR 97402-2668
Tel.: (541) 485-3111
Web Site: http://www.fresnovalves.com
Sales Range: $10-24.9 Million
Emp.: 36
Mfr of Valves & Pipe Fittings
N.A.I.C.S.: 332919

**FRESNO-MADERA FARM
CREDIT ASSOCIATION**
4635 W Spruce, Fresno, CA 93722
Tel.: (559) 277-7000
Web Site:
   https://www.fmfarmcredit.com
Sales Range: $25-49.9 Million
Emp.: 70
Production Credit Association, Agri-
cultural
N.A.I.C.S.: 522299
Dan Kiggens *(Chief Credit Officer &
Sr VP)*
Stephanie Graham *(Chief Admin Offi-
cer & Sr VP)*
David Ylarregui *(Sr VP-Relationship
Mgmt)*
Jeff Jue *(Chm)*
Victor Sahatdjian *(Vice Chm)*

FREUD, INC.
218 Feld Ave, High Point, NC 27263-
1930
Tel.: (336) 434-3171   **NC**

Web Site: https://www.freudtools.com
Year Founded: 1971
Sales Range: $10-24.9 Million
Emp.: 60
Hardware & Related Products Mfr
N.A.I.C.S.: 423710

FREUND & COMPANY INC.
15460 E Batavia Dr, Aurora, CO
80011
Tel.: (303) 341-9310
Sales Range: $10-24.9 Million
Emp.: 25
Warm Air Heating & Air Conditioning
Contractor
N.A.I.C.S.: 238220
Joseph D. Freund *(Pres)*

FREY & ASSOCIATES, LLC
100 2nd Ave S Ste 206 N, Saint Pe-
tersburg, FL 33701
Tel.: (727) 471-0654
Web Site: http://freymasterson.com
Sales Range: $1-9.9 Million
Emp.: 3
Investment Advisory Services
N.A.I.C.S.: 528940
Matthew Frey *(Owner & Partner)*

**FRHAM SAFETY PRODUCTS
INC.**
171 Grayson Rd, Rock Hill, SC
29732
Tel.: (803) 366-5131
Web Site:
   https://www.frhamsafety.com
Rev.: $15,161,516
Emp.: 40
Safety Equipment
N.A.I.C.S.: 423830
Trip McGarity *(Mgr-Sls)*
Cathy Robertson *(Comptroller)*
John H. McGarity Jr. *(Pres)*

FRICK SERVICES INC.
3154 Depot St, Wawaka, IN 46794
Tel.: (260) 761-3311   **IN**
Web Site:
   https://www.frickservices.com
Year Founded: 1952
Sales Range: $10-24.9 Million
Emp.: 100
Farm Supply Services
N.A.I.C.S.: 424910
Merrill B. Frick *(Pres)*

**FRICTIONLESS SOLUTIONS,
INC.**
415 W Golf Rd Ste 28, Arlington
Heights, IL 60005
Tel.: (847) 233-1060
Web Site:
   http://www.frictionlesssolutions.com
Year Founded: 2014
Sales Range: $10-24.9 Million
Emp.: 18
Software Development Services
N.A.I.C.S.: 541511
Mike McCauley *(Pres)*

FRIDAY OIL CO. INC.
1812 Culver Rd, Tuscaloosa, AL
35401
Tel.: (205) 759-4291
Rev.: $16,162,014
Emp.: 12
Petroleum Bulk Stations & Terminals
N.A.I.C.S.: 424710
Todd Turner *(Mgr)*

**FRIEDLER CONSTRUCTION
COMPANY**
2525 N Elston Ave Ste D230, Chicago, IL 60647-9349
Tel.: (773) 489-1818

Web Site:
http://www.friedlerconstruction.com
Sales Range: $10-24.9 Million
Emp.: 12
Nonresidential Construction Services
N.A.I.C.S.: 236220
Eric Friedler *(Pres)*

FRIEDMAN LLP
1700 Broadway, New York, NY 10019
Tel.: (212) 842-7000
Web Site: http://www.friedmanllp.com
Year Founded: 1924
Sales Range: $50-74.9 Million
Emp.: 300
Financial Services
N.A.I.C.S.: 541211
Marc P. Eidelberg *(Partner-New Jersey)*
Michael Goldman *(Partner-New Jersey)*
Barry Eckenthal *(Partner-New Jersey)*
Claudette Spano *(CFO)*
Carl H. Bagell *(Mng Partner-South Jersey)*
Neil I. Levine *(Partner-New Jersey)*
Jason Tang *(Partner-New Jersey & New York)*
Robert E. Fiorentino *(Partner-New Jersey)*
Ronald Frimmer *(Partner)*
Harriet Greenberg *(Co-Mng Partner)*
Jay L. Goldstein *(Partner)*
James Lee *(Principal)*
Glenn M. Josephs *(Partner-New Jersey)*
Frederick R. Berk *(Mng Partner-New York)*
Diane Gitto *(Partner-Linwood)*
Jerald Jacobik *(Partner-New York)*
Seth Marin *(Partner-New Jersey)*
Justin Van Fleet *(Partner-Marlton)*
Michael Sacco *(Partner)*
John M. Bono *(Partner-Tax Svcs Dept)*
Brian Kristiansen *(Partner-Tax Svcs Dept)*
Scott Stavin *(Partner-Tax Svcs Dept)*
Geoffrey Wilson *(Partner-Tax Svcs Dept)*
Susan Miano *(Partner-Forensic Acctg, Litigation Support & Valuation Svcs Grp)*
Randall Paulikens *(Partner-East Hanover)*
George Fanourakis *(Principal)*
Muriel Cheng *(Partner)*
Phillip A. Bottari *(Partner)*
Tom Corrie *(Principal)*
Marie DeCicco *(Principal)*
Noelene T. Sheridan *(Principal-Tax-Uniondale)*
Jo Anna M. Fellon *(Principal)*
Shaji Varghese *(Partner-Audit)*
Brandon Baker *(Principal-Tax)*
Scott Croff *(Principal-Tax)*

FRIEDMAN RECYCLING COMPANY
3640 W Lincoln St, Phoenix, AZ 85009
Tel.: (602) 269-9324
Web Site:
http://www.friedmanrecycling.com
Sales Range: $10-24.9 Million
Emp.: 70
Recycling Services
N.A.I.C.S.: 562920
David Friedman *(Co-Owner)*
Bret Burrer *(Plant Mgr)*
Morris Friedman *(Co-Owner)*

FRIEDOMTECH LLC
461 Oak Glen Rd, Howell, NJ 07731
Tel.: (732) 730-7777
Web Site: http://www.tech-keys.com

Year Founded: 2009
Sales Range: $10-24.9 Million
Emp.: 52
Information Technology Development Services
N.A.I.C.S.: 541511
Michael Fried *(Pres & CEO)*

FRIEL LUMBER CO.
100 Friel Pl, Queenstown, MD 21658
Tel.: (410) 827-8811
Web Site:
https://www.friellumber.com
Sales Range: $25-49.9 Million
Emp.: 150
Packaged Vegetables
N.A.I.C.S.: 311421
James R. Friel Jr. *(Partner)*

FRIEND FAMILY HEALTH CENTER, INC.
800 E 55th St, Chicago, IL 60615
Tel.: (773) 702-0660   IL
Web Site: https://www.friendfhc.org
Year Founded: 1997
Sales Range: $10-24.9 Million
Emp.: 178
Community Health Care Services
N.A.I.C.S.: 621498
Barbara K. Williams *(Dir-Resource Dev & External Affairs)*
Sabrina G. Moore *(CFO)*
Verneda Bachus *(CEO)*
Sean Harden *(Vice Chm)*
Andre Rawls *(Sec)*
Thomas Jones *(Chm)*
Carlos Meyers *(Treas)*

FRIEND SKOLER & CO., INC.
250 Pehle Ave Ste 205 Park 80 W Plz 1, Saddle Brook, NJ 07663
Tel.: (201) 712-0075
Web Site:
http://www.friendskoler.com
Year Founded: 1998
Sales Range: $25-49.9 Million
Emp.: 8
Privater Equity Firm
N.A.I.C.S.: 523999
Alexander A. Friend *(Mng Dir)*
Steven F. Skoler *(Mng Dir)*

FRIENDFINDER NETWORKS INC.
910E Hamilton Ave 6th Fl, Campbell, CA 95008
Tel.: (408) 745-5400   NV
Web Site: http://www.ffn.com
Year Founded: 1965
Sales Range: $300-349.9 Million
Social Networking & Multimedia Entertainment Services
N.A.I.C.S.: 518210
Ezra Shashoua *(CFO)*
Andrew Conru *(Founder & Chm)*
Jonathan Buckheit *(CEO)*

Subsidiaries:

Friendfinder Ventures, Inc.   (1)
6800 Broken Sound Pkwy, Boca Raton, FL 33487
Tel.: (561) 988-1733
Web Site:
http://www.friendfinderventures.com
Custom Computer Programming Services
N.A.I.C.S.: 541511
Daniel C. Staton *(Chm)*

Various, Inc.   (1)
220 Humboldt Ct, Sunnyvale, CA 94089
Tel.: (408) 745-5400
Web Site: http://www.various.com
Emp.: 250
Online & Social Networking Services
N.A.I.C.S.: 518210
Roger Lerrick *(Chief Acctg Officer)*
Christy Lam *(Project Mgr)*

FRIENDLY CHECK CASHING CORP.
701 N Frank E Roger Blvd, Harrison, NJ 07129
Tel.: (973) 482-0001
Year Founded: 1970
Sales Range: $25-49.9 Million
Emp.: 2
Personal Financial Services
N.A.I.C.S.: 522390
Jose Fernandez *(Pres)*

FRIENDLY CHEVROLET CO. INC.
2754 N Stemmons Fwy, Dallas, TX 75207-2213
Tel.: (214) 920-1956   TX
Web Site:
https://www.friendlychevy.com
Year Founded: 1963
Sales Range: $125-149.9 Million
Emp.: 165
Retailer of New & Used Automobiles & Trucks
N.A.I.C.S.: 441110
Mark A. Eddins *(Pres & CEO)*

FRIENDLY CHEVROLET, INC.
2540 Prairie Crossing Dr, Springfield, IL 62711
Tel.: (217) 953-4913
Web Site:
http://www.susanautomall.com
Sales Range: $10-24.9 Million
Emp.: 65
New Car Dealers
N.A.I.C.S.: 441110
Susan Langheim *(Owner)*
Mark Greenwood *(Controller)*

FRIENDLY CHRYSLER JEEP
32899 Van Dyke Ave, Warren, MI 48093-8139
Tel.: (586) 554-2006
Web Site:
https://www.jimriehlsfriendly chryslerjeep.com
Sales Range: $25-49.9 Million
Emp.: 120
Car Whslr
N.A.I.C.S.: 441110
James Riehl Jr. *(Pres)*

FRIENDLY ENERGY EXPLORATION
502 N Division St, Carson City, NV 89703
Tel.: (702) 953-0411   NV
Year Founded: 1993
Sales Range: Less than $1 Million
Emp.: 2
Natural Gas Extraction Services
N.A.I.C.S.: 211130

FRIENDLY FORD
660 N Decatur Blvd, Las Vegas, NV 89107
Tel.: (702) 870-7221
Web Site:
http://www.friendlyfordlv.com
Sales Range: $150-199.9 Million
Emp.: 350
New Car Dealers
N.A.I.C.S.: 441110
Jason Male *(Mgr-Contract)*

FRIENDLY FORD, INC.
2800 N Telegraph Rd, Monroe, MI 48162
Tel.: (734) 243-6000
Web Site:
https://www.yourfriendlyford.com
Sales Range: $10-24.9 Million
Emp.: 85
Car Dealership
N.A.I.C.S.: 441110

Thomas E. Shankie *(Pres)*
Jodi Lesinszki *(Office Mgr)*

FRIENDLY FUELS INC.
1190 Sunset Blvd NE Ste F, Renton, WA 98056
Tel.: (425) 228-1825
Rev.: $18,000,000
Emp.: 1
Land Subdividers & Developers, Commercial
N.A.I.C.S.: 237210
Adam M. Sims *(Pres)*

FRIENDLY SERVICE STATION INC.
1624 Dixwell Ave, Hamden, CT 06514-3614
Tel.: (203) 287-9433
Year Founded: 1975
Sales Range: $10-24.9 Million
Emp.: 125
Gasoline Sales
N.A.I.C.S.: 457120
Richard Wiehl *(Pres)*

FRIENDS CHILD CARE CENTER
1501 Cherry St, Philadelphia, PA 19102
Tel.: (215) 241-7011   PA
Web Site:
http://www.friendschildcare.org
Year Founded: 1978
Sales Range: $1-9.9 Million
Emp.: 29
Child Care Services
N.A.I.C.S.: 624110
Raechel O'Neal Coats *(Exec Dir)*

FRIENDS HOMES INC.
925 New Garden Rd, Greensboro, NC 27410
Tel.: (336) 292-8187
Web Site:
https://www.friendshomes.org
Year Founded: 1958
Sales Range: $50-74.9 Million
Emp.: 400
Retirement Home Operation
N.A.I.C.S.: 531110
Cham Dickey *(Controller)*
Marie Brown *(Dir-Admissions)*
Pat Manuel *(Dir-HR)*
Wilson M. Sheldon Jr. *(CEO)*

FRIENDS LIFE CARE
531 Plymouth Rd Ste 500, Plymouth Meeting, PA 19462
Tel.: (215) 628-8964   PA
Web Site:
http://www.friendslifecare.org
Year Founded: 1985
Sales Range: $10-24.9 Million
Emp.: 48
Disability Assistance Services
N.A.I.C.S.: 624120
Carol A. Barbour *(Pres)*

FRIENDS OF MOSDOT GOOR, INC
1310 48th St, Brooklyn, NY 11219
Tel.: (718) 435-8989   NY
Year Founded: 1991
Sales Range: $10-24.9 Million
Passover Assistance Services
N.A.I.C.S.: 812220
Issac Gottesman *(Pres)*
Moshe Steinberg *(Treas & VP)*
Yedidya Greenstein *(Sec)*

FRIENDS OF YOUTH
13116 NE 132nd St, Kirkland, WA 98034-2306
Tel.: (425) 869-6490   WA

Friends of Youth—(Continued)

Web Site:
https://www.friendsofyouth.org
Year Founded: 1951
Sales Range: $10-24.9 Million
Emp.: 259
Youth Care Services
N.A.I.C.S.: 624110
Derek Wentorf (Dir-Homeless Youth Svcs)
Cindy Sullivan (CFO)
Janet Turpen (Vice Chm)
Carol Almero (Dir-Residential Treatment Svcs)
Andrew Bartram (Treas)
Deann Adams (Dir-Specialized Residential Svcs)
Darlene Connor (Dir-HR)
Phil Crocker (Sec)
Paul Lwali (CEO)

FRIENDSHIP AUTOMOTIVE INC.
1855 Volunteer Pkwy, Bristol, TN 37620-6308
Tel.: (423) 652-6200   TN
Web Site:
http://www.friendshipauto.com
Year Founded: 1993
Sales Range: $25-49.9 Million
Emp.: 200
New & Used Car Dealers
N.A.I.C.S.: 441110
Mitch Walters (Owner & Pres)
David A. Snyder (Controller)
Audrey Spangler (Office Mgr)
Donnnie Rasnake (Dir-Parts)
Denny Fruth (Gen Mgr-Ford)

FRIENDSHIP COMMUNITY
1149 E Oregon Rd, Lititz, PA 17543-8366
Tel.: (717) 656-2466   PA
Web Site: https://www.friendshipcommunity.net
Year Founded: 1987
Sales Range: $10-24.9 Million
Emp.: 508
Disability Assistance Services
N.A.I.C.S.: 624120
Cynthia Beebe (Dir-Dev)
Gwen Schuit (CEO)
Robert Redcay (Dir-HR)

FRIENDSHIP HAVEN, INC.
420 Kenyon Rd, Fort Dodge, IA 50501
Tel.: (515) 573-6000   IA
Web Site:
http://www.friendshiphaven.org
Year Founded: 1946
Sales Range: $10-24.9 Million
Emp.: 433
Adult Care Services
N.A.I.C.S.: 623312
Mel Smith (VP-Campus Support Svcs)
Rollie Peterson (VP-Residential Ops)
Julie Thorson (Pres & CEO)
Tim J. Burns (Chm)

FRIENDSHIP HOUSE
1509 Maple St, Scranton, PA 18505
Tel.: (570) 342-8305   PA
Web Site:
https://www.friendshiphousepa.org
Year Founded: 1873
Sales Range: $10-24.9 Million
Emp.: 355
Behavioral Healthcare Services
N.A.I.C.S.: 623220
Patrick Ackourey (Exec VP)
Christine Gilroy (Exec VP)
Timothy McGrane (Dir-Program Dev & Design)
Alex J. Hazzouri (Pres & CEO)

Chyleen Chumard (Program Dir)
Debbie Zielinski (Chief HR Officer & VP)
Erin Connelly (Asst Program Dir-Autism)
James R. Martin (COO & VP)
Jeff Briggs (Mng Dir)
Keisha Moeller (Program Dir-Autism)
Megan Boettcher (Dir-Clinical Svcs)
Varsha Pandya (Dir-Medical)

FRIENDSHIP STATE BANK
5908 Main St, Friendship, IN 47021
Tel.: (812) 667-5103   IN
Web Site:
http://www.friendshipstatebank.com
Year Founded: 1912
Sales Range: $10-24.9 Million
Emp.: 70
Banking Services
N.A.I.C.S.: 522110
James William Lemon (Pres & CEO)
Greg Hughes (Branch Mgr)
Katie Sparks (Branch Mgr)

FRIEZE ADVERTISING INC.
48 Yorktown Rd, East Brunswick, NJ 08816-3325
Tel.: (732) 828-5800
Year Founded: 1971
Sales Range: $25-49.9 Million
Emp.: 3
Broadcast, Business-To-Business, Cable T.V., Exhibit/Trade Shows, Newspaper, Trade & Consumer Magazines
N.A.I.C.S.: 541810
Gerald Frieze (Pres)
Clara Baumann (Dir-Creative)
Linda Kasowsky (Media Dir)

FRIGHT-RAGS, INC.
1356 Buffalo Rd, Rochester, NY 14624
Tel.: (585) 730-8280
Web Site: http://www.fright-rags.com
Year Founded: 2003
Tee Shirt Producer & Online Retailer
N.A.I.C.S.: 315250
Benjamin Scrivens (Owner)
Tim Kilmer (Mgr-Shipping)

FRINGE BENEFIT GROUP LP
11910 Anderson Mill Rd Ste 401, Austin, TX 78726
Tel.: (800) 662-6177
Web Site: https://fbg.com
Year Founded: 1983
Emp.: 100
Benefits Administration Services
N.A.I.C.S.: 561499
Travis West (CEO)
Adam Bonsky (Exec VP)
Brian Robertson (Exec VP)
Erica A. Wolff (VP-HR)

Subsidiaries:

Century Healthcare LLC   (1)
6300 Fallwater Trl Ste 120, The Colony, TX 75056-2628
Tel.: (469) 341-0999
Direct Life Insurance Carriers
N.A.I.C.S.: 524113

FRIO REGIONAL HOSPITAL
200 S IH 35, Pearsall, TX 78061
Tel.: (830) 334-3617   TX
Web Site:
https://www.frioregionalhospital.com
Year Founded: 2002
Sales Range: $10-24.9 Million
Health Care Srvices
N.A.I.C.S.: 622110
Nancy Ortiz (Dir-HR & Mktg)
Louisa Martinez (Dir-Nursing)
Andy Williams (CEO)

FRIONA INDUSTRIES, LP
500 S Taylor St Ste 601, Amarillo, TX 79101-2442
Tel.: (806) 374-1811   DE
Web Site: http://www.frionaind.com
Year Founded: 1967
Sales Range: $50-74.9 Million
Emp.: 17
Agricultural Services
N.A.I.C.S.: 115210
James E. Herring (Pres & CEO)
Dal C. Reid (CFO)
Brad Stout (Mgr-Procurement)

Subsidiaries:

Friona Agriculture Credit Corp.   (1)
PO Box 15568, Amarillo, TX 79105-5568   (100%)
Tel.: (806) 220-2855
Web Site: http://www.frionaind.com
Sales Range: $25-49.9 Million
Emp.: 15
Cattle Feeding
N.A.I.C.S.: 522299
Brad Stout (Mgr-Cattle Procurement)

Friona Feed Yard   (1)
2370 FM 3140, Friona, TX 79035-0806
Tel.: (806) 265-3574
Sales Range: $10-24.9 Million
Cattle Feedlots
N.A.I.C.S.: 112112

Hi-Pro Feeds   (1)
1201 E 11th St, Friona, TX 79035-0519
Tel.: (806) 250-2791
Web Site: http://www.hiprofeeds.com
Marketing of Animal Feed
N.A.I.C.S.: 311119
Mark Osborn (Plant Mgr)
Mark Teel (Mgr-Food Safety & Quality Sys)

Littlefield Feed Yard   (1)
RR 1, Amherst, TX 79312-9614   (100%)
Tel.: (806) 385-5141
Web Site: http://www.frionaind.com
Sales Range: $10-24.9 Million
Cattle Feeding, Animal Health Products & Live Stock Feed
N.A.I.C.S.: 112112
John Vanwey (Gen Mgr)

Randall County Feed Yard   (1)
15000 FM 2219, Amarillo, TX 79119
Tel.: (806) 499-3701
Web Site: http://www.frionaindustries.com
Cattle Feeding & Meat Processing
N.A.I.C.S.: 112112
Barry Chew (Mgr-Feedyard)

Swisher County Cattle Co.   (1)
6656 FM 214, Happy, TX 79042
Tel.: (806) 627-4231
Web Site: http://www.frionaind.com
Sales Range: $10-24.9 Million
Feed Yard
N.A.I.C.S.: 112112
James Hairing (CEO)

FRISCHHERTZ ELECTRIC COMPANY, INC.
4240 Toulouse St, New Orleans, LA 70119
Tel.: (504) 482-1146
Web Site:
https://www.frischhertz.com
Year Founded: 1995
Sales Range: $25-49.9 Million
Emp.: 50
Electrical Wiring Services
N.A.I.C.S.: 238210
Steve Frischhertz (Pres)

FRIT INCORPORATED
1792 Jodie Parker Rd, Ozark, AL 36360-1589
Tel.: (334) 774-2515
Web Site: https://www.fritinc.com
Year Founded: 1989
Sales Range: $25-49.9 Million
Emp.: 250
Holding Company
N.A.I.C.S.: 551112

Shelton E Allred (Pres)
Carl Schauble (Exec VP)

Subsidiaries:

Frit Car Inc.   (1)
1965 S Blvd, Brewton, AL 36427
Tel.: (251) 867-7752
Web Site: http://www.fritcar.com
Sales Range: $10-24.9 Million
Emp.: 75
Distr of Railroad Cars
N.A.I.C.S.: 488210
Larry Lanham (Pres & CEO)
Jimmy Blankenship (Mgr-Ops)
Michael Newby (VP)
Harvey Wyatt (Dir-Ops)
Andy Lisabelle (Mgr-Quality Assurance)
David Turner (Dir-Safety)
A. J. Daugherty (Asst Gen Mgr)
Randy Cooke (Mgr-Quality Assurance)

Frit Industries Inc.   (1)
1792 Jodie Parker Rd, Ozark, AL 36360
Tel.: (334) 774-2515
Web Site: http://www.frit.com
Sales Range: $10-24.9 Million
Emp.: 40
Mfr of Fertilizers
N.A.I.C.S.: 325311

Green Sol Inc.   (1)
PO Box 1589, Ozark, AL 36360
Tel.: (334) 774-2515
Web Site: http://www.greensol.com
Sales Range: $10-24.9 Million
Emp.: 30
Farm Supplies
N.A.I.C.S.: 424910

Pro Sol Inc.   (1)
1792 Jodie Parker Rd, Ozark, AL 36360
Tel.: (334) 774-2515
Web Site: http://www.4prosol.com
Sales Range: $10-24.9 Million
Emp.: 30
Processor of Fertilizers
N.A.I.C.S.: 325314
Carl E Shauble (Exec VP)
Shelton E Allred (Pres)

FRITCH INC.
116 River St, Bethlehem, PA 18018
Tel.: (610) 691-1212   PA
Web Site: https://www.fritch.com
Year Founded: 1920
Sales Range: $10-24.9 Million
Emp.: 55
Heating Oil Distr
N.A.I.C.S.: 457210
Anthony Mauser (Pres)

FRITZ COMPANY
1912 Hastings Ave, Burnsville, MN 55055
Tel.: (651) 459-9751
Web Site: http://www.fritziefresh.com
Sales Range: $10-24.9 Million
Emp.: 8
Confectionery
N.A.I.C.S.: 424450
Keith Youngquist (CFO)

Subsidiaries:

Click Distributing Co Inc.   (1)
1912 Hastings Ave, Newport, MN 55055
Tel.: (608) 784-4110
Cigars
N.A.I.C.S.: 424940

FRITZ ENTERPRISES
1600 Broadway, Kerrville, TX 78028
Tel.: (830) 257-6464   TX
Year Founded: 1976
Sales Range: $10-24.9 Million
Emp.: 3
Grocery & Convenience Stores
N.A.I.C.S.: 445131

FRITZ ENTERPRISES INC.
1650 W Jefferson Ave, Trenton, MI
48183
Tel.: (734) 362-3200
Web Site: https://www.fritzinc.com
Year Founded: 1971
Rev.: $21,900,000
Emp.: 400
Ferrous Metal Scrap & Waste
N.A.I.C.S.: 423930
Leonard Fritz *(Pres)*
Eric Fritz *(Exec VP)*

FRITZ INDUSTRIES INC.
500 N Sam Houston Rd, Mesquite,
TX 75149-2789
Tel.: (972) 285-5471   TX
Web Site: http://www.fritzind.com
Year Founded: 1956
Sales Range: $100-124.9 Million
Emp.: 300
Mfr of Industrial Inorganic Materials;
Terrazzo Floor Tile, Oilfield Additives,
Aquaculture Products, Pet Products;
Wholesale Nondurable Goods
N.A.I.C.S.: 325998
Brian Ross *(VP-Safety & Environment)*

FRIZZELL CONSTRUCTION CO. INC.
1501 Bluff City Hwy, Bristol, TN
37620
Tel.: (423) 764-5107
Web Site:
   http://www.frizzellconstruction.com
Year Founded: 1960
Sales Range: $10-24.9 Million
Emp.: 54
Commercial & Office Building, New
Construction
N.A.I.C.S.: 236220
Sherie Horton *(CFO)*
Ben M. Frizzell Jr. *(Owner & Pres)*

FROEDTERT MEMORIAL LU-THERAN HOSPITAL, INC.
3200 Pleasant Vly Rd, West Bend,
WI 53095-3095
Tel.: (414) 805-3666
Web Site: http://www.froedtert.com
Emp.: 100
General Medical & Surgical Hospitals
N.A.I.C.S.: 622110
Anne King *(Project Mgr)*

Subsidiaries:

THEDACARE INC.   (1)
122 E College Ave, Appleton, WI 54911
Tel.: (920) 735-5560
Sales Range: $250-299.9 Million
Emp.: 100
Community Health Care Services
N.A.I.C.S.: 621498
Tim Olson *(CFO-Sys & VP)*
Gregory Devine *(Sr VP-Provider Strategies
& Sys of Care)*
Maureen Pistone *(Sr VP-Talent Mgmt)*
Keith Livingston *(CIO & Sr VP)*
Brian Burmeister *(Sr VP-Physician & Rural
Svcs)*
Julie Kressin *(VP-Revenue Mgmt)*
Randy Roeper *(COO-Physicians)*
Courtney Weiland *(VP-Philanthropy)*

FROEHLING & ROBERTSON INC.
3015 Dumbarton Rd, Richmond, VA
23228
Tel.: (804) 264-2701
Web Site: http://www.fandr.com
Sales Range: $50-74.9 Million
Emp.: 450
Engineering Testing Laboratories
N.A.I.C.S.: 541715
Marving Farmer *(Branch Mgr-Chesapeake)*
Bob Hill *(Mgr-Engrg)*

FROGGER, LLC
1400 Fashion Island Blvd Suite 1050,
Redwood City, CA 94063
Web Site:
   https://www.froggergolf.com
Year Founded: 2005
Sales Range: $1-9.9 Million
Emp.: 4
Designs, Mfr & Distributes Proprietary
Golf Accessory Products & Apparel
N.A.I.C.S.: 458110
Jeremiah Bohannon *(Founder &
Pres)*

FROMM ELECTRIC SUPPLY CORPORATION
2101 Center Ave, Reading, PA
19605-5147
Tel.: (610) 374-4441   PA
Web Site:
   https://www.frommelectric.com
Year Founded: 1958
Sales Range: $10-24.9 Million
Emp.: 115
Electrical Apparatus & Equipment
N.A.I.C.S.: 423610
Michael Fromm *(CEO)*
Lou Fromm *(VP-Business Development)*

FROMM FAMILY PET FOODS, INC.
13145 N Green Bay Rd 56 W, Me-
quon, WI 53092
Tel.: (262) 242-2200   WI
Web Site:
   https://www.frommfamily.com
Year Founded: 1904
Sales Range: $1-9.9 Million
Emp.: 90
Premium Pet Foods Mfr
N.A.I.C.S.: 311111
Tom Nieman *(Pres & Head Chef)*
Kathryn Nieman *(Controller)*
Jim Glassford *(Coord-Sls & Mktg)*

FRONK OIL CO. INC.
14950 Hwy 23, Booker, TX 79005
Tel.: (806) 658-4565
Web Site: https://www.fronkoil.com
Sales Range: $10-24.9 Million
Emp.: 50
Gases, Liquefied Petroleum, Propane
N.A.I.C.S.: 424720
Keith Fronk *(VP)*

FRONT BURNER BRANDS, INC.
8810 Twin Lakes Blvd, Tampa, FL
33614
Tel.: (813) 881-0055
Web Site:
   http://www.frontburnerbrands.com
Sales Range: $200-249.9 Million
Emp.: 700
Restaurant Owner & Franchisor
N.A.I.C.S.: 722511
Dan Stone *(Chief Bus & People Dev
Officer)*
Sandy D'Elosua *(Dir-Mktg & Comm)*
Bob Johnston *(Chm & CEO)*
Mike Johnston *(VP)*
Jim Sullivan *(VP-Real Estate)*
Scott Pierce *(CFO)*
Mark Johnston *(Pres & Chief Con-
cept Officer)*
Alisha dos Santos *(Mgr-Comm)*
Bud Culp *(Gen Counsel)*
Maryellen Torres *(Chief Brand Officer)*
Michele Whaley *(VP-Mktg)*
Randy Barnett *(VP-IT)*
Jennifer Dodd *(VP-Ops)*

Subsidiaries:

The Melting Pot Restaurants Inc.   (1)
7886 Woodland Ctr Blvd, Tampa, FL 33614

Tel.: (813) 881-0055
Web Site: http://www.meltingpot.com
Emp.: 45
Restaurant Owner & Franchisor
N.A.I.C.S.: 722511
Mike Lester *(Pres)*

FRONT PORCH MARKETING LLC
109 N Main St Ste 700, Dayton, OH
45402
Tel.: (937) 890-5311
Web Site: https://www.tricomb2b.com
Year Founded: 1984
Sales Range: $1-9.9 Million
Emp.: 29
Business-To-Business Advertising
N.A.I.C.S.: 541810
John Buscemi *(Principal)*
Chris Eifert *(Principal)*
Kara Cox *(Coord-Traffic)*

FRONT ROW MOTORSPORTS, INC.
2670 Peachtree Rd, Statesville, NC
28625
Tel.: (704) 873-6445
Web Site: http://www.teamfirm.com
Year Founded: 2005
Sales Range: $1-9.9 Million
Emp.: 55
NASCAR Sprint Cup Series Team
Operations
N.A.I.C.S.: 711219
Robin Johnson *(CMO)*
Mike Laheta *(Dir-Mktg & Bus Affairs)*

FRONTENAC COMPANY LLC
1 S Walker Ste 2980, Chicago, IL
60606
Tel.: (312) 368-0044
Web Site: http://www.frontenac.com
Year Founded: 1971
Emp.: 40
Privater Equity Firm
N.A.I.C.S.: 523999
Paul D. Carbery *(Mng Dir)*
Julie A. Bender *(CFO, Chief Com-
plaince Officer & VP)*
Walter C. Florence *(Mng Dir)*
Kristen L. Trotta *(Controller)*
Ronald W. Kuehl *(Mng Dir)*
Michael S. Langdon *(Mng Dir)*
Elizabeth C. Williamson *(Mng Dir)*
Joseph R. Rondinelli *(Principal)*
Neal G. Sahney *(Principal)*
Kenneth R. Kluckman *(VP)*
Markie L. Masri *(VP)*
Gilyana Lidzheeva *(Dir-Portfolio Ops)*
Teri D. Tadros *(Dir-Dev)*

Subsidiaries:

Bearing Engineers, Inc.   (1)
27 Argonaut, Aliso Viejo, CA 92656
Tel.: (949) 586-7442
Web Site: http://www.bearingengineers.com
Mechanical & Electrical Components Mfr
N.A.I.C.S.: 333613
Robert Bloom *(CEO)*
Eric Horne *(Acct Mgr)*
Bill Lackey *(Mgr-Motion Control Grp)*
Harold Katz *(Pres)*

CoCreativ Corp.   (1)
32 Ave of the Americas Fl 22, New York,
NY 10013
Tel.: (212) 792-2700
Web Site: http://www.cocreativ.co
Marketing & Digital Production Services
N.A.I.C.S.: 541613
Mathieu Champigny *(CEO)*

Subsidiary (Domestic):

Industrial Color Productions, Inc.   (2)
32 Ave of the Americas, Fl 22, New York,
NY 10013
Tel.: (212) 792-2700
Web Site: https://industrialcolor.com
Advertising Services

N.A.I.C.S.: 323111

Integrated Openings Solutions,
LLC   (1)
28120 Hunters Rdg Blvd 4, Bonita Springs,
FL 34135
Tel.: (239) 488-3667
Web Site: https://www.integratedopenings.com
Emp.: 100
Commercial & Architectural Metal, Wood
Doors, Frames & Other Hardware Products
Distr & Marketer
N.A.I.C.S.: 561621

Subsidiary (Domestic):

Atlass Hardware Corporation   (2)
4800 S W 51st St Ste 104, Davie, FL
33314
Tel.: (954) 316-6160
Web Site:
   http://www.atlasshardwarecorp.com
Rev.: $2,200,000
Emp.: 15
Wood Window & Door Mfr
N.A.I.C.S.: 321911
Robert Atlass *(Pres & CEO)*
Neil Martin *(Project Mgr)*
William Hays *(VP)*

Integris   (1)
11400 Cronridge Dr Ste A, Owings Mills,
MD 21117
Tel.: (888) 330-8808
Web Site: http://www.integrisit.com
Holding Company; Managed Information
Technology, Cybersecurity, Cloud & Net-
work Services
N.A.I.C.S.: 551112
Rashaad Bajwa *(CEO)*
John Marinac *(CTO)*
Joseph O'Hara *(CFO)*
Jason Erickson *(Chief Strategy Officer)*
Bill McCharen *(Chief People Officer)*
Hamish Davidson *(Mng Dir-Georgia)*
Mike Fowler *(COO)*
Chris Hoose *(VP-Growth)*
Tony Miller *(VP-Svc)*
Nick Nyberg *(VP-Middle Market Sls)*
Sitima Fowler *(VP-Branding)*

Subsidiary (Domestic):

CalTech Software Systems, LLC   (2)
4152 S Jackson St, San Angelo, TX 76903-
9337
Tel.: (325) 223-6100
Web Site: https://www.caltech.com
Computer Peripheral Whslr
N.A.I.C.S.: 423430
Will Welch *(CEO)*

CompuDyne Corporation   (2)
306 W Michigan St Ste 200, Duluth, MN
55802
Tel.: (410) 712-0275
Web Site: http://www.compudyne.com
Sales Range: $75-99.9 Million
Emp.: 707
Integrated Electronics, Attack Protection,
Public Safety & Institutional Security Sys-
tems Services & Products Mfr
N.A.I.C.S.: 334511

Domain Technology Partners,
Inc.   (2)
1 Corporate Dr, Cranbury, NJ 08512
Tel.: (732) 828-2340
Web Site: http://www.computerhelpnj.com
Sales Range: $1-9.9 Million
Emp.: 12
Computer System Design Services
N.A.I.C.S.: 541512
Rashaad Bajwa *(Pres)*

Iconic IT, LLC   (2)
656 Kreag Rd, Pittsford, NY 14534
Tel.: (585) 546-4120
Web Site: http://iconicit.com
Information Technology Services
N.A.I.C.S.: 519290
Nick Nyberg *(VP-Sls-Denver)*

Subsidiary (Domestic):

Capstone Information Technologies
Incorporated   (3)
252 Plymouth Ave S, Rochester, NY 14608
Tel.: (585) 546-4120

Frontenac Company LLC—(Continued)

Web Site: http://www.capstoneitinc.com
Rev.: $1,500,000
Emp.: 6
Data Processing, Hosting & Related Services
N.A.I.C.S.: 518210
Sitima Fowler (Co-CEO)
Matthew Walker (Engr-Tech Support)
Nicolaos Mitrousis (Engr-Tech Support)
Ankit Desai (Engr-Tech Support)
Lisa Nazarenko (Acct Coord)
Mike Fowler (Co-CEO)

Choose Networks, Inc. (3)
410 N St Francis, Wichita, KS 67202
Tel.: (316) 773-0920
Web Site: http://www.choosenetworks.com
IT Solutions & Services
N.A.I.C.S.: 513210
Chris Hoose (Pres & CEO)
Dawn McCallie (Controller)

Live Consulting, LLC (3)
7245 Gilpin Way Ste 100, Denver, CO
80229-6532
Tel.: (303) 217-3000
Web Site: http://www.liveconsulting.com
Process, Physical Distribution & Logistics
Consulting Services
N.A.I.C.S.: 541614
Tony Miller (Mgr)

Subsidiary (Domestic):

Modular Technology LLC (2)
1804 Rutherford Ln, Austin, TX 78754
Tel.: (512) 472-6000
Web Site: http://www.myitpros.com
Information Technology, Cloud & Security
Services
N.A.I.C.S.: 518210
Bill McCharen (CEO)
Stefanie D'Aulizio (Dir-Client Success)

Subsidiary (Domestic):

Solis Security Inc. (3)
300 E Highland Mall Blvd Ste 300, Austin,
TX 78752
Tel.: (512) 614-2040
Web Site: http://www.gosolis.com
Information Security Services
N.A.I.C.S.: 561621
Terry Oehring (CEO)

Subsidiary (Domestic):

Network People, Inc. (2)
13075 US Hwy 19 N, Clearwater, FL 33764
Tel.: (727) 446-4564
Web Site: http://www.networkpeople.com
Sales Range: $1-9.9 Million
Emp.: 12
Computer Support Services; Computer
Equipment Distr
N.A.I.C.S.: 541519
Kelly Freeman (CEO)
Elias Leslie (Dir-IT)

ProviDyn Inc. (2)
2812 Spring Rd SE Ste 130, Atlanta, GA
30339
Tel.: (404) 551-5492
Web Site: http://www.providyn.com
Sales Range: $1-9.9 Million
Emp.: 12
Information Technology Support Services
N.A.I.C.S.: 541512
Ralph Auriemmo (Dir-Ops)
Hamish Davidson (Pres & CEO)
Linda Messing Williams (Dir-Client Svcs)

Motion & Control Enterprises
LLC (1)
100 Williams Dr, Zelienople, PA 16063-2602
Tel.: (724) 452-6000
Web Site: http://mceautomation.com
Hydraulics, Pneumatics & Electromechnical
Products & Services
N.A.I.C.S.: 423830
Michelle Burnett (CFO)
Tom Savignac (COO)
Charles Hale (Chm & CEO)

Subsidiary (Domestic):

Applied Industrial Controls, Inc. (2)
1860 S Lee Ct, Buford, GA 30518-6094
Tel.: (770) 614-7022

Web Site: http://www.aic-controls.com
Electrical Apparatus & Equipment, Wiring
Supplies & Related Equipment Merchant
Whslr
N.A.I.C.S.: 423610

Daughtridge Sales Co., Inc. (2)
501 S Pine St, Rocky Mount, NC 27803
Tel.: (252) 977-1131
Web Site: http://www.dascosales.com
Rev.: $7,500,000
Emp.: 24
Industrial Supplies Merchant Whslr
N.A.I.C.S.: 423840
Bernadette Brooks (Treas)
Alan Anderson (Mgr-Quality & Tech)

Fluid Systems Engineering, Inc. (2)
18855 E 14 Mile Rd, Clinton Township, MI
48035
Tel.: (586) 790-8880
Web Site:
http://fluidsystemsengineering.com
Hydraulic Component & Pneumatic Product
Distr
N.A.I.C.S.: 423840

Ives Equipment Corporation (2)
601 Croton Rd, King of Prussia, PA 19406
Tel.: (610) 768-1600
Web Site: http://www.ivesequipment.com
Rev.: $21,000,000
Emp.: 60
Valves & Fittings
N.A.I.C.S.: 423830
David Oschwald (Engr-Sls)

Nova Hydraulics Inc. (2)
6212 Parliament Dr, Indianapolis, IN 46220
Tel.: (317) 322-0242
Web Site: http://www.novahydraulics.com
Rev.: $2,850,000
Emp.: 5
Industrial Supplies Merchant Whslr
N.A.I.C.S.: 423840

Primet Fluid Power Company,
Inc. (2)
7917 New Jersey Ave, Hammond, IN 46323
Tel.: (219) 844-4224
Web Site: http://www.primetfluidpower.com
Hydraulic, Pneumatic, Lubrication Systems
& Automation Components Distr
N.A.I.C.S.: 423830
William Bestow (Pres)
Dan Lafontaine (Mgr-Inside Sls)

Tri-State Hose & Fitting, Inc. (2)
616 Progress Ave, Munster, IN 46321-2872
Tel.: (219) 922-9700
Web Site: http://www.tristatehose.com
Rev.: $3,300,000
Emp.: 12
Rubber & Plastic Hose & Belting Industrial
Supplies Mfr
N.A.I.C.S.: 326220
Mike Webber (Mgr-ParkerStore)
Ray Thompson (Mgr-Sls)

Prime Technology Group, Inc. (1)
940 W Valley Rd Ste 1500, Wayne, PA
19087
Tel.: (610) 205-8740
Web Site: http://www.2xprime.com
Sales Range: $1-9.9 Million
Emp.: 250
Tests, Implements & Maintains Software in
the Financial & Life Sciences Industries
N.A.I.C.S.: 541519
Sudhakar Goverdhanam (Co-Founder &
CEO)
G. Shakuntala Rao (Co-Founder & Mng Dir)
G. Ramakrishna Rao (Co-Founder & VP-
Fin)

Subsidiary (Non-US):

Prime KI Software Solutions Pvt
Ltd. (2)
Krishe Sapphire 4th & 5th Floor Survey No
88 Madhapur Serilingampali, MLA Colony
Banjara Hills, Hyderabad, 500081, India
Tel.: (91) 4040327469
Web Site: http://www.primetgi.com
Software Programming Services
N.A.I.C.S.: 541511
Shakuntala Roa (Gen Mgr)

RCG Global Services, Inc. (1)
99 Wood Ave S, 9th Fl, Iselin, NJ 08830
Tel.: (732) 744-3500

Web Site: https://rcgglobalservices.com
Computer System Design Services
N.A.I.C.S.: 541512
Rob Simplot (Pres & CEO)

Subsidiary (Domestic):

Woodridge Advisors LLC (2)
320 S Teller Street Ste 250, Lakewood, CO
80226
Tel.: (720) 403-9454
Web Site:
http://www.woodridgesoftware.com
Mobile Application Development Services
N.A.I.C.S.: 541511
Kaj Gronholm (CEO)
Scott Holdeman (VP-Design & Strategy)
Jennifer Mcadams (VP-Ops & Mktg)
Paul Glauthier (VP-Dev)
Lynn Haney (Specialist-Security)

Salient Federal Solutions, Inc. (1)
4000 Legato Rd Ste 600, Fairfax, VA
22033-2893
Tel.: (703) 891-8200
Web Site: http://www.salientcrgt.com
Emp.: 1,600
Government Agency IT & Engineering Ser-
vices
N.A.I.C.S.: 541512
Keith Hoback (VP-Benefits & Security Solu-
tions)
Kay R. Curling (Chief HR Officer & Sr VP)
Charles Sowell (Sr VP-Natl Security & Sy-
ber Solutions)
J. D. Kuhn (CFO & Sr VP)
Larry Rose (Sr VP-Comml Ops)
Tom Ferrando (Pres & CEO)
PC Manning (Sr VP-C4US Urgent Solu-
tions)
Mark Colturi (Sr VP-Federal Modernization
of Sys & Svcs)
Manoj Gandhi (Sr VP-Enterprise Solutions
Grp)
Linda Harris (Sr VP-Responsive Mission
Support Solutions)
Ken Raffel (Sr VP-Data Analytics & Bus So-
lutions)
Phil Nolan (Chm)
John Anderson (Pres-Defense & Intel Agen-
cies Div)
Rebecca Miller (Pres-Health & Civilian
Agencies Div)
Atacan Donmez (Sr VP-Civilian Svcs Grp)
Rory Schultz (Exec Dir-Strategic Programs-
Civilian Svcs Grp)

Subsidiary (Domestic):

Command Information, Inc. (2)
2034 Eisenhower Ave Ste 222, Alexandria,
VA 22314
Tel.: (703) 224-2866
Sales Range: $10-24.9 Million
Computer Network Design & Information
Technology Support Services
N.A.I.C.S.: 541512

Subsidiary (Domestic):

AnviCom-Command Federal,
Inc. (3)
2034 Eisenhower Ave, Alexandria, VA
22314
Tel.: (703) 224-2866
Web Site: http://www.anvi.com
Computer Network Design & Information
Technology Support Services to the U.S.
Department of Defense
N.A.I.C.S.: 541512

Subsidiary (Domestic):

LIST Innovative Solutions, Inc. (2)
13921 Park Center Rd Ste 500, Herndon,
VA 20171
Tel.: (703) 467-0100
Web Site: http://www.listinc.com
Sales Range: $10-24.9 Million
Emp.: 90
Application Software Solutions
N.A.I.C.S.: 541690

Schlotterbeck & Foss, LLC (1)
3 Ledgeview Dr, Westbrook, ME 04092
Tel.: (207) 772-4666
Web Site: http://www.schlotterbeck-foss.com
Emp.: 85
Spice & Extract Mfr
N.A.I.C.S.: 311942

Subsidiary (Domestic):

Drew's LLC (2)
926 Vermont Rte 103 S, Chester, VT 05143
Tel.: (802) 875-1184
Web Site: http://www.chefdrew.com
Grocery Whslr
N.A.I.C.S.: 424490
David Hambright (Mgr)

TPC Training Systems, Inc. (1)
750 W Lake Cook Rd Ste 350, Buffalo
Grove, IL 60089
Tel.: (847) 808-4000
Web Site: http://www.tpctraining.com
Online & In-person Technical, Maintenance
& Continuing Education Industrial Skills
Training
N.A.I.C.S.: 611710
Holly Falcaro (VP-Sls)

Subsidiary (Domestic):

National Environmental Trainers
Inc. (2)
207 W Millbrook Rd Ste 115, Raleigh, NC
27609
Tel.: (919) 781-4591
Web Site: http://www.natlenvtrainers.com
Online & Onsite Training
N.A.I.C.S.: 611430
Clay Bednarz (Pres)

Whitebridge Pet Brands, LLC (1)
1224 Fern Ridge Pkwy Ste 200, Saint
Louis, MO 63141
Web Site:
http://www.whitebridgepetbrands.com
Pet Food Mfr
N.A.I.C.S.: 311111
Olivier Amice (CEO)

Subsidiary (Domestic):

Cardinal Laboratories, LLC (2)
710 S Ayon Ave, Azusa, CA 91702
Tel.: (626) 969-3305
Web Site: http://www.cardinalpet.com
Sales Range: $1-9.9 Million
Emp.: 70
Health Care & Pet Grooming Services; Ani-
mal Food Products Mfr & Marketer
N.A.I.C.S.: 311111
Tony DeVos (Pres)
R. Foster (VP-Sls)

XanEdu Publishing, Inc. (1)
4750 Venture Dr Ste 400, Ann Arbor, MI
48108
Tel.: (734) 302-6500
Web Site: http://www.xanedu.com
Education Services
N.A.I.C.S.: 611710
John DeBoer (CEO)
Jason Plackowski (CFO)
Marc Steinberg (CTO)
Brett Costello (Sr VP-Sls & Mktg)
Lance Westbrook (Sr VP-Corp & Bus Dev)
Kevin Woodman (Sr VP-Ops)
Natalie Danner (VP-Custom Solutions)
Mark Nelson (COO)
Jeff Letson (VP-Mktg)
Rich Foley (Sr VP-Strategy & Corp Dev)

FRONTIER AG, INC.
415 W 2nd, Oakley, KS 67748-1545
Tel.: (785) 672-3300 **KS**
Web Site:
http://www.frontieraginc.com
Year Founded: 1968
Sales Range: $300-349.9 Million
Grain, Petroleum & Farm Supplies
Wholesale Distr
N.A.I.C.S.: 424510
Mike Stephens (Chm)
Joe McIlnay (Sec)

**FRONTIER BEHAVIORAL
HEALTH**
107 S Division, Spokane, WA 99202
Tel.: (509) 838-4651 **WA**
Web Site: https://www.fbhwa.org
Year Founded: 1969
Sales Range: $25-49.9 Million
Emp.: 496
Behavioral Healthcare Services

N.A.I.C.S.: 623220

FRONTIER CAPITAL LLC
525 N Tryon St Ste 1900, Charlotte, NC 28202
Tel.: (704) 414-2880
Web Site:
http://www.frontiercapital.com
Year Founded: 1999
Rev.: $3,115,000
Emp.: 12
Venture Capital Firm Services
N.A.I.C.S.: 523999
Andrew Lindner (Mng Partner)
Richard MacLean (Mng Partner)
Michael Ramich (Partner)
Joel Lanik (Partner)
Scott Hoch (Partner)
Seth Harward (Partner)
Lori Shell (Chief Compliance Officer & Exec VP-Fin & Ops)
Jessica Warzybok (Mgr-Human Rels)
Dave Pandullo (VP)
Mason McVerry (Dir-Bus Dev)

Subsidiaries:

Healthx, Inc. (1)
9339 Priority Way West Dr Ste 150, Indianapolis, IN 46240
Tel.: (317) 843-3990
Web Site: http://www.healthx.com
Sales Range: $10-24.9 Million
Emp.: 150
Builds & Operates Web-Based Health Care Information Portals for Employers, Insurance Companies & HMO's
N.A.I.C.S.: 541512
Chuck Rolfsen (Chief Revenue Officer)
Nancy Wallace (VP-HR Svcs)
Matt Hay (Controller)
Thomas Millay (COO)
Chad Brake (VP-Engrg Ops)
Michael Gordon (Chief Product & Strategy Officer)
Ellen Humphrey (Chief People Officer)
Gene Cattarina (CEO)
Mark Rapoport (CFO)

FRONTIER COMMUNICATIONS CORPORATION
17650 E 32nd Place Unit 10A, Aurora, CO 80011
Tel.: (303) 390-3600   CO
Web Site: http://www.fbponline.com
Year Founded: 1979
Information Technology & Services
N.A.I.C.S.: 513210
Carol D. Mitschke (Pres)

FRONTIER COMMUNITY BUILDERS
10100 Trinity Pkwy Ste 420, Stockton, CA 95219
Tel.: (209) 957-8112
Web Site: https://www.fcbhomes.com
Sales Range: $75-99.9 Million
Emp.: 14
Single-Family Housing Construction
N.A.I.C.S.: 236115
Tom Doucette (Pres)
George Gibson (Sr VP)

FRONTIER COMMUNITY SERVICES
43335 K-Beach Rd Ste 36, Soldotna, AK 99669
Tel.: (907) 262-6331   AR
Web Site: https://www.fcsonline.org
Year Founded: 1983
Sales Range: $1-9.9 Million
Emp.: 358
Disability Assistance Services
N.A.I.C.S.: 624120
Larae Paxton (Dir-Finance)

FRONTIER COMMUNITY SERVICES

12127 Pleasant Valley Rd, Chillicothe, OH 45601
Tel.: (740) 772-1396   OH
Web Site:
https://www.frontiercommunity.com
Year Founded: 1977
Sales Range: $10-24.9 Million
Emp.: 260
Developmental Disability Assistance Services
N.A.I.C.S.: 623210
Gregory J. Arcaro (CEO)
Samuel C. Wood (CFO)

FRONTIER COMPUTER CORP.
1275 Business Park Dr, Traverse City, MI 49686
Tel.: (231) 929-1386
Web Site:
https://www.frontiercomputer corp.com
Year Founded: 1976
Rev.: $19,000,000
Emp.: 37
Computer Related Consulting Services
N.A.I.C.S.: 541690

Subsidiaries:

Frontier Computer Corp. B.V. (1)
Bijsterhuizen 1120a unit B, 6546 AS, Nijmegen, Netherlands
Tel.: (31) 24 3660012
Computer Related Consulting Services
N.A.I.C.S.: 541690
Richard Koenders (Mng Dir)

Frontier Computer Corp. UK Ltd. (1)
1 Steyning Way, Hounslow, TW4 6DL, Middlesex, United Kingdom
Tel.: (44) 208 572 9676
Computer Related Consulting Services
N.A.I.C.S.: 541690

FRONTIER COOPERATIVE COMPANY, INC.
211 S Lincoln St, Brainard, NE 68626
Tel.: (402) 545-2811   NE
Web Site:
http://www.frontiercooperative.com
Year Founded: 1915
Sales Range: $75-99.9 Million
Emp.: 200
Grain Wholesaler; Farm Supplies, Fertilizers & Related Materials
N.A.I.C.S.: 424510
Randy Robeson (CEO & Gen Mgr)
Jared DeWispelare (Mgr-IT)
Mel Bomar (Mgr-Credit)

Subsidiaries:

Midwest Farmers Cooperative (1)
304 S 3rd St, Elmwood, NE 68345
Tel.: (402) 994-2585
Web Site: http://www.midwestfarmers.coop
Sales Range: $10-24.9 Million
Emp.: 80
Agricultural Services
N.A.I.C.S.: 424510
Dale Piper (CEO & Gen Mgr)
John Crook (Vice Chm)
Tim Junge (Controller)

FRONTIER ENTERPRISES, INC.
8520 Crownhill Blvd, San Antonio, TX 78209-1119
Tel.: (210) 828-1493   TX
Web Site:
https://www.jimsrestaurants.com
Year Founded: 1950
Sales Range: $300-349.9 Million
Emp.: 1,400
Operator of Restaurants
N.A.I.C.S.: 722513
Ron Riemenschneider (Controller)
Jan Nikel (Sec)
Jeff Morrow (Dir-Ops)

FRONTIER FORD
3701 Stevens Creek Blvd, Santa Clara, CA 95051
Tel.: (408) 241-1800
Web Site:
https://www.frontierford.com
Sales Range: $100-124.9 Million
Emp.: 125
New & Used Car Dealers
N.A.I.C.S.: 441110
Keith Morgan (Controller)
Hal Arnon (Gen Mgr)

FRONTIER FS COOPERATIVE
222 E Puerner St, Jefferson, WI 53549
Tel.: (920) 674-7000
Web Site:
http://www.frontierservcofs.com
Sales Range: $50-74.9 Million
Emp.: 70
Feed
N.A.I.C.S.: 424910
Wendy Bolger (Asst Controller)
J. Dan Rohrer (Mgr-Sls-Feed)
Dave Thomsen (Mgr-Grain Dept)

Subsidiaries:

Frontier FS Cooperative (1)
3895 Crop Care Ct, Amherst Junction, WI 54407
Tel.: (920) 674-7000
Web Site: http://www.frontierfscoop.com
Sales Range: $25-49.9 Million
Emp.: 33
Supplier of Lubricants, Animal Feed & Other Farm & Garden Products
N.A.I.C.S.: 424910

FRONTIER FUNDS
25568 Genesee Trail Rd, Golden, CO 80401
Tel.: (303) 454-5500   DE
Year Founded: 2003
Rev.: $15,880
Assets: $12,021,523
Liabilities: $853,588
Net Worth: $11,167,935
Earnings: ($1,017,440)
Fiscal Year-end: 12/31/23
Investment Fund Services
N.A.I.C.S.: 525910

FRONTIER HEALTH
PO Box 9054, Gray, TN 37615
Tel.: (423) 467-3600   TN
Web Site:
https://www.frontierhealth.org
Year Founded: 1974
Sales Range: $50-74.9 Million
Emp.: 1,335
Behavioral Healthcare Services
N.A.I.C.S.: 621420
C. Allen Musil Jr. (Dir-Medical & Sr VP-Medical Svcs)

FRONTIER INDUSTRIES INC.
1911 Commercial Ave, Anacortes, WA 98221
Tel.: (360) 293-4588
Web Site: https://www.fbs.us
Rev.: $10,300,000
Emp.: 14
Lumber & Other Building Materials
N.A.I.C.S.: 423310
Michael Johnson (Pres)

FRONTIER INTERNATIONAL TRUCKS
1023 N Garnett Rd, Tulsa, OK 74116
Tel.: (918) 438-2000
Web Site: http://www.frontier-intltrucks.com
Rev.: $19,800,000
Emp.: 68
Trucks, Commercial
N.A.I.C.S.: 423110

Mike Owens (Gen Mgr)

FRONTIER LOGISTICS, LP
101 E Barbours Cut Blvd, Morgan's Point, TX 77571
Tel.: (281) 307-2000
Web Site:
http://www.frontierlogistics.com
Year Founded: 1997
Sales Range: $10-24.9 Million
Emp.: 100
Supply Chain Management Services
N.A.I.C.S.: 484121
John Black (Dir-Public Relations)

FRONTIER MANAGEMENT LLC
7420 Bridgeport Rd Ste 105, Portland, OR 97224
Tel.: (503) 443-1818
Web Site:
http://www.frontiermgmt.com
Sales Range: $10-24.9 Million
Emp.: 1,500
Management of Retirement & Assisted Living Communities
N.A.I.C.S.: 561499
Gregory A. Roderick (Pres & CEO)
Matthew Dunham (VP)

FRONTIER MEDICAL, INC.
1401 S Brookhurst Rd, Fullerton, CA 92801
Tel.: (714) 738-0051   CA
Year Founded: 1986
Sales Range: $1-9.9 Million
Emp.: 30
Distribution of Home Orthopedic Rehabilitation Equipment
N.A.I.C.S.: 532283
Matthew Bock (Pres)

FRONTIER NATURAL PRODUCTS CO-OP
3021 78th St, Norway, IA 52318
Tel.: (319) 227-7996
Web Site:
https://www.frontiercoop.com
Sales Range: $10-24.9 Million
Emp.: 200
Herbs & Spices, Aromatherapy
N.A.I.C.S.: 311942
Tony Bedard (CEO)
Clint Landis (CMO)
Ravin Donald (VP-Quality Assurance & R&D)
Kory Kazimour (Brand Mgr)

FRONTIER PRECISION INC.
2020 Frontier Dr, Bismarck, ND 58504
Tel.: (701) 222-2030
Web Site:
http://www.frontierprecision.com
Sales Range: $10-24.9 Million
Emp.: 15
Engineering Equipment & Supplies
N.A.I.C.S.: 423490
Dennis Kemmesat (Pres)

FRONTIER SCIENCE & TECHNOLOGY RESEARCH FOUNDATION, INC.
4033 Maple Rd, Amherst, NY 14226
Tel.: (716) 834-0900   NY
Web Site: http://www.fstrf.org
Year Founded: 1975
Sales Range: $25-49.9 Million
Emp.: 400
Research & Development Services
N.A.I.C.S.: 541720
Diana Sabra (CFO)

FRONTIER TECHNOLOGY LLC
8160 S Hardy Dr, Tempe, AZ 85284
Tel.: (480) 366-2200
Web Site: http://www.microage.com
Sales Range: $1-9.9 Million

Frontier Technology LLC—(Continued)

Emp.: 75
Integrated Computer Design Systems
N.A.I.C.S.: 541512
Mark McKeever (COO)
Roger Rouse (CFO)

Subsidiaries:

Custom Storage, Inc. (1)
4300 N Miller Rd Ste 146, Scottsdale, AZ 85251-3621
Tel.: (480) 941-4026
Web Site: https://cstor.com
Rev.: $4,700,000
Emp.: 7
Data Center & Consulting Solutions
N.A.I.C.S.: 518210
William Nowlin (Pres & CEO)

MicroAge, Inc. (1)
8160 S Hardy Dr Ste 101, Tempe, AZ 85284
Tel.: (480) 366-2000
Web Site: http://www.microage.com
Computers & Business Machines Retailer & Mfr
N.A.I.C.S.: 541512
Tracey M. Hayes (VP-Sls)

Custom Storage, Inc. (1)
4300 N Miller Rd Ste 146, Scottsdale, AZ 85251-3621
Tel.: (480) 941-4026
Web Site: https://cstor.com
Rev.: $4,700,000
Emp.: 7
Data Center & Consulting Solutions
N.A.I.C.S.: 518210
William Nowlin (Pres & CEO)

FRONTIER TRUCK GEAR
PO Box 277, Center Point, TX 78010-0277
Tel.: (830) 634-3037
Web Site: http://www.frontier-gear.com
Year Founded: 2001
Sales Range: $1-9.9 Million
Emp.: 47
Heavy Duty Aftermarket Accessories for Trucks & SUVs
N.A.I.C.S.: 336120
Roscoe Marshall (Owner)

FRONTIER WEALTH ENTER-PRISES, LLC
4435 Main St, Kansas City, MO 64111
Tel.: (816) 753-5100 MO
Web Site:
 http://www.frontierwealth.com
Holding Company; Investment Management & Advisory Services
N.A.I.C.S.: 551112
Nick Blasi (CEO)
Brandon Sifers (CFO)
Aaron Anson (Dir-Ops)

FRONTLINE ADVERTISING, INC.
890 Westfall Rd Ste C, Rochester, NY 14618
Tel.: (585) 244-1300 NY
Year Founded: 1994
Rev.: $12,300,000
Emp.: 10
N.A.I.C.S.: 541810
Frank Contestabile (Pres)
Lisa Daeffler (Mgr-Production)
John Brown (Creative Dir)
June Provenzano (Dir-Media)

FRONTLINE AG LLC
127 S Main St, Conrad, MT 59425
Tel.: (406) 278-5531 MT
Web Site:
 https://www.frontlineag.com
Year Founded: 2005
Sales Range: $1-9.9 Million
Emp.: 25

Farm & Garden Machinery & Equipment Distr
N.A.I.C.S.: 423820
Karl Tafelmeyer (Mgr-Parts)
Brad Fenger (Mgr-Svc)
Craig Broesder (Mgr-Svc)
Dale Larson (Mgr-Svc)
Daniel Jones (Mgr-Aftermarket)
Don Rogers (Mgr-Parts)
Drew Lesnik (Mgr-Sls)
Ken Brown (Mgr-Parts)
Wes Wrathall (Mgr-Parts)
Timothy Lewis (Mgr-Parts Corp)
Bryon Klose (Mgr-Parts Dept)
Josh Alkire (Mgr-Parts-Columbus)
James Coffman (Mgr-Parts-Columbus)
Trevor Dorner (Mgr-Parts-Columbus)
Tony Sebek (Mgr-Parts-Columbus)
Stephen Hartley (Mgr-Svc-Columbus)
Jerry Hoffmann (Mgr-Svc-Columbus)
Dave Stokes (Mgr-Svc-Columbus)

Subsidiaries:

Frontline Ag Solutions - Lewistown (1)
80335 US-87, Lewistown, MT 59457
Tel.: (406) 538-5433
Web Site:
 http://www.frontlineagsolutions.com
Farm Equipment & Supplies Distr
N.A.I.C.S.: 459999
Steve Moodie (Mgr-Store)
Tony Sebek (Mgr-Parts)
Dave Dieziger (Mgr-Svc)

FRONTLINE FREIGHT, INC.
13007 Crossroads S, City of Industry, CA 91746
Tel.: (562) 236-1440
Web Site:
 http://www.frontlinefreightinc.com
Year Founded: 1989
Sales Range: $10-24.9 Million
Emp.: 130
Freight Transportation Services
N.A.I.C.S.: 488510
Matt Hunter (VP-Sls & Ops)

FRONTLINE SELLING, LLC
6505 Shiloh Rd 3rd Fl, Alpharetta, GA 30005
Tel.: (678) 638-7300
Web Site:
 https://www.frontlineselling.com
Year Founded: 2002
Computer Software Publisher & Marketing Consulting Services
N.A.I.C.S.: 541613
Mike Scher (Co-Founder & Chief Sls Architect)
Dan McCann (Co-Founder & COO)
Tom Dunn (CEO)
Lauren Kornitsky (VP-Ops)
Meredith Buckley (Dir-Mktg)

FRONTPOINT PARTNERS LLC
80 Field Point Rd Ste 1, Greenwich, CT 06830
Tel.: (203) 622-5200
Sales Range: $25-49.9 Million
Emp.: 50
Portfolio Management
N.A.I.C.S.: 523940
Phil Duff (CEO)

FRONTSTREAM HOLDINGS LLC
11480 Commerce Park Dr Ste 300, Reston, VA 20191
Tel.: (202) 903-2585
Web Site:
 https://www.frontstream.com
Holding Company; Payment Processing Services
N.A.I.C.S.: 551112

Nina Vellayan (CEO)
Terry Lopresti (CTO)
Mark Sutton (CMO)
Liz Starliper (VP-Ops)
Tracy Harder (VP-HR)
William C. Wood (Pres)
Mark Herrington (Chm)

FROSCH INTERNATIONAL TRAVEL INC.
1 Greenway Plz Ste 800, Houston, TX 77046
Tel.: (713) 850-1566
Web Site: http://www.frosch.com
Sales Range: $10-24.9 Million
Emp.: 2,000
Travel Planning Services
N.A.I.C.S.: 561599
Richard Liebman (Chm)
Bryan D. Leibman (Pres & CEO)
Lara Leibman (Exec VP)
Marc Kazlauskas (Pres-Leisure Division & US Branch Ops)
Judith A. Allen (Pres-Global Corp & Energy Travel Mgmt)
Maggie Kealey (Pres-Global Entertainment Div)
Rachel L. Epstein (Pres-Grp Travel)
Kevin Landry (Exec VP-Trng, Partners & IC Support Svcs)
Sridhar Balaji (Exec VP-Engrg)
Brett Leslie (Sr VP-Bus Dev, Global Corp & Energy Travel Mgmt)
Paul Pua (Sr VP-Fin Analysis)
Janet Fernette (Sr VP-HR)
Diana Kearns (Sr VP-Exec Svcs)
Chris Evans (VP-IT-Network Ops)
Brian Buttigieg (Gen Counsel)

Subsidiaries:

All Horizons Travel Inc. (1)
160 Main St, Los Altos, CA 94022-2905
Tel.: (650) 941-5810
Web Site: http://www.allhorizonstvl.com
Travel Management Services
N.A.I.C.S.: 561510
Maureen Jones (Co-Founder)
Roy Jones (Co-Founder)

Luxe Travel Management, Inc. (1)
16450 Bake Pkwy Ste 100, Irvine, CA 92618
Tel.: (949) 336-1000
Web Site: http://www.luxetm.com
Travel Agency
N.A.I.C.S.: 561510
Craig Carter (Pres & CEO)

Division (Domestic):

Map Marketing & Incentives, LLC (2)
1500 Rosecrans Ave Ste 414, Manhattan Beach, CA 90266
Tel.: (310) 481-7992
Web Site: http://mapluxetm.com
Travel Promotions & Incentatives
N.A.I.C.S.: 561920
Jim McGory (Pres)
Lisa Yaremchuk (Sr VP)
Louise Georgeson (Dir-Incentive Travel)
Liz Wolf (Dir-Travel Svcs)
Shari Mogren (Mgr-Promotions & Branding)

Valerie Wilson Travel, Inc. (1)
475 Park Ave S Fl 34, New York, NY 10016-6901
Tel.: (212) 532-3400
Web Site: http://www.vwti.com
Sales Range: $100-124.9 Million
Emp.: 270
Travel Agencies
N.A.I.C.S.: 561510
Valerie Ann Wilson (Founder, Co-Owner, Chm & CEO)
Jennifer Wilson-Buttigieg (Co-Owner & Co-Pres)
Kimberly Wilson-Witty (Co-Owner & Co-Pres)
Dan Beschloss (Exec Dir-Corp Affairs)
Louis Rodriguez (Dir-IT & Trng)
Brian Buttigieg (COO)
Marc Jacobsen (VP-Tech)

FROST BROWN TODD LLC
3300 Great American Tower 301 E 4th St, Cincinnati, OH 45202-4118
Tel.: (513) 651-6800
Web Site:
 http://www.frostbrowntodd.com
Year Founded: 1956
Sales Range: $25-49.9 Million
Emp.: 394
Provider of Legal Services
N.A.I.C.S.: 541110
Robert V. Sartin (Chm)
Adam P. Hall (CEO)
Jacob R. Morvay (CFO)
Michael Severini (CIO)
Jill P. Meyer (Partner)

FROST ELECTRIC SUPPLY COMPANY INC.
2429 Schuetz Rd, Maryland Heights, MO 63043
Tel.: (314) 567-4004 MO
Web Site:
 https://www.frostelectric.com
Year Founded: 1945
Sales Range: $10-24.9 Million
Emp.: 91
Electrical Apparatus & Equipment Distr
N.A.I.C.S.: 423610
John Frost (Pres)
Mike Arb (Mgr-Sls)

FROST INC.
2020 Bristol NW, Grand Rapids, MI 49504
Tel.: (616) 453-7781 MI
Web Site: https://www.frostinc.com
Year Founded: 1913
Sales Range: $50-74.9 Million
Emp.: 50
Overhead Conveyor Components Mfr
N.A.I.C.S.: 333922
Chad Frost (Pres)
Paula Miller (VP)

Subsidiaries:

Frost Europe, S.L. (1)
Pol Ind Can Salvatella C/Comadran 19 naves B3 y B8, 08210, Barbera del Valles, Barcelona, Spain
Tel.: (34) 93 719 24 05
Web Site: http://www.frosteurope.com
Conveyor & Conveying Equipment Mfr
N.A.I.C.S.: 333922

Frost Links, Inc. (1)
2900 Northridge Dr NW, Grand Rapids, MI 49544
Tel.: (616) 785-9030
Web Site: http://www.frostlinks.com
Emp.: 6
Conveyor & Conveying Equipment Mfr
N.A.I.C.S.: 333922
Paula Miller (VP)

Production Industries Inc. (1)
1048 Main St, Frankfort, MI 49635
Tel.: (231) 352-7500
Web Site: http://www.prodind.com
Emp.: 8
Conveyor & Conveying Equipment Mfr
N.A.I.C.S.: 333922
Todd Frazee (Mgr)

FROST OIL CO
1430 S 28th St, Van Buren, AR 72956
Tel.: (479) 471-9992
Web Site: https://www.frostoil.com
Sales Range: $25-49.9 Million
Emp.: 50
Petroleum Bulk Stations
N.A.I.C.S.: 424710
Jeff Frost (Owner & Pres)
LaDonna Frost (Treas-Corp Tax & Acctg)

FROSTY ACRES BRANDS, INC.

1225 Old Alpharetta Rd Ste 235, Alpharetta, GA 30005
Tel.: (678) 356-5400
Web Site: http://www.frostyacres.com
Year Founded: 1954
Sales Range: $25-49.9 Million
Emp.: 55
National Marketing & Food Buying Cooperative
N.A.I.C.S.: 424420
Jake Marsh (Reg VP-South)
Cindy Naes (Sr VP-Procurement & Mktg)
Georgia Barber (Mgr-Mktg)
Philli Eakinf (CFO & VP)
Barry Pearson (Chm)
Ship Walker (Pres & CEO)

FROSTY TREATS INC.

620 E Linwood Blvd, Kansas City, MO 64109
Tel.: (816) 931-9969
Web Site: http://www.frostytreats.com
Rev.: $10,500,000
Emp.: 8
Ice Cream & Ices
N.A.I.C.S.: 424430
Carl S. Long III (Pres)

FROZEN FOOD EXPRESS INDUSTRIES, INC.

1145 Empire Central Pl, Dallas, TX 75247-4305
Tel.: (214) 630-8090   TX
Web Site: http://www.ffex.net
Year Founded: 1946
Sales Range: $350-399.9 Million
Emp.: 2,183
Holding Company for Refrigerated Transportation Carriers
N.A.I.C.S.: 484122
John T. Hickerson (COO & Exec VP)
Steven D. Stedman (Controller & VP-Fin)
Terry W. Thornton (CFO & Treas)
Janet Price (Sec)
Vince A. Schott (VP & Gen Mgr)
Joe Jaska (VP-Ops)

Subsidiaries:

AM Can   (1)
1145 Empire Central Pl, Dallas, TX
75247   (100%)
Tel.: (214) 819-5530
Sales Range: $25-49.9 Million
Emp.: 7
Truck Broker
N.A.I.C.S.: 484122

Conwell Corp.   (1)
1145 Empire Central Pl PO Box 655888,
Dallas, TX 75265-5888   (100%)
Tel.: (214) 630-8090
Lease Tractors with Drivers & Trailers
N.A.I.C.S.: 484110

Subsidiary (Domestic):

Conwell, LLC   (2)
1145 Empire Central Pl, Dallas, TX 75247
Tel.: (214) 630-8090
Temperature Controlled Transportation Services
N.A.I.C.S.: 484122

FFE Transportation Services, Inc.   (1)
PO Box 655888, Dallas, TX
75265-5888   (100%)
Tel.: (214) 630-8090
Web Site: http://www.ffeinc.com
Sales Range: $125-149.9 Million
Emp.: 300
Transportation of Perishable & Nonperishable Commodities in 48 States
N.A.I.C.S.: 484230
Mark Rhea (Dir-Academy)

Lisa Motor Lines, Inc.   (1)

1145 Empire Central Place, Dallas, TX 75247-4309
Tel.: (800) 569-9200
Web Site: http://www.lisamtc.com
Sales Range: $1-9.9 Million
Emp.: 347
Refrigerated Trucking Services
N.A.I.C.S.: 484230

FROZEN GOURMET INC.

5800 Airport Rd, Redding, CA 96002-9359
Tel.: (530) 226-0908
Web Site:
    https://www.frozengourmetinc.com
Rev.: $15,000,000
Emp.: 20
Ice Cream & Ices
N.A.I.C.S.: 424430
William A. Kohn (Pres)
David McDaniel (Mgr-Warehouse)

FROZSUN INC.

701 W Kimberly St Ste 210, Placentia, CA 92870
Tel.: (714) 630-2170
Web Site: http://www.frozsun.com
Year Founded: 1987
Sales Range: $10-24.9 Million
Emp.: 20
Sales of Fruits & Fruit Products
N.A.I.C.S.: 311421
Dave Yvanovich (VP-Sls)
Erwin Hettervik (VP-Ops)

FRS MECHANICAL CORP.

5845 Enterprise Pkwy, Fort Myers, FL 33905
Tel.: (239) 694-2711
Year Founded: 1992
Rev.: $11,100,000
Emp.: 125
Air Conditioning Contractors & Systems
N.A.I.C.S.: 238220
Fred Schuman (Pres)
Jeff Conrod (VP)

FRS SOFTWARE

5212 Concord Hwy, Monroe, NC 28110
Tel.: (704) 289-6424
Web Site:
    https://www.frssoftware.com
Sales Range: $1-9.9 Million
Emp.: 13
Background Screening Software Development Services
N.A.I.C.S.: 541511
Phil Chapman (Pres)
Lynn Chapman (VP)
Nichole Disser (Dir-Client Svcs)
Elaine Golde (Dir-Sls)
Kevin Scott (Mgr-Sys Architecture)
Leon Mayberry (Mgr-Strategic Svc)
Chris Jeffcoat (Controller)
Rebecca Melton (Mgr-Quality Assurance Software Testing & Custom Projects)

FRT INTERNATIONAL INCORPORATED

1700 N Alameda St, Compton, CA 90222
Tel.: (310) 604-8208
Web Site: https://www.frontier-logistics.com
Rev.: $17,056,038
Emp.: 7
Deep Sea Foreign Transportation Of Freigh
N.A.I.C.S.: 483111
Brian Chung (Pres & CEO)
Jeff J. Woo (Controller)
Daniel H. Park (Gen Mgr)

FRUIT BASKET GARDENS INC.

765 28th St SW, Grand Rapids, MI 49509
Tel.: (616) 532-5934
Web Site:
    http://www.myflowerland.com
Sales Range: $10-24.9 Million
Emp.: 65
Garden Supplies & Tools
N.A.I.C.S.: 444240
Ric Vuyst (Chm)

FRUIT DYNAMICS LLC.

4206 Mercantile Ave, Naples, FL 34104
Tel.: (239) 280-3717
Web Site:
    http://www.incrediblefresh.com
Sales Range: $10-24.9 Million
Emp.: 136
Fruit & Vegetable Canning Services
N.A.I.C.S.: 311421
Rich Cahoon (Mgr)

FRUIT GROWERS SUPPLY CO.

27770 N Entertainment Dr, Valencia, CA 91355
Tel.: (818) 986-6480   CA
Web Site:
    https://www.fruitgrowerssupply.com
Year Founded: 1907
Sales Range: $100-124.9 Million
Emp.: 200
Agricultural Supply Company
N.A.I.C.S.: 322211
Nazir Khan (Pres & CEO)

Subsidiaries:

Fruit Growers Supply Co. - FGS Ontario Carton Plant   (1)
225 S Wineville Ave, Ontario, CA 91761-7891
Tel.: (909) 390-0190
Web Site: http://www.foodgrowers.com
Emp.: 82
Farm Machinery Supplier
N.A.I.C.S.: 423820
Stephen Moore (Plant Mgr)

United Wholesale Lumber Co.   (1)
8009 Doe Ave, Visalia, CA 93291
Tel.: (559) 651-2037
Web Site: http://www.uwlco.com
Emp.: 35
Pallet Mfr
N.A.I.C.S.: 321920
Rick Hopper (Gen Mgr)

FRUIT OF THE EARTH INC.

3101 High River Rd Ste 175, Fort Worth, TX 76155
Tel.: (972) 790-0808
Web Site: http://www.fote.com
Rev.: $15,800,000
Emp.: 30
Cosmetics
N.A.I.C.S.: 424210
Leonard Shepley (CFO)
Thomas E. McCurry Sr. (CEO)
Tom McCurry Jr. (Pres)

FRUITA CONSUMERS COOP ASSOCIATION

1650 Hwy 6 and 50, Fruita, CO 81521
Tel.: (970) 858-3667
Web Site: http://www.fruitacoop.org
Sales Range: $10-24.9 Million
Emp.: 55
Fertilizer
N.A.I.C.S.: 457120

FRUITCROWN PRODUCTS CORP.

250 Adams Blvd, Farmingdale, NY 11735

Tel.: (631) 694-5800
Web Site: https://www.fruitcrown.com
Year Founded: 1945
Sales Range: $10-24.9 Million
Emp.: 75
Packaged Fruit
N.A.I.C.S.: 311421
Robert Jagenburg (Pres)
Bruce Jagenburg (VP)
Frank Poma (VP-Ops)
Eric Ducey (Dir-Ops)

FRUITION PARTNERS

168 N Clinton Ste 600, Chicago, IL 60661
Tel.: (312) 448-6777
Web Site:
    http://www.fruitionpartners.com
Year Founded: 2003
Sales Range: $10-24.9 Million
Emp.: 132
Information Technology Support Services
N.A.I.C.S.: 541512
Marc Talluto (Co-Founder & CEO)
Patrick Stonelake (Co-Founder & Chief Growth Officer)
Bill Carroll (VP-Global Delivery)
J. P. Bartley (Gen Counsel)
Heidi Farrell (VP-HR)
Sean Barrins (Dir-Sls-West)
Timothy Currie (CIO-Svcs & VP-Advisory)
Andy Richardson (Dir-Delivery-UK)
Angela Bachor (Dir-Delivery-Central)
Paul Cash (Mng Dir-UK)
Peggy Seery (Dir-Delivery-East)
Rick Bakewell (CFO)
Rob Schaffer (Dir-Sls-East)
Thomas Lundon (Dir-Sls-Canada)
Tim Dear (Dir-Delivery-West)

FRUITION.NET

201 Fillmore St Ste 200, Denver, CO 80206
Tel.: (303) 395-1880
Web Site: http://www.fruition.net
Sales Range: $1-9.9 Million
Internet Marketing Services
N.A.I.C.S.: 541613
Brad Anderson (Founder & CEO)
Jeff Williams (Project Mgr)
Todd Atkins (Sr Project Mgr)
Joe Malouff (Dir-Website Design & Dev)
Melanie Davidson (Pres)

FRUTH, INC.

4016 Ohio River Rd, Point Pleasant, WV 25550
Tel.: (304) 675-1612   WV
Web Site:
    https://www.fruthpharmacy.com
Year Founded: 1952
Sales Range: $50-74.9 Million
Emp.: 800
Pharmacy Operator
N.A.I.C.S.: 456110
Lynne Fruth (Pres)

FRY COMMUNICATIONS INC.

800 W Church Rd, Mechanicsburg, PA 17055-3179
Tel.: (717) 766-0211   PA
Web Site: https://www.frycomm.com
Year Founded: 1934
Sales Range: $75-99.9 Million
Emp.: 1,000
Printing Services
N.A.I.C.S.: 323111
Michael T. Lukas (CEO)
David Fry (CTO)
Terry Yeh (Mgr-Mgmt Info Sys)
Harry Warner (Dir-Quality Assurance-Compliance)

Fry Communications Inc.—(Continued)

Dave Landwehr *(Plant Mgr-Building One)*
Gary Deremer *(Plant Mgr-Building Two)*
Christopher Wawrzyniak *(CFO)*
Cheri Stryker *(VP-Sales)*
Steve Brandenburg *(Asst VP-Sales-Catalogs)*

FRY KRISP COMPANY
3360 Spring Arbor Rd, Jackson, MI 49203-3636
Tel.: (517) 784-8531
Web Site: http://www.frykrisp.com
Year Founded: 1950
Sales Range: $10-24.9 Million
Emp.: 10
Batter & Seasoning Mixes Mfr
N.A.I.C.S.: 311824
Richard G. Neuenfeldt *(Pres)*
Richard J. Neuenfeldt *(VP)*

FRY REGLET CORPORATION
12342 Hawkins St Santa Fe Spring California, Alhambra, CA 90670
Tel.: (626) 289-4744
Web Site: http://www.fryreglet.com
Sales Range: $10-24.9 Million
Emp.: 36
Aluminum Extruded Products
N.A.I.C.S.: 331318
Stephen Reed *(CEO)*

FRY'S ELECTRONICS, INC.
600 E Brokaw, San Jose, CA 95112
Tel.: (408) 350-1484   CA
Web Site: http://www.frys.com
Year Founded: 1985
Sales Range: Less than $1 Million
Consumer Electronics Retailer
N.A.I.C.S.: 449210
Randy Fry *(Founder)*

Subsidiaries:

Cyberian Outpost, Inc.   (1)
23 N Main St, Kent, CT 06757
Tel.: (860) 927-2050
Web Site: http://www.outpost.com
Computer & Software Retail
N.A.I.C.S.: 449210

FRY-WAGNER SYSTEMS INC.
3700 Rider Trl S, Earth City, MO 63045
Tel.: (314) 291-4100
Web Site: https://www.fry-wagner.com
Sales Range: $10-24.9 Million
Emp.: 65
Trucking Service
N.A.I.C.S.: 484121
Katy Drews *(Mgr-HR)*

FRYE BUILDERS & ASSOCIATES, INC.
2213 2nd Ave, Muscatine, IA 52761
Tel.: (563) 264-5045
Web Site:
https://www.fryebuilders.com
Sales Range: $25-49.9 Million
Emp.: 35
Commercial & Institutional Building Construction
N.A.I.C.S.: 236220
Jeff Frye *(VP)*
Mike Frye *(Pres)*
Steve Blaser *(VP)*

FRYE ROOFING, INC.
2000 Princeton Ave, Bluefield, WV 24701
Tel.: (304) 327-5314   WV
Web Site:
https://www.fryeroofing.com
Year Founded: 1900

Sales Range: $1-9.9 Million
Emp.: 40
Roofing Contractors
N.A.I.C.S.: 238160
Joseph P. Burmer *(CEO)*
Henry Malkin *(Mgr-Ops)*
Jeremiah Robinson *(VP-Sls)*

Subsidiaries:

Frye Roofing, Inc. - Beckley   (1)
1126 Harper Rd, Beckley, WV 25801
Tel.: (304) 256-1930
Web Site: http://www.fryroofing.com
Sales Range: $10-24.9 Million
Emp.: 10
Roofing Services
N.A.I.C.S.: 238160

FS CREDIT REAL ESTATE INCOME TRUST, INC.
201 Rouse Blvd, Philadelphia, PA 19112
Tel.: (215) 495-1150   MD
Web Site: http://fsinvestments.com
Year Founded: 2016
Rev.: $187,171,000
Assets: $8,337,816,000
Liabilities: $6,020,659,000
Net Worth: $2,317,157,000
Earnings: $126,363,000
Fiscal Year-end: 12/31/22
Real Estate Investment Services
N.A.I.C.S.: 531210
Michael C. Forman *(Chm, Pres & CEO)*
Stephen S. Sypherd *(Treas, Sec & VP)*
James Volk *(Chief Compliance Officer)*
Christopher Condelles *(CFO)*

FSC BANCSHARES, INC.
124 E 3rd St, Cameron, MO 64429
Tel.: (816) 632-6641   MO
Web Site: http://www.fscbank.com
Year Founded: 1983
Sales Range: $10-24.9 Million
Emp.: 68
Bank Holding Company
N.A.I.C.S.: 551111
R. Michael Poland *(Pres & CEO)*

Subsidiaries:

Farmers State Bank   (1)
124 E 3rd St, Cameron, MO 64429
Tel.: (816) 632-6641
Web Site: http://www.fscbank.com
Commericial Banking
N.A.I.C.S.: 522110
R. Michael Poland *(Pres & CEO)*
Tom Nance *(CFO & Sr VP)*

FSC MARKETING COMMUNICATIONS
Gulf Tower 707 Grant St, Ste 2900, Pittsburgh, PA 15222
Tel.: (412) 471-3700   PA
Web Site: http://www.fscmc.com
Year Founded: 1956
Rev.: $22,646,000
Emp.: 10
Consumer Marketing, New Product Development, Sales Promotion
N.A.I.C.S.: 541810
Donna Majewski *(Office Mgr)*
Lisa Sabol *(Creative Dir)*
Bryan Brunsell *(Creative Dir)*
Rich Hurey *(Controller, Mgr-HR & Mgr-IT)*

FSG FACILITY SOLUTIONS GROUP
4401 Westgate Blvd Ste 310, Austin, TX 78745-1494
Tel.: (512) 440-7985   TX
Web Site: http://www1.fsgi.com
Year Founded: 1982

Sales Range: $100-124.9 Million
Emp.: 2,300
Electrical Apparatus & Equipment
N.A.I.C.S.: 423610
William D. Graham *(CEO)*
Bob Graham *(CMO & Chief Sls Officer)*

FSG, INC.
500 Boylston St Ste 600, Boston, MA 02116
Tel.: (617) 357-4000   MA
Web Site: http://www.fsg.org
Year Founded: 2005
Sales Range: $10-24.9 Million
Emp.: 133
Social Advocacy Services
N.A.I.C.S.: 813319
Greg Hills *(Co-CEO)*
Michael E. Porter *(Co-Founder)*
Marcy Pfitzer *(Mng Dir-Geneva)*
Lauren Smith *(Co-CEO)*

FSK LAND CORPORATION
3910 Keswick Rd, Baltimore, MD 21211
Tel.: (443) 997-3737   MD
Year Founded: 1984
Sales Range: $10-24.9 Million
Title Holding Company
N.A.I.C.S.: 531390
Ronald R. Peterson *(Chm)*
Brian Dembeck *(Pres)*
Samuel Clark *(Sec)*
Terrence Warner *(Treas)*

FSO ONSITE OUTSOURCING
19 W 44th St 9th Fl, New York, NY 10036
Tel.: (212) 204-1193
Web Site: http://www.fso-outsourcing.com
Year Founded: 1976
Sales Range: $50-74.9 Million
Emp.: 1,134
Enterprise-Wide Staffing & Onsite Sourcing Services
N.A.I.C.S.: 561320
Mitchell D. Weiner *(Co-Owner & Chief Happiness Officer)*
Kimberly Shephard *(Sr VP-People Solutions)*
Lyon Goultiex *(Dir-Sls-Mid Atlantic)*

Subsidiaries:

FSO Outsourcing   (1)
1776 I St NW Suite 900, Washington, DC 20006   (100%)
Tel.: (703) 801-9476
Web Site: http://www.fso-outsourcing.com
Outsourcing & Staffing Solutions
N.A.I.C.S.: 561311
Pat Mustico *(VP-Natl Sls)*

FSO Outsourcing   (1)
22 W Washington Suite 1500, Chicago, IL 60602   (100%)
Tel.: (516) 637-3889
Web Site: http://www.fso-outsourcing.com
Outsourcing & Staffing Solutions
N.A.I.C.S.: 561311
Debra Gerard *(Dir-Central Reg)*

FSS Staffing Solutions   (1)
19 W 44th St 9th Fl, New York, NY 10036   (100%)
Tel.: (212) 986-3600
Web Site: http://www.fss-staffing.com
Staffing & Hiring Solutions
N.A.I.C.S.: 561311
Mitchell D. Weiner *(Owner & CEO)*

FSP 303 EAST WACKER DRIVE CORP.
401 Edgewater Pl, Wakefield, MA 01880
Tel.: (781) 557-1300   DE
Year Founded: 2006
Real Estate Investment Services

N.A.I.C.S.: 531210
John G. Demeritt *(CFO & Exec VP)*

FSS, INC.
5202 Moundview Dr, Red Wing, MN 55066
Tel.: (651) 388-5568
Web Site:
https://www.foodservicespecialties.com
Year Founded: 1985
Sales Range: $10-24.9 Million
Emp.: 49
Pasta & Sauce Mfr
N.A.I.C.S.: 311991
Don Leick *(Owner)*
Stephen Lineer *(Pres)*
Jerry Jirik *(Mgr-Pur)*

FST LOGISTICS INC.
2040 Atlas St, Columbus, OH 43228
Tel.: (614) 529-7900
Web Site: http://www.fstlogistics.com
Rev.: $10,000,000
Emp.: 200
Provider of Trucking Services
N.A.I.C.S.: 484110
Art DeCrane *(Owner)*
Dave Kent *(Pres)*
Bill Bell *(VP)*
Susan Seever *(VP-HR)*

Subsidiaries:

Hyway Trucking Company   (1)
10060 Sr 224 W, Findlay, OH 45840
Tel.: (419) 423-7145
Web Site: http://www.hywaytrucking.com
General Freight Trucking
N.A.I.C.S.: 484122
Roger Lenhart *(Pres)*

FT. MYERS TOYOTA INC.
2555 Colonial Blvd, Fort Myers, FL 33907
Tel.: (239) 936-4114
Web Site: http://www.smtoyota.com
Sales Range: $10-24.9 Million
Emp.: 370
Automobiles, New & Used
N.A.I.C.S.: 441110

FT. WAYNE PLASTICS INC.
510 Sumpter Dr, Fort Wayne, IN 46804
Tel.: (260) 432-2520
Web Site:
http://www.fortwayneplastics.com
Year Founded: 1997
Sales Range: $10-24.9 Million
Emp.: 50
Plastics Product Mfr
N.A.I.C.S.: 326199
Robb Robertson *(Pres)*

FTD COMPANIES, INC.
3113 Woodcreek Dr, Downers Grove, IL 60515
Tel.: (630) 719-7800   DE
Web Site: http://www.ftd.com
Year Founded: 2008
Rev.: $1,014,244,000
Assets: $386,980,000
Liabilities: $388,380,000
Net Worth: ($1,400,000)
Earnings: ($224,729,000)
Emp.: 1,333
Fiscal Year-end: 12/31/18
Holding Company; Flowers & Specialty Gifts Marketer & Floral Network Operator
N.A.I.C.S.: 551112
Scott D. Levin *(Vice Chm, Chief Admin Officer & Gen Counsel)*
Rhys J. Hughes *(Pres-Interflora British Unit & Head-Intl Div)*
Tom D. Moeller *(Exec VP-Florist Div)*
Steven D. Barnhart *(CFO & Exec VP)*

Dale Perrott *(Chief Supply Chain Officer & Exec VP)*
Elizabeth Cimaroli *(Sr VP-Strategy & Bus Dev)*
Jeff Clarke *(Chm)*

Subsidiaries:

Bloom That, Inc. **(1)**
645 Harrison St Ste 200, San Francisco, CA 94107
Tel.: (415) 231-5739
Web Site: http://www.bloomthat.com
Florist Services
N.A.I.C.S.: 459310
David Bladow *(Founder & CEO)*

FTD India Private Limited **(1)**
Block D-Wing II 5th Floor Cyber Gateway Building, Hitech City Madhapur Village Serilingampally, Hyderabad, 500 081, India
Tel.: (91) 4066030303
Emp.: 130
Gift Store Operator
N.A.I.C.S.: 459420

FTL CORPORATION
1580 Woodlane Dr, Saint Paul, MN 55125
Tel.: (651) 730-0377
Web Site: http://www.a-toast-to-you.com
Sales Range: $10-24.9 Million
Emp.: 7
Beer & Wine Distributors
N.A.I.C.S.: 445320
John J. Lanners *(Pres)*
Dan Pertile *(Gen Mgr)*

FTS FINANCIAL, INC.
510 Elm St, Williamsburg, IA 52361
Tel.: (319) 668-2525   IA
Web Site: http://www.ftsbia.com
Year Founded: 1982
Sales Range: $1-9.9 Million
Emp.: 17
Bank Holding Company
N.A.I.C.S.: 551111
John R. Jones *(Chm, Pres & CEO)*

Subsidiaries:

Farmers Trust & Savings Bank **(1)**
510 Elm St, Williamsburg, IA 52361
Tel.: (319) 668-2525
Web Site: http://www.ftsbia.com
Sales Range: $1-9.9 Million
Commericial Banking
N.A.I.C.S.: 522110
John R. Jones *(Chm, Pres & CEO)*
David J. Malloy *(Officer-Bank Security & VP)*
David J. Volkens *(Officer-Bus Dev & VP)*

FTS INTERNATIONAL EXPRESS INC.
400 Country Club Dr, Bensenville, IL 60106
Tel.: (630) 694-0644
Web Site: http://www.fts.com
Sales Range: $10-24.9 Million
Emp.: 34
Freight Forwarding
N.A.I.C.S.: 484110
John Chiu *(CEO)*

FTS INTERNATIONAL, INC.
777 Main St Ste 2900, Fort Worth, TX 76102
Tel.: (817) 862-2000   DE
Web Site: http://www.ftsi.com
Year Founded: 2000
Rev.: $776,600,000
Assets: $639,300,000
Liabilities: $601,600,000
Net Worth: $37,700,000
Earnings: ($72,900,000)
Emp.: 1,250
Fiscal Year-end: 12/31/19
Holding Company; Oil & Natural Gas Exploration

N.A.I.C.S.: 551112
Yong Siang Goh *(Chm)*
Michael J. Doss *(CEO)*
Lance D. Turner *(CFO & Treas)*
Buddy Petersen *(COO)*
Karen D. Thornton *(Chief Admin Officer)*
Jennifer L. Keefe *(Chief Compliance Officer, Gen Counsel & Sr VP)*

FTS LEESONA, INCORPORATED
2727 Tucker St, Burlington, NC 27215
Tel.: (336) 226-5511   NC
Web Site: https://www.leesona.com
Year Founded: 1986
Sales Range: $10-24.9 Million
Emp.: 40
Mfr of Textile Machinery
N.A.I.C.S.: 333319
Jim Arrington *(VP-Sls)*
Robert Charles Clark *(Pres)*

FTV MANAGEMENT COMPANY LP
555 California Ste 2850, San Francisco, CA 94104
Tel.: (415) 229-3000   DE
Web Site: http://www.ftvcapital.com
Year Founded: 1998
Miscellaneous Intermediation
N.A.I.C.S.: 523910
James C. Hale *(Mng Dir)*

FU DA INTERNATIONAL LTD
525 7th Ave 23rd Fl, New York, NY 10018
Tel.: (212) 292-8088
Rev.: $50,000,000
Emp.: 35
Men & Boys' Clothing
N.A.I.C.S.: 424350
Jing Deng *(Pres)*
Henderson Russell *(Mgr-AR)*
Jin Liu *(Asst Controller)*

FUCCILLO AUTOMOTIVE GROUP INC.
10524 US Route 11, Adams, NY 13605
Tel.: (315) 232-3222
Web Site: https://www.fuccillo.com
Year Founded: 1997
Sales Range: $10-24.9 Million
Emp.: 70
Car Whslr
N.A.I.C.S.: 441110
Scott Fox *(Gen Mgr)*
Cathy Rivers *(Sec)*

FUCCILLO CHEVROLET PONTIAC BUICK
10499 US Rte 11, Adams, NY 13605
Tel.: (315) 232-4503
Web Site: http://www.fuccillogm.com
Sales Range: $10-24.9 Million
Emp.: 60
New Car Dealers
N.A.I.C.S.: 441110
William B. Fuccillo *(Pres & Treas)*
Bruce Lewis *(CFO)*
Christina Bachar *(Controller)*

FUCCILLO CHRYSLER OF NELLISTON, INC.
6460 State Highway 5, Nelliston, NY 13410
Tel.: (518) 993-5555
Web Site: http://www.fuccillochryslerofnelliston.com
Rev.: $19,000,000
Emp.: 25
Automobiles, New & Used
N.A.I.C.S.: 441110

William B. Fuccillo *(Pres)*
Todd Dillon *(Gen Mgr)*

FUEL AGENCY, INC.
1300 Clay St 6th Fl, Oakland, CA 94612
Tel.: (510) 834-1400
Web Site: http://www.fuelagency.com
Year Founded: 1989
Rev.: $12,000,000
Emp.: 12
Advetising Agency
N.A.I.C.S.: 541810
Diane Manning *(Partner & Head Strategist)*
Guy Needham *(Dir-Creative)*
Pedro Bexiga *(Dir-Creative & Dir-Art)*
Marcelo Lourenco *(Copywriter & Dir-Creative)*
Richard Warrell *(Copywriter)*
Antonio Silva *(Dir-Art)*
Artur Pinheiro *(Dir-Art)*

FUEL CONTROLS INC.
3605 E Spring St, Long Beach, CA 90806
Tel.: (562) 498-1482
Rev.: $10,000,000
Emp.: 40
Aircraft Fueling Services
N.A.I.C.S.: 424720
Harold Reed *(Pres)*

FUEL FEED PLAZA HOME CENTERS
601 Nevan Rd, Virginia Beach, VA 23451
Tel.: (757) 491-9000
Web Site: http://www.taylorsdoit.com
Sales Range: $100-124.9 Million
Emp.: 130
Independent Hardware Retailer
N.A.I.C.S.: 449129
R. Dawson Taylor *(Chm)*
Joseph Taylor *(Pres)*

FUEL INTERACTIVE
1705 N Oak St, Myrtle Beach, SC 29577
Tel.: (843) 839-1456
Web Site: http://www.fuelinteractive.com
Sales Range: $10-24.9 Million
Emp.: 20
Consulting, Digital/Interactive, Email, Local Marketing, Media Relations, Search Engine Optimization, Web (Banner Ads, Pop-ups, etc.)
N.A.I.C.S.: 541810
Stuart Butler *(COO)*
David Day *(CTO)*
Pete Dimaio *(VP-Bus Strategy)*
Nick McNeill *(Chief Creative Officer)*
Lauren Prentice *(Mgr-Traffic)*
Antonia Leverton *(Controller)*

FUEL MANAGERS INC.
10711 E 11th St Ste 3, Tulsa, OK 74128
Tel.: (918) 877-5000
Web Site: http://www.fuelmanagers.com
Sales Range: $450-499.9 Million
Emp.: 35
Petroleum Brokers
N.A.I.C.S.: 424720
Cameron Long *(CFO & VP)*

FUEL PERFORMANCE SOLUTIONS, INC.
7777 Bonhomme Ave Ste 1920, Saint Louis, MO 63105
Tel.: (314) 863-3000   NV
Web Site: http://www.fuelperformancesolutions.com

Year Founded: 1996
Sales Range: Less than $1 Million
Liquid Fuel Additive Product Mfr
N.A.I.C.S.: 211130
Jonathan R. Burst *(CEO)*
Stuart D. Beath *(CFO)*
Thomas M. Powell *(Treas)*
Axel J. Farhi *(Dir-Global Bus Dev)*
James Lodge *(Mgr-Technical)*

FUEL TALENT, LLC
500 Union St Ste 940, Seattle, WA 98101
Tel.: (206) 465-2000
Web Site: http://www.fueltalent.com
Year Founded: 2013
Sales Range: $1-9.9 Million
Emp.: 35
Recruiting Firm Services
N.A.I.C.S.: 561311
Shauna Swerland *(CEO)*
Mindy Blakeslee *(Mktg Dir)*

FUELFX, LLC
1811 Bering Dr, Houston, TX 77057
Tel.: (855) 472-7316
Web Site: http://www.fuelfx.com
Year Founded: 2007
Sales Range: $1-9.9 Million
Emp.: 31
Digital Marketing & Communications Specializing in 3D Graphics, Interactive Applications & Presentations for the Oil & Gas Industry
N.A.I.C.S.: 541613
Oliver Diaz *(Pres & CEO)*

FUELLGRAF ELECTRIC CO.
245 Pittsburgh Rd Ste 100, Butler, PA 16001
Tel.: (724) 282-4800
Web Site: http://www.fuellgraf.com
Year Founded: 1946
Sales Range: $10-24.9 Million
Emp.: 68
Electrical Contractor
N.A.I.C.S.: 238210
Paul A. Harmon *(Controller)*
Charles L. Fuellgraf Jr. *(CEO & Treas)*
Charles L. Fuellgraf III *(Pres)*

FUELS & SUPPLIES INC.
617 E Emma Ave, Springdale, AR 72764
Tel.: (479) 751-2206
Web Site: https://www.fuelsandsupplies.com
Rev.: $33,000,000
Emp.: 30
Petroleum Products
N.A.I.C.S.: 424720
Jerry Brown *(CEO)*

FUELS, INC.
PO Box 917, Casper, WY 82602
Tel.: (307) 472-3000   WY
Year Founded: 1999
Oil & Gas Exploration
N.A.I.C.S.: 211120
Roy C. Smith *(Pres)*
Michael R. Butler *(Treas & Sec)*

FUESSLER GROUP INC.
73 Louder's Ln, Jamaica Plain, MA 02130
Tel.: (617) 522-0550
Web Site: http://www.fuessler.com
Year Founded: 1984
Sales Range: $10-24.9 Million
Emp.: 2
Public Relations Agency
N.A.I.C.S.: 541820
Rolf A. Fuessler *(Pres)*

FUGAZY INTERNATIONAL CORPORATION

Fugazy International Corporation—(Continued)

1270 Ave of the Americas, New York, NY 10020
Tel.: (212) 661-4155 NY
Web Site: http://www.fugazy.com
Year Founded: 1870
Sales Range: $10-24.9 Million
Emp.: 600
Travel & Tourism Services
N.A.I.C.S.: 485320
Roy D. Fugazy (Pres)

Subsidiaries:

Fugazy Transportation Inc (1)
1270 Avenue Of Americas, New York, NY 10020
Tel.: (212) 661-0100
Sales Range: $10-24.9 Million
Emp.: 1
Limousine Service
N.A.I.C.S.: 485320
Pat Loviso (Gen Mgr)

Fugazy Travel (1)
1270 Ave of the Americas 15th Fl, New York, NY 10020
Tel.: (212) 897-5000
Web Site: http://www.fugazy.com
Travel Agency
N.A.I.C.S.: 485320

FULCO, INC.
30 Broad St, Denville, NJ 07834
Tel.: (973) 627-2427 NJ
Web Site: https://www.fulcoinc.com
Year Founded: 1981
Sales Range: $1-9.9 Million
Emp.: 30
Data Processing & Preparation Custom Computer Programming
N.A.I.C.S.: 518210
James Duffy (Pres)
Kathy Gillen (Mgr-Client Svcs)
Jim Heath (Mgr-Client Svc)
Michael Wattley (Dir-IT & Gen Mgr)

FULCRUM ANALYTICS, INC.
70 W 40th St, New York, NY 10018
Tel.: (212) 651-7000
Web Site:
http://www.fulcrumanalytics.com
Year Founded: 1993
Sales Range: $10-24.9 Million
Emp.: 35
Customized Software Systems for Customer Management
N.A.I.C.S.: 541910
David King (CEO)

FULCRUM BIOENERGY, INC.
4900 Hopyard Rd Ste 220, Pleasanton, CA 94588
Tel.: (925) 730-0150 DE
Web Site: https://www.fulcrum-bioenergy.com
Year Founded: 2007
Sales Range: $25-49.9 Million
Emp.: 17
Biofuel Production
N.A.I.C.S.: 325194
E. James Macias (Pres & CEO)
Eric N. Pryor (CFO & VP)
Richard D. Barraza (VP-Admin)
Theodore M. Kniesche (VP-Bus Dev)
Lewis Lee Rich (VP-Engrg & Ops)
James A. C. McDermott (Founder)

FULCRUM DIGITAL INC.
111 Town Square Pl Ste 1215, Jersey City, NJ 07310
Tel.: (201) 523-7555
Web Site:
http://www.fulcrumdigital.com
Year Founded: 1999
Sales Range: $10-24.9 Million
Emp.: 1,000
Information Technology Development Services

Willis E. Pollo (Chm)
Rajesh Sinha (Founder & Chm)
Robert Butler (Partner-Client)

FULCRUM LOGIC, INC.
111 Town Sq Pl Ste 1215, Jersey City, NJ 07310
Tel.: (973) 379-3050
Web Site:
http://www.fulcrumlogic.com
Year Founded: 1999
Sales Range: $10-24.9 Million
Emp.: 700
Computer Programming Services
N.A.I.C.S.: 561110
Rajesh Sinha (Founder & CEO)
S. Balakrishnan (Exec VP)
S. Mukundhan (CFO)

FULCRUM RESEARCH GROUP, LLC
230 3rd Ave 4th Fl, Waltham, MA 02451
Tel.: (781) 209-5327
Web Site:
https://www.fulcrumresearch group.com
Year Founded: 2010
Marketing Research & Public Opinion Polling
N.A.I.C.S.: 541910
Rebecca Gould (VP)

FULCRUM TECHNOLOGIES INC.
712 Aurora Ave N, Seattle, WA 98109
Tel.: (206) 336-5656
Web Site: http://www.fulcrum.net
Rev.: $14,000,000
Emp.: 50
Custom Computer Programming Services
N.A.I.C.S.: 541511
Brent Bauer (Chm, Pres & CEO)
Mark Bourgoin (VP-Sls)

FULD & COMPANY, INC.
131 Oliver St 3rd Fl, Boston, MA 02110
Tel.: (617) 492-5900
Web Site: http://www.fuld.com
Marketing Research & Public Opinion Polling
N.A.I.C.S.: 541910
Diane Borska (Pres & CEO)
Alok Tayal (Chm)
Elaine Pratt (CMO)

FULFILLMENT STRATEGIES INTERNATIONAL
7800 The Bluffs Ste C, Austell, GA 30168
Tel.: (678) 391-5980
Web Site:
http://www.fsifulfillment.com
Year Founded: 1996
Rev.: $5,400,000
Emp.: 30
Packing & Crating Service
N.A.I.C.S.: 488991
Ken Marbutt (Pres)
Daryl Gramling (Dir-IT)
Hope Hemmila (Coord-Implementation)
Carleen Blakes (Dir-Admin)

FULFORD CONSTRUCTION INC.
775 Sunset Blvd Ste A, O'Fallon, IL 62269
Tel.: (618) 632-5779
Web Site:
http://www.fulfordhomes.com
Rev.: $12,782,680
Emp.: 30

New Construction, Single-Family Houses
N.A.I.C.S.: 236115
Mark Fulford (Founder)

FULHAM & CO., INC.
593 Washington St, Wellesley, MA 02482
Tel.: (781) 235-2266
Web Site: https://www.fulhamco.com
Private Investment Firm
N.A.I.C.S.: 551112
Timothy W. Fulham (Mng Partner)
Susan Sullivan (CFO)
Angelo L. Ciavarella (Operating Partner)
James P. Miller (Operating Partner)
John C. Rich (Partner)
John N. Fulham III (Mng Partner)

Subsidiaries:

Trombetta Motion Technologies, Inc. (1)
8111 N 87th St, Milwaukee, WI 53224
Tel.: (414) 410-0300
Web Site: http://www.trombetta.com
Power Switching & Power Management Products Mfr
N.A.I.C.S.: 334419
James L. Liberty (CEO)

Subsidiary (Domestic):

Electronic Design, Inc. (2)
211 Forest Ave, Sheboygan Falls, WI 53085
Tel.: (920) 550-2315
Web Site:
http://www.electronicdesigninc.com
Sales Range: $1-9.9 Million
Emp.: 20
Electronic Controls Designer & Mfr
N.A.I.C.S.: 335314
Mike Hassinger (Mgr-Sls)
Eric Vant Hul (Mgr-Quality)
Gregg Lulloff (Mgr-Pur)
Nathan Watson (Mgr-Engrg)

FULL CIRCLE AG
520 Vander Horck, Britton, SD 57430
Tel.: (605) 448-2231
Web Site:
https://www.fullcircleag.com
Sales Range: $25-49.9 Million
Emp.: 45
Agricltural Chemicals
N.A.I.C.S.: 424910
Dave Andreses (Mng Dir)

FULL CIRCLE BREWING CO., LTD.
620 F St, Fresno, CA 93706-3413
Tel.: (559) 319-8195
Web Site:
https://www.fullcirclebrewing.com
Year Founded: 2016
Breweries
N.A.I.C.S.: 312120
Don C. Anderson (Owner)

Subsidiaries:

Brewmaster, Inc. (1)
1195 Evans Ave Ste A, San Francisco, CA 94124
Tel.: (415) 238-0009
Web Site: https://goodbeer.com
Sales Range: $1-9.9 Million
Emp.: 11
Breweries
N.A.I.C.S.: 312120

FULL CIRCLE HOME LLC
131 W 35th St 8th Fl, New York, NY 10001
Tel.: (212) 432-0001
Web Site:
http://www.fullcirclehome.com
Cleaning Product Mfr
N.A.I.C.S.: 339999
Tal Chitayat (Founder & CEO)

Subsidiaries:

Soma Water, Inc. (1)
131 W 35th St, New York, NY 10001
Tel.: (925) 360-4149
Web Site: http://www.drinksoma.com
Glass Carafe & Plant-based Water Filter Mfr
N.A.I.C.S.: 327213
Tal Chitayat (CEO)

FULL COMPASS SYSTEMS LTD. INC.
9770 Silicon Prairie Pkwy, Madison, WI 53593
Tel.: (608) 831-7330 WI
Web Site:
https://www.fullcompass.com
Year Founded: 1977
Sales Range: $25-49.9 Million
Emp.: 160
National Reseller of Audio, Video, AV & Lighting Equipment
N.A.I.C.S.: 423610
Mark Nash (Pres)
Kyle Kjensrud (Gen Mgr-Mdsg)
Michelle Grabel-Komar (VP-Sls)
Doug Carnell (COO)

Subsidiaries:

Full Compass Systems Contractors LLC (1)
9770 Silicon Prairie Pkwy, Madison, WI 53593 (100%)
Tel.: (608) 831-7330
Web Site: http://www.fullcompass.com
Sales Range: $25-49.9 Million
Emp.: 350
Computer Systems, Lighting Design & Equipment Rental Services
N.A.I.C.S.: 423690
Mark Nash (Pres)

FULL GOSPEL BUSINESS MEN'S FELLOWSHIP INTERNATIONAL
2600 Michelson Dr Ste1700, Irvine, CA 92612
Tel.: (949) 419-3870
Web Site: http://www.fgbmfi.org
Year Founded: 1953
Emp.: 6
Religious Organizations
N.A.I.C.S.: 813110
Richard Shakarian (Pres)
Dan Sanders (Controller)

FULL IN PARTNERS MANAGEMENT, LLC
551 Madison Ave, Floor 11, New York, NY 10022
Web Site: https://fullinpartners.com
Emp.: 100
Private Equity
N.A.I.C.S.: 523940

FULL LIFE CARE
800 Jefferson St Ste 620, Seattle, WA 98104
Tel.: (206) 528-5315 WA
Web Site: http://www.fulllifecare.org
Year Founded: 1980
Sales Range: $10-24.9 Million
Emp.: 563
Disability Assistance Services
N.A.I.C.S.: 624120
Jesse Bond (Pres)

FULL LINE EXHAUST INC.
151 Tinker Ct, Dothan, AL 36303
Tel.: (334) 793-6367
Web Site:
https://www.fulllineexhaust.com
Year Founded: 1988
Rev.: $10,000,000
Emp.: 100
Exhaust Systems Mfr
N.A.I.C.S.: 423120
Ronnie R. Johns (Owner)
Caren Goodson (Controller)

FULL ON PRODUCTIONS, INC.
7512 Dr Phillips Blvd Ste 50-414, Orlando, FL 32819
Tel.: (407) 888-8064
Web Site:
https://www.fullonproductions.tv
Year Founded: 2005
Emp.: 100
Video Production
N.A.I.C.S.: 541810
John Calvert (Co-Founder)
Ren Williams (Co-Founder)

FULL PERSPECTIVE VIDEO SERVICES INC.
6902 Hawthorn Pk Dr, Indianapolis, IN 46220
Tel.: (317) 579-0400
Web Site:
http://www.fpservicesinc.com
Rev.: $10,368,031
Emp.: 30
Video Tape Production
N.A.I.C.S.: 334610
Anne-Marie Lawrence (Mgr-Acctg)
Chris Whetzel (Pres)

FULL SAIL BREWING CO.
408 Columbia St, Hood River, OR 97031
Tel.: (541) 386-2281
Web Site:
https://www.fullsailbrewing.com
Brewery
N.A.I.C.S.: 312120
Irene Firmat (Founder & CEO)

FULL SERVICE AUTO PARTS OF SAN ANTONIO
4737 Broom St, San Antonio, TX 78217
Tel.: (210) 590-6793
Web Site:
http://www.fullserviceap.org
Rev.: $37,800,000
Emp.: 47
Automotive Supplies & Parts
N.A.I.C.S.: 423120
Phillip Hooge (Mgr-IS)
Howard Huff (Pres)

FULL SERVICE INSURANCE AGENCY, INC.
423 Broadway, Buxton, ND 58218
Tel.: (701) 847-2600   ND
Year Founded: 1972
Bank Holding Company
N.A.I.C.S.: 551111
Paul H. Marchell (Chm)

Subsidiaries:

First State Bank   (1)
423 Broadway, Buxton, ND 58218
Tel.: (701) 847-2600
Web Site: http://www.firststatebanks.com
Commericial Banking
N.A.I.C.S.: 522110
Paul H. Marchell (Chm)
John D. Marchell (Pres)

The First & Farmers Bank   (1)
509 Parke Ave, Portland, ND 58274
Tel.: (701) 788-3791
Web Site: http://www.ffbnk.com
Commericial Banking
N.A.I.C.S.: 522110
Tom Capouch (Pres)

FULL SERVICE TRAVEL INC.
1890 Hacienda Dr, Vista, CA 92081
Tel.: (760) 745-2700
Web Site:
http://www.andersontravel.com
Year Founded: 1973
Sales Range: $10-24.9 Million
Emp.: 135
Provider of Travel Services
N.A.I.C.S.: 561510

Brad Anderson (Co-Pres)
Van Anderson (Co-Pres)

FULL THROTTLE INDOOR KART RACING INC.
4950 S Yosemite St F2 3339, Greenwood Village, CO 80111
Tel.: (303) 221-7223   CO
Web Site:
http://www.fullthrottleikr.com
Year Founded: 2009
Indoor Racing
N.A.I.C.S.: 711212
Mark Ryan (Chm)
Tim Cousineau (Sec)
Lawrence Kopf (CFO)
Will Sumners (Treas)
Richard Jay Herrera (Pres & CEO)

FULL THROTTLE SALOON
12997 State Hwy 34, Sturgis, SD 57785-6400
Tel.: (731) 882-1883
Web Site:
http://www.fullthrottlesaloon.com
Sales Range: $1-9.9 Million
Bar Owner & Operator
N.A.I.C.S.: 722410
Angie Carlson (Dir-Mktg)
Randy Westendorf (Mgr)

FULL-O-PEP APPLIANCES INCORPORATED
1436 Liberty Dr, Bloomington, IN 47403
Tel.: (812) 333-7496
Web Site:
http://www.americanrentals.com
Sales Range: $10-24.9 Million
Emp.: 350
Provider of Home Appliance, Furniture & Entertainment Rental Services
N.A.I.C.S.: 561320
Raouf Bishay (CTO & CIO)

FULLBLOOM BAKING COMPANY
6500 Overlake Pl, Newark, CA 94560
Tel.: (650) 325-6200
Web Site: http://www.fullbloom.com
Year Founded: 1989
Sales Range: $50-74.9 Million
Emp.: 286
Bakery Products Mfr
N.A.I.C.S.: 311812
Jose Carlos Santiago (Plant Mgr)
Natalia Hunter (Mgr-Quality Assurance)
Thomas Troy (Mgr-Maintenance)

FULLCONTACT, INC.
1624 Market St Ste 226 PMB 45057, Denver, CO 80202-2523
Tel.: (888) 330-6943
Web Site: http://www.fullcontact.com
Year Founded: 2010
Cloud Based Technology Services
N.A.I.C.S.: 513210
Bart Lorang (Co-Founder & CEO)
Christopher Harrison (Pres)
Kurt Hawks (Chief Risk Officer)
Mary Hennen (VP-Mktg)
Khristin Dickey (Sr Dir-Customer Success)

Subsidiaries:

Mattermark, Inc.   (1)
61 Moraga Way Ste 6, Orinda, CA 94563
Tel.: (415) 347-8666
Web Site: http://www.mattermark.com
Software Developer
N.A.I.C.S.: 513210

FULLEN DOCK & WAREHOUSE INC.
382 Klinke Rd, Memphis, TN 38127

Tel.: (901) 358-9544
Web Site: https://www.fullendock.com
Year Founded: 1949
Rev.: $15,347,608
Emp.: 35
Limestone
N.A.I.C.S.: 423320
M. Frick (Gen Mgr)
Roy R. (Mgr-Aggregate Sls)
L. Chalk (Mgr-Terminal)

FULLER BOX COMPANY INC.
1152 High St, Central Falls, RI 02863
Tel.: (401) 725-4300
Web Site: https://www.fullerbox.com
Rev.: $20,000,000
Emp.: 50
Jewelry Cases
N.A.I.C.S.: 316990
Peter Fuller (Pres)

FULLER COMMUNICATIONS INC.
7804 Sprinkle Rd, Portage, MI 49002
Tel.: (269) 998-9300
Web Site: http://fullerinc.us
Year Founded: 1976
Sales Range: $10-24.9 Million
Emp.: 20
Telephone & Communication Line Construction
N.A.I.C.S.: 237130
Larry W. Fuller (Pres)

FULLER FORD, INC.
900 W 8th St, Cincinnati, OH 45203
Tel.: (513) 407-4719
Web Site: https://fullerisford.com
Year Founded: 1939
Sales Range: $10-24.9 Million
Emp.: 55
Car Whslr
N.A.I.C.S.: 441110

FULLER MARKET BASKET INC.
1126 S Gold St Ste 211, Centralia, WA 98531
Tel.: (360) 330-0310
Sales Range: $50-74.9 Million
Emp.: 300
Independent Supermarket
N.A.I.C.S.: 445110

FULLER SUPPLY CO. INC.
3500 Messer Airport Hwy, Birmingham, AL 35222
Tel.: (205) 323-4431
Web Site:
http://www.fullersupplyco.com
Sales Range: $10-24.9 Million
Emp.: 50
Agricultural Supply
N.A.I.C.S.: 424210
William S. Fuller Jr. (Pres)

FULLERTON LUMBER COMPANY
13605 1st Ave N Ste 2000, Plymouth, MN 55441-5463
Tel.: (763) 543-2700
Web Site:
http://www.fullertonlumber.com
Sales Range: $25-49.9 Million
Emp.: 260
Lumber & Other Building Materials
N.A.I.C.S.: 423310
Jess Howe (Pres)
Jeff Cropp (CFO)
Dave Walock (Pres)

FULLFILLMENT SYSTEMS, INC.
1282 Hammerwood Ave, Sunnyvale, CA 94089
Tel.: (408) 541-0382   CA

Year Founded: 1983
Sales Range: $10-24.9 Million
Emp.: 5
Provider of Food Products & Services
N.A.I.C.S.: 722511
Donald D'Ambrosio (Co-Pres)
John D'Ambrosio (Owner)

FULLHOUSE INTERACTIVE
207 N Milwaukee St, Milwaukee, WI 53202
Tel.: (414) 271-4001
Web Site:
http://www.fullhouseinteractive.com
Emp.: 60
Advertising Services
N.A.I.C.S.: 541810

Subsidiaries:

Fullhouse   (1)
300 S Wacker Dr, Chicago, IL 60606
Tel.: (312) 624-6908
N.A.I.C.S.: 541810

FULLMER CONSTRUCTION INC.
1725 S Grove Ave, Ontario, CA 91761-4565
Tel.: (909) 947-9467   CA
Web Site: https://www.fullmerco.com
Year Founded: 1946
Rev.: $10,339,701
Emp.: 210
Provider of Construction Services
N.A.I.C.S.: 236210
Robert Fullmer (Pres)
Gary L. Fullmer (VP)

FULLY ACCOUNTABLE, LLC
2680 W Market St, Fairlawn, OH 44333
Web Site:
http://www.fullyaccountable.com
Year Founded: 2014
Sales Range: $1-9.9 Million
Emp.: 30
Accounting Services
N.A.I.C.S.: 541219
Chris Giorgio (Founder, Pres & Co-CEO)
Vinnie Fisher (Co-CEO)
Rachel Scava (COO)
Corey Niggel (Co-CFO)
Kevin Phillips (Co-CFO)

FULMER LOGISTICS SERVICES, INC.
1895 90th Ave, Vero Beach, FL 32966-6619
Tel.: (772) 569-0410   FL
Web Site: http://www.fulmerls.com
Year Founded: 1983
Sales Range: $25-49.9 Million
Emp.: 42
Freight Transportation Arrangement
N.A.I.C.S.: 488510
Zack Fulmer (Pres)

FULTON COUNTY MEDICAL CENTER
214 Peach Orchard Rd, McConnellsburg, PA 17233
Tel.: (717) 485-3155   PA
Web Site: https://www.fcmcpa.org
Year Founded: 1947
Sales Range: $25-49.9 Million
Emp.: 446
Health Care Srvices
N.A.I.C.S.: 622110
Jason F. Hawkins (Pres)
Deborah Shughart (CFO)
Kimberly Slee (COO)
Michael D. Makosky (CEO)
Timothy R. McGarvey Jr. (Treas)

FULTON COUNTY RURAL

FULTON COUNTY RURAL —(CONTINUED)

ELECTRIC MEMBERSHIP CORPORATION
PO Box 230, Rochester, IN 46975
Tel.: (574) 223-3156　　　　　IN
Web Site:
　http://www.fultoncountyremc.coop
Year Founded: 1936
Sales Range: $10-24.9 Million
Emp.: 18
Electric Transmission Services
N.A.I.C.S.: 221122
Ron Jana *(Pres)*
Dennis Burton *(VP)*
Leander Hoover *(Treas & Sec)*
Joe Koch *(CEO)*
Greg Bitterling *(Dir-Member Svcs)*

FULTON INDUSTRIES INC.
135 E Linfoot St, Wauseon, OH
43567-1005
Tel.: (419) 335-3015　　　　　OH
Web Site:
　https://www.fultonindoh.com
Year Founded: 1939
Sales Range: $75-99.9 Million
Emp.: 130
Metal Stamping
N.A.I.C.S.: 332119
Jim Bauman *(Mgr-Sls)*

FULTON OUTFITTERS, INC.
1292 Fulton St, Brooklyn, NY 11216
Tel.: (718) 622-6278　　　　　NY
Web Site:
　http://www.thefultonstores.com
Year Founded: 1966
Sales Range: $10-24.9 Million
Emp.: 90
Furniture & Household Sales
N.A.I.C.S.: 449110
Jeffrey Katz *(Treas & Principal)*

FULTON SAVINGS BANK INC.
75 S 1st St, Fulton, NY 13069
Tel.: (315) 592-4201　　　　　NY
Web Site:
　http://www.fultonsavings.com
Sales Range: $50-74.9 Million
Emp.: 110
Federal Savings Institutions
N.A.I.C.S.: 522180
Michael J. Pollock *(Pres & CEO)*
Roberta M. Dunn *(Officer-Security & VP-Branch Admin)*
David W. Holden *(Mgr-Fin Ops)*
Wendy S. Tetro *(Sr VP & Controller)*
Julie A. Merritt *(Mgr-Loan Ops)*
Rita K. Loperfido *(VP-Residential Mortgage Lending)*
Melissa Keller *(CFO & Sr VP)*
Thomas J. Johnston III *(Chm)*

FULTON SUPPLY COMPANY INC.
342 Nelson St SW, Atlanta, GA
30313
Tel.: (404) 688-3400　　　　　GA
Web Site:
　http://www.fultonsupply.com
Year Founded: 1914
Sales Range: $1-9.9 Million
Emp.: 15
Industrial Supplies Distr
N.A.I.C.S.: 423840
Joel L. Roth *(Pres)*
Pete Colson *(Mgr-Matls)*
Jim Litchfield *(Engr-Sls)*

FUN AND FUNCTION LLC
PO Box 11, Merion Station, PA 19066
Tel.: (866) 343-6863
Web Site:
　http://www.funandfunction.com
Year Founded: 2005

Sales Range: $1-9.9 Million
Emp.: 3
Designs Therapeutic Toys & Tools for Children with Autism, ADHD & Sensory Integration Disorders
N.A.I.C.S.: 923110
Aviva Weiss *(Co-Founder)*
Haskel Weiss *(Co-Founder)*

FUN BEVERAGE INC.
175 Schoolhouse Loop, Kalispell, MT
59901
Tel.: (406) 752-1455
Web Site:
　https://www.funbeverage.com
Year Founded: 1981
Sales Range: $10-24.9 Million
Emp.: 70
Beer & Other Fermented Malt Liquors & Wine
N.A.I.C.S.: 424810
Brian Clark *(Pres & Gen Mgr)*
Kim A. Clausen *(VP-Sls)*
Gary McClarty *(Mgr-Non-Alcohol)*

FUN COUNTRY RV'S & MARINE, INC.
8800 S Desert Blvd, Anthony, TX
79821
Tel.: (915) 886-3500
Web Site:
　https://www.funcountryrvs.com
Sales Range: $10-24.9 Million
Emp.: 12
Recreational Vehicle Dealers
N.A.I.C.S.: 441210
Dave Pool *(Owner)*

FUN SPOT OF FLORIDA, INC.
5700 Fun Spot Way, Orlando, FL
32819
Tel.: (407) 363-3867　　　　　FL
Web Site: http://www.fun-spot.com
Year Founded: 1993
Sales Range: $1-9.9 Million
Emp.: 285
Amusement Park
N.A.I.C.S.: 713110
Renee Ambos *(Dir-Sls)*
Albert Cabuco *(Sr VP-Food & Beverage)*
Jennifer Collier *(Dir-HR)*
John Arie Jr. *(Pres & CEO)*

FUN TOWN RV LP
2200 US 67 E Business, Cleburne,
TX 76031
Tel.: (855) 867-1433
Web Site: http://www.funtownrv.com
Car Dealer
N.A.I.C.S.: 441110
Raul Ramirez *(VP-Sales)*

Subsidiaries:

Northtown Motor Homes, Inc.　　(1)
10947 Northland Dr NE, Rockford, MI
49341
Tel.: (616) 866-4300
Web Site:
　http://www.northtownmotorhomes.com
Sales Range: $1-9.9 Million
Emp.: 11
Motor Homes & Camper Trailers
N.A.I.C.S.: 441210
Gerald O'Neil *(Pres)*

FUN TOWN SPLASH TOWN USA
774 Portland Rd, Saco, ME 04072
Tel.: (207) 284-5139
Web Site:
　https://www.funtownsplashtown
　usa.com
Rev.: $26,700,000
Emp.: 500
Amusement Park
N.A.I.C.S.: 713110

Kenneth D. Cormier *(Founder & Pres)*

FUNCTIONAL PATHWAYS, LLC.
10133 Sherrill Blvd Ste 200, Knoxville, TN 37932
Tel.: (865) 531-2204
Web Site:
　http://www.functionalpathways.com
Sales Range: $50-74.9 Million
Emp.: 1,073
Contract Rehabilitation & Therapy Management Services
N.A.I.C.S.: 621498
Marcus Miller *(VP-Ops)*
Paula Hargis *(Dir-HR)*
Traci McCullough *(CFO)*
Gina Tomcsik *(Officer-Privacy & Dir-Compliance)*
Kellie Buchanan *(VP-Client Retention)*
Tina Jackson *(VP-HR)*

FUND EVALUATION GROUP, LLC
201 E 5th St Ste 1600, Cincinnati,
OH 45202-2628
Tel.: (513) 977-4400
Web Site: https://www.feg.com
Year Founded: 1988
Investment Advisory Firm
N.A.I.C.S.: 523940
Ralph F. Doering *(VP)*
Matthew R. Veith *(VP)*
Andrew M. Zach *(VP)*
Brian A. Hooper *(VP)*
Ross W. Neltner *(VP)*
Michael A. Condon *(VP)*
Alan L. Bergin *(VP)*
Dave J. Germain *(VP)*
David D. Center *(VP)*
David L. Mason *(VP)*
Douglas J. Walouke *(VP)*
Emily B. Crail *(VP)*
G. Scott Tabor *(VP)*
Jeffrey A. Davis *(VP)*
John F. Labmeier *(VP)*
Kevin J. Conroy *(VP)*
Kevin M. Kersting *(VP)*
Larry J. Thompson *(VP)*
Matt DenBleyker *(VP)*
Matthew S. Schwier *(VP)*
Michael J. Aluise *(VP)*
Nicola M. Da Roza *(VP)*
Pete R. Salvator *(VP)*
Phillip A. Scherrer *(VP)*
Robin L. Harmon *(VP)*
Schwier S. Wheeler *(VP)*
Sean P. McChesney *(VP)*
Stephen M. Hodson *(VP)*

FUND FOR THE PUBLIC INTEREST, INC.
294 Washington St Ste 500, Boston,
MA 02108
Tel.: (617) 292-8050　　　　　MA
Web Site:
　https://www.fundforthepublicin
　terest.org
Year Founded: 1982
Sales Range: $25-49.9 Million
Emp.: 11,603
Social Welfare Services
N.A.I.C.S.: 923130
Douglas Phelps *(Exec Dir)*

FUNDABLE LLC
1322 Manning Pkwy, Powell, OH
43065
Tel.: (800) 799-6998
Web Site: http://www.fundable.com
Emp.: 40
Software Platform for Business Funding
N.A.I.C.S.: 513210

Wil Schroter *(Founder & CEO)*

Subsidiaries:

LaunchRock, Inc.　　　　　　　(1)
340 S Lemon Ave #3434, Walnut, CA
91789
Tel.: (855) 467-7532
Web Site: http://www.launchrock.com
Sales Range: $1-9.9 Million
Software Publisher
N.A.I.C.S.: 513210
Jameson Detweiler *(CEO)*
Nate Munger *(Dir-Customer Satisfaction)*

FUNDACION PARA EL DESAROLLO DEL HOGAR PROPIO, INC
Ave Luis Munoz Marin Esq Georgetti Angora Park Plz, Caguas, PR 00725
Tel.: (787) 746-1600　　　　　PR
Web Site: http://www.fdhp.org
Year Founded: 1992
Sales Range: $10-24.9 Million
Individual & Family Support Services
N.A.I.C.S.: 624190
Maria Del Pilar Seijo *(Chm)*
Maria Cotto *(Treas)*
Lucy Bonilla *(Sec)*

FUNDAMENTAL ADVISORS LP
745 5th Ave 25th Fl, New York, NY
10151
Tel.: (212) 205-5000　　　　　DE
Web Site: http://fundamental.com
Investment Services
N.A.I.C.S.: 523999
Laurence Gottlieb *(Chm & CEO)*

Subsidiaries:

MMA Capital Holdings, LLC　　(1)
3600 O Donnell St Ste 600, Baltimore, MD
21224
Tel.: (443) 263-2900
Web Site:
　http://www.mmacapitalholdings.com
Rev.: $42,014,000
Assets: $533,062,000
Liabilities: $243,178,000
Net Worth: $289,884,000
Earnings: $8,374,000
Fiscal Year-end: 12/31/2020
Real Estate Investment Trust
N.A.I.C.S.: 525990
Laurence Gottlieb *(Chm & CEO)*
Justin Vinci *(CFO)*

Subsidiary (Non-US):

International Housing Solutions S.a
r.l　　　　　　　　　　　　　(2)
54 Peter Place Peter Place Office Park, PO
Box 2125, Block G Glassgow House
Ground Floor, Bryanston, 2191, Gauteng,
South Africa
Tel.: (27) 113008600
Web Site: http://www.ihsinvestments.co.za
Financial Service Provider
N.A.I.C.S.: 525990

Subsidiary (Domestic):

MMA Energy Capital, LLC　　　(2)
1755 Prospector Dr Ste 202, Park City, UT
84060
Tel.: (435) 604-0336
Web Site:
　http://www.mmaenergycapital.com
Management Consulting Services
N.A.I.C.S.: 541618
Kevin Panzica *(VP)*
David Felix *(VP)*
Bob Hopper *(Mng Dir)*
Danielle Thompson *(VP)*
Mark Domine *(VP)*
Joshua Turner *(VP)*

MMA Financial TC, LLC　　　　(2)
621 E Pratt St Ste 300, Baltimore, MD
21202
Tel.: (410) 727-5387
Financial Management Services
N.A.I.C.S.: 541611

MMA Realty Capital, Inc.　　　　(2)

621 E Pratt St, Baltimore, MD 21202
Tel.: (443) 263-2900
Web Site: http://www.mmarealtycapital.com
Sales Range: $1-4.9 Billion
Commercial Real Estate Financing & Investment Services
N.A.I.C.S.: 522310

MMA Renewable Ventures, LLC   **(2)**
44 Montgomery St Ste 2400, San Francisco, CA 94104
Tel.: (415) 986-8038
Web Site:
   http://www.mmarenewableventures.com
Emp.: 100
Plumbing, Heating Equipment Merchant Whslr
N.A.I.C.S.: 423720

FUNDAMENTAL GLOBAL IN-VESTORS, LLC
4201 Congress St Ste 140, Charlotte, NC 28209
Tel.: (239) 434-7434   NC
Web Site:
   http://www.fundamentalglobal.com
Investment Services
N.A.I.C.S.: 523999
Jeff Sutton *(COO)*
Richard Knepfler *(CFO)*
Joe Moglia *(Co-Founder, Chm & Partner)*
Daniel Kyle Cerminara *(CEO & Partner)*
Lewis McKay Johnson *(Pres & Partner)*
Blaine Ferguson *(Partner)*
William Beynon *(Partner)*

FUNDAMENTAL LONG TERM CARE HOLDINGS
920 Ridgebrook Rd, Sparks Glencoe, MD 21152
Tel.: (410) 773-1000
Web Site: http://www.fundltc.com
Sales Range: $100-124.9 Million
Home Health Care Holdings Company
N.A.I.C.S.: 621610
Karen Miller *(VP-HR)*

FUNDCORE INSTITUTIONAL INCOME TRUST INC.
One World Financial Ctr 30th Fl, New York, NY 10281
Tel.: (212) 909-5897   MD
Year Founded: 2010
Real Estate Investment Trust Services
N.A.I.C.S.: 525990
Steven A. Ball *(Pres & Chief Investment Officer)*
Lee J. Taragin *(CFO & COO)*
Michael C. Vessels *(Sec & Exec VP)*

FUNDCORP, INC.
550 Bailey Ave Ste 650, Fort Worth, TX 76147
Tel.: (817) 735-4777
Web Site:
   https://www.fundcorpinc.com
Private Investment Manager
N.A.I.C.S.: 523999
Michael Poates *(Vice Chm)*

Subsidiaries:

Gigi's Cupcakes   **(1)**
3065 Mallory Ln Ste 106, Franklin, TN 37067
Tel.: (615) 472-1508
Web Site: http://www.gigiscupcakesusa.com
Retail Bakeries
N.A.I.C.S.: 311811
Gina Butler *(Founder)*
Judy Renfrow *(Pres & COO)*

FUNDERA INC.
123 William St 21st Fl, New York, NY 10038

Web Site: http://www.fundera.com
Year Founded: 2013
Sales Range: $10-24.9 Million
Emp.: 96
Financial Services
N.A.I.C.S.: 522291
Jared Hecht *(CEO)*

FUNDERBURK'S PHARMACY, INC.
134 W Commerce St, Hernando, MS 38632
Tel.: (662) 429-5337
Sales Range: $1-9.9 Million
Emp.: 15
Medicine & Drug Distr
N.A.I.C.S.: 456110
Cheryl Sudduth *(Owner)*
Billy L. Sudduth *(Treas & VP)*

FUNDINGSHIELD LLC
1655 Palm Beach Lakes Blvd #808, West Palm Beach, FL 33401
Tel.: (800) 295-0135
Web Site:
   http://www.fundingshield.com
Sales Range: $1-9.9 Million
Emp.: 10
Residential Mortgages & Loan Funding Data Analysis
N.A.I.C.S.: 531390
Shad Quraishi *(Co-Founder)*
Steven Kornblau *(Co-Founder)*

FUNDOS GROUP LLC
2750 Rasmussen Rd, Park City, UT 84098
Tel.: (435) 565-1272   UT
Web Site: http://www.rlgcap.com
Privater Equity Firm
N.A.I.C.S.: 523999
Mark Lisonbee *(Co-Founder & Mng Partner)*
Greg Robinson *(Co-Founder & Mng Partner)*
Mark Nelson *(Partner & CFO)*

Subsidiaries:

eLearning Brothers, LLC   **(1)**
732 E Utah Vly Dr Ste 130, American Fork, UT 84003
Tel.: (801) 796-8323
Web Site:
   http://www.eLearningBrothers.com
Sales Range: $1-9.9 Million
Emp.: 32
Online Learning & Development Services
N.A.I.C.S.: 611691
Andrew Scivally *(Co-Founder & CEO)*
Curtis Morley *(Pres)*
Todd Cummings *(Dir-Custom Dev)*
Scott Condie *(Partner-Custom Solutions)*
John Blackmon *(CTO)*

Subsidiary (Domestic):

Edulence Corporation   **(2)**
79 Madison Ave 15th Fl, New York, NY 10016
Tel.: (212) 792-5800
Web Site: http://www.Edulence.com
Sales Range: $1-9.9 Million
Emp.: 15
Web Search Portal Operator
N.A.I.C.S.: 519290
Jon Tota *(CEO)*
Peter Getchell *(VP-Sls)*
Moki Goyal *(VP-Product Dev)*
Carolyn Haggerty *(VP-Bus Mgmt)*
Yoomi Chun *(VP-Mktg & Dir-Creative)*
Karlene Readinger *(Acct Mgr)*
Megan Niffenegger *(Project Mgr)*
Cindy Tanton *(Dir-Monitoring & Evaluation-Trng)*
Harry Altman *(Acct Exec)*
Joey Davenport *(Chief Dev Officer & Principal)*
Laurie Ann Thorne *(Dir-Ops)*

Division (Domestic):

The Game Agency LLC   **(2)**

470 West Ave Ste 2011, Stamford, CT 06902
Tel.: (212) 931-8552
Web Site: http://www.thegameagency.com
Sales Range: $1-9.9 Million
Emp.: 32
Game Development Services
N.A.I.C.S.: 513210
Stephen Baer *(Mng Partner & Head-Creative)*
Joseph McDonald *(Founder, Mng Partner & Head-Production)*
Richard Lowenthal *(Mng Partner & Head-Bus Ops)*
Jordan Duvall *(Mgr-Support)*
J. D. Fox *(Mgr-Ops)*
James Lange *(Mgr-Tech)*

Subsidiary (Domestic):

Trivantis Corporation   **(2)**
400 Fairway Dr Ste 101, Deerfield Beach, FL 33441
Tel.: (513) 929-0188
Web Site: http://www.trivantis.com
Software Publisher
N.A.I.C.S.: 513210
Jennifer Valley *(Community Mgr)*
Laura Silver *(Dir-Product Mgmt)*

FUNITURE ROW LLC
5641 Broadway, Denver, CO 80216-1021
Tel.: (303) 371-8560
Web Site:
   http://www.furniturerow.com
Rev.: $60,500,000
Emp.: 2
Nonresidential Building Operators
N.A.I.C.S.: 449110
Barney Visser *(Partner)*

Subsidiaries:

Denver Mattress Company   **(1)**
5000 N 27th St, Lincoln, NE 68521
Tel.: (402) 476-4100
Web Site: http://www.denvermattress.com
Online Shopping Services
N.A.I.C.S.: 449110

Pillow Kingdom Inc.   **(1)**
24000 E 19th Ave, Aurora, CO
80019-3705   **(100%)**
Tel.: (303) 371-8560
Emp.: 100
Wood Household Furniture
N.A.I.C.S.: 337122
Barney Visser *(Owner)*

FUNK/LEVIS & ASSOCIATES
1045 Willamette St, Eugene, OR 97401
Tel.: (541) 485-1932
Web Site: http://www.funklevis.com
Year Founded: 1980
Rev.: $13,000,000
Emp.: 11
Advertising Agencies, Brand Development, Communications, Corporate Identity, Graphic Design, Logo & Package Design
N.A.I.C.S.: 541810
Anne Marie Levis *(Pres)*
Jeannette Crocker *(Gen Mgr)*
Tonya Watts *(Mgr-Production)*
Christopher Berner *(Sr Designer)*
Jason Anderson *(Graphic Designer)*
Sherisha Htuira *(Mgr-Acct)*

FUNMOBILITY, INC.
4234 Hacienda Dr Ste 200, Pleasanton, CA 94588-2721
Tel.: (925) 598-9700
Web Site:
   https://www.funmobility.com
Year Founded: 1999
Mobile Phone Application Developer
N.A.I.C.S.: 513210
Adam Lavine *(Co-Founder & CEO)*
Dennis Chen *(Co-Founder & CTO)*

FUNNELBOX INC

712 Main St Ste 100, Oregon City, OR 97045
Tel.: (503) 595-5901
Web Site: http://www.funnelbox.com
Year Founded: 1999
Sales Range: $1-9.9 Million
Emp.: 27
Video Production
N.A.I.C.S.: 512110
Robb Crocker *(Founder & CEO)*
Kirk Vanderleest *(VP)*

FUR BREEDERS AGRICUL-TURAL COOPERATIVE
8700 S 700 W, Sandy, UT 84070-2520
Tel.: (801) 255-4228
Sales Range: $10-24.9 Million
Emp.: 40
Animal Feed Mfr
N.A.I.C.S.: 311119
Dane Dikson *(CEO)*

FURBAY ELECTRIC SUPPLY CO.
208 Schroyer Ave SW, Canton, OH 44702
Tel.: (330) 454-3033
Web Site: https://www.furbay.com
Sales Range: $10-24.9 Million
Emp.: 34
Electrical Supplies
N.A.I.C.S.: 449129
Tim Furbay *(Pres)*
Cheryl Manko *(Controller)*

FURBER ADVERTISING
1718 Fairview St, Houston, TX 77006
Tel.: (713) 524-0382
Year Founded: 2003
Sales Range: $10-24.9 Million
Emp.: 5
Advertising Agency
N.A.I.C.S.: 541810
Paola Furber *(Principal)*
Elisabeth Wiedner *(Mgr-Mktg Strategy)*

FURINO & SONS INC.
66 Columbia Rd, Branchburg, NJ 08876-3519
Tel.: (908) 756-7736   NJ
Web Site:
   http://www.furinoandsons.com
Year Founded: 1929
Sales Range: $10-24.9 Million
Emp.: 122
Construction Services
N.A.I.C.S.: 236220
Thomas Furino *(Pres)*
Randy Furino *(VP)*
Greg Furino *(VP)*
David Furino *(VP)*

FURMAN ROTH ADVERTISING
801 2nd Ave 14th Fl, New York, NY 10017-4706
Tel.: (212) 687-2300   NY
Web Site: http://www.furmanroth.com
Year Founded: 1954
Sales Range: $10-24.9 Million
Emp.: 25
Advertising Agency
N.A.I.C.S.: 541810
Ernie Roth *(Pres & CEO)*
Mark Leftkowitz *(Exec VP, Partner & Media Dir)*
Jacki Friedman *(Sr VP, Acct Svcs Dir & Partner)*
Barry Glenn *(Art Dir-Creative Supvr)*
Maria LoPiccolo *(Sr VP & Acct Supvr)*
Peter Saluk *(Creative Dir)*
Dennis Short *(Sr Dir-Art)*
Vilma Sindoni *(Controller)*
Sally Mutafopulos *(Office Mgr)*

Furman Roth Advertising—(Continued)

Subsidiaries:

Furman, Feiner Advertising (1)
560 Sylvan Ave, Englewood Cliffs, NJ 07632
Tel.: (201) 568-1634
Web Site: http://www.furmanroth.com
Sales Range: $10-24.9 Million
Emp.: 15
N.A.I.C.S.: 541810
Robb Crocker (Pres & CEO)
Ernie Roth (Pres & CEO)
Vilma Sindoni (Exec VP)
Mark Lefkowitz (Partner, Exec VP & Dir-Media)
Jacki Friedman (Sr VP, Partner & Dir-Acct Svcs)
Barry Glenn (Supvr-Creative)
Mark Lenz (Acct Mgr)
Peter Saluk (Creative Dir)

FURMAN'S, INC.
1663 Mound St, Sarasota, FL 34236-7715
Tel.: (941) 365-7891   FL
Year Founded: 1959
Sales Range: $25-49.9 Million
Emp.: 800
Provider of Restaurant Services
N.A.I.C.S.: 722513
Robert G. Furman (Pres)
Steven Rusincovitch (CFO & Controller)

FURMANO FOODS, INC.
770 Cannery Rd, Northumberland, PA 17857
Tel.: (570) 473-3516   PA
Web Site: https://www.furmanos.com
Year Founded: 1921
Sales Range: $100-124.9 Million
Emp.: 300
Processed Tomatoes & Vegetables
N.A.I.C.S.: 311421
Chad Geise (Pres & CEO)

FURNACE AND TUBE SERVICE INC.
13130 Hwy 44, Gonzales, LA 70737
Tel.: (225) 621-4500
Web Site: https://www.furnaceandtube.com
Sales Range: $10-24.9 Million
Emp.: 81
Boiler & Boiler Shop Work
N.A.I.C.S.: 332410
Lonnie Maulden (Pres)

FURNISHED QUARTERS LLC
158 W 27th St 7th Fl, New York, NY 10001
Tel.: (212) 367-9400
Web Site: https://www.furnishedquarters.com
Sales Range: $10-24.9 Million
Emp.: 100
Furnished Room Rental
N.A.I.C.S.: 316110
Cory Haber (Dir-Mktg)
Lorraine Sullivan (CFO)
Steven Saide (Exec VP-Design)
Steven Brown (CEO)
Annette Clement (Exec VP & Gen Mgr-Massachusetts)
Jason Antoniazzi (VP-HR)

FURNITURE & THINGS INC.
15612 Jarvis St NW, Elk River, MN 55330
Tel.: (763) 441-7011
Web Site: https://www.furnitureandthings.com
Sales Range: $10-24.9 Million
Emp.: 50
Furniture Retailer
N.A.I.C.S.: 449110
Larry Hickman (Pres)

FURNITURE CONSULTANTS LLC
1450 Broadway 25th Fl, New York, NY 10018
Tel.: (212) 229-4500
Web Site: http://www.fcifurnitureconsultants.com
Year Founded: 1978
Sales Range: $75-99.9 Million
Emp.: 25
Contract Furniture Distr
N.A.I.C.S.: 423210
Michael J. Eble (Pres)

FURNITURE DISTRIBUTORS INC.
4524-C S Blvd, Charlotte, NC 28209-2841
Tel.: (704) 523-3424
Web Site: http://www.kimbrells.com
Year Founded: 1915
Sales Range: $50-74.9 Million
Emp.: 600
Operator of Furniture Distr
N.A.I.C.S.: 449110

Subsidiaries:

Kimbrell Investments Inc. (1)
4524 S Blvd, Charlotte, NC 28209-2841
Tel.: (704) 523-3424
Web Site: http://www.kimbrells.com
Sales Range: $25-49.9 Million
Emp.: 30
Furniture Distributors
N.A.I.C.S.: 551112
Ken Thornpurg (Pres)

FURNITURE ENTERPRISES OF ALASKA
940 E 38th Ave, Anchorage, AK 99503
Tel.: (907) 272-5800
Web Site: http://www.sadlers.com
Sales Range: $25-49.9 Million
Emp.: 100
La-Z-Boy Furniture Stores
N.A.I.C.S.: 449110
Dave Cavitt (Pres)

FURNITURE FAIR INC.
507 Bell Fork Rd, Jacksonville, NC 28541
Tel.: (910) 455-9595
Web Site: https://www.furniture-fair.net
Rev.: $11,900,000
Emp.: 100
Furniture Retailer
N.A.I.C.S.: 449110
Ivins Popkin (Pres)
Steve Foley (Mgr-Store)

FURNITURE MARKETING GROUP INC.
6100 W Plano Pkwy Ste 1400, Plano, TX 75093
Tel.: (214) 556-4700
Web Site: https://www.fmgi.com
Rev.: $64,600,000
Emp.: 100
Office Furniture
N.A.I.C.S.: 423210
Greg Almond (Pres)
Bob Bacic (CFO)
Don Harrell (Project Mgr)
Scott Bailey (Acct Mgr-New Bus Dev)
Sean Corrington (VP-Sls)

Subsidiaries:

Contract Associates Inc. (1)
219 Central Ave Nw Ste 101, Albuquerque, NM 87102
Tel.: (505) 881-8070
Web Site: http://www.contractassociatesnm.com
Rev.: $11,400,000
Emp.: 35

Floor Coverings
N.A.I.C.S.: 532490
Maria Griego-Raby (Pres)
Bruno Ienni (Controller)
Jennifer McMath (COO)

FURNITURE ON CONSIGNMENT INC.
4911 S 72nd St, Omaha, NE 68127
Tel.: (402) 339-7848
Sales Range: $10-24.9 Million
Emp.: 100
Owner & Operator of Furniture Stores
N.A.I.C.S.: 449110

FURNITURE OUTLETS USA
140 E Hinks Ln, Sioux Falls, SD 57104-0434
Tel.: (605) 336-5000
Web Site: http://www.thefurnituremart.com
Furniture Store Owner & Operator
N.A.I.C.S.: 449110
Dave Whisler (Dir-Info Sys)
Brandon Eberhard (Exec Dir-Ancillary Ops-Furniture Mart USA)
Troy Eichmann (CEO-Furniture Mart USA)
Kristen Stengel (Mng Dir-Furniture Mart USA)

FURNITURE RENTAL ASSOCIATES
60-2059 Pl, New York, NY 11378
Tel.: (212) 868-0300
Web Site: http://www.furniture4rent.com
Year Founded: 1941
Sales Range: $10-24.9 Million
Emp.: 50
Furniture Rental Services
N.A.I.C.S.: 449110

FURNITURE ROW
1701 Market Place Dr, Great Falls, MT 59404
Tel.: (406) 771-1400
Web Site: http://www.furniturerow.com
Furniture Retailer
N.A.I.C.S.: 449110
Alex Colson (Mgr)

Subsidiaries:

Sofa Mart, LLC (1)
5671 Broadway, Denver, CO 80216
Tel.: (303) 296-9524
Web Site: http://www.furniturerow.com
Furniture Retailer
N.A.I.C.S.: 449110

FURNITURELAND SOUTH, INC.
5635 Riverdale Dr, Jamestown, NC 27282-9171
Tel.: (336) 841-4328   NC
Web Site: https://www.furniturelandsouth.com
Year Founded: 1970
Sales Range: $125-149.9 Million
Emp.: 500
Sales & Service of Furniture
N.A.I.C.S.: 449110
Jeff Harris (Pres & COO)

FURNLITE, INC.
PO Box 159, Fallston, NC 28042
Tel.: (704) 538-3193
Web Site: https://www.furnlite.com
Sales Range: $10-24.9 Million
Emp.: 35
Residential Lighting Fixture Mfr
N.A.I.C.S.: 335131
Gary Alsobrook (Co-Founder, Pres & CEO)
Ritta Green (Controller)
Curtis Bailey (VP-Sls)

Doug Clay (Product Mgr)
Rusty Helme (Gen Mgr)
Marcia Alsobrook (Co-Founder)

FURST ENTERPRISES INC.
708 W N Temple St, Salt Lake City, UT 84116
Tel.: (801) 972-3838   UT
Web Site: https://www.furstconstruction.com
Year Founded: 1990
Sales Range: $10-24.9 Million
Emp.: 25
Construction & Contracting Services
N.A.I.C.S.: 236220
Robert Furstenau (Chm)
Trish Harris (Dir-Admin & Office Mgr)
Dean Jarman (Dir-Construction & Project Mgr)
Chris Furstenau (Pres)

Subsidiaries:

Furst Construction Co. Inc. (1)
708 W North Temple, Salt Lake City, UT 84116
Tel.: (801) 972-3838
Web Site: http://www.furstconstruction.com
Sales Range: $10-24.9 Million
Emp.: 20
Construction & Contracting Services
N.A.I.C.S.: 236220
Robert Furstenau (Founder & Chm)
Trish Harris (Dir-Admin & Office Mgr)

FURST-MCNESS COMPANY
120 E Clark St, Freeport, IL 61032
Tel.: (815) 235-6151   IL
Web Site: https://www.mcness.com
Year Founded: 1908
Sales Range: $100-124.9 Million
Emp.: 270
Feed Premix Products, Feed Commodities & Wet Brewers Grain for Swine, Dairy & Beef Mfr & Distr
N.A.I.C.S.: 311119
Frank E. Furst (Chm)
Martha Furst (Vice Chm)
Matthew Heinrich (Pres & CEO)
Matthew Hartman (CFO)
Kevin Gyland (Exec VP)
Shelley Martin (VP-Agribus Div)
Webb Howerton (Mgr-Commodities-Mid-Southern)
Steve England (VP)

Subsidiaries:

Aero Group, Inc. (1)
120 E Clark St, Freeport, IL 61032
Tel.: (815) 233-3387
Web Site: http://www.aeroinc.net
Emp.: 12
Computer Networking Services
N.A.I.C.S.: 541512
Adam Schulz (Gen Mgr)

Furst-McNess of Canada (1)
30 Wilson Street Ingersoll, Ingersoll, N5C 4E8, ON, Canada (100%)
Tel.: (519) 659-8600
Web Site: http://www.mcness.com
Sales Range: $10-24.9 Million
Emp.: 12
Dairy & Beef Feeds
N.A.I.C.S.: 311611

FURSTSTAFFING, INC.
2580 Charles St, Rockford, IL 61108
Tel.: (815) 229-7810
Web Site: http://www.furststaff.com
Sales Range: $10-24.9 Million
Emp.: 34
Temporary Employment Services
N.A.I.C.S.: 561320
Darlene J. Furst (Pres)
Ashley Bender (Coord-Assignment)
Dewey Everts (Mgr-Risk)

FURTHER GLOBAL CAPITAL MANAGEMENT, L.P.

445 Park Ave 14th Fl, New York, NY 10022
Tel.: (646) 661-1888
Web Site:
http://www.furtherglobal.com
Privater Equity Firm
N.A.I.C.S.: 523999
Olivier Sarkozy *(Founder & Mng Partner)*

Subsidiaries:

Payment Alliance International,
Inc. (1)
2101 High Wickham Pl Ste 101, Louisville, KY 40245
Tel.: (502) 212-4000
Web Site: http://www.gopai.com
Payment Solutions & Financial Transactions Services
N.A.I.C.S.: 522320
Scott McFarland *(VP-Sls-Merchant Alliance)*
Michael W. Hammer *(VP-Application Dev)*
Dale Herb *(Chief Talent Officer & Sr VP-HR)*
Dale A. Jones *(CTO & Sr VP)*
Sean Metcalf *(Acct Exec-Insurance)*
Shellon Hooten *(Acct Exec-Insurance)*
Eric McPheeters *(Acct Exec-Insurance)*
Justina Schaffer *(Acct Exec-Insurance)*
Todd Schroerlucke *(Acct Exec-Insurance)*
Jalen Boyd *(Acct Exec-Insurance)*
Daniel Willis *(Acct Exec-Insurance)*
Neil Clark *(CEO-ATM Bus)*
John J. Leehy III *(Pres & CEO)*
James C. Comis III *(Chm)*

Subsidiary (Domestic):

Eclipse Cash Systems, LLC (2)
6150 W Gila Springs Pl Ste 14, Chandler, AZ 85226-3493
Tel.: (480) 829-1294
Automated Teller Machine Products & Services
N.A.I.C.S.: 334118
Chris Biedrzycki *(CEO)*

ProSight Global, Inc. (1)
412 Mt Kemble Ave Ste 300, Morristown, NJ 07960
Tel.: (973) 532-1900
Web Site: http://www.prosightspecialty.com
Rev.: $817,090,000
Assets: $3,050,712,000
Liabilities: $2,426,744,000
Net Worth: $623,968,000
Earnings: $22,228,000
Emp.: 351
Fiscal Year-end: 12/31/2020
General Insurance Services
N.A.I.C.S.: 524210
Vivienne Zimmermann *(Chief Customer Experience Officer)*
Frank D. Papalia *(Chief Legal Officer)*
Kari Hilder *(Chief HR Officer)*
Lee Kraemer *(Chief Actuary Officer)*
Anthony S. Piszel *(CFO)*
Erin Cullen *(Pres-Customer Segment)*
Darryl Siry *(COO & CTO)*
Ric Victores *(Chief Sls & Mktg Officer)*
Joe Finnegan *(Pres-Customer Segment)*
Rob Bednarik *(Pres-Customer Segment)*
Donna Biondich *(Chief Claims Officer)*
Lee Lloyd *(Officer-Field Ops)*
Kevin Topper *(Pres-Customer Segment)*
Nico Santini *(Chief Investment Officer)*
Jeff Arricale *(Head-Capital Markets)*
Darryl Siry *(COO & CTO)*
Jonathan Ritz *(CEO)*
Stan Galanski *(Chm)*
Hunter Morgan *(Sr VP-Excess Casualty)*
Tim Ryan *(Pres)*
Christine Doherty *(VP)*
Philip Yung *(VP)*
Keith Lavigne *(Sr VP-Exec Liability)*

FURY MOTORS INC.
1000 Concord St S, South Saint Paul, MN 55075
Tel.: (651) 351-8200
Web Site: http://www.furymotors.com
Rev.: $26,412,639
Emp.: 70
New & Used Car Dealers
N.A.I.C.S.: 441110
Dick Reineck *(Mgr-Fleet & Comml)*

FUSCO PERSONNEL, INC.
4 Executive Park Dr, Albany, NY 12203
Tel.: (518) 869-6100   NY
Web Site:
https://www.fuscopersonnel.net
Year Founded: 1994
Sales Range: $10-24.9 Million
Emp.: 11
Temporary Help Service
N.A.I.C.S.: 561320
Patricia Fusco *(Pres)*

FUSE LLC
PO Box 4509, Burlington, VT 05406
Tel.: (802) 864-7123
Web Site:
http://www.fusemarketing.com
Year Founded: 1995
Sales Range: $1-9.9 Million
Emp.: 30
Public Relations & Event Marketing
N.A.I.C.S.: 541820
Brett Smith *(Partner)*
Bill Carter *(Partner)*
Issa Sawabini *(Partner)*

FUSE/IDEAS
8 Winchester Pl Ste 302, Winchester, MA 01890
Tel.: (617) 776-5800
Web Site: https://www.fuseideas.com
Sales Range: $10-24.9 Million
Emp.: 15
Advertising Agencies
N.A.I.C.S.: 541810
Dennis Franczak *(Founder, Pres & CEO)*
Rich Malak *(Dir-Engrg)*
Vanessa Levin *(Dir-Creative)*

FUSE3 SOLUTIONS LLC
914 N Broadway Ste 250, Oklahoma City, OK 73102
Tel.: (405) 455-2633   OK
Web Site:
http://www.fuse3solutions.com
Year Founded: 2013
Sales Range: $1-9.9 Million
Emp.: 15
Human Resource Consulting Services
N.A.I.C.S.: 541612
Ryan Albee *(Co-Owner & Dir-Bus Dev)*
Adam Giddens *(Co-Owner & Dir-Recruiting)*
Krista Collier *(Mgr-Fin & Acctg)*
Kelsey Sohrabi *(Mgr-Bus Dev)*
Tiffany Hebert *(Office Mgr)*

FUSION ACADEMY & LEARN-ING CENTER
512 Via De La Valle Ste 201, Solana Beach, CA 92075-2714
Tel.: (858) 792-2300
Web Site:
http://www.fusionacademy.com
Year Founded: 1989
Sales Range: $1-9.9 Million
Emp.: 40
Customized & Specialized Academic High School Programs
N.A.I.C.S.: 923110
Michelle Rose Gilman *(Founder & Pres)*
Jennifer Rumack *(Reg Dir)*
Karina Neal *(Reg Dir-Ops)*
Tyeler Viel *(Reg Dir-Community Dev)*

FUSION B2B, INC.
1548 Bond St Ste 114, Naperville, IL 60563
Tel.: (630) 579-8300
Web Site: http://www.fusionb2b.com
Sales Range: $1-9.9 Million

Emp.: 12
Advetising Agency
N.A.I.C.S.: 541810
Laurie Olesky *(Mng Dir)*

FUSION CONNECT, INC.
210 Interstate N Pkwy Ste 200, Atlanta, GA 30339
Tel.: (866) 424-5100   DE
Web Site:
http://www.fusionconnect.com
Year Founded: 1997
Sales Range: Less than $1 Million
Communication & Internet Technologies
N.A.I.C.S.: 517121
Brian Crotty *(CEO)*
Mario DeRiggi *(Chief Revenue Officer)*
Brian George *(CTO)*
John Dobbins *(COO)*
Samantha Zuniga *(VP-Channel Ops & Programs)*
Diane Frazzetta *(VP-Channel Sls-East)*
Jorel Potts *(Sr Mgr-Channel-West)*
Rick Ribas *(Sr VP-Channels & Alliances)*
Ruzanna Tantushyan *(Dir-Corp Comm)*
Brian McClintock *(CFO)*
Chris Updegraft *(CIO)*
James P. Prenetta Jr. *(Gen Counsel & Exec VP)*

Subsidiaries:

Birch Communications, Inc. (1)
3060 Peachtree Rd NW Ste 1065, Atlanta, GA 30305
Tel.: (866) 424-5544
Web Site: http://www.birch.com
Bundled Telecommunications Services
N.A.I.C.S.: 517810
Tony Tomae *(Pres & CEO)*

Network Billing Systems, LLC (1)
155 Willowbrook Blvd, Wayne, NJ 07470
Tel.: (973) 256-2020
Web Site: http://www.fusionconnect.com
Telecommunication Servicesb
N.A.I.C.S.: 517810

Technology For Business Corp. (1)
1112 Ocean Dr Ste 202, Manhattan Beach, CA 90266   (100%)
Tel.: (310) 491-3800
Web Site: http://www.tfbc.com
Sales Range: $1-9.9 Million
Emp.: 3
Comprehensive, Customized & Turnkey CTI Applications, IVR & Flexible Software Modules for Call Centers, Healthcare, Education, Government & Security Services
N.A.I.C.S.: 541511
Charles Cuggino *(CEO)*
William Jones *(VP-Sls)*

FUSION CONSULTING INC
5215 N O'Connor Blvd Ste 650, Irving, TX 75039
Tel.: (214) 649-2920
Web Site:
http://www.fusionconsultinginc.com
Year Founded: 2006
Sales Range: $1-9.9 Million
Emp.: 35
Data Processing Services
N.A.I.C.S.: 518210
Jeff Wilhelm *(Pres)*
Jaime Heller *(CFO & VP)*

FUSION HEALTH TECHNOLO-GIES CORPORATION
10 Woodbridge Ctr Dr Ste 200, Woodbridge, NJ 07095
Tel.: (732) 218-5705
Web Site: http://www.fusionehr.com
Year Founded: 2006
Sales Range: $1-9.9 Million
Emp.: 12

Health Care Consulting Services
N.A.I.C.S.: 621610
Bryan J. Jakovcic *(Pres)*

Subsidiaries:

Kalos, Inc. (1)
3518 SE 21st St, Topeka, KS 66607
Tel.: (785) 232-3606
Web Site: http://www.kalos-inc.com
Stationery & Office Supplies Merchant Whslr
N.A.I.C.S.: 424120
Josh Powell *(Engr-Software)*

FUSION OEM
6951 High Grove Blvd, Burr Ridge, IL 60527
Tel.: (630) 323-4115
Web Site:
https://www.fusionoem.com
Year Founded: 2002
Sales Range: $1-9.9 Million
Emp.: 50
Manufactures Industrial Products for the Packaging, Medical & Printing Industries
N.A.I.C.S.: 333248
Craig Zoberis *(Founder, Pres & CEO)*

FUSION OPTIX, INC.
19 Wheeling Ave, Woburn, MA 01801
Tel.: (781) 995-0805
Web Site: http://www.fusionoptix.com
Year Founded: 2003
Sales Range: $1-9.9 Million
Emp.: 15
Lighting Technology Services
N.A.I.C.S.: 541490
Terence Yeo *(Founder & CEO)*

FUSION PPT LLC
8245 Boone Blvd Ste 200, Vienna, VA 22182
Web Site: https://www.fusionppt.com
Sales Range: $1-9.9 Million
Software Publisher
N.A.I.C.S.: 513210
Michael Biddick *(CEO)*

FUSION PUBLIC RELATIONS
570 7th Ave 9th Fl, New York, NY 10018
Tel.: (212) 651-4200   NY
Web Site: http://www.fusionpr.com
Sales Range: $1-9.9 Million
Emp.: 35
Communications, Branding, Marketing & Public Relations
N.A.I.C.S.: 541820
Robert Geller *(Pres)*

Subsidiaries:

Fusion Public Relations, Inc. (1)
12121 Wilshire Blvd Ste 303, Los Angeles, CA 90025
Tel.: (310) 481-1431
Web Site: http://www.fusionpr.com
Emp.: 10
Public Relations
N.A.I.C.S.: 541820
Sara Preto *(VP)*

FUSION RECRUITING LABS, INC.
280 Hwy 35 S Ste 302, Red Bank, NJ 07701
Tel.: (732) 663-9777
Web Site: http://www.fusionrl.com
Year Founded: 2015
Sales Range: $1-9.9 Million
Emp.: 45
Human Resource Consulting Services
N.A.I.C.S.: 541612
Mike Kret *(Sr VP-Ops & IT)*
Matthew Zeto *(VP-Sls)*

Fusion Recruiting Labs, Inc.—(Continued)

Alex McKeown *(CEO)*
Thomas Lynch *(CFO)*
Bruno Stanziale *(Chm & Pres)*

FUSION SOLUTIONS, INC.
16901 N Dallas Pkwy Ste 114, Addison, TX 75001
Tel.: (972) 764-1708
Web Site:
http://www.fusionsolutionsinc.com
Year Founded: 2002
Sales Range: $10-24.9 Million
Emp.: 170
Telecom & IT Industry Consulting & Staffing Services
N.A.I.C.S.: 541690
Tahir Hussain *(Founder, Pres & CEO)*
Vic Velevis *(Head-Bus & Market Dev)*
John Manukian *(Head-Recruiting Initiatives)*

FUSION TRADE, INC.
10 Fan Pier Blvd 5th Fl, Boston, MA 02210
Tel.: (617) 502-4100   DE
Web Site: https://www.fusionww.com
Year Founded: 2001
Sales Range: $10-24.9 Million
Emp.: 600
Other Electronic Parts & Equipment Merchant Wholesalers
N.A.I.C.S.: 423690
Peter LeSaffre *(CEO)*
Paul Romano *(COO)*
Tobey Gonnerman *(Pres)*

Subsidiaries:

Fusion Trade HK Limited   (1)
Unit 27/F Unit 04 Cable TV Tower 9 Hoi Shing Road, Tsuen Wan, NT, China (Hong Kong)   **(100%)**
Tel.: (852) 24990267
Web Site: http://www.fusiontrade.com
Computer & Software Distribution Center
N.A.I.C.S.: 334610
Jeffrey Hong *(Mng Dir)*

FUSION92
440 W Ontario St, Chicago, IL 60654
Web Site: https://www.fusion92.com
Year Founded: 1999
Emp.: 55
Marketing Agency
N.A.I.C.S.: 541613
Matt Murphy *(Founder)*
Jon Dean *(Exec VP)*
Debbie Van Ooteghem *(Exec VP)*
Dave Clark *(VP & Dir-Creative)*
Christina Downey *(VP-Client Partnership)*
Meghan McCarthy *(Sr VP-Media & Activation Svcs)*
Jacob Beckley *(Exec VP-Product & Innovation)*
Tom Zanoni *(VP-Bus Transformation)*
Paul Semper *(VP-Project Excellence)*
Tom Patrevito *(Sr VP-Channel Integration)*
Phil Bellini *(VP-Bus Dev)*
Frank Nicodem *(VP-Bus Ops)*
Doug Dome *(Pres)*
Joseph Shavit *(Sr VP-Product)*

FUSIONAPPS, LLC
110A Meadowlands Pkwy Ste 101, Secaucus, NJ 07094
Tel.: (201) 537-8023
Web Site: http://www.fusionapps.com
Year Founded: 2000
Sales Range: $1-9.9 Million
Emp.: 15
Consulting Firm For Technical Web Development
N.A.I.C.S.: 541512

Chad Pugsley *(Founder & Principal)*
Tony Barroqueiro *(Mgr-Network Ops)*

FUSIONARY MEDIA
220 Grandville Ave SW, Grand Rapids, MI 49503
Tel.: (616) 469-4424
Web Site: https://www.fusionary.com
Year Founded: 1995
Sales Range: $1-9.9 Million
Emp.: 9
Computer System Design Services
N.A.I.C.S.: 541512
Jack Baty *(Partner)*

FUSIONBOX, INC.
2031 Curtis St, Denver, CO 80205
Tel.: (303) 952-7490
Web Site: http://www.fusionbox.com
Year Founded: 2001
Sales Range: $1-9.9 Million
Emp.: 20
Interactive Advertising
N.A.I.C.S.: 541810
Alexander Groth *(Pres)*
Ivy Hastings *(VP-Strategy)*
Paula Lee *(Office Mgr)*

FUSIONWARE CORP.
2815 E Lake Ave E Ste 300, Seattle, WA 98102
Tel.: (206) 903-1855
Year Founded: 2001
Sales Range: $1-9.9 Million
Emp.: 27
Custom Computer Programming Services
N.A.I.C.S.: 541511
Alan Davis *(CEO)*

FUSIONWORKS, INC.
120 Condado Ave Pico Ctr Ste 102, San Juan, PR 00907-2755
Tel.: (787) 721-1039
Web Site: http://www.fwpr.com
Year Founded: 2002
Rev.: $5,800,000
Emp.: 43
Computer Related Consulting Services
N.A.I.C.S.: 541512

FUSZ, LOUIS NISSAN-MAZDA, INC.
1025 N Lindbergh Blvd, Saint Louis, MO 63132
Tel.: (314) 994-3400
Web Site: http://www.fusz.com
Sales Range: $25-49.9 Million
Emp.: 60
New Car Dealers
N.A.I.C.S.: 441110
Pete Fusz *(Gen Mgr)*
David Arbogast *(Mgr-Sls)*
Glen Goepel *(Mgr-Subaru Svc)*

FUTAI USA INC.
7 Parkway Pl, Edison, NJ 08837
Tel.: (732) 225-1717
Web Site: http://www.futaiusa.com
Year Founded: 1991
Sales Range: $10-24.9 Million
Emp.: 40
Women's & Children's Accessories Distributors
N.A.I.C.S.: 424350
T. F. Chen *(Chm)*
Chandra Khemani *(Mgr-IT)*

FUTRON CORPORATION
7315 Wisconsin Ave Ste 900 W, Bethesda, MD 20814
Tel.: (301) 913-9372
Web Site: http://www.futron.com
Sales Range: $25-49.9 Million
Emp.: 100

Management Consulting Services
N.A.I.C.S.: 541618
Joe Fuller Jr. *(Pres & CEO)*
Kevin Fuller *(Dir-Mktg)*
Peggy Pslye *(Dir-Telecomm Div)*

FUTTERMAN, LANZA & PASCULLI, LLP
180 E Main St Ste 101, Smithtown, NY 11787
Tel.: (631) 979-4300
Web Site:
http://www.trustedattorneys.com
Law firm
N.A.I.C.S.: 541110
Ronald Lanza *(Partner)*
Aaron Futterman *(Partner)*

FUTURA CORPORATION
380 E Parkcenter Blvd Ste 230, Boise, ID 83706
Tel.: (208) 336-0150
Sales Range: $50-74.9 Million
Emp.: 4
Aluminum Extruded Products
N.A.I.C.S.: 331318
Yvonne Goundry *(Controller)*

Subsidiaries:

Alliance Title & Escrow Corporation   (1)
380 E Park Center Blvd Ste 105, Boise, ID 83706
Tel.: (208) 388-8881
Web Site: http://www.alliancetitle.com
Sales Range: $25-49.9 Million
Emp.: 35
Title & Escrow Insurance
N.A.I.C.S.: 524210
Larry Matney *(Pres & CEO)*
Kathy Brashear *(Chief HR Officer & Sr VP)*
Mark Mills *(CFO & Sr VP)*
Jason Jacobson *(CIO & Sr VP)*
Michael Greear *(Engr-IT Sys)*
Kevin Haro *(Accountant)*
Jenny Martin *(Sr VP & Dir-Corp Bus Dev)*
Robin Aberasturi *(Officer-Compliance & Sr VP)*
Katherine Nielsen *(VP & Gen Mgr-Pocatello)*
Karena Boesel *(VP & Sls Mgr-Residential-Ada County)*

FUTURA SERVICES
515 Pennsylvania Ave, Fort Washington, PA 19034
Tel.: (215) 642-3363
Web Site:
http://www.futuraservices.net
Year Founded: 1992
Rev.: $8,300,000
Emp.: 41
Public Relations Services
N.A.I.C.S.: 541820
Dominic Sambucci *(COO)*
Eric Nolan *(Dir-Bus Dev)*
Joseph Fares *(CFO)*
Janet E. Denicola *(Founder & Pres)*

FUTURAMIC TOOL & ENGINEERING COMPANY INC.
24680 Gibson Dr, Warren, MI 48089-4313
Tel.: (586) 497-8850
Web Site: http://www.futuramic.com
Year Founded: 1955
Sales Range: $10-24.9 Million
Emp.: 220
Special Dies, Tools & Fixtures Mfr
N.A.I.C.S.: 333514
H. B. Stowe Jr. *(Mgr-Aerospace Ops)*

Subsidiaries:

Capital Welding Inc.   (1)
21800 W 8 Mile Rd, Southfield, MI 48075-5624   **(100%)**
Tel.: (248) 355-0410
Web Site: http://www.capital-welding.com

Sales Range: $10-24.9 Million
Emp.: 38
Provider of Fabricated Plate Work
N.A.I.C.S.: 332313

FUTURE CAPITAL HOLDING CORPORATION
4250 Keith Bridge Rd, Cumming, GA 30041
Tel.: (770) 720-4622
Sales Range: $10-24.9 Million
Emp.: 4
Commercial & Institutional Building Construction Services
N.A.I.C.S.: 236220
Randy Eaton *(CEO)*

FUTURE COMPUTING SOLUTIONS INC.
23800 Via Del Rio, Yorba Linda, CA 92887-2726
Tel.: (714) 692-9120
Web Site: https://www.fcsinet.com
Year Founded: 1989
Sales Range: $10-24.9 Million
Emp.: 40
Provider of Computers, Peripherals & Software
N.A.I.C.S.: 423430
Bicky Singh *(CEO)*

FUTURE ENERGY SOLUTIONS
5400 NW 35th Ave Prospect Park, Fort Lauderdale, FL 33309
Tel.: (954) 714-0300
Web Site: http://www.feslighting.com
Year Founded: 2009
Sales Range: $1-9.9 Million
Emp.: 70
Lighting Product Mfr
N.A.I.C.S.: 335132
Daniel Gold *(CEO)*
Anthony Lyons *(Chm)*
Simon Conway *(COO)*
Lydia Greenstein *(Dir-Comml)*
Chris Dorn *(Dir-Ops)*
Wayne Burrell *(Dir-Sls-Natl)*
Andrew Duffus *(Head-Procurement)*
Denise Smith *(Dir-Project Admin)*
Josef Levy *(CTO & Dir-Engrg)*
Marcus Brodin *(Dir-Comml)*
Leon Scott *(Mgr-Procurement)*
Tim Jones *(Mgr-Warehouse)*

FUTURE FOAM, INC.
1610 Avenue N, Council Bluffs, IA 51501-1071
Tel.: (712) 323-9122   NE
Web Site:
https://www.futurefoam.com
Year Founded: 1958
Sales Range: $25-49.9 Million
Emp.: 550
Mfr of Polyurethane Foam for Furniture, Bedding, Packaging & Carpet Padding
N.A.I.C.S.: 326150
Charles Schneider *(Chm)*
Bruce Schneider *(Pres & CEO)*
Rob Heller *(VP)*
Mike Blatt *(Treas & Controller)*
Al Diamond *(Gen Mgr)*

Subsidiaries:

American Poly-Foam Co. Ltd   (1)
22300 Hathaway Ave A, Hayward, CA 94541
Tel.: (510) 786-3626
Polyurethane Foam Product Mfr
N.A.I.C.S.: 326150
Foam Craft, Inc.   (1)
9230 Harrison Park Ct, Indianapolis, IN 46216   **(100%)**
Tel.: (317) 545-3626
Web Site: http://www.foamcraftinc.com

Sales Range: $25-49.9 Million
Emp.: 175
Fabrication of Polyurethane Foam
N.A.I.C.S.: 314120

Future Foam, Inc. - Council Bluffs Pouring Plant (1)
400 N 10th St, Council Bluffs, IA 51503
Tel.: (712) 323-6718
Polyurethane Foam Product Mfr
N.A.I.C.S.: 326150

Future Foam, Inc. - Dallas Fabrication Plant (1)
8611 Ambassador Row Ste A, Dallas, TX 75247
Tel.: (214) 905-6043
Polyurethane Foam Product Mfr
N.A.I.C.S.: 326150

Future Foam, Inc. - Denver Fabrication Plant (1)
11475 E 40th Ave, Denver, CO 80239
Tel.: (303) 371-1492
Polyurethane Foam Product Mfr
N.A.I.C.S.: 326150

Future Foam, Inc. - Fullerton Pouring Plant (1)
2451 Cypress Way, Fullerton, CA 92831
Tel.: (714) 871-2344
Polyurethane Foam Product Mfr
N.A.I.C.S.: 326150

Future Foam, Inc. - High Point Pouring Plant (1)
1300 Prospect, High Point, NC 27260
Tel.: (336) 885-4121
Chemical Products Mfr
N.A.I.C.S.: 325998
Tim Hagan *(Mgr-Plant)*

Future Foam, Inc. - Kansas City Fabrication Plant (1)
1207 Macon Rd, Kansas City, MO 64116
Tel.: (816) 842-5745
Chemical Products Mfr
N.A.I.C.S.: 325998

Future Foam, Inc. - Middleton Fabrication Plant (1)
8430 Murphy Dr, Middleton, WI 53562
Tel.: (608) 827-0550
Sales Range: $25-49.9 Million
Emp.: 40
Chemical Products Mfr
N.A.I.C.S.: 325998

Future Foam, Inc. - Newton Pouring Plant (1)
520 S Payton St, Newton, KS 67114
Tel.: (316) 283-8600
Web Site: http://www.futurefoam.com
Chemical Products Mfr
N.A.I.C.S.: 325998

Future Foam, Inc. - Oklahoma City Fabrication Plant (1)
1101 Metropolitan Ave, Oklahoma City, OK 73108
Tel.: (405) 948-0001
Chemical Products Mfr
N.A.I.C.S.: 325998

Future Foam, Inc. - Omaha Fabrication Plant (1)
6425 N 16th St, Omaha, NE 68110
Tel.: (402) 455-6343
Chemical Products Mfr
N.A.I.C.S.: 325998

Future Foam, Inc. - Springfield Fabrication Plant (1)
1947 E Meadowmere, Springfield, MO 65804
Tel.: (417) 865-2930
Chemical Products Mfr
N.A.I.C.S.: 325998

FUTURE FORCE PERSONNEL SERVICES
5705 NW 158th St, Miami Lakes, FL 33014
Tel.: (786) 369-8379
Web Site:
  https://www.futureforceperson nel.com
Year Founded: 1992

Sales Range: $10-24.9 Million
Emp.: 20
Full Service Staffing Solutions
N.A.I.C.S.: 561311
Henry Gonzalez *(Mgr-Ops)*
Helen Valero *(VP)*

FUTURE FORD OF CONCORD, LLC.
2285 Diamond Blvd, Concord, CA 94520-5705
Tel.: (925) 686-5000
Web Site:
  https://www.futurefordofconcord.com
Year Founded: 2004
Sales Range: $10-24.9 Million
Emp.: 80
New Car Retailer
N.A.I.C.S.: 441110
Geoff Dettlinger *(Mgr-Fleet)*
Sandy Zukowski *(Mgr-Fleet)*

FUTURE FUND INVESTMENT INC.
295 Governor St, Paterson, NJ 07501
Tel.: (973) 345-4600
Web Site: http://www.ffi.com
Sales Range: $10-24.9 Million
Emp.: 19
Investment Services
N.A.I.C.S.: 523940
Tassos Manitaras *(Pres & CEO)*

FUTURE GRAPHICS LLC
655 N Central Ave Ste 1550, Glendale, CA 91203
Tel.: (818) 837-8100
Web Site:
  http://www.futuregraphics.com
Sales Range: $10-24.9 Million
Emp.: 225
Laser Systems & Equipment
N.A.I.C.S.: 335999
Julie Shives *(Sr Acct Exec)*

FUTURE LEADERS OF AMERICA FOUNDATION, INC
320 W Ohio St Ste 4W, Chicago, IL 60654
Tel.: (312) 322-9999   IL
Web Site:
  https://www.nslcleaders.org
Year Founded: 1989
Sales Range: $10-24.9 Million
Educational Support Services
N.A.I.C.S.: 611710
Michael Bennett *(Sec)*
Richard Duffy *(Chm)*
Stephen McGue *(Treas)*

FUTURE MEDIA CONCEPTS, INC.
299 Broadway Ste 1510, New York, NY 10007
Tel.: (212) 233-3500
Web Site:
  https://www.fmctraining.com
Year Founded: 1994
Rev.: $5,500,000
Emp.: 28
Fine Arts Schools
N.A.I.C.S.: 611610
Jeff Rothberg *(Co-Founder & Co-Pres)*
Ben Kozuch *(Co-Founder & Co-Pres)*
Tom Willson *(Dir-Trng)*
Brad Rothberg *(Branch Mgr)*
Liron Golan *(Mgr-IT)*

FUTURE RESEARCH, CORPORATION
675 Discovery Dr Bldg 2 Ste 102, Huntsville, AL 35806
Tel.: (256) 430-4304   AL

Web Site: http://www.future-research.com
Year Founded: 1995
Sales Range: $25-49.9 Million
Emp.: 220
Ballistic Missile Defense System Engineering Services
N.A.I.C.S.: 541330
Jesse W. Nunn *(Pres & CEO)*
Karen Edney *(CFO & VP)*
James Williams *(VP-Engrg Programs)*
Kim McDaniel *(Dir-HR)*

FUTURE SHERIDAN FORD SALES INC.
4001 Kirkwood Hwy, Wilmington, DE 19808
Tel.: (302) 999-0261
Web Site:
  http://sheridanfordsales.com
Sales Range: $10-24.9 Million
Emp.: 100
Automobiles, New & Used
N.A.I.C.S.: 441110
Joseph E. Sheridan *(Pres)*

FUTUREDONTICS, INC.
6060 Ctr Dr 7th Fl, Los Angeles, CA 90045-1596
Tel.: (310) 215-6400
Web Site:
  http://www.futuredontics.com
Year Founded: 1986
Sales Range: $100-124.9 Million
Emp.: 225
Dental Referral Network
N.A.I.C.S.: 541613
Fred Joyal *(Founder & Pres)*
Bret McAllister *(CTO)*
David Call *(Exec VP-Membership)*

FUTURENET GROUP, INC.
12801 Auburn St, Detroit, MI 48223
Tel.: (313) 544-7117
Web Site:
  http://www.futurenetgroup.com
Year Founded: 1994
Sales Range: $10-24.9 Million
Emp.: 40
Commercial & Institutional Building Construction
N.A.I.C.S.: 236220
Perry Mehta *(Pres & CEO)*
Jay Mehta *(Sr VP-Tech)*
Dipkia Mehta *(Treas)*
Lisa Salvador *(Dir-Proposals)*
Krishal Dalal *(VP-Corp Affairs)*
Joginder Singh *(CEO)*

FUTURES HOME INC.
3450 State Highway 16 W, Bremerton, WA 98312-5012
Tel.: (360) 479-4663
Web Site:
  http://www.futurehomes.com
Rev.: $10,000,000
Emp.: 10
Mobile Home Dealers
N.A.I.C.S.: 459930
Duane Henning *(Pres)*

FUTURES WITHOUT VIOLENCE
100 Montgomery St The Presidio, San Francisco, CA 94129
Tel.: (415) 678-5500   CA
Web Site:
  https://www.futureswithoutviol ence.org
Year Founded: 1989
Sales Range: $10-24.9 Million
Emp.: 48
Domestic Violence Prevention Services
N.A.I.C.S.: 813410

Debbie Lee *(Sr VP)*
Rachael Smith Fals *(Sr VP)*
Patrice Cochran *(Controller)*
Minjung Kwok *(CFO & COO)*
Ruth Wooden *(Chm)*
Esta Soler *(Pres)*
Susan Leal *(Sec)*
Nathan Brostrom *(Treas)*
Judi Kanter *(Vice Chm)*

FUTURESOFT, INC.
1660 Townhurst Dr Ste E, Houston, TX 77043
Tel.: (281) 496-9400   TX
Web Site: https://www.futuresoft.com
Year Founded: 1982
Sales Range: $25-49.9 Million
Emp.: 10
Computer Software
N.A.I.C.S.: 423430
Warren White *(Co-Owner)*
Tim Farrell *(Co-Founder, Co-Chm & CEO)*
Claire Shaw *(Dir-Bus Dev)*

FUTUREX INDUSTRIES INC.
80 E Smith St, Bloomingdale, IN 47832
Tel.: (765) 498-3900   DE
Web Site: https://www.futurexind.com
Year Founded: 1969
Sales Range: $25-49.9 Million
Emp.: 250
Mfr of Custom Sheet Metal & Plastic Products
N.A.I.C.S.: 326113
Brent Thompson *(Pres)*

FUTURUM, LLC.
11517 Emerald Falls Dr., Austin, TX 78738
Tel.: (817) 480-3038
Web Site:
  https://futurumresearch.com
Year Founded: 2016
Holding Company: Research Services
N.A.I.C.S.: 551112
Daniel Newman *(CEO & Principal)*

Subsidiaries:

Evaluator Group, Inc. (1)
3825 Iris Ave. Ste 150W, Boulder, CO 80301
Tel.: (303) 221-7867
Web Site: http://www.evaluatorgroup.com
Sales Range: $1-9.9 Million
Emp.: 11
Computer System Design Services
N.A.I.C.S.: 541512
Camberley Bates *(Mng Dir)*
John Webster *(Sr Partner)*
Russ Fellows *(Sr Partner)*

FUZZIBUNZ LLC
1318 Camellia Blvd, Lafayette, LA 70508
Web Site: http://shop.fuzzibunz.com
Year Founded: 2000
Sales Range: $1-9.9 Million
Emp.: 12
Cloth Diapers & Accessories
N.A.I.C.S.: 458110
Tereson Dupuy *(Founder & CEO)*

FUZZY LOGIX, LLC
10735 David Taylor Dr Ste 130, Charlotte, NC 28262
Tel.: (704) 512-0478
Web Site: http://www.fuzzyl.com
Sales Range: $1-9.9 Million
Business Analytical Software Publisher & Services
N.A.I.C.S.: 513210
Partha Sen *(CEO)*
Michael Upchurch *(COO & Chief Culture Officer)*
Munir Bondre *(CTO)*
Vivek Mohindra *(Chm)*

FVLCRUM PARTNERS LLC

FVLCRUM PARTNERS LLC—(Continued)

2600 Tower Oaks Blvd Ste 230,
Rockville, MD 20852
Tel.: (202) 960-1170
Web Site: https://fvlcrum.com
Privater Equity Firm
N.A.I.C.S.: 523940
Chijoke Asomugha (Partner)

Subsidiaries:

Burrell Communications Group,
LLC   (1)
233 N Michigan Ave Ste 2900, Chicago, IL
60601
Tel.: (312) 297-9600
Web Site: http://www.burrell.com
Emp.: 150
Advetising Agency
N.A.I.C.S.: 541810
Charlene Guss (VP-HR)
Terrence Burrell (Interim Chief Creative Officer)
Tuwisha Rogers-Simpson (VP-Brand Dev)
Channing Johnson (Chm)
Tara DeVeaux (CEO)

Unit (Domestic):

BEM (Burrell Engagement
Marketing)   (2)
233 N Michigan Ave Ste 2900, Chicago, IL
60601
Tel.: (312) 297-9600
Web Site: http://www.burrell.com
Sales Range: $25-49.9 Million
Emp.: 130
Advertising & Marketing Services
N.A.I.C.S.: 541810
McGhee Osse (CEO)

Branch (Domestic):

Burrell Communications Group, LLC -
Atlanta   (2)
1447 Peachtree St Ne Ste 820, Atlanta, GA
30309-3029
Tel.: (404) 875-1683
Web Site: http://www.burrell.com
Sales Range: $25-49.9 Million
Emp.: 2
Advetising Agency
N.A.I.C.S.: 541810

**FVM STRATEGIC COMMUNI-
CATIONS**
630 W Germantown Park Ste 400,
Plymouth Meeting, PA 19462
Tel.: (610) 941-0395
Web Site: http://www.thinkfvm.com
Sales Range: $1-9.9 Million
Emp.: 21
Advertising & Communications
Agency
N.A.I.C.S.: 541810
Jon Cohen (Exec VP-Client Svcs)
Paul Fleming (CEO)
Alexandra Pickel (Dir-Client Svcs)
Karen Murphy (Dir-Media & Campaigns)
Jordy Pickel (Dir-Digital Dev)
Laurie Van Metre (Pres)
Helen Smith (Exec VP & Bus Mgr)
Brian Taylor (Sr Acct Exec)
Christina Travaglini (Sr Acct Exec)
Nick Stile (Acct Exec)
Tom OBrien (Mktg Mgr)

FVTS ACQUISITION CO., INC.
5668 Neubert Rd, Appleton, WI
54913
Tel.: (920) 757-9400
Sales Range: $10-24.9 Million
Emp.: 86
Car Whslr
N.A.I.C.S.: 441110
Mark Arft (Gen Mgr)
Dan Toppins (Pres)

**FXC CHRYSLER PLYMOUTH
INC.**

18476 US Rte 11, Watertown, NY
13601
Tel.: (315) 788-7400
Web Site: http://www.fxCaprara.com
Sales Range: $10-24.9 Million
Emp.: 80
New & Used Automobiles
N.A.I.C.S.: 441110
Brad Charlton (Gen Mgr)

FYBERCOM, LLC
3780 N Yellowstone Hwy, Idaho Falls,
ID 83401
Tel.: (208) 403-0505
Web Site: http://www.fybercom.net
Year Founded: 2012
Sales Range: $1-9.9 Million
Emp.: 36
Telecommunication Servicesb
N.A.I.C.S.: 517810
Vince Calkins (COO)

FYI SYSTEMS, INC.
35 Waterview Blvd, Parsippany, NJ
07054
Tel.: (973) 331-9050
Web Site: http://www.fyisolutions.com
Year Founded: 1984
Sales Range: $10-24.9 Million
Emp.: 79
Financial Staffing & Information Technology Consulting Services
N.A.I.C.S.: 561320
Mindy Rosner Zaziski (Chm, Pres &
CEO)

FYPON, LTD.
960 W Barre Rd, Archbold, OH
43502
Tel.: (419) 445-0116   PA
Web Site: http://www.fypon.com
Year Founded: 1997
Sales Range: $25-49.9 Million
Emp.: 340
Mfr of Plastic Products
N.A.I.C.S.: 423100
Tim Grieser (Dir-Operations)

G & D INTEGRATED
50 Commerce Dr, Morton, IL 61550-
9196
Tel.: (309) 266-1177   IL
Web Site:
   https://www.gdintegrated.com
Year Founded: 1984
Sales Range: $25-49.9 Million
Emp.: 900
Provider of Trucking Services
N.A.I.C.S.: 484121
Andrea Noel (Dir-HR)
Isaac Aldrich (Dir-Contract Logistics)
Les Nelson (CFO)
Jeff Cohen (COO)
Elizabeth Brune (VP-Contract Logistics)

G & K MANAGEMENT
5150 Overland Ave, Culver City, CA
90230
Tel.: (310) 204-2050
Year Founded: 1974
Sales Range: $10-24.9 Million
Emp.: 276
Land Subdividing Services
N.A.I.C.S.: 237210
Jona Goldrich (Owner)

**G & M SALES OF EASTERN
NC, INC.**
103 Industry Ct, Goldsboro, NC
27530
Tel.: (919) 734-1062
Web Site: https://www.g-msales.com
Year Founded: 1958
Sales Range: $10-24.9 Million
Emp.: 42

Farm & Garden Machinery Equipment Whslr
N.A.I.C.S.: 423820
Sandra J. Murphy (Pres)

**G L MORRIS GENERAL
BUILDING CONTRACTORS**
PO Box 3632, Chatsworth, CA 91313
Tel.: (818) 341-5135
Sales Range: $10-24.9 Million
Emp.: 150
Civil Engineering Services
N.A.I.C.S.: 236220
J. Morris (VP)

G ROE WM & SONS INC.
PO Box 900, Winter Haven, FL
33882
Tel.: (863) 294-3577
Web Site: http://www.noblejuice.com
Sales Range: $25-49.9 Million
Emp.: 500
Fruit & Vegetable Canning Services
N.A.I.C.S.: 311421
William G. Roe (VP)
Quentin J. Roe (Pres)
Carol Roe (Mgr-HR)

G S HARRIS CO., INC.
2810 Pennsylvania Ave, Ogden, UT
84401
Tel.: (801) 621-1380
Web Site: https://www.harristone.com
Year Founded: 1966
Sales Range: $300-349.9 Million
Emp.: 1,283
Hardwood Veneer & Plywood Mfr
N.A.I.C.S.: 321211
Grant Harris (Owner)

G STREET FABRICS
12220 Wilkins Ave, Rockville, MD
20852-1853
Tel.: (240) 283-8300
Web Site:
   https://www.gstreetfabrics.com
Rev.: $21,487,113
Emp.: 125
Fabric Store Operator
N.A.I.C.S.: 459130
Joel Greenzaid (CEO)
Brenda Howell (Dir-Education Dept)
Dory Perez (Gen Mgr)
Robin Herrera (Mgr-Store)

G&A OUTSOURCING, INC.
17220 Katy Fwy Ste 350, Houston,
TX 77094
Tel.: (888) 715-8199
Web Site:
   http://www.gnapartners.com
Year Founded: 1995
Emp.: 147
Employment Agencies
N.A.I.C.S.: 561320
John W. Allen (Pres & CEO)
Aaron Call (COO)
Matthew Walus (VP-Sls-Midwest)
Lloyd Closson (CTO)
Liz Grail (VP-Implementation & Support)

Subsidiaries:

Employer Advantage, LLC.   (1)
1230 E 7th St, Joplin, MO 64801
Tel.: (417) 782-3909
Web Site:
   http://www.employeradvantage.com
Accounting, Auditing, And Bookkeeping
N.A.I.C.S.: 541219
Aaron Mayfield (Mgr)
Jared Young (Pres & CEO)

G&B OIL COMPANY INC.
667 N Bridge St, Elkin, NC 28621-
3004
Tel.: (336) 835-3607   NC

Web Site: https://www.gbenergy.com
Year Founded: 1962
Sales Range: $25-49.9 Million
Emp.: 135
Petroleum Services
N.A.I.C.S.: 424710
Fred Eidson (Chm)
Jeff Eidson (Pres)

G&C MARKETING CO.
26 Lakeview Dr, Easton, CT 06612
Tel.: (203) 373-9599
Web Site: http://www.jj-sales.com
Rev.: $80,000,000
Emp.: 4
Bond Brokers
N.A.I.C.S.: 424410
James Cianci (Pres)

**G&D COMMUNICATIONS COR-
PORATION**
422 Oliver Dr, Troy, MI 48084-5401
Tel.: (248) 362-2750   MI
Year Founded: 1962
Sales Range: $25-49.9 Million
Emp.: 16
Advertising Agencies, Audio/Visual,
Automotive, Consulting, Consumer
Marketing, Corporate Identity,
Exhibit/Trade Shows, Merchandising,
Sales Promotion
N.A.I.C.S.: 541810
Al Virzi (CEO)
K. Sharp (CFO)

G&G ADVERTISING
2804 3rd Ave N, Billings, MT 59101
Tel.: (406) 294-8113   FL
Web Site: http://www.gng.net
Year Founded: 1991
Rev.: $29,900,000
Emp.: 10
Advetising Agency
N.A.I.C.S.: 541810
Michele Gray (Pres & Dir-Creative)

G&G ADVERTISING, INC.
811 Silver SW, Albuquerque, NM
87102
Tel.: (505) 843-8113   NM
Web Site: http://www.gng.net
Year Founded: 1997
Sales Range: $10-24.9 Million
Emp.: 16
Advertising Agency
N.A.I.C.S.: 541810
Michael J. Gray (Pres & Dir-Creative)
Joani Gray (Dir-Art)
Mike Kindsfater (Dir-Art)
Gerald Gray Jr. (VP)

Subsidiaries:

G&G Advertising   (1)
2804 3rd Ave N, Billings, MT 59101
Tel.: (406) 294-8113
Web Site: http://www.gng.net
Emp.: 10
N.A.I.C.S.: 541810
Gerald Gray Jr. (VP)

**G&G ELECTRIC & PLUMBING
DISTRIBUTORS**
1900 NE 78th St Ste 101, Vancouver,
WA 98665
Tel.: (360) 696-4676
Web Site:
   http://www.groverelectric.com
Rev.: $42,600,000
Emp.: 150
Electrical Construction Materials
N.A.I.C.S.: 423610
Dave Blaydon (Pres)
Vicki Ferguson-Siemer (CFO)

G&G INCORPORATED
404 S 2nd Ave, Dodge City, KS
67801

Tel.: (620) 225-4126
Web Site:
https://www.buyggautos.com
Sales Range: $10-24.9 Million
Emp.: 40
New & Used Car Dealers
N.A.I.C.S.: 441110

G&G MANUFACTURING CO.
4432 McKinley St, Omaha, NE
68112-2086
Tel.: (402) 453-9595   NE
Web Site: https://www.ggmfg.com
Year Founded: 1943
Rev.: $11,700,000
Emp.: 100
Farm Machinery & Equipment
N.A.I.C.S.: 333111
Roxann Tucker (Pres)
Cynthia Smith (Co-Owner)
Lee Graske (Owner)

G&G OUTFITTERS INC.
4901 Forbes Blvd, Lanham, MD
20706
Tel.: (301) 731-2099
Web Site: http://www.ggoutfitters.com
Sales Range: Less than $1 Million
Emp.: 5
N.A.I.C.S.: 541810
Doug Gardner (Principal)
Rich Gergar (Founder & Exec VP)
Denise Wittmeyer (Dir-Motorsports
Div)
John A. Lamon III (Sr Account)
Robert W. Crowe Jr. (Pres-Licensed
Sports Grp)

G&G STEEL
15825 Hwy 243, Russellville, AL
35653
Tel.: (256) 332-6652
Web Site: https://www.ggsteel.com
Sales Range: $10-24.9 Million
Emp.: 200
Mfr of Building Components & Struc-
tural Steel
N.A.I.C.S.: 332322
Danny Gist (Owner & Pres)
Shey Tomkins (Controller)
Jimmy Taylor (Mgr-QA & QC)
Randy Lindsey (Project Mgr-
Estimating)
Raymond McNatt (Mgr-Traffic)

G&G TECHNICAL INC.
202 S Northkill Rd, Bernville, PA
19506-8447
Tel.: (410) 995-1200
Web Site:
http://www.ggtechnical.com
All Other Support Services
N.A.I.C.S.: 561990
Shawn MacDuff (Mgr)

Subsidiaries:

Tyler Griffin Co., Inc.   (1)
46 Darby Rd, Paoli, PA 19301
Tel.: (610) 647-1550
Web Site: http://www.ggtechnical.com
Industrial & Electronic Parts & Equipment
Mfr
N.A.I.C.S.: 423690

G&H DIVERSIFIED MANUFAC-
TURING LP
11660 Brittmoore Pk Dr, Houston, TX
77041
Tel.: (713) 849-2111
Web Site: http://www.ghdiv.com
Sales Range: $10-24.9 Million
Emp.: 75
Special Dies & Tools
N.A.I.C.S.: 333514
Ed Kash (Pres)
Angelia Gamble (Acct Mgr)

G&H TOWING CO. INC.
200 Pennzoil Rd, Galveston, TX
77554-2802
Tel.: (409) 744-6311
Web Site:
https://www.gandhtowing.com
Year Founded: 1934
Sales Range: $10-24.9 Million
Emp.: 275
Provider of Towing Services
N.A.I.C.S.: 488999
Steve Huffman (Pres)

G&J BROOKS ENTERPRISE,
INC.
608 Adams St NE, Albuquerque, NM
87198-6222
Tel.: (505) 268-4123   NM
Web Site:
http://www.johnbrooksfoods.com
Year Founded: 1920
Sales Range: $10-24.9 Million
Emp.: 200
Retail Supermarkets
N.A.I.C.S.: 445110
John H. Brooks (CEO)
James Flynn (Sec)

G&J PEPSI-COLA BOTTLERS
INC.
9435 Waterson Blvd Ste 390, Cincin-
nati, OH 45249
Tel.: (513) 785-6060
Web Site: https://www.gjpepsi.com
Sales Range: $100-124.9 Million
Emp.: 1,500
Bottler of Soft Drinks
N.A.I.C.S.: 312111
Stanley Kaplan (Chm)
Dale Watkins (CFO)
Tim Hardid (COO)
Michael McDonald (Sr VP-Sls)

G&J SEIBERLICH & CO., LLP
3264 Villa Ln, Napa, CA 94558
Tel.: (707) 224-7948
Web Site: https://www.gjs.cpa
Year Founded: 1949
Accounting Firm
N.A.I.C.S.: 541211
Greg A. Bennett (Partner)
Wendell R. Coats (Partner)
Julia Chandler (Partner)
Laura Wintz (Partner)
Leonard L. LaBranche Jr. (Partner &
Head-Calistoga Office)

G&K MANAGEMENT COM-
PANY
5150 Overland Ave, Culver City, CA
90230
Tel.: (310) 204-2050
Web Site: http://www.gkind.com
Rev.: $10,000,000
Emp.: 150
Real Estate Managers
N.A.I.C.S.: 531210
Carole Glodney (Pres)
Mike Drandel (CFO)

Subsidiaries:

Goldrich & Kest Industries LLC   (1)
5150 Overland Ave, Culver City, CA
90230   (100%)
Tel.: (310) 204-2050
Web Site: http://www.goldrichkest.com
Emp.: 200
Subdividers & Developers
N.A.I.C.S.: 237210
Stephine Kushner (Office Mgr)

G&L AUTO SALES INC.
28990 Groesbeck Hwy, Roseville, MI
48066
Tel.: (586) 773-8100
Web Site:
http://www.gandlautosales.com

Sales Range: $25-49.9 Million
Emp.: 35
Sales of Used Cars
N.A.I.C.S.: 441120
Larry Ring (VP)

G&L REALTY CORP.
439 N Bedford Dr, Beverly Hills, CA
90210-4302
Tel.: (310) 273-9930   MD
Web Site: http://www.glrealty.com
Year Founded: 1975
Sales Range: $25-49.9 Million
Emp.: 29
Healthcare Property Acquisition, De-
velopment, Management & Leasing
Services
N.A.I.C.S.: 525990
Steven D. Lebowitz (Co-Chm & Pres)
Daniel M. Gottlieb (Co-Chm & CEO)
Richard Gottlieb (Exec VP)
Andrew Lebowitz (Exec VP)
Paul Schneider (Sr VP-Ops)

Subsidiaries:

G&L Senior Care Properties,
LLC   (1)
439 N Bedford Dr, Beverly Hills, CA 90210
Tel.: (310) 273-9930
Sales Range: $10-24.9 Million
Ownership of Senior Care Facilities
N.A.I.C.S.: 623990
Steven D. Lebowitz (Owner & Pres)

G&M ELECTRICAL CONTRAC-
TORS CO. INC.
1746 N Richmond St, Chicago, IL
60647-5124
Tel.: (773) 278-8200   IL
Web Site: http://www.gm-electric.com
Year Founded: 1945
Sales Range: $25-49.9 Million
Emp.: 220
Electrical Work
N.A.I.C.S.: 238210
Adam Gooze (VP-Electrical Ops)
Bill Klier (Dir-Safety)

G&M OIL CO. INC.
76 Old 25 E, Barbourville, KY 40906
Tel.: (606) 546-3909
Sales Range: $10-24.9 Million
Emp.: 40
Petroleum Products Distr
N.A.I.C.S.: 424710
Jerry Garland (Pres)
Rick Allen (Controller)

G&M OIL COMPANY INC.
16868 A St, Huntington Beach, CA
92647-4831
Tel.: (714) 375-4700
Web Site: http://www.gmoc.com
Year Founded: 1969
Sales Range: $50-74.9 Million
Emp.: 350
Gasoline Services
N.A.I.C.S.: 457120
George Pearson (Pres)

G&S METAL PRODUCTS CO.
INC.
3330 E 79th St, Cleveland, OH
44127-1831
Tel.: (216) 441-0700   OH
Web Site: https://www.gsmetal.com
Year Founded: 1949
Sales Range: $25-49.9 Million
Emp.: 200
Metal Cans Mfr
N.A.I.C.S.: 332431
Bob Greenberger (Sr Exec VP)

Subsidiaries:

Porcelen Limited Connecticut
LLC   (1)
333 Welton St, Hamden, CT 06517-3934

Tel.: (203) 248-6346
Web Site: http://www.specral.com
Sales Range: $10-24.9 Million
Emp.: 70
Architectural Kynar Finishing
N.A.I.C.S.: 423510
William Battz (Gen Mgr)

G&S SERVICES COMPANY
6800 S Dawson Cir Ste 200, Centen-
nial, CO 80112-4266
Tel.: (303) 693-4474
Web Site: https://www.gsoil.com
Rev.: $24,200,000
Emp.: 8
Petroleum Product Distr
N.A.I.C.S.: 424720
Meyer J. Susman (Pres)

G&T INDUSTRIES INC.
1001 76th St SW, Byron Center, MI
49315-7956
Tel.: (616) 452-8611   MI
Web Site:
https://www.gtindustries.com
Year Founded: 1954
Sales Range: $25-49.9 Million
Emp.: 200
Piece Goods & Notions Mfr
N.A.I.C.S.: 314999
Rol Grit (Pres)

Subsidiaries:

G&T Industries of Indiana Inc.   (1)
290 E 30th St, Jasper, IN 47546
Tel.: (812) 634-2252
Web Site:
http://www.foamproductsgroup.com
Sales Range: $25-49.9 Million
Emp.: 65
Foam Products Mfr
N.A.I.C.S.: 326150
John Yoder (Branch Mgr)

World Resource Partners   (1)
1001 76th St SW, Byron Center, MI 49315
Tel.: (616) 452-8611
Web Site: http://www.wrpglobal.com
Sales Range: $10-24.9 Million
Emp.: 25
Resourcing & Logistics Support for Busi-
nesses
N.A.I.C.S.: 561499
Drew Schramm (Pres)

G&W ELECTRIC COMPANY
305 W Crossroads Pkwy, Boling-
brook, IL 60440
Tel.: (708) 388-5010   IL
Web Site: http://www.gwelec.com
Year Founded: 1905
Sales Range: $100-124.9 Million
Emp.: 300
Electric Power Equipment Distr
N.A.I.C.S.: 335313
Anthony Woon (VP-Malaysia)

Subsidiaries:

G&W Canada Corporation   (1)
2600 Argentia Road, Mississauga, L5N5V4,
ON, Canada
Tel.: (905) 542-2000
Web Site:
http://www.canadapowerproducts.com
Switchgear Mfr
N.A.I.C.S.: 335313
Paul Stirpe (VP)

Shanghai G&W Electric Ltd.   (1)
No 8 Lane 1505 Zu Chong Zhi Road,
Zhang Jiang Pudong, Shanghai, 201210,
China
Tel.: (86) 2158958648
Web Site: http://www.gwelec.com.cn
Electric Power Equipment Supplier
N.A.I.C.S.: 221118

G&W EQUIPMENT, INC.
600 Lawton Rd, Charlotte, NC 28216
Tel.: (704) 394-6316
Web Site: https://www.gwequip.com
Year Founded: 1963

G&W Equipment, Inc.—(Continued)
Sales Range: $10-24.9 Million
Emp.: 200
Provider of Sales, Service & Rentals
of Industrial Forklifts
N.A.I.C.S.: 423830
Mike Sabbagh (CEO)
Lyndon Kennedy (Controller)
Geoff Hadden (Mgr-Sls Field)

G&W LABORATORIES INC.
301 Helen St, South Plainfield, NJ
07080-3801
Tel.: (908) 753-2000   NJ
Web Site: http://www.gwlabs.com
Year Founded: 1918
Sales Range: $25-49.9 Million
Emp.: 250
Pharmaceutical Preparations
N.A.I.C.S.: 325412
Ronald Greenblatt (Chm)
Hemant Kumar (CIO)
James H. Coy (Chief Integration Officer & VP)
Joseph Greer (VP)
Kumar Kantheti (VP)
Matthew Handel (VP)
Jay Galeota (Pres & COO)
Carl Greenblatt (Founder)
Aaron Greenblatt (CEO)

G-A MASONRY CORP.OF NEW YORK
7014 Hughes Ave, Crestwood, KY
40014
Tel.: (502) 241-8456
Rev.: $28,200,000
Emp.: 300
Bricklaying
N.A.I.C.S.: 238140
Eugene George (Pres)

G-L VENEER CO. INC.
2224 E Slauson Ave, Huntington
Park, CA 90255
Tel.: (323) 582-5203
Web Site: https://www.glveneer.com
Rev.: $29,030,454
Emp.: 120
Hardwood Veneer & Plywood
N.A.I.C.S.: 321211
Jeffrey B. Levin (Pres)

G-P DISTRIBUTING INC.
3112 5th Ave S, Fort Dodge, IA
50501
Tel.: (515) 573-4233
Rev.: $15,100,000
Emp.: 112
All Other General Merchandise
Stores
N.A.I.C.S.: 455219
James Schmidt (Pres)

G-TECH SERVICES, INC.
17101 Michigan Ave, Dearborn, MI
48126
Tel.: (313) 441-3600
Web Site: https://www.gogtech.com
Rev.: $29,160,133
Emp.: 25
Temporary Help Service
N.A.I.C.S.: 561320
John Whelan (Mgr-HR)

G. BAILEY COMPANY INC.
814 W Diamond Ave Ste 200, Gaithersburg, MD 20878
Tel.: (301) 258-9386
Web Site:
   http://www.gbaileycompany.com
Sales Range: $10-24.9 Million
Emp.: 3
Provider of Carpentry Services
N.A.I.C.S.: 238130

Gary L. Bailey (Founder)
Michael Gresco (Controller)

G. F. TRUSS, INC.
PO Box 5514, Grand Forks, ND
58203
Tel.: (701) 775-3173
Sales Range: $10-24.9 Million
Emp.: 30
Truss Mfr
N.A.I.C.S.: 321215
Stu Johnson (Owner)

G. FRIED FLOORING AMERICA
4608 S Tamiami Trl, Sarasota, FL
34231
Tel.: (941) 584-8757   FL
Web Site: http://www.gfriedfa.com
Year Founded: 1997
Sales Range: $1-9.9 Million
Emp.: 18
Floor Covering Stores
N.A.I.C.S.: 449121
Mike Haber (Mgr-Ops)
Rusus Ashby (Pres)
Ron Gibson (Mgr-Ops-Tampa)
Mike Solmonson (Mgr-Retail Store-Tampa)
Mike Cosgrove (Gen Mgr-Orlando)
Pam Kendrick (Office Mgr-Tampa)
Andy Clarkson (Mgr-Warehouse-Tampa)
Keith Ogden (Mgr-Sls)

G. J. CHEMICAL CO. INC.
40 Veronica Ave, Somerset, NJ
08873
Tel.: (973) 589-1450
Web Site:
   https://www.gjchemical.com
Sales Range: $10-24.9 Million
Emp.: 19
Industrial Chemicals
N.A.I.C.S.: 424690
Diane Colonna (Pres)
Robert Masci (Owner)
Sonia Rosado-Iannitelli (Mgr-Inventory)
Regina Hoy (Sr Acct Mgr)

G. JOANNOU CYCLE CO. INC.
151 Ludlow Ave, Northvale, NJ
07647-2305
Tel.: (201) 768-9050   NJ
Web Site: http://www.jamisbikes.com
Year Founded: 1937
Sales Range: $10-24.9 Million
Emp.: 80
Bicycle Whslr
N.A.I.C.S.: 423910
Carine Joannou (Pres & CEO)
Madeline Joannou (VP)
Dave Rosen (Dir-Adv & Mktg)

G.A. BLANCO & SONS INC.
Route 71 at the Alford Line, Great
Barrington, MA 01230
Tel.: (413) 528-9500
Web Site: http://www.gablanco.com
Year Founded: 1976
Sales Range: $25-49.9 Million
Emp.: 50
Computer Supplies, Office Supplies,
Computer Hardware & Peripherals,
Office Furniture & Seating Distr
N.A.I.C.S.: 424120
Edward L. Blanco (Pres)
John Heummer (CFO & VP)

G.A. FOOD SERVICES OF PINELLAS COUNTY INC.
12200 32nd Ct N, Saint Petersburg,
FL 33716
Tel.: (727) 573-2211   FL

Web Site:
   https://www.sunmeadow.com
Year Founded: 1973
Frozen Specialty Foods Mfr
N.A.I.C.S.: 311412
Ken Lobianco (Co-Founder & CEO)
Jim Lobianco (Co-Founder)
Eileen Grady (Gen Mgr)
Frank Curto (Dir-Quality)
Rafael Spratling (Dir-Customer Care)
Glenn A. Davenport (Pres)

G.A. WEST & COMPANY INC.
12526 Celeste Rd, Chunchula, AL
36521
Tel.: (251) 679-1965
Web Site: http://www.gawest.com
Sales Range: $10-24.9 Million
Emp.: 600
Industrial Building Construction
N.A.I.C.S.: 236210
Gary West (Owner & Pres)
Rex Parnell (Dir-Safety)
Sonny Beasley (Mgr)
Suzie Hagan (Controller)
Randy Rowe (Mgr-Bus Dev)

G.A. WILLIAMS & SONS INC.
39 Adams St, Braintree, MA 02185
Tel.: (781) 394-9680
Web Site:
   https://www.mywilliamsenergy.com
Sales Range: $10-24.9 Million
Emp.: 35
Fuel Oil Dealers
N.A.I.C.S.: 457210
Brian Williams (Pres)
Don Sheehan (Mgr-Svc)
Rose McHugh (Controller)

G.A. WINTZER AND SON COMPANY
204 W Auglaize St, Wapakoneta, OH
45895-1402
Tel.: (419) 738-3771
Web Site: http://www.gawintzer.com
Sales Range: $10-24.9 Million
Emp.: 100
Feeds From Meat Vegetable Meals
N.A.I.C.S.: 311119
Gustave S. Wintzer (Pres)
Kirk Azbell (Mgr)

G.A.S. CAPITAL, INC.
9 Lydia Ct, Hawthorn Woods, IL
60047
Tel.: (847) 847-3600   IL
Investment Holding Company
N.A.I.C.S.: 551112
Daniel O. Dickinson (Pres & CEO)

Subsidiaries:

GAS/Wilson, L.P.   (1)
430 Kelso, Bakersfield, CA 93312   (45%)
Tel.: (661) 829-2170
Buyer, Seller, Leaser & Rebuilder of Commuter Class Aircraft
N.A.I.C.S.: 532411
Bud Wilson (Partner)

General Aviation Services, L.L.C.   (1)
110 N Brockway St Ste 310, Palatine, IL
60067   (75%)
Tel.: (847) 726-5000
Web Site: http://www.genav.com
Sales Range: $10-24.9 Million
Emp.: 7
Aircraft Brokerage, Sales & Consulting Services
N.A.I.C.S.: 425120
Greg Duckson (Pres)
Dale Lundeen (VP)

General Aviation Technologies,
L.P.   (1)
1155 Ensell Rd, Lake Zurich, IL
60047-1538   (75%)
Tel.: (847) 726-5000
Web Site: http://www.genad.com

Sales Range: $10-24.9 Million
Emp.: 8
Buyer, Seller, Broker & Leaser of Airline
Equipment & Engines
N.A.I.C.S.: 423860

General Helicopters International,
Inc.   (1)
1836 County Rd 411, Proctorville, OH
45669
Tel.: (740) 886-2992
Emp.: 2
Helicopter Leasing Services
N.A.I.C.S.: 532411
Jim Sturm (Pres & CEO)

G.C. HANFORD MANUFAC-TURING COMPANY
304 Oneida St, Syracuse, NY 13202-
3433
Tel.: (315) 476-7418
Web Site: https://www.hanford.com
Year Founded: 1846
Sales Range: $75-99.9 Million
Emp.: 125
Antibiotics & Health Care Products
Mfr
N.A.I.C.S.: 325412
George R. Hanford (Chm)
George W. Hanford (CEO)

G.D. BARRI & ASSOCIATES INC.
6860 W Peoria Ave, Peoria, AZ
85345
Tel.: (623) 773-0410
Web Site: https://www.gdbarri.com
Rev.: $10,816,129
Emp.: 300
Engineering Help Service
N.A.I.C.S.: 561320
Georgia D. Barri (Pres)
Rick W. Duff (COO & VP)
Alexandria M. Dorsey (CFO & Exec
VP)

G.D. HEIL INC.
1031 Segovia Cir, Placentia, CA
92870
Tel.: (714) 687-9100
Web Site: https://www.gdheil.com
Rev.: $10,000,000
Emp.: 90
Demolition, Buildings & Other Structures
N.A.I.C.S.: 238910
Mark Barela (Project Mgr)
Laura Heil (Pres)

G.D.C., INC.
6933 Colchester Park Dr, Manassas,
VA 20112
Tel.: (703) 497-2717
Web Site: http://www.gdctruck.com
Sales Range: $10-24.9 Million
Emp.: 110
Dump Truck Hauling & Rental Services, Snow Removal & Salt Transportation Services
N.A.I.C.S.: 484220
Gerald D. Cooper (Pres)

G.E. JOHNSON CONSTRUC-TION COMPANY, INC.
25 N Cascade Ave Ste 400, Colorado
Springs, CO 80903
Tel.: (719) 473-5321   CO
Web Site: http://www.gejohnson.com
Year Founded: 1967
Sales Range: $200-249.9 Million
Emp.: 450
Contracting & Construction Services
N.A.I.C.S.: 236220
David Ivis (Exec VP)
Steve Eikanger (Dir-Integrated Svcs)
Paul Sweeney (Mgr-MEP)
Laura Rinker (Dir-Mktg)

William Jones *(Mgr-Project Dev)*
Trey Nobles *(Sr VP-Rocky Mountain)*
Ron McInroy *(Mgr-Project Dev)*
Caryn Becker *(Sr Project Mgr-Dev)*
Randy Nance *(Gen Mgr)*
Nick Siakotos *(VP)*

G.E. RICHARDS GRAPHIC SUPPLIES CO. INC.
928 Links Ave, Landisville, PA 17538
Tel.: (717) 898-3151   PA
Web Site:
    https://www.gerichards.com
Year Founded: 1977
Sales Range: $10-24.9 Million
Emp.: 130
Graphic Supplies Distr
N.A.I.C.S.: 423830
Larry Wagner *(Pres)*

G.E. WALKER, INC.
4420 E Adamo Dr Ste 206, Tampa, FL 33605
Tel.: (813) 623-2481
Web Site: http://www.gewalker.com
Year Founded: 1976
Sales Range: $10-24.9 Million
Emp.: 50
X-Ray Machines & Tubes
N.A.I.C.S.: 423450
George E. Walker *(Pres & Owner)*
Andy Fields *(Engr-Fields Svc)*

G.F. VAUGHAN TOBACCO CO. INC.
1247 Versailles Rd, Lexington, KY 40508
Tel.: (859) 252-1733
Sales Range: $25-49.9 Million
Emp.: 60
Tobacco Warehousing & Storage
N.A.I.C.S.: 493130
Derek Vaughan *(CEO)*
Conrad Whitaker *(Pres)*
Elizabeth Hill *(Asst Controller)*

G.G. MCGUIGGAN CORP.
45 S 7th St Plz, Minneapolis, MN 55402
Tel.: (651) 646-4544
Sales Range: $10-24.9 Million
Emp.: 420
Converted Paper Product Mfr
N.A.I.C.S.: 322299
John Hickey *(CEO)*

G.L. MEZZETTA INC.
105 Mezzetta Ct, American Canyon, CA 94503
Tel.: (707) 648-1050
Web Site: https://www.mezzetta.com
Sales Range: $10-24.9 Million
Emp.: 120
Olives, Brined: Bulk
N.A.I.C.S.: 311421
Paul Betti *(Mgr-Matls)*
Joe Polivka *(Mgr-Retail)*
Robert Wallington *(Mgr-Sls-West)*
Peter Thomsen *(Dir-Sls)*

G.L. SAYRE INCORPORATED
1231 W Ridge Pke, Conshohocken, PA 19428
Tel.: (610) 277-4054
Web Site: http://www.glsayre.com
Year Founded: 1942
Sales Range: $25-49.9 Million
Emp.: 45
International, Peterbilt & UD Truck Dealer
N.A.I.C.S.: 441110
Ryan Nosia *(Mgr-Svc)*
Bill Tornetta *(Mgr-Body Shop)*
Jim R. Sayre Jr. *(Pres)*

G.L. SEAMAN & COMPANY

4201 International Pkwy, Carrollton, TX 75007
Tel.: (214) 764-6400
Web Site: http://www.glsc.com
Year Founded: 1984
Rev.: $40,000,000
Emp.: 80
Office Furniture Distr
N.A.I.C.S.: 423210
Ashley Lowrance *(Pres-Dallas)*
Rebecca Lutz *(CEO)*

Subsidiaries:

G.L. Seaman & Company-Fort Worth   **(1)**
100 N Forest Park Blvd, Fort Worth, TX 76102
Tel.: (817) 336-5400
Web Site:
    http://www.glseamancompany.com
Sales Range: $25-49.9 Million
Emp.: 60
Quality Furniture Mfr
N.A.I.C.S.: 423210
Mary Edward *(Pres)*

G.L. WILSON BUILDING COMPANY
190 Wilson Park Rd, Statesville, NC 28625-8506
Tel.: (704) 872-2411   NC
Web Site: https://www.glwilson.com
Year Founded: 1945
Sales Range: $10-24.9 Million
Emp.: 130
Contracting Services
N.A.I.C.S.: 236210
Thomas L. Wilson *(Pres)*
Julia D. Wilson *(Exec VP)*

G.M. CRISALLI ASSOCIATES, INC.
843 Hiawatha Blvd W, Syracuse, NY 13204
Tel.: (315) 454-0000
Web Site: https://www.gmca.com
Sales Range: $25-49.9 Million
Emp.: 30
Nonresidential Construction Services
N.A.I.C.S.: 236220
Gary Crisalli *(Pres)*

G.M. MCCROSSIN INC.
2780 Benner Pike, Bellefonte, PA 16823
Tel.: (814) 355-4848   PA
Web Site:
    http://www.gmmccrossin.com
Year Founded: 1950
Sales Range: $25-49.9 Million
Emp.: 300
Provider of Construction Services
N.A.I.C.S.: 236220
Joseph J. Leahey *(VP)*

G.M. NORTHRUP CORPORATION
15950 Franklin Trl SE, Prior Lake, MN 55372
Tel.: (952) 226-3090
Web Site:
    https://www.gmnorthrup.com
Year Founded: 1982
Sales Range: $10-24.9 Million
Emp.: 40
Commercial & Office Building, New Construction
N.A.I.C.S.: 236220
Michael Northrup *(Pres)*
John Northrup *(Controller)*
Jason Schultz *(Controller)*

G.O. CARLSON, INC.
175 Main St, Oil City, PA 16301-2063
Tel.: (610) 384-2800
Web Site: http://www.gocarlson.com
Year Founded: 1936

Sales Range: $125-149.9 Million
Emp.: 9
Nonferrous Rolling & Drawing
N.A.I.C.S.: 331110
Tracy Rudolph *(COO)*

G.R. KIRK COMPANY
201 Saint Helens Ave, Tacoma, WA 98402
Tel.: (253) 627-2133   WA
Web Site:
    http://www.kirkcompany.com
Year Founded: 1923
Sales Range: $10-24.9 Million
Emp.: 50
Christmas Tree Nursery & Whslr
N.A.I.C.S.: 111421
Gary Snyder *(Owner & Mgr-Production)*
Ralph Nilssen *(VP-Sls)*

G.R. MITCHELL INC.
14 Beaver Valley Pike, Willow Street, PA 17584
Tel.: (717) 464-2999
Web Site: https://www.grmitchell.com
Year Founded: 1969
Sales Range: $10-24.9 Million
Emp.: 50
Lumber & Plywood Products Whslr
N.A.I.C.S.: 423310
Steven D. Mitchell *(Pres)*
Betty Marley *(VP-Fin)*

G.R.H. MAIDEN INC.
7031 Hwy 6 N, Houston, TX 77095
Tel.: (281) 656-2095
Rev.: $20,000,000
Emp.: 3
Liquor Stores
N.A.I.C.S.: 445320

G.S. SCHWARTZ & CO. INC.
470 Park Ave S 10th Fl S, New York, NY 10016-6819
Tel.: (212) 725-4500
Year Founded: 1981
Sales Range: $10-24.9 Million
Emp.: 40
Public Relations Agency
N.A.I.C.S.: 541820
Gerald S. Schwartz *(Pres)*
Rachel Lyn Honig *(COO)*
Debra Berliner *(Mng Dir)*
Cathy Loos *(VP)*

G.STONE MOTORS, INC.
36 Boardman St, Middlebury, VT 05753
Tel.: (802) 388-6718
Web Site:
    https://www.gstonemotors.com
Year Founded: 1974
Sales Range: $10-24.9 Million
Emp.: 50
Car Whslr
N.A.I.C.S.: 441110
Gardner Stone *(Pres)*

G.V. MOORE LUMBER CO., INC.
22 W Main St, Ayer, MA 01432
Tel.: (978) 772-0900   MA
Web Site:
    http://www.moorelumber.com
Year Founded: 1985
Sales Range: $25-49.9 Million
Emp.: 100
Lumber & Other Building Materials Mfr
N.A.I.C.S.: 423310
Karen Patterson *(Dir-HR & Controller)*
Wendy Bowers *(Dir-HR)*

G.W. BERKHEIMER CO. INC.

6000 Southport Rd, Portage, IN 46368
Tel.: (219) 764-5200
Web Site:
    https://www.gwberkheimer.com
Rev.: $100,000,000
Emp.: 70
Warm Air Heating & Air Conditioning
N.A.I.C.S.: 423730
Brian Cobble *(Pres)*
Aaron Braun *(Dir-IT)*
Justin Bjankini *(Mgr-Store)*
Phil Arnold *(VP-Ops)*
Ted Heneka *(VP-Inventory Mgmt)*

G.W. HOFFMAN MARKETING & COMMUNICATIONS
757-767 Post Rd, Darien, CT 06820-4720
Tel.: (203) 655-8321   CT
Web Site: http://www.gwhoffman.com
Year Founded: 1981
Sales Range: $1-9.9 Million
Emp.: 27
Advetising Agency
N.A.I.C.S.: 541810
Karen Goyette *(Pres & Mng Dir)*

G.W. LISK COMPANY, INC.
2 South St, Clifton Springs, NY 14432
Tel.: (315) 462-2611
Web Site: https://www.gwlisk.com
Year Founded: 1953
Sales Range: $25-49.9 Million
Emp.: 600
Marketer & Designer of Electronic Component Mfr
N.A.I.C.S.: 334419
Roger Root *(Sys Engr-Manufacturing)*

Subsidiaries:

Finger Lakes Ambulance EMS Inc.   **(1)**
20 Crane St, Clifton Springs, NY 14432-1004   **(100%)**
Tel.: (315) 462-5701
Web Site:
    http://www.fingerlakesambulance.com
Rev.: $720,000
Emp.: 70
Emergency Medical Transportation
N.A.I.C.S.: 485999
William Comella *(Dir-Ops)*

Lisk Control Technology (Suzhou) Co., LTD   **(1)**
Suzhou Industrial Park SIP No 9 Hongfeng Road, Suzhou, 215021, Jiangsu, China
Tel.: (86) 512 62990128
Web Site: http://www.gwlisk.com
Emp.: 30
Electronic Components Mfr
N.A.I.C.S.: 334419
Benny Tiang *(Gen Mgr)*

Lisk Ireland LTD   **(1)**
Ennis Road, Gort, Galway, H91 P2V9, Ireland
Tel.: (353) 91 631711
Web Site: http://www.gwlisk.ie
Electronic Components Mfr
N.A.I.C.S.: 334419
John Tully *(Gen Mgr)*

G.W. PALMER LOGISTICS, LLC.
19 McHue Rd., Batesville, AR 72501-8802
Tel.: (870) 793-0006
Web Site: http://www.gwpl.com
Year Founded: 2008
Sales Range: $10-24.9 Million
Emp.: 32
Freight Transportation Arrangement Services
N.A.I.C.S.: 488510
Bobby McClure *(Pres & CEO)*
Beth Jones *(Controller)*
Alston Palmer *(VP)*

G.W. Palmer Logistics, LLC.—(Continued)

Mike Shannon (Gen Mgr)
Gregory S. Mohlke (VP-Ops)
Teresa Robinson (Controller)
Lisa Slisher (Mgr-HR & Office Mgr)
Steve Ryan (CFO)
Ellie Johnson (Sr Acct Mgr)
Terry Cross (Acct Mgr)
Bobby Power (Acct Mgr)
Mary Williams (Acct Mgr)

G/S LEASING INC.
3290 W Big Beaver Rd Ste 200,
Troy, MI 48084
Tel.: (248) 649-5560
Web Site: http://www.gslease.com
Year Founded: 1981
Sales Range: $10-24.9 Million
Emp.: 22
Retailer of Computers
N.A.I.C.S.: 423430
Michael J. Maiman (Chm)
Dennis Cuyrus (Pres)
Dale Racz (CFO)

G1 THERAPEUTICS, INC.
700 Park Offices Dr Ste 200, Re-
search Triangle Park, NC 27709
Tel.: (919) 213-9835   DE
Web Site:
   https://www.g1therapeutics.com
Year Founded: 2008
GTHX— (NASDAQ)
Rev.: $51,301,000
Assets: $187,965,000
Liabilities: $119,218,000
Net Worth: $68,747,000
Earnings: ($147,559,000)
Emp.: 170
Fiscal Year-end: 12/31/22
Biotechnology Research & Develop-
ment Services
N.A.I.C.S.: 325412
Joshua B. Franklin (Grp Pres, CEO &
Dir)
John E. Bailey Jr. (Pres & CEO)
Garry A. Nicholson (Chm)

G2 BUILDERS, LLC.
1300 Greenbrook Blvd Ste 101, Ha-
nover Park, IL 60133
Tel.: (630) 289-7304
Web Site: http://www.g2builders.net
Sales Range: $10-24.9 Million
Emp.: 25
Nonresidential Construction Services
N.A.I.C.S.: 236220
Oscar Garcia (Pres)

G2 CONSULTING GROUP, LLC
1866 Woodslee St, Troy, MI 48083
Tel.: (248) 680-0400   MI
Web Site:
   https://www.g2consultinggroup.com
Year Founded: 1994
Sales Range: $10-24.9 Million
Emp.: 54
Geotechnical, Environmental & Con-
struction Engineering Services
N.A.I.C.S.: 541690
Mark Smolinski (Principal)
Amy Schneider (Project Mgr)
Jason Stoops (Office Mgr-Ann Arbor)
Noel Hargrave-Thomas (Principal)
Bruce Wilberding (Principal)
Chris Nicol (Project Mgr)
Anthony Poisson (Office Mgr-
Chicago)
Mark Stapleton (Project Mgr)

G2, INC.
2075 17 Mile Rd NE, Cedar Springs,
MI 49319
Tel.: (616) 696-9581
Web Site: http://www.g2erectors.com
Year Founded: 2005

Sales Range: $1-9.9 Million
Emp.: 35
Commercial & Institutional Building
Construction
N.A.I.C.S.: 236220
Gordon Gilchrist (Pres)

GA BRAUN INC.
79 General Irwin Blvd, North Syra-
cuse, NY 13212
Tel.: (315) 475-3123
Web Site: https://www.gabraun.com
Sales Range: $10-24.9 Million
Emp.: 150
Washing Machines, Laundry: Com-
mercial, Coin-Operated
N.A.I.C.S.: 333310
Gerry Knotek (COO)
James Cain (Mgr-Production)

GA COMMUNICATIONS INC.
2196 W Park Ct, Stone Mountain, GA
30087
Tel.: (770) 498-4091   GA
Web Site:
   http://www.gasolutions.com
Year Founded: 1968
Sales Range: $25-49.9 Million
Emp.: 200
Advertising Services
N.A.I.C.S.: 541810
Andy Sung (Chief Digital Officer)
George Russell (CEO)

Subsidiaries:

GA Communications   (1)
490 Lapp Rd, Malvern, PA 19355
Tel.: (610) 889-9281
Web Site: http://www.gasolutions.com
Emp.: 30
N.A.I.C.S.: 541810

GA Communications   (1)
2630 Shea Center Dr, Livermore, CA
94551-7546
Tel.: (925) 294-5846
Web Site: http://www.gasolutions.com
N.A.I.C.S.: 541810

GA Communications   (1)
129 Robbins Station Rd, North Huntingdon,
PA 15642
Tel.: (724) 861-4300
Web Site: http://www.gasolutions.com
Emp.: 8
N.A.I.C.S.: 541810
Paul Baker (Gen Mgr)

Pure Red Creative   (1)
5243 Royal Woods Pkwy Ste 200, Atlanta,
GA 30084
Tel.: (770) 491-3353
Web Site: http://www.pureredcreative.com
Sales Range: $10-24.9 Million
Emp.: 35
N.A.I.C.S.: 541890
David Mimbs (VP-New Bus)

GA TELESIS LLC
1850 Nw 49th St, Fort Lauderdale,
FL 33309-3004
Tel.: (954) 676-3111
Web Site: http://www.gatelesis.com
Year Founded: 2002
Sales Range: $125-149.9 Million
Emp.: 400
Air Transportation Components Distr
& Maintenance Services for Aircraft
N.A.I.C.S.: 423860
Kevin M. Larson (CIO-Global & Sr
VP)
Abdol Moabery (Pres & CEO)
Russell Bonnell (Pres-Maintenance,
Repair & Ops)
Alvin Khoo (CFO, CIO & Sr VP)
Basil Papayoti (Pres-GA Telesis En-
gine Svcs Oy)
Jason Reed (Pres-CSG)

Carsten Holm (Mng Dir-GA Telesis
Engine Svcs)
Marc Cho (Chief Investment Officer)
Pastor Lopez (Pres-MRO Svcs)
Dave Dicken (VP-Airframe Solutions
Grp)
Frederic Denise (Sr VP-Strategy &
Corp Dev)
Alex Tuttle (COO)
Andreas Bauer (Sr VP-Ops, Logistics
& Quality Component Solutions Grp)
Kevin Geissler (VP-Aviation Lease
Solutions)
Priscilla Ang (Dir-Bus Dev-Asia Pa-
cific)
David Byrne (Dir-Asset Remarketing-
Dublin)
John Wales (Dir-APU Product Line)
Russell Shelton (Pres-Engine Strat-
egy Grp)
Rainford Knight (Chief Digital Trans-
formation Officer)
Jim Sokol (Sr VP-Sls-Flight Solutions
Grp-Americas)
Fabian Robinson (VP & Gen Mgr-
MRO Svcs)
Amir Taher (VP-GAT Logistics Solu-
tions Grp)

Subsidiaries:

GA Telesis Composite Repair Group
Southeast   (1)
3420 NW 53rd St, Fort Lauderdale, FL
33309
Tel.: (954) 486-8797
Web Site: http://www.gatelesis.com
Sales Range: $10-24.9 Million
Emp.: 51
Maintenance, Repair, Overhaul & Logistics
Support Services to Commercial & Military
Rotor & Fixed Wing Aircraft Markets
N.A.I.C.S.: 488190
Brad Herring (Gen Mgr)

GA Telesis UK Ltd.   (1)
Hanger 103 aviation Way, Christchurch,
Dorset, BH23 6NW, United Kingdom
Tel.: (44) 1202894945
Web Site: http://www.gatelesis.com
Sales Range: $10-24.9 Million
Emp.: 9
Aviation Maintenance & Solution-Based
Services; Distr of Aircraft, Engines & Com-
ponents
N.A.I.C.S.: 488190
Nigel Christie (Mng Dir)

GAAS LABS, LLC
28013 Arastradero Rd, Los Altos, CA
94022
Tel.: (650) 387-1425   CA
Web Site: http://www.gaaslabs.com
Year Founded: 2007
Semiconductor Industry-Focused Pri-
vate Equity Firm
N.A.I.C.S.: 523999
John L. Ocampo (Pres)
Susan Ocampo (Treas, Sec & VP)
Jerry Quinnell (Head-Corp Dev & In-
vestments)
Jerry Quinnell (Head-Corp Dev & In-
vestments)
Clay B. Simpson (Head-Legal)

GAB EMPACADORA INC.
9330 San Mateo Dr, Laredo, TX
78045
Tel.: (956) 727-0100
Rev.: $17,170,310
Emp.: 10
Frozen Vegetables Mfr
N.A.I.C.S.: 424420
Javier Usabiaga (Pres)

GABBA LLC
1008 W Ninth Ave, King of Prussia,
PA 19406
Tel.: (610) 756-2100

Web Site:
   http://www.invisionsecuritygroup.com
Year Founded: 2010
Sales Range: $10-24.9 Million
Emp.: 28
Electronic Security System Services
N.A.I.C.S.: 561621
Brandon Smith (Co-Founder & CEO)
Annette Smith (Co-Founder & COO)
Dave Charles (VP-Sls & Bus Dev)
Mark Eichlin (Project Mgr)
Rebecca So (Office Mgr-Fin)

GABRIEL PROPERTIES, LLC.
1302 Joe Yenni Blvd, Kenner, LA
70065
Tel.: (504) 466-9788
Sales Range: $25-49.9 Million
Emp.: 15
Land Subdividing Services
N.A.I.C.S.: 237210
Bryan Krantz (Principal)

GABRIEL'S HOLDINGS LTD.
10903 Industry Dr, San Antonio, TX
78217
Tel.: (210) 646-9992
Web Site:
   http://www.gabrielsliquor.com
Year Founded: 1983
Sales Range: $10-24.9 Million
Emp.: 165
Holding Company: Wines & Spirits
N.A.I.C.S.: 551112
Robert Sigafoos (CFO)

Subsidiaries:

Dons & Bens Inc.   (1)
10903 Industry Dr, San Antonio, TX 78217
Tel.: (210) 646-9992
Web Site: http://www.donsandbens.com
Hard Liquor
N.A.I.C.S.: 445320

GABRIELLA WHITE LLC
7000 Hwy 25, Montevallo, AL 35115
Web Site: http://gabbyhome.com
Year Founded: 1978
Home Interior Furniture Mfr
N.A.I.C.S.: 337126
Bew White (Founder & CEO)

Subsidiaries:

Stanford Furniture Corp.   (1)
2860 N Oxford St, Claremont, NC 28610
Tel.: (828) 459-1992
Web Site: http://www.stanfordfurniture.com
Upholstered Household Furniture
N.A.I.C.S.: 337121
Randy Short (Founder& Pres)

**GABRIELLI TRUCK SALES
LTD.**
153-20 S Conduit Ave, Jamaica, NY
11434
Tel.: (718) 977-7350
Web Site:
   https://www.gabriellitruck.com
Sales Range: $50-74.9 Million
Emp.: 50
New & Used Trucks, Tractors & Trail-
ers
N.A.I.C.S.: 441110
Armando Gabrielli (Pres)
Carlo Gabrielli (CFO)
Rick Pesto (Mgr-Sls)
John Guglielmi (Mgr-Svcs)

GAC AUTO GROUP, INC.
677 Ala Moana Blvd Ste 808, Hono-
lulu, HI 96813-5502
Tel.: (808) 564-9100   HI
Year Founded: 2009
Sales Range: $10-24.9 Million
Emp.: 85
Car Whslr
N.A.I.C.S.: 441110

Marc Cutter *(Pres & CEO)*
Art Toorinjian *(Gen Mgr)*

GAC CHEMICAL CORP.
Ste 3 5415 Monroe St, Toledo, OH
43623-2877
Tel.: (419) 865-8000   IN
Web Site:
http://www.gacchemical.com
Year Founded: 1978
Sales Range: $75-99.9 Million
Emp.: 120
Mfr of Chemical Products
N.A.I.C.S.: 331313
David M. Colter *(Pres & CEO)*

Subsidiaries:

GAC Chemical Corp   (1)
Kidder Point Rd, Searsport, ME
04974   **(100%)**
Tel.: (207) 548-2525
Web Site: http://www.gacchemical.com
Sales Range: $50-74.9 Million
Emp.: 60
Chemicals Manufacturing
N.A.I.C.S.: 325998
Jim Poure *(Founder & Chm)*

GAC CONTRACTORS
4116 N Hwy 231, Panama City, FL
32404
Tel.: (850) 769-9414   FL
Web Site:
http://www.gaccontractors.com
Year Founded: 1958
Sales Range: $25-49.9 Million
Emp.: 200
Operator of Franchised Motels
N.A.I.C.S.: 237310
Derwin White *(VP)*
Jim Haney *(Sr Project Mgr)*
L. Charles Hilton *(Founder, Chm &
CEO)*
Allan G. Bense *(Pres & Partner)*

GADABOUT INC.
3501 E Kleindale Rd, Tucson, AZ
85716
Tel.: (520) 322-9434
Web Site: http://www.gadabout.com
Rev.: $10,385,274
Emp.: 250
Beauty Shops
N.A.I.C.S.: 812112
Pam McNair *(Owner)*

GADDIE-SHAMROCK LLC
Hwy 55 S, Columbia, KY 42728
Tel.: (270) 384-2451
Sales Range: $10-24.9 Million
Emp.: 65
General Contractor Highway & Street
Construction
N.A.I.C.S.: 237310
Pat Judd *(Gen Mgr)*
Majel Harris *(Mgr-HR)*
Nicole Legg *(Supvr-Quality Control)*

GADDIS CAPITAL CORPORA-
TION
221 W Oakland Park Blvd, Fort Lau-
derdale, FL 33311
Tel.: (954) 565-8900
Sales Range: $75-99.9 Million
Emp.: 100
Equipment & Vehicle Finance Leas-
ing Companies
N.A.I.C.S.: 522220
Jesse Gaddis *(Pres)*
Jim Murray *(Controller)*

GADELLNET CONSULTING
SERVICES, LLC
1254 Hanley Industrial Ct, Brentwood, MO 63144
Tel.: (314) 431-0358
Web Site: http://www.gadellnet.com

Year Founded: 2003
Sales Range: $10-24.9 Million
Emp.: 18
Information Technology Consulting
Services
N.A.I.C.S.: 541512
Joe Gadell *(Co-Owner & CTO)*
Nick Smarrelli *(Co-Owner & COO)*
Tom Stemm *(CEO)*
Ashley Pyle *(Mgr-Acct)*
Luke Dudenhoeffer *(VP-Sls)*
Matthew Green *(Engr-Svc Desk)*
Lucky Jackson *(Engr-Svc Desk)*
Jim Shoulberg *(Engr-Software)*
Tyler Smallman *(Engr-Client Site)*
Tim Snyder *(Engr-Project)*
Jason Eshleman *(Dir-Strategic Part-
nerships)*

Subsidiaries:

Blue Key Technology LLC   (1)
9001 Technology Dr, Fishers, IN 46038
Tel.: (317) 845-5000
Web Site:
http://www.bluekeytechnology.com
Information Technology Services
N.A.I.C.S.: 518210
Nick Robinson *(Mng Partner)*

GADGITKIDS, LLC
10823 Seminole Blvd Ste 2A, Largo,
FL 33778
Tel.: (727) 258-4897
Web Site: http://www.gadgitkids.com
Sales Range: $1-9.9 Million
Technical Consulting & Training
N.A.I.C.S.: 541690
Amanda Cole *(Pres)*
Jamie Goetz *(Dir-Mktg)*
Kara Tucker *(Gen Counsel)*
Cecilia A. Tucker *(Founder)*

GADNIUM GROUP LLC
PO Box 122589, San Diego, CA
92112
Tel.: (949) 200-7084
Sales Range: Less than $1 Million
Emp.: 2
Integrated Marketing, Interactive, Me-
dia Buying Services, Media Planning,
Outdoor, Out-of-Home Media, Radio,
T.V., Web (Banner Ads, Pop-ups,
etc.)
N.A.I.C.S.: 541830
Brendan Kyle *(Partner)*

GADZOOKS INC.
4121 International Pkwy, Carrollton,
TX 75007
Tel.: (972) 307-5555
Web Site: http://www.gadzooks.com
Year Founded: 1982
Rev.: $136,900,000
Emp.: 974
Casual Apparel & Accessories Re-
tailer
N.A.I.C.S.: 315990
Carol G. Gigli *(Pres & CMO)*
Lee Frilot *(Sec)*
James A. Motley *(VP & Sec)*
Jeffrey P. Creecy *(VP-Info Sys)*
Mike Caddell *(VP)*
Shahrzad Bagheri *(VP)*
Georgia Taylor *(VP)*
George S. Sotirin *(VP-Store Ops)*
Standifer Monty *(VP)*
David Gruenn *(VP)*
Wade Thurman *(Mgr-IT)*
Christine Gates *(Mgr-Pur)*
Paula Y. Masters *(Mgr-Mktg)*
Sherry Andrus *(Gen Mgr-Mdse)*
William S. Kotch III *(Sr VP & Pres-
Real Estate & Construction)*

GAEDEKE HOLDINGS LTD.
3710 Rawlins St Ste 1100, Dallas, TX
75219

Tel.: (214) 528-8883
Web Site: https://www.gaedeke.com
Rev.: $26,000,000
Emp.: 20
Real Estate Managers
N.A.I.C.S.: 531210
Sabine Gaedeke Stener *(Owner &
CEO)*
Kirk R. Fetter *(VP-Leasing)*

GAF MATERIALS CORPORA-
TION
1 Campus Dr, Parsippany, NJ 07054
Tel.: (973) 628-3000   DE
Web Site: http://www.gaf.com
Year Founded: 1886
Sales Range: $1-4.9 Billion
Emp.: 3,700
Roofing Products Mfr & Marketer
N.A.I.C.S.: 551112
Michael Baker *(VP-Legal)*
Brian Kimber *(Exec VP-Sls)*
John Altmeyer *(Chm-Comml Roofing)*
Alma Garnett *(Sr VP-Comml Roofing
Sls)*
Pete Vollmar *(Sr VP-Sls Ops)*
John W. Altmeyer *(CEO)*

Subsidiaries:

Building Materials Corporation of
America   (1)
1361 Alps Rd, Wayne, NJ
07470-3700   **(100%)**
Tel.: (973) 628-3000
Web Site: http://www.gaf.com
Sales Range: $1-4.9 Billion
Asphalt & Polymer Based Roofing Products
& Accessories Mfr
N.A.I.C.S.: 324122

Subsidiary (Domestic):

ElkCorp.   (2)
14911 Quorum Dr Ste 600, Dallas, TX
75254   **(100%)**
Tel.: (972) 851-0500
Sales Range: $900-999.9 Million
Emp.: 1,496
Roofing & Architectural Products Mfr
N.A.I.C.S.: 324122

Subsidiary (Domestic):

Elk Premium Building Products,
Inc.   (3)
14911 Quorum Dr Ste 600, Dallas, TX
75254   **(100%)**
Tel.: (972) 851-0500
Web Site: http://www.gaf.com
Architectural Roofing Shingles & Accessory
Products Mfr
N.A.I.C.S.: 324122

Subsidiary (Domestic):

GAF Decking Systems LLC   (2)
8 Morin St, Biddeford, ME 04005   **(100%)**
Tel.: (207) 284-5600
Sales Range: $10-24.9 Million
Emp.: 55
Composite Decking Products Mfr
N.A.I.C.S.: 321918

LL Building Products, Inc.   (2)
295 McKoy Rd, Burgaw, NC 28425
Tel.: (910) 259-6374
Web Site: http://www.gaf.com
Rev.: $56,000,000
Emp.: 280
Mfr of Home Improvement Building Prod-
ucts
N.A.I.C.S.: 335210

Icopal ApS   (1)
Lyskaer 5, DK 2730, Herlev,
Denmark   **(100%)**
Tel.: (45) 4488 5500
Web Site: http://www.icopal.com
Emp.: 5,000
Roofing & Waterproofing Membranes Mfr
N.A.I.C.S.: 324122
Henrik Hansen *(CFO)*
Soren Drewsen *(Grp Mng Dir-North Europe
& VP)*

Bob Abildgaard-Jorgensen *(Head-Process
Mgmt-London)*
Anne Mette Trinskjaer *(Mgr-Comm Grp)*

Subsidiary (Non-US):

Icopal AB   (2)
Skeppsbron 11, PO Box 848, 201 80,
Malmo, Sweden   **(100%)**
Tel.: (46) 40 24 74 00
Web Site: http://www.icopal.se
Emp.: 1
Roofing & Waterproofing Membrane Mfr
N.A.I.C.S.: 324122
Magnus Eriksson *(Sls Mgr)*
Johan Bauer *(Head-Sls)*

Subsidiary (Domestic):

Icopal Entreprenad AB   (3)
Lodgatan 10, PO Box 848, 201 80, Malmo,
Sweden
Tel.: (46) 40247400
Web Site: http://www.icopalentreprenad.se
Construction & Roofing Installation
N.A.I.C.S.: 238160
Jimmy Adlerberth *(CEO)*
Thomas Nilsson *(Mgr-Construction-West)*

Subsidiary (Non-US):

Icopal AS   (2)
Fjellhamarveien 52, Fjellhamar, 1472, Nor-
way
Tel.: (47) 67 97 90 00
Web Site: http://www.icopal.no
Roofing & Waterproofing Membranes Mfr
N.A.I.C.S.: 324122
Trond Falao *(Sls Mgr)*
Ole Hakon Olavsrud *(Mgr-Ostfold)*
Lars Erik Ekeberg *(Mgr-Oslo, Akershus &
Buskerud)*
Havard Tande *(Mgr-Akershus, Hedmark &
Oppland)*
Dag Atle Engo *(Mgr-Vestfold, Telemark &
Aust-Agder)*

Subsidiary (Domestic):

Icopal Danmark ApS   (2)
Lyskaer 5, 2730, Herlev, Denmark
Tel.: (45) 44885500
Web Site: http://www.icopal.dk
Roofing & Waterproofing Membrane Mfr
N.A.I.C.S.: 332322
Jorgen Knudsen *(Mgr-Warehouse)*

Subsidiary (Non-US):

Icopal GmbH   (2)
Capeller Strasse 150, D-59368, Werne,
Germany
Tel.: (49) 238979700
Web Site: http://www.icopal.de
Roofing & Waterproofing Membranes Mfr
N.A.I.C.S.: 324122
Carsten Roemgens *(Mng Dir)*
Markus Kircher *(Mng Dir)*

Subsidiary (Domestic):

Feumas GmbH   (3)
Lucie Bolte Strasse 6, 66793, Saarnellin-
gen, Germany
Tel.: (49) 6838863160
Web Site: http://www.icopal.com
Roofing & Waterproofing Membranes Mfr
N.A.I.C.S.: 324122

Subsidiary (Non-US):

Icopal Kft.   (2)
Zrinyi M u 6, HU 8900, Zalaegerszeg, Hun-
gary
Tel.: (36) 92 550 351
Web Site: http://www.icopal.hu
Roofing & Waterproofing Membrane Mfr
N.A.I.C.S.: 238160
Norbert Ponyi *(Gen Mgr-SBU & Dir)*
Edit Taplo Kocsis *(Dir-Production)*
Fincza Ilona Moriczne *(Dir-Economic)*
Peter Tuboly *(Controller)*
Petra Gosztolai *(Sls Mgr-Eastern Hungary)*
Gitta Hadnagyne Avas *(Mgr-Fin & Acctg)*
Istvan Horvath *(Mgr-Warehouse)*
Thaier Saleh *(Mgr-Quality)*
Beata Kovacsova *(Coord-Intra Grp)*

Icopal Ltd   (2)
Barton Dock Road Stretford, Manchester,
M32 0YL, Lancashire, United Kingdom

GAF Materials Corporation—(Continued)
Tel.: (44) 1618654444
Web Site: http://www.icopal.co.uk
Emp.: 200
Roofing Product Mfr
N.A.I.C.S.: 324122
Andrew Lawton (Mng Dir)
Neil Harrison (Dir-Technical)
Mike Rimmer (Dir-Ops)
Paul Stel (CFO)
Simon Wood (Sls Dir-UK & Ireland)
Richard Thorne (Sls Dir-Builders Merchant & Monarflex)
David Dacres (Dir-Bus Dev)
Brian Dunn (Sls Dir-North Reg)
Jay Hollands (Sls Dir-South Reg)

Icopal Oy   (2)
Lantinen Teollisuuskatu 10, Espoo, 2920, Finland
Tel.: (358) 207436200
Web Site: http://www.icopal.fi
Roofing & Waterproofing Membranes Mfr
N.A.I.C.S.: 324122
Harri Vuoritsalo (Pres & CEO)
Jari Kortesalmi (Sls Mgr)
Jussi Pylkas (Reg Mgr-Western Finland)
Mikael Risikko (Reg Mgr-Eastern Finland)

Icopal S.A.   (2)
ZI des Hauts Sarts Rue de Hermee 186, 4040, Herstal, Belgium
Tel.: (32) 42405151
Web Site: http://www.icopal.be
Roofing & Waterproofing Membranes Mfr
N.A.I.C.S.: 332322
Janus Pagh (CEO)
Nicolas Marx (CFO)
Michel Falcone (Dir-Ops)

Icopal S.r.l.   (2)
Via Fratelli Gracchi 27, 20092, Cinisello Balsamo, Italy
Tel.: (39) 0266045029
Web Site: http://www.icopal.it
Roofing & Waterproofing Membranes Mfr
N.A.I.C.S.: 324122

Icopal Siplast SAS   (2)
12 rue de la Renaissance, 92160, Antony, France
Tel.: (33) 140963500
Web Site: http://www.siplast.fr
Sales Range: $150-199.9 Million
Emp.: 380
Roofing & Waterproofing Membranes Mfr
N.A.I.C.S.: 324122
Laurent Fischer (Dir Gen & Comml Dir-France)
Damien Soler (Comml Dir-Export)
Claire Racape (Dir-Product Dev)
Yannick Tenneguin (Dir-Supply Chain & Info Sys)
Jean-Christophe Roche (Dir-Indus)

Subsidiary (US):

Siplast Icopal Inc.   (3)
1000 E Rochelle Blvd, Irving, TX 75062-3940
Tel.: (469) 995-2200
Web Site: http://www.siplast.com
Roofing & Waterproofing Membranes Mfr
N.A.I.C.S.: 324122
Kirk Goodrum (Mgr-R&D)

Subsidiary (Non-US):

Icopal Sp. z o.o.   (2)
Ul Laska 169-197, 98 220, Zdunska Wola, Poland
Tel.: (48) 438234111
Web Site: http://www.icopal.pl
Roofing & Waterproofing Membranes Mfr
N.A.I.C.S.: 324122
Leszek Bajko (Comml Dir)
Grzegorz Gladkiewicz (Head-Technical Advisory)
Piotr Konieczny (Sls Mgr-K&S)
Piotr Macigowski (Sls Mgr)
Marek Wolanski (Sls Mgr)
Adam Gil (Mgr-Logistics & Customer Svc)

Monarflex s.r.o.   (2)
Tovarenska 1, 943 03, Sturovo, Slovakia
Tel.: (421) 367563865
Web Site: http://www.monarflex.com
Polyethylene Sheeting & Roofing Material Mfr

N.A.I.C.S.: 324122
Tibor Balogh (Fin Mgr)
Jozef Meszaros (Plant Mgr)
Adriana Juhaszova (Mgr-Quality)
Erik Hevo (Mgr-Group Plastics Category & Procurement)
Richard Larsen (Product Mgr-Group)
Norbert Tegen (Mgr-Logistics)

GAFCON INC.
5960 Corner Stone Ct W, San Diego, CA 92121
Tel.: (619) 231-6100
Web Site: http://www.gafcon.com
Year Founded: 1987
Sales Range: $10-24.9 Million
Emp.: 107
Construction Consulting Services
N.A.I.C.S.: 541618
Yehudi Gaffen (CEO)
Robin Duveen (COO)
Pam Gaffen (Pres & COO)
Bryan Benso (Chief Dev Officer)
Taunya Moen (Dir-Mktg)

GAFFNEY BUICK-GMC, INC.
730 Chesnee Hwy, Gaffney, SC 29341
Tel.: (864) 487-4227
Web Site: http://www.gaffneybuickgmc.com
Year Founded: 2007
Sales Range: $10-24.9 Million
Emp.: 65
Car Whslr
N.A.I.C.S.: 441110
Scott Hensley (Owner)

GAFFNEY-KROESE SUPPLY CORP.
50 Randolph Rd, Somerset, NJ 08873
Tel.: (732) 885-9000
Web Site: http://www.gaffney-kroese.com
Year Founded: 1931
Sales Range: $100-124.9 Million
Industrial Equipment Distr
N.A.I.C.S.: 423830
Bob Jouas (COO)

Subsidiaries:

Gaffney-Kroese Supply India Private Limited   (1)
307 3rd Floor Exhibition-cum-Marketing Development & Business Park, ECIL Post Kushaiguda, Hyderabad, 500062, India
Tel.: (91) 40 27138006
Web Site: http://www.gaffney-kroese.com
Emp.: 15
Industrial Machinery & Equipment Supplier
N.A.I.C.S.: 423830
Amarendra Prabhala (Dir)

Gaffney-Kroese Supply Private Limited   (1)
25 Loyang Crescent Loyang Offshore Supply Base Block 302 03-10, Mailbox 5089, Singapore, 508988, Singapore
Tel.: (65) 6542 3787
Industrial Machinery & Equipment Supplier
N.A.I.C.S.: 423830

Gaffney-Kroese Trinidad Limited   (1)
Lot 5 Southern Main Road McBean, Couva, Trinidad & Tobago
Tel.: (868) 6794704
Industrial Machinery & Equipment Supplier
N.A.I.C.S.: 423830

Gaffney-Kroese UK Ltd   (1)
15B Bell Yard Mews 159 Bermondsey Street, London, SE1 3TY, United Kingdom
Tel.: (44) 203 371 0956
Web Site: http://www.gaffney-kroese.com
Industrial Machinery & Equipment Supplier
N.A.I.C.S.: 423830

GAFFOGLIO FAMILY METAL-CRAFTERS INC.

11161 Slater Ave, Fountain Valley, CA 92708
Tel.: (714) 444-2000
Web Site: http://www.metalcrafters.com
Sales Range: $10-24.9 Million
Emp.: 200
Mfr of Prototype Concept Cars
N.A.I.C.S.: 336110
George Gaffoglio (CEO)
John Gaffoglio (Founder)
Dante Lamastra (Gen Mgr-Transparency Programs)

GAFFOS INC.
40 Bayview Ave, Inwood, NY 11096
Web Site: http://www.gaffos.com
Year Founded: 2007
Sales Range: $1-9.9 Million
Emp.: 15
Sunglasses & Optical Frames Retailer
N.A.I.C.S.: 456130
Jonathan Muller (Co-Founder & CEO)
Nathan Rosenberg (Co-Founder & Pres)
Matthew Choy (COO)

GAGE
10000 Hwy 55, Minneapolis, MN 55441-6300
Tel.: (763) 595-3800   MN
Web Site: https://www.gage.com
Year Founded: 1992
Sales Range: $75-99.9 Million
Emp.: 125
Advetising Agency
N.A.I.C.S.: 541810
Thomas Belle (Pres & CEO)
Chris Curry (Gen Counsel)
Jane Blanco (Sr VP)
Mark Kurtz (Chief Growth Officer & VP-New Media)
David Morrisette (VP-Strategic Acct Dev)
Jeffery Cannata (Mgr-Emerging Mktg)
Russ Nolan (Dir-Bus Dev)
Tony Rivera (Mgr-Customer Success-Plymouth)
Mark Iverson (Chief Revenue Officer & VP-Bus Dev)
Michelle Hoffman (Mgr-Pub Rels)
Jennifer Cole (Sr Project Mgr-Market Platform)
Liz Miller (Project Mgr)
Paige Black (Mgr-Engagement)
John Fox (VP-Global Customer Success)
Eric Paradis (Dir-Customer Experience)

Subsidiaries:

Gage-West   (1)
2535 152nd Ave NE, Redmond, WA 98052
Tel.: (425) 968-5039
Web Site: http://www.gage.com
Emp.: 12
Advetising Agency
N.A.I.C.S.: 541810

GAGE CHEVROLET INC.
1701 S Beacon Blvd, Grand Haven, MI 49417
Tel.: (616) 842-2250   MI
Web Site: http://www.gagemotormall.com
Year Founded: 1962
Sales Range: $25-49.9 Million
Emp.: 75
Sales & Service of New & Used Automobiles
N.A.I.C.S.: 441110
Edward A. Gage Jr. (Pres)

GAGE CHRYSLER-PLYMOUTH-DODGE INC.

1625 S Beacon Blvd, Grand Haven, MI 49417
Tel.: (616) 842-2250
Rev.: $12,200,000
Emp.: 60
New Car Dealers
N.A.I.C.S.: 441110
Edward A. Gage Jr. (Pres & Treas)

GAGE CORPORATION
821 Wanda St, Ferndale, MI 48220
Tel.: (248) 541-3824
Web Site: https://www.gageproducts.com
Sales Range: $25-49.9 Million
Emp.: 120
Organic Solvents
N.A.I.C.S.: 325199
Fred Lenz (CFO)

Subsidiaries:

Dell Marking Systems Inc.   (1)
721 Wanda St, Ferndale, MI 48220
Tel.: (248) 547-7750
Web Site: http://www.dellid.com
Rev.: $3,500,000
Emp.: 11
Marking Machines
N.A.I.C.S.: 333517

Gage Global Services   (1)
4200 Waterside Solihull Parkway Birmingham Business Park, Birmingham, B37 7YN, United Kingdom
Tel.: (44) 121 717 4740
Chemical Products Distr
N.A.I.C.S.: 424690
Garry Yesinkas (Mgr)

Gage Products Company   (1)
821 Wanda St, Ferndale, MI 48220
Tel.: (248) 541-3824
Web Site: http://www.gageproducts.com
Sales Range: $10-24.9 Million
Emp.: 85
Solvents, Organic
N.A.I.C.S.: 325199
Tony Stark (VP-Ops)

Gage Products Company de Mexico, S. de R.L. de C.V.   (1)
Calle Presidente Masaryk 111 Piso 1 Colonia Chapultepec, Morales, 11570, Mexico, Mexico
Tel.: (52) 5277 3047
Chemical Products Distr
N.A.I.C.S.: 424690

Gage do Brasil Ltda.   (1)
Av Alberto Soaes Sampaio 1240, Maua, 09380-000, Brazil
Tel.: (55) 11 4547 1111
Web Site: http://www.gagedobrasil.com.br
Chemical Products Distr
N.A.I.C.S.: 424690

GAGE INDUSTRIES INC.
1709 SE 3rd AVE, Lake Oswego, OR 97035
Tel.: (503) 639-2177
Web Site: http://www.gageindustries.com
Sales Range: $25-49.9 Million
Emp.: 140
Thermoformed Finished Plastics Products
N.A.I.C.S.: 326199
Jeff Gage (CEO)

GAGE'S FERTILIZER & GRAIN, INC.
105 S High St, Stanberry, MO 64489
Tel.: (660) 783-2167   MO
Web Site: http://www.gagesfertilizer.com
Year Founded: 1982
Sales Range: $10-24.9 Million
Emp.: 20
Feed Mfr
N.A.I.C.S.: 424910
Steven Gage (CEO)
Doug Mc Winn (Controller)

GAGMARS INC.
1211 W College Ave, Santa Rosa, CA 95401
Tel.: (707) 546-6877
Sales Range: $25-49.9 Million
Emp.: 365
Independent Supermarket
N.A.I.C.S.: 445110
Dick Gong (VP)
Lee Gong (VP)

GAGNON INCORPORATED
2315 Hampden Ave, Saint Paul, MN 55114
Tel.: (651) 644-4301
Web Site: https://www.gagnon-inc.com
Sales Range: $10-24.9 Million
Emp.: 50
Boiler Maintenance Contractor
N.A.I.C.S.: 238220
Ronald Gagnon (Pres)

GAIL'S HARLEY-DAVIDSON INC
5900 E 150 Hwy, Grandview, MO 64030
Tel.: (816) 966-2222
Web Site:
http://www.feelthepower.com
Sales Range: $10-24.9 Million
Emp.: 42
Motorcycles
N.A.I.C.S.: 441227
Gail Worth (Pres)
Dee Austin (Mgr-HR)

GAILLARD PERFORMANCE HALL FOUNDATION
40 Calhoun St Ste 230, Charleston, SC 29401
Tel.: (843) 718-1578   SC
Web Site:
http://www.gaillardfoundation.org
Year Founded: 2010
Sales Range: $25-49.9 Million
Fundraising Services
N.A.I.C.S.: 813211
Doerte McManus (Exec Dir)

GAIN CITIES LIMITED
5575 La Jolla Blvd, La Jolla, CA 92037
Tel.: (360) 878-9625   NV
Year Founded: 2014
GCTY—(OTCBB)
Emp.: 1
Investment Services
N.A.I.C.S.: 523999
James Oliver (Chm, Pres, CEO, CFO, Treas & Sec)
Benjamin Teare (COO)

GAINES MOTOR LINES INCORPORATED
2349 13th Ave SW, Hickory, NC 28602
Tel.: (828) 322-2000
Web Site: http://www.gainesml.com
Sales Range: $10-24.9 Million
Emp.: 100
Contract Haulers
N.A.I.C.S.: 484121
Tim Gaines (Owner)
Roger Short (Dir-Ops)
Camille Hawn (Coord-Backhaul)

GAINESVILLE REGIONAL UTILITIES INC.
301 SE 4th Ave, Gainesville, FL 32601
Tel.: (352) 334-3400
Web Site: http://www.gru.com
Year Founded: 1912
Sales Range: $25-49.9 Million
Emp.: 800

Combination Utility Services
N.A.I.C.S.: 221118
David E. Beaulieu (Asst Gen Mgr-Energy Delivery)
Cheryl McBride (Dir-HR)
William J. Shepherd (Chief Customer Officer)
David E. Owens (Officer-Compliance)
J. Lewis Walton (Chief Bus Svcs Officer)
Justin Locke (CFO)
Margaret A. Crawford (Dir-Comm)
Michelle Smith Lambert (Chief Change Officer)
Thomas R. Brown (COO)
Yvette Carter (Dir-Community Rels)
Justin Lock (CFO)
Tom Prone (COO)
Walter Banks (CIO)

GAINLINE CAPITAL PARTNERS LP
700 Canal St 5th Fl, Stamford, CT 06902
Tel.: (212) 319-3023
Web Site:
http://www.gainlinecapital.com
Year Founded: 2015
Privater Equity Firm
N.A.I.C.S.: 523999
Allan D. L. Weinstein (Mng Partner)
Rick Sullivan (Founder & Partner)
Brian Nethercott (Dir-Origination)
Tatiana Mishin (VP)
Brian O'reilly (COO)

Subsidiaries:

Integrated Energy Services LLC   (1)
450 Lexington Ave 4th Fl, New York, NY 10017
Tel.: (888) 971-9244
Web Site: https://www.iesmach.com
Computer Software Services
N.A.I.C.S.: 513210
Chris Ziccardi (CEO)

Subsidiary (Domestic):

MACH Energy   (2)
505 14th St Ste 450, Oakland, CA 94612
Tel.: (833) 935-5782
Web Site: http://www.machenergy.com
Energy Monitoring & Software Management Services
N.A.I.C.S.: 541618

SourceHOV L.L.C.   (1)
2701 E Grauwyler Rd, Irving, TX 75061
Tel.: (866) 321-5854
Web Site: http://www.sourcehov.com
Business Process Outsourcing Services
N.A.I.C.S.: 561499
James G. Reynolds (Co-Chm)
Sanjay Kulkarni (CTO)
Shrukant Sortur (Sr VP-Global Fin)

Subsidiary (Domestic):

BancTec, Inc.   (2)
2701 E Grauwyler Rd, Irving, TX 75061-3414
Tel.: (972) 821-4000
Document & Content Processing, Payment Processing & Information Technology Services
N.A.I.C.S.: 518210

Holding (Non-US):

BancTec Ltd.   (3)
Jarman House, Mathiesen Way, Colnbrook, SL3 0HF, Berkshire, United Kingdom
Tel.: (44) 1753 778888
Web Site: http://www.banctec.co.uk
Sales Range: $50-74.9 Million
Marketing & Maintenance of Computerized Document Processing Systems
N.A.I.C.S.: 518210
Stephen J. Downey (Sr VP-UK & Ireland & Gen Mgr)
Vitalie Robu (Sr VP-Ops-EMEA)
David J. Ogden (Dir-Sls)

Subsidiary (Domestic):

Rust Consulting, Inc.   (2)
625 Marquette Ave Ste 900, Minneapolis, MN 55402
Tel.: (612) 359-2000
Web Site: http://www.rustconsulting.com
Class Action Settlement & Bankruptcy Claims Administration Services
N.A.I.C.S.: 541618
David C. Holland (Exec VP)
Paul Vogel (CFO & Exec VP)
Robert T. Beedie (Sr VP)
Eric Bishop (Sr VP)
Tiffaney A. Janowicz (Sr VP)
James M. Parks (Sr VP)
Jonathan Paul (Sr VP)
Kendall Zylstra (Sr VP)
Justin Parks (Dir-Bus Dev)
Kim Schmidt (Sr VP)

TransCentra, Inc.   (2)
4855 Peachtree Industrial Blvd, Norcross, GA 30092
Tel.: (678) 728-2500
Web Site: http://www.transcentra.com
Emp.: 1,400
Billing & Payments Software & Services
N.A.I.C.S.: 518210
Michelle Krack (Controller)

Southern Motion, Inc.   (1)
161 Prestige Dr, Pontotoc, MS 38863
Tel.: (662) 488-4007
Web Site: http://www.southernmotion.com
Sales Range: $10-24.9 Million
Reclining Upholstered Furniture Mfr
N.A.I.C.S.: 337121
G. Lipscomb (Exec VP-Sls & Mktg)
Roger Bland (Pres & CEO)
Kelly Magnussen (Dir-Strategic Accts)
Jennifer Davis (VP-Mdsg)

GAITHER MANAGEMENT GROUP
1703 S Park Ave, Alexandria, IN 46001
Tel.: (765) 724-8400
Web Site:
http://www.gaithermusic.com
Year Founded: 1971
Sales Range: $10-24.9 Million
Emp.: 100
Production & Stage Performances
N.A.I.C.S.: 711130
Barry Jennings (Pres)

GAITHERSBURG FARMERS SUPPLY
700 E Diamond Ave, Gaithersburg, MD 20877
Tel.: (301) 670-9300
Web Site:
http://www.gaithersburgequipment.com
Rev: $20,748,201
Farm Tractors
N.A.I.C.S.: 459999
David E. Rippeon (Pres)

GAL-TEX HOTEL CORPORATION
2302 Postoffice St Ste 500, Galveston, TX 77550-1936
Tel.: (409) 763-8536
Web Site:
https://1859historichotels.com
Year Founded: 1940
Sales Range: $550-599.9 Million
Emp.: 3,000
Hotel Owner & Operator
N.A.I.C.S.: 551112
Eugene Lucas (Pres)
Dan Dick (CFO)
Joyce Dundee (Sec)

Subsidiaries:

1859 Historic Hotels, Ltd.   (1)
2302 Post Office St Ste 500, Galveston, TX 77550-1936
Tel.: (409) 763-8536
Web Site: http://www.1859historichotels.com

Sales Range: $10-24.9 Million
Emp.: 14
Home Management Services
N.A.I.C.S.: 721110
Eugene Lucas (Pres)

Holding (Domestic):

Hilton Houston Hobby Airport Hotel   (2)
8181 Airport Blvd, Houston, TX 77061
Tel.: (713) 645-3000
Web Site:
http://www.houstonhobbyairport.hilton.com
Hotel Operations
N.A.I.C.S.: 721110

Menger Hotel   (2)
204 Alamo Plz, San Antonio, TX 78205
Tel.: (210) 223-4361
Web Site: http://www.mengerhotel.com
Hotel Operator
N.A.I.C.S.: 721110
Eugene Lucas (Pres)
Loretta Delarosa (Mgr)

Mountain Lake Hotel   (2)
115 Hotel Cir, Pembroke, VA 24136
Tel.: (540) 626-7121
Web Site:
http://www.mountainlakehotel.com
Hotel Operations
N.A.I.C.S.: 721110
Jessica Coker (Mgr)
Marsha Stevers (Controller)

South Shore Harbour Resort & Conference Center   (2)
2500 S Shore Blvd, League City, TX 77573
Tel.: (281) 334-1000
Web Site: http://www.sshr.com
Hotel Operations
N.A.I.C.S.: 721110
Roy Green (Gen Mgr)
Bridget Bear (Dir-Sls & Catering)
Karen George (Dir-Reservations & Mgr-Revenue)

The Crockett Hotel   (2)
320 Bonham, San Antonio, TX 78205
Tel.: (210) 225-6500
Web Site: http://www.crocketthotel.com
Hotel Operations
N.A.I.C.S.: 721110
Maya Haller (Mgr-Sls)

Y.O. Ranch Resort Hotel & Conference Center   (2)
2033 Sidney Baker Hwy 16, Kerrville, TX 78028
Tel.: (830) 257-4440
Web Site: http://www.yoresort.com
Hotel Operations
N.A.I.C.S.: 721110
John Helm (Gen Mgr)
Fay Faure (Dir-Sls)

GALA CAPITAL PARTNERS, LLC
3191 Red Hill Ave, Costa Mesa, CA 92626
Tel.: (800) 653-3517
Web Site:
http://www.galacapitalpartners.com
Private Investment Firm
N.A.I.C.S.: 523940
Anand Gala (Founder & Mng Partner)

Subsidiaries:

Dunn Bros Coffee, Inc.   (1)
1569 Grand Ave, Saint Paul, MN 55105
Tel.: (651) 698-0618
Web Site: http://www.dunnbrosgrand.com
Sales Range: $1-9.9 Million
Emp.: 47
Coffee Mfr
N.A.I.C.S.: 311920
Lucinda Becker (Mgr-Ops)
Laura Ochsendorf (Owner & Mgr)

MOOYAH Franchising, LLC   (1)
6865 Windcrest Dr Ste 400, Plano, TX 75024
Tel.: (214) 310-0768
Web Site: http://www.mooyah.com
Casual Dining
N.A.I.C.S.: 722513

Gala Capital Partners, LLC—(Continued)

Natalie Anderson *(VP-Mktg)*
Pamela Parham *(Mktg Mgr)*

GALA PHARMACEUTICAL, INC.
18881 Von Karman Ave Ste 1440, Irvine, CA 92612
Tel.: (775) 321-8238   NV
Web Site: http://www.gala-global.org
Year Founded: 2010
Rev.: $4,675
Assets: $262,158
Liabilities: $1,120,864
Net Worth: ($858,706)
Earnings: ($1,858,877)
Emp.: 2
Fiscal Year-end: 11/30/18
Hemp-based Products Mfr
N.A.I.C.S.: 621511

GALADCO CO. INC.
263 Lakeview Rd, Edgemont, AR 72044
Tel.: (870) 948-2565
Sales Range: $25-49.9 Million
Emp.: 3
Commercial & Office Building Contractors
N.A.I.C.S.: 722513
Dennis Porter *(Pres)*

GALARDI GROUP, INC.
7700 Irvine Center Dr Ste 550, Irvine, CA 92618-3036
Tel.: (949) 892-2699   CA
Web Site:
http://www.wienerschnitzel.com
Year Founded: 1961
Sales Range: $200-249.9 Million
Emp.: 48
Fast Food Restaurants
N.A.I.C.S.: 533110
John R. Galardi *(Pres)*
Cindy Galardi Culpepper *(CEO)*

Subsidiaries:

Tastee Freez LLC   (1)
4501 Jamboree Rd, Newport Beach, CA 92660
Tel.: (949) 752-9626
Web Site: http://www.tastee-freez.com
Sales Range: $10-24.9 Million
Emp.: 11
Franchising of Quick Serve Restaurants
N.A.I.C.S.: 722513
Brian Huish *(Owner)*

GALASSO TRUCKING, INC.
2 Galasso Pl, Maspeth, NY 11378
Tel.: (718) 456-1800
Web Site: http://www.galasso.com
Sales Range: $10-24.9 Million
Emp.: 75
General Freight Trucking Services
N.A.I.C.S.: 484110
Frank Galasso *(Pres)*
Stephen Doran *(Sr VP)*
Greg Galasso *(VP)*
Richard Kaye *(VP-Sls)*
Nancy Bonet *(Mgr)*
Michael Degar *(Project Mgr)*
Susan D'Onofrio *(Office Mgr)*
Peter Van Galen *(Mgr-Billing)*
Ernest Llerena *(Mgr-Dispatch)*
Josh Gelles *(Mgr-Logistics Sls)*
Lou Mangia *(Mgr-Ops)*
Wildy Patino *(Mgr-Ops)*
Jeremy Razack *(Project Coord)*
Woodrow Gaskin *(Project Mgr)*

GALATI YACHT SALES
900 S Bay Blvd, Anna Maria, FL 34216
Tel.: (941) 778-0755   FL
Web Site:
https://www.galatiyachts.com

Year Founded: 1970
Sales Range: $10-24.9 Million
Emp.: 150
Yacht Sales & Services
N.A.I.C.S.: 441222
Stan Hoynowski *(Mgr-Sls)*
Carmine Galati *(VP-Sales)*

GALATIAN INC.
10420 Eastex Fwy, Houston, TX 77093-4904
Tel.: (713) 697-2904
Year Founded: 1967
Sales Range: $25-49.9 Million
Emp.: 175
Provider of Groceries & Merchandise
N.A.I.C.S.: 445110
Richard H. Galatian *(Pres & CFO)*
Garlon Pierce *(Mgr-Adv)*

GALAXIE CORPORATION
5170 Galaxie, Jackson, MS 39206-2608
Tel.: (601) 366-8465   MS
Year Founded: 1985
Sales Range: $10-24.9 Million
Emp.: 3
Bulk Petroleum Distr
N.A.I.C.S.: 424710
Matthew L. Holleman III *(Chm, Pres & CEO)*

GALAXY DESSERTS
1100 Marina Way S Ste D, Richmond, CA 94804
Tel.: (510) 439-3160
Web Site:
https://www.galaxydesserts.com
Year Founded: 1998
Sales Range: $25-49.9 Million
Emp.: 200
Frozen Bakery Products Mfr
N.A.I.C.S.: 311813
Jean-Yves Charon *(Co-Founder & VP)*
Lisa Weaver *(Dir-Sls)*
Paul Levitan *(Co-Founder, Pres & CEO)*

GALAXY ENTERPRISES INC.
1701 Charles Iam Ct, Las Vegas, NV 89117
Tel.: (702) 596-9628   WY
Year Founded: 2021
Assets: $15,638
Liabilities: $39,152
Net Worth: ($23,514)
Earnings: ($20,135)
Fiscal Year-end: 07/31/24
Advertising Agency Services
N.A.I.C.S.: 541810
Gregory Navone *(Pres & CEO)*
James C. Shaw *(CFO, Treas & Sec)*

GALAXY GLASS & ALUMINUM INC.
300 E Industrial Park Dr, Manchester, NH 03109
Tel.: (603) 626-1800
Web Site:
https://www.galaxyglass.biz
Rev.: $10,528,452
Emp.: 62
Glass & Glazing Work
N.A.I.C.S.: 444180
Daniel Simpson *(Pres)*
Paul Bissonnette *(Project Mgr)*

GALAXY INTERNATIONAL INC.
2400 Art Moore Blvd, Pittsburgh, PA 15221
Tel.: (412) 271-0620
Web Site:
http://www.galaxyinternational.com
Year Founded: 1978

Sales Range: $50-74.9 Million
Emp.: 12
Supplier of Packaged Frozen Goods
N.A.I.C.S.: 445240
Stan L. Shaw *(Controller)*
Gloria Fiore *(Mgr-Admin)*

GALAXY MARKETING
7100 Sophia Ave, Van Nuys, CA 91406
Tel.: (818) 786-6467
Web Site:
http://www.galaxymarketing.biz
Year Founded: 1989
Sales Range: $10-24.9 Million
Emp.: 50
Sells & Markets Electronics
N.A.I.C.S.: 423690
Dori Mizrahi *(Pres)*

GALAXY MARKETING SOLUTIONS LLC
420 S Garden Ave Ste 100, Clearwater, FL 33756
Tel.: (727) 531-7171
Web Site:
http://www.galaxymarketingsolutions.com
Sales Range: $1-9.9 Million
Emp.: 6
Dental Marketing Services
N.A.I.C.S.: 541890
Jyrki Ikonen *(CEO)*
Susan D. Wells *(CFO & VP)*

GALAXY MULTI RIDES
7431 Sawyer Cir, Port Charlotte, FL 33981
Tel.: (941) 697-0324
Web Site:
https://www.galaxymultirides.com
Sales Range: $1-9.9 Million
Emp.: 20
Mechanical Bulls & Other Rides Mfr & Sales
N.A.I.C.S.: 339999
Robin Whincup *(Owner)*

GALAXY PARTNERS LLC
16233 Kenyon Ave Ste 210, Lakeville, MN 55044
Tel.: (952) 431-0404
Sales Range: $25-49.9 Million
Emp.: 7
Investment Holding Company
N.A.I.C.S.: 523999
Timothy S. Krieger *(Mgr)*

GALAXY SOFTWARE SOLUTIONS INC.
5820 N Lilley Rd Ste 8, Canton, MI 48187
Tel.: (734) 983-9030
Web Site: https://www.galaxy-soft.com
Year Founded: 2004
Sales Range: $1-9.9 Million
Emp.: 145
IT Staffing, IT Training & Software Development
N.A.I.C.S.: 561311
Dileep Tiwari *(VP)*

GALAXY TECHNOLOGIES CORP.
109 W Dudley Town Rd, Bloomfield, CT 06002
Tel.: (860) 769-6900
Rev.: $10,000,000
Emp.: 2
Machine Tools & Metalworking Machinery
N.A.I.C.S.: 423830

Subsidiaries:

Millstar LLC   (1)

30200 Ryan Rd, Warren, MI 48092
Tel.: (586) 573-9450
Web Site: http://www.millstar.com
Machine Tool Accessories
N.A.I.C.S.: 333515

GALAXY TOYOTA
700 Route 36 Ste 750, Eatontown, NJ 07724
Tel.: (732) 544-1000
Web Site:
http://www.galaxytoyota.net
Year Founded: 1971
Sales Range: $10-24.9 Million
Emp.: 70
Car Whslr
N.A.I.C.S.: 441110
Robert G. Ciasulli *(Owner)*

GALE FORCE HOLDINGS, LP
1400 Edwards Mill Rd, Raleigh, NC 27607-3624
Tel.: (919) 861-2300   DE
Year Founded: 1998
Holding Company; Sports Arena Owner & Operator
N.A.I.C.S.: 551112
Jim Rutherford *(Pres)*

Subsidiaries:

Gale Force Sports & Entertainment, LLC   (1)
1400 Edwards Mill Rd, Raleigh, NC 27607-3624
Tel.: (919) 861-2300
Web Site: http://www.thepncarena.com
Sports & Entertainment Arena Operator
N.A.I.C.S.: 711310

GALE FORCE SOFTWARE CORPORATION
11800 Exit 5 Pkwy Ste 102, Fishers, IN 46037-7989
Tel.: (317) 570-4900
Web Site:
http://www.galeforcecorp.com
Custom Computer Programming Services
N.A.I.C.S.: 541511
Fran Gale *(Owner & Principal)*

Subsidiaries:

Smallponds, LLC   (1)
11800 Exit 5 Pkwy Ste 102, Fishers, IN 46037
Tel.: (317) 570-4900
Web Site: http://www.smallpondllc.com
Custom Computer Programming Services
N.A.I.C.S.: 541511
Scott Rulong *(Pres)*

GALE TOYOTA
50 Palomba Dr, Enfield, CT 06082
Tel.: (860) 269-3608
Web Site:
https://www.galetoyota.com
Year Founded: 1969
Sales Range: $10-24.9 Million
Emp.: 40
Car Whslr
N.A.I.C.S.: 441110
Bob Green *(Owner)*

GALEANA AUTOMOTIVE GROUP
28400 Van Dyke Ave, Warren, MI 48093
Tel.: (586) 573-4000
Web Site:
http://www.galeanaauto.com
Sales Range: $10-24.9 Million
Emp.: 75
Holding Company
N.A.I.C.S.: 441227
Carl Galeana *(VP)*

Subsidiaries:

Galeana Chrysler Dodge Jeep   (1)
14375 S Tamiami Trl, Fort Myers, FL 33912

Tel.: (239) 236-8915
Web Site: http://www.galeanachrysler.com
New & Used Automobiles
N.A.I.C.S.: 441110
Gary Haas *(Mgr-Sls, Small Bus, Comml & Fleet)*
Juan Agront *(Mgr-Bus)*

GALEN PARTNERS, L.P.
680 Washington Blvd 10th Fl, Stamford, CT 06901
Tel.: (203) 653-6400   DE
Web Site: https://www.galen.com
Healthcare Private Equity Firm
N.A.I.C.S.: 523999
David W. Jahns *(Mng Partner)*
Terrance H. Gregg *(Venture Partner)*
Stacey Bauer *(CFO)*
Steve Shapiro *(Partner-Venture)*
Bill Williams *(Partner-Venture)*
Ravinder Singh *(Controller)*
Michael R. Burcham *(Partner-Venture)*
Ken Davidson *(Partner-Venture)*
Zubeen P. Shroff *(Mng Dir)*
Judith E. Starkey *(Venture Partner)*

Subsidiaries:

Acura Pharmaceuticals, Inc.   (1)
616 N North Ct Ste 120, Palatine, IL
60067   (77%)
Tel.: (847) 705-7709
Web Site: https://www.acurapharm.com
Rev.: $3,570,000
Assets: $1,736,000
Liabilities: $7,627,000
Net Worth: ($5,891,000)
Earnings: ($1,208,000)
Emp.: 12
Fiscal Year-end: 12/31/2020
Abuse Deterrent Products Mfr
N.A.I.C.S.: 325412
Peter A. Clemens *(CFO, Sec & Sr VP)*
Robert A. Seiser *(Treas, VP & Controller)*
John G. Gilkay *(Dir-EHS & Engrg)*
Ronald L. Leech *(Sr Dir-Quality & Analytical Chemistry)*
Albert W. Brzeczko *(VP-Pharmaceutical Sciences)*

Subsidiary (Domestic):

Acura Pharmaceutical Technologies, Inc.   (2)
Andrew D Reddick Research & Development Ctr 16235 State Rd 17, Culver, IN
46511
Tel.: (574) 842-3305
Web Site: http://www.investors.acurapharm.com
Pharmaceuticals Product Mfr
N.A.I.C.S.: 325412

Consensys Imaging Service, Inc. (1)
1150 Catamount Dr, Golden, CO 80403
Tel.: (847) 462-2030
Web Site: http://www.unisynmedical.com
Sales Range: $25-49.9 Million
Emp.: 70
Medical Equipment Field Repair & Refurbishment Services
N.A.I.C.S.: 811210
Jim Spearman *(Pres)*
Derek Giulianelli *(Dir-Sls)*

GALENA ASSOCIATES, LLC
25 Main St 4th Fl, Hartford, CT
06106
Tel.: (860) 244-9310
Web Site: http://www.vioc.com
Sales Range: $125-149.9 Million
Emp.: 400
Oil Change Franchise Owner
N.A.I.C.S.: 811191
Andy Leiberman *(Dir-Mktg)*
Paul John Ferri *(Mgr)*

GALENFEHA, INC.
420 Throckmorton St Ste 200, Fort
Worth, TX 76102
Tel.: (817) 945-6448   NV
Web Site: http://www.galenfeha.com

Year Founded: 2013
Rev.: $3,335,330
Assets: $2,289,915
Liabilities: $2,313,408
Net Worth: ($23,493)
Earnings: $84,456
Fiscal Year-end: 12/31/18
Engineering Services For Energy
Producers
N.A.I.C.S.: 237990
LaNell Armour *(Treas & Sec)*

GALESBURG MANUFACTURING CO.
1835 Lacon Dr, Galesburg, IL 61401
Tel.: (309) 342-3173
Rev.: $11,500,000
Emp.: 4
Car Washing Machinery
N.A.I.C.S.: 333310
David Tukel *(Pres)*

GALESBURG NISSAN
2080 N Henderson St, Galesburg, IL
61401-4518
Tel.: (309) 342-4121
Web Site:
  https://www.galesburgcars.com
Year Founded: 1985
Sales Range: $10-24.9 Million
Emp.: 25
Car Whslr
N.A.I.C.S.: 441110
Jeffrey Klink *(Pres)*

GALESI GROUP
695 Rotterdam Indus Park,
Schenectady, NY 12306-1984
Tel.: (518) 356-4445   NY
Web Site: http://www.galesi.com
Year Founded: 1969
Real Estate Developers
N.A.I.C.S.: 531390
Thomas M. Owens *(Gen Counsel & VP)*

Subsidiaries:

Colonie Ventures, Inc.   (1)
PO Box 98, Guilderland Center, NY 12085-0098
Tel.: (518) 356-4445
Web Site: http://www.galesi.com
Sales Range: $10-24.9 Million
Emp.: 30
Owner & Operator of Nonresidential Building
N.A.I.C.S.: 531210
David M. Buicko *(Pres)*

Rotterdam Ventures Inc.   (1)
PO Box 98, Guilderland Center, NY 12085-0098
Tel.: (518) 356-4445
Web Site: http://www.galesi.com
Sales Range: $25-49.9 Million
Emp.: 100
General Warehousing & Storage; Logistics Management Real Property Lessors; Apartment Complexes & Condominium Development; Telecommunications
N.A.I.C.S.: 531120
David M. Buicko *(COO)*
Gerald J. Hennigan *(CFO)*

Subsidiary (Domestic):

Columbia Executive Associates   (2)
Guilderland Ctr, Guilderland Center, NY
12085-0098   (50%)
Tel.: (518) 356-4445
Sales Range: $25-49.9 Million
Office Building Development & Sales
N.A.I.C.S.: 531390

Distribution Unlimited, Inc.   (2)
695 Duanespurg, Rotterdam, NY
12306   (100%)
Tel.: (518) 356-4445
Sales Range: $10-24.9 Million
Emp.: 45
Contract Warehousing & Logistics Management

N.A.I.C.S.: 493110
David M Buicko *(COO)*
David Ahl *(VP)*

Galesi Group   (2)
Duanesburg Rd, Schenectady, NY 12306
Tel.: (518) 356-4445
Web Site: http://www.galesi.com
Sales Range: $25-49.9 Million
Emp.: 15
Apartment Building Operator
N.A.I.C.S.: 531110

Lake George Ventures Inc.   (2)
695 Rotterdam Industrial Pkwy,
Schenectady, NY 12306
Tel.: (518) 356-4445
Sales Range: $25-49.9 Million
Emp.: 1
Operative Builders
N.A.I.C.S.: 236116
David Buick *(Gen Mgr)*

Division (Domestic):

Rotterdam Industrial Park   (2)
PO Box 98, Guilderland Center, NY 12085-0098
Tel.: (518) 356-4445
Web Site: http://www.galesigroup.com
Sales Range: $25-49.9 Million
Emp.: 100
General Warehousing, Industrial & Office
Real Property Rental
N.A.I.C.S.: 531120
David M. Buicko *(COO)*

Subsidiary (Domestic):

Scotia Industrial Park, Inc.   (2)
695 Rotterdam Industrial Park,
Schenectady, NY 12306-0098   (100%)
Tel.: (518) 356-5175
Sales Range: $25-49.9 Million
Emp.: 15
General Warehousing & Industrial & Office
Real Property Rental
N.A.I.C.S.: 531120
David M. Buicko *(Pres)*

GALGON INDUSTRIES INC.
37399 Centralmont Pl, Fremont, CA
94536
Tel.: (510) 792-8211
Year Founded: 1967
Sales Range: $25-49.9 Million
Emp.: 420
Metal Tools Mfr
N.A.I.C.S.: 332721
Manfred K. Galgon *(Pres)*

GALI SERVICE INDUSTRIES, INC.
12312 Wilkins Ave, Rockville, MD
20852
Tel.: (301) 986-8890
Web Site: http://www.galiservice.com
Sales Range: $150-199.9 Million
Emp.: 1,000
Contract Management, Staffing, Employee Training & Consulting Services
N.A.I.C.S.: 541618
Francisco Gali *(Chm & CEO)*
Mark E. Terrenzi *(CFO)*
Eric L. Kelly *(Dir-Mktg)*

GALILEO GLOBAL ADVISORS, LLC
10 Rockefeller Plz Ste 1001, New
York, NY 10001
Tel.: (212) 332-6055   NY
Web Site:
  http://www.galileoglobaladvisor.com
Sales Range: $1-9.9 Million
Investment Banking & Advisory Services
N.A.I.C.S.: 523940
Georges Ugeux *(Chm & CEO)*
Francois Pages *(Mng Partner)*
Vicky Liao *(Sr VP)*
Katrina Panoutsopoulos *(CFO)*
Daniel Grasman *(Mng Dir)*

Jean-Claude Gruffat *(Mng Dir)*
Masazumi Nakayama *(Mng Dir)*
Thomas Fallows *(Mng Dir)*

Subsidiaries:

Galileo Global Securities, LLC   (1)
10 Rockefeller Plz Ste 1001, New York, NY
10020
Tel.: (212) 332-6055
Web Site:
  http://www.galileoglobalsecurities.com
Sales Range: $1-9.9 Million
Emp.: 3
Security Dealing & Brokerage Services
N.A.I.C.S.: 523150
Francois Pages *(Co-CEO & Mng Partner)*
Georges Ugeux *(Chm & Co-CEO)*
Thomas Fallows *(Mng Dir)*
Daniel Grasman *(Mng Dir)*
Jean-Claude Gruffat *(Mng Dir)*
Masazumi Nakayama *(Mng Dir)*
Katarina Panoutsopoulos *(CFO)*

GALIOT INSURANCE SERVICES, INC.
1700 Post Oak Blvd 2BLVD Pl Ste
600, Houston, TX 77056
Tel.: (713) 999-4849
Web Site:
  http://www.galiotinsurance.com
Insurance Agents
N.A.I.C.S.: 524298
Brian Toglia *(Pres & CEO)*

Subsidiaries:

Higginbotham Insurance Agency,
LLC   (1)
500 W 13th St, Fort Worth, TX 76102
Tel.: (817) 336-2377
Web Site: http://www.higginbotham.net
Insurance Brokerage, Risk Management &
Employee Benefits Services
N.A.I.C.S.: 524210
James Hubbard *(Mng Dir-Employee Benefits)*
James A. Krause *(CFO)*
Morgan Woodruff *(Mng Dir-Bus Insurance)*
Michael Parks *(Mng Dir & COO-Financial Svcs)*
Chris Rooker *(Mng Dir & COO-Bus Insurance)*
Mary Russell *(Mng Dir & Chief Admin Officer-Personal Insurance)*
Steve Addkison *(Mng Dir)*
Troy Ahrens *(Mng Dir)*
Blake Barnes *(Mng Dir)*
Christina MaGee *(Dir-Corp Comm)*
Drew Apperson *(Mng Dir)*
Jay Awtrey *(Mng Dir)*
Mike Bateman *(Mng Dir-Sls)*
William Blanchard *(Mng Dir)*
Matt Brand *(Mng Dir)*
Rob Causey *(Mng Dir)*
Edwin T. Coker *(Mng Dir)*
John Collins *(Mng Dir)*
Ryan Edgmon *(Mng Dir)*
Rob Fraiche *(Mng Dir)*
William Gammon *(Mng Dir)*
Matt Heinzelmann *(Mng Dir)*
John Huggins *(Mng Dir)*
Bart Johnson *(Mng Dir)*
Dana Jones *(Mng Dir)*
Vance Lee *(Mng Dir)*
Jason Littlejohn *(Mng Dir)*
Curtis Page *(Mng Dir)*
Brian Penny *(Mng Dir)*
Tami Rodgers *(Mng Dir)*
Dan Rybak *(Mng Dir)*
Mike Simon *(Mng Dir)*
Jeff Strahan *(Mng Dir)*
Trey Tollett *(Mng Dir)*
Mark Vann *(Mng Dir)*
Wayne Six *(Mng Dir)*
Randy Geving *(Mng Dir)*
Rusty Reid *(Chm & CEO)*
Matt Berry Sr. *(Mng Dir)*

Subsidiary (Domestic):

Americap Insurance Group, LLC   (2)
12720 Hillcrest Rd Ste 450, Dallas, TX
75230
Tel.: (800) 247-0712
Web Site: http://www.higginbotham.net
Insurance Related Activities

Galiot Insurance Services, Inc.—(Continued)
N.A.I.C.S.: 524298
Victor Malveaux *(Mng Dir-Benefit Svcs)*

Amerman Insurance Services, LLC (2)
14400 Northbrook Dr, San Antonio, TX 78232-5038
Tel.: (210) 298-6888
Web Site: http://www.amermaninsurance.com
Insurance Agencies & Brokerages
N.A.I.C.S.: 524210
Matt Amerman *(Owner)*

Brown & Co Insurance Services LP (2)
1825 Brothers Blvd, College Station, TX 77845-5413
Tel.: (979) 694-6900
Web Site: http://www.bcins.net
Insurance Agencies & Brokerages
N.A.I.C.S.: 524210
Bryan Brown *(VP)*

Capps Insurance Agency-Mt. Pleasant Ltd. (2)
1610 Shadywood Ln, Mount Pleasant, TX 75455
Tel.: (903) 572-4366
Web Site: http://www.higginbotham.net
Insurance Agents
N.A.I.C.S.: 524210

Cassidy & Company, LLC (2)
614 W Bay St, Tampa, FL 33609-1879
Tel.: (813) 877-7766
Web Site: https://www.cassidy-co.com
Sales Range: $1-9.9 Million
Emp.: 10
Wealth Management & Benefit Services
N.A.I.C.S.: 523940
William A. Cassidy *(Pres)*

Cress Insurance Consultants, Inc. (2)
6101 Moon St NE Ste 1000, Albuquerque, NM 87111
Tel.: (505) 822-8114
Web Site: http://www.cressinsurance.com
Sales Range: $1-9.9 Million
Emp.: 20
Insurance Agencies & Brokerages
N.A.I.C.S.: 524210
Tom Cress *(Pres)*
Cara Cress *(VP)*
Mark Maldonado *(Mgr-Mktg)*
Melissa Thompson *(Office Mgr)*
Pam Wilson *(CFO & Controller)*
Ray Strom *(COO)*

Eagan Insurance Agency, Inc. (2)
2629 N Causeway Blvd, Metairie, LA 70002
Tel.: (504) 836-5048
Web Site: http://www.eaganins.com
Emp.: 74
Insurance Agency & Brokerage Services
N.A.I.C.S.: 524210
Christopher F. Trapani *(Exec VP)*
Marc F. Eagan *(Pres)*
Chuck Strassel *(Exec VP & Mgr-Sls)*
Ed Duvernay *(Sr VP)*
Timothy R. Avegno *(VP)*
Rachel Foster *(Acct Exec)*
Erin Hurst *(Acct Exec)*
Joyce Shugg *(Mgr-Bus Dev)*
Ashley Lotz *(VP)*
Dooki Brooks *(Acct Exec)*
Jack Duvernay *(VP)*
Jordan D. Eagan *(VP)*
Julie Bell *(Acct Exec)*
Kristen Brunet *(Acct Exec)*
Lisa Forsythe *(Comptroller)*
Mandy Arnone *(Acct Exec)*
Tracy Cambre *(Mgr-Acctg)*
Wayne Roussel *(VP)*

Exploration Insurance Group, LLC (2)
100 Independence Way, Tyler, TX 75703-1310
Tel.: (903) 504-5405
Web Site: http://www.explorationig.com
Insurance Agencies
N.A.I.C.S.: 524210

Glenn Harris & Associates, Inc. (2)
7301 Broadway Ext Ste 200, Oklahoma City, OK 73116

Tel.: (405) 842-5385
Web Site: http://www.ghainsurance.com
Sales Range: $1-9.9 Million
Emp.: 20
Insurance Agencies & Brokerages
N.A.I.C.S.: 524210
Lona Evans *(Acct Mgr-Comml Lines)*
Jacquie Ford *(Acct Mgr-Comml Lines)*
Debra Hightower *(Acct Mgr-Comml Lines)*
Laura Mathes *(Acct Mgr-Comml Lines)*
Maryjo Miller *(Acct Mgr-Comml Lines)*
Dorothy Thomas *(Acct Mgr-Comml Lines)*
Tammie Hillian-Kates *(Acct Mgr-Personal Lines)*
Tonda Walters *(Acct Mgr-Personal Lines)*
Donna Smith *(Office Mgr)*

Higginbotham Insurance Group, Inc. (2)
500 W 13th St, Fort Worth, TX 76102
Web Site: http://www.higginbotham.net
Emp.: 100
Holding Company
N.A.I.C.S.: 551112
James Hubbard *(Mng Dir-Employee Benefits)*
James A. Krause *(CFO)*
Morgan Woodruff *(Mng Dir-Bus Insurance)*
James Reid *(Chm, Pres & CEO)*

Lipscomb & Pitts Insurance, LLC (2)
2670 Union Ave, Memphis, TN 38112
Tel.: (901) 321-1000
Web Site: http://www.lpinsurance.com
Sales Range: $200-249.9 Million
Emp.: 105
Insurance Agency & Brokerage Services
N.A.I.C.S.: 524210
Allison Carson *(Mgr-Comm)*
Andrew Bartolotta *(Mgr-Comm)*

Painter & Johnson Financial (2)
201 W Adams Ste 111, Brownwood, TX 76801
Tel.: (325) 646-2959
Web Site: http://www.painterandjohnson.com
Insurance & Financial Services
N.A.I.C.S.: 524210
Bart Johnson *(Pres & Principal)*
Blake Johnson *(VP-Sls & Client Svcs)*
Karen McQueary *(Chief Admin Officer-Sls & Client Svcs)*

Six & Geving Insurance, Inc. (2)
3630 Sinton Rd Ste 200, Colorado Springs, CO 80907-5077
Tel.: (719) 590-9990
Web Site: http://www.six-geving.com
Sales Range: $1-9.9 Million
Emp.: 46
Insurance Brokerage Services
N.A.I.C.S.: 524210
Randy Geving *(Co-Founder)*
Wayne Six *(Co-Founder)*
Joe Doyle *(VP)*

Stahl & Associates Insurance, Inc. (2)
110 Carillon Pkwy, Saint Petersburg, FL 33716
Tel.: (727) 391-9791
Web Site: http://www.stahlinsurance.com
Emp.: 130
Insurance Brokerage Services
N.A.I.C.S.: 524210
Robert L. Stahl *(Pres)*
Kelly Petzold *(Sr VP)*
Ken Williams *(Sr VP)*
Chuck Davies *(VP-Sls)*
Sandie Grimes *(VP)*
Jason Slack *(VP)*
Liz Antaya *(Acct Exec)*
Tony Martinez *(VP-Comml Lines Sls)*
Robert S. Bodolay *(VP-Employee Benefits)*

Subsidiary (Domestic):

Stahl & Associates Insurance (3)
3939 Tampa Rd, Oldsmar, FL 34677
Tel.: (813) 818-5300
Web Site: http://www.stal.com
Sales Range: $25-49.9 Million
Emp.: 20
Insurance Brokerage Services
N.A.I.C.S.: 524210
Candi O'Brien *(VP & Mgr-Branch)*
Patsy Penn *(Acct Mgr-Comml)*
Sandie Grimes *(VP-Sls)*

Stahl & Associates Insurance Inc. (3)
91 Lake Morton Dr, Lakeland, FL 33801
Tel.: (863) 688-5495
Web Site: http://www.stahlinsurance.com
Insurance Agents
N.A.I.C.S.: 524210

Stahl, Bowles & Associates, Inc. (3)
250 International Pkwy Ste 128, Lake Mary, FL 32746-5050
Tel.: (407) 833-8998
Web Site: http://www.stahlinsurance.com
Sales Range: $25-49.9 Million
Emp.: 4
Insurance Brokerage Services
N.A.I.C.S.: 524210
Robert Bowles *(Pres)*

Subsidiary (Domestic):

WRM Group, LLC (2)
1700 4th Ave, Jasper, AL 35501
Tel.: (205) 221-3621
Insurance Services
N.A.I.C.S.: 524298
W. Haig Wright II *(CEO)*

Subsidiary (Domestic):

Byars-Wright, Inc. (3)
1700 4th Ave S, Jasper, AL 35501
Tel.: (205) 221-3621
Web Site: https://www.byarswright.com
Sales Range: $1-9.9 Million
Emp.: 20
Insurance Agencies & Brokerages
N.A.I.C.S.: 524210
W. Haig Wright II *(CEO)*
Andy Byars *(VP)*
John Byars *(VP & Branch Mgr)*
Skip Roberts *(Sr VP)*
Gabe Clement *(Pres)*

Flowers Insurance Agency, LLC (3)
2501 W Main St Ste 500, Dothan, AL 36301
Tel.: (334) 794-8646
Web Site: http://www.flowersinsurance.com
Sales Range: $1-9.9 Million
Emp.: 13
Insurance Agencies & Brokerages
N.A.I.C.S.: 524210
Beth Granger *(Controller)*
Mike Worthington *(Branch Mgr)*
Shane Sinquefield *(Mng Partner)*

Pritchett-Moore, Inc. (3)
1120 Queen City Ave, Tuscaloosa, AL 35401
Tel.: (205) 758-4441
Web Site: http://www.pritchett-moore.com
Insurance & Real Estate
N.A.I.C.S.: 524210
Marlin Moore *(Chm)*
Gentry Williams *(Pres)*

GALLADE CHEMICAL INC.
1230 E St Gertrude Pl, Santa Ana, CA 92707-3030
Tel.: (714) 546-9901
Web Site: https://www.galladechem.com
Year Founded: 1964
Rev.: $42,000,000
Emp.: 70
Chemicals & Allied Products Mfr
N.A.I.C.S.: 424690
Rick Gallade *(Pres & CFO)*
Joni Harada *(Mgr-Acctg)*

GALLAGHER & BURK INC.
344 High St, Oakland, CA 94601
Tel.: (925) 829-9220
Web Site: https://www.gallagherburk.com
Year Founded: 1920
Rev.: $11,000,000
Emp.: 65
Excavation & Grading, Building Construction
N.A.I.C.S.: 237310
David DeSilva *(Pres)*

GALLAGHER & HENRY, INC.
6280 Joliet Rd, Countryside, IL 60525

Tel.: (708) 482-8900   IL
Web Site: https://www.gallagherandhenry.com
Year Founded: 1954
Sales Range: $10-24.9 Million
Emp.: 30
New Housing Construction
N.A.I.C.S.: 236115
John Gallagher *(Pres)*

GALLAGHER ASPHALT CORPORATION
18100 Indiana Ave, Thornton, IL 60476-1276
Tel.: (708) 877-7160   IL
Web Site: https://www.gallagherasphalt.com
Year Founded: 1927
Sales Range: $25-49.9 Million
Emp.: 175
Highway & Street Construction
N.A.I.C.S.: 237310
Mark Riester *(CFO)*
Pat Faster *(Dir-Natl Sls-Hot-in-Place Recycling Div)*
Paul Bulmann *(Superintendent-Construction)*

GALLAGHER FLUID SEALS INC.
500 Hertzog Blvd, King of Prussia, PA 19406
Tel.: (610) 277-8200
Web Site: https://www.gallagherseals.com
Year Founded: 1956
Sales Range: $10-24.9 Million
Emp.: 31
Fluid Seals Mfr
N.A.I.C.S.: 339991
John Kates *(Controller)*

Subsidiaries:

Johnson Packings & Industrial Products Inc. (1)
21 Deer Pk Dr, East Longmeadow, MA 01028
Tel.: (413) 525-5555
Web Site: http://www.johnsonpackings.com
Sales Range: $10-24.9 Million
Emp.: 25
Industrial Supplies
N.A.I.C.S.: 423840
Lorry Maznicky *(Controller)*
Joe Gallagher *(Pres)*

GALLAGHER TIRE INC.
1610 Hanford St, Levittown, PA 19057
Tel.: (215) 943-9911
Web Site: http://www.gallaghertire.com
Year Founded: 1968
Sales Range: $10-24.9 Million
Emp.: 60
Automobile Tires & Tubes Whslr
N.A.I.C.S.: 423130
John P. Gallagher *(Pres)*
Amanda Mendez *(Office Mgr)*

GALLAGHER-KAISER CORPORATION
777 Chicago Rd, Troy, MI 48083
Tel.: (313) 368-3100   MI
Web Site: https://www.gkcorp.com
Year Founded: 1952
Sales Range: $25-49.9 Million
Emp.: 125
Paint Finishing Systems & Equipment, Ventilation Systems, Dust Collection Equipment & Acoustical Panel Systems Mfr
N.A.I.C.S.: 332322
Joseph P. Kaiser *(VP)*
Robert S. Kaiser *(CEO)*
Tracy E. Roberts *(COO)*
Mark R. Dunn *(Exec VP-Sls)*

Subsidiaries:

Universal Piping Industries, LLC   (1)
12900 Capital St, Oak Park, MI 48237
Tel.: (248) 548-4900
Web Site: http://www.universalpiping.com
Sales Range: $1-9.9 Million
Mechanical Engineering Services
N.A.I.C.S.: 541330
Barbara Ann Libbrecht (Controller)
Joshua Henderson (Project Mgr)

GALLAHAN OIL COMPANY INC.

2916 N 100 N, Peru, IN 46970
Tel.: (765) 472-1963
Rev.: $15,000,000
Emp.: 90
Whslr of Petroleum Products
N.A.I.C.S.: 424720
Lance Gallahan (VP)
Kevin Gallahan (VP)

GALLAHER & ASSOCIATES, INC.

3351 Regal Dr, Alcoa, TN 37701
Tel.: (865) 970-2471
Web Site: http://www.gallaher-
    assoc.com
Year Founded: 1973
Rev.: $11,200,000
Emp.: 94
Electrical Contractor Services
N.A.I.C.S.: 238210
Roy T. Gallaher Jr. (CEO)
Roy T. Gallaher III (Pres)

GALLANT CAPITAL PART-NERS, LLC

1800 Ave of the Stars Ste 625, Los
Angeles, CA 90067
Tel.: (310) 362-3303   DE
Web Site:
    http://www.gallantcapital.com
Year Founded: 2018
Holding Company
N.A.I.C.S.: 551112
Jon Gimbel (Partner)

Subsidiaries:

Cassavant Machining, Inc.   (1)
3641 E La Salle St, Phoenix, AZ 85040
Tel.: (602) 437-4005
Web Site: http://www.cassmac.com
Sales Range: $1-9.9 Million
Emp.: 33
Commercial & Service Industry Machinery
Mfr
N.A.I.C.S.: 333310
Joe Cassavant (Gen Mgr)
Mike Nevitt (Mgr-Quality)

Subsidiary (Domestic):

Systems 3, Inc.   (2)
1515 W 17th St, Tempe, AZ 85281-6206
Tel.: (480) 894-2581
Web Site: http://www.systems3.net
Rev.: $2,700,000
Emp.: 40
Aircraft Parts & Auxiliary Equipment Mfr
N.A.I.C.S.: 336413
Craig Berland (Pres)
Bill Heisterberg (Mgr-Engrg)

Pro-Vac, LLC   (1)
2511 Inter Ave, Puyallup, WA 98372
Tel.: (888) 565-5665
Web Site: https://www.pro-vac.com
Environmental Services
N.A.I.C.S.: 237110

Subsidiary (Domestic):

Hydromax USA, LLC   (2)
3700 River Walk Dr Ste 145, Flower
Mound, TX 75028
Tel.: (812) 925-3930
Web Site: https://www.hydromaxusa.com
Water, Wadtewater & Natural Gas Convey-
ance Systems Data Collection & Assess-
ment Services
N.A.I.C.S.: 541990

Steve Lacy (CEO)

Subsidiary (Domestic):

Hydromax Plumbing, Inc.   (3)
2501 S Kentucky Ave, Evansville, IN 47714
Tel.: (812) 925-3930
Sales Range: $1-9.9 Million
Plumbing Services
N.A.I.C.S.: 238220
Nathan Bass (Mgr)

Quality Built, LLC   (1)
401 SE 12th St Ste 200, Fort Lauderdale,
FL 33316-1901
Tel.: (954) 358-3500
Web Site: http://www.qualitybuilt.com
Building Inspection Services
N.A.I.C.S.: 541350
Frank Ferrentino (Pres)
John Leonard (CFO)
Brendan Ong (COO)
Renee Leonard (Chief HR Officer)
Gregory F. Rzonca (CEO)
John Ballard (Chief Revenue Officer)

Subsidiary (Domestic):

DuctTesters, Inc.   (2)
615 13th St, Modesto, CA 95354
Tel.: (209) 579-5000
Web Site: http://www.ducttesters.com
Plumbing, Heating & Air-Conditioning Con-
tractors
N.A.I.C.S.: 238220
Dave Hegarty (Founder & CEO)

SMC Systems, Inc.   (2)
9570 Regency Square Blvd, Jacksonville,
FL 32225
Tel.: (904) 482-4260
Web Site: http://www.skyetec.com
Sales Range: $1-9.9 Million
Emp.: 80
Appliance Repair & Maintenance
N.A.I.C.S.: 811412
Christopher Uhland (CEO)

GALLATIN POINT CAPITAL LLC

660 Steamboat Rd First Fl, Green-
wich, CT 06830
Tel.: (203) 742-0200   DE
Web Site:
    http://www.gallatinpoint.com
Year Founded: 2017
Private Investment Firm
N.A.I.C.S.: 523999
Lewis A. Sachs (Co-Founder & Mng
Partner)
Matthew B. Botein (Co-Founder &
Mng Partner)

Subsidiaries:

First Investors Financial Services
Group, Inc.   (1)
5757 Woodway Dr Ste 400, Houston, TX
77057-2129
Tel.: (713) 977-2600
Web Site: http://www.fifsg.com
Emp.: 217
Automobile Financing Services
N.A.I.C.S.: 522291
Bennie H. Duck (CFO & Exec VP)
Blaise G. Rodon (Co-COO & Sr VP)
David L. Satterfield (Co-COO & Sr VP)
Thomas P. Redding (Sr VP & Dir-Risk
Mgmt)
Scott A. Fath (Sr VP & Dir-Fin)
Perry A. Sexton (CIO & Sr VP)
Tommy A. Moore Jr. (Founder, Pres & CEO)

GALLEGOS CORPORATION

100 Yacht Club Dr, Wolcott, CO
81655
Tel.: (970) 926-3737
Web Site:
    https://www.gallegoscorp.com
Sales Range: $25-49.9 Million
Emp.: 550
Masonry & Other Stonework
N.A.I.C.S.: 238140
Gary Woodworth (CEO)

GALLEGOS SANITATION, INC.

1941 Heath Pkwy Ste 2, Fort Collins,
CO 80524
Tel.: (970) 484-5556
Web Site:
    http://www.gallegossanitation.com
Year Founded: 1959
Sales Range: $10-24.9 Million
Emp.: 95
Solid Waste Landfill Services
N.A.I.C.S.: 562212
Arthur Gallegos (Co-Owner & VP)
Rudolph Gallegos (Co-Owner, Treas
& Sec)

GALLERY 63, INC.

4577 Roswell Rd, Atlanta, GA 30342
Tel.: (404) 252-2555
Web Site: http://www.gallery63.net
Sales Range: $10-24.9 Million
Emp.: 4
Antique Dealer
N.A.I.C.S.: 459510
Paul Brown (Owner)
Cindy Scott (Mgr)

GALLERY AUTOMOTIVE GROUP, LLC

918 920 Providence Hwy, Norwood,
MA 02062
Tel.: (781) 769-9600
Web Site:
    http://www.gallerygroup.com
Sales Range: $25-49.9 Million
Emp.: 25
Automobiles, New & Used
N.A.I.C.S.: 441110
Bill Frank (Mgr-Process)
Ken Dale (Dir-Fin)
Kevin Cuzzi (Mgr-Facilities)
Tsunoda Takashi-Bosmmsi (Pres)
Steve Martin (Mgr-Bus Dev)

GALLERY INDUSTRIES INC.

3001 S Ocean Dr Ste 1423, Holly-
wood, FL 33019
Tel.: (954) 929-8770
Web Site:
    http://www.galleryindustries.com
Year Founded: 1956
Sales Range: $25-49.9 Million
Emp.: 150
Women's & Children's Clothing
N.A.I.C.S.: 315250
Robert Alexander (CEO)

GALLERY MODEL HOMES, INC.

6006 N Fwy, Houston, TX 77076-
4029
Tel.: (713) 694-5570   TX
Web Site:
    https://www.galleryfurniture.com
Year Founded: 1981
Sales Range: $150-199.9 Million
Emp.: 300
Home Furnishings & Electronics Re-
tailer
N.A.I.C.S.: 449110
James McIngvale (Pres, CEO &
Founder)

GALLERY OF HISTORY, INC.

3601 W Sahara Ave Ste 207, Las
Vegas, NV 89102-5822
Tel.: (702) 364-1000   NV
Web Site:
    http://www.historyforsales.com
Year Founded: 1981
Sales Range: Less than $1 Million
Emp.: 7
Historical Memorabilia Marketer &
Auctions
N.A.I.C.S.: 459999
Todd M. Axelrod (Chm, Pres & CEO)

Subsidiaries:

Gallery of History Auctions, Inc.   (1)
3601 W Sahara Ave Ste 207, Las Vegas,
NV 89102-5822
Tel.: (702) 364-1000
Web Site: http://www.historyforsale.com
Live Auction House Services
N.A.I.C.S.: 459999
Todd M. Axelrod (CEO)

GALLES CHEVROLET

1601 Lomas Blvd NE, Albuquerque,
NM 87102-2710
Tel.: (505) 766-6800   NM
Web Site: http://www.galles.com
Year Founded: 1932
Sales Range: $125-149.9 Million
Emp.: 210
Car Dealership
N.A.I.C.S.: 441110
Larry Altergott (Mgr-Parts Dept)

GALLES CHEVROLET COM-PANY

1601 Lomas Blvd NE, Albuquerque,
NM 87102
Tel.: (505) 766-6800
Web Site:
    http://www.galleschevy.com
Year Founded: 1940
Sales Range: $50-74.9 Million
Emp.: 210
Car Whslr
N.A.I.C.S.: 441110
Jamie Galles (Gen Mgr)

GALLIKER DAIRY COMPANY INC.

143 Donald Ln, Johnstown, PA
15907-0159
Tel.: (814) 266-8702   PA
Web Site: https://www.gallikers.com
Year Founded: 1914
Sales Range: $25-49.9 Million
Emp.: 300
Wholesale Distributors of Dairy Prod-
ucts
N.A.I.C.S.: 311511
Louis G. Galliker (Chm)
George Pisula (VP-Ops)

GALLIOT ACQUISITION CORP.

4 Embarcadero Ctr Ste 2100, San
Francisco, CA 94111
Tel.: (415) 780-9975   DE
Year Founded: 2021
Investment Services
N.A.I.C.S.: 523999
Rufina A. Adams (CFO & Sec)
James H. Greene Jr. (Chm & CEO)

GALLO CORPORATION

3850 N Causeway Blvd Ste 1300,
Metairie, LA 70002
Tel.: (504) 944-6736
Rev.: $26,354,573
Emp.: 26
Mechanical Contractor
N.A.I.C.S.: 238220
David Gallo (Pres)
August R. Gallo Jr. (CEO)

Subsidiaries:

Gallo Mechanical Contractors   (1)
3850 N Cswy Blvd Ste 1300 Metairie, New
Orleans, LA 70002
Tel.: (504) 944-6736
Web Site: http://www.gallomech.com
Mechanical Contractor
N.A.I.C.S.: 238220
David R. Gallo (Pres)

GALLO EQUIPMENT CO.

11835 S Avenue O, Chicago, IL
60617

Gallo Equipment Co.—(Continued)

Tel.: (773) 374-5515
Web Site:
   https://www.galloequipment.com
Year Founded: 1969
Sales Range: $10-24.9 Million
Emp.: 54
Lift Trucks & Parts
N.A.I.C.S.: 423830
Christyne Cacich (Mgr-HR Ops)

GALLO MOTOR CENTER CORP.
70 Goldstar Blvd, Worcester, MA 01606
Tel.: (508) 791-3678
Web Site: http://www.gallocars.com
Rev.: $34,200,000
Emp.: 36
Automobiles, New & Used
N.A.I.C.S.: 441110
Nick Gallo (Pres)
David Patrick (Pres)

GALLO WINE SALES OF NJ INC.
520 Division St, Elizabeth, NJ 07201
Tel.: (908) 289-8000
Rev.: $68,600,000
Emp.: 150
Wine Distr
N.A.I.C.S.: 424820
Cindy Stevens (Coord-On-Sale)

GALLOWAY FAMILY OF DEALERSHIPS
1800 Boy Scout Dr, Fort Myers, FL 33907-2113
Tel.: (239) 936-3673   **FL**
Web Site:
   http://www.gallowayfamily.com
Year Founded: 1927
Sales Range: $200-249.9 Million
Emp.: 370
Automobile Dealership Services
N.A.I.C.S.: 441110
Sam M. Galloway Jr. (Pres)

GALLOWAY RIDGE, INC.
3000 Galloway Rdg, Pittsboro, NC 27312
Tel.: (919) 545-2215   **NC**
Web Site:
   https://www.gallowayridge.com
Year Founded: 2001
Sales Range: $10-24.9 Million
Emp.: 415
Continuing Care Retirement Facility Operator
N.A.I.C.S.: 623311

GALLUP LUMBER & SUPPLY
1724 S 2nd, Gallup, NM 87301
Tel.: (505) 863-4475
Year Founded: 1939
Sales Range: $10-24.9 Million
Emp.: 62
Lumber & Building Material Whslr
N.A.I.C.S.: 444110
Gordon McGehee (Principal)

GALPIN FORD INCORPORATED
1000 Sandretto Dr, Prescott, AZ 86305
Tel.: (928) 445-3673   **AZ**
Web Site:
   http://www.galpinfordinc.com
Sales Range: $650-699.9 Million
Emp.: 65
New & Used Car Dealers
N.A.I.C.S.: 441110
Gregory Galpin (Pres)

GALPIN MOTORS, INC.

15505 Roscoe Blvd, North Hills, CA 91343-6503
Tel.: (818) 787-3800   **CA**
Web Site: http://www.gogalpin.com
Year Founded: 1946
Sales Range: $500-549.9 Million
Emp.: 1,000
Retail Sales, Lease, Rental & Service of New & Used Motor Vehicles
N.A.I.C.S.: 441110
Bert Boeckmann (Pres)

GALT FOUNDATION
2405 Front St NE Ste 220, Salem, OR 97301
Tel.: (503) 361-1277   **OR**
Web Site:
   https://www.galtfoundation.org
Year Founded: 1998
Sales Range: $10-24.9 Million
Emp.: 20
Disability Assistance Services
N.A.I.C.S.: 624120
Stephen Mock (Dir-Mktg & Dev)
Tricia Miller (Dir-Staffing)

GALT PETROLEUM, INC.
175 S Main St 15th Fl, Salt Lake City, UT 84111
Tel.: (801) 719-7258   **NV**
Sales Range: Less than $1 Million
Oil & Gas Exploration
N.A.I.C.S.: 211120
Cary Valerio (Pres, CEO, CFO, Treas & Sec)
Mark Baca (Chm & Principal Acctg Officer)

GALVANEK & WAHL LLC
842 New Charleston Dr, Fuquay Varina, NC 27526
Tel.: (908) 722-3534
Web Site:
   http://www.gwadagency.com
Year Founded: 2003
Sales Range: Less than $1 Million
Emp.: 5
N.A.I.C.S.: 541810
Paxton Galvanek (CEO & Partner)

GALYPSO INTERNATIONAL
231 Gazelle Leap, San Antonio, TX 78258-4881
Tel.: (210) 499-5100
Year Founded: 1999
Sales Range: $1-9.9 Million
Emp.: 5
International Procurement, Sourcing & Vendor Development Services to Customers in Integrated Beverage Markets
N.A.I.C.S.: 424820
Joaquin Galan (CEO & VP-Sls)
Crystin McCormick (Owner & Gen Mgr)

GAMBOAS BODY & FRAME INC.
1101 N D St, Sacramento, CA 95814
Tel.: (916) 448-9721
Web Site: http://www.gamboas.com
Sales Range: $10-24.9 Million
Emp.: 20
Body Shop, Automotive
N.A.I.C.S.: 811121
Lee Gamboa (VP & Gen Mgr)
Rick Caron (Gen Mgr)

GAME PLAN HOLDINGS, INC.
112 Water St Ste 500, Boston, MA 02110
Tel.: (617) 512-4453   **NV**
Web Site: http://www.hazzsports.com
Sales Range: Less than $1 Million
Emp.: 5

Sports-Related Social Networking Website
N.A.I.C.S.: 551112
Alexander Karsos (CFO & Sec)
Brett Maloley (Chief Sls Officer)

GAME SOURCE, INC.
446 Towne Ave, Los Angeles, CA 90013
Tel.: (213) 683-9700
Web Site:
   http://www.gamesourceinc.com
Year Founded: 1997
Rev.: $29,300,000
Emp.: 40
Toy, Hobby Goods & Supplies Merchant Whslr
N.A.I.C.S.: 423920
Rohollah Ahdoot (Founder & Pres)
Prescy Morales (Mgr-Sls-North America)

GAMEBASE, INC.
14901 Bogle Dr 2nd Fl, Chantilly, VA 20151
Tel.: (703) 817-0567
Online Entertainment Services
N.A.I.C.S.: 517810

Subsidiaries:

Sandbox.com, Inc.   **(1)**
247 Route 100 Ste 2004, Somers, NY 10589
Tel.: (914) 232-1239
Sales Range: $10-24.9 Million
Emp.: 15
Online Gambling Services
N.A.I.C.S.: 517810

GAMECHANGER PRODUCTS LLC
2207 Harbor Bay Pkwy, Alameda, CA 94502
Tel.: (510) 521-7985
Web Site:
   https://www.gamechanger.net
Year Founded: 2007
Sales Range: $1-9.9 Million
Emp.: 24
Innovation & Growth Consulting Services
N.A.I.C.S.: 541618
Larry Popelka (CEO)
Sandy Brawley (Pres)

GAMEFLY, INC.
5340 Alla Rd Ste 110, Los Angeles, CA 90066
Tel.: (310) 664-6400   **DE**
Web Site: http://www.gamefly.com
Year Founded: 2002
Sales Range: $75-99.9 Million
Emp.: 186
Computer Game Rental Services
N.A.I.C.S.: 532282
David Hodess (Chm, Pres & CEO)
Sean Spector (Sr VP-Bus Dev & Content)
Scott Paterra (VP-Adv Sls)
Stacey Peterson (CFO & Sr VP)
Nilesh Seth (Sr VP-Product Dev & Tech)
Michael Gimlett (Sr VP-Mdsg & Logistics)
Terri Luke (Sr VP-Ops)
Rachel Silverstein (VP-Mktg)

GAMEPLAN FINANCIAL MARKETING, LLC
300 ParkBrooke Pl Ste 200, Woodstock, GA 30189
Tel.: (770) 517-2765
Web Site:
   http://www.gameplanfinancial.com
Sales Range: $25-49.9 Million
Emp.: 60

Insurance Brokers & Financial Marketing Services
N.A.I.C.S.: 524210
Greg Addison (Mgr-Fin)

GAMEWOOD TECHNOLOGY GROUP, INC.
165 Deer Run Rd, Danville, VA 24540
Tel.: (434) 799-8407   **VA**
Web Site: http://www.gamewood.net
Sales Range: $10-24.9 Million
Telecommunication Servicesb
N.A.I.C.S.: 517121
Bill Moore (Assoc Dir)
Cathy Taylor (Dir-Admin)
David Willette (Mgr-Technical Svcs)
Ed Wilborne (CIO)
Gary Ashburn (Mgr-Project)
Robert Taylor (CEO)
Webb Maddux (Mgr)

GAMING ENTERTAINMENT INTERNATIONAL, INC.
11700 W Charleston Blvd Ave 170, Las Vegas, NV 89135
Tel.: (702) 755-3745   **NV**
Web Site: http://www.gamingei.com
Sales Range: Less than $1 Million
Gambling Operations
N.A.I.C.S.: 713290
Sylvain Desrosiers (Pres & CEO)
William W. Noll (CFO & Treas)

GAMING LABORATORIES INTERNATIONAL LLC
600 Airport Rd, Lakewood, NJ 08701
Tel.: (732) 942-3999
Web Site:
   https://www.gaminglabs.com
Year Founded: 1989
Gaming Assessment, Testing & Certification Services
N.A.I.C.S.: 713290
James Maida (Pres & CEO)
Pierre Otto (Gen Mgr-South Africa)
Devon Dalbock (COO-Europe, Middle East & Africa)
Christie Eickelman (VP-Global Mktg)

Subsidiaries:

Public Knowledge, LLC   **(1)**
1911 SW Campus Dr Ste 457, Federal Way, WA 98023-6473
Tel.: (253) 231-1725
Web Site: http://www.pubknow.com
General Management Consulting Services
N.A.I.C.S.: 541611
Ken Disbrow (Partner)
Kristin Sparks (CFO)

SeNet International Corporation   **(1)**
3040 Williams Dr Ste 510, Fairfax, VA 22031
Tel.: (703) 206-9383
Data Processing, Hosting & Related Services
N.A.I.C.S.: 518210
Toly Kozushin (Co-Founder & Pres)

GAMMA CONSTRUCTION COMPANY INC.
2808 Joanel St, Houston, TX 77027-5306
Tel.: (303) 394-4892   **TX**
Web Site:
   http://www.gammaconst.com
Year Founded: 1985
Sales Range: $10-24.9 Million
Emp.: 120
Nonresidential Construction Services
N.A.I.C.S.: 236220
Keith Williams (Pres & CEO)

GAMMA SPORTS
200 Waterfront Dr, Pittsburgh, PA 15222

Tel.: (412) 323-0335
Web Site:
https://www.gammasports.com
Rev.: $14,731,541
Emp.: 40
Tennis Equipment & Supplies
N.A.I.C.S.: 339920
Douglasse Sieber (Mgr)

GAMMEX RMI INC.
7600 Discovery Dr, Middleton, WI
53562-2610
Tel.: (608) 828-7000
Web Site: http://www.gammex.com
Year Founded: 1969
Sales Range: $75-99.9 Million
Emp.: 60
Mfr of Laser Positioning Equipment &
Quality Assurance Products
N.A.I.C.S.: 334519
Pamela Durden (Coord-Adv & Show)
Jim Mailander (VP)

Subsidiaries:

Gammex RMI GmbH   (1)
Frankfurt Str 15, Giessen, 35390, Hessen,
Germany   (100%)
Tel.: (49) 2257823
Web Site: http://www.gammex.com
Laser Positioning Equipment
N.A.I.C.S.: 334510

Gammex RMI Limited   (1)
Broadway Business Centre, 32A Stoney
Street, Nottingham, NG1 1LL, United
Kingdom   (100%)
Tel.: (44) 1159247188
Web Site: http://www.gammex.com
Laser Positioning Equipment
N.A.I.C.S.: 334510
Ron Carney (Pres)

**GAMMON EQUIPMENT COM-
PANY INC.**
2918 E Blaine St, Springfield, MO
65803
Tel.: (417) 866-3528
Web Site: http://www.gammoneq.com
Sales Range: $10-24.9 Million
Emp.: 97
Industrial Machinery & Equipment
N.A.I.C.S.: 423830
Greg Gammon (Pres)
Tommy Buterbaugh (Controller)

**GAMUT CAPITAL MANAGE-
MENT, L.P.**
250 W 55th St 36th Fl, New York, NY
10019
Tel.: (212) 309-2600   DE
Web Site:
http://www.gamutcapital.com
Privater Equity Firm
N.A.I.C.S.: 523999
Stan Parker (Partner)
Jordan Zaken (Partner)

Subsidiaries:

Grede Holdings LLC   (1)
20750 Civic Ctr Dr Ste 100, Southfield, MI
48076
Tel.: (313) 758-2000
Web Site: http://www.grede.com
Holding Company; Cast, Forged & Ma-
chined Iron & Other Metal Components De-
signer, Developer & Mfr
N.A.I.C.S.: 551112
Marlo Cockroft (Mgr-Fin Svcs)
Michael Meyer (Gen Mgr)

Subsidiary (Domestic):

Advanced Cast Products, Inc.   (2)
18700 Mill St, Meadville, PA 16335
Tel.: (814) 724-2600
Web Site: http://www.advancedcast.com
Sales Range: $25-49.9 Million
Emp.: 150
Ductile Iron Foundry
N.A.I.C.S.: 331511

Carolyn Harned (Controller)
Roxie Fucci (Coord-AP)

Subsidiary (Non-US):

Novocast, S. de R.L. de C.V.   (2)
Carretera Monterry - Monclova 12 Int 0 S C
Localidad economica, El Carmen, Monter-
rey, NL, Mexico
Tel.: (52) 81 8288 5800
Iron Foundry; Iron Castings
N.A.I.C.S.: 331511

GAMZIO MOBILE INC.
123 W Nye Ln Ste 129, Carson City,
NV 89706
Tel.: (415) 839-1055   NV
Year Founded: 2007
Social Casino Gaming Services
N.A.I.C.S.: 513210
Monika Sagar (CFO & Sec)
Andrew Strauss (CTO)
Jason Deiboldt (Pres)

GAN CORPORATION
11247 S Memorial Pkwy, Huntsville,
AL 35803
Tel.: (256) 489-2471   AL
Web Site: http://www.gancorp.com
Year Founded: 2004
Sales Range: $1-9.9 Million
Emp.: 53
Engineeering Services
N.A.I.C.S.: 541330
Jonn Kim (Pres & CEO)
Tonya Sitko (Mgr-Bus Dev)
Myles Hathcock (Engr-Software)
Nate Grinstead (Engr-Aerospace)

GANAHL LUMBER COMPANY
1220 E Ball Rd, Anaheim, CA 92805-
5921
Tel.: (714) 772-5444   CA
Web Site:
https://www.ganahllumber.com
Year Founded: 1884
Sales Range: $200-249.9 Million
Emp.: 680
Retailer of Lumber, Building Materials
& Hardware
N.A.I.C.S.: 423310
Peter Ganahl (Mgr-Store-Los Alami-
tos)
Alex Uniack (Mgr-Store-Laguna
Beach)
Barrett Burt (Mgr-Site-Pasadena)
Chad Kidder (Mgr-Store-Los Alami-
tos)

**GANDARA MENTAL HEALTH
CENTER, INC.**
147 Norman St, West Springfield, MA
01089
Tel.: (413) 736-8329   MA
Web Site:
http://www.gandaracenter.org
Year Founded: 1977
Sales Range: $10-24.9 Million
Emp.: 678
Mental Health Assistance Services
N.A.I.C.S.: 623220
Henry J. East-Trou (Exec Dir)
Sterling Hall (Treas)
Vanessa Martinez (VP)

**GANDER MOUNTAIN COM-
PANY**
180 E 5th St Ste 1300, Saint Paul,
MN 55101-1664
Tel.: (651) 325-4300   MN
Web Site:
http://www.gandermountain.com
Year Founded: 1960
Sales Range: $5-14.9 Billion
Emp.: 2,325
Retailer of Hunting, Fishing, Boating
& Camping Equipment
N.A.I.C.S.: 459110

David C. Pratt (Chm & CEO)
Kerry D. Graskewicz (Sr VP-Inventory
Mgmt)
Jay Tibbets (COO & Exec VP)
Derek Siddons (Pres)
Lisa Schmidt (Exec VP-Store Ops,
Store Design & Dev)
Brian D. Kohlbeck (CFO & Sr VP)
Carissa Rollins (CIO & Sr VP)
Jeff Csuy (Sr VP-Softlines Mdsg &
Product Dev)
Ron Stoupa (Sr VP-Mktg & ECom-
merce)
Carissa L. Rollins (CIO, Exec VP-HR
& Sr VP)
Eric R. Jacobsen (Chief Admin Offi-
cer, Gen Counsel & Exec VP)

Subsidiaries:

Overton's Inc.   (1)
111 Red Bank Rd, Greenville, NC 27858
Tel.: (252) 355-7600
Web Site: http://www.overtons.com
Sales Range: $75-99.9 Million
Emp.: 255
Boating & Water Sports Equipment Retailer
N.A.I.C.S.: 459110
John Daigle (Pres)

GANDER, INC.
2801 W Coast Hwy Ste 260, Newport
Beach, CA 92663
Tel.: (949) 574-7600
Web Site:
http://www.crowsnestyachts.com
Sales Range: $10-24.9 Million
Emp.: 32
Boat Dealers
N.A.I.C.S.: 441222
Anthony Shieh (CEO)
John Lee (CFO)
Joel Swan (Parker Product Mgr)
Jeff Hall (Mktg Mgr)
Rod Halperin (Dir-Bus Dev)

GANDY COMPANY
815 Rice Lake St, Owatonna, MN
55060-0528
Tel.: (507) 451-5430
Web Site: https://www.gandy.net
Year Founded: 1936
Sales Range: $50-74.9 Million
Emp.: 25
Granular Chemical Applicators, Fertil-
izer Spreaders & Air Seeders Mfr
N.A.I.C.S.: 333111
Dale E. Gandrud (Pres)
Randy Vargason (Mgr-Sls & Mktg)

GANGLOFF INDUSTRIES, INC.
1041 W County Rd 250 S, Logan-
sport, IN 46947
Tel.: (574) 722-3888
Year Founded: 1992
Sales Range: $10-24.9 Million
Emp.: 25
General Freight Services
N.A.I.C.S.: 484121
Randy Ferguson (CEO)
Mark A. Gangloff (Treas & Sec)

**GANLEY CHRYSLER JEEP
DODGE RAM, INC.**
310 Broadway Ave, Bedford, OH
44146-2131
Tel.: (440) 232-2121
Web Site:
https://www.ganleychryslerjeep
dodge.com
Sales Range: $25-49.9 Million
Emp.: 35
New & Used Car Dealership
N.A.I.C.S.: 441110
Rick Heller (Gen Mgr)
John Livingston (Mgr-Gen Sls & Fin)
Jay Hoegler (Mgr-Used Car Sls)

Bob Wittig (Mgr-Parts)
Johnny Sestan (Mgr-Sls)
Paul Cunningham III (Mgr-Internet
Sls)

GANLEY EAST INC.
28840 Euclid Ave, Wickliffe, OH
44092
Tel.: (440) 585-1000
Web Site:
http://www.ganleyeastsubaru.com
Sales Range: $10-24.9 Million
Emp.: 50
Car Whslr
N.A.I.C.S.: 441110
Kenneth Ganley (Pres)
Chris Johnson (Gen Mgr)

**GANS INK & SUPPLY COM-
PANY, INC.**
1441 Boyd St, Los Angeles, CA
90033-3714
Tel.: (323) 264-2200   CA
Web Site: https://www.gansink.com
Year Founded: 1950
Sales Range: $100-124.9 Million
Emp.: 220
Printing Inks Mfr
N.A.I.C.S.: 325910
Jeff Koppelman (Pres)

GANT USA CORPORATION
20 W 55th St 11th Fl, New York, NY
10019
Tel.: (212) 230-1949
Web Site: http://www.gant.com
Rev.: $10,000,000
Emp.: 10
Men's & Boys' Clothing Stores
N.A.I.C.S.: 458110
Ari Hoffman (CEO)
Spencer Singer (Dir-Wholesale)
Teddy Schwartz (Mgr-Mdsg)
Cecilia Saggio (Office Mgr)
Liz Wong (Mgr-E-Commerce)
Rene Martinez (Mgr-Store)
David Arbuthnot (CEO)
Robert Mocase (Mgr-Retail-Natl)

GANTRADE CORPORATION
210 Summit Ave, Montvale, NJ
07645-1526
Tel.: (201) 573-1955   NY
Web Site: https://www.gantrade.com
Sales Range: $800-899.9 Million
Emp.: 2,000
Distr of Organic Industrial Chemicals
N.A.I.C.S.: 424690
Aaron Parekh (VP)
Mehendra Parekh (Pres & CEO)

Subsidiaries:

Gantrade Europe, Ltd.   (1)
Birch House Fairfield Avenue, Staines-
upon-Thames, TW18 4AB, Middlesex,
United Kingdom
Tel.: (44) 1279 755 775
Emp.: 10
Organic Chemical Distr
N.A.I.C.S.: 424690
Paul Fitzgerald (Mgr-Supply Chain)

GAP INTELLIGENCE
2448 Historic Decatur Rd Ste 105,
San Diego, CA 92106
Tel.: (619) 574-1100
Web Site:
http://www.gapintelligence.com
Year Founded: 2003
Sales Range: $1-9.9 Million
Emp.: 30
Market & Customer Research & Ana-
lytic Services
N.A.I.C.S.: 541613

Gap Intelligence—(Continued)

Gary Peterson *(Founder, Pres & CEO)*
Chris Barnes *(VP)*
Tom Young *(Dir-Bus Dev)*

GAP ROOFING INC.
4444 Hunt St MAIP, Pryor, OK 74361
Tel.: (918) 825-5200
Web Site: http://www.gaproofing.com
Rev.: $21,877,280
Emp.: 100
Roofing Felts, Cements, or Coatings
N.A.I.C.S.: 324122
Barbara Chupp *(CFO)*
Glen Passmore Jr. *(Pres)*

GARAGE ISLA VERDE, INC.
RR Ste 1, Carolina, PR 00979
Tel.: (787) 791-1313
Web Site:
http://www.garageislaverde.com
Sales Range: $50-74.9 Million
Emp.: 122
Car Whslr
N.A.I.C.S.: 441110
Carlos Quinones *(Pres)*

GARAGE MANAGEMENT CORPORATION CO
770 Lexington Ste 1102, New York, NY 10065
Tel.: (212) 888-7400
Web Site:
http://www.gmcparking.com
Rev.: $14,800,000
Emp.: 30
Parking Garage
N.A.I.C.S.: 812930
Richard Chapman *(Pres)*

GARAGETEK INC.
5 Aerial Way Ste 200, Syosset, NY 11791
Tel.: (516) 621-4300
Web Site: http://www.garagetek.com
Year Founded: 2000
Sales Range: $10-24.9 Million
Emp.: 13
Garage Organization & Storage System
N.A.I.C.S.: 533110
Marc Shuman *(Pres)*
Nick Paglino *(Gen Mgr)*
John Maxworthy *(Dir-Engrg)*

GARBAGEMAN CO
13895 Industrial Park Blvd Ste 100, Plymouth, MN 55441
Tel.: (763) 269-8182
Web Site:
http://www.garbagemanco.com
Year Founded: 2007
Sales Range: $1-9.9 Million
Emp.: 20
Garbage Collection Services
N.A.I.C.S.: 562111
Andrew Sorensen *(Pres & CEO)*
Steve Marik *(VP-Sls)*
James Marik *(Dir-Corp Ops)*
Jonathon Huber *(Dir-Field Ops)*

GARBER & GOODMAN ADVERTISING, INC.
300 W 41st St Ste 214, Miami Beach, FL 33140-3627
Tel.: (305) 673-5177 FL
Year Founded: 1963
Sales Range: $10-24.9 Million
Emp.: 13
Financial, Full Service, Industrial, Public Relations, Real Estate, Travel & Tourism
N.A.I.C.S.: 541810
Robert Goodman *(Pres & Acct Supvr)*
Diane Goodman *(Office Mgr)*

GARBER BROS INC.
Rte 139 at Kayway, Stoughton, MA 02072
Tel.: (781) 341-0800 MA
Web Site: http://www.garberbros.com
Year Founded: 1947
Sales Range: $25-49.9 Million
Emp.: 220
Convenience Shop Owner & Operator
N.A.I.C.S.: 424940
Debra Law *(Mgr-Customer Svc)*
Michael Piscione *(Mgr-Food Svc)*
John Poulakis *(VP-Sls)*
Jim Young *(Mgr-Plng & Analysis)*

GARBER BUICK GMC
5255 S US Hwy 1, Fort Pierce, FL 34982
Tel.: (772) 467-0835
Web Site:
http://www.garberbuickgmc.com
Emp.: 50
Car Whslr
N.A.I.C.S.: 441110
Eric Delee *(Sls Mgr-New Car)*
James Negvesky *(Sls Mgr-Used Car)*
James Pena *(Mgr-Internet)*
Michael Mantovi *(Mgr-Factory Trained Svc)*
Jude Forte *(Asst Mgr-Factory Trained Svc)*
Tom Camlet *(Asst Mgr-Factory Trained Svc)*
Jason Senk *(Mgr-Parts)*
Justin Hardison *(Fin Mgr)*
Mario Triana *(Mgr-Body Shop)*
Ralph Lenoci *(Gen Mgr)*

GARBER ELECTRICAL CONTRACTORS INC.
100 Rockridge Rd, Englewood, OH 45322
Tel.: (937) 771-5202
Web Site:
http://www.garberelectric.com
Electrical Contractor
N.A.I.C.S.: 238210
Marcus Brubaker *(Pres)*

Subsidiaries:

Miller Adams Electric Inc. (1)
819 Factory Rd Ste 1, Beavercreek, OH 45434
Tel.: (937) 427-0201
Web Site: http://www.garberelectric.com
Electrical Contractor
N.A.I.C.S.: 238210
Crystal Phillips *(Mgr-HR)*

GARBER FARMS
3405 Descannes Hwy, Iota, LA 70543-3118
Tel.: (337) 824-6328
Year Founded: 1978
Sales Range: $10-24.9 Million
Emp.: 20
Production of Rice, Soybeans & Sweet Potato
N.A.I.C.S.: 111160
Wayne T. Garber *(Pres & Partner)*

GARBER MANAGEMENT GROUP INC.
999 S Washington, Saginaw, MI 48601
Tel.: (989) 790-9090 MI
Web Site: http://www.garberauto.com
Year Founded: 1907
Sales Range: $250-299.9 Million
Emp.: 1,200
Car Dealership Owner & Operator
N.A.I.C.S.: 441110
Patrick Hengesbach *(COO)*
Richard J. Garber Jr. *(Owner & Pres)*

Subsidiaries:

Garber Buick Company Inc. (1)
5925 State St, Saginaw, MI 48603
Tel.: (989) 497-4444
Web Site: http://www.garberbuick.com
Sales Range: $25-49.9 Million
Emp.: 100
Dealer of New & Used Cars
N.A.I.C.S.: 441120
Chad Forster *(Mgr-Used Car)*
Ed Schneller *(Mgr-Parts)*
Rich Perdue *(Gen Mgr)*
Mike Weinert *(Gen Mgr)*
Ashley Revard *(Office Mgr)*
Richard J. Garber Jr. *(Owner & Pres)*

Garber Chevrolet Inc. (1)
1700 N Saginaw Rd, Midland, MI 48640-2652
Tel.: (989) 839-9944
Web Site: http://www.garberchevrolet.com
Sales Range: $25-49.9 Million
Emp.: 60
Dealer of New & Used Cars
N.A.I.C.S.: 441110
Toni Hubbard *(Mgr-Parts)*
Craig Lang *(Gen Mgr)*
Darin Crook *(Mgr-Body Shop)*
Jim McCrum *(Mgr-Svc)*
Brent Blanck *(Mgr-Used Car Fin)*
Juan Bush *(Mgr-Used Car Sls)*
Laura Fortino *(Asst Mgr-Body Shop)*
Kevin Humerickhouse *(Mgr-New Car Sls)*
Brian Strong *(Mgr-Fleet & Comml Sls)*

Garber Ford Mercury Inc. (1)
3380 Hwy 17, Green Cove Springs, FL 32043 (100%)
Tel.: (904) 284-3023
Web Site: http://www.garberautomall.com
Sales Range: $25-49.9 Million
Emp.: 100
Dealer of New & Used Cars
N.A.I.C.S.: 441227
Ronald Harris *(Mng Partner)*
Paul Bobo *(Dir-Svc)*
Pat Brewer *(Office Mgr)*
John Butt *(Mgr-Sls)*
Mike Fitzgerald *(Mgr-Body Shop)*
Mike Marcolini *(Mgr-Fin)*
Jerry Smith *(Mgr-Sls)*
Mike Weinert *(Gen Mgr-Sls)*

Garber Nissan Inc. (1)
5450 Bay Rd, Saginaw, MI 48604-2514
Tel.: (989) 790-0120
Web Site: http://www.garberbayroad.com
Sales Range: $10-24.9 Million
Emp.: 25
Dealer of New & Used Card
N.A.I.C.S.: 441110
Richard J. Garber Jr. *(Pres)*

Sunrise Chevrolet (1)
14640 Cicero Ave, Midlothian, IL 60445-2557
Tel.: (708) 389-0600
Web Site: http://www.sunrisechevy.com
Sales Range: $50-74.9 Million
Emp.: 158
Used & New Automobiles Retailer
N.A.I.C.S.: 441110
Dan Kurtz *(Gen Mgr)*

GARCIA & ORTIZ, PA
888 Executive Center Dr W Ste 101, Saint Petersburg, FL 33702
Tel.: (727) 576-1245
Web Site:
https://www.garciaortiz.com
Year Founded: 1972
Sales Range: $1-9.9 Million
Emp.: 28
Certified Public Accountants
N.A.I.C.S.: 541211
Louis P. Oritz *(Principal)*
J. Edward Del Rio *(Sr Partner)*
Clayton Kreis *(Mng Dir)*
Luis Garcia *(Principal & Dir-Health Care Svcs)*
James P. Waters *(Principal & Dir-Tax Svcs)*
Stephen H. Tondreault *(Principal)*
Suzanne M. Reiber *(Principal & Dir-Litigation)*

C. Burt Linthicum *(Principal)*
Erin D. Connors *(Mgr)*
Marianne O. Touger *(Mgr)*
William J. Metz *(Mgr-Audit)*

GARCIA IMPORTS INC.
8301 Lomas Blvd NE, Albuquerque, NM 87110
Tel.: (505) 268-8400
Web Site: http://www.garciacars.com
Rev.: $19,400,000
Emp.: 40
Automobiles, New & Used
N.A.I.C.S.: 441110
Sheilah Garcia *(Pres)*
Ed Garcia *(Owner)*

GARCIA ROOFING & SHEET METAL
18219 Swamp Rd, Prairieville, LA 70769
Tel.: (225) 756-3100
Web Site:
https://www.garciadidmyroof.com
Year Founded: 1992
Rev.: $15,800,000
Emp.: 25
Roofing & Sheet Metal Products
N.A.I.C.S.: 238160
Gabriel Garcia *(Founder)*
Maricell Dean *(Project Mgr-Re-Roof Div)*
Andrew Goldberg *(Gen Mgr)*

GARCO CONSTRUCTION, INC.
4114 E Broadway St, Spokane, WA 99202
Tel.: (509) 535-4688
Web Site: https://www.garco.com
Year Founded: 1978
Sales Range: $10-24.9 Million
Emp.: 310
General Contracting & Construction Management Services
N.A.I.C.S.: 236220
Tim Welsh *(CEO)*
Clancy Welsh *(Pres)*
Hollis Barnett *(VP)*
James T. Welsh Jr. *(VP)*

GARD ROGARD INC.
250 Williams St, Carpentersville, IL 60110
Tel.: (847) 836-7700
Web Site: http://www.gardrogard.com
Rev.: $12,800,000
Emp.: 69
Pesticide & Other Agricultural Chemical Mfg
N.A.I.C.S.: 325320
Nancy Klehm *(Sec)*
Howard Klehm Sr. *(Pres)*

GARDEL FOOD EQUIPMENT & CUTLERY
101 Mystic Ave, Medford, MA 02155
Tel.: (781) 396-1022
Year Founded: 1933
Sales Range: $10-24.9 Million
Emp.: 67
Food Equipment & Cutlery
N.A.I.C.S.: 333241
Lawrence Maganzini *(Pres)*

GARDEN CITY GROUP COMMUNICATIONS
5335 SW Meadows Rd Kruse Woods II Ste 365, Lake Oswego, OR 97035
Tel.: (503) 858-1096
Web Site:
http://www.gardencitygroup.com
Year Founded: 1998
Sales Range: $10-24.9 Million
Emp.: 10
In House Advertising Agency
N.A.I.C.S.: 541810

Tammy Ollivier *(Sr Project Mgr & Media Buyer)*

GARDEN CITY HOTEL INC.
45 7th St, Garden City, NY 11530
Tel.: (516) 747-3000
Web Site:
  https://www.gardencityhotel.com
Year Founded: 1874
Rev.: $16,000,000
Emp.: 475
Owner & Operator of Hotels
N.A.I.C.S.: 721110
Catherine Nelkin Miller *(Owner & Pres)*
Patrick Smalley *(Exec VP)*
Sara Anne Fingerman *(Mgr-Mktg & PR)*

GARDEN CITY PLUMBING & HEATING
4025 Flynn Ln, Missoula, MT 59808
Tel.: (406) 728-5550
Web Site:
  http://www.gardencityplumbing.com
Year Founded: 1985
Sales Range: $10-24.9 Million
Emp.: 60
Provider of Plumbing Services
N.A.I.C.S.: 238220
Bill Schaff *(Pres)*
Daniel Stuber *(Controller)*

GARDEN OF E
125 E Baker St Ste 190, Costa Mesa, CA 92626
Tel.: (714) 545-4630
Web Site: http://www.gardenofe.com
Year Founded: 2000
Rev.: $2,000,000
Emp.: 20
Fiscal Year-end: 12/31/06
Internet/Web Design, Search Engine Optimization, Web (Banner Ads, Pop-ups, etc.)
N.A.I.C.S.: 541810

GARDEN OF LIFE, INC.
5500 Village Blvd Ste 202, West Palm Beach, FL 33407
Tel.: (561) 748-2477
Web Site:
  http://www.gardenoflife.com
Year Founded: 2000
Sales Range: $25-49.9 Million
Emp.: 150
Nutritional & Herbal Supplement Mfr; Healthy Living Publisher
N.A.I.C.S.: 325412
Brian Ray *(Pres)*
Teresa M. Miller *(Sr Dir-HR & Quality)*
Erik Schmitt *(VP-Fin)*
Kent Keyser *(VP-Sls & Mktg)*
Jeff Brams *(Gen Counsel & VP-Intl)*

GARDEN RIDGE POTTERY
19411 Atrium Pl Ste 170, Houston, TX 77084
Tel.: (281) 579-7901
Web Site:
  http://www.gardenridge.com
Sales Range: $125-149.9 Million
Emp.: 3,510
Toy & Hobby Goods Whslr
N.A.I.C.S.: 459120
Al Troutman *(Dir-Stores)*

GARDEN SPOT VILLAGE
433 S Kinzer Ave, New Holland, PA 17557
Tel.: (717) 355-6000 PA
Web Site:
  https://www.gardenspotvillage.org
Year Founded: 1996
Sales Range: $25-49.9 Million
Emp.: 598

Elderly People Housing Services
N.A.I.C.S.: 624120
Scott Miller *(CMO)*
Linda Dodge *(Dir-Dev)*
Dale Beiler *(CFO)*
Steve Lindsey *(CEO)*
Bryan Groff *(Dir-HR)*
Jeff Goss *(Vice Chm)*
John Smucker *(Treas)*
Daryl Groff *(Sec)*
John Farber *(COO)*
Marlin Groff *(Chm)*

GARDEN STATE ENGINE & EQUIPMENT CO.
3509 US Hwy 22, Somerville, NJ 08876
Tel.: (908) 534-5444
Web Site: http://www.gsee-crane.com
Year Founded: 1977
Sales Range: $10-24.9 Million
Emp.: 25
General Construction Machinery & Equipment
N.A.I.C.S.: 423810
Paul Baldasarre *(Pres)*

GARDEN STATE SECURITIES INC.
328 Newman Springs Rd, Red Bank, NJ 07701
Tel.: (732) 280-6886
Web Site:
  https://www.gardenstatesecurities.com
Sales Range: $10-24.9 Million
Emp.: 38
Brokers Security
N.A.I.C.S.: 523150
Ian P. Ferrato *(VP-Investments)*
Susan Filingeri *(Mgr-Ops)*
Scott H. Sari *(Co-Owner)*
Mindy A. Horowitz *(CFO)*
Steven D. Trigili *(Chief Compliance Officer)*
Ernest Pellegrino *(Dir-Corp Fin)*
Fred Haas *(Exec VP-Bus Dev)*
Louis Lucky Perrotto Jr. *(Owner & CEO)*

GARDEN STATE TILE DISTRIBUTORS
5001 Industrial Rd, Wall, NJ 07727
Tel.: (732) 938-6675
Web Site: https://www.gstile.com
Sales Range: $10-24.9 Million
Emp.: 95
Ceramic Wall & Floor Tile Distr
N.A.I.C.S.: 423320
Steve Fischer *(Pres)*
David Stockhammer *(Controller)*
David Kepner *(Mgr-Sls-Dealer Div)*

GARDEN STREET IRON & METAL
3350 Metro Pkwy, Fort Myers, FL 33916
Tel.: (239) 337-5865
Web Site: http://www.gardenst.com
Rev.: $12,000,000
Emp.: 38
Metal Scrap & Waste Materials
N.A.I.C.S.: 423930
Sarah Weber *(Office Mgr)*
Earl J. Weber Jr. *(Pres)*

GARDEN VALLEY CORPORATION
850 Garden Vly Cir, Sutherlin, OR 97479
Tel.: (541) 459-9565
Web Site: http://www.gvcbeans.com
Year Founded: 1994
Sales Range: $10-24.9 Million
Emp.: 25
Dehydrated Legume Mfr

N.A.I.C.S.: 311423
Perry Sterner *(Pres-Engrg-R&D)*

GARDEN VALLEY TELEPHONE COMPANY
201 Ross Ave, Erskine, MN 56535
Tel.: (218) 687-5251 MN
Web Site: http://www.gvtel.com
Year Founded: 1906
Sales Range: $10-24.9 Million
Emp.: 109
Telecommunication Servicesb
N.A.I.C.S.: 517111
Byron V. Ness *(Sec)*

GARDEN-FRESH FOODS INC.
726 S 12th St, Milwaukee, WI 53204
Tel.: (414) 645-1000
Web Site: https://www.garden-freshfoods.com
Rev.: $15,200,000
Emp.: 90
Fresh Fruit & Vegetable Merchant Whslr
N.A.I.C.S.: 424480
Thomas H. Hughes *(Owner)*
Victoria S. Hughes *(Sec)*

GARDEN-WISE DISTRIBUTORS INC.
1515 E 29th St N, Wichita, KS 67219
Tel.: (316) 838-1451
Web Site: http://www.gardnwise.com
Sales Range: $10-24.9 Million
Emp.: 16
Garden Supplies
N.A.I.C.S.: 424910

GARDENER'S SUPPLY COMPANY
128 Intervale Rd, Burlington, VT 05401
Tel.: (802) 660-3500 VT
Web Site: https://www.gardeners.com
Year Founded: 1983
Mail Order Garden Services
N.A.I.C.S.: 424910
Rebecca Gray *(CEO)*

GARDENS ALIVE!, INC.
PO Box 4028, Lawrenceburg, IN 47025-2181
Tel.: (513) 354-1482 IN
Web Site:
  http://www.gardensalive.com
Year Founded: 1987
Sales Range: $25-49.9 Million
Emp.: 150
Organic Gardening Products
N.A.I.C.S.: 333112
Niles Kinerk *(Founder & Pres)*

GARDENS REGIONAL HOSPITAL & MEDICAL CENTER
21530 S Pioneer Blvd, Hawaiian Gardens, CA 90716
Tel.: (562) 860-0401 CA
Web Site: http://www.grhmc.org
Year Founded: 1997
Sales Range: $200-249.9 Million
Emp.: 5
Health Care Srvices
N.A.I.C.S.: 622110
Jim Sherman *(Pres & CEO)*

GARDINERS HOME FURNISHING CENTER
4241 Brookhill Rd, Baltimore, MD 21215
Tel.: (410) 358-1730
Web Site: http://www.gardiners.com
Year Founded: 1956
Sales Range: $25-49.9 Million
Emp.: 200
Operators of Furniture Stores
N.A.I.C.S.: 449110

Gregory Mullaney *(Pres & CEO)*

GARDNER & WHITE CORPORATION
201 W 103rd St Ste 505, Indianapolis, IN 46290
Tel.: (317) 581-1580
Web Site: http://www.gardnerwhite.com
Sales Range: $10-24.9 Million
Emp.: 50
Insurance Brokers
N.A.I.C.S.: 524210
Glenda Neff *(Treas & Controller)*
Holly Irwin *(VP & Natl Practice Mgr-Grp Benefits)*

GARDNER BUSINESS MEDIA INC.
6915 Valley Ave, Cincinnati, OH 45244-3029
Tel.: (513) 527-8800 OH
Web Site:
  https://www.gardnerweb.com
Year Founded: 1928
Sales Range: $10-24.9 Million
Emp.: 110
Trade Journals & Books Publisher
N.A.I.C.S.: 513120
Ernie Brubaker *(VP & Controller)*
Brian E. Wertheimer *(Acct Mgr)*
David Necessary *(Dir-Mktg)*
Richard G. Kline Sr. *(Pres)*

GARDNER DISTRIBUTING CO.
7225 Entryway Dr, Billings, MT 59101
Tel.: (406) 656-5000
Web Site:
  http://www.gardnerdistributing.com
Sales Range: $10-24.9 Million
Emp.: 28
Pet Foods
N.A.I.C.S.: 424490
Rob Chouinard *(Pres)*
Tim Benjamin *(Dir-Sls)*

GARDNER GLASS PRODUCTS INC.
300 Elkin Hwy, North Wilkesboro, NC 28659
Tel.: (336) 651-9300
Web Site: http://www.gardnerglass.com
Rev.: $70,000,000
Emp.: 175
Mirror Manufacturer & Glass Fabricator
N.A.I.C.S.: 327215
Randy Brooks *(Pres)*
Melissa Lackey *(CFO, CIO & Exec VP)*
Michael Krumel *(Mgr-Sls-Oklahoma & Texas)*
Jim Ventre *(VP-Sls-Central US)*

GARDNER INC.
3641 Interchange Rd, Columbus, OH 43204
Tel.: (614) 456-4000 OH
Web Site:
  https://www.gardnerinc.com
Year Founded: 1944
Sales Range: $25-49.9 Million
Emp.: 180
Industrial Machinery & Equipment
N.A.I.C.S.: 423830
John F. Finn *(Chm)*
Ted Finn *(CFO)*
Don Nye *(Mgr-HR)*
Don Thornton *(VP)*

GARDNER MARSH GAS EQUIPMENT COMPANY, INC.
8209 Brownleigh Dr, Raleigh, NC 27617
Tel.: (919) 787-8214
Web Site:
  https://www.gardnermarsh.com

Gardner Marsh Gas Equipment Company,
Inc.—(Continued)
Year Founded: 1961
Sales Range: $10-24.9 Million
Emp.: 30
Gas Equipment & Appliances Distr
N.A.I.C.S.: 423840
Dale M. Gardner *(Pres)*
Laura Kedzierawski *(Treas & Control-
ler)*

GARDNER NELSON & PART-
NERS
432 Park Ave S 2nd Fl, New York,
NY 10016
Tel.: (212) 584-9100
Web Site: http://www.gardner-
nelson.com
Year Founded: 1999
Rev.: $135,000,000
Emp.: 30
Advetising Agency
N.A.I.C.S.: 541810
Steve Gardner *(Pres)*
Bill Ivey *(Partner & Dir-Print Svcs)*

GARDNER NEWS INC.
309 Central St, Gardner, MA 01440
Tel.: (978) 919-4099
Web Site:
https://www.thegardnernews.com
Sales Range: $10-24.9 Million
Emp.: 50
Newspaper Publishers
N.A.I.C.S.: 513110
Alberta Bell *(Publr)*

GARDNER OIL COMPANY INC.
110 Crackerbox Ln, Hot Springs, AR
71913
Tel.: (501) 767-9982   AR
Year Founded: 1967
Sales Range: $25-49.9 Million
Emp.: 140
Oil Refinement
N.A.I.C.S.: 324110
Lewis Gardner *(Pres)*

GARDNER STANDARD LLC
885 3rd Ave Ste 2403, New York, NY
10022
Tel.: (212) 398-9139
Web Site:
http://www.gardnerstandard.com
Privater Equity Firm
N.A.I.C.S.: 523940
Kathy M. Sturgeon *(Mgr-Ops)*

Subsidiaries:

Shadin, LP   (1)
6831 Oxford St, Saint Louis Park, MN
55426
Tel.: (952) 927-6500
Web Site: http://www.shadin.com
Sales Range: $1-9.9 Million
Emp.: 80
Measuring & Controlling Device Mfr
N.A.I.C.S.: 334519
Dan Nelson *(CEO)*
Shadin Avionics *(Product Mgr)*

Wisconsin Elevator Company,
LLC   (1)
1726 N Ballard Rd Ste 1, Appleton, WI
54911-2404
Web Site: https://www.foxvalleyelevator.com
Residential Elevators & Dumbwaiters Mfr
N.A.I.C.S.: 333921

Subsidiary (Domestic):

Waupaca Elevator Co, Inc.   (2)
1726 N Ballard Rd, Appleton, WI 54911
Tel.: (920) 991-9082
Web Site: http://www.waupacaelevator.com
Sales Range: $1-9.9 Million
Emp.: 75
Mfg Elevators/Escalators
N.A.I.C.S.: 333921

Larry Rice *(Treas)*
Rubhen Rice *(Asst Gen Mgr)*
Gary Ziebell *(Dir-Ops)*

GARDNER TELECOMMUNICA-
TIONS, INC.
555 S Town East Blvd, Mesquite, TX
75149
Tel.: (972) 329-9933
Web Site:
http://www.gardner100.com
Year Founded: 1998
Sales Range: $10-24.9 Million
Emp.: 100
Electrical & Other Wiring Installation
Contracting Services
N.A.I.C.S.: 238210
Steve Gardner *(Pres)*

GARDUNOS RESTAURANT
2100 Louisiana Blvd NE, Albuquer-
que, NM 87110
Tel.: (505) 880-0055   MX
Web Site:
http://gardunosrestaurants.com
Year Founded: 1981
Mexican Restaurant
N.A.I.C.S.: 722511

GARELICK MANUFACTURING
CO.
644 2nd St, Saint Paul Park, MN
55071
Tel.: (651) 459-9795
Web Site: http://www.garelick.com
Sales Range: $10-24.9 Million
Emp.: 200
Metal Ladders
N.A.I.C.S.: 332999
Kenneth D. Garelick *(Pres)*
Richard Garelick *(VP)*

GARFF ENTERPRISES, INC.
111 E Broadway Ste 900, Salt Lake
City, UT 84111
Tel.: (801) 257-3400   UT
Web Site: http://www.kengarff.com
Year Founded: 1949
Sales Range: $350-399.9 Million
Emp.: 2,500
New & Used Car Dealerships Owner
& Operator
N.A.I.C.S.: 441110
John Garff *(Pres)*

Subsidiaries:

Ken Garff Nissan of Salt Lake   (1)
777 SW Temple, Salt Lake City, UT
84101   (51%)
Tel.: (801) 322-5663
Web Site: http://www.kengarffnissan.com
Rev.: $34,527,872
Emp.: 50
Automobiles, New & Used
N.A.I.C.S.: 441110
John Garff *(Pres)*

Ken Garff St. George Ford
Lincoln   (1)
145 Hilton Dr, Saint George, UT 84770-
6737
Tel.: (435) 674-3200
Web Site: http://www.sgford.com
Sales Range: $10-24.9 Million
Emp.: 126
Automobile Sales
N.A.I.C.S.: 441110
Greg Nelson *(Controller)*
Mark Emley *(Gen Mgr)*

GARGIULO, INC.
15000 Old 41 N, Naples, FL 34110-
8415
Tel.: (239) 597-3131   FL
Year Founded: 1992
Sales Range: $75-99.9 Million
Emp.: 20
Fresh Produce
N.A.I.C.S.: 424480

Christian Leleu *(Pres)*
Michael Sullivan *(CFO)*
Joyce Collins *(Controller)*
Rob Pearson *(VP-Sls)*
Robert Elliott *(Mgr-Sls)*

GARICH INC.
6336 Greenwich Dr Ste 100, San Di-
ego, CA 92122
Tel.: (858) 597-4000   CA
Web Site: http://www.tristaff.com
Year Founded: 1971
Employment Agencies
N.A.I.C.S.: 561311
Gary van Eik *(CEO)*
Rich Papike *(Pres)*
Chris Papike *(VP-Media)*
Alex Papike *(VP)*
Jill Martinelli *(Dir-Technical Recruit-
ment, Hardware Engrg, Mfg & Tech)*
Kanani Masterson *(Dir-Tech & Exec
Search, Technology, Mktg & Soft-
ware)*
Kelly Lucas *(Dir-Acctg & Fin)*
Mike Wilson *(Dir-Banking Div)*
Jennifer Smith *(Mgr-Bus Dev & Exec
Recruiter)*

GARKANE ENERGY COOP-
ERATIVE, INC.
120 W 300 S, Loa, UT 84747
Tel.: (435) 836-2795
Web Site:
https://www.garkaneenergy.com
Year Founded: 1938
Rev.: $12,574,720
Emp.: 60
Eletric Power Generation Services
N.A.I.C.S.: 221122
Terry Griffiths *(Sec & Treas)*
Dan McClendon *(CEO & Gen Mgr)*
Nanell Robinson *(Treas & Sec)*
Mike Avant *(COO)*

GARLAND INDUSTRIES INC.
3800 E 91st St, Cleveland, OH
44105-2103
Tel.: (216) 641-7500
Web Site: https://www.garlandco.com
Year Founded: 1974
Sales Range: $25-49.9 Million
Emp.: 160
Mfr of Roofing Materials
N.A.I.C.S.: 324122
David M. Sokol *(Pres)*
Bill Oley *(Reg Mgr)*
Chuck Ripepi *(Controller)*
Joe Orlando *(VP)*

Subsidiaries:

Design-Build Solutions, Inc.   (1)
3800 E 91st St, Cleveland, OH 44105
Web Site: http://www.dbsgarland.com
Institutional Building Construction Services
N.A.I.C.S.: 236220
Michael Heekin *(Dir-Sls & Dev)*

GMX   (1)
3800 E 91st St, Cleveland, OH
44105-2103   (100%)
Tel.: (216) 641-7502
Web Site: http://www.gmxwaterproofing.com
Sales Range: $10-24.9 Million
Emp.: 125
Asphalt Felts & Coatings Mfr
N.A.I.C.S.: 324122
Dave Sokol *(Pres)*

Garland Canada Inc.   (1)
209 Carrier Drive, Toronto, M9W 5Y8, ON,
Canada
Tel.: (416) 747-7995
Web Site: http://www.garlandco.com
Emp.: 7
Roofing Material Distr
N.A.I.C.S.: 423310
Charbel Bluol *(Gen Mgr)*

The Garland Company Inc.   (1)
3800 E 91st St, Cleveland, OH 44105-2103

Tel.: (216) 641-7500
Web Site: http://www.garlandco.com
Sales Range: $10-24.9 Million
Emp.: 100
Mfr of Asphalt Felts & Coatings
N.A.I.C.S.: 324122
David M. Sokol *(Pres)*

The Garland Company UK
Limited   (1)
Glevum Works Upton Street, Gloucester,
GL1 4LA, Gloucestershire, United Kingdom
Tel.: (44) 1452 330646
Web Site: http://www.garlandukltd.co.uk
Emp.: 30
Roofing Material Distr
N.A.I.C.S.: 423310
Stacey Sibbald *(Office Mgr)*
Stacey Jeffries *(Office Mgr)*

GARLAND INSULATING COM-
PANY
10912 Sanden Dr, Dallas, TX 75238
Tel.: (214) 341-0254   TX
Web Site:
https://www.garlandinsulating.com
Year Founded: 1980
Sales Range: $10-24.9 Million
Emp.: 75
Carpentry Work
N.A.I.C.S.: 238130
Ferrell D. Drum *(Pres)*

GARLAND SALES INC.
1800 Antioch Rd, Dalton, GA 30121
Tel.: (706) 278-7880
Web Site:
https://www.garlandrug.com
Sales Range: $25-49.9 Million
Emp.: 250
Rugs Mfr
N.A.I.C.S.: 423220
Kathy Bennett *(Mgr-Traffic)*

GARLAND'S, INC.
2501 26th Ave S, Minneapolis, MN
55406-1246
Tel.: (612) 333-3469
Web Site:
http://www.garlandsinc.com
Year Founded: 1944
Sales Range: $10-24.9 Million
Emp.: 50
Industrial Machinery & Equipment
Whslr
N.A.I.C.S.: 423830
Joanna Holland *(Mgr-Mktg)*

GARLING CONSTRUCTION
INC.
1120 11th St, Belle Plaine, IA 52208
Tel.: (319) 444-3409
Web Site:
https://www.garlingconstruction.com
Year Founded: 1971
Sales Range: $10-24.9 Million
Emp.: 45
Commercial & Office Building Con-
struction
N.A.I.C.S.: 236220
Brian Mumby *(Project Mgr)*
Troy Pins *(Pres)*

GARLINGHOUSE COMPANY
2121 Boundary St Ste 208, Beaufort,
SC 29902
Tel.: (843) 271-6107   VA
Web Site:
http://www.garlinghouse.com
Year Founded: 1907
Sales Range: $10-24.9 Million
Emp.: 25
Home & Residential Building Plans
Publisher
N.A.I.C.S.: 513120
Jarret Magbee *(Pres & CEO)*

GARLYN O. SHELTON INC.
5700 SW HK Dodgen Loop 363,
Temple, TX 76504
Tel.: (254) 771-0128
Web Site:
http://www.garlynshelton.com
Rev.: $35,400,000
Emp.: 60
New & Used Car Dealers
N.A.I.C.S.: 441110
Garlyn O. Shelton (Pres)
Jennifer Green (Controller)

GARMAN CABINET & MILL-WORK, INC.
137 Cross Center Rd Ste 318, Denver, NC 28037
Tel.: (704) 489-2798   NC
Year Founded: 1996
Sales Range: Less than $1 Million
Emp.: 14
Architectural Woodwork
N.A.I.C.S.: 337212
Valerie Garman (Pres & CEO)

GARNER ENVIRONMENTAL SERVICES
1717 W 13th St, Deer Park, TX
77536
Tel.: (281) 930-1200
Web Site: https://www.garner-es.com
Rev.: $29,742,430
Emp.: 100
Toxic or Hazardous Waste Cleanup
N.A.I.C.S.: 562910
Lyndal D. Garner (Pres)
Ed Crook (VP-Disaster Response)
Neal Overstreet (Exec VP)
Curtis Galloway (Mgr)

GARNER REBUILT WATER PUMPS INCORPORATED
5871 Bartlett Stage Rd, Bartlett, TN
38134
Tel.: (901) 386-0150
Rev.: $27,400,000
Emp.: 8
Motor Vehicle Water Pump Mfr
N.A.I.C.S.: 336310

GARNER TRANSPORTATION GROUP, INC.
9291 County Rd 313, Findlay, OH
45839
Tel.: (419) 422-5742
Web Site:
https://www.garnertrucking.com
Year Founded: 1960
Sales Range: $10-24.9 Million
Emp.: 115
Freight Trucking Services
N.A.I.C.S.: 484121
Sheri Garner Brumbaugh (Pres & CEO)
Tim Chrulski (Dir-Ops)
Cheryl Thompson (Supvr-Acctg)
Barb Zimmerman (Mgr-HR)
Ed McKinley (Dir-Sls & Mktg)
Kim Fredritz (Mgr-Customer Svc)
Justin Conrad (Mgr-IT)

GARNET ELECTRIC CO., INC.
1615 E State St, Sheffield, AL 35660-3523
Tel.: (256) 381-4062
Web Site:
https://www.garnetelectric.com
Sales Range: $10-24.9 Million
Emp.: 120
Electrical Wiring Services
N.A.I.C.S.: 238210
Charles Crow (Pres)

GARNETT & HELFRICH CAPITAL, LLC
1875 S Grant St Suite 920, San Mateo, CA 94402
Tel.: (650) 234-4200
Web Site:
http://www.garnetthelfrich.com
Year Founded: 2004
Privater Equity Firm
N.A.I.C.S.: 523999
David Helfrich (Mng Dir)

GARNETT STATION PARTNERS, LLC
853 Broadway 16th Fl, New York, NY
10003
Tel.: (917) 671-9731
Web Site: https://garnettstation.com
Investment Services
N.A.I.C.S.: 523999
Matthew Terker Perelman (Co-Founder & Mng Partner)

Subsidiaries:

Authentic Restaurant Brands   (1)
853 Broadway 16th Fl, New York, NY
10003
Tel.: (917) 671-9731
Web Site: https://authenticrb.com
Holding Company
N.A.I.C.S.: 551112
Felipe A. Athayde (CEO)

Subsidiary (Domestic):

Fiesta Restaurant Group, Inc.   (2)
14800 Landmark Blvd Ste 500, Dallas, TX
75254-7013
Tel.: (972) 702-9300
Web Site: https://www.frgi.com
Rev.: $357,277,000
Assets: $367,113,000
Liabilities: $212,242,000
Net Worth: $154,871,000
Earnings: $10,370,000
Emp.: 4,480
Fiscal Year-end: 01/02/2022
Holding Company; Fast Food Restaurants
Owner, Operator & Franchisor
N.A.I.C.S.: 551112
Dirk A. Montgomery (Pres, CEO & Dir)

Subsidiary (Domestic):

Cabana Grill, Inc.   (3)
1077 Central Pkwy S Ste 600, San Antonio,
TX 78232
Tel.: (904) 886-3206
Restaurant
N.A.I.C.S.: 722511

Pollo Operations, Inc.   (3)
7255 Center Dr N Kendall Dr Fl 8, Miami,
FL 33126
Tel.: (305) 670-7696
Web Site: http://www.pollotropical.com
Sales Range: $100-124.9 Million
Emp.: 3,000
Fast Food Restaurant Operator
N.A.I.C.S.: 722513
Daniel O'Grady (VP-Franchise Devel)

GARNEY HOLDING COMPANY, INC.
1333 NW Vivion Rd, Kansas City,
MO 64118-4554
Tel.: (816) 741-4600   MO
Web Site: http://www.garney.com
Year Founded: 1961
Sales Range: $50-74.9 Million
Emp.: 1,300
Water Treatment & Water Main & Sewer Line Construction
N.A.I.C.S.: 237110
Charles A. Garney (Chm)
Stephen M. McCandless (Dir-Special Projects)
Jeff Lacy (CFO)
Mark Kelly (Dir-Bus Dev)
Bill E. Williams (Dir-Ops-Northern California)
Steve Ford (VP)
Matt Foster (VP)

Greg Harris (VP)
Tony Kempf (VP)
Jay McQuillen Jr. (Dir-Federal Ops)

Subsidiaries:

Encore Construction Group, Inc.   (1)
370 E Crown Point Rd, Winter Garden, FL
34787
Tel.: (407) 877-5903
Web Site: http://www.encorecc.com
Sales Range: $75-99.9 Million
Emp.: 185
Construction Engineering Services
N.A.I.C.S.: 541330
Timothy M. Behler (Sr VP)
Mark A. Kelly (VP-Pre-Construction)

Garney Companies, Inc.   (1)
1333 NW Vivion Rd, Kansas City, MO
64118-4554
Tel.: (816) 741-4600
Web Site: http://www.garney.com
Sales Range: $25-49.9 Million
Emp.: 35
Water & Wastewater Construction for Public, Private, Industrial & Federal Clients
N.A.I.C.S.: 562998
Michael Heitmann (Pres)

Garney Construction Company   (1)
7911 Shaffer Pkwy, Littleton, CO 80127
Tel.: (303) 791-3600
Web Site: http://www.garney.com
Sales Range: $10-24.9 Million
Emp.: 125
Water, Sewer & Utility Lines
N.A.I.C.S.: 238990
Wayne O'Brien (COO-Western Plant Ops)
Timothy Behler (COO-Eastern Plant Ops)
Mike Heitmann (CEO)
Mark Kelly (Dir-Bus Dev)
Meggan Krase (VP)
Jeff Lacy (CFO)
Scott Parrish (Pres)
Tom Roberts (Dir-Fin Reporting)
Jason Seubert (COO-Eastern Pipe Ops)
Austin Delimont (Asst Controller-Ops)
Mike Strong (Gen Counsel)
Jay McQuillen Jr. (Dir-Federal Ops)

GARRAND & COMPANY
75 Washington Ave, Portland, ME
04101-2665
Tel.: (207) 772-3119   ME
Web Site: http://www.garrand.com
Year Founded: 1989
Sales Range: $25-49.9 Million
Emp.: 20
Advertising Agencies
N.A.I.C.S.: 541810
Brenda Garrand (Chm)
Emily Trescot (Mgr-Asset & Designer)
Jon Hutter (Dir-Acct Plng)
Kevin Moehlenkamp (CEO & Chief Creative Officer)
Matt Caffelle (Dir-Creative)

GARRATT-CALLAHAN COMPANY
50 Ingold Rd, Burlingame, CA 94010
Tel.: (650) 697-5811
Web Site:
https://www.garrattcallahan.com
Sales Range: $10-24.9 Million
Emp.: 320
Water Treating Compounds
N.A.I.C.S.: 325998
Jeffrey S. Garratt (Pres)
Mathew Garrett (VP)
Malcolm McDowell (Mgr-Hiring)
Lia Maafu (Dir-HR & Compliance)

GARRETT CONSTRUCTION COMPANY
Garrett Rd Off Fm 2725, Ingleside,
TX 78362
Tel.: (361) 776-7575
Web Site:
http://www.garrettconstruction.com
Sales Range: $10-24.9 Million
Emp.: 65

Marine Construction
N.A.I.C.S.: 236210
Jon J. Garrett (Pres)
Grant Garrett (VP)

GARRETT ENTERPRISES INC.
707 S 75 Hwy, Sabetha, KS 66534
Tel.: (785) 284-2167
Rev.: $12,000,000
Emp.: 200
Grocery Stores
N.A.I.C.S.: 445110
Dennis Garrett (Pres)

Subsidiaries:

Genes Thriftway Inc.   (1)
707 S 75 Hwy, Sabetha, KS 66534
Tel.: (785) 284-2167
Web Site: http://www.garettenterprises.com
Grocery Stores
N.A.I.C.S.: 445110
Dennis Garrett (Owner)

GARRETT REALTY SERVICES, INC.
3723 E C-30A, Santa Rosa Beach,
FL 32459
Tel.: (850) 231-1544
Web Site:
http://www.garrettrealty.com
Year Founded: 1987
Sales Range: $1-9.9 Million
Emp.: 20
Real Estate Brokerage & Property Management
N.A.I.C.S.: 531210
Cathy Pickle (Mgr-Ops)
Darla Jones (Mgr-Front Desk)
Kathy Strickland (Owner-Acctg)

GARRIS-EVANS LUMBER CO. INC.
701 W 14th St, Greenville, NC 27834
Tel.: (252) 752-2106
Web Site:
https://www.garrisevans.com
Sales Range: $10-24.9 Million
Emp.: 70
Lumber & Other Building Materials
N.A.I.C.S.: 423310
John Evans (Pres)
Carol Pickens (Office Mgr)
David A. Evans Jr. (Chm)

GARRISON INVESTMENT GROUP LP
1290 Avenue Of The Americas Ste
914, New York, NY 10104
Tel.: (212) 372-9500   DE
Web Site: http://www.garrisoninv.com
Year Founded: 2007
Equity Investment Firm
N.A.I.C.S.: 523999
Joseph B. Tansey (Founder & Chief Investment Officer)
Brian S. Chase (CFO & COO)

Subsidiaries:

Bristol Compressors International,
Inc.   (1)
15185 Industrial Park Rd, Bristol, VA 24202
Tel.: (276) 466-4121
Web Site:
http://www.bristolcompressors.com
Sales Range: $75-99.9 Million
Emp.: 700
Compressor Mfr
N.A.I.C.S.: 333912
Velma Mays (Mgr-Customer Svc Sys)
Chris Robinson (Dir-Intl Sls & Mktg)
Joel Moseley (Sr VP-Global Sls & Mktg)
Vicky Kiser (CFO)
John Young (VP-Supply Chain)
Lewis Ankeny (VP-Supply Chain Mgmt)
Robbie Eades (VP-Quality & Reliability)
Kevin Mumpower (VP-Product Dev Engrg)
Rick Nunley (Exec Dir-HR)
Cindy Hagemann (Mgr-Mktg)
Luka Lojk (VP-Sls & Mktg)

Garrison Investment Group LP—(Continued)

TNCI Operating Company, LLC (1)
114 E Haley St Ste A, Santa Barbara, CA
93101
Tel.: (805) 966-1801
Telecommunication Servicesb
N.A.I.C.S.: 517810
Jeff Compton (Pres & CEO)
Bill Farwell (CFO)
Victor Flores (VP-Network Ops)

Subsidiary (Domestic):

Impact Telecom, Inc. (2)
9000 E Nichols Ave Ste 230, Englewood,
CO 80112
Tel.: (301) 610-4354
Web Site: http://www.impacttelecom.com
Telecommunications Resellers
N.A.I.C.S.: 517121
Robert Beaty (Pres)
Chuck Griffin (CEO)
Doug Funsch (Chief Revenue Officer)
Brian McClintock (CFO)
Patrick Reilly (VP-Carrier Svcs)
Jason Welch (Exec VP-Carrier Svcs)
Bob Imhoff (VP-Bus Dev-Intl)

Subsidiary (Domestic):

AmericaTel Corporation (3)
11300 Rockville Pike Ste 900, Rockville,
MD 20855
Tel.: (800) 221-3020
Web Site: http://www.americatel.com
Telecommunication Servicesb
N.A.I.C.S.: 517810

Matrix Telecom, LLC (3)
433 E Las Colinas Blvd Ste 500, Irving, TX
75039
Tel.: (866) 728-7490
Web Site: http://www.matrixbt.com
Business Voice, Data & Internet Telecom-
munications Services
N.A.I.C.S.: 517112

Subsidiary (Domestic):

Excel Telecommunications (4)
433 Las Colinas Blvd Ste 500, Irving, TX
75039
Tel.: (972) 910-1900
Web Site: http://www.excel.com
Voice & Data Communication Products &
Services
N.A.I.C.S.: 517810
Don Eben (Sr Dir-Network Plng)

Division (Domestic):

TNCI (2)
2 Charlesgate W, Boston, MA 02215
Tel.: (617) 369-1000
Web Site: http://www.tncii.com
Telecommunication Servicesb
N.A.I.C.S.: 517810

**GARRITY ASPHALT RECLAIM-
ING INC.**
22 Peters Rd, Bloomfield, CT 06002
Tel.: (860) 243-2300
Web Site:
https://www.garrityasphalt.com
Sales Range: $10-24.9 Million
Emp.: 64
Highway & Street Construction Ser-
vices
N.A.I.C.S.: 237310
Kevin Sheehan (Gen Mgr)

**GARROTT BROTHERS CON-
TINUOUS MIX, INC.**
375 Red River Rd, Gallatin, TN
37066
Tel.: (615) 452-2385
Web Site:
https://www.garrottbros.com
Year Founded: 1950
Sales Range: $10-24.9 Million
Emp.: 60
Readymix Concrete Mfr
N.A.I.C.S.: 327320

Johnny Garrott (Pres)
Daniel Bugbee (Mgr-Ops)
Jeff Carnes (VP-Fin)
Chris Tuck (Mgr-Sls)

GARROW OIL CORP.
504 W Edgewood Dr, Appleton, WI
54913-9725
Tel.: (920) 733-8877
Web Site: https://www.garrowoil.com
Year Founded: 1972
Sales Range: $10-24.9 Million
Emp.: 15
Provider of Gas Services
N.A.I.C.S.: 424710
William Garrow (Pres & Treas)
Chuck Pluger (Controller)

**GARRY STRUTHERS ASSOCI-
ATES, INC.**
2059 135th Pl Se, Bellevue, WA
98005-4002
Tel.: (425) 519-0300
Web Site: http://www.gsassoc-
inc.com
Sales Range: $10-24.9 Million
Emp.: 100
Engineering, Environmental & Con-
struction Services
N.A.I.C.S.: 541330
Garry Struthers (Pres)

GARTEN SERVICES, INC.
500 Hawthorne Ave SE, Salem, OR
97309
Tel.: (503) 581-1984   OR
Web Site: https://www.garten.org
Year Founded: 1970
Sales Range: $10-24.9 Million
Emp.: 273
Developmental Disability Assistance
Services
N.A.I.C.S.: 624120
Marianna Bushnell (Mgr-HR)
Dave Chambers (Mgr-IT)
Matt Grams (Mgr-Packaging & As-
sembly)
Steve Babcock (Mgr-Mail Svcs)
Tim Rocak (CEO)
Grace Walborn (Treas)
Kathy Moreland (Pres)
Marin Arreola (VP)
Mary Lynn Morgan (Sec)
Pamela Best (CFO)
Garten Dallas (Mgr-Dallas Branch)
William Posegate (COO)

GARTNER STUDIOS, INC.
220 E Myrtle St, Stillwater, MN 55082
Tel.: (651) 351-7700
Web Site:
http://www.gartnerstudios.com
Year Founded: 1998
Sales Range: $25-49.9 Million
Emp.: 120
Stationery, Greeting Cards & Invita-
tions
N.A.I.C.S.: 322230
Russell Slygh (Dir-IT)
Angie Holmstrom (Product Mgr)
Timothy Carroll (Coord-Sls)

GARTON TRACTOR INC.
2400 N Golden State Blvd, Turlock,
CA 95382
Tel.: (209) 632-3931
Web Site:
https://www.gartontractor.com
Rev.: $35,243,743
Emp.: 52
Farm Machinery Sales
N.A.I.C.S.: 459999
Mike Converse (Gen Mgr)

GARVEY VOLKSWAGEN INC.

483 Quaker Rd, Queensbury, NY
12804
Tel.: (518) 665-8192
Web Site: http://www.garveyvw.com
Car Whslr
N.A.I.C.S.: 441110
Rachel Blanchard (Office Mgr)
JP Garvey (Sls Mgr)
Lee Garrand (Sls Mgr)
Larry Brown (Mgr-Svc)
Doug Lloyd (Mgr-Parts)
Martin Kunath (Mgr-Fin)
Matt Willis (Asst Mgr-Fin)

**GARVEY'S OFFICE PROD-
UCTS**
7500 N Caldwell Ave, Niles, IL
60714-3808
Tel.: (847) 588-1690
Web Site:
https://www.getgarveys.com
Year Founded: 1926
Rev.: $25,500,000
Emp.: 150
Stationery & Office Supplies
N.A.I.C.S.: 424120
Bernard Garvey Jr. (Pres)
Rick Lannert (Acct Exec)

GARVIN OIL COMPANY INC.
4154 Festival Trail Rd, Wagener, SC
29164
Tel.: (803) 564-5944
Web Site: http://www.garvinoil.com
Sales Range: $10-24.9 Million
Emp.: 250
Convenience Stores, Independent
N.A.I.C.S.: 445131
Kent Ingram (Chm)
Chad Ingram (Pres)

**GARY AMOTH TRUCKING,
INC.**
1874 Highland Ave E, Twin Falls, ID
83301
Tel.: (208) 733-1545
Web Site:
https://www.garyamothtrucking.com
Sales Range: $10-24.9 Million
Emp.: 90
General Freight Trucking, Long-
Distance, Truckload Services
N.A.I.C.S.: 484121
David Whaley (Mgr-Maxi Fleet)

**GARY COMMUNITY INVEST-
MENT COMPANY**
1705 17th St Ste 200, Denver, CO
80202
Tel.: (303) 628-3800
Web Site:
http://www.garycommunity.org
Sales Range: $25-49.9 Million
Emp.: 40
Investment Services
N.A.I.C.S.: 523999
Samuel Gary (Chm)
David Younggren (Sr VP)

Subsidiaries:

Gary-Williams Production Co.   (1)
1705 17th St Ste 200, Denver, CO 80202-
5653
Tel.: (303) 628-3800
Sales Range: $25-49.9 Million
Emp.: 21
Gas Exploration & Production
N.A.I.C.S.: 213112
Samuel Gary (Chm)
David Younggren (Sr VP)
Christy Kredera (Office Mgr)

**GARY D. NELSON ASSOCI-
ATES, INC.**
19080 Lomita Ave, Sonoma, CA
95476-5453
Tel.: (707) 935-6113   CA

Web Site: http://www.nelsonhr.com
Year Founded: 1970
Sales Range: $200-249.9 Million
Emp.: 200
Employment Placement, Executive
Recruiting & Workforce Management
Consulting Services
N.A.I.C.S.: 561311
Gary D. Nelson (Founder)
Tony Bartenetti (Pres-Bus Dev &
Strategic Partnerships)
Jack Unroe (CEO)
Joe Prusko (CFO)
Craig Nelson (Chm)
Joe Madigan (Exec VP)
Lisa Marie Johnson (VP-HR)
Christina Russo (VP-Mktg)
Rachel MacNeill (VP-Tech & Bus
Solutions)

**GARY MATHEWS MOTORS
INC.**
1100 New Ashland City Rd, Clarks-
ville, TN 37040-4299
Tel.: (931) 820-0067
Web Site:
https://www.garymathewsmotors.com
Rev.: $42,000,000
Emp.: 145
New & Used Car Dealers
N.A.I.C.S.: 441110
Gary Mathews (Pres)

**GARY MERLINO CONSTRUC-
TION CO., INC.**
9125 10th Ave S, Seattle, WA 98108
Tel.: (206) 762-9125   WA
Year Founded: 1961
Sales Range: $100-124.9 Million
Emp.: 325
Highway & Street Construction
N.A.I.C.S.: 237310
Gary M. Merlino (Pres)
Trevor Settlage (Project Mgr)
Charlie Oliver (VP)
Don Robertson (Mgr-Safety & Risk)

**GARY METALS MANUFAC-
TURING LLC**
2700 E 5th Ave, Gary, IN 46402
Tel.: (219) 885-3232
Rev.: $14,500,000
Emp.: 95
Heater & Air Conditioner Mfr
N.A.I.C.S.: 332322
David Strilich (Mng Partner)

**GARY SURDYKE MOTOR-
CYCLE INC.**
1305 Highway 61, Festus, MO 63028
Tel.: (636) 931-9166
Web Site: http://www.surdyke.com
Sales Range: $10-24.9 Million
Emp.: 50
Motorcycle Dealers
N.A.I.C.S.: 441227
Mat Surdyke (Owner)

GARY V. BURROWS INC.
416 N Lemoore Ave, Lemoore, CA
93245
Tel.: (559) 924-2064
Web Site: http://gvburrowsinc.com
Rev.: $10,000,000
Emp.: 12
Diesel Fuel
N.A.I.C.S.: 424720
Darryl Archer (Mgr)

GARY W. CURRY, INC.
6245 Clark Ctr Ave Ste J, Sarasota,
FL 34238
Tel.: (941) 921-9111   FL
Web Site:
http://www.roofingbycurry.com
Year Founded: 1990

Sales Range: $10-24.9 Million
Emp.: 90
Roofing Contractors
N.A.I.C.S.: 238160
Gary W. Curry (Pres)

GARY WOOD ASSOCIATES, INC.
1180 Ave of the Americas 8th Fl, New York, NY 10036
Tel.: (212) 792-9530
Web Site: http://www.gwaonline.net
Year Founded: 1956
Insurance Agents
N.A.I.C.S.: 524210
David S. Wood (Pres)
Eric Wood (Partner)

GARY YAMAMOTO CUSTOM BAITS
849 S Copper Mine Rd, Page, AZ 86040
Tel.: (928) 645-3812
Web Site: http://www.baits.com
Sales Range: $50-74.9 Million
Emp.: 130
Fishing Tackle
N.A.I.C.S.: 423910
Gary Yamamoto (CEO)
Bonny Colby (Mgr-Internal Sls)

GARY YEOMANS FORD INC.
1420 N Tomoka Farms Rd, Daytona Beach, FL 32124
Tel.: (386) 274-6700
Web Site: https://www.garyyeomansford.com
Sales Range: $100-124.9 Million
Emp.: 350
Automobiles New & Used Service & Parts
N.A.I.C.S.: 441110
Joseph Maenza (Fin Dir)
Roy Miller (Gen Mgr-Sls)
Michael Albrecht (Mgr-Sls)
Troy Lerdo (Dir-Internet)
Jeromie Allan (Gen Mgr)
Rick Tredo (Mgr-Bus Preferred)
Gary Coombs (Mgr-Floor)
Buddy Hall (Mgr-Floor)
Dustin Ketchum (Mgr-Floor)
Anthony Macchia (Mgr-Floor)
Mario Recupido (Mgr-Sls)

GARY'S & COMPANY NEW-PORT BEACH
1065 Newport Ctr Dr, Newport Beach, CA 92660
Tel.: (949) 759-1622
Web Site: http://www.garysonline.com
Year Founded: 1986
Sales Range: $25-49.9 Million
Emp.: 50
Retailer of Men & Boy's Clothing & Accessories
N.A.I.C.S.: 458110
Richard Braeger (Pres)
Bruce Tomiyama (CFO)

GARY'S WINE & MARKET-PLACE
121 Main St, Madison, NJ 07940-2115
Tel.: (973) 822-0200
Web Site: https://www.garyswine.com
Year Founded: 1995
Sales Range: $25-49.9 Million
Emp.: 200
Wine Retailer
N.A.I.C.S.: 445320
Gary Fisch (Founder & CEO)
Bryan McCall (Dir-Wine-St. Helena)

GARZA CREATIVE GROUP

2601 Hibernia St Ste 200, Dallas, TX 75204
Tel.: (214) 720-3888   TX
Web Site: http://www.garzacreative.com
Year Founded: 1991
Sales Range: Less than $1 Million
Emp.: 3
N.A.I.C.S.: 541810
Paco Garza (Sr Dir-Creative)
Vicki Garza (Dir-Mktg)
Daniel Garza (Graphic Designer)

GAS DEPOT OIL CO.
8930 N Waukegan Rd Ste 230, Morton Grove, IL 60053
Tel.: (847) 581-0303
Web Site: https://www.gasdepot.com
Year Founded: 1999
Sales Range: $150-199.9 Million
Emp.: 15
Distributes Gasoline & Diesel Fuel to Retail Service Gas Stations
N.A.I.C.S.: 457120
Nick Tanglis (CFO)

GAS EQUIPMENT COMPANY, INC.
11616 Harry Hines Blvd, Dallas, TX 75229-2203
Tel.: (972) 241-2333   TX
Web Site: http://www.gasequipment.com
Year Founded: 1937
Sales Range: $200-249.9 Million
Emp.: 425
Measuring & Controlling Devices & Industrial Machinery & Equipment Mfr & Whslr
N.A.I.C.S.: 423830
Gijs Majoor (CEO)
Jason Steichen (VP-Fin)

Subsidiaries:

Gas Equipment Company Inc.   (1)
1440 Lakes Pkwy Ste 300, Lawrenceville, GA 30043
Tel.: (770) 995-1131
Web Site: http://www.gasequipment.com
Sales Range: $25-49.9 Million
Emp.: 20
Provider of Industrial Supply Services
N.A.I.C.S.: 423840

Medidores Internacionales Rochester S.A. de C.V.   (1)
Calle 26A No 6 Parque Industrial Vallejo, Tlalnepantla, 54170, Edo de Mexico, Mexico
Tel.: (52) 5530030970
Web Site: http://www.rochester-mexico.com
Sales Range: $10-24.9 Million
Emp.: 100
Mfr of Measuring & Controlling Devices & Wholesale Industrial Machinery & Equipment
N.A.I.C.S.: 334519
Nicolas Salfaro (Mgr)

Rochester Gauges International   (1)
6 Avenue Lavoisier, Zone Industrielle Nord, 1300, Wavre, Belgium   (100%)
Tel.: (32) 10241010
Web Site: http://www.rochester-gauges.be
Sales Range: $10-24.9 Million
Emp.: 50
Measuring & Controlling Devices & Wholesale Industrial Machinery & Equipment Mfr
N.A.I.C.S.: 334519
Fredrick Gottard (Mgr-Sls)

GAS INCORPORATED
107 Mattox Ct, Lagrange, GA 30241
Tel.: (706) 885-9573
Web Site: http://www.gasincorporated.com
Rev.: $22,419,085
Emp.: 60
Butane Gas, Bottled
N.A.I.C.S.: 457210
Kendrick W. Mattox Jr. (Pres & CEO)

GAS INNOVATIONS INC.
18005 E Hwy 225, La Porte, TX 77571
Tel.: (281) 471-2200   TX
Web Site: https://www.gasinnovations.com
Year Founded: 2002
Sales Range: $25-49.9 Million
Industrial Gas Whslr
N.A.I.C.S.: 424690
Ashley Madray (Owner)
Dennis Frings (CFO)
Don Bobyk (VP-Mktg & Sls)

Subsidiaries:

Willingham Welding Solutions, Inc.   (1)
18005 E Highway 225, La Porte, TX 77571
Tel.: (281) 471-2200
Welding Equipment & Supplies Whslr
N.A.I.C.S.: 423840

GAS LAMP MEDIA
363 5th Ave Ste 300, San Diego, CA 92101
Tel.: (619) 955-6995
Web Site: http://www.gaslampmedia.com
Sales Range: Less than $1 Million
Emp.: 12
N.A.I.C.S.: 541810
Christopher Shaughnessy (Partner)
Thai Yin (Partner)

GAS LAND PETROLEUM INC.
785 Broadway, Kingston, NY 12401
Tel.: (845) 331-7545
Rev.: $44,248,353
Emp.: 6
Gasoline
N.A.I.C.S.: 424720
Majed Nesheiwat (Pres & CEO)
Hayita Nesheiwat (VP)

Subsidiaries:

Gas Land Trucking Inc.   (1)
785 Broadway, Kingston, NY 12401
Tel.: (845) 331-7545
Rev.: $210,000
Emp.: 4
Gas Delivery Services
N.A.I.C.S.: 484220
Rheem Nesheiwha (Controller)

GAS MONKEY GARAGE
2330 Merrell Rd, Dallas, TX 75229
Tel.: (972) 243-6659
Web Site: http://www.gasmonkeygarage.com
Sales Range: $1-9.9 Million
Automotive Custom Fabrication & Repair Services
N.A.I.C.S.: 811198
Richard Rawlings (Owner)

GAS PURIFICATION ENGINEERING CORPORATION
8925 Research Dr, Irvine, CA 92618
Tel.: (949) 660-1131
Web Site: https://www.gaspurification.com
Sales Range: $10-24.9 Million
Emp.: 8
Natural Gas Distr
N.A.I.C.S.: 221210
Hassan Mahdara (Pres)

GAS RECOVERY SYSTEMS INC.
5717 Brisa St, Livermore, CA 94550
Tel.: (925) 606-3700   CA
Web Site: http://www.grsi.net
Year Founded: 1997
Sales Range: $25-49.9 Million
Emp.: 60
Gasoline Field Services
N.A.I.C.S.: 213112

Rick Williams (VP-Ops)
Alan Siegwarth (Dir)

GAS TECHNOLOGY INSTITUTE
1700 S Mt Prospect Rd, Des Plaines, IL 60018-1804
Tel.: (847) 768-0500   IL
Web Site: http://www.gastechnology.org
Year Founded: 1941
Sales Range: $25-49.9 Million
Emp.: 250
Research Services
N.A.I.C.S.: 541715
William Liss (Mng Dir-Energy Delivery & Utilization)
Ron Snedic (Sr VP-Corp Dev)
Rodney Rinholm (Exec Dir-Bus Dev & Education)
Richard Kaelin (VP-Govt Affairs)
Jim Ingold (CFO, Treas & VP-Fin)
Edward Johnston (Sr VP-Res & Tech Dev)
Don Stevenson (VP-Govt Affairs)
Bret Lane (Chm)
Paula Gant (Sr VP-Corp Strategy & Innovation)

Subsidiaries:

Bevilacqua-Knight, Inc.   (1)
1000 Broadway Ste 410, Oakland, CA 94607
Tel.: (510) 444-8707
Web Site: http://www.bki.com
Sales Range: $1-9.9 Million
Emp.: 30
Engineering Services
N.A.I.C.S.: 541330
Richard Myhre (VP)
Rebecca Brown (Program Mgr)
Scott Fable (Sr Program Mgr)
Brian Gitt (Pres & CEO)

Davis Energy Group, Inc.   (1)
123 C St, Davis, CA 95616
Tel.: (530) 753-1100
Web Site: http://www.davisenergy.com
Sales Range: $1-9.9 Million
Emp.: 23
Heating & Air-Conditioning System Design Services
N.A.I.C.S.: 238220
David A. Springer (Principal)
Jeremy Springer (CFO)
Bill Dakin (Dir-Building Res & Energy Consulting)
Marc Hoeschele (Dir-Tech & Assessment Standards)
Pepper Smith (Dir-Residential Programs)

Endesco Services Corporation   (1)
1700 S Mount Prospect Rd, Des Plaines, IL 60018-1804
Tel.: (847) 768-0588
Rev.: $820,000
Emp.: 3
Business Services
N.A.I.C.S.: 561499

GAS TURBINE EFFICIENCY, LLC
300 Sunport Ln, Orlando, FL 32809
Tel.: (407) 304-5200
Web Site: https://www.gtefficiency.com
Sales Range: $10-24.9 Million
Emp.: 40
Industrial Engineering Services
N.A.I.C.S.: 541330
Dan Rashy (VP-Fin)
John Brooks (Exec VP)
Bob Knott (VP-Special Projects)
Michael Thomas (Pres)
Fred Chamness (Dir-Quality Production)

Subsidiaries:

Gas Turbine Efficiency AB   (1)
Datavagen 9A, Jarfalla, 175 27, Uppland, Sweden

Gas Turbine Efficiency, LLC—(Continued)

Tel.: (46) 854610500
Web Site: http://www.gtefficiency.com
Sales Range: $10-24.9 Million
Emp.: 20
Gas Turbine Mfr
N.A.I.C.S.: 333611
Par Krossling (Mng Dir)

GAS-FIRED PRODUCTS, INC.
305 Doggett St, Charlotte, NC 28203-4923
Tel.: (704) 372-3485   NC
Web Site:
    http://www.gasfiredproducts.com
Year Founded: 1949
Sales Range: $50-74.9 Million
Emp.: 100
Gas-Fired Heating Equipment Mfr
N.A.I.C.S.: 333414
Jay Ruschli (Controller)
Martin Brice (VP-Engrg)
Frank L. Horne Jr. (Pres)

Subsidiaries:

Gas-Fired Products (U.K.) Ltd.   (1)
4 6 Chapel Ln, Claydon, Ipswich, IP6 0JL,
United Kingdom   (100%)
Tel.: (44) 1473830551
Web Site: http://www.spaceray.co.uk
Sales Range: $10-24.9 Million
Emp.: 14
Mfr of Heating Apparatus
N.A.I.C.S.: 333414
Damien Oakley (Mng Dir)

GASBARRE PRODUCTS INC.
590 Division St, Du Bois, PA 15801
Tel.: (814) 371-3015
Web Site: https://www.gasbarre.com
Year Founded: 1973
Sales Range: $10-24.9 Million
Emp.: 140
Designer, Mfr & Marketer of Powder
Compaction & Sizing Presses for the
Powder Metallurgy Industry
N.A.I.C.S.: 333517
Thomas G. Gasbarre (CEO & CFO)
William Gasbarre (Sec)
Steve Wendel (Mgr-Engrg)
Jake Verdoux (Mgr-Mfg-Indus Furnace Sys)

Subsidiaries:

C.I. Hayes   (1)
33 Freeway Dr, Cranston, RI 02920
Tel.: (401) 467-5200
Web Site: http://www.cihayes.com
Sales Range: $10-24.9 Million
Emp.: 60
Heat Treating Solutions
N.A.I.C.S.: 333994
P. Parker (Mgr-Replacement Parts Sls)
Matthew Marzullo (Mgr-Capital Equipment Sls)
Steven Smith (Pres)
Bob Brodeur (Engr)
Mark Thomason (Mgr-Sls-Intl)

Gasbarre Products   (1)
590 Division St, Du Bois, PA 15801
Tel.: (814) 371-3015
Web Site: http://www.gasbarre.com
Sales Range: $10-24.9 Million
Emp.: 100
Hydraulic Powder Compaction Presses
N.A.I.C.S.: 333998
Andrew Whyte (Engr-Applications)
Tom Gasbarre (CEO & CFO)

Gasbarre Products Inc., McKee Carbide Tool Division   (1)
159 McKee Rd, Olanta, PA 16863
Tel.: (814) 236-3108
Web Site: http://www.gasbarre.com
Emp.: 30
Tooling & Precision Machined Components
N.A.I.C.S.: 333514

Gasbarre Products Inc., Sinterite Furnace Division   (1)
310 State Rd, Saint Marys, PA 15857

Tel.: (814) 371-3015
Web Site: http://www.gasbarre.com
Sales Range: $10-24.9 Million
Emp.: 13
Continuous Belt Sintering Furnaces
N.A.I.C.S.: 333994
Steve Smith (Pres)

Subsidiary (Domestic):

J.L. Becker Company   (2)
41150 Joy Rd, Plymouth, MI 48170
Tel.: (734) 656-2000
Web Site: http://www.jlbecker.com
Heat Tracing Equipment Mfr
N.A.I.C.S.: 333994
Ben Crawford (Mgr-Sls)

PTX-Pentronix, Inc.   (1)
41160 Joy Rd, Plymouth, MI 48170
Tel.: (734) 946-5850
Web Site: http://www.ptx.com
Sales Range: $10-24.9 Million
Emp.: 5
Mfr of High Speed & High Precision Powder
Compacting Presses, Robotic Parts Loaders & Other Products for the Powder Compacting Industry
N.A.I.C.S.: 333517

GASCH PRINTING LLC
1780 Crossroads Dr, Odenton, MD 21113
Tel.: (301) 362-0700
Web Site:
    https://www.gaschprinting.com
Year Founded: 1982
Sales Range: $1-9.9 Million
Emp.: 15
Commercial Lithographic Printing
N.A.I.C.S.: 323111
Linda Gasch (CEO)

GASCO ENERGY, INC.
7979 Tufts Ave Ste 1150, Denver, CO 80237
Tel.: (303) 483-0044
Web Site:
    http://www.gascoenergy.com
Sales Range: $1-9.9 Million
Emp.: 25
Oil & Gas Exploration & Production Services
N.A.I.C.S.: 211120
Michael K. Decker (COO & Exec VP)
Robin Dean (Mgr-Geological)
David R. Smith (Mgr-Land)
Camille A. Gerard (Sec & Controller)
Richard P. Crist (VP-Bus Dev & Exploration)
Diane Westerberg (Mgr-Land)
Richard S. Langdon (Interim Pres & Interim CEO)

Subsidiaries:

Gasco Production Company   (1)
8 Inverness Dr Ste 100, Englewood, CO 80112
Tel.: (303) 483-0044
Web Site: http://www.gascoenergy.com
Gas Production Services
N.A.I.C.S.: 211120

GASCOSAGE ELECTRIC CO-OPERATIVE
803 S Ellen St, Dixon, MO 65459
Tel.: (573) 759-7146
Web Site: http://www.gascosage.com
Year Founded: 1939
Sales Range: $10-24.9 Million
Emp.: 40
Electric Power Distribution Services
N.A.I.C.S.: 221122
Jimmy Clark (Mgr-Ops)

GASETERIA OIL CORP.
364 Maspeth Ave, Brooklyn, NY 11211-1704
Tel.: (718) 782-4200
Web Site: http://www.largavista.com
Year Founded: 1981

Sales Range: $10-24.9 Million
Emp.: 85
Gasoline Services
N.A.I.C.S.: 457120
Marcello Porcelli (Pres)

Subsidiaries:

4DDDD Corporation   (1)
364 Maspeth Ave, Brooklyn, NY 11211-1704   (100%)
Tel.: (718) 782-4200
Web Site: http://www.gaseteria.com
Sales Range: $10-24.9 Million
Emp.: 20
Grocery Stores
N.A.I.C.S.: 445131

Ditmas Oil Associates Inc.   (1)
275 Madison Ave Fl 37, New York, NY 10016
Tel.: (718) 782-4200
Sales Range: $10-24.9 Million
Emp.: 10
Mfr of Petroleum Products
N.A.I.C.S.: 424720
Marcello Porcelli (Pres)

GASHO OF JAPAN INTERNATIONAL LTD.
365 RR 32, Central Valley, NY 10917
Tel.: (845) 928-2387
Web Site: http://www.gasho.com
Rev.: $10,299,200
Emp.: 40
Japanese Restaurant
N.A.I.C.S.: 722511
Shiro Aoki (Chm)

Subsidiaries:

Gasho of Japan Long Island   (1)
356 Vanderbilt Motor Pkwy, Hauppauge, NY 11788
Tel.: (631) 231-3400
Web Site: http://www.gasho.com
Sales Range: $10-24.9 Million
Emp.: 31
Eating Place
N.A.I.C.S.: 722511

Hida Japanese Restaurant   (1)
6 Saw Mill River Rd, Hawthorne, NY 10532
Tel.: (914) 592-5900
Web Site: http://www.hidany.com
Food Catering Services & Restaurant Operator
N.A.I.C.S.: 722511

GASMART USA INC.
10777 Barkley St Ste 200, Overland Park, KS 66211
Tel.: (913) 599-5800
Web Site:
    http://www.gasmartusa.com
Year Founded: 1995
Rev.: $25,000,000
Emp.: 275
Convenience Store Services
N.A.I.C.S.: 445131
Kevin Lott (VP)
Louise Tilghman (Mgr-HR)
Marcus Morgan (CFO & Controller)
Michael George (VP)
David George (Pres)
John Tittle (CEO)
Dawn Walser (Controller)
Marie Remlinger (Mgr-District 1-Chicago)
Kim Fielder (Mgr-District 1-Omaha)
Syed Aslam (Mgr-District 2-Chicago)

GASPARI NUTRA LLC
8004 NW 154th St Ste 261, Miami Lakes, FL 33016
Tel.: (732) 364-3777   FL
Web Site:
    https://www.gasparinutrition.com
Year Founded: 2018
Holding Company; Nutritional Supplement Mfr & Marketer
N.A.I.C.S.: 551112
Richard S. Gaspari (Owner)

Subsidiaries:

Gaspari Nutrition, Inc.   (1)
575 Prospect St, Lakewood, NJ 08701
Tel.: (732) 364-3777
Web Site: http://www.gasparinutrition.com
Nutritional Supplement Mfr & Marketer
N.A.I.C.S.: 325411
Richard S. Gaspari (CEO)

GASPARILLA INN, INC.
500 Palm Ave, Boca Grande, FL 33921
Tel.: (941) 964-4500
Web Site: https://www.the-gasparilla-inn.com
Sales Range: $25-49.9 Million
Emp.: 325
Hotel Operations
N.A.I.C.S.: 721110
William Farish (Owner)

GASPARILLA ISLAND CONSERVATION & IMPROVEMENT ASSOCIATION, INC.
131 First St W Office 8, Boca Grande, FL 33921
Tel.: (941) 964-2667   FL
Web Site: https://www.thegicia.org
Year Founded: 1971
Sales Range: $10-24.9 Million
Emp.: 4
Environment & Land Preservation Services
N.A.I.C.S.: 813312
Bruce Carbonari (Pres)
Penn Branin (Sec)
Henry Pankratz (Treas)
Claudia Thomas (VP)
Misty Nabers Nichols (Exec Dir)

GASQUE ADVERTISING, INC.
3195 Leaphart Rd, West Columbia, SC 29169-3001
Tel.: (803) 791-0952   SC
Web Site: http://www.gasque.com
Year Founded: 1973
Sales Range: $10-24.9 Million
Emp.: 6
Brand Development, Business Publications, Business-To-Business, Strategic Planning
N.A.I.C.S.: 541810
Ken Gasque (Brand Developer-Designer & Mktg Planner)
Mary Gasque (Office Mgr)

GASSER & SONS, INC.
440 Moreland Rd, Commack, NY 11725
Tel.: (631) 543-6600
Web Site: https://www.gasser.com
Year Founded: 1916
Sales Range: $75-99.9 Million
Emp.: 65
Deep-draw Metal Fabrication Specialists
N.A.I.C.S.: 332119
Richard F. Gasser (Chm & Pres)
Jack W. Gasser (VP)

GASSER CHAIR COMPANY INC.
4136 Logan Way, Youngstown, OH 44505
Tel.: (330) 759-2234
Web Site:
    https://www.gasserchair.com
Rev.: $25,000,000
Emp.: 170
Chair Mfr
N.A.I.C.S.: 337127
Evelyn Mihin (COO)

GASTON & SHEEHAN AUCTIONEERS, INC.
1420 FM 685, Pflugerville, TX 78660

Tel.: (512) 251-2780
Web Site: https://www.txauction.com
Year Founded: 1988
Sales Range: $10-24.9 Million
Emp.: 10
Operator of Auction & Storage Facilities
N.A.I.C.S.: 561990
Bob Sheehan *(Owner)*

GASTON ADVERTISING

730 W Randolph St Ste 400, Chicago, IL 60661
Tel.: (312) 382-0800
Web Site: http://www.gastonad.com
Sales Range: $10-24.9 Million
Emp.: 10
Advertising Agencies
N.A.I.C.S.: 541810
Dave Gaston *(Founder & Pres)*
Jack Gniadecki *(VP & Dir-Creative)*

GASTON COUNTY DYEING MACHINE COMPANY

1310 Charles Raper Jonas Hwy, Mount Holly, NC 28120-1234
Tel.: (704) 822-5000   NC
Web Site: https://www.gaston-county.com
Year Founded: 1921
Sales Range: $50-74.9 Million
Emp.: 70
Mfr of Textile Wet-Processing Machinery & Controls
N.A.I.C.S.: 335314
David R. Craig *(CFO)*
Chip McGill *(VP-Sls)*

GASTONIA SHEET METAL

1535 W May Ave, Gastonia, NC 28052-1409
Tel.: (704) 864-0344
Web Site:
    http://www.gastoniasheetmetal.com
Year Founded: 1967
Sales Range: $10-24.9 Million
Emp.: 100
Roofing Installation Services
N.A.I.C.S.: 238390
Steven D. Long *(Owner)*
Joel Long *(Owner)*

GASTRO HEALTH, LLC

9500 S Dadeland Blvd Ste 200, Miami, FL 33156
Tel.: (305) 468-4180
Web Site:
    http://www.gastrohealth.com
Emp.: 100
Office Of Physician
N.A.I.C.S.: 621111
Alan B. Oliver *(COO)*
Pedro Marzocca *(VP-Revenue Cycle Management)*
Lawrence G. Freni *(CFO)*
Joseph Garcia *(CEO)*
James Leavitt *(Dir-Clinical Quality & Outcomes)*
Frank Manes *(Sr VP-Bus Dev)*
Christina Sullivan *(VP-HR)*
Jason Wallace *(Chief Compliance Officer & VP-Legal Affairs)*
John Rutherford *(VP-Payor Contracting)*

Subsidiaries:

Gastroenterology Associates of
Northern Virginia, LLC   (1)
3028 Javier Rd Ste 300, Fairfax, VA 22031
Tel.: (703) 698-8960
Offices of Physicians (except Mental Health Specialists)
N.A.I.C.S.: 621111

GASTRONOMY INC.

48 W Market St Ste 200, Salt Lake City, UT 84101-2103
Tel.: (801) 322-2020   UT
Web Site: http://www.ginc.com
Year Founded: 1980
Sales Range: $25-49.9 Million
Emp.: 700
Restaurant Operators
N.A.I.C.S.: 722511
Will Pliler *(Gen Mgr)*

GATE CITY BANK

500 2nd Ave N, Fargo, ND 58102
Tel.: (701) 293-2400
Web Site:
    http://www.gatecitybank.com
Year Founded: 1923
Sales Range: $10-24.9 Million
Emp.: 310
Federal Savings Bank
N.A.I.C.S.: 522180
Steven J. Swiontek *(Chm, Pres & CEO)*
Lance R. Wolf *(Dir-Retail Banking)*
Alan E. Erickson *(Dir-Fin, Strategic Plng & Risk Mgmt)*
Marcus Boykin *(Office Mgr)*
Steve Walker *(Mgr-Insurance Svc)*
Patricia A. Kotta *(Controller)*
Kimberly R. Meyer *(Dir-Admin)*
Karin J. Rudd *(Dir-Dev & Customer Rels)*
Kevin J. Hanson *(Dir-Lending)*
Maureen E. Jelinek *(Dir-Tech)*
Greg W. Ellwein *(Mgr-Bismarck Office)*
Kevin M. Warner *(Mgr-Bus Lending)*
Tavia K. Smith *(Mgr-Customer Svc Center)*
Jennifer L. Dirk *(Mgr-Deposit Admin & Servicing)*
Susan K. Anderson *(Mgr-Property Mgmt & Lending Solutions)*
Stephanie Dinius *(Asst VP)*
Shannon Nelson *(Asst VP)*
Lezan Tahir *(Asst VP)*
Jacob Thielges *(Asst VP)*
Lora Stebleton *(VP-Payment Svcs)*
Tanya Cox *(VP-Customer Svc Center)*
Amy Durbin *(VP-Mktg & Bus Intelligence)*
Megan Meis *(Asst VP-Fraud Mitigation)*
Sam Jelleberg *(Asst VP)*
David VanBruggen *(Asst VP)*
Robert Ross *(Asst VP-Office Svcs & Security)*
Teresa Jesten *(Asst VP)*
Patty Blozinski *(Sr VP-BSA & Fraud)*

GATE CITY LINCOLN MERCURY

300 N Church St, Greensboro, NC 27401
Tel.: (336) 274-0195
Year Founded: 1914
Sales Range: $25-49.9 Million
Emp.: 55
New Car Whslr
N.A.I.C.S.: 441110
David Brown *(Pres)*

GATE PETROLEUM COMPANY

9540 San Jose Blvd, Jacksonville, FL 32257
Tel.: (904) 737-7220   FL
Web Site: https://www.gatepetro.com
Year Founded: 1960
Sales Range: $1-4.9 Billion
Emp.: 3,000
Diversified Holding Company; Gasoline Stations, Architectural Products Mfr & Real Estate
N.A.I.C.S.: 551112
Herbert Hill Peyton *(Founder)*

Subsidiaries:

Epping Forest Yacht Club   (1)
1830 Epping Forest Dr, Jacksonville, FL
32217   (100%)
Tel.: (904) 739-7200
Web Site: http://www.efyc.com
Sales Range: $25-49.9 Million
Emp.: 50
Yacht Club
N.A.I.C.S.: 713930
Linda Henry *(Dir-Catering Sls)*

Gate Maritime Properties, Inc.   (1)
9540 San Jose Blvd, Jacksonville, FL
32241-3627
Tel.: (904) 737-7220
Web Site: http://www.gatepetro.com
Sales Range: $100-124.9 Million
Emp.: 1,800
Real Estate Services
N.A.I.C.S.: 531390
Jack C. Lueders Jr. *(Pres)*

Gate Marketing   (1)
9540 San Jose Blvd, Jacksonville, FL
32257   (100%)
Tel.: (904) 737-7220
Sales Range: $50-74.9 Million
Emp.: 500
Multi-Purpose Marketing Functions, Including Fuel Distribution, Convenience Stores & Other Services
N.A.I.C.S.: 457120
David Bill *(Pres)*

Gate Petroleum - Development
Division   (1)
9540 San Jose Blvd, Jacksonville, FL
32241-3627
Tel.: (904) 737-7220
Web Site: http://www.gatepetro.com
Sales Range: $25-49.9 Million
Emp.: 300
Residential & Commercial Real Estate Development
N.A.I.C.S.: 457120

Gate Precast Company   (1)
9540 San Jose Blvd, Jacksonville, FL
32257
Tel.: (904) 732-7668
Web Site: http://www.gateprecast.com
Sales Range: $25-49.9 Million
Emp.: 5
Pre-Cast Concrete Products
N.A.I.C.S.: 327390
Dean Gwin *(Pres & COO)*
Wright Mo *(Dir-Mktg)*
Mukarim Syed *(Mgr-Engrg-Southeast)*
Steve Brock *(Sr VP-Engrg)*
Tom Newton *(VP-Ops)*

Unit (Domestic):

Gate Precast Co.   (2)
810 Sawdust Trl, Kissimmee, FL 34744-1418
Tel.: (407) 847-5285
Web Site: http://www.gateprecast.com
Sales Range: $25-49.9 Million
Concrete Products
N.A.I.C.S.: 327390
Bryant Luke *(VP-Ops)*

Gate Precast Co.   (2)
101 7th St, Winchester, KY 40391
Tel.: (859) 744-9481
Web Site: http://www.gateprecast.com
Sales Range: $10-24.9 Million
Pre-Cast Concrete Products
N.A.I.C.S.: 327390
Tom Townes *(VP-Estimating)*
Jim Lewis *(Dir-Mktg)*
Mark Tedron *(VP-Ops)*
Steve Schweitzer *(VP & Mgr-Ops)*

Gate Precast Co.   (2)
1 Bluegrass Dr, Ashland City, TN 37015
Tel.: (615) 792-4871
Web Site: http://www.gateprecast.com
Sales Range: $10-24.9 Million
Pre-Cast Concrete Products
N.A.I.C.S.: 327390

Gate Precast Co.   (2)
3201 Veterans Dr, Pearland, TX 77584
Tel.: (281) 485-3273
Web Site: http://www.gateprecast.com

Sales Range: $10-24.9 Million
Concrete Products
N.A.I.C.S.: 327390
Peter Gemmill *(Plant Superintendent)*

Gate Precast Co.   (2)
3800 Oxford Loop, Oxford, NC 27565
Tel.: (919) 603-1633
Web Site: http://www.gateprecast.com
Sales Range: $25-49.9 Million
Concrete Products
N.A.I.C.S.: 327390
Dean Gwin *(Pres & COO)*
Earl Shimp *(Sr VP-Ops)*

Division (Domestic):

Gate Precast Company -
Jacksonville   (2)
402 Zoo Pkwy, Jacksonville, FL 32226
Tel.: (904) 757-0860
Web Site: http://www.gateprecast.com
Hollow-Core & Prestree Concrete Products Mfr
N.A.I.C.S.: 327390
Brian Griffins *(Mgr-Southeast Regional Sls & Mktg)*

Gate Riverplace Company   (1)
1301 River Pl Blvd, Jacksonville, FL 32207
Tel.: (904) 396-1111
Web Site: http://www.gateriverplace.com
Sales Range: $10-24.9 Million
Emp.: 9
Operator of Office Complex
N.A.I.C.S.: 531120

Ponte Vedra Beach Inn & Club   (1)
200 Ponte Vedra Blvd, Ponte Vedra Beach,
FL 32082
Tel.: (904) 285-1111
Web Site: http://www.pontevedra.com
Sales Range: $50-74.9 Million
Emp.: 700
Resort & Lodge
N.A.I.C.S.: 721110
Dale Haney *(Pres)*
Lauren Dooley *(Mgr-Sls)*

Ponte Vedra Lodge & Club   (1)
607 Ponte Vedra Blvd, Ponte Vedra Beach,
FL 32082
Tel.: (904) 273-9500
Web Site: http://www.pontevedra.com
Sales Range: $25-49.9 Million
Emp.: 180
Lodge & Resort
N.A.I.C.S.: 721110
Thayer Kern *(Gen Mgr)*

GATEHOUSE COMPANIES, INC.

120 Forbes Blvd, Mansfield, MA 02048
Tel.: (508) 337-2500
Web Site:
    https://www.gatehousemgt.com
Rev.: $16,400,000
Emp.: 146
Land Subdividers & Developers Residential
N.A.I.C.S.: 237210
Mark Plonskier *(Pres-Gatehouse Grp)*
Roger Yorkshaitis *(CFO)*

GATEONE, INC.

201 Aviation Way Hngr 11n, Fort Worth, TX 76106
Tel.: (817) 625-2366   TX
Year Founded: 1995
Sales Range: $1-9.9 Million
Emp.: 32
Petroleum & Petroleum Products Merchant Whslr (except Bulk Stations & Terminals)
N.A.I.C.S.: 424720
Thomas Mathew *(Pres & CEO)*

GATES & SONS INCORPORATED

90 S Fox St, Denver, CO 80223
Tel.: (303) 744-6185
Web Site:
    https://www.gatesconcreteforms.com

Gates & Sons Incorporated—(Continued)

Year Founded: 1948
Structural Wood Members
N.A.I.C.S.: 321215
Jim Huscroft Work *(Pres)*
Gloria Cross *(VP)*
Gary Winkler *(Plant Mgr)*
Tiffiny Annis *(VP-HR)*

GATES AUTOMOTIVE CENTER

50 Thruway Park Dr, West Henrietta, NY 14586
Tel.: (585) 247-3844
Web Site:
http://www.gatesautocenter.com
Year Founded: 1990
Sales Range: $1-9.9 Million
Emp.: 65
Services Consumer & Fleet Vehicles
N.A.I.C.S.: 811111
Anthony Ardillo *(VP-Ops)*
Teena Speck *(Area Mgr)*

GATES GROUP CAPITAL PARTNERS, LLC

6120 Parkland Blvd Ste 202, Mayfield Heights, OH 44124
Tel.: (440) 684-9900
Web Site:
http://www.gatesgroupcp.com
Emp.: 4
Privater Equity Firm
N.A.I.C.S.: 523999
Walter Stuelpe *(Chm)*

GATESMAN, INC.

444 Liberty Ave Ste 700, Pittsburgh, PA 15222
Tel.: (412) 381-5400   **PA**
Web Site:
https://www.gatesmanagency.com
Year Founded: 2006
Advertising & Public Relations Agency
N.A.I.C.S.: 541810
John Gatesman *(Founder & CEO)*
Shannon Baker *(Pres)*
Debbie Zappia *(Sr VP & Dir-Ops)*
Rodney Deloe *(CFO & Exec VP)*
Kathy Oldaker *(Sr VP & Dir-Media)*
Tim Friez *(Sr VP/Dir-IT & Cyber Security)*
Beth Thompson *(VP & Grp Acct Dir)*
Desiree Bartoe *(VP & Grp Acct Dir)*
Karen McKinley *(Chief Creative Officer & Exec VP)*
Richard Sanderson *(Exec VP & Gen Mgr)*
John Berka *(Sr VP & Grp Acct Dir)*
Susan English *(Sr VP & Dir-PR & Social Media)*
Jay Giesen *(Sr VP & Creative Dir)*
Emily Hamill *(Sr VP/Dir-Connections Strategy)*
Sara Ahuja *(VP & Grp Acct Dir)*
Demar Anderson *(VP & Dir-Mktg)*
Craig Ferrence *(Sr VP & Creative Dir)*
Christy Kelly *(Sr VP & Dir-Chicago Accts)*
Nancy Banasik *(Sr VP & Grp Acct Dir)*
Mark Dipietro *(VP & Creative Dir)*
Kirk Banasik *(Sr VP & Grp Acct Dir)*

Subsidiaries:

Gatesman, Inc. - Chicago   **(1)**
200 E Randolph St 52nd Fl, Chicago, IL 60601
Tel.: (312) 670-2900
Web Site: http://www.gatesmannoble.com
Advertising & Public Relations Agency
N.A.I.C.S.: 541810
Michael Jensen *(VP & Grp Acct Dir)*
Kirk Banasik *(VP-Acct Svc)*
Ruth Coyne *(Dir-Acct-Grp)*

Leslie Hutter *(Sr VP-Insights & Strategy)*
Maggie McKeon *(Dir-Art)*
John Scroggins *(VP-Integrated Comm)*
Tiffany White *(Supvr-Mgmt)*

Gatesman, Inc. - Springfield   **(1)**
2215 W Chesterfield Blvd, Springfield, MO 65807-8683
Tel.: (417) 875-5000
Web Site: http://www.gatesmanagency.com
Advertising & Public Relations Agency
N.A.I.C.S.: 541810
Nancy Banasik *(Sr VP & Grp Dir)*
Karen Frost *(VP & Dir-Creative)*

GATEWAY BUICK GMC

11438 LBJ Fwy, Dallas, TX 75238-5244
Tel.: (214) 342-7002   **MO**
Web Site:
https://www.gatewaybuickgmc.com
Year Founded: 1977
Sales Range: $125-149.9 Million
Emp.: 200
New & Used Car Dealer
N.A.I.C.S.: 441110
Mike Meyr *(Gen Sls Mgr)*
Mike Brotherton *(Dir-Ops)*
Charles Cooksey *(Mng Partner)*

GATEWAY COMPANY

6425 Graham Rd, Saint Louis, MO 63134
Tel.: (314) 524-7440
Web Site:
https://www.gatewaycompany.com
Sales Range: $10-24.9 Million
Emp.: 77
Industrial Painting
N.A.I.C.S.: 238320

GATEWAY CON FORMING SYSTEMS

11124 N Industrial Dr, Thiensville, WI 53092
Tel.: (262) 242-1600
Rev.: $12,000,000
Emp.: 35
Concrete Work
N.A.I.C.S.: 238110

GATEWAY ECONOMIC DEVELOPMENT CORPORATION OF GREATER CLEVELAND

758 Bolivar Rd, Cleveland, OH 44115
Tel.: (216) 420-4072   **OH**
Web Site:
http://www.gatewaysportscomplex.org
Year Founded: 1990
Sales Range: $10-24.9 Million
Emp.: 12
Economic Development Services
N.A.I.C.S.: 813410
Marchelle Jackson *(Mgr-Special Event)*
Joe Amberik *(Mgr-Ballpark)*
Todd Greathouse *(Exec Dir)*
Brian Kelly *(Controller)*
Timothy Offtermatt *(Chm)*
Daniella Nunnally *(Dir-Ops)*

GATEWAY ENERGY COMPANY, LLC

1415 Louisiana St Ste 4100, Houston, TX 77002
Tel.: (713) 336-0844   **DE**
Web Site:
http://www.gatewayenergy.com
Sales Range: $1-9.9 Million
Emp.: 3
Gas Transmission & Distr
N.A.I.C.S.: 486210
Frederick M. Pevow Jr. *(Chm, Pres & CEO)*

Subsidiaries:

Eclipse Energy Inc.   **(1)**

333 N Sam Houston Pkwy E # 610, Houston, TX 77060
Tel.: (281) 999-8200
Web Site: http://www.gatewayenergy.com
Natural Gas Production
N.A.I.C.S.: 211130

Gateway Pipeline Company   **(1)**
500 Dallas St Ste 2615, Houston, TX 77002
Tel.: (713) 336-0844
Web Site: http://www.gatewayenergy.com
Natural Gas Distr
N.A.I.C.S.: 221210

GATEWAY FOODS INC.

26285 Hwy 195, Double Springs, AL 35553
Tel.: (205) 489-8888
Sales Range: $10-24.9 Million
Emp.: 300
Grocery Stores, Independent
N.A.I.C.S.: 445110
Greg Waldorp *(VP)*
Audrey Early *(Controller)*
Harold Garrett *(Pres)*

GATEWAY FS, INC.

221 E Pine St, Red Bud, IL 62278-1548
Tel.: (618) 282-4000   **IL**
Web Site: https://www.gatewayfs.com
Year Founded: 1990
Sales Range: $75-99.9 Million
Emp.: 100
Field Seeding, Ferterlizer, Chemical & Grain Merchandise
N.A.I.C.S.: 424510
Don Schrader *(Sec)*
Jeff Heckert *(Treas)*
Dennis Neuhaus Hoyleton *(VP)*
Brian Perez *(CFO & Controller)*

GATEWAY GROUP ONE

604-608 Market S, Newark, NJ 07105
Tel.: (973) 465-8006
Web Site:
https://www.gatewaygroupone.com
Year Founded: 1979
Sales Range: $75-99.9 Million
Emp.: 4,000
Security Guards & Patrol Services
N.A.I.C.S.: 561612
Kurus Elavia *(CEO)*

Subsidiaries:

Gateway Group One   **(1)**
5757 Century BlvdSte810, Los Angeles, CA 90045   **(100%)**
Tel.: (310) 410-0790
Web Site: http://www.gatewaygroupone.com
Asset Protection, Aviation Terminal Services & Parking Management
N.A.I.C.S.: 561612

GATEWAY HOMES LTD

7676 Hillmont St Ste 345, Houston, TX 77040
Tel.: (713) 622-3737   **TX**
Web Site:
http://www.gatewayhomes.com
Year Founded: 1990
Sales Range: $10-24.9 Million
Emp.: 50
Family Home Construction
N.A.I.C.S.: 236115
Tom Walker *(Pres)*
Allen Blacksher *(VP-Construction)*
Paul Petropolis *(VP-Sls-Mktg)*
Tom Stancik *(CFO)*

GATEWAY LINCOLN-MERCURY INCORPORATED

1300 5th Ave, Columbus, GA 31902
Tel.: (706) 322-5575
Web Site: http://www.gatewaylmi.net
Rev.: $22,596,820
Emp.: 60
Automobiles, New & Used
N.A.I.C.S.: 441110

Daniel R. Snow *(Pres)*

GATEWAY MANAGEMENT SERVICES LTD

190 Charlois Blvd Ste 200 B, Winston Salem, NC 27103
Tel.: (336) 759-3352
Web Site:
http://www.premium2000.com
Year Founded: 1995
Sales Range: $1-9.9 Million
Emp.: 25
Truck Dealers
N.A.I.C.S.: 441110
Lynn Murphy *(Pres & CEO)*

GATEWAY MORTGAGE GROUP LLC

6910 E 14th St, Tulsa, OK 74112
Tel.: (918) 712-9000
Web Site:
http://www.gatewayloan.com
Year Founded: 2000
Sales Range: $10-24.9 Million
Emp.: 160
Mortgage Services
N.A.I.C.S.: 522310
David Robinson *(Dir-Alternative Sls Channels)*
Steve Frink *(Exec VP)*
Mike Goyer *(COO)*
Jared Edmonds *(VP-Natl Production-Correspondent Lending Div)*
Tyler Kobler *(Mgr-Wichita)*
Joanne Posen *(Mgr-Sls-Texas & New Mexico)*
Pete Tamoney *(Mgr-Sls-Mid Atlantic & Eastern Midwest)*
Fred Elflein *(Reg VP)*
Stephen Curry *(Chm)*
Steven Patrick *(Chief Risk Officer)*
Ken Harrison *(VP-Agency Rels)*
Jacquelyn Pardue *(Dir-Pur & Vendor Mgmt)*
Christopher G. Treece *(CFO)*
Jake Carlisle *(Reg VP-Pacific Northwest)*
Tina Knaut *(VP-Southwest Reg)*
Chris Dunlap *(VP-North Central)*
Mark Revard *(Exec VP-East)*
Jeff Schmidt *(Reg VP-North Texas)*
Steve Thompson *(Reg VP-South Texas)*
Steven Plaisance *(Pres-Mortgage Banking)*

GATEWAY MOTORSPORTS PARK

700 Raceway Blvd, Madison, IL 62060
Tel.: (618) 215-8888   **IL**
Web Site:
http://www.gatewaymsp.com
Motor Sport Facility
N.A.I.C.S.: 561210
Curtis Francois *(Owner)*
Chris Blair *(Exec VP & Gen Mgr)*
Matthew Dunscombe *(Comptroller)*
John Bisci *(Dir-Pub Rels)*
Scott Winter *(Sls Mgr)*
Taylor Deckard *(Grp Sls & Svcs Mgr)*
Sarah Kay Broeker *(Sls & Activation Mgr)*
George Whitaker *(Drag Strip Mgr)*
Declan O'Niell *(VP-Bus Dev)*

GATEWAY PRESS, INC.

4500 Robards Ln, Louisville, KY 40218-4537
Tel.: (502) 454-0431   **KY**
Web Site:
https://www.gatewaypressinc.com
Year Founded: 1950
Sales Range: $100-124.9 Million
Emp.: 170

Provider of Commercial Printing
N.A.I.C.S.: 323111
Ed Ryan *(VP)*
Darrell Embry *(Sr VP-Sls)*

GATEWAY PRINTING & OF-FICE SUPPLY, INC.

315 S Closner, Edinburg, TX 78539
Tel.: (956) 383-3861
Web Site: http://www.gatewayp.com
Sales Range: $10-24.9 Million
Emp.: 140
Office Supplies Distr; Commercial Printing Services
N.A.I.C.S.: 423420
Lin Miller *(Pres)*
Sonia Garcia *(VP-Printing Ops)*
Larry Talbert *(Mgr-Sls Furniture)*
Teresa Stouton *(Mgr-HR)*
Janie Bodden *(Mgr-Retail Store-Brownsville)*
Rudy Castilleja *(Mgr-Retail Store)*
Kelly Tijerina *(Mgr-Print Shop)*
Edel Diaz *(Branch Mgr)*
Norman Valicek *(Supvr-Customer Svc)*
Subsidiaries:
Jones & Cook Stationers, Inc.   **(1)**
106 S Broadway St, McAllen, TX 78501
Tel.: (956) 686-6578
Web Site: http://www.jonescook.com
Sales Range: $10-24.9 Million
Emp.: 40
Office Forms & Supplies
N.A.I.C.S.: 423420
S. Foss Jones *(Pres)*

GATEWAY RADIOLOGY CON-SULTANTS, P.A.

4800 Park Blvd, Pinellas Park, FL 33781
Tel.: (727) 525-2121
Web Site:
    https://www.gatewayradiology.com
Year Founded: 1976
Sales Range: $1-9.9 Million
Emp.: 35
Radiology Services
N.A.I.C.S.: 621111
Ray Hayduke *(Mgr-Radiology Ops)*

GATEWAY REHABILITATION CENTER

311 Rouser Rd, Moon Township, PA 15108-2719
Tel.: (412) 604-8900   PA
Web Site:
    http://www.gatewayrehab.org
Year Founded: 1972
Sales Range: $25-49.9 Million
Emp.: 691
Individual & Family Support Services
N.A.I.C.S.: 624190
Neil A. Capretto *(Dir-Medical)*
Paul Sweeney *(Chm)*
Richard F. Galardini *(Vice Chm)*
Joseph A. Massaro III *(Sec)*

GATEWAY SUPPLY COMPANY INC.

1312 Hamrick St, Columbia, SC 29201
Tel.: (803) 771-7160
Web Site:
    https://www.gatewaysupply.net
Year Founded: 1964
Rev.: $38,473,717
Emp.: 200
Plumbing Supplier
N.A.I.C.S.: 423720
Chris Williams *(Pres)*
Leonard Moore *(VP)*

GATEWAY TICKETING SYS-TEMS, INC.

445 County Line Rd, Gilbertsville, PA 19525
Tel.: (610) 987-4000
Web Site:
    https://www.gatewayticketing.com
Year Founded: 1988
Rev.: $15,200,000
Emp.: 101
Computer System Design Services
N.A.I.C.S.: 541512
Darryl L. Moser *(Exec VP)*
Nancy Bohn *(Dir-HR)*
Michael M. Andre *(Pres)*
Kevin Howard *(CFO)*
Shawn Ridgway *(Dir-Product Dev)*

GATEWAY TIRE OF ARKAN-SAS INC.

2528 S Caraway Rd, Jonesboro, AR 72402
Tel.: (870) 932-4523
Web Site: http://www.dktire.com
Rev.: $13,288,945
Emp.: 35
Tires & Tubes
N.A.I.C.S.: 423130
Robert H. Dunlap *(Pres)*
Barry Vaughn *(Mgr-Warehouse)*

GATEWAY TRANSPORT

5655 Lindero Canyon Rd, Westlake Village, CA 91362
Tel.: (310) 673-9770
Web Site:
    http://www.gatewaytransport.com
Rev.: $1,208,000
Emp.: 8
General Freight Trucking, Long-Distance, Truckload
N.A.I.C.S.: 484121
Jim Hession *(Founder)*

GATEWAY WAREHOUSE INC.

10009 Office Center Ave Ste 200, Saint Louis, MO 63128
Tel.: (314) 843-6455
Web Site: http://www.faurebros.com
Year Founded: 1998
Rev.: $14,900,000
Emp.: 100
Industrial Buildings & Warehouses
N.A.I.C.S.: 236220
Charles Koenig *(Pres)*

GATEWAY-LONGVIEW, INC.

10 Symphony Cir, Buffalo, NY 14201
Tel.: (716) 783-3100   NY
Web Site: https://www.gateway-longview.org
Year Founded: 1890
Sales Range: $25-49.9 Million
Emp.: 666
Child & Family Support Services
N.A.I.C.S.: 624190
Tim Girard *(VP-Educational Svcs)*
Erin Bice *(VP-HR)*
Pamela Rouse *(VP-Corp Compli-ance)*
Larry W. Perry *(VP-Tech)*
Keith McGriff *(Dir-Residential Svcs)*
Andrea Moran *(VP-Foundation & Or-ganizational Advancement)*
Kristy D'Angelo *(VP-Behavioral Health Svcs)*
Michelle Federowicz *(VP-Foster Care & Preventive Svcs)*
Mike Kelly *(CFO & VP-Fin)*
Carolyne Defranco *(Pres & CEO)*
Christopher Henning *(Dir-Residential Treatment)*
James Grande *(Dir-Behavioral Health Clinic)*
Kristin Rivera *(Dir-Clinical Svcs-Residential Treatment)*
Michael Trillizio *(Dir-Community Sup-port Svcs)*

Matthew Veazie *(Dir-Foster Care & Permanency Svcs)*
Shannon Ochal *(Dir-Therapeutic Pre-school)*
Keith Somerville *(Asst Dir-Residential Svcs)*
Ivan Sosa *(Dir-Residential Svcs)*

GATEWAYS HOSPITAL AND MENTAL HEALTH CENTER

1891 Effie St, Los Angeles, CA 90026
Tel.: (323) 644-2000   CA
Web Site:
    https://www.gatewayshospital.org
Year Founded: 1953
Sales Range: $25-49.9 Million
Emp.: 449
Behavioral Healthcare Services
N.A.I.C.S.: 621420
William McSweeney *(VP)*
Barry Steinhardt *(Pres)*
Hal Espinosa *(Treas)*
Mark Gottesman *(Sec)*

GATEWAYS INDUSTRIES

6000 Mahoning Ave Ste 234, Youngs-town, OH 44515
Tel.: (330) 792-2854   OH
Web Site:
    https://www.gatewaystbl.com
Year Founded: 2007
Sales Range: $1-9.9 Million
Disabled People Assisted Living Ser-vices
N.A.I.C.S.: 623312
James Linert *(CFO)*
Karl Ware *(Program Dir)*
Steven Snyder *(Vice Chm)*
James Dietz *(Sec)*

GATEWORKS, CORP.

3026 S Higuera St, San Luis Obispo, CA 93449
Tel.: (805) 781-2000   CA
Web Site:
    https://www.gateworks.com
Year Founded: 1996
Sales Range: $1-9.9 Million
Emp.: 25
Computer Component Manufacturer
N.A.I.C.S.: 334513
Doug Hollingsworth *(VP-Engrg)*
Chris Lang *(Dir-Ops)*
Gordon Edmonds *(Pres & CEO)*

GATHER WORKSPACES, LLC

313 E Broad, Richmond, VA 23219
Tel.: (804) 937-3287
Web Site:
    http://www.workatgather.com
Year Founded: 2014
Sales Range: $1-9.9 Million
Emp.: 9
Hospitality Operator
N.A.I.C.S.: 721110
Tariq Crumbly *(Mgr-Community)*
Lindsey Wrable *(Mgr-Community)*

GATOR AIR CONDITIONING

6216 28th St E Ste 1, Bradenton, FL 34203
Tel.: (941) 749-6000
Web Site: https://www.gatorac.com
Sales Range: $1-9.9 Million
Emp.: 25
Air Conditioning Contractor
N.A.I.C.S.: 238220
James Pomroy *(Owner)*
Dave Loyd *(Supvr-Svc Field)*

GATOR CAPITAL MANAGE-MENT LLC

100 S. Ashley Dr., Ste 895, Tampa, FL 33602
Tel.: (813) 282-7870
Web Site: https://gatorcapital.com

Year Founded: 2008
Investment Management
N.A.I.C.S.: 523999
Derek Pilecki *(Founder & Portfolio Mgr)*

GATOR CHRYSLER INC.

300 E Nasa Blvd, Melbourne, FL 32901-1940
Tel.: (321) 727-7711
Web Site:
    http://www.gatorchrysler.net
Year Founded: 1970
Sales Range: $10-24.9 Million
Emp.: 100
Car Whslr
N.A.I.C.S.: 441110
Carlos Menendez *(VP)*

GATOR FORD TRUCK SALES INC.

11780 Tampa Gateway Blvd, Seffner, FL 33584
Tel.: (813) 565-1732
Web Site: https://www.gatorford.com
Sales Range: $25-49.9 Million
Emp.: 85
Car & Truck Dealership Owner & Operator
N.A.I.C.S.: 441110
David Kilcoyne *(Pres)*
Pat Cooper *(Mgr-Sls)*

GATOR FOURE INC.

425 Fuller Ave NE, Grand Rapids, MI 49503
Tel.: (616) 459-4128
Rev.: $16,000,000
Emp.: 45
Supermarket Operator
N.A.I.C.S.: 445110

GATOR OF FLORIDA INCOR-PORATED

5002 N Howard Ave, Tampa, FL 33603
Tel.: (813) 877-8267
Web Site:
    http://www.gatoroflorida.com
Rev.: $23,861,150
Emp.: 12
Women's & Children's Sportswear
N.A.I.C.S.: 424350

GATOR VET INC.

1168 Indian Hills Blvd, Venice, FL 34293
Tel.: (941) 942-9692
Web Site:
    http://www.venicepinesvet.com
Sales Range: $1-9.9 Million
Emp.: 15
Veterinary Services
N.A.I.C.S.: 541940
Beth Crosley *(Office Mgr)*

GATSKI COMMERCIAL REAL ESTATE SERVICES

4755 Dean Martin Dr, Las Vegas, NV 89103
Tel.: (702) 221-8226   NV
Web Site:
    http://www.gatskicommercial.com
Year Founded: 1993
Sales Range: $1-9.9 Million
Emp.: 70
Commercial Real Estate
N.A.I.C.S.: 531210
Frank P. Gatski *(Pres & CEO)*
Diana Bachmura *(Dir-Res & Mktg)*
Gabe Telles *(Mng Dir & Sr VP)*
David Bauman *(Mng Dir-Property Mgmt)*

GAUBERT OIL COMPANY IN-CORPORATED

Gaubert Oil Company Incorporated—(Continued)

1201 Saint Patrick St, Thibodaux, LA 70301
Tel.: (985) 447-3811
Web Site: http://www.gaubertoil.com
Sales Range: $10-24.9 Million
Emp.: 40
Provider of Petroleum Products
N.A.I.C.S.: 424720
Grady K. Gaubert *(Pres)*
Josh Isbill *(VP-Sls)*
Ray Mayon Jr. *(Acct Mgr-Sls)*

GAUDENZIA, INC.
106 W Main St, Norristown, PA 19401
Tel.: (610) 239-9600   PA
Web Site: https://www.gaudenzia.org
Year Founded: 1968
Sales Range: $50-74.9 Million
Emp.: 1,172
Addiction Treatment & Recovery Services
N.A.I.C.S.: 622210

GAUGE CAPITAL LLC
1256 Main St Ste 256, Southlake, TX 76092
Tel.: (682) 334-5800   DE
Web Site:
  http://www.gaugecapital.com
Privater Equity Firm
N.A.I.C.S.: 523999
Drew Johnson *(Co-Founder & Mng Partner)*
Tom McKelvey *(Co-Founder & Mng Partner)*

Subsidiaries:

Teachers of Tomorrow LLC   (1)
2401 Fountain View Dr Ste 700, Houston, TX 77057
Tel.: (877) 888-2640
Web Site:
  http://www.teachersoftomorrow.org
Education Management Services
N.A.I.C.S.: 923110
Phillip Braithwaite *(CEO)*

Subsidiary (Domestic):

Infosource Inc.   (2)
1300 City View Ctr, Oviedo, FL 32765
Tel.: (407) 677-0300
Web Site: http://www.simplek12.com
Sales Range: $10-24.9 Million
Emp.: 60
Computer Software Development
N.A.I.C.S.: 541511
Linda O'Reily *(VP-Fin)*
Michael Werner *(CEO)*
Tom Warrner *(Pres)*
Ernie Spadaro *(VP-Product Dev)*

Urology America, LLC   (1)
8240 N. Mopac Expy Ste 100, Austin, TX 78759
Tel.: (512) 477-5905
Web Site: https://www.urologyamerica.com
Hospitals & Health Care
N.A.I.C.S.: 621610

Subsidiary (Domestic):

The Conrad / Pearson Clinic, P.C.   (2)
125 Guthrie Dr, Southaven, MS 38671-5829
Tel.: (662) 349-1964
Web Site: http://www.conradpearson.com
Offices of Physicians (except Mental Health Specialists)
N.A.I.C.S.: 621111

GAUGER + ASSOCIATES
360 Post St Ste 901, San Francisco, CA 94108
Tel.: (415) 434-0303   CA
Web Site: http://www.gauger-associates.com
Year Founded: 1974
Sales Range: $25-49.9 Million

Emp.: 30
Advertising Agencies, Brand Development, Graphic Design, New Product Development, Public Relations, Strategic Planning/Research
N.A.I.C.S.: 541810
David Gauger *(Pres & Creative Dir)*
Isabelle Laporte *(Sr Dir-Art)*
Lori Murphy *(Sr Dir-Art)*
Sam Matza *(VP & Media Dir)*
Iza Ellis *(VP & Gen Mgr)*
Heidi Oas *(Acct Mgr)*
Carol Muth *(Sr Copywriter)*
John F. Porter *(Controller)*
Dana Klumb *(Art Dir)*
Adam Zloto *(Mgr-Creative)*
Marcus Young *(Exec VP)*

GAULT CHEVROLET CO. INC.
2507 N St, Endicott, NY 13760
Tel.: (607) 748-8244
Web Site: http://www.gaultauto.com
Sales Range: $25-49.9 Million
Emp.: 200
Automobiles, New & Used
N.A.I.C.S.: 441110
Robert J. Gault *(Pres)*
Jim Mushock *(Bus Mgr)*

GAUTHIER MARKETING
5317 Brooklawn Dr, Toledo, OH 43623-2708
Tel.: (419) 255-6770
Web Site:
  http://www.gauthiermarketing.com
Year Founded: 1988
Sales Range: $10-24.9 Million
Emp.: 5
Collateral, Full Service, Graphic Design, Logo & Package Design
N.A.I.C.S.: 541810
John Gauthier *(Pres)*
Tony Thiros *(Dir-Client Svcs)*
Michele Bobich *(Gen Mgr)*
Scott Grosteffon *(Dir-Creative)*

GAVEL INTERNATIONAL CORPORATION
935 Lakeview Parkway Ste 190, Vernon Hills, IL 60061
Tel.: (847) 945-8150   IL
Web Site: http://www.gavelintl.com
Year Founded: 1985
Sales Range: $10-24.9 Million
Emp.: 30
Management Services
N.A.I.C.S.: 541611
Michael Richardson *(Exec VP)*
Hob Reichenbach *(Mng Dir)*

GAVIAL ENGINEERING & MANUFACTURING
1435 W McCoy Ln, Santa Maria, CA 93455
Tel.: (805) 614-0060
Web Site: https://www.gavial.com
Relay & Industrial Control Mfr
N.A.I.C.S.: 335314
Scott Barton *(Ops Mgr)*

Subsidiaries:

Gavial ITC   (1)
869 Ward Dr, Santa Barbara, CA 93111-2920
Tel.: (805) 357-2522
Web Site: http://www.gavial.com
Acoustic Transducer Mfr
N.A.I.C.S.: 334511
Scott Barton *(Ops Mgr)*

GAWK, INCORPORATED
5300 Melrose Ave Ste 42, Los Angeles, CA 90038
Tel.: (632) 893-8909   NV
Web Site: http://www.gawkinc.com
Year Founded: 2011
Rev.: $5,637,900

Assets: $3,088,564
Liabilities: $7,940,024
Net Worth: ($4,851,460)
Earnings: ($12,303,664)
Emp.: 11
Fiscal Year-end: 01/31/17
Digital Media Streaming Services
N.A.I.C.S.: 516210

Subsidiaries:

Net D Consulting, Inc.   (1)
7575 W Washington Ave Ste 127-364, Las Vegas, NV 89128
Tel.: (714) 289-4444
Web Site: http://www.netdinc.com
Telecommunications Consulting Services
N.A.I.C.S.: 541690
Christopher G. Hall *(Pres)*

GAY & SON MASONRY INC.
3080 W Washington St, Stephenville, TX 76401
Tel.: (254) 431-3426
Web Site:
  https://www.gayandsonmason.com
Year Founded: 1994
Sales Range: $10-24.9 Million
Emp.: 150
Masonry Services
N.A.I.C.S.: 238140
Susie Gay *(Office Mgr)*
Trent Gay *(Pres)*

GAY JOHNSON'S, INC.
1154 N 4th St, Grand Junction, CO 81501-7518
Tel.: (970) 245-7992   CO
Year Founded: 1941
Sales Range: $75-99.9 Million
Emp.: 63
Provider of Automotive & Food Services
N.A.I.C.S.: 457210
Berton Johnson *(Pres)*
Dee A. Brinegar *(CFO)*
Gaynell Johnson Colaric *(Treas, Sec & VP)*
Web Site: http://www.fairacrefarms.com

GAY MEN'S HEALTH CRISIS, INC.
446 W. 33rd St, New York, NY 10001-2601
Tel.: (212) 367-1000   NY
Web Site: http://www.gmhc.org
Year Founded: 1982
Sales Range: $10-24.9 Million
Emp.: 208
HIV Prevention & Awareness Services
N.A.I.C.S.: 622110

GAYLA INDUSTRIES, INC.
6401 Antoine Dr, Houston, TX 77091
Tel.: (713) 681-2411   TX
Web Site: http://www.gaylainc.com
Year Founded: 1961
Sales Range: $10-24.9 Million
Emp.: 40
Balloons, Advertising & Toy: Rubber
N.A.I.C.S.: 326299

GAYLE MANUFACTURING CO. INC.
1455 E Kentucky Ave, Woodland, CA 95776
Tel.: (530) 662-0284
Web Site: http://www.gaylemfg.com
Sales Range: $10-24.9 Million
Emp.: 100
Fabricator of Structural Steel
N.A.I.C.S.: 332312
Gary Glen *(Pres)*

GAYLOR INC.
5750 Castle Creek Pkwy N Dr Ste 400, Indianapolis, IN 46250-4337

Tel.: (317) 843-0577   IN
Web Site: https://www.gaylor.com
Year Founded: 1984
Sales Range: $75-99.9 Million
Emp.: 690
Electrical Construction
N.A.I.C.S.: 238210
John C. Gaylor *(Pres & CEO)*

Subsidiaries:

Gaylor Inc. - Utility Division   (1)
9231 Castlegate Dr, Indianapolis, IN 46256
Tel.: (317) 225-5010
Electric Power Distribution Services
N.A.I.C.S.: 221122

GAYLORD HOSPITAL
50 Gaylord Farm Rd, Wallingford, CT 06492
Tel.: (203) 284-2800   CT
Web Site: https://www.gaylord.org
Year Founded: 1991
Sales Range: $50-74.9 Million
Emp.: 916
Health Care Srvices
N.A.I.C.S.: 622110
Keith Dixon *(Dir-Medical)*
Jacqueline A. Epright *(Dir-Outpatient)*
Lisa Kalafus *(Chief Nursing Officer)*
George Kyriacou *(Pres/CEO-Gaylord Specialty Healthcare)*
Barbara Banning *(Dir-Pharmacy)*
Leigh Golembiewski *(Mgr-Process Improvement & Project Plng)*
Peter Grevelding *(VP-Clinical Ops)*
Jacob Hunter *(Dir-Outpatient Svcs)*
Margaret Kelley *(Dir-Administrative-Medical Svcs & Psychology)*
Kimberly Thompson *(Mgr-PR & Mktg)*
Lori Vickers *(Dir-Inpatient Therapy)*

GAYLORD INTEREST, LLC
5851 San Felipe St Ste 900, Houston, TX 77057
Tel.: (713) 974-5000
Sales Range: $25-49.9 Million
Emp.: 50
Holding Company
N.A.I.C.S.: 551112
Edward O. Gaylord *(Chm & Pres)*

GAZELLE TRANSPORTATION INC.
4939 Gazelle Ave, Bakersfield, CA 93308
Tel.: (661) 322-8868
Web Site:
  http://www.gazelletrans.com
Year Founded: 1993
Sales Range: $25-49.9 Million
Emp.: 255
Transportation of Crude Oil & Logistics Monitoring Services
N.A.I.C.S.: 486110
Ron Lallo *(Pres & CEO)*
Tony Castiglione *(Dir-Safety & Compliance)*

GAZELLE, INC.
25 Thomson Place, Boston, MA 02210
Web Site: http://www.gazelle.com
Year Founded: 2006
Sales Range: $25-49.9 Million
Emp.: 120
Exchanges Consumers' Gently-Used Cell Phones & Other Electronic Gadgets for Cash, Then Resells Or Recycles Them
N.A.I.C.S.: 532210
Chris Sullivan *(CEO)*

GAZELLES INC.
44031 Pipeline Plz Ste 200, Ashburn, VA 20147
Tel.: (703) 858-2400

Web Site: http://www.gazelles.com
Year Founded: 1996
Sales Range: $25-49.9 Million
Emp.: 10
Executive Education, Coaching &
Technology Services
N.A.I.C.S.: 541618
Verne Harnish *(Founder & CEO)*
Keith Cupp *(Pres-Intl)*
Joanne Costello *(Head-Ops)*
Donna Whitwell *(Mgr-Production)*

GAZOO ENERGY GROUP, INC.
2569 McCabe Way, Irvine, CA 92614-6243
Tel.: (949) 379-1210   NV
Investment Services
N.A.I.C.S.: 523999
Alan B. Miller *(Pres)*
Chip Hackley *(CEO)*
Lewis Kurtz *(Sec)*

GB 500 SATELLITE INC.
5701 Foster Ave, Brooklyn, NY 11234
Tel.: (718) 451-2210
Rev.: $10,300,000
Emp.: 70
Motor Vehicle Supplies & New Parts
Merchant Whslr
N.A.I.C.S.: 423120
Annette Morgenroth *(Pres)*
Lawrence Morgenroth *(Treas & Sec)*

GB COLLECTS, LLC
1253 Haddonfiled Berlin Rd, Voorhees, NJ 08043-4847
Tel.: (856) 768-9995
Web Site: https://www.gbcollects.com
Year Founded: 2001
Sales Range: $1-9.9 Million
Emp.: 50
Collection Services
N.A.I.C.S.: 561440
Gilbert L. Fisher *(COO)*
Jon P. Dame *(VP-Sls)*
George Bresler *(CEO)*

GB MANAGEMENT SYSTEMS, INC.
931 Interchange Dr, Holland, MI 49423
Tel.: (616) 396-1453
Web Site:
   https://www.transwayinc.com
Rev.: $11,067,417
Emp.: 133
Trucking Service
N.A.I.C.S.: 484121
Brenda Langston *(Dir-IT)*

GB TECH, INC.
2200 Space Park Dr Ste 400, Houston, TX 77058
Tel.: (281) 333-3703
Web Site: http://www.gbtech.net
Sales Range: $10-24.9 Million
Emp.: 50
Technical Consulting Services
N.A.I.C.S.: 541690
Randy Parker *(VP-Bus Mgmt)*

GBG INC. OF PENNSYLVANIA
1525 Beaver Ave, Pittsburgh, PA 15233
Tel.: (412) 321-8300
Web Site: https://www.gbgsupply.com
Year Founded: 1972
Sales Range: $10-24.9 Million
Emp.: 40
Warm Air Heating & Air Conditioning
N.A.I.C.S.: 423730
Wayne Castor *(Pres)*
David McIlwaine *(Owner)*

GBH COMMUNICATIONS INC.

1309 S Myrtle Ave, Monrovia, CA 91016
Tel.: (818) 246-9900
Web Site: http://www.gbh.com
Year Founded: 1986
Sales Range: $10-24.9 Million
Emp.: 25
Supplier of Electronic Parts & Equipment
N.A.I.C.S.: 423690
Von Bedikian *(Founder, Pres & CEO)*
Kelli Lowery *(Mgr-Enterprise Sls)*
Stacy Yacono *(Dir-Order Mgmt)*
Jose De La Paz *(CTO)*
Michael Laurin *(Dir-Solutions Architecture)*
Mitch Moore *(Exec VP-Sls)*

GBK CORP.
6733 S Yale Ave, Tulsa, OK 74136
Tel.: (918) 494-0000
Rev.: $521,400,000
Emp.: 300
Crude Petroleum Production
N.A.I.C.S.: 211120

GBL SYSTEMS CORPORATION
760 Paseo Camarillo Ste 401, Camarillo, CA 93010
Tel.: (805) 987-4345   NY
Web Site: https://www.gblsys.com
Year Founded: 1990
Sales Range: $1-9.9 Million
Emp.: 23
Computer System Design Services
N.A.I.C.S.: 541512
James Buscemi *(Founder & CEO)*
James Bak *(Chief Engr-Software)*
Kathy Smith *(VP-Engrg)*

GBRITT P.R. & MARKETING
505 Ocean St, South Portland, ME 04106
Tel.: (207) 775-2126
Web Site: http://www.gbritt.com
Sales Range: Less than $1 Million
Emp.: 5
Public Relations
N.A.I.C.S.: 541820
Gillian Britt *(Principal)*
James Britt *(Principal)*

GBS CORP.
7233 Freedom Ave NW, North Canton, OH 44720-0340
Tel.: (330) 494-5330   OH
Web Site: https://www.gbscorp.com
Year Founded: 1971
Sales Range: $50-74.9 Million
Emp.: 400
Paper & Office Supplies Distr
N.A.I.C.S.: 424120
Laurence A. Merriman *(Chm)*
Michele Benson *(VP-Fin)*
Pam McGrew *(Asst Mgr-Info Sys)*
Wanda Weinman *(Acct Mgr)*

GBU FINANCIAL LIFE
4254 Saw Mill Run Blvd, Pittsburgh, PA 15227-3394
Tel.: (814) 504-3562   PA
Web Site: https://www.gbu.org
Year Founded: 1892
Sales Range: $25-49.9 Million
Emp.: 50
Insurance Services
N.A.I.C.S.: 524113
Jacqueline Alaimo *(Supvr-Customer Svc)*

GC BUILDERS INC
11023 Eucalyptus St, Rancho Cucamonga, CA 91730
Tel.: (909) 944-6446

Web Site: http://www.gcbuilders.com
Rev.: $17,018,965
Emp.: 40
Commercial & Office Building, New Construction
N.A.I.C.S.: 237210
Ryan Hall *(Mgr-Acctg)*
Tom Fesenmeyer *(Controller)*

GC PARTNERS INC.
3816 Forrestgate Dr, Winston Salem, NC 27103
Tel.: (336) 767-1600
Web Site: http://www.gcpartners.com
Sales Range: $10-24.9 Million
Emp.: 700
Restaurant Services
N.A.I.C.S.: 722511
Tracy Tedder *(Sec)*
Susan Marie Cook *(Coord-Mktg)*
Stewart Degruchy *(Gen Mgr)*

GC SERVICES LP
6330 Gulfton St, Houston, TX 77081
Tel.: (713) 777-4441
Web Site: http://www.gcserv.com
Year Founded: 1957
Sales Range: $100-124.9 Million
Emp.: 3,000
Provider of Business Management Services
N.A.I.C.S.: 523999
Jerold B. Katz *(Founder)*
Frank A. Taylor *(Pres)*
Mike Sullivan *(Asst VP)*
Dan Cook *(Exec VP-Third Party Ops)*
Gary Hopkins *(Exec VP-Student Loan Ops Div)*
Michael D. Jones *(CFO & Exec VP-Fin)*
Brad C. Batig *(Chief Compliance Officer)*
Meagan M. Conway *(Exec VP-HR & Employee Rels)*
Craig M. Cappelle *(Sr VP-IT Applications)*
Robert D. Wilson *(Sr VP-IT Infrastructure)*
Scott M. Cole *(Sr VP-Sls & Mktg)*
Linda M. Spellicy *(Sr VP-Treasury)*

GC&E SYSTEMS GROUP, INC.
5835 Peachtree Corners E Ste A, Peachtree Corners, GA 30092
Tel.: (770) 448-3908
Web Site: https://www.gcesg.com
Year Founded: 1999
Sales Range: $10-24.9 Million
Emp.: 125
Communications & Electrical Services
N.A.I.C.S.: 335921
Daniel O'Sullivan *(Owner)*
Dennis Bristol *(Pres & COO)*
Alan Doble *(Mgr-Pur)*

GCA CHEMICAL CORPORATION
3655 Cortez Rd W, Bradenton, FL 34210
Tel.: (941) 748-6090
Rev.: $21,900,000
Emp.: 4
Chemical & Allied Products Merchant Whslr
N.A.I.C.S.: 424690
Phyllis Dernarging *(Mgr)*

GCC DACOTAH INC.
501 N St Onge St, Rapid City, SD 57702
Tel.: (605) 721-7100
Web Site: https://www.gcc.com
Rev.: $44,200,000
Emp.: 200
Natural Cement Mfr
N.A.I.C.S.: 327310
Steve Zellmer *(Pres)*

GCF, INC.
119 Rockland Ave, Northvale, NJ 07647
Tel.: (201) 767-6100
Year Founded: 1982
Rev.: $14,000,000
Emp.: 30
Industrial Machinery & Equipment
N.A.I.C.S.: 423830
Chip Nobile *(VP-Outside Sls & VP-Sls)*
Michael Felletter *(VP)*
Frank Messar *(Mgr-Bus Dev)*
Mark D'Andrea *(Dir-Engrg)*
Chip Nobile *(VP-Sls)*

GCG ADVERTISING
1612 Summit Ave Ste 410, Fort Worth, TX 76102-5916
Tel.: (817) 332-4600   TX
Web Site:
   http://www.gcgadvertising.com
Year Founded: 1973
Rev.: $23,860,000
Emp.: 23
Advetising Agency
N.A.I.C.S.: 541810
Scott Turner *(CEO)*
Becky Johnson *(Dir-Medical Education)*
Pat Gabriel *(Dir-Creative)*
Brian Wilburn *(Sr Dir-Art)*
Neil Foster *(Pres)*
Allyson Cross *(Acct Svcs Dir)*
Kris Copeland *(Dir-Art)*
Doug Mangold *(Assoc Art Dir)*
Scott Porter *(Copywriter)*
Bruce Natale *(Dir-Web Programming)*

GCG CONSTRUCTION INC.
9200 Estero Park Commons Blvd Ste 1, Estero, FL 33928
Tel.: (239) 454-7304
Web Site: http://www.gcgbuilds.com
Sales Range: $1-9.9 Million
Emp.: 6
Commercial Construction
N.A.I.C.S.: 236220
Teely Byrd *(Co-Owner)*
Lerin Byrd *(Co-Owner)*

GCG CONSTRUCTION, INC.
9200 Estero Park Commons Blvd Ste 1, Estero, FL 33928
Tel.: (239) 454-7304   FL
Web Site: http://www.gcgbuilds.com
Year Founded: 2000
Sales Range: $10-24.9 Million
Emp.: 8
Real Estate, Construction & Consulting Services
N.A.I.C.S.: 531390
Lerin Byrd *(CEO)*
Andrew Solon *(Project Mgr)*

GCI SYSTEMS
655 County Rd EW, Saint Paul, MN 55126
Tel.: (651) 604-5700
Web Site: http://www.gcisystems.com
Year Founded: 1988
Sales Range: $25-49.9 Million
Emp.: 30
Technology Management Services
N.A.I.C.S.: 541519
Sanjay Kuba *(Co-Founder, Chm & Pres)*
Terence Johnson *(Engr-Advanced Sys)*
Erik Buhl *(Dir-Sls & Mktg-Pacific Northwest)*

GCJ ENTERPRISES INC.
928 N Ferdon Blvd, Crestview, FL 32536

GCJ Enterprises Inc.—(Continued)

Tel.: (850) 682-8337
Rev.: $24,800,000
Emp.: 200
Supermarkets & Other Grocery
Stores
N.A.I.C.S.: 445110
Thomas M. Lalor (VP)
Gary C. Jones (CEO)
Richard Twitty (Pres)

GCM CONTRACTING SOLU-TIONS, INC.
16121 Lee Rd Ste 101, Fort Myers,
FL 33912
Tel.: (239) 334-8800 FL
Web Site:
https://www.gcmcontracting.com
Year Founded: 1988
Sales Range: $1-9.9 Million
Emp.: 30
General Construction Contractor
N.A.I.C.S.: 236220
Robert Brown (Pres)
Gregory S. Coleman (Project Mgr)
Kim Freel (Project Mgr-Acctg)
Kevin Berth (CFO)

GCP CAPITAL PARTNERS HOLDINGS LLC
600 Lexington Ave 31st Fl, New York,
NY 10022
Tel.: (212) 894-0600 DE
Web Site: https://www.gcpcapital.com
Year Founded: 2009
Rev.: $1,700,000,000
Emp.: 20
Holding Company; Private Equity
Firm
N.A.I.C.S.: 551112
Boris M. Gutin (Mng Dir)
Victor Frank Pottow (Mng Dir)
Cyrus B. Hormazdi (Mng Dir)
Michele Gursky (Controller)

Subsidiaries:

Alkeme Insurance Services, Inc. (1)
111 Corporate Drive Suite 200, Ladera
Ranch, CA 92694
Tel.: (949) 285-2612
Web Site: https://alkemeins.com
Emp.: 100
Insurance Brokerage
N.A.I.C.S.: 524210
Curtis Barton (Founder & CEO)

Subsidiary (Domestic):

ACW Group, LLC (2)
1000 Bishop St Ste 600, Honolulu, HI
96813-4206
Tel.: (808) 535-5050
Web Site: http://www.acwhawaii.com
Insurance Agencies & Brokerages
N.A.I.C.S.: 524210
Kirk Christman (Owner)

Mark Edward Partners LLC (2)
505 Park Ave, New York, NY 10022
Tel.: (212) 355-5005
Web Site:
http://www.markedwardpartners.com
Insurance Agencies & Brokerages
N.A.I.C.S.: 524210
Colleen Quiggle-Miskulin (Sr VP)
Mark Freitas (Pres & CEO)

Robert Bell Insurance Brokers,
Inc. (2)
605 E Alvarado St Ste 200, Fallbrook, CA
92028-2315
Tel.: (760) 631-5191
Web Site: http://www.bellinsgrp.com
Insurance Agencies & Brokerages
N.A.I.C.S.: 524210
Michael Bell (VP)

Snapp & Associates (2)
438 Camino Del Rio S Ste 112, San Diego,
CA 92108-3546
Tel.: (619) 908-3100
Web Site: https://snappassociates.com

Insurance Agencies & Brokerages
N.A.I.C.S.: 524210

Wharton Lyon & Lyon (2)
101 S Livingston Ave, Livingston, NJ 07039
Tel.: (973) 992-5775
Web Site: http://www.whartoninsurance.com
Sales Range: $1-9.9 Million
Emp.: 55
Insurance Agencies & Brokerages
N.A.I.C.S.: 524210
Albert Klein (Chm)
Tara Schwartz (Supvr-Personal Lines)

Chergey Insurance (1)
1489 E Thousand Oaks Blvd Ste 5, Thou-
sand Oaks, CA 91362-6210
Tel.: (805) 497-1290
Web Site: http://www.chergeyinsurance.com
Insurance Agencies & Brokerages
N.A.I.C.S.: 524210
Dan Chergey (Owner)

GCP Capital Partners Europe
Limited (1)
Lansdowne House 57 Berkeley Square,
London, W1J 6ER, United Kingdom
Tel.: (44) 2071987400
Web Site: http://www.gcpcapital.com
Privater Equity Firm
N.A.I.C.S.: 523999

GCP Capital Partners LLC (1)
600 Lexington Ave 31st Fl, New York, NY
10022
Tel.: (212) 894-0600
Web Site: http://www.gcpcapital.com
Rev.: $1,200,000,000
Emp.: 12
Privater Equity Firm
N.A.I.C.S.: 523999
Boris M. Gutin (Mng Partner)
Victor Frank Pottow (Mng Dir)
Cyrus B. Hormazdi (Mng Dir)
Robert Henry Niehaus (Chm)

Subsidiary (Domestic):

Kurtzman Carson Consultants
LLC (2)
2335 Alaska Ave, El Segundo, CA 90245
Tel.: (310) 823-9000
Web Site: http://www.kccllc.com
Sales Range: $10-24.9 Million
Emp.: 130
Legal & Financial Software
N.A.I.C.S.: 513210
James Le (Exec VP-Class Action Svcs)
Josh C. Wilson (VP-Restructuring Support
Svcs)
Drake D. Foster (Gen Counsel)
Bryan Butvick (CEO)
Patrick M. Passarella (Sr VP-Class Action
Svcs)
Joseph Bunning (Dir-Comm & Restructuring
Support Svcs)
Daniel Burke (Exec VP-Class Action Svcs)
Lance Cavallo (Sr Mgr-Project-Class Action
Svcs)
Rebecca Cook (Sr Dir-Corp Restructuring
Svcs)
Beth Friedman (Sr Dir-Corp Restructuring
Svcs)
Frank Gatto (VP-Mass Tort Svcs)
Evan Gershbein (Sr VP-Corp Restructuring
Svcs)
Francine Gordon-Durrer (Mng Dir-Corp Re-
structuring Svcs)
David Hartie (Mng Dir-Pub Securities Svcs)
Robert Jordan (Mng Dir-Corp Restructuring
Svcs)
Albert H. Kass (Sr Exec VP-Corp Restruc-
turing Svcs)
Joe P. Morrow (VP-Corp Restructuring
Svcs)
Gerry Mullins (Pres)
Angela Nguyen (Dir-Corp Restructuring
Svcs)
Carla Peak (VP-Legal Notification Svcs)

GCP Venture Partners LLC (1)
300 Park Ave 22nd Fl, New York, NY 10022
Tel.: (212) 389-1600
Web Site: http://www.gsavp.com
Early-Stage Equity Investment Firm
N.A.I.C.S.: 523999
Steve Brotman (Mng Partner)

GCS TECHNOLOGIES, INC.

8701 N Mopac Blve Ste 115, Austin,
TX 78759
Tel.: (512) 249-6080
Web Site: http://www.gcsaustin.com
Year Founded: 2000
Sales Range: $1-9.9 Million
Emp.: 32
IT Services, Technology Consulting &
Network Assessments
N.A.I.C.S.: 541690
Joseph Gleinser (Co-Founder & Pres)
Daryl Gleinser (Co-Founder & Dir-
Managed Svcs)
Marty Satterfield (VP-Bus Dev)
Shane Gronniger (Dir-Professional
Svcs)
Marquis Calmes (Dir-Tech)

GDB INTERNATIONAL, INC.
1 Home News Row, New Brunswick,
NJ 08901
Tel.: (732) 246-3001
Web Site: https://gdb.international
Year Founded: 1993
Sales Range: $100-124.9 Million
Emp.: 32
Exporter of Liquidated & Recycled
Products Including Paints, Metal,
Goods, Plastics & Paper
N.A.I.C.S.: 423930
Sunil Bagaria (Pres)
Albert Umali (Mgr-Sls-Intl)
Rajesh Dhir (Sr VP)
Victoria Hodge (VP-Strategy Product
Stewardship)

GDC CONSTRUCTION INC.
1031 Silverado St, La Jolla, CA
92037
Tel.: (858) 551-5222
Web Site:
https://www.gdcconstruction.com
Sales Range: $10-24.9 Million
Emp.: 15
Commercial & Office Buildings, Reno-
vation & Repair
N.A.I.C.S.: 236220
Jester Dewhurst (Pres)

GDC PROPERTIES, LLC
245 Saw Mill River Rd, Hawthorne,
NY 10532
Tel.: (914) 747-4000
Web Site:
https://www.gdcproperties.com
Year Founded: 1994
Sales Range: $10-24.9 Million
Emp.: 100
Commercial Constuction, Develop-
ment, Management & Investment
N.A.I.C.S.: 236220
Samuel Ginsburg (Co-Chm)
Adam Ginsburg (Co-Chm)
William Ingraham (Pres)
Richard DeMarco (Dir-Ops)
Maribeth McCauley (Dir-Asset Mgmt)
Raymond McNeal (Controller)
Mostafa Rizk (Sr Dir-Architecture &
Construction)
Christine McWalters (CFO)

GDH CONSULTING, INC.
4200 E Skelly Ste 650, Tulsa, OK
74135
Tel.: (918) 491-0600
Web Site:
http://www.gdhconsulting.com
Year Founded: 2001
Sales Range: $10-24.9 Million
Emp.: 40
IT Contracting Services
N.A.I.C.S.: 561320
Gerald Hurley (CEO)
Blake Reeves (Branch Mgr)

GDKN CORPORATION

1779 N University Dr Ste 102, Pem-
broke Pines, FL 33024
Tel.: (954) 985-6650
Web Site: http://www.gdkn.com
Sales Range: $25-49.9 Million
Emp.: 350
Telecommunications
N.A.I.C.S.: 517810
Jay Narang (VP)
Vic Narang (Pres & Principal)
Donna Harris-Gill (Mgr-Recruiting
Ops)

GDMI INC.
2763 Marquis Dr, Garland, TX 75042
Tel.: (972) 494-7477
Web Site: https://www.gdmiinc.com
Rev.: $11,000,000
Emp.: 60
Mfr of Cosmetics, Health & Beauty
Products
N.A.I.C.S.: 325620
Mike Ferrall (Pres)
Gina Ferrall (Co-Owner)
Carlos A. Sanchez-Caro (Dir-R&D &
Quality)

GE FOODLAND, INC.
1105 Beltline Rd, Carrollton, TX
75006
Tel.: (972) 245-0470
Web Site:
https://www.gefoodland.com
Year Founded: 1977
Sales Range: $25-49.9 Million
Emp.: 300
Grocery Store Services
N.A.I.C.S.: 424410
Dan McCann (Pres)
John Beckman (VP)

GEAR AID, INC.
1411 Meador Ave, Bellingham, WA
98229
Tel.: (360) 671-2227 WA
Web Site: https://www.gearaid.com
Year Founded: 1981
Marine & Sporting Rain Gear & Ac-
cessories Mfr
N.A.I.C.S.: 339920
Cheriss Faiola (Mgr-Mktg & PR)

Subsidiaries:

McNett Europe (1)
PO Box 1144, D-29684, Schwarmstedt,
Germany
Tel.: (49) 5071 80 00 72
Web Site: http://www.mcnetteurope.com
Manufacture & Sale of Outdoor Products
N.A.I.C.S.: 459110

GEAR COMPANY OF AMERICA, INC.
14300 Lorain Ave, Cleveland, OH
44111
Tel.: (216) 671-5400
Year Founded: 1946
Sales Range: $50-74.9 Million
Emp.: 50
Mfr of Gears & Automatic Screw Ma-
chine Products
N.A.I.C.S.: 332111
Scott Britvec (Gen Mgr)
Ed Morel (Pres)

GEARBOX EXPRESS, LLC
608 N Shore Dr, Hartland, WI 53029
Tel.: (262) 378-4303
Web Site:
http://www.gearboxexpress.com
Year Founded: 2011
Emp.: 100
Industrial Machinery Mfr
N.A.I.C.S.: 333248
Brian Hastings (Co-Founder & CFO)
Bruce Neumiller (Co-Founder & CEO)

GEARHEAD OUTFITTERS, INC.
230 S Main St, Jonesboro, AR 72401
Tel.: (870) 910-5569
Web Site:
https://www.gearheadoutfitters.com
Sporting Goods Retailer
N.A.I.C.S.: 459110
Ted Herget *(Owner)*

Subsidiaries:

Uncle Dans, Ltd (1)
1600 Sherman Ave, Evanston, IL 60201
Tel.: (847) 475-7100
Web Site: http://www.udans.com
Clothing Retailer
N.A.I.C.S.: 458110

GEARHEART COMMUNICA-TIONS COMPANY, INC.
20 Laynesville Rd, Harold, KY 41635
Tel.: (606) 478-9401
Web Site: https://www.gearheart.com
Sales Range: $25-49.9 Million
Emp.: 75
Telephone, Internet, Cable Television
& Home Security Services
N.A.I.C.S.: 516210

Subsidiaries:

Inter Mountain Cable Inc. (1)
20 Laynesville Rd, Harold, KY 41635
Tel.: (606) 478-9406
Web Site: http://www.imctv.com
Sales Range: $10-24.9 Million
Emp.: 35
Cable Television Services
N.A.I.C.S.: 516210

GEARON HOFFMAN INC.
88 Broad St, Boston, MA 02110
Tel.: (617) 247-1522   MA
Year Founded: 1982
Rev.: $73,000,000
Emp.: 35
Advetising Agency
N.A.I.C.S.: 541810
Dan Gearon *(Chm & CEO)*
Robert Hoffman *(Pres & Chief Creative Officer)*
Heidi Currier Ferris *(Dir-Media Channel)*
Kathy Gehring-Carino *(Sr VP & Dir-Client Svcs)*
Gerry L'Heureux *(VP & Controller)*
Samantha Bartfield *(VP & Acct Supvr)*
Sara O'Reilly *(Acct Exec)*
Holly Smith *(VP & Controller).*

GEARY LSF GROUP, INC.
655 Montgomery St Ste 1600, San Francisco, CA 94111
Tel.: (650) 616-8226   DE
Web Site: http://www.gearylsf.com
Year Founded: 1999
Emp.: 200
Online Marketing & Advertising Services
N.A.I.C.S.: 541810
Daniel Laury *(Founder)*
Paul McKnight *(CFO)*
Ramsay Crooks *(Exec VP-Product)*
Karen Kovaleski *(Pres & CEO)*
Kevin Hird *(Creative Dir-North America)*
Elizabeth Serafin *(VP-Interactive Media)*
Bob Yakominich *(Exec VP-Sls & Mktg)*
Brayden Beverage *(Acct Exec)*
Jennifer Fleck *(Mgr-Integrated Svcs)*
Katie Colleton *(Dir-Mktg)*
Kendra Losee *(Sr VP-Client Svcs)*
Lindsay Romanelli *(Coord-Media)*

Melissa Kielty *(VP-Engrg)*
Michelle Zimmerman *(Acct Dir)*
Neil Hicks *(Sr Dir-Partnerships & Dev)*

Subsidiaries:

Geary LSF Group, Inc. - San Diego (1)
401 W A St Ste 360, San Diego, CA 92101
Tel.: (760) 431-8594
Web Site: http://www.gearylsf.com
Online Marketing & Advertising Services
N.A.I.C.S.: 541810

GEARY PACIFIC CORPORA-TION
1360 N Hancock St, Anaheim, CA 92807
Tel.: (714) 279-2950
Web Site:
http://www.gearypacific.com
Year Founded: 1961
Sales Range: $10-24.9 Million
Emp.: 70
Heating & Air Conditioning Equipment Whslr
N.A.I.C.S.: 423730
Layne Miller *(CEO)*

Subsidiaries:

Geary Pacific Supply - Sacramento (1)
4365 Jetway Ct, North Highlands, CA 95660-5701
Tel.: (916) 481-0244
Web Site: http://www.gearypacific.com
Heating & Air Conditioning Equipment Whslr
N.A.I.C.S.: 423730
David Radmand *(Branch Mgr)*

Geary Pacific of Arizona - Fort Mojave (1)
5106 S Lakewood Rd, Fort Mohave, AZ 86427
Tel.: (928) 768-7177
Web Site: http://www.gearypacific.com
Emp.: 15
Heating & Air Conditioning Equipment & Supplies Whslr
N.A.I.C.S.: 423730
George Taylor *(Branch Mgr)*

HVAC Supply (1)
5901 N Broadway, Denver, CO 80216
Tel.: (303) 292-3025
Web Site: http://www.hvacsupply.net
Emp.: 75
Heating & Air Conditioning Equipment Whslr
N.A.I.C.S.: 423720
Jason Charles *(COO)*

GEAUGA SAVINGS BANK INC.
10800 Kinsman Rd, Newbury, OH 44065
Tel.: (440) 564-9441
Web Site:
http://www.geaugasavings.com
Rev.: $11,228,000
Emp.: 75
Savings & Loan Associations, Not Federally Chartered
N.A.I.C.S.: 522180
Betty Kimbrew *(Mgr-Community Rels-Newbury)*
Jennifer Brickman *(Treas)*
Robert Breslow *(CFO)*
James Kleinfelter *(Pres & CEO)*
Dell Duncan *(Exec VP)*
Bob Bloom *(Chm)*

GEBHARDT AUTOMOTIVE INC.
2470 49th St, Boulder, CO 80301
Tel.: (303) 447-8000
Web Site: http://www.gebauto.com
Sales Range: $10-24.9 Million
Emp.: 115
Car Dealership
N.A.I.C.S.: 441110
James P. Gebhardt *(Pres)*

GEBO DISTRIBUTING CO., INC.
3109 Olton Rd, Plainview, TX 79072-6763
Tel.: (806) 293-4212   TX
Web Site: http://www.gebos.com
Year Founded: 1958
Sales Range: $100-124.9 Million
Emp.: 150
Retail Farm & Home Supplies; Clothing; Automotive Supplies Including Tires & Batteries
N.A.I.C.S.: 459999
Mike Phillips *(Mgr-Ops)*

GEC, INC.
8282 Goodwood Blvd, Baton Rouge, LA 70806
Tel.: (225) 612-3000
Web Site: https://www.gecinc.com
Year Founded: 1986
Engineeering Services
N.A.I.C.S.: 541330
Brian Buckel *(Sr VP-Construction Div)*
Nancy Moeller *(Sr VP-Admin Div)*
Sherri LeBas *(Sr VP-Project Mgmt)*
Robert Hall *(CFO)*
Anthony Marino *(VP)*
Jeff Melby *(VP)*
Michael Walther *(VP)*
Cary Bourgeois *(Sr VP-Engrg Div)*
Jeff Robinson *(Sr VP-Coastal, Environmental & Water Resources)*
Ronald M. Noble *(Pres & CEO)*

Subsidiaries:

Noble Consultants, Inc. (1)
359 Bel Marin Keys Blvd Ste 9, Novato, CA 94949
Tel.: (415) 884-0727
Web Site: http://www.nobleconsultants.com
Sales Range: $1-9.9 Million
Emp.: 10
Engineeering Services
N.A.I.C.S.: 541330

GEE CONSULTANTS, INC.
10046 Monroe Dr, Dallas, TX 75229
Tel.: (214) 352-5433
Web Site:
http://www.geeconsultants.com
Year Founded: 1993
Scientific & Technical Consulting Services
N.A.I.C.S.: 541690
Richard W. Gee *(Pres)*

Subsidiaries:

Texas CMT Inc. (1)
10046 Monroe Dr, Dallas, TX 75229
Tel.: (214) 352-6957
Schools & Educational Services
N.A.I.C.S.: 611710

GEEKDOM
110 E Houston St 7th Fl, San Antonio, TX 78205
Tel.: (210) 373-6730
Web Site: http://www.geekdom.com
Business Consulting Services
N.A.I.C.S.: 541611
Charles Woodin *(CEO)*
Phillip Hernandez *(COO)*
Brooke Rodriguez *(Mgr-Ops)*
Joyce Dueley *(Program Mgr)*
Jon Ryan Garcia *(Mgr-Mktg)*
Matthew Espinoza *(Mgr-Membership)*
Leslie Chasnoff *(Program Mgr-CivTechSA)*
Graham Weston *(Co-Founder)*
Nick Longo *(Co-Founder)*
Lorenzo Gomez III *(Chm)*

GEEKS ON CALL HOLDINGS, INC.

7100 E Pleasant Valley Rd Ste 300, Independence, OH 44131
Tel.: (800) 905-4335   DE
Web Site:
http://www.geeksoncall.com
Sales Range: $1-9.9 Million
Emp.: 55
Computer Services & Solutions
N.A.I.C.S.: 541519
Richard T. Cole *(Chm & CEO)*

GEENIUS, INC.
4464 Long Lake Rd, Melbourne, FL 32934
Tel.: (321) 308-5330   NV
Web Site: http://www.geenius.com
Year Founded: 2009
Sales Range: Less than $1 Million
Emp.: 3
Computer Related Consulting Services
N.A.I.C.S.: 541690
Tom Rudmik *(Pres)*
Andy Rudmik *(CEO & CTO)*

GEERPRES INC.
1780 Harvey St, Muskegon, MI 49442-5378
Tel.: (231) 773-3211
Web Site: https://www.geerpres.com
Year Founded: 1935
Sales Range: $50-74.9 Million
Emp.: 28
Cleaning Equipment Mfr
N.A.I.C.S.: 333310
Bryan Depree *(CFO)*
Sam Waites *(VP-Sls & Mktg)*

GEF ACQUISITION CORPORA-TION
2 Bethesda Metro Ctr Ste 440, Bethesda, MD 20814
Tel.: (240) 482-8900   IL
Year Founded: 2015
Emp.: 4
Investment Services
N.A.I.C.S.: 523999
H. Jeffrey Leonard *(Chm & CEO)*
Daniel Prawda *(Mng Dir)*
Brian J. Foist *(CFO)*
Stuart Barkoff *(Chief Legal Officer, Chief Compliance Officer & Sec)*

GEI GLOBAL ENERGY CORP.
6060 Covered Wagon Trl, Flint, MI 48532
Tel.: (810) 610-2816   NV
Web Site: http://www.geiglobal.com
Year Founded: 2010
Emp.: 3
Fuel Cell Systems Mfr
N.A.I.C.S.: 335311
K. Joel Berry *(Founder & CEO)*

GEIGER BROTHERS
70 Mount Hope Ave, Lewiston, ME 04240
Tel.: (207) 755-2000   ME
Web Site: http://www.geiger.com
Year Founded: 1878
Sales Range: $150-199.9 Million
Emp.: 500
Print, Bookbinding & Leather Products, Calendars, Diaries, Year Books, Almanacs & Specialities for Advertising Mfr
N.A.I.C.S.: 339950
Peter Geiger *(Exec VP)*
Robert Blaisdell *(CFO)*
Fred Snyder *(Reg VP-Sls)*
Joan Lantz *(COO)*
Janet McMaster *(VP-Sls-MidAtlantic & Carolinas)*
Gene Geiger *(Pres & CEO)*
Chris McKee *(VP-Sls & Mktg)*
Craig Hughes *(VP-Sls-West)*

Geiger Brothers—(Continued)

Cathy Miller *(VP-Sls-South)*
Jamie Ondrejko *(VP-Sls-Southwest)*
Kerry Worden *(VP-Sls-Southeastern)*

Subsidiaries:

Almanac Publishing Co. **(1)**
70 Mount Hope Ave, Lewiston, ME 04240
Tel.: (207) 755-2292
Web Site: http://www.farmersalmanac.com
Periodical Publishers
N.A.I.C.S.: 513120

GEIGER EXCAVATING, INC.
5755 Jordan Rd, Woodland, MI
48897-9718
Tel.: (260) 459-2005
Web Site:
http://www.geigerexcavating.com
Emp.: 100
Site Preparation Contractor
N.A.I.C.S.: 238910
Roger Geiger *(Owner)*

GEIGER READY MIX COMPANY INCORPORATED
1333 S 2nd St, Leavenworth, KS
66048
Tel.: (913) 772-4010
Web Site:
http://www.geigerreadymix.com
Rev.: $14,300,000
Emp.: 50
Ready Mixed Concrete
N.A.I.C.S.: 327320
Steve McDonald *(Pres)*
Jim Jauernig *(Mgr)*

GEILE/LEON MARKETING COMMUNICATIONS
5257 Shaw Ave Ste 102, Saint Louis,
MO 63110
Tel.: (314) 727-5850
Web Site: http://www.geileon.com
Year Founded: 1989
Sales Range: $1-9.9 Million
Emp.: 15
Advetising Agency
N.A.I.C.S.: 541810
Tim Leon *(Pres)*
Dave Geile *(Mng Partner & Dir-Creative)*
Kathy Leonard *(VP-PR)*
Ben Edmonson *(Sr Dir-Art)*

GEISINGER HEALTH SYSTEM
100 N Academy Ave, Danville, PA
17822
Tel.: (570) 271-6211
Web Site: https://www.geisinger.org
Year Founded: 1915
Health Care Services Organization
N.A.I.C.S.: 813910
Steven R. Youso *(Pres/CEO-Geisinger Health Plan)*
Lynn Miller *(Exec VP-Clinical Ops)*
David H. Ledbetter *(Exec VP & Chief Scientific Officer)*
Susan M. Robel *(Chief Nursing Officer, Chief Patient Experience Officer & Exec VP)*
Amy Brayford *(Chief HR Officer, Exec VP & Chief of Staff)*
Jaewon Ryu *(Pres & CEO)*
Dominic Moffa *(Chief Strategy Officer & Exec VP)*
Heather M. Acker *(Vice Chm)*
Steven J. Scheinman *(Chief Academic Officer)*
Kevin Roberts *(CFO & Exec VP)*
David Felicio *(Exec VP & Chief Legal Officer)*
Karen Murphy *(Chief Innovation Officer & Exec VP)*
Huntington F. Willard *(Dir-Geisinger Natl Precision Health)*

Erica Ramos *(Dir/Head-Clinical & Bus Dev-Geisinger Natl Precision Health)*
Don Stanziano *(Chief Mktg Officer)*

Subsidiaries:

AtlantiCare Health System, Inc. **(1)**
2500 English Creek Ave, Egg Harbor Township, NJ 08234
Tel.: (609) 407-2300
Web Site: http://www.atlanticare.org
Emp.: 5,800
Health Care Services Organization
N.A.I.C.S.: 813910
Jatin Motiwal *(VP-Physician Grp & Reg Network)*
Margaret Belfield *(COO & Exec VP)*
Lori Herndon *(Pres & CEO)*
Jennifer Tornetta *(Dir-Media Rels & Pub Affairs)*

Subsidiary (Domestic):

AtlantiCare Behavorial Health, Inc. **(2)**
6010 Black Horse Pike, Egg Harbor Township, NJ 08234
Tel.: (609) 645-7600
Web Site: http://www.atlanticare.org
Behavioral Healthcare Services
N.A.I.C.S.: 621420

Unit (Domestic):

AtlantiCare Occupational Health **(2)**
2500 English Creek Ave Bldg 900 Ste 908,
Egg Harbor Township, NJ 08234
Tel.: (609) 677-7200
Web Site: http://www.atlanticare.org
Occupational Therapy Services
N.A.I.C.S.: 621340

Subsidiary (Domestic):

AtlantiCare Regional Medical Center, Inc. **(2)**
1925 Pacific Ave, Atlantic City, NJ 08401
Tel.: (609) 345-4000
Web Site: http://www.atlanticare.org
Hospital Operator
N.A.I.C.S.: 622110

Geisinger - Bloomsburg Hospital **(1)**
549 Fair St, Bloomsburg, PA 17815
Tel.: (570) 387-2100
Web Site: http://www.bloomhealth.net
Sales Range: $25-49.9 Million
Emp.: 505
Health Care Srvices
N.A.I.C.S.: 622110
Lissa Bryan-Smith *(Chief Admin Officer)*
Timothy Guschel *(Dir-Pharmacy)*
Joseph Devito *(CFO)*

Geisinger Health Plan **(1)**
100 N Academy Ave, Danville, PA 17822
Tel.: (570) 214-1552
Web Site: http://www.geisinger.org
Health Insurance Products & Services
N.A.I.C.S.: 524114
Steven R. Youso *(Pres & CEO)*
Lisa Hartman *(Assoc VP-Mktg & PR)*
Mark C. Gilger *(Coord-Mktg & PR)*

Geisinger HealthSouth Rehabilitation Hospital **(1)**
64 Rehab Ln, Danville, PA 17821-8498
Tel.: (570) 271-6110
Web Site:
http://www.geisingerhealthsouth.com
Vocational Rehabilitation Services
N.A.I.C.S.: 624310
Lori Dillon *(Pres)*

International Shared Services, Inc. **(1)**
2010 Cabot Blvd W, Langhorne, PA 19047
Tel.: (215) 752-2221
Web Site: http://www.isssolutions.com
Sales Range: $25-49.9 Million
Emp.: 200
Technology Lifecycle Management Solutions to Healthcare, Government, Education & Commercial Clients
N.A.I.C.S.: 541512
Peter Brooks *(CEO)*
Joseph A. Hardisky *(VP-Clinical Engrg)*
John Jones *(Head-IT)*
D. Michael Jones *(CFO)*
D. Michael Jones *(CFO)*

Subsidiary (Domestic):

Paradigm Technology Consulting, LLC **(2)**
22 S Main Street, Allentown, NJ 08501
Tel.: (609) 890-4150
Web Site: http://www.ptcllc.com
Executive Search Service
N.A.I.C.S.: 561312
Bridgette Hobart *(Pres)*

GEISSLER'S SUPERMARKET INCORPORATED
110 Bridge St, East Windsor, CT
06088-0887
Tel.: (860) 623-0176   CT
Web Site: http://www.geisslers.com
Year Founded: 1949
Sales Range: $50-74.9 Million
Emp.: 425
Grocery Services
N.A.I.C.S.: 445110
Dan Nilson *(VP)*
James H. Nilson Jr. *(Pres)*

GEKAY SALES & SERVICE CO. INC.
15 Dana Way, Ludlow, MA 01056
Tel.: (413) 583-7720
Web Site: https://www.gekay.com
Sales Range: $10-24.9 Million
Emp.: 54
Vending Machines & Supplies
N.A.I.C.S.: 423850
Marc Katz *(Pres)*

GEL-PAK LLC
31398 Huntwood Ave, Hayward, CA
94544
Tel.: (510) 576-2220
Web Site: https://www.gelpak.com
Rev.: $10,000,000
Emp.: 200
Mfr of Plastic Packaging Products
N.A.I.C.S.: 326199
Jeanne Beacham *(Pres)*
Diana Morgan *(CFO)*

GELBER GROUP LLC
141 W Jackson Blvd, Chicago, IL
60604
Tel.: (312) 427-7100
Web Site:
http://www.gelbergroup.com
Rev.: $18,892,000
Emp.: 300
Futures Brokers & Dealers, Commodity
N.A.I.C.S.: 523160
Brian Gelber *(Chm & Pres)*

GELFAND RENNERT & FELDMAN LLP
1880 Century Park E Ste 1600, Los
Angeles, CA 90067
Tel.: (310) 553-1707
Web Site: https://www.grfllp.com
Sales Range: $10-24.9 Million
Emp.: 180
Certified Public Accountants
N.A.I.C.S.: 541211
David Jackel *(Mng Partner)*
Irwin Rennert *(Partner)*
Adriane Hibbert *(Mng Dir)*
Cary MacMiller *(Mng Dir)*
Jeff Gillman *(Mng Dir)*
Lois Wecker *(Mng Dir)*
Mario Testani *(Mng Dir)*
Melissa Morton *(Mng Dir)*
Richard Mozenter *(Mng Dir)*
Ronald E. Nash *(Mng Partner-New York & Nashville)*
Todd Gelfand *(CEO)*
Tyson Beem *(Mng Dir)*
William Harper Jr. *(Mng Dir)*

GELIA-MEDIA, INC.

390 S Youngs Rd, Williamsville, NY
14221
Tel.: (716) 629-3200
Web Site: http://www.gelia.com
Year Founded: 1961
Rev.: $52,500,000
Emp.: 85
Advertising Agency
N.A.I.C.S.: 541810
James L. Phipps *(Pres & CEO)*
Cameron Macon *(Dir-Interactive Strategies)*

GELLER & CO.
909 3rd Ave, New York, NY 10022
Tel.: (212) 583-6000
Web Site: https://www.gellerco.com
Financial Management Services
N.A.I.C.S.: 541611

GELLER & COMPANY
909 3rd Ave, New York, NY 10022
Tel.: (212) 583-6000
Web Site: http://www.gellerco.com
Law firm
N.A.I.C.S.: 541110
Joseph Geller *(Partner)*

GELLERT GLOBAL GROUP
1 Atalanta Pl, Elizabeth, NJ 07206
Tel.: (908) 351-8000
Web Site:
https://www.gellertglobalgroup.com
Emp.: 100
Holding Company
N.A.I.C.S.: 551112

Subsidiaries:

Atalanta Corporation **(1)**
1 Atalanta Plz, Elizabeth, NJ 07206
Tel.: (908) 351-8000
Web Site: https://www.atalantacorp.com
Sales Range: $800-899.9 Million
Emp.: 370
Canned & Frozen Specialty Food Products
Importer & Distr
N.A.I.C.S.: 424490
Thomas Gellert *(Pres)*
Gaby Gaiz *(Mgr-Sls)*
Ellie Brown *(Mgr-Sls)*
Thomas Gellert *(Pres)*

Subsidiary (Non-US):

Atalanta Furniture SRL **(2)**
18 Aviator Mircea Zorileanu Street 4th Floor
Atalanta Building, District 1, Bucharest, Romania
Tel.: (40) 212242254
Web Site: http://www.atalanta1.com
International & Local Furniture Trading & Distribution
N.A.I.C.S.: 238990
Marin Pirvu *(Dir Gen)*
Serban Bucur *(VP)*

Atalanta Nova SRL **(2)**
18 Aviator Mircea Zorileanu Street 5th
Floor, Atalanta Building District 1, Bucharest, Romania
Tel.: (40) 212240251
Web Site: http://www.atalanta1.com
Commodity Trading
N.A.I.C.S.: 926140

Subsidiary (Domestic):

Camerican International, Inc. **(2)**
45 Eisenhower Dr, Paramus, NJ 07652-1452
Tel.: (201) 587-0101
Web Site: http://www.camerican.com
Processing of Tuna, Pineapple & Specialty Foods
N.A.I.C.S.: 424490
Larry Abramson *(CEO)*

Subsidiary (Domestic):

KH International, Inc. **(3)**
1649 N Decatur Rd NE, Atlanta, GA 30307
Tel.: (404) 371-9797
Web Site: http://www.khinternational.com
Grocery Whslr
N.A.I.C.S.: 424410
Karen Holzberg *(Founder)*

Subsidiary (Domestic):

JA Kirsch Corporation (2)
1086 Teaneck Rd Ste 2E, Teaneck, NJ
07666-4857
Tel.: (201) 862-0100
Web Site: http://www.jakirsch.com
Bottled Water Mfr
N.A.I.C.S.: 312112
Mark Gruenbaum (CEO)

Subsidiary (Non-US):

Lemarco S.A. (2)
12 Visarion Street District 1, Bucharest,
10424, Romania (50%)
Tel.: (40) 213119714
Emp.: 60
Agricultural Commodities: Sugar, Grains &
Vegetable Oils
N.A.I.C.S.: 523160
Mircea Radina (Pres)
Neculai Maratas (VP)
Dan Popovici (Dir-Comml)

GELMART INDUSTRIES INC.
136 Madison Ave 4th Fl, New York,
NY 10016
Tel.: (212) 743-6900
Web Site: http://www.gelmart.com
Sales Range: $25-49.9 Million
Emp.: 200
Bras, Girdles & Allied Garments
N.A.I.C.S.: 424990
Ilan Djemal (Dir-Mgmt Info Sys)
Leon Fisher (Dir-Mgmt Info Sys)
Ron Karger (Asst Controller)
Micheal DeBiase (Product Mgr)

GELSIGHT, INC.
179 Bear Hill Rd Ste 202, Waltham,
MA 02451
Tel.: (781) 790-1905
Web Site: https://www.gelsight.com
Year Founded: 2011
Analytical Laboratory Instrument Mfr
N.A.I.C.S.: 334516
Janos Rohaly (Co-Founder & CTO)
Youssef Benmokhtar (CEO)
Kimo Johnson (Co-Founder & Chief
Product Officer)
Dennis Lang (Chief Bus Officer)
Edward Adelson (Co-Founder)

GEM EQUIPMENT OF OR-EGON INC.
2150 Progress Way, Woodburn, OR
97071
Tel.: (503) 982-9902
Web Site:
https://www.gemequipment.com
Sales Range: $10-24.9 Million
Emp.: 150
Mfr, Designer & Installer of Custom
Food Processing Systems
N.A.I.C.S.: 333241
Edward T. Mckenney (Pres)
Steve Ross (CEO)
Donald Harmon (Project Mgr)
Brian Pikl (Project Mgr)
Josh Price (Engr-Mechanical)

GEM GROUP INC.
9 International Way, Lawrence, MA
01843
Tel.: (978) 691-2000
Web Site: https://www.gemline.com
Rev.: $16,500,000
Emp.: 225
Provider of Travel & Tote Bags
N.A.I.C.S.: 323113
Jonathan Isaacson (Owner & Pres)
Jean O'Connor (Coord-AP)

GEM INDUSTRIES CORPORA-TION
Hwy 123 N, Toccoa, GA 30577
Tel.: (706) 886-8431 DE
Year Founded: 1911

Sales Range: $150-199.9 Million
Emp.: 120
Holding Company
N.A.I.C.S.: 332510
M.F. Rolla (Pres & COO)
Mike Ramsey (Controller)

Subsidiaries:

Gem Industries (1)
PO Box 450061, Sunrise, FL
33351 (100%)
Tel.: (706) 886-8431
Web Site: http://www.gem-industries.com
Sales Range: $25-49.9 Million
Metal Furniture & Hardware Mfr
N.A.I.C.S.: 332510

Gem Southeast, Inc. (1)
5349 Hwy 123 N, Toccoa, GA
30577 (100%)
Tel.: (706) 886-8431
Sales Range: $25-49.9 Million
Mfr of Work Aids, Metal Furniture, Hardware
& Nursing Home Beds
N.A.I.C.S.: 332613
Barry Roberts (Plant Mgr)
Sally Walker (Mgr-HR & Safety)

GEM JEWELRY INC.
28 Main St, East Hartford, CT 06118
Tel.: (860) 568-7900
Web Site: http://www.gemjewelry.com
Rev.: $11,000,000
Emp.: 11
Jewelry, Precious Stones & Precious
Metals
N.A.I.C.S.: 458310
Stanley Frank (Pres)

GEM MINNEAPOLIS
5780 Lincoln Dr Ste 150, Edina, MN
55436
Tel.: (952) 831-6313 GA
Web Site: https://www.gemmpls.com
Year Founded: 1958
Creative Design Services
N.A.I.C.S.: 541810
David Kuettel (Owner & CEO)
Merrilee Riley (VP & Admin-HR)

GEM REFRIGERATOR COM-PANY, INC.
7340 Milnor St, Philadelphia, PA
19136
Tel.: (215) 426-8700
Web Site: http://www.gemref.com
Year Founded: 1925
Sales Range: Less than $1 Million
Emp.: 30
Refrigerators, Freezers & Equipment
for Commercial Use Mfr
N.A.I.C.S.: 333415
Bruce Gruhler (Pres)

GEM STATE DISTRIBUTORS INCORPORATED
350 Indus Ln, Pocatello, ID 83201
Tel.: (208) 237-5151
Web Site:
http://www.gemstatecandy.com
Sales Range: $10-24.9 Million
Emp.: 40
Tobacco & Tobacco Products Mfr
N.A.I.C.S.: 424940
D. Paul Noorda (Pres & CEO)

GEM-DANDY, INC.
200 W Academy St, Madison, NC
27025
Tel.: (336) 548-9624 NC
Web Site: https://www.gem-dandy.com
Year Founded: 1921
Suspenders, Belts & Small Leather
Products
N.A.I.C.S.: 315990
Brad Penn (Pres & CEO)
Paul Walter (VP-Fin)

GEMCO CONSTRUCTORS, LLC
6525 Guion Rd, Indianapolis, IN
46268
Tel.: (317) 537-0993
Web Site: http://www.gem-constructors.com
Year Founded: 2014
Mechanical, Electrical & Plumbing
Contractor
N.A.I.C.S.: 238220
Andrew Toth (CFO)
William Bates (CEO)
Jim Bates (COO)
Jason Kilgore (Dir-HR)
KC McDonald (Dir-Bus Dev)
Tom Fine (Dir-Service)
Emily Bates (Dir-Mktg & Comm)
Kris Nasser (Dir-Safety)
David Smith (Dir-IT)
Brad Kendall (Dir-Plumbing)

Subsidiaries:

Real Mechanical Inc. (1)
475 Gradle Dr, Carmel, IN 46032
Tel.: (317) 846-9299
Web Site: http://www.realmechanical.com
Electrical Contractor
N.A.I.C.S.: 238210
Thomas E. Fine (Sec)

GEMCRAFT HOMES INC.
2205 A Commerce Rd, Forest Hill,
MD 21050
Tel.: (410) 893-8458
Web Site:
http://www.gemcrafthomes.com
Sales Range: $25-49.9 Million
Emp.: 100
Residential Construction Services
N.A.I.C.S.: 236115
Vickie Luther (Pres-Administration)
Sharon Babcock (Owner)
Judy Cade (Sls Mgr)
William Luther Jr. (Pres)

GEMINI ALUMINUM CORPO-RATION
3255 Pomona Blvd, Pomona, CA
91768-3291
Tel.: (909) 595-7403 CA
Year Founded: 1979
Sales Range: $50-74.9 Million
Emp.: 25
Aluminum Products Mfr
N.A.I.C.S.: 331318
Allan J. Hardy (Pres)

GEMINI COMMUNICATIONS
28 Wells Ave 4th Fl, Yonkers, NY
10701
Tel.: (212) 689-8200 DE
Year Founded: 1932
Sales Range: $50-74.9 Million
Emp.: 48
Holding Company; Newspaper Adver-tising Services
N.A.I.C.S.: 551112
Phyllis Cavaliere (Principal)
Michael Baratoff (Principal)
Nili De Bono (VP-Fin-Admin)

Subsidiaries:

Metro Newspaper Advertising Ser-vices, Inc. (1)
28 Wells Ave 4th Fl, Yonkers, NY 10701
Tel.: (212) 689-8200
Web Site: http://www.metrosn.com
Sales & Marketing of Newspapers
N.A.I.C.S.: 424920
Phyllis Cavaliere (Principal)
Michael Baratoff (Principal)
Kim Aiello (Exec VP-Ops)
Tack Prashad (Exec VP-Client Svcs)
James Magee (Dir-Bus Dev)
Maluri Fernandez (Dir-Digital Plng)
Kathy Jahns (VP-Sls-Western)
Russell Mirman (VP-Bus Dev)

Unit (Domestic):

Metro Newspaper Advertising Ser-vices, Inc. (2)
15305 Dallas Pkwy Ste 300, Addison, TX
75001
Tel.: (972) 387-7477
Sales & Marketing of Newspapers
N.A.I.C.S.: 424920

Metro Sunday Newspapers (2)
8 W 38th St 4th Fl, New York, NY 10018
Tel.: (212) 689-8200
Web Site: http://www.metrosn.com
Rev.: $10,000,000
Emp.: 30
Sunday Newspaper Sales
N.A.I.C.S.: 541840
Phyllis Cavaliere (Pres & CEO)
Nili De Bono (VP-Fin & Admin)
Michael Baratoff (Pres & COO)
Bill Huck (VP-Eastern Adv Dir)

Metro-Puck Comics Network (2)
28 Wells Ave 4th Fl, New York, NY 10701
Tel.: (212) 689-8200
Web Site: http://www.metrosn.com
Sales Range: $1-9.9 Million
Sunday Comics Sections for Newspapers
N.A.I.C.S.: 541840
Bill Huck (Sr VP)

GEMINI COSMETICS, INC.
152 W 57th St Ste 2601, New York,
NY 10019-3310
Tel.: (212) 586-0100
Sales Range: $10-24.9 Million
Fragrance Developer
N.A.I.C.S.: 325620
Sam Endy (CFO)
Frank Fazzinga (Pres & CEO)
Joanne Cardello (VP-Mktg)

GEMINI GROUP SERVICE CORPORATION
5108 Pegasus Ct Ste A, Frederick,
MD 21074
Tel.: (240) 566-5280
Web Site:
http://www.geminicorporation.com
Year Founded: 1998
Sales Range: $1-9.9 Million
Emp.: 260
Commercial Building Cleaning Ser-vices
N.A.I.C.S.: 561720
Alan Dykstra (Founder & CEO)
Aracely Vargas (Mgr-Ops)
Simeon Hernandez (Area Mgr)
Courtney Dykstra (Dir-Mktg)
Rocio Moghaddam (Office Mgr)
Jennifer Dykstra (Dir-Insurance &
Loss Control)
Thomas Ingersoll (Pres)

GEMINI GROUP, INC.
175 Thompson Rd, Bad Axe, MI
48413
Tel.: (248) 435-7271
Web Site:
https://www.geminigroup.net
Year Founded: 1977
Sales Range: $25-49.9 Million
Emp.: 480
Plastic Products Mfr
N.A.I.C.S.: 541611
T. L. Bushey (CFO)
Lynette Drake (Pres)

Subsidiaries:

Axly Production Machining Inc. (1)
727 Skinner St, Bad Axe, MI 48413
Tel.: (989) 269-7791
Machine Tools Mfr
N.A.I.C.S.: 333517

Briney Tooling Systems, Inc. (1)
700 E Soper Rd, Bad Axe, MI 48413
Tel.: (800) 752-8035
Web Site: http://www.brineytooling.com
Emp.: 100
Machine Tools Mfr

Gemini Group, Inc.—(Continued)

N.A.I.C.S.: 333517
Tammy Gwisdalla (Office Mgr)

CKS Precision Machining, Inc. (1)
700 E Soper Rd, Bad Axe, MI 48413
Tel.: (800) 292-0268
Web Site: http://www.geminigroup.com
Machine Tools Mfr
N.A.I.C.S.: 333517
Mike Ornowski (Product Mgr)

Consolidated Tool, Inc. (1)
333 E Washington Ave, Muscle Shoals, AL
35661
Tel.: (256) 381-9420
Sales Range: $1-9.9 Million
Emp.: 20
Machine Tools Mfr
N.A.I.C.S.: 333517
Michael Greenhill (Plant Mgr)
Rick Lansdell (Mgr-Quality Control)

**Gemini Plastics de Mexico S. de R.L.
de C.V.** (1)
Parque Industrial Angostura Carretera
Saltillo Zacatecas km 4 5 sn, Nave 39 40 y
41, 25315, Saltillo, Coahuila, Mexico
Tel.: (52) 844 482 6863
Machine Tools Mfr
N.A.I.C.S.: 333517

Gemini Plastics, Inc. (1)
4385 Garfield St, Ubly, MI 48475
Tel.: (989) 658-8557
Machine Tools Mfr
N.A.I.C.S.: 333517
Eric Sweeney (Engr-Tooling)

Thumb Plastics Inc. (1)
400 Liberty St, Bad Axe, MI 48413-9490
Tel.: (248) 435-7271
Web Site: http://www.geminigroup.net
Sales Range: $10-24.9 Million
Emp.: 100
Injection Molding & Tooling Design Mfr
N.A.I.C.S.: 326199
Tom Heiman (Exec VP)

Thumb Tool & Engineering Co. (1)
354 Liberty St, Bad Axe, MI 48413
Tel.: (989) 269-9731
Web Site: http://www.geminigroup.net
Emp.: 200
Machine Tools Mfr
N.A.I.C.S.: 333517
John Moll (CEO)
Lynette Drake (Chm & Pres)
Anthony A. Trecapelli (Exec VP)
Brian Cubitt (Exec VP)
Tom Heiman (Exec VP)

Valley Enterprises, Inc. (1)
2147 Leppek Rd, Ubly, MI 48475
Tel.: (989) 658-3200
Automotive Interior Trim Mfr
N.A.I.C.S.: 336360

GEMINI INCORPORATED
103 Mensing Way, Cannon Falls, MN
55009
Tel.: (507) 263-3957
Web Site: http://www.signletters.com
Sales Range: $50-74.9 Million
Emp.: 150
Injection Molding Of Plastics
N.A.I.C.S.: 326199
James R. Weinel (Pres)
Wayne Meyer (Mgr-Matls & Project
Engr)
Frederick Oss (Pres)
David Schmitt (VP & Mgr-Ops)

GEMINI INDUSTRIES INC.
2300 SW Holloway St, El Reno, OK
73036
Tel.: (405) 262-5710
Web Site: http://www.gemini-
coatings.com
Sales Range: $25-49.9 Million
Emp.: 140
Paint & Related Products Mfr
N.A.I.C.S.: 325510
Rodney Wickersham (Mgr-Mktg)
Rick McGee (CFO)
Chris Hicks (Pres & CEO)

GEMINI INVESTORS LLC
20 William St Ste 250, Wellesley, MA
02481
Tel.: (781) 237-7001 DE
Web Site: https://www.gemini-
investors.com
Year Founded: 1993
Sales Range: $25-49.9 Million
Emp.: 13
Privater Equity Firm
N.A.I.C.S.: 523999
James J. Goodman (Pres)
David F. Millet (Mng Dir)
Jeffrey T. Newton (Mng Dir)
Matthew E. Keis (Mng Dir)
James T. Rich (Mng Dir)
Dean S. Pernisie (Principal)
Robert P. Menn (Principal)
Ellen V. Winston (VP-Fin)
Penney Ryan (Dir-Admin)
Penny L. Foote (Office Mgr)
Scott M. Johnson (VP)

Subsidiaries:

**Conditioned Air Company of Naples
LLC** (1)
3786 Mercantile Ave, Naples, FL 34104
Tel.: (239) 758-7255
Web Site: https://www.conditionedair.com
Plumbing, Heating & Air-Conditioning Con-
tractors
N.A.I.C.S.: 238220
Greg Johnson (Exec Chm & CEO)

Subsidiary (Domestic):

AC Designs, Inc. (2)
6656 Columbia Park Dr Ste 1, Jacksonville,
FL 32258
Tel.: (904) 829-8898
Web Site: http://www.acdesignsinc.net
Sales Range: $1-9.9 Million
Emp.: 50
Plumbing, Heating & Air-Conditioning Con-
tractors
N.A.I.C.S.: 238220
Corey Tennant (Pres)

FabEnCo, Inc. (1)
2002 Karbach St, Houston, TX 77092
Tel.: (713) 686-6620
Web Site: http://www.fabenco.com
Sales Range: $10-24.9 Million
Metal Safety Gate Mfr
N.A.I.C.S.: 332323
David H. LaCook (CEO)
Donald Henderson (Exec VP)
Scott Friedman (Sls Mgr)
Donna Dennis (Controller)
Philippe Suhas (Chm)

GEMINI LEGAL SUPPORT,
INC.
6020 W Oaks Blvd Ste 310, Rocklin,
CA 95765
Tel.: (559) 739-7481 CA
Web Site: https://gemini.legal
Year Founded: 2004
Law firm
N.A.I.C.S.: 541199
Dan Mora (CEO & Founder)
Jeff Pierce (Dir-Ops)
Frank Smithson (Dir-Sls)
Brian Milanese (Mgr-Reg Sls)
Richard Conteras (Mgr-Territory)
Hannah Pence (Mgr-Mktg)
Rochelle Hohn (Mgr-Acct)
Sara Noorzad (Acct Mgr)
Yoshi Warita (Mgr-Acct)
Tony Daugherty (Pres)

Subsidiaries:

Sayler Legal Service, Inc. (1)
2511 Garden Rd Ste B-100, Monterey, CA
93940
Tel.: (831) 384-4030
Web Site: http://www.saylerlegal.com
Legal Service Provider
N.A.I.C.S.: 541199
Stephanie Sayler (Founder & CEO)

GEMINI SOUND PRODUCTS
CORP.
107 Trumbull St Bldg F8 Fl 2, Eliza-
beth, NJ 07206
Tel.: (732) 346-0061 NJ
Web Site:
http://www.geminisound.com
Year Founded: 1974
Sales Range: $10-24.9 Million
Emp.: 20
Provider of Household Audio & Video
Equipment
N.A.I.C.S.: 334310
Arte Cabasso (CEO)

GEMINI VALVE
2 Otter Ct, Raymond, NH 03077
Tel.: (603) 895-4761
Web Site:
https://www.geminivalve.com
Sales Range: $10-24.9 Million
Emp.: 55
Screw Machine Products
N.A.I.C.S.: 332721
Daniel Packard (Pres)
Cor Osseweijer (Mng Dir)
Rebecca Shirtz (Controller)
Judy Frost (Mgr-Pur)
Harry Millette (VP-Mktg & Sls)
Kenneth Madden (VP-Ops)

GEMISYS FINANCIAL
7103 S Revere Pkwy, Centennial, CO
80112
Tel.: (303) 705-6000
Web Site: http://www.gemisys.com
Rev.: $10,300,000
Emp.: 121
Stock Transfer Agents
N.A.I.C.S.: 523999
Douglas Thaxton (Pres)

GEMLINE FRAME CO. INC.
15700 S Main St, Gardena, CA
90248
Tel.: (323) 223-1178
Web Site:
http://www.gemlineframe.com
Sales Range: $10-24.9 Million
Emp.: 35
Picture & Mirror Frames, Wood
N.A.I.C.S.: 339999

GEMMEL RX
143 N Euclid Ave, Ontario, CA 91762
Tel.: (909) 986-1129
Web Site: http://www.gemmelrx.com
Rev.: $12,700,000
Emp.: 135
Retail Prescription, Sterile & Non-
Sterile Compounding & Medical
Equipment Mfr
N.A.I.C.S.: 339112
Phic Lim (Sec)

GEMSHARES PHYSICAL DIA-
MOND TRUST
1330 W Monroe St, Chicago, IL
60607
Tel.: (312) 226-3139 NY
Year Founded: 2013
Investment Trust Services
N.A.I.C.S.: 523999
Victor Feldman (CEO)
Sharon Karsten (CFO & Principal
Acctg Officer)

GEMSPRING CAPITAL MAN-
AGEMENT, LLC
54 Wilton Rd, Westport, CT 06880
Tel.: (203) 842-8886 DE
Web Site: http://www.gemspring.com
Year Founded: 2015
Rev.: $1,500,000,000
Privater Equity Firm
N.A.I.C.S.: 523999

Malcolm Appelbaum (Mng Dir, CFO &
Chief Compliance Officer)
Ravdeep Chanana (Mng Dir)
Thomas Zanios (Mng Dir)
Geoff Broglio (Mng Dir)
Aron Grossman (Mng Dir)
Kerri Hagen (Dir-Bus Dev)
Alexander Shakibnia (Mng Dir)
Matthew Shuman (Mng Dir)
Bret Wiener (Founder & Mng Partner)
Donald Gerne (Mng Dir)
Charles Fraas (Mng Dir & Head-
Portfolio Ops)
Russ Spieler (Mng Dir)

Subsidiaries:

AINS Inc. (1)
1355 Piccard Dr Ste 300, Rockville, MD
20850
Tel.: (301) 670-2300
Web Site: http://www.ains-inc.com
Rev.: $8,000,000
Emp.: 60
Software Publisher
N.A.I.C.S.: 513210
Cindy Dillow (Dir-IT Support Svcs)
Mohinder Goswami (CEO)
Mohan Srinivasan (CFO)

AMPAM Parks Mechanical, Inc. (1)
1060 Wilmington Blvd, Wilmington, CA
90744
Tel.: (310) 835-1532
Web Site: http://www.parksmechanical.com
Emp.: 1,000
Plumbing Services
N.A.I.C.S.: 238220
Roland Kazandjian (Dir-Matls)
Buddy Parks (Chm)
Jason Parks (VP-CAD)
James Parks (VP-Reconstruction)
John Parks (VP)

Subsidiary (Domestic):

Multi Mechanical, Inc. (2)
1210 N Barsten Way, Anaheim, CA 92806-
1822
Tel.: (714) 632-7404
Web Site: http://www.multimechanical.com
Sales Range: $1-9.9 Million
Emp.: 15
Plumbing, Heating & Air-Conditioning Con-
tractors
N.A.I.C.S.: 238220

Avi Integrators Inc. (1)
1520 N Powerline Rd, Pompano Beach, FL
33069
Tel.: (954) 984-4282
Web Site: http://www.security101.com
Rev.: $4,000,000
Emp.: 13
Security Systems Services, except Lock-
smiths
N.A.I.C.S.: 561621
Richard Montalvo (Owner)
Jim Flisek (Dir-Tech)
Steve Crespo (Pres, CEO & Mng Partner)
Michael Walton (VP-Ops)
Mike Trilk (VP-Sls)
Tom Echols (Pres & Gen Mgr)

ClearCompany, Inc. (1)
11 Beacon St 13th Fl, Boston, MA 02108
Tel.: (617) 938-3801
Web Site: http://info.clearcompany.com
Sales Range: $1-9.9 Million
Human Resource Consulting Services
N.A.I.C.S.: 541612
Andre Lavoie (Co-Founder & CEO)
Colin Kingsbury (Co-Founder & Pres)
Django Bliss (CTO)
Sylvie Woolf (Dir-Client Svc)
Sara Pollock (Dir-Mktg)

Fenceworks Inc. (1)
870 N Main St, Riverside, CA 92501-1016
Tel.: (951) 788-5620
Web Site: https://www.fenceworks.us
Sales Range: $25-49.9 Million
Emp.: 275
Fences & Gates Sales & Installation
N.A.I.C.S.: 238990
Javier Venezuela (VP)
Dawn Smith (Office Mgr)
Jason Ostrander (CEO)

Maria Chavez (Dir-HR)
Gary Hansen (VP)
Michael Rice (Mgr-Safety)

Midland Industries. Co., Inc. (1)
3145 Oak St, Kansas City, MO 64111
Tel.: (800) 821-5725
Fittings, Couplings, Valves, Hoses & Related Products Mfr & Distr
N.A.I.C.S.: 332996

Subsidiary (Domestic):

Anderson Metals, LLC (2)
1701 Southern Rd, Kansas City, MO 64120
Tel.: (816) 471-2600
Web Site: http://www.midlandindustries.com
Plumbing Fixtures & Fittings Equipment Mfr
N.A.I.C.S.: 332913

Mid-America Fittings, Inc. (2)
7604 Wedd St,, Overland Park, KS 66204
Tel.: (913) 962-7277
Web Site: http://www.midamericafittings.com
Brass Fittings, Valves & Custom Components Mfr
N.A.I.C.S.: 332919
Scott Shane (CEO)

Midland Metal Mfg. Co., Inc. (2)
3145 Oak St, Kansas City, MO 64111
Tel.: (800) 821-5725
Web Site: http://midlandmetal.com
Plumbing Fixture Fitting & Trim Mfr
N.A.I.C.S.: 332913

RAB Aggregator, LLC (1)
1500 Providence Hwy Unit 26, Norwood, MA 02062
Tel.: (800) 764-5010
Web Site: https://amplix.com
Technology Advisory & Consulting Services
N.A.I.C.S.: 541690
Joe DeStefano (CEO)

Subsidiary (Domestic):

Go2 Communications, Inc. (2)
8 Cedar St, Woburn, MA 01810
Tel.: (781) 376-2100
Web Site:
   http://www.go2communications.com
Rev.: $7,600,000
Emp.: 5
Technologies & Business Information Solutions
N.A.I.C.S.: 813910
Michael E. Chapman (VP-Sls)
Erick Johnson (Dir-Mobility Svcs)
David L. Cosentino (Founder & CEO)
Tim Clough (Partner)

Rapid Displays, Inc. (1)
4300 W 47th St, Chicago, IL 60632-4439
Tel.: (773) 927-5000
Web Site: http://www.rapiddisplays.com
Provider of Mounting & Die Cutting of Point of Purchase Advertising Displays
N.A.I.C.S.: 322130
Ray Gottschalk (VP-Bus Dev-Western US)
Alan Foshay (VP-Bus Dev-Midwest/Eastern)

Division (Domestic):

Rapid Displays - Union City (2)
33195 Lewis St, Union City, CA 94587-2201   (100%)
Tel.: (510) 487-0700
Web Site: http://www.rapiddisplays.com
Advertising Displays Mfr
N.A.I.C.S.: 339950
Ray Gottschalk (VP-Bus Dev-West Coast)

Shrieve Chemical Company LLC (1)
1755 Woodstead Ct, Woodlands, TX 77380-0964
Tel.: (281) 367-4226
Web Site: http://www.shrieve.com
Sales Range: $10-24.9 Million
Emp.: 27
Industrial Chemical & Synthetic Fluid Distr
N.A.I.C.S.: 424690
Jim Coffey (Treas)
George Fuller (CEO)

Subsidiary (Domestic):

Gilbert & Jones Co., Inc. (2)
35 Peter Ct, New Britain, CT 06051
Tel.: (860) 832-8550
Web Site: http://www.gilbertandjones.net

Sales Range: $1-9.9 Million
Emp.: 20
Chemical & Allied Product Whslr
N.A.I.C.S.: 424690
George Gilbert (CEO)

Subsidiary (Non-US):

Shrieve Chemical (Shanghai) Ltd. (2)
Room 3301 Junling Plaza 500 North Chengdu Road, Shanghai, 200003, China
Tel.: (86) 2163598216
Web Site: http://www.shrieve.com.cn
Chemical Product Whslr
N.A.I.C.S.: 424690

Subsidiary (Domestic):

Shrieve Chemical Products Inc. (2)
1755 Woodstead Ct, Spring, TX 77380-1448   (100%)
Tel.: (281) 367-4226
Web Site: http://www.shrieve.com
Sales Range: $10-24.9 Million
Marketing of Chemical Preparations
N.A.I.C.S.: 325998
Veronica Levet (Mgr-Ops)

Subsidiary (Non-US):

Shrieve Products International Limited (2)
Suite 39 40 Churchill Square, Kings Hill, West Malling, ME19 4YU, Kent, United Kingdom
Tel.: (44) 1732520600
Web Site: http://www.shrieve.com
Chemical Product Whslr
N.A.I.C.S.: 424690

Shrieve Quimica do Brasil Ltda. (2)
Av Dr Jose Bonifacio Coutinho Nogueira 150 Terreo, Campinas, 13091-611, Brazil
Tel.: (55) 1935781177
Chemical Product Whslr
N.A.I.C.S.: 424690
Paulo Frare (Gen Mgr)

Subsidiary (Domestic):

Tlc Ingredients, Inc. (2)
1 Genstar Ln Ste D, Joliet, IL 60435-2675
Tel.: (815) 723-9900
Web Site: http://www.tlcingredients.com
Rev.: $1,400,000
Emp.: 9
Chemical & Allied Products Merchant Whslr
N.A.I.C.S.: 424690
Thomas B. Turriff (Pres)
Peter Lorusso (VP-Sls & Mktg)

TMP Worldwide Advertising & Communications LLC (1)
1 Battery Park Plz Ste 2710, New York, NY 10004-1405
Tel.: (646) 613-2000
Web Site: https://www.radancy.com
Emp.: 850
Advertising Agency
N.A.I.C.S.: 541810
Michelle Abbey (Pres & CEO)
Mike Newell (Pres-North America)
Sherry Jacobson (Exec VP)
Matt Lamphear (Exec VP-Digital Products & Strategy)
Lynda Harden (COO-Global Delivery)
Russell Miyaki (Sr VP-Creative Svcs)
Steven Z. Ehrlich (Sr VP-Client Dev-Global)
Michael Littlewood (Chief Revenue Officer & Exec VP-Sls-Global)
Jason Day (CFO)
Dennis Parrington (CTO)

Subsidiary (Non-US):

Associates in Advertising Limited (2)
200 Aldersgate Street, London, EC1A 4HD, United Kingdom
Tel.: (44) 20 7993 1300
Advetising Agency
N.A.I.C.S.: 541810
Steven Z. Ehrlich (Sr VP-European New Bus)
Sherry Jacobson (Exec VP)
Russell Miyaki (Sr VP-Creative Svcs)
Mike Littlewood (Exec VP-New Bus-Global)
Michelle Abbey (Pres & CEO)
Matt Lamphear (Exec VP-Digital Products & Strategy)

Lynda Harden (COO-Delivery-Global)
Dennis Parrington (CTO)
Emerson Moore II (Gen Counsel & Exec VP)

Subsidiary (Domestic):

CKR Interactive, Inc. (2)
399 N 3rd St, Campbell, CA 95008
Tel.: (408) 517-1400
Web Site: http://www.ckrinteractive.com
Advetising Agency
N.A.I.C.S.: 541810
Curtis Rogers (Pres & CEO)
Kasey Sixt (VP-Branding)
Brandon Spencer (Dir-Interactive Svcs)
Laurie Severino (Dir-Bus Dev)

Branch (Domestic):

CKR Interactive (3)
1499 S Federal Hwy Unit 312, Poynton, FL 33435
Tel.: (954) 252-6666
Web Site: http://www.ckrinteractive.com
Sales Range: Less than $1 Million
Emp.: 10
Advetising Agency
N.A.I.C.S.: 541810

Branch (Domestic):

TMP Worldwide/Advertising & Communications (2)
525 Market St Ste 1460, San Francisco, CA 94105
Tel.: (415) 820-7800
Advertising Services
N.A.I.C.S.: 541810
Michelle Abbey (Pres & CEO)
Gareth Edwards (Exec VP-Europe)
Lynda Harden (COO-Delivery-Global)
Matt Lamphear (Exec VP-Digital Products & Strategy)
Mike Littlewood (Exec VP-New Bus-Global)
Mike Newell (Pres-North America)
Russell Miyaki (Sr VP-Creative Svcs)
Sherry Jacobson (Exec VP)
Steven Z. Ehrlich (Sr VP-European New Bus)
Emerson Moore II (Gen Counsel & Exec VP)

TMP Worldwide/Advertising & Communications (2)
10 Glenlake S Ste 100, Atlanta, GA 30328
Tel.: (770) 280-4811
Advertising Services
N.A.I.C.S.: 541810

TMP Worldwide/Advertising & Communications (2)
1075 Main St Ste 110, Waltham, MA 02451
Tel.: (781) 895-4000
Advertising Services
N.A.I.C.S.: 541810

TMP Worldwide/Advertising & Communications (2)
1200 Ponce de Leon Blvd Ste 1005, Coral Gables, FL 33134
Tel.: (305) 704-4788
Advertising Services
N.A.I.C.S.: 541810

Branch (Non-US):

TMP Worldwide/Advertising & Communications (2)
The Exchange Tower 130 King Street West Suite 1800, Toronto, M5X 1E3, ON, Canada
Tel.: (416) 861-8679
Advertising Services
N.A.I.C.S.: 541810

TMP Worldwide/Advertising & Communications (2)
1275 W 6th Ave, Vancouver, V6H 1A6, BC, Canada
Tel.: (604) 688-2441
Advertising Services
N.A.I.C.S.: 541810

TMP Worldwide/Advertising & Communications (2)
Hillview House Gilford Road, Dublin, Ireland
Tel.: (353) 1 218 6800
Advertising Services
N.A.I.C.S.: 541810

Branch (Domestic):

TMP Worldwide/Advertising & Communications (2)
The Elsby 115 E Spring St Ste 600, New Albany, IN 47150
Tel.: (812) 945-9780
Advertising Services
N.A.I.C.S.: 541810

TMP Worldwide/Advertising & Communications (2)
330 N Brand Blvd Ste 1050, Glendale, CA 91203
Tel.: (818) 539-2002
Advertising Services
N.A.I.C.S.: 541810
Michelle Abbey (Pres & CEO)
Lynda Harden (COO-Delivery-Global)
Matt Lamphear (Exec VP-Digital Products & Strategy)
Mike Littlewood (Exec VP-Global New Bus)
Russell Miyaki (Sr VP-Creative Svcs)
Sherry Jacobson (Exec VP)
Dennis Parrington (CTO)
Emerson Moore II (Gen Counsel & Exec VP)

TMP Worldwide/Advertising & Communications (2)
205 N Michigan Ave Ste 4000, Chicago, IL 60601
Tel.: (312) 467-9350
Advertising Services
N.A.I.C.S.: 541810

TMP Worldwide/Directional Marketing (2)
10 Glenlake S Ste 100, Atlanta, GA 30328
Tel.: (414) 918-6503
Advertising Services
N.A.I.C.S.: 541810

Zavation Medical Products, LLC (1)
220 Lakeland Pkwy, Flowood, MS 39232
Tel.: (601) 919-1119
Web Site: http://www.zavation.com
Medical Device Mfr & Distr
N.A.I.C.S.: 339112
Jeffrey Johnson (Pres & CEO)

GEN CAP AMERICA, INC.
40 Burton Hills Blvd Ste 420, Nashville, TN 37215
Tel.: (615) 256-0231
Web Site:
   http://www.gencapamerica.com
Year Founded: 1988
Privater Equity Firm
N.A.I.C.S.: 523999
Barney D. Byrd (Pres & CEO)
Christopher T. Godwin (Mng Dir)
J. Matthew Lane (Sr VP)
Mark E. Isaacs (Mng Dir)
Andrew L. Ginsberg (Dir)
Stacey J. Turner (VP-Fin)
Donald D. Napier III (Exec VP)
MacLin P. Davis III (Controller)

Subsidiaries:

Canfield Technologies, LLC (1)
1 Crossman Rd, Sayreville, NJ 08872
Tel.: (732) 316-2100
Web Site: http://www.canfieldmetals.com
Lead Free Industrial Alloys Mfr
N.A.I.C.S.: 331492

Day Motor Sports LLC (1)
6100 US Hwy 69 N, Tyler, TX 75706-6830
Tel.: (903) 593-9815
Web Site: http://www.daymotorsports.com
Emp.: 25
Online Distr of Automotive Parts & Accessories
N.A.I.C.S.: 441330
Joe Francis (Pres & CEO)

Frontier Packaging, Inc. (1)
1201 Andover Park E Ste 101, Tukwila, WA 98188
Tel.: (206) 575-7772
Web Site: http://www.frontierpackaging.com
Industrial & Personal Service Paper Merchant Whslr
N.A.I.C.S.: 424130

Gen Cap America, Inc.—(Continued)

Rod Meussner *(Pres & CEO)*
Dennis O'Donnell *(Exec VP-Strategy & New Bus Dev)*
John Merritt *(VP-Sls)*

Gared Holdings, LLC   (1)
9200 E 146th St Bldg A, Noblesville, IN 46060
Tel.: (317) 774-9840
Web Site: http://www.garedsports.com
Holding Company
N.A.I.C.S.: 339920
Charlie Sasse *(Dir-Sls-Intl)*

Division (Domestic):

Gared Sports   (2)
9200 E 146th St Bldg A, Noblesville, IN 46060
Tel.: (317) 774-9840
Web Site: http://www.garedsports.com
Sporting Goods Whslr
N.A.I.C.S.: 339920
Richard Gregor *(Project Mgr)*
Kevin Needler *(Gen Mgr)*
Laura St. Geroge *(Exec VP-Sls & Mktg)*

Subsidiary (Domestic):

Performance Sports Systems, Inc.   (2)
9200 E 146th St Ste A, Noblesville, IN 46060
Tel.: (317) 774-9840
Web Site: http://www.perfsports.com
Emp.: 100
Sporting Goods Mfr
N.A.I.C.S.: 339920

Mayflower Sales Co.,LLC   (1)
614 Bergen St, Brooklyn, NY 11238
Tel.: (718) 622-8785
Web Site: http://www.mfsales.com
Sales Range: $1-9.9 Million
Cosmetics, Beauty Supplies & Perfume Stores
N.A.I.C.S.: 456120

Pyramyd Air Ltd.   (1)
5135 Naiman Pkwy, Solon, OH 44139
Tel.: (216) 896-0893
Web Site: http://www.pyramydair.com
Sales Range: $1-9.9 Million
Air Guns, Ammunition & Accessories Distr & Retailer
N.A.I.C.S.: 423910
Joshua D. Ungier *(CEO)*

The Bargain Barn Inc.   (1)
2924 Lee Hwy, Athens, TN 37303
Tel.: (423) 746-0022
Web Site: http://www.myugo.com
Grocery Stores
N.A.I.C.S.: 445110

GEN MEDIA PARTNERS LLC
1 Grand Central Place 60 E 42nd St Ste 3020, New York, NY 10165
Tel.: (212) 400-7430
Web Site:
   http://www.genmediapartners.com
Integrated Sales & Marketing Services
N.A.I.C.S.: 541613
Kevin Garrity *(CEO)*
Billy McEntee *(CFO)*
Clark Logan *(Pres-HRN Media Networks)*
Leta Mork *(Dir-Sls Support)*
Debbie Cazel *(Dir-Creative & Tech Services)*
Anny Mansfield *(Dir-Mktg Res)*

Subsidiaries:

Sun Broadcast Group   (1)
363 7th Ave Fl 2, New York, NY 10001
Tel.: (800) 871-6163
Web Site: https://gognetworks.com
Sales Range: $1-9.9 Million
Radio Broadcasting Services
N.A.I.C.S.: 516110
Ann Bailey *(Dir-Bus Ops)*
Erich Siqueira *(Coord-Sr Sls)*
Paul Capodanno *(VP-Mktg & Digital)*

India Weatherspoon *(Acct Mgr-Digital)*
Megan Hermensky *(Asst Mgr-Mktg)*
Laura Orkin *(VP-Bus Ops)*

GEN SERV, INC.
112 N Curry St, Carson City, NV 89703
Tel.: (954) 568-1234   NV
Year Founded: 2013
Emp.: 1
Business & Residential Concierge Services
N.A.I.C.S.: 561499
Christopher Riker *(Pres, Sec & Treas)*

GENCO ENERGY SERVICES, INC.
1701 W Hwy 107, McAllen, TX 78504
Tel.: (956) 380-3710
Web Site: https://www.genco.us
Year Founded: 1980
Sales Range: $10-24.9 Million
Emp.: 80
Oil & Gas Support Services
N.A.I.C.S.: 213112
Murray Meggison *(Owner & Pres)*
Rodney Youngblood *(Mgr-Sls)*
Aaron Garza *(Mgr-Ops)*
Becky Bergh *(Office Mgr)*
Jimmy Mueller *(Mgr-McAllen Ops)*

GENCO INC.
4853 Cordell Ave, Bethesda, MD 20814
Tel.: (301) 657-3340
Web Site:
   https://www.genmason.com
Year Founded: 1929
Sales Range: $10-24.9 Million
Emp.: 15
Construction Equipment Repair
N.A.I.C.S.: 811210
Steven R. Sullivan *(Pres)*

GENE B. GLICK COMPANY, INC.
8425 Woodfield Crossing Ste 300, Indianapolis, IN 46240-2495
Tel.: (317) 469-0400   IN
Web Site: http://www.genebglick.com
Year Founded: 1947
Sales Range: $10-24.9 Million
Emp.: 650
Builder & Manager of Apartments
N.A.I.C.S.: 531210
James T. Bisesi *(Sr VP-Construction)*
Thomas J. Grande *(Sr VP-Investments & Risk Mgmt)*
Anita S. Smith *(CFO, Treas & Exec VP)*
David O. Barrett *(Chm, Pres & CEO)*
Adam Richter *(Gen Counsel & VP)*
Colin Atkinson *(VP-Asset Mgmt)*
Doug Elmore *(VP-Ops & Maintenance)*
Hyacinth Garrison *(Dir-Payroll & Benefits Acctg)*
Jason Whittington *(VP-Bus Solutions)*
Jennifer Juskow *(Dir-Acctg)*
Julie Doss *(Dir-Trng)*
Kathy Overbey *(Sr VP-Asset Mgmt)*
Maggie Swift *(Dir-Ops Support)*
Chad A. Greiwe *(Exec VP-Ops)*
John Ehrhardt *(VP-Property Mgmt)*
Lisa Rees *(VP-HR)*
Ryan Tolle *(VP-Asset Mgmt)*
Sarah Wood *(VP-Property Mgmt Ops)*
Stacey Sunderman *(VP-Acctg & Fin Ops)*
Ceceily Brickley *(Dir-Resident Success)*

GENE HARRIS PETROLEUM INC.

12901 S I35 W, Burleson, TX 76028
Tel.: (817) 295-1091
Sales Range: $10-24.9 Million
Emp.: 50
Petroleum Bulk Stations
N.A.I.C.S.: 424710

GENE LATTA FORD INC.
Rte 94 N Carlisle Pike, Hanover, PA 17331
Tel.: (717) 633-1999
Web Site:
   http://www.genelattaford.com
Sales Range: $25-49.9 Million
Emp.: 90
Sales of New & Used Automobiles
N.A.I.C.S.: 441110
Steve Latta *(Pres)*

GENE LATTA FORD, INC.
1565 Carlisle Pike, Hanover, PA 17331
Tel.: (717) 633-7272
Web Site: http://www.genelatta-ford.com
Year Founded: 1973
Sales Range: $10-24.9 Million
Emp.: 50
Car Whslr
N.A.I.C.S.: 441110
Steve Latta *(Pres)*

GENE STEVENS HONDA
1033 Bright Rd, Findlay, OH 45840
Tel.: (419) 422-3511
Web Site:
   http://www.genestevensauto.com
Sales Range: $10-24.9 Million
Emp.: 50
Car Whslr
N.A.I.C.S.: 441110
Gene Stevens *(Owner)*
Scott Stevens *(Principal)*

GENE STIMSON'S OF ARKANSAS
1355 Lynnfield Rd Ste 286, Memphis, TN 38119
Tel.: (901) 761-2906
Web Site:
   http://genestimsonbigstar.com
Sales Range: $10-24.9 Million
Emp.: 5
Grocery Stores, Independent
N.A.I.C.S.: 445110
Buddy Stimson *(VP)*
Stephen Weston *(VP)*

GENE TAYLOR'S SPORTSMEN SUPPLY, INC.
445 W Gunnison Ave, Grand Junction, CO 81501
Tel.: (970) 242-8165
Sales Range: $10-24.9 Million
Emp.: 20
Skiing & Sporting Equipment
N.A.I.C.S.: 459110
Duke O. Taylor *(Pres)*
Anthony Taylor *(VP)*

GENECA, LLC
1111 W 22nd St Ste 270, Oakbrook Terrace, IL 60523
Tel.: (630) 599-0900
Web Site: http://www.geneca.com
Rev.: $11,114,000
Emp.: 50
Corporate IT Services
N.A.I.C.S.: 541519
Mark Hattas *(Chm)*
Joel Basgall *(Pres & CEO)*
David Katauskas *(CTO)*

GENENDER INTERNATIONAL INC.

225 Larkin Drive Unit 1, Wheeling, IL 60090-6050
Tel.: (847) 541-3333   IL
Web Site: http://www.gennco.com
Year Founded: 1936
Sales Range: $10-24.9 Million
Emp.: 5
Provider of Jewelry, Watches & Clocks
N.A.I.C.S.: 423940
Kenneth J. Genender *(Pres)*

GENERAL AIR SERVICE & SUPPLY CO.
1105 Zuni St, Denver, CO 80204
Tel.: (303) 892-7003
Web Site: https://www.generalair.com
Sales Range: $10-24.9 Million
Emp.: 118
Supplier of Industrial Gases
N.A.I.C.S.: 424690
Mark Greggory *(VP-Operations)*

GENERAL ASP INC.
8001 Lincoln Ave Ste 704, Skokie, IL 60077
Tel.: (847) 475-2283
Web Site:
   http://www.aspexsolutions.com
Year Founded: 1998
Sales Range: $1-9.9 Million
Emp.: 11
Software Services
N.A.I.C.S.: 513210
Matt Barclay *(Dir-Client Svcs)*
Adrienne Wagner *(Bus Mgr)*

GENERAL ASPHALT CO., INC.
4850 NW 72nd Ave, Miami, FL 33166
Tel.: (305) 592-3480
Rev.: $46,000,000
Emp.: 140
Construction Machinery Mfr
N.A.I.C.S.: 333120
Robert A. Lopez *(Pres)*
Curtis Simpson *(CFO)*
Albert Lopez *(VP)*

GENERAL ATLANTIC SERVICE COMPANY, L.P.
Park Ave Plz 55 E 52nd St 33rd Fl, New York, NY 10055
Tel.: (212) 715-4000   DE
Web Site:
   http://www.generalatlantic.com
Privater Equity Firm
N.A.I.C.S.: 523999
Justin Sunshine *(Mng Dir)*
Kell Reilly *(Mng Dir)*
Gabriel Caillaux *(Pres-Europe, Middle East & Africa & Head-Europe, Middle East & Africa)*
Sandeep Naik *(Mng Dir & Head-India & Southeast Asia)*
Graves Tompkins *(Head-Capital Partnering & Human Capital-Global)*
Samir Assaf *(Chm-Middle East & North Africa)*
David Hodgson *(Vice Chm)*
David C. Hodgson *(Vice Chm)*
William E. Ford *(Chm & CEO)*
Catherine M. Engelbert *(Vice Chm)*

Subsidiaries:

Actis LLP   (1)
2 More London Riverside, London, SE1 2JT, United Kingdom
Tel.: (44) 20 7234 5000
Web Site: http://www.act.is
Rev.: $5,000,000,000
Emp.: 300
Privater Equity Firm
N.A.I.C.S.: 523999
Michael Till *(Partner & Co-Head-Energy-Sao Paulo)*
Patrick Ledoux *(Partner-Sao Paulo)*
Meng Ann Lim *(Partner & Head-China & Southeast Asia)*

Alistair Mackintosh (Partner)
Peter Schmid (Head-Private Equity)
Amanda Jean-Baptiste (Partner-Real Estate)
David Morley (Partner & Head-Real Estate)
Torbjorn Caesar (Sr Partner)
David Grylls (Partner-Energy)
Mikael Karlsson (Partner-Energy)
Paul Owers (Partner & Gen Counsel)
Lou Baran (Chief HR Officer & Dir)
Sachin Korantak (Head-Indus)
Shami Nissan (Head-Responsible Investment)
Andrew Newington (COO, CIO & Partner)
Carlton Byrd (Dir-Investor Dev Grp-New York)
Adiba Ighodaro (Partner & Head-New York)
Glen Matsumoto (Partner-Real Assets Bus-New York)
Gaurav Sood (CEO)
Virginia Doble (Head-Investor Dev Grp-Europe, Middle East & Africa)
Neil Brown (Partner & Head-Investor Dev Grp-Global)
Ellen Li (Mng Dir & Head-Investor Dev Grp-Asia)

Holding (Non-US):

AES Sonel S.A. (2)
Bonanjo Avenue Charles de Gaulle, BP 4077, Douala, Cameroon
Tel.: (237) 3342 1553
Web Site: http://www.aessoneltoday.com
Sales Range: $200-249.9 Million
Power Generation
N.A.I.C.S.: 221112

Branch (Non-US):

Actis LLP - Beijing Office (2)
713 China World Tower 2 No 1 Jianguomenwai Avenue, Chaoyang District, Beijing, 100004, China
Tel.: (86) 10 6535 4800
Web Site: http://www.act.is
Emp.: 17
Privater Equity Firm
N.A.I.C.S.: 523999
Meng Ann Lim (Partner & Head-China & Southeast Asia)
Dong Zhong (Partner-Consumer)
Max Lin (Exec Dir)
Paul Leung (Dir-Ops-Asia)

Actis LLP - Mumbai Office (2)
12th Floor Birla Aurora Dr Annie Besant Road, Worli, Mumbai, 400 030, India
Tel.: (91) 22 6146 7900
Web Site: http://www.act.is
Emp.: 26
Privater Equity Firm
N.A.I.C.S.: 523999
Sanjiv Aggarwal (Partner-Energy)
Mahesh Chhabria (Partner-Private Equity)
Asanka Rodrigo (Partner-Private Equity)
Ashish Singh (Partner-Real Estate)

Actis LLP - Sao Paulo Office (2)
Rua Sao Tome 86 8th Floor Vila Olimpia, 04551-080, Sao Paulo, Brazil
Tel.: (55) 11 3844 6300
Web Site: http://www.act.is
Emp.: 10
Private Equity Firm Services
N.A.I.C.S.: 523999
Patrick Ledoux (Partner-Private Equity)
Beatriz Amary (Dir-Private Equity)
Nelson Bechara (Dir-Value Creation Grp)

Holding (Non-US):

Atlantic Energias Renovaveis S/A (2)
Al Dr Carlos de Carvalho 555, Curitiba, 80430-180, Brazil
Tel.: (55) 41 3079 7100
Web Site: http://www.atlanticenergias.com.br
Wind Electric Power Generation Services
N.A.I.C.S.: 221115
Marcelo Leite Marder (Pres)
Thiago Correa Marder (Dir-Admin & Fin)
Miguel Seoane (Mgr-Construction & Ops)
Sergio Brandao (Pres-Mgmt Bd)
Victor Nogueira Garcia (Member-Mgmt Bd)
Michael Andrew Simon Till (Member-Mgmt Bd)
Jose Roberto de Moraes (Member-Mgmt Bd)

Luiz Cruz Schneider (Member-Mgmt Bd)
Edvaldo Alves de Santana (Member-Mgmt Bd)

GHL Systems Berhad (2)
C-G-15 Block C Jln Dataran SD1 Dataran SD PJU 9, Bandar Sri Damansara, 52200, Kuala Lumpur, Malaysia **(63.51%)**
Tel.: (60) 362863388
Web Site: https://www.ghl.com
Rev.: $86,862,044
Assets: $164,885,679
Liabilities: $56,562,605
Net Worth: $108,323,074
Earnings: $5,994,701
Emp.: 899
Fiscal Year-end: 12/31/2022
Payment Solutions
N.A.I.C.S.: 522320
Simon Wee Hian Loh (Vice Chm)
Wai Foong Wong (Co-Sec)
Chih Ming Yap (CFO)
Te Hock Wee (Co-Sec)

Subsidiary (Domestic):

Card Pay Sdn. Bhd. (3)
Unit L8 C-G-15 Block C Jalan Dataran SD1 Dataran SD PJU 9, Bandar Sri Damansara, Kuala Lumpur, 52200, Malaysia
Tel.: (60) 3 62863388
Electronic Financial Transaction Services
N.A.I.C.S.: 522320

Subsidiary (Non-US):

GHL (China) Co. Ltd. (3)
Room 1003 10/F Trendy Centre 682-684 Castle Peak Road, Kowloon, China (Hong Kong)
Tel.: (852) 2370 1070
Web Site: http://www.ghl.com
Electrical Wiring Services
N.A.I.C.S.: 238210

Subsidiary (Non-US):

GHL (Beijing) Co. Ltd. (4)
3rd Floor Office Building of Liao Ning Hotel No 3 Deshengmenwai Dajie, Xi Cheng District, Beijing, 100088, China
Tel.: (86) 1082525080
Web Site: http://www.ghl.com
Electrical Wiring Services
N.A.I.C.S.: 238210

Subsidiary (Non-US):

GHL (Thailand) Co. Ltd. (3)
77/117-118, 28th Fl Sinn Sathorn Tower Krungthonburi Rd Klongtonsai, Bangkok, 10600, Thailand
Tel.: (66) 24400588
Web Site: http://www.ghl.com
Sales Range: $25-49.9 Million
Emp.: 30
Electrical Wiring Services
N.A.I.C.S.: 238210

Subsidiary (Domestic):

GHL Transact Sdn. Bhd. (3)
Unit L8 C-G-15 Blok C Jalan Dataran Sd 1, Dataran Sd Pju 9 Bandara, Sri Damansara, Kuala Lumpur, 52200, Malaysia
Tel.: (60) 362863388
Sales Range: $100-124.9 Million
Electrical Wiring Services
N.A.I.C.S.: 238210
Loh Wee Simon (Mng Dir)

Subsidiary (Non-US):

GHLSYS Philippines Inc. (3)
16/F Lepanto Condominium 8747 Paseo de Roxas, 1226, Makati, Philippines
Tel.: (63) 28560850
Web Site: http://www.ghl.com
Sales Range: $50-74.9 Million
Emp.: 60
Financial Transaction Management & Networking Services

e-pay Asia Pty. Ltd. (3)
Level 28 St Martins Tower 31 Market Street, Sydney, 2000, NSW, Australia
Tel.: (61) 292674633
Sales Range: $10-24.9 Million
Electronic Payment Services
N.A.I.C.S.: 522320

Robert Lees (Sec)
Simon Loh (Chm & CEO)
Eng Sun Sam (CTO)

Subsidiary (Non-US):

e-pay (M) Sdn. Bhd. (4)
16-18 Jalan PJS 11/28A, Bandar Sunway, 47500, Subang Jaya, Selangor, Malaysia
Tel.: (60) 56236000
Web Site: http://www.e-pay.com.my
Electronic Payment Services
N.A.I.C.S.: 522320

Holding (Non-US):

Globeleq Generation Limited (2)
11 New Street, Saint Peter Port, GY1 2PF, Guernsey
Tel.: (44) 1481 726 034
Holding Company; Electric Power Generation
N.A.I.C.S.: 221118

Subsidiary (Non-US):

Globeleq Advisors Limited (3)
2 More London Riverside, London, SE1 2JT, United Kingdom
Tel.: (44) 20 7 234 5400
Web Site: http://www.globeleq.com
Advisory & Support Services
N.A.I.C.S.: 561499
Paul Kunert (Head-Bus Dev-Africa)
Jake McConnell (VP-Engrg)
Chris Ford (Head-Asset Mgmt Africa)

Subsidiary (US):

Globeleq Inc. (3)
9801 Westheimer Ste 302, Houston, TX 77042
Tel.: (713) 355-3450
Web Site: http://www.globeleq.com
Emp.: 55
Administrative Management & General Management Consulting Services; Energy & Power Solutions
N.A.I.C.S.: 541611
Jake McConnell (VP-Engrg)
Mikael Karlsson (CEO)
Susan Wilkins (CFO)

Subsidiary (Non-US):

Songas Limited (3)
Corner Nelson Mandela & Morogoro Road, Dar es Salaam, Tanzania
Tel.: (255) 222452160
Web Site: http://www.globeleq.com
Natural Gas Operations
N.A.I.C.S.: 486210

Holding (Non-US):

Paycorp Payment Solutions Pty Ltd (2)
Sandhavon Office Park 12 Pongola Crescent Eastgate Ext 17, 2199, Johannesburg, South Africa
Tel.: (27) 11 531 5300
Web Site: http://www.paycorp.co.za
Electronic Payment Services
N.A.I.C.S.: 522320
Steven Kark (CEO)

Tracker Ltd. (2)
340 Repulic Road Stonemill Office Park, Darrenwood Entrance 2 Building Echo 1 Cresta, Randburg, South Africa
Tel.: (27) 11 380 0300
Web Site: http://www.tracker.co.za
Tracking Device Mfr
N.A.I.C.S.: 335999
Tulani Hlabangana (Exec Dir-HR)

Vlisco Netherlands B.V. (2)
Binnen Parallelweg 27, 5701 PH, Helmond, Netherlands
Tel.: (31) 492570922
Web Site: http://www.vlisco.com
Sales Range: $200-249.9 Million
Emp.: 2,100
Wax Print & Java Print Sale Marketing & Mfr
N.A.I.C.S.: 314910
Hans Ouwendijk (CEO)

Subsidiary (Non-US):

John Walkden et Compagnie S.A. (3)

Rue du Governeur General Roume, PO Box 24, Cotonou, Benin
Tel.: (229) 21313037
Web Site: http://www.vlisco.com
Wax Prints & Java Prints Sales, Marketing & Mfr
N.A.I.C.S.: 313230

Niger-Afrique S.A. (3)
Ave Du President Luebke, PO Box 11 050, Niamey, 00227, Niger
Tel.: (227) 20 73 33 19
Web Site: http://www.vlisco.com
Sales Range: $25-49.9 Million
Emp.: 11
Wax Prints & Java Prints Sales, Marketing & Mfr
N.A.I.C.S.: 313230

VAC Ghana (3)
PO Box 606, Tema, Ghana
Tel.: (233) 22304234
Web Site: http://www.vlisco.com
Wax Prints & Java Prints Sales, Marketing & Mfr
N.A.I.C.S.: 313230

Subsidiary (Domestic):

Ghana Textile Printing Company Ltd. (4)
PO Box 606, Tema, Ghana
Tel.: (233) 303 30 42 34
Web Site: http://www.vlisco.nl
Sales Range: $75-99.9 Million
Wax Prints & Java Prints Sales, Marketing & Mfr
N.A.I.C.S.: 313230

Subsidiary (Non-US):

VAC-Togo S.A. (3)
16 Rue du Commerce, PO Box 345, Lome, Togo
Tel.: (228) 2212800
Web Site: http://www.vlisco.nl
Wax Prints & Java Prints Sales, Marketing & Mfr
N.A.I.C.S.: 313230

Vlisco France S.A. (3)
5 Bis Rue Du Cirque, 750008, Paris, France
Tel.: (33) 142259425
Web Site: http://www.vlisco.nl
Sales Range: $25-49.9 Million
Emp.: 5
Wax Prints & Java Prints Sales, Marketing & Mfr
N.A.I.C.S.: 313230

Subsidiary (Domestic):

Vlisco Helmond B.V. (3)
Binnen Barallelweg 27, 5701 PH, Helmond, Netherlands
Tel.: (31) 492570922
Fabrics Mfr
N.A.I.C.S.: 313210

Subsidiary (Non-US):

Wintex-Department Vlisco (3)
Avenue du General de Gaulle 01, BP 5855, BP 5855, Abidjan, Cote d'Ivoire
Tel.: (225) 8309274
Web Site: http://www.vlisco.com
Wax Prints & Java Prints Sales, Marketing & Mfr
N.A.I.C.S.: 339999

General Atlantic L.P. (1)
677 Washington Blvd 8th Fl, Stamford, CT 06901
Tel.: (203) 629-8600
Web Site: http://www.generalatlantic.com
Privater Equity Firm
N.A.I.C.S.: 523999
William E. Ford (CEO)
Robert Vorhoff (Mng Dir & Head-Healthcare-Global)
Steven A. Denning (Chm)
Mark F. Dzialga (Mng Dir-Greenwich)
Rene Marc Kern (Mng Dir/Mng Dir-New York)
Anton Jonathan Levy (Mng Dir, Mng Dir & Head/Head-Internet & Tech-Global)
Drew Pearson (Mng Dir & Head-Portfolio Mgmt-Global)
Thomas Murphy (Mng Dir & CFO)

General Atlantic Service Company, L.P.—(Continued)

David Rosenstein (Mng Dir & Gen Counsel-New York)
Chris Lanning (Mng Dir-Legal-New York)
Cory A. Eaves (Operating Partner)
Aaron Goldman (Co-Head-Investments-Fin Svcs,London)
Sandeep Naik (Mng Dir, Mng Dir & Head/Head-India & Asia Pacific)
Alok Misra (Sr VP-Mumbai)
Andrew Crawford (Mng Dir & Head-Consumer Sector-Global)
Graves Tompkins (Mng Dir & Head-Capital Partnering-Global)
Chris Caulkin (Principal-London)
Peter Munzig (Principal)
Paul Stamas (Co-Head-Investments-Fin Svcs,New York)
Roni Elchahal (Principal)
Andrew Ferrer (Principal)
Rajat Sood (Principal)
Achim Berg (Operating Partner-Munich)
Hilary Hoffman (VP-New York)
Luiz Ribeiro (VP-Sao Paulo)
Martin Escobari (Mng Dir & Head-Latin America)
Melissa Heng (VP-Singapore)
Montes Piard (VP & Controller-Investment Funds-Global)
Eric Zhang (Mng Dir & Head-China)
Michelle Dipp (Mng Dir)
Wai Hoong Fock (Mng Dir)
Pierre Samec (Operating Partner)
Luis Cervantes (Principal)
Christian Figge (Principal)
David George (Principal)
Anna Golynskaya (Principal)
Shaw Joseph (VP)
Melis Kahya (Principal)
Whitney Cacase (Chief HR Officer-New York)
Jenny Farrelly (Chief Mktg & Comm Officer-New York)
Ke Wei (Mng Dir-Hong Kong)
Shantanu Rastogi (Mng Dir-Mumbai)
Alex Crisses (Mng Dir-New York)
Erin Chang (Principal-Hong Kong)
Alan Ghelberg (Principal-New York)
David Caluori (Principal-New York)
Roger Gao (VP-Beijing)
David Buckley (VP-Greenwich)
Tom Hussey (VP-London)
Varun Talukdar (VP-Mumbai)
Brandon Kerns (VP-New York)
Jeff Machlin (VP-New York)
Mei Shi (VP)
Raphael Osnoss (Mng Dir & VP-New York)
Zachary Kaplan (VP-New York)
Rodrigo Catunda (VP-Sao Paulo)
Piti Hongsaranagon (VP-Singapore)
Vittorio Colao (Vice Chm)
Justin Kotzin (Operating Partner-Debt Capital Markets & Head-Debt Capital Markets-New York)
Pedro Parente (Chm-Brazil)
Justin Sunshine (Mng Dir-New York)
Tanzeen Syed (Mng Dir)
Robert Perez (Operating Partner-New York)
Robert J. Perez (Operating Partner-New York)
Gary M. Reiner (Operating Partner)

Joint Venture (Domestic):

A Place For Mom, Inc. (2)
701 5th Ave Ste 3200, Seattle, WA 98104
Tel.: (206) 285-4666
Web Site: http://www.aplaceformom.com
Sales Range: $50-74.9 Million
Senior Care Referral Services
N.A.I.C.S.: 624190
Lawrence Kutscher (CEO)
Dan Willis (Sr VP-Partner Svcs)
Camille Cleveland (Gen Counsel & Sr VP)
Ted Ellis (CTO)
Allen Hsieh (CFO)
Jennifer Mellet (Chief Sls Officer)
Eric Seifert (COO)
Scott Booker (Pres & Chief Product Officer)
Lawrence Kutscher (CEO)

Joint Venture (Non-US):

Arco Platform Limited (2)
Rua Augusta 2840 9th Floor Suite 91, Consolacao, Sao Paulo, 01412-100, Brazil
Tel.: (55) 1130472655
Rev.: $341,325,841

Assets: $1,106,092,688
Liabilities: $741,311,771
Net Worth: $364,780,918
Earnings: $7,591,760
Emp.: 2,935
Fiscal Year-end: 12/31/2022
Educational Software Development Services
N.A.I.C.S.: 541511

Subsidiary (Domestic):

Nave a Vela Ltda. (3)
R Augusta 2840 - Jardins, Sao Paulo, SP, Brazil
Tel.: (55) 11988828432
Web Site: https://www.naveavela.com.br
Education Training Services
N.A.I.C.S.: 611110
Tadeu Omae (Product Mgr)

SAE Digital S.A. (3)
Rua Joao Domachoski 5 Mossungue, Curitiba, 81200-150, Parana, Brazil
Tel.: (55) 8007259797
Web Site: https://sae.digital
Education Training Services
N.A.I.C.S.: 611110

Joint Venture (Non-US):

Argus Media Limited (2)
Lacon House 84 Theobald's Road, London, WC1X 8NL, United Kingdom
Tel.: (44) 2077804200
Web Site: http://www.argusmedia.com
Emp.: 850
Price & Availability Information for Energy Related Products
N.A.I.C.S.: 519290
Adrian Binks (Chm & CEO)
Andrew Given (CFO)
Matthew Burkley (COO)
Jeffrey Amos (Compliance Officer)
Stuart Ashman (Chief Risk Officer & Sec)
Chris Fosberry (CTO)
Philip Shaw (Head-Ops)
Lucy Sladojevic (Head-Legal)
Matthew Thompson (Chief Strategy Officer & Bus Dev Officer)
Jim Nicholson (Sr VP-Editorial)
Simon Smith (Head-Govt & Regulatory Affairs)
Seana Lanigan (Mgr-Strategic Mktg)
Jo Loudiadis (Sr VP-Comml-Europe & Africa)
Peter Ramsay (Mng Editor-Europe & Africa)
Christina Vassil Wimmer (Sr VP-Sls)
Chuck Venezia (Sr VP-Petrochemicals-Global)
David Brooks (Sr VP-Metals)
Jamie Balderston (Sr VP-Conferences)
Kristine Klavers (Sr VP-Consulting)
Lauren Williamson (Sr VP-Fertilizers-Global)
Lloyd Thomas (Sr VP-Consulting Svcs)
Lori Ann Foertsch (Corp Counsel)
Miles Weigel (Sr VP)
Tania Ellery (Chief HR Officer)
Vanessa Viola (Sr VP-Latin America)
Jim Washer (Editor-in-Chief)

Subsidiary (Non-US):

Argus Media Ltd. - Japan (3)
22 Malacca St, 10-02 Royal Brothers Bldg, Singapore, 48980, Singapore
Tel.: (65) 65333638
Web Site: http://www.argusmediagroup.com
Sales Range: $25-49.9 Million
Emp.: 20
Price & Availability Information for Energy Related Products
N.A.I.C.S.: 519290

Argus Media Ltd. - Russia (3)
Ul Prechistenka 40/2 Entr 2 Fl 7, 119034, Moscow, Russia
Tel.: (7) 959337571
Web Site: http://www.argus.ru
Sales Range: $25-49.9 Million
Emp.: 100
Price & Availability Information for Energy Related Products
N.A.I.C.S.: 519290

Subsidiary (US):

Argus Media, Inc. (3)
2929 Allen Pkwy Ste 700, Houston, TX 77019 **(100%)**

Tel.: (713) 622-3996
Web Site: http://www.argusmediagroup.com
Sales Range: $25-49.9 Million
Emp.: 100
Price & Availability Information for Energy Related Products
N.A.I.C.S.: 513199
Euan Craik (CEO)

Branch (Domestic):

Argus Media, Inc. - New York (4)
500 5th Ave Ste 2410, New York, NY 10110
Tel.: (646) 376-6130
Web Site: http://www.argusmedia.com
Sales Range: $25-49.9 Million
Emp.: 17
Price & Availability Information for Energy Related Products
N.A.I.C.S.: 513199
Miles Weigel (Gen Mgr)

Argus Media, Inc. - Washington, D.C. (4)
1012 14th St NW Ste 1500, Washington, DC 20005
Tel.: (202) 775-0240
Web Site: http://www.argusmedia.com
Price & Availability Information for Energy Related Products
N.A.I.C.S.: 711510

Subsidiary (Domestic):

DeWitt & Company Incorporated (4)
601 Sawyer St Ste 750, Houston, TX 77007
Tel.: (713) 360-7500
Web Site: http://www.dewittworld.com
Sales Range: $10-24.9 Million
Emp.: 50
Petrochemical Consulting Services
N.A.I.C.S.: 541690
Charles Venezia (VP-Benzene & Derivatives)
Steve Weber (VP-BTX Economics Projects)
Mike Smith (VP-Propylene & Derivatives)
Paul E. Brisson (VP-C4 & Derivatives)

Subsidiary (US):

Mercaris Company (3)
8070 Georgia Ave, Silver Spring, MD 20910
Tel.: (240) 354-7114
Web Site: https://mercaris.com
Information Services
N.A.I.C.S.: 519290
Kellee James (Founder & CEO)

TABrewer Consulting, Inc. (3)
363 Wycliffe Dr, Houston, TX 77079-7146
Tel.: (713) 562-1109
Business Consulting Services
N.A.I.C.S.: 541611

Holding (Domestic):

CareMeTX, LLC (2)
6931 Arlington Rd Ste 308, Bethesda, MD 20814
Tel.: (301) 656-1080
Web Site: http://www.caremetx.com
Health Care Srvices
N.A.I.C.S.: 621610
Robert K. Dresing (Co-Founder)
Mark D. Hansan (Co-Founder & Chm)
Elizabeth Dresing (Chief People Officer)
Greg Lahens (Chief Innovation Officer & VP-IT)
Bill Lambros (CFO)
Shabbir Ahmed (Chief Comml Officer)
Craig Kephart (COO)
Jim Maguire (CIO & Sr VP-IT)
Catina Cox (VP-Hub Ops & Sr Dir-Hub Ops)
Dia Hernandez (VP-Assistance Programs & Implementation)
Tanvi Kachhy (VP-Tech Strategy & Assoc VP-IT)
Dan Desmarais (Sr VP & Gen Mgr)
Jim Long (Sr VP & Gen Mgr)
Jim Rowe (Pres & CEO)

Subsidiary (Domestic):

VirMedica Inc. (3)
708 Mercers Mill Ln, West Chester, PA 19382
Tel.: (610) 429-2499
Web Site: http://www.virmedica.com

Holding Company; Pharmaceutical Technology Developer
N.A.I.C.S.: 325412
Stephen J. Henricks (VP-Mktg)

Subsidiary (Domestic):

TransEngen, Inc. (4)
6 Research Dr Ste 210, Shelton, CT 06484
Tel.: (203) 845-0551
Web Site: http://www.transengen.com
Benefits Verification Software Publishers
N.A.I.C.S.: 513210
Buck Rogers (Pres & CEO)
Stephen J. Henricks (VP-Mktg)
Gregory Morris (Founder & Chief Strategy Officer)
Maggie O'Hara (Sr VP-Ops)

Holding (Domestic):

EN Engineering, LLC (2)
28100 Torch Pkwy Ste 400, Warrenville, IL 60555
Tel.: (630) 353-4000
Web Site: http://www.enengineering.com
Emp.: 1,000
Engineering, Automation & Consulting Services
N.A.I.C.S.: 541330
Thomas C. Ziegenfuss (Vice Chm)
Mitchell Hulet (COO)
David J. Klimas (Sr VP & Chief Engr-Project Svcs)
Adam Biggam (VP)
Mark Chadd (VP)
Anthony Gambony (VP-Western)
William Mampre (VP)
Keith Johnson (VP-Baltimore)
Jesse Rodriguez (VP-Transmission)
Gary Blevins (VP & Sr Project Mgr)
David Gibson (VP)
Chris Wiehe (Dir-Bus Dev)
Anil Arora (CFO)
Michael Simpson (Chief HR Officer)
Rick Grant (CMO & Chief Sls Officer)
Steve Knowles (CEO)

Subsidiary (Domestic):

QC Data LLC (3)
8000 E Maplewood Ave Ste 300, Greenwood Village, CO 80111
Tel.: (303) 783-8888
Web Site: http://www.qcdata.com
Outsourcing Services
N.A.I.C.S.: 561499
Michael L. Pfeiffer (Pres & CEO)
Glen Helin (Exec VP)
Jamie Curtin (Sr VP-Corp Dev)

Russell Corrosion Consultants, Inc. (3)
7130 Minstrel Way Ste 230, Columbia, MD 21045
Tel.: (410) 997-4481
Web Site: http://www.russellcorrosion.com
Corrosion Engineering Services
N.A.I.C.S.: 541330
Richard Grant (Co-Owner & Principal)
Maureen Grant (Co-Owner & Pres)
Michael Szeliga (Sr Project Mgr)
Steve Nikolakakos (Principal & Sr Project Mgr)
Thomas Fowler (Project Mgr)
Mike Choi (Mgr-Natl Accts)
Paul S. Rothman (Principal & Sr Project Mgr)
Ronald L. Bianchetti (Mgr-West Coast)
Duane Stewart (Sr Engr-Corrosion)
David Dawson (Sr Engr-Corrosion)
Yaofu Zhang (Corrosion Engr)
David R. Creque (Corrosion Engr)

Joint Venture (Domestic):

HireRight Holdings Corporation (2)
100 Centerview Dr Ste 300, Nashville, TN 37214
Tel.: (615) 320-9800
Web Site: https://www.hireright.com
Rev.: $806,668,000
Assets: $1,605,747,000
Liabilities: $1,037,429,000
Net Worth: $568,318,000
Earnings: $144,574,000
Emp.: 3,078
Fiscal Year-end: 12/31/2022
Holding Company
N.A.I.C.S.: 551112

Guy Abramo *(Pres & CEO)*
Thomas Spaeth *(CFO)*
Mark Dzialga *(Chm)*
Laurie Blanton *(Chief Acctg Officer & Sr VP)*

Subsidiary (Domestic):

Dexter Group Holdings LLC (3)
2900 Industrial Pkwy E, Elkhart, IN 46516
Tel.: (574) 295-7888
Web Site: https://www.dextergroup.com
Trailer Parts Mfr & Distr
N.A.I.C.S.: 336212

Fingerprint Solutions, LLC (3)
917 Chapin Rd, Chapin, SC 29036
Web Site:
    https://www.fingerprintsolutions.com
Background Check Services
N.A.I.C.S.: 561611

Subsidiary (Non-US):

HireRight AU Pty Ltd (3)
PO Box 40, Boolaroo, Lake Macquarie, 2284, NSW, Australia
Tel.: (61) 240230603
Background Check Services
N.A.I.C.S.: 561611

HireRight Background Screening India LLP (3)
Unit No 13 - 16 Level 7 Innovator Building ITPB Whitefield Main Rd, Bengaluru, 560066, India
Tel.: (91) 2249054399
Human Resouce Services
N.A.I.C.S.: 541612

HireRight UK Holding Limited (3)
15 Westferry Circus Canary Wharf, London, E14 4HD, United Kingdom
Tel.: (44) 2077672400
Human Resource Services
N.A.I.C.S.: 541612

Holding (Domestic):

Marathon Health, LLC (2)
20 Winooski Falls Way, Winooski, VT 05404
Tel.: (802) 857-0400
Web Site: http://www.marathon-health.com
Health Care Srvices
N.A.I.C.S.: 813212
Pierce Graham-Jones *(Chief Strategy Officer)*
Mandy Lee Berman *(COO)*
Venkataraman Chittoor *(Chief Product & Tech Officer)*
Jeff Wells *(Co-Founder & CEO)*
Ben Evans *(Co-Founder & Exec Chm)*
Meghan MacDerment *(Acting COO)*
Pat Murphy *(CFO & Exec VP)*
Christina Wahlig *(Gen Counsel)*
Debby Routt *(Chief People Experience Officer)*
Chad Ashcraft *(Chief Growth Officer)*
Shelly Towns *(CMO)*

Joint Venture (Domestic):

MedExpress Urgent Care (2)
1751 Earl Core Rd, Morgantown, WV 26505
Tel.: (304) 225-2500
Web Site: http://www.medexpress.com
Sales Range: $150-199.9 Million
Urgent Care Clinics
N.A.I.C.S.: 621498
Bryan Stuchell *(Owner)*
Troy Steckler *(VP-Clinical Ops)*
Russ Sullivan *(VP-HR)*
Tim Bugin *(VP-Payor Contracting & Reimbursement)*

Pantherx Specialty, LLC (2)
24 Summit Park Dr, Pittsburgh, PA 15275
Tel.: (412) 547-3483
Web Site: https://www.pantherxrare.com
Sales Range: $25-49.9 Million
Pharmaceuticals Product Mfr
N.A.I.C.S.: 325412
Timothy Davis *(Sr VP-Special Project)*
Austin Russian *(VP-Program Management)*
Robert Snyder *(Pres)*

Subsidiary (Non-US):

Plusgrade Parent L.P. (2)

1130 Sherbrooke Street West Suite 1500, Montreal, H3A 2M8, QC, Canada
Tel.: (917) 740-7291
Web Site: https://www.plusgrade.com
Ancillary Revenue Management Services
N.A.I.C.S.: 513210

Subsidiary (Domestic):

Points.com Inc. (3)
111 Richmond St W Suite 700, Toronto, M5H 2G4, ON, Canada
Tel.: (416) 596-6370
Web Site: https://www.points.com
Rev.: $217,387,000
Assets: $112,030,000
Liabilities: $76,811,000
Net Worth: $35,219,000
Earnings: ($5,357,000)
Emp.: 265
Fiscal Year-end: 12/31/2020
Reward-Program Management
N.A.I.C.S.: 491110
Christopher J. D. Barnard *(Founder & Pres)*
Inez Murdoch *(Chief People Officer)*
David Adams *(Chm)*
Jay Malowney *(Chief Comml Officer)*
Erick Georgiou *(CFO)*
Don Dew *(CTO)*
Chris Boyd *(Head-Product)*
Danielle Brown *(CMO)*

Holding (Domestic):

Sandy Hill Kennels, Inc. (2)
551 Sandy Hill Rd, Valencia, PA 16059-2727
Tel.: (724) 898-2895
Web Site: http://www.sandyhillkennels.com
Pet Care Services
N.A.I.C.S.: 812910

TriNet Group, Inc. (2)
1 Park Pl Ste 600, Dublin, CA 94568
Tel.: (510) 352-5000
Web Site: https://www.trinet.com
Rev.: $4,885,000,000
Assets: $3,443,000,000
Liabilities: $2,668,000,000
Net Worth: $775,000,000
Earnings: $355,000,000
Emp.: 3,600
Fiscal Year-end: 12/31/2022
Payroll, Employee Benefits & Human Resource Outsourcing Services
N.A.I.C.S.: 561499
Michael Q. Simonds *(Pres & CEO)*
Kelly L. Tuminelli *(CFO, Principal Acctg Officer & Exec VP)*
Jeff Hayward *(CTO)*
Thomas Rose *(Sr VP-Customer Success & Operations)*
Jay Venkat *(Chief Digital Officer & Chief Innovation Officer)*
Tim Nimmer *(Sr VP-Insurance Svcs & Operations)*
Shea Treadway *(Chief Revenue Officer)*
Michael Mendenhall *(CMO, Chief Comm Officer & Sr VP)*
Catherine M. Wragg *(Sr VP-HR)*
Catherine M. Wragg *(Sr VP-HR)*
Sidney Majalya *(Chief Legal Officer, Sec & Sr VP)*

Subsidiary (Domestic):

Ambrose Employer Group, LLC (3)
199 Water St Fl 28 909 3rd Ave, New York, NY 10022
Tel.: (646) 356-8607
Web Site: http://www.ambrose.com
Sales Range: $1-9.9 Million
Emp.: 48
Employee Leasing Services
N.A.I.C.S.: 561330

Strategic Outsourcing, Inc. (3)
1100 San Leandro Blvd Ste 400, San Leandro, CA 94577
Tel.: (704) 523-2191
Human Resources & Administration Support Services
N.A.I.C.S.: 561499

Division (Domestic):

TriNet - Bradenton (3)
9000 Town Center Pkwy, Bradenton, FL 34202-4101
Tel.: (941) 741-4540

Web Site: http://www.trinet.com
Sales Range: $500-549.9 Million
Human Resources Services; Payroll Administration, Risk Management, Benefits Administration, Unemployment Services
N.A.I.C.S.: 923130

Subsidiary (Domestic):

YourPeople, Inc. (3)
50 Beale St, San Francisco, CA 94105
Web Site: http://www.zenefits.com
Emp.: 1,000
Human Resources Software Developer
N.A.I.C.S.: 513210
Jay Fulcher *(Chm & CEO)*
Jeff Carr *(COO)*
Beth Steinberg *(Chief People Officer)*
Lisa Reeves *(Sr VP-Product)*
Kevin Marasco *(CMO)*
Shaun Wiley *(CFO & Sr VP)*

GENERAL ATOMICS

3550 General Atomics Ct, San Diego, CA 92121-1122
Tel.: (858) 455-3000   CA
Web Site: https://www.ga.com
Year Founded: 1982
Emp.: 12,500
Holding Company; Research & Development in the Physical, Engineering & Life Sciences
N.A.I.C.S.: 551112
Evin Powell *(Engr-Composite Mfg)*
Dennis Garegnani *(VP)*
Michael Hawman *(CIO & VP)*
Vivek Lall *(CEO-Corp-Global)*
Anantha Krishnan *(Sr VP-Energy Bus)*

Subsidiaries:

Commonwealth Computer Research Inc. (1)
1422 Sachem Pl Unit 1, Charlottesville, VA 22901-2498
Tel.: (434) 977-0600
Web Site: http://www.ccri.com
Custom Computer Programming Services
N.A.I.C.S.: 541511
David E. Sappington *(Treas & VP)*

ConverDyn (1)
7800 E Dorado Pl Ste 200, Englewood, CO 80111-2306
Tel.: (303) 770-0957
Web Site: http://www.converdyne.com
Sales Range: $10-24.9 Million
Emp.: 10
N.A.I.C.S.: 336611
Malcolm Critchley *(Pres & CEO)*

Cotter Corporation (1)
7800 E Dorado Pl Ste 210, Englewood, CO 80111-2306   (100%)
Tel.: (720) 554-6200
Sales Range: $25-49.9 Million
Emp.: 105
Uranium Mining
N.A.I.C.S.: 212290

Diazyme Laboratories, Inc. (1)
12889 Gregg Ct, Poway, CA 92064
Tel.: (858) 455-4768
Web Site: http://www.diazyme.com
Diagnostic Reagent Mfr
N.A.I.C.S.: 325998
Yuan Chong *(Mng Dir)*

General Atomics (1)
73 El Mirage Airport Rd Ste B, Adelanto, CA 92301-9540
Tel.: (760) 388-8100
Web Site: http://www.gat.com
Aeronautics Research & Development
N.A.I.C.S.: 334511
Nicholas Kendrick *(Supvr-Propulsion & Fuel Engrg)*

General Atomics - Cryotech Deicing Technology Division (1)
6103 Orthoway, Fort Madison, IA 52627
Tel.: (319) 372-6012
Web Site: http://www.cryotech.com
Propylene Glycol Mfr
N.A.I.C.S.: 325199
Craig Starwalt *(Pres & CEO)*

General Atomics Aeronautical Systems Inc. (1)
16761 Via Del Campo Ct, San Diego, CA 92127-1713
Tel.: (858) 762-6700
Web Site: http://www.ga-asi.com
Sales Range: $100-124.9 Million
Emp.: 800
Aircraft Mfr
N.A.I.C.S.: 336411
Elizabeth S. Patrick *(Coord-Mktg & Adv)*
David Wade *(Engr-HPC & CFD)*

General Atomics Electronic Systems, Inc. (1)
4949 Greencraig Ln, San Diego, CA 92123
Tel.: (858) 522-8300
Web Site: http://www.ga-esi.com
Business Support Services
N.A.I.C.S.: 561499
Rolf Ziesing *(VP-Programs)*
Scott Forney *(Pres)*

Subsidiary (Domestic):

Neva Ridge Technologies, Inc. (2)
6685 Gunpark Dr Ste 230, Boulder, CO 80301-3343
Tel.: (303) 443-9966
Web Site: http://www.nevaridge.com
Engineeering Services
N.A.I.C.S.: 541330
Richard Carande *(Pres)*

General Atomics Systems Integration, LLC (1)
1343 W Flint Meadow Dr Ste 2, Kaysville, UT 84037
Tel.: (801) 546-8100
Web Site: http://www.ga-si.com
Surveillance & Reconnaissance Services
N.A.I.C.S.: 334511
Doug Dawson *(Dir-Intl Bus Dev)*
Michael Allen *(Pres)*

Heathgate Resources Pty, Ltd. (1)
Level 7 25 Grenfell St, Adelaide, 5000, SA, Australia
Tel.: (61) 8 8110 0500
Web Site: http://www.heathgate.com.au
Emp.: 50
Uranium Mining Services
N.A.I.C.S.: 212290

Nuclear Fuels Corporation (1)
3550 General Atomics Ct, San Diego, CA 92121
Tel.: (858) 455-3000
Web Site: http://www.ga.com
Rev.: $620,000
Emp.: 16
Uranium Development & Marketing Services
N.A.I.C.S.: 212290

Rio Grande Holdings (1)
3550 General Atomics Ct, San Diego, CA 92121-1122
Tel.: (858) 455-3000
Web Site: http://www.ga.com
Rev.: $6,500,000
Emp.: 2
Primary Metal Products
N.A.I.C.S.: 331110

Rio Grande Resources Corporation (1)
4 Miles E on Fm 81, Hobson, TX 78117
Tel.: (830) 780-3911
Web Site: http://www.generalatomics.com
Sales Range: $10-24.9 Million
Emp.: 20
Primary Metal Products
N.A.I.C.S.: 331110

Spezialtechnik Dresden GmbH (1)
Zum Windkanal 21, 01109, Dresden, Germany
Tel.: (49) 351 886 5000
Web Site: http://www.spezialtechnik.de
Sales Range: $10-24.9 Million
Emp.: 15
Ammunition Disposal Services
N.A.I.C.S.: 562211
Harald Ropl *(Mng Dir)*

Subsidiary (Domestic):

B+F Beton- und Fertigteilgesellschaft mbH Lauchhammer (2)

General Atomics—(Continued)

Bockwitzer Strasse 85, 1979, Lauchhammer, Germany
Tel.: (49) 3574 7804 0
Web Site: http://www.bfl-gmbh.de
Emp.: 80
Precast Concrete Products Mfr
N.A.I.C.S.: 327390
Hermann Stenzhorn (Gen Mgr)

EST Energetics GmbH   (2)
Zweite Allee 1, 2929, Rothenburg, Germany
Tel.: (49) 35891 41 0
Web Site: http://www.est-steinbach.com
Explosive Chemical Disposal Services
N.A.I.C.S.: 562211

SGL Spezial- und Bergbau-
Servicegesellschaft Lauchhammer
mbH   (2)
Bockwitzer Strasse 85, 01979, Lauchhammer, Germany
Tel.: (49) 3574 7827 0
Web Site: http://www.sgl-mbh.de
Mining Support & Engineering Services
N.A.I.C.S.: 213114

Spreewerk Lubben GmbH   (2)
Bornichen 99, 15907, Lubben, Germany
Tel.: (49) 3546 28 200
Web Site: http://www.spreewerk.com
Ammunition Disposal Services
N.A.I.C.S.: 562211

Umwelt- und Ingenieurtechnik GmbH
Dresden   (1)
Zum Windkanal 21, 01109, Dresden, Germany
Tel.: (49) 351 88646 00
Web Site: http://www.uit-gmbh.de
Sales Range: $10-24.9 Million
Emp.: 25
Smart Sensor Probe Mfr
N.A.I.C.S.: 334510
Horst Marten (Gen Mgr)

GENERAL BANDAGES, INC.
4155 N Rockwell St, Chicago, IL 60618
Tel.: (847) 966-8383
Web Site:
   http://www.generalbandages.com
Year Founded: 1977
Sales Range: $100-124.9 Million
Emp.: 30
Self-Adhering Gauze Tape, Safety
Tape, First Aid Kits & Supplies
N.A.I.C.S.: 339113

GENERAL BUILDING MAINTENANCE, INC.
3835 Presidential Pkwy Ste 200, Atlanta, GA 30340
Tel.: (770) 457-5678
Web Site: https://www.gbmweb.com
Sales Range: $25-49.9 Million
Emp.: 560
Janitorial Services
N.A.I.C.S.: 561720
Sunny K. Park (CEO)
Tammy Scott (Controller)

GENERAL CATALYST PARTNERS
20 University Rd Ste 450, Cambridge, MA 02138
Tel.: (617) 234-7000   DE
Web Site:
   http://www.generalcatalyst.com
Year Founded: 1999
Sales Range: $25-49.9 Million
Emp.: 40
Capital Investment Company Services
N.A.I.C.S.: 523910
Joel Cutler (Co-Founder & Mng Dir)
William J. Fitzgerald (Co-Founder, Mng Dir & COO)
Lawrence S. Bohn (Mng Dir)
Adam Valkin (Mng Dir)
John Kim (Mng Dir)

Kenneth C. Frazier (Chm-Health Assurance Initiatives)
Hemant Taneja (Mng Partner-Health Assurance)

Subsidiaries:

Athletes First, LLC   (1)
23091 Mill Creek Dr, Laguna Hills, CA 92653-1258
Tel.: (949) 475-1006
Web Site: http://www.athletesfirst.net
Business Associations
N.A.I.C.S.: 813910
Brian Murphy (CEO)
Rudy Cline-Thomas (Chm)
Jene Elzie (Chief Growth Officer)

WC SACD One, Inc.   (1)
15 Network Dr, Burlington, MA 01803
Tel.: (617) 818-1887
Vehicle Company
N.A.I.C.S.: 523940

Subsidiary (Domestic):

Intersections Inc.   (2)
2553 Dulles View Dr 4th Fl, Herndon, VA 20171
Tel.: (703) 488-6100
Web Site: http://www.auracompany.com
Identity Management Solutions
N.A.I.C.S.: 518210
Stephen Ruggieri (VP-Partner Solutions)

Subsidiary (Domestic):

American Background Services, Inc.   (3)
629 Cedar Creek Grade Ste C, Winchester, VA 22601
Tel.: (540) 665-8056
Web Site:
   http://www.americanbackground.com
Sales Range: $100-124.9 Million
Background Screening
N.A.I.C.S.: 561611

Captira Analytical, LLC   (3)
3 E Comm Sq 11 Pruyn St, Albany, NY 12207
Tel.: (518) 312-4163
Web Site: http://www.captira.com
Sales Range: $10-24.9 Million
Emp.: 20
Software & Automated Service Solutions for Bail Bond Industry
N.A.I.C.S.: 513210
Steven Alan Sjoblad (Chm & CEO)

Intersections Insurance Services Inc.   (3)
315 W University Dr, Arlington Heights, IL 60004-1811
Tel.: (847) 797-8500
Web Site:
   http://www.intersectionsinsurance.com
Insurance Brokerage Services
N.A.I.C.S.: 524210

Net Enforcers, Inc.   (3)
2633 E Indian School Rd Ste 270, Phoenix, AZ 85016
Tel.: (270) 721-5491
Web Site: http://www.netenforcers.com
Sales Range: $10-24.9 Million
Emp.: 25
Brand Protection Services
N.A.I.C.S.: 541519

i4c Innovations Inc.   (3)
3800 Concorde Pkwy Ste 400, Chantilly, VA 20151
Tel.: (703) 961-6596
Web Site: http://www.voyce.com
Animal Production Services
N.A.I.C.S.: 112990

GENERAL COATINGS CORPORATION
6711 Nancy Ridge Dr, San Diego, CA 92121
Tel.: (858) 587-1277
Web Site: https://www.gencoat.com
Sales Range: $10-24.9 Million
Emp.: 200
Painting, Waterproofing & Wall Covering Contractor

N.A.I.C.S.: 238320
Craig Kinsman (Pres)

GENERAL COATINGS TECHNOLOGIES
24 Woodward Ave, Ridgewood, NY 11385
Tel.: (718) 821-1232
Year Founded: 1983
Sales Range: $10-24.9 Million
Emp.: 25
Paints & Paint Additives
N.A.I.C.S.: 325510
Michael Ghitelman (Pres)

GENERAL COLOR & CHEMICAL CO., INC.
350 Bridge St, Minerva, OH 44657
Tel.: (330) 868-4161
Web Site:
   https://www.generalcolor.com
Year Founded: 1938
Sales Range: $10-24.9 Million
Emp.: 20
Inorganic Dye & Pigment Mfr
N.A.I.C.S.: 325130
Keith W. Gartner (Pres)

GENERAL CONTROL EQUIPMENT COMPANY
PO Box 7066, Charlotte, NC 28273
Tel.: (704) 588-0484
Sales Range: $1-9.9 Million
Emp.: 15
Carburetor, Piston, Piston Ring & Valve Mfr
N.A.I.C.S.: 332911
Beth E. Young (VP)
William B. Young Jr. (Pres)

GENERAL DEVICES CO. INC.
1410 S Post Rd, Indianapolis, IN 46239-9632
Tel.: (317) 897-7000
Web Site:
   https://www.generaldevices.com
Year Founded: 1953
Sales Range: $10-24.9 Million
Emp.: 170
Electronic Packaging Hardware Mfr
N.A.I.C.S.: 334514
Maxwell S. Fall (Pres & CEO)

GENERAL DIE CASTERS INC.
2150 Highland Rd, Twinsburg, OH 44087
Tel.: (330) 657-2300
Web Site:
   https://www.generaldie.com
Year Founded: 1957
Rev.: $12,100,000
Emp.: 155
Aluminum Die-Castings
N.A.I.C.S.: 331523
James Mathias (CEO & Pres)
Chuck Long (Superintendent-Casting)
Dan Owens (Coord-Safety)
Ryan Hamric (Engr-Tooling)
Jose Camacho (Supvr-Die Casting)

GENERAL DISTRIBUTORS INC.
800 E Indianapolis, Wichita, KS 67206-1292
Tel.: (316) 267-2255
Web Site:
   http://www.generaldistributorsinc.net
Year Founded: 1949
Rev.: $11,800,000
Emp.: 40
Home Furnishing Wholesalers
N.A.I.C.S.: 423220
Larry K. Arbuckle (Pres)
Aaron Arbuckle (Pres)
Steven C. Bailey (Treas)

GENERAL DOORS CORP.
1 Monroe St, Bristol, PA 19007-0205
Tel.: (215) 788-9277
Web Site: https://www.general-doors.com
Year Founded: 1947
Sales Range: $10-24.9 Million
Emp.: 92
Wood Window & Door Mfr
N.A.I.C.S.: 321911
Francis Kane (Dir-IT & Mgr-Pur)

GENERAL ELECTRIC CREDIT UNION
10485 Reading Rd, Cincinnati, OH 45241
Tel.: (513) 243-4328
Web Site:
   https://www.gecreditunion.org
Rev.: $32,384,025
Emp.: 100
Federal Credit Union Services
N.A.I.C.S.: 522130
Ashley Weaver (Mgr-Bus Dev)
Matthew Dole (Dir-HR)
Patrick L. Taylor (CEO)

GENERAL ENGINES COMPANY INC.
14893 Hwy 27, Lake Wales, FL 33859
Tel.: (863) 638-1421   NJ
Web Site:
   https://www.eagerbeavertrailers.com
Year Founded: 1946
Sales Range: $50-74.9 Million
Emp.: 120
Trailer Mfr
N.A.I.C.S.: 336212
Frank Flowers (Pres)
Jim Anesh (Controller)

GENERAL EQUIPMENT & SUPPLIES INC.
4300 Main Ave, Fargo, ND 58103-1013
Tel.: (701) 282-2662
Web Site: https://www.genequip.com
Year Founded: 1984
Sales Range: $10-24.9 Million
Emp.: 75
Construction & Mining Machinery Mfr
N.A.I.C.S.: 423810
Don Shilling (Chm)
Mark Johnson (Mgr-Sls-Used Equipment)
Josh Wurgler (Mgr-Fargo Parts)
Steve Stafki (VP-Svc)

Subsidiaries:

General Aggregate Equipment Sales ULC   (1)
841 Oak Point Highway, Winnipeg, R3C 2E6, MB, Canada
Tel.: (204) 697-9600
Web Site: http://www.genagg.ca
Emp.: 8
Construction Equipment Rental Services
N.A.I.C.S.: 532412
Don Kern (VP)
Jon Shilling (Pres)
Tanya Groft (VP)
Sara Frith (VP)

Specialized Carrier Co. Inc.   (1)
4300 Main Ave, Fargo, ND 58103-1013
Tel.: (701) 282-6649
Web Site: http://www.generalequipment.com
Rev.: $1,200,000
Emp.: 2
Provider of Local Trucking Without Storage
N.A.I.C.S.: 484110
Kevin Paulson (Mgr)

GENERAL EQUITIES INC.
318 Main St, Kensington, CT 06037
Tel.: (860) 828-0333

Web Site:
http://www.newbritaincandy.com
Rev.: $32,300,000
Emp.: 40
Convenience Store
N.A.I.C.S.: 445131
Raymond Hill *(Pres)*
Ted Leaf *(Mgr-Transportation)*

GENERAL EXCAVATING COMPANY

6701 Cornhusker Hwy, Lincoln, NE 68507
Tel.: (402) 467-1627
Web Site:
https://www.generalexcavating.com
Sales Range: $10-24.9 Million
Emp.: 100
Underground Utilities Contractor Services
N.A.I.C.S.: 237110
Scott Fitzgerald *(Pres)*
Joe D'Amico *(VP & Div Mgr)*
Kenneth D. Imig *(Project Mgr)*

GENERAL EXTRUSIONS INC.

PO Box 3460, Youngstown, OH 44513-3488
Tel.: (330) 783-0270
Web Site: http://www.genext.com
Year Founded: 1950
Sales Range: $25-49.9 Million
Emp.: 58
Aluminum Extruded Products Mfr
N.A.I.C.S.: 331318
Herbert F. Schuler *(Chm)*
Beato Frank *(Gen Mgr)*
Jason Andre *(Dir-Ops)*
Jonathon Whaley *(Mgr-IT)*
Rosemary Athey *(CFO)*

GENERAL FABRICS COMPANY

45 47 Washington St, Pawtucket, RI 02860
Tel.: (401) 728-4200
Sales Range: $10-24.9 Million
Emp.: 25
Piece Goods & Other Fabrics
N.A.I.C.S.: 424310
Edward P. Odessa *(Pres)*
David Odessa *(VP)*

GENERAL FASTENERS COMPANY INC.

37584 Amrhein Rd, Livonia, MI 48150
Tel.: (734) 452-2400
Web Site: https://www.genfast.com
Year Founded: 1952
Sales Range: $100-124.9 Million
Emp.: 233
Hardware Distr
N.A.I.C.S.: 423710
Jill Baron *(Pres)*
Ken DiLaura *(CFO)*

GENERAL FILMS, INC.

645 S High St, Covington, OH 45318
Tel.: (937) 473-2051
Web Site:
https://www.generalfilms.com
Year Founded: 1947
Sales Range: $10-24.9 Million
Emp.: 80
Unsupported Plastic Film & Sheet Mfr
N.A.I.C.S.: 326113
Tom Granata *(VP-Sls)*
Joe Sprouse *(Mgr-Ops)*
Nicole Hutson *(Dir-HR)*

GENERAL FILTERS, INC.

43800 Grand River Ave, Novi, MI 48375-1115
Tel.: (248) 476-5100   MI
Web Site:
https://www.generalfilters.com

Year Founded: 1937
Sales Range: $50-74.9 Million
Emp.: 49
Filters for Heating Fuel, Hydraulic & Lubricating Oils, Residential Humidifiers, Air Filters & Accessories
N.A.I.C.S.: 333415
John A. Redner *(Owner & VP-Ops)*
Carl Redner *(Pres)*

Subsidiaries:

Canadian General Filters Limited **(1)**
400 Midwest Rd, Toronto, M1P 3A9, ON, Canada   **(100%)**
Tel.: (416) 757-3691
Web Site: https://generalaireiaq.ca
Sales Range: $10-24.9 Million
Emp.: 14
Air Filtration Product Mfr
N.A.I.C.S.: 333998

GENERAL FLOOR INDUSTRIES INC.

190 Benigno Blvd, Bellmawr, NJ 08031-2516
Tel.: (856) 931-0012
Web Site:
https://www.generalfloor.com
Rev.: $23,690,099
Emp.: 40
Wholesale Floor Coverings
N.A.I.C.S.: 449121
David Cometz *(Pres)*
Joey Garrous *(Branch Mgr)*
Dawn Sylvester *(Mgr-Internal Sls)*
Jim Smith *(CFO)*
Casey Spence *(Coord-Mktg)*

GENERAL FOAM PLASTICS CORP.

3321 E Princess Anne Rd, Norfolk, VA 23502-1502
Tel.: (757) 857-0153   VA
Web Site: http://www.genfoam.com
Year Founded: 1960
Sales Range: $200-249.9 Million
Emp.: 1,500
Plastics Product Mfr
N.A.I.C.S.: 339999
Margaret A. Heuisler *(Mgr-Liability Claims & Product Svc)*
Alan Swenson *(Mgr-Production)*
Beverly Smith *(Office Mgr-Sls)*
Bob Semmens *(VP-Product Dev)*

Subsidiaries:

Beckett Corporation **(1)**
3250 N Skyway Cir Dr, Irving, TX 75063-2306
Tel.: (972) 871-8000
Rev.: $50,000,000
Emp.: 8
Pumps Mfr
N.A.I.C.S.: 333996
Wingate Sung *(COO & Exec VP)*

GENERAL GERMAN AGED PEOPLE'S HOME OF BALTIMORE

800 Southerly Rd, Towson, MD 21286
Tel.: (410) 339-6000   MD
Web Site: https://www.edenwald.org
Year Founded: 1881
Sales Range: $10-24.9 Million
Emp.: 471
Health Care Srvices
N.A.I.C.S.: 622110
Kenneth L. Bullock *(VP-Fin)*
Diane L. Stinchcomb *(Dir-Sls)*
Andrew T. Jones *(VP)*
Salvatore Molite Jr. *(Pres)*
William Garrett Jr. *(Exec VP)*

GENERAL GLASS INTERNATIONAL CORP.

101 Venture Way, Secaucus, NJ 07094-1808
Tel.: (201) 553-1850
Web Site:
https://www.generalglass.com
Year Founded: 1900
Sales Range: $10-24.9 Million
Emp.: 250
Glass Products Supplier, Mfr & Importer
N.A.I.C.S.: 423310
David S. Balik *(Pres)*
Richard Balik *(VP)*

GENERAL HEALTH SYSTEM INC.

8490 Picardy, Baton Rouge, LA 70809
Tel.: (225) 237-1500
Web Site: http://www.brgeneral.org
Year Founded: 1945
Sales Range: $150-199.9 Million
Emp.: 3,000
Management Services
N.A.I.C.S.: 561110
Mark Flyter *(CEO)*
Tonya Jineaux *(Treas)*
G. Douglas Say *(Chm-Medicine Svcs)*
Jeffrey Littleton *(Chm-Surgical Svcs)*
Joseph E. Juban *(Chm)*
Phyllis McLaurin *(Vice Chm)*

Subsidiaries:

General Health System Foundation, Inc.   **(1)**
8490 Picardy Ave, Baton Rouge, LA 70809-3731
Tel.: (225) 237-1500
Web Site: http://www.brgeneral.org
Sales Range: $250-299.9 Million
Non-Profit Fountain Supporting Baton Rouge General
N.A.I.C.S.: 561110

GENERAL HOUSING CORPORATION

4650 E Wilder Rd, Bay City, MI 48706
Tel.: (989) 684-8078
Web Site: https://www.genhouse.com
Sales Range: $10-24.9 Million
Emp.: 45
Prefabricated Buildings, Wood
N.A.I.C.S.: 321992
Brad Sullivan *(Controller)*

GENERAL INFORMATICS

8000 GSRI Rd Bldg 3000, Baton Rouge, LA 70820
Tel.: (225) 767-7670
Web Site: http://www.geninf.com
Year Founded: 2001
Rev.: $2,600,000
Emp.: 22
Custom Computer Programming Services
N.A.I.C.S.: 541511
Mohit Vij *(Pres)*
Huy Du *(Engr-Sys)*
Colby Klein *(Engr-Network)*
Melenie Uesea *(Mgr-Ops)*

GENERAL INSULATION CO. INC.

278 Mystic Ave Ste 209, Medford, MA 02155
Tel.: (781) 391-2070
Web Site:
https://www.generalinsulation.com
Year Founded: 1981
Sales Range: $50-74.9 Million
Emp.: 180
Roofing, Siding & Insulation Materials
N.A.I.C.S.: 423330

Lawrence D. Murphy *(Pres-FIOX)*
Mark T. O'Neil *(Pres-Comml Products)*
Jeff Gentilotti *(CFO & VP)*
Frank R. Granara Jr. *(Pres)*

GENERAL ISRAEL ORPHAN HOME FOR GIRLS JERUSALEM

132 Nassau St Ste 725, New York, NY 10038
Tel.: (212) 267-7222   NY
Web Site: http://www.gioh.org
Year Founded: 1949
Sales Range: $1-9.9 Million
Emp.: 4
Orphanage Operator
N.A.I.C.S.: 623990
Eliezer Weingarten *(Chm)*

GENERAL JOHN J PERSHING MEMORIAL HOSPITAL ASSOCIATION

180 E Lockling, Brookfield, MO 64628
Tel.: (660) 258-2222   MO
Web Site:
http://www.pershinghealthsystems.com
Year Founded: 1955
Sales Range: $10-24.9 Million
Emp.: 182
Health Care Srvices
N.A.I.C.S.: 622110
Gail Turner *(Treas)*
William Thudium *(VP)*
Angela P. Littrell *(Sec)*

GENERAL LABOR STAFFING SERVICES INC.

1709 Banks Rd, Margate, FL 33063-7744
Tel.: (954) 973-8350
Web Site: https://www.glstaffing.com
Year Founded: 2001
Sales Range: $1-9.9 Million
Emp.: 1,000
Employment Agencies
N.A.I.C.S.: 561311
Gerry Califano *(Pres & CEO)*
Lawrence J. Minei *(CFO)*

GENERAL MACHINERY COMPANY INC.

921 1st Ave N, Birmingham, AL 35203
Tel.: (205) 251-9243
Web Site:
https://www.generalmachinery.com
Rev.: $21,715,159
Emp.: 45
Industrial Machinery & Equipment
N.A.I.C.S.: 423830
Paul Crockard *(VP)*

GENERAL MAGNAPLATE CORPORATION

1331 W Edgar Rd, Linden, NJ 07036
Tel.: (908) 862-6200   NJ
Web Site:
http://www.magnaplate.com
Year Founded: 1952
Sales Range: $10-24.9 Million
Emp.: 130
Mfr of High-Technology Composite Coatings For Industrial Metal Parts
N.A.I.C.S.: 332812
Candida C. Aversenti *(CEO)*
Edmund V. Aversenti *(COO)*
Valerie Corigliano *(Coord-Mktg)*

Subsidiaries:

General Magnaplate California **(1)**
1331 W Edgar Rd, Linden, NJ 07036   **(100%)**
Tel.: (908) 862-6200
Web Site: http://www.magnaplate.com

General Magnaplate Corporation—(Continued)

Sales Range: $10-24.9 Million
Emp.: 19
Materials Technology/Metal Finishing
N.A.I.C.S.: 332812

General Magnaplate Canada
Ltd. (1)
72 Orchard Road, Ajax, L1S6L1, ON,
Canada (100%)
Tel.: (905) 686-2277
Web Site: http://www.magnaplate.com
Metal Processing
N.A.I.C.S.: 332812

General Magnaplate Texas (1)
801 Ave G, Arlington, TX
76011-7709 (100%)
Tel.: (817) 649-8989
Web Site: http://www.magnaplate.com
Sales Range: $10-24.9 Million
Emp.: 30
Materials Technology/Metal Finishing
N.A.I.C.S.: 332812
John Larsen (VP & Gen Mgr)

GENERAL MECHANICAL CONTRACTORS INC

8107 Interstate 30, Little Rock, AR
72209
Tel.: (501) 562-5511
Sales Range: $10-24.9 Million
Emp.: 30
Warm Air Heating & Air Conditioning
N.A.I.C.S.: 238220
Bryce Swindler (Pres)
Anita Weber (Controller)
Wayne Williamson (Project Mgr)

GENERAL MICROSYSTEMS, INC.

13430 N Black Canyon hwy, Phoenix,
AZ 85029
Tel.: (480) 998-0555
Web Site: http://www.gmi.com
Rev.: $32,100,000
Emp.: 20
Computer & Computer Peripheral
Equipment & Software Merchant
Whslr
N.A.I.C.S.: 423430
Earl W. Overstreet II (Pres)
Barbara L. Overstreet (CFO)
Matthew Jolma (Dir-Sls)
Gregg Davis (Sr VP-Delivery)

Subsidiaries:

Alagen LLC (1)
1407 E San Miguel Ave, Phoenix, AZ
85014-2423
Tel.: (602) 345-1815
Web Site: http://www.alagen.com
Scientific & Technical Consulting Services
N.A.I.C.S.: 541690
Jason Rowland (Dir-Bus Dev)
Gregg Davis (Founder & CEO)

GENERAL MOLY, INC.

1726 Cole Blvd Ste 115, Lakewood,
CO 80401
Tel.: (303) 928-8599　　　　DE
Web Site:
http://www.generalmoly.com
Year Founded: 1925
Assets: $344,227,000
Liabilities: $248,074,000
Net Worth: $96,153,000
Earnings: ($7,878,000)
Emp.: 12
Fiscal Year-end: 12/31/19
Molybdenum Mineral Exploration, Development & Mining Services
N.A.I.C.S.: 212290
Michael K. Branstetter (Gen Counsel
& Sec)
Patrick C. Rogers (VP-Permitting &
Environmental Compliance)
Robert I. Pennington (COO)
R. Scott Roswell (Interim Chief Restructuring Officer)

GENERAL NOVELTY LTD.

420 E 58th Ave, Denver, CO 80216
Tel.: (303) 292-5537
Web Site:
http://www.coachhousegifts.net
Sales Range: $50-74.9 Million
Emp.: 40
Gift Shop
N.A.I.C.S.: 459420
Frederic Ieuter (VP-Fin)

GENERAL PACKAGING CORPORATION

200 E Arapaho Rd, Richardson, TX
75081
Tel.: (972) 234-5499
Web Site: https://www.gpctexas.com
Year Founded: 1960
Sales Range: $10-24.9 Million
Emp.: 153
Corrugated & Solid Fiber Box Mfr
N.A.I.C.S.: 322211
James W. Brown (Founder & Chm)
Jeff E. Brown (Exec VP)
James W. Brown III (Pres)

GENERAL PACKAGING PRODUCTS INC.

1700 S Canal St, Chicago, IL 60616-
1189
Tel.: (312) 226-5611
Web Site: http://www.generalpk.com
Year Founded: 1932
Sales Range: $10-24.9 Million
Emp.: 90
Commercial Gravure Printing Services
N.A.I.C.S.: 323111
Debbie Sands (Mgr-Customer Svc)

GENERAL PARTS OF MINNESOTA INC.

11311 Hampshire Ave S, Bloomington, MN 55438
Tel.: (952) 944-5800
Web Site:
https://www.generalparts.com
Sales Range: $10-24.9 Million
Emp.: 175
Industrial Machine Parts
N.A.I.C.S.: 423830
Jeff Weber (VP-Sls)

GENERAL PATTERN CO. INC.

3075 84th Ln NE, Blaine, MN 55449
Tel.: (763) 780-3518
Web Site:
https://www.generalpattern.com
Sales Range: $25-49.9 Million
Emp.: 200
Plastics Processing
N.A.I.C.S.: 326199
Denny Reiland (Pres)
Mark Tobler (Dir-Ops)
Mike Mether (Mgr-Facilities)
Mike Peterson (Mgr-QA)

GENERAL PENCIL COMPANY

67 Fleet St, Jersey City, NJ 07306-
2213
Tel.: (201) 653-5351　　　　NJ
Web Site:
http://www.generalpencil.com
Year Founded: 1889
Sales Range: $1-9.9 Million
Emp.: 50
Lead, Drawing, Colored & Office Pencils, Cosmetic Pencils, Ball Pens,
Markers, Erasers & Art Materials Mfr
N.A.I.C.S.: 339940
Jim Wienbaum (Pres)

Subsidiaries:

General Pencil Co. (1)
3168 Bay Rd, Redwood City, CA 94063-
0311

Tel.: (650) 369-4889
Web Site: http://www.generalpencil.com
Mfr of Lead Pencils
N.A.I.C.S.: 493110

GENERAL PERFUME & COSMETICS DISTRIBUTORS INC.

1504 S Flower St, Los Angeles, CA
90015-2906
Tel.: (213) 744-0074　　　　CA
Web Site:
https://www.generalperfume.com
Year Founded: 1987
Sales Range: $10-24.9 Million
Emp.: 30
Providers of Perfume
N.A.I.C.S.: 424210
Isaac Cohen (Pres)
Ronnie Cohen (VP)
Ilanit Tamam (Mgr-Accts Receivable)

GENERAL PETROLEUM INCORPORATED

7404 Disalle Blvd, Fort Wayne, IN
46825
Tel.: (260) 489-8504
Web Site: https://www.genpet.com
Sales Range: $10-24.9 Million
Emp.: 20
Lubricating Oils & Greases Mfr
N.A.I.C.S.: 424720
Cindy Vanderwall (Pres)

GENERAL PLASTICS & COMPOSITES LP

5727 Ledbetter St, Houston, TX
77087
Tel.: (713) 644-1449
Web Site: http://www.genplastics.com
Rev.: $13,000,000
Emp.: 200
Laminated Plastics Mfr
N.A.I.C.S.: 332710
David Walstad (Owner & CEO)
George Bulliner (Acct Mgr)
Tom McKernan (Controller)

GENERAL PLASTICS MANUFACTURING COMPANY

4910 Burlington Way, Tacoma, WA
98409
Tel.: (253) 473-5000
Web Site:
https://www.generalplastics.com
Rev.: $12,700,000
Emp.: 134
Urethane & Other Foam Product Mfr
N.A.I.C.S.: 326150
Mitchell Johnson (Pres & CEO)
Jeff Brown (VP-Ops & Engrg)
Dave Watt (Mgr-Bus Dev & Sls)

GENERAL PLUG & MANUFACTURING CO.

455 N Main, Grafton, OH 44044
Tel.: (440) 926-2411
Web Site:
http://www.generalplug.com
Year Founded: 1955
Sales Range: $10-24.9 Million
Emp.: 135
Metal Valve & Pipe Fitting Mfr
N.A.I.C.S.: 332919
Kevin J. Flanigan (Pres)

GENERAL PLUMBING SUPPLY

980 New Durham Rd, Edison, NJ
08817
Tel.: (732) 248-1000
Web Site:
https://www.generalplumbing
supply.net
Rev.: $29,660,918
Emp.: 65
Plumbing & Hydronic Heating Supplies

N.A.I.C.S.: 423720
Bruce Tucker (Pres)
Joe Novak (Pres)
Wanda Acosta (Mgr-Showroom)
Tom Mazzola (Dir-Pur)
Pat Saverino (Mgr)
Jay Setlow (Asst Mgr-Sls)
Ken Yanow (Controller)
Susan Benedetto (Mgr-Acctg)
Donna Damico (Mgr-Credit)
Jeff Friedman (Mgr-Showroom)
Sam Ninivaggi (Mgr-Showroom)
Scott Pashaian (Mgr-Showroom)
Ada Saharig (Mgr-Showroom)
Lori Stoll (Mgr-Showroom)
Gary Kuperstein (Sr VP)
Justin Freedman (VP)

GENERAL PLUMBING SUPPLY COMPANY INC.

1530 San Luis Rd, Walnut Creek, CA
94597
Tel.: (925) 939-4622
Web Site:
https://www.generalplumbing
supply.com
Year Founded: 1965
Sales Range: $10-24.9 Million
Emp.: 100
Plumbing Fixtures, Equipment & Supplies Whslr
N.A.I.C.S.: 423720
Bill Knaus (Mgr-Pur)
Madalene Rivera (Mgr-AP)
Richard Amaro Sr. (Pres)

GENERAL POLYMERIC CORP.

1136 Morgantown Rd, Reading, PA
19607
Tel.: (610) 374-5171
Web Site: https://www.genpore.com
Rev.: $11,000,000
Emp.: 62
Plastic Materials & Resins Mfr
N.A.I.C.S.: 325211
Joseph E. Ferri (Pres)

GENERAL PRODUCE CO. LTD.

1330 N B St, Sacramento, CA 95814
Tel.: (916) 441-6431　　　　CA
Web Site:
http://www.generalproduce.com
Year Founded: 1933
Sales Range: $25-49.9 Million
Emp.: 225
Provider of Fruit & Vegetable Gifts
N.A.I.C.S.: 424480
Daniel Chan (Mgr-Procurement)
Thomas Chan (CEO)
Cliff Rubens (Mgr-Acctg)
Linda Luka (Dir-Marketing-
Communications)
Mike McGonigle (Mgr-Export)
Traci Ennis (Dir-Procurement)

GENERAL PRODUCTS PARTNERS INC.

739 Wall Rd, Brownsboro, AL 35741
Tel.: (256) 859-5114　　　　DE
Web Site: https://www.gp-llc.com
Year Founded: 1971
Sales Range: $25-49.9 Million
Emp.: 40
Aerospace & Defense Components
Mfr
N.A.I.C.S.: 332999
Jeff Hunter (VP-Sls & Mktg)
Mike Tucker (Gen Mgr)

GENERAL PROPELLER COMPANY, INC.

1415 9th Ave E, Bradenton, FL 34208
Tel.: (941) 748-1527　　　　FL
Web Site: http://www.gpcprop.com
Year Founded: 1945

Sales Range: $1-9.9 Million
Emp.: 35
Propellers & Marine Hardware Mfr
N.A.I.C.S.: 332710
Paul Fox (Pres)

GENERAL PURPOSE STEEL INC.
505 Braddock Ave, Turtle Creek, PA 15145
Tel.: (412) 823-2600
Rev.: $17,000,000
Emp.: 8
Plates, Metal
N.A.I.C.S.: 423510
Lance Chatkin (Pres)
Dick Diamondstone (Mgr-Quality Control)

GENERAL RUBBER PLASTICS OF LOUISVILLE
3118 Preston Hwy, Louisville, KY 40213
Tel.: (502) 635-2605
Web Site: http://www.grplou.com
Sales Range: $10-24.9 Million
Emp.: 40
Industrial Supplies
N.A.I.C.S.: 423840
Randy Ramey (Mgr-Sls)

GENERAL RV CENTER INC.
48500 W 12 Mi Rd, Wixom, MI 48393
Tel.: (248) 349-0900
Web Site: http://www.generalrv.com
Sales Range: $100-124.9 Million
Emp.: 70
Recreational Vehicle Dealers
N.A.I.C.S.: 441210
Bill Brown (Asst Mgr-Sls)
Cathy Klekner (Asst Mgr-Svc)
Chris Dietrich (VP-Svc Ops)
Mike Thrower (Mgr-Sls)
Spencer Hallett (Mgr-Fin & Insurance)
Donnie MacKinnon (Mgr-Parts)
Dustin Olds (Mgr-IT)
John Demick (Dir-Rental)
Jeremy Miller (Mgr-Sls)
Roberta Angelo (VP-Client Rels)

Subsidiaries:

Independence RV Sales & Services, Inc (1)
12705 W Colonial Dr, Winter Garden, FL 34787
Tel.: (407) 877-7878
Web Site: http://www.independencerv.com
Recreational Vehicle Dealers
N.A.I.C.S.: 441210
Dan Healy (Dir-Mktg)

GENERAL SCIENTIFIC SAFETY EQUIPMENT CO.
2553 E Somerset St Fl 1, Philadelphia, PA 19134-5925
Tel.: (215) 739-7559
Year Founded: 1988
Sales Range: $75-99.9 Million
Emp.: 2
Distr of First Aid, Medical & Personal Safety Supplies & Equipment
N.A.I.C.S.: 423450
Angela D'Amico (VP)

Subsidiaries:

Industrial Drug Service Div. (1)
2553 E Somerset St 1st Fl, Philadelphia, PA 19134
Tel.: (215) 739-7559
First Aid & Medical Supply Distr for Various Manufacturers
N.A.I.C.S.: 423450

GENERAL SECURITY SERVICES CORPORATION

9110 Meadowview Rd, Minneapolis, MN 55425-2458
Tel.: (952) 858-5000   MN
Web Site: https://www.gssc.net
Year Founded: 1946
Sales Range: $25-49.9 Million
Emp.: 2,600
Customized Security Solutions
N.A.I.C.S.: 561612
Brenda Shaw (Asst Controller)
Doug Cresto (Supvr-Patrol)
Tom Bates (Project Mgr)

GENERAL SECURITY, INC.
100 Fairchild Ave, Plainview, NY 11803
Tel.: (516) 997-6464
Web Site: https://www.gensecurity.com
Rev.: $10,200,000
Emp.: 50
Hardware Merchant Whslr
N.A.I.C.S.: 423710
Peter Allen (Gen Mgr)

GENERAL SERVICES CORPORATION (GSC)
2922 Hathaway Rd, Richmond, VA 23225-1733
Tel.: (804) 320-7101   VA
Web Site: http://www.gscapartments.com
Year Founded: 1975
Sales Range: $200-249.9 Million
Emp.: 350
Apartment Rentals & Apartment Management Services
N.A.I.C.S.: 531110
Jonathan S. Perel (Pres)
Rene Bryant (Asst Treas)
Van Ferguson (CFO)

GENERAL SPORTS & ENTERTAINMENT, LLC
400 Water St Ste 250, Rochester, MI 48307
Tel.: (248) 601-2200
Web Site: http://www.generalsports.com
Sports & Entertainment Services
N.A.I.C.S.: 711211
Andrew D. Appleby (Chm & CEO-Gen)
Josh Hartman (Dir-Sls, Sponsorships & Mktg)

GENERAL SPORTSWEAR CO. INC.
2 Elting Ct, Ellenville, NY 12428
Tel.: (845) 647-4411
Web Site: https://www.generalsportwear.com
Year Founded: 1927
Sales Range: $10-24.9 Million
Emp.: 75
Clothing Mfr
N.A.I.C.S.: 315250
Herb Rosenstock (CEO)

Subsidiaries:

Devil Dog Manufacturing Co., Inc. (1)
23 Market St, Ellenville, NY 12428
Tel.: (919) 269-7485
Web Site: http://www.generalsportwear.com
Rev.: $12,800,000
Emp.: 6
Sportswear Mfr
N.A.I.C.S.: 315250

GENERAL STEAMSHIP AGENCIES
575 Redwood Hwy Ste 200, Mill Valley, CA 94941
Tel.: (415) 389-5200
Web Site: https://www.gensteam.com
Sales Range: $10-24.9 Million

Emp.: 350
Shipping Agents
N.A.I.C.S.: 488510
G. Scott Jones (Chm)
Janis R. Mahoney (VP)

GENERAL STEEL INC.
4131 Broadway, Macon, GA 31206
Tel.: (478) 746-2794
Web Site: http://www.steeldeal.com
Sales Range: $10-24.9 Million
Emp.: 1,000
Iron & Steel Products
N.A.I.C.S.: 423510
Charlie Boswell (Div Mgr-Rebar)

GENERAL SULLIVAN GROUP INC.
370 Sullivan Way, Trenton, NJ 08628
Tel.: (609) 882-7380
Year Founded: 1919
Sales Range: $10-24.9 Million
Emp.: 81
Metals Mfr
N.A.I.C.S.: 423510

Subsidiaries:

General Sullivan Corp. (1)
370 Sullivan Way, Trenton, NJ 08628
Tel.: (609) 882-7380
Sales Range: $10-24.9 Million
Emp.: 30
Industrial Machinery & Equipment Distr
N.A.I.C.S.: 423830

GENERAL SUPPLY COMPANY
2651 Baglyos Cir, Bethlehem, PA 18020-9626
Tel.: (610) 882-2141
Web Site: http://www.generalsupplycompany.com
Year Founded: 1903
Sales Range: $10-24.9 Million
Emp.: 60
Building Materials Distr
N.A.I.C.S.: 423310
John J. Simon (Pres & CEO)

GENERAL TOOL COMPANY INC.
101 Landy Ln, Cincinnati, OH 45215-3441
Tel.: (513) 733-5500   OH
Web Site: http://www.gentool.com
Year Founded: 1947
Sales Range: $10-24.9 Million
Emp.: 220
Industrial Machinery Services
N.A.I.C.S.: 332710
Ron Grzegorzewski (VP-Bus Dev)
William Kramer III (Pres)

GENERAL TOURS WORLD TRAVELER, INC.
53 Summer St, Keene, NH 03431-3318
Tel.: (603) 357-5033   NH
Web Site: http://www.generaltours.com
Year Founded: 1947
Sales Range: $1-9.9 Million
Emp.: 47
Tour Operator
N.A.I.C.S.: 561520
Alex Harris (Chm)

GENERAL TRADING CO., INC.
455 16th St, Carlstadt, NJ 07072-1922
Tel.: (201) 935-4460
Web Site: http://www.general-tradingco.com
Sales Range: $200-249.9 Million
Emp.: 500
Grocery Whslr
N.A.I.C.S.: 424410

George Abad (Pres)
Johnathan Abad (VP)

GENERAL TRAILER PARTS LLC
1420 S B St, Springfield, OR 97477
Tel.: (541) 746-8218
Web Site: http://www.generaltrailerparts.com
Sales Range: $10-24.9 Million
Emp.: 52
Trailer Parts & Accessories
N.A.I.C.S.: 423120
Eric Thompson (Owner)
Jim Fritz (Gen Mgr)

GENERAL TRANSPORTATION SERVICES
0255 Southwest Pkwy, Portland, OR 97225
Tel.: (503) 297-0119
Web Site: http://www.generaltransportation.com
Sales Range: $10-24.9 Million
Emp.: 15
Truck Transportation Brokers
N.A.I.C.S.: 488510
Robert Thompson (VP)
Richard Finks (Co-Owner)
Edward L. Kropp III (Co-Owner)

GENERAL TRANSPORTATION, INC.
2505 Industrial Park Rd, Van Buren, AR 72956-6009
Tel.: (479) 471-1200   AR
Year Founded: 1989
Sales Range: $10-24.9 Million
Emp.: 10
Freight Transportation Arrangement Services
N.A.I.C.S.: 488510
Margaret Decker (VP)
Roger Decker (Pres)

GENERAL TRUCK EQUIPMENT & TRAILER SALES
5310 Broadway Ave, Jacksonville, FL 32254
Tel.: (904) 389-5541
Web Site: https://www.generaltruckequipment.com
Sales Range: $10-24.9 Million
Emp.: 35
Truck Tractors
N.A.I.C.S.: 423120

GENERAL TRUCK PARTS & EQUIPMENT CO.
4040 W 40th St, Chicago, IL 60632
Tel.: (773) 247-6900
Web Site: https://www.generaltruckparts.com
Year Founded: 1971
Truck Parts & Accessories Whslr & Distr
N.A.I.C.S.: 423120
Jerry Dixon (Mgr-Shop)
Gregg Chudacoff (Pres)
Barry Brave (VP & Controller)
Eric Sjoerdsma (Sls Mgr-Natl)
Michael Parks (Sls Mgr-Local)
Curt Ladendorf (Mgr-Warranty Claims)
Brian Blum (Mgr-Freight)
Cynthia Renteria (Mgr-Credit)

GENERAL TRUCK SALES & SERVICE
1973 E Brooks Rd, Memphis, TN 38116
Tel.: (901) 345-3270
Web Site: https://www.generaltruck.com
Rev.: $38,000,000

General Truck Sales & Service—(Continued)

Emp.: 115
Trucks, Tractors & Trailers; New &
Used
N.A.I.C.S.: 441110
Jim McCullough (Owner)

GENERAL WAX CO. INC.
6858 Beck Ave, North Hollywood, CA
91605
Tel.: (818) 765-5800
Web Site:
   http://www.generalwax.com
Rev.: $19,673,131
Emp.: 110
Candles
N.A.I.C.S.: 339999
Jerry Baker (VP-Mfg)

**GENERAL WELDING WORKS
INC.**
2060 N Loop W Ste 200, Houston,
TX 77018
Tel.: (713) 869-6401
Web Site:
   http://www.generalwelding.com
Sales Range: $10-24.9 Million
Emp.: 120
Mfr of Process Vessels
N.A.I.C.S.: 332313
Phil Hybner (Mgr-Pur-Traffic)

**GENERAL WHOLESALE COM-
PANY, INC.**
1271 Tacoma Dr NW A, Atlanta, GA
30318-4145
Tel.: (404) 351-3626   GA
Year Founded: 1982
Sales Range: $125-149.9 Million
Emp.: 300
Wholesale Distribution of Liquor,
Wine, Beer & Other Fermented Malt
Liquors; Spirits
N.A.I.C.S.: 424820
Jane H. Young (Chm)
E. Howard Young (VP)
Dale Lowenstein (Sls Mgr)
Mike Blaine (Controller)
William D. Young Sr. (Pres & CEO)
William D. Young Jr. (Sec & VP)

Subsidiaries:

General Wholesale Company   (1)
615 Stonehill Dr SW, Atlanta, GA
30336   (100%)
Tel.: (404) 350-6543
Web Site: http://www.gwc-atl.com
Sales Range: $25-49.9 Million
Emp.: 35
Wholesale Distributor of Liquor, Wine, Beer
& Other Fermented Malt Liquors
N.A.I.C.S.: 424810

General Wholesale Company,
Inc.   (1)
813 5th St, Augusta, GA
30901-2414   (100%)
Tel.: (706) 724-4338
Sales Range: $25-49.9 Million
Emp.: 25
N.A.I.C.S.: 445320
Bill Young (Pres)

**GENERAL WHOLESALE DIS-
TRIBUTORS**
2299 Rdg Rd, Greenville, SC 29607
Tel.: (864) 277-9900
Web Site: http://www.gwd-ac.com
Sales Range: $25-49.9 Million
Emp.: 38
Warm Air Heating & Air Conditioning
N.A.I.C.S.: 423730
Sam Williams (VP-Pricing)
Chris Umberger (VP & Controller)

**GENERAL WOODWORKING
INC.**

---

105 Pevey St, Lowell, MA 01851
Tel.: (978) 458-6625
Web Site: https://www.genwood.com
Rev.: $10,597,754
Emp.: 33
Work Benches, Factory
N.A.I.C.S.: 337127
John Thompson (Pres)
Gary Merksamer (Project Mgr)
Rick Chenel (Project Mgr)

GENERATION 3 CAPITAL, LLC
1327 Barclay Blvd, Buffalo Grove, IL
60089
Tel.: (847) 250-6225
Web Site: http://gen3cap.com
Privater Equity Firm
N.A.I.C.S.: 523999
Brandon Nagler (Founder & Principal)
William Vranek (Principal & CFO)
James Coleman (Principal)
David Coleman (Principal)

**GENERATION GROWTH CAPI-
TAL, INC.**
411 E Wisconsin Ave Ste 1710, Mil-
waukee, WI 53202
Tel.: (414) 291-8908   WI
Web Site:
   http://www.generationgrowth.com
Year Founded: 2007
Privater Equity Firm
N.A.I.C.S.: 523940
Cory L. Nettles (Founder & Mng Dir)
John K. Reinke (Mng Dir)
Thomas P. Nye (Dir)
Laura J. Poll (Office Mgr)

Subsidiaries:

Bestmark, Inc.   (1)
5500 Feltl Rd, Minnetonka, MN 55343
Tel.: (952) 922-2205
Web Site: http://www.bestmark.com
Management Consulting & Marketing Re-
search Services
N.A.I.C.S.: 541910
Meredith Harper (Sr Mgr-Program)
Muriel Wirz (Editor-Quality Assurance)
Fred Ketcho (CEO)

Harrell's Car Wash Systems   (1)
1339 Country Club Rd, Indianapolis, IN
46234-1820
Tel.: (317) 271-0017
Web Site: http://www.hcws.com
Emp.: 60
Cosmetics, Beauty Supplies & Perfume
Stores
N.A.I.C.S.: 456120
Chad Tarman (Pres)

Model 2 Machining, Inc.   (1)
S82 W18762 Gemini Dr, Muskego, WI
53150
Tel.: (262) 679-4600
Machinery & Equipment Mfr
N.A.I.C.S.: 333517
Jerry Webb (Pres & CEO)

Rockford Specialties Co.   (1)
5601 Industrial Ave, Rockford, IL 61111
Tel.: (815) 877-6000
Web Site:
   http://www.rockfordspecialties.com
Rev.: $6,000,000
Emp.: 40
All Other Miscellaneous Electrical Equip-
ment & Component Mfr
N.A.I.C.S.: 335999
Lisa Stankey (Pres)

**GENERATION NEXT FRAN-
CHISE BRANDS, INC.**
2620 Financial Ct Ste 100, San Di-
ego, CA 92117
Tel.: (858) 210-4200   NV
Year Founded: 2011
VEND—(OTCBB)
Rev.: $18,397,434
Assets: $15,818,499
Liabilities: $45,707,889
Net Worth: ($29,889,390)

Earnings: ($18,958,100)
Emp.: 49
Fiscal Year-end: 06/30/19
Investment Services
N.A.I.C.S.: 445132

Subsidiaries:

Reis & Irvy's, Inc.   (1)
2620 Financial Ct Ste 100, San Diego, CA
92117
Tel.: (855) 385-5333
Web Site: http://www.reisandirvys.com
Frozen Dessert Mfr
N.A.I.C.S.: 311520
Paul Schmidt (CMO)

GENERATION PARTNERS
2 Latayette Ct, Greenwich, CT 06831
Tel.: (203) 442-8215
Web Site: http://www.generation.com
Year Founded: 1995
Privater Equity Firm
N.A.I.C.S.: 523999
Mark E. Jennings (Mng Partner)
John Hawkins (Mng Partner)
Andrew Hertzmark (Mng Partner)
Louis Marino (CFO & Sr VP)

**GENERATION ZERO GROUP,
INC.**
13663 Providence Rd Ste 253, Wed-
dington, NC 28104
Tel.: (470) 809-0707   NV
Web Site:
   http://www.generationzerogroup.com
Year Founded: 2006
Sales Range: Less than $1 Million
Internet Search Engine Services
N.A.I.C.S.: 519290
Christine B. Cheney (CFO)
Richard M. Morrell (Pres & CEO)

**GENERATIONAL EQUITY
GROUP, INC.**
3400 N Central Expy Ste 100, Rich-
ardson, TX 75080
Tel.: (972) 232-1121   TX
Web Site:
   http://www.genequityco.com
Year Founded: 1987
Holding Company; Corporate Merg-
ers & Acquisitions Advisory Services
N.A.I.C.S.: 551112
Ryan L. Binkley (Pres & CEO)
Elizabeth Lampkin (VP-Client Experi-
ence)
Jay Hellwig (Chief Experience Offi-
cer)
Heath Flock (COO)

Subsidiaries:

Generational Capital, LLC   (1)
3400 N Central Expy Ste 100, Richardson,
TX 75080
Tel.: (972) 232-1121
Web Site: http://www.generational.com
Mergers & Acquisitions Advisory Services
N.A.I.C.S.: 541611
Ryan Binkley (Pres & CEO)
Paul Blake (CIO)
Rita Boyko (Dir-Conference Ops)
Thomas Braun (Exec Mng Dir)
Rick Buchoz (Sr Mng Dir)

Subsidiary (Domestic):

Talis Advisory Services LLC   (2)
6205 Chapel Hill, Plano, TX 75093-8443
Tel.: (972) 378-1795
Web Site: http://www.talisadvisors.com
Investment Advice
N.A.I.C.S.: 523940

Generational Equity, LLC   (1)
14241 Dallas Pkwy Ste 700, Dallas, TX
75254
Tel.: (972) 232-1100
Web Site: http://www.genequityco.com
Corporate Mergers & Acquisitions Advisory
Services

N.A.I.C.S.: 541611
Ryan L. Binkley (Pres)
Thomas D. Farrell (Exec VP)
Dwight Jacobs (Exec VP-Mergers & Acq)
William White (Sr VP-Client Svcs)
Paul Blake (VP-Ops)
Steve Schrieber (VP-Bus Dev)
Beth Little (VP-Fin)
David McCreary (Chief Legal Officer)
Bob Berry (Mng Dir-Corp Valuations)
Marte Phillips (Dir-HR)
Rob Aldridge (Sr Mng Dir-Exit Strategy Ad-
visors)
Brian Ault (Sr Mng Dir-Exit Strategy Advi-
sors)
Thomas Braun (Sr Mng Dir-Exit Strategy
Advisors)
Robert Brenner (Sr Mng Dir-Exit Strategy
Advisors)
Rick Buchoz (Mng Dir-Exit Strategy Advi-
sors)
Carl Doerksen (Dir-Corp Dev)
Jay Hellwig (VP-Corp Rels)
Jessica Mead (Dir-Buyer Svcs)
Stephen Crisham (Mng Dir-Mergers & Acq)
James Carr (Sr Mng Dir-Exit Strategy Advi-
sors)
Roger Dean (Sr Mng Dir-Exit Strategy Advi-
sors)
Mark Fuhrer (Mng Dir-Exit Strategy Advi-
sors)
Gerry Gacek (Sr Mng Dir-Exit Strategy Ad-
visors)
Thomas Hamm (Sr Mng Dir-Exit Strategy
Advisors)
Brian Hendershot (Sr Mng Dir-Exit Strategy
Advisors)
Randy Kamin (Exec Mng Dir-Exit Strategy
Advisors)
Bill Kaushnir (Exec Mng Dir-Exit Strategy
Advisors)
Michael Lorence (Sr Mng Dir-Exit Strategy
Advisors)
Doug Morrow (Sr Mng Dir-Exit Strategy Ad-
visors)
Everett Poe (Sr Mng Dir-Exit Strategy Advi-
sors)
Terry Stidham (Sr Mng Dir-Exit Strategy Ad-
visors)
Michael Sullivan (Sr Mng Dir-Exit Strategy
Advisors)
Joe Van Voorhis (Sr Mng Dir-Exit Strategy
Advisors)
Edward Weber (Exec Mng Dir-Exit Strategy
Advisors)
Glenn Wenzel (Sr Mng Dir-Exit Strategy
Advisors)

**GENERATIONS FAMILY
HEALTH CENTER, INC.**
40 Mansfield Ave, Willimantic, CT
06226-1948
Tel.: (860) 450-7471   CT
Web Site: https://www.genhealth.org
Year Founded: 1991
Sales Range: $10-24.9 Million
Emp.: 201
Family Health Care Services
N.A.I.C.S.: 624190
Arvind Shaw (CEO)
Debra Daviau Savoie (CFO)
Jenelle Frappier (Dir-Patient Rev-
enue)
Melissa Bonsall (COO)
Natalie Haarala (Dir-Dental Ops)
Susan Beauregard (Dir-Fin Ops)
Beth Ober (Vice Chm)
John Schwenk (Sec)
Lynne Ide (Chm)
Jennifer Mendes Hramiak (Chief Be-
havioral Health Officer)
Morton Glasser (Chief Medical Offi-
cer)
Danielle DiGeronimo (Chief Quality
Officer)

GENESAR INC.
2800 Baltimore Ave, Ocean City, MD
21842
Tel.: (410) 289-1100
Web Site:
   https://www.dunesmanor.com
Sales Range: $10-24.9 Million

Emp.: 105
Owner & Operator of Hotels & Motels
N.A.I.C.S.: 721110
Kyle Johnson *(Gen Mgr)*

GENESEE CERAMIC TILE DISTRIBUTORS

1307 N Belsay Rd, Burton, MI 48509
Tel.: (810) 742-4611　　　　　MI
Web Site: http://www.genesee.com
Year Founded: 1973
Rev.: $13,236,240
Emp.: 18
Ceramic Tiles Distr
N.A.I.C.S.: 423320
James C. Cokley *(Pres)*
Linda Lick *(Controller)*

GENESEE CUT STONE & MARBLE CO.

5276 S Saginaw Rd, Grand Blanc, MI 48507
Tel.: (810) 743-1800　　　　　MI
Web Site: https://www.gcsm.com
Year Founded: 1954
Sales Range: $10-24.9 Million
Emp.: 45
Provider of Masonry Materials & Supplies
N.A.I.C.S.: 444180
David K. Stites *(Co-Partner)*
Eva Hemple *(CFO)*
John Peters *(Engr)*
Bob Paul *(Partner)*

GENESEE GROUP, INC.

1470 Ave Grand, Grand Prairie, TX 75050
Tel.: (972) 623-2004
Web Site:
　　http://www.geneseegroup.com
Rev.: $23,676,524
Emp.: 65
Metal Stamping Services
N.A.I.C.S.: 332119

Subsidiaries:

Genesee A & B, Inc.　　　　　**(1)**
8111 Eastgate Blvd, Mount Juliet, TN 37122
Tel.: (615) 547-0330
Sales Range: $10-24.9 Million
Emp.: 40
Mfr of Metal Stamps
N.A.I.C.S.: 333514
Bruce Ball *(Mgr-Acctg)*
Dan Ferguson *(Owner)*

Genesee Global Group, Inc.　　**(1)**
975 John St W, West Henrietta, NY 14586-9780
Tel.: (585) 475-0450
Web Site: http://www.geneseeglobal.com
Sales Range: $10-24.9 Million
Emp.: 60
Metal Stamping
N.A.I.C.S.: 332119
Jeff Dibble *(VP & Gen Mgr)*

Genesee Stamping & Fabricating, Inc.　　　　　　　　　　　**(1)**
1470 Ave T, Grand Prairie, TX 75050-1222
Tel.: (972) 623-2004
Web Site: http://www.geneseegroup.com
Sales Range: $10-24.9 Million
Fabrication of Metal Products
N.A.I.C.S.: 332322

GENESEE PACKAGING INC.

2010 N Dort Hwy, Flint, MI 48506
Tel.: (810) 235-6120
Web Site:
　　http://www.genpackaging.com
Rev.: $23,131,977
Emp.: 100
Packaging & Labeling Services
N.A.I.C.S.: 561910
Jane Worthing *(COO)*

GENESIS ATC

600 N Loop 1604 E, San Antonio, TX 78232
Tel.: (210) 489-6600
Web Site: http://www.genesisatc.com
Year Founded: 2008
Sales Range: $800-899.9 Million
Emp.: 500
Industrial Equipment Mfr
N.A.I.C.S.: 333998
Angela Miller *(Dir-Human Resources)*

GENESIS BIOTECHNOLOGY GROUP, LLC

1000 Waterview Dr, Hamilton, NJ 08691
Web Site:
　　http://www.genesisbiotechgroup.com
Holding Company; Biotechnology Research
N.A.I.C.S.: 551112
Eli Mordechai *(Founder & CEO)*
Martin E. Adelson *(COO)*
Ben Bandaru *(Dir-Corp Dev)*
Joseph Donovan *(CFO)*
Mark A. Lieberman *(Gen Counsel)*
Janet Cohen *(CIO)*
Christin Knox *(Dir-HR)*
Stephanie S. Thompson *(Dir-Mktg)*
Olesia Buiakova *(Chief Scientific Officer-Genesis Drug Discovery & Development)*

Subsidiaries:

Genesis Drug Discovery & Development LLC　　　　　　　　　**(1)**
1000 Waterview Dr, Hamilton, NJ 08691
Tel.: (844) 272-8234
Clinical Support Services
N.A.I.C.S.: 325412
Eli Mordechai *(CEO)*

Holding (Domestic):

BioBlocks, Inc.　　　　　　　**(2)**
9885 Mesa Rim Rd Ste 101, San Diego, CA 92121
Tel.: (858) 558-5900
Web Site: http://www.bioblocks.com
Drug Discovery Services
N.A.I.C.S.: 325412
Peter Pallai *(Founder, Pres & CEO)*
Warren Wade *(Dir-Medicinal Chemistry)*

Subsidiary (Non-US):

JSS Medical Research, Inc.　　**(2)**
9400 Henri-Bourassa Boulevard West Saint-Laurent, Montréal, H4S 1N8, QC, Canada
Tel.: (514) 934-6116
Web Site: http://www.jssresearch.com
Contract Medical Research & Development Services
N.A.I.C.S.: 541715
John S. Sampalis *(CEO & Officer-Scientific)*
Stella Boukas *(COO)*
Emmanouil Rampakakis *(Exec VP)*
Louise Bussieres *(Pres & CFO)*
Peter Heessel *(VP)*
Renu Razdan *(VP)*

Holding (Domestic):

STATKING Consulting, Inc.　　**(2)**
759 Wessel Dr Ste 6, Fairfield, OH 45014
Tel.: (513) 858-2989
Web Site: http://www.statkingconsulting.com
Drugs & Druggists' Sundries Merchant Whslr
N.A.I.C.S.: 424210
Dennis W. King *(Pres & CEO)*

PharmOptima, LLC　　　　　**(1)**
6710 Quality Way, Portage, MI 49002
Tel.: (269) 329-4370
Web Site: http://www.pharmoptima.com
Sales Range: $1-9.9 Million
Emp.: 22
Research & Development in Biotechnology
N.A.I.C.S.: 541714
Douglas E. Decker *(VP & Dir-Biochemistry & Cell Biology)*

Steven J. Weber *(Pres & CEO)*
Joseph A. Peters *(CFO & VP)*
Roger A. Poorman *(Chief Scientific Officer & VP)*

GENESIS CONSULTING PARTNERS, LLC

5207 Hickory Park Dr Ste E, Glen Allen, VA 23059
Tel.: (804) 523-8007
Web Site:
　　http://www.genesisconsulting.com
Year Founded: 2008
Sales Range: $10-24.9 Million
Emp.: 50
Management Consulting Services
N.A.I.C.S.: 541618
Jason Fair *(CEO)*
Nick Coticchia *(COO)*
Cameron Chaplin *(VP-Bus Ops)*

GENESIS CORP.

950 3rd Ave 26th Fl, New York, NY 10022
Tel.: (212) 688-5522
Web Site:
　　https://www.genesis10.com
Sales Range: $100-124.9 Million
Emp.: 100
Computer Related Consulting Services
N.A.I.C.S.: 541512
Harley Lippman *(Founder & CEO)*
Glenn Klyne *(CFO)*
Janet-Lee Hatt *(Mng Dir)*
Colleen McIntyre *(Mng Dir-Central Texas)*

Subsidiaries:

Infinity Info Systems Corp.　　**(1)**
535 Eighth Ave 17th Fl, New York, NY 10018
Tel.: (212) 563-4400
Web Site: http://www.infinityinfo.com
Sales Range: $10-24.9 Million
Emp.: 83
Client Centric Solutions Specialist in Customer Relationship Management (CRM) & Business Analytics
N.A.I.C.S.: 541611
Harley Lippman *(CEO)*
Lynn Henderson *(COO)*
Yacov Wrocherinsky *(Founder & Pres)*

GENESIS GROUP INC.

2507 Callaway Rd Ste 100, Tallahassee, FL 32303
Tel.: (850) 224-4400
Web Site:
　　http://www.genesisgroup.com
Year Founded: 1987
Sales Range: $1-9.9 Million
Emp.: 35
Engineeering Services
N.A.I.C.S.: 541330
Mark T. Llewellyn *(Pres)*
Bruce Kaschyk *(Sr VP)*

GENESIS HEALTH, INC.

3599 University Blvd S Ste 1000, Jacksonville, FL 32216-4252
Tel.: (904) 345-7235
Web Site:
　　http://www.brookshealth.org
Year Founded: 1970
Holding Company; Medical Rehabilitation, Home Health Care & Other Care Services
N.A.I.C.S.: 551112
Douglas M. Baer *(Pres & CEO)*

Subsidiaries:

Genesis Rehabilitation Hospital, Inc.　　　　　　　　　　　**(1)**
3599 University Blvd S, Jacksonville, FL 32216
Tel.: (904) 345-7600
Web Site: http://www.brooksrehab.org

Physical Rehabilitation Services
N.A.I.C.S.: 623210
Douglas M. Baer *(CEO)*
Bruce M. Johnson *(Chm)*
Michael Spigel *(Pres & COO)*
Howard C. Serkin *(Vice Chm)*
Kerry Maher *(VP-Physical Medicine, Rehabilitation Consulting & Physician Rels)*
Kathy Barbour *(VP-Mktg Comm)*

GENESIS HEALTHCARE SYSTEM

2951 Maple Ave, Zanesville, OH 43701-2882
Tel.: (740) 454-4000　　　　　OH
Web Site:
　　https://www.genesishcs.org
Year Founded: 1997
Sales Range: Less than $1 Million
Emp.: 3,000
Non-Profit Hospital Operator & Specialized Health Care Services
N.A.I.C.S.: 813212
Matt Perry *(Pres)*
Sharon Parker *(COO-Hospital Ops)*

Subsidiaries:

Genesis CareGivers　　　　　**(1)**
2503 Maple Ave, Zanesville, OH 43701-1833
Tel.: (740) 454-1370
Web Site: http://www.genesishcs.org
Non-Profit Home Health Care Services
N.A.I.C.S.: 813212

Northside Oxygen & Medical Equipment　　　　　　　　　**(1)**
702 Wabash Ave, Zanesville, OH 43701
Tel.: (740) 453-0693
Web Site: http://www.northsideoxygen.com
Medical & Respiratory Equipment Distr
N.A.I.C.S.: 423450
Martin Jones *(Pres & Mgr)*

GENESIS NETWORKS ENTERPRISES, LLC

600 N Loop 1604 E, San Antonio, TX 78232
Tel.: (210) 489-6600
Web Site: http://www.genesisnet.com
Sales Range: $400-449.9 Million
Emp.: 700
Communications Network, IT & Supply Chain Solutions
N.A.I.C.S.: 513210
James Goodman *(CEO)*
Sean Nelson *(Pres-Corp Div)*

Subsidiaries:

Austin Tele-Services Partners, L.P.　　　　　　　　　　　**(1)**
4209 S Industrial Dr Ste 300, Austin, TX 78744
Tel.: (512) 329-8799
Web Site: http://www.genesis-ats.com
Sales Range: $25-49.9 Million
Emp.: 35
Telecommunications Equipment & Services
N.A.I.C.S.: 517810
Charles J. Roesslein *(CEO)*
Kirk Miller *(CEO)*

GENESIS PARK, LP

2000 Edwards St Ste B, Houston, TX 77007
Tel.: (713) 489-4650
Web Site: https://www.genesis-park.com
Year Founded: 1999
Privater Equity Firm
N.A.I.C.S.: 523999
Peter T. Shaper *(Partner)*
Steve Gibson *(Partner)*
Cathy Leeson *(CFO)*
Christy Hartman *(Principal)*
Parel Patel *(Principal)*
Christina Smith *(Principal)*
Jonathan E. Baliff *(Operating Partner)*
Paul William Hobby *(Founder & Mng Partner)*

Genesis Park, LP—(Continued)

GENESIS PRODUCTS, INC.
2608 Almac Ct, Elkhart, IN 46514
Tel.: (574) 266-8292
Web Site:
https://www.genesisproductsinc.com
Year Founded: 2002
Sales Range: $50-74.9 Million
Emp.: 230
Wood Component Supplier & Mfr
N.A.I.C.S.: 337212
Jonathan Wenger (CEO)
Bo Ledbetter (Engr-Maintenance)

GENESIS TECHNOLOGIES, INC.
2942 Macarthur Blvd, Northbrook, IL 60062-2005
Tel.: (847) 498-0606
Web Site: http://www.gentechol.com
Year Founded: 1991
Sales Range: $10-24.9 Million
Emp.: 54
Computer Equipment & Software Whslr
N.A.I.C.S.: 423430
Michael J. Kahn (Pres & CEO)

GENESIS TODAY INC.
6800 Burleson Rd Bldg 310 Ste 180, Austin, TX 78744
Tel.: (512) 858-1977
Web Site:
http://www.genesistoday.com
Year Founded: 2001
Sales Range: $50-74.9 Million
Emp.: 40
Nutritional Food & Drink Supplements
N.A.I.C.S.: 456191
Darcy Ramey (Mgr-Field & Retail Sls)
William R. Meissner (CEO)
Drew Lamprich (Dir-Sales)
Jeff Brucker (VP-Mktg)

GENESIS TRANSPORTATION INC.
300 Lionville Station Rd, Chester Springs, PA 19425-9601
Tel.: (484) 713-1500
Web Site:
http://www.genesistrans.net
Year Founded: 1997
Sales Range: $10-24.9 Million
Emp.: 400
Local Trucking Services
N.A.I.C.S.: 484110
Jack Williams (COO)

GENESIS VII INC.
1605 White Dr, Titusville, FL 32780
Tel.: (321) 383-4813
Web Site: https://www.genesisvii.com
Sales Range: $10-24.9 Million
Emp.: 8
Industrial Supplies
N.A.I.C.S.: 423840
Robert Jordan (Pres)

GENEST CONCRETE WORKS INC.
36 Wilson St, Sanford, ME 04073
Tel.: (207) 324-3250
Web Site: https://www.genest-concrete.com
Rev.: $12,000,000
Emp.: 76
Ready Mixed Concrete
N.A.I.C.S.: 327331
Michael R. Genest (Pres)
David Genest (VP)
Mike Parker (Controller)

GENESYSWORKS
14400 Memorial Dr Ste 200, Houston, TX 77079

Tel.: (713) 337-0522   TX
Web Site:
http://www.genesysworks.org
Year Founded: 2001
Sales Range: $1-9.9 Million
Emp.: 19
Education & Development Services
N.A.I.C.S.: 611430

GENET PROPERTY GROUP, INC.
5701 N Pine Island Rd Ste 370, Tamarac, FL 33321
Tel.: (954) 572-9159
Web Site:
http://www.genetgroup.com
Year Founded: 2001
Sales Range: $10-24.9 Million
Emp.: 11
Commercial Property Leasing & Management
N.A.I.C.S.: 531120
Ben Genet (Pres)
Ivonne Lindao (Mgr-Property)
Joan Richards (Controller)

GENEVA CORPORATION
300 N Greene St Ste 2100, Greensboro, NC 27401-2181
Tel.: (336) 275-9936   NC
Year Founded: 1979
Sales Range: $125-149.9 Million
Emp.: 3
Distr of Diesel Engines & Generators
N.A.I.C.S.: 423830
F. James Becher Jr. (Chm, Pres & CEO)
Ronald Stanler Jr. (VP & CFO)

Subsidiaries:

Nixon Power Services Company   (1)
5038 Thoroughbred Ln, Brentwood, TN 37027
Tel.: (615) 309-5823
Web Site: http://www.nixonpower.com
Power Generator Distr
N.A.I.C.S.: 423610
Ron Stanley (CEO)

Subsidiary (Domestic):

Nixon Energy Solutions   (2)
14300 S Lakes Dr, Charlotte, NC 28273
Tel.: (704) 588-1043
Web Site: http://www.nixonenergy.com
Industrial Equipment Distr
N.A.I.C.S.: 423830
Pat Jolley (Dir-Sls-NC & SC)

GENEVA INTERNATIONAL CORPORATION
200 Larkin Dr Ste F, Wheeling, IL 60090-6498
Tel.: (847) 520-9970
Rev.: $18,364,130
Emp.: 37
Piano Distr
N.A.I.C.S.: 459140
Ken Young (Controller)

GENEVA MANAGEMENT INC.
1100 S Glebe Rd, Arlington, VA 22204-4309
Tel.: (703) 553-4300   VA
Year Founded: 1954
Sales Range: $50-74.9 Million
Emp.: 20
Retail Sales of New & Used Automobiles
N.A.I.C.S.: 561110
Robert M. Rosenthal (Chm)
Donald B. Baverly (Pres)
Tony Estrella (Pres-Adv)

GENEVA SUPPLY, INC.
1501 E Wisconsin St, Delavan, WI 53115
Tel.: (262) 435-4935

Web Site:
http://www.genevasupply.com
Year Founded: 2009
Brand Strategy, Digital Marketing Services & Supply Chain Solutions
N.A.I.C.S.: 541613
Jeff Peterson (Co-Founder & CEO)

Subsidiaries:

Cascio Music Company Inc.   (1)
13819 W National Ave, New Berlin, WI 53151
Tel.: (262) 786-6249
Web Site: http://www.interstatemusic.com
Musical Instruments
N.A.I.C.S.: 423990
Elwood Winn (CFO)
Michael Houser (CEO)

GENEVA WATCH GROUP
1407 Broadway Ste 400, New York, NY 10018
Tel.: (718) 729-8600   MI
Web Site:
http://www.genevawatchgroup.com
Year Founded: 1974
Sales Range: $10-24.9 Million
Emp.: 200
Watches, Clocks, Watchcases & Parts Marketer
N.A.I.C.S.: 334519
Amanda Bitetto (Sr VP-Sales)

GENEVA WORLDWIDE, INC.
261 W 35th St Ste 700, New York, NY 10001
Tel.: (212) 255-8400
Web Site:
http://www.genevaworldwide.com
Year Founded: 1903
Sales Range: $1-9.9 Million
Emp.: 30
Translation Services
N.A.I.C.S.: 541930
Joel Buckstein (Pres)
Lisa Bukowski (Supvr)

GENEVE HOLDINGS CORP.
96 Cummings Point Rd, Stamford, CT 06902
Tel.: (203) 358-8000
Sales Range: $150-199.9 Million
Emp.: 40
Holding Company
N.A.I.C.S.: 551112

Subsidiaries:

Cummings Point Investors Corp   (1)
96 Cummings Point Rd, Stamford, CT 06902
Sales Range: $25-49.9 Million
Fraternal Life Insurance Organization
N.A.I.C.S.: 524113

Geneve Corporation   (1)
96 Cummings Point Rd, Stamford, CT 06902-7912
Tel.: (203) 358-8000
Web Site:
http://www.independenceholding.com
Sales Range: $50-74.9 Million
Emp.: 34
Private Holding Company
N.A.I.C.S.: 551112
Brian R. Schlier (Sr VP-Taxation)

Subsidiary (Domestic):

Geneve Capital Group Inc.   (2)
96 Cummings Point Rd, Stamford, CT 06902-7912
Tel.: (203) 358-8000
Web Site: http://www.ihcgroup.com
Sales Range: $50-74.9 Million
Emp.: 30
Insurance
N.A.I.C.S.: 524210
Steven B. Lapin (Pres & CEO)

Independence Holding Company   (2)
96 Cummings Point Rd, Stamford, CT 06902-7919   (62.3%)

Tel.: (203) 358-8000
Web Site: https://www.ihcgroup.com
Rev.: $443,864,000
Assets: $1,083,156,000
Liabilities: $613,350,000
Net Worth: $469,806,000
Earnings: $18,881,000
Emp.: 550
Fiscal Year-end: 12/31/2020
Holding Company; Financial & Insurance Services
N.A.I.C.S.: 551112
Steven B. Lapin (Bd of Dirs & Vice Chm)
Roy T. K. Thung (Chm & CEO)
Teresa A. Herbert (Pres)
Colleen P. Maggi (CFO & VP)

Subsidiary (Domestic):

Madison National Life Insurance Co., Inc.   (3)
1241 John Q Hammons Dr, Madison, WI 53717   (100%)
Tel.: (608) 830-2000
Web Site: http://www.madisonlife.com
Sales Range: $1-9.9 Million
Emp.: 93
Life Credit & Group Insurance Services
N.A.I.C.S.: 524113
Robert Stubbe (Exec VP)
Daryl Zee (Sr VP)

Subsidiary (Domestic):

American Independence Corp.   (4)
485 Madison Ave, New York, NY 10022   (100%)
Tel.: (212) 355-4141
Web Site:
http://www.americanindependencecorp.com
Rev.: $183,266,000
Assets: $196,974,000
Liabilities: $89,776,000
Net Worth: $107,198,000
Earnings: $3,815,000
Emp.: 268
Fiscal Year-end: 12/31/2015
Insurance Holding Company Engaged in the Health Insurance & Reinsurance Business; owned 48% by Independence Holding Company
N.A.I.C.S.: 551112
Roy T. K. Thung (CEO)
Dave Keeler (Pres & COO)

IHC Financial Group, Inc.   (4)
3508 Far W Blvd Ste 360, Austin, TX 78731
Tel.: (512) 346-4610
Web Site: http://www.ihcfinancial.com
Insurance Brokerage Services
N.A.I.C.S.: 524210
Mark Saccomanno (Asst Dir-Agencies)
Val Majewski (VP-Sls & Mktg)

Subsidiary (Domestic):

Standard Security Life Insurance Company of New York   (3)
485 Madison Ave, New York, NY 10022-5872
Tel.: (212) 355-4141
Web Site: http://www.sslicny.com
Sales Range: $250-299.9 Million
Emp.: 350
Insurance Services
N.A.I.C.S.: 524113
Gary J. Balzofiore (Pres)

Subsidiary (Domestic):

Health Plan Administrators, Inc.   (4)
3703 N Main St, Rockford, IL 61103-1679
Tel.: (815) 633-5800
Health Insurance Services
N.A.I.C.S.: 524114

IHC Administrative Services, Inc.   (4)
2101 W Peoria Ave Ste 100, Phoenix, AZ 85029
Tel.: (602) 870-1400
Insurance Brokerage Services
N.A.I.C.S.: 524210

Subsidiary (Domestic):

Insurers Administrative Corporation   (5)
PO Box 39119, Phoenix, AZ 85069
Tel.: (602) 395-7095
Web Site: http://www.iacusa.com

Sales Range: $125-149.9 Million
Emp.: 300
Medical Insurance Claim Processing Services
N.A.I.C.S.: 524292
Michael K. Brown *(VP-Underwriting)*
Brad Waldrop *(VP-Sls)*

Subsidiary (Domestic):

Majestic Underwriters LLC (4)
550 Stephens Hwy Ste 407, Troy, MI 48083
Tel.: (248) 583-4488
Sales Range: Less than $1 Million
Emp.: 14
Healthcare Reinsurance Underwriting Services
N.A.I.C.S.: 524298

Standard Security Investors
Corporation (4)
485 Madison Ave Fl 14, New York, NY 10022
Tel.: (212) 355-4141
Investment Management Service
N.A.I.C.S.: 523150

Subsidiary (Domestic):

The Aristotle Corporation (2)
96 Cummings Point Rd, Stamford, CT 06902 (90%)
Tel.: (203) 358-8000
Web Site: http://www.aristotlecorp.net
Sales Range: $200-249.9 Million
Mfr & Distr Educational, Health, Medical Technology & Agricultural Products
N.A.I.C.S.: 339112
Brian R. Schlier *(VP-Taxation)*
H. William Smith *(Gen Counsel, Sec & VP)*
Dean T. Johnson *(CFO & Sr VP)*
W. Phillip Niemeyer *(Pres-Nasco Div)*
Todd Weisbrod *(Treas)*

Subsidiary (Domestic):

American Educational Products
LLC (3)
401 W Hickory St, Fort Collins, CO 80522
Tel.: (970) 484-7445
Web Site: http://www.amep.com
Sales Range: $10-24.9 Million
Emp.: 35
Educational Products Mfr
N.A.I.C.S.: 611710
Michael Warring *(Pres)*
Candace Coffman *(Mgr-Natl Sls & Mktg)*
Danelle Maestas *(Mgr-Sls)*
Barbara Gipple *(Mgr-Sls & Mktg-Natl)*

Division (Domestic):

Hubbard Scientific (4)
1120 Halbleib Rd, Chippewa Falls, WI 54729
Tel.: (715) 723-4427
Web Site: http://www.hubbardscientific.com
Mfr & Marketer Educational Products
N.A.I.C.S.: 339999

Scott Resources (4)
401 Hickory St, Fort Collins, CO 80522
Tel.: (970) 484-7445
Web Site: http://www.amep.com
Mfr & Marketer of Educational Products
N.A.I.C.S.: 512110
Candy Coffman *(Mgr-Sls & Mktg)*

Subsidiary (Domestic):

Nasco International, Inc. (3)
901 Janesville Ave, Fort Atkinson, WI 53538-2402
Tel.: (920) 563-2446
Web Site: http://www.enasco.com
Sales Range: $50-74.9 Million
Emp.: 500
Agricultural, Home Economics & Educational Supplies Mfr
N.A.I.C.S.: 423820
Jack Marshall *(Dir-Pur)*
Bob Elliott *(Dir-Modesto)*
Barbara George *(Dir-Fort Atkinson)*
Chuck Miller *(Dir-Fort Atkinson)*
Jim Felt *(Dir-Modesto)*
Jim Romenesko *(Dir-Fort Atkinson)*
Kris Bakke *(Dir-Fort Atkinson)*
Kelly Jacobson *(Dir-Educational Sls)*
Connie Kolander *(Dir-Educational Sls)*
Rhonda Hutchison *(Dir-Fort Atkinson)*

Rhonda Rigney *(Dir-Modesto)*
Tim Taggart *(Dir-Fort Atkinson)*
Wendy Lucht *(Dir-Fort Atkinson)*
Dixie Behlke *(Dir-Mathematics Sls)*

Subsidiary (Domestic):

Nasco Modesto (4)
4825 Stoddard Rd, Modesto, CA 95356-9318
Tel.: (209) 545-1600
Web Site: http://www.enasco.com
Sales Range: $1-9.9 Million
Educational Products for Various Organizations
N.A.I.C.S.: 611710
Tom Hudson *(Controller)*

Honor Capital Corp. (1)
96 Cummings Pt Rd, Stamford, CT 06902
Tel.: (203) 358-8000
Sales Range: $25-49.9 Million
Life Insurance
N.A.I.C.S.: 524113
Teresa A. Herbert *(Treas)*
Stephen Lapin *(Pres & Dir)*
Roy T. K. Thung *(VP & Dir)*

GENGHIS GRILL
18900 Dallas Pkwy Ste 125, Dallas, TX 75287
Tel.: (214) 774-4240
Web Site:
http://www.genghisgrill.com
Year Founded: 1998
Rev.: $29,500,000
Emp.: 500
Full-Service Restaurants
N.A.I.C.S.: 722511
Al Bhakta *(CEO)*

GENGRAS MOTOR CARS, INC.
300 Connecticut Blvd, East Hartford, CT 06108
Tel.: (860) 289-3461
Web Site: http://www.gengras.com
Year Founded: 1985
Sales Range: $10-24.9 Million
Emp.: 50
Car Whslr
N.A.I.C.S.: 441110
E. Clayton Gengras Jr. *(Owner)*

GENIANT, LLC
1651 N Collins Blvd Ste 150, Richardson, TX 75080
Tel.: (972) 383-2600
Web Site: http://www.geniant.com
Rev.: $4,000,000
Emp.: 30
Computer System Design Services
N.A.I.C.S.: 541512
David A. Lancashire *(Chm & Co-CEO)*
Keith Jacobs *(Co-CEO)*

Subsidiaries:

Eastlake Studio Inc. (1)
435 N Michigan Ave, Chicago, IL 60611
Tel.: (312) 527-0200
Web Site: http://www.eastlakestudio.com
Sales Range: $10-24.9 Million
Emp.: 10
Architectural Services
N.A.I.C.S.: 541310
Tom Zurowski *(Mng Principal)*
Carla Arroyo-Guerrero *(Coord-Technical)*
Mia DiMeo *(Coord-Mktg)*
Christina Brown *(Principal)*
Jon Salzmann *(Principal)*
Kevin Kamien *(Principal)*

GENICA CORPORATION
1890 Ord Way, Oceanside, CA 92056
Tel.: (760) 726-7700
Web Site: http://www.genica.com
Rev.: $113,065,863
Emp.: 2
Computer Peripheral Equipment
N.A.I.C.S.: 423430

Frank Segler *(Founder, Chm & CEO)*
Scott Kusel *(Pres & CEO)*
Patrick Thompson *(Sec & Controller)*
Geoff Hildebrandt *(CFO)*

GENIE ELECTRONICS COMPANY
1087 Valley View Rd, York, PA 17406
Tel.: (717) 840-6999
Web Site:
https://www.genieelectronics.com
Year Founded: 1972
Sales Range: $10-24.9 Million
Emp.: 50
Electronic Circuit Boards
N.A.I.C.S.: 334412
B. Robert Snyder *(Pres)*

GENIE GATEWAY
4570 S Eastern Ave Ste 26-221, Las Vegas, NV 89119
Web Site: http://www.ggwy.info
Rev.: $803,583
Assets: $1,058,504
Liabilities: $235,504
Net Worth: $823,000
Earnings: $33,991
Emp.: 6
Fiscal Year-end: 12/31/15
Telecommunication Servicesb
N.A.I.C.S.: 517810
Thomas E. Skala *(Pres & CEO)*

GENIS PRODUCTIONS, INC.
10727 Riverside Dr, Toluca Lake, CA 91602
Tel.: (818) 762-3911
Web Site:
http://www.eventmakers.com
Year Founded: 1990
Sales Range: $10-24.9 Million
Emp.: 6
Live Events, Trade Show Booth Design & Fabrication, Convention Logistics, Business Theater & Destination Management Marketing Services
N.A.I.C.S.: 541890
Guy Genis *(Founder & CEO)*
Mark Genis *(CFO & VP)*
Craig Weida *(Gen Mgr)*
Jessica Peterson *(Dir-Event)*

GENISYS CONTROLS, LLC
5757 Farinon Dr, San Antonio, TX 78249
Tel.: (210) 495-9772 DE
Web Site:
https://www.genisyscontrols.com
Holding Company; Investment Services
N.A.I.C.S.: 551112

Subsidiaries:

EControls Group, Inc. (1)
3523 Crosspoint, San Antonio, TX 78217
Tel.: (210) 495-9772
Web Site: http://www.econtrols.com
Sales Range: $1-9.9 Million
Emp.: 35
Motor Vehicle Parts And Accessories
N.A.I.C.S.: 336390
Stephen D. Ott *(Mgr-CNC)*
Victor Martinez *(Engr-Test)*
Albert Cottle *(Mgr-Production)*
Kennon H. Guglielmo *(Pres)*

Subsidiary (Domestic):

IMPCO Technologies, Inc. (2)
3030 S Susan St, Santa Ana, CA 92704-6435
Tel.: (714) 656-1200
Web Site:
http://www.impcotechnologies.com
Alternative Gaseous Fuel Systems Technologies & Components Designer & Mfr
N.A.I.C.S.: 333618
Nikhil Shaligram *(Mgr)*

Subsidiary (Non-US):

IMPCO Technologies (Japan) Co, Ltd. (3)
4-3-9 Morooka, Hakata-Ku, Fukuoka, 816-0094, Fukuoka, Japan
Tel.: (81) 925927270
Web Site: http://www.impco.co.jp
Alternative Fuel System Components Mfr
N.A.I.C.S.: 333618

IMPCO Technologies B.V. (3)
Distributieweg 9, Delfgauw, 2645 EG, Netherlands
Tel.: (31) 152742550
Web Site: http://www.impco.eu
Industrial Fuel Systems & Engine
N.A.I.C.S.: 332420

GENISYS CREDIT UNION
2100 Executive Hills Blvd, Auburn Hills, MI 48326
Tel.: (248) 322-9800 MI
Web Site: https://www.genisyscu.org
Year Founded: 1953
Sales Range: $50-74.9 Million
Emp.: 382
Financial Management Services
N.A.I.C.S.: 522130
Gerald Strausbaugh *(CFO & Sr VP)*
Jacqueline Buchanan *(Pres & CEO)*
Brian Zabowski *(Vice Chm)*
David Stolk *(Treas)*
Patrick Shaffer *(Chm)*
Gregory Melega *(Sec)*
Jim Fagan *(VP-Real Estate Lending)*

GENISYS GROUP INC.
256 Seaboard Ln Ste B 101, Franklin, TN 37067
Tel.: (615) 591-4015
Web Site:
http://www.genisysgroup.com
Sales Range: $25-49.9 Million
Emp.: 17
Computer & Software Stores
N.A.I.C.S.: 449210
Clyde Cutrer *(Owner & CEO)*
Amy Levy *(VP-Ops)*

GENIUS JONES INC.
2800 NE 2nd Ave, Miami, FL 33137
Tel.: (305) 571-2000
Web Site:
http://www.geniusjones.com
Year Founded: 2002
Sales Range: $1-9.9 Million
Emp.: 5
Computer Peripheral Equipment & Software Merchant Whslrs
N.A.I.C.S.: 423430
Daniel Kron *(Founder)*

GENIUS.COM, INCORPORATED
1400 Fashion Island Blvd Ste 510, San Mateo, CA 94404
Tel.: (650) 212-2050
Web Site: http://www.genius.com
Year Founded: 2004
Sales Range: $1-9.9 Million
Emp.: 61
Computer Software
N.A.I.C.S.: 513210
Yina Mersy *(Mgr-Fin)*
Sam Weber *(CEO)*
Rick Gustafson *(CFO)*
Matt West *(Sr Dir-Mktg)*
Omer Saeed *(Dir-Product & Svcs)*
Even Walser *(Dir-Corp Sls)*
Rajeev Dave *(Dir-Engrg)*
Dave Hunsinger *(Dir-Technical Ops)*

Subsidiaries:

Genius.com UK (1)
Stanley House The Boulevard Clarence Dock, Leeds, LS10 1PZ, United Kingdom
Tel.: (44) 845 680 5409
Web Site: http://www.genius.com

Genius.com, Incorporated—(Continued)

Software Publisher
N.A.I.C.S.: 513210
Mark Donkin (Mng Dir)

GENLABS
5568 Schaefer Ave, Chino, CA 91710
Tel.: (909) 591-8451
Web Site:
　　https://www.genlabscorp.com
Year Founded: 1973
Sales Range: $10-24.9 Million
Emp.: 150
Polishes & Sanitation Goods
N.A.I.C.S.: 325612
David D. Dobbins (Pres)
Bruce Gutterman (VP-Sls)
Leo Alon (Mgr-Quality Assurance)
Richard Balaban (VP-Contract Pkg)

GENNX360 CAPITAL PARTNERS, L.P.
200 Madison Ave Ste 2110, New York, NY 10016
Tel.: (212) 257-6772　　　　　DE
Web Site: http://www.gennx360.com
Year Founded: 2006
Privater Equity Firm
N.A.I.C.S.: 523999
Latasha M. Akoma (Operating Partner)
Lloyd G. Trotter (Co-Founder & Mng Partner)
Ronald E. Blaylock (Co-Founder & Mng Partner)
James Shepard (Co-Founder & Mng Partner)
Charles Castine (Mng Partner)
Daphne J. Dufresne (Mng Partner)
Monty Yort (Mng Partner)
Sumit Tony (CFO & Chief Compliance Officer)

Subsidiaries:

AeroRepair Corp.　　　　　　　　(1)
14 Tinker Ave, Londonderry, NH 03053
Tel.: (603) 657-7336
Web Site: http://www.aerorepaircorp.com
Emp.: 200
Aircraft Component Repair & Maintenance Services
N.A.I.C.S.: 811310
Alvin Sproul (COO)
Daniel M. Bell (CEO)
Harry Banks (CFO)
Paul Severin (Exec VP)

Division (Domestic):

AeroRepair　　　　　　　　　　(2)
902 S Pine Hill Rd, Griffin, GA 30224
Tel.: (678) 692-2001
Web Site: http://www.aogatlanta.com
Emp.: 19
Aircraft Accessory Overhaul & Repair Services
N.A.I.C.S.: 488190
Darrell Dotson (Coord-Repair Station)
Dran Crenshaw (Mgr)
Robbie Upchurch (Mgr-Battery)
Angie Haire (Mgr-Parts)

B2B Industrial Packaging, LLC　(1)
313 S Rohlwing Road, Addison, IL 60101
Tel.: (630) 396-6200
Web Site: http://www.b2bind.com
Packaging Equipment & Supplies Distr
N.A.I.C.S.: 423830
Bill Drake (CEO)

Subsidiary (Domestic):

Allen Packaging Co.　　　　　　(2)
1150 Valencia Ave, Tustin, CA 92780
Tel.: (714) 259-0100
Web Site: http://www.allenpkg.com
Rev.: $8,000,000
Emp.: 32
Paper, except Newsprint, Mills
N.A.I.C.S.: 322120

James Allen (CEO)
Cheryl Centonze (COO)
Scot Obler (Pres)

Rubin Industrial Co. Inc.　　　　(2)
3307 N 6th St, Harrisburg, PA 17110
Tel.: (717) 234-2409
Web Site:
　　http://www.lewisindustrialsupply.com
Sales Range: $10-24.9 Million
Emp.: 42
Holding Company; Safety Equipment & Supplies
N.A.I.C.S.: 551112
Berton L. Rubin (Pres)

CRS Temporary Housing　　　　(1)
10851 N Black Canyon Hwy Ste 700, Phoenix, AZ 85029
Tel.: (602) 943-3555
Web Site: http://www.crsth.com
Temporary Hosuing & Relocation Services
N.A.I.C.S.: 624221

GenServe Inc.　　　　　　　　　(1)
100 Newtown Rd, Plainview, NY 11803
Tel.: (800) 247-7215
Web Site: http://www.genserveinc.com
Industrial Generator Installation & Emergency & Contract Maintenance Services
N.A.I.C.S.: 811210
Joseph Flynn (CFO)
Michael Vahling (Pres & CEO)
Frank Gasparino (Branch Mgr-Fairfield,NJ)
Joe Voigt (Branch Mgr-Pennsauken,NJ)
Scott Bogart (Branch Mgr-Plainview,NY)

Subsidiary (Domestic):

Scan-Am Marine Services, Inc.　(2)
373 N River Dr, Deerfield Beach, FL 33441
Tel.: (954) 428-9990
Web Site: http://www.okgenerators.com
Sales Range: $1-9.9 Million
Emp.: 20
Electrical Apparatus & Equipment, Wiring Supplies & Related Equipment Merchant Whslr
N.A.I.C.S.: 423610

ITsavvy LLC　　　　　　　　　　(1)
313 S Rohlwing Rd, Addison, IL 60101
Tel.: (630) 396-6300
Web Site: https://www.itsavvy.com
Information Technology Consulting Services
N.A.I.C.S.: 519290
Munu Gandhi (CEO)

Subsidiary (Domestic):

INOC LLC　　　　　　　　　　　(2)
500 Skokie Blvd Ste 585, Northbrook, IL 60062
Tel.: (608) 663-4555
Web Site: http://www.inoc.com
Rev.: $2,737,000
Emp.: 17
Data Processing, Hosting & Related Services
N.A.I.C.S.: 518210
Prasad Ravi (CEO)
Prasad Rao (Pres & COO)

Miller Environmental Group, Inc.　(1)
538 Edwards Ave, Calverton, NY 11933
Tel.: (631) 369-4900
Web Site: http://www.millerenv.com
Oil Spill Cleanup & Groundwater Recovery Services
N.A.I.C.S.: 562910
Ronald E. Blaylock (Chm)
Jerry Coogan (COO)
Olga Longan (CFO)
Rudy Streng (CEO)
Jeff Dutzer (Chief Comml Officer)

Subsidiary (Domestic):

Environmental Products & Services of Vermont, Inc.　　　　　　　　　(2)
532 State Fair Blvd, Syracuse, NY 13204
Tel.: (315) 451-6666
Web Site: http://www.epsofvermont.com
Sales Range: $10-24.9 Million
Emp.: 125
Environmental Remediation Services
N.A.I.C.S.: 541620
Anthony M. Melfi (Pres)
Christopher D. Parzych (VP)

Nutra Med Packaging, Inc.　　　(1)

385 Franklin Ave Ste E, Rockaway, NJ 07866
Tel.: (973) 625-2274
Web Site: http://www.nutra-med.com
Sales Range: $1-9.9 Million
Emp.: 25
Packaging Service Specializing In Pharmaceuticals
N.A.I.C.S.: 561910
Mahesh Gupta (Pres)
Priteshkumar Patel (Supvr-Production)
Kunal Gupta (CEO)

Precision Aviation Group, Inc.　(1)
495 Lk Mirror Rd Bldg 800, Atlanta, GA 30349
Tel.: (404) 768-9090
Web Site:
　　http://www.precisionaviationgroup.com
Sales Range: $25-49.9 Million
Emp.: 42
Aircraft Repair & Maintenance Services
N.A.I.C.S.: 488190
David Mast (Pres & CEO)
Ketan Desai (VP-Sls & Mktg)
Chad Lemke (VP-Supply Chain-Global)
K. T. MacIntosh (CFO)

Subsidiary (Domestic):

Gardner Aviation Specialist, Inc.　(2)
500 Aviation Way B-5, Peachtree City, GA 30269
Tel.: (770) 486-6061
Web Site:
　　http://www.precisionaviationservices.com
Sales Range: $25-49.9 Million
Emp.: 19
Other Support Activities for Air Transportation
N.A.I.C.S.: 488190

Trace Aviation, Inc.　　　　　　(2)
Jackson Intl Airport Taxiway C7 116 S Hangar Dr, Jackson, MS 39208
Tel.: (601) 936-3599
Web Site: http://www.traceaviation.com
Other Airport Operations
N.A.I.C.S.: 488119
Mike Pigott (Pres)

Salford Group, Inc.　　　　　　(1)
925 Furnas Dr, Osceola, IA 50213-9690
Tel.: (519) 485-1293
Web Site: http://www.salfordgroup.com
Truck Trailer Mfr
N.A.I.C.S.: 336212

Subsea Global Solutions LLC　　(1)
12062 NW 27th Ave, Miami, FL 33167
Tel.: (305) 571-9700
Web Site:
　　http://www.subseaglobalsolutions.com
Underwater Ship Repair Services
N.A.I.C.S.: 336611
Rick Shilling (Exec VP-Technical Svcs)
Harun Duzgoren (Chief Comml Officer)
Paul Peters (CEO)
Douglas Hurst (Dir-Diving)
Elizabeth Tejeda (CFO)
Satnam Kumar (COO)

Subsidiary (Domestic):

Miami Diver LLC　　　　　　　　(2)
2994 N Miami Ave, Miami, FL 33127
Tel.: (305) 571-9700
Web Site: http://www.miamidiver.com
Sales Range: $1-9.9 Million
Emp.: 15
Commercial & Industrial Machinery & Equipment (except Automotive & Electronic) Repair & Maintenance
N.A.I.C.S.: 811310

Muldoon Marine Services, Inc.　(2)
1725 W Pier D St, Long Beach, CA 90802
Tel.: (562) 436-2701
Shipbuilding & Repairing
N.A.I.C.S.: 336611

Sea Sub Systems Inc.　　　　　(2)
10890 75 St N, Saint Petersburg, FL 33777-1424
Tel.: (727) 393-6114
Web Site: http://www.seasubsystems.com
All Other Support Services
N.A.I.C.S.: 561990
Dick N. Massari (Gen Mgr)

The Horsburgh & Scott Co.　　(1)

5114 Hamilton Ave, Cleveland, OH 44114-3985
Tel.: (216) 431-3900
Web Site: http://www.horsburgh-scott.com
Sales Range: $50-74.9 Million
Emp.: 200
Speed Changer, Industrial High-Speed Drive & Gear Mfr
N.A.I.C.S.: 333612
Lloyd G. Trotter (Chm)

Tooling Technology, LLC　　　　(1)
100 Enterprise Dr, Fort Loramie, OH 45845
Tel.: (937) 295-3672
Web Site: http://www.toolingtechgroup.com
Machined Tooling Services
N.A.I.C.S.: 333517
Anthony C. Seger (Founder)

Subsidiary (Domestic):

Majestic Industries Inc.　　　　(2)
15378 Hallmark Ct, Macomb, MI 48042
Tel.: (586) 786-9100
Web Site: http://www.majesticind.net
Sales Range: $1-9.9 Million
Special Die & Tool, Die Set, Jig & Fixture Mfr
N.A.I.C.S.: 333514

Trimaster Manufacturing, Inc.　(1)
95 Curtis Drive, Guelph, N1K 1E1, ON, Canada
Tel.: (519) 823-2661
Web Site: http://www.trimastermfg.com
Sales Range: $25-49.9 Million
Emp.: 170
Precision Component & Assembly Mfr
N.A.I.C.S.: 332999
Howard Singleton (CEO)

Vintage Parts, Inc.　　　　　　(1)
25011 W Ave Stanford Unit C, Valencia, CA 91355
Tel.: (818) 500-8778
Web Site: http://www.vintagepartsinc.com
Sales Range: $1-9.9 Million
Emp.: 100
Automotive Parts & Accessories Stores
N.A.I.C.S.: 441330

GENO LLC
45 1st Ave, Waltham, MA 02451
Tel.: (781) 466-6530　　　　DE
Web Site: http://www.genollc.com
Year Founded: 2006
Sales Range: Less than $1 Million
Emp.: 28
Biopharmaceutical Mfr
N.A.I.C.S.: 325414
Farzad Parsaie (COO)
Mark Wedel (Chief Medical Officer & VP-Clinical Affairs)
Jack Whiting (Gen Counsel, Sec & VP)

GENOA CONSTRUCTION SERVICES, INC.
1000 Mansell Exchange W Ste 300, Alpharetta, GA 30022
Tel.: (770) 984-2337
Web Site: http://www.genoaco.com
Year Founded: 1993
Land Subdividers & Developers, Commercial
N.A.I.C.S.: 237210
Kevin McSherry (VP)
Ray D. Moses (Owner & Pres)
Jason Allinson (VP)
Steven Lathem (CFO)

GENOA HEALTHCARE LLC
707 S Grady Way Ste 700, Renton, WA 98057
Tel.: (800) 519-1139　　　　PA
Web Site:
　　http://www.genoahealthcare.com
Year Founded: 1999
Specialized Pharmacy Services
N.A.I.C.S.: 456110
Dale Masten (VP-Govt Affairs)

Subsidiaries:

QoL meds, LLC (1)
4900 Perry Hwy Bldg 2, Pittsburgh, PA 15229
Web Site: http://www.qolmeds.com
Ambulatory Health Care Services
N.A.I.C.S.: 621999
Michael Vanderzee (Dir-Client Mgmt)

GENOA MOTORS INC.
22110 State Route 51 W, Genoa, OH 43430
Tel.: (419) 855-8366
Web Site:
https://www.baumannautogroup.com
Sales Range: $25-49.9 Million
Emp.: 25
Automobiles, New & Used
N.A.I.C.S.: 441110
Terry Paul (Pres)
Chris Danyi (Mgr-Svcs)
Jeff Brown (Mgr-Sls)

GENOMATICA, INC.
10520 Wateridge Cir, San Diego, CA 92121
Tel.: (858) 824-1771   DE
Web Site:
http://www.genomatica.com
Year Founded: 1998
Sales Range: Less than $1 Million
Emp.: 69
Chemicals Mfr
N.A.I.C.S.: 325998
Christophe H. Schilling (Founder & CEO)
Michael E. Keane (CFO & Exec VP)
Mark J. Burk (CTO & Exec VP)
Joseph P. Kuterbach (VP-Ops & Tech Transfer)
Damien A. Perriman (VP-Bus Dev)
Kaspar Evertz (Exec VP-Comml)
Carlos A. Cabrera (Chm)
William H. Baum (Bd of Dirs, Executives)
Shawnte Mitchell (Chief Legal Officer & Gen Counsel)

GENOVA & PARTNERS, INC.
487 E Main St Ste 324, Mount Kisco, NY 10549
Tel.: (914) 666-3982   CT
Year Founded: 1990
Rev.: $6,000,000
Emp.: 8
Fiscal Year-end: 12/31/03
Advertising Agencies, Brand Development, Business-To-Business, Communications, Consumer Marketing, Financial, Media Buying Services, Print, Radio, Travel & Tourism
N.A.I.C.S.: 541810
Joseph Genova (Pres & Exec Dir-Creative)
Enza Dattero (VP & Acct Dir)

GENOVA PRODUCTS, INC.
7034 E Court St, Davison, MI 48423
Tel.: (810) 744-4500   MI
Web Site:
http://www.genovaproducts.com
Year Founded: 1962
Sales Range: $150-199.9 Million
Emp.: 500
Mfr of Plumbing Pipe, Fittings & Related Products, Raingutters & Vinyl Fencing
N.A.I.C.S.: 326199
Robert F. Williams (Founder)

Subsidiaries:

Genova East Europe (1)
Draugystes Str 19, LT 51230, Kaunas, Lithuania
Tel.: (370) 37400052
Web Site: http://www.genovaee.com

Sales Range: $10-24.9 Million
Emp.: 6
Plumbing Pipe, Fittings & Related Products, Raingutters & Vinyl Fencing Mfr
N.A.I.C.S.: 332913

Genova Products, Inc. - Genova Minnesota Factory (1)
500 NW 12th St, Faribault, MN 55021-3743
Tel.: (507) 332-7421
Web Site: http://www.genovaproducts.com
Sales Range: $25-49.9 Million
Emp.: 120
Plastic Tank Mfr
N.A.I.C.S.: 326122

Genova Products, Inc. - Genova Nevada Factory (1)
1150 Southern Way, Sparks, NV 89431-6129
Tel.: (775) 358-4111
Plastic Tank Mfr
N.A.I.C.S.: 326122

Genova Products, Inc. - Rensselaer Plastics Factory (1)
1100 E Elm St, Rensselaer, IN 47978-2363
Tel.: (219) 866-5136
Web Site: http://www.genovaproducts.com
Sales Range: $25-49.9 Million
Emp.: 100
Plastic Tank Mfr
N.A.I.C.S.: 326122
Greg Biggs (Plant Mgr)

Genova Western Europe (1)
Redwell House Redwell Ln, Ightham, TN15 9EE, Kent, United Kingdom
Tel.: (44) 01732886060
Web Site: http://www.genovaproducts.com
Sales Range: $10-24.9 Million
Emp.: 2
Plumbing Pipe, Fittings & Related Products, Raingutters & Vinyl Fencing Mfr
N.A.I.C.S.: 332913

Genova-Indiana, Inc. (1)
9501 Airport Dr, Fort Wayne, IN 46809-3001   (100%)
Tel.: (260) 478-1639
Web Site: http://www.genovaproducts.com
Rev.: $3,000,000
Emp.: 50
Mfr of Plumbing Pipe & Fittings, Warehousing
N.A.I.C.S.: 493110

Genova-Minnesota, Inc. (1)
500 12th St NW, Faribault, MN 55021-3743   (100%)
Tel.: (507) 332-7421
Sales Range: $25-49.9 Million
Emp.: 150
Mfr of Plumbing Pipe, Fittings & Related Products
N.A.I.C.S.: 326191

Genova-Nevada (1)
1150 Southern Way, Sparks, NV 89431-6129   (100%)
Tel.: (775) 358-4111
Web Site: http://www.genovaproducts.com
Sales Range: $25-49.9 Million
Emp.: 10
Mfg. Facility
N.A.I.C.S.: 326122

Genova-Pennsylvania, Inc. (1)
502 4th Rd, Hazleton, PA 18202   (100%)
Tel.: (570) 459-1436
Web Site: http://www.genovaproducts.com
Sales Range: $25-49.9 Million
Emp.: 100
Mfr of Plumbing Pipe, Fittings & Related Products
N.A.I.C.S.: 326122

Wiltic Chemical Manufacturing (1)
422 Rising St, Davison, MI 48423   (100%)
Tel.: (810) 653-1890
Sales Range: $50-74.9 Million
Emp.: 4
Mfr of Solvents, Adhesives & Cleaners
N.A.I.C.S.: 325520

GENPRO TRANSPORTATION INC.
201 Rte 17 N Ste 900, Rutherford, NJ 07070

Tel.: (201) 729-9400
Web Site: http://www.genproinc.com
Sales Range: $25-49.9 Million
Emp.: 25
Truck Transportation Brokers
N.A.I.C.S.: 488510
Robert Goldstein (Pres)
Joe Kouten (VP-Ops)

GENQUEST, INC.
1503 N Rio Grande Blvd NW Ste B, Albuquerque, NM 87104
Tel.: (505) 246-2829   NM
Web Site:
http://www.genquestinc.com
Year Founded: 2001
Sales Range: $1-9.9 Million
Emp.: 55
Administrative Management & General Management Consulting Service
N.A.I.C.S.: 541611
Terri Giron-Gordon (Pres)
Lillian Alllack (Mgr-HR)

GENSCO INC.
4405 20th St E, Tacoma, WA 98424-1815
Tel.: (253) 620-8203   WA
Web Site: http://www.gensco.com
Year Founded: 1947
Sales Range: $50-74.9 Million
Emp.: 450
Plumbing Fixtures, Equipment & Supplies Distr
N.A.I.C.S.: 423720
Marcie Butterfield (Dir-HR)
Tracy Keller (Bus Dir-Parts)
Leeann Davis (Coord-Mktg)
Charles E. Walters Jr. (CEO)

GENSINGER MOTORS INC.
842 Valley Rd, Clifton, NJ 07013
Tel.: (973) 778-8500
Web Site:
https://www.gensingervw.com
Year Founded: 1950
Sales Range: $10-24.9 Million
Emp.: 40
Car Whslr
N.A.I.C.S.: 441110
Ken Gensinger (Owner)

GENSTAR CAPITAL, LLC
4 Embarcadero Ctr Ste 1900, San Francisco, CA 94111
Tel.: (415) 834-2350   DE
Web Site: http://www.gencap.com
Year Founded: 1987
Privater Equity Firm
N.A.I.C.S.: 523999
Jean-Pierre L. Conte (Chm & Mng Partner)
J. Ryan Clark (Pres & Mng Dir)
Eli Weiss (Mng Dir)
Anthony J. Salewski (Mng Partner)
David J. Golde (Mng Dir)
Katie Solomon (Mng Dir-Talent Mgmt)
Robert S. Rutledge (Mng Dir)
Scott Niehaus (Dir)
David Graham (Dir-Debt Capital Market)
Sid Ramarkrishnan (Dir)

Subsidiaries:

Abracon LLC (1)
5101 Hidden Creek Ln, Spicewood, TX 78699
Tel.: (512) 371-6159
Web Site: http://www.abracon.com
Frequency Control & Magnetic Components Supplier
N.A.I.C.S.: 423690
Syed Raza (Dir-Engrg)
Dean Clark (Sr Mgr-Technical)
Tony Roybal (Pres & CEO)
Tim Fedorov (VP-Corp Dev)
Cole Sikes (VP-Global Distr)
Mike White (VP-Global Sls)

Subsidiary (Domestic):

NEL Frequency Controls, Inc. (2)
357 Beloit St, Burlington, WI 53105
Tel.: (262) 763-3591
Web Site: http://www.nelfc.com
Sales Range: $1-9.9 Million
Emp.: 85
Electronic Components Mfr
N.A.I.C.S.: 334419

Advarra, Inc. (1)
6940 Columbia Gateway Dr Ste 110, Columbia, MD 21046
Tel.: (513) 761-4100
Web Site: http://www.advarra.com
Clinical Research Review Services
N.A.I.C.S.: 561499
John W. Hubbard (Chm)
David Golde (Chm)
Gadi Saarony (CEO)
Scott Uebele (Pres & Chief Review Svcs Officer)
Steven Buonaiuto (CFO)
James Riddle (VP-Res Svcs & Strategic Consulting)

Subsidiary (Domestic):

Bio-Optronics, Inc. (2)
1890 S Winton Rd Ste 190, Rochester, NY 14623
Tel.: (585) 272-1960
Web Site: http://www.bio-optronics.com
Sales Range: $1-9.9 Million
Emp.: 25
Computer System Design Services
N.A.I.C.S.: 541512
Daniel I. Kerpelman (Pres & CEO)
Maria Durkin (VP)
Mike Kamish (CTO & VP)

IRB Company Inc. (2)
7001 Vlg Way Ste 260, Buena Park, CA 90621
Web Site: http://www.irbco.com
Clinical Research Review Services
N.A.I.C.S.: 561499
Anil Sharma (CEO)

IntegReview, LLC (2)
3815 S Capital of Texas Hwy Ste 320, Austin, TX 78704
Tel.: (512) 326-3001
Web Site: http://www.integreview.com
Ethical Review & Consulting Services
N.A.I.C.S.: 541990
Betty Maldonado (Mgr-Regulatory Compliance)
Lynn Meyer (Mng Partner)

Watermark Research Partners, Inc. (2)
8123 Castleton Rd, Indianapolis, IN 46250-2006
Tel.: (317) 576-1818
Web Site: http://www.watermarkdsmb.com
Research & Development in the Social Sciences & Humanities
N.A.I.C.S.: 541720
Amanda Richardson (Project Coord)

YourEncore, Inc. (2)
20 NMeridian St Ste 800, Indianapolis, IN 46204
Tel.: (317) 885-6983
Web Site: http://www.yourencore.com
Human Resource Consulting Services
N.A.I.C.S.: 541612
Chuck Hinshaw (Controller)
Joseph Lamendola (Sr VP-Regulatory Practice)
Brad Lawson (Pres)

Alera Group, Inc. (1)
3 Pkwy N Ste 500, Deerfield, IL 60015
Tel.: (847) 582-4501
Web Site: http://www.aleragroup.com
Holding Company; Employee Benefits Consulting & Insurance Brokerage Services
N.A.I.C.S.: 551112
Alan J. Levitz (CEO)
William Corrigan (CFO)
Robert J. Lieblein (Chief Dev Officer)
Bill Doucette (VP-Organization Development)
Jim Blue (Pres)
Danielle Capilla (VP-Compliance & Employee Benefits)
Matt Kistler (VP-Bus Dev)

Genstar Capital, LLC—(Continued)

Tina Santelli *(VP-Voluntary Benefits & Enrollment Solutions)*
Jim Wochele *(VP-Sls Dev)*
Brian Sweeney *(VP-Merger & Acq)*
Robert Svenson *(VP-Tech)*
Tina Hohman *(Exec VP-Wealth Services)*
Taylor Wirth *(Project Mgr-Employee Benefits-Natl)*
Sally Prather *(Exec VP-Employee Benefits)*
Debra Martinez *(Chief HR Officer)*
Brian Parker *(VP-Employee Benefits Tech & Svcs)*
Monica Evans *(Sr VP & Dir-Property & Casualty Solutions)*
Mark Englert *(Exec VP)*
John Mollica *(Chief Info & Innovation Officer)*
Mervin McCormack *(Sr VP & Dir-Property & Casualty Market Relationships)*
Peter Marathas Jr. *(Chief Legal Officer)*

Subsidiary (Domestic):

A&B Insurance and Financial, LLC (2)
1408 N Westshore Blvd Ste 708, Tampa, FL 33607
Tel.: (813) 288-9500
Web Site: http://www.ab-financialgroup.com
Insurance & Financial Services
N.A.I.C.S.: 524210
Ruth Ladas *(Mgr-Agent)*

American Insurance Administrators, Inc. (2)
4550 Lena Dr, Mechanicsburg, PA 17055
Tel.: (717) 591-8280
Web Site: http://www.aiabrg.com
Insurance Agencies & Brokerages
N.A.I.C.S.: 524210
Kevin Krause *(COO & Principal)*
Jamie Tedor *(Sr VP)*
Ashley Tedor *(Sr VP)*

Armstrong/Robitaille/Riegle Business & Insurance Solutions (2)
830 Roosevelt Ste 200, Irvine, CA 92620
Tel.: (949) 381-7700
Web Site: http://www.ar-ins.com
Insurance Brokerage & Related Services
N.A.I.C.S.: 524210
Roger Armstrong *(CEO)*

Bailey & Company Benefits Group (2)
The Baldwin Ctr 625 Eden Park Dr Ste 250, Cincinnati, OH 45202
Tel.: (513) 579-9800
Web Site:
    https://baileyandco.aleragroup.com
Lessors of Residential Buildings & Dwellings
N.A.I.C.S.: 531110

Barnes Insurance & Financial Services (2)
1582 Airport Blvd, Pensacola, FL 32504
Tel.: (850) 473-1500
Web Site: http://www.biafs.com
Health, Dental, Life, Disability, Supplemental Policies & Financial Services
N.A.I.C.S.: 524298
Dennis E. Barnes *(Pres)*
Glenn Little *(VP)*
Bill Roberts *(Mng Dir)*
Johnnie Dahlinger *(Account Manager)*

Benefit Commerce Group (2)
16220 N Scottsdale Rd Ste 100, 85254, Scottsdale, AZ
Tel.: (480) 515-5010
Web Site:
    https://benefitcommerce.aleragroup.com
Employee Welfare Consulting Services
N.A.I.C.S.: 525120
Scott M. Wood *(Mng Partner & Principal)*

Benico, Ltd. (2)
11715 E Main St, Huntley, IL 60142-6913
Tel.: (847) 669-4800
Web Site: http://www.benico.com
Insurance Agencies & Brokerages
N.A.I.C.S.: 524210
John Garven *(Founder & Pres)*
Mary Bieker *(Sr Acct Mgr)*

Brio Benefit Consulting, Inc. (2)
30 Broad St 35th Fl, New York, NY 10004

Tel.: (212) 803-7160
Web Site: http://www.briobenefits.com
Sales Range: $1-9.9 Million
Emp.: 18
Insurance Agency Services
N.A.I.C.S.: 524210
Kevin Ritchie *(Chief Bus Officer)*
Jordan Cohen *(Mgr-Strategy)*
Matthew R. Compton *(Dir-Retirement Svcs)*
Raymond Burett *(Exec VP)*
Alexandra Horneman *(Mgr-Client Solutions)*

Burnham Benefit Advisors (2)
2038 Saranac Ave, Lake Placid, NY 12946
Tel.: (518) 523-8100
Web Site: https://bba.aleragroup.com
Insurance Related Activities
N.A.I.C.S.: 524298

C.M. Smith Agency, LLC (2)
100 Pearl St 3rd Fl W Tower, Hartford, CT 06103
Tel.: (860) 990-6400
Web Site: http://www.cmsmith.com
Emp.: 35
Insurance Agencies & Brokerages
N.A.I.C.S.: 524210
Denis Lynch *(Partner)*
John O'Connell *(Sr Partner)*
John Giliberto *(Partner)*
Barbara Aiudi *(Principal)*
Andy Hintz *(Dir-Client Svcs)*
Michael Martin *(Dir-Data Analytics)*
Scott Stauffer *(Dir-Fin Ops)*
Paul Grady *(Principal)*
Brigid Gunn *(Mgr-HR & Ops)*
Mary Hollanda *(Mgr-Acct)*
Katie LaBonia *(Mgr-Acct)*
Karen Lathrop *(Mgr-Acct)*
Ashley Hrubala *(Mgr-Client Svc)*

Clifford R. Zinn & Son, Inc. (2)
16 E Main Ave, Myerstown, PA 17067
Tel.: (717) 866-5717
Web Site: http://www.zinn.com
Sales Range: $1-9.9 Million
Insurance Brokerage & Risk Services
N.A.I.C.S.: 524210
Gregory J. Zinn *(Pres)*

Coury Health Services, LLC (2)
1 Oxford Ctr 301 Grant St Ste 300, Pittsburgh, PA 15219
Tel.: (412) 430-3070
Web Site: http://chs.aleragroup.com
Benefit Consulting Services
N.A.I.C.S.: 541618
Kandy Dudek *(Acct Exec)*
Donald Balla *(Exec VP)*

Direct Benefits, Inc. (2)
325 Cedar St, Saint Paul, MN 55101
Tel.: (651) 259-6240
Web Site: http://www.directbenefits.com
Insurance Agencies & Brokerages
N.A.I.C.S.: 524210
Dave Bortem *(Pres, CEO & COO)*

Distinctive Insurance (2)
8375 W Flamingo Rd Ste 102, Las Vegas, NV 89147-4149
Tel.: (702) 396-4844
Web Site: http://distinctive.net
Insurance Agencies & Brokerages
N.A.I.C.S.: 524210
Jonathan Johnson *(Principal)*
Alexa Olenick *(Project Mgr)*
Allison Ivie *(Acct Mgr)*

Dohrmann Insurance Agency Inc. (2)
3415 Brookside Rd, Stockton, CA 95219
Tel.: (209) 478-1400
Web Site: http://www.dohrins.com
Insurance Agencies & Brokerages
N.A.I.C.S.: 524210
Angelo Giannini *(VP-Employee Benefits)*

FIRM, Inc. (2)
1 Lethbridge Plz Ste 30, Mahwah, NJ 07430
Tel.: (201) 831-0505
Web Site: http://www.firminsurance.com
Insurance Agents
N.A.I.C.S.: 524210

Flexible Benefits System Inc. (2)
400 WillowBrook Ofc Park Ste 400, Fairport, NY 14450-4223
Tel.: (585) 248-8720

Web Site:
    http://www.relphbenefitadvisors.com
Scientific & Technical Consulting Services
N.A.I.C.S.: 541690
Robert Relph *(Pres & Chief Strategy Officer)*

GCG Financial, LLC (2)
3 Pkwy N Ste 500, Deerfield, IL 60015-2567
Tel.: (847) 457-3000
Web Site: http://www.gcgfinancial.com
Employee Benefits, Risk Management & Insurance Services
N.A.I.C.S.: 524210
Richard S. Levitz *(Mng Partner & Pres-Wealth Mgmt)*
David Levitz *(Mng Partner)*
Michael Gluck *(Dir-Mktg)*
Sheldon R. Bender *(VP-Wealth Mgmt)*
Jim Berman *(VP-Benefits Consulting)*
Natalie L. Blatnick *(Dir-Recruiting)*
Krista Bommarito *(Chief Compliance Officer)*
Brian Carlson *(VP-Wealth Mgmt)*
Brian Crane *(VP-Benefits Consulting)*
Pam S. Davis *(VP-Wealth Mgmt)*
Carla DeMello *(Pres-Employee Benefits)*
John Eichmann *(Mng Dir-Private Equity Practice)*
Steve Felker *(Pres-Risk Mgmt)*
Teddy Felker *(Mng Dir-Private Equity Practice)*
Bruce Friedman *(VP-Wealth Mgmt)*
Robert Janson *(Sr VP-Wealth Mgmt)*
Rick Loudenback *(Exec VP-Wealth Mgmt)*
Rosemary O'Brien *(Dir-Personal Risk Mgmt)*
Jill Olshefke *(Dir-Select Accts)*
Arthur D. Chantier Jr. *(VP-Benefits Consulting)*

GLB Insurance Group of Nevada (2)
4455 S Pecos Rd, Las Vegas, NV 89121
Tel.: (702) 735-9333
Web Site: http://www.glbins.com
Insurance Related Activities
N.A.I.C.S.: 524298
Russ Swain *(Pres)*
Gary K. Prater *(VP)*
Geoffrey W. Holmes *(Principal)*

Group Benefits LLC (2)
855 Rdg Lk Blvd Ste 410, Memphis, TN 38120
Tel.: (901) 259-7999
Web Site: http://www.groupbenefitsllc.com
Employee Benefits Consulting Firm
N.A.I.C.S.: 541611
Pat Jameson *(Dir-Ops & Compliance)*
Alexandra C. Finnell *(Creative Dir)*
Hallie Hastings *(Acct Mgr)*
Debbie Vopel *(Coord-Client Svcs)*
Cheryl W. Nunes *(Acct Mgr)*
Dee Ann Fletcher *(Acct Mgr)*
M. Diane Coleman *(Acct Mgr)*
Eddie McDoniel *(Acct Mgr)*
Amy T. Crippen *(Acct Mgr)*

Group Services, LLC (2)
3066 Victoria St, Bettendorf, IA 52722
Tel.: (563) 332-5552
Web Site: http://www.groupservices.com
Insurance Agencies & Brokerages
N.A.I.C.S.: 524210
Tom Schuetz *(Co-Pres)*
Ranae Warren *(Co-Pres)*
Catherine Hughes *(Dir-Bus Relationship)*
Doug Petersma *(Dir-HR/Compliance Consulting)*
Jessie Kelley *(Acct Mgr)*
Brenda Kleinston-Heber *(Mgr-Claims)*
Debra Schmidt *(Controller)*
Steve Felker *(Pres-Risk Mgmt)*

HMK Insurance (2)
54 S Commerce Way Ste 150, Bethlehem, PA 18017-8619
Tel.: (610) 868-8507
Web Site: http://www.hmk-ins.com
Insurance Agencies & Brokerages
N.A.I.C.S.: 524210
Tim Kurtz *(VP)*
William C. Kreitz *(Pres)*
David Dyson *(VP-Sls & Mktg)*
George Mowrer *(CFO)*
Maureen O'Meara *(Dir-Bus Dev)*
Todd Linn *(Mgr-Grp Benefits Div)*
Susan Hartranft-Bittinger *(Mgr-Claims)*
Tara Silfies *(COO)*
Jade Simmers *(Dir-Risk Mgmt)*

INGROUP Associates, LLC (2)
448 Murry Hill Cir, Lancaster, PA 17601
Tel.: (717) 509-8803
Web Site: http://www.ingroupassociates.com
Employee Benefits & Human Resource Technology Solutions Services
N.A.I.C.S.: 541611
Arlene Kime *(Acct Mgr)*
Christine Judith *(Mgr-Agency Ops)*
Diana Law *(Acct Mgr)*
Barbi Cottingham *(Coord-Sls & Mktg)*
Stephanie Chase *(Acct Mgr)*
Adrienne Gavin *(Acct Mgr)*
Gina Wood *(Acct Mgr)*
Patrick T. Moran II *(Founder & Pres)*

J.A. Counter & Associates, Inc. (2)
1477 S Knowles Ave Ste 200, New Richmond, WI 54017
Tel.: (715) 246-3811
Web Site: http://www.jacounter.com
Insurance Agencies & Brokerages
N.A.I.C.S.: 524210
Deb Henke *(COO)*
Jamie Pearson *(Acct Mgr)*
Alyssa Little *(Office Mgr)*
Edna Perkins *(Acct Mgr)*
Karrie Demulling *(Acct Mgr-Small Grp)*
Kristi Cherney *(Chief Client Officer)*
Jessica Langeness *(Coord-Acct)*
Shannon Mehls *(Mgr-Brokerage)*
James Counter *(Founder)*
Linda M. Skoglund *(Pres)*
Cindy Fodroczi *(Acct Mgr-Individual & Small Grp)*

John Hackney Agency, Inc. (2)
3700 Nash St NW, Wilson, NC 27896
Tel.: (252) 291-3111
Web Site:
    http://www.johnhackneyagency.com
Insurance Related Activities
N.A.I.C.S.: 524298
John Hackney III *(Partner)*

Menath Insurance, An Alera Group Agency, LLC (2)
333 Vlg Blvd Ste 203, Incline Village, NV 89451
Tel.: (775) 831-3132
Web Site:
    http://www.menath.aleragroup.com
Insurance Agency & Brokerage
N.A.I.C.S.: 524210
Michael Menath *(Pres)*
Michael Rohr *(Acct Mgr)*

Noyle W. Johnson Insurance Agency, Inc. (2)
119 River St, Montpelier, VT 05601
Tel.: (802) 223-7735
Web Site: http://www.nwjinsurance.com
Sales Range: $25-49.9 Million
Emp.: 40
Insurance Agents
N.A.I.C.S.: 524210
Timothy Ayer *(Pres)*
Peter O. Hood *(Treas)*

Orion Risk Management Insurance Services, Inc. (2)
1800 Quail St Ste 110, Newport Beach, CA 92660
Tel.: (7) 9492638850
Web Site: https://orionrisk.com
Insurance Agent/Broker
N.A.I.C.S.: 524210
Clifford A. Davis *(Pres)*

PWA Insurance Services, LLC (2)
2377 Gold Meadow Way Ste #250, Gold River, CA 95670
Tel.: (916) 631-7887
Web Site: http://www.pwadmin.com
General Insurance Services
N.A.I.C.S.: 524210
Conny Michael Saab *(VP)*
Jeffrey P. Gardenhire *(VP)*
Conny K. Saab *(CEO)*

Professional Risk, an Alera Group Agency, LLC (2)
8213 W 20th St, Greeley, CO 80634-3031
Tel.: (970) 356-8030
Web Site: http://www.rcins-co.com
Insurance Agents
N.A.I.C.S.: 524210
Mike Schmitt *(Gen Mgr)*

Rick Young & Associates, Inc. (2)

2993 Corinthia Dr Ste A, Rochester, MI
48309
Tel.: (248) 844-9110
Web Site:
http://www.rickyounginsurance.com
Sales Range: $1-9.9 Million
Emp.: 11
Insurance Agent/Broker
N.A.I.C.S.: 524210
Rick Young *(Founder)*

Shirazi Benefits LLC (2)
8205 W 20th St, Greeley, CO 80634
Tel.: (970) 356-5151
Web Site: http://www.shirazibenefits.com
Insurance Agencies & Brokerages
N.A.I.C.S.: 524210
Vicki Steiner *(Sr Acct Mgr)*
Ty Miller *(Principal)*
Masoud Shirazi *(Principal)*
Hossein Shirazi *(Principal)*
Sarah Thomas *(Acct Mgr)*
Jennifer Wambolt *(Acct Mgr)*
Monica Lauer *(Acct Mgr)*
Christine Muller *(Acct Mgr)*

Sutter, McLellan & Gilbreath, Inc. (2)
33 Buford Vlg Way 329, Buford, GA 30518
Tel.: (770) 246-8300
Web Site: http://www.smginsurance.com
Rev.: $1,800,000
Emp.: 42
Insurance Agencies & Brokerages
N.A.I.C.S.: 524210
Deborah Miller *(VP)*
Drew Gilbreath *(VP-Ops)*

The Avon-Dixon Agency, LLC (2)
28640 Marys Ct Ste 100, Easton, MD
21601-6005
Tel.: (410) 822-0506
Web Site: http://www.avondixon.com
Insurance Agencies & Brokerages
N.A.I.C.S.: 524210
Deanna Blanch *(Pres)*

The Centennial Group, LLC (2)
1500 Quail St Ste 100, Newport Beach, CA
92660
Tel.: (714) 740-1111
Web Site: http://www.thecentennial.com
Risk Managemeng Srvices
N.A.I.C.S.: 541611
Matthew Hanson *(Pres)*
Vickie Melfi *(COO)*
Ryan Miller *(Dir-Sls & Mktg)*

Virtus Benefits, LLC (2)
2910 Sidco Dr, Nashville, TN 37204
Tel.: (615) 806-6293
Web Site: http://www.virtusbenefits.com
Insurance Agencies & Brokerages
N.A.I.C.S.: 524210
David T. Johnson *(Sr Partner)*

Wilson, Washburn & Forster, Inc. (2)
10301 S Dixie Hwy Ste 300, Miami, FL
33156
Tel.: (305) 666-6636
Web Site: http://www.wwfins.com
Sales Range: $1-9.9 Million
Emp.: 16
Insurance Agencies & Brokerages
N.A.I.C.S.: 524210
Sarah Washburn *(Pres)*
Phil Yanan *(Acct Exec)*

Altegris Investments, Inc. (1)
1200 Prospect St Ste 400, La Jolla, CA
92037
Tel.: (858) 459-7040
Web Site: http://www.altegris.com
Rev.: $2,430,000,000
Alternative Investment Management Services
N.A.I.C.S.: 523940
Jon C. Sundt *(Founder & Chm)*
Jack Leon Rivkin *(Chief Investment Officer)*
Ken McGuire *(Co-Pres)*
David Mathews *(Gen Counsel & Sr VP)*
Laura Pyle *(Sr VP & Chief of Staff)*
Robert J. Murphy *(Deputy Chief Investment Officer)*

Subsidiary (Domestic):

Altegris Advisors, LLC (2)
1200 Prospect St Ste 400, La Jolla, CA
92037
Tel.: (858) 459-7040

Web Site: http://www.altegris.com
Investment Advisory Services
N.A.I.C.S.: 523940
Allen Cheng *(Chief Investment Officer, Sr VP & Portfolio Mgr)*
Jack Leon Rivkin *(Vice Chm & CEO)*
Kenneth Ives McGuire *(Pres & COO)*
Robert Naka *(COO)*

Altegris Portfolio Management, Inc. (2)
1200 Prospect St Ste 400, La Jolla, CA
92037
Tel.: (858) 459-7040
Web Site: http://www.altegris.com
Portfolio Management Services
N.A.I.C.S.: 523940
Jon C. Sundt *(Pres & CEO)*
Allen Cheng *(Sr VP & Co-Portfolio Mgr-Mutual Funds)*

Ascensus, LLC (1)
200 Dryden Rd, Dresher, PA 19025
Tel.: (800) 346-3860
Web Site: https://www.ascensus.com
Financial Retirement Services
N.A.I.C.S.: 524292
Raghav Nandagopal *(Chief Corp Dev Officer)*
James M. Lucania *(CFO)*
Joe Dansky *(Chief Compliance Officer, Chief Legal Officer & Chief Risk Officer)*
Amy Walker *(Chief HR Officer)*
David L. Musto *(Pres & CEO)*
Carl Negin *(CMO)*
Kevin Cox *(Pres-Retirement & Head-Retirement Bus)*
Peg Creonte *(Head-Gov Savings)*
Jim Gearin *(COO)*
Kurt Laning *(Pres-Institutional Solutions)*
James Lucania *(CFO)*
Clay Kennedy *(VP-Insurance & Nonqualified Retirement Plan Sls)*

Subsidiary (Domestic):

Beneco Systems, Inc. (2)
8655 East Via de Ventura Ste G-200,
Scottsdale, AZ 85258
Tel.: (800) 965-2702
Web Site: http://www.beneco.com
Human Resources & Executive Search
Consulting Services
N.A.I.C.S.: 541612

Benefits of Missouri Inc. (2)
14323 S Outer 40 Ste 600N, Chesterfield,
MO 63017-5747
Tel.: (314) 576-5880
Portfolio Management
N.A.I.C.S.: 523940

Intac Actuarial Services, Inc. (2)
50 Tice Blvd Ste 151, Woodcliff Lake, NJ
07677
Tel.: (201) 447-2525
Web Site: http://www.intacinc.com
Human Resources & Executive Search
Consulting Services
N.A.I.C.S.: 541612
Harry Rosenberg *(VP)*

National Retirement Services, Inc. (2)
5832 Bolsa Ave 100, Huntington Beach, CA
92649
Tel.: (714) 622-3188
Pension Funds & Retirement Services
N.A.I.C.S.: 525110

Polycomp Administrative Services, Inc. (2)
3000 Lava Ridge Ct Ste 130, Roseville, CA
95661
Tel.: (916) 773-3480
Web Site: http://www.polycomp.net
Insurance Services
N.A.I.C.S.: 524298
NaKendra Stewart *(Dir-Qualified Plans)*
Christopher Mastrianni *(Dir-Benefit Trust Svcs)*

Provident Trust Group, LLC (2)
8880 W Sunset Rd Ste 250, Las Vegas, NV
89148
Tel.: (702) 434-0023
Web Site: http://www.trustprovident.com
Trust, Custody, Administration & Escrow
Services
N.A.I.C.S.: 523991

Michael Vavruska *(Mgr-Sr Bus Dev)*

Qualified Plans, LLC (2)
2702 Whatley Ave Ste A-1, Savannah, GA
31404
Tel.: (912) 356-1120
Web Site: http://www.qplans.com
Third Party Retirement Plan Services
N.A.I.C.S.: 623311
Joanna M. Fenske *(Partner)*

TCFCW, LLC (2)
113 Seaboard Ln Ste B150, Franklin, TN
37067
Tel.: (615) 467-7090
HR Consulting Services
N.A.I.C.S.: 541612

The Newport Group, Inc. (2)
1350 Treat Blvd Ste 300, Walnut Creek, CA
94597
Tel.: (925) 328-4540
Web Site: http://www.newportgroup.com
Emp.: 1,200
Asset Management, Retirement Plans &
Insurance Services
N.A.I.C.S.: 524113
Amy K. Parker *(Mng Dir-Fiduciary Consulting Svcs)*
Greg Tschider *(CEO)*
Laura Ramanis *(COO)*
Sean N. Hardin *(CFO)*
Jacqueline Ward *(Chief HR Officer)*
Kurt J. Laning *(Exec VP)*
Micah DiSalvo *(Sr VP-Institutional Sls)*
Whitney Ames *(Gen Counsel)*
Geraldine O'Brien *(VP-Comm)*
Andre Mintz *(Chief Info Security Officer)*

Subsidiary (Domestic):

Plan Administrators, Inc. (3)
1300 Enterprise Dr, De Pere, WI 54115
Tel.: (920) 337-9906
Web Site: http://www.pai.com
Sales Range: $1-9.9 Million
Emp.: 100
Management Consulting Services
N.A.I.C.S.: 541611
Michael Kiley *(VP-Sls & Mktg)*
Kelly Skenandore-Holtz *(Coord-Trng & Dev)*
Drew Meyers *(Dir-Customer Care Center)*
Tracy Ruh *(CEO)*

Subsidiary (Domestic):

United Retirement Plan Consultants, Inc. (2)
545 Metro Pl S Ste 240, Dublin, OH 43017
Tel.: (614) 923-8822
Web Site: http://www.unitedretirement.com
Sales Range: $25-49.9 Million
Retirement, Pension Administration & Investment Management Services
N.A.I.C.S.: 524292

Subsidiary (Domestic):

MGA Consultants, Inc. (3)
6031 University Blvd Ste 300, Ellicott City,
MD 21043
Tel.: (301) 614-0957
Web Site: http://www.mgaconsultants.net
Financial Services
N.A.I.C.S.: 525990
Lee Bachu *(CEO)*

Asset International Inc. (1)
1055 Washington Blvd, Stamford, CT 06901
Tel.: (203) 595-3200
Web Site: http://www.strategic-i.com
Sales Range: $10-24.9 Million
B2B Information & Technology Services
N.A.I.C.S.: 519290
Phil Herzog *(CIO & Exec VP)*
SooJin Chun Buzelli *(Sr VP & Dir-Creative)*
Quinn Keeler *(Sr VP-Res)*
Stephen Moylan *(Exec VP-Sls & Mktg)*
Avi Nachmany *(Exec VP & Dir-Res)*
Jim Casella *(Chm)*
Joel Mandelbaum *(CEO)*
Mike Garity *(VP-Global Event Strategy & Bus Dev)*
Susan Belle *(VP-Mktg)*
Robert Ainsworth *(Sr VP & Controller)*
Terry Beadle *(Chief Revenue Officer)*
Tony White *(Chief Content Officer)*
Andrew Guillette *(Chief Data & Res Officer & Mgr-Global Product)*
Garry Hodnett *(Dir-Human Capital)*

Leonie Alsop *(Dir-Global Mktg)*
Karl Jaeger *(CFO)*
Charles A. Ruffel *(Founder)*

Subsidiary (Non-US):

AI Financial Information UK Limited (2)
Upper Ground Floor South, 200 Aldersgate
Street, London, EC1A 4HD, United Kingdom
Tel.: (44) 20 7397 3800
Web Site: http://www.assetinternational.com
B2B Information & Technology Services
N.A.I.C.S.: 519290
John Lee *(Mng Dir-Europe)*
Amit Dass *(Dir-Fin-EMEA)*

Asset International Australia Pty Ltd (2)
217 Blackburn Rd, Mount Waverley, 3149,
VIC, Australia
Tel.: (61) 3 9886 4400
Web Site: http://www.assetinternational.com
Emp.: 10
B2B Information & Technology Services
N.A.I.C.S.: 519290
Rael Solomon *(Gen Mgr)*

Asset International Hong Kong Ltd. (2)
4607-11 The Center 99 Queens Road, Central, China (Hong Kong)
Tel.: (852) 3796 7258
B2B Information & Technology Services
N.A.I.C.S.: 519290

Subsidiary (Domestic):

Strategic Insight, Inc. (2)
805 3rd Ave, New York, NY 10022
Tel.: (212) 944-4455
Web Site: http://www.sionline.com
Sales Range: $1-9.9 Million
Emp.: 40
Management Consulting Services
N.A.I.C.S.: 541611

Bracket Global LLC (1)
575 E Swedesford Rd Ste 200, Wayne, PA
19087
Tel.: (610) 225-5900
Web Site: http://www.bracketglobal.com
Support Services for Pharmaceutical Research & Clinical Trials
N.A.I.C.S.: 541519
Christopher Crucitti *(Chief Comml Officer)*
Michael P. Nolte *(CEO)*
David G. Daniel *(Chief Medical Officer & Sr VP)*
James Jay *(Gen Mgr & Sr VP-Endpoint Solutions)*
Thomas Barlow *(VP-Total Quality Mgmt)*
Mitch Blumenfeld *(CFO)*
Susie Robinson *(Chief People Officer)*
Lawrence Miller *(CTO)*
Nicole Kerr *(VP-Product Mgmt)*
James Primerano Jr. *(Sr VP & Gen Mgr-eClinical)*

Subsidiary (Non-US):

Bracket Global, s.r.o. (2)
Slezska 2127/13, 12000, Prague, 2, Czech
Republic
Tel.: (420) 221 001 733
Web Site: http://www.bracketglobal.com
Automated Clinical Trial Management Systems Using Voice Response (IVR) & Web-Based Technologies
N.A.I.C.S.: 541519

Subsidiary (Domestic):

Clinapps, Inc. (2)
9530 Towne Ctr Dr Ste 100, San Diego, CA
91361
Tel.: (858) 866-0228
Pharmaceutical Software Solutions & Consulting Services
N.A.I.C.S.: 541511

Clintara, LLC (2)
11 Beacon St Ste 600, Boston, MA 02108
Tel.: (617) 603-7580
Web Site: http://www.clintara.com
Drugs & Druggists' Sundries Merchant
Whslr
N.A.I.C.S.: 424210
Michael Nolte *(Mgr)*

Genstar Capital, LLC—(Continued)

Brook & Whittle Limited (1)
260 Branford Rd, North Branford, CT 06471
Tel.: (203) 483-5602
Web Site: http://www.brookandwhittle.com
Packaging, Label & Shrink Sleeve Design
N.A.I.C.S.: 561910
Steve T. Stewart (Founder)
Mark Pollard (CEO)
Don Sturdivant (Chm)

Subsidiary (Domestic):

Digital Label Solutions, LLC (2)
22745 Old Canal Rd, Yorba Linda, CA
92887
Tel.: (714) 982-5000
Web Site:
   http://www.digitallabelsolutions.com
Sales Range: $1-9.9 Million
Emp.: 26
Digital Printing Services
N.A.I.C.S.: 323111

Gilbreth Packaging Systems (2)
3001 State Rd, Croydon, PA
19021-6962 (100%)
Tel.: (215) 785-3350
Web Site: http://www.gilbrethusa.com
Marketer of Packaging & Labeling System
& Machinery Mfr
N.A.I.C.S.: 323111
Brian Riley (VP-Fin)

Label Impression, Inc. (2)
1831 W Sequoia Ave, Orange, CA 92868
Tel.: (714) 634-3466
Web Site: http://www.labelimpressions.com
Commercial Printing
N.A.I.C.S.: 323111

Paradigm Label, Inc (2)
10258 Birtcher Dr, Mira Loma, CA 91752
Tel.: (951) 372-9212
Web Site: http://www.paradigmlabel.com
Commercial Flexographic Printing
N.A.I.C.S.: 323111
Curtis Harton (CEO)

Cerity Partners LLC (1)
335 Madison Ave 23rd Fl, New York, NY
10017
Tel.: (212) 850-4260
Web Site: http://www.ceritypartners.com
Emp.: 425
Investment & Wealth Management Services
N.A.I.C.S.: 523940
Benjamin A. Pace (Partner)
Kurt Miscinski (Pres & CEO)

Subsidiary (Domestic):

Blue Prairie Group LLC (2)
65 E Wacker Pl, Chicago, IL 60601
Tel.: (312) 645-1899
Web Site: http://www.blueprairiegroup.com
Human Resource Consulting Services
N.A.I.C.S.: 541612
Matthew Gnabasik (Founder)
Gary M. Silverman (Chief Investment Officer)
Ty Parrish (Mng Partner)

Executive Monetary Management, LLC
220 E 42nd St Fl 32, New York, NY 10017
Tel.: (212) 476-5555
Web Site: http://www.emmwealth.com
Sales Range: $1-9.9 Million
Emp.: 36
Accounting Services
N.A.I.C.S.: 541219
Lloyd Abramowitz (Co-CEO)
David Aaron (Co-CEO & CIO)
Thomas O'Brien (CFO)

Permit Capital Advisors, LLC (2)
100 Frnt St Ste 900, West Conshohocken,
PA 19428
Tel.: (610) 941-5006
Web Site: http://www.permitcapital.com
Miscellaneous Financial Investment Activities
N.A.I.C.S.: 523999

Cetera Financial Holdings, Inc. (1)
2301 Rosecrans Ave Ste 5100, El Segundo,
CA 90245
Web Site: https://www.ceteraholdings.com
Holding Company

N.A.I.C.S.: 551112

Subsidiary (Domestic):

Avantax, Inc. (2)
3200 Olympus Blvd Ste 100, Dallas, TX
75019
Tel.: (972) 870-6000
Web Site: https://www.avantax.com
Rev.: $885,200,000
Assets: $1,071,943,000
Liabilities: $730,321,000
Net Worth: $341,622,000
Earnings: $7,757,000
Emp.: 1,100
Fiscal Year-end: 12/31/2021
Internet-enabled Tax Solutions & Financial
Services
N.A.I.C.S.: 518210

Subsidiary (Domestic):

2nd Story Software, Inc. (3)
1425 60th St NE Ste 300, Cedar Rapids, IA
52402
Tel.: (319) 373-3600
Web Site: https://www.taxact.com
Tax Preparation Software Development
Services
N.A.I.C.S.: 541213

Avantax Planning Partners, Inc. (3)
3390 Asbury Rd, Dubuque, IA 52002
Tel.: (563) 582-2855
Web Site: http://www.hkfs.com
Portfolio Management
N.A.I.C.S.: 523940

Subsidiary (Domestic):

Headquarters Advisory Group, LLC (4)
77 E Halsey Rd, Parsippany, NJ 07054
Tel.: (973) 560-0110
Web Site: http://www.hqadvisorygroup.com
Portfolio Management
N.A.I.C.S.: 523940

Subsidiary (Domestic):

Avantax Wealth Management, Inc. (3)
6333 N State Hwy 161 4th Fl, Irving, TX
75038
Tel.: (972) 870-6000
Web Site: http://www.avantaxwealthmanagement.com
Financial Management Services
N.A.I.C.S.: 541611
Enrique Vasquez (Pres-Wealth Mgmt)
Casey Griffin (Chief Compliance Officer)
Tim Stewart (VP-Bus Dev)
Amber Bird (Mgr-Compliance Svcs)
Todd Mckay (Pres)

H.D. Vest, Inc. (3)
6333 N State Hwy 161 4th Fl, Irving, TX
75038-2216
Tel.: (866) 218-8206
Web Site: http://www.hdvest.com
Financial Planning Services
N.A.I.C.S.: 523150
Scott Rawlins (Pres)
David L. Peavler (Gen Counsel)
Crystal Clifford (COO)
Marc Brasher (Head-Tech)
Tim Stewart (Head-Bus Dev)

HDV Holdings, Inc. (3)
6333 N State Hwy 161 4th Fl, Irving, TX
75038
Tel.: (972) 870-6000
Holding Company
N.A.I.C.S.: 551112

HowStuffWorks, Inc. (3)
4235 Redwood Ave, Marina Del Rey, CA
90066
Tel.: (404) 760-4729
Web Site: https://www.howstuffworks.com
Sales Range: $50-74.9 Million
Emp.: 160
Online Publishing
N.A.I.C.S.: 513199
Sarah Gleim (Mgr-Content)

TaxACT, Inc. (3)
1425 60th St NE, Cedar Rapids, IA 52402
Tel.: (319) 373-3600
Web Site: https://www.taxact.com
Software Development Services

N.A.I.C.S.: 513210
Curtis Campbell (Pres)

Subsidiary (Domestic):

Cetera Financial Group, Inc. (2)
200 Pacific Coast Hwy Ste 1200, El Segundo, CA 90245
Tel.: (866) 489-3100
Web Site: http://www.cetera.com
Investment Management Service
N.A.I.C.S.: 523940
Adam Antoniades (CEO)
Timothy E. M. Stinson (Head-Wealth Mgmt)
Jeffrey R. Buchheister (CFO)
Joseph Neary (Chief Risk Officer)
Sheila Woelfel (Head-Portfolio Solutions)
Thomas Taylor (Pres/CEO-Cetera Advisor
Networks)
Michael Ragunas (CIO)
Michael Zuna (CMO)
Ben Brigeman (Chm)
Jeannie Finkel (Chief HR Officer)
Patrick Jancsy (Head-Advisory Bus Consulting)
Catherine M. Bonneau (COO)
Andy Gill (Chief Strategy & Execution Officer)
David Greene (Gen Counsel)

Subsidiary (Domestic):

Cetera Advisor Networks LLC (3)
200 N Sepulveda Blvd Ste 1300, El Segundo, CA 90245
Tel.: (310) 326-3100
Web Site:
   http://www.ceteraadvisornetworks.com
Investment Advisory & Management Services
N.A.I.C.S.: 523940
Thomas B. Taylor (Pres & CEO)
Craig Markham (Sr VP-Advisor Experience)
Summer Pretzer (Head-Supervision)
Timothy P. Stone (COO)
Patricia R. McCallop (Chief Compliance Officer & Sr VP)

Cetera Advisors LLC (3)
4600 S Syracuse St Ste 600, Denver, CO
80203-2122
Tel.: (720) 509-2400
Web Site: http://www.multifinancial.com
Sales Range: $75-99.9 Million
Emp.: 60
Investment Management Service
N.A.I.C.S.: 523940
Brett L. Harrison (Pres & CEO)
Bernard Breton (Chief Compliance Officer)
Amanda L. Tawney (Dir-Ops & Svcs)
Cathy Maestas (Dir-Svc)
George Mulwee (Dir-Supervision)
Joseph Vinson (VP-New Bus Dev)

Cetera Investment Services LLC (3)
400 1st St S Ste 300, Saint Cloud, MN
56301-3661
Tel.: (320) 656-4300
Web Site:
   http://www.ceterafinancialinstitutions.com
Rev.: $21,500,000,000
Emp.: 200
Investment Management Service
N.A.I.C.S.: 523940
Catherine Bonneau (CEO)
Sean Casey (Dir-Bus Dev)
Mark Shelson (CFO)
Kim Holweger (COO)
Kevin Larson (Chief Compliance Officer)
Leann Rummel (Pres & CEO)

Voya Financial Advisors, Inc. (3)
909 Locust St, Des Moines, IA 50309-2803
Tel.: (515) 698-7300
Sales Range: $25-49.9 Million
Emp.: 100
Securities Brokerage
N.A.I.C.S.: 523150
Karl S. Lindberg (CEO)
Ed Pollis (Head-Practice Mgmt)

Clarience Technologies, LLC (1)
20600 Civic Center Dr, Southfield, MI
48076
Tel.: (877) 537-3820
Web Site:
   https://www.clariencetechnologies.com
Electronics, Technology, Telematics Mfr &
Data Analytics
N.A.I.C.S.: 334111

Doug Wolma (Pres)

Subsidiary (Domestic):

Pressure Systems International, Inc. (2)
3023 Interstate Dr, San Antonio, TX 78219
Tel.: (210) 222-1926
All Other Motor Vehicle Parts Mfr
N.A.I.C.S.: 336390
Steve Ottemann (CFO & VP-Ops)
Tim Musgrave (Pres & CEO)
Mike McIver (VP-Mfg)
Frank Sonzala (Exec VP-Sls & Mktg)
James Sharkey (Dir-Strategic Initiatives)
Jim Herzog (Sls Mgr-South Central)
Jonathan Gravell (Dir-Technical Svcs &
Customer Support)
Kevin Hennig (VP-Product Dev & Technical
Sls)
Mike Niemeyer (Dir-Strategic Accts)
Scott Burckhard (Sls Dir-West & Canada)

Safe Fleet Holdings LLC (2)
6800 E 163rd St, Belton, MO 64012
Tel.: (844) 258-8178
Web Site: http://www.safefleet.net
Safety & Productivity Solutions Provider to
Fleet Vehicles
N.A.I.C.S.: 561621
Mike Schulte (Pres)

Subsidiary (Domestic):

American Midwest Fleet Solutions (3)
1955 W US Highway 50, Lone Jack, MO
64070
Tel.: (816) 566-3420
Web Site: http://www.ammfleetsolutions.com
Recreational Vehicle Dealers
N.A.I.C.S.: 441210
David Miller (Co-Founder)
Teresa Miller (Co-Founder)

Roll-Rite, LLC (3)
650 Industrial Dr, Gladwin, MI 48624
Tel.: (989) 345-3434
Web Site: http://www.rollrite.com
Sales Range: $1-9.9 Million
Emp.: 50
Tarpaulin Mfr
N.A.I.C.S.: 314910
Cindy Cook (Mgr-Mktg Comm)
Brad Templeman (Pres)
Jim Kenyon (VP-Sls & Mktg)
Erl Henry (Mgr-Sls-Solid Waste & Recycling)
Dave Andrews (Mgr-Natl Svc)
Scott Kartes (Dir-Engrg)
Eric Bladecki (Mgr-Mfg)
Keith Lowe (Mgr-Accts-Natl)
Jeff Neubauer (Mgr-Municipal Sls)

Subsidiary (Domestic):

Truck-Lite Co., LLC (2)
310 E Elmwood Ave, Falconer, NY 14733
Tel.: (716) 665-6214
Web Site: http://www.truck-lite.com
Sales Range: $25-49.9 Million
Signal Light Mfr for Heavy-Duty Trucks,
Trailers & Commercial Vehicles
N.A.I.C.S.: 336320
Brian Kupchella (CEO)
Beth W. English (VP-Mktg)
Jillian C. Evanko (CFO & VP)
Aaron Justice (VP-Ops)

Subsidiary (Domestic):

JST Performance, Inc. (3)
779 N Colorado St, Gilbert, AZ 85233
Tel.: (480) 655-0100
Web Site: http://www.rigidindustries.com
Light Emitting Diode (LED) Products Mfr
N.A.I.C.S.: 334413
Taylor Anderson (VP-Branding)

Lumitec LLC (3)
1405 Poinsettia Dr Ste 10, Delray Beach,
FL 33444
Tel.: (561) 272-9840
Web Site: http://www.lumiteclighting.com
Lighting Equipment Mfr
N.A.I.C.S.: 335139
John Kujawa (Pres)

Trackpoint Systems LLC (3)

4717 Centennial Blvd, Nashville, TN 37203-3462
Tel.: (615) 469-5152
Tracking Products Mfr
N.A.I.C.S.: 334519

Subsidiary (Non-US):

Truck-Lite Europe Ltd. (3)
Barrows Road, Harlow, CM19 5FA, Essex, United Kingdom
Tel.: (44) 01279406406
Web Site: http://www.truck-lite.eu.com
Sales Range: $25-49.9 Million
Lighting Components Mfr for the Automotive Industry
N.A.I.C.S.: 336320

Foreside Financial Group LLC (1)
3 Canal Plz Ste 100, Portland, ME 04101
Tel.: (207) 553-7110
Web Site: http://www.foreside.com
Regulatory Compliance Services to Investment Management Industry
N.A.I.C.S.: 561499
Mark A. Fairbanks (Head-Distr Svcs)
David Whitaker (Pres)
Trudance L. C. Bakke (CFO)
Richard J. Berthy (CEO)
Jennifer E. Hoopes (Head-Consulting & Global Bus)
Christopher Lanza (COO)
Samantha Swift (Mng Dir-Risk & Corp Compliance)
Chuck Todd (Head-Fund Officer Svcs)
Josef Valdman (Mng Dir-Bus Dev & Capital Introductions)
Judith Coye Beressi (Dir-HR)
Bill Cox (Chief Admin Officer)

Subsidiary (Domestic):

Alaric Compliance Services LLC (2)
150 Broadway Ste 302, New York, NY 10038
Tel.: (646) 747-3182
Web Site: http://www.alariccompliance.com
Investment Advisory, Business Development & Financial Services
N.A.I.C.S.: 541611
Guy F. Talarico (CEO)

Capital Markets Compliance LLC (2)
3525 Holcomb Bridge Rd, Norcross, GA 30092
Tel.: (770) 263-7300
Web Site: http://www.cmcompliance.com
Rev.: $3,100,000
Emp.: 30
Investment Banking & Securities Dealing Services
N.A.I.C.S.: 523150
Jonathan A. Self (CFO)

Cipperman Compliance Services LLC (2)
480 E. Swedesford Road, Suite 220, Wayne, PA 19087
Tel.: (610) 687-5320
Web Site: https://www.cipperman.com
All Other Support Services
N.A.I.C.S.: 561990

Hardin Compliance Consulting, LLC (2)
Stonewood Commons II 103 Bradford Rd Ste 200, Wexford, PA 15090
Tel.: (833) 942-2218
Web Site: http://www.hardincompliance.com
General Management Consulting Services
N.A.I.C.S.: 541611
Matthew S. Hardin (Pres & CEO)
Jill Grenda (Mng Dir)
David Blue (Mng Dir-Strategic Plng)

Infinite RF Holdings, Inc. (1)
17802 Fitch, Irvine, CA 92614
Tel.: (866) 727-8376
Web Site: http://www.infiniterf.com
Supplier of Radio Frequency Technology Components
N.A.I.C.S.: 334419
David Collier (COO)
Alexander Arrieta (Chief HR Officer)
Penny Cotner (Pres & CEO)

Subsidiary (Domestic):

L-com, Inc. (2)

50 High St W Mill 3rd Fl Ste 30, North Andover, MA 01845
Tel.: (978) 682-6936
Web Site: http://www.l-com.com
Communication Equipment Mfr
N.A.I.C.S.: 334220

Subsidiary (Domestic):

L-com Global Connectivity Corp. - Florida (3)
1615 S Congress Ave Ste 202, Delray Beach, FL 33445
Tel.: (978) 682-6936
Web Site: http://www.l-com.com
Emp.: 350
Communication Equipment Mfr
N.A.I.C.S.: 334220
Mark Spinney (Gen Mgr)

Mercer Advisors Inc. (1)
1200 17th St Ste 500, Denver, CO 80202
Tel.: (888) 885-8101
Web Site: https://www.merceradvisors.com
Wealth Management & Advisory Services
N.A.I.C.S.: 523940
Loren Pierson (COO)
Dave Welling (CEO)
Daniel Gourvitch (Pres)

Subsidiary (Domestic):

Bell Wealth Management Inc. (2)
2901 Bee Cave Rd Ste F, Austin, TX 78746
Tel.: (512) 347-9500
Wealth Management & Investment Consulting Services
N.A.I.C.S.: 523940
Colin A. Bell (Pres)

Day & Ennis LLC (2)
125 Plantation Centre S Ste 400B, Macon, GA 31210-1906
Tel.: (478) 474-7480
Web Site: http://www.dayandennis.com
Investment Advice
N.A.I.C.S.: 523940

Jackson Financial Management, Inc. (2)
151 Kalmus Dr Ste H-7, Costa Mesa, CA 92626
Tel.: (714) 434-6900
Web Site: https://www.merceradvisors.com
Portfolio Management
N.A.I.C.S.: 523940

Kanaly Trust (2)
5555 San Felipe St Ste 200, Houston, TX 77056-2760 **(100%)**
Tel.: (713) 561-9300
Web Site: http://www.kanaly.com
Investment Management & Financial Planning Services
N.A.I.C.S.: 523999
Drew Kanaly (Mgr-Relationship)
Betty Keddington (COO & Chief Compliance Officer)
Linda Halcomb (Sr VP & Mgr-Trust Ops)
Todd Hunter (VP & Controller)

Mercer Global Advisors Inc. (2)
200 17th St Ste 500, Denver, CO 80202
Tel.: (805) 565-1681
Web Site: http://www.merceradvisors.com
Investment Advisory Services
N.A.I.C.S.: 523940
Deb Atwater-Robles (Dir-Incentive Compensation)
Aaron Langston (Reg VP)
Bryan Powers (VP)
David Barton (Vice Chm)
Donald Calcagni (Chief Investment Officer)
Dave Welling (CEO)

Subsidiary (Domestic):

Adam Financial Associates Inc. (3)
2500 N Military Trl Ste 306, Boca Raton, FL 33431
Tel.: (561) 417-0001
Web Site: http://www.adamfinl.com
Financial Planning & Wealth Management Services
N.A.I.C.S.: 523940
Mari Adam (Founder & Pres)

Atlanta Financial Associates Inc. (3)
5901 Peachtree Dunwdy NE Ste B275, Atlanta, GA 30328-7148

Tel.: (770) 261-5380
Web Site: http://www.atlantafinancial.com
Investment Advice
N.A.I.C.S.: 523940
Julianne F. Andrews (Principal)

ClearRock Capital, LLC (3)
131 4th St E, Ketchum, ID 83340
Tel.: (208) 726-8858
Web Site: http://www.clearrockcapital.com
Investment Advice
N.A.I.C.S.: 523940
Mark Eshman (Chm & CEO)

Empyrion Wealth Management, Inc. (3)
3741 Douglas Blvd Ste 130, Roseville, CA 95661
Tel.: (916) 786-7626
Web Site: http://www.empyrionwealth.com
Investment Management Service
N.A.I.C.S.: 523999
Renee Morrison (Dir-Client Svcs)
Kimberly Foss (Founder & Pres)
Marcy Gorton (Mgr-Ops)

Fure Financial Corp. (3)
8500 Normandale Lake Blvd Ste 950, Bloomington, MN 55437
Tel.: (952) 944-8250
Web Site: http://www.furefinancial.com
Portfolio Management
N.A.I.C.S.: 523940
Dale L. Acton (VP)
Johannes C. Fure (Founder, Pres & Chief Investment Officer)
Grant A. Meyer (Mgr-IT)

Goldstein Munger & Associates (3)
18 Crow Canyon Ct Ste 250, San Ramon, CA 94583
Tel.: (925) 552-1400
Web Site: http://www.goldsteinmunger.com
Investment Advice
N.A.I.C.S.: 523940
Bob Munger (Owner)

HawsGoodwin Investment Management, LLC (3)
5000 Meridian Blvd Ste 530, Franklin, TN 37067
Tel.: (615) 771-1012
Web Site: http://www.hawsgoodwin.com
Financial Services
N.A.I.C.S.: 523999
C. Arthur Haws (Co-Founder, CEO & Mng Partner)
W. Cam Goodwin (Co-Founder, Pres & Mng Partner)
Lisa Butler (Dir-Client Relationships)
Tom Weatherman (Dir-Insurance Svcs)

Kingfisher Capital, LLC (3)
201 S College St, Charlotte, NC 28244
Tel.: (704) 333-1710
Web Site: http://www.kingfishercapital.com
Securities Brokerage Services
N.A.I.C.S.: 523150
Chad Frk (Dir-AS)

M.J. Smith & Associates, Inc. (3)
5613 DTC Pkwy Ste 650, Greenwood Village, CO 80111
Tel.: (303) 768-0007
Web Site: http://www.mj-smith.com
Emp.: 11
Portfolio Management
N.A.I.C.S.: 523940
Mark J. Smith (Pres)

Private Asset Management, Inc. (3)
11995 El Camino Real, San Diego, CA 92130
Tel.: (858) 792-3800
Web Site: http://www.pamgmt.com
Sales Range: $1-9.9 Million
Emp.: 28
Investment Advice
N.A.I.C.S.: 523940
Gary Pulford (Sr VP & Portfolio Mgr)
Jeff Witt (Dir-Res)
Jonathan Elsberry (Corp VP & Mgr)
Michael D. Berlin (Gen Counsel & VP)
Stephen Cohen (Mgr-Asset)
John Harrington (Sr VP & Portfolio Mgr)
Michael Love (Portfolio Mgr)
Michael N. McGreevy (Mng Dir-Indian Wells)
Michael Ramirez (Portfolio Mgr)
Teresa Whorton (Mgr-Acctg)
Victor Calise (Sr VP-Mktg)

Quest Capital Management Inc (3)
8235 Douglas Ave, Dallas, TX 75225
Tel.: (214) 691-6090
Web Site: http://questadvisor.com
Rev.: $4,400,000
Emp.: 30
Portfolio Management
N.A.I.C.S.: 523940
Dennis J. Moore (Mgr)

Resource Planning Group Ltd. (3)
10 Glenlake Pkwy S Tower, Ste 150, Atlanta, GA 30328
Tel.: (770) 671-9500
Web Site: http://www.rpgplanner.com
Rev.: $2,490,000
Emp.: 6
Portfolio Management
N.A.I.C.S.: 523940
John E. Howard (Owner)

Starks Financial Group Inc. (3)
56 Clayton St, Asheville, NC 28801-2424
Tel.: (828) 285-8777
Web Site: http://www.starksfinancial.com
Miscellaneous Financial Investment Activities
N.A.I.C.S.: 523999
Dawn Starks (Pres)

The Asset Advisory Group, Inc. (3)
4600 McAuley Pl Ste 140, Cincinnati, OH 45242-4765
Tel.: (513) 771-7222
Web Site: http://www.taaginc.com
Miscellaneous Financial Investment Activities
N.A.I.C.S.: 523999
Gregg Jones (Mgr-Ops)
Chip Workman (Pres)

Transitions Wealth Management LLC (3)
8101 E Prentice Ave, Greenwood Village, CO 93550-4036
Tel.: (303) 221-4867
Web Site: https://transitionswm.com
Miscellaneous Intermediation
N.A.I.C.S.: 523910

Wrenn Financial Strategies, Inc. (3)
8352 6 Forks Rd Ste 201, Raleigh, NC 27615
Tel.: (919) 848-9999
Web Site: http://www.wrennfinancial.com
Financial Investment Activities
N.A.I.C.S.: 523999
Janice Wrenn (Co-Founder & VP)
Maxie E. Wrenn Jr. (Co-Founder & Pres)

Subsidiary (Domestic):

Regis Management Company LLC (2)
873 Santa Cruz Avenue, Ste 206, Menlo Park, CA 94025
Tel.: (650) 838-1030
Web Site: http://www.regisllc.com
Intermediation
N.A.I.C.S.: 523910
Steven Go (COO & Chief Compliance Officer)

Numerix LLC (1)
99 Park Ave 5th Fl, New York, NY 10016
Tel.: (212) 302-2220
Web Site: http://www.numerix.com
Sales Range: $25-49.9 Million
Emp.: 215
Asset Management Services
N.A.I.C.S.: 523940
James Jockle (CMO & Sr VP-Global Mktg & Corp Comm)
Gregory Whitten (Chm)
Mark A. Shornick (CFO)
Dawn Patrick (COO & Exec VP-Global Ops)
Meng Lu (Sr VP-Fin Engrg)
Benjamin Meyvin (Sr VP-Product Dev Grp & Head-Product Dev)
Satyam Kancharla (Chief Strategy Officer & Sr VP-Client Solutions Grp)
Elaine McKiernan (Sr VP-Global Bus Dev)
Yukiko Nakamura (Sr VP-Japan, Korea & Tokyo Office)
Erdem Ozgul (Sr VP-Singapore Office)
Steven R. O'Hanlon (Vice Chm)
Jennifer Bonelli (Sr VP-HR)
Saul Stepner (Sr VP-Americas Direct Sls)
Scott Haney (Sr VP-Enterprise Sys Analytics)

Genstar Capital, LLC—(Continued)

Joseph Gruna (Sr VP-IT)
Emanuele Conti (CEO)
Joseph Saporito (Exec VP-Global Direct Sls)

Subsidiary (Domestic):

Kynex Inc (2)
17 17 Route 208, Fair Lawn, NJ 07410
Tel.: (201) 796-4900
Web Site: http://www.kynex.com
Rev.: $2,936,000
Emp.: 8
Portfolio Management
N.A.I.C.S.: 523940
Pheroza Arcot (Pres)

PolyPaths, LLC (2)
45 Rockefeller Plz Ste 2325, New York, NY 10111
Tel.: (212) 332-6288
Web Site: http://www.polypaths.com
Sales Range: $1-9.9 Million
Emp.: 17
Financial Risk Analytics Services
N.A.I.C.S.: 561499
Stanley Diller (Principal)
James Golan (Product Mgr)
Kelli Sayres (Sr Mng Dir)
Gene Park (Mng Dir)

OEConnection LLC (1)
4205 Highlander Pkwy, Richfield, OH 44286-9077 (70%)
Web Site: http://www.oeconnection.com
Automobile Replacement Parts Sales & Service
N.A.I.C.S.: 423120
Penny Dickos (VP-Fin)
Ike Herman (Chief Product Officer & Exec VP)
Chuck Rotuno (Chm)
Philip Firrell (Exec VP-Mergers & Acq)
Paul Johnson (Exec VP-Bus Integration)
Amy French (Chief Admin Officer & Exec VP)
Bill Lopez (VP & Gen Mgr-Collision)
John Kovac (Dir-Natl Accts)
Kyle McChesney (Exec VP-Natl Accts)
Katherine Golden (CTO & Exec VP)
Dave Pankow (Dir-Bus Dev)
Jon Palazzo (VP & Gen Mgr-Mechanical)
Patrick C. Brown (Pres & CEO)

Ohio Transmission Corporation (1)
1900 Jetway Blvd, Columbus, OH 43219
Tel.: (800) 837-6827
Web Site: http://www.otpnet.com
Industrial Fluid Power, Pump, Power Transmission, Motion Control & Electrical Equipment Distr
N.A.I.C.S.: 423830
Matt Piatt (CFO & COO)
Philip Derrow (Pres & CEO)
Rob Webb (Pres-OTP Industrial Solutions)

Subsidiary (Domestic):

Air Technologies, Inc. (2)
1900 Jetway Blvd, Columbus, OH 43219
Tel.: (614) 342-6247
Web Site: http://www.aircompressors.com
Emp.: 25
Air Compressor Distr
N.A.I.C.S.: 423830
Kurt Lang (Pres)

Buckeye Pumps Inc. (2)
1311 Freese Works Pl, Galion, OH 44833
Tel.: (419) 468-7866
Web Site: http://www.buckeyepumps.com
Pumps & Pumping Equipment Distr
N.A.I.C.S.: 423830
Dave Falk (VP)
Ryan Hoffman (Engr-Municipal Application)
Todd Sweitzer (Dir-Svc)
Zach Baker (Engr-Application)
Josh Mullins (Mgr-Inside Sls)
Bruce Whitmyre (Engr-Application)
Matt Spring (Engr-Application)
Greg Mueller (Acct Mgr)
Ken Miracle (Acct Mgr)
Sean O'Toole (Acct Mgr)
John Miller (Mgr-Municipal Market)
Dustin Renner (Acct Mgr)

Filter & Coating Technology, Inc. (2)
5706 W River Rd NE, Belmont, MI 49306

Tel.: (616) 784-3228
Web Site: https://fact.otcindustrial.com
Warm Air Heating And Air Conditioning
N.A.I.C.S.: 423730

Furey Filter & Pump Inc. (2)
N117 W19237 Fulton Dr, Germantown, WI 53022
Tel.: (414) 358-5555
Web Site: http://www.fureyfp.com
Sales Range: $10-24.9 Million
Emp.: 50
Pumps & Pumping Equipment Whslr
N.A.I.C.S.: 423830
George Furey (Pres)
Jack Furey (VP)

Laron, Inc. (2)
4255 Santa Fe Dr, Kingman, AZ 86401
Tel.: (928) 757-8424
Web Site: http://www.laron.com
Electric Equipment Mfr
N.A.I.C.S.: 335999
Glenn Thoroughman (CEO)
Larry Tree (Pres)
John Hansen (COO)
Gary Maclay (CFO)

Midway Industrial Supply, Inc. (2)
4759 Old Highway 8, Saint Paul, MN 55112
Tel.: (763) 780-3000
Web Site: http://www.midwayis.com
Industrial Machinery & Equipment
N.A.I.C.S.: 423830

Subsidiary (Domestic):

Contrast Equipment, Inc. (3)
1449 N Topping Ave, Kansas City, MO 64120
Tel.: (816) 241-2412
Web Site:
http://www.contrastequipment.com
Sales Range: $1-9.9 Million
Emp.: 12
Industrial Fluid Handling & Finishing Equipment
N.A.I.C.S.: 423830
Jeff Brady (Mgr-Sls)
Neil Cortus (Sr Project Mgr)

Subsidiary (Domestic):

Tape Industrial Sales Inc. (2)
13450 Parkview Ct, Louisville, KY 40223
Tel.: (502) 254-0305
Web Site: http://www.tapeindustrial.com
Industrial Paint Spray Equipment Sales
N.A.I.C.S.: 424950
Susan Estes (Office Mgr)

Tri-Power Mpt, Inc. (2)
1447 S Main St, Akron, OH 44301
Tel.: (330) 773-3307
Web Site: http://www.tri-power.com
Electric Equipment Mfr
N.A.I.C.S.: 423610
Richard Wiley (Pres & Mgr-Div)

PSKW, LLC (1)
The Crossings at Jefferson Park 200 Jefferson Park, Whippany, NJ 07981
Tel.: (908) 809-6100
Web Site: http://www.connectiverx.com
Pharmaceutical Marketing Services
N.A.I.C.S.: 541613
Chris Dowd (Exec VP-Market & Product Dev)
Jim Corrigan (CEO)
Harry Totonis (Chm)
Frank Dana (Pres & Chief Comml Officer)
Danielle Daly (Chief Mktg & Comm Officer)

Prometheus Group Enterprises, LLC (1)
1101 Haynes St Ste 218, Raleigh, NC 27610
Tel.: (919) 835-0810
Web Site: http://www.prometheusgroup.com
Computer Software Services
N.A.I.C.S.: 513210
Steve Mankoff (Gen Partner)
Eric Huang (CEO)

Subsidiary (Non-US):

VIZIYA Corporation (2)
50 Dundas Street East Suite 201, Hamilton, L9H 7K6, ON, Canada
Tel.: (905) 544-4144
Web Site: http://www.viziya.com

Enterprise Asset Management Services
N.A.I.C.S.: 518210
John Vujicic (Founder)
Sean Licata (VP-Mktg & Bus Dev)
Dejan Obradovic (VP-Tech)
Paul Lupinacci (VP-Dev)
Paul Sunderland (Interim Pres & Interim CEO)

Subsidiary (Domestic):

Work Technology Corporation (2)
1 Mercer Cir, Somerville, MA 02144
Tel.: (617) 625-5888
Web Site: http://www.worktech.com
Time & Attendance Software & Cost Tracking Services
N.A.I.C.S.: 541511
Jack Hall (Pres & CEO)

SPay, Inc. (1)
5360 Legacy Dr Ste #150, Plano, TX 75024
Tel.: (972) 372-0777
Web Site: http://stacksports.com
Holding Company; Youth Sports Organization Management Services
N.A.I.C.S.: 551112
Casey Amidon (Chief People Officer)
Brandon Flora (VP-Strategic Programs)
Jeff Young (CEO)
Jonathan Dussault (CFO)
Todd Reynolds (CTO)
Jeff Brunsberg (Chief Revenue Officer & Chief Strategy Officer)

Subsidiary (Domestic):

Affinity Sports, LLC (2)
225 Broadway Ste 800, San Diego, CA 92101
Tel.: (800) 808-7195
Web Site: http://www.affinity-sports.com
Data Management Services
N.A.I.C.S.: 518210
Mark Skeen (CEO)
Shannon Stewart (VP)
Joel Myers (Acct Mgr)

Blue Sombrero, LLC (2)
746 Willoughby Way NE, Atlanta, GA 30307-2276
Web Site: http://www.bluesombrero.com
Software Development Services
N.A.I.C.S.: 541511
Benton Carper (VP-Ops)

End Result Company LLC (2)
3426 Towne Pointe Dr, Bettendorf, IA 52722
Tel.: (818) 784-1572
Web Site: http://www.theendresultco.com
Chip Timing & Data Management Services
N.A.I.C.S.: 541511

RaceWire LLC (2)
150 Wood Rd Ste 308, Braintree, MA 02184
Tel.: (855) 722-3947
Web Site: http://www.racewire.com
Event Management Services
N.A.I.C.S.: 711310
John Adams (Sr Acct Mgr)
John Ware (Mgr-Road Race Event)

STACK, Inc. (2)
1228 Euclid Ave Ste 1000, Cleveland, OH 44115
Tel.: (216) 861-7000
Web Site: http://www.stack.com
Television Broadcasting
N.A.I.C.S.: 516120

Skyhawks Sports Academy, Inc. (2)
1826 E Sprague Ave, Spokane, WA 99202
Tel.: (509) 466-6590
Web Site: http://www.skyhawks.com
Recreational & Vacation Camps (except Campgrounds)
N.A.I.C.S.: 721214
Jason Frazier (Pres & COO)
Josh Kaiel (VP-Franchising)
Matt Perham (VP-Ops)
Tracy Umbrell (Exec Dir-Fin)
Andrew Chapman (Exec Dir-Bus Dev)
Ryan Weaver (Dir-Mktg)
Matt Junior (Dir-Natl Sls)

Sequest Technologies, Inc. (1)
801 Warrenville Rd Ste 350, Lisle, IL 60532
Tel.: (630) 577-9003
Web Site: http://www.sequest.net
Rev.: $1,500,000

Emp.: 16
Software Developer
N.A.I.C.S.: 513210

Tekni-Plex, Inc. (1)
460 E Swedesford Rd Ste 3000, Wayne, PA 19087
Tel.: (484) 690-1520
Web Site: http://www.tekni-plex.com
Food, Cosmetics & Pharmaceutical Packaging Materials Mfr
N.A.I.C.S.: 322220
John Seifert (CFO)
David Waksman (Chief Legal Officer & Sr VP)
Rochelle Gesoff Krombolz (Chief HR Officer & Sr VP)
Steve Penn (Sr VP-Sls & Mktg)
Phil Bourgeois (Sr VP-Global Technology & Regulatory Affairs)
Suj Mehta (Sr VP-Corporate Devt & Mergers & Acquisitions)
Jeff Rishel (VP-Global Information Tech)
Lance Novotny (VP-Mfg & Engrg)
Kirk H. Rumsey (VP-Procurement)
Brenda Chamulak (Pres & CEO)
Chris Qualters (CEO-Healthcare)
Eldon Schaffer (CEO-Consumer Products)

Subsidiary (Non-US):

Action Technology Belgium (2)
Industrielaan 37, 9320, Erembodegem, Belgium
Tel.: (32) 53650711
Web Site: http://www.tekni-plex.be
Plastic Packaging Products Mfr
N.A.I.C.S.: 326199
Luc Vercruyssen (Mng Dir)

Subsidiary (Domestic):

Colorite Polymers (2)
101 Railroad Ave, Ridgefield, NJ 07657
Tel.: (800) 631-1577
Web Site: http://www.tekni-plex.com
Vinyl Compounds Mfr
N.A.I.C.S.: 326220

Colorite Specialty Resins (2)
101 Railroad Ave, Ridgefield, NJ 07657-2312
Tel.: (800) 631-1577
Web Site: http://www.tekni-plex.com
Resin Mfr
N.A.I.C.S.: 325991

Dolco Packaging (2)
252 Hosea Rd, Lawrenceville, GA 30046
Tel.: (770) 963-6191
Web Site: http://www.tekni-plex.com
Foam Packaging Mfr
N.A.I.C.S.: 326199

Plant (Domestic):

Dolco Packaging (3)
2110 Patterson St, Decatur, IN 46733-1892
Tel.: (260) 728-2161
Web Site: http://www.tekni-plex.com
Foam Packaging Mfr
N.A.I.C.S.: 326199
James Moser (Coord-Warehouse)
Linzi Reynolds (Mgr-Cost & Plng)

Subsidiary (Domestic):

Fibro Corporation (2)
3101 S Tacoma Way, Tacoma, WA 98409
Tel.: (509) 888-8866
Web Site: http://www.fibrocorp.com
Molded-Fiber Packaging Services
N.A.I.C.S.: 561910
Paul Zhang (Pres)

Subsidiary (Non-US):

Grupo Phoenix (2)
Calle 17F 126-90, Bogota, 110921, Colombia
Tel.: (57) 1 4222000
Web Site: http://www.grupophoenix.com
Sales Range: $750-799.9 Million
Emp.: 4,000
Plastic Packaging Mfr
N.A.I.C.S.: 326112
Alberto Peisach (CEO)
Jaime Lederman (COO)

Subsidiary (Domestic):

Multidimensionales S.A. (3)
Calle 17F 126-90, Bogota, 110921, Colombia
Tel.: (57) 1 422 2000
Emp.: 2,000
Plastic Food Packaging Products Mfr & Distr
N.A.I.C.S.: 326199
Juan Felipe Martinez *(Country Mgr-Colombia)*

PHOENIX PACKAGING CARIBE S.A.S. (3)
KM 9 Via Mamonal Zona Franca La Candelaria Etapa 2, Bolivar, Cartagena, Colombia
Tel.: (57) 14222000
Plastic Packaging Mfr
N.A.I.C.S.: 326112

PHOENIX PAPER PACKAGING COLOMBIA S.A.S. (3)
Calle 98 Sur No 48-225 Bodega 115, Centro Industrial Puerta del Sur La Estrella, Antioquia, Colombia
Tel.: (57) 44446052
Plastic Packaging Mfr
N.A.I.C.S.: 326112

Subsidiary (Non-US):

PHOENIX PAPER PACKAGING MEXICO, S. DE R.L. DE C.V. (3)
Carretera Nacional Km 206 1 Col Gil de Leyva, Montemorelos, Nuevo Leon, Mexico
Tel.: (52) 8262638154
Plastic Packaging Mfr
N.A.I.C.S.: 326112

Subsidiary (US):

Phoenix Packaging LLC (3)
3900 Dembroke Rd, Hollywood, FL 33020
Tel.: (954) 241-0023
Plastics Product Mfr
N.A.I.C.S.: 326199

Subsidiary (Non-US):

Phoenix Packaging Mexico, S.A. de C.V. (3)
Km 39 3 autopista Mexico Queretaro Parque Industrial La Luz, Cuautitlan Izcalli Edo de, Mexico, 54716, Mexico
Tel.: (52) 55 5063 9800
Web Site: http://www.grupophoenix.com
Emp.: 700
Plastic Packaging Container Mfr
N.A.I.C.S.: 326199

Branch (Non-US):

Phoenix Venezuela (3)
Av Francisco de Miranda Edificio Seguros Venezuela Piso 10, Urbanizacion Campo Alegre, Caracas, Venezuela
Tel.: (58) 212 953 4106
Web Site: http://www.grupophoenix.com
Regional Managing Office; Packaging Products Mfr & Distr
N.A.I.C.S.: 551114

Subsidiary (Domestic):

Natvar Tekni-Plex, Inc. (2)
19555 E Arenth Ave, City of Industry, CA 91748
Tel.: (909) 594-3660
Web Site: http://www.tekni-plex.com
Medical Tubing Mfr
N.A.I.C.S.: 326199

Seisa Medical, Inc. (2)
9005 Montana Ave, El Paso, TX 79925
Tel.: (915) 774-4321
Web Site: http://www.seisa.com
Emp.: 2,500
Medical Device Design, Development & Component Mfr
N.A.I.C.S.: 339112
Julio Chiu *(Founder & CEO)*

Subsidiary (Domestic):

Peridot Corporation (3)
1072 Serpentine Ln Ste D, Pleasanton, CA 94566
Tel.: (925) 461-8830
Web Site: http://www.peridotcorp.com

Sales Range: $1-9.9 Million
Emp.: 43
Fabricated Plate Work (Boiler Shop)
N.A.I.C.S.: 332313
Debra Pickerell *(VP)*
Anthony Cano *(Mgr-Production)*

Subsidiary (Domestic):

The Bruna Corporation (2)
2800 NW 105 Ave, Doral, FL 33172
Tel.: (305) 233-5553
Web Site: http://www.tekni-plex.com
Sales Range: $10-24.9 Million
Miscellaneous Nondurable Goods Whslr
N.A.I.C.S.: 424990
Antonio E. Bruna IV *(Owner)*

Tri-Seal, Inc. (2)
900 Bradley Hill Rd, Blauvelt, NY 10913
Tel.: (845) 353-3300
Web Site: http://www.tekni-plex.com
Plastic Packaging Products Mfr
N.A.I.C.S.: 326113

Subsidiary (Domestic):

SANCAP Liner Technology, Inc. (3)
16123 Armour St NE, Alliance, OH 44601 **(100%)**
Tel.: (330) 821-1166
Web Site: http://www.sancapliner.com
Emp.: 100
Heat-Seal, Pressure-Sensitive & Gasket-Sealing Liners for Pharmaceutical & Food Applications Mfr
N.A.I.C.S.: 561910
Mark Fueger *(Natl Sls Mgr)*

Branch (Domestic):

Tri-Seal, Inc. (3)
112 Church St, Flemington, NJ 08822
Tel.: (908) 782-4000
Web Site: http://www.tri-seal.com
Plastic Packaging Products Mfr
N.A.I.C.S.: 326113

Telestream, LLC (1)
848 Gold Flat Rd, Nevada City, CA 95959
Tel.: (530) 470-1300
Web Site: http://www.telestream.net
Digital Video Transcoding Software & High-Quality Media Exchange Services
N.A.I.C.S.: 513210
Dan Castles *(CEO)*
Shawn Carnahan *(Co-Founder & CTO)*
Steve Tilly *(Co-Founder & VP-Engrg)*
Anna Greco *(VP-Client Svcs-Enterprise Products)*
Jamie Lefebvre *(Dir-HR)*
Paul Turner *(VP-Enterprise Product Mgmt)*
Scott Murray *(Mgr-Corp Mktg & Desktop Products)*
Mark Wronski *(VP-Amercas Sls-Enterprise Products)*
George Boath *(VP-Intl Sls-Enterprise Products)*
Kyle Ford *(Pres & COO)*
Chris Drake *(VP-Bus & Corp Dev)*
Diana Horowitz *(VP-Sls-East)*
Benjamin Desbois *(Chief Sls Officer & Sr VP)*

Subsidiary (Domestic):

IneoQuest Technologies, Inc. (2)
170 Forbes Blvd, Mansfield, MA 02048
Tel.: (508) 339-2497
End-to-End Quality, Services & New Assurance Solutions for Video Users
N.A.I.C.S.: 541519
Satish Yellanki *(Dir-Product Dev)*

Subsidiary (Non-US):

IneoQuest Technologies Deutschland GmbH (3)
Im Breitspiel 21, 69126, Heidelberg, Germany
Tel.: (49) 80318076680
Hands-On Demonstration & Technical Training Facility
N.A.I.C.S.: 611420

IneoQuest Technologies Ltd. (3)
The Magdalen Centre Oxford Science Park, Robert Robinson Ave, Oxford, OX4 4GA, United Kingdom
Tel.: (44) 1865784322
Sales Support Center

N.A.I.C.S.: 541990

Vector Solutions, Inc. (1)
4890 W Kennedy Blvd Ste 300, Tampa, FL 33609
Tel.: (813) 286-7992
Web Site: http://www.vectorsolutions.com
Computer System Design Services
N.A.I.C.S.: 541512
Jonathan Cherins *(CEO)*

Subsidiary (Domestic):

RedVector.com, LLC (2)
4890 W Kennedy Blvd Ste 300, Tampa, FL 33609
Tel.: (800) 418-6789
Web Site: http://www.redvector.com
IT Training
N.A.I.C.S.: 611420
Jeff Gordon *(CEO)*

Slate Solutions, Inc. (2)
954 S Madison St, Hinsdale, IL 60521
Tel.: (847) 521-0850
Web Site: https://pathwayos.com
Education Administration Services
N.A.I.C.S.: 923110
Cecilia Retelle Zywicki *(CEO)*
Jimmy McDermott *(Founder & CTO)*

Subsidiary (Domestic):

PresenceLearning, Inc. (3)
530 7th Ave Ste 501, New York, NY 10018
Tel.: (415) 512-9000
Web Site: http://www.presencelearning.com
Online Speech & Occupational Therapy, Behavioral & Mental Health Services
N.A.I.C.S.: 624190
Aaron Skiles *(VP-Ops)*
Russ Greenspan *(CTO)*
Anthony Pane *(CFO)*
Laura Sullivan *(VP-Mktg & Comm)*

GENSTAR DEVELOPMENT COMPANY
12770 El Camino Real Ste 220, San Diego, CA 92130
Tel.: (858) 523-9090
Web Site: https://www.genstar.com
Land Development Partnership
N.A.I.C.S.: 112990
Frank Thomas *(CEO)*
Gina R. Papandrea *(CFO & Exec VP)*
Paul Boskovich *(Pres)*
Mike Kilgallon *(Pres-Atlanta Communities)*
John Crawford *(Controller)*
Dave Boles *(VP-Winnipeg Communities)*
Leigh Melnychuk *(VP-Edmonton Communities)*
Marcello Chiacchia *(VP-Calgary Communities)*
Ray Cunliffe *(VP-Atlanta Communities)*
Dave Waters *(VP-California Bus Dev)*

GENSUN CASUAL LIVING
1219 E Locust St, Ontario, CA 91761-4566
Tel.: (909) 230-9698
Web Site:
   http://www.gensuncasual.com
Sales Range: $10-24.9 Million
Emp.: 13
Outdoor Furnishings
N.A.I.C.S.: 337126
David Liu *(Pres)*

GENTECH ASSOCIATES, INC.
8103 E US Hwy 36 Ste 166, Avon, IN 46123
Tel.: (317) 547-4809
Web Site:
   http://www.gentechassociates.com
Year Founded: 2011
Sales Range: $1-9.9 Million
Emp.: 23
Government Support Services
N.A.I.C.S.: 921190

Scott Chaplin *(Pres & CEO)*
Tom Byers *(Mng Dir & Sr VP)*
Kimberly D. Whitfield *(Dir-Ops)*
Tiffany Villaveces *(Mgr-HR)*
Katelyn Heston *(Mgr-Talent Acquisition)*

GENTEX CORPORATION
324 Main St, Simpson, PA 18407
Tel.: (570) 282-3550   DE
Web Site:
   https://www.gentexcorp.com
Year Founded: 1995
Sales Range: $50-74.9 Million
Emp.: 570
Commercial & Military Equipment Designer & Mfr
N.A.I.C.S.: 334519
Heather M. Acker *(CFO & Exec VP)*

Subsidiaries:

Artisent, LLC (1)
15 Channel Ctr St, Boston, MA 02210
Tel.: (617) 423-4613
Web Site: http://www.artisent.com
Commercial & Military Headgear Designer & Mfr
N.A.I.C.S.: 339113
David Rogers *(Grp VP-Concept Dev)*

Ops-Core Inc. (1)
12 Channel St Ste 901, Boston, MA 02210
Tel.: (617) 423-4613
Web Site: http://www.gentexcorp.com
Emp.: 140
Commercial & Military Headgear Designer & Mfr
N.A.I.C.S.: 339113
David Rogers *(Grp VP-Concept Dev)*

GENTLE GIANT MOVING CO. INC.
29 Harding St, Somerville, MA 02143
Tel.: (617) 661-3333
Web Site:
   https://www.gentlegiant.com
Year Founded: 1980
Rev.: $12,368,327
Emp.: 90
Local Trucking & Storage Services
N.A.I.C.S.: 484110
Pat Inman *(Dir-Ops)*

GENTLEBROOK, INC.
880 Sunnyside St SW, Hartville, OH 44632
Tel.: (330) 877-7700   OH
Web Site:
   https://www.gentlebrook.org
Year Founded: 1974
Sales Range: $10-24.9 Million
Emp.: 603
Developmental Disability Assistance Services
N.A.I.C.S.: 623210
Dianna Huckestein *(Exec Dir-Corp Comm & Senior Living Svc)*
Norman Wengerd *(CEO)*
Michael Sleutz *(COO)*
Tom Gibbins *(VP)*

GENTNER INC.
9685 W Michigan Ave, Saline, MI 48176
Tel.: (734) 944-0362   MI
Sales Range: $10-24.9 Million
Emp.: 98
Trucking Services
N.A.I.C.S.: 484110
William Gentner *(Pres)*
Robert Gentner *(VP)*
Joseph Gentner *(Sr VP)*

GENTRY FINANCE CORPORATION
25331 I10 W Ste 101, San Antonio, TX 78257

Gentry Finance Corporation—(Continued)

Tel.: (210) 698-0448
Rev.: $35,447,237
Emp.: 4
Provider of Lending Services
N.A.I.C.S.: 522291
A. P. Gentry *(Pres)*

Subsidiaries:

Noble Finance Corporation **(1)**
13135 Dairy Ashford Ste 800, Sugar Land, TX 77478 **(100%)**
Tel.: (281) 276-6100
Rev.: $1,407,269,000
Assets: $5,212,224,000
Liabilities: $1,621,775,000
Net Worth: $3,590,449,000
Earnings: $243,957,000
Emp.: 3,799
Fiscal Year-end: 12/31/2022
Consumer Finance Companies
N.A.I.C.S.: 522291

Noble Finance Corporation **(1)**
308 N Conway Ave Ste 1, Mission, TX 78572-5412
Tel.: (956) 583-2941
Rev.: $210,000
Emp.: 3
Management Consulting Services
N.A.I.C.S.: 541611

Royal Finance Corp **(1)**
26254 I H 10th St W Ste 200, Boerne, TX 78006
Tel.: (210) 698-0448
Sales Range: $25-49.9 Million
Renting Services
N.A.I.C.S.: 522291

Vista Finance Inc. **(1)**
7946 S State St, Midvale, UT 84047
Tel.: (801) 568-0955
Rev.: $130,000
Emp.: 2
Provider of Lending Services
N.A.I.C.S.: 522291

Your Credit Inc. **(1)**
25331 IH 10 MN 31, Boerne, TX 78257
Tel.: (210) 698-0448
Provider of Lending Services
N.A.I.C.S.: 522291
A. P. Gentry *(Pres)*

GENTRY HOMES LTD
560 N Nimitz Hwy, Honolulu, HI 96817
Tel.: (808) 599-5558
Web Site:
http://www.gentryhawaii.com
Sales Range: $25-49.9 Million
Emp.: 80
Land Subdividers & Developers, Residential
N.A.I.C.S.: 236115
Art Pelkaus *(Mgr-Customer Svc)*
Debra Luning *(Dir-Govt Affairs & Community Rels)*
Marlene Eberharrt *(Coord-Community)*
Sheridan Albeso *(Coord-Community)*
Tosh Hosoda *(Sr VP-Plng)*
Rick Hobson *(VP-Sls & Mktg)*

GENTRY PACIFIC, LTD.
PO Box 295, Honolulu, HI 96809
Tel.: (808) 599-5558
Year Founded: 1971
Sales Range: $125-149.9 Million
Emp.: 80
Land Subdividing Services
N.A.I.C.S.: 237210
Dawn Suyenaga *(Sr VP)*

GENTZLER ELECTRIC
11450 Pagemill Rd, Dallas, TX 75243-5506
Tel.: (214) 341-2890
Web Site:
http://www.gentzlerelectric.com
Sales Range: $10-24.9 Million
Emp.: 210
Electrical Wiring Services
N.A.I.C.S.: 238210
Stan Gentzler *(Principal)*
George Guzman *(Dir-Safety & Personnel)*
Dennis Bishop *(Mgr-Svc)*
Jay Zorn *(Project Mgr)*
Ron Moore *(VP-Fin & Admin Dept)*
Tricia Cannon *(Controller)*
Rodney Tomlinson *(Mgr-Production)*
Scott Newell *(VP)*

GENUINE BIO-FUEL, INC.
17250 SW RailRd Ave, Indiantown, FL 34956
Tel.: (772) 597-0228
Web Site:
http://www.genuinebiofuel.com
Year Founded: 2007
Sales Range: $1-9.9 Million
Emp.: 10
Bio-Diesel Fuel Production
N.A.I.C.S.: 324199
Christopher Burdett *(Pres)*
Jeff Longo *(COO)*
George LaCourse *(VP-Admin)*

GENUINE MOTORCARS, INC.
3170 24th Ave N, Saint Petersburg, FL 33713
Tel.: (727) 877-1057
Web Site:
https://www.genuinemotorcars.com
Sales Range: $10-24.9 Million
Emp.: 3
Used Car Retailer
N.A.I.C.S.: 441120
Joe Kase *(Owner & Pres)*

GENXMEX FOODS, INC.
116C May Rd, Wentzville, MO 63385
Tel.: (636) 332-0448
Web Site: http://www.genxmex.com
Sales Range: $10-24.9 Million
Emp.: 5
Fast Food Restaurants & Stands
N.A.I.C.S.: 722513
Craig Wilds *(Dir-Asset Protection)*

GENZINK STEEL SUPPLY & WELDING CO.
40 E 64th St, Holland, MI 49423
Tel.: (616) 392-1437
Web Site:
http://www.genzinksteel.com
Year Founded: 1961
Sales Range: $25-49.9 Million
Emp.: 130
Fabricated Structural Metal
N.A.I.C.S.: 332312
Kenneth Genzink *(Chm)*
Brock Mahler *(COO)*

GEO DRILLING FLUIDS INC.
1431 Union Ave, Bakersfield, CA 93305
Tel.: (661) 325-5919
Web Site: https://www.geodf.com
Sales Range: $10-24.9 Million
Emp.: 80
Chemicals & Allied Products
N.A.I.C.S.: 424690
Jim Clifford *(Pres)*
Tom Needham *(VP-Ops)*
Robert McNabb *(Engr-Drilling Fluids)*

GEO GRADEL CO.
3135 Frnt St, Toledo, OH 43605
Tel.: (419) 691-7123
Web Site:
http://georgegradelco.tripod.com
Rev.: $13,636,216
Emp.: 60
Excavation & Grading, Building Construction

N.A.I.C.S.: 238910
John F. Gradel *(Pres)*

GEO GRAPHICS, INC.
3450 Browns Mill Rd, Atlanta, GA 30354
Tel.: (404) 768-5805 GA
Web Site:
https://www.geographicsinc.com
Year Founded: 1976
Commercial Printing
N.A.I.C.S.: 323111
Norvin C. Hagan *(Founder)*
Jack Schero *(Acct Exec)*
Lindsey Gibb *(Acct Exec)*

GEO-LOGICAL INC.
6551 Industrial Ave, Port Richey, FL 34668
Tel.: (727) 232-8000
Web Site: http://www.geo-logical.com
Year Founded: 2005
Sales Range: $1-9.9 Million
Emp.: 30
Foundation & Remediation Contractor
N.A.I.C.S.: 238110
Chad Dudeck *(Pres)*
Steve Pashoian *(Gen Mgr-Sls)*
Angel Montagna *(Dir-Mktg)*
John Detviler *(Mgr-Customer Rels)*
Judi Ottonello *(Controller)*

GEO-SOLUTIONS INC.
1250 5th Ave, New Kensington, PA 15068
Tel.: (724) 335-7273
Web Site: https://www.geo-solutions.com
Year Founded: 1996
Sales Range: $10-24.9 Million
Emp.: 40
Trains Construction Companies Worldwide to Perform Specialized Work in Soil & Groundwater
N.A.I.C.S.: 237990
Pete Maltese *(VP-Field Ops)*
Kenneth B. Andromalos *(VP-Engrg)*
Robert Schindler *(Pres)*

GEO-SYNTHETICS, INC.
2401 Pewaukee Rd, Waukesha, WI 53188
Tel.: (262) 524-7979
Web Site: https://www.geo-synthetics.com
Year Founded: 1971
Designer, Mfr & Installer of Geo-Synthetic Products & Erosion Control Materials & Systems
N.A.I.C.S.: 541620
John O'Connell *(Pres)*
Randy Hart *(Sls Mgr)*
Dave Clausen *(Project Mgr)*
Randy Pit *(Dir-Bus Dev)*

GEO. BYERS SONS HOLDING INC.
465 S Hamilton, Columbus, OH 43213
Tel.: (614) 228-5111
Web Site: http://www.byersauto.com
Sales Range: $200-249.9 Million
Emp.: 700
Car Dealership Owner & Operator
N.A.I.C.S.: 441110
Gwenna Carter *(Mgr-Acctg)*
Tim England *(Mgr-Parts)*
George W. Byers III *(Pres)*

GEO. GROWNEY MOTORS, INC.
1160 Main St, Red Bluff, CA 96080-2739
Tel.: (530) 527-1034
Web Site:
http://www.geogrowney.com

Sales Range: $10-24.9 Million
Emp.: 17
Car Whslr
N.A.I.C.S.: 441110
Mike Growney *(Pres)*

GEO. R. PIERCE INC.
3800 Pierce Pkwy, Billings, MT 59102
Tel.: (406) 655-8000
Web Site:
https://www.piercehome.com
Rev.: $10,965,511
Emp.: 200
Mobile Home Dealers
N.A.I.C.S.: 459930
G. Ron Pierce *(Pres)*

GEOCEL CORPORATION
2504 Marina Dr, Elkhart, IN 46514-8325
Tel.: (574) 264-0645 IN
Web Site:
https://www.geocelusa.com
Year Founded: 1974
Sales Range: $1-9.9 Million
Emp.: 65
High Performance Sealants & Caulks Mfr
N.A.I.C.S.: 325520
John Bencsics *(Dir-Mktg Svcs)*
Stephen Blacklaw *(Mgr-Sls Ops)*
Kurt Hostetler *(Mgr-Sls-Natl)*
Bruce Kulp *(Mgr-Pur)*

GEOCHEM INTERNATIONAL CORP.
137 Rowayton Ave Ste 330, Norwalk, CT 06853
Tel.: (203) 854-9979
Sales Range: $50-74.9 Million
Emp.: 12
Synthetic Resins, Rubber & Plastic Materials
N.A.I.C.S.: 424690

GEOGRAPHIC SOLUTIONS, INC.
1001 Omaha Cir, Palm Harbor, FL 34683
Tel.: (727) 786-7955 FL
Web Site:
http://www.geographicsolutions.com
Year Founded: 1992
Sales Range: $10-24.9 Million
Emp.: 140
Workforce Solutions Software
N.A.I.C.S.: 513210
Paul Toomey *(Founder & Pres)*
Tim Himes *(Mgr-Ops)*
Hallie Leverich *(Coord-Mktg)*
Mitchell Dimler *(Dir-Data Svcs)*

GEOLOGICS CORP.
5285 Shawnee Rd Ste 300, Alexandria, VA 22312
Tel.: (703) 750-4000
Web Site: http://www.geologics.com
Sales Range: $50-74.9 Million
Emp.: 600
Custom Computer Programming Services
N.A.I.C.S.: 541511
Fernando Arroyo *(Pres)*
Mary Balash-Melrod *(Dir-Mktg)*
Tim Mulcare *(Dir-Sys)*
Robert Lopez-Aparicio *(VP)*
William D. Winkler *(Dir-HR & Risk Mgmt)*
Ann Webb *(Dir-Acctg & Fin)*

GEOMETRICA, INC.
12300 Dundee Ct Ste 200, Cypress, TX 77429

Tel.: (832) 220-1200
Web Site:
   https://www.geometrica.com
Year Founded: 1992
Sales Range: $125-149.9 Million
Emp.: 208
Industrial Building Construction Services
N.A.I.C.S.: 236210
Francisco Castano *(CEO)*
Raul Del Toro *(Dir-Engrg)*
Cecilio Zalba *(Mgr-Sls)*
Gerardo Zamora *(Dir-Projects)*
Rogelio Contreras *(Plant Mgr)*
Gerardo Mendez *(CFO)*
Victoria Rios *(Mgr-Pur)*

GEONERCO INC.
400 N 34th St Ste 300, Seattle, WA 98103
Tel.: (206) 352-2020   WA
Web Site: http://www.geonerco.com
Year Founded: 1983
Sales Range: $25-49.9 Million
Emp.: 150
Home Construction Services
N.A.I.C.S.: 236115
George Neffner III *(Pres)*

GEONETRIC, INC.
415 12th Ave SE, Cedar Rapids, IA 52401
Tel.: (319) 221-1667
Web Site: https://www.geonetric.com
Year Founded: 1999
Rev.: $3,700,000
Emp.: 55
Wired Telecommunications Carriers
N.A.I.C.S.: 517111
Linda Barnes *(VP-Mktg & Comm)*
Ben Dillon *(VP)*
Eric Engelmann *(Founder, Pres & CEO)*

GEONOSTICS, INC.
25 Tri State International Ste 150, Lincolnshire, IL 60069
Tel.: (847) 914-0203
Web Site: http://www.geonostics.com
Sales Range: $10-24.9 Million
Emp.: 10
Micro-Sample Blood Diagnostic Services
N.A.I.C.S.: 621511
David Fleisner *(CEO)*

Subsidiaries:

Flexsite Diagnostics, Inc.   (1)
3543 SW Corporate Pkwy, Palm City, FL 34990
Tel.: (772) 221-8893
Sales Range: $10-24.9 Million
Laboratory Services
N.A.I.C.S.: 621511

GEOPETRO RESOURCES COMPANY
150 California St Ste 600, San Francisco, CA 94111-4564
Tel.: (415) 398-8186   CA
Web Site: http://www.geopetro.com
Emp.: 4
Oil & Gas Exploration, Development & Production
N.A.I.C.S.: 213112
Stuart J. Doshi *(Chm & CEO)*

Subsidiaries:

GeoPetro Alaska LLC   (1)
150 California St Ste 600, San Francisco, CA 94111-4564
Tel.: (415) 398-8186
Web Site: http://www.geopetro.com
Sales Range: $50-74.9 Million
Emp.: 3
Crude Petroleum & Natural Gas Extracting Services
N.A.I.C.S.: 211120

GEOPHYSICAL ELECTRICAL SUPPLY, INC.
6410 Mayfair St, Houston, TX 77087
Tel.: (713) 645-5999
Web Site: https://www.gesco-e.com
Sales Range: $10-24.9 Million
Emp.: 13
Electrical Apparatus & Equipment, Wiring Supplies & Related Equipment Whslr
N.A.I.C.S.: 423610
Duggan Hartzog *(VP)*

GEOPOINT SURVEYING, INC.
213 Hobbs St, Tampa, FL 33619
Tel.: (813) 248-8888   FL
Web Site:
   https://www.geopointsurvey.com
Engineering Services
N.A.I.C.S.: 541330
David A. Williams Jr. *(Pres)*

Subsidiaries:

Emerald Coast Associates, Inc.   (1)
12605 US Highway 98 W, Destin, FL 32550
Tel.: (850) 837-8242
Sales Range: $1-9.9 Million
Emp.: 44
Engineering Services
N.A.I.C.S.: 541330
Dean Burgis *(Pres)*
Daryl Burgis *(Treas & Exec VP)*
Dexter Lundy *(Sec & Exec VP)*
Danny Ross *(Supvr-Field Crew)*

GEORGE & LYNCH, INC.
150 Lafferty Ln, Dover, DE 19901-7205
Tel.: (302) 736-3031   DE
Web Site: https://www.geolyn.com
Year Founded: 1923
Sales Range: $125-149.9 Million
Emp.: 247
Heavy & Highway Contractor, Marine Construction Site Development, Structural Concrete & Environmental Remediation
N.A.I.C.S.: 237310
Dennis J. Dinger *(Pres & CEO)*
David W. McGuigan *(VP-Bus Dev)*
Christopher W. Baker *(VP-Ops)*
Michael Megonigal *(Mgr-Process & Utilities)*
Stephanie Preece *(CFO & Treas)*
Ken Heinsch *(Dir-Safety)*
Leonard J. Brooks *(VP-Bus Dev & Admin Svcs)*
Jeffrey L. Norman *(VP-Estimating)*
Christina Funk *(Co-CFO & Treas)*

GEORGE A. GRANT, INC.
1333 Gillespie St, Richland, WA 99352
Tel.: (509) 946-6188
Web Site: http://www.gagrantinc.com
Year Founded: 1957
Sales Range: $25-49.9 Million
Emp.: 25
Nonresidential Construction Services
N.A.I.C.S.: 236220
Dick Richter *(Owner)*

GEORGE B. WOODCOCK & CO.
9667 Canogo Ave, Chatsworth, CA 91311
Tel.: (818) 998-3774
Web Site:
   http://www.gbwoodcock.com
Sales Range: $10-24.9 Million
Emp.: 50
Packaging Materials
N.A.I.C.S.: 424990
Charles R. Northcross *(Chm)*

GEORGE BALLENTINE FORD INC.
1305 Highway 72 Byp, Greenwood, SC 29649
Tel.: (864) 223-4351
Web Site:
   http://www.georgeballentine.com
Rev.: $43,000,000
Emp.: 60
Automobiles, New & Used
N.A.I.C.S.: 441110
George W. Ballentine Sr. *(Pres)*

GEORGE BRAZILLER, INC.
277 Broadway Ste 708, New York, NY 10007
Tel.: (212) 260-9265
Web Site:
   http://www.georgebraziller.com
Year Founded: 1955
Sales Range: $75-99.9 Million
Emp.: 7
Art, Architectural, Literature, Fiction, Non-Fiction & Poetry Book Publisher
N.A.I.C.S.: 513130
George Braziller *(Founder & Editor-at-Large)*
Michael Braziller *(Pres & Editor)*
Joel Braziller *(Treas & Sec)*

GEORGE C. BRANDT INC.
2975 Long Lk Rd, Saint Paul, MN 55113
Tel.: (651) 636-6500
Web Site: http://www.gcbinc.com
Sales Range: $10-24.9 Million
Emp.: 15
Chemicals & Allied Products, Nec
N.A.I.C.S.: 424690
J. Chris Brandt *(CEO)*

GEORGE C. HOPKINS CONSTRUCTION COMPANY, INC.
919 W Glenoaks Blvd, Glendale, CA 91202-2725
Tel.: (818) 956-0533
Web Site:
   https://www.hopkinsconstruction.com
Year Founded: 1981
Sales Range: $10-24.9 Million
Emp.: 23
Industrial Building Construction Services
N.A.I.C.S.: 236210
Gary Hopkins *(CEO)*

GEORGE C. STAFFORD & SONS INC.
231 Ct St, Laconia, NH 03246
Tel.: (603) 524-1480   NH
Web Site: https://www.staffordoil.com
Year Founded: 1942
Sales Range: $10-24.9 Million
Emp.: 12
Petroleum Products Mfr
N.A.I.C.S.: 424720
Charles D. Stafford *(Pres)*
Jeff Pearson *(Owner & VP)*

GEORGE CHEVROLET A CALIFORNIA CORPORATION
17000 Lakewood Blvd, Bellflower, CA 90706-5594
Tel.: (562) 925-2500
Sales Range: $50-74.9 Million
Emp.: 100
Car Whslr
N.A.I.C.S.: 441110
Jeff Estabrooks *(Owner)*

GEORGE COLEMAN MOTOR CO., INC.
47 Plz Dr, Travelers Rest, SC 29690
Tel.: (864) 689-2048
Web Site:
   https://www.georgecolemanford.com
Sales Range: $10-24.9 Million

Emp.: 45
Car Whslr
N.A.I.C.S.: 441110
Gregg Coleman *(Pres)*

GEORGE DELALLO COMPANY, INC.
6390 Route 30, Jeannette, PA 15644
Tel.: (724) 613-5400   PA
Web Site: https://www.delallo.com
Year Founded: 1954
Sales Range: $10-24.9 Million
Emp.: 120
Specialty Italian Food Products
N.A.I.C.S.: 424490
Philip M. Polsinelli *(Treas & VP)*

GEORGE E. BOOTH CO., INC.
8202 W 10th St, Indianapolis, IN 46214
Tel.: (317) 247-0100
Web Site: https://www.gebooth.com
Year Founded: 1963
Sales Range: $10-24.9 Million
Emp.: 38
Process Instrumentation Products & Related Services Distr
N.A.I.C.S.: 423830
Virgil L. Cross *(VP-Fin)*
Douglas Manning *(Mgr-Tech Svcs)*
Troy Daves *(Mgr-Terminal)*
George E. Booth Jr. *(Pres & CEO)*

GEORGE E. MASKER, INC.
887 71st Ave, Oakland, CA 94621
Tel.: (510) 568-1206
Web Site:
   http://www.maskerpainting.com
Sales Range: $10-24.9 Million
Emp.: 100
Exterior Commercial Painting Contracting Services
N.A.I.C.S.: 238320
Alan Bjerke *(Pres)*
Oscar Chagoya *(Office Mgr)*
Newt Millward *(Project Mgr)*

GEORGE E. WARREN CORPORATION
3001 Ocean Dr Ste 203, Vero Beach, FL 32963-1953
Tel.: (772) 778-7100   FL
Web Site: https://www.gewarren.com
Year Founded: 1908
Sales Range: $1-4.9 Billion
Emp.: 35
Petroleum Products Whslr & Distr
N.A.I.C.S.: 424710
Thomas L. Corr *(Pres & CEO)*
Michael George *(Treas & Controller)*
Jack Virtus *(Mgr-Credit)*
Michele Murphy *(Mgr-Tax)*

GEORGE F. BROCKE & SONS, INC.
901 Hwy 3 W PO Box 159, Kendrick, ID 83537-0159
Tel.: (208) 289-4231   ID
Web Site: http://www.gfbrocke.com
Year Founded: 1948
Sales Range: $10-24.9 Million
Emp.: 35
Vegetable Processing Services
N.A.I.C.S.: 115114
Berton Brocke *(Mgr-Sls Ops)*

GEORGE F. KEMPF SUPPLY CO.
5200 Grays Ave, Philadelphia, PA 19143-5817
Tel.: (215) 724-8000
Web Site:
   http://www.kempfsupply.com
Year Founded: 1950
Sales Range: $10-24.9 Million
Emp.: 60
Other Construction Material Whslr

George F. Kempf Supply Co.—(Continued)
N.A.I.C.S.: 423390
Bob Kempf (Pres)

GEORGE F. YOUNG, INC.

299 Dr Martin Luther King Jr St, Saint Petersburg, FL 33701
Tel.: (727) 822-4317
Web Site:
   https://www.georgefyoung.com
Year Founded: 1919
Sales Range: $10-24.9 Million
Emp.: 110
Architectural Services
N.A.I.C.S.: 541310
James M. King (Sr VP)
Lewis H. Kent (Chm & CEO)
William D. Kent (Pres)
Robin Matson (VP-Client Liaison)

Subsidiaries:

Commercial Partners Realty Inc.   (1)
299 Dr Martin Luther King Jr St N, Saint Petersburg, FL 33701
Tel.: (727) 822-4715
Web Site: http://www.cprteam.com
Real Estate Broker
N.A.I.C.S.: 531210
Scott Clendening (Pres)

GEORGE G. SHARP INC.

160 Broadway 8th Fl, New York, NY 10038
Tel.: (212) 732-2800   DE
Web Site:
   http://www.georgesharp.com
Year Founded: 1920
Sales Range: $25-49.9 Million
Emp.: 850
Provider of Shipbuilding, Repairing, Design & Consulting Services
N.A.I.C.S.: 336611
Hilary Rolih (Chm)
Allen Chin (Pres)

GEORGE GEE AUTOMOTIVE

21502 E Mission Ln, Liberty Lake, WA 99019
Tel.: (509) 927-1000
Web Site: http://www.goseegee.com
Sales Range: $10-24.9 Million
Emp.: 55
Automobiles, New & Used
N.A.I.C.S.: 441110
George Gee (Owner & CEO)
Ryan Gee (Pres)
Valerie Christiansen (Controller)

GEORGE GLOVE CO., INC.

301 Greenwood Ave, Midland Park, NJ 07432-1446
Tel.: (201) 251-1200   NJ
Web Site:
   http://www.georgeglove.com
Year Founded: 1932
Sales Range: $1-9.9 Million
Emp.: 8
Gloves Mfr & Distr
N.A.I.C.S.: 315990
Clark Bullock (CEO)

GEORGE GROUP INC

13355 Neol Rd Ste 1100, Dallas, TX 75240
Tel.: (972) 661-8066
Rev.: $14,200,000
Emp.: 50
Business Consulting Services
N.A.I.C.S.: 561499

GEORGE H & IRENE L WALKER HOME FOR CHILDREN INCORPORATED

1968 Central Ave, Needham, MA 02192
Tel.: (781) 449-4500   MA

Web Site: http://walkercares.org
Year Founded: 1930
Sales Range: $10-24.9 Million
Emp.: 447
Child Care Services
N.A.I.C.S.: 624110
Susan M. Getman (Pres & CEO)
Maureen O. Kelly (Vice Chm)
Paul G. Shorthose (Vice Chm)
Steven M. Tannenbaum (Treas)
Scott M. Preston (VP-Performance Improvement)
Russell Livingston (Dir-Medical)
Edie Janas (Sr Dir-Residential & Educational Programs)
Patricia Cedrone (Sr Dir-Behavioral Health & Community Svcs)
Barbara Bjornson (VP-Fin)
Karl H. Trieschman (Chm)
Sonya Hamori (Sec)
Roberta Goldman Wilkinson (VP-HR & Admin)

GEORGE H. BLOUCH FUEL SERVICE

440 S 9th St, Lebanon, PA 17042
Tel.: (717) 273-7677
Web Site: http://www.blouchfuel.com
Year Founded: 1969
Sales Range: $10-24.9 Million
Emp.: 48
Provider of Gasoline Sevice
N.A.I.C.S.: 424720
David Blouch Jr. (Dir-Ops)

GEORGE HARMS CONSTRUCTION COMPANY, INC.

62 Yellowbrook Rd, Howell, NJ 07731
Tel.: (732) 938-4004
Web Site: http://www.ghcci.com
Year Founded: 1960
Sales Range: $25-49.9 Million
Emp.: 150
Highway & Street Construction Contracting Services
N.A.I.C.S.: 237310
George Harms (CEO)

GEORGE HARTE NISSAN INC.

426 Derby Ave, West Haven, CT 06516
Tel.: (203) 389-5701
Web Site:
   http://www.georgehartenissan.com
Sales Range: $10-24.9 Million
Emp.: 80
Automobiles, New & Used
N.A.I.C.S.: 441110
Donald Boucher (Mgr-Parts)
Lori Tomlinson (Mgr-Customer Svc)
Vincent Sumpter (Mgr)
George Harte Jr. (Pres)

GEORGE I. REITZ & SONS INC.

RR 17214 Rte 36, Brookville, PA 15825
Tel.: (814) 849-2308
Web Site: http://www.gireitz.com
Rev.: $11,466,495
Emp.: 50
Tanks, Pumps & Pumping Equipment Mfr
N.A.I.C.S.: 423830
Alan Reitz (Pres)
Brian Reitz (VP-Sls)
Rob Painter (Office Mgr)

GEORGE J. FOSTER CO. INC.

150 Venture Dr, Dover, NH 03820
Tel.: (603) 742-4455
Web Site: http://www.fosters.com
Rev.: $13,800,000
Emp.: 300
Newspapers, Publishing & Printing
N.A.I.C.S.: 513110

Patrice D. Foster (Owner)
Simeon Broughton (Mgr-IT)
Michelle Lester (VP-Adv)

GEORGE J. HAYDEN INC.

235 E Maple St, Hazleton, PA 18201
Tel.: (570) 455-6109
Web Site:
   http://www.haydenelectric.com
Year Founded: 1975
Sales Range: $10-24.9 Million
Emp.: 95
General Electrical Contractor & Telecommunication
N.A.I.C.S.: 238210
George J. Hayden (Co-Pres)
Usbaldo Trevino (VP)
George F. Hayden Jr. (Co-Pres)

GEORGE J. IGEL & COMPANY, INC.

2040 Alum Creek Dr, Columbus, OH 43207
Tel.: (614) 445-8421
Web Site: http://www.igelco.com
Year Founded: 1911
Sales Range: $50-74.9 Million
Emp.: 300
Site Preparation Contracting Services
N.A.I.C.S.: 238910
John Igel (Pres)

GEORGE K. BAUM HOLDINGS, INC.

4801 Main St ste 500, Kansas City, MO 64112
Tel.: (816) 474-1100
Web Site: http://www.gkbaum.com
Year Founded: 1928
Sales Range: $25-49.9 Million
Emp.: 250
Investment Services
N.A.I.C.S.: 551112
Jonathan E. Baum (Chm & Pres)
William H. Coughlin (Pres)
Dana L. Bjornson (CFO, Chief Admin Officer & Exec VP)
Nick Quatrochi (Exec VP & Dir-Info Svcs/Ops)
Robert K. Dalton (Vice Chm)
John Archuleta (Sr VP-New Mexico Pub Fin-Albuquerque)
Thomas K. Beckett (Sr VP-Philadelphia)
Joe Bosch (Exec VP & Mgr-Pub Fin-New York)
John Crandall (Exec VP & Mgr-Municipal Fin Grp-Utah)
Roger Edgar (Exec VP)
Anthony Fratto (Exec VP & Mgr-Pub Fin-Chicago)
Thomas Rupert (Sr VP-Quantitative Fin Grp)
Lynn Paquin (VP-Sacramento)
Charles Procknow (Exec VP-Boston)
Donna LoCascio (Sr VP-Res)
Charles Youtz (Exec VP & Mgr-Pub Fin-California)
Julia Sayre Donnelly (VP)
Lee White (Exec VP & Mgr-Education & Non-Profit Fin Grp)

Subsidiaries:

George K. Baum Merchant Banc   (1)
4801 Main St Ste 500, Kansas City, MO 64112
Tel.: (816) 474-1100
Web Site: http://www.gkbaum.com
Investment Services
N.A.I.C.S.: 523999
Jonathan E. Baum (Chm & CEO)

GEORGE KLEITZ + ASSOCIATES, INC., PUBLIC RELATIONS DIVISION

PO Box 4014, Wheaton, IL 60189-4014
Tel.: (630) 417-4737   IL
Year Founded: 1991
Sales Range: $10-24.9 Million
Emp.: 3
Advertising & Public Relations Agency
N.A.I.C.S.: 541820
George F. Kleitz (Pres & Dir)

GEORGE M. TAYLOR & SON, INC.

28 Tinkertown Rd, Dover Plains, NY 12522
Tel.: (845) 877-9343
Web Site:
   https://www.gmtayloroil.com
Rev.: $15,000,000
Emp.: 30
Heating Oil Dealers
N.A.I.C.S.: 457210
Thomas A. Taylor (Pres)
Kevin Taylor (Mgr-Ops)

GEORGE M. YOCUM, INCORPORATED

323 E Main St, Lansdale, PA 19446
Tel.: (215) 855-1153
Web Site: http://www.yocumford.com
Year Founded: 1921
Sales Range: $10-24.9 Million
Emp.: 45
Car Whslr
N.A.I.C.S.: 441110
G. Mack Yocum (Owner)

GEORGE NAHAS OLDSMOBILE INC.

200 E Burleigh Blvd, Tavares, FL 32778
Tel.: (352) 343-5005
Rev.: $10,400,000
Emp.: 22
New Car Dealers
N.A.I.C.S.: 441110
George E. Nahas (Pres)
John Danielson (Gen Mgr)
Jean Hutchison (Sec)

GEORGE O. PASQUEL CO.

1416 SW Adams St, Peoria, IL 61602
Tel.: (309) 673-7467
Web Site: http://www.pasquel.com
Rev.: $14,500,000
Emp.: 46
Groceries, General Line
N.A.I.C.S.: 424410
Brian Frank (Dir-Pur)

GEORGE P. BANE, INC.

3402 N NE Loop 323, Tyler, TX 75708
Tel.: (903) 597-6641
Web Site:
   http://www.banemachinery.com
Year Founded: 1963
Emp.: 50
Construction Equipment Sales & Rental
N.A.I.C.S.: 532412
George P. Bane III (Pres)

Subsidiaries:

Bane Machinery Fort Worth, LP   (1)
10505 North Fwy, Fort Worth, TX 76177
Tel.: (817) 847-5894
Web Site: http://www.banemachinery.com
Rev.: $3,600,000
Emp.: 12
Construction & Mining, except Oil Well, Machinery & Equipment Merchant Whslr
N.A.I.C.S.: 423810
George P. Bane III (Pres)

GEORGE P. REINTJES CO., INC.

3800 Summit St, Kansas City, MO 64111
Tel.: (816) 756-2150
Holding Company
N.A.I.C.S.: 551112
Bob Riley *(Project Mgr)*
Robert J. Reintjes Sr. *(Chm & Pres)*

Subsidiaries:

Reintjes Services Inc.   (1)
3800 Summit St, Kansas City, MO 64111
Tel.: (816) 756-2150
Rev.: $23,179,845
Emp.: 3
Refractory & Corrosion Resistant Materials Installation Services
N.A.I.C.S.: 238140

GEORGE R. BROWN PARTNERSHIP

1001 Fannin St Ste 4700 1st City Tower, Houston, TX 77002
Tel.: (713) 652-4901
Rev.: $14,100,000
Emp.: 20
Crude Petroleum Production
N.A.I.C.S.: 211120
Fred Gibson *(Gen Mgr)*

Subsidiaries:

Frio Pipe Line Company Inc.   (1)
1001 Fannin St, Houston, TX 77002
Tel.: (713) 652-4901
Rev.: $1,200,000
Emp.: 2
Gas Transmission & Distribution
N.A.I.C.S.: 221210

GEORGE S. COYNE CHEMICAL CO. INC.

3015 State Rd, Croydon, PA 19021-6697
Tel.: (215) 785-3000   PA
Web Site:
    https://www.coynechemical.com
Year Founded: 1868
Sales Range: $10-24.9 Million
Emp.: 105
Chemicals & Allied Product Distr
N.A.I.C.S.: 424690
Donald C. Helwig *(CFO)*
Thomas H. Coyne Sr. *(Pres & CEO)*
Thomas H. Coyne Jr. *(VP-Sls)*

Subsidiaries:

Kitchenman Terminal Co.   (1)
180 Canal Rd, Fairless Hills, PA 19030-4304
Tel.: (215) 295-2945
Web Site: http://www.coynechemical.com
Sales Range: $10-24.9 Million
Emp.: 20
Provider of Business Services
N.A.I.C.S.: 561499

GEORGE SCHMITT & CO. INC.

251 Boston Post Rd, Guilford, CT 06437
Tel.: (203) 453-4334
Web Site:
    https://www.georgeschmitt.com
Year Founded: 1874
Rev.: $21,900,000
Emp.: 69
Rotogravure Printing
N.A.I.C.S.: 323111
William G. Gunther *(Pres)*
Barbara Kohl *(Acct Mgr)*
James Rickert *(VP-Mfg)*

GEORGE SOLLITT CONSTRUCTION

790 N Central Ave, Wood Dale, IL 60191-1266
Tel.: (630) 860-7333   IL
Web Site: http://www.sollitt.com
Year Founded: 1838
Sales Range: $10-24.9 Million

Emp.: 150
Provider of Contracting & Construction Services
N.A.I.C.S.: 236220
John Pridmore *(Pres)*

GEORGE STREET PHOTO & VIDEO, LLC

230 W Huron St 3W, Chicago, IL 60654
Tel.: (866) 831-4103   DE
Web Site:
    http://www.georgestreetphoto.com
Year Founded: 2004
Sales Range: $10-24.9 Million
Emp.: 65
Photojournalistic Wedding Photography & Videography
N.A.I.C.S.: 541921
Michael McMahon *(Co-Founder & CEO)*
Dan Creviston *(Co-Founder, CMO & VP-Sls)*
Tim Muller *(Co-Founder & CFO)*

GEORGE T. HALL CO. INC.

1605 E Gene Autry Way, Anaheim, CA 92805-6727
Tel.: (714) 939-7100
Web Site:
    https://www.georgethall.com
Rev.: $11,600,000
Emp.: 25
Warm Air Heating & Air Conditioning
N.A.I.C.S.: 423730
Jim Martin *(VP)*
John Monaghan *(Coord-Ops)*

GEORGE T. SANDERS COMPANY

10201 W 49th Ave, Wheat Ridge, CO 80033
Tel.: (303) 423-9660
Web Site: https://www.gtsanders.com
Sales Range: $25-49.9 Million
Emp.: 130
Plumbing Fittings & Supplies
N.A.I.C.S.: 423720

GEORGE T. SCHMIDT, INC.

6151 W Howard St, Niles, IL 60714-3401
Tel.: (847) 647-7117   IL
Web Site: https://www.gtschmidt.com
Year Founded: 1895
Sales Range: $75-99.9 Million
Emp.: 70
Permanent Marking Identification Systems Mfr
N.A.I.C.S.: 333517
Neal O'Connor *(Pres)*
Tony Hill *(Controller)*
Kate Burgeson *(Mgr-Mktg)*

Subsidiaries:

Precise Machine Company Inc.   (1)
6151 W Howard St, Niles, IL 60714
Tel.: (847) 647-6125
Web Site:
    http://www.precisemachinecompany.com
Sales Range: $10-24.9 Million
Emp.: 20
Industrial Machinery
N.A.I.C.S.: 336390
Paul Bolenbaugh *(Pres)*

GEORGE T. WILKINSON, INC.

405 VFW Dr, Rockland, MA 02370
Tel.: (781) 335-2622
Web Site: http://www.gtwilkinson.com
Year Founded: 1952
Sales Range: $10-24.9 Million
Emp.: 42
Plumbing Services
N.A.I.C.S.: 238220
Geoffrey C. Wilkinson *(Pres)*

GEORGE UHE COMPANY, INC.

230 W Pkwy Ste 5, Pompton Plains, NJ 07444
Tel.: (201) 843-4000   NJ
Web Site: https://www.uhe.com
Year Founded: 1921
Emp.: 10
Broker of Essential Oils & Aromatic Chemicals & Distr of Raw Materials to the Pharmaceutical Industry
N.A.I.C.S.: 424690
Kevin C. Poehlmann *(Pres)*
Liz Vazquez *(Dir-Global Procurement)*

GEORGE VETESNIK MOTORS INC.

27475 US Hwy 14, Richland Center, WI 53581
Tel.: (608) 647-8808
Web Site: http://www.vetesnik.com
Sales Range: $10-24.9 Million
Emp.: 30
Automobiles, New & Used
N.A.I.C.S.: 441110
Greg Vetesnik *(Pres)*

GEORGE W. AUCH COMPANY

65 University Dr, Pontiac, MI 48342
Tel.: (248) 334-2000   MI
Web Site:
    https://www.auchconstruction.com
Year Founded: 1908
Sales Range: $75-99.9 Million
Emp.: 125
Construction Management, General Contracting, Commercial & Institutional Construction Services
N.A.I.C.S.: 541618
Vince Deleonardis *(Pres & CEO)*

GEORGE W. LOWRY INC.

4612 Kiernan Ct, Salida, CA 95368
Tel.: (209) 545-0791
Web Site: http://www.lowryoil.com
Year Founded: 1932
Rev.: $12,000,000
Emp.: 9
Distr of Petroleum Products
N.A.I.C.S.: 424720
Mark DeWane *(Mgr-Sls)*
Alicia Biedermann *(Mgr-Card Lock)*

GEORGE W. PARK SEED COMPANY, INC.

1 Parkton Ave, Greenwood, SC 29647
Tel.: (864) 223-8555   SC
Web Site: http://www.parkseed.com
Year Founded: 1868
Sales Range: $100-124.9 Million
Emp.: 200
Provider of Retail & Mail Order Seeds, Bulbs, Plants & Accessories
N.A.I.C.S.: 444240
Richard Pope *(CEO)*

GEORGE W. WARDEN COMPANY INCORPORATED

19810 141st Place NE Building D, Woodinville, WA 98072
Tel.: (206) 633-0382
Web Site: http://www.sun-source.com
Rev.: $10,950,000
Emp.: 500
Pneumatic Tools & Equipment Distr
N.A.I.C.S.: 423830
Jerry Helmick *(Gen Mgr)*

GEORGE WASHINGTON'S MOUNT VERNON

3200 Mount Vernon Memorial Hwy, Mount Vernon, VA 22121
Tel.: (703) 780-2000
Web Site:
    https://www.mountvernon.org
Year Founded: 1853

Museum Exhibition Services
N.A.I.C.S.: 711510

GEORGE WEBER CHEVROLET COMPANY

701 Old State Route 3, Columbia, IL 62236-2651
Tel.: (618) 281-5111
Sales Range: $50-74.9 Million
Emp.: 76
Car Whslr
N.A.I.C.S.: 441110
David Vogel *(Gen Mgr)*
George Weber *(Pres)*

GEORGE WEST MENTAL HEALTH FOUNDATION

1961 N Druid Hills Rd NE, Atlanta, GA 30329
Tel.: (404) 315-8333   GA
Web Site: http://www.skylandtrail.org
Year Founded: 1982
Sales Range: $10-24.9 Million
Emp.: 170
Mental Health Care Services
N.A.I.C.S.: 623220
Chris Cline *(VP-Clinical Svcs)*
Ray Kotwicki *(Chief Medical Officer)*
Cynthia Odom *(VP-Mktg & Comm)*
Beth Finnerty *(Pres & CEO)*
Elizabeth Alexander *(Dir-Grateful Families Program & Planned Giving)*

GEORGE'S INC.

402 W Robinson Ave, Springdale, AR 72764
Tel.: (479) 927-7000   AR
Web Site: http://www.georgesinc.com
Poultry Processing
N.A.I.C.S.: 311615
Gary Charles George *(Chm, Co-Pres & Co-CEO)*
Devin Cole *(Chief Strategy Officer & Chief Comml Officer)*
Carl George *(Co-Pres & Co-CEO)*
David Jetter *(VP-Culinary Innovation & Product Dev)*
Brian Coan *(Chief Customer Officer)*
Susan White *(CFO)*
John Gomes *(Gen Mgr)*
Beth Moore *(Sls Mgr)*

Subsidiaries:

George's Farms Inc.   (1)
402 W Robinson Ave, Springdale, AR 72764
Tel.: (479) 927-7000
Sales Range: $10-24.9 Million
Emp.: 100
Processor of Poultry
N.A.I.C.S.: 112320

George's Gas Co. Inc.   (1)
401 W Robinson Ave, Springdale, AR 72764
Tel.: (479) 927-7000
Sales Range: $10-24.9 Million
Emp.: 6
Retailer of Liquefied Petroleum Gas
N.A.I.C.S.: 457210
Jim Hall *(Mgr-Gas Dept)*

George's Inc. - Cassville Feed Mill   (1)
9225 State Hwy W, Cassville, MO 65625
Tel.: (417) 442-0266
Animal Feed Mfr
N.A.I.C.S.: 311119

George's Inc. - Cassville Processing Plant (1)
9066 State Hwy W, Cassville, MO 65625
Tel.: (417) 442-3500
Poultry Processing Services
N.A.I.C.S.: 311615

George's Inc. - Edinburg Processing Plant (1)
19992 Senedo Rd, Edinburg, VA 22801
Tel.: (540) 984-4121
Poultry Processing Services

George's Inc.—(Continued)

N.A.I.C.S.: 311615

George's Inc. - Harrisonburg Feed Mill (1)
61 Kratzer Rd, Harrisonburg, VA 22802
Tel.: (540) 568-1570
Animal Feed Mfr
N.A.I.C.S.: 311119

George's Inc. - Harrisonburg Processing Plant (1)
501 N Liberty St, Harrisonburg, VA 22802
Tel.: (540) 433-0720
Poultry Processing Services
N.A.I.C.S.: 311615

George's Inc. - Mount Jackson Feed Mill (1)
560 Caverns Rd, Mount Jackson, VA 22842
Tel.: (540) 477-3181
Animal Feed Mfr
N.A.I.C.S.: 311119

George's Inc. - Springdale Feed Mill (1)
200 W Robinson Ave, Springdale, AR 72764
Tel.: (429) 927-7400
Animal Feed Mfr
N.A.I.C.S.: 311119

George's Inc. - Springdale Plant (1)
1306 N Kansas St, Springdale, AR 72764
Tel.: (479) 927-7600
Poultry Processing Services
N.A.I.C.S.: 311615

George's Processing Inc. (1)
1306 N Kansas St, Springdale, AR 72764-3193 (100%)
Tel.: (479) 927-7000
Sales Range: $10-24.9 Million
Emp.: 70
Processor of Poultry
N.A.I.C.S.: 311615
Troy Green (Plant Mgr)

Ozark Mountain Poultry, Inc. (1)
750 W Easy St, Rogers, AR 72756
Tel.: (479) 633-8700
Web Site:
http://www.ozarkmountainpoultry.com
Poultry Processing
N.A.I.C.S.: 311615

GEORGECO INC.
2609 Willowbrook Rd, Dallas, TX 75220-4422
Tel.: (214) 352-9091
Web Site: http://www.barnsco.com
Year Founded: 1996
Sales Range: $10-24.9 Million
Emp.: 105
Brick, Stone & Related Materials Mfr
N.A.I.C.S.: 423320
Jeff Barnes (Pres)
Marcus Miller (CFO)

Subsidiaries:

Barnsco (1)
975 Ladd Rd, Walled Lake, MI 48390 (100%)
Tel.: (248) 668-1010
Web Site: http://www.barnsco.com
Sales Range: $10-24.9 Million
Emp.: 25
Brick, Stone & Related Materials Mfr
N.A.I.C.S.: 423320

Erect-A-Line Inc. (1)
121 La Paz, Dallas, TX 75217
Tel.: (214) 630-1154
Web Site: http://www.erectaline.com
Sales Range: $10-24.9 Million
Emp.: 8
Concrete Products & Brick, Stone & Related Materials Mfr
N.A.I.C.S.: 327390

GEORGETOWN MANOR INC.
8353 Kempwood Dr, Houston, TX 77055
Tel.: (713) 464-4460 TX
Web Site: http://www.ethanallen.com

Year Founded: 1968
Sales Range: $10-24.9 Million
Emp.: 100
Owner & Operator of Furniture Stores
N.A.I.C.S.: 449110
Ed Rush (Controller)
Robert Chesnick (VP)
H. Joseph Chesnick Sr. (Chm)
H. J. Chesnick Jr. (Pres)

GEORGETTE'S FASHIONS, INC.
141 S Dale Mabry, Tampa, FL 33609
Tel.: (813) 254-1141
Web Site:
http://www.georgettesfashions.com
Sales Range: $1-9.9 Million
Emp.: 8
Women's Clothing & Shoe Retailer
N.A.I.C.S.: 458110
Georgette Diaz (Pres)
Tashia Diaz (Office Mgr)

GEORGIA CORRECTIONAL INDUSTRIES
2984 Clifton Springs Rd, Decatur, GA 30034-3820
Tel.: (404) 244-5100 GA
Web Site: http://www.gci-ga.com
Year Founded: 1960
Sales Range: $10-24.9 Million
Emp.: 170
Mfr of Office Furniture
N.A.I.C.S.: 337214
Lawrence Defloria (Mgr-Field Svcs-Safety)

GEORGIA CRATE & BASKET COMPANY
1200 Parnell St, Thomasville, GA 31792
Tel.: (229) 226-2541
Web Site: http://www.georgiafacts.net
Sales Range: $10-24.9 Million
Emp.: 140
Food Containers, Wood Wirebound
N.A.I.C.S.: 321920
Ellis Fletcher (Chm)

GEORGIA CROWN DISTRIBUTING CO.
100 Georgia Crown Dr, McDonough, GA 30253
Tel.: (706) 568-4580 GA
Web Site:
http://www.georgiacrown.com
Year Founded: 1949
Sales Range: $25-49.9 Million
Emp.: 1,700
Whslr & Distr of Alcoholic Beverages & Bottled Water
N.A.I.C.S.: 424820
Bob Jones (Mgr-Sls)
Janice Petrella (Office Mgr-Georgia)
Nicolas Montgomery (Coord-Chain Acct)
John Nalley (Gen Mgr-Sls-Off Premise Spirits Div)
Lauren Iovanella (Dir-Events)
David Hubbard (Gen Mgr)

GEORGIA ELECTRIC MEMBERSHIP CORPORATION
2100 E Exchange Pl Ste 510, Tucker, GA 30084
Tel.: (770) 270-6950
Web Site:
https://www.georgiaemc.com
Sales Range: $10-24.9 Million
Emp.: 45
Electric, System & Transmission Trade Association
N.A.I.C.S.: 813910
Terri Statham (Mgr-Media Rels)

GEORGIA ENERGY COOPERATIVE
2100 E Exchange Pl Ste 300, Tucker, GA 30084-5313
Tel.: (770) 270-7500 GA
Web Site:
https://www.georgiaenergycoop.com
Year Founded: 2001
Sales Range: $200-249.9 Million
Emp.: 4
Electric Power Distr
N.A.I.C.S.: 221122
Gleen Loomer (Pres & CEO)
Melissa L. Calzada (VP-Fin & Admin)
John Winskie (VP-Power Supply)
Bob Jernigan (Chm)

GEORGIA FARM BUREAU FEDERATION
1620 Bass Rd, Macon, GA 31209
Tel.: (478) 474-8411 GA
Web Site: http://www.gfb.org
Year Founded: 1937
Sales Range: $10-24.9 Million
Emp.: 100
Farmer Welfare Services
N.A.I.C.S.: 813910
Daniel L. Johnson (VP-South Georgia)
Gerald Long (Pres)
Bernard Sims (VP)
Duke Groover (Gen Counsel)
Jon Huffmaster (Chief Admin Officer & Corp Sec)
David Jolley (CFO & Treas)
Robert Fountain Jr. (First VP)

GEORGIA FARM BUREAU MUTUAL INSURANCE CO.
1620 Bass Rd, Macon, GA 31210
Tel.: (478) 474-8411
Web Site: http://www.gfb.org
Rev.: $356,591,345
Emp.: 500
Fire, Marine & Casualty Insurance
N.A.I.C.S.: 524126
Wayne Daniels (Treas & Sec)
Mike Cook (Gen Mgr)
Amy Pendley (Mgr-Benefits & Compensation)
Howard Poarch (Asst Dir-IT)
Keith Stone (Mgr-Agency)
Scott Bowden (Mgr-Tech Svcs)
George Monk (Exec Dir-Insurance Company Ops)
Geri Powell (Exec Dir-Bus & Strategic Dev)

GEORGIA FENCE WHOLESALE INC.
1617 Blanchard Blvd, Columbus, GA 31901
Tel.: (706) 327-3661
Web Site: https://www.gafence.net
Rev.: $10,865,613
Emp.: 50
Wire Fence, Gates & Accessories Distr
N.A.I.C.S.: 423390
Steve Lowery (Pres)
Jane Redmond (Treas)
Susie Munch (Office Mgr)

GEORGIA GOAL SCHOLARSHIP PROGRAM, INC.
5 Concourse Pkwy Ste 200, Atlanta, GA 30328
Tel.: (770) 828-4625 GA
Web Site:
http://www.goalscholarship.org
Year Founded: 2006
Sales Range: $10-24.9 Million
Emp.: 13
Education Scholarship Provider
N.A.I.C.S.: 813211

Allison Saxby (Dir-Client Svcs)
Kate Saylor (Dir-Marketing-Communications)
Lisa Kelly (Pres)
Rick Gilbert (Chm)

GEORGIA LEGAL SERVICES PROGRAM
104 Marietta St NW, Atlanta, GA 30303
Tel.: (404) 206-5175 GA
Web Site: http://www.glsp.org
Year Founded: 1971
Sales Range: $10-24.9 Million
Emp.: 153
Law firm
N.A.I.C.S.: 541199
Lisa J. Krisher (Dir-Litigation)

GEORGIA MOTOR TRUCKS INC.
3068 Hwy 36 W, Jackson, GA 30233
Tel.: (770) 775-7772
Web Site:
http://www.georgiatrucks.com
Sales Range: $10-24.9 Million
Emp.: 8
Truck Leasing Services
N.A.I.C.S.: 532120
Janice Letson (Pres)

GEORGIA MUSEUMS, INC.
PO Box 3248, Cartersville, GA 30120
Tel.: (678) 721-0251 GA
Year Founded: 2004
Sales Range: $10-24.9 Million
Emp.: 157
Museum Operator
N.A.I.C.S.: 712110
Cathy Lee Eckert (Dir-Ops)
Seth Hopkins (Exec Dir)
Jonathan Oscher (Pres)
Forrest McClain (Treas & Sec)
Lorraine McClain (VP)
Dorothy Oscher (VP)

GEORGIA NORTH FOODS INC.
942 Tallulah Falls Scenic Loop, Tallulah Falls, GA 30573
Tel.: (706) 754-5464
Web Site:
http://www.northgafoodsinc.org
Sales Range: $10-24.9 Million
Emp.: 30
Fast Food Services
N.A.I.C.S.: 722513
Johnny M. Irvin (Co-Owner & Pres)
David L. Irvin (Co-Owner)

GEORGIA NUT COMPANY
7500 N Linder Ave, Skokie, IL 60077
Tel.: (847) 677-6887
Web Site: http://www.georgianut.com
Year Founded: 1945
Sales Range: $50-74.9 Million
Emp.: 325
Candy Mfr
N.A.I.C.S.: 311919
Steven Musso (Mgr-Retail)

GEORGIA TRANSMISSION CORPORATION
2100 E Exchange Pl, Tucker, GA 30084
Tel.: (770) 270-7400 GA
Web Site: http://www.gatrans.com
Year Founded: 1974
Rev.: $305,746,000
Assets: $2,789,792,000
Liabilities: $323,388,000
Net Worth: $2,466,404,000
Earnings: $15,167,000
Emp.: 284
Fiscal Year-end: 12/31/18
Electric Power Transmission
N.A.I.C.S.: 221118

Barbara Hampton (CFO & Sr VP)
Jerry Donovan (Pres & CEO)
Charles Fendley (Chm)
Otis Jones (Treas & Sec)
Keith Daniel (Sr VP-Transmission Policy)
John Raese (VP-Project Svcs)
Angela Sheffield (Chief Regulatory Compliance Officer, VP & Auditor)
Angie Farsee (VP-HR)
Joe Sowell (VP-Sys Plng)
Steve Rawl Sr. (Vice Chm)

GEORGIA UNITED CREDIT UNION

6705 Sugarloaf Pkwy, Duluth, GA 30097
Tel.: (770) 476-6400   GA
Web Site:
http://www.georgiaunitedcu.org
Year Founded: 1958
Emp.: 230
Credit Union
N.A.I.C.S.: 522130
Debbie Smith (CEO)
Michael Mason (VP-Consumer Lending)
Amanda Whitson (Sr VP-Consumer Lending)
Stephanie Zuleger (Chief Lending Officer)
Bob Bogart (CFO & Exec VP)
Sophia Rollins (Sr VP-Risk Mgmt)
Linda Landis (VP-Compliance & Bank Secrecy Act)
Janis W. Johnson (Gen Counsel)
Laura King (Pres)

GEORGIA WORLD CONGRESS CENTER AUTHORITY

285 Andrew Young Intl Blvd NW, Atlanta, GA 30313-1591
Tel.: (404) 223-4000   GA
Web Site: http://www.gwcc.com
Year Founded: 1976
Sales Range: $50-74.9 Million
Emp.: 458
Convention Site for Trade Shows & Exhibitions
N.A.I.C.S.: 722511
Kevin Duvall (COO)
Frank Poe (Exec Dir)
Mark Geiger (Mgr-Adv Sls)
Janet Arsenault (Sr Dir-Fin)
Jennifer LeMaster (Chief Admin Officer)
Brian Ramm (Dir-Concessions)
Carla Sayeh (Dir-Internal Audits)
Joiel Alexander (Dir-Sls)
Lidija Ahmetovic (Mgr-Sls)
Joe Bocherer (Chief Comml Officer)

GEORGIA'S OWN CREDIT UNION

1155 Peachtree St NE Ste 600, Atlanta, GA 30309
Tel.: (404) 874-1166   GA
Web Site:
http://www.georgiasown.org
Year Founded: 1934
Sales Range: $75-99.9 Million
Emp.: 476
Credit Union Operator
N.A.I.C.S.: 522130
Kelly M. Garmon (Chief Membership Officer)
Patrick H. Casey (Treas)
Joan K. Sims (Sec)
Michael W. Baumgartner (Vice Chm)
Eric Broome (Gen Counsel & Sr VP-Enterprise Risk Mgmt)
John Carew III (Sr VP-Strategy)

GEORGIA/ATLANTIC CONTRACTORS, INC

4193 Rufus Pl, Doraville, GA 30340
Tel.: (770) 409-0040
Year Founded: 1986
Sales Range: $10-24.9 Million
Emp.: 11
Commercial & Office Building, New Construction
N.A.I.C.S.: 236220
Kimberly Bailey (Pres)

GEORGINO INDUSTRIAL SUPPLY

14892 Bennetts Valley Hwy, Penfield, PA 15849
Tel.: (814) 637-5301   DE
Web Site: https://www.georgino.com
Year Founded: 1958
Sales Range: $10-24.9 Million
Emp.: 40
Provider of Mining Machinery & Equipment
N.A.I.C.S.: 423810
Ronald Hetrick (CFO & Gen Mgr)

GEOSYNTEC CONSULTANTS, INC.

2002 Summit Blvd NE Ste 885, Atlanta, GA 30319
Tel.: (404) 267-1101
Web Site: http://www.geosyntec.com
Year Founded: 1983
Sales Range: $75-99.9 Million
Emp.: 1,000
Environmental Consulting Services
N.A.I.C.S.: 541620
Rudy Bonaparte (Sr Engr)
Peter Anderson (Principal)
Mike McKibben (Principal)
Tom Wurzinger (Engr-Environmental)
Debora Shelton (Office Mgr)
Andrea Braga (Principal)
Jamie deLemos (Sr Principal)
Chris Greene (Sr Principal)
Julianna Connolly (Sr Principal)

Subsidiaries:

Geosyntec Consultants, Inc. - Acton   (1)
289 Great Rd Ste 202, Acton, MA 01720
Tel.: (978) 263-9588
Web Site: http://www.geosyntec.com
Sales Range: $10-24.9 Million
Emp.: 30
Environmental Consulting Services
N.A.I.C.S.: 541620
Juan M. Pestana (Sr Principal)

Geosyntec Consultants, Inc. - Colorado   (1)
5670 Greenwood Plz Blvd Ste 540, Greenwood Village, CO 80111
Tel.: (303) 790-1340
Web Site: http://www.geosyntec.com
Environmental Science & Engineering Consulting Services
N.A.I.C.S.: 541620
David J. Folkes (Sr Principal)

GEOTAG INC.

2591 Dallas Pkwy Ste 505, Frisco, TX 75034
Tel.: (469) 888-5580   DE
Web Site: http://www.geotag.com
Year Founded: 2010
Sales Range: $1-9.9 Million
Emp.: 2
Geo-Location Technology
N.A.I.C.S.: 334511
John W. Veenstra (CEO)

GEOTECH ENVIRONMENTAL EQUIPMENT, INC.

2650 E 40th Ave, Denver, CO 80205
Tel.: (303) 320-4764   CO
Web Site:
http://www.geotechenv.com
Year Founded: 1956
Sales Range: $10-24.9 Million

Emp.: 125
Mfr & Distr of Sampling, Filtration, Analytical & Remediation Products for Ground & Surface Water Industries
N.A.I.C.S.: 334513
Jerry L. Popiel (Chm)
Jeffrey L. Popiel (Pres & CEO)

Subsidiaries:

Geotech Instruments   (1)
1099 E Grand River Rd Ste 6, Williamston, MI 48895-1211   (100%)
Tel.: (517) 655-5616
Web Site: http://www.geotechenv.com
Sales Range: $10-24.9 Million
Emp.: 6
Mfr & Designer of Instrumentation for Groundwater Testing
N.A.I.C.S.: 334513
Eric Sanchez (Gen Mgr)

GEOTEMPS INC.

970 Caughlin Crossing Ste 102, Reno, NV 89519
Tel.: (775) 746-7146
Web Site: https://www.geotemps.com
Year Founded: 1986
Emp.: 100
Recruiting & Employing Geotechnical Personnel
N.A.I.C.S.: 561320
Lance I. Taylor (Pres & CEO)

GEOTEXT TRANSLATIONS, INC.

259 W 30th St 17th Fl, New York, NY 10001
Tel.: (212) 631-7432
Web Site: http://www.geotext.com
Sales Range: $10-24.9 Million
Emp.: 36
Business Consulting Services
N.A.I.C.S.: 611710
Joseph E. Duncan (Founder & Gen Mgr)
Matt Dineen (Dir-Client Svc)
Jason Starr (Dir-Client Svc)
Kevin Kraus (Dir-Client Svc)
Karen Wilson (Dir-Client Svc-London)
Nick Carpenter (Dir-Client Svc)

Subsidiaries:

Geotext Translations, Inc.   (1)
220 Montgomery St Ste 605, San Francisco, CA 94104
Tel.: (415) 576-9500
Web Site: http://www.geotext.com
Sales Range: $10-24.9 Million
Emp.: 10
Business Consulting Services
N.A.I.C.S.: 541618
Joe Duncan (CEO)

GEOVIC MINING CORP.

5500 E Yale Ave Ste 302, Denver, CO 80222
Tel.: (303) 476-6455   DE
Sales Range: Less than $1 Million
Emp.: 49
Cobalt Mining Exploration & Development
N.A.I.C.S.: 212290
Andrew C. Hoffman (VP-IR)
William Alan Buckovic (Exec VP-Exploration)
Michael T. Mason (Chm & CEO)
Gary R. Morris (Sr VP)
Shelia I. Short (Sec)
Christopher Arthur Serin (CFO, Interim Chief Acctg Officer & Sec)

GEOWAGGLE, LLC

5706 Benjamin Ctr Dr, Tampa, FL 33634
Tel.: (813) 340-1211
Web Site:
http://www.mamabearapp.com
Sales Range: $1-9.9 Million

Internet Child Protection Software Application
N.A.I.C.S.: 513210
Robyn Spoto (Co-Founder)
Steve Wilson (VP-Tech)
Steve MacDonald (Co-Founder)
Tom Cardy (Co-Founder)
Stuart Kime (Co-Founder)
Melvin Leiner (Vice Chm, Sec & Exec VP)

GEPCO, LTD.

9025 Carlton Hills Blvd Ste B, Santee, CA 92071
Tel.: (909) 708-4303   NV
Web Site: http://www.gepcoltd.com
Year Founded: 2008
Diamond Retailer
N.A.I.C.S.: 423940
Trisha Malone (Pres, CFO & Sec)

GERACE CONSTRUCTION COMPANY INC.

4055 S Saginaw Rd, Midland, MI 48640-8501
Tel.: (989) 496-2440   MI
Web Site:
https://www.geraceconstruction.com
Year Founded: 1963
Sales Range: $25-49.9 Million
Emp.: 119
Construction Services
N.A.I.C.S.: 236210
Thomas Valent (Pres & CEO)
Blake Hine (CFO)
John Waskevich (Project Mgr)

GERALD GRAIN CENTER INC.

14540 County Rd U, Napoleon, OH 43545-9747
Tel.: (419) 598-8015   OH
Web Site:
https://www.geraldgrain.com
Year Founded: 1931
Sales Range: $10-24.9 Million
Emp.: 18
Grain & Field Beans Distr
N.A.I.C.S.: 424510
Chester Phillips (Gen Mgr)
Randy Heldman (Mgr-Feed Dept)

GERALD H. PHIPPS, INC.

5995 Greenwood Plaza Blvd Ste 100, Greenwood Village, CO 80111-4710
Tel.: (303) 571-5377   CO
Web Site: https://ghphipps.com
Year Founded: 1952
Sales Range: $200-249.9 Million
Emp.: 350
General Contractors
N.A.I.C.S.: 236220
John A. Gibbs (Dir-Mktg)
Todd Ruff (VP-Preconstruction)

GERALD JONES VOLKSWAGEN INC.

4022 Washington Rd, Martinez, GA 30907
Tel.: (706) 228-6900
Web Site:
http://www.geraldjonesvolkswagen.com
Rev.: $18,800,000
Emp.: 46
Automobiles, New & Used
N.A.I.C.S.: 441110
Anthony E. Jones (Pres)

GERALD METALS INC.

Ste 10 680 Washington Blvd, Stamford, CT 06901-3727
Tel.: (203) 609-8300
Web Site: http://www.gerald.com
Year Founded: 1962
Sales Range: $50-74.9 Million
Emp.: 859
Metals Distr

Gerald Metals Inc.—(Continued)

N.A.I.C.S.: 423510
Janet Brown (Coord-Acctg)
Robert Liberati (Controller)
Fabio Calia (COO & Exec VP)

Subsidiaries:

Gerald Financial Group Inc.   (1)
680 Washington Blvd, Stamford, CT 06905-1327
Tel.: (203) 609-8300
Web Site: http://www.gerald.com
Sales Range: $50-74.9 Million
Emp.: 70
Commodity Contract Brokerage Services
N.A.I.C.S.: 523160

Gerald Metals S.A.   (1)
Rue De La Gare 29, Morges, 1110, Switzerland
Tel.: (41) 21 811 33 00
Web Site: http://www.gerald.com
Emp.: 30
Nonferrous Metal Whslr
N.A.I.C.S.: 423990
Alejandro Skidelsky (Gen Counsel & VP)

GERALD NISSAN OF NORTH AURORA

213 Hansen Blvd, North Aurora, IL 60542
Tel.: (630) 907-0800
Web Site:
 https://www.geraldnissannorth
 aurora.com
Sales Range: $10-24.9 Million
Emp.: 50
New Car Retailer
N.A.I.C.S.: 441110
Deen Collins (Partner)
Scott Wolf (Gen Mgr-Sls)
Rene Peyton (Mgr-Sls)
Yasser Ibrahim (Mgr-Sls)
Christopher Brischetto (Mgr-Svc)
Lee Cuomo (Mgr-Sls)
Tamer Shams (Mgr-Fin)
Mark Wieckowski (Mgr-Parts)

GERARD DESIGN

28371 Davis Pkwy Ste 100, Warrenville, IL 60555
Tel.: (630) 355-0775
Web Site:
 http://www.gerarddesign.com
Year Founded: 1995
Sales Range: $1-9.9 Million
Emp.: 20
Commercial Art & Graphic Design Services
N.A.I.C.S.: 541430
Carolyn Gerard (Principal)
Mark Manzo (Dir-Copy)
Kenton Gerard (Principal)
Patrick Schab (Dir-Creative)
Christina Steva (Dir-Creative)
Tony Ballinger (Dir-Interactive)

GERARD KLUYSKENS COMPANY INC.

295 5th Ave Ste 403, New York, NY 10016
Tel.: (212) 685-5710
Web Site: https://www.gkci.com
Rev.: $11,200,000
Emp.: 12
Abrasives
N.A.I.C.S.: 423840
Ed Quesada (Pres)
Paul Roman (VP)

GERARDI CONSTRUCTION, INC.

1604 N 19th St, Tampa, FL 33605
Tel.: (813) 248-4341
Web Site:
 https://www.gerardiconstruction.com
Year Founded: 1998

Sales Range: $10-24.9 Million
Emp.: 25
Commercial & Institutional Building Construction Services
N.A.I.C.S.: 236220
Phillip H. Gerardi (Founder)

GERBER & SONS INC.

100 S Ray St, Baltic, OH 43804
Tel.: (330) 897-6201
Web Site:
 http://www.gerberandsons.com
Sales Range: $10-24.9 Million
Emp.: 40
Livestock Feeds
N.A.I.C.S.: 311119
Doug Davis (Gen Mgr)
Doug Burrier (Mgr-Acctg Dept)
Bill Bartz (Mgr-Ops)
Todd Wise (Mgr-Sls)

GERBER AGRI INTERNATIONAL, LLC

1000 Parkwood Cir Ste 335, Atlanta, GA 30339
Tel.: (770) 952-4187
Web Site: https://www.gerberatl.com
Year Founded: 1981
Meat & Food Products Exporter
N.A.I.C.S.: 424470
Laura Tabanelli (Owner)

GERBER CHILDRENSWEAR LLC

445 State St, Fremont, MI 49413-0001
Tel.: (212) 863-2400   DE
Web Site:
 http://www.gerberchildrenswear.com
Sales Range: $1-9.9 Million
Emp.: 120
Children's Apparel, Bed & Bath Items Marketer
N.A.I.C.S.: 424350

Subsidiaries:

Gerber Childrenswear LLC - Greenville Operations Center   (1)
7005 Pelham Rd, Greenville, SC 29615
Tel.: (864) 987-5200
Web Site:
 http://www.gerberchildrenswear.com
Children's Apparel, Bed & Bath Items Marketer
N.A.I.C.S.: 424350
Vincent Rutledge (Dir-Sourced Plng)

Triboro Quilt Manufacturing Corp.   (1)
172 S Broadway, White Plains, NY 10605-1809
Tel.: (914) 428-7551
Web Site: http://www.triboro.com
Women's & Children's Underwear Mfr
N.A.I.C.S.: 314120
Joel Kaplan (Pres)
Alvin Kaplan (VP)
Marc Zuckernan (VP-Fin & Ops)

GERBER PLUMBING FIXTURES CORPORATION

2500 Internationale Pkwy, Woodridge, IL 60517
Tel.: (630) 679-1420   IN
Web Site:
 http://www.gerberonline.com
Year Founded: 1932
Sales Range: $100-124.9 Million
Emp.: 900
Plumbing Fixture Mfr
N.A.I.C.S.: 332913
Kevin McJoynt (Dir-Mktg)
Eric Peterson (VP-Sls-Wholesale Div)

GERBER TRADE FINANCE, INC.

488 Madison Ave Fl 800, New York, NY 10022-5728

Tel.: (212) 888-1533   NY
Web Site:
 http://www.gerberfinance.com
Year Founded: 1937
Sales Range: $75-99.9 Million
Emp.: 10
Trade Finance & Asset-Based Loans Lender
N.A.I.C.S.: 522299
Gerald L. Joseph (Pres & CEO)

GERDT FURNITURE & INTERIORS

2115 E Southport Rd, Indianapolis, IN 46227
Tel.: (317) 788-4236
Web Site: http://www.gerdt.com
Sales Range: $10-24.9 Million
Emp.: 50
Home Furnishings
N.A.I.C.S.: 449110
John Gerdt (Pres)
Frank Shoemaker (COO)
Kenneth Johnson (Gen Mgr)

GERELCO ELECTRICAL CONTRACTORS

560 NW Enterprise Dr, Port Saint Lucie, FL 34986
Tel.: (772) 340-7474
Web Site: https://www.gerelco.com
Year Founded: 1955
Sales Range: $10-24.9 Million
Emp.: 150
General Electrical Contractor
N.A.I.C.S.: 238210
Kenneth A. Geremia (Pres)

GEREMIA POOLS

7901 14th Ave, Sacramento, CA 95826
Tel.: (916) 914-7800
Web Site:
 https://www.geremiapools.com
Year Founded: 1922
Sales Range: $10-24.9 Million
Emp.: 100
Swimming Pool Construction
N.A.I.C.S.: 238990
Tim Murray (Controller)
Mike Geremia (Owner)

GERIATRIC SERVICES, INC.

300 Teaneck Rd, Teaneck, NJ 07666
Tel.: (201) 692-1000
Web Site:
 http://www.seniorhousingser
 vices.org
Year Founded: 1990
Elderly Assisted Living Facility Operator
N.A.I.C.S.: 623312
Mary Ann Van Clief (Pres)
Kay Lucas (VP)
Carolyn L. Larke (Treas)
Fran Monteleone (Sec)

GERICARE MEDICAL SUPPLY INC.

521 Whetstone St, Monroeville, AL 36460
Tel.: (251) 743-3844
Web Site:
 https://www.gericaremedical
 supply.com
Sales Range: $10-24.9 Million
Emp.: 32
Medical Equipment & Supplies Mfr
N.A.I.C.S.: 423450
Lynn Patterson (COO)
Bob Miller (VP-Sls)
Billy Jones (Pres)
Marty Miller (Mgr-Warehouse)

GERKEN MATERIALS INC.

9072 County Road 424, Napoleon, OH 43545-9732
Tel.: (419) 533-2421
Web Site:
 http://www.gerkenpaving.com
Year Founded: 1959
Sales Range: $25-49.9 Million
Emp.: 250
Highway & Street Construction
N.A.I.C.S.: 237310
Brent Gerken (Pres)
Joe Knepley (Mgr-Matls)

Subsidiaries:

Gerken Paving Inc.   (1)
424 County Rd, Napoleon, OH 43545-9732
Tel.: (419) 533-7701
Web Site: http://www.gerkencompanies.com
Sales Range: $10-24.9 Million
Emp.: 20
Highway & Street Construction
N.A.I.C.S.: 237310

GERLI & CO., INC.

41 Madison Ave, New York, NY 10010
Tel.: (212) 213-1919
Year Founded: 1978
Sales Range: $10-24.9 Million
Emp.: 180
Furnishing Fabric Mfr & Distr
N.A.I.C.S.: 313310
John M. Sullivan (Chm)
Robin Slough (Pres)
Cynthia Clark-Douthit (VP-Design)

GERLINGER STEEL & SUPPLY COMPANY, CO.

1527 Sacramento St, Redding, CA 96001-1914
Tel.: (530) 243-1053
Web Site: https://www.gerlinger.com
Year Founded: 1929
Sales Range: $10-24.9 Million
Emp.: 55
Industrial Services, Metalworking Machinery & Supplies Distr
N.A.I.C.S.: 423830
Fred M. Gerlinger (Pres)

GERLOFF COMPANY INC.

14955 Bulverde Rd, San Antonio, TX 78247
Tel.: (210) 490-2777
Web Site: https://www.gerloffinc.com
Year Founded: 1985
Sales Range: $10-24.9 Million
Emp.: 145
Fire Damage Repair Services
N.A.I.C.S.: 236118
Darren W. Gerloff (Chm)
James Gregory (Pres)

GERMAIN MOTOR COMPANY

4200 Morse Crossing, Columbus, OH 43219
Tel.: (614) 416-3377   DE
Web Site: http://www.germain.com
Year Founded: 1947
Emp.: 500
New & Used Car Dealerships Owner & Operator
N.A.I.C.S.: 441110
Stephen L. Germain (Pres & CEO)

Subsidiaries:

Columbus Motor Car Company, Inc.   (1)
4200 Morse Crossing, Columbus, OH 43219-3024
Tel.: (614) 421-2007
Web Site:
 http://www.germaincadillacofeaston.com
Sales Range: $10-24.9 Million
Emp.: 39
New & Used Automobile Dealer
N.A.I.C.S.: 441110
Mike Visocky (Gen Mgr)
Aaron Spiers (Mgr-Parts)

Germain Automotive Partnership, Inc. (1)
3885 W Dublin Granville Rd, Dublin, OH 43017
Tel.: (614) 383-4692
Holding Company; New & Used Car Dealerships
N.A.I.C.S.: 551112
Robert L. Germain Jr. *(Pres)*

Subsidiary (Domestic):

Germain Ford of Columbus, LLC (2)
7250 Sawmill Rd, Columbus, OH 43235
Tel.: (614) 889-7777
Web Site: http://www.germainford.com
Sales Range: $25-49.9 Million
Emp.: 135
New & Used Automobile Dealer
N.A.I.C.S.: 441110
Mitchell Gadd *(Gen Mgr)*
Joe Evener *(Mgr-Pre-owned Sls)*
James Soto *(Mgr-New Car & Internet Sls)*
Tasha Carnes *(Mgr-Customer Rels)*
Heather Blevins *(Mgr-Body Shop)*
John Carl *(Mgr-Pre-Owned Sls)*
Doug Carnes *(Mgr-F&I)*
Zane Hall *(Office Mgr)*
Randy Hellmann *(Mgr-Parts)*
Dave Henry *(Mgr-New Car)*
Spencer Monroe *(Mgr-F&I)*
Nick Rowland *(Mgr-New Car)*
Chad Secrest *(Gen Mgr)*
Bob Tschappat *(Mgr-F&I)*

Unit (Domestic):

Germain Lexus of Dublin (2)
3885 W Dublin Granville Rd, Dublin, OH 43017
Tel.: (614) 452-9775
Web Site:
http://www.germainlexusdublin.com
Sales Range: $10-24.9 Million
Emp.: 63
New & Used Automobile Dealer
N.A.I.C.S.: 441110
Rick Germain *(COO)*
Roberto Vazquez *(Gen Mgr)*

Germain Lexus of Easton (2)
4130 Morse Xing, Columbus, OH 43219
Tel.: (614) 504-8838
Web Site: http://www.lexusofeaston.com
Emp.: 50
New & Used Automobile Dealer
N.A.I.C.S.: 441110
Ken Collins *(Mgr-Lexus)*
Erv Konrad *(Dir-Parts)*
Josh Miller *(Gen Mgr)*
Bennie Fornash *(Mgr-New Car Sls)*
Kathy Armstrong *(Mgr-Customer Care)*
Lyn Starcher *(Mgr-Customer Rels, Accessories & Aftermarket Sls)*
Shane Kitts *(Mgr-Pre-Owned Sls)*
Ted Santagata *(Dir-Pre-Owned Sls)*
Dan Medley *(Mgr-Ground Ops & Inventory)*

Subsidiary (Domestic):

Germain Nissan of New Albany, Inc. (2)
4300 Morse Rd, Columbus, OH 43230
Tel.: (614) 383-4355
Web Site: http://www.germainnissan.com
Sales Range: $10-24.9 Million
Emp.: 50
New & Used Automobile Dealer
N.A.I.C.S.: 441110
John Germain *(Gen Mgr)*
Ladonshay Jackson *(Mgr-F&I)*

Affiliate (Domestic):

Germain of Naples, Inc. (2)
13491 Tamiami Trl N, Naples, FL 34110-6338
Tel.: (239) 592-5533
Web Site: http://www.lexusofnaples.com
Sales Range: $25-49.9 Million
Emp.: 80
New & Used Automobile Dealer
N.A.I.C.S.: 441110
Dave Camposano *(Gen Mgr)*
Trish Cano *(Gen Mgr-Sls)*
Robert L. Germain Jr. *(Pres)*

Germain on Tamiami, LLC (1)
11286 Tamiami Trl N, Naples, FL 34110-1622

Tel.: (260) 747-7524
Web Site: http://www.fillrite.com
Rev.: $9,705,000
Emp.: 15
New & Used Automobile Distr
N.A.I.C.S.: 441110
Sam Rusinik *(Coord-Lease End)*
Flavio Galasso *(Gen Mgr)*
Kevin Browne *(Mgr-Pre-Owned Sls)*
John Cathey *(Mgr-Parts)*
Paul Cullinan *(Gen Mgr-Sls)*
Bill Emerson *(Mgr-Svc)*
Francesca Zupancic *(Mgr-New Vehicle Sls)*

Staten Island Yacht Club, Inc. (1)
147 Mansion Ave, Staten Island, NY 10308
Tel.: (718) 948-9508
Web Site: http://www.siyachts.com
Sales Range: $1-9.9 Million
Emp.: 94
Marinas
N.A.I.C.S.: 713930
David King *(Founder)*

GERMANE SYSTEMS LC
3680 Centerview Dr, Chantilly, VA 20151
Tel.: (703) 502-8890
Web Site:
http://www.germanesys.com
Year Founded: 1997
Rev.: $24,931,493
Emp.: 100
Computer Systems Design & Integration Services
N.A.I.C.S.: 541512
Brian Hellems *(VP-Sls & Mktg & Customer Svc)*
Jim Armstrong *(CFO)*
Kerry Green *(Founder & CEO)*

GERMANIA FARM MUTUAL INSURANCE ASSOCIATION
507 Hwy 290 E, Brenham, TX 77833
Tel.: (979) 836-5224
Web Site:
https://www.germaniainsurance.com
Sales Range: $300-349.9 Million
Emp.: 300
Fire, Marine & Casualty Insurance
N.A.I.C.S.: 524126
Derrell Krebs *(CFO, Treas & Sec)*
Blake Lovelace *(First VP)*

GERMANOW-SIMON CORPORATION
408 St Paul St, Rochester, NY 14605
Tel.: (585) 232-1440
Web Site: http://www.gssupplies.com
Rev.: $10,000,000
Emp.: 96
Plastics Processing
N.A.I.C.S.: 326199
Andy Germanow *(Chm & Pres)*

GERMANTOWN LIFE ENRICHMENT CENTER
5722 Greene St, Philadelphia, PA 19144
Tel.: (215) 844-3281
Web Site:
http://www.germantownlifeenrichmentcenter.org
Year Founded: 1871
Sales Range: $1-9.9 Million
Emp.: 79
Christian Ministry Services
N.A.I.C.S.: 813110
Chester Williams *(First VP)*
Jesse W. Brown *(Pres)*

GERMFREE LABORATORIES INC.
17 Sunshine Blvd, Ormond Beach, FL 32174
Tel.: (386) 677-7742
Web Site: http://www.germfree.com
Rev.: $5,600,000
Emp.: 25
Surgical & Medical Instrument Mfr

N.A.I.C.S.: 339112
Jerome J. Landy *(Pres)*
Brandon Rosendahl *(Assoc Dir-Sls)*

Subsidiaries:

Arcoplast Inc. (1)
1873 Williamstown Dr, Saint Peters, MO 63376-8101
Tel.: (636) 978-7781
Web Site: http://www.arcoplast.com
Automatic Environmental Control Mfr for Residential, Commercial & Appliance Use
N.A.I.C.S.: 334512
Ghislain Beauregard *(Pres)*

GERNATT ASPHALT PRODUCTS INC.
13870 Taylor Hollow Rd, Collins, NY 14034
Tel.: (716) 532-3371
Web Site: https://www.gernatt.com
Rev.: $14,200,000
Emp.: 20
Asphalt Paving Mixtures & Blocks
N.A.I.C.S.: 324121
Bill Schmitz *(VP-Sls)*
Randall Best *(VP-Bus Dev)*
Susan DeGolier *(Office Mgr)*
Mark Smith *(VP-Land Acq & Mgmt)*
Jim Garner *(Comptroller)*
Ken Ziccarelli *(VP-Regulatory Affairs & Ops)*

GEROME MANUFACTURING COMPANY, INC.
80 Laurel View Dr, Smithfield, PA 15478
Tel.: (724) 438-8544
Web Site:
http://www.geromemfg.com
Sales Range: $10-24.9 Million
Emp.: 90
Sheet Metalwork
N.A.I.C.S.: 332322
Joseph Putila *(Pres)*
Jim Angry *(Plant Mgr)*

GEROTECH INC.
29220 Commerce Dr, Flat Rock, MI 48134-2749
Tel.: (734) 379-7788   MI
Web Site:
http://www.gerotechinc.com
Year Founded: 1987
Rev.: $54,456,292
Emp.: 75
Industrial Machinery & Equipment; Turnkey Solution Provider
N.A.I.C.S.: 423830
Roger Gauthier *(Owner)*
Donald O. Wood *(Mgr-Sls)*
Jim Fitzpatrick *(Engr-Applications)*
Patrick Lynch *(Engr-Sls)*
Richard Corteville *(Engr-Sls)*

Subsidiaries:

Haas Factory Outlet (1)
2716 Courier Dr NW, Grand Rapids, MI 49544-1271   (100%)
Tel.: (616) 453-4050
Web Site: http://www.hfogerotech.com
Sales Range: $25-49.9 Million
Emp.: 6
Industrial Machinery & Equipment; Turnkey Solution Provider
N.A.I.C.S.: 423830
Jay Haas *(Pres)*
Tom Dawson *(Engr-Sls-Southwest Michigan)*

Haas Factory Outlet (1)
29220 Commerce Dr, Flat Rock, MI 48134-2749
Tel.: (734) 379-7788
Web Site: http://www.gerotechinc.com
Sales Range: $25-49.9 Million
Emp.: 42
Industrial Machinery & Equipment; Turnkey Solution Provider
N.A.I.C.S.: 423830

GERRISH HONDA
369 Miracle Mile, Lebanon, NH 03766
Tel.: (603) 448-6969
Web Site:
http://www.gerrishhonda.com
Year Founded: 1957
Sales Range: $10-24.9 Million
Emp.: 41
Car Dealer
N.A.I.C.S.: 441110
Kurt Gerrish *(Pres)*
Robert Nicolson *(Gen Mgr-Sls)*

GERRITY COMPANY INCORPORATED
90 Oak St, Newton, MA 02464-1439
Tel.: (617) 928-3330
Year Founded: 1950
Sales Range: $10-24.9 Million
Emp.: 65
Lessor of Real Property
N.A.I.C.S.: 531190
James Gerrity *(Pres)*

Subsidiaries:

Dayken Pallet Company, Inc. (1)
152 Bog Rd, Leeds, ME 04263
Tel.: (207) 933-2804
Web Site: http://www.gerrityindustries.com
Sales Range: $10-24.9 Million
Emp.: 60
Mfr of Wood Pallets & Skids
N.A.I.C.S.: 321920

Gerrity Stone Inc. (1)
225 B Merrimac St, Woburn, MA 01801-1756
Tel.: (781) 938-1820
Web Site: http://www.gerritystone.com
Provider of Brick, Stone & Related Material
N.A.I.C.S.: 423320
James Gerrity *(Owner)*

Warren Trask Company Inc. (1)
1481 Central St, Stoughton, MA 02072-4415
Tel.: (781) 341-2426
Web Site: http://www.wtrask.com
Sales Range: $10-24.9 Million
Emp.: 35
Provider of Lumber, Plywood & Millwork
N.A.I.C.S.: 423310
Vincent Micale *(Pres)*

GERRITY'S SUPERMARKETS INC.
950 N S Rd, Scranton, PA 18504
Tel.: (570) 342-4144
Web Site: http://www.gerritygifts.com
Rev.: $114,293,678
Emp.: 14
Grocery Stores, Independent
N.A.I.C.S.: 445110
Joyce A. Fasula *(Pres)*
Anna Corcoran *(Mgr-Acctg)*

GERRY RED INC.
3008 State Hwy 155, Palestine, TX 75803
Tel.: (903) 729-6571
Sales Range: $10-24.9 Million
Emp.: 130
Convenience Store
N.A.I.C.S.: 445131
Gerald C. Blevins *(Pres)*

GERRY WOOD AUTOMOTIVE, LLC.
529 Jake Alexander Blvd S, Salisbury, NC 28147
Tel.: (704) 216-3401
Web Site:
https://www.gerrywoodauto.com
Year Founded: 1994
Sales Range: $10-24.9 Million
Emp.: 150
New Car Dealers
N.A.I.C.S.: 441110

Gerry Wood Automotive, LLC.—(Continued)

Gerald Wood *(Principal)*
Brad Wood *(Gen Mgr)*

GERSH ACADEMY, INC.
21 Sweet Hollow Rd Ste 1, Huntington, NY 11743
Tel.: (631) 385-3342
Web Site:
   https://www.gershacademy.org
Year Founded: 1999
Sales Range: $1-9.9 Million
Emp.: 70
Educational Institute
N.A.I.C.S.: 611699
Kevin Gersh *(Pres)*
Valerie Vlacancich *(CFO & COO)*

GERSHMAN MORTGAGE CORPORATION
7 N Bemiston Ave, Saint Louis, MO 63105
Tel.: (314) 889-0600
Web Site: http://www.gershman.com
Sales Range: $10-24.9 Million
Emp.: 150
Mortgage Services
N.A.I.C.S.: 522292
William C. Nass *(VP)*
Scott Ripple *(VP)*
David Bell *(VP)*
Paul Olson *(VP-Chicago)*
Dan Main *(VP-Saint Peters)*
Jeff Berger *(VP)*
Michael Thomas *(VP-Multifamily & Sr Housing)*
Charlie Nager *(Acct Exec)*
Jennifer Smerek *(VP)*
Justin Berger *(Officer-Loan)*
Nancy Williams *(Asst VP)*
Shari Wynn *(VP)*
Todd Wemhoener *(Asst VP)*
Adam J. Mason *(COO & Exec VP)*
Cory Timblin *(Mgr-HR)*
Bryan W. Marx *(VP/Mgr-Florida)*
Douglas Smith *(VP)*
Chris Gianino *(VP)*
Bethny Harwell *(VP)*
Jack Langley *(VP)*
Jason Larson *(VP)*

GERSHOW RECYCLING CORPORATION
71 Peconic Ave, Medford, NY 11763
Tel.: (631) 289-6188
Web Site:
   http://www.gershowrecycling.com
Year Founded: 1964
Rev.: $14,000,000
Emp.: 200
Provider of Recycling Services
N.A.I.C.S.: 562920
Sam Gershowitz *(Founder)*
Kevin Gershowitz *(Pres)*
Elliot Gershowitz *(Controller)*
Scott Bohan *(CFO)*

GERSON & GERSON, INC.
100 W 33rd St Ste 911, New York, NY 10001-0101
Tel.: (212) 244-6775   NY
Web Site:
   https://www.gersonandgerson.com
Year Founded: 1935
Sales Range: $75-99.9 Million
Emp.: 50
Mfr of Infants' & Children's Dresses
N.A.I.C.S.: 315250
Lauren Ruderman *(Product Mgr)*
Magaly Sosa *(Mgr-Sewing Room)*
Shelley Striar *(Mgr-Production)*
Terrince Autry *(Mgr-Customer Svc)*
Jack Dabby *(Dir-IT)*

GERSTAD BUILDERS INC.

1600 Reagan Blvd, McHenry, IL 60051
Tel.: (815) 344-1050
Web Site:
   http://www.gerstadbuilders.com
Year Founded: 1985
Sales Range: Less than $1 Million
Emp.: 5
Home Construction Services
N.A.I.C.S.: 236115
Roger O. Gerstad *(Pres)*
Tom Roach *(Mgr-Sls)*
Trisha Sayler *(Mgr-Sls)*

GERTEN GREENHOUSES & GARDEN CENTER, INC.
5715 Blaine Ave E, Grove Heights, MN 55076-1212
Tel.: (651) 450-1501
Web Site: https://www.gertens.com
Year Founded: 1997
Sales Range: $10-24.9 Million
Emp.: 450
Nursery, Garden Center & Farm Supply Services
N.A.I.C.S.: 444240
Lewis Gerten *(Pres)*

GERTRUDE HAWK CHOCOLATES, INC.
901 Keystone Industrial Park Rd, Dunmore, PA 18512-1516
Tel.: (570) 342-7556   PA
Web Site:
   http://www.gertrudehawk.com
Year Founded: 1936
Sales Range: $450-499.9 Million
Emp.: 2,000
Candy & Confectionery Products Mfr
N.A.I.C.S.: 311351
David W. Hawk *(Chm)*
William E. Aubrey II *(Pres-Alternative Investments)*

GERVAIS LINCOLN MERCURY INC.
24 Reiss Ave, Lowell, MA 01851
Tel.: (978) 454-5696
Web Site:
   https://www.gervaislincoln.net
Sales Range: $10-24.9 Million
Emp.: 30
Car Whslr
N.A.I.C.S.: 441110
Peter Jarvis *(Gen Mgr)*

GES GROUNDWATER & ENVIRONMENTAL SERVICES, INC.
1340 Campus Pkwy Bldg B, Neptune, NJ 07753
Tel.: (732) 919-0100
Web Site: http://www.gesonline.com
Year Founded: 1985
Sales Range: $125-149.9 Million
Emp.: 700
Environmental Consulting Services
N.A.I.C.S.: 541620
Tony Kull *(Founder & CEO)*

GESA CREDIT UNION
51 Gage Blvd, Richland, WA 99352
Tel.: (509) 378-3382   WA
Web Site: http://www.gesa.com
Year Founded: 1953
Sales Range: $50-74.9 Million
Emp.: 442
Credit Union
N.A.I.C.S.: 522130
Bob Follett *(Vice Chm)*
Bill Melberg *(Sec)*
Don Miller *(Pres & CEO)*

GESD CAPITAL PARTNERS
221 Main St Ste 1450, San Francisco, CA 94105
Tel.: (415) 477-8200

Web Site: http://www.gesd.net
Rev.: $20,000,000
Emp.: 212
Securities Brokerage
N.A.I.C.S.: 523150
Louis J. Giraudo *(Co-Founder & Partner)*
Sharon B. Duvall *(Co-Founder & Partner)*
Mark L. Briggs *(Co-Founder & Partner)*
Daniel J. Stromberg *(Co-Founder & Partner)*
William R. Dozier *(CFO)*

GESSNER INDUSTRIES INC.
384 Faggart Ave, Concord, NC 28027-6069
Tel.: (704) 782-3100   NC
Web Site:
   https://www.gessnerwj.syntha
   site.com
Year Founded: 1984
Sales Range: Less than $1 Million
Emp.: 7
Textile Machinery
N.A.I.C.S.: 811210
Frances Phillips *(Gen Mgr)*
Linda Shaver *(Mgr-Accts)*

GET IN SHAPE FOR WOMEN, INC.
75 2nd Ave Ste 220, Needham, MA 02494
Tel.: (781) 444-1913
Web Site: http://www.getinshapefor
   women.com
Year Founded: 2006
Sales Range: $1-9.9 Million
Emp.: 300
Weight Training Services
N.A.I.C.S.: 713940
Brian Cook *(Founder & CEO)*
Dave Dembinski *(Dir-Franchise Dev)*

GET INCORPORATED
901 A E Thomas St, Wausau, WI 54403
Tel.: (715) 845-2531
Web Site:
   http://www.classiccleaners.com
Rev.: $12,500,000
Emp.: 2
Dry Cleaning Services
N.A.I.C.S.: 812320
Tim Jolliffe *(Owner)*

GET MATCHES LLC
PO Box 1290, Little Falls, NJ 07424
Tel.: (973) 785-3350
Web Site:
   http://www.getmatches.com
Branded Match Boxes, Match Books & Paper Promotional Products Mfr
N.A.I.C.S.: 322211
Joe Dadon *(Pres)*

GET SOLUTIONS, INC.
5465 Greenwich Rd, Virginia Beach, VA 23462
Tel.: (757) 518-1703
Web Site:
   https://www.getsolutionsinc.com
Sales Range: $10-24.9 Million
Emp.: 85
Engineeering Services
N.A.I.C.S.: 541330

GET SPIFFY, INC.
4518 S Miami Blvd Ste 180, Durham, NC 27703
Tel.: (844) 438-7743   DE
Web Site: http://www.getspiffy.com
Year Founded: 2014
Mobile Car Wash & Detailing Services
N.A.I.C.S.: 811192

Mitchell Scot Wingo *(Co-Founder & CEO)*
Joe Procopio *(Chief Product Officer)*

Subsidiaries:

Your Location Lubrication, LLC   **(1)**
4225 Frontage Rd N, Lakeland, FL 33810
Tel.: (863) 937-9717
Web Site:
   http://www.yourlocationlubrication.com
Automotive Repair & Maintenance Services
N.A.I.C.S.: 811111

GETBLEND INC.
200 S Figueroa St, Los Angeles, CA 90012
Tel.: (800) 720-3722   DE
Web Site: http://www.getblend.com
Year Founded: 2008
Translation & Localization Services
N.A.I.C.S.: 541930
Yair Tal *(CEO)*

Subsidiaries:

GM Voices, Inc.   **(1)**
6515 Shiloh Rd 4th Fl, Alpharetta, GA 30005
Tel.: (770) 752-4500
Web Site: http://www.gmvoices.com
Rev.: $1,800,000
Emp.: 21
Telecommunication Servicesb
N.A.I.C.S.: 517810
Marcus Graham *(Founder & CEO)*

GETELMAN CORP.
2235 E Flamingo Rd Ste 355, Las Vegas, NV 89119
Tel.: (725) 777-0799   NV
Year Founded: 2015
Sales Range: Less than $1 Million
Corporate Event Planning Services
N.A.I.C.S.: 561920
Mark Gitelman *(CFO & Chief Acctg Officer)*
Anders Thange Nordlund *(Pres, CEO, Treas & Sec)*

GETHMANN CONSTRUCTION COMPANY
313 Font St, Gladbrook, IA 50635
Tel.: (641) 473-2323
Web Site: http://www.gethman.com
Sales Range: $10-24.9 Million
Emp.: 30
Construction Services
N.A.I.C.S.: 236210
Orville Brekke *(Treas)*

GETMAN CORPORATION
59750 34th Ave, Bangor, MI 49013
Tel.: (269) 427-5611
Web Site: https://www.getman.com
Year Founded: 1956
Rev.: $11,162,403
Emp.: 42
Mine Cars, Plows, Loaders, Feeders & Similar Equipment
N.A.I.C.S.: 333131
Dana S. Getman *(CEO)*
Erik VanAllen *(Pres)*

GETMYHOMESVALUE.COM
221 Rohrerstown Rd, Lancaster, PA 17603
Year Founded: 2003
Rev.: $2,700,000
Emp.: 30
Advertising & Marketing
N.A.I.C.S.: 541810
Mark Boyd *(Acct Mgr)*
Audrey Mack *(Acct Mgr)*

GETO & DEMILLY INC.
276 5th Ave Ste 806, New York, NY 10001
Tel.: (212) 686-4551   NY

Web Site:
https://www.getodemilly.com
Year Founded: 1980
Sales Range: $1-9.9 Million
Emp.: 25
Public Relations Agency
N.A.I.C.S.: 541820
Ethan Geto *(Pres)*
Michele de Milly *(Principal)*
Joyce Baumgarten *(Sr VP)*
Julie Hendricks *(VP)*

**GETTEL AUTOMOTIVE MAN-
AGEMENT GROUP**
5959 E State Rd 64, Bradenton, FL
34208
Tel.: (941) 417-5269
Web Site: https://www.gettel.com
Year Founded: 1990
Sales Range: $500-549.9 Million
Emp.: 570
Automobile Dealership
N.A.I.C.S.: 441110
James C. Gettel *(Pres)*
Ellen Walther *(Dir-PR)*
Fred Bartholomew *(Dir-Fixed Ops)*
Laura Hammer *(Controller)*
Mary Heraty *(Controller)*
Erin Siemer *(Dir-Trng & Implementa-
tion)*
Kurt Fisher *(Mgr-Used Vehicle Ops)*

GETTEL ENTERPRISE INC.
985 N Main St, Gainesville, FL 32609
Tel.: (352) 376-3262
Web Site:
http://www.gatorlandtoyota.com
Sales Range: $10-24.9 Million
Emp.: 500
Automobiles, New & Used
N.A.I.C.S.: 441110
Mary Ann *(Controller)*
Chris Trotti *(Gen Mgr)*

GETTEL FORD-MERCURY INC.
651 Unionville Rd, Sebewaing, MI
487591632
Tel.: (989) 883-2710
Rev.: $14,300,000
Emp.: 50
New Car Dealers
N.A.I.C.S.: 441110
James C. Gettel *(Pres)*

GETTLE, INC.
325 Busser Rd, Emigsville, PA
17318-0337
Tel.: (717) 843-1231
Web Site: https://www.gettle.com
Sales Range: $10-24.9 Million
Emp.: 280
Electronic Services
N.A.I.C.S.: 238210
P. Michael Walburn *(VP)*
Tom Furman *(Dir-Bus Dev)*

GETWELLNETWORK, INC.
7700 Old Georgetown Rd 4th Fl,
Bethesda, MD 20814-2500
Tel.: (240) 482-3200
Web Site:
https://www.getwellnetwork.com
Sales Range: $10-24.9 Million
Emp.: 200
Interactive Patient Care Solutions
N.A.I.C.S.: 513210
Robin Cavanaugh *(CTO)*
David Wright *(Sr VP-Govt Svcs)*
David D. Bennett *(Chief Info & Inno-
vation Officer)*
Karen Drenkard *(Chief Clinical &
Nursing Officer)*
John George *(Chief Growth Officer &
Sr VP)*
Scott Filion *(Pres)*

Sharon S. Kaufman *(Chief People
Officer)*
Carrie Ivers Reeuwijk *(Chief Strategy
Officer)*
Bill Roselli *(CFO, COO & Sr VP)*
Nikia Bergan *(Chief Revenue Officer)*
Michael B. O'Neil Jr. *(Founder &
CEO)*

GETWIRELESS, LLC
10901 Red Cir Dr Ste 325, Minne-
tonka, MN 55343
Tel.: (952) 890-6669
Web Site:
http://www.getwirelessllc.com
Year Founded: 2001
Sales Range: $25-49.9 Million
Emp.: 20
Distr of Cellular Solutions Offering
Landline Functionality Through Exist-
ing Cellular Networks
N.A.I.C.S.: 517112
Brian Taney *(CEO)*
Bryan Rasmussen *(Co-Founder &
COO)*
Tom Hoyt *(Dir-Bus Dev)*
Craig Linder *(Dir-Product Mgmt)*
Scott Davis *(Sr VP-Strategic Dev)*
Terra Bastolich *(VP-Mktg)*

GETZS, INC.
218 S Front St Ste 220, Marquette,
MI 49855-4680
Tel.: (906) 226-3561
Web Site: https://www.getzs.com
Sales Range: $1-9.9 Million
Emp.: 51
Outdoor Clothing, Products & Work
Wear Store & Online Retailer
N.A.I.C.S.: 458110
Richard Caden *(Pres)*

GEWEKE CO.
871 E Onstott Rd, Yuba City, CA
95991
Tel.: (530) 821-2121
Web Site:
http://www.larrygewekeford.com
Year Founded: 1966
Rev.: $40,000,000
Emp.: 80
Automobiles, New & Used
N.A.I.C.S.: 441110
Larry Geweke *(CEO)*

GEYEN GROUP, INC.
33606 W Cypress Rd, Tampa, FL
33634
Tel.: (813) 882-9655
Web Site:
http://www.geyengroup.com
Sales Range: $1-9.9 Million
Emp.: 15
Commercial Cleaning Services
N.A.I.C.S.: 561740
Marleen Geyen *(Pres)*

GEYERS MARKETS INC.
660 Diamond St, Mansfield, OH
44903
Tel.: (419) 552-6331
Web Site: http://www.geyers.com
Rev.: $34,491,789
Emp.: 8
Provider of Grocery Services
N.A.I.C.S.: 445110

GEZON MOTORS, INC.
3985 Plainfield Ave NE, Grand Rap-
ids, MI 49525-1627
Tel.: (616) 361-7361
Web Site: https://www.gezonvw.com
Year Founded: 1979
Sales Range: $10-24.9 Million
Emp.: 47
Car Dealer

N.A.I.C.S.: 441110
Mary Gezon *(Gen Mgr)*
David H. Gezon *(Chm)*

GF ACQUISITION CORP.
39 East Union St, Pasadena, CA
91103
Tel.: (626) 204-6298   DE
Year Founded: 2008
Investment Services
N.A.I.C.S.: 523999
Ronald F. Valenta *(Co-Chm, Pres &
CEO)*

**GF CAPITAL MANAGEMENT &
ADVISORS, LLC**
767 Fifth Ave 46th Fl, New York, NY
10153
Tel.: (212) 433-1234
Web Site: http://www.gfcap.com
Emp.: 20
Private Equity, Real Estate Invest-
ment & Wealth Management Services
N.A.I.C.S.: 523999
Gary Fuhrman *(Co-Founder, Chm &
CEO)*
Erik Baker *(Co-Founder & Mng Dir)*
Neil Shapiro *(Co-Founder, Mng Dir &
CFO)*
Brian Anderson *(VP)*
Christina Hull *(VP)*
James Taussig *(Mng Dir)*

Subsidiaries:

Airborne, Inc.   (1)
PO Box 1120, Chanhassen, MN 55317-
1120
Web Site: http://www.airbornehealth.com
Sales Range: $100-124.9 Million
Emp.: 23
Herbal Healthcare Products Mfr & Distr
N.A.I.C.S.: 325414

MAR (MD), LLC   (1)
1803 Research Blvd Ste 204, Rockville, MD
20850-0100
Tel.: (301) 231-0100
Web Site: http://www.marinc.com
Information Technology, Intelligence, Sys-
tems Engineering & Facilities Management
Services
N.A.I.C.S.: 541990
Samuel Sunukjian *(VP-IT & Cybersecurity
Svcs)*
Arlette Mitchell *(Dir-Intelligence & Special
Programs)*
Michael P. Norcio *(Chm & CEO)*
Franni Price *(Controller)*
Laura A. Evans *(VP-HR & Administration)*
Daniel K. Hackenberg *(Sr VP, CTO & Dir-
Engrg)*
Mary Lee Pence *(Dir-Contracts & Pur)*
Gwyneth Hill *(Mgr-Proposal Svcs)*

GF HEALTH PRODUCTS, INC.
1 Graham-Field Way, Atlanta, GA
30340
Tel.: (770) 368-4700   GA
Web Site:
http://www.gograhamfield.com
Year Founded: 1946
Sales Range: $200-249.9 Million
Emp.: 330
Medical & Home Health Care Prod-
ucts Mfr & Distr
N.A.I.C.S.: 423450
Cherie L. Antoniazzi *(Sr VP-Quality &
Risk Mgmt)*
Lawrence de la Haba *(Sr VP-Bus
Dev)*
Kenneth Spett *(Pres & CEO)*
David Walton *(Sr VP-Long-Term
Care)*
Kurt Hellman *(Sr VP-Mfg Ops)*
Marc Bernstein *(Sr VP-Consumer
Sls)*
Lori Kirschner *(Sr VP-HR & Admin)*
Alan Spett *(Sr VP-Ops)*

Subsidiaries:

Basic American Metal Products   (1)
336 Trowbridge Dr, Fond Du Lac, WI 54937
Tel.: (920) 929-8200
Web Site: http://www.bampwi.com
Sales Range: $100-124.9 Million
Emp.: 300
Metal Product Roll Forming, Fabricating,
Tube Bending, Welding, Powder Coating,
Assembly & Warehousing Services
N.A.I.C.S.: 332999
Kurt Hellman *(Sr VP-Mfg Ops & Gen Mgr)*

Gendron Inc.   (1)
520 W Mulberry St Ste 100, Bryan, OH
43506
Tel.: (419) 636-0848
Web Site: http://www.gendroninc.com
Rev.: $7,000,000
Emp.: 67
Medical, Dental & Hospital Equipment &
Supplies Merchant Whslr
N.A.I.C.S.: 423450

GF MANAGEMENT, INC.
1628 John F Kennedy Blvd 8 Penn
Ctr 23rd Fl, Philadelphia, PA 19103
Tel.: (215) 972-2222   PA
Web Site: http://www.gfhotels.com
Year Founded: 1988
Holding Company; Hotels, Catering
Facilities, Golf Courses & Other Hos-
pitality Assets Owner & Operator
N.A.I.C.S.: 551112
Kenneth Kochenour *(Pres & CEO)*
Barbara Evans *(Exec VP-Fin)*
Andrew S. Tod *(Exec VP)*
Jeffrey Kolessar *(Sr VP-Dev)*
Joseph A. Wellenbusher *(CFO)*
Andrew Taymans *(VP-Asset & Rev-
enue Mgmt)*
Vineet Nayyar *(COO)*
Kevin Corprew *(Reg Dir-Ops)*
John Rubino *(Exec VP-Ops)*
Robert E. Keith Jr. *(Vice Chm)*
Robert E. Keith Jr. *(Vice Chm)*
Ira M. Lubert *(Co-Founder)*
Ira M. Lubert *(Co-Founder)*

Subsidiaries:

GF Management, LLC   (1)
1628 John F Kennedy Blvd 8 Penn Ctr 23rd
Fl, Philadelphia, PA 19103
Tel.: (215) 972-2222
Web Site: http://www.gfhotels.com
Hotels, Catering Facilities, Golf Courses &
Other Hospitality Assets Operator
N.A.I.C.S.: 561110
Kenneth Kochenour *(Pres & CEO)*
Richard C. Henrikson *(Sr VP-Ops)*
Matthew S. Pica *(COO)*
Stan Glander *(Exec VP-Ops-North America)*
Mike Bowman *(Sr VP)*
M. Daniel Hatch *(Sr VP)*

GFA INCORPORATED
26 E Clinton Ave, Tenafly, NJ 07670
Tel.: (201) 655-7474   NJ
Web Site: http://www.gfany.com
Year Founded: 1994
Sales Range: $10-24.9 Million
Emp.: 8
General Warehousing & Storage
N.A.I.C.S.: 493110
Steve H. Hong *(Pres)*
Steve Hong *(Pres)*

GFC CONSTRUCTION INC.
10474 Hwy 82 E, Duncanville, AL
35456
Tel.: (205) 758-1948
Rev.: $14,100,000
Emp.: 75
Site Preparation Contractor
N.A.I.C.S.: 238910
William Godwin *(VP)*
John C. Free *(Pres)*
Cynthia K. Free *(Treas & Sec)*
Kay Free *(Mgr)*

GFC Construction Inc.—(Continued)

GFF INC.
145 Willow Ave, City of Industry, CA
91746-2047
Tel.: (323) 846-2700
Web Site:
https://www.girardsdressings.com
Sales Range: $10-24.9 Million
Emp.: 50
Pickles, Sauces & Salad Dressings
N.A.I.C.S.: 311941
Evan Beattie *(Sr Principal)*

GFRC SHELTERS, INC.
3725 E Texas St, Bossier City, LA
71111
Tel.: (318) 747-5598
Web Site: http://www.gfrc.com
Sales Range: $50-74.9 Million
Emp.: 100
Concrete & Precast Products
N.A.I.C.S.: 327390

GFS CHEMICALS, INC.
3041 Home Rd, Powell, OH 43065
Tel.: (740) 881-5501   OH
Web Site:
http://www.gfschemicals.com
Year Founded: 1928
Sales Range: $10-24.9 Million
Emp.: 90
Fine & Specialty Chemicals Mfr
N.A.I.C.S.: 325180
J.S. Hutchinson *(Owner & Pres)*
M. R. Pierron *(VP-Plant Ops)*
Martha Kiser *(Controller)*
David Baust *(Gen Mgr-Organic Chemical Mfg Div)*
Harry Ruster *(Dir-Mktg & Sls)*

GGMC PARKING, LLC
1651 3rd Ave, New York, NY 10128
Tel.: (212) 996-6363
Web Site:
https://www.ggmcparking.com
Rev.: $24,000,000
Emp.: 22
Parking Garage Services
N.A.I.C.S.: 812930
Nathan Jakub *(VP-Ops)*
Katherine Briganti *(Coord-Mktg)*
Oryan Kochavi *(Dir-Tech)*
Bordy Bissila *(Mgr)*

GHA TECHNOLOGIES, INC.
8998 E Raintree Dr, Scottsdale, AZ
85260
Tel.: (480) 951-6865
Web Site: https://www.gha-associates.com
Rev.: $95,000,000
Emp.: 100
Computer Reseller & Systems Integrator
N.A.I.C.S.: 423430
George Hertzberg *(Pres)*
Christine Wilson *(Mgr-Payroll)*
Gayle Loy *(Mgr-Credit)*
Michelle Dunn *(VP)*
Steve Nevins *(Exec VP)*

GHAFARI ASSOCIATES, L.L.C.
17101 Michigan Ave, Dearborn, MI
48126-2736
Tel.: (313) 441-3000   MI
Web Site: http://www.ghafari.com
Year Founded: 1982
Architectural, Engineering, CAD &
Computer Services Supplier
N.A.I.C.S.: 541330
Yousif B. Ghafari *(Founder & Chm)*
Kouhaila G. Hammer *(Pres & CEO)*
Jim Jobes *(Exec VP)*
Robert Bell *(CIO)*

Christine McDermott *(Chief HR Officer)*
Keith Sherman *(CFO)*
Tom Tooley *(Exec VP)*

Subsidiaries:

CDGGR, P.C.   (1)
89 Monroe Center St NW, Grand Rapids,
MI 49503
Tel.: (616) 771-0909
Web Site:
http://www.conceptdesigngroup.net
Architectural Services
N.A.I.C.S.: 541310
Stephen Fry *(Owner)*

Elton Anderson Associates   (1)
3159 Woodward Ave Ste 200, Detroit, MI
48201
Tel.: (313) 833-9148
Architectural, Engineering, CAD & Computer Services
N.A.I.C.S.: 541330

Ghafari Associates LLC   (1)
8606 Allisonville Rd Ste 355, Indianapolis,
IN 46250   (100%)
Tel.: (317) 845-9666
Web Site: http://www.ghafari.com
Sales Range: $10-24.9 Million
Emp.: 6
Architectural Engineering CAD Intergraph
Interpro 2020 & Computer Services
N.A.I.C.S.: 541310

GHAR INC.
5348 Vegas Dr, Las Vegas, NV
89108   NV
Year Founded: 2018
Assets: $5,306
Liabilities: $63,245
Net Worth: ($57,939)
Earnings: ($116,334)
Emp.: 1
Fiscal Year-end: 03/31/20
Online Marketing Services
N.A.I.C.S.: 531311
Wenjin Li *(Pres, CEO, CFO, Treas & Sec)*

**GHENT CHEVROLET CADIL-
LAC**
2715 35th Ave, Greeley, CO 80634
Tel.: (970) 673-7952
Web Site:
http://www.ghentmotors.com
Year Founded: 1989
Sales Range: $25-49.9 Million
Emp.: 53
New & Used Automobile Dealer
N.A.I.C.S.: 441110
Bob Ghent *(Owner)*
John Syracuse *(Dir-Internet Sls)*

GHENT MOTOR CO.
35th Ave & Hwy 34 Bypass, Greeley,
CO 80634
Tel.: (970) 339-2438
Web Site:
http://www.ghentmotors.com
Year Founded: 1989
Sales Range: $10-24.9 Million
Emp.: 50
Car Whslr
N.A.I.C.S.: 441110
Robert D. Ghent *(Pres)*

GHETTO FILM SCHOOL, INC.
79 Alexander Ave 4th Fl, Bronx, NY
10454
Tel.: (718) 589-5470   NY
Web Site: https://www.ghettofilm.org
Year Founded: 2000
Sales Range: $1-9.9 Million
Emp.: 7
Art School
N.A.I.C.S.: 611519
Evan Shapiro *(Chm)*
Joe Hall *(Founder & Pres)*

Katherine Oliver *(Sec)*
Neal Arthur *(Vice Chm)*
Tiffany R. Warren *(Treas)*

**GHI AUTOMOTIVE SERVICES
INC.**
3056 Eastern Ave SE, Grand Rapids,
MI 49508
Tel.: (616) 241-3980
Web Site: http://hitchesbygeorge.com
Rev.: $13,000,000
Emp.: 80
Automotive Supplies & Parts
N.A.I.C.S.: 423120
James Peterman *(Pres)*
Ron Norman *(VP)*

GHI HOLDINGS INC.
15455 Dallas Pkwy Ste 1000, Addison, TX 75001
Tel.: (214) 750-6528
Web Site:
http://www.grandhomes.com
Year Founded: 1986
Single-Family Housing Construction
N.A.I.C.S.: 236115
Stephen H. Brooks *(CEO)*

GHILOTTI BROS INC.
525 Jacoby St, San Rafael, CA
94901
Tel.: (415) 454-7011
Web Site: http://www.ghilottibros.com
Sales Range: $50-74.9 Million
Emp.: 200
Provider of Surfacing & Paving Services
N.A.I.C.S.: 237310
Michael Ghilotti *(Pres)*
Michael Maxson *(Mgr-IT)*
Dante Ghilotti *(CEO)*
Mike Llamas *(VP-Construction)*

**GHILOTTI CONSTRUCTION
COMPANY INC.**
246 Ghillotti Ave, Santa Rosa, CA
95407-8152
Tel.: (707) 585-1221   CA
Web Site: https://www.ghilotti.com
Year Founded: 1914
Sales Range: $75-99.9 Million
Emp.: 225
Highway & Street Construction
N.A.I.C.S.: 236210
Richard Ghilotti *(Owner & Pres)*
Brian Ongaro *(Sr VP-Ops)*
Brad Simpkins *(VP-Private & Comml Construction)*

GHK CAPITAL PARTNERS LP
28 Havemeyer Pl 3rd Fl, Greenwich,
CT 06830
Tel.: (203) 409-0900
Web Site: http://www.ghk.com
Privater Equity Firm
N.A.I.C.S.: 523999
Gilbert H. Klemann *(Mng Partner)*
Elena Sherman *(CFO & Chief Compliance Officer)*
Benjamin K. Stolbach *(Partner)*
Keith R. Adcock *(VP)*
Lucas M. Viola *(VP)*
John A. Luke *(VP)*
Gurinder Bhangu *(Controller)*

Subsidiaries:

Auto-Vehicle Parts LLC   (1)
100 Homan Dr, Cold Spring, KY 41076
Tel.: (859) 341-6450
Web Site: http://www.auveco.com
Automotive Stampings
N.A.I.C.S.: 336370
Joseph Hohe *(Mgr-Ops)*
Jeff Gilkinson *(CEO)*

Dura Supreme LLC   (1)
300 Dura Dr, Howard Lake, MN 55349

Tel.: (320) 543-3872
Web Site: http://www.durasupreme.com
Household Durable Goods Mfr
N.A.I.C.S.: 332215
Perry Fails *(Pres & COO)*

Hasa, Inc.   (1)
23119 Drayton St, Saugus, CA 91350
Tel.: (661) 259-5848
Web Site: http://www.hasapool.com
Water Treament Products Mfr & Distr
N.A.I.C.S.: 424690
Ken Ward *(CFO)*
Christopher Brink *(Pres & CEO)*
Rob Bzdil *(Chief Comml Officer & Pres-Chlor-Alkali)*
Angela Tran *(Chief Strategy Officer)*
Rick Sawin *(Sr VP-Sls, Pool & Distr)*
Alma Bunch *(COO)*
Mark Adams *(COO)*
David Johnson *(Sr VP-Engrg, Compliance & R&D)*
Randy Johnson *(VP-Sls, Pool & Distr)*
Jarred Morgan *(VP-Sls & Ancillary Products)*
Eric Knight *(VP-Pro Mktg)*

Subsidiary (Domestic):

Inter Valley Pool Supply, Inc.   (2)
1415 E 3rd St, Pomona, CA 91766
Tel.: (626) 969-5657
Web Site: http://www.ivpsinc.com
Sporting & Recreational Goods & Supplies
Merchant Whslr
N.A.I.C.S.: 423910

ITS Logistics, Inc.   (1)
555 Vista Blvd, Sparks, NV 89434
Tel.: (775) 358-5300
Web Site: http://www.its4logistics.com
Sales Range: $1-9.9 Million
Emp.: 100
Transportation Arrangement Services
N.A.I.C.S.: 488510
Darryl Bader *(VP-Ops)*
Jamie Lawson *(CFO)*
Mike Crawford *(Pres-Freight Brokerage Div)*
Jim Dingman *(Pres-Fleet Ops)*
Patrick McFarland *(Dir-Mktg)*
Scott Pruneau *(CEO)*

WSB & Associates, Inc.   (1)
4140 Thielman Ln, Saint Cloud, MN 56301
Tel.: (320) 252-4900
Web Site: http://www.wsbeng.com
Rev.: $1,896,000
Emp.: 12
Engineeering Services
N.A.I.C.S.: 541330
John Mackiewicz *(Principal & Grp Mgr-IT & GIS)*
Bret Weiss *(CEO)*

GHM CORP.
1651 N Glenville Dr Ste 214, Richardson, TX 75081
Tel.: (972) 864-7300   NV
Web Site: http://www.morganusa.com
Year Founded: 1960
Sales Range: $75-99.9 Million
Emp.: 75
Holding Company
N.A.I.C.S.: 551112
Guy H. Morgan *(Pres & CEO)*

Subsidiaries:

Morgan Buildings & Spas, Inc.   (1)
12700 Hillcrest Rd Ste 278, Dallas, TX
75230
Tel.: (972) 864-7300
Web Site: http://www.morganusa.com
Holding Company; Prefabricated Wood &
Metal Modular Building Construction & Installation Services
N.A.I.C.S.: 551112
Guy H. Morgan *(Pres & CEO)*
Hicks B. Morgan *(Gen Counsel, Treas & Sec)*

Subsidiary (Domestic):

Morgan Building & Spa Manufacturing Corporation   (2)
1651 N Glenville Dr, Richardson, TX 75081
Tel.: (972) 864-7341
Web Site: http://www.morganusa.com

Prefabricated Wood & Metal Modular Building Construction & Installation Services
N.A.I.C.S.: 321992
Guy H. Morgan *(Pres & CEO)*
Hicks B. Morgan *(Gen Counsel, Treas & Sec)*
Jim Schilligo *(Gen Sls Mgr-Comml)*

Morgan Building Transport Corp. (2)
1651 N Glenvile Dr Ste 214, Richardson, TX 75081
Tel.: (972) 864-7300
Web Site: http://www.morganusa.com
Emp.: 10
Modular Building Trucking Services
N.A.I.C.S.: 484220
Guy H. Morgan *(Pres & CEO)*

Morgan Management Corporation (2)
12700 Hillcrest Rd Ste 278, Dallas, TX 75230
Tel.: (972) 864-7300
Office Administrative & Bookkeeping Services
N.A.I.C.S.: 561110
Guy H. Morgan *(Pres & CEO)*

GHM INDUSTRIES, INC.
100A Sturbridge Rd, Charlton, MA 01507
Tel.: (508) 248-3941
Web Site: http://www.millerproducts.net
Year Founded: 1992
Heavy Equipment Mfr
N.A.I.C.S.: 333248

Subsidiaries:

GHM Industries, Inc. - Miller Lifting Products Divsion (1)
100A Sturbridge Rd, Charlton, MA 01507
Tel.: (508) 248-3941
Emp.: 20
Lifting Machinery Mfr
N.A.I.C.S.: 333998

Gessner/Miller Corporation (1)
100 A Sturbage Rd, Charlton, MA 01507
Tel.: (508) 248-3941
Mfr of Textile Finishing; Packaging & Carpet Shearing Machinery
N.A.I.C.S.: 333248
Paul Jankovic *(Pres)*

Miller Products, Inc. (1)
100 A Sturbridge Rd, Charlton, MA 01507-2360
Tel.: (508) 248-3941
Web Site: http://www.millerproducts.net
Sales Range: $10-24.9 Million
N.A.I.C.S.: 333248
Paul Jankovic *(Pres)*

GHP MEDIA, INC.
475 Heffernan Dr, West Haven, CT 06516
Tel.: (203) 479-7500   CT
Web Site: https://www.ghpmedia.com
Year Founded: 1935
Sales Range: $10-24.9 Million
Emp.: 170
Advertising & Commercial Printing
N.A.I.C.S.: 323111
Fred Hoxsie *(Partner)*
John Robinson *(CEO)*
Steve Bortner *(VP-Sls)*
Leena Davis *(Mgr-Admin)*
Bill Hahn *(CTO)*
Andy Robinson *(Mgr-Printing & Finishing Production)*
Lupi Robinson *(Dir-Mktg)*
John Vesia *(VP-Mfg)*
Cheryl Vincent *(Mgr-Client Svcs)*
David Springer *(Mgr-IT)*
Marc Server *(VP-New York & New Jersey Div)*
Sherri Fiordelisi *(Mgr-Mailing)*

GHS CORP.
2813 Wilbur Ave, Battle Creek, MI 49037

Tel.: (269) 968-3351
Web Site:
  https://www.ghsstrings.com
Sales Range: $10-24.9 Million
Emp.: 120
Strings & Musical Instruments Mfr
N.A.I.C.S.: 339992
Russell McFee *(Pres)*

GI DYNAMICS, INC.
320 Congress St 3rd Fl, Boston, MA 02210
Tel.: (781) 357-3300   DE
Web Site: http://www.gidynamics.com
Year Founded: 2003
Rev.: $236,000
Assets: $4,476,000
Liabilities: $5,011,000
Net Worth: ($535,000)
Earnings: ($11,136,000)
Emp.: 12
Fiscal Year-end: 12/31/20
Medical Device Mfr
N.A.I.C.S.: 339112
Scott W. Schorer *(Pres & CEO)*
Charles R. Carter *(CFO, Treas & Sec)*
Stephen Linhares *(VP-Clinical & Regulatory Affairs)*
Joseph Virgilio *(COO)*

GI INDUSTRIES, INC.
525 Fan Hill Rd Ste G, Monroe, CT 06468-1346
Tel.: (203) 452-1944   CT
Web Site: https://www.giind.com
Year Founded: 1966
Industrial Machinery Equipment Mfr
N.A.I.C.S.: 423830

GI MANAGER L.P.
4 Embarcadero Ctr 3200, San Francisco, CA 94111
Tel.: (415) 688-4800   DE
Web Site: http://www.gipartners.com
Year Founded: 2001
Privater Equity Firm
N.A.I.C.S.: 523999
Hoon Cho *(Co-Head-Private Equity)*
Jeff Sheu *(Mng Dir)*
Achi Yaffe *(Mng Dir-Portfolio Ops)*
Howard Park *(Mng Dir)*
Richard A. Magnuson *(Founder)*
David Mace *(Mng Dir)*
David Smolen *(Chief Compliance Officer, Gen Counsel & Mng Dir)*
Philip Yau *(Mng Dir)*
Patrick Welch *(Dir-IT)*
John Wang *(Principal & VP)*
Angela Zhang *(VP & Dir)*
Travis Pearson *(Mng Dir & Co-Head-Private Equity)*
Sendil Rajendran *(Mng Dir)*
Agnes Krygier *(Dir)*
Sandesh Shettar *(VP)*

Subsidiaries:

Atlas Technical Consultants, Inc. (1)
13215 Bee Cave Pkwy Bldg B Ste 230, Austin, TX 78738
Tel.: (512) 851-1501
Web Site: https://www.oneatlas.com
Rev.: $604,765,000
Assets: $487,360,000
Liabilities: $613,720,000
Net Worth: ($126,360,000)
Earnings: ($8,070,000)
Emp.: 3,450
Fiscal Year-end: 12/30/2022
Investment Services
N.A.I.C.S.: 523999
Hoon Cho *(Chm)*
Jacqueline C. Hinman *(CEO)*
John Alex Mollere *(Chief Admin Officer)*
Jamie Myers *(Chief Diversity Officer)*
Ken Burns Jr. *(COO)*
Jeanne DiBella *(CFO)*
Sarah Hilty *(Chief Legal Officer)*

Harshal Desai *(Chief Growth Officer)*
Shannon Rowley *(Chief HR Officer)*
David D. Quinn Sr. *(CFO)*

Subsidiary (Domestic):

1 Alliance Geomatics, LLC (2)
625 Strander Blvd Ste E, Seattle, WA 98188-2900
Tel.: (425) 502-8171
Web Site: http://www.1-alliance.com
Surveying & Mapping Services
N.A.I.C.S.: 541370
Jason T. Nakamura *(Pres)*

ATC Group Services (CT) Inc. (2)
290 Roberts St Ste 301, East Hartford, CT 06108
Tel.: (860) 282-9924
Environmental Consulting Services
N.A.I.C.S.: 541620
Scott Johnson *(Ops Mgr)*

Alta Vista Solutions (2)
555 12th St Ste 910, Oakland, CA 94607
Tel.: (510) 594-0510
Web Site: http://www.altavistasolutions.com
Engineeering Services
N.A.I.C.S.: 541330
Mazen Wahbeh *(Chm)*
Patrick Lowry *(Pres)*
Jinesh Mehta *(Exec VP)*
Bahjat Dagher *(COO)*
Rami Boundouki *(VP)*
Angel Marquez *(Dir-Rail Svcs)*
Suda Lee *(Mgr-Gen Ledger Acctg)*
Ian Broddrick *(Project Mgr)*
Patrick Young *(Project Mgr)*
Elisabeth Miller *(Ops Mgr)*
Justin Cocolicchio *(Mgr-Bus Dev)*
Megan Lawrence *(Mgr-HR)*
Courtney Saefong *(Comm Mgr)*

Atlantic Engineering Laboratories Inc. (2)
21 Randolph Ave, Avenel, NJ 07001
Tel.: (732) 815-0400
Web Site: https://www.aelinc.net
Testing Laboratories
N.A.I.C.S.: 541380
Fred A. Zimmerman *(VP-Mktg)*
Christopher T. O'Malley *(VP)*
Fidel Nieto *(Mgr-Laboratory)*
Jorge Arteaga *(Sr Project Mgr)*
Fawzy Salib *(Mgr-Mechanical Svcs)*
Stacey Ward *(Dir-Ops)*

Atlas Intermediate Holdings LLC (2)
13215 Bee Cave Pkwy Bldg B Ste 230, Austin, TX 78738
Web Site: http://www.oneatlas.com
Design, Management & Engineering Solutions Services Provider
N.A.I.C.S.: 541330
David Miller *(Chief Strategy Officer)*

Subsidiary (Domestic):

Moreland Altobelli Associates, Inc. (3)
2450 Commerce Ave NW Ste 100, Duluth, GA 30096
Tel.: (770) 263-5945
Web Site: http://www.maai.net
Engineering Management Services
N.A.I.C.S.: 541330
David Phillips *(Dir-IT)*

Pavetex Engineering LLC (3)
1500 Broadway Ave Ste 1117, Lubbock, TX 79401
Tel.: (806) 853-8693
Web Site: http://www.pavetex.com
Research & Development in the Physical, Engineering & Life Sciences
N.A.I.C.S.: 541715

Subsidiary (Domestic):

Dexter ATC Field Services LLC (2)
505 Orleans St Ste 400, Beaumont, TX 77701
Web Site: http://www.dexterfs.com
Oil & Gas Industrial Field Services
N.A.I.C.S.: 213112
Brett Kriley *(Pres)*
Judah Fontenot *(Dir-Bus Dev)*
Nick James *(Dir-Ops)*
Nicole Morrow *(Dir-Support Svcs)*

Geosphere Consultants, Inc. (2)
2001 Crow Canyon Rd Ste 210, San Ramon, CA 94583
Tel.: (925) 314-7180
Web Site: http://www.geosphereinc.net
Engineering Testing Services
N.A.I.C.S.: 541380
Corey Dare *(Mng Principal)*
Terese Salas *(Mktg Mgr)*
Marlene K. Jackson *(Engr-Geotechnical)*

Long Engineering, LLC (2)
2550 Heritage Ct SE Ste 250, Atlanta, GA 30339
Tel.: (770) 951-2495
Web Site: https://www.longeng.com
Emp.: 130
Civil Engineering Services
N.A.I.C.S.: 541330
Shepherd Long *(CEO)*
Joseph Severin *(Pres)*
Mike Thurman *(Sr VP)*
Dana Butterworth *(VP)*
Anthony Kamburis *(VP-Transportation)*

TranSmart Technologies, Inc. (2)
100 S Wacker Dr Ste 400, Chicago, IL 60606
Tel.: (312) 922-1700
Web Site: http://www.trafficonline.com
Construction & Engineering Services
N.A.I.C.S.: 541330
Charles Wade *(Dir-Plng Svcs)*

Subsidiary (Domestic):

EJM Engineering, Inc. (3)
411 S Wells St, Chicago, IL 60607
Tel.: (312) 922-1700
Web Site: http://www.ejmengineering.com
Sales Range: $1-9.9 Million
Emp.: 100
Construction & Engineering Services
N.A.I.C.S.: 541330
Joan Berry *(Pres)*

Subsidiary (Domestic):

WesTest, LLC (2)
627 Sheridan Blvd, Lakewood, CO 80214
Tel.: (303) 975-9959
Web Site: https://www.westest.net
Consulting Engineering Services
N.A.I.C.S.: 541330

California Cryobank LLC (1)
11915 La Grange Ave, Los Angeles, CA 90025
Tel.: (310) 443-5244
Web Site: https://www.cryobank.com
Sales Range: $10-24.9 Million
Reproductive & Stem Cell Management Services
N.A.I.C.S.: 621991
Cappy M. Rothman *(Co-Founder & Dir-Medical)*
Charles Sims *(Co-Founder, CEO & Dir-Corp Medical)*
Jaime Shamonki *(Dir-Medical)*
Scott Brown *(Dir-Client Experience & Comm)*
Kaj Rydman *(VP-Ops)*

Subsidiary (Domestic):

Southern Cord Inc. (2)
601 Genome Way NW Ste 1200, Huntsville, AL 35806
Tel.: (256) 564-7088
Web Site: http://www.southerncord.com
Blood & Organ Banks
N.A.I.C.S.: 621991
Chakri Deverapalli *(Pres & CEO)*

Cbr Systems, Inc. (1)
1200 Bayhill Dr 3rd Fl, San Bruno, CA 94066
Tel.: (650) 635-1420
Web Site: http://www.cordblood.com
Health Care Srvices
N.A.I.C.S.: 621610
Todd Van Horn *(Gen Mgr)*
Heather Brown *(VP-Scientific & Medical Affairs)*

Clinical Ink Inc. (1)
100 N Cherry St Ste 520, Winston Salem, NC 27101
Tel.: (336) 714-7402
Web Site: http://www.clinicalink.com

GI Manager L.P.—(Continued)

Software Publisher
N.A.I.C.S.: 513210
Doug Pierce (Pres)
Jonathan Andrus (Chief Data Officer)
Ed Seguine (CEO)
Stephen Boccardo (Chief Comml Officer)
Scott Miltenberger (CFO)
Joe Alea (CTO)

Subsidiary (Domestic):

Digital Artefacts LLC　　(2)
201 E Washington St Ste 1302, Iowa City,
IA 52240
Tel.: (319) 335-4985
Web Site: http://www.digitalartefacts.com
Comprehensive Digital Platform for Clinical
Studies
N.A.I.C.S.: 541715
Joan Severson (Pres)

Consilio, LLC　　(1)
1828 L St NW Ste 1070, Washington, DC
20036
Tel.: (202) 822-6222
Web Site: http://www.consilio.com
Computer Forensic & Litigation Research
Services
N.A.I.C.S.: 541199
Andrew Macdonald (CEO)
Raj Chandrasekar (CTO)
Michael Flanagan (Gen Counsel)
Adam Pollitt (Exec VP)
Amy Hinzmann (Chief Client Experience &
Diversity Officer)
Natalie Stute (Chief HR Officer)
Meredith Kildow (Chief Revenue Officer)

Subsidiary (Non-US):

Consilio HL (UK) Limited　　(2)
3rd Floor 10 Aldersgate Street, London,
EC1A 4HJ, United Kingdom
Tel.: (44) 2036950200
Web Site: http://www.consilio.com
Legal Consulting Services
N.A.I.C.S.: 541199

Subsidiary (Domestic):

DiscoverReady, LLC　　(2)
200 S College St 10th Fl, Charlotte, NC
28202
Tel.: (212) 699-3960
Web Site: http://www.discoverready.com
Business Document Review Services
N.A.I.C.S.: 518210
John Ritter (Pres & COO)
Phil Richards (CTO)
Todd Tennell (CFO)

DQE Communications LLC　　(1)
424 S 27th St Ste 220, Pittsburgh, PA
15203
Tel.: (412) 393-1033
Web Site: http://www.dqecom.com
Sales Range: $500-549.9 Million
Emp.: 1,500
Fiber-Optics Distr
N.A.I.C.S.: 457210
Michael T. Sicoli (CEO)
Michael T. Sicoli (CEO)

Daxko, LLC　　(1)
600 University Park Pl Ste 500, Birming-
ham, AL 35209-6729
Tel.: (205) 437-1400
Web Site: http://www.daxko.com
Sales Range: $10-24.9 Million
Management Software Publisher & Support
Services
N.A.I.C.S.: 513210
Matt Cowell (Sr VP-Ops)
Winston Gillum (CFO)
Bjorn Bjerkoe (CTO)
Brittany Foust (Sr VP-Svcs)
Jeff Vandixhorn (Sr VP & Gen Mgr-Club
Automation)
Ronald L. Lamb (CEO)
Saranda West (VP-Product Mgmt)
Rudy Nieto (Chief Revenue Officer)
Wendy White (CMO)

Division (Domestic):

CSI Software　　(2)
5252 Westchester Suite 250, Houston, TX
77005
Tel.: (713) 942-7779

Web Site: http://www.csisoftwareusa.com
Sales Range: $1-9.9 Million
Emp.: 30
Mobile Application Software Developer
N.A.I.C.S.: 541511
Ken Heineman (Dir-Sls)
David Molina (Dir-Product Dev)
Ryan Wehmeyer (Dir-Mktg)
Scott Wimberley (Mgr-Implementation)

Subsidiary (Domestic):

Motionsoft, Inc.　　(2)
1451 Rockville Pike Ste 500, Rockville, MD
20852
Tel.: (301) 255-6400
Web Site: http://www.motionsoft.net
Software Development Services
N.A.I.C.S.: 541511
Al Noshirvani (Co-Founder, Chm & Chief
Strategy Officer)
Hossein Noshirvani (Co-Founder & Head-
Mktg Team)
Ed Darwish (Exec VP-Fin Svcs & Compli-
ance)
Benson Fine (Chm)
Grant Otto (CTO)
Waseem Khan (Exec VP-Pro Svcs)
Bob Skinner (Exec VP-Sls & Mktg)
Dharmesh Trivedi (VP-Ops)
John Cramp (CEO)
Brian Daum (CFO)
Brent Zempel (Chief Product Officer)

Doxim Inc.　　(1)
220 Spring St, Herndon, VA 20170
Tel.: (866) 475-9876
Web Site: http://www.doxim.com
Customer Communications & Engagement
Technology Services
N.A.I.C.S.: 541511
Chris Rasmussen (Founder & Chm)
Michael Rogalski (Pres & CEO)

Subsidiary (Domestic):

Ancor Information Management
LLC　　(2)
1911 Woodslee Dr, Troy, MI 48083-2236
Tel.: (248) 740-8866
Web Site: http://www.ancorinfo.com
Data Processing Services
N.A.I.C.S.: 518210
Gary Zavislak (Pres)
Allie Graham Bunch (Acct Mgr)
Kristen Shankster (Acct Mgr)
April Lardie (Project Mgr)

Direct Technologies, Inc.　　(2)
600 Satellite Blvd, Suwanee, GA 30024
Tel.: (678) 288-1700
Web Site: http://www.dirtech.com
Sales Range: $10-24.9 Million
Emp.: 78
Printing Services
N.A.I.C.S.: 323111
David Jacobson (Co-Founder & Pres)
Brett Coltman (Co-Founder)
Richard Hawes (Gen Mgr)

Laser Print Plus, Inc.　　(2)
1261 1st Street South Ext, Columbia, SC
29209
Tel.: (803) 695-7090
Web Site: http://www.laserprintplus.com
Sales Range: $1-9.9 Million
Emp.: 35
Digital Printing Services
N.A.I.C.S.: 323111
Mark McNeill (VP & Gen Mgr)
Nash Patel (Mgr-DP)
Tim Delaney (Pres)
Richard Brazell (Supvr-Production)

Level One LLC　　(2)
53 General Warren Blvd, Malvern, PA
19355
Tel.: (610) 229-9200
Web Site: http://www.golevelone.com
Data Processing Services
N.A.I.C.S.: 518210
John Boland (Pres)

Pinnacle Data Systems, LLC　　(2)
350 Automation Way, Birmingham, AL
35210
Web Site:
　http://www.pinnacledatasystems.com
Computer Related Services
N.A.I.C.S.: 541519

John Cookson (Mgr-Compliance)
Robert Reddinger (CEO)

Striata, Inc.　　(2)
48 Wall St Ste 1100, New York, NY 10005
Tel.: (646) 448-8369
Web Site: http://www.striata.com
Sales Range: $1-9.9 Million
Emp.: 12
Prepackaged Software
N.A.I.C.S.: 513210
Michael Wright (CEO)
Alison Treadaway (Dir-South Africa)
Andrea Marsh (Project Mgr-eBus-Chubb
Insurance)
Jacqui Michelson (CFO)
Keith Russell (Dir-Sls-Asia Pacific)
Alex Papadopulos (Head-Ops-Americas)
Brent Haumann (Head-Dev)
Debi S. Ballard (Mgr-Fin Shared Svcs)
Elizabeth Stephen (Head-Sls-Americas)
Linda Misauer (Head-Global Solutions)
Lucy Lehmann (Head-Ops-UK)
Nic Ramage (CTO)
Paul Elliot (VP-Customer Svcs)
Stergios Saltas (Mng Dir-South Africa)
Tamara Hanley (Head-Global Mktg)

Far Niente Winery　　(1)
1350 Acacia Dr, Oakville, CA 94562
Tel.: (707) 944-2861
Web Site: http://www.farniente.com
Vineyard & Wine Mfr
N.A.I.C.S.: 111332
Michael A. Beindorff (Pres & Principal)
Mary Grace (VP-Mktg & Comm)

GI Partners U.K. Limited　　(1)
5th Floor 35 Portman Square, London,
W1H 6LR, United Kingdom
Tel.: (44) 2070341120
Web Site: http://www.gipartners.co.uk
Sales Range: $50-74.9 Million
Emp.: 20
Privater Equity Firm
N.A.I.C.S.: 523999
Brad Altberger (Mng Dir)
Al Foglio (Mng Dir)
Phil Kaziewicz (Mng Dir)
Mark Tagliaferri (Mng Dir)

GTY Technology Holdings Inc.　　(1)
363 W Erie St Fl 7, Chicago, IL 60654
Tel.: (702) 945-2898
Web Site: https://eunasolutions.com
Rev: $60,453,000
Assets: $394,944,000
Liabilities: $128,007,000
Net Worth: $266,937,000
Earnings: ($53,828,000)
Emp.: 3
Fiscal Year-end: 12/31/2021
Investment Services
N.A.I.C.S.: 523999
John J. Curran (CFO & Exec VP)
Tom Amburgey (CEO)
Brian Haney (Chief Customer Officer)
Brenna Lenchak (Gen Counsel & Sr VP)
Rob Crocker (CFO)
Mo Trezies (CTO)
James Ha (Chief Growth Officer)
Harry L. You (Co-Founder)

Subsidiary (Domestic):

Ion Wave Technologies, Inc.　　(2)
3653 S Ave., Springfield, MO 65807
Tel.: (417) 823-7773
Web Site: http://www.ionwave.net
Rev: $1,000,000
Emp.: 20
Custom Computer Programming Services
N.A.I.C.S.: 541511
Darren Henderson (CEO)
John Alexander (CFO)

Insurity, Inc.　　(1)
170 Huyshope Ave, Hartford, CT 06106
Tel.: (860) 616-7721
Web Site: http://www.insurity.com
Property & Casualty Insurance Technology
& Services
N.A.I.C.S.: 513210
Bob Larew (COO)
Doreen Tyburski (Chief HR Officer)
Jonathan Victor (CIO)
Mark Adessky (Gen Counsel)
Michele Shepard (Chief Revenue Officer)
Mitchell Wasserman (Chief Product Officer)
Craig Campestre (Chief Sls Officer)
Christopher J. Lafond (CEO & CFO)

Subsidiary (Non-US):

Oceanwide Inc.　　(2)
3400 De Maisonneuve W Ste 1450, Tower
1 Place Alexis Nihon, Montreal, H3Z 3B8,
QC, Canada
Tel.: (514) 289-9090
Web Site: http://www.oceanwide.com
Software Publisher
N.A.I.C.S.: 513210
Mitchell Wasserman (CEO)
Mark Adessky (Pres)
Mark Orosz (CIO & Chief Scientific Officer)
Jonathan Victor (COO)
Martin Bechard (CTO)
Denis Fragias (CIO)
Gabriel Suissa (Sr VP)
Alisa Morris (VP-Sls)
Vanessa Cheong (VP-Acct Mgmt)

Subsidiary (Non-US):

Oceanwide Europe Limited　　(3)
14 Devonshire Sq First Floor, London,
EC2M 4YT, United Kingdom
Tel.: (44) 203 1786610
Web Site: http://www.oceanwide.com
Insurance Software Development Services
N.A.I.C.S.: 541511
Mitchell Wasserman (CEO)

Subsidiary (Domestic):

Tropics Software Technologies,
Inc.　　(2)
7349 Merchant Ct, Sarasota, FL 34240
Tel.: (941) 955-1234
Web Site: http://www.gotropics.com
Software Development Services
N.A.I.C.S.: 541511
Jeremy Williams (COO)
Claire Stone (Dir-Conversion)
Robert Sillett (Dir-Tech)
Kelly Hinsberg (Dir-Support & Pro Svcs)
Mike Mobar (Pres & CEO)
David Chase (Mgr-Quality Assurance)
David Robertson (Mgr-Dev)
Jamie Schwartz-Gurley (Mgr)
Michele Doodnaught (Mgr)

LightEdge Solutions, Inc.　　(1)
215 10th St Ste 1000, Des Moines, IA
50309
Tel.: (515) 471-1000
Web Site: http://www.lightedge.com
Telecommunication Servicesb
N.A.I.C.S.: 517111
Jeffrey Springborn (Pres & COO)
Jim Masterson (CEO)
Tom Prosia (Sr VP-Mktg & Bus Dev)

Subsidiary (Domestic):

Cavern Technologies Inc.　　(2)
17501 W 98th St Pillar Ste 2533, Lenexa,
KS 66219
Tel.: (913) 227-0660
Web Site:
　http://www.caverntechnologies.com
Software Publisher
N.A.I.C.S.: 513210
John Clune (Founder & CEO)

Connectria LLC　　(2)
10845 Olive Blvd Ste 300, Saint Louis, MO
63141
Tel.: (314) 587-7000
Web Site: https://www.connectria.com
Sales Range: $10-24.9 Million
Emp.: 78
Server Support Services
N.A.I.C.S.: 541519
Richard S. Waidmann (Chm, Pres & CEO)
Denny Hug (VP)
Robert J. Strobing (CFO & VP)
Rusty Putzler (COO & VP)
Scott J. Azzolina (VP-Mktg)

OnRamp Access, LLC　　(2)
2916 Montopolis Dr Ste 300, Austin, TX
78741
Tel.: (512) 457-9000
Web Site: http://www.lightedge.com
Hosting & Colocation Services; Cloud Pro-
vider
N.A.I.C.S.: 518210
Ryan Robinson (CEO)
John Thurik (Dir-Technical Svcs)
Joshua Berman (Sr Coord-Mktg)
Matt Hammons (VP-Ops)

Kirk Wright *(VP-Mktg)*
Bobby Boughton *(VP-Sls)*
Jack D'Angelo *(VP-Fin & Corp Dev)*

Logibec Inc. (1)
1500-1010 de la Gauchetiere West, Montreal, H3B 2N2, QC, Canada
Tel.: (514) 766-0134
Web Site: https://www.logibec.com
Emp.: 350
Health & Social Information Systems Marketer & Support Services
N.A.I.C.S.: 513210
Michel Desgagne *(Pres)*
Eric Bergevin *(CFO)*
Simon L. Charest *(Chief Product Officer)*
Franco Sicilia *(Chief Comml Officer)*
Jean-François Chartrain *(VP)*
Virginia Bronsard *(VP)*

MRI Software, LLC (1)
28925 Fountain Pkwy, Solon, OH 44139
Tel.: (800) 321-8770
Web Site: http://www.mrisoftware.com
Emp.: 3,000
Property Management Software
N.A.I.C.S.: 513210
John Ensign *(Pres & Exec Mng Dir-North America)*
Patrick Ghilani *(CEO)*
Marc DiCapua *(Sr VP-Client Support, Merger & Acq)*
Brian Zrimsek *(Principal-Industry)*
Phil Trudeau *(Chief Sls Officer)*
Mandira Mehra *(CMO)*
Sarah Zinkie *(Mng Dir-Canada & VP-Client Success)*
Mark Fairweather *(Mng Dir-South Africa)*
Roman Telerman *(CFO)*
David Bowie *(Mng Dir & Sr VP-Asia Pacific)*

Subsidiary (Domestic):

AMTdirect, LLC (2)
17039 Kenton Dr Suite 200, Cornelius, NC 28031
Tel.: (704) 896-3118
Lease Administration & Accounting Software Publisher
N.A.I.C.S.: 513210

Subsidiary (Domestic):

NETfacilities, Inc. (3)
3605 Long Beach Blvd Ste 416, Long Beach, CA 90807-4026
Tel.: (562) 437-3000
Software Publisher
N.A.I.C.S.: 513210

Joint Venture (Domestic):

CTM Software Corp. (2)
6275 Simms St Ste 300, Arvada, CO 80004-4485
Tel.: (303) 399-3579
Web Site: http://www.ctmsoftware.com
Electronics Stores
N.A.I.C.S.: 449210
Claudio Riello *(CEO)*

Subsidiary (Domestic):

HAB, Inc. (2)
85 Milwaukee St, La Crosse, WI 54603
Tel.: (608) 785-7650
Web Site: http://www.habinc.com
Housing Management Software Solutions
N.A.I.C.S.: 541519
Dave Nutter *(VP-Sls)*

IPM Software, Inc. (2)
4008-C Vista Rd Ste 250, Pasadena, TX 77504
Tel.: (800) 944-5572
Web Site: http://www.ipm-software.net
Software Company
N.A.I.C.S.: 513210
Bill Sullivan *(Pres)*

Link Systems, Inc. (2)
1 Dock St, Stamford, CT 06902
Application Software Development Services
N.A.I.C.S.: 541511

Subsidiary (Non-US):

MRI Software Limited (2)
17th Floor Dashwood House 69 Old Broad Street, London, EC2M 1QS, United Kingdom

Tel.: (44) 2072564090
Web Site: http://www.mrisoftware.com
Property Management Software
N.A.I.C.S.: 513210

Subsidiary (Domestic):

Castleton Technology plc (3)
Douglas House 1 Emmanuel Court, Reddicroft, Sutton Coldfield, B73 6AZ, United Kingdom
Tel.: (44) 845 241 0220
Web Site: http://www.castletonplc.com
Rev.: $33,447,560
Assets: $63,320,291
Liabilities: $31,206,471
Net Worth: $32,113,820
Earnings: $5,197,906
Emp.: 177
Fiscal Year-end: 03/31/2019
Software Support & Consulting
N.A.I.C.S.: 541519
James Massey *(Dir-Client Strategy)*
Ian Niblock *(Dir-Integration Dev)*

Subsidiary (Domestic):

Redstone Group Holdings Ltd (4)
160 Centennial Pk Centennial Ave, Elstree Way, London, WD6 3SG, United Kingdom (100%)
Tel.: (44) 8452002200
Web Site: http://www.redstone.co.uk
Sales Range: $250-299.9 Million
Emp.: 900
Holding Company
N.A.I.C.S.: 551112

Division (Domestic):

Redstone Communications Ltd (5)
Newton House Cambridge Business Park, Cowley Road, Cambridge, CB4 0WZ, United Kingdom (100%)
Tel.: (44) 8452002200
Web Site: http://www.redstone.co.uk
Sales Range: $100-124.9 Million
Telecommunications Solutions
N.A.I.C.S.: 517810

Subsidiary (Domestic):

Macmunnis, Inc. (2)
321 N Clark Ste 90, Chicago, IL 60201
Tel.: (312) 858-8100
Web Site: http://www.macmunnis.com
Rev.: $1,200,000
Emp.: 13
Administrative Management & General Management Consulting Service
N.A.I.C.S.: 541611
Brice Weeks *(Principal)*
Stephanie Weeks *(Co-Founder)*

Subsidiary (Non-US):

Proptech Group Limited (2)
333 George St, Sydney, 2000, NSW, Australia
Tel.: (61) 396284122
Web Site: http://www.realestateinvestar.com.au
Rev.: $8,911,079
Assets: $29,239,995
Liabilities: $7,075,242
Net Worth: $22,164,753
Earnings: ($767,227)
Emp.: 103
Fiscal Year-end: 06/30/2021
Real Estate Investment Services
N.A.I.C.S.: 531390
Karen Austin *(Mgr-Customer Success)*
James Lawrence *(Mgr-Digital Mktg)*
Marietta Fiocco *(Accountant)*

Qube Global Software Ltd. (2)
9 King Street, London, EC2V 8EA, United Kingdom
Tel.: (44) 20 3861 7100
Web Site: http://www.qubeglobal.com
Emp.: 285
Real Estate Software Solutions
N.A.I.C.S.: 513210
John Cuppello *(Exec Mng Dir)*
Ben Lerner *(Mng Dir-Ops)*
David Makins *(Fin Dir)*
Paul Manning *(Mng Dir-EMEA Sls)*
James Lavery *(Mktg Dir)*
Jacqui Adams *(Dir-HR)*
Neil Harrison *(Dir-Product)*

Alastair Clunas *(Dir-Ops)*
Colin Greer *(Dir-Customer Svc)*
Trevor Youens *(Dir-Residential Svcs)*

Real Asset Management Ltd (2)
South Block Central Court Knoll Rise, Orpington, BR6 0JA, Kent, United Kingdom
Tel.: (44) 1689 892 100
Web Site: http://www.realassetmgt.co.uk
Asset Management Software Publisher
N.A.I.C.S.: 513210

Subsidiary (US):

Real Asset Management, Inc. (3)
309 Ct Ave Ste 244, Des Moines, IA 50309
Tel.: (515) 699-8574
Web Site: http://www.realassetmgt.com
Emp.: 200
Asset Management Software Publisher
N.A.I.C.S.: 513210

Subsidiary (Domestic):

Rental History Reports (2)
7900 W 78th St Ste 400, Edina, MN 55439
Tel.: (952) 545-3953
Web Site: https://www.myrentalhistoryreport.com
Screening Company; Residential & Tenant Screening; State & Federal Background & Criminal Checks
N.A.I.C.S.: 541618

Netsmart Technologies, Inc. (1)
11100 Nall Ave, Overland Park, KS 66211
Web Site: http://www.ntst.com
Emp.: 2,100
Health & Human Services Software Developer, Marketer & Technical Support Services
N.A.I.C.S.: 513210
Kevin Scalia *(Exec VP-Corp Dev)*
Paul Anderson *(Exec VP-Client Org)*
Michael Brand *(Exec VP-Engrg)*
Tom Herzog *(COO)*
Dawn Iddings *(Mng Dir & Sr VP)*
Scott Green *(Mng Dir & Sr VP-Careguidance)*
Mike Valentine *(CEO)*

Subsidiary (Domestic):

DeVero, Inc. (2)
300 Park Ave 2nd Fl, San Jose, CA 95110
Web Site: http://www.devero.com
Sales Range: $10-24.9 Million
Healthcare Software Development Services
N.A.I.C.S.: 541511

McBee Associates Inc. (2)
565 East Swedesford Rd, Suite 100, Wayne, PA 19087
Tel.: (610) 964-9680
Web Site: http://www.mcbeeassociates.com
Health Care Services & Consulting Firm
N.A.I.C.S.: 621491
Mike Dordick *(Pres)*
Keith Boroch *(VP-Advisory Consulting)*
Bob Braun *(Sr VP-Sls)*

Netsmart Technologies, Inc. - Missouri (2)
5100 N Town Centre Dr, Ozark, MO 65721
Tel.: (417) 799-6600
Web Site: http://www.ntst.com
Software Publisher
N.A.I.C.S.: 513210
Carol Reynolds *(Exec VP-Client Experience)*

Patriot Growth Partners, LLC (1)
501 Office Center DrSte 215, Washington, PA 19034
Tel.: (215) 600-1357
Web Site: https://patriotgis.com
Insurance Company
N.A.I.C.S.: 524210
Matt Gardener *(CEO)*

Subsidiary (Domestic):

Bagatta Associates, Inc. (2)
823 W Jericho Tpke Ste 1A, Smithtown, NY 11787
Tel.: (631) 864-1111
Web Site: http://www.bagatta.com
Insurance Agencies & Brokerages
N.A.I.C.S.: 524210
Frank Bagatta *(Pres)*

Benefits Alliance Insurance Services, LLC (2)
31248 Oak Crest Dr Ste 140, Westlake Village, CA 91361
Tel.: (800) 532-5941
Insurance Brokerage Services
N.A.I.C.S.: 524210
Aaryn Lamos *(Sr Acct Mgr-Benefits)*

Subsidiary (Domestic):

Bridgeport Benefits (3)
5210 Lewis Rd Ste 14, Agoura Hills, CA 91301-2662
Tel.: (818) 865-6800
Web Site: http://www.bridgeportbenefits.com
Insurance Agencies & Brokerages
N.A.I.C.S.: 524210
Kyle Blasman *(Dir-Bus Dev)*

Corporate Benefit Marketing (3)
18801 Ventura Blvd Ste 201, Tarzana, CA 91356-3343
Tel.: (818) 380-2500
Web Site: http://www.corporatebenefitmarketing.com
Insurance Agencies & Brokerages
N.A.I.C.S.: 524210
David Style *(Pres)*

Subsidiary (Domestic):

The Dougherty Company Inc. (2)
PO Box 7277, Long Beach, CA 90807
Tel.: (562) 424-1621
Web Site: http://www.daughertyinc.com
Insurance Agencies & Brokerages
N.A.I.C.S.: 524210
Lonna MacKay *(Mgr-Mktg)*

Peak 10, Inc. (1)
8809 Lenox Point Dr Ste G, Charlotte, NC 28273
Tel.: (704) 264-1010
Web Site: http://www.peak10.com
Sales Range: $25-49.9 Million
Web Hosting Services
N.A.I.C.S.: 518210
David H. Jones *(Chm)*
Brian Noonan *(CFO & Exec VP)*
Jeff Biggs *(Exec VP-Tech & Ops)*
Jeff Spalding *(COO & Exec VP)*
Allen Skipper *(Chief Comml Officer)*
Joe Deney *(Sr VP-Customer Ops)*
Mike Belote *(VP)*
Karin Davies *(Sr VP-HR)*
Tricia Ory *(VP-Fin)*
Steve Harris *(Sr VP-Natl Alliances)*
Mark McCrary *(VP & Gen Mgr)*
Michael Fuhrman *(CTO)*
Chris Downie *(CEO)*
Dave Sroka *(VP-Channel Sls)*
Steve Renda *(VP-Product)*
P. J. Kiggins *(VP-Sls)*
Dennis Musolino *(Sr VP-Sls)*

Subsidiary (Domestic):

Flexential Colorado Corp. (2)
6400 S Fiddlers Green Cir Ste 2000, Greenwood Village, CO 80111
Tel.: (720) 891-1000
Web Site: http://www.flexential.com
Data Center Services
N.A.I.C.S.: 518210
Chris Downie *(CEO)*
Ryan Mallory *(COO-Colocation Svcs)*
Sherri Liebo *(Sr VP & Head-Mktg)*
Garth Williams *(CFO)*

Subsidiary (Domestic):

Applied Trust Engineering, Inc. (3)
1033 Walnut St Ste 300, Boulder, CO 80302
Tel.: (303) 245-4545
Web Site: http://www.appliedtrust.com
Emp.: 50
Information Technology Consulting Services
N.A.I.C.S.: 541512
Randy Else *(Dir-Infrastructure Engrg)*
Steve Hathaway *(Dir-Resource Integration)*
Dan Mackin *(VP-Ops)*
Paul Nelson *(Chief Architect)*
Chris Rossi *(Dir-Governance, Risk & Compliance)*
Kasim Esmail *(Dir-Network Architecture)*
Scott Seidel *(Dir-Resource Dev)*
Sean Pearcy *(Dir-Incident Response)*
Tyller Bell *(Dir-Application Security)*

GI Manager L.P.—(Continued)

Aaron Ott *(Sr Engr)*
Bo Pearce *(Sr Engr)*
Jeff Wright *(Sr Engr)*
David Leonard *(Sr Engr)*
Warren Campbell *(Engr)*
Becky Schovanec *(Dir-Client PMO)*
Jason Rader *(Dir-Process Improvement)*
Megan Killpack *(Project Mgr)*

Single Digits, Inc.   **(1)**
4 Bedford Farms Ste 210, Bedford, NH
03110
Tel.: (603) 580-1539
Web Site: http://www.singledigits.com
Telephone Communications & High Speed
Internet Access
N.A.I.C.S.: 517810
Stephen A. Singlar *(Co-Founder)*
Robert Goldstein *(CEO)*
Joe Hartnett *(CEO)*
Jerry Grove *(VP/Gen Mgr-Senior Living)*
Mike Sargent *(CEO)*

Subsidiary (Domestic):

BSG Wireless Limited   **(2)**
7411 John Smith Dr Ste 1500, San Antonio,
TX 78229
Tel.: (210) 949-7000
Web Site: http://www.bsgwireless.com
Wireless Telecommunications Carriers
N.A.I.C.S.: 517112
June Semel *(Pres)*

Togetherwork Holdings, LLC   **(1)**
55 Washington St Ste 626, Brooklyn, NY
11201
Tel.: (888) 554-6634
Web Site: http://www.togetherwork.com
Portfolio Management: Group Management
Software Developer & Payments Solutions
N.A.I.C.S.: 513210
Neil Platt *(CEO)*
Andrew Stern *(Sr VP-Bus & Dev)*
Jesse Williamson *(Sr VP-Corp Dev)*
Karen Gil *(VP-Payments)*
Traci Laney *(VP-HR)*
Priyanka Singh *(CFO)*
Pat McGlynn *(Chief Revenue Officer)*

Subsidiary (Domestic):

Fonteva Inc.   **(2)**
4420 N Fairfax Dr Ste 500, Arlington, VA
22201
Tel.: (202) 618-6028
Web Site: http://www.fonteva.com
Professional, Scientific & Technical Services
N.A.I.C.S.: 541990
Dan Madigan *(Sr Project Mgr)*
Chris Noone *(VP-Bus Dev)*
Paul Lundy *(Co-Founder & Chief Customer
Officer)*
Evan Thomas *(Mgr-Mktg Comm)*
Suvro Khan *(Sr VP-Customers for Life)*
Jerry Huskins *(Co-Founder & CEO)*
Pat McGlynn *(Pres)*

Omega Financial, LLC   **(2)**
1300 Sixth Ave, Columbus, GA 31901
Tel.: (706) 571-0083
Web Site: http://www.omegafi.com
Investment Services
N.A.I.C.S.: 523999
Sheryl Bell *(Dir-Partner Success)*
Laura Cole *(VP-Strategic Initiatives)*
Krystee Edwards *(Chief Customer Officer)*
Jennifer Hadden *(VP-Ops)*
Fred Maglione *(CEO)*
Heather McLeod *(Dir-Client Svcs)*
Tara Pepper *(COO)*
Mathew Tooker *(Dir-Bus Intelligence)*
Trey Trotter *(Dir-Partner Succes)*

Subsidiary (Domestic):

Greek Resource Services, Inc.   **(3)**
2118 8th St, Tuscaloosa, AL 35401-2134
Tel.: (205) 758-7754
Web Site:
  http://www.greekresourceservices.com
Professional, Scientific & Technical Services
N.A.I.C.S.: 541990

Valet Living, LLC   **(1)**
100 S Ashley Dr Ste 700, Tampa, FL 33602
Tel.: (813) 248-1327
Web Site: http://valetliving.com

Doorstep Trash & Recycling Collection
N.A.I.C.S.: 562119
Shawn Handrahan *(Pres & CEO)*
Syd McDonald *(Sr VP-Sls)*
Brett Brown *(CFO)*
Kelly Veatch *(Sr VP-Ops)*
Steve Davis *(Exec VP-Strategic Dev)*
Henry Toledo *(Chief People Officer)*
Isorys Dilone *(Exec VP & Gen Counsel)*
Robert Casagrande *(CIO)*
Anthony Hylton *(Sr VP-Ops)*

Subsidiary (Domestic):

Concierge Services of Atlanta,
Inc.   **(2)**
3330 Cumberland Blvd Ste 500, Atlanta,
GA 30339
Tel.: (404) 816-1677
Web Site: http://www.csoa.com
Other Health & Personal Care Stores
N.A.I.C.S.: 456199
Lendy Fedors *(VP & Gen Mgr)*
Penny Morriss Campbell *(Owner & Pres)*
Lisa Whitlow *(Dir-Corp Ops)*
John Upshaw *(Dir-Corp Ops)*

Invisible Waste Services LLC   **(2)**
11334 Boggy Creek Rd Ste 127, Orlando,
FL 32824
Tel.: (407) 251-1552
Web Site:
  http://www.invisiblewasteservices.com
Residential Waste Collection Services
N.A.I.C.S.: 562119

GI PROPERTIES INC.
6610 Melton Rd, Portage, IN 46368
Tel.: (219) 763-1177
Sales Range: $10-24.9 Million
Emp.: 5
Pipeline Construction
N.A.I.C.S.: 237110
Todd Rubel *(Gen Mgr)*

GIA ENTERPRISES
10575 NE 4th St, Bellevue, WA
98004
Tel.: (425) 454-3663
Rev.: $23,054,250
Emp.: 10
Holding Company: Fast-Food Ser-
vices
N.A.I.C.S.: 551112
Len Giannola *(Pres)*
Tracy Dang *(Mgr-Guest Svc Dept)*

GIA-AIR HOLDINGS CORP.
3201 Griffin Rd Fl 4, Fort Lauderdale,
FL 33312-6970
Tel.: (954) 985-1500
Web Site:
  http://www.gulfstreamair.com
Rev.: $84,000,000
Emp.: 550
Air Passenger Carrier, Scheduled
N.A.I.C.S.: 481111
Thomas L. Cooper *(Pres-Intl Div)*
David Hackett *(Pres & CEO)*

GIALAMAS COMPANY INCOR-
PORATED
8040 Excelsior Dr Ste 200, Madison,
WI 53717
Tel.: (608) 836-8000
Web Site: https://www.gialamas.com
Sales Range: $10-24.9 Million
Emp.: 15
Land Subdividers & Developers,
Commercial
N.A.I.C.S.: 237210
George Gialamas *(Co-Founder &
CEO)*
Brenda Miller *(Controller)*
Andy Van Haren *(VP & Dir-
Construction & Facility Mgmt)*
Rob Bethke *(Coord-Facilities Mainte-
nance)*
Dennis Sandora *(Pres)*
Aristotle Gialamas *(VP-Sls)*
Cathy O'Donnell *(VP-Ops)*

GIAMBRONE + PARTNERS
5177 Salem Hills Ln, Cincinnati, OH
45230
Tel.: (513) 231-5146
Web Site:
  http://www.giambroneandpart
  ners.com
Year Founded: 2002
Sales Range: Less than $1 Million
Emp.: 8
Advetising Agency
N.A.I.C.S.: 541810
Ken Giambrone *(Principal & Exec
Dir-Creative)*
Mark Giambrone *(Principal & Exec
Dir-Creative)*

GIANT AUTOMOTIVE GROUP
1001 S Ben Maddox Way, Visalia,
CA 93292-3656
Tel.: (559) 733-1100
Web Site:
  https://www.giantautomotive.com
Sales Range: $25-49.9 Million
Emp.: 60
Automobiles, New & Used
N.A.I.C.S.: 441110
James Petty *(Pres)*

GIANT CHEVROLET COM-
PANY
1001 S Ben Maddox Way, Visalia,
CA 93292-3656
Tel.: (559) 733-1100
Web Site:
  https://www.giantautomotive.com
Year Founded: 1961
Sales Range: $10-24.9 Million
Emp.: 60
Car Whslr
N.A.I.C.S.: 441110
James Petty *(Pres)*

GIANT DISCOUNT FOOD INC.
580 N Davis Dr, Warner Robins, GA
31093
Tel.: (478) 929-0675
Year Founded: 1976
Sales Range: $10-24.9 Million
Emp.: 75
Owner & Operator of Grocery Stores
N.A.I.C.S.: 445110
Mike Howell *(Owner)*

GIANT EAGLE, INC.
700 Cranberry Woods Dr, Cranberry
Township, PA 16066
Tel.: (412) 871-2097   PA
Web Site:
  https://www.gianteagle.com
Year Founded: 1931
Sales Range: $5-14.9 Billion
Emp.: 36,000
Supermarkets & Other Grocery Re-
tailers (except Convenience Retail-
ers)
N.A.I.C.S.: 445110
David S. Shapira *(Chm)*
Kirk Ball *(CIO & Exec VP)*
Bill Artman *(CEO)*

Subsidiaries:

Aetos Construction Company   **(1)**
261 Kappa Dr, Pittsburgh, PA 15238-0591
Tel.: (412) 963-7740
Sales Range: $50-74.9 Million
Emp.: 60
N.A.I.C.S.: 457110

Butler Refrigerated Meats, Inc.   **(1)**
690 Perry Hwy, Harmony, PA 16037-8412
Tel.: (724) 452-8936
Web Site: http://www.gianteagle.com
Sales Range: $25-49.9 Million
Emp.: 150
Meat Whslr & Distr
N.A.I.C.S.: 424470

Giant Eagle American Seaway
Foods   **(1)**
900 Northfield Rd, Bedford, OH 44146
Tel.: (440) 439-1800
Web Site: http://www.gianteagle.com
Sales Range: $700-749.9 Million
Emp.: 5,800
Food Distr
N.A.I.C.S.: 445110
Jean C. Colarik *(Dir-Retail HR)*
Kevin Srigley *(VP-Adv)*
Larry Sevich *(VP-Warehouse Ops)*

Subsidiary (Domestic):

Giant Eagle   **(2)**
5300 Richmond Rd, Cleveland, OH
44146-1335   **(99.99%)**
Tel.: (216) 292-7000
Grocery Retailer & Wholesale
N.A.I.C.S.: 445110

Subsidiary (Domestic):

American Seaway Foods, Inc.   **(3)**
5300 Richmond Rd, Bedford, OH
44146-1335   **(100%)**
Tel.: (216) 292-7000
Web Site: http://www.gianteagle.com
Sales Range: $150-199.9 Million
Emp.: 1,000
Wholesale Food Distribution
N.A.I.C.S.: 445110
Anthnoy Regal *(CEO)*

Ricker Oil Company Inc.   **(1)**
30 W 11th St, Anderson, IN 46016
Tel.: (765) 643-3016
Web Site: http://www.rickers.net
Sales Range: $50-74.9 Million
Whslr of Petroleum Products; Owner & Op-
erator of Convenience Stores
N.A.I.C.S.: 424710
Jarod Downing *(CFO)*

Riser Foods Company   **(1)**
5300 Richmond Rd, Cleveland, OH 44146
Tel.: (216) 292-7000
Web Site: http://www.gianteagle.com
Grocery Store Operator
N.A.I.C.S.: 445110
Anthony Rego *(CEO)*

Tamarkin Co., Inc.   **(1)**
375 Victoria Rd, Youngstown, OH 44501
Tel.: (330) 792-3811
Convenience Store
N.A.I.C.S.: 457110

GIANT FLOOR & WALL COV-
ERING CO., INC.
1345 Hwy 315, Wilkes Barre, PA
18702
Tel.: (570) 825-3435
Web Site: https://www.giantfloor.com
Sales Range: $10-24.9 Million
Emp.: 52
Floor Coverings Whslr
N.A.I.C.S.: 449121
Helena Tanona *(Dir-Fixed Ops)*

GIANT GROUP LTD.
9440 Santa Monica Blvd Ste 407,
Beverly Hills, CA 90210
Tel.: (310) 273-5678
Rev.: $72,631,000
Emp.: 140
Investment Holding Companies, Ex-
cept Banks
N.A.I.C.S.: 523999
Burt Sugarman *(Chm)*

GIANT IDEAS
100 1st Ave Ste 200, Pittsburgh, PA
15222
Tel.: (412) 566-5756
Web Site: http://www.giantideas.com
Year Founded: 2001
Sales Range: $50-74.9 Million
Emp.: 20
Advetising Agency
N.A.I.C.S.: 541810

Bryan Ward *(Founder & CEO)*
Gary Kalinosky *(Dir-Creative)*
Ronda Zegarelli *(Dir-Bus Connections)*

GIANT INDUSTRIES, INC.
900 N Westwood Ave, Toledo, OH
43607-3261
Tel.: (419) 531-4600   OH
Web Site:
   https://www.giantpumps.com
Year Founded: 1934
Sales Range: $50-74.9 Million
Emp.: 30
Triplex Pumps & Accessories Mfr
N.A.I.C.S.: 333914
Edward Simon *(Pres)*
Debbie Harrison *(Controller)*

GIANT INLAND EMPIRE RV CENTER
9150 Benson Ave, Montclair, CA
91763
Tel.: (909) 323-0665
Web Site: https://www.giantrv.com
Rev.: $97,726,414
Emp.: 35
Sales of Recreational Vehicle Parts &
Accessories
N.A.I.C.S.: 441210
Bob Barouti *(Pres)*

GIANT MAGELLAN TELE-SCOPE ORGANIZATION
251 S Lake Ave Ste 300, Pasadena,
CA 91101
Tel.: (626) 204-0500   DE
Web Site: http://www.gmto.org
Year Founded: 2007
Sales Range: $25-49.9 Million
Emp.: 33
Astronomical Research Services
N.A.I.C.S.: 541715
Taft Armandroff *(Vice Chm)*
Walter E. Massey *(Chm)*
Robert N. Shelton *(Pres)*

GIANT OAK CORPORATION
1177 Avenue of the Americas 5th Fl,
New York, NY 10036
Tel.: (646) 452-7220   VG
Year Founded: 2018
Assets: $61,075
Liabilities: $52,098
Net Worth: $8,977
Earnings: ($14,373)
Emp.: 2
Fiscal Year-end: 03/31/21
Investment Services
N.A.I.C.S.: 523150
Lei Zhang *(CEO & Chm)*
Changjiang Chi *(CFO)*

GIANT OIL INC.
1806 N Franklin St, Tampa, FL 33602
Tel.: (813) 740-0422
Web Site: https://www.giantoil.com
Sales Range: $10-24.9 Million
Emp.: 30
Distribution of Petroleum Products
N.A.I.C.S.: 424720
Basem I. Ali *(Pres)*
Pat Carano *(VP)*
Ernie Gonzalez *(Dir-IT & Area Mgr)*

GIANT PARTNERS
2475 Townsgate Rd Ste 150, West-
lake Village, CA 91361
Tel.: (800) 370-0799
Web Site:
   http://www.giantpartners.com
Year Founded: 2006
Sales Range: $1-9.9 Million
Emp.: 55
Internet Marketing Services, Search
Engine Optimization & Custom Lists

N.A.I.C.S.: 541613
Giovanni Barile *(CEO)*

GIANTMICROBES INC.
78 Harvard Ave Ste 300, Stamford,
CT 06902
Web Site:
   https://www.giantmicrobes.com
Sales Range: $1-9.9 Million
Plush Toy Mfr
N.A.I.C.S.: 339930
Drew Oliver *(CEO)*

Subsidiaries:

Giantmicrobes UK Limited   (1)
Chene Court Poundwell Street, Modbury,
Devon, PL21 0RQ, United Kingdom
Tel.: (44) 1548 831070
Plush Toy Mfr
N.A.I.C.S.: 339930

GIAQUINTO ASSOCIATES INC.
2912 Pacific Dr, Norcross, GA 30071-
1808
Tel.: (770) 441-8292
Year Founded: 1973
Sales Range: $10-24.9 Million
Emp.: 85
Retailer of Hardware Stores
N.A.I.C.S.: 444140
Richie Giaquinto *(Controller)*

GIBBONS P.C.
1 Gateway Ctr, Newark, NJ 07102-
5310
Tel.: (973) 596-4500
Web Site:
   https://www.gibbonslaw.com
Year Founded: 1926
Sales Range: $100-124.9 Million
Emp.: 226
Law firm
N.A.I.C.S.: 541110
Guy V. Amoresano *(Atty)*
Dale E. Barney *(Dir-Fin Restructuring & Creditors Rights)*
Ivette P. Alvarado *(Dir-Real Property & Environmental)*
Christine A. Amalfe *(Atty)*
Frederick W. Alworth *(Dir-Bus & Commercial Litigation)*
Scott J. Etish *(Dir-Bus & Comml Litigation)*

GIBBS & SOELL, INC.
60 E 42nd St 44th Fl, New York, NY
10165
Tel.: (212) 697-2600   NY
Web Site:
   http://www.gscommunications.com
Year Founded: 1971
Sales Range: $10-24.9 Million
Emp.: 47
Public Relations Agency
N.A.I.C.S.: 541820
Luke Lambert *(Pres & CEO)*
Mary C. Buhay *(Sr VP-Mktg)*
Ron Loch *(Mng Dir-Chicago)*
Audra Hession *(Mng Dir-New York)*
Doug Hampel *(Mng Dir-Client Svc)*
Jeff Altheide *(Exec VP)*
Catherine Carlson Kadar *(Dir-Media Rels)*
Kate J. Threewitts *(Sr VP-HR)*
Kiersten Williams *(VP)*
Ann Camden *(Mng Dir)*
Brad Bremer *(VP)*
Brian Hall *(Mng Dir)*
Caryn Caratelli *(VP)*
Emily Bunce *(Dir-Insights)*
Seth Niessen *(CFO)*
Stephanie D. Moore *(VP)*
Steve Halsey *(Chief Growth Officer)*
Meredith Topalanchik *(Mng Dir-New York City)*
Ralph Katz *(Exec VP)*
Rachael Adler *(Sr VP)*

Katy Hendricks *(VP-Growth & Crop Comm)*
Chris Martin *(VP-Creative & Brand Experience)*
Dana Ferrell *(Mng Dir-Raleigh)*
Anne Green *(Principal & Mng Dir-Bus Consulting)*

Subsidiaries:

Gibbs & Soell - Chicago   (1)
125 S Wacker Dr Ste 2600, Chicago, IL
60606
Tel.: (312) 648-6700
Web Site:
   http://www.gscommunications.com
Sales Range: Less than $1 Million
Emp.: 34
Public Relations Agency
N.A.I.C.S.: 541820
Ron Loch *(Mng Dir)*
Doug Hampel *(Sr VP)*
Jeff Altheide *(Exec VP)*
Emily Bunce *(Dir-Insights)*
Ann Camden *(Mng Dir-Client Svcs)*
Peter Donnelly *(VP-Creative)*
Kerry Henderson *(Mng Dir-Raleigh)*
Audra Hession *(Mng Dir-New York)*
Luke Lambert *(Pres & CEO)*
Seth Niessen *(Controller)*
Mike Samec *(VP-Digital Strategy)*
Kate Threewitts *(VP-HR)*

Gibbs & Soell - Raleigh   (1)
8521 6 Forks Rd Ste 300, Raleigh, NC
27615
Tel.: (919) 870-5718
Web Site: http://www.gibbs-soell.com
Sales Range: $10-24.9 Million
Emp.: 40
Public Relations Agency
N.A.I.C.S.: 541820
Ann Camden *(Mng Dir-Client Svc)*
Kerry Henderson *(Mng Dir-Raleigh)*
Caryn Caratelli *(Sr VP)*
Stephanie D. Moore *(Sr VP)*
Jeff Altheide *(COO)*
Mary C. Buhay *(Sr VP-Mktg)*
Seth Niessen *(Controller)*
Mike Samec *(VP-Digital Strategy)*

Gibbs & Soell GmbH   (1)
Saint Johanns Vorstadt 22, 4056, Basel,
Switzerland
Tel.: (41) 61 264 8410
Web Site:
   http://www.gscommunications.com
Emp.: 3
Public Relations Agency
N.A.I.C.S.: 541820

Morgan & Myers, Inc.   (1)
N16 W23233 Stone Rdg Dr Ste 200,
Waukesha, WI 53188
Tel.: (262) 650-7260
Web Site: http://www.morganmyers.com
Sales Range: $50-74.9 Million
Emp.: 33
Advertising Services
N.A.I.C.S.: 541810
Janine Stewart *(Mng Dir)*
Tim Oliver *(Pres & Principal)*
Linda Basse Wenck *(Principal & Dir-Corp Affairs)*
Max Wenck *(Principal & Dir-Agriculture & Pasture-to-Plate Practice)*
Mary Steptoe *(Accountant)*

Branch (Domestic):

Morgan & Myers, Inc.   (2)
1005 Stratford Ave, Waterloo, IA 50701-
1952
Tel.: (319) 233-0502
Web Site: https://www.morganmyers.com
Sales Range: Less than $1 Million
Emp.: 30
Agriculture, Business-To-Business, Finan-
cial, Food Service
N.A.I.C.S.: 541810
Janine Stewart *(Dir-Integrated Mktg Comm Practice)*
Linda Basse Wenck *(Dir-Corp Affairs)*

GIBBS CALIFORNIA WILD RICE
10400 Billings Rd, Live Oak, CA
95953

Tel.: (530) 695-1612
Web Site: http://www.gwrice.com
Sales Range: $10-24.9 Million
Emp.: 7
Rice Milling
N.A.I.C.S.: 424510
Larry Erickson *(Pres)*

GIBBS INTERNATIONAL TRUCK CENTERS INCORPORATED
2201 E Ventura Blvd, Oxnard, CA
93030
Tel.: (805) 485-0551
Web Site:
   http://www.gibbstrucks.com
Year Founded: 1970
Rev.: $43,000,000
Emp.: 42
Distr of 18-Wheel Trucks
N.A.I.C.S.: 441110
Edward A. Gibbs *(Pres)*

GIBBS WIRE & STEEL COM-PANY, INC.
4 Metals Dr., Southington, CT 06489
Tel.: (860) 621-0121   CT
Web Site: https://www.gibbswire.com
Year Founded: 1956
Sales Range: $50-74.9 Million
Emp.: 170
Distr & Processor of Metal
N.A.I.C.S.: 423510
William Torres *(Pres & CEO)*

Subsidiaries:

Gibbs Wire & Steel Co.   (1)
3751 Olive Rd, South Bend, IN 46628-1523
Tel.: (574) 234-6071
Web Site: http://www.gibbswire.com
Sales Range: $25-49.9 Million
Emp.: 40
Metals Service Center
N.A.I.C.S.: 423510
Don Gibbs *(VP-Sls-Western Reg)*

Gibbs Wire & Steel Co.   (1)
3050 N Great SW Pkwy, Grand Prairie, TX
75050-6484
Tel.: (972) 602-0230
Web Site: http://www.gibbswire.com
Sales Range: $25-49.9 Million
Emp.: 30
Metals Service Center
N.A.I.C.S.: 423510
Bill Torres *(Pres & CEO)*

Gibbs Wire & Steel Co.   (1)
14020 Unit 520, Chino, CA 91710
Tel.: (909) 548-4420
Web Site: http://www.gibbswire.com
Sales Range: $25-49.9 Million
Emp.: 5
Metals Service Center
N.A.I.C.S.: 423510

Gibbs Wire & Steel Co.   (1)
5230 Westinghouse Blvd, Charlotte, NC
28273
Tel.: (704) 587-9666
Web Site: http://www.gibbswire.com
Sales Range: $25-49.9 Million
Emp.: 11
Metals Service Center
N.A.I.C.S.: 423510
Ben Leary *(Mgr-Ops & Quality)*

Gibbs Wire & Steel Company of
Canada Ltd.   (1)
250 Chrysler Drive Unit One, Brampton,
L6S6B6, ON, Canada   (100%)
Tel.: (905) 791-6811
Web Site: http://www.gibbswire.com
Sales Range: $10-24.9 Million
Emp.: 8
Metals Service Center
N.A.I.C.S.: 423510
Roger Forsyth *(Gen Mgr)*

GIBRALTAR CONSTRUCTION CO. INC.
42 Hudson St Ste 107, Annapolis,
MD 21401

Gibraltar Construction Co. Inc.—(Continued)
Tel.: (410) 573-1000
Web Site:
http://www.gibraltarconstruction
company.com
Year Founded: 1972
Sales Range: $1-9.9 Million
Emp.: 50
Mfr of Building Products
N.A.I.C.S.: 236118
Nathan Nelson (Mgr)

GIBRALTAR CONSTRUCTION, CORP.
88 S Lakeview Dr Bldg 3, Gibbsboro, NJ 08026
Tel.: (856) 435-4411   NJ
Year Founded: 1991
Sales Range: $25-49.9 Million
Emp.: 100
Commercial Construction
N.A.I.C.S.: 236220
Lee S. Babitt (Pres)
Arnold Cohen (CFO)
Dana Lazar (Project Mgr)
Jeffrey Heinsheimer (Dir-Sls)
Linda Roadknight (Dir-Info Mgmt)
Michael Clark (Project Mgr)
Michael McVey (Dir-Ops)
Tom Gilmore (Gen Mgr)
William Cyr (Principal & Gen Mgr-Ops)

GIBRALTAR IT, LLC
2 Market Plaza Way #6, Mechanicsburg, PA 17055
Web Site: https://www.gibraltarit.com
Year Founded: 1995
Sales Range: $1-9.9 Million
Emp.: 24
Extensive IT Consulting Services & Client Support
N.A.I.C.S.: 541618
Thomas Hogue (CEO)
Rachelle Hogue (Dir-Rels)
Matt Oswald (CFO & COO)
Joe Timko (Mgr-Helpdesk)
Adam Fogelstrom (Mgr-Technical Ops)

GIBRALTAR TRADE CENTER INC.
15525 Racho Blvd, Taylor, MI 48180
Tel.: (734) 287-2000
Web Site:
http://www.gibraltartrade.com
Year Founded: 1980
Rev.: $10,800,000
Emp.: 140
Shopping Center Operation Services
N.A.I.C.S.: 531120
James A. Koester (Pres)

GIBRALTAR US, INC.
4303 Innovation Loop, Marble Falls, TX 78654
Tel.: (830) 798-5444   TX
Web Site: http://www.gibraltarus.com
Barrier & Fencing Products Mfr & Whslr
N.A.I.C.S.: 332999
Bill Neusch (Owner & CEO)
Jim Bryer (CFO)
Jim Castello (Pres)
Peter D. Lewellen (VP-Products & Bus Dev)
Joseph Hauss (Pres-Material Distr)

GIBSON BRANDS, INC.
309 Plus Pk Blvd, Nashville, TN 37217
Tel.: (615) 871-4500   MI
Web Site: http://www.gibson.com
Year Founded: 1894

Musical Instruments & Accessories Mfr & Marketer
N.A.I.C.S.: 339992
Cesar Gueikian (Pres & Interim CEO)
Armin Boehm (Chief Comml Officer)
Jeremy Freckleton (Chief Production Officer)
Nat Zilkha (Chm)

Subsidiaries:

Baldwin Piano, Inc.   (1)
309 Plus Park Blvd, Nashville, TN 37217
Tel.: (615) 871-4500
Web Site: http://www2.gibson.com
Sales Range: $75-99.9 Million
Emp.: 1,500
Organs & Pianos Mfr & Sales
N.A.I.C.S.: 339992

Gibson Acoustic   (1)
1894 Orville Way, Bozeman, MT 59715
Tel.: (406) 587-4117
Web Site: http://www.gibson.com
Sales Range: $10-24.9 Million
Emp.: 130
Musical Instruments
N.A.I.C.S.: 339992

Gibson Custom, Art & Historic   (1)
1612 Elm Hill Pike, Nashville, TN 37210
Tel.: (615) 871-4500
Web Site: http://www.gibson.com
Custom Guitars Mfr
N.A.I.C.S.: 339992

Gibson Gear   (1)
641 Massman Dr, Nashville, TN 37210-3721
Tel.: (847) 741-7315
Web Site: http://www.gibson.com
Sales Range: $10-24.9 Million
Emp.: 100
Musical Instrument Sales
N.A.I.C.S.: 339992

Gibson Guitar Corp. - Entertainment Relations   (1)
9350 Civic Ctr, Beverly Hills, CA 90210
Tel.: (310) 300-2369
Web Site: http://www.gibson.com
Entertainment Services
N.A.I.C.S.: 713990

Gibson Guitar Corp. - Entertainment Relations   (1)
421 W 54th St Fl 1, New York, NY 10019-7413
Tel.: (212) 459-0801
Web Site: http://www.gibson.com
Sales Range: $10-24.9 Million
Emp.: 5
Entertainment Services
N.A.I.C.S.: 713990
Jim Felber (Mng Dir)

Gibson Guitar Corp. - Entertainment Relations   (1)
3rd Floor 20-35 Rathbone Street, London, W1T 1NJ, United Kingdom
Tel.: (44) 2071672140
Web Site: http://www.gibson.com
Entertainment Services
N.A.I.C.S.: 713990

Gibson Guitar Corp. - Entertainment Relations   (1)
14 Rue Chaptal, 75009, Paris, France   (100%)
Tel.: (33) 148743505
Web Site: http://www.gibson.com
Sales Range: $50-74.9 Million
Emp.: 2
Entertainment Services
N.A.I.C.S.: 713990

SM Speaker Corp.   (1)
772 S Military Trl, Deerfield Beach, FL 33442
Tel.: (954) 949-9600
Web Site: http://www.stantondj.com
Sales Range: $10-24.9 Million
Emp.: 100
Holding Company; Audio Equipment Mfr
N.A.I.C.S.: 551112
Timothy Dorwardt (CEO)

Subsidiary (Domestic):
Cerwin-Vega, Inc.   (2)

772 S Military Trl, Deerfield Beach, FL 33442-3025
Tel.: (954) 316-1501
Web Site: http://www.cerwin-vega.com
Speaker Systems Mfr
N.A.I.C.S.: 334310

Stanton Magnetics, Inc.   (2)
772 S Military Trail, Deerfield Beach, FL 33442
Tel.: (954) 949-9600
Web Site: http://www.stantondj.com
Sales Range: $10-24.9 Million
Emp.: 30
Audio Equipment, Electronic Cartridges, Headphones, Preamplifiers, Stanton Record Care Products Mfr
N.A.I.C.S.: 334610

The Epiphone Company   (1)
309 Plus Park Blvd, Nashville, TN 37217
Tel.: (615) 871-4500
Sales Range: $10-24.9 Million
Emp.: 60
Musical Instrument Mfr
N.A.I.C.S.: 339992
Henry Juszkiewicz (CEO)

GIBSON ELECTRIC MEMBER-SHIP CORP.
1207 S College St, Trenton, TN 38382-0047
Tel.: (731) 855-4740   TN
Web Site:
https://www.gibsonemc.com
Year Founded: 1936
Sales Range: $25-49.9 Million
Emp.: 83
Electric Services
N.A.I.C.S.: 221122
Kerry Watson (VP-Customer Care)
Steve Sanders (Chm)

GIBSON INSURANCE AGENCY INC.
333 E Jefferson, Plymouth, IN 46563
Tel.: (574) 936-2122   IN
Web Site: http://www.gibsonins.com
Year Founded: 1933
Sales Range: $25-49.9 Million
Emp.: 80
Insurance Agents
N.A.I.C.S.: 524210
Robert Sturtevant (VP)
Tania M. Bengtsson (Dir-Mktg)
Tim Leman (Chm & CEO)

Subsidiaries:

Insurance Network, LC   (1)
5005 S 900 E Ste 200, Salt Lake City, UT 84117-5791
Tel.: (801) 266-6800
Web Site:
http://www.insurancenetworklc.com
Sales Range: $1-9.9 Million
Emp.: 16
Insurance Brokerage Services
N.A.I.C.S.: 524210
Paul L. Holbrook (Principal)
Michael S. Tingey (Principal)

GIBSON MERCHANDISE GROUP INC.
2321 W Loop 281, Longview, TX 75604-2563
Tel.: (903) 297-0766   TX
Year Founded: 1981
Sales Range: $75-99.9 Million
Emp.: 450
Provider of Drugs & Pharmaceuticals
N.A.I.C.S.: 456110
Richard H. Gibson (Vice Chm)
Sammy Culpepper (Pres)

Subsidiaries:

Drug Emporium   (1)
2550 Barrow St, Abilene, TX 79605   (100%)
Tel.: (325) 698-0242
Web Site: http://www.drugemporiuminc.com

Sales Range: $25-49.9 Million
Emp.: 40
Retailer of Drugs & Proprietaries
N.A.I.C.S.: 456110

Emporium Drug Mart Inc. of Amarillo   (1)
4210B SW 45th Ave, Amarillo, TX 79109
Tel.: (806) 358-6228
Sales Range: $25-49.9 Million
Emp.: 50
Retailer of Drugs & Proprietaries
N.A.I.C.S.: 456110
Gregorry Dunckan (Mgr-Store)

Emporium Drug Mart Inc. of Lafayette   (1)
505 Bertrand Dr, Lafayette, LA 70506
Tel.: (337) 261-0051
Sales Range: $25-49.9 Million
Emp.: 70
Retailer of Drugs & Toiletries
N.A.I.C.S.: 456110

Emporium Drug Mart Inc. of Longview   (1)
2321 W Loop 281, Longview, TX 75604
Tel.: (903) 297-0966
Web Site: http://www.drugemporiuminc.com
Sales Range: $25-49.9 Million
Emp.: 40
Retailer of Drugs & Proprietaries
N.A.I.C.S.: 456110
Sammy Colpepper (Pres)

Emporium Drug Mart Inc. of Lubbock   (1)
5109 82nd St, Lubbock, TX 79424
Tel.: (806) 794-0022
Sales Range: $25-49.9 Million
Emp.: 70
Retailer of Drugs & Proprietaries
N.A.I.C.S.: 456110
Philip Craycraft (Gen Mgr)

Emporium Drug Mart Inc. of Shreveport   (1)
5819 E Kings Hwy, Shreveport, LA 71105
Tel.: (318) 861-7896
Sales Range: $25-49.9 Million
Emp.: 40
Retailer of Drugs & Proprietaries
N.A.I.C.S.: 456110
George Harvison (Gen Mgr)

Emporium Drug Mart Inc. of Tyler   (1)
5614 S Broadway Ave, Tyler, TX 75703
Tel.: (903) 534-9105
Sales Range: $25-49.9 Million
Emp.: 25
Retailer of Drugs & Proprietaries
N.A.I.C.S.: 456110

Emporium Drug Mart Inc. of Waco   (1)
5900 Bosque Blvd, Waco, TX 76710
Tel.: (254) 772-0011
Web Site: http://www.vitamins-plus.net
Sales Range: $25-49.9 Million
Emp.: 30
Retailer of Drugs & Proprietaries
N.A.I.C.S.: 456110

Gibson Properties Inc.   (1)
2321A W Loop 281, Longview, TX 75604-2563
Tel.: (903) 297-0766
Web Site: http://www.drugemporiuminc.com
Sales Range: $10-24.9 Million
Emp.: 12
Provider of Property Management Services
N.A.I.C.S.: 531120
Sammy Bulpper (Pres)

GIBSON OIL CO.
901 W Keiser Ave, Osceola, AR 72370-2911
Tel.: (870) 563-1200
Sales Range: $50-74.9 Million
Emp.: 8
Provider of Gasoline
N.A.I.C.S.: 424720
Bruce Gibson (CEO)
Shayla Gibson (Owner)

GIBSON WINE COMPANY
1720 Academy Ave, Sanger, CA 93657-3704
Tel.: (559) 875-2505   CA

Year Founded: 1939
Sales Range: $75-99.9 Million
Emp.: 9
Mfr & Distribution of Wines & Alcoholic Beverages
N.A.I.C.S.: 312130
Kim Spruance *(Gen Mgr)*
Leland Herman *(Pres)*

GIBSON, DUNN & CRUTCHER

200 Park Ave, New York, NY 10166-0193
Tel.: (212) 351-4000
Web Site:
  https://www.gibsondunn.com
Year Founded: 1890
Sales Range: $1-4.9 Billion
Emp.: 1,030
Law firm
N.A.I.C.S.: 541110
Robert F. Serio *(Partner)*
Steven R. Shoemate *(Partner)*
Beau Stark *(Partner-Denver)*
Brad Roach *(Partner-Singapore)*
Shaalu Mehra *(Partner-Palo Alto)*
Charles J. Stevens *(Partner)*
John W. F. Chesley *(Partner)*
Matthew S. Kahn *(Partner)*
Joshua A. Jessen *(Partner)*
Stuart M. Rosenberg *(Partner)*
Ken Doran *(Chm & Mng Partner)*
Mylan L. Denerstein *(Partner)*
Stacie B. Fletcher *(Partner-Washington)*
Marian J. Lee *(Partner-Washington)*
Deepak Nanda *(Partner-Orange County)*
Eric B. Sloan *(Partner)*
Eric J. Stock *(Partner)*
Aaron F. Adams *(Partner-New York)*
Chezard F. Ameer *(Partner-Dubai)*
Daniel Angel *(Partner-New York)*
Dora R. Arash *(Partner-Los Angeles)*
Dennis B. Arnold *(Partner-Los Angeles)*
Howard Adler *(Partner-Washington)*
D. Jarrett Arp *(Partner-Washington)*
Lisa A. Alfaro *(Partner)*
Nicholas Aleksander *(Partner-London)*
Peter Alexiadis *(Partner)*
John M. Pollack *(Partner)*
M. Kendall Day *(Partner-Washington)*
F. Joseph Warin *(Chm-White Collar Defense & Investigations Practice Grp)*
Jeffrey Jakubiak *(Partner-Washington)*
Jason Meltzer *(Partner-Washington)*
Jeremy Robison *(Partner-Washington)*
Jeffrey Steiner *(Partner-Washington)*
Daniel Zygielbaum *(Partner-Washington)*
Allison Kidd *(Partner)*
Elizabeth Papez *(Partner-Washington)*

GIBSON, DUNN & CRUTCHER LLP

333 S Grand Ave, Los Angeles, CA 94105-0921
Tel.: (213) 229-7000
Web Site:
  http://www.gibsondunn.com
Year Founded: 1890
Emp.: 1,077
Law firm
N.A.I.C.S.: 541110
Howard Adler *(Partner & Atty)*
Aaron F. Adams *(Partner & Atty)*
Lisa A. Alfaro *(Partner & Atty)*
Nicholas Aleksander *(Partner & Atty)*
Peter Alexiadis *(Partner & Atty)*
Richard J. Birns *(Partner & Atty)*
Stuart A. Graiwer *(Partner & Atty)*

Winston Y. Chan *(Partner & Atty)*
Jonathan L. Corsico *(Partner-Washington & Atty)*
Stacie B. Fletcher *(Partner-Washington & Atty)*
Neema Jalali *(Partner & Atty)*
Joshua S. Lipshutz *(Partner & Atty)*
Penny Madden *(Partner & Atty)*
Susan M. Marcella *(Partner & Atty)*
Karl G. Nelson *(Partner & Atty)*
Linda Noonan *(Atty)*
Philip Rocher *(Partner & Atty)*
Amy G. Rudnick *(Partner & Atty)*
William Rustum *(Partner & Atty)*
Saptak Santra *(Partner & Atty)*
Michael J. Scanlon *(Partner & Atty)*
Janet Vance *(Partner & Atty)*
Patrick Stokes *(Partner)*
Kristin Linsley *(Partner-Litigation)*
Ken Doran *(Chm & Mng Partner)*

GICON PUMPS & EQUIPMENT, LLC

17922 N Interstate 27, Abernathy, TX 79311
Tel.: (806) 298-2024
Web Site: http://www.gpeltd.com
Rev.: $15,000,000
Emp.: 8
Industrial Water Pumps Mfr
N.A.I.C.S.: 423830
Mark Durham *(COO)*
Bobie Louise *(Mgr-Distr)*
Candice Brewer *(Dir-HR)*
Joe Riker *(Mgr-Ops)*
Cary Harris *(Mgr-Website)*
Jason Evans *(Mgr-Market Dev)*
Ronnie Hensley *(Gen Mgr-Engineered Products)*

GICON PUMPS & EQUIPMENT, LTD.

17922 N Interstate 27, Abernathy, TX 79311
Tel.: (806) 298-2024
Web Site:
  http://www.giconpumps.com
Sales Range: $1-9.9 Million
Emp.: 60
Industrial Machinery & Equipment Whslr
N.A.I.C.S.: 423830
Vance Grant *(CFO)*

GID INVESTMENT ADVISOR LLC

125 High St, Boston, MA 02110
Tel.: (617) 973-9680
Web Site: http://www.gid.com
Year Founded: 1960
Rev.: $200,000,000
Emp.: 500
Real Estate Owner & Managers
N.A.I.C.S.: 531110
Robert E. DeWitt *(Vice Chm, Pres & CEO)*
W. Gardner Wallace *(Chm)*
Jeffrey A. Harris *(Pres-Windsor Mgmt & Exec VP)*
William H. Roberts *(Exec VP-GID Portfolio Mgmt)*
Gary Kroll *(VP-Real Estate Acq)*
Brian T. O'Herlihy *(CFO)*
Thad D. Palmer *(Exec VP)*

Subsidiaries:

Windsor Property Management
Company   **(1)**
125 High St Fl 27, Boston, MA
02110-2704   **(100%)**
Tel.: (617) 973-9680
Web Site:
  http://www.windsorcommunities.com
Rev.: $12,400,000
Emp.: 100
Apartment Building Operator
N.A.I.C.S.: 551112

Robert E. Dewitt *(Pres)*
Garner Wallace *(Chm)*

GIER OIL CO. INC.

301 E Eigth St, Eldon, MO 65026
Tel.: (573) 392-6150
Web Site: http://www.uhaul.com
Rev.: $23,442,260
Emp.: 6
Fuel Oil Distr
N.A.I.C.S.: 424720
Del Kliethmers *(Mgr)*

GIERTSEN COMPANY

8385 10th Ave N, Golden Valley, MN 55427
Tel.: (763) 546-1300   **MN**
Web Site:
  https://www.giertsenco.com
Year Founded: 1918
Sales Range: $10-24.9 Million
Emp.: 150
Fire Damage Repair Services
N.A.I.C.S.: 236118
David Egan *(Controller)*

GIF SERVICES INC.

2525 Brunswick Ave, Linden, NJ 07036
Tel.: (908) 474-1270
Web Site: http://www.gifservices.com
Sales Range: Less than $1 Million
Emp.: 7
Customhouse Brokers
N.A.I.C.S.: 488510
John Callea *(Pres)*

GIFFORDS FAMOUS ICE CREAM

25 Hathaway St, Skowhegan, ME 04976
Tel.: (207) 474-9821
Web Site:
  https://www.giffordsicecream.com
Sales Range: $10-24.9 Million
Emp.: 75
Ice Cream Stands Or Dairy Bars
N.A.I.C.S.: 722513
John Gifford *(Treas, Mgr & Co-Owner)*
Roger Gifford *(Pres, Mgr & Co-Owner)*

GIFT OF HOPE ORGAN & TISSUE DONOR NETWORK

425 Spring Lake Dr, Itasca, IL 60143
Tel.: (630) 758-2600   **IL**
Web Site: https://www.giftofhope.org
Year Founded: 1987
Sales Range: $50-74.9 Million
Emp.: 299
Organ & Tissue Donation Services
N.A.I.C.S.: 621991
Evelyn Schultz *(VP-Internal Ops)*
Michael Harmon *(Dir-Organ Recovery Ops)*
Kevin Cmunt *(Pres & CEO)*
Martin Jendrisak *(VP-R&D & Dir-Medical)*
Ross Raspopovich *(CFO & VP-Bus Dev)*
John Lunz *(Dir-Histocompatibility & Immunogenetics Laboratory)*
Edward Lesh *(Sr Mgr-Transportation & Facilities)*
Jack Lynch *(Dir-Community Affairs)*
Edward Marchewka *(Dir-IT Svcs)*
Ron Skolek *(Dir-Hospital Dev)*
Lori Malatesta *(VP-HR & Orgal Dev)*
Maureen Kwiecinski *(Gen Counsel & VP-External Affairs)*

GIFTCARDRESCUE.COM, LLC

6230 Old Dobbin Lane Suite 190, Columbia, MD 21045
Tel.: (877) 800-4413

Web Site:
  http://www.giftcardrescue.com
Year Founded: 2008
Sales Range: $1-9.9 Million
Emp.: 10
Buys Unused Gift Cards From Consumers Up to 90 percent of the Cards' Value & Resells Them Online for Less Than Face Value
N.A.I.C.S.: 459999
Kwame Kuadey *(Founder & CEO)*
Alex Gould *(Mgr-Bus Dev)*
Natalyn Obey *(Mgr-Ops & Customer Svc)*
Ngutifafa Paka *(CIO)*

GIGAFAST INC.

2033 Gateway Pl Ste 500, San Jose, CA 95110
Tel.: (408) 392-2333
Web Site: http://www.gigafast.com
Year Founded: 1997
Rev.: $4,000,000
Emp.: 25
Mfr of Networking Products
N.A.I.C.S.: 334112
Karen Chang *(Pres)*

GIGAHERTZ LLC

1749 Painters Run Rd, Pittsburgh, PA 15241
Tel.: (412) 257-2800   **PA**
Web Site:
  http://www.gigahertzllc.com
Sales Range: $10-24.9 Million
Emp.: 4
Radio Frequency Transmission Equipment Designer, Mfr & Consulting Services
N.A.I.C.S.: 334220
Robert M. Unetich *(Founder)*

Subsidiaries:

Axcera, LLC   **(1)**
103 Freedom Dr, Lawrence, PA 15055
Tel.: (724) 873-8100
Web Site: http://www.axcera.com
Television Broadcast Transmission, Mobile Media & Broadband Wireless Telecommunication Systems Mfr & Distr
N.A.I.C.S.: 334220

GIGANTE VAZ PARTNERS ADVERTISING, INC.

295 Lafayette St Fl 7, New York, NY 10012
Tel.: (212) 343-0004
Web Site: http://www.gigantevaz.com
Year Founded: 1989
Rev.: $61,000,000
Emp.: 23
N.A.I.C.S.: 541810
Paul Gigante *(CEO & Chief Compliance Officer)*
Madeline Vaz *(COO)*
Jim McHugh *(Pres)*

GIGGLE, INC.

158 W 27th St 8th Fl, New York, NY 10001
Web Site: http://www.giggle.com
Marketing Consulting Services
N.A.I.C.S.: 541613

Subsidiaries:

LMC Right Start, Inc.   **(1)**
3000 E 3rd Ave Unit 15, Denver, CO 80206
Tel.: (303) 320-8312
Web Site: http://www.rightstart.com
Juvenile Products Mfr & Distr
N.A.I.C.S.: 424350
Puneet Vedi *(Dir-IT)*

GIGGLES N HUGS, INC.

3222 Glendale Galleria Way, Glendale, CA 91210
Tel.: (818) 956-4847   **NV**

Giggles N Hugs, Inc.—(Continued)

Web Site:
http://www.gigglesnhugs.com
Year Founded: 2004
Rev.: $2,431,903
Assets: $614,424
Liabilities: $2,616,525
Net Worth: ($2,002,101)
Earnings: ($691,369)
Emp.: 53
Fiscal Year-end: 12/30/18
Children's Themed Restaurants
N.A.I.C.S.: 722513
Joey Parsi (Founder, CEO, CFO, Treas & Co-Sec)

GIGLIO DISTRIBUTING COMPANY, INC.
155 S Martin Luther King Pkwy, Beaumont, TX 77701
Tel.: (409) 838-1654
Web Site:
https://www.gigliodistributing.com
Rev.: $26,000,000
Emp.: 105
Beer & Ale Merchant Whslr
N.A.I.C.S.: 424810
Charles J. Giglio (Pres & CEO)

GIL HAUGAN CONSTRUCTION, INC.
200 E 60th St N, Sioux Falls, SD 57104-0433
Tel.: (605) 336-6082
Web Site: http://www.gilhaugan.com
Year Founded: 1960
Sales Range: $10-24.9 Million
Emp.: 80
Provider of Nonresidential Construction Services
N.A.I.C.S.: 236220
Kevin Eigenberg (Controller)
Gilbert Haugan Jr. (Pres)

Subsidiaries:

Gil Haugan Construction   (1)
200 E 60th St N, Sioux Falls, SD 57104-0433
Tel.: (605) 336-6088
Web Site: http://www.gilhaugan.com
Producer of Masonry & Other Stonework
N.A.I.C.S.: 236220
Gil Haugan (Pres)

GIL-BAR INDUSTRIES, INC.
5 W 19th St Fl 7, New York, NY 10011
Tel.: (212) 645-9720   NY
Web Site: http://www.gil-bar.com
Year Founded: 1986
Sales Range: $1-9.9 Million
Emp.: 22
Warm Air Heating & Air-Conditioning Equipment & Supplies Merchant Whslr
N.A.I.C.S.: 423730
John Gill (Pres)
Chris Bisaccia (Partner)
Eric Mueller (CEO-Sls-NJ)
Greg Peifer (Sls Mgr-Philadelphia)

Subsidiaries:

GBS Ltd.   (1)
321 Snyder Ave, Berkeley Heights, NJ 07922
Tel.: (732) 981-9400
Web Site: http://www.gbs-ltd.net
Rev.: $2,820,000
Emp.: 15
Heating, Ventilation & Air-Conditioning Services
N.A.I.C.S.: 423730
Corey Graney (Mgr)

GIL-MAR MANUFACTURING CO.
7925 Ronda Dr, Canton, MI 48187

Tel.: (734) 459-4803
Web Site: https://www.gil-mar.com
Sales Range: $10-24.9 Million
Emp.: 90
Precision Machined Part Distr
N.A.I.C.S.: 423830
Gary Gorski (Treas)
Gildo Ruicci (Pres)

GILBANE, INC.
7 Jackson Walkway, Providence, RI 02903
Tel.: (401) 456-5800
Web Site: https://www.gilbaneco.com
Year Founded: 1873
Sales Range: $1-4.9 Billion
Emp.: 3,534
Industrial Building Construction
N.A.I.C.S.: 236210
Robert V. Gilbane (VP)
William J. Gilbane Jr. (Vice Chm & VP)
Nicole Looney (Dir-Interiors Grp-Boston)
Ryan Hutchins (Sr VP)
Daniel P. Reynolds (Exec VP)
Karen A. Higgins-Carter (Chief Info & Digital Officer & Exec VP)
Robert J. Murray (CFO)
Adam R. Jelen (Pres)
Paul J. Choquette Jr. (Vice Chm)

Subsidiaries:

Gilbane Building Company   (1)
7 Jackson Walkway, Providence, RI 02903-3623   (100%)
Tel.: (401) 456-5800
Web Site: http://www.gilbaneco.com
Sales Range: $5-14.9 Billion
Emp.: 400
Commercial Construction Management & General Contractors
N.A.I.C.S.: 236220
Thomas F. Gilbane Jr. (Chm)
William J. Gilbane Jr. (Vice Chm)
Adam R. Jelen (CEO)
Dennis Cornick (Exec VP & Dir-Sls & Mktg-Global)
Jeff George (VP)
Scott Orr (Sr VP)
Brett Meyer (VP)
Robert Hayes (VP-Florida)
Lisa Martin (VP & Dir-Sls Svcs)
Michael D. Brown (Sr VP)
Karen Medeiros (CMO & Exec VP-Sls-Global)
Matt Tierney (Sr VP)
Paul Sullivan (VP)
Michael R. Bohn (Exec VP)
John Sinnott (VP)
Daniel P. Reynolds (Exec VP)
Rebecca A. Severson (Dir-Corp Safety)
Jason Burt (Mgr-Ops-Florida Div)
Matt McGarry (Controller-Project)
Brandon Reed (Superintendent)
David Childress (Dir-Interiors)
Emre Ozcan (VP-Washington)
Jennifer Sisak (Mgr-Bus Dev-North Carolina)
Carlos Torres (Dir-Corp & Public Markets-Atlanta)
Michael Kennedy (VP & Sr Dir-Bus Dev)
Raj Bhangoo (Sr Mgr-Bus Dev-Boston)
Shawn Carlin (VP)
Jim Carpenter (Ops Mgr-Philadelphia)
Greg Permison (Mgr-Bus Dev-Locust Point)
Nancy Ly (Mgr-Bus Dev)
Evan Synstad (Mgr-Bus Dev-Charlotte)
Karen A. Higgins-Carter (Chief Info & Digital Officer & Exec VP)
Dan Gilbane (Sr VP & Dir-Strategic Initiatives)
Heidi DeBenedetti (COO)
Cary Shippert (Dir-Healthcare, Science & Tech-Southeast)
Danny Patton (VP-Georgia & South Carolina)
Brian Steed (VP-Atlanta Bus Unit)
Yvette Stevens (VP-Economic Inclusion)
Ryan Hutchins (Reg Pres)
Kristen Costello (Mgr-Bus Dev-Richmond-VA)
Meagan Charbonneau (Mgr-Bus Dev-Massachusetts Bus Unit)

Mike O'Brien (Sr VP)
David Kristjanson (Mgr-Bus Dev-Boca Raton)
Tom Thrasher (Sr VP-Florida Bus Unit)
Nikki Rao (Mgr-Bus Dev-Boca Raton)
Charles Lines (Dir-Bus Dev-Clients-Natl)
Tonya Byrd (Mgr-Bus Dev-Atlanta)
Raquel Diaz (Mgr-Pub Sector-New York City)
John LaRow (Sr VP)
Carol Horne Penn (Sr Mgr-Bus Dev)
Jose Jimenez (Dir-Life Sciences-Mid-Atlantic Div)
Dan Keaveney (VP & Area Mgr-Arizona)
Tuyet Le (VP-Bus Dev & Strategy-West)
Alex Gutman (CTO)
Rawle Sawh (Dir-Ops Tech)
Tyler Swartzwelder (VP)
Joe Orr (Sr Mgr-Bus Dev-Central Florida)
Shanika Baughman (Dir-Economic Inclusion)
Thomas M. Laird Jr. (Pres)
Paul J. Choquette III (Pres-Mid Atlantic)

Subsidiary (Domestic):

Gilbane Development Company   (2)
7 Jackson Walkway, Providence, RI 02903-3623   (100%)
Tel.: (401) 456-5890
Web Site:
http://www.gilbanedevelopment.com
Sales Range: $25-49.9 Million
Emp.: 80
Real Estate Developers
N.A.I.C.S.: 531390
Edward Broderick (Pres & CEO)
Bob Gagliardi (Mgr-Property Mgmt)
Matthew P. Lawrence (CFO & Sr VP)
Karissa Schminky (Portfolio Mgr-Mktg)
Russell Broderick (Sr VP & Head-Next Level of Student Housing Dev Program)
Jim McCurdy (VP-Fin)
Doris Gantos (VP & Dir-Multifamily-Mid Atlantic)
Chandler Aden (VP & Dir-Dev-Multifamily)

Division (Domestic):

Gilbane, Inc.   (2)
1751 Mound St Ste 106, Sarasota, FL 34236
Tel.: (941) 758-6441
Web Site: http://www.gilbaneco.com
Construction Management & Related Services
N.A.I.C.S.: 236220
Timothy D. Hensey (VP)

Subsidiary (Domestic):

Innovative Technical Solutions, Inc.   (2)
1655 Grand Ste 12 Fl, Walnut Creek, CA 94520   (100%)
Tel.: (925) 946-3100
Web Site: http://www.itsi.com
Sales Range: $10-24.9 Million
Emp.: 350
Design, Infrastructure & Environmental Engineering Services
N.A.I.C.S.: 541330
Devendra K. Shukla (Founder & Pres)
Sallie Mellor Tedesco (Supvr-AR)

GILBERT CHEVROLET INC.
3550 Hwy 441 S, Okeechobee, FL 34974
Tel.: (863) 594-2083
Web Site:
https://www.gilbertchevrolet.com
Rev.: $14,000,000
Emp.: 50
New Car Dealers
N.A.I.C.S.: 441110
Christa Luna (Gen Mgr)
Roger Rice (Gen Mgr-Sls)
Gilbert H. Culbreth Jr. (Pres)

GILBERT DISPLAY INC.
110 Spagnoli Rd, Melville, NY 11747
Tel.: (631) 577-1100
Web Site:
http://www.gilbertdisplays.com
Rev.: $12,000,000
Emp.: 140

Store & Office Display Cases & Fixtures
N.A.I.C.S.: 337212
Barry Ballen (Pres)
Tony Colombo (Controller)

GILBERT GLOBAL EQUITY PARTNERS
767 5th Ave 15th Fl, New York, NY 10153-0028
Tel.: (212) 584-6200
Web Site:
https://www.gilbertglobal.com
Year Founded: 1997
Privater Equity Firm
N.A.I.C.S.: 523999
Steven J. Gilbert (Founder & Chm)

Subsidiaries:

CPM Holdings, Inc.   (1)
2975 Airline Cir, Waterloo, IA 50703
Tel.: (319) 232-8444
Web Site: http://www.cpmroskamp.com
Sales Range: $500-549.9 Million
Emp.: 75
Industrial Machinery Mfr
N.A.I.C.S.: 333111
Doug Ostrich (CFO)
Jim Hughes (Gen Mgr)
Emily Chase (Gen Counsel)

Subsidiary (Domestic):

Beta Raven Inc.   (2)
40 S Corporate Hill Dr, Saint Charles, MO 63301
Tel.: (636) 255-1600
Web Site: http://www.betaraven.com
Sales Range: $10-24.9 Million
Feedmill & Bakery Automation Services
N.A.I.C.S.: 335314

Subsidiary (Non-US):

CPM Europe B.V.   (2)
Distelweg 89, 1031 HD, Amsterdam, 1031HD, Netherlands
Tel.: (31) 204946111
Web Site: http://www.cpmeurope.nl
Sales Range: $25-49.9 Million
Pelleting Grinding & Flaking Equipment Mfr
N.A.I.C.S.: 333241

CPM Europe Ltd.   (2)
Industrial Estate, Wexford, Whitemill, Ireland   (100%)
Tel.: (353) 5323633
Web Site: http://www.cpm-europe.ie
Sales Range: $10-24.9 Million
Mfr of Pelleting, Grinding & Flaking Equipment
N.A.I.C.S.: 333241

Subsidiary (Domestic):

CPM Wolverine Proctor LLC   (2)
251 Gibraltar Rd, Horsham, PA 19044-2305
Tel.: (215) 443-5200
Web Site:
http://www.cpmwolverineproctor.com
Sales Range: $25-49.9 Million
Food, Chemical, Tobacco, Textile & Web Processing Equipment Mfr
N.A.I.C.S.: 333994
Paul Smith (VP-Sls & Mktg)

Unit (Domestic):

CPM Wolverine Proctor LLC - Lexington   (3)
121 Proctor Ln, Lexington, NC 27292
Tel.: (336) 248-5181
Web Site: http://www.wolverineproctor.com
Food, Chemical, Tobacco, Textile & Web Processing Equipment Mfr
N.A.I.C.S.: 333994
Harrison Danze (Coord-Outsource)

Subsidiary (Non-US):

CPM Wolverine Proctor Ltd.   (3)
3 Langlands Ave, Kelvin South Business Park, East Kilbride, G75 0YG, Glasgow, United Kingdom
Tel.: (44) 1355575350
Web Site: http://www.wolverineproctor.com

Sales Range: $25-49.9 Million
Food, Chemical, Tobacco, Textile & Web Processing Equipment Mfr
N.A.I.C.S.: 333994
Robin Holding *(Mng Dir)*

Subsidiary (Domestic):

California Pellet Mill Co. (2)
1114 E Wabash Ave, Crawfordsville, IN 47933-2635
Tel.: (765) 362-2600
Web Site: http://www.cpm.net
Emp.: 50
Oilseed & Animal Feed Production Process Equipment Mfr
N.A.I.C.S.: 333248
Carl Allis *(Plant Mgr)*
Michael Middleton *(Plant Mgr)*

Crown Iron Works Company (2)
2500 County Rd C, Roseville, MN 55113
Tel.: (651) 639-8900
Web Site: http://www.crowniron.com
Sales Range: $50-74.9 Million
Holding Company; Manufacturer of Heavy Machinery, Metalworking Machinery & Special Industrial Machinery
N.A.I.C.S.: 333248
George Anderson *(VP-Engrg)*
Jeff Scott *(VP-Mktg & Sls)*
Paul C. Ell *(Mgr-Parts)*
Ann Loveland *(Controller)*
Gary Koerbitz *(VP-Ops)*

Roskamp Champion (2)
2975 Airline Cir, Waterloo, IA 50703
Tel.: (319) 232-8444
Web Site: http://www.cpm.net
Sales Range: $25-49.9 Million
Mfr of Pelleting & Particle-Size Reduction Machinery
N.A.I.C.S.: 333519
Ted D. Waitman *(Pres & CEO)*

TSA Griddle Systems Inc. (2)
2009 McKenzie Dr Ste 116, Carrollton, TX 75006
Tel.: (972) 243-8070
Web Site: http://www.griddlesystems.com
Griddle Machinery Mfr
N.A.I.C.S.: 333998
Ryan Poling *(Gen Mgr)*
Mike Niemczyk *(Mgr-Sls & Bus Dev)*

GILBERT H. WILD & SON, LLC
2944 State Highway 37, Reeds, MO 64859
Tel.: (417) 548-3514   MO
Web Site: https://www.gilberthwild.com
Year Founded: 1885
Sales Range: $75-99.9 Million
Emp.: 70
Daylily, Iris & Peonies Plants Grower & Whlsr
N.A.I.C.S.: 424930
Gregory P. Jones *(Pres)*

GILBERT HARDWOODS INC.
12990 Trinity Rd, Trinity, NC 27370
Tel.: (336) 431-2127
Sales Range: $10-24.9 Million
Emp.: 8
Provider of Rough, Dressed & Finished Lumber
N.A.I.C.S.: 423310
John Henderson *(Owner & Gen Mgr)*

Subsidiaries:

Gilbert Hardwood Centers Inc. of Tennessee (1)
100 Harless Dr, Huntland, TN 37345
Tel.: (931) 469-7508
Lumber: Rough, Dressed & Finished
N.A.I.C.S.: 423310

GILBERT HOSPITAL LLC
5656 South Power Rd, Gilbert, AZ 85295
Tel.: (480) 984-2000   AZ
Web Site: http://www.gilberter.com
Year Founded: 2006
Hospital Services

N.A.I.C.S.: 622110
Dennis Rutherford *(CEO & Member-Mgmt Bd)*
Kim Casillas *(Chief Nursing Officer)*
Lou Schroeder *(CFO)*
Timothy Johns *(Chief Medical Officer)*
Scott Cluff *(Mgr-Plant Ops)*
Melinda Lopez *(Mgr-Admitting)*
Deborah Nordyk *(Dir-Diagnostic Svcs)*
Travis Stynes *(Dir-Nursing)*
Bradley L. Newswander *(Chm-Mgmt Bd)*
Bryan McCormick *(Member-Mgmt Bd)*
Robert Mead *(Member-Mgmt Bd)*
Alphonse M. Ambrosia *(Member-Mgmt Bd)*

Subsidiaries:

Florence Hospital at Anthem, LLC (1)
4545 N Hunt Hwy, Florence, AZ 85132
Tel.: (520) 868-3333
Web Site: http://www.fhanthem.com
General Medical & Surgical Hospitals
N.A.I.C.S.: 622110
Dennis Rutherford *(CEO & Member-Mgmt Bd)*
Kim Casillas *(Chief Nursing Officer)*
Lou Schroeder *(CFO)*
Timothy Johns *(Chief Medical Officer)*
Scott Cluff *(Mgr-Plant Ops)*
Melinda Lopez *(Mgr-Admitting)*
Deborah Nordyk *(Dir-Diagnostic Svcs)*
Bradley L. Newswander *(Chm-Mgmt Bd)*
Bryan McCormick *(Member-Mgmt Bd)*
Robert Mead *(Member-Mgmt Bd)*
Alphonse M. Ambrosia *(Member-Mgmt Bd)*

GILBERT MARTIN WOODWORKING COMPANY, INC.
2345 Britannia Blvd, San Diego, CA 92154-8223
Tel.: (619) 671-5100   CA
Web Site: https://www.martinfurniture.com
Year Founded: 1980
Sales Range: $10-24.9 Million
Emp.: 300
Wood Household & Office Furniture
N.A.I.C.S.: 337122
Gilbert Martin *(Founder, Pres & CEO)*
Patrick Hayes *(VP-Imports)*

GILBOY FORD MERCURY INC.
2805 MacArthur Rd, Whitehall, PA 18052
Tel.: (610) 434-4211
Web Site: http://www.gilboyvw.com
Rev.: $30,000,000
Emp.: 85
Automobiles, New & Used
N.A.I.C.S.: 441110
Sarah Gaspar *(Controller)*
John P. Gilboy Jr. *(Pres)*

GILCHRIST ENTERPRISES
1711 35th St Ste 108, Orlando, FL 32839
Tel.: (407) 428-0961
Sales Range: $10-24.9 Million
Emp.: 450
Fast Food Franchise Operator
N.A.I.C.S.: 722513
James Gilchrist *(Pres)*
Ginger Wright *(Mgr-HR)*

GILCHRIST HOSPICE CARE INC.
11311 McCormick Rd Ste 350, Hunt Valley, MD 21031
Tel.: (443) 849-8200   MD
Web Site: http://www.gilchristhospice.org
Year Founded: 1993
Sales Range: $25-49.9 Million
Emp.: 473
Hospice Care Services

N.A.I.C.S.: 621610
Regina S. Bodnar *(Dir-Clinical Svcs)*
Lori D. Mulligan *(Mktg & Community Svcs)*
R. Wayne Barth *(Controller)*

GILCREST ELECTRIC & SUPPLY CO.
570 Ternes Ln, Elyria, OH 44035
Tel.: (440) 366-6587
Web Site: http://www.gilcrest.net
Sales Range: $1-9.9 Million
Emp.: 53
Electrical Contractor
N.A.I.C.S.: 238210
Sam Gilbert *(Pres)*

GILDNER AUTO GROUP
1407 N 10th St, Arkadelphia, AR 71923-2511
Tel.: (870) 246-4508
Web Site: http://www.gildnerauto.com
Year Founded: 1985
Sales Range: $10-24.9 Million
Emp.: 50
Car Whlsr
N.A.I.C.S.: 441110
Neal Gildner *(Owner)*

GILEAD COMMUNITY SERVICES, INC.
222 Main St, Middletown, CT 06457
Tel.: (860) 343-5300   CT
Web Site: https://www.gileadcs.org
Year Founded: 1968
Sales Range: $10-24.9 Million
Emp.: 289
Community Care Services
N.A.I.C.S.: 624190
Lucy McMillan *(Dir-Dev & PR)*
Dan Osborne *(CEO)*
Janel Segui *(COO)*
Ed Sokaitis *(Dir-HR)*
Fran Ludwig *(Pres)*
Kim Earles *(Dir-Facilities)*
Ray Bourret *(Treas)*
Joe Mascolo *(Dir-IT)*
Linda Walsh *(Dir-Contracts & Licensing)*
Stu Forman *(Dir-Medical)*
Rob Snyder *(Dir-Quality Assurance)*

GILES & KENDALL INC.
3470 Maysville Rd Northeast, Huntsville, AL 35811
Tel.: (256) 776-2979
Web Site: http://www.cedarsafeclosets.com
Sales Range: $25-49.9 Million
Emp.: 75
Wood Millworking
N.A.I.C.S.: 321918
Blake Austin *(Pres)*

GILES & RANSOME, INC.
2975 Galloway Rd, Bensalem, PA 19020-2327
Tel.: (215) 639-4300   PA
Web Site: http://www.ransome.com
Year Founded: 1916
Sales Range: $100-124.9 Million
Emp.: 600
Construction Equipment & Engines Dealer & Rental Services
N.A.I.C.S.: 423810
Dennis R. Runyen *(COO)*
Carl Wanjek *(CFO)*
Wayne L. Bromley *(Owner & Pres)*

Subsidiaries:

Giles & Ransome, Inc. - Allentown Facility (1)
211 Lloyd St, Allentown, PA 18109
Tel.: (610) 266-1029
Web Site: http://www.ransome.com

Sales Range: $25-49.9 Million
Emp.: 9
Construction Equipment Rental Services
N.A.I.C.S.: 532412
Zachary Blazer *(Gen Mgr)*

Ransome Engine (1)
2975 Galloway Rd, Bensalem, PA 19020   (100%)
Tel.: (215) 639-4300
Web Site: http://www.ransome.com
Sales Range: $25-49.9 Million
Emp.: 300
Construction Equipment Engine & Power Systems Distr
N.A.I.C.S.: 423810

Ransome Rents (1)
2975 Galloway Rd, Bensalem, PA 19020-2327
Tel.: (215) 639-4300
Web Site: http://www.ransome.com
Sales Range: $50-74.9 Million
Emp.: 400
Construction Equipment Rental Services
N.A.I.C.S.: 532412
Ken Bryant *(VP)*
Denise Runyen *(VP)*

GILES AUTOMOTIVE GROUP, INC.
6137 Johnston St, Lafayette, LA 70503
Tel.: (337) 210-9001
Web Site: https://www.gilesauto.com
Year Founded: 1989
Sales Range: $25-49.9 Million
Emp.: 300
Provider of Passenger Car Rental
N.A.I.C.S.: 532111
Robert E. Giles *(Owner)*

GILES CHEMICAL CORP.
102 Commerce St, Waynesville, NC 28786
Tel.: (828) 452-4784
Web Site: http://www.gileschemical.com
Year Founded: 1950
Sales Range: $150-199.9 Million
Emp.: 250
Producer of Epsom & Magnesium Sulfate Solutions; Marketer of Sodium Sulfate
N.A.I.C.S.: 311942
Darrel Clark *(Controller)*
Dan Dougherty *(Mgr-Natl Sls)*
Jason Bumgarner *(Mgr-Production)*

GILFORD CORPORATION
4600 Powder Mill Rd Ste 350, Beltsville, MD 20705
Tel.: (301) 931-3900
Web Site: https://www.gilfordcorp.com
Rev.: $25,700,000
Emp.: 15
Commercial & Institutional Building Construction
N.A.I.C.S.: 236220
Han Nguyen *(Project Mgr)*

GILFORD GRAPHICS INTERNATIONAL
PO Box 1023, Toms River, NJ 08753
Tel.: (732) 349-6854
Year Founded: 1996
Retail Advertisement Printing
N.A.I.C.S.: 323111

Subsidiaries:

Greenwich Village Gazette (1)
PO Box 1023, Island Heights, NJ 08732
Tel.: (732) 349-6854
Sales Range: Less than $1 Million
Emp.: 12
Online Provider of New York City News & Information
N.A.I.C.S.: 517810
Howard Flysher *(Dir-Mktg & Adv)*

Gilford Graphics International—(Continued)

GILFORD SECURITIES INC.
777 3rd Ave, New York, NY 10017
Tel.: (212) 888-6400
Web Site:
  http://www.gilfordsecurities.com
Rev.: $26,887,270
Emp.: 100
Brokers Security
N.A.I.C.S.: 523150
Randy A. Daniels (Vice Chm)
John Richter (VP-Sls & Mktg)
Robert A. Maley (Pres)
Robert J. Kropp (Sec & Sr VP)

GILFORD-JOHNSON FLOOR-ING LLC
3001 Hamburg Pike, Jeffersonville, IN 47130
Tel.: (800) 852-5454
Web Site: http://gilfordjohnson.com
Year Founded: 1991
Flooring Wholesale Distr
N.A.I.C.S.: 238330
David Dobbs (Sr VP-Supply Chain & Customer Support)
Christopher Nelson (VP-Mktg & Bus Ops)
Shahn Hall (VP-Ops)
Bill Schollmeyer (Pres)
Scott Hanks (Sr VP-Fin & Admin)

Subsidiaries:

Mastercraft Flooring Distributors, Inc. (1)
13001 NW 38th Ave, Opa Locka, FL 33054
Tel.: (800) 728-7770
Web Site: http://www.mastercraftfd.com
Floor Coverings Whslr
N.A.I.C.S.: 423220
Harvey Johnson (Founder & CEO)
Angel Lierena (Sls Mgr)
Brad Johnson (VP-Ops)

GILKEY WINDOW COMPANY INC.
3625 Hauck Rd, Cincinnati, OH 45241
Tel.: (513) 769-4527
Web Site: https://www.gilkey.com
Year Founded: 1978
Sales Range: $10-24.9 Million
Emp.: 140
Mfr & Distributor of Vinyl Windows
N.A.I.C.S.: 326199

GILL AUTOMOTIVE GROUP, INC.
5790 Anthony, Tranquillity, CA 93668
Tel.: (559) 698-7453
Web Site:
  http://www.gillautogroup.com
Year Founded: 2003
Sales Range: $1-9.9 Million
Emp.: 12
New Car Dealers
N.A.I.C.S.: 441110
Jagroop Gill (Pres & CEO)

Subsidiaries:

H & J Chevrolet Inc. (1)
14680 W Whitesbridge Ave, Kerman, CA 93630-1196
Tel.: (559) 846-9335
New Car Dealers
N.A.I.C.S.: 441110
John Tixeira (Owner)

GILL INDUSTRIES INC.
5271 Plainfield Ave NE, Grand Rapids, MI 49525-1046
Tel.: (616) 559-2700
Web Site: http://www.gill-industries.com
Year Founded: 1964
Sales Range: $200-249.9 Million
Emp.: 1,500

Automotive Stampings
N.A.I.C.S.: 336370

Subsidiaries:

GR Spring & Stamping Inc. (1)
706 Bond Ave NW, Grand Rapids, MI 49503
Tel.: (616) 453-4491
Web Site: http://www.grs-s.com
Sales Range: $100-124.9 Million
Emp.: 600
Metal Stampings, Assemblies & Slide-Formed Products Mfr
N.A.I.C.S.: 332119
Michael Libby (Coord-CI)
Chris Bloss (Mgr-Design)
Mike Santoski (Mgr-Acct)
Merle Emery (Pres)

Gill Queretaro S de RL de CV (1)
Vialidad Benito Juarez #118 Parque Industrial Queretaro, Santa Rosa Jauregui, Queretaro, 76220, Mexico
Tel.: (52) 55 5090 4835
Emp.: 130
Mfr of Specialty Mechanical Assemblies, Metal Stampings & Welded Components for Automotive Industry
N.A.I.C.S.: 336370

GILL-SIMPSON INCORPO-RATED
2834 Loch Raven Rd, Baltimore, MD 21218
Tel.: (410) 467-3335
Sales Range: $25-49.9 Million
Emp.: 300
Electrical Work
N.A.I.C.S.: 238210
Kenneth K. Gill (Chm)
E. Christopher Odell (Pres)
Albert Nocar (VP)

GILLAND CHEVROLET-PONTIAC-GMC INC.
3071 S US Hwy 231, Ozark, AL 36360-0855
Tel.: (334) 774-9030
Web Site:
  https://www.gillandchevrolet.com
Year Founded: 1991
Sales Range: $25-49.9 Million
Emp.: 60
Car Whslr
N.A.I.C.S.: 441110
John Gilland (Pres)

GILLEBAARD USA CORPORA-TION
6831 Silsbee, Houston, TX 77033
Tel.: (713) 644-1966
Web Site: https://www.hollandsw.com
Sales Range: $10-24.9 Million
Emp.: 15
Hardboard
N.A.I.C.S.: 423310
Bob Gillebaard (Chm)
Lori Sepulvado (Controller)
Butch Finnell (Gen Mgr-Sls)
Sandy Fondaw (Mgr-Traffic)
JoAnn Gillebaard (Pres & CEO)
Robert J. Gillebaard (VP)

GILLELAND CHEVROLET INC.
3019 W Division St, Saint Cloud, MN 56301
Tel.: (320) 251-4943
Web Site:
  http://www.gillelandchevrolet.com
Sales Range: $50-74.9 Million
Emp.: 128
Automobiles, New & Used
N.A.I.C.S.: 441110
Duane Gilleland (Pres)
Allen Marthaler (Controller)
Zane Johnson (Mgr-Comml & Fleet Sls)

GILLESPIE POWERS REFRIG-ERATION & ENGINEERING
9550 True Dr, Saint Louis, MO 63132
Tel.: (314) 423-9460
Web Site:
  https://www.gillespiepowers.com
Year Founded: 1943
Sales Range: $10-24.9 Million
Emp.: 20
Boiler & Furnace Contractors
N.A.I.C.S.: 238220
David Schenato (CFO & VP)
Laurie Thornsberry (Mgr-Acctg-HR)
Fred Cornell (Chief Engr)
John Peterman (Project Mgr & Engr-Sys)
Mark Roberts (Sr Engr-Combustion)
Rob Nash (Mgr-Construction)
Joe Maassen (Engr-Electrical & Combustion)
Bob Redmon (Mgr-Warehouse)
Derek Poston (Coord-Safety)
Mark Burke (Mgr-Construction)

Subsidiaries:

Gillespie & Powers Inc. (1)
9550 True Dr, Saint Louis, MO 63132
Tel.: (314) 423-9460
Web Site: http://www.gillespiepowers.com
Furnace Equipment Mfr & Distr
N.A.I.C.S.: 333994
John B. Gillespie (COO)
David Schenato (CFO & VP)
Laurie Thornsberry (Mgr-Acctg & HR)

GILLIAM BELL MOSER LLP
813 Chapel Hill Rd, Burlington, NC 27215
Tel.: (336) 227-6283
Year Founded: 2020
Emp.: 44
Accounting Firm
N.A.I.C.S.: 541219
Scott Williams (Mng Partner)

Subsidiaries:

Apple Bell Johnson & Co. PA (1)
1211 S Main St, Burlington, NC 27215-5762
Tel.: (336) 227-2022
Web Site: http://www.abjcpa.com
Offices of Certified Public Accountants
N.A.I.C.S.: 541211
Glenn S. Van Fleet (Partner)

Gilliam Coble & Moser LLP (1)
800 Green Vly Rd Ste 306, Greensboro, NC 27408-7030
Tel.: (336) 623-0804
Web Site: http://www.gcmllp.com
Offices of Certified Public Accountants
N.A.I.C.S.: 541211
Brad Moser (Partner)

GILLIE HYDE AUTO GROUP
610 Happy Valley Rd, Glasgow, KY 42141
Tel.: (270) 651-2125
Web Site: https://www.gilliehyde.com
Year Founded: 1953
Sales Range: $10-24.9 Million
Emp.: 60
Auto Operator & Services
N.A.I.C.S.: 441110
Mike Hyde (Pres & CEO)
Virginia Settle (Mgr)
Wes Gentry (Mgr-Sls-GM & Imports)
Lynn Larkin (Mgr-Fin)

GILLIGAN & FERNEMAN, LLC
1754 Business Center Lane, Kissimmee, FL 34758
Web Site:
  http://www.gilliganandferneman.com
Year Founded: 2007
Sales Range: $1-9.9 Million
Emp.: 5
Operates Six e-Commerce Sites that Sell Cooling & Wicking Daywear, Sleepwear & Temperature Regulating & Cooling Bedding

N.A.I.C.S.: 459999
William Gilligan (Co-Founder & CTO)
Michael Ferneman (Co-Founder & COO)

GILLIS GILKERSON INC.
212 W Main St Ste 305, Salisbury, MD 21801
Tel.: (410) 749-4821
Web Site:
  http://www.gillisgilkerson.com
Rev.: $37,065,760
Emp.: 55
Industrial Buildings & Warehouses
N.A.I.C.S.: 236220
Palmer Gillis (CEO)
Don Murray (Project Mgr)
Mike Truitt (Project Mgr)

GILLISS & GILLISS INC.
5819 United States Hwy 19, New Port Richey, FL 34652
Tel.: (727) 815-9611
Web Site: http://www.friendlykia.com
Rev.: $23,000,000
Emp.: 175
Automobiles, New & Used
N.A.I.C.S.: 441110
John Gilliss (Pres)

GILLMAN COMPANIES
10595 W Sam Houston Pkwy S, Houston, TX 77099
Tel.: (713) 776-7000
Web Site:
  http://www.gillmanauto.com
Year Founded: 1938
Rev.: $215,594,595
Emp.: 1,000
Automobiles, New & Used
N.A.I.C.S.: 441110
Stacey Gillman Wimbish (Pres)
Patrick York (COO)
Jason Gillman (Exec VP)

Subsidiaries:

Gillco Finance Company (1)
10595 W Sam Houston Pkwy S, Houston, TX 77099
Tel.: (713) 776-7079
Web Site: http://www.gillmanauto.com
Sales Range: Less than $1 Million
Emp.: 2
Financing Of Dealers By Motor Vehicle Manufacturers Organ.
N.A.I.C.S.: 522299
Ramsey H. Gillman (Pres)

Gillman Chrysler Jeep Dodge Ram (1)
10585 W Sam Houston Pkwy S, Houston, TX 77099
Tel.: (713) 776-4900
Web Site:
  http://www.gillmanchryslerjeepdodge.com
Sales Range: $10-24.9 Million
Car Dealership
N.A.I.C.S.: 441110
Matt Chapman (Gen Mgr)

Gillman Imports North Inc. (1)
18010 N Fwy, Houston, TX 77090
Tel.: (281) 821-2600
Web Site: http://www.gillmanauto.com
Sales Range: $10-24.9 Million
Emp.: 45
Automobiles, New & Used
N.A.I.C.S.: 441110
Stacey Gillman (CEO)

Gillman North Inc. (1)
18010 N Freeway, Houston, TX 77090
Tel.: (281) 821-1100
Web Site: http://www.gillmanacura.com
Rev.: $3,983,152
Emp.: 50
Automobiles, New & Used
N.A.I.C.S.: 441110
Stacey Gillman (Pres)

GILMAN BUILDING PRODUCTS COMPANY

581705 White Oak Rd, Yulee, FL 32097-2145
Tel.: (904) 548-1050   NH
Sales Range: $75-99.9 Million
Emp.: 50
Mfr of Lumber
N.A.I.C.S.: 551112
Victor Garrett (Pres)
Dominick Sorrentino (CFO)
Philip Skoropat (VP-Sls)

GILMAN CHEESE CORPORA-TION
300 S Riverside Dr, Gilman, WI 54433
Tel.: (715) 447-8241
Web Site:
  https://www.gilmancheese.com
Rev.: $13,500,000
Emp.: 71
Processed Cheese Mfr
N.A.I.C.S.: 311513
Thomas P. Hand (Pres & CEO)

GILMAN YACHT SALES, INC.
203 6th St, West Palm Beach, FL 33401-4003
Tel.: (561) 626-1790
Web Site:
  http://www.gilmanyachts.com
Year Founded: 1968
Sales Range: $50-74.9 Million
Emp.: 16
Seller of Yachts
N.A.I.C.S.: 441222
David Gilman (Pres)
Don Gilman (VP & Broker)

Subsidiaries:

Gilman Yachts of Fort Lauderdale, Inc.   (1)
1510 SE 17th St Ste 300, Fort Lauderdale, FL 33316-1737
Tel.: (954) 525-8112
Web Site: http://www.gilmanyachts.com
Sales Range: $10-24.9 Million
Emp.: 10
Builder & Brokerage of Luxury World Class Yachts
N.A.I.C.S.: 441222
Jeffrey W. Stanley (Owner)
Joe Majcherek (Partner)

GILMORE & ASSOCIATES INC.
65 E Butler Ave Ste 100, New Britain, PA 18901-5106
Tel.: (215) 345-4330
Web Site: https://www.gilmore-assoc.com
Year Founded: 1918
Sales Range: $1-9.9 Million
Full-Service Civil Engineering & Consulting
N.A.I.C.S.: 541330
Scott C. Muller (Pres)
Steven D. Gilmore (CEO)
Russell S. Dunlevy (Sr Exec VP)
Craig D. Kennard (COO)
Richard J. DeCarolis (CFO)

Subsidiaries:

Gilmore & Associates, Inc.   (1)
5100 Tilghman St Suite 150, Allentown, PA 18104
Tel.: (610) 366-8064
Web Site: http://www.gilmore-assoc.com
Emp.: 20
Municipal & Civil Engineering
N.A.I.C.S.: 237990
Scott C. Muller (Exec VP)

GILMORE & QUINN INDUS-TRIES INC.
265 Ballard Rd, Middletown, NY 10941-3034
Tel.: (201) 487-4492   NJ
Year Founded: 1990
Sales Range: $75-99.9 Million

Emp.: 20
Belt Backings, Beltings & Plastic Extrusions
N.A.I.C.S.: 316110
Robert Siegel (Pres)
Joshua Gat (VP & Gen Mgr)

GILO VENTURES, LLC
61 E Main St Ste A, Los Gatos, CA 95301
Tel.: (408) 399-7590
Rev.: $1,200,000,000
Emp.: 10
Privater Equity Firm
N.A.I.C.S.: 523999
Gil Peretz (CEO)
Robert Graifman (CFO)
Avraham Fischer (Chm)
Stephen Phillip Pezzola (Gen Counsel)
Ilan Judkiewicz (Mng Dir)
Emiko Higashi (Co-Founder)

Subsidiaries:

Javelin Innovations Inc.   (1)
6225 The Corners Pkwy Ste 100, Norcross, GA 30092
Tel.: (303) 792-2030
Sales Range: $1-9.9 Million
Wireless Broadband Access Systems Mfr
N.A.I.C.S.: 334290

Subsidiary (Non-US):

Vyyo Ltd.   (2)
4 Ha'Negev Street, PO Box 197, 70100, Lod, Israel
Tel.: (972) 39769888
Emp.: 7
Wireless Broadband Access Systems Research & Development
N.A.I.C.S.: 517810
Gabi Magnizi (Mng Dir)

GILROY CHEVROLET CADIL-LAC INC.
6720 Automall Ct, Gilroy, CA 95020
Tel.: (408) 842-9301
Web Site: http://www.gilroychevy.com
Sales Range: $10-24.9 Million
Emp.: 50
Car Dealership Owner & Operator
N.A.I.C.S.: 441110

GILROY HONDA, INC.
6700 Chestnut St, Gilroy, CA 95020
Tel.: (408) 848-3000
Web Site:
  http://www.gilroyhonda.com
Sales Range: $10-24.9 Million
Emp.: 45
Car Whslr
N.A.I.C.S.: 441110
Jim Hammer (Gen Mgr-Sls)

GILSBAR INC.
2100 Covington Ctr, Covington, LA 70433
Tel.: (985) 892-3520
Web Site: http://www.gilsbar.com
Year Founded: 1959
Sales Range: $100-124.9 Million
Emp.: 325
Insurance Information & Consulting Services
N.A.I.C.S.: 524298
Doug Layman (Pres-Health & Life)
Kim Randazzo (VP-Health & Life & Sr Dir-Client Svcs)
Judy Schott (COO & VP)
Paul Johnson (VP-Health & Life & Sr Dir-Population Health Mgmt)
Ryan Haun (Pres & CEO)

Subsidiaries:

MedCom Care Management, Inc.   (1)
2100 Covington Ctr, Covington, LA 70433   (100%)

Tel.: (985) 892-3520
Web Site: http://www.gilsbar.com
Sales Range: $50-74.9 Million
Emp.: 250
Developer of Cost Containment Programs for Employer Sponsored Plans Marketed by Gilsbar, Inc.
N.A.I.C.S.: 524298

GILSON COMPANY, INC.
7975 N Central Dr, Lewis Center, OH 43035
Tel.: (740) 548-7298
Web Site:
  https://www.globalgilson.com
Year Founded: 1939
Rev.: $13,000,000
Emp.: 50
Testing Equipment Mfr & Distr
N.A.I.C.S.: 423490
Trent R. Smith (Pres & CEO)

GILSON ENGINEERING SALES, INC.
535 Rochester Rd, Pittsburgh, PA 15237
Tel.: (412) 369-0100   PA
Web Site: http://www.gilsoneng.com
Year Founded: 1964
Sales Range: $10-24.9 Million
Emp.: 30
Manufactures' Representative for Flow, Pressure, Level, Analytical, Data Acquisition & Automation Products
N.A.I.C.S.: 423610
Dolly McDonald (Office Mgr)

GILSON, INC.
3000 Parmenter St, Middleton, WI 53562-0027
Tel.: (608) 836-1551
Web Site: https://www.gilson.com
Year Founded: 1947
Sales Range: $25-49.9 Million
Emp.: 340
Analytical Instrument Mfr
N.A.I.C.S.: 334516
Kevin Barrett (Sr VP-Strategic Bus Dev)
Nicolas Paris (CEO)

GILSTER-MARY LEE CORPO-RATION
1037 State St, Chester, IL 62233
Tel.: (618) 826-2361   IL
Web Site:
  https://www.gilstermarylee.com
Year Founded: 1895
Sales Range: $650-699.9 Million
Emp.: 4,000
Private Label & Contract Mfr of Cake Mixes, Dry Drink Mixes, Dry Cereals, Macaroni, Potato Products, Popcorn & Pasta
N.A.I.C.S.: 311824

Subsidiaries:

Gilster-Mary Lee Corporation   (1)
305 E Washington St, Momence, IL 60954-1615
Tel.: (618) 826-2361
Web Site: http://www.gilstermarylee.com
Sales Range: $25-49.9 Million
Emp.: 80
Chocolate Products, Including Hot Cocoa Mixes, Chocolate Syrup & Chocolate Drink Mixes Mfr
N.A.I.C.S.: 311999
Brian Van Hoveln (Plant Mgr)

Mary Lee Packaging Corporation   (1)
615 Old Saint Marys Rd, Perryville, MO 63775
Tel.: (573) 547-1705
Sales Range: $350-399.9 Million
Emp.: 500
Cereal Breakfast Foods
N.A.I.C.S.: 311230

GILVIN-TERRILL INC.
PO Box 9027, Amarillo, TX 79105-9027
Tel.: (806) 944-5200   TX
Year Founded: 1953
Sales Range: $75-99.9 Million
Emp.: 52
Heavy Highway Construction; Aggregate & Hot Mix Production
N.A.I.C.S.: 237310
F.C. Chow (Pres)

Subsidiaries:

Safety Signs Inc.   (1)
4401 Raes Rd, Amarillo, TX 79111 (100%)
Tel.: (806) 335-1114
Sales Range: $10-24.9 Million
Emp.: 4
Mfr of Road Construction Signs
N.A.I.C.S.: 339950

GIMMAL GROUP, INC.
10505 Town & Country Way Ste 79788, Houston, TX 77024
Tel.: (713) 586-6500   TX
Web Site: https://www.gimmal.com
Year Founded: 2002
Sales Range: $10-24.9 Million
Emp.: 100
Holding Company; Information, Records & Enterprise Management Software Publisher & Services
N.A.I.C.S.: 551112
Michael R. Alsup (Sr VP)
Cynthia Wood (Sr VP-Demand Generation)
Nancy Bratic (Gen Counsel)
Art Bellis (VP-Sls & Alliances)
Brad Teed (CTO)
Brian McLaurin (Chief Revenue Officer)
Chris Caplinger (Co-CTO)
Mark Johnson (Pres)

Subsidiaries:

Gimmal LLC   (1)
24 Greenway Plz Ste 1000, Houston, TX 77046
Tel.: (713) 586-6500
Web Site: http://www.gimmal.com
Information, Records & Enterprise Management Software Publisher & Services
N.A.I.C.S.: 513210
Cynthia Wood (Sr VP-Sls & Mktg)
Danae Stephenson (VP-Admin)
K. David Quackenbush (CEO)
Michael R. Alsup (Sr VP)
Brad Teed (CTO)
Eric Anderson (VP-ERP-Link Products)
Art Bellis (VP-Sls & Alliances)
Nancy Bratic (Gen Counsel)
Thor Schueler (VP-Product Delivery)
John Flaherty (VP-Pro Svcs)
Diana Massaro (VP-Mktg & Product Mgmt)
Jeff Skiba (VP-Pro Svcs)
Dwayne Sablatura (VP-Pro Svcs)
Brian K. McLaurin (Chief Revenue Officer)

GINGER BAY SALON GROUP, LTD.
439 S Kirkwood Rd, Saint Louis, MO 63122
Tel.: (314) 966-0655   MO
Web Site: http://www.gingerbay.com
Year Founded: 1991
Rev.: $4,300,000
Emp.: 62
Beauty Salon & Spa
N.A.I.C.S.: 812112
Laura A. Ortmann (Co-Founder & CEO)

GINKGO RESIDENTIAL TRUST INC.
1023 W Morehead St Ste 301, Charlotte, NC 28208
Tel.: (704) 944-0100   MD
Web Site: http://www.ginkgores.com
Sales Range: $50-74.9 Million

Ginkgo Residential Trust Inc.—(Continued)

Emp.: 422
Real Estate Investment Services
N.A.I.C.S.: 525990
Philip S. Payne *(CEO & Principal)*
D. Scott Wilkerson *(COO)*
Eric S. Rohm *(COO & Principal)*
Phillip S. Foley *(Dir-Project Svc)*

GINN CHEVROLET

8153 Access Rd NW, Covington, GA
30014-2099
Tel.: (770) 786-3421
Web Site: http://www.ginnchevy.com
Sales Range: $10-24.9 Million
Emp.: 80
New Car Whslr
N.A.I.C.S.: 441110
Tim Cartledge *(Gen Mgr)*
Rusty Angel *(Coord-Bodyshop Parts)*

GINO MORENA ENTER-PRISES, LLC

PO Box 191, South San Francisco,
CA 94083
Tel.: (650) 871-0363
Web Site:
http://www.ginomorena.com
Sales Range: $25-49.9 Million
Emp.: 1,700
Barber Shops & Hair Salons
N.A.I.C.S.: 812111
Rex Moreno *(Pres)*
Chantanee Saejao *(Coord-Mktg)*
Thomas Hebert *(Mgr-Ops)*

GINOP SALES INC.

11274 M 68 W, Alanson, MI 49706
Tel.: (231) 548-2272   MI
Web Site:
https://www.ginopsales.com
Year Founded: 1959
Sales Range: $10-24.9 Million
Emp.: 30
Sales of Tractors & Farm Equipment
Supplies
N.A.I.C.S.: 459999
Lawrence Ginop *(Pres)*
Cindy Bowen *(Treas & Sec)*
Jim Thompson *(Mgr-Helman)*

GINSBERG'S INSTITUTIONAL FOODS, INC.

29 Ginsbergs Ln, Hudson, NY 12534
Tel.: (518) 828-4004   NY
Web Site: https://www.ginsbergs.com
Year Founded: 1909
Sales Range: $50-74.9 Million
Emp.: 170
Distr of Institutional Food Supplies
N.A.I.C.S.: 424410
David Ginsberg *(Pres & CEO)*
Suzanne Rajczi *(COO)*
Tracy Cantele *(Mgr-Mktg)*

GINSBURG DEVELOPMENT CORP.

100 Summit Lake Dr, Valhalla, NY
10595
Tel.: (914) 747-3600
Web Site: http://www.gdc-homes.com
Year Founded: 1985
Sales Range: $10-24.9 Million
Emp.: 50
Provider of Property Development
Services
N.A.I.C.S.: 237210
Martin Ginsburg *(Founder)*

Subsidiaries:

SMG Associates   (1)
100 Summit Lake Dr, Valhalla, NY 10595
Tel.: (914) 747-3600
Sales Range: $10-24.9 Million
Emp.: 30
Provider of Property Development Services

N.A.I.C.S.: 237210

GINSEY INDUSTRIES, INC.

2078 Ctr Sq Rd, Swedesboro, NJ
08031
Tel.: (856) 933-1300
Web Site: http://www.ginsey.com
Year Founded: 1952
Sales Range: $10-24.9 Million
Emp.: 135
Wood Products Mfr
N.A.I.C.S.: 321999
Herb Briggs *(CEO)*

GINZAMARKETS, INC.

25 Taylor St, San Francisco, CA
94102
Tel.: (650) 421-3390
Web Site:
http://www.ginzametrics.com
Sales Range: $1-9.9 Million
Search Engine Optimization Services
N.A.I.C.S.: 541519
Ray Grieselhuber *(Founder & CEO)*
Erin Robbins O'Brien *(COO)*

GIOIA SAILS INC.

1951 Rutgers University Blvd, Lake-
wood, NJ 08701
Tel.: (732) 901-6770
Web Site: https://www.gioiasails.com
Year Founded: 1966
Sales Range: $10-24.9 Million
Emp.: 45
Canvas & Related Product Mills
N.A.I.C.S.: 314910
Donald Gioia *(Pres)*

GIORDANO CONSTRUCTION CO., INC.

3018 Nashua Rd, New Castle, PA
16105
Tel.: (724) 652-5055
Web Site: https://www.giordano-
cc.com
Year Founded: 1974
Sales Range: $10-24.9 Million
Emp.: 30
Commercial Contracting & Construc-
tion Services
N.A.I.C.S.: 236220
Tom Giordano *(VP)*

GIORDANO'S ENTERPRISES, INC.

308 W Randolph St, Chicago, IL
60606-1710
Tel.: (312) 641-6500
Web Site: http://www.giordanos.com
Year Founded: 1974
Sales Range: $75-99.9 Million
Emp.: 1,000
Restaurant
N.A.I.C.S.: 722513

GIORGI BROS

211 Baden Ave, South San Fran-
cisco, CA 94080
Tel.: (650) 588-4621
Web Site: https://www.giorgibros.com
Sales Range: $10-24.9 Million
Emp.: 20
Furniture Retailer
N.A.I.C.S.: 449110
Robert Giorgi *(Chm)*

GIORGIO FOODS INC

Blandon Rd, Temple, PA 19560
Tel.: (610) 926-2139
Web Site:
http://www.giorgiofoods.com
Sales Range: $1-9.9 Million
Emp.: 300
Mushroom Processing Services
N.A.I.C.S.: 424480

Ron Hoffman *(Sr VP-Sls & Mktg-
FoodSvc & Industry)*
Dave Sensenig *(Dir-Retail Sls & Corp
Mktg)*
Dawn Fedorchak *(Mgr-Customer Svc
Dept)*
Lisa Hemker *(Reg Mgr-Sls)*
Bill Litvin *(Sr VP-Sls)*
Paul Tucker *(VP-School Food Svc
Sls & Mfg)*
Doug Stewart *(VP-Sls)*
Brian Loiseau *(Sr VP-Sls & Bus Dev)*

GIORGIO HEALTH & WEL-FARE PLAN

PO Box 96, Temple, PA 19560
Tel.: (610) 926-2139   PA
Year Founded: 1979
Sales Range: $10-24.9 Million
Health & Welfare Benefit Services
N.A.I.C.S.: 525120
Philip Impink *(CFO-Giorgio Foods)*

GIOVANNI FOOD COMPANY, INC.

8800 Sixty Rd, Baldwinsville, NY
13027
Tel.: (315) 457-2373   NY
Web Site:
https://www.giovannifoods.com
Year Founded: 1934
Sales Range: $10-24.9 Million
Emp.: 60
Mfr Tomato Based Products for Retail
& Foodservice Industries
N.A.I.C.S.: 311421
Mary Dement *(Pres)*
Timothy Budd *(Plant Mgr)*
Louis DeMent *(CEO)*

GIRARD FORD

450 W Thames St, Norwich, CT
06360
Tel.: (860) 800-6777
Web Site: https://www.girardford.com
Year Founded: 2007
Sales Range: $10-24.9 Million
Emp.: 50
Car Whslr
N.A.I.C.S.: 441110
Charles Antonino *(Treas & Sec)*
Alice Preston *(Coord-Customer Care)*

GIRARD WOOD PRODUCTS INC.

802 E Main, Puyallup, WA 98372
Tel.: (253) 845-0505
Web Site:
https://www.girardwoodproduct.com
Year Founded: 2002
Rev.: $10,348,676
Emp.: 34
Provider of Wood Products
N.A.I.C.S.: 321920
Dave Loden *(Mgr-Sls)*
David Comfort *(Controller)*
Anthony Hubbs *(Plant Mgr)*
Dave Loden *(Mgr-Sls)*

GIRKIN DEVELOPMENT, LLC

810 Morgantown Rd, Bowling Green,
KY 42102-9011
Tel.: (270) 781-3378   KY
Web Site: https://www.minitmart.com
Year Founded: 1969
Sales Range: $25-49.9 Million
Emp.: 400
Property Development Services
N.A.I.C.S.: 237210
Fred Higgins *(Pres & CEO)*

GIS SURVEYORS, INC.

12120 Tech Center Dr Ste D, Poway,
CA 92064
Tel.: (858) 679-1732

Web Site:
http://www.gissurveyors.com
Year Founded: 2013
Sales Range: $1-9.9 Million
Emp.: 38
Engineeering Services
N.A.I.C.S.: 541330
Paul Loska *(CEO)*
Matthew Van Eck *(CTO)*

GIS WORKSHOP, LLC

4949 NW 1st St Ste 1, Lincoln, NE
68521
Tel.: (402) 436-2150   DE
Web Site: http://www.gworks.com
Year Founded: 1999
Application Development & GIS Data
Services
N.A.I.C.S.: 541511
Joseph Heieck *(CEO)*
Janelle Heuton *(COO)*
Geneie Andrews *(Sr Acct Exec)*
Derek Waskel *(Engr)*
Leslie Aldag *(Acct Mgr)*

GISH OIL CO.

1329 W Hill Ave, Valdosta, GA 31601
Tel.: (229) 242-8191
Sales Range: $10-24.9 Million
Emp.: 13
Wholesale Distributor of Petroleum
Products
N.A.I.C.S.: 424710
Mark Gish *(Pres)*

GISH, SHERWOOD & FRIENDS, INC.

209 10th Ave S Ste 222, Nashville,
TN 37203
Tel.: (615) 385-1100
Web Site: https://www.gsandf.com
Year Founded: 1978
Rev.: $52,000,000
Emp.: 115
Advetising Agency
N.A.I.C.S.: 541810
Roland Gibbons *(Chief Creative Offi-
cer & Exec VP)*
Laramey Lawson *(Sr VP & Dir-Media)*
Gregg Boling *(Pres)*
Chad Grant *(Dir-Information Technol-
ogy)*
Joe Dougherty *(Mgr-Quality Assur-
ance)*
Dana Haynes *(VP-Accounting)*
Elena Griffo *(Acct Coord-PR)*
Emilie Guthrie *(Dir-Account Manage-
ment & VP)*
Evanne Lindley *(Dir-Interactive Prod-
ucts & Svcs)*

GIST & ERDMANN, INC.

1978 The Alameda, San Jose, CA
95126
Tel.: (408) 551-0290
Year Founded: 1988
Sales Range: $10-24.9 Million
Emp.: 10
High Technology, Information Tech-
nology
N.A.I.C.S.: 541810
Gerald Gist *(Partner)*

GIST COMMUNICATIONS, INC.

84 Wooster St Ste 602, New York,
NY 10012-4325
Tel.: (212) 965-1999
Year Founded: 1996
Sales Range: $10-24.9 Million
Emp.: 45
Software Applications for Digital Tele-
vision
N.A.I.C.S.: 517810
Dave Ekhaus *(Chief Software Archi-
tect)*

GIST, INC.
4385 Pleasant Valley Rd, Placerville, CA 95667
Tel.: (530) 644-8000   CA
Web Site:
  https://www.gistsilversmiths.com
Year Founded: 1967
Sales Range: $10-24.9 Million
Emp.: 80
Silver & Gold Belt Buckles, Jewelry & Equestrian Accessories Mfr
N.A.I.C.S.: 339993
Jennifer Folsom *(VP-Mktg & Bus Dev)*
Wende Heinen *(Dir-Sls & Media Comm)*

GIT-N-GO CONVENIENCE STORES
2716 Indianola Ave, Des Moines, IA 50315
Tel.: (515) 288-8565
Sales Range: $25-49.9 Million
Emp.: 200
Convenience Store
N.A.I.C.S.: 445131
Dennis Flora *(Pres)*

GITTINGS PROTECTIVE SECURITY, INC.
104 N Center St, Ebensburg, PA 15931
Web Site:
  https://www.gittingssecurity.com
Year Founded: 1989
Sales Range: $1-9.9 Million
Emp.: 65
Full-Service Private Detective & Private Security Services
N.A.I.C.S.: 561612
Dean C. Gittings *(Founder)*

GIUFFRE
8904 5th Ave, Brooklyn, NY 11214
Tel.: (718) 748-5367
Web Site:
  http://www.giuffrehyundai.com
Sales Range: $10-24.9 Million
Emp.: 30
New Car Retailer
N.A.I.C.S.: 441110
Ignazio Giuffre *(VP)*
Greg Rossomando *(Mgr-Sls)*
Trudi Hinds *(Mgr-Internet)*

GIUFFRE BROS CRANES, INC.
6635 S 13th St, Milwaukee, WI 53221-5248
Tel.: (414) 764-9200
Web Site: https://www.giuffre.com
Year Founded: 1963
Sales Range: $10-24.9 Million
Emp.: 40
Mfr of Industrial Machinery & Equipment
N.A.I.C.S.: 423830

Subsidiaries:

Coast Crane Of Utah Inc.   (1)
1905 Fremont Dr, Salt Lake City, UT 84104
Tel.: (801) 973-7939
Web Site: http://www.giuffre.com
Sales Range: $10-24.9 Million
Emp.: 3
Industrial Machinery & Equipment Mfr
N.A.I.C.S.: 423830
Frank Giuffre *(Chm)*

GIUFFRE VOLVO INC.
1030 S Dirksen Pkwy, Springfield, IL 62703
Tel.: (217) 788-2400
Web Site:
  http://www.giuffrevolvo.com
Sales Range: $10-24.9 Million
Emp.: 36
New Car Dealers

N.A.I.C.S.: 441110
Roger C. Sables *(Pres)*

GIULIANI PARTNERS LLC
200 Park Ave, New York, NY 10166
Tel.: (212) 931-7300
Web Site:
  http://www.giulianipartners.com
Year Founded: 2002
Sales Range: $25-49.9 Million
Emp.: 55
Management Consulting Services
N.A.I.C.S.: 541611
Rudolph W. Giuliani *(Chm & CEO)*

GIULIANO'S DELICATESSEN & BAKERY
1117 E Walnut St, Carson, CA 90746
Tel.: (310) 537-7700   CA
Web Site: http://www.giulianos.com
Year Founded: 1974
Rev.: $11,600,000
Emp.: 100
Delicatessen & Wholesale Bakery
N.A.I.C.S.: 311811
Nancy Ritmire Giuliano *(CEO)*

GIULIANO-PAGANO CORPORATION
1117 E Walnut St, Carson, CA 90746-1317
Tel.: (310) 537-7700
Web Site: http://www.giulianos.com
Sales Range: $10-24.9 Million
Emp.: 100
Bakery Products Mfr
N.A.I.C.S.: 311812
Gregory Ritmire *(Owner)*
Glenn Martin *(Mgr)*

GIUMARRA VINEYARDS CORPORATION
11220 Edison Hwy, Bakersfield, CA 93307
Tel.: (661) 395-7000   CA
Web Site:
  https://www.giumarravineyards.com
Year Founded: 1939
Grower, Distr & Marketer of Wines
N.A.I.C.S.: 111332
Mike Rodgers *(Dir-East Coast Operations)*

GIUNTA BROTHERS INC.
3715 31st Ave, Astoria, NY 11103
Tel.: (516) 256-3100
Sales Range: $10-24.9 Million
Emp.: 62
Independent Supermarket
N.A.I.C.S.: 445110
John Giunta *(Treas)*

GIUSTO SPECIALTY FOODS INC.
344 Littlefield Ave, South San Francisco, CA 94080
Tel.: (650) 873-6566
Web Site: https://www.giustos.com
Rev.: $10,000,000
Emp.: 24
Flour Mills, Cereal (Except Rice)
N.A.I.C.S.: 311211
Craig Moore *(Pres)*

GIVE KIDS THE WORLD, INC.
210 S Bass Rd, Kissimmee, FL 34746
Tel.: (407) 396-1114   FL
Web Site: https://www.gktw.org
Year Founded: 1986
Sales Range: $25-49.9 Million
Emp.: 176
Child Care Services
N.A.I.C.S.: 624110
Amy Racicot *(CFO)*
Jeff Vahle *(Chm)*

Pamela Landwirth *(Pres & CEO)*
Kathleen Tagle *(Chief Strategy Officer)*
Henri Landwirth *(Founder)*
Christopher Moyson *(VP-IT)*
Caroline Schumacher *(VP-Ops)*

GIVE SOMETHING BACK LLC
7730 Pabe Ln, Oakland, CA 94621
Tel.: (510) 635-5500
Web Site:
  http://www.givesomethingback.com
Rev.: $20,380,965
Emp.: 50
Office Forms & Supplies
N.A.I.C.S.: 424120
Mike Hannigan *(Founder & Partner)*
Sean Marx *(CEO & Partner)*
Kelly Dun *(Exec Dir-Mid Atlantic)*

GIVE2ASIA
340 Pine St Ste 501, San Francisco, CA 94104
Tel.: (415) 967-6300   CA
Web Site: http://www.give2asia.org
Year Founded: 2000
Sales Range: $25-49.9 Million
Grantmaking Services
N.A.I.C.S.: 813219
Birger Stamperdahl *(Pres & CEO)*
Ta-lin Hsu *(Chm)*

GIZA TECHNOLOGIES INC.
600 Meadowlands Pkwy Ste 22B, Secaucus, NJ 07094
Tel.: (201) 867-2777
Web Site: https://www.gizatech.com
Sales Range: $10-24.9 Million
Emp.: 12
Electronic Parts & Equipment
N.A.I.C.S.: 423690
Zeki Bilmen *(Owner)*

GJ&L INC.
2804 Wylds Rd Ext, Augusta, GA 30909
Tel.: (706) 737-9191
Web Site:
  http://www.borderequipment.com
Sales Range: $10-24.9 Million
Emp.: 8
Tractors & Farm Equipment Lease & Sales
N.A.I.C.S.: 423820
Brian Rich *(Mgr-Atlanta)*
Dwayne Collins *(Mgr-Augusta)*
Johnny Urrutia *(Mgr-Savannah)*
Bud Lawrence *(Mgr-Svc-Augusta)*
Scott Misico *(Mgr-Svc-Atlanta)*

GJOVIK CHEVROLET BUICK PONTIAC GMC, INC.
2780 E Route 34, Sandwich, IL 60548-1904
Tel.: (815) 786-2177
Web Site: http://www.gjovikauto.com
Year Founded: 1968
Sales Range: $10-24.9 Million
Emp.: 40
New Car Whslr
N.A.I.C.S.: 441110
Bruce Snyder *(Mgr-Used Car)*

GJOVIK FORD-MERCURY, INC.
2600 US Route 34 E, Sandwich, IL 60548-1911
Tel.: (630) 552-8058
Web Site: http://www.gjovikford.com
Sales Range: $25-49.9 Million
Emp.: 50
Car Whslr
N.A.I.C.S.: 441110
Scott Gjovik *(Pres)*

GK ENTERPRISES, INC.

26000 Whiting Way, Monee, IL 60449-8060
Tel.: (708) 596-6600   IL
Web Site:
  http://www.whitingcorp.com
Year Founded: 1988
Sales Range: $50-74.9 Million
Emp.: 150
Hoists, Cranes & Monorails Mfr
N.A.I.C.S.: 551112
Jeffrey L. Kahn *(Pres)*

Subsidiaries:

Swenson Technology, Inc.   (1)
26000 S Whiting Way, Monee, IL 60449-8060
Tel.: (708) 587-2300
Web Site:
  http://www.swensontechnology.com
Sales Range: $25-49.9 Million
Emp.: 25
Designing Equipments For Chemical Industries
N.A.I.C.S.: 333248
Timothy Nordahl *(Pres)*

Whiting Corporation   (1)
26000 Whiting Way, Monee, IL 60449-8060
Tel.: (708) 587-2000
Web Site: http://www.whitingcorp.com
Sales Range: $25-49.9 Million
Emp.: 145
Overhead Cranes, Foundry Equipment & Rail Transportation Maintenance Equipment Mfr
N.A.I.C.S.: 333248
Jeffrey L. Kahn *(Pres)*
Ed Slota *(Product Mgr)*
Perry Pabich *(Sr VP)*

Holding (Non-US):

Whiting Equipment Canada, Inc.   (2)
350 Alexander St, Welland, L3B 2R3, ON, Canada   (100%)
Tel.: (905) 732-7585
Web Site: https://www.whiting.ca
Sales Range: $25-49.9 Million
Emp.: 60
Heavy Industrial Equipment Designer & Mfr
N.A.I.C.S.: 333248
Nick Sestili *(CFO & Treas)*

Subsidiary (Domestic):

Whiting Equipment Services Co. Ltd.   (3)
350 Alexander Street, Welland, L3B 2R3, ON, Canada
Tel.: (905) 732-7585
Web Site: http://www.whiting.ca
Sales Range: $10-24.9 Million
Emp.: 50
Maintenance & Inspection Services for Overhead Traveling Cranes
N.A.I.C.S.: 811310
Rudi Kroeker *(Pres)*

Subsidiary (Domestic):

Whiting Services Inc.   (2)
26000 Whiting Way, Monee, IL 60449-8060
Tel.: (708) 587-2230
Web Site: http://www.whiting-serv.com
Sales Range: $1-9.9 Million
Emp.: 7
Maintenance & Inspection Services for Overhead Traveling Cranes
N.A.I.C.S.: 811310
Jeffrey L. Kahn *(Pres)*
Warren Jones *(Mgr-Midwest Reg)*

GK PACKAGING INC.
7680 Commerce Pl, Plain City, OH 43064-9222
Tel.: (614) 873-3900
Web Site:
  https://www.gkpackaging.com
Sales Range: $25-49.9 Million
Emp.: 27
Containers; Paper & Disposable Plastic
N.A.I.C.S.: 424130
Eugene Kuzma *(Pres)*
Robert Kellerman *(CFO)*

GK Packaging Inc.—(Continued)

Tristan Herstol *(Engr-Design)*
Jason Blann *(Mgr-Warehouse)*
Ted Niswonger *(Mgr-Ops)*

GKI INCORPORATED

6204 Factory Rd, Crystal Lake, IL 60014
Tel.: (815) 459-2330
Web Site: http://www.gkitool.com
Year Founded: 1971
Rev.: $6,100,000
Emp.: 50
Industrial Machinery & Equipment Mfr
N.A.I.C.S.: 332710
Kevin Began *(Mgr-Sls)*
Jackie Jesse *(Office Mgr)*
Olaf Klutke *(Pres)*
Eric Klutke *(VP)*

GKKWORKS CONSTRUCTION SERVICES, INC

2355 Main St Ste 220, Irvine, CA 92614
Tel.: (949) 250-1500
Web Site: http://www.gkkworks.com
Year Founded: 1991
Sales Range: $125-149.9 Million
Emp.: 312
Architectural Services
N.A.I.C.S.: 541310
Praful Kulkarni *(Pres & CEO)*
Vanann Allan *(Project Dir-Construction Svcs)*
Stephen R. Dunn *(Dir-Preconstruction Svcs)*
Mahmoud Mehrabian *(Dir-Design)*
Ncarb Faia *(Principal)*
Sam Porter *(CFO)*

GKV COMMUNICATIONS

1500 Whetstone Way 4th Fl, Baltimore, MD 21230
Tel.: (410) 539-5400
Web Site: https://www.gkv.com
Year Founded: 1981
Rev.: $150,000,000
Emp.: 85
N.A.I.C.S.: 541810
Roger L. Gray *(CEO & Partner)*
Jeffrey I. Millman *(Chief Creative Officer & Partner)*
Kevin Kempske *(Partner & Exec VP-PR & Grassroots Outreach)*
Dan Collins *(Partner & Sr VP-Strategic Plng & Res)*
Cathy Kowalewski *(CFO, Partner & VP)*
Daniel Robinson *(Sr VP & Dir-Media)*
Dave Broscious *(Partner & Assoc Dir-Creative)*
Garry Raim *(Partner)*
David Blum *(Sr VP & Dir-Acct Mgmt)*
Andrew Robinson *(Acct Supvr)*
Mike Lugat *(Asst Acct Exec)*
Katie Linder *(Asst Acct Exec)*
Amelia Miller *(Acct Exec)*
Julia D'Esterre *(Asst Acct Exec-Grassroots & Outreach Dept)*
Stacey Wynia *(VP & Dir-PR & Social Media)*
Courtney Dick *(Coord-Digital Project)*
Alexei Yukna *(Chief Digital Officer, Partner & Sr VP)*
Mark Rosica *(Partner & Dir-Creative)*

GL GROUP, INC.

1230 Macklind Ave, Saint Louis, MO 63110
Web Site:
 https://www.goodluckgroup.com
Year Founded: 1974
Sales Range: $50-74.9 Million
Emp.: 194

Holding Company Operates Four Separate Children's Book Publisher
N.A.I.C.S.: 551112
Gary Jaffe *(CEO)*
Mark Rygelski *(CFO)*
Greg Bonebrake *(Dir-IT)*

Subsidiaries:

The Booksource Inc.   (1)
1230 Macklind Ave, Saint Louis, MO 63110-1432
Tel.: (314) 647-0600
Web Site: http://www.booksource.com
Sales Range: $25-49.9 Million
Emp.: 60
Retailer of Books, Periodicals & Newspapers
N.A.I.C.S.: 424920
Sanford Jaffe *(Owner)*
Neil Jaffe *(Pres-Educational Div)*
Mark Rygelski *(CFO)*

Subsidiary (Domestic):

San Val Inc.   (2)
1230 Macklind Ave, Saint Louis, MO 63110-1432
Tel.: (314) 644-2622
Sales Range: $10-24.9 Million
Emp.: 4
Bookbinding & Related Work
N.A.I.C.S.: 323120
Sanford Jaffe *(Pres)*

The Peaceable Kingdom Press, Inc.   (1)
950 Gilman St, Berkeley, CA 94710
Tel.: (510) 558-2051
Web Site: http://www.pkpress.com
Sales Range: $1-9.9 Million
Emp.: 20
Greeting Cards
N.A.I.C.S.: 513191

GL HOMES OF FLORIDA CORP.

1600 S Corp Pkwy, Sunrise, FL 33323
Tel.: (954) 753-1730
Web Site: http://www.glhomes.com
Year Founded: 1976
Sales Range: $300-349.9 Million
Emp.: 280
Residential Construction
N.A.I.C.S.: 236115
Jill DiDonna *(Sr VP-Sls & Mktg)*
Alan Gremillion *(Mgr-Contracts)*
Howard Langshaw *(CIO)*
Ed Rodriguez *(Project Mgr)*
Jason Smith *(Mgr-Contracts)*
Julie Boulos *(Dir-Mktg)*
Robert Carr *(Mgr-Construction)*
Tambra Wolfe *(VP & Project Mgr)*
Theresa Fowler *(VP & Project Mgr)*
Janice Cruz *(Asst Controller)*
Mike Lintner *(Dir-Construction)*
Paul Vonderheide *(Dir-Construction)*
Kevin Homer *(Mgr-Contracts)*
Brandy Granacki *(Mgr-Mktg)*
Cindy Penn *(Mgr-Pur)*
Glenn Ryals *(VP)*
Maria Menendez *(CFO)*
Celine Odelein *(Coord-Options)*
Joe McKeon *(Dir-Construction)*
Oliver Isaac *(Mgr-Contracts)*
Tom Gillan *(VP-Contracts)*

GLABMAN FURNITURE INC.

10984 Santa Monica Blvd, Los Angeles, CA 90061
Tel.: (310) 478-9700
Web Site: http://www.glabman.com
Rev.: $11,600,000
Emp.: 45
Furniture Retailer
N.A.I.C.S.: 449110
Kathy Akins *(Mgr-Admin)*

GLACIAL PLAINS COOPERATIVE

543 Van Norman Ave, Murdock, MN 56271
Tel.: (320) 875-2811   MN
Web Site:
 https://www.glacialplains.com
Year Founded: 1909
Sales Range: $10-24.9 Million
Emp.: 25
Agricultural Services
N.A.I.C.S.: 424510
Vicki DeBoer *(Controller)*
Tom Traen *(Gen Mgr)*
Joel James *(Mgr-Energy & Crop Insurance)*
Dustin Skogstad *(Mgr-Agronomy Ops)*
Randy Simmonds *(Mgr-Feed & Birdseed)*
Jason Walsh *(Mgr-Benson Agronomy)*
Jeff Syverson *(Mgr-Sunburg)*
Tim Molden *(Mgr-Benson Shop)*
Lyndon Skogstad *(Mgr-Agronomy)*
Jane Saulsbury *(Mgr-C-Store)*
James Johnson *(Mgr-Clontarf)*

GLACIER BAY TECHNOLOGY

2930 Faber St, Union City, CA 94587
Tel.: (510) 437-9100
Web Site:
 http://www.glacierbaytechnology.com
Year Founded: 1990
Sales Range: $10-24.9 Million
Emp.: 100
Refrigeration & Heating Mfr
N.A.I.C.S.: 333415
G. Alston *(Pres)*
Derek Kaufman *(CEO)*
Anthony Van Grol *(VP-Engrg)*
Dina Folkman *(VP-HR)*
Chris Coughlin *(VP-Govt Affairs)*
Bill Dewes *(VP-Fin)*
Charles Fetter *(VP-Sls & Gen Mgr-ClimaCab)*
Tom Gottlieb *(VP-Ops)*

GLACIER HILLS SENIOR LIVING COMMUNITY

1200 Earhart Rd, Ann Arbor, MI 48105
Tel.: (734) 769-6410   MI
Web Site: http://www.glacierhills.org
Year Founded: 1966
Sales Range: $25-49.9 Million
Emp.: 654
Elder Care Services
N.A.I.C.S.: 624120
Ray Rabidoux *(CEO)*
Larry Petroskey *(Sr VP-Bus Strategies)*
Margaret A. Reynolds *(Chm)*
Reed Vander Slik *(Pres)*

GLACIER RESTAURANT GROUP LLC

911 Wisconsin Ave Ste 103, Whitefish, MT 59937
Tel.: (406) 862-5245
Web Site: http://www.grgfood.com
Restaurant Services
N.A.I.C.S.: 722511
Brad Ridgeway *(Pres)*

Subsidiaries:

Max & Erma's Restaurants, Inc.   (1)
4849 Evanswood Dr, Columbus, OH 43229-6206
Tel.: (614) 431-5800
Web Site: http://www.maxandermas.com
Sales Range: $125-149.9 Million
Restaurant Operators
N.A.I.C.S.: 722511

GLACIER SALES INC.

316 N 3rd St, Yakima, WA 98901
Tel.: (509) 248-2866

Web Site:
 https://www.glaciersales.com
Rev.: $34,703,397
Emp.: 12
Packaged Frozen Goods
N.A.I.C.S.: 424420
Bruce Bacon *(Pres)*
Doug Kanyer *(Mng Partner)*

GLACIER VILLAGE SUPERMARKET

9103 Mendenhall Mall Rd, Juneau, AK 99801
Tel.: (907) 789-0173
Rev.: $14,500,000
Emp.: 80
Independent Supermarket
N.A.I.C.S.: 445110

GLACIER WORLDWIDE, INC.

10390 Santa Monica Blvd, Los Angeles, CA 90025
Tel.: (310) 359-6791   NV
Web Site: https://www.postads.com
Year Founded: 2013
Assets: $173,139
Liabilities: $111,247
Net Worth: $61,892
Earnings: ($79,075)
Emp.: 1
Fiscal Year-end: 12/31/21
Online Auction & Advertising Services
N.A.I.C.S.: 481112
Breyon Prescott *(Pres & CEO)*

GLADES ELECTRIC COOPERATIVE

1190 Hwy 27 E, Moore Haven, FL 33471
Tel.: (863) 946-0061
Web Site: http://www.gladesec.com
Rev.: $28,454,185
Emp.: 75
Electric Power Distr
N.A.I.C.S.: 221122
Tommy Todd *(CEO & Gen Mgr)*
Jeffery Brewington *(CEO)*

GLADIEUX TRADING AND MARKETING CO. LP

4133 New Haven Ave, Fort Wayne, IN 46803
Tel.: (260) 423-4477
Sales Range: $125-149.9 Million
Emp.: 50
Petroleum Marketing
N.A.I.C.S.: 424710
James Gladieux *(Partner)*
Steven Uebelhoer *(Pres)*

GLADIFI

13428 Maxella Ave #224, Marina Del Rey, CA 90292
Tel.: (310) 577-8255   DE
Web Site: http://www.gladifi.com
Year Founded: 1986
Sales Range: $1-9.9 Million
Emp.: 24
Advertising Management & Solution Services
N.A.I.C.S.: 541890
Daniel Nadeau *(VP-Software Engrg)*
Eli Rousso *(CTO & Exec VP)*
Jeffrey Baudo *(COO & Sr VP)*
Leslie Bernhard *(Pres & CEO)*
William Bernhard *(VP-Ops)*
Al Cortez *(VP-Tech Ops)*

Subsidiaries:

Edgil Associates, Inc.   (1)
6 Fortune Dr Ste 201, Billerica, MA 01821
Tel.: (978) 262-9799
Web Site: http://www.edgil.com
Software Applications Developer for Publishing Industry
N.A.I.C.S.: 561499

GLADSON INTERACTIVE, LLC
1973 Ohio St, Lisle, IL 60532
Tel.: (630) 435-2200
Web Site: http://www.gladson.com
Year Founded: 1971
Sales Range: $10-24.9 Million
Emp.: 100
Product Images, Product Content & Related Services
N.A.I.C.S.: 541890
Paul Salay *(CEO)*
Kevin Koontz *(VP-Fin & Admin)*
Greg Gates *(Sr VP-Product & Segment Sls)*
Isabel DuPont *(Sr VP-Product)*
Jason Howard *(Sr VP-Tech & B2c Market)*
Steve Swanson *(VP-Market Sls)*
Justin Hartanov *(Chief Comml Officer)*

GLADSTONE MANAGEMENT CORPORATION
1521 Westbranch Dr Ste 200,
McLean, VA 22102
Tel.: (703) 287-5800   DE
Web Site:
http://www.gladstonecompanies.com
Investment Fund Management Services
N.A.I.C.S.: 523940
David J. Gladstone *(Founder, Chm & CEO)*
Terry Lee Brubaker *(COO & Vice Chm)*
Paula Novara *(Head-HR, Facilities, Office Mgmt, and IT)*

Subsidiaries:

Gladstone Capital Corporation   (1)
1521 Westbranch Dr Ste 100, McLean, VA 22102
Tel.: (703) 287-5800
Web Site: https://www.gladstonecapital.com
Rev.: $86,434,000
Assets: $719,498,000
Liabilities: $310,803,000
Net Worth: $408,695,000
Earnings: $41,020,000
Fiscal Year-end: 09/30/2023
Closed-End Investment Fund
N.A.I.C.S.: 525990
David J. Gladstone *(Founder, Chm & CEO)*
Paula Novara *(Head-Resource Mgmt)*
Michael B. LiCalsi *(Gen Counsel & Sec)*
Jennifer Smith *(Chief Valuation Officer)*
Jack Dellafiora Jr. *(Chief Compliance Officer)*
Jay Beckhorn *(Asst Treas)*
Nicole Schaltenbrand *(CFO & Treas)*
Eric Maloy *(Mng Dir)*
Laura Gladstone *(Mng Dir)*
Mike McQuigg *(Sr Mng Dir & Exec VP)*
John Sateri *(Mng Dir)*
Andrew Ahlberg *(Mng Dir)*
Robert L. Marcotte *(Pres)*
Robert L. Marcotte *(Pres)*

Subsidiary (Domestic):

Kansas Cable Holdings, Inc.   (2)
6700 SW Topeka Blvd, Topeka, KS 66619
Tel.: (785) 862-1950
Investment Management Service
N.A.I.C.S.: 551112

Sunshine Media Group, Inc   (2)
12225 Morrison St, Valley Village, CA 91607
Tel.: (323) 465-6102
Web Site:
http://www.sunshinemediagroup.com
Online Marketing Services
N.A.I.C.S.: 512191

Gladstone Commercial
Corporation   (1)
1521 Westbranch Dr Ste 100, McLean, VA 22102
Tel.: (703) 287-5800
Web Site:
https://www.gladstonecommercial.com
Rev.: $147,584,000

Assets: $1,133,471,000
Liabilities: $809,164,000
Net Worth: $324,307,000
Earnings: ($7,738,000)
Emp.: 69
Fiscal Year-end: 12/31/2023
Real Estate Investment Trust
N.A.I.C.S.: 525990
David J. Gladstone *(Founder, Chm & CEO)*
Buzz Cooper *(Exec VP & Head-South Central Reg)*
Terry Lee Brubaker *(COO)*
Paula Novara *(Head-Resource Mgmt)*
Jay Beckhorn *(Treas)*
Ryan Carter *(Exec VP)*
E. J. Wislar *(Chief Investment Officer)*
Robert G. Cutlip *(Pres)*

Subsidiary (Domestic):

Gladstone Commercial Partners,
LLC   (2)
1521 Westbranch Dr Ste 200, McLean, VA 22102
Tel.: (703) 287-5893
Web Site:
http://gladstonecommercial.investor room.com
Emp.: 40
Real Estate Investment Trust
N.A.I.C.S.: 525990
David J. Gladstone *(Chm & CEO)*
Buzz Cooper *(Mng Dir)*
Mike Sodo *(CFO)*

Gladstone Investment
Corporation   (1)
1521 Westbranch Dr Ste 100, McLean, VA 22102
Tel.: (703) 287-5893
Web Site:
https://www.gladstoneinvestment.com
Rev.: $72,552,000
Assets: $740,412,000
Liabilities: $294,582,000
Net Worth: $445,830,000
Earnings: $14,990,000
Fiscal Year-end: 03/31/2022
Closed-End Investment Fund
N.A.I.C.S.: 525990
David J. Gladstone *(Chm & CEO)*
David A. R. Dullum *(Co-Pres)*
Paula Novara *(Head-Resource Mgmt)*
Michael B. LiCalsi *(Co-Pres, Gen Counsel & Sec)*
Jennifer Smith *(Chief Valuation Officer)*
Jack Dellafiora Jr. *(Chief Compliance Officer)*
Jay Beckhorn *(Asst Treas)*
David Glazer *(Mng Dir)*
Erika Highland *(Mng Dir)*
Christopher Lee *(Mng Dir)*

Holding (Domestic):

Edge Adhesives, Inc.   (2)
5117 Northeast Pkwy, Fort Worth, TX 76106
Tel.: (817) 232-2026
Web Site: http://www.edgeadhesives.com
Emp.: 95
Adhesive & Sealant Products Mfr
N.A.I.C.S.: 325520
Dave Burger *(Pres & CEO)*
Chris Arnoldt *(Dir-Tech & Dev)*
John Thomas *(VP-Ops)*

Subsidiary (Domestic):

PARR Technologies, LLC   (3)
24087 CR 6 E, Elkhart, IN 46514
Tel.: (574) 264-9614
Sales Range: $1-9.9 Million
Emp.: 20
Adhesive Mfr
N.A.I.C.S.: 325520
Joe Hoppert *(Mgr-Sls)*

Rubex, Inc.   (3)
3709 Grove City Rd, Grove City, OH 43123
Tel.: (614) 875-6343
Adhesives & Sealants Mfr
N.A.I.C.S.: 325520
Paul Swingle *(Plant Mgr)*

Holding (Domestic):

Head Country Inc.   (2)
2116 N Ash St, Ponca City, OK 74601
Tel.: (580) 762-1227

Web Site: http://www.headcountry.com
Sales Range: $1-9.9 Million
Barbecue Sauce Mfr & Distr
N.A.I.C.S.: 311941
Rocky Flick *(Pres & CEO)*
Paul Schatte *(VP)*
Linda Groth *(Office Mgr)*

Joint Venture (Domestic):

J.R. Johnson, Inc.   (2)
9425 N Burrage Ave, Portland, OR 97217-6966
Tel.: (503) 240-3388
Web Site: http://www.jrjohnsoninc.com
Sales Range: $1-9.9 Million
Building Repair & Restoration Services
N.A.I.C.S.: 238990
Clint Arp *(Co-Pres & Partner)*
Del Starr *(Co-Pres & Partner)*

Holding (Domestic):

Mason West Inc.   (2)
1601 E Miraloma Ave, Placentia, CA 92870
Tel.: (714) 630-0701
Web Site: http://www.masonwest.com
Sales Range: $10-24.9 Million
Emp.: 50
Instruments & Control Equipment
N.A.I.C.S.: 423830
Bobbie Irby *(Office Mgr)*

Meridian Rack & Pinion, Inc.   (2)
6740 Cobra Way, San Diego, CA 92121
Tel.: (858) 587-8777
Web Site: http://www.meridianautoparts.com
Sales Range: $10-24.9 Million
Automobile Parts Distr
N.A.I.C.S.: 423120
Jean-Pierre Gilbertz *(Founder)*
Matt Glauber *(Pres & COO)*
Dara Greaney *(CEO)*

PSI Molded Plastics New Hampshire,
Inc.   (2)
5 Wickers Dr, Wolfeboro, NH 03894
Tel.: (603) 569-5100
Web Site: https://www.psimp.com
Molded Plastics Mfr
N.A.I.C.S.: 326199
Jim Bolton *(Mgr-Finishing)*
Daniel Mills *(Pres & CEO)*

Subsidiary (Domestic):

Precision Southeast Inc.   (3)
4900 Hwy 501, Myrtle Beach, SC 29579
Tel.: (843) 347-4218
Web Site:
http://www.precisionsoutheast.com
Rev.: $19,906,253
Emp.: 120
Injection Molding Of Plastics
N.A.I.C.S.: 326199
Dick Averette *(Pres)*
Erica Sparks *(Coord-Inside Sls)*
Thomas Horne *(Mgr-Tool Room)*
Shane Prince *(Supvr)*

Holding (Domestic):

SBS Industries, Inc.   (2)
1843 N 106th E Ave, Tulsa, OK 74116
Tel.: (918) 836-7756
Web Site: http://www.sbsindustries.com
Sales Range: $10-24.9 Million
Emp.: 120
Precision Turned Product Mfr
N.A.I.C.S.: 332721
Jeff Greer *(CEO)*

Specialized Fabrication Equipment
Group, LLC   (2)
4433 S Dr, Houston, TX 77053
Tel.: (713) 747-8502
Web Site: https://www.sfe-brands.com
Pipe Fabrication, Precision Engineered Applications & Cutting Solutions Services
N.A.I.C.S.: 332996
Vinay Varma *(CEO)*
Aidan Tagliaferro *(Pres)*

Subsidiary (Domestic):

CLIMAX Portable Machine Tools,
Inc.   (3)
2712 E 2nd St, Newberg, OR 97132-8210
Tel.: (503) 538-2185
Web Site: http://www.climaxportable.com

Sales Range: $25-49.9 Million
Emp.: 100
Portable Machine Tool Mfr
N.A.I.C.S.: 333517
Tom Cunningham *(Pres & CEO)*
Scott Thiel *(VP-Ops, Engrg, and R&D)*
John Hazlett *(CFO)*

Subsidiary (Non-US):

Climax GmbH   (4)
Am Langen Graben 8, Duren, 52353, Germany
Tel.: (49) 242191770
Web Site: http://www.climaxportable.com
Sales Range: $10-24.9 Million
Portable Machine Tool Mfr
N.A.I.C.S.: 333517

Subsidiary (Domestic):

Mathey Dearman, Inc.   (3)
4344 S Maybelle Ave, Tulsa, OK 74107
Tel.: (918) 447-1288
Web Site: http://www.mathey.com
Sales Range: $1-9.9 Million
Emp.: 32
Oil & Gas Machinery Mfr
N.A.I.C.S.: 333132
Doug Hughes *(Pres & CEO)*
Gary Gamino *(CFO)*
Kevin Dooley *(VP-Sls)*
Brandon Boyd *(Mgr-North American Sls)*
Chris Patterson *(Mgr-Sls Acct-Intl)*
Debbie Brace *(Mgr-Customer Svc)*
Frank McCauley *(VP-Ops)*
Freddy Blakely *(Mgr-Sls Acct-Intl)*
Heather Wing *(Mgr-Domestic Sls Acct)*
Josh Wilson *(Engr-Technical Sls)*
Mike Brace *(Mgr-Key Acct)*
Svatopluk Jezek *(Mgr-Bus Dev-Eastern European)*
Will Jansen *(Dir-Engrg)*

Holding (Domestic):

The Maids International, LLC   (2)
9394 W Dodge Rd Ste 140, Omaha, NE 68114-3326
Tel.: (402) 558-5555
Web Site: http://www.maids.com
Rev.: $11,665,152
Emp.: 46
Franchise
N.A.I.C.S.: 533110
Daniel J. Bishop *(Founder & Chm)*
Daniel F. Kirwan *(Pres & CEO)*

The Mountain Corporation   (2)
59 Optical Ave, Keene, NH 03431
Tel.: (603) 355-3700
Web Site: http://www.themountain.com
T-Shirt Mfr & Marketer
N.A.I.C.S.: 424350
Michael McGloin *(Art Dir & Creative Dir)*

Gladstone Land Corporation   (1)
1521 Westbranch Dr Ste 100, McLean, VA 22102
Tel.: (703) 287-5800
Web Site: https://www.gladstonefarms.com
Rev.: $90,398,000
Assets: $1,387,324,000
Liabilities: $667,711,000
Net Worth: $719,613,000
Earnings: ($9,852,000)
Emp.: 69
Fiscal Year-end: 12/31/2023
Farms & Farm Related Real Estate Investment Services
N.A.I.C.S.: 523999
David J. Gladstone *(Founder, Chm, Pres & CEO)*
Terry Lee Brubaker *(COO)*
Paula Novara *(Head-Resource Mgmt)*
Michael B. LiCalsi *(Gen Counsel & Sec)*
Jennifer Smith *(Chief Valuation Officer)*
Jack Dellafiora Jr. *(Chief Compliance Officer)*
Jay Beckhorn *(Treas)*
Lewis Parrish *(CFO & Asst Treas)*
William Reiman *(Exec VP-West Coast Ops)*
Bill Frisbie *(Exec VP-East Coast Ops)*

GLADWIN MACHINERY & SUPPLY CO
5170 Main St NE, Minneapolis, MN 55421
Tel.: (763) 574-9000

Gladwin Machinery & Supply
Co—(Continued)

Web Site:
http://www.gladwinmachinery.com
Year Founded: 1973
Rev.: $10,400,000
Emp.: 43
Metal Fabrication Equipment Mfr
N.A.I.C.S.: 332312
Todd King (Pres)
Brad Bannister (Mgr-Warehouse)

GLAM MEDIA, INC.
2000 Sierra Point Pkwy Fl 10, Brisbane, CA 94005-1866
Tel.: (650) 244-4000
Web Site: http://www.glam.com
Sales Range: $10-24.9 Million
Emp.: 10
Lifestyle Websites & Online Media
Network
N.A.I.C.S.: 541810
Samir Arora (Founder & CEO)
Fernando Ruarte (Co-Founder-Native
Ad Platform Engrg, CTO & Exec VP)
Raj Narayan (Co-Founder-Consumer
Products Engrg & Sr VP)
Jack Rotolo (Exec VP-Content &
Video Sls & Ops)
Bianca Posterli (Dir-Editorial)
Jill Byron (Sr VP-Mktg)

Subsidiaries:

Ning, Inc.   (1)
285 Hamilton Ave Ste 400, Palo Alto, CA
94301-2540
Tel.: (650) 289-0606
Web Site: http://www.ning.com
Sales Range: $10-24.9 Million
Social Networking Website Operator
N.A.I.C.S.: 516210
Gina L. Bianchini (Founder)

GLAMORISE FOUNDATIONS, INC.
135 Madison Ave, New York, NY
10016-6712
Tel.: (212) 684-5025   **NY**
Web Site: http://www.glamorise.com
Year Founded: 1921
Sales Range: $100-124.9 Million
Emp.: 200
Intimate Apparel for Full-Figured
Women Mfr
N.A.I.C.S.: 315250
Jon R. Pundyk (CEO)
Martin Gresack (Sr VP)
Angela Martin-Fehr (VP-Mktg)
Sol Neuman (Dir-Tech Engrg)
Sven Saller (Sr VP)

GLANCE NETWORKS, INC.
1167 Massachusetts Ave, Arlington,
MA 02476
Tel.: (781) 646-8505
Web Site: http://www.glance.net
Year Founded: 2001
Rev.: $5,800,000
Emp.: 12
Custom Computer Programming Services
N.A.I.C.S.: 541511
Rich Baker (Founder & CTO)
Tom Martin (CEO)

GLASER'S COLLISION CENTER
3331 Preston Hwy, Louisville, KY
40213-1331
Tel.: (502) 266-5905
Web Site:
http://www.glaserscollision.com
Emp.: 100
Automotive Body, Paint & Interior Repair & Maintenance
N.A.I.C.S.: 811121
Gene Glaser (Owner)

Subsidiaries:

Oldham Collision Center   (1)
6408 Hwy 329, Crestwood, KY 40014-8558
Tel.: (502) 224-1124
Web Site: http://www.oldhamcollision.com
Automotive Body, Paint & Interior Repair &
Maintenance
N.A.I.C.S.: 811121
Nick Moser (Mgr)

GLASER-MILLER CO. INC.
421 Exton Commons, Exton, PA
19341
Tel.: (610) 873-2415
Web Site: https://www.glaser-miller.com
Year Founded: 1952
Sales Range: $25-49.9 Million
Emp.: 9
Metal Castings & Plastic Products
N.A.I.C.S.: 423510
Sharon Davidson (Office Mgr)

GLASFLOSS INDUSTRIES
420 E Danieldale Rd, Desoto, TX
75115
Tel.: (214) 741-7056
Web Site: https://www.glasfloss.com
Rev.: $13,300,000
Emp.: 200
Furnace & Air Conditioning Equipment Mfr
N.A.I.C.S.: 333413
Scott Lange (Pres)
Bill McKnight (Dir-Pur)
Cheryl Thompson (VP-Admin Svcs)
Juby Alexander (Mgr-IT)
Don Kingston (CEO)
Mike Woolsey (Mgr-Natl Sls-ARW)
Chuck Watts (VP-Mfg)
Mark Filewood (VP-Sls & Mktg)

GLASGOW INC.
104 Willow Grove Ave, Glenside, PA
19038-1089
Tel.: (215) 884-8800
Web Site: http://www.glasgowinc.com
Rev.: $100,000,000
Emp.: 80
Provider of Road Paving Materials
N.A.I.C.S.: 324121
Bruce B. Rambo (Pres)
Aileen Gibson (Mgr-Credit)
Matt Uliasz (Engr-Civil)
Tim McCool (Mgr-Equipment)

GLASS & DOOR INTERNATIONAL
2002 Brittmoore Rd, Houston, TX
77043
Tel.: (713) 690-8282
Web Site: https://www.glasscraft.com
Sales Range: $10-24.9 Million
Emp.: 100
Glass Construction Materials
N.A.I.C.S.: 423390
John Plummer (Pres)

GLASS & SASH INC.
425 Irwin St, San Rafael, CA 94901
Tel.: (415) 456-2240
Web Site:
https://www.glassandsash.com
Sales Range: $75-99.9 Million
Emp.: 20
Glass & Glazing Work
N.A.I.C.S.: 238150
Nick Something (Pres)
Tom Hess (VP)

GLASS CONSTRUCTION
3307 Connecticut Ave NW, Washington, DC 20008
Tel.: (202) 362-6012
Web Site:
https://www.glassconstruction.biz

Year Founded: 1991
Rev.: $8,100,000
Emp.: 18
New Single-Family Housing Construction
N.A.I.C.S.: 236115
Thomas D. Glass (Owner & Pres)
Gary Myers (Gen Mgr)

GLASS FAB INC.
257 Ormond St, Rochester, NY
14605
Tel.: (585) 262-4000
Web Site: https://www.glassfab.com
Year Founded: 1974
Sales Range: $1-9.9 Million
Emp.: 45
Optical Lenses Mfr
N.A.I.C.S.: 333310
Daniel Saltzman (Pres)
Wayne Leon (Gen Mgr)
Robert Saltzman (Founder & CEO)

GLASS GARDENS INC.
220 W Passaic St, Rochelle Park, NJ
07662-3118
Tel.: (201) 843-1424   **NJ**
Web Site: https://www.shoprite.com
Year Founded: 1955
Sales Range: $125-149.9 Million
Emp.: 1,500
Grocery Stores Owner & Operator
N.A.I.C.S.: 445110
Terry Glass (Co-Owner)
Irv Glass (Co-Owner)
Sal Ndiaye (Asst Dir)

Subsidiaries:

Pearl River Shop Rite Associates
Inc.   (1)
244 W Passaic St Ste 202, Rochelle Park,
NJ 07662-3118
Tel.: (201) 843-1364
Sales Range: $10-24.9 Million
Emp.: 13
Grocery Stores
N.A.I.C.S.: 445110
Irving Glass (Exec VP)
Ben Focarino (Gen Mgr)
Ed Smith (Dir-Fin)

Rockaway ShopRite Associates,
Inc.   (1)
437 Route 46, Dover, NJ 07801-3709
Tel.: (973) 366-3343
Sales Range: $25-49.9 Million
Emp.: 150
Grocery Stores
N.A.I.C.S.: 445110
John Lombardo (Gen Mgr)

GLASS MCCLURE
2700 J St 2nd Fl, Sacramento, CA
95816
Tel.: (916) 448-6956
Web Site:
http://www.glassmcclure.com
Year Founded: 1991
Sales Range: $10-24.9 Million
Emp.: 35
N.A.I.C.S.: 541810
Greg Glass (CEO)
Siobhann Mansour (VP & Dir-Media)
Brantley Payne (VP & Dir-Creative)

GLASS MOUNTAIN CAPITAL, LLC
1930 Thoreau Dr Ste 100, Schaumburg, IL 60173
Tel.: (877) 214-0276
Web Site:
http://www.glassmountaincapital.com
Year Founded: 2005
Sales Range: $1-9.9 Million
Emp.: 140
Debt Collection Services
N.A.I.C.S.: 561440

David C. Ansani (Gen Counsel)
Ed Carfora (Sr VP-Ops)
Anthony P. Nuzzo Jr. (CEO)

GLASS PRO INC.
101 Pond Cypress Rd, Venice, FL
34292
Tel.: (941) 488-4586
Web Site:
http://www.zapskimboards.com
Year Founded: 1983
Sales Range: $1-9.9 Million
Emp.: 20
Skimboard Mfr
N.A.I.C.S.: 339920
Bob Smetts (Pres)

GLASS RECYCLERS INC.
6465 Wyoming St, Dearborn, MI
48126
Tel.: (313) 584-3434
Web Site:
https://www.glassrecyclers.net
Sales Range: $10-24.9 Million
Emp.: 65
Recycling Glass
N.A.I.C.S.: 562920
Robert S. Rahaim (Pres)
Douglas Rahaim (VP)
Jerry Murray (Controller)

GLASSHOUSE TECHNOLOGIES, INC.
200 Crossing Blvd, Framingham, MA
01702
Tel.: (508) 879-5729   **DE**
Web Site:
http://www.glasshouse.com
Sales Range: $125-149.9 Million
Emp.: 600
Information Technology Infrastructure
Consulting Services
N.A.I.C.S.: 541512
Rick Cameron (VP-GlassHouse Technologies)
James Damoulakis (CTO)
Debralee Donovan (Mgr-Mktg Events)
Michael Burstein (Sr VP-Bus Dev-Intl
Div)
Jeff Wakely (CFO)
Dave Malcolmson (Sr VP-Global Sls)
Robert Bongi (Sr VP-Worldwide Svc
Delivery)
Steve Sharp (CEO)

Subsidiaries:

GlassHouse Technologies (UK)
Limited   (1)
Ocean House, Bourne Business Park, Weybridge, KT15 2QW, Surrey, United
Kingdom   (100%)
Tel.: (44) 8707770017
Web Site: http://www.glasshouse.com
Sales Range: $25-49.9 Million
Emp.: 145
Information Technology Infrastructure Consulting Services
N.A.I.C.S.: 541512

GlassHouse Technologies Ltd.   (1)
Hayetsira 13 3 Htidhar Street, Petah Tiqwa,
Israel
Tel.: (972) 97622700
Sales Range: $25-49.9 Million
Emp.: 200
Information Technology Services
N.A.I.C.S.: 541512

GLASSMAN AUTOMOTIVE GROUP
28000 Telegraph Rd, Southfield, MI
48034
Tel.: (248) 354-3300
Year Founded: 1969
Sales Range: $25-49.9 Million
Emp.: 90
Car Whslr
N.A.I.C.S.: 441110

George H. Glassman *(Pres)*

GLASSMAN OLDSMOBILE INC.
28000 Telegraph Rd, Southfield, MI 48034
Tel.: (248) 354-3300
Web Site: http://www.glassmanautogroup.com
Rev.: $22,400,000
Emp.: 90
Automobiles, New & Used
N.A.I.C.S.: 441110
George Glassman *(Pres)*

GLASSMASTER CONTROLS COMPANY, INC.
831 Cobb Ave, Kalamazoo, MI 49007-2444
Tel.: (269) 382-2010   MI
Web Site: http://www.gcontrols.com
Year Founded: 1921
Flexible Steel Wire Controls & Molded Plastic Control Panels, Electronic Controls & Circuit Mfr
N.A.I.C.S.: 332618

GLASSMERE FUEL SERVICE INC.
1967 Saxonburg Blvd, Tarentum, PA 15032
Tel.: (724) 224-0880   PA
Web Site: https://www.glassmerefuel.com
Sales Range: $50-74.9 Million
Emp.: 40
Dealers of Gasoline & Fuel Oil Services
N.A.I.C.S.: 424720
Dell M. Cromie *(Pres)*
Chris Burkhiser *(Controller)*
Kelly Mago *(Mgr-Credit)*

GLASSTECH INC.
995 4th St, Perrysburg, OH 43551-4321
Tel.: (419) 661-9500
Web Site: https://www.glasstech.com
Year Founded: 1971
Sales Range: $10-24.9 Million
Emp.: 100
Mfr of Industrial Furnaces & Ovens
N.A.I.C.S.: 541330
Mark Christman *(Pres & CEO)*
Harry I. Freund *(Vice Chm)*
Jay S. Goldsmith *(Chm)*

GLASSWERKS LA CO.
8600 Rheem Ave S Gate, Los Angeles, CA 90280
Tel.: (323) 789-7800
Web Site: http://www.glasswerks.com
Rev.: $6,666,666
Emp.: 50
Flat Glass Mfr
N.A.I.C.S.: 327211
Randy Steinberg *(Owner)*
Mike Torres *(Controller)*

Subsidiaries:

Northwestern Industries-Arizona, Inc.   (1)
7595 E 30th St, Yuma, AZ 85365
Tel.: (206) 285-3140
Web Site: http://www.nwiglass.com
Glass Mfr
N.A.I.C.S.: 327211
John Butler *(Mgr)*

GLATT AIR TECHNIQUES, INC.
20 Spear Rd, Ramsey, NJ 07446-1221
Tel.: (201) 825-8700
Web Site: http://www.glatt.com
Year Founded: 1973
Solid Pharmaceutical Dosage Forms Develops & Producer

N.A.I.C.S.: 325412
James Ahearn *(Reg Sls Mgr)*

GLAUBER EQUIPMENT CORP.
1600 Commerce Pkwy, Lancaster, NY 14086
Tel.: (716) 681-1234
Web Site: http://www.glauber.com
Year Founded: 1960
Sales Range: $10-24.9 Million
Emp.: 48
Mfr of Compressors
N.A.I.C.S.: 423830
Peter Glauber *(Pres)*
P. J. Glauber *(VP)*

GLAZER'S FAMILY OF COMPANIES
14911 Quorum Dr, Dallas, TX 75254
Tel.: (972) 392-8200
Web Site: http://www.southernglazers.com
Emp.: 7,000
Holding Company; Wine & Distilled Beverage Wholesale Distr
N.A.I.C.S.: 551112
Sheldon I. Stein *(Pres/CEO-Glazer's Distributors)*
Bennett J. Glazer *(Chm & CEO)*
Mike Glazer *(Sec & Exec VP)*
Barkley Stuart *(Asst Sec & Exec VP)*

Subsidiaries:

Glazer's Beer and Beverage, LLC   (1)
14911 Quorum Dr Ste 200, Dallas, TX 75254
Tel.: (972) 392-8090
Web Site: http://www.glazersbeer.com
Beer Distr
N.A.I.C.S.: 424810
Sheldon Stein *(CEO)*
Bennett Glazer *(Chm)*
Phil Meacham *(Pres & COO)*
Orman Anderson *(CFO)*
Don Gallian *(Sr VP-Sls & Ops)*

Subsidiary (Domestic):

KC Distributing, LLC   (2)
10615 Fishtrap Rd, Aubrey, TX 76227-5263
Tel.: (940) 440-0616
Web Site: http://www.kcdistributing.com
Advertising Material Distribution Services
N.A.I.C.S.: 541870

Glazer's Distributors of Texas, Inc.   (1)
14911 Quorum Dr Ste 150, Dallas, TX 75380-9013
Tel.: (972) 392-8200
Web Site: http://www.southernglazers.com
Sales Range: $1-4.9 Billion
Emp.: 5,800
Wine, Beer & Distilled Beverage Wholesale Distr
N.A.I.C.S.: 424820
Bennett J. Glazer *(Chm & CEO)*
Mike McLaughlin *(Exec VP-Sls & Mktg)*

Subsidiary (Domestic):

Cenla Beverage Company, LLC   (2)
4001 Lakeside Dr, Alexandria, LA 71315
Tel.: (318) 487-8596
Wine & Distilled Beverage Wholesale Distr
N.A.I.C.S.: 424820

Glazer's Distributors of Arkansas, Inc.   (2)
11101 Smitty Ln, North Little Rock, AR 72117-5390
Tel.: (501) 955-2903
Web Site: http://www.glazers.com
Sales Range: $1-9.9 Million
Emp.: 100
Wine & Distilled Beverage Wholesale Distr
N.A.I.C.S.: 424820
Jason Bazin *(Dir-Ops)*

Glazer's Distributors of Indiana, LLC   (2)
5337 W 78th St, Indianapolis, IN 46268-4148

Tel.: (317) 876-1188
Web Site: http://www.glazers.com
Emp.: 50
Wine & Distilled Beverage Wholesale Distr
N.A.I.C.S.: 424820
Candace Ford *(Portfolio Mgr)*

Glazer's Distributors of Iowa, Inc.   (2)
4377 112th St, Urbandale, IA 50322-2073
Tel.: (515) 252-7173
Web Site: http://www.glazers.com
Sales Range: $1-9.9 Million
Wine & Distilled Beverage Wholesale Distr
N.A.I.C.S.: 424820

Branch (Domestic):

Glazer's Distributors of Iowa, Inc. - Cedar Rapids   (3)
6425 7th St Ct SW Ste H, Cedar Rapids, IA 52404-7054
Tel.: (319) 366-4333
Web Site: http://www.glazers.com
Wine, Beer & Distilled Beverage Wholesale Distr
N.A.I.C.S.: 424820

Subsidiary (Domestic):

Glazer's Distributors of Missouri, Inc.   (2)
1 Glazers Way, Saint Charles, MO 63301-4367
Tel.: (636) 925-8800
Web Site: http://www.glazers.com
Sales Range: $125-149.9 Million
Emp.: 400
Wine & Distilled Beverage Wholesale Distr
N.A.I.C.S.: 424820
Steven R. Becker *(Treas & Exec VP-Compliance)*
Harvey Chaplin *(Chm)*
Wayne Chaplin *(CEO)*
Mel Dick *(Pres-Wine Div & Sr VP)*
Lee F. Hager *(Sec & Exec VP-Admin)*
Brad Vassar *(COO & Exec VP)*

Branch (Domestic):

Glazer's Distributors of Missouri, Inc. - Springfield   (3)
1128 N Farm Rd 123, Springfield, MO 65802-6668
Tel.: (417) 869-5512
Web Site: http://www.southernglazers.com
Sales Range: $10-24.9 Million
Emp.: 75
Wine, Beer & Distilled Beverage Wholesale Distr
N.A.I.C.S.: 424820
Dave Quigley *(Dir-Sls)*

Branch (Domestic):

Glazer's Distributors of Texas, Inc. - Dallas   (2)
2001 Diplomat Dr, Farmers Branch, TX 75234-8919
Tel.: (972) 277-2000
Web Site: http://www.southernglazers.com
Wine, Beer & Distilled Beverage Wholesale Distr
N.A.I.C.S.: 424820
Jalinda Ruiz *(Office Mgr)*

Glazer's Distributors of Texas, Inc. - Prestige Sales Division   (2)
13995 Diplomat Dr Ste 200, Farmers Branch, TX 75234-8805
Tel.: (214) 823-9272
Web Site: http://www.glazers.com
Rev.: $10,400,000
Emp.: 8
Wine & Distilled Beverage Wholesale Distr
N.A.I.C.S.: 424820
Bill Stowe *(VP)*
Chad Butler *(Gen Mgr)*

Glazer's Distributors of Texas, Inc. - San Antonio   (2)
1002 S Callaghan Rd, San Antonio, TX 78227
Tel.: (210) 224-4291
Web Site: http://www.glazers.com
Wine, Beer & Distilled Beverage Wholesale Distr
N.A.I.C.S.: 424820
David Kitchen *(Branch Mgr)*

Subsidiary (Domestic):

Premier Beverage Inc.   (2)
1100 Blake St, Edwardsville, KS 66111-3824
Tel.: (913) 745-2900
Web Site: http://www.glazers.com
Sales Range: $25-49.9 Million
Emp.: 140
Wine & Distilled Beverage Wholesale Distr
N.A.I.C.S.: 424820
James C. Baird *(Branch Mgr)*
Jim Dorsey *(Pres)*

Victor L. Robilio Company, Inc.   (2)
3680 Air Park St, Memphis, TN 38118
Tel.: (901) 362-0933
Web Site: http://www.robilio.com
Wine & Distilled Beverage Wholesale Distr
N.A.I.C.S.: 424820
Marne Anderson *(Gen Mgr-Sls)*

Southern Glazer's Wine & Spirits, LLC   (1)
1600 NW 163rd St, Miami, FL 33169-5641
Tel.: (305) 625-4171
Web Site: https://www.southernglazers.com
Emp.: 24,000
Wine & Distilled Alcoholic Beverage Merchant Wholesalers
N.A.I.C.S.: 424820
Sheldon I. Stein *(Pres)*
Harvey R. Chaplin *(Chm)*
Wayne E. Chaplin *(CEO)*
Steven R. Becker *(Exec VP & Treas)*
Lee F. Hager *(Sec & Exec VP)*
Melvin Dick *(Pres-Wine Div & Sr VP)*
Brad Vassar *(COO & Exec VP)*
Bobby Burg *(Chief Supply Chain Officer & Sr VP)*
Patrick Daul *(Pres-West)*
Gene Sullivan *(Pres-East)*
John Landry *(Exec VP/Gen Mgr- Nevada)*
Randy Barnhart *(VP-Govt Affairs-East)*
John Wittig *(Chief Transformation Officer)*
John Klein *(Exec VP/Gen Mgr-Pacific Northwest)*
Larry Ruvo *(Sr Mng Dir-Nevada)*
Bennett Glazer *(Vice Chm)*
Thomas Greenlee *(Exec VP-Fin)*
Alan Greespan *(Gen Counsel & Exec VP)*
Amy Grantland *(Sr VP-Revenue Mgmt)*
Cindy Haas *(VP-Comm & CSR)*
Shawn Thurman *(Exec VP-Natl Accounts)*
Ray Lombard *(Exec VP-Supplier Mgmt & Bus Dev)*
Mike McLaughlin *(Pres-Central)*
Scott Oppenheimer *(Pres-Control States & Canada Reg)*
Rahul Sathe *(Sr VP-Comml Effectiveness)*
Jennifer Hanlon *(Mgr-PR)*
Scott Westerman *(Exec VP/Gen Mgr-North Central Sub-Reg)*
Soren Sorensen *(VP/Gen Mgr-Minnesota)*
Stephanie Silvestre *(Sr VP-Supply Chain)*
Cindy Leonard *(Sr VP-Supplier Mgmt & Bus Dev)*
Zach Poelma *(Sr VP-Supplier Strategy & Bus Dev)*
Kim Scarpone *(Sr VP-Spirits-Nevada)*
Kim Beto *(Sr VP-Wine-Nevada)*
Jamie Gruwer *(VP-Supplier & Customer Collaboration)*
Mark Chaplin *(VP-Sls & Mktg)*
Christina Reed *(VP/Gen Mgr-Alaska)*
Allison Graham *(Sr VP-Sls & Mktg-Canada)*
Doug Wieland *(Pres-Canada)*
Casey McQuaid *(VP & Gen Mgr-Oregon)*
Sofia Estevez *(Mgr-Comm & CSR)*

Division (Domestic):

Southern Glazer's Wine & Spirits of Hawaii   (2)
155 Kapalulu Pl Ste 300, Honolulu, HI 96819-1806
Tel.: (808) 591-8825
Wine & Distilled Beverages Whslr
N.A.I.C.S.: 424820
Warren Shon *(Exec VP & Gen Mgr)*
Ryan Sipe *(VP & Gen Mgr-Sls-Ocean Pacific Div)*
Derek Nobu *(Portfolio Mgr-Off Premise)*
Roberto Viernes *(Gen Mgr-Artisinal Spirits & Fine Wines Div)*
Kevin Burkett *(VP & Mgr-Wine-Atlantic Div)*
Kimo Correa *(Gen Sls Mgr-Transatlantic Div)*

Glazer's Family of Companies—(Continued)

Southern Glazer's Wine & Spirits of Illinois (2)
300 E Crossroads Pkwy, Bolingbrook, IL 60440-3516
Tel.: (630) 685-3000
Wine Distr
N.A.I.C.S.: 424820
Dave Carini (VP & Gen Mgr- Artisanal & Fine Wines Div)
Terry Brick (Sr VP & Gen Mgr)
Gene Krusenoski (VP-American Liberty Div)
Al Larose (VP & Portfolio Mgr)
Janine Dettbarn (VP & Gen Mgr-Transatlantic Div)

Subsidiary (Domestic):

Southern Glazer's Wine & Spirits of Illinois- Direct Warehouse Sales (3)
250 N Artesian Ave, Chicago, IL 60612
Tel.: (630) 685-3000
Wine Distr
N.A.I.C.S.: 424820

Division (Domestic):

Southern Glazer's Wine & Spirits of New York (2)
313 Underhill Blvd, Syosset, NY 11791-3411
Tel.: (516) 921-9005
Wine & Alcoholic Beverage Whslr
N.A.I.C.S.: 424820
Larry Goodrich (Exec VP & Gen Mgr-SGWS Div)
Larry Romer (VP & Gen Mgr-Spirits)
Steven Bonavita (VP & Gen Sls Mgr-Artisanal Spirits & Fine Wines Div)
Greg Clement (VP-American Liberty Div)
Damian Caruana (VP & General Sls Mgr-Atlantic Div)
Bob Danzi (VP & Gen Mgr-Transatlantic Div)

Subsidiary (Domestic):

Southern Glazer's Wine & Spirits of New York - Syracuse (3)
3063 Court St, Syracuse, NY 13208
Tel.: (315) 428-2100
Emp.: 200
Wine & Spirit Whslr
N.A.I.C.S.: 424820

Division (Domestic):

Southern Glazer's Wine & Spirits of Pennsylvania (2)
460 American Ave, King of Prussia, PA 19406-1405
Tel.: (610) 265-6800
Emp.: 85
Distr of Wine & Distilled Beverages
N.A.I.C.S.: 424820
Brad Waxman (Exec VP & Gen Mgr-SGWS Div)
Ryan DeVecchio (Gen Sls Mgr-American Liberty)
Chuck Silio (Exec VP-Artisanal Spirits & Fine Wines Div)
Beth Lewandowski (VP & Gen Sls Mgr-Atlantic Div)
Brad Reynolds (VP & Gen Mgr-NASWB PA)
Zach Waxman (Gen Sls Mgr-Transatlantic Div)

GLAZER-KENNEDY INSIDER'S CIRCLE, LLC
401 Jefferson Ave, Towson, MD 21286
Tel.: (410) 825-8600
Web Site:
http://www.dankennedy.com
Year Founded: 2004
Rev.: $15,000,000
Emp.: 27
Management Consulting Services
N.A.I.C.S.: 541613
Tonya Pszcolka (Mgr-Mktg)

GLAZIER FOODS COMPANY
11303 Antoine Dr, Houston, TX 77066-4429
Tel.: (713) 869-6411　　　　TX

Web Site:
http://www.glazierfoods.com
Year Founded: 1936
Sales Range: $125-149.9 Million
Emp.: 250
Provider of Packaged Frozen Goods
N.A.I.C.S.: 424420
Art Innis (VP-Fin & HR)

GLE ASSOCIATES, INC.
5405 Cypress Centre Dr Ste 110, Tampa, FL 33609
Tel.: (813) 241-8350
Web Site:
https://www.gleassociates.com
Year Founded: 1989
Sales Range: $1-9.9 Million
Emp.: 60
Facilities & Environmental Consulting Services
N.A.I.C.S.: 541620
Robert B. Greene (Pres)
Donna Douglas (Mgr-Mktg)
Amber Ward (Mgr-Employee Dev & HR)

GLEANER LIFE INSURANCE SOCIETY INC.
5200 W US Hwy 223, Adrian, MI 49221-9461
Tel.: (517) 265-7745
Web Site: https://www.gleanerlife.org
Year Founded: 1894
Sales Range: $100-124.9 Million
Emp.: 564
Provider of Life Insurance
N.A.I.C.S.: 524113
Kevin A. Marti (Pres & CEO)
Suann D. Hammersmith (Chm)
Terry L. Garner (Vice Chm)

GLEASON CORPORATION
10474 Santa Monica Blvd Ste 400, Los Angeles, CA 90025
Tel.: (310) 470-6001　　　　CA
Web Site:
http://www.gleasoncorporation.com
Rev.: $128,100,000
Emp.: 500
Provider of Flares & Fireworks
N.A.I.C.S.: 325998
Sakya Schuler (Dir-Client Experiences)

Subsidiaries:

Algoma Net Company (1)
1525 Mueller St, Algoma, WI 54201
Tel.: (920) 487-5577
Web Site: http://www.algomanet.com
Emp.: 18
Hammock Mfr
N.A.I.C.S.: 314994
David Schoenborn (Mgr-Natl Sls)

Gleason Industrial Products Inc. (1)
8575 Forest Home Ave Ste 100, Greenfield, WI 53228-3417
Tel.: (414) 529-8357
Web Site:
http://www.milwaukeehandtrucks.com
Sales Range: $10-24.9 Million
Emp.: 8
Tubular Steel Products; Hand Trucks; Dollies; Specialty Material Handling Manual Equipment Mfr & Distr
N.A.I.C.S.: 423120
Jay Kvasnicka (VP-Sls & Mktg)

Precision Products, Inc. (1)
316 Limit St, Lincoln, IL 62656
Tel.: (217) 735-1590
Web Site: http://www.precisionprodinc.com
Emp.: 200
Lawn & Garden Equipment Mfr
N.A.I.C.S.: 333112
Brooke Feld (Mgr-Sls)

GLEASON CORPORATION
1000 University Ave, Rochester, NY 14607-1239

Tel.: (585) 473-1000　　　　DE
Web Site: https://www.gleason.com
Year Founded: 1865
Sales Range: $350-399.9 Million
Emp.: 2,600
Holding Company
N.A.I.C.S.: 423830
James S. Gleason (Chm)
John J. Perrotti (Pres & CEO)
Edward J. Pelta (Gen Counsel, Sec & VP)
John W. Pysnack (Treas & VP-Fin)
William J. Simpson (VP-Supply Chain-Global)
Nanci Malin-Peck (VP-Corp HR)
Robert P. Phillips (Sr VP-Tooling Products Grp)

Subsidiaries:

Distech Systems, Inc. (1)
1005 Mount Read Blvd, Rochester, NY 14606
Tel.: (585) 254-7020
Web Site: http://www.distechsystems.com
Sales Range: $1-9.9 Million
Industrial Tray Stacking Machinery Mfr & Whslr
N.A.I.C.S.: 333998
Daniel J. Schwab (Pres)

Gleason - M&M Precision Systems Corporation (1)
300 Progress Rd, West Carrollton, OH 45449
Tel.: (937) 859-8273
Web Site: http://www.precision.com
Sales Range: $10-24.9 Million
Emp.: 60
Mfr Precision Motion Systems, Rotary Tables & Metrology Systems
N.A.I.C.S.: 334519
Doug Beerck (VP & Gen Mgr)
Dennis Traynor (Mgr-Sls)

Gleason Corporation - Gleason K2 Plastics Plant (1)
8210 Buffalo Rd, Bergen, NY 14416
Tel.: (585) 494-2470
Web Site: http://www.gleason.com
Sales Range: $25-49.9 Million
Emp.: 7
Injection Molded Plastic Products Mfr
N.A.I.C.S.: 326199

Gleason Cutting Tools Corporation (1)
1351 Windsor Rd, Loves Park, IL 61111-4294　　　(100%)
Tel.: (815) 877-8900
Web Site: http://www.gleason.com
Sales Range: $25-49.9 Million
Emp.: 310
Cutting Tool Mfr
N.A.I.C.S.: 333515

Gleason Gear Technology (Suzhou) Co., Ltd. (1)
No 85 Yangpu Road Suzhou Industrial Park, Suzhou, 215024, Jiangsu, China
Tel.: (86) 512 6732 5806
Web Site: http://www.gleason.com
Gear Cutting Tool & Hobbing Machine Mfr
N.A.I.C.S.: 333517

Gleason Metrology Systems Corporation (1)
300 Progress Rd, Dayton, OH 45449
Tel.: (937) 859-8273
Web Site: http://www.gleason.com
Emp.: 60
Gear Whslr
N.A.I.C.S.: 423840
Dennis Traynor (Mgr-Sls)

Gleason Milano (1)
Via Caldera 21 E 2, I-20153, Milan, Italy　　　(100%)
Tel.: (39) 024828571
Web Site: http://www.gleason.com
Sales & Marketing of Machine Tools
N.A.I.C.S.: 423830

Gleason Works (India) Private Ltd. (1)
Plot No 37 Doddenakundi Industrial Area, Whitefield Road, Mahadevapura, 560 048,

Bangalore, India　　　(100%)
Tel.: (91) 8028524315
Web Site: http://www.gleason.com
Sales Range: $10-24.9 Million
Emp.: 65
Cutting Tool Mfr
N.A.I.C.S.: 332216
Pradeep Kumar Agarwal (Gen Mgr)

Gleason-Hurth Maschinen und Werkzeuge GmbH (1)
Moosacher Str 42-46, Munich, 80809, Germany
Tel.: (49) 89 35401 0
Web Site: http://www.gleason.com
Sales Range: $25-49.9 Million
Emp.: 200
Machine Tool Whslr
N.A.I.C.S.: 423840
Jens Mucki (Mng Dir)

Gleason-Pfauter Maschinenfabrik GmbH (1)
Buetigen St 80, Studen, 2557, Switzerland　　　(100%)
Tel.: (41) 323666171
Web Site: http://www.gleason.com
Sales Range: $1-9.9 Million
Emp.: 55
Mfr of Cutting Tools
N.A.I.C.S.: 333515
Rudolf Moser (Mng Dir-Ops)

Gleason-Pfauter Maschinenfabrik GmbH (1)
Daimlerstrasse 14, Ludwigsburg, 71636, Germany
Tel.: (49) 71414040
Web Site: http://www.gleason.com
Mfr of Gear Hobbing & Finishing Machines, Shaping Machines, Spline Hobbing Machines; Worm Gear Hobbing Machines
N.A.I.C.S.: 333517

The Gleason Works (1)
1000 University Ave, Rochester, NY 14692-2970
Tel.: (585) 473-1000
Web Site: http://www.gleason.com
Bevel Gear, Curvic Coupling, Spur & Helical Machinery Mfr
N.A.I.C.S.: 333517
Doug Beerck (VP & Gen Mgr)

GLEASON INDUSTRIES, INC.
1277 Santa Anita Ct, Woodland, CA 95776
Tel.: (530) 406-1982
Year Founded: 1949
Sales Range: $10-24.9 Million
Emp.: 70
Paperboard Product Mfr & Distr
N.A.I.C.S.: 322130
John Maher (Treas)

GLEASON WOODWORK, INC.
2850 N Pulaski Rd, Chicago, IL 60641
Tel.: (773) 205-2260
Web Site:
http://www.gleasonwoodwork.com
Year Founded: 2002
Rev.: $9,900,000
Emp.: 27
Lumber, Plywood & Millwork
N.A.I.C.S.: 423310
Thomas M. Gleason (Pres)
Chuck Slatkoff (Project Mgr)
Steve Skupien (Engr-Design)

GLEIM THE JEWELER INC.
540 University Ave Ste 100, Palo Alto, CA 94301-1914
Tel.: (650) 323-1331
Web Site:
http://www.gleimjewelers.com
Sales Range: $10-24.9 Million
Emp.: 37
Jewelry Stores
N.A.I.C.S.: 458310
Georgie Gleim (Pres)
David Loudy (VP)

GLEN BUILDERS INC.
Uppr Westside Rd, North Conway, NH 03860
Tel.: (603) 356-3401
Web Site:
http://www.glenbuilders.com
Sales Range: $10-24.9 Million
Emp.: 50
Provider of Commercial Construction Services
N.A.I.C.S.: 236220
David Miller *(Pres)*

GLEN COVE PROPERTIES LTD. INC.
235 Glencove Blvd, Lake Ozark, MO 65049
Tel.: (573) 365-4001
Web Site:
http://www.glencovemarine.com
Sales Range: $10-24.9 Million
Emp.: 45
Boat Dealers
N.A.I.C.S.: 441222
Brynda Waller *(Bus Mgr)*
Barb Niedergerke *(Mgr-Sls & Fin)*
Steve Stoufer *(Mgr-Svc)*

GLEN OAK COUNTRY CLUB
21 W 451 Hill Ave, Glen Ellyn, IL 60137
Tel.: (630) 469-5600   IL
Web Site:
https://www.glenoakcountryclub.org
Year Founded: 1911
Sales Range: $1-9.9 Million
Emp.: 208
Country Club
N.A.I.C.S.: 713910
David Knapp *(Dir-PY)*
Gerard Buccino *(VP)*
James Bridgman *(Dir-PY)*
Jeff Scott *(Dir-PY)*
Kevin Riordan *(Treas)*
David Knapp *(Dir-PY)*
Gerard Buccino *(VP)*
James Bridgman *(Dir-PY)*
Jeff Scott *(Dir-PY)*
Kevin Riordan *(Treas)*
Marc Raymond *(Gen Mgr)*
Robert Tillman *(Second VP)*
Stan Gaffey *(Dir-PY)*
Thomas Mikrut *(Treas-PY)*
Tony Dupasquier *(Sec)*
William Muckian *(Pres)*

GLEN OAK LUMBER & MILLING INC.
N2885 County Rd F, Montello, WI 53949
Tel.: (608) 297-2161   WI
Web Site:
http://www.glenoaklumber.com
Year Founded: 1979
Sales Range: $10-24.9 Million
Emp.: 140
Producer of Wood Products
N.A.I.C.S.: 321912
Tom Talbot *(Owner)*
Doug Isberner *(Mgr-Sls)*
Dusty Lee Gray *(Dir-Svcs)*

GLEN OAKS CLUB
175 Post Rd, Old Westbury, NY 11568-0249
Tel.: (516) 626-2900   NY
Web Site:
https://www.glenoaksclub.org
Year Founded: 1924
Sales Range: $10-24.9 Million
Emp.: 219
Golf Club Operator
N.A.I.C.S.: 713910
Jeffrey Riegler *(Gen Mgr)*

GLEN RAVEN, INC.

1831 N Park Ave, Glen Raven, NC 27217
Tel.: (336) 227-6211   NC
Web Site: http://www.glenraven.com
Year Founded: 1880
Sales Range: $75-99.9 Million
Emp.: 115
Textile Mill Products Mfr; Specialty Yarns, Upholstery Fabrics Mfr & Marketer; Dyeing & Finishing Operations
N.A.I.C.S.: 313110
Gary Smith *(CFO, Treas & Sr VP)*
Derek Steed *(Gen Counsel, Sec & Sr VP)*
Ethan Lane *(CIO)*

Subsidiaries:

Glen Raven Custom Fabrics, L.L.C.   (1)
1831 N Park Ave, Burlington, NC 27217-1137
Tel.: (336) 227-6211
Web Site: http://www.glenraven.com
Sales Range: $25-49.9 Million
Mfr of Marine Furniture & Industrial Fabrics
N.A.I.C.S.: 459130
Vince Hankins *(Dir-Bus Dev)*
Hal Hunnicut *(VP-Mktg)*
Greg Rosendale *(Mgr-Residential Furniture Fabrics)*
Suzie Roberts *(VP-Sls-Americas)*
Alexis Maklakoff *(Bus Mgr-Decorative Fabrics)*
Steve Pawl *(CMO)*
David Swers *(Pres & COO)*
Allen Gant III *(Mgr-Casual Market)*

Plant (Domestic):

Glen Raven Custom Fabrics, LLC - Plant One   (2)
142 Glen Raven Rd, Glen Raven, NC 27217-1100
Tel.: (336) 227-6211
Textile Fabric Mfr
N.A.I.C.S.: 313310

Glen Raven Custom Fabrics, LLC - Anderson Plant   (1)
4665 Liberty Hwy, Anderson, SC 29621
Tel.: (864) 224-1671
Textile Fabric Mfr
N.A.I.C.S.: 313310

Glen Raven Custom Fabrics, LLC - Norlina Plant   (1)
Hwy US 1 S, Norlina, NC 27563-0518
Tel.: (252) 456-4141
Textile Fabric Mfr
N.A.I.C.S.: 313310

Glen Raven Filament Fabrics LLC   (1)
73 E United States Hwy 19E, Burnsville, NC 28714
Tel.: (828) 682-2142
Sales Range: $25-49.9 Million
Marketing & Sales for the Filament Fabrics Division
N.A.I.C.S.: 313210

Glen Raven Logistics, Inc.   (1)
3726 Altamahaw Union Rdg Rd, Altamahaw, NC 27202
Tel.: (800) 729-0081
Web Site: http://www.glenravenlogistics.com
Logistics Consulting Servies
N.A.I.C.S.: 541614

Glen Raven Technical Fabrics, LLC   (1)
73 E Hwy 19 E PO Box 100, Burnsville, NC 28714-0100
Tel.: (828) 682-2142
Web Site: http://www.glenraven.com
Produces Filament Fabrics Woven for Outerwear, Sport & Leisure Gear, Luggage, Interlinings, Pocketing, Upholstery, Flags & Industrial Uses
N.A.I.C.S.: 313210
Randy Blackston *(VP)*
Patrick Hennessy *(Dir-Mktg)*

Plant (Domestic):

Glen Raven Technical Fabrics, LLC - Park Avenue Facility   (2)

1821 N Park Ave, Glen Raven, NC 27217-1100
Tel.: (336) 229-5576
Textile Fabric Mfr
N.A.I.C.S.: 313310
Allen Giant *(Pres)*

Glen Raven Transportation Inc.   (1)
3726 Altamahaw Union Ridge Rd, Altamahaw, NC 27202
Tel.: (336) 513-2586
Web Site: http://www.glenraventrans.com
Sales Range: $10-24.9 Million
Emp.: 30
Provider of Transportation Services
N.A.I.C.S.: 484121

Glen Raven, Inc.   (1)
Avenida Arocena 1591 Apartment 203, Carrasco, Montevideo, 11500, Uruguay
Tel.: (598) 26013143
Sales Range: $10-24.9 Million
Emp.: 2
Fabric Distr & Whslr
N.A.I.C.S.: 313310

Glen Raven, Inc.   (1)
11th Floor Mayapada Tower Jalan Jenderal Sudirman Kav 28, Jakarta, 12920, Indonesia
Tel.: (62) 2152897393
Web Site: http://www.glenraven.com
Sales Range: $10-24.9 Million
Emp.: 3
Textile Fabric Mfr
N.A.I.C.S.: 313310
Simon J. Jatliss *(Gen Mgr)*

Sunbury Textiles Mills, Inc.   (1)
1150 Walnut St Ext, Sunbury, PA 17801-0768
Tel.: (570) 286-3800
Web Site: http://www.glenraven.com
Textile Mfr
N.A.I.C.S.: 313210

The Glen Raven Technical Fabrics LLC   (1)
1831 N Park Ave, Glen Raven, NC 27217-1100   (100%)
Tel.: (336) 227-6211
Web Site: http://www.glenraven.com
Sales Range: $10-24.9 Million
Emp.: 18
Commision Dyer & Finisher Specializing in Knitted, Woven & Nonwoven Fabrics
N.A.I.C.S.: 424310
Harold W. Hill *(Pres)*
Ron Payne *(Mgr-Bus Dev-GlenGuard®-Longview)*
Jeff Michel *(VP-Protective Fabrics)*
Rich Lippert *(Dir-Technical-Protective Fabrics)*
Andrew Medley *(Mgr-Bus-Protective Fabrics)*

Trivantage, LLC   (1)
1831 N Park Ave, Glen Raven, NC 27217-1100
Tel.: (336) 227-6211
Web Site: http://www.trivantage.com
Specialty Fabrics Distr
N.A.I.C.S.: 424310
Rett Haigler *(Mgr-Shade Solutions Bus)*

GLEN ROCK SAVINGS BANK
175 Rock Rd, Glen Rock, NJ 07452
Tel.: (201) 652-8776
Web Site:
http://www.glenrockonline.com
Year Founded: 1922
Sales Range: $1-9.9 Million
Emp.: 21
Savings Bank
N.A.I.C.S.: 522180
Ferdinand Viaud *(CFO & Exec VP)*
James D. Smith Sr. *(Exec VP)*

GLENAIR INC.
1211 Air Way, Glendale, CA 91201-2497
Tel.: (818) 247-6000   CA
Web Site: https://www.glenair.com
Year Founded: 1956
Sales Range: $25-49.9 Million
Emp.: 500

Current-Carrying Wiring Devices
N.A.I.C.S.: 335931
Peter D. Kaufman *(Chm & CEO)*

Subsidiaries:

Glenair UK Ltd.   (1)
40 Lower Oakham Way Oakham Business Park, Mansfield, NG18 5BY, Notts, United Kingdom
Tel.: (44) 1623 638100
Web Site: http://www.glenair.co.uk
Emp.: 450
Electronic Connector Mfr
N.A.I.C.S.: 335999
Tony Birks *(Mng Dir)*

GLENCOE CAPITAL LLC
200 N LaSalle St Ste 2150, Chicago, IL 60601
Tel.: (312) 795-6300
Web Site: http://www.glencap.com
Year Founded: 1993
Sales Range: $10-24.9 Million
Emp.: 25
Holding Company
N.A.I.C.S.: 523910
David S. Evans *(Chm & CIO)*
Jason L. Duzan *(Mng Dir)*
G. Douglas Patterson *(Mng Dir)*
Yana Krivozus *(VP)*
Timothy J. Flannery *(VP)*
Julie Vuotto *(CFO)*
Judy Slater *(Chief Compliance Officer & VP)*
Nicholas Iovino *(Asst Controller)*
Douglas S. Kearney *(CEO-DialogDirect)*
Jim Boyle *(Portfolio Fin Officer)*

Subsidiaries:

Child Development Schools, Inc.   (1)
6053 Veterans Pkwy Bldg 300, Columbus, GA 31909
Tel.: (706) 562-8600
Web Site: http://www.childcarenetwork.net
Child Day Care Services
N.A.I.C.S.: 624410
J. Scott Cotter *(Pres & CEO)*

Cincinnati Preserving Company Inc.   (1)
3015 E Kemper Rd, Sharonville, OH 45241
Tel.: (513) 771-2000
Web Site: http://www.clearbrookfarms.com
Fruit & Vegetable Canning Services
N.A.I.C.S.: 311421

Robert Rothschild Farm LLC   (1)
3015 E Kemper Rd, Cincinnati, OH 45241
Tel.: (800) 222-9966
Web Site: http://www.robertrothschild.com
Sales Range: $10-24.9 Million
Emp.: 45
Farm Products Mfr & Distr
N.A.I.C.S.: 111334

GLENCOE REGIONAL HEALTH SERVICES
1805 Hennepin Ave N, Glencoe, MN 55336
Tel.: (320) 864-3121   MN
Web Site: https://www.grhsonline.org
Year Founded: 1999
Sales Range: $25-49.9 Million
Emp.: 640
Health Care Srvices
N.A.I.C.S.: 622110
John Doidge *(VP-Finance)*

GLENCROFT
8611 N 67th Ave, Glendale, AZ 85302
Tel.: (623) 939-9475   AZ
Web Site: https://www.glencroft.com
Year Founded: 1970
Sales Range: $10-24.9 Million
Emp.: 532
Elder Care Services
N.A.I.C.S.: 624120

Glencroft—(Continued)

Heidi Hokanson *(VP-HR)*
Susan M. Hornbostel *(CFO & Sr VP)*
John N. Wenzlau *(Pres & CEO)*
Michael A. McCammond *(CIO)*
Ronald W. Harrold *(Sr Dir-Special Projects)*

GLENDALE DODGE CHRYSLER JEEP
900 S Brand Blvd, Glendale, CA 91204
Tel.: (818) 242-4161
Year Founded: 1980
Sales Range: $10-24.9 Million
Emp.: 52
Car Whslr
N.A.I.C.S.: 441110
Jerry Gordon *(Dir-Svc)*

GLENDALE IRON & METAL CO.
6210 N 55th Ave, Glendale, AZ 85301
Tel.: (623) 931-3701
Web Site: http://www.glendaleironandmetal.com
Rev.: $14,000,000
Emp.: 30
Provider of Recycling Services
N.A.I.C.S.: 562920
Keith Kosier *(VP)*

GLENDALE PLUMBING & FIRE SUPPLY, INC.
11120 Sherman Way, Sun Valley, CA 91352
Tel.: (818) 764-9800
Web Site: https://www.gpfsupply.com
Rev.: $11,300,000
Emp.: 31
Service Establishment Equipment & Supplies Merchant Whslr
N.A.I.C.S.: 423850
Armond Sarkisian *(CEO)*

GLENDIVE MEDICAL CENTER
202 Prospect Dr, Glendive, MT 59330
Tel.: (406) 345-3306   MT
Web Site: https://www.gmc.org
Year Founded: 1964
Sales Range: $25-49.9 Million
Emp.: 565
Health Care Srvices
N.A.I.C.S.: 622110
Sam Hubbard *(VP-Ops)*
Parker Powell *(CEO)*
Jill Domek *(VP-Patient Care Svcs)*
Shawna Dorwart *(VP-Patient Care Svcs)*

GLENDONTODD CAPITAL LLC
2101 Cedar Springs Rd Ste 1540, Dallas, TX 75201
Tel.: (214) 310-1094   TX
Web Site: http://www.gtc.group
Emp.: 12
Equity Investment Firm
N.A.I.C.S.: 523999
Todd Furniss *(CEO & Mng Partner)*
Mary Hatcher *(CFO & Chief Compliance Officer)*
Art Stewart *(Mng Dir)*

Subsidiaries:

Enterra Solutions LLC   (1)
17 Blacksmith Rd Ste 200, Newtown, PA 18940
Tel.: (571) 336-0072
Web Site: http://www.enterrasolutions.com
Sales Range: $1-9.9 Million
Supply Chain Software Publisher
N.A.I.C.S.: 513210
Denise McAuliffe *(VP-HR)*
Stephen DeAngelis *(Pres & CEO)*
Jason Glazier *(CTO & Sr VP)*

Nolan Sklute *(Chief Admin Officer & Gen Counsel)*
Samir Rohatgi *(Sr VP-Client Svcs)*
Glenn Elias *(VP-Client Ops Grp)*
Bradd C. Hayes *(Sr Dir-Comm & Res)*
Keith S. Henry *(Sr VP-Strategic Consulting & Bus Dev)*
Daniel Shaffer *(Sr VP-Consumer Products & Retail Indus Grp)*
Kevin Cunningham *(CFO)*
Kady O'Grady *(Chief People & Culture Officer)*
Yolanda Li *(Mng Dir)*
Roch Boucher *(VP-Platform Dev)*

GLENFARNE GROUP, LLC
292 Madison Ave 19th Fl, New York, NY 10017
Tel.: (212) 500-5454   DE
Web Site: http://www.glenfarnegroup.com
Infrastructure Asset Management & Investment Services
N.A.I.C.S.: 523999
Brendan Duval *(Mng Partner)*

Subsidiaries:

IACX Energy LLC   (1)
Heritage II 5001 LBJ Fwy Ste 300, Dallas, TX 75244
Tel.: (972) 960-3210
Web Site: http://www.iacx.com
Midstream Services
N.A.I.C.S.: 213112
Rex W. Canon *(CEO)*
Jeremy Jordan *(Sr VP-Comml)*
Tony Hines *(Sr VP-Ops)*
Herbert Reinhold *(CTO)*

GLENHILL ADVISORS, LLC
600 5th Ave 11th Fl, New York, NY 10020
Tel.: (646) 432-0600   DE
Holding Company; Investment Advisory & Hedge Fund Management Services
N.A.I.C.S.: 551112
Glenn J. Krevlin *(Mng Partner)*

Subsidiaries:

Glenhill Capital Advisors, LLC   (1)
600 5th Ave 11th Fl, New York, NY 10020
Tel.: (646) 432-0600
Web Site: http://www.glenhillcap.com
Investment Advisory & Hedge Fund Management Services
N.A.I.C.S.: 523940
Glenn J. Krevlin *(Mng Partner)*

Subsidiary (Domestic):

Glenhill Capital Management, LLC   (2)
600 5th Ave 11th Fl, New York, NY 10020
Tel.: (646) 432-0600
Web Site: http://www.glenhillcap.com
Emp.: 17
Hedge Funds Management Services
N.A.I.C.S.: 523940
Glenn J. Krevlin *(Co-Founder & Mng Partner)*

GLENMEADOW, INC.
24 Tabor Crossing, Longmeadow, MA 01106
Tel.: (413) 567-7800   MA
Web Site: https://www.glenmeadow.org
Year Founded: 1884
Sales Range: $1-9.9 Million
Emp.: 256
Elder Care Services
N.A.I.C.S.: 623312
JoAnn Paier *(Dir-Nursing)*
David Leslie *(Controller)*
Linda Edwards *(Dir-Mktg)*
Meghan Reynolds *(Dir-Resident Svcs)*
Dusty Hoyt *(Vice Chm)*
Everett Brown *(Dir-Plant Ops)*

Mark Cress *(Treas)*
Paul Nicholson *(Chm)*
Anne Thomas *(Pres & CEO)*

GLENMORE DISTILLERIES CO
PO Box 1069, Owensboro, KY 42302
Tel.: (270) 926-1110
Web Site: http://www.sazerac.com
Sales Range: $10-24.9 Million
Emp.: 180
Distilled & Blended Liquor Mfr
N.A.I.C.S.: 312140
John Goldring *(Pres)*

GLENN & WRIGHT, INC.
2836 Mary Taylor Rd, Birmingham, AL 35210
Tel.: (205) 836-0188
Web Site: https://www.gwsys.net
Sales Range: $25-49.9 Million
Emp.: 250
Industrial Building Construction Services
N.A.I.C.S.: 236210
A. W. Wright III *(Founder)*
Francis E. Glenn Jr. *(Founder)*

GLENN C BARBER & ASOC.
2801 Plant St, Rapid City, SD 57702-0335
Tel.: (605) 342-7006
Year Founded: 2000
Sales Range: $10-24.9 Million
Emp.: 50
Housing Construction Services
N.A.I.C.S.: 236117
William Barber *(Pres)*

GLENN DISTRIBUTOR INC.
1301 N Wenatchee Ave, Wenatchee, WA 98801-1537
Tel.: (509) 663-7173
Web Site: http://www.glenndistributor.com
Rev.: $94,800,000
Emp.: 19
Petroleum & Petroleum Products Merchant Whslr
N.A.I.C.S.: 424720
Ray Glenn *(Pres)*
Pegi Glenn *(Treas & Sec)*

GLENN E. THOMAS CHRYSLER DODGE JEEP
2100 E Spring St, Signal Hill, CA 90755
Tel.: (562) 426-5111
Web Site: https://www.getdodge.com
Year Founded: 1901
Sales Range: $50-74.9 Million
Emp.: 80
New Car Retailer
N.A.I.C.S.: 441110
Allen King *(CFO)*
Brad Davis *(VP)*
Tom Bonnstetter *(Mgr-Svc)*
Chris Brodeur *(Mgr-Parts)*

GLENN FUQUA, INC.
5698 FM 3455, Navasota, TX 77868
Tel.: (936) 825-7153
Web Site: http://www.glennfuquainc.com
Year Founded: 1973
Sales Range: $10-24.9 Million
Emp.: 85
Highway, Street & Bridge Construction Services
N.A.I.C.S.: 237310
Josh Sechelski *(Project Mgr)*
Daphne Day *(Sec & Office Mgr)*

GLENN H. JOHNSON CONSTRUCTION
1776 Winthrop Dr, Des Plaines, IL 60018

Tel.: (847) 297-4700
Web Site: https://www.ghjohnson.com
Year Founded: 1967
Sales Range: $10-24.9 Million
Emp.: 40
Commercial & Institutional Building Construction Services
N.A.I.C.S.: 236220
Donald J. Voss *(Pres)*
Richard D. Hill *(VP)*
John H. Erickson *(VP)*
Sheroll Ritchie *(Controller & Dir-Info Sys)*

GLENN JONES AUTO CENTER
1932 N Pinal Ave, Casa Grande, AZ 85122
Tel.: (520) 836-3100
Web Site: https://www.jonesautocenters.com
Sales Range: $10-24.9 Million
Emp.: 50
Car Whslr
N.A.I.C.S.: 441110
Terry Behrens *(Mgr-Sls)*

GLENN MACHINE WORKS, INC.
734 Hwy 45 S, Columbus, MS 39701
Tel.: (662) 328-4611
Web Site: https://www.glennmachineworks.com
Year Founded: 1957
Machine Shops
N.A.I.C.S.: 332710
Lisa Burchfield *(COO)*

GLENN NISSAN INC.
3360 Richmond Rd, Lexington, KY 40509
Tel.: (859) 263-5020
Web Site: http://www.glennnissan.com
Sales Range: $25-49.9 Million
Emp.: 70
Car Dealership
N.A.I.C.S.: 441110
Barry Henderson *(Dir-Nissan Parts)*
Jason Branham *(Gen Mgr)*

GLENN O. HAWBAKER, INC.
1952 Waddle Rd Ste 203, State College, PA 16803-1649
Tel.: (814) 237-1444   PA
Web Site: https://www.goh-inc.com
Year Founded: 1952
Sales Range: $75-99.9 Million
Emp.: 120
Crushed Stone & Paving Product Service
N.A.I.C.S.: 237310
Daniel R. Hawbaker *(Pres & CEO)*
D. Michael Hawbaker *(Exec VP)*
Michael Hawbaker *(Exec VP)*
Patrick Hawbaker *(Exec VP)*

Subsidiaries:

Hawbaker Engineering, LLC   (1)
1952 Waddle Rd Ste 201, State College, PA 16803
Tel.: (800) 284-8590
Web Site: http://www.hawbakerengineering.com
Civil Engineering Services
N.A.I.C.S.: 541330

GLENN POLK AUTOPLEX, INC.
4320 N I 35, Gainesville, TX 76240
Tel.: (940) 665-3461
Web Site: http://www.glennpolkautoplex.net
Sales Range: $10-24.9 Million
Emp.: 30
Car Whslr
N.A.I.C.S.: 441110

Glenn Polk *(Pres)*

GLENN RIEDER, INC.
3420 W Capitol Dr, Milwaukee, WI
53216
Tel.: (414) 449-2888
Web Site: http://www.glennrieder.com
Year Founded: 1945
Sales Range: $10-24.9 Million
Emp.: 100
Millwork Services
N.A.I.C.S.: 321918
Dan Carey *(VP-Estimating & Global
Procurement)*
Pat Murphy *(Gen Mgr-Sls)*
Michael Floyd *(CEO)*
James Caragher *(COO & Gen Counsel)*
Nicholas P. Willems *(CFO)*

Subsidiaries:

Palm City Millwork, Inc.   **(1)**
3313 SW 42nd Ave, Palm City, FL 34991
Tel.: (772) 288-7086
Web Site: http://www.palmcitymillwork.com
Wood Window & Door Mfr.
N.A.I.C.S.: 321911
Frank J. Carr *(Pres)*

GLENN SALES COMPANY INC.
6425 Powers Ferry Rd NW, Atlanta,
GA 30339-2913
Tel.: (770) 952-9292   **GA**
Web Site: http://www.glennsales.com
Year Founded: 1954
Sales Range: $10-24.9 Million
Emp.: 10
Supplier of Fish & Seafoods
N.A.I.C.S.: 424460
Bruce Pearlman *(Pres)*
Cliff Cohen *(VP)*

GLENN THURMAN, INC.
3212 Pioneer Rd, Mesquite, TX
75185
Tel.: (972) 286-6333   **TX**
Web Site:
    http://www.glennthurmaninc.com
Year Founded: 1972
Sales Range: $25-49.9 Million
Emp.: 150
Heavy Highway & Street Construction
Contractor
N.A.I.C.S.: 237310
C. Glenn Thurman *(Pres)*
Bobby Clark *(Mgr-Shop)*
Gary Maynor *(Exec VP)*
Ronnie Millar *(Project Mgr)*
Chad San Juan *(Project Mgr)*
Tom Pennell *(Mgr-QA & QC)*
Les Foster *(COO & Exec VP)*

GLENNON BITTAN INVESTMENTS
631 Dickinson Ave Ste B, Greenville,
NC 27834
Tel.: (252) 321-8780
Year Founded: 1992
Sales Range: $10-24.9 Million
Emp.: 7
Real Estate Investors
N.A.I.C.S.: 523999
Thomas Glennon *(Pres)*

GLENPOINTE ASSOCIATES II LLC
25 Main St, Hackensack, NJ 07601
Tel.: (201) 342-2777
Web Site: http://www.sanzari.com
Rev.: $13,500,000
Emp.: 35
Commercial & Industrial Building Operation
N.A.I.C.S.: 531120
John Colardi *(CFO)*

GLENRO INC.
39 McBride Ave, Paterson, NJ 07501
Tel.: (973) 279-5900
Web Site: https://www.glenro.com
Year Founded: 1958
Sales Range: $10-24.9 Million
Emp.: 80
Heat Transfer Systems
N.A.I.C.S.: 333994
John Rasmussen *(Mgr-Svc)*
Eric Hummel *(Reg Mgr-Sls)*
Mike Papapietro *(Mgr-Ops)*

GLENROY CONSTRUCTION CO. INC.
450 S Ritter Ave, Indianapolis, IN
46219-7123
Tel.: (317) 359-9501   **IN**
Web Site:
    https://www.glenroyconstruction.com
Year Founded: 1945
Sales Range: $75-99.9 Million
Emp.: 25
Provider of Construction & Contracting Services
N.A.I.C.S.: 236210
C. Lane Slaughter *(Pres)*

GLENROY INC.
W 158 N 9332 Nor-X-Way, Menomonee Falls, WI 53051
Tel.: (262) 255-4422
Web Site: http://www.glenroy.com
Sales Range: $25-49.9 Million
Emp.: 200
Packaging Mfr
N.A.I.C.S.: 326113
Kimberly Weiss *(Acct Mgr)*
Tom Danneker *(Pres & CEO)*
William Dopp *(CFO)*
Teri Green *(Dir-HR & Organizational
Dev)*
Brian Hodek *(Dir-Food & Beverage)*
Steve Nichols *(VP-Sls & Mktg)*

GLENS FOOD CENTER INCORPORATED
205 E Warren, Luverne, MN 56156
Tel.: (507) 283-4429
Web Site: http://www.glens-food.com
Sales Range: $10-24.9 Million
Emp.: 85
Grocery Stores, Independent
N.A.I.C.S.: 445110
Glen Gust *(Owner)*

GLENWAY DISTRIBUTION
73 Station Rd, Cranbury, NJ 08512
Tel.: (732) 593-0010
Web Site:
    https://www.glenwaydistribution.com
Year Founded: 2001
Integrated Logistics, Warehousing &
Distribution Services
N.A.I.C.S.: 493110
Tracey Murnane *(Mgr-Logistics)*

GLENWAY MOTOR CAR CO., INC.
6135 Harrison Ave, Cincinnati, OH
45247
Tel.: (513) 251-5555
Web Site: https://www.glenway.com
Sales Range: $10-24.9 Million
Emp.: 65
Car Whslr
N.A.I.C.S.: 441110
Mark Ackerman *(Co-Owner)*
Phillip Purkiser *(Co-Owner)*

GLENWOOD LLC
PO Box 5419, Englewood, NJ 07631-
5419
Tel.: (201) 569-0050

Web Site: http://www.glenwood-
llc.com
Year Founded: 1997
Sales Range: $10-24.9 Million
Emp.: 20
Pharmaceutical Preparation Mfr
N.A.I.C.S.: 325412
Judith Gacita *(Controller)*

GLENWOOD SPRINGS FORD, INC.
55 Storm King Rd, Glenwood
Springs, CO 81601
Tel.: (970) 945-2317   **CO**
Web Site:
    http://www.glenwoodspringsford.com
Year Founded: 1978
Sales Range: $50-74.9 Million
Emp.: 70
Automobiles, New & Used
N.A.I.C.S.: 441110
Jeff Carlson *(Pres)*
Steve Nilsson *(Gen Mgr)*
Ryan White *(Controller)*

GLESBY BUILDING MATERIALS CO.
15119 Oxnard St, Van Nuys, CA
91411
Tel.: (818) 785-2166
Web Site: http://www.glesby.com
Sales Range: $10-24.9 Million
Emp.: 45
Provider of Building Materials
N.A.I.C.S.: 423310
Anne Hunt *(Controller)*

GLESBY-MARKS LTD
10200 Richmond Ave Ste 100, Houston, TX 77042
Tel.: (713) 361-0011
Web Site:
    https://www.glesbymarks.com
Rev.: $92,800,000
Emp.: 20
Leasing Company
N.A.I.C.S.: 522220

GLIMCHER GROUP INCORPORATED
500 Grant St BNY Mellon Ctr Ste
2000, Pittsburgh, PA 15219
Tel.: (412) 765-3333   **PA**
Web Site:
    http://www.glimchergroup.com
Year Founded: 1984
Retail Shopping Centers Acquisition,
Development & Property Management Services
N.A.I.C.S.: 531390
Craig A. Polard *(VP-Leasing & Brokerage)*
Diane E. DiGuilio *(VP & Controller)*
Robert I. Glimcher *(Pres)*
Matthew G. Cochran *(VP-Asset
Mgmt)*

GLIMMER, INC.
9 S Columbia St, Naperville, IL 60540
Tel.: (630) 330-8747
Year Founded: 2004
Sales Range: Less than $1 Million
Emp.: 11
Advertising Services
N.A.I.C.S.: 541890
Brian Eveslage *(Pres)*

GLINES & RHODES, INC.
189 E St, Attleboro, MA 02703-4210
Tel.: (508) 226-2000   **MA**
Web Site:
    https://www.glinesandrhodes.com
Year Founded: 1915
Sales Range: $10-24.9 Million
Emp.: 28
Processor of Precious Metals

N.A.I.C.S.: 331410
Ralph Crowell *(Pres)*
Douglas Jost *(VP-Mfg)*
Richard Lunn *(VP-Fin)*
Michael Powers *(VP-Sls)*

GLISSEN CHEMICAL CO. INC.
1321 58th St, Brooklyn, NY 11219
Tel.: (718) 436-4200
Sales Range: $10-24.9 Million
Emp.: 100
Producer of Detergents
N.A.I.C.S.: 325611
Joseph W. Lehr *(CEO)*
Barbara Lehr *(Pres)*

GLK FOODS, LLC
400 Clark St, Bear Creek, WI 54922
Tel.: (715) 752-4105   **WI**
Web Site: http://www.krispkraut.com
Year Founded: 1900
Sales Range: $100-124.9 Million
Emp.: 200
Mfr of Sauerkraut
N.A.I.C.S.: 311421
Ryan M. Downs *(Gen Mgr)*

GLM LANDSCAPE SUPPLY, LLC
13975 Hwy 9 N, Alpharetta, GA
30004-3239
Tel.: (770) 066-8200
Web Site: http://www.glmsod.com
Landscaping Services
N.A.I.C.S.: 561730
Garry Gallas *(Owner)*
Britt Thomas *(Pres-Div)*

Subsidiaries:

Rock Yard Inc.   **(1)**
2348 Monroe Dr, Gainesville, GA 30507-
7368
Tel.: (770) 232-0154
Web Site: http://www.therockyardinc.com
Brick, Stone & Related Construction Materials Whslr
N.A.I.C.S.: 423320

GLN INC.
207 S Broadway St, Checotah, OK
74426
Tel.: (918) 473-2369
Web Site: http://www.glninc.com
Sales Range: $25-49.9 Million
Emp.: 9
Grocery Stores, Independent
N.A.I.C.S.: 445110
Gary L. Nichols *(Pres)*

GLOBAL ACCESS UNLIMITED INC.
4205 116th Ter N, Clearwater, FL
33762-4972
Tel.: (727) 538-2528
Web Site: http://www.gauinc.com
Sales Range: $10-24.9 Million
Emp.: 3
Electronic Parts & Equipment, Nec
N.A.I.C.S.: 423690
Dana Bauer *(Pres)*
Charlie Bauer *(VP)*

GLOBAL ADVERTISING STRATEGIES, INC.
55 Broad St 19th Fl, New York, NY
10004
Tel.: (212) 964-0030
Web Site: http://www.global-ny.com
Year Founded: 1999
Rev.: $18,600,000
Emp.: 45
N.A.I.C.S.: 541810
Givi Topchishvili *(Founder & Pres)*
Leiann S. Kaytmaz *(Dir-HR)*
Olena Kushch *(Acct Dir)*

Global Advertising Strategies, Inc.—(Continued)

Jesse Williamson *(Dir-Bus Dev)*
Lena Feygin *(Dir-Special Projects)*
Alexander Aksenov *(Exec Dir-Creative)*

Subsidiaries:

Prime Access, Inc. (1)
345 7th Ave, New York, NY 10001
Tel.: (212) 868-6800
Web Site: http://www.prime-access.com
Advertising Services
N.A.I.C.S.: 541810
Howard Buford *(Pres)*
Jose Monfort *(CFO & VP)*
Sharman Davis *(Dir-Media)*
Angela Walker Campbell *(VP & Exec Dir-Creative)*
Sophy Regelous *(VP & Dir-Digital Media)*
Andy Bagnall *(VP & Grp Acct Dir)*
Chip Weinstein *(CEO)*
Harrisen Kim *(VP-Creative Svcs)*
Deborah Katz *(Sr VP-Client Svcs)*

GLOBAL AG ASSOCIATES INC.
2650 W Market St, York, PA 17404
Tel.: (717) 792-2481
Rev.: $12,000,000
Emp.: 150
Garden Supplies & Tools
N.A.I.C.S.: 444240
Hank Yohe *(Owner)*

GLOBAL AIRCRAFT SERVICE, INC.
320 Andover Park E Ste 100, Seattle, WA 98188
Tel.: (425) 264-0335
Web Site: http://www.gairservices.com
Year Founded: 2000
Sales Range: $10-24.9 Million
Emp.: 5
Placement for New & Used Jet Aircraft
N.A.I.C.S.: 488190
Kenneth A. Moninski *(Pres)*
Marshall Frantz *(Gen Mgr)*

GLOBAL AXCESS CORP.
7800 Belfort Pkwy Ste 165, Jacksonville, FL 32256
Tel.: (904) 280-3950   NV
Web Site: http://www.globalaxcess.biz
Year Founded: 1984
Sales Range: $25-49.9 Million
Emp.: 45
Holding Company; Automated Teller Machine & DVD Self-Service Kiosk Management Services
N.A.I.C.S.: 551112

Subsidiaries:

Nationwide Ntertainment Services, Inc. (1)
7800 Belfort Pkwy Ste 165, Jacksonville, FL 32256
Tel.: (904) 280-3950
Web Site: http://www.nationwidentertainment.com
DVD Self-Service Kiosk Management Services
N.A.I.C.S.: 561499

GLOBAL BEAUTY IMAGE, INC.
4897 W Waters Ave Ste F, Tampa, FL 33634
Tel.: (813) 374-9180
Web Site: http://www.globalbeautyimage.com
Sales Range: $10-24.9 Million
Emp.: 14
Hair Care Products Distr
N.A.I.C.S.: 424690
Juan Angarita *(Co-Owner)*
Marcela Angarita *(Co-Owner)*

GLOBAL BEHAVIORAL SOLUTIONS LLC
3565 Piedmont Rd Bldg 2 Ste 700, Atlanta, GA 30305
Tel.: (404) 949-0541
Web Site: https://www.gbehavior.com
Year Founded: 2003
Wellness, Safety Incentive Programs & Rewards Fullfilment Services
N.A.I.C.S.: 923120
Don Doster *(CEO)*

Subsidiaries:

RivalHealth, LLC (1)
1174 1121 Situs Ct Ste 190, Raleigh, NC 27606,
Tel.: (888) 949-1001
Web Site: http://www.rivalhealth.com
Fitness & Nutrition Solutions
N.A.I.C.S.: 713940

GLOBAL BRIGADES, INC.
1099 E Champlain Dr Ste A176, Fresno, CA 93720
Tel.: (206) 489-4798   CA
Web Site: https://www.globalbrigades.org
Year Founded: 2007
Sales Range: $10-24.9 Million
Emp.: 1
Foster Care Services
N.A.I.C.S.: 624110
Vanessa Lopez *(Pres & CEO)*
Leonel Quinteros *(Dir-Tech)*
Duffy Casey *(Co-Founder)*
Catherine Berman *(Co-Founder)*
Nancy Amador *(Chief Compliance Officer)*
Pallav Vora *(Chief Legal Officer)*
Shital Vora *(CEO)*

GLOBAL BUSINESS CENTERS CORP.
468 N Camden Dr 2nd Fl, Beverly Hills, CA 90210
Tel.: (310) 858-5558
Web Site: https://www.gbcone.com
Year Founded: 1995
Sales Range: $1-9.9 Million
Emp.: 13
Virtual Offices & Services
N.A.I.C.S.: 561499
Dan Maayan *(Pres)*

GLOBAL BUSINESS CONSULTING SERVICES, INC.
489 Plainfield Rd, Edison, NJ 08820
Tel.: (732) 548-4000
Web Site: http://www.gbcs-usa.com
Year Founded: 2003
Sales Range: $10-24.9 Million
Emp.: 70
Business & IT Consulting Services
N.A.I.C.S.: 541618
Pradeep Nigam *(CEO)*

GLOBAL BUSINESS SOLUTIONS, INC.
2400 W Michigan Ave Ste 4, Pensacola, FL 32526
Tel.: (850) 944-7579
Web Site: https://www.gbsi.com
Year Founded: 1995
Sales Range: $10-24.9 Million
Emp.: 102
IT Consulting & Support Services
N.A.I.C.S.: 541519
Randy Ramos *(CEO)*
Frank Smith *(Dir-Bus Dev)*
Johnson Warwick *(Dir-Global Brdcst Svcs)*
Steve Greunke *(Mgr-Bus Dev)*

GLOBAL BUSINESS SUPPORT SYSTEMS, INC.

6310 Nancy Ridge Dr Ste 103, San Diego, CA 92121-3209
Tel.: (858) 784-6904
Web Site: http://www.testcountry.com
Year Founded: 2002
Sales Range: $1-9.9 Million
Emp.: 13
Drug Testing & Laboratory Services
N.A.I.C.S.: 541380
Serhat Pala *(CEO)*

GLOBAL BUSINESS TRAVEL ASSOCIATION
123 N Pitt St, Alexandria, VA 22314
Tel.: (703) 684-0836   NY
Web Site: http://www.gbta.org
Year Founded: 1968
Sales Range: $10-24.9 Million
Emp.: 67
Educational Association
N.A.I.C.S.: 813910
Rebecca Bateman *(Sr Mgr-Event Ops)*
Hema Shah *(CFO & Sr VP)*
Getnesh Amde *(Fin Mgr)*
Liz Huh *(VP-Ops)*
Scott A. Solombrino *(CEO)*
Bhart Sarin *(Pres)*

GLOBAL CAPITAL CORP.
140 E Stewart Huston Dr, Coatesville, PA 19320
Tel.: (610) 857-1900
Web Site: http://www.ramkmasters.com
Rev.: $13,000,000
Emp.: 32
Provider of Trucks & Construction Equipment
N.A.I.C.S.: 333924
Mike Wilkinson *(Pres)*
Robert G. Watkins Jr. *(Chm)*

Subsidiaries:

General Transervice Inc. (1)
140 Stewart Huston Dr, Coatesville, PA 19320
Tel.: (610) 857-1900
Web Site: http://www.rampmasters.com
Rev.: $4,000,000
Emp.: 30
Provider of Trucks & Construction Equipment
N.A.I.C.S.: 333924
Dan Watkins *(CFO)*
Kevin Ward *(VP-Sls & Mktg)*
Mike Matza *(VP-Tech & Bus Process)*
Tim Porter *(Mgr-Production)*
Ed Sell *(Dir-Engrg)*
Owen Watkins *(COO)*
Robert Watkins *(Founder & Chm)*
Mike Wilkinson *(Co-CEO)*
Leighton Yohannan *(Co-CEO)*

Omni American Inc. (1)
211 W Stewart Huston Dr, Coatesville, PA, 19320
Tel.: (610) 857-1900
Provider of Truck Leasing Services
N.A.I.C.S.: 532120

GLOBAL CAPITAL LIMITED
205 W Wacker Dr Ste 730, Chicago, IL 60606
Tel.: (312) 846-6918
Web Site: http://www.globalcapitalltd.com
Year Founded: 1999
Sales Range: $10-24.9 Million
Emp.: 5
Asset Management & Leasing Services
N.A.I.C.S.: 525990
Terri McNally *(Pres & CEO)*

GLOBAL CELLULAR INC.
6485 Shiloh Rd Bldg B-100, Alpharetta, GA 30005
Tel.: (678) 513-4020

Web Site: https://www.cellairis.com
Sales Range: $10-24.9 Million
Emp.: 230
Mobile Device Accessory Retailer
N.A.I.C.S.: 423690
Taki Skouras *(CEO)*

GLOBAL CHEM INTERNATIONAL INC.
103 Holmes Rd, Ridgefield, CT 06877
Tel.: (203) 431-4500
Rev.: $15,464,825
Emp.: 3
Resin Mfr
N.A.I.C.S.: 424610
Stephen Shiller *(Pres)*

GLOBAL CLOTHING NETWORK INC.
600 Meadowlands Pkwy 17, Secaucus, NJ 07094
Tel.: (201) 422-7400
Sales Range: $10-24.9 Million
Emp.: 5
Men's & Boy's Clothing
N.A.I.C.S.: 424350
Michael T Mehta *(Pres)*
P. K. Thenna *(Vp)*

GLOBAL COMMERCE & INFORMATION, INC.
7008 Security Blvd Ste 210, Windsor Mill, MD 21244
Tel.: (410) 363-0161
Web Site: http://www.globalci.com
Year Founded: 1992
Data Processing, Hosting & Related Services
N.A.I.C.S.: 518210
Mike Ziman *(Founder & CEO)*
Juanita Thomas *(Mgr-HR)*
Michael Parrish *(COO)*
Stanley Soldz *(CFO)*
Chris Crouse *(CIO)*
Kurt Seiden *(Mgr-Bus Dev & Acct)*
Bill Monachino *(Head-Comml Bus Div & Exec VP)*

Subsidiaries:

MMY Consulting, Inc. (1)
5719 Lawton Loop E Dr #103, Indianapolis, IN 46216
Tel.: (317) 846-9500
Web Site: http://www.mmyconsulting.com
Technology Consulting Firm
N.A.I.C.S.: 541690
Kelly Butler *(Mgr-Bus Dev)*

GLOBAL COMMUNICATION NETWORKS INC.
4699 N Federal Highway #105, Pompano Beach, FL 33064
Web Site: http://www.gcnsolutions.com
Year Founded: 1997
Sales Range: $1-9.9 Million
Emp.: 9
Voice, Data, Colocation & Managed Data Center Services Solutions
N.A.I.C.S.: 518210
Christopher Palermo *(CEO, Founder & Pres)*

GLOBAL COMMUNICATIONS GROUP, INC.
10333 E Dry Creek Rd Ste 320, Englewood, CO 80112
Tel.: (303) 865-9000
Web Site: http://www.gcgcom.com
Year Founded: 2003
Sales Range: $1-9.9 Million
Emp.: 24
Telecommunication Management Consulting Services
N.A.I.C.S.: 541618

Joel Saint-Germain *(CEO)*
Heidi Humphreys *(VP-Ops)*
Bob West *(VP-Mktg)*

GLOBAL CONCEPTS ENTER-PRISE

785 Waverly Ct, Holland, MI 49423
Tel.: (616) 355-7657
Web Site:
https://www.globalconcepts.com
Sales Range: $25-49.9 Million
Emp.: 55
Industrial Machinery & Equipment
N.A.I.C.S.: 423830
Robert Rynbrandt *(Pres)*
Barry Slinkman *(Mgr-Production)*

GLOBAL CONSTRUCTORS LLC.

3900 C St Ste 303, Anchorage, AK 99503
Tel.: (907) 339-6725
Rev.: $800,000
Emp.: 5
Commercial & Institutional Building Construction
N.A.I.C.S.: 236220
Roberta Quintavell *(Mgr)*

GLOBAL CONSUMER ACQUI-SITION CORP.

1926 Rand Ridge Ct, Marietta, GA 30062
Tel.: (404) 939-9419   DE
Year Founded: 2020
Assets: $183,907,872
Liabilities: $197,133,434
Net Worth: ($13,225,562)
Earnings: $1,143,620
Emp.: 1
Fiscal Year-end: 12/31/21
Investment Services
N.A.I.C.S.: 523999
Rohan Ajila *(Co-Chm, CEO & CFO)*
Gautham Pai *(Co-Chm)*

GLOBAL CONVERGENCE SO-LUTIONS, INC.

239 Prospect Plains Rd Ste A101, Monroe Township, NJ 08831
Tel.: (732) 853-0510   DE
Web Site:
http://www.globalconverge.com
Sales Range: $1-9.9 Million
Emp.: 12
Information Technology Services
N.A.I.C.S.: 541512
Jay Meranchik *(CTO & Pres)*
Chris Birdsall *(Exec VP-Worldwide Sls)*

GLOBAL CONVERGENCE, INC.

700 Brooker Creek Blvd Ste 1000, Oldsmar, FL 34677
Tel.: (813) 925-6021   FL
Web Site:
http://www.globalconvergence.com
Year Founded: 2008
Emp.: 200
Holding Company; Information Tech-nology Products & Services
N.A.I.C.S.: 551112
James Bradshaw *(Chm & CEO)*
Peter A. Cammick *(Sr VP-Sls-Global)*
Vic Berggren *(CTO)*
Richard Lewis *(Sr VP-OEM Svcs-Global & Dev)*
John Medaska *(Chief Revenue Offi-cer)*
John Keenan *(Exec VP-Svc Strategy & Architecture)*

Subsidiaries:

Interlink Communication Systems, Inc.   (1)

700 Brooker Creek Blvd Ste 1000, Oldsmar, FL 34677-2934
Tel.: (813) 818-8597
Web Site: http://www.interlinkweb.com
Sales Range: $10-24.9 Million
Emp.: 70
Specialty Information Technology Products & Services Distr
N.A.I.C.S.: 423430
James Bradshaw *(Chm & CEO)*
Ann Schaner *(Dir-Mktg)*
John Jeromin *(CFO)*
Joseph Serra Jr. *(Pres & COO)*

Network Dynamics Inc.   (1)
700 Brooker Creek Blvd Ste 1000, Oldsmar, FL 34677
Tel.: (813) 818-8597
Web Site: http://www.ndiwebsite.com
Emp.: 110
Information Technology Support Services
N.A.I.C.S.: 541990
James Bradshaw *(Chm & CEO)*
Richard Lewis *(Sr VP-Strategic Sls)*
John Keenan *(Exec VP-Svc Strategy & Ar-chitecture)*
Vic Berggren *(CTO)*
Jim Blackman *(Sr VP-Strategic Sls)*
John Medaska *(Chief Revenue Officer)*

GLOBAL CORNERSTONE HOLDINGS LIMITED

352 Park Ave S 13th Fl, New York, NY 10010
Tel.: (212) 822-8165   VG
Web Site:
http://www.globalcornerstone.com
Year Founded: 2011
Sales Range: Less than $1 Million
Investment Services
N.A.I.C.S.: 523999
Byron I. Sproule *(CFO & Exec VP)*
James D. Dunning Jr. *(Chm & CEO)*

GLOBAL CREDIT UNION

1520 W 3rd Ave, Spokane, WA 99201
Tel.: (509) 455-4700
Web Site: http://www.globalcu.org
Rev.: $19,700,000
Emp.: 150
Credit Union
N.A.I.C.S.: 522130
Jack L. Fallis Jr. *(Treas)*

GLOBAL DATA MANAGEMENT SYSTEMS, LLC

1816 West Point Pike #210, Lans-dale, PA 19446
Tel.: (877) 866-2747
Web Site: http://www.globaldms.com
Year Founded: 2003
Sales Range: $1-9.9 Million
Emp.: 20
Develops Commercial & Residential Real Estate Appraisal Software & Collateral Management Technologies
N.A.I.C.S.: 513210
Vladimir Bien-Aime *(Pres & CEO)*
Matt McHale *(Chief Revenue Officer)*
Mac Chiles *(Exec VP-Sls)*
Michael Quaranto *(VP-Dev)*
Julie Bussey *(Dir-Accts-Natl)*

GLOBAL DATA SYSTEMS INC.

310 Laser Ln, Lafayette, LA 70507
Tel.: (337) 291-6500
Web Site: https://www.getgds.com
Year Founded: 1987
Sales Range: $25-49.9 Million
Emp.: 100
Computer & Communication System Design Services
N.A.I.C.S.: 541512
Charles Vincent *(Chm & CEO)*
Chris Vincent *(Pres)*
Robert Guidry *(CTO)*
Mark Ditsious *(CFO)*
Ned Fasullo *(CMO)*
Rich Stewart *(Dir-HR/HSE)*

Vaughn Crisp *(VP-Sls-Energy Sector)*
Wade Berzas *(VP-Sls)*
Toby DuBois *(Chief Mktg Officer)*

GLOBAL DATA VAULT, LLC

900 Jackson St Ste 220, Dallas, TX 75202
Tel.: (214) 363-1900
Web Site:
http://www.globaldatavault.com
Year Founded: 2004
Sales Range: $1-9.9 Million
Emp.: 10
Information Technology Development Services
N.A.I.C.S.: 541511
Will Baccich *(CEO)*

GLOBAL DIVERSIFIED INDUS-TRIES, INC.

1200 Airport Dr, Chowchilla, CA 93610
Tel.: (559) 665-5800   NV
Web Site: http://www.gdvi.net
Sales Range: Less than $1 Million
Emp.: 50
Modular Construction Services
N.A.I.C.S.: 321991
Philip Hamilton *(Chm, Pres & CEO)*
Adam DeBard *(Treas & Sec)*

GLOBAL DIVING & SALVAGE, INC.

3840 W Marginal Way SW, Seattle, WA 98106
Tel.: (206) 623-0621
Web Site: http://www.gdiving.com
Rev.: $29,300,000
Emp.: 250
Remediation Services
N.A.I.C.S.: 562910
Bruce Humberstone *(Mgr-Off Shores)*
John Graham *(Founder)*
Mike Langen *(VP-Marine Construc-tions)*
Tim Beaver *(Founder)*
Trinity Ng-Yeung *(VP-Fin & Admin)*
Devon Grennan *(Pres & CEO)*
Ben Daily *(Mgr-Dive Ops-Alaska)*
Jennifer Jensen *(VP-Quality Assur-ance)*
Mike Brown *(VP-Energy Svcs-Houston)*
Renee Gowdy *(VP-Marine Construc-tion, Engrg & Tech)*
Dan Pierson *(VP-Ops)*
Alisa Preston *(Dir-Marine Tech)*

GLOBAL DOMAINS INTERNA-TIONAL, INC.

701 Palomar Airport Rd Ste 300, Carlsbad, CA 92011
Tel.: (760) 602-3000
Web Site: http://www.website.ws
Year Founded: 1996
Rev.: $10,000,000
Emp.: 35
Sales of Website Domains
N.A.I.C.S.: 517810
Chris Murch *(Dir-Military Out Reach Program)*

GLOBAL DRILLING SUPPLI-ERS INC.

12101 Centron Pl, Cincinnati, OH 45246
Tel.: (513) 671-8700
Web Site:
http://www.globaldrilsup.com
Sales Range: $10-24.9 Million
Emp.: 30
Mining Machinery
N.A.I.C.S.: 423810
Mark Kuenning *(Pres & Treas)*
Brian Walker *(Gen Mgr)*

GLOBAL EDM SUPPLIES, INC.

7697 Innovation Way Ste 400, Ma-son, OH 45040
Web Site: http://www.gedms.com
Sales Range: $1-9.9 Million
Emp.: 50
Electrical Discharge Machine Distr
N.A.I.C.S.: 423830
Gregg Lund *(CEO)*

Subsidiaries:

EDM Supplies, Inc.   (1)
9806 Everest St, Downey, CA 90242
Tel.: (562) 803-6563
Web Site: http://www.edmsupply.com
Provider of Industrial Supplies
N.A.I.C.S.: 423840

GLOBAL EMPLOYMENT HOLDINGS, INC.

10375 Park Mdws Ste 475, Lone Tree, CO 80124-6760
Tel.: (303) 216-9500   DE
Year Founded: 1998
Sales Range: $150-199.9 Million
Emp.: 15,000
Staffing, Executive Search & Human Resource Consulting Services
N.A.I.C.S.: 561320

Subsidiaries:

Fahrenheit IT, Inc.   (1)
103 Pk Meadows Dr Ste 475, Littleton, CO 80124
Tel.: (770) 500-1615
Web Site: http://www.fahrenheitit.com
Professional Employer Organizations
N.A.I.C.S.: 561330

Subsidiary (Domestic):

Information Technology Engineering Corp.   (2)
9635 Maroon Cir Ste 420, Englewood, CO 80112
Tel.: (303) 261-3371
Web Site: http://www.teamitec.com
Sales Range: $1-9.9 Million
Emp.: 20
Staffing Services
N.A.I.C.S.: 561311
John Allen *(Founder & CEO)*
Randy Dingle *(Exec VP & COO)*

The Halo Group, LLC   (2)
39475 W 13 Mile Rd Ste 201, Novi, MI 48377-2359
Tel.: (877) 456-4256
Web Site: http://fahrenheitit.com
Computer System Design Services
N.A.I.C.S.: 541512

GLOBAL ENGINEERING SO-LUTIONS, INC.

6700 A Rockledge Dr Ste 301, Bethesda, MD 20817
Tel.: (301) 216-2871
Web Site: http://www.theges.com
Year Founded: 2002
Sales Range: $1-9.9 Million
Emp.: 35
Engineeering Services
N.A.I.C.S.: 541330
Laleh Zargarinejad *(Pres)*

GLOBAL EQUITY CAPITAL, LLC

6260 Lookout Rd, Boulder, CO 80301
Tel.: (303) 531-1000
Privater Equity Firm
N.A.I.C.S.: 523999
Michael Adkins *(Sr VP-Ops)*
Edmund Aston *(Sr VP-European Ops)*
Angela Blatteis *(Mng Dir)*
Alan Byrne *(Sr VP-HR)*
Michael Hirano *(Exec VP-Ops)*

Global Equity Capital, LLC—(Continued)

Catherine Babon Scanlon *(Mng Dir & CFO)*
Thomas Waldman *(Exec VP-Legal)*
Lindsay Wynter *(Sr VP-Fin)*

Subsidiaries:

Essintial Enterprise Solutions (1)
1 Sterling Pl 100 Sterling Pkwy Ste 100,
Mechanicsburg, PA 17050
Tel.: (717) 610-3200
Web Site: http://www.essintial.com
Information Technology Services
N.A.I.C.S.: 541519
Tom York *(CEO)*
Craig Heck *(Gen Mgr)*
Greg Lorenzen *(VP-Bus Dev)*
Tom Clauser *(VP-Bus Intelligence & Solutions)*
Dale Drendall *(CFO)*
Jerry Hooks *(CIO)*

GLOBAL ESCIENCE CORP.
350 S Ctr Ste 500, Reno, NV 89501
Tel.: (775) 321-8211
Wireless Telecommunication Services
N.A.I.C.S.: 517112
Virgil Hentz *(Chm & CEO)*

GLOBAL EXECUTIVE SOLUTIONS GROUP, LLC
3505 Embassy Pkwy Ste 200, Fairlawn, OH 44333
Tel.: (330) 666-3354   OH
Web Site: https://www.globalesg.com
Year Founded: 2001
Sales Range: $1-9.9 Million
Emp.: 27
Executive Placement Services
N.A.I.C.S.: 541612
Jim Chadbourne *(Mng Partner)*
Scott Chadbourne *(Mng Dir)*

GLOBAL FOCUS GROUP
55 Champlain Ct, Manahawkin, NJ 08050
Tel.: (917) 653-0154
Year Founded: 2008
Sales Range: Less than $1 Million
Emp.: 2
Advetising Agency
N.A.I.C.S.: 541810
Edward Juarez *(Pres)*

GLOBAL FORWARDING ENTERPRISES LIMITED LIABILITY COMPANY
348 Rt 9 N Suite G, Manalapan, NJ 07726
Web Site:
   http://www.globalforwarding.com
Year Founded: 2008
Sales Range: $1-9.9 Million
Emp.: 20
Logistics Specialists in Carrier, Supply Chain & Warehouse Management
N.A.I.C.S.: 488510
Pavel Kapelnikov *(Pres & CEO)*

GLOBAL FUND INVESTMENTS LLC
4125 NW 88th Ave, Sunrise, FL 33351
Tel.: (305) 535-6305
Web Site:
   https://www.gfinvestments.com
Sales Range: $1-9.9 Million
Emp.: 20
Commercial Real Estate Investment & Management Services
N.A.I.C.S.: 531390
Doron Valero *(Mng Partner)*
Alan Merkur *(Principal)*
Rafi Zitvar *(Principal)*
Stephen Frazier *(Mgr-Real Estate-Florida)*

Stephanie Rippe *(Sr Mgr-Property-Dallas)*
Kevin Buth *(Mgr-Florida Assets)*
Douglas Wolfe *(Dir-Leasing-Florida)*
Adam Blustein *(VP-Leasing-Texas)*
Abril Martinez *(Mgr-Property)*
Daniel Bittel *(Mgr-Property)*
Randy Tulepan *(Dir-Leasing)*
Nikolas Kozy *(Dir-Acq)*
Silvana Motta *(Corp Controller)*

GLOBAL GAMING SOLUTIONS, LLC
1921 Cradduck Rd, Ada, OK 74820
Tel.: (580) 559-0886   DE
Web Site:
   https://www.globalgamingsol.com
Year Founded: 2008
Venture Capital Investment Services
N.A.I.C.S.: 523910
Skip Seeley *(CEO)*
Robert Lannert *(COO)*
Scott Wells *(Pres & Gen Mgr)*
Tiffany Frye *(VP-Fin)*

Subsidiaries:

Global Gaming RP, LLC (1)
1 Remington Pl, Oklahoma City, OK 73110
Tel.: (405) 424-1000
Web Site: http://www.remingtonpark.com
Sales Range: $75-99.9 Million
Emp.: 250
Horse Racetrack & Casino Operator
N.A.I.C.S.: 711212
Scott Wells *(Pres & Gen Mgr)*
Melanie Allcorn *(Dir-Surveillance)*
Cardell Barkus *(Dir-IT)*
Kyle Cates *(Dir-Food & Beverage)*
Mike Chapple *(VP-Gaming Ops)*
Mark Enos *(Dir-Casino Ops)*
Kathy Luman *(Dir-HR)*
Christy McCormack *(Dir-Sls)*
Yenni Vance *(Dir-Digital Comm & Social Media)*
Skip Seeley *(CEO)*
Roy Corby *(COO)*
Trent Roberts *(CFO)*

Lone Star Race Park, Ltd. (1)
1000 Lone Star Pkwy, Grand Prairie, TX 75050
Tel.: (972) 263-7223
Web Site: http://www.lonestarpark.com
Sales Range: $50-74.9 Million
Emp.: 700
Horse Racetrack Operator
N.A.I.C.S.: 711212

GLOBAL GATE PROPERTY CORP.
400 Park Ave Ste 1440, New York, NY 10022
Tel.: (860) 604-5892   NV
Web Site:
   http://www.globalgateproperty.com
Sales Range: Less than $1 Million
Emp.: 3
Real Estate Services
N.A.I.C.S.: 531390
Gary S. Ohlbaum *(Pres, CEO & CFO)*

GLOBAL GENES
28 Argonaut Ste 150, Aliso Viejo, CA 92656
Tel.: (949) 248-7273   CA
Web Site:
   https://www.globalgenes.org
Year Founded: 2008
Sales Range: $1-9.9 Million
Emp.: 3
Disease Awareness Services
N.A.I.C.S.: 813212
Nicole Boice *(Founder)*
Caroline M. Loewy *(Bd of Dirs, Executives)*

GLOBAL GEOPHYSICAL SERVICES, INC.

13927 S Gessner Rd, Missouri City, TX 77489
Tel.: (713) 972-9200   DE
Web Site:
   http://www.globalgeophysical.com
Year Founded: 2003
Seismic Data Acquisition Services
N.A.I.C.S.: 518210
Tim Schield *(Sls Mgr-North America)*
Sean M. Gore *(CFO & Sr VP)*
Bill McLain *(VP-Seismic Processing)*
Charles Sicking *(VP-R&D)*
Jan Vermilye *(Mgr-Ambient Seismic Processing & Interpretation)*
Rick Burnett *(Gen Counsel, Sec & VP)*
Chad Baillie *(Mgr-Consulting)*
Jerry Lawson *(Mgr-Seismic Acq-North America)*
Guilherme Castilho *(Country Mgr-Brazil)*
Aldo Caballero *(Country Mgr-Paraguay)*

Subsidiaries:

Autoseis, Inc. (1)
13927 S Gessner Rd, Missouri City, TX 77489
Tel.: (713) 972-9200
Web Site: http://www.globalgeophysical.com
Emp.: 200
Oil & Gas Field Exploration Services
N.A.I.C.S.: 213112
Richard White *(Pres)*

Global Geophysical Services, Sp. z.o.o. (1)
Ul Warowna 3-1, Warsaw, 02-654, Poland
Tel.: (48) 224930135
Oil & Gas Field Exploration Services
N.A.I.C.S.: 213112

Global Servicos Geofisicos, Ltda. (1)
Rua Jornalista Ricardo Marinho 360, Sala 106/107 Ed, Rio de Janeiro, 22631-350, CEP, Brazil
Tel.: (55) 2133447662
Geophysical Mapping Services
N.A.I.C.S.: 541360

GLOBAL GUARDIAN, LLC
8280 Greensboro Dr Ste 750, McLean, VA 22102
Tel.: (703) 566-9463
Web Site:
   https://www.globalguardian.com
Sports Team Management Software Development Services
N.A.I.C.S.: 561612
Dale Buckner *(Pres & CEO)*
Matt Boccia *(COO)*
Jimmy Hester *(VP-Intl Ops)*
Williem Straatman *(CFO)*
Spencer Livingston *(Pres-Air Ambulance Card)*
John Fitzgibbons *(Chm)*

Subsidiaries:

Global Guardian Air Ambulance (1)
8280 Greensboro Dr Ste 100, McLean, VA 22102
Tel.: (703) 566-9481
Web Site: http://www.airambulancecard.com
Emp.: 25
Aeromedical Transportation Services
N.A.I.C.S.: 532411
Kyndal Melvin Robertson *(Dir-Membership Svcs)*

GLOBAL HEALTH TECHNOLOGIES, INC.
112 N Curry St, Carson City, NV 89703
Tel.: (800) 473-7665   NV
Web Site:
   http://www.globalhealthtech.net
Year Founded: 2013
Medical Device Mfr
N.A.I.C.S.: 339112

Martin J. Mair *(Pres, CEO, CFO, Principal Acctg Officer, Treas & Sec)*

GLOBAL HUNGER PROJECT
5 Union Sq W 7th Fl, New York, NY 10003
Tel.: (212) 251-9100   CA
Web Site: http://www.thp.org
Year Founded: 1977
Sales Range: $10-24.9 Million
Emp.: 20
Hunger Relief Services
N.A.I.C.S.: 624210
John Coonrod *(Exec VP)*
Charles Deull *(Sec)*

GLOBAL IMAGING HOLDINGS REALTY, LLC
51 Industrial Dr, North Smithfield, RI 02896-8032
Tel.: (401) 762-3800   DE
Sales Range: $25-49.9 Million
Emp.: 50
Real Estate Holdings
N.A.I.C.S.: 531390
William Ulmschneider *(Pres)*

Subsidiaries:

Narragansett Imaging (1)
51 Industrial Dr, North Smithfield, RI 02896-0278
Tel.: (401) 762-3800
Web Site: http://www.nimaging.com
Emp.: 15
Optical Devices
N.A.I.C.S.: 334419
Frank A. Epps *(Co-Founder)*

GLOBAL IMPEX, INC.
2055 North Brown Rd Ste 235, Lawrenceville, GA 30043
Tel.: (678) 584-5345
Web Site: http://www.globalimpex.net
Sales Range: $10-24.9 Million
Emp.: 10
Recycling Material Whslr
N.A.I.C.S.: 423930
Siraj Kazani *(CEO)*
Suhel Kazani *(CFO)*
Gulnaz Kazani *(Sec)*

GLOBAL INDEMNITY INSURANCE AGENCY, INC.
20 Highland Ave, Metuchen, NJ 08840
Tel.: (732) 632-2790   PA
Web Site:
   https://www.globalindemnityinsurance.com
Year Founded: 1988
Sales Range: $10-24.9 Million
Insurance Agents
N.A.I.C.S.: 524210
Timothy J. Wagner *(Pres)*
Maria Rocha *(Office Mgr-Metuchen)*

GLOBAL INDUSTRIAL COMPONENTS
705 College St, Woodbury, TN 37190
Tel.: (615) 563-5120
Web Site: https://www.gic-co.com
Sales Range: $10-24.9 Million
Emp.: 39
Fasteners & Fastening Equipment
N.A.I.C.S.: 423840
Gerald Toledo *(Pres)*
Kevin Hochstetler *(Gen Mgr)*
David Vance *(Product Mgr-Automotive)*
Dottie Mason *(Supvr-Mfg)*
Melissa Talley *(Coord-PPAP)*
Zachary Cannon *(Mgr-Bus Dev)*

GLOBAL INDUSTRIES INC.
17 W Stow Rd, Marlton, NJ 08053
Tel.: (856) 596-3390

Web Site:
http://www.globaltotaloffice.com
Rev.: $340,000,000
Emp.: 180
Mfr of Office Furniture
N.A.I.C.S.: 337214
John Ibraham *(CFO)*

GLOBAL INFRASTRUCTURE SOLUTIONS, INC.
660 Newport Ctr Dr Ste 940, Newport Beach, CA 92660
Tel.: (213) 640-8159
Web Site: https://www.gisi.com
Emp.: 100
Engineering & Construction Services
N.A.I.C.S.: 541330
Dick Newman *(Exec Chm)*
Rick Newman *(Pres & CEO)*

Subsidiaries:

GEI Consultants, Inc. (1)
400 Unicorn Park Dr, Woburn, MA 01801
Tel.: (781) 721-4000
Web Site: https://www.geiconsultants.com
Engineering & Environmental Consulting Services
N.A.I.C.S.: 541690
Raymond Hart *(VP)*
Ronald P. Palmieri *(Pres & CEO)*
Cameron Davis *(VP)*
Scott J. Wallington *(Chief Dev Officer)*

Subsidiary (Domestic):

Resource Management Associates, Inc (2)
4171 Suisun Valley Rd, Fairfield, CA 94534
Tel.: (707) 864-2950
Web Site: http://www.rmanet.com
Rev.: $1,533,000
Emp.: 8
Engineering Services
N.A.I.C.S.: 541330
John DeGeorge *(Pres)*

Hill International Inc. (1)
1 Commerce Sq 2005 Market St 17th Fl, Philadelphia, PA 19103
Tel.: (215) 309-7700
Web Site: https://www.hillintl.com
Rev.: $377,438,000
Assets: $283,057,000
Liabilities: $179,818,000
Net Worth: $103,239,000
Earnings: ($4,271,000)
Emp.: 2,578
Fiscal Year-end: 12/31/2021
Construction Management, Project Management & Construction Claims Management Services
N.A.I.C.S.: 541330
William H. Dengler Jr. *(Chief Admin Officer & Exec VP)*
Vic Spinabelli Jr. *(Sr VP & Reg Mgr)*
Luis Lugo Jr. *(Sr VP & Reg Mgr-Southeast)*

Subsidiary (Non-US):

Beijing Hill Construction Consulting Co., Ltd. (2)
Rm 017 Unit DE1 8th Floor Tower B No 18 Xiaguangli East, 3rd Ring North Rd Chaoyang District, Beijing, 100027, China
Tel.: (86) 13910307983
Construction Management Services
N.A.I.C.S.: 236220

Binnington Copeland & Associates (Pty.) Ltd. (2)
4 Fricker Road, Illovo, 2196, South Africa
Tel.: (27) 117317000
Web Site: http://www.bca.co.za
Construction Management & Consulting Services
N.A.I.C.S.: 237990
Terry Rensen *(Chm)*

Hill Engineering Consultancy, LLC (2)
Office 206 Tamimah Building 3rd floor Al Nahdah Street, Wattayah, Muscat, Oman
Tel.: (968) 24562570
Construction Management & Consulting Services
N.A.I.C.S.: 237990

Hill International (2)
Sarkuysan-Ak Business Center Kisikli Cad No 4, Block A 4th Floor No 10 Altunizade Uskudar, 34662, Istanbul, Turkiye
Tel.: (90) 2166517770
Construction Management & Consulting Services
N.A.I.C.S.: 237990
Ezgi Ulku *(Office Mgr)*

Hill International (Bucharest) S.R.L. (2)
Dr Iacob Felix 17-19 3rd floor, Bucharest, 011031, Romania
Tel.: (40) 213195248
Web Site: http://www.hillintl.com
Emp.: 15
Construction Claims Consulting Services
N.A.I.C.S.: 541618

Hill International (Colombia) SAS (2)
Carrera 7 No 71 -21 Torre B Piso 13, Bogota, 111511, Colombia
Tel.: (57) 13192670
Engineering Services
N.A.I.C.S.: 541330

Hill International (Germany) GmbH (2)
Taunusstrasse 44, 65183, Wiesbaden, Germany
Tel.: (49) 61189043668
Web Site: http://www.hill-international.de
Personnel & Executive Search Services
N.A.I.C.S.: 561312

Hill International (Hellas) S.A. (2)
37A Kifissias Avenue 2nd Floor Office 203, Maroussi, 151 23, Athens, Greece
Tel.: (30) 210 610 5171
Web Site: http://www.hillintl.com
Project Management & Construction Claim Consulting Services
N.A.I.C.S.: 541618

Hill International (Hong Kong) Ltd. (2)
Conson Business Center Room 1101 11th Floor Tower 1, 883 Cheun Sha Wan Road, Kowloon, China (Hong Kong)
Tel.: (852) 97251683
Construction Management Services
N.A.I.C.S.: 236220

Hill International (Libya) Ltd. (2)
Hay Alandalus Behind Peoples Hall, PO Box 82958, Tripoli, Libya
Tel.: (218) 214776502
Construction & Project Management Services
N.A.I.C.S.: 541330

Subsidiary (Domestic):

Hill International (New England) Inc. (2)
330 Congress St 6th Fl, Boston, MA 02210
Tel.: (617) 778-0900
Construction Management & Consulting Services
N.A.I.C.S.: 237990

Subsidiary (Non-US):

Hill International (North Africa) Ltd. (2)
Parcel no 140 NCFC Building Banks Zone, 1st District 5th Settlement, New Cairo, Cairo, Egypt
Tel.: (20) 22 322 0000
Web Site: http://www.hillintl.com
Sales Range: $75-99.9 Million
Emp.: 250
Construction Engineering Services
N.A.I.C.S.: 541330

Hill International (Spain) S.A. (2)
Monday Diagonal Carrer de la Riera de Sant Miquel 1 BIS, 08006, Barcelona, Spain (100%)
Tel.: (34) 91 431 0196
Web Site: http://www.hillintl.com
Emp.: 10
Construction Claims Consulting Services
N.A.I.C.S.: 541618

Subsidiary (Non-US):

Hill International de Mexico, S.A. de C.V. (3)

Arquimedes 15 Col Polanco V Seccion, Del Miguel Hidalgo, 11560, Mexico, Mexico
Tel.: (52) 558 310 9551
Web Site: http://www.hillinternational.com
Emp.: 50
Construction Claims Consulting Services
N.A.I.C.S.: 541618

Subsidiary (Non-US):

Hill International (UK), Ltd. (2)
Level 7 1 London Bridge, London, SE19BG, United Kingdom (100%)
Tel.: (44) 2070897020
Rev.: $3,000,000
Emp.: 80
N.A.I.C.S.: 541611

Hill International BH do.o (2)
S b Basagica 67, 71000, Sarajevo, Bosnia & Herzegovina
Tel.: (387) 33572180
Web Site: http://www.hill-international.com
Management Consulting Services
N.A.I.C.S.: 541618

Hill International Engineering Consultancy, LLC (2)
Office No 15 1st Floor Al Mashraq Building 18 November St, Muscat, Oman
Tel.: (968) 24613609
Engineering Services
N.A.I.C.S.: 541330

Branch (Non-US):

Hill International Inc.- Abu Dhabi, U.A.E. (2)
Ste 1601 16th Fl D O Buttti Al Otaiba Bldg Sheikh Khalifa St, PO Box 5201, Abu Dhabi, United Arab Emirates (100%)
Tel.: (971) 43372145
Sales Range: $10-24.9 Million
Emp.: 50
N.A.I.C.S.: 541611
David Brodie-Stedman *(Sr VP-Construction Claims Grp)*
David Merritt *(Sr VP)*
Benjamin Highfield *(Sr VP-Construction Claims Grp-Dubai)*
Christopher Pedersen *(Sr VP-Construction Claims Grp-Dubai)*
James A. McCarthy *(VP-Construction Claims Grp-Dubai)*
Brian C. Meyrick *(VP-Construction Claims Grp-Dubai)*
William E. Trembath *(VP-Fin-Middle East)*
Samer T. Tamimi *(Sr VP-Project Mgmt Grp)*

Branch (Domestic):

Hill International Inc.-California (2)
1 Sansome St Ste2940, San Francisco, CA 94104
Tel.: (925) 275-9870
Web Site: http://www.hillintl.com
Sales Range: $1-9.9 Million
Emp.: 10
Construction Consulting
N.A.I.C.S.: 541618

Hill International Inc.-District of Columbia (2)
1225 I St NW Ste 601, Washington, DC 20005-5961 (100%)
Tel.: (202) 408-3000
Web Site: http://www.hillintl.com
Sales Range: $10-24.9 Million
Emp.: 45
Construction Management
N.A.I.C.S.: 541690

Hill International Inc.-Florida (2)
5100 Lemmon St, Tampa, FL 33619-4357
Tel.: (813) 288-0531
Web Site: http://www.hillintl.com
Sales Range: $300-349.9 Million
Emp.: 2,000
Construction Management
N.A.I.C.S.: 541618

Branch (Non-US):

Hill International Inc.-Greece (2)
62 Kifissias Ave, Athens, 151 25, Greece
Tel.: (30) 106105171
Web Site: http://www.hillintl.com
Sales Range: $50-74.9 Million
N.A.I.C.S.: 541611

Branch (Domestic):

Hill International Inc.-New York (2)
1 Penn Plz Ste 3415, New York, NY 10119-0002
Tel.: (212) 244-3700
Web Site: http://www.hillintl.com
Sales Range: $10-24.9 Million
Emp.: 30
Construction Management
N.A.I.C.S.: 541618

Hill International Inc.-Pennsylvania (2)
30 S 15th St Ste 1300, Philadelphia, PA 19102 (100%)
Tel.: (215) 557-3240
Sales Range: $350-399.9 Million
Emp.: 2,500
N.A.I.C.S.: 541611
Michael Griffin *(Sr VP)*
Peter J. Wallace *(Sr VP-Construction Claims Grp)*
Michael E. Radbill *(VP-Project Mgmt Grp)*
James P. Donnelly *(VP-Project Mgmt Grp)*
Wayne J. Germscheid *(VP-Project Mgmt Grp)*
Mark A. Stout *(VP-Project Mgmt Grp-Bethel Park)*
Mark Purcell *(VP)*

Subsidiary (Non-US):

Hill International Proje Yonetimi ve Danismanlik A.S. (2)
Buyukdere Caddesi Ali Kaya Sokak Polat Plaza B Blok Kat 10, Levent, 34394, Istanbul, Turkiye
Tel.: (90) 2122709650
Engineering Services
N.A.I.C.S.: 541330

Hill International Project Management (India) Private Limited (2)
1st Floor Building 10-B Cyber City Phase III, Gurgaon, Haryana, India
Tel.: (91) 1244076312
Engineering Services
N.A.I.C.S.: 541330

Hill International Vietnam Co. Limited (2)
Room 404 Floor 4 Danang Software Park 15 Quang Trung, Hai Chau District, Da Nang, Vietnam
Tel.: (84) 839252298
Engineering Services
N.A.I.C.S.: 541330

Subsidiary (Domestic):

HillStone International, LLC (2)
3801 PGA Blvd Ste 805, Palm Beach Gardens, FL 33410
Tel.: (561) 899-2200
Web Site: http://www.hillintl.com
Steel Mesh & Reinforced Concrete Provider
N.A.I.C.S.: 238120

GLOBAL INTELLISYSTEMS, LLC
1153 Bergen Pkwy #455, Evergreen, CO 80439
Tel.: (970) 315-3637
Web Site: http://www.gliq.com
Sales Range: $1-9.9 Million
Software Publisher
N.A.I.C.S.: 513210
John Brogan *(CEO)*

GLOBAL INVESTMENT RECOVERY, INC.
5409 E Henry Ave, Tampa, FL 33610
Tel.: (813) 620-1507
Web Site: http://www.girpm.com
Sales Range: $1-9.9 Million
Emp.: 13
Hazardous Waste Treatment & Disposal
N.A.I.C.S.: 562211
David Ritter *(Owner)*
Jay Woodall *(Dir-Natl Sls)*
Lisa Collins *(Reg Dir-Sls)*
Paul Sweeney *(Mgr-Environ Affairs)*

Global Logistics Inc.—(Continued)

GLOBAL LOGISTICS INC.
99 W Hawthorne Ave L-12, Valley Stream, NY 11580
Tel.: (516) 825-2922
Web Site: https://www.globallog.com
Rev.: $12,000,000
Emp.: 8
Purchasing Service
N.A.I.C.S.: 561499
Avi Auslander *(Pres)*
Shay Tsouri *(VP)*

GLOBAL MACRO TRUST
c/o Millburn Corp 411 W Putnam Ave, Greenwich, CT 06830
Tel.: (203) 625-7554   DE
Rev.: $1,489,408
Assets: $112,410,212
Liabilities: $4,231,284
Net Worth: $108,178,928
Earnings: $16,021,844
Fiscal Year-end: 12/31/22
Investment Services
N.A.I.C.S.: 523999
Harvey Beker *(Chm)*

GLOBAL MANUFACTURING & ASSEMBLY
1801 Wildwood Ave, Jackson, MI 49202
Tel.: (517) 789-8116
Rev.: $10,900,000
Emp.: 3
Plastic Containers Mfr
N.A.I.C.S.: 326199
Armida Pearse *(Founder & Pres)*

GLOBAL MECHANICAL, INC.
225 Scarlet Rd, Kennett Square, PA 19348
Tel.: (610) 444-2100
Web Site:
    http://www.globalmechanical.net
Wood Container & Pallet Mfr
N.A.I.C.S.: 321920
Robert D. Powell *(Pres)*
Barry Smith *(VP)*

GLOBAL MEDIA OUTREACH
910 E Hamilton Ave Ste 145, Campbell, CA 95008
Tel.: (972) 975-9444   CA
Web Site: http://www.globalmediaout
    reach.com
Year Founded: 2006
Sales Range: $10-24.9 Million
Emp.: 57
Christian Ministry Services
N.A.I.C.S.: 813110
Michelle Diedrich *(CMO)*
Walt Wilson *(Founder & Chm)*
Scott Begin *(Dir-Dev)*
Jeff Gowler *(CEO)*

GLOBAL MEDICAL SOLUTIONS, LTD.
14140 Ventura Blvd Ste 201, Sherman Oaks, CA 91423
Tel.: (818) 783-2915
Web Site:
    http://www.globalmedicalsolu
    tions.com
Year Founded: 2003
Sales Range: $50-74.9 Million
Emp.: 200
Pharmaceuticals Product Mfr
N.A.I.C.S.: 325412
Haig S. Bagerdjian *(Chm & CEO)*
John S. Baumann *(Sr VP-Bus Dev & Legal Affairs)*
Neal Cannon *(CFO)*
Jean Stoiberg *(Controller)*

GLOBAL MEMORY PROCURE-MENT CORP.
216 Avenida Fabricante Ste 103, San Clemente, CA 92672
Tel.: (949) 485-5525
Web Site: http://www.memory.net
Year Founded: 2000
Sales Range: $10-24.9 Million
Emp.: 11
Computer Hardware Distr
N.A.I.C.S.: 423430
Mike Johnson *(Pres)*

GLOBAL MERCHANT FUND CORP.
20807 Biscayne Blvd Ste 203, Aventura, FL 33180
Tel.: (786) 279-2900
Web Site:
    http://www.globalmerchantfund.com
Financial Services
N.A.I.C.S.: 523999
Marius Silvasan *(CEO)*

Subsidiaries:

Accutrac Capital Solutions, Inc.   (1)
174 West Street South, Orillia, L3V 6L4, ON, Canada
Tel.: (866) 531-2615
Consumer Lending
N.A.I.C.S.: 522291

Bibby Financial Services (Holdings) Inc   (1)
1901 S Congress Ave Suite 110, Boynton Beach, FL 33426
Tel.: (877) 882-4229
Web Site: http://www.bibbyusa.com
Emp.: 100
Financial Advisory Services
N.A.I.C.S.: 523940
Barry Kastner *(Exec VP)*
Mohammad Rasian *(Sr VP-Underwriting)*
Ian Watson *(Pres-North America)*
Jim Vargo *(Sr VP-Bus Dev)*
Jeff Guldner *(Chief Credit Officer-North America)*
Bret Hill *(CFO-North America)*
Jeff Morse *(COO-North America)*
David Ciccolo *(Mng Dir-Factoring & Asset Based Lending Bus-Atlanta)*

GLOBAL MOTOR SPORT GROUP, INC.
155 E Main Ave Ste 150, Morgan Hill, CA 95037
Tel.: (408) 778-0500   CA
Web Site:
    http://www.customchrome.com
Value Added Distr of Harley Davidson Motorcycle Parts & Accessories
N.A.I.C.S.: 336991

Subsidiaries:

Custom Chrome Incorporated   (1)
18225 Serene Dr Ste 150, Morgan Hill, CA 95037   (100%)
Tel.: (408) 778-0500
Web Site: http://www.customchrome.com
Motorcycle Exhausts, Frames, Oiltanks & Other Parts Mfr
N.A.I.C.S.: 336991
Holger Mohr *(Pres & CEO)*

GLOBAL NETWORK SYSTEMS, INC.
2400 Research Blvd Ste 115, Rockville, MD 20850
Tel.: (301) 921-4467
Web Site: http://www.gns-us.com
Year Founded: 1998
Sales Range: $1-9.9 Million
Emp.: 32
Information Technology Services for Government Agencies
N.A.I.C.S.: 541512
Peyman Goldoust *(Owner & Sr VP)*
Tony Ingelido *(Dir-Ops)*

GLOBAL OFFICE SOLUTIONS
22759 Heslip Dr, Novi, MI 48375
Web Site:
    https://www.globalofficesolu
    tions.com
Year Founded: 1998
Sales Range: $10-24.9 Million
Emp.: 20
Office Supplies & Furniture
N.A.I.C.S.: 459410
Reuben Levy *(Pres)*
Jeff Summers *(COO)*

GLOBAL OPERATIONS AND DEVELOPMENT
8332 Commonwealth Ave, Buena Park, CA 90621
Tel.: (714) 523-4454   CA
Web Site: http://www.gchope.org
Year Founded: 1982
Sales Range: $25-49.9 Million
Emp.: 23
Child Care & Development Services
N.A.I.C.S.: 624110
Sean Lawrence *(Exec Dir)*
Joe Bergfalk *(Dir-Budgets & Fin)*

GLOBAL ORDNANCE LLC
2150 Whitfield Ave Buildings A&B, Sarasota, FL 34243
Tel.: (941) 549-8388
Web Site:
    https://www.globalordnance.com
Defense Military Products Mfr
N.A.I.C.S.: 928110
Marc Morales *(Pres)*

Subsidiaries:

Chemring Military Products, Inc.   (1)
10625 Puckett Road Perry, Marshall, TX 75672
Tel.: (903) 934-9200
Web Site: http://www.chemringmp.com
Ammunition Mfr
N.A.I.C.S.: 332993

GLOBAL ORGANIC SPE-CIALTY SOURCE, INC.
6284 McIntosh Rd, Sarasota, FL 34238
Tel.: (941) 358-6555
Web Site:
    http://www.globalorganics.ws
Year Founded: 1999
Sales Range: $25-49.9 Million
Emp.: 100
Organic Fruit & Vegetable Supplier
N.A.I.C.S.: 424480
Mitchell Blumenthal *(Owner & Pres)*
George Caldwell *(Dir-Pur)*

GLOBAL OUTREACH INTER-NATIONAL, INC.
74 Kings Hwy, Pontotoc, MS 38863
Tel.: (662) 842-4615   MS
Web Site:
    https://www.globaloutreach.org
Year Founded: 2001
Sales Range: $10-24.9 Million
Emp.: 112
Life Care Services
N.A.I.C.S.: 813110

GLOBAL PACIFIC PRODUCE, INC.
11500 S Eastern Ave Ste 120, Henderson, NV 89052
Tel.: (702) 898-8051
Web Site:
    http://www.globalpacificproduce.com
Rev.: $121,500,000
Emp.: 22
Fruit Whslr
N.A.I.C.S.: 424480

Ken Zueger *(Mgr-Fin)*
Marco Nuques *(Mgr-Trading-Latin America)*
Michelle Marquez *(Asst Mgr-Fin)*

GLOBAL PACKAGING SOLU-TIONS, INC.
1590 Continental St Ste 109, San Diego, CA 92154
Tel.: (619) 710-2661
Web Site: http://www.globlsoln.com
Year Founded: 2006
Sales Range: $10-24.9 Million
Emp.: 280
Corrugated & Solid Fiber Box Mfr
N.A.I.C.S.: 322211
Jawed Ghias *(Pres)*

GLOBAL PERFORMANCE
Patewood Plz I 30 Patewood Dr Ste 200, Greenville, SC 29615
Tel.: (864) 288-3009
Web Site:
    http://www.globalperformance.net
Year Founded: 1999
Sales Range: $125-149.9 Million
Emp.: 300
Automotive Manufacturing
N.A.I.C.S.: 811114
Tim Griffin *(Pres)*

GLOBAL POVERTY PROJECT, INC.
594 Broadway Ste 207, New York, NY 10012
Tel.: (646) 943-4745   NY
Web Site:
    http://www.globalpovertyproject.com
Year Founded: 2010
Sales Range: $10-24.9 Million
Emp.: 17
Anti-Poverty Advocacy Services
N.A.I.C.S.: 813319
Jane Atkinson *(Dir-Comm)*
Wei Soo *(Mng Dir-Ops)*
Simon Moss *(Mng Dir-Programs)*
Hugh Evans *(CEO)*
Liza Henshaw *(COO)*

GLOBAL POWER GROUP, INC.
12060 Woodside Ave, Lakeside, CA 92040
Tel.: (619) 579-1221   CA
Web Site:
    http://www.globalpowergroup.net
Year Founded: 2005
Sales Range: $10-24.9 Million
Emp.: 66
General Engineering & Electrical Contractor
N.A.I.C.S.: 238990
Terry Mammen *(CEO)*
John U. Moorhead *(Mng Dir)*
Salvatore Martorana *(Pres)*
Salvador Ceballos *(CFO)*

GLOBAL POWER SUPPLY, LLC
136 W Canon Perdido, Santa Barbara, CA 93101
Tel.: (805) 683-3828   CA
Web Site: https://www.globalpwr.com
Year Founded: 2004
Sales Range: $25-49.9 Million
Emp.: 20
Electric Power Distr
N.A.I.C.S.: 221118
Ron Zamir *(Pres & CEO)*
Mike Wolfe *(VP-Power Solutions)*
Scott Feinberg *(Dir-Production)*
Robert Feinberg *(Dir-Ops)*
Rob Hansen *(Dir-Mission Critical Facilities Div)*

GLOBAL PRINTER SERVICES INC.
5315 Paulson Rd, McFarland, WI 53558
Tel.: (608) 838-5070
Web Site:
http://www.globalprinter.com
Rev.: $10,000,000
Emp.: 40
HP LaserJet & Laser Printer Parts Sales
N.A.I.C.S.: 423430
Bruce Andre (Pres)
Paul Walters (Acct Mgr)

GLOBAL PRODUCTS INC.
21 Cherokee Dr, Saint Peters, MO 63376
Tel.: (636) 939-1622
Web Site: http://www.gpii.com
Rev.: $16,100,000
Emp.: 120
Custom & Licensed Products Designer, Mfr & Distr
N.A.I.C.S.: 315250
Rebecca L. Herwick (Pres & CEO)
John D. Stratman (Co-Owner)
James D. Stratman (Co-Owner)

GLOBAL PV SPECIALISTS
PO Box 478, Woodland Hills, CA 91365
Tel.: (818) 882-2152
Year Founded: 1967
Sales Range: $10-24.9 Million
Emp.: 35
Mfr, Developer & Engineering of Photovoltaic Products
N.A.I.C.S.: 335999
Elias Kady (VP-Intl Bus Dev)

GLOBAL REAL ESTATE HOLDINGS, INC.
125 Wolf Rd Ste 123, Albany, NY 12205
Tel.: (800) 373-5910   NV
Year Founded: 2012
Emp.: 3
Real Estate Investment Services
N.A.I.C.S.: 523999
Dipendra K. Singh (Chm, Pres & CEO)
Kurt D. Benedict (CFO & Treas)
James M. Male (Sec)

GLOBAL REALTY SERVICES GROUP LLC
300 Spectrum Center Dr Ste 145, Irvine, CA 92629
Tel.: (213) 908-2173   CA
Web Site: http://www.grs-global.com
Year Founded: 2009
Sales Range: $25-49.9 Million
Emp.: 600
Commercial Real Estate Services
N.A.I.C.S.: 531210
Noreen Clindinning (Pres)
Charles Victor (CEO)
Andy Brownstein (CFO & Gen Counsel)
Mark Halloran (Dir-Key Accts-GRS/Corteq)

GLOBAL RECRUITERS NETWORK, INC.
200 S Wacker Dr, Chicago, IL 60606
Tel.: (630) 663-1900
Web Site: https://www.grncorp.com
Sales Range: $10-24.9 Million
Emp.: 30
Executive Placement Services
N.A.I.C.S.: 541612
John Israel (VP-Customer Rels)
Glen Louthan (CFO & COO)

GLOBAL RECYCLING INC.
2800 N Tryon St, Charlotte, NC 28206
Tel.: (704) 376-2370
Web Site:
http://www.globalrecyclinginc.com
Sales Range: $10-24.9 Million
Emp.: 5
Recycling Services
N.A.I.C.S.: 423930

GLOBAL REDEMPTION INC.
Lancaster Baptist Church 201 Richmond St, Lancaster, KY 40444
Tel.: (859) 354-7937
Web Site:
https://www.globalredemption.com
Investment Management Service
N.A.I.C.S.: 523999

GLOBAL RESALE LLC
2214 W Braker Ln, Austin, TX 78758
Tel.: (512) 355-6719   DE
Web Site:
http://www.globalresale.com
Lifecycle Management Solutions Services
N.A.I.C.S.: 561499
Jeff Zeigler (CEO)

GLOBAL RESOURCE MANAGEMENT INC.
3851 200st Potsl Rif Te 30093, Suwanee, GA 30024
Tel.: (678) 456-6992
Web Site: http://www.grmi.net
Year Founded: 1993
Sales Range: $50-74.9 Million
Emp.: 517
Human Resource Management Consulting Services
N.A.I.C.S.: 541612
Naheed Syed (Founder & CEO)
Tariq Sultan (COO-Indian Ops)

GLOBAL RESPONSE CORPORATION
777 S State Rd 7, Margate, FL 33068
Tel.: (954) 973-7300
Web Site:
http://www.globalresponse.com
Year Founded: 1974
Sales Range: $25-49.9 Million
Emp.: 1,200
Customer Contact & Fulfillment Services
N.A.I.C.S.: 561421
Herman Shooster (Founder)
Barbara Turner (VP-Call Center Ops)
Joey Johnson (Chief Security Officer)
Dimas Rodriguez (CTO)
Phillip Crowe (Dir-Social Media)
Bryan Czerwinski (Mgr-Contact Center Ops)
Dawn Racz (Project Mgr-Southeast Toyota)
Aaron Linder (Supvr-Customer Svc)
Annabelle Miller (VP-Bus Dev)

GLOBAL RETIREMENT PARTNERS, LLC
4340 Redwood Hwy Ste B-60, San Rafael, CA 94903
Tel.: (415) 526-2750
Web Site:
http://www.grpfinancial.com
Year Founded: 2014
Sales Range: $1-9.9 Million
Emp.: 50
Investment Advisory Services
N.A.I.C.S.: 523940
Geoff White (CEO)
Russ Frierson (COO)
Cosmo Gould (Pres & Chief Compliance Officer)
Stefanie Rzepecki (Dir-Bus Dev)
Pat Destein (Dir-Compliance)

GLOBAL RISK SOLUTIONS, INC.
1000 Trickle Ave Ste 1020, Miami, FL 33131
Tel.: (305) 523-6365
Web Site:
http://www.globalrisksolutions.com
Year Founded: 2002
Sales Range: $10-24.9 Million
Emp.: 35
Insurance Claims Management Services; Litigation Support Consulting & Data Discovery Services
N.A.I.C.S.: 524298
Arthur Radigan (CEO)
Vincent Levito (CFO)
Alex Neiman (Mgr)
Colm Keenan (Exec VP)
Suzanne McClellan Ziemann (Chief Client Officer & Sr VP)
Antoine Green (VP-Sls)
Chris Reeves (Head-Quantity Surveying)

Subsidiaries:

Tailored Adjustment Services, Inc.   (1)
51 Village Ln, Colleyville, TX 76034
Tel.: (972) 751-5510
Sales Range: $1-9.9 Million
Emp.: 30
IInsurance Agencies & Brokerages
N.A.I.C.S.: 524210
James Buchachan (Pres)

GLOBAL SCIENCE & TECHNOLOGY INC.
7855 Walker Dr Ste 200, Greenbelt, MD 20770
Tel.: (301) 474-9696
Web Site: http://www.gst.com
Rev.: $30,000,000
Emp.: 250
Provider of Earth & Space Consulting Services
N.A.I.C.S.: 541330
Chieh-San Cheng (Pres & CEO)
Christopher Moren (Dir-Technical Programs)

GLOBAL SEAFOOD TECHNOLOGIES
211 Caillavet St, Biloxi, MS 39530
Tel.: (228) 435-3632
Sales Range: $10-24.9 Million
Emp.: 100
Shrimp Processing Services
N.A.I.C.S.: 311710
Clayton Gutierrez (Sec & Sr VP)

Subsidiaries:

Custom Pack Inc.   (1)
555 Bayview Ave, Biloxi, MS 39530
Tel.: (228) 435-3632
Shrimp Processing Services
N.A.I.C.S.: 311710

Killer Bee Inc.   (1)
555 Bayview Ave, Biloxi, MS 39530
Tel.: (228) 435-3632
Rev.: $5,600,000
Emp.: 8
Fishing Bait Sales
N.A.I.C.S.: 424990

GLOBAL SECURITY AGENCY INC.
12818 Hwy #105 W Ste 2-G, Conroe, TX 77304
Tel.: (936) 447-4229   NV
Web Site:
http://www.globalsecurityagency.org
Year Founded: 2006
Sales Range: $1-9.9 Million
Emp.: 4
Security Solutions & Risk Management Services
N.A.I.C.S.: 561621

Larry E. Lunger (CEO)
Ronald H. Reif (Pres)
John D. Kuykendall (CFO)
George M. Rock Rutherford (Sec)

GLOBAL SERVICE SOLUTIONS, INC.
3420 Oakcliff Rd Ste 115, Doraville, GA 30340
Tel.: (770) 457-3048
Web Site: http://www.gotprepaid.com
Year Founded: 2000
Sales Range: $250-299.9 Million
Emp.: 10
Prepaid Cellular Products & Services Including Cards & Pins to Distr, Whslr & Retailers
N.A.I.C.S.: 525990
David Sparks (Pres & CEO)
Ivan Sarembock (Controller-Fin)

GLOBAL SMOOTHIE SUPPLY, INC.
4516 Lovers Ln 144, Dallas, TX 75225
Tel.: (214) 769-0836   TX
Web Site: http://www.gssww.com
Sales Range: Less than $1 Million
Fresh-Fruit Smoothie Systems Supplier
N.A.I.C.S.: 333241
David C. Tiller (Chm & CEO)
Donald M. Roberts (Vice Chm, CFO & Treas)
Harry B. Ireland (Vice Chm, Chief Legal Officer & Sec)

GLOBAL SOLAR ENERGY, INC.
8500 S Rita Rd, Tucson, AZ 85747
Tel.: (520) 546-6313
Web Site: http://www.globalsolar.com
Sales Range: $10-24.9 Million
Emp.: 110
Solar Panel & Module Mfr
N.A.I.C.S.: 221118
Timothy Teich (VP-Ops)

Subsidiaries:

Global Solar Energy Deutschland GmbH   (1)
Am Studio 16, Berlin, 12489, Germany
Tel.: (49) 3081879101
Web Site: http://www.globalsolar.com
Solar Panel Mfr
N.A.I.C.S.: 221118

GLOBAL SOURCING GROUP, INC.
10621 S 51 St Ste 103, Phoenix, AZ 85044
Tel.: (480) 893-1888
Year Founded: 1998
Sales Range: $25-49.9 Million
Emp.: 150
Offshore Sourcing & International Supply Chain Management Services
N.A.I.C.S.: 423830
Steven McNeely (Co-Founder & Pres)
Edward Tian (Co-Founder & VP)

GLOBAL SOURCING INC.
150 E 52nd St, New York, NY 10022
Tel.: (212) 572-9820
Web Site: https://www.gs-ny.com
Year Founded: 1987
Rev.: $15,342,140
Emp.: 4
Exporter & Importer of Industrial Machinery & Equipment
N.A.I.C.S.: 423830
Mark Oravec (Pres)

Global Sourcing Inc.—(Continued)

GLOBAL SPECIALTY CON-TRACTORS
3220 Terminal Dr, Saint Paul, MN 55121
Tel.: (651) 406-8232
Sales Range: $10-24.9 Million
Emp.: 100
Highway & Street Sign Installation
N.A.I.C.S.: 237310
Zach Brazier *(Project Mgr)*

GLOBAL STRATEGIC MAN-AGEMENT INSTITUTE (GSMI)
1501 India St Ste 103-60, San Diego, CA 92101
Web Site: https://www.gsmiweb.com
Year Founded: 2008
Sales Range: $1-9.9 Million
Emp.: 8
Developer of Executive Conferences, Workshops, Training Sessions & Exhibitions
N.A.I.C.S.: 611430
Byron Mignanelli *(CEO)*
Luke Vinci *(Pres)*
Kara M. Mignanelli *(Sr VP-People & Gen Counsel)*
Breanna Jacobs *(VP-Digital Mktg Div)*

GLOBAL STRATEGIES, IN-CORPORATED
1600 Tysons Blvd 8th Fl, McLean, VA 22102
Tel.: (703) 818-7191
Web Site:
   http://www.gsiprotection.com
Year Founded: 2003
Sales Range: $1-9.9 Million
Emp.: 20
Global Security Consulting Services
N.A.I.C.S.: 541618
Christopher Simovich *(CEO)*
Thomas J. Woods *(Chief Medical Officer)*

Subsidiaries:

Global Strategies   (1)
39 Vantis Dr, Aliso Viejo, CA 92656   (100%)
Tel.: (949) 643-3929
Web Site: http://www.gsiprotection.com
Security & Executive Protection Services
N.A.I.C.S.: 928110

GLOBAL STUDIO
285 E Parr Blvd, Reno, NV 89512-1003
Tel.: (775) 853-8333
Web Site:
   http://www.globalstudio.com
Sales Range: $10-24.9 Million
Emp.: 15
N.A.I.C.S.: 541810
Michael Reynolds *(Principal)*

GLOBAL SUPPLY CHAIN SO-LUTIONS INC.
11494 Luna Rd Ste 100, Farmers Branch, TX 75234-9429
Tel.: (972) 401-4727
Web Site: http://www.gscsinc.com
Sales Range: $25-49.9 Million
Emp.: 25
Managed Materials Solutions
N.A.I.C.S.: 541512
Paul Peck *(CEO)*

GLOBAL SUPPLY LLC
500 Division St, Campbell, CA 95008-6919
Tel.: (408) 978-4180
Web Site:
   http://www.globalsupplyllc.com
Advertising Material Distribution Services

N.A.I.C.S.: 541870
Lance Archer *(Pres)*

Subsidiaries:

Innovative Plastics Corporation   (1)
400 Route 303, Orangeburg, NY 10962
Tel.: (845) 359-7500
Web Site: http://www.innovative-plastics.com
Sales Range: $100-124.9 Million
Emp.: 250
Plastic Packaging Mfr
N.A.I.C.S.: 326112
Judith Hershaft *(Pres & CEO)*
Steve Hershaft *(VP)*
Peter Streitman *(CFO)*

Subsidiary (Domestic):

Innovative Plastics   (2)
2900 Old Franklin Rd, Antioch, TN 37013-3114   (100%)
Tel.: (615) 501-9100
Web Site: http://www.innovative-plastics.com
Sales Range: $10-24.9 Million
Emp.: 55
Mfr of Plastic Packaging
N.A.I.C.S.: 326113
James Parrish *(Pres)*

Innovative Plastics West Corp.   (2)
10199 W Van Buren Ste 12, Tolleson, AZ 85353
Tel.: (623) 742-9999
Packaging Services
N.A.I.C.S.: 561910

GLOBAL SUPPLY SOLUTIONS LLC
1569 Diamond Springs Rd Ste C, Virginia Beach, VA 23455
Tel.: (757) 227-6757
Web Site: http://www.gssgear.com
Year Founded: 2004
Sales Range: $10-24.9 Million
Emp.: 40
Military & Tactical Products
N.A.I.C.S.: 336992
Emily Whittaker *(CEO)*
Rob Banta *(COO)*

GLOBAL TECH LED LLC
8901 Quality Rd, Bonita Springs, FL 34135
Tel.: (877) 748-5533
Web Site:
   http://www.globaltechled.com
Sales Range: $10-24.9 Million
Emp.: 30
LED Lighting Designer & Mfr
N.A.I.C.S.: 334419
Jeffrey Newman *(Pres)*
Gary Mart Jr. *(CEO)*

GLOBAL TECH SOLUTIONS, INC.
80713 Alexandria Ct, Indio, CA 92201
Tel.: (714) 473-9728   NV
Year Founded: 2012
Computer & Mobile Device Software Developer & Distr
N.A.I.C.S.: 423430
Kenneth Johnson *(Chm, Pres & Sec)*

GLOBAL TECHNICAL SER-VICES, INC.
4000 Sandshell Dr, Fort Worth, TX 76137-2422
Tel.: (817) 847-6673   TX
Web Site: http://www.teamglobal.com
Year Founded: 1989
Sales Range: $10-24.9 Million
Emp.: 24
Technical Staffing Services
N.A.I.C.S.: 561330
Gene Rhoades *(CFO & Exec VP)*
Scott J. Kostelecky *(CIO & Facility Security Officer)*

Rick Davis *(Bus Mgr-Aviation Div)*
Valerie White *(Bus Mgr-Engrg Div)*
Glenda Harrison *(Bus Mgr-Light Indus & Pro Svcs)*

GLOBAL TECHNICAL SYS-TEMS
784 Lynnhaven Pkwy, Virginia Beach, VA 23452-7315
Tel.: (757) 468-8751
Web Site: http://www.gtshq.com
Year Founded: 1997
Sales Range: $50-74.9 Million
Emp.: 41
Management Services
N.A.I.C.S.: 541512
Christine Boettger *(Sr Dir-Contracts & Compliance)*

Subsidiaries:

Global Technical Systems - GTS Information and Sensor Systems Facility   (1)
11200 Dr Martin Luther King Jr St N, Saint Petersburg, FL 33716-2349
Tel.: (727) 329-1500
Engineering Support Services
N.A.I.C.S.: 561990

GLOBAL TECHNOLOGY AS-SOCIATES, LTD.
1 Parklane Blvd, Dearborn, MI 48126
Tel.: (313) 593-0600   MI
Web Site: http://www.gta.jobs
Year Founded: 1988
Sales Range: $10-24.9 Million
Emp.: 200
Staffing Services for Auto Industry
N.A.I.C.S.: 541330
Marcia Ulrich *(Controller)*
Leo Hagan *(Pres & COO)*
Burl C. Adkins *(Founder, Chm & CEO)*

GLOBAL TELESOURCING, LLC
4301 N Fairfax Dr 320, Arlington, VA 22203
Tel.: (703) 684-1141
Web Site:
   http://www.globaltelesourcing.com
Sales Range: $1-9.9 Million
Emp.: 285
Telemarketing Services
N.A.I.C.S.: 561422
Tom Herrity *(Co-Founder & Chm)*
Bill Colton *(Co-Founder & CEO)*
Riyad Abu-Sharr *(CFO)*
Mariana Ramos *(Sr VP-Ops & Country Dir)*

GLOBAL TEST SUPPLY, LLC
3310 Ste 100 Kitty Hawk Rd, Wilmington, NC 28405
Tel.: (910) 442-2164
Web Site:
   http://www.globaltestsupply.com
Sales Range: $1-9.9 Million
Emp.: 60
Scientific Instruments & Laboratory Supplier & Service
N.A.I.C.S.: 541990
David Reed *(Owner)*

GLOBAL TEXTILE SERVICES LLC
120 Keen Dr, Dalton, GA 30720
Tel.: (706) 226-5647
Web Site: http://www.global-textile.net
Sales Range: $10-24.9 Million
Emp.: 155
Finishers of Tufted Carpets & Rugs
N.A.I.C.S.: 314110
Tom Peeples *(Pres)*

GLOBAL TRAVEL INTERNA-TIONAL, INC.
2600 Lake Lucien Dr Ste 201, Maitland, FL 32751
Tel.: (407) 660-7800
Web Site:
   http://www.globaltravel.com
Year Founded: 1994
Sales Range: $100-124.9 Million
Emp.: 70
Travel Agency
N.A.I.C.S.: 561510
Diane Steenman *(COO)*
Kim Johnson *(Dir-Acctg Ops)*
Jeff Church *(Office Mgr)*

GLOBAL UNICORN HOLD-INGS, INC.
387 S 520 W Ste 200, Lindon, UT 84042
Tel.: (801) 224-7199   DE
Web Site: http://www.zyto.com
Sales Range: $1-9.9 Million
Holding Company; Personal Health & Wellness Software & Integrated Computer Hardware Products Mfr
N.A.I.C.S.: 551112
Kami J. Howard *(Pres & CEO)*
Vaughn R. Cook *(Founder & Chm)*

Subsidiaries:

Kailo Energy   (1)
437 E 1000 S, Pleasant Grove, UT 84062
Tel.: (385) 985-4390
Web Site: http://www.kailoenergy.com
Residential Solar Power Equipment & Software Developer, Mfr & Whslr
N.A.I.C.S.: 334413
Ryan Shepherd *(CEO)*

GLOBAL UPSIDE, INC.
4906 El Camino Real Ste 201, San Jose, CA 95129
Tel.: (650) 954-4820
Web Site:
   http://www.globalupside.com
Temporary Staffing Services
N.A.I.C.S.: 561499
Ragu Bhargava *(CEO & Founder)*

Subsidiaries:

Montgomery Professional Services Corp.   (1)
75 E Santa Clara Ste 1388, San Jose, CA 95113
Tel.: (650) 574-7573
Web Site: http://www.montgomerypsc.com
Sales Range: $1-9.9 Million
Emp.: 20
Temporary Staffing Services
N.A.I.C.S.: 561110
Rick Giorgetti *(Pres)*
Steve Jimenez *(Dir-Remote Acctg Svcs)*
Bryan Lucey *(Dir-Remote Acctg Svcs)*
Lynne DeHart-Duston *(Dir-Recruiting Search)*

GLOBAL USED TRUCK SALES, LLC
4182 E Hillsborough Ave, Tampa, FL 33610
Tel.: (813) 333-2219
Web Site:
   http://www.globalusedtrucksales.com
Sales Range: $1-9.9 Million
Emp.: 2
Used Truck Dealership
N.A.I.C.S.: 441227
Brian Donley *(Pres)*
Elizabeth Donley *(VP)*

GLOBAL WARRANTY GROUP, LLC
500 Middle Country Rd, Saint James, NY 11780
Tel.: (631) 750-0300

Web Site:
http://www.globalwarrantygroup.com
Sales Range: $25-49.9 Million
Emp.: 45
Warranty Administration Services
N.A.I.C.S.: 524298
Michael Deluca *(Mgr-Facilities)*

GLOBAL WEDGE, INC.
8807 Mesa Oak Dr, Riverside, CA 92508
Tel.: (951) 413-1482
Web Site:
http://www.globalwedge.com
Year Founded: 2001
Sales Range: $10-24.9 Million
Emp.: 4
Developer & Distr of Solar Power Projects, Solar Photovoltaic Raw Materials & Solar Modules & Panels
N.A.I.C.S.: 221118
Rao Marella *(Owner & Pres)*

GLOBAL WILDLIFE CONSERVATION
PO Box 129, Austin, TX 78767-0129
Tel.: (512) 593-1883   CA
Web Site:
http://www.globalwildlife.org
Year Founded: 2008
Sales Range: $1-9.9 Million
Emp.: 7
Animal Welfare Services
N.A.I.C.S.: 812910
Sam Reza *(Mgr-Fin)*
Leeanne E. Alonso *(Dir-Global Biodiversity Exploration)*
James P. Lewis *(Dir-Conservation Program)*
Brian Shelth *(Chm)*
Wes Sechrest *(CEO)*
Don Church *(Pres & Dir-Conservation)*
Alex Quintero *(COO)*
Russ Mittermeier *(Chief Conservation Officer)*

GLOBAL-5, INC.
2180 W State Rd 434 Ste 1150, Longwood, FL 32779
Tel.: (407) 571-6760   FL
Web Site: https://www.global-5.com
Year Founded: 1995
Sales Range: $10-24.9 Million
Emp.: 12
Advertising, Affiliate Marketing, Automotive, Aviation & Aerospace, Brand Development & Integration, Broadcast, Business Publications, Business-To-Business, Collateral, Commercial Photography
N.A.I.C.S.: 541820
Jenni Luke *(CFO)*
Mary Hamill *(Pres & CEO)*
Matt Hamill *(Exec VP & COO)*

GLOBALFLUENCY
1494 Hamilton Way, San Jose, CA 95125
Tel.: (408) 677-5300   CA
Web Site:
https://www.globalfluency.com
Year Founded: 1987
Sales Range: $1-9.9 Million
Emp.: 27
Public Relations & Advertising Agency
N.A.I.C.S.: 541820
Donovan Neale-May *(Pres)*
Liz Miller *(Sr VP)*
Bryan DeRose *(VP-Bus Dev)*
Natalie Fleisher *(Creative Dir)*
David Murray *(Exec VP)*
David Murray *(Exec VP)*

Subsidiaries:

GlobalFluency   (1)
80 N Moore St Ste 33D, New York, NY 10013
Tel.: (212) 213-5400
Web Site: http://www.globalfluency.com
Emp.: 1
Public Relations & Advertising Agency
N.A.I.C.S.: 541820
Donovan Neale-May *(Pres, CEO & Mng Partner)*
Liz Miller *(Sr VP)*
Dave Murray *(Exec VP)*
Bryan DeRose *(VP-Bus Dev)*
Natalie Fleisher *(Dir-Creative)*
Mary Anne Hensley *(Dir-Content & Mktg Programs)*
Tom Murphy *(Dir-Editorial)*
Monica Noriega *(Controller-Fin)*
Heidi Sue *(Chief Entertainment Officer)*
Kevin Sugarman *(Dir-Media Rels)*

GLOBALISE
1025 Connecticut Ave Nw Ste 1000, Washington, DC 20036
Tel.: (202) 857-9746   CT
Web Site: http://www.globalise.org
Year Founded: 2009
Sales Range: $1-9.9 Million
Emp.: 2
Educational Support Services
N.A.I.C.S.: 611710
Roger A. Riske *(CEO & Exec Dir)*

GLOBALIZATION PARTNERS INTERNATIONAL
1600 Tysons Blvd 8th Fl, McLean, VA 22102
Tel.: (703) 286-2193
Web Site:
http://www.globalizationpartner.com
Year Founded: 2001
Sales Range: $1-9.9 Million
Emp.: 25
Language Software
N.A.I.C.S.: 513210
Martin Spethman *(Founder & Mng Partner)*
Natalie Galvin *(Controller)*
Peter Betts *(Dir-Bus Dev-Global)*
Nancy Cremins *(Gen Counsel)*
Nicole Sahin *(CEO)*
Teresa James *(Sr Dir-Info Sys)*
Nicole Forbes *(Dir-Global Client Svcs & Assoc Gen Counsel)*
David Hughson *(Dir-Bus Dev-Natl)*
Jane Booth *(Sr Dir-Sls)*
Debbie Millin *(COO)*

GLOBALMED GROUP, LLC.
15020 N 74th St, Scottsdale, AZ 85260
Tel.: (480) 922-0044
Web Site: http://www.globalmed.com
Year Founded: 2002
Sales Range: $25-49.9 Million
Emp.: 113
Healthcare Software Development Services
N.A.I.C.S.: 541511
Joel E. Barthelemy *(Mng Dir)*
Brad Schmidt *(Dir-Bus Dev)*
Neal Schoenbach *(Dir-Sls-North America)*
Robert Rennie *(VP-EMEA)*

GLOBALMEDIA GROUP LLC
15020 N 74th St, Scottsdale, AZ 85260
Tel.: (480) 922-0044
Web Site:
http://www.globalmedia.com
Year Founded: 2002
Sales Range: $10-24.9 Million
Emp.: 100
Software Developing Services
N.A.I.C.S.: 423430

Joel E. Barthelemy *(Mng Dir)*
Michael Harris *(Dir-Dev)*
Brad Schmidt *(Dir-Global Mktg)*

GLOBALOGIX, INC.
13831 NW Freeway Ste 600, Houston, TX 77040
Tel.: (713) 987-7630
Web Site: http://www.globlx.com
Year Founded: 2004
Sales Range: $10-24.9 Million
Emp.: 150
Control & Automation Engineering Design & Implementation Services to Oil, Gas Exploration & Production Companies
N.A.I.C.S.: 213112
Robert Burkhardt *(VP-Acctg & Fin)*
Horacio Tinoco *(Dir-Tech)*
Gina Meins *(Dir-Engrg)*
Jake Eckert *(Dir-Ops)*
Shawn Lain *(Mgr-Barnet Shale Area)*
Charles Drobny Jr. *(Pres & CEO)*

GLOBALPAYNET HOLDINGS INC.
Columbia Tower 701 5th Ave Ste 4200, Seattle, WA 98104
Tel.: (206) 262-7533   NV
Web Site:
http://www.globalpaynet.com
Sales Range: Less than $1 Million
Payment Processing Services
N.A.I.C.S.: 522320

GLOBALSIM, INC.
9735 S 500 W, Sandy, UT 84070
Tel.: (801) 571-9094   UT
Web Site: https://www.globalsim.com
Crane & Custom Simulation Systems Developer, Mfr & Whslr
N.A.I.C.S.: 333310
Brad Ball *(VP-Sls & Mktg)*
Jonathan McCurdy *(Pres & CEO)*
Dan Olson *(VP-Ops)*
Kolby Baron *(VP-Fin)*

GLOBALSTREAMS, INC.
20353 W 108th St, Olathe, KS 66061-2893
Tel.: (314) 997-5100   DE
Web Site:
http://www.globalstreams.com
Year Founded: 2000
Sales Range: $10-24.9 Million
Emp.: 3
Video Communications Products Mfr
N.A.I.C.S.: 541611
Tom Webb *(Sr VP-Intl Sls)*

GLOBALTECH INDUSTRIES INC.
418 Hwy 441 Business, Cornelia, GA 30531
Tel.: (706) 776-1912
Web Site:
https://www.globaltechindustry.com
Year Founded: 1995
Sales Range: $10-24.9 Million
Emp.: 9
Scented Candles Mfr
N.A.I.C.S.: 339999
Jim Bruce *(Pres)*
Jeff Lewis *(Mgr-Sls-Natl)*
Nathan Carter *(Mgr-Process & Mechanical Engrg & Testing)*
Sam F. Dayton *(Owner)*

GLOBALWARE SOLUTIONS INC.
200 Ward Hill Ave, Haverhill, MA 01835
Tel.: (978) 469-7500
Web Site:
http://www.globalwaresolutions.com
Rev.: $123,894,800

Emp.: 375
Printing & Software Distribution & Documentation
N.A.I.C.S.: 541519
John P. Viliesis *(CFO)*
Daren Courter *(Gen Mgr & VP)*

Subsidiaries:

Global Ware Solutions   (1)
200 Ward Hill Ave, Haverhill, MA 01835
Tel.: (978) 469-7500
Web Site:
http://www.globalwaresolutions.com
Technical Manuals: Publishing & Printing
N.A.I.C.S.: 541519
Jerry Alexander *(Acct Mgr-Project & Product)*
Dan Dewar *(Sr Acct Mgr)*

Globalware Solutions   (1)
1089 Mills Way, Redwood City, CA 94063
Tel.: (650) 363-2200
Web Site:
http://www.globalwaresolutions.com
Rev.: $15,900,000
Emp.: 199
Disk & Diskette Conversion Service
N.A.I.C.S.: 541519

GLOBALWORKS
220 5th Ave, New York, NY 10001
Tel.: (212) 252-8800
Web Site:
http://www.globalworks.com
Emp.: 70
Advetising Agency
N.A.I.C.S.: 541810
Yuri Radzievsky *(CEO & Sr Partner)*
Anna Radzievsky *(Sr Partner & Chief Creative Officer)*
Mans Angantyr *(Sr Partner & Chief Digital Officer)*
Takashi Omura *(Partner & COO)*
Caroline Fish *(Dir-Creative)*
Brian Ng *(Partner)*
Jose Velez-Silva *(Partner, Dir-Client Svcs)*
John Mustin *(Partner & CMO)*
Ashley Laing *(Partner & CTO)*

GLOBE BUSINESS INTERIORS
6454 Centre Park Dr, West Chester, OH 45069
Tel.: (513) 771-5550
Web Site:
http://www.thercfgroup.com
Sales Range: $10-24.9 Million
Emp.: 100
Office Furniture
N.A.I.C.S.: 423210
Scott Robertson *(CEO)*
Bryan Lindholz *(Pres)*

GLOBE EXPRESS SERVICES LTD.
8025 Arrowridge Blvd, Charlotte, NC 28273
Tel.: (704) 357-3223
Web Site:
http://www.globeexpress.com
Rev.: $70,000,000
Emp.: 100
Freight Forwarding
N.A.I.C.S.: 488510
Mustapha Kawam *(Pres & CEO)*

GLOBE MECHANICAL, INC.
20 W 7th St, New Albany, IN 47150
Tel.: (812) 949-2001
Web Site:
http://www.globemechanical.com
Year Founded: 1984
Sales Range: $10-24.9 Million
Emp.: 99
Fabricated Pipe & Pipe Fitting Mfr
N.A.I.C.S.: 332996

Globe Mechanical, Inc.—(Continued)

Marlin Andres *(Pres)*

GLOBE MORTGAGE AMERICA, LLC
475 Grand Ave, Englewood, NJ 07631-4965
Tel.: (201) 816-5900   DE
Year Founded: 1957
Sales Range: $150-199.9 Million
Emp.: 25
Mortage Banking & Related Services
N.A.I.C.S.: 522292

GLOBE STORAGE & MOVING CO. INC.
665 Broadway, New York, NY 10012
Tel.: (212) 925-3555
Web Site:
http://www1.globemoving.com
Rev.: $13,649,624
Emp.: 54
Moving Services
N.A.I.C.S.: 484210
Vincent Cibrano *(Pres)*
Dennis Annunziata *(Controller)*

GLOBE TRAILER MANUFAC-TURING, INC.
3101 59th Ave Dr E, Bradenton, FL 34203
Tel.: (941) 753-2199   FL
Web Site:
http://www.globetrailers.com
Year Founded: 2004
Sales Range: $10-24.9 Million
Emp.: 60
Heavy Equipment Hauling Trailers Mfr
N.A.I.C.S.: 333924
Jeffrey K. Walters *(Pres)*

GLOBE TRAILERS OF FLORIDA, INC.
3101 59th Ave Dr E, Bradenton, FL 34203
Tel.: (941) 753-2199
Web Site:
http://www.globetrailers.com
Sales Range: $10-24.9 Million
Emp.: 75
Truck Trailer Mfr
N.A.I.C.S.: 336212
Jeff Walters Sr. *(Pres)*

GLOBENET INTERNATIONAL CORPORATION
4995 NW 72 Ave Ste 303, Miami, FL 33166
Tel.: (305) 513-0323
Web Site:
http://www.globenetcorp.com
Year Founded: 2001
Rev.: $3,300,000
Emp.: 13
Computers, Peripherals & Software
N.A.I.C.S.: 423430
Nestor Salvo *(Acct Mgr)*
Manuel Vibanco *(COO)*
Ahmed Cruz *(VP)*

GLOBOTEK HOLDINGS INC.
25 Jenna Ln, New York, NY 10304
Tel.: (917) 684-2422   NV
Web Site:
http://www.globotekholdingsinc.com
Sales Range: $1-9.9 Million
Emp.: 47
Oil & Gas Production
N.A.I.C.S.: 213112
Vladislav Feliksovich Tenenbaum *(Chm & Pres)*
Dmitry Viktorovich Lukin *(CEO)*
Alexandr Nikolaevich Lapkin *(Chief Science Officer & Principal Engr)*

Sergey Alexandrovich Lapkin *(CTO, Principal Engr & Dir-Tech)*
Alexander Viktorovich Lukin *(Chief Production Officer & Dir-Producing & Construction)*
Sergey Viktorovich Lukin *(CFO)*
Alexandr Vladimirivich Auxtin *(Dir-Corp Mgmt & Relations)*
Elena Alexandrova Lapkina *(Head-Project Dept)*

GLOBTEK, INC.
186 Veterans Dr, Northvale, NJ 07647
Tel.: (201) 784-1000
Web Site: https://www.globtek.com
Year Founded: 1984
Sales Range: $25-49.9 Million
Emp.: 4,365
Power Supplies Mfr & Distr
N.A.I.C.S.: 335311
Anna Kaplan *(CEO)*
Hans Moritz *(Mgr-Quality Assurance)*
Linda Chiandusse *(Mgr-Customer Svc)*
Rosario Mendez *(Engr-Quality Assur-ance)*

GLOBUS RELIEF
1775 W 1500 S, Salt Lake City, UT 84104
Tel.: (801) 977-0444   UT
Web Site: http://www.globusrelief.org
Year Founded: 1996
Sales Range: $100-124.9 Million
Emp.: 36
Health Care Srvices
N.A.I.C.S.: 622110

GLOBYS INC.
705 5th Ave S Ste 700, Seattle, WA 98104
Tel.: (206) 352-3055   WA
Web Site: http://www.globys.com
Year Founded: 1996
Sales Range: $10-24.9 Million
Emp.: 35
Contextual Marketing Solutions
N.A.I.C.S.: 513210
Derek Edwards *(CEO)*

GLOCKNER CHEVROLET CO. INC.
4368 US Hwy 23, Portsmouth, OH 45662-8801
Tel.: (740) 353-2161
Web Site: http://www.glockner.com
Year Founded: 1927
Sales Range: $10-24.9 Million
Emp.: 250
Petroleum Product Distr
N.A.I.C.S.: 424720
Mike Glockner *(Owner & Dir-Svc)*

Subsidiaries:

Andys Car And Truck Center, Inc.   (1)
2867 US Rte 23, Portsmouth, OH 45662
Tel.: (740) 354-3255
Web Site: http://www.glockner.com
Dealer of New & Used Cars
N.A.I.C.S.: 441110
Jim Donnely *(Pres)*

Glockner Oil Company Inc.   (1)
4407 US Hwy 23 S, Piketon, OH 45661-9703
Tel.: (740) 289-2979
Web Site: http://www.glockneroilco.com
Sales Range: $10-24.9 Million
Emp.: 30
Petroleum Product Whslr
N.A.I.C.S.: 424720
Richard Puckett *(Pres)*
Todd Ramey *(Mgr-Fuel)*

Glockner Quality Leasing   (1)
4746 Old Scioto Trl, Portsmouth, OH 45662
Tel.: (740) 355-5327

Web Site: http://www.qualityleasinginc.com
Automobile Finance Leasing Services
N.A.I.C.S.: 522220

The J.A.M.S. Agency Corporation   (1)
4368 US Hwy 23, Portsmouth, OH 45662-8801   (100%)
Tel.: (740) 353-2161
Web Site: http://www.j.a.m.s.com
Provider of Building Operation Services
N.A.I.C.S.: 531120

GLOHAB, INC.
3111 Camino del Rio N Ste 400, San Diego, CA 92108
Tel.: (619) 884-5953   DE
Web Site: http://www.glohab.com
Year Founded: 1997
Emp.: 4
Construction Services
N.A.I.C.S.: 236220
Daniel D. Correa *(Pres, CEO & Sec)*
Tabitha U. Correa *(Sec & VP-Mktg)*
James E. Slayton *(CFO & Controller)*
Carmen Burns *(Office Mgr)*

GLORIA LANCE INC.
15616 S Broadway St, Gardena, CA 90248
Tel.: (310) 767-4400
Web Site: http://www.glorialance.com
Rev.: $23,276,000
Emp.: 90
Provider of Women's & Juniors' Blouses
N.A.I.C.S.: 315250
Luz Lerman *(Mgr-AR)*
Miguel Lopez *(Owner)*
Sharon Weinstock *(VP & Gen Mgr)*

GLORIA NILSON, INC.
350 Route 35, Middletown, NJ 07701
Tel.: (732) 450-2300   NJ
Web Site:
http://www.glorianilson.com
Year Founded: 1980
Sales Range: $50-74.9 Million
Emp.: 700
Real Estate Agency
N.A.I.C.S.: 531210
Gary Foulks *(Reg VP)*
Pat Bell *(Pres & CEO)*
Sharon DiMonaco *(Mgr-Mktg)*
Richard Schlott *(Owner, Chm & CEO)*

GLORY DAYS GRILL
9426 Stewartown Rd Ste 2E, Gaith-ersburg, MD 20879   VA
Web Site:
https://www.glorydaysgrill.com
Year Founded: 1996
Family Restaurants
N.A.I.C.S.: 722511
Beth Rydzewski *(VP-Fin)*
Tony Cochones *(VP-Culinary Ops)*
Maribeth Harper *(Mktg Mgr)*
Gary M. Cohen *(Exec VP-Ops)*
Charissa E. Costa *(Dir-Mktg)*
Katie Easterbrook *(Mktg Mgr)*
Renee O'Neill *(Asst Mgr-Mktg)*
Jim Klavis *(Mgr-Franchise)*
Chris Verdecchia *(VP-Acctg & Fin)*
Tommy Boehm *(Controller)*

GLOSTEN, INC.
1201 Western Ave Ste 200, Seattle, WA 98101-2921
Tel.: (206) 624-7850   WA
Web Site: https://www.glosten.com
Year Founded: 1958
Sales Range: $10-24.9 Million
Emp.: 69
Consulting & Engineering Services
N.A.I.C.S.: 541330
Carmen Williams *(Controller)*
John L. R. Edgar *(Dir-R&D)*

Nicole A. Fortener *(Office Mgr & Mgr-HR)*
Zenzile Brooks *(Mgr-Mktg)*
Lisa N. Renehan *(VP)*
David W. Larsen *(Dir-Engrg)*
Josh Horst *(Mgr-Production Svcs)*
Kenneth Lane *(Dir-Production Svcs)*
Rick Strong *(Dir-Ops)*
Tom Robertson *(Mgr-IT)*
John Springer *(Pres)*
William L. Hurley Jr. *(Chm)*

Subsidiaries:

Noise Control Engineering, LLC   (1)
85 Rangeway Rd Bldg 2 Fl 2, Billerica, MA 01862
Tel.: (978) 670-5339
Web Site: http://www.noise-control.com
Sales Range: $1-9.9 Million
Emp.: 17
Consulting & Engineering Services
N.A.I.C.S.: 541330
Raymond Fischer *(Founder)*
Jeffrey Komrower *(Sr Engr)*
Jesse Spence *(Pres)*
Leo Boroditsky *(Chief Engr)*
Ann Marie Fischer *(Office Mgr)*

GLOSTREAM, INC.
1050 Wilshire Dr Ste 200, Troy, MI 48084
Tel.: (248) 227-9167
Web Site: http://www.glostream.com
Year Founded: 2006
Sales Range: $25-49.9 Million
Computer Technology Development Services
N.A.I.C.S.: 541511
Michael J. Sappington *(Chm & Mng Partner)*
Yaw Kwakye *(Sr VP-Client Support & Cloud)*
Milind Ghyar *(Co-Founder & Mng Dir)*

GLOTFELTY ENTERPRISES INC.
14161 Garrett Hwy, Oakland, MD 21550
Tel.: (301) 334-3911
Web Site: http://www.glotfeltytire.net
Sales Range: $10-24.9 Million
Emp.: 37
Power Supplies & Services
N.A.I.C.S.: 441330

GLOVER FOODS, INC.
119 Old Andersonville Rd, Americus, GA 31709
Tel.: (229) 924-2974   GA
Year Founded: 1957
Sales Range: $10-24.9 Million
Emp.: 101
Food Distribution Services
N.A.I.C.S.: 424410
Bryan McMichael *(Exec VP)*
William S. Harris *(Chm)*
Lorenzo Waters *(Mgr-CIS)*
Riley Purser *(VP-Sls)*
Ed Shattles *(Pres)*

GLOVER MAINTENANCE
913 W 14600 S, Bluffdale, UT 84065
Tel.: (801) 679-4266
Web Site: http://www.goglover.com
Year Founded: 2008
Sales Range: $10-24.9 Million
Emp.: 85
Property Construction & Maintenance Services
N.A.I.C.S.: 236220
Matt Glover *(Owner)*

GLOVES INTERNATIONAL INC.
2445 State Hwy 30, Mayfield, NY 12117

Tel.: (518) 661-6675
Web Site:
https://www.glovesinternational.com
Sales Range: $10-24.9 Million
Emp.: 25
Gloves, Women's & Children's
N.A.I.C.S.: 424350
Ben Kline (Pres)

GLOW INTERACTIVE, INC.
105 Chambers St Fl 2, New York, NY 10007
Tel.: (212) 206-7370
Web Site:
http://www.glowinteractive.com
Year Founded: 1999
Sales Range: $10-24.9 Million
Emp.: 25
Telephone Communication, Except Radio
N.A.I.C.S.: 541810
Peter Levin (Pres)
Neil Voss (Design Technologist)
Howard Kleinberg (Pres-Digital)

GLOW NETWORKS, INC.
2140 Lake Park Blvd Ste 113, Richardson, TX 75080-2290
Tel.: (972) 699-1994
Web Site:
http://www.glownetworks.com
Year Founded: 2000
Sales Range: $10-24.9 Million
Communications & Engineering
N.A.I.C.S.: 541330
Raj Malhotra (Co-Founder)

Subsidiaries:

Glow Networks Pvt Ltd (1)
No 42 2dn Fl Block B Brigade Software Park, Banashankari 2nd Stage, Bengaluru, 560070, India
Tel.: (91) 8026715817
Web Site: http://www.glownetworks.com
Sales Range: $10-24.9 Million
Emp.: 110
Communication & Engineering Services
N.A.I.C.S.: 541330
Vaidyanath Shanker (Gen Mgr-Asia Pacific Markets)

GLOWAC, HARRIS, MADISON INC.
330 S Whitney Way Ste 300, Madison, WI 53705
Tel.: (608) 232-9696
Year Founded: 2004
Rev.: $15,000,000
Emp.: 12
Advertising, Brand Development & Integration, Consulting, Market Research
N.A.I.C.S.: 541810
Wayne Glowac (CEO)
Wayne Harris (Pres)

GLOWTOUCH TECHNOLOGIES
The Summit II 4360 Brownsboro Rd Ste 200, Louisville, KY 40207
Tel.: (502) 410-1732
Web Site: https://www.glowtouch.com
Year Founded: 2004
Sales Range: $1-9.9 Million
Emp.: 1,500
Outsourced Information Technology Services
N.A.I.C.S.: 541519
V. Ravichandran (CEO)
Vidya Ravichandran (Founder & CEO)
Vik Chadha (Co-Founder & Mng Dir)
Paul Kuamoo (VP-Continuous Improvement)
Yogish Pai (Sr Mgr-Sys Admin)
Brian Schmidt (VP-Sls & Bus Dev)
Linda Ruffenach (Exec VP-Customer Care)

GLOWWORM INC.
200 Crescent CT Ste 1600, Dallas, TX 75201
Tel.: (214) 965-7999
Rev.: $70,000,000
Emp.: 70
Computer Software Development
N.A.I.C.S.: 541511
John Ware (Pres)

GLT INC.
3341 Successful Way, Dayton, OH 45414
Tel.: (937) 237-0055
Web Site: https://www.gltonline.com
Sales Range: $10-24.9 Million
Emp.: 60
Special Warehousing & Storage
N.A.I.C.S.: 493190
Kevin Knight (Pres)
Michelle Dornbusch (Mgr-HR)
Jason Heggs (Engr-Mfg)

GLUEFAST COMPANY, INC.
3535 State Rte 66 Bldg 1, Neptune, NJ 07753
Tel.: (732) 918-4600   DE
Web Site: https://www.gluefast.com
Year Founded: 1939
Sales Range: $1-9.9 Million
Emp.: 12
Labeling Equipment, Glues & Adhesives Moisteners
N.A.I.C.S.: 325520
Lester Mallet (Pres)
Joe Benenati (Gen Mgr)
Laura Hincapie (Office Mgr)
Amy Altman (VP)

GLY CONSTRUCTION INC.
200 112th Ave NE Ste 300, Bellevue, WA 98004-5878
Tel.: (425) 451-8877
Web Site: https://www.gly.com
Rev.: $228,700,000
Emp.: 250
Commercial & Institutional Building Construction
N.A.I.C.S.: 236220
Jim Elliott (Principal-Healthcare)
Ted Herb (CEO)
Mark Kane (COO)
Steve Peterson (CFO)
Aaron Helmers (Project Engr)
Amy Bergman (Project Mgr)
Andrew Johnson (Project Engr)
Barney Melnrick (Sr Project Engr)
Brian Caudle (Sr Project Engr)
Bryan Haakenson (Principal)
Tim Campbell (Principal)
Bill DeJarlais (Principal)
Monty Kilcup (Principal)
Steve Hoffmann (Principal)
Tyler Tonkin (Principal)

GLYECO, INC.
PO Box 10112, Rock Hill, SC 29731   NV
Web Site: https://www.glyeco.com
GLYE—(OTCBB)
Sales Range: $1-9.9 Million
Emp.: 18
Hazardous Waste Processing & Recycling
N.A.I.C.S.: 562211

Subsidiaries:

GlyEco Acquisition Corp #7 (1)
8464 Ardwick Ardmore Rd, Landover, MD 20785
Tel.: (301) 341-7907
Transportation Services
N.A.I.C.S.: 484230

GLYNNDEVINS ADVERTISING & MARKETING
11230 College Blvd, Overland Park, KS 66210-2700

Tel.: (913) 491-0600   KS
Web Site:
http://www.glynndevins.com
Year Founded: 1987
Rev.: $80,000,000
Emp.: 76
N.A.I.C.S.: 541810
George D. Devins (Principal)
Janel Wait (Dir-Digital Svcs)
Lea Ann Hodson (VP-Client Svc)
Teresa Carter (VP-Production Ops & Project Mgmt)
Molly White (VP-Brand Strategy)
Mika Cohn (Dir-Acct)
Charles Harris (Dir-Creative)
Brandi Towns (Dir-Content Strategy-Reputation & Social)
Candice Yagmin (VP-Client Svc)
Dana Compagnone (Acct Supvr)
Jen White (VP-Creative Svcs)
Mark Johnston (Sr VP)
Rob Adams (Sr VP)
Jeremy Johnson (VP-Creative)
Sue McClure (Pres & COO)
Laura McIntosh (VP-Talent Dev)
Beth Simos (VP)
Rhonda Stewart (Mng Dir-Brooks Adams & VP)
Lisa Legeer (Sr VP-Res & Healthcare Consulting)

GLYNWOOD CENTER, INC.
PO Box 157, Cold Spring, NY 10516
Tel.: (845) 265-3338   NY
Web Site: http://www.glynwood.org
Year Founded: 1929
Sales Range: $25-49.9 Million
Emp.: 30
Community Farming & Food Services
N.A.I.C.S.: 624210
Kathleen Frith (Pres)
Alexander Reese (Chm)

GM PETROLEUM DISTRIBUTORS INC.
2100 1st Ave S, Billings, MT 59101
Tel.: (406) 252-4661   MT
Web Site:
http://www.gmpetroleum.com
Year Founded: 1964
Sales Range: $10-24.9 Million
Emp.: 65
Petroleum Services
N.A.I.C.S.: 424710
Dennis Whitmore (Pres)

GM PLACE INC.
225 Summit Blvd, Birmingham, AL 35243
Tel.: (205) 252-7474
Web Site: http://www.gusmayer.com
Sales Range: $10-24.9 Million
Emp.: 50
Sales of Women's Accessories
N.A.I.C.S.: 458110
Richard Pizitz (CEO)

GMA ACCESSORIES/CAPELLI OF NEW YORK
1 E 33rd St Fl 9, New York, NY 10016-5011
Tel.: (212) 684-3344
Year Founded: 1986
Sales Range: $25-49.9 Million
Emp.: 155
Mfr of Women's, Children's & Infants' Clothing
N.A.I.C.S.: 424350
George Altirs (Pres)

Subsidiaries:

Capelli Europe GmbH (1)
Elisabethstrasse 17, 40880, Ratingen, Germany
Tel.: (49) 2102 4349 0
Web Site: http://www.capelli.shop.de
Emp.: 40

Women's & Children's Apparel Whslr
N.A.I.C.S.: 424350
Dimitrios Kokkinos (Acct Mgr)

Capelli of New York Inc. (1)
1 E 33rd St Fl 9, New York, NY 10016-5011
Tel.: (212) 684-3344
Web Site: http://www.capellinewyork.com
Sales Range: $25-49.9 Million
Mfr of Womens Childrens & Infants' Clothing
N.A.I.C.S.: 424350
Hani Afif (Mgr-Ops & IT)
Jemisin Rodriguez (Product Mgr-Design)

Shanghai GMA Factory Co., Ltd. (1)
Room 802 No 18 Hualing Building Lane 3062 Yan an Road W, Shanghai, 201103, China
Tel.: (86) 21 6103 1555
Web Site: http://www.gmashanghai.com.cn
Emp.: 200
Fashion Accessory Mfr
N.A.I.C.S.: 315250

GMC HARDWOODS INC.
30 Springdale Ave, Dover, MA 02030-0218
Tel.: (508) 785-1140   MA
Web Site:
http://www.gmchardwoods.com
Year Founded: 1965
Sales Range: $10-24.9 Million
Emp.: 13
Lumber & Millwork
N.A.I.C.S.: 423310
Samuel F. Glidden (VP)
Arthur Boynton Glidden III (Pres)

GMC+COMPANY
365 Canal St Ste 2950, New Orleans, LA 70130
Tel.: (504) 524-8117
Web Site:
http://www.gmcadvertising.com
Sales Range: Less than $1 Million
Emp.: 5
N.A.I.C.S.: 541810
Glenda McKinley English (Founder & Pres)
Randy Reyes (Sr Acct Exec)

GMDI LEASING CORP.
100 Renaissance Ctr, Detroit, MI 48265-0001
Tel.: (313) 667-6136
Web Site: http://www.gm-dileasing.com
Year Founded: 1968
Sales Range: $10-24.9 Million
Emp.: 25
Leasing of Signs
N.A.I.C.S.: 532490

GMF CAPITAL LLC
650 Madison Ave, New York, NY 10022
Tel.: (212) 300-1270
Web Site: http://gmfcapital.com
Year Founded: 2013
Investment Management
N.A.I.C.S.: 523999

Subsidiaries:

Motorsport Network, LLC (1)
5972 NE 4th Ave, Miami, FL 33137
Tel.: (305) 507-8799
Web Site:
http://www.motorsportnetwork.com
Digital & Traditional Media Services to Motorsport Fans & Automotive Consumers
N.A.I.C.S.: 519290
Ben Block (CEO)

Subsidiary (Domestic):

Motorsport Games Inc. (2)
5972 NE 4th Ave, Miami, FL 33137
Tel.: (305) 507-8799
Web Site:
https://www.motorsportgames.com
Rev.: $10,324,559

GMF Capital LLC—(Continued)

Assets: $18,897,792
Liabilities: $16,994,394
Net Worth: $1,903,398
Earnings: ($35,990,805)
Emp.: 133
Fiscal Year-end: 12/31/2022
Holding Company
N.A.I.C.S.: 551112
Stephen Hood (Pres & CEO)

duPont Publishing, Inc. (2)
4600 140th Ave N Ste 210, Clearwater, FL 33762
Tel.: (727) 573-9339
Web Site: http://www.dupontregistry.com
Sales Range: $10-24.9 Million
Emp.: 80
Magazine Publisher
N.A.I.C.S.: 513120
Thomas L. duPont (Publr)
Manuel O. Obordo (CTO)
J. Douglas Baldridge (Gen Counsel)
William Chapman (CEO)
Steven Chapman Jr. (Pres)

Division (Domestic):

duPont Registry (3)
3051 Tech Dr, Saint Petersburg, FL 33716
(100%)
Tel.: (727) 573-9339
Web Site: http://www.dupontregistry.com
Magazine Publisher
N.A.I.C.S.: 513120
Thomas L. duPont (Publr)
Kit Jeerapaet (Pres-A Buyers Gallery of Fine Automobiles)
Hal Reddick (VP-Sls)
Tim Breaux (VP-Sls)
Sherri L. Norris (VP-Sls)

GMH ASSOCIATES INC.
10 Campus Blvd, Newtown Square, PA 19073
Tel.: (610) 355-8000 **PA**
Web Site: http://www.gmh-inc.com
Year Founded: 1985
Sales Range: $25-49.9 Million
Emp.: 144
Real Estate Owner, Developer & Manager
N.A.I.C.S.: 531210
Robert DiGiuseppe (CFO & Exec VP)
Joseph Macchione (Exec VP)
Mike Holloway (Exec VP)
Jim Kirby (Exec VP)
Dennis O'Leary (Exec VP)
James Kennedy (Gen Counsel & Sr VP)
Rand A. Ginsburg (COO)
David R. Forrest (Sr VP-Investment Sls)
Nick Lee (Chief Acq Officer)
Gary M. Holloway Jr. (Exec VP)
Gary Holloway Sr. (Founder, Pres & CEO)

GMI
222 Rampart St, Charlotte, NC 28203
Tel.: (704) 940-7755
Web Site: http://www.gmi3.com
Year Founded: 2002
Rev.: $17,800,000
Emp.: 70
Medical, Dental, Hospital Equipment & Supplies Merchant Whslr
N.A.I.C.S.: 423450
Scott Ray (Owner)

GMI COMPANIES, INC.
2999 Henkle Dr, Lebanon, OH 45036-9260
Tel.: (513) 932-3445 **OH**
Web Site: https://gmicompanies.com
Year Founded: 1976
Sales Range: $100-124.9 Million
Emp.: 190
Visual Communication & Presentation Aids Mfr
N.A.I.C.S.: 337127

Mark Leasure (CEO)

Subsidiaries:

Waddell Display Cases (1)
512 S Washington St, Greenfield, OH 45123-1645
(100%)
Tel.: (937) 981-7724
Web Site: http://www.waddellfurniture.com
Sales Range: $25-49.9 Million
Emp.: 27
Mfr of Display Cases
N.A.I.C.S.: 337212
George L. Leasure (Pres)

GMI HOLDING, INC.
104 Maxwell Ave, Greenwood, SC 29646
Tel.: (864) 941-4044
Holding Company
N.A.I.C.S.: 551112
A. Self (CEO)

Subsidiaries:

Greenwood Communities & Resorts, Inc. (1)
104 Maxwell Ave, Greenwood, SC 29646
(100%)
Tel.: (864) 941-4044
Web Site: http://www.greenwoodcr.com
Sales Range: $75-99.9 Million
Emp.: 12
Real Estate Development
N.A.I.C.S.: 237210
Bill Watkins (Gen Counsel & VP)

Greenwood Mills, Inc. (1)
300 Morgan Ave, Greenwood, SC 29646-2641
Tel.: (864) 229-2571
Web Site: http://www.greenwoodmills.com
Sales Range: $75-99.9 Million
Emp.: 500
Mfr of Fabrics for Men's, Women's & Children's Wear; Uniform & Career Apparel; Home Furnishings
N.A.I.C.S.: 313210
Thomas J. Davis (CFO & Exec VP)
Gary Niederauer (VP-Sls)
Warren L. Moore (VP-HR)
Lisa McMillan (Dir-Human Reis)
Barry Putnam (Mgr-Pur)
James C. Self III (Pres & COO)

Subsidiary (Domestic):

SingleSource Apparel, Inc. (2)
300 Morgan Ave, Greenwood, SC 29646
Tel.: (864) 227-2121
Web Site: http://www.ssapparel.com
Apparels Mfr
N.A.I.C.S.: 313210

GMLV-GLOBAL MARKETING WITH A LOCAL VISION
53 Edison Pl Level 3, Newark, NJ 07102
Tel.: (973) 848-1100
Web Site: http://www.gmlv.co
Year Founded: 2007
Marketing & Advertising Agency
N.A.I.C.S.: 541810
Steven Manise (Account Mgr)

Subsidiaries:

The Byne Group (1)
75 Montebello Rd, Suffern, NY 10901
Tel.: (845) 369-0945
Web Site: http://www.thebynegroup.com
Advertising Agency Services
N.A.I.C.S.: 541810
Ann Byne (Principal)
Melissa Lipovsky (VP & Dir-Creative)

GMM CAPITAL LLC
Fl 14 689 5th Ave, New York, NY 10022-3148
Tel.: (212) 688-8288 **DE**
Privater Equity Firm
N.A.I.C.S.: 523999
Isaac Dabah (CEO)

Subsidiaries:

Delta Galil Industries Ltd. (1)
45 Ha Eshel St Southern Industrial Zone, Caesarea, 30889, Israel (54%)
Tel.: (972) 768177000
Web Site: https://www.deltagalil.com
Rev.: $1,857,682,000
Assets: $1,788,587,000
Liabilities: $1,020,205,000
Net Worth: $768,382,000
Earnings: $85,341,000
Emp.: 24,320
Fiscal Year-end: 12/31/2023
Intimate Apparel, Men's Underwear & Socks Mfr
N.A.I.C.S.: 315250
Isaac Dabah (Vice Chm & CEO)
Gil Shimon (Pres-Global Upper Market Bus)
Noam Lautman (Chm)
Anat Bogner (CEO-Delta Israel)
Miki Laxer (Sec, VP-Finance & Accountant)
Inbar Schwartz (Sr VP & Dir-Bus Dev)
Yaniv Benedek (CFO)
Michal Segal (Chief HR Officer & Sr VP)
Paul Gelb (Chief Admin Officer & Gen Counsel)
Iric L. Browndorf (Exec VP-Global Sourcing & Production)
Itzhak Weinstock (COO & COO)

Subsidiary (Non-US):

Delta Galil Germany GmbH (2)
Zeppelinallee 47, 60487, Frankfurt am Main, Germany
Tel.: (49) 69 79405
Web Site: http://www.deltagalil.com
Intimate Apparel, Men's Underwear & Socks Mfr
N.A.I.C.S.: 315250

Subsidiary (Domestic):

Schiesser AG (3)
Schutzenstrasse 18, Radolfzell, 78315, Germany (100%)
Tel.: (49) 7732 90 0
Web Site: http://www.schiesserag.com
Sales Range: $150-199.9 Million
Underwear Marketer Mfr
N.A.I.C.S.: 315210
Karl-Achim Klein (Member-Mgmt Bd)
Isaac Dabah (Chm-Supervisory Bd)
Andreas Lindemann (Chm-Mgmt Bd)

Subsidiary (Non-US):

Pleas a.s. (4)
Havirska 144, 581 27, Havlickuv Brod, Czech Republic (100%)
Tel.: (420) 569463111
Web Site: http://www.pleas.eu
Sales Range: $150-199.9 Million
Emp.: 700
Innerwear Mfr
N.A.I.C.S.: 315120
Johannes Molzberger (Member-Exec Bd)
Eugen Bohl (Member-Exec Bd)
Petr Nobst (Member-Exec Bd)

S.A. Schiesser International N.V. (4)
Nijverheidslaan 2, 1853, Strombeek-Bever, Belgium (100%)
Tel.: (32) 2 2 63 01 70
Web Site: http://www.schiesser.be
Sales Range: $100-124.9 Million
Emp.: 13
Underwear Mfr & Marketer
N.A.I.C.S.: 315250
Anne Decooman (Gen Mgr)

Schiesser Body Fashion Center s.r.o. (4)
Na Porici 25, 11000, Prague, Czech Republic (100%)
Tel.: (420) 222827702
Web Site: http://www.schiesser.cz
Intimate Apparel
N.A.I.C.S.: 458110

Schiesser International Ltd. (4)
6 Fl Fortune Indus Bldg, 35 Tai Yip St, Kowloon, China (Hong Kong) (100%)
Tel.: (852) 27991230
Sales Range: $50-74.9 Million
Emp.: 15
Mfr of Underwear
N.A.I.C.S.: 315120

Schiesser International Nederland BV (4)
Valutaboulevard 20, 3825 BT, Amersfoort, Netherlands (100%)
Tel.: (31) 33 4 96 86 00
Emp.: 12
Underwear Marketing & Sales
N.A.I.C.S.: 424350

Schiesser Schweiz AG (4)
Hafenstrasse 6, 8280, Kreuzlingen, Switzerland (100%)
Tel.: (41) 71 6 77 08 60
Sales Range: $50-74.9 Million
Emp.: 30
Innerwear Mfr
N.A.I.C.S.: 315120
Uschi Riget (Mng Dir)

Subsidiary (US):

Delta Galil USA Inc. (2)
1 Harmon Plz 5th Fl, Secaucus, NJ 07094-3619
Tel.: (201) 902-0055
Web Site: http://www.deltagalil.com
Sales Range: $25-49.9 Million
Emp.: 150
Mfr of Womens & Childrens Underwear
N.A.I.C.S.: 315250
Steve Lockulf (CFO)

Division (Domestic):

7 For All Mankind (3)
777 S Alameda St Bldg 1 4th Fl, Los Angeles, CA 90021
Tel.: (213) 747-7002
Web Site: http://www.7forallmankind.com
Mens & Womens Clothing Mfr
N.A.I.C.S.: 315250
Simon James Spurr (Creative Dir-Global)
Margaret Maldonado (Sr Dir-Design-Women's Ready-to-Wear)
Larissa Noble (Dir-Women's Design)
Wes Austin (Dir-Men's Design)

Subsidiary (Domestic):

Auburn Hosiery Mills, Inc. (3)
113 E Main St, Auburn, KY 42206-5106
Tel.: (270) 542-4175
Sales Range: $25-49.9 Million
Emp.: 50
Mfr of Men's, Ladies' & Children's Socks
N.A.I.C.S.: 424350

Burlen Corp. (3)
1904 McCormick Dr, Tifton, GA 31794
Tel.: (229) 382-4100
Web Site: http://www.burlen.com
Sales Range: $25-49.9 Million
Emp.: 200
Women's & Children's Undergarments
N.A.I.C.S.: 315250
Steve Klein (Pres & CEO)

Delta Textiles New York Ltd. (3)
6 E 32nd St, New York, NY 10016 (100%)
Tel.: (212) 481-3550
Web Site: http://www.deltagalil.com
Sales Range: $25-49.9 Million
Emp.: 7
Mfr of Undergarments & Nightwear
N.A.I.C.S.: 314120

Division (Domestic):

Ella Moss (3)
777 S Alameda St 4th Fl, Los Angeles, CA 90021
Tel.: (213) 747-7002
Web Site: http://www.ellamoss.com
Apparel Designer & Whslr
N.A.I.C.S.: 315250

Subsidiary (Domestic):

Loomworks Apparel Inc. (3)
16912 Von Karman Ave, Irvine, CA 92606-4923
Tel.: (949) 296-0380
Web Site: http://www.pjsalvage.com
Women's Loungewear & Lingerie Mfr
N.A.I.C.S.: 315250
Peter Burke (Pres)

Division (Domestic):

Splendid (3)

777 S Alameda St 4th Fl, Los Angeles, CA 90021
Tel.: (213) 747-7002
Web Site: http://www.splendid.com
Apparels Mfr
N.A.I.C.S.: 315250

Subsidiary (Non-US):

Eminence S.A.S. (2)
Route De Gallargues, BP 30, 30470, Aimargues, France
Tel.: (33) 466736565
Web Site: https://www.eminence.fr
Women's Undergarments Mfr & Sales
N.A.I.C.S.: 315210

Subsidiary (Non-US):

Eminence Benelux S.A. (3)
Chaussee de Louvain 490, 1380, Lasne, Belgium (100%)
Tel.: (32) 22630290
Web Site: http://www.eminencebenelux.be
Women's Undergarments Mfr & Sales
N.A.I.C.S.: 315120
Renata Gerneenen (Mng Dir)

GMPC
11390 W Olympic Blvd Ste 400, Los Angeles, CA 90064
Tel.: (310) 392-4070
Web Site: http://www.gmpc.com
Sales Range: $25-49.9 Million
Emp.: 40
Advertising Novelties
N.A.I.C.S.: 339950
Gary Mandel (Co-Pres)
Mark Lipschitz (CFO)
Sharon Seyoum (Controller)

GMS MINE REPAIR & MAINTENANCE
32 Enterprise Dr, Oakland, MD 21550
Tel.: (301) 334-8186
Web Site: https://www.gmsminerepair.com
Rev.: $13,600,000
Emp.: 1,500
Industrial Machinery & Equipment Repair
N.A.I.C.S.: 811210
Mike Fleece (Coord-GMS North Reg)
Susan Bealko (Dir-Safety)
Mike Thomas (Gen Mgr)
Lester Tupper (Dir-GMS Midwest)

GMSS HOLDINGS, LLC
28 Torrice Dr, Woburn, MA 01801
Tel.: (781) 305-3144 DE
Year Founded: 2020
Holding Company
N.A.I.C.S.: 551112
Jeffrey Siegal (CEO)

Subsidiaries:

Emily Corporation (1)
11800 28th St N, Saint Petersburg, FL 33716-1815
Web Site: http://www.ddpmedical.com
Medical, Dental & Hospital Equipment & Supplies Merchant Whslr
N.A.I.C.S.: 423450
Joseph W. Difabio (CEO)

Geriatric Medical & Surgical Supply, Inc. (1)
28 Torrice Dr, Woburn, MA 01801
Web Site: http://www.geriatricmedical.com
Medical, Dental & Hospital Equipment & Supplies Merchant Whslr
N.A.I.C.S.: 423450
Arthur Siegal (Pres)

GMST, LLC
45 Winsted Rd, Torrington, CT 06790
Tel.: (888) 869-5889
Web Site: http://www.gengrassubaru.com
Auto Dealership
N.A.I.C.S.: 441110

Jonathan Gengras (Co-Owner)
E. Clayton Gengras Jr. (Co-Owner)

Subsidiaries:

Center Subaru (1)
45 Winsted Rd, Torrington, CT 06790
Tel.: (860) 489-1268
Web Site: http://www.centersubaru.com
Car Whslr
N.A.I.C.S.: 441110
R. Phil Porter (Pres)

GMT CAPITAL CORP.
2100 Riveredge Pkwy Nw, Atlanta, GA 30328
Tel.: (770) 989-8261
Web Site: https://gmtcapital.com
Rev.: $1,400,000
Emp.: 14
Investment Banking & Securities Dealing
N.A.I.C.S.: 523150
Thomas E. Claugus (Founder & Pres)

GMT CORPORATION
2116 E Bremer Ave, Waverly, IA 50677-0358
Tel.: (319) 352-1509 IA
Web Site: https://www.gmtcorporation.com
Year Founded: 1973
Sales Range: $25-49.9 Million
Emp.: 400
Provider of Industrial Machinery
N.A.I.C.S.: 332710
Jared Graening (Mgr-Sls & Mktg)

GMX INC.
741 Boston Post Rd Ste 200, Guilford, CT 06437-2714
Tel.: (203) 453-5026
Rev.: $10,000,000
Emp.: 4
Investors, Nec
N.A.I.C.S.: 523999
Charles A. Robertson (Pres)

GMX RESOURCES INC.
1 Benham Pl 9400 N Broadway Ste 600, Oklahoma City, OK 73114-7422
Tel.: (405) 254-5838 OK
Year Founded: 1998
Sales Range: $100-124.9 Million
Emp.: 112
Oil & Gas Exploration Services
N.A.I.C.S.: 211310
Keith Leffel (VP-Gas Mktg)
Gary D. Jackson (VP)
James A. Merrill (CFO)
David C. Baggett (CEO)
Michael J. Rohleder (Pres)
Harry C. Stahel Jr. (VP-Fin)

Subsidiaries:

Endeavor Pipeline, Inc. (1)
1 Benham Pl Ste 600, Oklahoma City, OK 73114
Tel.: (405) 600-0711
Sales Range: $50-74.9 Million
Emp.: 75
Gas Exploration & Development
N.A.I.C.S.: 211120

GN US HOLDINGS INC.
8001 E Bloomington Freeway, Minneapolis, MN 55420
Tel.: (952) 769-8000
Web Site: http://www.gnresound.com
Rev.: $26,600,000
Emp.: 250
Hearing Aids
N.A.I.C.S.: 334510
Todd Marie (Pres)

GNB BANCORPORATION
529 G Ave Box 246, Grundy Center, IA 50638
Tel.: (319) 824-5431

Web Site: http://www.gnbbank.com
Year Founded: 1981
National Commercial Banks
N.A.I.C.S.: 522110
Kevin Swalley (Pres & CEO)

GNCO, INC.
1395 Valley Belt Rd, Brooklyn Heights, OH 44131
Tel.: (216) 749-6800
Web Site: https://gncoinc.com
Year Founded: 1965
Holding Company
N.A.I.C.S.: 551112
Matt Adams (Pres)

Subsidiaries:

FMH Material Handling Solutions (1)
5165 Vasquez Blvd, Denver, CO 80216
Tel.: (303) 920-1653
Web Site: https://www.fmhsolutions.com
Sales Range: $25-49.9 Million
Emp.: 238
Materials Handling Machinery
N.A.I.C.S.: 423830
Cathy Yeager (Mgr-AP)

GNO INTERNATIONAL LLC
608 Iona St, Metairie, LA 70005
Tel.: (504) 828-3939
Sales Range: $10-24.9 Million
Emp.: 5
Men's & Boy's Clothing
N.A.I.C.S.: 424350
Kenneth Gordon (Pres)

GNOSTECH, INC.
650 Louis Dr Ste 190, Warminster, PA 18974
Tel.: (215) 443-8660
Web Site: http://www.gnostech.com
Year Founded: 1981
Sales Range: $10-24.9 Million
Emp.: 65
Mechanical Engineering Services
N.A.I.C.S.: 541330
Sarah Carter (VP)

Subsidiaries:

Gnostech, Inc. - San Diego (1)
2468 Historic Decatur Rd Ste 230, San Diego, CA 92106
Tel.: (619) 220-0896
Web Site: http://www.gnostech.com
Sales Range: $10-24.9 Million
Emp.: 10
Mechanical Engineering Services
N.A.I.C.S.: 541330
Joseph M. Spahn (Mgr-Info)

GO COMPANIES, LLC
4215 Worth Ave Ste 320, Columbus, OH 43219
Tel.: (614) 383-7367 DE
Year Founded: 2021
Holding Company; Real Estate Credit
N.A.I.C.S.: 551112
Michael Isaacs (CEO)
Andrew Panagos (Pres & COO)

Subsidiaries:

Go Mortgage, LLC (1)
4215 Worth Ave, Columbus, OH 43219
Tel.: (614) 383-7367
Web Site: https://gomortgage.com
Sales Range: $10-24.9 Million
Emp.: 14
Mortgage Lending & Brokerage Firm
N.A.I.C.S.: 522292
Michael Isaacs (CEO)
Andrew Panagos (Pres & COO)
Nicholas Capretta (VP-Retail Sls)

GO ENERGISTICS LLC
2101 Cedar Springs Rd Ste 1050, Dallas, TX 75201
Tel.: (214) 347-0590
Web Site: http://www.goenergistics.com

Year Founded: 2011
Sales Range: $10-24.9 Million
Emp.: 46
Healthcare Related Construction Services
N.A.I.C.S.: 236220
Adam Shepherd (Pres & CEO)
Aaron Card (Project Mgr)
Teri Dorsey-Porter (Dir-Mktg & Proposals)
Dave Giles (Exec Dir-Design)

GO JO INDUSTRIES, INC.
1 GOJO Plz Ste 500, Akron, OH 44311
Tel.: (330) 255-6000 OH
Web Site: https://www.gojo.com
Year Founded: 1946
Mfr of Hand Soaps
N.A.I.C.S.: 325612

GO MINI'S LLC
13611 McQueen's Ct, Jacksonville, FL 32225
Tel.: (866) 466-4647
Web Site: http://www.gominis.com
Year Founded: 2002
Sales Range: $1-9.9 Million
Emp.: 2
Portable Moving & Storage Container Mfr & Sales
N.A.I.C.S.: 493190
Sheila Norris (CFO)

GO MODULAR, INC.
294 Albion Rd, Lincoln, RI 02865
Tel.: (508) 992-1655
Web Site: https://www.gomodularhomes.com
Year Founded: 1986
Sales Range: $10-24.9 Million
Emp.: 19
Lumber & Building Material Whslr
N.A.I.C.S.: 444110
Chris Pitliangas (Gen Mgr)

GO MORTGAGE GROUP, LLC
9308 S Mooreland Rd, Richmond, VA 23229
Tel.: (804) 915-8843 VA
Web Site: http://www.gomortgagegroup.net
Year Founded: 2005
Digital Home Lending Services
N.A.I.C.S.: 522292
Christopher H. Stephenson (Pres)

GO WELSH
3055 Yellow Goose Rd, Lancaster, PA 17601
Tel.: (717) 898-9000
Web Site: http://www.gowelsh.com
Sales Range: Less than $1 Million
Emp.: 5
Advertising, Graphic Design, Public Relations
N.A.I.C.S.: 541810
Craig Welsh (Owner)

GO-GO BABYZ, CORP.
3530 Charter Park Dr, San Jose, CA 95136
Tel.: (408) 360-0653
Web Site: http://www.gogobabyz.com
Year Founded: 2003
Sales Range: $1-9.9 Million
Emp.: 9
Toy & Children Vehicle Mfr
N.A.I.C.S.: 339930
Kerry Williams (Founder, Pres & COO)

GO-MART, INC.
915 Riverside Dr, Gassaway, WV 26624
Tel.: (304) 364-8000 WV

Go-Mart, Inc.—(Continued)

Sales Range: $300-349.9 Million
Emp.: 50
Convenience Stores Owner & Operator
N.A.I.C.S.: 445131
John D. Heater (Pres & CEO)

GO2CALL.COM, INC.

807 Davis St Unit 2207, Evanston, IL
60201-7104
Tel.: (847) 864-4123   IL
Web Site: http://www.go2call.com
Year Founded: 1998
Sales Range: $10-24.9 Million
Emp.: 23
Internet-Based Telephone Calling
N.A.I.C.S.: 541690

GOAL FINANCIAL, LLC

401 W A St Ste 1300, San Diego, CA
92101-7906
Tel.: (866) 290-4222
Web Site:
   http://www.goalfinancial.net
Year Founded: 2001
Sales Range: $10-24.9 Million
Emp.: 250
Educational Loan Services
N.A.I.C.S.: 522310
Ryan Katz (Founder & CEO)
Ken Ruggiero (CFO)
Andre Kostadinov (CIO)
Michael Middleton (VP-Product Dev)
Mark Jacobs (VP-Bus Dev)
Seamus Garland (Treas & VP-Capital
Markets)
Pam Daly (VP-Sls)
Ravi Rajaratnam (VP-Project Mgmt
Office)
Alan Komensky (Gen Counsel)

GOBRANDGO, LLC

8221 Minnesota Ave, Saint Louis, MO
63111
Tel.: (314) 754-8712
Web Site: http://www.gobrandgo.com
Year Founded: 2003
Sales Range: $1-9.9 Million
Emp.: 50
Marketing & Advertising Services
N.A.I.C.S.: 541810
Brandon Dempsey (Partner)
Jamie Rule (VP-Strategy)
Nicole Turner (Creative Dir)
Olivia Oppelt (Acct Mgr)

GOBRANDS, INC.

537 N 3rd St, Philadelphia, PA 19123
Tel.: (855) 400-7833
Web Site: http://gopuff.com
Emp.: 1,000
Delivery Service
N.A.I.C.S.: 492110
Yakir Gola (Founder)
Bryan Batista (Sr VP-Intl)

Subsidiaries:

Beverages & More Inc.   (1)
1401 Willow Pass Rd, Concord, CA 94520
Tel.: (925) 609-6000
Web Site: http://www.bevmo.com
Sales Range: $300-349.9 Million
Retailer of Wine Beer Liquor Non-Alcoholic
Beverage & Snack Food DISTR
N.A.I.C.S.: 445320
Bob Paulinsky (Sr VP-Mdsg)

GOC LTD.

801 Riderwood Dr, Butler, AL 36904
Tel.: (205) 459-2727
Web Site: https://www.gocltd.com
Rev.: $10,900,000
Emp.: 8
Convenience Store
N.A.I.C.S.: 445131

Sam Y. Gibson (Owner & Pres)
Kay Mosley (Mgr)

GOCONVERGENCE

4545 36th St, Orlando, FL 32811
Tel.: (407) 235-3210
Web Site:
   http://www.goconvergence.com
Rev.: $18,000,000
Emp.: 32
Advetising Agency
N.A.I.C.S.: 541810
Brian Townsend (Sr Dir-Sls & Mktg)

GOD'S PIT CREW

2499 N Main St, Danville, VA 24540
Tel.: (434) 836-4472   VA
Web Site:
   https://www.godspitcrew.org
Year Founded: 2000
Sales Range: $10-24.9 Million
Emp.: 7
Disaster Relief Services
N.A.I.C.S.: 624230
Rhonda Zola (VP-Advancement Ops)
Roger Ewing (Sec)
Tim Nuckles (Chm)
James Hodge (Treas)
Tracy Stone (Vice Chm)

GOD'S WORLD PUBLICA-TIONS INC.

12 All Souls Cres, Asheville, NC
28803
Tel.: (828) 253-8063
Web Site: http://www.gwnews.com
Year Founded: 1981
Sales Range: $10-24.9 Million
Emp.: 50
Book Club, Mail Order & News Publisher
N.A.I.C.S.: 513120
Kevin Martin (CEO)

GODBY HOME FURNISHINGS INC.

17828 United States Hwy 31 N,
Westfield, IN 46074
Tel.: (317) 896-3832
Web Site:
   http://www.godbyfurniture.com
Rev.: $11,370,746
Emp.: 65
Furniture Retailer
N.A.I.C.S.: 449110
Mary Ann Cooper (Coord-Adv)
Kellie Price (Mgr-Ops)

GODENGO, INC.

2855 Telegraph Ave Ste 203, Berkeley, CA 94705
Tel.: (510) 594-2570
Web Site: http://www.godengo.com
Sales Range: $10-24.9 Million
Emp.: 5
Online Publishing Platform
N.A.I.C.S.: 541810
Peter Stilson (Pres & CEO)

Subsidiaries:

Texterity Inc.   (1)
144 Turnpike Rd, Southborough, MA 01772-2104
Tel.: (508) 804-3000
Web Site: http://www.texterity.com
Sales Range: $10-24.9 Million
Systems & Services for Creation, Delivery &
Tracking of Digital Editions of Magazines
N.A.I.C.S.: 541690

GODFATHER'S PIZZA, INC.

2808 N 108th St, Omaha, NE 68164
Tel.: (402) 391-1452   DE
Web Site:
   https://www.godfathers.com
Year Founded: 1973
Sales Range: $800-899.9 Million

Emp.: 2,500
Operator of Pizza Restaurants
N.A.I.C.S.: 722511
Ronald B. Gartlan (Pres & CEO)
Connie Cajka (Dir-Sls)
Jan Sammons (Dir-Mktg)
Ginny Allumbaugh (Mgr-Franchise
Mktg)

GODFREY & KAHN, S.C.

833 E Michigan St Ste 1800, Milwaukee, WI 53202-5615
Tel.: (414) 273-3500
Web Site: https://www.gklaw.com
Sales Range: $25-49.9 Million
Emp.: 400
Law firm
N.A.I.C.S.: 541110
Kelly Conrardy (Dir-Atty Recruiting &
Retention)
Jon Anderson (Mng Partner-Madison
Office & Atty)
Nicholas P. Wahl (Mng Partner)
Robert M. Mueller (COO)
Susan E. Steberl (Dir-Mktg)
Thomas R. Dressel (Dir-IT)
Todd M. Womack (CFO)
Merry Lee Lison (Dir-HR)
Andrew Spillane (Atty-Banking & Fin
Institutions Practice Grp)
Charles Allenstein (Dir-IT)
Kimberly P. Thekan (Chief Talent
Officer)

GODFREY ADVERTISING, INC.

40 N Christian St, Lancaster, PA
17602
Tel.: (717) 393-3831   PA
Web Site: https://www.godfrey.com
Year Founded: 1947
Sales Range: $10-24.9 Million
Emp.: 93
Advetising Agency
N.A.I.C.S.: 541810
Ken Jones (Partner & Exec VP)
Stacy Whisel (Pres)
Erin Michalak (Sr VP & Dir-Acct Svc)
Josh Albert (Dir-Bus Dev)

GODIGITAL MEDIA GROUP, LLC

233 Wilshire Blvd Ste 100, Santa
Monica, CA 90401-1217
Tel.: (310) 394-9610   CA
Web Site:
   http://www.godigitalmg.com
Year Founded: 2006
Advertising Agencies
N.A.I.C.S.: 541810
Jason Peterson (Founder, Chm &
CEO)

Subsidiaries:

Bob's Stores, LLC   (1)
160 Corporate Ct, Meriden, CT 06450
Tel.: (203) 235-5775
Web Site: http://www.bobstores.com
Retail Apparel Stores
N.A.I.C.S.: 458110

Cinq Music Group, LLC   (1)
4712 Admiralty Way Ste 533, Marina Del
Rey, CA 90292
Tel.: (310) 394-9610
Web Site: https://cinqmusic.com
Music Publisher, Record Production & Distribution Services
N.A.I.C.S.: 512250

Subsidiary (Domestic):

Cinq Music Publishing, LLC   (2)
4712 Admiralty Way Ste 533, Marina Del
Rey, CA 90292
Tel.: (310) 394-9610
Web Site: https://cinqmusic.com
Music Publishers
N.A.I.C.S.: 512230

Eastern Mountain Sports, LLC   (1)

160 Corporate Ct, Meriden, CT 06450
Tel.: (203) 379-2233
Web Site: http://www.ems.com
Outdoors Clothing & Equipment Whslr
N.A.I.C.S.: 459110

GODINGER SILVER ART CO. LTD.

6315 Traffic Ave, Ridgewood, NY
11385
Tel.: (718) 418-1000
Web Site: https://www.godinger.com
Rev.: $18,400,000
Emp.: 50
Gifts & Novelties
N.A.I.C.S.: 339910
Arnold Godinger (Pres)
David Cohen (VP)

GODISH.COM

10041 Regal Row Ste 100, Houston,
TX 77040
Tel.: (713) 983-2200
Web Site: http://www.godish.meats
Year Founded: 1996
Sales Range: $25-49.9 Million
Emp.: 150
Cable & Other Subscription Programming Services
N.A.I.C.S.: 516210
Dale Dickey (CTO)
Mark McGuire (Mgr-Sls & Ops)
Kimberly McZeal (Supvr-Client Svcs)
Dusty Meador (Mgr-Client Svc)

GODLAN, INC.

15399 Canal Rd, Clinton Township,
MI 48038
Tel.: (586) 464-4400   MI
Web Site: https://www.godlan.com
Year Founded: 1984
Enterprise Resource Planning Software Publisher
N.A.I.C.S.: 513210
Steve Sandy (Project Mgr)
Shane Grumbles (Sr Acct Exec)
Chris Worley (Dir-Strategic Initiatives)

Subsidiaries:

Godlan, Inc. - Regional Office   (1)
1212 Haywood Rd Ste 200, Greenville, SC
29615
Tel.: (864) 286-9000
Web Site: http://www.godlan.com
Computer & Software Stores
N.A.I.C.S.: 513210
Ron Clontz (VP-Solutions & Corp Strategy)

GODLEY AUCTION COMPANY, INC.

4918 Rozzelles Ferry Rd, Charlotte,
NC 28216
Tel.: (704) 399-6111
Sales Range: $10-24.9 Million
Electronic Auctions
N.A.I.C.S.: 459999
Frankie Godley (Treas)
Johnny Godley (Pres)

GODSELL CONSTRUCTION CORP.

351 Duffy Ave, Hicksville, NY 11801
Tel.: (516) 939-0280
Web Site: https://www.godsellcc.com
Sales Range: $10-24.9 Million
Emp.: 50
Nonresidential Construction
N.A.I.C.S.: 236220

GODSHALL QUALITY MEATS INC.

675 Mill Rd, Telford, PA 18969
Tel.: (215) 256-8867
Web Site: https://www.godshalls.com
Year Founded: 1945
Sales Range: $10-24.9 Million
Emp.: 74

Meats & Meat Products
N.A.I.C.S.: 424470
Mark Godshall *(Pres)*
Floyd Kratz *(VP)*

GODSIL CONSTRUCTION, INC.
1182 Teaneck Rd, Teaneck, NJ 07666
Tel.: (201) 837-0800
Web Site:
  http://www.godsilconstruction.com
Year Founded: 1997
Sales Range: $10-24.9 Million
Emp.: 8
General Contracting & Construction Management Services
N.A.I.C.S.: 236220
Gerard M. Godsil *(Pres & Gen Mgr)*
Darrell Hostvedt *(VP)*
Paul Burgunder *(Project Mgr)*

GODSPEED CAPITAL MAN-AGEMENT LP
1055 Thomas Jefferson St NW, Washington, DC 20007
Tel.: (202) 765-1010
Web Site:
  http://www.godspeedcm.com
Privater Equity Firm
N.A.I.C.S.: 523999
Nathaniel T. G. Fogg *(Partner)*
Douglas T. Lake Jr. *(Founder & Mng Partner)*

Subsidiaries:

Exceptional Software Strategies, Inc.   (1)
1302 Concourse Dr Ste 304, Linthicum, MD 21090
Tel.: (410) 694-0240
Web Site:
  http://www.exceptionalsoftware.com
Computer Consulting Services
N.A.I.C.S.: 541611
Paul J. Stasko *(Founder & Pres)*

Huckabee Architects LP   (1)
801 Cherry St Ste 500, Fort Worth, TX 76102
Tel.: (817) 377-2969
Web Site: https://www.huckabee-inc.com
Architecture, Engineering & Consulting Services
N.A.I.C.S.: 541310
Christopher M. Huckabee *(CEO)*

Subsidiary (Domestic):

Image Engineering Group, Ltd.   (2)
1301 Solana Blvd Bldg 1 Ste 1420, West-lake, TX 76262
Tel.: (817) 410-2858
Web Site: http://www.iegltd.com
Sales Range: $1-9.9 Million
Emp.: 30
Engineeering Services
N.A.I.C.S.: 541330
Don Penn *(Founder)*
Jonathan Penn *(Pres)*

Prime ABA, LP   (1)
100 Royal Palm Way, Palm Beach, FL 33480
Tel.: (202) 765-1040
Holding Company; Engineering, Surveying, Consulting & Construction Management Services
N.A.I.C.S.: 551112

Subsidiary (Domestic):

Austin Brockenbrough & Associates, LLP   (2)
1011 Boulder Springs Dr Ste 200, Rich-mond, VA 23225-4950
Tel.: (804) 592-3900
Web Site: http://www.brockenbrough.com
Engineering Services
N.A.I.C.S.: 541330
Craig Matthews *(Principal)*
Bob Polino *(Mng Principal & Dir-Site Dev)*
Paul Shope *(Dir-Buildings)*
Jeff King *(Dir-Fuels Infrastructure)*

Shelia Wharam *(Dir-Acctg)*
Bruce Sadler *(Principal)*
Vince Benedetti *(Principal)*

SilverEdge Government Solutions   (1)
6708 Alexander Bell Dr Ste 200, Columbia, MD 21046
Tel.: (410) 290-8008
Web Site: https://silveredge-gs.com
Cybersecurity, Software & Intelligence Solutions Provider
N.A.I.C.S.: 513210
Robert J. Miller III *(CEO)*
Kelly Douglas *(VP-Talent Acq)*
Vishal Desai *(CTO)*
David Baer *(Pres)*

Subsidiary (Domestic):

QVine LLC   (2)
11720 Sunrise Valley Dr Ste 310, Reston, VA 20191-1415
Tel.: (703) 349-0600
Web Site: http://www.qvine.com
Data Processing, Hosting & Related Services
N.A.I.C.S.: 518210
Greg Bobby *(CEO)*

Varen Technologies, Inc.   (2)
9841 Brokenland Pkwy, Columbia, MD 21046
Tel.: (410) 290-8008
Web Site: http://www.varentech.com
Rev.: $1,800,000
Emp.: 35
Custom Computer Programming Services
N.A.I.C.S.: 541511
Martin Leshin *(Pres & CEO)*
Debra L. Bowman *(Dir-Bus & Sys Integration)*
Doug Zwiselsberger *(Dir-Defense Health Sys)*
Kenneth L. Cortese *(Dir-Software & IT Svcs)*
Teresa Smith *(Dir-Fin)*

Special Aerospace Services LLC   (1)
3005 30th St, Boulder, CO 80301
Tel.: (303) 625-1010
Web Site:
  http://www.specialaerospaceservices.com
Sales Range: $1-9.9 Million
Emp.: 60
Aerospace Engineering Services
N.A.I.C.S.: 541330
Heather L. Bulk *(Co-Founder & CEO)*
Timothy A. Bulk *(Co-Founder & CTO)*
N. Wayne Hale *(Dir-Human Spaceflight & Energy Svcs)*
Fred A. Ouellette *(Mgr-Program-Human Spaceflight & Energy Svcs)*
Kenneth D. Lindas *(Mgr-Program Ops)*

Subsidiary (Domestic):

Quintron Systems, Inc.   (2)
2105 S Blosser Rd, Santa Maria, CA 93458-7311
Tel.: (805) 928-4343
Web Site: http://www.quintron.com
Sales Range: $10-24.9 Million
Emp.: 70
Provider of Telecommunications Systems
N.A.I.C.S.: 334210

Willbrook Solutions, Inc.   (2)
4811 A Bradford Dr, Huntsville, AL 35805-1948
Tel.: (256) 864-8731
Web Site: http://www.willbrook.com
Computer System Design Services
N.A.I.C.S.: 541512
Bonita Phillips *(Pres & CEO)*

Stengel Hill Architecture, Inc   (1)
1764 Frankfort Ave, Louisville, KY 40206
Tel.: (502) 893-1875
Web Site: http://www.stengelhill.com
Rev.: $1,510,000
Emp.: 10
Architectural Services
N.A.I.C.S.: 541310
Charles A. Hill *(Co-Owner, Partner & Principal)*
James Zwissler *(Principal)*
Bradford P. Stengel *(Co-Owner, Partner & Principal)*
Christopher E. Gilbert *(Partner & Principal)*

Christopher M. Malicki *(Partner & Principal)*
James T. Watkins *(Partner & Principal)*
Mark L. Spies *(Partner & Principal)*
Paul W. Edwards *(Partner & Principal)*
Todd W. Wieringa *(Partner & Principal)*

Subsidiary (Domestic):

Mason Blau & Associates, Inc.   (2)
4625 E Bay Dr Ste 228, Clearwater, FL 33764
Tel.: (727) 530-0570
Web Site: http://www.masonblau.com
Sales Range: $1-9.9 Million
Emp.: 13
Architectural Services
N.A.I.C.S.: 541310
Michael R. Mason *(Pres)*
Robert H. Blau *(VP)*

Smith Consulting Architects   (2)
12220 El Camino Real, San Diego, CA 92130
Tel.: (858) 793-4777
Web Site: http://www.sca-sd.com
Sales Range: $1-9.9 Million
Emp.: 30
Architectural Services
N.A.I.C.S.: 541310

The Donkey Barn, LLC   (1)
512 Linden Ave, Carlisle, OH 45005
Tel.: (703) 955-5374
Web Site: https://crimsonphoenix.com
Data Processing, Hosting & Related Services
N.A.I.C.S.: 518210

Subsidiary (Domestic):

Cyberspace Solutions, LLC   (2)
12021 Sunset Hills Rd Ste 110, Reston, VA 20190-6013
Tel.: (210) 862-4639
Scientific & Technical Consulting Services
N.A.I.C.S.: 541690
Robert Osterloh *(Pres & CFO)*

Seaford Consulting, LLC   (2)
9050 Roaring Spring Loop, Bristow, VA 20136-1254
Tel.: (571) 225-3641
Web Site: http://www.seafordconsulting.com
General Management Consulting Services
N.A.I.C.S.: 541611
Tommy Seaford *(Founder & CEO)*

Tekmasters LLC   (2)
4437 Brookfield Corp Dr St, Chantilly, VA 20151
Tel.: (703) 349-1110
Web Site: http://www.tekmasters.com
Scientific & Technical Consulting Services
N.A.I.C.S.: 541690
Brad DeVore *(Mgr-Network Ops)*

GODWIN & REESE INSUR-ANCE AGENCY, INC.
905 Battleground Ave, Greensboro, NC 27408
Tel.: (336) 379-8640
Web Site:
  https://www.godwinagency.com
Year Founded: 1953
Sales Range: $10-24.9 Million
Emp.: 18
Insurance Brokerage Services
N.A.I.C.S.: 524210
Shirley Ray *(Pres)*
Teresa Owens *(VP)*

GODWIN ADVERTISING AGENCY, INC.
1 Jackson Pl 188 E Capitol St Ste 800, Jackson, MS 39201
Tel.: (601) 954-8475   MS
Web Site: http://www.godwin.com
Year Founded: 1937
Rev.: $67,000,000
Emp.: 80
Advetising Agency
N.A.I.C.S.: 541810
Donna Ritchey *(Chief Strategy Officer & Partner)*
Jeff Russell *(Pres)*

Lee Ragland *(VP & Dir-PR)*
John McKie *(Chief Integrated Mktg Officer & Partner)*
Susan Graves *(CFO & Chief Network Officer)*
Steve Alderman *(Sr Mgr-PR)*
Tal McNeill *(Exec Dir-Creative)*
Glenn Owens *(Sr VP-Digital Strategy & User Experience)*

Subsidiaries:

GodwinGroup   (1)
1617 25th Ave, Gulfport, MS 39501
Tel.: (601) 354-5711
Web Site: http://www.godwin.com
Sales Range: $10-24.9 Million
Emp.: 55
Financial, Health Care, Travel & Tourism
N.A.I.C.S.: 541810
Kami Wert *(Gen Mgr-Gulf Coast)*
Philip Shirley *(Chm, CEO & Sr Partner)*
Donna L. Ritchey *(Vice Chm)*
Susan Graves *(CFO, Chief Network Officer & Partner)*
John McKie *(Chief Integrated Mktg Officer & Mng Partner)*
Tal McNeill *(Exec Dir-Creative)*
Lee Ragland *(VP & Dir-PR)*
Jeff Russell *(Pres & Sr Partner)*

GODWIN HARDWARE, INC.
3703 Division Ave S, Grand Rapids, MI 49548
Tel.: (616) 243-3131
Web Site:
  https://www.godwinplumbing.com
Rev.: $13,900,000
Emp.: 130
Hardware Stores
N.A.I.C.S.: 444140
Tim Buist *(Pres)*

Subsidiaries:

Godwin Plumbing Inc.   (1)
3703 Division Ave S, Grand Rapids, MI 49548
Tel.: (616) 243-3131
Web Site: http://www.godwinplumbing.com
Plumbing Contractor
N.A.I.C.S.: 238220

GODWIN'S GATORLAND, INC.
14501 S Orange Blossom Trl, Or-lando, FL 32837
Tel.: (407) 855-5496
Web Site: https://www.gatorland.com
Year Founded: 1949
Sales Range: $1-9.9 Million
Emp.: 90
Theme Park
N.A.I.C.S.: 713110
Michelle Harris *(Mgr-Mktg)*
Owen Godwin *(Owner)*
Jennifer Gallagher *(Dir-Sls)*
Brandon Fisher *(Dir-Media Production)*

GOEBEL FIXTURE CO.
528 Dale St, Hutchinson, MN 55350
Tel.: (320) 587-2112   MN
Web Site: http://www.gf.com
Year Founded: 1935
Custom Woodwork & Architectural Millwork Mfr
N.A.I.C.S.: 337212
Matt Field *(Pres & CEO)*
Karen Kentrell *(VP-Bus Dev)*
Rob DeLeers *(Mgr-Bus Dev)*
Timothy Gill *(Project Engr)*

GOECART
Park City Plz 10 Middle St, Bridge-port, CT 06604
Tel.: (203) 336-2284
Web Site: http://www.goecart.com
Year Founded: 2000
Sales Range: $10-24.9 Million
Integrated On-Demand Ecommerce Solutions

GoECart—(Continued)
N.A.I.C.S.: 513210
Manish Chowdhary (CEO)

GOELLNER, INC.
2500 Latham St, Rockford, IL 61103-3963
Tel.: (815) 962-6076
Web Site: http://www.ame.com
Year Founded: 1966
Sales Range: $10-24.9 Million
Emp.: 10
Engineeering Services
N.A.I.C.S.: 541330
Willy Goellner (Founder)
Deb Boland (Mgr-HR)

GOETZ ENERGY CORPORATION
1319 Military Rd, Tonawanda, NY 14217
Tel.: (716) 876-4324   NY
Web Site:
https://www.goetzenergy.com
Year Founded: 1960
Sales Range: $10-24.9 Million
Emp.: 70
Petroleum Products Mfr
N.A.I.C.S.: 424720
John Deleo (Controller)

GOETZE DENTAL
3939 NE 33rd Ter Ste J, Kansas City, MO 64117-2689
Tel.: (816) 413-1200
Web Site:
https://www.goetzedental.com
Sales Range: $25-49.9 Million
Emp.: 115
Dental Equipment & Supplies
N.A.I.C.S.: 423450
Don Brunker (Pres & CEO)
Curtis Cramer (Mgr-Warehouse)
Cathy Reardon (Coord-Sls Support)

GOEX CORPORATION
2532 Foster Ave, Janesville, WI 53545
Tel.: (608) 754-3303
Web Site: http://www.goex.com
Rev.: $13,100,000
Emp.: 100
Unlaminated Plastics Film & Sheet
N.A.I.C.S.: 326113
Joshua D. Gray (Pres & CEO)
Joseph T. Pregont (Owner)
Ken Trapp (Dir-Fin)
Robert Waddell (Dir-Sls)
Diane Day (Sec)

GOFBA, INC.
3281 E Guasti Rd Ste 700, Ontario, CA 91761
Tel.: (909) 212-7989   CA
Web Site: http://www.gofba.com
Year Founded: 2008
Assets: $3,598,000
Liabilities: $16,915,000
Net Worth: ($13,317,000)
Earnings: ($3,233,000)
Fiscal Year-end: 12/31/22
Online Information Services
N.A.I.C.S.: 513199
Anna Chin (Founder, Chm, Pres & CFO)
William DeLisi (CFO & Sec)
John Larsen (VP)

GOFEN & GLOSSBERG, LLC
455 N Cityfront Plaza Dr Ste 3200, Chicago, IL 60611
Tel.: (312) 828-1100   DE
Web Site: https://www.gofen.com
Year Founded: 1932
Sales Range: $1-4.9 Billion
Emp.: 40

Investment Advisory & Portfolio Management Services
N.A.I.C.S.: 523940
James G. Borovsky (Principal)
Mark A. Brown (Principal & Gen Counsel)
Michael A. Gawlik (Principal)
Joseph B. Glossberg (Principal)
Charles S. Gofen (Principal)
William H. Gofen (Principal)
Mark R. Goodman (Principal)
Peter B. Kupferberg (Principal)
John W. Myers (Principal)
Daniel J. Sobol (Principal)
Michael J. Stelmacki (Principal & Dir-Res)
Jonathan T. Vree (Principal)
Mary Pat Burke (Principal)
Alex Wang (CIO)
Deborah Johnson (Dir-HR)

GOFF CAPITAL, INC.
500 Commerce St Ste 700, Fort Worth, TX 76102
Tel.: (817) 509-3951   TX
Investment Holding Company
N.A.I.C.S.: 551112
John C. Goff (Founder & Owner)

Subsidiaries:

Crescent Real Estate LLC   (1)
777 Main St Ste 2260, Fort Worth, TX 76102
Tel.: (817) 321-2100
Real Estate Investment & Management Services
N.A.I.C.S.: 531390
John C. Goff (Chm)
Jason E. Anderson (Co-CEO)
Conrad Suszynski (Co-CEO)
Suzanne M. Stevens (Mng Dir & CFO)

Subsidiary (Domestic):

Mira Vista Golf Club, L.C.   (2)
6600 Mira Vista Blvd, Fort Worth, TX 76132
Tel.: (817) 294-6600
Web Site:
http://www.miravista.clubhouseonline-e3.com
Emp.: 100
Golf Course & Country Club Operator
N.A.I.C.S.: 713910
Courtney Connell (Head-Golf Pro)
Brad Ibbott (Head-Tennis)

Obsidian Holdings LLC   (2)
9709 178th Pl NE Unit 2, Redmond, WA 98052-6972
Tel.: (425) 299-3031
Investment Management Service
N.A.I.C.S.: 523999

Parkside Townhomes, LLC   (2)
1122 Millview Dr, Arlington, TX 76012
Tel.: (817) 422-0118
Web Site: http://www.parksidearlington.com
Residential Construction Services
N.A.I.C.S.: 236115

Rhode Investments LLC   (2)
690 N Cooper Rd Ste 101, Gilbert, AZ 85233
Tel.: (480) 656-7814
Investment Management Service
N.A.I.C.S.: 523999

Sonoma Golf Club, LLC   (2)
17700 Arnold Dr, Sonoma, CA 95476
Tel.: (707) 939-4100
Web Site: http://www.sonomagolfclub.com
Golf Course & Country Club Operator
N.A.I.C.S.: 713910

Taurus Investments LLC   (2)
185 Village Sq, Baltimore, MD 21204
Tel.: (410) 532-9501
Investment Management Service
N.A.I.C.S.: 523999

The Park at One Riverfront, LLC   (2)
1690 Little Raven St, Denver, CO 80202
Tel.: (303) 988-4200
Commercial Building Construction Services
N.A.I.C.S.: 236220

Townhomes at Riverfront Park, LLC   (2)
1400 Little Raven St, Denver, CO 80202
Tel.: (303) 988-4200
Commercial Building Construction Services
N.A.I.C.S.: 236220

GOFF COMMUNICATIONS INC.
6711 26th Center E, Sarasota, FL 34243
Tel.: (941) 955-7106
Web Site:
https://www.goffcommunication.com
Year Founded: 1958
Sales Range: $10-24.9 Million
Emp.: 35
Wireless Communication Services, Engineering & Construction Management & Network Systems Integration
N.A.I.C.S.: 237130
James E. Goff (Pres & CEO)
Donald Bibb (Controller)
Rick Clark (VP)
Mohammad Khawaja (Engr-Structural Design)

GOFF INC.
12216 NS 3520, Seminole, OK 74868
Tel.: (405) 278-6203   OK
Web Site: http://www.goff-inc.com
Year Founded: 1973
Industrial Machinery Mfr
N.A.I.C.S.: 333248
David Zehren (Sls Mgr)
Belinda Adams (Coord-Marketing)

GOFF'S ENTERPRISES INC.
700 Hickory St, Pewaukee, WI 53072
Tel.: (262) 691-4998
Web Site:
https://www.goffscurtainwalls.com
Year Founded: 1987
Sales Range: $1-9.9 Million
Emp.: 30
Industrial Equipment Mfr
N.A.I.C.S.: 332999
Tony Goff (Pres)
Robert Goff (CEO)
Candi Caya (Controller)
Marcus Mohwinkel (VP-Sls & Mktg)
Wells Wells (Mgr-Dealer Dev)

GOG FOUNDATION, INC.
2127 Espey Ct Ste 100, Crofton, MD 21114
Tel.: (410) 721-7126   DC
Web Site: https://www.gog.org
Year Founded: 2002
Sales Range: $25-49.9 Million
Emp.: 28
Clinical Training Services
N.A.I.C.S.: 611310
Catherine Galoppo (Mgr-Info Sys)
Larry J. Copeland (Treas & VP)

GOGERTY STARK MARRIOTT
2900 Century Sq 1501 4th Ave Ste 2900, Seattle, WA 98101
Tel.: (206) 292-3000
Web Site: http://www.gsminc.com
Year Founded: 1978
Sales Range: $25-49.9 Million
Emp.: 20
Public Relations Agency
N.A.I.C.S.: 541820
Donald E. Stark (Founder)
Glenn Belcher (CFO)
Robert E. Gogerty (Chm & Partner)
David M. Marriott (Partner)

GOGLANIAN BAKERIES INC.
3401 W Segerstrom Ave, Santa Ana, CA 92704
Tel.: (714) 444-3500
Web Site: http://goglanian.com
Rev.: $77,400,000
Emp.: 500

Bakery Products
N.A.I.C.S.: 424490
George Goglanian (Pres)
Karen Smith (Mgr-Customer Svc)

GOHMANN ASPHALT & CONSTRUCTION INC.
PO Box 2428, Clarksville, IN 47131
Tel.: (812) 282-1349   IN
Web Site:
https://www.gohmannasphalt.com
Year Founded: 1950
Sales Range: $75-99.9 Million
Emp.: 453
Asphaltic & Highway Construction Materials; Trucking; Quarrying Mfr
N.A.I.C.S.: 237310
Richard L. Cripe (Controller)

Subsidiaries:

Riverton Truckers, Inc.   (1)
6211 Gheens Mill Rd, Jeffersonville, IN 47130-9214   (100%)
Tel.: (812) 284-1515
Web Site: http://www.rivertontruckers.com
Sales Range: $25-49.9 Million
Emp.: 140
Aggregate Transportation
N.A.I.C.S.: 484220
Jennifer Haycraft (Office Mgr)
George Grenon (Mgr-Ops)

Sellersburg Stone Company, Inc.   (1)
1019 E Utica, Sellersburg, IN 47172   (100%)
Tel.: (812) 246-3383
Web Site: http://www.sellersburgstone.com
Sales Range: $25-49.9 Million
Emp.: 70
Mfr of Stone
N.A.I.C.S.: 212312
Kenneth Rush (Gen Mgr)

GOIN' POSTAL FRANCHISE CORPORATION
4941 4th St, Zephyrhills, FL 33542
Tel.: (813) 782-1500   FL
Web Site:
https://www.goinpostal.com
Year Founded: 2002
Sales Range: $1-9.9 Million
Emp.: 25
Franchisor & Shipping Services
N.A.I.C.S.: 533110
Marcus Price (CEO)
Larry Kottke (VP)
Mike Bork (Mgr-Trng)

GOJO INDUSTRIES, INC.
1 Gojo Plz Ste 500, Akron, OH 44311
Tel.: (330) 255-6000
Web Site: https://www.gojo.com
Year Founded: 1946
Rev.: $83,300,000
Emp.: 700
Skin Health & Hygiene Solutions Mgr
N.A.I.C.S.: 325611
Stephen A. Schultz (Pres & COO-North America)

GOLD & DIAMOND SOURCE
3800 Ulmerton Rd, Clearwater, FL 33762
Tel.: (727) 573-9351   FL
Web Site:
http://www.goldanddiamond.com
Year Founded: 1984
Sales Range: $25-49.9 Million
Emp.: 60
Jewelry Stores
N.A.I.C.S.: 458310
Lynn Canavan (Mgr-Ops & HR)
Steven F. Weintraub (Pres & CEO)
Julie Weintraub (VP)
Patty Weintraub (Mgr-Sls)

Brian Johnson (Gen Mgr-Retail Ops)
Pat Kelly (Mgr-Store)
Dee Mantzaris (Coord-Event)

GOLD & SILVER BUYERS

1122 Spring Cypress Rd, Spring, TX 77373
Tel.: (281) 288-3273
Web Site:
http://www.goldandsilverbuyers.com
Year Founded: 2010
Sales Range: $10-24.9 Million
Emp.: 81
Gold, Silver & Platinum Dealers
N.A.I.C.S.: 458310
Amelia Culwell (Co-Owner)
Brian Culwell (Co-Owner)

GOLD & SILVER COIN SHOP, INC.

713 Las Vegas Blvd S, Las Vegas, NV 89101-6755
Tel.: (702) 385-7912
Web Site: https://www.gspawn.com
Year Founded: 1981
Sales Range: $1-9.9 Million
Emp.: 40
Pawn Shop Owner
N.A.I.C.S.: 459510
Richard Harrison (Co-Owner)
Rick K. Harrison (Co-Owner)
Corey Harrison (Mgr-Ops)

GOLD AVIATION SERVICES, INC.

1420 Lee Wagener Blvd, Fort Lauderdale, FL 33315
Tel.: (954) 359-9919
Web Site:
https://www.goldaviation.com
Year Founded: 1995
Aircraft Charter Services
N.A.I.C.S.: 481211
Leonard Goldberg (Pres & CEO)
William Wing (Dir-Charter Sls & Mktg)
Keith Drake (Dir-Ops)
Jeff Evans (Dir-Maintenance)

GOLD BELT INCORPORATED

3025 Clinton Dr, Juneau, AK 99801-7109
Tel.: (907) 790-4990   AK
Web Site: https://www.goldbelt.com
Year Founded: 1974
Sales Range: $10-24.9 Million
Emp.: 91
Provider of Water Passenger Transportation
N.A.I.C.S.: 487210
Lisa Fisher (Dir-Fin & Acctg)
Lisa-Marie Ikonomov (Sec)
Randy Wanamaker (Treas)
Barbara Fujimoto (Dir-Small Bus Govt Contracting Compliance)
Philip M. Livingston (Gen Counsel)
Elliott Wimberly (Pres & CEO)
Mchugh Pierre (VP-Ops-Alaska)
Bruce Swagler (VP-Technical Svcs)
Ben Johnson (CIO)
Kathleen Moran (CFO)

Subsidiaries:

CP Marine, Inc.   (1)
76 Egan Drove, Juneau, AK 99801
Tel.: (907) 463-8811
Web Site: http://www.goldbelt.com
Marine Transportation Services
N.A.I.C.S.: 488390
McHugh Pierre (VP-Ops)

Facility Support Services, LLC   (1)
5475 Wllliam Flynn Hwy, Gibsonia, PA 15044
Tel.: (724) 502-4394
Web Site: http://www.gbfss.com
Emp.: 75
Commercial Building Construction Services
N.A.I.C.S.: 236220

Tammy Demarco (Supvr-Estimating)
Beth Cheberenchick (Mgr-Bus Dev)
Nick Kochis (Mgr-Ops)
Thomas G. Ali (Pres)

Glacier Park Marine Services
Inc.   (1)
107 W Denny Way Ste 303, Seattle, WA 98119
Tel.: (206) 623-7110
Sales Range: $10-24.9 Million
Emp.: 1
Holding Companies
N.A.I.C.S.: 487210

Goldbelt Eagle, LLC   (1)
2101 Executive Dr Tower Box 36 Suite 5-D, Hampton, VA 23666
Tel.: (757) 873-0019
Web Site: http://www.gbeagle.com
Management Consulting Services
N.A.I.C.S.: 541611

Goldbelt Falcon, LLC   (1)
860 Greenbrier Cir Ste 410, Chesapeake, VA 23320
Tel.: (757) 873-7647
Web Site: http://www.goldbeltfalcon.com
Technical Support Services
N.A.I.C.S.: 541990
Latoya Green (Mgr-Acctg)
Michael Blume (Pres)
Terri Seese (Dir-HR)
Troy Yoho (Mgr-Program)

Goldbelt Glacier Health Services,
LLC   (1)
5510 Cherokee Ave Ste 150, Alexandria, VA 22312
Tel.: (703) 854-1869
Web Site: http://www.gbg-hs.com
Health Care Srvices
N.A.I.C.S.: 621999
Elliott Wimberly (Pres)
Paige M. Blache (Mgr-Ops)
Virginia Torsch (Dir-Bus Dev)
John Kirk (Pres)

Goldbelt Hawk, LLC   (1)
740 Thimble Shoals Blvd Ste G, Newport News, VA 23606
Tel.: (757) 874-1067
Web Site: http://www.goldbelthawk.com
Emp.: 20
Information Technology Consulting Services
N.A.I.C.S.: 541512
Bruce Swagler (Pres)

Goldbelt Orca, LLC   (1)
7051 Muirkirk Meadows Dr Ste A-1, Beltsville, MD 20705
Tel.: (301) 210-4700
Web Site: http://www.goldbeltorca.com
Engineering Consulting Services
N.A.I.C.S.: 541330
Fred Hawkins (Pres)

Goldbelt Raven, LLC   (1)
13900 Lincoln Park Dr Ste 310, Herndon, VA 20171
Tel.: (703) 871-2091
Web Site: http://www.goldbeltraven.com
Information Technology Consulting Services
N.A.I.C.S.: 541512
Darryl Rekemeyer (Dir-Capture Mgmt)
Elliott Wimberly (Pres)
Michael Soto (VP-Frederick Ops)

Goldbelt Security Services, LLC   (1)
8585 Old Dairy Rd Ste 201, Juneau, AK 99801
Tel.: (907) 790-1435
Web Site: http://www.goldbelt.com
Emp.: 30
Security Guard Services
N.A.I.C.S.: 561612
Steven Stewart (Mgr-Ops)

Goldbelt Wolf, LLC   (1)
5500 Cherokee Ave Ste 100, Alexandria, VA 22312
Tel.: (703) 584-8889
Web Site: http://www.goldbeltwolf.com
Emp.: 15
Management Consulting Services
N.A.I.C.S.: 541612
James B. Jones (Pres)
Todd J. Kelsey (VP-Product Solutions)

LifeSource Biomedical, LLC   (1)

PO Box 339, Moffett Field, CA 94035
Tel.: (650) 604-4682
Web Site: http://www.lifesourcebiomed.com
Drug Research & Development Services
N.A.I.C.S.: 541715

Mount Roberts Tramway, Ltd.   (1)
490 S Franklin St, Juneau, AK 99801
Tel.: (907) 463-1338
Tour Operator
N.A.I.C.S.: 561520

Nisga'a Data Systems, LLC   (1)
14900 Bogle Dr Ste 300, Chantilly, VA 20151
Tel.: (703) 871-2091
Web Site: http://www.ndsystems.com
General Management Consulting Services
N.A.I.C.S.: 541611

Peregrine Technical Services,
LLC   (1)
114 Ballard St, Yorktown, VA 23690
Tel.: (757) 234-6664
Web Site: http://www.gbpts.com
Technical Support Services
N.A.I.C.S.: 541990
David Wolfe (COO & VP)
Edwin Armistead (Pres)

GOLD BOND INC.

5485 Hixson Pike, Hixson, TN 37343
Tel.: (423) 842-5844
Web Site:
http://www.goldbondinc.com
Year Founded: 1947
Sales Range: $25-49.9 Million
Emp.: 230
Promotional Products, Advertising Displays & Novelties
N.A.I.C.S.: 323111
Mark Godsey (Pres)
Chris Crowe (Dir-Pur)
Mike Davis (Mgr-Ops)
Kristin Fuller (Controller)
Lisa Garrison (Acct Mgr)
Mark Tipton (Mgr-Natl Sls)
Melissa Wallin (Asst Mgr-Customer Svc)
Donna McDowell (Mgr-IT & Telecom Office)
Gabe McGraw (Mgr-Golf Vendor Rels)
Melinda Moses (Asst Mgr-Customer Svc)
Michael Beaumont (Acct Mgr)
Matt Price (Mgr-IS)
Tracey Pruett (Dir-Golf)
Britney Godsey (VP-Sls)
Brooke Standefer (Mgr-Inside Sls Team)

Subsidiaries:

World Wide Line, Inc.   (1)
128 Industrial Rd N, Covington, TN 38019
Tel.: (901) 476-9797
Web Site: http://www.worldwideline.com
Sales Range: $1-9.9 Million
Emp.: 93
Promotional Products Supplier
N.A.I.C.S.: 323113
Kim Newell (Pres)

GOLD COAST BEVERAGE DISTRIBUTORS INC.

10055 NW 12th St, Doral, FL 33172
Tel.: (305) 591-9800
Web Site:
http://www.goldcoastbeverage.com
Year Founded: 1946
Beer, Ale & Water Whslr & Distr
N.A.I.C.S.: 424810

GOLD COAST EAGLE DISTRIBUTING L.P.

7051 Wireless Ct, Sarasota, FL 34240
Tel.: (941) 355-7685
Web Site: https://www.gceagle.com
Year Founded: 1996
Sales Range: $75-99.9 Million

Emp.: 165
Beer Distr
N.A.I.C.S.: 424810
Allen Pagan (CFO)

GOLD COAST INGREDIENTS, INC.

2429 Yates Ave, Commerce, CA 90040-1917
Tel.: (323) 724-8935
Web Site:
https://www.goldcoastinc.com
Year Founded: 1985
Sales Range: $10-24.9 Million
Emp.: 20
Food Flavours & Colors Mfr
N.A.I.C.S.: 311942
Chuck Brasher (CEO)
James Sgro (Pres)
Steve Torsky (Mgr-Quality Assurance)
Stephanie Spates (Mgr-Quality Assurance)
Kenneth Chu (VP)
Tina Moore (Acct Mgr)
Ted Rodriguez (Mgr-Pur)
Michelle Trent (Mgr-Corp Sls)

GOLD CRAFT JEWELRY CORP.

640 S Hill St Ste 650, Los Angeles, CA 90014
Tel.: (213) 623-8673
Sales Range: $10-24.9 Million
Emp.: 37
Jewelry Mfr
N.A.I.C.S.: 339910
Vahi Urun (Pres)
Tonya Badema (Office Mgr)

GOLD CROSS SERVICES INC.

1717 S Redwood Rd, Salt Lake City, UT 84104
Tel.: (801) 972-3600
Web Site:
https://www.goldcrossservices.com
Year Founded: 1968
Sales Range: $10-24.9 Million
Emp.: 330
Ambulance Services
N.A.I.C.S.: 621910
Gene Moffitt (Chm)

GOLD CRUST BAKING COMPANY, INC.

6200 Columbia Park Rd, Landover, MD 20785
Tel.: (703) 549-0420
Sales Range: $10-24.9 Million
Emp.: 110
Bakery Products Mfr
N.A.I.C.S.: 311812
Bennet Helfgott (Gen Mgr)

GOLD DYNAMICS CORP.

2248 Meridian Blvd Ste H, Minden, NV 89423
Tel.: (949) 419-6588
Year Founded: 2006
Liabilities: $98,064
Net Worth: ($98,064)
Earnings: ($4,375)
Fiscal Year-end: 07/31/15
Metal Ore Resource Services
N.A.I.C.S.: 212290
Tie Ming Li (CEO)

GOLD EAGLE COMPANY

4400 S Kildare Ave, Chicago, IL 60632-4356
Tel.: (773) 376-4400   IL
Web Site: https://www.goldeagle.com
Year Founded: 1932
Sales Range: $100-124.9 Million
Emp.: 200
Automotive Additives, Cleaners & Fluids Developer, Mfr, Marketer & Distr

Gold Eagle Company—(Continued)

N.A.I.C.S.: 325998
Robert F. Hirsch *(Chm)*
Marc Blackman *(CEO)*
Howard Donnally *(Pres-Gold Eagle Brands)*
Rich Hirsch *(Sr VP)*
Dan Stewart *(VP-HR)*
Tyler Rossdeutcher *(Mgr-Sls-Natl)*
Kevin Krueger *(CFO)*

Subsidiaries:

Gold Eagle Company - International Division .... (1)
4400SKildare Ave, Chicago, IL 60632-4356
Tel.: (773) 376-4400
Web Site: http://www.goldeagle.com
Sales Range: $10-24.9 Million
Emp.: 180
Automotive Additives, Cleaners & Fluids
N.A.I.C.S.: 324191
Mark Blackman *(Pres & CEO)*

Gold Eagle Company - Private Label Division .... (1)
4400 S Kildare Ave, Chicago, IL 60632-4356
Tel.: (773) 376-4400
Web Site: http://www.goldeagleco.com
Automotive Additives, Cleaners & Fluids
N.A.I.C.S.: 324191
Rich Hirsch *(VP)*
Tom Novacek *(Sr Dir-Sls)*
Jim Sill *(VP-Operational Dev)*
Tom Bingham *(Sr Dir-Mktg)*
Bob Hirsch *(Chm)*

Gold Eagle Company - The Golden Touch Division .... (1)
4400 S Kildare Ave, Chicago, IL 60632-4356
Tel.: (773) 376-4400
Web Site: http://www.goldeagleco.com
Automotive Additives, Cleaners & Fluids
N.A.I.C.S.: 324191

Gold Eagle Company - Wholesale/Retail Division .... (1)
4400 S Kildare Ave, Chicago, IL 60632
Tel.: (773) 376-4400
Web Site: http://www.goldeagle.com
Automotive Additives, Cleaners & Fluids
N.A.I.C.S.: 324191
Marc Blackman *(CEO)*

TriNova Inc. .... (1)
4485 Laughlin Dr S, Mobile, AL 36693
Tel.: (251) 378-7837
Web Site: http://www.trinovainc.com
Industrial Machinery & Equipment Whslr
N.A.I.C.S.: 423830
Steve Wimmer *(Brand Mgr)*

GOLD EXPRESS, LLC.
1150 Shelton Rd NW, Concord, NC 28027-9532
Tel.: (704) 788-1603
Year Founded: 1987
Sales Range: $10-24.9 Million
Emp.: 125
Highway & Street Construction Services
N.A.I.C.S.: 237310
Kerry D. Beaver *(Partner)*
Richard A. Jordan *(Pres)*
Ron Richardson *(Principal)*

GOLD HILL RESOURCES, INC.
3751 Seneca Ave, Pahrump, NV 89048
Tel.: (775) 751-6931 .... NV
Web Site:
    http://goldhillresources.com
Year Founded: 2001
Sales Range: Less than $1 Million
Emp.: 12
Gold Mining
N.A.I.C.S.: 212220
Jason Lieber *(Pres)*
Wayne Good *(CEO)*
Kenneth S. Bailey *(CTO)*

GOLD KEY/PHR, LLC
300 32nd St, Virginia Beach, VA 23451-3990
Tel.: (757) 491-3000 .... VA
Web Site:
    https://www.goldkeyphr.com
Emp.: 2,400
Hotels, Restaurants & Resorts Management Services
N.A.I.C.S.: 721110
Bryan D. Cuffee *(VP-Dev)*
Bruce L. Thompson *(CEO)*
Brian Carson *(CFO)*
Robert M. Howard *(Chief Investment Officer)*

GOLD MEDAL HAIR PRODUCTS, INC.
104 Allen Blvd Ste H, Farmingdale, NY 11735
Tel.: (631) 465-0202 .... NY
Web Site:
    http://www.goldmedalhair.com
Year Founded: 1942
Sales Range: $75-99.9 Million
Emp.: 10
Hair-Care Products, Curling Irons & Skin-Care Products Mfr & Mail Order Catalog Retailer
N.A.I.C.S.: 325620

GOLD MEDAL PRODUCTS CO.
10700 Medallion Dr, Cincinnati, OH 45241-4807
Tel.: (513) 769-7676 .... OH
Web Site: http://www.gmpopcorn.com
Year Founded: 1931
Sales Range: $75-99.9 Million
Emp.: 350
Concession & Snack Bar Installations
N.A.I.C.S.: 333241
Dan Kroeger *(Chm & CEO)*
Chris Petroff *(Mgr-Sls-Natl)*
Stephanie Goodin *(VP-Mktg)*
James Adam Browning *(Pres)*
Andy Shang *(VP-Engrg)*
Brandon James *(Gen Counsel)*
Joe Macaluso *(VP-Sls & Concession-US & Canada)*
John Evans Jr. *(Sr VP)*

GOLD MOTORS, INC.
1422 N Coast Hwy, Newport, OR 97365-2440
Tel.: (541) 265-7731 .... OR
Web Site: http://www.goldmotors.com
Sales Range: $10-24.9 Million
Emp.: 45
Car Whslr
N.A.I.C.S.: 441110
Mike Gold *(Owner)*

GOLD POINT LODGING AND REALTY, INC.
53 View Ln, Breckenridge, CO 80424
Tel.: (970) 453-1910
Web Site: http://www.goldpoint.com
Sales Range: $25-49.9 Million
Emp.: 200
Land Subdividers & Developers, Residential
N.A.I.C.S.: 531390
Michael C. Millisor *(Owner)*
David Stroeve *(Dir-Mktg)*

GOLD STANDARD ENTERPRISES INC.
5100 W Dempster, Skokie, IL 60077
Tel.: (847) 933-7600
Web Site: http://www.binnys.com
Year Founded: 1949
Sales Range: $25-49.9 Million
Emp.: 300
Wine, Cheese & Gourmet Products Retailer
N.A.I.C.S.: 445320

Tim Smith *(Controller)*

Subsidiaries:

Binny's Inc. .... (1)
71 N Greenbay Rd, Glencoe, IL 60022
Tel.: (847) 835-3900
Web Site: http://www.binnys.com
Sales Range: Less than $1 Million
Emp.: 4
Alcoholic Beverage Retailer
N.A.I.C.S.: 445320
Barbara Baskin *(Gen Mgr)*

GOLD STANDARD MINING COMPANY
226 N Cottonwood Dr, Gilbert, AZ 85234
Tel.: (801) 830-8288 .... NV
Year Founded: 2016
Sales Range: Less than $1 Million
N.A.I.C.S.:
Kim D. Southworth *(Founder)*
Lisa Averbuch *(Pres, Treas & Sec)*

GOLD STAR CHILI INC.
650 Lunken Park Dr, Cincinnati, OH 45226
Tel.: (513) 231-4541
Web Site:
    https://www.goldstarchili.com
Sales Range: $75-99.9 Million
Emp.: 150
Food Preparations & Vending
N.A.I.C.S.: 311999
Kim Olden *(Controller)*
Mike Mason *(Dir-Ops)*
Mike Rohrkemper *(CEO)*
Charlie Howard *(Dir-Mktg)*
Dave Mayerik *(VP-Ops)*

GOLD STAR FS INC.
101 NE St, Cambridge, IL 61238
Tel.: (309) 937-3369
Web Site: http://www.goldstarfs.com
Sales Range: $50-74.9 Million
Emp.: 13
Grain Elevators
N.A.I.C.S.: 424510
Steve Swanstrom *(CEO)*

GOLD STAR MORTGAGE FINANCIAL GROUP CORP.
100 Phoenix Dr Ste 300, Ann Arbor, MI 48108
Tel.: (734) 971-2300 .... MI
Web Site:
    https://www.goldstarfinancial.com
Year Founded: 2000
Sales Range: $50-74.9 Million
Emp.: 456
Mortgage & Nonmortgage Loan Brokers
N.A.I.C.S.: 522310
Daniel Milstein *(Founder & CEO)*
Daniel Sugg *(Pres)*

GOLD STAR PRODUCTS
21680 Coolidge Hwy, Oak Park, MI 48237
Tel.: (248) 548-9840
Web Site:
    https://www.goldstarproducts.com
Year Founded: 1923
Rev.: $15,000,000
Emp.: 35
Commercial Cooking & Food Service Equipment
N.A.I.C.S.: 423440
Jeffrey Applebaum *(Pres)*
Kerry Gluckman *(Head-Interior Design)*
Tom Jabrocki *(Mgr-Ops)*

GOLD STAR TRANSPORTATION INC.

9424 Reeds Rd Ste 201, Shawnee Mission, KS 66207
Tel.: (913) 341-0081
Web Site:
    http://www.goldstartrans.com
Sales Range: $10-24.9 Million
Emp.: 35
Transportation Services
N.A.I.C.S.: 488510
Rayla Erding *(Pres)*

GOLD STAR TUTORING SERVICES, INC.
2385 Orange Blossom Dr, Naples, FL 34109
Tel.: (239) 404-9410 .... FL
Web Site:
    http://www.goldstartutoring.com
Year Founded: 2007
Sales Range: Less than $1 Million
Tutoring Services
N.A.I.C.S.: 611691
Mindy Kline *(Chm, Pres & CEO)*
Robert M. Kline *(CFO, Treas & Sec)*

GOLD TORRENT, INC.
960 Broadway Ave Ste 530, Boise, ID 83706
Tel.: (208) 343-1413 .... NV
Year Founded: 2006
Assets: $2,143,577
Liabilities: $2,831,847
Net Worth: ($688,270)
Earnings: ($1,946,671)
Emp.: 3
Fiscal Year-end: 03/31/17
Gold Exploration Services
N.A.I.C.S.: 212220
Alexander Gregory Kunz *(CFO)*

GOLD-EAGLE COOPERATIVE INC.
515 N Locust, Goldfield, IA 50542
Tel.: (515) 825-3161
Web Site:
    https://www.goldeaglecoop.com
Year Founded: 1908
Sales Range: $75-99.9 Million
Emp.: 115
Grain & Field Beans Distr
N.A.I.C.S.: 424510
John Stelzer *(Controller)*
Chris Petersen *(Mgr-Sls-Seeds)*

GOLDBERG & OSBORNE
4423 E Thomas Rd Ste 3, Phoenix, AZ 85018-7615
Tel.: (602) 234-1111 .... AZ
Web Site:
    http://www.goldbergandosborne.com
Year Founded: 1989
Sales Range: $25-49.9 Million
Emp.: 150
Law firm
N.A.I.C.S.: 541110
Mark Goldberg *(Owner)*
John Osborne *(Mng Partner)*

GOLDBERG LINDSAY & CO., LLC
630 5th Ave, New York, NY 10111
Tel.: (212) 651-1100 .... DE
Web Site:
    https://www.lindsaygoldbergllc.com
Year Founded: 2001
Private Equity Investment Firm
N.A.I.C.S.: 523999
Robert D. Lindsay *(Co-Founder & Chm)*
Russell Triedman *(Mng Partner)*
Norman L. Rosenthal *(Partner)*
Michael W. Dees *(Mng Partner)*
Krishna K. Agrawal *(Partner)*
Eric Fry *(Partner)*
Ali Nensi *(Partner)*
Vincent C. Ley *(Partner)*

Jacob Lew *(Mng Partner)*
Alan E. Goldberg *(Co-Founder & CEO)*

Subsidiaries:

Affordable Suites of America, Inc. (1)
117 W Perry Rd, Myrtle Beach, SC 29579
Tel.: (843) 236-9998
Web Site: https://www.affordablesuites.com
Hotels & Motels Services
N.A.I.C.S.: 721110
Gary DeLapp *(CEO)*

Brock Holdings III, Inc. (1)
10343 Sam Houston Park Dr Ste 200, Houston, TX 77064
Tel.: (281) 807-8200
Web Site: http://www.brockgroup.com
Sales Range: $700-749.9 Million
Emp.: 15,000
Holding Company; Industrial Engineering, Construction & Maintenance Services
N.A.I.C.S.: 551112

Creation Technologies LP (1)
One Beacon St 23rd Fl, Boston, MA 02108 **(70%)**
Tel.: (877) 734-7456
Web Site: http://www.creationtech.com
Sales Range: $300-349.9 Million
Contract Electronic Manufacturing Services Including Design Support & New Product Assembly
N.A.I.C.S.: 334419
Stephen P. DeFalco *(Chm & CEO)*
Ashley Dafel *(Pres & CEO)*
Mike Conway *(Exec VP-Global Sls & Mktg)*
Todd Baggett *(COO)*
Heather Ohlinger *(Exec VP-People & Culture)*
David Longshore *(Chief Mktg Officer & Chief Sls Officer)*
Annette Cusworth *(CFO)*
Ana Cantu *(Exec VP-Supply Chain Mgmt)*
Ben Wong *(Sr VP-Changzhou & Vancouver)*

Subsidiary (Domestic):

Applied Technical Services Corporation (2)
6300 Merrill Creek Pkwy A-100, Everett, WA 98203
Tel.: (425) 249-5555
Web Site: http://www.atscorp.net
Rev.: $69,600,000
Emp.: 240
Printed Circuit Assembly Mfr
N.A.I.C.S.: 334418
George Hamilton *(CEO)*
Mike Kelly *(VP-Strategic Acct Mgmt)*
Steve Canzano *(VP-Engrg & Design)*
Suzette McClelland *(VP-HR & Admin)*

IEC Electronics Corp. (2)
105 Norton St, Newark, NY 14513
Tel.: (315) 331-7742
Web Site: http://www.iec-electronics.com
Rev.: $182,714,000
Assets: $122,964,000
Liabilities: $83,809,000
Net Worth: $39,155,000
Earnings: $6,753,000
Emp.: 860
Fiscal Year-end: 09/30/2020
Printed Circuit Board Assemblies, Electronic Products & Systems Mfr
N.A.I.C.S.: 334412
Jeremy R. Nowak *(Chm)*
Debbie Cardon *(VP-HR)*

Subsidiary (Domestic):

Celmet Company, Inc. (3)
1365 Emerson St, Rochester, NY 14606
Tel.: (585) 647-1760
Web Site: http://www.celmet.com
Sales Range: $1-9.9 Million
Emp.: 45
Sheet Metal Work Mfg
N.A.I.C.S.: 332322

IEC Electronics - Albuquerque (3)
1450 Mission Ave NE, Albuquerque, NM 87107
Tel.: (505) 345-5591
Web Site: http://www.iec-electronics.com

High-Quality, High-Electronic Cards, Boxes, Sub-Systems & Systems for the Aerospace, Space, Medical, Communications & Defense Markets Mfr
N.A.I.C.S.: 334419

Southern California Braiding, Inc. (3)
PO Box 2068, Bell Gardens, CA 90202
Tel.: (562) 927-5531
Web Site: http://www.socalbraid.com
Electronic Components Mfr
N.A.I.C.S.: 334510

Golden West Packaging Group LLC (1)
15400 Don Julian Rd, City of Industry, CA 91745
Tel.: (888) 501-5893
Web Site: http://www.goldenwestpackaging.com
Holding Company; Specialty Packaging Services
N.A.I.C.S.: 551112
Michele L. Burks *(Controller & Dir-Corp Credit & Collections)*
Jason Benson *(Mgr-Fin Plng & Analysis)*
Steve Strickland *(CEO)*
Brad Jordan *(Pres)*

Subsidiary (Domestic):

Berry Pack Inc. (2)
6 Quail Run Cir Ste 101, Salinas, CA 93907
Tel.: (805) 922-4432
Web Site: http://www.berrypack.com
Packaging Services
N.A.I.C.S.: 561910
Brenda Guillen *(Mgr)*
Barry Johnston *(Founder)*

Cal Sheets, LLC (2)
1212 Performance Dr, Stockton, CA 95206
Tel.: (209) 234-3300
Web Site: http://www.calsheets.com
Corrugated & Solid Fiber Box Mfr
N.A.I.C.S.: 322211
Pete Brodie *(CFO)*

PackageOne, Inc. (2)
401 S Granada Dr, Madera, CA 93637
Tel.: (559) 662-1910
Web Site: http://www.packageone.com
Corrugated & Solid Fiber Boxes Mfr
N.A.I.C.S.: 322211
Scott McIlravy *(Acct Mgr)*

Packaging Innovators, LLC (2)
6650 National Dr, Livermore, CA 94550
Tel.: (925) 371-2000
Web Site: http://www.packaginginnovators.com
High End Graphics Packaging Services
N.A.I.C.S.: 561910
Mark Mazzocco *(VP)*

Montebello Container Corporation (1)
13220 Molette St, Santa Fe Springs, CA 90670
Tel.: (562) 404-6221
Web Site: http://www.montcc.com
Corrugated Sheet Mfr
N.A.I.C.S.: 322211
Anthony Salcido *(Pres)*
Joe Salcido *(Mgr-Production)*
John Salcido *(VP)*

Pike Corporation (1)
100 Pike Way, Mount Airy, NC 27030
Tel.: (336) 789-2171
Web Site: http://www.pike.com
Sales Range: $800-899.9 Million
Electrical Contracting Services
N.A.I.C.S.: 238210
J. Eric Pike *(Chm & CEO)*
Kevin Boatrigh *(VP-Pike Electric-South)*
Edward Scott *(VP-Pike Electric-West)*
Matt Fisher *(Sr VP-Pike Electric-South)*
Will Pike *(Sr VP-Pike Electric-West)*

Subsidiary (Domestic):

Klondyke Construction LLC (2)
2640 W Lone Cactus Dr, Phoenix, AZ 85027
Tel.: (623) 580-5440
Web Site: http://www.klondykeinc.com
Electric Power Generation & Distribution Services
N.A.I.C.S.: 221122

Brian Rall *(Mgr-Estimating Div)*
Brandon Adams *(Project Mgr)*
Nicholas S. Visel *(Sr VP-Power Contracting)*

Pike Electric, LLC (2)
100 Pike Way, Mount Airy, NC 27030-8147
Tel.: (336) 789-2171
Web Site: http://www.pike.com
Electrical Contractor Services
N.A.I.C.S.: 238210
Jim Benfield *(Pres)*
Stan Marion *(Reg VP)*
Matt Simmons *(Reg VP)*
David McDuffie *(VP-Ops)*
Stacey Nobles *(VP-Ops-Substation, Transmission & Distr)*
Fred Thornton *(Bus Mgr-Line)*
David Bartlett *(Mgr-East)*
Ronnie Gilbert *(VP-Ops-OH, IN, MO, KY, TN, WV, VA)*
James Lawrence *(Mgr-NC & SC)*
Jim McCloud *(Mgr-GA, FL, AL & MS)*
Neal Sanders *(VP-Ops-FL)*
David Condrey *(VP-Ops-AL, MS, FL & LA)*
Donald Anderson *(VP-Ops-NC & SC)*
Gene Walden *(VP-Ops-MD, VA, NC & SC)*

Pixelle Specialty Solutions LLC (1)
228 S Main St, Spring Grove, PA 17362
Tel.: (717) 225-4711
Web Site: http://www.pixelle.com
Paper & Forest Products Mfr
N.A.I.C.S.: 322120
Tim Hess *(Pres)*

Subsidiary (Domestic):

Pixelle Androscoggin LLC (2)
300 Riley Rd, Jay, ME 04239 **(100%)**
Tel.: (207) 897-3431
Web Site: http://www.pixelle.com
Coated Groundwood & Freesheet Paper Mill
N.A.I.C.S.: 322120

Plant (Domestic):

Verso Corporation - Stevens Point Mill (3)
707 Arlington Pl, Stevens Point, WI 54481
Tel.: (715) 345-8060
Emp.: 240
Paper Mfr
N.A.I.C.S.: 322120

The Kleinfelder Group, Inc. (1)
550 W C St Ste 1200, San Diego, CA 92101
Tel.: (619) 831-4600
Web Site: http://www.kleinfelder.com
Engineeering Services
N.A.I.C.S.: 541330
Linda Lannen *(Sr VP & Dir-Corp Svcs)*
Daniel Harpstead *(Sr VP & Dir-Technical & Quality)*
John A. Murphy *(CFO & Exec VP)*
Andrea Baker *(VP-Mktg & Bus Dev)*
Patrick Schaffner *(Sr VP & Dir-HR)*
Louis Armstrong *(Pres & CEO)*
Lisa Millet *(Exec VP-Central Div)*
Rita Fordiani *(Sr VP & Mgr-Water Natl Market)*
Ashraf Jahangir *(Dir-Markets)*
Jeremy Larsen *(Sr VP & Mgr-Natl CoMET Svcs)*
Richard C. Wells *(Sr VP & Mgr-Transportation Natl Market)*
Deborah Butera *(Gen Counsel & Sr VP)*
Sally Miller *(Sr VP & Dir-Health & Safety)*
Jeff Hill *(Exec VP & Dir-East Div)*
Dustin Esposito *(Comm Mgr)*
Rebecca Katzke *(Sr VP & Natl Mgr-Water Market)*

Subsidiary (Domestic):

Doucet & Associates, Inc. (2)
7401 W Hwy, Austin, TX 78735
Tel.: (512) 583-2600
Web Site: http://www.doucetandassociates.com
Sales Range: $1-9.9 Million
Emp.: 91
Professional Engineering Services
N.A.I.C.S.: 541330
Amy Doucet *(CEO)*
John Doucet *(Pres)*
Sydney Xinos *(VP)*
Craig Cox *(CFO)*

Garcia & Associates, Inc. (2)
1 Saunders Ave, San Anselmo, CA 94960
Tel.: (415) 458-5803
Web Site: http://www.garciaandassociates.com
Rev.: $7,600,000
Emp.: 60
Fiscal Year-end: 12/31/2006
Environmental Consulting
N.A.I.C.S.: 541690

Gas Transmission Systems, Inc. (2)
575 Lennon Ln Ste 250, Walnut Creek, CA 94598
Tel.: (530) 893-6711
Web Site: http://www.gtsinc.us
Sales Range: $1-9.9 Million
Emp.: 11
Engineering Services
N.A.I.C.S.: 541330
Katie Clapp *(Mgr)*
Jason Berry *(Project Mgr)*
Ben Campbell *(Pres)*

Kleinfelder Central, Inc. (2)
11529 W 79th St Bldg 21, Lenexa, KS 66214
Tel.: (913) 962-0909
Web Site: http://www.braunintertec.com
Emp.: 20
Engineering Services
N.A.I.C.S.: 541330
Scott Beadleston *(Mgr-Environmental Grp)*

Kleinfelder East, Inc. (2)
5015 Shoreham Pl, San Diego, CA 92122
Tel.: (858) 320-2000
Web Site: http://www.kleinfelder.com
Management Consulting Services
N.A.I.C.S.: 541618
William C. Siegel *(Pres & CEO)*

Subsidiary (Domestic):

Kleinfelder Northeast, Inc. (3)
215 1st St Ste 320, Cambridge, MA 02142
Tel.: (617) 497-7800
Web Site: http://www.kleinfelder.com
Emp.: 2,200
Engineering Services
N.A.I.C.S.: 541330
George Pierson *(CEO)*

Kleinfelder Southeast, Inc. (3)
9009 Perimeter Woods Dr Ste H, Charlotte, NC 28216
Tel.: (704) 598-1049
Web Site: http://www.kleinfelder.com
Emp.: 30
Engineering Services
N.A.I.C.S.: 541330
Colin Davis *(Sr Project Mgr)*

Subsidiary (Domestic):

Kleinfelder International, Inc. (2)
5015 Shoreham Pl, San Diego, CA 92122
Tel.: (858) 320-2000
Holding Company; Engineering Services
N.A.I.C.S.: 551112

Subsidiary (Non-US):

Kleinfelder Australia Pty LTD (3)
Level 13 200 Queen Street, Melbourne, 3000, VIC, Australia
Tel.: (61) 3 8648 6460
Engineering Services
N.A.I.C.S.: 541330

Subsidiary (Domestic):

Kleinfelder Guam, LLC (3)
600 Harmon Loop Rd Ste 108, Dededo, GU 96929
Tel.: (671) 300-8040
Engineering Services
N.A.I.C.S.: 541330

Branch (Non-US):

Kleinfelder International, Inc.-Calgary (3)
144-4 Avenue SW Suite 1600, Calgary, T2P 3N4, AB, Canada
Tel.: (403) 269-2700

Goldberg Lindsay & Co., LLC—(Continued)

Web Site: http://www.kleinfelder.com
Emp.: 1
Engineeering Services
N.A.I.C.S.: 541330
Paul Deppe (Office Mgr)

Subsidiary (Domestic):

Kleinfelder West, Inc. **(2)**
5015 Shoreham Pl, San Diego, CA 92122
Tel.: (858) 320-2000
Engineeering Services
N.A.I.C.S.: 541330
William C. Seigel (Pres & CEO)
Chuck Cleeves (Mgr-Environmental Ping &
Permitting Program)

Omni Environmental LLC **(2)**
Research Park 321 Wall St, Princeton, NJ
08540
Tel.: (609) 924-8821
Sales Range: $10-24.9 Million
Emp.: 15
Environmental Consulting Services
N.A.I.C.S.: 541620
James F. Cosgrove Jr. (VP)
Timothy D. Bradley (VP)

GOLDEN 1 CREDIT UNION

8945 Cal Center Dr, Sacramento, CA
95826
Tel.: (916) 732-2900   CA
Web Site: https://www.golden1.com
Year Founded: 1933
Sales Range: $100-124.9 Million
Emp.: 1,600
Credit Union
N.A.I.C.S.: 522130
Donna Bland (Pres & CEO)
Richard Musci (Chief Products Officer
& Exec VP)
Dustin Luton (CFO & Sr VP)
Erica Taylor (VP-Communications-
Community Relations)
Doug Aguiar (CMO & Sr VP)
Courtney Linn (Sr VP & Gen Coun-
sel)
Allyson Hill (CFO)
Chad Carrington (Sr VP-Security,
Tech Infrastructure & Facilities)

GOLDEN AGE INC.

2901 Hwy 82 E, Greenwood, MS
38930-6072
Tel.: (662) 453-6323   MS
Web Site:
     https://www.goldenageinc.org
Year Founded: 1954
Sales Range: $10-24.9 Million
Emp.: 343
Senior Living Services
N.A.I.C.S.: 623311
Bobbie Methvin (Bus Mgr)
Tynisha Stransberry (Mgr-Care Team)
Beverly Lawson-Wilson (Dir-Activity)
Patsy Pruett (Mgr-Care Team)
Carole Upchurch (Mgr-Care Team)

GOLDEN ARCH ENTERPRISES

1334 Fall River Ave, Seekonk, MA
02771
Tel.: (508) 336-6230
Rev.: $14,100,000
Emp.: 5
Fast-Food Restaurant, Chain
N.A.I.C.S.: 722513
Louis Provenzano (Owner)
Cathy Sthalen (Office Mgr)

GOLDEN BEVERAGE COM-
PANY LLC

2361 B Ave, Ogden, UT 84401
Tel.: (801) 399-3773
Web Site:
     http://www.goldenbeverage.com
Sales Range: $10-24.9 Million
Emp.: 45
Beer & Food Distr

N.A.I.C.S.: 424810
Terrence M. White (Owner)

GOLDEN CARRIERS INC.

200 Route 22 E, Hillside, NJ 07205
Tel.: (973) 926-3200
Web Site:
     http://www.goldencarriers.com
Sales Range: $10-24.9 Million
Emp.: 40
Trucking Except Local
N.A.I.C.S.: 484121
Charles Stein (Pres)
Mary Roque (Mgr-Ops)
Jeff Bader (CEO)

GOLDEN CROWN DEPOT

6900 NW 43rd St, Miami, FL 33166
Tel.: (305) 640-1799
Web Site:
     https://www.goldencrowndepot.com
Rev.: $12,100,000
Emp.: 15
Fresh Fruit & Vegetable Merchant
Whslr
N.A.I.C.S.: 424480
Leslie Ellzey (VP)
Ernesto Ruiz-Sierra (Pres)
Harry Lee (Treas & Sec)

GOLDEN EAGLE DISTRIBUT-
ING CO.

9669 Hwy 168, Hannibal, MO 63401
Tel.: (573) 221-0908
Sales Range: $50-74.9 Million
Emp.: 100
Beer & Other Fermented Malt Liquors
N.A.I.C.S.: 424810
Richard A. Risenback (Owner)

Subsidiaries:

Golden Eagle Distributing **(1)**
500 Golden Eagle Dr, Mount Pleasant, IA
52641
Tel.: (319) 385-7900
Sales Range: $25-49.9 Million
Emp.: 30
Whslr of Beer & Other Fermented Malt Li-
quors
N.A.I.C.S.: 424810
Rich Riesenbeck (Pres)
Kent Spratt (Mgr-Warehouse)

GOLDEN EAGLE DISTRIBU-
TORS, INC.

PO Box 27506, Tucson, AZ 85726-
7506
Tel.: (520) 884-5999   AZ
Web Site: http://www.gedaz.com
Year Founded: 1975
Beverage Distr
N.A.I.C.S.: 424810
Christopher Clements (CEO)
Kimberly Clements (Pres)

GOLDEN EAGLE EXPRESS
INC.

2555 E Olympic Blvd, Los Angeles,
CA 90023-2605
Tel.: (909) 282-7000
Web Site: http://www.gees.com
Rev.: $29,000,000
Emp.: 62
Trucking Service
N.A.I.C.S.: 484110
John Jelaco (Pres & CEO)

GOLDEN EAGLE EXTRU-
SIONS INC.

1762 State Rte 131, Milford, OH
45150
Tel.: (513) 248-8292
Web Site:
     https://www.goldeneagleextru
     sions.com
Sales Range: $10-24.9 Million
Emp.: 12

Plastics Film
N.A.I.C.S.: 424610
Paul Eagle (Chm)

GOLDEN EAGLE LOG HOMES,
INC.

4421 Plover Rd, Wisconsin Rapids,
WI 54494
Tel.: (715) 421-3392
Web Site:
     https://www.goldeneaglelog
     homes.com
Year Founded: 1966
Sales Range: $10-24.9 Million
Emp.: 75
Wood Building Mfr
N.A.I.C.S.: 321992
Tod Parmeter (Owner)
Daniel Zech (Mgr-Sls)

GOLDEN EQUITY INVEST-
MENTS LLC

700 12th St, Golden, CO 80401
Tel.: (720) 328-9055
Web Site:
     http://9thstreetinvestments.com
Privater Equity Firm
N.A.I.C.S.: 523999
Andrew Coors (Principal)
Mark Petty (Principal)
Darden Coors (Sec)

Subsidiaries:

Goosecross Cellars, Inc. **(1)**
1119 State Ln, Yountville, CA 94599
Tel.: (707) 944-1986
Web Site: http://www.goosecross.com
Sales Range: $25-49.9 Million
Emp.: 10
Winery
N.A.I.C.S.: 312130
Christi Coors Ficeli (CEO)
Phil Borgmeyer (CFO)

GOLDEN FURROW FERTIL-
IZER INC.

311 Elm St, Eldon, IA 52554
Tel.: (641) 652-3535
Web Site:
     http://www.goldenfurrow.com
Sales Range: $10-24.9 Million
Emp.: 62
Fertilizer & Pesticide Application Ser-
vices, Agriculture Consulting & Crop
Scouting
N.A.I.C.S.: 115116
Russ Fullenkamp (VP-Southwest
Reg)
Terry Clark (VP-Eastern Reg)

Subsidiaries:

Golden Furrow Fertilizer -
Bloomfield **(1)**
906 Karr Ave, Bloomfield, IA 52537-2055
Tel.: (641) 664-1045
Web Site: http://www.goldenfurrow.com
Sales Range: $1-9.9 Million
Emp.: 20
Fertilizer & Pesticide Application Services,
Agriculture Consulting & Crop Scouting
N.A.I.C.S.: 424910
Russ Fullenkamp (VP-Southwest Reg)
Bob Lawson (Mgr)
Ryan Anderson (Mgr)
Dick Drebenstedt (Mgr-Ops)
Kirk Secrest (Mgr)

GOLDEN GATE BRIDGE HIGH-
WAY & TRANSPORTATION
DISTRICT

PO Box 9000, San Francisco, CA
94129-9000
Tel.: (415) 921-5858
Web Site: http://www.goldengate.org
Year Founded: 1928
Sales Range: $25-49.9 Million
Emp.: 912
Transportation Services

N.A.I.C.S.: 488490
Kary Witt (Bridge Mgr)
Joseph M. Wire (Controller)
Denis Mulligan (Gen Mgr)
Mary Currie (Dir-Pub Affairs)

GOLDEN GATE CAPITAL MAN-
AGEMENT II, LLC

1 Embarcadero Ctr 39th Fl, San
Francisco, CA 94111
Tel.: (415) 983-2700   DE
Web Site:
     http://www.goldengatecap.com
Privater Equity Firm
N.A.I.C.S.: 523999
David C. Dominik (Mng Dir)
John Olshansky (Mng Dir)
Felix Lo (Mng Dir)
Mike Montgomery (Principal)
Josh Cohen (Mng Dir)
Jim Rauh (Mng Dir)
Rob Little (COO & Mng Dir)
Rishi Chandna (Mng Dir)
Doug Ceto (Principal)
Steve Oetgen (Mng Dir, Gen Counsel
& Exec VP)
Greg Mason (Mng Dir)
Chris Collins (Principal)
Anant Gupta (Principal)
Dan Hecht (Principal)
Chris Lawler (Principal)

Subsidiaries:

ANGUS Chemical Company **(1)**
1500 E Lk Cook Rd, Buffalo Grove, IL
60089
Tel.: (844) 474-9969
Web Site: http://www.angus.com
Nitroparaffin-Based Chemicals & Deriva-
tives Mfr & Marketer
N.A.I.C.S.: 325199
Michael Lewis (VP-Bus-United States &
Canada)
Liam Doherty (VP-Bus-Europe, Middle East,
Africa & India)
Scott Hinkle (CFO)
David Green (VP-Res & Dev)
Ernest Green (VP-Mfg & Engrg)
Robert Kirby (Chm)
Dave Neuberger (Pres & CEO)
James Huang (VP-Bus-Asia Pacific)

Subsidiary (Non-US):

ANGUS Chemie GmbH **(2)**
Zeppelinstrasse 30, D 49479, Ibbenburen,
Germany
Tel.: (49) 5459560
Web Site: http://www.angus.com
Fine Chemicals Mfr
N.A.I.C.S.: 325110

Expression Systems, LLC **(2)**
Tel.: (530) 747-2035
Web Site:
     http://www.expressionsystems.com
Chemicals Mfr
N.A.I.C.S.: 325998
David Hedin (CEO)

Active Minerals International,
LLC **(1)**
4 Loveton Cir Ste 100, Sparks, MD 21152
Tel.: (410) 825-2920
Web Site: http://www.activeminerals.com
Emp.: 20
Mineral Services
N.A.I.C.S.: 423520
Don Uphouse (Controller)
Bob Purcell (VP-Sls)
Dennis Parker (Pres & CEO)

Angel Island Capital, L.P. **(1)**
1 Embarcadero Ctr Ste 2110, San Fran-
cisco, CA 94111
Tel.: (415) 616-7500
Web Site: http://www.aicap.com
Holding Company; Private Equity & Finan-
cial Services
N.A.I.C.S.: 551112
Lynette Vanderwarker (Chief Strategy Offi-
cer)
Dev Gopalan (CEO)
Jonathan Cohen (Head-Bus Dev)
Nicole Macarchuk (COO & Gen Counsel)
Robert Ryan (CFO)

Subsidiary (Domestic):

Angel Island Capital Management, LLC (2)
1 Embarcadero Ctr Ste 2150, San Francisco, CA 94111
Tel.: (415) 616-7500
Web Site: http://www.aicap.com
Rev.: $3,000,000,000
Privater Equity Firm
N.A.I.C.S.: 523999
Prescott Ashe (Pres)
Rob Stobo (Sr Portfolio Mgr)
Asif Chaudhry (VP)
Sonya Li (VP)
Adam Wueger (VP)
Jim O'Connor (Chief Compliance Officer)
Nick Stangl (CFO)

ArrMaz Products, LP (1)
4800 State Rd 60 E, Mulberry, FL 33860
Tel.: (863) 578-1206
Web Site: http://www.arrmaz.com
Specialty Chemicals Mfr
N.A.I.C.S.: 325199
Patricia Yonker Arscott (VP-HR)
Patrick Lavin (Pres-Road Science)
Doug Van Orsdale (VP-Strategic Projects)
Jeff Walker (Sr VP-Corp Dev)
Dan Partin (VP-Africa & Middle East)
Ron Lueptow (CFO)
Dave Keselica (CEO)
Vido Vareika (VP-Sls-Fertilizer & Mining)
Chris Day (VP-Mktg & Bus Dev)
Frank Mastria (Sr VP-Ops)
Paul Williams (VP-Tech & Innovation)

Bob Evans Restaurants, LLC (1)
8111 Smith's Mill Rd, New Albany, OH 43054 (100%)
Web Site: http://www.bobevans.com
Sales Range: $1-4.9 Billion
Emp.: 300
Family Restaurant Operator
N.A.I.C.S.: 722511
Saed Mohseni (CEO)

California Pizza Kitchen Inc. (1)
12181 Bluff Creek Dr 5th Fl, Playa Vista, CA 90094
Tel.: (310) 342-5000
Web Site: http://www.cpk.com
Sales Range: $900-999.9 Million
Emp.: 14,000
Restaurant Operators
N.A.I.C.S.: 722511
Jim Hyatt (Pres)
Scott Hargrove (CMO-Global & Exec VP)
Giorgio Minardi (Exec VP-Global Dev & Franchise Ops)
Judd Tirnauer (CFO & Exec VP)
Michael P. O'Donnell (Chm)
Jeff Warne (CEO)

Catalog Holdings, Inc. (1)
1 Embarcadero Ctr 39th Fl, San Francisco, CA 94111 (100%)
Tel.: (415) 627-4500
Sales Range: $50-74.9 Million
Emp.: 13
Holding Company
N.A.I.C.S.: 551112
Sue Breedlove (CFO)

Holding (Domestic):

Venus Swimwear, Inc. (2)
11711 Marco Beach Dr, Jacksonville, FL 32224
Tel.: (904) 645-6000
Web Site: http://www.venus.com
Sales Range: $100-124.9 Million
Mail Order Women's Apparel & Swimsuits
N.A.I.C.S.: 424350
Daryle Scott (Pres & CEO)
Laura Morris (Dir-Mktg)

Escalate Retail, Inc. (1)
9890 Towne Centre Dr Ste 100, San Diego, CA 92121
Tel.: (858) 457-3888
Sales Range: $25-49.9 Million
Emp.: 500
Customer-Focused Software Solutions
N.A.I.C.S.: 513210
Tom Mudd (VP-Software Dev)

Express Oil Change LLC (1)
1880 Southpark Dr, Birmingham, AL 35244
Tel.: (205) 945-1771
Web Site: http://www.expressoil.com
Oil Change & Automotive Maintenance Services Franchise
N.A.I.C.S.: 811191
Richard A. Brooks (CEO)
Kathy Palmer (Mgr-HR)
Josh Henderson (Exec VP-Mktg)

Subsidiary (Domestic):

Mavis Tire Express Services Corp. (2)
358 Sawmill River Rd, Millwood, NY 10546
Tel.: (914) 984-2500
Web Site: http://www.mavistire.com
Automotive Tires Sales
N.A.I.C.S.: 441340
Fred Christensen (CFO)

Subsidiary (Domestic):

Tire Kingdom, Inc. (3)
823 Donald Ross Rd, Juno Beach, FL 33408-1605
Tel.: (561) 383-3000
Web Site: http://www.tirekingdom.com
Sales Range: $150-199.9 Million
Emp.: 7,000
Operator of Tire Stores & Automotive Service Centers
N.A.I.C.S.: 441340

Subsidiary (Domestic):

TBC (4)
4770 Hickory Hill Rd, Memphis, TN 38141
Tel.: (901) 363-8030
Retail Tire & Automotive Centers
N.A.I.C.S.: 441340

Subsidiary (Domestic):

Savannah Tire & Rubber Company, Inc. (2)
PO Box 7089, Savannah, GA 31418-7089
Tel.: (912) 966-0303
Web Site: http://www.savannahtire.com
Tire Dealers
N.A.I.C.S.: 441340
David Wall (Pres)
Trey Cook (COO)

Invo HealthCare Associates, Inc. (1)
1780 Kendarbren Dr, Jamison, PA 18929
Tel.: (215) 489-8760
Web Site: http://www.invohealthcare.com
Staffing for Specialized Education Services
N.A.I.C.S.: 561311
Anthony L. Manley (CEO)
Jason T. Ralph (COO)
Lisa Orlando (Sr VP-Mktg & Strategy)
Matt Stringer (Pres)
Jim Paul (CFO)
Andrew B. Post (Chief Innovation Officer)

Subsidiary (Domestic):

Progressus Therapy, Inc. (2)
2701 N Rocky Point Dr Ste 650, Tampa, FL 33607
Tel.: (813) 288-8131
Web Site:
http://www.progressustherapy.com
Emp.: 600
Speech-Language Pathology, Occupational Therapy & Physical Therapy Staffing
N.A.I.C.S.: 561311
Donna Orlando (Dir-HR)
Anthony L. Manley (CEO)

Lexicon Marketing Corporation (1)
6380 Wilshire Blvd Ste 1400, Los Angeles, CA 90048-5018
Tel.: (323) 782-8282
Web Site: http://www.lexiconmarketing.com
Sales Range: $150-199.9 Million
Emp.: 1,500
Retailer of English Language Learning Programs
N.A.I.C.S.: 611630
Marcia Tula (Dir-Sls)
Robert Ro (CFO)
Jorge Azpiazu Beristain (Dir-Creative)
Rosa N. Hernandez (VP-Ops & HR)
Yngriborg Richter-Tantalean (Dir-Media)

Nassau Reinsurance Group Holdings L.P. (1)
1 American Row, Hartford, CT 06102-5056
Tel.: (860) 403-5000
Web Site: http://www.nsre.com
Holding Company; Insurance Products & Services
N.A.I.C.S.: 551112
Phillip J. Gass (Co-Founder, Chm & CEO)
Kostas Cheliotis (Co-Founder, COO & Gen Counsel)

Subsidiary (Domestic):

Constitution Life Insurance Co. (2)
1064 Greenwood Blvd Ste 200, Lake Mary, FL 32746
Tel.: (877) 504-3918
Web Site:
http://www.constitutionlife.nsre.com
Emp.: 50
Insurance Services
N.A.I.C.S.: 524113
Rich Cannone (CFO & Sr VP-Fin)
Steve Carlton (Chief Privacy Officer, Gen Counsel, Sec & VP)

Nassau Financial Group, LP (2)
1 American Row, Hartford, CT 06102-5056
Tel.: (800) 541-0171
Web Site: http://www.nsre.com
Financial Services
N.A.I.C.S.: 522320
Christine A. Janofsky (CFO)
Phil Gass (Chm & CEO)

Subsidiary (Domestic):

Foresters Financial Holding Company, Inc. (3)
40 Wall St 10th Fl, New York, NY 10005
Tel.: (212) 858-8000
Web Site: http://www.forestersfinancial.com
Holding Company; Investment Management, Mutual Fund Distribution & Insurance Product Distribution Services
N.A.I.C.S.: 551112
Robert Lamoureux (Chm)
Blake Moore (Pres-Asset Mgmt-North America)
Alvin Sharma (CFO-Global)

Subsidiary (Domestic):

Foresters Financial Services, Inc. (4)
40 Wall St 10th Fl, New York, NY 10005-1343 (100%)
Tel.: (212) 858-8000
Web Site: http://www.forestersfinancial.com
Investment & Insurance Products Broker & Dealer
N.A.I.C.S.: 523150

Foresters Investment Management Company, Inc. (4)
40 Wall St 10th Fl, New York, NY 10005-1343
Tel.: (212) 858-8000
Web Site: http://www.forestersfinancial.com
Mutual Fund Investment Advisory & Management Services
N.A.I.C.S.: 523940

Foresters Investor Services, Inc. (4)
Raritan Plz I 110 Fieldcrest Ave 8th Fl, Edison, NJ 08837-3620 (100%)
Tel.: (732) 855-2500
Investment Transfer Services
N.A.I.C.S.: 523999
Greg Walter (Sr VP)

Foresters Life Insurance & Annuity Company (4)
40 Wall St, New York, NY 10005-1343
Tel.: (212) 858-8200
Web Site: http://www.forestersfinancial.com
N.A.I.C.S.: 524113

Subsidiary (Non-US):

Foresters Life Insurance Company (4)
789 Don Mills Road, Toronto, M3C 1T9, ON, Canada
Tel.: (800) 828-1540
Web Site: https://www.foresters.com
General Insurance Services
N.A.I.C.S.: 524210

Subsidiary (Domestic):

The Phoenix Companies, Inc. (2)
1 American Row, Hartford, CT 06102-5056 (100%)
Tel.: (860) 403-5000
Web Site: http://www.phoenix.nsre.com
Sales Range: $1-4.9 Billion
Emp.: 1,000
Holding Company; Life Insurance & Annuity Products
N.A.I.C.S.: 551112
Christopher M. Wilkos (Chief Investment Officer & Exec VP)
Thomas M. Buckingham (COO & Exec VP-Product & Ops)
Robert J. Lombardi (Chief Actuary & Sr VP)
Jody A. Beresin (Chief Admin Officer & Exec VP)
Joseph Tedone (VP)
Gina Collopy O'Connell (Chief Risk Officer & Sr VP)
Justin Banulski (VP-Investment Acctg)
Phillip Gass (CEO)
Kostas Cheliotis (Gen Counsel)
Ernest McNeill Jr. (CFO, Chief Acctg Officer & Sr VP)

Subsidiary (Domestic):

PHL Variable Insurance Company (3)
1 American Row, Hartford, CT 06102-5056 (100%)
Tel.: (860) 403-5000
Web Site: http://phoenix.nsre.com
Insurance Services
N.A.I.C.S.: 524113

Phoenix Founders, Inc. (3)
1 American Row, Hartford, CT 06102
Tel.: (860) 403-5000
Insurance Services
N.A.I.C.S.: 524113

Pacific Sunwear of California, LLC (1)
3450 E Miraloma Ave, Anaheim, CA 92806-2101
Tel.: (714) 414-4000
Web Site: http://www.pacsun.com
Shoes, Clothing & Accessories Retailer
N.A.I.C.S.: 458110
Jon Brewer (Sr VP-Ops)
Alfred Chang (Pres)
Brieane Olson (Chief Mdsg Officer/Exec VP-Men's and Women's Div)
Ernie Sibal (VP-Real Estate & Store Optimization)
Joel Quill (VP-Stores)
Chris Ota (VP-Loss Prevention)

Subsidiary (Domestic):

Pacific Sunwear Stores LLC (2)
3450 E Miraloma Ave, Anaheim, CA 92806-2101
Tel.: (714) 414-4000
Shoes, Clothing & Accessories Retailer
N.A.I.C.S.: 458210

Red Lobster Hospitality LLC (1)
450 S Orange Ave Ste 800, Orlando, FL 32801-3383
Tel.: (407) 245-4000
Web Site: https://www.redlobster.com
Sales Range: $25-49.9 Million
Emp.: 350
Seafood Restaurant Services
N.A.I.C.S.: 722511
Salli Setta (Pres & Chief Concept Officer)
Thomas Gathers (COO)
Nelson Griffin (Chief Supply Chain Officer & Sr VP)
Rittirong Boonmechote (Chm)
Patty Trevino (CMO)
Horace G. Dawson III (Gen Counsel & Exec VP-External Rels)

Rocket Dog Brands, LLC (1)
11854 S Alameda St, Lynwood, CA 90262
Web Site: http://www.rocketdog.com
Footwear Designer, Developer & Distr
N.A.I.C.S.: 316210

The Learning Experience (1)
210 Hillsboro Technology Dr, Deerfield Beach, FL 33441
Tel.: (888) 865-7775
Web Site:
http://www.thelearningexperience.com
Childcare & Early Childhood Development Services

Golden Gate Capital Management II,
LLC—(Continued)

N.A.I.C.S.: 923110
Michael Weissman *(Co-Founder)*
Linda Weissman *(Co-Founder & Exec VP-Mktg)*
Richard Weissman *(Co-Founder, Chm & CEO)*

The Sierra-Cedar Group, Inc. (1)
1255 Alderman Dr, Alpharetta, GA 30005
Tel.: (678) 385-7540
Web Site: http://www.cedarcrestone.com
Sales Range: $125-149.9 Million
Emp.: 600
Computer Related Consulting & Management Services
N.A.I.C.S.: 541512
Cal Yonker *(Pres & CEO)*
Chris Ahern *(Gen Mgr-Higher Education)*
Daniel Frye *(Sr Mgr-Security & Compliance)*
Kurt Bachelder *(Assoc Dir-Managed Svcs)*

Tronair, Inc. (1)
1740 Eber Rd Ste E, Holland, OH 43528   (100%)
Tel.: (419) 866-6301
Web Site: http://www.tronair.com
Sales Range: $10-24.9 Million
Emp.: 200
Aircraft Ground Support Equipment Mfr
N.A.I.C.S.: 336413
Harley Kaplan *(Pres & CEO)*
Ken Green *(CFO & VP-Strategic Plng)*

Vantage Elevator Solutions (1)
50 E 153rd St, Bronx, NY 10451
Tel.: (347) 226-4558
Web Site: http://www.vantageelevation.com
Elevator Components & Systems Mfr & Distr
N.A.I.C.S.: 333921
Mark Boelhouwer *(Pres & CEO)*

Subsidiary (Domestic):

Bore-Max Corp. (2)
3380 Gilman Rd, El Monte, CA 91732
Tel.: (626) 443-8616
Web Site: http://www.bore-max.com
Hydraulic Elevator Component Mfr
N.A.I.C.S.: 333998
Steven Sturm *(Pres)*

GAL Manufacturing Corporation (2)
50 E 153rd St, Bronx, NY 10451
Tel.: (718) 292-9000
Web Site: http://www.gal.com
Elevator Door Equipment, Controls & Signal Fixtures Mfr
N.A.I.C.S.: 333921
Frank Marchese *(Dir-Prod Dev)*

Subsidiary (Domestic):

Comprehensive Manufacturing Services, LLC (3)
3044 Lambdin Ave, Saint Louis, MO 63115
Tel.: (314) 533-5700
Web Site: http://www.couriondoors.com
Freight Elevator, Window & Door Mfr
N.A.I.C.S.: 332321

Subsidiary (Non-US):

GAL Canada Elevator Products Corp. (3)
6500 Gottardo Court, Mississauga, L5T 2A2, ON, Canada
Tel.: (416) 747-7967
Web Site: https://www.galcanada.com
Elevators & Moving Stairways Parts Mfr
N.A.I.C.S.: 333921

Subsidiary (Domestic):

Vertical Dimensions, LLC (2)
1115 Andover Park W, Tukwila, WA 98188
Tel.: (206) 767-8022
Web Site: http://www.verticaldimensions.net
Sales Range: $1-9.9 Million
Emp.: 14
Elevator & Moving Stairway Mfr
N.A.I.C.S.: 333921
Steve McBride *(Pres)*

GOLDEN GATE NATIONAL PARKS CONSERVANCY

201 Fort Mason, San Francisco, CA 94123
Tel.: (415) 561-3000   CA
Web Site:
    https://www.parksconservancy.org
Year Founded: 1981
Sales Range: $25-49.9 Million
Emp.: 392
Environmental Conservation Services
N.A.I.C.S.: 813312
Robert Lieber *(VP-Interpretive Sls)*
Randi Fisher *(Chm)*
Lynn Mellen Wendell *(Vice Chm)*
Larry Low *(Sec)*
Gordon Ritter *(Treas)*

GOLDEN GATE PETROLEUM CO.

1340 Arnold Dr Ste 231, Martinez, CA 94553-4189
Tel.: (925) 228-2222
Web Site:
    http://www.ggpetroleum.com
Sales Range: $50-74.9 Million
Emp.: 275
Gasoline
N.A.I.C.S.: 424720
Dennis O'Keefe *(Pres & CEO)*
Deloris Williams *(Mgr-Customer Svc)*

GOLDEN GATE REGIONAL CENTER INC.

875 Stevenson St, San Francisco, CA 94103
Tel.: (415) 546-9222   CA
Web Site: http://www.ggrc.org
Year Founded: 1966
Sales Range: $10-24.9 Million
Emp.: 175
Individual & Family Services
N.A.I.C.S.: 624190

GOLDEN GLOBAL CORP.

21573 San Germain Dr, Boca Raton, FL 33433
Tel.: (561) 430-5935   NV
Web Site:
    http://www.goldenglobalcorp.com
Year Founded: 2009
Rev.: $173,447
Assets: $1,939
Liabilities: $1,934,999
Net Worth: ($1,933,060)
Earnings: ($425,282)
Emp.: 2
Fiscal Year-end: 06/30/17
Gold Mining Services
N.A.I.C.S.: 212220

GOLDEN GRAIN ENERGY, LLC

1822 43rd St SW, Mason City, IA 50401
Tel.: (641) 423-8525   IA
Web Site: https://ggecorn.com
Year Founded: 2002
Rev.: $303,435,418
Assets: $164,396,537
Liabilities: $19,560,658
Net Worth: $144,835,879
Earnings: $24,497,974
Emp.: 53
Fiscal Year-end: 10/31/21
Fuel-Grade Ethanol Plant Constructor, Owner & Operator; Ethanol & Distillers Grains Producer
N.A.I.C.S.: 325199

GOLDEN HARVEST FOOD BANK

3310 Commerce Dr, Augusta, GA 30909
Tel.: (706) 736-1199   GA
Web Site:
    https://www.goldenharvest.org
Year Founded: 1982
Sales Range: $25-49.9 Million

Emp.: 59
Community Food Services
N.A.I.C.S.: 624210

GOLDEN HOTEL LIMITED PARTNERSHIP

18700 MacArthur Blvd, Irvine, CA 92612
Tel.: (949) 833-2770   CA
Web Site:
    https://www.atriumhotel.com
Year Founded: 1992
Sales Range: $1-9.9 Million
Emp.: 140
Hotel/Motel Operation
N.A.I.C.S.: 721110
Steve Hostter *(Gen Mgr)*

GOLDEN INDUSTRIES INC.

613 N Grant Ave Apt 3C, York, NE 68467
Tel.: (402) 366-1374   NE
Web Site: http://www.cumblr.com
Sales Range: $10-24.9 Million
Emp.: 1
Cans & Bottles Purchaser & Seller
N.A.I.C.S.: 423930
Joseph Gold *(Pres & CEO)*

GOLDEN ISLES CUSTOM HOMES LLC

PO Box 21098, Saint Simons Island, GA 31522
Tel.: (912) 230-6770
Web Site:
    http://www.goldenislescustom
    homes.com
Year Founded: 2007
Sales Range: $1-9.9 Million
Emp.: 2
Custom Home Builder & Remodeler
N.A.I.C.S.: 236117
John Hodor *(Co-Founder)*
Brad Brumbach *(Co-Founder)*

GOLDEN KEY GROUP, LLC

11400 Commerce Park Dr Ste 250, Reston, VA 20191
Tel.: (703) 815-0290
Web Site:
    http://www.goldenkeygroup.com
Year Founded: 2002
Sales Range: $10-24.9 Million
Emp.: 160
HR Support & Consulting Services
N.A.I.C.S.: 541612
Bruce Tarpinian *(CEO)*
Glenn Duncan *(VP-IT)*
Gretchen McCracken *(Partner)*
Larry McCracken *(VP)*
Pat Pearson *(VP)*
Michael McGregor *(VP-Client Engagement & Bus Optimization)*

GOLDEN LIGHTING COMPANY

2851 Industrial Plaza Dr, Tallahassee, FL 32301
Tel.: (850) 877-8265
Web Site:
    https://www.goldenlighting.com
Sales Range: $10-24.9 Million
Lighting Product Distr
N.A.I.C.S.: 423610
Yuh-Mei Hutt *(Pres)*

GOLDEN M CO. INC.

1101 Opal Ct Ste 315, Hagerstown, MD 21740
Tel.: (301) 766-7100
Rev.: $10,167,682
Emp.: 150
Fast Food Restaurant Operator
N.A.I.C.S.: 722513
Mark Levine *(Pres)*

GOLDEN MEDIA

6720 SW Macadam Suite 300, Portland, OR 97219
Tel.: (503) 293-8000
Web Site:
    http://www.goldenmedia.com
Year Founded: 2002
Sales Range: $10-24.9 Million
Emp.: 10
Advertising Agencies
N.A.I.C.S.: 541830
Susan Golden *(Pres)*

GOLDEN NEO LIFE DIAMITE INTERNATIONAL

3500 Gateway Blvd, Fremont, CA 94538
Tel.: (510) 651-0405
Web Site: http://www.gnld.com
Year Founded: 1958
Rev.: $30,100,000
Emp.: 80
Vitamins & Minerals
N.A.I.C.S.: 424210
Jerry Brassfield *(Founder)*

GOLDEN PACIFIC HOMES INC.

165 S Pacific Hwy, Woodburn, OR 97071
Tel.: (503) 982-3000
Web Site:
    http://www.goldenpacifichomes.com
Rev.: $20,000,000
Emp.: 8
Sales of Mobile Homes
N.A.I.C.S.: 459930
Larry L. Marple *(Pres)*

GOLDEN PHOENIX MINERALS, INC.

7770 Duneville St No 11, Las Vegas, NV 89139
Tel.: (702) 589-7475   NV
Web Site:
    http://www.goldenphoenix.us
Sales Range: $1-9.9 Million
Gold, Silver & Other Metal Mining Services
N.A.I.C.S.: 212220

GOLDEN RAIN FOUNDATION

1001 Golden Rain Rd, Walnut Creek, CA 94595
Tel.: (925) 988-7700
Web Site: https://www.rossmoor.com
Sales Range: $25-49.9 Million
Emp.: 350
Manager of Senior Living Community
N.A.I.C.S.: 813990
Rick Chakoff *(CFO)*

GOLDEN RESERVE, LLC

6037 Frantz Rd Ste 106, Dublin, OH 43017
Tel.: (614) 254-6561
Web Site:
    http://www.goldenreserve.com
Year Founded: 2011
Sales Range: $1-9.9 Million
Emp.: 10
Financial Investment Services
N.A.I.C.S.: 523940
Patrick Schmidt *(Partner)*
Bart Patterson *(Partner)*
Rick Shibko *(Dir-Analytics)*
Chanda Hunter *(Coord-Mktg)*
Michelle Thompson *(Controller)*

GOLDEN ROD BROILERS INC.

85 13th St NE, Cullman, AL 35055-5907
Tel.: (256) 734-0851   AL
Year Founded: 1959
Sales Range: $75-99.9 Million
Emp.: 1,010
Producer of Chickens
N.A.I.C.S.: 112320

Louie Ayers *(Gen Mgr)*

GOLDEN ROYAL DEVELOP-MENT, INC.

80 Main St Ste 415, West Orange, NJ 07052   DE
Year Founded: 2016
Liabilities: $197,666
Net Worth: ($197,666)
Earnings: ($63,340)
Emp.: 1
Fiscal Year-end: 09/30/22
Mineral Asset Leasing Services
N.A.I.C.S.: 533110
Jacob Roth *(Chm, Pres, CEO, CFO & Chief Acctg Officer)*
Bernard Rosenberg *(Sec)*

GOLDEN SOURCE CORPORA-TION

22 Cortlandt St Fl 22, New York, NY 10007
Tel.: (212) 798-7100
Web Site:
http://www.thegoldensource.com
Rev.: $50,331,051
Emp.: 100
Computer Software Development
N.A.I.C.S.: 541511
Mark Zill *(Exec VP-Client Ops-Global)*
John H. Eley *(CEO)*

GOLDEN STAR CORPORA-TION

99 Hudson St 5th Fl, New York, NY 10013
Tel.: (646) 706-5365   Ky
Year Founded: 2021
Emp.: 2
Investment Services
N.A.I.C.S.: 523999
Linjun Guo *(CEO & Chm)*
Kenneth Lam *(CFO)*

GOLDEN STAR INC.

4770 N Belleview Ave Ste 209, Kansas City, MO 64116-4303
Tel.: (816) 842-0233   KS
Web Site: http://www.goldenstar.com
Year Founded: 1908
Sales Range: $150-199.9 Million
Emp.: 450
Mfr of Textile & Chemical Cleaning Products
N.A.I.C.S.: 339994
William Gradinger *(VP)*

GOLDEN STATE ENGINEER-ING INC.

15338 S Garfield Ave, Paramount, CA 90723
Tel.: (562) 634-3125
Web Site:
https://www.goldenstateeng.com
Rev.: $8,800,000
Emp.: 120
Metalworking Machines Mfr
N.A.I.C.S.: 333519
Eugenio Rostovski *(Pres)*
Alexandra Rostovski *(CEO)*

GOLDEN STATE FARM CREDIT

1580 Ellis St, Kingsburg, CA 93631
Tel.: (559) 897-5814
Web Site:
http://www.gsfarmcredit.com
Year Founded: 1916
Sales Range: $10-24.9 Million
Agricultural Financing
N.A.I.C.S.: 522390
Scott Anderson *(Pres & CEO)*

GOLDEN STATE FOODS CORP.

18301 Von Karman Ave Ste 1100, Irvine, CA 92612
Tel.: (949) 247-8000   DE
Web Site:
https://www.goldenstatefoods.com
Year Founded: 1947
Sales Range: $1-4.9 Billion
Emp.: 6,000
Other Miscellaneous Nondurable Goods Merchant Wholesalers
N.A.I.C.S.: 424990
Mike Waitukaitis *(Vice Chm)*
Larry McGill *(VP)*
John Page *(Chief Corp Social Responsibility & Legal Officer & Sr VP)*
Wayne Morgan *(Pres & VP-Protein Products Grp)*
Shellie Frey *(VP-Corp Comm)*
John Broekhuis *(VP-Intl)*
Joe Heffington *(Chief Acctg Officer)*
Guilda Javaheri *(CIO)*
Brian Dick *(COO & Exec VP)*
Jeff Steiner *(Sr VP-McDonalds Distr)*
Ed Savard *(Grp VP-Food Safety, Compliance & Engrg)*
Amy Zurborg *(Grp VP-Sls & Mktg)*
Carol Fawcett *(CIO & VP)*
Campbell Cooper *(Pres-Intl Bus Grp)*
Hugues Labrecque *(VP-Sls)*
Trisha McRoberts *(Grp VP-Strategic Sourcing)*
Shane Blanchette *(Grp VP-Continuous Improvement-Quality Custom Distr)*
Stephen Wetterau *(VP-Logistics-Quality Custom Distr)*
Ed Rodriguez *(Chief HR Officer & Sr VP)*
Kate Starr *(Grp VP-Comm)*

Subsidiaries:

CFM Logistics   (1)
11500 Olive Blvd Ste 276, Saint Louis, MO 63141
Tel.: (314) 428-9900
Web Site: http://www.cfmlogistics.com
Logistics Consulting Servies
N.A.I.C.S.: 541614
Bill Gibson *(Principal)*

Centralized Leasing Corporation   (1)
1 Mid Rivers Mall Dr Ste 256, Saint Peters, MO 63376
Tel.: (636) 397-0384
Web Site: http://www.goldenstatefoods.com
Emp.: 5
Food Product Mfr & Whslr
N.A.I.C.S.: 424420
Bill Pocilujko *(Gen Mgr)*

Golden State Foods-City of Industry Division   (1)
21489 Baker Pkwy, City of Industry, CA 91789
Tel.: (909) 595-6262
Rev.: $189,379,000
Emp.: 325
Mfr & Distributor of Meats, Dairy Products, Syrups & Condiments
N.A.I.C.S.: 424470

Golden State Foods-Georgia Division   (1)
1525 Old Covington Rd NE, Conyers, GA 30013-5001   (100%)
Tel.: (770) 483-0711
Web Site: http://www.gsf.com
Sales Range: $25-49.9 Million
Emp.: 282
Meat Processing; Syrups; Baking Goods
N.A.I.C.S.: 311612

Golden State Foods-Hawaii Division   (1)
94 554 Ukee St, Waipahu, HI 96797-4213
Tel.: (808) 671-4017
Web Site: http://www.goldenstatefoods.com
Sales Range: $25-49.9 Million
Emp.: 72
Food Distribution Center
N.A.I.C.S.: 424470
Mark Wetterau *(CEO)*

Golden State Foods-Northwest Division   (1)

1409 Puyallup St, Sumner, WA 98390-1635
Tel.: (253) 863-3800
Sales Range: $25-49.9 Million
Emp.: 80
Distribution Center
N.A.I.C.S.: 424470

Golden State Foods-Oak Brook   (1)
2211 York Rd Ste 208, Oak Brook, IL 60523-4028
Tel.: (630) 575-2070
Web Site: http://www.goldenstatefoods.com
Sales Range: $10-24.9 Million
Emp.: 4
Mfr & Distributor of Food Products
N.A.I.C.S.: 541611

Golden State Foods-Phoenix Division   (1)
5516 W Buchanan St, Phoenix, AZ 85043-4625   (100%)
Tel.: (602) 233-1511
Web Site: http://www.goldenstatefoods.com
Sales Range: $25-49.9 Million
Emp.: 67
Distribution Center
N.A.I.C.S.: 424410

Golden State Foods-Rochester Division   (1)
41 Cook Dr, Rochester, NY 14623-3509
Tel.: (585) 334-2400
Web Site: http://www.goldenstatefoods.com
Sales Range: $25-49.9 Million
Emp.: 58
Distribution Center
N.A.I.C.S.: 424410
Tom Hank *(Gen Mgr)*

Golden State Foods-South Carolina Division   (1)
2588 Old 2 Notch Rd, Lexington, SC 29072   (100%)
Tel.: (803) 957-9811
Web Site: http://www.goldenstatefoods.com
Sales Range: $10-24.9 Million
Emp.: 120
Distribution Center for McDonalds
N.A.I.C.S.: 493110

Golden State Service Industries, Inc.   (1)
9310 N Harborgate St, Portland, OR 97203
Tel.: (503) 283-4400
Web Site: http://www.goldenstatefoods.com
Emp.: 100
Fast Food Restaurant Operator
N.A.I.C.S.: 722513
Mike Ehlers *(Mgr)*

Quality Custom Distribution - Suffolk   (1)
1391 Progress Rd, Suffolk, VA 23434-2154
Tel.: (757) 942-2810
Web Site: http://www.goldenstatefoods.com
Sales Range: $25-49.9 Million
Emp.: 65
Food Products Distr
N.A.I.C.S.: 424490
Jery Wilson *(Gen Mgr)*

GOLDEN STATE IRRIGATION SERVICES

4500 E Fremont St, Stockton, CA 95215
Tel.: (209) 943-7774
Web Site:
https://www.goldenstateirr.com
Year Founded: 1985
Sales Range: $10-24.9 Million
Emp.: 30
Irrigation Equipment Mfr
N.A.I.C.S.: 423820
Peter Bernadicou *(Owner)*

GOLDEN STATE LUMBER INC.

38801 Cherry St, Newark, CA 94560
Tel.: (707) 769-0181
Web Site:
http://www.goldenstatelumber.com
Year Founded: 1954
Sales Range: $25-49.9 Million
Emp.: 450
Building Materials Distr
N.A.I.C.S.: 423310

Rick Zalsove *(Pres)*
Jilleun Eglin *(Mgr-Mktg)*
Dennis R. Finnie *(Controller)*
Rob Scerri *(COO)*
Dave Houck *(Mgr-Yard)*
Bob Bowler *(CFO)*
Tamara Heath *(Controller)*
Eric Schmies *(Gen Mgr)*
Brandon Deering *(Mgr-Fleet & Safety)*
Rich Wheeler *(Gen Mgr)*
Wendi Dunton *(Mgr-Mktg)*

GOLDEN STATE MEDICARE HEALTH PLAN

4000 MacArthur Blvd Ste 1025, Newport Beach, CA 92660
Tel.: (562) 799-0319   CA
Web Site:
http://www.goldenstatemhp.com
Elderly Services
N.A.I.C.S.: 624120
Sanjay Patil *(CEO)*
Ash Damle *(Chief Strategy Officer)*
Holly Brenier *(CFO)*
Jim Boyle *(COO)*

GOLDEN STATE WARRIORS, LLC

1011 Broadway, Oakland, CA 94607
Tel.: (510) 986-2200   CA
Web Site: http://www.nba.com
Year Founded: 1946
Professional Basketball Team
N.A.I.C.S.: 711211
Travis Schlenk *(Asst Gen Mgr)*
Vivek Y. Ranadive *(Vice Chm)*
Lachlan Penfold *(Head-Physical Performance & Sports Medicine)*
Bob Myers *(Gen Mgr)*
Kirk Lacob *(Asst Gen Mgr)*
Larry Harris *(Dir-Player Personnel)*
Frederic Welts *(Pres & COO)*

GOLDEN SUN, INC.

26529 Ruether Ave, Santa Clarita, CA 91350
Tel.: (661) 250-1111
Web Site:
http://www.labellabeauty.com
Year Founded: 1976
Sales Range: $10-24.9 Million
Emp.: 27
Toilet Preparation Mfr
N.A.I.C.S.: 325620
Alcides Rodriguez *(Founder)*

GOLDEN TADCO INTERNA-TIONAL CORPORATION

251 Herrod Blvd, Dayton, NJ 08810
Tel.: (732) 230-5005   NJ
Web Site:
https://www.goldentadco.com
Year Founded: 1981
Sales Range: $10-24.9 Million
Emp.: 58
Homefurnishings
N.A.I.C.S.: 423220
Bettywu Gallistel *(Pres)*

GOLDEN TOUCH IMPORTS, INC.

1410 Broadway 8th Fl, New York, NY 10018-9362
Tel.: (212) 643-9048   NY
Year Founded: 1975
Holding Company
N.A.I.C.S.: 551112
Bruce Fischer *(Pres & CEO)*

Subsidiaries:

Global Gold, Inc.   (1)
1410 Broadway Fl 8, New York, NY 10018
Tel.: (212) 239-4657

Golden Touch Imports, Inc.—(Continued)

Sales Range: $1-9.9 Million
Emp.: 38
Womens And Misses Suits And Coats, Nsk
N.A.I.C.S.: 315250
Bruce Fisher *(Pres & CEO)*

Jaclyn, Inc.   **(1)**
197 W Spring Valley Ave, Maywood, NJ
07607
Tel.: (201) 909-6000
Sales Range: $150-199.9 Million
Apparel, Backpacks, Handbags, Sport
Bags, Travel Bags, Premiums & Related
Accessories for Men, Women & Children
N.A.I.C.S.: 315210
Anthony Christon *(CFO)*

Subsidiary (Domestic):

Bonnie International   **(2)**
197 W Spring Valley Ave, Maywood, NJ
07607
Tel.: (201) 909-6000
Web Site: http://www.bonnie-
international.com
Handbags Mfr
N.A.I.C.S.: 424350
Gina Labartino *(Exec Dir)*

**GOLDEN TRIANGLE DAIRY
QUEENS, INC.**
3525 Preston Ave, Pasadena, TX
77505-2008
Tel.: (409) 866-3781   **TX**
Web Site:
    http://www.dqpasadena.com
Year Founded: 1971
Limited Service Restaurant Franchi-
see
N.A.I.C.S.: 722513
Wesley R. Howard *(Pres)*

**GOLDEN VALLEY ELECTRIC
ASSOCIATION**
758 Illinois St, Fairbanks, AK 99701
Tel.: (907) 452-1151
Web Site: https://www.gvea.com
Year Founded: 1903
Sales Range: $75-99.9 Million
Emp.: 250
Electric Power Company
N.A.I.C.S.: 221118
Cory Borgeson *(Pres & CEO)*

**GOLDEN VALLEY GRAPE
JUICE & WINE**
11770 Rd 27 1/2, Madera, CA 93637
Tel.: (559) 661-4657
Web Site:
    https://goldenvalleywine.com
Sales Range: $10-24.9 Million
Emp.: 40
Concentrate, Juice & Wine Mfr
N.A.I.C.S.: 311411
Gerald D. Homolka *(Plant Mgr)*
Jerry Holomka *(Mgr)*
Doren Lee *(Mgr-Quality Assurance)*

GOLDEN VILLA HOMES INC.
2394 Hwy 6 And 50, Grand Junction,
CO 81505-1340
Tel.: (970) 245-9039
Web Site:
    http://www.goldenvillahomes.com
Sales Range: $10-24.9 Million
Emp.: 9
Mobile Home Dealers
N.A.I.C.S.: 459930
Michael F. Ruse *(Pres)*

**GOLDEN WEST IRRIGATION &
EQUIPMENT LLC**
2256 S Hwy 191, Rexburg, ID 83440
Tel.: (208) 356-9318
Web Site:
    http://www.goldenwest.valley
    dealers.com
Sales Range: $10-24.9 Million

Emp.: 20
Dealer Of Irrigation Equipment
N.A.I.C.S.: 423820
Richard McGary *(Controller)*

GOLDEN WEST NUTS INC.
1555 Warren Rd, Ripon, CA 95366-
9532
Tel.: (209) 599-6193   **CA**
Web Site:
    http://www.goldenwestnuts.com
Year Founded: 1983
Sales Range: $10-24.9 Million
Emp.: 100
Provider of Roasted & Salted Nuts
N.A.I.C.S.: 115114
Mark Vanlerberghe *(Controller)*
Steve Gikas *(Owner & Mgr-Sls)*
Lorie Bolme *(Mgr-Acctg)*

**GOLDEN WEST PIPE & SUP-
PLY CO.**
11700 Woodruff Ave, Downey, CA
90241
Tel.: (562) 803-4321
Web Site:
    https://www.goldenwestpipe.com
Sales Range: $10-24.9 Million
Emp.: 22
Mfr of Piping & Plumbing Equipment
N.A.I.C.S.: 423720
Shirley Lutgen *(Pres)*

**GOLDEN WEST TELECOMMU-
NICATIONS**
415 Crown St, Wall, SD 57790
Tel.: (605) 279-2161
Web Site:
    https://www.goldenwest.com
Year Founded: 1952
Sales Range: $10-24.9 Million
Emp.: 50
Provider of Telecommunications Ser-
vices
N.A.I.C.S.: 517121
Jody Bielmaier *(Mgr-Svcs)*
Denny Law *(CEO)*
Gordy Kraut *(CFO)*

**GOLDENTREE ASSET MAN-
AGEMENT LP**
300 Park Ave 21st Fl, New York, NY
10022
Tel.: (212) 847-3500   **DE**
Web Site:
    https://www.goldentree.com
Year Founded: 2000
Rev.: $21,000,000,000
Emp.: 190
Holding Company; Investment Man-
agement Services
N.A.I.C.S.: 551112
Lee Kruter *(Partner & Sr Portfolio
Mgr)*
Kathryn Sutherland *(CEO & Partner)*
Taro Ueda *(Mng Dir-Tokyo)*
Chad Plotke *(Principal)*
Steve Tananbaum *(Founder, Mng
Partner & Chief Investment Officer)*

Subsidiaries:

GoldenTree Asset Management
LLC   **(1)**
300 Park Ave 21st Fl, New York, NY 10022
Tel.: (212) 847-3500
Web Site: http://www.goldentree.com
Investment Management Service
N.A.I.C.S.: 523940
Casey Shanley *(Portfolio Mgr)*
Robert Matza *(Pres & Partner)*
Steven A. Tananbaum *(Founder, Mng Part-
ner & Chief Investment Officer)*
Joseph Naggar *(Partner & Sr Portfolio Mgr)*
Steven Todd Shapiro *(Partner & Sr Portfolio
Mgr)*
Frederick S. Haddad *(Partner & Sr Portfolio
Mgr)*
Lee Kruter *(Partner & Sr Portfolio Mgr)*

Pierre De Chillaz *(Partner & Head-Bus Dev)*
Kathryn Sutherland *(CEO & Partner)*
Alysia Love *(Partner & Chief Talent Officer)*
Shawn Mathew *(Partner & Head-Corp Strat-
egy)*

GoldenTree Asset Management Sin-
gapore Pte. Ltd.   **(1)**
12 Marina Boulevard #17-01 Marina Bay
Financial Centre Tower 3, Singapore,
018982, Singapore
Tel.: (65) 6809 5070
Web Site: http://www.goldentree.com
Investment Management Service
N.A.I.C.S.: 523940

GoldenTree Asset Management UK
LLP   **(1)**
33 Davies Street 4th Floor, London, W1K
4LR, United Kingdom
Tel.: (44) 207 925 8800
Web Site: http://www.goldentree.com
Investment Management Service
N.A.I.C.S.: 523940

Hamburg Commercial Bank AG   **(1)**
Gerhart-Hauptmann Platz 50, 20095, Ham-
burg, Germany   **(12.49%)**
Tel.: (49) 4033330
Web Site: http://www.hcob-bank.de
Rev.: $2,462,572,140
Assets: $53,430,760,320
Liabilities: $47,048,678,180
Net Worth: $6,382,082,140
Earnings: $13,438,320
Emp.: 1,482
Fiscal Year-end: 12/31/2019
Commericial Banking
N.A.I.C.S.: 522110
Stefan Ermisch *(CEO & Member-Mgmt Bd)*
Uwe-Jens Werner *(Head-Savings Banks &
Institutional Clients)*
Judith Steinhoff *(Head-HR)*
Ralf Lowe *(Head-Treasury)*
Peter Axmann *(Head-Real Estate-Global)*
Barbara Himmel *(Head-Legal & Taxes)*
Oliver Waldeck *(Head-Bus Origination)*
Bernd Gabor *(Head-Shipping-Europe &
Americas)*
Loukas Lagaras *(Head-Shipping-Athens
Branch)*
Jutta Arlt *(Head-Cash & Trade Svcs)*
Ulrik Lackschewitz *(Deputy CEO, Chief Risk
Officer & Member-Mgmt Bd)*
Michael Rothehuser *(Head-Trade, Food,
Commodities, Industry & Svcs)*
Martin Jonas *(Head-IR)*
Franziska von Scholz *(Head-Strategic Proj-
ects)*
Stephan Otto *(Head-Risk Mgmt)*
Ian Banwell *(CFO & Member-Mgmt Bd)*
Nicolas Blanchard *(Chief Clients & Products
Officer & Member-Mgmt Bd)*
Christopher Brody *(Chief Investment Officer
& Member-Mgmt Bd)*
Thomas Jakob *(Head-Corp Banking & Advi-
sory)*
Stephen Scheuer *(Head-Corp Fin & Work-
ing Capital Solution)*
Inka Klinger *(Head-Infrastructure Project
Fin-Global)*
Jan-Philipp Rohr *(Head-Shipping-Global)*
Donald Banks *(Head-Capital Markets)*
Tilo Kraus *(Head-Sls & Syndicate-Global)*
Monika Feher *(Head-Middle Office & Bus
Dev)*
Markus Best *(Head-Transaction Banking)*
Nicole Neumann *(Head-Mktg & Digital Me-
dia)*
Katrin Steinbacher *(Head-Press)*
Eileen Maschmann *(Head-Corp & Securities
Compliance)*
Dirk von Thaden *(Head-Acctg)*
Jorg Reinicke *(Head-Regulatory Reporting)*
Henrik Stein *(Head-Internal Auditing)*
Svenja Neuhaus *(Head-Law)*
Juan Rodriguez Inciarte *(Chm-Supervisory
Bd)*

Subsidiary (Domestic):

CAPCELLENCE Holding GmbH &
Co. KG   **(2)**
Gasstrasse 4, 22761, Hamburg, Germany
Tel.: (49) 40 30700700
Financial Management Services
N.A.I.C.S.: 551112

HSH Facility Management
GmbH   **(2)**

Rosenstr 11, Hamburg; 20095, Germany
Tel.: (49) 40 33330
Financial Management Services
N.A.I.C.S.: 551112

HSH Move+More GmbH   **(2)**
Martensdamm 6, 24103, Kiel, Schleswig-
Holstein, Germany
Tel.: (49) 43190001
Logistics Services & Consulting Services
N.A.I.C.S.: 541614

Subsidiary (US):

HSH N Financial Securities LLC   **(2)**
230 Park Ave, New York, NY 10169
Tel.: (212) 407-6000
Financial Management Services
N.A.I.C.S.: 551112

Representative Office (Non-US):

HSH Nordbank AG
(Luxembourg)   **(2)**
2 rue Jean Monnet, L-2180, Luxembourg,
Luxembourg
Tel.: (352) 424137
Web Site: http://www.hsh-nordbank.lu
Banking Services
N.A.I.C.S.: 522110

Subsidiary (Non-US):

HSH Nordbank Securities S.A.   **(2)**
2 Rue Jean Monnet, Luxembourg, 2180,
Luxembourg
Tel.: (352) 42414111
Web Site: http://www.hshn-securities.com
Sales Range: $100-124.9 Million
Emp.: 145
Private Banking Services
N.A.I.C.S.: 522320
Carsten Backer *(Chm-Mgmt Bd, CFO &
Chief Risk Officer)*
Jan Luhrs-Behnke *(Mng Dir & Head-Bus
Unit)*
Franz-Josef Glauben *(Member-Mgmt Bd)*

Subsidiary (Domestic):

Kontora Family Office GmbH   **(2)**
Ballindamm 39, 20095, Hamburg, Germany
Tel.: (49) 4032908880
Web Site: http://www.kontora-advisory.com
Financial Management Services
N.A.I.C.S.: 551112

Syncora Guarantee Inc.   **(1)**
135 W 50th St 20 Fl, New York, NY 10020.
Tel.: (212) 478-3400
Financial Guarantee & Credit Enhancement
Services
N.A.I.C.S.: 522299

Subsidiary (Domestic):

Swap Financial Group LLC   **(2)**
135 W 50th St 20th Fl, New York, NY
10020   **(80%)**
Tel.: (212) 478-3700
Web Site: http://www.swapfinancial.com
Bond & Other Financial Instrument Advisory
Services
N.A.I.C.S.: 523940
Peter Shapiro *(Sr Mng Dir)*
Nathaniel R. Singer *(Sr Mng Dir)*
Peter Clerc *(Mng Dir)*
Gerri Magie *(Mng Dir)*
James Murphy *(Mng Dir)*

**GOLDENWEST DIAMOND
CORPORATION**
15732 Tustin Village Way, Tustin, CA
92780-8320
Tel.: (714) 542-9000   **CA**
Web Site:
    https://www.jewelryexchange.com
Year Founded: 1977
Sales Range: $25-49.9 Million
Emp.: 132
Jewelry Services
N.A.I.C.S.: 458310
William S. Doddridge *(Pres & CEO)*

**GOLDENWEST LUBRICANTS,
INC.**

1937 Mount Vernon Ave, Pomona, CA 91768
Tel.: (909) 865-3081   CA
Web Site:
 http://www.goldenwestlubricant.com
Year Founded: 1985
Sales Range: $1-9.9 Million
Petroleum Product Whslr
N.A.I.C.S.: 424720
Edith Camacho *(Dir-Global Sls)*
Claudine Abdelkassa *(Mgr)*

GOLDEO INC.

5100 Washington St Ste 202, Hollywood, FL 33021
Tel.: (754) 816-6371   FL
Year Founded: 2011
Sales Range: $10-24.9 Million
Emp.: 1
Online Precious Metals Platform
N.A.I.C.S.: 425120
Brandon Wynn *(Pres)*

GOLDFIELDS INTERNATIONAL INC.

8022 S Rainbow Blvd Ste 417, Las Vegas, NV 89139
Tel.: (800) 315-6551   NV
Web Site:
 http://www.goldfieldscorp.com
Year Founded: 2001
Gold Mining Services
N.A.I.C.S.: 212220
Jared Beebe *(Interim Pres, Treas & Sec)*

GOLDFISH SWIM SCHOOL FRANCHISING LLC

2388 Cole St Ste 101, Birmingham, MI 48009
Tel.: (248) 243-4897
Web Site:
 https://www.goldfishschool.com
Year Founded: 2006
Sales Range: $1-9.9 Million
Emp.: 50
Swim School Franchise Operation
N.A.I.C.S.: 611699
Jenny McCuiston *(Co-Founder)*
Christopher McCuiston *(Co-Founder)*

Subsidiaries:

Goldfish Swim School   (1)
2388 Cole St Ste 101, Birmingham, MI 48009
Tel.: (248) 644-1914
Web Site:
 http://www.goldfishswimschool.com
Swim School Programs
N.A.I.C.S.: 923110
Jenny McCuiston *(Co-Founder)*
Christopher McCuiston *(Co-Founder)*

GOLDING FARMS FOODS, INC.

6061 Gun Club Rd, Winston Salem, NC 27103
Tel.: (336) 766-6161
Web Site:
 http://www.goldingfarmsfoods.com
Sauce & Condiment Mfr
N.A.I.C.S.: 311941
John Frostad *(CEO)*

Subsidiaries:

Arcobasso Foods, Inc.   (1)
8850 Pershall Rd, Hazelwood, MO 63042
Tel.: (314) 381-8083
Web Site: http://www.arcobasso.com
Dressing, Marinade, Sauce Bottler & Mfr
N.A.I.C.S.: 311941
Pat Newsham *(Pres & Partner)*
Mark Miner *(Partner & Sr VP-Sls)*
Lindsay Rosenthal *(Sr Mgr-Mktg & Mgr-Bus Dev)*
Stephanie Gabrian *(Sr Mgr-Admin & Sourcing)*
Matt Pudlowski *(COO & CfO)*

GOLDMAN & ASSOCIATES

500 E Plume St Ste 406, Norfolk, VA 23510
Tel.: (757) 625-2518   VA
Web Site:
 http://www.goldmanandassocs.com
Year Founded: 1967
Sales Range: $10-24.9 Million
Emp.: 11
Public Relations Agency
N.A.I.C.S.: 541820
Dean S. Goldman *(Pres)*
Audrey Knoth *(Exec VP)*
Scott McCaskey *(Acct Dir)*

GOLDMAN EQUIPMENT CO., LLC.

8144 US Hwy 65, Waterproof, LA 71375
Tel.: (318) 749-3205
Web Site:
 http://www.goldmanequipment.com
Rev.: $80,900,000
Emp.: 80
All Other Miscellaneous Store Retailers
N.A.I.C.S.: 459999
Ken Vines *(VP)*
Mac Hazlip *(Pres)*
Harry T. Goldman III *(Treas & Sec)*

GOLDMAN PROPERTIES

804 Ocean Dr 2nd Fl, Miami Beach, FL 33139
Tel.: (305) 531-4411
Web Site:
 http://www.goldmanproperties.com
Sales Range: $1-9.9 Million
Real Estate Investment & Management Services
N.A.I.C.S.: 531390
Jessica Goldman Srebnick *(CEO & Principal)*
Marlo Courtney *(Sr Mng Dir)*
Daniele Lomoriello *(Dir-Fin)*
Victor Sanchez *(Sr Project Mgr)*
Elizabeth Periche *(Dir-HR)*
Janet Goldman *(Chm & Principal)*
Joey Goldman *(Principal)*
Marite Iglesias *(Mgr-Arts)*
Zack Tagani *(Mng Dir-New York)*
Joseph Furst *(Mng Dir-Wynwood)*

GOLDMAN SACHS PRIVATE CREDIT CORP.

200 W St, New York, NY 10282
Tel.: (312) 655-4419   DE
Year Founded: 2022
Rev.: $83,548,000
Assets: $1,905,900,000
Liabilities: $315,063,000
Net Worth: $1,590,837,000
Earnings: $67,777,000
Fiscal Year-end: 12/31/23
Investment Management Service
N.A.I.C.S.: 523999

GOLDNER ASSOCIATES, INC.

231 Venture Cir, Nashville, TN 37228
Tel.: (615) 244-3007
Web Site:
 https://www.goldnerassociates.com
Sales Range: $10-24.9 Million
Emp.: 70
Promotional Products Distr
N.A.I.C.S.: 424990
Jim Straus *(CEO)*
Andy Strauss *(CEO)*
Laurie Aronoff *(Dir-Mktg)*

GOLDNER HAWN JOHNSON & MORRISON INC.

3700 Wells Fargo Ctr 90 S 7th St, Minneapolis, MN 55402-4128
Tel.: (612) 338-5912   MN
Web Site: http://www.ghjm.com

Year Founded: 1989
Emp.: 10
Privater Equity Firm
N.A.I.C.S.: 523999
Van Zandt Hawn *(Founder & Mng Dir)*
Timothy D. Johnson *(Mng Dir)*
John L. Morrison *(Mng Dir)*
Joseph M. Heinen *(Mng Dir)*
Jason T. Brass *(Mng Dir)*
Grace N. Haagenson *(Treas)*
Mark J. Emmen *(CFO)*
Chad M. Cornell *(Mng Dir)*
Peter J. Settle *(Mng Dir)*
Joseph P. Helms *(VP)*
Andrew M. Tomashek *(VP)*

Subsidiaries:

Applied Products, Inc.   (1)
6035 Baker Rd, Minnetonka, MN 55345
Tel.: (952) 933-2224
Web Site: http://www.applied-adhesives.com
Sales Range: $10-24.9 Million
Adhesive Mfr & Whslr
N.A.I.C.S.: 325520
Dan Horner *(CEO)*
Brian Webb *(Pres)*
Andy Lutz *(Dir-Tech Svc)*
Douglas J. Moore *(CFO & COO)*
John Feriancek *(CFO)*

Mid Valley Industries, LLC   (1)
1151 Delanglade St, Kaukauna, WI 54130-4122
Tel.: (920) 759-0314
Web Site: http://www.mvii.com
Sales Range: $25-49.9 Million
Emp.: 100
Precision Machined & Fabricated Metal Components Mfr
N.A.I.C.S.: 332710
Kevin Schmid *(Pres)*
Jeff Stilt *(Exec VP)*

GOLDRIVER ORCHARDS, INC.

5640 River Rd, Oakdale, CA 95361
Tel.: (209) 847-1367
Web Site:
 http://www.goldriverorchards.com
Year Founded: 1912
Sales Range: $10-24.9 Million
Emp.: 10
Postharvest Crop Activities (except Cotton Ginning)
N.A.I.C.S.: 115114
Manuel Teixeira *(Plant Mgr)*
Danae Romero *(Mgr)*
Anthony Mello *(CFO)*
Donald L. Barton *(Pres & Mng Partner)*

GOLDSBORO MILLING COMPANY

938 Millers Chapel Rd, Goldsboro, NC 27534-7772
Tel.: (919) 778-3130   NC
Web Site: http://www.work4gmc.com
Year Founded: 1916
Sales Range: $200-249.9 Million
Emp.: 875
Processing Plant for Turkeys, Breeders & Hogs
N.A.I.C.S.: 311119
Tom Howell *(Controller)*
James L. Maxwell Jr. *(Chm)*
Hugh G Maxwell III *(Pres)*
Walter Pelletier III *(CEO)*

GOLDSTAR NORTHAMERICAN MINING INC.

4600 E Washington Ste 300, Phoenix, AZ 85034
Tel.: (602) 772-3968
Web Site:
 http://www.goldstarmining.com
Sales Range: $1-9.9 Million
Gold Mining
N.A.I.C.S.: 212220
Craig L. Parkinson *(CEO)*

GOLDSTEIN ENTERPRISES INC.

1754 Central Ave, Albany, NY 12205
Tel.: (518) 869-1250
Web Site:
 http://www.goldsteinauto.com
Sales Range: $50-74.9 Million
Emp.: 240
Automobiles, New & Used
N.A.I.C.S.: 441110
Alan Goldstein *(Pres)*
Tracy Springer *(Controller)*

GOLDSTONE HOSIERY CO. INC.

10 W 33rd St Rm 1016, New York, NY 10001
Tel.: (212) 239-1233
Web Site: http://www.goldenlegs.com
Rev.: $11,444,330
Emp.: 10
Men's & Boys' Hosiery Mfr
N.A.I.C.S.: 424350
Zoltan Goldstein *(Pres)*

GOLETA WATER DISTRICT

4699 Hollister Ave, Santa Barbara, CA 93110
Tel.: (805) 964-6761
Web Site:
 https://www.goletawater.com
Year Founded: 1944
Sales Range: $10-24.9 Million
Emp.: 44
Water Supply
N.A.I.C.S.: 221310
David Matson *(Asst Gen Mgr)*
Ryan Drake *(Mgr-Water Supply-Conservation)*

GOLF & SKI WAREHOUSE INC.

290 Plainfield Rd, West Lebanon, NH 03784
Tel.: (603) 298-8282
Web Site:
 https://www.golfskiwarehouse.com
Year Founded: 1988
Sales Range: $10-24.9 Million
Emp.: 50
Golf Goods & Equipment
N.A.I.C.S.: 459110
Scott Peters *(Pres)*
Steve Ewald *(Controller)*
Ned Waters *(CEO)*

GOLF APPAREL BRANDS, INC.

13301 S Main St, Los Angeles, CA 90061-1611
Tel.: (310) 327-5188   CA
Web Site: http://www.lamode.com
Year Founded: 1977
Sales Range: $10-24.9 Million
Emp.: 20
Men's & Boys' Clothing Mfr
N.A.I.C.S.: 315250
Eddie Kahn *(Owner & Pres)*

GOLF CORPORATION

5233 Hohman Ave, Hammond, IN 46320
Tel.: (219) 937-4653
Rev.: $11,700,000
Emp.: 10
Commercial & Office Buildings, Renovation & Repair
N.A.I.C.S.: 236220
Diane Chakos *(Pres)*

GOLF COURSE MEDIA NETWORK

7380 Sand Lake Rd Ste 500, Orlando, FL 32819

Golf Course Media Network—(Continued)

Web Site:
http://www.golfcoursemedia.com
Rev.: $20,000,000
Emp.: 137
N.A.I.C.S.: 541890
Bill Hanson *(Mgr-Natl Adv)*

GOLF COURSE SUPERINTENDENTS ASSOCIATION OF AMERICA
1421 Research Park Dr, Lawrence, KS 66049
Tel.: (785) 841-2240
Web Site: https://www.gcsaa.org
Year Founded: 1928
Sales Range: $10-24.9 Million
Emp.: 93
Professional Association
N.A.I.C.S.: 813920
J. D. Dockstader *(COO)*
J. Rhett Evans *(CEO)*
Eileen Bangalan *(Sr Dir-Bus Strategy)*
Cameron Oury *(CFO)*
Shari Koehler *(Dir-Pro Dev)*
John J. O'Keefe *(Pres)*

GOLF DISCOUNT OF ST. LOUIS INCORPORATED
4100 Mid Rivers Mall Dr, Manchester, MO 63011
Tel.: (636) 527-3334
Web Site:
http://www.golfdiscountstl.com
Year Founded: 1976
Sales Range: $10-24.9 Million
Emp.: 14
Golf Goods & Equipment
N.A.I.C.S.: 459110
Ned Byron Story *(Pres)*
Richard Helmstetter *(Sr Exec VP-Res)*
Josh Morris *(Coord-Mktg)*
Michael Bernal *(Gen Mgr)*

GOLF ETC. OF AMERICA, INC.
2201 Commercial Ln, Granbury, TX 76048
Tel.: (817) 279-7888
Web Site: http://www.golfetc.com
Year Founded: 1992
Sales Range: $1-9.9 Million
Emp.: 10
Franchisor of Golf Equipment & Accessories Stores
N.A.I.C.S.: 459110
Jeremy Glanzer *(CEO)*

GOLF MART INC.
1408 S Village Way, Santa Ana, CA 92705
Tel.: (714) 834-0430
Web Site: http://www.rdgolf.com
Rev.: $26,333,182
Emp.: 75
Golf Goods & Equipment
N.A.I.C.S.: 459110

GOLF MILL FORD
9401 N Milwaukee Ave, Niles, IL 60714-1209
Tel.: (847) 470-9800
Web Site:
https://www.golfmillford.com
Year Founded: 2005
Sales Range: $25-49.9 Million
Emp.: 102
Car Whslr
N.A.I.C.S.: 441110
Gus Kreatsoulas *(Owner)*
Nick Sfikas *(Gen Mgr-Sls)*
Mario Sosnowski *(Gen Mgr)*

GOLFBALLS.COM, INC.

126 Arnould Blvd, Lafayette, LA 70506
Tel.: (337) 210-4653
Web Site: http://www.golfballs.com
Year Founded: 1995
Sales Range: $10-24.9 Million
Emp.: 40
New, Used & Custom Golf Balls, Golf Clubs & Apparel Online Retailer
N.A.I.C.S.: 459110
Tom Cox *(CEO)*
Johnny Cox *(Dir-Ops)*
Robin Bonin *(Dir-Tech)*
Greg Palmer *(Pres)*

GOLFLAND ENTERTAINMENT CENTERS
155 W Hampton Ave, Mesa, AZ 85210
Tel.: (480) 834-8319
Web Site: https://www.golfland.com
Sales Range: $10-24.9 Million
Emp.: 1,000
Investment Holding Companies, Upgrades Family Entertainment Centers
N.A.I.C.S.: 551112
Mario Arreola *(Mgr-Maintenance)*
Royce Stine *(Controller-Fin)*
Stephen Carlston *(Dir-Projects)*
Corrie Curtis *(Mgr-Ops)*

GOLICK MARTINS INC.
140 Sylvan Ave Ste 7, Englewood Cliffs, NJ 07632-2514
Tel.: (201) 592-8800
Web Site:
http://www.golickmartinsinc.com
Year Founded: 1968
Sales Range: $10-24.9 Million
Emp.: 100
Sales of Groceries
N.A.I.C.S.: 424410
Brian Mallahan *(Acct Mgr)*
Joe Lanzilli *(Exec VP)*
Fran Pizzo *(Acct Mgr)*
Harold Greiner *(Acct Mgr)*
Debbie Greene *(VP)*
Raul Francisco *(Mng Partner)*
Paul O'Donnell *(VP)*

GOLIVE! MOBILE, LLC
10940 S Parker Rd Ste 736, Parker, CO 80134-7440
Tel.: (303) 500-0000
Web Site: http://www.shipito.com
Year Founded: 2006
Sales Range: $25-49.9 Million
Emp.: 102
Cellular Telephone Service & Suppliers
N.A.I.C.S.: 517112
Robert Austine *(Owner)*

GOLLING PONTIAC GMC TRUCK INC.
1491 S Lapeer Rd, Lake Orion, MI 48360
Tel.: (248) 693-5900
Web Site: http://www.bg.com
Sales Range: $10-24.9 Million
Emp.: 200
Sales of New & Used Automobiles
N.A.I.C.S.: 441110
John Cooper *(Gen Mgr)*
A. William Golling III *(Pres)*

GOLUB & CO
625 N Michigan Ave Ste 2000, Chicago, IL 60611-3179
Tel.: (312) 440-8800
Web Site:
http://www.golubandcompany.com
Year Founded: 1960
Sales Range: $75-99.9 Million
Emp.: 55
Real Estate Investment & Development Services

N.A.I.C.S.: 237210
Eugene Golub *(Chm)*
Michael Newman *(Pres, CEO & Principal)*
Lee Golub *(Principal & Exec VP)*
Michael Goldman *(Sr VP-Fin & Acq)*
John Ferguson *(Sr VP-Leasing & Mktg)*
Paula Harris *(Principal & Sr VP)*
Bruce Armstrong *(Sr VP-Dev)*
Adam Short *(VP-Acquisitions)*
Michael Glazier *(Sr VP-Dev)*
Laura Newman *(Asst Mgr-Ops)*
Samantha Patinkin *(Mgr-HR)*
Kristin Nason *(Portfolio Mgr-Residential)*
Mark Segal *(Sr VP)*
Deborah Frank *(Sr VP-Leasing)*
Josh Patinkin *(VP-Capital Resources)*
Sandy Macaluso *(VP-Leasing)*

Subsidiaries:

Golub Realty Services LLC **(1)**
625 N Michigan Ave, Chicago, IL 60611
Tel.: (312) 440-8800
Real Estate Brokerage Services
N.A.I.C.S.: 531390

GOLUB CAPITAL DIRECT LENDING UNLEVERED CORPORATION
200 Park Ave 25th Fl, New York, NY 10166
Tel.: (212) 750-6060
Year Founded: 2021
Rev.: $26,412,000
Assets: $314,078,000
Liabilities: $7,884,000
Net Worth: $306,194,000
Earnings: $24,653,000
Fiscal Year-end: 09/30/24
Asset Management Services
N.A.I.C.S.: 523999

GOLUB CAPITAL, INC.
200 Park Avenue 25th Fl, New York, NY 10166
Tel.: (212) 750-6060
Web Site:
http://www.golubcapital.com
Year Founded: 1994
Sales Range: $25-49.9 Million
Emp.: 500
Privater Equity Firm
N.A.I.C.S.: 523999
David B. Golub *(Vice Chm & Pres)*
Lawrence E. Golub *(CEO)*
Jason J. Van Dussen *(Mng Dir & Head-Capital Markets)*
Frank P. Straub *(CFO & Chief Admin Officer-Chicago)*
Andrew H. Steuerman *(Head-Middle Market Lending & Late Stage Lending)*
Spyro G. Alexopoulos *(Co-Head-Direct Lending)*
Paul Armsby *(Principal-Chicago)*
Gregory W. Cashman *(Co-Head-Direct Lending)*
Nicholas C. Chan *(Principal)*
Peter B. Fair *(Mng Dir)*
Jeffrey C. Gabuzda *(Mng Dir)*
Alissa Grad *(Mng Dir & Co-Head-Investor Partners Grp)*
Patrick W. Hayes *(Mng Dir)*
Richard D. Jacobson *(Mng Dir)*
Gregory A. Robbins *(Mng Dir & Co-Head-Investor Partners Grp)*
Marc C. Robinson *(Mng Dir & Co-Head-Underwriting-Chicago)*
Robert G. Tuchscherer *(Mng Dir & Co-Head-Underwriting-Chicago)*
Ross Van der Linden *(Mng Dir-Bus Dev Grp-Charlotte)*
Josh Haldi *(Dir-Middle Market Lending Team)*

Michael Nebel *(Dir-Middle Market Lending Team)*
Michele D. Joyeux *(Mng Dir-Investor Partners Grp & Head-Bus Dev)*
Hyun J. Chang *(Mng Dir-Middle Market Lending)*
Jon A. Charette *(Mng Dir-Capital Markets)*
Daniel B. Derman *(Mng Dir-Capital Markets)*
Matthew B. Fulk *(Sr Mng Dir & Head-Originations)*
Michael M. Meagher *(Mng Dir-Middle Mktg Lending)*
Christina D. Jamieson *(Mng Dir)*
Craig Benton *(Sr Mng Dir & Head-Investor Partners Grp)*
Joshua M. Levinson *(Chief Compliance Officer & Gen Counsel)*
Chris Born *(Sr VP-Sls & Trading)*
Josh F. Morgan *(Sr VP-Capital Markets)*
Amy Chiang *(Mng Dir-Greater China & Southeast Asia)*

Subsidiaries:

Golub Capital BDC, Inc. **(1)**
200 Park Ave 25th Fl, New York, NY 10166
Tel.: (212) 750-6060
Web Site: https://www.golubcapitalbdc.com
Rev.: $724,677,000
Assets: $8,705,978,000
Liabilities: $4,691,449,000
Net Worth: $4,014,529,000
Earnings: $382,436,000
Fiscal Year-end: 09/30/2024
Investment Services
N.A.I.C.S.: 523999
David B. Golub *(Pres & CEO)*
Lawrence E. Golub *(Chm)*
Gregory A. Robbins *(Mng Dir)*
Matthew W. Benton *(Mng Dir & COO)*
Christopher C. Ericson *(CFO & Treas)*
Joshua M. Levinson *(Chief Compliance Officer & Sec)*
Jon Simmons *(Mng Dir-Strategy)*
Tim Topicz *(Dir)*

Subsidiary (Domestic):

GC SBIC V, L.P. **(2)**
666 5th Ave 18th Fl, New York, NY 10103
Tel.: (212) 750-6060
Investment Management Service
N.A.I.C.S.: 523940

Golub Capital BDC Revolver Funding LLC **(2)**
1011 Centre Rd Ste 200, Wilmington, DE 19805
Tel.: (312) 205-5050
Financial Investment Services
N.A.I.C.S.: 523999

GOLUB CORPORATION
461 Nott St, Schenectady, NY 12308
Tel.: (518) 355-5000
Web Site:
http://www.pricechopper.com
Year Founded: 1932
Sales Range: $5-14.9 Billion
Emp.: 24,500
Retail Grocery Chain
N.A.I.C.S.: 457110
David B. Golub *(VP-Store Ops)*
Neil M. Golub *(Chm)*
Scott Grimmett *(Pres & CEO)*

Subsidiaries:

Golub Service Stations, Inc. **(1)**
501 Duanesburg Rd, Schenectady, NY 12306-1058 **(100%)**
Tel.: (518) 355-5000
Provide Gas & Petroleum; Snack Food Retail Outlet
N.A.I.C.S.: 457120

Price Chopper Golub Corporation **(1)**
461 Nott St, Schenectady, NY 12308 **(100%)**
Tel.: (518) 355-5000

Sales Range: $10-24.9 Million
Emp.: 50
Retail Grocery Stores
N.A.I.C.S.: 445110
Rick Mausert (Dir-Pur)
Mark Brown (Grp VP-Fresh Food Mdsg)
Christine Daniels (VP-Legal Svcs)
Sean Weiss (Dir-Bus Intelligence & Pricing)

Subsidiary (Domestic):

Tops Markets, LLC   (2)
5274 Main & Union, Williamsville, NY 14221
Tel.: (716) 632-7411
Web Site: http://www.topsmarkets.com
Sales Range: $250-299.9 Million
Emp.: 14,000
Supermarket Retailer
N.A.I.C.S.: 445110
Frank Curci (Chm & CEO)

Price Chopper Operating Co. of Mas-
sachusetts, Inc.   (1)
461 Nott St, Schenectady, NY
12308   (100%)
Tel.: (518) 355-5000
Web Site: http://www.pricechopper.com
Retail Grocery Stores
N.A.I.C.S.: 445110
Neil M. Golub (Pres & CEO)

Price Chopper Operating Co.,
Inc.   (1)
1640 Eastern Pkwy, Schenectady, NY
12306   (100%)
Tel.: (518) 355-5000
Web Site: http://www.pricechopper.com
Sales Range: $25-49.9 Million
Emp.: 100
Retail Grocery Stores
N.A.I.C.S.: 445110

Price Chopper Supermarket   (1)
1640 Eastern Pkwy, Schenectady, NY
12309   (100%)
Tel.: (518) 372-6553
Web Site: http://www.pricechopper.com
Distr of Food Products & Services
N.A.I.C.S.: 445110
Ryan C. Hill (VP-Construction & Engrg)
Tracy Nolan (CIO & Sr VP)

GOMEZ CONSTRUCTION COMPANY
7100 SW 44th St, Miami, FL 33155
Tel.: (305) 661-7660
Web Site:
    https://www.gomezconstruction.com
Rev.: $21,000,000
Emp.: 40
Commercial & Office Building, New
Construction
N.A.I.C.S.: 236220
Juan Gomez (CFO)
Orlando J. Gomez Sr. (Pres)

GOMEZ FLOOR COVERING, INC.
3816 Binz Engleman Ste B 125, San
Antonio, TX 78219
Tel.: (210) 651-5002
Web Site: https://www.gomezfc.com
Year Founded: 1996
Rev.: $12,055,871
Emp.: 40
Floor Laying Services
N.A.I.C.S.: 238330
Bobby Coldiron (Project Mgr-Dallas)
Jerry Burrows (Acct Mgr-Dallas)
Jeff Carter (Branch Mgr-Dallas)
Gene Hartley (Controller)
Brian Whitener (Project Mgr-San An-
tonio)
Steve Whitener (CFO)
Linda Gomez-Whitener (Pres)
Americo Garcia (Mgr-Production)
Darinda Dear-Gunnells (Project
Coord-San Antonio)
Jim Walker (Project Mgr-San Antonio)
Mary Jean Garcia (Mgr-Acctg)
Randy Whitener (VP-San Antonio)

ReDonna Mendez (Sr Project Mgr-
San Antonio)
Robert Nocito (Mgr-HR)
Kevin Whitener (VP-Dallas)

GONG'S MARKET OF SANGER INC.
1825 Academy Ave, Sanger, CA
93657
Tel.: (559) 875-5576
Sales Range: $10-24.9 Million
Emp.: 10
Provider of Retail Services
N.A.I.C.S.: 531120

Subsidiaries:

Gong Ventures Inc.   (1)
1825 Academy Ave, Sanger, CA 93657
Tel.: (559) 875-5576
Independent Supermarket
N.A.I.C.S.: 445110

GONGCO FOODS
1115 W Olive Ave, Merced, CA 95348
Tel.: (209) 725-2150
Web Site: http://www.food4less.com
Rev.: $12,200,000
Emp.: 100
Supermarkets, Chain
N.A.I.C.S.: 445110
Joe Gong (Pres)

GONGOS RESEARCH
2365 Pontiac Rd, Auburn Hills, MI
48326
Tel.: (248) 239-2300
Web Site: http://www.gongos.com
Year Founded: 1991
Sales Range: $10-24.9 Million
Emp.: 125
Marketing Research & Public Opinion
Polling
N.A.I.C.S.: 541910
Susan Scarlet (VP-Strategic Brand-
ing)
Camille Nicita (Pres & CEO)
Cheryl Halverson (Chief People Offi-
cer)
Bob Yazbeck (VP-Digital Methods)
Greg Heist (Chief Innovation Officer)
Katherine Ephlin (COO)
Joe Cardador (VP-Decision Sciences)
Jason Solack (VP-Data Sciences
Practice-O2 Integrated)
Crystle Uyeda (VP-Growth Strategy)
Amy Perifanos (VP-Artifact)
Jennifer Yu (Coord-Mktg & Indus En-
gagement)
Paula Sprowl (Sr Dir-Res)
Meaghan Hafner (VP-Health Care)
Megan Cuellar (VP)

GONNELLA BAKING COM-PANY
2361 Palmer Dr, Schaumburg, IL
60173
Tel.: (312) 733-2020   IL
Web Site: http://www.gonnella.com
Year Founded: 1886
Sales Range: $200-249.9 Million
Emp.: 600
French Bread & Rolls
N.A.I.C.S.: 311812

Subsidiaries:

Gonnella Frozen Products   (1)
1117 E Wiley Rd, Schaumburg, IL 60173-
4337
Tel.: (847) 884-8829
Web Site: http://www.gonella.com
Sales Range: $25-49.9 Million
Emp.: 150
Bakery
N.A.I.C.S.: 311812
Ronald Lucchesi (Pres)

GONSALVES & SANTUCCI INC.
5141 Commercial Cir, Concord, CA
94520-8585
Tel.: (925) 685-6799
Web Site:
    http://www.theconcocompanies.com
Year Founded: 1959
Sales Range: $100-124.9 Million
Emp.: 1,500
Industrial Building & Warehouse Con-
tracting Services
N.A.I.C.S.: 236220
Steven Gonsalves (Pres & CEO)
Joe Santucci (VP)
Holly Bertuccelli (CFO)

GONZALES CONSULTING SERVICES, INC.
633 17th St Ste 2600, Denver, CO
80202-3627
Tel.: (303) 383-5500
Web Site: http://www.gcs-usa.com
Sales Range: $10-24.9 Million
Emp.: 11
Certified Public Accountants
N.A.I.C.S.: 541611
Albert C. Gonzales (Pres & CEO)
John Klennert (CFO)
Bruce Roberts (VP)

Subsidiaries:

Tele-Images Inc.   (1)
5690 Dtc Blvd Ste 560 E, Greenwood Vil-
lage, CO 80111
Tel.: (303) 383-5500
Web Site: http://www.gcs-usa.com
Rev.: $100,000
Telecommunications Consultant
N.A.I.C.S.: 541690

GONZALES LABOR SYSTEMS INC.
112 W Randol Mill Rd Ste 100, Ar-
lington, TX 76011
Tel.: (817) 261-5005
Web Site: https://www.glstemps.com
Sales Range: $10-24.9 Million
Emp.: 15
Temporary Help Service
N.A.I.C.S.: 561320
Cecilia Gonzales (Pres)
Dee Cavazos (Mgr-Safety & Risk)

GONZALEZ DESIGN ENGI-NEERING COMPANY INC.
29401 Stephenson Hwy, Madison
Heights, MI 48071-2331
Tel.: (248) 548-6010   MI
Web Site: http://www.gonzalez-
    group.com
Year Founded: 1977
Sales Range: $25-49.9 Million
Emp.: 365
Engineering Services
N.A.I.C.S.: 541330
Gary H. Gonzalez (Pres)

Subsidiaries:

Gonzalez Pico Systems Inc.   (1)
110 Allen Dr, Lake Orion, MI 48359
Tel.: (248) 209-4780
Sales Range: $10-24.9 Million
Emp.: 16
Provider of Building Equipment
N.A.I.C.S.: 333995

Semi-Kinetics Inc.   (1)
20191 Windrow Dr Ste A, Lake Forest, CA
92630-8157
Tel.: (949) 830-7364
Web Site: http://www.semi-kinetics.com
Sales Range: $10-24.9 Million
Emp.: 75
Printed Circuit Boards Mfr
N.A.I.C.S.: 334412
Mike Perdue (VP-Ops & Gen Mgr)

GONZALEZ MANUFACTURING TECHNOLOGIES
2555 Clark St, Detroit, MI 48226
Tel.: (248) 209-4791
Rev.: $23,621,063
Emp.: 75
Boxes For Packing & Shipping, Metal
N.A.I.C.S.: 541330
Eric Baranek (Mgr-Design)

GOOD ADVERTISING, INC.
5100 Poplar Ave Ste 1700, Memphis,
TN 38137
Tel.: (901) 761-0741
Web Site:
    http://www.goodadvertising.com
Year Founded: 1982
Rev.: $10,000,000
Emp.: 25
Business-To-Business, Consumer
Marketing, Public Relations,
Publicity/Promotions, Retail
N.A.I.C.S.: 541810
Dale Cox (Pres)
Barney Street (Exec VP & Controller)
Ellen Isaacman (Exec VP-Creative)
Mary Adams (Mgr-Acctg)
Audra Bloom (Sr Acct Mgr)

GOOD BROTHERS FLOORING PLUS
2217 Sunset Blvd Ste 705, Rocklin,
CA 95765-4782
Tel.: (916) 435-1920
Web Site: https://www.goodbros.com
Flooring Contractors
N.A.I.C.S.: 238330
Tom Good (Owner)

GOOD COMMERCE ACQUISI-TION CORP.
23 La Cuesta Dr, Greenbrae, CA
94904
Tel.: (415) 849-5748   Ky
Year Founded: 2021
Investment Services
N.A.I.C.S.: 523999
Art Peck (Chm & CEO)
Gary Wassner (Vice Chm)
Abinta Malik (Pres)

GOOD COMPANIES
1118 E 223rd St, Carson, CA 90745-
4210
Tel.: (310) 549-2160   CA
Web Site:
    http://www.goodcompanies.com
Year Founded: 1956
Sales Range: $350-399.9 Million
Emp.: 1,000
Occasional Wood Furniture; Tables,
Bookcases & Bedroom Casegoods
N.A.I.C.S.: 337122

Subsidiaries:

Muebles Fino Bueno S.A.   (1)
Blvd San Martin Y Calle La Primera, Pracc
La Ciengla, 22660, Tijuana, BC,
Mexico   (100%)
Tel.: (52) 6646893110
Wood Furniture Mfr
N.A.I.C.S.: 337215

GOOD EARTH, INC.
PO Box 290, Lancaster, NY 14086-
0266
Tel.: (716) 684-8111   NY
Web Site: http://www.goodearth.org
Year Founded: 1958
Sales Range: $100-124.9 Million
Emp.: 150
Products for Lawns & Gardens; Horti-
cultural Products Mfr & Distr
N.A.I.C.S.: 112519
Monika Burkhardt (VP-Marketing)

Good Earth, Inc.—(Continued)

Subsidiaries:

A.H. Hoffman, Inc.   (1)
PO Box 290, Lancaster, NY 14086 **(100%)**
Tel.: (716) 684-8111
Web Site: http://www.ahhoffman.com
Sales Range: $10-24.9 Million
Emp.: 50
Producer of Horticultural Specialty Products
N.A.I.C.S.: 424490
Guenter H. Burkhardt (Pres)
Monika Burkhardt (VP-Mktg)

Good Earth Canada Limited   (1)
459 Escuminac Point Ch, Escuminac, E9A
1V8, NB, Canada
Tel.: (506) 228-3205
Fertilizer Mfr
N.A.I.C.S.: 325314

GOOD FOOD HOLDINGS LLC
915 E 230th St, Carson, CA 90745
Tel.: (310) 233-4700
Web Site:
http://www.goodfoodholdings.com
Holding Company; Food Retailing
Services
N.A.I.C.S.: 551112
Neil Stern (CEO)

Subsidiaries:

New Seasons Market, LLC   (1)
2004 N Vancouver Ave, Portland, OR
97227-1917
Tel.: (503) 230-4949
Web Site:
http://www.newseasonsmarket.com
Discount Department Stores
N.A.I.C.S.: 455110
Howard Vandivner (Mgr-Sea Food)
Kristi McFarland (Pres & Chief Strategy Officer)

GOOD LIFE COMPANIES LLC
2395 Lancaster Pike, Reading, PA
19607
Tel.: (610) 898-6927   PA
Web Site: http://www.goodlifeco.com
Year Founded: 2012
Sales Range: $10-24.9 Million
Emp.: 58
Financial Advisory Services
N.A.I.C.S.: 523940
Conor Delaney (Co-Founder & CEO)
Courtnie Nein (Co-Founder & Pres)
Aelish Brooks (Dir-HR & Controller)
Kelsey Fox (Coord-HR)
Louise Ludwig (Coord-Community
Outreach)

GOOD NEWS PEST SOLUTIONS
1080 Enterprise Ct Ste A, North Venice, FL 34275
Tel.: (941) 412-9610
Web Site:
https://www.goodnewspestsolutions.com
Year Founded: 1989
Sales Range: $1-9.9 Million
Emp.: 40
Exterminating & Pest Control Services
N.A.I.C.S.: 561710
Dean Burnside (Owner, Pres & CEO)
Deborah Adams (Controller)
Matt Van Landuyt (Mgr-Svc)
John Macy (Founder & Dir-Relationships)

GOOD NEWS PUBLISHERS
1300 Crescent St, Wheaton, IL 60187
Tel.: (630) 682-4300   IL
Year Founded: 1938
Sales Range: $10-24.9 Million
Emp.: 103
Religious Organizations
N.A.I.C.S.: 813110

Raymond Elliott (Exec Dir-Media Architecture)
Randall D. Jahns (Sr VP-Bible Rels)
Dallas Richards (Dir-Bible Production)
Dane Ortlund (Sr VP-Bible Publ)
Justin Taylor (Sr VP-Book Publ)
Josh Dennis (VP-Design Svcs)
James Fellowes (Treas)
Allan Fisher (Mgr-Bible Licensing)
Dan Kok (Sr VP-Ops)
Paul Thomas (Sr VP-Fin)
M. Ebeth Dennis (Sr VP-Publ Min)
Lane T. Dennis (Pres)
James Kinnard (Dir-Mktg)
Mark Hendrie (Dir-IT)
Geoffrey L. Dennis (COO, Sec & Exec VP)

GOOD OIL CO. INC.
1201 N United States Hwy 35,
Winamac, IN 46996
Tel.: (574) 946-4863
Web Site:
http://www.goodoilcompany.com
Sales Range: $25-49.9 Million
Emp.: 150
Petroleum Bulk Stations
N.A.I.C.S.: 424710
Don A. Good (Pres)
Laurie Henry (Brand Mgr)

GOOD OLD DAYS FOODS, INC.
3300 S Polk St, Little Rock, AR
72204
Tel.: (501) 565-1257
Web Site:
https://www.goodolddaysfoods.com
Year Founded: 1975
Sales Range: $10-24.9 Million
Emp.: 75
Ice Cream & Frozen Desserts Production
N.A.I.C.S.: 311520
Carroll Elder (Chm & CEO)
John Zachariason (CFO)
Mel Whitney (Reg Mgr)

GOOD SHEPHERD HEALTH CARE SYSTEM
610 NW 11th St, Hermiston, OR
97838
Tel.: (541) 667-3400   OR
Web Site: https://www.gshealth.org
Year Founded: 1953
Sales Range: $75-99.9 Million
Emp.: 607
Health Care Srvices
N.A.I.C.S.: 622110
Theresa L. Brock (VP-Nursing)
Kelly B. Sanders (VP-HR)
Dennis E. Burke (Pres & CEO)
Steve Eldrige (Chm)
Derek Earl (Sec)
Tom Wamsley (Treas)
Nancy Mabry (Vice Chm)
Jim Schlenker (COO)
Nick Bejarano (Dir-Mktg & Comm)
Jan D. Peter (CFO & VP-Fiscal Svcs)

GOOD SHEPHERD SERVICES
305 7th Ave Fl 9, New York, NY
10001
Tel.: (212) 243-7070   NY
Web Site:
https://www.goodshepherds.org
Year Founded: 1947
Sales Range: $50-74.9 Million
Emp.: 2,927
Community Action Services
N.A.I.C.S.: 624190
Paulette LoMonaco (Exec Dir)
Greghan Fischer (CFO)
Michele Wyman (Pres & CEO)

GOOD SOLUTIONS GROUP

456 E Orange Grove Blvd Suite 302,
Pasadena, CA 91104
Tel.: (626) 229-9991
Web Site:
http://www.goodsolutionsgroup.com
Year Founded: 2003
Sales Range: $1-9.9 Million
Emp.: 10
Marketing Programs for Corporate
Clients & Brands
N.A.I.C.S.: 541613
Shari Boyer (CEO)
Christopher Boyer (COO)
Emily Eisenberg (Dir-Product)

GOOD SPORTSMAN MARKETING, LLC
5250 Frye Rd, Irving, TX 75061
Tel.: (877) 269-8490   DE
Web Site:
http://www.gsmoutdoors.com
Outdoor Consumer Products Mfr &
Marketer
N.A.I.C.S.: 423990
Eddie Castro (CEO)
Ben Smith (Sr VP-Sls & Mktg)

Subsidiaries:

TRUGLO, Inc.   (1)
710 Presidential Dr, Richardson, TX 75081
Tel.: (972) 774-0300
Web Site: http://truglo.com
Sales Range: $1-9.9 Million
Emp.: 45
Archery & Firearm Products Distr
N.A.I.C.S.: 423990
Paul Lorocco (Pres)
Aaron Dusek (Mgr-Sls-Natl)

GOOD TIRE SERVICE INC.
401 S Water St, Kittanning, PA 16201
Tel.: (724) 543-2010
Web Site: https://www.goodtire.com
Sales Range: $10-24.9 Million
Emp.: 110
Automotive Tires
N.A.I.C.S.: 441340
Denton J. Good (Pres)

GOOD TRANSPORT SERVICES, INC.
4668 Breezyview Rd, Columbia, PA
17512
Tel.: (717) 684-2228
Year Founded: 1943
Sales Range: $10-24.9 Million
Emp.: 50
Freight Trucking Services
N.A.I.C.S.: 484121
Daniel F. Good (Sec & VP)
Lester F. Good (Pres)

GOOD WHEELS AUTOMOTIVE GROUP LLC
2824 Elkhart Rd, Goshen, IN 46526
Tel.: (574) 534-2521
Sales Range: $10-24.9 Million
Emp.: 49
New Car Dealers
N.A.I.C.S.: 441110
Chad Lochmandy (VP & Dir)
Kirk Lochmandy (Pres)

GOOD WILL PUBLISHERS INC.
1520 S York Rd, Gastonia, NC 28053
Tel.: (704) 865-1256
Web Site:
https://www.goodwillpublishers.com
Sales Range: Less than $1 Million
Emp.: 150
Provider of Publishing Services
N.A.I.C.S.: 513130
Daniel Bartlett (VP)
Joe Bentley (VP)
William Schiffiano (Pres-Community
Svcs of America)

GOOD-NITE INN INC.
11500 W Olympic Blvd #345, Los Angeles, CA 90064
Tel.: (310) 235-2745
Web Site: http://www.goodnite.com
Rev.: $20,159,335
Emp.: 10
Hotel
N.A.I.C.S.: 721110
Phillip Ho (Pres)
Nicholas Contreras (Mgr-Ops)
Sergio Luna (Asst Mgr)
Tamara Upshaw (Gen Mgr)
Patrick Kataoka (Treas)

GOOD360
675 N Washington St Ste 330, Alexandria, VA 22314
Tel.: (703) 836-2121   VA
Web Site: https://www.good360.org
Year Founded: 1984
Sales Range: $300-349.9 Million
Emp.: 45
Other Grantmaking & Giving Services
N.A.I.C.S.: 813219
Richard Barney (Exec VP-Bus Dev)
Jason Boon (Dir-Logistics)
Vicki Dorsey (Mgr-Admin & HR)
Michael Avis (CFO & CAO)
Mikel Durham (Vice Chm)
Shabab Gruberg (Pres)
Kathleen Coartney (Mgr-Production &
Ops)
Monica Erwin (Mgr-Nonprofit Programs)
Howard Sherman (CEO)
Shari Rudolph (CMO)
John Grugan (Chm)

GOODALL MFG. LLC
7558 Washington Ave S, Eden Prairie, MN 55344-3705
Tel.: (952) 941-6666
Web Site: http://www.goodallmfg.com
Year Founded: 1939
Sales Range: $400-449.9 Million
Emp.: 26
Motor Vehicle Electrical & Electronic
Equipment Mfr
N.A.I.C.S.: 336320
Kate Karja (Mgr-HR)

GOODBEE AND ASSOCIATES, INC.
13909 E Maplewood Pl, Centennial,
CO 80111
Tel.: (303) 765-2634
Web Site:
http://www.goodbeeassoc.com
Year Founded: 1994
Sales Range: $10-24.9 Million
Emp.: 15
Technical Consulting Services
N.A.I.C.S.: 541690
Lisa A. Goodbee (Pres & Principal)
Elissa T. Roselyn (Sr Project Mgr)

GOODBERRY CREAMERY INC.
PO Box 58307, Raleigh, NC 27658
Tel.: (919) 878-8870
Web Site: http://www.goodberrys.com
Rev.: $11,700,000
Emp.: 10
Frozen Custard; Retail
N.A.I.C.S.: 311520
Harry Brathwaite (Pres)

GOODDATA CORPORATION
660 3rd St, San Francisco, CA 94107
Tel.: (415) 200-0186
Web Site: http://www.gooddata.com
Year Founded: 2007
Sales Range: $25-49.9 Million
Emp.: 15
Computer Related & Data Processing
Services

N.A.I.C.S.: 541519
Roman Stanek (Founder & CEO)
Zdenek Svoboda (VP-Platform)
Radovan Janecek (Sr VP)
Blaine Mathieu (CMO)
James Smith (CMO)
Garry Olah (Sr VP-Bus Dev)
Ryan Snyder (Chief Customer Officer)

Subsidiaries:

GoodData Pty Ltd   (1)
Suite 12 Level 1 857-859 Doncaster Rd,
Doncaster, 3109, VIC, Australia
Tel.: (61) 3 9026 0850
Web Site: http://www.gooddata.com
Computer Related & Data Processing Services
N.A.I.C.S.: 541519

GOODE COMPANIES, INC.
6305 Ivy Ln Ste 720, Greenbelt, MD 20770
Tel.: (301) 486-7501
Web Site:
    http://www.goodecompanies.com
Year Founded: 1991
Sales Range: $10-24.9 Million
Emp.: 100
Trash Removal & Recycling Collection Services
N.A.I.C.S.: 562111
Willie K. Goode (Pres)

GOODE PARTNERS, LLC
767 3rd Ave 22nd Fl, New York, NY 10017
Tel.: (646) 722-9450
Web Site:
    https://www.goodepartners.com
Year Founded: 2005
Sales Range: $1-9.9 Million
Emp.: 11
Investment Advisory Services
N.A.I.C.S.: 523940
Paula G. Semelmacher (CFO)
Michael Stanley (Principal)
Daniel Bonoff (Partner)
David Oddi (Partner)
Joe Ferreira (Partner)
Keith Miller (Partner)
Reyna Posada (Office Mgr)
Andres Rodriguez (Controller)

Subsidiaries:

Forman Mills, Inc.   (1)
1070 Thomas Busch Memorial Hwy, Pennsauken, NJ 08110-2313
Tel.: (856) 486-1447
Web Site: http://www.formanmills.com
Miscellaneous Apparel & Accessory Sales
N.A.I.C.S.: 458110
Scott Sanford (Dir-Loss Prevention)

Stonefire Grill Inc.   (1)
5655 Lindero Canyon Rd Ste 204, Westlake Village, CA 91362-4044
Tel.: (818) 991-4054
Web Site: http://www.stonefiregrill.com
Emp.: 100
Limited-Service Restaurants
N.A.I.C.S.: 722513
Patti Monson (Gen Mgr)
Mary Harrigan (Co-Founder)
Kaduri Shemtov (Co-Founder)

GOODE-COOK INC.
2422 Bartlett St, Houston, TX 77098
Tel.: (713) 529-4616
Web Site:
    https://www.goodecompany.com
Year Founded: 1977
Rev.: $16,886,248
Emp.: 20
Barbecue Restaurant
N.A.I.C.S.: 722511
James D. Goode (Pres)

GOODFELLOW BROS., INC.

1407 Walla Walla Ave, Wenatchee, WA 98801-1530
Tel.: (509) 662-7111   WA
Web Site:
    http://www.goodfellowbros.com
Year Founded: 1923
Sales Range: $50-74.9 Million
Emp.: 300
Highway & Street Construction
N.A.I.C.S.: 237310
Chad S. Goodfellow (CEO)
Dan Goodfellow (VP)
Bo McKuin (Reg Mgr)

Subsidiaries:

Top Grade Construction, Inc.   (1)
50 Contractors St, Livermore, CA 94551
Tel.: (925) 449-5764
Web Site:
    http://www.topgradeconstruction.com
Sales Range: $10-24.9 Million
Emp.: 80
Construction Services
N.A.I.C.S.: 237990
Brian Gates (Exec VP & Gen Mgr)
John Copriviza (VP-Estimating)
Frank Williams (VP-Field Ops)

GOODGUYS TIRE CENTERS INC.
6770 N Blackstone Ave, Fresno, CA 93710
Tel.: (559) 498-7705
Web Site: https://www.goodguys-tire.com
Sales Range: $50-74.9 Million
Emp.: 83
Automotive Tires
N.A.I.C.S.: 441340
Scott Shubin (Gen Mgr)

GOODHART NATIONAL GORMAN AGENCY, INC.
598 Tuckahoe Rd, Yonkers, NY 10710
Tel.: (914) 779-0500
Year Founded: 1904
Sales Range: $10-24.9 Million
Emp.: 20
Insurance Agency & Brokerage Services
N.A.I.C.S.: 524210
Michael Berr (CEO)
Patricia Carpanzano (Pres & COO)
Donna Boonjamalik (Asst VP)
Dana Lehane (Supvr-Claims)

GOODHUE HAWKINS NAVY YARD, LLC
244 Sewall Rd, Wolfeboro, NH 03894
Tel.: (603) 569-2371   NH
Web Site:
    http://www.goodhueandhawkins.com
Year Founded: 1903
Sales Range: $10-24.9 Million
Emp.: 20
Dealers of Boats
N.A.I.C.S.: 441222
Cameron Pratt (Owner)

GOODIES FROM GOODMAN, INC.
11390 Grissom Ln, Dallas, TX 75229-2350
Tel.: (972) 484-3236
Web Site:
    http://www.goodiesfromgoodman.com
Year Founded: 1916
Sales Range: $10-24.9 Million
Emp.: 6
Provider of Catalog Mail Order Specialty Goods & Gifts
N.A.I.C.S.: 722320
Bobby Goodman (CEO)
Charles Goodman (Pres)

GOODIN COMPANY
2700 2nd St N, Minneapolis, MN 55411-1602
Tel.: (612) 588-7811   MN
Web Site: https://www.goodinco.com
Year Founded: 1937
Sales Range: $75-99.9 Million
Emp.: 100
Provider of Plumbing Supplies
N.A.I.C.S.: 423720
Greg Skagerberg (Chm & CEO)
Steve Kelly (Pres)
Brian Sand (Treas)
Bruce Oelfke (Branch Mgr)
Lance Cole (Mgr-Heating Div-Minneapolis)
Mylo Gustafson (Mgr-Credit)
Jim VanVoorhis (Mgr-St. Cloud)
Brian Ashland (Mgr-Eau Claire)
Ken Wickre (Branch Mgr)
Mike Grunklee (Treas & Controller)

GOODING & COMPANY, INC.
1517 20th St, Santa Monica, CA 90404
Tel.: (310) 899-1960
Web Site:
    https://www.goodingco.com
Car Auctions
N.A.I.C.S.: 441227
David Gooding (Pres & CEO)
Morgan Carter (CFO & VP)
Dawn Ahrens (Dir-Mktg)

GOODMAN FAMILY OF BUILDERS
5808 W Plano Pkwy, Plano, TX 75093-4636
Tel.: (469) 737-1400   TX
Web Site: http://www.khov.com
Year Founded: 1979
Sales Range: $100-124.9 Million
Emp.: 171
Single-Family Housing Construction
N.A.I.C.S.: 236115
Jimmy Brownley (Gen Mgr)

GOODMAN FOOD PRODUCTS INC.
200 E Beach Ave, Inglewood, CA 90302
Tel.: (310) 674-3180
Web Site:
    http://www.donleefarms.com
Rev.: $23,200,000
Emp.: 200
Frozen Specialties
N.A.I.C.S.: 311412
Donald Goodman (Pres & CEO)

GOODMAN NETWORKS, INC.
2801 Network Blvd Ste 300, Frisco, TX 75034
Tel.: (972) 406-9692   TX
Web Site:
    http://www.goodmannetworks.com
Year Founded: 2000
Sales Range: $700-749.9 Million
Emp.: 3,400
Telecommunication Network Design & Installation Services
N.A.I.C.S.: 517810
Jason A. Goodman (Pres & COO-Field Svcs)
Ajay Ramaswami (Exec VP-Infrastructure Svcs)
Caren Gates (Exec VP-Infrastructure Svcs-East Reg)
Anthony J. Rao (Gen Counsel & Exec VP)

Subsidiaries:

Multiband Corporation   (1)
5605 Green Circle Dr, Minnetonka, MN 55343
Tel.: (763) 504-3060

Web Site: http://www.multibandusa.com
Rev.: $305,624,000
Assets: $140,474,000
Liabilities: $93,801,000
Net Worth: $46,673,000
Earnings: $2,606,000
Emp.: 4,069
Fiscal Year-end: 12/31/2012
Video, Data & Voice Systems Services
N.A.I.C.S.: 517121
Steven M. Bell (CFO & Gen Counsel)

Subsidiary (Domestic):

Multiband NC Inc.   (2)
801 Industrial Ave, Mount Pleasant, MI 48858-4645   (80%)
Tel.: (989) 317-4861
Sales Range: $10-24.9 Million
Emp.: 32
Antennas & Satellite Dish Retailer & Installer
N.A.I.C.S.: 449210

GOODMAN TRUCK & TRACTOR COMPANY, INC.
17020 Patrick Henry Hwy, Amelia, VA 23002
Tel.: (804) 561-2141
Web Site:
    https://www.goodmantruck.com
Year Founded: 1951
Sales Range: $10-24.9 Million
Emp.: 46
New Car Dealers
N.A.I.C.S.: 441110
Clem Goodman (Mgr-Sls)
Chad Vaughn (Dir-Svc)
Dwayne Lenhart (Mgr)
Adam Russell (Mgr-Parts)

GOODMANS, INC.
1400 E Indian School Rd, Phoenix, AZ 85014-4928
Tel.: (602) 263-1110   AZ
Web Site:
    https://www.goodmans.com
Year Founded: 1953
Sales Range: $125-149.9 Million
Emp.: 300
Office Furniture Whslr
N.A.I.C.S.: 423210
Adam Goodman (Pres & CEO)
Allison Van Dyke (Dir-Mktg)
Brian Turner (Dir-HR)
Clarke Rea (CFO)
Jeff Kiewel (Gen Mgr)
Stuart Hamilton (Gen Mgr)

Subsidiaries:

Goodmans Interior Structures   (1)
3925 N Business Center Dr, Tucson, AZ 85705-2981   (100%)
Tel.: (520) 888-1117
Web Site: http://www.goodmans.info
Sales Range: $10-24.9 Million
Emp.: 30
Selling Office Furniture
N.A.I.C.S.: 449110
Adam Goodman (Pres & CEO)
Jen Scrivner (COO)
Jeff Kiewel (Dir-Corp Accts)
Clarke Rea (CFO)
Jacqui Sabo (VP-Sls)
Steve Miller (CIO)
Brian Turner (Dir-HR)
Allison Van Dyke (Dir-Mktg)

Goodmans Office Furniture   (1)
4860 Pan American Freeway NE, Albuquerque, NM 87109
Tel.: (505) 889-0195
Web Site: http://www.goodmansinc.com
Sales Range: $10-24.9 Million
Emp.: 25
Showroom Sales of Office Furniture
N.A.I.C.S.: 449110
Adam Goodman (Pres & CEO)
Jeff Kiewel (Gen Mgr-Tucson)
Steve Miller (CIO)
Clarke Rea (CFO)
Jen Scrivner (COO)
Brian Turner (Dir-HR)
Allison Van Dyke (VP-Mktg)

Goodmans, Inc.—(Continued)

Goodmans Office Furniture (1)
1400 E Indian School Rd, Phoenix, AZ
85014-4928
Tel.: (602) 263-1110
Web Site: http://www.goodmans.info.com
Sales Range: $10-24.9 Million
Emp.: 100
N.A.I.C.S.: 449110
Murray Goodman (Owner)

Workspace Dynamics, Inc. (1)
4711 Lomas Blvd NE, Albuquerque, NM
87110
Tel.: (505) 254-2000
Web Site: http://www.wsdnm.com
Furniture Retailer
N.A.I.C.S.: 449110
Mary Escobar (Principal)
Mike McCory (Mgr-Ops)
Mary Jury (Founder)

GOODNESS GREENESS
5959 S Lowe Ave, Chicago, IL 60621
Tel.: (773) 224-4411
Web Site:
http://www.goodnessgreeness.com
Year Founded: 1991
Sales Range: $10-24.9 Million
Emp.: 50
Fresh Fruit & Vegetable Production
Services
N.A.I.C.S.: 111419

**GOODNIGHT BROTHERS
PRODUCE CO., INC.**
372 Industrial Park Dr, Boone, NC
28607
Tel.: (828) 264-8892
Web Site:
https://www.goodnightbrothers.com
Year Founded: 1948
Sales Range: $10-24.9 Million
Emp.: 120
Meat Product Whslr
N.A.I.C.S.: 424470
Tony Snow (Mgr-Sls)

**GOODNIGHT INTERNATIONAL,
LLC**
5160 William Mills St, Jacksonville,
FL 32226
Tel.: (904) 757-2260
Web Site:
http://www.goodnightintl.com
Year Founded: 2002
Freight Transportation Services
N.A.I.C.S.: 488510
Mary J. Mackey (Pres)
Gary MacKey (COO)

**GOODRICH RADIO AND THE-
ATERS INC.**
4417 Broadmoor Ave SE, Grand
Rapids, MI 49512-5367
Tel.: (616) 698-7733   MI
Web Site: http://www.gqti.com
Year Founded: 1960
Sales Range: $75-99.9 Million
Emp.: 1,200
Motion Picture Theater
N.A.I.C.S.: 512131
Robert Emmett Goodrich (Pres &
Sec)
Ross Pettinga (CFO & Treas)
Sue Howard (Controller)

Subsidiaries:

Goodrich Quality Theaters Inc. (1)
4417 Broadmoor Ave SE, Grand Rapids, MI
49512-5367
Tel.: (616) 698-7733
Web Site: http://www.gqti.com
Sales Range: $10-24.9 Million
Emp.: 40
Provider of Motion Picture Services
N.A.I.C.S.: 512131

Robert Goodrich (Pres)
Tom McCall (Mgr-Acctg)
Patricia Lintner (Mgr-HR)

Goodrich Radio Marketing Inc. (1)
4417 Broadmoor Ave SE, Grand Rapids, MI
49512-5367
Tel.: (616) 698-7733
Sales Range: $10-24.9 Million
Emp.: 17
Provider of Radio Broadcasting Services
N.A.I.C.S.: 516110
Robert Goodrich (Owner)

**GOODS FURNITURE HOUSE
INC.**
200 N Main St, Kewanee, IL 61443
Tel.: (309) 937-5656
Web Site:
https://www.goodsfurniture.com
Rev.: $20,000,000
Emp.: 90
Furniture Retailer
N.A.I.C.S.: 449110
Phil Good (CEO)

**GOODSONS SUPERMARKETS
INC.**
US Rte 52, Welch, WV 24801
Tel.: (304) 436-8481
Rev.: $21,579,123
Emp.: 60
Provider of Grocery Services
N.A.I.C.S.: 445110
W. M. Goodson (Pres)

GOODSUITE
21109 Oxnard St, Woodland Hills, CA
91367
Tel.: (818) 874-1200   CA
Web Site: https://www.goodsuite.com
Year Founded: 1999
Miscellaneous Retail Stores
N.A.I.C.S.: 459999
Chris Strull (Founder & CEO)
Christianne Strull (CFO)
Dan Strull (CEO)

Subsidiaries:

Select Business Systems, Inc. (1)
7560 N Del Mar Ave, Fresno, CA 93711
Tel.: (559) 446-0123
Web Site: http://selectbusinesssystems.com
Office Equipment
N.A.I.C.S.: 423420
Todd Mumma (Pres)

Strata Information Technology
Inc. (1)
17328 Ventura Blvd Ste 336, Encino, CA
91316-3904
Tel.: (818) 321-0854
Web Site: http://www.stratait.com
Technology Consulting Firm
N.A.I.C.S.: 541513
Keith Stark (Pres)

**GOODWAY GRAPHICS OF VA
INC.**
6628 Electronic Dr, Springfield, VA
22151
Tel.: (703) 941-1160
Year Founded: 1963
Rev.: $18,600,000
Emp.: 180
Commercial Printing, Lithographic
N.A.I.C.S.: 323111

**GOODWAY TECHNOLOGIES
CORPORATION**
420 W Ave, Stamford, CT 06902-
6384
Tel.: (203) 359-4708   CT
Web Site: https://www.goodway.com
Year Founded: 1966
Sales Range: $10-24.9 Million
Emp.: 65

Tube Cleaning Systems, Pressure
Washers, Drain Cleaners, Vacuums,
Floor Machines & Duct Cleaning Sys-
tems Mfr
N.A.I.C.S.: 333310
Timothy J. Kane (Pres)
Timothy Robb (Dir-Mktg & Strategic
Bus Dev)
Frank Intrieri Jr. (VP-Sls)

**GOODWILL INDUSTRIES IN-
TERNATIONAL, INC.**
15810 Indianola Dr, Rockville, MD
20855
Tel.: (301) 530-6500   MA
Web Site: http://www.goodwill.org
Year Founded: 1902
Sales Range: $1-4.9 Billion
Emp.: 82,300
Used Merchandise Retailer; Voca-
tional Rehabilitation Services
N.A.I.C.S.: 455219
Marla Jackson (CFO)
Steve Lufburrow (Pres/CEO-Houston)
Katy Gaul-Stigge (Pres/CEO-Greater
New York & Northern New Jersey)
Dale Jenkins (Chm)
Steven C. Preston (Pres & CEO)
David Eagles (COO)
Doug Newsome (VP-Admin-Middle
Georgia & CSRA)
Dru Rai (CIO)
Onney Crawley (CMO)
Audrey D. Hollingsworth (VP-People
Svcs)

Subsidiaries:

Goodwill Industries of Central Indi-
ana, Inc. (1)
1635 W Michigan St, Indianapolis, IN 46222
Tel.: (317) 524-4313
Non-Profit Charity Services
N.A.I.C.S.: 561990
Kyle Lanham (Chief Advancement Officer &
VP-Community Engagement)
Jay Lytle (CIO)

Goodwill Industries of the Valleys,
Inc. (1)
2502 Melrose Ave NW Ste A, Roanoke, VA
24017
Tel.: (540) 581-0620
Web Site: http://www.goodwillvalleys.com
Disabled People Employment Services
N.A.I.C.S.: 561311
Jackson Green (COO)
Phil Jones (Sr VP-Admin)
Steven Kelley (CFO)
Frank Rogan (Chief Dev Officer)
Kelly Sandridge (VP-Mktg)
Deb Saunders (Chief Compliance Officer)
Richmond Vincent Jr. (Pres & CEO)
Robert Jeffrey Jr. (Chm)

Goodwill Keystone Area, Inc. (1)
1150 Goodwill Dr, Harrisburg, PA 17101
Tel.: (717) 232-1831
Web Site: http://www.yourgoodwill.org
Disabled People Employment Services
N.A.I.C.S.: 561311
Harris Booker (Chm)
Richard W. Conley (Vice Chm)
James Perano (Vice Chm)
John McHenry (Pres & CEO)

Tacoma Goodwill Industries, Inc. (1)
714 S 27th St, Tacoma, WA 98409
Tel.: (253) 573-6500
Web Site: http://www.goodwillwa.org
Sales Range: $100-124.9 Million
Emp.: 1,500
Placement Support Services
N.A.I.C.S.: 561311
Terry A. Hayes (CEO)
C. W. Herchold (Chm)
Judy Swain (Sec)
Scott Waner (Treas)

**GOODWILL INDUSTRIES OF
KANAWHA VALLEY, INC.**
209 Virginia St W, Charleston, WV
25302

Tel.: (304) 346-0811   WV
Web Site: http://www.goodwillkv.com
Year Founded: 1950
Sales Range: $1-9.9 Million
Emp.: 336
Vocational Rehabilitation Services
N.A.I.C.S.: 624310
Cheryl Bever (Pres & CEO)
John Taylor (Dir-Mission Svcs)

Subsidiaries:

Sw Resources, Inc. (1)
1007 Mary St, Parkersburg, WV 26101
Tel.: (304) 428-6344
Web Site: http://www.swresources.com
Sales Range: $1-9.9 Million
Emp.: 200
Vocational Rehabilitation Services
N.A.I.C.S.: 624310
Gloria Cox (Pres & CEO)

**GOODWILL INDUSTRIES-
MANASOTA, INC.**
7501 15th St E, Sarasota, FL 34243
Tel.: (941) 355-2721
Web Site:
http://www.discovergoodwill.com
Sales Range: $25-49.9 Million
Emp.: 1,000
Charitable Organization; Used Mer-
chandise Retailer
N.A.I.C.S.: 813319
Adrian Gessen (VP-HR & Risk Mgmt)
Ray Couch (VP-Real Estate & Market
Dev)
Deborah Vaughn (Mgr-Risk Mgmt &
Safety)
Dave Wells (VP-OD)
Veronica Brandon Miller (VP-
Foundation)
Margie Genter (VP-Mission Svcs)
Amy Confer (VP-Support Svcs)
Bill Thielen (Dir-Risk Mgmt)

**GOODWILL INDUSTRIES-
SUNCOAST, INC.**
10596 Gandy Blvd, Saint Petersburg,
FL 33702
Tel.: (727) 523-1512
Web Site: https://www.goodwill-
suncoast.org
Year Founded: 1954
Sales Range: $50-74.9 Million
Emp.: 1,362
Nonprofit Organization; Used Mer-
chandise Store Operator; Housing &
Workforce Placement Services
N.A.I.C.S.: 813410
R. Lee Waits (Pres)
Lee C. Zeh (Sec & VP-Bd Dev)
Gary Hebert (CFO & Treas)
Deborah A. Passerini (Pres)
Jacqueline R. Miller (VP-HR)
James Williams (VP-Fund Dev)
Stefanie Anna (VP-Corp Affairs &
Governance)
Heather Ceresoli (Chm)
Carole Philipson (Sec)
Allen Starr (CIO & VP-IT)
Paul M. Norris (VP-Corrections &
Housing)
Kris Rawson (VP-Workforce Dev)

**GOODWILL OF GREATER
WASHINGTON**
2200 S Dakota Ave NE, Washington,
DC 20018
Tel.: (202) 636-4225
Web Site: http://www.dcgoodwill.org
Sales Range: $25-49.9 Million
Emp.: 500
Surplus & Salvage Store Operator
N.A.I.C.S.: 455219
Michael Frohm (COO)
Catherine Meloy (Pres & CEO)

Dave Sullivan (VP-Donations & Retail Sls)
Rosa Proctor (CFO)
Jeff Cole (CIO)

GOODWILL OF NORTH FLORIDA
4527 Lenox Ave, Jacksonville, FL 32205
Tel.: (904) 384-1361
Web Site: https://www.goodwilljax.org
Sales Range: $25-49.9 Million
Emp.: 400
Clothing, Secondhand
N.A.I.C.S.: 459510
Robert H. Thayer (CEO)
Dolly Sedwick (VP-Contracts)
Jim Wadsworth (COO)
Karen L. Phillips (VP-Mktg & Admin)

GOODWILL RETIREMENT COMMUNITY
891 Dorsey Hotel Rd, Grantsville, MD 21536
Tel.: (301) 895-5194   MD
Web Site:
   https://www.goodwillhome.org
Year Founded: 1958
Sales Range: $10-24.9 Million
Emp.: 227
Continuing Care Retirement Community Operator
N.A.I.C.S.: 623311
Gary Bunnell (Dir-Environmental Svcs)
Patricia Knopsnyder (Dir-Activities)
Linda Bender (Dir-Dietary Svcs)

GOODWIN AMMONIA COMPANY
12102 Industry St, Garden Grove, CA 92841
Tel.: (714) 894-0531
Web Site:
   https://www.goodwininc.com
Sales Range: $10-24.9 Million
Emp.: 15
Polishes & Sanitation Goods
N.A.I.C.S.: 325612
Tom Goodwin (Pres)

GOODWIN PROCTER LLP
100 Northern Ave, Boston, MA 02210
Tel.: (617) 570-1000   MA
Web Site:
   https://www.goodwinlaw.com
Year Founded: 1912
Sales Range: $75-99.9 Million
Emp.: 2,000
Law Firm
N.A.I.C.S.: 541110
Regina M. Pisa (Partner)
Dean C. Pappas (Partner)
Mark J. Abate (Partner)
Karen L. Febeo (Mng Dir-Pro Dev & Trng)
Carolyn D. Rosenthal (Sr Mgr-Pro Bono)
Anne M. Stemlar (Mng Dir-Res & Knowledge Mgmt)
Michael D. Maline (Partner)
Heidi Goldstein Shepherd (Chief HR Officer)
Matthew S. Sheldon (Partner)
Paul J. Delligatti (Partner)
Lynda T. Galligan (Chm-Silicon Valley & Partner)
Brenda R. Sharton (Chm-Bus Litigation & Partner)
Robert E. Puopolo (Partner)
Michael R. Caplan (COO)
Adam P. Small (Partner)
Adam Slutsky (Partner)
Joseph P. Rockers (Partner)
David H. Roberts (Partner)
James L. Donohue (Partner)

Yvonne W. Chan (Partner)
Shane Brun (Partner)
Natascha S. George (Partner)
Brett M. Schuman (Partner)
Andrew H. Goodman (Partner)
Jay Schifferli (Partner)
Marcia H. Sundeen (Partner)
Chauncey M. Swalwell (Partner)
Richard Lever (Partner)
James T. Barrett (Partner-Private Equity Grp)
Simon Fulbrook (Partner-London)
Fredrich N. Lim (Partner-Private Equity Grp-San Francisco)
Jeffrey A. Simes (Chm-Litigation Dept & Partner)
Lucianna Aquino-Hagedorn (Partner)
Elizabeth Roberts (Partner)
Koray J. Bulut (Partner-Labor & Employment Grp-San Francisco)
Michael S. Russell (Partner)
Heiko Penndorf (Partner-Tax-Frankfurt)
Alessandra K. Murata (Partner)
Konstantin A. Shishkin (Chief Comm Officer)
Veronica McGregor (Partner-Fin Indus & Fin Tech Practices-San Francisco)
Brian Burgess (Partner)
David Fleming (CIO)
Jon P. Kanter (CFO)
Nancy L. Kostakos (CMO)
Eric Goldstein (Partner-Private Equity & Private Investment Funds Practice)
Ilan Nissan (Sr Partner-Private Equity Practice)
A. J. Weidhaas (Chm-Private Equity Practice)
Diana Brummer (Partner-New York)
Gregor Klenk (Partner-Frankfurt)
Stephan Kock (Chm-Frankfurt)
Joshua Soszynski (Partner-New York)
Lars Jessen (Founder & Partner-Frankfurt)
Paul Lyons (Co-Chm-London)
Robert Young (Partner-London)
Samantha Lake Coghlan (Co-Chm-London)
Lily Wound (Partner-New York)
Mitch Bloom (Chm-Life Sciences Practice)
Stuart Cable (Partner & Chm-Merger & Acq-Global)
Rob Insolia (Chm)
Laurie A. Burlingame (Partner)
Mark Bettencourt (Mng Partner)

GOODWIN'S CHEVROLET COMPANY
195 Pleasant St, Brunswick, ME 04011
Tel.: (207) 729-1611
Web Site:
   http://www.goodwinchevyme.com
Year Founded: 1932
Sales Range: $10-24.9 Million
Emp.: 45
Car Whslr
N.A.I.C.S.: 441110
Frank Goodwin (Owner)
Rick Kimball (Mgr-Ops)

GOOSENECK IMPLEMENT COMPANY
1425 Highway 2 Byp E, Minot, ND 58701
Tel.: (701) 852-0767
Web Site:
   http://www.gooseneckimplement.com
Year Founded: 1988
Sales Range: $50-74.9 Million
Emp.: 49
Agricultural Machinery Dealer

N.A.I.C.S.: 423820
Kevin Borud (Pres)
Jamie Melgaard (Gen Mgr)

GOPHER NEWS COMPANY
9000 Tenth Ave N, Minneapolis, MN 55427-4322
Tel.: (763) 546-5300   MN
Web Site:
   http://www.gophernews.com
Year Founded: 1906
Sales Range: $10-24.9 Million
Emp.: 94
Periodicals & Newspapers
N.A.I.C.S.: 424920
Don Webber (Pres)

GOPPERT FINANCIAL CORP.
106 E 5th St, Garnett, KS 66032
Tel.: (785) 448-3111   KS
Year Founded: 1954
Sales Range: $10-24.9 Million
Emp.: 88
Bank Holding Company
N.A.I.C.S.: 551111
M. Charles Kellogg (Pres)
Thomas A. Goppert (Chm & CEO)

Subsidiaries:

Goppert Financial Bank   (1)
710 Oak St, Lathrop, MO 64465
Tel.: (816) 528-4296
Web Site: http://www.goppertfb.com
Sales Range: $1-9.9 Million
Emp.: 23
Retail & Commercial Banking Services
N.A.I.C.S.: 522110
Billy Campbell (Pres)
Michael Corey Strider (Exec VP)

Goppert State Service Bank   (1)
106 E 5th St, Garnett, KS 66032
Tel.: (785) 448-3111
Web Site: http://www.gssb.us.com
Sales Range: $1-9.9 Million
Emp.: 36
Retail & Commercial Banking
N.A.I.C.S.: 522110
Jeff McAdam (VP)

The Pleasant Hill Bank   (1)
101 S State Route 7, Pleasant Hill, MO 64080
Tel.: (816) 540-5101
Web Site: http://www.goppertfb.com
Sales Range: $1-9.9 Million
Emp.: 18
Retail & Commercial Banking
N.A.I.C.S.: 522110
Billie Ragner (VP)

GORA/MCGAHEY ARCHITECTS
43 Barkley Cir Ste 202, Fort Myers, FL 33907
Tel.: (239) 275-0225
Web Site:
   https://www.gmaarchitect.com
Year Founded: 1981
Sales Range: $10-24.9 Million
Emp.: 10
Architectural Services
N.A.I.C.S.: 541310
Dan McGahey (Pres & Principal)
Becky Gibbard (Office Mgr-Mktg)

GORANT CANDIES INC.
8301 Market St, Boardman, OH 44512
Tel.: (330) 726-8821
Web Site: https://www.gorant.com
Year Founded: 1949
Rev.: $18,000,000
Emp.: 130
Candy, Nut & Confectionery Stores
N.A.I.C.S.: 445292
Mary Ann Bailey (Office Mgr)
Joe Miller (Owner)

GORDON & REES LLP

275 Battery St Ste 2000, San Francisco, CA 94111
Tel.: (415) 986-5900
Web Site:
   http://www.gordonrees.com
Year Founded: 1974
Sales Range: $150-199.9 Million
Emp.: 776
Attorney Services
N.A.I.C.S.: 541110
P. Gerhardt Zacher (Mng Partner)
Kendra S. Canape (Partner-Orange County)

GORDON ALUMINUM INDUSTRIES, INC.
1000 Mason St, Schofield, WI 54476-0109
Tel.: (715) 359-6101
Web Site:
   https://www.gordonaluminum.com
Year Founded: 1959
Sales Range: $750-799.9 Million
Emp.: 150
Mfr of Aluminum Extruded Products
N.A.I.C.S.: 331318
Jack Gordon (CEO)
Bruce Pregont (Mgr-Estimating)
Brian Kling (Mgr-IT)

GORDON BROTHERS GROUP, LLC
Prudential Twr 800 Boylston St 27th Fl, Boston, MA 02199
Tel.: (617) 426-3233   DE
Web Site:
   http://www.gordonbrothers.com
Year Founded: 1903
Sales Range: $250-299.9 Million
Emp.: 150
Holding Company; Corporate Consulting, Financial Restructuring, Investment Advisory, Valuation & Appraisal Services Firm
N.A.I.C.S.: 551112
Mitchell H. Cohen (Sr Mng Dir)
Michael D. Chartock (Gen Counsel)
Robert M. Himmel (Sr Mng Dir)
Kenneth S. Frieze (Chm)
Michael L. Caplan (CIO)
Lee L. Cote (Sr Mng Dir-Retail)
Richard P. Edwards (Pres-Retail)
Rafael Klotz (Sr Mng Dir-Intl)
Leonard R. Polivy (Mng Dir-Jewelry Valuations)
Frank Grimaldi (Sr Mng Dir & Sls Mgr-North America)
Francis Garvin (Dir-Bus Dev)
John Dattilo (Dir-Indus Real Estate)
Marcos Brandt (Sr Mng Dir)
Christopher Koenig (Dir-Comml & Indus Div)
Bob Maroney (Pres-Comml & Indus)
Eli Appelbaum (Mng Dir)
Colleen Arons (Mng Dir)
Yoshiyuki Fujikawa (Mng Dir)
Olaf Galler (Mng Dir)
Norikazu Harada (Mng Dir)
Hideaki Horiuchi (Sr Mng Dir-Sourcing & Mktg)
Jim Lightburn (Sr Mng Dir-Comml & Indus)
Tom Lonabocker (Mng Dir)
Joe McLeish (Mng Dir)
Tricia Parent (Sr Mng Dir)
Liz Sarhaddi-Blue (Mng Dir)
Rick Schmitt (Pres-Valuations)
Tim Stewart (Mng Dir)
Andy Stone (Mng Dir)
Isao Tamamoto (Mng Dir & Chief Admin Officer)
Nick Taylor (Sr Mng Dir-Retail)
Norma Kuntz (CEO)
Steven Holstein (Head-Bus Dev)
Evren Ozargun (Mng Dir-Corp Dev & Credit)

Gordon Brothers Group, LLC—(Continued)

Larry Sax (COO)
Kyle C. Shonak (Mng Dir-Retail)
Dennis Bolton (Mng Dir-Comml & Indus)
Thomas Pedulla (Pres-Real Estate)
Ramez Toubassy (Pres-Brands)
Frank Morton (Chief Investment Officer)
Nick Kitchin (Mng Dir)
Joseph Malfitano (Sr Mng Dir)
Samantha Schackman (Dir-Bus Dev)

Subsidiaries:

DJM Asset Management, LLC (1)
445 Broadhollow Rd Ste 225, Melville, NY
11747-3601 **(100%)**
Tel.: (631) 752-1100
Web Site: http://www.djmrealty.com
Sales Range: $10-24.9 Million
Emp.: 22
Retail Real Estate Consulting
N.A.I.C.S.: 541618
Ed Zimmer (Sr Mng Dir & Gen Counsel)
James Avallone (Sr Mng Dir)
Thomas Laczay (Sr Mng Dir)
Andrew Couch (Mng Dir)
Neill J. Kelly (Pres)

Durkin Group & Associates LLC (1)
9 Campus Dr, Parsippany, NJ 07054
Tel.: (973) 575-8339
Web Site: http://www.durkingroup.com
Financial Due Diligence, Field Examination,
Accounting & Auditing Services
N.A.I.C.S.: 541690
Kevin P. Durkin (Mng Dir)

**Emerald Technology Valuations,
LLC** (1)
231 Sansome St 5th Fl, San Francisco, CA
94104
Tel.: (415) 773-6310
Web Site: http://www.emerald-tech.com
Equipment Assessment Services
N.A.I.C.S.: 541990
Robert Hamner (Mng Dir)
Kyle Pesonen (Dir-Client Rels)

Enhanced Retail Funding, LLC (1)
Prudential Twr 800 Boylston St, Boston, MA
02199
Tel.: (617) 426-3233
Web Site: http://www.gordonbrothers.com
Emp.: 300
Asset Buyer Lending To Retailers
N.A.I.C.S.: 522310

**Gordon Brothers Asset Advisors,
LLC** (1)
800 Boylston 27th Fl, Boston, MA
02199 **(100%)**
Tel.: (617) 426-3233
Web Site: http://www.gordonbrothers.com
Sales Range: $10-24.9 Million
Emp.: 20
Corporate Appraisal Services
N.A.I.C.S.: 531320

Gordon Brothers Europe (1)
13 Hanover Square, London, W1S 1HN,
United Kingdom
Tel.: (44) 207 647 5120
Web Site: http://www.gordonbrothers.co.uk
Investment Services
N.A.I.C.S.: 523999
Frank Morton (CEO-Intl)
Angus Collett (CFO-Intl)
Heinz Weber (Pres)
Duncan Ainscough (Mng Dir-Valuation &
Indus)
Federica Pietrogrande (Mng Dir-Intl)
Nimit N. R. Shah (Mng Dir-Fin Plng &
Analysis)

Holding (Domestic):

TS Operations Limited (2)
Harefield Place The Drive, Uxbridge, UB10
8AQ, United Kingdom
Tel.: (44) 1895258866
Web Site: http://www.blockbuster.co.uk
Sales Range: $1-4.9 Billion
Video Rental & Retail Services
N.A.I.C.S.: 532282

Subsidiary (Domestic):

**Blockbuster Entertainment
Limited** (3)

Harefield Place The Drive, Ickenham, Uxbridge, UB10 8AQ, Middlesex, United Kingdom
Tel.: (44) 1895 258866
Web Site: http://www.blockbuster.co.uk
Videos & DVDs Rental & Sales
N.A.I.C.S.: 532282

**Gordon Brothers International,
LLC** (1)
Prudential Twr 800 Boylston St, Boston, MA
02199 **(100%)**
Tel.: (617) 426-3233
Web Site: http://www.gordonbrothers.com
Corporate Consulting Services
N.A.I.C.S.: 541611

**Gordon Brothers Retail Partners,
LLC** (1)
800 Boylston 27th Fl, Boston, MA
02199 **(100%)**
Tel.: (617) 426-3233
Web Site:
    http://www.gordonbrothersgroup.com
Sales Range: $10-24.9 Million
Emp.: 100
Retail Industry Corporate Consulting Services
N.A.I.C.S.: 541611
Richard P. Edwards (Pres)

Laura Ashley Holdings plc (1)
27 Bagleys Lane Fulham, London, SW6
2QA, United Kingdom
Tel.: (44) 2078805100
Web Site: http://www.lauraashley.com
Holding Company; Ladies' & Children's
Clothing & Accessories & Home Furnishings
N.A.I.C.S.: 551112
Kwan Cheong Ng (CEO)
Sean Anglim (CFO, Co-COO & Dir-Fin)
Nick Kaloyirou (Co-COO)
Jonathan Gwilt (Sec)

Subsidiary (Non-US):

Laura Ashley CER Countries BV (2)
Oude Stadsgracht 1, NL-5611 DD, Eindhoven, Netherlands **(100%)**
Tel.: (31) 402435022
Web Site: http://www.lauraashley.com
Sales Range: $50-74.9 Million
Emp.: 70
Holding Company
N.A.I.C.S.: 551112

Subsidiary (Non-US):

Laura Ashley (Ireland) Ltd. (3)
60/61 Grafton Street, Dublin, 2,
Ireland **(100%)**
Tel.: (353) 35316330050
Web Site: http://www.lauraashley.com
Retail of Women's & Children's Clothing &
Home Furnishings
N.A.I.C.S.: 458110

Laura Ashley Espana SA (3)
Calle Calvo Sotelo 10, 26003, Logrono,
Spain
Tel.: (34) 941587676
Web Site: http://www.lauraashley.es
Emp.: 7
Retail of Women's & Children's Clothing &
Home Furnishings
N.A.I.C.S.: 458110
Alberto Gomez (Mgr)

Laura Ashley NV (3)
Rue De Namur 45, Brussels, 1000,
Belgium **(100%)**
Tel.: (32) 25120447
Web Site: http://www.lauraashley.com
Sales Range: $25-49.9 Million
Emp.: 5
Retail Women's Cothing & Home Furnishings
N.A.I.C.S.: 458110

Laura Ashley S.p.A. (3)
Via Brera 4, 20121, Milan, Italy **(100%)**
Tel.: (39) 0286463532
Web Site: http://www.lauraashley.com
Retail Women's Clothing & Home Furnishings
N.A.I.C.S.: 458110

Laura Ashley SA (3)

8 Rue De Verdaine, 1204, Geneva,
Switzerland **(100%)**
Tel.: (41) 223113494
Web Site: http://www.lauraashley.com
Retail Women's Clothing & Home Furnishings
N.A.I.C.S.: 458110

Laura Ashley SA (3)
94 Rue De Rennes, 75006, Paris,
France **(100%)**
Tel.: (33) 145484389
Web Site: http://www.lauraashley.com
Sales Range: $25-49.9 Million
Emp.: 15
Retail Women's Clothing & Home Furnishings
N.A.I.C.S.: 458110

Subsidiary (Non-US):

Laura Ashley Japan Co., Ltd. (2)
Honey Building 2 Fl Aoyama 3 35 8 Jingumae, Sibuya Ku, Tokyo, 150 0001,
Japan **(100%)**
Tel.: (81) 354742642
Web Site: http://www.laura-ashley.co.jp
Sales Range: $25-49.9 Million
Emp.: 70
Women's Apparel Stores; Joint Venture of
Laura Ashley Holdings plc & Jusco Co., Ltd.
N.A.I.C.S.: 458110
Koji Maekawa (Pres)

Subsidiary (Domestic):

Laura Ashley Ltd. (2)
27 Bagleys Lane, Fulham, London, SW6
2QA, United Kingdom **(100%)**
Tel.: (44) 2078805100
Web Site: http://www.lauraashley.com
Sales Range: $25-49.9 Million
Emp.: 200
Mfr & Retail of Ladies' & Children's Clothing
& Home Furnishings & Accessories
N.A.I.C.S.: 315210

Subsidiary (US):

Laura Ashley, Inc. (2)
7000 Regent Pkwy, Fort Mill, SC
29715-8313 **(100%)**
Tel.: (803) 396-7700
Sales Range: $25-49.9 Million
Emp.: 7
Retailer of Ladies' & Children's Clothing &
Home Furnishings
N.A.I.C.S.: 458110

Polaroid Corporation (1)
4350 Baker Rd Ste 180, Minnetonka, MN
55343
Tel.: (952) 641-1020
Web Site: http://www.polaroid.com
Sales Range: $125-149.9 Million
Camera & Optical Instrument Mfr
N.A.I.C.S.: 333310

Subsidiary (Non-US):

**Nippon Polaroid Kabushiki
Kaisha** (2)
Toranomon Marine Building, 3-18-19 Toranomon, Minato-ku, Tokyo, 105 0001, Japan
Tel.: (81) 334388811
Photographic Cameras, Films, Light Polarizing Filters, Lenses & Diversified Chemical,
Optical & Commercial Products Mfr
N.A.I.C.S.: 333310

Polaroid (Espana) S.A. (2)
Camino de las Ceudas 2 bis, Ctra de La
Coruna Km 22 300, 28230, Madrid, Spain
Tel.: (34) 91 636 3521
Sales Range: $1-9.9 Million
Emp.: 6
Photographic Cameras, Films, Light Polarizing Filters, Lenses & Diversified Chemical,
Optical & Commercial Products Mfr
N.A.I.C.S.: 333310

Polaroid (U.K.) Limited (2)
7th Floor Ziggurat 25 Grosvenor Road, AL1
3BW, Saint Albans, Hertfordshire, United
Kingdom - England
Tel.: (44) 1727792250
Photographic Cameras, Films, Light Polarizing Filters, Lenses & Diversified Chemical,
Optical & Commercial Products Mfr
N.A.I.C.S.: 333310

Polaroid GmbH (2)
Robert Bosch Str 32, 63303, Dreieich,
Sprendlingen, Germany
Tel.: (49) 6966901800
Web Site: http://www.polaroid.com
Sales Range: $25-49.9 Million
Emp.: 6
Photographic Cameras, Films, Light Polarizing Filters, Lenses & Diversified Chemical,
Optical & Commercial Products Mfr
N.A.I.C.S.: 333310

Polaroid de Mexico S.A. de C.V. (2)
Torre Presidente Reforma, Andres Bello 45
22nd Fl, 11550, Mexico, DF, Mexico
Tel.: (52) 5552795555
Sales Range: $25-49.9 Million
Emp.: 14
Photographic Cameras, Films, Light Polarizing Filters, Lenses & Diversified Chemical,
Optical & Commercial Products Mfr
N.A.I.C.S.: 333310

Things Remembered, Inc. (1)
5500 Avion Park Dr, Highland Heights, OH
44143
Tel.: (440) 473-2000
Web Site:
    http://www.thingsremembered.com
Sales Range: $300-349.9 Million
Engraved & Personalized Gifts Retailer
N.A.I.C.S.: 459420
Alice Guiney (VP-HR)
Nelson Tejada (Pres)

**GORDON BRUSH MFG CO,
INC.**
6247 Randolph St, Los Angeles, CA
90040
Tel.: (323) 724-7777   CA
Web Site:
    http://www.gordonbrush.com
Year Founded: 1998
Sales Range: $1-9.9 Million
Emp.: 58
Broom, Brush & Mop Mfr
N.A.I.C.S.: 339994
Kenneth Rakusin (Pres)
Bill Loitz (Dir-Special Projects)
Paul Fidler (Mgr-Ops)

Subsidiaries:

Michigan Brush Manufacturing Company, Inc. (1)
7446 Central Ave, Detroit, MI 48210
Tel.: (313) 834-1070
Web Site: http://www.mi-brush.com
Sales Range: $1-9.9 Million
Emp.: 20
Mfg Brooms/Brushes
N.A.I.C.S.: 339994

GORDON CHEVROLET CO.
2031 Gordon Hwy, Augusta, GA
30909
Tel.: (706) 733-9411
Web Site:
    http://www.malcolmcunningham
    chevrolet.com
Sales Range: $25-49.9 Million
Emp.: 100
New & Used Automobile Dealer
N.A.I.C.S.: 441110
Malcolm Cunningham (Pres)
Keith Payton (Mgr-Used Car)

GORDON CHEVROLET-GEO
16414 N Dale Mabry Hwy, Tampa, FL
33618-1343
Tel.: (813) 969-2600
Web Site:
    http://www.gordontampa.com
Year Founded: 1990
Sales Range: $10-24.9 Million
Emp.: 80
Car Whslr
N.A.I.C.S.: 441110
Arthur Smith (VP & Gen Mgr)
Skip Greaney (Dir-Fixed Ops)

GORDON COMPANIES INC.
85 Innsbruck Dr, Buffalo, NY 14227

Tel.: (716) 447-0100
Web Site:
http://www.christmascentral.com
Rev.: $14,000,000
Emp.: 20
Hobby & Craft Supplies
N.A.I.C.S.: 459120
David Gordon (Pres)
Ed Pilarz (Controller)
Leah Marie (Mgr-HR)
Matt Pilarski (Mgr-Store)
Angela Berghoefer (Dir-E-Commerce)

GORDON DOCUMENT PRODUCTS INC.

2141 Powers Ferry Rd Ste 250, Marietta, GA 30067
Tel.: (770) 563-8400
Web Site: https://www.gdp.com
Year Founded: 1987
Sales Range: $1-9.9 Million
Emp.: 50
Copier & Document Management Services
N.A.I.C.S.: 561439
John C. Gordon Sr. (Co-Founder, Pres & CEO)
John Gordon Jr. (Sls Mgr)

GORDON FLESCH COMPANY, INC.

2675 Research Park Dr, Madison, WI 53711
Tel.: (608) 271-2100   WI
Web Site: https://www.gflesch.com
Year Founded: 1956
Sales Range: $50-74.9 Million
Emp.: 700
Retailer of Office Equipment
N.A.I.C.S.: 423420
Thomas Flesch (Chm)
Mark Flesch (COO)
William Flesch (Chief Dev Officer)
Patrick Flesch (Pres & CEO)
Kelly Dolphin (CFO)
Kelly Glaser (VP-Sls & Mktg)
Travis Lemke (VP-Leasing)
Brad Olm (VP-Shared Services)
Brad Samuel (VP-Service)

Subsidiaries:

Advanced Systems Inc.   (1)
5801 Westminster Dr, Cedar Falls, IA 50613
Tel.: (319) 260-4100
Web Site: http://www.asiowa.com
Rev.: $12,700,000
Emp.: 60
Miscellaneous Store Retailers
N.A.I.C.S.: 459999
Tony Love (Pres)

Indiana Business Equipment, LLC   (1)
1301 Ohio St, Terre Haute, IN 47807
Tel.: (812) 232-7784
Office Equipment Merchant Whslr
N.A.I.C.S.: 423420

Information Technology Professionals, LLC   (1)
345 W Washington Ste 403, Madison, WI 53703
Tel.: (608) 251-6755
Web Site: http://www.itprosusa.com
Information Technology Consulting Services
N.A.I.C.S.: 541512
Paul Hager (Pres & CEO)

GORDON FOOD SERVICE INC.

1300 Gezon Pkwy SW, Wyoming, MI 49509
Tel.: (616) 530-7000   MI
Web Site: https://www.gfs.com
Year Founded: 1897
Sales Range: $100-124.9 Million
Emp.: 22,000
Food Service Contractors
N.A.I.C.S.: 722310

Tim Fatum (Dir-HR)
Alan Hooker (Dir-Treasury Ops)
Jeff Maddox (CFO)
Rich Wolowski (Pres & CEO)

Subsidiaries:

Distal Inc.   (1)
414 Boulevard Raymond, Beauport, G1C 7S4, QC, Canada
Tel.: (418) 666-5575
Grocery Distr
N.A.I.C.S.: 424410

GFS Ontario   (1)
2999 James Snow Parkway N, Milton, L9T 5G4, ON, Canada
Tel.: (905) 864-3700
Web Site: http://www.gfscanada.com
Sales Range: $50-74.9 Million
Emp.: 600
Food Distr
N.A.I.C.S.: 424410

Gordon Food Service   (1)
1700 Cliveden Ave, Delta, V3M 6T2, BC, Canada
Tel.: (604) 540-3701
Web Site: http://www.gfs.com
Sales Range: $50-74.9 Million
Emp.: 700
Food Distr
N.A.I.C.S.: 424410

Gordon Food Service - Florida   (1)
2850 NW 120th Ter, Miami, FL 33167
Tel.: (305) 685-5851
Web Site: http://www.gfs.com
Sales Range: $50-74.9 Million
Emp.: 510
Food Distr
N.A.I.C.S.: 424490
Scott Nicholson (Pres)
Kirk Zell (Gen Mgr)

Gordon Food Service Inc.   (1)
290212 Township Road 216 Rockyveiw County, Calgary, T4A 0V6, AB, Canada
Tel.: (403) 235-8555
Web Site: https://gfs.ca
Grocery Distr
N.A.I.C.S.: 424410
David Barber (Pres)

M&S Food Service Ltd.   (1)
38 Industrial Park Drive, Amherst, B4H 4R5, NS, Canada
Tel.: (902) 664-3700
Web Site: http://www.gssatlantic.com
Sales Range: $10-24.9 Million
Emp.: 80
Food Distr
N.A.I.C.S.: 424410
Cam Godin (Pres)

GORDON HANRAHAN, INC.

150 N Michigan Ave Ste 600, Chicago, IL 60601-7570
Tel.: (312) 372-0935   IL
Year Founded: 1987
Sales Range: Less than $1 Million
Emp.: 15
Advetising Agency
N.A.I.C.S.: 541810
Michael Gordon (Partner)
Mary Ellen Hanrahan (Owner)
Tom Sanpakit (Partner)
Valerie Ester (Controller)
Molly Berggren (Acct Supvr)
Heather Simms (Sr Dir-Art)
Dawn Johnson (Dir-Creative)
Megan Warmouth (Project Mgr)
Heather Kaplan (Copywriter)
Karen Lubinski (Dir-Creative)

GORDON PAPER COMPANY INCORPORATED

5713 Ward Ave, Virginia Beach, VA 23455
Tel.: (757) 464-3581
Web Site:
https://www.gordonpaper.com
Sales Range: $10-24.9 Million
Emp.: 100

Converted Paper Products
N.A.I.C.S.: 322299
Tavia F. Gordon (Pres)
Stephen Gordon (Mgr-Indus Sls)

GORDON RESEARCH CONFERENCES

512 Liberty Ln, West Kingston, RI 02892
Tel.: (401) 783-4011   RI
Web Site: https://www.grc.org
Year Founded: 2009
Sales Range: $25-49.9 Million
Emp.: 92
Biotechnology Research Services
N.A.I.C.S.: 541714
Nancy Ryan Gray (Pres & CEO)

GORDON-DARBY INC.

2410 Ampere Dr, Louisville, KY 40299
Tel.: (502) 266-5797
Web Site: https://www.gordon-darby.com
Rev.: $26,100,000
Emp.: 200
Emissions Testing Without Repairs, Automotive
N.A.I.C.S.: 811198
Stanley J. Gordon (Pres)
Jess Yowell (Mgr-Software Dev)
Jesse Campbell (Engr-Software)
Jay Gordon (Pres)

GORDONS WALTHAM LIQUOR STORES INC.

894 Main St, Waltham, MA 02451
Tel.: (781) 893-1900
Web Site:
https://www.gordonswine.com
Sales Range: $10-24.9 Million
Emp.: 30
Beer
N.A.I.C.S.: 445320
Richard Gordon (Pres)

GORDY'S, INC.

362 Ashford St, Worthington, MN 56187-1665
Tel.: (507) 376-3727   MN
Year Founded: 1963
Sales Range: $200-249.9 Million
Emp.: 800
Retail Groceries
N.A.I.C.S.: 445110
Thomas G. Anderson (Chm & Pres)
Jerry Junker (Mgr-Employee Benefits)

GORES INC.

1300 E Mill Ave, Comanche, TX 76442
Tel.: (915) 356-3045
Rev.: $73,343,250
Emp.: 170
Cereal, Grain & Seed-Based Feeds
N.A.I.C.S.: 311119

GORGES MOTOR COMPANY INC.

2660 S Oliver Rd, Wichita, KS 67210
Tel.: (316) 685-2201
Web Site:
http://www.carbuyingfun.com
Year Founded: 1958
Sales Range: $10-24.9 Million
Emp.: 50
New & Used Car Dealers
N.A.I.C.S.: 441110

GORHAM BANCORP, MHC

10 Wentwood Dr, Gorham, ME 04038
Tel.: (207) 839-4796
Web Site:
https://www.gorhamsavings.bank
Emp.: 100
Bank Holding Company

N.A.I.C.S.: 551111

Subsidiaries:

Gorham Savings Bank   (1)
10 Wentwood Dr, Gorham, ME 04038
Tel.: (207) 839-4796
Web Site:
http://www.gorhamsavingsbank.com
Sales Range: $10-24.9 Million
Emp.: 175
State Savings Bank
N.A.I.C.S.: 522110
Dan Hunter (COO)
Chris Emmons (Pres & CEO)
Matt White (VP)
Matt White (VP)

GORILLA CAPITAL

1342 High St, Eugene, OR 97401
Tel.: (541) 344-7867
Web Site:
https://www.gorillacapital.com
Year Founded: 2006
Sales Range: $75-99.9 Million
Emp.: 35
Acquisitions of Distressed Residential Properties
N.A.I.C.S.: 531390
John Helmick (CEO)

GORILLA COMMERCE

111 W Jackson Blvd Ste 300, Chicago, IL 60604
Tel.: (312) 243-8777
Web Site:
http://www.gorillagroup.com
Sales Range: $1-9.9 Million
Emp.: 89
Website Development Services
N.A.I.C.S.: 541511
Brian Grady (CEO)
Justin Finnegan (COO)
Justin Saviano (Dir-Bus Dev)
Adam Brown (Exec Dir-Creative)
Allison Kehm (Dir-HR)
Amanda LaBonar (Sr Project Mgr)
Andrey Davydov (Mgr-Facility)
Bryan Herhold (Dir-Ops-Montreal)
Chad Carlson (Dir-Tech)
Chris Kostakis (Dir-Enterprise Architecture)
Christina Quirin (Project Mgr)

GORILLA GLUE CO.

4550 Red Bank Expy, Cincinnati, OH 45227
Tel.: (513) 271-3300   OH
Web Site:
http://www.gorillatough.com
Rev.: $4,000,000
Emp.: 120
Glue Distr
N.A.I.C.S.: 332216
Peter Ragland (Pres)
Lauren Connley (Dir-Creative)
Joe Ragland (COO)
Simon Damp (Mng Dir-Europe)
Mark Mercurio (VP-Mktg & Innovation)

GORILLA LOGIC, INC.

1500 Pearl St Ste 300, Boulder, CO 80302
Tel.: (303) 974-7088
Web Site: http://www.gorillalogic.com
Sales Range: $1-9.9 Million
Emp.: 53
Software Development Services
N.A.I.C.S.: 541511
Stu Stern (Pres)
Ed Schwarz (VP-Engrg)
Rachel Beisel (VP-Mktg)
Tess Manderson (Global VP-Talent Ops)
Daniel Berg (CEO)
Dave Barr (VP-Svc Delivery-Global)

Gorilla Logic, Inc.—(Continued)

GORILLA NATION MEDIA, LLC
5140 W Goldleaf Cir Fl 3, Los Angeles, CA 90056
Tel.: (310) 449-1890
Web Site:
http://www.gorillanation.com
Sales Range: $50-74.9 Million
Emp.: 120
Advetising Agency
N.A.I.C.S.: 541810
Brian Fitzgerald (Co-Founder & Pres)
Aaron Broder (Co-Founder & CEO)
Jessica Fong (Dir-Sls Plng)
John Hoffman (Strategic Acct Mgr)
Brad Agens (Sr VP-Natl Sls)
Aimee Geary (Sr Acct Mgr)
Neda LaMarr (Acct Exec-Inside Sls)
Sharyn Alcaraz (Sr Counsel)
Sharon Reese (VP-HR)
Kyle Fletcher (VP-GNKids)
Moises Magana (Sr VP-Fin)
John Ellingwood (Gen Counsel)
Richard Rocca (VP & Dir-Bus Dev)
Susan Mandell (Sr Acct Exec)
Elain Chang (Acct Dir)
Alex Godelman (CTO)

GORILLA STATIONERS LLC
10860 Walker St, Cypress, CA 90630
Web Site:
http://www.gorillastationers.com
Year Founded: 2012
Stationery & Office Supplies Merchant Whslr
N.A.I.C.S.: 424120
RoseMary Czopek (Founder)

GORMAN & COMPANY INC.
200 N Main St, Oregon, WI 53575
Tel.: (608) 835-3900
Web Site:
https://www.gormanusa.com
Year Founded: 1984
Sales Range: $10-24.9 Million
Emp.: 130
Residential Land Development
N.A.I.C.S.: 237210
Gary J. Gorman (Founder, Chm & Co-CEO)
Tom Capp (Vice Chm & COO)
Joyce Wuetrich (Dir-Asset Mgmt)
Kathleen Bahman (Dir-Sls & Mktg)
Brian Swanton (Pres & Co-CEO)
Ted Matkom (Pres-Wisconsin Market)

GORMAN BROTHERS INC.
200 Church St, Albany, NY 12202
Tel.: (518) 462-5401
Web Site:
https://www.gormanroads.com
Rev.: $18,500,000
Emp.: 20
General Contractor, Highway & Street Construction
N.A.I.C.S.: 237310
Albert M. Gorman (Pres)

GORMAN FOODS INC.
9265 Redwood Rd B, West Jordan, UT 84088
Tel.: (801) 352-9559
Rev.: $18,023,421
Emp.: 5
Supermarkets, Chain
N.A.I.C.S.: 445110

GORMAN LEARNING CENTER, INC.
1826 Orange Tree Ln, Redlands, CA 92374
Tel.: (909) 307-6312
Web Site: http://www.gormanlc.org
Year Founded: 2000
Sales Range: $10-24.9 Million
Emp.: 197

Educational Support Services
N.A.I.C.S.: 611710
Antoine Hawkins (Chief Bus Officer)
Kim McClellan (Pres)
Susan Nesbitt (Treas & Sec)

GORMAN MILLING CO. INC.
502 E Lubbock, Gorman, TX 76454
Tel.: (254) 734-2252
Web Site:
http://www.redchainfeeds.com
Sales Range: $10-24.9 Million
Emp.: 84
Prepared Feeds
N.A.I.C.S.: 311119
Harold Fritts (Pres)
John Fritts (VP)

GORMAN'S FURNITURE INC.
29145 Telegraph Rd, Southfield, MI 48034
Tel.: (248) 353-9880
Web Site: https://www.gormans.com
Year Founded: 1987
Sales Range: $10-24.9 Million
Emp.: 20
Furniture Retailer
N.A.I.C.S.: 449110
Bernard D. Moray (Chm & CEO)
Tom Lias (Pres & COO)

GORNO FORD
22025 Allen Rd, Woodhaven, MI 48183
Tel.: (734) 676-2200
Web Site: https://www.gornoford.com
Sales Range: $25-49.9 Million
Emp.: 115
Car Whslr
N.A.I.C.S.: 441110
George M. Gorno (Mgr-Sls)
Ed Jolliffe (Gen Mgr)

GORSUCH LTD.
263 E Gore Creek Dr, Vail, CO 81657
Tel.: (970) 476-2294   CO
Web Site: https://www.gorsuch.com
Year Founded: 1966
Sales Range: $25-49.9 Million
Emp.: 75
Clothing Stores
N.A.I.C.S.: 458110
Genii Gatter (CFO)

GOSECURE INC.
4225 Exec Sq Ste 1600, La Jolla, CA 92037
Tel.: (855) 893-5428
Web Site: http://www.gosecure.net
Year Founded: 2002
Sales Range: $1-9.9 Million
Emp.: 20
Cyber Security Services
N.A.I.C.S.: 518210
Rajendra Dodhiawala (Chief Product Officer)
Michael Davis (CTO)
Neal Creighton (CEO)
Matthew Addington (Exec VP-Federal Bus)
Robert J. McCullen (Chm)
David DeRuff (CFO)

Subsidiaries:

EdgeWave Inc.   **(1)**
15333 Ave of Science Ste 100, San Diego, CA 92128
Tel.: (858) 676-2277
Web Site: http://www.edgewave.com
Sales Range: $10-24.9 Million
Emp.: 111
Secure Content Management Software Developer, Publisher & Marketer
N.A.I.C.S.: 513210
Bob Crowe (Sr VP-Engrg)
Louis E. Ryan (Chm)

Thalia R. Gietzen (COO)
Steve Kelley (CEO)
Mike Walls (Mng Dir-Security Ops & Analysis)

GOSH ENTERPRISES, INC.
2500 Farmers Dr Ste 140, Columbus, OH 43235-5706
Tel.: (614) 923-4700
Web Site: http://www.charleys.com
Year Founded: 1986
Sales Range: $25-49.9 Million
Emp.: 6,500
Fast Food & Quick Service Restaurants
N.A.I.C.S.: 722513
Charley Shin (Founder, Pres & CEO)

GOSHEN HEALTH SYSTEM
PO Box 139, Goshen, IN 46527-0139
Tel.: (574) 533-2141
Year Founded: 1909
Sales Range: $10-24.9 Million
Emp.: 1,100
Pharmaceutical Product Whslr
N.A.I.C.S.: 424210
Addi Kaminskis (Coord-Pain Mgmt)
Pam Karsen (VP-Nursing)
Dan Nafziger (Chief Medical Officer-Goshen Hospital)

GOSHEN HOSPITAL & HEALTH CARE FOUNDATION INC.
1926 W Lincoln Ste A, Goshen, IN 46526
Tel.: (574) 533-4500   IN
Web Site:
http://www.givetogoshen.org
Year Founded: 1969
Sales Range: $1-9.9 Million
Emp.: 4
Community Health Care Services
N.A.I.C.S.: 621498
Clare Krabill (CEO)
Grace Bonewitz (Dir-Comm)

GOSHEN MEDICAL CENTER, INC.
119 Crossover Rd, Beulaville, NC 28518
Tel.: (910) 298-3125   NC
Web Site:
http://www.goshenmedical.org
Year Founded: 1979
Sales Range: $10-24.9 Million
Emp.: 224
Health Care Srvices
N.A.I.C.S.: 622110
Gregory M. Bounds (CEO)
Christian Holmes (Project Mgr)
Rhonda Barwick (Dir-Ops)

GOSIGER INC.
108 McDonough St, Dayton, OH 45402-2246
Tel.: (937) 228-5174   OH
Web Site: https://www.gosiger.com
Year Founded: 1922
Sales Range: $100-124.9 Million
Emp.: 300
Distr of Machine Tools & Machinery
N.A.I.C.S.: 423830
Jane Gosiger Haley (Chm)
John R. Haley (CEO)

GOSPEL LIGHT PUBLICATIONS
1957 Eastman Ave, Ventura, CA 93003
Tel.: (805) 644-9721
Web Site: http://www.gospellight.com
Rev.: $22,800,000
Emp.: 84
Book Publishing & Printing
N.A.I.C.S.: 513130

Ken Lorenz (Dir-Sls)
Jackie Morales (Coord-Mktg)
Peter Bundy (Dir-Ops)
Peter Germann (Mgr-Production)
Al Harvey (Dir-IT)
Brenda Usery (Mgr-Production)
Alice Coryell (Assoc Dir-HR)
Mario Pacifici (VP-Mktg & Web Svcs)
Rachel Fudge (Coord-Sls)

GOSS DODGE INC.
1485 Shelburne Rd, South Burlington, VT 05403-7714
Tel.: (802) 210-1377
Web Site: http://www.gosscars.com
Year Founded: 1979
Sales Range: $10-24.9 Million
Emp.: 55
Car Whslr
N.A.I.C.S.: 441110
Brian Hoar (Gen Mgr)
Douglas W. Hoar (Pres)

GOSS DODGE, INC.
1485 Shelburne Rd, South Burlington, VT 05403
Tel.: (802) 658-0120
Web Site: http://www.gosscars.com
Sales Range: $25-49.9 Million
Emp.: 51
Car Whslr
N.A.I.C.S.: 441110
Brian Hoar (VP)
Douglas W. Hoar (Pres)

GOSSETT MOTOR CARS INC.
1900 Covington Pke Rd, Memphis, TN 38128
Tel.: (901) 388-8989
Web Site:
http://www.gossetmotors.com
Rev.: $132,608,000
Emp.: 350
Automobiles, New & Used
N.A.I.C.S.: 441110
Al Gossett (Pres)
Dan Fields (Dir-IT)
David Kirby (Mgr-Sls)
Terry Hawkins (Dir-Parts)

Subsidiaries:

Infiniti of Memphis, Inc.   **(1)**
3060 North Germantown Rd, Memphis, TN 38133
Tel.: (901) 432-8200
Web Site: http://www.infinitiofmemphis.com
New Car Dealers
N.A.I.C.S.: 441110
Al Gossett (Pres)
John Pfund (Mgr-Mktg)
Johanna Ellis Reisinger (Principal-Dealer)

GOT-RACK.COM INC.
5210 Causeway Blvd, Tampa, FL 33619
Tel.: (813) 246-5800
Web Site: https://www.got-rack.com
Sales Range: $10-24.9 Million
Online Material Handling & Warehouse Racking Systems Retailer
N.A.I.C.S.: 423830
Alan Bridges (Owner)

GOTHAM CIGARS, LLC
1606 NW 84th Ave, Miami, FL 33126
Tel.: (305) 597-1501
Web Site:
http://www.gothamcigars.com
Year Founded: 2001
Sales Range: $1-9.9 Million
Emp.: 15
Online Retailer of Cigars & Cigar Accessories
N.A.I.C.S.: 459991
Manny Balani (Pres & CEO)

Subsidiaries:

American Fitness Wholesalers LLC (1)
860 Lakemont Dr, Louisville, TN 37777-5342
Tel.: (865) 977-8017
Web Site: http://www.a1supplements.com
Toy & Hobby Goods & Supplies Merchant Whslr
N.A.I.C.S.: 423920
Manny Balani *(CEO)*

GOTHAM ORGANIZATION INC.
432 Park Ave S Fl 2, New York, NY 10016
Tel.: (212) 599-0520
Web Site: http://www.gothamorg.com
Sales Range: $10-24.9 Million
Emp.: 30
Subdividers & Developers
N.A.I.C.S.: 237210
Joel I. Picket *(Chm & CEO)*

GOTHAM TECHNOLOGY GROUP, LLC
1 Paragon Dr Ste 200, Montvale, NJ 07645
Tel.: (201) 474-4200   NY
Web Site: http://www.gothamtg.com
Year Founded: 2001
IT Consulting Services
N.A.I.C.S.: 423430
Ira Silverman *(CEO)*
Steve Kilcoyne *(Mgr-Comm)*
Adam Silverman *(Pres)*
Richard Silverman *(Chm)*
Kenneth Phelan *(CTO)*
Christopher Passaretti *(Dir-Sls)*

GOTHIC LANDSCAPE, INC.
27413 Tourney Rd, Santa Clarita, CA 91355
Tel.: (661) 678-1400
Web Site:
   https://www.gothiclandscape.com
Year Founded: 1984
Landscaping Services
N.A.I.C.S.: 561730
Jon Georgio *(Pres & CEO)*
Clarke La Vine *(CFO)*
Nick Arena *(VP-Admin)*
Dan Cullen *(Dir-IT)*
Sandi Malmquist *(Dir-HR)*
Ron Georgio *(Pres-Maintenance Div)*

Subsidiaries:

Terra Pacific Landscape, Inc. (1)
1627 E Wilshire Ave, Santa Ana, CA 92705
Tel.: (714) 567-0177
Web Site: http://www.terrapac.com
Landscape Services
N.A.I.C.S.: 541320

GOTHIC LANDSCAPING INC.
27502 Ave Scott, Valencia, CA 91355-3968
Tel.: (661) 257-1266   CA
Web Site:
   https://www.gothiclandscape.com
Year Founded: 1997
Sales Range: $25-49.9 Million
Emp.: 500
Commercial Landscaping Services
N.A.I.C.S.: 561730
Jon Georgio *(Pres)*

GOTT COMPANY INC.
PO Box 2810, Prince Frederick, MD 20646
Tel.: (410) 535-1717
Web Site: http://www.gottco.com
Year Founded: 1945
Rev.: $22,600,000
Emp.: 20
Liquefied Petroleum Gas Dealers
N.A.I.C.S.: 457210
John M. Gott Jr. *(Pres)*

GOTUWIRED, INC.
1621 S Rancho Santa Fe Rd Ste D, San Marcos, CA 92078
Tel.: (858) 999-2031
Web Site: http://www.gotuwired.com
Year Founded: 2007
Sales Range: $1-9.9 Million
Emp.: 17
Management Consulting Services
N.A.I.C.S.: 541618
Ari Bajaj *(Dir-Customer Rels)*

GOTWALS INC.
12 Gotwals Ln, Oley, PA 19547
Tel.: (610) 987-6284
Web Site:
   https://www.brookledge.com
Sales Range: $10-24.9 Million
Emp.: 200
Long Distance Heavy Hauling Services
N.A.I.C.S.: 484220
Robert S. Gotwals *(Owner & Pres)*
Dennis Rittenhouse *(Controller)*

Subsidiaries:

Brook Ledge Inc (1)
12 Gotwals Ln, Oley, PA 19547
Tel.: (610) 987-6284
Web Site: http://www.brookledge.com
Sales Range: $10-24.9 Million
Emp.: 35
Long Distance Heavy Hauling Services
N.A.I.C.S.: 484220
Dennis Rittenhouse *(Controller)*

GOUGH INC.
2200 E 88th Dr, Merrillville, IN 46410
Tel.: (219) 756-2200
Web Site: http://www.goughinc.com
Sales Range: $25-49.9 Million
Emp.: 80
Operative Builders
N.A.I.C.S.: 236117
Raymond Gough *(Pres)*
Charlie Blink *(Dir-Safety)*
Dave Warren *(Project Mgr)*
Luis Garcia *(Project Mgr)*

GOULD & ASSOCIATES GLOBAL SERVICES, INC.
412 Violet St, Golden, CO 80401
Tel.: (216) 831-0135   OH
Web Site:
   http://www.gouldglobal.com
Year Founded: 2001
Sales Range: $1-9.9 Million
Emp.: 43
Management Consulting Services & Contract Staffing
N.A.I.C.S.: 541611
Stephen A. Gould *(Pres & CEO)*

GOULD CHEVROLET
3939 Chelsea Rd W, Monticello, MN 55362-3310
Tel.: (763) 295-2911
Web Site:
   http://www.cornerstonechevrolet.com
Year Founded: 1927
Sales Range: $50-74.9 Million
Emp.: 65
Car Whslr
N.A.I.C.S.: 441110
Darrin Berg *(Gen Mgr-Sls)*

GOULD EVANS AFFILIATES P.A.
706 Massachusetts St, Lawrence, KS 66044-2344
Tel.: (785) 842-3800   KS
Web Site:
   http://www.gouldevans.com
Year Founded: 1974
Sales Range: $10-24.9 Million
Emp.: 225

Architectural Services
N.A.I.C.S.: 541310
John Wilkins *(Principal)*
David Reid *(Principal)*
Becky Rimmer *(CFO & Sec)*
Anthony Rohr *(Mng Principal)*
Trudi Hummel *(Chm & Principal)*
Robert Riccardi *(Principal)*
Lauren Maass *(Assoc Principal)*
Sean Zaudke *(Assoc Principal)*
Bob Baum *(Principal)*
Dennis Strait *(Principal)*
Douglas Thornley *(Principal)*
Graham Smith *(Assoc Principal)*
Krista Shepherd *(Principal)*
Steve Carpenter *(Principal)*
John Dimmel *(VP)*
Debra Ford *(VP)*
Richard Kniss *(VP)*
Daniel Zeller *(Principal)*
Kelly Dreyer *(Assoc Principal)*
Emily Harrold *(Assoc Principal)*
Aaron Herring *(Assoc Principal)*

Subsidiaries:

Gould Evans Associates LLC (1)
3136 North 3rd Ave, Phoenix, AZ 85013
Tel.: (602) 234-1140
Web Site: http://www.gouldevans.com
Rev.: $770,000
Emp.: 34
Architectural Services
N.A.I.C.S.: 541310
Amanda Harper *(Dir-Canary)*
Melissa Alexander *(Dir-Canary)*
Eduardo Perez *(Assoc Principal)*
Jim Miller *(Assoc Principal)*

GOULD PAPER CORPORATION
99 Park Ave, New York, NY 10016
Tel.: (212) 301-0000   NY
Web Site:
   https://www.gouldpaper.com
Year Founded: 1924
Printing Papers & Paper Board Mfr & Distr
N.A.I.C.S.: 323113
Michael Duncan *(Pres)*
David H. Berkowitz *(Pres & CEO)*
Joe Ryan *(Exec VP-North America)*
Michael Trachtenberg *(Exec VP-Intl)*
Ed Silver *(CFO)*

Subsidiaries:

BRW Paper Co., Inc. (1)
1435 Bradley Ln Ste 130, Carrollton, TX 75007-3438
Tel.: (469) 568-5000
Web Site: http://www.gouldpaper.com
Emp.: 40
Mfr of Papers
N.A.I.C.S.: 424110
Joe Ryan *(Pres)*

Communications Papers (1)
15 East State St, Doylestown, PA 18901   (100%)
Tel.: (215) 230-3535
Paper Products
N.A.I.C.S.: 424130

Diamond Paper Corporation (1)
21955 Cascades Pkwy, Sterling, VA 20167-1049   (100%)
Tel.: (703) 450-0000
Web Site: http://www.diamondpaper.com
Sales Range: $10-24.9 Million
Emp.: 20
N.A.I.C.S.: 322120

Gould International Packaging (1)
11 Madison Ave Fl 14l, New York, NY 10010-3670
Tel.: (203) 661-9091
Web Site: http://www.gouldpaper.com
Sales Range: $10-24.9 Million
Emp.: 5
Paper Brokers
N.A.I.C.S.: 424110

Gould Paper Company of Maryland LLC (1)
3973 Woods Edge Dr, Davidsonville, MD 21035   (100%)
Tel.: (410) 798-1349
Web Site: http://www.gouldpaper.com
Sales Range: $10-24.9 Million
Emp.: 5
Paper Merchant
N.A.I.C.S.: 424130

Gould Paper Corp. - Chicago (1)
11 Madison Ave, New York, NY 10010   (100%)
Tel.: (212) 301-0001
Web Site: http://www.gouldpaper.com
Specialty Paper Mfr
N.A.I.C.S.: 322120

Gould Paper Corp. - Metro (1)
100 Executive Ave, Edison, NJ 08817-6016   (100%)
Tel.: (732) 248-7800
Web Site: http://www.gouldpaper.com
Sales Range: $10-24.9 Million
Emp.: 25
Newsprint Mill
N.A.I.C.S.: 322120
Mike Duncan *(Mgr-Div)*

Gould Paper Corp. - Mid Atlantic (1)
405 Lakeside Park, Southampton, PA 18966-4077   (100%)
Tel.: (215) 887-9660
Sales Range: $10-24.9 Million
Emp.: 6
Direct Distribution of Paper
N.A.I.C.S.: 424130

Gould Paper North America (1)
25 E St, Winchester, MA 01890
Tel.: (781) 729-2059
Web Site: http://www.gouldpaper.com
Sales Range: $10-24.9 Million
Emp.: 10
Paper Products
N.A.I.C.S.: 424110
Jeff Haut *(VP)*
Tom Ryan *(Pres)*

Legion Paper Corporation (1)
11 Madison Ave, New York, NY 10010-3643
Tel.: (212) 683-6990
Web Site: http://www.legionpaper.com
Sales Range: $10-24.9 Million
Emp.: 12
N.A.I.C.S.: 322120
Michael Ginsburg *(Pres)*
Len Levine *(Treas & VP)*

GOULSTON & STORRS PC
400 Atlantic Ave, Boston, MA 02110-3333
Tel.: (617) 482-1776   MA
Web Site:
   https://www.goulstonstorrs.com
Year Founded: 1900
Sales Range: $100-124.9 Million
Emp.: 201
Legal Advisory Services
N.A.I.C.S.: 541110
Beth Marie Cuzzone *(Dir-Client Svc & Bus Dev)*
Robert DeFabrizio *(Mgr-Library Svcs)*
Elizabeth L. Foster-Nolan *(Dir-Pro Dev)*
Marianne Monagle *(Dir-HR)*
Nancy Needle *(Dir-Legal Recruitment)*
Francis X. Robinson *(Dir-Fiduciary Svcs)*
Jeff Scalzi *(Assoc Dir-Mktg)*
Kevin Smith *(CFO)*
David Avitabile *(Dir-Washington)*
Adam Hundley *(Dir-Boston)*
Kerry Scarlott *(Dir-Boston)*
Michelle Porter *(Dir-Boston)*
William Dillon *(Dir-Boston)*
Gerret Baur *(Dir-Tax Grp)*
Pamela MacKenzie *(Chm-Corp Practice Grp)*
Jennifer Furey *(Chm-Litigation Practice Grp)*

Goulston & Storrs PC—(Continued)

Nordo Nissi *(Head-Electronic Discovery & Litigation Tech)*
Christopher Ende *(Chief Value Officer)*

GOURMET BOUTIQUE
144-02 158th St, Jamaica, NY 11434
Tel.: (718) 977-1200
Web Site:
https://www.gourmetboutique.com
Year Founded: 1995
Sales Range: $25-49.9 Million
Emp.: 348
Salad & Side Dish Mfr
N.A.I.C.S.: 311991
Andrew Murphy *(VP-Ops)*
Vanessa Lindsay *(Dir-Food Safety & Quality Assurance)*
Jan Sussman *(Pres)*
Jody Crystall *(Dir-Customer Svcs)*
Andrew Meidl *(Engr-Plant)*
Noemi Diaz *(Dir-HR)*

GOURMET EXPRESS LLC
204 N Ford St, Gridley, IL 61744-3902
Tel.: (309) 747-4401
Web Site:
http://www.gourmetdining.net
Rev.: $11,800,000
Emp.: 120
Mfr of Frozen Food Specialties
N.A.I.C.S.: 311412
Kevin Scully *(CFO)*

GOURMET GARAGE
52 Greene St, New York, NY 10013
Tel.: (212) 595-5850
Web Site:
http://www.gourmetgarage.com
Rev.: $33,000,000
Emp.: 25
Gourmet Food Stores & Catering Services
N.A.I.C.S.: 445298

GOURMET SERVICES INC.
82 Piedmont Ave, Atlanta, GA 30303
Tel.: (404) 876-5700
Web Site:
http://www.gourmetservicesinc.com
Sales Range: $125-149.9 Million
Emp.: 1,500
Food Service Management
N.A.I.C.S.: 722514
Raymond McClendon *(Pres-Gourmet Hospitality Grp)*
Nathaniel R. Goldston III *(Founder, Chm & CEO)*

GOURMET VEG-PAQ, INC.
4395 Davidson Ave, Gilroy, CA 95020-9519
Tel.: (408) 847-3755
Sales Range: $25-49.9 Million
Emp.: 60
Fruit & Vegetable Whslr
N.A.I.C.S.: 424480
Santos Martinez *(Pres)*
Sara Disney *(CFO)*

GOURMETGIFTBASKETS.COM
60 Gourmet Pl, Exeter, NH 03833
Tel.: (603) 606-5269
Web Site:
https://www.gourmetgiftbaskets.com
Year Founded: 2002
Sales Range: $1-9.9 Million
Emp.: 41
Specialty Food & Drink Gift Baskets Online
N.A.I.C.S.: 459420
Ryan Abood *(CEO)*

GOVDOCS, INC.

355 Randolph Ave Ste 200, Saint Paul, MN 55102
Tel.: (888) 273-3274   MN
Web Site: http://www.govdocs.com
Year Founded: 1999
Labor Law & Human Resource Compliance Information Services
N.A.I.C.S.: 519290
Zach Stabenow *(Co-Founder & CEO)*
Dawn Thompson *(Dir-Inside Sls & Op)*
Kara Kanis *(VP-Growth)*
Mark Richards *(VP-Operations & Fin)*
Kelly Knight *(Dir-Product Dev)*
Ryan Sutter *(Dir-Software Engrng)*
Patricia Mumford *(Dir-Product Compliance)*
Kristen McCabe *(Dir- Client Svcs)*
Sherry Schmidt *(Dir-HR)*
Kaitlyn Weed *(Dir-Production & Fulfillment)*
Ryan Stilwell *(Sr Dir-Acct)*
Jamie Johnson *(Mgr-Shipping)*
Erica Kritsberg *(Mgr-Product Mktg)*

GOVERNMENT ACCOUNTABILITY INSTITUTE
PO Box 12594, Tallahassee, FL 32317-2594
Tel.: (850) 329-7259   DE
Web Site: https://www.g-a-i.org
Year Founded: 2012
Sales Range: $1-9.9 Million
Emp.: 26
Civic & Social Organization
N.A.I.C.S.: 813410
Peter Schweizer *(Pres)*
Stephen K. Bannon *(Chm)*

GOVERNMENT ACQUISITIONS, INC.
720 E Pete Rose Way Ste 360, Cincinnati, OH 45202
Tel.: (513) 721-8700   OH
Web Site: http://www.gov-acq.com
Year Founded: 1989
Sales Range: $100-124.9 Million
Emp.: 50
IT Solutions, Integration & Logistics Services
N.A.I.C.S.: 541519
Bruce Erney *(CFO)*
Jay Lambke *(Pres)*
Jacy Peters *(Acct Exec)*

GOVERNMENT CAPITAL CORPORATION
345 Miron Dr, Southlake, TX 76092
Tel.: (817) 421-5400   TX
Web Site: https://www.govcap.com
Year Founded: 1992
Sales Range: $25-49.9 Million
Emp.: 35
Provider of Credit Services
N.A.I.C.S.: 522299
Stewart Shirey *(Sr VP)*
Tim Temple *(Pres)*

Subsidiaries:

Government Capital Corporation-South Texas   **(1)**
2384 Hwy 59 E, Beeville, TX 78102
Tel.: (361) 362-2760
Provider of Credit Services
N.A.I.C.S.: 522299

Government Capital Corporation-Southeastern Region   **(1)**
303 Hwy 51 S, Brookhaven, MS 39601
Tel.: (601) 823-6000
Web Site: http://www.govcap.com
Sales Range: $50-74.9 Million
Emp.: 3
Provider of Credit Services
N.A.I.C.S.: 522291

GOVERNMENT CONTRACT

SOLUTIONS, INC.
8251 Greensboro Dr Ste 500, McLean, VA 22102
Tel.: (703) 749-2223   VA
Web Site: http://www.gcsinfo.com
Year Founded: 1995
Sales Range: $10-24.9 Million
Emp.: 250
Professional Services & Solutions to Federal Government & Industry Clients
N.A.I.C.S.: 921190
Nicole Geller *(Founder & CEO)*
Tanaz Shahrzad *(VP-Civilian Solutions Grp)*
Gary Polston *(Dir-Missions Support Grp)*
Jennifer Iams *(Dir-HR)*
Mike Murphy *(VP-Intelligence)*
Stephen Passuth *(VP-Fin & Contracts)*

GOVERNMENT CONTRACT-ING RESOURCES, INC.
315 Page Rd Box 7, Pinehurst, NC 28374
Tel.: (910) 215-1900   VA
Web Site: http://www.gcrinc.net
Year Founded: 1984
Sales Range: $25-49.9 Million
Facilities Maintenance & Logistics Management Support Services
N.A.I.C.S.: 561210
J. Don Albritton *(Pres)*
Michael P. Albritton *(VP-Bus Dev)*
Kevin Jernigan *(VP-Mgmt Info & Reporting)*
Mark Gapetz *(VP-Bus Ops)*
Somer Nelson *(VP-Fin & Acctg)*
Tom Amburgey *(CEO)*
Malinda Kelley *(Dir-Mktg)*

Subsidiaries:

PCC Technology Group, LLC   **(1)**
100 Northfield Dr Ste 300, Windsor, CT 06095
Tel.: (860) 242-3299
Web Site: http://www.pcctg.com
Emp.: 200
Develops & Implements Technology Solutions for State & Local Governments & the Energy & Education Sectors
N.A.I.C.S.: 513210
Anand Balasubramanian *(Mgr-Div)*
John Bastin *(Chief Sls Officer)*
Todd Bouillion *(COO)*
Michael Wons *(Pres)*

GOVERNMENT EMPLOYEES HEALTH ASSOCIATION, INC.
310 NE Mulberry St, Lees Summit, MO 64086
Tel.: (816) 257-5500   MO
Web Site: https://www.geha.com
Year Founded: 1939
Non-Profit Federal Health Insurance Association
N.A.I.C.S.: 813910
Aileen Wilkins *(VP-People-Culture)*
Mary Beth Vitale *(Chm)*

GOVERNMENT PERSONNEL MUTUAL LIFE INSURANCE COMPANY
2211 NE Loop 410, San Antonio, TX 78217-4630
Tel.: (210) 357-2222
Web Site: https://www.gpmlife.com
Sales Range: $75-99.9 Million
Emp.: 100
Life Insurance Carrier
N.A.I.C.S.: 524113
Pamela A. Hutchins *(Chief Actuary, Chief Actuary, Sr VP & Sr VP)*
Maria de Lourdes Mendoza *(Treas & VP)*
Robert R. Draper *(VP)*

Peter J. Hennessey III *(Pres, CEO & Chm)*
Peter J. Hennessey IV *(Sr VP-Mktg)*

GOVERNMENT SOURCING SOLUTIONS
3752 Jocelyn St NW, Washington, DC 20015
Tel.: (202) 244-1820
Web Site:
http://www.govsourcing.com
Year Founded: 2005
Sales Range: $1-9.9 Million
Emp.: 6
Government Support Services
N.A.I.C.S.: 921190
David Yarkin *(Pres)*
Mike Smith *(VP-Midwest)*
Courtney A. Carlson *(CFO)*
Nicole Smith *(Dir-Res)*
Nicole Kenney *(VP-Northeast)*
Jane Benton *(VP-South)*
Debra Warren *(Chief Revenue Officer)*
Jason Soza *(VP-West)*

GOVERNMENTAL & EDUCA-TIONAL ASSISTANCE CORPO-RATION
7900 Excelsior Blvd Ste 250, Hopkins, MN 55343
Tel.: (952) 837-0540   AR
Web Site: http://www.vistaprairie.org
Year Founded: 1997
Sales Range: $50-74.9 Million
Emp.: 530
Elder Care Services
N.A.I.C.S.: 623312
Morris E. Knopf *(Pres)*

GOVIND DEVELOPMENT, LLC.
9359 IH 37 Ste A, Corpus Christi, TX 78409
Tel.: (361) 241-2777
Web Site:
https://www.govinddevelopment.com
Year Founded: 2007
Sales Range: $10-24.9 Million
Emp.: 145
Engineeering Services
N.A.I.C.S.: 541330
Govind Nadkarni *(Pres & CEO)*
Andy Bennett *(Exec VP)*
Christian Penuela *(VP-Technical Svcs-South East Asia & Middle East Ops)*

GOVPLACE, INC.
1886 Metro Ctr Dr Ste 100, Reston, VA 20190
Tel.: (703) 435-6195   DE
Web Site: http://www.govplace.com
Year Founded: 1995
Sales Range: $25-49.9 Million
Emp.: 55
Government Information Technology Software & Services
N.A.I.C.S.: 541511
Brian C. Seagrave *(VP & Gen Mgr-Svcs & Solutions)*
Steve Hoffman *(VP-Sls)*
Suzanne Liscouski *(VP-Strategy & Bus Dev)*
Patrick Herwig *(Sr VP-Sls)*
Jim Evans *(Sr Dir-DoD Sls)*
Shannon Edwards *(Mktg Mgr)*
Ronnie Vliet *(VP-Tech)*
Simone Feldman *(CEO)*

GOWAN COMPANY LLC
370 S Main St, Yuma, AZ 85364-2312
Tel.: (928) 783-8844
Web Site: http://www.gowanco.com
Year Founded: 1990

Sales Range: $10-24.9 Million
Emp.: 90
Farm Supplies Distr
N.A.I.C.S.: 424910
Chad Dyer *(Product Mgr-Justice)*
Olivier Deneufbourg *(Gen Mgr-EUMENA)*

Subsidiaries:

Isagro S.p.A. **(1)**
Via Caldera 21, 20153, Milan, Italy
Tel.: (39) 02409011
Web Site: https://www.isagro.com
Rev.: $120,407,347
Assets: $235,124,686
Liabilities: $133,195,029
Net Worth: $101,929,657
Earnings: ($15,573,893)
Emp.: 343
Fiscal Year-end: 12/31/2019
Agrochemical Mfr
N.A.I.C.S.: 325320
Roberto Bonetti *(Chm & CEO)*
Alessandro Chieffi *(Sec)*
Gianluca Fusco *(COO)*
Ruggero Gambini *(CFO)*
Maria Teresa Agazzani *(Grp Dir-HR & Comm)*
Lorenzo Campioni *(Grp Dir-Sls)*
Antonino Ferrario *(Grp Dir-Regulatory Affairs)*
Claudio Notaristefano *(Grp Dir-Mktg & Bus Dev)*
Francesco Sasso *(Grp Dir-Supply Chain)*

Subsidiary (Non-US):

Isagro Hellas Ltd **(2)**
39 Pindou Str, 18344, Moschato, Athens, Greece
Tel.: (30) 2104813637
Web Site: http://www.isagrohellas.com
Sales Range: $25-49.9 Million
Emp.: 2
Basic Inorganic Chemical Mfr
N.A.I.C.S.: 325180

Subsidiary (Domestic):

Isagro Italia S.R.L. **(2)**
Via Caldera 21d, 20153, Milano, Italy
Tel.: (39) 02452801
Web Site: http://www.isagro.com
Chemical Industry

Subsidiary (US):

Isagro USA, Inc. **(2)**
430 Davis Dr Ste 240, Morrisville, NC
27560-6802 **(100%)**
Tel.: (919) 321-5200
Web Site: http://www.isagro-usa.com
Sales Range: $25-49.9 Million
Emp.: 11
Pesticide & Agricultural Chemical Mfr
N.A.I.C.S.: 325320

Affiliate (Domestic):

Siapa S.r.l. **(2)**
Via Caldera 21d, 20153, Milan, Italy
Tel.: (39) 02409461
Web Site: http://www.siapa.mi.it
Sales Range: $25-49.9 Million
Emp.: 50
Basic Inorganic Chemical Mfr
N.A.I.C.S.: 325180

GOWER CORPORATION
355 Woodruff Rd Ste 106, Greenville, SC 29607
Web Site: http://www.gower.com
Year Founded: 1955
Sales Range: $10-24.9 Million
Emp.: 260
Mfr of Conveyors & Conveying Equipment
N.A.I.C.S.: 333922
Carl Whitmer *(Pres)*

Subsidiaries:

Engineered Products LLC **(1)**
355 Woodruff Rd Highland Park Ste 204, Greenville, SC 29607
Tel.: (864) 234-4888
Web Site: http://www.engprod.com

Mfr of Material Handling Equipment
N.A.I.C.S.: 337126
Barry Templeton *(VP-Sls)*

MP Husky Corporation **(1)**
204 Old Piedmont Hwy, Greenville, SC
29605
Tel.: (864) 234-4800
Web Site: http://www.mphusky.com
Sales Range: $10-24.9 Million
Emp.: 100
Mfr of Fabricated Plate Work
N.A.I.C.S.: 332313
Dusty Henry *(Pres)*

The Jobscope Corporation **(1)**
355 Woodruff Rd Ste 210, Greenville, SC
29607-3494 **(100%)**
Tel.: (864) 458-3100
Web Site: http://www.jobscope.com
Sales Range: $10-24.9 Million
Emp.: 25
Prepackaged Software Mfr
N.A.I.C.S.: 513210
Hank Sanders *(Pres)*

GOWIRELESS, INC.,
9970 W Cheyenne Ave, Las Vegas, NV 89129
Tel.: (866) 487-1222
Web Site: http://www.gowireless.com
Year Founded: 1995
Sales Range: $10-24.9 Million
Emp.: 1,001
Retailer of Verizon Wireless Products
N.A.I.C.S.: 517112

GOYA FOODS, INC.
100 Seaview Dr, Secaucus, NJ
07094-1800
Tel.: (201) 348-4900　　　　　**NY**
Web Site: http://www.goya.com
Year Founded: 1936
Sales Range: $1-4.9 Billion
Emp.: 2,500
Food Products Mfr & Distr
N.A.I.C.S.: 424410
Conrad O. Colon *(VP)*
Joseph Perez *(Sr VP)*
Alvaro Serrano *(Product Mgr)*
Robert Unanue *(Pres)*

Subsidiaries:

Goya En Espana S.A. **(1)**
Carretera Sevilla Malaga KM 5 4, PO Box
60, Alcala De Guadaira, 41500, Seville,
Spain
Tel.: (34) 955632032
Web Site: http://www.goya.com
Sales Range: $10-24.9 Million
Emp.: 28
Food Processing Services
N.A.I.C.S.: 311999

Goya Foods Inc. **(1)**
5 Goya Dr, Webster, MA 01570
Tel.: (508) 949-6100
Web Site: http://www.goya.com
Sales Range: $10-24.9 Million
Emp.: 20
Food Processing Services
N.A.I.C.S.: 424490
Carlos Mangual *(Gen Mgr)*

Goya Foods of California **(1)**
15320 Salt Lake Ave, City of Industry, CA
91745
Tel.: (626) 961-6161
Web Site: http://www.goya.com
Sales Range: $25-49.9 Million
Emp.: 150
Food Processing Services
N.A.I.C.S.: 424410
Robert Anthony Unanue *(Mgr-Emerging Markets)*
Ralph de Leon *(Mgr-Ops)*

Goya Foods of Florida **(1)**
13300 NW 25th St, Miami, FL 33182
Tel.: (305) 592-3150
Web Site: http://www.goyafoods.com
Sales Range: $25-49.9 Million
Emp.: 200
Distr of Food
N.A.I.C.S.: 424820

Robert Unanue *(Pres)*
Cynthia Chipi *(Dir-Mktg)*
Raul Zabala *(Controller)*
Roberto Echavarria *(Supvr-Sls)*

Goya Foods of Florida **(1)**
10425 S Orange Ave, Orlando, FL 32824
Tel.: (407) 816-7776
Web Site: http://www.goya.com
Sales Range: $10-24.9 Million
Emp.: 30
Food Processing Services
N.A.I.C.S.: 424410
Lenmim Cardemas *(Gen Mgr)*

Goya Foods of Great Lakes New
York **(1)**
200 S Main St, Angola, NY 14006-1534
Tel.: (716) 549-0076
Web Site: http://www.goyafoods.com
Rev.: $15,000,000
Emp.: 100
Canned Foods, Dried Beans, Sloppy Joe
Mix, Tomato Sauce, Corned Beef & Chicken
N.A.I.C.S.: 311421
Robert J. Drago *(Pres)*

Goya Foods of Illinois **(1)**
1401 Remington Blvd, Bolingbrook, IL
60490
Tel.: (815) 230-1400
Web Site: http://www.goya.com
Sales Range: $25-49.9 Million
Emp.: 115
Food Processing Services
N.A.I.C.S.: 424410
Rafael Rodriguez *(Gen Mgr)*

Goya Foods of Long Island **(1)**
201 Gruman Rd, Bethpage, NY 11714
Tel.: (516) 349-9752
Web Site: http://www.goya.com
Sales Range: $10-24.9 Million
Emp.: 110
Food Processing Services
N.A.I.C.S.: 424410

Goya Foods of Madrid **(1)**
Avenida Constitucion 115 Poligono Industrial Monte Boyal, Casarrubios Del Monte,
45950, Toledo, Spain
Tel.: (34) 918188000
Web Site: http://www.goya.com
Purveyor of Spanish Food Product Distr
N.A.I.C.S.: 445110

Goya Foods of Puerto Rico **(1)**
Industrial Park Luchetti Francisco J Goya
Ave, Bayamon, PR 00961
Tel.: (787) 740-4900
Web Site: http://www.goya.com
Sales Range: $50-74.9 Million
Emp.: 600
Food Processing Services
N.A.I.C.S.: 311422
Carlos A. Unanue *(Pres)*

Goya Foods of South Jersey **(1)**
1 Industrial Way, Pedricktown, NJ 08067
Tel.: (856) 423-9300
Web Site: http://www.goya.com
Sales Range: $10-24.9 Million
Emp.: 70
Food Processing Services
N.A.I.C.S.: 424410

Goya Foods of Texas **(1)**
30602 Goya Rd, Brookshire, TX 77041
Tel.: (713) 266-9834
Web Site: http://www.goya.com
Sales Range: $10-24.9 Million
Emp.: 40
Food Processing Services
N.A.I.C.S.: 424410
Evelio Fernandez *(Gen Mgr)*

Goya Foods of the Dominican Republic, S.A. **(1)**
Kilometro 17 Autopista 6 de Noviembre,
San Cristobal, Santo Domingo, Dominican
Republic
Tel.: (809) 5414900
Web Site: http://www.goya.com
Food Processing Services
N.A.I.C.S.: 311999
Rose Reyes *(Gen Mgr)*

GOYETTE MECHANICAL
3842 Gorey Ave, Flint, MI 48506

Tel.: (810) 743-6883
Web Site:
　　https://www.goyettemechanical.com
Sales Range: $50-74.9 Million
Emp.: 150
Mechanical Contractor
N.A.I.C.S.: 238220
Dominic Goyette *(Pres & CEO)*
Curtis William LaLonde *(VP & Gen
Mgr-Svc)*
Carl Matt Burke *(Sr Mgr-Acct)*
Tammy Langley *(Controller)*
Mike Anson *(Mgr-Residential Svc)*
Tom Goyette *(Dir-Safety)*
Leif Johnson *(Mgr-Comml & Industrial
Svc)*
Cherie Parks *(Mgr-Office & Personnel)*
Randy Porter *(Mgr-Building Controls)*
Matt Wendling *(Project Mgr-Facility)*
Kameron Williams *(Mgr-Customer
Care)*

GP COMPANIES INC.
1174 Northland Dr, Mendota Heights,
MN 55120
Tel.: (651) 454-6500
Web Site:
　　http://www.generalpump.com
Sales Range: $10-24.9 Million
Emp.: 100
Pumps & Floor Machine Products
N.A.I.C.S.: 332721
Eric Stenborg *(Engr-Design)*
Jared Grymaloski *(Mgr-Bus Unit)*
Marc Palecek *(Mgr-Sls)*
Reed Peterson *(Mgr-Bus Unit)*
Mark Halverson *(Product Mgr)*

GP DESIGN, INC.
1185 W Mahalo Pl, Compton, CA
90220-5444
Tel.: (310) 638-8731
Sales Range: $10-24.9 Million
Emp.: 15
Miscellaneous Textile Product Mfr
N.A.I.C.S.: 314999
Glenn Aoyama *(Pres)*
Margaret Aoyama *(Treas & Sec)*

GP LAND & CARPET CORPORATION
32 Marway Cir, Rochester, NY 14624
Tel.: (585) 637-2828
Web Site:
　　http://www.gpflooringsolutions.com
Year Founded: 1989
Sales Range: $10-24.9 Million
Emp.: 34
Flooring Installation Services
N.A.I.C.S.: 238330
Abby Reinhard *(Owner & Pres)*
Scott Baker *(Dir-Ops)*
Tim Glassbrook *(Dir-Sls)*
Linda Nauerth *(Mgr-Admin)*
Josh Reinhard *(Dir-Project Mgmt)*

GPA TECHNOLOGIES, INC.
2368 Eastman Ave Ste 8, Ventura,
CA 93003-5770
Tel.: (805) 643-7878
Web Site: https://www.gpatech.com
Year Founded: 1993
Sales Range: $1-9.9 Million
Emp.: 50
Engineering & IT Services
N.A.I.C.S.: 541330
Michael Vaswani *(Pres & CEO)*
Darrell Boynton *(Program Mgr)*

**GPA, SPECIALTY SUBSTRATE
SOLUTIONS**
8740 W 50th St, McCook, IL 60525
Tel.: (773) 650-2020
Web Site: http://www.askgpa.com
Rev.: $21,000,000

GPA, Specialty Substrate Solutions—(Continued)

Emp.: 55
Industrial & Personal Service Paper
N.A.I.C.S.: 424130
Bob Niesen (Pres & CEO)
Mary Ann Geers (Sr VP-Corp Strategy)
David Maucieri (Sr VP-Sls)
Karol Mountcastle (Mgr-Bus Dev)
Kevin Cooper (VP-South Central)
Anna Ruffolo (Sr VP-Fin & Ops & Head-Acctg, Ops & Pur Depts)
Julie Shakoor (Mgr-Bus Dev)
Mike McConville (VP-Northeast)
Jules Gonzales (VP-Central Reg)
Trina May (Dir-Bus Dev-Client Mktg Svcs)
Wendy Sherbondy (Mgr-Bus Dev)
Jim Bender (VP-West)
Rob Olson (Mgr-Bus Dev)

GPB CAPITAL HOLDINGS, LLC
535 West 24th St Fl 4th, New York, NY 10011
Tel.: (212) 235-2650
Year Founded: 2013
Private Investment Firm
N.A.I.C.S.: 523999
David Gentile (CEO)
Robert Yaeger (VP-Fin Strategy)

Subsidiaries:

Alliance Physical Therapy Partners, LLC   (1)
3030 N Rocky Point Dr W Ste 670, Tampa, FL 33607
Tel.: (877) 392-3036
Web Site: http://www.allianceptp.com
Financial & Management Solutions Services
N.A.I.C.S.: 523999
Mark Andrzejewski (CEO)
Mark Marriage (CFO)
Viera Vorasarn (VP-Ops)
Shannon Hofmeister (Dir-Bus Dev)
Kenneth Chu (Dir-Acctg)
Scott Knowlson (Dir-Compliance)
Kevin McAlpin (Dir-Recruiting)

Subsidiary (Domestic):

Back In Motion Physical Therapy   (2)
94 Main St, Gorham, ME 04038-1340
Tel.: (207) 699-4111
Web Site:
http://www.mainephysicaltherapy.com
Offices of All Other Miscellaneous Health Practitioners
N.A.I.C.S.: 621399
Michel Brunet (Owner)

MatrixOneSource, LLC   (1)
9016 Philips Hwy, Jacksonville, FL 32256
Tel.: (866) 453-2722
Web Site: http://www.matrixonesource.com
PEO Services, Payroll, Human Resources & Risk Management & Services
N.A.I.C.S.: 561499

Prime Motor Group   (1)
375 Providence Hwy, Westwood, MA 02090
Tel.: (781) 688-1000
Web Site: http://www.driveprime.com
Car Dealership
N.A.I.C.S.: 441110
Todd Skelton (Pres & CEO)

Surge Resources Inc.   (1)
300 Hanover St, Manchester, NH 03104
Web Site: http://www.surgehrs.com
Human Resources & Executive Search Consulting Services
N.A.I.C.S.: 541612
George Attar (Pres)

GPBC INC.
120 W Washington St Ste 1, Ann Arbor, MI 48104-1356
Tel.: (734) 741-7325
Sales Range: $10-24.9 Million
Emp.: 120
Brewery Mfr

N.A.I.C.S.: 312120
Jon Carlson (Co-Pres)
Scott Keller (Mgr)
Kelly Carmody (Mgr)

GPC INTERNATIONAL, INC.
510 Broadhollow Rd, Melville, NY 11747
Tel.: (631) 752-9600   DE
Web Site:
http://www.northamericancapital.com
Sales Range: $10-24.9 Million
Emp.: 10
Holding Company
N.A.I.C.S.: 337214
Stanley Roth (Chm)
Michael Berman (Controller)

Subsidiaries:

Chartpak Inc   (1)
1 River Rd, Leeds, MA 01053
Tel.: (413) 584-5446
Web Site: http://www.chartpak.com
Tape, Pressure Sensitive: Made From Purchased Materials
N.A.I.C.S.: 322220
Steven W. Roth (Pres)

GPD GROUP
520 S Main St Ste 2531, Akron, OH 44311
Tel.: (330) 572-2100
Web Site: https://www.gpdgroup.com
Rev.: $14,000,000
Emp.: 175
Architectural Services
N.A.I.C.S.: 541310
Mo Darwish (Dir-Plng)
James R. Shives (CFO)
Joseph Kidder (Dir-Mktg)

Subsidiaries:

Timmerman Geotechnical Group Inc   (1)
2685 Gilchrist Rd, Akron, OH 44305
Tel.: (330) 733-6054
Engineeering Services
N.A.I.C.S.: 541330
David Timmerman (Pres)

GPD, PC
2291 W Broadway Ste 4, Missoula, MT 59802
Tel.: (406) 721-5936   MT
Web Site: http://www.gpdinc.com
Year Founded: 1979
Sales Range: $25-49.9 Million
Emp.: 16
Engineering, Design & Management Services
N.A.I.C.S.: 541490
Glen Sparks (Sr Engr-Mechanical)
Carl Rummel (Principal)

GPG CONSTRUCTION & MODULAR HOMES, LLC.
370 Hope St Ste 2302, Stamford, CT 06906
Tel.: (203) 965-0084
Year Founded: 1980
Sales Range: $10-24.9 Million
Emp.: 10
Housing Construction Services
N.A.I.C.S.: 236117
Kai Young (VP-Ops)

GPM ASSOCIATES LLC
45 High Tech Dr, Rush, NY 14543
Tel.: (800) 836-7237
Web Site:
http://www.forbesproducts.com
Emp.: 100
Looseleaf Binders & Devices
N.A.I.C.S.: 323111

John Dobberton (VP-Fin)
Thomas C. McDermott (Owner)
Jim McDermott (Pres)

GPM INDUSTRIES, INC.
110 Gateway Dr, Macon, GA 31210
Tel.: (478) 471-7867
Web Site:
http://www.gpmindustries.com
Sales Range: $10-24.9 Million
Emp.: 50
Industrial Machinery & Equipment
N.A.I.C.S.: 423830
Dave Herrick (Engr-Application)
Bob Cooper (Engr-Outside Sls)

GPOD OF IDAHO
865 E 1400 N, Shelley, ID 83274
Tel.: (208) 357-7646
Year Founded: 1968
Sales Range: $50-74.9 Million
Emp.: 150
Potato Whslr
N.A.I.C.S.: 424590
Kevin Searle (Gen Mgr)

GPODS, INC.
1308 Oak Ave, Carlsbad, CA 92008
Tel.: (760) 681-6665   NV
Year Founded: 2017
Assets: $97,629
Liabilities: $1,424,709
Net Worth: ($1,327,080)
Earnings: ($453,942)
Emp.: 3
Fiscal Year-end: 03/31/23
Office Furniture Designing & Mfr
N.A.I.C.S.: 337211
Robert L. Dolan (Founder, Chm, Pres, CEO, CFO & Treas)

GPROULX INC.
3275 SW 42nd St, Fort Lauderdale, FL 33312
Tel.: (954) 327-3465
Web Site: http://www.g-proulx.com
Sales Range: $25-49.9 Million
Emp.: 55
Drywall Materials
N.A.I.C.S.: 423320
Jocelyn Vinet (Pres)

GR WOOD INC.
518 S Park Dr, Mooresville, IN 46158
Tel.: (317) 831-8060
Web Site: http://www.grwood.net
Rev.: $14,000,000
Emp.: 5
Veneer
N.A.I.C.S.: 423310
Gunther Rodatz (Owner)

GRA, INC.
2317 Falling Creek Rd, Silver Spring, MD 20904
Tel.: (940) 668-2506
Web Site: http://www.grainc.com
Year Founded: 1995
Rev.: $11,300,000
Emp.: 124
Management Consulting Services
N.A.I.C.S.: 541612
Pete Dickson (VP-Admin)
Gary Koca (Principal)
Tim Dirks (Chm)
Daliza Salas (Pres & CEO)
Joan P. Fegan (VP-Strategic Rels)

GRABIAK CHEVROLET, INC.
Route 22, New Alexandria, PA 15670
Tel.: (724) 668-2231
Web Site: http://www.grabiak.com
Sales Range: $10-24.9 Million
Emp.: 20
Car Whslr
N.A.I.C.S.: 441110

Joe Policastro (COO)

GRABILL CABINET COMPANY
13844 Sawmill Rd, Grabill, IN 46741
Tel.: (260) 376-1500
Web Site:
https://www.grabillcabinets.com
Year Founded: 1946
Sales Range: $10-24.9 Million
Emp.: 210
Millwork Services
N.A.I.C.S.: 321918
Vilas Schertz (Founder)
Martin Heiny (Pres)

GRABLE & ASSOCIATES REALTY
201 N Line St, Columbia City, IN 46725
Tel.: (260) 244-7299
Web Site:
http://www.grableandassociates.com
Sales Range: $10-24.9 Million
Emp.: 12
Real Estate Agency Services
N.A.I.C.S.: 531210
Angela Grable Garcia (Pres)

GRABOYES COMMERCIAL WINDOW COMPANY
4050 S 26 St Ste160, Philadelphia, PA 19112
Tel.: (215) 625-8810
Web Site: http://www.graboyes.com
Year Founded: 1984
Sales Range: $25-49.9 Million
Emp.: 42
Lumber, Plywood, Millwork & Wood Panel Merchant Whslr
N.A.I.C.S.: 423310
John Scott (Dir-Fin)
Bill Steedle (Dir-Sls & Estimating)
Terry Graboyes (Pres & CEO)
Les Schlemback (Project Mgr)

GRACE ALASKA INC.
6689 Changepoint Dr, Anchorage, AK 99518
Tel.: (907) 646-4800   AK
Web Site:
https://www.changepointalaska.com
Year Founded: 2001
Sales Range: $10-24.9 Million
Religious Services
N.A.I.C.S.: 813110
Brenda Hanson (Fin Dir)

GRACE BROTHERS LTD.
1560 Sherman Ave Ste 900, Evanston, IL 60201-4809
Tel.: (847) 733-1230   IL
Year Founded: 1986
Sales Range: $100-124.9 Million
Emp.: 15
Provider of Investment Services
N.A.I.C.S.: 523150
Karen Arredondo (Office Mgr)
Chris Rogoski (Portfolio Mgr)
Christopher Rogowski (Portfolio Mgr)
Bradford Todd Whitmore (Mng Partner)

GRACE DISCOUNT FOODS INC.
17171 Clay County Hwy, Red Boiling Springs, TN 37150
Tel.: (615) 699-3523
Sales Range: $10-24.9 Million
Emp.: 184
Provider of Grocery Services
N.A.I.C.S.: 445110
Melvin Grace (Pres)

GRACE ENERGY CORP.
2485 W Old 66 Blvd, Carthage, MO 64836
Tel.: (417) 358-7300

Web Site:
http://www.graceenergy.com
Rev.: $70,000,000
Emp.: 35
Petroleum Bulk Stations
N.A.I.C.S.: 424710
Jerry Perry *(Pres & CEO)*
Brent Smith *(Comptroller)*
Wayne Gruenewald *(Dir-Corp Mdsg)*
Mike Thomas *(VP & Dir-HR)*
Greg Vestal *(Dir-Motor Fuels)*

GRACE HEALTH
181 W Emmett St, Battle Creek, MI
49037-2963
Tel.: (269) 965-8866   MI
Web Site:
https://www.gracehealthmi.org
Year Founded: 1986
Emp.: 300
Family Health Care Services
N.A.I.C.S.: 621498
Scott Hutchings *(CFO & VP)*
A. J. Jones *(Pres & CEO)*
Peter Chang *(Chief Medical Officer & VP)*
Tera Wilson *(COO-Core Svcs & VP)*
Jill Wise *(COO-Specialty Svcs & VP)*
Sonja Elder *(CIO & VP)*
Rose Miller *(Chm)*
Barbara Comai *(Vice Chm)*
James Reed *(Sec)*

GRACE HEALTHCARE, LLC
801 Broad Ste 300, Chattanooga, TN
37402
Tel.: (423) 308-1845   TN
Web Site: http://www.grace-healthcare.com
Year Founded: 1997
Sales Range: $75-99.9 Million
Emp.: 2,310
Owns/Manages Nursing & Assisted
Living Facilities
N.A.I.C.S.: 623110
Craig D. Taylor *(Sec & Chief Credit Officer)*
Sue Birchett *(Dir-Quality Assurance)*
Tracy Surdyk *(Dir-HR & Corp Compliance)*
Brigetta Nethery *(Dir-Clinical Svcs)*
Mike Carson *(VP-Clinical Svcs)*
John P. O'Brien Jr. *(CEO & Principal)*

Subsidiaries:

Grace Healthcare of Tucker   (1)
2165 Idlewood Rd, Tucker, GA 30084
Tel.: (770) 934-3172
Web Site: http://www.gracehctucker.com
Sales Range: $25-49.9 Million
Emp.: 150
Nursing Care Facility Operator
N.A.I.C.S.: 623311

GRACE HOMES COLORADO
786 Valley Ct, Grand Junction, CO
81505
Tel.: (970) 523-5555
Sales Range: $10-24.9 Million
Emp.: 45
New Single Family Housing Construction Services
N.A.I.C.S.: 236115
Terry Lawernce *(Pres)*

GRACE HOSPICE
2141 E Broadway Dr Ste 118,
Tempe, AZ 85282
Tel.: (480) 775-2599   OK
Web Site:
http://www.gracehospiceaz.com
Year Founded: 2009
Sales Range: $10-24.9 Million
Emp.: 222
Hospice Care Services
N.A.I.C.S.: 621610
April Bolles *(Exec Dir)*

GRACE HOSPITAL
2307 W 14th St, Cleveland, OH
44113
Tel.: (216) 687-1500   OH
Web Site:
https://www.gracehospital.org
Year Founded: 1910
Sales Range: $25-49.9 Million
Emp.: 257
Health Care Srvices
N.A.I.C.S.: 622110
Michelle Hennis *(Dir-Fin)*
Rajive Khanna *(Pres & CEO)*

GRACE INVESTMENT COMPANY, INC.
518 College Ave, Alva, OK 73717
Tel.: (580) 327-3300   OK
Year Founded: 1978
Sales Range: $10-24.9 Million
Emp.: 60
Bank Holding Company
N.A.I.C.S.: 551111
Ken Schultz *(Pres/CEO-Banks)*
Peggy Jean Wisdom *(Chm & CEO)*

Subsidiaries:

Alva State Bank & Trust
Company   (1)
518 College Ave, Alva, OK 73717
Tel.: (580) 327-3300
Web Site: http://www.alvastatebank.com
Sales Range: $1-9.9 Million
Emp.: 38
Commericial Banking
N.A.I.C.S.: 522110
Ken Schultz *(Pres & CEO)*

First National Bank in Okeene   (1)
124 N Main, Okeene, OK 73763
Tel.: (580) 822-3300
Web Site: http://www.fnbokeene.com
Sales Range: $1-9.9 Million
Emp.: 10
Commericial Banking
N.A.I.C.S.: 522110
Ken Schultz *(Pres & CEO)*
Mark Hoffman *(VP)*
Matt Boeckman *(Asst VP)*

The First State Bank, Kiowa,
Kansas   (1)
546 Main St, Kiowa, KS 67070
Tel.: (620) 825-4147
Web Site: http://www.fstbanc.com
Sales Range: $1-9.9 Million
Emp.: 13
Commericial Banking
N.A.I.C.S.: 522110
Ken Schultz *(Pres & CEO)*
Peggy Jean Wisdom *(Chm)*

GRACE LIMOUSINE, LLC
995 Goffstown Rd, Manchester, NH
03102
Tel.: (603) 666-0203   NH
Web Site: https://www.gracelimo.com
Year Founded: 1990
Sales Range: $1-9.9 Million
Emp.: 50
Limousine Service
N.A.I.C.S.: 485320
Michael Campbell *(Pres & CEO)*

Subsidiaries:

Black Tie Limousine Inc.   (1)
Ward Hill Business Park 25 Bond St, Haverhill, MA 01835
Web Site: http://www.blacktielimo.com
Rev.: $3,800,000
All Other Transit & Ground Passenger
Transportation
N.A.I.C.S.: 485999

GRACE LUTHERAN FOUNDATION
3410 Sky Park Blvd, Eau Claire, WI
54702
Tel.: (715) 832-3003   WI

Web Site:
https://www.graceluthfound.com
Year Founded: 1961
Sales Range: $10-24.9 Million
Emp.: 522
Elderly People Assisted Living Services
N.A.I.C.S.: 623312

GRACE MANAGEMENT GROUP, LLC
951 S Pine St Ste 200, Spartanburg,
SC 29302
Tel.: (864) 515-9515
Web Site: https://www.gracemg.com
Year Founded: 1975
Sales Range: $75-99.9 Million
Emp.: 300
Holding Company; Candles, Cosmetics & Clothing Accessories Retailer
N.A.I.C.S.: 551112
Robert E. Caldwell Sr. *(Pres)*
Stacey Petty *(Coord-Fragrance Lab)*
Shannon Redish *(Product Mgr)*

Subsidiaries:

Greenleaf, Inc.   (1)
951 S Pine St, Spartanburg, SC 29302
Tel.: (864) 515-9515
Web Site: http://www.greenleafgifts.com
Sales Range: $10-24.9 Million
Emp.: 20
Fragrance & Beauty Supplies Retailer
N.A.I.C.S.: 456120
Robert E. Caldwell Sr. *(Pres)*

The Bridgewater Candle Company,
LLC   (1)
951 S Pine St Ste 105, Spartanburg, SC
29302
Tel.: (864) 542-8062
Web Site:
http://www.bridgewatercandles.com
Sales Range: $1-9.9 Million
Emp.: 25
Candle Retailer
N.A.I.C.S.: 459999
Robert E. Caldwell Sr. *(Pres)*

Votivo, LLC   (1)
951 S Pine St Ste 135, Spartanburg, SC
29302
Tel.: (864) 515-9515
Web Site: http://www.votivo.com
Sales Range: $1-9.9 Million
Candle Retailer
N.A.I.C.S.: 459999
Robert E. Caldwell Sr. *(Pres)*

GRACE MEDICAL HOME, INC.
51 Pennsylvania St, Orlando, FL
32806
Tel.: (407) 936-2785
Web Site:
http://www.gracemedicalhome.org
Sales Range: $1-9.9 Million
Primary Care Facility
N.A.I.C.S.: 621999
Stephanie Nelson Garris *(Exec Dir)*
Johnathan Lein *(Case Mgr)*
Lynn Ivanek Fleming *(Dir-Philanthropy)*

GRACELAND COLLEGE CENTER FOR PROFESSIONAL DEVELOPMENT AND LIFELONG LEARNING, INC.
6900 Squibb Rd, Mission, KS 66202
Tel.: (913) 748-5082   MO
Web Site: https://www.skillpath.com
Year Founded: 1994
Sales Range: $25-49.9 Million
Emp.: 252
Business & Professional Training
Services
N.A.I.C.S.: 611430

GRACELAND FRUIT INC.
1123 Main St, Frankfort, MI 49635
Tel.: (231) 352-7181

Web Site:
https://www.gracelandfruit.com
Sales Range: $25-49.9 Million
Emp.: 140
Fruit Distr
N.A.I.C.S.: 311423

GRACIANO CORPORATION
209 Sigma Dr, Pittsburgh, PA 15238-2826
Tel.: (412) 963-8400
Web Site: http://www.graciano.com
Year Founded: 1916
Sales Range: $10-24.9 Million
Emp.: 30
Masonry & Other Stonework Services
N.A.I.C.S.: 238140
Glenn Foglio *(Pres)*

GRACIE SQUARE HOSPITAL
420 E 76th St, New York, NY 10021
Tel.: (212) 434-5300   NY
Web Site: https://www.nygsh.org
Year Founded: 1958
Sales Range: $25-49.9 Million
Emp.: 317
Mental Health Care Services
N.A.I.C.S.: 623220
David Wiecks *(CFO)*
Roger Wolfsohn *(Dir-Medical)*
Frank Bruno *(CEO)*

GRACON CORPORATION
7221 E US Hwy 34, Loveland, CO
80537
Tel.: (970) 667-2203
Web Site: http://www.graconllc.com
Year Founded: 1981
Rev.: $12,245,861
Emp.: 35
General Contractors
N.A.I.C.S.: 238220
Matthew Hannah *(Project Mgr)*
Derek Dykstra *(Pres)*

GRADCO HOLDINGS, LLC
371 Coronado Center Dr Ste 200,
Henderson, NV 89052
Tel.: (702) 940-2266   NV
Web Site: http://www.gradco.com
Year Founded: 1973
Sales Range: $10-24.9 Million
Emp.: 35
Supplier of Paper Handling Equipment to the Office Automation Market
N.A.I.C.S.: 333248
Darcy Hollinger *(Controller)*

Subsidiaries:

Gradco (Japan), Ltd.   (1)
Shin-Osaki Kangyo Bldg 5F 1-6-4 Osaki,
Shinagawa-ku, Tokyo, 141-0032,
Japan   (100%)
Tel.: (81) 357591501
Web Site: http://www.gradco.co.jp
Office Machines Mfr & Sales
N.A.I.C.S.: 333310

Gradco (USA), Inc.   (1)
871 Coronado Center Dr Ste 200, Henderson, NV 89052   (100%)
Tel.: (702) 940-2266
Web Site: http://www.gradco.co.jp
Holding Company; Supplier of Paper Handling Equipment to the Office Automation
Market
N.A.I.C.S.: 333310

GRADE A MARKET INC.
360 Connecticut Ave, Norwalk, CT
06854
Tel.: (203) 838-0504
Web Site: http://www.shoprite.com
Sales Range: $150-199.9 Million
Emp.: 1,000
Independent Supermarket
N.A.I.C.S.: 445110

Grade A Market Inc.—(Continued)

Rocco Cingari (Pres)
Jim Tarantio (CFO)
Robert Procaccini (Mgr-Adv)

GRADE EIGHT CORP
4060 E Plano Pkwy Ste B, Plano, TX
75074
Tel.: (855) 928-8222
Web Site:
https://www.gradeeight.com
Emp.: 100
Industrial Equipment Whsr
N.A.I.C.S.: 423840
John B. Smart III (Pres & CEO)

GRADEX INC.
12900 N Meridian St Ste 120, Car-
mel, IN 46032
Tel.: (317) 573-3970 IN
Web Site: http://gradexinc.com
Year Founded: 1981
Sales Range: $75-99.9 Million
Emp.: 400
Provider of Excavation Services
N.A.I.C.S.: 238910
Thomas E. Dapp (CEO, Founder &
Chm)

GRADUATE PLASTICS, INC.
15800 NW 15th Ave, Miami, FL
33169
Tel.: (305) 687-0405
Web Site:
https://www.quantumstorage.com
Year Founded: 1992
Sales Range: $10-24.9 Million
Emp.: 226
Plastics Product Mfr
N.A.I.C.S.: 326199
Anthony Cohen (Pres)

GRADY BRITTON, INC.
107 SE Washington St Ste 300, Port-
land, OR 97214-2613
Tel.: (503) 228-4118 OR
Web Site:
http://www.gradybritton.com
Year Founded: 1974
Advetising Agency
N.A.I.C.S.: 541810
Frank Grady (Pres)
Kelly Burns (Sr Acct Mgr)
Paige McCarthy (Partner & Dir-Acct
Svcs)
Andy Askren (Partner & Dir-Creative)
Sarah Prince (Dir-Media)
Dayn Wilberding (Dir-Digital Culture)
Emma Oliver (Dir-Fin)
Frances Kershaw (Acct Coord)
Michelle Blinkhorn (Dir-Acct)
Ben Peters (Dir-Digital)

GRADY BROTHER'S, INC.
915 S Somerset Ave, Indianapolis, IN
46241
Tel.: (317) 244-3343
Web Site: https://www.gradybros.com
Year Founded: 1935
Sales Range: $150-199.9 Million
Emp.: 50
Highway & Street Construction Ser-
vices
N.A.I.C.S.: 237310
Thomas Grady (Owner)

GRADY CRAWFORD CON-STRUCTION CO., INC. OF BA-TON ROUGE
12290 Greenwell Springs Rd, Baton
Rouge, LA 70814-6335
Tel.: (225) 275-7334
Web Site:
https://www.gradycrawford.com
Year Founded: 1976

Sales Range: $25-49.9 Million
Emp.: 220
Provider of Water Sewer & Utility
Line Setting Svcs.
N.A.I.C.S.: 237110
Terry Head (Mgr)

Subsidiaries:

Grady Crawford Construction
Co. (1)
45256 Hwy 445, Robert, LA 70455
Tel.: (985) 542-7349
Web Site: http://www.gradycrawford.com
Sales Range: $25-49.9 Million
Emp.: 50
Provider of Water Sewer & Utility Line Set-
ting Services
N.A.I.C.S.: 237130
Hugh J. Johnson (Pres)

GRADY ELECTRIC MEMBER-SHIP CORPORATION
1499 Hwy 84 W, Cairo, GA 39828
Tel.: (229) 377-4182 GA
Web Site: https://www.gradyemc.com
Year Founded: 1937
Sales Range: $25-49.9 Million
Emp.: 76
Electric Power Distr
N.A.I.C.S.: 221122
Wayne Windham (Mgr-Ops)
Donnie Prince (Mgr-Member Svcs)
Rex Robinson (Mgr-Engrg)
Claire Chason (Atty)
Robert E. Lee (Vice Chm)
Lamar Carlton (Chm)
Pat Reed (CFO)
John Long (Interim CEO)
Dewey Brock Jr. (Treas & Sec)

GRADY-WHITE BOATS, INC.
PO Box 1527, Greenville, NC 27835-
1527
Tel.: (252) 752-2111
Web Site: http://www.gradywhite.com
Sales Range: $75-99.9 Million
Emp.: 300
Boat Mfr
N.A.I.C.S.: 336612
Shelley Tubaugh (VP-Marketing)

GRAE-CON CONSTRUCTION, INC.
880 Kingsdale Rd, Steubenville, OH
43952-4361
Tel.: (740) 282-6830
Web Site: https://www.graecon.com
Year Founded: 1987
Sales Range: $10-24.9 Million
Emp.: 80
Commercial & Institutional Building
Construction Services
N.A.I.C.S.: 236220
Robert A. Gribben Jr. (Pres & CEO)
John A. Humpe III (VP)
Robert A. Gribben III (VP)

GRAEBEL COMPANIES, INC.
16346 Airport Cir, Aurora, CO 80011
Tel.: (303) 214-6683 DE
Web Site: https://www.graebel.com
Year Founded: 2001
Holding Company; Commercial Relo-
cation Services & Storage Facilities
Operator
N.A.I.C.S.: 551112
David W. Graebel (Founder)
William H. Graebel (Chm & CEO)
Brad Siler (CFO)
Ron Dunlap (COO)
Bill Nemer (Pres-Relocation Svcs)
Dale Collins (Chief Strategy Officer &
Mng Dir-EMEA)
George Bates (Chief Revenue Offi-
cer)
Richard Payne (Chief Compliance
Officer & Chief Risk Officer)

Scott Snead (Sr VP-Comml Svcs)
Sue Diltz (CIO, Chief Security Officer
& Chief Privacy Officer)
Mary Dymond (Chief Talent Officer)
Katrin Razzano (VP-Consulting Svcs)

GRAEBEL DENVER MOVERS, INC.
16456 E Airport Cir, Aurora, CO
80011
Tel.: (303) 214-6600
Web Site: http://www.graebel.com
Year Founded: 1950
Sales Range: $125-149.9 Million
Emp.: 1,771
General Freight Truck Operating Ser-
vices
N.A.I.C.S.: 484122

GRAEF-USA, INC.
275 W Wisconsin Ave Ste 300, Mil-
waukee, WI 53203
Tel.: (414) 259-1500 WI
Web Site: http://www.graef-usa.com
Year Founded: 1961
Emp.: 254
Engineering, Planning & Consulting
Services
N.A.I.C.S.: 541330
Jenny Christel (Dir-HR)
John Kissinger (Pres & CEO)
Kenneth Grebe (COO)
Richard Bub (Chm)
Brent Otto (CFO)
Brent Pitcher (Infrastructure Group
Leader)
Burt Naumann (Regional Office
Leader)
George Podrebarac (Office Leader-
Chicago Loop)
Jim Hansen (Office Leader-Sarasota,
Turks and Caicos)
Jon Schwichtenberg (Office Leader-
Minneapolis)

GRAETER'S, INC.
2145 Reading Rd, Cincinnati, OH
45202-1417
Tel.: (513) 721-3323 OH
Web Site: http://www.graeters.com
Year Founded: 1870
Sales Range: $200-249.9 Million
Emp.: 350
Packaged Ice Cream & Related Prod-
ucts Mfr
N.A.I.C.S.: 311520
Richard Graeter (Pres & CEO)
Bob Graeter (Owner & VP)
Bill Hanavan (Mgr-Ops-Natl)
James Lee (Gen Mgr)

GRAF AIR FREIGHT INCOR-PORATION
550 W Taylor St, Chicago, IL 60607
Tel.: (312) 987-9960
Web Site:
http://www.grafairfreight.com
Sales Range: $10-24.9 Million
Emp.: 15
Freight Forwarding
N.A.I.C.S.: 488510
Odette Alaniz (Mgr-Acctg)

GRAF CREAMERY INC.
N4051 Creamery St, Bonduel, WI
54107
Tel.: (715) 758-2137
Web Site:
https://www.grafcreamery.com
Rev.: $50,000,000
Emp.: 60
Creamery Butter Mfr
N.A.I.C.S.: 311512
Jim Bleick (Pres)
Ruth Bleick (Treas & Sec)

GRAFF CHEVROLET COM-PANY
1405 E Main St, Grand Prairie, TX
75050
Tel.: (972) 343-1200 DE
Web Site:
http://www.graffchevrolet.com
Rev.: $41,400,000
Emp.: 500
New & Used Car Dealers
N.A.I.C.S.: 441110
Stanley V. Graff (CEO)

GRAFF MOTOR SALES INC.
1100 W Cedar Ave, Gladwin, MI
48624
Tel.: (989) 426-9292
Web Site:
http://www.graffgladwinchevrolet.com
Sales Range: $10-24.9 Million
Emp.: 70
Car Whslr
N.A.I.C.S.: 441110
Chris Griff (Owner)

GRAFF TRUCK CENTERS INC.
1401 S Saginaw St, Flint, MI 48503
Tel.: (810) 239-8300
Web Site:
http://www.grafftruckcenter.com
Rev.: $12,000,000
Emp.: 40
Trucks, Tractors & Trailers: New &
Used
N.A.I.C.S.: 441110
Keith Whitmore (Gen Mgr & Mgr-Sls)

GRAFFMANS INC.
203 Madison Ave, Skowhegan, ME
04976
Tel.: (207) 474-7075 ME
Web Site:
http://www.motorsupplyautoparts.com
Year Founded: 1996
Sales Range: $10-24.9 Million
Emp.: 100
Sales of Automotive Supplies & Parts
N.A.I.C.S.: 423120
Robert J. York (Pres)
Valerie McCarty (Owner)
Tim Williams (Gen Mgr)

GRAFICAGROUP
525 E Main St, Chester, NJ 07930-
2627
Tel.: (908) 879-2169
Year Founded: 1986
Rev.: $14,168,660
Emp.: 37
Advetising Agency
N.A.I.C.S.: 541810
Debra A. Taeschler (Pres & CEO)
John Puglionisi (VP & Dir-Creative)
Colleen Ritchie (VP-Production)
Ed Miller (CFO)
Michael Burchill (Dir-Creative Digital
Technologies)

GRAFICAINTER.ACTIVE, LTD.
525 E Main St, Chester, NJ 07930-
2627
Tel.: (908) 879-2169 NJ
Year Founded: 1996
Rev.: $14,100,000
Emp.: 27
Advetising Agency
N.A.I.C.S.: 541810
Debra A. Taeschler (Pres & CEO)
John Puglionisi (VP & Dir-Creative)
Cathy Conway (Dir-Acct)
Quinnie Wong (CMO)
Colleen Ritchie (VP-Production)
Steven Paige (VP-Acct Svcs)

GRAFIK MARKETING COMMU-NICATIONS LTD.

1199 N Fairfax St Ste 700, Alexandria, VA 22314
Tel.: (703) 299-4500
Web Site: http://www.grafik.com
Sales Range: $10-24.9 Million
Emp.: 25
Advertising Services
N.A.I.C.S.: 541810
Judy Kirpich (Founder)
Lynn Umemoto (Principal-Client Strategy)
Lance Wain (Pres & Principal)
Gregg Glaviano (Principal & Dir-Creative)
David Collins (Principal & Dir-Creative)
Johnny Viotorovich (Dir-Creative)
Cheryl Haar (VP-Client Strategy)
Hal Swetnam (Chief Creative Officer)
Mikah Sellers (Chief Digital Officer)
Maxine Noyes (Controller)
Milagros Arrisueno (Dir-Art)
Arthur Hsu (Dir-Art)
Rob King (Dir-Art)
Efrat Levush (Dir-Art)
George Nicholas (Dir-Creative)
Ladonna Thompson (Dir-HR & Office Mgr)
Amanda Brooks (Mgr-Client Strategy)
Greg Spraker (Sr Dir-Art)

GRAFT SALES AND SERVICE INC.
301 N Broadway St, Scottdale, PA 15683
Tel.: (724) 887-7800   PA
Web Site: http://www.graftsales.com
Year Founded: 1976
Sales Range: $10-24.9 Million
Emp.: 12
Car Dealership
N.A.I.C.S.: 441110
Douglas Graft (Owner)
Ken Bell (Mgr-Svc)
Jim Clarkson (Mgr-Parts)
Greg Hrimnock (Mgr-Body Shop)

GRAFTON CITY HOSPITAL
500 Market St, Grafton, WV 26354
Tel.: (304) 265-0400   WV
Web Site:
http://www.graftonhospital.com
Year Founded: 1972
Sales Range: $10-24.9 Million
Emp.: 486
Health Care Srvices
N.A.I.C.S.: 622110
Pat Shaw (Co-CEO)

GRAGG ADVERTISING
450 E 4th St Ste 100, Kansas City, MO 64106
Tel.: (816) 931-0050
Web Site: http://www.graggadv.com
Year Founded: 1993
Sales Range: $75-99.9 Million
Emp.: 51
Advetising Agency
N.A.I.C.S.: 541810
Darryl Mattox (Pres)
Lisa Olmedo (Dir-New Bus Dev)
Angie Claycomb (Coord-Mktg)
Stacy Scott (Dir-Acct Svcs)
Stephanie Oehlert (Dir-Media)
Erica Wright (Dir-Ops)
Mike Schuler (Dir-IT)
Todd Prehm (Mgr-Sls)
Cathryn Vaughn (Dir-Digital Mktg Grp)
Bryan Durham (Mgr-Integration & Data Svcs)
Fred Frantz (Exec VP)

GRAHAM ADVERTISING
525 Communication Cir, Colorado Springs, CO 80905-1736

Tel.: (719) 635-7335   CO
Web Site: http://www.grahamadv.com
Year Founded: 1977
Rev.: $40,000,000
Emp.: 55
Advertising Agency
N.A.I.C.S.: 541810
Jerry A. Graham (Founder)
Sandy Emmert (Pres)
Kirk Oleson (CEO)
Sarah Davison (Exec VP & Art Dir)
Rhonda Maehara (Exec VP-Media & Res)
Jack Rostollan (Dir-Client Svcs)
Bill Leonard (Dir-Creative)
Scott Beer (Dir-Art)
Matt Barrett (Mgr-Bus)

GRAHAM AUTOMALL
1515 W 4th St, Mansfield, OH 44906
Tel.: (419) 529-1800
Web Site:
https://www.grahamautomall.com
Sales Range: $75-99.9 Million
Emp.: 150
Car Dealership
N.A.I.C.S.: 441110
Ken Williams (VP & Gen Mgr)
Aaron Breudigam (Mgr-Sls)
Graham Brock (Dir-Svc)
Scot Osborne (Dir-Fin-Mansfield)

GRAHAM C- STORES COMPANY
33978 N US Hwy 45, Grayslake, IL 60030-1714
Tel.: (847) 726-8188   IL
Web Site:
http://www.grahamcstores.com
Year Founded: 1992
Sales Range: $10-24.9 Million
Emp.: 120
Petroleum Services
N.A.I.C.S.: 424720
John O. Graham (Pres)

GRAHAM CAPITAL GROUP, LLC
950 N 72nd St Ste 100, Seattle, WA 98103
Tel.: (206) 812-1033
Web Site: https://www.grahamcapital group.com
Sales Range: $10-24.9 Million
Emp.: 4
Privater Equity Firm
N.A.I.C.S.: 523999
Paul A. Raidna (Mng Dir)

Subsidiaries:

Simon Metals LLC   (1)
2202 E River St, Tacoma, WA 98421-1502
Tel.: (253) 272-9364
Web Site: http://www.jsimonandsons.com
Sales Range: $25-49.9 Million
Scrap Metal Collection & Recycling Services
N.A.I.C.S.: 423930

GRAHAM COUNTY ELECTRIC COOPERATIVE, INC.
9 West Ctr, Pima, AZ 85543
Tel.: (928) 485-2451   AZ
Web Site: https://gce.coop
Year Founded: 1946
Rev.: $11,089,285
Emp.: 40
Distribution, Electric Power
N.A.I.C.S.: 221122
Steve Lines (Gen Mgr)
Gene Robert Larson (Pres)

GRAHAM ENTERPRISE INC.
PO Box 246, Meridian, MS 39302-0246
Tel.: (601) 553-0555   IL

Web Site:
https://www.grahamenterprises.com
Year Founded: 1990
Sales Range: $10-24.9 Million
Emp.: 125
Petroleum Products Mfr
N.A.I.C.S.: 424720

GRAHAM GULF, INC.
6590 Half Mile Rd, Irvington, AL 36544
Tel.: (251) 957-1012   AL
Web Site: http://www.grahamgulf.com
Year Founded: 1996
Sales Range: $10-24.9 Million
Emp.: 100
Marine Freight Transportation Services
N.A.I.C.S.: 483111
Janson Graham (Owner)
A. Keith Hayles (CEO)
Barbara Griggs (VP)

GRAHAM MOTORS AND CONTROLS
11394 James Watt Dr Ste 304, El Paso, TX 79936
Tel.: (915) 599-2727
Web Site:
http://www.grahammotorsand controls.com
Year Founded: 1936
Sales Range: Less than $1 Million
Emp.: 20
Industrial Power Transmission Equipment Mfr
N.A.I.C.S.: 336350
Matthew Kelly (Mgr-Ops)

GRAIL PARTNERS LLC
885 3rd Ave Ste 3180, New York, NY 10022
Tel.: (212) 916-7422
Web Site:
http://www.grailpartners.com
Year Founded: 2005
Sales Range: $25-49.9 Million
Emp.: 25
Investment Services
N.A.I.C.S.: 523999
Donald H. Putnam (Mng Partner)
J. Clarke Gray (CFO)
S. Craig Cognetti (Partner)

GRAIN MANAGEMENT, LLC
100 N Washington Blvd Ste 201, Sarasota, FL 34236
Tel.: (941) 373-0033
Web Site: https://graingp.com
Emp.: 100
Private Equity Firm; Wired Telecommunications Carriers
N.A.I.C.S.: 523999
David J. Grain (Founder & CEO)
Chad Crank (Mng Dir)
Michael McKenzie (Mng Dir)

Subsidiaries:

E. Ritter Agribusiness Holdings, Inc.   (1)
10 Elm St, Marked Tree, AR 72365
Tel.: (870) 358-7333
Web Site: http://www.ritterag.com
Holding Company; Farm Management Services
N.A.I.C.S.: 551112
Kevin Wright (Pres)

Subsidiary (Domestic):

E. Ritter Farm Management, Inc.   (2)
10 Elm St, Marked Tree, AR 72365
Tel.: (870) 358-7333
Web Site: http://www.ritterag.com
Farm Management Services
N.A.I.C.S.: 115116

Kevin Wright (Pres)
Jason Brewer (Gen Mgr)
Phil Negri (Mgr-Farm)
Woody Ray (Project Mgr)

E. Ritter Communications Holdings, Inc.   (1)
30 Elm St, Marked Tree, AR 72365
Tel.: (870) 358-4400
Web Site:
http://www.rittercommunications.com
Holding Company; Telecommunications Services
N.A.I.C.S.: 551112
Jeff Chapman (VP/Gen Mgr-Fiber-to-the-Home Bus)
Alan Morse (CEO)

Subsidiary (Domestic):

E. Ritter Communications, Inc.   (2)
30 Elm St, Marked Tree, AR 72365
Tel.: (870) 358-4400
Web Site:
http://www.rittercommunications.com
Radio Telephone Communication & Internet Access Services
N.A.I.C.S.: 517112

Subsidiary (Domestic):

E. Ritter Telephone Company   (3)
30 Elm St, Marked Tree, AR 72365
Tel.: (870) 358-4400
Web Site:
http://www.rittercommunications.com
Wired Telephone Communication Services
N.A.I.C.S.: 517121

LightRiver Technologies, Inc.   (1)
2150 John Glenn Dr Ste 200, Concord, CA 94520
Tel.: (925) 363-9000
Web Site: http://www.lightriver.com
Rev.: $15,000,000
Emp.: 100
Communication Signal Enhancement Network Services
N.A.I.C.S.: 517810
Glenn A. Johansen (Pres & CEO)
Michael P. Jonas (Pres-Global Sls & Mktg)
David Courtney (VP-Pro Svcs)
Howard H. Yang (CIO)
Dean L. Campbell (CTO)
Walt Paskowski (Sr VP-Vertical Sls)
Brian Hasegawa (CFO)

Spectrotel, Inc.   (1)
655 Shrewsbury Ave, Shrewsbury, NJ 07702
Tel.: (732) 345-7000
Web Site: https://www.spectrotel.com
Sales Range: $1-9.9 Million
Emp.: 65
Telecommunications Resellers
N.A.I.C.S.: 517121
Jacob B. Dayan (Founder & CEO)
David Zahka (CFO)
Ross Artale (CEO)

GRAIN MILLERS, INC.
10400 Viking Dr Ste 301, Eden Prairie, MN 55344
Tel.: (952) 829-8821
Web Site:
https://www.grainmillers.com
Rev.: $42,000,000
Emp.: 370
Oat Milling Services
N.A.I.C.S.: 311211
Kris Nelson (Mgr-Sales)

Subsidiaries:

Agricor Inc.   (1)
1626 S Joaquin Dr, Marion, IN 46953
Tel.: (765) 662-0606
Web Site: http://www.grainmillers.com
Sales Range: $10-24.9 Million
Emp.: 60
Corn Flour Milling
N.A.I.C.S.: 311211
Steve Wickes (Pres)
Bill Cramer (Dir-Maintenance)
Duane Hudson (Coord-Sls)

GRAINGER HONDA

Grainger Honda—(Continued)

1596 Chatham Pkwy, Savannah, GA
31408
Tel.: (912) 790-5444
Web Site:
https://www.graingerhonda.com
Year Founded: 1997
Sales Range: $10-24.9 Million
Emp.: 70
Car Whslr
N.A.I.C.S.: 441110
Mark Grainger *(Gen Mgr & VP)*

GRAINLAND COOPERATIVE
421 S Colorado, Haxtun, CO 80731
Tel.: (970) 774-6166
Web Site:
http://www.chsgrainland.com
Year Founded: 1903
Farm Supplies
N.A.I.C.S.: 424910
Rick Cumming *(Controller)*
Bob Schaefer *(Mgr-Operations)*
Todd Workman *(Dir-Safety)*

Subsidiaries:

Grainland Cooperative - Amherst (1)
34661 County Rd, Amherst, CO 80721
Tel.: (970) 854-3141
Web Site: http://www.grainland.coop
Sales Range: $10-24.9 Million
Emp.: 25
Grain Elevators
N.A.I.C.S.: 424510

GRAINLAND COOPERATIVE
927 County Hwy 3, Eureka, IL 61530
Tel.: (309) 467-2355
Web Site:
https://www.grainlandcooperative.com
Sales Range: $10-24.9 Million
Emp.: 12
Provider of Grain Elevators
N.A.I.C.S.: 424510
Jeffrey K. Brooks *(Gen Mgr)*
Lance Gehlbach *(Mgr-Ops)*
Lori Miller *(Mgr-Relationship)*
John Hood *(Mgr-Ops-Minier)*
Johnathan Schertz *(Treas)*
Fred Wyss *(Sec)*

GRAMAG LLC
470 E High St, London, OH 43140
Tel.: (740) 490-1000
Web Site: http://www.gramag.com
Sales Range: $25-49.9 Million
Emp.: 25
Provider of Automotive Seats
N.A.I.C.S.: 336360
David Higgs *(Pres)*

GRAMMARLY, INC.
548 Market St #35410, San Francisco, CA 94104
Tel.: (415) 857-1560
Web Site: http://www.grammarly.com
Year Founded: 2008
Sales Range: $1-9.9 Million
Emp.: 50
Online Automated Proofreader & Editor
N.A.I.C.S.: 611710
Brad Hoover *(CEO)*
Max Lytvyn *(Co-Founder)*
Alex Shevchenko *(Co-Founder)*

GRAND & BENEDICTS INC.
6140 SE Macadam Ave, Portland,
OR 97239
Tel.: (503) 232-1988
Web Site: https://www.grand-benedicts.com
Sales Range: $10-24.9 Million
Emp.: 85
Store Fixtures
N.A.I.C.S.: 423440

John V. Phillips *(Pres)*
Joe Thompson *(Project Mgr)*
Ken Gibson *(Mgr-Sls)*
Nancy Thompson *(Mgr-Acctg)*

GRAND AIRE EXPRESS INC.
11777 W Airport Service Rd, Swanton, OH 43558-9387
Tel.: (419) 865-1760   OH
Web Site: https://www.grandaire.com
Year Founded: 1985
Sales Range: $1-9.9 Million
Emp.: 15
Air Charter Management
N.A.I.C.S.: 481212
Tahir Cheema *(Founder)*

GRAND BANCORP, INC.
1022 S Main St, Grove, OK 74344
Tel.: (918) 786-2203   OK
Web Site:
http://www.grandsavingsbank.com
Year Founded: 2013
Bank Holding Company
N.A.I.C.S.: 551111
Guy Cable *(CEO)*

Subsidiaries:

Grand Savings Bank (1)
1022 S Main St, Grove, OK 74344
Tel.: (918) 786-2203
Web Site:
http://www.grandsavingsbank.com
Sales Range: $25-49.9 Million
Emp.: 155
Commercial Banking
N.A.I.C.S.: 522110
Elaine Gardner *(CFO)*
Guy Cable *(Pres & CEO)*
Tyler Steele *(Vice Chm)*
Leah Morgan *(COO & Sr VP)*
John Williams *(Chief Credit Officer & Chief Lending Officer)*
Natalie Bartholomew *(Chief Admin Officer & VP)*
Pam Hulion *(Chief Risk Officer & Sr VP)*

GRAND BLANC CEMENT PRODUCTS
10709 Ctr Rd, Grand Blanc, MI
48439
Tel.: (810) 694-7500
Web Site:
http://www.grandblanccement.com
Sales Range: $10-24.9 Million
Emp.: 49
Cement Products Mfr
N.A.I.C.S.: 327331
Michael Hicks *(VP)*
Ron Hunt *(Mgr-Sls)*

GRAND BUICK GMC KIA
2000 W 104th Ave, Denver, CO
80234
Tel.: (303) 460-8000
Web Site:
http://www.grandbuickgmckia.com
Year Founded: 1989
Sales Range: $50-74.9 Million
Emp.: 90
Car Dealer
N.A.I.C.S.: 441110
W. D. Moreland *(Pres)*
Tree King *(Mgr-Customer Svc)*

GRAND BUICK, INC.
2901 28th St SW, Grandville, MI
49418
Tel.: (616) 530-9191   MI
Web Site:
http://www.grandautofamily.com
Rev.: $75,000,000
Emp.: 150
Automobiles, New & Used
N.A.I.C.S.: 441110
Harvey Koning *(Founder)*
Jerry Dykhuis *(Mgr-Fin)*

GRAND CANYON RAILWAY INC.
1201 W Route 66 Ste 200, Flagstaff,
AZ 86001
Tel.: (928) 773-1976
Web Site: http://www.thetrain.com
Sales Range: $25-49.9 Million
Emp.: 400
Passenger Rail Transportation
N.A.I.C.S.: 485112

GRAND CENTRAL BAKERY
21 S Nevada St, Seattle, WA 98134
Tel.: (206) 768-0320
Web Site:
http://www.grandcentralbakery.com
Year Founded: 1972
Sales Range: $25-49.9 Million
Emp.: 180
Bakery Product Whslr
N.A.I.C.S.: 424490
Gillian Allen-White *(Owner & Gen Mgr)*
Claire Randall *(Owner)*
Laura Ohm *(Mgr-Cuisine)*

GRAND CENTRAL DISTRICT MANAGEMENT ASSOCIATION, INC.
122 E 42nd St Ste 601, New York,
NY 10168
Tel.: (212) 883-2420   NY
Web Site:
http://www.grandcentralpartnership.org
Year Founded: 1988
Sales Range: $10-24.9 Million
Economic Development Services
N.A.I.C.S.: 541720
Michael Buzzy O'Keeffe *(Owner)*

GRAND CIRCLE CORPORATION
347 Congress St, Boston, MA 02210
Tel.: (617) 350-7500
Web Site: https://www.gct.com
Rev.: $78,300,000
Emp.: 100
Travel Agency
N.A.I.C.S.: 561510
Alan E. Lewis *(Chm)*
Harriet Lewis *(Vice Chm)*

GRAND ELY LODGE LLC
400 N Pioneer Rd, Ely, MN 55731
Tel.: (218) 365-6565
Web Site:
https://www.grandelylodge.com
Sales Range: $10-24.9 Million
Emp.: 50
Holding Company
N.A.I.C.S.: 721110
Denise Jordan *(Gen Mgr)*
Dan Koegstad *(Dir-Event Plng)*

Subsidiaries:

Grand Ely Lodge (1)
400 N Pioneer Rd, Ely, MN
55731-1057   (100%)
Tel.: (218) 365-6565
Web Site: http://www.grandelylodge.com
Sales Range: $10-24.9 Million
Resort Services
N.A.I.C.S.: 721110
Mary Zuanich *(Gen Mgr)*

GRAND ENERGY, INC.
15303 Dallas Pkwy Ste 1010, Addison, TX 75001
Tel.: (972) 788-2080
Web Site:
http://www.grandenergy.com
Rev.: $20,200,000
Emp.: 22
Crude Petroleum & Natural Gas Extraction
N.A.I.C.S.: 211120

James L. Harris *(Pres)*
Claudia K. Young *(CFO)*

GRAND ENTRANCE
1001 W Bayaud Ave, Denver, CO
80223
Tel.: (303) 893-4001
Web Site:
http://www.thegrandentrance.com
Year Founded: 1997
Sales Range: $1-9.9 Million
Emp.: 55
Custom Door & Window Manufacturing
N.A.I.C.S.: 321911
Frank Meyer *(Pres)*

GRAND FURNITURE DISCOUNT STORES
1305 Baker Rd, Virginia Beach, VA
23455
Tel.: (757) 460-3800
Web Site:
http://www.grandfurniture.com
Sales Range: $25-49.9 Million
Emp.: 450
Furniture Retailer
N.A.I.C.S.: 449110
Craig Stein *(Owner)*
Craig Kendle *(Mgr-Warehouse)*

GRAND HAVEN BOARD OF LIGHT & POWER
1700 Eaton Dr, Grand Haven, MI
49417
Tel.: (616) 846-6250
Web Site: https://www.ghblp.org
Sales Range: $25-49.9 Million
Emp.: 69
Electric Power Administration Organization
N.A.I.C.S.: 926130
Renee Molyneux *(Mgr-Admin Svcs)*
David Walters *(Gen Mgr)*

GRAND HERITAGE HOTEL GROUP, LLC
39 Bay Dr, Annapolis, MD 21403
Tel.: (410) 280-9800
Web Site:
http://www.grandheritage.com
Year Founded: 1989
Owner & Operator of Hotels
N.A.I.C.S.: 721110
Stephen Moore *(Mng Dir)*
Jean Patrick Thiry *(Mng Dir-Europe)*
Joy Gladwell *(Controller)*
Pierre-Marie Vasseur *(Dir-Bus Dev-Europe)*
Kenneth Gay *(VP-IT)*
Dan Swanson *(Dir-e-Commerce)*
Cresta Shafer *(Controller)*
Damien Boynton *(VP-Revenue)*
Jorge Tostado *(Dir-HR)*
Reed Rowley *(VP-Bus Dev)*
Christopher Vesper *(Dir-Fin)*
Francesca Lupo *(Reg Dir-HR)*
John W. Cullen IV *(Founder & Pres)*

Subsidiaries:

McCamly Plaza Hotel (1)
50 Capital Ave SW, Battle Creek, MI 49017
Tel.: (269) 963-7050
Web Site: http://www.mccamlyplaza.com
Sales Range: $10-24.9 Million
Emp.: 170
Hotel
N.A.I.C.S.: 721110
Chris Black *(Chief Engr)*

GRAND HOTEL, LLC
286 Grand Ave, Mackinac Island, MI
49757
Tel.: (906) 847-3331
Web Site: http://www.grandhotel.com
Year Founded: 1887

Sales Range: $25-49.9 Million
Emp.: 500
Hotel & Resort Services
N.A.I.C.S.: 721110
Ken Hayward (Mng Dir & Exec VP)
Dana Orlando (VP-Sls & Mktg)
Doug Dean (Exec VP-Ops)
R. D. Musser III (Pres)

GRAND INCENTIVES, INC.
7560 Commerce Ct, Sarasota, FL 34243
Tel.: (941) 552-7885
Web Site:
  http://www.grandincentives.com
Sales Range: $1-9.9 Million
Travel Incentive Programs
N.A.I.C.S.: 561599
Cynthia Taylor (VP-Bus Admin)

GRAND ISLAND EXPRESS INC.
432 S Stuhr Rd, Grand Island, NE 68801
Tel.: (308) 384-8555
Web Site: https://www.giexpress.com
Year Founded: 1967
Sales Range: $250-299.9 Million
Emp.: 175
Provider of Contract Hauling Services
N.A.I.C.S.: 484121
J. Thomas Pirnie (Pres)
Keith Pirnie (VP)
Sue Pirnie (Treas & Sec)
Paula Dush (Controller)

GRAND KAHN ELECTRIC, LLC
16760 S Richmond, Chicago, IL 60612
Tel.: (312) 298-1500   IL
Web Site: http://www.grandkahn.com
Year Founded: 1962
Sales Range: $10-24.9 Million
Emp.: 15
Electrical Contractor
N.A.I.C.S.: 238210
James Gallagher (Owner & Pres)

GRAND LAKE MENTAL HEALTH CENTER, INC.
114 W Delaware, Nowata, OK 74048
Tel.: (918) 273-1841   OK
Web Site: http://www.glmhc.net
Year Founded: 1977
Sales Range: $10-24.9 Million
Emp.: 227
Behavioral Healthcare Services
N.A.I.C.S.: 621420
Larry Smith (COO)
Lissa James (Dir-Clinical)

Subsidiaries:

12 & 12, Inc.   (1)
6333 E Skelly Dr, Tulsa, OK 74135
Tel.: (918) 664-4224
Web Site: http://www.12and12.org
Sales Range: $1-9.9 Million
Emp.: 120
Residential Mental Health & Substance Abuse Facilities
N.A.I.C.S.: 623220
Bryan Day (CEO)

GRAND PRAIRIE SERVICES
17746 Oak Park Ave, Tinley Park, IL 60477
Tel.: (708) 444-1012   IL
Web Site: https://www.gpsbh.org
Year Founded: 1950
Sales Range: $10-24.9 Million
Emp.: 193
Behavioral Healthcare Services
N.A.I.C.S.: 623220
Sharronne Ward (Pres & CEO)

GRAND PRIX PERFORMANCE OF HICKSVILLE
500 S Broadway, Hicksville, NY 11801
Tel.: (516) 822-6800
Web Site:
  http://www.grandprixautogroup.com
Rev.: $17,200,000
Emp.: 25
Automobiles, New & Used
N.A.I.C.S.: 441110
Daniel Ross (Office Mgr)

GRAND RAPIDS FOAM TECHNOLOGIES, INC.
2788 Remico St SW, Wyoming, MI 49519
Tel.: (616) 726-1677   MI
Web Site: https://www.grft.com
Year Founded: 1949
Sales Range: $100-124.9 Million
Emp.: 200
Foam Products Mfr
N.A.I.C.S.: 326150
Benjamin Amann (Pres)

GRAND RAPIDS GRAVEL CO.
2700 28th St SW, Grand Rapids, MI 49509
Tel.: (616) 538-9000
Web Site: https://www.grgravel.com
Rev.: $34,330,326
Emp.: 120
Ready Mixed Concrete
N.A.I.C.S.: 327320
Denny Baskin (Asst Mgr-Ops)
Dave Moore (Gen Mgr-Sls)
Gary Bos (Mgr-Ops)

GRAND RAPIDS LABEL CO.
2351 Oak Industrial Dr NE, Grand Rapids, MI 49505
Tel.: (616) 459-8134
Web Site: http://www.grlabel.com
Sales Range: $10-24.9 Million
Emp.: 70
Flexographic Printing
N.A.I.C.S.: 323111
W. W. Muir (Pres)
John Laninga (CFO & Controller)
John Crosby (VP-Ops)
Bill Bergstrom (VP-Sls & Mktg)

GRAND RAPIDS PRINTING INK COMPANY
4920 Starr St SE, Grand Rapids, MI 49546
Tel.: (616) 241-5681   MI
Web Site: https://www.grpi.net
Year Founded: 1995
Sales Range: $10-24.9 Million
Emp.: 25
Printing Ink Mfr
N.A.I.C.S.: 325910
John Toigo (Pres & CEO)

Subsidiaries:

Miller-Cooper Printing Ink Company LLC   (1)
5187 Merriam Dr, Merriam, KS 66203
Tel.: (913) 312-5020
Web Site: http://www.mcink.com
Sales Range: $10-24.9 Million
Printing Ink & Pressroom Supplies Distr
N.A.I.C.S.: 424120

GRAND RAPIDS SYMPHONY SOCIETY
300 Ottawa Ave NW Ste 100, Grand Rapids, MI 49503
Tel.: (616) 454-9451
Web Site:
  https://www.grsymphony.org
Year Founded: 1930
Sales Range: $10-24.9 Million
Emp.: 100
Symphony Orchestra
N.A.I.C.S.: 711130

Claire Van Brandeghen (Dir-Education)
Marcelo Lehninger (Dir-Music)
Charles Frayer (Chm)
W. Michael Van Haren (Sec)
Diane Lobbestael (VP-Dev)

GRAND RIVER DAM AUTHORITY
226 W Dwain Willis Ave PO Box 409, Vinita, OK 74301-0409
Tel.: (918) 256-5545   OK
Web Site: http://www.grda.com
Year Founded: 1935
Sales Range: $400-449.9 Million
Emp.: 551
Dam & Electrical Power Generation Administrative Organization
N.A.I.C.S.: 926130
Carolyn Dougherty (CFO & Treas)
Joseph Vandevier (Chm)
Dan Sullivan (Pres & CEO)
Tim Brown (COO)
Ellen Edwards (Gen Counsel)
Charles Barney (Asst Gen Mgr-Fuel & Generation Projects)
Mike Herron (Asst Gen Mgr-Engrg, Sys Ops & Reliability)
Darrell Townsend (Asst Gen Mgr-Ecosystems & Lake Mgmt)
John Goodwin (Asst Gen Mgr-HR)
Brian Edwards (Asst Gen Mgr)
Justin Alberty (Dir-Corp Comm)
Steven R. Jacoby (Asst Gen Mgr-Hydroelectric Projects & Chief Engr-Hydro)

GRAND RIVER MUTUAL TELEPHONE CORPORATION
1001 Kentucky St, Princeton, MO 64673
Tel.: (660) 748-3231
Web Site: http://www.grm.net
Sales Range: $10-24.9 Million
Emp.: 99
Telephone Communication, Except Radio
N.A.I.C.S.: 517121
Ken Roberts (Controller)
Gregg Davis (Pres)

GRAND RIVER, INC.
3045 Miller Rd, Ann Arbor, MI 48103
Tel.: (734) 913-8000
Web Site:
  http://www.thegrandriver.com
Year Founded: 2007
Sales Range: $1-9.9 Million
Emp.: 45
Electronic Commerce Services
N.A.I.C.S.: 459999
Scott Robertson (Co-Founder & CEO)
Betsy Petrovic (VP-Strategic Svcs)
Steve Thallman (Co-Founder & COO)
Judy Foster (Exec Creative Dir)

GRAND STRAND WATER & SEWER AUTHORITY
170 Jackson Bluff Rd, Conway, SC 29526
Tel.: (843) 443-8200
Web Site: http://www.gswsa.com
Sales Range: $25-49.9 Million
Emp.: 200
Water Supply Regulation Organization
N.A.I.C.S.: 924110
Fred Richardson (CEO)
Marguerite Carroll (CFO)
Sidney F. Thompson (Chm)
Benjy Hardee (Vice Chm)
John Griggs (Sec)
Christy Everett (COO)

GRAND VIN LTD.
8000 Southpark Ter, Littleton, CO 80120-5605
Tel.: (303) 794-2422
Web Site: http://www.grandvin.co.uk
Rev.: $25,000,000
Winery
N.A.I.C.S.: 424820
Jim Smith (Pres)

Subsidiaries:

Provin Ltd   (1)
4301 S Federal Blvd # 108, Englewood, CO 80110
Tel.: (303) 797-2208
Web Site: http://grandvin.com
Rev.: $490,000
Emp.: 3
Winery
N.A.I.C.S.: 424820

GRAND WIRELESS INC.
267 Boston Rd, North Billerica, MA 01862
Tel.: (978) 663-9600
Web Site:
  http://www.grandwireless.com
Rev.: $10,305,000
Emp.: 60
Telephone & Communication Equipment
N.A.I.C.S.: 449210

GRANDE CHEESE COMPANY
250 Camelot Dr, Fond Du Lac, WI 54935
Tel.: (920) 269-7200
Web Site: https://www.grande.com
Year Founded: 1941
Sales Range: $50-74.9 Million
Emp.: 750
Cheese Mfr & Distr
N.A.I.C.S.: 311513
Sheryl Williams (Mgr-Transportation Team)
Todd Koss (CFO)
Eileen Blanckaert (Mgr-Corp Safety & Health)
Courtney Zitlow (Mgr-Talent)
Patrick Cardiff (Dir-Mfg Process Innovation)
Dick DeZwarte (Dir-Engrg)

GRANDE CHEESE COMPANY INC.
Hwy 49 and Dairy Rd, Brownsville, WI 53006
Tel.: (920) 269-7200   WI
Web Site: http://www.grande.com
Year Founded: 1967
Sales Range: $25-49.9 Million
Emp.: 750
Cheese Products Mfr
N.A.I.C.S.: 311513
Wayne Matzki (Pres)

GRANDE FOODS CALIFORNIA CORPORATION
11630 Pike St, Santa Fe Springs, CA 90670-2938
Tel.: (714) 978-0061   CA
Web Site:
  http://www.grandefoods.com
Year Founded: 1950
Sales Range: $10-24.9 Million
Emp.: 130
Mfr of Potato Chips & Similar Snacks
N.A.I.C.S.: 311919

Subsidiaries:

G&A Snack Distributing Inc.   (1)
8521 Loch Lomond Dr, Pico Rivera, CA 90660-2509
Tel.: (323) 720-1040
Web Site: http://gasnacks.com

Grande Foods California
Corporation—(Continued)

Sales Range: $10-24.9 Million
Emp.: 100
Provider of Confectionery
N.A.I.C.S.: 424450

GRANDESIGN ADVERTISING FIRM, INC.

125 14th St, San Diego, CA 92101
Tel.: (800) 270-2084   FL
Web Site: http://www.grandesign.com
Alternative Marketing & Advertising
N.A.I.C.S.: 541810
Aaron Gaeir *(CEO)*

Subsidiaries:

Hadley Media Inc.   (1)
1665 South Rancho Santa Fe, San Marcos,
CA 92078
Tel.: (310) 492-9798
Promotional Service
N.A.I.C.S.: 541810
Patrick Hadley *(Pres)*

GRANDMA'S COUNTRY FOODS

386 W 9400 S, Sandy, UT 84070
Tel.: (801) 748-0808
Web Site:
    http://www.grandmascountry
    foods.com
Year Founded: 1993
Sales Range: $10-24.9 Million
Emp.: 25
Spice & Extract Mfr
N.A.I.C.S.: 311942
Michelle Kwon *(Office Mgr)*

GRANDMA'S RESTAURANT CO.

525 S Lake Ave, Duluth, MN 55802
Tel.: (218) 727-2250
Web Site:
    https://www.grandmasrestau
    rants.com
Year Founded: 1976
Sales Range: $25-49.9 Million
Steak Restaurant
N.A.I.C.S.: 722511
Tony Bronson *(Reg Mgr)*

GRANDOR CORPORATION

814 S Main St, Corsicana, TX 75110
Tel.: (903) 872-6571
Web Site: https://www.ociw.com
Rev.: $17,600,000
Emp.: 200
Gray & Ductile Iron Foundries
N.A.I.C.S.: 331511
Eric Meyers *(Chm)*

GRANDPA BRANDS COMPANY

1820 Airport Exchange Blvd, Er-
langer, KY 41018-3192
Tel.: (859) 647-0777   OH
Web Site:
    http://www.grandpabrands.com
Year Founded: 1936
Sales Range: $50-74.9 Million
Emp.: 15
Pine Tar Soap & Dental Aids Mfr
N.A.I.C.S.: 325412
Richard D. Oliver *(Chm, Pres & CEO)*
Margaret Sharp *(VP-Ops)*

Subsidiaries:

Grandpa Soap Company   (1)
1820 Airport Exchange Blvd, Erlanger, KY
41018-3192
Tel.: (859) 647-0777
Web Site: http://www.grandpabrands.com
Sales Range: $10-24.9 Million
Soap Mfr
N.A.I.C.S.: 325611
Richard D. Oliver *(Pres)*
Marget Sharp *(VP-Ops)*

GRANDPARENTS.COM, INC.

589 8th Ave 6th Fl, New York, NY
10018
Tel.: (646) 839-8800   DE
Year Founded: 2007
Family-Oriented Social Media Web-
site
N.A.I.C.S.: 516210
Joe Rutledge *(Chief Marketing Strate-
gist)*

Subsidiaries:

Grandcorp Inc   (1)
PO Box 404, Valparaiso, IN 46384
Tel.: (219) 465-7065
Web Site: http://www.grandcorp.net
Property Leasing Services
N.A.I.C.S.: 531110

Grandparents Insurance Solutions
LLC   (1)
10018 Biscayne Blvd Ste 750, Miami, FL
33161
Tel.: (305) 899-0404
Insurance Services
N.A.I.C.S.: 524298

GRANDSTREAM NETWORKS, INC.

1297 Beacon St Fl 2, Brookline, MA
02446
Tel.: (617) 566-9300
Web Site:
    http://www.grandstream.com
Year Founded: 2002
Rev.: $23,000,000
Emp.: 50
Computer Peripheral Equipment Mfr
N.A.I.C.S.: 334118
Bruce Macaloney *(VP-Sls)*

GRANDVIEW PRODUCTS CO.

1601 Superior Dr, Parsons, KS
67357
Tel.: (620) 421-6950
Web Site:
    http://www.grandviewcabinets.com
Sales Range: $25-49.9 Million
Emp.: 150
Wood Kitchen Cabinet Mfr
N.A.I.C.S.: 337110
Emil Frank Zetmeir *(Pres)*
Gary Haynes *(Mgr-Natl Sls)*
Greg Chalker *(Mgr-Multi Family Sls)*
Teresa Hays *(Mgr-Payroll & Corp
Sec)*

GRANDVILLE PRINTING COMPANY

4719 Ivanrest Ave SW, Grandville, MI
49418-9321
Tel.: (616) 534-8647   MI
Web Site: https://www.gpco.com
Year Founded: 1956
Sales Range: $10-24.9 Million
Emp.: 275
Printer of Advertising Inserts & News-
papers
N.A.I.C.S.: 323111
Jeff Brewer *(Chm & CEO)*
Pat Brewer *(Pres)*
Rick Durham *(VP-Ops)*
Anthony Trevino *(VP-Retail Customer
Dev)*
Dennis Kucharczyk *(Mgr-Production)*
Chris E. Nunez *(Dir-Digital Printing)*

GRANE TRANSPORTATION LINES

1001 S Laramie Ave, Chicago, IL
60644
Tel.: (773) 379-9700   IL
Web Site:
    http://www.granetransportation.com
Year Founded: 1925
Sales Range: $10-24.9 Million
Emp.: 75

Provider of Vehicular Delivery Service
N.A.I.C.S.: 484110
Joe Garza *(Controller)*

GRANGE COOPERATIVE SUPPLY ASSOCIATION

PO Box 3637, Central Point, OR
97502
Tel.: (541) 664-1261
Web Site:
    https://www.grangecoop.com
Sales Range: $50-74.9 Million
Emp.: 200
Feed & Farm Supplies Distr
N.A.I.C.S.: 459999
Barry Repino *(Pres)*

GRANGE MUTUAL CASUALTY COMPANY

67 S High St, Columbus, OH 43206-
1014
Tel.: (614) 445-2900   OH
Web Site:
    http://www.grangeinsurance.com
Year Founded: 1935
Sales Range: $200-249.9 Million
Emp.: 1,400
Holding Company; Insurance Prod-
ucts & Services
N.A.I.C.S.: 551112
LaVawn Coleman *(Gen Counsel, Sec
& Exec VP)*
M. Marnette Perry *(Chm)*
Carrie Maun-Smith *(Asst VP-
Community Rels, Diversity, Equity &
Inclusion)*
Paul McCaffrey *(CFO & Exec VP)*
Linda Roubinek *(Chief Customer In-
teractions Officer & Exec VP)*
Doreen Delaney Crawley *(COO &
Exec VP)*
John Ammendola *(Pres & CEO)*
Mike Winner *(Pres-Comml Lines)*
Theresa Mason *(Pres-Grange Life)*
Jill Wagner *(Pres-Integrity)*
Amy Nichols *(Asst VP-Corp Comm)*

Subsidiaries:

Grange Indemnity Insurance
Company   (1)
671 S High St, Columbus, OH 43206
Tel.: (614) 445-2900
Web Site: http://www.grangeinsurance.com
Reinsurance Products & Services
N.A.I.C.S.: 524130
Mike Winner *(Pres)*

Grange Property & Casualty Insur-
ance Company   (1)
671 S High St, Columbus, OH 43206-1014
Tel.: (614) 445-2900
Web Site: http://www.grangeinsurance.com
Emp.: 1,000
Property & Casualty Insurance Products &
Services
N.A.I.C.S.: 524126
John Ammendola *(Pres & CEO)*
Amy Nichols *(Mgr-Corp Comm)*

Subsidiary (Domestic):

Trustgard Insurance Company   (2)
671 S High St, Columbus, OH 43206-1014
Tel.: (614) 445-2900
Emp.: 1,000
Property & Casualty Insurance Products &
Services
N.A.I.C.S.: 524126
John North *(Pres)*

Integrity Mutual Insurance
Company   (1)
2121 E Capitol Dr, Appleton, WI 54911-
8726
Tel.: (920) 734-4511
Web Site: http://www.integrityinsurance.com
Sales Range: $200-249.9 Million
Holding Company; Property & Casualty In-
surance Products & Services
N.A.I.C.S.: 551112

Jill Wagner *(Pres)*
Brent Hammer *(Treas & Controller)*
Christian Martin *(VP-Claims & Sls)*
Andy Ott *(VP-Comml Lines)*
Katey Smith *(VP-HR & Admin)*

GRANGER ASSOCIATES, INC.

16980 Wood Rd, Lansing, MI 48906-
1044
Tel.: (517) 372-2800   MI
Web Site: http://www.grangernet.com
Year Founded: 1974
Sales Range: $100-124.9 Million
Emp.: 150
Environmental Services Company
Involved Principally in Waste & Recy-
cling
N.A.I.C.S.: 562211

Subsidiaries:

Granger Compost Services   (1)
3125 Wood Rd, Lansing, MI 48906-1044
Tel.: (517) 484-2724
Web Site: http://www.grangernet.com
Sales Range: $50-74.9 Million
Emp.: 4
Waste Management & Disposal Services
N.A.I.C.S.: 237110

Granger Container Service, Inc.   (1)
16980 Wood Rd, Lansing, MI 48906-1044
Tel.: (517) 372-2800
Web Site: http://www.graingernet.com
Sales Range: $75-99.9 Million
Waste Management & Disposal
N.A.I.C.S.: 237110
Keith Granger *(CEO)*

Granger Land Development Co.   (1)
16980 Wood Rd, Lansing, MI
48906-1044   (100%)
Tel.: (517) 372-2800
Web Site: http://www.grangernet.com
Sales Range: $75-99.9 Million
Waste Management & Disposal
N.A.I.C.S.: 237110
Tonia Olson *(Dir-HR & Admin)*

Granger Waste Management Co.   (1)
16980 Wood Rd, Lansing, MI
48906-1044   (100%)
Tel.: (517) 372-2800
Web Site: http://www.grangernet.com
Sales Range: $25-49.9 Million
Waste Management & Disposal
N.A.I.C.S.: 562212

GRANGER CONSTRUCTION COMPANY

6267 Aurelius Rd, Lansing, MI 48911
Tel.: (517) 393-1670   MI
Web Site:
    https://www.grangerconstruction.com
Year Founded: 1960
Sales Range: $250-299.9 Million
Emp.: 300
Construction, Management & General
Contracting Services
N.A.I.C.S.: 236220
Alton Granger *(Chm)*
Glenn D. Granger *(Pres & CEO)*
Darryl Massa *(Exec VP-Ops)*
Dennis Carignan *(VP)*
Tim Variantwerp *(VP)*
Jerry Brand *(VP)*
Glenn Simon *(VP)*
Rob Train *(VP)*

GRANGETTO FARM & GARDEN SUPPLY CO.

1105 W Mission Ave, Escondido, CA
92025
Tel.: (760) 745-4671   CA
Web Site:
    https://www.grangettos.com
Year Founded: 1952
Sales Range: $10-24.9 Million
Emp.: 55
Farm Supplies
N.A.I.C.S.: 424910
Kevin Grangetto *(Owner)*

GRANI INSTALLATION INC.

5411 Comml Dr, Huntington Beach, CA 92649
Tel.: (714) 898-0441
Web Site: https://www.grani.biz
Sales Range: $25-49.9 Million
Emp.: 200
Commercial & Office Buildings, Renovation & Repair
N.A.I.C.S.: 236220
Maggie Brown (Office Mgr)

GRANITE BANK

202 2nd Ave S, Cold Spring, 56320, MN
Tel.: (320) 685-8611
Web Site: https://granitebank.com
Emp.: 66
Bank Holding Company
N.A.I.C.S.: 551111

Subsidiaries:

First Bancshares Inc of Cold
Spring   **(1)**
301 Main St, Cold Spring, MN 56320
Tel.: (320) 685-8611
Web Site: http://www.fnbcs.com
Rev.: $3,800,000
Emp.: 28
Fiscal Year-end: 12/31/2009
Commericial Banking
N.A.I.C.S.: 522110
Daniel Tial (VP)
Anton Muggli (Pres)
Gerald Reiter (Pres & CEO)

GRANITE BRIDGE PARTNERS LLC

420 Lexington Ave Ste 290, New York, NY 10170
Tel.: (646) 599-9900
Web Site:
   http://www.granitebridgepartners.com
Privater Equity Firm
N.A.I.C.S.: 523999
Peter Petrillo (Mng Partner)
Jeff Gerson (Partner)

GRANITE CITY ELECTRIC SUPPLY CO., INC.

19 Quincy Ave, Quincy, MA 02169-6709
Tel.: (617) 472-6500   **MA**
Web Site:
   http://www.granitecityelectric.com
Year Founded: 1923
Electrical Apparatus & Equipment Mfr
N.A.I.C.S.: 423610
Phyllis Papani Godwin (CEO, Treas & Sec)
Steve Helle (Pres)
Cori Slade (CFO)
Adrian R. Grundy (COO)

Subsidiaries:

Baynes Electric Supply Co. Inc. **(1)**
900 W Chestnut St, Brockton, MA 02301
Tel.: (508) 586-1040
Web Site: http://www.bayneselectric.com
Electrical Supplies
N.A.I.C.S.: 423610
William Arnone (Exec VP)
Dennis Todisco (VP-Natl Acct)

GRANITE CREEK CAPITAL PARTNERS, LLC

222 W Adams St Ste 1980, Chicago, IL 60606
Tel.: (312) 895-4500
Web Site:
   http://www.granitecreek.com
Privater Equity Firm
N.A.I.C.S.: 523999
James F. Clark (Partner)
Andrew Kearney (Dir)
Mark A. Radzik (Co-Founder & Mng Partner)

Brian B. Boorstein (Co-Founder & Mng Partner)
Peter G. Lehman (Co-Founder & Mng Partner)
Michael Barry (Operating Partner)
Angie Kuna (CFO)
Ting Wang (Dir)

Subsidiaries:

Diamond Blade Warehouse Inc. **(1)**
588 Lakeview Pkwy, Vernon Hills, IL 60061
Tel.: (847) 229-7970
Web Site:
   http://www.diamondbladewarehouse.com
Mfr of Saw Blades
N.A.I.C.S.: 423710
Michael I. Levy (Dir-Ops)
Jon Hartmann (Mgr-Sls-Natl)
W. James Farrell (Chm)
James M. Farrell (CEO)

NYP, LLC   **(1)**
805 E Grand St, Elizabeth, NJ 07201
Tel.: (908) 351-6550
Web Site: http://nyp-corp.com
Sales Range: $1-9.9 Million
Emp.: 100
Textile Bag Mills
N.A.I.C.S.: 314910
Jerry Labelle (VP & Mgr-Natl Sls)
Robert Dahl (CEO)

Sunset Pacific Transportation, Inc. **(1)**
13875 Norton Ave, Chino, CA 91710
Tel.: (909) 464-1677
Web Site: http://www.sunsetpacific.com
Local Trucking with Storage
N.A.I.C.S.: 484110
Josh Craig (CEO)

GRANITE EQUITY PARTNERS LLC

122 12th Ave N Ste 201, Saint Cloud, MN 56303
Tel.: (320) 251-1800
Web Site:
   http://www.graniteequity.com
Privater Equity Firm
N.A.I.C.S.: 523999
Richard L. Bauerly (Mng Partner)
Patrick K. Edeburn (Partner)
Arthur R. Monaghan (Partner)
Shelly Bauerly Kopel (Partner)
Greg Schumacher (Partner)
Angie Krtnick Complin (Dir-Talent)

Subsidiaries:

All Flex Flexible Ciruits, LLC **(1)**
1705 Cannon Ln, Northfield, MN 55057
Tel.: (507) 663-7162
Web Site: http://www.allflexinc.com
Sales Range: $25-49.9 Million
Emp.: 134
Circuit Board Mfr
N.A.I.C.S.: 334418
Dave Becker (Mgr-Sls)
Greg Closser (Pres & CEO)
John Fallon (CFO)
Chris Eisenberg (Mgr-Bus Dev)

DeZURIK, Inc. **(1)**
250 Riverside Ave N, Sartell, MN 56377
Tel.: (320) 259-2000
Web Site: http://www.dezurik.com
Sales Range: $50-74.9 Million
Emp.: 340
Valve Mfr
N.A.I.C.S.: 332911
Duane Gasser (Exec VP-Sls & Mktg)
Dan Welz (Dir-IT)
Aaron Zulkosky (Engr-Intl Applications)
Dale Grebinoski (Dir-Quality)
Clarence Jarnot (Coord-Tech Sls-Intl)
William Cogliano (Dir-Supply Chain)

Subsidiary (Domestic):

Hilton Valve, Inc. **(2)**
14520 NE 91St, Redmond, WA 98052
Tel.: (425) 883-7000
Web Site: http://www.hiltonvalve.com
Valve Mfr
N.A.I.C.S.: 332911

Leonard Elliott (VP-Sls)

Red Valve Co., Inc. **(2)**
750 Holiday Dr Ste 400, Pittsburgh, PA 15220
Tel.: (412) 279-0044
Web Site: http://www.redvalve.com
Sales Range: $25-49.9 Million
Emp.: 55
Pressure Valves & Regulators, Industrial
N.A.I.C.S.: 332911
Chris Raftis (Pres)

Valve & Primer Corporation **(2)**
1100 Via Callejon, San Clemente, CA 92673
Tel.: (949) 361-9900
Web Site: http://www.apcovalves.com
Sales Range: $25-49.9 Million
Emp.: 85
Valve Mfr
N.A.I.C.S.: 332911

GEOTEK, Inc. **(1)**
1421 2nd Ave NW, Stewartville, MN 55976
Tel.: (507) 533-6076
Web Site: http://www.geotekinc.com
Sales Range: $25-49.9 Million
Emp.: 50
Reinforced Fiberglass Pultrusion Product Mfr
N.A.I.C.S.: 326199
Conrad F. Fingerson (CEO)

Massman Automation Designs, LLC **(1)**
1010 E Lake St, Villard, MN 56385
Tel.: (320) 554-3611
Web Site: http://www.massmanllc.com
Sales Range: $25-49.9 Million
Emp.: 170
Packaging Machinery Mfr
N.A.I.C.S.: 333993
Jeff Bigger (Pres & CEO)
Mark Suchy (VP-Sls & Mktg)

Subsidiary (Domestic):

DTM Packaging, LLC **(2)**
150 Recreation Park Dr, Hingham, MA 02043
Tel.: (781) 749-1866
Web Site: http://www.dtmpackaging.com
Broom, Brush & Mop Mfr
N.A.I.C.S.: 339994
Scott MacKenzie (VP-Ops)

EDL Massman, LLC **(2)**
1260 Parkview Rd, Green Bay, WI 54304
Tel.: (920) 336-7744
Web Site: http://www.edlpackaging.com
Packaging Equipment Designer & Mfr
N.A.I.C.S.: 333993
Toni Nigrelli-LaFleur (Mgr-Bus Dev)
Matt Tresp (Sls Mgr-Midwest Reg)
Jarlath Harkin (Product Mgr-Bagged Products)
Greg Gorski (VP & Gen Mgr)

Elliott Manufacturing Company, Inc. **(2)**
2664 S Cherry Ave, Fresno, CA 93706
Tel.: (559) 233-6235
Web Site: http://www.elliott-mfg.com
Sales Range: $1-9.9 Million
Emp.: 46
Packaging Equipment Mfr
N.A.I.C.S.: 333993
John M. Rea (Mgr-Sls-Natl)
Terry Aluisi (Pres & CEO)

New England Machinery, Inc. **(2)**
6204 29th St E, Bradenton, FL 34203-5304
Tel.: (941) 755-5550
Web Site: http://www.neminc.com
Sales Range: $1-9.9 Million
Emp.: 46
Mfr of Packaging Machinery & Equipment
N.A.I.C.S.: 333993
Marge Bonura (Dir-Sls & Mktg)
Geza F. Bankuty (VP)
Judith Nickse (Pres)

GRANITE FALLS ENERGY, LLC

Tel.: (320) 564-3100
Web Site:
   https://www.granitefallsenergy.com

Year Founded: 2000
Rev.: $309,615,376
Assets: $145,136,914
Liabilities: $71,215,181
Net Worth: $73,921,733
Earnings: $23,657,081
Emp.: 82
Fiscal Year-end: 10/31/21
Methanol Mfr
N.A.I.C.S.: 325193
Paul Enstad (Chm)
Dean Buesing (Sec)
Philip Coffin (Mgr)
Cory Heinrich (Plant Mgr)
Angela Paulson (Asst Controller)
Kim Buysse (Sr Accountant/Accountant-Staff)
Elizabeth Lewison (Accountant-Staff & Investor Services & Coord-Investor Svcs)
Martin Seifert (Governor-Alternate)
Michael Green (CEO)
Matt Clausen (Mgr-Risk)
Sherry Larson (Vice Chm)
Sam Hansen (Governor)
Kevin Sharkey (Governor)

Subsidiaries:

Heron Lake BioEnergy, LLC **(1)**
91246 390th Ave, Heron Lake, MN 56137-1375 **(100%)**
Tel.: (507) 793-0077
Web Site:
   https://www.heronlakebioenergy.com
Rev.: $76,029,841
Assets: $63,080,181
Liabilities: $29,955,313
Net Worth: $33,124,868
Earnings: ($14,318,810)
Emp.: 40
Fiscal Year-end: 10/31/2020
Methanol Mfr
N.A.I.C.S.: 325193
Stacie Schuler (CFO)
Brodie McKeown (Plant Mgr)
Michael Green (CEO)
Richard Doescher (Mgr-Environmental Health & Safety)

GRANITE FURNITURE CO

1475 W 9000 S, West Jordan, UT 84088
Tel.: (801) 566-4444   **UT**
Web Site:
   http://www.granitefurniture.com
Year Founded: 1910
Sales Range: Less than $1 Million
Emp.: 6
Home Furnishings Retailer
N.A.I.C.S.: 449110
Roger T. Richards (CFO & Sec)
John D. Richards Jr. (CEO)

GRANITE GROUP WHOLESALE LLC

6 Storrs St, Concord, NH 03301-4837
Tel.: (603) 224-1901   **NH**
Web Site:
   http://www.thegranitegroup.com
Year Founded: 1998
Sales Range: $125-149.9 Million
Emp.: 400
Plumbing & Heating Supplies
N.A.I.C.S.: 423720
Kevin Condron (Pres & CEO)

Subsidiaries:

Granite Group Wholesale, LLC **(1)**
37 Amoskeag St, Manchester, NH 03102
Tel.: (603) 518-1501
Web Site: http://www.thegranitegroup.com
Sales Range: $10-24.9 Million
Emp.: 12
Wholesale Distributor of Plumbing & Heating Supplies
N.A.I.C.S.: 423720

Shetucket Plumbing Supply Inc. **(1)**
75 Jefferson Ave, New London, CT 06320
Tel.: (860) 442-4348

Granite Group Wholesale LLC—(Continued)

Web Site:
http://www.shetucketindustrial.com
Sales Range: $10-24.9 Million
Emp.: 23
Plumbing Fittings & Supplies
N.A.I.C.S.: 423720

GRANITE MICROSYSTEMS INC.

10202 N Enterprise Dr, Mequon, WI 53092
Tel.: (262) 242-8800
Web Site:
http://www.granitemicrosystem.com
Rev.: $45,000,000
Emp.: 105
Electronic Computer Mfr
N.A.I.C.S.: 334111
Clint Hanson (VP)
Michael McDonald (Bus Mgr)
Michael Shore (Mgr)
Daniel P. Armbrust (CEO)
Bruce Hurwitz (VP)
Todd Sweet (VP)

GRANITE PACKAGING SUPPLY ONE CO.

111 Whittendale Dr, Moorestown, NJ 08057
Tel.: (856) 727-1010
Web Site: http://www.supplyone.com
Sales Range: $10-24.9 Million
Emp.: 80
Packaging Materials
N.A.I.C.S.: 424990
Bill Leith (Pres)

GRANITE ROCK COMPANY

350 Technology Dr, Watsonville, CA 95077-5001
Tel.: (831) 768-2000
Web Site:
https://www.graniterock.com
Year Founded: 1900
Sales Range: $50-74.9 Million
Emp.: 900
Construction Sand & Gravel
N.A.I.C.S.: 212321
Bruce W. Woolpert (Pres & CEO)

GRANITE RUN BUICK GMC, INC.

1056 E Baltimore Pike, Media, PA 19063
Tel.: (484) 443-5350
Web Site: https://www.graniterun.com
Year Founded: 1954
Sales Range: $10-24.9 Million
Emp.: 45
New Car Retailer
N.A.I.C.S.: 441110
Peter Irish (Owner)
Ryan Irish (Gen Mgr-Sls)
Mark O'Brien (Mgr-Sls-New Car)
Dave Gaudino (Mgr-Used Car)
Peter Croyle (Mgr-Fin)
Dave Cunningham (Mgr-Svc)
James Davidson (Mgr-Parts)

GRANITE TELECOMMUNICATIONS, LLC

100 Newport Ave Ext, Quincy, MA 02171
Tel.: (617) 933-5500
Web Site: http://www.granitenet.com
Year Founded: 2002
Sales Range: $250-299.9 Million
Emp.: 900
Telephone, Broadband & Inside Wire Service Whslr, Specializing in Multi-Location Businesses & Offering Consolidated Billing
N.A.I.C.S.: 517111
Jack McCadden (VP)
Geoff Cookman (Dir-Carrier Rels)

Lauren Grenier (Mktg Dir)
Sana Sheikh (VP-Transformation)
Rob Hale Jr. (Pres & CEO)

GRANITO ACQUISITION I, INC.

3414 Pino Dr, Las Vegas, NV 89121
Tel.: (702) 738-8614
Year Founded: 2014
Investment Services
N.A.I.C.S.: 523999
Frank Underhill Sr. (Pres, CEO, CFO, Chief Acctg Officer, Treas & Sec)

GRANT AVENUE CAPITAL, LLC

65 E 55th St 33rd Fl, New York, NY 10022
Tel.: (212) 630-5037
Web Site: http://www.grantave.com
Healthcare Private Equity Firm
N.A.I.C.S.: 523999
Buddy Gumina (Founder & Mng Partner)
Preston Brice (Partner)

Subsidiaries:

Quorum Health Resources, LLC   (1)
1573 Mallory Ln Ste 200, Brentwood, TN 37027
Tel.: (615) 371-7979
Web Site: http://www.qhr.com
Sales Range: $75-99.9 Million
Health Care Srvices
N.A.I.C.S.: 622110
Timothy J. Ryan (CFO)
William Donatelli (VP-West Ops)
Matthew Hayes (Reg VP)
David Jensen (Principal-Revenue Cycle)
Dan Hamman (VP-Strategic Integrated Resources Group)
Lisa Boston (Dir-Compliance)
Brendan Rokke (Mgr-Strategy)
David Perry (VP & Dir-Healthcare Fin & Reimbursement)
Michael Donahue (Mgr-Healthcare Fin & Reimbursement)
Michele Mayes (Sr VP-Consulting)
Jody Pigg (VP-Fin Practice)
Chip Holmes (VP-Div)
Ron Vigus (Reg VP)
David Yackell (Reg VP)
Sam Brown (Assoc VP)
Ken Ward (Assoc VP)
Herb Winters (Assoc VP)
Lynn Collins (Dir-Clinical & Operational Improvement)
Michael Corbett (Assoc VP-Clinical & Operational Improvement)
Mark Henning (Dir-Clinical & Operational Performance Improvement)
Judy Krempin (Dir-Clinical & Operational Improvement)
Cathy Stern (Mgr-Clinical Ops)
Theresa Lewis (Assoc VP-Physician Svcs & Strategy Consulting)
Pamela Wells (Sr Mgr-Clinical & Operational Improvement)
Wanda Wright (Dir-Managed Care)
Robin Bradbury (Sr VP)
Dwayne Gunter (Pres & CEO)

Subsidiary (Domestic):

Resolution Consulting, Inc.   (2)
2655 W Midway Blvd Ste 235, Broomfield, CO 80020
Tel.: (303) 530-0396
Web Site: http://www.ereso.com
Sales Range: $1-9.9 Million
Emp.: 60
Billing Management Solutions
N.A.I.C.S.: 561499
Robin Bradbury (Pres)
Michael A. Rönning (VP-Client Svcs)

GRANT AVIATION INC.

4451 Aircraft Dr Ste A, Anchorage, AK 99502
Tel.: (907) 248-7025
Web Site: http://www.flygrant.com
Sales Range: $10-24.9 Million
Emp.: 125

Provider of Airline Transportation Services
N.A.I.C.S.: 481211

GRANT BANCSHARES, INC.

814 Washington St, Natchitoches, LA 71457
Tel.: (318) 352-3060
Web Site: http://www.bofm.com
Year Founded: 2003
Sales Range: $10-24.9 Million
Bank Holding Company
N.A.I.C.S.: 551111
Richard Kent Hale (Pres & CEO)

Subsidiaries:

Bank of Montgomery   (1)
1000 Caddo St, Montgomery, LA 71454
Tel.: (318) 646-3386
Web Site: http://www.bofm.com
Sales Range: $10-24.9 Million
Commericial Banking
N.A.I.C.S.: 522110
Richard Kent Hale (Pres & CEO)

GRANT CONSTRUCTION, INC.

3335 Henry Ln, Bakersfield, CA 93308
Tel.: (661) 588-4586
Web Site: http://www.gciframing.com
Sales Range: $10-24.9 Million
Emp.: 100
New Single-Family Housing Construction
N.A.I.C.S.: 236115
Julio C. Vega (Controller)
Hugo Montoya (Mgr-Acctg)

GRANT HARTFORD CORPORATION

2620 Connery Way, Missoula, MT 59808-1325
Tel.: (303) 506-6822
Web Site:
http://www.granthartford.com
Year Founded: 2007
Sales Range: $25-49.9 Million
Emp.: 4
Gold Mining & Exploration Services
N.A.I.C.S.: 212220
David Gilmer (Treas & Sec)
J. Robert Flesher (VP-Geology)
Aaron Charlton (Chm & CEO)
David Rodli (Pres & COO)

GRANT INDUSTRIAL CONTROLS INC.

200 Industry Dr, Pittsburgh, PA 15275
Tel.: (412) 787-9770
Web Site:
https://www.grantindustrial.com
Year Founded: 1981
Emp.: 130
Factory Automation & Motor Controls
N.A.I.C.S.: 334513
William G. Harrington (Pres & Owner)
William Small (VP & Gen Mgr)
Gail Cunningham (Controller)
Roy Chilson (Branch Mgr)
Tom Fitzgerald (Pur Mgr)
Barbara Giblock (VP-Fin)
Steve Young (Mgr-Networking & Automation)

GRANT INDUSTRIES INC.

125 Main Ave, Elmwood Park, NJ 07407
Tel.: (201) 791-6700
Web Site: https://www.grantinc.com
Rev.: $12,600,000
Emp.: 52
Manufacture Chemicals
N.A.I.C.S.: 325412
Mike Granatell (CEO)
Carlos Santiago (Dir-Tech R&D)
Thomas Hrubec (Dir-R&D)

GRANT INDUSTRIES INCORPORATED

33415 Groesbeck Hwy Ste 4203, Fraser, MI 48026
Tel.: (586) 293-9200
Web Site: https://www.grantgrp.com
Rev.: $13,000,000
Emp.: 45
Automotive Stampings
N.A.I.C.S.: 336370
Robert Grant (Pres)

GRANT MARKETING

2020 Commonwealth Ave, Newton, MA 02466
Tel.: (617) 796-0186
Web Site:
http://www.grantmarketing.com
Year Founded: 1986
Sales Range: Less than $1 Million
Emp.: 8
Advetising Agency
N.A.I.C.S.: 541810
Bob Grant (Founder, Principal & Brand Strategist)
Grant Penny (Dir-Art)
Paul Jarosik (VP-New Bus Dev)
Jacinta Carrion-Williams (Mgr-Office & Traffic)
Bob Jaczko (Dir-Creative)

GRANT MEMORIAL HOSPITAL

117 Hospital Dr, Petersburg, WV 26847
Tel.: (304) 257-1026
Web Site:
http://www.grantmemorial.com
Year Founded: 1957
Sales Range: $25-49.9 Million
Emp.: 416
Healtcare Services
N.A.I.C.S.: 622110
Joe A. Barnes (CFO)
Robert W. Milvet (CEO)

GRANT PARK FUTURES FUND LIMITED PARTNERSHIP

555 W Jackson Blvd Ste 600, Chicago, IL 60661
Tel.: (312) 756-4450
Web Site:
http://www.grantparkfunds.com
Year Founded: 1989
Rev.: $412,124
Assets: $38,367,940
Liabilities: $918,273
Net Worth: $37,449,667
Earnings: $128,438
Fiscal Year-end: 12/31/22
Investment Services
N.A.I.C.S.: 523999

GRANT ROAD LUMBER CO. INC.

2543 E Grant Rd, Tucson, AZ 85716
Tel.: (520) 795-4160
Web Site:
http://www.grantroadlumber.com
Rev.: $11,824,946
Emp.: 40
Lumber: Rough, Dressed & Finished
N.A.I.C.S.: 423310
Sam Hauert (Pres)

GRANT THORNTON LLP - USA

175 W Jackson Blvd 20th Fl, Chicago, IL 60604
Tel.: (312) 856-0200
Web Site:
http://www.grantthornton.com
Year Founded: 1924
Accounting, Auditing, Tax & Management Consulting Services
N.A.I.C.S.: 541211

Mike McGuire (CEO)
Steven R. Perkins (Mng Dir-Tech-Natl)
Jeffrey L. Burgess (Mng Partner-Audit Svcs-Natl)
Jeff T. French (Mng Partner-Consumer & Indus Products-Natl)
Srikant Sastry (Mng Principal-Advisory Svcs-Natl)
Dexter Manning (Partner)
Warren W. Stippich (Partner)
Erich Pugh (Partner-Tax Svcs)
Sean Denham (Partner)
Kim O'Connor (Mng Partner-Boston)
Oliver Dennison (Mng Dir)
Angelica Roiz (Partner-Philadelphia)
Zeynep Koller (Principal-Strategy & Transformation Practice-Boston)
Scott Davis (Mng Partner-Fin Advisor Svcs-Natl)
Ricci L. Mulligan (Dir-Public Sector Healthcare practice)
Sharif Ambrose (Mng Principal-Public Sector Healthcare practice)
David Hazels (Mng Partner-Advisory Svcs-Natl)
Jim Peko (COO)
Renato Zanichelli (Mng Partner-Tax Svcs-National)
Nichole Jordan (Mng Partner-Central Region)
Brad Preber (CEO)
Keith Nickels (Partner-Tax)
Beatrix Bernauer (Chief Risk & Compliance Officer & Deputy Gen Counsel)
Sven Stumbauer (Mng Dir-Advisory Svcs)
Paul Melville (Mng Principal-Integrity, Investigations & Restructuring Solutions-Natl)
Mark Margulies (Mng Partner-South Florida)

Subsidiaries:

TayganPoint Consulting Group, Inc. (1)
1118 General Washington Memorial Blvd, Washington Crossing, PA 18977
Tel.: (215) 302-2500
Web Site: http://www.tayganpoint.com
Management Consulting Services
N.A.I.C.S.: 541618
Joy E. Taylor (Co-Founder & CEO)
John Cassimatis (Co-Founder & Pres)
Adam Berman (Sr Dir-Talent Mgmt)
Jim Szakacs (Chief Admin Officer)
Barry Rudner (Dir-HR)
Debbie Neuscheler (Chief Consulting Officer)
Amy Flynn (Mng Dir)
Andrew Hunter (Mng Dir)

GRANT VICTOR
854 W 450 N Ste 4, Kaysville, UT 84037
Tel.: (801) 444-5959
Web Site:
   https://www.grantvictor.com
Year Founded: 2000
Sales Range: $25-49.9 Million
Emp.: 44
Retail Automatic Teller Machine Distr
N.A.I.C.S.: 423420
Sam Anderson (Dir-Mktg)

Subsidiaries:

ATMEquipment.com (1)
854 W 450 N Ste 4, Kaysville, UT 84037
Tel.: (801) 546-4146
Web Site: http://www.atmequipment.com
Sales Range: $10-24.9 Million
Emp.: 20
Wholesale Supplier of Retail ATM Machines
N.A.I.C.S.: 525990
James Ethridge (Pres)

GRANT-BLACKFORD MENTAL HEALTH, INC.

505 Wabash Ave, Marion, IN 46952-2608
Tel.: (765) 662-3971   IN
Year Founded: 1969
Sales Range: $10-24.9 Million
Emp.: 213
Emotion Consultation & Treatment Services
N.A.I.C.S.: 623220
Paul Kuczora (CEO)

GRANTHAM DISTRIBUTING COMPANY, INC.
2685 Hansrob Rd, Orlando, FL 32804-3317
Tel.: (407) 299-6446   FL
Year Founded: 1956
Sales Range: $50-74.9 Million
Emp.: 145
Distr of Beer, Wine & Liquor
N.A.I.C.S.: 424820

GRANTHAM, MAYO, VAN OT-TERLOO & CO. LLC
40 Rowes Wharf, Boston, MA 02110
Tel.: (617) 330-7500   MA
Web Site: https://www.gmo.com
Year Founded: 1977
Rev.: $71,000,000,000
Emp.: 500
Investment Management & Advisory Services
N.A.I.C.S.: 523940
Jeremy Grantham (Co-Founder)
Urban Mueller (Head-Global Client Rels)
Amit Bhartia (Portfolio Mgr-Emerging Markets Equity)
Tom Hancock (Head-Focused Equity)
Drew Spangler (Head-Intl Active)
Jason Halliwell (Head-Systematic Global Macro)
Sean Gleason (Portfolio Mgr-Systematic Global Macro)
Scott Hayward (CEO)
Greg A. Shell Sr. (Portfolio Mgr)

Subsidiaries:

Grantham, Mayo, Van Otterloo & Co. LLC - San Francisco (1)
2150 Shattuck Ave Ste 900, Berkeley, CA 94704
Tel.: (510) 649-6030
Web Site: http://www.gmo.com
Investment Management & Advisory Services
N.A.I.C.S.: 523940
Arjun Divecha (Head-Emerging Markets Equity)

GRANUM COMMUNICATIONS
200 Schultz Dr, Red Bank, NJ 07701-6776
Tel.: (732) 933-2626   NJ
Year Founded: 1996
Radio Consulting Management Advisory Services
N.A.I.C.S.: 541690

GRANUM INC.
600 S Brandon St, Seattle, WA 98108
Tel.: (206) 525-0051
Web Site:
   http://www.choiceorganicteas.com
Organic Tea Whslr
N.A.I.C.S.: 424490
Ray Lacorte (VP-Ops)

GRAPE EXPECTATIONS INC.
1091 Essex Ave, Richmond, CA 94801
Tel.: (510) 412-5969
Web Site: http://www.grapex.com
Sales Range: $10-24.9 Million
Emp.: 60
Wine Whslr

N.A.I.C.S.: 424820
Allen Pricco (Pres)
Deborah Cooper (Sec)

GRAPEVINE COMMUNICA-TIONS INTERNATIONAL INC.
5201 Paylor Ln, Sarasota, FL 34240
Tel.: (941) 351-0024
Web Site: http://www.grapeinc.com
Sales Range: $10-24.9 Million
Emp.: 14
Advertising, Marketing & Public Relations
N.A.I.C.S.: 541810
Angela Massarro-Fain (Founder, Pres & Partner)
John Fain (Partner & Exec VP)
Eric Buchanan (Dir-Art)
John Butzko (Dir-Comm)
Lisa E. Dahlquist (Sr Mgr-Client Rels)
Lisa Grasso (Sr Dir-Art)
Miranda Spinner (Mgr-PR & Media)
Gabriele Vest (VP-Bus Dev)
Joan Burnell (Mgr-Production & Traffic)
Kristie OKon (Mgr-Client Rels)
Heidi Cook (Dir-Ops)

GRAPEVINE DODGE CHRYS-LER JEEP
2601 William D Tate Ave, Grapevine, TX 76051
Tel.: (817) 784-7399
Web Site:
   http://www.grapevinedcj.com
Sales Range: $10-24.9 Million
Emp.: 70
Car Whslr
N.A.I.C.S.: 441110
Nicole Kelley (Comptroller)

GRAPHIC ANGELS DESIGN GROUP
370 Turrell Ave, South Orange, NJ 07079
Tel.: (973) 378-3394
Web Site:
   http://www.graphicangels.com
Year Founded: 1997
Sales Range: Less than $1 Million
Emp.: 3
Advetising Agency
N.A.I.C.S.: 541810
Tomm Scalera (Dir-Creative)
Holly Scalera (Dir-Sls)

GRAPHIC COMMUNICATIONS HOLDINGS
16 B Journey, Aliso Viejo, CA 92656
Tel.: (949) 215-9300
Web Site:
   http://www.graphiccommunications.com
Year Founded: 1985
Sales Range: $500-549.9 Million
Emp.: 10
Broker of Paper
N.A.I.C.S.: 424110
Ken Russell (Asst Controller)
Matt Dawley (Pres)

GRAPHIC CONVERTING INC.
877 N Larch Ave, Elmhurst, IL 60126
Tel.: (630) 758-4100   IL
Web Site:
   http://www.graphicconverting.com
Year Founded: 1976
Sales Range: $50-74.9 Million
Emp.: 200
Holding Company; Trading Card & Packaging Mfr
N.A.I.C.S.: 551112
John Tinnon (Founder & Chm)
Steve Skalski (Pres & CEO)
Joe Yaney (CFO)

Subsidiaries:

GC Packaging, LLC (1)
877 N Larch Ave, Elmhurst, IL 60126   (100%)
Tel.: (630) 758-4100
Web Site: http://www.gcpackaging.com
Emp.: 3
Trading Card Packaging Products Mfr
N.A.I.C.S.: 322220
John Tinnon (Chm)
Steve Skalski (Pres & CEO)
Joe Yaney (CFO & Controller)

GRAPHIC INFORMATION SYS-TEMS INC.
17300 SW Upper Boones Ferry Rd Ste 130, Portland, OR 97224
Tel.: (503) 682-1322   OR
Web Site:
   https://www.gisimarketing.com
Year Founded: 1968
Sales Range: $10-24.9 Million
Emp.: 100
Photocopying & Duplicating Services
N.A.I.C.S.: 323111
Eben Swett (Pres & CEO)

GRAPHIC INNOVATORS INC.
855 Morse Ave, Elk Grove Village, IL 60007
Tel.: (847) 718-1516
Web Site:
   http://www.graphicinnovators.com
Year Founded: 1991
Printing Trades Machinery
N.A.I.C.S.: 333248
Joe Pierobon (Sr Dir-Global Proj Mgmt)
John Bankson (VP-Ops)
Duane Harris (Mgr-Traffic)
Tom Riley (Sr VP-Sls)
Paul Lange (VP-Sls)

GRAPHIC LAMINATING, INC.
6185 Cochran Rd, Solon, OH 44139-3305
Tel.: (440) 498-3400
Web Site:
   http://www.graphiclaminating.com
Sales Range: $75-99.9 Million
Emp.: 50
Laminating Film & Equipment Mfr
N.A.I.C.S.: 424610
Michael Hannon (Pres)

GRAPHIC MEDIA PRODUCTS INC.
750 Commerce Dr, Gulf Shores, AL 36542
Tel.: (251) 967-3456
Web Site: http://www.gmpinc.com
Sales Range: $10-24.9 Million
Emp.: 2
Industrial Machinery Mfr
N.A.I.C.S.: 333248
Carl Champion (VP)
Joyce Freeman (Pres)

GRAPHIC PRODUCTS COR-PORATION
455 Maple Ave, Carpentersville, IL 60110
Tel.: (847) 836-9600
Web Site:
   https://www.gpcpapers.com
Year Founded: 1962
Rev.: $10,000,000
Emp.: 15
Graphic Arts Products Mfr & Whslr
N.A.I.C.S.: 424130
Douglas Trullinger (Mgr-Warehouse)

GRAPHIC RESEARCH INC
9334 Mason Ave, Chatsworth, CA 91311-5201

Graphic Research Inc—(Continued)

Tel.: (818) 886-7340
Web Site:
   http://www.graphicresearch.com
Year Founded: 1966
Sales Range: $50-74.9 Million
Emp.: 75
Printed Circuit Boards Mfr
N.A.I.C.S.: 334412
Beverley Hector (VP-Sls & Mktg)
Pete Vaghashia (Pres)

GRAPHIC SCIENCES INC.
7515 Northeast Ambassador Pl Ste L,
Portland, OR 97220
Tel.: (503) 460-0203
Web Site:
   http://www.graphicsciences.com
Year Founded: 1987
Sales Range: $25-49.9 Million
Emp.: 65
Printing Services
N.A.I.C.S.: 325910
Kent Wishart (Pres)
Cindy Hill (CFO & VP)
Qingjiang Zhou (CTO)
Jeff Ashburn (VP-Sls & Mktg)
Ed Caskey (VP-Primary Mfg)
Jie Wang (Gen Mgr)
Eric Aldridge (Plant Mgr)
James Blanton (Acct Mgr)
Julian Gonzalez (Plant Mgr)
Renda Grogan (Reg Acct Mgr)
Jimmy Nix (Plant Mgr)
Lino Nunez (Plant Mgr-Tech Sls)
Pat Mullin (Plant Mgr)
Melisa Stark (Reg Acct Mgr)

GRAPHIC SYSTEMS INC.
7200 Goodlett Farms Pkwy Ste 102,
Cordova, TN 38016-4948
Tel.: (901) 937-5500
Web Site: http://www.yesgsi.com
Sales Range: $10-24.9 Million
Emp.: 15
Printing Broker Services
N.A.I.C.S.: 541990
Dennis Kopcial (Pres)

**GRAPHIC VISUAL SOLU-
TIONS, INC.**
4301 Waterleaf Ct, Greensboro, NC
27410
Tel.: (336) 292-4000
Web Site:
   http://www.graphicvisualsolu
   tions.com
Year Founded: 1985
Sales Range: $1-9.9 Million
Emp.: 150
Printing Services
N.A.I.C.S.: 323111
Bryan T. Hall (Pres)
Beverly Allred (CFO)
Jack Brown (CTO)
R. J. Landry (Exec VP-HR & Ops)

**GRAPHIC WEST PACKAGING
MACHINERY, LLC**
115 Progress Dr, Manchester, CT
06042
Tel.: (860) 645-7178   CT
Web Site:
   http://www.graphicwestpm.com
Packaging Machinery Mfr
N.A.I.C.S.: 333993
Carmen Martocchio (Owner)

GRAPHICODE INC.
1924 Bickford Ave Ste 201, Snohom-
ish, WA 98290-1753
Tel.: (360) 282-4888
Web Site: http://www.graphicode.com
Year Founded: 1987

Electronics Manufacturing Software
Solutions
N.A.I.C.S.: 513210
Adam Brockman (Mgr-Sls & Mktg)

GRAPHICS GROUP LTD.
2425 NE Riverside Way, Portland,
OR 97211
Tel.: (503) 248-2060
Sales Range: $10-24.9 Million
Emp.: 125
Embroidery & Screen Printing Ser-
vices
N.A.I.C.S.: 323113
Larie Thomas (Mgr-Sls)
Jon C. Biro (Sec)
Joe R. Davis (Pres)

**GRAPHICS INTERNATIONAL
INC.**
2318 Crown Center Dr, Charlotte, NC
28227
Tel.: (704) 847-8282
Web Site:
   https://www.graphicsinterna
   tional.com
Sales Range: $10-24.9 Million
Emp.: 16
Printing Trades Machinery, Equip-
ment & Supplies
N.A.I.C.S.: 423830
William B. Troutman (Founder &
CEO)

**GRAPHICS SYSTEMS CORP.
(GXSC)**
W133 N5138 Campbell Dr, Menom-
onee Falls, WI 53051
Tel.: (262) 790-1080   WI
Web Site: http://www.gxsc.com
Year Founded: 1990
Sales Range: $10-24.9 Million
Emp.: 38
3D Engineering Technology for De-
sign, Management, Simulation &
Communication
N.A.I.C.S.: 541512
David M. Kasinskas (Pres & CEO)
David Vedder (VP-Engrg & Tech)

GRAPHITE CORP.
616 Corporate Way Ste 2-9011, Val-
ley Cottage, NY 10989   NV
Web Site: http://www.graphenz.com
Year Founded: 2007
Emp.: 2
Graphite Mfr
N.A.I.C.S.: 335991
Yehuda Eliraz (Chm)

**GRAPHITE METALLIZING
CORPORATION**
1050 Nepperhan Ave, Yonkers, NY
10703
Tel.: (914) 968-8400
Web Site: http://www.graphalloy.com
Year Founded: 1913
Sales Range: $25-49.9 Million
Emp.: 60
Graphalloy Mechanical & Electro-
Mechanical Products Mfr
N.A.I.C.S.: 335991
Eben Walker (Gen Mgr)
Dennis Rawle (Dir-Sls-Europe)
Andrew Ondish (Mgr-Sls-New Jersey,
Eastern Pennsylvania, Delaware,
Maryland &)
John Warhoover (Mgr-Sls-Missouri,
Southern Illinois, Kansas, Oklahoma,
Nebraska,)
Joe Conyers (Sls Mgr-California, Ne-
vada & Arizona)

GRAPHITE SALES, INC.
16710 W Park Cir Dr, Chagrin Falls,
OH 44023

Tel.: (440) 543-8221   OH
Web Site:
   http://www.graphitesales.com
Year Founded: 1971
Sales Range: $10-24.9 Million
Emp.: 50
Carbon & Graphite Products
N.A.I.C.S.: 335991
Kevin Burmeister (Pres)
Arthur Martin (VP-Graphite Tech)
John Johnson (Mgr-Quality Assur-
ance)
Micheal Slabe (CFO)

GRAPHNET INC.
30 Broad St Fl 43, New York, NY
10004
Tel.: (212) 994-1100
Web Site: http://www.graphnet.com
Year Founded: 1989
Rev.: $50,000,000
Emp.: 100
Data Messaging Technologies
N.A.I.C.S.: 518210
Idan Elkon (COO)
Guy Conte (VP-Fin)

**GRASS & MORE OUTDOOR
SERVICES, INC.**
1730 Bledsoe Dr, Dalton, GA 30721
Tel.: (706) 259-9349
Web Site:
   https://www.grassandmoreout
   door.com
Sales Range: $1-9.9 Million
Emp.: 15
Landscape Services
N.A.I.C.S.: 561730
David Smith (Pres)
Lisa Smith (Sec)

GRASSBURGER, LLC
726 1/2 Main Ave, Durango, CO
81301
Tel.: (970) 247-1081   CO
Web Site:
   http://www.eatgrassburger.com
Year Founded: 2014
Sales Range: $1-9.9 Million
Emp.: 50
Food & Beverage Product Distr
N.A.I.C.S.: 445298
Jessie Kileen (Founder & CEO)

**GRASSLAND DAIRY PROD-
UCTS, INC.**
N8790 Fairground Ave, Greenwood,
WI 54437-7668
Tel.: (715) 267-6182
Web Site: https://www.grassland.com
Year Founded: 1904
Sales Range: $50-74.9 Million
Emp.: 200
Dairy Products Mfr
N.A.I.C.S.: 112120
Dallas L. Wuethrich (Pres)
Laurie Horn (Dir-Sls-Natl)
Tammy Jacobs (Coord-Logistics)
Eric Vorpahl (Mgr-Sls-Natl)

Subsidiaries:

West Point Dairy Products, LLC   (1)
1715 E Rd, West Point, NE 68788
Tel.: (402) 372-5551
Web Site: http://www.westpointdairy.com
Dairy Products Mfr
N.A.I.C.S.: 311512
Rob Jackson (Plant Mgr)

**GRASSLAND EQUIPMENT &
IRRIGATION CORPORATION**
892-898 Troy Schenectady Rd,
Latham, NY 12110
Tel.: (518) 785-5841   NY
Web Site:
   https://www.grasslandcorp.com
Year Founded: 1961

Sales Range: $1-9.9 Million
Emp.: 50
Lawn & Garden Machinery Equip-
ment Whlsr
N.A.I.C.S.: 423820
Chris Pogge (Mgr-Sales-Eastern NY)

Subsidiaries:

Grassland Equipment & Irrigation
Corp.   (1)
270 Lake Ave, Blasdell, NY 14219-1500
Tel.: (716) 822-2020
Web Site: http://www.grasslandcorp.com
Outdoor Power Equipment, Golf Course
Equipment & Supplies Whlsr
N.A.I.C.S.: 423820

Grassland Equipment & Irrigation
Corp.   (1)
315 Commerce Blvd, Liverpool, NY 13088-
4512
Tel.: (315) 457-0181
Web Site: http://www.grasslandcorp.com
Emp.: 12
Irrigation Equipment Distr
N.A.I.C.S.: 423820
Roger Lind (Mgr-Comml Sls)

**GRASSROOTS ENTERPRISE,
INC.**
1875 Eye St NW Ste 900, Washing-
ton, DC 20006
Tel.: (202) 371-0200
Web Site: http://www.grassroots.com
Year Founded: 1999
Sales Range: $25-49.9 Million
Emp.: 45
Nonpartisan Political Action Website
& Online Community
N.A.I.C.S.: 513110
Alex Tomlinson (VP-Client Svcs)
Sherry Reilly (Dir-Comm)

GRATES CORPORATION
25614 Jefferson Ave, Saint Clair
Shores, MI 48081-2316
Tel.: (586) 777-7775
Web Site: http://www.grates.net
Sales Range: $10-24.9 Million
Emp.: 12
Mfr Medical Equipment & Supplies
N.A.I.C.S.: 423450
Michael Grates (Pres)
Kevin Malone (VP)

**GRATWICK ENTERPRISES
INC.**
21 Donald B Dean Dr, South Port-
land, ME 04106
Tel.: (207) 773-3829
Web Site:
   https://www.bonneystaffing.com
Rev.: $13,000,000
Emp.: 15
Employment Agencies
N.A.I.C.S.: 561311
Joel Gratwick (CEO)

GRAVA OF MEDFORD, INC.
29 Mystic Ave, Medford, MA 02155
Tel.: (781) 391-8950
Year Founded: 1983
Sales Range: $10-24.9 Million
Emp.: 58
Car Whlsr
N.A.I.C.S.: 441110
Peter M. Grava (Pres)

**GRAVES & GRAVES CON-
STRUCTION CO., INC.**
1267 W Main St, Parsons, TN 38363
Tel.: (731) 847-6391
Web Site:
   https://www.gravesandgraves.com
Year Founded: 1983
Sales Range: $10-24.9 Million
Emp.: 150
Commercial & Institutional Building
Construction Services
N.A.I.C.S.: 236220

Danny L. Graves *(Pres)*
Jon Graves *(VP)*

GRAVES OIL COMPANY
226 Pearson St PO Box 112, Batesville, MS 38606
Tel.: (662) 563-4604
Web Site: https://www.gravesoil.com
Year Founded: 1982
Sales Range: $25-49.9 Million
Emp.: 40
Provider of Petroleum Bulk Stations
N.A.I.C.S.: 424710

GRAVES SUPER MARKETS INC.
797 Main St, Presque Isle, ME 04769
Tel.: (207) 769-2181
Web Site: http://shopnsave.com
Rev.: $15,000,000
Emp.: 175
Grocery Stores
N.A.I.C.S.: 445110
Robert D. Graves *(Pres)*
Gregory Graves *(VP)*

GRAVITY PAYMENTS
1455 NW Leary Way Ste 200, Seattle, WA 98107
Web Site:
    http://www.gravitypayments.com
Year Founded: 2004
Sales Range: $1-9.9 Million
Emp.: 80
Payment Processing Services, Including Debit & Credit Card Processing, Electronic Check Payments & e-Commerce Services
N.A.I.C.S.: 522320
Dan Price *(Founder & CEO)*

GRAY & COMPANY
3325 W Polk Rd, Hart, MI 49420
Tel.: (231) 873-5628   OR
Web Site:
    https://www.grayandcompany.us
Year Founded: 1908
Packaged Maraschino Cherry, Glazed Fruit & Coconut Mfr & Distr
N.A.I.C.S.: 424490

GRAY & OSBORNE, INC.
701 Dexter Ave N Ste 200, Seattle, WA 98109
Tel.: (206) 284-0860
Web Site: http://www.g-o.com
Rev.: $13,100,000
Emp.: 160
Engineering Consulting Services
N.A.I.C.S.: 541330
Keith Stewart *(Engr-Design)*
Nancy Lockett *(Project Mgr)*
Tom Zerkel *(Project Mgr)*
John Wilson *(Project Mgr)*

GRAY & PAPE, INC.
1318 Main St, Cincinnati, OH 45202
Tel.: (513) 287-7700   OH
Web Site: https://www.graypape.com
Year Founded: 1991
Sales Range: $10-24.9 Million
Emp.: 58
Cultural Resources Management & Historic Preservation Services
N.A.I.C.S.: 541620
Cinder Miller *(VP-Ops)*
Madonna Ledford *(Sr Mgr-Technical Svcs Grp)*
Michael Striker *(Sr Mgr-Archaeology)*

GRAY AMERICA CORP.
3050 Dryden Rd, Dayton, OH 45439-1620
Tel.: (937) 293-9313   OH
Web Site:
    https://www.grayamerica.com

Year Founded: 1978
Sales Range: $10-24.9 Million
Emp.: 150
Industrial Services
N.A.I.C.S.: 331110
John C. Gray *(Pres & CEO)*

Subsidiaries:

A-Lab Corp.   (1)
3050 Dryden Rd, Dayton, OH 45439-1620   (100%)
Tel.: (937) 293-0333
Web Site: http://www.a-labcorp.com
Sales Range: $10-24.9 Million
Emp.: 17
Testing Services
N.A.I.C.S.: 541380
John William *(Gen Mgr)*

L&H Threaded Rods Corp.   (1)
3050 Dryden Rd, Dayton, OH 45439-1620   (100%)
Tel.: (937) 294-6666
Web Site: http://www.lhrods.com
Sales Range: $10-24.9 Million
Emp.: 130
Steel Services
N.A.I.C.S.: 331110

New Dimension Metals Corp.   (1)
3050 Dryden Rd, Dayton, OH 45439-1620   (100%)
Tel.: (937) 299-2233
Web Site: http://www.ndmetals.com
Sales Range: $10-24.9 Million
Emp.: 100
Steel Services
N.A.I.C.S.: 331221
Randall R. Fox *(Pres)*
Bill Abbott *(Mgr-Production)*
Ronald D. Griffith Jr. *(Supvr-Production)*

Scarlet & Gray Corp.   (1)
3050 Dryden Rd, Dayton, OH 45439-1620
Tel.: (937) 293-3207
Web Site: http://www.grayamerica.com
Sales Range: $10-24.9 Million
Emp.: 12
Trucking Service
N.A.I.C.S.: 484121

GRAY INC.
10 Quality St, Lexington, KY 40507-1450
Tel.: (859) 281-5000
Web Site: https://www.gray.com
Year Founded: 1960
Sales Range: $25-49.9 Million
Emp.: 2,000
Offices of Other Holding Companies
N.A.I.C.S.: 551112
Jill Wilson *(VP-Comm & Mktg)*
Stephen Gray *(Pres & CEO)*
Scott Parker *(CFO)*
Brian Jones *(COO)*
Bob Lowry *(Sr VP-Engrg)*
Brian Silver *(CFO & Sec-West)*
Eric Berg *(COO-West)*
Jeff Bischoff *(Exec VP-Bus Dev)*
Jim Grant *(VP-Safety & Field Ops)*
Phil Seale *(Exec VP-Mfg Market, Food & Beverage Market)*
Robert A. Moore *(Pres-West Reg)*
Susan Brewer *(VP-HR)*
Steve Renshaw *(Pres-Ohio Valley Reg Office)*
Steve Summers *(Exec VP)*
Randall Vaughn *(VP-A&E Pro Svcs)*
Anne Gorham *(Gen Counsel & Exec VP)*

Subsidiaries:

Anderson & Dahlen Inc.   (1)
6850 Sunwood Dr NW, Ramsey, MN 55303-5303
Tel.: (763) 852-4700
Web Site: http://www.andersondahlen.com
Sheet Metal Work Mfg
N.A.I.C.S.: 332322
David Knoll *(CFO & VP)*

Gray Construction, Inc.   (1)
10 Quality St, Lexington, KY 40507-1443

Tel.: (859) 281-5000
Web Site: http://www.gray.com
Sales Range: $50-74.9 Million
Emp.: 300
Design, Engineering & Construction Services
N.A.I.C.S.: 236220
Scott Parker *(CFO & VP)*
Robert J. Lowry *(Sr VP-Architecture & En-grg)*
Jill Wilson *(VP-Comm & Mktg)*
Kim Leonardis *(CFO)*
Susan Brewer *(Dir-HR)*
Phil Seale *(Exec VP-Mfg, Food & Beverage Market)*
Brian Jones *(COO)*
Jeff Bischoff *(Exec VP-Bus Dev)*
Jim Grant *(VP-Safety & Field Ops)*
Stephen Gray *(Pres & CEO)*
Bob Moore *(Pres-West)*
Robert Simpson *(Dir-IT)*
Steve Summers *(Exec VP)*
Patrick McCowan *(Mgr-Southeast)*

Unit (Domestic):

Gray-I.C.E. Builders   (2)
421 E Cerritos Ave, Anaheim, CA 92805
Tel.: (714) 491-1317
Web Site: http://www.gray.com
Rev.: $41,935,406
Emp.: 100
Retail, Hospitality, Commercial & Industrial Contractor
N.A.I.C.S.: 236220
Robert A. Moore *(Pres & CEO)*

WS Construction Inc   (1)
109 Fieldview Dr, Versailles, KY 40383
Tel.: (859) 873-7840
Construction Engineering Services
N.A.I.C.S.: 541330
Jill Wilson *(VP-Comm & Mktg)*

GRAY INSURANCE COMPANY
3601 N Interstate 10 Service Rd W, Metairie, LA 70002
Tel.: (504) 888-7790
Web Site: http://www.grayinsco.com
Sales Range: $1-9.9 Million
Emp.: 100
Fire, Marine & Casualty Insurance
N.A.I.C.S.: 524126
Mark Manguno *(Dir-HR)*
Michael Townsend Gray *(Pres)*

GRAY LIFT INCORPORATED
4646 E Jensen Ave, Fresno, CA 93725
Tel.: (559) 268-6621
Web Site: http://www.graylift.com
Sales Range: $75-99.9 Million
Emp.: 85
Industrial Machinery & Equipment
N.A.I.C.S.: 423830
Mike Kutka *(Mgr-Credit)*
Roy Hobock *(Mgr-Parts)*
Richard Waugh *(VP-Sls)*
John L. Waugh Sr. *(Founder & Chm)*

GRAY LUMBER COMPANY INC.
3800 6th Ave, Tacoma, WA 98406
Tel.: (253) 752-7000   WA
Web Site:
    https://www.graylumber.com
Year Founded: 1903
Sales Range: $25-49.9 Million
Emp.: 50
Lumber & Other Building Materials
N.A.I.C.S.: 423310
Steve Gray *(Treas & Sec)*

GRAY SUPPLY CORP.
199 Franklin Rd, Randolph, NJ 07869
Tel.: (973) 366-7272
Web Site:
    http://www.graysupplycorp.com
Year Founded: 1916
Rev.: $14,000,000
Emp.: 35
Underground Utilities Contractor

N.A.I.C.S.: 237110
Brad Heimburger *(Office Mgr)*
Scott Eberenz *(Mgr-Equipment)*
R. W. Herms Jr. *(Pres)*

GRAY TRANSPORTATION INC.
2459 GT Dr, Waterloo, IA 50703
Tel.: (319) 234-3930
Web Site: https://www.graytran.com
Rev.: $20,000,000
Emp.: 180
Trucking Except Local
N.A.I.C.S.: 484121
Darrin Gray *(VP)*
Leroy L. Gray Jr. *(Owner & Pres)*

GRAY'S FOODS INC.
3214 Auburn St, Rockford, IL 61101
Tel.: (815) 962-7700
Rev.: $25,000,000
Emp.: 300
Owner & Operator of Grocery Stores
N.A.I.C.S.: 445110
Clifford Gray *(Pres)*
Jeff Gray *(VP)*
Joan Gray *(Treas & Sec)*

GRAY, BILL AUTOMOTIVE ENTERPRISES INC.
2897 Washington Rd, Canonsburg, PA 15317
Tel.: (412) 343-1222
Year Founded: 1985
Sales Range: $10-24.9 Million
Emp.: 60
Car Whslr
N.A.I.C.S.: 441110
William L. Gray *(Owner)*

GRAY-DANIELS FORD
201 Octavia Dr, Brandon, MS 39042
Tel.: (601) 825-2801
Web Site:
    http://www.graydaniels.com
Rev.: $68,400,000
Emp.: 180
New & Used Car Dealers
N.A.I.C.S.: 441110
Clint Campbell *(Mgr-Internet Sls)*

GRAY-HODGES CORPORATION
103 Jessamine St, Knoxville, TN 37917
Tel.: (865) 522-3113
Web Site:
    http://www.grayhodges.com
Sales Range: $10-24.9 Million
Emp.: 25
Plumbing & Hydronic Heating Supplies
N.A.I.C.S.: 423720
Tony Rose *(VP)*
Justin Ward *(Dir-Pur)*

GRAYBACH, LLC
227 Stark St, Cincinnati, OH 45214
Tel.: (513) 381-4868
Web Site: http://www.graybach.com
Year Founded: 2007
Sales Range: $1-9.9 Million
Emp.: 13
Construction Management Services
N.A.I.C.S.: 236220
Pete Subach *(Owner)*
Tyson Grace *(Owner)*
Nathan Williams *(Project Mgr)*
Erica Grace *(Mgr-Ops)*

GRAYBAR ELECTRIC COMPANY, INC.
34 N Meramec Ave, Saint Louis, MO 63105
Tel.: (314) 573-9200   NY
Web Site: https://www.graybar.com

Graybar Electric Company, Inc.—(Continued)

Year Founded: 1925
Rev.: $10,534,400,000
Assets: $3,749,100,000
Liabilities: $2,223,500,000
Net Worth: $1,525,600,000
Earnings: $452,900,000
Emp.: 9,400
Fiscal Year-end: 12/31/22
Electrical Apparatus & Equipment, Wiring Supplies & Related Equipment Merchant Wholesalers
N.A.I.C.S.: 423610
Kathleen M. Mazzarella *(Chm, Pres & CEO)*
Dennis E. DeSousa *(Sr VP & Gen Mgr)*
Matthew W. Geekie *(Gen Counsel, Sec & Sr VP)*
William P. Mansfield *(Sr VP-Mktg)*
Beverly L. Propst *(Sr VP-HR)*
David G. Maxwell *(Sr VP-Sls)*
Scott S. Clifford *(CFO & Sr VP)*
Richard H. Harvey *(VP-New York)*

Subsidiaries:

Advantage Industrial Automation Inc. **(1)**
4775 River Green Pkwy, Duluth, GA 30096
Tel.: (770) 447-4474
Web Site: https://www.advantageind.com
Automation System Mfr
N.A.I.C.S.: 423610

Blazer Electric Supply Company of Colorado Springs **(1)**
6125 Omaha Blvd, Colorado Springs, CO 80915-2811
Tel.: (719) 596-1333
Web Site: https://www.buyblazer.com
Electrical Apparatus & Related Equipment Merchant Whslr
N.A.I.C.S.: 423610
Steve Blazer *(Pres)*

Cape Electrical Supply Inc. **(1)**
489 Kell Farm Rd, Cape Girardeau, MO 63701
Tel.: (573) 334-7786
Web Site: https://www.capeelectric.com
Sales Range: $125-149.9 Million
Emp.: 50
Electrical Apparatus & Equipment Supplier
N.A.I.C.S.: 423610
Ryan Weissmueller *(Pres)*

Electro-Mag Inc. **(1)**
5445 rue Rideau Suite 110, Quebec, G2E 5V9, QC, Canada
Tel.: (418) 651-9880
Mechanical Engineering Services
N.A.I.C.S.: 541330

Graybar Canada Limited **(1)**
3600 Joseph Howe Drive, PO Box 9078, Halifax, B3L 4H7, NS, Canada
Tel.: (902) 457-8787
Web Site: https://www.graybarcanada.com
Sales Range: $10-24.9 Million
Emp.: 70
Electronic Services
N.A.I.C.S.: 423610
Peter Horncastle *(Sr VP-Sls & Mktg)*
Cory Morris *(Reg VP-Atlantic)*
Amanda Canning *(Ops Mgr)*
Bill Jones *(VP)*
Nick Malone *(VP)*

Graybar Electric Canada Limited **(1)**
260 Brownlow Avenue, Dartmouth, B3B 1V9, NS, Canada
Tel.: (902) 468-6665
Electrical Equipment Distr
N.A.I.C.S.: 423610

Graybar Energy Limited **(1)**
130 Hayward Avenue, PO Box 1000, Kitchener, N2C 2E4, ON, Canada
Tel.: (519) 576-4050
Web Site: http://www.graybarenergy.com
Electric Power Distribution Services
N.A.I.C.S.: 221122

Graybar Financial Services, Inc. **(1)**
1185 Lackland, Saint Louis, MO 63146

Tel.: (314) 573-9200
Web Site: http://v1.graybar.com
Sales Range: $25-49.9 Million
Emp.: 10
Electrical & Communication Product Financing
N.A.I.C.S.: 522220
Kathleen M. Mazzarella *(Pres)*

Graybar International, Inc. **(1)**
11885 Lackland Rd, Saint Louis, MO 63146
Tel.: (314) 573-5700
Web Site: http://www.graybar.com
Electrical Products
N.A.I.C.S.: 335999

Richmond Electrical Supply, LLC **(1)**
233 N Keeneland Dr, Richmond, KY 40475-8523
Tel.: (859) 626-8600
Web Site: http://www.richmondelectricalsupply.com
Rev.: $4,000,000
Emp.: 5
Electronic Parts & Equipment Merchant Whslr
N.A.I.C.S.: 423690
Larry Day *(Principal)*

Shepherd Electric Supply Company **(1)**
7401 Pulaski Hwy, Baltimore, MD 21237-2529
Tel.: (410) 866-6000
Web Site: http://www.shepherdelec.com
Sales Range: $75-99.9 Million
Emp.: 115
Electrical Apparatus & Equipment Distr
N.A.I.C.S.: 423610
Charles Vogel *(CEO)*
Scott Vogel *(VP)*
Stuart Vogel *(Pres)*
Jim Shearer *(Branch Mgr)*

Shingle & Gibb Automation LLC **(1)**
845 Lancer Dr, Moorestown, NJ 08057
Tel.: (856) 234-8500
Web Site: https://www.shingle.com
Electric Power Transmission Equipment
N.A.I.C.S.: 423610

Subsidiary (Domestic):

KOM Automation, Inc. **(2)**
355 Commerce Dr, Amherst, NY 14228
Tel.: (877) 266-8765
Web Site: http://www.komautomation.com
Electronic Parts & Equipment Merchant Whslr
N.A.I.C.S.: 423690
Bruce Bucher *(Product Mgr)*

NED Liquidating Inc. **(2)**
115 Water St, Southington, CT 06489
Tel.: (860) 621-7335
Web Site: http://www.nedrives.com
Electrical Apparatus & Related Equipment Merchant Whslr
N.A.I.C.S.: 423610
Mike Rogers *(Gen Mgr)*

St. Louis-Metro Electrical Supply, Inc. **(1)**
6801 Hoffman, Saint Louis, MO 63139
Tel.: (314) 645-9000
Web Site: https://www.metroelectricsupply.com
Electrical Products Distr
N.A.I.C.S.: 423610

Valin Corporation **(1)**
1941 Ringwood Ave, San Jose, CA 95131
Tel.: (408) 730-9850
Web Site: http://www.valinonline.com
Sales Range: $10-24.9 Million
Emp.: 100
Industrial Machinery & Equipment Mfr
N.A.I.C.S.: 423830
Joseph C. Nettemeyer *(Pres & CEO)*
David Hefler *(CFO & VP)*

Subsidiary (Domestic):

Disco Associates Inc. **(2)**
4015 S Howick St, Salt Lake City, UT 84107
Tel.: (801) 268-3500
Web Site: http://www.discoassociates.com
Sales Range: $1-9.9 Million
Emp.: 15

Heat Tracing Products & Other Control Equipment Mfr
N.A.I.C.S.: 334519
Bruce Bain *(Pres)*

Walker Industrial Products, Inc. **(1)**
117 Mt Pleasant Rd, Newtown, CT 06470-1541
Web Site: http://www.walkeremd.com
Electrical Apparatus & Related Equipment Merchant Whslr
N.A.I.C.S.: 423610
Eaton Durant *(Pres-Series Count Control)*

GRAYBOW COMMUNICATIONS GROUP, INC.
1000 Boone Ave N Ste 700, Golden Valley, MN 55427
Tel.: (952) 544-5555
Web Site: http://www.graybow.com
Sales Range: $10-24.9 Million
Emp.: 40
Audio Visual Equipment Design, Installation, Sale & Rental
N.A.I.C.S.: 423690
Jeff Jacobson *(Pres)*
Andrew DiPilato *(Dir-Mktg & Sls)*
Julie Phillips *(Controller)*
Kendra Lettau *(Dir-Resource Mgmt)*
Loren Sposito *(Sr Acct Exec)*
Warren Pasbrig *(Mgr-Rental)*
Tedd Enger *(Project Mgr)*

GRAYCLIFF ENTERPRISES, INC.
3300 Battleground Ave Ste 100,
Greensboro, NC 27410   **NC**
Tel.: (336) 288-9464
Web Site: http://www.graycliffent.com
Year Founded: 2003
Sales Range: $10-24.9 Million
Telecommunication & Utility Infrastructure Engineering, Consulting, Installation, Integration & Maintenance Services
N.A.I.C.S.: 541330
Raymond L. Galtelli *(Founder & Pres)*
James Frederick Robertson *(VP)*

Subsidiaries:

Graycliff Enterprises, Inc. - Tucson Office **(1)**
4242 W Jeremy Pl Lot 1, Tucson, AZ 85741-2220
Tel.: (520) 579-6500
Web Site: http://www.graycliffent.com
Emp.: 30
Telecommunication & Utility Infrastructure Engineering, Consulting, Installation, Integration & Maintenance Services
N.A.I.C.S.: 541330
Richard Maben *(Project Mgr)*
William Lawton *(Project Mgr)*
Ron Baker *(Mgr)*
Melissa Myers *(Office Mgr)*

GRAYCLIFF PARTNERS LP
500 5th Ave 47th Fl, New York, NY 10110   **DE**
Tel.: (212) 300-2900
Web Site: http://www.graycliffpartners.com
Year Founded: 2011
Private Equity & Mezzanine Investment Firm
N.A.I.C.S.: 523999
Stephen C. Hindmarch *(Mng Partner)*
James W. Marley *(Mng Partner)*
Andrew P. Trigg *(Mng Partner)*
Will Henderson *(Mng Dir)*
Duke M. Punhong *(Mng Dir)*
Carl Barcoma *(Principal)*
Brandon C. Martindale *(Mng Dir)*
David Frederick Mullen *(Mng Dir)*
Garrett Wentzell *(Principal)*
Frank Cacace *(VP)*
Greg Olson *(Partner-Ops)*

Brian O'Reilly *(Mng Dir)*
Troy Iskarpatyoti *(VP)*
Dan Schaefer *(CFO)*

Subsidiaries:

Ballymore Co., Inc. **(1)**
501 Gunnard Carlson Dr, Coatesville, PA 19320
Tel.: (610) 593-5062
Web Site: http://www.ballymore.com
Sales Range: $1-9.9 Million
Emp.: 50
Rolling Safety Ladders Mfr
N.A.I.C.S.: 332999
William Frame *(CEO)*

Electro-Mechanical Corporation **(1)**
329 Williams St, Bristol, VA 24201-4510
Tel.: (276) 466-8200
Web Site: http://www.electro-mechanical.com
Sales Range: $25-49.9 Million
Emp.: 624
Provider of Power Distribution Services
N.A.I.C.S.: 335311
Chris Ambrose *(Product Mgr-Switchgear)*
Angie Adkins *(Engr-Sls & Application)*
Jack Phillips *(Mgr-Sls)*
Jody Dutcher *(Dir-Mktg)*
Justin Davis *(Engr-R&D)*
Laura Boardwine *(Mgr-HR)*
Mike Stollings *(Dir-HR Employee Rels & Trng)*
Robert Nelson *(Mgr-Engrg)*
Russell Leonard *(Pres & COO)*
Gary Stachelski *(VP-Sls & Mktg)*

Gerard Daniel Worldwide, Inc. **(1)**
34 Barnhart Dr, Hanover, PA 17331-9586
Tel.: (717) 637-5901
Web Site: http://www.gerarddaniel.com
Provider of Holding Company Services
N.A.I.C.S.: 423510
Nancy Bankert *(Mgr-HR)*
Lloyd Runkle *(Project Mgr)*
Hank Decker *(VP-IT)*
Justin Nicholson *(Mgr-Warehouse)*
Tim Kardish *(CEO)*

Division (Non-US):

GDW Canadian Division **(2)**
205 Courtneypark Drive W, Mississauga, L5W 0A5, ON, Canada
Tel.: (905) 670-8558
Web Site: http://www.gerarddaniel.ca
Emp.: 15
Industrial Supplies Whslr
N.A.I.C.S.: 423840
Adil Mohamed *(Mgr-Ops)*

GDW European Division **(2)**
Mountmahon Industrial Estate Abbeyfeale Co, Limerick, Ireland
Tel.: (353) 68 31284
Web Site: http://www.gerarddaniel.com
Emp.: 32
Industrial Supplies Whslr
N.A.I.C.S.: 423840
Redmond Quigley *(Gen Mgr)*

Division (Domestic):

GDW Western Division **(2)**
13055 Jurupa Ave, Fontana, CA 92337-6982
Tel.: (951) 361-1111
Industrial Supplies Whslr
N.A.I.C.S.: 423840

Subsidiary (Domestic):

Gerard Daniel Worldwide **(2)**
13055 Jurupa Ave, Fontana, CA 92337   **(100%)**
Tel.: (951) 361-1111
Web Site: http://www.gerarddaniel.com
Sales Range: $25-49.9 Million
Emp.: 150
Mfr of Miscellaneous Fabricated Wire Products
N.A.I.C.S.: 423510
Todd Snelbaker *(Gen Mgr)*

Langley Wire Cloth Products **(1)**
161 Mount Pleasant Rd, Collierville, TN 38027-0201
Tel.: (901) 853-0748

Web Site: http://www.langleywirecloth.com
Rev.: $9,702,000
Emp.: 30
All Other Miscellaneous Chemical Product & Preparation Mfr
N.A.I.C.S.: 325998
Paul Talkington *(Mgr-Sls)*

Wire Cloth Manufacturers, Inc. **(2)**
110 Iron Mountain Rd, Mine Hill, NJ 07803
Tel.: (973) 328-1000
Web Site: http://www.wireclothman.com
Sales Range: $1-9.9 Million
Emp.: 31
Mfg Misc Fabricated Wire Products
Blowers/Fans Valves/Pipe Fittings
N.A.I.C.S.: 332618
James Hegarty *(Pres)*
Kathy Blaber *(COO)*

Impresa Aerospace, LLC **(1)**
344 W 157th St, Gardena, CA 90248
Tel.: (310) 354-1200
Web Site:
   http://www.impresaaerospace.com
Sales Range: $25-49.9 Million
Aerospace Component Mfr
N.A.I.C.S.: 336413
Sheila Hsu *(Mgr-HR)*
Vince Flores *(Dir-Quality-Gardena)*

Oberfields LLC **(1)**
528 London Rd, Delaware, OH 43015
Tel.: (740) 369-7644
Web Site: http://www.oberfields.com
Concrete Block & Precast Concrete Products Mfr & Distr
N.A.I.C.S.: 327331
Randy Tackett *(Mgr-Dispatch, Fleet Maintainance & Transportation)*
Tim Schilling *(Mgr-Territory)*
Jeffrey Vagnier *(CFO)*
Mark Selhorst *(Mgr-Masonry Ops)*

Pebble Technology, Inc. **(1)**
15540 N 77th St, Scottsdale, AZ 85260
Tel.: (480) 948-5058
Web Site: http://www.pebbletec.com
Pebble Pool Finishes
N.A.I.C.S.: 423320

Sweeteners Plus LLC **(1)**
5768 Sweetners Blvd, Lakeville, NY 14480
Tel.: (585) 346-2318
Web Site: http://www.sweetenersplus.com
Cane Sugar Mfr
N.A.I.C.S.: 311314
Douglas C. Wagner *(Pres & CEO)*

TS Industries Inc. **(1)**
1022 N Stadem Dr, Tempe, AZ 85281
Tel.: (480) 968-1930
Web Site: http://www.goldtechind.com
Gold Plating
N.A.I.C.S.: 332813
Daniel A. Skinner *(CEO)*

GRAYCO, INC.
20 Sams Point Rd, Beaufort, SC 29907
Tel.: (843) 522-9994
Web Site: https://www.graycoinc.com
Rev.: $17,900,000
Emp.: 80
Lumber & Other Building Materials
N.A.I.C.S.: 423310
Herbert G. Gray *(Pres & CEO)*
Joseph Hawley *(Mgr-Inventory)*

GRAYCOR INC.
Two Mid America Plz Ste 400, Oakbrook Terrace, IL 60181
Tel.: (630) 684-7110   IL
Web Site: http://www.graycor.com
Year Founded: 1921
Sales Range: $400-449.9 Million
Emp.: 1,500
Holding Company; Commercial Construction Contractor Services
N.A.I.C.S.: 551112
John Shannon *(Mgr-Bus Dev)*
Dave Wing *(Pres)*

Subsidiaries:

Graycor Blasting Company Inc. **(1)**

12233 S Ave O, Chicago, IL 60633-1106   **(100%)**
Tel.: (773) 933-1100
Sales Range: $10-24.9 Million
Emp.: 10
Dynamiting & Demolition
N.A.I.C.S.: 238910

Graycor Industrial Constructors Inc. **(1)**
2 Mid America Plz Ste 400, Oakbrook Terrace, IL 60181   **(100%)**
Tel.: (708) 206-0500
Sales Range: $50-74.9 Million
Emp.: 900
General Building Contractors, Heavy Construction, Machinery Installations, Precision Blasting & Steel & Aluminum Mill Services
N.A.I.C.S.: 236220

Graycor International Inc. **(1)**
1 Graycor Dr, Homewood, IL 60430-4618   **(100%)**
Tel.: (708) 206-0500
Sales Range: $25-49.9 Million
Emp.: 130
General Contractors
N.A.I.C.S.: 236210

GRAYHAWK LLC
2424 Merchant St, Lexington, KY 40511
Tel.: (859) 255-2754
Web Site: https://www.grayhawk-ky.com
Year Founded: 1967
Sales Range: $10-24.9 Million
Emp.: 100
Drywall
N.A.I.C.S.: 238310
Mark Mabity *(CEO)*
Kurt Stenzel *(VP)*
Benny Tompkins *(VP)*

GRAYHILL INC.
561 W Hillgrove Ave, La Grange, IL 60525-5914
Tel.: (708) 354-1040   DE
Web Site: https://www.grayhill.com
Year Founded: 1943
Sales Range: $600-649.9 Million
Emp.: 600
Relays, Industrial Controls & Electric Components
N.A.I.C.S.: 335313
Brian Mey *(Pres)*
Keith Hansen *(VP-Operator Interface Products)*
Rick O'Grady *(Mgr-Automation Products)*

GRAYLING INDUSTRIES INC.
1008 Branch Dr, Alpharetta, GA 30004
Tel.: (770) 751-9095
Web Site:
   http://www.graylingindustries.com
Sales Range: $25-49.9 Million
Emp.: 200
Converter of Custom Plastic Films, Bags & Liners
N.A.I.C.S.: 326111
Ben Greene *(Dir-Mktg)*

GRAYMILLS CORPORATION
3705 N Lincoln Ave, Chicago, IL 60613-3515
Tel.: (773) 477-4100   IL
Web Site: http://www.graymills.com
Year Founded: 1939
Sales Range: $10-24.9 Million
Emp.: 130
Pumping Parts, Cleaning Units & Systems for the Printing & Machine Tool Industries Mfr
N.A.I.C.S.: 333914
John Bosselli *(VP-Mktg)*
Greg Giles *(Controller)*

GRAYROBINSON, P.A.

301 E Pine St Ste 1400, Orlando, FL 32802-3068
Tel.: (407) 843-8880
Web Site: https://www.gray-robinson.com
Year Founded: 1970
Sales Range: $125-149.9 Million
Emp.: 620
Law Firm
N.A.I.C.S.: 541110
Mayanne Downs *(Gen Counsel)*
Rob Shave *(Dir-Govt Affairs-Tallahassee & Fort Myers)*
Dean Cannon *(Pres & CEO)*

GRAYS HARBOR PUD NO. 1
2720 Sumner Ave, Aberdeen, WA 98520
Tel.: (360) 532-4220
Web Site: https://www.ghpud.org
Year Founded: 1938
Electric Power Distr
N.A.I.C.S.: 221122
Dave Ward *(Gen Mgr)*
Arie Callaghan *(Commissioner)*
Russ Skolrood *(Commissioner)*
Dave Timmons *(Commissioner)*

GRAYS PEAK CAPITAL LP
320 Park Ave 18th Fl, New York, NY 10022
Tel.: (212) 506-7050   DE
Web Site:
   http://grayspeakcapital.com
Privater Equity Firm
N.A.I.C.S.: 523999
Scott Stevens *(Partner)*

Subsidiaries:

McMurray Stern Inc. **(1)**
15511 Carmenita Rd, Santa Fe Springs, CA 90670
Tel.: (562) 623-3000
Web Site: http://www.mcmurraystern.com
Rev.: $3,700,000
Emp.: 50
Design & Build Services
N.A.I.C.S.: 238130
Linda Stern *(CEO)*
Matt Zirkle *(Gen Mgr)*
Shaun Ferguson *(Dir-Fin)*
John Fisher *(VP-Sls & Mktg)*

Solid Restoration Inc. **(1)**
912 S Andreasen Dr Ste 111, Vista, CA 20774-8900
Tel.: (760) 724-0454
Carpet & Upholstery Cleaning Services
N.A.I.C.S.: 561740
Shirley Gonzales *(Mgr)*

GRAYSON HYUNDAI-SUBARU
8729 Kingston Pike, Knoxville, TN 37923
Tel.: (865) 693-4550
Web Site:
   https://www.graysonauto.com
Year Founded: 2003
Sales Range: $10-24.9 Million
Emp.: 75
Car Whslr
N.A.I.C.S.: 441110
Walter Grayson *(Owner)*
Brandon McDerman *(Gen Mgr-Sls)*

GRAYSON-COLLIN ELECTRIC COOPERATIVE, INC.
1096 N Waco St, Van Alstyne, TX 75495
Tel.: (903) 482-7100   TX
Web Site: http://www.gcec.net
Year Founded: 1937
Sales Range: $100-124.9 Million
Emp.: 113
Electric Power Distr
N.A.I.C.S.: 221122
Tracy Begley *(Mgr-HR)*
David McGinnis *(CEO & Gen Mgr)*
Mike Rolandt *(CFO)*

Dennis Ferguson *(Mgr-Overhead Construction)*
Bruce Stevens *(Mgr-Maintenance & Ops)*
Jeff Smith *(Mgr-Information Technology)*
Doug Yates *(Mgr-Underground Construction)*
Michael Lauer *(Mgr-Economic Dev)*

GRAYSTAR LLC
9 Simmonsville Rd, Bluffton, SC 29910
Tel.: (843) 815-5600
Web Site: http://www.graystarllc.com
Year Founded: 1991
Sales Range: $10-24.9 Million
Emp.: 8
Abrasive Grains & Ceramic Materials Distr
N.A.I.C.S.: 424690
Kevin Fellinger *(Pres)*
Nick Macropoulos *(VP)*
Tracy Cook *(Mgr-Ops & Customer Svc)*
Dave Johnson *(Mgr-Sls & Mktg)*
Rob Previte *(Mgr-Quality)*
Tom Murphy *(Mgr-Sls-Distr)*

GRC ENTERPRISES, INC.
3477 Watling St, East Chicago, IN 46312-1708
Tel.: (219) 932-2220
Sales Range: $1-9.9 Million
Emp.: 15
Industrial Link-Type Chains Mfr
N.A.I.C.S.: 332618
Gerhard Volkmann *(Pres)*
Robert Volkmann *(VP-Sls)*
Fred Craute *(Dir-Sls)*
Jennifer Volkmann *(Controller)*

GRC INC.
10 E 3rd St Ste 400, Tulsa, OK 74103
Tel.: (918) 584-1471
Rev.: $21,300,000
Emp.: 5
Instruments & Control Equipment
N.A.I.C.S.: 423830
Robert W. Langholz *(Chm)*
Jeanell Rinas *(Controller)*

GRE VENTURES, INC.
1062 E Main St PO Box 69, Clarion, PA 16214
Tel.: (814) 226-6911   DE
Year Founded: 1991
Investment Holding Company
N.A.I.C.S.: 551112
Gary C. Wilson *(Pres)*

Subsidiaries:

C&K Coal Company **(1)**
1062 E Main St, Clarion, PA 16214   **(100%)**
Tel.: (814) 226-6911
Emp.: 2
Coal Mining
N.A.I.C.S.: 212114
Gary C. Wilson *(Pres)*

GREAAT SCHOOLS INC.
660 Burton Ave SE, Grand Rapids, MI 49507
Tel.: (616) 551-3049   MI
Web Site:
   http://www.greaatschools.com
Year Founded: 2008
Sales Range: $1-9.9 Million
Emp.: 69
Educational Support Services
N.A.I.C.S.: 611710
Dominique Taylor *(Dir-Preparatory Academy & Athletics)*
Angela Wallace *(Dir-Special Populations & Social Worker)*

GREAAT Schools Inc.—(Continued)

Krystle Hunter (Dir-Extended Learning)
Mary Johnston (Dir-Tech)
Cornelius Prince (Dir-Security & Facilities)

GREAT AMERICAN BANK
33050 W 83rd St, De Soto, KS 66018
Tel.: (913) 585-1131
Web Site:
    http://www.greatambank.com
Rev.: $1,300,000
Emp.: 11
Commericial Banking
N.A.I.C.S.: 522110
Cathy McGivern (VP)
Al Wiley (Officer-Comml Loan & Sr VP)
Ryan Nugent (Asst VP & Branch Mgr)
Todd Harris (Chief Lending Officer, Officer-Comml Loan & Sr VP)
Matthew G. Little (VP & Officer-IT)
David M. Clark (Sr VP)
Ben Compton (Asst VP)
Donna Nuccio (Asst VP & Mgr-Lake Lotawana)

GREAT AMERICAN DUCK RACES, INC.
16444 N 91st St, Scottsdale, AZ 85260
Tel.: (602) 957-3825   AZ
Web Site: http://www.game-group.com
Year Founded: 1988
Sales Range: $10-24.9 Million
Emp.: 36
Retailer of Entertainment Parks Merchandise
N.A.I.C.S.: 459999
Bob Ives (COO)
Eric Schechter (Pres)

GREAT AMERICAN FOODS CORP.
3684 FM 161 N, Hughes Springs, TX 75656
Tel.: (903) 639-1482
Rev.: $21,000,000
Emp.: 5
Seafood Restaurants
N.A.I.C.S.: 722511
David Beard (Chm)

GREAT AMERICAN INDUS-TRIES, INC.
300 Plaza Dr, Vestal, NY 13850-3647
Tel.: (607) 729-9331   DE
Year Founded: 1926
Sales Range: $75-99.9 Million
Emp.: 4
Holding Company
N.A.I.C.S.: 326150
Burton I. Koffman (Chm & Pres)

GREAT AMERICAN MARKET-ING CO.
1224 N Post Oak Rd Ste 160B, Houston, TX 77055
Tel.: (713) 682-6471
Web Site: http://www.valero.com
Sales Range: $10-24.9 Million
Emp.: 80
Freezer Provisioning & Meat Marketing Services
N.A.I.C.S.: 445240
William Horton (Partner)

GREAT AMERICAN RESTAU-RANTS, INC.
3060 Williams Dr Ste 405, Fairfax, VA 22031-4667
Tel.: (703) 645-0700   VA

Web Site:
    https://www.greatamericanrestaurants.com
Year Founded: 1979
Sales Range: $10-24.9 Million
Casual Dining Restaurant Owner & Operator
N.A.I.C.S.: 722511
Randy R. Norton III (Chm)

GREAT AMERICAN TITLE AGENCY, INC.
7720 N 16th St Ste 450, Phoenix, AZ 85020
Tel.: (602) 445-5525
Web Site: https://www.azgat.com
Year Founded: 1998
Sales Range: $1-9.9 Million
Emp.: 66
Title & Escrow Services for Mortgage Refinancing
N.A.I.C.S.: 921130
Bruce Beverly (CEO)
Tom Connaker (Pres)
Donna Lanocha (VP & Mgr-HR)
Jimmy Connor (VP & Mgr-Sls & Mktg)
Kim Batty (Mgr-Escrow Acctg)
Sheryl Stone (VP & Branch Mgr)
Donna Walt (VP & Branch Mgr)
James Kempf (Sr VP)

GREAT BASIN SCIENTIFIC, INC.
2441 S 3850 W, Salt Lake City, UT 84120
Tel.: (801) 307-4881   DE
Web Site: https://www.gbscience.com
Year Founded: 2003
GBSN—(OTCBB)
Sales Range: $1-9.9 Million
Emp.: 190
Molecular Diagnostic Testing Equipment Mfr
N.A.I.C.S.: 339112

GREAT BAY DISTRIBUTORS INC.
2750 Eagle Ave N, Saint Petersburg, FL 33716
Tel.: (727) 584-8626
Web Site:
    https://www.greatbaybud.com
Year Founded: 1968
Sales Range: $150-199.9 Million
Emp.: 300
Beer Distr
N.A.I.C.S.: 424810
Ronald R. Petrini (Pres & CEO)
Craig Rubright (CFO)
Bill Carmen (VP-Sls & Mktg)

GREAT BEND COOPERATIVE ASSOCIATION
606 Main St, Great Bend, KS 67530
Tel.: (620) 793-3531
Web Site:
    http://www.greatbendcoop.com
Sales Range: $50-74.9 Million
Emp.: 80
Grain & Farm Supplies Whslr
N.A.I.C.S.: 424510
Frank Riedl (Gen Mgr)
Dennis Neeland (Mgr-Ops)
John Sullivan (Controller)

GREAT BRITAIN TILE, INC.
9533 Land O'Lakes Blvd, Lutz, FL 34638
Tel.: (813) 235-9775
Web Site:
    http://www.greatbritaintile.com
Year Founded: 1986
Sales Range: $1-9.9 Million
Emp.: 7

Floor Tile Supplier & Installation Services
N.A.I.C.S.: 444180
George Clamp (Pres)
Josh Hogan (Project Mgr)

GREAT CIRCLE
330 N Gore Ave, Saint Louis, MO 63119
Tel.: (314) 968-2060
Web Site: https://www.greatcircle.org
Year Founded: 2009
Behavioral Health Care Services Organization
N.A.I.C.S.: 813920
Julia Adami (Chief Program Officer & VP)
Paula Fleming (COO)
Leroy Nunn (CFO & VP)
Phillury Platte (Chief Advancement Officer & VP)
Mary Sherfy (CMO & VP)
Clay Thornhill (Chief HR Officer & VP)

Subsidiaries:

Butterfield Youth Services, Inc.   (1)
1126 Hwy W, Marshall, MO 65340
Tel.: (660) 886-2253
Web Site: http://www.bys-kids.org
Sales Range: $1-9.9 Million
Emp.: 150
Residential Care
N.A.I.C.S.: 623990
John Carton (Exec Dir)

GREAT CIRCLE FAMILY FOODS LLC
300 S Gland Ste 2600, Los Angeles, CA 90071
Tel.: (213) 489-2340
Year Founded: 1937
Sales Range: $75-99.9 Million
Emp.: 20
Provider of Doughnuts
N.A.I.C.S.: 311812
Brett Garlinghouse (Pres)
Bill Britt (Mgr-Facilty)
Romie Garcia (Gen Mgr)

GREAT CLIPS, INC.
7700 France Ave S Ste 425, Minneapolis, MN 55435
Tel.: (952) 893-9088   MN
Web Site: http://www.greatclips.com
Year Founded: 1982
Sales Range: $75-99.9 Million
Emp.: 200
Hair Salons Franchiser
N.A.I.C.S.: 812112
Ray Barton (Chm)
Steve Overholser (CFO & Treas)
Terry Miller (Sr VP-Mktg & Comm)
Nancy Uden (Sr VP-Franchise Svcs & HR)
Stephen Hockett (Pres)
Rob Goggins (COO)
Yvonne Mercer (VP-Bus Svcs)
Rachelle Markey Johnson (VP-Fin)
Michelle Sack (VP-Learning & Dev)
Adam Husemann (VP-Facilities & Franchise Dev)
Lisa Hake (VP-Mktg & Comm)
Sandra Anderson (Chief Legal Officer)

GREAT COMMUNICATORS, INC.
2625 Ponce de Leon Blvd Ste 101, Coral Gables, FL 33134
Tel.: (305) 448-1456
Web Site: http://www.greatcom.com
Year Founded: 1990
Sales Range: $10-24.9 Million
Emp.: 7
Advetising Agency
N.A.I.C.S.: 541810

Anay Villar (Acct Exec)

GREAT DANE POWER EQUIP-MENT
PO Box 33358, Raleigh, NC 27636-3358
Tel.: (919) 567-6400
Web Site:
    http://www.greatdanemowers.com
Rev.: $12,000,000
Emp.: 43
Provider of Lawn & Garden Equipment
N.A.I.C.S.: 444240
Philip Kirwan-Hamilton (Pres)

GREAT DAY IMPROVEMENTS LLC
700 E Highland Rd, Macedonia, OH 44056-2112
Tel.: (330) 468-0700   OH
Web Site:
    https://www.greatdayimprovements.com
Year Founded: 1966
Sales Range: $25-49.9 Million
Emp.: 360
Prefabricated Metal Buildings
N.A.I.C.S.: 332311
Steve White (Mng Dir)
Larry Napolitan (CFO)
Michael Hoy (Pres & CEO)

Subsidiaries:

Judson Enterprises, LLC   (1)
2440 Gold River Rd, Rancho Cordova, CA 95670
Tel.: (916) 853-7400
Web Site: http://www.k-designers.com
Rev.: $65,600,000
Emp.: 750
Residential Remodeler
N.A.I.C.S.: 236118
Mike Burgess (VP-Sls)
Larry D. Judson (Pres & CEO)

Your Home Improvement, Co.   (1)
1619 32nd Ave N, Saint Cloud, MN 56303
Tel.: (320) 290-8488
Web Site:
    http://www.yourhomeimprovementco.com
Sales Range: $1-9.9 Million
Emp.: 12
Residential Remodeler
N.A.I.C.S.: 236118
Steve Little (Pres)

GREAT DAY RADIO
8335 Sunset Blvd Ste 220, Los Angeles, CA 90069
Tel.: (323) 337-9033
Web Site:
    http://www.greatdayradio.com
Sales Range: Less than $1 Million
Emp.: 8
N.A.I.C.S.: 541810
Michael Niles (Dir-Creative & Exec Producer)

Subsidiaries:

Great Day Advertising   (1)
28312 Constellation Rd Ste 200, Valencia, CA 91355
Tel.: (661) 362-5970
Advetising Agency
N.A.I.C.S.: 541810
Michael Niles (Pres)
John Stein (Dir-Creative)
Scott Berry (Dir-New Media)
Alex Alba (Dir-Creative Hispanic Market)
Rob Reyes (Dir-Art)
Catherine Liddane (Dir-Acct)

GREAT EASTERN COLOR LITHOGRAPHIC
46 Violet Ave, Poughkepsie, NY 12601
Tel.: (845) 454-7420
Rev.: $15,500,000
Emp.: 100
Lithographic Printing Services

N.A.I.C.S.: 323111

GREAT ECOLOGY, INC.

315 W 36th St, New York, NY 10018
Tel.: (212) 579-6800
Web Site:
http://www.greatecology.com
Year Founded: 2001
Sales Range: $1-9.9 Million
Emp.: 40
Ecological Consulting, Restoration,
Planning & Design of Natural & Urban Environments
N.A.I.C.S.: 541620
Mark S. Laska *(Founder & Pres)*
Lilia Gavrilenko *(Controller)*

Subsidiaries:

Great Ecology, Inc. **(1)**
1020 Prospect St Ste 310, La Jolla, CA
92037 **(100%)**
Tel.: (858) 750-3201
Web Site: http://www.greatecology.com
Emp.: 12
Ecological Consulting, Restoration, Planning
& Design of Natural & Urban Environments
N.A.I.C.S.: 541620
Mark S. Laska *(Pres & Founder)*

Great Ecology, Inc. **(1)**
1435 Larimer St Ste 200, Denver, CO
80202 **(100%)**
Tel.: (303) 872-0927
Web Site: http://www.greatecology.com
Emp.: 6
Ecological Consulting, Restoration, Planning
& Design of Natural & Urban Environments
N.A.I.C.S.: 541620
Joshua Eldridge *(Gen Mgr)*

Great Ecology, Inc. **(1)**
2000 "O" St Suite 200, Sacramento, CA
95811 **(100%)**
Tel.: (916) 376-7691
Web Site: http://www.greatecology.com
Ecological Consulting, Restoration, Planning
& Design of Natural & Urban Environments
N.A.I.C.S.: 541620
Trey Munday *(COO & CFO)*

GREAT HARVEST FRANCHISING, INC.

28 S Montana St, Dillon, MT 59725
Tel.: (406) 683-6842
Web Site:
http://www.greatharvest.com
Year Founded: 1976
Sales Range: $25-49.9 Million
Emp.: 32
Bakery Franchiser
N.A.I.C.S.: 311812
J. Michael Ferretti *(Chm & CEO)*
Mark Peterson *(Dir-Corp Baking &
Live Trng)*
Janet Tatarka *(Dir-Bakery Cafe Trng)*
Eric Keshin *(Pres & CMO)*
Kay Roach *(CFO)*

Subsidiaries:

Montana Mills Bread Co. **(1)**
28 S Montana St, Dillon, MT 59725-2434
Tel.: (585) 242-7540
Web Site: http://www.montanamills.com
Bakery Products
N.A.I.C.S.: 311811

GREAT HILL PARTNERS, L.P.

200 Clarendon St 29th Fl, Boston,
MA 02116
Tel.: (617) 790-9400　　　**MA**
Web Site:
http://www.greathillpartners.com
Year Founded: 1998
Privater Equity Firm
N.A.I.C.S.: 523999
Christopher S. Gaffney *(Co-Founder
& Mng Partner)*
Michael A. Kumin *(Mng Dir)*
Peter L. Garran *(Partner)*
Matthew T. Vettel *(Mng Partner)*

Christopher M. Busby *(Mng Dir)*
Nicholas R. Cayer *(Partner)*
Mark Taber *(Mng Dir)*
Drew C. Loucks *(Mng Dir)*
Rafael Cofino *(Partner)*
Craig K. Byrnes *(Principal)*
Mary Kate Bertke *(Dir-IR)*
John S. Dwyer *(CFO & Chief Compliance Officer)*
Steven K. Achatz *(VP)*
Eric A. Ahlgren *(VP)*
Rebecca A. Keddy *(Controller)*
Jesse Hertzberg *(Operating Partner)*
Michael Thompson *(Operating Partner)*
Joseph D. Germanese *(VP)*
Cristopher G. Govey *(VP)*
Alison M. Holmes *(VP)*
Kevin M. Magan *(VP)*
Marc D. Patrician *(VP)*
Derek Schoettle *(Operating Partner)*
Heather Fox Ewing *(Dir-Talent)*
Derek Schoettle *(Partner-Growth)*
Suaad Sait *(Partner-Growth)*
Joe Farhat *(Dir-Tech)*
David Roberts *(Mng Dir)*

Subsidiaries:

All Web Leads, Inc. **(1)**
7300 Rm 2222 Bldg 2 Ste 100, Austin, TX
78730
Tel.: (888) 522-7355
Web Site: http://www.allwebleads.com
Sales Range: $50-74.9 Million
Sales Leads for the Insurance Industry
N.A.I.C.S.: 524298
Bill Daniel *(Pres & CEO)*
Erik Josowitz *(Sr VP-Tech & Strategy)*
Charlie Brock *(Sr VP-Sls & Mktg)*
Cortney Johnson *(CFO & Sr VP-Fin)*
Dan Atkinson *(VP-Bus Intelligence)*
J. R. Attick *(VP-Sls)*

EnterpriseDB Corporation **(1)**
34 Crosby Dr Ste 201, Bedford, MA 01730
Tel.: (732) 331-1300
Web Site: http://www.enterprisedb.com
Database Management Systems Producer
N.A.I.C.S.: 541519
Ed Boyajian *(Pres & CEO)*
Marc Linster *(Sr VP-Product & Svcs)*
Mike Huseman *(Sr VP-Global Sls & Bus Dev)*
Paul Blondin *(CFO & Sr VP)*
Keith Alsheimer *(VP-Ops)*
Andrew Astor *(Co-Founder)*

Esroc, LLC **(1)**
989 Old Eagle School Rd Ste 815, Wayne,
PA 19087
Tel.: (610) 964-8000
Web Site: http://www.evolveip.net
Call Center Operator
N.A.I.C.S.: 518210
Michael Peterson *(Co-Founder & Vice Chm)*
Timothy Allen *(CMO, Chief Sls Officer & Partner)*
Scott Kinka *(CTO, Chief Product Officer & Partner)*
Jeff Coursen *(CFO)*
Pete Stevenson *(CEO)*
Randal Thompson *(Chief Revenue Officer)*
Thomas J. Gravina *(Co-Founder & Chm)*

Footage Firm, Inc. **(1)**
1515 N Courthouse Rd Ste 1000, Arlington,
VA 22201
Web Site: http://www.storyblocks.com
Sales Range: $1-9.9 Million
Emp.: 15
Subscription-Based Stock Media Services
N.A.I.C.S.: 512120
Joel Holland *(Founder)*
TJ Leonard *(CEO)*

Fusion Risk Management, Inc. **(1)**
3601 Algonquin Rd Ste 510, Rolling Meadows, IL 60008
Tel.: (847) 632-1002
Web Site: http://www.fusionrm.com
Scientific & Technical Consulting Services
N.A.I.C.S.: 541690
Andy Mercker *(VP-Bus Dev)*
Kurt Spangler *(VP-Product Mktg)*
Scott Arthur *(Mgr-Sls-Canada)*

Cory Cowgill *(CTO & Sr VP)*
David Nolan *(Founder)*
Paul Ybarra *(Chief Revenue Officer)*
Jim Stewart *(CFO & Sr VP)*
Steve Richardson *(Chief Product Officer & Sr VP)*
Joanna Zvirbulis *(Chief People Officer & Sr VP)*
Bill Bould *(Gen Mgr-Europe)*
Michael Campbell *(CEO)*
Terese Fernandez *(CMO)*

Go Media, Inc. **(1)**
1290 Avenue of the Americas, New York,
NY 10104
Tel.: (646) 214-7895
Web Site: https://g-omedia.com
Sales Range: $1-9.9 Million
Emp.: 25
Periodical Publishers
N.A.I.C.S.: 513120
Zachary Seward *(Gen Mgr & Editor-in-Chief)*
James Giddings *(Pres)*

Subsidiary (Domestic):

Quartz Media, Inc. **(2)**
675 Ave of the Americas, New York, NY
10010
Tel.: (202) 266-7000
Web Site: http://www.qz.com
News Organization Services
N.A.I.C.S.: 516210
Zachary Seward *(Co-Founder & CEO)*
Katherine Bell *(Editor-in-Chief)*

One, Inc. **(1)**
620 Coolidge Dr Ste 200, Folsom, CA
95630
Web Site: http://www.oneincsystems.com
Human Resource Consulting Services
N.A.I.C.S.: 541612
Christopher Ewing *(Pres & CEO)*

Subsidiary (Domestic):

Invenger Technologies, Inc. **(2)**
2775 Tapo St Ste 204, Simi Valley, CA
93063-0467
Tel.: (855) 467-8772
Web Site: http://www.invenger.com
Electronics Stores
N.A.I.C.S.: 449210
Sumeet Nayak *(Mgr)*
Krishna Mohan Pai *(CEO)*

PartsSource, Inc. **(1)**
777 Lena Dr, Aurora, OH 44202
Tel.: (330) 562-9900
Web Site: http://www.partssource.com
Medical Procurement Services
N.A.I.C.S.: 423450
Philip Settimi *(Pres & CEO)*
Jina Tweed *(VP-Quality Assurance)*
David Brennan *(VP & Gen Mgr-Svc)*
Joseph Zaluzney *(Chief Revenue Officer & Sr VP)*
Patrick Blake *(CFO & Treas)*
Mark Tomasetti *(CTO)*

Prodege, LLC **(1)**
100 N Pacific Coast Hwy 8th Fl, El Segundo, CA 90245
Tel.: (310) 294-9599
Web Site: http://www.prodege.com
Advertising & Marketing
N.A.I.C.S.: 541890
Josef Gorowitz *(Founder & Pres)*
Chuck Davis *(Chm & CEO)*
Stacey Olliff *(Sr VP-Legal & Bus Affairs)*
Brad Kates *(CFO)*
David Weinrot *(COO)*
Shane O'Neill *(CTO)*
Joe DeTuno *(Chief Content Officer)*
Mendy Orimland *(Sr VP-Revenue)*
Lonna Rimestad *(Sr VP-Fin & Acctg)*
Irma Mena *(Sr VP-HR)*
Stefan DeCota *(Sr VP-Revenue, Shop & Discover)*

Subsidiary (Domestic):

AdGate Media LLC **(2)**
241 W 37 St Ste 923, New York, NY 10018
Tel.: (646) 681-4156
Web Site: http://www.adgatemedia.com
Sales Range: $1-9.9 Million
Emp.: 6
Application Software Development Services

N.A.I.C.S.: 541511
Andrew Song *(Acct Mgr)*
Andy Chan *(Acct Mgr)*
Dan Sapozhnikov *(Co-Founder)*
Ephi Blanshey *(Sr Engr-Software)*
Jayden Xue *(Mgr-Billing)*

CotterWeb Enterprises, Inc. **(2)**
1295 Northland Dr Ste 300, Mendota
Heights, MN 55120
Tel.: (651) 289-0724
Web Site: http://corporate.inboxdollars.com
Internet Marketing
N.A.I.C.S.: 541910
Daren Cotter *(Founder & CEO)*

Upromise, Inc. **(2)**
85 Wells Ave Ste 110, Newton, MA 02459
Tel.: (800) 587-7309
Web Site: http://www.upromise.com
Educational Financing Services
N.A.I.C.S.: 523999
David O'Connell *(Pres)*

SheKnows LLC **(1)**
443 Park Ave S, New York, NY 10016
Tel.: (480) 237-7100
Women's Entertainment Website
N.A.I.C.S.: 424350

Subsidiary (Domestic):

BlogHer Inc. **(2)**
805 Veterans Blvd Ste 305, Redwood City,
CA 94063
Tel.: (650) 363-2564
Web Site: http://www.blogher.com
Online Media Publishing Services
N.A.I.C.S.: 516210
Julie Ross Godar *(Exec Dir-Editorial)*
Christine Arel *(Editor-Lifestyle)*
Rita Arens *(Mng Editor)*
Karen Ballum *(Mgr-Community)*

TodayTix Inc. **(1)**
64 Wooster St Fl 23, New York, NY 10013
Tel.: (860) 307-4278
Web Site: http://www.todaytix.com
Software Publisher
N.A.I.C.S.: 513210
Max Talbot-Minkin *(VP-Strategy & Design)*
Brian Fenty *(CEO)*

Subsidiary (Non-US):

Encore Tickets Ltd. **(2)**
2nd Floor North Harling House 47-51 Great
Suffolk Street, London, SE1 0BS, United
Kingdom
Tel.: (44) 2074001255
Web Site: http://www.encoretickets.co.uk
Theatre & Other Attraction Tickets Retailer
N.A.I.C.S.: 561599
John Wales *(Co-Founder & CEO)*
Ashley Herman *(Co-Founder & Deputy Chm)*
Chris Ryan *(Comml Dir)*
Johan Oosterveld *(Dir-Sls & Ops)*
Richard Woolliss *(Mgr-E-Commerce Sls)*
Susan Grobbelaar *(Fin Dir)*
Mat Hart *(Mktg Dir)*
Cameron Lund *(Mgr-E-Commerce Sls)*
Richard Segal *(Chm)*
Paramjot Jassal *(CIO)*

Subsidiary (Domestic):

West End Theatre Bookings
Limited **(3)**
Barnard's Inn 86 Fetter Lane, London,
EC4A 1 EN, United Kingdom
Tel.: (44) 20 7492 9969
Web Site:
http://www.westendtheatrebookings.com
Theatre & Other Attraction Tickets Retailer
N.A.I.C.S.: 561599

VersaPay Corporation **(1)**
18 th Floor 18 King Street East, Toronto,
M5C 1C4, ON, Canada
Tel.: (647) 258-9380
Web Site: http://www.versapay.com
Rev.: $3,474,572
Assets: $24,083,116
Liabilities: $16,242,244
Net Worth: $7,840,873
Earnings: ($9,481,350)
Emp.: 75
Fiscal Year-end: 12/31/2018

Great Hill Partners, L.P.—(Continued)

Credit & Debit Card Merchant Payment Processing Service
N.A.I.C.S.: 522390
Kevin Short (*Founder & CIO*)
Craig O'Neill (*CEO*)
John McLeod (*Chief Mktg Officer*)
Geoff Coutts (*VP-Sls*)
Frank Opat (*VP-Software Architecture*)
Eddie Chan (*CTO*)
Shouvik Roy (*CFO*)
Jason Read (*Chief Product Officer*)
Flynn Fishman (*VP-Software Engrg*)
Harry Rose (*Sr VP-Strategic Partners*)
Carey O'Connor Kolaja (*CEO*)

GREAT HIRE INC.
14241 Firestone Blvd Ste 400, La Mirada, CA 90638
Tel.: (562) 735-0035
Web Site:
    http://www.staffingagenciesca.com
Year Founded: 2012
Sales Range: $10-24.9 Million
Emp.: 15
Human Resource Consulting Services
N.A.I.C.S.: 541612
Jason Bivins (*Pres*)

GREAT IDEA CORP.
2724 Otter Creek Ct 101, Las Vegas, NV 89117
Tel.: (702) 767-5131   NV
Year Founded: 2011
Investment Services
N.A.I.C.S.: 523999
Nishon Petrossian (*Pres, CEO, CFO, Chief Acctg Officer & Sec*)

GREAT LAKE WOODS INC.
3303 John F Donnelly Dr, Holland, MI 49424
Tel.: (616) 399-3300
Web Site:
    http://www.greatlakewoods.com
Rev.: $32,000,000
Emp.: 150
Paint & Coating Mfg
N.A.I.C.S.: 325510
Keith Malmstadt (*Owner & Pres*)
Karl Zwaanstra (*Mgr-Quality Control*)
Dave Wilson (*Mgr-Pur*)

GREAT LAKES AUTO AUCTION, INC.
25784 State Rd 2, South Bend, IN 46619
Tel.: (574) 289-7767
Web Site:
    https://www.greatlakesaa.com
Emp.: 100
Motor Vehicles Mfr
N.A.I.C.S.: 336211
Ryan Clark (*Pres*)

Subsidiaries:

Wolfe's Evansville Auto Auction
Inc.   (1)
2229 S Kentucky Ave, Evansville, IN 47714
Tel.: (812) 425-4576
Sales Range: $1-9.9 Million
Emp.: 74
Automobile Whslr
N.A.I.C.S.: 441110
R. Tony (*Pres*)
Jeffrey R. Wolfe (*Gen Mgr*)
Susan Wolfe (*Sec*)

GREAT LAKES BEHAVIORAL RESEARCH INSTITUTE
9515 Goehring Rd, Cranberry Township, PA 16066
Tel.: (724) 584-5100   PA
Web Site:
    https://www.greatlakesresearch.com
Year Founded: 1977
Sales Range: $10-24.9 Million

Emp.: 202
Information Management & Human Resource Consulting Services
N.A.I.C.S.: 541612
Richard Meltzer (*Pres*)

GREAT LAKES BEVERAGE
1600 Modern St, Detroit, MI 48203
Tel.: (313) 865-3900
Web Site:
    http://www.greatlakesbev.com
Rev.: $22,300,000
Emp.: 100
Beer & Ale Merchant Whslr
N.A.I.C.S.: 424810
Frank Hayden (*Mgr-Fleet*)
Howard Wolpin (*Owner*)
Lucas Pagalos (*VP-Sls & Mktg*)
Nancy Mulligan (*Office Mgr*)
Randy Rogers (*Gen Mgr*)
Wally Shammami (*Mgr-Sls*)

GREAT LAKES CASE & CABINET CO., INC.
PO Box 551, Edinboro, PA 16412
Tel.: (814) 734-7303
Web Site:
    http://www.greatcabinets.com
Year Founded: 1985
Sales Range: $25-49.9 Million
Emp.: 100
Cabinet Enclosures, Racks & Open-Frame Workstations Mfr
N.A.I.C.S.: 332999
Rick Trombetta (*VP*)
Kevin Holzwart (*VP*)

GREAT LAKES CLEANING INC.
1405 Combermere Dr, Troy, MI 48083
Tel.: (586) 465-4420
Web Site:
    http://www.newimagebldg.com
Rev.: $2,170,000
Emp.: 70
Janitorial Services
N.A.I.C.S.: 561720
Mike Harris (*Owner*)

GREAT LAKES COMPUTER CORP.
33675 Lear Indus Pkwy, Avon, OH 44011
Tel.: (440) 937-1100
Web Site: http://www.grlakes.com
Sales Range: $10-24.9 Million
Emp.: 50
Computer & Software Stores
N.A.I.C.S.: 449210
James Manco (*CEO*)
Robert A. Martin (*Pres*)
David Doucette (*Mgr-Ops*)

GREAT LAKES COMPUTER SOURCE, INC.
5555 Corporate Exchange Ct SE, Grand Rapids, MI 49512
Tel.: (616) 698-1100   MI
Web Site: http://www.glcomp.com
Year Founded: 1986
Rev.: $70,000,000
Emp.: 55
Provider of Used Computers & Accessory Services
N.A.I.C.S.: 459510
Frank Kwiatek (*CFO*)
Matt Burch (*Mgr-Sls*)

GREAT LAKES CREDIT UNION
2525 Green Bay Rd, North Chicago, IL 60064
Tel.: (847) 578-7000
Web Site: http://www1.glcu.org
Sales Range: $50-74.9 Million
Emp.: 145

Credit Union
N.A.I.C.S.: 522130
Steven J. Bugg (*Pres & CEO*)

GREAT LAKES CUSTOM TOOL MFG, INC.
101 N Old Peshtigo Rd, Peshtigo, WI 54157-0152
Tel.: (715) 582-3884
Web Site: https://www.glct.com
Rev.: $10,800,000
Emp.: 80
Hardware Merchant Whslr
N.A.I.C.S.: 423710
Gloria Kuhnlein (*Controller*)
Russell L. Martin (*Pres & CEO*)

GREAT LAKES DIE CAST CORPORATION
701 W Laketon Ave, Muskegon, MI 49441
Tel.: (231) 726-4002
Web Site: http://www.gldiecast.com
Year Founded: 1974
Sales Range: $10-24.9 Million
Emp.: 150
Aluminum Die Castings & Injection Molding of Plastics Mfr
N.A.I.C.S.: 331523
Con Nolan (*Pres*)
Denise Marz (*VP-HR*)
Sherrie Couch (*Controller*)

GREAT LAKES ENERGY COOPERATIVE
1323 Boyne Ave, Boyne City, MI 49712
Tel.: (231) 582-6521
Web Site: https://www.gtlakes.com
Sales Range: $75-99.9 Million
Emp.: 350
Electric Power Distr
N.A.I.C.S.: 221122
Steven L. Boeckman (*Pres & CEO*)
Sherry Joles (*Mgr-Mktg*)
Mark Carson (*Vice Chm*)

GREAT LAKES FASTENERS, INC.
2057 Case Pkwy, Twinsburg, OH 44087-4087
Tel.: (330) 425-4488
Web Site: http://www.glftechnical.com
Emp.: 100
Support Activities for Transportation
N.A.I.C.S.: 488999
Justin Taylor (*Reg Mgr-Sls*)

Subsidiaries:

Frontier Fastener Inc.   (1)
4324 Bailey Ave, Buffalo, NY 14226
Tel.: (716) 835-3000
Rev.: $3,654,000
Emp.: 100
Hardware Stores
N.A.I.C.S.: 444140
Dennis Perry (*Mgr*)

GREAT LAKES FISHERY COMMISSION
2100 Commonwealth Blvd Ste 100, Ann Arbor, MI 48105
Tel.: (734) 662-3209   MI
Web Site: http://www.glfc.org
Year Founded: 1955
Sales Range: $25-49.9 Million
Emp.: 22
Fishery Management Services
N.A.I.C.S.: 541715
Steve Domeracki (*Dir-Corp Svcs*)
Marc Gaden (*Dir-Comm & Legislative Liaison*)
Sean Martineau (*Mgr-Fin Acctg*)
Andrew Muir (*Dir-Science*)
John Dettmers (*Dir-Fisheries Mgmt*)
Michael Siefkes (*Mgr-Sea Lamprey Control Program*)

Dale Burkett (*Dir-Sea Lamprey Program*)
Jill Wingfield (*Mgr-Comm Program*)
Pete Hrodey (*Mgr-Sea Lamprey Info*)

GREAT LAKES GYPSUM SUPPLY
1099 Doris Rd, Auburn, MI 48326
Tel.: (248) 377-1770
Web Site: http://www.glgsupply.com
Sales Range: $10-24.9 Million
Emp.: 15
Construction & Mining, except Oil Well, Machinery & Equipment Merchant Whslr
N.A.I.C.S.: 423810
Wayne Buchanan (*Mgr*)

GREAT LAKES HOTEL SUPPLY CO.
24101 W Nine Mile Rd, Southfield, MI 48033
Tel.: (313) 962-9176
Web Site: https://www.glhsco.com
Sales Range: $10-24.9 Million
Emp.: 28
Food Service Equipment Installation
N.A.I.C.S.: 238990
Mark Israel (*Pres*)
David Israel (*VP*)
Myrna Marceau (*Acct Supvr*)

GREAT LAKES ICE CREAM INC.
12355 S Kedvale Ave, Alsip, IL 60803
Tel.: (708) 371-1999
Web Site:
    http://www.greatlakesicecream.com
Rev.: $20,200,000
Emp.: 80
Dairy Product Merchant Whslr
N.A.I.C.S.: 424430
Majid Amorajabi (*Pres*)

GREAT LAKES INTEGRATED
4005 Clark Ave, Cleveland, OH 44109-1186
Tel.: (216) 651-1500   OH
Web Site:
    http://www.glintegrated.com
Year Founded: 1931
Sales Range: $100-124.9 Million
Emp.: 140
Commercial Lithographic Printing
N.A.I.C.S.: 323111
James R. Schultz (*Chm & CEO*)
Robert J. Schultz (*Exec VP & Gen Mgr-Print Div*)
Kostika Radivoj (*Exec VP*)
Anthony Sanson (*VP-Fin & HR*)
Thomas Schultz (*Exec VP-Mktg*)
Jason Schultz (*VP-Mktg*)
Carrie Higgins (*Dir-PreMedia Svcs*)
Brian Kellum (*Mgr-Digital Print*)
Bob Wisard (*Mgr-Estimating*)
Doug Kaminski (*Mgr-Mailroom*)
Steve Caskey (*Mgr-Warehouse & Fulfillment*)
Mike Stewart (*Sr VP & Gen Mgr-Fulfillment & Tech*)
Paul Doerfler (*VP-Sls*)
Scot D. Adkins (*Pres & COO*)

Subsidiaries:

GL Direct   (1)
33625 Pin Oak Pkwy, Avon Lake, OH 44012-2321   (100%)
Tel.: (440) 892-7760
Web Site: http://www.gldirect.com
Sales Range: $10-24.9 Million
Emp.: 12
Computerized Inventory Management, Warehousing & Fulfillment, Mailing & Distribution Services
N.A.I.C.S.: 323111

GREAT LAKES MDF, LLC.

300 Commerce Dr, Lackawanna, NY 14218
Tel.: (716) 827-3008
Sales Range: $1-9.9 Million
Emp.: 100
Wood Products Mfr
N.A.I.C.S.: 321999
Greg Maher *(Pres)*
Karen Schroth *(CFO)*
Tom Clennon *(VP-Sls & Mktg)*

GREAT LAKES PACKAGING CORP.

W190 N 11393 Carnegie Dr, Germantown, WI 53022
Tel.: (262) 255-2100
Web Site: http://www.glpc.com
Sales Range: $10-24.9 Million
Emp.: 112
Mfr of Corrugated Boxes
N.A.I.C.S.: 322211
Bob Boden *(VP-Sls & Design)*
James Nelson *(Pres)*
Deanna Scheunemann *(Coord-Graphic Design)*

GREAT LAKES PETERBILT, GMC

5900 Southport Rd, Portage, IN 46368-6407
Tel.: (219) 763-7227   IN
Web Site: http://www.glpete.com
Year Founded: 1960
Sales Range: $25-49.9 Million
Emp.: 60
New & Used Trucks & Truck Parts Retailer; Service & Body Shop
N.A.I.C.S.: 441227
Rick Kerley *(Mgr-Parts)*

GREAT LAKES PETROLEUM CO.

4478 Johnston Pkwy, Cleveland, OH 44128
Tel.: (216) 478-0501
Web Site: http://www.greatlakespetroleum.com
Sales Range: $10-24.9 Million
Emp.: 15
Petroleum Services
N.A.I.C.S.: 424710
Tom Arcoria *(Pres)*
Jeffrey Platko *(COO & Gen Counsel)*
Louise Kirk *(CFO)*

GREAT LAKES PLUMBING & HEATING CO. INC.

4521 W Diversey Ave, Chicago, IL 60639-1925
Tel.: (773) 489-0400   IL
Web Site: https://www.glph.com
Year Founded: 1946
Sales Range: $25-49.9 Million
Emp.: 350
Mechanical Contractor
N.A.I.C.S.: 238220
Kevin J. Condon *(Pres)*

GREAT LAKES POWER PRODUCTS INC.

7455 Tyler Blvd, Mentor, OH 44060-5401
Tel.: (440) 951-5111   OH
Web Site: https://www.glpower.com
Year Founded: 1973
Industrial Supplies
N.A.I.C.S.: 423840
Richard J. Pennza *(Pres & CEO)*
David Allen *(VP-Service Ops)*
Stephen Allen *(VP & Mgr-Regional Sls)*

GREAT LAKES PUBLISHING COMPANY

1422 Euclid Ave Ste 730, Cleveland, OH 44115
Tel.: (216) 771-2833
Web Site:
    https://www.glpublishing.com
Sales Range: $10-24.9 Million
Emp.: 70
Magazine Publisher
N.A.I.C.S.: 513120
Betsy Brock *(Sr Acct Exec)*
Evanthia Sevastakis *(Mgr-Events)*

Subsidiaries:

Cleveland Scene Publishing LLC   **(1)**
1468 W 9th St, Cleveland, OH 44113
Tel.: (216) 802-7205
Rev.: $5,500,000
Emp.: 60
Newspaper Publishers
N.A.I.C.S.: 513110
Johnny Angell *(Acct Exec)*

GREAT LAKES REALTY CORP.

28900 Schoolcraft Rd, Livonia, MI 48150-2209
Tel.: (734) 425-4870   MI
Year Founded: 1959
Sales Range: $75-99.9 Million
Emp.: 300
Bowling Centers
N.A.I.C.S.: 713950
Barbara Fritz *(VP & Controller)*

Subsidiaries:

Cloverlanes, Inc.   **(1)**
28900 Schoolcraft Rd, Livonia, MI 48150-2209
Tel.: (734) 427-6410
Web Site: http://www.cloverlanes.com
Sales Range: $10-24.9 Million
Emp.: 35
Bowling Centers
N.A.I.C.S.: 713950

Fairlanes Bowl, Inc.   **(1)**
29600 Stephenson Hwy, Madison Heights, MI 48071-2339
Tel.: (248) 548-9333
Sales Range: $10-24.9 Million
Emp.: 28
Bowling Centers
N.A.I.C.S.: 713950

Ypsi-Arbor Lanes   **(1)**
2985 Washtenaw Rd, Ypsilanti, MI 48197-1552
Tel.: (734) 434-1110
Sales Range: $10-24.9 Million
Emp.: 20
Bowling Centers
N.A.I.C.S.: 713950

GREAT LAKES RUBBER & SUPPLY

6150 N Flint Rd, Glendale, WI 53209-0860
Tel.: (414) 352-8800
Web Site:
    https://www.greatlakesrubber.com
Rev.: $12,000,000
Emp.: 39
Rubber Goods, Mechanical
N.A.I.C.S.: 423840
Thomas H. Baumann *(Pres)*
Ed Kelley *(VP-Sls & Mktg)*

GREAT LAKES TEXTILES INCORPORATED

6810 Cochran Rd, Solon, OH 44139
Tel.: (440) 914-1122
Web Site:
    https://www.gltproducts.com
Rev.: $15,000,000
Emp.: 34
Polyvinylidene Chloride Resins
N.A.I.C.S.: 325211

GREAT LAKES TISSUE COMPANY, INC.

437 S Main St, Cheboygan, MI 49721

Tel.: (231) 627-0200
Web Site:
    http://www.greatlakestissue.com
Sales Range: $10-24.9 Million
Emp.: 100
Tissue Mfr
N.A.I.C.S.: 322291
Clarence Roznowski *(Owner)*

GREAT LAKES WINE & SPIRITS, LLC

373 Victor Ave, Highland Park, MI 48203-3117
Tel.: (313) 453-2200   MI
Web Site: https://www.glwas.com
Year Founded: 2007
Sales Range: $50-74.9 Million
Emp.: 900
Wine & Distilled Alcoholic Beverage Distr
N.A.I.C.S.: 424820
Rick Lopus *(VP-Sls)*
Thomas Pringle *(Supvr-Warehouse)*
Bill Przytulski *(VP-Ops)*
J. Lewis Cooper III *(Co-CEO)*

GREAT LAKES WIRE & CABLE, INC.

800 Tech Row, Madison Heights, MI 48071
Tel.: (586) 979-0022   MI
Web Site: http://www.greatwire.com
Year Founded: 1998
Sales Range: $10-24.9 Million
Emp.: 31
Wire, Cable & Connectivity Products Mfr & Distr
N.A.I.C.S.: 335929
James Holth *(Dir-Engrg)*
Karen Glutting *(Mgr-Pur)*
Oscar Ferrari *(Mgr-Bus Dev)*

GREAT MIDWEST BANK, S.S.B.

15900 W Bluemound Rd, Brookfield, WI 53005
Tel.: (262) 784-4400
Web Site:
    https://www.greatmidwestbank.com
Sales Range: $25-49.9 Million
Emp.: 100
Savings Bank
N.A.I.C.S.: 522180
Dennis J. Doyle *(Pres)*
Mark Loneffel *(VP)*

GREAT MIDWEST NEWS LLC.

2571 Saradan Dr, Jackson, MI 49202
Tel.: (517) 784-7163
Web Site: http://www.tng.com
Sales Range: $100-124.9 Million
Emp.: 800
Book, Periodical & Newspaper Merchant Whslr
N.A.I.C.S.: 424920
John Swett *(Sr VP)*

GREAT MILL ROCK LLC

667 Madison Ave, New York, NY 10065
Tel.: (212) 764-7740
Web Site: http://www.millrockcap.com
Year Founded: 2018
Financial Services
N.A.I.C.S.: 523999
Bob Feeser *(Sr Partner)*
Ed Rose *(Sr Partner)*
Christopher Whalen *(Co-Founder)*
Adi Pekmezovic *(Co-Founder)*
Diane Parisi *(Sr Principal)*
Eric Popham *(Sr Principal)*
Charles Heskett *(Sr Partner)*

Subsidiaries:

Asbury Carbons, Inc.   **(1)**

405 Old Main St, Asbury, NJ 08802-0144
Tel.: (908) 537-2155
Web Site: http://www.asbury.com
Sales Range: $50-74.9 Million
Emp.: 80
Carbon & Graphite Product Mfr & Distr
N.A.I.C.S.: 335991
Nicholas T. Mares *(VP-Mktg)*
Albert V. Tamashausky *(Dir-Tech Svcs)*
Lance R. Miller *(Mgr-Technical-Specialty Products)*
Lisa A. Hoover *(Gen Mgr)*
Lewis S. Fish *(VP-Sls)*
Stephen A. Polgar *(Mgr-Facilities)*
Carlos Aguirre *(Gen Mgr)*
Jim Roberts *(Plant Mgr)*
Jon L. Silvis *(Plant Mgr)*
Robert A. Smart *(Plant Mgr)*
Noah A. Nicholson *(Pres & COO)*
M. Susan Rish *(CFO)*
Eric Walmet *(Sr VP-Ops)*
Scott Palm *(Sr VP-Strategy & Innovation)*
Gregg A. Jones *(Chm & CEO)*

Subsidiary (Domestic):

Anthracite Industries, Inc.   **(2)**
Anthracite Rd, Sunbury, PA 17801-0112
Tel.: (570) 286-2176
Web Site: http://www.asbury.com
Sales Range: $10-24.9 Million
Emp.: 36
Coal & Petroleum Coke Producer
N.A.I.C.S.: 324199
Timothy L. Hendricks *(Gen Mgr)*
Lisa A. Hoover *(Office Mgr)*
Lewis Fish *(VP-Sls)*
John Reardon *(Mgr-Quality)*

Asbury Carbons, Inc.   **(2)**
103 Foulk Rd Ste 202, Wilmington, DE 19803
Tel.: (302) 652-0266
Sales Range: $10-24.9 Million
Emp.: 2
Graphite Mining
N.A.I.C.S.: 212390

Division (Non-US):

Asbury Carbons, Inc. - Graphitos Mexicanos de Asbury Division   **(2)**
Blvd Jose Maria Morelos No 389 Nte Local 03 Plaza Guayacanes, Colinas del Bacho, 83148, Hermosillo, Sonora, Mexico
Tel.: (52) 6622678598
Graphite Product Mfr
N.A.I.C.S.: 335991

Division (Domestic):

Asbury Carbons, Inc. - Southwestern Graphite Division   **(2)**
2564 Highway 12, Dequincy, LA 70633
Tel.: (337) 786-5905
Graphite Product Mfr
N.A.I.C.S.: 335991
Robert A. Smart *(Plant Mgr)*
Dan Buxton *(Mgr-Quality)*

Subsidiary (Domestic):

Asbury Equipment   **(2)**
280 Lendy Rd, Kittanning, PA 16201-7519   **(100%)**
Tel.: (724) 543-1343
Web Site: http://www.asbury.com
Sales Range: $10-24.9 Million
Emp.: 50
Mfr of Injection Equipment
N.A.I.C.S.: 327992
Noah Nicholason *(Pres)*

Asbury Graphite   **(2)**
405 Old Main St, Asbury, NJ 08802-1077   **(100%)**
Tel.: (908) 537-2155
Web Site: http://www.asburystore.com
Supplier of Fluxes & Salts to Aluminum Smelters & Foundries
N.A.I.C.S.: 327992
Carol A. Kalmar *(Pres)*
Stephen A. Riddle *(CEO)*
H. Marvin Riddle *(Chm)*
Stephen A. Polgar *(Mgr-Quality)*

Asbury Graphite Inc. of California   **(2)**
2855 Franklin Canyon Rd, Rodeo, CA 94572-2116   **(100%)**

Great Mill Rock LLC—(Continued)
Tel.: (510) 799-3636
Web Site: http://www.asbury.com
Sales Range: $10-24.9 Million
Emp.: 30
Processor & Supplier of Petroleum Coke,
Coal & Graphite to Steel Industries
N.A.I.C.S.: 324110
Tony Perez (Mgr-Quality)
James Roberts (Plant Mgr)

Asbury Graphite Mills, Inc. (2)
405 Old Main St, Asbury, NJ
08802-0144 **(100%)**
Tel.: (908) 537-2155
Web Site: http://www.asburygraphite.com
Sales Range: $10-24.9 Million
Ground & Treated Minerals
N.A.I.C.S.: 327992
Stephen A. Riddle (CEO)
Albert Tamashausky (Dir-Technical Svcs)
Carol A. Kalmar (Pres)
Lu Fish (VP-Sls)

Plant (Domestic):

**Asbury Graphite Mills, Inc. - Asbury
Plant** (3)
156 Asbury W Portal Rd, Asbury, NJ 08802
Tel.: (908) 537-2157
Carbon & Graphite Product Mfr
N.A.I.C.S.: 335991

**Asbury Graphite Mills, Inc. - Kittan-
ning Plant** (3)
280 Linde Rd, Kittanning, PA 16201
Tel.: (724) 543-1343
Emp.: 62
Carbon & Graphite Product Mfr
N.A.I.C.S.: 335991
John Silvis (Plant Mgr)

Subsidiary (Domestic):

Asbury Louisiana, Inc. (2)
2564 Hwy 12, Dequincy, LA 70633 **(100%)**
Tel.: (337) 786-5905
Web Site: http://www.asbury.com
Sales Range: $10-24.9 Million
Emp.: 40
Processor & Supplier of Petroleum Coke
Coal & Graphite to Steel Mill Mfr
N.A.I.C.S.: 335991
Stephen A. Riddle (CEO)

Subsidiary (Non-US):

Asbury Wilkinson, Inc. (2)
1115 Sutton Drive, Burlington, L7L 5Z8, ON,
Canada **(100%)**
Tel.: (905) 332-0862
Web Site: http://www.asbury.com
Sales Range: $1-9.9 Million
Emp.: 10
Foundry Industry Distr
N.A.I.C.S.: 423830
Allan Barnwell (Gen Mgr)

Plant (Domestic):

**Asbury Wilkinson, Inc. - Burlington
Plant** (3)
1115 Sutton Drive, Burlington, L7L 5Z8, ON,
Canada
Tel.: (905) 332-0862
Activated Carbon Mfr
N.A.I.C.S.: 335991

Subsidiary (Domestic):

Cummings-Moore Graphite Co. (2)
1646 N Green St, Detroit, MI
48209-2069 **(100%)**
Tel.: (313) 841-1615
Sales Range: $10-24.9 Million
Emp.: 28
Supplier of Graphite to Drilling Industry
N.A.I.C.S.: 327992

Southwestern Graphite Co. (2)
405 Old Main St, Asbury, NJ
08802 **(100%)**
Tel.: (908) 537-2155
Web Site: http://www.asbury.com
Sales Range: $10-24.9 Million
Emp.: 30
Mines & Refines Graphite
N.A.I.C.S.: 327992
Dan Buxton (Mgr-Quality)

**Mill Rock Packaging Partners
LLC** (1)
667 Madison Ave, New York, NY 10065
Tel.: (212) 763-7440
Web Site: https://millrockpackaging.com
Specialty Packaging Platform
N.A.I.C.S.: 561910
Bob Feeser (Vice Chm)
Ed Rose (Chm)
Steve Rice (CIO)
Allen Ennis (CEO)

Subsidiary (Domestic):

All Packaging Company (2)
14806 E 33rd Pl, Aurora, CO 80011
Tel.: (303) 373-1222
Web Site: http://www.allpack.com
Sales Range: $1-9.9 Million
Emp.: 65
Folding Paperboard Box Mfr
N.A.I.C.S.: 322212
Alan Kramer (Controller)
Kenneth Pepper (Pres)

Impressions Incorporated (2)
1050 Westgate Dr, Saint Paul, MN 55114
Tel.: (651) 646-1050
Web Site: http://www.i-i.com
Sales Range: $25-49.9 Million
Emp.: 300
Mfr of Folding Paperboard Boxes
N.A.I.C.S.: 322212
Mark Allan Jorgensen (CEO)
Steve Holupchinski (CFO)
Jenna Hazaert (Dir-Sls & Dev)

**Keystone Paper & Box Company,
Inc.** (2)
31 Edwin Rd, South Windsor, CT 06074-
6074
Web Site:
　　http://www.keystonepaperbox.com
Folding Cartons & Packaging Boxes Mfr
N.A.I.C.S.: 322130
Richard Joao (Plant Mgr)
Jim Rutt (Pres)

Trojan Lithograph Corporation (2)
800 SW 27th St, Renton, WA 98057
Tel.: (425) 873-2200
Web Site: http://www.trojanlitho.com
Paper & Coated & Laminated Packaging
N.A.I.C.S.: 322220
Ian May (Pres & CEO)

Tandym Group, LLC (1)
675 3rd Ave 5th Fl, New York, NY 10017
Tel.: (212) 922-1001
Web Site: https://tandymgroup.com
Human Resources & Executive Search
Consulting Services
N.A.I.C.S.: 541612
Edward Fleischman (Founder)
Guido Gabriele (Corp Counsel)
Kyle W. Mattice (Chief Comml Officer)
Larry Stabler (CFO)
Vaishali Rathod (Chief People Officer)
Heather Schimmel (COO)
Len Lombardo (CIO)
Hannah Jaeger (CMO)
Corin Best (VP-Tech)
Dave Muller (Pres)
Charles Heskett (Exec Chm & CEO)

Subsidiary (Domestic):

**Aetea Information Technology
Inc.** (2)
1445 Research Blvd Ste 300, Rockville, MD
20850
Tel.: (301) 721-4200
Web Site: http://www.aetea.com
Sales Range: $300-349.9 Million
Emp.: 250
Computer Related Consulting Services
N.A.I.C.S.: 541512
Charles V. Brown (CFO)

Longford & Company Inc. (2)
75 State St Ste 100, 02109, Boston, MA
Tel.: (617) 553-5555
Web Site: http://www.longfordco.com
Business Management Consulting Services
N.A.I.C.S.: 541618
Sean McCourt (Founder & Mng Dir)
Mike Regenye (Mgr-Recruiting & Delivery)

Metro Systems Inc. (2)

209 Madison St Ste 400, Alexandria, VA
22314-1764
Tel.: (703) 299-6203
Web Site: http://www.metrosystemsinc.com
Temporary Help Service
N.A.I.C.S.: 561320
Don Fisher (Mgr)
Kirk Casey (Co-CEO)
Dave Steinbraker (Co-CEO)

Techlink, Inc. (2)
10 Mountainview Rd, Upper Saddle River,
NJ 07458
Tel.: (201) 786-2400
Data Processing, Hosting & Related Ser-
vices
N.A.I.C.S.: 518210

GREAT NECK SAW MANUFAC-
TURERS, INC.
165 E 2nd St, Mineola, NY 11501-
3523
Tel.: (901) 221-4024　　　　　　　**NY**
Web Site:
　　https://www.greatnecksaw.com
Year Founded: 1919
Sales Range: $200-249.9 Million
Emp.: 700
Mfr of Hand Tools
N.A.I.C.S.: 423710
Daniel Jacoff (VP-Engrg)
Bob Jacoff (VP)
Bob Demers (VP-Automotive Sls)
Bill Kilduff (VP-Aftermarket Sls)
Bruce Baum (VP-Sls-Eastern Reg)
Jim Hoenscheidt (VP-Sls-Western
Reg)
Steve Morgan (VP-Sls-Intl)
Jorge Serrano (VP-Sls-Intl)

GREAT NORTHERN BUILDING
PRODUCTS, LLC
901 S 15th St, Louisville, KY 40210
Tel.: (502) 266-6662
Web Site: http://www.gnbuilding.com
Year Founded: 1999
Sales Range: $1-9.9 Million
Emp.: 75
Manufactures & Distributes Niche
Products for the Residential & Com-
mercial Construction Industries
N.A.I.C.S.: 321999
James Horn (Sls Mgr)
Brian McMahan (Mgr-HR)

GREAT NORTHERN CORPO-
RATION
395 Stroebe Rd, Appleton, WI 54914-
8782
Tel.: (920) 739-3671　　　　　　　**WI**
Web Site:
　　http://www.greatnortherncorp.com
Year Founded: 1962
Sales Range: $10-24.9 Million
Emp.: 900
Provider of Storage Products
N.A.I.C.S.: 322211
John R. Davis (CEO)
Gary Hietpas (Pres)
Mark Radue (CFO)
Jeremy Stimpson (VP & Gen Mgr)
Jeff Michels (Pres-Packaging & In-
store)

GREAT NORTHERN INDUS-
TRIES INC.
266 Beacon St, Boston, MA 02116
Tel.: (617) 262-4314
Rev.: $14,900,000
Emp.: 174
Stationery Products
N.A.I.C.S.: 322230

GREAT NORTHERN PROD-
UCTS, LTD.
804 Centerville Rd, Warwick, RI
02886-4397
Tel.: (401) 821-2400　　　　　　　**RI**

Web Site:
　　http://www.northernproducts.com
Year Founded: 1989
Sales Range: $50-74.9 Million
Emp.: 24
Seafood, Meats, Cheese & Fruit Con-
centrates
N.A.I.C.S.: 424410
George Nolan (Pres)

GREAT NORTHWEST INSUR-
ANCE COMPANY
332 Minnesota St Ste W1800, Saint
Paul, MN 55101-1313
Tel.: (651) 325-0060
Web Site:
　　http://www.greatnorthwest.com
Sales Range: $10-24.9 Million
Emp.: 13
Insurance Underwriting Services
N.A.I.C.S.: 524298

Subsidiaries:

**Hawaiian Insurance & Guaranty
Company, Ltd.** (1)
1001 Bishop St ASB Twr Ste 500, Honolulu,
HI 96813-3429 **(100%)**
Tel.: (808) 536-2777
Web Site: http://www.higltd.com
Insurance Underwriting Services
N.A.I.C.S.: 524298

GREAT OUTDOOR PROVISION
CO.
2017 Cameron St, Raleigh, NC
27605
Tel.: (919) 833-1741
Web Site:
　　https://www.greatoutdoorpro
　　vision.com
Rev.: $12,600,000
Emp.: 30
Sporting Goods & Bicycle Shops
N.A.I.C.S.: 459110
Thomas F. Valone (Founder)
Chad Pickens (Mgr-Store)
Corey Van Dlac (Asst Mgr-Store)
Rob Arends (Mgr-Greensboro)
Bill Mauney (VP-Retail Mgmt)

GREAT
PERFORMANCES/ARTISTS AS
WAITRESSES, INC.
304 Hudson St, New York, NY 10013
Tel.: (212) 727-2424
Web Site:
　　http://www.greatperformances.com
Year Founded: 1979
Sales Range: $10-24.9 Million
Emp.: 300
Caterers
N.A.I.C.S.: 722320
Liz Neumark (CEO)
Dean Martinus (Pres)
Bob Paul (Controller)

GREAT PLAINS COMPANIES,
INC.
1 Carlson Pkwy N Ste 120, Plymouth,
MN 55447-4453
Tel.: (763) 208-9760　　　　　　　**MN**
Web Site:
　　http://www.greatplainsmfg.com
Year Founded: 1989
Sales Range: $25-49.9 Million
Emp.: 250
Holding Company; Residential Con-
struction Contractors
N.A.I.C.S.: 551112
Michael R. Wigley (CEO)
Dave Franze (CFO & Controller)

Subsidiaries:

TerraDek Lighting Inc. (1)
2050 E Center Cir Ste 100, Plymouth, MN
55441-3802
Tel.: (763) 577-2425
Web Site: http://www.terradek.com

Sales Range: $10-24.9 Million
Emp.: 10
N.A.I.C.S.: 444110

GREAT PLAINS HEALTH ALLIANCE INC.
625 3rd St, Phillipsburg, KS 67661-2138
Tel.: (785) 543-2111
Web Site: http://www.gpha.com
Sales Range: $50-74.9 Million
Emp.: 1,097
Non-Profit Management System
N.A.I.C.S.: 541611
Kerry Kellerman (Mgr-Network)
Brenda Olson (VP-Health Info Mgmt)
Eldon Schumacher (VP-Reimbursement)
J. H. Seitz (VP-Reg Ops)
Darin D. Walk (VP-Info Sys)
Robert E. Hamilton (Sec)
Thomas E. Keller (Chm)
Mike Ruggiero (VP-Reg Ops)
David Dellasega (Pres & CEO)
Les Lacy (VP-Reg Ops)
John Terrill (Second VP)
Tim Kerr (VP-Pharmacy Svcs)

GREAT PLAINS MEDIA, INC.
2023 Cape Lacroix Rd, Cape Girardeau, MO 63701
Tel.: (573) 651-0707   MO
Year Founded: 2004
Sales Range: $10-24.9 Million
Emp.: 100
Holding Company; Radio Broadcasting Stations Owner & Operator
N.A.I.C.S.: 551112
Jerry Zimmer (Pres)

Subsidiaries:

Cookeville Communications, LLC (1)
698 S Willow Ave, Cookeville, TN 38501-3802
Tel.: (931) 526-7144
Web Site: http://www.countrygiant.com
Sales Range: $10-24.9 Million
Emp.: 30
Radio Broadcasting Stations
N.A.I.C.S.: 516110
Jerome R. Zimmer (Owner)

Great Plains Media - Lawrence (1)
3125 W 6th St, Lawrence, KS 66049
Tel.: (785) 843-1320
Web Site: http://www.klwn.com
Radio Broadcasting Stations
N.A.I.C.S.: 516110
Tim Robisch (Regional Mgr-Sls)

GREAT PLAINS SERVICE, INC.
642 Hwy 6, Ashland, NE 68003
Tel.: (402) 944-3349   NE
Web Site:
https://www.greatplainspropane.com
Year Founded: 1955
Sales Range: $1-9.9 Million
Emp.: 25
Bottled Gas Dealer
N.A.I.C.S.: 457210
Dan Chudomelka (Pres)

GREAT PLAINS VENTURES, INC.
3504 N Great Plains St, Wichita, KS 67203-3400
Tel.: (316) 684-1540   KS
Web Site: http://www.gplains.com
Year Founded: 1972
Sales Range: $25-49.9 Million
Emp.: 200
Investment Holding Company
N.A.I.C.S.: 551112
Susayn Brandes (CEO)

Subsidiaries:

Aerospace Systems & Components Inc. (1)

5201 E 36th St N, Wichita, KS 67220
Tel.: (316) 686-7392
Web Site: http://www.asc-aero.com
Sales Range: $10-24.9 Million
Emp.: 75
Mfr of Aircraft Parts & Equipment
N.A.I.C.S.: 336413
Vicki Hickman (Mgr-Admin & Fin)
Eddie Morrison (Pres)

Great Plains Industries, Inc. (1)
5252 E 36th St N, Wichita, KS 67220-3205   (100%)
Tel.: (316) 686-7361
Web Site: http://www.gpi.net
Measuring & Dispensing Pumps
N.A.I.C.S.: 333914
Victor Lukic (CEO)

PowderTech, LLC (1)
800 E 37th St N, Wichita, KS 67219
Tel.: (316) 832-9210
Web Site:
http://www.powdertechwichita.com
Powder Coating Mfr
N.A.I.C.S.: 325510

GREAT POINT PARTNERS, LLC
165 Mason St 3rd Fl, Greenwich, CT 06830
Tel.: (203) 971-3300
Web Site: http://www.gppfunds.com
Year Founded: 2003
Private Equity Firm; Financial Services
N.A.I.C.S.: 523999
Jeffrey R. Jay (Mng Dir)
David E. Kroin (Mng Dir)
Adam B. Dolder (Mng Dir)
Rohan Saikia (Mng Dir)
Ron Panzier (Chief Compliance Officer & CFO)
Noah F. Rhodes III (Mng Dir)

Subsidiaries:

American Surgical Holdings, Inc. (1)
7324 SW Fwy #1550, Houston, TX 77074
Tel.: (713) 779-9800
Web Site: http://www.amerisurg.com
Holding Company; Professional Surgical Assistant Services To Patients, Surgeons & Healthcare Institutions
N.A.I.C.S.: 551111
Tom Kirk (Chm & CEO)
David Richardson (CFO)
Matt French (VP-Surgical Ops)
Jimmy Gailes (VP-HR)
Kevin Leaverton (Dir-IT)

Subsidiary (Domestic):

Chesapeake Medical Staffing, LLC (2)
2401 York Rd, Lutherville Timonium, MD 21093-2220
Tel.: (410) 321-4267
Web Site: http://www.cms24-7.com
Medical Staffing Network Company
N.A.I.C.S.: 561311
Missy Blankenship (Exec VP)

Aris Teleradiology, LLC (1)
5655 Hudson Dr Ste 210, Hudson, OH 44236
Tel.: (886) 521-2747
Radiology Services
N.A.I.C.S.: 621511
Carl J. Kozlowski (Pres & CEO)

Subsidiary (Domestic):

Optimal IMX, Inc. (2)
28 White Bridge Rd Ste 316, Nashville, TN 37205-1467
Tel.: (877) 833-2242
Web Site: http://www.optimalrad.com
Radiology Services
N.A.I.C.S.: 621512
Jonathan Grimes (CEO)
Alan Taylor (COO)
Chad Calendine (Chief Medical Officer)
Derek Hunley (Chief Dev Officer)

Citra Health Solutions, Inc. (1)

10151 Deerwood Park Blvd Bldg 300, Jacksonville, FL 32256
Web Site: http://www.citrahealth.com
IT Enabled Healthcare Solutions
N.A.I.C.S.: 541519
Howard Buff (Founder)
Mark Brockelman (CFO)
Scott Sanner (CEO)
Gina Brier (Sr VP-Tech Ops)
David Morris (Chief Comml Officer & Exec VP)
Frank Waterhouse (CFO)

Subsidiary (Domestic):

Datawing Software, LLC (2)
1717 NE 42nd Ave, Portland, OR 97213
Tel.: (503) 345-1891
Web Site: http://www.datawingsoftware.com
Custom Computer Programming Services
N.A.I.C.S.: 541511
Jerry Porter (Pres)

SironaHealth, Inc. (2)
500 Southborough Dr, South Portland, ME 04106
Tel.: (888) 674-7662
Web Site: http://www.sironahealth.com
Emp.: 150
Clinical Care Management Services
N.A.I.C.S.: 541519
Jeffrey Forbes (CEO)
Travis Hersom (CIO)
Dan Roy (VP-Ops)
Richard Walker (CFO)
Lorie Whittemore (VP-Quality & Trng)

Health Systems International, LLC (1)
5975 Castle Creek Pkwy Ste 100, Indianapolis, IN 46250
Tel.: (317) 806-2000
Web Site: http://www.us-hsi.com
Sales Range: $25-49.9 Million
Emp.: 25
Medical Claims Cost Control Solutions & Services
N.A.I.C.S.: 541519
Russell W. Sherlock (Founder & Chm)

MLM Medical Labs GmbH (1)
Dohrweg 63, 41066, Monchengladbach, Germany
Tel.: (49) 2161 4642 0
Web Site: http://www.mlm-labs.com
Biopharmaceutical Services
N.A.I.C.S.: 541714
Stephan Voswinkel (Mng Dir)

Subsidiary (US):

MD Biosciences, Inc. (2)
3510 Hopkins Pl N, Oakdale, MN 55128
Tel.: (651) 641-1770
Web Site: http://www.mdbiosciences.com
Research & Development in the Physical, Engineering & Life Sciences
N.A.I.C.S.: 541715
Amy Clausen (VP-Bus Dev)
Eddie Moradian (CEO)

GREAT RANGE CAPITAL, LLC
11250 Tomahawk Creek Pkwy, Leawood, KS 66211
Tel.: (913) 378-0850
Web Site:
http://www.greatrangecapital.com
Financial Investment Services
N.A.I.C.S.: 525990
Ryan Sprott (Mng Partner)
Paul Maxwell (Mng Partner)
Tracy Christian (CFO)

Subsidiaries:

Fairbank Equipment, Inc. (1)
3700 W Jewell St, Wichita, KS 67213
Tel.: (316) 943-2247
Web Site:
http://www.fairbankequipment.com
Sales Range: $1-9.9 Million
Emp.: 40
Industrial Equipment Distr
N.A.I.C.S.: 423810
Steve Taylor (Mgr-Sls)

LLL Transport, Inc. (1)

6950 Squibb Rd Ste 520, Mission, KS 66202
Tel.: (913) 777-5400
Web Site: http://www.llltransport.com
Sales Range: $10-24.9 Million
Emp.: 200
Hazardous Material Trucking Services
N.A.I.C.S.: 484110
Gary Waller (CEO)
J. B. Britton (VP)

SSG, Inc. (1)
1520 E Evergreen, Springfield, MO 65803
Tel.: (417) 889-5533
Web Site:
http://www.salonservicegroup.com
Full-service Beauty Supply Distr
N.A.I.C.S.: 456120
Debbie Duval (Mgr-Acctg)
Gino Barbo (CEO)

GREAT RECIPES COMPANY, INC.
PO Box 647, Beaverton, OR 97075
Tel.: (503) 590-1108
Web Site:
http://www.firenzamixes.com
Sales Range: $10-24.9 Million
Emp.: 2
Frozen Specialty Food Mfr
N.A.I.C.S.: 311412
Mark Bonebrake (Owner)

GREAT RIVER ENERGY
12300 Elm Creek Blvd, Maple Grove, MN 55369-4718
Tel.: (763) 445-5000   MN
Web Site:
https://www.greatriverenergy.com
Sales Range: $900-999.9 Million
Emp.: 880
Electric Utility Providing Services
N.A.I.C.S.: 221118
David Saggau (Pres & CEO)
Eric Olsen (Gen Counsel & VP)
Jud Goerss (Mgr-Field Svcs)
Michelle Strobel (CFO & VP)
Gary Connett (Dir-Member Svcs & Mktg)
Priti Patel (Chief Transmission Officer & VP)

Subsidiaries:

Blue Flint Ethanol LLC (1)
2841 3rd St SW, Underwood, ND 58576
Tel.: (701) 442-7500
Web Site: http://www.blueflintethanol.com
Methanol Mfr
N.A.I.C.S.: 325193
Michael Grosz (CFO)

GREAT RIVER HOLDING COMPANY
14633 Edgewood Dr, Baxter, MN 56425
Tel.: (218) 824-8400
Web Site:
http://www.riverwoodbank.com
Year Founded: 2003
Sales Range: $10-24.9 Million
Emp.: 75
Bank Holding Company
N.A.I.C.S.: 551111
David G. Landgrebe (Pres)

Subsidiaries:

RiverWood Bank (1)
14091 Baxter Dr Ste 117, Baxter, MN 56425
Tel.: (218) 824-8400
Web Site: http://www.riverwoodbank.com
Assets: $335,000,000
Emp.: 9
Banking Services
N.A.I.C.S.: 522110
David G. Landgrebe (Pres & CEO)
Lisa Finken (Mgr-HR)

GREAT SALT LAKE ELECTRIC INCORPORATED

Great Salt Lake Electric Incorporated—(Continued)

8540 Sandy Pkwy, Sandy, UT 84070-6422
Tel.: (801) 565-0088   UT
Web Site: https://www.gslelectric.com
Year Founded: 1981
Sales Range: $25-49.9 Million
Emp.: 375
Electrical Work
N.A.I.C.S.: 238210
Lance Capell (CEO)
Kurt Jensen (COO & Sr VP-Ops)
Bob Lifferth (Mgr-Contract)

Subsidiaries:

GSL Electric   (1)
5100 Sobb Ave, Las Vegas, NV 89118
Tel.: (702) 364-5313
Web Site: http://www.gslelectric.com
Sales Range: $10-24.9 Million
Emp.: 85
Electrical Wiring
N.A.I.C.S.: 811210
Tom Jensen (VP & Branch Mgr)
Tom Ewing (Pres)
Dustin Williams (Mgr-Special Projects Dept)
Lance Capell (CEO)
Kurt Jensen (COO & Exec VP)
Craig Taft (Chm)

GREAT SOUTH TEXAS CORPORATION

814 Arion Pkwy, San Antonio, TX 78216
Tel.: (210) 369-0300   MD
Web Site: http://www.comsoltx.com
Year Founded: 1984
Sales Range: $25-49.9 Million
Emp.: 50
Computer Services
N.A.I.C.S.: 423430
Caroline Labatt (Owner)
Bryce Walker (Pres)

GREAT SOUTHERN CAPITAL CORP.

218 22nd Ave S, Meridian, MS 39301
Tel.: (601) 693-5141
Web Site: http://www.gsnb.com
Sales Range: $10-24.9 Million
Emp.: 132
Bank Holding Company
N.A.I.C.S.: 551111
Dancy Sykes (CFO)

Subsidiaries:

Great Southern Bank   (1)
218 22nd Ave S, Meridian, MS 39302
Tel.: (601) 693-5141
Web Site: http://www.gsnb.com
Sales Range: $10-24.9 Million
Commericial Banking
N.A.I.C.S.: 522110
Dancy Sykes (CFO)
Angie Sowers (Asst VP)
Lisa Dearman (Asst VP-Quitman)
Michael Gibson (Sr VP)
Von Burt (Pres-Meridian)
Jeff McCoy (Pres & CEO)
Michelle Rowland (VP)
Shawntal M. Stamper (Officer-Mktg & Asst VP-Decatur)
Ken Lee (Pres-Hattiesburg)
Brett Phillips (Officer-Loan-Hattiesburg)
Brenda Gough (Sr VP-Meridian)
Christy Quick (Officer-Mortgage Loan & Asst VP-Meridian)
Anthony Thomas (Officer-Loan-Quitman)
Becky Campbell (VP-Waynesboro)
Mike Evans (Pres-Waynesboro)
Chris Odom (VP-Waynesboro)
Mildred Smith (Asst VP-Waynesboro)

GREAT SOUTHERN INDUSTRIES INC.

1320 Boling St, Jackson, MS 39209
Tel.: (601) 948-5700

Web Site: http://www.greatsouthernindustriesinc.com
Sales Range: $10-24.9 Million
Emp.: 105
Corrugated Boxes
N.A.I.C.S.: 322211
Joe Russell (Controller)
Charles W. Ellis Sr. (Pres)

GREAT SOUTHERN WOOD PRESERVING, INCORPORATED

1100 US Hwy 431 N, Abbeville, AL 36310
Tel.: (334) 585-2291   AL
Web Site: http://www.yellawood.com
Year Founded: 1971
Rev.: $61,000,000
Emp.: 250
Wood Preserving Services
N.A.I.C.S.: 321114
James W. Rane (Founder, Owner, Pres & CEO)

Subsidiaries:

Escue Wood Preserving, Inc.   (1)
164 Post Millwood Rd, Millwood, KY 42762
Tel.: (270) 879-3411
Web Site:
 http://www.escuewoodpreserving.com
Wood Preservation
N.A.I.C.S.: 321114
Chris Brown (Mgr-Sls & Mktg)

GREAT UNIVERSAL INCORPORATED

23 280 Park Ave, New York, NY 10017-1216
Tel.: (212) 355-3440
Rev.: $174,705,000
Emp.: 1,000
Cellular Telephone Services
N.A.I.C.S.: 531210

Subsidiaries:

Innova International Corp.   (1)
153 E 53rd St Ste 5900, New York, NY 10022
Tel.: (212) 355-3440
Telecommunications Consultant
N.A.I.C.S.: 541690

Mach USA Inc.   (1)
153 E 53rd St Ste 5900, New York, NY 10022
Tel.: (212) 702-4570
Rev.: $1,000,000
Emp.: 5
Telephone Communication, Except Radio
N.A.I.C.S.: 517121

Primetime 24 Joint Venture   (1)
89 Summit Ave Fl 2, Summit, NJ 07901
Tel.: (908) 378-2860
Emp.: 2
Fiscal Year-end: 12/01/2006
Satellite Earth Stations
N.A.I.C.S.: 517410
Gillien Murrey (Mgr-HR)

GREAT VALLEY ADVISOR GROUP, INC.

1200 Pennsylvania Ave Ste 202, Wilmington, DE 19806
Tel.: (302) 483-7200
Web Site:
 http://www.greatvalleyadvisors.com
Offices of Certified Public Accountants
N.A.I.C.S.: 541211
Peter Holtz (Owner)

Subsidiaries:

U.S. Financial Advisors LLC   (1)
139 Wood Rd, Braintree, MA 02184
Tel.: (781) 849-9200
Rev.: $1,600,000
Emp.: 14
Administrative Management & General Management Consulting Service

N.A.I.C.S.: 541611
George T. Clarke (CFO)

GREAT WESTERN DINING SERVICE, INC.

111 W Moniteau St, Tipton, MO 65081
Tel.: (660) 433-2298   MO
Web Site: http://gwdining.net
Sales Range: $10-24.9 Million
Emp.: 8
Contract Food Services
N.A.I.C.S.: 722310
Robert E. Nold (VP)

GREAT WESTERN ERECTORS CO.

9207 Sovereign Row, Dallas, TX 75247-4513
Tel.: (214) 637-2500
Web Site:
 http://www.greatwesternerectors.com
Year Founded: 1984
Sales Range: $10-24.9 Million
Emp.: 100
Sub Contractor of Structural Steel Erection
N.A.I.C.S.: 238120
Earl Fishel (Mgr-Area)
Howard Parsons (Mgr-Area)
Mark Meyer (Gen Mgr)

GREAT WESTERN INK, INC.

2100 NW 22nd Ave, Portland, OR 97210
Tel.: (503) 226-3595
Web Site: https://www.gw-inks.com
Year Founded: 1925
Sales Range: $10-24.9 Million
Emp.: 50
Ink Mfr
N.A.I.C.S.: 325910
Keith Voigt (Pres)

GREAT WESTERN LEASING & SALES, LLC

14212 Vly Blvd, Fontana, CA 92335
Tel.: (866) 649-1612   DE
Web Site:
 https://www.greatwesterntrailer.com
Year Founded: 1971
New & Used Travel Trailers Sales
N.A.I.C.S.: 532120
David Arnovitz (VP-Credit & Collections)

Subsidiaries:

Pacific Truck & Trailer   (1)
4826 Monument Dr, Grants Pass, OR 97526-8502   (100%)
Tel.: (541) 471-4450
Web Site:
 http://www.pacifictruckandtrailer.com
Emp.: 80
Sales of New & Used Semi Trailers & Used Semi Trucks
N.A.I.C.S.: 333924
Robert L. Grover Sr. (Pres)

Quality Trailer Sales Corp.   (1)
13501 Central Ave NW, Albuquerque, NM 87121
Tel.: (505) 833-5000
Web Site: http://www.qualitytrailersales.com
Sales Range: $1-9.9 Million
Emp.: 12
Truck Trailer Sls & Service
N.A.I.C.S.: 423120
Larry Gilbert (Pres)

Trinity Trailer Sales & Service, Inc.   (1)
6410 Singleton Blvd, Dallas, TX 75212
Tel.: (214) 630-7051
Web Site: http://www.trinitytrailersales.com
Trucks, Tractors & Trailers Sales & Services
N.A.I.C.S.: 441110

GREAT WESTERN SUPPLY, INC.

2626 Industrial Dr, Ogden, UT 84401
Tel.: (801) 621-5412
Web Site: https://www.gwsupply.com
Sales Range: $1-9.9 Million
Emp.: 48
Plumbing & Industrial Whslr
N.A.I.C.S.: 423720
Glen Jenkins (Mgr-Store-Retail)
Mark Jenkins (Mgr-Store-Retail)
Brent Zeluf (Mgr-Shipping)
Doug Jamison (Mgr)
Taylor Proctor (Mgr-HR)
Gary Tyler (Mgr-HR)
Jennie Adams (Mgr-Showroom)
Jenna Nielsen (Mgr-Showroom)
Fernando Herrara (Mgr-Warehouse)
Jeremy Rose (Mgr-Warehouse-Receiving)
Heidi Knight (Office Mgr)

GREAT WHITE SHARK ENTERPRISES, INC.

2041 Vista Pkwy Level 2, West Palm Beach, FL 33411
Tel.: (561) 640-7000   FL
Web Site: http://www.shark.com
Year Founded: 1984
Holding Company
N.A.I.C.S.: 551112
Jack Schneider (Pres)

Subsidiaries:

Greg Norman Golf Course Design Company   (1)
2041 Vista Pkwy Level 2, West Palm Beach, FL 33411   (100%)
Tel.: (561) 640-7000
Web Site: http://www.gngcd.com
Sales Range: $25-49.9 Million
Emp.: 50
Golf Course Design & Development Services
N.A.I.C.S.: 541490
Gregory J. Norman (Chm & CEO)

Medalist Village Club, Inc.   (1)
7380 SE Medalist Pl, Hobe Sound, FL 33455
Tel.: (772) 546-2337
Private Country Club & Spa
N.A.I.C.S.: 713910

Medallist Developments Pty. Limited   (1)
Level 12 1 Martin Place, Sydney, 2000, NSW, Australia
Tel.: (61) 800 667 626
Sales Range: $1-9.9 Million
Emp.: 53
Golf Course Real Estate Developer & Residential Housing Construction; Owned by Great White Shark Enterprises, Inc. & by Macquarie Group Limited
N.A.I.C.S.: 237210

Subsidiary (US):

Medallist Developments Inc.   (2)
200 Blue Moon Crossing Ste 100, Pooler, GA 31322
Tel.: (912) 450-2280
Web Site: http://www.medallist.com
Golf Course Real Estate Developer & Residential Housing Construction
N.A.I.C.S.: 237210

GREAT WORKS INTERNET

8 Pomerleau St, Biddeford, ME 04005
Tel.: (207) 496-1287
Web Site: https://www.gwi.net
Year Founded: 1994
Sales Range: $10-24.9 Million
Emp.: 96
Telecommunication Servicesb
N.A.I.C.S.: 517810
Fletcher Kittredge (Founder & CEO)

GREATAMERICA LEASING

CORPORATION
625 1st St SE, Cedar Rapids, IA 52401
Tel.: (319) 365-8000
Web Site:
  https://www.greatamerica.com
Rev.: $47,627,737
Emp.: 325
Provider of Machinery & Equipment Leasing Services
N.A.I.C.S.: 522220
Tony Golobic *(Chm & CEO)*
Deb Ferguson *(VP-HR & Org Dev)*
Jim Burns *(VP-IT)*
David Pohlman *(COO & Exec VP)*
Stan Herkelman *(Pres)*
Lane Wolbe *(Sr VP-Tactical Sls Dev)*
Greg VanDeWalker *(Sr VP & Gen Mgr-Unified Comm & IT Grp)*
Brett Steffen *(Controller)*
Matthew Doty *(Dir-Corp Comm)*
Marty Klees *(Chief Risk Officer & Sr VP-Ops)*
Joe Terfler *(CFO & Exec VP)*
Jennie Fisher *(Sr VP & Gen Mgr-Office Equipment Grp)*

GREATER AUSTIN DEVELOP-MENT
4105 Eck Ln, Austin, TX 78734
Tel.: (512) 310-9300
Sales Range: $10-24.9 Million
Emp.: 300
Concrete Finishing Services
N.A.I.C.S.: 238140
Bobby Finley *(Owner)*
Kerry Collins *(VP)*
Michelle Conger *(Coord-Resource)*
Doug Mathews *(Mgr-Special Projects)*

GREATER BATON ROUGE FOOD BANK
10600 S Chotaw Dr, Baton Rouge, LA 70815
Tel.: (225) 359-9940   LA
Web Site:
  https://www.brfoodbank.org
Year Founded: 1985
Sales Range: $10-24.9 Million
Emp.: 41
Community Food Services
N.A.I.C.S.: 624210
Charlene Guarisco Montelaro *(Sr VP-Dev & Philanthropy)*
Mike Manning *(Pres & CEO)*
Jude Guerin *(Treas)*
Eddie Hughes *(Chm)*
Ed Collins *(Sec)*
Bob Kanas *(COO)*
Jenna Schexnayder *(CFO)*

GREATER BERKS FOOD BANK
117 Morgan Dr, Reading, PA 19608
Tel.: (610) 926-5802   PA
Web Site:
  http://www.berksfoodbank.org
Year Founded: 1983
Sales Range: $10-24.9 Million
Emp.: 17
Community Food Services
N.A.I.C.S.: 624210
Peg Bianca *(Exec Dir)*
Timothy Becker *(Mgr-Ops)*
Deb Gehris *(Mgr-Fin)*
Deb Mest *(Mgr-Agency & Volunteer Svcs)*
Bryan Geiger *(VP)*
Joshua Weiss *(Treas)*
Lori Endy *(Pres)*
Vickie Kintzer *(Sec)*

GREATER BOSTON LEGAL SERVICES, INC.
197 Friend St, Boston, MA 02114

Tel.: (617) 371-1234   MA
Web Site: http://www.gbls.org
Year Founded: 1900
Sales Range: $10-24.9 Million
Emp.: 157
Law firm
N.A.I.C.S.: 541199
Sonia Marquez *(Dir-HR)*
Jacquelynne J. Bowman *(Exec Dir)*
Joanne Sanders *(Dir-Fin)*
Jeffrey M. Stoler *(Treas)*

GREATER CEDAR RAPIDS COMMUNITY FOUNDATION
324 3rd St SE, Cedar Rapids, IA 52401-1841
Tel.: (319) 366-2862   IA
Web Site: http://www.gcrcf.org
Year Founded: 1987
Sales Range: $10-24.9 Million
Emp.: 18
Grantmaking Services
N.A.I.C.S.: 813211
Michelle Beisker *(VP-Dev)*
Karla Twedt-Ball *(Sr VP)*
Josie Velles *(Dir-Dev Svcs)*
Jean Brenneman *(CFO)*
Carrie Walker *(Coord-Non-Profit Network)*
Corinne Ramler *(Dir-Mktg & Comm)*
Rochelle Naylor *(Officer-Program)*
Les Garner Jr. *(Pres & CEO)*

GREATER CHICAGO FOOD DEPOSITORY
4100 W Ann Lurie Pl, Chicago, IL 60632
Tel.: (773) 247-3663   IL
Web Site:
  http://www.chicagosfoodbank.org
Year Founded: 1978
Sales Range: $100-124.9 Million
Emp.: 259
Hunger Relief Services
N.A.I.C.S.: 624210
Jill Zimmerman *(VP-Dev)*
Norman M. Leon *(Vice Chm)*
Patrick M. Mulhern *(Co-Chm)*
Peter G. Johnson *(Co-Chm)*
Sheila Creghin *(VP-Ops)*
Dennis James *(CFO)*
Jill A. Rahman *(COO)*
Joan K. Chow *(CMO)*

GREATER CLEVELAND RE-GIONAL TRANSIT AUTHORITY
1240 W 6th St, Cleveland, OH 44113-1302
Tel.: (216) 566-5285
Web Site: http://www.riderta.com
Year Founded: 1975
Sales Range: $25-49.9 Million
Emp.: 2,700
Provider of Transportation Services
N.A.I.C.S.: 485119
Michael J. Schipper *(Deputy Gen Mgr-Engrg & Project Mgmt)*
Bruce Hampton *(Deputy Gen Mgr-HR)*
Sheryl King Benford *(Gen Counsel & Deputy Gen Mgr-Legal Affairs)*
Danielle Bennett *(Sec)*
Peter Anderson *(CIO & Exec Dir-IT)*
Frank Polivka *(Dir-Procurement)*
Jenice Contreras *(Exec Dir)*
Anthony Garofoli *(Exec Dir-Internal Audit)*
Stephen J. Bitto *(Exec Dir-Mktg & Comm)*
Herlinda Bradley *(Mgr)*
Linda Scardilli Krecic *(Mgr-Media Rels)*
Dennis M. Clough *(VP)*
Leo Serrano *(Exec Dir)*
Floun'say Caver *(Interim CEO & Interim Gen Mgr)*

GREATER DICKSON GAS AU-THORITY
605 E Walnut St, Dickson, TN 37055-2505
Tel.: (615) 441-2830
Web Site: https://www.gdga.com
Sales Range: $25-49.9 Million
Emp.: 70
Natural Gas Distr
N.A.I.C.S.: 221210
Donald R. Richardson *(Chm)*
Jesse Davis *(Dir-Ops)*
John Duke *(Sec & Treas)*
Stephanie Bates *(Sec)*

GREATER GEORGIA PRINT-ERS, INC.
1263 Athens Rd, Crawford, GA 30630
Tel.: (706) 743-8155
Web Site:
  https://www.georgiaprinters.com
Year Founded: 1969
Emp.: 34
Printing Services
N.A.I.C.S.: 323111
Bobby Miller *(Gen Mgr)*
J. Kevin Miller *(Plant Mgr)*

Subsidiaries:

ABC Printing Co.   (1)
2175 W Broad St, Athens, GA 30606
Tel.: (706) 353-2225
Web Site: http://www.abc-printing.com
Emp.: 9
Commercial Printing Services
N.A.I.C.S.: 323111

GREATER HARLEM NURSING HOME & REHABILITATION CENTER INC.
30 W 138th St, New York, NY 10037
Tel.: (212) 690-7400   NY
Year Founded: 1973
Sales Range: $10-24.9 Million
Emp.: 236
Nursing & Rehabilitation Services
N.A.I.C.S.: 624120
Steven J. Cohen *(CFO)*
Thomas Foristall *(CEO)*

GREATER KANSAS CITY COMMUNITY FOUNDATION
1055 Broadway Blvd Ste 130, Kansas City, MO 64105
Tel.: (816) 842-0944   MO
Web Site:
  https://www.growyourgiving.org
Year Founded: 1978
Sales Range: $300-349.9 Million
Emp.: 67
Charity Services
N.A.I.C.S.: 813219
Julie Barry *(VP-Fin)*
Leanne Breiby *(Dir-Comm)*
Jeremy Brewer *(Dir-Tech)*
David Anderson *(Dir-Investments)*
Katie Gray *(Sr VP-Fin & Foundation Svcs)*
Debbie Wilkerson *(Pres & CEO)*

GREATER LAWRENCE COM-MUNITY ACTION COUNCIL, INC.
305 Essex St 4th Fl, Lawrence, MA 01840
Tel.: (978) 681-4900   MA
Web Site: https://www.glcac.org
Year Founded: 1966
Sales Range: $25-49.9 Million
Emp.: 379
Community Action Services
N.A.I.C.S.: 624190
William Buckley *(Pres)*
Natalie Coon *(Treas)*
Helen Ann A. Knepper *(Sec)*

GREATER LAWRENCE FAMILY HEALTH CENTER, INC.
34 Haverhill St, Lawrence, MA 01841-2884
Tel.: (978) 686-0090   MA
Web Site: https://www.glfhc.org
Year Founded: 1980
Sales Range: $50-74.9 Million
Emp.: 660
Healtcare Services
N.A.I.C.S.: 622110
Ann Marie Borgesi *(Chief HR Officer & Sr VP)*
Robert Ingala *(Pres & CEO)*
Patrick Grotton *(CIO & Sr VP)*
Saifur Rahman *(COO & Sr VP)*

GREATER LYNN SENIOR SER-VICES, INC.
8 Silsbee St, Lynn, MA 01901
Tel.: (781) 599-0110   MA
Web Site: http://www.glss.net
Year Founded: 1975
Sales Range: $50-74.9 Million
Emp.: 751
Senior Care Services
N.A.I.C.S.: 623312
Edward Purtz *(Treas)*
Kenneth C. Haltkin *(CFO)*
Valerie Parker Callahan *(Dir-Plng & Dev)*
Kathryn C. Burns *(CEO)*
John Baker *(Pres)*

GREATER MIAMI CONVEN-TION & VISITORS BUREAU
701 Brickell Ave Ste 2700, Miami, FL 33131
Tel.: (305) 539-3000
Web Site:
  https://www.miamiandbeaches.com
Year Founded: 1985
Sales Range: $75-99.9 Million
Emp.: 75
Convention & Visitors Bureau
N.A.I.C.S.: 561591
Rolando Aedo *(COO)*
Barry Moskowitz *(VP-Convention Sls)*
Ileana Castillo *(Assoc VP-Convention Sls)*
Sonia Fong *(Assoc VP-Convention Sls)*
Ita Moriarty *(Sr VP-Convention Sls)*
Pam Payano *(Mgr-Corp Sls)*
Keon Hardemon *(Chm)*
Eve Gardiner *(Co-Mng Dir-First PR)*
Elizabeth MacKinlay *(Partner & Mgr-Acct)*
Gisela Marti *(VP-Mktg & Tourism)*
Connie Valenti *(VP-Multicultural Tourism & Dev)*
William D. Talbert III *(Pres & CEO)*

GREATER MILWAUKEE FOUN-DATION
101 W Pleasant St Ste 210, Milwaukee, WI 53212
Tel.: (414) 272-5805   WI
Web Site:
  http://www.greatermilwaukeefoundation.org
Year Founded: 1989
Sales Range: $75-99.9 Million
Emp.: 37
Fundraising Organization
N.A.I.C.S.: 813211
Claudia Scholl *(Mgr-Event & Hospitality)*
Ellen M. Gilligan *(Pres & CEO)*
Marcus White *(VP-Civic Engagement)*
Kathryn J. Dunn *(VP-Community Investment)*
Liliane McFarlane *(Mgr-Grants)*
Janel M. Hines *(Dir-Grants)*
Kenneth Robertson *(CFO & VP)*

Greater Minneapolis Convention & Visitors Association—(Continued)

GREATER MINNEAPOLIS CONVENTION & VISITORS ASSOCIATION
250 Marquette Ave S Ste 1300, Minneapolis, MN 55401
Tel.: (612) 767-8000 MN
Web Site: http://www.minneapolis.org
Year Founded: 1987
Sales Range: $10-24.9 Million
Emp.: 74
Convention & Visitor Bureau Services
N.A.I.C.S.: 561591
David Nguyen (Mgr-IT)
Bill Deef (VP-Intl Rels)
Madonna Carr (VP-Destination Svcs)
Brent Foerster (Sr VP-Destination Sls)
Sylvia Olson (Dir-Employee Experience & Ops)
Kevin Hanstad (Dir-Market Res)
Edi Hasan (Mgr-Accounting)
Melvin Tennant (Pres & CEO)
Amy Alegi (Sr VP-Destination Branding & Strategy)
Scott M. Romane (Exec Dir-Sports)
Matthew Teichert (Mgr-Market Research Project)
Donya L. Dawson (Project Mgr)

GREATER MISSOURI BUILDERS
1551 Wall St Ste 220, Saint Charles, MO 63303
Tel.: (636) 946-1341
Web Site: http://www.gmb-inc.com
Year Founded: 1966
Sales Range: $25-49.9 Million
Emp.: 25
Subdividers & Developers
N.A.I.C.S.: 237210
Todd Ellison (Dir-Construction)
Ben Ashburn (Dir-Pur)
James Walker (Mgr)
Debbie Terwilliger (Mgr-Community Sls)
Howard Newsome (Superintendent)
Diane Hawkins (Asst Controller)
Sharon Sommer (Asst Controller)
Robin Teemul (Supvr-Maintenance)
Scott Campbell (VP)

GREATER NEVADA CREDIT UNION
PO Box 2128, Carson City, NV 89702
Tel.: (775) 882-2060 NV
Web Site: http://www.gncu.org
Year Founded: 1949
Sales Range: $25-49.9 Million
Emp.: 282
Credit Union
N.A.I.C.S.: 522130
Rob Joiner (Vice Chm)
Alex Talmant (Treas)
Bill Arensdorf (Sec)
Paul Richey (Chm)

GREATER NEW YORK HOSPITAL ASSOCIATION
555 W 57th St, New York, NY 10019
Tel.: (212) 246-7100 NY
Year Founded: 1904
Sales Range: $25-49.9 Million
Emp.: 4
Hospital Association
N.A.I.C.S.: 813910
Bridgette A. Ingraham (VP-Govt Affairs)
Lloyd C. Bishop (VP-Community Health Initiative & Govt Affairs)
Karen S. Heller (Exec VP-Economics & Fin)

Jonathan Cooper (VP-Govt Affairs)
Susan C. Waltman (Gen Counsel & Exec VP)

GREATER NEW YORK MUTUAL INSURANCE COMPANY
200 Madison Ave, New York, NY 10016
Tel.: (212) 683-9700 NY
Web Site: http://www.gny.com
Year Founded: 1914
Sales Range: $250-299.9 Million
Emp.: 330
Mutual Holding Company; Property & Casualty Insurance Products & Services
N.A.I.C.S.: 551112
Gerard Ragusa (Exec VP-Claims)
Ray Lee (VP-Loss Control)
Susan D'Onofrio (VP-Underwriting)
Elizabeth Heck (Pres & CEO)
Kathleen Zarzycki (CIO & VP-IT)
Chris McNulty (CFO, Treas & Exec VP)
Lucas Sheldon (Chief Underwriting Officer & Sr VP)
Margaret G. Klein (VP-Legal)
Michael Meyer (VP-Customer Experience & Operational Excellence)

Subsidiaries:

Insurance Company of Greater New York   (1)
200 Madison Ave, New York, NY 10016-3903   (100%)
Tel.: (212) 683-9700
Web Site: http://www.gny.com
Sales Range: $50-74.9 Million
Emp.: 200
Property & Casualty Insurance Company
N.A.I.C.S.: 524126
Rosie Roman Cortez (Office Mgr)

GREATER OMAHA PACKING CO. INC.
3001 L St, Omaha, NE 68107
Tel.: (402) 731-1700 NE
Web Site:
    https://www.greateromaha.com
Year Founded: 1952
Sales Range: $150-199.9 Million
Emp.: 660
Meat Slaughtering Plant
N.A.I.C.S.: 311611
Henry A. Davis (Pres)
Carol Mesenbrink (Mgr-Credit)
Angelo Fili (Exec VP)
Angel Besta (Mgr-Technical Res)
Dan Jensen (VP-Sls)

GREATER ORLANDO AVIATION AUTHORITY INC.
1 Jeff Fuqua Blvd, Orlando, FL 32827-4392
Tel.: (407) 825-2001 FL
Web Site:
    https://www.orlandoairports.net
Year Founded: 1975
Sales Range: $300-349.9 Million
Emp.: 650
Airport Operations
N.A.I.C.S.: 488119
Phillip N. Brown (Exec Dir)
Ronald N. Lewis (Deputy Exec Dir-Ops)
Dayci S. Burnette-Snyder (Asst Sec)
Marcos Marchena (Gen Counsel)
Morton Carson Good (Chm)

GREATER PHILADELPHIA HEALTH ACTION
432 N 6th St, Philadelphia, PA 19123
Tel.: (215) 925-2400 PA
Web Site: http://www.gphainc.org
Year Founded: 1970
Sales Range: $25-49.9 Million

Emp.: 513
Health Care Srvices
N.A.I.C.S.: 622110
Brian Clark (CFO & COO)
Charles Jeorger (Chief HR Officer)
Royal E. Brown (Chm)
Paula D. Jackson (Sec)
Celeste A. Johns (Dir-Reimbursement)
Dennis Carter (Dir-Maintenance)
Janet E. Young (Dir-Medical & Chief Medical Officer)
Latisha Lee (Mgr-Call Center)
Markisha Myers (Dir-Marketing)
Sharon Neilson (Dir-Daycare Svcs)
Sheila Saylor (Mgr-Dental Ops)
Maggie Lyons Johnson (Chief Behavioral Health Officer)
Zel Negassa (CIO)

GREATER PITTSBURGH CONVENTION & VISITORS BUREAU
120 5th Ave Ste 2800 5th Ave Pl, Pittsburgh, PA 15222
Tel.: (412) 281-7711 PA
Web Site:
    https://www.visitpittsburgh.com
Year Founded: 1997
Sales Range: $10-24.9 Million
Emp.: 55
Convention & Visitor Bureau Services
N.A.I.C.S.: 561591
Karen Fisher (CFO)
Karl Pietrzak (VP-Convention Sls)
David Atkins (VP-Digital Mktg)
Ashley Steckel (Dir-Adv Sls)
Brenda Hill (VP-Convention Svcs)

GREATER RIDGEWOOD YOUTH COUNCIL INC.
5903 Summerfield St, Ridgewood, NY 11385
Tel.: (718) 456-5437 NY
Year Founded: 1980
Sales Range: $1-9.9 Million
Emp.: 236
Community Welfare Services
N.A.I.C.S.: 624110
Robert J. Monahan (Pres)

GREATER TAMPA CHAMBER OF COMMERCE
201 N Franklin St Ste 201, Tampa, FL 33602
Tel.: (813) 228-7777 FL
Web Site:
    http://www.tampachamber.com
Year Founded: 1894
Sales Range: $50-74.9 Million
Emp.: 20
Economic Development Services
N.A.I.C.S.: 926110
Wendy Wiemert (Dir-Database)
Steven M. Bernstein (Chm)
Karen Arnold (COO)
Robert J. Rohrlack Jr. (Pres & CEO)

GREATER TEXAS FOUNDATION
6100 Foundation Place Dr, Bryan, TX 77807
Tel.: (979) 779-6100 TX
Web Site:
    https://www.greatertexasfounda tion.org
Year Founded: 1973
Sales Range: $10-24.9 Million
Emp.: 14
Grantmaking Services
N.A.I.C.S.: 813211
Carol Miller (Mgr-Grants)
Erin Arnold (Accountant)
Leslie Gurrola (Mgr-Strategy)
Amber Bass (Controller)

GREATER THAN ONE, INC.
395 Hudson St 4th Fl, New York, NY 10014
Tel.: (212) 252-1999 DE
Web Site:
    http://www.greaterthanone.com
Year Founded: 2000
Advetising Agency
N.A.I.C.S.: 541810
Elizabeth Izard Apelles (Founder & CEO)
Richard Newman (Pres)
Steve Longbons (Partner-Tech)
Christa Toole (Partner-Search & Analytics)
John Mahler (Partner-Strategy & Insights)
Pilar Belhumeur (Partner-Experience Design)
Carol Fraser (Chief People Officer)
Chris Mycek (Sr VP-Strategy & Growth)

GREATLAND CORPORATION
2480 Walker Ave NW, Grand Rapids, MI 49544-1302
Tel.: (616) 791-0100 MI
Web Site: https://www.greatland.com
Year Founded: 1974
Emp.: 135
Printed & Electronic Documents Products; Software & Support Services
N.A.I.C.S.: 459410
Robert Nault (Chm, Pres & CEO)
Phil Kirchner (Dir-Dev & IT)
Kerry Mungons (Dir-Sls, Mktg & Fulfillment)

Subsidiaries:

JAT Software, Inc.   (1)
440 Route 22 E, Bridgewater, NJ 08807
Tel.: (908) 725-0111
Web Site: http://www.jatsoftware.com
Emp.: 16
Computer Related Consulting Services
N.A.I.C.S.: 541512
Jack Felicio (Pres)

GREATMATS.COM CORPORATION
117 Industrial Ave, Milltown, WI 54858
Tel.: (715) 653-6100
Web Site: https://www.greatmats.com
Year Founded: 1999
Rev.: $6,100,000
Emp.: 8
Floor Covering Stores
N.A.I.C.S.: 449121
David W. Butler (Pres)

GREEK CATHOLIC UNION OF THE U.S.A.
5400 Tuscarawas Rd, Beaver, PA 15009
Web Site: https://www.gcuusa.com
Year Founded: 1892
Sales Range: $300-349.9 Million
Fraternal Life Insurance Organization
N.A.I.C.S.: 524113
George N. Juba (Pres & CEO)
Deborah Tatro (COO & Exec VP)
Gregory N. Vladika (Chm)
George A. Kofel (Vice Chm)

GREEKTOWN HOLDINGS, LLC
555 E Lafayette St, Detroit, MI 48226
Tel.: (313) 223-2999 DE
Web Site:
    http://www.greektowncasino.com
Year Founded: 2010
Sales Range: $350-399.9 Million
Emp.: 1,824
Casino Hotel Operator
N.A.I.C.S.: 721120
Glen Tomaszewski (CFO, Treas & Sr VP)

Charles M. Moore *(Vice Chm)*
Daniel Gilbert *(Chm)*
Matthew P. Cullen *(Pres & CEO)*

GREEN & CHAPMAN, INC.
4033 E Broadway St, North Little
Rock, AR 72114
Tel.: (501) 945-4555   AR
Year Founded: 1956
Rev.: $15,660,750
Emp.: 6
Petroleum Terminal
N.A.I.C.S.: 424710
Timothy D. Green *(VP)*
Steven J. Green *(Pres)*

GREEN ACRES CONTRACT-ING CO. INC.
148 Pennsylvania Ave, Scottdale, PA
15683
Tel.: (724) 887-8096
Web Site:
  https://www.greenacrescontrac
  ting.com
Rev.: $29,020,450
Emp.: 123
Guardrail Construction, Highways
N.A.I.C.S.: 237310
Gregory Pisula *(Pres)*

GREEN AUTOMOTIVE COM-PANY
5495 Wilson St, Riverside, CA
92509   NV
Web Site:
  http://www.thegreenautomotive
  company.com
Year Founded: 1996
Sales Range: $1-9.9 Million
Emp.: 60
Electric Car Mfr
N.A.I.C.S.: 336110
Fred Graves Luke *(Pres & Sec)*

Subsidiaries:

Blackhawk Manufacturing, Inc.   **(1)**
3122 S Riverside Ave, Bloomington, CA
92316
Tel.: (909) 874-9962
Web Site:
  http://www.blackhawkmanufacturing.net
Sales Range: $1-9.9 Million
Emp.: 75
Ffiberglass, Urethane & Vacuum Formed
Parts Mfr
N.A.I.C.S.: 326199
Floyd Sanders *(Pres)*

GREEN BALLAST, INC.
2620 Thousand Oaks Blvd Ste 4000,
Memphis, TN 38118
Tel.: (901) 260-4400   DE
Web Site:
  http://www.greenballastinc.com
Year Founded: 2011
Sales Range: Less than $1 Million
Emp.: 1
Electronic Ballast Mfr
N.A.I.C.S.: 334419
J. Kevin Adams *(Pres & CEO)*
J. Philip Jones *(Gen Counsel)*
Penelope Springer *(Chief Acctg Offi-cer)*

GREEN BAY PACKAGING INC.
1700 N Webster Ct, Green Bay, WI
54302-1166
Tel.: (920) 433-5111   WI
Web Site: https://www.gbp.com
Year Founded: 1933
Sales Range: $800-899.9 Million
Emp.: 3,500
Corrugated & Paper Board & Coded
Label Stock Mfr
N.A.I.C.S.: 322130
Rick Luftman *(VP-Natl Sls & Mktg)*

Subsidiaries:

Archbold Container Corporation   **(1)**
800 W Barre Rd, Archbold, OH 43502
Tel.: (419) 445-8865
Web Site: http://www.archboldcontainer.com
Emp.: 150
Retail Display Mfr
N.A.I.C.S.: 337215

Green Bay Packaging Inc. - Arkansas
Kraft Division   **(1)**
338 Highway 113 S, Morrilton, AR 72110
Tel.: (501) 354-4521
Paperboard Packaging Product Mfr
N.A.I.C.S.: 322219

Green Bay Packaging Inc. - Baird
Display Division   **(1)**
W220N507 Springdale Rd, Waukesha, WI
53186-3186
Tel.: (262) 650-6100
Web Site: https://www.bairddisplay.com
Point-of-Purchase Display Mfr
N.A.I.C.S.: 339950
Jeffrey Eckoldt *(Project Mgr)*

Green Bay Packaging Inc. - Baltimore
Division   **(1)**
11000 Gilroy Rd, Hunt Valley, MD 21031-
1309
Tel.: (410) 785-2233
Paperboard Packaging Product Mfr
N.A.I.C.S.: 322219

Green Bay Packaging Inc. - California
Division   **(1)**
10727 7th St Ste A, Rancho Cucamonga,
CA 91730
Tel.: (909) 466-3501
Paperboard Packaging Product Mfr
N.A.I.C.S.: 332216

Green Bay Packaging Inc. - Chickasha Division   **(1)**
1800 Charles Allen Dr, Chickasha, OK
73018
Tel.: (405) 222-2306
Paperboard Packaging Product Mfr
N.A.I.C.S.: 322219

Green Bay Packaging Inc. - Cincin-
nati Division   **(1)**
760 Kingsview Dr, Lebanon, OH 45036
Tel.: (513) 489-8700
Web Site: http://www.gbp.com
Emp.: 100
Paperboard Packaging Product Mfr
N.A.I.C.S.: 322219
Wayne Petersen *(VP & Gen Mgr)*

Green Bay Packaging Inc. - De Pere
Division   **(1)**
2001 American Blvd, De Pere, WI 54115
Tel.: (920) 337-6900
Paperboard Packaging Product Mfr
N.A.I.C.S.: 322219

Green Bay Packaging Inc. - El Paso
Division   **(1)**
10515 Railroad Dr, El Paso, TX 79924
Tel.: (915) 822-9700
Web Site: http://www.gbp.com
Sales Range: $25-49.9 Million
Emp.: 150
Paperboard Packaging Product Mfr
N.A.I.C.S.: 322212
Eddie Sigala *(Gen Mgr)*

Green Bay Packaging Inc. - Fiber
Resource Division   **(1)**
1001 E Broadway St, Morrilton, AR 72110
Tel.: (501) 354-2461
Paperboard Packaging Product Mfr
N.A.I.C.S.: 322219

Green Bay Packaging Inc. - Folding
Carton Division   **(1)**
2275 American Blvd, De Pere, WI 54115-
8490
Tel.: (920) 498-4000
Web Site: http://www.gbp.com
Paperboard Packaging Product Mfr
N.A.I.C.S.: 322212

Green Bay Packaging Inc. - Fort
Worth Division   **(1)**
7901 S Freeway, Fort Worth, TX 76134-
5102

Tel.: (817) 551-1934
Paperboard Packaging Product Mfr
N.A.I.C.S.: 322219

Green Bay Packaging Inc. - Fremont
Division   **(1)**
2323 Commerce Dr, Fremont, OH 43420-
0650
Tel.: (419) 332-5593
Paperboard Packaging Product Mfr
N.A.I.C.S.: 322219
Gary Fry *(Production Mgr)*

Green Bay Packaging Inc. - Green
Bay Coated Products Division   **(1)**
3250 S Ridge Rd, Green Bay, WI 54304-
5643
Tel.: (920) 337-1800
Paperboard Packaging Product Mfr
N.A.I.C.S.: 322219

Green Bay Packaging Inc. - Green
Bay Division   **(1)**
831 Radisson St, Green Bay, WI 54307-
1388
Tel.: (920) 433-5399
Sales Range: $25-49.9 Million
Emp.: 300
Paperboard Packaging Product Mfr
N.A.I.C.S.: 322212
Roy Schneider *(Gen Mgr)*

Green Bay Packaging Inc. - Green
Bay Mill Division   **(1)**
1601 N Quincy St, Green Bay, WI 54307-
9017
Tel.: (920) 433-5000
Web Site: http://www.gbp.com
Paperboard Packaging Product Mfr
N.A.I.C.S.: 322219
Bill Dyer *(Coord-Info Sys)*

Green Bay Packaging Inc. - Kalama-
zoo Division   **(1)**
5350 E Kilgore Rd, Kalamazoo, MI 49003
Tel.: (269) 552-1000
Web Site: http://www.gbp.com
Emp.: 200
Paperboard Packaging Product Mfr
N.A.I.C.S.: 322219
Dan Murphy *(Gen Mgr)*

Green Bay Packaging Inc. - Kansas
City Division   **(1)**
4342 NW Belgium Blvd, Riverside, MO
64150
Tel.: (816) 746-0808
Web Site:
  http://www.greenbaypackaging.com
Emp.: 35
Paperboard Packaging Product Mfr
N.A.I.C.S.: 322212

Green Bay Packaging Inc. - Minne-
apolis Division   **(1)**
555 87th Ln NW, Minneapolis, MN 55433
Tel.: (763) 786-7446
Web Site: http://www.gbp.com
Paperboard Packaging Product Mfr
N.A.I.C.S.: 322219

Green Bay Packaging Inc. - Pinecrest
Lumber Division   **(1)**
3610 Highway 64 E, Plumerville, AR 72127
Tel.: (501) 354-4627
Paperboard Packaging Product Mfr
N.A.I.C.S.: 322219

Green Bay Packaging Inc. - Tulsa
Division   **(1)**
6106 W 68th St, Tulsa, OK 74131-2429
Tel.: (918) 446-3341
Paperboard Packaging Product Mfr
N.A.I.C.S.: 322219

Green Bay Packaging Inc. - Twin Cit-
ies Division   **(1)**
6801 Shingle Creek Pkwy, Brooklyn Center,
MN 55430-1417
Tel.: (763) 566-1882
Paperboard Packaging Product Mfr
N.A.I.C.S.: 322212
Brain Hoppe *(Mgr)*

Green Bay Packaging Inc. - Wausau
Division   **(1)**
6845 Packer Dr, Wausau, WI 54402-1587
Tel.: (715) 845-4201
Web Site: http://www.gbp.com

Paperboard Packaging Product Mfr
N.A.I.C.S.: 322212
Devn Decker *(Gen Mgr)*

Green Bay Packaging Inc. - Win-
chester Division   **(1)**
285 Park Ctr Dr, Winchester, VA 22603
Tel.: (540) 678-2600
Paperboard Packaging Product Mfr
N.A.I.C.S.: 322219

GREEN BAY PACKERS, INC.
1265 Lombardi Ave, Green Bay, WI
54304-3927
Tel.: (920) 569-7500   WI
Web Site: https://www.packers.com
Year Founded: 1919
Sales Range: $150-199.9 Million
Emp.: 500
Professional Football Franchise
N.A.I.C.S.: 711211
Mark H. Murphy *(Pres & CEO)*
Russ Ball *(VP-Football Ops & Player
Fin)*
Brian Gutekunst *(Gen Mgr)*
Thomas L. Olson *(VP)*

GREEN BAY REMODELING, INC.
1170 Burnett Ave, Concord, CA
94520
Web Site:
  http://www.greenbayremodeling.com
Year Founded: 2012
Sales Range: $1-9.9 Million
Emp.: 20
General Contractor Services
N.A.I.C.S.: 236210
Adir Hazan *(Project Mgr)*
Allen Tal *(Project Mgr)*
Arial Ben-Shimon *(Project Mgr)*
Daniel Atal *(Project Mgr)*
David Bar *(Project Mgr)*

GREEN BAY WATER UTILITY
631 S Adams St, Green Bay, WI
54301
Tel.: (920) 448-3480
Web Site: http://www.ci.green-
  bay.wi.us
Sales Range: $10-24.9 Million
Emp.: 60
Water Supply Administration Services
N.A.I.C.S.: 924110
Kim Couillard *(Coord-Customer Bill-
ing)*
John Lake *(Coord-Equipment Mainte-
nance)*
Brian Powell *(Mgr-Engrg Svcs)*

GREEN BEANS COFFEE COM-PANY, INC.
4300 Redwood Hwy Ste100, San Ra-
fael, CA 94903
Tel.: (415) 461-4023
Web Site:
  http://www.greenbeanscoffee.com
Year Founded: 1996
Sales Range: $125-149.9 Million
Emp.: 250
Coffeehouse Operator
N.A.I.C.S.: 722513
Jason Araghi *(Pres)*
Jon Araghi *(VP)*

GREEN BOX FOODS
4355 International Blvd Ste 150, Nor-
cross, GA 30093
Tel.: (678) 739-4800
Web Site:
  http://www.greenboxfoods.com
Year Founded: 1981
Sales Range: $250-299.9 Million
Emp.: 221
Nutrition Wellness Products Grown
Naturally & Organically
N.A.I.C.S.: 456191

Green Box Foods—(Continued)

Brian Boles (Founder & Partner)
Keith Kantor (CEO)
Michael Cohen (CMO)
James Backstrom (COO)

GREEN BUILDERS, INC.
3613 Williams Dr Ste 206, George-
town, TX 78628
Tel.: (512) 688-5055
Web Site:
http://www.georgetownvillage.com
Year Founded: 1848
Real Estate Investment & Residential
Housing Development & Construction
Services
N.A.I.C.S.: 236116
William E. Weber (Pres & CEO)
Alex Hayes (Bus Mgr & Fin Mgr)

GREEN BUILDING CERTIFICA-
TION INSTITUTE
2101 L St NW Ste 500, Washington,
DC 20037
Tel.: (202) 828-1145   DC
Web Site: http://www.gbci.org
Year Founded: 2007
Sales Range: $25-49.9 Million
Energy & Environmental Design Cer-
tification Services
N.A.I.C.S.: 541620

GREEN CHEVROLET, INC.
8017 N Knoxville Ave, Peoria, IL
61615
Tel.: (309) 322-6739   DE
Web Site:
https://www.chevystore.com
Sales Range: $25-49.9 Million
Emp.: 130
New & Used Car Dealer
N.A.I.C.S.: 441110
Anthony Ficociello (Partner)
Drake Green (Owner)

GREEN CHEVROLET-BUICK-
GMC, INC.
1700 W Morton Ave, Jacksonville, IL
62650
Tel.: (217) 245-4117   DE
Web Site:
http://www.greeninjacksonville.com
Sales Range: $10-24.9 Million
Emp.: 37
New & Used Car Dealer
N.A.I.C.S.: 441110
Todd Green (Pres)

GREEN CHIMNEYS CHIL-
DREN'S SERVICES, INC.
400 Doansburg Rd, Brewster, NY
10509
Tel.: (845) 279-2995   NY
Web Site:
https://www.greenchimneys.org
Year Founded: 1947
Sales Range: $25-49.9 Million
Emp.: 600
Child & Youth Care Services
N.A.I.C.S.: 624110
Donna Kessler (Dir-HR)
Kristin Dionne (Dir-Dev)
Debbie MacCarry (Dir-Quality Assur-
ance & Compliance)

GREEN CIRCLE BIO ENERGY
INC.
2500 Green Cir Pkwy, Cottondale, FL
32431
Tel.: (850) 557-7357
Web Site:
http://www.greencirclebio.com
Sales Range: $1-9.9 Million
Emp.: 77
Alternative Energy

N.A.I.C.S.: 221117
Kelly Parker (Mgr-HR & Safety)
James Cole (Project Mgr-Ops)
Paula Smith (Mgr-Acctg)
Bobby Adams (Area Mgr)

GREEN CLOUD TECHNOLO-
GIES, LLC
411 University Ridge Ste 201, Green-
ville, SC 29601
Tel.: (864) 214-0913
Web Site:
http://www.gogreencloud.com
Sales Range: $1-9.9 Million
Emp.: 70
Cloud-Based Technology Solutions
N.A.I.C.S.: 541519
Charles S. Houser (Chm)
Shaler P. Houser (Founder)
Keith Coker (Founder & CEO)
Charles L. Houser (Founder & Exec
VP-Sls & Mktg)
Eric Hester (VP-Engrg)
Cathy McDowell (Dir-Fin)
Eric Bost (Mgr-Natl Channel)
Jonathan Nalley (Mgr-Network Ops)
Joshua Sbardella (Mgr-Customer
Ops)
Kendale Miller (Dir-Mktg)
Stephen Rieck (VP-Sls)
Jonathan Philipsen (Sr VP-Sls)

GREEN COURTE PARTNERS,
LLC
840 S Waukegan Rd Ste 222, Lake
Forest, IL 60045
Tel.: (847) 582-9400   IL
Web Site:
http://www.greencourtepartners.com
Sales Range: $25-49.9 Million
Emp.: 30
Private Equity Real Estate Investment
Firm
N.A.I.C.S.: 523999
Randall K. Rowe (Founder, Chm &
Mng Principal)
Kelly L. Stonebraker (Mng Dir & Gen
Counsel)
Stephen F. Douglass (Mng Dir-Asset
Mgmt)
David B. Lentz (Mng Dir, COO & Mng
Principal)
Antonia A. Anagnostopoulos (VP &
Controller-Portfolio)
Stephen E. Ehrlich (Mng Dir-Legal &
Deputy Gen Counsel)
Mark E. Scully (Mng Dir-Acquisitions)
William Glascott (Mng Dir-Investment)
Marnie C. Helfand (Mng Dir-Capital
Markets-Investor Relations)
Jordan T. Kerger (Mng Dir-
Acquisitions)
Tom E. Jasica (VP-Acctg &
Controller-Portfolio)
Braden L. Rudolph (Mng Dir-Portfolio
Mgmt)
Matthew J. Pyzyk (Mng Dir-
Acquisitions)
Mark K. Engel (Mng Dir & CFO)
Jeff Foland (Mng Dir)

Subsidiaries:

American Land Lease, Inc.   (1)
380 Park Pl Blvd Ste 200, Clearwater, FL
33759
Tel.: (727) 726-8868
Web Site:
http://www.americanlandlease.com
Sales Range: $25-49.9 Million
Residential Real Estate Investment Trust
N.A.I.C.S.: 525990
David B. Lentz (Pres)
Karen J. Dearingchief (Officer-Fin)

Subsidiary (Domestic):

All Homes Corp.   (2)

380 Park Place Blvd Ste 200, Clearwater,
FL 33759-4929
Tel.: (727) 726-8868
Residential Land-Lease Communities Man-
agement Services
N.A.I.C.S.: 531311
David B. Lentz (Pres)

TPS Parking Management, LLC   (1)
200 W Monroe St, Chicago, IL 60606
Tel.: (312) 453-1700
Web Site: http://www.theparkingspot.com
Sales Range: $50-74.9 Million
Holding Company; Airport Parking Facilities
Owner & Operator
N.A.I.C.S.: 551112
Mark P. Wildman (Sr VP-Mktg)
Tim Holic (Sr VP)
Todd Johnson (Sr VP-Ops)
Mary Ruberry (Sr VP-HR)
Thom Zak (VP-Sls)
John Lyons (VP-Dev)
Jeff Foland (Pres & CEO)

Subsidiary (Domestic):

PRG Parking Century, LLC   (2)
5701 W Century Blvd, Los Angeles, CA
90045
Tel.: (310) 642-0947
Web Site: http://www.theparkingspot.com
Airport Parking Facilities Operator
N.A.I.C.S.: 812930
Matt Seymour (Gen Mgr)

Unit (Domestic):

PRG Parking Management, LLC -
Atlanta   (2)
2741 Camp Creek Pkwy, Atlanta, GA 30337
Tel.: (404) 761-3300
Web Site: http://www.theparkingspot.com
Airport Parking Facilities Operator
N.A.I.C.S.: 812930
Jeff Leonard (Gen Mgr)

PRG Parking Management, LLC -
Dallas-Cedar Springs   (2)
6900 Cedar Springs Rd, Dallas, TX 75235
Tel.: (214) 350-2410
Web Site: http://www.theparkingspot.com
Airport Parking Facilities Operator
N.A.I.C.S.: 812930
Corey Bugay (Gen Mgr)

PRG Parking Management, LLC -
Dallas-Plaza Drive   (2)
6900 Cedar Springs Rd, Dallas, TX 75235
Tel.: (214) 350-2410
Web Site: http://www.theparkingspot.com
Airport Parking Facilities Operator
N.A.I.C.S.: 812930
David Cale (Gen Mgr)

PRG Parking Management, LLC -
Dallas-Valley View   (2)
1945 Valley View Ln, Irving, TX 75061
Tel.: (972) 399-7768
Web Site: http://www.theparkingspot.com
Airport Parking Facilities Operator
N.A.I.C.S.: 812930

PRG Parking Management, LLC -
Orlando   (2)
5500 Hazeltine National Dr, Orlando, FL
32812
Tel.: (407) 851-5500
Web Site: http://www.theparkingspot.com
Sales Range: $10-24.9 Million
Airport Parking Facilities Operator
N.A.I.C.S.: 812930

Subsidiary (Domestic):

Park 'N Fly, Inc.   (2)
2060 Mount Paran Rd NW Ste 207, Atlanta,
GA 30327-2935
Tel.: (404) 763-3185
Web Site: http://www.pnf.com
Real Estate Agent & Manager Services
N.A.I.C.S.: 812930
Tony Paalz (CEO)
Michael Deaderick (CFO & CTO)

GREEN CROW CORPORATION
727 E 8th St, Port Angeles, WA
98362-6448
Tel.: (360) 452-3325   WA

Web Site:
https://www.greencrow.com
Year Founded: 1983
Sales Range: $10-24.9 Million
Emp.: 59
Supplier of Durable Goods
N.A.I.C.S.: 423990
John David Crow (Co-Founder &
Chm)
Randy Johnson (Co-Founder & Gen
Mgr)
Gretchen Crow (Co-Founder & Sr
Partner)
Tyler Crow (Pres & CEO)

GREEN DIAMOND RESOURCE
COMPANY
1301 5th Ave Ste 2700, Seattle, WA
98101-2613
Tel.: (206) 224-5800
Web Site:
https://www.greendiamond.com
Timber Tract Operations
N.A.I.C.S.: 113110
Douglas Reed (Pres)
Dale Sowell (VP & CFO)
Jason Carlson (COO)
Pete Jackson (VP-California & Gen
Mgr-California)
Colin Moseley (Chm)

GREEN DOT ADVERTISING &
MARKETING
1819 W Ave Ste 5, Miami Beach, FL
33139
Tel.: (305) 674-8406
Web Site:
http://www.greendotadvertising.com
Year Founded: 1995
Sales Range: $10-24.9 Million
Emp.: 5
N.A.I.C.S.: 541810
Mario Behr (Pres)

GREEN EARTH TECHNOLO-
GIES, INC.
PO Box 4644, Greenwich, CT 06831
Tel.: (203) 918-1894   DE
Web Site: http://www.getg.com
Emp.: 1
Environmentally Safe Cleaning &
Lawn Care Products Mfr & Marketer
N.A.I.C.S.: 325612
David M. Buicko (Chm)
Walter Francis Raquet (CEO-Interim)

GREEN ENDEAVORS, INC.
59 W 100 S 2nd Fl, Salt Lake City,
UT 84101
Tel.: (801) 575-8073   UT
Salon Owner & Operator
N.A.I.C.S.: 812112
Richard D. Surber (CEO)

GREEN ENERGY MANAGE-
MENT SERVICES HOLDINGS,
INC.
575 Lexington Ave 4th Fl, New York,
NY 10022
Tel.: (212) 319-8400   DE
Web Site:
http://www.gempowered.com
Sales Range: Less than $1 Million
Emp.: 1
Energy-Saving & Water Conservation
Technologies
N.A.I.C.S.: 238210
Robert Thomson (Chm & Acting
CFO)
Barry P. Korn (CEO)

GREEN FAMILY STORES, INC.
PO Box 13315, Springfield, IL 62791
Tel.: (217) 698-3100

Web Site:
    http://greenfamilystores.com
Sales Range: $10-24.9 Million
Emp.: 36
Car Whslr
N.A.I.C.S.: 441110
Mylas Copeland (Gen Mgr-Sls)
Todd Green (Pres)
Shane Speagle (Owner & Pres)
Shane Steigel (Principal)

GREEN FORD INC.
3800 W Wendover Ave, Greensboro,
NC 27407
Tel.: (336) 439-3886
Web Site: https://www.greenford.com
Sales Range: $50-74.9 Million
Emp.: 140
Sales of Motor Vehicles
N.A.I.C.S.: 441110
H. Dean Green (Owner)

GREEN FORD SALES INC.
2104 N Buckeye Ave, Abilene, KS
67410
Tel.: (785) 263-3015
Sales Range: $25-49.9 Million
Emp.: 50
Sell & Service New & Used Automobiles
N.A.I.C.S.: 441110
Lease Duckwall (Pres)
Aileen Duckwall (VP)

GREEN GIFFORD MOTOR CORP.
2747 N Military Hwy, Norfolk, VA
23518
Tel.: (757) 855-2277
Web Site:
    http://www.greengifford.com
Sales Range: $50-74.9 Million
Emp.: 150
Car Whslr
N.A.I.C.S.: 441110
Michael Galloway (CEO)

GREEN GROUP HOLDINGS LLC
8811 Westgate Park Dr, Raleigh, NC
27617
Tel.: (919) 571-9990
Web Site:
    http://greengroupcompanies.com
Lawn Care Serviices
N.A.I.C.S.: 811411
Keith Freeman (CEO)

Subsidiaries:

Lawn Tech Inc.   (1)
302 W Smith St, Cleburne, TX 76033-5450
Tel.: (817) 558-6688
Web Site: http://www.lawntechinc.com
Architectural Services
N.A.I.C.S.: 541310
Darryle Taylor (Owner)

GREEN HILL INC.
103 Pleasant Valley Way, West Orange, NJ 07052
Tel.: (973) 731-2300   NJ
Web Site: http://www.green-hill.com
Year Founded: 1866
Sales Range: $10-24.9 Million
Emp.: 283
Lifecare Retirement Community Services
N.A.I.C.S.: 623311
Marcella M. Spezzacatena (Dir-Dining Svcs)
Iesha Carter (Dir-Nursing Svc)
Diane Lambert (Dir-Environmental Svcs)
Stephanie Hogan (Dir-Mktg)
Jackie Colao (Dir-Social Svc)
Karen E. Jung (Dir-Fin)

Donna Drake (Mgr-Home Health Nurse)
Manmah Johnson (Dir-Assisted Living Ops)
Donna Lazartic (Pres)
Lori Braender (Chm)
Raymond Williams Jr. (Dir-Plant)

GREEN HILLS SOFTWARE INC.
30 W Sola St, Santa Barbara, CA
93101-2526
Tel.: (805) 965-6044   CA
Web Site: https://www.ghs.com
Year Founded: 1982
Sales Range: $100-124.9 Million
Emp.: 160
Custom Computer Programming Services
N.A.I.C.S.: 541511
David Chandler (Sr VP-Sales)

Subsidiaries:

Green Hills Software (Israel) Ltd   (1)
Ackerstein Towers B 11 Hamenofim Street,
PO Box 12151, Herzliyya, 46733, Israel
Tel.: (972) 9 9584060
Web Site: http://www.ghs.com
Software Development Services
N.A.I.C.S.: 541511

Green Hills Software AB   (1)
Isafjordsgatan 22 B, SE 222 24, Lund,
Sweden   (100%)
Tel.: (46) 462113370
Web Site: http://www.ghs.com
Sales Range: $10-24.9 Million
Emp.: 4
Sales of Software Distr
N.A.I.C.S.: 449210

Green Hills Software BV   (1)
FokkerStraat 11, Leusden, 3833 LD,
Netherlands   (100%)
Tel.: (31) 334613363
Web Site: http://www.ghs.nl
Sales Range: $10-24.9 Million
Emp.: 10
Sales of Software
N.A.I.C.S.: 449210
Frank Vandenberg (Mng Dir)
Jeremy Flann (VP-Sls-EMEA)

Green Hills Software GmbH   (1)
Unterreut 6, Karlsruhe, 76135,
Germany   (100%)
Tel.: (49) 7219862580
Web Site: http://www.greenhills.com
Sales Range: $10-24.9 Million
Emp.: 20
Sales of Software
N.A.I.C.S.: 449210

Green Hills Software Ltd.   (1)
Fleming Business Centre, Leigh Road,
Eastleigh, SO50 9PD, Hants, United
Kingdom   (100%)
Tel.: (44) 2380649660
Web Site: http://www.ghs.com
Sales Range: $10-24.9 Million
Emp.: 4
Marketer of Software
N.A.I.C.S.: 541511

Green Hills Software Ltd.   (1)
Goodsons Mews Wellington Street, Thame,
OX9 3BX, Oxon, United Kingdom   (100%)
Tel.: (44) 1844267950
Web Site: http://www.ghs.com
Sales Range: $10-24.9 Million
Emp.: 45
Sales of Software
N.A.I.C.S.: 449210
John Williams (Gen Mgr)

Green Hills Software S.A.R.L.   (1)
4 rue de la Pierre Levee, 75011, Paris,
France   (100%)
Tel.: (33) 143 143 700
Web Site: http://www.ghs.com
Sales Range: $10-24.9 Million
Emp.: 4
Sales of Software Products
N.A.I.C.S.: 541519

Green Hills Software, Laguna
Hills   (1)

23046 Avenida De La Carlota Ste 600, Laguna Hills, CA 92653-1537
Tel.: (949) 460-6442
Web Site: http://www.ghs.com
N.A.I.C.S.: 541511

Green Hills Software, Palm
Harbor   (1)
34125 US Hwy 19 N Ste 100, Palm Harbor,
FL 34684
Tel.: (727) 781-4909
Web Site: http://www.ghs.com
Sales Range: $25-49.9 Million
Emp.: 30
Software Devolepment
N.A.I.C.S.: 541511
Jason Isaacs (Gen Counsel)
Jeffrey Hazarian (CFO)

INTEGRITY Global Security, LLC   (1)
30 W Sola St, Santa Barbara, CA 93101
Tel.: (805) 882-2500
Web Site:
    http://www.integrityglobalsecurity.com
Information Technology Consulting Services
N.A.I.C.S.: 541512
David W. Chandler (CEO)
Jimmy Sorrells (Sr VP)
Tom Zavisca (Dir-Dev)

GREEN INNOVATIONS LTD.
3208 Chiquita Blvd S Ste 216, Cape
Coral, FL 33914
Tel.: (239) 829-4372   NV
Web Site:
    http://www.greeninnovationsltd.com
Year Founded: 2008
Sales Range: $1-9.9 Million
Emp.: 4
Hygienic Household Bamboo-Based
Paper Products Mfr
N.A.I.C.S.: 322291
Bruce Harmon (Chm & Interim CFO)
Jeff Thurgood (CEO)
Alyce B. Schreiber (Pres, Interim
CEO, Treas & Sec)

GREEN LAWN FERTILIZING, INC.
1004 Saunders Lane, West Chester,
PA 19380
Web Site:
    http://www.greenlawnfertilizing.com
Year Founded: 2004
Sales Range: $1-9.9 Million
Emp.: 75
Lawn, Tree & Pest Services
N.A.I.C.S.: 561710
Matt Jesson (Owner, Pres & CEO)
Tom Knopsnyder (VP-Lawn Care
Association-Pennsylvania)
Josh Willey (CFO)

GREEN LINE EQUIPMENT, INC.
3990 W US Hwy 30, Grand Island,
NE 68803-5039
Tel.: (308) 384-8777   NE
Web Site:
    http://www.greenlineequip.com
Year Founded: 1967
Sales Range: $10-24.9 Million
Emp.: 90
Farm & Garden Machinery Dealer
N.A.I.C.S.: 441227
Russ Rerucha (Gen Mgr)
Lynos Rerucha (Pres)

Subsidiaries:

Green Line Equipment - Albion   (1)
2361 State Hwy 91, Albion, NE 68620
Tel.: (402) 395-2173
Web Site: http://www.greenlineequip.com
Sales Range: $10-24.9 Million
Emp.: 25
Farm & Garden Machinery Dealer
N.A.I.C.S.: 333111
Jim Sock (Mgr-Site)

Green Line Equipment - Norfolk   (1)
W Hwy 275, Norfolk, NE 68702-1146

Tel.: (402) 371-7333
Web Site: http://www.greenlineequip.com
Farm & Garden Machinery Dealer
N.A.I.C.S.: 441227
Dennis Smydra (Gen Mgr)

Green Line Equipment -
Spalding   (1)
N Mill St, Spalding, NE 68665
Tel.: (308) 497-2511
Web Site: http://www.greenlineequip.com
Sales Range: $1-9.9 Million
Emp.: 30
Farm & Garden Machinery Dealer
N.A.I.C.S.: 441227
Ed Bauer (Mgr-Store)

GREEN LINES TRANSPORTATION
7089 Alliance Rd NW, Malvern, OH
44644
Tel.: (330) 863-2111
Web Site: https://www.greenlines.net
Sales Range: $10-24.9 Million
Emp.: 110
Trucking Except Local
N.A.I.C.S.: 484121
Roger A. Bettis (Pres)
Brad Yoder (VP)

GREEN MOUNTAIN KNITTING INC.
28 Industrial Dr, Milton, VT 05468-3234
Tel.: (802) 865-3697
Web Site:
    http://www.greenmountainknitting.com
Year Founded: 1985
Sales Range: $10-24.9 Million
Emp.: 25
Broadwoven Fabric Mills
N.A.I.C.S.: 313210
Richard Pinchuk (Pres & CEO)
Richard Giguere (Dir-Sls & Product Dev)

GREEN OIL CO. INC.
PO Box 800, Lincoln, IL 62656-0800
Tel.: (217) 732-4107   IL
Year Founded: 1991
Sales Range: $10-24.9 Million
Emp.: 200
Provider of Petroleum Services
N.A.I.C.S.: 457120
Bob Green (Pres)

GREEN PARTS INTERNATIONAL, INC.
844 Regina Dr, Atlanta, GA 30318
Tel.: (404) 589-8000   NV
Web Site: http://www.greenparts.com
Year Founded: 1998
Rev.: $7,282,983
Assets: $5,123,813
Liabilities: $7,014,056
Net Worth: ($1,890,243)
Earnings: ($3,349,118)
Emp.: 9
Fiscal Year-end: 12/31/15
Recyclable Material Whslr
N.A.I.C.S.: 423930

GREEN POWER EMC
2100 E Exchange Pl, Tucker, GA
30084
Tel.: (770) 270-6950   GA
Web Site:
    http://www.greenpoweremc.com
Year Founded: 2001
Sales Range: $10-24.9 Million
Electric Power Distribution Services
N.A.I.C.S.: 221121
Jeff Pratt (Pres)
Chris Dillard (Vice Chm)
Wendy H. Sellers (Chm)
Randy Crenshaw (Treas & Sec)

GREEN PRODUCTS CO. INC.

Green Products Co. Inc.—(Continued)

16902 290th St, Conrad, IA 50621
Tel.: (641) 366-2001
Web Site: http://www.greenpet.com
Rev.: $10,000,000
Emp.: 48
Contract Haulers
N.A.I.C.S.: 115114
Matt Schryver (Pres)

GREEN RESOURCE, LLC.
5204 Highgreen Ct, Colfax, NC 27235
Tel.: (336) 855-6363
Web Site: https://www.green-resource.com
Year Founded: 1994
Sales Range: $10-24.9 Million
Emp.: 64
Farm Supplier & Whslr
N.A.I.C.S.: 424910
Jonathan Annas (Principal)
Todd McPeak (Principal)
Ben Holcomb (CFO)
Robert Herring (Dir-Sls & Mktg)

GREEN SPOT, INC.
100 S Cambridge Ave, Claremont, CA 91711-4842
Tel.: (909) 625-8771   CA
Web Site: https://www.greenspotusa.com
Year Founded: 1934
Sales Range: $1-9.9 Million
Emp.: 15
Fruit Drink Concentrates & Flavors Mfr & Distr
N.A.I.C.S.: 424490
Terry Hughes (VP-Sls)

GREEN STAR EXTERIORS, LLC
1914 Parker Ave, Holmes, PA 19043
Web Site: http://www.greenstarexteriors.com
Year Founded: 2014
Sales Range: $10-24.9 Million
Emp.: 50
Exterior Home Improvement Services
N.A.I.C.S.: 236118
Justin Fiordimondo (Owner & Pres)

GREEN STREET POWER PARTNERS LLC
1 Landmark Sq Ste 320, Stamford, CT 06901
Tel.: (203) 496-8950
Web Site: http://www.gspp.com
Year Founded: 2014
Sales Range: $25-49.9 Million
Emp.: 50
Solar Energy Power Generation Services
N.A.I.C.S.: 221114
Scott Kerner (CEO)
Jason Kuflik (Pres)
Debi Galler (Gen Counsel)
Christine Sheridan (CFO)
Max Whitacre (Chief Capital Markets Officer)

GREEN TEAM ADVERTISING, INC.
286 5th Ave 12th Fl, New York, NY 10001
Tel.: (212) 966-6365   NY
Web Site: http://www.greenteamusa.com
Year Founded: 1993
Sales Range: $10-24.9 Million
Emp.: 10
Advetising Agency
N.A.I.C.S.: 541810
Hugh Hough (Pres & Partner)
Jimmie Stone (Partner & Chief Creative Strategist)

Milton Kapelus (Partner & Dir-Client Svcs)
Hank Stewart (VP-Brand Strategy)
Nubia Zagami (Controller-Fin)
Joy Burka (Media Planner)
Lauren Mann (Copywriter)
Erika Perry (Sr Dir-Art)
Alison Gartner (Dir-Creative)

GREEN TECHNOLOGY SOLUTIONS, INC.
2880 Zanker Rd Ste 203, San Jose, CA 95134
Tel.: (408) 432-7285   NV
Emp.: 1
Environmentally Friendly Mining Technologies
N.A.I.C.S.: 213114
Kathleen Delaney (Interim Pres)

GREEN THREADS, LLC
6002 Loganwood Rd, Rockville, MD 20852
Tel.: (240) 461-6099
Web Site: http://www.greenthreadsllc.com
Year Founded: 2014
Sales Range: $1-9.9 Million
Emp.: 10
Identity & Access Management Services
N.A.I.C.S.: 561621
Nimish Shah (Pres & Mng Partner)
Steve Dickson (Mng Partner-Solution)
Marat Sklyarov (Mng Partner-Solution)

GREEN TOYOTA OF LEXINGTON INC.
630 New Circle Rd, Lexington, KY 40505
Tel.: (859) 254-5751
Web Site: http://www.greensbestprice.com
Year Founded: 1966
Sales Range: $75-99.9 Million
Emp.: 210
Automobiles, New & Used
N.A.I.C.S.: 441110
Curtis Green (Owner)

GREEN TREE ELECTRONIC RECYCLING, LLC
28052 Camino Capistrano, Laguna Niguel, CA 92677
Web Site: https://www.greentreeelectronicrecycling.com
Waste Recycling Services
N.A.I.C.S.: 562998

Subsidiaries:

Trinity Recyclers LLC   (1)
28052 Camino Capistrano Ste 107, Laguna Niguel, CA 92677-1106
Tel.: (949) 364-9200
Web Site: http://www.californiasrecycler.com
Nonhazardous Waste Treatment & Disposal
N.A.I.C.S.: 562219

GREEN VALLEY CHEMICAL CORP.
1284 N Cherry St Rd, Creston, IA 50801
Tel.: (641) 782-7041
Web Site: https://www.greenvalleychemical.com
Sales Range: $10-24.9 Million
Emp.: 45
Anhydrous Ammonia
N.A.I.C.S.: 325311
Doug Plambeck (COO & Plant Mgr)
Maurice Greene (Mgr-Ops)
Dwayne Smith (Mgr-Maintenance)

Jeff Hodge (Mgr-Lab)
Chris Loudon (Mgr-Ice Plant)
Brett Chapman (Mgr-IT)

GREEN VALLEY GROCERIES
1580 S Jones Blvd, Las Vegas, NV 89146-1237
Tel.: (702) 367-0056   NV
Year Founded: 1978
Sales Range: $25-49.9 Million
Emp.: 250
Convenience Store
N.A.I.C.S.: 445131
Richard Crawford (Pres)

GREEN VALLEY ONION COMPANY
310 County Route 12, New Hampton, NY 10958
Tel.: (845) 726-3315
Web Site: http://www.greenvalleyonion.com
Sales Range: $10-24.9 Million
Emp.: 24
Onion Production & Distribution Services
N.A.I.C.S.: 111219
Ed Sobiech (Pres)
Ellen Blaikner (Office Mgr)

GREEN ZEBRA MEDIA
23 Corporate Plz Dr Ste 150, Newport Beach, CA 92660-7908
Tel.: (949) 872-1965
Web Site: http://www.greenzebramedia.com
Marketing Consulting Services
N.A.I.C.S.: 541613
William C. Smith (CEO)

GREEN'S SUZUKI
674 E New Cir Rd, Lexington, KY 40505
Tel.: (859) 254-2391
Year Founded: 1991
Sales Range: $25-49.9 Million
Emp.: 70
Car Whslr
N.A.I.C.S.: 441110
Tammy Goodwin (Office Mgr)
Curtis C. Green (Pres)
C. Clay Green (VP)

GREENAUER HOLDING INC.
2699 Transit Rd, Elma, NY 14059
Tel.: (716) 675-9434
Sales Range: $10-24.9 Million
Emp.: 50
Holding Company
N.A.I.C.S.: 551112
Norman R. Merriman (Pres)
Michael J. Higgins (Treas & VP)
Charles E. Bowen (Sec & VP)

Subsidiaries:

Tom Greenauer Development, Inc.   (1)
2699 Transit Rd, Elma, NY 14059-9633
Tel.: (716) 675-9434
Commercial Surfacing & Paving Contractor
N.A.I.C.S.: 238110
Norman R. Merriman (Pres)

GREENBACKER RENEWABLE ENERGY COMPANY LLC
11 East 44th St Ste 1200, New York, NY 10017
Tel.: (646) 237-7884   DE
Web Site: http://www.greenbackerrenewableenergy.com
Year Founded: 2012
Rev.: $32,551,137
Assets: $1,582,559,120
Liabilities: $143,248,488
Net Worth: $1,439,310,632

Earnings: $2,655,809
Fiscal Year-end: 12/31/21
Investment Management Service
N.A.I.C.S.: 523940
Charles Wheeler (Chm, Pres & CEO)
Spencer Mash (Exec VP)
Michael Landenberger (Chief Acctg Officer & Chief Acctg Officer-Greenbacker Administration LLC)

Subsidiaries:

Lighthouse Finance LLC   (1)
370 Interlocken Blvd Ste 525, Broomfield, CO 80021
Tel.: (303) 444-1818
Web Site: http://www.lighthousefinancialllc.com
Financial Services
N.A.I.C.S.: 523940

GREENBACKER RENEWABLE ENERGY CORPORATION
570 Lexington Ave 48th Fl, New York, NY 10022
Tel.: (646) 651-1623   MD
Energy Related Services
N.A.I.C.S.: 221118
Charles Wheeler (Pres & CEO)
Richard Butt (CFO)

GREENBALL CORPORATION
222 S Harbor Blvd Ste 700, Anaheim, CA 92805
Tel.: (310) 669-2626   CA
Web Site: http://www.greenball.com
Year Founded: 1976
Emp.: 100
Tires & Tubes Whslr & Distr
N.A.I.C.S.: 423130
Chris Tsai (Pres)
Jenny Tsai (Sr VP)
Richard Kearney (Mgr-Product & Sls)
Michelle Roberts (Acct Mgr-Svcs)

GREENBAUM HOME FURNISHINGS
929 118th Ave SE, Bellevue, WA 98005
Tel.: (425) 454-2474
Web Site: http://www.differentbydesign.com
Year Founded: 1989
Rev.: $14,773,174
Emp.: 42
Furniture Retailer
N.A.I.C.S.: 449110
Steve S. Greenbaum (Pres)

GREENBAX ENTERPRISES INC.
176 Croghan Spur, Charleston, SC 29407
Tel.: (843) 554-9880
Web Site: http://www.thepig.net
Rev.: $458,847,673
Emp.: 15
Trading Stamp Promotion
N.A.I.C.S.: 561990
David School (Pres)
Connie Couch (VP-Acctg)
Dolly Droze (Dir-Corp Acctg)
Melody Hasch (Dir-Info Svcs)

GREENBELT CAPITAL MANAGEMENT L.P.
301 Congress Ave Ste 2050, Austin, TX 78701
Tel.: (512) 362-6260   DE
Web Site: https://www.greenbeltcapital.com
Privater Equity Firm
N.A.I.C.S.: 523999
Chris Murphy (Partner)
Sam Graham (Principal)

Subsidiaries:

Saber Power Services, LLC   (1)
3309 Texas St, Houston, TX 77003-3330
Tel.: (713) 222-9102

Web Site: http://www.saberpower.com
Architectural Services
N.A.I.C.S.: 541310
Phil Collins (Mgr)

GREENBERG FARROW AR-CHITECTURE INCORPORATED
1430 W Peachtree St NW Ste 200,
Atlanta, GA 30309
Tel.: (404) 601-4000   GA
Web Site:
http://www.greenbergfarrow.com
Year Founded: 1974
Sales Range: $50-74.9 Million
Emp.: 250
Architectural, Engineering & Real Estate Development & Consulting Firm
N.A.I.C.S.: 541330
Subsidiaries:

Greenberg Farrow Architecture Inc.,
California   (1)
19000 Macarthur Ste 250, Irvine, CA 92612
Tel.: (949) 296-0450
Web Site: http://www.greenbergfarrow.com
Sales Range: $10-24.9 Million
Emp.: 40
Providing Architectural Services
N.A.I.C.S.: 541310

Greenberg Farrow Architecture Inc.,
Illinois   (1)
21 S Evergreen Ave Ste 200, Arlington
Heights, IL 60005-1090
Tel.: (847) 788-9200
Web Site: http://www.greenbergfarrow.com
Sales Range: $25-49.9 Million
Emp.: 163
N.A.I.C.S.: 541310

Greenberg Farrow Architecture Inc.,
New York   (1)
44 W 28 St Fl 15, New York, NY 10001
Tel.: (212) 725-9530
Web Site: http://www.greenbergfarrow.com
Sales Range: $10-24.9 Million
Emp.: 16
Architectural Firm
N.A.I.C.S.: 541310

Greenberg Farrow Architecture Inc.,
Texas   (1)
Ste 125 2611 Internet Blvd, Frisco, TX
75034-9085
Tel.: (214) 975-3200
Web Site: http://www.greenbergfarrow.com
Sales Range: $10-24.9 Million
Emp.: 10
Architectural Services
N.A.I.C.S.: 541310

GREENBERG INC.
1250 53rd St Ste 5, Emeryville, CA
94608
Tel.: (510) 446-8200
Web Site:
https://www.greenberginc.com
Year Founded: 1997
Sales Range: $1-9.9 Million
Emp.: 40
Advertising & Marketing
N.A.I.C.S.: 541810
Andrew Greenberg (Founder & CEO)
Anita Kanal (VP-Brand Strategy)
Iwan Thomis (Chief Strategy Officer)
Nick Collins (Chief Client Officer-Strategy)

GREENBERG SPORTS GROUP INC.
112 Medlar Field at Lubrano Park,
University Park, PA 16802
Tel.: (814) 272-1711   PA
Web Site:
http://www.statecollegespikes.com
Year Founded: 2008
Sales Range: $25-49.9 Million
Emp.: 10
Sports Investment Holding Company
N.A.I.C.S.: 551112

Charles M. Greenberg (Owner, Pres
& CEO)
Subsidiaries:

Greensons Baseball II Inc.   (1)
1251 21st Ave N, Myrtle Beach, SC 29577
Tel.: (843) 918-6077
Sales Range: $50-74.9 Million
Holding Company; Professional Baseball
Clubs Owner & Operator
N.A.I.C.S.: 551112

Unit (Domestic):

Myrtle Beach Pelicans Baseball
Club   (2)
9550 16th St N, Saint Petersburg, FL 33716
Web Site: http://www.milb.com
Sales Range: $25-49.9 Million
Professional Baseball Club
N.A.I.C.S.: 711211
Charles M. Greenberg (Chm, Mng Partner
& Dir-League)
Fernando G. Aguirre (Executives)

Spikes Baseball LP   (1)
112 Medlar Field at Lubrano Park, University Park, PA 16802
Tel.: (814) 272-1711
Web Site:
http://www.statecollegespikes.com
Sales Range: $50-74.9 Million
Holding Company; Professional Baseball
Club Owner & Operator
N.A.I.C.S.: 551112
Charles M. Greenberg (Mng Partner)

Unit (Domestic):

State College Spikes Baseball
Club   (2)
112 Medlar Field at Lubrano Park, University Park, PA 16802
Tel.: (814) 272-1711
Web Site:
http://www.statecollegespikes.com
Sales Range: $25-49.9 Million
Professional Baseball Club
N.A.I.C.S.: 711211
Charles M. Greenberg (Chm & Mng Partner)
Rick Janac (Exec VP)
John Donley (CFO)
Dan Petrazzolo (Mgr-Ballpark Ops)
Joe Putnam (Mgr-Media Rels)
Ben Love (Mgr-Community Rels)

GREENBERG TRAURIG, LLP
1 Vanderbilt Ave, New York, NY
10017
Tel.: (212) 801-9200   NY
Web Site: https://www.gtlaw.com
Year Founded: 1999
Sales Range: $1-4.9 Billion
Emp.: 2,500
Law firm
N.A.I.C.S.: 541110
Richard A. Rosenbaum (Chm)
Martin I. Kaminsky (Gen Counsel)
Christopher J. Del Giudice (Dir-Govt
Law & Policy Practice-Albany)
Jaroslaw Grzesiak (Mng Partner-Poland)
Lejb Fogelman (Head-Mergers & Acq
Practice-Poland & Sr Partner)
Liz Dudek (Dir-Healthcare Affairs-Tallahassee)
Robert Gago (Head-Competition
Practice)
Daniel Seiden (Chm-Govt Law &
Policy Grp-Phoenix)
Brad Kaufman (Co-Pres)
John Eliason (Co-Head-Energy Project Fin-Washington D. C.)
Jeff Chester (Co-Head-Energy Project Fin-Global)
Ernest L. Greer (Co-Pres & Chm-Washington D. C.)
Subsidiaries:

Greenberg Traurig, P.A.   (1)
333 SE 2nd Ave Ste 4400, Miami, FL
33131

Tel.: (305) 579-0500
Web Site: https://www.gtlaw.com
Sales Range: $1-4.9 Billion
Emp.: 2,500
Law firm
N.A.I.C.S.: 541110
Cesar L. Alvarez (Co-Chm)
Cesar L. Alvarez (Co-Chm)
Halle R. Alexander (Atty)
Alan R. Greenfield (Atty)
Alexandra Aguirre (Atty)
William R. Clayton (Atty)
Ryan D. Bailine (Atty)
Andrew E. Balog (Atty)
David A. Barkus (Atty)
Christopher L. Barnett (Atty)
Kerri L. Barsh (Atty)

GREENBERG'S JEWELERS INC.
600 4th St Ste 1003, Sioux City, IA
51101
Tel.: (712) 255-5013   IA
Web Site:
http://www.greenbergsjewelers.com
Year Founded: 1900
Sales Range: $10-24.9 Million
Emp.: 18
Jewelry, Precious Stones & Precious
Metals Mfr
N.A.I.C.S.: 458310
Amy Greenberg-Sachnoff (Co-Pres)
Elice Greenberg (Co-Pres)
Raymond Greenberg (Dir)
Brian Maas (Dir-Ops)

GREENBRIAR EQUITY GROUP, L.P.
555 Theodore Fremd Ave Ste A 201,
Rye, NY 10580
Tel.: (914) 925-9600   DE
Web Site:
http://www.greenbriarequity.com
Year Founded: 1999
Privater Equity Firm
N.A.I.C.S.: 523999
Niall McComiskey (Mng Partner)
Jill C. Raker (Mng Partner)
Michael Weiss (Mng Partner)
Gerald Greenwald (Operating Partner)
Noah Roy (Mng Partner)
David L. Dyckman (Operating Partner)
John Anderson (Operating Partner)
Noah Blitzer (Mng Dir & Principal)
Nathan Irwin (Dir)
Michael Wang (Mng Dir)
John Clarke (CFO)
Reginald L. Jones III (Co-Founder &
Mng Partner)
Subsidiaries:

Applied Aerospace Structures,
Corp.   (1)
3437 S. Airport Wy, Stockton, CA 95206
Web Site: http://www.aascworld.com
Other Guided Missile & Space Vehicle Parts
& Auxiliary Equipment Manufacturing
N.A.I.C.S.: 336419
John Regan (Mgr-Mktg)

Arotech Corporation   (1)
1229 Oak Valley Dr, Ann Arbor, MI 48108
Tel.: (734) 761-5836
Web Site: http://www.arotech.com
Rev.: $96,599,741
Assets: $117,963,645
Liabilities: $41,187,928
Net Worth: $76,775,717
Earnings: $1,869,955
Emp.: 472
Fiscal Year-end: 12/31/2018
Zinc-Air Batteries & Vehicle Armor Mfr; Multimedia & Interactive Digital Training Systems
N.A.I.C.S.: 423830
David Modeen (Pres-Power Sys Div-United
States)
Dean M. Krutty (Pres & CEO)
Kurt A. Flosky (Pres-Trng & Simulation Div)

Yaakov Har-Oz (Gen Counsel, Sec & Sr
VP)
Jon B. Kutler (Chm)
Kelli L. Kellar (CFO & VP-Fin)
Ronen Badichi (Gen Mgr-Power Sys Div-Europe & Asia)
Colin Gallagher (Chief Acctg Officer & Controller)

Subsidiary (Domestic):

Electric Fuel Battery Corporation   (2)
354 Industry Dr, Auburn, AL 36832
Tel.: (334) 502-9001
Web Site: http://www.electric-fuel.com
Sales Range: $100-124.9 Million
Lithium Batteries Mfr
N.A.I.C.S.: 335910

Subsidiary (Non-US):

Epsilor-Electric Fuel Limited   (3)
Western Industrial Park 1 Battery Street,
Beit Shemesh, 99000, Israel
Tel.: (972) 29906666
Web Site: http://www.electric-fuel.com
Sales Range: $25-49.9 Million
Emp.: 45
Lifejacket & Electric Vehicle Mfr
N.A.I.C.S.: 336320

Subsidiary (Domestic):

FAAC, Incorporated   (2)
1229 Oak Valley Dr, Ann Arbor, MI 48108
Tel.: (734) 761-5836
Web Site: http://www.faac.com
Sales Range: $100-124.9 Million
Emp.: 125
Developer of Simulation Software
N.A.I.C.S.: 513210
Kurt A. Flosky (Pres)

Inter-Coastal Electronics, LLC   (2)
5750 E McKellips Rd, Mesa, AZ 85215
Tel.: (480) 981-6898
Web Site: http://www.inter-coastal.net
Sales Range: $10-24.9 Million
Emp.: 81
Electronic Research
N.A.I.C.S.: 541715
C. R. Kirkpatrick (Founder & CEO)
Shawn Kirkpatrick (Pres)
Evan Mussemann (Exec VP-Engrg)
Mark McKearn (VP-Programs)
Gregory Kraak (VP-Programs)

MDT Armor Corporation   (2)
308 Alabama St, Auburn, AL 36832
Tel.: (334) 321-0762
Web Site: http://www.mdt-armor.com
Sales Range: $50-74.9 Million
Emp.: 43
Mfr of Armor
N.A.I.C.S.: 336992
Jonathan Whartman (Exec VP)

UEC Electronics, LLC   (2)
5914 Howard St, Hanahan, SC 29410
Tel.: (843) 552-8682
Web Site: http://www.uec-electronics.com
Sales Range: $10-24.9 Million
Emp.: 107
Engineeering Design & Rapid Prototyping
Services
N.A.I.C.S.: 334419
Nancy Straight (Dir-Strategic Plng)
Francisca Soares (Dir-Quality Sys)

Subsidiary (Domestic):

UST-Aldetec Group   (3)
17 01 Pollitt Dr, Fair Lawn, NJ 07410
Web Site: http://www.ust-aldetec.com
Electronic Components, Sub-Assemblies &
High Performance RF/Microwave & Power
Applications Designs & Mfr
N.A.I.C.S.: 334419
Paul Skolnick (VP-Sls)

Subsidiary (Domestic):

Aldetec, Inc.   (4)
3560 Business Dr Ste 100, Sacramento, CA
95820
Tel.: (916) 453-3382
Web Site: http://www.aldetec.com
Electronic Components Mfr
N.A.I.C.S.: 334419

Greenbriar Equity Group, L.P.—(Continued)

Subsidiary (Domestic):

Pioneer Magnetics Inc. (5)
17-01 Pollitt Dr, Fair Lawn, NJ 07410
Tel.: (201) 475-8700
Web Site: http://www.pioneermagnetics.com
Electronic Parts & Equipment Merchant
Whslr
N.A.I.C.S.: 423690

Subsidiary (Domestic):

U.S. Technologies Inc. (4)
1701 Pollitt Dr, Fair Lawn, NJ 07410
Tel.: (201) 475-8700
Web Site: http://www.ustechnologies.com
Electronics Mfr
N.A.I.C.S.: 334419
Gary Grutkowski (Pres)

Chicago Switchboard Co., Inc. (1)
470 West Wrightwood Ave, Elmhurst, IL
60126
Tel.: (630) 833-2266
Web Site: http://www.chiswbd.com
Rev.: $4,578,864
Emp.: 28
Switchgear & Switchboard Apparatus Mfr
N.A.I.C.S.: 335313
Domenick Pellegrino (Engr-Sls)
Don Johnson (VP-Mfg & Engrg)
Bill Blomquist (Exec VP)
Bill Eder (VP)

JEGS Automotive Inc. (1)
101 Jegs Pl, Delaware, OH 43015
Tel.: (614) 294-5050
Web Site: http://www.jegs.com
Automotive Part & Supply Mfr & Mail-Order
Retailer
N.A.I.C.S.: 423120
George Gow (Controller)
Jeg Coughlin III (Pres)

Lube Management Corporation (1)
4511 Willow Rd, Pleasanton, CA 94588
Tel.: (925) 734-5800
Web Site: http://www.oilchangerinc.com
Provider of Oil Change Services for Auto-
mobiles
N.A.I.C.S.: 811191
Lawrence Read (Pres & CEO)
Charlie N. Pass (CFO)

Subsidiary (Domestic):

Oil Changer Inc. (2)
4511 Willow Rd Ste 1, Pleasanton, CA
94588
Tel.: (925) 734-5800
Web Site: http://www.oilchangers.com
Automotive Lubrication Service
N.A.I.C.S.: 811191
Lawrence Read (Chm, CEO & Pres)

Nordco, Inc. (1)
245 W Forest Hill Ave, Oak Creek, WI
53154
Tel.: (414) 766-2180
Web Site: http://www.nordco.com
Sales Range: $25-49.9 Million
Emp.: 175
Track Maintenance Machinery Mfr
N.A.I.C.S.: 336510
Bruce Boczkiewicz (Pres & CEO)
Jeff Roschyk (Pres-Rail)

Subsidiary (Domestic):

Royal Tractor Co., Inc. (2)
109 Overland Park Pl, New Century, KS
66031
Tel.: (913) 782-2598
Web Site: http://www.royaltractor.com
Rev.: $8,500,000
Emp.: 50
Industrial Truck, Tractor, Trailer & Stacker
Machinery Mfr
N.A.I.C.S.: 333924
Jim Hardwick (CEO)

PCX Aerostructures, LLC (1)
300 Fenn Rd, Newington, CT 06111-2244
Tel.: (860) 666-2471
Web Site: http://www.pcxaero.com
Sales Range: $75-99.9 Million
Aerospace Component Mfr
N.A.I.C.S.: 336413

Jeffry D. Frisby (Exec Chm)
Trevor Hartman (VP-Sls & Mktg)
Thomas Holzthum (CEO)

Subsidiary (Domestic):

**PCX Aerosystems – Manchester
LLC** (2)
586 Hilliard St, Manchester, CT 06042
Tel.: (860) 649-0000
Web Site: https://aerodrivesystems.com
Aircraft Engine Parts Mfr
N.A.I.C.S.: 336412

SEKO Enterprises, LLC (1)
1100 Arlington Heights Rd Ste 600, Itasca,
IL 60143
Tel.: (630) 919-4800
Web Site: http://www.sekologistics.com
Sales Range: $300-349.9 Million
Emp.: 131
Freight Transportation Arrangement
N.A.I.C.S.: 488510
Randy Sinker (Exec Mng Dir & COO)
Dan Sarna (CFO)
Shawn Richard (VP-Air Freight-Global-Seko
Logistics)
Terry Unrein (Chief Comml Officer-Seko Lo-
gistics)
James T. Gagne (Pres & CEO)
Brian Bourke (VP-Mktg)
Alfred Hofmann (Sr VP-Global Ocean
Freight)
Steen Christensen (COO-Intl)

Subsidiary (Domestic):

Air-City Inc. (2)
210 E Sunrise Hwy, Valley Stream, NY
11581
Tel.: (718) 949-2900
Web Site: http://www.air-city.com
Sales Range: $10-24.9 Million
Emp.: 20
Freight Transportation Arrangement
N.A.I.C.S.: 488510
Frank Casano (Principal & Exec VP-Intl
Forwarding Grp)
Donna Sciame (Mgr-Customer Svc)
Erika Shum (Controller)
Irene Cheung (Mgr)
William Pho (Mgr)
Chris Zheng (Exec VP)

Spireon, Inc. (1)
16802 Aston St Ste #100, Irvine, CA 92606
Tel.: (800) 557-1449
Web Site: http://www.spireon.com
Mobile Resource Management Services
N.A.I.C.S.: 541519
Tim Welch (COO & Exec VP-Shared Svcs)
Brad Jarvis (Chief Strategy Officer)
Rita Parvaneh (CFO)
Sam Balooch (CIO)
Jamie Slattery (Sr VP-Software Engrg)
Kevin Weiss (CEO)
Ed Suski (Sr VP-Hardware Engrg)
Jason Penkethman (Chief Product Officer)
Reggie Ponsford (Sr VP-Sls-Automotive
Solutions Grp)
Bob Burden (Sr VP-Sls-Fleet Div)
John Krumheuer (Pres)
Prem Hareesh (CTO)

Subsidiary (Domestic):

Inilex, Inc. (2)
4908 E McDowell Rd Ste 103, Phoenix, AZ
85008
Tel.: (480) 889-5676
Web Site: http://www.inilex.com
Sales Range: $1-9.9 Million
Emp.: 11
Security System Services
N.A.I.C.S.: 561621
Thomas Gordy (Sr VP-Customer Svc)
Michael Maledon (Pres & CEO)
Cathy Wutkowski (Dir-Ops)
Robert Chichon (CTO)
David Van Driel (Dir-Natl Bus-Fleet Div)
Cory Pace (CFO)
Brad Walls (VP-Sls)
Emily Morris (VP-Bus Dev)

Sun Auto Tire & Service, Inc. (1)
2910 North Swan Road Suite 110, Tucson,
AZ 85712
Tel.: (888) 398-8863
Web Site: https://sun.auto
Automotive Repair Services

N.A.I.C.S.: 811121
Frank Kneller (CEO)

Subsidiary (Domestic):

Boyd's Tire & Service (2)
7038 Northgate Way, Westerville, OH
43082
Tel.: (614) 899-2693
Web Site: http://www.boydstire.com
Sales Range: $1-9.9 Million
Emp.: 70
Tire Dealer Services
N.A.I.C.S.: 441340

Sun Devil Auto Parts Inc. (2)
1830 E Elliot Rd Ste 104, Tempe, AZ 85284
Tel.: (480) 491-4246
Web Site: http://www.sundevilauto.com
Rev.: $10,900,000
Emp.: 200
General Automotive Repair Shops
N.A.I.C.S.: 811111
Joel Higginbotham (Founder & Pres)

**The Facilities Group National
LLC** (1)
217 N Howard Ave Ste 200, Tampa, FL
33606
Tel.: (813) 321-7420
Web Site: https://www.thefacilitiesgroup.com
Facilities Services
N.A.I.C.S.: 561210

Subsidiary (Domestic):

**National Healthcare Resources,
Inc** (2)
535 Dock St Ste 114, Tacoma, WA 98402-
4629
Graphic Design Services
N.A.I.C.S.: 541430
Eric Hokol (Pres)

Towne Park Ltd (1)
One Park Pl Ste 200, Annapolis, MD 21401
Tel.: (410) 267-6111
Web Site: http://www.townepark.com
Sales Range: $150-199.9 Million
Valet Parking, Parking Management & Hos-
pitality Staffing Services
N.A.I.C.S.: 561320
Jerry B. South (Founder)
Andrew C. Kerin (CEO)
Andrew C. Kerin (CEO)
Steve Duffy (Sr VP-Natl Accts)
Frank Pikus (Exec VP-Ops-Healthcare)
Chuck Heskett (Pres)
Matt Cahill (Exec VP)
Dave Nichols (Vice Chm)
Mark Norwicz (CFO)
John Daniels (Sr VP-Ops)
Todd Tucker (VP-Ops)
Misti Mukherjee (Gen Counsel & Exec VP)
Beverly Valltos (Exec VP-HR)
Bryan DeCort (Sr VP-Southern Grp & Corp
Mktg)
Anthony Brown (Sr VP-HR)
Brad Miller (Sr Dir-Corp Comm)

Western Peterbilt, Inc. (1)
3801 Airport Way S, Seattle, WA 98108
Tel.: (206) 624-7383
Web Site: http://www.westernpeterbilt.com
Rev.: $79,000,000
Emp.: 50
New & Used Heavy & Medium Trucks
Sales, Leasing, Short-Term Rental, New
Parts Sales & Maintenance Services
N.A.I.C.S.: 441110
Gayle Smith (Dir-HR)
Roger Martindell (Mgr-IT)
Jim Audette (Mgr-Credit)
Cory Carneau (CFO)
Alan Womack (Mgr-Fin)
Frank Anglin (Pres & CEO)

Unit (Domestic):

Western Pacific PacLease (2)
3801 Airport Way S, Seattle, WA 98108
Tel.: (206) 624-7383
Web Site: http://www.westernpeterbilt.com
Sales Range: $25-49.9 Million
Emp.: 25
Truck Rental & Leasing Services
N.A.I.C.S.: 532120
Frank England (CEO)

Subsidiary (Domestic):

**Western Truck Parts & Equipment
Company LLC** (2)

825 Stillwater Rd, West Sacramento, CA
95605
Tel.: (916) 441-6151
Web Site: http://www.wtpe.com
Emp.: 20
Aftermarket Parts Sales, Truck Mainte-
nance, Repairs & Refuse Systems Services
N.A.I.C.S.: 423120
Frank Anglin (Pres & CEO)

Whitcraft LLC (1)
76 County Rd, Eastford, CT 06242
Tel.: (860) 289-2520
Web Site: https://www.whitcraft.com
Aerospace & Aircraft Engine Parts Mfr
N.A.I.C.S.: 336412
Jacqueline Gallo (Mgr-Strategic Ops)

GREENBRIER FARMS, INC.
225 Sign Pine Rd, Chesapeake, VA
23322
Tel.: (757) 421-2141
Web Site:
http://www.greenbrierfarms.info
Year Founded: 1916
Sales Range: $75-99.9 Million
Emp.: 8
Horticultural Products & Nursery
Stock
N.A.I.C.S.: 561730
Ryan Baker (Mgr-Ops)

**GREENCHEM INDUSTRIES
LLC**
222 Clematis St Ste 207, West Palm
Beach, FL 33401
Tel.: (561) 659-2236
Web Site:
https://www.greenchemindus
tries.com
Year Founded: 2008
Sales Range: $50-74.9 Million
Emp.: 15
Full-Service Wholesale Chemical
Distr
N.A.I.C.S.: 325110
John Lagae (Partner)
Eric Kriegisch (Gen Mgr)
Daniel Lobo (VP-Sls & Mktg)

GREENE BEVERAGE CO. INC.
6000 Grover Burchfield Dr, Tusca-
loosa, AL 35401
Tel.: (205) 345-6950
Web Site: http://greenebeverage.com
Rev.: $28,000,000
Emp.: 80
Beer & Other Fermented Malt Liquors
N.A.I.C.S.: 424810
Philip Mullin (Pres)

GREENE GROUP INC.
1300 McFarland Blvd NE Ste 300,
Tuscaloosa, AL 35406
Tel.: (205) 345-5600   AL
Year Founded: 1980
Sales Range: $25-49.9 Million
Emp.: 21
Insurance Services
N.A.I.C.S.: 524130
Scott Phelps (Pres)

Subsidiaries:

Alabama Reassurance Co. Inc. (1)
1300 McFarland Blvd Northeast Ste 300,
Tuscaloosa, AL 35406
Tel.: (205) 345-5600
Sales Range: $25-49.9 Million
Emp.: 10
Insurance Services
N.A.I.C.S.: 524113

**Texas Parimutuel Management
Inc.** (1)
1300 MacFarland Blvd, Tuscaloosa, AL
35401-1599   (100%)
Tel.: (205) 345-5600
Sales Range: $10-24.9 Million
Emp.: 11
Racing Services
N.A.I.C.S.: 457120

GREENE RESOURCES, INC.
805-400 Spring Forest Rd, Raleigh, NC 27609
Tel.: (919) 862-8602
Web Site:
http://www.greeneresources.com
Year Founded: 2000
Rev.: $33,800,000
Emp.: 32
Employment Placement Agencies
N.A.I.C.S.: 561311
Angela Grey (Div Mgr-IT & Internet Support)
Gary Greene (Pres & CEO)
Loren Nowoc (Mgr)
Sam Dufford (CFO)

GREENE RUBBER COMPANY
20 Cross St, Woburn, MA 01801
Tel.: (781) 937-9909
Web Site:
https://www.greenerubber.com
Year Founded: 1931
Emp.: 50
Molded & Fabricated Rubber Components Mfr
N.A.I.C.S.: 423840
Kevin McInerney (Mgr-Bus Dev)
Paul Gagnon (Mgr-Engrg)

GREENE'S ENERGY CORP.
1610 St Etienne Rd, Broussard, LA 70518
Tel.: (337) 232-1830
Web Site:
http://www.greenenerge.com
Year Founded: 1953
Rev.: $17,696,265
Emp.: 600
Oil Field Services
N.A.I.C.S.: 213112
Maury Dumba (Sr VP-Bus Dev)
Brad Farnsworth (CFO)
Bob Vilyus (CEO)
Antwan McMillian (Mgr-Testing & Svcs)
Terry Hatcher (VP-HR)
Brian Cooper (Key Acct Mgr)
Michael Hayes (VP & Gen Mgr-Pressure Testing, Svcs & Engrg Grp-Houston)

GREENE, TWEED & CO.
2075 Detwiler Rd, Kulpsville, PA 19443
Tel.: (215) 256-9521   PA
Web Site: https://www.gtweed.com
Year Founded: 1863
Sales Range: $150-199.9 Million
Emp.: 1,200
Gaskets, Packing & Sealing Devices
N.A.I.C.S.: 339991
Adnan Khawaja (Engr-Aerospace Product Dev)
Barry Chadwick (Mgr-Global Sls)
Glenn Doell (Sr Mgr-Advanced Tech & Bus Dev)
Les Moser (Superintendent-Maintenance)
Travis Mease (Engr-Aerospace Composites Sls)

Subsidiaries:

Greene, Tweed & Co France SAS   (1)
19 Rue Des Beaux Soleils, PO Box 409, Cergy-Pontoise, 95527, Osny, Cedex, France
Tel.: (33) 1 30 73 54 44
Industrial Machinery Mfr
N.A.I.C.S.: 333248

Greene, Tweed & Co. (Suisse) SA   (1)
Z I Le Bey 16, 1400, Yverdon-les-Bains, Switzerland
Tel.: (41) 24 447 35 70
Industrial Machinery Mfr

N.A.I.C.S.: 333248
Christian Rheault (CEO)

Greene, Tweed & Co. GmbH   (1)
Nordring 12, 65719, Hofheim, Germany
Tel.: (49) 6192 929950
Industrial Machinery Mfr
N.A.I.C.S.: 333248

Greene, Tweed & Co. Italia S.r.l.   (1)
Via Gaetano Crespi 12, 20134, Milan, Italy
Tel.: (39) 02 21 05 17 1
Industrial Machinery Mfr
N.A.I.C.S.: 333248

Greene, Tweed & Co. Japan   (1)
12F PMO Tamachi 5-31-17 Shiba, Minato-ku, Tokyo, 108-0014, Japan
Tel.: (81) 3 3454 3501
Industrial Machinery Mfr
N.A.I.C.S.: 333248

Greene, Tweed & Co. Pte Ltd.   (1)
2 Serangoon North Ave 5 04-01, Singapore, 554911, Singapore
Tel.: (65) 6555 4828
Web Site: http://www.gtweed.com
Industrial Machinery Mfr
N.A.I.C.S.: 333248

Greene, Tweed & Co., Benelux B.V.   (1)
Vang 12, Halsteren, Netherlands
Tel.: (31) 164 612 123
Web Site: http://www.gtweed.com
Emp.: 1
Industrial Machinery Mfr
N.A.I.C.S.: 333248

Greene, Tweed & Co., Korea Ltd.   (1)
22 Teheran-Ro 87-gil, Gangnam-gu, Seoul, 135 728, Korea (South)
Tel.: (82) 2 566 5244
Web Site: http://www.gtweed.com
Emp.: 16
Industrial Machinery Mfr
N.A.I.C.S.: 333248
Michael Delfino (Pres)

Greene, Tweed & Co., Limited   (1)
Ruddington Fields, Ruddington, Nottingham, NG11 6JS, United Kingdom
Tel.: (44) 115 9315 777
Industrial Machinery Mfr
N.A.I.C.S.: 333248

Palmetto Inc.   (1)
25 Engerman Ave, Denton, MD 21629-2035   (100%)
Tel.: (410) 479-2244
Rev.: $5,000,000
Emp.: 20
Mfr of Gaskets, Packing & Sealing Devices
N.A.I.C.S.: 339991

GREENELL CORP.
4243 Lonat Dr, Nazareth, PA 18064
Tel.: (908) 387-1440
Web Site:
https://www.kitchenmagic.com
Year Founded: 1979
Rev.: $10,959,763
Emp.: 190
Custom Kitchen Cabinets
N.A.I.C.S.: 337110
Brett W. Bacho (Pres)

GREENER PASTURES GROUP LLC
7700 Irvine Center Dr Ste 230, Irvine, CA 92618
Web Site:
http://www.gpgadvisers.com
Year Founded: 2009
Emp.: 20
Real Estate Advisory Services
N.A.I.C.S.: 531390
Quinn Munton (Exec Dir)

Subsidiaries:

GPG Lupine Partners   (1)
13901 Midway Rd Ste 102-428, Farmers Branch, TX 75244
Tel.: (214) 953-1032
Web Site: http://www.lupinepartners.com

Sales Range: $1-9.9 Million
Emp.: 9
Real Estate Consulting Service
N.A.I.C.S.: 531390
David Wolfe (Pres)
Brian Wood (Dir-IT)

Palazzo, Inc.   (1)
999 18th St Ste 3200, Denver, CO 80202
Tel.: (303) 575-6770
Web Site: http://www.palazzoinc.com
Sales Range: $1-9.9 Million
Emp.: 30
Real Estate Consulting Service
N.A.I.C.S.: 531390
Ed Stephens (Mgr-Fin)

GREENERPRINTER
1003 Canal Blvd, Richmond, CA 94804
Tel.: (510) 898-0000
Web Site:
https://www.greenerprinter.com
Year Founded: 1987
Sales Range: $1-9.9 Million
Emp.: 30
Printing Machinery Mfr
N.A.I.C.S.: 333248
Sarah Marth (Controller & Mgr-Fin)
Mario Assadi (CEO)

GREENEVILLE LIGHT & POWER SYSTEM
110 N College St, Greeneville, TN 37743
Tel.: (423) 636-6200
Web Site: https://www.glps.net
Year Founded: 1945
Sales Range: $50-74.9 Million
Emp.: 75
Distribution, Electric Power
N.A.I.C.S.: 221122
William Carroll (Gen Mgr)
W. T. Daniels (Chm)
Jim Glaze (Dir-Customer Svcs & Mktg)
Allen Tweed (Dir-Engrg)
Duane Wells (Dir-Tech Svcs)

GREENEVILLE OIL & PETRO-LEUM INC.
860 W Andrew Johnson Hwy, Greeneville, TN 37745
Tel.: (423) 638-3145
Web Site:
https://www.greeneville oil.com
Sales Range: $25-49.9 Million
Emp.: 400
Crude Oil Distributor
N.A.I.C.S.: 424720
Allen Johnson (Owner & Pres)

GREENFIELD BANCORPORA-TION LTD.
214 S 1st St, Greenfield, IA 50849-1470
Tel.: (641) 343-7310
Web Site: http://www.usbgfd.com
Offices of Bank Holding Companies
N.A.I.C.S.: 551111
Peg Scott (CEO)

Subsidiaries:

Union State Bank   (1)
214 S 1st St, Greenfield, IA 50849
Tel.: (641) 343-7310
Web Site: https://www.usbgfd.com
Commercial Banking Services
N.A.I.C.S.: 522110
Matt Mensing (Pres)

GREENFIELD BANCSHARES INC.
1920 N State St, Greenfield, IN 46140
Tel.: (317) 462-1431
Web Site: https://www.gbcbank.com
Rev.: $15,436,056

Emp.: 150
Bank Holding Company
N.A.I.C.S.: 551111
Bradley J. Herndon (VP)
Marcia Foster (VP)
Vickie M. Mattox (Sr VP)
Judy J. Swift (Asst VP)
Ronald D. Ward (VP)
Janie Fink (Asst Branch Mgr)
Stephen E. Wilson (VP)
Renee Rupley (VP & Dir-Mktg)
Deborah Shipp (Mgr-Acctg)
Anecea Woodrow (Asst Dir-Mktg)
Leslie Frady (Asst VP & Mgr)
Mark Griffin (Asst VP & Loan Officer)
Rosemary Robertson (Dir-HR)
Patricia Jessie (VP)
Susan Davis (Asst Branch Mgr)
John Kennedy (Pres & CEO)

Subsidiaries:

Greenfield Banking Company   (1)
1920 N State St, Greenfield, IN 46140
Tel.: (317) 462-1431
Web Site: http://www.gbcbank.com
Sales Range: $250-299.9 Million
Emp.: 56
State Commercial Banks
N.A.I.C.S.: 522110
John M. Kennedy (Pres & CEO)
John Lee (Officer-Trust & VP)
Jeffrey E. Somers (Officer-Bus Dev & VP)
Susan Wildey (Officer-Trust & VP)
Victor A. Melchiorre (Chief Risk Officer)
Brad McClarnon (Officer-Loan & Asst VP)
Michelle Webb (Officer-Compliance, CRA, HMDA & Privacy)
Miranda Cook (Officer-Trust)
Stacey Wixson (Officer-Trust)

GREENFIELD GOLF, L.L.C.
10325 Greenfield Blvd, Bradenton, FL 34212
Tel.: (941) 747-9432
Web Site:
http://www.linksatgreenfieldplantation.com
Sales Range: $1-9.9 Million
Golf Course Owner & Operator
N.A.I.C.S.: 713910
Anthony Soletti (Owner)
Andrew Dlugos (Gen Mgr)

GREENFIELD PARTNERS LLC
2 Post Rd W, Westport, CT 06880
Tel.: (203) 354-5000
Web Site:
https://www.greenfieldpartners.com
Sales Range: $25-49.9 Million
Emp.: 45
Private Equity Firm
N.A.I.C.S.: 523999
Eugene A. Gorab (Founder, Pres & CEO)
Dean A. Sotter (COO)
Paul Altieri (CFO & Principal)
Barry P. Marcus (Principal)
Michael B. Bradley (Chief Investment Officer)
Rajesh Menon (Principal)
James Stan Nix (Principal)
Frank Cartolano (Mng Dir)
Jeff Usas (Mng Dir)
Alex Ching (Mng Dir)
Brandon Bass (VP)
Brian Orr (Chief Acctg Officer)
Bridget Bartmann (VP-IR)
Eli Boyajian (CTO)
Elizabeth C. Wohlleb (Mng Dir)
Eric Freeman (Mng Dir)
Gary Dienst (Mng Dir)
Matthew Lewis (VP)
Michael Paloian (VP)
Michael Baldwin (VP)
Robert A. Hernandez (VP)
Trevor K. Oliff (VP)

GREENFIELD RESEARCH, INC.

Greenfield Research, Inc.—(Continued)

347 Edgewood Ave, Greenfield, OH
45123
Tel.: (937) 981-2154
Web Site: http://www.greenfield-
research.com
Year Founded: 1968
Sales Range: $10-24.9 Million
Emp.: 300
Mfr of Cut & Sew Trim, Wires & Rein-
forcement Products
N.A.I.C.S.: 314999
Michael Penn *(Pres)*
Robert Snider *(Treas)*
Bruce Decker *(Mgr-Operating)*
Marcus Bradley *(Controller)*

GREENFIELD SAVINGS BANK
400 Main St, Greenfield, MA 01301
Tel.: (413) 774-3191
Web Site:
http://www.greenfieldsavings.com
Sales Range: $10-24.9 Million
Emp.: 100
Savings Institutions, Except Federal
N.A.I.C.S.: 522180
William Granger *(CIO)*
Kevin DeRosa *(VP-Retail Distr Net-
work)*
Thomas Meshako *(Pres & CEO)*
John Fortier III *(Mgr-Fin Reporting)*

**GREENFIELD SENIOR LIVING
INC.**
6312 Seven Corners Ctr #161, Falls
Church, VA 22044-2409
Tel.: (703) 237-5606
Web Site:
http://www.greenfieldseniorli
ving.com
Senior Living Facilities
N.A.I.C.S.: 623110
Mathew A. Peponis *(Chm & CEO)*
Thomas K. Scanlon *(CFO)*
Jonathan Barbieri *(VP-Mktg)*
Kevin J. Bonello *(VP-IT)*

GREENFIELD WINE COMPANY
205 Jim Oswald Way Ste B, Ameri-
can Canyon, CA 94503
Tel.: (707) 552-5984
Sales Range: $10-24.9 Million
Emp.: 50
Winery
N.A.I.C.S.: 424820
Tony Cartlidge *(Pres)*

**GREENFIELDS PETROLEUM
CORPORATION**
2001 Timberloch Pl Ste 500, The
Woodlands, TX 77380
Tel.: (832) 234-0800   DE
Web Site: http://www.greenfields-
petroleum.com
Year Founded: 2010
Rev.: $30,962,000
Assets: $193,471,000
Liabilities: $70,202,000
Net Worth: $123,269,000
Earnings: $10,655,000
Fiscal Year-end: 12/31/18
Petroleum Exploration Services
N.A.I.C.S.: 211120
John W. Harkins *(Pres, CEO & COO)*
Sanjay Swarup *(CFO & Treas)*

GREENGEEKS, LLC.
5739 Kanan Rd Ste 300, Agoura
Hills, CA 91301
Tel.: (310) 496-8946
Web Site:
http://www.greengeeks.com
Year Founded: 2008
Sales Range: $1-9.9 Million
Emp.: 28
Web Hosting Services

N.A.I.C.S.: 518210
Trey Gardner *(CEO)*

**GREENHECK FAN CORPORA-
TION**
1100 Greenheck Dr, Schofield, WI
54476-1854
Tel.: (715) 355-6171   WI
Web Site: http://www.greenheck.com
Year Founded: 1947
Sales Range: $350-399.9 Million
Emp.: 2,200
Air Moving & Control Equipment Mfr
N.A.I.C.S.: 333413
Robert C. Greenheck *(Chm)*

GREENHILL AIR, INC.
2220 S Burleson Blvd, Burleson, TX
76028
Tel.: (817) 293-2322
Web Site: http://www.greenhillair.com
Year Founded: 1999
Sales Range: $10-24.9 Million
Emp.: 7
Air Conditioning Contractor
N.A.I.C.S.: 238220
David Greenhill *(Pres)*
Mike Greenhill *(VP)*

GREENHOUSE SCHOLARS
1881 9th St Ste 200, Boulder, CO
80302
Tel.: (720) 449-7444   CO
Web Site:
http://www.greenhousescholars.org
Year Founded: 2005
Sales Range: $1-9.9 Million
Emp.: 16
Leadership Development Association
N.A.I.C.S.: 813920
Andra Pool *(Chief Relationship &
Community Officer)*
Pete Burridge *(Pres & CEO)*

**GREENHOUSE SOFTWARE,
INC.**
18 W 18th St 11th Fl, New York, NY
10011
Tel.: (917) 780-4130
Web Site: http://www.greenhouse.io
Year Founded: 2012
Sales Range: $25-49.9 Million
Emp.: 267
Software Development Services
N.A.I.C.S.: 541511
Daniel Chait *(Founder & CEO)*

**GREENHUNTER RESOURCES,
INC.**
1048 Texan Trail, Grapevine, TX
76051
Tel.: (972) 410-1044   DE
Web Site: http://www.greenhunterre
sources.com
Year Founded: 2005
Sales Range: $25-49.9 Million
Renewable Energy Resources
N.A.I.C.S.: 221122
Kirk J. Trosclair *(COO)*
Paul Falgoust *(VP-Environmental So-
lutions Bus)*
Melissa Pagen *(Asst VP-Investor
Comm)*
Robert Sloan *(Sr VP-Ops)*
Morgan F. Johnston *(Gen Counsel,
Sec & Sr VP)*
Morgan F. Johnston *(Gen Counsel,
Sec & Sr VP)*
Ronald McClung *(CFO & Sr VP)*

Subsidiaries:

Blue Water Energy Solutions,   (1)
LLC
3459 Acworth Due W Rd Ste 206, Acworth,
GA 30101
Tel.: (678) 594-2058

Web Site:
http://www.bluewaterenergysolutions.com
Management Consulting Services
N.A.I.C.S.: 541618

GreenHunter Environmental Solu-   (1)
tions, LLC
1048 Texan Trail, Grapevine, TX 76051
Tel.: (972) 410-1044
Oil & Gas Tank Cleaning Services
N.A.I.C.S.: 213112
Paul Falgoust *(VP-Bus Dev & Ops)*

Hunter Disposal, LLC   (1)
38505 Marietta Rd, Dexter City, OH 45727
Tel.: (740) 783-2233
Oil & Gas Exploration Services
N.A.I.C.S.: 213112

**GREENHUT CONSTRUCTION
COMPANY, INC.**
23 S A St, Pensacola, FL 32502
Tel.: (850) 433-5421   FL
Web Site: https://www.greenhut.com
Year Founded: 1946
Sales Range: $25-49.9 Million
Emp.: 50
Commercial & Office Building, New
Construction
N.A.I.C.S.: 236220
Dudley H. Greenhut *(Founder, Chm &
CEO)*
Rachel Reyes *(CFO)*
Bill Greenhut *(Pres)*

GREENIX LLC
1280 S 800 E, Orem, UT 84097
Tel.: (614) 328-8013
Web Site: http://www.greenixpc.com
Year Founded: 2011
Sales Range: $10-24.9 Million
Emp.: 617
Environmental Services
N.A.I.C.S.: 541620
Parker Steffensen *(Sls Mgr-Area)*

GREENLAND (AMERICA) INC.
1905 Woodstock Rd Ste 2200, Ro-
swell, GA 30075
Tel.: (770) 435-1100
Web Site:
https://www.greenlandamerica.com
Year Founded: 1996
Rev.: $79,300,000
Emp.: 30
Recyclable Material Merchant Whslr
N.A.I.C.S.: 423930
Vishal Jatia *(Mgr-Pur)*
Suresh Jatia *(Pres)*
Dhaval Virpariya *(Mgr-Logistics)*

**GREENLEAF BOOK GROUP,
LLC**
PO Box 91869, Austin, TX 78709
Tel.: (512) 891-6100   TX
Web Site: https://www.greenleafbook
group.com
Year Founded: 1997
Sales Range: $25-49.9 Million
Emp.: 35
Book Publishing & Consulting Ser-
vices
N.A.I.C.S.: 513130
Nathan DeLacretaz *(Mgr-Info Sys)*
Tanya Hall *(CEO)*
Brian Viktorin *(CFO)*
Corrin Foster *(Dir-Mktg & Branding)*
Neil Gonzalez *(Dir-Art)*
Carrie Jones *(Dir-Production)*
Tyler LeBleu *(Mgr-Production)*
Jen Glynn *(Project Mgr)*

GREENLEAF CORPORATION
18695 Greenleaf Dr, Saegertown, PA
16433
Tel.: (814) 763-2915
Web Site:
http://www.greenleafcorporation.com

Year Founded: 1945
Sales Range: $10-24.9 Million
Emp.: 282
Machine Tool Accessories Whslr
N.A.I.C.S.: 333515
Kari Carpenter *(Asst Mgr-Mktg)*
Daniel Duckworth *(Mgr-Laboratories)*
Jack Kohler *(Engr-Applications)*
Jim Wyant *(Engr-Applications & Proj-
ect Dev)*
Travis Biggs *(Reg Mgr)*
Greg Bronson *(Engr-Sls & Svc)*
Joseph Mawn *(Plant Mgr)*
Jan Andersson *(Global Mgr-Tech &
Mktg)*
Bernie McConnell *(Exec VP-Comml)*

**GREENLEAF ENVIRONMEN-
TAL GROUP, INC.**
4943 Austin Park Ave, Buford, GA
30518
Tel.: (678) 714-8420
Web Site:
http://www.greenleafgroup.net
Year Founded: 2001
Sales Range: $25-49.9 Million
Emp.: 30
Environmental Services
N.A.I.C.S.: 562910

**GREENLEAF NURSERY CO.
INC.**
28406 Highway 82, Park Hill, OK
74451-2845
Tel.: (918) 457-5172   OK
Web Site:
https://www.greenleafnursery.com
Year Founded: 1945
Sales Range: $25-49.9 Million
Emp.: 1,200
Ornamental Nursery Products
N.A.I.C.S.: 111421
Randy Davis *(Pres)*

**GREENLEAF WHOLESALE
FLORIST INC.**
2112 Leeland St, Houston, TX 77003
Tel.: (303) 659-8000   CA
Web Site:
http://www.greenleafwholesale.com
Year Founded: 1959
Sales Range: $25-49.9 Million
Emp.: 270
Flowers & Florists Supplies
N.A.I.C.S.: 424930
Conrad Gaboriau *(Controller-Fin)*
Geoff Wiltjer *(Mgr-IT)*
Robert Kitayama *(Pres)*
Rob Spikol *(COO)*

**GREENLEAF-TNX SIKH SO-
LAR, LLC**
3325 Melendy Dr, San Carlos, CA
94070
Tel.: (650) 576-6876
Web Site:
http://www.greenleaftnx.com
Year Founded: 2011
Solar Power & Other Renewable En-
ergy Asset Management Services
N.A.I.C.S.: 523940
Charlie Fiechter *(Mgr)*
Linda Kong *(Mgr)*
Thomas Yap *(Mgr)*

GREENLIGHT CAPITAL, INC.
2 Grand Central Tower 140 E 45th St
24th Fl, New York, NY 10017
Tel.: (212) 973-1900   DE
Web Site:
http://www.greenlightcapital.com
Year Founded: 1996
Emp.: 45
Investment Management Service

N.A.I.C.S.: 523940
Sean Farrell *(Chief Compliance Officer)*
David Michael Einhorn *(Pres)*

GREENLINK FINANCIAL, LLC
3 MacArthur Pl Ste 1000, Santa Ana, CA 92707
Tel.: (949) 396-0923
Web Site:
http://www.greenlinkfunding.com
Year Founded: 2014
Sales Range: $25-49.9 Million
Emp.: 60
Financial Investment Services
N.A.I.C.S.: 523940
Eric Heller *(Mng Partner)*

GREENLINKS GOLF VILLAS
7995 Mahagony Run Ln, Naples, FL 34113-1624
Tel.: (239) 732-9920
Web Site:
https://www.greenlinksnaples.com
Sales Range: $10-24.9 Million
Emp.: 15
Golf Resort
N.A.I.C.S.: 721110
Randy A. Bayard *(Gen Mgr)*
Dan Sullivan *(Dir-Sls & Mktg)*
Samantha Hendricks *(Mgr-Guest Svcs)*

GREENLOGIC ENERGY
425 Country Rd 39A Ste 101, Southampton, NY 11968
Tel.: (631) 771-5152
Web Site: http://www.greenlogic.com
Year Founded: 2005
Sales Range: $10-24.9 Million
Emp.: 40
Alternative Energy Solutions & Installations
N.A.I.C.S.: 221118
Marc Clejan *(Co-Founder & Mng Dir)*
Nesim Albukrek *(Co-Founder & Mng Dir)*
Jean Pierre Clejan *(Mgr-Sls & Engr)*
Cheryl Monter *(Mgr-Ops)*

GREENLOOP IT, INC.
1800 Paxton St, Harrisburg, PA 17104
Tel.: (717) 233-6650
Web Site: http://greenloopit.com
Year Founded: 1991
Sales Range: $10-24.9 Million
Emp.: 71
Holding Company: Environmentally-Conscious Technology After-Market Products
N.A.I.C.S.: 551112
George H. Crist *(CEO)*
Adam B. Crockett *(Pres-GreenLoop IT & Sr VP-Sls/Mktg-PC Parts)*

Subsidiaries:

PC Parts, Inc. (1)
1800 Paxton St, Harrisburg, PA 17104
Tel.: (717) 233-6650
Web Site: http://www.pcpartsinc.com
Out-of-Warranty IT Replacement & Spare Parts & Computer Peripheral Equipment & Software Merchant Distr
N.A.I.C.S.: 423430
George H. Crist *(Pres & CFO)*
Adam B. Crockett *(Sr VP-Sls & Mktg)*
Adam Akers *(Dir-IT)*
Matt Arnold *(Dir-Sls & Mktg)*

GREENMAN-PEDERSEN, INC.
325 W Main St, Babylon, NY 11702
Tel.: (631) 587-5060
Web Site: https://www.gpinet.com
Engineeering Services
N.A.I.C.S.: 541330

Christer Ericsson *(Pres & CEO)*
Steve Greenman *(Chm)*

Subsidiaries:

Horizon Engineering Group, Inc. (1)
2500 Maitland Center Pkwy, Maitland, FL 32751
Tel.: (407) 644-7755
Web Site: http://www.horizoncivil.com
Rev.: $1,200,000
Emp.: 15
Engineeering Services
N.A.I.C.S.: 541330
Michele Verner *(Controller & Mgr-Bus)*
Chris McDaniel *(Dir-Mktg)*

GREENOAKS CAPITAL PARTNERS LLC
1 Letterman Dr Bldg A Ste 500, San Francisco, CA 94129
Tel.: (415) 942-5322   DE
Web Site: https://greenoaks.com
Privater Equity Firm
N.A.I.C.S.: 523999

Subsidiaries:

Farfetch Limited (1)
The Bower 211 Old Street, London, EC1V 9NR, United Kingdom
Tel.: (44) 2035100670
Web Site: https://www.farfetch.com
Rev.: $2,316,680,000
Assets: $3,675,916,000
Liabilities: $2,770,295,000
Net Worth: $905,621,000
Earnings: $344,855,000
Emp.: 6,728
Fiscal Year-end: 12/31/2022
Online Fashion Retailer
N.A.I.C.S.: 458110
Jose Neves *(Founder, Chm & CEO)*

Subsidiary (Non-US):

Farfetch Portugal - Unipessoal, Lda (2)
Rua Da Lionesa N 446 Edificio G12, Leca Do Balio, 4465-671, Porto, Portugal
Tel.: (351) 220430530
Web Site: https://www.farfetch.com
N.A.I.C.S.: 458110

New Guards Group Holding S.p.A (2)
Via Filippo Turati 12, 20121, Milan, Italy
Tel.: (39) 0283997000
Web Site: https://newguardsgroup.com
N.A.I.C.S.: 315990

GREENOUGH COMMUNICATIONS
1 Brook St, Watertown, MA 02472
Tel.: (617) 275-6500
Web Site: http://www.greenough.biz
Year Founded: 1999
Sales Range: $10-24.9 Million
Emp.: 50
Public Relations & Communications
N.A.I.C.S.: 541820
Phil Greenough *(Founder & CEO)*
Scott Bauman *(Exec VP & Gen Mgr)*
Ed Coletti *(Exec VP-Ops)*
Paul Greenough *(VP-IT)*
Amy McHugh *(VP)*
Rachel Robbins *(Sr VP)*

GREENPAGES, INC.
33 Badgers Is W, Kittery, ME 03904
Tel.: (207) 439-7310
Web Site:
http://www.greenpages.com
Sales Range: $125-149.9 Million
Emp.: 190
Computer System Integration Services
N.A.I.C.S.: 541512
Ron Dupler *(CEO)*
Andrew Lally *(Pres)*
Stephen Manero *(CFO)*
Joshua Dinneen *(Pres-Strategic Svcs)*

Jay Keating *(Sr VP-Svc Delivery & Managed Svcs)*
Jeanne Raney *(Sr VP-HR)*

Subsidiaries:

GreenPages (1)
5680 W Cypress St Ste 5680, Tampa, FL 33607
Tel.: (813) 387-5444
Web Site: http://www.greenpages.com
Sales Range: $10-24.9 Million
Emp.: 8
Communication Equipment Mfr
N.A.I.C.S.: 334290
Daniel Boone *(Dir-Sls)*

Sovereign Systems LLC (1)
3930 E Jones Bridge Rd, Norcross, GA 30092
Tel.: (844) 727-3622
Web Site: http://www.sovsystems.com
Sales Range: $25-49.9 Million
Emp.: 15
It Consulting
N.A.I.C.S.: 541690

GREENPATH INC
36500 Corporate Dr, Farmington Hills, MI 48331
Tel.: (248) 553-5400
Web Site: https://www.greenpath.com
Sales Range: $10-24.9 Million
Emp.: 200
Debt Counseling Or Adjustment Service Individuals
N.A.I.C.S.: 812990
Jane E. McNamara *(Pres & CEO)*
Nicole Bladzik *(Mgr-Bus Analyst)*
Danielle Crane *(Dir-HR)*

GREENPEACE, INC.
702 H St NW Ste 300, Washington, DC 20001
Tel.: (202) 462-1177
Web Site:
https://www.greenpeace.org
Sales Range: $25-49.9 Million
Emp.: 185
Environmental Conservation Organization
N.A.I.C.S.: 813312
Britt Cocanour *(Dir-Pub Outreach)*
Corrine Barr *(Mgr-Gift Plng)*
Michael Leon Guerrero *(Treas)*
Karen Topakian *(Chm)*

GREENPOWER INTERNATIONAL GROUP LIMITED
1311 S Bromley Ave, West Covina, CA 91790
Tel.: (312) 622-7670   DE
Sales Range: Less than $1 Million
Emp.: 2
LED Lighting Mfr
N.A.I.C.S.: 335132
Xiaoping Liu *(Pres & CEO)*

GREENRIDGE INVESTMENT PARTNERS
3600 N Capital of Texas Hwy Bldg B Ste 150, Austin, TX 78746
Tel.: (512) 505-4113
Web Site:
http://www.greenridgeinv.com
Investment Services
N.A.I.C.S.: 523999
Jack Cardwell *(Co-Founder & Partner)*
Ben Moss *(Co-Founder & Partner)*
Gary Loudamy *(Operating Partner)*
James Baker *(VP)*

Subsidiaries:

GrowthZone, Inc. (1)
4837 County Rd 77, Nisswa, MN 56468
Tel.: (218) 825-9200
Web Site: http://www.growthzone.com
Association Management Software
N.A.I.C.S.: 513210

Scott Juranek *(CEO)*
John Cook *(VP-Mktg)*

Subsidiary (Domestic):

BuilderFusion, Inc. (2)
424 W 800 N Ste 202, Orem, UT 84057-3728
Tel.: (801) 765-8017
Web Site: http://www.builderfusion.com
Software & Technology Development Services
N.A.I.C.S.: 513210
Craig Weston *(Founder & Pres)*
David Baird *(Gen Mgr)*

GREENROPE, LLC
249 S Hwy 101 Ste 525 Solana Beach, San Diego, CA 92075
Tel.: (442) 333-7577
Web Site: http://www.greenrope.com
Year Founded: 2008
Business Marketing Software
N.A.I.C.S.: 513210
Lars Helgeson *(CEO & Founder)*
Alessandra Ceresa *(Mgr-Mktg)*
Lyle Hopkins *(CTO)*
Matt Stewart *(Mgr-Sales)*
Ryan Bahl *(Creative Dir)*
Diana Kohan *(Mgr-Client Svcs)*
Jill Dimel *(Mgr-ISP Rels)*
Melissa Filich *(Program Mgr-GreenRope Certification)*

GREENRUBINO
1938 Fairview Ave E Ste 200, Seattle, WA 98102
Tel.: (206) 447-4747
Web Site:
http://www.greenrubino.com
Year Founded: 1977
Rev.: $21,500,000
Emp.: 45
N.A.I.C.S.: 541810
Cameron Green *(CEO & Creative Dir)*
Mark DeJarnett *(Media Dir)*
John Rubino *(Pres)*
Chris Dressler *(Dir-Digital Interactive)*
Hamilton McCulloh *(Dir-PR)*
Crystal Inge *(Dir-Acct Svc)*
Kevin Dillon *(Dir-New Bus)*
Phil Stafford *(Dir-Retail Strategy)*
Dennis C. Budell *(Assoc Dir-Creative)*

GREENS FARMS CAPITAL LLC
17 Harding Ln, Westport, CT 06880
Tel.: (917) 743-0527
Web Site:
https://www.greensfarmscapital.com
Privater Equity Firm
N.A.I.C.S.: 523999

Subsidiaries:

919 Marketing Company (1)
102 Avent Ferry Rd, Holly Springs, NC 27540
Tel.: (919) 557-7890
Web Site: http://www.919marketing.com
Sales Range: $1-9.9 Million
Emp.: 50
Marketing Services
N.A.I.C.S.: 541613
David Chapman *(Founder & CEO)*
Sue Yannello *(Exec VP)*
Graham Chapman *(VP-Acct Svcs)*
Scott Curkin *(VP-Acct Svcs)*
Nancy Bostrom *(Sr Acct Mgr)*

Subsidiary (Domestic):

Fish Consulting, LLC (2)
117 NE 2nd St, Fort Lauderdale, FL 33301
Tel.: (954) 893-9150
Web Site: http://www.fish-consulting.com
Public Relations Services
N.A.I.C.S.: 541820
Jenna Kantrowitz *(COO & Sr VP)*
Chad Cohen *(Sr VP)*
Kim Ryan *(VP)*

Greens Farms Capital LLC—(Continued)

Becky Peterson (Sr Acct Dir)
Lorne Fisher (CEO & Mng Partner)
Samantha Russo (Acct Mgr)
Ellie Mannix (Acct Mgr)
Tiffany Trilli (Acct Coord)
Sloane Fistel (Acct Exec)
Andie Biederman (Mgr-Acct)
Ashley Reynolds (Mgr-Social Media)
Claibourne Smith (Mgr-Acct)
Elayne Sommers (Sr Acct Mgr)
Rachel Tabacnic (Sr Acct Mgr)
Amanda Bortzfield (Sr Dir-Acct)
Lauren Simo (Sr Dir-Acct)
Julia Block (Dir-Acct)
Michelle Estevam (Sr Acct Mgr)
Courtney Whelan (Acct Exec)
Caitlin Willard (Acct Exec)
Chelsea Bear (Coord-Acct)

GREENSBORO COUNTRY CLUB

410 Sunset Dr, Greensboro, NC 27408
Tel.: (336) 275-8506 NC
Web Site:
https://www.greensborocc.org
Year Founded: 1941
Sales Range: $10-24.9 Million
Emp.: 400
Country Club Operator
N.A.I.C.S.: 713910
William E. Stone (CFO)
C. Earl Anderson (Gen Mgr)
Jim Deaton (Dir-Golf)

GREENSCAPE, INC.

2360 Broad St, Holly Springs, NC 27540
Tel.: (919) 552-7742 NC
Web Site:
https://www.greenscapeinc.com
Year Founded: 1979
Emp.: 100
Landscaping Services
N.A.I.C.S.: 561730
Daniel Currin (Pres & CEO)

Subsidiaries:

Turftenders Landscape Services
Inc (1)
2610 Rowland Rd, Raleigh, NC 27615
Tel.: (919) 878-4441
Web Site: http://www.turftenders.com
Landscaping Services
N.A.I.C.S.: 561730
Steve Hill (Pres)

GREENSCAPES OF SOUTH-WEST FLORIDA, INC.

14370 Collier Blvd, Naples, FL 34119
Tel.: (239) 643-4471 FL
Web Site:
http://www.greenscapesfl.com
Year Founded: 1962
Sales Range: $10-24.9 Million
Emp.: 2,340
Landscaping Services
N.A.I.C.S.: 561730
Linda Rae Nelson (Pres)
Jami McGarvey (VP-Client Svcs)
Rafael Jimenez (Dir-Ops)
Dusty Fontaine (Dir-Irrigation)

GREENSOURCE CORPORATION

677 7th Ave Ste 410, San Diego, CA 92101
Tel.: (760) 390-8350
Sales Range: $10-24.9 Million
Sustainable Development Services
N.A.I.C.S.: 541620
Tad Simmons (Pres & CEO)

Subsidiaries:

GS EnviroServices, Inc. (1)
411 Hackensack Ave, Hackensack, NJ 07601

Tel.: (424) 341-2522
Emp.: 1
Wastewater Treatment Technologies
N.A.I.C.S.: 562219
Kevin E. Kreisler (CEO & CFO)

GREENSPOON MARDER LLP

200 E Broward Blvd Ste 1800, Fort Lauderdale, FL 33301
Tel.: (954) 491-1120
Web Site: http://www.gmlaw.com
Year Founded: 1981
Law firm
N.A.I.C.S.: 541110
William Berger (Partner)
Alan B. Cohn (Partner)
Joseph Geller (Partner)
Michael J. Alman (Partner)
Rebecca Faith Bratter (Deputy Mng Partner)
Leonard Lubart (Partner)
Mark Lynn (Partner)
David Merkur (Partner)
Steven Wherry (Partner)
Lee F. Lasris (Partner)
Richard W. Epstein (Partner & Chm-Litigation)
Gene K. Glasser (Partner)
Haas Hatic (Partner)
Evan B. Klinek (Partner)
Jessica Wasserman (Partner-Washington)
Germain D. Labat (Partner-Los Angeles)
Michael Marder (Co-Mng Dir)
Myrna Maysonet (Partner & Chief Diversity Officer)
Gerald Greenspoon (Co-Mng Dir)
John A. Gelety (Atty)

Subsidiaries:

Handal & Associates, Inc. (1)
401 W A St Ste 1150, San Diego, CA 92101
Tel.: (619) 544-6400
Web Site: http://www.gmlaw.com
Law firm
N.A.I.C.S.: 541199
Anton N. Handal (Partner)

GREENSPRING AT MT. SNOW HOMEOWNER'S ASSOCIATION, INC.

Route 100, West Dover, VT 05356
Tel.: (802) 464-7111
Web Site:
http://www.greenspringhoa.net
Sales Range: $10-24.9 Million
Emp.: 14
Real Estate Management & Development
N.A.I.C.S.: 531390

GREENSPRING ENERGY LLC

30 W Aylesbury Rd, Timonium, MD 21093
Tel.: (443) 322-7000
Web Site:
http://www.greenspringenergy.com
Sales Range: $10-24.9 Million
Emp.: 40
Solar Power Structure Installation & Maintenance Services
N.A.I.C.S.: 237130
Jake Albert (Area Mgr-Sls)
Jay Radcliffe (Reg Pres)
Paul Wittemann (Owner)

GREENSTONE FARM CREDIT SERVICES

3515 West Rd, East Lansing, MI 48823-7312
Tel.: (517) 318-4100
Web Site:
https://www.greenstonefcs.com
Year Founded: 1917
Sales Range: $100-124.9 Million
Emp.: 450

Agricultural Credit Institutions
N.A.I.C.S.: 522299
David Armstrong (Pres & CEO)
Melissa A. Stolicker (Exec VP)
Jeff Pavlik (Mng Dir-Capital Markets & Sr VP)
Edward Reed (Vice Chm)
Travis Jones (CFO & Exec VP)
Paul Anderson (Chief Credit Officer & Exec VP)
Steve Junglas (CIO, Chief Security Officer & Exec VP)
Peter Lemmer (Exec VP)
John Jones (Sr VP-Comml Lending)
Ian McGonigal (Sr VP-Sls)

GREENSTREET REAL ESTATE PARTNERS, L.P.

2601 S Bayshore Dr Ste 900, Coconut Grove, FL 33133
Tel.: (305) 858-4225
Web Site:
http://www.greenstreetre.com
Sales Range: $10-24.9 Million
Emp.: 30
Commercial Real Estate Investment & Asset Management Services
N.A.I.C.S.: 531390
Jeffrey Alan Safchik (CFO & Mng Dir)
Randal Rombeiro (Head-Fin)
Kristie P. Barrios (Controller)

GREENSTRIPE MEDIA, INC.

424 N Newport Blvd, Newport Beach, CA 92663-4211
Tel.: (949) 650-5081
Year Founded: 1977
Sales Range: $10-24.9 Million
Emp.: 8
N.A.I.C.S.: 541810
Joe Winkelmann (Pres & CEO)
Tony De Dios (Media Buyer)

GREENTECH TRANSPORTATION INDUSTRIES INC.

7000 Merrill Ave Ste 31, Chino, CA 91710
Tel.: (909) 614-7007 NV
Year Founded: 2010
Hybrid, Electric, Alternative Fuel Heavy Duty Transit Buses, Luxury Motor Coaches & Tour Buses Retailer
N.A.I.C.S.: 441227
Ian B. McAvoy (CEO)

GREENTREE MORTGAGE COMPANY L P

2 Eastwick Dr, Gibbsboro, NJ 08026
Tel.: (856) 596-8858
Web Site:
http://www.hipotecalatina.com
Rev.: $11,500,000
Emp.: 55
Mortgage Banker
N.A.I.C.S.: 522292
Andrea Warren (Sr VP)

GREENTREE MOTORS DANBURY INC.

87 Federal Rd, Danbury, CT 06811
Tel.: (203) 730-4040
Web Site:
http://www.greentreemotors.com
Sales Range: $25-49.9 Million
New & Used Automobile Dealers
N.A.I.C.S.: 441110
Chris Morgado (Dir-Svc)
Keith Frank (Mgr-Inventory)
Armando Muniz (Gen Sls Mgr)
Douglas Deakin (Sls Mgr)
Frank Nieves (Sls Mgr)
Howard Luna (Sls Mgr)
Maxwell Tanabaum (Gen Mgr)

GREENVIEW LANDSCAPING, INC.

PO Box 12668, Saint Petersburg, FL 33733
Tel.: (727) 906-8864
Web Site:
https://www.greenviewfl.com
Year Founded: 1984
Emp.: 25
Landscaping Services
N.A.I.C.S.: 561730
Larry Rhum (Pres)

GREENVILLE COUNTRY CLUB

239 Byrd Blvd, Greenville, SC 29605
Tel.: (864) 232-6771 SC
Web Site: https://www.gccsc.com
Year Founded: 1905
Sales Range: $10-24.9 Million
Emp.: 270
Golf & Tennis Club
N.A.I.C.S.: 713910
David Holly (Dir-Tennis)
Greg Hobbs (Gen Mgr & COO)

GREENVILLE HOSPITAL SYSTEM INC.

701 Grove Rd, Greenville, SC 29605-5611
Tel.: (864) 455-7000 SC
Web Site: http://www.ghs.org
Sales Range: $750-799.9 Million
Emp.: 7,300
Operates Hospital & Health Care Services
N.A.I.C.S.: 622110
D. Douglas Dorman (Chief HR Officer & VP-HR)
Sally Foister (Dir-Mktg Comm)
Brenda J. Thames (VP-Academic & Faculty Affairs)

GREENVILLE NATIONAL BANK

446 S Broadway St, Greenville, OH 45331
Tel.: (937) 548-1114
Web Site:
http://www.greenvillenational bank.com
Sales Range: $25-49.9 Million
Emp.: 102
Bank Holding Company
N.A.I.C.S.: 522110
Kent A. James (Pres & CEO)
Gloria A. Harpest (Head-HR)
Curt Brooks (Asst VP-Ansonia)

GREENVILLE REGIONAL HOSPITAL

200 Health Dr, Greenville, IL 62246
Tel.: (618) 664-1230 IL
Web Site:
https://www.greenvilleregionalhos pital.com
Year Founded: 1956
Sales Range: $25-49.9 Million
Emp.: 573
Health Care Srvices
N.A.I.C.S.: 622110
Vicki Kloeckner (Dir-HR)
Mark Ennen (Dir-Acctg)
Bart Caldieraro (Sec)
Rosie York (Treas)
Jeff Mollet (Chm)
Brian Nall (COO & Exec VP)
Tammy Lett (Chief Nursing Officer)

GREENWASTE RECOVERY INC.

625 Charles St, San Jose, CA 95112
Tel.: (408) 283-4800
Web Site:
http://www.greenwaste.com
Rev.: $12,797,566
Emp.: 500
Rubbish Collection & Disposal

N.A.I.C.S.: 562111
Richard Christina *(Pres)*
Murray Hall *(VP)*
Ricardo Lopez *(Mgr-MRF Ops-GreenWaste)*
Tracy Adams *(Chief Admin Officer)*
Valerie Chavez *(Mgr-Customer Svc)*
Dave Tilton *(CFO)*
Frank Weigel *(Co-COO & Sec)*

GREENWAVE REALITY, INC.

200 Spectrum Center Dr 15th Fl, Irvine, CA 92618
Tel.: (714) 805-9283
Web Site:
http://www.greenwavesystems.com
Year Founded: 2008
Software Developer & Information Technology Services
N.A.I.C.S.: 513210
Martin Manniche *(Co-Founder, Chm & CEO)*
Tim Lyons *(Sr VP-Engrg)*
Christos Lagomichos *(COO)*
Peter Wilmar Christensen *(Co-Founder, CFO & Gen Mgr-EMEA)*
Mark E. Harrington *(Exec VP, Gen Counsel & Sec)*
Eskild Hansen *(Chief Design Officer)*
Troy Pliska *(Exec VP-Ops)*
Sharon Wang *(Exec VP-Program Mgmt Office)*
Siddhartha Dattagupta *(Sr VP-Global Engrg)*
Varun Arora *(Gen Mggr-Singapore & VP-Bus Dev-APAC)*
Bryan Sun *(VP-Corp Bus Dev)*

GREENWAY CO-OP SERVICE COMPANY

PO Box 6878, Rochester, MN 55903-6878
Tel.: (507) 289-4086   MN
Web Site: http://www.greenway.coop
Year Founded: 1930
Sales Range: $150-199.9 Million
Emp.: 60
Grain, Farm Supplies, Propane & Fuel Oil Whslr
N.A.I.C.S.: 424510
Jeff Lund *(Mgr-Energy)*

GREENWAY ENTERPRISES INCORPORATED

608 W Lincoln Rd, Helena, MT 59604
Tel.: (406) 458-9411
Web Site:
https://www.greenwayent.com
Sales Range: $10-24.9 Million
Emp.: 20
Commercial & Office Building, New Construction
N.A.I.C.S.: 236220
YuVonne D. Hoovestal *(Pres)*
Vickie Tasha *(Controller)*
Gary E. Hoovestal *(CEO)*
Viki Peccia *(Controller)*

GREENWAY EQUIPMENT, INC.

412 S Van Buren, Weiner, AR 72479
Tel.: (870) 684-7720   AR
Web Site:
https://www.gogreenway.com
Sales Range: $10-24.9 Million
Emp.: 130
Agricultural & Farming Machinery & Equipment Sales & Services
N.A.I.C.S.: 441227
Marshall Stewart *(Pres)*
Tommy Hall *(VP-Svc)*
Steve Shepard *(Reg VP)*
Rick Bormann *(Sr VP)*
Stan Vardell *(VP-Parts Ops)*
Steve Smith *(CFO)*

Bill Simmons *(Mgr-Remarketing)*
Brad Nash *(Reg VP)*
Chad Sandoval *(Reg VP)*

GREENWAY FORD, INC.

9001 E Colonial Dr, Orlando, FL 32817
Tel.: (407) 275-3200
Web Site:
http://www.greenwayford.com
Year Founded: 1973
Sales Range: $10-24.9 Million
Emp.: 25
New Car Dealers
N.A.I.C.S.: 441110
Lee Mitchell *(Gen Mgr)*

GREENWAY INVESTMENT COMPANY

2808 Fairmount Ste 100, Dallas, TX 75201
Tel.: (214) 880-9009
Web Site:
https://www.greenwayinvestment.com
Year Founded: 1979
Subdividers & Developers
N.A.I.C.S.: 237210
Jerry Stool *(Pres)*
Stein LaRee *(Dir-Asset Mgmt)*
John Erspamer *(Controller)*
Christy Hammons *(VP)*
Mark Hardaway *(VP)*
Todd Petty *(COO)*

GREENWAY PARTNERS, LP

150 E 57th St, New York, NY 10022
Tel.: (212) 355-6800   DE
Sales Range: $150-199.9 Million
Emp.: 5
Investment Company
N.A.I.C.S.: 523150
Alfred D. Kingsley *(Gen Partner)*

GREENWAY TRANSPORTA-TION SERVICES

14807 N 73rd St Ste 102, Scottsdale, AZ 85260-3194
Tel.: (480) 443-8800
Web Site:
http://www.shipgreenway.com
Year Founded: 1982
Sales Range: $10-24.9 Million
Emp.: 10
Truck Transportation Brokers
N.A.I.C.S.: 488510
Craig Skillicorn *(Pres)*
Georgie Bourgeois *(Office Mgr)*
Steve Phelps *(Mgr-LTL Svcs)*

GREENWAY-MALDEN EQUIP-MENT CO.

20919 State Hwy 114, Dexter, MO 63841
Tel.: (573) 624-7467
Sales Range: $10-24.9 Million
Emp.: 18
Agricultural Machinery & Equipment Sales
N.A.I.C.S.: 423820
Charles Chilcutt *(Pres)*

GREENWELL ENERGY SOLU-TIONS LLC

2000 B Edwards St, Houston, TX 77007
Tel.: (713) 993-7772
Web Site:
http://greenwellsolutions.com
Specialty Chemical Supplier
N.A.I.C.S.: 325998
David Kippie *(VP-Chemicals)*
Parel Patel *(VP-Fin)*
Ron Long *(VP-Ops)*
Christy Hartman *(VP-Mktg)*

Dean Murdock *(Mgr-Ops)*
Keith Pope *(VP-Completions)*
James Kiser *(VP-Wholesale Oilfield Equipment)*

GREENWICH AEROGROUP, INC.

1701 S Hoover Rd Ste 200, Wichita, KS 67209
Tel.: (316) 201-3020   DE
Web Site:
http://www.greenwichaerogroup.com
Year Founded: 2007
Holding Company; Aviation Services
N.A.I.C.S.: 551112
James Ziegler *(Vice Chm)*
Gene Juris *(CFO)*
Daniel Lafrance *(VP & Gen Mgr)*
Phil Winters *(VP-Aircraft Sls & Charter Mgmt)*
Frank Cowle *(Sr VP-Distr)*
Ralph Kunz *(COO)*

Subsidiaries:

Alamo Aerospace, LP   **(1)**
351 Airport Dr PO Box 1209, Decatur, TX 76234
Tel.: (940) 627-6709
Web Site: http://www.alamoaerospace.com
Development & Improvements to General Aviation Aircraft & Products
N.A.I.C.S.: 541330

Helivia Aero Taxi SA   **(1)**
Rua Barao De Flamengo 32-2nd Andar, Rio de Janeiro, 22220-080, Brazil
Tel.: (55) 2122857335
Passenger Air Transportation industry
N.A.I.C.S.: 481211

Matrix Aviation, Inc.   **(1)**
1701 S Hoover Rd, Wichita, KS
67209-2813   **(100%)**
Tel.: (316) 942-0844
Web Site: http://www.matrixaviation.com
Sales Range: $10-24.9 Million
Emp.: 14
Avionics, Instrumentation & Radar Systems Supplier for Aviation Industry
N.A.I.C.S.: 423860
Chuck Wilds *(Dir-Quality Control)*
John Bobetsky *(Dir-Sls-Northeast US & South Central US)*
Daniel Boen *(Dir-Sls-Southwest US & Northwest US)*

Professional Aircraft Accessories, Inc.   **(1)**
7035 Ctr Ln, Titusville, FL 32780
Tel.: (321) 267-1040
Web Site: https://www.gopaa.com
Sales Range: $25-49.9 Million
Emp.: 200
Aircraft Accessories Supplier & Repair Service
N.A.I.C.S.: 811210
Keith Johnson *(VP)*

Professional Aviation Associates, Inc.   **(1)**
105 Southfield Pkwy Ste 300, Forest Park, GA 30297
Tel.: (404) 767-0282
Web Site: https://www.proaviation.com
Sales Range: $25-49.9 Million
Emp.: 30
Avionics, Landing Gear, Hydraulic Components, Engine Accessories, Electrical Items & Other Airframe Components Distr
N.A.I.C.S.: 423860
Hibo Linares *(Dir-Quality)*
Shelly Gehl *(Mgr-Sls Acct)*
Wesley Hunter *(Mgr-Sls Acct)*
Daniel Lafrance *(VP)*

Western Aircraft, Inc.   **(1)**
4300 S Kennedy St, Boise, ID 83705-6542
Tel.: (208) 338-1800
Web Site: https://www.westair.com
Sales Range: $25-49.9 Million
Emp.: 175
Aircraft Service Including Maintenance Aircraft Sales Avionics Sale & Installation Aircraft Parts Sale Airline Fueling Aircraft Charter & Aircraft Management Distr

N.A.I.C.S.: 423860
Austin Shontz *(VP & Gen Mgr)*
Peter Woodke *(Mgr-Contracts)*
Kevin Kaye *(VP)*

GREENWICH AUTOMOTIVE ENTERPRISES

468 W Putnam Ave, Greenwich, CT 06830
Tel.: (203) 869-6666
Web Site:
http://www.greenwichjeep.com
Sales Range: $25-49.9 Million
Emp.: 100
New & Used Auto Service & Sales
N.A.I.C.S.: 441110
Jonathon Wade *(Pres)*

GREENWICH HONDA

289 Mason St, Greenwich, CT 06830
Tel.: (203) 622-0600
Web Site:
http://www.greenwichhonda.com
Sales Range: $10-24.9 Million
Emp.: 35
New Car Dealers
N.A.I.C.S.: 441110
Scott E. Jordan *(Gen Mgr)*
Louis Sollecito *(Pres)*

GREENWICH WORKSHOP INC.

151 Main St, Seymour, CT 06483
Tel.: (203) 881-7724
Web Site:
https://www.greenwichworkshop.com
Sales Range: $10-24.9 Million
Emp.: 30
Art Goods
N.A.I.C.S.: 424990
Scott Usher *(Pres)*

GREENWOOD CREDIT UNION

2669 Post Rd, Warwick, RI 02886
Tel.: (401) 739-4600   RI
Web Site:
http://www.greenwoodcu.org
Year Founded: 1948
Sales Range: $10-24.9 Million
Emp.: 86
Credit Union
N.A.I.C.S.: 522130
Holly E. Ferrara *(VP-Comml Lending)*
Lori Coletta *(VP-HR)*
Joseph Lajoie *(CFO & Exec VP)*
Will Thibodeau *(VP-Retail Lending)*
Stephen Elias *(VP-Indirect Lending)*
Frederick Reinhardt *(Pres & CEO)*
Karen S. D. Grande *(Sec)*
Peter E. D'Orsi Jr. *(Treas)*

GREENWOOD FABRICATING & PLATING

215 Mill Ave, Greenwood, SC 29646
Tel.: (864) 229-1225
Web Site: https://www.gfpi.com
Year Founded: 1986
Sales Range: $50-74.9 Million
Emp.: 90
Electroplating of Metals or Formed Products
N.A.I.C.S.: 332813
Tim Fender *(Pres)*
Kirk Husser *(COO)*

GREENWOOD GENETIC CEN-TER INC.

106 Gregor Mendel Cir, Greenwood, SC 29646-2315
Tel.: (864) 941-8100
Web Site: http://www.ggc.org
Rev.: $11,080,704
Emp.: 60
Biological Research
N.A.I.C.S.: 541720
Charles Schwartz *(Dir-Res)*
Leta M. Tribble *(Dir-Education)*

Greenwood Genetic Center Inc.—(Continued)

Jennifer Lee *(Dir-Lead Molecular Diagnostic Laboratory)*
Laura Pollard *(Assoc Dir-Biochemical Genetics Lab & Medical Genetics Trng)*
Alka Chaubey *(Dir-Cytogenetic Laboratory)*
Barbara DuPont *(Sr Dir-Cytogenetic Laboratory)*
Julie Jones *(Dir-Clinical Genomic Sequencing Program)*
Michael J. Lyons *(Dir-Clinical Svcs)*
Tim Wood *(Dir-Biochemical Genetics Laboratory)*
Michael J. Friez *(Dir-Diagnostic Laboratory)*
William Tiller *(Exec Dir-Greenwood Genetic Center Foundation)*
Steve Skinner *(Mng Dir)*

GREENWOOD INC.
2507 Wade Hampton Blvd, Greenville, SC 29615-1167
Tel.: (864) 244-9669
Web Site: http://www.gwood.com
Year Founded: 1993
Sales Range: $50-74.9 Million
Emp.: 460
Provider of Industrial Building & Warehouse Contracting Services
N.A.I.C.S.: 236220
Laura Lipscomb *(CEO)*
Eric Burnette *(Dir-Sls & Mktg)*
Brad Wood *(Pres)*
Chris Hemmings *(CFO)*
Chip Scammon *(Dir-Ops)*
Dana Spadafora *(Dir-HR)*
Shannon McKamey *(Project Mgr-GE Power-Greenville & South Carolina)*
Bo Hastings *(Dir-Construction Ops)*
Kevin Crittendon *(Dir-Continuous Improvement)*
Mike Simmons *(Dir-Safety)*

GREENWOOD INDUSTRIES
640 Linken St, Worcester, MA 01605
Tel.: (508) 865-4040
Web Site: http://www.greenwood-industries.com
Year Founded: 1992
Rev.: $32,300,000
Emp.: 190
Roofing Contractors
N.A.I.C.S.: 238160
John D'Elia *(VP-Esitmating & Sls)*
David Klein *(Owner)*

Subsidiaries:

Hudson Valley Roofing & Sheetmetal, Inc. **(1)**
214 Mac Arthur Ave, New Windsor, NY 12553
Tel.: (845) 565-6700
Web Site: http://hudsonvalleyroofing.com
Sales Range: $10-24.9 Million
Roofing Contractors
N.A.I.C.S.: 238160

GREENWOODS FINANCIAL GROUP, INC.
117 N Main St, Lake Mills, WI 53551
Tel.: (920) 648-2324
Web Site: http://www.greenwoodsstatebank.com
Year Founded: 2006
Sales Range: $1-9.9 Million
Emp.: 35
Bank Holding Company
N.A.I.C.S.: 551111
Bill McDonald *(Pres & CEO)*

Subsidiaries:

The Greenwood's State Bank **(1)**
117 N Main St, Lake Mills, WI 53551
Tel.: (920) 648-2324
Web Site: http://www.greenwoods.bank
Commericial Banking
N.A.I.C.S.: 522110
Becky Anhalt *(Sr VP-Retail & Admin)*
Bill McDonald *(Chm & CEO)*
Barb Bakshis *(Sr VP-Comml Banking)*
Bob Murray *(Sr VP-Comml Banking)*
David Barnett *(Sr VP-Comml Banking)*
Jennifer Blumer *(CFO)*
Jon Eyler *(Officer-Loan)*
Keith Pollek *(Exec VP-Comml Banking)*
Nate Salas *(Sr VP-Comml Banking)*
Rob Cera *(Pres)*

GREENWORKS SERVICE COMPANY
1910 Pacific Ave Ste 16800, Dallas, TX 75201
Tel.: (214) 823-2585
Web Site: http://www.greenworksinspections.com
Year Founded: 2011
Sales Range: $1-9.9 Million
Emp.: 28
Real Estate Manangement Services
N.A.I.C.S.: 531390
Harmony Brown *(Mng Partner)*
Damon Durham *(COO)*
Jessica Hendricks *(Dir-Ops)*
Jennifer Pillar *(CFO)*
Allison Singleton *(Chief Bus Dev Officer)*

GREER INDUSTRIES INC.
570 Canyon Rd, Morgantown, WV 26508
Tel.: (304) 594-1768
Web Site: http://www.greerindustries.com
Year Founded: 1917
Sales Range: $25-49.9 Million
Emp.: 450
Crushed & Broken Limestone
N.A.I.C.S.: 327410
James M. Troy *(CFO)*

Subsidiaries:

Greer Limestone Company **(1)**
598 Canyon Rd, Morgantown, WV 26508-9065
Tel.: (304) 296-1751
Web Site: http://www.greerlimestone.com
Sales Range: $25-49.9 Million
N.A.I.C.S.: 331221

Greer Steel Company **(1)**
624 Blvd, Dover, OH 44622
Tel.: (330) 343-8811
Web Site: http://www.greersteel.com
Sales Range: $25-49.9 Million
Emp.: 1,200
Cold Rolled Strip Steel & Flat Wire Mfr
N.A.I.C.S.: 331221
Charlie Eames *(Mgr-Admin Sls)*

West Virginia Newspaper Publishing Company **(1)**
1251 Earl L Core Rd, Morgantown, WV 26501
Tel.: (304) 291-9417
Sales Range: $1-9.9 Million
Newspaper Publishers
N.A.I.C.S.: 513110

GREG BUICK PONTIAC CADILLAC
2008 N Belt Hwy, Saint Joseph, MO 64506
Tel.: (816) 232-4413
Year Founded: 1974
Sales Range: $10-24.9 Million
Emp.: 75
Car Whslr
N.A.I.C.S.: 441110
Josh Benight *(Bus Mgr)*
Greg Ronchetti *(Owner & Pres)*

GREG LEBLANC INC.
1772 Martin Luther King Blvd, Houma, LA 70360
Tel.: (985) 447-1111
Web Site: http://www.gregleblanc.com
Rev.: $25,124,497
Emp.: 50
New & Used Car Dealers
N.A.I.C.S.: 441110
Gregory Leblanc *(Pres)*

GREG WEBER, INC.
9220 Bonita Beach Rd Ste 200, Bonita Springs, FL 34135
Tel.: (239) 333-4001
Web Site: http://www.gregweberinc.com
Sales Range: Less than $1 Million
Emp.: 1
Custom Home Designer
N.A.I.C.S.: 236115
Greg Weber *(Owner)*

GREG WEEKS INC.
10881 State Hwy 149, West Frankfort, IL 62896
Tel.: (618) 937-2446
Web Site: https://www.gregweeks.com
Sales Range: $50-74.9 Million
Emp.: 70
New & Used Automobiles
N.A.I.C.S.: 441110

GREGAN CONSTRUCTION CORP.
4970 SW 72nd Ave Ste 102, Miami, FL 33155
Tel.: (305) 663-1122
Web Site: http://www.greganconstruction.com
Sales Range: $10-24.9 Million
Emp.: 20
New Single Family Housing Construction Services
N.A.I.C.S.: 236115
Eduardo Goudie *(Pres)*

GREGERSON'S FOODS INC.
272 N 3rd St, Gadsden, AL 35901
Tel.: (256) 549-0644
Year Founded: 1969
Sales Range: $25-49.9 Million
Emp.: 100
Provider of Grocery Services
N.A.I.C.S.: 445110
Leanne Blackmon *(Controller)*
Peter V. Gregerson Jr. *(Pres)*

GREGG DRILLING & TESTING INC.
2726 Walnut Ave, Signal Hill, CA 90755
Tel.: (562) 427-6899
Web Site: https://www.greggdrilling.com
Year Founded: 1985
Sales Range: $10-24.9 Million
Emp.: 100
Water Well Drilling Services
N.A.I.C.S.: 238990
John M. Gregg *(Pres)*
Patrick Keating *(VP)*
Chris Christensen *(VP)*
Brian Savela *(Mgr-Ops)*
Ron Boggess *(Mgr-Ops)*
Terry Shewchuk *(Mgr-Ops)*

GREGG INDUSTRIES INC.
201 Estes Dr, Longview, TX 75602
Tel.: (903) 757-5754
Web Site: http://www.gregg-merico.com
Sales Range: $25-49.9 Million
Emp.: 1,800
Insulation; Commercial Buildings
N.A.I.C.S.: 238310
Thomas C. Merritt *(Pres)*
David Brook *(VP)*

Subsidiaries:

Gregg Industrial Insulators **(1)**
201 Estes Dr, Longview, TX 75602
Tel.: (903) 757-5754
Web Site: http://www.gregg-merico.com
Sales Range: $50-74.9 Million
Emp.: 441
Industrial Insulation Services
N.A.I.C.S.: 238990
Diane Hokit *(Mgr-Acctg Dept)*

Merritt Safety Environmental Management **(1)**
201 Estes Dr, Longview, TX 75602
Tel.: (903) 758-0562
Web Site: http://www.gregg-merico.com
Sales Range: $10-24.9 Million
Emp.: 9
Safety, Health & Environmental Consultant
N.A.I.C.S.: 238990

GREGG SMITH FORD LINCOLN MERCURY INC.
1316 N Price Ln, Clinton, MO 64735
Tel.: (660) 885-5505
Web Site: https://www.greggsmithford.com
Rev.: $10,800,000
Emp.: 24
New Car Dealers
N.A.I.C.S.: 441110
Gregg Smith *(Pres)*
Preston Smith *(Gen Mgr)*

GREGG'S GREENLAKE CYCLE INC.
7007 Woodlawn Ave NE, Seattle, WA 98115
Tel.: (206) 523-1822
Web Site: https://www.greggscycles.com
Rev.: $10,620,176
Emp.: 75
Bicycle & Bicycle Parts
N.A.I.C.S.: 459110
Marty Pluth *(VP & Gen Mgr)*
Kelsey Curtis *(Mgr-Svc)*
Leif Thorsen *(Mgr-Store)*
Stanley Gregg Jr. *(Owner)*

GREGGO & FERRARA INC.
4048 New Castle Ave, New Castle, DE 19720
Tel.: (302) 658-5241
Rev.: $25,200,000
Emp.: 200
General Contractor, Highway & Street Construction
N.A.I.C.S.: 237310
Ellen Rohrbach *(Engr-Construction)*
John Long *(Mgr-Acctg)*
Joseph DeJuliis *(CFO)*

GREGMAR, INC.
4312 S Georgia Pl, Oklahoma City, OK 73129-7972
Tel.: (405) 677-6633
Web Site: http://www.otl-upt.com
Sales Range: $25-49.9 Million
Emp.: 300
Local Trucking Services
N.A.I.C.S.: 484220
Greg Price *(Pres & CEO)*
Kevin Price *(VP)*
David Keegan *(VP-Maintenance)*
Rod Radcliffe *(VP-Sls)*
Tim Rains *(CFO & VP-Fin & Admin)*
Kerry Willingham *(Controller)*

Subsidiaries:

United Petroleum Transports, Inc. **(1)**
4312 S Georgia Pl, Oklahoma City, OK 73129

Tel.: (405) 677-6633
Web Site: http://www.otl-upt.com
Oil Transportation Services
N.A.I.C.S.: 484220
Gregory Price *(Chm)*
David Price *(VP-Chemical Svcs Div)*
Matthew K. Price *(VP-Mktg & Corp Culture)*
Matt Herndon *(Pres & CEO)*
Kevin Price *(VP- Natl Acct)*
Scott Hunt *(COO)*
Andrew Mantey *(CFO & VP-Admin/Acctg)*
Rod Radcliffe *(VP-Sls & Bus Dev)*
David Keegan *(VP-Maintenance)*
Robert Moore *(VP-Risk Mgt)*
David Withers *(Dir-Driver Recruiting)*
Joanne Miley *(Dir-HR)*
Carl Bailey *(VP-Crude Svcs Div)*
Kaleb Robinson *(Mgr-Bus Process Improvement)*
Joe Hill *(Dir-Compliance)*
Kevin Lansford *(Mgr-Pur TPFL)*
Alfredo Alvarez *(Dir-Western Reg Safety)*
Michael Hulsey *(Dir-Southern Reg Safety)*
Derek Martin *(Dir-Northern Reg Safety)*
Joe Nation *(Dir-Crude Svcs Safety)*
Rosemarie Hocking *(Mgr-Trng & Instructional Design)*
Charlie Stein *(Mgr-Bus Dev-Southern Texas)*
Kevin Hogan *(Mgr-Bus Dev-Western Reg)*
Brian Bajema *(Mgr-Bus Dev-Northern & Central Reg)*
Adam Gentis *(Dir-Crude Pricing)*
Donna DaValt *(Mgr-Claims)*
Eric Lewis *(Dir-Acctg)*
Kristie Murphy *(Mgr-Accts Payable & Accountant)*
Veronica Towe *(Mgr-Payroll/Settlements)*
Susan Cates *(Supvr-Collections)*
Laurie Williams *(Supvr-Billing)*

Subsidiary (Domestic):

Patriot Transportation Holding,
Inc.   **(2)**
200 W Forsyth St 7th Fl, Jacksonville, FL
32202
Tel.: (904) 396-5733
Web Site: https://www.patriottrans.com
Rev.: $94,785,000
Assets: $52,667,000
Liabilities: $18,336,000
Net Worth: $34,331,000
Earnings: $2,673,000
Emp.: 466
Fiscal Year-end: 09/30/2023
Holding Company
N.A.I.C.S.: 551112
Robert E. Sandlin *(Pres & CEO)*
John D. Klopfenstein *(Chief Acctg Officer, Treas & Controller)*
Jeff Anthony *(VP-HR)*
John Wagner *(CIO)*
James N. Anderson IV *(VP-Risk Mgmt & Safety)*

GREGORIS NISSAN
555 W Merrick Rd, Valley Stream, NY
11580
Tel.: (516) 825-8700
Web Site:
    http://www.gregorisnissan.com
Sales Range: $10-24.9 Million
Emp.: 48
Car Whslr
N.A.I.C.S.: 441110
Gerard DeGregoris *(Pres)*

GREGORY ELECTRIC CO. INC.
2124 College St, Columbia, SC
29205-1023
Tel.: (803) 748-1122   SC
Web Site:
    https://www.gregoryelectric.com
Year Founded: 1949
Sales Range: $25-49.9 Million
Emp.: 450
Electrical Work
N.A.I.C.S.: 238210
Randy Taylor *(Sr Project Mgr)*
Lisa Phillips *(VP-Infrastructure)*
Glenn Greer *(VP-Indus)*

GREGORY FCA

27 W Athens Ave Ste 200, Ardmore,
PA 19003
Tel.: (610) 642-8253
Web Site: http://www.gregoryfca.com
Year Founded: 1991
Sales Range: $1-9.9 Million
Emp.: 40
Public Relations Agency
N.A.I.C.S.: 541820
Gregory Matusky *(Founder, Pres & CEO)*
Doug Rose *(COO)*
Mike Lizun *(Sr VP)*
Joseph Anthony *(Pres-Fin Svcs)*
Joe Hassett *(Sr VP)*
Matthew McLoughlin *(VP)*
Jimmy Moock *(Sr VP)*
Alexandra Silks *(Acct Coord)*
Brian McDermott *(Assoc VP)*
Haley Rosa *(Acct Coord)*
Jacob Tulsky *(Mgr-Bus Dev)*
Jesse Kennedy *(Dir-Creative)*
Kerry Davis *(VP)*
Kim Harmsen *(VP)*
Lauren Davis *(Assoc VP)*
Leigh Minnier *(VP)*
Heather Crowell *(Exec VP)*
Brittany Bevacqua *(Mng Dir-New York)*
Nicole Sullivan *(Assoc VP)*
Katie Kennedy *(Sr VP)*

GREGORY INDUSTRIES, INC.
4100 13th St SW, Canton, OH 44710
Tel.: (330) 477-4800
Web Site:
    https://www.gregorycorp.com
Year Founded: 1957
Sales Range: $10-24.9 Million
Emp.: 100
Fabricated Metal Products Mfr
N.A.I.C.S.: 332999
T. Raymond Gregory *(Founder)*
Andrew Artar *(VP-Sls & Mktg)*
Kevin R. Mally *(Mgr-Mktg)*
Terrence Brown *(Supvr-Inside Svc & Sls)*

GREGORY, SHARER & STUART, P.A.
100 2nd Ave S Ste 600, Saint Petersburg, FL 33701
Tel.: (727) 821-6161   FL
Web Site: http://www.gsscpa.com
Year Founded: 1984
Sales Range: $1-9.9 Million
Emp.: 48
Accounting Services
N.A.I.C.S.: 541211
Charles L. Stuart *(Co-Founder)*
James Newman *(Mng Partner)*
Thomas H. Gregory *(Partner)*
Troy Kimbrough *(Dir-Healthcare Indus Svcs Team)*
M. Timothy Farrell *(Dir-Construction & Real Estate Dev Indus Svcs Team)*
Paula D. Popovich *(Dir-Tax & Acctg)*
Deborah C. Fallucca *(Principal)*
Larry W. Sharer *(Co-Founder)*

GREINER PONTIAC-BUICK, INC.
14555 Civic Dr Ste A, Victorville, CA
92394
Tel.: (760) 245-3451   DE
Web Site: http://www.greinergm.com
Year Founded: 1984
Sales Range: $10-24.9 Million
Emp.: 65
New Car Dealers
N.A.I.C.S.: 441110
Colt Gaxiola *(Mgr-Fin)*

GREINER SCHMIDT MOTOR COMPANY
3333 Cy Ave, Casper, WY 82604

Tel.: (307) 224-4136
Web Site:
    https://www.greinerford.com
Rev.: $28,800,000
Emp.: 130
Sales & Service of New & Used Automobiles
N.A.I.C.S.: 441110
Philip A. Schmidt *(Pres & CEO)*

GREINER'S INC.
117 Whiting St, Tampa, FL 33602
Tel.: (813) 226-3207
Web Site:
    https://www.greinersclothing.com
Year Founded: 1981
Sales Range: $1-9.9 Million
Emp.: 6
Men's Clothing Retailer
N.A.I.C.S.: 424350
Christopher T. Blowers *(Owner)*

GREKA ENERGY CORPORATION
630 5th Ave Ste 1501, New York, NY
10111-0100
Tel.: (212) 218-4680   CO
Sales Range: $25-49.9 Million
Emp.: 126
Producer & Developer of Oil & Gas
N.A.I.C.S.: 211120
Richard Lembcke *(VP-Upstream Opers)*
Randeep Singh Grewal *(Chm, Pres & CEO)*

Subsidiaries:

Greka Energy, California   **(1)**
6527 Dominion Rd, Santa Maria, CA 93454
Tel.: (805) 347-8700
Sales Range: $10-24.9 Million
Emp.: 20
Oil & Gas Exploitation, Production & Development
N.A.I.C.S.: 334515
Veronica Hilbrant *(Mgr-HR)*

Greka Energy, China   **(1)**
Frenchship Hotel 62932, Beijing, 100873,
China
Tel.: (86) 1068498487
Sales Range: $25-49.9 Million
Emp.: 20
Oil & Gas Production & Development
N.A.I.C.S.: 213112

GRELTON ELEVATOR INC.
6944 County Rd M, Grelton, OH
43523
Tel.: (419) 256-6381
Year Founded: 1972
Sales Range: $10-24.9 Million
Emp.: 7
Grain Elevators
N.A.I.C.S.: 424510
Steve Beck *(Pres)*
Mike Beck *(Controller)*

GREMADA INDUSTRIES INC.
825 28th St S Ste E, Fargo, ND
58103
Tel.: (701) 356-0814
Web Site: http://www.gremada.com
Sales Range: $10-24.9 Million
Emp.: 100
Machine Shop, Jobbing & Repair
N.A.I.C.S.: 332710
Steven F. Walker *(Pres & CEO)*
Kimberly Glidden *(CFO)*
Jim Giles *(Gen Mgr-Aaseby Indus Machining)*
John Triplett *(Gen Mgr-Whelan Machine & Tool)*

Subsidiaries:

Aaseby Industrial Machining;
LLC   **(1)**
301 6th St S, Wahpeton, ND 58075-4636

Tel.: (701) 642-8820
Web Site: http://www.aimachining.com
Emp.: 22
Industrial Supplies Whslr
N.A.I.C.S.: 423840
Jim Giles *(Gen Mgr)*
Pam Knapper *(Office Mgr)*
Dana Wiertzema *(Mgr-Sls)*

Schaffer Precision Machine Shop,
Inc.   **(1)**
7470 Miller Rd Ste 2, Houston, TX 77049
Tel.: (281) 457-3564
Web Site: http://www.schafferprecision.com
Sales Range: $10-24.9 Million
Emp.: 14
Machining, Fabricating & Manufacturing
Services
N.A.I.C.S.: 332999

Whelan Machine & Tool, LLC   **(1)**
134 Rochester Dr, Louisville, KY 40214
Tel.: (502) 364-6370
Web Site: http://www.whelanmachine.com
Emp.: 35
Machine Tools Mfr
N.A.I.C.S.: 333517
John Triplett *(Mgr-Ops)*

GRENO INDUSTRIES INC.
2820 Amsterdam Rd, Scotia, NY
12302
Tel.: (518) 393-4195
Web Site: http://www.greno.com
Sales Range: $10-24.9 Million
Emp.: 77
Machine Shop, Jobbing & Repair
N.A.I.C.S.: 332710
Robert W. Golden *(CEO)*
Eileen Guarino *(Pres & COO)*
Vincent Guarino *(Founder)*
Peter Bennice *(Mgr-Global Sls)*
Pauline Caldarone *(Mgr-Acctg)*

GRESCO UTILITY SUPPLY INC.
1135 Rumble Rd, Forsyth, GA 31029
Tel.: (478) 315-0850
Web Site: https://www.gresco.com
Sales Range: $75-99.9 Million
Emp.: 99
Whslr of Electrical Apparatus &
Equipment
N.A.I.C.S.: 423610
Steve Gramling *(Pres & CEO)*
Melissa Sanders *(CFO)*
Mike Williams *(Sr VP-Pub Power Georgia)*
Chad Capps *(Sr VP-Tech Solutions)*

GRESHAM OUTLOOK
1190 NE Division St, Gresham, OR
97030-0185
Tel.: (503) 665-2181
Web Site:
    http://www.theoutlookonline.com
Sales Range: $100-124.9 Million
Emp.: 150
Weekly Newspaper
N.A.I.C.S.: 513110
Steve Clark *(Pres)*
Steve Brown *(Mng Editor)*

GRESHAM PETROLEUM CO.
415 Pershing Ave, Indianola, MS
38751
Tel.: (662) 887-2160
Web Site:
    https://www.greshampetroleum.com
Sales Range: $25-49.9 Million
Emp.: 47
Petroleum Bulk Stations
N.A.I.C.S.: 424710
William W. Gresham Jr. *(Pres)*

GRESHAM, SMITH & PARTNERS
511 Union St Ste 1400, Nashville, TN
37219-1733

Gresham, Smith & Partners—(Continued)

Tel.: (615) 770-8100   **TN**
Year Founded: 1967
Sales Range: $25-49.9 Million
Emp.: 800
Architectural & Engineering Services
N.A.I.C.S.: 541310
James Bearden (Chm & CEO)
John Reidy (VP-Water Resources)
Kelly Knight Hodges (VP-Corp & Urban Design)
Jim Brennan (Principal-Design)
Joel Ratekin (Sr VP-Workplace Strategies)
Ken Zyga (Exec VP)
Mickey Sullivan (Exec VP)
Sonja Thompson (Project Mgr-Transportation Market)
Dawn Polley (Project Mgr-Transportation Market)
Sammy Harton (Engr-Transportation)
Sam Allen (Project Mgr-Transportation Market)
Devan Hill (Sr Project Mgr-Transportation)
Doug Kiesler (Sr Engr-Electrical)
Ram Vadarevu (Engr-Transportation)
Colleen Dolan (Sr Coord-PR-Corp Comm)
Eric Huber (Mgr-Risk-Risk Mgmt)
Layton Meng (Dir-Corp Comm)
Randy Hulsey (Sr VP)
Patricia West (Sr VP-Bus Dev)
Tom Lambert (Sr Engr-Transportation)
Jim Langlois (Exec VP-Healthcare Market)
Keith Beserud (Dir-Digital Innovation)
David Verner (Exec VP-Indus Market)
Jeff Nash (Exec VP-Water & Environment)
Scott Ribble (Sr Engr-Electrical-Transportation)
Greg Poston (Mgr-Transportation)
Tonya Spry (Dir-HR)

Subsidiaries:

Gresham, Smith & Partners, Atlanta Office   (1)
2325 Lakeview Pkwy Ste 300, Alpharetta, GA 30004-7940
Tel.: (770) 754-0755
Web Site: http://www.greshamsmith.com
Sales Range: $25-49.9 Million
Emp.: 60
Architectural & Engineering Services
N.A.I.C.S.: 541310
Peter Oram (VP-South)
Shawn Reese (Sr VP)
Nithin Gomez (Sr Engr-Transportation Market)

Gresham, Smith & Partners, Birmingham Office   (1)
3595 Grandview Pkwy Ste 300, Birmingham, AL 35243-1927
Tel.: (205) 298-9200
Sales Range: $10-24.9 Million
Emp.: 29
Architectural Services
N.A.I.C.S.: 541310
Derrick Murphy (Mgr-Water Resources Project & Client Svc)

Gresham, Smith & Partners, Charlotte Office   (1)
15720 John J Delaney Dr Ste 480, Charlotte, NC 28277
Tel.: (704) 752-1011
Sales Range: $10-24.9 Million
Emp.: 12
Architectural Services
N.A.I.C.S.: 541310
Mary Clayton (Sr VP)

Gresham, Smith & Partners, Dallas Office   (1)
2811 McKinney Ave Ste 300, Dallas, TX 75204
Tel.: (214) 350-1500
Web Site: http://www.greshamsmith.com

Sales Range: $10-24.9 Million
Emp.: 20
Architectural & Engineering Services
N.A.I.C.S.: 541310
Al Pranuk (VP)
Lauren J. Seydewitz (Partner)

Gresham, Smith & Partners, Jacksonville Office   (1)
225 Water St Ste 2200, Jacksonville, FL 32256-6018
Tel.: (904) 332-6699
Rev.: $14,004,884
Emp.: 40
Architectural Services
N.A.I.C.S.: 541310
James Bearden (CEO)
Trevor Lee (Mng Principal)
Jaime Abreu (Sr Engr-Water Resources)

Gresham, Smith & Partners, Louisville Office   (1)
101 S 5th Ste 1400, Louisville, KY 40202-3207
Tel.: (502) 627-8900
Sales Range: $10-24.9 Million
Emp.: 17
Environmental Transportation And Land Planning
N.A.I.C.S.: 541310
Mickey Sullivan (Exec VP-Land Plng & Design)
David West (Exec VP-Federal)
William J. Whitson (Exec VP-Water Resources)
Ken Zyga (Exec VP-Indus)
Tony Young (Sr Engr)
John A. Lengel Jr. (Exec VP-Aviation & Environ Svcs)

Gresham, Smith & Partners, Memphis Office   (1)
1138 N Germantown Pkwy Ste 101-341, Cordova, TN 38016
Tel.: (901) 753-5590
Sales Range: $50-74.9 Million
Emp.: 750
Architectural Services
N.A.I.C.S.: 541310

Gresham, Smith & Partners, Richmond Office   (1)
10 S 6th St Ste 100, Richmond, VA 23219   **(100%)**
Tel.: (770) 754-0755
Sales Range: $10-24.9 Million
Emp.: 26
Architectural Services
N.A.I.C.S.: 541310
David King (Office Mgr)

Gresham, Smith & Partners, Tampa Office   (1)
302 Knights Run Ave, Tampa, FL 33602
Tel.: (813) 251-6838
Sales Range: $10-24.9 Million
Emp.: 48
Architectural Services
N.A.I.C.S.: 541310
Joseph Barksdale (Sr VP-Water Svcs)
Grant J. Clifford (Sr VP)
Leith Oatman (Sr VP)
Jeremy Ashlock (Sr Engr-Transportation)
Jose Castellanos (Sr VP)

GRESHAM-PRUETT LUMBER EXCHANGE
1647 Mcfarland Blvd, Tuscaloosa, AL 35406
Tel.: (205) 349-4973
Sales Range: $10-24.9 Million
Emp.: 7
Lumber, Plywood & Millwork
N.A.I.C.S.: 423310
Henry Pruett (Pres)

GRETEMAN GROUP
1425 E Douglas 2nd Fl, Wichita, KS 67211
Tel.: (316) 263-1004
Web Site:
  http://www.gretemangroup.com
Year Founded: 1989
Sales Range: $25-49.9 Million
Emp.: 21
N.A.I.C.S.: 541810

Sonia Greteman (Pres & Dir-Creative)
Deanna Harms (Exec VP)
Garrett Fresh (Sr Dir-Art)
Chris Parks (Sr Dir-Art)
Lori Heinz (Mgr-Production)
Ashley Bowen Cook (Assoc VP & Brand Dir)
C. Shelley Straub (Brand Mgr)
Todd Gimlin (Interactive Developer)
Randy Bradbury (Sr Writer)
Shelley Downs (Brand Mgr)
Chaney Kimball (Sr Dir-Digital)
Jared Brickman (Specialist-Digital)
Donna Grow (Sr Designer-Production)
Kevin Jenks (Dir-Mktg)
Jordan Walker (Dir-Digital)
Joshua Wood (Editor)

GREY EAGLE DISTRIBUTORS INC.
2340 Millpark Dr, Maryland Heights, MO 63043-3530
Tel.: (314) 429-9100   **MO**
Web Site: https://www.greyeagle.com
Year Founded: 1963
Sales Range: $10-24.9 Million
Emp.: 200
Beer Distr
N.A.I.C.S.: 424810
David M. Stokes (CEO)

Subsidiaries:

Illinois Distributing Co.   (1)
2222 Cornell Ave, Montgomery, IL 60538
Tel.: (630) 966-8915
Beverage Distr
N.A.I.C.S.: 541614

GREY MOUNTAIN PARTNERS, LLC
1470 Walnut St Ste 400, Boulder, CO 80302
Tel.: (303) 449-5692   **DE**
Web Site:
  http://www.greymountain.com
Year Founded: 2003
Privater Equity Firm
N.A.I.C.S.: 523999
Jeff Kuo (Co-Founder & Mng Partner)
Rob Wright (Co-Founder & Mng Partner)
Rob Dellinger (Mng Dir & VP)

Subsidiaries:

Bolttech Mannings, Inc.   (1)
501 Mosside Blvd, North Versailles, PA 15137
Tel.: (724) 872-4873
Web Site: http://www.bolttechmannings.com
Industrial Bolt & Heat Treating Equipment, Whslr & On-Site Services
N.A.I.C.S.: 423840
Ed Komoski (Pres & CEO)
Aidan Graham (VP-Ops)
Tim Baxter (Engr-Electrical)

Subsidiary (Domestic):

Bone Frontier Company   (2)
190 W Southern St, Brighton, CO 80601
Tel.: (303) 659-4611
Web Site: http://www.bonefrontier.com
Industrial Induction Heating Systems Mfr
N.A.I.C.S.: 333994

Consolidated Glass Holding   (1)
1 Gateway Blvd, Pedricktown, NJ 08067
Web Site: http://cghinc.com
Holding Company
N.A.I.C.S.: 551112
Angela Beach (Sr Mgr-Mktg)

Subsidiary (Domestic):

Columbia Commercial Building Products LLC   (2)
1200 E Washington St, Rockwall, TX 75087-4717
Tel.: (972) 771-7100

Web Site: http://www.ccbpwin.com
Sales Range: $1-9.9 Million
Aluminum Commercial Window & Door Mfr
N.A.I.C.S.: 332321
Jason Pratt (VP & Gen Mgr)
Lance Hamilton (Pres)

Dlubak Specialty Glass Corporation   (2)
520 Chestnut St, Blairsville, PA 15717
Tel.: (724) 459-9540
Web Site: http://www.dlubakglass.com
Curved Glass & Specialty Flat Glass Laminates Mfr
N.A.I.C.S.: 327215
Chris J. Cotton (Gen Mgr)
Gary McDonald (Acct Mgr)

Frogco Amphibious Equipment, LLC   (1)
2280 Coteau Rd, Houma, LA 70364
Tel.: (985) 853-2200
Web Site: http://www.frogco-amphibious.com
Emp.: 25
Construction Equipment Mfr
N.A.I.C.S.: 333120
Garrett Naquin (Pres)

Global Security Glazing LLC   (1)
616 Selfield Rd, Selma, AL 36703   **(100%)**
Tel.: (334) 875-1900
Web Site: http://www.security-glazing.com
Architectural & Security Glass & Glass-Clad Polycarbonate Products Mfr
N.A.I.C.S.: 327211
Jacob Glann (Mgr-Matls)

Honsador Lumber LLC   (1)
91151 Malakole Rd, Kapolei, HI 96707
Tel.: (808) 682-2011
Web Site: http://www.honsador.com
Lumber, Plywood & Millwork Whslr
N.A.I.C.S.: 423310

Insulpane of Connecticut, Inc.   (1)
30 Edmund St, Hamden, CT 06517
Tel.: (203) 865-6021
Web Site: http://www.solarsales.com
Architectural Glass Product Mfr
N.A.I.C.S.: 332321
Paul Cody (Pres)

Mann Lake Ltd.   (1)
501 1st St S, Hackensack, MN 56452
Web Site: http://www.mannlakeltd.com
Beekeeping Supply Mfr
N.A.I.C.S.: 333111
Betty Thomas (Co-Founder)
Jack Thomas (Co-Founder)

Subsidiary (Domestic):

Stromberg's Unlimited, Inc.   (2)
501 1st St S, Hackensack, MN 56452
Tel.: (800) 720-1134
Web Site:
  http://www.strombergschickens.com
Poultry Product Distr
N.A.I.C.S.: 424440

GREYLOCK PARTNERS
2550 Sand Hill Rd, Menlo Park, CA 94025
Tel.: (650) 493-5525
Web Site: http://www.greylock.com
Year Founded: 1965
Sales Range: $25-49.9 Million
Emp.: 50
Private Equity Investments
N.A.I.C.S.: 523999
Reid G. Hoffman (Gen Partner)
Don Sullivan (Partner-Admin & Fin)
William W. Helman IV (Gen Partner)
Asheem Chandna (Partner)
Jerry Chen (Partner)
Joseph Ansanelli (Partner)
John Lilly (Partner-Venture)
Simon Rothman (Partner)
Sarah Guo (Gen Partner)
Elisa Schreiber (Partner-Mktg)
David Strohm (Partner)
James Slavet (Partner)

GREYMART METAL COMPANY INC.

974 Meeker Ave, Brooklyn, NY 11222
Tel.: (718) 388-1432
Web Site:
  https://greymartmetalco.com
Year Founded: 1926
Sales Range: $10-24.9 Million
Emp.: 18
Recycling Services
N.A.I.C.S.: 562920
Steven Nalaboff (Pres)

Subsidiaries:

Enviro Shred Inc   (1)
974 Meeker Ave, Brooklyn, NY 11222
Tel.: (718) 384-2144
Web Site: http://www.enviro-shred.com
Rev.: $450,000
Emp.: 6
Document & Office Record Destruction
N.A.I.C.S.: 561499

GREYROCK CAPITAL GROUP, LLC

230 W Monroe St Ste 2000, Chicago,
IL 60606
Tel.: (312) 849-0006   DE
Web Site: http://www.greyrockcapital
  group.com
Equity Investment Firm
N.A.I.C.S.: 523999
Todd Osburn (Partner)
Tracy Perkins (Partner)
Jeff Birch (CFO & VP)
Daniel Kapnick (VP)

GREYSTAR REAL ESTATE PARTNERS, LLC

465 Meeting St Ste 500, Charleston,
SC 29403
Tel.: (843) 579-9400   DE
Web Site: http://www.greystar.com
Year Founded: 1993
Holding Company; Residential Real
Estate Investment, Development &
Property Management Services
N.A.I.C.S.: 551112
Bob Faith (Founder, Chm & CEO)
Derek Ramsey (Exec Mng Dir)
Bill Maddux (Exec Mng Dir)
Wes Fuller (Exec Mng Dir-Investment
Mgmt)
Andrew Livingstone (Exec Mng Dir-
Property Mgmt)
Scott Wise (Exec Mng Dir-Dev &
Construction Svcs)
Jodi Bearden (Sr Mng Dir-Enterprise
Svcs)
Todd Wigfield (Sr Mng Dir-Dev)
Yale Dieckmann (Mng Dir-Dev)
Chris MacNaughton (Sr Mng Dir-
Portfolio Mgmt)
Kevin Scelfo (Mng Dir-Portfolio Mgmt)
John Clarkson (Mng Dir-Dev-Mid-
Atlantic)
Pia Cornejo (Sr Mng Dir-Global
People & Culture)
Scott Berka (Sr Mng Dir)

Subsidiaries:

Education Realty Trust, Inc.   (1)
999 S Shady Grove Rd Ste 600, Memphis,
TN 38120
Tel.: (901) 259-2500
Web Site: http://www.EdRTrust.com
Rev.: $331,066,000
Assets: $3,015,164,000
Liabilities: $1,169,199,000
Net Worth: $1,845,965,000
Earnings: $47,440,000
Emp.: 1,265
Fiscal Year-end: 12/31/2017
Ownership, Development & Management of
Student Housing
N.A.I.C.S.: 721310
Christine D. Richards (COO & Exec VP)
James Kenner (VP-Design)
Liz Keough (Gen Counsel, Sec & Sr VP)
Lindsey Mackie (Chief Acctg Officer & Sr
VP)

Scott P. Casey (CTO & Sr VP-Strategic Bus
Dev)
Matthew S. Fulton (Sr VP-Ops)
Steve Schnoor (Sr VP-Western Dev)
Randy Schnoor (Chief Info Sys Officer & Sr
VP)
Julie Skolnicki (Sr VP-University Partner-
ships)
Scott Barton (Sr VP-Acquisitions & Dev)
Bob Earwood (Sr VP-Construction & Engrg
Svcs)
Mark Grambergs (VP-Real Estate Dev)
Jason Taylor (Sr VP-University Partner-
ships)
Jared Everett (VP-University Partnerships)
Kim Grisvard (VP-Sls & Mktg)
Sonja Harris (VP-HR)
Scott Jones (VP-IT)
Rodney J. King (VP-Real Estate Dev)
Patrick Parsons (VP-Dev)
Dawn Ray (VP-Corp Comm & Mktg)
Jeffrey Resetco (VP-Real Estate Dev &
Construction)
Jennifer E. Worsham (VP-Ops)
Joshua J. Wilson (VP-Real Estate Dev)
Agnes Webb (VP-Tax Compliance)
Steve Simonetti (VP-Land Acquisition &
Dev)
Brad Shaw (VP-Client Rels)

Subsidiary (Domestic):

319 Bragg Student Housing Auburn
AL LLC   (2)
319 Bragg Ave, Auburn, AL 36830
Tel.: (334) 826-6868
Emp.: 22
Boarding House Management Services
N.A.I.C.S.: 721310

Allen & O'Hara Education Services,
Inc.   (2)
530 Oak Ct Dr, Memphis, TN
38117   (100%)
Tel.: (901) 259-2500
Web Site: http://www.aoinc.com
Sales Range: $25-49.9 Million
Emp.: 112
Collegiate Student Housing
N.A.I.C.S.: 624229
Randy Churchey (Pres)

EDR Auburn, LLC   (2)
1255 S College St, Auburn, AL 36832-5809
Tel.: (334) 826-1202
Web Site:
  http://www.reserveonsouthcollege.com
Residential Building Rental & Leasing Ser-
vices
N.A.I.C.S.: 531110
Allyson Robinson (Mgr-Community)

EDR Management Inc.   (2)
700 Greenbag Rd, Morgantown, WV 26508
Tel.: (304) 296-0688
Trust, Fiduciary & Custody Services
N.A.I.C.S.: 523991
Ryan Sullivan (Reg Dir & Mgr-Community)

EDR Syracuse, LLC   (2)
315 Small Rd, Syracuse, NY 13210
Tel.: (315) 424-1047
Web Site: http://www.uvcolvin.com
Emp.: 11
Real Estate Management Services
N.A.I.C.S.: 531210
Jaimee Morrissey (Gen Mgr)

GM Westberry, LLC   (2)
2855 W Bowie St, Fort Worth, TX 76109
Tel.: (817) 924-2900
Web Site: http://www.grandmarctcu.com
Sales Range: $25-49.9 Million
Emp.: 17
Real Estate Management Services
N.A.I.C.S.: 531210
Ajax Atzinter (Mgr-Property)

River Pointe (DE), LLC   (2)
915 Lovvorn Rd, Carrollton, GA 30117
Tel.: (770) 834-9393
Web Site: http://www.riveruwga.com
Residential Building Rental & Leasing Ser-
vices
N.A.I.C.S.: 531110
Marcus Duvall (Mgr-Mktg & Leasing)

University Village Towers, LLC   (2)
3500 Iowa Ave, Riverside, CA 92507
Tel.: (951) 276-2929

Web Site:
  http://www.universityvillagetowers.com
Emp.: 10
Real Estate Management Services
N.A.I.C.S.: 531110

Greystar Development & Construc-
tion, L.P.   (1)
750 Bering Dr Ste 400, Houston, TX 77057
Tel.: (713) 966-5000
Web Site: http://www.greystar.com
Sales Range: $100-124.9 Million
Residential Property Development & Multi-
Family Housing Construction
N.A.I.C.S.: 236117

Greystar Growth & Income Fund,
LP   (1)
18 Broad St 3rd Fl, Charleston, SC 29401
Tel.: (843) 579-9400
Closed-End Investment Fund
N.A.I.C.S.: 525990
Robert A. Faith (Chm & CEO)

Greystar Management Services,
L.P.   (1)
750 Bering Dr Ste 400, Houston, TX 77057
Tel.: (713) 966-5000
Web Site: http://www.greystar.com
Residential Property Management & Real
Estate Services
N.A.I.C.S.: 531311
Stacy Hunt (Exec Dir-Natl Client Rels &
New Bus Dev)
Andrew Livingstone (Exec Dir-Real Estate
Svcs)

Pinnacle at Union Hills LLC   (1)
4750 E Union Hills Dr, Phoenix, AZ 85050-
3363
Tel.: (602) 313-0140
Web Site:
  http://www.pinnacleatunionhills.com
Emp.: 6
Multifamily Residential Property Manager
N.A.I.C.S.: 531311
Lisa Bergeron (Mgr)

Riverstone Residential Group,
LLC   (1)
1201 Elm St Ste 1600, Dallas, TX 75270
Tel.: (214) 965-6000
Web Site: http://www.riverstoneres.com
Emp.: 4,700
Multifamily Residential Property Manager
N.A.I.C.S.: 531311
Terry Danner (CEO)
MarySusan Wanich (COO)
Peggy Bertsch (Chief Acctg Officer)
Mike Dow (Chief Client Relations Officer)
Mel Barks (Chief Performance Officer)
Laurie Brashear (Chief HR Officer)
Tom Daniels (Div Pres-Northwest)
Stephanie Brock (Div Pres-Central)
Maura Bilafer (Div Pres-East)
Gardner Rees (Div Pres-Ancillary Svcs)
Stephanie Fuhrman (Exec VP-Property
Svcs)
Lisa Ellis (Exec VP-Client Rels)
Dave Denslow (Exec VP-Property Mainte-
nance Svcs)
Katie Sibbern (CMO)

GREYSTON BAKERY INC.

104 Alexander St, Yonkers, NY 10701
Tel.: (914) 375-1510
Web Site:
  http://www.greystonbakery.com
Year Founded: 1982
Sales Range: $1-9.9 Million
Emp.: 53
Bakery Product Mfr & Distr
N.A.I.C.S.: 327910
Gregg Lerner (Chm)
Joel Frank (Treas)
Mike Brady (Pres & CEO)
Lisa Saltzman (Dir-Sls & Mktg)
Ariella Gastel (Mgr-Acctg)

GREYSTONE & CO., INC.

152 W 57th St Fl 60, New York, NY
10019
Tel.: (212) 649-9700   NY
Web Site: http://www.greyco.com
Sales Range: $650-699.9 Million

Emp.: 3,000
Investment Bankers
N.A.I.C.S.: 523150
Stephen Rosenberg (Founder &
CEO)
Robert Barolak (Co-COO)
Rick Wolf (Sr Mng Dir & Head-
Production-West Coast)
Joe Mosley (Exec VP-Fannie Mae &
Freddie Mac Lending)
Claudia Schiepers (CMO)
Arthur Hatzopoulos (Mng Dir)
Karen Marotta (Dir-Comm)
Nikhil Kanodia (Head-FHA Lending)
Robert Russell (Head-CMBS Produc-
tion)
Steven Caligor (Sr Mng Dir-
Structured Fin)
Jim McDevitt (Pres-Multifamily Sls
Advisory)
Sharon Briskman (Exec VP-Servicing
& Asset Mgmt)
Betsy Vartanian (Exec VP)
Charlie Baxter (Chief Lending Officer)
Jonathan D. Coven (Mng Dir)
Lisa Schwartz (Gen Counsel)
Serafino Tobia (Dir-CMBS & Bond
Trading)
Victoria Spevacek (Chief Talent Offi-
cer)
Dan Frink (Mng Dir-FHA Lending)
Scott Thurman (Sr Mng Dir)
Jerry Muir (Mng Dir)
Ana Ramos (Mng Dir & Head-Small
Loan Production-West Coast)
Shana Daby (Mng Dir-FHA Lending)
Kelley Klobetanz (Mng Dir-FHA
Team-Denver)
Michael Doran (Mng Dir-Atlanta)
Mark R. Jarrell (Head-Portfolio Lend-
ing Grp)
Anthony Alicea (Head-Production-
Portfolio Lending Grp)
Marc Zimmet (Mng Dir-Healthcare
Lending Grp)
Bryan Foxley (Mng Dir-Kirkland)
Billy Posey (Head-Lending Ops)
Paul Smyth (Mng Dir-CMBS Platform-
Irving)
Cary Williams (Mng Dir-CMBS
Platform-Irving)
Paul Jankovsky (Mng Dir-CMBS
Platform-Irving)
Robert Farrington (Dir-CMBS
Platform-Irving)
Matthew Downs (Mng Dir-CMBS)
Chip Hudson (CEO-Agency Lending)
David E. Friedman (Sr Mng Dir &
Head-Institutional Lending)
C. Lamar Seats (Sr VP-FHA Produc-
tion)
David Goodwin (Mng Dir-Portfolio
Lending Grp)
Steve Germano (Sr Mng Dir-Atlanta)
Niraj Patel (CIO & Head-Tech)
Curt Pollock (Co-COO)
Marc A. Fox (CFO)
Jared Noordyk (Head-Securitization)
Natalie Grainger (Chief Credit Officer)
Rich Highfield (Head-CMBS)
Clive Lipshitz (Mng Dir-Corp Fin Grp)
Jeffrey Baevsky (Exec Mng Dir-Corp
Fin)
Lance Wright (Mng Dir-Dallas)
Vince Mejia (Sr VP-Agency Produc-
tion)
John Sloot (Mng Dir-Dallas)
Debby Jenkins (Exec Mng Dir)

Subsidiaries:

Greystone Affordable Housing Initiatives, LLC   (1)
4025 Lake Boone Trl Ste 209, Raleigh, NC
27607
Tel.: (919) 573-7500
Financial Management Services

Greystone & Co., Inc.—(Continued)

N.A.I.C.S.: 523940

Greystone Housing Impact Investors LP   (1)
14301 FNB Pkwy Ste No 211, Omaha, NE 68154
Tel.: (402) 952-1235
Web Site: https://www.ghinvestors.com
Rev.: $104,900,664
Assets: $1,513,400,702
Liabilities: $1,164,093,994
Net Worth: $349,306,708
Earnings: $51,143,118
Emp.: 16
Fiscal Year-end: 12/31/2023
Financial Services
N.A.I.C.S.: 523999
Neil Bo (Mng Dir)
Frank Bravo (Mng Dir)
Andy Grier (Sr VP)
Robert Schultz (Mng Dir)
Brett Southworth (Mng Dir)
Jason Kaye (Mng Dir)
Jesse A. Coury (CFO)
Kenneth C. Rogozinski (CEO)

Greystone Servicing Corporation, Inc.   (1)
419 Belle Air Ln, Warrenton, VA 20186
Tel.: (540) 341-2100
Web Site: http://www.greystoneusa.com
Sales Range: $50-74.9 Million
Emp.: 200
Real Estate Loan Asset Management Services
N.A.I.C.S.: 523940
Betsy Vartanian (Exec VP)

GREYSTONE CONSTRUCTION COMPANY
500 Marschall Rd Ste 300, Shakopee, MN 55379-2690
Tel.: (952) 496-2227
Web Site: http://www.greystoneconstruction.com
Year Founded: 1986
Sales Range: $10-24.9 Million
Emp.: 80
Provider of Industrial Building & Warehouse Services
N.A.I.C.S.: 236220
Kevin O'Brien (Pres)
Chad Schmit (Superintendent-Shop)

GREYSTONE GRAPHICS, INC.
101 Greystone Ave, Kansas City, KS 66103-1325
Tel.: (913) 342-1393   KS
Year Founded: 1922
Sales Range: $100-124.9 Million
Emp.: 170
Printers Specializing In Multi-color Sheetfed & Web 40″ to 60″ Sheet Size; Also Direct Mail & Finishing Operation
N.A.I.C.S.: 323111
Eugene Reynolds (Pres & CEO)
Kevin Walsh (Chm)

Subsidiaries:

Coleridge Design & Imaging, Inc. (1)
101 Greyston Ave, Kansas City, KS 66103   (100%)
Tel.: (816) 878-6060
Sales Range: $10-24.9 Million
Emp.: 6
Graphic Design Illustration Photography, Copywriting & Multi Media
N.A.I.C.S.: 323120

GREYSTONE HEALTHCARE MANAGEMENT CORP.
4042 Park Oaks Blvd Ste 300, Tampa, FL 33610-9536
Tel.: (813) 635-9500
Web Site: http://www.greystonehealth.com
Year Founded: 2001
Sales Range: $100-124.9 Million

Emp.: 3,000
Health Care Management Services
N.A.I.C.S.: 541618
Steve Rosenberg (Pres)
Jean Nelson (Reg Dir-Clinical Ops)
Connie Bessler (CEO)
Melissa Purvis (Chief Nursing Officer)

GREYSTONE INCORPORATED
7 Wellington Rd, Lincoln, RI 02865
Tel.: (401) 333-0444   RI
Web Site: https://www.greyst.com
Holding Company; Metal Plating Services
N.A.I.C.S.: 551112
Everett H. Fernald Jr. (Owner & Pres)

Subsidiaries:

Induplate, LLC   (1)
1 Greystone Dr, North Providence, RI 02911
Tel.: (401) 231-5770
Web Site: http://www.greyst.com
Sales Range: $10-24.9 Million
Emp.: 75
Plating Metal Mfr
N.A.I.C.S.: 332813

GREYSTONE POWER CORPORATION
4040 Bankhead Hwy, Douglasville, GA 30134-4313
Tel.: (770) 942-6576
Web Site: http://www.greystonepower.com
Year Founded: 1936
Sales Range: $25-49.9 Million
Emp.: 275
Provider of Electric Services
N.A.I.C.S.: 221118
Gary Miller (Pres & CEO)

GREYSTONE PROGRAMS, INC.
36 Violet Ave, Poughkeepsie, NY 12601
Tel.: (845) 452-5772   NY
Web Site: http://www.greystoneprograms.org
Year Founded: 1979
Sales Range: $10-24.9 Million
Emp.: 453
Developmental Disability Assistance Services
N.A.I.C.S.: 623210
Pattiann LaVeglia (Dir-Clinical Svcs)
Julius Jones (Sec)
Robert Dietz (Co-Pres)

GRID ALTERNATIVES
1171 Ocean Ave Ste 200, Oakland, CA 94608
Tel.: (510) 731-1310   CA
Web Site: https://www.gridalternatives.org
Year Founded: 2002
Sales Range: $25-49.9 Million
Emp.: 121
Solar Electric System Installation Services
N.A.I.C.S.: 238160
Tim Sears (Co-Founder & COO)
Erica Mackie (Co-Founder & CEO)
Anna Bautista (VP-Construction & Workforce Dev)
Stanley Greschner (VP-Govt Rels & Market Dev)
Dan Dumovich (Mgr-Program)
Katie Kerr (Dir-HR)
Maura McKnight (Dir-Corp Partnership)
Julian Foley (Dir-Comm)
Katelyn McClintock (Mgr-Digital Comm)
Tim Willink (Dir-Tribal Programs)
Carla Estrada (Country Mgr)
Jenean Smith (Dir-Intl Programs)

Karen Edson (Pres)
Ben Tarbell (Sec)
Phyllis Currie (VP)
Jeff Coleman (VP-Outreach)

GRIDIRON CAPITAL, LLC
220 Elm St, New Canaan, CT 06840
Tel.: (203) 972-1100
Web Site: http://www.gridironcapital.com
Year Founded: 2006
Privater Equity Firm
N.A.I.C.S.: 523999
Geoffrey D. Spillane (Mng Dir)
Owen G. Tharrington (Mng Dir)
William Hausberg (Mng Dir)
Sean M. Kelley (Mng Dir-Bus Dev)
Kevin Jackson (Mng Partner)
Kallie Hapgood (Mng Dir)
Christopher M. King (Principal)
Scott C. Harrison (Mng Dir & COO)
Douglas Rosenstein (Principal)
Bradley S. Skaf (VP)
John Warner (Mng Dir)
John Nives (Operating Partner)
Jeff Steinhorn (Operating Partner)
Thomas A. Burger Jr. (Co-Founder & Mng Partner)
Eugene P. Conese Jr. (Co-Founder & Mng Partner)
Joseph A. Saldutti Jr. (Mng Dir)

Subsidiaries:

Class Valuation, LLC   (1)
2600 Bellingham Ste 100, Troy, MI 48083
Tel.: (248) 220-2360
Web Site: http://www.classappraisalsorders.com
Real Estate Appraisal Management Services
N.A.I.C.S.: 531320
Stephanie Holdsworth (COO)
John Fraas (CEO)

Subsidiary (Domestic):

Landmark Network Inc.   (2)
5805 Sepulveda Blvd Ste 801, Van Nuys, CA 91411
Web Site: http://landmarknetwork.com
Sales Range: $1-9.9 Million
Emp.: 36
Real Estate Appraisal Management Services
N.A.I.C.S.: 531390
Hunter Gorog (Partner)
Lou Franzini (CFO)

Market Data Service LLC   (2)
765 E Gordon Ave, Layton, UT 84041
Tel.: (801) 657-5769
Web Site: http://www.datamasterusa.com
Software Development Services
N.A.I.C.S.: 541511
Rick Lifferth (CEO)
Ryan Lifferth (VP-Dev & Tech)
Mitch Dorius (VP-Sls & Mktg)
Derek Lamb (Mgr-Sls)
Nathan Kane (Dir-Software Engrg)

Dent Wizard International Corp.   (1)
4710 Earth City Expy, Bridgeton, MO 63044
Tel.: (314) 592-1800
Web Site: http://www.dentwizard.com
Paintless Dent Removal Services
N.A.I.C.S.: 811121
Mike Black (CEO)
Terry R. Koebbe (Chm)
Michael Fedorowich (VP-Northeast US & Canada)
Matt Boyd (Dir-Ops-Canada)
Jim Powers (CFO)
Dave Harness (VP-IT)
Cory Lyda (VP-Key Ops)
Addison Thomas (Pres)
Andy Trommer (CTO)
Adam Nebeker (COO)

Subsidiary (Non-US):

Dent Wizard GmbH   (2)
Siemensstrasse 55A, 25462, Rellingen, Germany
Tel.: (49) 410178920

Web Site: http://www.dentwizard.de
Automotive Dent Removal Services
N.A.I.C.S.: 811121
Thomas Kuesel (Mng Dir)
Haiko Eichhorn (Mng Dir)
Bernd Lonne (Mng Dir)

Dent Wizard S.A.S.   (2)
20 Boulevard Eugene Deruelle, Le Britannia - Bat A, 69432, Lyon, Cedex 03, France
Tel.: (33) 437913222
Web Site: http://www.dentwizard.fr
Emp.: 100
Automotive Accessories
N.A.I.C.S.: 441330
Xavier Goutille (Mgr-Fin)

McKenzie Sports Products LLC   (1)
1910 St Luke Church Rd, Salisbury, NC 28146
Tel.: (704) 279-7985
Web Site: http://www.mckenziesp.com
Sales Range: $50-74.9 Million
Taxidermy Product Mfr & Distr
N.A.I.C.S.: 423920
Kevin McKenzie (Chm)
Dave Sachs (CFO)

Subsidiary (Domestic):

Van Dyke Supply Co., Inc.   (2)
39771 SD Hwy 34 E, Woonsocket, SD 57385
Tel.: (605) 796-4425
Web Site: http://www.vandykestaxidermy.com
Sales Range: $100-124.9 Million
Emp.: 70
Mail Order Catalog Company
N.A.I.C.S.: 423850

Ramsey Industries Inc.   (1)
4707 N Mingo Rd, Tulsa, OK 74117
Tel.: (918) 438-2760
Web Site: http://www.ramsey.com
Construction Machinery
N.A.I.C.S.: 333923
John Celoni (CEO)
Bryan Fleming (CFO)

Subsidiary (Domestic):

Auto Crane Company   (2)
4707 N Mingo Rd, Tulsa, OK 74117-5904
Tel.: (918) 836-0463
Web Site: http://www.autocrane.com
Truck Mounted Field Service Electric & Hydraulic Telescopic Cranes, Hydraulic Articulating Cranes, Crane Service Bodies & Hydraulic Air Compressors
N.A.I.C.S.: 333924
Michael Gelsthorpe (Reg Mgr-Sls)

Ramsey Winch Company Inc.   (2)
4707 N Mingo Rd, Tulsa, OK 74117-5904
Tel.: (918) 438-2760
Web Site: http://www.ramsey.com
Construction Machinery
N.A.I.C.S.: 333923
Lori McCauley (Mgr-HR)

Vertical Supply Group   (1)
496 Gallimore Dairy Rd Ste D, Greensboro, NC 27409
Tel.: (336) 378-0444
Web Site: https://www.verticalsupplygroup.com
Arborist Tools & Equipment Distr
N.A.I.C.S.: 423820
Tripp Wyckoff (CEO)

Subsidiary (Domestic):

Sherrill, Inc.   (2)
496 Gallimore Dairy Rd Ste D, Greensboro, NC 27406
Tel.: (800) 525-8873
Web Site: http://www.sherrilltree.com
Farm & Garden Machinery & Equipment Merchant Whslr
N.A.I.C.S.: 423820

GRIFFIN & ASSOCIATES
119 Dartmouth Dr SE, Albuquerque, NM 87106
Tel.: (505) 764-4444
Web Site: http://www.griffinassoc.com
Year Founded: 1990
Sales Range: $1-9.9 Million
Emp.: 15

Public Relations & Marketing Services
N.A.I.C.S.: 541820
Joanie Griffin *(Pres & CEO)*
Patricia Garrett *(Controller)*
Jamie Dickerman *(VP-IR)*
David Dabney *(Dir-Digital Solutions)*
Floyd Vasquez Jr. *(Acct Mgr)*

Subsidiaries:

Griffin & Associates **(1)**
1422 Animas View Dr #28, Durango, CO 81301 **(100%)**
Tel.: (970) 817-9981
Web Site: http://www.griffinassoc.com
Public Relations & Advertising Services
N.A.I.C.S.: 541820
Patricia Garrett *(Controller)*

GRIFFIN BEVERAGE CO.
1901 Dam Rd, West Branch, MI 48661
Tel.: (989) 345-0540
Web Site: https://www.griffinbev.com
Sales Range: $10-24.9 Million
Emp.: 25
Provider of Beer & Other Fermented Malt Liquors
N.A.I.C.S.: 424810
Robert Griffin *(Pres)*
Jeff Gronda *(Acct Mgr)*

GRIFFIN CAPITAL CORPORATION
Griffin Capital Plaza 1520 E Grand Ave, El Segundo, CA 90245
Tel.: (310) 469-6100 CA
Web Site:
http://www.griffincapital.com
Year Founded: 1995
Emp.: 200
Real Estate Investment & Portfolio Management; Securities Brokerage & Dealing Services
N.A.I.C.S.: 523940
Kevin A. Shields *(Chm & CEO)*
Michael J. Escalante *(Chief Investment Officer)*
David C. Rupert *(Pres)*
Howard S. Hirsch *(Gen Counsel-Securities)*
Joseph E. Miller *(CFO & COO)*
Mary P. Higgins *(Gen Counsel-Real Estate)*
Eric J. Kaplan *(Mng Dir-Acq)*
Don G. Pescara *(Mng Dir-Acq)*
Scott A. Tausk *(Mng Dir-Asset Mgmt)*
Julie A. Treinen *(Mng Dir-Asset Mgmt)*
Louis K. Sohn *(Mng Dir-Acquisition)*
Shawn R. Carstens *(VP-Acq)*
Travis W. Bushman *(VP)*
Lily Fong *(Sr VP)*
Mark M. Goldberg *(Exec VP)*
Jennifer Nahas *(VP-Mktg)*
Chester P. White *(Founder)*

Subsidiaries:

American Healthcare REIT, Inc. **(1)**
18191 Von Karman Ave 3rd Fl, Irvine, CA 92612
Tel.: (949) 270-9200
Web Site:
https://www.americanhealthcarereit.com
Rev.: $1,643,175,000
Assets: $4,786,698,000
Liabilities: $3,137,335,000
Net Worth: $1,567,765,000
Earnings: ($73,383,000)
Emp.: 113
Fiscal Year-end: 12/31/2022
Healthcare Industry Real Estate Investment Trust
N.A.I.C.S.: 525990
Danny Prosky *(Pres & CEO)*
Brian S. Peay *(CFO)*
Gabe Willhite *(COO)*
Mark Foster *(Gen Counsel, Sec & Exec VP)*
Stefan Oh *(Chief Investment Officer)*

Kenny Lin *(Chief Acctg Officer, Deputy CFO & Exec VP)*
Wendie Newman *(Exec VP-Asset Mgmt)*
Ray Oborn *(Exec VP-Asset Mgmt)*
Charlynn Diapo *(Sr VP-Accounting & Finance)*

Subsidiary (Domestic):

Griffin-American Healthcare REIT III, Inc. **(2)**
18191 Von Karman Ave Ste 300, Irvine, CA 92612
Tel.: (949) 270-9200
Web Site: http://www.healthcarereit3.com
Rev.: $1,244,301,000
Assets: $3,234,937,000
Liabilities: $2,200,454,000
Net Worth: $1,034,483,000
Earnings: $2,163,000
Emp.: 50
Fiscal Year-end: 12/31/2020
Healthcare Industry Real Estate Investment Trust
N.A.I.C.S.: 525990
Jeffrey T. Hanson *(Chm & CEO)*
Danny Prosky *(Pres & COO)*
Brian S. Peay *(CFO)*
Mathieu B. Streiff *(Gen Counsel & Exec VP)*
Stefan K. L. Oh *(Sr VP-Acquisitions)*
Cora Lo *(Sec)*

Joint Venture (Domestic):

Trilogy Health Services LLC **(3)**
303 N Hurstbourne Pkwy Ste 200, Louisville, KY 40222 **(70%)**
Tel.: (502) 412-5847
Web Site: https://www.trilogyhs.com
Women Healthcare Services
N.A.I.C.S.: 532283
Randall J. Bufford *(Pres & CEO)*

Griffin Capital Essential Asset REIT II, Inc. **(1)**
Griffin Capital Plz 1520 E Grand Ave, El Segundo, CA 90245
Tel.: (310) 469-6100
Web Site: http://www.griffincapital.com
Rev.: $106,394,000
Assets: $1,137,335,000
Liabilities: $620,827,000
Net Worth: $516,508,000
Earnings: ($3,281,000)
Emp.: 50
Fiscal Year-end: 12/31/2018
Real Estate Investment Trust
N.A.I.C.S.: 525990
Kevin A. Shields *(Chm & CEO)*
Michael J. Escalante *(Pres)*
David C. Rupert *(Pres & VP)*
Howard S. Hirsch *(Sec & VP)*
Mary P. Higgins *(Gen Counsel & VP)*
Don G. Pescara *(VP-Acquisitions)*
Julie A. Treinen *(VP-Asset Mgmt)*
Javier F. Bitar *(CFO & Treas)*

Griffin Capital Securities, Inc. **(1)**
18191 Von Karman Ave Ste 300, Irvine, CA 92612
Tel.: (949) 270-9300
Web Site: http://www.griffincapital.com
Emp.: 40
Securities Broker & Dealer
N.A.I.C.S.: 523150
Kevin A. Shields *(Chm)*
Charles Huang *(COO & Chief Compliance Officer)*
Deron Richens *(VP-Internal Sls)*
Howard Hirsch *(Gen Counsel)*
Vere Reynolds-Hale *(Mng Dir-Natl Accts)*
Jennifer Nahas *(VP-Mktg-Griffin Capital Company, LLC)*
Mark M. Goldberg *(CEO)*
Adam Hanson *(Sr VP-Independent Broker Dealer Channel-Florida)*
Cory Calvert *(Dir-Sls-Natl)*

Peakstone Realty Trust **(1)**
1520 E Grand Ave, El Segundo, CA 90245
Tel.: (310) 606-3200
Web Site: https://www.pkst.com
Rev.: $416,485,000
Assets: $3,633,376,000
Liabilities: $1,776,053,000
Net Worth: $1,857,323,000
Earnings: ($411,909,000)
Emp.: 36
Fiscal Year-end: 12/31/2022

Real Estate Investment Trust
N.A.I.C.S.: 525990
Michael J. Escalante *(Pres & CEO)*
Javier F. Bitar *(CFO & Treas)*
Nina Momtazee Sitzer *(COO & Chief Legal Officer)*
Casey Wold *(Chm)*
Lily Fong *(Sr VP)*
Mikayla Lynch *(Sr VP)*
Carrie DiTolla *(Sr VP & Controller)*
Travis Bushman *(Mng Dir)*
Jay Venzon *(Mng Dir)*
Marina Braccio *(VP)*
Courtney Pierre *(VP)*
Adam Sickley *(VP)*
Stacie O'Connor *(VP-Human Resources)*
Dan Ranchigoda *(VP-Investor Relations)*
Nick Goggin *(Assoc VP)*
Rich Hoopis *(Sr Dir)*
Max Kaminsky *(Sr Dir)*
Kirsten Urakami *(Acct Mgr)*
Jon Paul Johnson *(Acct Mgr)*
Jasmine Lozano *(Supvr-Financial Reporting)*
David Carballo *(Sr Accountant)*
Daisy Burgos *(Sr Accountant)*
Kenneth Ng *(Accountant-Staff)*
Maria Mojica *(Accountant-Staff)*

GRIFFIN CHRYSLER DODGE JEEP
961 E US Hwy 74, Hamlet, NC 28345-9704
Tel.: (910) 582-1200
Web Site:
http://www.mikegriffincars.com
Year Founded: 1994
Sales Range: $10-24.9 Million
Emp.: 50
New Car Whslr
N.A.I.C.S.: 441110
Debra Pate *(Mgr-Customer Rels)*

GRIFFIN COMMUNICATIONS, LLC
7401 N Kelly Ave, Oklahoma City, OK 73111-8420
Tel.: (405) 843-6641
Web Site:
http://www.griffincommunications.net
Year Founded: 1953
Sales Range: $25-49.9 Million
Emp.: 300
Holding Company; Television Broadcasting Stations
N.A.I.C.S.: 551112
David F. Griffin *(Pres & CEO)*
Ted Strickland *(COO)*
Wade Deaver *(VP-Sls)*
Chad Woolbright *(Dir-Sls-Tulsa)*
Stephanie Clark *(Mgr-Local Sls-News 9)*
Tony Lopresto *(CFO & VP)*
Steve Hunter *(Dir-Radio Ops & Programming)*
Randy Smith *(Dir-Radio Sls)*

Subsidiaries:

KHTT **(1)**
303 N Boston Ave, Tulsa, OK 74103
Tel.: (918) 743-7814
Web Site: http://www.khits.com
Radio Stations
N.A.I.C.S.: 516110
Randy Smith *(Gen Mgr-Sls)*
Dan Smith *(Mgr-Sls-Local)*
Steve Hunter *(Mgr-Ops)*
Tabatha Grammer *(Dir-Program)*

KOTV Inc. **(1)**
303 N Boston Ave, Tulsa, OK 74103
Tel.: (918) 732-6000
Web Site: http://www.newson6.com
Sales Range: $25-49.9 Million
Emp.: 140
Television Broadcaster
N.A.I.C.S.: 516120
Rob Krier *(COO & VP)*
Jeff Bardach *(Dir-content)*

GRIFFIN FORD INC.
1940 E Main St, Waukesha, WI 53186
Tel.: (262) 542-5781
Web Site: https://www.griffinford.com
Year Founded: 1960
Sales Range: $25-49.9 Million
Emp.: 125
Car Dealer
N.A.I.C.S.: 441110
John Griffin *(Gen Mgr)*
Jim Griffin *(Pres)*
Kip Rupple *(Mgr-New Vehicle Sls)*
Mark Doedens *(Mgr-New Cars)*
Loren Sweeney *(Mgr-Pre-Owned Sls)*
Anton Lak *(Mgr-Pre-Owned Sls)*
Jim Stein *(Mgr-Fleet)*
Kay Horn *(Mgr-Fin)*
Karen Kluczynski *(Mgr-Fin)*
Rob Jarecki *(Mgr-Svc)*

GRIFFIN FORD-LINCOLN-MERCURY, INC.
511 W 7th St, Tifton, GA 31794
Tel.: (229) 382-1300
Web Site: http://www.griffinford.net
Year Founded: 1986
Sales Range: $25-49.9 Million
Emp.: 40
Owner & Operator of Car Dealerships
N.A.I.C.S.: 441110
Myra Wiggins *(Office Mgr)*

GRIFFIN GREENHOUSE & NURSERY SUPPLIES, INC.
1619 Main St, Tewksbury, MA 01876
Tel.: (978) 851-4346 MA
Web Site: http://www.griffins.com
Year Founded: 1947
Sales Range: $75-99.9 Million
Emp.: 75
Greenhouse & Nursery Supplies
N.A.I.C.S.: 424930
Rick Hyslip *(Pres & CFO)*
Craig Hyslip *(COO)*
Chris Layne *(Mgr-Customer Svc)*
Dan Morrissey *(Mgr-Construction)*
Duane Salenger *(Dir-Ops)*
Ken Turrentine *(Dir-Mktg)*
Len Roux *(Dir-HR)*
Liz Janik *(Mgr-Bus Ops)*
Lou DeSisto *(Dir-Tech Knowledge)*
Melissa Liakas *(Dir-Fin)*
Rick Layne *(Mgr-Risk Compliance)*
Rick Yates *(Mgr-GGSPro Technical Support)*
T. J. Magnan *(Dir-Sls)*
Kenneth M. Hyslip Sr. *(CEO)*
Ken Hyslip Jr. *(Exec VP)*
Bob Hawkes Jr. *(Mgr-Pur)*

Subsidiaries:

Griffin Greenhouse & Nursery Supplies, Inc. - Connecticut **(1)**
20 Grandview Ct, Cheshire, CT 06410-1261
Tel.: (203) 699-0919
Web Site: http://www.griffins.com
Sales Range: $25-49.9 Million
Emp.: 7
Sale of Greenhouse Supplies
N.A.I.C.S.: 424910
Bill Page *(Gen Mgr)*

Griffin Greenhouse & Nursery Supplies, Inc. - Maine **(1)**
50 W Gray Rd, Gray, ME 04039-9772
Tel.: (207) 657-5442
Web Site: http://www.griffins.com
Sales Range: $25-49.9 Million
Emp.: 7
Greenhouse Supply Whslr
N.A.I.C.S.: 424910
Bob Corey *(Branch Mgr)*

Griffin Greenhouse & Nursery Supplies, Inc. - New Jersey **(1)**
1005 Whitehead Rd Ext, Ewing, NJ 08638-2424
Tel.: (609) 530-9120
Web Site: http://www.griffins.com

Griffin Greenhouse & Nursery Supplies, Inc.—(Continued)
Sales Range: $25-49.9 Million
Emp.: 5
Greenhouse Supplies
N.A.I.C.S.: 424910

Griffin Greenhouse & Nursery Supplies, Inc. - New York-Central (1)
1 Ellis Dr, Auburn, NY 13021-8588
Tel.: (315) 255-1450
Web Site: http://www.griffins.com
Sales Range: $25-49.9 Million
Emp.: 7
Nursery Supplies Whslr
N.A.I.C.S.: 444240
Mike Hamm (Branch Mgr)

Griffin Greenhouse & Nursery Supplies, Inc. - New York-East (1)
126 Van Guysling Ave, Schenectady, NY 12305
Tel.: (518) 381-7120
Web Site: http://www.griffins.com
Sales Range: $25-49.9 Million
Emp.: 14
Nursery Supplies Whslr
N.A.I.C.S.: 444240
Rick Hyslip (Pres)

Griffin Greenhouse & Nursery Supplies, Inc. - Pennsylvania (1)
200 Mountain View Rd, Morgantown, PA 19543
Tel.: (610) 286-0046
Web Site: http://www.griffins.com
Nursery Supply Distr
N.A.I.C.S.: 444240

Griffin Greenhouse & Nursery Supplies, Inc. - Virginia (1)
5612 Pride Rd, Richmond, VA 23224-1028
Tel.: (804) 233-3454
Web Site: http://www.griffins.com
Sales Range: $25-49.9 Million
Emp.: 8
Nursery Supply Distr
N.A.I.C.S.: 424910
Corey Patterson (Branch Mgr)

GRIFFIN HEALTH SERVICES CORPORATION
130 Division St, Derby, CT 06418-1326
Tel.: (203) 735-7421   CT
Web Site:
  https://www.griffinhealth.org
Year Founded: 1901
Sales Range: $75-99.9 Million
Emp.: 1,381
Hospital & Health Care Services
N.A.I.C.S.: 622110
Patrick Charmel (Pres & CEO)
Barbara Stumpo (VP-Patient Care Svcs)
Margaret Deegan (VP-Ambulatory Svcs)
Matthew Milardo (Dir-Revenue Cycle)
Kathleen Martin (VP-Patient Safety & Care Improvement)
Gene DeLaurentis (Dir-Environmental Svcs)
Christine Cooper (Dir-Radiology, Cardiology & Neurology)
Royce York (Dir-Respiratory Svcs)
John J. Zaprzalka (Vice Chm)
Ken Roberts (Dir-Comm & Pub Affairs)
Mark O'Neill (VP-Fin)
W. Neil Pearson (VP-Medical Staff)
Eileen Carino (Dir-Inpatient Psychiatry)
James Downey (Dir-Fin)
Michael Devito (Dir-Laboratory Svcs)
Myra Odenwaelder (Dir-Rehabilitation Svcs)
Patricia Degennaro (Dir-Infusion Svcs)
Adam Dworkin (VP-Ambulatory Svcs)

GRIFFIN HOLDINGS INC.

---

111 S Cherokee St, Muskogee, OK 74403
Tel.: (918) 687-6311
Web Site: http://www.griffinfoods.com
Year Founded: 1908
Rev.: $27,000,000
Emp.: 70
Investment Holding Company
N.A.I.C.S.: 551112

Subsidiaries:

Griffin Food Company (1)
111 S Cherokee St, Muskogee, OK 74403
Tel.: (918) 687-6311
Web Site: http://www.griffinfoods.com
Mfr of Waffle Syrup, Coconut & Canned Foods, Preserves, Jellies, Salad Dressing & Mustards
N.A.I.C.S.: 311999
John W. Griffin (Founder & Pres)

JDG Television Inc. (1)
4624 Kelley Hwy, Fort Smith, AR 72904
Tel.: (479) 785-2400
Web Site: http://www.jnwa.com
Rev.: $5,100,000
Emp.: 42
Television Translator Station
N.A.I.C.S.: 516120

GRIFFIN HOLDINGS, LLC
2121 Avenue of the Stars Ste 2575, Los Angeles, CA 90064
Tel.: (424) 245-4423   CA
Web Site: http://www.griffinhld.com
Year Founded: 2004
Privater Equity Firm
N.A.I.C.S.: 523999
Egal Gabbay (Mgr)
Samuel McCullough (Chm, Pres & CEO)

Subsidiaries:

Tufco Technologies, Inc. (1)
3161 S Ridge Rd, Green Bay, WI 54305
Tel.: (920) 336-0054
Web Site: http://www.tufco.com
Rev.: $99,287,639
Assets: $41,864,106
Liabilities: $10,070,996
Net Worth: $31,793,110
Earnings: ($3,980,768)
Emp.: 264
Fiscal Year-end: 09/30/2013
Converted Paper Product Mfr Specialty
Printing Services Business Imaging Paper Product Mfr
N.A.I.C.S.: 322299
James F. Robinson (Pres & CEO)
John Michaud (VP-Sls & Mktg)
Tim Spittgerber (CFO & VP)
Shaun Gabbay (Chm)

Subsidiary (Domestic):

Hamco Manufacturing & Distributing LLC (2)
1205 Burris Rd, Newton, NC 28658
Tel.: (828) 464-6730
Web Site: http://www.hamco.com
Sales Range: $300-349.9 Million
Emp.: 75
Printing Paper Products Distr
N.A.I.C.S.: 424120
Gary Isom (Gen Mgr)

GRIFFIN INTEGRATED COMMUNICATIONS
260 5th Ave 6th Fl, New York, NY 10001
Tel.: (212) 481-3456
Web Site: http://www.griffinpr.com
Year Founded: 1982
Sales Range: $1-9.9 Million
Emp.: 15
Public Relations & Advertising Agency
N.A.I.C.S.: 541820
Robert J. Griffin (Pres)

GRIFFIN INTERNATIONAL COMPANIES

5980 Golden Hills Dr, Minneapolis, MN 55416-1040
Tel.: (612) 344-4700
Web Site: http://www.griffinintl.com
Sales Range: $10-24.9 Million
Emp.: 25
Marketing, Product Development & Sourcing Services
N.A.I.C.S.: 541613
Bob Griffin (Pres & CEO)

GRIFFIN KBIK STEPHENS & THOMPSON
233 S Wacker Dr Ste 300, Chicago, IL 60606
Tel.: (312) 441-2500
Web Site: http://www.gkst.com
Rev.: $10,400,000
Emp.: 95
Investment Banking Services
N.A.I.C.S.: 523150
David G. Thompson (Pres)
Jim Kubik (Mng Dir-Pub Fin-BMO Capital Markets)
Mary Corrigan (Mng Dir & Head-Ops-BMO Capital Markets)
Derek J. Bonifer (VP-BMO Capital Markets)
Michael Boisvert (Mng Dir-Pub Fin Grp-BMO Capital Markets)
David DeYoung (Sr VP & Mgr)
Michael Hallmann (VP)
Kristyn Harrell (VP)
Ann Koch (VP-BMO Capital Markets)
James Rachlin (Mng Dir-BMO Capital Markets)
Amy Movitz (Asst VP)
Holly Wiemken (VP)

GRIFFIN MEDICAL PRODUCTS INC.
80 Manheim Ave, Bridgeton, NJ 08302
Tel.: (856) 455-6870
Web Site:
  http://www.buddiesbygriffin.com
Year Founded: 1984
Rev.: $10,000,000
Emp.: 100
Disposable Garments & Accessories
N.A.I.C.S.: 315250
Bruno A. Basile (Pres)

GRIFFIN PARTNERS, INC.
1177 W Loop S Ste 1750, Houston, TX 77027
Tel.: (713) 622-7714   TX
Web Site:
  http://www.griffinpartners.com
Year Founded: 1986
Emp.: 75
Commercial Real Estate Investment, Development & Property Management Services
N.A.I.C.S.: 531390
Fred B. Griffin (Chm)
David Magee (Dir-Engrg)
Jacquie McCombs (CFO)
Janie Snider (Sr VP-Property Mgmt)
Josh Cheatham (Sr VP)
Andrew Montgomery (Exec VP & Head-Acq)
Chris Broussard (Exec VP-Construction)
Terry Early (Mng Dir-Dev)
Edward Griffin (Pres & CEO)
Lee Moreland (Exec VP-Asset Mgmt)
Brian Pimley (Sr Mgr-Construction)
Fred J. Heyne IV (Mgr-Acq)

GRIFFIN TELEVISION, INC.
7401 N Kelley, Oklahoma City, OK 73113
Tel.: (405) 843-6641
Web Site: http://www.newsok.com
Year Founded: 1953

Sales Range: $10-24.9 Million
Emp.: 216
Broadcasting Services
N.A.I.C.S.: 516120
David Griffin (Pres)

GRIFFIN THERMAL PRODUCTS INC.
100 Hurricane Creek Rd, Piedmont, SC 29673
Tel.: (864) 845-5000
Web Site: http://www.griffinrad.com
Sales Range: $100-124.9 Million
Emp.: 80
Radiators & Radiator Shells & Cores, Motor Vehicle
N.A.I.C.S.: 336390
Steve Beebe (Dir-Mktg)
James Burns (Head-Engrg)
Tom Beebe (VP)

GRIFFIN'S HUB CHRYSLER JEEP DODGE
5700 S 27th St, Milwaukee, WI 53221
Tel.: (414) 253-3907
Web Site:
  https://www.griffinshubchrysler
  jeepdodge.com
Sales Range: $10-24.9 Million
Emp.: 40
Automobiles, New & Used
N.A.I.C.S.: 441110
Jim Griffin (Pres)

GRIFFIS BLESSING INC.
102 N Cascade Ave Ste 550, Colorado Springs, CO 80903-1409
Tel.: (719) 520-1234
Web Site:
  https://www.griffisblessing.com
Rev.: $29,628,340
Emp.: 100
Real Estate Brokers & Agents
N.A.I.C.S.: 531210
Marty Galindo (Sr VP-Construction Svcs)
David C. Bunkers (CFO & Sr VP-Fin Svcs)
Kelly Clay (Portfolio Mgr)
Doris Donahue Wall (VP)
Julie Romeo (Mgr-Property)
Becky Deeter (Mgr-Property)
Suzan Parra (Portfolio Mgr)
Penny Gettler (Mgr-Multifamily Property Svcs Grp)
Erin Moroney (Dir-Bus Dev & Mktg Admin)
Steve Engel (Principal-Investment Svcs)
Liz Seeger (Portfolio Mgr)
Richard K. Davidson (Sr VP-Comml Property Svcs)
Patricia A. Stanforth (Sr VP-Multifamily Property Svcs)

GRIFFIS INC.
2630 US Hwy 441 S, Douglas, GA 31535
Tel.: (912) 383-6250
Sales Range: $10-24.9 Million
Emp.: 110
Convenience Store
N.A.I.C.S.: 445131
Aden Griffis (Pres)

GRIFFITH & COE ADVERTISING, INC.
801 Jerry Ct, Martinsburg, WV 25401
Tel.: (304) 263-1453   MD
Year Founded: 1983
Sales Range: $10-24.9 Million
Emp.: 9
Business-To-Business, Industrial
N.A.I.C.S.: 541810
James A. Coe (Co-Founder & Pres)

GRIFFITH COMPANY

12200 Bloomfield Ave, Santa Fe
Springs, CA 90670-0150
Tel.: (562) 929-1128
Web Site:
https://www.griffithcompany.net
Rev.: $70,000,000
Emp.: 300
Highway & Street Construction
N.A.I.C.S.: 237310
Tom Foss *(Pres & CEO)*

GRIFFITH ELECTRIC SUPPLY COMPANY

5 2nd St, Trenton, NJ 08611
Tel.: (609) 695-6121
Web Site: https://www.griffithelec.com
Rev.: $13,000,000
Emp.: 55
Electrical Supplies
N.A.I.C.S.: 423610
Bill Goodwin *(Pres)*
Ron Lim *(VP-Sls & Mktg)*
Paul Mauro *(Branch Mgr)*
Ron Kaczmarek *(VP-Pur)*

GRIFFITH HOLDINGS INC.

3021 Weymouth Rd, Medina, OH
44256
Tel.: (330) 723-3136
Web Site:
http://www.griffithholdings.com
Year Founded: 1993
Sales Range: $10-24.9 Million
Emp.: 34
Holding Company; Internet Related
Services
N.A.I.C.S.: 551112
Jeff Reusser *(CFO)*

GRIFFITH LABORATORIES, INC.

1 Griffith Ctr, Alsip, IL 60803-3408
Tel.: (708) 371-0900   IL
Web Site:
http://www.griffithlaboratories.com
Year Founded: 1919
Sales Range: $1-4.9 Billion
Emp.: 2,500
Food Ingredient Mfr
N.A.I.C.S.: 311942
Dean Griffith *(Chm)*
Joe Maslick *(CFO & Exec VP)*
Drew M. Bandusky *(Sr VP-Global Bus Performance)*
James S. Legg *(Gen Counsel & VP)*
Herve de la Vauvre *(Pres & CEO-Worldwide)*
Jennifer Convery *(Pres-US)*
Christine Carr *(Sr VP-Mktg & Global Comm)*
William Frost *(Sr VP)*
Brian Griffith *(Pres-Asia)*
Don Bernacchi *(VP-Creative Dev)*
Steve Hubbard *(VP-Global Mktg)*
Christopher Wood *(VP-Sls)*
Oscar Lizarazu *(Pres-Central & South America)*
Stelio Paschalidis *(Pres-Europe)*
Chris Savage *(Pres-Canada)*
Eugenio Torres *(Pres-Mexico)*
Anibal De La Cruz *(Mktg Dir)*
Steve Lee *(Sr VP-HR-Global)*

Subsidiaries:

Custom Culinary, Inc.   (1)
2505 S Finley Rd, Lombard, IL
60148   (100%)
Tel.: (630) 928-4898
Web Site: http://www.customculinary.com
Sales Range: $25-49.9 Million
Emp.: 56
Private-Label Soup Bases, Gravies &
Sauces Mfr
N.A.I.C.S.: 311999
Jim Legg *(Gen Counsel & VP)*
Elisa Loconte *(Mgr-Quality Sys)*

Mike Zelski *(Mgr-R&D Grp)*
Kevin Drees *(Plant Mgr)*
Tom Nemanich *(Reg Mgr-Sls)*
Ray Keltner *(Supvr-Maintenance)*
David Love *(VP-Supply Chain & Ops)*

Griffith Colombia S.A.   (1)
Autopista Medellin Bogota Km 39, Marinilla,
Antioquia, 54020, Medellin,
Colombia   (100%)
Tel.: (57) 45698000
Web Site: http://www.griffithfoods.com
Sales Range: $50-74.9 Million
Emp.: 220
Food Ingredient Mfr
N.A.I.C.S.: 311423
Oscar Patino *(Gen Dir)*

Griffith Laboratories (Phils.) Inc.   (1)
Building No 2 Honeydew Road, FT Com-
plex, Tagig, Manila, Philippines
Tel.: (63) 2 838 4935
Sales Range: $50-74.9 Million
Emp.: 200
Food Ingredient Mfr
N.A.I.C.S.: 311423

Griffith Laboratories Limited   (1)
Cotes Park Estate, Somercotes, Derby,
DE55 4NN, Derbyshire, United
Kingdom   (100%)
Tel.: (44) 1773837000
Web Site: http://www.griffithlabs.com
Sales Range: $50-74.9 Million
Emp.: 175
Food Ingredient Mfr
N.A.I.C.S.: 311423

Griffith Laboratories Ltd.   (1)
757 Pharmacy Ave, Scarborough, M1L 3J8,
ON, Canada
Tel.: (416) 288-3050
Web Site: http://www.griffithlaboratories.com
Sales Range: $50-74.9 Million
Emp.: 250
Mfr of Food Preparations; Rice Milling;
Food Products Machinery
N.A.I.C.S.: 311423
Chris Savage *(Pres)*
Don Bernacchi *(VP-Creative Dev)*
Wendy Tai *(Mgr-HR)*
Joyce Ballou *(Sr Dir-HR)*
Joseph Tavares *(VP-Sls & Mktg)*

Griffith Laboratories, Inc. - Innova
Division   (1)
1437 W 37th St, Chicago, IL 60609
Tel.: (630) 928-4800
Web Site: http://www.innovaflavors.com
Food Flavor Mfr
N.A.I.C.S.: 311999
Enrique Medina *(Pres)*

Griffith Laboratories, K.K.   (1)
NSS Bldg 13 31 Kohnan 2 Chome, Minato
Ku, Tokyo, 108 0075, Japan   (100%)
Tel.: (81) 334501231
Web Site: http://www.griffithlaboratories.com
Sales Range: $25-49.9 Million
Emp.: 60
Food Ingredient Mfr
N.A.I.C.S.: 311423

Laboratorios Griffith de Centro
America S.A.   (1)
1.5 km al Oeste des Jardines del Recuerdo,
Lagunilla, San Jose, Heredia, Costa Rica
Tel.: (506) 22777000
Web Site: http://www.griffithlaboratories.com
Sales Range: $50-74.9 Million
Emp.: 200
Food Ingredient Mfr
N.A.I.C.S.: 311423

Laboratorios Griffith de Mexico S.A.
de C.V.   (1)
Carr Monterrey-Saltillo Pio XII, Santa Cata-
rina, 66350, Nuevo Leon, Mexico
Tel.: (52) 8183804400
Food Products Mfr
N.A.I.C.S.: 311999

N.V. Griffith Laboratories S.A.   (1)
Toekomstlaan Wolfstee Industriepark, 2200,
Herentals, Belgium   (100%)
Tel.: (32) 14254211
Sales Range: $50-74.9 Million
Emp.: 200
Food Ingredient Mfr
N.A.I.C.S.: 311423

Win Deno *(Gen Mgr)*
Inge De Belder *(Mgr-Fin)*

GRIFFITH MOTOR COMPANY

1300 W Harmony St, Neosho, MO
64850
Tel.: (417) 451-2626
Web Site:
https://www.griffithmotor.com
Sales Range: $25-49.9 Million
Emp.: 40
New & Used Automobile Service &
Parts
N.A.I.C.S.: 441110
Jerry Griffith *(Pres)*

GRIFFITH MOTORS INC.

523 E 3rd St, The Dalles, OR 97058
Tel.: (541) 296-2271
Web Site:
http://www.griffithmotors.com
Sales Range: $10-24.9 Million
Emp.: 30
Automobiles, New & Used
N.A.I.C.S.: 441110
Mike Swartz *(Mgr-Parts)*

GRIFFITH RUBBER MILLS INC.

2625 NW Industrial St, Portland, OR
97210-1826
Tel.: (503) 226-6971
Web Site:
http://www.griffithrubber.com
Year Founded: 1988
Sales Range: $25-49.9 Million
Emp.: 300
Mfr of Mechanical Rubber Goods
N.A.I.C.S.: 326291
Timothy Gray *(VP-Sls & Mktg)*

Subsidiaries:

Griffith Rubber Mills of Garrett,
Inc.   (1)
400 N Taylor Rd, Garrett, IN
46738-1846   (100%)
Tel.: (260) 357-3125
Web Site: http://www.griffithrubber.com
Sales Range: $10-24.9 Million
Emp.: 45
Mfr of Mechanical Rubber Goods
N.A.I.C.S.: 326291

GRIFFITHS CORPORATION

2717 Niagara Ln N, Minneapolis, MN
55447-4844
Tel.: (763) 557-8935   MN
Web Site:
http://www.griffithscorp.com
Year Founded: 1966
Sales Range: $50-74.9 Million
Emp.: 800
Holding Company; Metal Stamping &
Fabricating Services
N.A.I.C.S.: 551112
Harold F. Griffiths *(Owner)*
Art Hahn *(VP)*

Subsidiaries:

K-Tek Corporation, Inc.   (1)
750 Vandeberg St, Baldwin, WI 54002
Tel.: (715) 684-3033
Web Site: http://www.ktek-net.com
Emp.: 110
Machine Tools Mfr
N.A.I.C.S.: 333517
Brandon Green *(Gen Mgr)*

Wrico Stamping of Arizona   (1)
1310 N Hobson St, Gilbert, AZ
85233-1207   (100%)
Tel.: (480) 892-7800
Web Site: http://www.wrico-net.com
Rev.: $2,300,000
Emp.: 65
Metal Stamping
N.A.I.C.S.: 332119
John Beutler *(Gen Mgr)*

Wrico Stamping of Florida   (1)

10659 Rocket Blvd, Orlando, FL 32824-
8517
Tel.: (407) 851-8342
Web Site: http://www.wrico-net.com
Sales Range: $10-24.9 Million
Emp.: 60
Metal Stamping
N.A.I.C.S.: 332119
Rick Albright *(Gen Mgr)*

Wrico Stamping of Minnesota   (1)
2727 Niagara Ln N, Minneapolis, MN
55447-4844
Tel.: (763) 559-2288
Web Site: http://www.wrico-net.com
Sales Range: $10-24.9 Million
Emp.: 70
Metal Stamping
N.A.I.C.S.: 332119
Paul Olson *(Gen Mgr)*

Wrico Stamping of North
Carolina   (1)
10134 Industrial Dr, Pineville, NC 28134
Tel.: (704) 554-9060
Web Site: http://www.wrico-net.com
Sales Range: $10-24.9 Million
Emp.: 70
Metal Stamping
N.A.I.C.S.: 332119

Wrico Stamping of Texas   (1)
650 Industrial Blvd, Grapevine, TX 76051-
3916
Tel.: (817) 488-6547
Sales Range: $10-24.9 Million
Emp.: 85
Metal Stamping Mfr
N.A.I.C.S.: 332119
Harold Griffith *(Owner)*

Wrico Stamping of Wisconsin   (1)
N 50 W 13471 Overview Dr, Menomonee
Falls, WI 53051-7041   (100%)
Tel.: (262) 781-4700
Web Site: http://www.wrico-net.com
Sales Range: $10-24.9 Million
Emp.: 125
Metal Stamping
N.A.I.C.S.: 332119
Dick Schultz *(Gen Mgr)*

GRILL CONCEPTS, INC.

6300 Canoga Ave Ste 600, Woodland
Hills, CA 91367
Tel.: (818) 251-7000   DE
Web Site:
http://www.grillconcepts.com
Year Founded: 1988
Sales Range: $75-99.9 Million
Emp.: 2,100
Owner & Manager of Fine & Casual
Dining Restaurants
N.A.I.C.S.: 722310
Chris Gehrke *(VP-Human Resources)*

Subsidiaries:

Grill Concepts-D.C., Inc.   (1)
1200 18th St NW, Washington, DC 20036
Tel.: (818) 251-7000
Web Site: http://www.grillconcepts.com
Sales Range: $10-24.9 Million
Emp.: 50
Manager of Fine & Casual Dining Restau-
rants
N.A.I.C.S.: 722511
Seth Merin *(Gen Mgr)*

GRIMALDI COMMERCIAL RE-ALTY CORP.

115 W Bearss Ave, Tampa, FL 33613
Tel.: (813) 882-0884
Web Site:
http://www.gcrproperties.com
Year Founded: 1975
Sales Range: $1-9.9 Million
Real Estate Broker
N.A.I.C.S.: 531210
Kari Grimaldi *(Pres)*
Kristy Marcelle *(Mgr-Property)*
Frank Grimaldi Sr. *(Founder)*

GRIMCO INC.

1585 Fencorp Dr, Fenton, MO 63026

Grimco Inc.—(Continued)

Web Site: http://www.grimco.com
Year Founded: 1875
Emp.: 500
Mfr of Digital Print Products, Signs &
Sign-Making Supplies
N.A.I.C.S.: 339950
Emily Martin (Dir-E-Commerce)

GRIMES ACE HARDWARE CO.
11 N Grand Ave, Fairborn, OH 45324
Tel.: (937) 879-0141
Sales Range: $10-24.9 Million
Emp.: 210
Hardware Stores
N.A.I.C.S.: 444140
David Grimes (Pres)

GRIMLEY FINANCIAL CORPO-RATION
30 Washington Ave Ste C-6, Haddon-
field, NJ 08033
Tel.: (856) 672-0265   NJ
Web Site: http://www.grimleyfc.com
Year Founded: 1986
Sales Range: $1-9.9 Million
Emp.: 24
Collection Agency Services
N.A.I.C.S.: 561440
Dawn Pinto (Exec Dir)
Charles D. Grimley III (Pres & CEO)

GRIMMER REALTY CO. INC.
200 Green Springs Hwy, Birmingham,
AL 35209-4906
Tel.: (205) 290-2712   AL
Year Founded: 1962
Sales Range: $75-99.9 Million
Emp.: 10
Provider of Real Estate Development
Services
N.A.I.C.S.: 531210
Park Grimmer (Pres)
Susan L. Grimmer (Treas & VP)
Rose J. Grimmer (Sec)

GRIMMWAY ENTERPRISES INC.
14141 Di Giorgio Rd, Arvin, CA
93203-9518
Tel.: (661) 854-6270
Web Site: http://www.grimmway.com
Year Founded: 1968
Sales Range: $450-499.9 Million
Emp.: 4,600
Vegetable Production & Sales
N.A.I.C.S.: 111219
Steve Antongiovanni (Controller)

GRINDER HAIZLIP CON-STRUCTION CO., INC.
1746 Thomas Rd, Memphis, TN
38134
Tel.: (901) 377-1000
Web Site:
  https://www.grinderhaizlip.com
Sales Range: $10-24.9 Million
Emp.: 90
Commercial & Institutional Building
Construction Services
N.A.I.C.S.: 236220
Brad Burford (Co-Owner)
Wilson Baird (Project Mgr)
Dorothy Jones (Treas & Sec)
Robert Nelson (VP)

GRINDSTONE PARTNERS, LLC
600 Cameron St Ste #303, Alexan-
dria, VA 22314
Tel.: (703) 627-9577
Web Site:
  http://grindstonepartners.com
Year Founded: 2009
Privater Equity Firm

N.A.I.C.S.: 523940
Michael D. Bluestein (Founder)

GRINER DRILLING SERVICE INC.
1014 Highway 98 Byp, Columbia, MS
39429
Tel.: (601) 736-6347
Web Site:
  https://www.grinerdrillingser
  vice.com
Sales Range: $10-24.9 Million
Emp.: 70
Water Well Drilling Services
N.A.I.C.S.: 237110
Ann Haddox (Office Mgr)
Charles H. Griner Jr. (Pres)

GRINER PONTIAC CADILLAC NISSEN
3715 Inner Perimeter Rd, Valdosta,
GA 31602
Tel.: (229) 242-7325
Web Site:
  http://www.grinerautogroup.com
Sales Range: $10-24.9 Million
Emp.: 41
Car Whslr
N.A.I.C.S.: 441110
Clay Griner (Principal)

GRINGO'S MEXICAN KITCHEN
2601 Underwood Dr, La Porte, TX
77571
Tel.: (281) 470-7900   TX
Web Site:
  http://www.gringostexmex.com
Year Founded: 1993
Restaurant Services
N.A.I.C.S.: 722511
Russell Ybarra (Pres & CEO)
Heather L. McKeon (VP-Mktg)
Jonathan Kim (Sr VP-Ops)
John Fernandez (VP-Ops)
Danny Hanks (VP-Ops)
Brian Jennings (CFO)
Al Flores (Gen Counsel)
Steve Ybarra (VP-Real Estate)

GRINNELL BANCSHARES, INC.
814 4th Ave, Grinnell, IA 50112
Tel.: (641) 236-3174   IA
Web Site:
  http://www.grinnellbank.com
Year Founded: 1982
Sales Range: $10-24.9 Million
Emp.: 4
Bank Holding Company
N.A.I.C.S.: 551111

Subsidiaries:

Grinnell State Bank   (1)
814 4th Ave, Grinnell, IA 50112
Tel.: (641) 236-3174
Web Site: http://www.grinnellbank.com
Sales Range: $10-24.9 Million
Emp.: 35
Retail & Commercial Banking
N.A.I.C.S.: 522110
F. Addison Jones (Chm)
David A. Jones (CEO)
F. Austin Jones (Pres & Chief Trust Officer)
Alison Murphy (COO, Exec VP & Sr Dir-HR)
Rusty Jones (CFO, Officer-Comml Loan &
Sr Exec VP)

GRINNELL MUTUAL REINSUR-ANCE COMPANY INC.
4215 Hwy 146 S, Grinnell, IA 50112
Tel.: (641) 236-6121   IA
Web Site:
  http://www.grinnellmutual.com
Year Founded: 1909
Sales Range: $400-449.9 Million
Emp.: 660

Property & Casualty Insurance & Re-
insurance Services
N.A.I.C.S.: 524126
Jeff Menary (Pres & CEO)
Dave Wingert (COO & Exec VP)
Chris Hansen (CFO & VP-Fin)
Roby Shay (CIO & VP-Enterprise
Solutions)

Subsidiaries:

Big M. Agency   (1)
4215 Hwy 146, Grinnell, IA
50112-0790   (100%)
Tel.: (641) 236-6121
Sales Range: $1-9.9 Million
Excess, Surplus, Non-Standardized Lines
N.A.I.C.S.: 561499

Grinnell Infosystems Inc.   (1)
4215 Hwy 146, Grinnell, IA 50112-8110
Tel.: (641) 236-6121
Web Site: http://www.grinnellmutual.com
Sales Range: $10-24.9 Million
Information System Services
N.A.I.C.S.: 541511
Larry Jansen (Pres & CEO)

Grinnell Select Insurance
Company   (1)
4215 Hwy 146, Grinnell, IA
50112-8110   (100%)
Tel.: (641) 236-6121
Web Site: http://www.grinnellmutual.com
Sales Range: $100-124.9 Million
Emp.: 650
Automobile Insurance
N.A.I.C.S.: 524210

GRIPPO POTATO CHIP COM-PANY, INC.
6750 Colerain Ave, Cincinnati, OH
45239-5542
Tel.: (513) 923-1900
Web Site: http://www.grippos.com
Sales Range: $1-9.9 Million
Emp.: 65
Snack Food Mfr
N.A.I.C.S.: 311919
Jerry Hawk (Mgr-Sls)

Subsidiaries:

Ballreich Snack Food Company   (1)
186 Ohio Ave, Tiffin, OH 44883
Tel.: (419) 447-1814
Web Site: https://www.ballreich.com
Snack Food Manufacturer & Distributor
N.A.I.C.S.: 311919

GRISANTI, INC.
Ste 304 333 E Main St, Louisville, KY
40202-1281
Tel.: (502) 429-0341   KY
Year Founded: 1980
Sales Range: $75-99.9 Million
Emp.: 300
Italian Restaurant Chain
N.A.I.C.S.: 722511
Michael J. Grisanti (Owner)

GRISHAM FARM PRODUCTS, INC.
7364 Newkirk Rd, Mountain Grove,
MO 65711-2540
Tel.: (417) 746-4834
Web Site:
  http://www.grishamfarms.com
Year Founded: 1994
Sales Range: $10-24.9 Million
Emp.: 163
Animal Feed Mfr
N.A.I.C.S.: 311119
Lexie Grisham (Pres)
Annabelle Grisham (Treas & Sec)
Rick Grisham (VP)

GRIST MAGAZINE, INC.
1201 Western Ave Ste 410, Seattle,
WA 98101
Tel.: (206) 876-2020   MA

Web Site: http://www.grist.org
Year Founded: 2002
Community Development Services
N.A.I.C.S.: 624190
Anne Lapora (Mgr-Ops)
Chip Giller (Founder & CEO)
Jamie Thayer (Dir-Dev)
John Alderman (Treas)
John Brosnan (Mgr-Foundation &
Corp Rels)

Subsidiaries:

Pacific Standard   (1)
804 Garden St, Santa Barbara, CA 93101-
2212
Tel.: (805) 568-1797
Web Site: http://www.psmag.com
Magazine Publisher
N.A.I.C.S.: 513120
Geane Delima (Exec Dir)

GRISWOLD CONTROLS
2803 Barranca Pkwy, Irvine, CA
92606
Tel.: (949) 559-6000
Web Site:
  http://www.griswoldcontrols.com
Sales Range: $25-49.9 Million
Emp.: 80
Valves & Pipe Fittings
N.A.I.C.S.: 332919
Doris Meyers (Sec)
Hemant Shah (Mgr-Pur)
Stefan Tuineag (Dir-Engrg)
Patrick Hennes (Dir-Ops)
Bryan Holloway (Engr-Design In-
ternernship)
Bob L. Powers (Pres)

GRISWOLD HOME CARE
120 W Germantown Pike Ste 200,
Plymouth Meeting, PA 19462
Tel.: (215) 261-7185
Web Site:
  http://www.griswoldhomecare.com
Year Founded: 1982
Sales Range: $25-49.9 Million
Emp.: 502
Non-Medical Home Care Services
N.A.I.C.S.: 621610
Joe Carr (VP-Mktg)
Ronald Patterson (VP-IT & Innova-
tion)
Michael Slupecki (CEO)
John Pouschine (Chm)
Christina Sommerfield (VP)
Matt Ericksen (Dir-Sls & Ops)
Shelley Kanther (Dir-Mktg)

GRISWOLD INDUSTRIES, INC.
1701 Placentia Ave, Costa Mesa, CA
92627-4416
Tel.: (949) 722-4800   CA
Web Site: https://www.cla-val.com
Year Founded: 1970
Sales Range: $150-199.9 Million
Emp.: 450
Automatic Hydraulic & Pneumatic
Control Valves Mfr
N.A.I.C.S.: 332912
Vic Roberts (VP-Sls & Mktg)
Larry Kolk (Reg Mgr-Western)
John Link (VP-Sls & Mktg)

Subsidiaries:

CLA-VAL Automatic Control
Valves   (1)
PO Box 1325, Newport Beach, CA
92659-0325   (100%)
Tel.: (949) 722-4800
Web Site: http://www.claval.com
Rev.: $25,000,000
Emp.: 400
Automatic Regulating Valves
N.A.I.C.S.: 332912
Martin Pickett (Pres)

Cla-Val Canada Corp.   (1)
4687 Christie Dr, Beamsville, L0R1B4, ON,
Canada
Tel.: (905) 563-4963

COMPANIES

GROOM & SONS' HARDWARE & LUMBER, INC.

Web Site: http://www.cla-val.ca
Emp.: 50
Fluid Power Valve & Hose Fitting Mfr
N.A.I.C.S.: 332912
Darryl Beck *(Gen Mgr)*

Cla-Val Pacific (1)
45 Kennaway Road, Christchurch, 8023,
Woolston, New Zealand
Tel.: (64) 39644860
Web Site: http://www.cla-val.com
Emp.: 5
Fluid Power Valve & Hose Fitting Mfr
N.A.I.C.S.: 332912
Glynn Nuthall *(Mgr-Asia-Pacific)*
Peter Olsen *(Mgr-District Sls)*

Soundcast Company (1)
1701 Placentia Ave, Costa Mesa, CA
92627-4416
Tel.: (949) 722-4800
Sales Range: $10-24.9 Million
Emp.: 100
Castings, Except Die; Copper & Copper-
base Alloys
N.A.I.C.S.: 331529
Mike Weaver *(Pres)*
Tom Dixon *(VP-Mktg)*

GRITMAN MEDICAL CENTER
700 S Main St, Moscow, ID 83843
Tel.: (208) 882-4511   ID
Web Site: https://www.gritman.org
Year Founded: 1939
Sales Range: $25-49.9 Million
Emp.: 552
Health Care Srvices
N.A.I.C.S.: 622110
Robin Woods *(Treas & Sec)*
Janie Nirk *(Vice Chm)*

GRIZZLY INDUSTRIAL INC.
1821 Valencia St, Bellingham, WA
98229
Tel.: (360) 647-0801
Web Site: https://www.grizzly.com
Rev.: $21,900,000
Emp.: 320
Tools Retailer
N.A.I.C.S.: 444140
Shiraz Balolia *(Pres)*
Don Osterloh *(VP)*

GRM INFORMATION MANAGE-
MENT SERVICES
215 Coles St, Jersey City, NJ 07310
Tel.: (201) 798-7100
Web Site: http://www.grmims.com
Rev.: $15,100,000
Emp.: 200
Document & Office Records Storage
N.A.I.C.S.: 493190
Jerry Glatt *(Pres)*
Walter Perez *(Gen Mgr)*
Ronen Grady *(Sr VP-Ops-Natl)*
Larry Reynolds *(VP-Sls & Digital Div)*
Yossi Harel *(Exec VP)*
Dave Symanski *(VP-Ops)*

Subsidiaries:

Recordkeeper Records Management
Systems Ltd. (1)
57 Littlefield St, Avon, MA 02322-1914
Tel.: (508) 588-1919
Web Site: http://www.recordkeeperrms.com
All Other Personal Services
N.A.I.C.S.: 812990
Thomas Walsh *(Owner)*

GRN FUNDS, LLC
1000 2nd Ave Ste 3900, Seattle, WA
98104
Tel.: (425) 830-1192   WA
Web Site: http://grnfunds.com
Privater Equity Firm
N.A.I.C.S.: 523999
Justin Costello *(CEO & Mgr)*

Subsidiaries:

GRN Holding Corporation (1)

21301 S Tamiami Trl Ste 320, Estero, FL
33928   **(55.65%)**
Tel.: (239) 273-3344
Web Site: http://www.grnholding.com
Rev.: $31,912
Assets: $58,265
Liabilities: $444,776
Net Worth: ($386,511)
Earnings: ($435,950)
Emp.: 1
Fiscal Year-end: 04/30/2020
Holding Company
N.A.I.C.S.: 551112
Donald Steinberg *(Chm, CEO, CFO & Sec)*

GRO ALLIANCE
613 N Randolph St, Cuba City, WI
53807-1070
Tel.: (608) 744-7333
Web Site: http://www.groalliance.com
Year Founded: 1941
Sales Range: $10-24.9 Million
Emp.: 70
Seed & Specialty Crop Production
Services
N.A.I.C.S.: 111199
Lou Schwagert *(CEO)*
Jim Schweigert *(Pres)*
Sherri Schweigert *(Mgr-HR & Admin)*
Jay Brant *(Mgr-Fin)*
Darrell Honn *(Dir-Ops)*

GRO-WELL BRANDS INC.
420 E Southern Ave, Tempe, AZ
85282
Tel.: (602) 792-0275
Web Site: http://www.gro-well.com
Lawn & Garden Products Mfr
N.A.I.C.S.: 444240
Tim Sellew *(Pres)*

Subsidiaries:

Pacific Topsoils Inc. (1)
805 80th St SW, Everett, WA 98203
Tel.: (425) 337-2700
Web Site: http://www.pacifictopsoils.com
Cut Stock Resawing Lumber & Planing
N.A.I.C.S.: 321912
Dave Forman *(Pres)*
Sandra Forman *(Treas & Sec)*
Thomas Finnerty *(Mgr-Construction)*

Western Organics Inc. (1)
PO Box 25406, Tempe, AZ 85282-5406
Tel.: (480) 966-4442
Web Site: http://www.gro-well.com
Sales Range: $10-24.9 Million
Emp.: 13
Fertilizer & Fertilizer Materials
N.A.I.C.S.: 424910
James Porter *(Pres)*

GROCERY HAULERS INC.
581 Main St, Woodbridge, NJ 07095
Tel.: (732) 499-3800
Web Site:
   http://www.groceryhaulers.com
Sales Range: $25-49.9 Million
Emp.: 500
Trucking Except Local
N.A.I.C.S.: 484121
Jack O'Brien *(Mgr-HR)*
Leesa Clark *(Mgr-Safety & Claims)*
Michael O'Malley *(VP-Engrg)*
Robert Cawley *(Mgr-Fleet Mainte-
nance)*
Tommy Merz *(Mgr-Terminal)*
Eddie Rishty *(CFO)*
Joel Clinton *(Engr-Indus)*
Robert Helmer *(VP-IT)*

GROCERY MARKETING INC.
Ste 437 601 N Congress Ave, Delray
Beach, FL 33445-4641
Tel.: (561) 276-1811
Year Founded: 1986
Sales Range: $10-24.9 Million
Emp.: 15
Sales of Groceries
N.A.I.C.S.: 424410

Alan Schuering *(Pres)*

GROEBNER & ASSOCIATES
INC.
9530 Fallon Ave NE, Monticello, MN
55362
Tel.: (763) 295-5355
Web Site: http://www.groebner.com
Rev.: $16,000,000
Emp.: 28
Sales of Industrial Supplies
N.A.I.C.S.: 423840
Joe Groebner *(Pres)*
Jane Covart *(Controller)*

GROEN BROTHERS AVIATION,
INC.
2640 W California Ave, Salt Lake
City, UT 84104-4593
Tel.: (801) 973-0177
Web Site: http://www.groenbros.com
Year Founded: 1986
Sales Range: Less than $1 Million
Emp.: 13
Aircraft Mfr
N.A.I.C.S.: 336411

GROENDYKE TRANSPORT,
INC.
2510 Rock Is Blvd, Enid, OK 73701
Tel.: (580) 234-4663   OK
Web Site: http://www.groendyke.com
Year Founded: 1932
Sales Range: $10-24.9 Million
Emp.: 1,300
Tank & Truck Carrier Services
N.A.I.C.S.: 484121
John D. Groendyke *(Chm & CEO)*
Don Querciagrossa *(VP)*
Martin Tewari *(Exec VP)*
Aaron Harmon *(VP-Performance &
Bus Analytics)*
Steven Jech *(Dir-Construction & Fa-
cilities)*
David H. Snapp *(COO)*

Subsidiaries:

McKenzie Tank Lines, Inc. (1)
1966 Commonwealth Ln, Tallahassee, FL
32303
Tel.: (800) 828-6495
Web Site: http://www.mckenzietank.com
Provider of Transportation Services &
Equipment
N.A.I.C.S.: 484230
Jim Shaeffer *(Pres & CEO)*

GROENEWOLD FUR & WOOL,
CO.
304 E Avon St, Forreston, IL 61030
Tel.: (815) 938-2381
Web Site: https://www.gfwco.com
Sales Range: $1-9.9 Million
Emp.: 20
Farm & Garden Machinery Whslr
N.A.I.C.S.: 424590
Guy Groenewold *(VP)*

GROESBECK BANCSHARES,
INC.
121 S Ellis St, Groesbeck, TX 76642
Tel.: (254) 729-3272   TX
Web Site:
   http://www.farmersstatebank
   texas.com
Year Founded: 1987
Sales Range: $1-9.9 Million
Emp.: 61
Bank Holding Company
N.A.I.C.S.: 551111
David Hughes *(Chm)*

Subsidiaries:

Farmers State Bank (1)
121 S Ellis St, Groesbeck, TX 76642
Tel.: (254) 729-3272

Web Site:
   http://www.farmersstatebanktexas.com
Sales Range: $1-9.9 Million
Commericial Banking
N.A.I.C.S.: 522110
David Hughes *(Chm)*
Morris DeFriend *(Vice Chm, Pres & CEO)*
Bryan Bradley *(VP & Mgr-Mexia)*
Jeri Penny *(Fin & Ops Officer, Sec & VP)*
Lori Bosley *(Branch Mgr)*
Eli Pratt *(Officer-Loan)*
June Wietzikoski *(Branch Mgr)*

GROESBECK LUMBER & SUP-
PLY, INC.
23155 Groesbeck Hwy, Warren, MI
48089-4249
Tel.: (586) 776-5410   MI
Year Founded: 1946
Sales Range: $10-24.9 Million
Emp.: 6
Provider of Millwork & Lumber
N.A.I.C.S.: 444110
Robert Maguja *(Pres)*
Crisostomo Amaba *(Controller &
Mgr-Credit)*

GROFF TRACTOR & EQUIP-
MENT, INC
6779 Carlisle Pike, Mechanicsburg,
PA 17050
Tel.: (717) 766-7671
Web Site:
   https://www.grofftractor.com
Year Founded: 1958
Construction Equipment Distr
N.A.I.C.S.: 333924
Mike Savastio *(Pres & CEO)*
Jim Price *(CFO)*

GROGANS TOWNE CHRYS-
LER DODGE INC.
6100 Telegraph Rd, Toledo, OH
43612-4575
Tel.: (419) 962-3690   OH
Web Site:
   https://www.groganstownechry
   slerdodge.com
Year Founded: 2008
Sales Range: $25-49.9 Million
Emp.: 90
Holding Company New & Used Car
Dealerships Owner & Operator
N.A.I.C.S.: 551112
Denny Amrhein *(Owner)*

Subsidiaries:

Grogan's Towne Chrysler Dodge
LLC (1)
6100 Telegraph Rd, Toledo, OH 43612
Tel.: (419) 476-0761
Web Site:
   http://www.groganstownechrysler.com
Sales Range: $25-49.9 Million
Emp.: 50
New & Used Car Dealer
N.A.I.C.S.: 441110
Denny Amrhein *(Gen Mgr)*

GROLMUS ENTERPRISES INC.
103 W Walnut St, Williamsburg, IA,
52361
Tel.: (319) 668-2535
Sales Range: $10-24.9 Million
Emp.: 60
Grocery Stores, Chain
N.A.I.C.S.: 445110
Steve Grolmus *(Pres)*
Julie Tippie *(Mgr)*
Cindy Schwating *(VP)*

GROOM & SONS' HARDWARE
& LUMBER, INC.
1310 S 3rd St, Mabank, TX 75147
Tel.: (903) 887-2408
Web Site:
   http://www.groomandsons.com
Sales Range: $10-24.9 Million
Emp.: 4

1791

Groom & Sons' Hardware & Lumber,
Inc.—(Continued)

Retailer of Lumber & Other Building
Materials
N.A.I.C.S.: 423310
Roger Groom *(Co-Owner)*
Terry Groom *(Co-Owner)*
Michael Rosen *(Co-Owner)*

GROOV-PIN CORPORATION
331 Farnum Pike, Smithfield, RI
02917
Tel.: (401) 232-3377
Web Site: https://www.groov-pin.com
Year Founded: 1926
Sales Range: $75-99.9 Million
Emp.: 100
Metal Fasteners & Precision Turned
Component Mfr
N.A.I.C.S.: 332722
Scot A. Jones *(CEO)*
Mark Ciuba *(Mgr-Sls)*
Jacky Beshar *(VP)*
Scott Bunn *(Plant Mgr)*

Subsidiaries:

Precision Turned Components   (1)
331 Farnum Pike, Smithfield, RI 02917
Tel.: (401) 232-3377
Fastener Mfr
N.A.I.C.S.: 339993

GROOVER SEMINARS, INC.
117 E 37th St Ste 580, Loveland, CO
80538
Tel.: (970) 377-2562
Web Site:
    http://www.rachaeljayne.com
Year Founded: 2010
Sales Range: $1-9.9 Million
Emp.: 13
Training Institute Operator
N.A.I.C.S.: 611430
Rachael Jayne Groover *(Founder &
CEO)*

GROPPETTI AUTOMOTIVE
PO Box 1431, Visalia, CA 93279
Tel.: (559) 627-4777
Web Site:
    http://www.groppettiauto.com
Year Founded: 1993
Sales Range: $10-24.9 Million
Emp.: 50
New Car Retailer
N.A.I.C.S.: 441110
Don Groppetti *(Pres)*
Mike Hagans *(Gen Mgr)*
Walter Jones *(Controller & Bus Mgr)*

GROQ, INC.
400 Castro St Ste 600, Mountain
View, CA 94041   DE
Web Site: https://groq.com
Year Founded: 2016
Emp.: 100
Information Technology System De-
sign Services
N.A.I.C.S.: 541512
Jonathan Ross *(Founder & CEO)*

Subsidiaries:

Maxeler Technologies, Inc.   (1)
2225 E Bayshore Rd Pacific Business Ctr
Ste 214, Palo Alto, CA 94303
Tel.: (650) 320-1614
Web Site: http://www.maxeler.com
Data Flow Computing Equipment Distr
N.A.I.C.S.: 423430
Stephen Weston *(Chief Dev Officer)*
Oskar Mencer *(Founder & CEO)*
Michael J. Flynn *(Chm)*
Steven Hutt *(VP-Data Analytics)*
Glenn Rosenberg *(VP-Ops)*
Georgi Gaydadjiev *(VP-Dataflow Software
Engrg)*
Itay Greenspon *(VP-Networking Tech)*
Simon Aglionby *(VP-Dataflow Sys)*

GROSCHOPP, INC.
420 15th St NE, Sioux Center, IA
51250-2100
Tel.: (712) 722-4135   IA
Web Site:
    https://www.groschopp.com
Year Founded: 1930
Fractional Horsepower AC & DC Mo-
tors, Gearmotors & Reducers Mfr
N.A.I.C.S.: 335312
Ed Tullar *(Sls Mgr)*
Connie Vander Ploeg *(Pres)*

GROSOLAR INC.
205 Billings Farm Rd Bldg 4, White
River Junction, VT 05001
Tel.: (802) 295-4415
Web Site: http://www.grosolar.com
Sales Range: $10-24.9 Million
Emp.: 50
Solar Power System Installation Ser-
vices
N.A.I.C.S.: 238990
James Resor *(CEO)*
Frank Griffin *(Exec VP-Engrg & Con-
struction)*
Rod Viens *(Exec VP)*
Robb Jetty *(VP-Bus Dev-Comml &
Industrial)*

GROSOUTH INC.
620 N McDonough St, Montgomery,
AL 36104
Tel.: (334) 265-8241
Web Site: https://www.grosouth.com
Rev.: $15,600,000
Emp.: 70
Farm Supplies Merchant Whslr
N.A.I.C.S.: 424910
John W. Morgan *(Pres)*
Scott J. Morgan *(VP-Sls)*
Cecil Dorsey Jr. *(VP)*
Arthur L. Morgan Jr. *(VP)*

GROSS ELECTRIC INC.
2807 N Reynolds Rd, Toledo, OH
43615
Tel.: (419) 537-1818
Web Site:
    https://www.grosselectric.com
Rev.: $16,831,376
Emp.: 60
Electrical Supplies
N.A.I.C.S.: 423610
Laurie Gross *(Pres)*
Colleen Braham *(Mgr-Sls)*
Sue Sweeney *(Dir-Mktg)*
Jessica Inwood *(Mgr-Store)*
Lenny Piojda *(Controller)*

GROSS MOTORS AUTOMO-
TIVE GROUP
404 E Division St, Neillsville, WI
54456
Tel.: (715) 743-3207
Web Site: https://www.grossauto.com
Year Founded: 1956
Emp.: 150
New & Used Car Sales
N.A.I.C.S.: 441110
Wayne Gross *(Co-Owner & Pres)*
Michael Gross *(Gen Mgr)*
Marcy Leggate *(Bus Mgr)*
Jerry Gross *(Co-Owner & Mgr-Svc)*

GROSS-KOBRICK CORP.
111 Linnet St, Bayonne, NJ 07002
Tel.: (718) 257-1212
Web Site: https://www.gkccorp.com
Sales Range: $10-24.9 Million
Emp.: 10
Cotton Goods
N.A.I.C.S.: 424310
Marvin M. Mendlowitz *(Pres)*
Sy Mendlowitz *(VP-Sls)*
Imran Latif *(Gen Mgr)*

GROSSENBURG IMPLEMENT,
INC.
31341 US Hwy 18, Winner, SD
57580-6484
Tel.: (605) 842-2040   SD
Web Site:
    https://www.grossenburg.com
Year Founded: 1937
Sales Range: $75-99.9 Million
Emp.: 75
Farm Machinery, Tires & Appliances
Mfr
N.A.I.C.S.: 423820
Barry Grossenburg *(CEO)*
Gene C. Grossenburg *(VP)*
Doug Percy *(Controller)*
Charlie Grossenburg *(Mgr-SD Reg)*
Ed Turgeon *(Mgr-Parts)*
Bob McCready *(Mgr-Tire Shop)*
Tad Vosika *(Mgr-Weld Shop)*
Brandy Biggins *(Mgr-HR)*

GROSSINGER CITY AU-
TOPLEX, INC.
1561 N Fremont St, Chicago, IL
60642-2527
Tel.: (312) 707-9500
Web Site:
    http://www.grossingercityauto
    plex.com
Sales Range: $10-24.9 Million
Emp.: 70
Car Whslr
N.A.I.C.S.: 441110
Gary Grossinger *(Pres)*
Van Ness *(Gen Mgr)*

GROSSINGER'S NORTH AU-
TOCORP, INC.
7225 N Cicero Ave, Lincolnwood, IL
60712-1611
Tel.: (847) 675-7100
Web Site: http://www.grossinger.com
Sales Range: $10-24.9 Million
Emp.: 45
Car Whslr
N.A.I.C.S.: 441110
Caroline Grossinger *(Pres)*

GROSSMAN CHEVROLET
300 Middlesex Tpke, Old Saybrook,
CT 06475
Tel.: (860) 339-4184
Web Site:
    https://www.grossmanchevy.com
Sales Range: $10-24.9 Million
Emp.: 34
Car Whslr
N.A.I.C.S.: 441110
John Grossman *(Pres)*

GROSSMAN COMPANY PROP-
ERTIES, INC.
3101 N Central Ave Ste 1390, Phoe-
nix, AZ 85012
Tel.: (602) 285-1300   AZ
Web Site:
    http://www.grossmancompany.com
Offices of Real Estate Agents & Bro-
kers
N.A.I.C.S.: 531210
Anne McGoldrick *(Sr VP-Mgmt)*
Chuck Carlise *(Dir)*
Larry Coltharp *(CFO & Sr VP)*
W. Matthew Crow *(CEO)*
John Grossman *(Pres)*
Richard Behr *(COO)*
A. Ennis Dale *(Sr VP)*
Stanley Gray *(Sr VP-Dev & Construc-
tion)*
Melanie Bast *(VP-Risk Mgmt)*
Andrea Rusing *(VP)*
Jake Gray *(VP-Acq & Dev)*
Sam Grossman *(Founder)*

Subsidiaries:

Classic Hotels & Resorts   (1)
8000 S Arizona Grand Pkwy, Phoenix, AZ
85044
Tel.: (866) 267-1321
Hotel & Resort Operator
N.A.I.C.S.: 721110
Carrie Deuchar Purner *(Dir-Revenue)*

Subsidiary (Domestic):

The Scott Resort & Spa   (2)
4925 N Scottsdale Rd, Scottsdale, AZ
85251
Tel.: (480) 945-7666
Web Site: http://www.thescottresort.com
Hotel, Resort & Spa Services
N.A.I.C.S.: 721110
David Oglesby *(Sls Mgr)*

GROSSMAN IRON & STEEL
COMPANY
5 N Market St, Saint Louis, MO
63102-1415
Tel.: (314) 231-9423   MO
Web Site:
    http://www.grossmaniron.com
Sales Range: $25-49.9 Million
Emp.: 180
Scrap Metal Processor
N.A.I.C.S.: 331410
Skip Grossman *(Exec VP)*
David Grossman *(Pres)*
Jackie Forshee *(VP-Mktg)*

GROSSMAN MARKETING
GROUP
30 Cobble Hill Rd, Somerville, MA
02143
Tel.: (617) 623-8000   MA
Web Site:
    https://www.grossmanmarketing.com
Year Founded: 1910
Sales Range: $75-99.9 Million
Emp.: 60
Full Service Marketing Communica-
tions Materials & Promotional Prod-
ucts
N.A.I.C.S.: 424120
Ben Grossman *(Pres)*

Subsidiaries:

ASAP, Inc.   (1)
13101 W Washington Blvd Ste 228, Los
Angeles, CA 90403
Tel.: (310) 578-6766
Web Site: http://www.asapla.com
Data Collection Services
N.A.I.C.S.: 561499

Links Marketing Group Inc.   (1)
7350 S Tamiami Trl, Sarasota, FL 34231-
7004
Tel.: (941) 926-4645
Web Site: http://www.linksmarketingusa.com
Marketing Consulting Services
N.A.I.C.S.: 541613

GROTBERG ELECTRIC, INC.
1109 W Main St, Valley City, ND
58072
Tel.: (701) 845-3010
Web Site:
    https://www.grotbergelectric.com
Year Founded: 1948
Sales Range: $10-24.9 Million
Emp.: 85
Electrical Contractor Services
N.A.I.C.S.: 238210
Steven Welken *(Pres)*

GROTE INDUSTRIES, INC.
2600 Lanier Dr, Madison, IN 47250
Tel.: (812) 273-1296   IN
Web Site: http://www.grote.com
Year Founded: 1901
Sales Range: $125-149.9 Million
Emp.: 688

Automotive Lighting Systems, Mirrors & Reflective Components Mfr
N.A.I.C.S.: 336320
Brian Blanton (CFO)

Subsidiaries:

Grote (Shanghai) Co., Ltd   (1)
485 Xin Run Road Xinqiao Township Song Jiang, Shanghai, 201612, China
Tel.: (86) 21 5774 9633
Sales Range: $10-24.9 Million
Emp.: 50
Motor Vehicle Safety Equipment Mfr
N.A.I.C.S.: 336390

Grote Electronics   (1)
95 Bathurst Dr, Waterloo, N2V 1N2, ON, Canada
Tel.: (519) 884-4991
Motor Vehicle Safety Equipment Mfr
N.A.I.C.S.: 336390
G. Louie (Gen Mgr)

Grote Industries Europe GmbH   (1)
Am Schaidweg 3, 94559, Niederwinkling, Germany
Tel.: (49) 9962 20008 0
Web Site: http://www.grote.com
Sales Range: $10-24.9 Million
Emp.: 50
Motor Vehicle Safety Equipment Mfr
N.A.I.C.S.: 336390
Klaus Vetterl (Gen Mgr)

Grote Industries de Mexico, S.A, DE C.V.   (1)
Ave. Rogelio Gonzalez Caballero 225, Parque Industrial Stiva Aeropuerto Apodaca, Nuevo Leon, Mexico
Tel.: (52) 8182624400
Web Site: http://www.grote.com
Automotive Lighting & Lamps
N.A.I.C.S.: 336320

Grote Industries, Co.   (1)
230 Travail Rd, Markham, L3S 3J1, ON, Canada   (100%)
Tel.: (905) 209-9744
Web Site: http://www.grote.com
Sales Range: $10-24.9 Million
Emp.: 95
Truck Lights & Emergency Light Mfr
N.A.I.C.S.: 336390

GROTECH VENTURES
230 Schilling Cir Ste 362, Hunt Valley, MD 21031
Tel.: (703) 637-9555   MD
Web Site: http://www.grotech.com
Year Founded: 1983
Rev.: $5,300,000
Emp.: 16
Venture Capital Investment Firm
N.A.I.C.S.: 523999
Sharon E. Gogol (VP & Controller)
Charles Cullen (COO & Gen Partner)
Joseph R. Zell (Gen Partner)
Stephen M. Fredrick (Gen Partner)
Frank A. Adams (Founder & Mng Gen Partner)
Lawson DeVries (Mng Gen Partner)
Don Rainey (Gen Partner)
Julia Taxin (Partner)
Meghan Pfeifer (Dir-Fin)
Andrew Winslow (VP)

Subsidiaries:

Sagittarius Brands, Inc.   (1)
1717 Elm Hill Pike Ste A1, Nashville, TN 37210
Tel.: (615) 231-2328
Sales Range: $900-999.9 Million
Holding Company; Limited Service Restaurants Franchisor & Operator
N.A.I.C.S.: 551112

GROTTO PIZZA INC.
20376 Coastal Hwy, Rehoboth Beach, DE 19971
Tel.: (302) 227-3567
Web Site:
    https://www.grottopizza.com
Sales Range: $50-74.9 Million

Emp.: 1,400
Pizzeria, Independent
N.A.I.C.S.: 722513
Jeff Gosnear (VP)
Glen Byrum (Dir-HR)
Adam Webster (Dir-Ops)

GROUNDS FOR SCULPTURE
80 Sculptors Way, Hamilton, NJ 08619
Tel.: (609) 586-0616   NJ
Web Site:
    https://www.groundsforsculpture.org
Year Founded: 1999
Sales Range: $1-9.9 Million
Emp.: 81
Architectural Services
N.A.I.C.S.: 541310
Gary Garrido Schneider (Exec Dir)
Lois Silagyi (Dir-HR & Acctg)
Rhonda DiMascio (Dir-Dev)
Claire Cossaboon (Mgr-Membership)
Barbara Lawrence (VP)
Robert C. Gross (CFO)
Faith McClellan (Dir-Collections & Exhibitions Mgmt)
Janis Martin-Hughes (Mgr-Corp Engagement)
Eric B. Ryan (Pres)
Marco B. Cucchi (Treas)
Seward Johnson (Founder)
Nancy Kieling (Sec)

GROUNDWATER & ENVIRONMENTAL SERVICES, INC.
101 E Southwest Pkwy Ste 114, Lewisville, TX 75067
Tel.: (800) 871-6417
Web Site: http://www.gesonline.com
Year Founded: 1985
Research & Development in Biotechnology
N.A.I.C.S.: 541714
Anthony Kull (Chm)
Edward Van Woudenberg (Pres & CEO)

GROUP & PENSION ADMINISTRATORS, INC.
Park Central 8 2nd Fl 12770 Merit Dr, Dallas, TX 75251
Tel.: (972) 238-7900
Web Site: http://www.gpatpa.com
Year Founded: 1968
Sales Range: $10-24.9 Million
Emp.: 137
Insurance Information & Consulting Services
N.A.I.C.S.: 524298
Jerry McPeters (Pres)
Kathy Enochs (COO)
J. W. Dewbre (VP)
Tommy McDaniel (CFO)

GROUP 5 WEST, INC.
810 W 2nd St, Little Rock, AR 72201-2118
Tel.: (501) 372-7151   AR
Web Site:
    https://www.groupfivewest.com
Year Founded: 1963
Sales Range: $25-49.9 Million
Emp.: 7
Advertising Agencies
N.A.I.C.S.: 541810
Richard Hinkle (Founder & Chm)
Lisa Hemme (Pres)

Subsidiaries:

Group 5 West, Inc.   (1)
197 Walnut Gardens Dr, Memphis, TN 38018-2907
Tel.: (901) 624-3956
Web Site: http://www.groupfivewest.com

Sales Range: Less than $1 Million
Emp.: 6
Advertising Agencies
N.A.I.C.S.: 541820
Lisa Hemme (VP)

GROUP BUILDERS INC.
511 Mokauea St, Honolulu, HI 96819
Tel.: (808) 832-0888   HI
Web Site:
    http://www.groupbuilders.net
Year Founded: 1980
Sales Range: $75-99.9 Million
Emp.: 250
Providers of Plastering; Plain or Ornamental
N.A.I.C.S.: 238310
Anacleto R. Alcantra (Owner & Pres)

GROUP DELPHI, INC.
950 W Tower Ave, Alameda, CA 94501
Tel.: (800) 536-4545
Year Founded: 1989
Marketing & Advertising Services
N.A.I.C.S.: 541890
Justin Hersh (CEO)

GROUP E LTD. INC.
2397 Bateman Ave, Duarte, CA 91010-3313
Tel.: (626) 301-0280
Web Site: http://www.esportia.com
Year Founded: 1985
Sales Range: $10-24.9 Million
Emp.: 35
Womens, Childrens & Infants Clothing
N.A.I.C.S.: 424350
David Ouyang (Pres)

GROUP EXCELLENCE
7616 LBJ Freeway Ste 515, Dallas, TX 75251
Tel.: (214) 570-3140
Web Site:
    http://www.groupexcellence.org
Year Founded: 2004
Sales Range: $10-24.9 Million
Emp.: 500
Tutoring & Mentoring
N.A.I.C.S.: 611691
Carl Dorvil (CEO)
Kimberly Golden-Bergstrand (Mgr-Acctg)
Yuritza Morales (Reg Mgr)

GROUP HEALTH COOPERATIVE OF EAU CLAIRE
2503 N Hillcrest Pkwy, Altoona, WI 54720
Tel.: (715) 552-4300   WI
Web Site: https://www.group-health.com
Year Founded: 1972
Sales Range: $250-299.9 Million
Emp.: 49
Community Health Care Services
N.A.I.C.S.: 621498
Darin McFadden (COO)
Michele Bauer (Chief Medical Officer)
Bob Tanner (CFO)
Peter Farrow (CEO & Gen Mgr)
Dessin Campbell (Treas)
Luke Salter (Sec)

GROUP HEALTH COOPERATIVE OF SOUTH CENTRAL WISCONSIN
1265 John Q Hammons Dr, Madison, WI 53717-1962
Tel.: (608) 251-4156   WI
Web Site: https://www.ghcscw.com
Year Founded: 1972
Sales Range: $250-299.9 Million
Emp.: 753

Health Care Srvices
N.A.I.C.S.: 622110
Mark Huth (Pres & CEO)

GROUP III INTERNATIONAL, LTD.
2981 W McNab Rd, Pompano Beach, FL 33069
Tel.: (954) 984-1607
Luggage Product Distr
N.A.I.C.S.: 424990
Joy Tong (Founder & Pres)

GROUP LOGIC, INC.
1100 N Glebe Rd Ste 800, Arlington, VA 22201
Tel.: (703) 528-1555
Web Site: http://www.grouplogic.com
Sales Range: $10-24.9 Million
Emp.: 33
Software Developer
N.A.I.C.S.: 513210
T. Reid Lewis (Pres)
Derick Naef (CTO)
Andrew M. Lewis III (Sr VP-Bus Dev)

GROUP MANUFACTURING SERVICES
1928 Hartog Dr, San Jose, CA 95131
Tel.: (408) 436-1040
Web Site:
    https://www.groupmanufacturing.com
Rev.: $10,000,000
Emp.: 78
Sheet Metalwork
N.A.I.C.S.: 332322
Curtis Molyneaux (Pres-Engrg)
Patty Thatcher (Mgr-Fin & Admin)
Jay Garrett (Dir-Sls & Matls)

GROUP MANUFACTURING SERVICES OF ARIZONA
3201 S Hardy Dr, Tempe, AZ 85282
Tel.: (480) 966-3952
Web Site: http://www.gmsaz.com
Rev.: $12,500,000
Emp.: 90
Sheet Metalwork
N.A.I.C.S.: 332322
Tim Maze (Pres)

GROUP MOBILE, INC.
5590 W Chandler Blvd Ste 3, Chandler, AZ 85226
Tel.: (480) 705-6100   AZ
Web Site:
    http://www.groupmobile.com
Year Founded: 2002
Sales Range: $1-9.9 Million
Emp.: 8
Computer & Computer Products Supplier
N.A.I.C.S.: 423430
Darin White (Pres)
Criss Cross (Sr VP-Pub Sector Sls)
Troy Ware (Mgr-Sls-Northeast)

GROUP NINE MEDIA, INC.
568 Brdwy Fl 10, New York, NY 10012
Tel.: (212) 966-2263
Web Site:
    http://www.groupninemedia.com
Digital Marketing
N.A.I.C.S.: 541810
Ben Lerer (CEO)

GROUP O INC.
4905 77th Ave E, Milan, IL 61264-3250
Tel.: (309) 736-8300   IL
Web Site: https://www.groupo.com
Year Founded: 1992
Sales Range: $50-74.9 Million
Emp.: 340
Supply chain & Logistic Services

Group O Inc.—(Continued)

N.A.I.C.S.: 541614
Gregg Ontiveros *(CEO)*
Kimberly Fox *(VP-HR)*
Bob Marriott *(CFO & Sr VP)*
Mark Herbert *(Dir-Reward Solutions)*
Mike Horan *(Exec Dir-Bus Analytics)*
Richard Resch *(Mgr-Sls-Packaging Solutions-Natl)*
Jeremy Aune *(VP)*
Kieran Keddy *(VP-Sls)*
Candy Wise *(Sr VP-Mktg Solutions)*
Eric Salisbury *(Sr VP-Supply Chain & Pkg Solutions)*
Mike De La Cruz *(Sr VP-Bus Dev)*
Mike Huntley *(CIO & VP)*
Robert Ontiveros *(Founder & Chm)*

Subsidiaries:

Bi-State Packaging Incorporated **(1)**
4905 77th Ave, Milan, IL 61264 **(100%)**
Tel.: (309) 736-8500
Web Site: http://www.groupo.com
Sales Range: $10-24.9 Million
Emp.: 30
Distr of Packaging Material
N.A.I.C.S.: 424990

Group O Direct Inc. **(1)**
4905 77th Ave E, Milan, IL 61264-3250 **(100%)**
Tel.: (309) 736-8100
Web Site: http://www.groupodirect.com
Rev.: $7,861,969
Emp.: 125
Direct Marketing Services
N.A.I.C.S.: 541860

GROUP ONE THOUSAND ONE, LLC

301 Pennsylvania Pkwy, Indianapolis, IN 46280
Tel.: (888) 594-2654 **IN**
Web Site: http://group1001.com
Year Founded: 2013
Insurance Holding Company
N.A.I.C.S.: 551112
Dan Towriss *(Pres & CEO)*
Jim Purvis *(COO)*
Andres Barragan *(Chief Experience Officer)*
Andrew Kenney *(CIO)*

Subsidiaries:

Lackawanna Casualty Company **(1)**
46 Public Sq Ste 501, Wilkes Barre, PA 18701-2609
Tel.: (570) 824-1400
Web Site: http://www.ligins.com
Insurance Agents, Brokers & Service
N.A.I.C.S.: 524210
Dave Kalinowski *(Mgr-Mktg)*

GROUP ONE TRADING, L.P.

11 Bdwy Ste 360, New York, NY 10006
Tel.: (646) 827-6000 **CA**
Web Site: http://www.group1.com
Year Founded: 1989
Sales Range: $25-49.9 Million
Emp.: 150
Securities Broker & Dealer
N.A.I.C.S.: 523150
John Gilmartin *(Co-CEO)*
Chad Grosam *(CFO)*
James Hutchinson *(Mng Dir)*
Ben Londergan *(Co-CEO)*
David McKenzie *(Mng Dir-Electronic Trading)*
Greg Shissler *(Mng Dir-Risk)*

Subsidiaries:

Group One Trading, L.P. - San Francisco **(1)**
220 Montgomery St Ste 600, San Francisco, CA 94104
Tel.: (312) 922-2620
Web Site: http://www.group1.com

Sales Range: $50-74.9 Million
Emp.: 40
Securities Broker & Dealer
N.A.I.C.S.: 523150

GROUP PUBLISHING INC.

1515 Cascade Ave, Loveland, CO 80538-8681
Tel.: (970) 669-3836 **CO**
Web Site: https://group.com
Year Founded: 1974
Sales Range: $25-49.9 Million
Emp.: 200
Provider of Publishing Services
N.A.I.C.S.: 513130
Jeff Lou *(CFO)*
Tom Schultz *(Founder, Chm & CEO)*
Rockey Gilmore *(Pres)*
Jeff Loop *(CFO)*

GROUP RHI

50 Milk St, Boston, MA 02110
Tel.: (214) 997-6046
Web Site: http://grouprhi.com
Retirement Services
N.A.I.C.S.: 525110
Tom Gaillard *(CEO)*

Subsidiaries:

Merit Benefits Group, Inc. **(1)**
2001 Midwest Rd Ste 306, Oak Brook, IL 60523
Tel.: (630) 792-0700
Web Site: http://www.meritbenefits.com
Insurance Agencies & Brokerages
N.A.I.C.S.: 524210
Carolyn Cumbee *(Gen Counsel)*

GROUP SIX CORPORATION

900 WestPark Dr Ste 300, Peachtree City, GA 30269
Tel.: (770) 389-9100
Web Site: http://www.groupvi.com
Sales Range: $10-24.9 Million
Emp.: 40
Industrial Buildings & Warehouses
N.A.I.C.S.: 236220
Ronald K. Williamson *(Co-Founder & Chm)*

GROUP SJR

22W 21st St 9th Floor, New York, NY 10010
Tel.: (917) 267-2930
Web Site: http://www.groupsjr.com
Year Founded: 2004
Sales Range: $10-24.9 Million
Emp.: 40
Specialized Communications Services
N.A.I.C.S.: 517810
Jen Wong *(Graphic Designer)*
Alexander Jutkowitz *(CEO)*
Brennan Kelley *(Editor)*
Christa Carone *(COO)*

GROUP TOOL & DIE CO. INC.

2200 W College Ave, Normal, IL 61761
Tel.: (309) 454-4146
Year Founded: 1973
Sales Range: $10-24.9 Million
Emp.: 52
Tools & Accessories For Machine Tools
N.A.I.C.S.: 326199

GROUP TWO ADVERTISING, INC.

2002 Ludlow St, Philadelphia, PA 19103
Tel.: (215) 561-2200 **PA**
Web Site: http://www.grouptwo.com
Year Founded: 1970
Sales Range: $10-24.9 Million
Emp.: 12
Advertising Agencies

N.A.I.C.S.: 541810
Megan Farrell *(Copywriter)*
Mollie Elkman *(Pres & Owner)*

GROUP VOYAGERS, INC.

5301 S Federal Cir, Littleton, CO 80123-2980
Tel.: (303) 797-2800 **CO**
Web Site:
   http://www.globusandcosmos.com
Year Founded: 1940
Sales Range: $25-49.9 Million
Emp.: 350
International Travel Tours
N.A.I.C.S.: 561520
Steve Born *(VP-Mktg)*
Jeff Canterbury *(Mgr-Engrg)*
Mark Liveris *(Mgr-Facilities)*

GROUP Z, INC.

9250 Bendix Rd N, Columbia, MD 21045
Tel.: (410) 772-0888
Web Site: http://www.group-z.net
Year Founded: 2001
Sales Range: $1-9.9 Million
Emp.: 25
Computer Facilities Management Services
N.A.I.C.S.: 518210
Anthie Zairis *(Founder, Pres & CEO)*
Nora Presti *(Owner, COO & VP)*

GROUP125 LLC

4532 W Kennedy Blvd Ste 114, Tampa, FL 33609
Tel.: (813) 321-7360
Web Site: https://www.group125.com
Sales Range: $1-9.9 Million
Business Advisory & Consulting Services
N.A.I.C.S.: 561499
Marshall J. Morris *(Mng Partner)*
Sarah Clendennen *(Mgr-Admin)*

GROUP9, INC.

2150 Cabot Blvd W, Langhorne, PA 19047
Tel.: (215) 555-1212
Web Site: http://www.group9.net
Year Founded: 2000
Sales Range: $25-49.9 Million
Emp.: 135
Mortgage & Lending Services
N.A.I.C.S.: 522310

GROUPHEALTHFLORIDA.COM

12651 N Dale Mabry Hwy, Tampa, FL 33688
Tel.: (813) 251-0222
Web Site:
   http://www.grouphealthflorida.com
Year Founded: 1984
Sales Range: $1-9.9 Million
Emp.: 26
Health Insurance Agency
N.A.I.C.S.: 524210
Thomas A. Kaspar *(Pres)*

GROUPSYSTEMS CORPORATION

520 Zang St Ste 211, Broomfield, CO 80021
Tel.: (303) 468-8680 **AZ**
Web Site:
   http://www.groupsystems.com
Year Founded: 1989
Sales Range: $10-24.9 Million
Emp.: 20
Developer of Collaborative Knowledge Software & Systems
N.A.I.C.S.: 513210
Jay F. Nunamaker Jr. *(Founder)*

GROUPWARE INTERNATIONAL INC.

1907 W Main St, Inverness, FL 34452
Tel.: (727) 462-5743
Web Site:
   http://www.gibroadband.com
Sales Range: $10-24.9 Million
Emp.: 475
Online Service Providers - Cable Installation
N.A.I.C.S.: 238210
Jason Lemon *(Reg VP)*

GROVE CITY DENTAL

4079 Grantz Rd Ste A, Grove City, OH 43123
Tel.: (614) 801-1000
Web Site:
   https://www.grovecitydental.com
Year Founded: 2004
Sales Range: $1-9.9 Million
Emp.: 15
General Cosmetic & Family Dentistry Practice
N.A.I.C.S.: 621210
Scott Schumann *(Owner)*

GROVE FARM COMPANY INC.

3-1850 Kaumualii Hwy, Puhi, HI 96766
Tel.: (808) 245-3678
Web Site: https://www.grovefarm.com
Sales Range: $10-24.9 Million
Emp.: 8
Selling Agent; Real Estate
N.A.I.C.S.: 531210
Warren H. Haruki *(Pres & CEO)*

GROVE LUMBER & BUILDING SUPPLIES INC.

13100 S Campus Ave, Ontario, CA 91761-4352
Tel.: (909) 947-0277
Web Site:
   http://www.grovelumber.com
Year Founded: 1979
Sales Range: $25-49.9 Million
Emp.: 100
Lumber, Plywood & Millwork Distr
N.A.I.C.S.: 444110
Raymond Groll Jr. *(Pres)*

GROVE SUPPLY INC.

106 Steamboat Dr, Warminster, PA 18974
Tel.: (215) 672-8666
Web Site:
   https://www.grovesupplyinc.com
Year Founded: 1948
Sales Range: $10-24.9 Million
Emp.: 50
Suppliers of Plumbing & Hydronic Heating Line of Products
N.A.I.C.S.: 423720
Carl M. Wolfe *(Pres & CEO)*
Bob Hamilton *(Controller)*
Chris Downey *(Mgr-Warehouse)*
Richard Scott *(Branch Mgr-Heating Sls)*

GROVE/ATLANTIC, INC.

154 W 14 St 12th Fl, New York, NY 10011
Tel.: (212) 614-7850 **NY**
Web Site:
   https://www.groveatlantic.com
Year Founded: 1917
Sales Range: $25-49.9 Million
Emp.: 50
Book Publishers
N.A.I.C.S.: 513130
Joan Bingham *(Exec Editor)*
Elisabeth Schmitz *(VP & Dir-Editorial)*

Subsidiaries:

Atlantic Books **(1)**
Ormond House 26 27 Boswell St, London,

WC1N 3JZ, United Kingdom   **(100%)**
Tel.: (44) 2072691610
Web Site: http://www.groveatlantic.co.uk
Sales Range: $10-24.9 Million
Emp.: 30
Book Publishers
N.A.I.C.S.: 513130
Peter Roche *(Chm)*

GROVER CORPORATION
2759 S 28th St, Milwaukee, WI
53215
Tel.: (414) 384-9472
Web Site: http://www.grovercorp.com
Sales Range: $10-24.9 Million
Emp.: 50
Manufacture Piston Rings
N.A.I.C.S.: 332710
Stuart E. Banghart *(Pres)*
Bob Chase *(Mgr-Acctg)*
Pat McCrory *(Mgr-Quality)*

GROVER GAMING, INC.
3506 Greenville Blvd NE, Greenville,
NC 27834
Tel.: (252) 329-7900
Web Site:
   http://www.grovergaming.com
Year Founded: 2013
Sales Range: $10-24.9 Million
Emp.: 140
Software Development Services
N.A.I.C.S.: 541511
Garrett Blackwelder *(Founder)*

GROVER INDUSTRIES INC.
219 Laurel Ave, Grover, NC 28073
Tel.: (704) 937-7434   NC
Web Site:
   http://www.groverindustries.com
Year Founded: 1970
Sales Range: $25-49.9 Million
Emp.: 90
Yarn Spinning Mills
N.A.I.C.S.: 313110
James A. Harry *(Pres)*
Greg Blalock *(CFO)*

GROVERT MOTOR CO.
7300 28th Ave, Newhall, IA 52315-
9638
Tel.: (319) 223-5141   IA
Web Site:
   http://www.bestpricechevy.com
Year Founded: 1918
Sales Range: $10-24.9 Million
Emp.: 18
Sales of New & Used Cars
N.A.I.C.S.: 441110
Bill Grovert *(Owner)*

**GROW FINANCIAL FEDERAL
CREDIT UNION**
PO Box 89909, Tampa, FL 33689-
0415
Tel.: (813) 837-2451
Web Site:
   https://www.growfinancial.org
Year Founded: 1955
Sales Range: $100-124.9 Million
Emp.: 560
Federal Credit Unions
N.A.I.C.S.: 522130
Katherine Peterson *(Asst VP-HR)*
Jim Esner *(Mgr-Underwriting)*
Irene Levell *(Supvr-Loan Servicing)*
Christian Gallardo *(Supvr-
Underwriting)*

GROW INTERACTIVE
427 Granby St, Norfolk, VA 23510
Tel.: (757) 248-5274
Web Site: http://www.thisisgrow.com
Sales Range: $10-24.9 Million
Emp.: 15
Advertising, Digital/Interactive
N.A.I.C.S.: 541810

Drew Ungvarsky *(Owner & Dir-
Creative)*
Matt Clack *(Dir-Art)*
Sonya Parker *(Project Mgr & Interac-
tive Producer)*

GROW MORE, INC.
15600 New Century Dr, Gardena, CA
90248
Tel.: (310) 515-1700
Web Site: http://www.growmore.com
Year Founded: 1918
Sales Range: $10-24.9 Million
Emp.: 50
Agricultural Chemical Mfr
N.A.I.C.S.: 325320
John Atwill *(Pres)*
Debbie Gerber *(Office Mgr)*
Irene Ahn *(Sec)*
Phil Nash *(Mgr-Retail Sls)*

GROWER SERVICES, LLC.
2321 Industrial Way, Vineland, NJ
08360
Tel.: (856) 690-9999
Web Site:
   https://www.growerservicesllc.com
Sales Range: $10-24.9 Million
Emp.: 6
Fresh Fruit & Vegetable Whslr
N.A.I.C.S.: 424480
Rusty Lucca *(Owner & CEO)*
Paul C. Massey *(Pres)*
Tony Gibson *(Mgr-Sls & Ops)*
John Heckman *(Mgr-Sls-Floral)*

GROWER'S ORGANIC LLC.
6400 Broadway Unit 11, Denver, CO
80221
Tel.: (303) 299-9500
Web Site:
   http://www.growersorganic.com
Year Founded: 2005
Sales Range: $10-24.9 Million
Emp.: 68
Food Product Whslr
N.A.I.C.S.: 424480
Brian Freeman *(Founder)*
Christina Stathos *(Mgr-Acctg)*
Bruno Dispoto *(Dir-Pur)*
Nancy Vitello *(Dir-Ops)*

GROWERS DIRECT
101 E 17th St, Costa Mesa, CA
92627-3779
Tel.: (949) 631-7880
Sales Range: $10-24.9 Million
Emp.: 35
Vegetable Distr
N.A.I.C.S.: 424480
Juan I. Caldera-Reveles *(Mgr-Ops)*

GROWERS EXPRESS LLC
150 Main St Ste 210, Salinas, CA
93901
Tel.: (831) 757-9700
Web Site:
   http://www.growersexpress.com
Rev.: $167,300,000
Emp.: 300
Vegetable & Melon Farming
N.A.I.C.S.: 111219
Mishalin Modena *(Mgr-Mktg)*
Oscar Chawdhry *(VP-Distr)*
Jamie Strachan *(CEO)*
Mark Dendle *(CEO)*
Tom Byrne *(Pres)*
Kirk Wagner *(COO & Gen Counsel)*

**GROWERS FERTILIZER COR-
PORATION**
312 N Buena Vista Dr, Lake Alfred,
FL 33850
Tel.: (863) 956-1101
Web Site:
   http://www.growersfertilizer.com

Year Founded: 1934
Sales Range: $25-49.9 Million
Emp.: 52
Phosphatic Fertilizer Mfr
N.A.I.C.S.: 325312
Brent Sutton *(Pres & Gen Mgr)*
Rick O'Steen *(Treas, Sec & Control-
ler)*
Larry Sparrow *(Mgr-Ops)*
Joe Alderman *(Mgr-Pur)*
Mark Wheaton *(Mgr-Turf & Ornamen-
tal Sls)*
Nancy Hrabal *(Office Mgr)*
Necole Weed *(Mgr-Retail Sls)*
Delmar Douglas *(Mgr-Warehouse)*

GROWEST INC.
1700 Growest Ave, Riverside, CA
92504-5307
Tel.: (951) 780-1552
Rev.: $15,040,588
Emp.: 12
Personal Service Agents, Brokers &
Bureaus
N.A.I.C.S.: 711410
John M. Bremer *(Pres)*

GROWING IN VOICES
2102 Business Center Dr Ste
130/180-D, Irvine, CA 92612
Tel.: (888) 508-6140   CA
Web Site: http://www.giv-
   foundation.org
Year Founded: 2009
Sales Range: $1-9.9 Million
Temporary Shelter Provider
N.A.I.C.S.: 624221
George Sanchez *(Pres)*
Yvonne Sanchez *(CFO & Sec)*

GROWING ROOM INC.
7270 Northlake Dr, Columbus, GA
31909
Tel.: (706) 596-1510
Web Site:
   http://www.growingroomusa.com
Year Founded: 1988
Sales Range: $10-24.9 Million
Emp.: 180
Child Day Care Centers
N.A.I.C.S.: 624410
Sheree W. Mitchell *(Founder)*
Brad Haines *(Sr VP)*
Jennifer Carpenter *(VP-Early Child-
hood Education)*

GROWMARK, INC.
1701 Towanda Ave, Bloomington, IL
61701-2090
Tel.: (309) 557-6000   DE
Web Site: http://www.growmark.com
Year Founded: 1927
Sales Range: $5-14.9 Billion
Emp.: 7,000
Agricultural Supply Cooperatives
N.A.I.C.S.: 926140
John Reifsteck *(Chm & Pres)*
Bob Phelps *(Vice Chm)*
Brent Ericson *(Sr VP-Member Svcs)*
Mark Orr *(VP-Agronomy)*
Jim Spradlin *(CEO)*
Barry Schmidt *(VP-Retail Bus)*
Mike Builta *(VP-Energy & Logistics)*
Kevin Herink *(Sec)*
Chet Esther Jr. *(Vice Chm)*

Subsidiaries:

GROWMARK FS, LLC   **(1)**
308 NE Front St, Milford, DE 19963
Tel.: (302) 422-3002
Web Site: http://www.growmarkfs.com
Fertilizer & Seed Distr
N.A.I.C.S.: 424910
Steve Buckalew *(CEO)*
Kandi Willey *(Mgr)*

Interprovincial Cooperative
Limited   **(1)**
945 Marion Street, Winnipeg, R2J 0K7, MB,
Canada
Tel.: (204) 233-3461
Web Site: https://www.ipco.ca
Agricultural Chemicals Mfr & Whslr
N.A.I.C.S.: 325320

MID-CO COMMODITIES, INC.   **(1)**
1701 Towanda Ave, Bloomington, IL 61701
Tel.: (309) 557-6001
Web Site: http://www.mid-co.com
Emp.: 12
Agricultural Commodity Trading Services
N.A.I.C.S.: 523160
John Cripe *(Dir-Commodity Risk Mgmt)*
Vanessa Youngmark *(Sr Mgr-Bus Ops)*
Cindy Hoerbert *(Sr Mgr-Bus Ops)*
Chad Richey *(Branch Mgr)*

Manito Transit LLC   **(1)**
405 N 2nd St, Ashkum, IL 60911
Tel.: (800) 252-6874
Web Site: http://www.manitotransit.com
Sales Range: $10-24.9 Million
Emp.: 25
Petroleum & Liquid Hauling Services
N.A.I.C.S.: 484220
Lee J. Louret *(Gen Mgr)*

STAR Energy   **(1)**
1006 1st Ave, Manson, IA 50563
Tel.: (712) 469-3708
Web Site: http://www.starnrgy.com
Emp.: 35
Fuel Distr
N.A.I.C.S.: 457210
Dave Brecher *(Gen Mgr)*

Seedway, LLC   **(1)**
1734 Railroad Pl, Hall, NY 14463
Web Site: http://www.seedway.com
Vegetable Seed Distr
N.A.I.C.S.: 424910

Sunrise FS   **(1)**
20735 IL Rte 125, Virginia, IL 62691
Tel.: (217) 452-7751
Web Site: http://home.sunriseagservice.com
Sales Range: $10-24.9 Million
Emp.: 125
Agricultural Supply Cooperative
N.A.I.C.S.: 424910
Randy Wilson *(Gen Mgr)*
Mike Beck *(Mgr-Grain)*
Tom Brooks *(Mgr-Energy Ops)*
Mark Scobble *(CFO)*
Glenda Postin *(Controller)*
Chad Shull *(Mgr-Energy/Retail Div)*
Dave Swigart *(Mgr-Ag Fin)*
Dawna McLain *(Asst Controller)*
Josh Ayres *(Asst Controller)*
Arlene Smith *(Mgr-Credit)*
Keith Fricke *(Mgr-Safety)*
Art Meunier *(Mgr-Agronomy Dept)*

UPI Energy LP   **(1)**
105 Silvercreek Parkway North Suite 200,
Guelph, N1H 8M1, ON, Canada
Tel.: (519) 821-2667
Web Site: http://www.upienergylp.com
Sales Range: $25-49.9 Million
Emp.: 50
Petroleum & Propane Product Marketer &
Distr; Owned by Suncor Energy Inc. &
Growmark, Inc.
N.A.I.C.S.: 424720
Robert P. Sicard *(Pres & CEO)*

**GROWTH ACCELERATION
PARTNERS, LLC**
8627 N MoPac Expy Ste 120, Austin,
TX 78759
Tel.: (512) 243-5754   TX
Web Site:
   http://www.growthacceleration
   partners.com
Year Founded: 2007
Sales Range: $1-9.9 Million
Emp.: 150
Custom Computer Programming &
Website Design
N.A.I.C.S.: 541511
Joyce R. Durst *(Co-Founder & CEO)*
Brett Bachman *(Co-Founder)*
Angela Marchant *(VP-Sls)*

Growth Acceleration Partners, LLC—(Continued)

Andres Molina (VP-Talent Acq)
Dave Moore (Chief Innovation Officer)
Jocelyn Sexton (VP-Mktg)
Michael Hull (VP-Sls)
Darryl Worsham (Chief Mktg & Revenue Officer)

Subsidiaries:

Mission Data LLC (1)
12910 Shelbyville Rd Ste 310, Louisville, KY 40243
Tel.: (502) 245-6756
Web Site: http://www.missiondata.com
Sales Range: $1-9.9 Million
Emp.: 20
Web Design & Development
N.A.I.C.S.: 541519
Carson McDonald (Partner)
Todd Budnikas (Dir-Creative)

GROWTH CATALYST PARTNERS, LLC
318 W Adams St 16th Fl, Chicago, IL 60606
Tel.: (312) 283-3689
Web Site:
http://www.growthcatalystpartners.com
Year Founded: 2015
Middle Market Private Equity Firm
N.A.I.C.S.: 551112
Scott Peters (Mng Partner)

Subsidiaries:

Government Executive Media Group LLC (1)
600 New Hampshire Ave Nw, Washington, DC 20037
Tel.: (202) 739-8500
Web Site:
http://www.govexecmediagroup.com
Periodical Publishers
N.A.I.C.S.: 513120

Risk & Strategic Management, Corp. (1)
209 Elden St Ste 206, Herndon, VA 20170-4846
Tel.: (703) 435-8572
Web Site: http://www.rsmconsulting.us
General Management Consulting Services
N.A.I.C.S.: 541611
Kristen Blyth (Pres)

GROWTH ENERGY
777 N Capitol St NE Ste 805, Washington, DC 20002
Tel.: (202) 545-4000   DC
Web Site:
http://www.growthenergy.org
Year Founded: 2008
Sales Range: $10-24.9 Million
Emp.: 23
Energy Conservation & Research Services
N.A.I.C.S.: 541690
Chris Bliley (Dir-Regulatory Affairs)
Kelly Manning (VP-Dev)
John Fuher (Dir-Govt Affairs)
Emily Skor (CEO)
Dan Sanders (Chm)
Mike Lorenz (Sr VP-Market Dev)
Jake Comer (VP-Market Dev)

GROWTH MANAGEMENT CORPORATION
4200 S 14th St, Lincoln, NE 68502-5943
Tel.: (402) 488-8500   NE
Web Site:
https://www.amigoskings.com
Year Founded: 1980
Sales Range: $10-24.9 Million
Emp.: 300
Eating Place
N.A.I.C.S.: 722511

Roger D. Moore (Pres)

GROWTH ORGANIZATION OF TOPEKA / SHAWNEE COUNTY, INC.
120 SE 6th Ave Ste 110, Topeka, KS 66603
Tel.: (785) 234-2644   KS
Web Site: http://www.gotopeka.com
Year Founded: 2000
Sales Range: $1-9.9 Million
Economic Development Services
N.A.I.C.S.: 813410
Scott Smathers (VP-Economic Dev)
Molly Howley (Dir-Bus Dev)
Matthew Lara (Specialist-Comm)

GROWTH PROPERTIES INVESTMENT MANAGERS, INC.
1329 Bristol Pike, Bensalem, PA 19020-6415
Tel.: (215) 546-5980
Web Site: https://www.gpim.net
Rev.: $10,000,000
Emp.: 475
Operator & Investor in Hotels
N.A.I.C.S.: 531210

GROWTH THROUGH SERVICE INTERIOR SUPPLY CO. INC.
10819 120th Ave NE, Kirkland, WA 98033-5434
Tel.: (425) 828-0608   WA
Web Site:
http://www.gtsinteriorsupply.com
Year Founded: 1986
Sales Range: $25-49.9 Million
Emp.: 200
Commercial & Residential Interior Finishing Products Distr
N.A.I.C.S.: 423310
Don Taylor (Pres)

GROWTHCURVE CAPITAL LP
1301 Ave of the Americas 38th Fl, 10019, New York, NY
Tel.: (212) 970-1900
Web Site:
https://www.growthcurvecapital.com
Year Founded: 2020
Holding Company
N.A.I.C.S.: 551112
Vignesh Aier (Head)

Subsidiaries:

Medical Reimbursements of America, Inc. (1)
7105 Moores Ln, Brentwood, TN 37027-2840
Tel.: (615) 905-2678
Web Site: https://revecore.com
Other Accounting Services
N.A.I.C.S.: 541219
Lyle Beasley (Pres)
Dave Wojczynski (CEO)

Subsidiary (Domestic):

Kemberton Healthcare Services LLC (2)
501 Corporate Ctr Ste 600, Franklin, TN 37067
Tel.: (877) 540-0749
Web Site: http://www.kemberton.net
Insurance Agencies & Brokerages
N.A.I.C.S.: 524210
George Abatjoglou (CEO)
Rainie Kleckner (Chief Customer Officer)
Deanna Gray (Sr VP-Customer Success)
Roze Seale (Reg VP-Sls)

Subsidiary (Domestic):

Advanced Patient Advocacy LLC (3)
175 Admiral Cochrane Dr Ste 403, Annapolis, MD 21401
Tel.: (410) 268-1577
Web Site: http://www.apallc.com
Sales Range: $10-24.9 Million
Emp.: 150

Helps Hospitals Match Uninsured & Under-insured Hospital Patients With Health Care Programs Such As Medicare, Medicaid & Cobra
N.A.I.C.S.: 524210
Kevin A. Groner (Founder & CEO)
Wendy Bennett (Pres)
Michael Wilmoth (COO)

GROWTHFORCE, LLC
800 Rockmead Suite 200, Kingwood, TX 77339
Tel.: (281) 358-2007
Web Site:
http://www.growthforce.com
Year Founded: 2004
Sales Range: $1-9.9 Million
Emp.: 35
Bookkeeping & Controller Services
N.A.I.C.S.: 525990
Stephen King (Pres & CEO)

GROWTHINK, INC.
6033 W Century Blvd Ste 150, Los Angeles, CA 90045
Tel.: (310) 846-5000   CA
Web Site: http://www.growthink.com
Year Founded: 2000
Sales Range: $1-9.9 Million
Emp.: 45
Management Consulting Services
N.A.I.C.S.: 541611
Jeff Jones (VP)

GROWTHPLAY LLC
30 W Monroe St Ste 400, Chicago, IL 60603
Tel.: (773) 230-7157
Web Site: http://www.growthplay.com
Sales Consulting Services
N.A.I.C.S.: 541611
Daniel J. Weinfurter (Founder & Partner-Channel)
Debra Baker (Mng Dir)
Eli Boufis (Chm)
Deb Knupp (Mng Dir)
Courtney Mohr (CEO)

Subsidiaries:

Force Management, LLC (1)
10815 Sikes Pl Ste 200, Charlotte, NC 28277
Tel.: (704) 246-2400
Web Site: http://www.forcemanagement.com
Sales Range: $1-9.9 Million
Emp.: 10
Sales Consulting Services
N.A.I.C.S.: 541611
John McMahon (VP)
Joe Schwartz (VP)
Kim Bastian (Dir-Mktg)
Tom Martin (Gen Mgr)
John Kaplan (Mng Dir)
Grant Wilson (Mng Dir & Chief Revenue Officer)
Debra Baker (Mng Dir)
Anne Bradley (CFO)
Amy Dordek (Mng Dir)
Tasneem Goodman (Mng Dir)
Matt Jordan (Mng Dir-Product Dev)
Deborah Knupp (Mng Dir)
Tracy LaLonde (Mng Dir)
Alycia Sutor (Mng Dir)
Christopher Wallace (Mng Dir)
Tracey Wik (VP-Dev Solutions)

SSS Consulting, Inc. (1)
3123 Research Blvd, Dayton, OH 45420
Tel.: (937) 259-1200
Web Site: http://www.chally.com
Sales Range: $1-9.9 Million
Emp.: 50
Human Resource Consulting Services
N.A.I.C.S.: 541612
Ken Carroll (CEO)
Robert Schwab (Pres)
Tracey Wik (VP-Dev Solutions)

GRP MEDIA, INC.
1 E Wacker Dr Ste 1600, Chicago, IL 60601-1905

Tel.: (312) 836-0995
Web Site: http://www.grpmedia.com
Year Founded: 1996
Sales Range: $75-99.9 Million
Emp.: 19
Media Buying Services
N.A.I.C.S.: 541830
Guy Lay (Pres & CEO)
John Reebel (Exec VP-Media Res)
Jennifer Lay (Sr VP & Dir-Media)
Wendy Smith (Exec VP & Dir-Strategy)

GRT CORPORATION
1177 Summer St 6th Fl, Stamford, CT 06905
Tel.: (203) 340-0277
Web Site: http://www.grtcorp.com
Year Founded: 1995
Sales Range: $1-9.9 Million
Emp.: 50
Information Technology Services
N.A.I.C.S.: 541512
Viktor Litvinov (Co-Founder & CIO)
Anna Rozinov (CEO)

GRUBBS INFINITI, LTD.
1661 W Airport Fwy, Euless, TX 76040
Tel.: (817) 318-1200
Web Site:
http://www.grubbsinfiniti.com
Year Founded: 1948
Rev.: $14,200,000
Emp.: 47
Automobile Dealers
N.A.I.C.S.: 441110
Joe O'Day (Mgr-Sls)
John Bastian (Mgr-Parts)

GRUBER HURST ELROD JOHANSEN HAIL SHANK LLP
Fountain Pl 1445 Ross Ave Ste 2500, Dallas, TX 75202
Tel.: (214) 855-6800   TX
Web Site: http://www.ghjhlaw.com
Year Founded: 2006
Emp.: 23
Law firm
N.A.I.C.S.: 541110
Mark L. Johansen (Partner)
G. Michael Gruber (Partner)
Brian N. Hail (Partner)
A. Shonn Brown (Partner)
Trey Crawford (Partner)
Michael Lang (Partner)
Jonathan Childers (Partner)
Orrin Harrison (Partner)
David W. Elrod (Partner)
David Wishnew (Partner)
Tricia R. DeLeon (Partner)
Jeffrey R. Erler (Partner)
Brian Farlow (Partner)
Anthony J. Magee (Partner)
Mark A. Shank (Partner)
Sam Stricklin (Partner)

GRUBER INDUSTRIES INC.
21439 N 2nd Ave, Phoenix, AZ 85027
Tel.: (602) 863-2655
Web Site: http://www.gruber.com
Year Founded: 1984
Rev.: $20,529,612
Emp.: 200
Communications Equipment
N.A.I.C.S.: 423690
Peter Gruber (Pres & CEO)
Steve Robinson (Sr Acct Mgr)

Subsidiaries:

Gruber Technical Inc. (1)
21439 N 2nd Ave, Phoenix, AZ 85027
Tel.: (602) 863-2655
Web Site: http://www.gruber.com
Sales Range: $1-9.9 Million
Emp.: 100
Computer Maintenance & Repair

N.A.I.C.S.: 811210
Linda Hall *(Mgr-Acctg)*

GRUBER SYSTEMS INC.
29083 The Old Rd, Valencia, CA 91355
Tel.: (661) 257-4060
Web Site: http://www.gruber-systems.com
Sales Range: $1-9.9 Million
Emp.: 45
Industrial Molds
N.A.I.C.S.: 333511
John Hoskinson *(CEO)*
Jim Thiessen *(Pres)*

GRUBMARKET, INC.
1925 Jerrold Ave, San Francisco, CA 94124
Tel.: (510) 556-4786
Web Site:
http://www.grubmarket.com
Year Founded: 2014
Online Storefront Website
N.A.I.C.S.: 445299
Mike Xu *(Founder, Pres & CEO)*
Genevieve Wang *(Chief Software Officer)*
Bryan Barsness *(Head-Software Sls)*

Subsidiaries:

Bengard Marketing, Inc.   (1)
PO Box 970, Kelseyville, CA 95451
Tel.: (707) 263-1990
Web Site: http://www.bengard.us
General Line Grocery Merchant Whslr
N.A.I.C.S.: 424410
James Bengard *(Owner)*
Broc Bengard *(CEO)*

Boston Organics LLC   (1)
50 Terminal St Bldg 2 Ste 105, Charlestown, MA 02129
Tel.: (617) 242-1700
Web Site: http://www.bostonorganics.com
Fresh Fruit & Vegetable Merchant Whslr
N.A.I.C.S.: 424480
Jeff Barry *(Founder & Pres)*

Custom Produce, Inc.   (1)
15628 E Nebraska Ave, Kingsburg, CA 93631
Tel.: (559) 897-1041
Web Site:
http://www.customproducesales.com
Fresh Fruit & Vegetable Merchant Whslr
N.A.I.C.S.: 424480
Bob Melenbacker *(CFO)*
Irasema Mejia *(Mgr-Acctg)*
Marvin Farris *(Pres)*
Brandy McNelly *(Supvr-Acctg)*

Freshtex Produce LLC   (1)
1300 W Business 83, Alamo, TX 78516
Tel.: (956) 283-9267
Web Site: http://www.freshtexproduce.com
Grocery Merchant Whslr
N.A.I.C.S.: 424410
Kenny Alford *(CEO)*

Hung San Foods, Inc.   (1)
22613 76th Ave S, Kent, WA 98032
Tel.: (206) 574-0144
Web Site: http://www.hungsanfoods.com
General Line Grocery Merchant Whslr
N.A.I.C.S.: 424410
Hung Tan *(CEO)*

London Fruit, Inc.   (1)
9010 S Cage Blvd, Pharr, TX 78577-9769
Tel.: (956) 781-7581
Web Site: http://www.londonfruit.com
Sales Range: $10-24.9 Million
Emp.: 60
Whslr of Fresh Fruits & Vegetables
N.A.I.C.S.: 424480
Barry London *(Pres)*
Emma Gonzalez *(Controller)*

Mendez International Tropical Foods, Inc.   (1)
152 Hunts Point Terminal Market, Bronx, NY 10474
Tel.: (718) 893-0100

Sales Range: $1-9.9 Million
Emp.: 11
Fresh Fruit & Vegetable Merchant Whslr
N.A.I.C.S.: 424480

Nova Libra, Inc.   (1)
8609 W Bryn Mawr Ave, Chicago, IL 60631
Tel.: (773) 714-1441
Web Site: http://www.novalibra.com
Custom Computer Programming Services
N.A.I.C.S.: 541511
Ken Harkleroad *(Project Mgr)*

Spring Valley Produce, Inc.   (1)
6001 S International Pkwy, 78504, Mcallen, TX
Tel.: (805) 474-8434
Fresh Fruits & Vegetables Whslr
N.A.I.C.S.: 424480
John Meena *(Founder & Pres)*

Sunfed Produce LLC   (1)
51 Kipper St, Rio Rico, AZ 85648-4191
Tel.: (520) 281-4689
Web Site: http://www.sunfed.net
Farm Product Raw Material Merchant Whslr
N.A.I.C.S.: 424590
Brett Burdsal *(VP-Mktg)*
Craig Slate *(VP-Sls)*
Mark Cassius *(Exec VP & Gen Mgr)*

VIP Wholesale, Inc.   (1)
4652 University Ave, San Diego, CA 92105-1915
Tel.: (619) 285-9592
All Other General Merchandise Stores
N.A.I.C.S.: 455211

GRUENINGER TOURS & CRUISES INC.
Meridian Tower 201 W 103rd St Ste 380, Indianapolis, IN 46290
Tel.: (317) 465-1122
Web Site:
http://www.grueningertours.com
Year Founded: 1954
Sales Range: $25-49.9 Million
Emp.: 20
Travel & Cruise Services
N.A.I.C.S.: 561510
Michael Grueninger *(Pres)*

Subsidiaries:

Ambassadair Travel Club, Inc.   (1)
9011 N Meridian St Ste 100, Indianapolis, IN 46260
Tel.: (317) 581-1122
Web Site: http://www.ambassadair.com
Sales Range: $10-24.9 Million
Membership Travel Club
N.A.I.C.S.: 713990
Erika Grueninger *(Owner)*

Amber Travel, Inc.   (1)
201 W 103rd St Ste 380, Indianapolis, IN 46290-1145
Tel.: (317) 465-1122
Web Site: http://www.ambertravel.com
Sales Range: $10-24.9 Million
Emp.: 30
Full Service Travel Agency
N.A.I.C.S.: 561510
Mike Grugninter *(Pres)*

Grueninger Music Tours   (1)
Meridian Twr 201 W 103rd St Ste 380, Indianapolis, IN 46290
Tel.: (317) 465-1122
Web Site: http://www.gogmt.com
Sales Range: $10-24.9 Million
Travel Agency
N.A.I.C.S.: 561510
Michael Grueninger *(Pres)*
Chris Richards *(Mgr-Bus Dev)*
Katharine Cox *(Acct Exec)*
Carole Greenawald *(Acct Exec)*
Othmar Grueninger *(Chm)*
Diana Hook *(Dir-Ops)*

GRUMMAN HILL GROUP, LLC
270 Greenwich Ave, Greenwich, CT 06830
Tel.: (405) 589-1695   DE
Web Site:
https://www.grummanhill.com
Privater Equity Firm

N.A.I.C.S.: 523999
James T. Kelsey *(Mng Partner)*
James T. Bunch *(Mng Partner)*

GRUNBERG REALTY
928 Broadway Ste 200, New York, NY 10010
Tel.: (212) 489-7198
Web Site:
http://www.grunbergrealty.com
Real Estate Investment Services
N.A.I.C.S.: 531190
Susan Donahue *(Dir-Comml Real Estate)*
Fanny Grunberg *(Founder & Principal)*
Michael Grunberg *(Principal)*
Ariel Grunberg *(Principal)*

GRUNDY ELECTRIC COOPERATIVE, INC.
4100 Oklahoma Ave, Trenton, MO 64683
Tel.: (660) 359-3941
Web Site: https://www.grundyec.com
Year Founded: 1938
Sales Range: $10-24.9 Million
Emp.: 45
Electric Power Distribution Services
N.A.I.C.S.: 221122
Dan Lentz *(Pres)*
Joe Hartley *(VP)*
Richard Moore *(Treas)*
Marvin Harding *(Sec)*
Eric Woodard *(Asst Sec)*

GRUNDY NATIONAL BANK
22112 River Side Dr, Grundy, VA 24614
Tel.: (276) 935-8111
Web Site:
http://www.grundynationalbank.com
Sales Range: $10-24.9 Million
Emp.: 100
Banking Services
N.A.I.C.S.: 522110
Ronald Delph *(VP)*

GRUNLEY CONSTRUCTION CO. INC.
15020 Shady Grove Rd Ste 500, Rockville, MD 20850
Tel.: (240) 399-2000   MD
Web Site: http://www.grunley.com
Year Founded: 1988
Sales Range: $25-49.9 Million
Emp.: 500
Nonresidential Construction
N.A.I.C.S.: 236220
Kenneth M. Grunley *(Pres & CEO)*
Sonya Y. Brown *(VP-Mktg & Bus Dev)*
George R. Rusk *(VP-Pur)*
Chris Odell *(CFO)*

GRUNWELL-CASHERO CO. INC.
1041 Major St, Detroit, MI 48217
Tel.: (313) 843-8440
Web Site:
https://www.gcbuildingrestoration.com
Sales Range: $10-24.9 Million
Emp.: 67
Commercial & Office Buildings, Renovation & Repair
N.A.I.C.S.: 236220
Scott Cashero *(Pres)*
Larry Darling *(Dir-Technical Svcs)*

GRUPE HOLDING COMPANY
3255 W March Ln Ste 400, Stockton, CA 95219-2352
Tel.: (209) 473-6000
Web Site: https://www.grupe.com
Year Founded: 1960

Sales Range: $50-74.9 Million
Emp.: 500
Real Estate Developers
N.A.I.C.S.: 236115
Kevin P. Huber *(Pres)*

Subsidiaries:

Green Home Solutions LLC   (1)
3255 W March Ln Ste 400, Stockton, CA 95219
Tel.: (877) 984-7873
Web Site: http://www.greenbygrupe.com
Consumer Electronics Repair & Maintenance Services
N.A.I.C.S.: 811210
Mark Fischer *(Pres)*
Chason Ishii *(Pres & Head-Bus Dev-Hawaii)*

Grupe Commercial Company   (1)
3255 W March Ln Ste 400, Stockton, CA 95219
Tel.: (209) 473-6200
Commercial Property Management Services
N.A.I.C.S.: 531312

Grupe Management Company   (1)
3255 W March Ln Ste 400, Stockton, CA 95219
Tel.: (209) 322-7475
Web Site:
http://www.grupemanagement.com
Home Rental Services
N.A.I.C.S.: 531110

The Grupe Company   (1)
3255 W March Ln Ste 400, Stockton, CA 95219-2304
Tel.: (209) 473-6000
Web Site: http://www.grupe.com
Sales Range: $25-49.9 Million
Emp.: 80
Construction Services
N.A.I.C.S.: 236220
Kevin Huber *(Pres & CEO)*
Dan Keyser *(Sr VP)*

GRUPO GALLEGOS
300 Pacific Coast Hwy Ste 200, Huntington Beach, CA 92648
Tel.: (562) 256-3600
Web Site:
http://www.grupogallegos.com
Year Founded: 2001
Rev.: $67,500,000
Emp.: 100
Hispanic Marketing
N.A.I.C.S.: 541810
John Gallegos *(Founder & CEO)*
Joe Da Silva *(Mng Dir)*
Andrew Delbridge *(Co-Pres & Chief Strategy & Engagement Officer)*
Sebastian Garin *(Exec Dir-Creative)*
Chris Mellow *(Exec Dir-Activation)*
Jennifer Mull *(CMO)*
Dave Damman *(Co-Pres & Chief Creative Officer)*

GRUSKIN GROUP
294 Morris Ave, Springfield, NJ 07081
Tel.: (973) 376-4411
Web Site:
https://www.gruskingroup.com
Year Founded: 1982
Rev.: $10,100,000
Emp.: 56
Leading Architectural Branding & Design Firm
N.A.I.C.S.: 541310
Ed James *(Dir-Tech-Industrial Design)*
Bob Lyons *(Dir-Mktg & Svcs)*
Joel Shulman *(Principal-Architecture)*
Jeff Barcan *(Dir-Creative Svcs)*
Kenneth A. Gruskin *(Principal)*

GRV GIBBS, INC.
34345 Hwy 46 N PO Box 277, Deer River, MN 56636
Tel.: (218) 246-8551
Sales Range: $25-49.9 Million
Emp.: 13

GRV Gibbs, Inc.—(Continued)

Processor of Wild Rice
N.A.I.C.S.: 424510
Greig Olson (Pres)

GRW ADVERTISING
28 W 25th St Second Fl, New York,
NY 10010-2705
Tel.: (212) 620-0519   **NY**
Year Founded: 1994
Sales Range: $10-24.9 Million
Emp.: 8
Advetising Agency
N.A.I.C.S.: 541810
Ed Ronk (Pres)
Glen Wielgus (Partner & Chief Creative Officer)

GRYPHON INVESTORS, LLC
1 Maritime Plz Ste 2300, San Francisco, CA 94111
Tel.: (415) 217-7400   **DE**
Web Site: http://www.gryphon-inv.com
Year Founded: 1995
Privater Equity Firm
N.A.I.C.S.: 523999
Nick Orum (Pres & CIO)
R. David Andrews (Founder & CEO)
Alex Earls (Partner-Deal & Head-Business Services Group)
James R. Gillette (Mng Dir & CFO)
Keith H. Stimson (Partner-Deal & Head-Heritage Fund)
Dorian Faust (Partner, Head-Capital Markets & Co-Head-Credit Fund)
Matt Farron (Partner-Deal, Principal & Head-Consumer Group)
Kevin Blank (Operating Partner-Healthcare Group)
John Geisler (Operating Partner-Emeritus, FP&A & Diligence)
Dell Larcen (Operating Partner-Human Capital Group)
Jim Gallagher (Mng Dir-Bus Dev)
Jon Cheek (Partner-Deal & Head-Software)
Carl Theobald (Operating Partner)
John Schumacher (Partner & Co-Head-Junior Capital Team)
Craig Nikrant (Operating Partner-Heritage Fund)

Subsidiaries:

3Cloud, LLC   (1)
3025 Highland Pkwy Ste 525, Downers Grove, IL 60515
Tel.: (888) 882-9873
Cloud Infrastructure & Advanced Analytics
N.A.I.C.S.: 513210
Mike Rocco (CEO)

Subsidiary (Domestic):

Bluegranite, Inc.   (2)
7950 Moorsbridge Rd Ste 201, Portridge, MI 49024-4420
Tel.: (269) 353-7512
Web Site: http://www.blue-granite.com
Sales Range: $1-9.9 Million
Emp.: 22
Computer System Design Services
N.A.I.C.S.: 541512
Matthew D. Mace (CEO)
Mike Depoian (VP)

Pragmatic Works Inc.   (2)
1845 Town Ctr Blvd Ste 505, Fleming Island, FL 32003
Tel.: (904) 413-1911
Web Site: http://www.pragmaticworks.com
IT Staffing, Training & Consulting
N.A.I.C.S.: 561311
Brian Knight (Founder & Owner)
Tim Moolic (COO)
Adam Jorgensen (Pres-Consulting)
Devin Knight (Pres-Training)
Robert Beatty (VP-Consulting Sls)

Chicago Protective Apparel, Inc.   (1)

3425 Cleveland St, Skokie, IL 60076
Tel.: (847) 674-7900
Web Site: http://www.chicagoprotective.com
Firefighting & Other Emergency Service Apparel Mfr
N.A.I.C.S.: 315250
Scott Sherman (Pres)
Carlos Perez (Mgr-Shipping)

ECG Management Consultants, Inc.   (1)
1111 3rd Ave Ste 2500, Seattle, WA 98101
Tel.: (206) 689-2200
Web Site: http://www.ecgmc.com
Emp.: 60
Health Care Consulting Services
N.A.I.C.S.: 541618
Gary Edmiston (Co-CEO)
Leonard Henzke (Principal-Seattle)
Michelle Holmes (Principal)
Kevin Kennedy (Principal-Seattle)
Dan Merlino (Principal)
Kenneth Roorda (Principal-Seattle)
Deirdre Baggot (Principal-Washington)
Jenni Bendfeldt (Mgr)
Clark Bosslet (Mgr)
Jessica Turgon (Principal-Washington)
John Bry (Mgr)
Andrew Davis (Mgr)
Craig Acosta (Principal-San Francisco)
Andrew Bachrodt (Principal-Dallas)
Jesse Balok (Principal-Minneapolis)
Christopher Collins (Principal-Boston)
Ben Colton (Principal-Seattle)
Scott J. Cullen (Principal-Boston)
John Fink (Principal-San Diego)
Carl Fleming (Principal-Atlanta)
Kevin Forster (Principal-San Francisco)
Leah Gassett (Principal-Boston)
Jennifer Gingrass (Principal-Chicago)
Keith Graff (Principal-Chicago)
Josh Halverson (Principal-Dallas)
Jeffrey Hoffman (Principal-San Francisco)
I. Naya Kehayes (Principal-Seattle)

Subsidiary (Domestic):

NeuStrategy, Inc.
17 N State St Ste 1700, Chicago, IL 60602
Tel.: (312) 644-4780
Web Site: http://www.neustrategy.com
Health Care Consulting Services
N.A.I.C.S.: 541618
Lisa J. Garvy (Sr Dir)
Theodore Michalke (Co-Founder)
Kevin Dunne (Co-Founder)

Ed's Supply Company Inc.   (1)
711 6th Ave S, Nashville, TN 37203
Tel.: (615) 244-2600
Web Site: http://www.edssupply.com
Rev.: $13,100,000
Emp.: 200
Warm Air Heating & Air Conditioning
N.A.I.C.S.: 423730
Jimmy Byron (Co-Pres)
Tucker Byram (Co-Pres)

Subsidiary (Domestic):

Controlled Temp Supply, LLC   (2)
15A County Rd 1014, Oxford, MS 38655-7726
Tel.: (662) 236-9015
Air-Conditioning, Warm Air Heating Equipment & Commercial & Industrial Refrigeration Equipment Mfr
N.A.I.C.S.: 333415

HEPACO Inc.   (1)
9335 Harris Corners Parkway, Charlotte, NC 28269
Tel.: (704) 598-9782
Web Site: http://www.hepaco.com
Environmental Contracting & Emergency Response
N.A.I.C.S.: 562211
Ken Knibbs (Chief Comml Officer)
Bryan Martin (VP-Midwest & Sr Dir)
Scott Metzger (Pres & COO)
Bill Mohl (Exec Chm)
Shayne Ingersoll (Chief HR Officer)

Subsidiary (Domestic):

Environmental Management Alternatives, Inc.
10627 Midwest Ind Blvd, Saint Louis, MO 63132
Tel.: (314) 785-6425

Web Site: http://www.ema-env.com
Sales Range: $1-9.9 Million
Emp.: 15
Business Services, Nec, Nsk
N.A.I.C.S.: 711410
Daniel Giesler (Pres)
William Cathey (Project Mgr)
Jeff Cosmano (Project Mgr)
Mike Hylla (Owner)
Timothy Hylla (Principal)

Environmental Management Specialists, Inc.   (2)
6909 Engle Rd Ste 331, Middleburg Heights, OH 44130
Tel.: (440) 816-1107
Web Site: http://www.emsonsite.com
Environmental Services; Emergency Spill Response & Waste Management
N.A.I.C.S.: 541620
Cherie Walsh (Mgr-Customer Svc)
Jon Ransom (Owner & Pres)
Lyndell Williams (Mgr-HR)
Kara Allison (Dir-Project Dev & Comm)

PetroChem Recovery Services, Inc.   (2)
635 Maltby Ave, Norfolk, VA 23504
Tel.: (757) 627-8791
Research & Development in Biotechnology
N.A.I.C.S.: 541714

The Evergreen Group, Inc.   (2)
7416 Hwy 329, Crestwood, KY 40014-8884
Tel.: (502) 241-4171
Web Site: http://www.evergreenaes.com
Waste Management Services
N.A.I.C.S.: 562998
Kris L. Smith (Office Mgr)

Jensen Hughes, Inc.   (1)
3610 Commerce Dr Ste 817, Baltimore, MD 21227-1652
Tel.: (410) 737-8677
Web Site: http://www.jensenhughes.com
Fire Protection Engineering & Security Consulting Services
N.A.I.C.S.: 541690
Steve Bassine (VP-Strategy & Bus Dev)
Raj Arora (CEO)
Pankaj Duggal (Pres & COO)
Sanford Tassel (CFO)
Heather Sanchez (Chief People Officer)

Subsidiary (Domestic):

CASE Forensics Corp.   (2)
23109 55th Ave W, Mountlake Terrace, WA 98043   (100%)
Tel.: (425) 775-5550
Web Site: http://www.case4n6.com
Sales Range: $1-9.9 Million
Emp.: 38
Forensic & Engineering Services
N.A.I.C.S.: 541330
Cynthia Raecker (Mgr-Bus Dev)
Paul Orveske (Pres)

Cygna Energy Services, Inc.   (2)
1600 S Main St Ste 120, Walnut Creek, CA 94596
Tel.: (925) 930-8324
Web Site: http://www.cygna.net
Database Management Product Services
N.A.I.C.S.: 541511
Glenn Smith (Pres & CEO)
Timothy Fay (CIO)

Erin Engineering & Research Inc.   (2)
2001 N Main St Ste 510, Walnut Creek, CA 94596
Tel.: (925) 943-7077
Web Site: http://www.erineng.com
Engineeering Services
N.A.I.C.S.: 541330
Edward Burns (VP)

Hillard Heintze, LLC   (2)
30 S Wacker Dr Ste 1400, Chicago, IL 60606
Tel.: (312) 869-8500
Web Site: http://www.hillardheintze.com
Security System Services
N.A.I.C.S.: 561621
Kenneth A. Bouche (COO)
Vicky L. Chatelain (Sr Dir-Comm)
Stephen C. Grant (Chief Comm Officer)
Steven M. Bova (Sr Dir-Security Risk Mgmt)
Arnette F. Heintze (Co-Founder & CEO)

Jennifer L. Mackovjak (Sr VP)
William V. Aslan (CFO)
Edward Hughes (Dir-Strategic Rels)
Jo Ann Ugolini (Dir-Threat & Violence Risk Mgmt)
Adam Zoll (Dir-Investigations)
Daniel M. Walsh (Dir-Security Risk Mgmt)
Carl J. Dobrich (Sr Dir-Investigations)
Matthew W. Doherty (Sr VP)
Howard Fisher (Sr VP-Strategic Relationships)
Debra K. Kirby (Sr VP-Law Enforcement Consulting Practice)
Rick Tanksley (VP-Law Enforcement Consulting)
Mark Brenzinger (VP-Forensic, Threat & Violence Risk Mgmt)
Christi L. Gullion (VP-Law Enforcement Consulting)
Diane Ragans (VP-Law Enforcement Consulting)
Robert Boehmer (VP-Law Enforcement Consulting)

J. D. Stevenson and Associates, Inc.   (2)
275 Mishawum Rd Ste 200, Woburn, MA 01801
Tel.: (781) 932-9580
Web Site: http://www.vecsa.com
Rev.: $4,100,000
Emp.: 20
Engineeering Services
N.A.I.C.S.: 541330
Walter Djordjevic (Pres)

Unit (Domestic):

JENSEN HUGHES, Inc. - Midwest   (2)
600 W Fulton St Ste 500, Chicago, IL 60661
Tel.: (312) 879-7200
Fire Protection Engineering Services
N.A.I.C.S.: 541330
Moriel Kaplan (VP-Bus Support Svcs)
Jim Bychowski (Sr VP-Bus Dev)
Don Mershon (VP-Comml Ops)
Renee Clemetsen (Sr Mgr-Mktg Tech)
Kelly Thomas (Mgr-Digital Mktg & Comm)
Raj Arora (Pres-Strategy & Bus Dev)
Pam Butziger (Sr VP-HR)
Pete Costa (Pres-Ops)
Paul Orzeske (CEO)
Dina Wong (Corp Counsel)

Subsidiary (Domestic):

Nexus Engineering   (2)
One Transam Plaza Dr Ste 200, Oakbrook Terrace, IL 60181
Tel.: (630) 627-2277
Web Site: http://www.nexus-tech.com
Engineeering Services
N.A.I.C.S.: 541330
Thomas McCormack (Pres)
James F. Limes (Sec)
Donald F. Mershon (Treas)

Technical Response Planning Corp.   (2)
2219 Sawdust Rd Ste 601, The Woodlands, TX 77380
Tel.: (281) 955-9600
Scientific & Technical Consulting Services
N.A.I.C.S.: 541690

Kano Laboratories Inc.   (1)
1000 E Thompson Ln, Nashville, TN 37211-2658
Tel.: (615) 210-5705
Web Site: http://www.kanolabs.com
Testing Laboratories
N.A.I.C.S.: 541380
Rose Zimmerman (Owner)
Sevan Demirdogen (CEO)

Lawler Foods Ltd.   (1)
1219 Carpenter Rd, Humble, TX 77396
Tel.: (281) 446-0059
Web Site: http://www.lawlers.com
Sales Range: $10-24.9 Million
Emp.: 300
Cakes, Pies & Pastries Mfr
N.A.I.C.S.: 311812
Fausto Hernandez (Mgr-Production)
Wes Stasny (Pres)
Gus Castillo (Mgr-Maintenance)
Tricia Mooney (Mgr-HR)

Learn It Systems LLC (1)
6225 Smith Ave. Suite 100/1A, Baltimore, MD 21209
Tel.: (410) 369-0000
Web Site: http://www.learnbehavioral.com
Behavioral Health & Applied Behavior Analysis Services
N.A.I.C.S.: 621498
Michael Maloney (Founder & CEO)
Sabrina Daneshvar (Sr VP-Clinical Services)
Justin Funches (Pres)
Meg Galletti (Chief People Officer)
Rob Haupt (Exec VP)

Subsidiary (Domestic):

Behavior Analysis Center for Autism (2)
9929 E 126th St, Fishers, IN 46038
Tel.: (317) 436-8961
Web Site: http://www.thebaca.com
Psychiatric & Substance Abuse Hospitals
N.A.I.C.S.: 622210
Devon Sundberg (Dir-Admin)

Total Spectrum, LLC (2)
650 W Grand Ave Ste 207, Elmhurst, IL 60126
Tel.: (844) 263-1613
Web Site: https://totalspectrumcare.com
Clinical-Based Applied Behavioral Analysis Services
N.A.I.C.S.: 621498
Jim Bogenreif (Pres & CEO)

Matrixx Initiatives, Inc. (2)
1 Grande Commons 440 Route 23 E Ste 130, Bridgewater, NJ 08807
Web Site: http://www.matrixxinc.com
Over-the-Counter Healthcare Products Developer & Marketer
N.A.I.C.S.: 325411
Timothy L. Clarot (Sr VP-R&D)
Sam Kamdar (CFO & COO)
Marc L. Rovner (CEO)
Phil Bramel (Sr VP-Sls)
Gulam Khan (VP-Mktg)
Craig Stoll (VP-Customer Strategy & Insights)

Subsidiary (Domestic):

Zicam LLC (2)
4742 N 24th St Ste 455, Phoenix, AZ 85016-4856
Web Site: http://www.zicam.com
Cold Remedies Mfr
N.A.I.C.S.: 325412

Nolan Transportation Group, Inc. (1)
400 Northridge Road, Suite 1000, Atlanta, GA 30350
Tel.: (770) 509-9611
Web Site: http://www.ntgfreight.com
Third-Party Logistics Services
N.A.I.C.S.: 488999
Kevin Nolan (Founder)
Geoff Kelley (Pres & COO)
Andrew Herpich (Chief Comml Officer)

Subsidiary (Domestic):

Eagle Transportation LLC (2)
7127 Hwy 98W Ste 50, Hattiesburg, MS 39402
Tel.: (601) 271-8337
Web Site: http://www.eagletran.com
Rev.: $1,400,000
Emp.: 30
Scenic & Sightseeing Transportation, Land
N.A.I.C.S.: 487110
Tory Bass (Pres)

Meridian Logistics LLC (2)
3307 Northland Dr Ste 360, Austin, TX 78731
Web Site: http://www.freightpros.com
Logistics & Transportation
N.A.I.C.S.: 488999
Chris Clever (Sr VP-LTL)
Scott Faust (Co-Founder & COO)

North American Essential Home Services (1)
28 Dunkirk Rd, St., Catharines, L2R 1A1, ON, Canada
Web Site: https://www.gryphon-inv.com
Holding Company
N.A.I.C.S.: 551112

Subsidiary (Domestic):

Right Time Group Inc. (2)
28 Dunkirk Rd, Saint Catharines, L2R 1A1, ON, Canada
Web Site: https://www.right-time.ca
HVAC Services; Installation, Maintenance & Repairs
N.A.I.C.S.: 238220

Subsidiary (US):

Southern Home Services LLC (2)
485 N Keller Rd Ste 515, Maitland, FL 32751
Tel.: (407) 519-3265
Web Site: https://www.southernhomeservices.com
HVAC Services
N.A.I.C.S.: 238220
Bryan Benak (CEO)

Subsidiary (Domestic):

Presidential Heating & Air Conditioning, Inc. (3)
8000 Cessna Ave, Gaithersburg, MD 20879
Tel.: (301) 774-3388
Web Site: http://www.presidentialheat.com
Rev.: $2,920,000
Emp.: 20
Heating & Air Conditioning Solutions Services
N.A.I.C.S.: 238220

Physical Rehabilitation Network, LLC (1)
2035 Corte Del Nogal Ste 200, Carlsbad, CA 92011
Tel.: (760) 239-6391
Web Site: http://www.prnpt.com
Holding Company; Physical Therapy Clinics Owner & Operator
N.A.I.C.S.: 551112
Erika Jacob (Chief Compliance Officer & Dir-Compliance)
Mike Rice (Chief Dev Officer)
Christina Sisco (VP-Revenue Cycle Mgmt)
Ajay Gupta (CEO)
Nick Poan (CFO)

Subsidiary (Domestic):

Albany Physical Therapy, PC (2)
948 San Pablo Ave, Albany, CA 94706-2010
Tel.: (510) 526-2353
Web Site: http://www.albanypt.com
Offices of Physical, Occupational & Speech Therapists & Audiologists
N.A.I.C.S.: 621340

Rio Rancho Physical Therapy (2)
4516 Arrowhead Rdg Dr SE, Rio Rancho, NM 87124-5932
Tel.: (505) 896-4978
Web Site: https://www.prnpt.com
Offices of Physical, Occupational & Speech Therapists & Audiologists
N.A.I.C.S.: 621340

Rocklin Physical Therapy, Inc. (2)
2217 Sunset Blvd, Rocklin, CA 95765
Tel.: (916) 435-3500
Web Site: http://www.rocklinpt.com
Process, Physical Distribution & Logistics Consulting Services
N.A.I.C.S.: 541614
John Zieour (Pres)

RegEd, Inc. (1)
2100 Gateway Centre Blvd Ste 200, Morrisville, NC 27560
Tel.: (919) 653-5200
Web Site: http://www.reged.com
Compliance Management Solutions Services
N.A.I.C.S.: 513210
John M. Schobel (Founder & CEO)
Margaret S. Fox (Gen Counsel)
Lorraine Smith Carver (Exec VP-Sls)
Debra Freitag (Chief Strategy Officer)
Pamela C. Parker (COO)
Brandi Brown (Sr VP-Regulatory Affairs)
Yogesh Periwal (CFO)
John Nichols (Sr VP-Sls)
Ann Robinson (Sr VP-Product Mgmt)
Mark Schlageter (Chm)

Shermco Industries, Inc. (1)

2425 E Pioneer Dr, Irving, TX 75061
Tel.: (972) 793-5523
Web Site: http://www.shermco.com
Engineering Services
N.A.I.C.S.: 541330
Philip V. Petrocelli (CEO)
Kevin R. Kohutek (CFO)
Gary Hill (COO)
Kim Drake-Loy (Chief Legal Officer & Chief Risk Officer)
Robert Harrison (Chief Comml Officer)

Subsidiary (Domestic):

Innovative Electric, Inc. (2)
12002 Beverly Park Rd Bldg C, Everett, WA 98204
Tel.: (425) 290-7803
Web Site: http://www.innovative-electric.com
Sales Range: $10-24.9 Million
Emp.: 10
Electrical Contractor
N.A.I.C.S.: 238210
Donna Petzold (Pres)

Sigma Six Solutions, Inc. (2)
2200 W Valley Hwy N, Auburn, WA 98001
Tel.: (253) 333-9730
Web Site: http://www.sigmasix.com
Sales Range: $1-9.9 Million
Emp.: 25
Engineering Services
N.A.I.C.S.: 541330
John Parker (Engr-Sls)
Chris Morgan (Gen Mgr)
Elisabeth Moore (CFO)

Sierra Research, Inc. (1)
1801 J St, Sacramento, CA 95811
Tel.: (916) 444-6666
Web Site: http://www.sierraresearch.com
Sales Range: $1-9.9 Million
Emp.: 550
Air Quality & Pollution Control Consulting Services
N.A.I.C.S.: 541620
Jim Lyons (Office Mgr)

Smile Brands, Inc. (1)
100 Spectrum Ctr Dr Ste 1500, Irvine, CA 92618
Tel.: (714) 668-1300
Web Site: http://www.smilebrands.com
Dental Management Services
N.A.I.C.S.: 621210
Steve C. Bilt (CEO)
Brad Schmidt (CFO)
George J. Suda (CIO)
Kim Marcus (Sr VP-Acctg & Fin)
Cheryl Dore (Chief HR Officer & Sr VP)
Robert C. Crim (Chief Dental Officer)
Stan Andrakowicz (COO & Sr VP-Ops)
Victoria Harvey (Chief Legal Officer & Sr VP)
Patrick Costello (Dir-Bus Dev)
Lucy Juarez (Natl VP-Specialty)
Lorilee Schmidt (Reg VP-West Reg)
Christy Englehart (Reg VP-East Reg)
April Cole (Reg VP-Central Reg)
Kevin Rogus (VP-Merger & Acq)

Subsidiary (Domestic):

A+ Dental Care (2)
1258 Coloma Way, Roseville, CA 95661
Tel.: (916) 784-1144
Web Site: http://www.rosevilledentist.com
Emp.: 30
Offices of Dentists
N.A.I.C.S.: 621210
Tim Herman (Founder)

Branch (Domestic):

A+ Dental Care (3)
4000 Foothills Blvd Ste 126, Roseville, CA 95747-7251
Tel.: (916) 771-7200
Web Site: http://rosevilledentist.com
Offices of Dentists
N.A.I.C.S.: 621210
Tim Herman (Founder)

Subsidiary (Domestic):

Castle Dental, Inc. (2)
5712 Kirby Dr, Houston, TX 77005
Tel.: (713) 521-3509
Web Site: http://www.castledental.com

General, Orthodontic & Multi-Specialty Dental Services
N.A.I.C.S.: 621210

Thermal Technology Distribution Solutions (1)
5150 Big Chief Dr., Cincinnati, OH 45227
Tel.: (513) 271-7411
Web Site: https://www.gobigchief.com
Electric Process Heating Distr
N.A.I.C.S.: 221122

Subsidiary (Domestic):

Applied Thermal Systems (2)
8401 73rd Ave N Ste 74, Brooklyn Park, MN 55428-1508
Tel.: (763) 535-5545
Web Site: http://www.apptherm.com
Sales Range: $1-9.9 Million
Emp.: 8
Plumbing & Heating Equipment & Supplies (Hydronics) Merchant Whslr
N.A.I.C.S.: 423720
Michael Roark (Pres)

Big Chief Inc. (2)
5150 Big Chief Dr., Cincinnati, OH 45227
Tel.: (513) 271-7411
Web Site: https://www.gobigchief.com
Plumbing, Heating & Air-Conditioning Contractors
N.A.I.C.S.: 238220

Proheat, Inc. (2)
117 E Adams St, La Grange, KY 40031-1229
Tel.: (502) 222-1402
Web Site: http://www.proheatinc.com
Electrical Apparatus & Equipment, Wiring Supplies & Related Equipment Merchant Whslr
N.A.I.C.S.: 423610
Steve Button (Pres)

Southwest Heater & Controls, Inc. (2)
10610 Control Pl, Dallas, TX 75238
Tel.: (214) 340-7500
Web Site: http://www.swhc.com
Sales Range: $1-9.9 Million
Emp.: 14
Industrial Machinery And Equipment
N.A.I.C.S.: 423830
Camille Hawkins (Pres)
Chris Hawkins (Gen Mgr)

Thermal Devices, Inc. (2)
1702 Back Acre Cir, Mount Airy, MD 21771
Tel.: (301) 831-7550
Web Site: https://www.thermaldevices.com
Sales Range: $1-9.9 Million
Emp.: 18
Industrial Machinery & Equipment Whslr
N.A.I.C.S.: 423830

Transportation Insight, LLC (1)
310 Main Ave Way SE, Hickory, NC 28602
Tel.: (828) 485-5000
Web Site: https://www.transportationinsight.com
Sales Range: $200-249.9 Million
Emp.: 2,300
Freight Transportation Arrangement
N.A.I.C.S.: 488510
Paul Thompson (Founder & Chm)
Reynolds Faulkner (CFO)
Rick Brumett (VP-Client Solutions)
Clay Gentry (VP & Gen Mgr-Truckload Ops)
Chris Mendenhall (VP-Pricing Svcs)
Charles Moore (VP-Parcel Pricing)
Jay Wilson (VP-Processing Svcs)
Sophie Dabbs (VP-Client Solutions)
Paul Schmitz (VP-Client Solutions)
Jim Taylor (VP-IT)
Ken Wacker (Exec VP-Enterprise Bus Solutions)
Josh Walker (VP-Org Dev)
Todd Benge (VP-Parcel Ops)
Scott Hagenkord (VP-Client Svcs)
Ken Beyer (CEO)

Subsidiary (Domestic):

CPA International, Inc. (2)
72 W Stafford Rd Brookside Professional Ctr Bldg III, Stafford Springs, CT 06076
Tel.: (860) 684-4288
Supply Chain Management Services
N.A.I.C.S.: 488510

Gryphon Investors, LLC—(Continued)

Spend Management Experts, LLC (2)
967 Buckingham Cir, Atlanta, GA 30327
Tel.: (404) 902-5390
Web Site: http://www.spendmanagementex perts.com
Sales Range: $1-9.9 Million
Expense Management Services
N.A.I.C.S.: 523940
John Haber (Founder & CEO)
Kim McQuilken (Pres-Sls & Mktg)
Paul Steiner (VP-Strategic Analysis)
Traci Doenitz (VP-Info Sys)
Gary Colangelo (VP-Client Svc)
Brian Broadhurst (VP-Transportation Solutions)
Melissa Runge (VP-Analytical Solutions)
Steve Clow (VP-Truckload)

Vetnique Labs LLC (1)
1864 High Grove Ln Ste 112, Naperville, IL 60540
Web Site: http://www.vetniquelabs.com
Sales Range: $1-9.9 Million
Emp.: 10
Pet Product Distr
N.A.I.C.S.: 459910
James Bascharon (CEO & Founder)

Wind River Environmental LLC (1)
46 Lizotte Dr Ste 1000, Marlborough, MA 01752
Tel.: (978) 841-5005
Web Site: http://www.wrenvironmental.com
Solid Waste Collection
N.A.I.C.S.: 562111
John P. O'Connell (CEO)
Dave Kline (Vice Chm)
Nathan Bernstein (CFO)
Jack Bailey (VP-Bus Dev)
Greg Seefeldt (VP-Sls & Mktg)
Adam Beck (VP-Ops)
Diana Newmier (VP-HR)

Subsidiary (Domestic):

SES Properties of Stanley, Inc. (2)
131 Mariposa Rd, Stanley, NC 28164-9645
Tel.: (704) 263-8186
Web Site: http://www.stanleyenviro.com
Septic System Services
N.A.I.C.S.: 562991
Jim Lanier (Pres & CEO)
Thomas Morrison (VP)

Wittichen Supply Company (1)
1600 3rd Ave S, Birmingham, AL 35233
Tel.: (205) 251-8500
Web Site: http://www.wittichen-supply.com
Sales Range: $25-49.9 Million
Emp.: 200
Wholesale Distributor of Air Conditioning, Heating, Refrigeration Equipment, Parts & Supplies
N.A.I.C.S.: 423740
David P. Henderson (Pres)
Marty Waddle (Mgr)
David Clough (Mgr)

Subsidiary (Domestic):

Benoist Brothers Supply Co (2)
1410 N 5th St, Union City, TN 38261
Tel.: (731) 884-1233
Web Site: http://www.benoist.com
Rev.: $5,000,000
Emp.: 18
Warm Air Heating & Air-Conditioning Equipment & Supplies Merchant Whslr
N.A.I.C.S.: 423730
Jack Benoist (Pres)

GRYYT, LLC
7350 E Progress Pl Ste 100, Greenwood Village, CO 80111
Tel.: (866) 720-3350
Web Site: http://www.gryyt.com
Social Impact Intelligence Company
N.A.I.C.S.: 813319
Stephen Deason (CEO)
Jonathan Bray (Chief Innovation Officer)
Angela Whaley (Chief Customer Officer)
Craig Schmieder (CTO)
Lisa Wilson (Dir-Fin & Ops)

Derrick DeCarlo (VP-Nonprofit and For-Purpose Partnerships)
Chelsie Blancas (Dir-Client Ops)
John Steuart (Exec Chm)

Subsidiaries:

Rally4, Inc. (1)
7000 E Belleview Ave Ste 220, Greenwood Village, CO 80111
Tel.: (866) 720-3350
Web Site: http://www.rally4.com
Mobile Fundraising Services
N.A.I.C.S.: 541519
Frank Richards (CEO)
Jonathan Bray (CIO)
Angela Whaley (VP-Client Strategies)

GS GLOBAL RESOURCES, INC.
926 Perkins Dr, Mukwonago, WI 53159
Tel.: (262) 378-5200
Web Site:
https://www.gsglobalresources.com
Year Founded: 1972
Hydraulic Systems Equipment & Supplies
N.A.I.C.S.: 423830
John Thornton (Pres)
Greg Jones (Supvr-Warehouse)
Steve Stoehr (Mgr-Engrg)
Aaron Thomsen (Engr)

GS INTER, INC.
1455 19th St, Santa Monica, CA 90404
Tel.: (310) 586-1100
Web Site: http://www.guitarsalon.com
Sales Range: $10-24.9 Million
Emp.: 20
Musical Equipment Whslr
N.A.I.C.S.: 423990
Tim Miklaucic (Owner & CEO)
David Collett (Pres)

GS MARKETING, INC.
1345 Enclave Pkwy, Houston, TX 77077
Tel.: (713) 580-3900
Web Site:
http://www.gsmarketing.com
Year Founded: 2002
Sales Range: $1-9.9 Million
Emp.: 80
Direct Mail Advertising Services
N.A.I.C.S.: 541860
Shelley Washburn (Pres)
Tom Heizer (VP-Bus Dev)
Claudia Esquivel (VP-Fin & Ops)
Kristi Pierce (Dir-Mktg Ops, Integration & Sourcing)
Michael Wirth (Dir-Sls-Natl)

GS&L ENTERPRISES INCORPORATED
408 Hwy 49 S, Jackson, MS 39218
Tel.: (601) 939-1000
Rev.: $105,700,000
Emp.: 650
General Construction Machinery & Equipment
N.A.I.C.S.: 423110
Gerald S. Swanson (Pres)

Subsidiaries:

Empire Truck Sales Inc (1)
373 Hwy 49 S, Jackson, MS 39218
Tel.: (601) 939-5000
Trucks, Tractors & Trailers: New & Used
N.A.I.C.S.: 441110
Gerald Swanson (Pres)

Stribling Equipment LLC (1)
408 Hwy 49 S, Jackson, MS 39218
Tel.: (601) 939-1000
Web Site:
http://www.striblingequipment.com
General Construction Machinery & Equipment

N.A.I.C.S.: 423810
Brien Craig (Mgr-Fin & Insurance)
Lee Cooke (Controller)

GSB DIGITAL INC.
33-01 Hunters Point Ave, Long Island City, NY 11101
Tel.: (212) 684-3600
Web Site: http://gsbdigital.com
Year Founded: 1991
Print & Litigation Support Services
N.A.I.C.S.: 323111
Stephan Steiner (Pres)

GSC ARCHITECTS
3100 Alvin Devane Blvd Bldg A Ste 200-B, Austin, TX 78741
Tel.: (512) 477-9417
Web Site:
https://www.gscarchitects.com
Year Founded: 1978
Sales Range: $10-24.9 Million
Emp.: 40
Architectural Design Services
N.A.I.C.S.: 541310
Thomas A. Cornelius (Pres & Principal)
Joe Larocca (Principal)
Julie Zitter (Project Mgr)
Phil Scott (Principal)

GSC ENTERPRISES, INC.
130 Hillcrest Dr, Sulphur Springs, TX 75482
Tel.: (903) 885-7621
Web Site:
http://www.grocerysupply.com
Year Founded: 1947
Sales Range: $25-49.9 Million
Emp.: 1,100
Holding Company; Grocery Distr & Money Order Fulfillment Services
N.A.I.C.S.: 551112
Michael K. McKenzie (Chm)
Kerry Law (CFO & VP-Fin)
Michael J. Bain (Pres & CEO)
Janet Price (VP-Risk Mgmt & Employee Svcs)
Ryan McKenzie (COO & VP-Ops)
Steve Rutherford (Gen Counsel)
Robert Cody (Controller)
Mark Pope (Mgr-Warehouse)

Subsidiaries:

Fidelity Express Money Order Company (1)
128 Jefferson St, Sulphur Springs, TX 75482
Tel.: (903) 885-1283
Web Site: http://www.fidelityexpress.com
Sales Range: $25-49.9 Million
Emp.: 60
Full-Service Money Order Company
N.A.I.C.S.: 424410
Dolly Gilliam (Mgr-Ops)
Terry Hair (Mgr-Mktg)
Tracey Fatland (Mgr-Customer Svc)

Grocery Supply Company (1)
130 Hillcrest Dr, Sulphur Springs, TX 75482 (100%)
Tel.: (903) 885-7621
Web Site: http://www.gsc.com
Sales Range: $50-74.9 Million
Emp.: 440
Groceries Supply
N.A.I.C.S.: 424410
John Prickette (Mgr-Div)
Nancy Bolton (Mgr-Customer Svcs)

Unit (Domestic):

Grocery Supply Company-San Antonio (2)
2330 Roosevelt Ave, San Antonio, TX 78210-4936 (100%)
Tel.: (210) 533-1281
Sales Range: $25-49.9 Million
Emp.: 300
Grocery Supply
N.A.I.C.S.: 424410

Grocery Supply Company-SouthEast (2)
4150 W Blount St, Pensacola, FL 32505
Tel.: (850) 438-9651
Sales Range: $50-74.9 Million
Emp.: 365
Warehousing & Transporting Grocery Products
N.A.I.C.S.: 424410

GSC GROUP
500 Campus Dr Ste 220, Florham Park, NJ 07932-1024
Tel.: (973) 437-1000
Year Founded: 1994
Sales Range: $250-299.9 Million
Emp.: 180
Equity Investment Firm
N.A.I.C.S.: 523999
Richard M. Hayden (Vice Chm)
Peter D. Firth (Mng Dir)
Seth M. Katzenstein (Sr Mng Dir & Co-Head-European Mezzanine Lending)
Nicolas Petrusic (Sr Mng Dir & Co-Head-European Mezzanine Lending)
Harvey E. Siegel (Mng Dir)
Alexander B. Wright (Mng Dir)
Sarah Blackwood (Office Mgr)

GSC LOGISTICS INC.
530 Water St 5th Fl, Oakland, CA 94607-3524
Tel.: (510) 844-3700
Web Site: http://www.gschq.com
Year Founded: 1988
Sales Range: $10-24.9 Million
Emp.: 60
General Warehousing & Local Freight Trucking
N.A.I.C.S.: 493110
Scott E. Taylor (Pres & CEO)
Joseph Zepko (VP-Sls & Bus Dev)
Laura Root (Dir-Bus Dev-Pacific Northwest)
Andy Garcia (Chm)
Richard Norton (VP-Ops)

Subsidiaries:

GSC Air Logistics Inc. (1)
530 Water St Ste 501, Oakland, CA 94607-3524
Tel.: (510) 844-3700
Web Site: http://www.gschq.com
Rev.: $110,000
Emp.: 30
Airfreight Loading & Unloading Services
N.A.I.C.S.: 488119

Macmillan-Piper LLC (1)
1762 6th Ave S, Seattle, WA 98134
Tel.: (206) 624-5135
Web Site: http://www.macpiper.com
Sales Range: $10-24.9 Million
Emp.: 68
Provider of Trucking Services; Operator of Container Freight Stations
N.A.I.C.S.: 488991
Suzanne Tilley (Mgr-Compliance & Assets)
Mark Miller (Pres)

GSC PACKAGING, INC.
575 Wharton Dr, Atlanta, GA 30336
Tel.: (404) 505-9925
Web Site:
http://www.gscpackaging.com
Year Founded: 2001
Sales Range: $100-124.9 Million
Emp.: 300
Packaging Services
N.A.I.C.S.: 561910
Robert Shapiro (Pres)
Ed Forrest (Dir-Ops)
Marisol Garcia (Dir-Quality)
Sheila Bettis (Office Mgr)
Charles Sallee (Dir-Natl Sls)

GSG DESIGN
33 E 17th St, New York, NY 10003

Tel.: (212) 242-8787
Year Founded: 1980
Emp.: 135
Advertising Services
N.A.I.C.S.: 541890
Ken Madsen *(Pres)*
Bill Hufstader *(CEO)*
Richard Paganello *(COO)*
Jan Stollerman *(Partner)*

GSM NATION LLC.
282 York St, New Haven, CT 06511
Tel.: (203) 660-1198
Year Founded: 2010
Sales Range: $10-24.9 Million
Emp.: 10
Miscellaneous Product Whslr
N.A.I.C.S.: 456120
Ahmed Khattak *(Owner)*

GSP INTERNATIONAL AIR-PORT
2000 GSP Dr Ste 1, Greer, SC 29651
Tel.: (864) 877-7426
Web Site: https://www.gspairport.com
Year Founded: 1962
Sales Range: $10-24.9 Million
Emp.: 100
Airport Operation Services
N.A.I.C.S.: 488119
Kevin Howell *(COO & VP)*
Rosylin Weston *(VP-Comml)*
Richard Piper *(Dir-Facilities)*
Michael A. Gula *(Dir-Ops)*
Fred Bright *(Mgr-Airport Ops Duty)*
Ronnie Bullard *(Mgr-Facilities)*
Nathan Garner *(Mgr-Aviation Svcs)*
Marsha Madore *(Mgr-HR)*
Kristie Weatherly *(Dir-Fin)*
Kim Davis *(Mgr-Customer Svc)*
Michael Kossover *(Dir-Ops)*
Scott Carr *(VP-Comml Bus & Properties)*
Basil Dosunmu *(CFO & Sr VP-Admin & Fin)*
David N. Edwards Jr. *(Pres & CEO)*

GSP MARKETING SERVICES, INC.
320 W Ohio St, Chicago, IL 60654
Tel.: (312) 944-3000   IL
Web Site:
   http://www.gspmarketing.com
Year Founded: 1978
Rev.: $210,000,000
Emp.: 50
Commercial Photography, Consumer Marketing, Direct Marketing, Full Service, Strategic Planning/Research
N.A.I.C.S.: 541810
Richard Grunsten *(Pres)*
Kelly Vetter *(Controller)*
Jim Clark *(VP)*

GSP MARKETING TECHNOLO-GIES, INC.
14055 46th St N Ste 1112, Clearwater, FL 33762
Tel.: (727) 532-0647   FL
Web Site: https://www.gspretail.com
Sales Range: $10-24.9 Million
Emp.: 170
Screen Printing, Retail Branding & Marketing Services
N.A.I.C.S.: 323113
Paul F. Neuhoff *(Chm)*
Geoff Neuhoff *(Pres & CEO)*
Steven Cohen *(VP-Creative Svcs)*
Margaret Sotrop *(Exec Dir-Creative-Design Svcs)*

Subsidiaries:

Great Big Pictures, Inc.   (1)
5701 Manufacturers Dr, Madison, WI 53704
Tel.: (608) 257-7071

Web Site: http://www.gbpinc.com
Sales Range: $10-24.9 Million
Emp.: 100
Large-Format Commercial Screen Printing & Retail Display Mfr
N.A.I.C.S.: 323113
Alice Torti *(VP & Gen Mgr)*
Shae Darvin *(Coord-Matls)*
Bobbie Stellner *(Project Mgr)*

GSPANN TECHNOLOGIES, INC.
362 Fairview Way, Milpitas, CA 95035
Tel.: (408) 263-3435
Web Site: https://www.gspann.com
Year Founded: 2004
Sales Range: $1-9.9 Million
Emp.: 174
Enterprise Content Management, Quality Assurance, Business Intelligence, Mobile & Web Development & Integrated Marketing Strategy Services
N.A.I.C.S.: 518210

GST INFORMATION TECHNOL-OGY SOLUTIONS
12881 166th St, Cerritos, CA 90703
Tel.: (562) 345-8700   CA
Web Site: http://www.gstes.com
Year Founded: 1983
Sales Range: $10-24.9 Million
Emp.: 80
Computer Integrated Systems Design
N.A.I.C.S.: 449210
Alice Wang *(Pres)*
Jia P. Wang *(CEO)*
Dennis Wang *(COO)*

GST NET INC.
4001 Main St, Vancouver, WA 98663
Tel.: (360) 906-7100   WA
Year Founded: 1996
Sales Range: $25-49.9 Million
Long Distance Telephone Communications
N.A.I.C.S.: 517121
Robert Ferchat *(Chm)*

GSTEK, INC.
1100 Madison Plz Ste A, Chesapeake, VA 23320
Tel.: (757) 548-1597
Web Site: http://www.gstekinc.com
Year Founded: 1992
Rev.: $22,900,000
Emp.: 257
Engineeering Services
N.A.I.C.S.: 541330
Burhl E. Strother Jr. *(Pres)*
Matthew Strother *(VP)*
Timothy J. Strother *(VP)*

GT ADVANCED TECHNOLO-GIES INC.
243 Daniel Webster Hwy, Merrimack, NH 03054
Tel.: (603) 883-5200   DE
Web Site: http://www.gtat.com
Year Founded: 1994
Sales Range: $250-299.9 Million
Emp.: 541
Silicon Wafer & Solar Cell Electronic & Industrial Equipment Mfr
N.A.I.C.S.: 334413
P. S. Raghavan *(CTO)*

Subsidiaries:

GT Advanced Cz LLC   (1)
1600 Park 370 Pl Ste 2, Hazelwood, MO 63042
Tel.: (314) 880-0888
Production of Monocrystalline Materials for Solar Panels
N.A.I.C.S.: 334413

GT Advanced Sapphire Systems Group LLC   (1)
27 Congress St, Salem, MA 01970
Tel.: (978) 745-0088
Mfr of Sapphire Material for LED Industry
N.A.I.C.S.: 212390

GT Advanced Technologies Inc. - Polysilicon Division   (1)
101 E Front Ste 401, Missoula, MT 59802
Tel.: (406) 532-0110
Web Site: http://www.gtat.com
Sales Range: $125-149.9 Million
Emp.: 68
Fabrication Equipment Mfr for Solar Power Generation Systems
N.A.I.C.S.: 333248
Dave Keck *(VP)*

GT Advanced Technologies Limited   (1)
13/F Tower 2 The Gateway Harbour City 25 Canton Road, Tsimshatsui, Kowloon, China (Hong Kong)
Tel.: (852) 21530858
Web Site: http://www.gtat.com
Silicon Wafer & Solar Cell Electronic & Industrial Equipment Mfr
N.A.I.C.S.: 334413

GT Advanced Technologies Taiwan Co., Ltd.   (1)
6F-10 No 38 Taiyuan St, Jhubei, 30265, Hsin-chu, Taiwan
Tel.: (886) 35600111
Electric Equipment Mfr
N.A.I.C.S.: 334511

GT Solar (Shanghai) Co., Ltd.   (1)
3201-3203 Park Place 1601 Nanjing Road West, Jing An District, Shanghai, 200040, China
Tel.: (86) 2162887272
Sales Range: $25-49.9 Million
Emp.: 60
Silicon Wafer & Solar Cell Electronic & Industrial Equipment Mfr
N.A.I.C.S.: 334413
Jeff Ford *(Gen Mgr)*

Thermal Technology Inc.   (1)
1911 Airport Blvd, Santa Rosa, CA 95403
Tel.: (707) 571-1911
Web Site:
   http://www.thermaltechnology.com
Sales Range: $10-24.9 Million
Emp.: 37
Vacuum Furnaces & Ovens Mfr
N.A.I.C.S.: 333994
David Hansinger *(Pres)*

GT CONTRACTING CORP
1447 Pennsylvania SE, Washington, DC 20003
Tel.: (202) 544-5155   NY
Year Founded: 1929
Sales Range: $10-24.9 Million
Emp.: 10
Building Contractors
N.A.I.C.S.: 236117
Jefferey Clum *(Exec VP)*
Gurlherne Tavares *(Pres)*
Fernando Barbosa *(Owner)*

GT SALES & MANUFACTUR-ING INC.
2202 S W St, Wichita, KS 67213-1114
Tel.: (316) 943-2171   KS
Web Site: https://www.gtmidwest.com
Year Founded: 1984
Sales Range: $25-49.9 Million
Emp.: 150
Industrial Supplies Distr
N.A.I.C.S.: 423840
Brad Hallet *(Mgr-Customer Rels)*
Bob McDaris *(Sys Engr-Sales)*
Jason Chambers *(Sys Engr-Sales)*
Jeff Jaeger *(Sys Engr-Sales)*
Jim Severin *(Sys Engr-Sales)*
Keith Fulton *(Sys Engr-Sales)*

GTC SYSTEMS INC.

9855 Business Park Ave, San Diego, CA 92131
Tel.: (858) 560-5800
Web Site: http://www.gtcsystems.com
Sales Range: $10-24.9 Million
Emp.: 20
Computers, Peripherals & Software
N.A.I.C.S.: 423430
Keith Esshaki *(CEO)*
Thaniel Noles *(CTO)*
Jonathan Bucud *(Engr-Sys)*
Monique Tuisamoa *(Mgr-Ops)*

GTCR LLC
300 N LaSalle St Ste 5600, Chicago, IL 60654
Tel.: (312) 382-2200   DE
Web Site: https://www.gtcr.com
Year Founded: 1980
Privater Equity Firm
N.A.I.C.S.: 523999
Anna May L. Trala *(Mng Dir & CFO)*
Aaron D. Cohen *(Mng Dir & Head-Fin Svcs & Tech)*
Mark A. Springer *(Chief Acctg Officer & Principal)*
Travis J. Krueger *(Mng Dir)*
Stephen J. Jeschke *(Mng Dir)*
John D. Kos *(Mng Dir)*
Jeffrey S. Wright *(Chief Legal Officer, Chief Compliance Officer & Principal)*
Michael S. Hollander *(Mng Dir)*
K. J. McConnell *(Mng Dir)*
Kathleen A. Keenan *(Dir-Events & Investor Meetings)*
Stephen P. Master *(Mng Dir)*
Jeffrey B. Heh *(Mng Dir)*
Faraz Ahmed *(Principal & Head-IT)*
Cameron Rouzer *(Dir)*
Christopher Smith *(Principal)*
Geoffrey Tresley *(Principal)*
David A. Donnini *(Mng Dir & Head-Consumer Svcs)*
Tom Ehrhart *(Principal)*
Benjamin J. Daverman *(Mng Dir & Co-Head-Healthcare)*
Constantine S. Mihas *(Co-CEO & Mng Dir)*
Sean L. Cunningham *(Mng Dir & Co-Head-Healthcare)*
Luke Marker *(Mng Dir)*
Mark M. Anderson *(Mng Dir & Co-Head-Media, Tech, and Telecom)*
Collin E. Roche *(Co-CEO & Mng Dir)*

Subsidiaries:

ADT Commercial LLC   (1)
1501 Yamato Rd, Boca Raton, FL 33431
Tel.: (855) 238-2666
Web Site: https://www.adt.com
Fire & Security Systems Installation, Maintenance & Monitoring Services
N.A.I.C.S.: 561621
Mike Compton *(CTO)*
Mark Foley *(CFO)*
Michael McWilliams *(Sr VP-Sls & Field Ops)*

Subsidiary (Domestic):

Alarm Tech Solutions LLC   (2)
8141 Telegraph Rd Ste F, Severn, MD 21144-3148
Tel.: (301) 912-1775
Web Site:
   http://www.alarmtechsolutions.com
Security System Services
N.A.I.C.S.: 561621

Apex Integrated Security Solutions, LLC   (2)
109 S 4th St, Boise, ID 83702-7226
Tel.: (208) 378-9650
Web Site:
   http://www.apexintegratedsecurity.com
Electrical Apparatus & Related Equipment Merchant Whslr
N.A.I.C.S.: 423610

GTCR LLC—(Continued)

Cal Ledbetter (Gen Mgr)

Design/Systems Group, Inc. (2)
402 S Center St, Grand Prairie, TX 75051
Tel.: (972) 262-3332
Web Site: http://www.dsgworld.net
Electrical Apparatus & Equipment, Wiring
Supplies & Related Equipment Merchant
Whslr
N.A.I.C.S.: 423610
Ovid Morphew (Owner)

Digiop Technologies, Ltd. (2)
3850 Priority Way Dr S, Indianapolis, IN
46240
Tel.: (317) 489-0413
Web Site: http://www.digiop.com
Rev.: $2,800,000
Emp.: 35
Data Processing, Hosting & Related Ser-
vices
N.A.I.C.S.: 518210
Mike Compton (Pres & CEO)
Cesar Gonzalez (VP-Sls)

**Diversified Protection Systems
Inc.** (2)
1241 N Barsten Way, Anaheim, CA 92806-
1822
Web Site: http://www.dps-sc.com
Specialty Trade Contractors
N.A.I.C.S.: 238990
Tony Milton (Pres)

Newtech Systems, Inc. (2)
1850 Dalton Ave, Ashland, KY 41102
Tel.: (606) 325-0306
Web Site: http://www.newtechashland.com
Sales Range: $10-24.9 Million
Emp.: 60
Electrical Apparatus & Equipment Whslr
N.A.I.C.S.: 423610
Mary Ware (CFO)
Michael Bryant (VP & Gen Mgr)
Tom Kibler (VP & Gen Mgr)

**Red Hawk Fire & Security (NY)
LLC** (2)
6 Skyline Dr, Hawthorne, NY 10532
Tel.: (914) 769-8900
Sales Range: $25-49.9 Million
Emp.: 60
Fire Alarm Systems
N.A.I.C.S.: 423610
William Nugent (Mgr-Engrg)

Tele-Tector of Maryland, Inc. (2)
6935 Oakland Mills Rd E, Columbia, MD
21045
Tel.: (410) 290-5600
Web Site: http://www.tele-tector.com
Sales Range: $1-9.9 Million
Other Communications Equipment Mfr
N.A.I.C.S.: 334290
Fred Pedrosa (CEO)

**AssetMark Financial Holdings,
Inc.** (1)
1655 Grant St 10th Fl, Concord, CA 94520
Tel.: (925) 521-2200
Rev.: $618,306,000
Assets: $1,502,930,000
Liabilities: $376,564,000
Net Worth: $1,126,366,000
Earnings: $103,261,000
Emp.: 980
Fiscal Year-end: 12/31/2022
Financial Services
N.A.I.C.S.: 523999
Gary Zyla (CFO & Exec VP)
David McNatt (Exec VP-Investment Solu-
tions)
Esi Minta-Jacobs (Exec VP-Human Re-
sources & Digital Product Solutions)
Ted Angus (Gen Counsel & Exec VP)
Carrie Hansen (COO & Exec VP)
Mukesh Mehta (CIO & Exec VP)
Michael Kim (Pres & CEO)
Lou Maiuri (Chm)

Subsidiary (Domestic):

**Adhesion Wealth Advisor Solutions,
Inc.** (2)
5925 Carnegie Blvd Ste 500, Charlotte, NC
28209
Web Site: http://www.adhesionwealth.com
Software Publisher

N.A.I.C.S.: 513210

AssuredPartners, Inc. (1)
450 S Orange Avenue 4th Floor, Orlando,
FL 32801
Tel.: (407) 804-5222
Web Site: http://www.assuredpartners.com
Emp.: 9,200
Holding Company; Insurance & Benefits
Brokerage Services
N.A.I.C.S.: 551112
Jim W. Henderson (Founder & Chm)
Paul Vredenburg (COO & Chief Acq Officer)
Stan Kinnett (Gen Counsel & Exec VP)
Steve Deal (Exec VP-Carrier Relationships)
Gerald B. Budde (VP-Corp Fin)
Joe Guercio (COO-Retail Operations)
Randy Larsen (Pres & CEO)
Michael J. Crawford (Sr VP)
Brian Bair (Pres-Retail)
Andrea Brogger (Chief HR Officer)
John Stephens (Regl Pres)
Mark Hammond (CFO)
Alush Garzon (Sr VP)
Ty Beba (Chief Revenue Officer)
Mike Randall (Exec VP-Vertical Strategies)
Jim Hartz (Sr VP)
Elizabeth Thrailkill (CMO)
Stephanie Lockwood (CFO-Retail)
Will Dierking (COO)

Subsidiary (Domestic):

Air Capital Insurance, LLC (2)
9860 E. 21st Street North, Wichita, KS
67206-3845
Tel.: (316) 858-1999
Web Site: http://www.aircapitalins.com
Insurance Related Activities
N.A.I.C.S.: 524298
Greg Hiser (Pres)

AirSouth Insurance, Inc. (2)
2434 Fortner St Ste 3, Dothan, AL 36301-
2156
Tel.: (334) 793-9802
Insurance Agencies & Brokerages
N.A.I.C.S.: 524210

**Alliance Marine Risk Managers of
Florida, Inc.** (2)
901 SE 10th Ave, Fort Lauderdale, FL
33316
Tel.: (954) 522-7755
Sales Range: $1-9.9 Million
Emp.: 18
Insurance Agencies & Brokerages
N.A.I.C.S.: 524210

Alpine Insurance Associates, Inc. (2)
6160 Plumas St, Reno, NV 89519
Tel.: (775) 829-2345
Web Site: http://www.alpine-insurance.com
Rev.: $4,000,000
Emp.: 35
All Other Insurance Related Activities
N.A.I.C.S.: 524298
Chris Gonfiantini (Pres)
Morre J. Hughes (Dir-Ops)
Ryan Garaventa (VP)

**American Westbrook Insurance Ser-
vices, LLC** (2)
4 Westbrook Corporate Ctr Ste 500,
Westchester, IL 60154
Web Site: http://www.amwestbrook.com
Property & Casualty Insurance Agency; Em-
ployee Benefits Administration Services
N.A.I.C.S.: 524210
Raymond John Rotolo (Exec VP-Employee
Benefits Practice)
Christine Seitz (VP & Dir-Comm)
Greg Crawford (VP-Human Capital Mgmt
Practice)
John Willenborg (CFO)
Karen Kozik (VP & Dir-HR)
Mary O'Neill Bresnahan (Dir-Private Client
Svcs)
Mike Melnick (VP)
Mike Schoch (Exec VP-Property & Casualty
Practice)
Robert Levy (Exec VP)
Anthony S. Pulgine (Pres)
Scott Walker (CTO)
Theodore G. Barlas (Exec VP)
Diana Jacobs (First VP)
Laurie Leggett (Mgr-Client Svcs)

Aniello Insurance Agency, Inc. (2)

3012 W Charleston Blvd, Las Vegas, NV
89102
Tel.: (702) 259-0250
Web Site: http://www.anielloinsurance.com
Sales Range: $1-9.9 Million
Emp.: 18
Insurance Agents, Brokers, And Service, N
N.A.I.C.S.: 524210
Debi Bennett (Office Mgr)
Kyle Tayrien (VP)

Archer A. Associates, Inc. (2)
1230 Hempstead Tpke, Franklin Square,
NY 11010
Tel.: (516) 328-0333
Web Site: http://www.archerins.com
Sales Range: $1-9.9 Million
Emp.: 21
Insurance Agents
N.A.I.C.S.: 524210
Charles R. Torsiello (Pres)
Bennett Palmeri (VP-Producer)
Rose Bruccoleri (Mgr-Ops)
Robert Lanciotti (VP)
Thomas D. Muscarella (VP)
Joseph D. Muscarella (VP)
Greg Milewczik (Mgr-Acctg)
Phyllis M. Rizzo (Mgr-Personal Lines)
JoAnn Babiak (Acct Exec-Comml)
Lisa Cassese (Acct Exec-Small Bus)
Sherri Checkla (Mgr-Ops)

AssureSouth, Inc. (2)
291 S Pine St, Spartanburg, SC 29302
Tel.: (864) 582-5481
Web Site: http://www.assuresouth.com
Sales Range: $1-9.9 Million
Emp.: 16
Insurance Agents
N.A.I.C.S.: 524210
Barbara A. Light (Mgr-Personal Lines)
Ben Taylor (CEO)

**Assured Neace Lukens Insurance
Agency, Inc.** (2)
2305 River Rd, Louisville, KY 40206
Tel.: (502) 894-2100
Web Site: http://www.neacelukens.com
Holding Company; Insurance Agencies Op-
erator
N.A.I.C.S.: 551112
Todd Stocksdale (Pres)

Subsidiary (Domestic):

Davis-Garvin Agency, Inc. (3)
1 Fernandina Ct, Columbia, SC 29212
Tel.: (803) 732-0060
Web Site: http://www.davisgarvin.com
Insurance Agents Brokers & Services
N.A.I.C.S.: 524210
Janice Bullock (Coord-Acct)
Vicki Johnson (Mgr-Acctg)

Subsidiary (Domestic):

B & H Insurance, LLC (2)
111 Ruthar Dr, Newark, DE 19711
Tel.: (302) 995-2247
Web Site: http://www.bhi365.com
Sales Range: $1-9.9 Million
Emp.: 26
Insurance Services
N.A.I.C.S.: 524210
John P. Boykin (Pres & CEO)
Kory R. Hitchens (Partner & Sls Mgr)
Brandon L. Grizzel (Dir-Ops)
Laura S. Hitchens (Dir-Claims Mgmt)
Craig C. Campbell (Dir-Risk Control)

Beimdiek Insurance Agency, Inc. (2)
303 W 3rd St, Carthage, MO 64836
Tel.: (417) 358-4007
Web Site: http://www.beimdiek.com
Insurance Agencies
N.A.I.C.S.: 524210
Tina Osborne (Acct Mgr-Comml)
Steve Beimdiek (CEO)
Carol Baker (Acct Mgr-Individual Health &
Claims)
Kristi Cates (Acct Mgr-Comml)
Lorie Downing (Acct Exec-Grp Health)
Kimberly Fullerton (CFO)
Terry Geller (Acct Mgr-Comml)
Chelsea Hoenshell (Acct Mgr-Personal)
Athena Hughes (Acct Mgr-Comml)
Dina Sarratt (Acct Mgr-Comml)

Benefit Resource Group (2)

5985 Home Gardens Dr Ste A, Reno, NV
89502-6276
Tel.: (775) 688-4400
Web Site: http://www.benresgroup.com
Health & Medical Insurance Carriers
N.A.I.C.S.: 524114
Todd Wilson (Founder & Pres)

Biddle Insurance Services, Inc. (2)
3650 Winding Way, Newtown Square, PA
19073
Tel.: (484) 427-8900
Web Site: http://www.biddleservices.net
Insurance Agencies & Brokerages
N.A.I.C.S.: 524210
Kate Flanagan (Pres)
Frederick A. Tucker (Chm)

**Centennial Surety Associates,
Inc.** (2)
251 Najoles Rd Ste H, Millersville, MD
21108
Tel.: (301) 725-1855
Web Site: http://www.centennialsurety.com
Sales Range: $1-9.9 Million
Emp.: 8
Insurance Agents
N.A.I.C.S.: 524210
Michael Schendel (Principal)

**Church Insurance & Financial Ser-
vices, Inc.** (2)
600 E Cuyahoga Falls Ave, Akron, OH
44310
Tel.: (330) 733-1800
Web Site: http://www.churchagency.com
Sales Range: $1-9.9 Million
Emp.: 8
Insurance Agents
N.A.I.C.S.: 524210

Clark Associates, Inc. (2)
2229 Rocky Ridge Rd, Birmingham, AL
35216
Tel.: (205) 823-2300
Web Site: http://www.clarkagent.com
Sales Range: $1-9.9 Million
Emp.: 14
Insurance Agents
N.A.I.C.S.: 524210
Lanelle Duncan (Mgr-Acctg)
Leroy Clark (Pres)

**Commercial Insurance Services,
Inc.** (2)
340 MacCorkle Ave SE, Charleston, WV
25314
Tel.: (304) 345-8000
Web Site: http://www.ciswv.com
Sales Range: $1-9.9 Million
Emp.: 36
Insurance Agencies & Brokerages
N.A.I.C.S.: 524210
Brent J. Burton (Sr VP-Gen Comml & Pub
Sector)
Raye King White (Pres, Partner, COO &
Principal)
Sandy L. Jenkins (VP-Property & Casualty
Svcs)
Paul S. White (Partner, Principal & Exec
VP)
Geoff S. Christian (Partner, Principal & Sr
VP)
Trip King (Sr VP-Gen Comml & Pub Sector)
Frank A. Baer III (Chm, CEO, Partner &
Principal)

Corkill Insurance Agency, Inc. (2)
25 NW Point Blvd, Elk Grove Village, IL
60007
Tel.: (847) 758-1000
Web Site: http://www.corkillinsurance.com
Insurance Agencies & Brokerages
N.A.I.C.S.: 524210
Joanne Helzer (Mgr-Benefits)

D.M. Lovitt Insurance Agency (2)
607 N 6th Ave, Tucson, AZ 85705
Tel.: (520) 798-1888
Web Site: http://www.dmlovitt.com
Sales Range: $1-9.9 Million
Emp.: 16
Insurance Agents
N.A.I.C.S.: 524210
David M. Lovitt Jr. (Pres)

Daly Merritt, Inc. (2)
3099 Biddle Ave, Wyandotte, MI 48192
Tel.: (734) 283-1400
Web Site: http://www.dalymerritt.com

Sales Range: $1-9.9 Million
Emp.: 35
Insurance Agencies & Brokerages
N.A.I.C.S.: 524210
Martin F. Daly (Pres & CEO)
Thomas J. Daly (Pres-Gibraltar Veterinary Hospital)

Dawson Companies (2)
1340 Depot St Ste 300, Cleveland, OH 44116
Tel.: (440) 333-9000
Web Site:
 http://www.dawsoncompanies.com
Sales Range: $50-74.9 Million
Insurance Brokers
N.A.I.C.S.: 524210
Trudie Gaal (VP-HR)
Eva Karl (Coord-Wellness & Sls)
Jeremy Ball (VP)
Lori Proch (VP)
Terry Johnson (Sr VP)
Michael J. Kmetz (CFO & Exec VP)

Subsidiary (Domestic):

Leonard Insurance Services Agency Inc. (3)
4244 Mount Pleasant St NW, Canton, OH 44720
Tel.: (330) 266-1904
Web Site: http://www.leonardinsurance.com
Sales Range: $10-24.9 Million
Emp.: 50
Insurance Brokerage Services
N.A.I.C.S.: 524210
Douglas R. Malcolm (VP)
Marlene E. McLendon (Treas)
Marsha Dunn (VP-Agency Ops)
Paul E. Cruciani (VP)
Kim A. Degiralomo (VP)
Darren J. Faye (VP)
Lee W. Framer (Sr VP)
David G. Ingalls (VP)
Linda A. Mazzaferri (Acct Exec)
Carly Mussey-Widener (Acct Exec)
J. Perry Schlabach (VP)
Josef C. Skemp (VP)
Jon D. Smith (VP)
Richard K. Martindale (Chm)
Fred W. Kloots Jr. (Pres)

Subsidiary (Domestic):

Early, Cassidy & Schilling, LLC (2)
15200 Omega Dr Ste 100, Rockville, MD 20850
Tel.: (301) 948-5800
Web Site: http://www.ecsinsure.com
Insurance Services
N.A.I.C.S.: 524210
Andrew G. Cassidy (Treas)
Sean K. Gormley (VP-Ops)
James Hodgson (CFO)
Lynne W. Cook (Sr VP-Surety)
Timothy A. Schilling (Pres & Sec)
Michael A. Fragola (VP-Bus Dev)
Patrick T. Duke (VP-Employee Benefits Practice)
Jamie Mooney (VP-Baltimore)
Matarie Broom (COO, Principal & Exec VP)

Evolve Consulting Group Inc. (2)
2142 Priest Bridge Ct Ste 3, Crofton, MD 21114-2545
Tel.: (877) 721-6677
Web Site:
 http://www.evolveconsultinginc.com
Direct Title Insurance Carriers
N.A.I.C.S.: 524127
Ronald C. Sroka (COO)

First Service Insurance Agents & Brokers, Inc. (2)
215 Estates Dr Ste 1, Roseville, CA 95678
Tel.: (800) 591-9692
Web Site: http://www.firstserviceweb.com
Insurance Agencies & Brokerages
N.A.I.C.S.: 524210

Fleet Risk Management, Inc. (2)
2485 Demere Rd Ste 100, Saint Simons Island, GA 31522
Tel.: (866) 638-8277
Web Site: http://www.fleetriskmgt.com
Insurance Agencies & Brokerages
N.A.I.C.S.: 524210
Bob Fuller (Pres)
Burt James (Mgr-Non-Fleet)

Tory Bolinger (Mgr-Cust Svc)
Missy Worth (Mgr-Ops)
Susan Petersen (Mgr-Fleet Mktg)

Front Range Insurance Group, LLC (2)
1100 Haxton Dr Unit 100, Fort Collins, CO 80525
Tel.: (970) 223-1804
Web Site: http://www.frig.net
Sales Range: $1-9.9 Million
Emp.: 15
Insurance Brokerage Services
N.A.I.C.S.: 524210
David Wooldridge (Partner)
Susan Roberts (Partner)
John Bell (Partner)
Steven Smith (Partner)

Glenn/Davis & Associates, Inc. (2)
23452 US Hwy 80 E, Statesboro, GA 30461-0844
Tel.: (912) 489-3716
Web Site: http://www.glenn-davis.com
Sales Range: $1-9.9 Million
Emp.: 28
Insurance Agents
N.A.I.C.S.: 524210
Brian Glenn (Pres)

GoodWorks Financial Group (2)
2534 Main Street, Glastonbury, CT 01230
Tel.: (860) 633-0241
Insurance Services
N.A.I.C.S.: 524298
Chad Yonker (Chm & CEO)

Subsidiary (Domestic):

Canary Blomstrom Insurance Agency, Inc. (3)
868 Springfield St, Feeding Hills, MA 01030
Tel.: (413) 789-3995
Web Site: http://www.canaryblomstrom.com
Insurance Related Activities
N.A.I.C.S.: 524298
Debbie Marino (Acct Mgr-Comml Lines)

Subsidiary (Domestic):

Group Alternatives Inc. (2)
1400 Opus Pl Ste 830, Downers Grove, IL 60515
Tel.: (847) 303-9900
Web Site: http://www.groupalt.com
Insurance Agencies & Brokerages
N.A.I.C.S.: 524210
Michael J. Baker (Pres)

Halstead Insurance Agency, Inc. (2)
11 Electric Ave, Fitchburg, MA 01420
Tel.: (978) 345-2505
Web Site:
 http://www.halsteadinsurance.com
Insurance Agencies & Brokerages
N.A.I.C.S.: 524210
Kevin Halstead (Mgr-Sls-New England)

Herbert L. Jamison & Co., LLC (2)
100 Executive Dr Ste 200, West Orange, NJ 07052-3362
Tel.: (973) 731-0806
Web Site: http://www.jamisongroup.com
Sales Range: $10-24.9 Million
Insurance Brokerage Services
N.A.I.C.S.: 524210
John O. McDonald (Co-CEO)
Robert M. Frattarola (Exec VP)
Roger P. Testa (Exec VP)
Vincent J. Curatolo (Exec VP)
Gloria J. Stalzer (Sr VP)
Joseph A. Zamarelli (Sr VP)
Diane L. Barreiro (VP-Comml Lines Insurance)
Joseph F. Bieniowski (Dir-Risk Mgmt)
Louis F. Barbaro (Sr VP)
Charles J. Caruso (Exec VP)
Dennis Duff (Sr VP)
Thomasina Peele (Exec VP)
Deena M. Johnson (VP-Pro Liability)
John P. Ferreira (Exec VP & Mgr)
Anthony F. Bavaro (Sr VP-Sls & Mktg)
Sean M. Pattwell (Co-CEO)
Eugene Bebout (CFO)
Theresa Vines (VP & Mgr)
Dwight Nystrom (Sr VP & Mgr-Agency Licensing & Regulatory Compliance)
Ellen Dunne (Sr VP & Mgr-Mgmt Info Sys)
Susan Darrah (VP-Technical Support)
Toni Lawson (Coord-Convention)

Houston Business Insurance Agency, Inc. (2)
3718 Mount Vernon, Houston, TX 77006
Tel.: (713) 979-1001
Web Site:
 http://www.houstonbusinessinsurance.com
Insurance & Brokerages Services
N.A.I.C.S.: 524210

Innovate360, Inc. (2)
3825 Henderson Blvd Ste 402, Tampa, FL 33629
Tel.: (813) 453-1980
Web Site:
 http://www.superiorbenefitsinc.com
Sales Range: $1-9.9 Million
Emp.: 12
Insurance Brokerage
N.A.I.C.S.: 524210

Insurance & Benefits Group LLC (2)
404 W Broadway Blvd, Sedalia, MO 65301
Tel.: (660) 827-2224
Web Site: http://www.ibgagent.com
Sales Range: $1-9.9 Million
Emp.: 31
General Insurance Agency
N.A.I.C.S.: 524210
Randy Raffal (Principal)

Insurance Marketing Center, Inc. (2)
6101 Executive Blvd Suite 120, Rockville, MD 20852
Tel.: (301) 468-8888
Web Site: http://www.imctr.com
Sales Range: $1-9.9 Million
Emp.: 25
Wholesale Distr of Group & Individual Health Products
N.A.I.C.S.: 524210
David Gimenez (VP)
Martin G. Rochkind (Exec VP)
Jodi Wrublik (VP-Grp Ops)
Lois Wishnia (Comptroller)
Adrienne Lupin (Dir-Acctg & Office Ops)
Julie N. Grafe (Dir-Sls & Mktg)
Antoinette Zopf (Dir-Comm)

Insurance Systems, Inc. (2)
1 Insurance Way, Ona, WV 25545
Tel.: (304) 736-2222
Web Site:
 http://www.insurancesystemsinc.com
Sales Range: $1-9.9 Million
Emp.: 20
Insurance Brokerage Services
N.A.I.C.S.: 524210
David Robinson (Branch Mgr)
Taylor MacCurdy (Pres & COO)

Italiano Insurance Services, Inc. (2)
3021 W Swann Ave, Tampa, FL 33609
Tel.: (813) 877-7799
Web Site: http://www.italianoinsurance.com
Sales Range: $25-49.9 Million
Emp.: 30
Insurance Brokers
N.A.I.C.S.: 524210
Jeffrey G. Italiano (Pres & Principal)
Nelson A. Italiano (Principal & VP)
Maggie Guerra (Controller)

J. Ryan Bonding, Inc. (2)
2920 Enloe St, Hudson, WI 54016
Tel.: (800) 535-0006
Web Site: http://www.jryanbonding.com
Insurance Agencies & Brokerages
N.A.I.C.S.: 524210
Aaron Sundeen (Acct Mgr)

Johnson-Locklin & Associates Insurance Corporation (2)
700 Corporate Pkwy, Birmingham, AL 35242
Tel.: (205) 980-8008
Web Site: http://www.johnson-locklin.com
Insurance Agents
N.A.I.C.S.: 524210
Andy Locklin (Founder & Pres)
Jimmy Magette (Sr VP-Sls)
Beth Horton (Mgr-Acctg & Office)

Kainos Partners Inc. (2)
16545 Vlg Dr Bldg B, Houston, TX 77040
Tel.: (281) 810-4900
Web Site: http://www.kainos-partners.com
Financial Investment Activities
N.A.I.C.S.: 523999
Rebecca Davis (VP-Sls)
Gary Jurney (Pres)

LJ Stein & Company Inc. (2)
71 E Fairmount Ave, Lakewood, NY 14750
Tel.: (716) 763-7100
Web Site: http://www.ljstein.com
Insurance Risk Management Services
N.A.I.C.S.: 524126
Patrick Kennedy (Pres)
David Stein (CEO)
Kyle Albert (Pres-LJ STein Canada)

Langley Agency, Inc. (2)
6100 Glades Rd Ste 206, Boca Raton, FL 33434
Tel.: (561) 482-2501
Insurance Agencies & Brokerages
N.A.I.C.S.: 524210
Brent Langley (Pres)

Lundstrom Insurance Agency, Inc. (2)
2205 Point Blvd, Elgin, IL 60123
Tel.: (847) 741-1000
Web Site:
 http://www.lundstrominsurance.com
Insurance Agencies & Brokerages
N.A.I.C.S.: 524210
Adam Wright (Sr Acct Exec)

MFI Companies, LLC (2)
21 East 5th Ave, Conshohocken, PA 19428
Tel.: (610) 862-4300
Web Site: http://www.mfirvine.com
Employee Benefits Insurance & Risk Management Services
N.A.I.C.S.: 524298
Michael F. Irvine (CEO & Principal)
Sean S. Sweeney (Principal)
Michael Devine (VP-Ops)

Mack Mack & Waltz Insurance Group, Inc. (2)
1211 S Military Trl, Deerfield Beach, FL 33442
Tel.: (954) 356-1980
Web Site: https://www.assuredpartners.com
Insurance Agencies & Brokerages
N.A.I.C.S.: 524210

Michael J. Hall & Co. (2)
19578 10th Ave NE, Poulsbo, WA 98370
Tel.: (360) 598-3700
Web Site:
 http://www.mjhallandcompany.com
Sales Range: $1-9.9 Million
Emp.: 46
Insurance Services
N.A.I.C.S.: 524298
Michael Hall (Pres)

Moscker Insurance Agency, Inc. (2)
302 Ritchie Hwy, Severna Park, MD 21146-1910
Tel.: (410) 544-6104
Web Site:
 http://www.mosckerinsurance.com
Sales Range: $1-9.9 Million
Emp.: 14
Insurance Agents
N.A.I.C.S.: 524210
Peter Moscker (Principal)

Nevada West Business Insurance Services (2)
4175 S Riley St Ste 200, Las Vegas, NV 89147
Tel.: (702) 597-5998
Web Site: http://www.nvwestinsurance.com
Insurance Related Activities
N.A.I.C.S.: 524298
Lanny Maren (Owner)

People's United Insurance Agency, Inc. (2)
1 Financial Plaza 755 Main St, Hartford, CT 06103-9932
Tel.: (860) 524-7600
Web Site: http://www.peoples.com
Insurance Agents & Brokers
N.A.I.C.S.: 524210

Subsidiary (Domestic):

Kesten-Brown Insurance, LLC (3)
277 Fairfield Ave 3rd Fl Bijou Sq, Bridgeport, CT 06604
Tel.: (203) 336-6302
Web Site: http://www.kestenbrown.com
Emp.: 155
Insurance Services
N.A.I.C.S.: 524210

GTCR LLC—(Continued)

Subsidiary (Domestic):

Pierce Group Benefits, LLC (2)
4928 Linksland Dr Ste 201, Holly Springs,
NC 27540
Tel.: (919) 577-0700
Web Site:
http://www.piercegroupbenefits.com
Insurance Agencies & Brokerages
N.A.I.C.S.: 524210
Quincy Caspar (Mgr-Print Production)
Chris Pierce (Pres)

Powderhorn Agency, Inc. (2)
353 Candlewood Lk Rd, Brookfield, CT
06804-1603
Tel.: (888) 354-0677
Web Site:
http://www.powderhornagency.com
Insurance Agencies & Brokerages
N.A.I.C.S.: 524210
Gary Missigman (Pres)

Preferred Guardian Insurance (2)
18383 Preston Rd Ste 330, Dallas, TX
75252
Tel.: (972) 331-5100
Web Site: http://www.preferredguardian.com
Sales Range: $1-9.9 Million
Insurance Agents & Brokers
N.A.I.C.S.: 524210
Barney Schwartz (CEO)

Premier Insurance Corporation,
Inc. (2)
3501 Del Prado Blvd., Suite 200, Cape
Coral, FL 33904
Tel.: (239) 542-1533
Web Site: https://www.assuredpartners.com
Insurance Related Activities
N.A.I.C.S.: 524298

Ramsey Insurance Agency, Inc. (2)
340 MacCorkle Ave SE, Charleston, WV
25314
Tel.: (304) 925-6789
Web Site: http://www.ramseyinsurance.com
Sales Range: $1-9.9 Million
Emp.: 20
Insurance Services
N.A.I.C.S.: 524210
Mary Kerns (Pres)

Rand-Tec Insurance Agency, Inc. (2)
977 Lakeview Pkwy Ste 105, Vernon Hills,
IL 60061
Tel.: (847) 367-2633
Web Site: http://www.rand-tec.com
Rev.: $8,000,000
Insurance Agencies & Brokerages
N.A.I.C.S.: 524210
Mary Bowman (VP)
Todd Silver (Pres)

Redmond General Insurance Agency,
Inc. (2)
16160 NE 80th St, Redmond, WA 98052
Tel.: (425) 885-2283
Web Site: http://www.rgia.com
Sales Range: $1-9.9 Million
Emp.: 28
Insurance Agents
N.A.I.C.S.: 524210
Keith W. Brewe (Pres)

Regal Aviation Insurance (2)
5625 NE Elam Young Pkwy Ste 100, Hills-
boro, OR 97124-6422
Tel.: (800) 275-7345
Web Site: http://www.regalaviation.com
Insurance Related Activities
N.A.I.C.S.: 524298

Roehrs & Company, Inc. (2)
736 Springdale Dr, Exton, PA 19341
Tel.: (610) 363-7999
Web Site: http://www.roehrs.com
Sales Range: $1-9.9 Million
Emp.: 12
Insurance Agents
N.A.I.C.S.: 524210
Stacey Roehrs (CFO)
Giles Roehrs (CEO)
Joe Giannetti (Mgr-Personal Lines)
Kim Rhodes (Mgr-Employee Benefits &
Claims)

Roemer Insurance, Inc. (2)

3912 Sunforest Ct, Toledo, OH 43623
Tel.: (419) 475-5151
Web Site: http://www.roemer-insurance.com
Nonresidential Building Leasing Services
N.A.I.C.S.: 531120
Wellington F. Roemer III (Pres & CEO)

SKCG Group, Inc. (2)
123 Main St Fl 14, White Plains, NY 10601
Tel.: (914) 761-9000
Web Site: http://www.skcg.com
Sales Range: $10-24.9 Million
Risk Management & Insurance Advisory
Services
N.A.I.C.S.: 541618
Thomas R. Kozera (Pres & CEO)

Safeguard Insurance LLC (2)
375 E Warm Springs Rd Ste 201, Las Ve-
gas, NV 89119
Tel.: (702) 638-0022
Web Site: http://www.safeguardme.com
Insurance Agent/Broker
N.A.I.C.S.: 524210
Kristopher Dye (CFO)

Stoudt Advisors, Inc. (2)
280 Granite Run Dr Ste 250, Lancaster, PA
17601
Tel.: (717) 581-8382
Web Site: http://www.stoudtadvisors.com
Sales Range: $1-9.9 Million
Emp.: 20
Employee Benefit Solutions; Insurance Bro-
kerage Services
N.A.I.C.S.: 524210
R. Scott Labrecque (VP-Client Solutions)
David K. Stoudt (Pres & CEO)

Surety Solutions Insurance Services
Inc. (2)
3225 Monier Cir Ste 100, Rancho Cordova,
CA 95742
Tel.: (916) 294-0044
Web Site: http://www.surety1.com
Direct Property & Casualty Insurance Ser-
vices
N.A.I.C.S.: 524126
John Page (Pres)

The Ranew Insurance Agency,
Inc. (2)
966 S Wickham Rd Ste 102, West Mel-
bourne, FL 32904
Tel.: (321) 722-2338
Web Site: http://www.ranewinsurance.com
Insurance Agencies & Brokerages
N.A.I.C.S.: 524210

Tutton Insurance Services, Inc. (2)
2913 Pullman St, Santa Ana, CA 92705
Tel.: (949) 261-5335
Web Site: http://www.tutton.com
Insurance Agents
N.A.I.C.S.: 524210
Bill Tutton (Pres)

Ventura Pacific Insurance
Services (2)
30077 Agoura Ct Ste 240, Thousand Oaks,
CA 91301
Tel.: (747) 204-2710
Insurance Agencies & Brokerages
N.A.I.C.S.: 524210

Williams & Williams, Inc. (2)
25 Manor Rd, Smithtown, NY 11787
Tel.: (631) 265-5511
Web Site:
http://www.williamsandwilliams.net
Insurance Agencies & Brokerages
N.A.I.C.S.: 524210
Glenn Williams (Pres)
Jonathan Tilden (VP)

Wilson H. Flock Insurance, Inc. (2)
464 Wyoming Ave, Wyoming, PA 18644
Tel.: (570) 693-1710
Web Site: http://www.flockinsurance.com
Sales Range: $1-9.9 Million
Emp.: 14
Insurance Agents
N.A.I.C.S.: 524210
William Flock Jr. (Pres)

Witkemper Insurance Group (2)
7740 East 88th Street Suite 100, Indianapolis, IN 46256
Tel.: (800) 039-5247
Web Site: https://www.witkempergroup.com

Insurance Agencies & Brokerages
N.A.I.C.S.: 524210
Mary Beth Meyer (Sr Acct Mgr-Comml
Lines)

WorkforceTactix, Inc. (2)
954 Ridgebrook Rd Ste 200, Sparks, MD
21152
Tel.: (443) 212-1540
Web Site: http://www.workforcetactix.com
Human Resources for Small to Mid-size
Employers
N.A.I.C.S.: 541612
Kathleen Janocha (VP-Acct Mgmt)
Amber Berry (Acct Mgr)
Sharon Barton (Acct Exec)
Chris Draghi (Acct Mgr)
Lesli Corbin (VP-HR Pro Svcs)
Donna Dellarose (Mgr-Acct)
Lizz Hatcher (Mgr-Acct)
Jeanne Smith (Mgr-Acct)
Salamon Cober (Acct Exec)

Blue Canyon Holdings AB (1)
c/o GTCR 300 N LaSalle St Ste 5600, Chi-
cago, IL 60654
Tel.: (312) 382-2200
Holding Company
N.A.I.C.S.: 551110

Callcredit Limited (1)
One Park Lane, Leeds, LS3 1EP, W York-
shire, United Kingdom
Tel.: (44) 1132424747
Web Site: http://www.callcredit.co.uk
Emp.: 700
Credit Reference & Marketing Consultation
Services
N.A.I.C.S.: 522390
Graham Lund (Mng Dir)
Elizabeth Richards (Dir-Fin)
Mark Davison (Dir-Technical Dev)
Emma Peach (Dir-Legal)
Ed Davies (Dir-Data & Client Svcs)
Tom Ilube (Mng Dir-Consumer Mktg)
Chris McDonald (Mng Dir-Mktg Solutions)
Peter Mansfield (Mng Dir-Credit Solutions)
Steve Humm (COO)

Subsidiary (Domestic):

Callcredit Marketing Limited (2)
One Park Lane, LS31EP, Leeds, West
Yorkshire, United Kingdom
Tel.: (44) 1132424747
Sales Range: $75-99.9 Million
Emp.: 700
Management Consulting Services
N.A.I.C.S.: 541618

DecisionMetrics Ltd. (2)
King George House, Comet Way, Hatfield,
AL10 9TF, United Kingdom
Tel.: (44) 1707282640
Web Site: http://www.decisionmetrics.co.uk
Sales Range: $25-49.9 Million
Emp.: 20
Credit Risk Market Consulting
N.A.I.C.S.: 541690

Legatio Technologies Ltd. (2)
One Park Lane, Leeds, LS3 1EP, West
Yorkshire, United Kingdom
Tel.: (44) 1133884300
Web Site: http://www.callcredit.co.uk
Software Publisher
N.A.I.C.S.: 513210
Robert Kenneth Campbell Munro (Dir &
Sec)
Michael Jon Gordon (Dir)

Cannondale Investments, Inc. (1)
372 Danbury Rd Ste 210, Wilton, CT 06897
Tel.: (203) 423-0648
Web Site:
https://www.cannondaleinvestments.com
Investment Holding Company
N.A.I.C.S.: 551112
Jonathan A. Flatow (Partner)
Robert E. Bies (CFO)
Hank Weghorst (CTO)
Steve Pogorzelski (CEO)
Joseph Ripp (Partner)
Charles Stryker (Partner)

Cole-Parmer Instrument Company,
LLC (1)
625 E Bunker Ct, Vernon Hills, IL 60061-
1844
Tel.: (847) 549-7600

Web Site: http://www.coleparmer.com
Scientific Instruments Mfr & Distr
N.A.I.C.S.: 334513
Michael Whitaker (Sr Mgr-Regulatory Com-
pliance & Safety)
Mike Sesterhenn (Dir-Warehouse Ops &
Facilities)
Bernd Brust (Chm & CEO)
Jaime Robles (Mgr-Customer Svc)
Jon Salkin (COO)
Nick Morse (CFO & Sr VP)
Mina Canning (Sr VP-HR & Integrations)

Subsidiary (Non-US):

Cole-Parmer India Pvt. Ltd (2)
403 A-Wing Delphi Hiranandani Business
Park Powai, Mumbai, 400076, India
Tel.: (91) 2261394444
Web Site: http://www.coleparmer.in
Laboratory Analytical Optical Instruments
Mfr & Distr
N.A.I.C.S.: 333310

Cole-Parmer Instrument Co. Ltd. (2)
9 Orion Court Ambuscade Road Colmworth
Business Park, Saint Neots, PE19 8YX,
Cambs, United Kingdom
Tel.: (44) 1480272279
Web Site: http://www.coleparmer.co.uk
Electrical Equipment & Component Mfr &
Distr
N.A.I.C.S.: 335999

Subsidiary (Domestic):

ZeptoMetrix Corporation (2)
878 Main St, Buffalo, NY 14202-1403
Tel.: (716) 882-0920
Web Site: http://www.zeptometrix.com
Integrated Biotechnology Company
N.A.I.C.S.: 325414
David Reinlander (Dir-Quality Assurance)
David Waterman (VP-Ops)
Diane Waterman (Dir-Analytical Svcs)
Douglas Mason (Dir-Immunology)
Heather Duffus (Dir-Matls Mgmt & Coord-
Website)
John Paul (VP-Ops)
Kelly A. Cycon (Dir-Virology)
Michael A. Hershfield (Dir-Sls & Mktg)
Shawn R. Smith (Pres & CEO)

Consumer Cellular, Inc. (1)
7204 SW Durham Rd Ste 300, Portland,
OR 97224
Tel.: (503) 675-8988
Web Site: http://www.consumercellular.com
Rev.: $65,000,000
Emp.: 1,000
Wireless Telecommunications Carriers
N.A.I.C.S.: 517112
John Marick (Founder & CEO)
Tami Marick (Sec)
Greg Pryor (CEO)

Corza Medical Inc. (1)
247 Station Dr Ste NE1, Westwood, MA
02090
Tel.: (781) 751-1000
Web Site: https://corza.com
Medical Equipment Mfr
N.A.I.C.S.: 339112
Henry Burmeister (CFO)
Tom Testa (CEO)
Gregory T. Lucier (Founder & Exec Chm)

Subsidiary (Domestic):

Barron Precision Instruments,
LLC (2)
8170 Embury Rd, Grand Blanc, MI 48439
Tel.: (973) 989-1600
Web Site: http://www.bpic.com
Surgical And Medical Instruments
N.A.I.C.S.: 339112
Mark Barron (Pres)

Surgical Specialties Corporation (2)
1100 Berkshire Blvd Ste 308, Wyomissing,
PA 19610
Tel.: (781) 602-6777
Web Site:
http://www.surgicalspecialties.com
Sales Range: $125-149.9 Million
Emp.: 331
Surgical & Medical Instruments Mfr
N.A.I.C.S.: 339112
Victor Diaz (Pres & COO)
Dan Sutherby (CFO)

Janet Hart *(VP-HR)*
Dan Croteau *(CEO)*
Joseph Siletto *(Chief Bus Officer)*

Curia, Inc. (1)
26 Corporate Cir, Albany, NY 12212
Tel.: (518) 512-2000
Web Site: http://curiaglobal.com
Contract Chemistry Research & Development Services
N.A.I.C.S.: 541715
Christopher Conway *(Pres-Res & Dev)*
Dawn Von Rohr *(Sr VP-Strategy)*
Joseph D. Sangregorio *(Chief HR Officer)*
Diane M. Beno *(Sr VP-Quality)*
John Ratliff *(Chm)*
Mike Kleppinger *(Chief Comml Officer)*
Jason Knoblauch *(CFO)*
Prakash Pandian *(CIO)*
Stacei Phillips *(Sec & Gen Counsel)*
Hua Tu *(CTO)*
Scott Wagner *(Sr VP-Global Ops)*
Scott Waldman *(Sr VP-Corp Dev)*
Niall Condon *(Pres-Mfg-Div)*
Philip Macnabb *(CEO)*
Gerald Auer *(CFO)*

Subsidiary (Domestic):

CURIA INDIANA, LLC (2)
3065 Kent Ave, West Lafayette, IN 47906-1076
Tel.: (765) 463-0112
Life Science, Physical, Engineering Research & Development Services
N.A.I.C.S.: 541715

Subsidiary (Non-US):

Curia France SAS (2)
Zone Industrielle de Laville, 47240, Bon Encontre, France
Tel.: (33) 553691300
Fine Chemicals Mfr
N.A.I.C.S.: 325998

Curia Germany GmbH (2)
Industriepark Hochst, 65926, Frankfurt, Germany
Tel.: (49) 6930522055
Pharmaceutical Ingredient Mfr
N.A.I.C.S.: 325199

Curia Holdings (UK) Limited (2)
Todd Campus West of Scotland Science Park, Glasgow, G20 OXA, Lanarkshire, United Kingdom
Tel.: (44) 1419458400
Drug Research & Development Services
N.A.I.C.S.: 541715

Subsidiary (Domestic):

Curia (Scotland) Limited (3)
Todd Campus West of Scotland Science Park, Glasgow, G20 0XA, Lanarkshire, United Kingdom
Tel.: (44) 1419458400
Aseptic Formulation Development & Drug Product Mfr
N.A.I.C.S.: 325412

Subsidiary (Non-US):

Curia India Private Limited (2)
Plot 9 MN Park Turkapally Shameerpet Genome Valley, RR District, Hyderabad, 500 078, India
Tel.: (91) 4066876666
Chemical & Pharmaceutical Research
N.A.I.C.S.: 541715

Subsidiary (Domestic):

Curia Massachusetts, Inc. (2)
99 S Bedford St, Burlington, MA 01803
Tel.: (781) 270-7900
Pharmaceutical Preparation Mfr
N.A.I.C.S.: 325412

Curia Missouri, Inc. (2)
2460 W Bennett St, Springfield, MO 65807-1229
Tel.: (417) 868-3458
Pharmaceutical Ingredient Mfr
N.A.I.C.S.: 325199

Curia New Mexico, LLC (2)
4401 Alexander Blvd NE, Albuquerque, NM 87107
Tel.: (505) 923-1500

Surgical & Medical Instrument Mfr
N.A.I.C.S.: 339112

Curia New York, Inc. (2)
33 Riverside Ave, Rensselaer, NY 12144
Tel.: (518) 433-7700
Pharmaceuticals Mfr
N.A.I.C.S.: 325412

Curia Services, Inc. (2)
26 Corporate Cir, Albany, NY 12203
Tel.: (518) 512-2000
Pharmaceuticals Product Mfr
N.A.I.C.S.: 325412

Curia Washington, Inc. (2)
26 Corporate Cir, Albany, NY 12203
Tel.: (518) 512-2000
Natural Products Drug Discovery & In Vitro Biology Research
N.A.I.C.S.: 541714

Cygnus Technologies, Inc. (1)
4705 Southport Supply Rd SE, Southport, NC 28461
Tel.: (910) 454-9442
Web Site:
   http://www.cygnustechnologies.com
Office Supplies & Stationery Stores
N.A.I.C.S.: 459410

EaglePicher Technologies, LLC (1)
120 S Central Ave Ste 200, Saint Louis, MO 63105
Tel.: (417) 623-8000
Web Site: http://www.eaglepicher.com
Batteries, Chargers, Electronics & Energetic Devices Mfr
N.A.I.C.S.: 335910
Greg Miller *(VP-Applications Engrg)*
Jesse Griggs *(VP-Quality)*
George Cintra *(VP-Res & Dev)*
Nate Rynas *(VP-Supply Chain)*
Rich Hunter *(CEO)*
Kurt Bruenning *(Pres & CFO)*
Jon Bagrosky *(Sr VP-Defense)*

Subsidiary (Non-US):

Diehl & EaglePicher GmbH (2)
Fischbachstrasse 20 ad Pegnitz, 90552, Rothenbach, Germany
Tel.: (49) 9119572073
Web Site: http://www.battery.de
Thermal Battery Mfr
N.A.I.C.S.: 335910

Wolverine Advanced Materials GmbH (2)
Verrenberger Weg 20, D-74613, Ohringen, Baden-Wurttemberg, Germany
Tel.: (49) 79416030
Web Site: http://www.wamglobal.com
Gasket Product Mfr
N.A.I.C.S.: 339991

Fairway Outdoor Advertising, LLC (1)
814 Duncan-Reidville Rd, Duncan, SC 29334
Tel.: (864) 485-1899
Web Site: http://fairwayoutdoor.com
Outdoor Advertising Services
N.A.I.C.S.: 541850
Rick Steele *(Gen Mgr)*
Jeff Hoyt *(Gen Sls Mgr)*
Garry Brown *(Sls Mgr)*
Mike Fleming *(Sls Mgr)*
Scott Arenz *(Gen Mgr)*
Terry Harkins *(Gen Mgr)*
Marshall Henderson *(Gen Mgr-Sls)*
Paul Hickman *(Gen Mgr)*
Mark Renier *(Gen Mgr)*
Brian Grant *(VP-HR)*
Abe Levine *(Sls Mgr)*
Rich Zecchino *(Gen Counsel & VP)*

Division (Domestic):

Fairway Outdoor Advertising, LLC - Athens (2)
3420 Jefferson Rd, Athens, GA 30607-1476
Tel.: (706) 543-0380
Web Site: http://fairwayoutdoor.com
Emp.: 32
Outdoor Advertising Services
N.A.I.C.S.: 541810
Terry Harkins *(Gen Mgr)*
Allyson Payne *(Acct Exec)*

Fairway Outdoor Advertising, LLC - Chattanooga (2)
18 W 28th St, Chattanooga, TN 37408-3000
Tel.: (423) 756-4200
Web Site: http://fairwayoutdoor.com
Outdoor Advertising Services
N.A.I.C.S.: 541810
Scott LaFoy *(Gen Mgr)*
Scott Hibberts *(Sls Mgr)*

Fairway Outdoor Advertising, LLC - Duncan (2)
814 Duncan Reidville Rd, Duncan, SC 29334-1900
Tel.: (800) 849-3247
Web Site: http://fairwayoutdoor.com
Outdoor Advertising Services
N.A.I.C.S.: 541810
Rick Steele *(Gen Mgr)*
Jeff Hoyt *(Gen Sls Mgr)*
Garry Brown *(Sls Mgr)*
Mike Fleming *(Sls Mgr)*

Fairway Outdoor Advertising, LLC - Greensboro (2)
105-A E JJ Dr, Greensboro, NC 27406
Tel.: (336) 292-4242
Web Site: http://www.fairwayoutdoor.com
Emp.: 25
Outdoor Advertising Services
N.A.I.C.S.: 541810
Brian Britland *(Mgr-Sls)*

Fairway Outdoor Advertising, LLC - Prestonsburg (2)
1749 US 23 N, Prestonsburg, KY 41653
Web Site: http://fairwayoutdoor.com
Outdoor Advertising Services
N.A.I.C.S.: 541850
Kevin Gleason *(CEO)*
Dan Streek *(CFO)*

Fairway Outdoor Advertising, LLC - Raleigh (2)
508 Capital Blvd, Raleigh, NC 27605
Tel.: (919) 755-1900
Web Site: http://fairwayoutdoor.com
Emp.: 50
Outdoor Advertising Services
N.A.I.C.S.: 541810
Paul Hickman *(Gen Mgr)*
Mike Russell *(Mgr-Mktg)*
Todd Allen *(Dir-Real Estate)*
Aaron Guyton *(Sls Mgr)*

Fairway Outdoor Advertising, LLC - Rochester (2)
3185 41st St NW, Rochester, MN 55901
Web Site: http://fairwayoutdoor.com
Outdoor Advertising Services
N.A.I.C.S.: 541850
Mary Niemeyer *(Gen Mgr)*

Fairway Outdoor Advertising, LLC - Valdosta (2)
369 Enterprise Dr, Valdosta, GA 31601
Web Site: http://www.fairwayoutdoor.com
Outdoor Advertising Services
N.A.I.C.S.: 541850
Mike Coleman *(Gen Mgr)*
Deborah Enfinger *(Sls Mgr)*

Foundation Source Philanthropic Services Inc. (1)
55 Walls Dr, Fairfield, CT 06824
Tel.: (203) 319-3700
Web Site: http://www.foundationsource.com
Administrative, Compliance, Advisory & Technology Solutions Services
N.A.I.C.S.: 541611
Daniel M. Schley *(Chm)*
Andrew C. Bangser *(Pres)*
Jeffrey D. Haskell *(Chief Legal Officer)*
Page Snow *(Chief Philanthropic Officer)*
William L. Brennan *(Head-Institutional Sls)*
Joseph M. Fuschillo *(Chief Distr Officer)*
Julie Binder *(Dir-Strategic Alliances)*
Hugh S. Asher *(Mng Dir-South)*
Kimberly Scott *(Sr Dir-Client Svcs)*
Scott Rose *(Mng Dir-Central Reg)*
Pascal Vincent *(CTO)*
Joseph Mrak III *(CEO)*

Subsidiary (Domestic):

PG Calc, Inc. (2)
129 Mount Auburn St, Cambridge, MA 02138

Tel.: (888) 497-4970
Web Site: http://www.pgcalc.com
Computer Software Services
N.A.I.C.S.: 541512
Gary Pforzheimer *(Pres)*

GTN Limited (1)
Level 42 Northpoint 100 Miller Street, North Sydney, 2060, NSW, Australia (50.84%)
Tel.: (61) 299553500
Web Site: https://www.gtnetwork.com.au
Rev.: $123,018,162
Assets: $199,853,765
Liabilities: $54,373,664
Net Worth: $145,480,101
Earnings: $3,781,384
Fiscal Year-end: 06/30/2024
Holding Company; Traffic Information Reporting Services
N.A.I.C.S.: 551112
Anna Sandham *(Co-Sec)*
Patrick Quinlan *(Co-Sec)*
Brent Henley *(CFO-Global)*
Sophie Jackson *(Gen Counsel)*
William L. Yde III *(Founder, CEO & Mng Dir)*

Subsidiary (Non-US):

Canadian Traffic Network (2)
1920 Yonge Street Suite 503, Toronto, M4S 3E2, ON, Canada
Tel.: (416) 849-9090
Web Site: https://trafficnet.ca
Traffic Information Reporting Services
N.A.I.C.S.: 519290
Michel Leblanc *(VP-Eastern Reg)*
Tracey Hemphill *(Natl Dir-Ops)*
Isabelle Viau *(Dir-Ops-Montreal)*
Amber Belzer *(Dir-Ops-Vancouver)*
Trudy Rennie *(Dir-Ops-Calgary)*
Justin Dervin *(Dir-Ops-Edmonton)*

Global Traffic Network (UK) Limited (2)
1st Floor Swan House, 52-53 Poland Street, London, W1F 7NH, United Kingdom (100%)
Tel.: (44) 2033014920
Web Site: http://www.gtn.uk.com
Emp.: 15
Traffic Information Reporting Services
N.A.I.C.S.: 519290
Denise Perry *(Dir-Sls)*
John Quinn *(COO)*
Andy Walker *(Mgr-Sls)*

Subsidiary (Domestic):

The Australian Traffic Network Pty. Limited (2)
Level 42 Northpoint 100 Miller Street, Sydney, 2060, NSW, Australia (100%)
Tel.: (61) 299553500
Web Site: http://www.trafficnet.com.au
Traffic Information Reporting Services
N.A.I.C.S.: 519290
Christopher Thornton *(Sls Dir-Natl)*
Victor Lorusso *(Ops Mgr)*
Kelly McIlwraith *(Dir-Sls & Mktg)*

Mega Broadband Investments, LLC (1)
5251 W 116th Place Ste 200, Leawood, KS 66211
Tel.: (312) 953-3305
Investment Company; Broadband Services
N.A.I.C.S.: 551112
Phil Spencer *(CEO)*
Rod Siemers *(CFO)*

Subsidiary (Domestic):

Northland Communications Corp. (2)
101 Stewart St Ste 700, Seattle, WA 98101
Tel.: (206) 621-1351
Web Site: http://www.yournorthland.com
High-speed Data, Voice Services & Television Services
N.A.I.C.S.: 516210
Paul Milan *(Gen Counsel)*

Subsidiary (Domestic):

Corsicana Media, Inc. (3)
1504 N Beaton St, Corsicana, TX 75110
Tel.: (903) 874-7421
Web Site: http://www.kand1340am.com
Sales Range: $10-24.9 Million
Emp.: 4

GTCR LLC—(Continued)

Provider of Radio Broadcasting Station Services
N.A.I.C.S.: 516110

Opus Global Holdings LLC   (1)
48 Wall St 6th Fl, New York, NY 10005
Tel.: (908) 981-0080
Web Site: http://www.opus.com
Holding Company
N.A.I.C.S.: 551112
Glenn Renzulli (CFO)
Mike Angle (CTO)
Mark DeLuca (Sr VP-Worldwide Sls)
Doug Udoff (Sr VP-Customer Success)
Stacey Bray (Mgr-HR)
Steve Ortman (VP-Data Ops)
Gabor Kralik (Head-Energy Div)

Subsidiary (Domestic):

Alacra, Inc.   (2)
48 Wall St 6th Fl, New York, NY 10005
Tel.: (212) 363-9620
Web Site: http://www.alacra.com
Online Business Information Aggregator
N.A.I.C.S.: 561499
Carol Ann Thomas (Mgr-Mktg)
Albert Tamayev (VP-Ops)
Craig Kissel (CFO)
Kelvin Dickenson (VP-Compliance Solutions)
Ajit Tharaken (Sr VP-Ops)
Steve Ortman (VP-Data Ops)

PPC Flexible Packaging LLC   (1)
1111 Busch Pkwy, Buffalo Grove, IL 60089
Tel.: (800) 837-2247
Web Site: http://www.ppcflex.com
Flexible Plastic Packaging Products Mfr
N.A.I.C.S.: 326111
Kevin Keneally (Pres & CEO)

Subsidiary (Domestic):

Plastic Packaging Technologies, LLC   (2)
750 S 65th St, Kansas City, KS 66111
Web Site: http://www.plaspack.com
Paper Bag & Coated & Treated Paper Mfr
N.A.I.C.S.: 322220
Jim Kennedy (Dir-Innovation)

Temkin International Inc.   (2)
213 Temkin Way, Payson, UT 84651
Tel.: (801) 465-1300
Web Site:
   http://www.temkininternational.com
Packaging Materials Mfr
N.A.I.C.S.: 322220
Danny Temkin (Founder)

Park Place Technologies, LLC   (1)
5910 Landerbrook Dr, Cleveland, OH 44124   (50%)
Tel.: (877) 778-8707
Web Site:
   http://www.parkplacetechnologies.com
Hardware Maintenance Services
N.A.I.C.S.: 541513
Chris Adams (Pres & CEO)
Hal Malstrom (Interim COO)
Jennifer Deutsch (CMO)
Michael Vedda (Chief Revenue Officer)

Subsidiary (Domestic):

Ardent Support Technologies, LLC   (2)
12 Crosby Rd, Dover, NH 03820
Web Site: http://www.ardentsupporttech.com
Computer Related Services
N.A.I.C.S.: 541519
Dave Daniels (Mgr-Tech Support)

Custom Hardware Engineering & Consulting, Inc.   (2)
1576 Fencorp Dr, Fenton, MO 63026
Tel.: (636) 305-9669
Web Site: http://www.checonsulting.com
Sales Range: $1-9.9 Million
Emp.: 90
Computer Maintenance/Repair
N.A.I.C.S.: 811210
David York (Pres & CEO)

Regatta Medical Holdings LLC   (1)
2275 Half Day Rd Ste 185, Bannockburn, IL 60016
Tel.: (224) 880-5662

Web Site: http://www.regattamedical.com
Privater Equity Firm
N.A.I.C.S.: 523999
Robert Hance (CEO)
Mark Weishaar (VP-Bus Dev)

Subsidiary (Domestic):

Resonetics, LLC   (2)
26 Whipple St, Nashua, NH 03060
Tel.: (800) 759-3330
Web Site: http://www.resonetics.com
Laser Micromachining Products & Services
N.A.I.C.S.: 332710
Thomas Burns (Chm)
Kevin Hartke (Chief Technical Officer)
Brett Reynolds (CFO)
Jessica Carreiro (VP-HR)
Kevin Kelly (Pres & CEO)

RevSpring, Inc.   (1)
38705 Seven Mile Rd Ste 450, Livonia, MI 48152
Tel.: (248) 567-7300
Web Site: http://www.revspringinc.com
Document Preparation & Processing Services
N.A.I.C.S.: 561410
John Carson (CFO & COO)
Martin Callahan (Pres-Healthcare Markets)
Barbara Rice (Chief HR Officer)
Bill Needham (CTO)
John Telford (Pres-Fin Svcs)
Robert Horwitz (Chief Compliance Officer & Gen Counsel)
Scott MacKenzie (CEO)
Steve Callis (Pres-Payments)
Valerie Schmidt Mondelli (Chief Comml Officer & Exec VP-Healthcare)

Subsidiary (Domestic):

Apex Print Technologies, LLC   (2)
100 S Owasso Blvd W, Saint Paul, MN 55117-1036
Tel.: (651) 287-8200
Technology Solutions for Print, Web & Mobile Delivery of Billing Information
N.A.I.C.S.: 541519
Elizabeth Geist (Chief Experience Officer)
Tom Ziel (Sr VP-Bus Dev)

Subsidiary (Domestic):

LetterLogic, LLC   (3)
1209 4th Ave S, Nashville, TN 37210-4107
Tel.: (615) 783-0070
Web Site: http://www.letterlogic.com
Emp.: 31
Payment Processing Services
N.A.I.C.S.: 522320
Kennon Askew (VP-Bus Dev)
Carrie Arkle (Mgr-Client Svcs)
Elizabeth Geist (Pres)
Daniel Harris (Reg Dir-Bus Dev)
Eric Hollingsworth (COO)

Unit (Domestic):

RevSpring, Inc. - Oaks   (2)
105 Montgomery Ave, Oaks, PA 19456
Tel.: (610) 650-3900
Web Site: http://revspringinc.com
Outsourced Billing & Transaction Services
N.A.I.C.S.: 522320

RevSpring, Inc. - Phoenix   (2)
23751 N 23rd Ave Ste 150, Phoenix, AZ 85085
Tel.: (623) 516-4700
Web Site: http://revspringinc.com
Electronic Billing & Payments Services
N.A.I.C.S.: 522320

Riverchase Dermatology & Cosmetic Surgery LLC   (1)
2750 Bahia Vista St Ste 250, Sarasota, FL 34239
Tel.: (239) 313-2553
Web Site: http://www.caryldunnmd.com
Offices of Dermatologists & Dermatology Services Including Cosmetic Surgery
N.A.I.C.S.: 621399
Candace Steiding (CEO)

Subsidiary (Domestic):

Riverchase Dermatology & Cosmetic Surgery - Pembroke Pines   (2)

603 N Flamingo Rd Ste 350, Pembroke Pines, FL 33028-1013
Tel.: (954) 435-5100
Web Site:
   http://www.riverchasedermatology.com
Dermatology Services
N.A.I.C.S.: 621111

Simplifi Holdings Inc.   (1)
1407 Texas St, Fort Worth, TX 76102
Tel.: (800) 840-0768
Web Site: http://www.simpli.fi
Digital Advertising Services
N.A.I.C.S.: 541810
Frost Prioleau (Co-Founder, Pres & CEO)
Paul Harrison (Co-Founder & CTO)
James Moore (Chief Revenue Officer)
Andries Marx (CFO)
Elizabeth Brockey (Chief Customer Officer)
Ryan Horn (VP-Mktg)

Ultimus Fund Solutions, LLC   (1)
225 Pictoria Dr Ste 450, Cincinnati, OH 45246
Tel.: (513) 587-3400
Web Site:
   http://www.ultimusfundsolutions.com
Rev.: $28,000,000,000
Emp.: 140
Mutual Fund & Securities Asset Management Services
N.A.I.C.S.: 523940
Kirk Littleton (VP & Dir-Bus Dev)
Robert G. Dorsey (Co-Founder, Co-CEO & Mng Dir)
Dave Carson (Pres-Ultimus Managers Trust, VP & Dir-Client Strategies)
Mark Seger (Co-Founder & Vice Chm)
Gary Tenkman (Co-CEO)
Bo Howell (VP & Dir-Fund Admin)
Doug Jones (VP & Dir-Broker Svcs)
Nancy Aleshire (VP & Dir-HR)
Stephen Preston (Chief Compliance Officer & VP)
Jason Stevens (CTO & VP)
Kris Lambert (VP & Controller)
Steve Nienhaus (VP-IT)
Bill Tomko (Dir-Fund Servicing)
Dina Tantra (Dir-Fund Admin & Compliance)
Nickolaus Darsch (Sr VP-Bus Dev)
David Felcyn (Dir-Transfer Agent Tech)
Ian Martin (Chief Admin Officer)

Subsidiary (Domestic):

Ultimus Asset Services, LLC   (2)
9465 Counselors Row Ste 200, Indianapolis, IN 46240   (100%)
Tel.: (317) 917-7003
Emp.: 75
Mutual Fund & Securities Asset Management Services
N.A.I.C.S.: 523940
Matt Miller (Asst VP-Relationship Mgmt)
Stacey Havens (Asst VP-Relationship Mgmt)

Subsidiary (Domestic):

Unified Financial Securities, LLC   (3)
9465 Counselors Row Ste 200, Indianapolis, IN 46240   (100%)
Tel.: (317) 917-7002
Security Brokerage & Dealing Services
N.A.I.C.S.: 523150

Wilton Industries, Inc.   (1)
2240 W 75th St, Woodridge, IL 60517-2333
Tel.: (630) 963-1818
Web Site: http://www.wilton.com
Sales Range: $75-99.9 Million
Mfr, Distr & Importer of Consumer Products; Baking & Decorating Cookware & Kitchenware & Picture Frames
N.A.I.C.S.: 423220

Subsidiary (Domestic):

Dimensions Holdings LLC   (2)
1801 N 12th St, Reading, PA 19604-1527
Tel.: (610) 939-9900
Web Site: http://www.dimensions-crafts.com
Sales Range: $25-49.9 Million
Designer, Producer & Distributor of Craft & Hobby Kits
N.A.I.C.S.: 339930

Subsidiary (Domestic):

K&Company, LLC   (3)

11125 NW Ambassador Dr Ste 200, Kansas City, MO 64153
Tel.: (816) 389-4150
Sales Range: $25-49.9 Million
Scrapbooking & Craft Products Designer & Developer
N.A.I.C.S.: 323111

Subsidiary (Domestic):

EK Success Ltd.   (2)
261 River Rd, Clifton, NJ 07014
Tel.: (973) 458-0092
Web Site: http://www.eksuccess.com
Gift Wrap & Novelties, Paper
N.A.I.C.S.: 322130

Worldpay, Inc.   (1)
8500 Governors Hill Dr, Symmes Township, OH 45249   (55%)
Tel.: (513) 900-5250
Web Site: http://www.worldpay.com
Rev.: $3,925,400,000
Assets: $24,888,500,000
Liabilities: $14,684,500,000
Net Worth: $10,204,000,000
Earnings: $19,600,000
Emp.: 8,186
Fiscal Year-end: 12/31/2018
Payment Systems, Alternative Payments, Risk Management, Currency Exchange & E-Commerce Services
N.A.I.C.S.: 522320
Robert Bartlett (CIO)
Charles D. Drucker (CEO)

Subsidiary (Domestic):

Mercury Payment Systems, LLC   (2)
150 Mercury Village Dr, Durango, CO 81301
Tel.: (970) 247-5557
Web Site: http://www.mercurypay.com
Rev.: $237,259,000
Assets: $130,512,000
Liabilities: $319,744,000
Net Worth: ($189,232,000)
Earnings: $42,653,000
Emp.: 646
Fiscal Year-end: 12/31/2013
Payment Processing Services
N.A.I.C.S.: 522320

National Processing Company   (2)
5100 Interchange Way, Louisville, KY 40229
Web Site: http://www.npc.net
Payment Processing Services
N.A.I.C.S.: 522320

Paymetric Inc.   (2)
300 Colonial Ctr Pkwy Ste 130, Atlanta, GA 30076
Tel.: (678) 242-5281
Web Site: http://www.paymetric.com
Payment Solutions Provider
N.A.I.C.S.: 522320

Pazien, Inc.   (2)
383 Elliot St Ste G, Newton, MA 02464
Tel.: (617) 300-8169
Web Site: http://www.pazien.com
Electronic Payment Services
N.A.I.C.S.: 522320

Vantiv, LLC   (2)
8500 Governors Hill Dr, Cincinnati, OH 45249
Tel.: (513) 900-5205
Electronic Integrated Payment Processing Services
N.A.I.C.S.: 522320

Subsidiary (Domestic):

NPC Group, Inc.   (3)
5100 Interchange Way, Louisville, KY 40229
Tel.: (877) 453-5933
Web Site: http://www.npc.net
Electronic Integrated Payment Processing Services
N.A.I.C.S.: 522320

Subsidiary (Domestic):

Worldpay Company, LLC   (2)
1 Riverfront Pl 20 NW 1st St, Evansville, IN 47708
Tel.: (812) 425-0072

Credit Card, Debit Card, Merchant & Private Label Program Services
N.A.I.C.S.: 522320

Xifin, Inc.   **(1)**
12225 El Camino Real, San Diego, CA 92130
Tel.: (858) 793-5700
Web Site: http://www.xifin.com
Sales Range: $1-9.9 Million
Emp.: 100
Financial Management Software
N.A.I.C.S.: 513210
Jeffrey Yates *(CTO)*
Mike Coats *(Exec VP)*
Steve Nielson *(VP-Sls)*
James C. Malone *(CFO & Exec VP)*
Nick Simanteris *(Sr VP-Customer Svcs)*
Jeff Carmichael *(VP-Engrg)*
Lee Ann Nichols *(Chief Customer Officer)*
Vicki DiFrancesco *(Chief Strategy Officer)*
Doug Wheeler *(CMO)*
Kyle Fetter *(Exec VP & Gen Mgr-Diagnostic Svcs)*
John Kelly *(CIO)*
Lale White *(Chm & CEO)*

Subsidiary (Domestic):

Computerized Management Services, Inc.   **(2)**
4100 Guardian St Ste 205, Simi Valley, CA 93063
Tel.: (805) 522-5940
Web Site: http://www.cmsmanagement.net
Sales Range: $1-9.9 Million
Emp.: 100
Office Administrative Services
N.A.I.C.S.: 561110
Daryl J. Favale *(Pres & CEO)*

VisualShare, LLC   **(2)**
350 E 500 S Ste 101, Salt Lake City, UT 84111-3346
Tel.: (801) 521-0257
Web Site: http://www.visualshare.com
Medical Imaging Software Developer
N.A.I.C.S.: 513210
Patricia Goede *(CEO)*
Jason Lauman *(VP-Engrg)*
Kurtis Bleeker *(VP-Technical Svcs)*
Larry Rigby *(Chm)*

GTE FINANCIAL
PO Box 172599, Tampa, FL 33672-0599
Tel.: (813) 871-2690
Web Site: http://www.gtefinancial.org
Year Founded: 1935
Sales Range: $50-74.9 Million
Credit Union
N.A.I.C.S.: 522130
Brad Baker *(CFO & Exec VP)*
Aaron Bresko *(Exec VP)*
Brian Best *(Pres & CEO)*
Mandy Zurbrick *(Chief Mktg Officer)*
Manuel Aguilar *(Sr VP-Comml & Advisory Svcs)*
Tedd Doucette *(VP-Admin)*
Dona Svehla *(Chief Lending Officer)*
Jennifer Maxfield *(Chief Strategy Officer)*
Gerhard Toth *(VP-Bus Banking)*

GTIS PARTNERS LP
45 Rockefeller Plz 31st Fl, New York, NY 10111
Tel.: (212) 220-5200
Web Site:
http://www.gtispartners.com
Year Founded: 2005
Rev.: $3,000,000,000
Emp.: 68
Real Estate Investment Services
N.A.I.C.S.: 523999
Tom Shapiro *(Pres & Chief Investment Officer)*
Thomas M. Feldstein *(Gen Counsel)*
Richard Cohen *(Mng Dir)*
Robert Rediker *(Mng Dir-Asset Mgmt)*
Robert Karnig Vahradian *(Partner & Sr Mng Dir)*
Amy Boyle *(Mng Dir & CFO)*

Dietrich Heidtmann *(Mng Dir & Head-Intl Capital Markets-Paris)*
David Pahl *(Mng Dir-Income Investments)*
Barry Howell *(Mng Dir-Income Investments)*
Thomas M. Baur *(Dir-Munich)*
Theodore Karatz *(Dir-Acq)*
Chaitali D. Patel *(Dir-IR)*
Ed McDowell *(Mng Dir-Acquisition-US)*
Alberto Pedrini *(Mng Dir-Construction & Design)*
Maristella Val Diniz *(Mng Dir-Dev)*
Josh Pristaw *(Sr Mng Dir & Co-Head-Brazil Acq, Asset Mgmt & Portfolio Mgmt)*
Joao Teixeira *(Sr Mng Dir & Head-Brazil Office)*

Subsidiaries:

GTIS Partners Brazil   **(1)**
Vista Faria Lima Rua Professor Atilio Innocenti 165-17th Floor, Sao Paulo, Brazil
Tel.: (55) 11 3043 6333
Web Site: http://www.gtispartners.com
Emp.: 25
Real Estate Investment Services
N.A.I.C.S.: 523999
Joao Teixeira *(Sr Mng Dir & Head-GTIS Brazil)*
Joshua H. Pristaw *(Sr Mng Dir & Head-Capital Markets-Brazil)*
Carlos Roberto D'Amato *(Mng Dir-Fin)*
Eduardo Klepacz *(Mng Dir & Head-Brazil Infrastructure)*
Robert McCall *(Mng Dir & Head-Brazil Acquisitions)*

Holding (Domestic):

BHG S.A. - Brazil Hospitality Group   **(2)**   **(70%)**
Av Rio Branco 01 sala 803, Rio de Janeiro, 04552-020, Brazil
Tel.: (55) 2135455445
Web Site: http://www.bhghoteis.com.br
Hotel Owner & Operator
N.A.I.C.S.: 721110
Eduardo de Salles Bartolomeo *(CEO)*
Andre Bellintani Tambosi *(Chief Comml Officer)*
Felipe Pinto Gomes *(CFO, Officer-IR & Dir-Bus Dev)*
Alexandre Solleiro *(Pres)*
Tomas Ramos *(Dir-Sls & Mktg)*
Eduardo de Salles Bartolomeo *(CEO)*

GTJ CO. INC.
60 Hempstead Ave, West Hempstead, NY 11552
Tel.: (516) 881-3535
Web Site: http://www.gtjreit.com
Year Founded: 1965
Sales Range: $25-49.9 Million
Emp.: 26
Provider of School Buses
N.A.I.C.S.: 485410
Dennis Connor *(Gen Mgr)*

GTJ REIT, INC.
1399 Franklin Ave Ste 100, Garden City, NY 11530
Tel.: (516) 693-5500   MD
Web Site: https://www.gtjreit.com
Year Founded: 2006
Rev.: $65,534,000
Assets: $521,117,000
Liabilities: $454,966,000
Net Worth: $66,151,000
Earnings: $15,425,000
Emp.: 12
Fiscal Year-end: 12/31/22
Real Estate Services
N.A.I.C.S.: 531390
Paul A. Cooper *(Chm & CEO)*
Louis Sheinker *(Pres, COO & Sec)*
Stuart M. Blau *(CFO & Treas)*
Carissa Covatti-Clark *(VP-Fin & Controller)*
Kristy Sariego *(Dir-Property Mgmt)*

Subsidiaries:

MetroClean Express Corp.   **(1)**
28-90 Review Ave, Long Island City, NY 11101-3236
Tel.: (718) 482-0080
Web Site:
http://www.metroexpressservices.com
Cleaning & Maintenance Services
N.A.I.C.S.: 561720

ShelterCLEAN, Inc.   **(1)**
11065 Penrose St, Sun Valley, CA 91352
Tel.: (818) 767-9162
Web Site:
http://www.sheltercleanservices.com
Cleaning & Maintenance Services
N.A.I.C.S.: 561720

The Bus Depot, Inc.   **(1)**
30 E 4th St, East Greenville, PA 18041
Tel.: (215) 234-8989
Web Site: https://www.busdepot.com
Automobile Parts Distr
N.A.I.C.S.: 441330

GTM PAYROLL SERVICES INC.
7 Executive Park Dr, Clifton Park, NY 12065
Tel.: (518) 373-4111
Web Site: http://www.gtm.com
Year Founded: 1991
Sales Range: $1-9.9 Million
Emp.: 37
Payroll Services
N.A.I.C.S.: 541214
Guy Maddalone *(Founder, Pres & CEO)*
Todd Maddalone *(VP-Ops)*
Erin Bandaru *(Gen Mgr-Household)*
Anne Johnson *(Mgr-Software & HR)*
Chris Chariton *(Dir-Mktg & Bus Dev)*
Kate Wolfe *(Mgr-Client Svcs)*
Dorothy Keesler *(Mgr-Insurance Svcs)*

GTM PLASTICS INC.
2405 S Shiloh, Garland, TX 75041
Tel.: (972) 278-9700
Web Site: http://www.gtmplastics.com
Year Founded: 1964
Sales Range: $10-24.9 Million
Emp.: 65
Mfr Thermoplastic Injection Molded Parts
N.A.I.C.S.: 333511
Bob Landers *(Controller)*
Ron Burton *(Engr-Mfg)*

GTM SPORTSWEAR
520 McCall Rd, Manhattan, KS 66502
Tel.: (877) 597-8066
Web Site:
http://www.gtmsportswear.com
Year Founded: 1989
Emp.: 900
Sportswear Retailer
N.A.I.C.S.: 424350
David Dreiling *(Founder & Owner)*
John Strawn *(CIO & Sr VP-Ops)*
Kyra Dreiling *(Dir-Retail)*

GTN TECHNICAL STAFFING
14800 Quorum Dr Ste 150, Dallas, TX 75254
Tel.: (214) 615-2600   TX
Web Site:
http://www.gtntechnicalstaffing.com
Year Founded: 2000
Sales Range: $10-24.9 Million
Emp.: 187
Technical & IT Staffing Services
N.A.I.C.S.: 561311
Greg Smith *(Owner)*
Jim Bright *(Dir-Sls)*

GTP GREEN BELL INC.

1801 Rutherford Rd, Greenville, SC 29609
Tel.: (864) 244-4110
Web Site:
http://www.globaltextilepartner.com
Sales Range: $25-49.9 Million
Emp.: 140
Textile Machinery & Equipment
N.A.I.C.S.: 423830

GTS HOLDINGS, INC.
255 Meadowlands Pkwy, Secaucus, NJ 07094-2316
Tel.: (201) 784-1200
Web Site: https://www.empirecls.com
Year Founded: 2005
Sales Range: $25-49.9 Million
Emp.: 800
Holding Company; Limousine Services
N.A.I.C.S.: 551112
David Seelinger *(Chm & CEO)*
Nat Buonfiglio *(CFO)*
Edward Martinez *(COO)*
Joey Phelps *(Sr Exec VP)*
Marissa Criaris *(Exec VP-Sls)*
Abbie Kelly *(Exec VP-Meetings & Events)*
Seth Marcus *(Exec VP-Meeting & Event Sls)*

Subsidiaries:

EmpireCLS Worldwide Chauffeured Services   **(1)**
225 Meadowlands Pkwy, Secaucus, NJ 07094
Tel.: (201) 784-1200
Web Site: http://www.empirecls.com
Sales Range: $100-124.9 Million
Chauffeured Services
N.A.I.C.S.: 485310
David Seelinger *(Chm & CEO)*
Seth Marcus *(Exec VP-Meeting & Event Sls)*
Joey Phelps *(Sr Exec VP)*
Gary Stevens *(Exec Dir-Sls & Mktg)*
Abbie Kelly *(Exec VP-Meeting & Events)*
Edward Martinez *(COO)*
Marissa Criaris *(Exec VP-Sls)*
Nat Buonfiglio *(CFO)*

GTT COMMUNICATIONS, INC.
7900 Tysons 1 Pl Ste 1450, McLean, VA 22102
Tel.: (703) 442-5500   DE
Web Site: http://www.gtt.net
Year Founded: 2005
Rev.: $1,727,800,000
Assets: $4,757,700,000
Liabilities: $4,466,600,000
Net Worth: $291,100,000
Earnings: ($105,900,000)
Emp.: 3,100
Fiscal Year-end: 12/31/19
Telecommunications; Cloud Networking & Internet Services
N.A.I.C.S.: 517111
Christopher McKee *(Gen Counsel & Exec VP-Corp Dev)*
Corey Eng *(Sr VP-Bus Ops & Sys)*
Jesper Aagaard *(Pres-Europe)*
Fletcher Keister *(Chief Product & Tech Officer)*
Frederique Arnold *(Sr VP-HR)*
Ernie Ortega *(Chief Revenue Officer)*
Beth Hollenback *(Sr VP-Client Experience)*
Tom Homer *(Sr VP-Europe)*
Donna Granato *(CFO)*
Valerie Green *(Gen Counsel)*
George Kuzmanovski *(COO)*
Ed Morche *(CEO)*
Charlie Lucas *(VP-Fin)*

Subsidiaries:

Accelerated Connections Inc.   **(1)**
123 Edward Street Suite 300, Toronto, M5G 0A8, ON, Canada

GTT Communications, Inc.—(Continued)

Tel.: (470) 264-5428
Telecommunication Servicesb
N.A.I.C.S.: 517810

Access Point Inc. (1)
1100 Crescent Green Dr 109, Cary, NC 27518
Tel.: (919) 851-4838
Web Site: http://www.accesspointinc.com
Sales Range: $10-24.9 Million
Emp.: 75
Provider of Long Distance, Local & Internet Phone Access
N.A.I.C.S.: 517121

GTT Communications HK Limited (1)
6th Floor Bonham Circus 40 Bonham Strand, Sheung Wan, China (Hong Kong)
Tel.: (852) 81071088
Telecommunication & Internet Services
N.A.I.C.S.: 517111

GTT GmbH (1)
Weismullerstrasse 26, 60314, Frankfurt, Germany
Tel.: (49) 69 24437 2255
Mobile & Digital Telecommunication Services
N.A.I.C.S.: 517810

GTT-EMEA, Ltd. (1)
5 Fleet Place 9th Floor, 9th Floor, London, EC4M 7RD, United Kingdom
Tel.: (44) 2074897200
Emp.: 57
Telecommunication Related Services
N.A.I.C.S.: 517810

Global Telecom & Technology Americas, Inc. (1)
8484 Westpark Dr Ste 720, McLean, VA 22102
Tel.: (703) 442-5500
Telecommunication Related Services
N.A.I.C.S.: 517810

Hibernia Atlantic Cable System Limited (1)
International Exchange Centre Clonshaugh Industrial Estate, Clonshaugh, Dublin, D17, AW86, Ireland
Tel.: (353) 18673600
Trans-Atlantic Fiber-Optic Cable Network Operator & Video Media Streaming Services
N.A.I.C.S.: 517810

IDC Global, Inc. (1)
Ste 947 26 Bdwy, New York, NY 10004
Tel.: (212) 514-8186
Web Site: http://www.idcglobal.com
Telecommunication Related Services
N.A.I.C.S.: 517810

Interoute Communications Limited (1)
3rd Floor New Castle House Castle Boulevard, Nottingham, NG7 1FT, United Kingdom
Tel.: (44) 2070259000
Fiber-Optic Network Operator
N.A.I.C.S.: 517810
Zoe Trubridge (Acct Mgr-Customer Svc)

Subsidiary (Non-US):

Interoute Austria GmbH (2)
Lembockgasse 63 Stiege 2, 1230, Vienna, Austria
Tel.: (43) 186753100
Telecommunication Servicesb
N.A.I.C.S.: 517810

Interoute Bulgaria JSCo (2)
Business Building Megapark 1st Floor 115G Tsarigradsko Shose Blvd, Sofia, 1784, Bulgaria
Tel.: (359) 249 108 20
Telecommunication Servicesb
N.A.I.C.S.: 517810

Interoute Czech s.r.o (2)
Siemensova 2717/4 City West, 155 00, Prague, Czech Republic
Tel.: (420) 225352111
Telecommunication Servicesb
N.A.I.C.S.: 517810

Interoute Finland Oy (2)
Teknobulevardi 3-5, Vantaa, 01530, Finland
Tel.: (358) 20 74 97 700
Telecommunication Servicesb
N.A.I.C.S.: 517810

Interoute France SAS (2)
34 rue des Gardinoux, 93300, Aubervilliers, France
Tel.: (33) 177497000
Telecommunication Servicesb
N.A.I.C.S.: 517810

Interoute Iberia S.A.U (2)
Pol Emp Herrera Oria Lezama 4, Madrid, 28034, Spain
Tel.: (34) 91 515 9680
Telecommunication Servicesb
N.A.I.C.S.: 517810

Interoute Magyarorszag Tavkozlesi Kft (2)
Victor Hugo u 18-22, 1132, Budapest, Hungary
Tel.: (36) 30 385 8575
Telecommunication Servicesb
N.A.I.C.S.: 517810

Interoute Managed Services Denmark A/S (2)
Niels Juels Gade 5 3 sal, DK-1059, Copenhagen, Denmark
Tel.: (45) 3213 3299
Telecommunication Servicesb
N.A.I.C.S.: 517810

Interoute Managed Services Sweden AB (2)
Sveavagen 163, 113 46, Stockholm, Sweden
Tel.: (46) 8 459 94 00
Telecommunication Servicesb
N.A.I.C.S.: 517810

Interoute Managed Services Switzerland Sarl (2)
Chemin de l'Epinglier 2, Meyrin, 1217, Geneva, Switzerland
Tel.: (41) 227836000
Computer Programming Services
N.A.I.C.S.: 541511

Interoute S.R.L (2)
Bd Pompeiu Dimitrie Prof 8 Bucuresti-Sector 2, 020337, Bucharest, Romania
Tel.: (40) 742 260 000
Telecommunication Servicesb
N.A.I.C.S.: 517810

Interoute Slovakia s.r.o. (2)
Kutlikova ulica 17, 852 50, Bratislava, Slovakia
Tel.: (421) 268286618
Telecommunication Servicesb
N.A.I.C.S.: 517112

Subsidiary (US):

Interoute USA Inc. (2)
60 Hudson St Ste 1213, New York, NY 10013
Tel.: (347) 774-0521
Telecommunication Servicesb
N.A.I.C.S.: 517810

KPN EuroRings B.V. (1)
PO Box 30000, 2500, Hague, Netherlands
Tel.: (31) 703438609
Web Site: http://www.kpn.com
Telecommunication Servicesb
N.A.I.C.S.: 517810

Subsidiary (Domestic):

KPN International (2)
PO Box 162, 1180 AD, Amstelveen, Netherlands (100%)
Tel.: (31) 20 5456 789
Web Site: http://www.kpn-international.com
Sales Range: $25-49.9 Million
Emp.: 60
Data & IP Communications
N.A.I.C.S.: 517810

Subsidiary (Non-US):

KPN International (2)
75 boulevard Haussmann, 75008, Paris, France
Tel.: (33) 142685094
Web Site: http://www.kpn-international.com

Sales Range: $25-49.9 Million
Telecommunication Servicesb
N.A.I.C.S.: 517810

KPN International (2)
4th Floor Regina House 1 Queen Street, London, United Kingdom
Tel.: (44) 2034177053
Web Site: http://www.kpn-international.com
Emp.: 50
Telecommunication Servicesb
N.A.I.C.S.: 517810

NT Network Services, LLC (1)
120 E FM 544, Murphy, TX 75094
Tel.: (214) 490-3175
Web Site: http://www.ntnetworkservices.net
Telecommunication Related Services
N.A.I.C.S.: 517810

Sparkplug, Inc. (1)
7575 E Redfield Rd Ste 137, Scottsdale, AZ 85260
Tel.: (602) 648-5000
Telecommunication Related Services
N.A.I.C.S.: 517810

Transbeam, Inc. (1)
8 W 38th St, New York, NY 10018
Tel.: (212) 631-8100
Telecommunications; Managed Data, Voice, IT & Event Solutions
N.A.I.C.S.: 517810
Brian Murray (Dir-Network Engrg)
Harpreet Chandhok (VP-Ops)
Sam Kashi (CEO)

WBS Connect, LLC (1)
700 N Colorado Blvd Ste 307, Denver, CO 80206
Tel.: (720) 259-3456
Web Site: http://www.wbsconnect.com
Telecommunication Related Services
N.A.I.C.S.: 517810
Michael Hollander (Co-Founder & Mng Partner)
Scott Charter (Co-Founder & Mng Partner)
Terri Jorgensen (Dir-Provisioning & Implementation)
Matthew Haentzschel (Dir-Sls)
Suzen Rodgers (CFO)

nLayer Communications, Inc. (1)
209 W Jackson Blvd Ste 700, Chicago, IL 60606-6936
Tel.: (312) 698-4800
Telecommunication Related Services
N.A.I.C.S.: 517810

GUADALUPE LUMBER & SUPPLY COMPANY, INC.
1547 S Zarzamora St, San Antonio, TX 78207
Tel.: (210) 223-4263
Web Site: https://www.guadalupelumberco.com
Sales Range: $10-24.9 Million
Emp.: 75
Lumber Whslr
N.A.I.C.S.: 444110
Andrew Dunk (Mgr-Store)
Roland Longoria (Asst Mgr)

GUADALUPE LUMBER CO.
1547 S Zarzamora, San Antonio, TX 78207
Tel.: (210) 223-4263
Web Site: https://www.guadalupelumberco.com
Year Founded: 1915
Sales Range: $10-24.9 Million
Emp.: 140
Lumber & Other Building Materials
N.A.I.C.S.: 423310
Deborah Grothues (Office Mgr)

GUADALUPE VALLEY ELECTRIC COOP
825 E Sarah Dewitt Dr, Gonzales, TX 78629
Tel.: (830) 857-1200
Web Site: https://www.gvec.org
Rev.: $77,493,378
Emp.: 150

Electric Power Distr
N.A.I.C.S.: 221122
Darren Schauer (CEO & Gen Mgr)
Melvin E. Strey (VP)
Sean Alvarez (COO)
Don Williams (Treas & Sec)
Gerri Lawing (Coord-Economic Dev)

GUADALUPE-BLANCO RIVER AUTHORITY
933 E Ct St, Seguin, TX 78155
Tel.: (830) 379-5822
Web Site: http://www.gbra.org
Year Founded: 1933
Rev.: $52,731,461
Assets: $306,015,170
Liabilities: $190,008,013
Net Worth: $116,007,157
Earnings: $9,820,268
Emp.: 210
Fiscal Year-end: 08/31/19
Water Resource Administration Services
N.A.I.C.S.: 924110
Dennis L. Patillo (Chm)
Don B. Meador (Vice Chm)
Kenneth A. Motl (Treas & Sec)
Kevin Patteson (CEO & Gen Mgr)
Randy Staats (CFO & Mgr-Fin)
Nathan Pence (Mgr-Environmental Science & Community Affairs)

GUAM POWER AUTHORITY
Rte 16, Harmon, GU 96932-2977
Tel.: (671) 647-5787
Web Site:
http://www.guampowerauthority.com
Year Founded: 1968
Sales Range: $200-249.9 Million
Emp.: 532
Energy Administration Services
N.A.I.C.S.: 926130
Joaquin C. Flores (Gen Mgr)
Randall V. Wiegand (CFO)
Simon Sanchez (Chm)
Benigno Palomo (Co-Vice Chm)
Gloria C. Nelson (Co-Vice Chm & Sec)

GUANHUA CORP.
5847 San Felipe Dr Ste 1700, Houston, TX 77057
Tel.: (713) 821-1755
Holding Company
N.A.I.C.S.: 551112
M. J. Shaheed (Chm, Pres & CEO)

GUAR GLOBAL LTD.
407 E Louisiana St, McKinney, TX 75069-4233
Tel.: (214) 380-9677
Year Founded: 2007
Guar Gum Producer
N.A.I.C.S.: 213112
Joe P. Moore Jr. (VP-Global Bus Dev)

GUARAGUAO TRUCK SALES INC.
Km 5 HM 1 RR 174, Bayamon, PR 00959
Tel.: (787) 780-0090
Web Site:
http://www.guaraguaotruck.com
Sales Range: $10-24.9 Million
Emp.: 80
Trucks, Tractors & Trailers: New & Used
N.A.I.C.S.: 441110
Oscar W. Covas (Pres)

GUARANTEE ELECTRICAL COMPANY
3405 Bent Ave, Saint Louis, MO 63116-2601
Tel.: (314) 772-5400
Web Site: https://www.geco.com

Year Founded: 1902
Sales Range: $75-99.9 Million
Emp.: 100
Industrial & Commercial Electrical
Contracting Services
N.A.I.C.S.: 238210
Richard Oertli *(Chm)*
Josh Voegtli *(CFO)*
Jason Wiegand *(VP-Preconstruction Svcs)*
Greg Crook *(Dir-HR-Corp Office)*
Sean James *(Mgr-BIM & Revit-GECO Engrg)*
Brian Wood *(Sr Engr-GECO Engrg)*
Perry Lorts *(Asst Project Mgr-MO Construction)*
Todd Cook *(Dir-Corp Safety)*
Erica Heinssen *(Dir-Field Safety)*
Don Brown *(VP-Bus Dev)*
Nick Arb *(Mgr-Dev-Missouri, Illinois, Colorado & California)*
Rich Ledbetter *(CEO)*
Emily Martin *(COO)*
Dave Gralike *(Pres)*

GUARANTEE INSURANCE GROUP, INC.
401 E Las Olas Blvd Ste 1540, Fort Lauderdale, FL 33301
Tel.: (954) 556-1600   DE
Web Site:
http://www.guaranteeins.com
Holding Company; Reinsurance Products & Services
N.A.I.C.S.: 551112
Charles K. Schuver *(Pres)*

Subsidiaries:

Guarantee Insurance Company   (1)
401 E Las Olas Blvd Ste 1540, Fort Lauderdale, FL 33301
Tel.: (954) 556-1600
Web Site: http://www.guaranteeins.com
Reinsurance Products & Services
N.A.I.C.S.: 524130
Charles K. Schuver *(Pres)*

GUARANTEE INTERIORS INC.
2914 Locust St, Saint Louis, MO 63103
Tel.: (314) 533-3500
Web Site: http://www.giiweb.com
Sales Range: $10-24.9 Million
Emp.: 100
Drywall
N.A.I.C.S.: 238310
Steven Farrell *(VP)*
Robert Farell Jr. *(VP)*

GUARANTEE SPECIALTIES INC.
9401 Carr Ave, Cleveland, OH 44108
Tel.: (216) 451-9744
Sales Range: $10-24.9 Million
Emp.: 30
Stampers Mfr
N.A.I.C.S.: 332112
Armando E. Pages *(Pres)*
John Gallagher *(Controller)*

GUARANTEE TITLE & TRUST COMPANY
50 W Town St Ste 350, Columbus, OH 43215-4197
Tel.: (513) 794-4020   OH
Year Founded: 1899
Sales Range: $1-4.9 Billion
Emp.: 1,000
Title Insurance Underwriter
N.A.I.C.S.: 524127
Mike Parlor *(VP)*
Hiram Blomquist *(Pres)*
Jim Diltz *(CFO)*

GUARANTEED HOME MORT-GAGE, INC.

108 Corporate Park Dr Ste 301, West Harrison, NY 10604-3822
Tel.: (914) 696-3400
Web Site:
http://www.guaranteedhome
mortgagecompanyinc.com
Sales Range: $10-24.9 Million
Emp.: 500
Mortgage Financing Services
N.A.I.C.S.: 522310
David A. Wind *(Founder, Chm & CEO)*

GUARANTEED RATE, INC.
3940 N Ravenswood, Chicago, IL 60613
Tel.: (773) 290-0358
Web Site:
http://www.guaranteedrate.com
Year Founded: 2000
Sales Range: $450-499.9 Million
Emp.: 2,700
Mortgage Banking & Related Services
N.A.I.C.S.: 522310
Ted Ahern *(Chief Investment Officer)*
Victor F. Ciardelli III *(Founder & CEO)*
Martin J. Logan *(CIO)*
Nikolaos Athanasiou *(COO)*
Elizabeth Garner *(Exec VP)*
Matthew Harmon *(Exec VP-Natl Retail Fulfillment)*
Jim Hettinger *(Exec VP)*
Kasey J. Marty *(Exec VP)*
Rebecca Blabolil *(Chief Compliance Officer)*
Scott Ubersox *(Dir-Real Estate & Facilities)*
James Elliott *(Pres-OriginPoint)*
Jim Linnane *(Dir-Natl Sls)*
Brian Logie *(Sr VP & Mgr-Maryland & Washington)*
Brian Fein *(Mgr-Annapolis)*
Craig Lombardi *(Pres-Online)*
Michael Harrington *(VP-Mortgage Lending)*
Paul Sellers *(VP-Mortgage Lending)*
Kai Bike *(VP-Mortgage Lending)*
Paul Anastos *(Chief Innovation Officer)*
Steve Moffat *(CMO)*
Tej Brar *(Exec VP-Tech)*
Suk Shah *(CFO)*
Charley Wickman *(Exec Creative Dir)*
Scott G. Stephen *(Chief Growth Officer)*
Ramesh Sarukkai *(Chief Product & Tech Officer)*
John Palmiotto *(Chief Retail Production Officer & Head-Sls)*
Ryan Ogata *(Mgr-Northwest Market)*
Tim Sorenson *(Mgr-Southwest Market)*
Pat Bolan *(Mgr-South Central)*

Subsidiaries:

Attorneys' Title Guaranty Fund, Inc.   (1)
2102 Windsor Pl, Champaign, IL 61820
Tel.: (217) 359-2000
Web Site: http://www.atgf.com
Sales Range: $25-49.9 Million
Emp.: 200
Title Insurance
N.A.I.C.S.: 524127
Peter J. Birnbaum *(Pres & CEO)*

Subsidiary (Domestic):

Attorneys' Title Guaranty Fund   (2)
2418 Crossroads Dr Ste 1600, Madison, WI 53718-2420
Tel.: (608) 442-8130
Sales Range: $10-24.9 Million
Emp.: 1
Real Estate Marketing & Sales Company
N.A.I.C.S.: 531210
Thomas Cullen *(VP)*

NLT Title, LLC   (2)
6885 Vistagreen Way, Rockford, IL 61107-6801
Tel.: (815) 654-6800
Web Site: http://www.nlt-title.com
Emp.: 5
Escrow Services
N.A.I.C.S.: 531390
Sheila Riportella *(Branch Mgr)*
Michael Moore *(Pres)*

GUARANTY CAPITAL CORP
217 Church St, Belzoni, MS 39038
Tel.: (662) 247-1454
Web Site: https://gbtonline.com
Bank Holding Company
N.A.I.C.S.: 551111
Huey L. Townsend *(Pres)*

Subsidiaries:

Guaranty Bank and Trust Company   (1)
210 N Hayden St, Belzoni, MA 39038
Tel.: (662) 247-1454
Web Site: https://gbtonline.com
Banking Services
N.A.I.C.S.: 522110

GUARANTY CHEVROLET-PONTIAC
20 Hwy 99 S, Junction City, OR 97448-9714
Tel.: (541) 998-2333   OR
Web Site:
https://www.guarantycars.com
Year Founded: 1966
Sales Range: $125-149.9 Million
Emp.: 300
Retailer of Automobiles
N.A.I.C.S.: 441210
Shannon Nill *(Owner)*

GUARANTY DEVELOPMENT COMPANY
120 N 2nd St, Livingston, MT 59047-2290
Tel.: (406) 222-2265   MT
Web Site: https://www.americanbank
montana.com
Rev.: $16,393,000
Emp.: 70
Bank Holding Company
N.A.I.C.S.: 551111
Bruce A. Erickson *(Chm)*
Tom Kuka *(Sr VP)*

Subsidiaries:

American Bank   (1)
120 N 2nd St, Livingston, MT 59047
Tel.: (406) 222-2265
Web Site:
http://www.americanbankmontana.com
Sales Range: $10-24.9 Million
Emp.: 73
Retail & Commercial Banking
N.A.I.C.S.: 522110
Jennifer Wilkinson *(Pres-San Antonio)*
Clayton Hoover *(Asst Mgr-Customer Rels-San Antonio)*
Stephen C. Raffaele *(Pres & CEO)*
Joseph T. Lee *(CIO)*

GUARANTY RV CENTERS
20 Hwy 99 S, Junction City, OR 97448-9714
Tel.: (541) 998-2333
Web Site: http://www.guaranty.com
Year Founded: 1966
Sales Range: $300-349.9 Million
Emp.: 320
New & Pre-owned RVs Retailers
N.A.I.C.S.: 441210
Shannon Nill *(Gen Mgr)*
Herb Nill *(Founder)*
Ed Morgan *(CFO)*

GUARD PUBLISHING COMPANY
3500 Chad Dr, Eugene, OR 97408

Tel.: (541) 485-1234
Web Site:
http://www.registerguard.com
Rev.: $25,900,000
Emp.: 200
Newspapers; Publishing & Printing
N.A.I.C.S.: 513110
Robert Ness *(CFO)*
N. Christian Anderson III *(Pres)*

GUARD-SYSTEMS, INC.
1190 Monterey Pass Rd, Monterey Park, CA 91754
Tel.: (323) 881-6711   CA
Web Site:
https://www.guardsystemsinc.com
Year Founded: 1956
Sales Range: $25-49.9 Million
Emp.: 20
Security Guard Services
N.A.I.C.S.: 561612
Theodore Haas *(Pres)*

GUARDIAN 8 HOLDINGS
7432 E Tierra Buena Ln Ste 102, Scottsdale, AZ 85260
Tel.: (913) 317-8887   NV
Web Site: http://www.guardian8.com
Year Founded: 2009
Sales Range: Less than $1 Million
Emp.: 17
Personal Security Device Mfr
N.A.I.C.S.: 561621
C. Stephen Cochennet *(Chm, Treas & Sec)*
James G. Miller *(Founder)*
Kathleen C. Hanrahan *(Interim CFO)*

GUARDIAN ALARM COMPANY
20800 Southfield Rd, Southfield, MI 48075-4238
Tel.: (248) 423-1000   MI
Web Site:
https://www.guardianalarm.com
Year Founded: 1930
Sales Range: $350-399.9 Million
Emp.: 2,000
Security System Services
N.A.I.C.S.: 561621
Milton Pierce *(Founder)*
Douglas Pierce *(Co-Owner)*
Karen Majeske *(Gen Mgr)*
Richard Pierce *(Co-Owner)*

Subsidiaries:

Guardian Alarm of Toledo   (1)
3222 W Central Ave, Toledo, OH 43606   (100%)
Tel.: (419) 255-8400
Web Site: http://www.guardianalarm.com
Sales Range: $25-49.9 Million
Emp.: 100
Security & Alarm System Monitoring Services
N.A.I.C.S.: 561621
Chris Zielinski *(Branch Mgr)*

GUARDIAN ANGELS HOME-CARE, LLC
405 Maple Ave Ste 1, Cheshire, CT 06410
Tel.: (203) 439-7731
Web Site:
http://myguardianangelshome
care.com
Year Founded: 1993
Home Care Services
N.A.I.C.S.: 621610
William Miska *(Dir)*

Subsidiaries:

Compassionate Care at Home LLC   (1)
1008 Main St Ste 3, Branford, CT 06405
Tel.: (203) 433-4325
Web Site: http://www.compassionatect.com
Women Healthcare Services
N.A.I.C.S.: 621610

Guardian Capital Partners, LLC—(Continued)

GUARDIAN CAPITAL PARTNERS, LLC
724 W Lancaster Ave Ste 120,
Wayne, PA 19087
Tel.: (610) 263-0100   DE
Web Site:
https://www.guardiancp.com
Privater Equity Firm
N.A.I.C.S.: 523999
Scott D. Evans (Mng Partner)
Peter H. Haabestad (Mng Partner)
Adrian R. Ironside (Partner)
Christopher S. Fugaro (VP)
Janet L. Stott (CFO)
Hugh Kenworthy III (Mng Partner)

Subsidiaries:

McCubbin Hosiery, LLC   (1)
5310 NW 5th St, Oklahoma City, OK
73127-5805
Tel.: (405) 236-8351
Web Site: http://www.mccubbin.com
Sales Range: $1-9.9 Million
Women's & Children's Socks, Tights & Slippers Designer, Mfr & Distr
N.A.I.C.S.: 424350
Mark H. McCubbin (CEO)
David McCubbin (Pres)
Tim Kanzler (Sr VP-Sls & Mktg)

R & D Circuits, Inc.   (1)
3601 S Clinton Ave, South Plainfield, NJ
07080
Tel.: (732) 549-4554
Sales Range: $25-49.9 Million
Emp.: 50
Printed Circuit Board Mfr
N.A.I.C.S.: 334412

Rio Brands, Inc.   (1)
10981 Decatur Rd, Philadelphia, PA 19154-3210
Tel.: (215) 632-2800
Web Site: http://www.riobrands.com
Sales Range: $25-49.9 Million
Aluminum Tables, Casual Outdoor Furniture, Folding Beds, Office Chairs, Sand
Chairs & Umbrellas Mfr
N.A.I.C.S.: 337126
Warren Cohen (Principal)
Ira Cohen (Pres)
Steve Haverstick (Mgr-Import)

WS Acquisition, LLC   (1)
830 Wilson St, Eugene, OR 97402
Tel.: (541) 344-7267
Web Site: https://westernshelter.com
Shelter Mfr & Field Support System
N.A.I.C.S.: 336214

Subsidiary (Domestic):

Air Rover, Inc.   (2)
12679 FM 3311, Tyler, TX 75708
Tel.: (903) 877-3430
Web Site: http://www.airrover.com
Rev.: $2,333,333
Emp.: 30
Air-Conditioning & Warm Air Heating Equipment & Commercial & Industrial Refrigeration Equipment Mfr
N.A.I.C.S.: 333415
Frances Stiles (Owner & Pres)

GUARDIAN COMMERCIAL REALTY
10940 Wilshire Blvd Ste 925, Los Angeles, CA 90024
Tel.: (310) 882-2050
Web Site: http://www.guardianusa.net
Year Founded: 2004
Sales Range: $1-9.9 Million
Emp.: 6
Real Estate Advisory Services
N.A.I.C.S.: 531390
Robert Chavez (Pres & CEO)

GUARDIAN COMPANIES INC.
1617 Matassino Rd, New Castle, DE
19720
Tel.: (302) 834-1000

Web Site:
https://www.guardianco.com
Rev.: $13,900,000
Emp.: 50
Underground Utilities Road Contractor
N.A.I.C.S.: 237110

Subsidiaries:

Guardian Companies Inc.   (1)
101 Rogers Rd Ste 101, Wilmington, DE
19801
Tel.: (302) 834-1000
Sales Range: $10-24.9 Million
Heavy Construction Equipment Rental
N.A.I.C.S.: 532412
Teresa Miller (Office Mgr)

GUARDIAN FALL PROTECTION, INC.
6305 S 231 St, Kent, WA 98032
Tel.: (253) 854-5877
Web Site:
http://www.guardianfall.com
Year Founded: 1985
Sales Range: $1-9.9 Million
Emp.: 18
Fall Protection Gear Mfr
N.A.I.C.S.: 332999
Ed Marquardt (Pres)
Douglas Boehm (Project Mgr-Engrg Svcs)
Tommy Lee (Mgr-Trng)
Larry Baker (Dir-QA)

Subsidiaries:

QC Industries, Inc.   (1)
60 Maple St, Mansfield, MA 02048
Tel.: (781) 344-1000
Web Site: http://www.qualcraft.com
Scaffolding Systems Mfr
N.A.I.C.S.: 332311

GUARDIAN FUELING TECHNOLOGIES
9452 Philips Hwy 35 Ste 2, Jacksonville, FL 32256
Tel.: (904) 680-0850
Web Site:
http://www.guardianfueltech.com
Rev.: $22,800,000
Emp.: 250
Garage & Service Station Contractors
N.A.I.C.S.: 236220
Patrick Reese (CFO)
Joey D. Batchelor (Pres & CEO)
Ken Weiss (VP-Sls)
David McMichael (VP-Svc-Southeast)
Eric Postma (Branch Mgr-Pensacola)
Rolando Gil (Branch Mgr)
Scott Blockinger (Branch Mgr-Jacksonville)
Joey Cheek (Exec VP)
Sterling Baker (Operating Partner)

GUARDIAN HOLDINGS INC.
3801 Sunset Ave, Rocky Mount, NC
27804-0397
Tel.: (252) 443-4101   NC
Year Founded: 1981
Sales Range: $25-49.9 Million
Emp.: 3
Holding Company; Fast Food Restaurants Owner & Operator
N.A.I.C.S.: 551112
Vince Andracchio (Partner)

GUARDIAN MOVING & STORAGE CO., INC.
1901 Light St, Baltimore, MD 21230-4994
Tel.: (410) 752-0500
Web Site:
https://www.guardianservices.com
Year Founded: 1946
Sales Range: $100-124.9 Million
Emp.: 113

General Freight Trucking Services
N.A.I.C.S.: 484110
Eugene W. Smoot (Pres)

GUARDIAN PHARMACY, LLC.
1776 Peachtree St NW, Atlanta, GA
30309
Tel.: (404) 810-0089
Web Site:
http://www.guardianpharmacy.net
Pharmacies & Drug Stores
N.A.I.C.S.: 456110
William E. Bindley (Bd of Dirs, Executives)
David Morris (CFO)
Fred Burke (CEO)
Gail Young (Dir-HR)
Robert Dunn (Pres)
Bob Weir (VP-Ops & Regulatory Support)
Chad Downey (Treas & VP)
Kendall Forbes (Exec VP-Sls & Ops)
Matt Hopp (Pres)
Michael Bahou (Sls Mgr-Natl)

Subsidiaries:

Guardian Pharmacy of Dallas-Fort
Worth   (1)
610 Magic Mile, Arlington, TX 76011
Tel.: (817) 633-6688
Web Site:
http://www.guardianpharmacydfw.com
Pharmacies & Drug Stores
N.A.I.C.S.: 456110
Melissa Deas (Pres)

GUARDIAN SAVINGS BANK FSB
5901 Colerain Ave, Cincinnati, OH
45239
Tel.: (513) 923-4100
Web Site:
https://www.guardiansavings
bank.com
Year Founded: 1895
Rev.: $21,039,000
Emp.: 110
Federal Savings Bank
N.A.I.C.S.: 522180
Louis Beck (Chm)
Richard Berkhardt (Pres)
Jared Bernard (VP)
Yvonne Rich (VP)
Kevin Martley (CFO)

GUARDIAN SECURITY SYSTEMS, INC.
1743 1st Ave S, Seattle, WA 98134
Tel.: (206) 622-6545
Web Site:
https://www.guardiansecurity.com
Rev.: $12,000,000
Emp.: 200
Security System Services
N.A.I.C.S.: 561621
Frank A. Close (Pres)
Marv Gere (Mgr-Ops)
Erik Isakson (Dir-Security Sls)
Lynda Whitton (Dir-Fin & Admin)

Subsidiaries:

Puget Sound Alarm Inc.   (1)
1743 1st Ave S, Seattle, WA 98134
Tel.: (206) 365-3155
Security System Services
N.A.I.C.S.: 561621

GUARDIAN SURVIVAL GEAR, INC.
527 McGregor Ct, Boise, ID 83705
Web Site:
http://www.wholesalesurvival.com
Year Founded: 2005
Sales Range: $1-9.9 Million
Emp.: 15
Emergency Preparedness Products
N.A.I.C.S.: 424210

Daniel Kunz (Pres)

GUARDIANLINK
2631 McCormick Dr Ste 103, Clearwater, FL 33759
Tel.: (800) 258-5123   WY
Year Founded: 2012
Personal Emergency Response Systems Subscription Services
N.A.I.C.S.: 561621
Mark Kelly (Pres)

GUARDIAR USA LLC
3309 S Kaufman Str, Ennis, TX
75119
Tel.: (972) 878-7000
Web Site: https://www.guardiar.com
Security Product Mfr & Distr
N.A.I.C.S.: 334290

GUENTHER-VORRUCKEN INC.
4915 S Tamiami Trl, Sarasota, FL
34231
Tel.: (941) 925-2673
Sales Range: $10-24.9 Million
Emp.: 30
Radio, Television & Electronic Stores
N.A.I.C.S.: 449210
Andrew Guenther (Pres)

GUERNSEY OFFICE PRODUCTS INC.
45070 Old Ox Rd Ste 100, Dallas, VA
20166-2343
Tel.: (703) 968-8200
Web Site:
http://www.guernseyop.com
Sales Range: $25-49.9 Million
Emp.: 140
Office Supplies Distr
N.A.I.C.S.: 459410
David M. Guernsey (Pres & CEO)

GUESS MOTORS, INC.
457 Steubenville Rd, Carrollton, OH
44615
Tel.: (330) 627-2146   OH
Web Site: http://www.guess-motors.com
Year Founded: 1965
Sales Range: $10-24.9 Million
Holding Company; New & Used Car Dealerships Owner & Operator
N.A.I.C.S.: 551112
Michael Guess (Owner & Pres)
Chris Eick (Office Mgr)

Subsidiaries:

Guess Ford, Inc.   (1)
457 Steubenville Rd SE, Carrollton, OH
44615
Tel.: (330) 627-2146
Web Site: http://www.buyguess.com
Sales Range: $10-24.9 Million
Emp.: 33
New & Used Car Dealer
N.A.I.C.S.: 441110
Scott Power (Mgr-Sls)
Chris Eick (Office Mgr)
Dustin Shockey (Mgr-Fin)
Mason Shreve (Mgr-Parts)
Eric Best (Mgr-Used Cars)
Mike Guess (Pres)

GUEST SERVICES, INC.
3055 Prosperity Ave, Fairfax, VA
22031
Tel.: (703) 849-9300   DC
Web Site:
http://www.guestservices.com
Year Founded: 1917
Sales Range: $200-249.9 Million
Emp.: 3,500
Lodging, Retail Food Services, Restaurants & Recreation Facilities Operator
N.A.I.C.S.: 721110
Gerard T. Gabrys (Chm)
Ken Lopez (Sr Mgr-New Bus Dev)

Scott Shepherd *(Chief Comml Officer & VP)*
Nico J. Foris *(Pres & CEO)*

Subsidiaries:

Guest Services Company of
Virginia **(1)**
3055 Prosperity Ave, Fairfax, VA
22031-2216 **(100%)**
Tel.: (703) 849-9300
Web Site: http://www.guestservices.com
Sales Range: $10-24.9 Million
Emp.: 75
Provider of Hospitality Services
N.A.I.C.S.: 722514
Gerald T. Gabrys *(CEO)*
Jeffery A. Marquis *(Pres & COO)*
Scott Shepherd *(Chief Comml Officer & VP)*
Rick Wayland *(VP-Ops Div)*

GUGGENHEIM BASEBALL MANAGEMENT, L.P.

1000 Elysian Park Ave, Los Angeles,
CA 90012-1199
Tel.: (323) 224-1500 **DE**
Year Founded: 2012
Investment Holding Company
N.A.I.C.S.: 551112
Mark R. Walter *(Mng Partner)*
Stan Kasten *(Partner)*
Earvin Johnson *(Partner)*
Peter Guber *(Partner)*
Todd Boehly *(Partner)*
Robert Patton Jr. *(Partner)*

Subsidiaries:

Los Angeles Dodgers LLC **(1)**
1000 Elysian Park Ave, Los Angeles, CA
90012-1199 **(100%)**
Tel.: (323) 224-1500
Web Site:
   http://losangeles.dodgers.mlb.com
Sales Range: $75-99.9 Million
Emp.: 1,200
Professional Baseball Club
N.A.I.C.S.: 711211
Mark R. Walter *(Chm)*
Stan Kasten *(Pres & CEO)*
Sam Fernandez *(Gen Counsel & Sr VP)*
Bill Hunter *(VP-Ticket Ops)*
Leonor Romero *(Coord-Payroll)*
Ellen Harrigan *(Dir-Baseball Admin)*
Tom Darin *(Dir-Brdcst Engrg)*
Joe Jareck *(Dir-PR)*
Jennifer Harris *(Sr Mgr-Payroll)*
David Siegel *(VP-Ticket Sls)*
Seth Bluman *(VP-Ticket Dev)*
Jenny Oh *(Sr Dir-Partnership Admin)*
Michael Young *(Sr VP-Corp Partnerships)*
Jon Weisman *(Dir-Digital & Print Content)*
Eric Hernandez *(VP-Fin)*
Earvin Johnson *(Partner)*
Peter Guber *(Partner)*
Todd Boehly *(Partner)*
Bob Wolfe *(Exec VP)*
Janet Marie Smith *(Sr VP-Plng & Dev)*
Steve Ethier *(Sr VP-Stadium Ops)*
Andrew Friedman *(Gen Mgr)*
Josh Byrnes *(Sr VP-Baseball Ops)*
Scott Akasaki *(Dir-Team Travel)*
Doug Fearing *(Dir-R&D)*
Andrew MacPhail *(Coord-Player Dev)*
Mitch Poole *(Mgr-Dodger Clubhouse)*
Alex Tamin *(Dir-Baseball Ops)*
Greg Taylor *(Dir-Production)*
Jerry Turner *(Mgr-Visiting Clubhouse)*
Ross Yoshida *(Dir-Graphic Design)*
Jeremy Zoll *(Sr VP-Player Dev)*
Brandon Gomes *(Dir-Player Dev)*
Ron Porterfield *(Dir-Player Health-Spring Training Facility)*
Jeff Kingston *(Asst Gen Mgr)*
Robert Patton Jr. *(Partner)*

GUGGENHEIM PARTNERS, LLC

227 W Monroe, Chicago, IL 60606
Tel.: (312) 827-0100 **DE**
Web Site:
   http://www.guggenheimpartners.com
Holding Company; Securities Trading,
Investment Advisory & Asset Management Services

N.A.I.C.S.: 551112
Mark R. Walter *(CEO)*
Michael Guss *(Mng Dir & Head-Alternative Investment Acctg)*
James Howley *(Mng Dir)*
Alan D. Schwartz *(Exec Chm)*
B. Scott Minerd *(Mng Partner)*
Gerald Donini *(COO)*
Thomas J. Irvin *(Mng Partner)*
Andrew M. Rosenfield *(Pres)*
Peter Mahn *(Mgr)*
Mark Van Lith *(CEO-Guggenheim Securities & Head-Investment Banking)*
Stefano Natella *(Head-Equities-Guggenheim Securities)*
Stephen D. Sautel *(Co-Founder-credit investing bus)*
Yatin Suneja *(Mng Dir-Guggenheim Securities)*
Robert S. Khuzami *(Mng Partner & Chief Legal Officer)*
Scott Green *(Sr Mng Dir-IT Svcs & Solutions & Outsourced Svcs Sectors)*
David Levin *(Sr Mng Dir-Equity Capital Markets-Guggenheim Securities)*
Michael Amez *(Sr Mng Dir-Guggenheim Securities)*
Peter O. Lawson-Johnston II *(Mng Partner)*

Subsidiaries:

API Heat Transfer, Inc. **(1)**
2777 Walden Ave, Buffalo, NY 14225-4748
Tel.: (716) 684-6700
Web Site: http://www.apiheattransfer.com
Sales Range: $75-99.9 Million
Emp.: 1,600
Industrial Heat Exchangers & Heat Transfer Systems
N.A.I.C.S.: 332410
Michael Sanders *(Pres-Shell & Tube Grp)*
Jeff Lennox *(VP-Fin & Admin)*
David Rice *(Dir-Global Supply Chain)*
Jill Kelly *(VP-HR)*
Arif Khan *(Dir-Product Dev)*
Ed Smouse *(VP-Mfg)*
Brett Border *(Chief Mfg Officer)*
John Malone *(VP-Mktg)*
Friedrich Schenker *(Mng Dir-Plate & Thermal Sys Grp)*
Guo Wei *(Mng Dir-China & Asia-Pacific)*
Stephen Rennie *(Pres & CEO)*
Steve Delaney *(Chm)*

Backstage LLC **(1)**
770 Broadway 7th Fl, New York, NY 10003
Tel.: (212) 493-4420
Web Site: http://www.backstage.com
Sales Range: $10-24.9 Million
Emp.: 70
Periodical Publishers
N.A.I.C.S.: 513120
Sherry Eaker *(Editor-in-Chief)*
Joshua Ellstein *(Pres & COO)*
Jim Jazwiecki *(CTO)*
Michael Felman *(CFO)*
David Grossman *(VP & Dir-Digital)*
Luke Crowe *(VP)*
Jessica Balaschak *(Dir-Design)*
Richard Burridge *(Mgr-Customer Svc)*
Kasey Howe *(Dir-Integrated Mktg)*
Tom Lapke *(Dir-Education & Events)*
Jeff Lilley *(VP-Engrg)*
Peter Rappaport *(CEO)*
James G. Reynolds *(VP-Engrg)*
Margaret Ruling *(Dir-Art)*
Gerry Sankner *(Sr Mgr-Bus Dev)*
Mark Stinson *(Mgr-Production)*

Subsidiary (Domestic):

Sonicbids Corporation **(2)**
500 Harrison Ave Fl 4 Ste 404R, Boston, MA 02118
Tel.: (617) 502-1300
Web Site: http://www.sonicbids.com
Sales Range: $1-9.9 Million
Emp.: 40
Live Entertainment Promotion & Networking Solutions
N.A.I.C.S.: 711320
Panos Panay *(Founder)*

Guggenheim Credit Income
Fund **(1)**
330 Madison Ave, New York, NY 10017
Tel.: (212) 739-0700
Web Site:
   https://www.guggenheiminvestments.com
Rev.: $8,958,000
Assets: $62,145,000
Liabilities: $872,000
Net Worth: $61,273,000
Earnings: $5,147,000
Emp.: 75
Fiscal Year-end: 12/31/2022
Closed-End Investment Fund
N.A.I.C.S.: 525990
James Howley *(CFO & Treas)*
Matthew S. Bloom *(CEO)*
John V. Palmer *(Pres)*
Brian E. Binder *(Sr VP)*
Amy J. Lee *(Chief Legal Officer & Sec)*
Joanna M. Catalucci *(Chief Compliance Officer)*

Guggenheim Life and Annuity
Company **(1)**
401 N Pennsylvania St Ste 200, Indianapolis, IN 46280
Tel.: (317) 574-6213
Web Site: http://www.guggenheimlife.com
Emp.: 150
Life Insurance
N.A.I.C.S.: 524113
Jim Pervis *(COO)*
Daniel Towriss *(Chief Operating Actuary)*

Millstein & Co., L.P. **(1)**
555 Madison Ave, New York, NY 10022
Tel.: (212) 416-5800
Web Site: http://www.millsteinandco.com
Corporate Consulting & Capital Investment Services
N.A.I.C.S.: 541611
Jim Millstein *(Founder & CEO)*
Mark Walker *(Mng Dir & Head-Sovereign Advisory)*
Jane Vris *(Mng Dir & Gen Counsel)*
Jim Wigand *(Mng Dir)*
Elizabeth Abrams *(Mng Dir)*
Brendan Hayes *(Mng Dir)*
Alice Chong *(VP)*
Jill Dauchy *(Mng Dir)*
Adam Preiss *(Mng Dir)*
Ashley Winston *(Mng Dir)*

Subsidiary (Domestic):

Mill Point Capital LLC **(2)**
104 W 40th St 5th Fl, New York, NY 10018
Tel.: (212) 416-5800
Web Site: http://www.millpoint.com
Privater Equity Firm
N.A.I.C.S.: 523999
Carl E. Vogel *(Exec Partner)*
Michael Duran *(Founder & Mng Partner)*
Richard Summers *(VP)*
Dustin Smith *(Partner)*
Timothy Chizak *(CFO)*
Mark Paolano *(VP)*
Jiaeh Kim *(Dir-IR)*

Affiliate (Domestic):

Aero Snow Removal, LLC **(3)**
165 Cantiague Rock Rd, Westbury, NY 11590
Tel.: (516) 944-3100
Web Site: http://www.aerosnow.com
Rev.: $3,100,000
Emp.: 100
Janitorial Services
N.A.I.C.S.: 561720
Ed Pontremoli *(Asst Mgr)*
Peter Dejana *(Founder, Owner & Pres)*

Subsidiary (Domestic):

Outworx Group **(4)**
165 Cantiague Rock Rd, Westbury, NY 11590
Tel.: (516) 266-7504
Cleaning & Waste Management Services
N.A.I.C.S.: 924110
Daryl Hendricks *(CEO)*

Subsidiary (Domestic):

Gold Landscape **(5)**
2454 Glenda Ln, Dallas, TX 75229
Tel.: (972) 241-7663
Web Site: http://www.goldlandscape.com

Sales Range: $1-9.9 Million
Emp.: 12
Landscaping Services
N.A.I.C.S.: 561730
Aaron Goldstein *(Dir)*
Cris Mckinney *(Mgr-Ops)*

Subsidiary (Domestic):

Tovar Snow Professionals, Inc. **(4)**
195 Penny Ave, East Dundee, IL 60118
Tel.: (847) 695-0080
Web Site: http://www.tovarsnow.com
Landscape Maintenance Services
N.A.I.C.S.: 561730
Steve Bednarz *(VP-Ops)*
Jeff Tovar *(Founder & Pres)*
Rick Lenth *(Pres)*

Holding (Domestic):

Anexinet Corp. **(3)**
4 Sentry Pkwy Ste 300, Blue Bell, PA 19422
Tel.: (610) 239-8100
Web Site: http://www.anexinet.com
Sales Range: $50-74.9 Million
Emp.: 200
IT Services
N.A.I.C.S.: 541511
John Kolimago *(Exec VP & Gen Mgr-Cloud Solutions)*
Brad Hokamp *(CEO)*
Al Sporer *(Exec VP-Digital & Analytics Svcs Bus Unit)*
Joti Balani *(VP-Mktg)*
Jeff Brownlow *(CIO & VP-Managed Svcs)*
Tim Malfara *(VP-Hybrid IT & Cloud Svcs)*
Diego F. Calderin *(Pres)*
Michael Cirafesi *(Exec VP & Gen Mgr)*

Subsidiary (Domestic):

ListenLogic, LLC **(4)**
4 Sentry Parkway Suite 300, Blue Bell, PA 19422 **(100%)**
Tel.: (215) 283-6393
Web Site: http://www.listenlogic.com
Emp.: 20
Unstructured Data Analytics, Social Intelligence & Real-Time Risk Sensing to Large Enterprises
N.A.I.C.S.: 513210
Mark Langsfeld *(Pres)*
Brian Atkiss *(VP-Ops)*

Holding (Domestic):

Construction Resources LLC **(3)**
196 Rio Cir, Decatur, GA 30030
Tel.: (404) 378-3132
Web Site:
   http://www.constructionresourcesusa.com
Stone Product Mfr
N.A.I.C.S.: 327991
Mitch Hires *(CFO & Sec)*

Subsidiary (Domestic):

United Materials, Inc. **(4)**
1959 Trade Center Way, Naples, FL 34109
Tel.: (239) 593-6995
Web Site: http://www.umistone.com
Brick, Stone & Related Construction Material Merchant Whslr
N.A.I.C.S.: 423320

Holding (Domestic):

Franklin Madison Group LLC **(3)**
801 Crescent Centre Drive Suite 500, Franklin, TN 37067-6228
Tel.: (800) 265-4407
Web Site: https://franklin-madison.com
Insurance Services
N.A.I.C.S.: 524298
Robert Dudacek *(Pres & CFO)*

Subsidiary (Domestic):

Sequel Response, LLC **(4)**
6870 Washington Ave S Ste 240, Eden Prairie, MN 55344
Tel.: (952) 564-6932
Web Site: http://www.sequelresponse.com
Marketing Research & Public Opinion Polling
N.A.I.C.S.: 541910
James Fussy *(VP-Data & Analytics)*
Chris Hofmann *(VP-Digital Svcs)*
Jay Carroll *(Co-Founder & CEO)*

Guggenheim Partners, LLC—(Continued)

Holding (Domestic):

Full Circle Fiber Partners, Inc. (3)
8600 Park Meadows Dr Ste 800, Lone Tree, CO 80124
Tel.: (720) 344-5577
Privater Equity Firm
N.A.I.C.S.: 523940
Carl E. Vogel (Exec Chm)
Wayne Davis (CEO)

Holding (Domestic):

Reel Telecommunication Services, LLC (4)
3232B SE Dixie Hwy, Stuart, FL 34997
Tel.: (772) 781-0003
Web Site: http://www.reeltele.com
Sales Range: $1-9.9 Million
Emp.: 21
Power & Communication Line & Related Structures Construction
N.A.I.C.S.: 237130
Donna L. Smith (Pres & Co-Founder)

Holding (Domestic):

GlacierPoint Enterprises, Inc. (3)
701 Zerega Avenue, Bronx, NY 10473
Tel.: (732) 225-1314
Web Site: https://glacierpointenterprises.com
Food & Beverage Distr
N.A.I.C.S.: 445298

Subsidiary (Domestic):

Joe & Ross Inc. (4)
7451 W 100th Place, Bridgeview, IL 60455
Tel.: (708) 656-6869
Web Site: https://www.joeandrossicecream.com
Dairy Product Merchant Whslr
N.A.I.C.S.: 424430
Gary Purpura (Pres)

Southern Ice Cream, Corp. (4)
13755 Greenland Dr, Stafford, TX 77477
Tel.: (281) 499-9837
Web Site: http://www.southernicecreamtx.com
Sales Range: $1-9.9 Million
Emp.: 9
Dairy Product Whslr
N.A.I.C.S.: 424430
Michael Johnston (Pres)
Sharon Johnston (CFO)

Holding (Domestic):

Government Revenue Solutions, LLC (3)
7625 N Palm Ave Ste 108, Fresno, CA 93711
Tel.: (559) 271-6800
Web Site: http://www.pragovernment.com
Holding Company; Government Revenue Enhancement, Technology & Consulting Services
N.A.I.C.S.: 551112
Craig Adler (Chm & CEO)

Subsidiary (Domestic):

MuniServices, LLC (4)
7625 N Palm Ave Ste 108, Fresno, CA 93711
Tel.: (559) 271-6800
Web Site: http://www.muniservices.com
Government Revenue Enhancement Services
N.A.I.C.S.: 541219
George Keels (Mgr-Client Svcs)

Division (Domestic):

Broussard Partners & Associates (5)
12301 Kurland Dr Ste 150, Houston, TX 77034
Tel.: (281) 335-8100
Web Site: http://www.broussardpa.com
Government Revenue Administration Support Services
N.A.I.C.S.: 541219
Lisa Broussard (VP-Ops)

Revenue Discovery Systems (5)
600 Beacon Pkwy W Ste 900, Birmingham, AL 35209

Tel.: (205) 532-0088
Web Site: http://www.revds.com
Emp.: 230
Government Revenue Enhancement Services
N.A.I.C.S.: 541219
Kennon Walthall (Grp COO & Sr VP-Ops)
Ashley Hancock (Acct Mgr)

Subsidiary (Domestic):

Ram Ware, LLC (4)
8282 Goodwood Blvd Ste W-1, Baton Rouge, LA 70806
Tel.: (225) 215-0100
Web Site: http://www.egovsystems.com
Sales Range: $10-24.9 Million
Government Electronic Filing & Collections Software Development & Consulting Services
N.A.I.C.S.: 513210
Rick Mekdessie (Founder, Pres & CEO)

Subsidiary (Domestic):

Antares Technology Solutions, Inc. (5)
8282 Goodwood Blvd Ste W-1, Baton Rouge, LA 70806
Tel.: (225) 922-7748
Web Site: http://www.antaresnet.com
Emp.: 45
Technology, Consulting & Custom Software Solutions Services
N.A.I.C.S.: 541512
Ralph S. Melian (Pres & CEO)
Laura P. Thomas (VP-Sls & Mktg)

Holding (Domestic):

Knight Enterprises, Inc. (3)
6056 Ulmerton Rd, Clearwater, FL 33760
Tel.: (727) 524-6235
Web Site: http://www.knight-enterprises.com
Sales Range: $10-24.9 Million
Emp.: 100
Communication Line & Transmission Tower Construction Services
N.A.I.C.S.: 237130
Donna Bentley (VP-Acctg & HR)
Jason Welz (CEO)
Charles Kwasnecki (VP-Ops)

Metal Powder Products, LLC (3)
14670 Cumberland Rd, Noblesville, IN 46060
Tel.: (317) 805-3764
Web Site: http://www.mppinnovation.com
Powder Metallurgy Product Mfr
N.A.I.C.S.: 332117
Dennis McKeen (CEO)
Steven Kahn (Dir-Pur)
Chuck Spears (Chm)
Tom Lunsford (CFO)

Plant (Domestic):

Metal Powder Products - Ford Road Division (4)
150 Ford Rd, Saint Marys, PA 15857-2931
Tel.: (814) 834-2886
Web Site: http://www.metalpowderproducts.com
Sales Range: $25-49.9 Million
Emp.: 80
Powder Metallurgy Product Mfr
N.A.I.C.S.: 332117

Subsidiary (Domestic):

NetShape Technologies, Inc. (4)
14670 Cumberland Rd, Noblesville, IN 46060
Tel.: (812) 248-9273
Web Site: http://www.mppinnovation.com
Powder Metallurgy & Metal Injection Molding Engineered Components Designer & Mfr
N.A.I.C.S.: 332117

Holding (Domestic):

Noble Broadband LLC (3)
2212 Lynnbrook Dr, Austin, TX 78748-2131
Tel.: (512) 291-9563
Web Site: http://www.noblerc.com
Administrative Management & General Management Consulting Services
N.A.I.C.S.: 541611
David Austin (Mgr)

Subsidiary (Domestic):

Nursery Supplies Inc. (3)
1415 Orchard Dr, Chambersburg, PA 17201
Tel.: (717) 263-7780
Web Site: http://www.nurserysupplies.com
Rev.: $41,100,000
Emp.: 125
Flower Pots, Plastics
N.A.I.C.S.: 326199
Robert Summers (VP-Sls)

Pioneer Custom Electrical Products Corp. (3)
10640 Springdale Ave, Santa Fe Springs, CA 90670
Tel.: (562) 944-0626
Web Site: http://www.pioneercep.com
Electric Equipment Mfr
N.A.I.C.S.: 423610
Kytchener Whyte (Pres)
Randy Schaal (Mgr-Production & Ops)
Lani Basa (Controller)
Jose Fidel Avitia (Mgr-Engrg)

Smart Source, LLC (3)
3813 Illinois Ave, Saint Charles, IL 60174
Tel.: (630) 818-1045
Web Site: http://www.smartsource-inc.com
Sales Range: $10-24.9 Million
Emp.: 30
Technical Staffing Services
N.A.I.C.S.: 561320
Joseph Iovinelli (CEO)
Tony Iovinelli (Pres)

Holding (Domestic):

United Road Towing, Inc. (3)
9550 Bormet Dr, Mokena, IL 60448
Tel.: (708) 390-2200
Web Site: http://www.unitedroadtowing.com
Motor Vehicle Towing
N.A.I.C.S.: 488410
Michael Mahar (CFO)

Subsidiary (Non-US):

Pioneer Transformers Ltd. (3)
612 Bernard Road, Granby, J2J 0H6, QC, Canada
Tel.: (450) 378-9018
Web Site: http://www.pioneertransformers.com
Liquid Filled Transformer Mfr
N.A.I.C.S.: 334416
Nathan J. Mazurek (Chm, Pres, CEO & VP-Sls & Mktg)

Subsidiary (US):

Jefferson Electric Inc. (3)
9650 S Franklin Dr, Franklin, WI 53132
Tel.: (414) 209-1620
Web Site: http://www.jeffersonelectric.com
Sales Range: $10-24.9 Million
Emp.: 35
Power & Distribution Transformers
N.A.I.C.S.: 335311

Security Benefit Corporation (1)
1 Security Benefit Pl, Topeka, KS 66636-0001
Tel.: (785) 438-3000
Web Site: http://www.securitybenefit.com
Rev.: $30,000,000,000
Emp.: 780
Retirement Planning, Insurance & Investment Services
N.A.I.C.S.: 523940
Albert J. Dal Porto (VP-Product Dev)
Michael Dolaher (Dir-Fin Institutions)
Mike Maghini (Sr VP & Head-Natl Accounts)
Michael Castino (Dir-PR)
Brianne Johnson (Mgr-Natl Accounts-Independent Broker Dealers)

Subsidiary (Domestic):

Se2 Inc. (2)
5801 SW 6th Ave, Topeka, KS 66636
Tel.: (785) 438-3000
Web Site: http://www.se2.com
Insurance & Financial Processing Systems Developer
N.A.I.C.S.: 561499
Tom Spencer (Sr VP-Bus Dev)
Vinod Kachroo (CIO)
Ashish Jain (CMO)
Kevin Paulson (COO)
Michele Trogni (Chm)
Mark Schultis (CEO)

Security Benefit Life Insurance Company (2)
1 Security Benefit Pl, Topeka, KS 66636-0001
Tel.: (785) 438-3000
Web Site: http://www.securitybenefit.com
Life Insurance
N.A.I.C.S.: 524113

Security Investors, LLC (1)
227 W Monroe St, Chicago, IL 60606
Tel.: (312) 827-0100
Web Site: http://www.guggenheiminvestments.com
Rev.: $202,000,000,000
Asset Management & Investment Advisory Services
N.A.I.C.S.: 523940
William Belden (Mng Dir & Head-Bus Dev-ETF)
Jerry W. Miller (Pres)
Brian E. Binder (Sr Mng Dir & Chief Admin Officer)
Scott Minerd (Chm)

Subsidiary (Domestic):

Guggenheim Funds Distributors, LLC (2)
805 King Farm Blvd Ste 600, Rockville, MD 20850
Tel.: (301) 296-5100
Web Site: http://www.currencyshares.com
Investment Fund Management Services
N.A.I.C.S.: 523940
Nikolaos Bonos (Mng Dir)
Joseph M. Arruda (Mng Dir-Fin)

Affiliate (Domestic):

Guggenheim Taxable Municipal Bond & Investment Grade Debt Trust (2)
227 W Monroe St, Chicago, IL 60606
Tel.: (312) 827-0100
Closed-End Investment Fund
N.A.I.C.S.: 525990
Ronald E. Toupin Jr. (Chm)

Sun Life Assurance Company of Canada - U.S. Operations Holdings, Inc. (1)
1 Sun Life Executive Park, Wellesley Hills, MA 02481 (100%)
Tel.: (781) 237-6030
Web Site: http://www.sunlife-usa.com
Life Insurance & Financial Services
N.A.I.C.S.: 524113
Scott M. Davis (Gen Counsel & Sr VP)
Terry Mullen (Sr VP-Distr)
Bob Klein (Sr VP-Multiline & Voluntary Benefits)
Scott Beliveau (Sr VP-Grp & Voluntary Insurance-Sun Life Fin)
David Healy (Sr VP-Ops)
Ed Milano (VP-Mktg)
Andrew Darfoor (Sr VP)
Cathy Liston (VP-Claims, Grp & Voluntary Insurance-Sun Life Fin)

Subsidiary (Domestic):

MFS Investment Management (2)
111 Huntington Ave, Boston, MA 02199-7618 (90%)
Tel.: (617) 954-5000
Web Site: http://www.mfs.com
Sales Range: $1-4.9 Billion
Mutual Fund Annuitie & Services
N.A.I.C.S.: 525910
Michael W. Roberge (CEO)
William J. Adams (Chief Investment Officer-Global Fixed Income)
Pilar Gomez-Bravo (Dir-Fixed Income-Europe)
Megan Poplowski (Dir-Municipal Res)
Joshua Marston (Portfolio Mgr)
Edward M. Maloney (Chief Investment Officer)
Robert J. Manning (Chm)

Subsidiary (Domestic):

MFS Service Center Inc. (3)
30 Dan Rd, Canton, MA 02021-2809 (100%)
Web Site: http://www.mfs.com
Financial Services
N.A.I.C.S.: 523940

Subsidiary (Domestic):

Sun Capital Advisers, LLC (2)
1 Sun Life Executive Park SC 1308,
Wellesley Hills, MA 02481   **(100%)**
Tel.: (781) 446-3330
Sales Range: $350-399.9 Million
Emp.: 1,500
Financial Advisor for Pension Funds & Investment Portfolios
N.A.I.C.S.: 523999
James M.A. Anderson (Pres)

**Sun Life Financial Employee Benefits
Group** (2)
1 Sun Life Executive Park, Wellesley Hills,
MA 02481
Tel.: (860) 737-7400
Sales Range: $700-749.9 Million
Emp.: 650
Accident, Health & Life Insurance
N.A.I.C.S.: 524113
Mark Donaphon (Mgr-Mktg)
Michael Joyce (Exec VP-Sls)

Sun Life Insurance & Annuity Company of New York (2)
60 E 42nd St Ste 1115, New York, NY
10165   **(100%)**
Tel.: (212) 983-6352
Web Site: http://www.sunlife-usa.com
Sales Range: $150-199.9 Million
Emp.: 15
Life Insurance & Financial Services
N.A.I.C.S.: 523150
Scott M. Davis (Gen Counsel & Sr VP)
Michele G. Van Leer (Sr VP & Gen Mgr)
Michael K. Moran (Chief Acctg Officer, VP &
Controller)

GUIDANT FINANCIAL GROUP, INC.
1100 112th Ave NE Ste 100, Bellevue, WA 98004
Tel.: (425) 289-3200   **WA**
Web Site:
    https://www.guidantfinancial.com
Year Founded: 2003
Sales Range: $10-24.9 Million
Emp.: 85
IRA's & Small Business Financing
N.A.I.C.S.: 523940
David Nilssen (Co-Founder & CEO)
Joshua Levell (Coord-Client)
Michelle Flandreau (VP-Mktg)
Devin Miller (Exec VP)
Jeremy Ames (Co-Founder & Pres)
Katie Burckhardt (VP-Sls)

GUIDANT PARTNERS
1410 Donelson Pike Ste B5, Nashville, TN 37217
Tel.: (615) 327-9111
Web Site:
    http://www.guidantpartners.com
Sales Range: $1-9.9 Million
Emp.: 26
Information Technology Services
N.A.I.C.S.: 423430
Steve Burgess (Founder & CEO)
Mike Neyman (VP-Strategic Plng)
Karen Nixon (VP-Ops)
Wade Givens (Dir-Solutions Advisors)
Michelle Burgess (Co-Founder &
Pres)

GUIDED DISCOVERIES INC.
232 W Harrison Ave, Claremont, CA
91711
Tel.: (909) 625-6194
Web Site:
    http://www.guideddiscoveries.org
Rev.: $10,020,653
Emp.: 200
Scuba, Sailing, Astronomy & Marine
Biology Educational Camps
N.A.I.C.S.: 721214
Jeff Chace (Program Dir)
Matt Mishalow (Dir-Summer Camp)

GUIDEONE INSURANCE COMPANY
1111 Ashworth Rd, West Des Moines,
IA 50265-3544
Tel.: (515) 267-5000   **IA**
Web Site: http://www.guideone.com
Year Founded: 1947
Sales Range: $650-699.9 Million
Emp.: 700
Property & Casualty Coverage Insurance
N.A.I.C.S.: 524298
Brian J. Hughes (Sr VP-Investments)
Dave Sours (VP-Claims)
Bernard Hengesbaugh (CEO)
Mike Faley (VP-HR & Organizational
Dev)
Joe Highbarger (VP)
Philip Cole (Chief Underwriting Officer & Sr VP)
Mark Groenheide (Sr VP-Specialty)
Christy Gooding (Dir-Mktg)
Ken Cademajori (CFO & Sr VP)
Andy Noga (Gen Counsel)

GUIDEPOST GROWTH MANAGEMENT COMPANY LLC
The Prudential Tower 800 Boylston St
Ste 1310, Boston, MA 02199
Tel.: (617) 807-8800
Web Site: http://guidepostgrowth.com
Year Founded: 2007
Privater Equity Firm
N.A.I.C.S.: 523999
Chris Cavanagh (Gen Partner)

GUIDEPOSTS ASSOCIATES, INC.
39 Seminary Hill Rd, Carmel, NY
10512-1990
Tel.: (845) 225-3681   **NY**
Web Site: http://www.guideposts.org
Year Founded: 1944
Sales Range: $150-199.9 Million
Emp.: 450
Publisher of Periodicals, Magazines &
Books
N.A.I.C.S.: 513120
Richard V. Hopple (Pres & CEO)
Philip Charles-Pierre (VP-Digital
Media)

GUIDESPARK, INC.
1350 Willow Rd Ste 201, Menlo Park,
CA 94025
Web Site: http://www.guidespark.com
Year Founded: 2008
Sales Range: $10-24.9 Million
Emp.: 174
Employee Communications & Engagement Software Publisher
N.A.I.C.S.: 513210
Joseph A. Larocque (Dir-Product
Mgmt)
Will Johnson (VP-Corp Dev & Strategy)
Keith Kitani (CEO)
Bob Benedict (CTO)
Shep Maher (Sr VP-Sls)
Linda Itskovitz (VP-Mktg)
Christopher Krook (CFO)
Stephanie Copeland Weber (VP-Ops)
Theresa Strickland (VP-People & Culture)
Dharam Rai (VP-Content Svcs)
Larry McAlister (VP-Talent-Global)

GUIDESTAR DIRECT CORP.
15510 Rockfield Blvd Ste A, Irvine,
CA 92618
Tel.: (949) 581-5100
Web Site:
    http://www.carneydirect.com
Year Founded: 1991
Sales Range: $1-9.9 Million
Emp.: 15

Direct Marketing Services
N.A.I.C.S.: 541860
Peter Carney (Pres & CEO)
Jennifer Le (Mgr-List)

GUIDESTAR USA, INC.
4801 Courthouse St Ste 220, Williamsburg, VA 23188
Tel.: (757) 229-4631
Web Site: http://www.guidestar.org
Year Founded: 1994
Sales Range: $10-24.9 Million
Emp.: 47
Information & Database Services on
Non-Profit Organizations
N.A.I.C.S.: 513140
James Dobrzeniecki (VP-IT)
Chuck McLean (VP-Res)
Debra Snider (VP-Ops)
Tom C. Tinsley (Treas)
Jacob Harold (Pres & CEO)
James Lum (CFO)
Charles Best (Sec)
Lindsay J. K. Nichols (Sr Dir-Mktg &
Comm)
Evan Paul (VP-Products)

GUIDEWELL MUTUAL HOLDING CORPORATION
4800 Deerwood Campus Pkwy DC 4
1, Jacksonville, FL 32246
Tel.: (904) 436-4201
Web Site: http://www.guidewell.com
Holding Company
N.A.I.C.S.: 551112
Patrick Geraghty (Pres & CEO)
Chuck Divita (Exec VP-Comml Markets)
Charlie Joseph (Chief Legal Officer &
Exec VP-Corp Affairs)
Gary Aderson (CIO & Sr VP)
John B. Ramil (Chm)

Subsidiaries:

**Blue Cross & Blue Shield of Florida,
Inc.** (1)
4800 Deerwood Campus Pkwy DC3-4,
Jacksonville, FL 32246
Web Site: http://www.floridablue.com
Health Insurance Services
N.A.I.C.S.: 524114
Beth Stambaugh (Sr Commun Consultant)
Susan B. Towler (VP & Exec Dir-Corp Responsibility)
Patrick J. Geraghty (CEO)
Camille Harrison (Chm)
Cynthia Griffin (Sec)
Kim Read (Treas)
Tim Cromwell (Dir-Fin & Ops)
Ryan Graff (Sr Mgr-Program)
Velma Monteiro-Tribble (Dir-Grants & Programs)

Joint Venture (Domestic):

Availity, LLC (2)
5555 Gate Pkwy Ste 110, Jacksonville, FL
32256
Tel.: (904) 470-4900
Web Site: https://www.availity.com
Sales Range: $10-24.9 Million
Emp.: 32
Health Information Services
N.A.I.C.S.: 519290
Julie D. Klapstein (Founder)
Russ Thomas (CEO)
Nathan von Colditz (Chief Strategy Officer)
Frank Petito (CFO)
Frank Manzella (Sr VP)
Bobbi Coluni (Chief Product Officer)
Leslie Antunes (Chief Growth Officer)
Jim McNary (COO)

Subsidiary (Domestic):

Capital Health Plan, Inc. (2)
PO Box 15349, Tallahassee, FL 32317
Tel.: (850) 383-3333
Web Site: http://www.capitalhealth.com
Rev.: $640,216,000
Assets: $450,666,000
Liabilities: $84,726,000

Net Worth: $365,940,000
Earnings: $13,762,000
Emp.: 400
Fiscal Year-end: 12/31/2013
Health Care Insurance Carrier
N.A.I.C.S.: 524114
Nancy Van Vessem (Chief Medical Officer)
Ken Boutwell (Chm)
Kristie Whitmore (Dir-Claims Ops)
Polly White (Sr VP-Mktg & Admin Svcs)
Tom Glennon (Sr VP-Bus & Community
Dev)

Diagnostic Clinic (2)
1301 2nd Ave SW, Largo, FL 33770
Tel.: (727) 584-7706
Web Site: http://www.dc-fl.com
Sales Range: $10-24.9 Million
Emp.: 100
Health Clinic
N.A.I.C.S.: 621111
Kathy Cates (Sec-Lab)
Charlie Campbell (CEO)
James F. Rivenbark III (COO & Chief Medical Officer)

Diversified Service Options Inc. (2)
532 Riverside Ave, Jacksonville, FL 32202
Tel.: (904) 791-6111
Web Site: http://www.dsocorp.com
Sales Range: $10-24.9 Million
Emp.: 20
Administrative Services for the Government
Sponsored Healthcare Market
N.A.I.C.S.: 923120

Subsidiary (Domestic):

First Coast Service Options Inc. (3)
532 Riverside Ave, Jacksonville, FL 32202
Tel.: (904) 791-8000
Web Site: http://www.fcso.com
Administration of Government Healthcare
Programs
N.A.I.C.S.: 923120
Sandra Coston (CEO)

Novitas Solutions Inc. (3)
532 Riverside Ave, Jacksonville, FL 32202
Tel.: (904) 791-8000
Web Site: http://www.novitas-solutions.com
Sales Range: $10-24.9 Million
Emp.: 15
Administration of Government Healthcare
Programs
N.A.I.C.S.: 923120

Affiliate (Domestic):

**Florida Combined Life Insurance
Company Inc.** (2)
4800 Deerwood Campus Pkwy Bldg 200
Ste 600, Jacksonville, FL 32246
Tel.: (904) 828-7800
Life Insurance
N.A.I.C.S.: 524113

Subsidiary (Domestic):

Florida Health Care Plan, Inc. (2)
1340 Ridgewood Ave, Holly Hill, FL 32117
Tel.: (386) 676-7100
Web Site: http://www.fhcp.com
Sales Range: $100-124.9 Million
Emp.: 800
HMO
N.A.I.C.S.: 524114
Wendy Myers (Pres & CEO)
David C. Schandel (Assoc CEO, CFO,
Treas & Sec)
Joseph Zuckerman (Chief Medical Officer)
Robert Gilliland (Officer-Compliance)
Tim Moylan (CIO & Chief Security Officer)
Shannon Osland (Dir-HR)
Pamela Thomas (Gen Counsel)

Affiliate (Domestic):

Florida True Health Inc. (2)
PO Box 30729, Palm Beach, FL 33420
Web Site: http://www.fltrueblue.com
Health Insurance Services
N.A.I.C.S.: 524114

Subsidiary (Domestic):

GuideWell Inc. (2)
4800 Deerwood Campus Pkwy DC 4-1,
Jacksonville, FL 32246
Tel.: (904) 791-6111
Web Site: http://www.guidewellconnect.com

GuideWell Mutual Holding
Corporation—(Continued)

Sales Range: $10-24.9 Million
Emp.: 20
Healthy Lifestyle Products & Services
N.A.I.C.S.: 456199
Jannifer Drake Harper (Chief Medical Officer)
Rene Lerer (Pres)

Affiliate (Domestic):

**Health Intelligence Company
LLC**   (2)
225 N Michigan Ave 9th Fl, Chicago, IL
60601
Tel.: (312) 540-5151
Web Site:
  http://www.bluehealthintelligence.com
Emp.: 50
Healthcare Database of Integrated Medical
& Pharmacy Claims
N.A.I.C.S.: 423430
Swati B. Abbott (Pres & CEO)
David King (VP-Info Tech)
Mary Henderson (Sr VP)

Subsidiary (Domestic):

Health Options, Inc.   (2)
4800 Deerwood Campus Pkwy, Jacksonville, FL 32246   (100%)
Tel.: (904) 791-6111
Web Site: http://www.bcbsfl.com
Emp.: 600
Individual, Family, Group & Medicare Health
Insurance Services
N.A.I.C.S.: 524114
Javelyn Arvay (Dir-Mktg)

Incepture Inc.   (2)
5011 Gate Parkway Bldg 100 Ste 100,
Jacksonville, FL 32256-8288
Web Site: http://www.incepture.com
Sales Range: $1-9.9 Million
Emp.: 75
Staffing & Managed Solutions
N.A.I.C.S.: 561311

Navigy Inc.   (2)
4800 Deerwood Campus Pkwy, Jacksonville, FL 32246
Tel.: (904) 791-6111
Sales Range: $10-24.9 Million
Emp.: 15
Web Centric Solutions
N.A.I.C.S.: 541519

Affiliate (Domestic):

Prestige Health Choice LLC   (2)
11631 Kew Gardens Ave Ste 200, Palm
Beach Gardens, FL 33410
Web Site:
  http://www.prestigehealthchoice.com
Affordable, Community Based Healthcare
N.A.I.C.S.: 621111
Sandra Schwemmer (Chief Medical Officer)
Dwight D. Chenette (Pres)

Prime Therapeutics, LLC   (2)
1305 Corporate Ctr Dr, Eagan, MN 55121
Tel.: (612) 777-4000
Web Site: http://www.primetherapeutics.com
Sales Range: $550-599.9 Million
Emp.: 2,400
Pharmacy Benefit Management Services
N.A.I.C.S.: 541611
Michael Showalter (CMO)
Jacqueline Chase (Sr VP-HR)
Cameron Olig (Sr VP-Comml Markets &
Sls)
Aaron Rodriguez (Sec)
Andrew C. Corbin (CFO)
Ann Tobin (Chief Compliance Officer)
Scott Fries (COO & Sr VP-Govt Programs)
Ellyn Hosch (CIO)
Maurice S. Smith (Chm)
Jonathan B. Gavras (Chief Medical Officer)
Christopher Vojta (Sr VP-Pharmacy & Network Svcs)
K. Alec Mahmood (CFO)
Georgia Eddleman Little (Chief Customer
Experience Officer & VP)
Mostafa Kamal (Pres & CEO)
John Drakulich (Chief Sls Officer)
Denise Lecher (Dir-PR)
Michael Kolar (Gen Counsel & Sr VP)
Timothy Vines (Vice Chm)

Sid Sahni (Chief Strategy Officer & Sr VP)
Maurice S. Smith (Chm)
Matt Patella (VP-Natl & Mid-Market Accounts & Gen Mgr-Natl & Mid-Market Accounts)
Dave Schlett (Pres-PBM Solutions & Exec
VP)

TriCenturion Inc.   (2)
7909 Parklane Rd Ste 190, Columbia, SC
29223
Tel.: (803) 264-7700
Web Site: http://www.tricenturion.com
Insurance Fraud & Abuse Investigations
N.A.I.C.S.: 524298

**Worldwide Insurance Services
LLC**   (2)
933 1st Ave, King of Prussia, PA 19406
Tel.: (610) 254-5304
Web Site: http://www.geo-blue.com
International Health Insurance Services
N.A.I.C.S.: 524114
Alan Krigstein (Chm)
Sheldon Kenton (Pres & CEO)
Ron Duld (CFO)
Frank Gillingham (Chief Medical Officer)
Doug Hilton (Chief HR Officer)
Lynn Pina (CMO)
Malcolm Wright (Chief Comml Officer)

**New Directions Behavioral Health
LLC**   (1)
6100 Sprint Pwy Ste 200, Overland Park,
KS 66211
Web Site: http://www.ndbh.com
Behavioral Healthcare Products & Services
N.A.I.C.S.: 621330
Peggy DeCarlis (Chief Innovation Officer &
Sr VP)
Griff Docking (CMO & Sr VP)
Deborah Happ (Sr VP-Clinical Svcs)
Andrea Auxier (Chief Comml Officer & Sr
VP)
Aron Halfin (Chief Medical Officer & Sr VP)
Charles Freed (VP & Dir-Medical-South)
Lyndon Good (VP & Dir-Medical-Central)
Deepak Rajpoot (Dir-Medical)
Diane Bigler (Dir-Performance Solutions)
Nibal Henderson (Dir-Corp Trng)
Timothy Hoffman (CIO)
Robin Jackson (Chief Fin & Admin Officer &
Sr VP)
Ann O'Grady (Chief Clinical Officer & Sr
VP)
Erin Scrapper (Chief Strategy Officer & Sr
VP)
Shana Hoffman (Pres & CEO)
Thurman Justice (Chm)
Lynn Merritt (Chief People Officer)

Subsidiary (Domestic):

E4 Health LLC   (2)
105 Decker Ct Ste 475, Irving, TX 75062
Tel.: (972) 810-3100
Web Site: http://www.e4healthinc.com
Health Care Consulting Services
N.A.I.C.S.: 541690
Ameet Patel (CIO)
Missy Schrib (CFO)
Brian Summers (Pres)
Karen Vincent (Chief Clinical Officer)

**GUIDING EYES FOR THE
BLIND, INC.**
611 Granite Springs Rd, Yorktown
Heights, NY 10598
Tel.: (914) 245-4024   NY
Web Site:
  https://www.guidingeyes.org
Year Founded: 1954
Sales Range: $25-49.9 Million
Emp.: 150
Visually Impaired People Assistance
Services
N.A.I.C.S.: 624120
Karen McClure (Sr Dir-Response
Mktg)
Thomas Panek (Pres & CEO)
Mary J. Conway (Vice Chm)
Wendy Aglietti (Chm)
Ellin Purcell (Dir-Special Needs Programs)
Jane Russenberger (Sr Dir-Genetics
& Breeding)

Linda Press (VP-Dev)
Kathryn Zubrycki (VP-Trng Programs)
James Gardner (Dir-Home Trng Programs)
Gail Resnikoff (Dir-Planned Giving)
Kimberly Benson (Officer-Special Gift)

GUIDO & COMPANIES
8526 Vidor Ave, San Antonio, TX
78216
Tel.: (210) 344-8321
Web Site:
  http://www.guidobrothersconstruction.com
Year Founded: 1927
Rev.: $35,246,661
Emp.: 60
Commercial & Office Building, New
Construction
N.A.I.C.S.: 236220
Cosmo F. Guido (Chm)

GUIDON PARTNERS, LP
5 Kanawha Rd, Richmond, VA 23226
Tel.: (757) 513-0915   VA
Web Site:
  http://www.guidonpartners.com
Privater Equity Firm
N.A.I.C.S.: 523999
Vicky B. Gregg (Co-Founder & Partner)
Greg Roth (Operating Partner)
Gregory W. Scott (Partner & Chief
Investment Officer)
James G. Carlson (Partner)
Timothy F. McDonald (Partner)
Nicholas J. Pace (Partner)

GUILD ASSOCIATES INC.
5750 Shier Rings Rd, Dublin, OH
43016
Tel.: (614) 798-8215
Web Site:
  https://www.guildassociates.com
Rev.: $15,000,000
Emp.: 100
Chemical Machinery & Equipment
N.A.I.C.S.: 333248
Salvatore T. Di Novo (Pres)
Buzz Alvey (Mgr-Quality)
Joe Rossin (Dir-Matls Dev)
Nick DiNovo (VP)
Rod Bishop (Supvr-Matl Acq & Control)
Travis Puchalski (Engr-Test)
Wayne Ballantyne (VP)

GUILDMASTER, INC.
1938 E Phelps, Springfield, MO
65802
Tel.: (417) 879-3326   DE
Web Site:
  http://www.guildmaster.com
Year Founded: 2000
Sales Range: $10-24.9 Million
Emp.: 554
Home Furnishing Whslr
N.A.I.C.S.: 337110
Stephen R. Crowder (CEO)
Margaret Powers (VP-Sls & Mktg)
Karen Kaminsky (VP-Mdsg)
Georgia Ipsen (Controller)

**GUILFORD CHILD DEVELOP-
MENT**
1200 Arlington St, Greensboro, NC
27406
Tel.: (336) 378-7700   NC
Web Site:
  https://www.guilfordchilddev.org
Year Founded: 1967
Sales Range: $10-24.9 Million
Emp.: 428
Child Care & Development Services
N.A.I.C.S.: 624110

Frank Workman (Dir-IT)
C. Robin Britt (Exec Dir)
Patricia Lynch (Dir-HR)
David Garriques (Dir-Fiscal)
Sherry Murr (Dir-Procurement)
Brad Huffstetler (Dir-Dev)
Bonita Sherrod (Treas)

GUILFORD SAVINGS BANK
1 Park St, Guilford, CT 06437
Tel.: (203) 453-2721
Web Site: https://www.gsb-
  yourbank.com
Sales Range: $25-49.9 Million
Emp.: 100
State Commercial Banks
N.A.I.C.S.: 522110

GUIRYS INC.
2121 S Colorado Blvd, Denver, CO
80222
Tel.: (303) 756-7714
Web Site: https://www.guirys.com
Rev.: $13,500,000
Emp.: 7
Artists' Supplies & Materials
N.A.I.C.S.: 459999
Sean Guiry (Owner)

**GUITAR SALON INTERNA-
TIONAL**
1455 19th St, Santa Monica, CA
90404
Tel.: (310) 586-1100
Web Site:
  https://www.guitarsalon.com
Sales Range: $10-24.9 Million
Emp.: 20
Durable Goods Whslr
N.A.I.C.S.: 423990
Tim Miklaucic (Owner & CEO)
David Collett (Pres)
Johnpaul Trotter (Mgr-Sls)

**GUITTARD CHOCOLATE COM-
PANY**
10 Guittard Rd, Burlingame, CA
94010-2203
Tel.: (650) 697-4427
Web Site: https://www.guittard.com
Year Founded: 1868
Sales Range: $50-74.9 Million
Emp.: 200
Chocolate Product Mfr
N.A.I.C.S.: 311351
Gary Guittard (Pres & CEO)
Mark Spini (Dir-Indus Sls)

**GULF BAY GROUP OF COM-
PANIES**
8156 Fiddler's Creek Pkwy, Naples,
FL 34114
Tel.: (239) 732-9400
Web Site: https://www.gulfbay.com
Year Founded: 1986
Sales Range: $10-24.9 Million
Real Estate Development & Management
N.A.I.C.S.: 237210
Aubrey Ferrao (CEO)

GULF BAY HOTELS INC.
3470 Club Ctr Blvd, Naples, FL
34114
Tel.: (239) 732-9400
Web Site: http://www.gulfbay.com
Rev.: $20,600,000
Emp.: 100
Commercial & Institutional Building
Construction
N.A.I.C.S.: 236220
Aubrey Ferrao (Pres & CEO)
Anthnoy Dinardo (CFO)

GULF BREEZE REAL ESTATE
1200 5th Ave S, Naples, FL 34102
Tel.: (239) 213-1620

Web Site:
http://www.gulfbreezenaples.com
Year Founded: 2001
Sales Range: $1-9.9 Million
Emp.: 50
Real Estate Broker
N.A.I.C.S.: 531210
Sue Myhelic *(Owner)*
Kristi Castle *(Owner)*

GULF BUILDING CORP.
633 S Federal Hwy Ste 500, Fort
Lauderdale, FL 33301
Tel.: (954) 492-9191
Web Site:
https://www.gulfbuilding.com
Sales Range: $10-24.9 Million
Emp.: 30
Commercial & Office Building Con-
tractors
N.A.I.C.S.: 236220
John Scherer *(Owner, Pres & CEO)*
Steve Hynds *(Superintendent)*
Shawn Quill *(CFO)*
Giovanna Alessi-Suarez *(VP-Mktg)*
Michael Lanciault *(VP-
Preconstruction)*
Jordana L. Jarjura *(Gen Counsel)*
Eric Squilla *(VP)*
Darrylle Hood Sr. *(Dir-Safety)*

GULF COAST BANK
221 S State St, Abbeville, LA 70510
Tel.: (337) 893-7733
Web Site: http://www.gcbank.com
Year Founded: 1971
Sales Range: $10-24.9 Million
Emp.: 98
State Commercial Banks
N.A.I.C.S.: 522110
Paul Patout *(Pres & CEO)*
Patrick Patout *(Chm)*
Chris Dardeau *(Officer-Loan & VP)*
Jason C. Patout *(VP)*
Angel Willis *(Officer-Loan & Mgr-
Maurice)*
Carey Chopin *(Officer-Loan & Bus
Dev & VP)*
Cathy Roy *(Officer-Loan, VP & Mgr-
Johnston Saint Lafayette)*
Charlene Soirez *(Officer-Loan & Asst
VP)*
Cheryl McManus *(Officer-Loan, Asst
VP & Mgr-West Congress Saint La-
fayette)*
Chris Bourque *(Officer-Loan & VP)*
Christine Juneau *(VP-Security & HR)*
Claire Trahan *(VP)*
Gregrory Harrrington *(Officer-Bus Dev
& VP)*
Heather Dawson *(Officer-Ops & Asst
VP)*
Jan Davis *(Officer-Loan, Asst VP &
Mgr-Delcambre)*
Jodi Bodin *(VP & Auditor)*
Joe Dore *(VP)*
Karen Broussard *(Officer-Customer
Svc)*
Karen Pierre *(Officer-Loan & Mgr-NE
Evangeline Thruway Carencro)*
Sharon Catalon *(Officer-Loan, Asst
VP & Mgr-Ambassador Caffery Pkwy
Lafayette)*
Stacey Perrodin *(Officer-Compliance)*
Tammie Romero *(Officer-Loan, Asst
VP & Mgr-Youngsville)*
Kim Carver *(Sr VP)*
Murphy Guilbeaux Jr. *(Officer-Bus
Dev)*
Ray L. Duagl III *(Officer-Loan, Asst
VP & Mgr-Erath)*

GULF COAST BANK & TRUST
COMPANY
200 St Charles Ave, New Orleans, LA
70130

Tel.: (504) 561-6124
Web Site: https://www.gulfbank.com
Sales Range: $75-99.9 Million
Emp.: 460
Banking Services
N.A.I.C.S.: 522110
Brian Behlar *(VP-Comml Lending)*
Bruce Falkenstein *(Chief Comml
Lending Officer & Exec VP-Veterans)*
Gary Littlefield *(Pres-Market-Baton
Rouge)*
Mickey Spencer *(Sr VP-Comml
Lending-Veterans)*
Rance Mangipano *(VP-Comml
Lending-St. Bernard)*
Sean Warner *(VP-Comml Lending-St.
Bernard)*
Effie Moore *(Sr VP)*
James Jones *(Mgr-Mktg Svcs)*
Jennifer Nugent *(Mgr-Ops)*
Kim Anthony *(VP-Deposit Ops)*
Rene Oubre *(Mgr-Market & Comml
Lending-Manhattan)*
Darlene Creppel *(Asst VP)*

GULF COAST COLLECTION
BUREAU, INC.
5630 Marquesas Cir, Sarasota, FL
34233
Tel.: (941) 927-6999
Web Site:
https://www.gulfcoastcollection.com
Year Founded: 1978
Sales Range: $1-9.9 Million
Emp.: 33
Collection Agency
N.A.I.C.S.: 561440
Jack Brown *(Pres & CEO)*
Marie St. James *(COO)*
Dick Mac Millan *(VP)*
James Aresk Hiles *(Gen Mgr)*

GULF COAST COMMUNITY
SERVICES ASSOCIATION
9320 Kirby Dr, Houston, TX 77054
Tel.: (713) 393-4700   TX
Web Site: https://www.gccsa.org
Year Founded: 1968
Sales Range: $10-24.9 Million
Emp.: 429
Grantmaking Services
N.A.I.C.S.: 813219
Al Maldonado *(Dir-Compliance-
Accountability)*

GULF COAST ELECTRIC CO-
OPERATIVE INC.
9434 Highway 77, Southport, FL
32409
Tel.: (850) 639-2216   FL
Web Site: https://www.gcec.com
Year Founded: 1941
Sales Range: $10-24.9 Million
Emp.: 75
Electric Power Distr
N.A.I.C.S.: 221118

GULF COAST EXPRESS PIPE-
LINE LLC
1001 Louisiana St Ste 1000, Hous-
ton, TX 77002
Tel.: (714) 560-4411   DE
Natural Gas Distribution Services
N.A.I.C.S.: 486210

GULF COAST MARINE SUP-
PLY COMPANY INC.
501 Stimrad Rd, Mobile, AL 36610-
4133
Tel.: (251) 452-8066   AL
Web Site:
http://www.gulfcoastmarine.com
Year Founded: 1935
Sales Range: $25-49.9 Million
Emp.: 300

Industrial Supplies
N.A.I.C.S.: 423840
John T. Mostellar *(Pres)*
Gordon Sanford *(Exec VP)*
Hugh O'Neil *(Comptroller)*

GULF COAST NUTRITIONALS,
INC.
6166 Taylor Rd Ste 103, Naples, FL
34109
Tel.: (239) 592-9388
Web Site: http://www.arknaturals.com
Sales Range: $1-9.9 Million
Emp.: 10
Pet Healthcare Products Mfr
N.A.I.C.S.: 325412
Susan D. Weiss *(Pres)*

GULF COAST OBSTETRICS
AND GYNECOLOGY OF SARA-
SOTA, LLC
1950 Arlington St Ste 203, Sarasota,
FL 32439
Tel.: (941) 379-6331
Web Site:
http://www.gulfcoastobstetrics.com
Year Founded: 1995
Sales Range: $1-9.9 Million
Emp.: 28
Obstetrics & Gynecology Services
N.A.I.C.S.: 621111
Gary Easterling *(Founder & Partner)*
Deanna Doyle *(Partner)*
Richard Jamison *(Partner)*
Kyle Garner *(Partner)*
Tara Wypiszynski *(Bus Mgr & Office
Mgr)*

GULF COAST OFFICE PROD-
UCTS, INC.
5801 River Oaks Rd S, New Orleans,
LA 70123
Tel.: (504) 733-3830
Web Site: https://www.gcopnet.com
Year Founded: 1977
Sales Range: $10-24.9 Million
Emp.: 80
Office Equipment Whslr
N.A.I.C.S.: 423420
Bill Kenny *(Owner)*

GULF COAST PET SUPPLIES,
INC.
4532 McAshton St, Sarasota, FL
34233
Tel.: (941) 921-7546
Web Site:
https://www.gulfcoastpetsup
plies.com
Year Founded: 2007
Sales Range: $1-9.9 Million
Emp.: 4
Online Pet Supplies Retailer
N.A.I.C.S.: 424990
Tricia Bolds *(Founder, Pres & CEO)*

GULF COAST PRE-STRESS,
INC.
494 N Market St, Pass Christian, MS
39571
Tel.: (228) 452-9486
Web Site:
https://www.gcprestress.com
Year Founded: 1967
Sales Range: $25-49.9 Million
Emp.: 150
Precast Prestressed Concrete Com-
ponent Mfr
N.A.I.C.S.: 327390
Peter S. Wareing *(Chm)*
Mike Spruill *(Pres)*

GULF COAST RENAISSANCE
CORPORATION

11975 Seaway Rd Ste A140, Gulf-
port, MS 39503
Tel.: (228) 896-3386   MS
Web Site: http://www.msgcrc.com
Year Founded: 2007
Sales Range: $10-24.9 Million
Emp.: 15
Community Housing Services
N.A.I.C.S.: 624229
Chuck Wall *(CFO)*
Kimberly La Rosa *(Pres & CEO)*

GULF COAST SOCIAL SER-
VICES
2400 Edenborn Ave, Metairie, LA
70001
Tel.: (504) 831-6561   LA
Web Site: http://www.gctfs.org
Year Founded: 1983
Sales Range: $10-24.9 Million
Emp.: 1,282
Community Support Services
N.A.I.C.S.: 624190
Stephen Villavaso *(Chm)*
Helen Siegel *(Treas)*
Rick Hardie *(Pres & CEO)*
Bruce Kuehne *(Vice Chm)*

GULF COAST SUPPLY & MFG.
INC.
14429 SW 2nd Pl Ste G30, New-
berry, FL 32669
Tel.: (352) 498-0778
Web Site:
https://www.gulfcoastsupply.com
Rev.: $15,000,000
Emp.: 100
Roofing, Siding & Insulation Material
Merchant Whslr
N.A.I.C.S.: 423330
John Sherrill *(Pres)*

GULF COAST TRUCK &
EQUIPMENT CO., INC.
2260 Halls Mill Rd, Mobile, AL 36606
Tel.: (251) 476-2744
Web Site:
https://www.gulfcoasttruck.com
Rev.: $60,000,000
Emp.: 60
Trucks; Tractors & Trailers: New &
Used
N.A.I.C.S.: 441110

GULF COAST WATER AU-
THORITY
3630 Hwy 1765, Texas City, TX
77591
Tel.: (409) 935-2438
Web Site:
http://www.gulfcoastwautho
rity.com
Sales Range: $10-24.9 Million
Emp.: 45
Water Supply Administration Services
N.A.I.C.S.: 924110
Russell C. Jones *(Pres)*
Bob Webb *(Bus Mgr)*
Ivan Langford *(Gen Mgr)*
Nancy Matthews *(Project Mgr-Sys)*
Brandon Wade *(Asst Gen Mgr)*
Brad Matlock *(Asst Sec)*
Bennie Jones Jr. *(Treas)*

GULF COAST YACHT SALES
INCORPORATED
101 16th Ave S, Saint Petersburg, FL
33701
Tel.: (727) 822-5516   FL
Web Site: https://www.gcyachts.com
Year Founded: 1997
Emp.: 50
Yacht Brokers & Financial Services
N.A.I.C.S.: 441222
Brenda E. Aldacosta *(Co-Owner &
Pres)*
Lauran Lee *(Co-Owner)*
Brenda Aldacosta *(Pres)*

Gulf Compress—(Continued)

GULF COMPRESS

201 N 19th St, Corpus Christi, TX 78408
Tel.: (361) 882-5489
Web Site:
   https://www.gulfcompress.com
Rev.: $14,666,492
Emp.: 48
Cotton Compresses & Warehouses
N.A.I.C.S.: 493130
Robert Swize *(CEO)*

GULF COPPER & MANUFAC-TURING CORP

7200 Highway 87, Port Arthur, TX 77642-0324
Tel.: (409) 983-1691
Web Site: http://www.gulfcopper.com
Sales Range: $10-24.9 Million
Emp.: 110
Commercial Cargo Ships, Building & Repairing
N.A.I.C.S.: 336611
Steve Hale *(Pres)*
Robert Irelan *(Dir-Federal Bus Dev)*

GULF CREDIT UNION

5140 W Pkwy St, Groves, TX 77619
Tel.: (409) 963-1191   TX
Web Site: https://www.gecu.org
Year Founded: 1939
Sales Range: $10-24.9 Million
Emp.: 111
Credit Union Operator
N.A.I.C.S.: 522130
Ron Burkhalter *(Pres & CEO)*

GULF DISTRIBUTING HOLD-INGS LLC

3378 Moffett Rd, Mobile, AL 36607
Tel.: (251) 476-9600
Web Site:
   https://www.gulfdistributinghold
   ings.com
Holding Company; Alcoholic & Non-Alcoholic Beverage Distr
N.A.I.C.S.: 551112
Elliot B. Maisel *(Chm & CEO)*
Tom Gangle *(Treas)*
Jimmy Marston *(COO)*
Evan Maisel *(Sr VP)*
Jeff Floyd *(Mng Dir-Chains)*
Amy Baldwin *(Mng Dir-Craft)*
Brian Illian *(Mng Dir-Ops)*
David Gaines *(Mng Dir-Craft)*
J. R. Ebbitt *(Mng Dir-Non-Alcoholic)*
Joey Irelan *(Mng Dir-Red Bull)*
Louis Maisel *(Sr VP)*
T. J. Dela Pena *(Mng Dir-Ops)*

Subsidiaries:

Allstate Beverage Company LLC   **(1)**
130 6th St, Montgomery, AL 36104-1633
Tel.: (334) 265-0507
Web Site: http://www.allstatebeverage.com
Sales Range: $10-24.9 Million
Emp.: 78
Beer & Soft Drink Distr
N.A.I.C.S.: 424810
Marc Kirklin *(Mng Dir & Gen Mgr)*

Energy Beverage Management LLC   **(1)**
159 Concourse Dr, Pearl, MS 39208
Tel.: (601) 936-4606
Web Site:
   http://www.energybeveragemanage
   ment.com
Energy Drink Distr
N.A.I.C.S.: 424410
David Gaines *(Mng Dir-Craft Div)*
J. R. Ebbitt *(Mng Dir-Non-Alcoholic)*
Jay Cox *(CFO)*
Joey Irelan *(Mng Dir-Red Bull)*
Louis Maisel *(Sr VP)*
Rebecca L. Maisel *(Gen Counsel & Sr VP)*
T. J. Dela Pena *(Mng Dir-Ops)*

Goldring Gulf Distributing Company, LLC   **(1)**
927 Mulberry Ave, Panama City, FL 32401
Tel.: (850) 769-3522
Web Site: http://www.goldringgulf.com
Sales Range: $1-9.9 Million
Emp.: 78
Beer & Ale Merchant Whslr
N.A.I.C.S.: 424810
Mike Johnson *(Mng Dir)*

Gulf Distributing Company of Mobile LLC   **(1)**
3378 Moffett Rd, Mobile, AL 36607
Tel.: (251) 476-9600
Web Site: http://www.gulfdistributing.com
Sales Range: $10-24.9 Million
Emp.: 110
Beer & Wine Distr
N.A.I.C.S.: 424810
James R. Cox *(CFO)*
Domenic Olson *(Mng Dir & Gen Mgr)*
Rebecca L. Maisel *(Gen Counsel & Sr VP)*

GULF ELECTROQUIP LTD.

425 N Wayside Dr, Houston, TX 77020-7598
Tel.: (713) 675-2525   TX
Web Site:
   https://www.gulfelectroquip.com
Year Founded: 1985
Electric Motors & Generators Mfr & Repair Services
N.A.I.C.S.: 335312
Jim Petersen Jr. *(Pres)*

Subsidiaries:

Ideal Electric Company   **(1)**
330 E 1st St, Mansfield, OH 44902
Tel.: (419) 522-3611
Web Site: http://theidealelectric.com
Motors, Generators & Switch Gear
N.A.I.C.S.: 335312
Nick Smollen *(Sls Dir)*

GULF ENERGY INFORMATION

2 Greenway Plz Ste 1020, Houston, TX 77046
Tel.: (713) 520-4498
Web Site:
   https://www.gulfenergyinfo.com
Year Founded: 1916
Periodical Publishers
N.A.I.C.S.: 513120
John Royall *(Pres & CEO)*
Alan Millis *(CFO)*
Andy McDowell *(VP & Publr-Wold Oil)*
Harry Brookby *(VP-Data Sls-Energy Web Atlas)*
Sheryl Stone *(VP-Production)*
Pamela Harvey *(VP-Fin & Ops)*
Roger Jordan *(Dir-Mktg & Audience Dev)*
Catherine Watkins *(Publr-Hydrocarbon & Gas Processing & LNG)*
Brian Nessen *(Publr-Pipeline & Gas Journal & Underground Construction)*
Scott Allgood *(Dir-Data Svcs)*
J. Russell Denson *(Chm)*

GULF ENGINEERING, LLC

611 Hill St, Jefferson, LA 70121
Tel.: (504) 733-1820
Web Site:
   http://www.gulfengineering.com
Year Founded: 1924
Sales Range: $10-24.9 Million
Machinery Dismantling
N.A.I.C.S.: 237990
Stuart Vint Massimini *(Pres)*

GULF EQUIPMENT CORPORA-TION

5535 Business Pkwy, Theodore, AL 36582
Tel.: (251) 653-5075

Web Site:
   http://www.gulfequipment.net
Sales Range: $10-24.9 Million
Emp.: 115
Provider of Commercial & New Con-struction Services
N.A.I.C.S.: 236220
J. Anthony Dees *(CFO & Sec)*
Lyman M. Ramsay *(COO & VP)*
John A. Ramsay *(Dir-Ops)*
Carol Gengo *(Office Mgr)*
James Davis *(Project Mgr)*
Chad Tubbs *(Project Mgr)*
Danny Brannan *(Project Mgr-Primary)*
Ashley Ramsay *(Treas)*
John C. Ramsay *(VP)*
J. Rhea Silvernail *(VP)*
Gene Sylvester *(Sr Project Mgr-Jackson)*
L. W. Ramsay Jr. *(Pres & CEO)*

GULF INTERNATIONAL COR-PORATION

Gulf Plz 16010 Barkers Point Ln Ste 600, Houston, TX 77079-9000
Tel.: (713) 850-3400
Web Site: http://www.gie.com
Holding Company; Oil & Gas Pipeline Engineering & Construction Manage-ment Services
N.A.I.C.S.: 551112
H. Douglas Evans *(Pres & CEO)*
Criss Shipman *(Sr VP)*

Subsidiaries:

Gulf Interstate Engineering Company   **(1)**
Gulf Plaza 16010 Barkers Point Ln Ste 600, Houston, TX 77079-9000
Tel.: (713) 850-3400
Web Site: http://www.gie.com
Sales Range: $50-74.9 Million
Emp.: 400
Oil & Gas Pipeline Engineering & Construc-tion Management Services
N.A.I.C.S.: 237120
H. Douglas Evans *(Chm)*
Criss Shipman *(Sr VP-Intl)*
Rick Barnard *(Pres & CEO)*
Bob Sprick *(Sr VP-Gulf Interstate Field Svcs)*
John Thomas *(CFO)*

Division (Domestic):

Gulf Interstate Field Services, Inc.   **(2)**
Gulf Plaza 16010 Barkers Point Ln Ste 600, Houston, TX 77079-9000   **(100%)**
Tel.: (713) 850-3500
Web Site: http://www.gifieldservices.com
Sales Range: $25-49.9 Million
Emp.: 7
Energy Transportation Construction Man-agement & Inspection Services
N.A.I.C.S.: 561990
Cathie Kramer *(Mgr-Field Svcs)*

Post Oak Graphics   **(2)**
Gulf Plz 16010 Barkers Point Ln Ste 150, Houston, TX 77079   **(100%)**
Tel.: (713) 850-3563
Web Site: http://www.postoakgraphics.com
Digital Copying, Reprographic Printing, Plot-ting, Document Binding & Web Design Ser-vices
N.A.I.C.S.: 323111
Brad Godwin *(Mgr-Mktg)*
Jay Pousson *(Mgr-Production)*

GULF INTERNATIONAL TRUCKS

2605 Port Lavaca Dr, Victoria, TX 77901
Tel.: (361) 575-1481
Web Site:
   https://www.kyrishtruckcenters.com
Sales Range: $10-24.9 Million
Emp.: 20
Car Whslr
N.A.I.C.S.: 441110

Jeff Kyrish *(Owner & Gen Mgr)*

GULF MARINE REPAIR COR-PORATION

1800 Grant St, Tampa, FL 33605
Tel.: (813) 247-3153
Web Site:
   http://www.gulfmarinerepair.com
Year Founded: 1988
Sales Range: $10-24.9 Million
Emp.: 250
Shipbuilding & Repairing Services
N.A.I.C.S.: 336611
John P. Gallagher *(Pres)*

GULF PACIFIC INC.

12010 Taylor Rd, Houston, TX 77041
Tel.: (713) 464-0606
Web Site: https://www.gulfpac.com
Rev.: $35,218,452
Emp.: 25
Rice, Unpolished
N.A.I.C.S.: 424510
Friedrich Brenckmann *(Pres)*

GULF RICE ARKANSAS, LLC.

12010 Taylor Rd, Houston, TX 77041-1239
Tel.: (713) 880-9197
Sales Range: $10-24.9 Million
Emp.: 90
Rice Milling Services
N.A.I.C.S.: 311212
Anthony Gracely *(Mgr)*
Thomas Stivers *(CFO)*

GULF SHORE TEL-COM INC.

13500 Fm 753, Athens, TX 75751-8857
Tel.: (903) 675-5599
Web Site:
   http://www.gulfshoretelcom.com
Sales Range: $10-24.9 Million
Emp.: 40
Telecommunication Construction
N.A.I.C.S.: 238990
Stace S. Smith *(Pres)*
Tonya Hannigan *(Controller)*

GULF SOUTH TECHNOLOGY SOLUTIONS, LLC.

5757 Corporate Blvd Ste 250, Baton Rouge, LA 70808
Tel.: (225) 216-2169
Web Site:
   http://www.gulfsouthtech.com
Year Founded: 2005
Sales Range: $1-9.9 Million
Emp.: 20
Sofetware Development Service
N.A.I.C.S.: 449210
James Moak Jr. *(Pres)*

GULF SPECIAL SERVICES, INC.

7455 Cullen Blvd, Houston, TX 77051
Tel.: (713) 733-4341
Web Site:
   http://www.gulfspecialservices.com
Sales Range: $10-24.9 Million
Emp.: 80
Construction & Mining Machinery & Equipment Merchant Whslr
N.A.I.C.S.: 423810
Reynaldo Santos *(Pres)*

GULF STANDARD ENERGY COMPANY, LLC

1414 W Swann Ave Ste 100, Tampa, FL 33606
Tel.: (813) 579-2009
Web Site: http://www.gulf-standard.com
Sales Range: $1-9.9 Million
Oil & Gas Investment Services
N.A.I.C.S.: 213112

GULF STATES CANNERS INC.

1006 Industrial Park Dr, Clinton, MS 39056-3210

Tel.: (601) 924-0511
Sales Range: $75-99.9 Million
Emp.: 75
Bottled & Canned Soft Drink Mfr
N.A.I.C.S.: 312111
Albert C. Clark (Pres)
Randy Lee (Controller)

GULF STATES FINANCIAL SERVICES, INC.
1345 Enclave Pkwy, Houston, TX 77077
Tel.: (713) 580-3000
Web Site: https://www.gsfsgroup.com
Rev.: $20,800,000
Emp.: 293
Advisory Services, Insurance
N.A.I.C.S.: 561510
Steve Amos (Pres & CEO)

GULF STATES HOLDINGS, INC.
1201 Camellia Blvd Ste 201, Lafayette, LA 70508
Tel.: (888) 277-0575
Web Site:
    http://www.gulfstatesinsure.com
Insurance & Brokerages Services
N.A.I.C.S.: 524210
Noel Bunol (Exec VP)
Crystal Bunol (VP)
Cindy Nezat (Office Mgr)
Melissa Dupre (Ops Mgr)
Parker Reaux (Acct Mgr)
Bill Gourgues (Claims Manager)
Erin Belk (Claims Manager)
Terri McCoy (Product & Systems Manager)
H Marcus Carter Jr. (Pres & CEO)

Subsidiaries:

Coastal American Insurance
Company   (1)
1105 30th Ave Ste 203, Gulfport, MS 39501
Tel.: (855) 836-4950
Web Site: http://www.caic-insco.com
Insurance Agencies & Brokerages
N.A.I.C.S.: 524210
Noel Bunol (Exec VP)
Crystal Bunol (VP)
Cindy Nezat (Office Mgr)
Melissa Dupre (Ops Mgr)
Parker Reaux (Acct Mgr)
Bill Gourgues (Claims Manager)
Erin Belk (Claims Manager)
Terri McCoy (Product & Systems Manager)
H Marcus Carter Jr. (Pres & CEO)
Marc Carter (Pres & CEO)

Gulf States Insurance Company,
Inc.   (1)
1201 Camellia Blvd Ste 201, Lafayette, LA 70508
Tel.: (888) 277-0575
Insurance & Brokerages Services
N.A.I.C.S.: 524210
Noel J Bunol IV (Exec VP)

GULF STREAM BUILDERS SUPPLY, INC.
1481 W 15 St, Riviera Beach, FL 33404
Tel.: (561) 472-9220   FL
Rev.: $28,450,000
Emp.: 69
Lumber & Other Building Materials Sales
N.A.I.C.S.: 423310
Skeith Graves (Chm)
Dennis Vlassis (Pres)

GULF STREAM COACH INC.
503 S Oakland Ave, Nappanee, IN 46550
Tel.: (574) 773-7761
Web Site:
    https://www.gulfstreamcoach.com
Year Founded: 1983
Sales Range: $25-49.9 Million

Emp.: 650
Provider of Trailers & Motor Homes
N.A.I.C.S.: 336213
Phil Sarvari (Pres)
Jeffrey Kloska (VP-Sls & Mktg)

GULF SYSTEMS INC.
7720 FM 1960 Rd E, Humble, TX 77346
Tel.: (281) 852-6700
Web Site:
    http://www.gulfpackaging.com
Sales Range: $10-24.9 Million
Emp.: 20
Packaging, Industrial
N.A.I.C.S.: 423840
Jeff Cutshall (Pres)
Don House (Mgr-Sls)

GULF TILE DISTRIBUTORS OF FLORIDA, INC.
2318 W Columbus Dr, Tampa, FL 33607-1642
Tel.: (813) 251-8807
Web Site: http://www.gulftile.com
Rev.: $15,000,000
Emp.: 40
Ceramic Wall & Floor Tile Distr
N.A.I.C.S.: 423320
Frank J. Garcia (Pres)
Eva Lockard (Dir-HR)

GULF WINDS INTERNATIONAL INC.
411 Brisbane St, Houston, TX 77061-5003
Tel.: (713) 747-4909
Web Site: http://www.gwii.com
Rev.: $12,891,801
Emp.: 130
General Warehousing & Trucking
N.A.I.C.S.: 493110
Todd Stewart (Pres)
Brandi Crawley (Controller)
B. J. Tarver (COO)
Cliff Robbins (Dir-Logistics Svcs)
Patrick Maher (Exec VP)
Dustin Hebrank (CFO)

GULF-GREAT LAKES PACKAGING CORPORATION
1040 Maryland Ave, Dolton, IL 60419
Tel.: (708) 849-8100
Web Site: http://www.gulfpack.com
Rev.: $22,000,000
Emp.: 50
Industrial Supplies Merchant Whslr
N.A.I.C.S.: 423840
Carl Fleck (Owner & Pres)
Steve Cummings (Mgr-Sls)
Robert Bisch (Mgr-Warehouse)

GULFCOAST COIN & JEWELRY, LLC
14181 S Tamiami Trl, Fort Myers, FL 33912
Tel.: (239) 939-5636
Web Site:
    https://www.gulfcoastcoin.com
Year Founded: 1975
Sales Range: $50-74.9 Million
Emp.: 25
Jewelry, Rare Coins, Gold & Silver
N.A.I.C.S.: 458310
Denise Joyce (Co-Owner)
Michael Joyce (Co-Owner)

GULFCOAST SPINE INSTITUTE, PA
2300 E Norvell Bryant Hwy, Hernando, FL 34442
Tel.: (352) 351-4778
Web Site:
    https://www.gulfcoastspine.net
Sales Range: $1-9.9 Million
Emp.: 20

Orthopaedic Services
N.A.I.C.S.: 621111
James J. Ronzo (Co-Owner)
Frank Bono (Co-Owner)

GULFEAGLE SUPPLY, INC.
2900 E 7th Ave Ste 200, Tampa, FL 33605
Tel.: (813) 636-9808   FL
Web Site:
    http://www.gulfeaglesupply.com
Year Founded: 1973
Roofing, Siding & Insulation Distr
N.A.I.C.S.: 423330
Chuck Everts (Mgr-Financial Services)

Subsidiaries:

Kimal Lumber Company   (1)
400 Riverview Dr S, Nokomis, FL 34275
Tel.: (941) 484-9721
Web Site: http://www.kimallumber.com
Lumber & Other Building Materials
N.A.I.C.S.: 423310

Division (Domestic):

Kimal Lumber Company   (2)
6520 Industrial Ln, Englewood, FL 34224
Tel.: (941) 474-7793
Web Site: http://www.kimallumber.com
Emp.: 17
Lumber & Other Building Materials
N.A.I.C.S.: 423310
Jeff Koerbel (Mgr-Ops)
Donny Thomas (Gen Mgr)

GULFSHORE INSURANCE, INC.
4100 Goodlette Rd N, Naples, FL 34103
Tel.: (239) 261-3646   FL
Web Site:
    https://www.gulfshoreinsurance.com
Year Founded: 1970
Sales Range: $10-24.9 Million
Emp.: 90
Insurance Agencies
N.A.I.C.S.: 524210
Michelle Gleeson (COO, Partner & Exec VP)
Brad Havemeier (Pres)
Greg Havemeier (Sr VP & Partner)
Jack Powers (Chief Sls Officer)
Kim Ovaitte (Sr VP-Comml Mktg)
John Caballero (Partner & Mgr-Risk)
Paige Moore (VP-Personal Svcs)
John Keller (VP-Comm Sls)
Heather MacDougall (VP-HR)
Jim Helton (VP-IT)
Holly McMaster (Controller)
Jan Allan (VP-Comml Svc)

GULFSIDE SUPPLY INC.
1565 Northgate Blvd, Sarasota, FL 34234
Tel.: (941) 355-7161
Rev.: $7,000,000
Emp.: 100
Roofing, Siding & Insulation Material Merchant Whslr
N.A.I.C.S.: 423330
Pat Runde (Mgr)

Subsidiaries:

Tri-Excellence, Inc.   (1)
12595 Belcher Rd S, Largo, FL 33773
Tel.: (727) 539-6455
Rev.: $3,745,000
Emp.: 35
Lumber, Plywood, Millwork & Wood Panel
Merchant Whslr
N.A.I.C.S.: 423310
Marc H. Banning (Pres)

GULISTAN CARPET INC.
3140 Hwy 5, Aberdeen, NC 28315
Tel.: (910) 944-2371   DE

Web Site: http://www.gulistan.com
Year Founded: 1924
Sales Range: $25-49.9 Million
Emp.: 470
Retail of Carpets & Rugs
N.A.I.C.S.: 314110
Tony Prestipino (VP-Res & Comml Sls)
Philip Essig (Pres & CEO)
Pete Kruyer (CFO)

GULL HOLDINGS, LTD.
3838 W Parkway Blvd, Salt Lake City, UT 84120-6336
Tel.: (801) 954-7100
Web Site: http://www.usana.com
Holding Company: Healthcare Management
N.A.I.C.S.: 551112
Myron W. Wentz (Chm & CEO)

Subsidiaries:

USANA Health Sciences, Inc.   (1)
3838 W Pkwy Blvd, Salt Lake City, UT 84120   (51.3%)
Tel.: (801) 954-7100
Web Site: https://www.usana.com
Rev.: $1,186,464,000
Assets: $577,740,000
Liabilities: $182,616,000
Net Worth: $395,124,000
Earnings: $116,505,000
Emp.: 1,978
Fiscal Year-end: 01/01/2022
Nutritional, Personal Care & Weight Management Product Developer & Mfr
N.A.I.C.S.: 325411
Myron W. Wentz (Founder)
Jim Brown (Pres)
Kevin G. Guest (Exec Chm)
Paul A. Jones (Chief People Officer)
Walter Noot (COO)
P. Joshua Foukas (Chief Legal Officer, Gen Counsel & Sec)
Robert A. Sinnott (Chief Scientific Officer)
Daniel A. Macuga Jr. (Chief Mktg & Comm Officer)

Subsidiary (Non-US):

BabyCare Ltd.   (2)
4th Floor Building A East Gate Plaza 9
Dong Zhong Street, Dong Cheng District, Beijing, 100027, China
Tel.: (86) 1064198869
Web Site: http://www.baoying.com
Nutritional Supplement Mfr & Distr
N.A.I.C.S.: 325411
Matthew Estes (Pres & CEO)

UHS Essential Health Philippines,
Inc.   (2)
24th Floor Tower 1 The Enterprise Center
6766 Ayala Avenue Corner, Paseo de Roxas, Makati, 1200, Philippines
Tel.: (63) 28584500
Nutritional Supplement Mfr & Distr
N.A.I.C.S.: 325411
Loudelle Cinco (Mgr-Fin)

UHS Products (Malaysia) SDN
BHD   (2)
Unit M 01 & M 02 Mezz Flr Menara Axis No 2 Jalan 51A/223, 46100, Petaling Jaya, Malaysia
Tel.: (60) 379538036
Nutritional Supplement Mfr & Distr
N.A.I.C.S.: 325411

USANA Australia Pty. Ltd.   (2)
3 Hudson Ave, Baulkham Hills, 2154, NSW, Australia
Tel.: (61) 298424600
Web Site: http://www.usana.com
Sales Range: $25-49.9 Million
Emp.: 100
Nutritional Supplements, Skin Care & Weight Loss Product Mfr
N.A.I.C.S.: 325412

USANA Canada Co.   (2)
80 Innovation Dr, Woodbridge, L4H 0T2, ON, Canada
Tel.: (905) 264-9873
Nutritional, Skin Care & Weight Loss Pharmaceuticals

Gull Holdings, Ltd.—(Continued)
N.A.I.C.S.: 325412

**USANA Health Sciences (NZ)
Corp.** (2)
25 Canaveral Dr, Auckland, New Zealand
Tel.: (64) 94152750
Web Site: http://www.usana.com
Sales Range: $25-49.9 Million
Emp.: 7
Nutritional Supplements, Skin Care &
Weight Loss Products Mfr
N.A.I.C.S.: 325412

**USANA Health Sciences Korea
Ltd.** (2)
143-39 Samsung-dong Kangnam-gu, 2nd
FL Sinil Bldg, Seoul, 135-877, Korea
(South)
Tel.: (82) 221927300
Web Site: http://www.usana.com
Nutritional Supplements, Skin Care &
Weight Loss Products Mfr
N.A.I.C.S.: 325412

**USANA Health Sciences Singapore
Pte, Ltd.** (2)
391B Orchard Road Ngee Ann City Tower B
19-01/02, Singapore, 238874, Singapore
Tel.: (65) 68208838
Web Site: http://www.usana.com
Sales Range: $25-49.9 Million
Emp.: 20
Nutritional Supplements, Skin Care &
Weight Loss Products Mfr
N.A.I.C.S.: 325412

USANA Hong Kong Ltd. (2)
Unit 2504-6, 25F World Trade Ctr, 280
Gloucester Rd, Causeway Bay, Hong Kong,
China (Hong Kong)
Tel.: (852) 21621880
Web Site: http://www.usana.com
Nutritional Supplement, Skin Care & Weight
Loss Products Mfr
N.A.I.C.S.: 325412
Brent Neidig (Exec VP)

USANA Japan, Inc. (2)
Yoyogi Crystal Building 4/5F 1-35-4 Yoyogi,
Shibuya-ku, Tokyo, 151-0053, Japan
Tel.: (81) 353544141
Web Site: http://www.usana.com
Nutritional Supplement, Skin Care & Weight
Loss Products Mfr
N.A.I.C.S.: 325412
Koji Kubota (Mng Dir)

GULLEY ENTERPRISES INC.
1001 S Douglas Hwy B, Gillette, WY
82718
Tel.: (307) 682-4421   NY
Sales Range: $10-24.9 Million
Emp.: 70
Operator of Family Restaurants
N.A.I.C.S.: 722511

**GULLY TRANSPORTATION
INC.**
3820 Wisman Ln, Quincy, IL 62305
Tel.: (217) 224-0770
Web Site: http://www.gullyicx.com
Rev.: $20,000,000
Emp.: 150
Trucking Except Local
N.A.I.C.S.: 484121
William Gully (Pres)
Michael Gully (VP)
Duane Seals (Dir-Safety)

GUM TREE FABRICS INC.
4002 S Eason Blvd, Tupelo, MS
38804
Tel.: (662) 844-9329
Web Site:
    https://www.gumtreefabrics.com
Rev.: $24,096,881
Emp.: 30
Upholstery Fabrics, Woven
N.A.I.C.S.: 424310
Donna Marecle (Pres)
Jane Livingston (Controller)

Greg Morgan (Dir-Sls & Product Dev)
Andrew Blassingame (Acct Exec)
Allison Wargowsky (Acct Exec)

GUMAS ADVERTISING
99 Shotwell St, San Francisco, CA
94103-3625
Tel.: (415) 621-7575   CA
Web Site: http://www.gumas.com
Year Founded: 1984
Rev.: $10,500,000
Emp.: 20
Advertising Agencies, Advertising
Specialties, Public Relations
N.A.I.C.S.: 541810
John Gumas (Founder & CEO)
Bob Bedbury (VP & Dir-Mktg)
Pat Demiris (VP & Dir-Ops)
Rebecca Favero (Acct Svcs Exec)
Rita Ipsen (Acct Mgr-Acct Svcs)
Erik Johnson (Brand Strategist)
Creighton Anderson (Interactive
Graphic Designer)
Craig Alexander (Pres)

GUMBLE BROTHERS INC.
Rte 507, Paupack, PA 18451
Tel.: (570) 226-4531
Web Site:
    http://www.gumblebrothers.com
Sales Range: $10-24.9 Million
Emp.: 30
Provider of Building Supplies
N.A.I.C.S.: 423310
Susan Campfield (Pres & CEO)
Dana Gumble (Owner)

**GUMBY'S PIZZA SYSTEMS
INC.**
8720 Sw 40th Ave, Gainesville, FL
32608-8698
Tel.: (352) 338-7775
Year Founded: 1985
Rev.: $16,500,000
Emp.: 1,300
Limited-Service Restaurants
N.A.I.C.S.: 722513
Jeff O'Brien (VP)
Frank Myles (Pres)
Chancellor Hippler (Sec)

**GUMMER WHOLESALE CO.
INC.**
1945 James Pkwy, Heath, OH 43056
Tel.: (740) 928-0415
Web Site:
    https://www.gummerwholesale.net
Sales Range: $200-249.9 Million
Emp.: 80
Full Line Convenience Store Distr
N.A.I.C.S.: 424990
Chad Gummer (Pres)
Richard Gummer (CEO)

GUMP'S CORP.
135 Post St, San Francisco, CA
94108-4701
Tel.: (415) 982-1616   CA
Web Site: http://www.gumps.com
Year Founded: 1861
Sales Range: $75-99.9 Million
Emp.: 100
Modern & Antique Gifts, Art Objects,
Jewelry, Home Furnishings & Decora-
tions Specialty Store Operator
N.A.I.C.S.: 459420
Carmen Roberson (Dir-Retail Mktg)

Subsidiaries:

Gump's By Mail, Inc. (1)
135 Post St, San Francisco, CA
94108-4701   (100%)
Tel.: (415) 982-1616
Web Site: http://www.gumps.com
Mail-Order Catalog Marketer
N.A.I.C.S.: 455219
Tony Lopez (COO & CFO)

GUN.IO INCORPORATED
1200 Clinton St Ste 225, Nashville,
TN 37203
Tel.: (615) 541-8095   TN
Web Site: https://www.gun.io
Year Founded: 2011
Online Job Search Portal for Soft-
ware Developers
N.A.I.C.S.: 561499
Teja Yenamandra (Founder & CEO)

**GUNDAKER COMMERCIAL
GROUP, INC.**
2458 Old Dorsett Rd Ste 311, Saint
Louis, MO 63043
Tel.: (636) 728-5100   MO
Web Site:
    https://www.gundakercommer
    cial.com
Sales Range: $75-99.9 Million
Emp.: 130
Real Estate Brokerage, Asset Man-
agement, Development & Construc-
tion Services
N.A.I.C.S.: 531390
Gordon A. Gundaker (Chm)
Mary E. Mercurio (CFO & Sr VP-Fin)
Donna Miller (Dir-HR)
Dean Burns (Sr VP)
Dave Wuenscher (VP)
Mark Hejna (VP)
Mike Hejna (Pres & CEO)
Anne Klene (Sr VP-Asset Mgmt)
Robert Busch (Exec VP)

**GUNDERSEN LUTHERAN
HEALTH SYSTEMS, INC.**
1900 South Ave, La Crosse, WI
54601
Tel.: (608) 782-7300
Web Site:
    https://www.gundersenhealth.org
Year Founded: 1995
Sales Range: $450-499.9 Million
Emp.: 5,500
Multi-Specialty Group Medical Prac-
tices & Regional Hospital Services
N.A.I.C.S.: 622110
Kathy Klock (Sr VP-HR & Clinical
Support Svcs)
Marilu Bintz (Sr VP-Population Health
& Strategy)
Michael J. Dolan (COO-Medical &
Exec VP)
Debra Rislow (COO-Admin)
Kari Adank (Chief Compliance Offi-
cer)
Jean Krause (Chief Officer-Quality &
Patient Safety)
Pamela Maas (Chief Officer-Bus Dev
& Mktg)
Mary Ellen McCartney (Chief Learn-
ing Officer)
Scott W. Rathgaber (CEO)
Lynnetta Kopp (Exec Dir)
Greg Thompson (Chief Medical Offi-
cer & Dir-Medical Education)

GUNDERSON MARINE LLC
4350 NW Front Ave, Portland, OR
97210
Tel.: (503) 972-5700   OR
Year Founded: 1993
Sales Range: $25-49.9 Million
Emp.: 1,300
Ocean-Going Cargo Vessels Builder
N.A.I.C.S.: 336611

GUNDERSON'S JEWELERS
Lakeport Commons 4830 Sergeant
Rd, Sioux City, IA 51106
Tel.: (712) 255-7229
Web Site:
    http://www.gundersons.com
Year Founded: 1945
Jewelry Stores

N.A.I.C.S.: 458310
Brian Gunderson (CEO)
George Gunderson (Founder)

GUNN-MOWERY, LLC
650 N 12th St, Lemoyne, PA 17043
Tel.: (717) 761-4600
Web Site:
    https://www.gunnmowery.com
Year Founded: 1985
Emp.: 70
Insurance Brokers
N.A.I.C.S.: 524210
G. Greg Gunn (Mng Partner)
Robert Snyder (VP-Fin)
Ted Mowery (Partner)
Pam Barbush (VP)
Gary Harshbarger (Sr VP)
Mark Yost (Acct Exec)

**GUNSTER, YOAKLEY &
STEWART, P.A.**
777 S Flagler Dr Ste 500 E, West
Palm Beach, FL 33401-6194
Tel.: (561) 655-1980
Web Site: https://www.gunster.com
Year Founded: 1925
Sales Range: $75-99.9 Million
Emp.: 340
Law firm
N.A.I.C.S.: 541110
Steve McDermott (CFO)

**GUNSTOCK RECREATION
AREA**
719 Cherry Valley Rd, Gilford, NH
03249
Tel.: (603) 293-4341   DE
Web Site: https://www.gunstock.com
Year Founded: 1936
Sales Range: $10-24.9 Million
Emp.: 35
Ski Area & Resort
N.A.I.C.S.: 721110
Gregg Goddard (Gen Mgr)

GUNTHER DOUGLAS, INC.
2601 Lk St Ste 400, Denver, CO
80205
Tel.: (303) 534-4441
Web Site:
    http://www.guntherdouglas.com
Sales Range: $1-9.9 Million
Emp.: 52
Information Technology Staffing
N.A.I.C.S.: 561311
Lisa Gunther (Co-Founder & Pres)
Douglas Payne (Co-Founder & Sr
VP)

GUNTHER MOTOR COMPANY
1660 S State Rd 7, Fort Lauderdale,
FL 33317
Tel.: (954) 797-1660
Web Site:
    https://www.gunthermotors.com
Rev.: $181,994,762
Emp.: 300
Automobiles, New & Used
N.A.I.C.S.: 441110
Joseph Gunther (Pres)
Julie Stevenson (Controller)

**GUNTHER VOLKSWAGON OF
COCONUT CREEK**
4300 N State Rd 7, Coconut Creek,
FL 33073
Tel.: (954) 590-3750
Web Site: https://www.gunthervw.net
Sales Range: $25-49.9 Million
Emp.: 200
New Car Dealers
N.A.I.C.S.: 441110
Robert Klein (Gen Mgr)
Moe Ali (Mgr-Sls)
Jeff Foreman (Mgr-Sls)
Gregg Freeman (Mgr-Bus)

Justin Dewar *(Bus Mgr)*
Phil Elios *(Dir-Fin)*
Emre Esmer *(Mgr-Inventory)*
Marcelo Gomez *(Mgr-Lot)*
Allan Hancock *(Mgr-Sls-VW Pre-Owned)*
Carlos Jimenez *(Mgr-Sls)*
Dewey Klein *(Mgr-VW Pre-Owned Sls)*
Steve Meadows *(Mgr-VW Pre-Owned Sls)*

GUNTON CORPORATION

26150 Richmond Rd, Bedford, OH 44146-1438
Tel.: (216) 831-2420   OH
Web Site:
   http://www.guntonpella.com
Year Founded: 1932
Sales Range: $25-49.9 Million
Emp.: 280
Lumber, Plywood & Millwork
N.A.I.C.S.: 423310
Andy Wollschleger *(Customer Support & Svc)*
Denise Joviak *(Mgr-Cleveland Collection)*
Mike Slates *(Mgr-IS)*
Randy McCoy *(Mgr-Collections-Philadelphia)*
Sarah Telischak *(Project Mgr)*
Soc Colovas *(Mgr-HR)*

GUPPY MEDIA INC

12443 Bel Red Rd Ste 320, Bellevue, WA 98005
Tel.: (425) 450-9494
Web Site:
   http://www.guppymedia.com
Year Founded: 2003
Sales Range: $1-9.9 Million
Emp.: 15
Online & Mobile Ad Network for Advertisers & Agencies
N.A.I.C.S.: 541890
Alex Choe *(Founder)*
Sam Sim *(CEO)*

GUPTA PERMOLD CORPORATION

234 Lott Rd, Pittsburgh, PA 15235
Tel.: (412) 793-3511   PA
Web Site:
   https://www.guptapermold.com
Year Founded: 1980
Sales Range: $10-24.9 Million
Emp.: 185
Provider of Aluminum Machinery Castings
N.A.I.C.S.: 331524
Lakshmi P. Gupta *(Pres)*

GURLEY MOTOR COMPANY

701 W Coal Ave, Gallup, NM 87301-6503
Tel.: (505) 722-6621   NM
Web Site:
   https://www.gurleymotorford.com
Year Founded: 1933
Sales Range: $100-124.9 Million
Emp.: 80
Retail Sale of New & Used Automobile Distr
N.A.I.C.S.: 441110
Steve Gurley *(Owner & Pres)*

Subsidiaries:

Southwest General Insurance
Company   (1)
701 W Coal Ave, Gallup, NM 87305-1377
Tel.: (505) 722-6621
Web Site: http://www.swgic.com
Insurance Brokerage Services
N.A.I.C.S.: 524210
Pat Gurley *(Pres)*
Steve Gurley *(VP)*
Cynthia Knight *(Mgr)*

GURLEY-LEEP BUICK-GMC TRUCK, INC

5302 N Grape Rd, Mishawaka, IN 46545
Tel.: (574) 272-0990   IN
Web Site: http://www.gurleyleep.com
Sales Range: $50-74.9 Million
Emp.: 200
Automobile & Automotive Parts Dealer
N.A.I.C.S.: 441330
Rick Torres *(Controller)*

Subsidiaries:

Rock Oldsmobile Cadillac   (1)
4004 Grape Rd, Mishawaka, IN 46545
Tel.: (574) 674-9703
Rev.: $140,000
Emp.: 1
New & Used Car Dealers
N.A.I.C.S.: 441110

GURNEE DODGE CHRYSLER JEEP, INC.

7255 Grand Ave, Gurnee, IL 60031
Tel.: (847) 623-3000
Web Site:
   http://www.gurneedodge.com
Sales Range: $10-24.9 Million
Emp.: 60
New Car Dealers
N.A.I.C.S.: 441110
Bill Brundage *(Mgr-Parts)*
Bret Matthews *(Co-Owner)*
Jim Spellman *(Co-Owner)*

GURNEE HYUNDAI MOTORS

6251 Grand Ave, Gurnee, IL 60031-1614
Tel.: (224) 637-1674
Web Site:
   https://www.gurneehyundai.com
Sales Range: $10-24.9 Million
Emp.: 35
Car Whslr
N.A.I.C.S.: 441110
Ricky Perez *(Gen Mgr)*

GURNET POINT CAPITAL LLC

55 Cambridge Pkwy Ste 401, Cambridge, MA 02142
Tel.: (617) 588-4900
Web Site:
   http://www.gurnetpointcapital.com
Private Investment Firm
N.A.I.C.S.: 523999
Travis Wilson *(Partner)*
David Moore *(Partner)*
Christopher Viehbacher *(Mng Partner)*
Sophie Kornowski *(Sr Partner)*
Ernesto Bertarelli *(Co-Founder)*
Christopher A. Viehbacher *(Co-Founder)*

Subsidiaries:

Corium International, Inc.   (1)
235 Constitution Dr, Menlo Park, CA 94025
Tel.: (650) 298-8255
Web Site: http://www.coriumgroup.com
Rev.: $31,864,000
Assets: $84,851,000
Liabilities: $68,639,000
Net Worth: $16,212,000
Earnings: ($47,793,000)
Emp.: 213
Fiscal Year-end: 09/30/2017
Pharmaceuticals Mfr
N.A.I.C.S.: 325412
Parminder Singh *(CTO & VP-R&D)*
Timothy Sweemer *(Chief Acctg Officer & VP-Admin)*
Robert S. Breuil *(CFO)*
Dan Arsulowicz *(VP-Ops-Grand Rapids)*
Christina Dickerson *(VP-Corp Dev)*

Innocoll Holdings plc   (1)
Unit 9 Block D Monksland Business Park, Monksland, Athlone, Ireland
Tel.: (353) 90 6486834

Web Site: http://www.innocoll.com
Sales Range: $1-9.9 Million
Pharmaceutical Preparation Mfr
N.A.I.C.S.: 325412
Charles F. Katzer *(Exec VP-Global Technical Ops)*
Kimball Hall *(Pres & CEO)*
Gwendolyn Niebler *(Chief Medical Officer)*
Beth A. Krewson *(Gen Counsel)*
Louis Pascarella *(Pres & CEO)*
Anthony Galdi *(Chief Comml Officer)*

Subsidiary (Non-US):

Syntacoll GmBH   (2)
Industriegebiet Saal Donaustrasse 24, 93342, Saal an der Donau, Germany
Tel.: (49) 9441 6860 0
Web Site: http://www.innocoll.com
Pharmaceutical Preparation Mfr
N.A.I.C.S.: 325412

Paratek Pharmaceuticals, Inc.   (1)
75 Park Plz, Boston, MA 02116
Tel.: (617) 807-6600
Web Site: https://www.paratekpharma.com
Rev.: $160,268,000
Assets: $172,538,000
Liabilities: $343,580,000
Net Worth: ($171,042,000)
Earnings: ($63,566,000)
Emp.: 268
Fiscal Year-end: 12/31/2022
Holding Company; Specialty Pharmaceutical Develpment & Marketing Services
N.A.I.C.S.: 551112
Walter A. Gilbert *(Founder)*
Adam Woodrow *(Pres & Chief Comml Officer)*
Randall Brenner *(Chief Dev & Regulatory Officer)*
William M. Haskel *(Chief Legal Officer, Gen Counsel & Sec)*
Sarah Higgins *(Principal Acctg Officer, VP-Fin & Controller)*
Chris Bostrom *(VP)*

Subsidiary (Domestic):

Paratek Pharmaceuticals, LLC   (2)
75 Park Plz 3rd Fl, Boston, MA 02116
Tel.: (617) 807-6600
Web Site: http://www.paratekpharma.com
Specialty Pharmaceutical Develpment & Marketing Services
N.A.I.C.S.: 325412

Radius Health, Inc.   (1)
22 Boston Wharf Rd 7th Fl, Boston, MA 02210
Tel.: (617) 551-4000
Web Site: https://www.radiuspharm.com
Rev.: $229,973,000
Assets: $181,542,000
Liabilities: $433,846,000
Net Worth: ($252,304,000)
Earnings: ($70,176,000)
Emp.: 293
Fiscal Year-end: 12/31/2021
Pharmaceuticals Mfr
N.A.I.C.S.: 325412
Mark Conley *(CFO, Treas & VP)*
Chhaya Shah *(Chief Bus Officer)*
Salvador Grausso III *(Chief Comml Officer, Sr VP & Head-Patient Access-US)*
Averi Price *(Chief Compliance Officer & Gen Counsel)*
Maureen Conlan *(Head-Oncology)*
Bruce Mitlak *(Chief Medical Officer & Head-Discovery Science)*

GURTLER INDUSTRIES INC

15475 S La Salle St, South Holland, IL 60473
Tel.: (708) 331-2550
Web Site: https://www.gurtler.com
Sales Range: $10-24.9 Million
Emp.: 65
Detergents, Synthetic Organic or Inorganic Alkaline
N.A.I.C.S.: 325611
Greg Gurtler *(Pres)*

GURU.COM

5001 Baum Blvd Ste 605, Pittsburgh, PA 15213
Tel.: (412) 687-2228

Web Site: https://www.guru.com
Year Founded: 1997
Rev.: $23,600,000
Emp.: 22
Business Products & Services
N.A.I.C.S.: 561320

GUS MACHADO ENTERPRISES, INC.

1200 W 49th St, Hialeah, FL 33012-3217
Tel.: (305) 822-8338   FL
Web Site:
   http://www.gusmachadofordof
   hialeah.com
Year Founded: 1982
Sales Range: $150-199.9 Million
Emp.: 180
Holding Company; New & Used Car Dealerships
N.A.I.C.S.: 551112
Lydia Machado *(Mgr-Customer Rels)*
Alex Garrido *(Mgr-Fleet)*
Carlos Cruz *(Mgr-Sls)*
Eddie Miranda *(Mgr-Sls)*
Gilbert Casanova *(Mgr-Fin)*
Jesus Alvarez *(Gen Mgr-Sls)*
Jesus Reyes *(Mgr-Used Car)*
Jose Mendez *(Mgr-Internet Sls)*
Luis Alonso *(Mgr-Body Shop)*
Nestor Gonzalez *(Mgr-Internet Sls)*

Subsidiaries:

Gus Machado Ford, Inc.   (1)
1200 W 49th St, Hialeah, FL 33012   (100%)
Tel.: (786) 393-6499
Web Site: http://www.gusmachadoford.com
Emp.: 100
New & Used Car Dealer
N.A.I.C.S.: 441110
Martha Capote *(Sec)*

GUSMER ENTERPRISES, INC.

1165 Globe Ave, Mountainside, NJ 07092-2903
Tel.: (908) 301-1811
Web Site:
   https://www.gusmerenterprises.com
Year Founded: 1929
Rev.: $29,300,000
Emp.: 170
Coatings & Filters for Beverage-Making Machinery Mfr
N.A.I.C.S.: 333998
Marla G. Jeffrey *(Pres)*

Subsidiaries:

Gusmer Enterprises, Inc.   (1)
81 M St, Fresno, CA 93721-3215
Tel.: (559) 256-5400
Web Site: http://www.gusmercellulo.com
Sales Range: $10-24.9 Million
Emp.: 64
Filters for Beverage-Making Machinery
N.A.I.C.S.: 333998

GUSTAVE A. LARSON COMPANY

233 N 2869 Roundy Cir W, Pewaukee, WI 53072-5794
Tel.: (262) 542-0200   WI
Web Site: https://www.galarson.com
Year Founded: 1936
Warm Air Heating & Air Conditioning
N.A.I.C.S.: 423730
Andrew Larson *(Chm & CEO)*
Scott Larson *(Pres)*

GUSWEILER GM CENTER

1132 State Rte 41 SW, Washington Court House, OH 43160
Tel.: (740) 335-2200
Web Site: http://www.gusweiler.com
Year Founded: 1984
Sales Range: $25-49.9 Million
Emp.: 65
Car Whslr
N.A.I.C.S.: 441110

Gusweiler GM Center—(Continued)

Jim Gusweiler *(Pres)*

GUTENBERG COMMUNICA-TIONS

555 Eighth Ave Ste 1509, New York, NY 10018
Tel.: (212) 239-8475
Web Site:
　http://www.gutenbergpr.com
Year Founded: 2004
Emp.: 100
Full-Service Strategic Communications, Public & Investor Relations Services
N.A.I.C.S.: 541820
Hugh Burnham *(Co-Founder & Co-CEO)*
Harjiv Singh *(Co-Founder & Co-CEO)*
Michael Gallo *(Mng Dir)*
Liana Hawes *(VP)*
Lavanya DJ *(VP)*
John Kreuzer *(VP)*
Ed Rebello *(VP)*
Kerri Hazama-Rider *(Dir)*
Max Liberty-Point *(Dir-Creative)*
J. Bonasia *(Sr Strategist-Comm)*

Subsidiaries:

Gutenberg Communications　　　(1)
A-85 East of Kailash, New Delhi, 110065, India
Tel.: (91) 11 4132 4969
Web Site: http://www.gutenbergpr.com
Public Relations
N.A.I.C.S.: 541820
Sonali Madbhavi *(Country Head & VP)*
Amardeep Singh *(Dir-Fin & Ops)*
Christina Daniels *(Dir-Content)*

GUTHRIE COUNTY RURAL ELECTRIC COOPERATIVE ASSOCIATION

1406 State St, Guthrie Center, IA 50115-0007
Tel.: (641) 747-2206
Web Site: https://www.guthrie-rec.coop
Sales Range: $10-24.9 Million
Emp.: 17
Electric Power Administration Organization
N.A.I.C.S.: 926130
Cozy Nelson *(Gen Mgr)*

GUTHRIE LUMBER SALES INC.

3300 Gonzales St, Austin, TX 78702
Tel.: (512) 247-2777
Web Site:
　http://www.guthrielumber.com
Sales Range: $10-24.9 Million
Emp.: 8
Lumber: Rough, Dressed & Finished
N.A.I.C.S.: 423310
Bobby Guthrie *(Founder & Owner)*
Greg Guthrie *(VP-Special Products)*

GUTHRIE/MAYES

710 W Main St, Louisville, KY 40202-2676
Tel.: (502) 584-0371
Web Site:
　http://www.guthriemayes.com
Year Founded: 1977
Sales Range: $10-24.9 Million
Emp.: 12
Public Relations Agency
N.A.I.C.S.: 541820
Jack Guthrie *(Founder)*
Clair Nichols *(Principal)*
Dan Hartlage *(Principal)*
Andy Eggers *(Principal)*
N. Gregory Pettit *(Mng Dir-Lexington)*

Drew Mitchell *(Assoc Acct Mgr-PR)*
McKenzi Loid *(Acct Mgr)*
Ashley Brauer *(Acct Mgr)*

GUTHY-RENKER CORPORA-TION

100 N Sepulveda Blvd Ste 1600, El Segundo, CA 90245
Tel.: (310) 581-6250　　　　CA
Web Site: https://www.guthy-renker.com
Year Founded: 1988
Sales Range: $1-4.9 Billion
Emp.: 825
Holding Company; Direct Marketing Services
N.A.I.C.S.: 551112
Bill Guthy *(Founder, Owner, Chm & Principal)*
Greg Renker *(Founder, Owner, Chm & Principal)*
Lenny Lieberman *(Founder & CEO)*
Bennet Van De Bunt *(Bd of Dirs, Executives)*

Subsidiaries:

Guthy-Renker Corp. - Santa Monica Office　　　　　　　　　　　　　(1)
3340 Ocean Park Blvd Ste 3055, Santa Monica, CA 90405-3268
Tel.: (310) 581-6250
Web Site: http://www.guthy-renker.com
Sales Range: $25-49.9 Million
Emp.: 160
Provider of Direct Marketing Services
N.A.I.C.S.: 423990
Bill Guthy *(Co-Pres)*
Greg Renker *(Co-Pres)*

GUTKNECHT CONSTRUCTION COMPANY

2280 Citygate Dr, Columbus, OH 43219
Tel.: (614) 532-5410
Web Site: https://www.gutknecht.com
Sales Range: $10-24.9 Million
Emp.: 50
Commercial & Office Building, New Construction
N.A.I.C.S.: 236220
Mike Poyer *(CFO & Controller)*
Tom Beddow *(Dir-Safety)*
Jeff Feinman *(Pres)*
Ben Lindsay *(VP)*

GUTTMAN HOLDINGS, INC.

200 Speers St, Belle Vernon, PA 15012
Tel.: (724) 489-5199　　　　DE
Web Site:
　https://www.guttmanenergy.com
Year Founded: 2022
Emp.: 220
Holding Company
N.A.I.C.S.: 551112
Joseph Lucot *(CEO)*

Subsidiaries:

Guttman Energy, Inc.　　　　　(1)
200 Speers St, Belle Vernon, PA 15012-1000
Tel.: (724) 483-3533
Web Site: https://www.guttmanenergy.com
Sales Range: $200-249.9 Million
Emp.: 700
Petroleum Products Marketer & Distr; Towing Services
N.A.I.C.S.: 424710
Richard M. Guttman *(Pres)*
Louis Quarto *(VP-Ops & VP-Supply)*
Alan R. Guttman *(Chm & CEO)*
Richard M. Guttman *(Vice Chm)*
Mark R. Harper *(Exec VP-Sls & Mktg)*
Gary Smelko *(Exec VP-Transportation & Terminals)*
W. Arthur Benson *(Sr VP)*
Louis Quarto *(VP-Supply)*
Shauna Huzicko *(VP-Supply & Trading)*
Lawrence A. Flannelly *(VP-Fleet Card Sls)*

Jeff Plymell *(Dir-Supply & Bus Dev-Fuels Div)*
Jeffrey Roberts *(Dir-Risk Mgmt)*
George Butler *(Sr Dir-Sls)*
David Wade *(VP-Sls & Mktg)*
William Benson Jr. *(VP-Supply & Program Sls)*
Web Site: http://www.guthy.com

Source One Transportation, LLC　(1)
200 Speers St, Belle Vernon, PA 15012
Tel.: (724) 483-3533
Web Site: http://www.source01.com
Fuel Transportation Services
N.A.I.C.S.: 484220

GUY BENNETT LUMBER COMPANY

2050 Wilma Dr, Clarkston, WA 99403
Tel.: (509) 758-5558
Web Site: http://www.bennett-lumber.com
Sales Range: $10-24.9 Million
Emp.: 350
Sawmills
N.A.I.C.S.: 321113
Frank Bennett *(Pres)*

GUY BROWN PRODUCTS

9003 Overlook Blvd, Brentwood, TN 37027
Tel.: (615) 777-1500
Web Site: http://www.guybrown.com
Year Founded: 1977
Sales Range: $10-24.9 Million
Emp.: 75
Recycled Laser Toner Cartridges Mfr, Sales & Distr
N.A.I.C.S.: 333248
Jay Chawan *(CFO)*
Maria Teresa Vazquez *(VP-Sls & Mktg)*

GUY CHEMICAL COMPANY, INC.

150 Dominion Dr, Somerset, PA 15501
Tel.: (814) 443-9455
Web Site:
　https://www.guychemical.com
Year Founded: 1995
Rev.: $15,600,000
Emp.: 50
Business Services
N.A.I.C.S.: 561910
Guy Berkebile *(Pres)*
Bruce Contino *(VP)*
Valerie Glover *(Mgr-Admin)*

GUY HOPKINS CONSTRUCTION CO., INC.

13855 W Amber Ave, Baton Rouge, LA 70809
Tel.: (225) 751-2158
Web Site:
　https://www.guyhopkins.com
Rev.: $14,800,000
Emp.: 50
Commercial & Institutional Building Construction
N.A.I.C.S.: 236220
Collette M. Lambert *(CFO)*
Henry G. Hopkins III *(Pres)*

GUY M. TURNER INC.

4514 S Holden Rd, Greensboro, NC 27406
Tel.: (336) 294-4660
Web Site:
　https://www.guymturner.com
Rev.: $32,856,577
Emp.: 125
Machine Moving & Rigging
N.A.I.C.S.: 238290
Mike Hoggard *(VP)*
Karen Faircloth *(Mgr-Contracting Admin)*
Doug Gilliam *(VP)*
Paul Lanier *(VP-Electrical)*

Joe Godwin *(Project Mgr)*
Jamie Warner *(Dir-Safety)*
Jeanette Landret *(CFO)*

GUYAN INTERNATIONAL INC.

5 Nichols Dr, Barboursville, WV 25504
Tel.: (304) 733-1029
Web Site:
　http://www.guyaninternational.com
Year Founded: 1985
Sales Range: $100-124.9 Million
Emp.: 265
Mfr of Fluid Power Pumps & Motors
N.A.I.C.S.: 332313
Carletta Fannin *(Dir-Affairs)*
Robert L. Shell Jr. *(Chm & CEO)*

GUYETTE, SCHMIDT & DEETER

24718 Beverly Rd, Saint Michaels, MD 21663
Tel.: (410) 745-0485
Web Site:
　http://www.guyetteandschmidt.com
Year Founded: 1984
Sales Range: $10-24.9 Million
Emp.: 7
Decoy Auctions
N.A.I.C.S.: 459510
Gary Guyette *(Owner)*
Lynda Brooks *(Office Mgr)*
Ed Kenney *(Mgr-Shipping)*

GUYS FLOOR SERVICE INCORPORATED

10275 E 47th Ave, Denver, CO 80238
Tel.: (303) 371-8900
Web Site: https://www.guysfloor.com
Rev.: $45,000,000
Emp.: 352
Floor Laying & Floor Work
N.A.I.C.S.: 238330
Edward Routzon *(Pres)*
Al Feldman *(CFO)*
Angie Stoehr *(Supvr-Customer Svc)*
Rich Youll *(VP)*

GVD INDUSTRIES LLC

3440 Windwuest Dr, Holland, MI 49424
Tel.: (616) 836-4067　　　　MI
Web Site: https://gvdindustries.com
Privater Equity Firm
N.A.I.C.S.: 523999
Gary Van Dyke *(Chm & CEO)*

GVH MANAGEMENT

2601 SE Loop 289, Lubbock, TX 79404
Tel.: (806) 795-2453
Web Site:
　http://www.gvhmanagement.com
Distribution Company
N.A.I.C.S.: 512250
Joseph Earl Schmidt *(CEO)*

Subsidiaries:

Miller Paper Company　　　　　(1)
6511 S Washington St, Amarillo, TX 79118
Tel.: (806) 353-0317
Web Site: http://www.millerpaper.com
Paper, Janitorial Supplies, Gift Wrap Supplies & Packaging Material Distr
N.A.I.C.S.: 424130
Joe Schmidt *(CEO & Mng Partner)*
Sean Wright *(Pres & Partner)*

GVM INC.

374 Heidlersburg Rd, Biglerville, PA 17307
Tel.: (717) 677-6197
Web Site: https://www.gvminc.com
Rev.: $15,000,000
Emp.: 60
Farm Machinery & Equipment

N.A.I.C.S.: 333111
Mark Anderson *(Owner & Pres)*
Jim Collins *(VP-Ops)*
Ronald Weigle *(Mgr-Fabrication)*

GVNA HEALTHCARE, INC.
34 Pearly Ln, Gardner, MA 01440
Tel.: (978) 632-1230   MA
Web Site:
   http://www.gvnahealthcare.org
Year Founded: 1906
Sales Range: $10-24.9 Million
Emp.: 219
Community Health Care Services
N.A.I.C.S.: 621498
Ann Racine *(VP-Dev & Community Rels)*
Laura LaBrack *(VP-Mktg & Bus Dev)*
Elaine T. Fluet *(Pres & CEO)*
Heather Layton *(Sec)*
Andrew Boucher *(Chm)*
Ken Tomasetti *(Vice Chm)*
Michael Gerry *(Treas)*
Dale DelleChiaie *(VP-HR)*
Patty Bean *(Dir-My Home Connection)*
Murielle Conway *(Program Dir-Gardner Adult Day Health)*
Karen Culkeen *(Dir-Healthy Families Program)*
Ann Marie D'Olimpio *(Program Dir-Fitchburg Adult Day Health)*
Kathy Kilhart *(Dir-Elder Svcs)*
Mark Lemcke *(Mgr-IT)*
Kelly Loescher *(Dir-Homecare Ops & Clinical IS)*
Kristin Mattson *(Dir-Homecare)*
Ricardo Muchiutti *(Dir-Compliance)*
Elizabeth Newton *(Dir-Admin Support)*
Pam Saulnier *(Dir-Nursing)*

GVTC COMMUNICATIONS
36101 FM 3159, New Braunfels, TX 78132-5906
Tel.: (830) 885-4411
Web Site: https://www.gvtc.com
Year Founded: 1951
Sales Range: $25-49.9 Million
Emp.: 225
Telephone Services
N.A.I.C.S.: 517121
Ritchie Sorrells *(Pres & CEO)*
Mark Gitter *(CFO)*
Jeff Mnick *(VP-Sales-Marketing)*
George O'Neal *(VP-Network Svcs)*
Josh Pettiette *(VP-Product-Business Development-Strategic Planning)*
Charles J. Knibbe *(Chm)*
Alan Buxkemper *(Treas & Sec)*

Subsidiaries:

Guadalupe Valley Telecommunications Cooperative   (1)
36101 Fm 3159, New Braunfels, TX 78132-5906
Tel.: (830) 885-4411
Web Site: http://www.gbtc.com
Sales Range: $25-49.9 Million
Provider of Communication Services
N.A.I.C.S.: 517121

GVW GROUP, LLC
625 Roger Williams Ave, Highland Park, IL 60035
Tel.: (847) 681-8417
Web Site: http://www.gvwgroup.com
Year Founded: 1993
Holding Company; Motor Vehicles & Car Bodies
N.A.I.C.S.: 551112
Andrew Taitz *(Chm)*
Gregory Martin *(CFO)*
Jeffrey Leeb *(Gen Counsel)*
Julie Teeters *(Dir-Talent Mgmt)*

GW & WADE

93 Worcester St, Wellesley, MA 02481
Tel.: (781) 239-1188
Web Site: http://www.gwwade.com
Year Founded: 1986
Sales Range: $10-24.9 Million
Emp.: 57
Financial Management Services
N.A.I.C.S.: 523999
David L. Brodsky *(Principal)*
James Da Silva *(Principal-Client Dev)*
Christopher J. K. Dolan *(Dir-Ops)*
Robert J. Emens *(Principal)*
Neil L. Goldberg *(Principal)*
Philip P. Jameson *(Principal)*
Ron W. Minassian *(Dir-Trading)*
John S. Murray *(Principal)*
Darren M. Norton *(Principal)*
Timothy Pinch *(Principal)*
Gerald A. Polcari *(Principal)*
Joseph P. Rigali *(Principal)*
Eric H. Rosenberg *(Principal)*
Beth Lehman *(Chief Compliance Officer & Gen Counsel)*
Gene E. Sinclair *(Principal)*
Alice Hsu *(VP-Client Dev-Palo Alto)*
Heather Mahoney *(VP-Ops)*
Robert J. DeFreitas *(VP-Client Dev)*
Ryan Bartholomew *(Principal)*
Sherman Moore *(VP-Client Dev-D.C. Metro)*
Laurie Wexler Gerber *(Mktg Dir)*
Robert F. Bodio Jr. *(Principal)*

GW FOODS INC.
2041 Railroad Dr, Willow Springs, MO 65793-1439
Tel.: (417) 469-4000   MO
Web Site:
   https://www.gwfoodsinc.com
Year Founded: 1981
Sales Range: $50-74.9 Million
Emp.: 430
Grocery Stores
N.A.I.C.S.: 445110

Subsidiaries:

Hudson's Super Markets, Inc.   (1)
609 N Main St, Harrison, AR 72601-2910
Tel.: (870) 741-2171
Sales Range: $25-49.9 Million
Emp.: 65
Grocery Stores
N.A.I.C.S.: 445110

GWI, INC.
8 Pomerleau St, Biddeford, ME 04005
Tel.: (207) 407-5721
Web Site: https://www.gwi.net
Sales Range: $10-24.9 Million
Emp.: 60
Telecommunication Servicesb
N.A.I.C.S.: 517810
Fletcher Kittredge *(CEO)*
David Allen *(VP-Tech)*
Heather Kelley *(VP-Ops)*
Remi Caron *(VP-Strategic Alliances)*
Patrick Sweeney *(CFO)*
Tom Kinney *(Chief Revenue Officer)*
Sean Byrne *(Dir-Comml Sls)*
Brad Dormanen *(Dir-IT)*
Eric Smith *(Dir-Svc Delivery & Customer Svc)*
Eric Samp *(Gen Counsel)*

GWIN DOBSON & FOREMAN INC.
3121 Fairway Dr, Altoona, PA 16602
Tel.: (814) 943-5214
Web Site:
   http://www.gdfengineers.com
Rev.: $9,480,000
Emp.: 60
Engineeering Services
N.A.I.C.S.: 541330

Mark Glenn *(Pres, CEO & Mgr-Engrg)*

Subsidiaries:

Pathline, Inc.   (1)
3121 Fairway Dr, Altoona, PA 16602
Tel.: (814) 941-0640
Web Site: http://www.pathline.com
Project Management & Construction Services
N.A.I.C.S.: 541618

GWINNETT HOSPITAL SYSTEM, INC.
1000 Medical Center Blvd, Lawrenceville, GA 30046
Tel.: (678) 312-1000   GA
Web Site:
   http://www.gwinnettmedicalcenter.org
Year Founded: 1992
Sales Range: $600-649.9 Million
Emp.: 4,665
Health Care Srvices
N.A.I.C.S.: 622110
Tommy McBride *(CFO & Exec VP)*
Alan Bier *(Chief Medical Officer & Exec VP)*
Carol Danielson *(Chief Nursing Officer & Sr VP)*
Jay Dennard *(COO)*

GWP INDUSTRIES INC.
3001 Gateman Dr, Parkersburg, WV 26101-1911
Tel.: (304) 422-3103   WV
Year Founded: 1950
Sales Range: $25-49.9 Million
Emp.: 200
Holding Company; Metals Service Centers
N.A.I.C.S.: 423510
E.R. Gateman *(Pres)*
Tim Kern *(CFO)*

GYANSYS INC.
8440 Woodfield Crossing Blvd Ste 290, Indianapolis, IN 46240
Tel.: (317) 580-4200
Web Site: http://www.gyansys.com
Year Founded: 2001
Sales Range: $1-9.9 Million
Emp.: 50
Consulting & Management Services
N.A.I.C.S.: 518210
Arun Kotagiri *(COO-Asia Ops)*
Rajkishore Una *(Pres & CEO)*
Anand Aboti *(Chief Bus Officer)*

GYK ANTLER
175 Canal St, Manchester, NH 03101
Tel.: (603) 625-5713
Web Site: http://www.gykantler.com
Year Founded: 1974
N.A.I.C.S.: 541810
Patrick W. Griffin *(Chm)*
Travis York *(Pres & CEO)*
Jen Jonsson *(COO)*

GYMBOGLOBAL CORPORATION
71 Stevenson St Ste 2200, San Francisco, CA 94105
Tel.: (415) 604-3094
Web Site:
   http://www.gymboreeclasses.com
Year Founded: 1976
Family Developmental Play, Music & Art Classes
N.A.I.C.S.: 713990
Dana Rich *(Mgr-Site)*

GYPSUM EXPRESS LTD.
8280 Sixty Rd, Baldwinsville, NY 13027
Tel.: (315) 638-2201

Web Site:
   https://www.gypsumexpress.com
Sales Range: $25-49.9 Million
Emp.: 720
Local Trucking, With Storage
N.A.I.C.S.: 484110
John C. Wight *(Owner & Pres)*
John Zink *(VP)*
Jerry Harris *(VP-Vans & Dedicated Ops)*
Dennis Plucinik *(Dir-Safety)*
Adrienne Deloff *(Mgr-HR-Baldwinsville)*
Amy Crysler *(Coord-Payroll)*
Candice Zaia *(Coord-Payroll)*
Kim Scaries *(Coord-Payroll)*
Kristen McGrew *(Mgr-Compliance)*
Phil Gorea *(Mgr-Ops-Baldwinsville)*
Ryan Smith *(Asst Dir-Safety)*

GYPSUM PRODUCTS INC.
1400 E 61st Ave, Denver, CO 80216
Tel.: (303) 227-3167
Web Site:
   http://www.gypsumproducts.com
Year Founded: 1985
Sales Range: $50-74.9 Million
Emp.: 76
Drywall, Steel & Acoustical Ceilings Whslr
N.A.I.C.S.: 423310
Larry Haligas *(VP-Sls)*
Jay Haddick *(Branch Mgr)*

GYPSUM SUPPLY CO.
1125 Harrison Ave, Rockford, IL 61104
Tel.: (815) 397-5718   IL
Web Site:
   http://www.gypsumsupply.net
Rev.: $37,297,143
Emp.: 20
Drywall & Plastering Materials Distr
N.A.I.C.S.: 423320
Jim Gabelbauer *(Pres)*
Mary Osborn *(VP-Legal)*

GYROTRON TECHNOLOGY INC.
3412 Progress Dr, Bensalem, PA 19020
Tel.: (215) 244-4740   DE
Web Site:
   https://www.gyrotrontech.com
Year Founded: 1998
Glass Laminating Machines & Equipment Mfr
N.A.I.C.S.: 333248
Vladislav Sklyarevich *(Pres & Treas)*

GZA GEOENVIRONMENTAL INC.
249 Vanderbilt Ave, Norwood, MA 02062-4674
Tel.: (781) 278-3700   DE
Web Site: http://www.gza.com
Year Founded: 1964
Sales Range: $75-99.9 Million
Emp.: 450
Environmental Consulting, Remediation Services, Geotechnical Services & Information Services
N.A.I.C.S.: 541330
W. Fred Lenz *(Sr Principal)*
William E. Hadge *(Pres & CEO)*
Douglas S. Roy *(Principal)*
Mary B. Hall *(Sr Principal)*
William H. Hover *(Sr Principal)*
Frank S. Vetere *(Principal)*
Christopher Snow *(Assoc Principal-Geotechnical)*
Kenneth R. Johnston *(Principal)*
Richard L. Ecord *(Assoc Principal & Dir-EHS)*
Paul G. Davis *(Principal)*

GZA GeoEnvironmental Inc.—(Continued)

John C. Murphy (COO)
Chad W. Cox (Principal-Dams & Levees)
Russell J. Morgan (Sr Principal)
Terese M. Kwiatkowski (Sr Principal-Geotechnical)
Anders B. Bjarngard (Principal)
John C. Osborne (Sr Principal)
Robert J. Palermo (Sr Principal)
David L. Palmerton (Principal)
Albert J. Ricciardelli (Sr Principal)
Patrick F. Sheehan (CEO)
Daniel C. Stapleton (Sr Principal)
Peter Baril (Principal)
Angela Cincotta (Chief Mktg & Comm Officer)
Paul J. Malagrifa (CIO)

Subsidiaries:

Ecosystem Consulting Service, Inc. **(1)**
30 Mason St, Coventry, CT 06238-3121
Tel.: (860) 742-0744
Web Site:
http://www.ecosystemconsulting.com
Sales Range: $1-9.9 Million
Emp.: 6
Commercial & Service Industry Machinery Mfr
N.A.I.C.S.: 333310
Mary S. Kortmann (VP)

Glorieta Geoscience, Inc. **(1)**
1723 2nd St, Santa Fe, NM 87505
Tel.: (505) 983-5446
Web Site: http://www.glorietageo.com
Geological Engineering Services
N.A.I.C.S.: 541330
Jay Lazarus (Pres)
Jim Riesterer (Project Mgr)
Tara Vander Dussen (Exec Dir-CAFOweb)
Patricia Lovato (Office Mgr)
Paul Drakos (VP)

Vieau Associates Inc. **(1)**
7710 Computer Ave Ste 102, Edina, MN 55435
Tel.: (952) 893-7931
Web Site: http://www.vieauassociates.com
Environment, Conservation & Wildlife Organizations
N.A.I.C.S.: 813312
Dave Vieau (Pres)

GZK INC.
660 Fame Rd, Dayton, OH 45449
Tel.: (937) 384-1960   OH
Web Site:
http://www.arbysdayton.com
Year Founded: 1959
Sales Range: $25-49.9 Million
Emp.: 1,300
Operator of Fast-Food Restaurant Chain
N.A.I.C.S.: 722513
Bonnie Mahaffy (Mgr-Payroll & Benefits)
Christine Koeller (CMO)
John Frueauf (COO)
Kevin Edwards (Reg Dir)
Steve Judge (VP-HR)
Brian Kaufman (Dir-Corp Dev)
Beth Plews (Controller)

H & C MOTORS, INC.
15531 Frederick Rd, Rockville, MD 20855
Tel.: (301) 340-3100
Web Site: http://www.hersonskia.com
Year Founded: 1982
Sales Range: $25-49.9 Million
Emp.: 54
New Car Dealers
N.A.I.C.S.: 441110
Nick Sanzone (Mgr)
John Samanski (Mgr-Ops)

H & H CHEVROLET OLDSMO-

BILE PONTIAC & CADILLAC
730 E King St, Shippensburg, PA 17257-1510
Tel.: (717) 327-4583
Web Site: https://hhchev.com
Sales Range: $10-24.9 Million
Emp.: 60
Car Whslr
N.A.I.C.S.: 441110
Eddie Coy (Dir-Sls)

H & L BLOOM, INC.
28 Grosvenor St, Taunton, MA 02780
Tel.: (508) 822-1991
Web Site: https://www.bloombus.com
Year Founded: 1946
Sales Range: $10-24.9 Million
Emp.: 260
Charter Bus Industry Services
N.A.I.C.S.: 485510
Mark Bloom (Treas & Pres)
Matthew Bloom (Sec)
Gerald Santos Jr. (VP)

H & L CHEVROLET, INC.
1416 Post Rd, Darien, CT 06820-5467
Tel.: (203) 202-3951
Web Site: https://www.hlchevy.com
Year Founded: 1955
Sales Range: $10-24.9 Million
Emp.: 32
New Car Dealers
N.A.I.C.S.: 441110
Daniel B. Haims (Pres)

H & M CONSTRUCTORS CO.
187 Deaverview Rd, Asheville, NC 28806
Tel.: (828) 254-6141
Web Site:
https://www.mbhaynes.com
Sales Range: $125-149.9 Million
Emp.: 90
Commercial & Institutional Building Construction Services
N.A.I.C.S.: 236220
Faison Hester (CFO)

H & T SEAFOOD, INC.
5598 Lindbergh Ln, Bell, CA 90201
Tel.: (323) 526-0888   CA
Web Site: https://www.htseafood.com
Year Founded: 1994
Sales Range: $10-24.9 Million
Emp.: 50
Fish/Seafood Mfr
N.A.I.C.S.: 424460
Thong Lu (Pres)
Linda Tang (Mgr-Pur)

H ENTERPRISES INTERNATIONAL INC.
1 Financial Plz Ste 2300, Minneapolis, MN 55402
Tel.: (612) 340-8849   DE
Web Site: http://www.heii.us
Year Founded: 1994
Sales Range: $10-24.9 Million
Emp.: 7
Provider of Industrial Machinery & Equipment
N.A.I.C.S.: 423830
Richard E. O'Leary (Chm)
John Byrne (Pres)

H&C ANIMAL HEALTH, LLC
18403 Longs Way Ste 102, Parker, CO 80134
Tel.: (757) 650-9338
Web Site: http://www.hc-animal-health.com
Year Founded: 2013
Sales Range: $10-24.9 Million
Emp.: 50
Consumer Products Distr

N.A.I.C.S.: 423620
Chuck Latham (CEO)

H&C HEADWEAR INC.
17145 Margay Ave, Carson, CA 90746-1209
Tel.: (310) 324-5263   CA
Web Site: http://www.kccaps.com
Year Founded: 1991
Emp.: 150
Provider of Hats & Golf Shirts
N.A.I.C.S.: 424350
John Lee (CEO)
Charles Schoonover (Controller)

Subsidiaries:

H&C Headwear-Atlanta Capco Sportswear **(1)**
5945 Shiloh Rd, Alpharetta, GA 30005-8352   **(100%)**
Tel.: (678) 947-5898
Web Site: http://www.kccaps.com
Sales Range: $10-24.9 Million
Emp.: 6
Provider of Hats & Golf Shirts
N.A.I.C.S.: 458110
Al Schultz (Gen Mgr)

H&C Headwear-Chicago **(1)**
1625 Todd Farm Dr, Elgin, IL 60123
Tel.: (847) 289-8512
Web Site: http://www.kccaps.com
Mfr of Hats & Golf Shirts
N.A.I.C.S.: 424350
John Lee (CEO)

H&C Headwear-Dallas **(1)**
2168 Diplomat Dr, Farmers Branch, TX 75234-8932   **(100%)**
Tel.: (972) 620-1717
Web Site: http://www.kcheadwear.com
Sales Range: $10-24.9 Million
Emp.: 6
Provider of Hats & Golf Shirts
N.A.I.C.S.: 424350
Susan Wayne (Acct Mgr)
Susan Wayne (Acct Mgr)

H&C Headwear-New York **(1)**
100 W Commercial Ave, Moonachie, NJ 07074-2304
Tel.: (201) 939-9228
Web Site: http://www.hcheadwear.com
Sales Range: $10-24.9 Million
Emp.: 15
Provider of Hats & Golf Shirts
N.A.I.C.S.: 424690

H&D STEEL SERVICE, INC.
9960 York Alpha Dr, North Royalton, OH 44133-3510
Tel.: (440) 237-3390   OH
Web Site: https://www.hdsteel.com
Year Founded: 1972
Sales Range: $25-49.9 Million
Emp.: 45
Provider of Steel Services
N.A.I.C.S.: 423510
Scott Sustar (Dir-Mktg)
Andy Gasbarre (Controller)

H&F GULF INC.
1834 Lincoln Hwy E, Lancaster, PA 17602
Tel.: (717) 392-6793
Web Site: https://www.hftires.com
Sales Range: $10-24.9 Million
Emp.: 40
Automobile Tires & Tubes
N.A.I.C.S.: 423130
Barry Lee Fitzgerald Sr. (Pres)

H&G SALES INC.
11635 Lackland Rd, Saint Louis, MO 63146
Tel.: (314) 432-8188
Web Site: http://www.h-gsales.com
Year Founded: 1967
Sales Range: $25-49.9 Million
Emp.: 85

Metal Doors; Wood Door; Hollow Metal Frames & Doors
N.A.I.C.S.: 423710
Irvin S. Hill (Chm)
Jay Manzo (Pres)
Tim Elam (Mgr-Engrg)
Joshua LaVigne (Project Mgr)

H&H AGENCY, INC.
PO Box 8208, Newport Beach, CA 92658
Tel.: (949) 851-6362
Web Site: http://www.dashers.com
Year Founded: 1969
Sales Range: $25-49.9 Million
Emp.: 107
Provider of Insurance Agents Brokers & Services
N.A.I.C.S.: 524210
Mike Weinstein (Pres)

Subsidiaries:

Sterling Casualty Insurance Company Inc. **(1)**
600 City Pkwy W Ste 800, Orange, CA 92868-1703   **(100%)**
Tel.: (949) 851-6362
Sales Range: $50-74.9 Million
Provider of Insurance Agents, Brokers & Services
N.A.I.C.S.: 524210

H&H CONTINENTAL MOTORS INC.
5750 S La Grange Rd, Countryside, IL 60525
Tel.: (708) 352-9200
Web Site:
http://www.continentalmotors.com
Rev.: $41,304,418
Emp.: 50
Automobiles, New & Used
N.A.I.C.S.: 441110
John F. Weinberger (Pres & CEO)

H&H DISTRIBUTING COMPANY, INC.
304 S Vine St, West Union, IA 52175-1437
Tel.: (563) 422-3846   IA
Year Founded: 1946
Sales Range: $75-99.9 Million
Emp.: 102
Distr of Groceries, Fresh Fruits, Vegetables, Candy, Tobacco & Restaurant Equipment & Supplies
N.A.I.C.S.: 424510
Sandra Kaye Baldwin (Pres & Treas)
Darrel Dolf (Controller & Dir-MIS)

H&H GROUP INC.
2801 Syene Rd, Madison, WI 53713
Tel.: (608) 273-3434
Web Site:
http://www.hhindustries.com
Sales Range: $25-49.9 Million
Emp.: 50
General Electrical Contractor
N.A.I.C.S.: 238210
William D. Plummer (Pres)

H&H GUN RANGE-SHOOTING SPORTS OUTLET
400 S Vermont Ave Ste 110, Oklahoma City, OK 73108
Tel.: (405) 947-3888   OK
Web Site:
http://www.hhgunrange.com
Year Founded: 1990
Sales Range: $10-24.9 Million
Emp.: 65
Retailer of Guns, Ammunition & Training Services
N.A.I.C.S.: 459110

Jayne Hall *(Co-Founder & Treas)*
Miles E. Hall *(Co-Founder & Pres)*
Michael Rust *(Mgr-Ops)*
Yvonne Cagle *(Mgr)*

**H&H INDUSTRIAL CORPORA-
TION**
7612 N Route 130, Pennsauken, NJ
08110
Tel.: (856) 663-4444   DE
Web Site:
   http://www.hhindustrial.com
Year Founded: 1950
Sales Range: $1-9.9 Million
Emp.: 42
Household Furniture (except Wood &
Metal) Mfr
N.A.I.C.S.: 337126
Gertrude Hajduk *(Pres)*

**H&H SHOOTING SPORTS
COMPLEX**
400 S Vermont Ave Ste 110, Okla-
homa City, OK 73108-1034
Tel.: (405) 947-3888
Web Site:
   https://www.hhshootingsports.com
Year Founded: 1981
Sales Range: $10-24.9 Million
Emp.: 86
Shooting Sports Club Operator
N.A.I.C.S.: 713940
Miles Hall *(Founder & Pres)*

**H&H SYSTEMS AND DESIGN
INC.**
135 W Market St, New Albany, IN
47150
Tel.: (812) 944-2396
Web Site: https://www.hhsd.com
Sales Range: $10-24.9 Million
Emp.: 25
Hospital Construction
N.A.I.C.S.: 236220
Mike Reed *(Mgr-Special Projects
Grp)*

H&H TRAILER, LLC
222 N 1st St, Clarinda, IA 51632
Tel.: (712) 542-2618
Web Site: http://www.hhtrailer.com
Year Founded: 1993
Sales Range: $10-24.9 Million
Emp.: 45
Trailer Bodies Mfr
N.A.I.C.S.: 336212

H&K GRAPHICS
8374 Market St Ste 489, Bradenton,
FL 34202
Tel.: (941) 758-2200
Web Site:
   http://www.hkgraphicsinc.com
Year Founded: 1989
Sales Range: Less than $1 Million
Emp.: 2
Advertising Agencies, Advertising
Specialties, Graphic Design, Legal
Services, Magazines, Media Buying
Services, Newspaper, Newspapers &
Magazines, Print
N.A.I.C.S.: 541810
William T. Kalter *(Pres)*
Janet Heller *(Controller)*

H&L MESABI COMPANY
1205 7th Ave E, Hibbing, MN 55746
Tel.: (218) 263-6845
Web Site: https://www.hlmesabi.com
Year Founded: 1985
Emp.: 13
Mining Supply, Distribution Sales &
Services
N.A.I.C.S.: 423810
Bernard Carey *(Pres)*
Caryl Gjerdahl *(CFO)*

H&L TOOTH COMPANY
1540 S Greenwood Ave, Montebello,
CA 90640
Tel.: (323) 721-5146
Web Site: http://www.hltooth.com
Sales Range: $10-24.9 Million
Emp.: 4
Commercial Construction Machinery
Mfr
N.A.I.C.S.: 333120
Richard L. Launder *(Chm)*

H&M COMPANY INC.
50 Security Dr, Jackson, TN 38305
Tel.: (731) 664-6300
Web Site:
   https://www.hmcompany.com
Year Founded: 1957
Sales Range: $300-349.9 Million
Emp.: 250
Engineering & Construction Services
N.A.I.C.S.: 236220
Roger Cook *(Sr VP)*
James Kirkland *(Sr Project Mgr)*

Subsidiaries:

H&M Industrial Service Inc.   **(1)**
50 Security Dr, Jackson, TN 38305
Tel.: (731) 422-5211
Web Site: http://www.hmcompany.com
Rev.: $42,072,101
Emp.: 200
Industrial Support Services, Including Engi-
neering, Procurement, Fabrication, Con-
crete Installation, Steel Fabrication & Pro-
cess Equipment Installation
N.A.I.C.S.: 541330

**H&M INTERNATIONAL TRANS-
PORTATION INC.**
485-C US 1 S Ste 330, Iselin, NJ
08830
Tel.: (732) 510-4640   NJ
Web Site: http://www.hmit.net
Year Founded: 1968
Sales Range: $25-49.9 Million
Emp.: 810
Provider of Transportation Services
N.A.I.C.S.: 488510
Charles T. Connors *(Pres & COO)*
Eric T. Witham *(VP-IT)*
Margaret Horne *(CFO-Fin)*

Subsidiaries:

American Terminals Distribution
Corp   **(1)**
700 Belleville Tpke, Kearny, NJ 07032
Tel.: (201) 997-4400
Web Site: http://www.hmit.com
Sales Range: $10-24.9 Million
Emp.: 75
Trucking Services
N.A.I.C.S.: 484110
Richard Werkmeister *(Dir-Warehousing)*

H&M WAGNER & SONS INC.
7204 May Wagner Ln, Glen Burnie,
MD 21061-2858
Tel.: (410) 766-1150
Web Site:
   https://www.hmwagner.com
Year Founded: 1964
Sales Range: $25-49.9 Million
Emp.: 149
Commercial Equipment Whslr
N.A.I.C.S.: 423440
Joe Black *(Gen Mgr)*
George Wagner *(VP)*

H&M WHOLESALE INC.
14727 SM 2154, College Station, TX
77845
Tel.: (979) 690-1245
Web Site:
   http://www.hmwholesale.com
Sales Range: $25-49.9 Million
Emp.: 20
Petroleum Bulk Stations

N.A.I.C.S.: 424710
Mary Alford Walker *(Pres)*

**H&N CHEVROLET BUICK CO.
INC.**
713 N Grand Ave, Spencer, IA
51301-3707
Tel.: (712) 262-3230   IA
Web Site: https://www.hnchevy.com
Year Founded: 1929
Sales Range: $10-24.9 Million
Emp.: 34
Sales of New & Used Cars
N.A.I.C.S.: 441110

**H&N FOODS INTERNATIONAL,
INC.**
5580 S Alameda St, Vernon, CA
90058-3426
Tel.: (323) 586-9388   CA
Web Site: https://www.hnfoods.com
Year Founded: 1981
Sales Range: $150-199.9 Million
Emp.: 300
Seafood Distr
N.A.I.C.S.: 424460
Hua T. Ngo *(Pres)*
Christine Ngo *(Exec VP)*
Bobby Ngo *(VP-Sls)*
Dat Trieu *(VP-Admin)*

H&Q ASIA PACIFIC, LTD.
228 Hamilton Ave 3 Fl, Palo Alto, CA
94301
Tel.: (650) 838-8088
Web Site: https://www.hqap.com
Sales Range: $25-49.9 Million
Emp.: 10
Privater Equity Firm
N.A.I.C.S.: 523999
Ta-Lin Hsu *(Founder & Chm)*
Jarlon Tsang *(COO & Mng Dir)*

Subsidiaries:

Fabrinet   **(1)**
One Nexus Way, Grand Cayman, Camana
Bay, KY1-9005, Cayman Islands   **(60%)**
Tel.: (345) 25249600
Web Site: https://www.fabrinet.com
Rev.: $2,882,967,000
Assets: $2,338,519,000
Liabilities: $592,774,000
Net Worth: $1,745,745,000
Earnings: $296,181,000
Emp.: 14,213
Fiscal Year-end: 06/28/2024
Optical Component, Module & Subsystem
Mfr
N.A.I.C.S.: 333310
David T. Mitchell *(Bd of Dirs, Executives)*
Harpal S. Gill *(Pres & COO)*
Colin R. Campbell *(Gen Counsel & VP)*
Seamus Grady *(CEO)*
Mark O'Connor *(Exec VP-Corp Dev)*
Edward T. Archer *(Exec VP-Mktg & Sls-
Global)*
Csaba Sverha *(CFO & Exec VP)*
Renaud Dupre de Boulois *(Dir-Automotive)*
Kevin Camelon *(Sr Dir-Worldwide Supply
Chain)*

Subsidiary (Non-US):

CASIX Inc.   **(2)**
PO Box 1103, Fuzhou, 350014, Fujian,
China   **(100%)**
Tel.: (86) 59183620115
Web Site: http://www.casix.com
Sales Range: $25-49.9 Million
Crystal & Precision Optics Products Mfr
N.A.I.C.S.: 333310
Toh-Seng Ng *(Gen Mgr)*
Ranjit Mand *(Dir-Sls & Mktg)*

Subsidiary (US):

VitroCom Inc.   **(2)**
8 Morris Ave, Mountain Lakes, NJ
07046-0125   **(100%)**
Tel.: (973) 402-1443
Web Site: http://www.vitrocom.com

Sales Range: $10-24.9 Million
Precision Glass Products Mfr
N.A.I.C.S.: 327215

H&R AGRI-POWER, INC.
4900 Eagle Way, Hopkinsville, KY
42241
Tel.: (270) 886-3918   KY
Web Site:
   https://www.hragripower.com
Year Founded: 1990
Sales Range: $25-49.9 Million
Emp.: 170
Farm & Garden Machinery Mfr
N.A.I.C.S.: 423820
Wayne Hunt *(Pres)*
Steve Hunt *(VP)*

**H&R AUTO RADIO SERVICE
INCORPORATED**
155 York Rd, Warminster, PA 18974
Tel.: (215) 672-3707   PA
Web Site:
   http://www.hrautoradio.com
Year Founded: 1963
Sales Range: $10-24.9 Million
Emp.: 125
Motor Vehicle Radios Mfr
N.A.I.C.S.: 423620
Stephen Houk *(Owner)*

H&S BAKERY INC.
601 S Caroline St, Baltimore, MD
21231
Tel.: (410) 276-7254   MD
Web Site: https://www.hsbakery.com
Year Founded: 1953
Sales Range: $25-49.9 Million
Emp.: 481
Bread, Cake & Related Products Pro-
ducer
N.A.I.C.S.: 311812
Bill Paterakis *(Pres)*

Subsidiaries:

Automatic Rolls of Baltimore,
Inc.   **(1)**
7111 Commercial Ave, Baltimore, MD 21237
Tel.: (410) 488-2550
Bakery Product Whslr
N.A.I.C.S.: 424490
Scott Moore *(Plant Mgr)*

Automatic Rolls of New England,
Inc.   **(1)**
328 Lake Rd, Dayville, CT 06241
Tel.: (877) 877-2867
Bakery Product Whslr
N.A.I.C.S.: 424490
Steve Elias *(Plant Mgr)*

Automatic Rolls of New Jersey,
Inc.   **(1)**
1 Gourmet Ln, Edison, NJ 08837
Tel.: (732) 549-2243
Web Site: http://www.nefoods.com
Bakery Product Whslr
N.A.I.C.S.: 424490
Wayne Chandler *(Plant Mgr)*

Automatic Rolls of North Carolina,
LLC   **(1)**
68 Harvest Mill Rd, Clayton, NC 27520
Tel.: (855) 300-2867
Web Site: http://www.nafoods.com
Emp.: 50
Bakery Product Whslr
N.A.I.C.S.: 424490
Rich Tommy *(Plant Mgr)*

Bake Rite Rolls, Inc.   **(1)**
2945 Samuel Dr, Bensalem, PA 19020
Tel.: (215) 638-2400
Web Site: http://www.nefoods.com
Emp.: 250
Bakery Product Whslr
N.A.I.C.S.: 424490
Jackie Eddis *(Plant Mgr)*

H&S Properties Development
Corporation   **(1)**

H&S Bakery Inc.—(Continued)

650 S Exeter St Ste 200, Baltimore, MD
21202-4631
Tel.: (410) 649-0030
Web Site: http://www.handsbakery.com
Sales Range: $25-49.9 Million
Emp.: 140
Hotels And Motels
N.A.I.C.S.: 237210

H&S CONSTRUCTORS INC.
1616 Corn Products Rd, Corpus
Christi, TX 78409-3017
Tel.: (361) 289-5272   TX
Web Site:
   http://www.hsconstructors.com
Year Founded: 1982
Sales Range: $25-49.9 Million
Emp.: 600
Construction Services
N.A.I.C.S.: 238220
Michael D. Scott (VP)

H&S FOREST PRODUCTS INC.
525 Metro Pl N Ste 200, Dublin, OH
43017
Tel.: (614) 459-9663
Web Site: http://www.hsforest.com
Year Founded: 1990
Sales Range: $25-49.9 Million
Emp.: 21
Lumber Products Mfr
N.A.I.C.S.: 423310
John Heller (Pres)
Bill Biersteker (VP)
John Romelfanger (CEO)
Gaylord Gardner (Controller)
Amy Mollenkopf (Mgr-Acctg)
Tim Foley (Mgr-Sls & Customer Svc-
West Virginia)
Paul Buchholtz (Mgr-Panel Bd Sls)

H&S OIL COMPANY INC.
308 Martin Luther King Dr, Andrews,
SC 29510
Tel.: (843) 264-3518
Web Site: https://www.handsoil.com
Sales Range: $10-24.9 Million
Emp.: 50
Petroleum Bulk Stations
N.A.I.C.S.: 424710
Bobby Atkinson (Bus Mgr)
H. Edsel Hemingway Sr. (Pres)

H&V COLLISION CENTER
7 Oakwood Ave, Troy, NY 12180
Tel.: (518) 273-1834
Web Site:
   http://www.handvcollision.com
Year Founded: 1973
Automotive Repair Shops
N.A.I.C.S.: 811111
Vartan Jerian Jr. (VP)
Vartan Jerian Sr. (Founder)

Subsidiaries:

H&V Collision Center - Clifton
Park   (1)
390 Clifton Park Center Rd, Clifton Park,
NY 12065
Tel.: (518) 383-3368
Web Site: http://www.handvcollision.com
Sales Range: $1-9.9 Million
Emp.: 50
Automotive Body, Paint & Interior Repair &
Maintenance
N.A.I.C.S.: 811121
Pat Donohue (Mgr-Shop)

H+A INTERNATIONAL, INC.
70 E Lake St Ste 1220, Chicago, IL
60601
Tel.: (312) 332-4650
Web Site: http://www.h-a-intl.com
Year Founded: 1984
Sales Range: $10-24.9 Million
Emp.: 8
Advetising Agency

N.A.I.C.S.: 541810
Roger Halligan (Founder & CEO)
Beate Halligan (Pres)

H-E-B, LP
646 S Flores, San Antonio, TX 78204
Tel.: (210) 938-7943   TX
Web Site: https://www.heb.com
Year Founded: 1905
Sales Range: $25-49.9 Billion
Emp.: 145,000
Supermarkets & Other Grocery (ex-
cept Convenience) Stores
N.A.I.C.S.: 445110
Charles Clarence Butt (Owner &
Chm)

**H-I-S PAINT MANUFACTURING
COMPANY INC.**
1801 W Reno, Oklahoma City, OK
73106
Tel.: (405) 232-2077
Web Site: https://www.hispaint.com
Year Founded: 1972
Sales Range: $10-24.9 Million
Emp.: 30
Paint & Coating Mfr
N.A.I.C.S.: 325510
Joe T. Cox (CEO)
Kirk Cox (Pres-Professional Coatings
Grp)
Tony Cox (Pres-Industrial Coatings
Grp)
J. Kent Cox (CFO & Pres-Operations)

H-K CONTRACTORS INC.
6350 S Yellowstone Hwy, Idaho Falls,
ID 83402-1450
Tel.: (208) 523-6600   ID
Web Site:
   https://www.hkcontractors.com
Year Founded: 1975
Highway & Street Construction Ser-
vices
N.A.I.C.S.: 237310
Jeff Trosper (Pres)

**H-O-H WATER TECHNOLOGY,
INC.**
500 S Vermont St, Palatine, IL 60067
Tel.: (847) 358-7400
Web Site:
   https://www.hohwatertechno
   logy.com
Year Founded: 1968
Sales Range: $10-24.9 Million
Emp.: 50
Chemicals, Equipment & Services for
Commercial, Institutional, Light Indus-
trial & Waste Treatment Facilities
N.A.I.C.S.: 325998
Thomas F. Hutchison (Pres)

H-P PRODUCTS, INC.
512 W Gorgas St, Louisville, OH
44641-1332
Tel.: (330) 875-5556   OH
Web Site: http://www.hpproducts.net
Year Founded: 1948
Sales Range: $100-124.9 Million
Emp.: 300
Fabricated Tubing Systems & Com-
ponents, H-P Tubing, Central Vacuum
Cleaning Systems & Offset Pipe
Bends Mfr
N.A.I.C.S.: 332996
Paul R. Bishop (Chm & CEO)
David L. Bishop (Vice Chm)
Allen Green (Pres & COO)
Amy Wesley (Mgr-Mktg)
Greg Calderone (VP & Gen Mgr-
Floorcare)

**H. ARNOLD WOOD TURNING
INC.**

220 White Plains Rd Ste 245, Tarry-
town, NY 10591
Tel.: (914) 381-0801
Web Site:
   https://www.arnoldwood.com
Year Founded: 1919
Wood Products Supplier & Distr
N.A.I.C.S.: 423310
Ann Arnold (CFO)

H. BETTI INDUSTRIES, INC.
303 Paterson Plank Rd, Carlstadt, NJ
07072
Tel.: (201) 438-1300
Web Site: https://www.betson.com
Year Founded: 1934
Sales Range: $200-249.9 Million
Emp.: 400
Coin-Operated Equipment Distr
N.A.I.C.S.: 445132
Peter Betti (Chm & CEO)
Steven Betti (Treas & Sec)
Robert Betti (Exec VP)
Robert Geschine (Pres)
Jonathan Betti (VP-Sls & Bus Dev)
Glenn Quaiver (COO)
Bill Seibert (Sr VP-Ops)
Bob Boals (Exec VP)

Subsidiaries:

Betson Enterprises   (1)
303 Paterson Plank Rd, Carlstadt, NJ
07072
Tel.: (201) 438-1300
Web Site: http://www.betson.com
Sales Range: $25-49.9 Million
Emp.: 150
Coin Operated Equipment Wholesale & Re-
pair Services
N.A.I.C.S.: 423440
Robert Boals (Exec VP)
Richard Kirby (Mng Dir & Exec VP-Div)
Richard Zayas-Bazan (VP-Betson Imperial
Parts & Svc)
Robert Betti (Exec VP)

Imperial International   (1)
303 Paterson Plank Rd E, Carlstadt, NJ
07072
Tel.: (201) 288-9199
Web Site: http://www.imperialusa.com
Rev.: $10,000,000
Emp.: 10
Billiard Equipment & Supplies Distr
N.A.I.C.S.: 423910
Michael Dimotta (Pres)
Mike Cetinich (Mgr-Sls)

H. BRUCE AND SONS INC.
930 Cass St, New Castle, PA 16101
Tel.: (724) 652-5566
Web Site:
   https://www.bruceandmerrilees.com
Year Founded: 1945
Sales Range: $100-124.9 Million
Emp.: 250
General Electrical Contractor
N.A.I.C.S.: 238210
Robert J. Bruce (Chm)
Jay H. Bruce (Pres & CEO)
Gary L. Bruce (VP)

H. C. RUSTIN CORPORATION
50 E Main St, Durant, OK 74701
Tel.: (580) 924-3260
Web Site:
   http://www.rustinconcrete.com
Year Founded: 1951
Sales Range: $10-24.9 Million
Emp.: 77
Readymix Concrete Mfr
N.A.I.C.S.: 327320
Jackie Williams (Plant Mgr)

H. CARR & SONS INC.
100 Royal Little Dr, Providence, RI
02904
Tel.: (401) 331-2277
Web Site: https://www.hcarr.com
Sales Range: $10-24.9 Million

Emp.: 250
Drywall
N.A.I.C.S.: 238310
Mary Anne Wood (CFO & Treas)
Angela Rossi (Sec)
James Carr Jr. (Pres & CEO)
Thomas E. Purcell Jr. (VP-Ops)

H. EIKENHOUT & SONS, INC.
346 Wealthy St SW, Grand Rapids,
MI 49503-4022
Tel.: (616) 459-4523   MI
Web Site:
   http://www.roofingsidingwindows.com
Year Founded: 1971
Sales Range: $10-24.9 Million
Emp.: 60
Roofing, Siding & Insulation Services
N.A.I.C.S.: 423330
Henry Schierbeek (Pres)
Greg Schierbeek (VP)

H. FREEMAN & SON, INC.
411 N Cranberry Rd, Westminster,
MD 21157
Tel.: (410) 857-5774   DE
Web Site:
   https://www.hfreemanco.com
Year Founded: 1885
Sales Range: $150-199.9 Million
Emp.: 425
Mens Tailored Clothing Mfr
N.A.I.C.S.: 315250
Mark Falcone (CEO)

H. GREENBERG & SON INC.
321 Main St, Bennington, VT 05201
Tel.: (802) 442-3131
Web Site:
   http://www.hgreenbergandson.com
Sales Range: $10-24.9 Million
Emp.: 40
Hardware Stores
N.A.I.C.S.: 444140
Norman Greenberg (Owner & Pres)
Robin James (VP)

H. KRAMER & CO.
1345 W 21st St, Chicago, IL 60608
Tel.: (312) 226-6600
Web Site: https://www.hkramer.com
Year Founded: 1888
Sales Range: $10-24.9 Million
Emp.: 140
Copper Based Alloy Mfr
N.A.I.C.S.: 331529
Howard Chapman (CEO)
William O'Brien (CFO)
Adam Chapman (Exec VP)
Randall Weil (Exec VP)

**H. LEE MOFFITT CANCER
CENTER & RESEARCH INSTI-
TUTE**
12902 USF Magnolia Dr, Tampa, FL
33612
Tel.: (813) 745-4673   FL
Web Site: http://www.moffitt.org
Sales Range: $700-749.9 Million
Emp.: 4,246
Specialty Hospitals
N.A.I.C.S.: 622310
L. David de la Parte (Gen Counsel &
Exec VP)
G. Douglas Letson (Exec VP)
Thomas Sellers (Exec VP)
Yvette Tremonti (Exec VP-Strategy &
Bus Dev)
Jane Fusilero (Chief Nursing Officer
& VP)
B. Lee Green (VP-Diversity)
Dana Rollison (Chief Data Officer, VP
& Assoc Dir-Data Science)
Susan Stern (VP-Foundation)

Braulio Vicente (Sr VP-Hospital & Physician Grp Ops)
Jamie Wilson (VP-Govt Rels)
T. Cole Peterson (Assoc Gen Counsel)
Diane Hammon (VP-Strategic Dev)
Joanna Weiss (VP-Revenue Cycle Mgmt)
Jennifer Greenman (CIO & VP)
Matt Bednar (VP-Ambulatory Ops)
Bob Keenan (Chief Medical Officer & VP-Quality)
Elizabeth S. Dunn (VP-Foundation)
Mariana Bugallo-Muros (Chief HR Officer & VP)
Don Futrell (VP-Facilities & Support Svcs)
Robert J. Keenan (CMO & VP-Quality)
Brian Springer (VP-Res Admin)
Dominic Seraphin (VP-Strategic Alliances & Network)
Maria Muller (Chief Philanthropy Officer, Pres-Foundation & Exec VP)
H. Lee Moffitt (Founder)
Tim Adams (Chm)
Patrick Hwu (Pres & CEO)
Terrence Wright (VP-Facilities & Support Svcs)
Santosh Mohan (VP-Digital)
Sarabdeep Singh (COO & Exec VP)
Jarett Rieger (Chief Innovation Officer & VP)
James Mule (Assoc Dir-Translational Science)

Subsidiaries:

M2Gen (1)
10902 N McKinley Dr, Tampa, FL 33612
Tel.: (813) 384-5000
Web Site: http://www.m2gen.com
Clinical Research
N.A.I.C.S.: 621511
William S. Dalton (Founder & Chm)
Daniel Sullivan (Chief Medical Officer)
Odalys Capote (Chief Admin Officer)
Naveen Kumar (VP-Strategy & Bus Dev)
Hongyue Dai (Chief Scientific & Bioinformatics Officer)
Joseph R. Smith (CFO)
Judy Barkal (Chief Tech & Medical Informatics Officer & VP)
Helge Bastian (Pres & CEO)

H. NAGEL & SON CO.

2428 Central Pkwy, Cincinnati, OH 45214
Tel.: (513) 665-4550
Sales Range: $10-24.9 Million
Emp.: 30
Flour Mfr
N.A.I.C.S.: 311212
Edward Nagel (VP)
Ted Nagel (Co-Pres)
Michael Norris (VP)
Jack Steinmetz (Mgr)
William Nagel (Co-Pres)

H. R. SPINNER CORPORATION

115 S 1st Ave, Yakima, WA 98902
Tel.: (509) 453-9111
Web Site: https://www.hrspinner.com
Year Founded: 1916
Sales Range: $10-24.9 Million
Emp.: 42
Industrial & Personal Service Paper Whslr
N.A.I.C.S.: 424130
Ed Jewett (Pres)
Shawn Graham (Gen Mgr)

H. SALT OF SOUTHERN CALIFORNIA, INC.

2540 Corporate Pl Ste B102, Monterey Park, CA 91754
Tel.: (323) 264-8766
Web Site: http://www.hsalt.com

Year Founded: 1965
Sales Range: $50-74.9 Million
Emp.: 3
Fast Food Restaurant Owner & Franchisor
N.A.I.C.S.: 722513
Tom Chang (Pres)
Frank Lin (Treas & Sec)

H. SQUARED, INC.

110 Edgewood Dr, Durham, NC 27713
Year Founded: 1986
Sales Range: $10-24.9 Million
Clothing Distr
N.A.I.C.S.: 458110
Carol S. Haynes (Pres)

H. W. HERRELL DISTRIBUTING COMPANY

1002 White Ave, Imperial, MO 63052
Tel.: (636) 464-0100
Web Site: http://www.hwherrell.com
Sales Range: $25-49.9 Million
Emp.: 50
Beer & Ale Merchant Whslr
N.A.I.C.S.: 424810
Donald H. Herrell (Pres)
Carol A. Schanz (Treas & Sec)

H.A. LANGER & ASSOCIATES

3950 N Elston Ave, Chicago, IL 60618
Tel.: (773) 929-1620
Web Site: http://www.halanger.com
Year Founded: 1969
Sales Range: $10-24.9 Million
Emp.: 30
Apartment Building Operator
N.A.I.C.S.: 531110
Harry A. Langer (Owner)

H.B. FRAZER COMPANY

514 Shoemaker Rd, King of Prussia, PA 19406
Tel.: (610) 768-0400
Web Site: http://www.hbfrazer.com
Year Founded: 1906
Rev.: $29,555,774
Emp.: 270
Electronic Services
N.A.I.C.S.: 238210
Frank Holleran (VP)
Scott Groh (Mgr)

H.B. MCCLURE COMPANY

600 S 17th St, Harrisburg, PA 17104
Tel.: (717) 232-4328
Web Site:
https://www.hbmcclure.com
Year Founded: 1914
Emp.: 388
Plumbing, Electrical, Heating, Ventilation & Air-Conditioning Contractor
N.A.I.C.S.: 238220
Todd Johns (VP-Residential Svcs)
Eric Crawford (COO)
Robert Whalen (Pres & CEO)
Robert F. McClure (Chm)
Tammy Halteman (Mgr-Residential Div)
Thomas Whalen (CFO)
Jim Saussaman (Pres-Harrisburg)
Kerrin Musselman (Pres-IT Landes Div)
Kyle Seaman (Sr VP-Corp Dev)
Brandy Shope (VP-Corp Comm)
Melissa Ural (VP-HR)

H.B. MELLOTT ESTATE, INC.

100 Mellott Dr Ste 100, Warfordsburg, PA 17267-8555
Tel.: (301) 678-2000
Web Site: http://www.mellotts.com
Year Founded: 1952
Sales Range: $150-199.9 Million

Emp.: 230
Provider of Crushed Limestone & Ready-Mix Concrete
N.A.I.C.S.: 212312
Paul Mellott (Chm & CEO)
Terry L. Randall (Vice Chm)
Brian Mellott (Sec & VP)
Herman B. Mellott (VP-Production & Corp Treas)

H.B. SMITH CO., INC.

47 Westfield Industrial Park Rd, Westfield, MA 01085
Tel.: (413) 568-3148
Web Site: http://www.hbsmith.com
Year Founded: 1853
Sales Range: $75-99.9 Million
Emp.: 10
Mfr of Cast Iron Heating Boilers
N.A.I.C.S.: 333414
Walter Pawulski (Treas)
Peter J. Stasz (Gen Counsel)
Edwin M. Smith (Pres)

H.B. STUBBS COMPANY

27027 Mound Rd, Warren, MI 48092
Tel.: (586) 574-9700
Sales Range: $25-49.9 Million
Emp.: 112
Displays & Cutouts, Window & Lobby
N.A.I.C.S.: 339950
Fred Sherry (VP-Strategic Plng)
Alan Wester (VP-Mktg)
Tim Childs (Supvr)

H.B.D. CONTRACTING INC.

5517 Manchester Ave, Saint Louis, MO 63110-1975
Tel.: (314) 781-8000
Web Site: http://www.hbdgc.com
Year Founded: 2005
Sales Range: $50-74.9 Million
Emp.: 125
Civil Engineering Services
N.A.I.C.S.: 237310
Michael J. Perry (CEO)

H.C. LA MARCHE ENTERPRISES

7089 Belgrave Ave, Garden Grove, CA 92841
Tel.: (949) 454-3700
Sales Range: $10-24.9 Million
Emp.: 10
Lumber Plywood & Millwork
N.A.I.C.S.: 423310
Philip La Marche (Gen Mgr)

H.C. LEWIS OIL COMPANY INC.

201 Route 52 N, Welch, WV 24801
Tel.: (304) 436-2148
Sales Range: $10-24.9 Million
Emp.: 19
Petroleum Bulk Stations
N.A.I.C.S.: 424710
Peggy Lewis (Office Mgr)
Hiram Carson Lewis Jr. (CEO)

H.C. MILLER COMPANY

3030 Lowell Dr, Green Bay, WI 54311
Tel.: (920) 465-3030
Web Site: http://www.hcmiller.com
Year Founded: 1888
Sales Range: $1-9.9 Million
Emp.: 66
Loose Leaf Binders & Indexes Mfr
N.A.I.C.S.: 332216
Tom Sonntag (CEO)

H.C. WAINWRIGHT & CO., LLC

430 Park Ave 4th Fl, New York, NY 10022
Tel.: (212) 356-0500

Web Site:
http://www.hcwainwright.com
Year Founded: 1868
Sales Range: $10-24.9 Million
Emp.: 40
Investment Banking & Advisory Services
N.A.I.C.S.: 523150
Aileen M. Gibbons (VP-Healthcare Investment Banking)
Jeffery R. Smith (VP-Healthcare Investment Banking)
Mark W. Viklund (CEO)
Ed Arce (Mng Dir-Equity Res)
Richard E. Gormley (Vice Chm & Pres-Capital Markets)

H.D. HUDSON MANUFACTURING COMPANY

500 N Michigan Ave, Chicago, IL 60611-3777
Tel.: (312) 644-2830
Web Site: http://www.hdhudson.com
Year Founded: 1905
Sales Range: $75-99.9 Million
Emp.: 225
Mfr of Agricultural Sprayers & Spraying Machines; Mechanical Dusters; Lawn & Garden Sprayers
N.A.I.C.S.: 333111
John C. Romans (Sec & Sr VP)
Robert J. Kosinski (CFO)
Ron Dorf (Pres)

Subsidiaries:

H.D. Hudson Asia Limited (1)
1 San Hop Lane Second Floor, Tuen Mun, China (Hong Kong)
Tel.: (852) 2462 1504
Web Site: http://www.hudsonasia.com
Sprayer Mfr & Distr
N.A.I.C.S.: 333111

H.D. SHELDON & COMPANY INC.

143 W 29th St Fl 12, New York, NY 10001
Tel.: (212) 924-6920
Web Site:
https://www.hdsheldon.com
Rev.: $21,328,040
Emp.: 24
Restaurant Equipment & Supplies
N.A.I.C.S.: 423740
Robert Metros (Pres)
M. Moulabi (Controller)
William Izbicki (Mgr-Sls-Europe)

H.D. SMITH WHOLESALE DRUG CO. INC.

4650 Industrial Dr, Springfield, IL 62703-5318
Tel.: (217) 753-1688
Web Site: http://www.hdsmith.com
Year Founded: 1954
Sales Range: $10-24.9 Million
Emp.: 80
Drugs & Pharmaceuticals Whslr
N.A.I.C.S.: 424210
J. Christopher Smith (Pres & COO)
Robert Appleby (Pres-Specialty Solutions)
Jeff Greer (VP-Sls)
Henry Dale Smith Jr. (Chm & CEO)

Subsidiaries:

H.D. Smith Wholesale Drug Co. Inc. (1)
1101 West Vickery Blvd, Fort Worth, TX 76104-1025
Tel.: (817) 335-5714
Web Site: http://www.hdsmith.com
Sales Range: $10-24.9 Million
Emp.: 50
Provider of Drugs & Drug Proprietaries
N.A.I.C.S.: 424210

Smith Medical Partners, LLC (1)

H.D. Smith Wholesale Drug Co. Inc.—(Continued)

960 Lively Blvd, Wood Dale, IL 60191
Tel.: (630) 227-9420
Web Site: http://www.smpspecialty.com
Pharmaceutical Product Whslr
N.A.I.C.S.: 424210
Joe Conda *(Pres)*

H.E. BUTT GROCERY COMPANY
646 S Fores Ave, San Antonio, TX 78204-1210
Tel.: (210) 938-8000　　TX
Web Site: http://www.heb.com
Year Founded: 1905
Sales Range: $5-14.9 Billion
Emp.: 76,000
Grocery Store Operator
N.A.I.C.S.: 445110
Charles C. Butt *(Chm & CEO)*
Susan Wade *(Exec VP-Retailing)*
Cory Basso *(VP-Mktg, Adv & Branding)*
Brooke Brownlow *(VP-Benefits & HR)*
Steve Harper *(Exec VP-Food Mfg, Procurement & Mdsg)*
Jeff Thomas *(Sr VP & Gen Mgr-Central Texas)*
Susan Ghertner *(Mgr-Environment)*
Leslie Lockett *(Dir-Pub Affairs)*
Dya Campos *(Dir-Pub Affairs)*
Craig Boyan *(Pres & COO)*
Jag Bath *(Chief Digital Officer)*
Mike Georgoff *(Chief Product Officer-Digital)*

H.E. CALLAHAN CONSTRUCTION CO.
2664 Turner Rd, Auburn, ME 04210
Tel.: (207) 784-6927
Web Site: https://www.hecallahan.com
Sales Range: $10-24.9 Million
Emp.: 50
Commercial & Institutional Building Construction Services
N.A.I.C.S.: 236220
Jonica Poole *(CFO)*

H.E. HUNEWILL CONSTRUCTION CO.
315 Artist View Rd, Wellington, NV, 89444
Tel.: (775) 465-2448
Sales Range: $10-24.9 Million
Emp.: 60
Provider of Earthmoving Contracting Services
N.A.I.C.S.: 236210
Loren Hunewill *(Pres)*
Wayne Sprague *(Mgr-Safety)*

H.E. MURDOCK CO. INC.
88 Main St, Waterville, ME 04901
Tel.: (207) 873-7036
Web Site: https://www.daysjewelers.com
Sales Range: $10-24.9 Million
Emp.: 100
Jewelry, Precious Stones & Precious Metals
N.A.I.C.S.: 458310
Nikia Levesque *(VP-Mktg)*
Joseph Corey *(Pres)*

H.E. NEUMANN CO.
100 Middle Creek Rd, Triadelphia, WV 26059
Tel.: (304) 232-3040
Web Site: https://www.heneumann.com
Year Founded: 1924
Emp.: 150
Plumbing, Heating & Air-Conditioning Contractors
N.A.I.C.S.: 238220

Don Wagenheim *(Chm)*
K. Scott Winters *(CEO & Owner)*

H.E. TURNER & CO., INC.
403 E Main St, Batavia, NY 14020
Tel.: (585) 343-8868
Web Site: https://www.bataviafuneral homes.com
Emp.: 100
Funeral Homes & Funeral Services
N.A.I.C.S.: 812210

Subsidiaries:

Gilmartin Funeral Home and Cremation Co., Inc.　　　　　(1)
329331 W Main St, Batavia, NY 14020
Tel.: (585) 343-8260
Web Site: http://www.gilmartinfuneralhome.com
Funeral Homes & Funeral Services
N.A.I.C.S.: 812210

H.E. WHITLOCK INC.
4808 Dillon Dr, Pueblo, CO 81008
Tel.: (719) 544-9475
Web Site: https://www.hewhitlock.com
Rev.: $16,700,000
Emp.: 47
Commercial & Office Building Construction Services
N.A.I.C.S.: 236220
Micky Bonham *(Pres)*

H.E. WILLIAMS, INC.
831 W Fairview Ave, Carthage, MO 64836-3736
Tel.: (417) 358-4065　　MO
Web Site: https://www.hew.com
Year Founded: 1921
Electrical Lighting Fixtures Mfr
N.A.I.C.S.: 335132
Paul Eckels *(COO)*

H.E.R.O.E.S. CARE
1306 R W Lark Industrial Dr, Fenton, MO 63026
Tel.: (636) 600-0096　　MO
Web Site: http://www.heroescare.org
Year Founded: 2007
Sales Range: $10-24.9 Million
Emp.: 5
Military Family Support Services
N.A.I.C.S.: 624190
Jon Jerome *(Pres & CEO)*

H.F. LONG AND ASSOCIATES, INC.
631 N Central Ave, Wood Dale, IL 60191-0905
Tel.: (630) 860-5664
Web Site: https://www.longgroup.com
Year Founded: 1980
Sales Range: $50-74.9 Million
Emp.: 15
Customhouse Brokers
N.A.I.C.S.: 488510
Bob Raney *(Pres)*

H.G. HASTINGS CO.
3420 Woodhill Dr, Peachtree Corners, GA 30092
Tel.: (404) 869-7447　　GA
Web Site: http://www.hastingsgardencenter.com
Year Founded: 1889
Rev.: $1,000,000
Emp.: 25
Holding Company; Garden Centers; Landscaping Services
N.A.I.C.S.: 551112
Kathy Bussey *(Pres)*

Subsidiaries:

Hastings Landscape & Design Group　　　　　　　　(1)

3420 Woodhill Dr, Peachtree Corners, GA 30092
Tel.: (404) 869-7447
Web Site: http://www.hastingsgardencenter.com
Sales Range: $10-24.9 Million
Landscaping Services
N.A.I.C.S.: 561730

Hastings Nature & Garden Center　　　　　　　　(1)
2350 Cheshire Bridge Rd., Atlanta, GA 30324
Tel.: (404) 321-1045
Gardening Services
N.A.I.C.S.: 111422

H.G. MAKELIM COMPANY
219 Shaw Rd, South San Francisco, CA 94080
Tel.: (650) 873-4757
Web Site: http://www.hgmakelim.com
Rev.: $18,000,000
Emp.: 48
Engines & Transportation Equipment
N.A.I.C.S.: 423830
Paul Hoffman *(CFO)*

H.G. REYNOLDS CO. INC.
113 Contract Dr, Aiken, SC 29801
Tel.: (803) 641-1401　　SC
Web Site: https://www.hgreynolds.net
Year Founded: 1948
Sales Range: $10-24.9 Million
Emp.: 110
General Contractors
N.A.I.C.S.: 236220
Leland Reynolds *(VP & Project Mgr)*

H.H. BENFIELD ELECTRIC SUPPLY COMPANY INC.
25 Lafayette Ave, White Plains, NY 10603-1613
Tel.: (914) 948-6660　　NY
Web Site: http://www.benfieldelectric.com
Year Founded: 1951
Rev.: $70,000,000
Emp.: 185
Electrical Apparatus & Equipment
N.A.I.C.S.: 423610
Roy C. Kohli *(Chm)*
Daniel J. McLaughlin *(Pres & CEO)*

Subsidiaries:

Benfield Control & Power Systems, Inc.　　　　　　　　(1)
55 Lafayette Ave, White Plains, NY 10603-1613
Tel.: (914) 948-3231
Web Site: http://www.benfieldcontrolsystems.com
Sales Range: $10-24.9 Million
Emp.: 15
Switchgear & Switchboard Apparatus
N.A.I.C.S.: 335313
William Raum *(Pres-HVAC Sls)*
Dominic DeVito *(Pres)*
Tom Gherardi *(Mgr-Sls)*
John Raum *(Mgr-Engrg)*

Benfield Electric International Ltd. Inc.　　　　　　　　(1)
25 Lafayette Ave, White Plains, NY 10603-1613
Tel.: (914) 948-0995
Web Site: http://www.benfieldelectric.com
Sales Range: $10-24.9 Million
Emp.: 15
Electrical Apparatus & Equipment
N.A.I.C.S.: 423610
Ralph J. Frickel *(Pres)*

Benfield Electric Japan Co. Ltd.　　(1)
Shibafuji Bldg 4F Shiba Daimon 1-1-15 Shiba Daimon, Minato-ku, Tokyo, 105-0012, Japan
Tel.: (81) 3 5472 5431
Web Site: http://www.benfield.co.jp
Electrical Equipment Distr
N.A.I.C.S.: 423610
Hidehito Ikoma *(Pres)*

Benfield Electric and Elevator Supply Corp.　　　　　　　　(1)
708-12 E 133rd St, Bronx, NY 10454
Tel.: (718) 706-8600
Industrial Supplies Whslr
N.A.I.C.S.: 423840

Benfield Lighting, Inc.　　　　(1)
100B Tec St, Hicksville, NY 11801
Tel.: (516) 822-8800
Web Site: http://www.benfieldelectric.com
Emp.: 15
Lighting Equipment Whslr
N.A.I.C.S.: 423610
Anthony Maiorana *(Gen Mgr)*

H.H. Benfield Electric Supply Company Inc. - Benfield Data Comm Division　　　　　　　　(1)
708-12 E 133rd St, Bronx, NY 10454
Tel.: (914) 285-0007
Telecommunications Equipment Mfr
N.A.I.C.S.: 334220

H.H. HUNT CORPORATION
800 Hethwood Blvd, Blacksburg, VA 24060-4207
Tel.: (540) 552-3515　　VA
Web Site: https://www.hhhunt.com
Year Founded: 1972
Sales Range: $50-74.9 Million
Emp.: 1,500
Apartment Building Operator
N.A.I.C.S.: 531110
Harry H. Hunt *(Founder & Chm)*
Paul Johnson *(Dir-IT Svcs)*
Steve Fritz *(Mgr-Raleigh Div)*
Jill Crews *(VP-Mktg & Branding)*

H.I.G. CAPITAL, LLC
1450 Brickell Ave 31st Fl, Miami, FL 33131
Tel.: (305) 379-2322　　FL
Web Site: http://www.higcapital.com
Year Founded: 1993
Privater Equity Firm
N.A.I.C.S.: 523999
John P. Bolduc *(Exec Mng Dir)*
Sami Mnaymneh *(Co-Founder & Co-CEO)*
Anthony Tamer *(Co-Founder & Co-CEO)*
Brian Schwartz *(Co-Pres)*
Rick Rosen *(Co-Pres)*
Aaron C. Tolson *(Mng Dir & Principal)*
Elliot Maluth *(Mng Dir-San Francisco)*
Raffaele Legnani *(Mng Dir & Head-Italy)*
Tenno Tsai *(Mng Dir-New York)*
Richard Siegel *(Chief Compliance Officer & Gen Counsel)*
Camilo E. Horvilleur *(Mng Dir-Miami)*
Anthony Chambers *(Principal-Miami)*
Jonathan Contos *(Principal-San Francisco)*
Amar Doshi *(Principal-New York)*
Rodrigo Feitosa *(Mng Dir-Rio de Janeiro)*
Shaun Fitzgibbon *(Principal)*
Jonathan Fox *(Principal-Miami)*
Michael Gallagher *(Mng Dir-Miami)*
Matthew Hankins *(Mng Dir-San Francisco)*
Matthew Kretzman *(Mng Dir-New York)*
Justin Reyna *(Mng Dir-San Francisco)*
Stefano Giambelli *(Principal-Middle Market-London)*
Markus Noe-Nordberg *(Mng Dir & Head-European Middle Market)*
Wolfgang Biedermann *(Exec Mng Dir & Head-Buyouts-Europe)*
John Harper *(Mng Dir & Head-Leveraged Buyouts-London)*
Pascal Meysson *(Mng Dir & Head-WhiteHorse & Direct Lending-Europe)*
Timur Akazhanov *(Mng Dir-Advantage Fund)*

Ed Pallesen *(Mng Dir & Co-Head-Infrastructure)*
Andrew Liau *(Co-Head-Infrastructure)*
Ahmad Atwan *(Mng Dir-Infrastructure)*
Ryan Kaplan *(Mng Dir)*
Todd Ofenloch *(Mng Dir)*
Jordan Peer Griffin *(Exec Mng Dir & Head-Capital Formation Grp-Global)*
Pankaj Gupta *(Pres)*
Javier Casillas *(Chief Credit Officer)*
Alejandra Arguello *(Mng Dir-Capital Formation)*
Carlos Soto *(Mng Dir & Head-Private Equity Bus Dev-US)*
Doug Berman *(Head-Private Equity-US)*
Benjamin Charon *(Mng Dir-Capital Formation Grp-New York)*
Kira Yugay *(Principal)*
Stuart D. Aronson *(Exec Mng Dir)*
Evan Karp *(Mng Dir-Growth Partners)*

Subsidiaries:

BECO Holding Company, Inc. (1)
10926 David Taylor Dr Ste 100, Charlotte, NC 28262
Tel.: (704) 916-3448
Web Site:
 https://www.brooksequipment.com
Critical Life Safety & Security Solutions
N.A.I.C.S.: 922160
Eric Smith *(CEO)*

Subsidiary (Domestic):

Brooks Equipment Company, LLC (2)
10926 David Taylor Dr Ste 300, Charlotte, NC 28269
Tel.: (704) 916-3448
Web Site: http://www.brooksequipment.com
Fire Equipment & Related Parts Distr
N.A.I.C.S.: 423830
Kathy Cullop *(Acct Mgr)*
Belinda Hunt *(Acct Mgr)*
Bob Mete *(Reg Sls Mgr)*
Cesar Covarrubias *(Sls Mgr-Export)*
Christy Honeycutt *(Acct Mgr)*
Ericka Matthews *(Acct Mgr)*
Jim Bartholomew *(Acct Mgr)*
Katie Lott *(Acct Mgr)*
Kelly Venable *(Dir-Inside Sls)*
Krissy Cowan *(Acct Mgr)*
Matt Cerveny *(Acct Mgr)*
Mel Casey *(Acct Mgr)*
Mike Cox *(Acct Mgr)*
Robert Hussey *(Acct Mgr-Territory)*
Sarah McManus *(Dir-Sls Ops)*
Todd Warner *(Product Mgr)*
Robert Bell Jr. *(Sls Mgr-Natl)*

Electronic Supply Company (2)
561 Holcombe Ave, Mobile, AL 36606-1599
Electronic Parts & Equipment Merchant Whslr
N.A.I.C.S.: 423690

Bayside Capital, Inc. (1)
1450 Brickell Ave, Miami, FL 33131
Tel.: (305) 379-8686
Web Site: http://www.bayside.com
Privater Equity Firm
N.A.I.C.S.: 523999
John P. Bolduc *(Exec Mng Dir)*
Andrew Scotland *(Mng Dir-London)*
Roman Krislav *(Mng Dir)*
Adam Schimel *(Mng Dir)*
Darryl Cregg *(Principal)*
Sami Mnaymneh *(Co-Founder & Co-CEO)*
Tony Tamer *(Co-Founder & Co-CEO)*

Holding (Domestic):

Esquire Deposition Solutions, LLC (2)
2700 Centennial Tower 101 Marietta St, Atlanta, GA 30303
Tel.: (404) 495-0777
Web Site: http://www.esquiresolutions.com
Litigation Solutions, Including Court Reporting, Legal Video, Hosted Review, Trial Software & Trial Consultation
N.A.I.C.S.: 561492
Avi Stadler *(Gen Counsel)*
Jim Ballowe *(CIO)*

Terrie Campbell *(CEO)*
Sara Quick *(CFO)*
Ron Carey *(Chief Revenue Officer)*
Michael Saltman *(Pres-Esquire Corp Solutions)*

Branch (Domestic):

Esquire Deposition Solutions, LLC - Chicago (3)
20 N Clark St Ste 500, Chicago, IL 60602
Tel.: (312) 782-8087
Emp.: 40
Court Reporting & Stenotype Services
N.A.I.C.S.: 561492
Elizabeth Murtha *(Mgr-Ops)*
Melanie Jakus *(Reg Mgr)*

Esquire Deposition Solutions, LLC - Long Island (3)
1225 Franklin Ave Ste 325, Garden City, NY 11530
Tel.: (212) 687-8010
Web Site: http://www.esquiresolutions.com
Sales Range: $25-49.9 Million
Emp.: 32
Court Reporting & Stenotype Services
N.A.I.C.S.: 561492
Alexander Gallo *(Pres)*

Esquire Deposition Solutions, LLC - Philadelphia (3)
1600 JFK Blvd Ste 1210, Philadelphia, PA 19103-7421
Tel.: (215) 569-1134
Sales Range: $25-49.9 Million
Emp.: 20
Legal Staffing Services
N.A.I.C.S.: 561110

Esquire Deposition Solutions, LLC - San Diego (3)
402 W Broadway Ste 1600, San Diego, CA 92101
Tel.: (619) 239-4111
Web Site: http://www.esquiresolutions.com
Sales Range: $1-9.9 Million
Emp.: 100
Court Reporting & Stenotype Services
N.A.I.C.S.: 561492
Perry Soloman *(Chm)*
Terrie Campbell *(CEO)*

Esquire Deposition Solutions, LLC - Woodbridge (3)
33 S Wood Ave, Iselin, NJ 08830
Tel.: (732) 283-1060
Web Site: http://www.esquiresolutions.com
Sales Range: $25-49.9 Million
Emp.: 1
Secretarial & Court Reporting
N.A.I.C.S.: 561492
Joshua Haggett *(Office Mgr)*

Holding (Domestic):

Flight Express Incorporated (2)
3122 C E Amelia St, Orlando, FL 32803
Tel.: (407) 895-0453
Rev.: $17,137,297
Emp.: 150
Air Cargo & Charter Flights
N.A.I.C.S.: 481112

CHA Consulting, Inc. (1)
575 Broadway Ste 301, Albany, NY 12207
Tel.: (518) 453-4500
Web Site: https://www.chacompanies.com
Emp.: 1,300
Full-service Engineering & Construction Management Firm
N.A.I.C.S.: 541330
Jay Wolverton *(Chief Growth Officer & Exec VP)*
Dom Bernardo *(CFO & Exec VP)*
John Achenbach *(Pres-Buildings)*
Greg Corso *(Pres-Power)*
John Hensley *(Pres-Infrastructure)*
Michael Platt *(Gen Counsel & Exec VP)*
Jim Stephenson *(Pres)*
Jennifer Chatt *(Chief People Officer & Exec VP)*
Jay Wolverton *(Chief Growth Officer & Exec VP)*

Subsidiary (Domestic):

A&P Consulting Transportation Engineers Corp. (2)

10305 NW 41st St Ste 115, Doral, FL 33178
Tel.: (305) 592-7283
Web Site: http://www.apcte.com
Sales Range: $10-24.9 Million
Emp.: 31
Construction Engineering Services
N.A.I.C.S.: 237310
Antonio G. Acosta *(Pres)*
Carlos Gil-Mera *(Principal)*
Eithel M. Sierra *(Sr Project Mgr)*
Alexander S. Yi *(Sr Project Mgr)*
Lazaro Ferrero *(Mgr-Water Resources Project)*
Nelson V. Perez *(Head-CEI-Dept)*
Alex Guon *(Sr Mgr-Electrical Project)*
Arnelio Alfonso *(Head-Water Resources Dept)*
Johnny Martinez *(Sr VP)*
Frank Lena *(Sr Project Mgr)*
Osmany Alfonso *(Head-Structural Dept)*
Eduardo Martinez *(Head-Electrical Dept)*

CHA Architecture, P.C. (2)
49 Dartmouth St, Portland, ME 04101
Tel.: (207) 775-1059
Web Site: http://www.chaarchitecture.com
Architecture, Interior Design, Master Planning & Designing Services
N.A.I.C.S.: 541310

Subsidiary (Non-US):

CHA Canada (2)
80 King Street Suite 404, Saint Catharines, L2R 7G1, ON, Canada
Tel.: (905) 984-8383
Web Site: http://www.chacanada.com
Mechanical Engineering Services
N.A.I.C.S.: 541330

Subsidiary (Domestic):

CME Associates, Inc. (2)
33 Wilbur Cross Wy Ste 105 Mansfield, Tolland, CT 06268
Tel.: (860) 885-1055
Web Site: http://www.chacompanies.com
Architectural Engineering Services
N.A.I.C.S.: 541330

D'Huy Engineering, Inc. (DEI) (2)
1 E Broad St Suite 310, Bethlehem, PA 18018
Tel.: (610) 865-3000
Web Site: http://www.dhuy.com
Emp.: 35
Structural Design & Analysis, Facilities Engineering, Forensic Engineering & Project Management
N.A.I.C.S.: 561210
Zachary S. Zazo *(Project Mgr)*

Eckler Engineering Inc (2)
4700 Riverside Dr, Coral Springs, FL 33067
Tel.: (954) 755-1351
Web Site: http://www.ecklerengineering.com
Rev.: $1,000,000
Emp.: 8
Engineeering Services
N.A.I.C.S.: 541330
Donald Eckler *(Pres)*

JBS Project Management LLC (2)
45 Main St Ste 526, Brooklyn, NY 11201
Tel.: (718) 643-3800
Office Administrative Services
N.A.I.C.S.: 561110

R.W. Armstrong & Associates LLC (2)
3500 S DuPont Hwy Ste W 101, Dover, DE 19901
Tel.: (302) 531-1139
Web Site: http://www.rwa.com
Engineeering Services
N.A.I.C.S.: 541330

Wolverton & Associates, Inc. (2)
6745 Sugarloaf Pkwy Ste 100, Duluth, GA 30097-4357
Tel.: (770) 447-8999
Landscape Architectural Services
N.A.I.C.S.: 541320

CLC Group Limited (1)
Unit 2 Northbrook Industrial Estate Vincent Avenue, Southampton, SO16 6PB, United Kingdom
Tel.: (44) 2380701111
Web Site: http://www.clcgroup.com

Holding Company; Property & Building Maintenance & Refurbishment Services
N.A.I.C.S.: 551112
Bill Childerstone *(Co-Founder)*
Bert Limbrick *(Co-Founder)*
Bill Cane *(Co-Founder)*

Subsidiary (Domestic):

CLC Contractors Ltd. (2)
Vincent Avenue, Shirley, Southampton, SO16 6PQ, Hants, United Kingdom
Tel.: (44) 2380701111
Web Site: http://www.clcgroup.com
Emp.: 50
Property & Building Maintenance & Refurbishment Services
N.A.I.C.S.: 561790
Peter B. Armitage *(Mng Dir)*
Nick Hilton *(Deputy Mng Dir)*

Capstone Logistics, LLC (1)
6525 The Corners Pkwy Ste 520, Norcross, GA 30092
Tel.: (770) 414-1929
Web Site: http://www.capstonelogistics.com
Logistics Management Consulting Services
N.A.I.C.S.: 541614
Steve Taylor *(CEO)*

Subsidiary (Domestic):

Priority Express Courier Inc. (2)
5 Chelsea Pkwy, Boothwyn, PA 19061
Tel.: (610) 364-3300
Web Site: http://www.priorityexpress.com
Couriers & Express Delivery Services
N.A.I.C.S.: 492110
Robert Johnstone *(Founder & Pres)*

Rapid Response Delivery Inc. (2)
6660 Security Blvd, Baltimore, MD 21207
Tel.: (800) 997-9060
Web Site: https://www.rapideast1.com
Rev.: $3,525,000
Emp.: 25
General Freight Trucking, Local
N.A.I.C.S.: 484110
Colin Withers *(Pres)*

Circle Graphics, Inc. (1)
120 9th Ave, Longmont, CO 80501
Tel.: (303) 532-2370
Web Site:
 http://www.circlegraphicsonline.com
Sales Range: $25-49.9 Million
Emp.: 800
Large-Format Digital Printing Services
N.A.I.C.S.: 323111
Andrew Cousin *(CEO)*
Judy Toran Cousin *(Chief Mktg & Innovation Officer)*

Subsidiary (Domestic):

Graphik Dimensions, LLC (2)
2103 Brentwood St, High Point, NC 27263
Tel.: (336) 887-3700
Web Site:
 http://www.graphikdimensions.com
All Other Miscellaneous Fabricated Metal Product Mfr
N.A.I.C.S.: 332999
David Krohto *(VP-Sls & Bus Dev)*
Geo Krieg *(Pres)*

Unit (Domestic):

Imagic (2)
2810 N Lima St, Burbank, CA 91504
Tel.: (818) 333-1670
Web Site: http://www.imagic.la
Sales Range: $1-9.9 Million
Emp.: 30
Digital Printing Services
N.A.I.C.S.: 323111
David Allman *(CEO)*

Estacionamientos Y Servicios, S.A. (1)
3 Edificio Mizar Planta 1, 28027, Madrid, Spain
Tel.: (34) 91 230 81 64
Web Site: https://eysaservicios.com
Emp.: 100
All Other Business Support Services
N.A.I.C.S.: 561499

H.I.G. BioVentures, LLC (1)
1450 Brickell Ave 31st Fl, Miami, FL 33131
Tel.: (305) 379-2322

H.I.G. Capital, LLC—(Continued)

Web Site: http://www.higbio.com
Sales Range: $100-124.9 Million
Emp.: 200
Investment Management Service
N.A.I.C.S.: 523940
Bruce C. Robertson (Mng Dir)
Michael Wasserman (Mng Dir)
Sami Mnaymneh (Co-Founder & Co-CEO)
Jorge Ramirez (VP)
Tony Tamer (Co-Founder & Co-CEO)
Alex Zisson (Mng Dir)

H.I.G. Brazil Investment Advisory Ltda. (1)
Avenida Ataulfo de Paiva 1251 9th and 10th Floors Leblon, Rio de Janeiro, 22440-034, Brazil
Tel.: (55) 21 2529 3550
Web Site: http://www.higcapital.com
Investment Management Service
N.A.I.C.S.: 523940
Daniel Nader (Mng Dir)

Holding (Domestic):

Cel Lep Idiomas (2)
Paulista Avenue 2006 1 andar, Sao Paulo, 01310-200, Brazil
Tel.: (55) 11 3742 7728
Language Training Services
N.A.I.C.S.: 611630

Elekeiroz S.A. (2)
392 Dr Edgardo de Azevedo Soares street 13, 13 224-030, Sao Paulo, Brazil
Tel.: (55) 1145968800
Web Site: http://www.elekeiroz.com.br
Chemicals & Synthetic Resin Mfr
N.A.I.C.S.: 325998
Ricardo Garcia (Head-Fin & IT)

H.I.G. Capital, LLC - Boston Office (1)
500 Boylston St 20th Fl, Boston, MA 02116
Tel.: (617) 262-8455
Web Site: http://www.higcapital.com
Sales Range: $50-74.9 Million
Emp.: 10
Portfolio Management
N.A.I.C.S.: 523940
John Black (Head-Growth Equity)
William Nolan (Mng Dir)
John Von Bargen (Mng Dir)
Todd J. Ofenloch (Mng Dir)

H.I.G. European Capital Partners GmbH (1)
Warburgstrasse 50, 20354, Hamburg, Germany
Tel.: (49) 40 41 33 06 100
Web Site: http://www.higeurope.com
Emp.: 15
Privater Equity Firm
N.A.I.C.S.: 523999
Jens Alsleben (Mng Dir)
Wolfgang Biedermann (Mng Dir)
Holger Kleingarn (Mng Dir)
Christian Kraul-von Renner (Principal)
Klaas Reineke (Mng Dir)

Holding (Non-US):

ARMetallizing N.V. (2)
Woudstraat 8, Genk, 3600, Belgium
Tel.: (32) 89 84 80 00
Web Site: http://www.armetallizing.com
Emp.: 100
Metallic Labeling & Packaging Mfr
N.A.I.C.S.: 327999
Bart Devos (CEO)

Subsidiary (US):

AR Metallizing Ltd. (3)
24 Forge Pk, Franklin, MA 02038
Tel.: (508) 541-7700
Web Site: http://www.armetallizing.com
Emp.: 80
Metallic Label & Packaging Mfr
N.A.I.C.S.: 327999

Subsidiary (Non-US):

AR Metallizing Srl (3)
Via Lombriasco 4-12, Casalgrasso, 12030, Cuneo, Italy
Tel.: (39) 011 97 51 54
Metallic Label & Packaging Mfr

N.A.I.C.S.: 327999

Holding (Domestic):

Der Grune Punkt - Duales System Deutschland GmbH (2)
Frankfurter Strasse 720-726, D 51145, Cologne, Germany
Tel.: (49) 22039370
Web Site: http://www.gruener-punkt.de
Sales Range: $800-899.9 Million
Plastics, Cardboard & Electronics Waste Collection, Materials Recovery & Recycling Services
N.A.I.C.S.: 562920
Michael Wiener (Chief Sls Officer & Member-Mgmt Bd)
Klaus Hillebrand (Head-Press Office & Dir-Comm)
Ulf Doster (Head-Fin)
Timothy Glaz (Head-Sustainability)

Haltermann Carless Deutschland GmbH (2)
Schlengendeich 17, 21107, Hamburg, Germany
Tel.: (49) 40 33 31 80
Web Site: http://www.haltermann-carless.com
Emp.: 450
Hydrocarbon Solvent Mfr
N.A.I.C.S.: 325199
Uwe Nickel (Co-CEO)
Peter Stubbe (Exec Dir)
Marc Heiden (Sr VP-HR, Legal & Compliance)
Henrik Krupper (Co-CEO)
Albrecht Spangenberg (Sr VP-Performance Solvents)
Daniel Jeffrey (Sr VP-Special Aromatics)
Bruno Pingel (Sr VP-Bus Unit Mobility)
Rene Tessmann (Sr VP-Bus Unit Industrial)

Holding (Non-US):

Petrochem Carless BVBA (2)
Orteliuskaai 2-4 Bus 26, 2000, Antwerp, Belgium
Tel.: (32) 3 205 9370
Sales Range: $10-24.9 Million
Emp.: 13
Chemical Solvent Mfr
N.A.I.C.S.: 325199

Holding (Domestic):

walter services GmbH (2)
Am Turm 42, 53721, Siegburg, Germany
Tel.: (49) 2241267450
Web Site: http://www.walterservices.com
Emp.: 6,400
Business Process Outsourcing Services
N.A.I.C.S.: 561499
Meinolf Brauer (Owner & CEO)
Benjamin Helbig (CIO)
Bjorn Hiemer (COO)
Michael Niedermeier (CFO)
Wolfgang Salzig (Chief HR Officer)

Subsidiary (Non-US):

walter services Poland Sp. z. o. o. (3)
Ul Taneczna 30 Onyx Building, PL-02-829, Warsaw, Poland
Tel.: (48) 22 345 55 55
Business Process Outsourcing Services
N.A.I.C.S.: 561499

walter services Swiss AG (3)
Zurichstrasse 131, CH-8600, Dubendorf, Switzerland
Tel.: (41) 43 355 25 25
Web Site: http://ch.walterservices.com
Sales Range: $25-49.9 Million
Business Process Outsourcing Services
N.A.I.C.S.: 561499
Daniel Mally (Mng Dir)

H.I.G. European Capital Partners LLP (1)
10 Grosvenor Street 2nd Floor, London, W1K 4QB, United Kingdom
Tel.: (44) 207 318 5700
Web Site: http://www.higeurope.com
Emp.: 130
Investment Management Service
N.A.I.C.S.: 523940

Holding (Domestic):

Bezier Limited (2)
Golden House, 30 Great Pulteney Street, London, W1F 9NN, United Kingdom
Tel.: (44) 207 534 8800
Web Site: http://www.bezier.co.uk
Sales Range: $150-199.9 Million
Emp.: 85
Advetising Agency
N.A.I.C.S.: 541810
Joe Garton (CEO)

DX (Group) PLC (2)
Ditton Park Riding Court Road, Datchet, SL3 9GL, Slough, United Kingdom
Tel.: (44) 1753630630
Web Site: https://www.dxdelivery.com
Rev.: $581,375,704
Assets: $294,489,468
Liabilities: $219,271,780
Net Worth: $75,217,688
Earnings: $19,008,080
Emp.: 4,100
Fiscal Year-end: 07/02/2022
Logistics & Parcel Distr
N.A.I.C.S.: 541614
Paul Ibbetson (CEO)
Will Wright (CFO)
Ian Bland (Mng Dir-DX Freight)
Martin Illidge (Mng Dir-DX Express)
Michael Sherry (Dir-Information Technology)
James Chuter (Sls Dir)
Elaine Phillips (Sls Dir-Logistics)
Tony Kells (Sls Dir-DX Express)
Kevin Galligan (Dir-Document Exchange UK & DX Ireland)
Patrick Clancy (Gen Mgr)

Silentnight Group Limited (2)
Long Ing Bus Park Long Ing Lane, Barnoldswick, BB18 6BJ, Lancashire, United Kingdom
Tel.: (44) 1282 813 051
Web Site: http://www.silentnightgroup.co.uk
Sales Range: $50-74.9 Million
Emp.: 700
Mattress Mfr
N.A.I.C.S.: 337910

Division (Domestic):

Silentnight Group Limited - Sealy UK Division (3)
Station Rd, Aspatria, Wigton, CA7 2AS, Cumbria, United Kingdom
Tel.: (44) 16973 20342
Web Site: http://www.sealy.co.uk
Sales Range: $50-74.9 Million
Emp.: 400
Bed & Mattress Mfr
N.A.I.C.S.: 337910
Steve Freeman (Mng Dir)
Graham Carberry (Mgr-Contracts)

Holding (Domestic):

Synseal Extrusions Limited (2)
Common Road, Huthwaite, Sutton in Ashfield, NG17 6AD, Nottinghamshire, United Kingdom
Tel.: (44) 1623 443200
Web Site: http://www.synseal.com
Window & Door Mfr
N.A.I.C.S.: 321911

H.I.G. European Capital Partners SAS (1)
2 Lord Byron, 75008, Paris, France
Tel.: (33) 1 53 57 50 60
Web Site: http://www.higeurope.com
Emp.: 10
Privater Equity Firm
N.A.I.C.S.: 523999
Olivier Boyadjian (Mng Dir-France)

Holding (Domestic):

ALTEO Holding SAS (2)
Route de Biver, PO Box 20062, 13541, Gardanne, Cedex, France
Tel.: (33) 4 4265 2222
Web Site: http://www.alteo-alumina.com
Sales Range: $400-449.9 Million
Specialty Alumina Products Mfr
N.A.I.C.S.: 325199
Frederic Rame (Gen Mgr)
Henri Thomas (Dir-PR & Sustainability)

H.I.G. European Capital Partners Spain, S.L.U. (1)

Calle Alfonso XII 38 5a Planta, 28014, Madrid, Spain
Tel.: (34) 91 737 50 50
Web Site: http://www.higcapital.com
Emp.: 14
Investment Management Service
N.A.I.C.S.: 523940
Jaime Bergel (Mng Dir)
Leopoldo Reano (Principal)

Holding (Domestic):

Standard Hidraulica, S.A.U. (2)
Avenida de la Ferreria 73-75 Pol Ind La Ferreria Apdo de Correos 67, 08110, Montcada i Reixac, Barcelona, Spain
Tel.: (34) 935 641 094
Web Site: http://www.standardhidraulica.com
Plumbing & Heating Equipment Mfr
N.A.I.C.S.: 332913

H.I.G. Private Equity (1)
1450 Brickell Ave 31st Fl, Miami, FL 33131
Tel.: (305) 379-2322
Web Site: http://www.higprivateequity.com
Privater Equity Firm
N.A.I.C.S.: 523999
Tony Tamer (Co-Founder)
Douglas Berman (Head-US)
Rick Rosen (Co-Pres)
Brian Schwartz (Co-Pres)
Tyler Levin (Principal-San Francisco)
Todd Ofenloch (Mng Dir-Boston)

Holding (Non-US):

ATX Networks Corp. (2)
1-501 Clements Road West, Ajax, L1S 7H4, ON, Canada
Tel.: (905) 428-6068
Web Site: https://atx.com
Designer, Mfr & Marketer of Products for Cable Television Industry
N.A.I.C.S.: 334419
Jay Lee (CTO & VP-Bus Dev)
Brad Nikkari (VP-Bus Dev-RF & Optical Solutions)
Linas Underys (VP-Bus Dev-Digital Video Products & Solutions)
Andrew Isherwood (Co-CTO & Chief Strategy Officer-Media Distr)
Jeffrey Liening (Chief Sls Officer)
Kim Lee (Exec VP-Mktg)
Bob Murphy (Sr VP)
Vince Martelli (CFO)
Brooke Mistry (Chief People Officer)
Don Rowley (CIO)
Matt Grimes (Sr VP)

Subsidiary (US):

Pico Digital Inc. (3)
8880 Rehco Rd, San Diego, CA 92121
Tel.: (858) 546-5050
Web Site: http://www.picodigital.com
Electronic Components Distr
N.A.I.C.S.: 423690
Carlos Shteremberg (Pres)
Ian A. Lerner (CEO)
Jose Rivero (VP-Brdcst)
Brian Trexel (VP-Engrg)
Andrew Isherwood (Chief Technical Officer)
Anthony Tibbs (CFO)

Holding (Domestic):

AirNet II, LLC (2)
3041 George Page Jr, Columbus, OH 43217
Tel.: (614) 409-4900
Web Site: http://www.airnet.com
Air Cargo Transportation Services
N.A.I.C.S.: 481112
Michael Utt (Ops Mgr-Airline)
Mark Simone (Gen Mgr)

American Pacific Corporation (2)
3883 Howard Hughes Pkwy Ste 700, Las Vegas, NV 89169
Tel.: (702) 735-2200
Web Site: http://www.ampac.us
Rev.: $215,085,000
Assets: $277,307,000
Liabilities: $165,970,000
Net Worth: $111,337,000
Earnings: $23,232,000
Emp.: 530
Fiscal Year-end: 09/30/2013
Chemicals Mfr

N.A.I.C.S.: 325180

Subsidiary (Domestic):

American Azide Corporation (3)
3770 Howard Hughes Pkwy Ste 300, Las Vegas, NV 89169 **(100%)**
Tel.: (702) 735-2200
Web Site: http://www.apfc.com
Sales Range: $50-74.9 Million
Emp.: 200
Chemical Gas for Auto Airbag Filler Mfr
N.A.I.C.S.: 325998

Halotron, Inc. (3)
3883 Howard Hughes Pkwy Ste 700, Las Vegas, NV 89169-0914 **(100%)**
Tel.: (702) 735-2200
Web Site: http://www.halotron.com
Sales Range: $25-49.9 Million
Emp.: 25
Mfr of Chemical Gas for Fire Extinguishers
N.A.I.C.S.: 325998

Western Electrochemical Company (3)
10622 West 6400 N, Cedar City, UT 84720-9016 **(100%)**
Tel.: (435) 865-5000
Web Site: http://www.apfc.com
Rev.: $75,000,000
Emp.: 180
Mfr of Inorganic Material
N.A.I.C.S.: 541618

Holding (Domestic):

Amsive LLC (2)
605 Territorial Dr Ste A B & C, Bolingbrook, IL 60440
Tel.: (331) 318-7800
Web Site: https://www.amsive.com
Advertising Services, Data Solutions, Creative, Direct Mail, Search, SEO, Email, Digital Media, Managed Social & Web Development Services
N.A.I.C.S.: 323111
Michael Coppola (Pres)
Laura Klimenko (Chief People Officer)
Daniel J. Fujii (CFO)
Keith Chadwell (CIO & Exec VP-Ops)
Brad Moore (CEO)
Mark Evans (CMO)

Subsidiary (Domestic):

Amsive Digital Inc. (3)
915 Broadway Ste 1003, New York, NY 10010
Tel.: (212) 661-8969
Web Site: https://www.amsivedigital.com
Emp.: 100
Digital Marketing Agency
N.A.I.C.S.: 541840
Michael Coppola (CEO)
Michelle LeWinter (VP-Ops, Sls & Strategy)
Michael Candullo (Exec VP-Digital Ops)
Rich Campanero (Sr VP-Digital Sls)
Jenny Chan (Dir-Fin & Ops)

Holding (Non-US):

Arctic Glacier Holdings Inc. (2)
625 Henry Avenue, Winnipeg, R3A 0V1, MB, Canada
Tel.: (204) 772-2473
Web Site: http://www.arcticglacier.com
Holding Company; Packaged Ice Mfr & Distr
N.A.I.C.S.: 551112
Neil Winther (VP-HR & Admin)

Subsidiary (Domestic):

Arctic Glacier Inc. (3)
625 Henry Ave, Winnipeg, R3A 0V1, MB, Canada
Tel.: (204) 772-2473
Web Site: https://www.arcticglacier.com
Sales Range: $100-124.9 Million
Emp.: 2,400
Packaged Ice Mfr & Distr
N.A.I.C.S.: 312113

Subsidiary (US):

Arctic Glacier Pennsylvania, Inc. (3)
1 Bala Plz Ste 622, Bala Cynwyd, PA 19004
Tel.: (800) 562-1990

Mfr & Distr of Packaged Ice, Ice Equipment & Related Svcs
N.A.I.C.S.: 312113
Richard Wyckoff (Pres & CEO)

Subsidiary (Domestic):

Southeastern Ice, Inc. (4)
1202 W Stovall Rd 1, Wilburton, OK 74578
Tel.: (918) 465-2500
Sales Range: $1-9.9 Million
Emp.: 20
Miscellaneous Store Retailers (except Tobacco Stores)
N.A.I.C.S.: 459999
Destry Harber (Founder & CEO)

Subsidiary (US):

Arctic Glacier U.S.A., Inc. (3)
1654 Marthaler Ln, West Saint Paul, MN 55118
Tel.: (651) 455-0410
Packaged Ice Product Mfr & Distr
N.A.I.C.S.: 312113

Subsidiary (Domestic):

Jack Frost Ice Service, Inc. (4)
1440 Coldwell Ave, Modesto, CA 95350
Tel.: (209) 524-3128
Web Site: http://www.arcticglacierinc.com
Rev.: $13,000,000
Emp.: 45
Mfr & Distr of Premium Quality Packaged Ice Products
N.A.I.C.S.: 312113

Mid Central Ice, LLC (4)
39072 County Hwy 49, Perham, MN 56573
Tel.: (218) 346-4423
Web Site: http://www.midcentralice.com
Sales Range: $1-9.9 Million
Emp.: 13
Miscellaneous Store Retailers (except Tobacco Stores)
N.A.I.C.S.: 459999
David Chase (Principal)

Holding (Domestic):

Atlantic Aluminum, LLC (2)
167 Stone Henge Dr, Dunn, NC 28334-7677
Tel.: (910) 359-0150
Aluminum Extruded Product Mfr
N.A.I.C.S.: 331318

Cablexpress Corporation (2)
5404 S Bay Rd, Syracuse, NY 13212 **(100%)**
Tel.: (315) 476-3000
Web Site: http://www.cablexpress.com
Distributes Computer Peripherals
N.A.I.C.S.: 423430
Robert Jordan (Architect-Data Center Infrastructure)
Rick Dallmann (Dir-Data Center Architecture)
Renee Duffy (VP-Mktg)
Barbara Ashkin (CFO & VP)
Jeff Williams (Exec VP-Sls)
Pete Belyea (Pres & CEO)
Tim Duffy (CTO)

Subsidiary (Domestic):

Atlantix Global Systems, LLC (3)
1 Sun Ct, Norcross, GA 30092-2851
Tel.: (888) 400-6994
Web Site: http://www.atlantixglobal.com
New & Used Computer & Computer Peripheral Equipment Distr
N.A.I.C.S.: 423430
Brian Glahn (Pres & CEO)
Jason Jellie (Exec VP-Sls)
Barbara Ashkin (CFO & VP)
Renee Duffy (VP & Mktg)

Holding (Domestic):

Continental Battery Company (2)
4919 Woodall St, Dallas, TX 75247
Tel.: (214) 631-5701
Web Site: http://www.continentalbattery.com
Sales Range: $10-24.9 Million
Emp.: 45
Whslr of Automotive Batteries
N.A.I.C.S.: 423120

James R. McCann (Pres)
Dave Nelson (CFO)
William McCann (VP)
Eric Royse (CEO)

Correct Care Solutions, LLC (2)
1283 Murfreesboro Rd Ste 500, Nashville, TN 37217
Tel.: (615) 324-5750
Web Site:
  http://www.correctcaresolutions.com
Sales Range: $500-549.9 Million
Emp.: 3,000
Correctional Facility Medical, Dental & Mental Health Care Services
N.A.I.C.S.: 623990
Patrick Cummiskey (Pres & Chief Strategy Officer)
Bob Martin (CIO & Sr VP)
Jon Bosch (Sr VP-Accreditation & Operational Compliance)
Chris Bove (COO)
Jorge Dominicis (CEO)
Kevin Jordan (Sr VP-Bus Support)
Scott A. Pustizzi (Chief HR Officer & Sr VP)
Carl Keldie (Chief Clinical Officer & Sr VP)
Cassandra Newkirk (Chief Psychiatric Officer & VP)
Stan Wofford (Sr VP-Local Detention)
Brad Dunbar (Exec VP-Local Detention Div)
Juan C. Perez (CFO)

Subsidiary (Domestic):

Conmed Healthcare Management, Inc. (3)
7250 Parkway Dr Ste 400, Hanover, MD 21076
Tel.: (410) 567-5520
Sales Range: $50-74.9 Million
Emp.: 587
Medical Devices
N.A.I.C.S.: 525120

Subsidiary (Domestic):

Conmed, Inc. (4)
7250 Parkway Dr Ste 400, Hanover, MD 21076-3400
Tel.: (410) 567-5520
Ambulatory Health Care Services
N.A.I.C.S.: 621999

Holding (Domestic):

DHISCO, Inc. (2)
3 Lincoln Ctr 5430 LBJ Frwy Ste 1100, Dallas, TX 75240
Tel.: (214) 234-4000
Holding Company; Hotel Transactions Processing & Hospitality Business Intelligence Software & Services
N.A.I.C.S.: 551112
Toni Portmann (Chm & CEO)
Charles Loop (CFO)
Greg Berman (Chief Strategy Officer)
Bryan Hadley (CIO)

Subsidiary (Domestic):

DHISCO Electronic Distribution, Inc. (3)
14000 N Pima Rd Ste 200, Scottsdale, AZ 85260
Tel.: (214) 234-4000
Web Site: http://www.pegasus.io
Hotel Transactions Processing & Hospitality Business Intelligence Software & Services
N.A.I.C.S.: 513210
Toni Portmann (Chm & CEO)
Charles Loop (CFO)
Bryan Bradley (CIO)
Greg Berman (Chief Strategy Officer)
Patty Woodhouse (Sr VP-Applications Dev)
Bryan Finney (VP-Fin)
Kyle Moore (Sr VP-Product Dev)
Anne Cole (VP-Content)
John Thomas (VP-Infrastructure)
Katherin Dockerill (VP-Mktg)
Amy Garr (VP-HR)

Holding (Domestic):

Desa LLC (2)
2701 Industrial Dr, Bowling Green, KY 42101-4065
Tel.: (270) 781-9600
Web Site: http://www.desaint.com

Sales Range: $200-249.9 Million
Heating Equipment, Portable Chain Saws, Security Lighting Door Bells & Specialty Tools Mfr
N.A.I.C.S.: 333414

Eruptr LLC (2)
16417 Cornwall Ln, Bradenton, FL 34202
Web Site: http://www.eruptr.com
General Marketing Services
N.A.I.C.S.: 541613
J. K. Lloyd (Co-Founder & Pres)
Kevin Minnelli (Co-Founder & CEO)
Lea Bizri (CFO)
Melissa Placzkowski (COO)
Adam Kruse (Dir-Tech)
Joel Cessna (VP-Sls)
Emma Therrien (Dir-Mktg)
Monica Patel (Dir-Client Svcs)

Escalate Media Holdings, LLC (2)
444 N Michigan Ave Ste 3550, Chicago, IL 60611
Tel.: (312) 396-1800
Web Site: http://www.escalatemedia.com
Holding Company; Website Publisher & Advertising Services
N.A.I.C.S.: 551112
Mark Kaufman (CEO)
Jodi Luber (Pres)

Subsidiary (Domestic):

Escalate Media, L.P. (3)
PO Box 591928, Houston, TX 77259
Web Site: http://www.escalatemedia.com
Advertising Website Publisher
N.A.I.C.S.: 541890

Group (Domestic):

Womensforum Media Group (3)
444 N Michigan Ave Ste 3550, Chicago, IL 60611
Tel.: (312) 396-1800
Web Site:
  http://www.womensforummediagroup.com
Holding Company; Website Publisher & Advertising Services
N.A.I.C.S.: 551112
Jodi Luber (Pres)

Holding (Domestic):

F.H.G. Corporation (2)
4637 Port Royal Rd, Spring Hill, TN 37174
Tel.: (931) 499-7070
Rev.: $9,283,000
Emp.: 25
Drugs & Druggists' Sundries Merchant Whslr
N.A.I.C.S.: 424210

Holland Services, LLC (2)
309 W 7th St Ste 200, Fort Worth, TX 76102
Tel.: (817) 698-9393
Web Site: http://www.hollandservices.com
Oil & Gas Support Services
N.A.I.C.S.: 213112
Robert Gaudin (Founder & CEO)
Taylor Gregg (CFO)
Bryan Gaudin (COO)
Brian Poe (Mgr-Houston)
Tiffany Booher (Sr Mgr-Project)
Nick Delacoma (Sr VP-Ops)
Clint Foutch (Sr Mgr-Project)
Tom Hower (Mgr-Bus Dev)
Andrew St. John (Gen Counsel)
Marc Jackson (Mgr-Denver)
Howard Seely (CFO)

InterDent, Inc. (2)
9800 S La Cienega Blvd, Inglewood, CA 90301-4440
Tel.: (310) 765-2400
Web Site: http://www.interdent.com
Sales Range: $200-249.9 Million
Accounting, Hiring, Training, Marketing, Scheduling & Information Management Services for Dentists
N.A.I.C.S.: 524114
Marshal Salomon (CEO)

Jenny Craig, Inc. (2)
5770 Fleet St, Carlsbad, CA 92008-9446
Tel.: (760) 696-4000
Web Site: http://www.jennycraig.com
Weight Management Centers
N.A.I.C.S.: 456191

H.I.G. Capital, LLC—(Continued)

Doug Battista *(Pres-Field Ops-North America)*
Jeff Burchfield *(Gen Counsel, Sec & VP)*
Jenny Craig *(Founder)*
Michelle Hodges *(Chief HR Officer)*
Monty Sharma *(Chm)*
Peter Noverr *(COO)*
David Pastrana *(CEO)*

Unit (Domestic):

Jenny Craig Distribution Center (3)
11335 Jersey Blvd Ste C, Rancho Cu-
camonga, CA 91730
Tel.: (909) 481-7766
Web Site: http://www.jennycraig.com
General Warehousing & Storage
N.A.I.C.S.: 493110

Subsidiary (Domestic):

Jenny Craig Operations, Inc. (3)
3311 N Sterling Ave Ste 7, Peoria, IL
61604-1840
Tel.: (309) 681-0100
Health Care Srvices
N.A.I.C.S.: 621999
Melinda Heinz *(Office Mgr)*

Subsidiary (Non-US):

**Jenny Craig Weight Loss Centres
(Canada) Company** (3)
411 Bayfield Street, Barrie, L4M 6E5, ON,
Canada
Tel.: (705) 728-7661
Personal Weight Loss Treatment & Nutri-
tional Service Centers Operator
N.A.I.C.S.: 812191

**Jenny Craig Weight Loss Centres
(NZ) Ltd.** (3)
Ground Floor 31-33 Great South Road
Newmarket, Auckland, 1051, New Zealand
Tel.: (64) 95205300
Web Site: http://www.jennycraig.co.nz
Personal Weight Loss Treatment & Nutri-
tional Service Centers Operator
N.A.I.C.S.: 812191

**Jenny Craig Weight Loss Centres
Pty. Ltd.** (3)
Level 2 468 Saint Kilda Rd, Melbourne,
3004, Australia
Tel.: (61) 398675644
Web Site: http://www.jennycraig.com.au
Sales Range: $25-49.9 Million
Emp.: 50
Personal Weight Loss Treatment & Nutri-
tional Service Centers Operator
N.A.I.C.S.: 812191
Ken Carter *(Mng Dir)*

Subsidiary (Domestic):

**Jenny Craig Weight Loss Centres,
Inc.** (3)
5770 Fleet St, Carlsbad, CA 92008-4700
Tel.: (760) 696-4000
Web Site: http://www.jennycraig.com
Sales Range: $300-349.9 Million
Personal Weight Loss Treatment & Nutri-
tional Service Centers Operator
N.A.I.C.S.: 812191

Holding (Domestic):

Lionbridge Technologies, Inc. (2)
1050 Winter St Ste 2300, Waltham, MA
02451
Tel.: (781) 434-6000
Web Site: http://www.lionbridge.com
Software, User Manuals & Web Content
Translation & Globalization Services
N.A.I.C.S.: 541519
Richard Patrick Tobin *(COO)*
John Fennelly *(CEO)*
Clemente Cohen *(CFO)*
Jim Weber *(Chief Revenue Officer)*
Tony Stoupas *(CTO)*
Kat McCabe *(Gen Counsel)*

Subsidiary (Non-US):

**Beijing Lionbridge Global Solutions
Technologies, Inc.** (3)
11F Futai Center, Chaoyang, Beijing,
100102, China

Tel.: (86) 1085186161
Web Site: http://www.lionbridge.com
Software, User Manuals & Web Content
Translation & Globalization Services
N.A.I.C.S.: 541519

Darwin Zone S.A. (3)
Oficentro Plaza Roble Edificio Las Terrazas
A Piso 4 San Rafael, Escazu, Costa Rica
Tel.: (506) 40701399
Software Development Services
N.A.I.C.S.: 541511

Lionbridge (Canada) Inc. (3)
7900-E W Taschereau Blvd Suite 204, Mon-
treal, J4X 1C2, QC, Canada
Tel.: (450) 923-5650
Web Site: http://www.lionbrige.com
Software, User Manuals & Web Content
Translation & Globalization Services
N.A.I.C.S.: 541519

Lionbridge (Slovakia) S.r.o. (3)
Murgasova 2, SK-01001, Zilina, Slovakia
Tel.: (421) 417242488
Web Site: http://www.lionbridge.com
Software, User Manuals & Web Content
Translation & Globalization Services
N.A.I.C.S.: 541519

Lionbridge (Thailand) Limited (3)
24th Floor Unit 5 Silom Complex Bldg 191
Silom Rd, Silom Bangrak, Bangkok, 10500,
Thailand
Tel.: (66) 26321530
Web Site: http://www.lionbridge.com
Software, User Manuals & Web Content
Translation & Globalization Services
N.A.I.C.S.: 541519

Lionbridge (UK) Ltd. (3)
Town Square Office 3, Willow Brook Centre
Bradley Stoke, Bristol, BS32 8FB, United
Kingdom
Tel.: (44) 1173729784
Web Site: http://www.lionbridge.com
Software, User Manuals & Web Content
Translation & Globalization Services
N.A.I.C.S.: 541519

Lionbridge Denmark A/S (3)
Lerso Parkalle 42, 2720, Vanlose, Denmark
Tel.: (45) 70142944
Web Site: http://www.lionbridge.com
Software, User Manuals & Web Content
Translation & Globalization Services
N.A.I.C.S.: 541519

Lionbridge Espana S.L. (3)
Edificio Ofipinar Caleruega 102-104 7th
floor, ES-28033, Madrid, Spain
Tel.: (34) 91 791 3443
Web Site: http://www.lionbridge.com
Software, User Manuals & Web Content
Translation & Globalization Services
N.A.I.C.S.: 541519

Lionbridge France SAS (3)
E Space Park Batiment D 45 Allee des
Ormes, BP 1200, 06254, Mougins, France
Tel.: (33) 492 952 001
Web Site: http://www.lionbridge.com
Software, User Manuals & Web Content
Translation & Globalization Services
N.A.I.C.S.: 541519

Lionbridge Holding GmbH (3)
Konsumstrasse 45, D-42285, Wuppertal,
Germany
Tel.: (49) 202 43047800
Web Site: http://www.lionbridge.com
Software, User Manuals & Web Content
Translation & Globalization Services
N.A.I.C.S.: 541519

Subsidiary (Domestic):

Lionbridge Deutschland GmbH (4)
Konsumstrasse 45, D-42285, Wuppertal,
Germany
Tel.: (49) 202 43047800
Web Site: http://www.lionbridge.com
Software, User Manuals & Web Content
Translation & Globalization Services
N.A.I.C.S.: 541519

Subsidiary (Non-US):

Lionbridge Ireland Limited (3)
3 West Pier Business Campus, Dun
Laoghaire, Co Dublin, Ireland

Tel.: (353) 12021200
Web Site: http://www.lionbridge.com
Software, User Manuals & Web Content
Translation & Globalization Services
N.A.I.C.S.: 541519

Lionbridge Japan III K.K. (3)
42nd Floor Yokohama Landmark Tower 2-2-
1-1 Minatomirai Nishisku, 2-2-1-1- Minato-
Mirai Nishi-ku, Yokohama, 220-8142, Japan
Tel.: (81) 456404250
Web Site: http://www.lionbridge.com
Software, User Manuals & Web Content
Translation & Globalization Services
N.A.I.C.S.: 541519

Lionbridge Japan KK (3)
2-1-1 Minatomirai 2-chome Nishi-ku, 220-
8142, Yokohama, Kanagawaken, Japan
Tel.: (81) 456404250
Computer Support Services
N.A.I.C.S.: 541519

Lionbridge Korea Co. Ltd. (3)
7th Floor Business Tower Nuritkum Square
Building 1605 Sangam-dong, Mapo-gu,
Seoul, 121-795, Korea (South)
Tel.: (82) 27879500
Web Site: http://www.lionbridge.com
Software User Manual & Web Content
Translation & Globalization Services
N.A.I.C.S.: 541519

Subsidiary (Domestic):

Lionbridge Midwest, LLC (3)
2601 Fortune Cir E Ste 200A, Indianapolis,
IN 46241
Tel.: (317) 484-2325
Web Site: http://www.lionbridge.com
Engineering Services
N.A.I.C.S.: 541330

Subsidiary (Non-US):

Lionbridge Nederland B.V. (3)
Overschiestraat 55, 1062 HN, Amsterdam,
Netherlands
Tel.: (31) 207083915
Web Site: http://www.lionbridge.com
Software, User Manuals & Web Content
Translation & Globalization Services
N.A.I.C.S.: 541519

Lionbridge Oy (3)
Puolikkotie 8, 5 krs, Espoo, FI-02230, Fin-
land
Tel.: (358) 942705600
Web Site: http://www.lionbridge.com
Software, User Manuals & Web Content
Translation & Globalization Services
N.A.I.C.S.: 541519

Lionbridge Poland Sp. z o.o. (3)
183 Jutrzenki St, Warsaw, 2231, Poland
Tel.: (48) 228659900
Web Site: http://www.lionbridge.com
Software, User Manuals & Web Content
Translation & Globalization Services
N.A.I.C.S.: 541519

Lionbridge Singapore Pte Ltd. (3)
8 Eu Tong Sen Street, #18-99 The Central,
Singapore, 059818, Singapore
Tel.: (65) 62711501
Web Site: http://www.lionbridge.com
Software, User Manuals & Web Content
Translation & Globalization Services
N.A.I.C.S.: 541519

Lionbridge Sweden Aktiebolag (3)
Karl Johansgatan 27, 41459, Gothenburg,
Sweden
Tel.: (46) 317756080
Web Site: http://www.lionbridge.com
Software, User Manuals & Web Content
Translation & Globalization Services
N.A.I.C.S.: 541519

**Lionbridge Technologies (France)
S.a.r.l.** (3)
Buropolis 1 1240 Route Des Dolines, So-
phia Antipolis, Valbonne, 06560, France
Tel.: (33) 492952000
Web Site: http://www.lionbridge.com
Software Consulting Services
N.A.I.C.S.: 541690

**Lionbridge Technologies Private
Limited** (3)
5th Floor Tower B Tek Meadows, 51 Rajiv

Gandhi Salai Sholinganallur, Chennai, 600
119, India
Tel.: (91) 4466785000
Web Site: http://www.lionbridge.com
Software, User Manuals & Web Content
Translation & Globalization Services
N.A.I.C.S.: 541519

Lionbridge Testing Services Oy (3)
Visiokatu 1, FI-33720, Tampere, Finland
Tel.: (358) 942705600
Web Site: http://www.lionbridge.com
Translation & Localization Services
N.A.I.C.S.: 541930

Subsidiary (Domestic):

Productive Resources, LLC (3)
1917 McKinley Ave, Columbus, IN 47201
Tel.: (812) 372-2551
Engineeering Services
N.A.I.C.S.: 541330

VeriTest, Inc. (3)
3535 Factoria Blvd SE, Bellevue, WA 98006
Tel.: (425) 688-1000
Business Support Services
N.A.I.C.S.: 561499

Holding (Domestic):

Lucas Associates Inc. (2)
3384 Peachtree Rd Ste 900, Atlanta, GA
30326
Tel.: (404) 239-5620
Web Site: http://www.lucasgroup.com
Rev.: $52,600,000
Emp.: 70
Executive Recruitment Services
N.A.I.C.S.: 561311
Amy Healey *(Dir-Sls Ops)*
Bob Prather *(Gen Mgr-Acctg & Fin)*
Joe Eiseman *(Mng Partner-IT Practice Grp-
New York)*
Tom McGee *(VP & Gen Mgr-Sls & Mktg
Practice Grp)*
Justin Laliberte *(Mng Partner-IT)*
Whitney Husby Worthington *(Mng Partner-
Branch)*
Nancy Neal *(Sr Partner-Sls & Mktg)*
Valerie Vincent Taylor *(Sr Partner-HR-Los
Angeles)*
Ann Reiling *(Mng Partner-HR)*
Laura Kesler *(Mng Partner-IT-San Diego,
Las Vegas & Phoenix)*
Steven Robinson *(Gen Mgr-IT)*
Jimmy Dwertman *(Mng Partner-Mfg Office-
Cincinnati)*
Charlie Wilgus *(Gen Mgr-Mfg Practice Grp)*
Danielle Edwards *(Project Mgr-Mktg)*
Mark Hinshaw *(CFO)*
Kate Naylor *(Mgr-HR Practice)*
Aram Lulla *(Gen Mgr-HR Exec Search
Practice)*
Shelton Blease *(Dir-HR Ops)*
Nick Buffini *(Mng Partner)*
Jamie Hersh *(Mng Partner)*
Carolina King *(Chief People Officer)*
Lori Layton *(Mng Partner)*
Christian Novissimo *(Mng Partner)*
Curt Webb *(Mng Partner)*
Don Wylie *(Mng Partner)*
Randy Marmon *(Pres & Grp CEO)*
Mir Ali *(CIO)*

Lucas Group (2)
18301 Von Karman Ave Ste 700, Irvine, CA
92612
Tel.: (949) 660-9450
Web Site: http://www.lucasgroup.com
Sales Range: $25-49.9 Million
Emp.: 30
Employment Placement Services
N.A.I.C.S.: 561311
Andrea Jennings *(Pres & CEO)*
Bob Prather *(Gen Mgr-Acctg & Fin)*
Scott Smith *(CMO)*
James Lose *(Mng Partner-Military Transi-
tion)*
Alex Hirschenfang *(Sr Partner-Acctg & Fin)*
Carl White *(Sr Partner-Acctg & Fin)*
Christian Novissimo *(Mng Partner-Acctg &
Fin)*
Curt Webb *(Mng Partner-Acctg & Fin)*
Don Wylie *(Mng Partner-Acctg & Fin)*
Jamie Hersh *(Mng Partner-Acctg & Fin)*
Ray Garcia *(Mng Partner-Acctg & Fin)*
Victor Palumbo *(Mng Partner-Acctg & Fin)*
Carolina King *(Chief HR Officer)*

Carly Gorman *(Mgr-Branch Practice-Sls & Mktg)*
Marc Wilder *(Mng Partner-IT-New York)*
Steven Robinson *(Gen Mgr-IT Exec Recruitment Svcs)*
Ana Hey-Colon *(Dir-Sls & Trng)*
Amdie Mengistu *(Mng Partner-Legal)*
Ann Reiling *(Mng Partner-HR)*
Bret Hamilton *(Mng Partner-IT)*
Carolyn Aberman *(Mng Partner-Legal)*
Dan McCall *(Mng Partner-Military Transition)*
Erik Kessinger *(Mng Partner-Mfg)*
J. T. Mackey *(Mng Partner-IT)*
Jeffrey Bloom *(Mng Partner-Legal)*
Jennifer Bowers *(Mng Partner-Mfg)*
Jimmy Dwertman *(Mng Partner-Mfg)*
Jim O'Neal *(Mng Partner-Military Transition)*
John Quinn *(Mng Partner-Military Transition)*
Justin Laliberte *(Mng Partner-IT)*
Justin Martinez *(Mng Partner-IT)*
Ken Martin *(Mng Partner-IT)*
Laura Kesler *(Mng Partner-IT)*
Mark Hinshaw *(CFO)*
Myra Mendizabal *(Mng Partner-Legal)*
Nick Buffini *(Mng Partner-Acctg & Fin)*
Paul Matthews *(Mng Partner-Mfg)*
Sam Henry *(Mng Partner-Mfg)*
Sam Peterson *(Mng Partner-Acctg & Fin)*
Scott Plumstead *(Mng Partner-Mfg)*
C. Thomas Williamson III *(Mng Partner-Legal)*

Milestone Technologies Inc. (2)
3101 Skwy Ct, Fremont, CA 94539
Tel.: (510) 651-2454
Web Site:
http://www.milestonepowered.com
Custom Computer Programming Services
N.A.I.C.S.: 541511
Rose Baldwin *(VP-People Ops)*
Edward Reginelli *(CFO)*
Doug Tracy *(Exec VP-Global Tech Ops)*
Prem Chand *(Founder)*
Sameer Kishore *(Pres & CEO)*
Elliot Maluth *(Chm)*

Subsidiary (Domestic):

Covestic, Inc. (3)
5555 Lakeview Dr Ste 100, Kirkland, WA 98033
Tel.: (425) 803-9889
Web Site: http://www.covestic.com
Sales Range: $10-24.9 Million
Emp.: 92
Computer System Design Services
N.A.I.C.S.: 541512
John Schaffer *(Pres & CEO)*

Holding (Domestic):

NCI, Inc. (2)
11730 Plaza America Dr, Reston, VA 20190-4764
Tel.: (703) 707-6900
Web Site: http://www.nciinc.com
Sales Range: $300-349.9 Million
Holding Company; Information Technology, Engineering, Professional Services & Solutions
N.A.I.C.S.: 551112
Charles K. Narang *(Chm)*
Michele R. Cappello *(Sr VP, Gen Counsel & Sec)*
Daniel R. Young *(Vice Chm)*
James D. Collier *(CFO, Treas & Exec VP)*
Brad Mascho *(Chief Artificial Intelligence Officer)*
Sandra Gillespie *(COO)*
Bridget Medeiros *(Sr VP-Bus Dev)*
Pamela Rothka *(CFO-Empower AI)*
Paul Harrington *(Chief Growth Officer)*
Jeff Bohling *(CEO)*

Subsidiary (Domestic):

Kruge-Air, Inc. (3)
7125 Northland Terrace N Ste 100, Brooklyn Park, MN 55428 **(100%)**
Tel.: (763) 424-0555
Web Site: http://www.krugeair.com
Compressors, After Coolers & Other Air Equipment Mfr
N.A.I.C.S.: 423830

Holding (Domestic):

Next Generation Vending, LLC (2)

800 Technology Ctr Dr Ste 110, Stoughton, MA 02072
Tel.: (781) 828-2345
Web Site:
http://www.nextgenerationone.com
Sales Range: $100-124.9 Million
Vending Machine Operators
N.A.I.C.S.: 445132
Lidia Fraga *(Coord-AP)*
Kenneth Strachan *(Gen Counsel)*

Oxford Global Resources, Inc. (2)
100 Cummings Ctr Ste 206L, Beverly, MA 01915
Tel.: (978) 236-1182
Web Site: http://www.oxfordcorp.com
Emp.: 55
Employment Placement Services
N.A.I.C.S.: 561311
Ted Hanson *(Pres)*

Polymer Additives, Inc. (2)
7500 E Pleasant Vly Rd, Independence, OH 44131
Tel.: (216) 875-7200
Web Site: http://valtris.com
Polymer Additives Mfr
N.A.I.C.S.: 325998
Steve Hughes *(VP-Comml)*
Paul Angus *(CEO)*
Craig Fitzpatrick *(CFO)*
Jim Mason *(VP-Ops)*
Brenda Hollo *(VP-Tech)*
Curt Tschantz *(VP-HR)*
Tim Harker *(Dir-Bus Ops)*

Holding (Non-US):

Project Informatica SRL (2)
Via C Cattaneo 6, 24040, Stezzano, Italy
Tel.: (39) 0352050301
Web Site: http://www.project.it
Sales Range: $200-249.9 Million
Emp.: 230
IT Services
N.A.I.C.S.: 541512
Valeria Mauri *(Mgr-Mktg)*
Alberto Ghisleni *(Founder & CEO)*

Subsidiary (Domestic):

Project Shop Land SpA (3)
Via C Cattaneo 6, 24040, Stezzano, BG, Italy
Tel.: (39) 0352050301
Web Site: http://www.projectshopland.com
Emp.: 200
IT Services
N.A.I.C.S.: 423430
Alberto Ghisleni *(CEO)*

Holding (Domestic):

Reliant Rehabilitation Holdings, Inc. (2)
5800 Granite Pkwy Ste 1000, Plano, TX 75024
Tel.: (972) 447-9800
Web Site: http://www.reliant-rehab.com
Rehabilitation Services; Physical, Occupational & Speech Therapy Services
N.A.I.C.S.: 624310
Christopher M. Bird *(CEO)*
Jeffrey B. Rosenthal *(CIO)*
David Tate *(Chief Strategy Officer)*
Peggy Gourgues *(COO)*
Austin Lanham *(Chief Legal Officer & Gen Counsel)*
Stephanie Parks *(Chief Development Officer)*
Amy Phipps *(Chief Compliance Officer & Chief Clinical Officer)*

Holding (Non-US):

Rolland Enterprises Inc. (2)
455 Avenue Rolland, CP 850, Saint-Jerome, J7Z 5S2, QC, Canada
Tel.: (450) 569-3900
Sales Range: $10-24.9 Million
Security Papers Mfr & Whslr
N.A.I.C.S.: 322120
Daniel Parrot *(Pres & COO)*

Holding (Domestic):

Rotorcraft Leasing Company, L.L.C. (2)
430 N Eola Rd, Broussard, LA 70518
Tel.: (337) 837-6038

Web Site: http://www.rotorcraftleasing.net
Helicopter Support Services
N.A.I.C.S.: 561499
Dru Milke *(Pres & CEO)*
Joan McCarthy *(CFO)*
Patrick Graves *(COO)*
Edie Hunt *(VP-HR)*
John Gilley *(VP-Sls & Mktg)*
James Gueringer *(VP & Dir-Maintenance)*
Pat Milam *(VP-Sls & Mktg)*
David Nezat *(Dir-Facilities)*
Jeff Peltier *(Dir-Supply Chain)*
Tom Young *(VP-Safety & Quality Assurance)*

SCRIBE MANUFACTURING, INC. (2)
14421 Myerlake Cir, Clearwater, FL 33760-2840
Tel.: (727) 536-7895
Stationery Product Mfr
N.A.I.C.S.: 322220
David Miller *(Treas)*
Camilo Horvilleur *(Sec)*
Jonathan Fox *(VP)*
David A. Klatt Jr. *(CEO)*

Shapes/Arch Holdings, LLC (2)
9000 River Rd, Delair, NJ 08110
Tel.: (856) 662-5500
Web Site: http://www.shapesllc.com
Sales Range: $250-299.9 Million
Holding Company
N.A.I.C.S.: 551112
Chris Boland *(VP-Comml)*

Subsidiary (Domestic):

Accu-Weld, LLC (3)
1211 Ford Rd, Bensalem, PA 19020
Tel.: (215) 245-6050
Web Site: http://www.accuweld.com
Sales Range: $25-49.9 Million
Emp.: 150
Vinyl Replacement Window & Steel Door Mfr & Dealer
N.A.I.C.S.: 444180

Aluminum Shapes, LLC (3)
9000 River Rd, Delair, NJ 08110-3204
Tel.: (856) 662-5500
Web Site: http://www.shapesllc.com
Sales Range: $75-99.9 Million
Aluminum Extruded Product Mfr
N.A.I.C.S.: 331318
James Rutherford *(VP-Mfg)*
Rick Mackessy *(CFO)*
David Pika *(Dir-HR)*

Delair Group, LLC (3)
8600 River Rd, Delair, NJ 08110-3328
Tel.: (856) 663-2900
Web Site: http://www.delairgroup.com
Sales Range: $25-49.9 Million
Swimming Pools, Pool Accessories & Aluminum Fencing Mfr
N.A.I.C.S.: 331318
Lynne Weinstein *(Office Mgr)*
Bill Mackenzie *(VP-Sls)*

Holding (Non-US):

Signature Aluminum Canada, Inc. (2)
1850 Clements Road, Pickering, L1W 3R8, ON, Canada
Tel.: (905) 427-6550
Web Site: https://www.signaturealum.com
Sales Range: $25-49.9 Million
Emp.: 200
Primary Aluminum Mfr
N.A.I.C.S.: 331313

Holding (Domestic):

Southern Quality Meats, Inc. (2)
266 W 8th St, Pontotoc, MS 38863
Tel.: (662) 489-1524
Pork Sausage Product Mfr
N.A.I.C.S.: 311615

Stant Corp. (2)
1620 Columbia Ave, Connersville, IN 47331-1672 **(100%)**
Tel.: (765) 825-3121
Web Site: http://www.stant.com
Sales Range: $200-249.9 Million
Fuel & Oil Cap Mfr
N.A.I.C.S.: 336390

Tim King *(Sr VP-Sls-Global)*
Michael Cowley *(VP-Engrg & Program Mgmt)*
Andy Anderson *(CIO)*
Tom Zambelli *(CFO)*

Symplicity Corporation (2)
1560 Wilson Blvd Suite 550, Arlington, VA 22209 **(100%)**
Tel.: (703) 351-0200
Web Site: http://www.symplicity.com
Rev.: $1,400,000
Emp.: 200
Development of Dynamic & Database-Driven Web Applications
N.A.I.C.S.: 513210
Zena Thomas *(Mgr-HR)*
Matthew Small *(Pres & CEO)*
Keval Patel *(Chm)*

T-Bird Restaurant Group, Inc. (2)
1250 Prospect St Ste 305, La Jolla, CA 92037
Tel.: (858) 456-2703
Web Site: http://www.outback.com
Owns & Operates Restaurants
N.A.I.C.S.: 722511
Mike Wong *(CFO)*
Thomas Shannon Jr. *(CEO)*

TestAmerica Laboratories, Inc. (2)
455 Pennsylvania Ave Ste 205, Fort Washington, PA 19034
Tel.: (215) 628-9601
Web Site: http://www.testamericainc.com
Sales Range: $350-399.9 Million
Emp.: 4
Environmental Testing Services
N.A.I.C.S.: 541380
Rachel Brydon Jannetta *(Chm & CEO)*
Scott Morris *(COO)*
Harry Behzadi *(VP-Ops)*
Kamrul Alam *(Dir-Technical)*
Fred Haley *(VP-Ops-West)*
Nick Mahmood *(CIO)*
James H. Miller *(Sr VP-Sls & Mktg)*
Chris Oprandi *(VP-Client Svc)*
Jenny L. Stewart *(VP-HR)*
Stuart Stoller *(CFO)*
Rusty Vicinie *(VP-Ops-Central)*

Subsidiary (Domestic):

METCO Environmental, Inc. (3)
3226 Commander Dr, Carrollton, TX 75006
Tel.: (972) 931-7127
Web Site: http://www.metcoenv.com
Sales Range: $10-24.9 Million
Source Emissions Testing Services
N.A.I.C.S.: 541380
Rob Patterson *(Pres)*
Byron C. Gies *(Mgr-Bus Dev)*
Mike Hutcherson *(Dir-Field Ops)*

Subsidiary (Non-US):

NCALABS Co., Ltd. (3)
Level 19 PM Tower 731 Asoke-Dindaeng Road, Dindaeng, Bangkok, 10400, Thailand
Tel.: (66) 22459660
Sales Range: $10-24.9 Million
Testing Laboratory
N.A.I.C.S.: 541380

Branch (Domestic):

TestAmerica Buffalo (3)
10 Hazelwood Dr, Buffalo, NY 14228
Tel.: (716) 691-2600
Web Site: http://www.testamericainc.com
Environmental Testing Services
N.A.I.C.S.: 541380
James H. Miller *(Sr VP)*
Mike Movinski *(Acct Exec)*

TestAmerica Denver (3)
4955 Yarrow St, Arvada, CO 80002-4517
Tel.: (303) 736-0100
Web Site: http://www.testamericainc.com
Sales Range: $25-49.9 Million
Emp.: 140
Environmental Lab Services
N.A.I.C.S.: 621511
William Cicero *(Dir-Laboratory)*
Michelle Johnston *(Project Mgr)*
Kevin Furman *(VP-PMO)*
Michael Sara *(Supvr-IT-NW)*
Brett Vandelinder *(Mgr-Program Mgmt)*

Subsidiary (Domestic):

TestAmerica Drilling Corp. (3)

H.I.G. Capital, LLC—(Continued)

1016 E Katela Ave, Anaheim, CA 92805
Tel.: (714) 939-6850
Web Site: http://www.westhazmat.com
Sales Range: $25-49.9 Million
Provider of Environmental & Geotechnical
Drilling Services to the Western United
States
N.A.I.C.S.: 237110

Holding (Domestic):

Thane International, Inc. (2)
78 140 Calle Tampico, La Quinta, CA 92253
Tel.: (760) 777-0217
Web Site: http://www.thaneinc.com
Consumer Product Marketing Services
N.A.I.C.S.: 561422

Subsidiary (Non-US):

Thane Direct UK Ltd. (3)
1 Fore Street Avenue, London, EC2Y 9DT,
United Kingdom
Tel.: (44) 3445717511
Web Site: http://www.thanedirect.co.uk
Recreational Goods Distr
N.A.I.C.S.: 423910

Holding (Domestic):

The Rossi Group, LLC (2)
213 Ct St Ste 603, Middletown, CT 06457
Tel.: (860) 632-3505
Web Site: http://www.rossigroup.net
Sales Range: $200-249.9 Million
Emp.: 20
Holding Company; Hardwood Lumber Saw-
mills & Products Mfr
N.A.I.C.S.: 551112
Andrew Becker (Gen Counsel)
John Read (Dir-Export Sls)
Matt Gauvrit (Dir-European Sls)

Subsidiary (Domestic):

Emporium Hardwoods, LLC (3)
15970 Route 120, Emporium, PA 15834-
9399
Tel.: (814) 486-3764
Sales Range: $25-49.9 Million
Hardwood Lumber & Other Wood Products
Mfr
N.A.I.C.S.: 321113
Jared Fowler (Gen Mgr)

Linden Lumber, LLC (3)
23741 US Hwy 43, Linden, AL 36748
Tel.: (334) 295-8751
Sales Range: $25-49.9 Million
Hardwood Lumber & Flooring Mfr
N.A.I.C.S.: 321113

Northern Hardwoods (3)
45807 Hwy M 26, South Range, MI 49963
Tel.: (906) 487-6400
Hardwood Lumber Mfr
N.A.I.C.S.: 321113

Rossi Lumber Company (3)
162 W St, Cromwell, CT 06416-2425
Tel.: (860) 632-3500
Emp.: 30
Hardwood Flooring & Furniture Material Mfr
N.A.I.C.S.: 321211
Theodore P. Rossi (Chm & CEO)

Holding (Domestic):

Town & Country Linen Corp. (2)
475 Oberlin Ave S, Lakewood, NJ 08701
Tel.: (732) 364-2000
Web Site: http://www.tncliving.com
Home Textile Furnishings Mfr & Whslr
N.A.I.C.S.: 314120
David J. Beyda (Chm)

Subsidiary (Domestic):

Home Dynamix LLC (3)
100 Porete Ave, North Arlington, NJ 07031
Tel.: (201) 955-6000
Web Site: http://www.homedynamix.com
Emp.: 300
Rugs Mfr & Distr
N.A.I.C.S.: 812331
Assia Slavova (Mgr-Design Product)
Steven Rosenberg (VP-Accts-Natl)

Holding (Domestic):

Trinity Services Group, Inc. (2)
477 Commerce Blvd, Oldsmar, FL 34677
Tel.: (813) 854-4264
Web Site:
http://www.trinityservicesgroup.com
Sales Range: $10-24.9 Million
Emp.: 55
Food Delivery Services
N.A.I.C.S.: 722310
Larry Vaughn (Pres)

Subsidiary (Domestic):

Swanson Services Corporation (3)
1133 Pennsylvania St, Denver, CO 80203
Tel.: (303) 832-3920
Web Site: http://www.swansons.net
Food Service Products
N.A.I.C.S.: 445131
Kelly Swanson (Pres)
Bridget Hall (Mgr-Client Rels-Software Sup-
port)
Chris Swanson (Mgr-Pur)
Marta Swanson (Treas & Sec)
Chuck Swanson Jr. (Chm)

Holding (Domestic):

USALCO, LLC (2)
2601 Cannery Ave, Baltimore, MD 21226
Tel.: (410) 918-2230
Web Site: http://www.usalco.com
Sales Range: $25-49.9 Million
Emp.: 50
Water & Wastewater Treatment Industries
N.A.I.C.S.: 325998
David Askew (Pres)
Ken Gayer (CEO)

Subsidiary (Domestic):

USALCO Ashtabula Plant, LLC (3)
3050 Lake Rd E, Ashtabula, OH 44004
Tel.: (440) 993-2721
Web Site: http://www.usalco.com
All Other Miscellaneous Chemical Product
& Preparation Mfr
N.A.I.C.S.: 325998
Brad Lovejoy (Mgr)

USALCO Baltimore Plant, LLC (3)
2601 Cannery Ave, Baltimore, MD 21226
Tel.: (410) 918-2230
Web Site: http://www.usalco.com
Chemical Products Mfr
N.A.I.C.S.: 325998
Terry Badwak (VP-Mktg & Sls)

USALCO Fairfield Plant, LLC (3)
3700 Dixie Hwy, Fairfield, OH 45014
Tel.: (513) 737-7100
Chemical Products Mfr
N.A.I.C.S.: 325998

USALCO Gahanna Plant, LLC (3)
1024 Enterprise Dr, Gahanna, OH 43230
Tel.: (614) 986-2001
Chemical Products Mfr
N.A.I.C.S.: 325998

USALCO Michigan City Plant,
LLC (3)
1750 E US Highway 12, Michigan City, IN
46360
Tel.: (219) 873-0914
Chemical Products Mfr
N.A.I.C.S.: 325998

USALCO Port Allen Plant, LLC (3)
1696 Catalyst Dr, Port Allen, LA 70767
Tel.: (225) 334-7808
Chemical Products Mfr
N.A.I.C.S.: 325998

Holding (Domestic):

VAS Aero Services, LLC (2)
645 Park of Commerce Way, Boca Raton,
FL 33487-8204
Tel.: (561) 998-9330
Web Site: http://www.vas.aero
Sales Range: $75-99.9 Million
Aircraft Parts & Components Aftermarket
Sales
N.A.I.C.S.: 423860
Tommy Hughes (CEO)
Kevin P. Hartney (Sr VP-Program Mgmt &
Legal Affairs)

Vantage Specialty Chemicals,
Inc. (2)
4650 South Racine Ave, Chicago, IL 60609
Tel.: (773) 376-9000
Web Site:
http://www.vantagespecialties.com
Natural Based Specialty Ingredients Mfr
N.A.I.C.S.: 311999
Richard McEvoy (CEO)
Allison Yake (CTO)

Subsidiary (Domestic):

Jeen International Corp. (3)
24 Madison Rd, Fairfield, NJ 07004-2309
Tel.: (973) 439-1401
Web Site: http://www.jeen.com
Sales Range: $1-9.9 Million
Emp.: 23
Specialty Chemicals Mfr
N.A.I.C.S.: 424690
Adam Perle (Pres)
Carl J. Cappabianca (Gen Mgr)

Vantage Specialties, Inc. (3)
3938 Porett Dr, Gurnee, IL 60031
Tel.: (847) 244-3410
Web Site:
http://www.vantagespecialties.com
Holding Company; Specialty Chemicals Mfr
N.A.I.C.S.: 551112
Noel Beavis (COO)
Tiffany Kyllmann (Sr VP-Performance Matls,
Sls & Mktg)
Patrick Brueggman (Sr VP & Gen Mgr-
Personal Care)
Richard McEvoy (Pres & CEO)
Craig Yuen (CFO)

Subsidiary (Domestic):

Desert Whale Jojoba Company,
Inc. (4)
2101 E Beverly Dr, Tucson, AZ 85719
Tel.: (520) 882-4195
Web Site: http://www.desertwhale.com
Sales Range: $50-74.9 Million
Emp.: 25
Jojoba Plant Farming, Processing & Or-
ganic Chemical Derivatives Mfr
N.A.I.C.S.: 311224
Amber Schwartz (Dir-Technical)

Unit (Domestic):

Lambent Technologies (4)
3938 Porett Dr, Gurnee, IL 60031
Tel.: (847) 249-6366
Web Site: http://www.petroferm.com
Sales Range: $10-24.9 Million
Specialty Chemicals
N.A.I.C.S.: 325998
Chris Fouts (Dir-Derivatives Tech)
Alex Georgevich (Dir-Fin)
Paul Gaines (Dir-Mktg)
Rich Twarowski (Mgr-QC)
Scott Jordan (Supvr-Mfg)

Subsidiary (Domestic):

Mallet & Company, Inc. (4)
51 Arch St, Carnegie, PA 15106
Tel.: (412) 276-9000
Web Site: http://www.malletoil.com
Oils, Ingredients & Custom Food Process-
ing Equipment
N.A.I.C.S.: 311999
Robert I. Mallet (CEO)

Petroferm Cleaning Products (4)
3938 Porett Dr, Gurnee, IL 60031
Tel.: (847) 249-6826
Web Site: http://www.petroferm.com
Specialty Cleaning Chemical Products Mfr
N.A.I.C.S.: 325998
John Marcolini (Reg Sls Mgr-Americas)
Bill Breault (Mgr-Aerospace & Precision
Market)
Gilbert Siu (Reg Sls Mgr-Asia)

The Amarna Co. (4)
1755 Gunnison Ave, Delta, CO 81416
Tel.: (970) 874-0388
Web Site: http://www.amarna.us
Water-based Cleaning Properties & Spray
Systems Mfr
N.A.I.C.S.: 311991
John Starr (Pres)
Joshua Starr (VP-Ops & Gen Mgr)

Drew Pope (VP-Sls & Support)
Wade Kallsen (Dir-Food Safety & Quality)
Stephanie McDonald (Mgr-Quality Assur-
ance)

Vantage Oleochemicals, Inc. (4)
4650 S Racine Ave, Chicago, IL 60609-
3321
Tel.: (773) 650-7600
Web Site: http://www.vantageoleo.com
Sales Range: $25-49.9 Million
Specialty Chemicals Mfr
N.A.I.C.S.: 325199
Bob Drennan (Chm)
Don Ciancio (Exec VP)
Steve Collier (Dir-IT)

Vantage Specialty Ingredients,
Inc. (4)
150 Mount Bethel Rd Bldg 2 Ste 200, War-
ren, NJ 07059
Tel.: (973) 345-8600
Web Site: http://www.lipochemicals.com
Industrial Organic Chemical Mfr & Distr
N.A.I.C.S.: 325199
Steven Richards (Acct Mgr-Strategic-North
America)
Diana Tang (Gen Mgr-Asia Pacfic)
Nancy Clements (VP-Global Mktg)
Richard McEvoy (CEO)
Smitha Rao (VP-Innovation-Personal Care-
Global)

Subsidiary (Domestic):

Ruger Chemical Company, Inc. (5)
1515 W Blancke St, Linden, NJ 07036
Tel.: (973) 926-0331
Web Site: http://www.rugerchemical.com
Chemical & Allied Products Merchant Whslr
N.A.I.C.S.: 424690

Holding (Non-US):

Vernacare Limited (2)
Folds Road, Bolton, BL1 2TX, Lancs,
United Kingdom
Tel.: (44) 1204 529 494
Web Site: http://www.vernacare.com
Healthcare Sanitation Products Mfr
N.A.I.C.S.: 339999
Matt Miller (CEO)
Paul Wright (CFO)

Holding (Domestic):

Wastequip, LLC (2)
6525 Morrison Blvd Ste 300, Charlotte, NC
28211
Web Site: http://www.wastequip.com
Waste & Material Handling Equipment Mfr
N.A.I.C.S.: 333248
John Defenbaugh (Pres-Comml)
Marty Bryant (CEO)
Steven Klueg (CFO)
Henry Retamal (Pres-Ops)
Amy Wright (Sr VP-Mktg & Bus Analytics)
Kristin Kinder (VP-Res & Waste Stream
Sustainability)
Richard Sedory (Gen Counsel)
Nick Wiseman (Chief HR Officer)
Mike Marchetti (CIO)
J.P. McLaughlin (VP-Natl Accts)
Chris Nicolazzo (Pres-Tarps & Parts)

Subsidiary (Non-US):

Cusco Fabricators, LLC (3)
305 Enford Rd, Richmond Hill, L4C 3E9,
ON, Canada
Tel.: (905) 883-1214
Web Site: http://www.wastequip-cusco.com
Industrial & Commercial Mobile Vacuum
Equipment Mfr
N.A.I.C.S.: 423440

Subsidiary (Domestic):

Pioneer Cover-all (3)
10 Boulder Pkwy, North Oxford, MA 01537
Web Site: http://www.pioneercoverall.com
Plastic Tarp & Covering Products Mfr
N.A.I.C.S.: 326199

Toter, LLC (3)
841 Meacham Rd, Statesville, NC 28677
Tel.: (704) 872-8171
Web Site: http://www.toter.com
Plastic Industrial Containers Mfr
N.A.I.C.S.: 326199

Skip Lynn *(Sr VP-Western Reg Sls)*
Jim Pickett *(Sr VP-Eastern Reg Sls)*
Derrick Masimer *(VP-Sls Ops)*

Wastebuilt Environmental Solutions, LLC — **(3)**
560 Territorial Dr, Bolingbrook, IL 60440
Tel.: (630) 485-2040
Web Site: http://www.wastebuilt.com
Holding Company; Waste Collection Truck & Equipment Distr
N.A.I.C.S.: 551112
Gregory L. Podell *(Vice Chm)*
Ed Carroll *(CFO)*
David E. McKeon *(COO)*
James J. Pfeiffer *(Exec VP & Head-Parts Segment)*

Subsidiary (Domestic):

Consolidated Disposal Systems — **(4)**
5595 Oakdale Rd SE, Smyrna, GA 30082
Tel.: (404) 696-1530
Web Site:
   http://www.consolidateddisposal.com
Disposal Equipment Whlsr
N.A.I.C.S.: 532120
Bob Keller *(Gen Mgr & VP)*

Stepp Equipment Company — **(4)**
5400 Stepp Dr, Summit, IL 60501
Tel.: (708) 458-7800
Web Site: http://www.steppequipment.com
Sales Range: $1-9.9 Million
Emp.: 45
Industrial Machinery Equipment Whslr
N.A.I.C.S.: 423830

Holding (Domestic):

Xtera Communications, Inc. — **(2)**
500 W Bethany Dr, Allen, TX 75013
Tel.: (972) 649-5000
Web Site: http://www.xtera.com
Emp.: 200
Optical Communications Mfr
N.A.I.C.S.: 334290
Jayesh Pankhania *(CFO)*
Joerg Schwartz *(Sr VP-Turnkey Sys)*
Keith Henderson *(CEO)*
Robert J. Richardson *(Founder & Chief Sls Officer)*
Stuart Barnes *(Chm & Chief Strategy Officer)*
Tony Frisch *(CTO)*
Lynsey Thomas *(VP-Sls-Global)*
Ricardo Franco *(VP-Sls-Americas Reg)*
Wayne Pelouch *(VP-Photonics)*
Paul Farrugia *(VP-Engrg for Submerged Equipment)*
Dylan Higginbotham *(VP-Ops)*
Bill McCutcheon *(VP-Cust Svc)*
Dave Winterburn *(Dir-Software Dev)*
Vijay Rudravajjala *(VP-Engrg)*
Leigh Frame *(COO)*

Health Network One, Inc. — **(1)**
2001 S. Andrews Ave., Ft, Lauderdale, FL 33316
Tel.: (800) 595-9631
Web Site: https://healthnetworkone.com
Hospitals & Health Care
N.A.I.C.S.: 621498
Marty Bilowich *(Pres & COO)*

Subsidiary (Domestic):

Premier Eye Care LLC — **(2)**
6501 Park of Commerce Blvd., First Fl,
Boca Raton, FL 33487
Tel.: (800) 337-9406
Web Site: http://www.premiereyecare.net
Sales Range: $50-74.9 Million
Emp.: 80
Optometric & Ophthalmologic Services
N.A.I.C.S.: 621320
Lorna Taylor *(Pres & CEO)*
Michael A. Hecht *(Dir-Medical)*
Jason Panos *(COO)*
C. Haas Gomez *(VP-Network Mgmt)*
Shari Basye *(Chief Collaboration Officer)*
Anna Pinera *(VP-Natl Network Mgmt)*
Moira Burke *(Dir-Medical)*
Dennis Poore *(Dir-IT Infrastructure & Security)*
Afrouz Motedaeiny *(Assoc Dir-Medical)*
Jeff Nowak *(Chief Solutions Officer)*
Melaunda Hall *(VP-Benefit Admin)*
Duane Carter *(VP-Info Mgmt & Solutions)*

Infinigate Holding AG — **(1)**
Grundstrasse 14, Rotkreuz, 6343, Switzerland
Tel.: (41) 417996969
Web Site: http://www.infinigate.com
Sales Range: $50-74.9 Million
Emp.: 20
Information Technology Security Services
N.A.I.C.S.: 541512
David Martinez *(Chm)*
Richard Huth *(CFO)*
Stephan Hassenbach *(CTO)*
Erik Walter *(COO)*
Klaus Schlichtherle *(CEO)*
Simon England *(Chief Growth Officer)*

Subsidiary (Non-US):

Infinigate Danmark A/S — **(2)**
Marielundvej 46 A 2, 2730, Herlev, Denmark
Tel.: (45) 70205656
Web Site: http://www.infinigate.dk
Sales Range: $25-49.9 Million
Emp.: 8
Information Technology Security Services
N.A.I.C.S.: 541512

Infinigate Deutschland GmbH — **(2)**
Grunwalder Weg 34, Oberhaching, D 82041, Munich, Germany
Tel.: (49) 89 89048 0
Web Site: http://www.infinigate.de
Information Technology Security Services
N.A.I.C.S.: 541512
Andreas Bechtold *(Mng Dir)*

Infinigate France SAS — **(2)**
88 Avenue du General Leclerc, 92100, Boulogne-Billancourt, France
Tel.: (33) 1 80 73 04 25
Web Site: http://www.infinigate.fr
Information Technology Consulting Services
N.A.I.C.S.: 541511
Patric Berger *(Gen Mgr)*

Infinigate Norge AS — **(2)**
Martin Linges Vei 25, N 1367, Snaroya, Norway
Tel.: (47) 67101800
Web Site: http://www.infinigate.no
Sales Range: $25-49.9 Million
Emp.: 16
Information Technology Security Services
N.A.I.C.S.: 541512
Thomas Hagelid *(Mng Dir)*

Infinigate Osterreich GmbH — **(2)**
Hirschstettner Strasse 19, 1220, Vienna, Austria
Tel.: (43) 1 890 21 97 0
Web Site: http://www.infinigate.at
Software Development Services
N.A.I.C.S.: 541511

Infinigate Sverige AB — **(2)**
Axel Johanssonsgata 4-6, 754 50, Uppsala, Sweden
Tel.: (46) 18655585
Web Site: http://www.infinigate.se
Sales Range: $25-49.9 Million
Emp.: 16
Information Technology Security Services
N.A.I.C.S.: 541512
Peter Strand *(Mng Dir-Sweden)*

Infinigate UK Ltd. — **(2)**
Arch 8 Chancel Street, London, SE1 0UR, United Kingdom
Tel.: (44) 845 4900 245
Web Site: http://www.infinigate.co.uk
Information Technology Consulting Services
N.A.I.C.S.: 541511
Alex Teh *(Founder & Mng Dir)*

Mainline Information Systems, Inc. — **(1)**
1700 Summit Lk Dr, Tallahassee, FL 32317
Tel.: (850) 219-5000
Web Site: http://www.mainline.com
Emp.: 100
Information Technology Systems Reseller
N.A.I.C.S.: 423430
Rick Kearney *(Founder & Chm)*
Beth Oberacker *(VP-HR)*
Joe Elebash *(CFO)*
Brian Showman *(Gen Counsel)*
Jeff Dobbelaere *(CEO)*
Perry Carfagna *(COO)*

Subsidiary (Non-US):

Mainline Systems do Brasil Ltda. — **(2)**
Rua Funchal 411 Conjunto 61, Sao Paulo, 04551 060, Brazil
Tel.: (55) 1130504400
Web Site: http://www.mainline.com
Emp.: 11
Information Technology Consulting Services
N.A.I.C.S.: 541512
Joao Alves *(Gen Mgr)*

Subsidiary (Domestic):

Software By Design, Inc. — **(2)**
800 Westchester Ave Ste 522, Rye Brook, NY 10573
Tel.: (914) 909-3105
Web Site: http://www.softwarebydesign.com
Sales Range: $1-9.9 Million
Emp.: 35
Technical Solutions & Business Consulting Services
N.A.I.C.S.: 541618

Mobileum, Inc. — **(1)**
20813 Stevens Creek Blvd Ste 200, Cupertino, CA 95014
Tel.: (408) 844-6600
Web Site: http://www.mobileum.com
Wireless Network Software & Services
N.A.I.C.S.: 513210
Bobby Srinivasan *(CEO)*
Andrew Warner *(CFO)*
Avnish Chauhan *(CTO)*
Sebastiano Tevarotto *(Chief Comml Officer)*

Subsidiary (Non-US):

SIGOS GmbH — **(2)**
Klingenhofstrasse 50d, 90411, Nuremberg, Germany
Tel.: (49) 911 95168 0
Web Site: http://www.sigos.com
Sales Range: $25-49.9 Million
Emp.: 270
Automated End-to-End Testing & Fraud Detection of Telecommunication Networks & Services
N.A.I.C.S.: 517810
Joachim Bamberger *(Exec VP-Sls)*
Adil Kaya *(CEO)*
Gerald Wittmann *(Head-R&D)*
Mark Stumpf *(CTO)*

Northwest Pump & Equipment Co. — **(1)**
2800 NW 31st Ave, Portland, OR 97210-1720
Tel.: (503) 227-7867
Web Site: http://www.nwpump.com
Rev.: $51,617,221
Emp.: 300
Industrial Machinery & Equipment
N.A.I.C.S.: 423830
Gregory W. Miller *(Pres)*
Mark Mathews *(Pres)*
Bob Mathews *(VP-Svcs)*
Stuart Trebelhorn *(VP-Indus Div)*

Subsidiary (Domestic):

D.R. Smith Co., Inc. — **(2)**
12428 Hwy 99 Ste 49, Everett, WA 98204
Tel.: (425) 743-2888
Sales Range: $1-9.9 Million
Emp.: 11
Industrial Machinery & Equipment Merchant Whslr
N.A.I.C.S.: 423830
Tom Braun *(Mng Dir)*

Penhall Company — **(1)**
1212 Corporate Dr Ste 500, Irving, TX 75038
Tel.: (714) 772-6450
Web Site: http://www.penhall.com
Sales Range: $10-24.9 Million
Emp.: 1,200
Holding Company; Concrete Cutting, Sawing, Breaking & Removal
N.A.I.C.S.: 532412

Subsidiary (Domestic):

Penhall Co. — **(2)**
1801 Penhall Way, Anaheim, CA 92801 — **(100%)**
Tel.: (714) 772-6450
Web Site: http://www.penhall.com

Demolition Company
N.A.I.C.S.: 532412
Jeff Long *(CEO)*
Lynn Schrier-Behler *(CFO)*

SMTC Corporation — **(1)**
7050 Woodbine Ave Suite 300, Markham, L3R 4G8, ON, Canada
Tel.: (905) 479-1810
Web Site: http://www.smtc.com
Rev.: $386,450,000
Assets: $229,939,000
Liabilities: $188,749,000
Net Worth: $41,190,000
Earnings: ($581,000)
Emp.: 2,881
Fiscal Year-end: 01/03/2021
Electronics Manufacturing Services
N.A.I.C.S.: 334412
Josh Chien *(Sr VP-Sls, Mktg & Customer Experience-Global)*
Carlos Diaz *(Sr VP-West)*
Edward John Smith *(Pres & CEO)*
Blair McInnis *(VP-Fin)*
Bob Miller *(VP-Customer Acquisition)*
Seth Choi *(VP-Supply Chain Mgmt & Procurement-Global)*
Kenny Lai *(VP & Gen Mgr-Fremont-California)*
Steven M. Waszak *(CFO & Sr VP-Mergers & Acquisition)*
Terry Wegman *(Sr VP-Sls & Mktg)*
Phil Wehrli *(Sr VP-Plng & Supply Chain-Global)*
Chuck Fries *(VP-Plng & Logistics-Global)*
Helen Ong *(VP-Fin)*
Baron Thrower *(VP-IT-Global)*

Subsidiary (US):

MC Test Service, Inc. — **(2)**
425 N Dr Melbourne, Palm Bay, FL 32905
Tel.: (321) 253-0541
Web Site: http://www.mcati.com
Sales Range: $250-299.9 Million
Electronics Components & Systems Mfr, Engineering, Repair & Testing Services
N.A.I.C.S.: 334418

Plant (Domestic):

MC Test Service, Inc. - Boston — **(3)**
21 ESt, Winchester, MA 01890
Tel.: (781) 218-7550
Web Site: http://www.mcati.com
Electronics Components & Systems Mfr, Engineering, Repair & Testing Services
N.A.I.C.S.: 334418

Plant (Non-US):

MC Test Service, Inc. - Mexico — **(3)**
Carr Fresnillo-Plateros Km 2, Fresnillo Zac, CP 99059, Zacatecas, Mexico
Tel.: (52) 493 935 7024
Web Site: http://www.mcati.com
Electronics Components & Systems Mfr, Engineering, Repair & Testing Services
N.A.I.C.S.: 334418

Subsidiary (Non-US):

SMTC Asia Ltd. — **(2)**
Rm 701 7/F Silvercord Twr 2 30 Canton Rd, Tsim Tsa Tsui, China (Hong Kong)
Tel.: (852) 21627390
Electronic Components Mfr
N.A.I.C.S.: 334419

SMTC Electronics (Suzhou) Company Limited — **(2)**
No 839 Yinzhong Road South, Wuzhong Economic Development Zone, Suzhou, 215124, Jiangsu, China
Tel.: (86) 512669830501
Electronic Components Mfr
N.A.I.C.S.: 334419

SMTC Electronics Dongguan Company Limited — **(2)**
No 61 Changdong Road Changan Town, Dongguan, 523841, China
Tel.: (86) 76985533451
Electronic Components Mfr
N.A.I.C.S.: 334419

Subsidiary (US):

SMTC Manufacturing Corporation of California — **(2)**

H.I.G. Capital, LLC—(Continued)

2302 Trade Zone Blvd, San Jose, CA
95131
Tel.: (408) 934-7100
Web Site: http://www.smtc.com
Sales Range: $50-74.9 Million
Emp.: 150
Printed Circuit Board Mfr
N.A.I.C.S.: 334412

Subsidiary (Domestic):

SMTC Manufacturing Corporation of
Canada   (2)
7100 Woodbine Avenue Suite 215,
Markham, ON, Canada
Tel.: (905) 479-1810
Bare Printed Circuit Board Mfr
N.A.I.C.S.: 334412

Subsidiary (US):

SMTC Mex Holdings, Inc.   (2)
1325 Pendale Rd, El Paso, TX 79936
Tel.: (915) 775-1428
Investment Management Service
N.A.I.C.S.: 523999
Rubin Alvarado (Mgr)

Subsidiary (Domestic):

SMTC Nova Scotia Company   (2)
7100 Woodbine Avenue Suite 215,
Markham, L3R 5J2, ON, Canada
Tel.: (905) 479-1810
Printed Circuit Board Mfr
N.A.I.C.S.: 334412

Subsidiary (Non-US):

SMTC de Chihuahua S.A. de
C.V.   (2)
Washington 3701 Building 20, Chihuahua,   (100%)
31200, Mexico
Tel.: (52) 6144391700
Web Site: http://www.smtc.com
Sales Range: $200-249.9 Million
Emp.: 1,000
Electronic Components Mfr
N.A.I.C.S.: 334419

Signature Flexible Packaging,
Inc.   (1)
5519 Jillson St, Commerce, CA 90040
Tel.: (323) 887-1997
Web Site: http://www.signatureflexible.com
Sales Range: $10-24.9 Million
Emp.: 65
Flexible Packaging Solutions
N.A.I.C.S.: 326112
Adrian Backer (Pres)
Jeff Sewell (VP-Sls & Mktg)
John Attayek (CEO)
Daniel Murillo (CFO)

Subsidiary (Domestic):

Atlapac Corp.   (2)
2901 E 4th Ave, Columbus, OH 43219
Tel.: (614) 252-2121
Web Site: http://www.atlapac.com
Bags: Plastic, Laminated, And Coated, Nsk
N.A.I.C.S.: 322220
James Staeck (Founder)
Daniela Williams (Controller)
David Healey (Dir-Techical)
Paul Unrue (Pres)
Tammy Lehar (Mgr-Bus Dev)
Bob Lightner (VP)
Stuart Staeck (CEO)

Chromatic Productions, Inc.   (2)
17032 Armstrong Ave, Irvine, CA 92614
Tel.: (949) 475-2300
Web Site: http://www.chromaticlabels.com
Instruments & Related Products Mfr
N.A.I.C.S.: 334513
Peter Pitchess (CEO)

Plant (Domestic):

Signature Flexible Packaging   (2)
1120 Sandhill Ave, Carson, CA 90746
Tel.: (310) 639-0800
Sales Range: $1-9.9 Million
Emp.: 17
Flexible Packaging Solutions
N.A.I.C.S.: 322220
Howard Applebaum (Pres)

Subsidiary (Domestic):

Techflex Packaging, LLC   (2)
13771 Gramercy Pl, Gardena, CA 98057
Tel.: (323) 242-8400
Web Site: http://www.tfpack.com
Sales Range: $1-9.9 Million
Emp.: 60
Electrical Industrial Apparatus, Nec, Nsk
N.A.I.C.S.: 335999
Katrina Serrano (Mgr)

The Safety Zone, LLC   (1)
385 Long Hill Rd, Guilford, CT 06437
Tel.: (203) 533-7700
Web Site: http://www.safety-zone.com
Apparel Accessories & Other Apparel Mfr
N.A.I.C.S.: 315990

Tower Engineering Professionals,
Inc.   (1)
326 Tryon Rd, Raleigh, NC 27603
Tel.: (919) 661-6351
Web Site: http://www.tepgroup.net
Emp.: 700
Engineeering Services
N.A.I.C.S.: 541330
Michael Gardner (VP)

USA DeBusk LLC   (1)
1005 W 8th St, Deer Park, TX 77536
Tel.: (281) 941-9670
Web Site: https://usadebusk.com
Mechanical & Industrial Cleaning Services
N.A.I.C.S.: 541330
Andrew DeBusk (CEO)
Martin Gilmour (VP-Ops)

Subsidiary (Domestic):

Nitro Lift Technologies, LLC   (2)
8980 Hwy 1 S, Mill Creek, OK 74856
Tel.: (580) 226-6600
Web Site: http://nitrolift.com
Rev.: $4,500,000
Emp.: 13
Industrial Gas Mfr
N.A.I.C.S.: 325120
Danny Daniels (CTO)

United Flow Technologies   (1)
27191 Burbank, Ste B, Foothill Ranch, CA
92610
Tel.: (949) 458-5555
Web Site:
   https://www.unitedflowtechnologies.com
Water Treatment Solutions & Services
N.A.I.C.S.: 221310
Matt Hart (CEO)

Subsidiary (Domestic):

Macaulay Controls Co   (2)
1036 Hercules Ave A, Houston, TX 77058
Tel.: (281) 282-0100
Web Site: http://www.macaulaycontrols.com
Rev.: $2,850,000
Emp.: 5
Industrial Supplies Merchant Whslr
N.A.I.C.S.: 423840
Kari Hollway (Pres-Sls)

Newman Regency Group, Inc.   (2)
12705 S Kirkwood Rd Ste 140, Stafford, TX
77477
Tel.: (281) 980-7448
Web Site:
   http://www.newmanregencygroup.com
Construction & Mining Machinery & Equipment Merchant Whslr
N.A.I.C.S.: 423810

Shape, Inc.   (2)
5115-A, Johnson Drive, Pleasanton, CA
94588
Tel.: (925) 485-9720
Web Site: http://www.shapecal.com
Sales Range: $1-9.9 Million
Emp.: 15
Industrial Machinery & Equipment Merchant
Whslr
N.A.I.C.S.: 423830
Jim Wilcox (Engr)
Nick Chavez (VP)

Southwest Valve & Equipment   (2)
402 West Bedford Suite 111, Fresno, CA
93711
Tel.: (559) 261-2703
Web Site: http://www.southwestvalve.com
Industrial Supplies Merchant Whslr

N.A.I.C.S.: 423840

Watchfire Signs, LLC   (1)
1015 Maple St, Danville, IL 61832
Tel.: (217) 442-0611
Web Site: http://www.watchfiresigns.com
Sales Range: $25-49.9 Million
Emp.: 300
Electronic Sign Mfr
N.A.I.C.S.: 339950

Subsidiary (Domestic):

Aerva, Inc.   (2)
1 Alewife Ctr Ste 120, Cambridge, MA
02140
Web Site: http://www.aerva.com
Software Developer
N.A.I.C.S.: 513210
Sanjay Manandhar (Founder)
David Crow (VP-Tech)

Zimmer Biomet Spine, LLC   (1)
310 Interlocken Pkwy Ste 120, Broomfield,
CO 80021
Tel.: (303) 443-7500
Sales Range: $1-9.9 Million
Emp.: 200
Surgical & Medical Instrument Mfr
N.A.I.C.S.: 339112

Branch (Domestic):

Zimmer Biomet Spine   (2)
7375 Bush Lake Rd, Minneapolis, MN
55439-2027
Tel.: (952) 832-5600
Sales Range: $25-49.9 Million
Spine Implant & Orthopaedic Surgical Prod-
uct Design & Mfr
N.A.I.C.S.: 339113

hibu Inc.   (1)
221 3rd Ave SE Ste 300, Cedar Rapids, IA
52401
Tel.: (319) 790-1100
Web Site: http://www.hibu.com
Telephone Directories Publisher & Advertis-
ing Services
N.A.I.C.S.: 513140
Kevin Jasper (CEO)

Subsidiary (Domestic):

RevLocal, LLC   (2)
PO Box 511, Mount Vernon, OH 43050
Tel.: (740) 263-5188
Web Site: http://www.revlocal.com
Sales Range: $1-9.9 Million
Emp.: 83
Internet Marketing Services
N.A.I.C.S.: 541613
Marc Hawk (CEO)
Aaron Boggs (Exec VP)
Patrick Dichter (Reg Mgr-Sls)
R. J. Lowery (Reg Mgr-Sls)
Diana Park-Alford (Reg Mgr Dev)
Michael Ford (Mgr-Bus Dev)
Brenda Reddy (Mgr-Sls)
Lara Seamon (Reg Mgr-Sls)
Greg Smith (Mgr-Bus Dev)
Chuck Lewis (Dir-Sls)
Austin Catherina (Mgr-Bus Dev)
Brandon Bivins (Mgr-Bus Dev)
Donald Biddings (Mgr-Bus Dev)
Doug Coyne (Mgr-Bus Dev)
Felicia Albanese (Mgr-Bus Dev)
John Berka (Mgr-Bus Dev)
Josh Cohen (Mgr-Bus Dev)
Michelle Breathitt (Mgr-Bus Dev)
Patrick Blas (Mgr-Bus Dev)
Richard Baldwin (Mgr-Bus Dev)
Robert Castel (Mgr-Bus Dev)
Ashley Munoz (Mgr-Bus Dev)
Alix Cochran (Dir-Corp Mktg)
Ben Dean (Chief Data Officer)

H.J. BAKER & BRO., INC.
2 Corporate Dr Ste 545, Shelton, CT
06484
Tel.: (203) 682-9200   DE
Web Site: https://www.hjbaker.com
Year Founded: 1850
Sales Range: $100-124.9 Million
Emp.: 125
Mfr of Animal Feed Concentrate; Dis-
tributor of Oils, Fats, Meals & Canned
& Frozen Foods; Wholesale Distribu-
tor of Fertilizers & Other Chemicals

N.A.I.C.S.: 311119
Christopher V. B. Smith (CEO)
David M. Smith (Exec VP)
Donald Cherry (Pres)
Martin Campfield (Dir-Intl Sls)
David Hans (Dir-Global Mktg)
Barbara Sullivan (VP-HR)
Scott Snyder (Mgr-Aquaculture Tech-
nical Svcs-Animal Health & Nutrition
Div)

Subsidiaries:

H.J. Baker & Bro., Inc. - Sulphur
Plant   (1)
1001 Schley Ave, Wilmington, CA 90744
Tel.: (562) 436-5341
Fertilizer Mfr
N.A.I.C.S.: 325314
Kevin Courtney (Plant Mgr)

Oxbow Sulphur Canada ULC   (1)
Suite 1020 606 4th Street SW, Calgary,
T2P 1T1, AB, Canada
Tel.: (403) 264-8954
Web Site: https://hjbaker.com
Sulphur Product Mfr
N.A.I.C.S.: 325312

H.J. KALIKOW & CO. LLC
101 Park Ave, New York, NY 10178
Tel.: (212) 808-7000
Web Site: https://www.hjkalikow.com
Rev.: $87,000,000
Emp.: 20
Real Estate Development & Manage-
ment Services
N.A.I.C.S.: 236220
Richard Gurvitz (CIO)

H.J. OLDENKAMP CO.
4669 E 8 Mile Rd, Warren, MI 48091
Tel.: (586) 756-0600   MI
Web Site: http://www.oldenkamp.com
Year Founded: 1946
Sales Range: $10-24.9 Million
Emp.: 65
Custom Cabinets Mfr
N.A.I.C.S.: 423310
Jeff Jensen (Mgr-Ops)

H.J. RUSSELL & COMPANY
504 Fair St SW, Atlanta, GA 30313-
2199
Tel.: (404) 330-1000   GA
Web Site: http://www.hjrussell.com
Year Founded: 1953
Sales Range: $200-249.9 Million
Emp.: 500
Provider of Real Estate Development
& Management & Construction Ser-
vices
N.A.I.C.S.: 236220
Michael B. Russell (CEO)
Jerome Russell (Pres)
Herman Jerome Russell (Founder &
Owner)
Yasmine Murray (Gen Counsel, Corp
Sec & Exec VP)
Elaine Ubakanma (VP-HR)
Mitchell Powell (CFO)
Paul Bryant (Dir-External Affairs)
Mack Hancock (Sr VP-Property Mgmt
& Dev Div)
Tiffanie Sanders-Lewis (VP-
Compliance & IT)
Lonoia Brooks (Dir-Mktg)
Delilah Wynn-Brown (Dir-Real Estate
Dev)
Curtis Wilson (VP-Transportation, In-
frastructure & Program Mgmt)

H.J. WALKER OIL CO. INC.
107 E 3rd St, South Pittsburg, TN
37380
Tel.: (423) 837-7939
Web Site:
   http://www.walkeroilcompany.com
Sales Range: $10-24.9 Million

Emp.: 20
Petroleum Bulk Stations
N.A.I.C.S.: 424710
Kim Walker Lappin (Pres)
Dennis White (Plant Mgr)

H.K. LANE PALM DESERT, INC.
74 199 El Paseo Ste 101 A, Palm Desert, CA 92260
Tel.: (760) 834-7500
Web Site: https://www.hklane.com
Year Founded: 2009
Emp.: 150
Real Estate Agency Operator
N.A.I.C.S.: 531210
Harvey Katofsky (Founder, Pres & CEO)
Ron Gerlich (COO, Principal & VP)
Rachel Markovitz (Exec VP-Mktg)

H.L. HUDSON FURNITURE INC.
6527 Main Circle St, Connelly Springs, NC 28612
Tel.: (828) 879-9732
Web Site:
   https://www.lindysfurniture.com
Sales Range: $10-24.9 Million
Emp.: 16
Furniture Retailer
N.A.I.C.S.: 449110
H. L. Hudson Sr. (Pres)

H.M. CRAGG CO.
7490 Bush Lk Rd, Edina, MN 55439-2801
Tel.: (952) 884-7775   MN
Web Site: http://www.hmcragg.com
Year Founded: 1968
Electrical Apparatus, Equipment & Wiring Supplies Distr & Services
N.A.I.C.S.: 423610
Tony Wand (COO)
Tim Foley (VP-Sales-Marketing)
Dan Pumarlo (VP-Operations-Svcs)
Mary Nutting (Head-Talent Mgmt)
Dan Loftus (Dir-Natl Sls)
George Wasielewski (Dir-AC Power Sls)
John Hanson (Dir-Generator Bus)

H.M. DUNN COMPANY INC.
3301 House Anderson Rd, Euless, TX 76040
Tel.: (817) 283-3722
Web Site: http://www.hmdunn.com
Sales Range: $75-99.9 Million
Emp.: 250
Machine Shops
N.A.I.C.S.: 332710
Ray Neuwirth (Engr-Quality)
Raffi Avakian (Program Mgr)

H.M. WHITE LLC
12855 Burt Rd, Detroit, MI 48223-3316
Tel.: (313) 531-8477   MI
Web Site: http://www.hmwhite.com
Year Founded: 1936
Sales Range: $25-49.9 Million
Emp.: 50
Sheet Metalwork
N.A.I.C.S.: 332322
William H. White (CEO)
Chris Hulbert (VP)

H.N. FUNKHOUSER & COMPANY INC.
2150 S Loudoun St, Winchester, VA 22601-3615
Tel.: (540) 773-2953   VA
Web Site:
   https://www.hnfunkhouser.com
Year Founded: 1962
Rev.: $44,000,000

Emp.: 170
Petroleum Products
N.A.I.C.S.: 424720
Robert Claytor (Pres)
Ken Rice (Exec VP & Gen Mgr-Ops)
Cary C. Nelson (Executives)

H.O. PENN MACHINERY COMPANY INC.
122 Noxon Rd, Poughkeepsie, NY 12603
Tel.: (845) 452-1200   NY
Web Site: https://www.hopenn.com
Year Founded: 1923
Sales Range: $200-249.9 Million
Emp.: 400
Retailer & Distributor of Earth Moving & Material Handling Equipment Power Systems
N.A.I.C.S.: 423810
Susan Steffanci (VP-HR)
Jeffrey Mitchell (Pres)
Robert Cleveland (CEO)
John Murphy (Mgr-Mktg & Bus Dev)

H.O. TRERICE COMPANY
12950 W 8 Mile Rd, Oak Park, MI 48237-3288
Tel.: (248) 399-8000   MI
Web Site: https://www.trerice.com
Year Founded: 1923
Sales Range: $50-74.9 Million
Emp.: 125
Pressure Gauges & Temperature Instruments Mfr
N.A.I.C.S.: 334513
Richard Picut (CEO)

H.O. ZIMMAN, INC.
152 Lynnway Seaport Landing, Lynn, MA 01902
Tel.: (781) 598-9230
Web Site: https://www.hozinc.com
Sales Range: $1-9.9 Million
Emp.: 15
Sports, Art, Travel, Medical & Catalogue Publishing
N.A.I.C.S.: 513120
Harriet Miller (VP-Natl Sls)
John Veneziano (Editor)
Kenneth Meifert (Sr Dir-Dev)
William E. Haase (Sr VP)
Jane Forbes Clark (Chm)
Joe L. Morgan (Vice Chm)
Kevin S. Moore (Treas)
Andre Christopher (Assoc Editor)
Sean J. Gahagan (VP-Retail Mktg & Licensing)
Jeffrey L. Idelson (Pres)

H.P. CUMMINGS CONSTRUCTION COMPANY INC.
14 Prospect St, Ware, MA 01082-1116
Tel.: (413) 967-6251   MA
Web Site:
   http://www.hpcummings.com
Year Founded: 1960
Sales Range: $10-24.9 Million
Emp.: 18
Industrial Building & Warehouse Construction
N.A.I.C.S.: 236220
John Harrington (Treas)
Benjamin Harrington Jr. (Pres)

H.P. KOPPLEMANN INC.
140 Van Block Ave, Hartford, CT 06141-0145
Tel.: (860) 549-6210
Web Site: https://www.hpknews.com
Rev.: $23,000,000
Emp.: 125
Wholesale Distributor of Books, Newspapers & Periodicals
N.A.I.C.S.: 424920

Neil K. Hauss (Pres)

H.P. NEMENZ FOOD STORES INC.
70 W McKinley Way, Poland, OH 44514
Tel.: (330) 757-8940
Sales Range: $10-24.9 Million
Emp.: 200
Grocery Sales
N.A.I.C.S.: 445110
Judith Gabriele (Pres)

H.P. STARR LUMBER COMPANY LLC
1011 Pittsburgh Rd, Valencia, PA 16059
Tel.: (724) 898-1501
Web Site: http://www.starrlumber.com
Year Founded: 1926
Sales Range: $10-24.9 Million
Emp.: 60
Lumber Yard
N.A.I.C.S.: 444110
Bruce Edwards (Pres, CEO & Gen Mgr)

H.R. CURRY COMPANY, INC.
801 Industrial Blvd, New Kensington, PA 15068
Tel.: (724) 335-1199
Web Site: http://www.hrcurry.com
Year Founded: 1946
Sales Range: $10-24.9 Million
Refractory Products Mfr & Distr
N.A.I.C.S.: 327120
Diane L. Curry (CFO & Treas)
Jeffrey P. Curry (Pres)

H.R. HANNAPEL DOOR CO.
805 Spruce St, Dowagiac, MI 49047
Tel.: (269) 782-7788   MI
Web Site: https://www.hannapel.com
Year Founded: 1967
Rev.: $13,000,000
Emp.: 40
Lumber & Other Building Materials Retailer
N.A.I.C.S.: 444110
Jerald L. Hannapel (Pres)
Thomas Carlson (VP)

H.R. LEWIS PETROLEUM CO.
1432 Cleveland St, Jacksonville, FL 32209
Tel.: (904) 356-0731
Web Site:
   https://www.lewispetroleum.com
Sales Range: $10-24.9 Million
Emp.: 75
Oil & Gasoline
N.A.I.C.S.: 424720
A. Brian Lewis (CFO & VP)

H.S. CROCKER CO., INC.
12100 Smith Dr, Huntley, IL 60142-9618
Tel.: (847) 669-3600   CA
Web Site: http://www.hscrocker.com
Year Founded: 1856
Sales Range: Less than $1 Million
Emp.: 200
Pharmaceutical & Pressure Sensitive Labels Printers & Folding Cartons & Portion Pack Lids Mfr
N.A.I.C.S.: 322220
Ron Giordano (Pres & CEO)

Subsidiaries:

H.S. Crocker Co., Inc.   (1)
Eagleview Corp Ctr 400 Eagleview Blvd Ste 106, Exton, PA 19341   (100%)
Tel.: (847) 669-3600
Web Site: http://www.hscrocker.com
Printers of Pharmaceutical & Pressure Sensitive Labels, Folding Cartons & Portion Pack Lids

N.A.I.C.S.: 323111

H.S. GERE & SONS INCORPORATED
115 Conz St, Northampton, MA 01060
Tel.: (413) 584-5000
Web Site: http://www.gazettenet.com
Sales Range: $10-24.9 Million
Emp.: 116
Newspapers, Publishing & Printing
N.A.I.C.S.: 513110
Jeffrey Morse (Controller)
Dennis Skoglund (Publr)

H.S. MORGAN LIMITED PARTNERSHIP
3158 Production Dr, Fairfield, OH 45014-4298
Tel.: (513) 870-4400
Web Site:
   http://www.hamiltonsorter.com
Sales Range: $10-24.9 Million
Emp.: 70
Holding Company; Office Furniture Mfr
N.A.I.C.S.: 551112
Thaddeus Jaroszewicz (CEO)
Jim Vanderzwaag (Controller)

Subsidiaries:

TAB Products Co. LLC   (1)
605 Fourth St, Mayville, WI 53050
Tel.: (920) 387-3131
Web Site: http://www.tab.com
Filing Equipment, Computer Accessory Products, Forms Handling Machines, Mobile Storage Systems, Labels, Folders & Filing Supplies, Office Furniture, File Services, Records Management Software
N.A.I.C.S.: 459410
Thaddeus Jaroszewicz (CEO)
John Palmer (Pres & CFO)
Carol Ann Hartnagle (VP-Sls)
Keith Weyer (VP-Mfg & Distr)
Betsy Streblow (VP-Client Svcs)
William Graham (Pres)
Dana Noel (Dir-HR)
Charles Stilwill (Sr VP-Sls)
Gregg Darsch (Sr VP)
Jon Eynon (VP-Pro Svcs & Tech)
Aggie Konciak-Jaggers (CFO)
Ross Nepean (VP-Worldwide Mktg)

Subsidiary (Domestic):

Jeter Systems   (2)
1 Cascade Plz Ste 110, Akron, OH 44308-1115
Tel.: (330) 773-8971
Web Site: http://www.jetersystems.com
Office Cabinets & Filing Systems
N.A.I.C.S.: 337214

Subsidiary (Non-US):

TAB Canada   (2)
130 King Street West 19th Floor, Willowdale, Toronto, M5X 1E3, ON, Canada   (100%)
Tel.: (416) 497-1552
Web Site: https://www.tab.ca
Distr of Filing Systems
N.A.I.C.S.: 337214

TAB Data File   (2)
Unit 4 41 Vore Street Silver Water, Sydney, 2128, NSW, Australia   (100%)
Tel.: (61) 293520800
Web Site: http://www.datafile.com.au
Sales Range: $1-9.9 Million
Emp.: 22
Office Supplies
N.A.I.C.S.: 322230
Sean Rudder (Gen Mgr)

TAB Products Europe B.V.   (2)
Hettenheuvelweg 8-10, 1101 BN, Amsterdam, 1101 BN, Netherlands   (100%)
Tel.: (31) 206975333
Web Site: http://www.tab.nl
Sales Range: $10-24.9 Million
Emp.: 3
Sales of Filing Systems & Data Entry Equipment

H.S. Morgan Limited Partnership—(Continued)

N.A.I.C.S.: 337214
Guido Nagtegaal *(Gen Mgr)*

Workstream Inc.   **(1)**
3158 Production Dr, Fairfield, OH 45014
Tel.: (513) 870-4400
Web Site: http://www.myworkstream.com
Sales Range: $10-24.9 Million
Emp.: 30
Furniture Mfr
N.A.I.C.S.: 337214
Thaddeus Jaroszewicz *(CEO)*

Subsidiary (Domestic):

Hamilton Sorter, Inc   **(2)**
3158 Production Dr, Fairfield, OH 45014
Web Site: http://www.hamiltonsorter.com
Office Furniture Mfr
N.A.I.C.S.: 337211
Jim Vanderzwaag *(CFO)*

New Maverick Desk Inc.   **(2)**
15100 S Figueroa St, Gardena, CA 90248
Tel.: (310) 217-1554
Web Site: http://www.maverickdesk.com
Wood Office Furniture
N.A.I.C.S.: 337211
Tony Pacheco *(Pres)*

H.W. DRUMMOND INC.

15383 Merry Cat Ln, Belle Haven, VA
23306
Tel.: (757) 442-6104
Web Site:
https://www.hwdrummond.com
Sales Range: $10-24.9 Million
Emp.: 35
Petroleum Products
N.A.I.C.S.: 424720
Harry D. Parker *(Pres)*

H.W. HUNTER INC.

1130 Auto Mall Dr, Lancaster, CA
93534-6302
Tel.: (661) 948-8411
Web Site:
http://www.hunterdodge.com
Year Founded: 1944
Rev.: $42,396,512
Emp.: 70
Car Dealership Owner & Operator
N.A.I.C.S.: 441110
Tim Fuller *(Pres)*
Tom Fuller *(VP)*
Sean Rodgers *(Mgr-Sls)*

H.W. JENKINS COMPANY

4155 Pidgeon Roost Rd, Memphis,
TN 38118
Tel.: (901) 363-7641
Web Site: http://www.hwjenkins.com
Rev.: $36,683,756
Emp.: 80
Lumber: Rough, Dressed & Finished
N.A.I.C.S.: 423310
Harold W. Jenkins Jr. *(Pres)*

H.W. KAUFMAN FINANCIAL GROUP, INC.

30833 NW Hwy Ste 220, Farmington
Hills, MI 48334
Tel.: (248) 932-9000   **MI**
Web Site:
http://www.burnsandwilcox.com
Year Founded: 1969
Sales Range: $250-299.9 Million
Emp.: 200
General Agents & Brokers of Spe-
cialty Insurance Products & Services
N.A.I.C.S.: 522220
Alan Jay Kaufman *(Chm, Pres & CEO)*
Chris Zoidis *(Exec VP)*
Steven D. Kaufman *(Dir-Mktg, Pro-mos & PR)*
Daniel T. Muldowney *(CFO & Exec VP)*
Daniel J. Kaufman *(Exec VP)*

Marc Fuhrman *(Mgr-Natl Relation-ship)*
Michael S. Paulin *(CIO & VP)*
Josh Hunegs *(VP)*
Christine M. Tricoli *(VP-HR)*
Renee S. Lerche *(Sr VP)*

Subsidiaries:

Atain Insurance Companies   **(1)**
220 Kaufman Financial Ctr 30833 North-
western Hwy, Farmington Hills, MI 48334
Tel.: (248) 538-4530
Web Site: http://www.atainins.com
Property & Casualty Insurance Services
N.A.I.C.S.: 524126
Chris Zoidis *(Pres & CEO)*
Ken Rice *(Dir-Underwriting)*
Emmanuel Manuelidis *(Assoc VP)*
Jessalynn Suda *(VP)*

Burns & Wilcox Ltd.   **(1)**
30833 Northwestern Hwy Ste 220, Farming-
ton, MI 48334-2582   **(100%)**
Tel.: (248) 932-9000
Web Site: http://www.burnsandwilcox.com
Underwriting Managers & Brokers
N.A.I.C.S.: 524126
Alan Jay Kaufman *(Chm & CEO)*
David J. Price *(Exec VP & Chief Underwrit-ing Officer)*
Elizabeth Gardiner *(Dir-Education, Trng & Dev)*
Marilyn A. Heckel *(Sec)*
Susie Parks *(VP-Arizona)*
Mary Mullen *(Mgr-Personal Insurance-Chicago)*
Gary Batten *(Exec VP)*
Donald Carson *(Exec VP)*
William Gatewood *(VP)*
Harvey Goldenberg *(Exec VP)*
Daniel Muldowney *(CFO & Exec VP)*
Michael Paulin *(CIO & VP)*
Marc Fuhrman *(Mgr-Natl Relationship)*
Suzette Torres *(Mng Dir)*
Gina Marquez *(Mgr-Ops)*
Blaise D'Antoni *(Mng Dir & Exec VP)*
Matthew Brady *(Mng Dir/VP-Dallas)*
David Gross *(Mng Dir-Brokerage-North Dal-las)*
Hector Collazo *(Mng Dir/VP-San Antonio)*
Michelle Clark *(Mng Dir-Denver)*
John Woods *(VP-Scottsdale)*
Daniel J. Kaufman *(Pres)*

Subsidiary (Domestic):

Burn & Wilcox Ltd.   **(2)**
21820 Burbank Blvd Ste 269, Woodland
Hills, CA 91367   **(100%)**
Tel.: (818) 737-3090
Web Site: http://www.burnsandwilcox.com
Sales Range: $50-74.9 Million
Emp.: 35
Insurance Brokers
N.A.I.C.S.: 524128
Timothy D. Burnett *(Mng Dir & VP)*
Dennis Fox *(Assoc Mng Dir)*

Burns & Wilcox   **(2)**
333 S 7th St Ste 1300, Minneapolis, MN
55402-2423   **(100%)**
Tel.: (651) 487-2800
Web Site: http://www2.burnsandwilcox.com
Sales Range: $50-74.9 Million
Emp.: 20
Insurance Brokerage Firm
N.A.I.C.S.: 524210
Heather Posner *(Assoc VP & Dir-High Net Worth)*
Tom O'Donnell *(Assoc Mng Dir)*

Subsidiary (Non-US):

Burns & Wilcox Canada   **(3)**
Bay Adelaide Centre West Tower Suite 850
333 Bay Street, Toronto, M5H 2R2, ON,
Canada
Tel.: (416) 774-2477
Web Site: http://www.burnsandwilcox.ca
Sales Range: $50-74.9 Million
Emp.: 15
Insurance Brokerage Services
N.A.I.C.S.: 524210
John McGlynn *(Dir-Transportation)*
Alan J. Kaufman *(Pres)*
Daniel Kaufman *(Pres)*
Harvey Goldenberg *(Exec VP)*
Blaise D'Antoni *(Exec VP)*

Denis Brady *(Pres)*
Jeff Diefenbach *(Sr VP)*
William Gatewood *(Sr VP)*
Rich Gobler *(Mng Dir)*
Christine Tricoli *(Chief HR Officer)*
Laura Bates *(Sr VP)*
Marc Fuhrman *(VP)*
Rich S. Fusinski *(CIO)*
Kevin Heckman *(CIO)*
Paul G. Smith *(Sr VP)*
Richard Shipley *(VP)*
Taylor Smith *(VP)*

Subsidiary (Domestic):

Burns & Wilcox   **(2)**
Brookhollow 1 2301 E Lamar Blvd 5th Fl,
Arlington, TX 76006-7422   **(100%)**
Tel.: (817) 652-1277
Web Site: http://www.burnsandwilcox.com
Emp.: 90
Insurance Brokerage
N.A.I.C.S.: 524126
Donald R. Carson *(Mng Dir & Exec VP)*
Alan Kaufman *(Chm, Pres & CEO)*
Daniel Muldowney *(CFO & Exec VP)*
Blaise D'Aantoni *(Sr VP)*
Chris Zoidis *(Sr VP)*
Harvey Goldenberg *(Mng Dir & Exec VP)*
Jeff Diefenbach *(Mng Dir & Sr VP)*
Jim Epting *(Mng Dir & Sr VP)*

Burns & Wilcox Ltd.   **(2)**
5005 Rockside Rd Ste 330, Independence,
OH 44131-2217   **(100%)**
Tel.: (216) 447-0858
Web Site: http://www.burnsandwilcox.com
Sales Range: $50-74.9 Million
Emp.: 12
Insurance Brokerage Services
N.A.I.C.S.: 524126

Royal Premium Budget, Inc. **(2)**
30833 Northwestern Hwy Ste 220, Farming-
ton Hills, MI 48334-2582   **(100%)**
Tel.: (248) 932-9000
Web Site: http://www.royalpremium.com
Sales Range: $50-74.9 Million
Emp.: 10
Financing of Commercial Insurance Policies
N.A.I.C.S.: 524210
Greg Ludwig *(Gen Mgr)*

Burns & Wilcox of San Francisco **(1)**
100 Pine St 23rd Fl, San Francisco, CA
94111   **(100%)**
Tel.: (415) 421-4244
Web Site: http://www.burns-wilcox.com
Sales Range: $25-49.9 Million
Emp.: 68
Insurance Brokers
N.A.I.C.S.: 524210
Susanne M. Waite *(VP)*
Denis Brady *(Pres-Brokerage)*
Jim Lynch *(VP-California Brokerage)*
Anthony Greene *(VP-Brokerage-New York)*

Cranbrook Underwriting Limited **(1)**
Upper Ground Floor 1 Minster Court Minc-
ing Lane, London, EC3R 7AA, United King-
dom
Tel.: (44) 2073373510
Web Site: http://www.cranbrookuw.com
Sales Range: $25-49.9 Million
Emp.: 7
Insurance Underwriting Services
N.A.I.C.S.: 524210
James Stevenson *(Mng Dir)*

Global Excess Partners   **(1)**
555 5th Ave Fl 10, New York, NY 10017
Tel.: (212) 338-9767
Web Site:
http://www.globalexcesspartners.com
Sales Range: $25-49.9 Million
Emp.: 20
Commercial Property Insurance Services
N.A.I.C.S.: 524126
Diarmuid Hogan *(Pres & CEO)*
Sharon Herbert-Conlon *(Sr VP)*

Rathbone, King & Seeley Insurance Services   **(1)**
7575 N Palm Ave Ste 200, Fresno, CA
93711-3516   **(100%)**
Tel.: (559) 448-1180
Web Site: http://www.burnandwilcox.com
Sales Range: $25-49.9 Million
Emp.: 20
Insurance Services

N.A.I.C.S.: 524210
Cathy L. Lee *(Dir-Branch Dev)*

H.W. LOCHNER, INC.

225 W Washington St 12th Fl, Chi-
cago, IL 60606
Tel.: (312) 372-7346
Web Site: http://www.hwlochner.com
Sales Range: $100-124.9 Million
Emp.: 520
Construction & Engineering Services
N.A.I.C.S.: 236220
Terry A. Ruhl *(Chm & CEO)*
Harry W. Lochner *(Chm)*
Jim Bisohop *(Pres & CEO)*
Roy D. Bruce *(Sr VP)*
John Cook *(VP & Dir-HR)*
Jeanne T. Cormier *(Sr VP)*
Chuck Craycraft *(Sr VP)*
Frank Powers *(Sr VP)*
David Twiddy *(VP)*
Pieter L. Lesterhuis *(CFO & Sr VP)*
John O'Neill *(VP)*

Subsidiaries:

Armstrong Consultants, Inc. **(1)**
6855 S Havana St Ste 635, Centennial, CO
80112
Tel.:- (970) 242-0101
Web Site:
http://www.armstrongconsultants.com
Engineering Services
N.A.I.C.S.: 541330
Dennis Corsi *(Pres)*

K Friese & Associates, Inc. **(1)**
1120 S Capital Texas Hwy Ste 100, West
Lake Hills, TX 78746-6464
Tel.: (512) 338-1704
Web Site: http://www.kfriese.com
Engineering Services
N.A.I.C.S.: 541330
Karen Friese *(Founder)*
Wayne S. Watts *(Dir-Pub Works)*
Charlotte Gilpin *(VP)*

KOA Corporation   **(1)**
1100 Corporate Ctr Dr Ste 201, Monterey
Park, CA 91754
Tel.: (323) 260-4703
Web Site: https://www.koacorporation.com
Engineering Services
N.A.I.C.S.: 541330
Joel Falter *(COO)*
Min Zhou *(Pres & CEO)*

**Triunity Engineering & Management,
Inc.**   **(1)**
621 17th St Ste 2101, Denver, CO 80202
Tel.: (303) 953-0320
Web Site: http://www.triunityeng.com
Sales Range: $1-9.9 Million
Emp.: 33
Engineering Services
N.A.I.C.S.: 541330
Jonnie L. Thomas *(Co-Founder & CEO)*
Marvin L. Thomas *(Co-Founder & Pres)*

H2 PERFORMANCE CONSULTING

222 W Main St Fl 3, Pensacola, FL
32502
Tel.: (866) 794-8239
Web Site: http://www.h2pc.com
Year Founded: 2005
Sales Range: $1-9.9 Million
Emp.: 17
Management & Technology Consult-
ing Services to Government & Com-
mercial Companies
N.A.I.C.S.: 921190
Hazel Wiggington *(Co-Founder, CEO & Mng Partner)*
Holly Smith *(Co-Founder, Pres & Mng Partner)*
Travis Goins *(VP)*

H2I GROUP, INC.

430 Industrial Blvd NE, Minneapolis, MN 55413
Tel.: (888) 239-8747
Web Site: https://h2igroup.com
Year Founded: 1924
Emp.: 271
Commercial & Institutional Building Construction Services
N.A.I.C.S.: 236220
Chris Miller *(Mgr)*
Sue Clineff *(Gen Mgr)*
Michael Propp *(Pres)*
Jared Judson *(Project Mgr)*
Megan Gruning *(Controller)*
Nathan Thiesfeld *(VP-Sls)*
Dan Moran *(Pres)*
Paul Fedje *(Chm)*

Subsidiaries:

Dow Diversified, Inc. **(1)**
1679 Placentia Ave, Costa Mesa, CA 92627
Tel.: (949) 650-9000
Web Site: http://www.dowdiversified.com
Engineeering Services
N.A.I.C.S.: 541330
Dean Dow *(Founder & Pres)*
Matt Dow *(Mgr-Ops)*

Paton - Miller LLC **(1)**
787 W Woodbury Rd Ste 10, Altadena, CA 91001
Tel.: (800) 826-0570
Web Site: http://www.patongroup.com
Technology Education Solutions Provider
N.A.I.C.S.: 611710

H2M ARCHITECTS + ENGINEERS

538 Broad Hollow Rd 4th Fl E, Melville, NY 11747
Tel.: (631) 756-8000
Web Site: https://www.h2m.com
Year Founded: 1933
Sales Range: $1-9.9 Million
Emp.: 125
Offices of Real Estate Agents & Brokers
N.A.I.C.S.: 531210
Richard Humann *(Pres & CEO)*

H2O INC.

841 Vincent Rd, Lafayette, LA 70508
Tel.: (337) 857-7203
Web Site:
   http://www.watermaker.com
Year Founded: 1980
Sales Range: $1-9.9 Million
Emp.: 40
Potable Water Solutions for Offshore Oil & Gas Operations, Including Hydroblaster, Storage Tank & Transfer Pump Rentals Supporting Offshore Coatings Markets
N.A.I.C.S.: 221310
Jess Fike *(Pres)*
David N. Dixon *(Project Mgr)*

H2O TO GO/OPAL SPRINGS WATER COMPANY INC.

815 B St, Culver, OR 97734
Tel.: (541) 389-1773   OR
Web Site:
   http://www.h2otogoopalsprings.com
Year Founded: 1986
Sales Range: Less than $1 Million
Emp.: 5
Bottled Spring Water Mfr
N.A.I.C.S.: 312112
Daryl Lonien *(Mgr-Ops)*
Ardena Lonien *(Office Mgr)*

H2OCEAN, INC.

7938 SW Jack James Dr, Stuart, FL 34997
Tel.: (772) 219-8183
Web Site: https://www.h2ocean.com
Sales Range: $1-9.9 Million
Emp.: 30

All Natural Sea Salt Health Care Products Mfr
N.A.I.C.S.: 325411
Eddie Kolos *(Pres)*

H2SCAN CORPORATION

27215 Turnberry Unit A, Valencia, CA 91355
Tel.: (661) 775-9575
Web Site: https://www.h2scan.com
Sales Range: $10-24.9 Million
Emp.: 40
Mfr of Hydrogen Sensing Equipment
N.A.I.C.S.: 334519
Dennis Reid *(Founder)*
Steve Hoviss *(Mgr-Mktg)*
Michael Nofal *(VP-Sls & Bus Dev)*
Michael Allman *(Chm & CEO)*
Bharat Vats *(Chief Growth Officer)*
David Meyers *(Pres & CEO)*

HA LOGISTICS, INC.

2333 San Ramon Valley Blvd Ste 345, San Ramon, CA 94583
Tel.: (925) 251-9300
Web Site: http://www.halogistics.com
Year Founded: 1985
Rev.: $22,271,864
Emp.: 40
Supply Chain Transportation Services
N.A.I.C.S.: 488510
Dennis Appelbaum *(CFO)*

HAART INC.

4550 N Blvd Ste 250, Baton Rouge, LA 70806
Tel.: (225) 927-1269   LA
Web Site: http://www.haartinc.org
Year Founded: 1995
Sales Range: $10-24.9 Million
Emp.: 57
Fundraising Services
N.A.I.C.S.: 813212
Cody King *(Sec)*

HAAS & HAAS, LLC

20400 Interstate 45 N, Spring, TX 77373
Tel.: (281) 297-7000   TX
Sales Range: $25-49.9 Million
Emp.: 320
Holding Company; Car Dealerships Owner & Operator
N.A.I.C.S.: 551112
Mark E. Haas *(Pres)*
Fred E. Haas Jr. *(CEO)*

Subsidiaries:

Fred Haas Motors, Ltd. **(1)**
20400 Interstate 45 N, Spring, TX 77373
Tel.: (281) 297-7000
Web Site: http://www.fredhaastoyota.com
New & Used Car Dealer
N.A.I.C.S.: 441110
Nate Murphy *(VP & Gen Mgr)*

Subsidiary (Domestic):

Fred Haas Country, L.P. **(2)**
22435 State Hwy 249, Houston, TX 77070-1530
Tel.: (281) 357-4000
Web Site:
   http://www.fredhaastoyotacountry.com
Emp.: 90
New & Used Car Dealer
N.A.I.C.S.: 441110
Robert Gaige *(Gen Mgr)*

Fred Haas Nissan, L.P. **(2)**
24202 State Hwy 249, Tomball, TX 77375-8217
Tel.: (281) 516-6700
Web Site: http://www.fredhaasnissan.com
New & Used Car Dealer
N.A.I.C.S.: 441110
John Hays *(Gen Mgr)*

HAAS BROTHERS, LTD.

75 Bdwy Ste 258, San Francisco, CA 94111
Tel.: (415) 282-8585
Web Site: http://www.haasbrothers.com
Year Founded: 1851
Imported & Domestic Distilled Spirits Whslr
N.A.I.C.S.: 424820
Jacob Lustig *(Dir-Natl Sls)*

HAAS CABINET CO. INC.

625 W Utica St, Sellersburg, IN 47172-1163
Tel.: (812) 246-4431
Web Site:
   https://www.haascabinet.com
Year Founded: 1939
Sales Range: $25-49.9 Million
Emp.: 400
Provider of Cabinetry Products & Services
N.A.I.C.S.: 337110
Todd Haas *(Founder & Pres)*
Carlos Haas *(Founder)*

Subsidiaries:

Haas Carriage Inc. **(1)**
625 W Utica St, Sellersburg, IN 47172-1163   **(100%)**
Tel.: (812) 246-4431
Web Site: http://www.haascabinet.com
Sales Range: $10-24.9 Million
Emp.: 35
Provider of Trucking Services
N.A.I.C.S.: 484121

HAAS DOOR COMPANY

320 Sycamore St, Wauseon, OH 43567
Tel.: (419) 337-9900
Web Site: http://www.haasdoor.com
Year Founded: 1995
Sales Range: $10-24.9 Million
Emp.: 200
Metal Window & Door Mfr
N.A.I.C.S.: 332321
Ed Nofziger *(Chm)*
Jeff Nofziger *(Pres)*

HAAS OUTDOORS INC.

200 E Main St, West Point, MS 39773-2953
Tel.: (662) 494-8859   MS
Web Site: https://www.mossyoak.com
Year Founded: 1986
Sales Range: $10-24.9 Million
Emp.: 100
Provider of Mens & Boys Clothing
N.A.I.C.S.: 424350
Toxey Haas *(Founder & CEO)*
Bill Sugg *(Pres)*
Chris Paradise *(Sr VP-Sls)*
Asif Sakhawat *(Sr VP-Sls & Licensing)*
Ronnie Strickland *(Sr VP-Television & Related Media)*

HAAS, JEFF MAZDA

11222 Katy Freeway, Houston, TX 77043
Tel.: (713) 932-6004
Web Site:
   http://www.jeffhaasmazda.com
Year Founded: 1991
Sales Range: $10-24.9 Million
Emp.: 75
Car Whslr
N.A.I.C.S.: 441110
Jeff Haas *(Principal)*

HAAS-ANDERSON CONSTRUCTION

1402 Holly Rd, Corpus Christi, TX 78417
Tel.: (361) 853-2535

Web Site:
   http://www.haasanderson.com
Sales Range: $10-24.9 Million
Emp.: 146
Land Preparation Construction
N.A.I.C.S.: 236210
Daryl O. Haas *(Pres)*
Floyd Conrad *(Mgr-Fleet)*

HABBERSTAD BMW INC.

945 E Jericho Tpke, Huntington Station, NY 11746
Tel.: (631) 647-6940
Web Site:
   https://www.habberstadbmw.com
Sales Range: $25-49.9 Million
Emp.: 100
Automobiles, New & Used
N.A.I.C.S.: 531120
Derek Cesani *(Mgr-Preowned BMW)*

HABERMAN & ASSOCIATES, INC.

430 1st Ave N Ste 216, Minneapolis, MN 55401-1741
Tel.: (612) 338-3900
Web Site:
   http://www.habermaninc.com
Sales Range: $10-24.9 Million
Emp.: 30
N.A.I.C.S.: 541810
Fred Haberman *(Co-Founder & CEO)*
Sarah Haberman *(Co-Founder)*
John Tuttle *(Dir-Tech)*
Jon Zurbey *(Partner & Modern Storyteller)*
Amanda Arens *(Partner)*
Claudine Enger Galloway *(Gen Mgr)*
Molly Gaines *(Partner & Acct Dir)*
Eric Davis *(Partner & Modern Storyteller)*
Brian Wachtler *(Mng Partner & Head-Acct Svc)*
Alex Seitz *(Acct Mgr)*
Sunny Fenton *(Dir-Bus Dev)*
Puja Shah *(Sr Dir-Art)*
Emalie Wichmann *(Assoc Dir-Creative)*

HABIB AMERICAN BANK

99 Madison Ave, New York, NY 10016
Tel.: (212) 532-4444
Web Site:
   http://www.habibamericanbank.com
Sales Range: $10-24.9 Million
Emp.: 55
State Commercial Banks
N.A.I.C.S.: 522110
A. G. Abbasi *(Chm)*
Rizwan Qureshi *(Chief Compliance Officer & Sr Exec VP)*
Arvid Nelson *(Vice Chm)*
Saleem Iqbal *(Pres & CEO)*
Mirza Ejaz Hussain *(Sr Exec VP & Head-Correspondent Banking)*
Javed Karim *(Officer-Credit & Exec VP)*
Zilay Wahidy *(Chief Market Officer & Exec VP)*
Abbas Somjee *(Sr VP & Controller-Fin)*
Amina Hashim *(Sec)*
Imran Habib *(Sr VP)*

HABITEC SECURITY INC.

2926 S Republic Blvd, Toledo, OH 43615
Tel.: (419) 537-6768
Web Site:
   http://www.habitecsecurity.com
Year Founded: 1972
Sales Range: $10-24.9 Million
Emp.: 75
Security System Services
N.A.I.C.S.: 561621

Habitec Security Inc.—(Continued)

James H. Smythe *(Founder & Pres)*
Mark Sprenger *(VP-Mktg)*
Bob Seymour *(Mgr-Comml Sls)*

HACHIK DISTRIBUTORS, INC.
100 Commerce Dr, Aston, PA 19014
Tel.: (610) 497-6460
Web Site: https://www.hachik.com
Year Founded: 1923
Sales Range: $1-9.9 Million
Emp.: 30
Recreational & Sporting Goods Whslr
N.A.I.C.S.: 423910
Nanette Zakian *(Pres)*
Coleen Velardi *(Mgr-AR)*
David McCune *(Mgr-Shipping)*

HACIENDA HOME CENTERS INC.
1160 Bosque Farms Blvd, Bosque Farms, NM 87068
Tel.: (505) 884-8811   NM
Web Site:
http://www.hacienda.doitbest.com
Year Founded: 1975
Sales Range: $25-49.9 Million
Emp.: 215
Lumber & Building Materials
N.A.I.C.S.: 444110
Gary Sanchez *(Pres)*

HACIENDA LIGHTING, INCORPORATED
15613 N Greenway Hayden Loop, Scottsdale, AZ 85260
Tel.: (480) 991-6767
Web Site:
http://www.haciendalighting.net
Sales Range: $10-24.9 Million
Emp.: 60
Electrical Apparatus & Equipment, Wiring Supplies & Related Equipment Whslr
N.A.I.C.S.: 423610
David Pritchett *(Pres)*

HACKBARTH DELIVERY SERVICE, INC.
3504 Brookdale Dr N, Mobile, AL 36618-1101
Tel.: (251) 478-1401
Web Site:
https://www.hackbarthdelivery.com
Sales Range: $10-24.9 Million
Emp.: 250
Same Day Courier & Logistics Services
N.A.I.C.S.: 492110
Kim Sweet *(Dir-PR & Mktg)*
Sean Sweet *(Dir-Svc Center)*
Chris Blackmon *(Coord-Bio Medical & Security)*
Latasha Hawkins *(Coord-Pharmaceutical)*
Scott Moller *(CFO)*
William Fonde *(Mgr-Terminal)*
Kelly Picard *(CEO)*

HACKENSACK MERIDIAN HEALTH, INC.
343 Thornall St, Edison, NJ 08837 NJ
Web Site:
https://www.hackensackmeridian health.org
Year Founded: 1997
Health Care Services Organization
N.A.I.C.S.: 813920
Gordon N. Litwin *(Chm)*
Peter S. Reinhart *(Vice Chm)*
Ann B. Gavzy *(Gen Counsel-Health Sys & Exec VP)*
Salvatore R. Inciardi *(Chief Bus Dev Officer)*
Russ Molloy *(Sr VP-Govt Rels)*

Joseph Lemaire *(Exec VP-Fin)*
Patrick Young *(Pres-Population Health Solutions)*
Joseph Mannion *(CIO & Sr VP)*
Sherrie String *(Sr VP-HR)*
Theodore Schlert *(Sr VP-Risk Mgmt)*
Chrisie A. Scott *(VP-Mktg & Corp Comm)*
Maureen Sintich *(Chief Nurse Officer-Network & Sr VP-Nursing)*
Robert C. Garrett *(CEO)*
Robert L. Glenning *(CFO & Pres-Fin Svcs Div)*
Andrew Pecora *(Chief Innovation Officer & Pres-Physician Svcs Div)*
Bonita Stanton *(Pres-Academic Enterprise & Dean-School of Medicine)*
Jon Fitzgerald *(Co-Chief Dev Officer-Foundation & Reg Pres-North)*
Joseph Stampe *(Pres & Co-Chief Dev Officer-Foundation)*
Cathy Ainora *(Chief Integration Officer & Exec VP)*
James Blazar *(Chief Strategy Officer & Exec VP)*
Nancy Corcoran-Davidoff *(Chief Experience Officer & Exec VP)*
Carol Barsky *(Chief Quality Officer & Sr VP)*
Steve Baker *(Pres-Post Acute Care)*
Audrey Murphy *(Gen Counsel-Hospital Enterprise & Exec VP)*
Mark D. Sparta *(VP-Population Health)*
Thomas Flynn *(Chief Compliance Officer & VP-Compliance)*
Jose Lozano *(VP-Corp Svcs & Governance & Chief of Staff)*
Marty Scott *(Chief Transformational Officer & Sr VP)*
Joseph Simunovich *(Co-Chm)*
Kenneth N. Sable *(Pres-South)*
Helen Cunning *(Co-Chief Dev Officer & Pres-North)*
David Reis *(Co-CIO & Exec VP)*
Rose R. Glenn *(CMO & Sr VP)*
Raymond F. Fredericks *(Pres-Central Market)*
Ihor Sawczuk *(Pres-North)*
Tim Hogan *(Pres-Care Transformation Svcs)*
Theresa M. Brodrick *(Exec VP)*
Tim O'Brien *(CEO-Mountainside Medical Center)*
Joyce P. Hendricks *(Chief Dev Officer-Network Philanthropy)*
Yang Linda Chen *(CFO-Mountainside Medical Center)*

Subsidiaries:

Carrier Clinic   (1)
252 County Rd 601, Belle Mead, NJ 08502
Tel.: (908) 281-1000
Web Site: http://www.carrierclinic.org
Sales Range: $75-99.9 Million
Emp.: 983
Psychiatric Treatment Services
N.A.I.C.S.: 622210
Donald J. Parker *(Pres & CEO)*
Thomas G. Amato *(Chm)*

Hackensack University Medical Center   (1)
30 Prospect Ave, Hackensack, NJ 07601
Tel.: (551) 996-2000
Web Site: http://www.hackensackmc.org
Hospital Operator
N.A.I.C.S.: 622110
Mark D. Sparta *(Pres)*

Ocean Medical Center   (1)
425 Jack Martin Blvd, Brick, NJ 08724
Tel.: (732) 840-2200
Web Site:
http://www.oceanmedicalcenter.com
Hospital Operator
N.A.I.C.S.: 622110
Dean Q. Lin *(Pres)*
Vincent Vivona *(VP-Clinical Effectiveness)*

Richard A. Epstein *(VP-Strategic Program Dev)*
Ellen Angelo *(VP-Nursing & Chief Nurse Exec)*
Cindy Lantz *(VP-Physician Dev)*
Marie Foley-Danecker *(Sr Mgr-Patient Svcs)*
Ken Souchek *(Sr Mgr-Rehab Svcs & Orthopedics)*

Riverview Medical Center   (1)
1 Riverview Plz, Red Bank, NJ 07701
Tel.: (732) 741-2700
Web Site:
http://www.riverviewmedicalcenter.com
Hospital Operator
N.A.I.C.S.: 622110
Timothy J. Hogan *(Reg Pres-Monmouth County Hospitals)*
Kelli O'Brien *(COO)*
Kathy McKean *(VP & Chief Nurse Exec)*
Joseph Reichman *(VP-Clinical Effectiveness & Medical Affairs)*
Sheila Hintze *(Sr Mgr-Ops)*
Rachel Weiss *(VP-Physician & Bus Dev)*
Todd Shellenberger *(Exec Dir-Hackensack Meridian-Foundation)*
Steve Scopellite *(Chm)*

Southern Ocean Medical Center   (1)
1140 Rte 72 W, Manahawkin, NJ 08050
Tel.: (609) 597-6011
Web Site: http://www.southernoceanmedical center.com
Hospital Operator
N.A.I.C.S.: 622110
Myrna Capabianco *(VP-Nursing & Ops & Chief Nurse Exec)*
Theodore G. Zaleski *(VP-Clinical Effecitveness)*
Kimberly Clements *(Sr Mgr-Patient Care Svcs)*
Michelle Morrison *(Sr Mgr-Ops)*
Regina M. Foley *(COO)*
Robert Adams Jr. *(Pres)*

HACKER INSTRUMENTS & INDUSTRIES INC.
1132 Kincaid Bridge Rd, Winnsboro, SC 29180
Tel.: (803) 712-6100
Web Site:
https://www.hackerinstruments.com
Year Founded: 1942
Sales Range: $75-99.9 Million
Emp.: 4
Microtomes, Cryostats, Microtome Knives, Fiber Optic Illuminators, Histology/Cytology Instruments, Mortuary/Autopsy Instruments, Slide Stainers, Tissue Processors, Robot Cover Slippers Mfr
N.A.I.C.S.: 423490
James Mullen Jr. *(VP & Gen Mgr)*

HACKER, JOHNSON & SMITH PA
500 N Westshore Blvd Ste 1000, Tampa, FL 33609
Tel.: (813) 286-2424   FL
Web Site:
https://www.hackerjohnson.com
Year Founded: 1982
Sales Range: $1-9.9 Million
Emp.: 34
Accounting, Auditing & Bookkeeping
N.A.I.C.S.: 541211
Edward F. Hacker *(Partner)*
Thomas D. Smith *(Partner)*
Robert W. Brink *(Partner)*
Stephen R. Kania *(Partner)*
Edward F. Hacker Jr. *(Partner)*

HACKLEY COMMUNITY CARE
2700 Baker St, Muskegon Heights, MI 49444
Tel.: (231) 737-1335   MI
Web Site:
https://www.hackleycommunity care.org
Year Founded: 1992
Sales Range: $10-24.9 Million

Emp.: 207
Community Health Care Services
N.A.I.C.S.: 621498
Dianna L. Anderson *(Chief HR Officer)*
Valerie J. Blondin *(CFO)*
Sheri L. Weglarz *(COO)*
Linda Juarez *(CEO)*
Wayne H. Kohn *(Chief Health Officer)*

HACKWORTH REPROGRAPHICS, INC.
1700 Liberty St, Chesapeake, VA 23324
Tel.: (757) 545-7675   VA
Web Site: https://www.hackworth.co
Year Founded: 1991
Rev.: $3,366,000
Emp.: 33
Other Business Service Centers, including Copy Shops
N.A.I.C.S.: 561439
Drew Little *(Dir-Crop Dev)*
Steve Kirnan *(Dir-Tech)*
Charles G. Hackworth II *(VP)*

Subsidiaries:

Creative Document Imaging, Inc.   (1)
4460 Brookfield Corporate Dr Ste G, Chantilly, VA 20151
Tel.: (703) 208-2212
Web Site: http://www.creativedoc.net
Other Business Service Centers, including Copy Shops
N.A.I.C.S.: 561439

HADADY CORPORATION
510 W 172nd St, South Holland, IL 60473-2717
Tel.: (708) 228-4735   DE
Web Site:
http://www.hadadycorp.com
Year Founded: 1973
Sales Range: $10-24.9 Million
Emp.: 250
Metal Products Distr
N.A.I.C.S.: 332999
Rodger Gorden *(Controller)*
Andy Miller *(Engr-Quality)*
Jeff Ladendorf *(Mgr-Engrg)*
Rose Sullivan *(Coord-Safety, Trng & HR)*
Nick Ferris *(VP-Matl Control)*
William Parks *(Mgr-IT)*
Mark Kordys *(Mgr-IT)*
Stan Burjek *(Mgr-Sls-Rail Div)*

HADASSAH, THE WOMEN'S ZIONIST ORGANIZATION OF AMERICA, INC.
40 Wall St, New York, NY 10005
Tel.: (212) 355-7900   NY
Web Site: https://www.hadassah.org
Year Founded: 1922
Sales Range: $10-24.9 Million
Emp.: 199
Woman Welfare Services
N.A.I.C.S.: 813410

HADDAD APPAREL GROUP, LTD.
100 W 33rd St Ste 1115, New York, NY 10001-2900
Tel.: (212) 630-3100   NY
Web Site: https://www.haddad.com
Year Founded: 1948
Sales Range: $200-249.9 Million
Emp.: 500
Children's & Infant Clothing Mfr
N.A.I.C.S.: 424350
Jack Haddad *(Principal)*

HADDAD DODGE
3000 Harris Rd, Bakersfield, CA 93313
Tel.: (661) 527-4318

Web Site:
https://www.haddaddodge.net
Rev.: $47,800,000
Emp.: 135
New Car Dealers
N.A.I.C.S.: 441110
Shanon Burtcher *(Mgr)*
John Haddad *(Gen Mgr)*
Elias W. Haddad *(Pres)*

HADDAD ORGANIZATION LTD.
90 E 5th St Ste 1, Bayonne, NJ
07002-4272
Tel.: (212) 685-4141
Rev.: $15,100,000
Emp.: 25
Men's & Boys Clothing
N.A.I.C.S.: 424350
Sam Haddad *(Sr VP)*

HADDAD RESTAURANT GROUP, INC.
3100 Gillham Rd, Kansas City, MO
64109-1712
Tel.: (816) 931-2261   KS
Year Founded: 1992
Sales Range: $150-199.9 Million
Emp.: 1,200
Holding Company; Franchise Restaurant Owner & Operator
N.A.I.C.S.: 551112
Nabil Haddad *(Chm)*
Bruce Campbell *(VP-Mktg-Pur)*
David W. Haddad *(Pres)*

Subsidiaries:

Haddad Specialty Restaurants,
Inc.   (1)
4717 Grand Ave Ste 200, Kansas City, MO
64112-2256   (100%)
Tel.: (816) 931-2261
Web Site:
http://www.plazaiiisteakhouse.com
Franchise Steakhouse Restaurant Operator
N.A.I.C.S.: 722511

HADDON SAVINGS BANK
201 White Horse Pike, Haddon
Heights, NJ 08035-1779
Tel.: (856) 547-3700
Web Site:
http://www.haddonsavings.com
Year Founded: 1905
Sales Range: $10-24.9 Million
Emp.: 35
Savings & Loan Associations
N.A.I.C.S.: 522180
Kevin Peterson *(Pres & CEO)*
Terri J. Krout *(Asst VP)*
Caroline Sapp *(Treas & Sec)*

HADDON-MCCLELLAN ASSOCIATES INC.
1838B Independence Sq, Atlanta, GA
30338
Tel.: (770) 399-6050
Web Site: http://www.haddon-mcclellan.com
Sales Range: $10-24.9 Million
Emp.: 6
Electrical Apparatus & Equipment
N.A.I.C.S.: 423610
Michael Haddon *(Pres)*
Michael McClellan *(VP)*

HADER INDUSTRIES INC.
15600 W Lincoln Ave, New Berlin, WI
53151-0260
Tel.: (262) 641-6000   WI
Web Site: https://www.haderinc.com
Year Founded: 1954
Sales Range: $10-24.9 Million
Emp.: 115
Provider of Pumps & Pumping Equipment
N.A.I.C.S.: 333914
Wayne K. Hader *(Pres & CEO)*

Subsidiaries:

Fabri-Tech Inc.   (1)
225 N Janacek Rd, Brookfield, WI
53045-6102   (100%)
Tel.: (262) 789-7370
Web Site: http://www.fabri-tech.net
Sales Range: $10-24.9 Million
Emp.: 47
Provider of Fabricated Metal
N.A.I.C.S.: 332312

Hader Inc.   (1)
15600 W Lincoln Ave, New Berlin, WI
53151-2823
Tel.: (262) 641-8000
Web Site: http://www.haderinc.com
Sales Range: $10-24.9 Million
Emp.: 20
Hydraulic Manufacturer
N.A.I.C.S.: 811210

Hader-Seitz Inc.   (1)
15600 W Lincoln Ave, New Berlin, WI
53151-2823
Tel.: (262) 641-6000
Web Site: http://www.haderind.com
Sales Range: $10-24.9 Million
Emp.: 65
Provider of Industrial Equipment
N.A.I.C.S.: 333995

Ram-Pac International Inc.   (1)
15600 W Lincoln Ave, New Berlin, WI
53151-2823
Tel.: (262) 641-6000
Sales Range: $10-24.9 Million
Emp.: 15
Provider of Pumps & Motors
N.A.I.C.S.: 333996

HADINGER CARPET INC.
6401 N Airport Rd, Naples, FL 34109
Tel.: (239) 566-7100
Web Site:
https://www.hadingerflooring.com
Year Founded: 1931
Sales Range: $10-24.9 Million
Emp.: 50
Floor Covering Stores
N.A.I.C.S.: 449121
Don Williamson *(CEO)*

HADLEY CAPITAL LLC
1200 Central Ave Ste 300, Wilmette,
IL 60091
Tel.: (847) 906-5300
Web Site:
http://www.hadleycapital.com
Investment Advice
N.A.I.C.S.: 523940
Thomas Haber *(Owner)*

Subsidiaries:

Centare Holdings Inc.   (1)
300 N Executive Dr Ste 100, Brookfield, WI
53005
Tel.: (262) 264-6106
Web Site: http://www.centare.com
Data Processing, Hosting & Related Services
N.A.I.C.S.: 518210
Chad Albrecht *(Pres)*
Tim Eiring *(CEO)*
Tim Dransfield *(Dir-Consulting)*
Ian Fox *(Dir-Dev Center)*

HADLEY EXHIBITS INC.
1700 Elmwood Ave, Buffalo, NY
14207
Tel.: (716) 874-3666
Web Site:
https://www.hadleyexhibits.com
Rev.: $10,588,465
Emp.: 100
Displays & Cutouts, Window & Lobby
N.A.I.C.S.: 339950
Dave Johnson *(Pres)*
Patrick Haggerty *(Dir-Design)*
Robert Riehle *(Project Mgr)*
Jim Dzielski *(Project Mgr)*

HADLEY HOUSE COMPANY

4816 Nicollet Ave S, Minneapolis, MN
55419
Tel.: (952) 943-8474
Web Site:
https://www.hadleyhouse.com
Sales Range: $25-49.9 Million
Emp.: 700
Carved & Turned Wood Products Mfr;
Sales of Art Framing & Giftware
N.A.I.C.S.: 321999

HADWIN WHITE PONTIAC - BUICK - GMC TRUCK
2325 E Hwy 501, Conway, SC
29526-9599
Tel.: (843) 347-4633
Web Site: https://www.hadwin-white.com
Year Founded: 1986
Sales Range: $10-24.9 Million
Emp.: 60
Car Whslr
N.A.I.C.S.: 441110
Jordan Hadwin *(Coord-Customer Care)*
Gary L. Hadwin *(Pres)*

HAEGER INDUSTRIES, INC.
7 Maiden Ln, Dundee, IL 60118-2307
Tel.: (847) 426-3441   IL
Web Site:
http://www.haegerpotteries.com
Year Founded: 1871
Sales Range: $300-349.9 Million
Emp.: 400
Holding Company; Ceramic Gifts & Decorative Accessories Mfr
N.A.I.C.S.: 551112
Alexandra H. Estes *(Chm & Pres)*
Terry Rosborough *(VP-Mfg)*
Gene McGahan *(VP-Mdsg, Mktg & Sls)*

Subsidiaries:

Haeger Potteries, Inc.   (1)
7 Maiden Ln, Dundee, IL 60118-2307
Tel.: (847) 426-3441
Web Site: http://www.haegerpotteries.com
Sales Range: $25-49.9 Million
Emp.: 145
Ceramic Gifts & Decorative Accessories Mfr
N.A.I.C.S.: 327110

Division (Domestic):

Haeger Potteries of Macomb Inc.   (2)
411 Calhoun, Macomb, IL 61455   (100%)
Tel.: (309) 833-2171
Web Site: http://www.haegerpotteries.com
Sales Range: $25-49.9 Million
Emp.: 85
Ceramic Gifts & Decorative Accessories Mfr
N.A.I.C.S.: 327110

HAFELE AMERICA CO. INC.
3901 Cheyenne Dr, Archdale, NC
27263-3157
Tel.: (336) 889-2322   OH
Web Site: http://www.hafele.com
Year Founded: 1973
Sales Range: $25-49.9 Million
Emp.: 250
Mfr of Hardware
N.A.I.C.S.: 423710
Gary Crysel *(Exec VP)*
Ursula Hafele *(Co-Owner)*
Paul K. Smith *(Pres)*
Natalie Davenport *(Head-Mktg-UK)*

HAFSA CORPORATION
13985 Live Oak Ave, Irwindale, CA
91706
Tel.: (626) 814-2900
Rev.: $24,876,972
Emp.: 3
Groceries, General Line
N.A.I.C.S.: 424410
Farid Shalabi *(Pres)*

HAGER CABINETS INCORPORATED
474 Eastern Bypass, Richmond, KY
40475
Tel.: (859) 623-8230
Web Site:
https://www.hagercabinets.com
Sales Range: $10-24.9 Million
Emp.: 60
Lumber & Other Building Materials
N.A.I.C.S.: 423310
Bob Hager *(Pres)*

HAGER GROUP INC.
1545 Marquette St SW, Grand Rapids, MI 49509
Tel.: (616) 247-7984   MI
Year Founded: 1967
Sales Range: $10-24.9 Million
Emp.: 115
Wholesalers of Lumber, Plywood & Millwork Siding
N.A.I.C.S.: 423310
Bob Branski *(CFO)*

Subsidiaries:

Marquette Lumbermens
Warehouse   (1)
1545 Marquette St SW, Grand Rapids, MI
49509
Tel.: (616) 247-7984
Sales Range: $10-24.9 Million
Emp.: 85
Lumber: Rough, Dressed & Finished
N.A.I.C.S.: 423310

Marquette Saginaw Warehouse   (1)
1545 Marquette St Southwest, Grand Rapids, MI 49509
Tel.: (616) 452-5151
Rev.: $17,000,000
Emp.: 100
Lumber, Plywood & Millwork
N.A.I.C.S.: 423310

HAGER SHARP INC.
1030 15th St NW Ste 600 E, Washington, DC 20005
Tel.: (202) 842-3600   DC
Web Site:
http://www.hagersharp.com
Year Founded: 1973
Sales Range: $1-9.9 Million
Emp.: 25
Public Relations Agency
N.A.I.C.S.: 541820
Walter Watts *(CFO)*
Aaron Murphy *(VP & Dir-Digital Design)*
Mike Gallagher *(Sr VP & Creative Dir)*
Christina Nicols *(Sr VP & Dir-Strategic Plng & Res)*
Jennifer Wayman *(Pres & CEO)*
Katherine Nicol *(Exec VP)*

HAGERMAN CONSTRUCTION CORPORATION
510 W Washington Blvd, Fort Wayne,
IN 46802-2918
Tel.: (260) 424-1470   IN
Web Site:
https://www.thehagermangroup.com
Year Founded: 1908
Sales Range: $125-149.9 Million
Emp.: 300
General Contracting & Construction Management
N.A.I.C.S.: 236220
Jeff Hagerman *(Chm)*

Subsidiaries:

The Hagerman Group   (1)
10315 Allisonville Rd, Fishers, IN 46038
Tel.: (317) 577-6836
Web Site:
http://www.thehagermangroup.com

Hagerman Construction
Corporation—(Continued)

Sales Range: $10-24.9 Million
Emp.: 60
General Contracting & Construction Man-
agement Service
N.A.I.C.S.: 541511
Jeff Hagerman *(Chm)*
Terry Greene *(Exec VP)*
Thomas White *(Chief Safety Officer)*
Rob Young *(VP-Bus Dev)*
Bruce Molter *(Pres)*
Brad Smith *(Exec VP)*
Melanie King *(CFO)*
Missy Hoover *(Chief Mktg Officer)*

HAGERTY, LOCKENVITZ AD-
VERTISING, INC.

901 E Grove Ste B, Bloomington, IL
61701
Tel.: (309) 827-8491   IL
Year Founded: 1978
Sales Range: $10-24.9 Million
Emp.: 5
N.A.I.C.S.: 541810
Ron Lockenvitz *(Pres)*
Brad Ochiltree *(Creative Dir)*
Bridget Hoffman *(Acct Dir)*

HAGGARD & STOCKING AS-
SOCIATES INC.

5318 Victory Dr, Indianapolis, IN
46203-5951
Tel.: (317) 788-4661
Web Site: http://www.haggard-
   stocking.com
Year Founded: 1973
Sales Range: $10-24.9 Million
Emp.: 72
Provider of Industrial Machinery &
Equipment
N.A.I.C.S.: 423830
Herbert C. Haggard *(Chm & CEO)*
Kevin D. Burnett *(Exec VP)*
Dan McNeely *(Mgr-IT)*
Paul Mills *(CFO)*

HAGIN INVESTMENT MANAG-
MENT

5138 Main St, Manchester Center,
VT 05255
Tel.: (802) 417-7664
Web Site: http://www.haginim.com
Investment Services
N.A.I.C.S.: 523999
Patrick R. Morris *(CEO)*
Shawn P. Harrington *(Sr VP & Mgr-
Wealth)*

HAGLE LUMBER COMPANY,
INC.

3100 Somis Rd, Somis, CA 93066
Tel.: (805) 987-3887
Web Site:
   https://www.haglelumber.com
Sales Range: $10-24.9 Million
Emp.: 33
Lumber Whslr
N.A.I.C.S.: 423310
Joe Ferreira *(VP & Gen Mgr)*

HAGOPIAN WORLD OF RUGS
INC.

14000 W 8 Mile Rd, Oak Park, MI
48237
Tel.: (248) 399-2323
Web Site:
   https://www.originalhagopian.com
Rev.: $11,600,000
Emp.: 90
Rugs
N.A.I.C.S.: 449121
Edmund Hagopian *(Pres)*
Brian Davis *(Mgr-Flooring)*

HAHN & CLAY, LTD.

5100 Clinton Dr, Houston, TX 77020

Tel.: (713) 672-1671   TX
Web Site: https://www.hahnclay.com
Year Founded: 1908
Metal Fabrication & Machine Shop
N.A.I.C.S.: 332710
Ward Sheffield *(Owner)*

HAHN AUTOMOTIVE WARE-
HOUSE, INC.

415 W Main St, Rochester, NY
14608-1944
Tel.: (585) 235-1595   NY
Year Founded: 1958
Sales Range: $125-149.9 Million
Automotive Aftermarket Parts Distr &
Retailer
N.A.I.C.S.: 423120
Daniel J. Chessin *(Co-Pres & CEO)*
Eli N. Futerman *(Co-Pres)*
Michael Piccolo *(CFO & VP-Fin)*
Clint Bentley *(VP-Ops)*

Subsidiaries:

Norwood Auto Parts   (1)
1760 Route 37 E, Toms River, NJ 08753
Tel.: (732) 573-0900
Emp.: 5
Automobile Parts Distr
N.A.I.C.S.: 441330

Prime Aurtomotive Parts Co.,
Inc.   (1)
89-17 Union Trnpk, Glendale, NY 11385-
8098
Tel.: (718) 846-8900
Web Site: http://www.primeauto.com
Automobile Parts Distr
N.A.I.C.S.: 423120

Subsidiary (Domestic):

E&L Battery & Ignition Co.   (2)
28 William St, Newark, NJ 07102
Tel.: (973) 623-0415
Web Site: http://www.elbattery.com
Sales Range: $10-24.9 Million
Emp.: 50
Automobile Parts Distr
N.A.I.C.S.: 423120

HAHN HOLDING CO.

90 W Main St, New Market, MD
21774
Tel.: (301) 865-5467
Sales Range: $10-24.9 Million
Emp.: 25
Contract Haulers
N.A.I.C.S.: 484121
Barbara Winter *(Pres)*

HAHNER FOREMAN & HAR-
NESS INC.

423 N Saint Francis St, Wichita, KS
67202
Tel.: (316) 264-0306
Web Site: http://www.hfh.com
Sales Range: $10-24.9 Million
Emp.: 15
Industrial Buildings & Warehouses
N.A.I.C.S.: 236220
David Foreman *(Pres)*

HAIG'S SERVICE CORPORA-
TION

211A US Highway 22 E, Green
Brook, NJ 08812
Tel.: (732) 968-6677   NJ
Web Site:
   http://www.haigservice.com
Year Founded: 1985
Sales Range: $1-9.9 Million
Emp.: 45
Security System Services
N.A.I.C.S.: 561621
Christopher Bernard *(VP)*
Thomas Solimani *(VP-Ops)*
Richard D. Haig Jr. *(Pres & CEO)*

HAIGHT BROWN & BONEST-
EEL, LLP

555 S Flower St 45th Fl, Los Ange-
les, CA 90071
Tel.: (213) 542-8000
Web Site: https://www.hbblaw.com
Year Founded: 1937
Law firm
N.A.I.C.S.: 541110
Peter A. Dubrawski *(Partner)*
Gary A. Bague *(Partner)*
Bruce Cleeland *(Partner)*
David W. Evans *(Partner)*
Kevin M. Osterberg *(Partner)*

HAIGHTS CROSS COMMUNI-
CATIONS, INC.

136 Madison Ave 8th Fl, New York,
NY 10016
Tel.: (212) 209-0500   DE
Web Site:
   http://www.haightscross.com
Year Founded: 1997
Sales Range: $150-199.9 Million
Emp.: 542
Educational Books, Periodicals, Audio
Products, Software & Online Products
Publisher
N.A.I.C.S.: 513120
Ken Collins *(CFO)*
Diane Curtin *(VP-HR)*
Dennis Cullen *(CFO)*

HAIGOOD & CAMPBELL LLC

108 E Walnut, Archer City, TX 76351
Tel.: (940) 574-4622
Web Site: https://www.haigood-
   campbell.com
Year Founded: 1947
Rev.: $30,322,389
Emp.: 20
Fuels, Propane & Lubricants Busi-
ness Services
N.A.I.C.S.: 561499
Ward Campbell *(Gen Mgr)*

HAINES & COMPANY, INC.

8050 Freedom Ave NW, North Can-
ton, OH 44720-6912
Tel.: (330) 494-9111   OH
Web Site: http://www.haines.com
Year Founded: 1932
Sales Range: $100-124.9 Million
Emp.: 300
Publisher of Cross References Trade-
name Directory Mailing List & CD
Roms Printing Design & Mailing Ser-
vices
N.A.I.C.S.: 513140
Ashley Williams *(CEO)*

Subsidiaries:

Haines & Company, Inc. - Americalist
Division   (1)
8050 Freedom Ave NW, Canton, OH 44720
Tel.: (888) 219-5478
Web Site: http://www.americalist.com
Direct Marketing Services
N.A.I.C.S.: 541613
Jenus Sibila *(Dir-New Market Dev)*

Haines & Company, Inc. - Haines Di-
rect Division   (1)
8050 Freedom Ave NW, North Canton, OH
44720
Tel.: (800) 726-9577
Web Site: http://www.haines-direct.com
Telemarketing Services
N.A.I.C.S.: 561422
Gina Sibila *(Dir-Client Svcs)*
Liz Lowe *(Acct Mgr)*
Suzanne Foughty *(Sec)*
Jennifer Quartz *(Acct Exec)*
Pete Forbes *(Dir-New Client Dev)*

HAINES & KIBBLEHOUSE INC.

2052 Lucon Rd, Skippack, PA 19474-
0196

Tel.: (610) 584-8500   DE
Web Site: https://www.hkgroup.com
Year Founded: 1968
Sales Range: $500-549.9 Million
Emp.: 1,900
Excavation, Demolition & Paving Ser-
vices
N.A.I.C.S.: 238910
Sam Jackson *(Mgr)*
Steve Bowers *(Mgr-Weld Shop)*
Tom Gusick *(Project Mgr)*
Kevin Propsner *(Supvr-Quality Con-
trol)*
Pete Roussin *(Project Mgr)*
Anthony Jeremias *(Dir-PR & Mktg)*
Bonnie Schatz *(Coord-Bid)*

Subsidiaries:

209 Enterprises   (1)
Route 209, Marshalls Creek, PA 18335
Tel.: (570) 223-8060
Crushed Stone Product Mfr
N.A.I.C.S.: 327991

ABE Materials - Easton   (1)
5137 Lower Mud Run Rd, Easton, PA
18040-9240
Tel.: (610) 250-7700
Stone Product & Asphalt Material Distr
N.A.I.C.S.: 423320

Architectural Stone   (1)
1 Quarry Rd, Douglassville, PA 19518
Tel.: (610) 705-5455
Landscape Stone Mfr & Whslr
N.A.I.C.S.: 327991

Atkinson Materials   (1)
HC1 Box 15 Owego Turnpike, Hawley, PA
18428
Tel.: (570) 226-4728
Crushed Stone Distr
N.A.I.C.S.: 423320

Bechtelsville Asphalt   (1)
1355 N Reading Ave, Bechtelsville, PA
19505
Tel.: (610) 367-7789
Asphalt Paving Mixture Mfr
N.A.I.C.S.: 324121

Bedrock Quarries, Inc.   (1)
SR 1003, Damascus, PA 18415
Tel.: (570) 224-6835
Stone Product Mfr
N.A.I.C.S.: 327991

Belvidere Sand & Gravel   (1)
487 CR 519, Belvidere, NJ 07823-0418
Tel.: (908) 475-8080
Construction Materials Distr
N.A.I.C.S.: 423320

Birdsboro Materials   (1)
1267 Haycreek Rd, Birdsboro, PA 19508
Tel.: (610) 404-8440
Sales Range: $1-9.9 Million
Emp.: 30
Crushed Stone Mfr
N.A.I.C.S.: 327991
Dale Martin *(Mgr)*

Blooming Glen Contractors Inc.   (1)
901 Minsi Trl, Blooming Glen, PA 18911
Tel.: (215) 257-9400
Web Site: http://www.hkgroup.com
Sales Range: $25-49.9 Million
Emp.: 200
Highway & Street Paving Services
N.A.I.C.S.: 237310
John B. Haines IV *(Pres)*

Blooming Glen Quarry   (1)
901 Minsi Trl, Blooming Glen, PA 18911
Tel.: (215) 257-5188
Aggregate Mfr
N.A.I.C.S.: 327992

Colony Materials Hardscape & Land-
scape Supplies   (1)
7144 Danboro-Point Pleasant Pike, Point
Pleasant, PA 18950
Tel.: (215) 297-8748
Web Site: http://www.hkgroup.com
Emp.: 1
Hardscape & Landscape Supplier
N.A.I.C.S.: 423320
Eric Weidemoyer *(Mgr)*

Colony Materials, L.L.C. (1)
7144 Danboro-Point Pleasant Pike, Point
Pleasant, PA 18950
Tel.: (215) 297-8111
Building Material Disposal Services
N.A.I.C.S.: 562998

Dagsboro Materials (1)
30548 Thorogoods Rd, Dagsboro, DE
19939
Tel.: (302) 934-7635
Crushed Stone Distr
N.A.I.C.S.: 423320

**Deck's Hardscape & Landscape
Supplies** (1)
316 New Schaefferstown Rd, Bernville, PA
19506
Tel.: (610) 488-7291
Sales Range: $10-24.9 Million
Emp.: 4
Hardscape & Landscape Supplier
N.A.I.C.S.: 423320
Chris Palumbo (Gen Mgr)

Delaware Valley Recycling, Inc. (1)
3107 S 61st St, Philadelphia, PA 19153
Tel.: (215) 724-2244
Crushed Stone Product Mfr
N.A.I.C.S.: 327991
Lee S. Detwiler (Pres)

Dunmore Materials (1)
950 Dunham Dr, Dunmore, PA 18512
Tel.: (570) 347-1800
Asphalt Paving Mixture Mfr
N.A.I.C.S.: 324121

Dushore Construction Materials (1)
8700 Route 220, Dushore, PA 18614
Tel.: (570) 928-8858
Construction Materials Supplier
N.A.I.C.S.: 423320

Easton Block & Supply (1)
5135 Lowr Mud Run Rd, Easton, PA 18040
Tel.: (610) 250-7703
Building Material Supplier
N.A.I.C.S.: 423390
Roy E. Kester (Gen Mgr)

Eckley Asphalt (1)
25 No 1 Ln, Weatherly, PA 18255
Tel.: (570) 636-1750
Sales Range: $10-24.9 Million
Emp.: 4
Asphalt Whslr
N.A.I.C.S.: 423320

Greger Topsoil (1)
1 Quarry Rd, Douglassville, PA 19518
Tel.: (610) 705-5455
Topsoil & Mulch Whslr
N.A.I.C.S.: 424910

H&K Materials (1)
300 Skunk Hollow Rd, Chalfont, PA 18914
Tel.: (215) 822-2200
Stone Product Mfr
N.A.I.C.S.: 327991

Harnden Group, LLC (1)
5010 Ritter Rd Ste 112, Mechanicsburg, PA
17055
Tel.: (717) 790-9843
Civil Engineering Services
N.A.I.C.S.: 541330

Hazleton Materials, L.L.C. (1)
10 No 1 Ln, Weatherly, PA 18255
Tel.: (570) 636-3300
Web Site: http://www.handjgroup.com
Crushed Stone Mfr
N.A.I.C.S.: 327991
John Haines (Gen Mgr)

Hazleton Site Contractors (1)
Humboldt Industrial Park - 40 Elm Rd,
Hazleton, PA 18202
Tel.: (570) 453-3900
Web Site: http://www.hkgroup.com
Emp.: 60
Site Contracting Services
N.A.I.C.S.: 238910
Vince Nahf (Superintendent)

Hilltop Quarry (1)
376 Quarry Hill Dr, Dalton, PA 18414
Tel.: (570) 586-7461
Web Site: http://www.hkgroup.com
Aggregate Mfr

N.A.I.C.S.: 327992

Kent Sand & Gravel, L.L.C. (1)
13505 Alexander Rd, Massey, MD 21650
Tel.: (410) 928-5522
Web Site: http://www.hkgroup.com
Sand & Gravel Distr
N.A.I.C.S.: 423320
Myles Bennet (Owner)
Dawn Hartzell (Plant Mgr)
Scott Haines (Pres)

**Landis C. Deck & Sons Site
Contractors** (1)
316 New Schaefferstown Rd, Bernville, PA
19506
Tel.: (610) 488-8929
Web Site: http://www.hk.com
Site Contracting Services
N.A.I.C.S.: 238910

Leeward Asphalt, L.L.C. (1)
9 Collan Way, Honesdale, PA 18431
Tel.: (570) 226-7623
Asphalt Mixture Whslr
N.A.I.C.S.: 423320

Locust Ridge Contractors (1)
2699 Locust Rdg Rd, Pocono Lake, PA
18347
Tel.: (570) 646-3324
Site Contracting & Excavating Services
N.A.I.C.S.: 238910
Ginny Terry (Engr-Cost)

Locust Ridge Quarry (1)
2699 Locust Rdg Rd, Pocono Lake, PA
18347
Tel.: (570) 643-5823
Crushed Stone Mfr
N.A.I.C.S.: 327991

Miniscalco Construction, L.L.C. (1)
2052 Lucon Rd, Skippack, PA 19474
Tel.: (610) 222-4090
Site Contracting Services
N.A.I.C.S.: 238910

Penn/MD Materials (1)
303 Quarry Rd, Peach Bottom, PA 17563
Tel.: (717) 548-2147
Stone Product Mfr
N.A.I.C.S.: 327991

**Pikes Creek Asphalt & Crushed
Stone** (1)
528 Trojan Rd, Hunlock Creek, PA 18621
Tel.: (570) 477-2919
Web Site: http://www.hkgroup.com
Emp.: 17
Asphalt & Paving Material Whslr
N.A.I.C.S.: 423320
Mick Serfim (Gen Mgr)

Pyramid Materials (1)
414 W Knowlton Rd, Media, PA 19063
Tel.: (610) 494-4722
Web Site: http://www.hkgroup.com
Sales Range: $10-24.9 Million
Emp.: 8
Site Contracting & Excavating Services
N.A.I.C.S.: 238910
Tom Welsh (Gen Mgr)

Rahns Construction Material Co. (1)
430 Rahns Rd Rahns, Perkiomen, PA
19426
Tel.: (610) 528-4060
Readymix Concrete Mfr
N.A.I.C.S.: 327320
Dan Condiles (Gen Mgr)

Reading Site Contractors (1)
392 N Sanatoga Rd, Pottstown, PA 19464
Tel.: (610) 705-0500
Site Contracting Services
N.A.I.C.S.: 238910
David Richards (Superintendent)
Ronald Burton (Superintendent-Site)

Silver Hill Quarry (1)
470 Yellow Hill Rd Ste 1, Narvon, PA 17555
Tel.: (717) 445-7430
Web Site: http://www.hkgroup.com
Sales Range: $10-24.9 Million
Emp.: 16
Crushed Stone Mfr
N.A.I.C.S.: 327991
Keith Martin (Gen Mgr)

South Reading Blacktop (1)

148 Angstadt Ln, Birdsboro, PA 19508
Tel.: (610) 373-5540
Sales Range: $10-24.9 Million
Emp.: 4
Asphalt Mixture Mfr
N.A.I.C.S.: 324121

**Stockertown Construction
Materials** (1)
SR 191 Center St, Stockertown, PA 18083-
0307
Tel.: (610) 614-1445
Stone Product Mfr
N.A.I.C.S.: 327991

Terra Structures (1)
1 Quarry Rd, Douglassville, PA 19518
Tel.: (610) 326-3098
Web Site: http://www.hkgroup.com
Emp.: 25
Paver Installation Services
N.A.I.C.S.: 238990

Top Shelf Drilling (1)
2082 Lucon Rd, Skippack, PA 19473
Tel.: (610) 222-3090
Drilling Services
N.A.I.C.S.: 237990

Warren Materials (1)
703 Route 57, Stewartsville, NJ 08886
Tel.: (908) 859-3333
Asphalt Product Mfr
N.A.I.C.S.: 324121

Windsor Service, Inc. (1)
2415 Kutztown Rd, Reading, PA 19605-
2957
Tel.: (610) 929-0716
Web Site: http://www.hkgroup.com
Sales Range: $25-49.9 Million
Emp.: 100
Mfr of Asphalt Products; Paving Contractor
N.A.I.C.S.: 532490

HAIRSTYLISTS MANAGEMENT
SYSTEMS
12700 Indus Park Blvd, Minneapolis,
MN 55441
Tel.: (763) 550-1332
Rev.: $13,000,000
Emp.: 8
Beauty Shops
N.A.I.C.S.: 812112
Michael Kunin (Pres)
Mike Brooks (Controller)

HAITAI, INC.
7227 Telegraph Rd, Montebello, CA
90640-6512
Tel.: (323) 890-0101
Web Site: http://www.haitaiusa.com
Year Founded: 1981
Sales Range: $10-24.9 Million
Emp.: 50
Packaged Frozen Food Distr
N.A.I.C.S.: 424420
Taeki Min (Pres)
Soon Cha (CFO)

HAITI ENTREPRENEURIAL INI-
TIATIVE
1043 Howland St, Franklin, TN 37064
Tel.: (615) 424-0878
Web Site: http://haitientrepreneuriali
tiative.com
Employment Services
N.A.I.C.S.: 561311
Will McGinniss (CEO)

HAKIMIANPOUR RESTAU-
RANT GROUP
11110 Ohio Ave Ste 107, Los Ange-
les, CA 90025
Tel.: (310) 575-3221
Sales Range: $10-24.9 Million
Emp.: 10
Fast-Food Restaurant, Chain
N.A.I.C.S.: 722513
Herbert Hakimianpour (Partner)

HAL HAYS CONSTRUCTION,
INC.
4181 Latham St, Riverside, CA
92501-1729
Tel.: (951) 788-0703
Web Site: https://www.halhays.com
Year Founded: 1991
Sales Range: $50-74.9 Million
Emp.: 110
Construction Engineering Services
N.A.I.C.S.: 541330
Elizabeth Cabral (VP-Mktg & Corp
Dev)
Hal Hays (Founder)
Tom Bailey (Project Mgr)

HAL JONES CONTRACTORS
INC.
720 Talleyrand Ave, Jacksonville, FL
32202
Tel.: (904) 355-5885
Web Site:
   http://www.haljonescontractor.com
Rev.: $33,200,000
Emp.: 60
Highway, Street & Bridge Construc-
tion
N.A.I.C.S.: 237310
Dennis E. Harrison (Pres)
Hal L. Jones III (VP & Project Mgr)

HAL MCBRIDE CAR SALES
INCORPORATED
1313 E Main St, Santa Maria, CA
93454
Tel.: (805) 928-7744
Web Site: http://www.home-
motors.net
Rev.: $42,943,174
Emp.: 90
New & Used Car Dealer
N.A.I.C.S.: 441110
Charles R. Hebard (Owner)
Nancy Sewell (Bus Mgr)
Mike McNulty (Owner)

HAL SMITH RESTAURANT
GROUP, INC.
3101 W Tecumseh Rd Ste 200, Nor-
man, OK 73072-1817
Tel.: (405) 321-2600   OK
Web Site: http://halsmith.com
Year Founded: 1992
Casual & Upscale Restaurant Opera-
tor
N.A.I.C.S.: 722511
Dave Brauckmann (CFO)
Hal Smith (CEO)
Mike Rogers (VP)
Diane Fair (Dir-Acctg)

HALABI INC.
2100 Huntington Dr, Fairfield, CA
94533
Tel.: (707) 402-1600
Web Site: http://www.duracite.com
Rev.: $25,000,000
Emp.: 290
Cut Stone & Stone Products
N.A.I.C.S.: 327991
Fadi Halabi (Pres)

HALCO INDUSTRIES, LLC
1015 Norcross Industrial Ct, Nor-
cross, GA 30071
Tel.: (770) 840-3480
Web Site:
   http://www.halcolubricants.com
Sales Range: $10-24.9 Million
Emp.: 45
Lubricants & Other Automotive
Chemical Products Distr
N.A.I.C.S.: 424720
Alan Parker (Pres)
Mike Parker (Mgr-Customer Svc)
Larry Hurst (Mgr-Sls)

Halco Industries, LLC—(Continued)

HALCYON CREEK INC.
3305 G St, Merced, CA 95348
Web Site: http://www.midvalleyit.com
Year Founded: 2007
Sales Range: $1-9.9 Million
Emp.: 16
Information Technology Services
N.A.I.C.S.: 541512
David Kamins *(Acct Mgr)*

HALDEMAN LINCOLN MER-CURY, INC.
2443 Lehigh St, Allentown, PA 18103
Tel.: (610) 791-4900
Sales Range: $10-24.9 Million
Emp.: 50
Car Whslr
N.A.I.C.S.: 441110
Paul Haldeman *(Owner)*

HALE CAPITAL PARTNERS, L.P.
17 State St Ste 3230, New York, NY 10004
Tel.: (212) 751-1201
Web Site: https://halecapital.com
Investment Services
N.A.I.C.S.: 523999

Subsidiaries:

Culmen International, LLC (1)
99 Canal Center Plz Ste 410, Alexandria, VA 22314
Tel.: (703) 224-7000
Web Site: https://www.culmen.com
Sales Range: $10-24.9 Million
Emp.: 43
Business Research & Development Services
N.A.I.C.S.: 541720
Dan Berkon *(Founder & CEO)*
Brian Jones *(VP-Bus Dev)*
Richard G. Irwin *(Pres & COO)*
Mark Dumas *(Chief Strategy Officer)*

Subsidiary (Domestic):

Centrifuge Systems, Inc. (2)
7926 Jones Branch Dr Ste 210, McLean, VA 22102
Tel.: (571) 830-1300
Web Site: http://www.centrifugesystems.com
Information Technology Services
N.A.I.C.S.: 541512
Casey Henderson *(Founder & CTO)*
Stan Dushko *(Chief Product Officer)*
Steve Panzer *(Sr VP-Govt Sector)*

Vysnova Partners, Inc. (2)
241 E 4th St Ste 106, Frederick, MD 21701-3605
Tel.: (301) 830-8875
Web Site: http://www.vysnova.com
General Management Consulting Services
N.A.I.C.S.: 541611
Carlos G. Rivera *(Pres & CEO)*
John Fallon *(COO)*

HALE KAUAI, LTD.
3371 Wilcox Rd Unit 102, Lihue, HI 96766
Tel.: (808) 639-2199 HI
Web Site: http://www.halekauai.com
Year Founded: 1950
Sales Range: $10-24.9 Million
Real Estate Investment & Development Firm
N.A.I.C.S.: 531390

HALE MAKUA
472 Kaulana St, Kahului, HI 96732
Tel.: (808) 877-2761
Web Site: https://www.halemakua.org
Rev.: $31,800,000
Emp.: 450
Nursing Care Facilities
N.A.I.C.S.: 623110

Margie Albete *(Dir-Admission)*
Jennifer Gardanier *(Mgr-Health Information Mgmt)*
Michael T. Munekiyo *(Chm)*
Roy Sakamoto *(Treas)*

HALE TRAILER BRAKE & WHEEL
Cooper Rd RR 73, Voorhees, NJ 08043
Tel.: (856) 768-1330
Web Site: http://www.haletrailer.com
Rev.: $72,000,000
Emp.: 300
Trucks, Tractors & Trailers: New & Used
N.A.I.C.S.: 336212
Barry J. Hale *(Pres)*
Hue Cunningham *(Controller)*
Ira Eckstein *(Mgr-Rental)*
Joe Frankenfield *(Dir-Sls Admin)*
William Fryer *(VP-Sls)*
Anthony Mascoveto *(Mgr-Credit & Collections)*
French Richendollar *(Mgr)*
David Tomasello *(Exec VP)*
Janis Walls *(Office Mgr)*
Bob DeWitt *(Mgr-Svc & Warehouse)*
Michael Sferrazza *(Mgr-IT)*
Gene Whitley *(Mgr-Svcs)*
Diane Small *(Mgr-Ops)*

HALEY & ALDRICH INC.
70 Blanchard Rd Ste 204, Burlington, MA 01803
Tel.: (617) 886-7400 MA
Web Site:
http://www.haleyaldrich.com
Year Founded: 1957
Sales Range: $50-74.9 Million
Emp.: 420
Engineeering Services
N.A.I.C.S.: 541330
James W. Little *(Sr VP & Gen Mgr-Mfg Bus Unit)*
Brian Fitzpatrick *(Dir-Health & Safety)*
Mehdi Miremadi *(Chief Client Officer & Sr VP)*
Ben Chandler *(Chief Innovation Officer)*
Marcel Guay *(COO)*
Stephen MacIntyre *(Chief Svcs Officer)*
Anne Nason *(Chief Mktg Officer)*
Erin Davies *(Chief Human Potential Officer)*
Marya Gorczyca *(Chief Learning & Dev Officer)*
Patricia McKee *(Gen Counsel)*
Philip J. Lagas *(Chief Client Officer & Exec VP)*
Robert Gabel *(CFO)*
Shawn Fiore *(Pres & CEO)*

Subsidiaries:

Cal Engineering & Geology Inc (1)
1870 Olympic Blvd, Walnut Creek, CA 94596
Tel.: (925) 935-9771
Web Site: http://www.caleng.com
Rev.: $1,000,000
Emp.: 9
Engineeering Services
N.A.I.C.S.: 541330
Phillip Gregory *(Founder & Sr Engr)*
Mark Myers *(Engr)*

Haley & Aldrich Construction Services, Inc. (1)
598 Byrne Industrial Dr, Rockford, MI 49341
Tel.: (616) 951-6250
Web Site: http://www.HaleyAldrich.com
Emp.: 6
Engineering Consulting Services
N.A.I.C.S.: 541330

Hart Crowser, Inc. (1)
1700 W Lk Ave N Ste 200, Seattle, WA 98109

Tel.: (206) 324-9530
Web Site: http://www.hartcrowser.com
Sales Range: $75-99.9 Million
Emp.: 74
Environmental Hazardous Waste Management Services
N.A.I.C.S.: 561210
Robert Jenson *(CFO)*
Susan Kemp *(Mgr-Mktg)*
Mike Bailey *(CEO)*
Janice Marsters *(Principal)*
Pam Gunther *(Mng Principal-Natural Resources)*
Alayna Martin *(Coord-Mktg)*
David Winter *(Pres & CEO)*

Division (Domestic):

Pentec Environmental (2)
190 W Daton Ste 201, Edmonds, WA 98020
Tel.: (425) 775-4682
Web Site: http://www.pentecenv.com
Sales Range: $10-24.9 Million
Emp.: 10
Environmental Consulting Firm
N.A.I.C.S.: 541690
David Winter *(CEO)*

HALEY CONSTRUCTION INC.
900 Orange Ave, Daytona Beach, FL 32114-4787
Tel.: (386) 944-0470 FL
Web Site:
http://www.haleyconstruction.com
Year Founded: 1986
Sales Range: $10-24.9 Million
Emp.: 50
Nonresidential Construction
N.A.I.C.S.: 236220
Daniel H. Haley *(Pres)*
Danielle Bruno *(Project Coord)*
Stacy McRitchie *(VP)*

HALEY MIRANDA GROUP
8654 Washington Blvd, Culver City, CA 90232
Tel.: (310) 842-7369 CA
Web Site:
http://www.haleymiranda.com
Year Founded: 1993
Sales Range: $1-9.9 Million
Emp.: 14
Advetising Agency
N.A.I.C.S.: 541810
Jed West *(Pres)*
Tina Hopkins *(Exec VP-Acct Svcs)*
Rob Buscher *(Dir-Creative)*
Donna Landau *(VP-Bus Dev & Client Svcs)*

HALEY OF FARMVILLE, INC.
1906 S Main St, Farmville, VA 23901-2563
Tel.: (434) 694-2062
Web Site:
https://www.haleyoffarmville.net
Year Founded: 1985
Sales Range: $10-24.9 Million
Emp.: 50
New Car Retailer
N.A.I.C.S.: 441110
Darryl Diffee *(Gen Mgr)*
Gene Kitchent *(VP)*
Jerry Flowers *(Gen Mgr)*

HALEY-GREER INC.
2257 C Lombardy Ln, Dallas, TX 75220
Tel.: (972) 556-1177
Web Site:
https://www.haleygreer.com
Year Founded: 1979
Sales Range: $25-49.9 Million
Emp.: 100
Glass & Glazing Work
N.A.I.C.S.: 238150
Donald E. Haley *(CEO)*
Letitia Haley Barker *(Pres)*

HALF PRICE BOOKS RE-CORDS MAGAZINES INC.
5803 E Northwest Hwy, Dallas, TX 75231-7416
Tel.: (214) 360-0833 TX
Web Site:
http://www.halfpricebooks.com
Year Founded: 1972
Sales Range: $100-124.9 Million
Emp.: 1,600
Used Books & Magazines Retail
N.A.I.C.S.: 459210
Sharon Anderson-Wright *(Pres & CEO)*
Jan Cornelius *(Exec VP & Mgr-Ops)*
Kathy Thomas *(Exec VP-Dev & Mktg)*

HALFACRE CONSTRUCTION COMPANY
7015 Professional Pkwy E, Sarasota, FL 34240
Tel.: (941) 907-9099
Web Site:
http://www.halfacreconstruction.com
Year Founded: 1970
Sales Range: $25-49.9 Million
Emp.: 22
Commercial & Institutional Building Construction
N.A.I.C.S.: 236220
Reed Giasson *(VP-Ops)*
Andy Stultz *(VP)*
Chelsea Gruber *(Mgr-Mktg & Bus Dev)*
Rick Milhoan *(Sr Project Mgr-Lakewood Ranch)*
Brian Berges *(Asst Project Mgr-Lakewood Ranch)*
Lindsay Roth *(Mgr-Comm, Mktg & Proposals)*

HALFF ASSOCIATES, INC.
1201 N Bowser Rd, Richardson, TX 75081-2275
Tel.: (214) 346-6200
Web Site: https://halff.com
Engineeering Services
N.A.I.C.S.: 541330

Subsidiaries:

Singhofen & Associates, Inc. (1)
11723 Orpington St Ste 100, Orlando, FL 32817-4620
Tel.: (407) 679-3001
Web Site: http://www.saiengineers.com
Engineeering Services
N.A.I.C.S.: 541330
Pete Singhofen *(Founder)*

HALFORD, NIEMIEC & FREE-MAN, L.L.P.
238 Rockmont Dr, Fort Mill, SC 29708
Tel.: (803) 547-6618
Web Site: http://www.fortmilllaw.com
Legal Firm & Services
N.A.I.C.S.: 541199
Becky Roof *(Office Mgr)*

HALIFAX ELECTRIC MEMBER-SHIP CORP.
208 Whitfield St, Enfield, NC 27823
Tel.: (252) 445-5111
Web Site:
https://www.halifaxemc.com
Rev.: $11,000,000
Emp.: 55
Distribution, Electric Power
N.A.I.C.S.: 221122
Charles H. Guerry *(Exec VP & Gen Mgr)*
Rod Bozard *(Mgr-Fin)*
Wanda Cooke *(Mgr-Fin)*
Brady Martin *(Mgr-Mktg & Economic Dev)*
Leona Padgette *(Mgr-HR & Facilities)*

HALIFAX MEDICAL CENTER

303 N Clyde Morris Blvd, Daytona
Beach, FL 32114   FL
Web Site:
   http://www.halifaxhealth.org
Sales Range: $250-299.9 Million
Emp.: 5,000
Hospital
N.A.I.C.S.: 622110
Jeff Feasel (Pres & CEO)
David Davidson (Gen Counsel)
Lori Delone (CIO)
William Griffin (Dir-Strategic Plng)
Joe Petrock (Exec Dir-Foundation)

HALJOHN INC.

704 E Wonsley Dr, Austin, TX 78753
Tel.: (512) 837-2551
Rev.: $15,800,000
Emp.: 20
Franchiser of Fast-Food Restaurants
N.A.I.C.S.: 722513
Harold A. Leverson (Pres)
Steven Neeley (Dir-Personnel)
Bryna Schulze (Mgr-Ops)

Subsidiaries:

Haljohn-San Antonio, Inc.   (1)
7300 Blanco Rd Ste 302, San Antonio, TX
78216
Tel.: (210) 344-9707
Sales Range: $10-24.9 Million
Emp.: 12
Fast-Food Restaurant, Chain
N.A.I.C.S.: 722513
John V. Bohling (Pres)
Virginia Bohling (VP)

HALL & HOUSE LUMBER CO. INC.

18030 US Hwy 31 N, Westfield, IN
46074
Tel.: (317) 896-2375
Web Site:
   http://www.hallandhouse.com
Year Founded: 1972
Sales Range: $25-49.9 Million
Emp.: 80
Lumber & Other Building Materials
N.A.I.C.S.: 423310

HALL AUTO WORLD INC.

441 Viking Dr, Virginia Beach, VA
23452-7309
Tel.: (757) 431-9930
Web Site: http://www.hallauto.com
Rev.: $21,500,000
Emp.: 23
Automobiles, New & Used
N.A.I.C.S.: 441110
Steven B. Fader (CEO)
Keith McCullers (Gen Mgr-Sls)

HALL AUTOMOTIVE

704 Bluemound Rd, Waukesha, WI
53188
Tel.: (262) 953-4641
Web Site:
   https://www.hallwaukesha.com
Sales Range: $50-74.9 Million
Emp.: 90
Car Dealership
N.A.I.C.S.: 441110
Andrew Hall (Pres)
Dan Soto (Mgr-Hall Automotive Svc)
Jim Herman (Asst Mgr-Parts)
Jerry Schienebeck (Gen Mgr-Sls)
Kent Smith (Mgr-Body Shop)
Mike Delmore (Exec VP & Controller)
Rick Riazi (Mgr-Pre-Owned Sls)
Andy Paszkiewicz (Mgr-Bus)
Brenda Santiago (Mgr-Bus)

Subsidiaries:

Hall Imports   (1)
19809 W Bluemound Rd, Brookfield, WI
53045

Tel.: (262) 782-5300
Web Site:
   http://www.hallcars.com
Rev.: $13,000,000
Emp.: 50
Automobiles, New & Used
N.A.I.C.S.: 441110
Andrew Hall (Pres)
Mike Delmore (Exec VP & Controller)
Charlie Hall (Gen Mgr)
Rick Riazi (Mgr-Pre-Owned Sls)
Jerry Schienebeck (Gen Mgr-Sls)

HALL CAPITAL, LLC

9225 Lake Hefner Pkwy Ste 200,
Oklahoma City, OK 73120
Tel.: (405) 231-2400   OK
Web Site: https://www.hall-capital.com
Holding Company; Private Equity &
Real Estate Investment Services
N.A.I.C.S.: 551112
Fred Hall (Chm & CEO)
Kirkland Hall (Vice Chm & CFO)
Brooks Hall Jr. (Vice Chm & Exec VP)

Subsidiaries:

Hall Capital Partners, LP   (1)
9225 Lake Hefner Pkwy Ste 200, Oklahoma
City, OK 73120
Tel.: (405) 231-2400
Web Site: http://www.hall-capital.com
Privater Equity Firm
N.A.I.C.S.: 523999
Fred J. Hall (Chm & CEO)
Kirkland Hall (Vice Chm & Grp CFO)
John Kobza (Mng Dir & COO)
Maya Lowder (Mng Dir & CFO)
Jonathan Adamson (Mng Dir)
Brian Devening (Mng Dir)
Tim Clark (Mng Dir)
David Holt (Mng Dir-IR)
Kathryn A. Hall (Co-Chm)
Brooks Hall Jr. (Vice Chm & Exec VP)

Joint Venture (Domestic):

JAC Holdings, LLC   (2)
3937 Campus Dr, Pontiac, MI 48341
Tel.: (248) 874-1800
Web Site: http://www.jacproducts.com
Holding Company; Plastic Injection Molding
Products Mfr
N.A.I.C.S.: 551112
Mike Wood (Pres & CEO)
Peter Steffes (CFO)

Subsidiary (Domestic):

JAC Products, Inc.   (3)
3937 Campus Dr, Pontiac, MI 48341
Tel.: (248) 874-1800
Web Site: http://www.jacproducts.com
Plastic Injection Molding Products Mfr
N.A.I.C.S.: 326199
Mike Wood (Pres & CEO)
Stuart McRobbie (COO)
Mike Gallico (VP-HR & Admin)
Gordon Michie (VP-Advanced Product Dev)
Alex Hall (Dir-Product Engrg)
Dennis Kirby (CFO)
Ricardo Neves (Mng Dir-Europe)
Tony Yuan (Mng Dir-China)

Plant (Domestic):

JAC Products, Inc. - JAC Molding
Plant   (4)
225 S Industrial Dr, Saline, MI 48176
Tel.: (734) 944-8844
Plastic Injection Molding Products Mfr
N.A.I.C.S.: 326199

HALL CONTRACTING CORP.

6415 Lakeview Rd, Charlotte, NC
28269-2602
Tel.: (704) 598-0818   KY
Web Site:
   https://www.hallcontracting.com
Year Founded: 1954
Sales Range: $75-99.9 Million
Emp.: 40
Contracting & Construction Services
N.A.I.C.S.: 237110
Kay Michael Hall (Owner & CEO)

HALL CONTRACTING OF KENTUCKY

3800 Crittenden Dr, Louisville, KY
40209
Tel.: (502) 367-6151
Web Site: https://www.hallky.com
Rev.: $24,000,000
Emp.: 250
Underground Utilities Contractor
N.A.I.C.S.: 237110
Stephen Mark Priebe (Pres)
Diane Underhill (Asst Sec & Supvr-Acctg)
Stephen Gerlach (Mgr-Equipment)

HALL FINANCIAL GROUP, LTD.

6801 Gaylord Pkwy Ste 100, Frisco,
TX 75034-8557
Tel.: (972) 377-1100
Web Site:
   http://www.hallfinancial.com
Year Founded: 1968
Sales Range: $25-49.9 Million
Emp.: 1,000
Real Estate Lending, Commercial
Development, Securities Investing,
Software, Oil & Gas, Vineyard & Winery Business Operations
N.A.I.C.S.: 523999
Donald Braun (Pres)
Craig Hall (Founder & Chm)
Mark Depker (Pres-Mgmt Div)
Larry Levey (Pres-Dev Div)
Mike Jaynes (Pres-Hall Structured Fin)
Kim Vincent Butler (Dir-Leasing)
Stephanie Byrd (Gen Counsel)
Travis Jeakins (VP-Dev)
Kymberley Scalia (VP-Mktg)
Larry Harris (VP-Property Mgmt)

Subsidiaries:

Hall Structured Finance   (1)
6801 Gaylord Pkwy Ste 100, Frisco, TX
75034   (100%)
Tel.: (972) 377-1100
Web Site:
   http://www.hallstructuredfinance.com
Sales Range: $75-99.9 Million
Emp.: 50
Real Estate Lending Services
N.A.I.C.S.: 522292
Donald Braun (Chm)
Mike Jaynes (Pres)
Allyson Van Blarcum (VP)
Brett McLeod (VP)

Hall Wines of Napa, L.P.   (1)
401 Saint Helena Hwy S, Saint Helena, CA
94574   (100%)
Tel.: (707) 967-2626
Web Site: http://www.hallwines.com
Sales Range: $25-49.9 Million
Emp.: 200
Vineyards & Wineries
N.A.I.C.S.: 312130
Mike Reynolds (Pres)
Don Munk (Dir-Vineyard Ops)
Steve Leveque (Dir-Winemaking)
Diem Doonan (Dir-Membership)
Kathleen Fidler (Controller)
Emily Harrison (Dir-Mktg)
Jocelyn Hoar (Dir-Hospitality-Saint Helena)
Whitney Jacobson (VP-Investments)

HALL MANAGEMENT COMPANY

441 Viking Dr, Virginia Beach, VA
23452-7309
Tel.: (757) 431-9944
Year Founded: 1971
Sales Range: $10-24.9 Million
Emp.: 65
New Car Whslr
N.A.I.C.S.: 441110
Chris Colbert (Mgr)

HALL NISSAN VIRGINIA BEACH

3757 Bonney Rd, Virginia Beach, VA
23452
Tel.: (757) 431-9944
Web Site:
   https://www.hallnissanofvirginia
   beach.com
Year Founded: 1970
Sales Range: $400-449.9 Million
Emp.: 1,100
New Car Whslr
N.A.I.C.S.: 441110
Nathen Warrior (Dir-IT)

HALL SHEET METAL WORKS, INC.

11 River St, Middleton, MA 01949
Tel.: (978) 739-3800
Web Site:
   https://www.hallsheetmetal.com
Year Founded: 1977
Sales Range: $10-24.9 Million
Emp.: 25
Sheet Metal Work Services
N.A.I.C.S.: 238390
Jeff Hall (Pres)

HALL SIGNS, INC.

4495 W Vernal Pike, Bloomington, IN
47404
Tel.: (812) 332-9355   IN
Web Site: https://www.hallsigns.com
Year Founded: 1949
Sales Range: $50-74.9 Million
Emp.: 65
Traffic Signs Mfr
N.A.I.C.S.: 339950
Larry W. Hall (Pres)

HALL TECHNOLOGIES INC.

6300 Bartmer Industrial Dr, Saint
Louis, MO 63130-2625
Tel.: (314) 725-2600
Web Site:
   https://www.halltechinc.com
Year Founded: 1963
Specialty Chemicals Distr
N.A.I.C.S.: 424690
Jeff Laurent (Pres)
Mark D. Loudenslager (VP-Mktg & Tech)
Chris Sexton (VP-Sls)
Oleg Afanasyev (Mgr-Technical Svc Laboratory)

HALL-IRWIN CORPORATION

301 Centennial Dr, Milliken, CO
80543
Tel.: (970) 587-7200
Web Site: http://www.hall-irwin.com
Year Founded: 1963
Sales Range: $10-24.9 Million
Emp.: 30
Water, Sewer & Utility Lines
N.A.I.C.S.: 237110
Rob Laidig (Mgr-Bus Dev)

HALLADAY MOTORS INC.

2100 Westland Rd, Cheyenne, WY
82001
Tel.: (307) 634-1511
Web Site:
   https://www.halladaymotors.com
Rev.: $25,400,000
Emp.: 85
New Car Dealers
N.A.I.C.S.: 441110
Terese Becker (Mgr-HR)
Richard Heiser (Mgr)
Tim Joannides (Pres)
Jim Casey (VP & Gen Mgr)
Deana Jessok (Office Mgr)
Rusty Lathen (CFO)
Heidi Dardano (Dir-Bus Dev)
Travis Vaughan (Mgr-Bus)

Halladay Motors Inc.—(Continued)

Wael Gomma *(Mgr-Internet Sls)*
Don Rodriguez *(Mgr-Nissan Svc)*
Nick Gartelos *(Mgr-Paint & Collision Center)*
Dennis Struebing *(Mgr-Subaru Parts)*
Mike Mullett Jr. *(Mgr-Nissan Sls)*

HALLAMORE CORPORATION

795 Plymouth St, Holbrook, MA 02343-1936
Tel.: (781) 767-2000   MA
Web Site: https://www.hallamore.com
Rigging, Heavy Hauling, Crane Rental, Specialty Contracting
N.A.I.C.S.: 484121
Sheldon Thompson *(CFO)*
Gary Spencer *(Gen Mgr)*
Paul Gaboury *(Reg Mgr)*
Philip O'Brien *(Dir-Safety)*

Subsidiaries:

B.T. Equipment Co., Inc.   (1)
115 Lydia Ann Rd, Smithfield, RI 02917-1943   **(100%)**
Tel.: (401) 232-1995
Web Site: http://www.hallamore.com
Sales Range: $25-49.9 Million
Emp.: 50
Sales & Rentals of Heavy Equipment
N.A.I.C.S.: 532412

HALLE ENTERPRISES INC.

2900 Linden Ln Ste 300, Silver Spring, MD 20910
Tel.: (301) 495-1520
Web Site:
   http://www.hallecompanies.com
Rev.: $18,200,000
Emp.: 50
Residential Construction
N.A.I.C.S.: 236115
Warren E. Halle *(Pres)*
Scott Supple *(Mgr-Fleet)*

HALLIDIE MACHINE TOOL SALES, INC.

2002 W Valley Hwy Ste 400, Auburn, WA 98002
Tel.: (253) 939-9020   WA
Web Site: http://www.hallidie.com
Year Founded: 1900
Machine Tools & Accessories Distr
N.A.I.C.S.: 423830
Scott Hanson *(Pres)*

HALLMAN & LORBER ASSOCIATES, INC.

70 E Sunrise Hwy Ste 411, Valley Stream, NY 11581-1233
Tel.: (516) 872-1000   NY
Web Site: http://www.nfp.com
Sales Range: $150-199.9 Million
Emp.: 12
Insurance Services
N.A.I.C.S.: 524298

HALLMAN LINDSAY PAINTS INC.

1717 N Bristol St, Sun Prairie, WI 53590
Tel.: (608) 834-8844
Web Site:
   http://www.hallmanlindsay.com
Sales Range: $10-24.9 Million
Emp.: 100
Paints & Allied Products Mfr
N.A.I.C.S.: 325510
Tim Mielcarek *(Pres)*
Linda Meyers *(Comptroller)*
Randy Mitchell *(Mgr-Admin Support)*
Mark Kowald *(Area Mgr-Sls)*

HALLMAN WOOD PRODUCTS INC.

127 Lowr Harmony Rd, Eatonton, GA 31024
Tel.: (706) 485-6951
Web Site:
   http://www.hallmanwood.com
Sales Range: $10-24.9 Million
Emp.: 30
Builders' Hardware
N.A.I.C.S.: 444140
John H. Hallman *(Pres)*

HALLMARK AVIATION SERVICES LP

5757 W Century Blvd Ste 860, Los Angeles, CA 90045
Tel.: (310) 215-0701
Web Site: https://www.hallmark-aviation.com
Year Founded: 1989
Sales Range: $10-24.9 Million
Emp.: 500
Airport Customer Service, Flight Operations & Training Services
N.A.I.C.S.: 561320
Hosi Kapadia *(VP-Mktg)*

HALLMARK BUILDING SUPPLIES, INC.

2120 Pewaukee Rd Ste 100, Waukesha, WI 53188
Tel.: (800) 642-2246
Web Site: http://www.hllmark.com
Year Founded: 1974
Sales Range: $10-24.9 Million
Building Materials Distr
N.A.I.C.S.: 444180
O. Joseph Balthazor *(Founder, Pres & CEO)*
Katie Sadorf *(VP-Mktg)*
Bobby Staats *(VP-Sls)*

HALLMARK CARDS, INC.

2501 McGee Trafficway MD 339, Kansas City, MO 64108
Tel.: (816) 274-5111   MO
Web Site: https://www.hallmark.com
Year Founded: 1910
Sales Range: $1-4.9 Billion
Emp.: 20,000
Greeting Card Publishers
N.A.I.C.S.: 513191
Donald J. Hall Jr. *(Chm)*
Brian E. Gardner *(Gen Counsel & Exec VP)*
David E. Hall *(Vice Chm)*
Evon L. Jones *(CIO & Sr VP-Tech & Bus Enablement)*
James Shay *(CFO & Exec VP)*
Molly Biwer *(Sr VP-Pub Affairs & Comm)*
Matt Dokman *(Dir-Info Security)*
Beth Sweetman *(Sr VP-HR)*
Martin Stallbaumer *(Mgr-Corp Svcs-Fleet & Relocation-Shawnee)*
Amy McAnarney *(VP & Gen Mgr)*

Subsidiaries:

Crayola LLC   (1)
1100 Church Ln, Easton, PA 18040   **(100%)**
Tel.: (610) 253-6271
Web Site: http://www.crayola.com
Sales Range: $75-99.9 Million
Emp.: 1,200
Toys & Artist Materials Mfr
N.A.I.C.S.: 339940
Chuck Linden *(Exec VP-Global Expansion)*
Connie Legath *(Acct Mgr)*
David Zapotocky *(Supvr-SAP Data & Reporting)*
Lisa Troxell *(Mgr-Payroll)*
Nicole Williams *(Mgr-Creative Design)*
Smith Holland *(Pres & CEO)*
Pete Ruggiero *(Exec VP-Global Ops & Info Solutions)*
Orville Trout *(Sr VP-HR, Corp Affairs & Admin)*
Melanie Boulden *(Executives)*

Branch (Non-US):

Crayola Canada   (2)
15 Mary St West, PO Box 120, Lindsay, K9V 4R8, ON, Canada   **(100%)**
Tel.: (705) 324-6105
Web Site: https://www.crayola.ca
Sales Range: $25-49.9 Million
Emp.: 215
Art Materials & Childrens Crafts Distr
N.A.I.C.S.: 339940

Crown Center Redevelopment Corp   (1)
2405 Grand Blvd Ste 200, Kansas City, MO 64108-2519   **(100%)**
Tel.: (816) 274-8444
Web Site: http://www.crowncenter.com
Sales Range: $10-24.9 Million
Emp.: 5,000
Develop & Manage Shopping & Office Complex
N.A.I.C.S.: 561110
Stacey Paine *(Pres)*
Brian Eskijian *(Controller)*
Rick Schroeder *(Project Mgr)*

Crown Media Holdings, Inc.   (1)
12700 Ventura Blvd Ste 200, Studio City, CA 91604   **(100%)**
Tel.: (818) 755-2400
Rev.: $478,734,000
Assets: $1,088,137,000
Liabilities: $508,574,000
Net Worth: $579,563,000
Earnings: $86,083,000
Emp.: 236
Fiscal Year-end: 12/31/2015
Holding Company; Cable & Other Pay Television Programming & Services
N.A.I.C.S.: 551112
Donald J. Hall Jr. *(Co-Chm)*
Brian E. Gardner *(Sec)*
Deanne R. Stedem *(Gen Counsel & Exec VP-Bus Affairs)*
Michelle Vicary *(Exec VP-Programming & Network Publicity)*
Herbert A. Granath *(Co-Chm)*
Susanne Smith McAvoy *(Exec VP-Mktg, Creative & Comm)*
Kristen Roberts *(Exec VP-Pricing, Plng & Revenue Mgmt)*
Mark Kern *(Sr VP-Corp Comm & Media Rels)*
Wonya Y. Lucas *(Pres & CEO)*

Subsidiary (Domestic):

Crown Media United States LLC   (2)
12700 Ventura Blvd Ste 200, Studio City, CA 91604
Tel.: (818) 755-2400
Sales Range: $25-49.9 Million
Emp.: 300
Cable & Other Pay Television Programming & Services
N.A.I.C.S.: 516210
Laura J. Lee *(VP-Network Distr & Svc-Hallmark Channel)*

DaySpring Cards, Inc.   (1)
21154 Hwy 16 E, Siloam Springs, AR 72761
Tel.: (479) 524-9301
Web Site: http://www.dayspring.com
Greeting Card Mfr
N.A.I.C.S.: 513191

Plant (Domestic):

Hallmark Canada, Inc.   (1)
501 Consumers Road, North York, M2J 5E2, ON, Canada   **(100%)**
Tel.: (416) 492-1300
Web Site: http://www.hallmark.com
Sales Range: $25-49.9 Million
Emp.: 800
Greeting Cards & Party Goods Mfr
N.A.I.C.S.: 323111

Hallmark Cards Australia Ltd.   (1)
10 Caribbean Dr, Scoresby, 3179, VIC, Australia   **(100%)**
Tel.: (61) 397304444
Sales Range: $25-49.9 Million
Emp.: 300
Greeting Cards & Party Goods Mfr
N.A.I.C.S.: 323111

Hallmark Cards Belgium NV   (1)
Ruiterijschool 5, 2930, Brasschaat, Belgium   **(100%)**

Tel.: (32) 36807251
Web Site: http://nl.hallmark.be
Sales Range: $10-24.9 Million
Emp.: 10
Greeting Card Publishers
N.A.I.C.S.: 513191
Christa Alders *(Dir Gen)*

Hallmark Cards Nederland, B.V.   (1)
Rietbaan 48, 2908 LP, Capelle aan den IJssel, Netherlands   **(100%)**
Tel.: (31) 104596566
Web Site: http://www.hallmark.nl
Sales Range: $25-49.9 Million
Emp.: 260
Mfr of Greeting Cards
N.A.I.C.S.: 323111

Hallmark Cards New Zealand Ltd.   (1)
Level 1 12 Hugo Johnston Drive, Penrose, Auckland, 1005, New Zealand
Tel.: (64) 9 5712110
Greeting Card Mfr
N.A.I.C.S.: 513191

Hallmark Cards, Inc. - Center Fixture Operations   (1)
1010 Logansport St, Center, TX 75935
Tel.: (936) 598-5644
Sales Range: $10-24.9 Million
Emp.: 80
Fixtures Mfr
N.A.I.C.S.: 332919

Hallmark Cards, Inc. - Enfield   (1)
PO Box 2100, Enfield, CT 06083-2100   **(100%)**
Tel.: (860) 741-9400
Web Site: http://www.hallmark.com
Sales Range: $50-74.9 Million
Emp.: 900
Distribution Center For Cards
N.A.I.C.S.: 424120

Hallmark Cards, Inc. - Lawrence Production Center   (1)
101 McDonald Dr, Lawrence, KS 66044-0099
Tel.: (785) 813-0300
Web Site:
   http://www.corporate.hallmark.com
Sales Range: $10-24.9 Million
Emp.: 800
Greeting Cards & Gift Articles Mfr
N.A.I.C.S.: 513191

Hallmark Cards, Inc. - Leavenworth Production Center   (1)
450 Eisenhower Rd, Leavenworth, KS 66048-5018
Tel.: (913) 727-6692
Web Site: http://www.hallmark.com
Sales Range: $25-49.9 Million
Emp.: 400
Card Services
N.A.I.C.S.: 513191

Hallmark Cards, Inc. - Liberty Distribution Center   (1)
2101 N Lightburne St, Liberty, MO 64068-9759
Tel.: (816) 792-7382
Greeting Card Sales & Mfr
N.A.I.C.S.: 322230

Hallmark International   (1)
2501 Mcgee, Kansas City, MO 64108
Tel.: (816) 274-5111
Web Site: http://www.hallmark.com
Sales Range: $300-349.9 Million
Emp.: 4,000
Gold & Silver Engraving Services
N.A.I.C.S.: 339910
Don Hall Jr. *(Pres)*

Hallmark Puerto Rico Inc.   (1)
43 Calle Diana Ste 2, Guaynabo, PR 00969   **(100%)**
Tel.: (787) 783-2300
Web Site: http://www.hallmark.com
Sales Range: $10-24.9 Million
Emp.: 23
Greeting Card Mfr
N.A.I.C.S.: 424120
Jorge Gonzalez *(Mgr-Sls & Svc)*

Halls Merchandising Inc.   (1)
2450 Grand Blvd Ste 3303, Kansas City, MO 64108-2509   **(100%)**

Tel.: (816) 274-8111
Web Site: http://www.hallskc.com
Sales Range: $25-49.9 Million
Emp.: 328
Specialty Retailing
N.A.I.C.S.: 455110
Kelly Cole (CEO)

La Carterie Hallmark (1)
7 Rue du Gabian, 98000, Monaco, 98000,
Monaco
Tel.: (377) 97778100
Web Site: http://www.hallmark.mc
Sales Range: $10-24.9 Million
Emp.: 2
Greeting Card, Stationery & Related Product Mfr
N.A.I.C.S.: 322230

Litho-Krome Company (1)
5700 Old Brim Dr, Midland, GA
31820 (100%)
Tel.: (706) 225-6600
Web Site: http://www.lithokrome.com
Sales Range: $10-24.9 Million
Emp.: 130
Printing Services
N.A.I.C.S.: 323111

Picture People Inc. (1)
1800 10th St Ste 300, Plano, TX
75074-8010 (100%)
Tel.: (800) 249-4083
Web Site: http://www.picturepeople.com
Sales Range: $10-24.9 Million
Emp.: 80
Photographic Studios
N.A.I.C.S.: 541921
Steve Putervaugh (VP)
Kurt Kendall (VP)

Sunrise Greetings
2501 McGee Trafficway, Kansas City, MO
64141 (100%)
Web Site: http://www.sunrisegreetings.com
Sales Range: $25-49.9 Million
Emp.: 150
Greeting Cards
N.A.I.C.S.: 513191

Topeka Production Center (1)
240 Madison St, Topeka, KS
66607-1147 (100%)
Tel.: (785) 233-3241
Sales Range: $25-49.9 Million
Emp.: 700
Publisher of Greeting Cards
N.A.I.C.S.: 322230

Westin Crown Center Hotel (1)
1 E Pershing Rd, Kansas City, MO 64108-
2503
Tel.: (816) 474-4400
Web Site: http://www.westin.com
Sales Range: $25-49.9 Million
Emp.: 433
Hotel & Motel Management
N.A.I.C.S.: 561110
Steve Shalit (Gen Mgr)

William E. Coutts Co., Ltd. (1)
501 Consumers Rd, Toronto, M2J 5E2, ON,
Canada (100%)
Tel.: (416) 492-1300
Web Site: http://www.hallmark.com
Sales Range: $25-49.9 Million
Emp.: 500
Greeting Cards
N.A.I.C.S.: 323111

HALLMARK DEVELOPMENT OF FLORIDA, INC.
4500 140th Ave N Ste 201, Clearwater, FL 33762
Tel.: (727) 539-7002
Web Site:
https://www.hallmarkdevelopment.net
Sales Range: $1-9.9 Million
Emp.: 8
Land Subdivision; Real Estate Management & Investment
N.A.I.C.S.: 237210
Steven Englehardt (Pres)
Paul Engelhardt (VP)

HALLMARK JEEP INC.

2431 Galaton Rd N, Madison, TN
37115
Tel.: (615) 859-3200
Web Site:
http://www.hallmarkauto.com
Sales Range: $10-24.9 Million
Emp.: 120
Automobiles, New & Used
N.A.I.C.S.: 441110
Rocky Hendrickson (Pres)

HALLMARK PARTNERS INC.
6675 Corporate Center Pkwy, Jacksonville, FL 32216
Tel.: (904) 363-9002
Web Site:
http://www.hallmarkpartners.com
Year Founded: 1993
Sales Range: $1-9.9 Million
Emp.: 25
Real Estate Development, Brokerage & Management
N.A.I.C.S.: 237210
Alex Coley (Principal)
Bryan Weber (Principal)
Jeffrey Conn (Co-Founder & Principal)
Coen V. Purvis (Sr VP-Dev)
Dave Auchter (COO & Exec VP)
Kristilee Adler (Dir-Mktg)
Patrick Thornton (Principal)
Keith Goldfaden (Principal)
Christian Harden (Principal)
Bryan J. Mickler (VP-Brokerage)
Carmen Mantay (VP-Brokerage & Dir-Intl)
Betsy W. Reichert (Sr VP-Property Mgmt)
Dane C. Hurst (Dir-Property Mgmt)
Vicki D. Barrett (Mgr-Property)
Ann Wilson (Controller)
Amie Sword (Dir-Property Acctg)
Daniel Burkhardt (VP-Brokerage)
Joe Scavetto (VP-Brokerage)
Kelsey Dalton (Coord-Office)

HALLMARK SYSTEMS INC.
Unit C 1002 Landfall Way, Johns Island, SC 29455-6332
Tel.: (770) 933-5500 GA
Year Founded: 1995
Sales Range: $10-24.9 Million
Emp.: 300
Hospital Management Services
N.A.I.C.S.: 561110

HALLMARK VOLKSWAGEN MITSUBISHI
2431 Gallatin Rd N, Madison, TN
37115
Tel.: (615) 859-3200
Web Site: http://www.hallmarkvw.com
Year Founded: 1989
Sales Range: $10-24.9 Million
Emp.: 120
Car Whslr
N.A.I.C.S.: 441110
Rocky Hendrickson (Pres)
Glenn Krueger (Gen Mgr)
Rob Salyers (Mgr-Sls)

HALLOCK AGENCY
2445 NW Irving St, Portland, OR
97210
Tel.: (503) 224-1711
Year Founded: 1959
Sales Range: Less than $1 Million
Emp.: 6
N.A.I.C.S.: 541810
Jackie Hallock (Pres & Dir-Creative)
Tracy Holstad (Dir-Art)
Jillian Forni (Dir-Client Svcs)
Suzanne Dumas (Dir-Ops)
Tiger Branch (CEO & Sr Writer)

HALLS DRIVE INS INC.

216 US Hwy 930 W, New Haven, IN
46774
Tel.: (260) 493-3522 IN
Web Site: http://www.donhalls.com
Year Founded: 1946
Sales Range: $10-24.9 Million
Emp.: 50
American Restaurant
N.A.I.C.S.: 722511
Jeff Black (Controller)

HALLS WAREHOUSE CORP.
501 Kentile Rd, South Plainfield, NJ
07080
Tel.: (908) 756-6242
Web Site:
http://www.hallswarehouse.com
Rev.: $28,868,676
Emp.: 70
General Warehousing
N.A.I.C.S.: 493110
Dan Channel (Mgr-Ops Trng)
Tom Brennan (COO)
Warren Tamaroff (CFO)
Marty Helfer (Coord-EDI)
Patricia Weiss (Mgr-Admin)
Patrick Sahradnik (Mgr-Pur & Resource Energy)
Michael Weinstein (VP-Acctg & Fin)
Salvatore LaBruno (Dir-Sls)
Wil Biscardi (Dir-IS)

HALLSTROM CONSTRUCTION INC.
101 E Long Ave, Du Bois, PA 15801
Tel.: (814) 371-4334
Web Site:
https://www.hallstromconstruction.com
Rev.: $15,000,000
Emp.: 60
Construction Services
N.A.I.C.S.: 236210
Robert E. Grieve (Pres)
Julianne Graham (CFO)
Brian R. Ganoe (Project Mgr)
Christian P. Satterlee (Project Mgr)

HALLUM INC.
114 W Hunt Ave, Flagstaff, AZ 86001-
3041
Tel.: (928) 774-0643 AZ
Year Founded: 1972
Sales Range: $10-24.9 Million
Emp.: 88
Petroleum Products Mfr
N.A.I.C.S.: 457120
Steve Hallum (Pres)

HALLWOOD GROUP, LLC
3710 Rawlins Ste 1500, Dallas, TX
75219
Tel.: (214) 528-5588 DE
Web Site: http://www.hallwood.com
Year Founded: 1981
Sales Range: $125-149.9 Million
Emp.: 439
Holding Company
N.A.I.C.S.: 551112
Anthony Joseph Gumbiner (Chm & CEO)
Joseph Koenig (Treas)
Richard Kelley (CFO)
William H. Marble (Chief Engrg Officer)
Gert Lessing (Pres/CEO-Leasing)
Celine Gumbiner Jacobson (Mng Dir)
Kelechi Ojukwu (COO)
Louis Castro (CFO)
Richard Reavley (Founder & CEO)
Russell Meduna (Pres)
Steve Davies (CTO)
William L. Guzzetti (Pres)

Subsidiaries:

Brookwood Companies Inc. (1)

485 Madison Ave 5 Fl, New York, NY
10022 (100%)
Tel.: (212) 551-0100
Web Site: http://www.brookwoodcos.com
Sales Range: $25-49.9 Million
Emp.: 36
Develops, Designs & Finishes Technically Oriented Woven Nylon Textiles; Military & Industrial Coating Processes
N.A.I.C.S.: 314999
Jeff Harris (Exec VP-Mktg)
Frank Montie (CEO)

Subsidiary (Domestic):

Kenyon Industries, Inc. (2)
36 Sherman Ave, Kenyon, RI
02836 (100%)
Tel.: (401) 364-3400
Web Site: http://www.brookwoodcos.com
Sales Range: $1-9.9 Million
Woven Fabrics Mfr
N.A.I.C.S.: 313310

HALMOS CAPITAL PARTNERS
362 9th Ave Ste 908, New York, NY
10001
Tel.: (212) 470-8049
Web Site:
https://www.halmoscapital.com
Privater Equity Firm
N.A.I.C.S.: 523999
Andrew Cohan (Founder & Partner)

Subsidiaries:

Thermal Concepts, LLC (1)
2201 College Ave, Davie, FL 33317
Tel.: (954) 472-4465
Web Site: https://thermalconcepts.com
Heating, Ventilation & Air-Conditioning Services
N.A.I.C.S.: 238220
Larry Maurer (Founder & CEO)

Subsidiary (Domestic):

Irvine Mechanical, Inc. (2)
1500 N Orange Blossom Trl, Orlando, FL
32804
Tel.: (407) 839-3630
Sales Range: $1-9.9 Million
Emp.: 26
Plumbing, Heating & Air-Conditioning Contractors
N.A.I.C.S.: 238220
Robert Irvine (Pres)

HALO ELECTRONICS INC.
2880 Lakeside Dr Ste 116, Santa
Clara, CA 95052
Tel.: (650) 903-3800 CA
Web Site:
http://www.haloelectronics.com
Year Founded: 1991
Sales Range: $10-24.9 Million
Emp.: 15
Electromagnetic Components Mfr
N.A.I.C.S.: 423690
James Heaton (Pres)
Jeff Heaton (VP)

HALO TECHNOLOGY HOLDINGS, INC.
1 Landmark Sq 5th Fl, Stamford, CT
06901
Tel.: (203) 391-7985
Web Site:
http://www.haloholdings.com
Sales Range: $25-49.9 Million
Emp.: 254
Holding Company
N.A.I.C.S.: 551112
Rodney A. Bienvenu Jr. (CEO & Mng Partner)

Subsidiaries:

Process Software, LLC (1)
959 Concord St, Framingham, MA
01701-4682 (100%)
Tel.: (508) 879-6994
Web Site: http://www.process.com

Halo Technology Holdings, Inc.—(Continued)
Sales Range: $10-24.9 Million
Emp.: 15
Supplier of Infrastructure Software Solutions to Mission Critical Environments
N.A.I.C.S.: 513210
Michael McCarthy *(VP-Global Sls)*
Lauren Maschio *(Sr VP-Mktg)*

HALOCARBON PRODUCTS CORPORATION
6525 The Corners Pkwy, Peachtree Corners, GA 30092
Tel.: (470) 419-6364   NJ
Web Site:
  https://www.halocarbon.com
Year Founded: 1950
Sales Range: $100-124.9 Million
Emp.: 150
Fluorochemicals, Inert Lubricants & Inhalation Anesthetics Mfr
N.A.I.C.S.: 325998
Ronald M. Epstein *(Dir-Sls)*
David Bacon *(CEO)*
H. Carl Walther *(Mgr-Technical Svcs)*

Subsidiaries:

Halocarbon Laboratories   (1)
887 Kinderkamack Rd, River Edge, NJ 07661-0661
Tel.: (201) 262-8899
Web Site: http://www.halocarbon.com
Sales Range: $10-24.9 Million
Emp.: 12
Mfr of Fluorinated Anesthetics
N.A.I.C.S.: 325199
Ron Epstein *(Dir-Medical Mktg)*

HALOSOURCE CORP.
1725 220th St SE Ste 103, Bothell, WA 98021
Tel.: (425) 881-6464
Web Site: http://www.halosource.com
Water Purification Technologies Developer, Mfr & Whslr
N.A.I.C.S.: 333310
James Allan Thompson *(CEO)*

Subsidiaries:

HaloSource, Inc.   (1)
1725 220th St SE Ste 103, Bothell, WA 98021
Tel.: (425) 881-6464
Web Site: http://www.halosource.com
Rev.: $1,969,000
Assets: $4,994,000
Liabilities: $3,853,000
Net Worth: $1,141,000
Earnings: ($5,719,000)
Emp.: 51
Fiscal Year-end: 12/31/2017
Water Purification Technologies Developer, Mfr & Whslr
N.A.I.C.S.: 333310
Jeffrey F. Williams *(Co-Founder)*
Timothy J. Joyce *(Mng Dir-Americas & VP)*
Jeanine Willis *(Dir-HR)*
Erik Baserman *(CTO & Sr VP)*
Robyn Adams *(Gen Counsel)*
Jason Zhao *(Mng Dir-Asia Pacific & VP)*

Subsidiary (Non-US):

HaloSource Technologies Pvt. Ltd.   (2)
Survey No 11 Devanahalli Rd off Old Madras Rd, Virgonagar Post, Bengaluru, 560 049, India   (100%)
Tel.: (91) 8028472828
Web Site: http://www.halosource.com
Water Purification Technologies
N.A.I.C.S.: 312112
Tamal Chaudhuri *(Gen Mgr)*

HaloSource Water Purification Technology (Shanghai) Co. Ltd.   (2)
Building No 3 No 288 Yuegong Rd, Caojing Jinshan District, Shanghai, 201507, China   (100%)
Tel.: (86) 2167256200
Web Site: http://www.halosource.com
Antimicrobial & Water Purification Technologies

N.A.I.C.S.: 312112

HALPERN ENTERPRISES, INC.
5269 Buford Hwy, Atlanta, GA 30340
Tel.: (770) 451-0318
Web Site: http://www.halpern-online.com
Sales Range: $25-49.9 Million
Emp.: 25
Shopping Center Investment, Management & Leasing
N.A.I.C.S.: 531390
C. Lisa Loften *(CFO)*
Tommy Tillman *(Mgr-Construction)*
Carolyn H. Oppenheimer *(Exec VP)*
John W. Brozovic *(Reg Dir-Leasing)*
Steve A. West *(VP-Dev)*
Glenn S. Caracappa *(VP-Ops)*
Daniel F. Gagne *(Reg Dir-Leasing)*
Jack N. Halpern *(Chm)*
Bill Brown *(Pres)*
Marc Kirchhoff *(VP-Build to Suit)*
Brad Oppenheimer *(Mng Partner)*
Charles N. Worthen *(Partner)*
Henry Pittman *(Mng Partner)*
Jimmy Cushman *(Mgr-Property)*
Kendall Ridley *(Dir-Mktg)*
Mary Hood *(Dir-Lease Admin)*
Mark McDermott *(Mgr-Property)*
Roger LeVine *(Controller)*

HALPERN IMPORT COMPANY INC.
2890 Amwiler Rd, Atlanta, GA 30360
Tel.: (770) 840-0444
Web Site:
  https://www.halpernimport.com
Rev.: $12,000,000
Emp.: 15
Lighters, Cigarette & Cigar
N.A.I.C.S.: 424990
Jay Halpern *(Pres)*

HALPERN'S STEAK & SEAFOOD CO.
4685 Welcome All Rd, Atlanta, GA 30349
Tel.: (404) 767-9229
Web Site: https://www.halperns.com
Year Founded: 2005
Rev.: $158,000,000
Emp.: 320
Full-Service Restaurants
N.A.I.C.S.: 722511
Howard I. Halpern *(Chm)*
Kirk Halpern *(CEO)*
Ray Hicks *(Pres & COO)*
Ray Farmer *(Exec VP)*
Jody Hicks *(VP)*

HALQUIST STONE COMPANY, INC.
N51W23563 Lisbon Rd N 51 W, Sussex, WI 53089
Tel.: (262) 246-9000   WI
Web Site:
  http://www.halquiststone.com
Year Founded: 1929
Sales Range: $1-9.9 Million
Emp.: 80
Crushed & Broken Limestone Mining & Quarrying
N.A.I.C.S.: 212312
Thomas Halquist *(Owner)*

HALREC INC.
4202 Stevens Creek Blvd, San Jose, CA 95129
Tel.: (408) 984-1234
Web Site: http://www.sctoyota.com
Rev.: $150,000,000
Emp.: 250
New & Used Car Dealers
N.A.I.C.S.: 441110
Harold Cornelius *(Chm)*

HALRON LUBRICANTS INC.
1618 State St, Green Bay, WI 54304
Tel.: (920) 436-4000   WI
Web Site: https://www.halron.com
Year Founded: 1927
Lubricants Products & Services Distr
N.A.I.C.S.: 424720
Kent Klein *(Controller)*
Glen Steinfeldt *(Mgr-Environmental Svcs)*
Kathy Diedrick *(Mgr-Inventory)*
Keith Van Pay *(Mgr-IT)*

HALSTAD ELEVATOR COMPANY
Hwy 75 N, Halstad, MN 56548
Tel.: (218) 456-2135
Web Site:
  http://www.halstadelevator.com
Sales Range: $10-24.9 Million
Emp.: 30
Grains
N.A.I.C.S.: 424510
Robin Stene *(Gen Mgr)*

HALSTEAD PROPERTY, LLC.
499 Park Ave, New York, NY 10022
Tel.: (212) 734-0010
Web Site: http://www.halstead.com
Year Founded: 1984
Sales Range: $10-24.9 Million
Emp.: 90
Real Estate Agents & Brokers
N.A.I.C.S.: 531210
Edward E. Saunders *(Exec Dir-Ops & Dir-Sls-Darien)*
Eugene Cordano *(VP & Exec Dir-Sls-New Jersey)*
Fritz Frigan *(Exec Dir-Sls & Leasing East Side)*
Gerald Makowski *(Exec VP-Mktg)*
Gregory J. Heym *(Exec VP)*
John DiCenzo *(Exec Dir-Sls-Westport & Wilton)*
John Goldman *(Mng Dir-Comml Div)*
John N. Wollberg *(Mng Dir & Exec VP)*
Matthew J. Leone *(Chief Brand & Mktg Officer)*
Michael A. Goldenberg *(Exec Dir-Sls-West Side)*
Richard J. Grossman *(Pres)*
Robyn Kammerer *(Exec Dir-Sls-Darien & Rowayton)*
Sharon Daley Maasdorp *(Exec Dir-Sls-New Canaan)*
Charlotte Felt *(Exec Dir-Sls-Darien & Rowayton)*
Clark P. Halstead *(Founder)*
James Cahill *(Chief IT Officer & Exec VP)*
Trish Martin *(Mng Dir-Sls-Brooklyn)*
Vincent D'Agostino *(Exec VP & Dir-Web Engrg)*
Diane M. Ramirez *(Chm & CEO)*
Gus Perry *(Exec Dir-Sls-Upper Manhattan & Riverdale)*
Joann P. Erb *(Exec Dir-Sls-Greenwich)*
Kimberly Barkoff *(Exec Dir-Global Svcs)*
Nancy Hardy *(Dir-Sls-Southampton)*
Sandy Wilson *(Exec Dir-Sls)*
Stephen G. Kliegerman *(Pres-Dev Mktg)*
Sara Rotter *(Exec Dir-Sls-Downtown)*
Robert Whalen *(Dir-Sls-Long Island City)*
Maya Kriet *(Dir-Comm)*
Itzy Garay *(Exec Dir-Sls-Park Avenue)*
Alan J. Kersner *(COO, Treas & Exec VP)*
Judy Caplan *(Sr VP-HR)*
Juliet Clapp *(Exec Dir-Sls-West Side)*

Subsidiaries:

Halstead Brooklyn, LLC   (1)
122 Montague St, Brooklyn, NY 11201
Tel.: (718) 613-2000
Web Site: http://www.halstead.com
Emp.: 25
Real Estate Services
N.A.I.C.S.: 531210
Tricia Martin *(Mng Dir-Sls)*

Halstead East Hampton, LLC   (1)
2 Newtown Lane, East Hampton, NY 11937
Tel.: (631) 324-6100
Web Site: http://www.halstead.com
Emp.: 30
Real Estate Services
N.A.I.C.S.: 531210
Philip O'Connell *(Mng Dir)*

Halstead Property Connecticut, LLC   (1)
671 Boston Post Rd, Darien, CT 06820
Tel.: (203) 655-1418
Web Site: http://www.halstead.com
Real Estate Services
N.A.I.C.S.: 531210
Edward E. Saunders *(Exec Dir-Ops)*
Tammy Felenstein *(Exec Dir-Sls)*
Diane Ramirez *(CEO)*

Halstead Property Hudson Valley, LLC   (1)
526 Warren St, Hudson, NY 12534
Tel.: (518) 828-0181
Web Site: http://www.halstead.com
Real Estate Services
N.A.I.C.S.: 531210
Nancy Feketto *(Mng Dir)*

Halstead Property New Jersey, LLC   (1)
200 Washington St, Hoboken, NJ 07030
Tel.: (201) 478-6700
Web Site: http://www.halstead.com
Emp.: 35
Real Estate Services
N.A.I.C.S.: 531210
Eugene Cordano *(VP & Exec Dir-Sls)*

Halstead Property Riverdale, LLC   (1)
3531 Johnson Ave, Riverdale, NY 10463
Tel.: (718) 787-1700
Real Estate Services
N.A.I.C.S.: 531210

Terra Development Marketing, LLC   (1)
445 Park Ave 10th Fl, New York, NY 10022
Tel.: (212) 253-9300
Web Site: http://www.hpdmny.com
Emp.: 30
Real Estate Services
N.A.I.C.S.: 531210
Stephen Kliegerman *(Pres-Dev)*

HALTOM'S JEWELERS INC.
317 Main St, Fort Worth, TX 76102
Tel.: (817) 336-4051   TX
Web Site: https://www.haltoms.com
Year Founded: 1983
Sales Range: $10-24.9 Million
Emp.: 45
Jewelry Stores
N.A.I.C.S.: 458310
Arna Posey *(Mgr)*

HALUS POWER SYSTEMS
2539 Grant Ave, San Leandro, CA 94579
Tel.: (510) 278-2212
Web Site: http://www.halus.com
Year Founded: 2000
Sales Range: $1-9.9 Million
Emp.: 10
Commercial Scale Wind Turbines ReMfr
N.A.I.C.S.: 333611
Louis A. Rigaud *(Founder & Gen Dir)*
Lindsay Kendall *(Dir-Engrg)*
Kenneth Fries *(Mgr-Technical Svcs)*

HALVIK CORP.

1600 Spring Hill Rd Ste 240, Vienna, VA 22182
Tel.: (703) 592-4444
Web Site: https://www.halvik.com
Year Founded: 2007
Sales Range: $75-99.9 Million
Emp.: 41
Information Technology Support Services
N.A.I.C.S.: 541512
Saju Varghese (*Sr VP-Federal Civilian & Health programs*)
Madhavi Bathula (*CEO*)
Vijay Bathula (*Pres*)
Peter Santighian (*Sr VP-Defense/Intel & Natl Security*)

HALVORSEN HOLDINGS LLC
851 S Federal Hwy Ste 201, Boca Raton, FL 33432
Tel.: (561) 367-9200
Web Site:
  http://www.halvorsenholdings.com
Emp.: 8
Retail Developer & Lessor
N.A.I.C.S.: 237210
Jeffrey T. Halvorsen (*Pres & CEO*)

HALYARD CAPITAL MANAGEMENT, LLC
140 E 45th St 37th Fl, New York, NY 10017
Tel.: (212) 554-2121   DE
Web Site: http://www.halyard.com
Sales Range: $25-49.9 Million
Emp.: 7
Privater Equity Firm
N.A.I.C.S.: 523999
Bruce A. Eatroff (*Founder & Partner*)
Jonathan P. Barnes (*Partner*)
Brendyn T. Grimaldi (*Principal*)
Sarah Kim (*Mng Dir*)
Robert B. Nolan Jr. (*Mng Partner*)

Subsidiaries:

Digital Forest, Inc.   (1)
12101 Tukwila International Blvd, Seattle, WA 98168
Tel.: (206) 838-1630
Web Site: http://digital.forest.net
Emp.: 30
Telephone Communications Custom Computer Programing
N.A.I.C.S.: 517810
Mark Ashida (*CEO*)

HAMAR-QUANDT CO. INC.
W7400 US Hwy 2, Quinnesec, MI 49876
Tel.: (906) 774-8882   MI
Web Site: http://www.41lumber.com
Year Founded: 1925
Sales Range: $10-24.9 Million
Emp.: 60
Mfr & Retailer of Lumber Services
N.A.I.C.S.: 423310
Stephen M. Quandt (*Pres*)
Al Butkovich (*Mgr*)
Craig Burkman (*Mgr*)
Daryll Williams (*Mgr*)
Jason Biddinger (*Mgr*)
Jeff Wood (*Mgr*)
Ruth Porter (*Mgr*)

HAMASPIK OF ROCKLAND COUNTY, INC.
58 Route 59 Ste 1, Monsey, NY 10952
Tel.: (845) 356-8400   NY
Web Site:
  http://www.hamaspikrockland.org
Year Founded: 1997
Sales Range: $25-49.9 Million
Emp.: 1,369
Developmental Disability Assistance Services
N.A.I.C.S.: 624120

Aron Rubinstein (*Mgr-Maintenance*)
Moshe Sabel (*Dir-Residential Svcs*)
Zalmen Stein (*Dir-Dev*)
Eliezer Eizikovits (*Dir-At-Home Services*)
Esty Schonfeld (*Dir-Day Hab*)
Sholoime Kornbluh (*Dir-Day & Employment Svcs*)
Zishe Muller (*Dir-Gazette & Pub Affairs*)
Asher Katz (*Dir-HamaspikCare*)
Eliezer Appel (*Dir-Quality Improvement*)
Meyer Wertheimer (*Exec Dir*)
Solomon Lebowitz (*Mgr-Home*)
Joel Friedman (*Dir-ASR*)
Zissy Reich (*Corp Compliance Officer*)
Kaila Mendlowitz (*Coord-HR*)

HAMBURG BROTHERS
333 E Carson St Ste 525, Pittsburgh, PA 15219
Tel.: (412) 488-4428   PA
Web Site:
  http://www.hamburgbrothers.com
Year Founded: 1920
Sales Range: $1-9.9 Million
Emp.: 12
Whslr of Consumer Electronics & Electrical Household Goods
N.A.I.C.S.: 423620
Dennis Holzer (*Co-Owner & Pres*)

HAMBY CHEVROLET-BUICK-GMC TRUCK
2000 Hwy 41 S, Perry, GA 31069
Tel.: (478) 997-8567
Web Site: https://www.hamby.com
Year Founded: 1981
Sales Range: $10-24.9 Million
Emp.: 35
Car Whslr
N.A.I.C.S.: 441110
Mark Hamby (*Pres*)

HAMEL & MCALISTER INC.
215 Middlesex Tpke, Burlington, MA 01803
Tel.: (781) 272-0100
Web Site: https://www.h-m-inc.com
Year Founded: 1994
Rev.: $62,603,240
Emp.: 200
Mechanical Contractor
N.A.I.C.S.: 238220
Ray Hamel (*Pres & Treas*)
Dave Lyons (*Exec VP*)

HAMEL BUILDERS
2520 Pennsylvania Avenue SE, Washington, DC 20020
Tel.: (202) 584-2100
Web Site:
  http://www.hamelbuilders.com
Sales Range: $10-24.9 Million
Emp.: 146
Nonresidential Construction Services
N.A.I.C.S.: 236220
Daniel Beegle (*Principal*)

HAMEL FOREST PRODUCTS, INC.
5401 County Rd D, Vesper, WI 54489
Tel.: (715) 569-4186
Year Founded: 1964
Sales Range: $10-24.9 Million
Emp.: 110
Wood Products Mfr
N.A.I.C.S.: 321999
Ralph Hamel (*Pres*)
Carol Hamel (*VP*)

HAMER TOYOTA INC.

11041 Sepulveda Blvd, Mission Hills, CA 91345
Tel.: (818) 365-9621
Web Site:
  https://www.hamertoyota.com
Year Founded: 1939
Sales Range: $50-74.9 Million
Emp.: 200
Owner & Operator of Car Dealerships
N.A.I.C.S.: 441110
Peter Fernandez (*Asst Mgr-Svcs*)
Darwin Ribadeneira (*Dir-Sls Ops*)

HAMILTON CASTER & MFG. CO.
1637 Dixie Hwy, Hamilton, OH 45011-4087
Tel.: (513) 863-3300   OH
Web Site:
  https://www.hamiltoncaster.com
Year Founded: 1907
Sales Range: $75-99.9 Million
Emp.: 78
Truck Casters, Wheels & Non-Powered Floor Trucks Mfr, Supplier & Distr
N.A.I.C.S.: 332999
James Lippert (*VP-Sls*)
Mark J. Lippert (*VP-Mktg*)

HAMILTON CENTER, INC.
620 8th Ave, Terre Haute, IN 47804
Tel.: (812) 231-8200   IN
Web Site:
  http://www.hamiltoncenter.org
Year Founded: 1966
Sales Range: $25-49.9 Million
Emp.: 796
Behavioral Healthcare Services
N.A.I.C.S.: 621420
David Hilton (*Dir-Medical*)

HAMILTON CO., INC.
4970 Energy Way, Reno, NV 89502-4123
Tel.: (775) 858-3000
Web Site:
  https://www.hamiltoncompany.com
Year Founded: 1953
Sales Range: $150-199.9 Million
Emp.: 2,500
Laboratory Instruments & Supplies Mfr & Designer
N.A.I.C.S.: 334516
Steven Hamilton (*Pres*)
Jaison March (*Dir-Mktg*)
Louis Rachal (*Mgr-IT*)

Subsidiaries:

HAMILTON Messtechnik GmbH   (1)
Forstelerstr 13, 64739, Hochst, Germany
Tel.: (49) 6163910495
Web Site: http://www.hamilton-messtechnik.de
Emp.: 5
Industrial Equipment Distr
N.A.I.C.S.: 423830

Hamilton Bonaduz AG   (1)
Veagrusch 8, PO Box 26, 7402, Bonaduz, Switzerland   (100%)
Tel.: (41) 816606060
Web Site: http://www.hamiltoncompany.ch
Sales Range: $25-49.9 Million
Mfr of Laboratory Instruments
N.A.I.C.S.: 334516

HAMILTON COMMUNICATIONS GROUP, INC.
20 N Wacker Dr Ste 1960, Chicago, IL 60606
Tel.: (312) 321-5000   IL
Web Site:
  http://www.hamiltongrp.com
Year Founded: 1982
Sales Range: $125-149.9 Million
Emp.: 45

Advertising Agencies
N.A.I.C.S.: 541810
James D. Lee (*Chief Strategic Officer*)

HAMILTON CONSTRUCTION CO. OREGON INC.
2213 S F, Springfield, OR 97477-0121
Tel.: (541) 746-2426   OR
Web Site: https://www.hamil.com
Year Founded: 1940
Sales Range: $25-49.9 Million
Emp.: 150
Provider of Heavy Construction Services
N.A.I.C.S.: 237310
Scott Williams (*Pres*)

HAMILTON COUNTY ELECTRIC COOPERATIVE
420 N Rice, Hamilton, TX 76531
Tel.: (254) 386-3123   TX
Web Site:
  http://www.hamiltonelectric.coop
Year Founded: 1938
Sales Range: $10-24.9 Million
Emp.: 44
Electric Power Distr
N.A.I.C.S.: 221122
Joe Raibourn (*Dir-Office Svcs*)
Brian Geeslin (*Mgr-Engrg*)
Sam Campbell (*VP*)

HAMILTON EQUIPMENT, INC.
567 S Reading Rd, Ephrata, PA 17522-1835
Tel.: (717) 733-7951   PA
Web Site: http://www.haminc.com
Year Founded: 1938
Sales Range: $10-24.9 Million
Emp.: 30
Lawn & Garden & Industrial Machinery & Equipment & Agricultural Machinery & Paints Whslr
N.A.I.C.S.: 424950
Jan D. Reddig (*Mgr-Sls*)
Robert J. Hamilton Jr. (*Pres*)

HAMILTON EXHIBITS LLC
9150 E 33rd St, Indianapolis, IN 46235
Tel.: (317) 898-9300
Web Site: http://www.hamilton-exhibits.com
Sales Range: $10-24.9 Million
Emp.: 78
Displays, Paint Process
N.A.I.C.S.: 339950
Daniel Cantor (*Chm*)
Paula Tinkey (*CFO*)
Kim Raby (*Sr Acct Mgr*)
Josh Halpern (*Dir-Client Team*)
Brenda Hurst (*Mgr-Health Care*)
Kevin Daugherty (*Mgr-Mktg Creative Svcs*)
Matt Farrell (*Dir-Client Team*)
Josh Frisbie (*Dir-Creative*)
Paul Quay (*Dir-Program Mgmt*)
Jim Obermeyer (*VP-Hamilton Chicago*)
Jason Weddle (*CEO*)
Lynne Damer (*VP-Strategy*)

HAMILTON FORM CO., LTD.
7009 Midway Rd, Fort Worth, TX 76118
Tel.: (817) 590-2111
Web Site:
  https://www.hamiltonform.com
Sales Range: $10-24.9 Million
Emp.: 100
Prestressed Concrete Products Mfr
N.A.I.C.S.: 327390
William F. Daily (*Pres*)
B. A. Plotnicki (*VP-Engrg*)

Hamilton Health Care System, Inc.—(Continued)

HAMILTON HEALTH CARE SYSTEM, INC.
PO Box 1900, Dalton, GA 30722-1900
Tel.: (706) 226-3003   **GA**
Web Site: https://vitruvianhealth.com
Year Founded: 1983
Sales Range: $10-24.9 Million
Emp.: 584
Health Care Srvices
N.A.I.C.S.: 622110

Subsidiaries:

Cleveland Tennessee Hospital Company, LLC   (1)
2305 Chambliss Ave NW, Cleveland, TN 37311
Tel.: (423) 559-6000
Web Site:
  https://www.tennovacleveland.com
Health Care Srvices
N.A.I.C.S.: 622110

HAMILTON IMPORTS
2200 Route 33, Trenton, NJ 08690
Tel.: (609) 587-7314
Web Site:
  http://www.hamiltonimports.com
Year Founded: 1981
Sales Range: $10-24.9 Million
Emp.: 45
Car Whslr
N.A.I.C.S.: 441110
David Brodtman (Gen Mgr)
Harris Wildstein (Owner)

HAMILTON LANE ADVISORS, LLC
1 Presdential Blvd 4th Fl, Bala Cynwyd, PA 19004
Tel.: (610) 934-2222   **PA**
Web Site:
  http://www.hamiltonlane.com
Year Founded: 1991
Rev.: $25,000,000,000
Emp.: 190
Private Equity Asset Management & Investment Advisory Services
N.A.I.C.S.: 523940
Janet Bauman (Mng Dir-Fund Investment Team)
Stephen R. Brennan (Head-Bus Dev)
Michael T. Donohue (Mng Dir & Controller-Fin)
David P. Helgerson (Mng Dir-Co-Investment Team)
Thomas J. Kerr (Head-Secondaries)
Andrea Anigati Kramer (Mng Dir & Interim Chief Risk Officer)
Kevin J. Lucey (COO)
Jeffrey S. Meeker (Chief Client Officer)
Randy M. Stilman (CFO & Treas)
Hartley Raymond Rogers (Chm)
Mario L. Giannini (CEO)
Erik R. Hirsch (Chief Investment Officer)
Frederick Shaw (Chief Compliance Officer)
Lydia Gavalis (Gen Counsel)
Brent Burnett (Mng Dir)
Christian Kallen (Mng Dir-Fund Investment Team)
Juan Delgado-Moreira (Mng Dir & Head-Asia Bus)
Keith Brittain (Mng Dir)
Miguel Luina (Principal-Fund Investment Team)
Ricardo Fernandez (Mng Dir-Fund Investment Team)
Richard Hope (Mng Dir-Fund Investment Team)
Robert Flanigan (Principal-Real Estate)
Scott Davies (Principal-Real Assets)

Steve Gruber (Mng Dir-Real Assets)
Tara Blackburn (Mng Dir)
Tarang Katira (Principal-Fund Investment Team)

Subsidiaries:

Hamilton Lane (Hong Kong) Limited   (1)
Room 1-2 10th Floor St George's Building, 2 Ice House Street, Central, China (Hong Kong)
Tel.: (852) 3987 7191
Web Site: http://www.hamiltonlane.com
Emp.: 10
Private Equity Asset Management & Investment Advisory Services
N.A.I.C.S.: 523940
Juan Delgado-Moreira (Mng Dir-Investments-Asia)
Josh Jacob (VP-Relationship Mgmt-Asia)
Joshua E. Kahn (Mng Dir-Co-Investment Team-Asia)
Matthew Silverio (VP-Relationship Mgmt-Asia)
Mingchen Xia (Principal-Fund Investment)

Hamilton Lane (Japan) Co., Ltd.   (1)
17F Imperial Tower 1-1-1 Uchisaiwai-cho, Chiyoda-ku, Tokyo, 100-0011, Japan
Tel.: (81) 3 3580 4000
Web Site: http://www.hamiltonlane.com
Emp.: 5
Private Equity Asset Management & Investment Advisory Services
N.A.I.C.S.: 523940
Tomoko Kitao (Dir)

Hamilton Lane (UK) Limited   (1)
8-10 Great George Street, London, SW1P 3AE, United Kingdom
Tel.: (44) 207 340 0100
Web Site: http://www.hamiltonlane.com
Emp.: 370
Private Equity Asset Management & Investment Advisory Services
N.A.I.C.S.: 523940
Richard Hope (Mng Dir)
Ana Lei Ortiz (Mng Dir-Relationship Mgmt-Europe)
Mitesh Pabari (Principal-Secondary Team)
Daniel Schoneveld (Principal)
Jim Strang (Head-EMEA)
Paul Waller (Sr Partner)
Carolin Blank (Principal)

Hamilton Lane Israel Ltd.   (1)
6 Hahoshlim Street Building C 7th Floor, PO Box 12279, Herzliya Pituach, 4672201, Israel
Tel.: (972) 732716610
Web Site: http://www.hamiltonlane.com
Private Equity Asset Management & Investment Advisory Services
N.A.I.C.S.: 523940
Limor Beker (Mng Dir-Relationship Mgmt-Middle East)
Zoe Nakash (Principal-Relationship Mgmt-Middle East)

Hamilton Lane do Brasil Ltda.   (1)
Avenida Niemeyer No 2 Sala 102 Leblon, CEP 22450-220, Rio de Janeiro, RJ, Brazil
Tel.: (55) 21 3520 8903
Web Site: http://www.hamiltonlane.com
Private Equity Asset Management & Investment Advisory Services
N.A.I.C.S.: 523940

HAMILTON MATERIALS INC.
345 W Meats Ave, Orange, CA 92865
Tel.: (714) 637-2770
Sales Range: $200-249.9 Million
Emp.: 165
Drywall Materials
N.A.I.C.S.: 327120
Willis D. Hamilton (Pres)

HAMILTON METALS INC.
29315 Katy Brookshire Rd, Katy, TX 77494
Tel.: (713) 474-9700
Web Site:
  https://www.hamiltonmetals.com
Sales Range: $25-49.9 Million
Emp.: 15

Steel
N.A.I.C.S.: 423510
Jim Millman (Owner)
Cindy Adkins (Mgr-Inside Sls-OCTG)
Drew Delaune (VP-Sls-Western Hemisphere Mechanical Products)
John Dickinson (Acct Mgr)
Gene Lockard (Mgr-Sls)
Chad Mills (Mgr-Expediting)

HAMILTON PARTNERS, INC.
300 Park Blvd Ste 201, Itasca, IL 60143-2635
Tel.: (630) 250-9700   **IL**
Web Site:
  https://www.hamiltonpartners.com
Year Founded: 1987
Sales Range: $25-49.9 Million
Emp.: 160
Real Estate Development Services
N.A.I.C.S.: 237210
Mark Hamilton (Partner)
Kirk Hamilton (Partner)

HAMILTON ROBINSON LLC
301 Tresser Blvd Ste 1333, Stamford, CT 06901
Tel.: (203) 602-0011   **DE**
Web Site: https://www.hrco.com
Sales Range: $10-24.9 Million
Emp.: 10
Privater Equity Firm
N.A.I.C.S.: 523999
Owen Steve Crihfield (Partner)
Christian E. Lund (Partner)
Carrie L. DiLauro (Chief Admin Officer)
Stephen B. Connor (Dir-Bus Dev)
Petter Ostberg (CFO)
Brandon Richter (Principal)
Scott I. Oakford Sr. (Mng Partner)

Subsidiaries:

Gray Matter Systems, LLC.   (1)
100 Global View Dr Ste 200, Warrendale, PA 15086
Tel.: (412) 741-2410
Web Site:
  http://www.graymattersystems.com
Sales Range: $1-9.9 Million
Emp.: 31
Computer & Computer Peripheral Equipment & Software Merchant Whslr
N.A.I.C.S.: 423430
James Gillespie (Co-Founder & CEO)
Mandy Urey (COO)
Carson Drake (Co-Founder & VP)
Kerry McQuone (CMO)
Alan Hinchman (Chief Revenue Officer)
Jim Terrell (CFO)
John Benitz (CTO)
Kemell Kassim (VP-Sls)
John Gehan (Dir-Customer Care)

Subsidiary (Domestic):

Automation & Control Concepts, Inc.   (2)
1310 Papin St Ste 1B, Saint Louis, MO 63103
Tel.: (314) 241-2581
Web Site: http://www.a-cc.com
Sales Range: $1-9.9 Million
Emp.: 24
Administrative Management & General Management Consulting Service
N.A.I.C.S.: 541611
Mark Hoffman (Principal)

Phantom Technical Services, Inc.   (2)
111 Outerbelt St, Columbus, OH 43213
Tel.: (614) 868-9920
Web Site: http://www.phantomtechnical.com
Sales Range: $1-9.9 Million
Emp.: 13
Engineering Services, Nsk
N.A.I.C.S.: 541330
William Yates (Pres)

Technical Marketing Manufacturing Inc.   (2)

5000 Robb St Ste A, Wheat Ridge, CO 80033-2300
Tel.: (303) 232-1516
Web Site: http://www.tmmi.com
Automatic Environmental Control Mfr for Residential, Commercial & Appliance Use
N.A.I.C.S.: 334512
Michael Karty (Pres)

HAMILTON SYSTEM DISTRIBUTORS
325 S River St, South Hackensack, NJ 07601
Tel.: (201) 441-4888
Rev.: $11,900,000
Emp.: 45
Books
N.A.I.C.S.: 424920
Charles Hughes (Pres & CEO)
Roger Ham (Controller)

HAMILTON'S UNIFORMS LLC
17660 S Tamiami Trl Ste 106, Fort Myers, FL 33908
Tel.: (239) 415-9099
Web Site:
  http://www.hamiltonsuniforms.com
Sales Range: $1-9.9 Million
Emp.: 15
Uniform Clothing Stores
N.A.I.C.S.: 458110
Hank Porterfield (Owner)

HAMILTON-PARKER COMPANY
1865 Leonard Ave, Columbus, OH 43219
Tel.: (614) 358-7800
Web Site:
  https://www.hamiltonparker.com
Year Founded: 1934
Sales Range: $10-24.9 Million
Emp.: 200
Diversed Products Distr
N.A.I.C.S.: 444110
Adam Lewin (Pres & Owner)

HAMILTON-RYKER COMPANY
947 E Main St, Martin, TN 38237
Tel.: (731) 587-3161
Web Site: https://www.hamilton-ryker.com
Year Founded: 1971
Employment Placement & Human Resources Consulting Services
N.A.I.C.S.: 561311
Wayne McCreight (Chm)
Kelly McCreight (CEO)
Dedra Walker (VP)
Shari Franey (COO)
L. J. Perry (CIO)

Subsidiaries:

Priority Personnel, Inc.   (1)
226 Wonder World Dr, San Marcos, TX 78666
Tel.: (512) 392-2323
Web Site: http://www.prioritypersonnel.com
Sales Range: $1-9.9 Million
Emp.: 70
Employment Placement Agency
N.A.I.C.S.: 561311
Dan Roy (CEO)
Mark Olsen (Pres)
Cristina Rendon (Acct Mgr)

Steverson & Company, Inc.   (1)
1155 Dairy Ashford St, Houston, TX 77079
Tel.: (281) 496-5313
Web Site: http://www.steversonstaffing.com
Sales Range: $10-24.9 Million
Emp.: 86
Staffing Services
N.A.I.C.S.: 561311
Mike Lejeune (Pres)

HAMLIN NEWCO, LLC
2741 Wingate Ave, Akron, OH 44314-1301

Tel.: (330) 753-7791
Web Site:
https://www.hnmetalstamping.com
Metal Stampings, Medium & Small
Assemblies
N.A.I.C.S.: 332119
Pierre Osborne *(Mgr-Engrg)*

HAMM MANAGEMENT CO.
205 W Maple St, Enid, OK 73701
Tel.: (580) 242-1876
Sales Range: $25-49.9 Million
Emp.: 430
Holding Company
N.A.I.C.S.: 484230
Justin Boyd *(Pres)*

Subsidiaries:

Hamm & Phillips Service
Company   (1)
205 W Maple Ste 600, Enid, OK 73701
Tel.: (580) 242-1876
Web Site: http://www.hammphillips.com
Sales Range: $25-49.9 Million
Emp.: 237
Oilfield Transportation Services
N.A.I.C.S.: 484230
Ron L. Boyd *(Pres)*

Stride Well Service   (1)
205 WestMaple Ste 600, Enid, OK 73701
Tel.: (580) 242-1876
Provider of Workover Rigs
N.A.I.C.S.: 213112
Cathy Sue Wood *(VP-Personal-Southern District)*
Randy Stebbins *(Exec VP)*
Joe Wood *(VP-Ops)*

HAMMACHER SCHLEMMER & CO., INC.
9307 N Milwaukee Ave, Niles, IL 60714
Tel.: (847) 581-8600   IL
Web Site:
https://www.hammacher.com
Year Founded: 1848
Sales Range: $100-124.9 Million
Emp.: 200
Housewares & Giftware Retailer
N.A.I.C.S.: 455219
Richard W. Tinberg *(CEO)*
Robert Bohlin *(Dir-Mdsg)*
Heather Zdan *(VP-Mktg)*

HAMMEL, GREEN & ABRA-HAMSON, INC.
420 N 5th St, Minneapolis, MN 55401-1180
Tel.: (612) 758-4000   MN
Web Site: https://www.hga.com
Year Founded: 1953
Sales Range: $150-199.9 Million
Emp.: 600
Provider of Architectural & Engineering Services
N.A.I.C.S.: 541330
Daniel L. Avchen *(Exec Dir-Strategic Growth)*
Kurt Spiering *(Principal)*
Loren Ahles *(Principal-Design)*
Bill Blanski *(Principal-Design)*
Tim Carl *(CEO)*
Hal L. Henderson *(Principal & Dir-Office-Rochester)*
John Cook *(VP)*
John K. Justus *(Principal)*
Debra Barnes *(Principal & Dir-Interior Design)*
Jeff Harris *(Dir-Mechanical Engrg)*
Erika Eklund *(Dir-Comm)*
James Goblirsch *(Principal)*
Kaveh Amirdelfan *(Principal)*
Mia Blanchett *(Principal)*
Scott Colson *(Principal & Dir-Office-San Jose)*
Stan Chiu *(Principal)*
William Hendrix *(Principal)*
V. Noel Bryan *(Assoc VP & Mgr-Ops-California)*
David Ainsworth *(Assoc VP & Sr Engr-Mechanical)*
Luther Blair *(Principal)*
Nancy Blankfard *(Principal)*
Mark Bultman *(Principal)*
Frank Cedarblade *(Principal)*
Rebecca Celis *(Principal)*
John Chapman *(Principal)*
Scott Davidson *(Principal)*
Kevin Farquhar *(Principal)*
Nima Gujar *(Principal)*
Jennifer Klund *(Principal)*
Joey Kragelund *(Principal)*
Marc L'Italien *(Principal)*
Lisa Macaluso *(Principal)*
Kent Mainquist *(CFO)*
James Matson *(Principal)*
Roxanne Nelson *(Principal)*
Greg Osecheck *(Principal)*
Rebecca Kleinbaum Sanders *(Principal)*
Richard Smith *(Principal)*
Steven Weir *(Principal)*
Douglas Whiteaker *(Principal)*
Paul Widlarz *(Principal)*
Alanna Carter *(Principal)*
Amy Douma *(Principal-Design)*
Bruno Grinwis *(Principal)*
Bryan Cannon *(Principal-Design)*
David Dailey *(Principal)*
David Feth *(Principal)*
Elizabeth Young *(Principal)*
Hayley Gibbons *(Principal)*
J. Patrick Halpin *(Principal)*
John Frane *(Principal-Design)*
Kevin Donaghey *(Principal)*
Meredith Hayes Gordon *(Principal)*
Peter Balistrieri *(Principal)*
Peter D. Cook *(Principal-Design)*
Peter Dahl *(Principal)*
Peter Erni *(Principal)*
Richard Hombsch *(Principal)*
Rich Bonnin *(Principal-Design)*
Robert Cull *(Principal)*
Steven Dwyer *(Principal-Design)*
Susan Foong *(Principal-Design)*
William Wilson *(Principal)*

Subsidiaries:

HGA Mid-Atlantic, Inc.   (1)
44 Canal Center Plz Ste 100, Alexandria, VA 22314
Tel.: (703) 836-7766
Architectural Services
N.A.I.C.S.: 541310
Pat Halpin *(Gen Mgr)*

HAMMER COMMERCIAL, INC.
1715 Cape Coral Pkwy Ste 8, Cape Coral, FL 33914
Tel.: (239) 573-0730
Web Site:
https://www.hammerconstruction.com
Year Founded: 1980
Sales Range: $1-9.9 Million
Emp.: 13
Commercial Construction & Custom Homebuilder
N.A.I.C.S.: 236220
Gerard Blain *(CEO)*

HAMMER CONSTRUCTION, INC.
4320 Adams Rd, Norman, OK 73069
Tel.: (405) 310-3160
Web Site:
https://www.hammerok.com
Sales Range: $10-24.9 Million
Emp.: 120
Oil & Gas Field Operation Services
N.A.I.C.S.: 213112
Shirley Hammer *(Owner & Pres)*
Robby Moore *(VP-Ops)*

Tommy VanHoose *(Mgr-Bridgeport-TX)*
Larry Hollingsworth *(Mgr-Asset)*
Steve Doss *(Mgr-Fleet Fueling & Cost Control)*
Mark Brown *(Sr Project Mgr)*

HAMMER CREATIVE
6311 Romaine St 3rd Fl, Los Angeles, CA 90038-2617
Tel.: (323) 606-4700
Web Site:
http://www.hammercreative.com
Year Founded: 1988
Sales Range: Less than $1 Million
Emp.: 30
Audio/Visual, Production (Ad, Film, Broadcast)
N.A.I.C.S.: 541810
Mark Pierce *(Founder & CEO)*
Jim Botko *(Head-Mktg)*
Scott Hayman *(Dir-Creative)*

HAMMER-WILLIAMS COMPANY
1710 W Willow Rd, Enid, OK 73703
Tel.: (580) 237-9600
Rev.: $15,800,000
Emp.: 20
Convenience Stores, Independent
N.A.I.C.S.: 445131
Kyle Williams *(Pres)*

HAMMERMAN & GAINER INC.
1340 Poydras St Ste 2000, New Orleans, LA 70112
Tel.: (504) 681-6135
Web Site: http://www.hng.com
Year Founded: 1929
Insurance Agents, Brokers & Service
N.A.I.C.S.: 524298
Larry D. Oney *(Chm & CEO)*
Vanessa James *(VP-Claims)*
Christopher Oney *(Exec VP)*

HAMMERS LLC
1415 Dinah Shore Blvd, Winchester, TN 37398
Tel.: (931) 967-3787
Web Site:
http://www.hammersstore.com
Sales Range: $10-24.9 Million
Emp.: 25
Department Stores, Discount
N.A.I.C.S.: 458110
W. Earl Hammer *(Gen Mgr)*

HAMMERSMITH DATA MANAGEMENT, INC.
23 Inverness Way E Ste 200, Englewood, CO 80112
Tel.: (303) 980-0700
Web Site:
https://www.ehammersmith.com
Year Founded: 1981
Sales Range: $1-9.9 Million
Emp.: 70
Real Estate Management Services
N.A.I.C.S.: 531390
John Hammersmith *(CEO)*

Subsidiaries:

Mountain Managers, Inc.   (1)
1121 N Dillon Dam Rd, Frisco, CO 80443
Tel.: (970) 668-3174
Web Site:
http://www.mountainmanagers.com
Sales Range: $1-9.9 Million
Emp.: 40
Lessors of Other Real Estate Property
N.A.I.C.S.: 531190

HAMMES PARTNERS WIS-CONSIN LP
18000 W Sarah Ln Ste 250, Brookfield, WI 53045
Tel.: (262) 792-5900

Web Site: http://www.hammesco.com
Sales Range: $10-24.9 Million
Emp.: 40
Land Subdividers & Developers, Commercial
N.A.I.C.S.: 237210
Jon Hammes *(Founder & Partner)*

HAMMILL MANUFACTURING COMPANY INC.
360 Tomahawk Dr, Maumee, OH 43537
Tel.: (419) 476-0789
Web Site:
http://www.hammillmfg.com
Sales Range: $10-24.9 Million
Emp.: 240
Special Dies, Tools, Jigs & Fixtures
N.A.I.C.S.: 333514
Dean Johnson *(Plant Mgr)*

HAMMONASSET FORD-LINCOLN-MERCURY INC.
191 Boston Post Rd, Madison, CT 06443
Tel.: (203) 245-8828
Web Site:
http://www.hammonassetford.com
Rev.: $14,800,000
Emp.: 43
New Car Dealers
N.A.I.C.S.: 441110
Al Mantilia *(Pres)*
Dana Fordyce *(Gen Mgr)*
David Mantilia *(Mgr)*
Steve Mantilia *(Mgr-Sls)*

HAMMOND ELECTRONICS INC.
1230 W Central Blvd, Orlando, FL 32805-1815
Tel.: (407) 849-6060   FL
Web Site:
http://www.hammondelec.com
Year Founded: 1947
Sales Range: $25-49.9 Million
Emp.: 210
Electronic Parts & Equipment Distr
N.A.I.C.S.: 423690
Dylan Brown *(Mgr)*

HAMMOND GROUP, INC.
1414 Field St Bldg B, Hammond, IN 46320-2664
Tel.: (219) 931-9360   IN
Web Site:
https://www.hmndgroup.com
Year Founded: 1930
Sales Range: $25-49.9 Million
Emp.: 150
Chemical & Lead Products Mfr
N.A.I.C.S.: 325180
Mel Prime *(Controller)*
Gordon C. Beckley *(CTO & VP)*
Terrence Murphy *(Pres & CEO)*

Subsidiaries:

Hammond Expanders Division - Malaysia Plant   (1)
No 1 Lebuh Sultan Mohammed 1 Selat Klang Utara, 42000, Port Klang, Selangor, Malaysia
Tel.: (60) 3 3176 4519
Emp.: 30
Electronic Components Mfr
N.A.I.C.S.: 334419

Hammond Lead Products   (1)
1414 Field St, Hammond, IN 46320
Tel.: (219) 931-9360
Web Site: http://www.hmndgroup.com
Sales Range: $25-49.9 Million
Emp.: 45
Inorganic Chemical Mfr
N.A.I.C.S.: 325180
Gerry Kaoukis *(MIS Mgr)*
Debbie Mangerson *(HR Mgr)*

Hammond Group, Inc.—(Continued)

Plant (Domestic):

Hammond Lead Products Division - Pottstown Plant (2)
10 S Grosstown Rd, Pottstown, PA 19464
Tel.: (610) 327-1400
Web Site: http://www.hammondlead.com
Lead Product Mfr
N.A.I.C.S.: 331491
Brian Vermeesch *(Plant Mgr-Ops)*

HAMMOND LUMBER COMPANY
25 Mill St, Belgrade, ME 04917
Tel.: (207) 495-3303
Web Site:
http://www.hammondlumber.com
Year Founded: 1953
Sales Range: $50-74.9 Million
Emp.: 340
Provider of Building Materials
N.A.I.C.S.: 423310
Connie Brock *(Branch Mgr & Asst Branch Mgr)*
Donald Hammond *(VP)*
Rod Bickford *(Controller)*
Scott Brock *(Branch Mgr & Asst Branch Mgr)*
Michael Hammond *(Pres & CEO)*

Subsidiaries:

Brocks Plywood Sales, Inc. (1)
298 N Main St, Rochester, NH 03867
Tel.: (603) 332-4065
Web Site: http://www.brocksonline.com
Clay Building Material & Refractories Mfr
N.A.I.C.S.: 327120

HAMMOND MACHINERY, INC.
1600 Douglas Ave, Kalamazoo, MI 49007-1630
Tel.: (269) 345-7151   MI
Web Site:
http://www.hammondmach.com
Year Founded: 1881
Rev.: $9,000,000
Emp.: 40
Abrasive Belt Grinders, Polishing & Buffing Machines, Dust Collectors Mfr
N.A.I.C.S.: 333517
Chuck J. Aldrich *(Mgr-Svc)*
Robert Hammond *(Pres)*

HAMMOND POWER SOLUTIONS, INC.
17715 Susana Road, Compton, CA 90221
Tel.: (310) 537-4690
Web Site:
http://www.hammondpowerso
lutions.com
Rev.: $6,666,666
Emp.: 100
Electronic Coil, Transformer & Other Inductor Mfr
N.A.I.C.S.: 334416

Subsidiaries:

Micron Industries Corp. (1)
1211 22nd St Ste 200, Oak Brook, IL 60523
Tel.: (630) 516-1222
Web Site: http://www.micronpower.com
Emp.: 100
Power, Distribution & Specialty Transformer Mfr
N.A.I.C.S.: 335311
Donald Clark *(Pres)*

HAMMOND TRACTOR COMPANY
216 Center Rd, Fairfield, ME 04937
Tel.: (207) 453-7131
Web Site:
http://www.hammondtractor.com
Rev.: $11,300,000
Emp.: 50

Farm & Garden Machinery & Equipment Merchant Whslr
N.A.I.C.S.: 423820
Laura Atwood *(Office Mgr)*
Dave Bryant *(Gen Mgr)*
Scott Gamage *(Mgr-Agricultural-Sls)*
Gary L. Hammond *(Owner & Pres)*
David Hammond *(Owner & VP)*
Dave Ponsant *(Mgr-Product Support)*
Dennis Weymouth *(Mgr-Consumer Svcs)*
Tim Covert *(Mgr-Consumer & Comml Sls Web Ops)*
Richard Ingraham *(Mgr-Consumer & Comml Sls)*
Pam Jacques *(Bus Mgr)*

HAMMOND, KENNEDY, WHITNEY & COMPANY, INC.
1 Indiana Sq Ste 2650, Indianapolis, IN 46204
Tel.: (317) 574-6900   NY
Web Site: http://www.hkwinc.com
Year Founded: 1903
Privater Equity Firm
N.A.I.C.S.: 523999
Mike Foisy *(Pres & Partner)*
Maria Evangelista *(Mgr-Acctg & Compliance)*
Kent W. Robinson *(Partner)*
Ted H. Kramer *(CEO & Partner)*
Jim Snyder *(Partner)*

Subsidiaries:

CIS Secure Computing, Inc. (1)
21050 Ashburn Crossing Dr Ste 145, Ashburn, VA 20147
Tel.: (703) 996-0500
Web Site: http://www.cissecure.com
Computing Services & Tactical Video Teleconferencing
N.A.I.C.S.: 541690
Bill Strang *(Chm & CEO)*
Jim Armstrong *(CFO)*
Dan Gavin *(Pres-CIS Labs)*
Jim Sisk *(Dir-Quality Assurance)*
Paula Adams *(Dir-Facilities)*
David Sawyer *(Dir-Ops)*
Robert Hoyecki *(COO)*
Jim Patterson *(CTO)*

Subsidiary (Domestic):

Intrepid Solutions and Services, LLC (2)
12950 Worldgate Dr Ste 710, 20170, Herndon, VA
Tel.: (703) 992-0386
General Management Consulting Services
N.A.I.C.S.: 541611

Subsidiary (Domestic):

BWM Outcomes, LLC (3)
16105 Gossum Ct, Haymarket, VA 20169
Tel.: (641) 590-2679
Cyber Security & Intelligence Analysis Services
N.A.I.C.S.: 561621

Darkblade Systems Corporation (3)
420 W Jubal Early Dr Ste 204, Winchester, VA 22601
Tel.: (540) 226-3393
Web Site: http://www.darkbladesystems.com
Research & Development in the Physical, Engineering & Life Sciences
N.A.I.C.S.: 541715
Fred Starkey *(Pres)*

Delta Solutions & Strategies, LLC (3)
565 Space Center Dr Ste 330, Colorado Springs, CO 80915
Tel.: (719) 475-0605
Web Site: http://www.deltasands.com
Sales Range: $10-24.9 Million
Emp.: 122
Systems Engineering & Technical Assistance (SETA) & Advisory & Assistance Services (A&AS)
N.A.I.C.S.: 541990
Gary Bain *(Pres)*

CMIT Solutions LLC (1)
9433 Bee Caves Rd Bldg 3 Ste 210, Austin, TX 78733
Tel.: (512) 879-4551
Web Site: http://www.cmitsolutions.com
Sales Range: $25-49.9 Million
Emp.: 350
Information Technology Services
N.A.I.C.S.: 561990
George Bobbitt *(COO)*
Jason Arabian *(Chief Strategy Officer)*
Roger Lewis *(CEO)*

Contract Land Staff LP (1)
2245 Texas Dr Ste 200, Sugar Land, TX 77479
Tel.: (281) 240-3370
Web Site: http://www.contractlandstaff.com
Sales Range: $10-24.9 Million
Emp.: 150
Land Management & Right of Way Consulting
N.A.I.C.S.: 541191
Brent Leftwich *(Pres & CEO)*
Mazie Leftwich *(Chief Admin Officer)*
Kerry Malone *(Sr VP-Special Projects)*
Rosie Dawson *(Sr VP-Special Projects)*
Leon Law *(VP-Tech Sls)*
Bruce Trepl *(VP-Pipeline Projects)*
Lori Bible *(Sr VP-Pub Sector)*
Mike Brantley *(Sr VP-Pipelines)*
Lesley Buentello *(Sr VP-HR)*
Michael Cummings *(VP-Electric Projects)*
Doug Holley *(VP-Projects)*
David Martin *(Sr VP-Special Projects)*
Halet Murphy *(CFO)*
Phil Pack *(Chief Projects Officer)*
Chris Thompson *(Sr VP-Canada)*
Rachel Siegert *(Mgr-St. Louis)*

Culture Partners (1)
27555 Ynez Rd Ste 200, Temecula, CA 92591
Tel.: (800) 504-6070
Web Site: https://culture.io
Sales Range: $1-9.9 Million
Emp.: 38
Management Consulting Services
N.A.I.C.S.: 541611
Roger Conners *(Co-Founder)*
Brad Starr *(VP)*
Tom Smith *(Co-Founder)*
Erez Yereslove *(CMO)*
Joe Terry *(CEO)*

Subsidiary (Non-US):

Paradigm Learning, Inc. (2)
Tel.: (813) 287-9330
Web Site: http://www.paradigmlearning.com
Professional & Management Development Training
N.A.I.C.S.: 611430
Raymond D. Green *(CEO)*
Catherine J. Rezak *(Chm)*
Robb J. Gomez *(Pres)*

Grobet File Company of America, Inc. (1)
750 Washington Ave, Carlstadt, NJ 07072-3008
Tel.: (201) 939-6700
Web Site: http://www.grobetusa.com
Sales Range: $25-49.9 Million
Emp.: 80
Industrial Machinery, Equipment & Supplies Mfr
N.A.I.C.S.: 423830
Ralph R. Whitney Jr. *(Chm)*

Hammond, Kennedy, Whitney & Company, Inc. - Indianapolis (1)
420 Lexington Ave Ste 2633, New York, NY 10170
Tel.: (212) 867-1010
Web Site: http://www.hkwinc.com
Sales Range: $10-24.9 Million
Emp.: 14
Privater Equity Firm
N.A.I.C.S.: 523999
Kent W. Robinson *(Partner-Ops)*
James C. Snyder *(Partner)*
John M. Carsello *(Partner)*
Jeffrey G. Wood *(Sr Partner)*
Ryan M. Grand *(VP-Deal Generation)*
Chris Eline *(Principal)*

John M. Floyd & Associates, Inc. (1)
1415 North Loop W Ste 500, Houston, TX 77008

Tel.: (800) 809-2307
Web Site: https://advantage-fi.com
Management Consulting Services
N.A.I.C.S.: 541611
Mark Roe *(Exec VP-Natl Sls)*
Cheryl Lawson *(Exec VP-Compliance Review)*
John Cohron *(CEO)*
Jennifer Peoples *(VP-Product Mgmt)*
Ed Wolfe *(Exec VP-Natl Sls)*
Kathy Morales *(Chief Admin Officer)*

Nyloncraft, Inc. (1)
616 W McKinley Ave, Mishawaka, IN 46545-5518
Tel.: (574) 256-1521
Web Site: http://www.nyloncraft.com
Sales Range: $25-49.9 Million
Emp.: 404
Injection-Molded Parts Mfr
N.A.I.C.S.: 326199
Samuel Taylor *(Engr-Mfg)*
William Graham *(Engr-Opsal Excellence)*
Gary Dockery *(Supvr-Shipping)*
Dennis Wasikowski *(VP-Matls & IT)*
Bob Brzozowski *(Pres)*

Division (Domestic):

Nyloncraft, Inc. (2)
100 N Graham Ave, Bowling Green, KY 42101-1137
Tel.: (270) 782-6224
Web Site: http://www.nyloncraft.com
Sales Range: $25-49.9 Million
Emp.: 83
Automotive Windows, Doors, Pistons & Other Parts Mfr
N.A.I.C.S.: 326199

Nyloncraft, Inc. - Jonesville (2)
1640 E Chicago Rd, Jonesville, MI 49250-0035
Tel.: (517) 849-9911
Web Site: http://www.nyloncraft.com
Plastic Injection Molding
N.A.I.C.S.: 326199
Tom Smith *(Plant Mgr)*

Panos Brands LLC (1)
395 W Passaic Str Ste 240 2nd Fl, Rochelle Park, NJ 07662
Tel.: (201) 843-8900
Web Site: http://www.panosbrands.com
Grocery Distr
N.A.I.C.S.: 424490
Dathan Swick *(Dir-Sls)*
Mike Foisy *(Chm)*
Darcy Zbinovec *(CEO)*

Subsidiary (Domestic):

Walden Farms, LLC (2)
1209 W St Georges Ave, Linden, NJ 07036
Tel.: (908) 925-9494
Web Site: http://www.waldenfarms.com
Salad Dressings, Dips & Fruit Spreads Mfr
N.A.I.C.S.: 311941

Subsidiary (Non-US):

Walden Farms Canada (3)
9000 Rue Pierre-Bonne, Montreal, H1E 6W5, QC, Canada
Tel.: (877) 276-1981
Web Site: http://www.waldenfarms.ca
Salad & Dressing Retailer
N.A.I.C.S.: 424490

Special Applications Technology Inc. (1)
3985 S Lincoln Ave Ste 100, Loveland, CO 80537
Tel.: (970) 663-1431
Web Site: http://www.satechnology.com
Sales Range: $1-9.9 Million
Emp.: 140
Remote-Control Robots Mfr
N.A.I.C.S.: 332312

HAMMONS PRODUCTS COMPANY
105 Hammons Dr, Stockton, MO 65785
Tel.: (417) 276-5181   MO
Web Site: https://www.black-walnuts.com
Year Founded: 1946

Sales Range: $1-9.9 Million
Emp.: 55
Processor & Supplier of Nuts & Nut Products
N.A.I.C.S.: 311911
Brian K. Hammons *(Pres)*

Subsidiaries:

Hammons Products Co. - Arkansas **(1)**
PO Box K, Gravette, AR 72736
Tel.: (501) 787-5227
Black Walnuts Grower
N.A.I.C.S.: 115114

HAMPEL OIL DISTRIBUTORS INC.

3727 SW St, Wichita, KS 67217
Tel.: (316) 529-1162
Web Site: http://www.hampeloil.com
Sales Range: $10-24.9 Million
Emp.: 45
Petroleum Bulk Stations
N.A.I.C.S.: 424710
William Hampel *(Chm)*
Jim Hintz *(Controller)*
Ken Hampel *(Exec Dir-Sls & Mktg)*
Ed Hampel *(Exec Dir-Pur & Product Mgmt)*

HAMPSHIRE EQUITY PARTNERS

520 Madison Ave Fl 33, New York, NY 10022
Tel.: (203) 769-5601
Web Site: http://www.hampep.com
Year Founded: 1990
Privater Equity Firm
N.A.I.C.S.: 523999
Gregory Flynn *(Mng Partner)*

HAMPSHIRE GROUP LIMITED

114 W 41st St, New York, NY 10036
Tel.: (212) 840-5666   DE
Web Site: http://www.hamp.com
Year Founded: 1956
Sales Range: $75-99.9 Million
Emp.: 633
Holding Company; Sweaters & Hosiery Mfr & Retailer
N.A.I.C.S.: 313310
Paul M. Buxbaum *(Chm, Pres & CEO)*
William Drozdowski *(CFO-Interim)*
Fred Buonocore *(Sr VP)*

Subsidiaries:

Hampshire Brands **(1)**
114 W 41st St 4th Fl, New York, NY 10018-1705   **(100%)**
Tel.: (212) 840-5666
Web Site: http://www.hamp.com
Sales Range: $75-99.9 Million
Emp.: 50
Mfr of Sweaters & Colesta Knit Shirts
N.A.I.C.S.: 424350
Ronald Siu *(Mgr-Tech Design)*

Hampshire Designers, Inc. NY **(1)**
114 W 41st St, New York, NY 10036   **(100%)**
Tel.: (212) 840-5666
Web Site: http://www.hamp.com
Sales Range: $50-74.9 Million
Emp.: 100
Sweaters, Skirts & Slacks Mfr
N.A.I.C.S.: 424350

Hampshire Designers, Inc. SC **(1)**
1924 Pearman Dairy Rd, Anderson, SC 29625   **(100%)**
Tel.: (864) 225-6232
Web Site: http://www.hamp.com
Sales Range: $50-74.9 Million
Emp.: 65
Mfr of Sweaters & Knit Apparel
N.A.I.C.S.: 424350

San Francisco Knitworks **(1)**
345 Alabama St, San Francisco, CA 94110-1312

Tel.: (415) 552-1421
Sales Range: $125-149.9 Million
Emp.: 290
Mfr of Sweaters & Knitwears
N.A.I.C.S.: 315120

HAMPTON AFFILIATES

9600 SW Barnes Rd Ste 200, Portland, OR 97225
Tel.: (503) 297-7691   OR
Web Site:
   https://www.hamptonlumber.com
Year Founded: 1942
Lumber & Wood Products; Tree Farms; Building Product Distribution
N.A.I.C.S.: 423310
Bob Bluhm *(CFO & VP-Fin)*
Carter Stinton *(VP-Sls & Ops)*
Mark Porter *(Pres-Sls)*
Steve Zika *(CEO)*
David Hampton *(Co-Owner)*
Elizabeth Hampton *(Co-Owner)*
Jamey Hampton *(Co-Owner)*
Vicki Shaylor *(Sec)*
Dave Salmon *(VP-HR)*
Doug Cooper *(VP-Resources)*
Bret Griffin *(VP-Mfg)*

Subsidiaries:

Hampton Affiliates - Morton - Cowlitz Division **(1)**
302 State Hwy 7, Morton, WA 98356
Tel.: (360) 496-5115
Web Site: http://www.hamptonlumber.com
Stud & Kiln Dried Lumber Mfr
N.A.I.C.S.: 321912

Hampton Affiliates - Randle - Cowlitz Division **(1)**
10166 US Hwy 12, Randle, WA 98377
Tel.: (360) 497-5030
Studs & Kiln Dried Lumber Mfr
N.A.I.C.S.: 321912
Ken Rankin *(Plant Mgr)*

Hampton Affiliates - Warrenton Division **(1)**
550 NE Skipanon Dr, Warrenton, OR 97146
Tel.: (503) 861-5320
Web Site: http://www.hamptonaffiliates.com
Emp.: 162
Kiln Dried Stud & Framing Lumber Mfr
N.A.I.C.S.: 321999
Cliff Tuttle *(Gen Mgr)*

Hampton Affiliates - Washington Mills **(1)**
46921 Sauk Prairie Rd, Darrington, WA 98241
Tel.: (360) 436-2022
Web Site: http://www.hamptonaffiliates.com
Emp.: 170
Timber Product Mfr
N.A.I.C.S.: 321912
Steve Zika *(Pres)*

Hampton Tree Farms, Inc. **(1)**
2001 Front St NE Ste A, Salem, OR 97301
Tel.: (503) 365-8400
Web Site: http://www.hamptonlumber.com
Emp.: 15
Lumber Product Whslr
N.A.I.C.S.: 423310
Doug Cooper *(VP)*

Tillamook Lumber Company **(1)**
3111 3rd St, Tillamook, OR 97141
Tel.: (503) 842-6641
Timber Product Mfr
N.A.I.C.S.: 321912

Willamina Lumber Co., Inc. **(1)**
1000 Willamina Creek Rd, Willamina, OR 97396
Tel.: (503) 876-2322
Web Site: http://www.hamptonaffiliates.com
Sales Range: $10-24.9 Million
Emp.: 200
Lumber & Wood Products
N.A.I.C.S.: 321212
Steve Zika *(CEO)*

HAMPTON CHEVROLET MAZDA

1073 W Mercury Blvd, Hampton, VA 23666
Tel.: (757) 790-4008
Web Site:
   https://www.hamptonchevy.com
Year Founded: 1988
Sales Range: $25-49.9 Million
Emp.: 95
New Car Whslr
N.A.I.C.S.: 441110
Abe Kent *(Dir-Sls)*

HAMPTON DISTRIBUTING CO.

7605 N University Ave, Peoria, IL 61614
Tel.: (309) 692-6250
Web Site:
   https://www.hamptonsshowrooms.com
Sales Range: $25-49.9 Million
Emp.: 30
Cabinets
N.A.I.C.S.: 337110
Larry Hampton *(VP)*

HAMPTON ENTERPRISES INC.

3701 Union Dr Ste 100, Lincoln, NE 68516-6629
Tel.: (402) 489-8858
Web Site:
   http://www.hamptonenterprises.com
Sales Range: $10-24.9 Million
Emp.: 50
Commercial & Industrial Building Operation
N.A.I.C.S.: 531120
Joseph R. Hampton *(Founder & Chm)*
Jeff Nicklas *(Project Mgr)*
Terry Zimmerman *(VP)*
Scott Lockard *(Pres-Construction)*
John Hyland *(Mgr-Bus Dev)*
Mike Lindberg *(CFO)*
Michelle Keogh *(Pres-Real Estate)*
Lincoln Zehr *(CEO)*

HAMPTON HOMES, LLC.

12206 1/2 Walraven Dr, Huffman, TX 77336
Tel.: (713) 366-3510
Web Site: http://www.hampton-homes.com
Rev.: $36,000,000
Emp.: 65
New Construction & Single-Family Houses
N.A.I.C.S.: 236115
Seth Lincoln *(CEO)*
Victor Alonso *(VP)*

HAMPTON ROADS COMMUNITY FOUNDATION

101 W Main St Ste 4500, Norfolk, VA 23510
Tel.: (757) 622-7951   VA
Web Site:
   https://www.hamptonroadscf.org
Year Founded: 1950
Sales Range: $10-24.9 Million
Emp.: 16
Grantmaking Services
N.A.I.C.S.: 813211
Robin C. Foreman *(VP-Admin & Scholarships)*
Lynn Watson Neumann *(Dir-Gift Plng)*
Kay A. Stine *(VP-Dev)*
Deborah M. DiCroce *(Pres, CEO & Sec)*
Jody M. Wagner *(Treas)*
Leigh Evans Davis *(VP-Donor Engagement)*
Frank Dunn *(VP-Special Projects)*
Sally Kirby Hartman *(VP-Comm)*
Tim McCarthy *(CFO)*
Debbi Steiger *(VP-Reg Outreach)*

HAMPTON ROADS ECONOMIC DEVELOPMENT ALLIANCE

500 E Main St Ste 1300, Norfolk, VA 23510-2206
Tel.: (757) 627-2315   VA
Web Site: http://www.hreda.com
Year Founded: 1984
Sales Range: $1-9.9 Million
Emp.: 10
Marketing, Business Recruitment & Economic Development
N.A.I.C.S.: 541613
Amy N. Parkhurst *(Sr VP-Bus Dev)*
Tom Elder *(Dir-Economic Dev-Wight County)*
Eric K. Miller *(Exec VP-Bus Dev)*
Steve Herbert *(Interim Pres & Interim CEO)*
Chris Lemmon *(Chief Mktg Officer & Exec VP)*

HAMPTON TEDDER ELECTRIC CO.

4571 State St, Montclair, CA 91763
Tel.: (909) 628-1253
Web Site:
   https://www.hamptontedder.com
Sales Range: $10-24.9 Million
Emp.: 40
Electrical Work
N.A.I.C.S.: 238210
Mary Larson *(Controller)*
Matt Tedderf *(Coord-Safety)*
Mike Campos *(Dir-Utility Ops)*
Jim Andersen *(Project Mgr)*
Jim Brenton *(VP)*

HAMPTON TOYOTA

6191 Johnston St, Lafayette, LA 70503
Tel.: (337) 984-5010
Web Site:
   https://www.hamptontoyota.com
Sales Range: $10-24.9 Million
Emp.: 71
New Car Retailer
N.A.I.C.S.: 441110
Michael Alfano *(Mgr-Sls)*
Charles Boatmon *(Bus Mgr)*
Jami Cormier *(Gen Mgr-Sls)*
Tom Jardell *(Mgr-Svc)*
Terry McCall *(Mgr-Parts)*
Kyle Vidrine *(Bus Mgr)*

HAMRICK INC.

742 Peachoid Rd, Gaffney, SC 29341-3440
Tel.: (864) 489-6095
Web Site: http://www.hamricks.com
Sales Range: $200-249.9 Million
Emp.: 440
Clothing Stores
N.A.I.C.S.: 458110
Barry L. Hamrick *(Pres)*
Dinah Hamrick *(VP)*
Lesesile Perry *(Controller)*

HAMSHAW LUMBER INC.

3 Bradco St, Keene, NH 03431
Tel.: (603) 352-6506
Web Site:
   https://www.hamshawlumber.com
Rev.: $25,787,316
Emp.: 88
Lumber & Other Building Materials
N.A.I.C.S.: 423310
Douglas P. Hamshaw *(Pres)*
Barbara Leatherman *(Controller)*
Steven M. Clark *(Gen Mgr)*
Frank Buckbee *(Mgr-Hardware)*
Pete Thayer *(Mgr-Installed Insulation)*
Bruce Dunham *(Supvr-Sls)*

HAMSTRA GROUP, INC.

12028 N 200 W, Wheatfield, IN 46392
Tel.: (219) 956-3111

Hamstra Group, Inc.—(Continued)

Web Site:
https://www.hamstragroup.com
Sales Range: $10-24.9 Million
Emp.: 90
Nonresidential Construction Services
N.A.I.C.S.: 236220
Eric E. Carlson (Mgr)

HANA SPORTS INC.

13942 Orange Ave, Paramount, CA
90723
Tel.: (562) 633-2626
Web Site:
https://www.hanasports.com
Sales Range: $10-24.9 Million
Emp.: 20
Footwear, Athletic
N.A.I.C.S.: 424340
Sang C. Chon (Pres)
Bruce Lee (VP)

HANAC, INC.

49 W 45th St 4th Fl, New York, NY
10036
Tel.: (212) 840-8005   NY
Web Site: http://www.hanac.org
Year Founded: 1972
Sales Range: $10-24.9 Million
Emp.: 296
Community Action Services
N.A.I.C.S.: 624190
Gail Carmichael (Dir-HR)
Lola Maroulis (Controller)
Zoe C. Agios (CEO)
Evangeline Douris (Chm)

HANCOCK & MOORE INC.

166 Hancock & Moore Ln, Hickory,
NC 28601
Tel.: (828) 495-8235
Web Site:
https://www.hancockandmoore.com
Sales Range: $10-24.9 Million
Emp.: 200
Couches Sofas & Davenports: Uphol-
stered On Wood Frames
N.A.I.C.S.: 337121
Jack Glasheen (Pres & CEO)
Tim Rogers (VP-Fin)
Tom O'Connell (VP-Fin)
Joy Bailey (VP)
Andy Coffey (VP)

HANCOCK CLAIMS CONSUL-
TANTS, LLC

6875 Shiloh Rd E, Alpharetta, GA
30005
Tel.: (770) 569-1669
Web Site:
http://www.hancockclaims.com
Year Founded: 2003
Sales Range: $25-49.9 Million
Emp.: 125
Building Inspection Services
N.A.I.C.S.: 541350
Brad McCarty (Owner & Specialist-
Claims)

HANCOCK COUNTY SAVINGS
BANK, F.S.B.

351 Carolina Ave, Chester, WV
26034
Tel.: (304) 387-1620
Web Site: https://www.hcsbank.com
Sales Range: $10-24.9 Million
Emp.: 80
Federal Savings Bank
N.A.I.C.S.: 522180
Harry Comm (Chm)
Jerry Linger (Vice Chm)
Mark Eckleberry (Sec)

HANCOCK FABRICS, INC.

1 Fashion Way, Baldwyn, MS 38824-
8547
Tel.: (662) 365-6000   DE
Web Site:
http://www.hancockfabrics.com
Year Founded: 1957
Sales Range: $250-299.9 Million
Emp.: 3,100
Fashion Textile & Home Decor Mate-
rials & Sewing Equipment Whslr &
Retailer
N.A.I.C.S.: 459130
O. Pierce Crockett (VP & Controller)
Rebecca Isbell Flick (CFO & Exec
VP)

HANCOCK LUMBER COM-
PANY, INC.

Rte 121, Casco, ME 04015
Tel.: (207) 627-4201   ME
Web Site:
http://www.hancocklumber.com
Year Founded: 1848
Sales Range: $200-249.9 Million
Emp.: 500
Provider of Building Materials & Sup-
plies
N.A.I.C.S.: 423310
Paul R. Wainman (Pres & CEO)
Kevin Hancock (Pres & CEO)
Wendy Scribner (Gen Mgr-HR)
Kevin Hynes (COO)

HANCOCK PARK ASSOCI-
ATES, LP

10350 Santa Monica Blvd Ste 295,
Los Angeles, CA 90025
Tel.: (310) 228-6900   CA
Web Site: http://www.hpcap.com
Year Founded: 1986
Emp.: 12
Privater Equity Firm
N.A.I.C.S.: 523999
Kenton S. Van Harten (Partner)
Kevin L. Listen (Partner)
Michael F. Gooch (VP-Fin)
Ted Fourticq (Principal)
Martin Irani (VP)
Michael J. Fourticq Sr. (Mng Partner)
Michael J. Fourticq Jr. (Partner)
Kenneth G. Watler Jr. (Partner)

Subsidiaries:

Soundcast LLC   (1)
881 Kuhn Dr Ste 200, Chula Vista, CA
91914-3563
Tel.: (281) 692-9095
Web Site: http://www.gosoundcast.com
Wireless Audio Speakers Mfr
N.A.I.C.S.: 334310
Oscar Ciornei (Pres & CEO)
Bob Dulsky (CFO)
Leonard Santos (COO)
Charity Hardwick (VP-Sls & Mktg)

The Markets LLC   (1)
4350 Cordata Pkwy, Bellingham, WA
98226-8190
Tel.: (360) 714-9797
Web Site: http://www.themarketswa.com
Sales Range: $200-249.9 Million
Grocery Store Operator
N.A.I.C.S.: 445110
Kevin Weatherill (Pres & CEO)

HANCOCK PARK CORPORATE
INCOME, INC.

10 S Wacker Dr Ste 2500, Chicago,
IL 60606
Tel.: (847) 734-2000   IL
Web Site: https://www.hancockparkin
come.com
Year Founded: 2015
Rev.: $5,570,461
Assets: $53,644,078
Liabilities: $31,626,131
Net Worth: $22,017,947
Earnings: $1,525,913

Emp.: 783
Fiscal Year-end: 12/31/22
Investment Services
N.A.I.C.S.: 523999
Mukya S. Porter (Chief Compliance
Officer)
Tod K. Reichert (Sec)
Vassili Cerny (CFO)
Kyle Spina (Chief Acctg Officer)
Bilal Rashid (Chm, Pres & CEO)

HANCOCK-WOOD ELECTRIC
COOP INC.

1399 Business Park Dr S, North Bal-
timore, OH 45872-0190
Tel.: (419) 257-3241
Web Site: https://www.hwe.coop
Rev.: $19,923,007
Emp.: 50
Electronic Services
N.A.I.C.S.: 221118
George Walton (Pres & CEO)

HANCOCKS PHARMACY &
SURGICAL

840 E Main St, Meriden, CT 06450
Tel.: (203) 235-6323
Web Site:
https://www.hancockpharmacy.com
Sales Range: $10-24.9 Million
Emp.: 68
Pharmaceutical Product Whslr
N.A.I.C.S.: 424210
Greg Hancock (Owner)

HAND CONSTRUCTION, LLC.

9445 Stevens Rd Ste 200, Shreve-
port, LA 71106
Tel.: (318) 686-4170
Web Site:
https://www.handconstruction.com
Year Founded: 1980
Sales Range: $25-49.9 Million
Emp.: 38
Commercial & Institutional Building
Construction Services
N.A.I.C.S.: 236220
M. Cayce Hand (Owner & Pres)
Kyle Hand (VP-Ops)
John I. Provost (VP-Construction
Ops)

HANDA PHARMACEUTICALS,
INC.

2025 Gateway Pl Ste 480, San Jose,
CA 95110
Tel.: (510) 354-2888
Year Founded: 2005
Pharmaceuticals Product Mfr
N.A.I.C.S.: 325412
Fangyu Bill Liu (Pres & CEO)

HANDCRAFTED WINES, LLC

17501 W 98 St 4627, Lenexa, KS
66219
Tel.: (913) 829-4500   KS
Web Site:
https://www.handcraftedwines.net
Year Founded: 1996
Sales Range: $10-24.9 Million
Emp.: 15
Wine & Distilled Spirits Distr
N.A.I.C.S.: 424820
Jonathan Pey (Principal)
Donald Brain (Principal & Gen Mgr)

Subsidiaries:

D'Vine Wine, Inc.   (1)
3315 NW 26th Ave, Portland, OR 97210
Tel.: (503) 228-9450
Web Site: http://www.d-vine.net
Sales Range: $1-9.9 Million
Emp.: 20
Wine Distr
N.A.I.C.S.: 424820
Greg Falk (Dir-Sls)
Greg Cantu (Mgr-Bus)

HANDEE MART FOOD
STORES INC.

3209 Geer Hwy, Marietta, SC 29661
Tel.: (864) 836-6333
Sales Range: $10-24.9 Million
Emp.: 48
Convenience Stores, Independent
N.A.I.C.S.: 445131
David League (VP)
Robert A. League Jr. (Pres & Owner)

HANDEX CONSULTING AND
REMEDIATION, LLC

2211 Lee Rd Ste 110, Winter Park,
FL 32789
Tel.: (321) 441-9801
Web Site: https://www.hcr-llc.com
Year Founded: 1968
Environmental Consulting & Reme-
diation Services
N.A.I.C.S.: 541620
Stephen Tomicki (Sr Mgr-Client Rela-
tionship)
Brett D. Fadeley (CEO)
Andy Shoulders (Pres & COO)
Mark Coleman (CFO)

HANDFORD GENERAL CON-
TRACTORS

261 Oak Grove Ave, Springfield, MA
01109
Tel.: (413) 733-7703
Web Site: http://handford-general-
contractors.sbcontract.com
Sales Range: $10-24.9 Million
Emp.: 17
Highway & Street Paving Contractor
N.A.I.C.S.: 237310
Lugrone Handford (Pres)

HANDI-HOUSE MANUFACTUR-
ING CO.

747 US Hwy 1, Swainsboro, GA
30401
Tel.: (478) 237-6708
Web Site:
https://www.handihouse.com
Sales Range: $10-24.9 Million
Emp.: 140
Buildings, Portable: Prefabricated
Metal
N.A.I.C.S.: 332311
Donald Flanders (Pres)

HANDI-RAMP

510 North Ave, Libertyville, IL 60048
Tel.: (847) 680-7700
Web Site: http://www.handiramp.com
Year Founded: 1958
Rev.: $5,200,000
Emp.: 34
Industrial Machinery & Equipment
Merchant Whslr
N.A.I.C.S.: 423830
Thomas Disch (Pres)

HANDL-IT INC.

5386 Majestic Pkwy Ste A, Cleve-
land, OH 44146
Tel.: (440) 786-2200
Web Site: http://www.handlit.com
Sales Range: $25-49.9 Million
Emp.: 40
General Warehousing & Storage
N.A.I.C.S.: 493110
Jerry Peters (Pres & COO)
Jeannie Sureck (Mgr-HR)

Subsidiaries:

VMR Service   (1)
7120 Krick Rd, Walton Hills, OH 44146
Tel.: (440) 232-0661
Rev.: $400,000
Emp.: 6
Industrial Machinery & Equipment Repair
N.A.I.C.S.: 811310

HANDLERY HOTELS INC.
180 Geary St Ste 700, San Francisco, CA 94108
Tel.: (415) 781-4550
Web Site: http://www.handlery.com
Sales Range: $10-24.9 Million
Emp.: 300
Hotel
N.A.I.C.S.: 721110
Michael Handlery (Sr VP)
Jon Handlery (Pres & Gen Mgr-San Francisco)
Arthur John Pekrul (CEO)
Mark Hyde (Dir-HR)

HANDLING SYSTEMS INC.
2659 E Magnolia St, Phoenix, AZ 85034
Tel.: (602) 275-2228
Web Site: http://www.handlingsystems.com
Year Founded: 1981
Sales Range: $10-24.9 Million
Emp.: 80
Sales & Service of Materials Handling Machinery
N.A.I.C.S.: 423830
Joe Schnurr (CFO & Controller)
Chris Stevens (VP-Major Accts & Sys Sls)
Daryl Forbes (VP-Product Support)
James Wilcox (Gen Mgr)

HANDS-ON LEARNING SOLUTIONS LLC
3617 Lonzalo Way, New Port Richey, FL 34655
Tel.: (866) 668-7505   FL
Web Site: http://www.learnondemandsystems.com
Information Technology Services
N.A.I.C.S.: 541511
Corey J. Hynes (CEO)

Subsidiaries:

Wadeware LLC   (1)
10400 NE 4th St Ste 500, Bellevue, WA 98004
Tel.: (425) 497-9833
Web Site: http://www.wadeware.net
Administrative Management & General Management Consulting Services
N.A.I.C.S.: 541611
William Wade (CEO)

HANDSON3, LLC
3003 Pennsylvania Ave, Santa Monica, CA 90404
Tel.: (424) 268-8900
Web Site: http://www.handson3.com
Buyout Funds & Investment Services
N.A.I.C.S.: 523999
Par Chadha (CEP & Chief Investment Officer)
Jim Reynolds (COO & CFO)
Ashim Ahuja (Mng Dir)
Andrej Jonovic (Mng Dir)

HANDSTAND INNOVATIONS LLC
980 Monroe Ave NW, Grand Rapids, MI 49503
Tel.: (616) 805-4816
Web Site: http://www.messagewrap.com
Year Founded: 2011
Sales Range: $1-9.9 Million
Emp.: 14
Advertising Agency Services
N.A.I.C.S.: 541810
Nathan Vanderploeg (Founder & CEO)

HANDY BUICK-GMC-CADILLAC INC.

405 Swanton Rd, Saint Albans, VT 05478-2611
Tel.: (802) 752-4606
Web Site: https://www.handygmc.com
Year Founded: 1958
Sales Range: $10-24.9 Million
Emp.: 25
Car Whslr
N.A.I.C.S.: 441110
Jeffrey L. Handy (Co-Owner)
David J. Handy (Co-Owner)
Tom Clark (Gen Mgr)

HANDY STORE FIXTURES, INC.
337 Sherman Ave, Newark, NJ 07114-1507
Tel.: (973) 242-1600   NJ
Web Site: http://www.handysf.com
Year Founded: 1952
Sales Range: $10-24.9 Million
Emp.: 250
Mfr of Store Fixtures
N.A.I.C.S.: 337126
Rayfield B. Kurland (Chm)
Ross Ciaglia (VP-Production)
Scott McClymont (CFO)

HANDY TV INC.
220 Distribution Dr, Birmingham, AL 35209-6458
Tel.: (205) 290-0300   AL
Web Site: http://www.handytv.com
Year Founded: 1976
Sales Range: $10-24.9 Million
Emp.: 85
Appliance & Electronics Stores
N.A.I.C.S.: 444230
Melody Pennington (Dir-IT)

HANDY WACKS CORPORATION
100 E Averill St, Sparta, MI 49345
Tel.: (616) 887-8268
Web Site: http://www.handywacks.com
Rev.: $15,000,000
Emp.: 50
Waxed Paper: Made From Purchased Material
N.A.I.C.S.: 322220
Paul Steffens (Mgr-Production)
Scott Gritter (Dir-Maintenance)
Sue Harrison (Mgr-Customer Svc)
Bruce Stevens (Dir-CIS)
Chris Roberts (Dir-Sls)
Henry B. Fairchild III (Pres)

HANENKRATT GRAIN CO., INC.
471 S 300 E, Monticello, IN 47960
Tel.: (574) 583-5044
Web Site: http://www.farmersedge.com
Year Founded: 1952
Sales Range: $10-24.9 Million
Emp.: 12
Grain Elevators
N.A.I.C.S.: 424510
R. Daniel Hanenkratt (Pres)
Cindy Hanenkratt (Sec)

HANES SUPPLY INC.
55 James E Casey Dr, Buffalo, NY 14206
Tel.: (716) 826-2636
Web Site: https://www.hanessupply.com
Sales Range: Less than $1 Million
Emp.: 50
Contractor's Materials
N.A.I.C.S.: 423810
William Hanes (Pres)
David Learn (VP)
Richard Streicher (VP-Sls)

HANFORD CHRYSLER-DODGE-JEEP, INC.
369 N 11th Ave, Hanford, CA 93230-4511
Tel.: (559) 583-7000
Web Site: http://www.hanfordchryslerdodgejeepram.net
Year Founded: 1991
Sales Range: $10-24.9 Million
Emp.: 43
New Car Dealers
N.A.I.C.S.: 441110
Dwight D. Nelson (Pres)
Rick Jacobs (Gen Mgr)

HANFORD HOTELS INC.
4 Corporate Plz Dr 102, Newport Beach, CA 92660
Tel.: (949) 640-8888
Rev.: $33,018,521
Emp.: 11
Real Estate Managers
N.A.I.C.S.: 531210
Donald Sodaro (Chm)
Jenny Stout (Dir-Pur)

HANFT RABOY & PARTNERS
205 Hudson St 7th Fl, New York, NY 10013
Tel.: (212) 674-3100   NY
Year Founded: 1981
Rev.: $100,000,000
Emp.: 50
Advetising Agency
N.A.I.C.S.: 541810
Doug Raboy (Mng Partner)
John Prendergast (Exec Dir-Media)
Allan Cohen (Exec Acct Dir)
Adam Hanft (Pres & Dir-Creative)

HANG UP SHOPPES INC.
3308 N Mitthoeffer Rd, Indianapolis, IN 46235-2332
Tel.: (317) 337-2121
Web Site: http://www.manalive.com
Year Founded: 1969
Sales Range: $25-49.9 Million
Emp.: 300
Men's & Boys' Clothing Stores
N.A.I.C.S.: 458110
Lou Spagna (Pres)

HANGER CLINIC-MOBILE
2700 Grant St, Mobile, AL 36606-4703
Tel.: (251) 473-7001
Web Site: http://hangerclinic.com
Health & Personal Care Stores
N.A.I.C.S.: 456199
Ronald Deckert (Treas & VP)

HANGOVER JOE'S HOLDING CORPORATION
9457 S University 349, Highlands Ranch, CO 80126
Tel.: (303) 872-5939   CO
Web Site: http://www.hangoverjoes.com
Year Founded: 2005
Sales Range: Less than $1 Million
Emp.: 2
Pharmaceutical Preparation Mfr
N.A.I.C.S.: 325412
Michael Jaynes (Chm & Dir-Ops)
Matthew A. Veal (CEO & CFO)

HANIG'S FOOTWEAR INC.
2754 N Clark St FL 1, Chicago, IL 60614
Tel.: (773) 248-1977
Web Site: http://www.hanigs.com
Sales Range: $10-24.9 Million
Emp.: 40
Shoe Stores
N.A.I.C.S.: 458210

Ted Koransky (Mgr-Store)

HANIGAN CHEVROLET
915 S Main St, Payette, ID 83661
Tel.: (208) 642-3348
Web Site: http://www.haniganchevrolet.com
Year Founded: 1925
Sales Range: $10-24.9 Million
Emp.: 36
Car Whslr
N.A.I.C.S.: 441110
Mike Hanigan (Pres)

HANK'S FURNITURE INC.
5708 Warden, Sherwood, AR 72120
Tel.: (501) 565-3561
Web Site: http://www.hanksfurniture.com
Rev.: $47,185,375
Emp.: 200
Furniture Retailer
N.A.I.C.S.: 449110
Henry C. Browne (Chm)
Tripp Estlinbaum (Mgr-Warehouse)

HANKEY GROUP
4751 Wilshire Blvd Ste 110, Los Angeles, CA 90010
Tel.: (323) 692-4053
Web Site: https://www.hankeygroup.com
Year Founded: 1972
Sales Range: $1-4.9 Billion
Emp.: 2,879
Holding Company Financial & Management Services
N.A.I.C.S.: 551112
Don Hankey (Founder, Chm & CEO)
Bret Hankey (Pres)
Amit Shah (COO)
Jay Kamdar (CTO)
Gracia Ang (CFO)

Subsidiaries:

Westlake Financial Services, LLC   (1)
4751 Wilshire Blvd Ste 110, Los Angeles, CA 90010   (100%)
Tel.: (888) 739-9192
Web Site: http://www.westlakefinancial.com
Financial & Franchise Services
N.A.I.C.S.: 523999
Ian Anderson (Grp Pres)
Don Hankey (Founder & Chm)

HANKIN GROUP
707 Eagleview Blvd Fl 4, Exton, PA 19341
Tel.: (610) 458-1900
Web Site: http://www.hankingroup.com
Year Founded: 1958
Sales Range: $25-49.9 Million
Emp.: 80
Provider of Speculative Building & Single-Family Houses
N.A.I.C.S.: 236115
Robert Hankin (CEO & Partner)
Christine M. Helmig (CFO)
Beverly Abbonizio (Dir-Mktg)
Neal Fisher (VP-Dev)
Lance Hillegas (VP-Design & Sustainable Dev)
Stacy Martin (VP-Comml Sls & Leasing)

HANKINS LUMBER COMPANY, INC.
Nat G Troutt Rd, Elliott, MS 38926
Tel.: (662) 226-2961   MS
Web Site: https://www.hankinslumber.com
Lumber Sales
N.A.I.C.S.: 423310
Jerry A. Pegg (CFO)

HANKISON INTERNATIONAL

Hankison International—(Continued)

1000 Philadelphia St, Canonsburg,
PA 15317-1700
Tel.: (724) 746-4240   DE
Web Site: http://www.spx.com
Year Founded: 1948
Sales Range: $25-49.9 Million
Emp.: 400
Air & Gas Compressors Mfr
N.A.I.C.S.: 333912
Jay Francis (Mgr-Mktg)

HANKOOK MOTORS INC.
2229 Benice Blvd, Los Angeles, CA
90006
Tel.: (213) 382-8464
Year Founded: 1973
Sales Range: $10-24.9 Million
Emp.: 10
Dealer of New & Used Automobiles
N.A.I.C.S.: 441110
Banny Yoon (Pres)

HANKSCRAFT INC.
300 Wengel Dr, Reedsburg, WI
53959
Tel.: (608) 524-4341
Web Site:
    https://www.hankscraft.com
Year Founded: 1920
Sales Range: $10-24.9 Million
Emp.: 300
Small Electrical Motors
N.A.I.C.S.: 335312
Dan Braun (Pres)
Mark Bloom (CFO)
Walt See (Mgr-Sls-H2O Products Div)
Ron Wright (VP-Ops)

Subsidiaries:

AJS & Associates Inc.   (1)
200 Industrial Dr, Random Lake, WI 53075
Tel.: (920) 994-4300
Web Site: http://www.hankscraft.com
Rev.: $3,900,000
Emp.: 30
Knobs, Wood
N.A.I.C.S.: 321999

HANLEES HILLTOP TOYOTA
3255 Auto Plz, Richmond, CA 94806-
1931
Tel.: (510) 243-2020
Web Site:
    https://www.hanleesrichmond
    toyota.com
Year Founded: 1995
Sales Range: $10-24.9 Million
Emp.: 69
Car Whslr
N.A.I.C.S.: 441110
Shawn Mosley (Gen Mgr)
Jason Tran (Principal)

Subsidiaries:

Napa Chrysler Jeep Dodge Ram
Volvo Kia   (1)
333 Soscol Ave, Napa, CA 94559-4005
Tel.: (707) 224-3166
Web Site: http://www.napaautodealer.com
Sales Range: $10-24.9 Million
Emp.: 35
New Car Whslr
N.A.I.C.S.: 441110

HANN ENTERPRISES, INC.
6555 18th St E Unit 103, Sarasota,
FL 34243
Tel.: (941) 756-8183
Web Site:
    http://www.hannpowerboats.com
Sales Range: $1-9.9 Million
Emp.: 6
Boat Building & Sales
N.A.I.C.S.: 336612
Russell Hann (Pres)
Kevin J. McLaughlin (VP)

HANNA & ASSOCIATES INC.
1090 E Lakeshore Dr, Coeur
D'Alene, ID 83814
Tel.: (208) 667-2428   ID
Web Site: http://www.hanna-
advertising.com
Year Founded: 1976
Emp.: 25
Advetising Agency
N.A.I.C.S.: 541810
Dayne G. Hanna (Pres)
John Baechler (VP & Dir-Creative)
Jeffrey Hanna (VP & Dir-Media)
Dwain Smart (Assoc Dir-Creative)
Shannon Pyle (Coord-Acctg)
Seth Weber (Dir-Art)

HANNA CYLINDERS
8901 102nd St, Pleasant Prairie, WI
53158
Tel.: (262) 764-8300
Web Site:
    https://www.hannacylinders.com
Year Founded: 1900
Pneumatic & Hydraulic Cylinders &
Limit Switch Assemblies Mfr
N.A.I.C.S.: 332313
Tom Shealy (Regional Sls Mgr)

HANNA HOLDINGS, INC.
119 Gamma Dr, Pittsburgh, PA 15238
Tel.: (412) 967-9000   PA
Web Site:
    http://www.howardhanna.com
Year Founded: 1981
Sales Range: $250-299.9 Million
Holding Company; Real Estate Bro-
kerage, Mortgage, Title, Closing &
Insurance Services
N.A.I.C.S.: 551112
Howard W. Hanna III (Pres & CEO)
Howard W. Hanna Jr. (Founder)

Subsidiaries:

Howard Hanna Company   (1)
119 Gamma Dr, Pittsburgh, PA 15238
Tel.: (412) 967-9000
Web Site: http://www.howardhanna.com
Real Estate Brokerage, Mortgage, Title,
Closing & Insurance Services
N.A.I.C.S.: 531210
Howard W. Hanna IV (Pres-Real Estate
Svcs)
Helen Hanna Casey (Pres & CEO-Real Es-
tate Brokerage)
Howard W. Hanna III (Chm & CEO)
Tracy Rossetti Delvaux (CFO)
Annie Hanna Cestra (COO & Exec VP-Real
Estate Svcs)
Annie Hanna Engel (Pres-Insurance Svcs)
Mark Steele (Pres-Fin)
Thomas M. Ceponis (Sr VP & Mgr-North
Pennsylvania Reg)
Gregory F. Hammill (Pres-Pennsylvania-
Real Estate Svcs)
Ronald L. Dishler (Sr VP-Franchising & Li-
censing)
Susan M. Sadowski (Sr VP-Franchising,
Merger & Acq)
Jean Hayes (VP & Dir-Pur & Ops)
Darlene Hunter (VP & Mgr-New
Construction-Real Estate Svcs)
Meredith C. Stephenson (Dir-HR)
Robina R. English (VP & Mgr-Northwest-
Real Estate Svcs)
Nick Bozovich (VP-IT)
Tal Crandell (VP & Mgr-Squirrel Hill)
Angela Wargelin-Fross (Mgr-Chester Town-
ship)
Dawn Rose-Sohnly (Mgr-Ohio)
Michelle Lantz-Echnat (VP & Dir-Sls-Fox
Chapel)
Sonya Clemente (Dir-Sls)
Cindy Criss (Mgr-Cranberry)
Trisha Fronczak (Mgr-North Hills)
Steve Walthius (Mgr-Carlisle)
Jim Vernon (Mgr-Elizabeth City)
Gail Coleman (Mgr-Southeast)
Justin Grant (Mgr-Great Neck)
Karen Leonardi (Sr VP-West)
Albert Picchi (Sr VP-East)

Denise Serbin (Sls Dir-East Suburban &
Monoreville)
Amy Norris (Mgr-Wooster)
Kristine Burdick (Pres-Midwest)
Ann Kyner (Mgr-South)
Armand D'Alfonso (Pres-New York)
Nan Malysza (VP-New York)
Bryant Magnien (Dir-Data Strategy)
Mike Regan (Dir-Innovation)
Fred Corsi (Pres-Western New York)
Karlton Utter (VP-Career Dev)
Jennifer Luzik (Sls Dir)
Yvonne Guthrie (VP-Pennsylvania North)
Howard W. Hanna Jr. (Founder)
Dennis Cestra Jr. (Pres-Pennsylvania)

Subsidiary (Domestic):

ALTA Financial Services, Inc.   (2)
6700 Fairview Rd Ste 300, Charlotte, NC
28210
Tel.: (704) 365-6910
Web Site: http://www.allentate.com
Real Estate Agent, Residential
N.A.I.C.S.: 531210
Pat Riley (Pres & CEO)
Chris Cope (Pres-Allen Tate Mortgage)
Mike Laruffa (Pres-Builder Services)
Eric Heintschel (CFO)
Sara Spencer (VP-Ops)
Sergio Gomez (CIO)
Stephanie Brown (CMO)

Subsidiary (Domestic):

Beverly-Hanks & Associates Inc.   (3)
300 Executive Park, Asheville, NC 28801
Tel.: (828) 254-7221
Web Site: http://www.beverly-hanks.com
Real Estate Brokers & Agents
N.A.I.C.S.: 531210
Larry Zapf (VP-Bus Dev)
Natalie Buckner (Mgr-Acctg)
Debbie Lane (Exec VP)
Amy Congdon (VP-Mortgage Svcs)
Holly Dahl (Dir-Career Dev)
Connie Edson (Coord-Relocation)
Amy Hanks (Pres-Mortgage Svcs)
Lesia Hensley (Mgr-Adv)
Richard Hoffart (Coord-Relocation Cus-
tomer Svc)
Michael Phelan (Chief Mktg & Tech Officer)
Amy Wardle (Coord-Relocation)
Josh Baker (Mgr-Creative Svcs)
Rachel Broadbent (Mktg Mgr)
Neal Hanks Jr. (Pres)

Blowing Rock Investment Properties,
Inc.   (3)
6236 US Hwy 321 S, Blowing Rock, NC
28605
Tel.: (828) 829-7337
Web Site: http://www.brips.com
Real Estate Brokerage Services
N.A.I.C.S.: 531210
Scott MacIntosh (Pres)

Subsidiary (Domestic):

Hanna Commercial Real Estate   (2)
1350 Euclid Ave Ste 700, Cleveland, OH
44115
Tel.: (216) 861-7200
Web Site: http://www.hannacre.com
Emp.: 100
Commercial & Industrial Real Estate Man-
agement & Brokerage Services
N.A.I.C.S.: 531210
Amy Wolf-Fischer (VP)
Mark Abood (Mng Dir & Principal)
Michael Berland (Mng Dir & Principal)
Amy Brocato (VP)
William Carothers (VP)
Andrew H. Chess (Sr VP)
Michael Clegg (Sr VP)
Anthony Delguyd (Sr VP)
Joseph Ditchman (Sr VP)
Joel Dutton (VP)
David R. Janka (Dir-Mktg)
Geoff F. Coyle III (Mng Partner)
David O'Neill Jr. (Exec Mng Dir-Corp Svcs)
William Nice Jr. (Mng Dir & Principal)

Branch (Domestic):

Howard Hanna Co. - Mentor   (2)
8396 Mentor Ave, Mentor, OH 44060
Tel.: (440) 974-9999
Web Site: http://www.howardhanna.com
Emp.: 120

Real Estate Brokerage, Mortgage, Title,
Closing & Insurance Services
N.A.I.C.S.: 531210
Melissa Crockett Willis (VP & Reg Mgr-
Northeast Ohio)

Subsidiary (Domestic):

Nothnagle REALTORS   (2)
217 W Main St, Rochester, NY 14614-1101
Tel.: (585) 756-7300
Web Site: http://www.nothnagle.com
Real Estate Services
N.A.I.C.S.: 531210
Phillip R. Nothnagle (Chm)
Rob Reimer (Sr Mgr-Sls)
Armand D'Alfonso (Pres)
Bob Maves (Sr Mgr-Sls & Branch Mgr-
Pittsford Office)
Jay Teresi (VP-Sls)
John Rummel (Reg Mgr-Buffalo)
Michelle Schlossel (Sr Mgr-Sls & Branch
Mgr-Batavia Office)
John Mitchell (Branch Mgr-Amherst)
Gail Vanderbrook (Branch Mgr-
Canandaigua, Geneva & Naples Offices)
Dan Cappa (Branch Mgr-Fairport Office)
Abramo Bianchi (Branch Mgr-Hilton &
Spencerport Office)
David Sharp (Branch Mgr-Mendon Honeoye
Falls & Nothnagle Academy)
Lisa Avery (Branch Mgr-Orchard Park Of-
fice)
Louis DiMartino (Branch Mgr-Webster Of-
fice)
Jeremy Havens (Branch Mgr-Penfield Of-
fice)
Frank Robusto (Branch Mgr-Ontario Office)
Jeffrey Pastorella (Branch Mgr-Irondequoit
Office)
Dan Head (Branch Mgr-Henrietta Office)
Nancy Cook (Branch Mgr-Gates Office)
Margaret Sullivan (Branch Mgr-Dansville
Office)
John Majchrzak (Branch Mgr-Chili-Ogden &
Brockport Office)
Donald Simonetti Jr. (Branch Mgr-Brighton)

Smythe, Cramer Co.   (2)
800 W Saint Clair Ave, Cleveland, OH
44113
Tel.: (216) 447-4477
Web Site: http://www.howardhanna.com
Sales Range: $25-49.9 Million
Emp.: 250
Real Estate Brokerage, Mortgage, Title,
Closing & Insurance Services
N.A.I.C.S.: 531210
Howard W. Hanna IV (Pres-Midwest-
Howard Hanna Grp & Reg)
Barbara Reynolds (VP-Brokerage Svcs)

The Edward Surovell Company   (2)
1884 W Stadium Blvd, Ann Arbor, MI 48103
Tel.: (734) 665-9800
Web Site: http://www.howardhanna.com
Emp.: 15
Real Estate Brokerage, Mortgage, Title,
Closing & Insurance Services
N.A.I.C.S.: 531210
Lisa Fleming (VP & Reg Mgr-Michigan)

HANNA INSTRUMENTS INC.
584 Park E Dr, Woonsocket, RI
02895
Tel.: (401) 765-7500
Web Site: https://www.hannainst.com
Year Founded: 1978
Sales Range: $10-24.9 Million
Emp.: 50
Instruments & Control Equipment Mfr
N.A.I.C.S.: 423830
Martino Nardo (Pres)

HANNA LEE COMMUNICA-
TIONS, INC.
575 Madison Ave 8th Fl, New York,
NY 10022
Tel.: (212) 721-2090
Web Site:
    http://www.hannaleecommunica
    tions.com
Year Founded: 2004
Sales Range: Less than $1 Million
Emp.: 10
Advetising Agency

N.A.I.C.S.: 541810
Hanna Lee *(Founder & Pres)*

HANNA STEEL CORPORATION
3812 Commerce Ave, Fairfield, AL 35064
Tel.: (205) 780-1111
Web Site:
https://www.hannasteel.com
Rev.: $69,600,000
Emp.: 200
Welded Pipe & Tubes
N.A.I.C.S.: 331210
Joe Yost *(Exec VP-Sls)*
Jimmy Gustin *(Pres)*

Subsidiaries:

Hanna Truck Line, Inc.   (1)
1700 Boone Blv, Northport, AL 35476
Web Site: http://www.hannatruck.com
General Freight Trucking, Long-Distance,
Truckload
N.A.I.C.S.: 484121
Pete Hanna *(Chm & Pres)*

HANNABERY ELECTRIC INC.
200 Schantz Rd, Allentown, PA 18104
Tel.: (610) 366-9400
Web Site:
https://www.hannabery.com
Year Founded: 1972
Sales Range: $10-24.9 Million
Emp.: 100
Warm Air Heating & Air Conditioning
Contractor
N.A.I.C.S.: 238220
Dave Valek *(VP-Sls)*

HANNAH MOTOR COMPANY INCORPORATED
3321 NE Auto Mall Dr, Vancouver, WA 98662
Tel.: (360) 944-3399   WA
Web Site:
http://www.dickhannah.com
Automobiles, New & Used
N.A.I.C.S.: 441110
Mike Phillips *(Gen Mgr)*
Nick Faust *(Gen Mgr-Sls)*
Alex Basett *(Dir-Svc)*
Pat Cassity *(Mgr-Used Car)*
Milton Copeland *(Mgr-Sls)*
Scott Hegney *(Mgr-Sls)*
Zeke Holpuch *(Mgr-Sls)*
Chris Nelson *(Mgr-Fin)*
Noah Rodeman *(Mgr-Fin)*
Paul Nickolas *(Mgr-Fin)*
Pavel Shevyakov *(Mgr-Fin)*
Jennifer Pennington *(Dir-Internet)*
Jeanne Riley *(Asst Gen Mgr)*
Elizabeth Barber *(Mgr-Customer Rels)*
Chuck Ansted *(Mgr-Team Svc)*
Michele Archuleta *(Mgr-Team Svc)*
Shawn Bonebrake *(Mgr-Team Svc)*
Natalie Chambers *(Mgr-Team Svc)*
Che Haluapo *(Mgr-Team Svc)*
Darin Kyle *(Mgr-Team Svc)*
Rob Loomis *(Mgr-Team Svc)*
Jeff Munson *(Mgr-Team Svc)*
Lisa Maunu *(Mgr-Team Svc)*

HANNAM CHAIN USA INC.
5301 Beach Blvd, Buena Park, CA 90621
Tel.: (213) 382-2922
Web Site:
http://www.hannamchain.com
Sales Range: $50-74.9 Million
Emp.: 90
Restaurant Equipment & Supplies
N.A.I.C.S.: 423440
Kee Whan Ha *(Pres)*
Jason Lee *(Chief Plng Officer)*

HANNAN SUPPLY COMPANY

1565 N 8th St, Paducah, KY 42001-1721
Tel.: (270) 442-5456
Web Site:
https://www.hannansupply.com
Sales Range: $10-24.9 Million
Emp.: 60
Electrical Supplies
N.A.I.C.S.: 423610
W. James Brockenborough *(Chm)*
Bruce P. Brockenborough *(Pres)*
Philip Haire *(Mgr)*
Katy Zaninovich *(CFO)*
Bruce Brockenborough *(CEO)*
Michael Hughes *(Mgr-Branch)*

HANNAY REELS INC.
553 State Rte 143, Westerlo, NY 12193-0159
Tel.: (518) 797-3791   NY
Web Site: http://www.hannay.com
Year Founded: 1933
Sales Range: $75-99.9 Million
Emp.: 150
Mfr of Reels to Handle Hose & Electric Cable
N.A.I.C.S.: 332999
Eric A. Hannay *(Pres & CEO)*

HANNER CHEVROLET PONTIAC
I-20 at FM 2047, Baird, TX 79504
Tel.: (325) 854-1133
Web Site:
http://www.hannerchevrolet.com
Rev.: $10,500,000
Emp.: 40
Automobiles, New & Used
N.A.I.C.S.: 441110
John Wheeler *(Mgr-Svcs)*

HANNIS T. BOURGEOIS, LLP
2322 Tremont Dr, Baton Rouge, LA 70809
Tel.: (225) 928-4770
Web Site: https://htbcpa.com
Emp.: 100
Accounting Services
N.A.I.C.S.: 541211
Jay Montalbano *(Mng Partner)*

Subsidiaries:

Daenen Henderson & Co.   (1)
5615 Jackson St Ext Ste C, Alexandria, LA 71303-2304
Tel.: (318) 445-4585
Web Site: http://www.dhc-cpas.com
Other Accounting Services
N.A.I.C.S.: 541219
Boyle J. Henderson Jr. *(Partner)*

HANNON COMPANY
1605 Waynesburg Dr SE, Canton, OH 44707
Tel.: (330) 456-4728
Web Site: http://www.hanco.com
Sales Range: $10-24.9 Million
Emp.: 125
Electric Motor Mfr
N.A.I.C.S.: 335312
Thomas W. Hannon *(Chm)*
Pat Hoover *(VP-Fin)*
C. Wood *(Treas)*

HANNON HILL CORPORATION
1720 Peachtree St NW Ste 405, Atlanta, GA 30309
Tel.: (678) 904-6900
Web Site: http://www.hannonhill.com
Year Founded: 2001
Sales Range: $25-49.9 Million
Emp.: 50
Web Marketing Solutions
N.A.I.C.S.: 513210
David Cummings *(Founder & Chm)*
Blaine Herman *(VP-Sls)*
Bradley Wagner *(VP-Engrg)*

Kat Liendgens *(CEO)*
Penny Kronz *(Dir-Professional Svcs)*
Tim Reilly *(Dir-Support)*
Laura Rives *(VP-Sls & Mktg)*

HANNON'S KENTUCKY FRIED CHICKEN, INC.
361 Edgewood Ter Dr, Jackson, MS 39206
Tel.: (601) 982-2552   MS
Year Founded: 1965
Sales Range: $10-24.9 Million
Emp.: 300
Fast-Food Restaurant, Chain
N.A.I.C.S.: 722513
Mike Hannon *(VP)*

HANNOUSH JEWELERS INC.
1655 Boston Rd Unit B7, Springfield, MA 01129-1155
Tel.: (413) 439-2886   MA
Web Site: https://www.hannoush.com
Year Founded: 1980
Sales Range: $50-74.9 Million
Emp.: 500
Sales of Jewelry
N.A.I.C.S.: 458310
Anthony Hannoush *(Pres)*
Mary Gancarz *(Reg Mgr)*
Elizabeth Singer *(Dir-Insurance Replacement)*

HANNUMS HARLEY-DAVIDSON SALES, INC.
1011 W Baltimore Pike, Media, PA 19063
Tel.: (610) 566-5562   PA
Web Site:
https://www.hannumshd.com
Sales Range: $10-24.9 Million
Emp.: 28
Motorcycles
N.A.I.C.S.: 441227
Thomas B. Hannum *(Owner)*
Tonda Di Pasquale *(Owner)*

HANOVER ENGINEERS PC INC.
9121 Dickey Dr, Mechanicsville, VA 23116-2808
Tel.: (804) 730-0011   VA
Web Site: http://www.hepc.com
Year Founded: 1968
Sales Range: $10-24.9 Million
Emp.: 15
Engineeering Services
N.A.I.C.S.: 541330
Tiffany Bryant *(Pres)*

HANOVER FIRE & CASUALTY INSURANCE COMPANY
295 S Gulph Rd, King of Prussia, PA 19406
Tel.: (610) 940-1165
Web Site:
https://www.hanoverfire.com
Year Founded: 1914
Fire, Marine & Casualty Insurance
N.A.I.C.S.: 524126
Ross D. Miller *(Pres & CEO)*
Laurence Barker *(CFO)*
Elizabeth Rultenberg *(VP-Claims)*
Brian Thompson *(Dir-Agency Dev)*

HANOVER LAND SERVICES, INC.
2001 Meadow Dr, Westminster, MD 21158-2706
Tel.: (410) 857-0210
Web Site:
http://www.hanoverlandservice.com
Engineeering Services
N.A.I.C.S.: 541330

Gary A. Gregory *(Pres)*
Keith Heindel *(VP & Dir-Surveys-Maryland & Pennsylvania)*

Subsidiaries:

Hanover Land Services, Inc.-Pennsylvania Office   (1)
585 Mcallister St, Hanover, PA 17331
Tel.: (717) 637-5674
Web Site:
http://www.hanoverlandservices.com
Surveying & Mapping Services
N.A.I.C.S.: 541360

HANOVER PARTNERS, INC.
201 B Ave Ste 270, Lake Oswego, OR 97034
Tel.: (503) 699-6410   OR
Web Site:
http://www.hanoverpartners.com
Year Founded: 1994
Privater Equity Firm
N.A.I.C.S.: 523999
Andrew N. Ford *(Co-Founder & Principal)*
John E. Palmer *(Co-Founder & Principal-California)*
Aaron C. Aiken *(Principal)*

Subsidiaries:

Blast Deflectors, Inc.   (1)
8620 Technology Way, Reno, NV 89521
Tel.: (775) 856-1928
Web Site: http://www.blastdeflectors.com
Jet Blast Deflector & Related Products Mfr
N.A.I.C.S.: 331222
Mike Sherman *(Dir-Fin)*

HANOVER R.S. LIMITED PARTNERSHIP
5847 San Felipe St Ste 3600, Houston, TX 77057-3263
Tel.: (713) 267-2100   TX
Web Site: http://www.hanoverco.com
Year Founded: 1994
Sales Range: $25-49.9 Million
Emp.: 300
Holding Company: Real Estate Development Services
N.A.I.C.S.: 551112
J. Murray Bowden *(Founder, Chm & CEO)*
Judi Hopper *(Chief Acctg Officer)*

Subsidiaries:

The Hanover Company   (1)
5847 San Felipe St, Houston, TX 77057-3000
Tel.: (713) 267-2100
Web Site: http://www.hanoverco.com
Sales Range: $50-74.9 Million
Real Estate Development Services
N.A.I.C.S.: 237210
Jeb Bowden *(COO)*
Howard Dyer-Smith *(Mng Partner-Construction)*
Brandt Bowden *(Chief Investment Officer)*
Murry Bowden *(Founder, Chm & CEO)*
Roxanne Cox *(VP-HR)*
Tim Ellwood *(Gen Counsel)*
John Garibaldi *(Mng Partner-Dev)*
Judi Hopper *(Chief Acctg Officer)*
John Nash *(Pres)*
Ben Whitman *(VP-Capital Markets)*

HANS HAGEN HOMES INC.
941 Hillwind Rd NE Ste 300, Fridley, MN 55432-5965
Tel.: (763) 572-9455   MN
Web Site:
http://www.hanshagenhomes.com
Year Founded: 1977
Sales Range: $10-24.9 Million
Emp.: 50
Single-Family Housing Construction Services
N.A.I.C.S.: 236115
Ted Hagen *(VP-Construction)*
Jim Lee *(Mgr-Sls)*

Hans Hagen Homes Inc.—(Continued)

Doug Smith (VP-Construction Ops)
Elizabeth Clapp (Mgr-Sls)
John Rask (VP-Land Dev)

HANS HOLTERBOSCH, INC.
375 Park Ave Ste 2503, New York,
NY 10152-0002
Tel.: (212) 421-3800
Sales Range: $75-99.9 Million
Emp.: 3
Real Estate Services
N.A.I.C.S.: 531390
H.D. Holterbosch (Pres)

HANSEL 'N GRETEL BRAND INC.
79-36 Cooper Ave, Glendale, NY
11385
Tel.: (718) 326-0041
Web Site: http://www.healthydeli.com
Sales Range: $10-24.9 Million
Emp.: 150
Processed Meat Mfr
N.A.I.C.S.: 311612
Steven Rosbosh (Dir-Fin)
Kris Brimski (Plant Engr)
Richie Fawcett (Mgr-Production)
James Roe (Product Mgr)

HANSEL HONDA
1310 Auto Center Dr, Petaluma, CA
94952-6507
Tel.: (707) 683-7873
Web Site:
    https://www.hanselhonda.com
Year Founded: 1996
Sales Range: $10-24.9 Million
Emp.: 80
Car Whslr
N.A.I.C.S.: 441110
General Manager (Principal)

HANSEN CHEVROLET CO.
1175 S Commerce Way, Brigham
City, UT 84302
Tel.: (435) 723-5255   UT
Web Site:
    http://www.hansenmotor.com
Rev.: $28,259,301
Emp.: 37
Automobiles, New & Used
N.A.I.C.S.: 441110
Byron Hansen (Pres)
Matthew Hansen (Gen Mgr)

HANSEN COMPANY INC.
5665 Greendale Rd Ste A, Johnston,
IA 50131
Tel.: (515) 270-1117
Web Site:
    https://www.hansencompany.com
Year Founded: 1979
Rev.: $16,000,000
Emp.: 20
Provider of Commercial & Office
Building Construction Services
N.A.I.C.S.: 236220
Craig W. Hansen (Pres)
Craig Faber (Pres)
Mike Halstead (Controller)

HANSEN ENGINEERING CO. INC.
24050 Frampton Ave, Harbor City,
CA 90710
Tel.: (310) 534-3870
Web Site:
    https://www.hansenengineering.com
Sales Range: $10-24.9 Million
Emp.: 40
Machine Shop, Jobbing & Repair
N.A.I.C.S.: 332710
Jody Lay (Pres)

HANSEN INTERNATIONAL INC.
130 Zenker Rd, Lexington, SC
29072-4600
Tel.: (803) 695-1500   SC
Web Site: https://www.hansenint.com
Year Founded: 1994
Sales Range: $10-24.9 Million
Emp.: 65
Provider of Special Industry Machinery
N.A.I.C.S.: 333248
Lisa Hansen Beebe (Pres)
Michael Coggins (COO)
Fanny Leung (Controller)
John Hillis (Dir-Sales)

HANSEN OIL CO.
411 East 2nd St, Soda Springs, ID
83276
Tel.: (208) 547-3692
Sales Range: $10-24.9 Million
Emp.: 6
Petroleum Bulk Stations
N.A.I.C.S.: 424710
Kirk Hansen (Pres)

HANSEN-MUELLER CO. INC.
12231 Emmet St, Omaha, NE 68164-4266
Tel.: (402) 491-3385   NE
Web Site:
    http://www.hansenmueller.com
Year Founded: 1979
Sales Range: $50-74.9 Million
Emp.: 150
Commodity Contracts, Brokers & Dealers
N.A.I.C.S.: 523160
Jack Hansen (Founder & Pres)

HANSENS IGA INCORPORATED
1800 Commercial St, Bangor, WI
54614
Tel.: (608) 486-2626
Web Site:
    http://www.hansensiga.com
Rev.: $14,000,000
Emp.: 50
Grocery Store Operator
N.A.I.C.S.: 445110
Leo Hansen (Owner & Pres)

HANSER & ASSOCIATES PUBLIC RELATIONS
Neptune Bldg Ste 212, West Des
Moines, IA 50266
Tel.: (515) 224-1086
Web Site: http://www.hanser.com
Year Founded: 1996
Emp.: 8
Public Relations Agency
N.A.I.C.S.: 541820
Ronald C. Hanser (Pres)
Bonnie K. Hanser (COO)
Amanda Mullin (Acct Mgr)
Jim Sroboda (Dir-Creative)

Subsidiaries:

Hanser & Associates Public
Relations   (1)
10031 Maple St, Omaha, NE 68134
Tel.: (402) 393-8131
Web Site: http://www.hanser.com
Rev.: $5,152,241,086
Emp.: 2
N.A.I.C.S.: 541820

HANSER HOLDINGS INTERNATIONAL
3015 Kustom Dr, Hebron, KY 41048
Tel.: (859) 817-7100
Sales Range: $50-74.9 Million
Emp.: 75

Holding Company; Music & Audio
Equipment Developer, Mfr, Distr &
Retailer
N.A.I.C.S.: 551112
Jack Hanser (Chm & CEO)
Sales Range: $10-24.9 Million
Emp.: 80

Subsidiaries:

B.C. Rich Guitars   (1)
3015 Kustom Dr, Hebron, KY 41048
Tel.: (859) 817-7100
Web Site: http://www.bcrich.com
Sales Range: $25-49.9 Million
Guitar Sales
N.A.I.C.S.: 459140
Jack Hanser (Chm & CEO)

The Davitt & Hanser Music Co.   (1)
3015 Kustom Dr, Hebron, KY 41048
Tel.: (859) 817-7100
Web Site:
    http://www.hansermusicgroup.com
Sales Range: $25-49.9 Million
Emp.: 65
Musical Instrument Distr
N.A.I.C.S.: 423990

HANSON & HANSON ENTERPRISES LLC
2099 S Pelzer Rd, Boonville, IN
47601
Tel.: (812) 897-7910
Year Founded: 1995
Sales Range: Less than $1 Million
Emp.: 3
N.A.I.C.S.: 541810
Brian L. Hanson (Owner)
Lulu Hanson (Owner & CEO)

HANSON COMMUNICATIONS INC.
227 S Main St, Clara City, MN 56222
Tel.: (320) 847-2211
Web Site: http://www.hcinet.net
Sales Range: $25-49.9 Million
Emp.: 6
Telephone Communication Services,
Except Radio
N.A.I.C.S.: 517121
Bruce Hanson (Owner)

Subsidiaries:

Fort Randall Telephone
Company   (1)
722 W Hwy 46, Wagner, SD 57380
Tel.: (605) 384-3993
Telephone Communication, Except Radio
N.A.I.C.S.: 517121

HANSON CONSTRUCTION CO, INC.
12514 NE 95th St Ste C 100, Vancouver, WA 98682
Tel.: (360) 883-0695
Web Site:
    http://www.hansonconstructionco.com
Year Founded: 1991
Sales Range: $1-9.9 Million
Emp.: 29
Home Remodeling & Restoration
Services
N.A.I.C.S.: 236118
John P. Hanson (Founder & Pres)

HANSON DISTRIBUTING COMPANY
10802 Rush St, South El Monte, CA
91733
Tel.: (626) 224-9800
Rev.: $25,575,943
Emp.: 200
Automotive Supplies & Parts
N.A.I.C.S.: 423120
Daniel L. Hanson (Pres & CEO)
William Hansen (CFO & VP)
Bill Copeland (Mgr-Sls)
Steven A. Cox (COO)

HANSON DODGE INC.

220 E Buffalo St, Milwaukee, WI
53202
Tel.: (414) 347-1266
Web Site:
    https://www.hansondodge.com
Sales Range: $10-24.9 Million
Emp.: 65
Advetising Agency
N.A.I.C.S.: 541810
Tim Dodge (Pres)
Sarah Van Elzen (Dir-Social Media)
Chris Buhrman (Exec Dir-Creative)
Nick Wesselman (CTO-Active Commerce)
Mike Stefaniak (Partner & VP-Brand
Engagement)
Sharon Hettinger (VP-Bus Ops)
Tom Flierl (VP-Mktg & Bus Strategy)
Angela Rothen (VP-Tech)

HANSON ELECTRIC OF BEMIDJI
3125 Bemidji Ave N, Bemidji, MN
56601
Tel.: (218) 751-5833   MN
Year Founded: 1981
Sales Range: $10-24.9 Million
Emp.: 118
Electrical Contract Services
N.A.I.C.S.: 238210
Stephen Hanson (Treas & Sec)
Richard Hansom (Mgr)

HANSON INTERNATIONAL INC.
2900 S State St, Saint Joseph, MI
49085
Tel.: (269) 982-0103   MI
Web Site:
    http://www.hansonmold.com
Year Founded: 1986
Rev.: $10,000,000
Emp.: 110
Special Dies & Tools; Industrial Molds
Mfr
N.A.I.C.S.: 333514
Merlin Hanson (Chm)
Thomas Crossman (CFO & VP)
Gregory Hanson (Sec)

HANSON LOGISTICS
2875 S Pipestone Rd, Sodus Point,
MI 49126
Tel.: (269) 925-0091
Web Site:
    http://www.hansoncoldstorage.com
Sales Range: $10-24.9 Million
Emp.: 200
Storage, Frozen or Refrigerated
Goods Mfr
N.A.I.C.S.: 493120
Matt Luckas (VP-Supply Chain Svc)
Jack White (CFO & VP)

HANSON PROFESSIONAL SERVICES, INC.
1525 S 6th St, Springfield, IL 62703-2801
Tel.: (217) 788-2450   DE
Web Site: http://www.hanson-inc.com
Year Founded: 1954
Sales Range: $50-74.9 Million
Emp.: 450
Architectural, Engineering, Scientific
& Program Management Consulting
Services
N.A.I.C.S.: 541618
Jeffery Ball (Pres)
James Sassin (Sr Project Mgr-Austin)

Subsidiaries:

Hanson Alaska LLC   (1)
801 B St Ste 400, Anchorage, AK 99501
Tel.: (907) 279-1282
Web Site: http://www.hanson-inc.com

Emp.: 6
Construction Engineering Services
N.A.I.C.S.: 541330
Tom Moll (VP)

HANSON TRUSS INCORPO-RATED

13950 Yorba Ave, Chino, CA 91710
Tel.: (909) 591-9256
Web Site:
   http://www.hansontruss.com
Year Founded: 1985
Rev.: $13,800,000
Emp.: 110
Wood Truss Mfr
N.A.I.C.S.: 321215
Donald R. Hanson (Pres)
Ana Reyes (Office Mgr)
Anthony Arubalcava (Dir-Engrg)
Phillip P. David (VP)

HANSON WATSON ASSOCI-ATES

1411 15th St, Moline, IL 61265
Tel.: (309) 764-8315   IL
Year Founded: 1945
Sales Range: $10-24.9 Million
Emp.: 6
N.A.I.C.S.: 541810
James C. Hanson (CEO)
James S. Watson (Pres)
Nanci Perkins (Bus Mgr)
Katherine Betcher (Dir-Art)
Tim Wilkinson (Dir-Bus Dev)

Subsidiaries:

Latin Connection   (1)
1411 15th St, Moline, IL 61265
Tel.: (309) 764-8315
N.A.I.C.S.: 541810
Nanci Perkins (Pres)
Katherine Betcher (Dir-Art)

HANSON'S AUTO & IMPLE-MENT INC.

14830 Hwy 17 W, Grafton, ND 58237
Tel.: (701) 352-3600
Web Site: https://www.hansonai.com
Sales Range: $10-24.9 Million
Emp.: 60
Farm Implements
N.A.I.C.S.: 423820
Brian Hanson (Pres & Gen Mgr)

HANSON, WALTER & ASSOCI-ATES, INC.

8 Broadway 104, Kissimmee, FL 34741-5481
Tel.: (407) 847-9433
Web Site:
   http://www.hansonwalter.com
Sales Range: $10-24.9 Million
Emp.: 25
Civil Engineering & Land Surveying
N.A.I.C.S.: 237990
Larry W. Walter (Pres)
Shawn D. Hindle (Sr VP-Engrg)
Mark Vincutonis (VP-Engrg)
Randy Hanson (Sr VP-Surveying)
Caroll Castleberry (VP-Surveying)
John Hughes (VP-Surveying)

HANTOVER INC.

5200 W 110th St Ste 200, Overland Park, KS 66211
Tel.: (816) 761-7800
Web Site: https://www.hantover.com
Sales Range: $25-49.9 Million
Emp.: 109
Food Industry Machinery
N.A.I.C.S.: 423830
Bernard Huff (Chm)
Dave Brockway (Acct Mgr-Natl)
Chris Ancell (Asst Mgr-Credit)
Cynthia Miller (Product Mgr)
David Vaught (Controller)

HANTZ GROUP, INC.

26200 American Dr, Southfield, MI 48034
Tel.: (248) 304-2855   MI
Web Site: http://www.hantzgroup.com
Holding Company
N.A.I.C.S.: 551112
John R. Hantz (Pres & CEO)
John Beebe (Sr VP)

Subsidiaries:

Hantz Air, LLC   (1)
49541 Ecorse Rd, Belleville, MI 48111
Tel.: (734) 893-6611
Web Site: http://www.hantzair.com
Sales Range: $1-9.9 Million
Emp.: 20
Private Jet Chartering & Aircraft Manage-ment Services
N.A.I.C.S.: 488190

Hantz Financial Services, Inc.   (1)
26200 American Dr, Southfield, MI 48034
Tel.: (248) 304-2855
Web Site: http://www.hantzgroup.com
Investment Advisory & Financial Services
N.A.I.C.S.: 523940
John F. Machcinski (Pres)
John R. Hantz (Chm & CEO)

HAP O'NEILL, INC.

6701 Sunshine Skywy Ln S, Saint Petersburg, FL 33711
Tel.: (727) 867-2585   FL
Web Site:
   https://www.oneillsmarina.com
Year Founded: 1954
Sales Range: $1-9.9 Million
Emp.: 15
Marina Operations
N.A.I.C.S.: 713930
John A. Phillips (Pres)

HAPCO FARMS INC.

889 Harrison Ave, Riverhead, NY 11901-2037
Tel.: (631) 369-7000   NY
Web Site:
   http://www.hapcofarms.com
Year Founded: 1945
Sales Range: $25-49.9 Million
Emp.: 140
Fresh Fruits & Vegetables Whslr
N.A.I.C.S.: 424480
Joseph Leuci (CFO)

HAPCO REAL ESTATE IN-VESTMENT

889 Harrison Ave, Riverhead, NY 11901
Tel.: (631) 369-7000
Sales Range: $25-49.9 Million
Emp.: 100
Real Estate Agents & Managers
N.A.I.C.S.: 531210
Andy Pollak (Pres)

HAPO COMMUNITY CREDIT UNION

601 Williams Blvd, Richland, WA 99354
Tel.: (509) 943-5676   WA
Web Site: https://www.hapo.org
Year Founded: 1953
Sales Range: $50-74.9 Million
Emp.: 417
Credit Union Operator
N.A.I.C.S.: 522130
John J. Schnellbach (CFO & Sr VP)
Ruby Campos (Chief Brand Officer & Sr VP)
Scott Mitchell (Chief Risk Officer & Sr VP)
Carolyn O'Niel (Chief Dev Officer & Sr VP-Product Dev & Delivery)

HAPPINESS INC.

521 W Bedford Euless Rd, Hurst, TX 76053
Tel.: (817) 268-2466
Web Site:
   http://www.Happinessgifts.com
Rev.: $10,000,000
Emp.: 20
Gifts & Novelties
N.A.I.C.S.: 459420
James Welborn (Chm)
Renee Zubroski (Pres)

HAPPY APPLE COMPANY

Hwy 47 S, Washington, MO 63090
Web Site:
   http://www.happyapples.com
Year Founded: 1960
Sales Range: $10-24.9 Million
Emp.: 10
Apple Farm & Confectioner Producer
N.A.I.C.S.: 311340
Dan Ahot (CFO)

HAPPY CHEF SYSTEMS, INC.

51646 US Hwy 169, Mankato, MN 56001-6584
Tel.: (507) 345-4571
Year Founded: 2008
Sales Range: $10-24.9 Million
Emp.: 25
Restaurant Operating Services
N.A.I.C.S.: 722511
Thomas P. Frederick (CEO)

HAPPY DAY CORPORATION

1619 16th Ave 703 9th St, Lewiston, ID 83501
Tel.: (208) 743-0583
Web Site:
   http://www.happydaycorp.com
Sales Range: $25-49.9 Million
Emp.: 400
Franchise Owner of Fast-Food Res-taurants & Mexican Restaurants
N.A.I.C.S.: 722511
Bruce Finch (Owner)
Mike Cooper (CFO)
Lori Dufour (Dir-HR)

HAPPY FOODS, INC.

6415 N Central Ave, Chicago, IL 60646
Tel.: (773) 774-4466
Web Site:
   http://www.happyfoodsinc.com
Rev.: $13,400,000
Emp.: 185
Grocery Stores, Independent
N.A.I.C.S.: 445110
William Tarant (Co-Owner)
Dale Eastman (Co-Owner)

HAPPY JACK INC.

2122 Hwy 258 S, Snow Hill, NC 28580
Tel.: (252) 747-2911
Web Site:
   https://www.happyjackinc.com
Year Founded: 1946
Sales Range: $10-24.9 Million
Emp.: 10
Pet Supplies Mfr & Distr
N.A.I.C.S.: 325412
Joe Exum (Pres & CEO)
Manning Exum (Controller)

HAPPY JOE'S PIZZA AND ICE CREAM PARLOR, INC.

2705 Happy Joe Dr, Bettendorf, IA 52722
Tel.: (563) 332-8811
Web Site:
   https://www.happyjoes.com
Rev.: $12,030,323
Emp.: 20
Pizzeria & Ice Cream Parlor
N.A.I.C.S.: 722513

Lawrence J. Whitty (Chm & Pres)
Hollie Matthys (Controller)
Walt Malik (Dir-Pur-Store Owners Operators)

HAPPYFAMILY

40 Fulton St 17th Fl, New York, NY 10038
Tel.: (212) 374-2779
Web Site:
   http://www.happyfamilybrands.com
Sales Range: $25-49.9 Million
Emp.: 75
Baby Food Product Retailer
N.A.I.C.S.: 445298
Shazi Visram (Founder & CEO)
Jessica Rolph (Founder, Partner & COO)
Helen Bernstein (VP-Mom-to-Mom Mktg)
Alton Bradshaw (Sr VP-Quality Assur-ance)
Bob Zimmerman (VP-Sls)
Julie Scharnhorst (Sr Dir-R&D)
Shauna Grob (Dir-Fin)

HARADEN MOTORCAR CORP.

175 Freemans Bridge Rd Rte 50, Scotia, NY 12302
Tel.: (518) 370-4911
Web Site:
   http://www.mohawkhonda.com
Rev.: $15,400,000
Emp.: 40
Automobiles, New & Used
N.A.I.C.S.: 441110
Steve Haraden (VP)
Joseph Haraden II (Chm)

HARALAMBOS DISTRIBUTING CO.

2300 Pellissier Pl, City of Industry, CA 90601
Tel.: (562) 347-4300
Web Site:
   http://www.haralambos.com
Sales Range: $25-49.9 Million
Emp.: 400
Beer & Other Alcoholic Beverage Distr
N.A.I.C.S.: 424810
Anthony Haralambos (Gen Mgr)

HARARI INC.

3617 Exposition Blvd, Los Angeles, CA 90016
Tel.: (323) 734-5302
Web Site: http://eharari.com
Sales Range: $10-24.9 Million
Emp.: 45
Women's Clothing Store
N.A.I.C.S.: 315250
Dan Harari (Owner)
Shoshana Botnick (COO)
Susan Farrell (Mgr)

HARBACH GILLAN & NIXON INC.

618 W Van Buren St, Clinton, IL 61727
Tel.: (217) 935-8378
Sales Range: $25-49.9 Million
Emp.: 25
Fertilizer & Fertilizer Materials Whslr
N.A.I.C.S.: 424910
Virgil T. Harbach (Pres)
Bob Anderson (Treas & Sec)
Gene Kaufman (Controller)

HARBERT MANAGEMENT CORPORATION

2100 3rd Ave N Ste 600, Birming-ham, AL 35203
Tel.: (205) 987-5500   AL
Web Site: https://www.harbert.net

Harbert Management Corporation—(Continued)

Year Founded: 1993
Sales Range: $75-99.9 Million
Emp.: 300
Holding Company; Real Estate, Private Equity & Other Investment Services
N.A.I.C.S.: 551112
John C. Harrison *(Sr Mng Dir-Credit Solutions Team)*
Raymond J. Harbert *(Chm & CEO)*
Charles D. Miller *(Exec VP & Head-Distr-Global)*
John W. McCullough *(Gen Counsel & Exec VP)*
Sonja J. Keeton *(CFO & Exec VP)*
J. Travis Pritchett *(Sr VP & Head-Real Assets-Global)*
Jeffrey B. Liles *(CIO)*
Melissa M. Babb *(Sr Mng Dir-Sls & Mktg)*
Michael C. Bauder *(Chief Compliance Officer & VP)*
Ryan M. Hughes *(Mng Dir-Leading Sls & Mktg)*
Jerry J. Phillips *(VP & Dir-Taxation)*
Raymond J. Harbert Jr. *(Sr VP-Fin & Admin)*
Richard F. Brereton Jr. *(Sr Mng Dir-Institutional IR)*

Subsidiaries:

Bally Total Fitness Holdings Corporation **(1)**
8700 W Bryn Mawr Ave 2rd Fl, Chicago, IL 60631-3512
Tel.: (773) 380-3000
Sales Range: $1-4.9 Billion
Holding Company; Physical Fitness Facilities
N.A.I.C.S.: 713940

Subsidiary (Domestic):

Bally Total Fitness Corporation **(2)**
8700 W Bryn Mawr Ave, Chicago, IL 60631-3512
Tel.: (773) 380-3000
Web Site: http://www.ballyfitness.com
Sales Range: $10-24.9 Million
Emp.: 100
Owner & Operator of Fitness Centers
N.A.I.C.S.: 713940

Dent-A-Med Inc. **(1)**
203 E Emma Ste A, Springdale, AR 72764
Tel.: (479) 750-6700
Web Site: http://www.helpcard.com
Sales Range: $25-49.9 Million
Emp.: 90
Specialty Consumer Medical Financing Services
N.A.I.C.S.: 522210
Cliff Scogin *(CFO & Exec VP)*

HMC Investors, LLC **(1)**
2100 3rd Ave N Ste 600, Birmingham, AL 35203
Tel.: (205) 987-5596
Web Site: http://www.harbert.net
Sales Range: $50-74.9 Million
Emp.: 120
Real Estate, Private Equity & Other Investment Services
N.A.I.C.S.: 523999

Unit (Domestic):

Harbert Mezzanine Capital **(2)**
2100 3rd Ave N Ste 360, Birmingham, AL 35203
Tel.: (205) 987-5500
Web Site: http://www.harbert.net
Equity Investment Firm
N.A.I.C.S.: 523999
John C. Harrison *(Sr Mng Dir)*
Robert A. Bourquin *(Mng Dir)*
John S. Scott *(Mng Dir)*
David A. Boutwell *(Vice Chm & Exec VP)*
Raymond J. Harbert *(Chm & CEO)*

Joint Venture (Domestic):

Candescent SoftBase, LLC **(3)**

20 Fall Pippin Ln Ste 202, Asheville, NC 28803
Tel.: (828) 670-9900
Web Site: http://www.softbase.com
Sales Range: $1-9.9 Million
Software Testing & Support Services
N.A.I.C.S.: 541519
Stephen Woodard *(CEO)*
Jim Spires *(Dir-Dev)*
Teresa Turbyfill *(Controller & Dir-HR)*

Unit (Domestic):

Harbert Venture Partners **(2)**
2100 3rd Ave N Ste 600, Birmingham, AL 35203
Tel.: (205) 987-5500
Web Site: http://www.harbert.net
Equity Investment Firm
N.A.I.C.S.: 523999
William W. Brooke *(Mng Partner)*
Wayne L. Hunter *(Mng Partner)*
Robert L. Crutchfield *(Venture Partner)*
Brian C. Carney *(Principal)*
Thomas D. Roberts III *(Partner)*

HARBIN CLINIC LLC
212 Technologies Pkwy NW, Rome, GA 30165
Tel.: (706) 295-5331
Web Site: http://www.harbinclinic.com
Sales Range: $150-199.9 Million
Emp.: 400
Health Care Facility & Provider
N.A.I.C.S.: 621111
Kenneth F. Davis *(Chm & Pres)*
Alfonso Diaz *(Dir-Medical)*
Sarah King *(Dir-Wellness)*
David Strain *(Mgr)*
Andrew Goodwin *(CIO)*
Kenna Stock *(CEO)*
Tom Diehl *(CFO)*
Liz Schoen *(Chief Compliance Officer & Gen Counsel)*
Wendy Pitts *(Chief Quality Officer)*
Charles Edward McBride III *(Chief Medical Officer)*

HARBIN LUMBER COMPANY INCORPORATED
560 Smith Rd, Lavonia, GA 30553
Tel.: (706) 356-5041
Web Site: https://www.harbinlumber.com
Rev.: $30,000,000
Emp.: 9
Lumber & Other Building Materials
N.A.I.C.S.: 423310
Barron C. Harbin *(Pres)*
Jody Page *(Gen Mgr)*

HARBINGER CAPITAL PARTNERS LLC
450 Park Ave 30th Fl, New York, NY 10022
Tel.: (212) 339-5800 DE
Web Site: http://www.harbingercapital.com
Year Founded: 2001
Emp.: 40
Privater Equity Firm
N.A.I.C.S.: 523999
Deborah Gollin *(Dir-Human Recruiting)*
Keith M. Hladek *(CFO & COO)*
Kathleen Murphy *(Sr VP)*

HARBINGER PARTNERS, INC.
855 Village Center Dr Ste 356, Saint Paul, MN 55127
Tel.: (651) 260-7805
Web Site: http://www.harbinger-partners.com
Sales Range: $10-24.9 Million
Emp.: 64
Information Technology Staffing Services
N.A.I.C.S.: 561311

Mike Dvorak *(Project Mgr)*
Cindy Nelson *(Office Mgr)*

HARBISON CORPORATION
15450 S Outer 40 Rd Ste 120, Chesterfield, MO 63017-2062
Tel.: (314) 727-8200
Web Site: http://www.pretiumpkg.com
Year Founded: 1992
Sales Range: $75-99.9 Million
Emp.: 1,000
Mfr of Plastic Products
N.A.I.C.S.: 326199
Keith S. Harbison *(Chm)*
Paul Keiser *(Chm)*

Subsidiaries:

Prentium Packaging LLC **(1)**
5235 E Hunter Ave, Anaheim, CA 92807-2052
Tel.: (314) 727-8200
Sales Range: $25-49.9 Million
Emp.: 185
Mfr of Plastic Products
N.A.I.C.S.: 326199

HARBOR AMERICA
21977 E Wallis Dr, Porter, TX 77365
Tel.: (281) 999-5544 TX
Web Site: https://www.hapeo.com
Year Founded: 1997
Sales Range: $100-124.9 Million
Emp.: 60
Providers of Employee Leasing Service
N.A.I.C.S.: 561330
Douglas L. Lowery *(Pres)*
Kelly Johnson *(Mgr-Safety & Loss Prevention Ops)*
Daisy Araujo *(Mgr-Benefits Ops)*
Joseph Little *(COO & Sr VP)*

HARBOR BEACH CAPITAL, LLC
401 E Las Olas Blvd Ste 2360, Fort Lauderdale, FL 33301
Tel.: (954) 594-8001 FL
Web Site: http://www.harborbeachcapital.com
Year Founded: 2016
Privater Equity Firm
N.A.I.C.S.: 523999
Brian Urbanek *(Founder & Mng Partner)*

Subsidiaries:

AVFX, LLC **(1)**
96 Holton St, Boston, MA 02135-1318
Tel.: (617) 254-0770
Web Site: http://www.avfix.com
Commercial & Industrial Machinery & Equipment Rental & Leasing
N.A.I.C.S.: 532490
Steve Halling *(CEO)*

Subsidiary (Domestic):

A V Matters **(2)**
6113 Anno Ave, Orlando, FL 32809
Tel.: (407) 240-0694
Web Site: http://www.avmatters.com
Rev.: $1,830,000
Emp.: 10
Consumer Electronics & Appliances Rental
N.A.I.C.S.: 532210

Atlantic Southern Paving & Sealcoating, Co. **(1)**
6301 W Sunrise Blvd, Plantation, FL 33313
Tel.: (954) 581-5805
Web Site: http://www.atlanticsouthernpaving.com
Sales Range: $10-24.9 Million
Emp.: 50
Pavement Maintenance Services
N.A.I.C.S.: 324121
Michael Curry *(CEO)*

Subsidiary (Domestic):

Emerald Acquisition, Inc. **(2)**

6381 Industry Way, Westminster, CA 92683-3693
Tel.: (714) 593-3054
Web Site: http://www.empave.com
Highway, Street & Bridge Construction
N.A.I.C.S.: 237310
Derek Davis *(CEO)*

Murphree Paving LLC **(2)**
1211 Nelle St, Tupelo, MS 38801
Tel.: (662) 844-2331
Web Site: http://www.murphreepaving.com
Rev.: $1,175,000
Emp.: 5
Highway, Street & Bridge Construction
N.A.I.C.S.: 237310
Michael Murphree *(Owner)*

Property Paving Inc. **(2)**
2618 Central Ave, Grand Prairie, TX 75050-6230
Tel.: (817) 792-4000
Web Site: http://www.propertypaving.com
Concrete Foundation & Structure Contractors
N.A.I.C.S.: 238110
David Wooldridge *(Pres)*

HARBOR BEACH COMMUNITY HOSPITAL, INC.
210 S 1st St, Harbor Beach, MI 48441
Tel.: (989) 479-3201 MI
Web Site: https://www.hbch.org
Year Founded: 1957
Sales Range: $10-24.9 Million
Emp.: 181
Community Health Care Services
N.A.I.C.S.: 621498
Jill Wehner *(COO & VP)*

HARBOR BUSINESS COMPLIANCE CORPORATION
1830 Colonial Village Ln, Lancaster, PA 17601
Web Site: http://www.harborcompliance.com
Year Founded: 2012
Sales Range: $1-9.9 Million
Emp.: 50
Software Development Services
N.A.I.C.S.: 541511
Mike Montali *(Co-Founder & CEO)*
Megan Danz *(Co-Founder & CIO)*
Brian Tully *(Pres)*

Subsidiaries:

Labyrinth Inc. **(1)**
841 Quince Orchard Blvd Ste F, Gaithersburg, MD 20878-1615
Tel.: (205) 242-7334
Web Site: http://www.labyrinthinc.com
Electronic Shopping
N.A.I.C.S.: 541511
Stephen Urich *(Pres)*

HARBOR CORP.
6629 W Central Ave, Toledo, OH 43617
Tel.: (419) 475-4449 OH
Web Site: http://www.harbor.org
Year Founded: 1946
Sales Range: $10-24.9 Million
Emp.: 400
Community Action & Youth Care Services
N.A.I.C.S.: 624190
John Tooson *(Treas)*
John Betts *(Exec Dir-Rural Health Dev)*
Jim Aulenbacher *(Exec Dir-Clinical Svcs)*
Steve Benjamin *(Sr VP-Clinical Svcs)*
Bushra Qureishi *(Dir-Medical)*
Jean Drees *(Exec Dir-Mktg & Community Affairs)*
Patrick Sheehan *(Pres)*

Subsidiaries:

Behavioral Connections of Wood County, Inc. **(1)**

PO Box 29, Bowling Green, OH 43402
Tel.: (419) 352-5387
Web Site:
    http://www.behavioralconnections.org
Sales Range: $1-9.9 Million
Emp.: 200
Behavioral Healthcare Services
N.A.I.C.S.: 623220
Sajid Khan (Pres)

HARBOR DEVELOPMENTAL DISABILITIES FOUNDATION, INC.

21231 Hawthorne Blvd, Torrance, CA
90503
Tel.: (310) 540-1711   CA
Web Site: https://www.harborrc.org
Year Founded: 1977
Sales Range: $125-149.9 Million
Emp.: 266
Developmental Disability Assistance
Services
N.A.I.C.S.: 624120
Judy Wada (CFO)
Richard Malin (Mgr-IT)
Patricia Del Monico (Exec Dir)
Georgia Thompson (Mgr-Rights Assurance)
Steven Hankow (Mgr-Virtual Charts)

HARBOR FOODS GROUP INC.

3901 Hogum Bay Rd NE, Lacey, WA
98516
Tel.: (360) 754-4484   WA
Web Site: https://harborfoods.com
Year Founded: 2019
Holding Company
N.A.I.C.S.: 551112

Subsidiaries:

Harbor Wholesale Grocery Inc.   (1)
3901 Hogum Bay Rd NE, Lacey, WA
98516-3136
Tel.: (541) 464-7808
Web Site: http://www.harborwholesale.com
General Line Grocery Merchant Whslr
N.A.I.C.S.: 424410
Rick Jensen (Pres)

Subsidiary (Domestic):

Halfon Candy Company, Inc.   (2)
9229 10th Ave S, Seattle, WA 98108
Tel.: (206) 763-2000
Web Site: http://www.halfoncandy.com
Sales Range: $1-9.9 Million
Emp.: 15
Confectionery, Nsk
N.A.I.C.S.: 424450

HARBOR FOOTWEAR GROUP, LTD.

55 Harbor Park Dr, Port Washington,
NY 11050-4659
Tel.: (516) 621-8400
Web Site: http://www.gbxshoe.com
Year Founded: 1969
Sales Range: $1-9.9 Million
Emp.: 105
Mfr of Footwear
N.A.I.C.S.: 424340
Dennis S. Lazar (Pres & CEO)
Israel Weintraub (CFO)
Jim McCormick (Pres-Bass Wholesale)

HARBOR FREIGHT TOOLS USA

3491 Mission Oaks Blvd, Camarillo,
CA 93012
Tel.: (805) 388-1000
Web Site:
    https://www.harborfreight.com
Sales Range: $10-24.9 Million
Emp.: 25,000
Hardware Retailer
N.A.I.C.S.: 444140
Eric Smidt (Founder, Pres, Pres,
CEO, CEO & CEO)

HARBOR GROUP INC

1520 N Main Ave, Sioux Center, IA
51250-2111
Tel.: (712) 722-1662
Web Site: http://www.interstates.com
Rev.: $47,800,000
Emp.: 80
Holding Company
N.A.I.C.S.: 238210
Larry Den Herder (Chm)
Scott Peterson (Pres)
Lisa Visser (Mgr-Mktg)

Subsidiaries:

Interstates Construction Services
Inc   (1)
1400 7th Ave NE, Sioux Center, IA
51250   (100%)
Tel.: (712) 722-1662
Web Site: http://www.interstates.com
Sales Range: $50-74.9 Million
Electrical Work
N.A.I.C.S.: 238210
Dave Crumrine (Pres)

Interstates Control Systems, Inc.   (1)
444 12th St NE, Sioux Center, IA
51250-2150   (100%)
Tel.: (712) 722-1663
Web Site: http://www.interstates.com
Sales Range: $10-24.9 Million
Emp.: 65
Automated Control Systems
N.A.I.C.S.: 334519
Catherine Bloom (CFO)
Dave Crumrine (Pres)
Larry Den Herder (Chm)
Scott Peterson (CEO)

Interstates Engineering   (1)
1520 N Main, Sioux Center, IA
51250-2111   (100%)
Tel.: (712) 722-1662
Web Site: http://www.interstates.com
Sales Range: $10-24.9 Million
Emp.: 20
Electrical Engineering Services
N.A.I.C.S.: 541330
Doug Post (Pres)

HARBOR GROUP INCORPORATED

1115 E Broadway Ave, Muskegon, MI
49444-2333
Tel.: (231) 739-7152
Web Site:
    https://www.harborsteel.com
Year Founded: 1983
Sales Range: $10-24.9 Million
Emp.: 130
Provider of Metals Service Centers &
Offices
N.A.I.C.S.: 423510
Joseph Gerhardt (CFO)

Subsidiaries:

Harbor Steel & Supply
Corporation   (1)
1115 E Broadway Ave, Muskegon, MI
49444-2333
Tel.: (231) 739-7152
Web Site: http://www.harborsteel.com
Sales Range: $10-24.9 Million
Emp.: 72
Metals Service Center
N.A.I.C.S.: 423510
Sindy Haverkamp (CEO)

HARBOR INDUSTRIES INC.

14130 172nd Ave, Grand Haven, MI
49417-9431
Tel.: (616) 842-5330   MI
Web Site: http://www.harborind.com
Year Founded: 1959
Sales Range: $25-49.9 Million
Emp.: 450
Provider of Wood Partitions & Shelving
N.A.I.C.S.: 337212
Fred Miller (Project Mgr)

HARBOR MOTORS

6660 Auto Center Dr, Ventura, CA
93003
Tel.: (805) 656-4030
Web Site:
    http://harbormotorsventura.com
Sales Range: $10-24.9 Million
Emp.: 53
New & Used Automobile Dealership
N.A.I.C.S.: 441110
Ted Katapodis (Pres)

HARBOR RETIREMENT ASSOCIATES, LLC

958 20th Pl 2nd Fl, Vero Beach, FL
32960
Tel.: (772) 492-5002
Web Site:
    https://www.hraseniorliving.com
Emp.: 1,700
Senior Living Facilities
N.A.I.C.S.: 623311
Tim Smick (Chm & Mng Partner)
Thomas Mitchell (CFO)
Charlie Jennings (Chief Dev Officer)
Sarabeth Hanson (Pres & CEO)
Dora Barber (VP-Sls & Mktg)
Bill Blouin (Dir-HR)
Chris Collins (Controller)
Merry Schellhase (VP-Hospitality &
Dining Svcs)
Sheila Wilson (Natl Dir-Health & Wellness)
Peggy Connelly (Natl Dir-Life Enrichment & Memory Care)
Judi Donovan (VP-Operational Transition)
Richard Baummer (Dir-Land Acquisition & Entitlements)
Kim Brawley (Reg Dir-Ops)
Jamie Mathews (Reg Dir-Ops)
Kimberly Ali (Reg Dir-Sls)
Mindi Kocurek (Corp Dir-Mktg)
James Richards (Dir-Dev)
Natalie Cardenas (Corp Dir-Training)
Christopher Thompson (Dir-Culinary
Svcs-Natl)
Gottfried Ernst (VP-Hospitality)
Karin Bateman (COO)

HARBOR SEAFOOD, INC.

969 Lakeville Rd, New Hyde Park,
NY 11040
Tel.: (516) 775-2400   NY
Web Site:
    https://www.harborseafood.com
Year Founded: 1975
Sales Range: $25-49.9 Million
Emp.: 40
Frozen Fish & Seafood Processor &
Whslr
N.A.I.C.S.: 424420
Peter V. Cardone (Owner, Pres &
CEO)
Michael Lemmon (Controller)

HARBOR VIEW HOLDINGS INC.

433 California St Fl 7, San Francisco,
CA 94104
Tel.: (415) 982-7777
Web Site: http://stanfordhotels.com
Rev.: $200,000,000
Emp.: 30
Hotel/Motel, New Construction
N.A.I.C.S.: 236220
Lawrence Lui (Pres)

Subsidiaries:

Cresleigh Homes Arizona Inc   (1)
7006 W Miner Trail, Peoria, AZ 85383
Tel.: (602) 231-0999
Web Site: http://www.cresleighhomes.com
Rev.: $1,100,000
Emp.: 4
Single-Family Housing Construction
N.A.I.C.S.: 236115

Wade J. Kempton (VP)

Cresleigh Management Inc   (1)
433 California St Ste 700, San Francisco,
CA 94104
Tel.: (415) 982-7777
Web Site: http://www.cresleighhomes.com
Rev.: $1,700,000
Emp.: 45
Management Services
N.A.I.C.S.: 237210
Lawrence Lui (Pres)

HARBOR-UCLA MEDICAL FOUNDATION, INC.

21840 S Normandie Ave Ste 100,
Torrance, CA 90502-2047
Tel.: (310) 222-5002   CA
Web Site:
    http://www.harborucladocs.org
Year Founded: 1983
Health Care Professional Organization & Referral Services
N.A.I.C.S.: 813920
Chester Choi (Chm)
John S. McDonald (Treas)
Mack B. Oliver (CEO)
William Stringer (Vice Chm)
Darrell Harrington (Sec)

Subsidiaries:

Harbor-UCLA Faculty Practice Plan,
A Medical Group, Inc.   (1)
21840 S Normandie Ave Ste 100, Torrance,
CA 90502-2047
Tel.: (310) 222-5101
Web Site: http://www.harborucladocs.org
Health Care Professional Referral Services
N.A.I.C.S.: 624190
Lydia Echeverria (Mgr)

HARBORLIGHT CAPITAL GROUP, LLC

8307 Gunn Hwy, Tampa, FL 33626
Tel.: (813) 443-4914   FL
Web Site:
    https://www.harborlightcapital.com
Investment Banking & Asset Management Services
N.A.I.C.S.: 523150
Dean G. Tanella (Pres & CEO)
Michael Freeman (Exec VP)

Subsidiaries:

HarborLight Capital Management,
LLC   (1)
8307 Gunn Hwy, Tampa, FL 33626
Tel.: (813) 443-4914
Web Site: http://www.harborlightcapital.com
Investment Management Service
N.A.I.C.S.: 523940
Dean G. Tanella (Pres)

HARBORSTONE CREDIT UNION

PO Box 4207, Tacoma, WA 98438-0207
Tel.: (253) 584-2260   WA
Web Site:
    https://www.harborstone.com
Year Founded: 1955
Sales Range: $25-49.9 Million
Emp.: 214
Credit Union
N.A.I.C.S.: 522130
Bonnie Kern (Chm)
Jim Buck (Vice Chm)
Ann Anderson (Sec)
Scott Beckwith (VP-Bus Lending)
Geoff Bullock (Pres & CEO)

HARBOUR CONTRACTORS, INC.

23830 W Main St, Plainfield, IL
60544-1909
Tel.: (815) 254-5500   IL
Web Site: https://www.harbour-cm.com
Year Founded: 1959

Harbour Contractors, Inc.—(Continued)

Sales Range: $50-74.9 Million
Emp.: 50
Provider of Contracting Services
N.A.I.C.S.: 541618
Patrick C. Harbour (Pres)
Janet Scott (Dir-Bus Dev)
Phil Farsalas (Engr-Resident)

HARBOUR GROUP INDUSTRIES, INC.
7733 Forsyth Blvd 23rd Fl, Saint
Louis, MO 63105
Tel.: (314) 727-5550   MO
Web Site:
   http://www.harbourgroup.com
Year Founded: 1976
Investment Holding Company
N.A.I.C.S.: 551112
Jeffrey L. Fox (Chm & CEO)
Jeff DePlanty (Sr VP-Fin)
Kevin Klebe (Mng Dir)

Subsidiaries:

ACS Group, Inc.   (1)
2900 S 160th St, New Berlin, WI 53151
Tel.: (262) 641-8600
Web Site: http://www.acsgroup.com
Sales Range: $75-99.9 Million
Emp.: 805
Holding Company; Designer, Manufacturer
& Marketer of Auxiliary Products for the
Plastics Processing Industry
N.A.I.C.S.: 333415
Dave Stewart (Grp VP-Aftermarket Bus)
Jim Holbrook (Pres & CEO)
Bob Andress (VP-Ops)

Subsidiary (Domestic):

AEC, Inc.   (2)
1100 E Woodfield Rd, Schaumburg, IL
60173
Tel.: (630) 595-1060
Web Site: http://www.aecinternet.com
Sales Range: $25-49.9 Million
Emp.: 100
Mfr of Water Cooling, Water Recovery &
Energy Recapture Products & Systems;
Automated Parts, Material Reclaim Systems; Automated Material Handling Systems, Conveyance Systems; Robots
N.A.I.C.S.: 333415
Keith Larson (VP-Sls & Mktg)

Cumberland Engineering
Corporation   (2)
2900 S 160th St, New Berlin, WI
53151   (100%)
Tel.: (262) 641-8600
Web Site:
   http://www.cumberlandplastics.com
Sales Range: $10-24.9 Million
Emp.: 35
Size Reduction & Material Recovery Machinery Mfr
N.A.I.C.S.: 333998

Subsidiary (Non-US):

Cumberland Europe Ltd.   (3)
Daniels Industrial Estate Bath Rd, Stroud,
GL5 3TJ, Glos, United Kingdom   (100%)
Tel.: (44) 1453768980
Web Site:
   http://www.cumberlandeurope.com
N.A.I.C.S.: 322120
Martin Knaptor (Mgr-Sls & Mktg)

Subsidiary (Domestic):

Sterling, Inc.   (2)
2900 S 160th St, New Berlin, WI 53151
Tel.: (262) 641-8600
Web Site: http://www.sterlco.com
Sales Range: $25-49.9 Million
Emp.: 140
Packaged Temperature Control System
Condensation Pump Control Valve Hydraulic Presse Granulator Automatic Part Removal Equipment Automatic Handling &
Processing Equipment Mfr
N.A.I.C.S.: 334513
Robert Wozniak (Controller)

Division (Domestic):

Ball & Jewell Division   (3)
2900 S 160th St, New Berlin, WI 53151
Tel.: (262) 641-8610
Web Site: http://www.acsgroup.com
Sales Range: $25-49.9 Million
Emp.: 125
Mfr of Material Reclaim Systems; Granulating & Size Reduction Machinery
N.A.I.C.S.: 333248
Jim Holbrook (Pres & CEO)

Subsidiary (Domestic):

Carver, Inc.   (3)
1569 Morris St, Wabash, IN 46992
Tel.: (260) 563-7577
Web Site: http://www.carverpress.com
Sales Range: $10-24.9 Million
Emp.: 57
Mfr of Hydraulic Presses
N.A.I.C.S.: 333517
Gary Herring (Reg Mgr-Sls)

Wabash Metal Products Inc   (3)
1569 Morris St, Wabash, IN 46992
Tel.: (260) 563-1184
Web Site: http://www.wabashmpi.com
Sales Range: $10-24.9 Million
Emp.: 75
Mfr of Hydraulic Presses & Other Machines
N.A.I.C.S.: 333248
Joel Kline (Reg Mgr-Sls)

Subsidiary (Domestic):

Walton/Stout, Inc.   (2)
2900 S 160th St, New Berlin, WI 53151
Tel.: (262) 641-8600
Web Site: http://www.waltonstout.com
Sales Range: $1-9.9 Million
Emp.: 30
Industrial Equipment Mfr
N.A.I.C.S.: 333248

Air Monitor Corp.   (1)
1050 Hopper Ave, Santa Rosa, CA 95406
Tel.: (707) 544-2706
Web Site: http://www.airmonitor.com
Industrial Machinery Mfr
N.A.I.C.S.: 333248

Americo Chemical Products, Inc.   (1)
1765 Holmes Rd., Elgin, IL 60123
Tel.: (847) 805-0830
Web Site: http://www.americochemical.com
Rev.: $5,005,000
Emp.: 5
Other Chemical & Allied Products Merchant
Whslr
N.A.I.C.S.: 424690
Chris Bozin (CEO)

CPS Products, Inc.   (1)
1010 E 31st St, Hialeah, FL 33013
Tel.: (305) 687-4121
Web Site: http://www.cpsproducts.com
Emp.: 200
Industrial Tools Mfr
N.A.I.C.S.: 333991
Nora Maria Zampieri (Controller)

Subsidiary (Domestic):

Star Envirotech, Inc.   (2)
17852 Gothard St, Huntington Beach, CA
92647-6217
Tel.: (714) 427-1244
Web Site: http://www.starenvirotech.com
Sales Range: $1-9.9 Million
Emp.: 20
Motor Vehicle Parts Whslr
N.A.I.C.S.: 423120
Richard Banyard (Dir-Tech & R&D)

Cattron Holdings, Inc.   (2)
655 N River Rd NW Ste A, Warren, OH
44483
Tel.: (234) 806-0018
Web Site: https://www.cattron.com
Industrial Wireless Remote Control Systems, Parts & Related Products Mfr
N.A.I.C.S.: 335314
Ryan Wooten (CEO)

Subsidiary (Domestic):

Bwi Eagle, Inc.   (2)
105 Bonnie Dr, Butler, PA 16002
Tel.: (724) 283-4681

Web Site: http://www.bwieagle.com
Rev.: $2,013,000
Emp.: 10
Relay & Industrial Control Mfr
N.A.I.C.S.: 335314
David Festog (Founder & Pres)

Cleaver-Brooks Inc.   (1)
221 Law St, Thomasville, GA 31792
Tel.: (229) 226-3024
Web Site: http://www.cleaverbrooks.com
Sales Range: $150-199.9 Million
Emp.: 1,000
Boilers, Burners & Heating Equipment Mfr &
Distr
N.A.I.C.S.: 332410
Paul M. Anderson (Sr VP-Sls & Mktg)
Bart A. Aitken (Pres & CEO)
Jimmy Sprouse (CFO)

Subsidiary (Domestic):

Cleaver-Brooks Sales and Service,
Inc.   (2)
1956 Singleton Blvd, Dallas, TX 75212-
3827
Tel.: (214) 637-0020
Web Site: http://www.cbservice.com
Sales Range: $25-49.9 Million
Emp.: 1,000
Boilers Sales & Service
N.A.I.C.S.: 423830
John Marrinucci (Pres & CEO)
Ron Settimi (Mgr-HR)
Dell Bardere (Dir-Safety)

Fleetgistics Holdings, Inc.   (1)
2251 Lynx Ln Ste 7, Orlando, FL 32804
Tel.: (407) 843-6505
Web Site: http://www.fleetgistics.com
Sales Range: $100-124.9 Million
Emp.: 25
Holding Company; Automotive Parts, Medical & Pharmaceutical Industry Logistics &
Delivery Services
N.A.I.C.S.: 551112
Jim Van Leenen (Pres & CEO)
Pat Grum (VP-Ops)

Subsidiary (Domestic):

Medifleet, Inc.   (2)
30 Railroad Ave, West Haven, CT 06516
Tel.: (888) 470-1218
Web Site: http://www.medifleet.com
Prescription Drug Delivery Services
N.A.I.C.S.: 492210

Partsfleet, Inc.   (2)
2251 Lynx Ln Ste 7, Orlando, FL 32804
Tel.: (407) 843-6505
Web Site: http://www.partsfleet.com
Automotive Parts Industry Delivery Services
N.A.I.C.S.: 492110

Scriptfleet, Inc.   (2)
13577 Feather Sound Dr Ste 200, Clearwater, FL 33762-5533
Tel.: (727) 539-8400
Web Site: http://www.scriptfleet.com
Sales Range: $25-49.9 Million
Emp.: 20
Prescription Drug Delivery Services
N.A.I.C.S.: 492210
Ted Johanson (Sr VP)
Richard Smith (Sr VP-Ops)

Harbour Group Limited of
Delaware   (1)
7733 Forsyth Blvd 23rd Fl, Saint Louis, MO
63105
Tel.: (314) 727-5550
Web Site: http://www.harbourgroup.com
Sales Range: $25-49.9 Million
Emp.: 500
Investment Firm
N.A.I.C.S.: 523999
Jeffrey L. Fox (Chm & CEO)

Industrial Lighting Products, LLC   (1)
519 Codisco Way, Sanford, FL 32771
Tel.: (407) 478-3759
Web Site: http://www.ilp-inc.com
Industrial Lighting Fixture Mfr
N.A.I.C.S.: 335132
Patrick Hayes (Mgr-Production)

LOFA Industries, LLC   (1)
250 Hembree Park Dr Ste 122, Roswell,
GA 30076

Tel.: (770) 569-9828
Industrial Machinery & Equipment Whslr
N.A.I.C.S.: 423830
Peter Herbrand (Co-Founder)
Hans Herbrand (Co-Founder)

Nationwide Industries, Inc.   (1)
10333 Windhorst Rd, Tampa, FL 33619
Tel.: (813) 988-2628
Web Site:
   http://www.nationwideindustries.com
Metal Hardware & Components Design &
Mfr
N.A.I.C.S.: 332510
Christopher Kliefoth (Pres)

ONICON Incorporated   (1)
11451 Belcher Rd S, Largo, FL 33773
Tel.: (727) 447-6140
Web Site: http://www.onicon.com
Measurement Instrument Mfr
N.A.I.C.S.: 334519
John Norris (Pres)

Subsidiary (Domestic):

Fox Thermal Instruments, Inc.   (2)
399 Reservation Rd, Marina, CA
93933   (100%)
Tel.: (831) 384-4300
Web Site: http://www.foxthermal.com
Sales Range: $1-9.9 Million
Emp.: 50
Thermal Gas Flow Meter Mfr
N.A.I.C.S.: 334514
Rich Cada (VP-Sls & Mktg)

Subsidiary (Non-US):

Greyline Instruments Inc.   (2)
16456 Sixsmith Drive, Long Sault, K0C
1P0, ON, Canada
Tel.: (613) 938-8956
Web Site: http://www.greyline.com
Emp.: 45
Flow Meters & Level Monitoring Instruments
Mfr
N.A.I.C.S.: 334513

Branch (US):

Greyline Instruments Inc.   (3)
105 Water St, Massena, NY 13662
Tel.: (315) 788-9500
Web Site: http://www.greyline.com
Sales Range: $1-9.9 Million
Emp.: 25
Flow Meters & Level Monitoring Instruments
Mfr
N.A.I.C.S.: 334513
Shawn Killoran (VP-Bus Dev)
William Robson (Pres)

Pearlman Corporation   (1)
6832 E Slauson Ave, Commerce, CA 90040
Tel.: (562) 927-5561
Web Site: http://www.pearlabrasive.com
Sales Range: $25-49.9 Million
Emp.: 70
Mfr & Whslr of Abrasives
N.A.I.C.S.: 423840
Tedd Skaff (Mgr-Sls & Mktg)
Rich Berry (Pres)

Subsidiary (Domestic):

Pearl Abrasive Company   (2)
4900 Zambrano St, Commerce, CA 90040
Tel.: (562) 927-5561
Web Site: http://www.pearlabrasive.com
Sales Range: $25-49.9 Million
Abrasives Mfr
N.A.I.C.S.: 327910
Rich Berry (Pres)

Phillips & Temro Industries, Inc.   (1)
9700 W 74th St, Eden Prairie, MN 55344
Tel.: (952) 941-9700
Web Site: http://www.phillipsandtemro.com
Motor Vehicle Heating, Cooling, Silencing &
Emission Products Mfr
N.A.I.C.S.: 336390
Thomas Meline (VP-Ops, Engrg & Quality)
Michael Ramsay (CFO)
Thomas Moser (Pres)

Subsidiary (Domestic):

Arctic Fox, LLC   (2)
570 S 7th St PO Box 309, Delano, MN
55328

Tel.: (763) 972-2758
Web Site: http://www.arctic-fox.com
Fuel & Fluid Heating Products for Heavy
Duty Trucks & Off-Highway Equipment Mfr
& Distr
N.A.I.C.S.: 333414

SP Industries Inc. (1)
935 Mearns Rd, Warminster, PA 18974-
2811
Tel.: (215) 672-7800
Web Site: http://www.spindustries.com
Emp.: 100
Pharmaceutical, Biotechnology, Educational,
Industrial Specialty Glassware & Equipment
N.A.I.C.S.: 327213
Brian Wright (COO)
Ian Whitehall (Chief Sls Officer)
Bill Roller (Chm)
Brian Larkin (Pres & CEO)

Subsidiary (Domestic):

Bel-Art Products, Inc. (2)
661 Rte 23 S, Wayne, NJ 07470
Tel.: (973) 694-0500
Web Site: http://www.belart.com
Molded & Fabricated Plastics Mfr for Sci-
ence & Industry
N.A.I.C.S.: 326199
Jill Guide (Mgr-Product)

Subsidiary (Domestic):

SP Ableware (3)
661 Rte 23 S, Wayne, NJ 07470
Tel.: (973) 628-7600
Web Site: http://www.maddak.com
Handicap Aids Mfr
N.A.I.C.S.: 423450
Susan Tulanowski (Mgr-Brand)

ShockWatch, Inc. (1)
510 Corporate Dr, Graham, TX 76450-2117
Tel.: (940) 549-2385
Web Site: http://www.shockwatch.com
Sales Range: $25-49.9 Million
Shock, Vibration & Temperature Detector
Devices Mfr
N.A.I.C.S.: 334519
Tony Fonk (Pres & CEO)
Reuben Isbitsky (Bus Dir-Temperature)

Subsidiary (Non-US):

LCR Hallcrest Ltd (2)
Riverside Building Dock Road, Connahs
Quay Flintshire, London, CH5 4DS, United
Kingdom
Tel.: (44) 1244817107
Temperature Control Products & Services
N.A.I.C.S.: 334513
Russell Booth (Mng Dir-European Bus)

Subsidiary (US):

LCR Hallcrest LLC (3)
1911 Pickwick Lne, Glenview, IL 60026
Tel.: (847) 998-8480
Temperature Control Products & Services
N.A.I.C.S.: 334513
Rocco Sapienza Jr. (VP-Ops)

Subsidiary (Domestic):

Biosynergy, Inc. (4)
1940 E Devon Ave, Elk Grove Village, IL
60007
Tel.: (847) 956-0471
Web Site: http://www.biosynergyinc.com
Rev.: $1,173,143
Assets: $1,891,514
Liabilities: $152,518
Net Worth: $1,738,996
Earnings: $15,795
Emp.: 5
Fiscal Year-end: 04/30/2021
Measuring & Controlling Product Mfr
N.A.I.C.S.: 334513
Lauane C. Addis (Corp Counsel & Sec)
Fred K. Suzuki Jr. (Chm, Pres, CEO, CFO,
Chief Acctg Officer & Dir-Mktg)

Subsidiary (Domestic):

Marathon Products, Inc. (2)
627 McCormick St, San Leandro, CA
94577-1109
Tel.: (510) 562-6450
Web Site: http://www.marathonproducts.com

Sales Range: $1-9.9 Million
Emp.: 26
Mfr, Designer & Global Supplier of Data
Collecting Devices & Sensor-Based Prod-
ucts in Monitoring Environmental Conditions
N.A.I.C.S.: 334512
Jon Y. Nakagawa (CEO)
John Perry (VP-Sls & Mktg)
Vikki K. Lisec (Pres)

HARBOUR HOMES LLC
400 N 34th St Ste 300, Seattle, WA
98103
Tel.: (206) 315-8130
Web Site:
    http://www.harbourhomes.com
Sales Range: $50-74.9 Million
Emp.: 150
New Single-Family Housing Con-
struction
N.A.I.C.S.: 236115
George Neffner IV (Treas & Sec)
George Neffner III (Pres)

**HARBOUR POINT MANAGE-
MENT LLC**
320 Boston Post Rd Ste 180 256,
Darien, CT 06820
Tel.: (646) 681-4600
Web Site:
    https://www.harbourpointcapital.com
Privater Equity Firm
N.A.I.C.S.: 523999
Bob Juneja (Co-Founder & Partner)
Bret Bowerman (Co-Founder & Part-
ner)
Ben Schlang (Operating Partner)
Adam Seiden (VP)

Subsidiaries:

Insight Telepsychiatry LLC (1)
1120 Rt 73 Ste 300, Mount Laurel, NJ
08054
Tel.: (856) 797-4772
Web Site:
    http://www.insighttelepsychiatry.com
Hospital-Based Telepsychiatry Services
N.A.I.C.S.: 622210
Geoffrey Boyce (CEO)

Subsidiary (Domestic):

Regroup Therapy, Inc. (2)
4525 N Ravenswood Ave, Chicago, IL
60640
Tel.: (224) 216-0726
Web Site: http://www.regrouptherapy.com
General Management Consulting Services
N.A.I.C.S.: 541611
David Cohn (Founder & CEO)
Tim Gustafson (VP-Bus Dev)

**HARBOURVEST PARTNERS,
LLC**
1 Financial Ctr, Boston, MA 02111-
2621
Tel.: (617) 348-3707   MA
Web Site:
    http://www.harbourvest.com
Year Founded: 1982
Sales Range: $250-299.9 Million
Emp.: 300
Venture Capital Investors
N.A.I.C.S.: 523940
Alex A. Rogers (Mng Dir)
Karin J. Lagerlund (Mng Dir & CFO-
Boston)
Robert M. Wadsworth (Mng Dir-
Boston)
Christopher J. Walker (Principal-
Boston)
Scott C. Voss (Mng Dir-Boston)
David Atterbury (Mng Dir-London)
Jeffrey R. Keay (Mng Dir-Boston)
Julie H. Ocko (Mng Dir-Boston)
Laura C. Thaxter (Mng Dir)
Julie Eiermann (Mng Dir & CIO)
Peter B. Lipson (Mng Dir)
John M. Fiato (Principal-Boston)

John G. Morris (Mng Dir-Boston)
Gregory V. Stento (Mng Dir-Boston)
Michael W. Taylor (Mng Dir)
Brett A. Gordon (Mng Dir)
Mary Traer (Mng Dir & Chief Admin
Officer)
Michael J. Pugatch (Mng Dir-Boston)
Jack Wagner (Treas & Sr VP)
Sally Shan (Mng Dir-Beijing)
Tim Flower (Mng Dir-Hong Kong)
Nate Bishop (Mng Dir-IR)
Minjun Chung (Mng Dir)
Bruce Pixler (Sr VP & Dir-Tax)
James Kase (Mng Dir & Head-IR-
Global)
Alex Barker (Principal-London)
Francisco Arboleda (Principal)
George Anson (Mng Dir-London)
Jessica Auchterlonie (Mgr-Distr-
Boston)
Kathleen Bacon (Mng Dir-London)
Monique Austin (VP-Boston)
Till Burges (Principal-London)
Tricia M. Mackechnie (CTO & Mng
Dir)
Paula Drake (Mng Dir & Gen Coun-
sel)
James Athanasoulas (Mng Dir)
Karen Simeone (Mng Dir-Credit Grp)
Pete Wilson (Mng Dir)
Craig MacDonald (Mng Dir)
Edward Holdsworth (Mng Dir)
Rich Campbell (Mng Dir)
Ian Lane (Mng Dir)
Matt HoganBruen (Mng Dir)
Peter Mahoney (Mng Dir & Head-
Fund Acctg)
John M. Toomey Jr. (Mng Dir)

Subsidiaries:

HarbourVest Horizon (1)
135 S LaSalle St, Chicago, IL 60603
Tel.: (312) 828-2278
Web Site: http://www.harbourvest.com
Investment Management Service
N.A.I.C.S.: 523940
Craig Fowler (Mng Dir)

**HarbourVest Investment Consulting
(Beijing) Company Limited** (1)
Suite 5608 56/F China World Tower A 1 Ji-
anguomenwai Ave, Chaoyang, Beijing,
100004, China
Tel.: (86) 1057068600
Web Site: http://www.harbourvest.com
Emp.: 6
Investment Consulting Services
N.A.I.C.S.: 525910
Shumin Gong (Principal)
Sally Shan (Mng Dir)

**HarbourVest Partners (Asia)
Limited** (1)
Champion Tower Suite 1207 3 Garden
Road, Central, Hong Kong, China (Hong
Kong)
Tel.: (852) 25252214
Investment Management Service
N.A.I.C.S.: 523940
Alex A. Rogers (Mng Dir)
Simon Lund (Principal)
Tim Flower (Mng Dir)
Kelvin Yap (Mng Dir)
Joseph Li (Principal)
Hemal Mirani (Mng Dir)

**HarbourVest Partners (Japan)
Limited** (1)
Marunouchi Building 34th Floor 2-4-1
Marunouchi, Chiyoda-ku, Tokyo, 100-6334,
Japan
Tel.: (81) 332844320
Web Site: http://www.harbourvest.com
Sales Range: $25-49.9 Million
Emp.: 3
Investment Management Service
N.A.I.C.S.: 523940
Tatsuya Kubo (Mng Dir & Co-Head)
Tadasu Matsuo (Mng Dir & Co-Head)

**HarbourVest Partners (U.K.)
Limited** (1)

33 Jermyn Street, London, SW1Y6DN,
United Kingdom
Tel.: (44) 20 7399 9820
Web Site: http://www.harbourvest.com
Sales Range: $25-49.9 Million
Emp.: 35
Venture Capital Services
N.A.I.C.S.: 523910
George Anson (Mng Dir)
David Atterbury (Mng Dir)
Kathleen Bacon (Mng Dir)
Alex Barker (Principal)
Carolina Espinal (Mng Dir)
Simon Jennings (Mng Dir)

HarbourVest Partners, LLC (1)
Oficina de Representacion Carrera 7 113 -
43, Oficina 904 Edificio Samsung, Bogota,
Colombia
Tel.: (57) 1 552 1400
Web Site: http://www.harbourvest.com
Emp.: 3
Investment Management Service
N.A.I.C.S.: 523940
Francisco Arboleda (Principal)
Nhora Otalora (Principal)

Sign Zone LLC (1)
6850 Shingle Creek Pkwy, Brooklyn Center,
MN 55430
Tel.: (763) 746-1350
Web Site: http://www.signzoneinc.com
Signs & Displays; Advertising Specialty &
Other Promotional Products Mfr
N.A.I.C.S.: 339950
Edward Flaherty (Pres & CEO)

**HARBURGER/SCOTT ADVER-
TISING**
72 Balmville Rd, Newburgh, NY
12550
Tel.: (845) 787-0031   NY
Year Founded: 1982
Sales Range: $10-24.9 Million
Emp.: 2
Advetising Agency
N.A.I.C.S.: 541810
Brenda Harburger (Pres & CEO)

HARCHELROAD MOTORS INC.
122 N Tecumseh, Wauneta, NE
69045
Tel.: (308) 394-5555
Web Site:
    http://www.harchelroadsmotors.com
Sales Range: $10-24.9 Million
Emp.: 15
Automobile Whslr
N.A.I.C.S.: 441110
Sid Harchelroad (Chm)
Louann Rector (Office Mgr)
Brian Harchelroad (VP)

HARCO DISTRIBUTORS INC.
1328 Old Post Rd, Havre De Grace,
MD 21078
Tel.: (410) 939-4433   MD
Year Founded: 1965
Sales Range: $10-24.9 Million
Emp.: 100
Soft Drinks Whslr
N.A.I.C.S.: 424490
Clark D. Connellee Jr. (Pres)

**HARCO INSURANCE SER-
VICES**
1077 NW Fwy Ste 700, Houston, TX
77092-7313
Tel.: (713) 681-2500
Web Site: https://www.harco-ins.com
Year Founded: 1969
Rev.: $14,000,000
Emp.: 30
Insurance Services
N.A.I.C.S.: 524210
Josh Hargrave (Pres)
Gerri Rougeau (VP)
Carolyn Demel (Sr Acct Mgr)
Linda Drake (Sr Acct Mgr)
Christopher L. Goff (VP)

HARCO Insurance Services—(Continued)

Peter Hamel *(Sr Acct Exec)*
Peggy Messamore *(Sr Acct Mgr)*
Candy Tilton *(Sr Acct Mgr)*
Carole Smith *(Mgr-Acctg & Coord-IT)*
Darlene Bugaj *(Mgr-Comml Dept)*
Jerry Campbell *(Sr Acct Mgr)*
Brenda Canenguez *(Sr Acct Mgr)*
Ruthie Mead *(Sr Acct Mgr)*
Jennifer Palermo *(Sr Acct Mgr)*
Alicia Velez *(Sr Acct Mgr)*
Anita Zatopek *(Sr Acct Mgr)*

HARCO MANUFACTURING COMPANY INC.

1000 Industrial Pkwy, Newberg, OR 97132
Tel.: (503) 537-0600
Web Site:
https://www.harcomanufacturing.com
Sales Range: $1-9.9 Million
Emp.: 22
Engineering & Environmental Products in the Industrial, Agricultural & Marine Arenas
N.A.I.C.S.: 541330
Rodney Harris *(Pres & CEO)*
Jeff Harris *(Mng Dir)*
Frank E. Harris Jr. *(VP)*

HARCO, LLC

12100 Blue Valley Pkwy, Overland Park, KS 66213
Tel.: (913) 451-8030   KS
Web Site: http://www.lukasliquor.com
Rev.: $11,000,000
Emp.: 40
Liquor Stores
N.A.I.C.S.: 445320
Harold Lukas *(Pres)*

Subsidiaries:

Colorado Superstores Llc   (1)
8457 S Yosemite St, Lone Tree, CO 80124
Tel.: (303) 792-2288
Sales Range: $10-24.9 Million
Emp.: 15
Hard Liquor
N.A.I.C.S.: 445320

HARCON INC.

1121 Alderman Dr Ste 101, Alpharetta, GA 30005-5470
Tel.: (770) 343-9998
Web Site:
http://www.harconforming.com
Rev.: $12,976,771
Emp.: 100
Concrete Work
N.A.I.C.S.: 238110
Brian Johnson *(Controller)*

HARCROS CHEMICALS INC.

5200 Speaker Rd, Kansas City, KS 66106-1048
Tel.: (913) 321-3131   DE
Web Site:
http://www.harcroschem.com
Year Founded: 1981
Sales Range: $350-399.9 Million
Emp.: 525
Specialty Chemical Mfr & Distr
N.A.I.C.S.: 325998
Kevin Mirner *(Pres & CEO)*
Smokey Skyrmes *(VP-Matls Mgmt)*
Lynne Bukovic *(VP-Mktg)*
David Goode *(Dir-Bus Dev)*
Dan Johnson *(Dir-Ops)*
Judy O'Dell *(Mgr-HR)*
Mark Loethen *(CFO)*
Steve Gripp *(Dir-Matls Mgmt)*
Martin Morgan *(VP & Gen Mgr-Distr Div)*
Peter Radford *(VP-Manufactured Products)*

Subsidiaries:

Harcros Chemicals Inc. - Organics Division   (1)
5200 Speaker Rd, Kansas City, KS 66106
Tel.: (913) 321-3131
Chemical Products Mfr
N.A.I.C.S.: 325199

HARD BEAT COMMUNICATIONS

1515 Broadway 11th Fl, New York, NY 10036
Tel.: (718) 476-3616
Web Site: http://www.caribpr.com
Year Founded: 2004
Sales Range: Less than $1 Million
Emp.: 3
Advetising Agency
N.A.I.C.S.: 541810
Felicia Persuad *(CEO)*

HARD DOLLAR CORPORATION

9977 N 90th St Ste 250, Scottsdale, AZ 85258
Tel.: (480) 776-2900
Web Site: http://www.harddollar.com
Year Founded: 1989
Sales Range: $1-9.9 Million
Emp.: 31
Computer & Computer Peripheral Equipment & Software Merchant Whslr
N.A.I.C.S.: 423430
Brad Barth *(VP)*

HARD DRIVES NORTHWEST, INC.

14315 NE 20th, Bellevue, WA 98007
Tel.: (425) 644-6474
Web Site: http://www.hdnw.com
Sales Range: $10-24.9 Million
Emp.: 65
Computer & Software Stores
N.A.I.C.S.: 449210
Toni Sawaya *(CEO)*

HARD ROCK TOOL INC.

1810 E Ball Rd, Anaheim, CA 92805
Tel.: (714) 772-2490
Web Site:
http://www.hardrocktool.com
Sales Range: $10-24.9 Million
Emp.: 37
Industrial Supplies
N.A.I.C.S.: 444140
Dan Develin *(Pres)*

HARDAGE INVESTMENTS, INC.

12671 High Bluff Dr Ste 300, San Diego, CA 92130-3018
Tel.: (858) 794-2338   DE
Year Founded: 1982
Sales Range: $10-24.9 Million
Emp.: 32
Home Management Services
N.A.I.C.S.: 721110
Ed Romanov *(CFO)*

Subsidiaries:

Hardage Hotels V LLC   (1)
12671 High Bluff Dr Ste 300, San Diego, CA 92130-3018
Tel.: (858) 794-2338
Web Site: http://www.hardagegroup.com
Rev.: $10,000,000
Emp.: 17
Hotels & Motels
N.A.I.C.S.: 721110

Woodfin Suite Hotels   (1)
Ste 300 12671 High Bluff Dr, San Diego, CA 92130-3018
Tel.: (858) 794-2338
Hotel Management & Franchising Services
N.A.I.C.S.: 721110

Samuel A. Hardage *(Owner)*
Thomas D. Farrell *(Exec VP, Dir-Acq & Devel)*

HARDAWAY GROUP, INC.

1001 Gallatin Ave, Nashville, TN 37206
Tel.: (615) 254-5461
Web Site: http://www.hardaway.net
Year Founded: 1924
Sales Range: $150-199.9 Million
Emp.: 50
Civil Engineering Services
N.A.I.C.S.: 237310

Subsidiaries:

Hardaway Construction Corp.   (1)
615 Main St, Nashville, TN 37206
Tel.: (615) 254-5461
Web Site: http://www.hardaway.net
Commercial & Office Building Construction
N.A.I.C.S.: 236220
Steve Webster *(Superintendent)*
Ed Bullington *(VP)*
Shaun Dickert *(Project Mgr)*
Sharon Hackett *(Office Mgr)*
Earline Simpson *(Dir-Insurance & HR)*
Bret Obrien *(VP)*
Gary Chesley *(VP)*
Stan H. Hardaway *(Pres)*
Scott Wilson *(Superintendent)*
Robert Rish *(Superintendent)*
Jack Cecil *(Superintendent)*
Stanton Zackery *(Asst Superintendent)*
Russell Jackson *(Superintendent)*

Hardaway Realty Co. Inc.   (1)
615 Main St, Nashville, TN 37206
Tel.: (615) 254-8096
Web Site: http://www.hardaway.com
Real Estate Brokers & Agents
N.A.I.C.S.: 531210
Stan Hardaway *(Pres)*

HARDBALL CAPITAL

984 Foxcroft Rd, Atlanta, GA 30327
Tel.: (404) 579-5786
Web Site:
https://www.hardballcapital.com
Privater Equity Firm
N.A.I.C.S.: 523999
Jason Freier *(Chm & CEO)*

HARDEE BY EVH MANUFACTURING COMPANY, LLC

4895 Red Bluff Rd, Loris, SC 29569
Tel.: (843) 756-2555
Web Site:
https://www.hardeebyevh.com
Year Founded: 1956
Farm Equipment; Agricultural Sprayers, Landscape Equipment & Nursery Equipment Mfr
N.A.I.C.S.: 333111

HARDEES SOUTHWEST MISSOURI INC.

608 Kathryn St, Nixa, MO 65714
Tel.: (417) 724-0250
Web Site: http://www.hardees.com
Sales Range: $10-24.9 Million
Emp.: 450
Fast-Food Restaurant, Chain
N.A.I.C.S.: 722513

HARDEL MUTUAL PLYWOOD CORPORATION

143 Maurin Rd, Chehalis, WA 98532-8716
Tel.: (360) 740-0232   WA
Web Site: https://www.hardel.com
Year Founded: 1953
Sales Range: $100-124.9 Million
Emp.: 275
Plywood Panel Mfr
N.A.I.C.S.: 321212
Tracy Trogden *(Mgr-Sls)*

Subsidiaries:

Hardel Builders Center   (1)
2321 Harrison Ave NW, Olympia, WA 98502-4542   (100%)
Tel.: (360) 357-6353
Web Site: http://www.hardel.doitbest.com
Sales Range: $25-49.9 Million
Emp.: 9
Plywood, Lumber, Hardware & Building Supplies Distr
N.A.I.C.S.: 444110
Emmanuel Piliaris *(Pres)*

HARDEMAN LANDSCAPE NURSERY, INC.

2207 W North A St, Tampa, FL 33606
Tel.: (813) 689-5160   FL
Web Site:
http://www.hardemanlandscape.com
Year Founded: 1986
Sales Range: $1-9.9 Million
Emp.: 70
Landscaping Services
N.A.I.C.S.: 561730
Jeffrey Hardeman *(Pres)*

HARDEN FURNITURE INC.

8550 Mill Pond Way, McConnellsville, NY 13401-1800
Tel.: (315) 245-1000   NY
Web Site: http://www.harden.com
Year Founded: 1844
Sales Range: $150-199.9 Million
Emp.: 350
Mfr of Solid Cherry & Upholstered Household & Office Furniture
N.A.I.C.S.: 337122
Janet Dixon *(Coord-Sls & Admin)*
Jim Schafer *(Dir-Costing)*
Karen Light *(Coord-Production)*
David McGowan *(Mgr-Lumber Sls & Pur)*
Pete Raynsford *(VP-Pur)*
Gregory M. Harden *(Pres & CEO)*

HARDENBERGH INSURANCE GROUP, INC.

8000 Sagemore Dr Ste 810, Marlton, NJ 08053
Tel.: (856) 489-9100   NJ
Web Site:
http://www.hardenberghins.com
Year Founded: 1954
Sales Range: $10-24.9 Million
Emp.: 55
Insurance Agencies & Brokerages
N.A.I.C.S.: 524210
Helen Goodwin *(Mgr-Acct-Pub Entity Div)*
Lori Kosyla *(Mgr-Acct-Bus Insurance Div)*
Kathy Ward *(Mgr-Acct-Personal Insurance Div)*
Pat Wheeler *(Mgr-Personal Lines-Personal Insurance Div)*
Brian Blaston *(Mgr-Comml Lines)*
Jon Sharp *(Pres)*
John McCrudden *(VP)*
Joe Haggerty *(Dir-Client Svcs)*
Kelly Velez *(Mgr-Acct-Bus Insurance Div)*
Matt Filer *(Supvr-Select Bus Unit-Bus Insurance Div)*
Bonnie Ridolfino *(Dir-Pub Entity Div)*
Christina Violetti *(Acct Mgr)*
Jamie Manners *(Acct Mgr)*
Karen Haskell *(Acct Mgr)*
Laura Lawrence *(Acct Mgr)*
Melissa Holliday *(Acct Mgr)*
Susan Miller *(Acct Mgr)*

HARDER CORP.

7029 Raywood Rd, Monona, WI 53713
Tel.: (608) 271-5127

Web Site:
https://www.hardercorp.com
Sales Range: $10-24.9 Million
Emp.: 48
Packaging Product Distr
N.A.I.C.S.: 424130
Richard Zimmerman (Owner)

HARDER MECHANICAL CONTRACTORS INC.
2148 NE Martin Luther King Blvd,
Portland, OR 97212-3724
Tel.: (503) 281-1112   OR
Web Site: http://www.harder.com
Year Founded: 1955
Sales Range: $100-124.9 Million
Emp.: 1,000
Provider of Plumbing, Heating & Air
Conditioning Contracting Services
N.A.I.C.S.: 238220
Steve Harder (CEO)
Todd Firestenberg (Mgr-Sheet Metal)

HARDESTY & HANOVER, LLC
1501 Broadway, New York, NY 10036
Tel.: (212) 944-1150   DE
Web Site:
https://www.hardestyhanover.com
Infrastructure Engineering Services
N.A.I.C.S.: 541330
Michael Harrison (Dir-Rail)
Sean A. Bluni (CEO)
Anna Volynsky (CFO)
Hank Pokigo (Principal)
Keith R. Griesing (Chief Tech Officer
& Head-Engrg)
Michael D. Hawkins (COO & Principal)
David S. Tuckman (Dir-Engrg)
Paul M. Skelton (Chief Dev Officer)
Brendan O'Shea (Pres-Construction
Svcs)
David J. DeLuca (Dir-Bus Dev)

Subsidiaries:

Corven Engineering, Inc.   (1)
2882 Remington Green Cir, Tallahassee, FL
32308
Tel.: (850) 386-6800
Web Site: http://www.corveneng.com
Rev.: $1,200,000
Emp.: 14
Engineeering Services
N.A.I.C.S.: 541330
John Corven (Pres)
Clif Nelson (Mgr-CADD)

Frederick P Clark Associates,
Inc.   (1)
350 Theodore Fremd Ave, Rye, NY 10580
Tel.: (914) 967-6540
Web Site: http://www.fpclark.com
Community Planning, Development, Environmental & Transportation Consulting Services
N.A.I.C.S.: 541618

P.E. Structural Consultants, Inc.   (1)
8436 Spicewood Springs Rd, Austin, TX
78759
Tel.: (512) 250-5200
Web Site: http://www.pestructural.com
Engineeering Services
N.A.I.C.S.: 541330
Lisa Carter Powell (Pres & Principal Engr)
Mary Theresa Cano-Arroyo (Sr Engr-QC)

The Heimburg Group, Inc.   (1)
5461 W Waters Ave Ste 910, Tampa, FL
33634
Tel.: (813) 749-0823
Web Site: http://www.heimburggroup.com
Transportation Infrastructure Engineering
Consulting Services
N.A.I.C.S.: 541330
Stephan Heimburg (Sec & VP)
Lisa Heimburg (Pres)

HARDIN BUICK PONTIAC GMC
1321 Auto Center Dr, Anaheim, CA
92806-5612
Tel.: (714) 635-2020
Web Site:
https://www.hardinbuickgmc.com
Sales Range: $10-24.9 Million
Emp.: 80
Car Whslr
N.A.I.C.S.: 441110
John Yakel (Gen Mgr-Sls)

HARDIN COUNTY BANCORPORATION
1202 Edgington Ave, Eldora, IA
50627-1739
Tel.: (641) 939-3407   IA
Web Site: https://www.hardincsb.com
Year Founded: 1980
Sales Range: $1-9.9 Million
Emp.: 31
Bank Holding Company
N.A.I.C.S.: 551111
James R. Brown (Pres)
Donna M. Lawler (Treas & Sr VP)
Larry Wolf (Sr VP)
David Vander Wilt (Sr VP-Insurance)
Tom Volding (VP)
Drew M. Lewis (Exec VP)

Subsidiaries:

Hardin County Savings Bank   (1)
1202 Edgington Ave, Eldora, IA 50627
Tel.: (641) 939-3407
Web Site: http://www.hardincsb.com
Sales Range: $1-9.9 Million
Emp.: 30
Commericial Banking
N.A.I.C.S.: 522110
James R. Brown (Pres)
Donna M. Lawler (Sr VP)
Larry Wolf (Sr VP)
David Vander Wilt (Sr VP-Insurance)

HARDIN HONDA
1381 S Auto Center Dr, Anaheim, CA
92806
Tel.: (714) 533-6200
Web Site:
https://www.hardinhonda.com
Sales Range: $75-99.9 Million
Emp.: 115
Automobiles, New & Used
N.A.I.C.S.: 441110
Dennis Hardin (Owner & Pres)
Roberta Hardin (Gen Mgr)

HARDING & HILL INC.
533 Allegan St, Plainwell, MI 49080-
1297
Tel.: (269) 685-5370   MI
Year Founded: 1975
Sales Range: $50-74.9 Million
Emp.: 600
Grocery Stores
N.A.I.C.S.: 445110
Martin Hill (Pres)

HARDING HOLDINGS INC.
184 E 53rd Ave, Anchorage, AK
99518-1222
Tel.: (907) 344-1577
Web Site: http://www.udelhoven.com
Year Founded: 1970
Sales Range: $50-74.9 Million
Emp.: 500
Holding Company; Oil & Gas Field
Services
N.A.I.C.S.: 237120
Tim Jacques (Pres)

Subsidiaries:

Udelhoven Oilfield Systems Services
Inc.   (1)
184 E 53rd Ave, Anchorage, AK 99518-
1222
Tel.: (281) 440-9909
Web Site: http://www.udelhoven.com

Sales Range: $50-74.9 Million
Supplier Of Industrial Buildings & Warehouses
N.A.I.C.S.: 236210
Jim Udelhoven (CEO)
Tim Jacques (Pres)

HARDINGER TRANSFER CO. INC.
1314 W 18th St, Erie, PA 16502
Tel.: (814) 453-6587
Web Site: https://www.team-h.com
Rev.: $12,478,364
Emp.: 140
Trucking Except Local
N.A.I.C.S.: 484121
Bill Schaal (Pres)

HARDINGS MARKET-WEST INC.
211 E Bannister St Ste E, Plainwell,
MI 49080-1372
Tel.: (269) 685-9807   MI
Web Site: http://www.hardings.com
Year Founded: 1987
Rev.: $75,700,000
Emp.: 700
Grocery Stores, Chain
N.A.I.C.S.: 445110
Brian Hettinghouse (Pres)

HARDINGS THOMAS MANAGEMENT
8960 E D Ave, Richland, MI 49083
Tel.: (269) 629-4596
Rev.: $43,100,000
Emp.: 9
Grocery Stores, Independent
N.A.I.C.S.: 445110
Thomas Harding (Pres)

HARDISON/DOWNEY CONSTRUCTION INC.
6150 N 16th St Ste A, Phoenix, AZ
85016
Tel.: (602) 861-0044
Web Site:
http://www.hardisondowney.com
Year Founded: 1985
Sales Range: $10-24.9 Million
Emp.: 50
Commercial & Office Building, New
Construction
N.A.I.C.S.: 236220
Pat Downey (Co-Founder & VP)
Jim Kurtzman (VP-Dev)
Mike Mongelli (COO & Sr VP)

HARDMAN SUPPLY COMPANY
102 Ct St, Spencer, WV 25276
Tel.: (304) 927-4701   WV
Web Site: http://www.hardmans.com
Year Founded: 1907
Sales Range: $25-49.9 Million
Emp.: 105
Builders' Materials & Services
N.A.I.C.S.: 444140
Randall Walker (Gen Mgr)
Fred C. Hardman (Treas & VP)
Thomas Hardman (Pres)

HARDRIVES OF DELRAY, INC.
2101 S Congress Ave, Delray Beach,
FL 33445
Tel.: (561) 278-0456
Web Site:
https://www.hardrivespaving.com
Year Founded: 1953
Sales Range: $25-49.9 Million
Emp.: 120
Highway, Street & Bridge Construction
N.A.I.C.S.: 237310
George Elmore (Pres)

HARDRIVES, INC.
14475 Quiram Dr, Rogers, MN 55374

Tel.: (763) 428-8886   MN
Web Site:
http://www.hardrivesinc.com
Year Founded: 1997
Highway & Street Construction Services
N.A.I.C.S.: 237310
Donald R. Hall (VP)
Brad Mehlhaff (Treas)
Steve Hall (Pres & CEO)

Subsidiaries:

Tower Asphalt Inc.   (1)
15001 Hudson Rd, Lakeland, MN 55043
Tel.: (651) 436-8444
Web Site: http://www.towerasphalt.com
Sales Range: $25-49.9 Million
Emp.: 80
Highway & Street Paving Contracting Services
N.A.I.C.S.: 237310
Steve Hall (Pres)

HARDWARE DISTRIBUTION WAREHOUSES, INC.
2938 Brown Rd, Marshall, TX 75672
Tel.: (318) 686-8527   LA
Web Site: http://www.hdwinc.com
Sales Range: $25-49.9 Million
Emp.: 170
Hardware Tools Plumbing & Ventilation Components Electrical Components Paint Housewares Industrial Supplies & Building Materials Distr
N.A.I.C.S.: 423710
James Coughlan (VP-Building Matl)
Billy Stapleton (Pres)

Subsidiaries:

HDW-Greenwood Distribution
Center   (1)
1100 Sycamore St, Greenwood, MS
38930   (100%)
Tel.: (662) 453-3221
Web Site: http://www.hdwinc.com
Hardware, Tools, Plumbing & Ventilation
Components, Electrical Components, Paint,
Housewares, Industrial Supplies & Building
Materials Distr
N.A.I.C.S.: 423710
Mary-Anne Stinson (Gen Mgr)

HARDWARE IMAGINATION-TECH
4300 NW 37th Ave, Miami, FL 33142
Tel.: (305) 635-3300   DE
Web Site:
https://www.hardwareimagination-tech.com
Sales Range: $100-124.9 Million
Emp.: 280
Flexible Foam Products Mfr & Marketer
N.A.I.C.S.: 326150
Luis Perez (VP)

HARDWARE SALES INC.
2034 James St, Bellingham, WA
98225
Tel.: (360) 734-6140
Web Site:
https://www.hardwaresales.net
Sales Range: $10-24.9 Million
Emp.: 125
Hardware Stores
N.A.I.C.S.: 444140
Alta McClellan (Treas)

HARDWARE SPECIALTY CO. INC.
4875 36th St, Long Island City, NY
11101-1917
Tel.: (718) 361-9393   NY
Web Site:
http://www.hardwarespecialty.com
Year Founded: 1932
Sales Range: $25-49.9 Million

Hardware Specialty Co. Inc.—(Continued)

Emp.: 230
Provider of Industrial Supply Services
N.A.I.C.S.: 423840
Jeffrey Kaufman (VP)
Tom Moranzoni (CFO)

HARDWARE SUPPLIERS OF AMERICA
1400 East Firetower Rd, Greenville, NC 27858
Tel.: (252) 355-9400
Web Site:
http://www.hardwaresuppliers.com
Year Founded: 1984
Sales Range: $10-24.9 Million
Emp.: 50
Hardware Mfr
N.A.I.C.S.: 423710
Thomas F. Taft (Chm)

HARDWICK CLOTHES INC.
3800 Old Tasso Rd, Cleveland, TN 37312
Tel.: (423) 476-6534　　　TN
Web Site:
http://www.hardwickclothes.com
Year Founded: 1880
Sales Range: $100-124.9 Million
Emp.: 225
Men's & Ladies' Clothing, Suits, Sport Coats & Slacks Mfr
N.A.I.C.S.: 315250
Bruce Bellusci (CEO)
John Diacatos (VP-Mfg)
Finn Wald-Jacobsen (Dir-Engrg)
Sheila Waddell (Mgr-Lean Mfg)

HARDWIRE LLC
1947 Clarke Ave, Pocomoke City, MD 21851
Tel.: (410) 957-3669
Web Site:
https://www.hardwirellc.com
Year Founded: 2002
Sales Range: $100-124.9 Million
Emp.: 48
Military/Government Facility Armor Developer & Mfr
N.A.I.C.S.: 336992
Tim Keller (Mgr)
Scott Kendall (Dir-Engrg)
George Tunis III (CEO)

HARDWOOD CREATIONS
1560 N Maple Ave, Corona, CA 92878
Tel.: (714) 936-5586
Web Site: https://www.hcirailings.com
Year Founded: 1981
Sales Range: $10-24.9 Million
Emp.: 70
Carpentry Work
N.A.I.C.S.: 238130
Thomas Steele (Pres)
Mahshid Aminian (Controller)
Melvin Grimes (Sec)
Jeremy Steele (Sls Mgr)

HARDWOOD INDUSTRIES INC.
20548 SW Wild Rd Pl, Sherwood, OR 97140
Tel.: (503) 692-6620
Web Site:
https://www.hardwoodind.com
Sales Range: $10-24.9 Million
Emp.: 60
Lumber: Rough, Dressed & Finished
N.A.I.C.S.: 423310
Jeffrey Wirkkala (Pres)
Jim Susbauer (Mgr-HR)
Scott Lilley (Mgr-Sls & Pur)

HARDY CHEVROLET, INC.
2115 Browns Bridge Rd, Gainesville, GA 30501-4743

Tel.: (770) 532-4389
Web Site:
https://www.hardychevrolet.com
Sales Range: $25-49.9 Million
Emp.: 90
Car Whslr
N.A.I.C.S.: 441110
Wayne Alexander (Gen Mgr)

HARDY COMMUNICATIONS DEVELOPMENT
16333 Ohio St, Omaha, NE 68116
Tel.: (402) 991-8823
Year Founded: 2005
Sales Range: Less than $1 Million
Emp.: 10
Advetising Agency
N.A.I.C.S.: 541810
John Hardy (Pres)
Neal Sapp (Dir-Creative & Mktg)

HARDY DIAGNOSTICS
1430 W McCoy Ln, Santa Maria, CA 93455
Tel.: (805) 346-2766
Web Site:
https://www.hardydiagnostics.com
Year Founded: 1980
Sales Range: $100-124.9 Million
Emp.: 200
Prepared & Powdered Culture Media Products & Microbiology Supply Items
N.A.I.C.S.: 423450
Jay R. Hardy (Pres)
Christopher Cantani (Dir-Sls, Mktg & Customer Svc)
Nathaniel Graessle (CFO)
Eddie Yubeta (Mgr-Customer Svc)

HARDY ENTERPRISES INCORPORATED
598 W 2600 S, Bountiful, UT 84010-7718
Tel.: (801) 298-1180　　　UT
Year Founded: 1966
Sales Range: $10-24.9 Million
Emp.: 12
Operator of Gasoline Service Stations & Convenience Stores
N.A.I.C.S.: 457120

HAREN CONSTRUCTION COMPANY INC
PO Box 350, Etowah, TN 37331
Tel.: (423) 263-5561
Web Site:
http://www.harenconstruction.com
Sales Range: $10-24.9 Million
Emp.: 125
Waste Water & Sewage Treatment Plant Construction
N.A.I.C.S.: 237110
Frank E. Haren (Pres)
Dan Berry (VP)

HARGER HOWE ADVERTISING
1800 St James Pl Ste 400, Houston, TX 77056
Tel.: (713) 623-2030
Web Site:
http://www.hargerhowe.com
Year Founded: 1984
Sales Range: $1-9.9 Million
Emp.: 40
Advetising Agency
N.A.I.C.S.: 541810
Jennifer Sopczak (Mng Partner)

Subsidiaries:

Harger Howe Advertising　　　(1)
3155 W Big Beaver Rd Ste 110, Troy, MI 48084
Web Site: http://www.hargerhowe.com
Advetising Agency

N.A.I.C.S.: 541810
Mark Wedes (Mng Partner)

Harger Howe Advertising　　　(1)
1 Van De Graaff Dr Ste 401, Burlington, MA 01803
Tel.: (781) 425-5005
Web Site:
http://www.inbound.hargerhowe.com
Advertising Agency Services
N.A.I.C.S.: 541810
Michael Walsh (Owner & Pres)

HARGROVE ENGINEERS & CONSTRUCTORS
20 S Royal St, Mobile, AL 36602
Tel.: (251) 476-0605
Web Site: http://www.web.hargrove-epc.com
Year Founded: 1997
Sales Range: $75-99.9 Million
Emp.: 685
Engineeering Services
N.A.I.C.S.: 541330
Patrick Smith (Sr Project Mgr)
Stephen Jackson (Engr-Mechanical & Piping)

HARGROVE ENGINEERS + CONSTRUCTORS
20 S Royal St, Mobile, AL 36602
Tel.: (251) 476-0605
Web Site: https://www.hargrove-epc.com
Year Founded: 1995
Emp.: 700
Industrial Engineering Services; Designs, Builds & Remodels Industrial Buildings
N.A.I.C.S.: 541330
Ralph A. Hargrove (Pres)
Jim Backes (VP & Sr Project Mgr)
Phil Hamilton (VP-Engrg)
R. Dennis Watson (VP-Project Mgmt)
Jeb Shell (CFO)

HARKCON INC.
1390 Chain Bridge Rd #570, McLean, VA 22101
Tel.: (800) 499-6456
Web Site: http://www.harkcon.com
Year Founded: 2005
Sales Range: $1-9.9 Million
Emp.: 22
Management Consulting
N.A.I.C.S.: 541611
Kevin D. Harkins (Pres & CEO)
Keith G. Curran (COO & Exec VP)
Laurie Mosier (Sr VP)
Mark Faller (CFO)
Kyle Moore (Pres)

HARKEN, INCORPORATED
1 Harken Way N15 W24983 Bluemound Rd, Pewaukee, WI 53072-3755
Tel.: (262) 691-3320　　　WI
Web Site: https://www.harken.com
Year Founded: 1967
Sailboat Hardware & Accessories Mfr & Distr
N.A.I.C.S.: 332510
Olaf Harken (Co-Founder & CEO)
Peter Harken (CEO-Global)

HARKINS AMUSEMENT ENTERPRISES, INC.
7511 E McDonald Dr, Scottsdale, AZ 85250
Tel.: (480) 627-7777　　　AZ
Web Site:
http://www.harkinstheaters.com
Year Founded: 1933
Sales Range: $25-49.9 Million
Emp.: 55
Holding Company; Motion Picture Theaters Owner & Operator

N.A.I.C.S.: 551112
Daniel E. Harkins (Chm & CEO)
Michael L. Bowers (Pres)

Subsidiaries:

Harkins Theatres, Inc.　　　(1)
7511 E McDonald Dr, Scottsdale, AZ 85250
Tel.: (480) 627-7777
Web Site: http://www.harkinstheaters.com
Motion Picture Theater Operator
N.A.I.C.S.: 512131
Daniel E. Harkins (Chm)
Michael L. Bowers (Pres & CEO)
Heather Morgan (VP-Content & Programming)

HARKINS BUILDERS, INC.
2201 Warwick Way, Marriottsville, MD 21104-1600
Tel.: (410) 750-2600　　　MD
Web Site:
http://www.harkinsbuilders.com
Year Founded: 1965
Sales Range: $200-249.9 Million
Emp.: 200
Apartment & Industrial Buildings & Commercial Construction
N.A.I.C.S.: 236117
Gary J. Garofalo (Pres & COQ)
Richard Lombardo (Chm & CEO)
Lawrence P. Kraemer (Exec VP)
John Dawson (Mgr-Comm)
David A. Borkowski (VP-Construction)
John A. Loftus (VP-Construction Excellence)
Thomas Capps (VP-Construction)
Mike Ebrahimi (Sr VP-Construction Ops)
Mark Tillotson (VP-Comml)
Omar Black (Dir-Preconstruction)
Jonathan Mowery (Mgr-Preconstruction-Charlotte)
Rick Kottke (VP)

Subsidiaries:

Carpentry & Hardware Services　　(1)
8919 McGaw Ct Ste 1, Columbia, MD 21045-4725
Tel.: (443) 539-9191
Sales Range: $25-49.9 Million
Emp.: 65
Carpentry Subcontractor & Hardware Supplier
N.A.I.C.S.: 238130

Harkins Builders, Inc.　　　(1)
610 E Baltimore Pike, Media, PA 19063-1735
Tel.: (610) 627-4945
Web Site: http://www.harkinsbuilders.com
Sales Range: $10-24.9 Million
Emp.: 10
Apartment & Industrial Buildings & Commercial Construction
N.A.I.C.S.: 236116
Richard M. Lombardo (CEO)
Larry Getz (Mgr-Reg Bus Dev)
Mark Tillotson (VP-Comml Construction)
Gary J. Garofalo (Pres & COO)
Jorge Otalora (Dir-Corp Safety)

Harkins Builders, Inc. Virginia　　(1)
2201 Warwick Way, Marriottsville, MD 21104-1600
Tel.: (757) 490-2160
Web Site: http://www.harkinsbuilders.com
Sales Range: $25-49.9 Million
Emp.: 10
Apartment, Industrial & Commercial Buildings Construction
N.A.I.C.S.: 236117

HARLAN BAKERIES LLC
7597 E US Hwy 36, Avon, IN 46123-7171
Tel.: (317) 272-3600
Web Site:
http://www.harlanbakeries.com
Year Founded: 1991
Sales Range: $50-74.9 Million
Emp.: 25

Retail Groceries & Related Products
N.A.I.C.S.: 424490
Hugh Harlan *(Pres)*
Doug Harlan *(Exec VP)*
Joseph E. Latouf *(Exec VP-Sls & Mktg)*
John Menni *(CFO)*

Subsidiaries:

AmeriQual Group, LLC **(1)**
18200 Hwy 41 N, Evansville, IN 47725
Tel.: (812) 867-1444
Web Site: http://www.ameriqual.com
Production, Packaging, Assembly & Distribution of Shelf-Stable Food Products
N.A.I.C.S.: 722310
Dennis Straub *(Pres)*
Daniel S. Hermann *(Founder)*

HARLAN ELECTRIC COMPANY INC.
441 Allied Dr, Nashville, TN 37211
Tel.: (615) 331-0007
Web Site: https://www.harlan-electric.com
Sales Range: $10-24.9 Million
Emp.: 190
General Electrical Contractor
N.A.I.C.S.: 238210
Keith Pugh *(Pres)*
Gary T. Keith *(Exec VP & Project Mgr)*

HARLAN SPRAGUE DAWLEY INC.
8520 Allison Pointe Ste 400, Indianapolis, IN 46250
Tel.: (317) 894-7521 IN
Web Site: http://www.harlan.com
Year Founded: 1931
Sales Range: $75-99.9 Million
Emp.: 1,350
Breeding & Sale of Laboratory Animals for Research Purposes
N.A.I.C.S.: 112990
Manuela Leone *(Pres-Contract Res Svcs)*

HARLAN-CUMBERLAND COAL COMPANY
Hwy 421 S, Grays Knob, KY 40829
Tel.: (606) 573-2233
Sales Range: $10-24.9 Million
Emp.: 90
Bituminous Coal Underground Mining
N.A.I.C.S.: 212115
Joseph T. Bennett *(Pres)*

HARLEM CHILDREN'S ZONE, INC.
35 E 125th St, New York, NY 10035
Tel.: (212) 360-3255 NY
Web Site: https://www.hcz.org
Year Founded: 1970
Sales Range: $125-149.9 Million
Emp.: 3,494
Community Care Services
N.A.I.C.S.: 624190
Tracey Costello *(CFO)*
Mindy Miller *(VP-Dev)*
Conrad Pinnock *(Dir-HR)*
Anne Williams-Isom *(CEO)*
Karen Sodomick *(Chief Comm Officer)*

HARLEY DAVIDSON OF FORT SMITH
6304 S 36th St, Fort Smith, AR 72908
Tel.: (479) 648-1666
Web Site: http://www.oldfortharleydavidson.com
Sales Range: $10-24.9 Million
Emp.: 85
Sales of Motorcycles

N.A.I.C.S.: 441227
Michael Crouch *(Pres)*

HARLEY DAVIDSON OF GLENDALE
3717 San Fernando Rd, Glendale, CA 91204
Tel.: (818) 423-4367
Web Site: https://www.glendaleharley.com
Rev.: $13,494,493
Emp.: 58
Motorcycles
N.A.I.C.S.: 441227
Oliver A. Shokouh *(Founder, Chm & Pres)*
Emily Vindeni *(Controller)*
Bobbi Rojas *(Coord-Event)*

HARLEY ELLIS DEVEREAUX CORPORATION
417 Montgomery St 400, San Francisco, CA 94104
Tel.: (415) 981-2345
Web Site: http://www.hed.design
Architectural Engineering & Planning Services
N.A.I.C.S.: 541310
Ronald Herzog *(Project Mgr)*
Susan DiMario *(Mgr-Bus Dev)*
Brett Paloutzian *(Mng Principal)*
Jerome Odell *(Principal-Los Angeles)*
Gregory Blackburn *(Principal)*
Peter Devereaux *(Chm & CEO)*

Subsidiaries:

Integrated Design Group, Inc. **(1)**
133 Federal St Fl 5, Boston, MA 02110
Tel.: (617) 338-1177
Web Site: http://www.idgroupae.com
Engineering & Architectural Services
N.A.I.C.S.: 541330
Gary Murphy *(Principal)*
Robert Stein *(Principal)*
Sara Martin *(Project Mgr-Boston & Dallas)*
Joseph F Maggio *(VP)*

Pacific Cornerstone Architects Inc. **(1)**
11750 Sorrento Vly Rd Ste 100, San Diego, CA 92121
Tel.: (858) 677-9880
Web Site: http://pacificcornerstonearchitects.com
Rev.: $1,510,000
Emp.: 10
Architectural Services
N.A.I.C.S.: 541310

Puchlik Design Associates, Inc. **(1)**
859 S Raymond Ave, Pasadena, CA 91105
Tel.: (626) 304-9215
Web Site: http://www.puchlikdesign.com
Architectural Services
N.A.I.C.S.: 541310
DeeAnna DeLelio *(Mgr-Bus Dev)*

HARLEY MARINE SERVICES INC.
910 SW Spokane St, Seattle, WA 98134
Tel.: (206) 628-0051
Web Site: http://www.harleymarine.com
Year Founded: 1987
Sales Range: $25-49.9 Million
Emp.: 200
Water Transportation Services
N.A.I.C.S.: 483211
Harley V. Franco *(Founder, Chm, Pres & CEO)*
Todd Prophet *(CFO & Sr VP)*
Bryon Fletcher *(Reg Dir-Petroleum Barge Ops)*
Kelly Moore *(Reg Dir-Petroleum Barge Ops)*
Jim Weimer *(Gen Mgr-Alaska)*
Rod Gullickson *(Sr VP-Ops)*
Bo Jun *(VP-Bus Dev)*
Steve Carlson *(VP-Engrg)*

HARLEY STANFIELD, INC.
1725 Eye St NW Ste 300, Washington, DC 20006
Tel.: (202) 349-3822
Web Site: http://www.harleystanfield.com
Year Founded: 2003
Sales Range: $25-49.9 Million
Emp.: 22
Real Estate Investment Services
N.A.I.C.S.: 523999
Cedric J. Franklin *(Chm & CEO)*
Gail L. Garnett *(COO & Exec VP)*

HARLEY-DAVIDSON OF CHARLOTTE
9205 E Independence Blvd, Matthews, NC 28105-4501
Tel.: (704) 847-4647
Web Site: http://www.harleydavidsonofcharlotte.com
Motorcycle, ATV & All Other Motor Vehicle Dealers
N.A.I.C.S.: 441227
Ginger Witherspoon *(Dir-Administration-Riding Academy)*

HARLEY-DAVIDSON OF MIAMI LLC
19400 NW 2nd Ave, Miami, FL 33169
Tel.: (305) 651-4811
Web Site: http://www.miamiharley.com
Year Founded: 1954
Sales Range: $25-49.9 Million
Emp.: 100
Retailer of Motorcycles
N.A.I.C.S.: 441227
Phil Peterson *(Pres)*
Dirk Peterson *(VP)*
Drew Peterson *(VP)*

HARLEY-DAVIDSON OF WASHINGTON, DC
9407 Livingston Rd, Fort Washington, MD 20744
Tel.: (301) 248-1200
Web Site: http://www.hdwash.com
Rev.: $19,555,367
Emp.: 59
Motorcycle Mfr, Sales & Rentals
N.A.I.C.S.: 441227
Donald Smolinski *(Pres)*
Thomas Moorehead *(Owner)*

HARLO CORPORATION
4210 Ferry St SW, Grandville, MI 49418
Tel.: (616) 538-0550
Web Site: https://www.harlo.com
Rev.: $23,555,229
Emp.: 110
Lift Trucks, Industrial: Fork, Platform, Straddle
N.A.I.C.S.: 333924
Mary Helen Crooks *(Pres & CEO)*

HARLOW AEROSTRUCTURES, LLC
1501 S McLean Blvd, Wichita, KS 67213-4303
Tel.: (316) 265-5268
Web Site: https://www.harlowair.com
Year Founded: 1954
Aircraft Part & Auxiliary Equipment Mfr
N.A.I.C.S.: 336413

Subsidiaries:

Aerospace Holdings, Inc. **(1)**
3401 E 69th St, Long Beach, CA 90805
Tel.: (562) 634-7392
Holding Company; Aerospace Component Mfr
N.A.I.C.S.: 336413

Subsidiary (Non-US):

GroupAero Mexico **(2)**
Ave Valle de Calafia S/N Nave III Modulo A Lote 3 Manz 4, Col. Abasolo CO, 21600, Mexicali, Mexico
Tel.: (52) 686 564 8465
Aerospace Component Mfr
N.A.I.C.S.: 336413

Subsidiary (Domestic):

NC Dynamics Inc. **(2)**
3400 E 69th St, Long Beach, CA 90805
Tel.: (562) 634-7392
Web Site: http://www.ncdi.aero
Aerospace Component Mfr
N.A.I.C.S.: 336413

STADCO **(2)**
107 S Ave 20, Los Angeles, CA 90031
Tel.: (323) 227-8888
Web Site: https://www.stadco.com
Emp.: 120
Aerospace Component Mfr
N.A.I.C.S.: 336413
Bret Matta *(VP-Contracts & Programs)*
Craig Sliwa *(Dir-Engrg)*
Scott Merrell *(Dir-Quality)*

Subsidiary (Non-US):

Survirn Engineering Ltd. **(2)**
1581 Bristol Road South, Birmingham, B45 9UA, United Kingdom
Tel.: (44) 121 453 7718
Web Site: http://www.survirn.co.uk
Aerospace Component Mfr
N.A.I.C.S.: 336413

Subsidiary (Domestic):

Valley Tool & Manufacturing, Inc. **(2)**
22 Prindle Hill Rd, Orange, CT 06477-0564
Tel.: (203) 799-8800
Web Site: http://www.valleytl.com
Aerospace Component Mfr
N.A.I.C.S.: 336413
Gary Greco *(Owner)*
Larry Feinn *(Pres)*

Best Lighting Products, Inc. **(1)**
1213 Etna Pkwy, Pataskala, OH 43062
Tel.: (740) 964-1198
Web Site: http://www.bestlighting.net
Commercial, Industrial & Residential Lighting Products Mfr
N.A.I.C.S.: 335139
Juna Cai *(CFO & Dir-HR)*
Jeff Katz *(CEO)*
Nate VanMeter *(VP-Sls)*
Jeremy Adkins *(Dir-IT & Telecom)*
George T. Jue *(Pres)*
Scott Stephens *(COO)*
Ana Perez *(Mgr-Logistics)*
Dave Melanson *(Mgr-Pur)*
Joe Cotugno *(Mgr-Warehouse)*

Hamilton Engineering, Inc. **(1)**
777 Post Oak Blvd Ste 400, Houston, TX 77056
Tel.: (713) 956-0956
Web Site: http://www.hamiltongroup.org
Sales Range: $75-99.9 Million
Emp.: 250
Oil & Gas Technical Consulting, Engineering & Well Drilling Services
N.A.I.C.S.: 541690
Keith Grimes *(CEO)*
Clyde Neely *(VP)*
Dan Hostler *(VP-Engrg)*
Claude Thorp Sr. *(VP-Bus Dev)*

Subsidiary (Domestic):

Petroleum Engineers, Inc. **(2)**
500 Dover Blvd, Lafayette, LA 70503
Tel.: (337) 984-2603
Web Site: http://www.peiinc.com
Emp.: 40
Petroleum Engineering & Consulting Services
N.A.I.C.S.: 213112
Mahlon LeBlanc *(Coord-Consulting)*
John Morgan *(CEO)*

HARMAC MEDICAL PRODUCTS INC.
2201 Bailey Ave, Buffalo, NY 14211

Harmac Medical Products Inc.—(Continued)

Tel.: (716) 897-4500
Web Site: https://www.harmac.com
Sales Range: $25-49.9 Million
Emp.: 350
Surgical & Medical Instruments
N.A.I.C.S.: 339112
Jeffrey Welch (Mgr-Supply Chain)

HARMAN PRESS
6840 Vineland Ave, North Hollywood, CA 91605
Tel.: (818) 432-0570   **CA**
Web Site: https://harmanpress.com
Year Founded: 1963
Sales Range: $1-9.9 Million
Emp.: 50
Lithographic Commercial Printing
N.A.I.C.S.: 323111
Philip Goldner (Pres)

Subsidiaries:

Fox Printing Company, Inc.   (1)
9330 San Fernando Rd, Sun Valley, CA 91352
Tel.: (818) 768-6110
Web Site: http://foxprtco.com
Sales Range: $1-9.9 Million
Emp.: 15
Commercial Printing Services
N.A.I.C.S.: 323111
Gary Fox (Pres)

HARMAR
2075 47th St, Sarasota, FL 34234
Tel.: (941) 351-2776   **FL**
Web Site: http://www.harmar.com
Year Founded: 1998
Sales Range: $25-49.9 Million
Emp.: 135
Industrial Truck, Tractor, Trailer & Stacker Machinery Mfr
N.A.I.C.S.: 333924
Mike Vogt (COO-Harmar Summit)
David Baxter (VP-Mktg)
Drew McCartney (Pres & CEO)

HARMELIN MEDIA
525 Righters Ferry Rd, Bala Cynwyd, PA 19004-1315
Tel.: (610) 668-7900   **PA**
Web Site: http://www.harmelin.com
Year Founded: 1983
Sales Range: $350-399.9 Million
Emp.: 137
Media Buying Services
N.A.I.C.S.: 541830
Joanne Harmelin (Founder & CEO)
Lyn Pierce Strickler (Exec VP)
Cheryl Klear (Sr VP-Brdcst)
John Camilleri (Sr VP-New Bus)
Scott Davis (Chief Revenue Officer)
Joe Waugh (Sr VP-Acct Mgmt)
Brad Bernard (VP-Innovation & Product Dev)
Irene Neveil (VP-Plng)
Janine Cross (VP-Digital)
Jamie Grim (Assoc VP)
Greg Ebbecke (VP-Bus Intelligence)
Dan DiZio (VP-Plng)
Conor Elliott (CTO & VP)
Karen Yerk (VP-Acctg)
Mary M. Meder (Pres)

HARMON CITY, INC.
3540 S 4000 W Ste 500, Salt Lake City, UT 84120-3296
Tel.: (801) 969-8261   **UT**
Web Site:
    http://www.harmonsgrocery.com
Year Founded: 1945
Sales Range: $250-299.9 Million
Emp.: 2,500
Retailer of Groceries
N.A.I.C.S.: 445110

Dean Peterson (Pres)
Lee Hussey (VP-IT)
Bob Harmon (VP-Mktg)
Laurie Harmon (VP-HR)

HARMON FOODS INC.
1255 W Morton Ave, Jacksonville, IL 62650-2619
Tel.: (217) 243-8615   **IL**
Year Founded: 1979
Sales Range: $50-74.9 Million
Emp.: 500
Grocery Stores
N.A.I.C.S.: 445110
Thomas Harmon (Owner)

HARMON GROUP
621-623 S State St, North Vernon, IN 47265
Tel.: (812) 346-2064
Web Site:
    http://www.harmongroup.com
Sales Range: $10-24.9 Million
Holding Company; Construction & Specialty Contractor Services
N.A.I.C.S.: 551112
William A. Harmon (CEO)
Thomas D. Harmon (Pres)

Subsidiaries:

Harmon Construction Incorporated   (1)
621 S State St, North Vernon, IN 47265
Tel.: (812) 346-2048
Web Site:
    http://www.harmonconstruction.com
Construction & General Contracting Services
N.A.I.C.S.: 238990
William A. Harmon (Co-Owner & Pres)
Thomas D. Harmon (Co-Owner & VP)
William B. Harmon (Co-Owner)

Harmon Steel, Inc.   (1)
1002 W Troy Ave, Indianapolis, IN 46225
Tel.: (317) 780-5025
Web Site: http://www.harmonsteel.com
Structural Steel Erection Services
N.A.I.C.S.: 238120
Thomas D. Harmon (Co-Pres)
William A. Harmon (Co-Pres)

Taylor Bros. Construction Co., Inc.   (1)
4555 Middle Rd, Columbus, IN 47203
Tel.: (812) 379-9547
Web Site: http://www.tbcci.com
Emp.: 35
Commercial & Institutional Building Construction
N.A.I.C.S.: 236220
Jeffrey A. Chandler (VP)
Thomas D. Harmon (Chm & CEO)
David A. Doup (Pres)
James C. Euler (Treas & Sec)

HARMONIA, INC
2020 Kraft Dr Ste 1000, Blacksburg, VA 24060
Tel.: (540) 951-5900
Web Site: http://www.harmonia.com
Year Founded: 1999
Rev.: $3,200,000
Emp.: 32
Custom Computer Programming Services
N.A.I.C.S.: 541511
Marc Abrams (Pres & CTO)
Michael Bame (Controller)
Pallabi Saboo (CEO)
Manish Khera (VP-Bus & Data Analytics)

HARMONIE CLUB OF THE CITY OF NEW YORK
4 E 60th St, New York, NY 10022
Tel.: (212) 355-7400   **NY**
Web Site:
    https://www.harmonieclub.org
Year Founded: 1852

Sales Range: $10-24.9 Million
Emp.: 175
Social Club
N.A.I.C.S.: 813410
Christopher O. Carey (Gen Mgr)

HARMONY COUNTRY COOPERATIVE
2327 W Veterans Pkwy, Marshfield, WI 54449
Tel.: (715) 223-2306
Web Site:
    http://www.harmonycountrycooperatives.com
Rev.: $18,464,549
Emp.: 200
Feed
N.A.I.C.S.: 424910
Rob Larson (Gen Mgr)

HARMONY DEVELOPMENT CO., LLC
3500 Harmony Sq Dr W, Harmony, FL 34773
Tel.: (407) 891-8358
Web Site: http://www.harmonyfl.com
Sales Range: $10-24.9 Million
Emp.: 2
Housing Developer
N.A.I.C.S.: 236116
Jim Lentz (Chm)

HARMONY HEALTHCARE INTERNATIONAL, INC.
430 Boston St Ste 104, Topsfield, MA 01983
Tel.: (978) 887-8919
Web Site: https://www.harmony-healthcare.com
Year Founded: 2001
Sales Range: $1-9.9 Million
Emp.: 25
Assists Long-Term Care Facilities with Maximizing Medicare Reimbursements Through Audits, Education & Training Programs
N.A.I.C.S.: 623990
Kris Mastrangelo (Pres & CEO)
Elisa Bovee (VP-Ops)
Beckie Dow (VP-Field Ops)
Diane Buckley (VP-Quality & Performance Improvement)
Howard Rich (Dir-Bus Dev)
Jon A. Di Gesu (VP-Mktg)
Joyce Sadewicz (VP-Field Ops)
Kim Steele (VP-Field Ops)
Matt McGarvey (Dir-Bus Dev)

HARMONY HOME HEALTH, LLC
13787 S Belcher Rd Ste 220, Largo, FL 33771
Tel.: (727) 723-7532
Web Site: http://www.harmonyhh.com
Year Founded: 2004
Sales Range: $1-9.9 Million
Emp.: 120
Women Healthcare Services
N.A.I.C.S.: 621610
Jonathan Bowman (CEO)
Carole Ware-McKenzie (Dir-Staff Dev)
Cathy Poston (Dir-Nursing)
Anita Trent (Coord-Acctg & HR)
Amanda Frady (Mgr-Recruitment)
Brittany Carter (Mgr-Client Svcs)

HARMS OIL COMPANY
411 10th Ave SW, Aberdeen, SD 57401
Tel.: (605) 696-5000
Web Site: http://www.harmsoil.net
Sales Range: $10-24.9 Million
Emp.: 105
Diesel Fuel
N.A.I.C.S.: 424720

Duane D. Harms (Pres)

HARNISH GROUP INC.
17035 W Vly Hwy, Tukwila, WA 98188
Tel.: (425) 251-9800
Web Site:
    http://www.ncmachinery.com
Sales Range: $400-449.9 Million
Emp.: 50
Construction & Mining Machinery
N.A.I.C.S.: 423810
Ralph Simonds (Mgr-Tech Svcs)

HARODITE INDUSTRIES, INC.
66 South St, Taunton, MA 02780
Tel.: (508) 824-6961   **MA**
Web Site: https://www.harodite.com
Year Founded: 1910
Sales Range: $75-99.9 Million
Emp.: 100
Finished Textile Mfr
N.A.I.C.S.: 313210
Michael P. Albert (Chm)
Donna Adams (VP-Quality)
Jean Jardim (VP-HR-Fin Dept)
Aaron M. Albert (Pres & CEO)
Tommy Bridges (VP)
Frank Grace (Dir-R&D)
Dale Fulgham (Reg Mgr-Sls)
Antonio Gomez (VP-Mexico & Latin America)

Subsidiaries:

Harodite Industries, Inc. - South Carolina   (1)
2 Henderson Ct, Travelers Rest, SC 29690
Tel.: (864) 834-9066
Web Site: http://www.harodite.com
Sales Range: $1-9.9 Million
Emp.: 20
Mfr of Interlinings & Converters
N.A.I.C.S.: 314999
Thomas Bridges (VP)

Harodite S.A. de C.V.   (1)
Gregorio Ruiz Velazco 203 Ciudad Industrial, 20290, Aguascalientes, Mexico
Tel.: (52) 449 971 1917
Web Site: http://www.harodite.com
Sales Range: $10-24.9 Million
Emp.: 10
Nonwoven Fabric Mfr
N.A.I.C.S.: 313210
Antonio Gomez (VP-Mexico & Latin America)

Harodite S.A. de C.V.   (1)
Zona Franca Miramar Km 30 5 Carretera al Aeropuerto International, Olocuilta, La Paz, El Salvador
Tel.: (503) 2389 8989
Nonwoven Fabric Mfr
N.A.I.C.S.: 313210

HAROL BROTHERS LLC
9204 Eisenhower Dr Ste 100, Apex, NC 27539
Web Site:
    http://www.lighthouselabservice.com
Year Founded: 2013
Sales Range: $1-9.9 Million
Clinical Laboratory Services
N.A.I.C.S.: 621511
Joe Kessler (Dir-Recruiting)
Tom Boyd (Dir-Consulting Solutions)

Subsidiaries:

Pathology Lab Solutions, Inc.   (1)
524 E Elm St, Conshohocken, PA 19428
Tel.: (610) 828-7100
Web Site: http://www.pathlabsolutions.com
Sales Range: $1-9.9 Million
Emp.: 7
Laboratory Equipment Distr
N.A.I.C.S.: 423450
Rod Glose (CEO)
Sarah Glose (Mgr-Mktg)
Ellen Harrison (Office Mgr)

HAROLD A. O'NEIL CO., INC.
1016 N Houston Ave, Humble, TX 77338

Tel.: (281) 548-0039
Web Site: http://www.haoneil.com
Year Founded: 1962
Sales Range: $10-24.9 Million
Emp.: 13
Sales of Metals
N.A.I.C.S.: 423510
James H. O'Neil *(Pres)*

HAROLD ALLEN'S MOBILE HOMES INC.

323 N Main St, Atmore, AL 36502
Tel.: (251) 368-8134
Web Site:
   http://www.haroldallenhome
   show.com
Rev.: $12,411,381
Emp.: 20
Mobile Home Dealers
N.A.I.C.S.: 459930
William H. Allen *(Pres)*

HAROLD FRIEDMAN INC.

530 Fairground Hill Rd, Butler, PA
16001-2634
Tel.: (724) 283-6030   PA
Web Site:
   http://www.friedmansfreshmar
   kets.com
Year Founded: 1900
Sales Range: $25-49.9 Million
Emp.: 120
Grocery Stores
N.A.I.C.S.: 445110
Carole F. Bitter *(Pres & CEO)*
David Crater *(Controller)*

HAROLD GRINSPOON FOUNDATION

67 Hunt St Ste 100, Agawam, MA
01001
Tel.: (413) 276-0700   MA
Web Site: https://www.hgf.org
Year Founded: 1991
Sales Range: $25-49.9 Million
Emp.: 82
Jewish Education Support Services
N.A.I.C.S.: 611710
Jim Baird *(Dir-Software Dev)*
Brian Buerkle *(Mgr-Publr Rels)*
Madeline Calabrese *(Dir-Voices & Visions)*
Tamar Remz *(Dir-Partnerships)*
Adrian Dion *(COO)*

HAROLD LEVINSON ASSOCIATES

21 Banfi Plz, Farmingdale, NY 11735-5356
Tel.: (631) 962-2400   NY
Web Site: https://www.hlacigars.com
Year Founded: 1975
Sales Range: $25-49.9 Million
Emp.: 300
Cigars & Related Tobacco Products
Mfr & Distr
N.A.I.C.S.: 424940
Amir Babazadeh *(Dir-IT)*
Marty Glick *(VP-Sls)*
Michael Berro *(VP-Corp Dev)*

HAROLD MATTHEWS NISSAN INC.

185 Hwy 76, Clarksville, TN 37043
Tel.: (931) 552-7555
Web Site:
   http://www.mathewsnissan.com
Sales Range: $10-24.9 Million
Emp.: 60
New & Used Car Dealers
N.A.I.C.S.: 441110
Gary Matthews *(Pres)*
Wayne Clardy *(Office Mgr)*

HAROLD T. ILLING CO. INC.

N114 W 18937 Clinton Dr, Germantown, WI 53022
Tel.: (262) 250-7566
Web Site:
   http://www.illingcompany.com
Sales Range: $10-24.9 Million
Emp.: 24
Containers: Glass, Metal Or Plastic
N.A.I.C.S.: 423990
Robert H. Illing *(Pres)*

HAROLD ZEIGLER AUTO GROUP, INC.

4201 Stadium Dr, Kalamazoo, MI
49008
Tel.: (269) 375-4500
Web Site: http://www.zeigler.com
Year Founded: 1975
Sales Range: $500-549.9 Million
Emp.: 2,200
Used & New Car Dealer
N.A.I.C.S.: 441110
Aaron Zeigler *(Owner & Pres)*

Subsidiaries:

McCarthy Ford Inc.   **(1)**
11400 S Pulaski Rd, Chicago, IL 60655
Tel.: (773) 239-7900
Web Site: http://www.mccarthyfordinc.net
Automotive Repair & Maintenance
N.A.I.C.S.: 811198
John Lefevour *(Pres)*

HAROLD ZEIGLER LINCOLN-MERCURY

4201 Stadium Dr, Kalamazoo, MI
49008
Tel.: (269) 375-4500
Web Site:
   http://www.hzkalamazoo.com
Sales Range: $75-99.9 Million
Emp.: 800
Sales of Automobiles
N.A.I.C.S.: 441110
Harold Ziegler *(Chm)*
Dan Scheid *(CFO)*
Erin Ziegler *(Pres)*

Subsidiaries:

Harold Zeigler Ford Lincoln Mercury
-Elkhart   **(1)**
2525 Bypass Rd, Elkhart, IN 46514-1519
Tel.: (574) 294-1563
Web Site: http://www.haroldzeigler.com
Sales Range: $25-49.9 Million
Emp.: 65
Sales of Automobiles
N.A.I.C.S.: 441110
Harold Ziegler *(Pres & Owner)*
Kathy Summers *(Controller & Office Mgr)*
Cathy Summers *(Gen Mgr)*

HARPAK-ULMA PACKAGING, LLC

175 John Quincy Adams Rd,
Taunton, MA 02780
Tel.: (508) 884-2500
Web Site: http://www.harpak-ulma.com
Year Founded: 1994
Sales Range: $10-24.9 Million
Emp.: 30
Packaging Machinery & Equipment
N.A.I.C.S.: 333993
Jim Ryan *(Sr VP)*
Dave Favret *(Product Mgr)*
Hugh Crouch *(Product Mgr)*

Subsidiaries:

Harpak-ULMA Engineering   **(1)**
2242 72nd Ave E, Sarasota, FL 34243
Tel.: (941) 527-3293
Web Site: http://www.harpak-ulma.com
Packaging Machinery
N.A.I.C.S.: 423830

HARPEL OIL COMPANY INC.

5480 Brighton Blvd, Commerce City,
CO 80022-3607
Tel.: (303) 294-0767   CO
Web Site: http://www.harpeloil.com
Year Founded: 1937
Sales Range: $25-49.9 Million
Emp.: 20
Petroleum Bulk Stations & Terminals
N.A.I.C.S.: 424710
Doug Harpel *(Pres)*

HARPER & TWO

2937 Cherry Ave, Signal Hill, CA
90755
Tel.: (562) 424-3030
Web Site:
   https://www.harperandtwo.com
Year Founded: 1990
Sales Range: $10-24.9 Million
Emp.: 28
Electronic Parts & Equipment Mfr
N.A.I.C.S.: 423690
Jim Quilty *(VP)*
Dan Kilstofte *(Pres & CEO)*
Joe Cottrell *(Partner)*

HARPER + SCOTT, LLC

915 Broadway Ste 1206, New York,
NY 10010
Web Site:
   http://www.harperandscott.com
Year Founded: 2014
Sales Range: $10-24.9 Million
Emp.: 32
Cut Paper Product Mfr
N.A.I.C.S.: 322230
Jon Alagem *(Founder)*

HARPER CHEVROLET-BUICK-GMC

200 Hwy 531, Minden, LA 71055
Tel.: (318) 377-0395
Web Site:
   https://www.harperminden.com
Year Founded: 1983
Sales Range: $10-24.9 Million
Emp.: 26
New Car Whslr
N.A.I.C.S.: 441110
Billy Davidson *(Dir-Sls)*

HARPER CONSTRUCTION COMPANY

2241 Kettner Blvd Ste 300, San Diego, CA 92101-1769
Tel.: (619) 233-7900
Web Site:
   https://www.harperconstruction.com
Year Founded: 1974
Sales Range: $100-124.9 Million
Emp.: 150
Contractor of Commercial, Office
Buildings & Military Housing
N.A.I.C.S.: 236220
Peter Wheeler *(Project Mgr)*
Brad Humphrey *(VP-Construction)*
Brian Crowley *(Mgr-Design)*
Harvey Rogoff *(Project Mgr)*

HARPER CORPORATION OF AMERICA

11625 Steele Creek, Charlotte, NC
28273
Tel.: (704) 588-3371
Web Site:
   https://www.harperimage.com
Sales Range: $10-24.9 Million
Emp.: 91
Printing Trades Machinery
N.A.I.C.S.: 333248
Ronald L. Harper *(Co-Founder)*
Katherine Harper *(Co-Founder)*
A. K. Mecklanberg *(Dir-Fin)*
Alexander James *(Mgr-Technical Graphic-Eastern Div)*

Mike Huey *(Mgr-Technical Graphic-Western Div)*
Josh Kiser *(Mgr-Technical OEM Accts)*
Ronald Kluttz *(Pres)*
Alan Rogers *(VP-Sls)*
Robbie King *(Sr Mgr-Sls & Technical-East)*
Craig Worman *(Mgr-Sls & Technical-Central)*
John Davis *(Mgr-Sls & Technical-West)*
Sean Teufler *(Dir-Technical)*
Bill Mulligan *(Acct Mgr-Technical-Northeast)*
Josh Sigmon *(Mgr-Sls & Technical-Eastern Hemisphere)*

HARPER ENGRAVING & PRINTING CO.

2626 Fisher Rd, Columbus, OH
43204
Tel.: (614) 276-0700
Web Site:
   http://www.harperengraving.com
Sales Range: $10-24.9 Million
Emp.: 80
Offset Printing & Engraving
N.A.I.C.S.: 323111
Donald J. Mueller *(Pres)*

HARPER INDUSTRIES INC.

960 N HC Mathis Dr, Paducah, KY
42001
Tel.: (270) 442-2753
Web Site: http://www.harper1.com
Year Founded: 1980
Sales Range: $125-149.9 Million
Emp.: 500
Ready-Mixed Concrete
N.A.I.C.S.: 327320
Billy Harper *(Pres & CEO)*
David Belt *(CFO)*
Laura Chastain *(Officer-Ethics)*
Amy Vick *(Office Mgr)*
Colette Buford *(Project Mgr-Viewpoint)*
Margee Shuemaker *(Treas)*
Ryan Bendick *(Mgr-IT)*
Tammy Partain *(Coord-Benefits & Wellness)*

HARPER INDUSTRIES INC.

645 SW Cherry Ln, Jesup, GA 31545
Tel.: (912) 427-6991
Web Site: http://harperpropane.com
Year Founded: 1973
Sales Range: $10-24.9 Million
Emp.: 5
Retailers of Propane Gas
N.A.I.C.S.: 424720
James L. Harper *(Pres)*

HARPER INDUSTRIES, INC.

151 E US Highway 160, Harper, KS
67058-8201
Tel.: (620) 896-7381   KS
Web Site: http://www.deweze.com
Year Founded: 1998
Sales Range: $75-99.9 Million
Emp.: 85
Agricultural Machinery, Round Bale
Handling & Feeding Equipment &
Grounds Maintenance Equipment Mfr
N.A.I.C.S.: 333111
A. Timothy Penner *(CEO)*
Heber Ramer *(Mgr-Engrg)*
Jennifer Rose *(Controller)*

HARPER OIL PRODUCTS INC.

7975 Kentucky Dr, Florence, KY
41042
Tel.: (859) 283-1001
Web Site: http://www.harperoil.com
Sales Range: $25-49.9 Million
Emp.: 25

Harper Oil Products Inc.—(Continued)

Petroleum Products
N.A.I.C.S.: 424720
Kevin Harper (Controller & Personnel Mgr)

HARPER TRUCKS, INC.
1522 S Florence St, Wichita, KS 67209
Tel.: (316) 942-1381
Web Site:
http://www.harpertrucks.com
Year Founded: 1940
Sales Range: $10-24.9 Million
Emp.: 50
Industrial Trucks & Tractors Mfr
N.A.I.C.S.: 333924
Darrell Neugebauer (Mgr-Sls-Natl)
Susie Ellis (Mgr-Customer Svc)

HARPER'S MAGAZINE FOUNDATION
666 Broadway 11th Fl, New York, NY 10012-2317
Tel.: (212) 420-5720
Web Site: https://www.harpers.org
Year Founded: 1850
Sales Range: $50-74.9 Million
Emp.: 30
Magazine Publisher
N.A.I.C.S.: 513120
Lynn Carlson (VP & Gen Mgr)
Ellen Rosenbush (Dir-Editorial)
Stacey D. Clarkson James (Editor-Visuals)
Shawn D. Green (VP-Circulation)
Giulia Melucci (VP-Mktg, Comm & PR)

HARPETH VALLEY UTILITIES DISTRICT OF DAVIDSON & WILLIAMSON COUNTIES
5838 River Rd, Nashville, TN 37209
Tel.: (615) 352-7076
Web Site: https://www.hvud.com
Year Founded: 1962
Sales Range: $10-24.9 Million
Emp.: 63
Water Supply & Sewage Administration Services
N.A.I.C.S.: 924110

HARPO, INC.
110 N Carpenter St, Chicago, IL 60607-2104
Tel.: (312) 633-1000
Web Site: http://www.oprah.com
Year Founded: 1986
Holding Company; Audio & Visual Entertainment Production, Publishing & Broadcasting Services
N.A.I.C.S.: 551112
Oprah Winfrey (Founder)
Bernard Gugar (Sr VP & Gen Counsel)
Ed Cuadrado (Mgr-IT Ops)

Subsidiaries:

Harpo Productions, Inc. **(1)**
110 N Carpenter St, Chicago, IL 60607-2104 **(100%)**
Tel.: (312) 633-1000
Web Site: http://www.oprah.com
Sales Range: $25-49.9 Million
Emp.: 176
Music, Audio & Interactive Content Publishing Services
N.A.I.C.S.: 512230

HARPS FOOD STORES, INC.
918 S Gutensohn Rd, Springdale, AR 72765-0048
Tel.: (479) 751-7601
Web Site: http://www.harpsfood.com
Year Founded: 1930
Sales Range: $1-4.9 Billion

Emp.: 3,000
Retail Groceries
N.A.I.C.S.: 445110
Kim Eskew (Chm)
Jim Antz (CFO & VP-Fin & Admin)
Frank Ray (VP-HR)
J. Max Van Hoose (VP-Store Plng)
Mike Thurow (VP-Store Sys)
Dean Payton (Dir-10Box Div)
Mike Roberts (Dir-Produce Ops)
David Ganoung (VP-Mktg)

HARPURE ENTERPRISES INC.
13560 Colombard Ct, Fontana, CA 92337
Tel.: (951) 681-9697
Chemical Product & Preparation Mfr
N.A.I.C.S.: 325998
Buck Long (Pres)

Subsidiaries:

Aqua-Serv Engineers Inc. **(1)**
13560 Colombard Ct, Fontana, CA 92337
Tel.: (951) 681-9696
Web Site: http://www.aqua-serv.com
Rev.: $2,700,000
Emp.: 50
Chemicals & Allied Products Blending
N.A.I.C.S.: 424690
Earl L. Harper (CEO)
Buck Long (Pres)

HARR MOTOR COMPANY
100 Gold Star Blvd, Worcester, MA 01606
Tel.: (508) 852-5111
Web Site: http://www.harr.com
Sales Range: $10-24.9 Million
Emp.: 300
Sales & Service Of New & Used Automobiles
N.A.I.C.S.: 441110
Charles Ribakoff (Chm)
Diane Mohieldin (CFO)

HARRELD CHEVROLET CO.
3096 S Liberty St, Canton, MS 39046-9211
Tel.: (601) 859-1611
Web Site:
http://www.harreldchevrolet.com
Rev.: $11,800,000
Emp.: 50
New & Used Automobiles & Trucks
N.A.I.C.S.: 441110
John Harreld (VP)
Brian King (Controller)

HARRELL & HARRELL INC.
4630 E Princess Anne Rd, Norfolk, VA 23502
Tel.: (757) 855-1616
Rev.: $24,100,000
Emp.: 40
Grocery Stores, Chain
N.A.I.C.S.: 445110
James L. Harrell III (Pres)

HARRELL HALL ENTERPRISES INC.
43 Airpark Ct, Alabaster, AL 35007
Tel.: (205) 664-9191
Web Site: https://www.hhsales.com
Year Founded: 1987
Sales Range: $10-24.9 Million
Emp.: 20
Building Services
N.A.I.C.S.: 444180
Wayne Hall (Pres)

Subsidiaries:

H&H Spas & Truck Covers **(1)**
698 N Eastern Blvd, Montgomery, AL 36117
Tel.: (334) 272-4447
Web Site: http://www.hhsales.com
Rev.: $450,000
Emp.: 4
Truck Parts & Accessories

N.A.I.C.S.: 423120
Wayne Hall (Owner)

HARRELL OIL CO. OF MOUNT AIRY
PO Box 1947, Mount Airy, NC 27030
Tel.: (336) 786-4107
Sales Range: $10-24.9 Million
Emp.: 37
Convenience Stores, Independent
N.A.I.C.S.: 445131
Joseph Harrell (Pres)
Jean Welch (Mgr)

HARRELLS INC.
5105 New Tampa Highway, Lakeland, FL 33815
Tel.: (863) 687-2774
Web Site: http://www.harrells.com
Sales Range: $600-649.9 Million
Emp.: 230
Fertilizers, Blending & Golf Courses
N.A.I.C.S.: 325314
Alex Barcia (VP-IT & HR)

HARREN EQUITY PARTNERS
123 E Main St, Charlottesville, VA 22902
Tel.: (434) 245-5800
Web Site:
http://www.harrenequity.com
Rev.: $3,168,000
Emp.: 8
Consumer Lending
N.A.I.C.S.: 522291
Thomas A. Carver (Mng Partner)
Taylor Coggin (Mgr-Mktg)
Jonathan Earnhardt (Partner)
Christian D. W. Codish (Office Mgr)
Christine Piorkowski Barth (CFO)
Ethan S. Caskey (VP)
Lee J. Monahan (Partner)
Shari S. Fowley (Controller)
C. Taylor Cole Jr. (Partner)

HARRIMAN ASSOCIATES
46 Harriman Dr, Auburn, ME 04210
Tel.: (207) 784-5100
Web Site: https://www.harriman.com
Year Founded: 1870
Sales Range: $10-24.9 Million
Emp.: 90
Architectural & Engineering Services
N.A.I.C.S.: 541310
Clifton W. Greim (Pres & CEO)
Michael Polley (Mgr-IT)
Daniel W. Cecil (Principal)
Carol F. Gillis (Principal)
Judy L. Johnson (Principal)
Jeffrey P. Larimer (Principal)
Mark D. Lee (Principal)
John W. Tarr (Principal)

HARRIMAN CREATIVE, INC
1310 NW Naito Pkwy Ste 111, Portland, OR 97209
Tel.: (503) 796-1813
Web Site:
http://www.harrimancreative.com
Year Founded: 1996
Sales Range: Less than $1 Million
Emp.: 2
N.A.I.C.S.: 541810
Brian R. Harriman (Pres)

HARRIMAN UTILITY BOARD
300 N Roane St, Harriman, TN 37748
Tel.: (865) 882-3242
Web Site: http://www.hubtn.com
Sales Range: $10-24.9 Million
Emp.: 74
Utility Administration Organization
N.A.I.C.S.: 926130
Bill Young (Gen Mgr)

HARRINGTON & KING PERFORATING COMPANY, INC.
5655 W Fillmore St, Chicago, IL 60644-5504
Tel.: (773) 626-1800
Web Site: https://www.hkperf.com
Year Founded: 1883
Sales Range: $75-99.9 Million
Emp.: 145
Mfr of Perforated Metal Sheets & Coils; Plates; Plastics
N.A.I.C.S.: 332119

Subsidiaries:

Harrington & King South, Inc. **(1)**
3939 Michigan Ave Rd NE, Cleveland, TN 37323-5903 **(100%)**
Tel.: (423) 479-8691
Web Site: http://www.hkperf.com
Sales Range: $10-24.9 Million
Emp.: 50
Perforated Materials
N.A.I.C.S.: 332119
Andrew Lovaas (Pres)

HARRINGTON BOTTLING COMPANY
1740 Holmes Ave, Butte, MT 59701
Tel.: (406) 494-3200
Sales Range: $10-24.9 Million
Emp.: 63
Carbonated Beverages
N.A.I.C.S.: 312111
Jim Bennett (VP)

HARRINGTON ENGINEERING, INC.
129 Mill Rock Rd, Old Saybrook, CT 06475
Web Site:
http://www.harringtonengineering.com
Year Founded: 1991
Rev.: $48,900,000
Emp.: 250
Sheet Metal Work Mfg
N.A.I.C.S.: 332322
Al Barone (Sr VP-Bus Dev)
Nicholas Gorra (Gen Counsel & Sr VP)
Sarah Johnson (Sec)
Todd McLeod (VP-Energy Svcs)
David Wilkie (Owner & CFO)

HARRINGTON HEALTHCARE SYSTEM
100 South St, Southbridge, MA 01550
Tel.: (508) 765-9771
Web Site:
https://www.harringtonhospital.org
Year Founded: 1928
Sales Range: $100-124.9 Million
Emp.: 1,381
Medical Devices
N.A.I.C.S.: 622110
Anthony Jay Detarando (Sec)
Edward Moore (Pres & CEO)
John G. Stagias (Vice Chm)
Jessica Calcidise (VP-Nursing & Ancillary Ops)

HARRINGTON HOUSE BEACH-FRONT BED & BREAKFAST INN
5626 Gulf Dr, Holmes Beach, FL 34217-1666
Tel.: (941) 778-5444
Web Site:
http://www.harringtonhouse.com
Sales Range: $10-24.9 Million
Emp.: 15
Hotel Operations
N.A.I.C.S.: 721110
Frank Davis (Co-Owner)
Jo Davis (Co-Owner)
Mark Davis (Gen Mgr)

HARRINGTONS OF VERMONT, INC.

210 E Main St, Richmond, VT 05477-7721
Tel.: (802) 434-4444   VT
Web Site:
https://www.harringtonham.com
Year Founded: 1873
Sales Range: $75-99.9 Million
Emp.: 30
Mail Order of Gourmet Foods
N.A.I.C.S.: 311612
Peter Klinkenberg (Owner & Pres)
Michael Barb (Controller)

HARRIS & FORD, LLC

9307 E 56th St, Indianapolis, IN 46216
Tel.: (317) 591-0000
Web Site:
https://www.harrisandford.com
Rev.: $105,000,000
Emp.: 50
Chemical & Allied Products Merchant Whslr
N.A.I.C.S.: 424690
Tim Harris (Co-Founder)
Joe Ford (Co-Founder)
Chris LaMothe (Co-Founder)

HARRIS & SON TRUCKING CO. INC.

178 Elon Rd, Madison Heights, VA 24572
Tel.: (434) 528-6700
Web Site:
http://www.harristrucking.com
Year Founded: 1969
Sales Range: $10-24.9 Million
Emp.: 250
Trucking Except Local
N.A.I.C.S.: 484121
Harris Trucking (CEO)
James R. Harris Jr. (Owner & Pres)

HARRIS BATTERY CO. INC.

10708 Industrial Pkwy NW, Bolivar, OH 44612
Tel.: (330) 874-0205
Web Site:
https://www.harrisbattery.com
Rev.: $14,500,000
Emp.: 15
Automotive Batteries
N.A.I.C.S.: 423120
Jerry Harris (Pres)
Chris Harris (Controller)

HARRIS BUSINESS GROUP INC.

13555 Bishops Ct Ste 300, Brookfield, WI 53005
Tel.: (262) 784-9099
Web Site: http://www.harrisdata.com
Year Founded: 1972
Sales Range: $25-49.9 Million
Emp.: 25
Mfr of Software
N.A.I.C.S.: 551112
Lane Nelson (Pres)
Henry Nelson (CEO)

Subsidiaries:

Harris Data Services of
Wisconsin   (1)
13555 Bishops Ct Ste 300, Brookfield, WI 53005
Tel.: (262) 784-9099
Web Site: http://www.harrisdata.com
Computer Software
N.A.I.C.S.: 423430
Lane Nelson (Pres)
Henry Nelson (CEO)

HARRIS CAPITAL GROUP, INC.

157 Yadkin Vly Rd Ste 100, Advance, NC 27006
Tel.: (336) 940-2022   NC
Year Founded: 1969
Sales Range: $10-24.9 Million
Emp.: 13
Commercial & Industrial Building Owner & Lessor
N.A.I.C.S.: 531120
Cleve Harris (Pres)

HARRIS COMPANIES

909 Montreal Cir, Saint Paul, MN 55102-4296
Tel.: (651) 602-6500   MN
Web Site:
https://www.harriscompany.com
Year Founded: 1954
Sales Range: $100-124.9 Million
Emp.: 500
Mechanical Contractor
N.A.I.C.S.: 238220
Greg Hosch (CEO)
Brenda Devlin (VP-Human Capital)
David Barnes (CFO)
Darrel Bugel (Sr VP)
Greg Donley (Sr VP)
Randy Richter (Sr VP)

Subsidiaries:

Capital City Controls   (1)
120 Westhampton Ave, Capitol Heights, MD 20743
Tel.: (301) 350-0241
Web Site: http://www.capitalcitycontrols.com
Building Automation Systems Services
N.A.I.C.S.: 238210
Todd Thiele (VP)
Jovel Ford (Sls Mgr)

Harris Companies - Harris Mechanical Southwest Division   (1)
21415 North 15th Ln Ste 105, Phoenix, AZ 85027
Tel.: (623) 344-1458
Sales Range: $25-49.9 Million
Emp.: 200
Mechanical Engineering Services
N.A.I.C.S.: 541330
John Krhin (Mgr-Ops)

Harris Companies - Wasatch Controls Division   (1)
1925 S Milestone Dr Ste E, Salt Lake City, UT 84104
Tel.: (801) 433-2640
Web Site: http://www.wcontrols.net
Sales Range: $10-24.9 Million
Emp.: 25
Building Automation & Security System Installation Services
N.A.I.C.S.: 561621
Jarvis Hofhines (Mgr-Sls)
Brett Parry (Acct Exec)
Jeff Keller (Acct Exec)
Mike Skinner (Mgr)
Todd Thiele (VP)

Harris Mechanical Service, LLC   (1)
909 Montreal Cir, Saint Paul, MN 55102
Tel.: (651) 602-6500
Web Site: http://www.harriscompany.com
Sales Range: $10-24.9 Million
Emp.: 1,600
Mechanical Engineering Services
N.A.I.C.S.: 541330
Tom Danley (Mgr-Svc)

HiMEC Conveyors Inc   (1)
1400 7th St NW, Rochester, MN 55901
Tel.: (507) 281-4000
Web Site: http://www.himec-conveyors.com
Sales Range: $10-24.9 Million
Emp.: 120
Conveyor Mfr
N.A.I.C.S.: 333922
Ryan Gillette (Mgr-Design)

R.M. Thornton, Inc.   (1)
120 Westhampton Ave, Capitol Heights, MD 20743
Tel.: (301) 350-5000
Web Site: http://www.harriscompany.com

Sales Range: $10-24.9 Million
Emp.: 100
Mechanical Engineering Services
N.A.I.C.S.: 541330
John Godblod (Mgr-HVAC Svc)

Superior Air Handling Corporation   (1)
2327 Grant Ave, Ogden, UT 84401
Tel.: (801) 776-1997
Web Site:
http://www.superiorairhandling.com
Sales Range: $25-49.9 Million
Emp.: 220
Engineeering Services
N.A.I.C.S.: 238390
Dan Bankhead (Gen Mgr)
Randy Richter (Pres)
J. L. Herndon (VP)

HARRIS CONNECT, LLC

1511 Rte 22 Ste C-25, Brewster, NY 10509   NY
Web Site:
http://www.bcharrispub.com
Year Founded: 1963
Sales Range: $100-124.9 Million
Emp.: 2,000
Alumni Directories Publisher
N.A.I.C.S.: 513140
Robert Gluck (CEO)
John Harris (CFO)

HARRIS COUNTY EMERGENCY CORPS

2800 Aldine Bender Rd, Houston, TX 77032
Tel.: (281) 449-3131   TX
Web Site: https://www.hcec.com
Year Founded: 2010
Sales Range: $10-24.9 Million
Emp.: 150
Emergency Medical Services
N.A.I.C.S.: 621910
Joe Cataneo (Dir-HR)
Brian Bayani (Dir-Clinical Svcs)
Amy Spoerle (Dir-Logistics)

HARRIS D. MCKINNEY, INC.

55 W Wacker Dr, Chicago, IL 60601
Tel.: (312) 506-5200
Web Site:
http://www.harrisdmckinney.com
Year Founded: 1936
Sales Range: $1-9.9 Million
Emp.: 25
Advetising Agency
N.A.I.C.S.: 541810
Dillon Allie (Sr VP-Client Svcs)
Hooshna Amaria (VP-Client Svcs)

Subsidiaries:

Zoomedia, Inc.   (1)
1620 Montgomery St Ste 250, San Francisco, CA 94111
Tel.: (415) 474-1192
Web Site: http://www.hdmz.com
Advetising Agency
N.A.I.C.S.: 541810
Karisa Juachon (Dir-Fin)

HARRIS FARMS, INC.

27366 W Oakland Ave, Coalinga, CA 93210-0420
Tel.: (559) 884-2859   CA
Web Site:
https://www.harrisfarms.com
Year Founded: 1937
Sales Range: $75-99.9 Million
Emp.: 1,500
Holding Company; Horses & Other Equine Production; Cattle Ranching & Farming Services
N.A.I.C.S.: 551112
David E. Wood (Pres)
John C. Harris (Chm)
Darren Filkins (CEO-Farm, Hotel, Restaurant & Thoroughbred Horse)

Subsidiaries:

Harris Ranch Inn & Restaurant   (1)
24505 W Dtorris Ave, Coalinga, CA 93210
Tel.: (559) 935-0717
Web Site: http://www.harrisranch.com
Sales Range: $25-49.9 Million
Emp.: 400
Hotel & Restaurant Operator
N.A.I.C.S.: 721110
Brad Reynolds (Gen Mgr)

HARRIS FORD, INC.

20006 64th Ave W, Lynnwood, WA 98036-5906
Tel.: (425) 774-4141   WA
Web Site: https://www.harrisford.com
Year Founded: 1955
Sales Range: $125-149.9 Million
Emp.: 150
Provider of Wholesale & Retail Automobiles & Trucks
N.A.I.C.S.: 441110
Rob Nobles (Controller)

HARRIS FREEMAN & CO. LP

3110 E Miraloma Ave, Anaheim, CA 92806
Tel.: (714) 765-1190
Web Site:
https://www.harrisfreeman.com
Sales Range: $25-49.9 Million
Emp.: 75
Tea, Coffee & Spices Importer
N.A.I.C.S.: 424490
Anil Shah (Principal)

HARRIS GROUP INC.

300 Elliott Ave W Ste 500, Seattle, WA 98119-4114
Tel.: (206) 494-9400
Web Site:
http://www.harrisgroup.com
Year Founded: 1975
Sales Range: $25-49.9 Million
Emp.: 200
Provider of Engineering Services
N.A.I.C.S.: 541330
Robert M. Harris (Founder & Chm)
Tony Davis (Gen Counsel & Sec)
Randy Hinton (Pres & CEO)
Chris Shockey (CFO & Treas)

HARRIS HOLDINGS INC.

1641 Lewis Way, Stone Mountain, GA 30083-1107
Tel.: (770) 939-2835
Web Site: https://www.insect-o-cutor.com
Year Founded: 1938
Sales Range: $50-74.9 Million
Emp.: 19
Electrical Flying Insect Control Equipment Mfr
N.A.I.C.S.: 335139

HARRIS MARKETING GROUP

102 Pierce St, Birmingham, MI 48009-6018
Tel.: (248) 723-6300
Web Site: http://www.harris-hmg.com
Year Founded: 1976
Sales Range: $10-24.9 Million
Emp.: 30
Advetising Agency
N.A.I.C.S.: 541810
Janice Rosenhaus (Owner)
Celeste Stachurski (VP-Ops)
Jeremy Tucker (Acct Exec)

HARRIS METALS COMPANY, LLC

2437 Hilham Rd, Cookeville, TN 38501-1085
Tel.: (931) 528-6483
Sales Range: $1-9.9 Million
Emp.: 53

Harris Metals Company, LLC—(Continued)

Aluminum Foundry
N.A.I.C.S.: 331523
Pete Koperski *(Mgr-Sls & Mktg)*

HARRIS OLDSMOBILE, IN-
CORPORATED
1151 N Broad St, Lansdale, PA
19446
Tel.: (215) 368-8500
Sales Range: $10-24.9 Million
Emp.: 31
Car Whslr
N.A.I.C.S.: 441110
H. Harris *(Pres)*

HARRIS ORIGINALS OF NY.,
INC.
800 Prime Pl, Hauppauge, NY 11788
Tel.: (631) 348-0303　　NY
Web Site:
　https://www.harrisjewelry.com
Year Founded: 1955
Sales Range: $100-124.9 Million
Emp.: 40
Jewelry Stores
N.A.I.C.S.: 458310

HARRIS PACKAGING CORPO-
RATION
1600 Carson St, Haltom City, TX
76117
Tel.: (817) 429-6262
Web Site:
　https://www.harrispackaging.com
Sales Range: $50-74.9 Million
Emp.: 116
Boxes Corrugated: Made From Pur-
chased Materials
N.A.I.C.S.: 322211
Harold Bivens *(Plant Mgr & Gen Mgr)*
Jenise Cox *(Pres)*

HARRIS PREFERRED CAPI-
TAL CORPORATION
111 W Monroe St, Chicago, IL 60603
Tel.: (312) 461-2121
Year Founded: 1997
Sales Range: $10-24.9 Million
Real Estate Investment Trust Ser-
vices
N.A.I.C.S.: 531190
Pamela C. Piarowski *(Chm, Pres & CEO)*

HARRIS STEEL CO.
1223 S 55th Ctr, Cicero, IL 60804-
1206
Tel.: (708) 656-5500　　IL
Web Site:
　https://www.harrissteelco.com
Year Founded: 1950
Sales Range: $25-49.9 Million
Emp.: 85
Marketer of Metal Products
N.A.I.C.S.: 423510
Jack Harris *(Chm)*
Thomas G. Eliasek *(Pres)*
Bernard McCudden *(VP-Fin)*

HARRIS TIRE COMPANY
1100 S Brundidge St, Troy, AL
36081-0888
Tel.: (334) 566-2691
Web Site: https://www.harristire.com
Year Founded: 1982
Sales Range: $10-24.9 Million
Emp.: 65
Mfr of Tires & Tubes
N.A.I.C.S.: 423130
Gary Berry *(Owner)*
Gary Wheeler *(Owner)*
Jason Berry *(CFO-Huntsville)*
Shane Pierce *(Asst Mgr-Huntsville)*
Ken Harris Jr. *(Owner)*

HARRIS VENTURES, INC.
863 Holcomb Bridge Rd, Roswell, GA
30076　　　　　　　　　　　　　GA
Web Site:
　http://www.thestaffzone.com
Staffing & Recruiting Services
N.A.I.C.S.: 561311
Sam Harris *(COO)*
Sherri Harris *(CEO)*

HARRIS, BAIO & MCCULL-
OUGH INC.
520 S Front St, Philadelphia, PA
19147-1723
Tel.: (215) 440-9800　　　　PA
Web Site: https://www.hbmadv.com
Year Founded: 1983
Sales Range: $50-74.9 Million
Emp.: 50
Advetising Agency
N.A.I.C.S.: 541820

Subsidiaries:

HB&M Sports, Inc.　　　　　　　(1)
1000 W Morehead St Ste 120, Charlotte,
NC 28208
Tel.: (704) 643-2020
Web Site: http://www.hbmsports.com
Sports Advertising & Marketing Services
N.A.I.C.S.: 541810

HARRISBURG NEWS COM-
PANY INC.
980 Briarsdale Rd, Harrisburg, PA
17109-5905
Tel.: (717) 561-8377
Web Site:
　http://www.harrisburgnewsco.com
Year Founded: 1975
Sales Range: $50-74.9 Million
Emp.: 400
Books, Periodicals & Newspapers Mfr
& Distr
N.A.I.C.S.: 424920
Jason Kieffer *(CFO)*
David S. Etter *(Chm)*
Joseph Murphy *(Sr VP)*

Subsidiaries:

Harrisburg News Company Inc.-
Harrisburg, PA　　　　　　　　(1)
37 S 8th St, Lebanon, PA 17042-5210
Tel.: (717) 273-6779
Sales Range: $10-24.9 Million
Emp.: 5
Distribution of Books Periodicals & Newspa-
pers
N.A.I.C.S.: 424920

HARRISON CREATIVE DIREC-
TION
2717 W Prairie Creek Dr, Richard-
son, TX 75080-2026
Tel.: (972) 783-4200
Year Founded: 1996
Sales Range: $10-24.9 Million
Emp.: 1
Electronic Media, Financial, Health
Care, High Technology, Restaurant
N.A.I.C.S.: 541810
Harry Harrison *(Dir-Creative)*

HARRISON FORD, INC.
820 N Main St, Wellington, OH 44090
Tel.: (440) 647-3614
Web Site:
　http://www.buyharrisonford.com
Year Founded: 1972
Sales Range: $10-24.9 Million
Emp.: 38
Car Whslr
N.A.I.C.S.: 441110
Rodney Harrison *(Pres)*

HARRISON FRENCH & ASSO-
CIATES, LTD.
1705 S Walton Blvd Ste 3, Benton-
ville, AR 72712
Tel.: (479) 273-7780
Web Site: http://www.hfa-ae.com
Architectural Services
N.A.I.C.S.: 541310
Chris Horton *(CFO & VP)*
Harrison French *(Founder)*
Larry Lott *(COO)*
Dave Wilgus *(Pres & CEO)*
Ryan Ray *(VP-Engrg)*
Daryl Whitmer *(Dir-Mktg & Bus Dev)*
Greg Schluterman *(VP)*
James Owens *(VP)*

Subsidiaries:

Allevato Architects Inc　　　　　(1)
31 Hayward St, Franklin, MA 02038
Tel.: (508) 528-0770
Web Site: http://www.allevatoarchitects.com
Rev.: $1,000,000
Emp.: 10
Architectural Services
N.A.I.C.S.: 541310
Lou Allevato *(Principal)*

HARRISON HOUSE
7498 E 46th Pl, Tulsa, OK 74145
Tel.: (918) 523-5700
Web Site:
　http://www.harrisonhouse.com
Rev.: $20,000,000
Emp.: 50
Book Publishing
N.A.I.C.S.: 513130
Julie Werner *(Mgr-Production)*
Christina Mussman *(Mgr-Info Sys)*
Stephen Hurt *(Dir-Sls)*

HARRISON INTERESTS LTD.
712 Main St Ste 1900, Houston, TX
77002-3220
Tel.: (713) 228-5911
Rev.: $13,700,000
Emp.: 50
Oil Gas Operator
N.A.I.C.S.: 211120
Ed K. Night *(Gen Mgr)*
Beth Aguirre *(Coord-Regulatory)*
Jim Schoerger *(Mgr-Petrolium Land)*
Dan J. Harrison III *(Gen Partner)*

HARRISON LEIFER DIMARCO,
INC.
100 Merrick Rd, Rockville Centre, NY
11570-4800
Tel.: (516) 536-2020
Year Founded: 1986
Rev.: $29,300,000
Emp.: 35
Advetising Agency
N.A.I.C.S.: 541810
Julie Gross Gelfand *(Exec VP & Dir-PR)*
Dale Moskowitz *(Dir-Fin)*
John H. Decker *(Creative Dir)*
Jeffrey Lipson *(Acct Exec)*
Barbara Roscoe *(Production Mgr)*
John Harper *(VP & Dir-Production Svcs)*
Roy DiMarco *(Pres & CEO)*
Ed Brennan *(Partner & Chief Creative Officer)*
David Rockwell *(Sr Copywriter)*
Don Miller *(VP-PR)*
Robert O'Regan *(Dir-Media)*
Frank Dinolfo *(Dir-Digital Svcs)*
Sam Custodio *(Sr Copywriter)*
Gina DiMarco *(Acct Mgr)*
Cathy Pollini *(Acct Mgr)*

Subsidiaries:

Harrison Leifer DiMarco Public
Relations　　　　　　　　　　　(1)
100 Merrick Rd, Rockville Centre, NY
11570
Tel.: (516) 536-2020
Emp.: 20

N.A.I.C.S.: 541820
Julie Gross Gelfand *(Exec VP & Dir-PR)*
Robert O'Regan *(Dir-Media)*

HARRISON OIL & TIRE CO.
124 W Academy St, Gainesville, GA
30501
Tel.: (770) 536-2361
Web Site:
　http://www.harrisontireservice.com
Sales Range: $10-24.9 Million
Emp.: 17
Gasoline
N.A.I.C.S.: 424720
James M. Harrison *(Pres & CEO)*

HARRISON PAINT COMPANY
1329 Harrison Ave SW, Canton, OH
44706
Tel.: (330) 455-5125　　　　OH
Web Site:
　https://www.harrisonpaint.com
Year Founded: 1911
Sales Range: $1-9.9 Million
Emp.: 30
Paint, Varnish & Specialty Coatings
Mfr
N.A.I.C.S.: 325510
Patrick Lauber *(Pres)*
Gloria Tomer *(Controller)*
Steve Laizure *(VP-Ops)*

Subsidiaries:

Harrison Paint Company - Excelsior
Coatings Division　　　　　　　(1)
1329 Harrison Ave SW, Canton, OH 44706
Tel.: (800) 292-5755
Coating Mfr
N.A.I.C.S.: 325510
Patrick Lauber *(Gen Mgr)*

HARRISON POULTRY INC.
107 Star St E, Bethlehem, GA 30620-
2119
Tel.: (770) 867-9105　　　　GA
Sales Range: $25-49.9 Million
Emp.: 1,100
Integrated Poultry Business
N.A.I.C.S.: 112340
Dennis Daniel *(Coord-Live Production HACCP)*
IsMarie Ripley *(Mgr-Bulk Commodity Sls)*
Nick Strange *(Mgr-Corp Pur)*
David Bleth *(Pres & CEO)*

HARRISON STEEL CASTINGS
CO.
900 S Mound St, Attica, IN 47918
Tel.: (765) 762-2481
Web Site: https://www.hscast.com
Sales Range: $50-74.9 Million
Emp.: 300
Steel Foundries
N.A.I.C.S.: 331513
Jeffrey Curtis *(VP & Gen Mgr)*

HARRISON WALKER &
HARPER LP
2510 S Church St, Paris, TX 75460
Tel.: (903) 785-1653
Web Site: http://www.webuild-
hwh.com
Year Founded: 1887
Rev.: $24,906,087
Emp.: 500
Commercial Construction
N.A.I.C.S.: 236220
Chip Harper *(CEO)*
James Proctor *(Mgr-IT)*
Alison Foster *(Mgr-Fin)*
Bill Restmeyer *(Dir-Mktg)*
Brandon Hoog *(CIO)*
Cory Wood *(Mgr-Bus Dev)*
Dave Osborne *(Mgr-Bus Dev)*
Melanie Hatcher *(Mgr-HR)*
Mike Anders *(CFO)*

Shea Johnson (Mgr-Bus Dev)
Jordan Harper (Co-CEO)
Holland Harper (Pres-Enterprise Bus Dev)
Jared Kinabrew (VP-Industrial)
Tim Glenn (VP-Ops)
Randall Stanley (VP-Pre-Construction)

HARRISON-HOGE INDUSTRIES, INC.
19 N Columbia St, Port Jefferson, NY 11777   NY
Web Site:
https://www.panthermartin.com
Fishing Lures & Inflatable Boats Importer & Mfr
N.A.I.C.S.: 423910

Subsidiaries:

Sea Eagle Boats, Inc.   (1)
19 N Columbia St, Port Jefferson, NY 11777-2165
Tel.: (631) 791-1799
Web Site: http://www.seaeagle.com
Emp.: 50
Inflatable Canoes & Dinghies Importer & Mfr
N.A.I.C.S.: 423910

HARRISON-ORR AIR CONDITIONING, INC.
4100 N Walnut, Oklahoma City, OK 73105
Tel.: (405) 528-3333
Web Site:
https://www.harrisonorr.com
Sales Range: $10-24.9 Million
Emp.: 120
Heating Systems Repair & Maintenance
N.A.I.C.S.: 238220
Joe McKenzie (Pres)

HARRISS & COVINGTON HOSIERY MILLS
1250 Hickory Chapel Rd, High Point, NC 27260-7187
Tel.: (336) 882-6811   NC
Web Site:
https://www.harrissandcov.com
Year Founded: 1920
Sales Range: $100-124.9 Million
Emp.: 250
Hosiery Mfr
N.A.I.C.S.: 315120
Ned Covington (Pres & CEO)
Darrell L. Frye (VP-Fin & Admin)
Danny McNair (VP-Mfg)
Tyler Covington (VP-Product Dev)

HARRISTOWN DEVELOPMENT CORPORATION
PO Box 1224, Harrisburg, PA 17108
Tel.: (717) 236-5061   PA
Year Founded: 1974
Sales Range: $10-24.9 Million
Emp.: 51
Community Development Services
N.A.I.C.S.: 624190
Andrew McCleaf (CFO, Treas & VP)
Bradley Jones (VP)
Patricia McPoyle (Asst Sec)
Carol Green Rossi (VP)
Neal West (Gen Counsel & Sr VP)

HARROD MANAGEMENT INC.
2411 Gateway Dr Ste 115, Irving, TX 75038
Tel.: (214) 614-7425
Sales Range: $10-24.9 Million
Sand & Gravel Distr
N.A.I.C.S.: 444180
Ted Harrod (CEO)

HARROGATE, INC.
400 Locust St, Lakewood, NJ 08701
Tel.: (732) 905-7070   NJ
Web Site: http://www.harrogate-lifecare.org
Year Founded: 1982
Sales Range: $10-24.9 Million
Emp.: 379
Continuing Care Retirement Community Operator
N.A.I.C.S.: 623311
Peter J. Wright (Asst Sec)
William J. Slivka (Treas & Exec VP)
Robert A. Roman (Sec)
Donald A. Johansen (Exec Dir)
Becky Harris (Mgr-Fitness)
Edwin J. O'Malley Jr. (Pres & Asst Sec)

HARRON COMMUNICATIONS, L.P.
70 E Lancaster Ave, Frazer, PA 19355
Tel.: (610) 644-7500
Web Site: https://www.harron.com
Year Founded: 1976
Cable Television Services
N.A.I.C.S.: 518210
Thomas M. Marturano (Pres & COO)
Ryan F. Pearson (Gen Counsel & Exec VP)
Shawn P. Flannery (CFO & Treas)
Danny L. Jobe (VP-Sys Ops)
Constance S. Prince (Chief Admin Officer)
Gregory V. Pucci (VP-Bus Support Sys)
Aaron Brace (VP-Engrg)
James J. Bruder Jr. (Chm & CEO)
Warren W. Beitel Jr. (VP-Customer Svcs)

HARROP INDUSTRIES, INC.
3470 E 5th Ave, Columbus, OH 43219-3816
Tel.: (614) 231-3621   OH
Web Site: https://www.harropusa.com
Year Founded: 1919
Sales Range: $75-99.9 Million
Emp.: 50
Civil Engineering Construction Services
N.A.I.C.S.: 237990
James E. Houseman (Pres)
Stephen D. Houseman (CEO)
Daniel A. O'Brien (VP)
Terry Henderson (Controller)

HARROW STORES INC.
627 Route 110, Melville, NY 11747
Tel.: (631) 756-2800
Web Site: https://www.harrows.com
Rev.: $42,750,000
Emp.: 35
Swimming Pools, Above Ground
N.A.I.C.S.: 459999

HARRY BOCK COMPANY INC.
6019 Berkshire Ln Ste 200, Dallas, TX 75225
Tel.: (214) 692-9000
Web Site: http://www.bachendorf.com
Sales Range: $25-49.9 Million
Emp.: 70
Jewelry Stores
N.A.I.C.S.: 423940
Julie Abbey (CFO)
Mike Tsou (Mgr-Jeweler Production)

HARRY COOPER SUPPLY COMPANY
605 N Sherman Pkwy, Springfield, MO 65802-3656
Tel.: (417) 865-8392   MO
Web Site:
https://www.harrycooper.com
Year Founded: 1914

Sales Range: $50-74.9 Million
Emp.: 250
Plumbing Fixtures, Equipment & Supplies
N.A.I.C.S.: 423720
Harry Cooper (Pres)
Stephen Reagan (CEO)
Larry McMullen (CFO & Controller)
John Cooper (VP)

Subsidiaries:

Joplin Supply Company   (1)
302 S Michigan, Joplin, MO 64801-2017
Tel.: (417) 624-2422
Web Site: http://www.harrycooper.com
Plumbing Fixtures, Equipment & Supplies
N.A.I.C.S.: 423720
Ron Hall (Gen Mgr)

Springfield Flying Service
Incorporated   (1)
2546 E Division St, Springfield, MO 65803-5138
Tel.: (417) 862-2418
Web Site: http://www.fly3dw.com
Rev.: $730,000
Emp.: 8
Airports, Flying Fields & Services
N.A.I.C.S.: 488190
Brad Byron (Gen Mgr)
John Cooper (Pres)

HARRY E. FERRYMAN ENTERPRISES
9110 NE Hwy 99, Vancouver, WA 98665
Tel.: (360) 574-0911
Sales Range: $10-24.9 Million
Emp.: 3
Motel Operator
N.A.I.C.S.: 721110
Shirley Klattenhoff (Controller)

HARRY E. ROBBINS ASSOCIATES, INC.
3733 S Tuttle Ave, Sarasota, FL 34239
Tel.: (941) 924-8346
Web Site:
https://www.robbinscommercial.com
Year Founded: 1971
Sales Range: $1-9.9 Million
Emp.: 10
Real Estate Broker
N.A.I.C.S.: 531210
Harry E. Robbins (Pres)
Loyd M. Robbins (VP)

HARRY F. ORTLIP COMPANY INC.
780 W Lancaster Ave, Bryn Mawr, PA 19010-3415
Tel.: (610) 527-7000
Year Founded: 1944
Sales Range: $25-49.9 Million
Emp.: 160
Electronic Services
N.A.I.C.S.: 238210

HARRY FOURTUNIS INC.
2 Pierpont Ave, Newburgh, NY 12550
Tel.: (845) 561-5246
Sales Range: $10-24.9 Million
Emp.: 25
Wholesale Distributor
N.A.I.C.S.: 424940
Harry Fourtunis (Pres)

HARRY GRODSKY & CO., INC.
33 Shaws Ln, Springfield, MA 01101
Tel.: (413) 785-1947   MA
Web Site: https://www.grodsky.com
Year Founded: 1918
Sales Range: $50-74.9 Million
Emp.: 250
Mechanical Contractor
N.A.I.C.S.: 238220

Ronald Grodsky (Pres)
Matthew Tucker (Coord-Mechanical)
Frank Spakoski (Coord-Cad Piping)
Dave Streeter (VP-Design Build)
Mahan Tom (Sr VP-Pre-Construction)
Douglas Leed (Project Mgr)
Leanne Barrett (Mgr-Warehouse)
Michael P. Lescarbeau (Mgr-Design)
Tricia LeBlanc Cole (Coord-Mechanical)
Mark Rose (Mgr-CAD Drafting Dept)
Jerry Gonsalves (Supvr)
Andrew Yuen (Controller)

Subsidiaries:

Grodsky Service, Inc.   (1)
64 Shaws Ln, Springfield, MA 01101
Tel.: (413) 785-1203
Industrial Equipment Maintenance Services
N.A.I.C.S.: 811310

Harry Grodsky & Co., Inc.-Hartford Office   (1)
92 Weston St Ste 7, Hartford, CT 06120-1519   (100%)
Tel.: (860) 560-1569
Web Site: http://www.grodsky.com
Sales Range: $25-49.9 Million
Emp.: 10
Mechanical Contractor
N.A.I.C.S.: 238220

HARRY HOLLAND & SON, INC.
7050 High Grove Blvd, Burr Ridge, IL 60527
Tel.: (630) 325-5130
Web Site:
https://www.hollandapt.com
Year Founded: 1903
Sales Range: $25-49.9 Million
Emp.: 65
Sanitary Process Components, Custom Modular Process Systems & Specialty Chemicals
N.A.I.C.S.: 423830

HARRY J. BOSWORTH COMPANY
7227 N Hamlin Ave, Skokie, IL 60076-3901
Tel.: (847) 679-3400
Web Site: http://www.bosworth.com
Year Founded: 1912
Dental Materials Mfr
N.A.I.C.S.: 339114
Herbert L. Pozen (VP-Sls & Mktg)

HARRY J. KLOEPPEL & ASSOCIATES
2399 S Foster Ave, Wheeling, IL 60090
Tel.: (847) 483-0133
Web Site: http://www.kloeppel.com
Sales Range: $10-24.9 Million
Emp.: 21
Contractor Of Laboratory Equipment
N.A.I.C.S.: 423490
Harry J. Kloeppel (Pres)
Mark Skole (Mgr-Sls-Indiana Div)
Cindy Detlof (Office Mgr)
Nick Proepper (Mgr-Sls-Illinois)

HARRY J. LAWALL & SON
8026 Frankford Ave 28, Philadelphia, PA 19136
Tel.: (215) 338-6611
Web Site: http://www.ont.com
Rev.: $15,300,000
Emp.: 110
Artificial Limbs Mfr
N.A.I.C.S.: 339113
John McDermott (Mgr-Production)
Joy Hymon (Acct Mgr-Patient)
Kristy Gangloff (Acct Mgr-Patient)
Tandra Ashely (Acct Mgr-Patient)

Harry J. Lawall & Son—(Continued)

HARRY J. RASHTI & CO. INC.
875 Avenue Of The Americas, New
York, NY 10001
Tel.: (212) 594-3733   NY
Web Site:
   http://www.rashtiandrashti.com
Year Founded: 1937
Sales Range: $25-49.9 Million
Emp.: 175
Mfr of Women's, Children's & Infant's
Clothes
N.A.I.C.S.: 424350
Michael Rashti (Chm & CEO)

HARRY KRANTZ COMPANY
100 13th Ave, Ronkonkoma, NY
11779
Tel.: (516) 742-6300
Web Site: http://www.harrykrantz.com
Year Founded: 1939
Sales Range: $10-24.9 Million
Emp.: 80
Other Electronic Part & Equipment
Whslr
N.A.I.C.S.: 423690
Cody Valentin (Dir-Supply Chain)
Camie Genna (Dir-Quality Control)

**HARRY MAJOR MACHINE &
TOOL CO.**
24801 Capital Blvd, Clinton Township,
MI 48036
Tel.: (586) 783-7030
Web Site:
   http://www.harrymajormachine.com
Rev.: $13,800,000
Emp.: 50
Conveyors & Conveying Equipment
N.A.I.C.S.: 333922
Curtis Major (Owner & Pres)

**HARRY RITCHIE JEWELER
INC.**
956 Willamette St, Eugene, OR
97401
Tel.: (541) 686-1787
Web Site:
   https://www.harryritchies.com
Sales Range: $10-24.9 Million
Emp.: 350
Jewelry Precious Stones & Precious
Metals
N.A.I.C.S.: 458310
Donald Ritchie (Pres)

**HARRY ROBINSON BUICK
GMC**
6000 S 36th St, Fort Smith, AR
72908
Tel.: (479) 646-8600
Web Site:
   https://www.harryrobinson.com
Year Founded: 1969
Sales Range: $10-24.9 Million
Emp.: 35
New Car & Truck Dealers
N.A.I.C.S.: 441110
Renee Durham (Gen Mgr)
Harry G. Robinson Jr. (Pres)

**HARRY S. EKLOF JR. & AS-
SOCIATES INC.**
3401 Pennsy Dr, Landover, MD
20785-1630
Tel.: (301) 772-1700
Web Site: https://www.harryeklof.com
Year Founded: 1968
Sales Range: $10-24.9 Million
Emp.: 53
Mfr of Plumbing Fixtures, Equipment
& Supplies
N.A.I.C.S.: 423720
David Knell (Mgr-Accts)

HARRY VIOLA ADVERTISING
650 From Rd Ste 375, Paramus, NJ
07652-3556
Tel.: (201) 267-8074   NJ
Web Site:
   http://www.intl.movado.com
Year Founded: 1972
Sales Range: $25-49.9 Million
Emp.: 15
In House Advertising Agency
N.A.I.C.S.: 541810
Mary Leach (CMO)
Diana Moran (VP-Media)
Donna Schweizer (Project Coord)

HARRY'S ELECTRONICS INC.
405 Convent Ave, Laredo, TX 78040-
5849
Tel.: (956) 727-8546
Year Founded: 1979
Sales Range: $10-24.9 Million
Emp.: 35
Electronic Parts & Equipment
N.A.I.C.S.: 423690
Elmer Lopez (Mgr)

HARRY'S HARDWARE INC.
3535 Magazine St, New Orleans, LA
70115
Tel.: (504) 895-7764
Sales Range: $10-24.9 Million
Emp.: 125
Retail Hardware
N.A.I.C.S.: 444140
Philip I. Deutch (Pres)
George Lapheart (Office Mgr)

HARRY'S OF AMERICA INC.
9995 Gate Pkwy N Ste 400B, Jack-
sonville, FL 32246
Tel.: (904) 642-2165
Web Site:
   https://www.hookedonharrys.com
Sales Range: $10-24.9 Million
Emp.: 450
Seafood Restaurants
N.A.I.C.S.: 722511
Louis Saig (Pres)

HARRY'S ON THE HILL
819 Patton Ave, Asheville, NC 28806-
3618
Tel.: (828) 252-3821
Web Site:
   https://www.harrysonthehill.com
Sales Range: $75-99.9 Million
Emp.: 100
New Car Dealers
N.A.I.C.S.: 441110
Chad Stamey (Asst Mgr-Sls)
Dionna Long (Comptroller)
Frank Leccese (Mgr-Fixed Ops)
Mark Wright (Gen Mgr-Sls)
Esther Sabatino (Dir-Guest Rels)
Les Ewald (Mgr-Fin)
Macon Cutshall (Mgr-Internet Sls)
Matt Hyder (Mgr-Used Car)
Mike Candler (Mgr-Parts)
Randy Schirmer (Mgr-Collision Re-
pair)
Tisha Murphy (Bus Mgr)

HARSCH INVESTMENT CORP.
1121 SW Salmon St, Portland, OR
97205-2000
Tel.: (503) 242-2900
Web Site: http://www.harsch.com
Year Founded: 1950
Sales Range: $25-49.9 Million
Emp.: 250
Apartment Building Operation Ser-
vices
N.A.I.C.S.: 531110
Jordan D. Schnitzer (Pres)
Brenda Davey (VP-HR)
Steve Roselli (Sr VP & Reg Mgr)

Bill Rodewald (Sr VP & Reg Mgr)
John Shorey (Sr VP & Reg Mgr)
Angela Williams (VP-Fin)
Bill Agnew (VP & Controller)
Chris McConnico (Asst VP & Mgr-
Leasing)
Delilah Richman (Reg VP)
Ed Kanter (VP & Controller-Property)
Eric Stein (Sr VP & Reg Mgr)
Jennifer Cole (VP)
John Gordon (Sr VP-Dev)
John Ramous (Sr VP & Reg Mgr)
Julie Remy (Sr VP & Reg Mgr)
Kathy Rose (VP & Dir-Property
Mgmt)
Michael Corbitt (Sr VP-Retail)
Monica Graham (Asst VP & Mgr-Ops)
Reed Gottesman (VP & Dir-Leasing-
Las Vegas)
Ryan Irwin (CFO & Sr VP)
Steve Barragar (VP & Dir-Leasing)
Susanne Orton (VP-Mktg & Comm)
Wanda Garwood (Dir-Ops)
Arlene Schnitzer (Exec VP)
Jim Sather (Sr VP-Dev)
Kyriacos Kitsis (CIO)
Rojita Raghubansh (Sr VP-HR & Risk
Mgmt)
Renee Dockweiler (VP-Tax)
Andrew Goodman (Asst VP-Dev)

Subsidiaries:

Harsch Investment Inc.   (1)
950 SW 21st Ave, Portland, OR
97205-1562   **(100%)**
Tel.: (503) 242-2900
Web Site: http://www.harsch.com
Sales Range: $10-24.9 Million
Emp.: 7
Apartment Building Operation Services
N.A.I.C.S.: 531110

King Tower Inc.   (1)
901 SW King Ave, Portland, OR
97205-1304   **(100%)**
Tel.: (503) 223-1458
Web Site: http://www.kingtower.com
Sales Range: $10-24.9 Million
Emp.: 5
Provider of Apartment Building Operation
Services
N.A.I.C.S.: 531110
Jason Polinger (Mgr-Sls)

HARSH INTERNATIONAL, INC.
600 Oak Ave, Eaton, CO 80615-3404
Tel.: (970) 454-2291   CO
Web Site:
   https://www.harshenviro.com
Year Founded: 1948
Rev.: $20,000,000
Emp.: 80
Hydraulic Cylinder Hoists, Mobile
Feed Mixers & Body Combination Mfr
N.A.I.C.S.: 333111

Subsidiaries:

Clark Truck Equipment   (1)
PO Box 27, Linden, IN 47955-0027
Tel.: (765) 362-4101
Web Site: http://www.clarktruck-in.com
Fluid Power Cylinders & Actuators
N.A.I.C.S.: 423110
Larry Smith (Mgr)

HARSHAW SERVICE INC.
12700 Plantside Dr, Louisville, KY
40299
Tel.: (502) 499-7000
Web Site:
   http://www.harshawtrane.com
Rev.: $19,000,000
Emp.: 110
Air Conditioning Equipment
N.A.I.C.S.: 238220
Frank Harshaw (Pres)

HART & VOGT INC.

5624 Airport Fwy, Fort Worth, TX
76117
Tel.: (817) 831-4222
Web Site: https://www.vogtrv.com
Sales Range: $25-49.9 Million
Emp.: 45
Sales of Recreational Vehicles
N.A.I.C.S.: 441210
Danny Vogt (Pres)

HART ASSOCIATES, INC.
1915 Indian Wood Cir, Maumee, OH
43537-4002
Tel.: (419) 893-9600   OH
Web Site: http://www.hartinc.com
Year Founded: 1965
Sales Range: $1-9.9 Million
Emp.: 48
Advetising Agency
N.A.I.C.S.: 541810
Michael K. Hart (CEO)
Rich Kretz (VP-Video Svcs)
Marc Paulenich (Pres)
Susan Degens (VP-Media)
Sean Rodman (VP & Dir-Creative)
Angela Beardsley (Dir-Fin & Admin)
Randy Phipps (Exec Dir-Creative)
Brian Newberry (VP-Brand Leader-
ship)
Rick Carey (VP & Dir-Creative)
Marcie Gabor (VP-Branding & Dir-
Design)

Subsidiaries:

MDB Communications, Inc.   (1)
1150 18th St NW, Washington, DC 20036-
5521
Tel.: (202) 835-0774
Web Site: http://www.mdbcomm.com
Sales Range: $10-24.9 Million
Emp.: 27
Advertising Services
N.A.I.C.S.: 541810
Seth Niman (Dir-Media Strategy)
Richard M. Coad (Chief Creative Officer-
Engagement)
Jodie Warren (Dir-Campaign Strategy)
Rob Gerds (VP & Dir-Client Svcs)

**HART ELECTRIC MEMBER-
SHIP CORPORATION**
1071 Elberton Hwy, Hartwell, GA
30643
Tel.: (706) 376-4714
Web Site: https://www.hartemc.com
Rev.: $38,621,694
Emp.: 130
Electric Power Distr
N.A.I.C.S.: 221122
Jeffrey B. Murphy (Pres & CEO)
Galen Mills (Chm)
Guerry Hall (Vice Chm)

**HART ENGINEERING CORPO-
RATION**
800 Scenic View Dr, Cumberland, RI
02864
Tel.: (401) 658-4600   RI
Web Site:
   https://www.hartcompanies.com
Year Founded: 1941
Sales Range: $75-99.9 Million
Emp.: 100
Mechanical Contracting, Process De-
sign & Engineering Services
N.A.I.C.S.: 541330
Frank Carnevale (CFO)
David Rampone (Pres)
Paul Rampone (Pres-Hart Design
Grp)
Michael DelleFave (VP-Process Con-
struction)
Michael Feldman (VP)
James Horwath (VP-Engrg)
Mark Lindgren (VP)
Robert Mulligan (VP-Municipal Con-
struction)

Robert Cole *(VP-Ops)*
C. Frank Rampone *(Founder & Chm)*
James M. Ramos *(VP)*
David DeStefano *(VP-Facilities Engrg & Design)*

HART FORD LINCOLN, INC.
117 Lk St, Roscommon, MI 48653
Tel.: (989) 275-8922
Web Site:
http://www.hartford.dealerconnection.com
Year Founded: 1992
Sales Range: $10-24.9 Million
Emp.: 50
New & Used Automobiles Dealer
N.A.I.C.S.: 441120
Scott McCarthy *(Gen Mgr)*
Chris Kalthoff *(Mgr-Parts)*
Jerry Whitfield *(Mgr-Svc)*

HART FURNITURE COMPANY INC.
420 E 3rd St, Siler City, NC 27344
Tel.: (919) 742-5515
Web Site:
http://www.hartfurnitureco.com
Sales Range: $10-24.9 Million
Emp.: 29
Household Furniture
N.A.I.C.S.: 449110
Lisa Staut *(Pres)*

HART INDUSTRIES INC.
931 Jeanette Ave, Middletown, OH 45044
Tel.: (513) 422-3639
Web Site: https://www.hose.com
Sales Range: $10-24.9 Million
Emp.: 100
Industrial Supplies Mfr & Distr
N.A.I.C.S.: 423840
Roger Hart *(Pres)*
Chris Hart *(CFO)*

HART INTERCIVIC INC.
15500 Wells Port Dr, Austin, TX 78728
Tel.: (512) 252-6400   TX
Web Site: http://www.hartic.com
Year Founded: 1912
Sales Range: $10-24.9 Million
Emp.: 49
Business Form & Card Printing, Lithographic Services
N.A.I.C.S.: 323111
Phillip Braithwaite *(Chm & CEO)*
Peter Lichtenheld *(VP-Ops)*
Karen Clakeley *(Dir-Strategic Acct)*
Julie Mathis *(Pres & CFO)*

HARTE INFINITI INC.
150 Weston St, Hartford, CT 06120
Tel.: (866) 568-0724
Web Site: http://www.harteinfiniti.com
Sales Range: $75-99.9 Million
Emp.: 200
New Car Dealers
N.A.I.C.S.: 441110
John Finelli *(Dir-Sls)*
Gregory Harte *(VP-Fin)*
Roseann Harte *(Sec)*

HARTE NISSAN, INC.
165 W Service Rd, Hartford, CT 06120
Tel.: (860) 549-2800
Web Site:
https://www.hartenissan.com
Year Founded: 1983
Sales Range: $10-24.9 Million
Emp.: 38
Car Whslr
N.A.I.C.S.: 441110
Erin Touponse *(Dir-Comm)*

HARTER HOUSE-GLENSTONE, INC.
1500 E Republic Rd, Springfield, MO 65804
Tel.: (417) 886-4410   MO
Web Site:
http://www.harterhouse.com
Year Founded: 1976
Supermarkets & Other Grocery (except Convenience) Stores
N.A.I.C.S.: 445110
Barbara Bettlach *(Owner)*
Don Smith *(Mgr-Night)*
Greg Allen *(Mgr-Meat)*
Marty Lower *(Asst Mgr-Meat)*
Michele Kauffman *(Office Mgr)*
Roxann Mann *(Mgr-Liquor)*
Sharon Baker *(Mgr-Dairy & Frozen Foods)*

HARTFIEL AUTOMATION
2600 Technology Dr Ste 300, Plano, TX 75074-7486
Tel.: (972) 633-0000
Web Site: https://www.hartfiel.com
Year Founded: 1958
Emp.: 230
Mfr of Pneumatic & Automation Solutions
N.A.I.C.S.: 334510
Patrick Schusted *(Pres)*
Myron Moser *(Founder, Chm & CEO)*
Jeff Murphy *(CFO, Treas & Sec)*
Gary Simonson *(VP-Ops)*

Subsidiaries:

Advanced Pneumatics Co., Inc.   (1)
9708 Ashley Dawn Ct, Fredericksburg, VA 22408   (100%)
Tel.: (540) 898-4511
Web Site: http://www.advpneumatics.com
Rev.: $3,400,000
Emp.: 200
Automation Components Mfr from Pneumatic Products
N.A.I.C.S.: 335999
Mark Santschi *(Mgr-Sls)*

Fiero Fluid Power Inc.   (1)
5280 Ward Rd, Arvada, CO 80002
Tel.: (303) 431-3600
Web Site: http://www.fierofluidpower.com
Distribute Pneumatic Pistons & Valves
N.A.I.C.S.: 423830
Michael Brooks *(Pres)*
Martin Steve *(Engr-Sls)*

HARTFORD CITY PAPER LLC
501 S Springs St, Hartford City, IN 47348-0030
Tel.: (765) 348-5440   DE
Year Founded: 1999
Sales Range: $10-24.9 Million
Emp.: 81
Paper Mill Services
N.A.I.C.S.: 322120
Erin Richards *(Controller)*

HARTFORD CPL CO-OP, INC.
376 Ledyard St, Hartford, CT 06114-3201
Tel.: (860) 296-5636
Sales Range: $10-24.9 Million
Emp.: 110
Bakery Products Mfr
N.A.I.C.S.: 311812
William Galatis *(Pres)*
William Ghio *(Treas)*
Dave Place *(CFO & Gen Mgr)*

HARTFORD DISTRIBUTORS INC.
PO Box 8400, Manchester, CT 06042-1633
Tel.: (860) 643-2337   CT
Sales Range: $100-124.9 Million
Emp.: 150
Beer Retailer & Distr

N.A.I.C.S.: 424810
Thomas Capobianco *(Mgr)*

HARTFORD ELECTRIC SUPPLY CO.
30 Inwood Rd Ste 1, Rocky Hill, CT 06067
Tel.: (860) 236-6363
Web Site: https://www.hesconet.com
Sales Range: $10-24.9 Million
Emp.: 50
Electrical Apparatus & Equipment
N.A.I.C.S.: 423610
Bill Patrick Depasquale *(Pres & CEO)*
Nancy Verdone *(CFO)*
Todd DePasquale *(Gen Mgr)*
Brake William *(VP-Sls)*

HARTFORD FOUNDATION FOR PUBLIC GIVING
10 Columbus Blvd 8th Fl, Hartford, CT 06106
Tel.: (860) 548-1888   CT
Web Site: http://www.hfpg.org
Year Founded: 1925
Rev.: $28,722,128
Assets: $933,276,490
Liabilities: $41,720,697
Net Worth: $891,555,793
Earnings: ($115,497,394)
Emp.: 55
Fiscal Year-end: 12/31/18
Grantmaking Services
N.A.I.C.S.: 813211
LouAnn Campanello *(Dir-Fin)*
Bonnie Malley *(VP-Fin & Admin)*
Rodney O. Powell *(Vice Chm)*
Elysa Gordon *(VP-Community Impact)*
Theodore Sergi *(Chm)*
Andrew Worthington *(Treas)*
Chari L. Chester Anderson *(Officer-Prospect Mgmt & Dev)*
Doretta Andonucci *(Officer-Comm)*
Juana Baribeau *(Assoc Mgr-Grants Ops)*
Yvette Bello *(Officer-Community Impact)*
Francesca Borges Gordon *(Officer-Dev)*
Tracy Bradley *(Coord-Office)*
Sarah E. Carlson *(Coord-Scholarship)*
Jacqueline Coleman *(Officer-Community Impact)*
Wanda Correa *(Officer-Dev)*
Susan Dana *(Dir-Dev-Major Gifts)*
Bradford Drazen *(VP-Comm & Mktg)*
Julie Feidner *(Mgr-Bd Rels)*
Erika Frank *(Officer-Community Impact)*
Betty Ann Grady *(Officer-Dev)*
Frank Gramuglia *(Dir-HR)*
Alison Granger *(Chief Investment Officer)*
Andrew Halpryn *(Officer-IT)*
Susan Harmon *(Accountant)*
Karen Hartenstein *(Program Mgr)*
Judy McBride *(Dir-Strategic Partnership Investments)*
Josephine Morrison *(Mgr-Acctg)*
Deborah Rothstein *(VP-Dev)*
Jay Williams *(Pres)*

HARTFORD HEALTHCARE CORPORATION
1 State St Ste 19, Hartford, CT 06103
Tel.: (860) 263-4100   CT
Web Site:
http://hartfordhealthcare.org
Year Founded: 1985
Sales Range: $1-4.9 Billion
Emp.: 18,277
Acute Care Health Services Organization
N.A.I.C.S.: 813910

Elliot Joseph *(CEO)*
Jeffrey A. Flaks *(Pres & COO)*
Tracy Church *(Chief HR Officer & Sr VP)*
Margaret Marchak *(Chief Legal Officer & Sr VP)*
James P. Cardon *(Chief Clinical Integration Officer & Exec VP)*
Richard T. Shirey *(CIO & Sr VP)*
Richard Stys *(Treas & Sr VP-Fin)*
Stuart Markowitz *(Sr VP)*
David Whitehead *(Chief Strategy Officer, Chief Transformation Officer & Sr VP)*
Patricia Rehmer *(Pres-Behavioral Health Network & Sr VP)*
Rita Parisi *(Sr VP-Community Network)*
Bimal Patel *(Pres-Hartford)*
Gary Havican *(Pres-Central)*
Janette Edwards *(VP-Ops-Central)*
John Rossi *(VP-Operation Integration)*
Donna Handley *(Pres-East)*
David P. Hess *(Chm)*
Gerald J. Boisvert *(Sr VP-Fin Ops)*
Karen Goyette *(Sr VP-Strategy & Sys Integration)*
Peter Paul Yu *(Sr VP)*
Sabet Hashim *(Sr VP)*
Patricia DeFusco *(Dir-Breast Program)*
Niamey Wilson *(Dir-Breast Surgery, Quality & Res)*
Gregory M. Jones *(VP-Community Health & Engagement)*
John Santopietro *(Sr VP)*
William M. Jennings *(Pres-Fairfield & Sr VP)*
Charles L. Johnson III *(CFO & Exec VP)*
Rocco Orlando III *(Chief Medical Officer & Sr VP)*
John J. Patrick Jr. *(Vice Chm)*

Subsidiaries:

Clinical Laboratory Partners, LLC   (1)
129 Patricia M Genova Dr, Newington, CT 06111-1543
Tel.: (860) 696-8050
Web Site: http://www.clpct.com
Medical Laboratories
N.A.I.C.S.: 621511
James Fantus *(Pres & CEO)*

HARTFORD SYMPHONY ORCHESTRA INC.
99 Pett St Ste 500, Hartford, CT 06103
Tel.: (860) 246-8742
Web Site:
http://www.hartfordsymphony.org
Sales Range: $75-99.9 Million
Emp.: 101
Symphony Orchestra
N.A.I.C.S.: 711130
Cheryl Anderson *(Dir-Fin & HR)*
Stephen Collins *(Pres & CEO)*
Jeff Verney *(Chm)*

HARTFORD TOYOTA SUPERSTORE
135 W Service Rd, Hartford, CT 06120
Tel.: (959) 223-4773
Web Site:
https://www.hartfordtoyota.com
Year Founded: 1978
Sales Range: $10-24.9 Million
Emp.: 44
Car Whslr
N.A.I.C.S.: 441110
Rich McAllister *(Pres)*
Alexander Benyi *(Mgr-Svc)*

HARTGERS DIAMONDS, LTD.

Hartgers Diamonds, Ltd.—(Continued)

699 Wyckoff Ave, Wyckoff, NJ 07481
Tel.: (201) 891-0044
Web Site:
  https://www.hartgersjewelers.com
Year Founded: 1898
Sales Range: $10-24.9 Million
Emp.: 9
Mfr, Retailer, Repairer & Appraiser of
Watches & Custom Jewelry
N.A.I.C.S.: 458310
John Hartgers (Pres)
Gregory Hartgers (Owner)

HARTLAND FUEL PRODUCTS, LLC

920 10th Ave N, Onalaska, WI 54650
Tel.: (608) 779-6540
Web Site:
  http://www.hartlandfuels.com
Rev.: $10,800,000
Emp.: 35
Petroleum & Petroleum Products
Merchant Whslr
N.A.I.C.S.: 424720
Beth Pederson (Dir-HR)
Bob Ploetz (VP)
Bob Mathy (Controller)

Subsidiaries:

Consolidated Energy Company (1)
910 Main St, Jesup, IA 50648
Tel.: (319) 827-1211
Web Site: http://www.cecgas.com
Sales Range: $25-49.9 Million
Emp.: 35
Gasoline, Diesel Fuel & Propane Distr
N.A.I.C.S.: 457210
Jeff Rummell (Pres & CFO)

HARTLEY COMPANY

319 Wheeling Ave, Cambridge, OH
43725
Tel.: (740) 432-2328
Sales Range: $100-124.9 Million
Emp.: 25
Petroleum Products
N.A.I.C.S.: 424720
Doug Hartley (Pres)

HARTMAN & CO. INC.

1200 E Woodhurst Dr Ste J200,
Springfield, MO 65804-4260
Tel.: (417) 882-2062
Web Site:
  http://www.hartmancomo.com
Sales Range: $25-49.9 Million
Emp.: 150
Concrete Work
N.A.I.C.S.: 238110
Dean Hartman (Pres)
Gerri Hartman (VP)
Dan Zimmerman (Controller)

HARTMAN NEWSPAPERS INC.

1914 4th St, Rosenberg, TX 77471
Tel.: (281) 342-8691
Rev.: $10,200,000
Emp.: 10
Newspapers, Publishing & Printing
N.A.I.C.S.: 513110
J. W. Hartman (Owner)
Mark Thormaehlen (Controller)

HARTMAN-WALSH CORPORATION

7144 N Market St, Saint Louis, MO
63133
Tel.: (314) 863-1800
Web Site:
  http://www.hartmanwalsh.com
Sales Range: $25-49.9 Million
Emp.: 150
Exterior Commercial Painting Contractor
N.A.I.C.S.: 238320
Edward Smith (Chm)

HARTMANN & FORBES

10655 SW Avery St, Tualatin, OR
97062
Tel.: (503) 692-9313
Web Site: http://www.hfshades.com
Year Founded: 1998
Rev.: $5,100,000
Emp.: 35
Custom Manufacturing
N.A.I.C.S.: 337126
Michael S. Jones (Founder & CEO)
Colleen Vohs (Mgr-Customer Rels)
Debbie Rhodes (Mgr-Showroom-
West Reg)

HARTMANN ELECTRIC COMPANY INC.

750 Lee St, Elk Grove Village, IL
60007
Tel.: (847) 734-1260
Web Site:
  http://www.hartmannelectric.com
Sales Range: $10-24.9 Million
Emp.: 80
General Electrical Contractor
N.A.I.C.S.: 238210
William R. Hartmann (Pres)

HARTSON-KENNEDY CABINET TOP CO. INC.

522 W 22nd St, Marion, IN 46953-
2926
Tel.: (765) 668-8144
Web Site: https://www.hartson-
  kennedy.com
Year Founded: 1948
Sales Range: $25-49.9 Million
Emp.: 520
Laminated Plastic Counter Tops Mfr
N.A.I.C.S.: 326130
Doug Burkhardt (Gen Mgr-Sls &
Mktg)
Nicole Schwartz (CFO)
Glen Devitt (Mgr-Ops)
Chris Kennedy (Co-Pres & CEO)
Mike Kennedy (Co-Pres)

Subsidiaries:

Hartson-Kennedy Cabinet Top Co.
Inc. - Luke AFB (1)
7676 N Glen Harbor Blvd, Luke AFB, AZ
85307
Tel.: (623) 772-0000
Web Site: http://www.hartson-kennedy.com
Sales Range: $10-24.9 Million
Emp.: 50
Laminated Plastic Counter Tops Mfr
N.A.I.C.S.: 326130

Hartson-Kennedy Cabinet Top Co.
Inc. - Macon (1)
4255 Interstate Dr, Macon, GA 31210
Tel.: (478) 474-0266
Web Site: http://www.hartson-kennedy.com
Sales Range: $10-24.9 Million
Emp.: 40
Laminated Plastic Counter Tops Mfr
N.A.I.C.S.: 326130
Jim Horton (Mgr)

HARTSVILLE OIL MILL

311 Washington St, Darlington, SC
29532
Tel.: (843) 393-1501
Web Site: http://www.homill.com
Sales Range: $25-49.9 Million
Emp.: 70
Cottonseed Oil Mills
N.A.I.C.S.: 311224
Dwain Watson (Controller)
Edgar H. Lawton III (Pres & Treas)

HARTUNG BROTHERS INC.

708 Hertland Trl Ste 2000, Madison,
WI 53717-2099
Tel.: (608) 829-6000
Web Site:
  https://www.hartungbrothers.com

Year Founded: 1975
Sales Range: $25-49.9 Million
Emp.: 150
Agribusiness Services
N.A.I.C.S.: 111150
Donald Hartung (VP)
Daniel Layton (Treas & Controller)

Subsidiaries:

H&N Transport (1)
708 Heartland Trl Ste 2000, Madison, WI
53717-2009
Tel.: (608) 829-6060
Web Site: http://www.hnlogisticsllc.com
Sales Range: $10-24.9 Million
Emp.: 70
Transportation & Logistic Services
N.A.I.C.S.: 541614

Hartung Brothers Inc. - Bowling
Green Cucumber Plant (1)
815 S Dunbridge Rd, Bowling Green, OH
43402
Tel.: (419) 352-3000
Cucumber Farming Services
N.A.I.C.S.: 111219

Hartung Brothers Inc. - Madison
Seed Plant (1)
2622 Blaney Rd, Madison, WI 53711
Tel.: (608) 278-8150
Corn Seed Production Services
N.A.I.C.S.: 111219

Hartung Brothers Inc. - Muncie Illinois
Seed Production and Distribution
Plant (1)
17558 N 500 East Rd, Fithian, IL 61844-
5136
Tel.: (217) 548-2117
Corn Seed Production Services
N.A.I.C.S.: 111219

Hartung Brothers, Inc.-Uvalde Cucumber Operations (1)
2199 W Hacienda Rd FM 2369, Uvalde, TX
78801
Tel.: (830) 278-4557
Web Site: http://www.hartungbrothers.com
Sales Range: $25-49.9 Million
Emp.: 12
Cucumber Processing
N.A.I.C.S.: 111219
Ryan Noltner (Gen Mgr)

HARTUNG GLASS INDUSTRIES, INC.

17830 W Vly Hwy, Tukwila, WA
98188
Tel.: (425) 656-2626
Web Site: http://www.hartung-
  glass.com
Sales Range: $25-49.9 Million
Emp.: 200
Glass Mfr
N.A.I.C.S.: 327211
Nick Sciola (Pres)

HARTWIG INC.

10617 Trenton Ave, Saint Louis, MO
63132-1633
Tel.: (314) 426-5300
Web Site: https://www.hartwiginc.com
Year Founded: 1972
Sales Range: $75-99.9 Million
Emp.: 150
Industrial Machinery & Equipment Mfr
N.A.I.C.S.: 423830
Geoff Hartwig (Pres)

HARTWIG TRANSIT INC.

9329 Bernice Ave, Schiller Park, IL
60176
Tel.: (847) 678-1085
Sales Range: $10-24.9 Million
Emp.: 230
Mail Carrier Services
N.A.I.C.S.: 484220

HARTY TRACTOR SERVICES, INC.

924 E Rhode Island Ave, Orange
City, FL 32774-1674
Tel.: (386) 775-1005
Web Site: http://www.hartytractor.com
Sales Range: $25-49.9 Million
Emp.: 50
Industrial Building Construction Services
N.A.I.C.S.: 236210
Thad Harty (Founder & Pres)
Debbie Braddock (Mgr-Contracts &
Asst Controller)
Tony Stover (Mgr-Fleet)

HARTZ CONSTRUCTION CO. INC.

9026 Heritage Pkwy, Woodridge, IL
60517-4993
Tel.: (630) 228-3800
Web Site:
  https://www.hartzhomes.com
Year Founded: 1960
Sales Range: $25-49.9 Million
Emp.: 150
Operative Builders
N.A.I.C.S.: 236115
Donald L. Hartz (Pres)

HARTZELL INDUSTRIES, INC.

1025 S Roosevelt Ave, Piqua, OH
45356
Tel.: (937) 773-6295
Web Site: http://www.hartzell.com
Sales Range: $10-24.9 Million
Emp.: 150
Veneer Stock, Hardwood
N.A.I.C.S.: 551112
Jane Farley (Sec)
Jeff Bannister (CEO)
James R. Hartzell (Chm)
Christopher J. Oliss (CFO)
Randi M. Pearson (CFO-Air Movement)
Sean M. Steimle (Pres-Air Movement)
Thomas J. Gustafson (CTO-Air
Movement)
J. Neil Cordonnier (VP-Air Movement)
Chuck Abramson (Dir-Sls)
Mike Ritze (Dir-Ops-Hardwoods)
Kelly R. Hostetter (Gen Mgr-
Hardwoods)
Thomas W. Coble (Dir-Sls-
Hardwoods)

Subsidiaries:

Hartzell Fan, Inc. (1)
910 S Downing St, Piqua, OH 45356
Tel.: (937) 773-7411
Web Site: http://www.hartzell.com
Blowers & Fans
N.A.I.C.S.: 333413

Hartzell Hardwoods, Inc. (1)
1025 S Roosevelt Ave, Piqua, OH 45356
Tel.: (937) 773-7054
Web Site:
  http://www.hartzellhardwoods.com
Sawmills
N.A.I.C.S.: 321113
Kelly Hostetter (Gen Mgr)

Hartzell Veneer Products, LLC (1)
282 Industrial Dr, Hillsdale, MI 49242
Tel.: (517) 437-3117
Web Site: http://www.theveneershop.com
Hardwood Veneer Mfr
N.A.I.C.S.: 321211

HARVARD BUSINESS SCHOOL PUBLISHING CORPORATION

20 Guest St Ste 700, Brighton, MA
02135
Tel.: (617) 783-7500
Web Site:
  https://www.harvardbusiness.org
Year Founded: 1994
Rev.: $96,074,080

Emp.: 260
Periodicals Publishing Only
N.A.I.C.S.: 513120
David A. Wan (Pres & CEO)
Matt Gardiner (Asst Dir-US Midwest)
Denise Lau (Mgr-Sls-Asia Pacific South)
Gabriela Allmi (Mgr-Sls-Southern Europe)
John Walton (Mgr-Inside Sls)
Ken Bayliss (Mgr-Inside Sls)
Luciano Durini (Mgr-Sls-Latin America)
Michael Cronin (Asst Dir-Northern Europe)
Vinay Hebbar (Mng Dir-India)
Jim Aisner (Dir-Media & PR)

Subsidiaries:

Harvard Business Review   (1)
75 Rockefeller Plz Ste 1501, New York, NY 10019-6908
Tel.: (212) 872-9280
Web Site: http://www.hpr.org
Sales Range: $10-24.9 Million
Emp.: 15
Publisher of Business Management Magazine
N.A.I.C.S.: 424920
David Wan (CEO)
Alex Clemente (Mng Dir-Analytic Svcs & Intl Adv)
Karen Dillon (Editor)
Gail Day (Assoc Publr)
Adi Ignatius (Editor-in-Chief)

HARVARD COOPERATIVE SOCIETY INC.

1400 Massachusetts Ave, Cambridge, MA 02138-3807
Tel.: (617) 499-2000   MA
Web Site: http://www.thecoop.com
Year Founded: 1882
Sales Range: $25-49.9 Million
Emp.: 80
Merchandise Cooperative Store
N.A.I.C.S.: 455110
Jerry Murphy (Pres)

HARVARD DEVELOPMENT COMPANY LLC

6569 Wild Oaks Dr, Toledo, OH 43615-1719
Tel.: (419) 843-2030
Sales Range: $25-49.9 Million
Emp.: 1
Land Subdividers & Developers
N.A.I.C.S.: 237210
Bruce Douglas (Pres)

HARVARD ILLINOIS BANCORP, INC.

205 Carson Dr, Poplar Grove, IL 61065
Tel.: (815) 871-5649   MD
Web Site:
http://www.harvardillinoisbancorpinc.com
Year Founded: 2009
Bank Holding Company
N.A.I.C.S.: 551111
Donn L. Claussen (Pres)

HARVARD IN-HOUSE AGENCY

1563 Massachusetts Ave, Cambridge, MA 02138-3701
Tel.: (617) 495-2924
Web Site: http://www.law.harvard.edu
Year Founded: 1910
Sales Range: $1-9.9 Million
Emp.: 12
In House Advertising Agency
N.A.I.C.S.: 541810
Linda Armstrong Cross (Dir-Pub Rel-Media Rel)

HARVARD JOLLY, INC.

2714 Dr Martin Luther King Jr St N, Saint Petersburg, FL 33704
Tel.: (727) 896-4611   FL
Web Site:
http://www.harvardjolly.com
Year Founded: 1938
Sales Range: $10-24.9 Million
Emp.: 53
Architectural Services
N.A.I.C.S.: 541310
Jeffrey E. Cobble (CEO)
Ward J. Friszolowski (Pres)
Michael K. Hart (Principal & Exec VP)
Jack Williams (Principal & Sr VP)
Philip L. Trezza (Principal & Sr VP)
Rene Tercilla (Principal & Sr VP)
Drazen Ahmedic (Principal & VP)
Alex F. Gonzalez (Sr VP)
Jacquelyn S. Spears (Sr VP)
William B. Harvard Jr. (Chm)
Stephen L. Johnson (Principal & Sr VP)

Subsidiaries:

Harvard Jolly Inc.   (1)
5201 W Kennedy Blvd Ste 515, Tampa, FL 33609
Tel.: (813) 286-8206
Web Site: http://www.harvardjolly.com
Sales Range: $10-24.9 Million
Emp.: 26
Architectural Services
N.A.I.C.S.: 541310
Michael K. Hart (Principal & Exec VP)
Jeffrey E. Cobble (CEO)
Ward J. Friszolowski (Pres)
William B. Harvard (Chm)

HARVARD MAINTENANCE, INC.

59 Maiden Ln Fl 17, New York, NY 10038
Tel.: (212) 730-0001
Web Site:
http://www.harvardmaint.com
Sales Range: $150-199.9 Million
Emp.: 3,000
Building Maintenance Services
N.A.I.C.S.: 561720
Stanley K. Doobin (Owner & Pres)
Patrick Mullin (Sr VP)
Brian Rauch (Gen Counsel)
David Domlija (Exec VP)
John Ravaris (Sr VP-Sls & Mktg)
Manuel Bautista (CIO)
W. Carl Drew (CFO)

HARVARD PILGRIM HEALTH CARE, INC.

93 Worcester St, Wellesley, MA 02481
Tel.: (617) 745-1000
Web Site:
http://www.harvardpilgrim.org
Sales Range: $1-4.9 Billion
Emp.: 1,400
HMO & Health Care Services
N.A.I.C.S.: 524114
Deborah A. Norton (CIO)
Beth-Ann Roberts (Sr VP-Enterprise Sls & Mktg)
Michael Sherman (Chief Medical Officer & Sr VP)
Karen Young (Chief Inclusion Officer)
Cynthia Ring (Chief HR Officer)
Charles Goheen (CFO)
Tisa Hughes (Chief Legal Officer)
Richard O'Connor (VP-Mktg)
Michael Carson (Pres & CEO)
Paul Bartosic (Dir-Sls-Connecticut)
Marianne E. Felice (Chm)
Heidi M. Brooks (COO)
William J. Graham (Sr VP-Pub Affairs & Govt Programs)
Kevin J. Rasch (VP-Govt Affairs & Program)

Subsidiaries:

Health Plans, Inc.   (1)
1500 W Park Dr Ste 330, Westborough, MA 01581
Tel.: (508) 752-2480
Web Site: http://www.healthplansinc.com
Benefit Plan Administration Services
N.A.I.C.S.: 923130
Michele Rood (Mgr-Enrollment & Billing Ops)
Kristin Manduca (Mgr-Ops Quality Assurance)
Christopher Parr (VP-Claims Ops & Customer Svc)
Deanna Demers (Acct Mgr)
Linda Munroe (Acct Mgr)
Deborah Hodges (Pres & CEO)
Carol Biron (VP-Bus Dev)
Joan Recore (VP-Fin Ops)
Chuck Moulter (CIO)
Todd Bailey (Sr VP)
Paul Forte (VP-Medical Mgmt & Health Strategies)
Karen Kenney (Dir-Strategic Mktg)
Catherine Lukas (Dir-Acct Ops)
Dianne Oldach (Dir-Medical Mgmt)
Camille Reams (Sr VP-Reg Markets)
Eileen Riethle (VP-Corp Compliance & Regulatory Affairs)
Mary Shea (VP-Client Svcs)
Lynn Stetson (Sr Acct Exec-Natl Client Mgmt)
Holly Weiske (VP-Natl Client Mgmt)
Su Doyle (Dir-Strategic Mktg)

Subsidiary (Domestic):

TrestleTree, Inc.   (2)
3715 Business Dr Ste 202, Fayetteville, AR 72703
Tel.: (479) 582-0777
Web Site: http://www.trestletree.com
Sales Range: $1-9.9 Million
Emp.: 40
Employee Health Coaching Solutions
N.A.I.C.S.: 541612
Cory Ward (Dir-IT)
Ted Borgstadt (CEO)
Becky Parker (VP-Coach Ops)
Lisa Stafford (VP-Client Ops)

HARVARD STUDENT AGENCIES, INC.

67 Mount Auburn St, Cambridge, MA 02138
Tel.: (617) 495-3030
Web Site: https://www.hsa.net
Year Founded: 1957
Sales Range: $10-24.9 Million
Emp.: 10
Student Run Business Services
N.A.I.C.S.: 561311
James McKellar (CEO & Gen Mgr)
Ali Dastjerdi (Pres)
Grace Chen (Treas)

Subsidiaries:

Let's Go Publications, Inc.   (1)
67 Mount Auburn St, Cambridge, MA 02138-4961
Tel.: (617) 495-9659
Web Site: http://www.letsgo.com
Sales Range: $10-24.9 Million
International Travel Guides Publisher
N.A.I.C.S.: 513199

HARVARD UNIVERSITY PRESS

79 Garden St, Cambridge, MA 02138-1423
Tel.: (617) 495-2650
Web Site:
https://www.hup.harvard.edu
Year Founded: 1913
Sales Range: $75-99.9 Million
Emp.: 80
Scholarly Books & Other Publications
N.A.I.C.S.: 513130
Janice Audet (Exec Editor-Life Sciences)
Ulysses S. Grant (Pres)

Subsidiaries:

Harvard University Press - London   (1)
Vernon House 23 Sicilian Avenue 11 Chenies St, London, WC1A 2QS, United Kingdom   **(100%)**
Tel.: (44) 2073060603
Web Site: http://www.hup.harvard.edu
Sales Range: $10-24.9 Million
Emp.: 7
Marketing Services for Harvard University Press
N.A.I.C.S.: 513130
Richard Howells (Dir-Sls & Mktg-Intl)

HARVEST CONSUMER INSULATION, INC.

641 Northpark Dr, Clinton, TN 37716
Tel.: (865) 463-6184
Web Site:
https://www.climashield.com
Year Founded: 2008
Sales Range: $10-24.9 Million
Emp.: 45
Converted Paper Product Mfr
N.A.I.C.S.: 322299
Ken Hardin (CEO)
Brian Emanuel (Gen Mgr)
Matt Schrantz (COO)

HARVEST CREATIVE

348 N Main St, Memphis, TN 38103
Tel.: (901) 526-6244
Web Site:
https://www.harvestcreative.com
Year Founded: 2006
Sales Range: $1-9.9 Million
Emp.: 10
Full Service Advertising & Design Agency
N.A.I.C.S.: 541810
Daniel Brown (Co-Owner & Creative Dir)
Andrew Holliday (Co-Owner)

HARVEST INTERNATIONAL INC.

401 W 20th St, Storm Lake, IA 51012-1012
Tel.: (712) 213-5100
Web Site:
http://www.harvestauger.com
Conveyor & Conveying Equipment Mfr
N.A.I.C.S.: 333922
Dustin K. Friesen (Reg Mgr-Sls)

HARVEST LAND CO-OP INC.

1435 NW 5th St, Richmond, IN 47374
Tel.: (765) 962-1527
Web Site:
http://www.harvestlandcoop.com
Sales Range: $200-249.9 Million
Emp.: 400
Local Agricultural Cooperative
N.A.I.C.S.: 424910
Bonnie Norris (Mgr-HR)
Brandon Bowser (Reg Mgr)
Ron Smith (Mgr-Grain Div)
Kim Buttery (Office Mgr)
Mark Richey (Asst Mgr)
Randal Reese (Mgr-Ops)

Subsidiaries:

Harvest Land Co-Op Inc.   (1)
141 W 500 N, Anderson, IN 46012-9500
Tel.: (765) 643-6639
Sales Range: $10-24.9 Million
Emp.: 125
Liquid Fuels
N.A.I.C.S.: 457210

HARVEST LAND COOPERATIVE

715 Frnt St, Morgan, MN 56266
Tel.: (507) 249-3196

Harvest Land Cooperative—(Continued)

Web Site:
   http://www.harvestland.com
Sales Range: $75-99.9 Million
Emp.: 120
Fiscal Year-end: 08/31/14
Grains
N.A.I.C.S.: 424510
Dave Stuk *(CEO)*
Timothy Sullivan *(Sec)*
Roger Kettner *(Chm)*
Mark Vogel *(Acct Mgr)*
Craig Fredin *(Acct Mgr-Comfrey)*
Rick Kastner *(Acct Mgr-Comfrey)*
Tony Dunn *(Acct Mgr-Lake Benton)*
Keegan Mammen *(Acct Mgr-Morton)*
Todd Beran *(Acct Mgr-Morton)*
Joel Heiling *(Acct Mgr-Springfield)*
Rob Dalsgaard *(Acct Mgr-Springfield)*
Jim Boyle *(Mgr-Crop Nutrients Div)*
Tim Woelfel *(Mgr-Crop Protection Div)*
Matt Peitig *(Mgr-Harvest Max-Precision Ag)*
Kristin Henning *(Mgr-HR)*
Lynn Button *(Mgr-Insurance)*
Pat Macht *(Mgr-Petroleum)*
Aaron Guggisberg *(Mgr-Safety)*
Brett Braulick *(Mgr-Seed Div)*
Lake Benton *(Acct Mgr)*

HARVEST PARTNERS L.P.
280 Park Ave 26th Fl, New York, NY 10017-1216
Tel.: (212) 599-6300   **NY**
Web Site:
   http://www.harvestpartners.com
Year Founded: 1981
Private Equity Firm
N.A.I.C.S.: 523999
Michael B. DeFlorio *(Pres)*
Andrew Schoenthal *(Partner)*
Jay Wilkins *(COO)*
Stephen Carlson *(Partner)*
Nicholas Romano *(Partner)*
Dan Glickman *(Partner)*

Subsidiaries:

ADCS Clinics, LLC   **(1)**
151 Southhall Ln Ste 300, Maitland, FL 32751
Tel.: (407) 875-2080
Web Site: http://www.advancedderm.com
Holding Company; Advanced Dermatology & Cosmetic Surgery Consultation & Surgical Services
N.A.I.C.S.: 551112
Matt L. Leavitt *(Founder & Chm)*
Justin Simoncini *(VP-Bus Dev)*
Daniel D. Crowley *(Chm, Pres & CEO)*
Brian Griffin *(CEO)*

Subsidiary (Domestic):

Leavitt Medical Associates of Florida, Inc.   **(2)**
2600 Lake Lucien Dr Ste 180, Maitland, FL 32751-7217
Tel.: (407) 875-2080
Web Site: http://www.advancedderm.com
Advanced Dermatology & Cosmetic Surgery Consultation & Surgical Services
N.A.I.C.S.: 621399
David Morrell *(Pres & COO)*
Justin Kuperberg *(VP-Bus Dev & Acq)*
Gia Concannon *(Dir-Billing)*
Sheila Cunningham *(Mgr-Accts Receivable)*
Erica Novak *(Dir-HR)*
Steven Grekin *(Chief Bus Dev Officer & Exec VP)*
Bobby Karegianes *(Dir-Ops & Aesthetics)*
Michael Oswalt *(Dir-IT)*
David Yoffee *(Controller)*
Paul Tuffy *(Dir-Mktg)*
Jennifer Bancroft *(VP-Aesthetics)*
Steve Essayan *(CIO)*
Matt Leavitt *(Founder & Chm)*
Cheryl Zelenak *(VP-Mktg)*
Karen Hornsby *(Chief Managed Care Officer)*

Brian T. Griffin *(CEO)*
Daniel Davison *(CFO)*
David Loschinskey *(Exec VP-Ops)*
David Polston *(CMO)*

Subsidiary (Domestic):

Bay Area Dermatology Associates   **(3)**
12 Professional Park, Webster, TX 77598
Tel.: (281) 332-8571
Web Site:
   http://www.usdermatologypartners.com
Dermatological Care Services
N.A.I.C.S.: 621111
Mary Fasel *(Office Mgr)*

Capital Dermatology, Ltd.   **(3)**
4660 Kenmore Ave Ste 500, Alexandria, VA 22304-1300
Tel.: (703) 370-0073
Web Site: http://www.703derm.com
Sales Range: $1-9.9 Million
Dermatological Health Care Services
N.A.I.C.S.: 621111
Lynda Stout *(Office Mgr)*

Dermatology of Northern Colorado, P.C.   **(3)**
3726 S Timberline Rd Ste 101, Fort Collins, CO 80525-4332
Tel.: (970) 221-5795
Web Site: http://www.dermofnoco.com
Sales Range: $1-9.9 Million
Dermatological Care Services
N.A.I.C.S.: 621111
Kathy Hahn *(Office Mgr)*
B. Lynn West *(Founder)*

Kalamazoo Dermatology, P.C.   **(3)**
6100 Newport Rd Ste 100, Portage, MI 49002
Tel.: (269) 343-4679
Web Site:
   http://www.kalamazoodermatology.com
Sales Range: $1-9.9 Million
Dermatological Care Services
N.A.I.C.S.: 621111
Lori Kollin *(Mgr-Practice)*
Gerald Karabin *(Principal)*

Mid-Michigan Dermatology, PLLC   **(3)**
416 S Creyts Rd Ste A, Lansing, MI 48917-8290
Tel.: (517) 721-7701
Web Site:
   http://www.lansingdermatologycenter.com
Sales Range: $1-9.9 Million
Dermatological Care Services
N.A.I.C.S.: 621111
Katie Greenfelder *(Office Mgr)*

Patrick T. Ottuso, M.D., F.A.A.D., P.A.   **(3)**
1955 22nd Ave, Vero Beach, FL 32960-3083
Tel.: (772) 299-0085
Sales Range: $1-9.9 Million
Dermatological Care Services
N.A.I.C.S.: 621111
Naomi Ottuso *(Office Mgr)*
Patrick T. Ottuso *(Principal)*

Skin Pathology Associates Inc.   **(3)**
3550 Independence Dr Ste B, Birmingham, AL 35209   **(100%)**
Tel.: (205) 949-2800
Web Site: http://www.skinpathology.net
Emp.: 80
Dermatopathology Labs, Skin Testing & Diagnosis
N.A.I.C.S.: 621511
James E. Elder *(Pres & Medical Officer)*
Anne H. Bussian *(Medical Officer)*

Western Wyoming Dermatology & Surgery   **(3)**
62 S Redmond St, Jackson, WY 83001-8664
Tel.: (307) 734-5864
Web Site:
   http://www.westernwyomingderm.com
Dermatological Care Services
N.A.I.C.S.: 621111
Michelle Gauthier *(Office Mgr)*
Christian Anderson *(Principal)*

Subsidiary (Domestic):

Oakland Dermatology Associates (2)

36700 Woodward Ave Ste 203, Bloomfield Hills, MI 48304-0930
Tel.: (248) 647-5750
Office Of Physician
N.A.I.C.S.: 621111

SkinTrust Dermatology   **(2)**
26 Roper Corners Cir, Greenville, SC 29615-4833
Tel.: (864) 234-7744
Web Site: http://www.theskintrust.com
Offices of Physicians (except Mental Health Specialists)
N.A.I.C.S.: 621111
Connie Gill *(Office Mgr)*
Eric James Baker *(Founder)*

APC Automotive Technologies, LLC   **(1)**
300 Dixie Trail, Goldsboro, NC 27530
Tel.: (919) 580-2000
Web Site: http://www.apcautotech.com
Underbody Vehicle Products Supplier
N.A.I.C.S.: 336340
James McCoy *(COO)*

AxelaCare Holdings, Inc.   **(1)**
15529 College Boulevard, Lenexa, KS 66219
Tel.: (913) 747-3700
Web Site: http://www.axelacare.com
Healtcare Services
N.A.I.C.S.: 621498
Ted Kramm *(Founder & CEO)*
Larry Freni *(CFO)*
Ron Lindahl *(Chief IT Officer)*
Brad Holliday *(Chief HR Officer)*
Brendan Beggin *(VP-Fin)*
David Maurer *(Chief Sls Officer)*
Michele Hartmann Tamene *(Chief Compliance Officer, Gen Counsel & VP)*
Joe Zavalishin *(Exec VP-Strategic Contracting & Payer Rels)*

Holding (Domestic):

Ambient Healthcare, Inc.   **(2)**
15951 SW 41st St Ste 500, Davie, FL 33331
Tel.: (954) 389-1126
Web Site: http://www.axelacare.com
Drugs & Druggists Sundries Merchant Whslr
N.A.I.C.S.: 424210

Fortis Solutions Group LLC   **(1)**
2505 Hawkeye Ct, Virginia Beach, VA 23452
Tel.: (757) 340-8893
Web Site:
   http://www.fortissolutionsgroup.com
Labels, Data Printing, Booklet Printing & Flexible Packaging Services
N.A.I.C.S.: 561910
John O. Wynne Jr. *(Pres & CEO)*

Subsidiary (Domestic):

Anchor Printing Company   **(2)**
800 Denison Ct, Bloomfield Hills, MI 48302
Tel.: (248) 335-7440
Web Site: http://www.anchorprinting.com
Sales Range: $1-9.9 Million
Emp.: 27
Flexographic & Commercial Offset Printing
N.A.I.C.S.: 323111
Daniel Fisher *(VP-Ops)*

Digital Dogma Corp.   **(2)**
13003 Los Nietos Rd, Santa Fe Springs, CA 90670-3013
Tel.: (562) 903-1533
Web Site: http://www.digital-dogma.com
Printing Services
N.A.I.C.S.: 323111

Label Tech, Inc.   **(2)**
16 Interstate Dr, Somersworth, NH 03878
Tel.: (603) 692-2005
Web Site: https://www.labeltechinc.com
Gravure Commercial Printing Mfg
Coated/Laminated Paper Mfg Packaging Paper/Film
N.A.I.C.S.: 323111
Peter Mullen *(Mgr-Plant)*
Pat Brady *(CEO)*

Insight Global, Inc.   **(1)**
4170 Ashford Dunwoody Rd NE Ste 250, Atlanta, GA 30319

Tel.: (404) 257-7900
Web Site: http://www.insightglobal.net
Sales Range: $300-349.9 Million
Technical Staff Recruiting Services
N.A.I.C.S.: 561311
Glenn Johnson *(Chm)*
Scott Madden *(COO)*
Rich Lingle *(CEO)*

Lazer Spot, Inc.   **(1)**
6525 Shiloh Rd Ste 900, Alpharetta, GA 30005-0005
Tel.: (770) 886-6851
Web Site: http://www.lazerspot.com
Yard Management Services & Solutions
N.A.I.C.S.: 561499
Adam Newsome *(CEO)*
Jerry Edwards *(Exec VP-Ops)*
Phil Newsome *(COO)*
Will Rozeboom *(VP-Pricing & Customer Solutions)*
Bob Wright *(Exec VP-Fleet Ops)*
David Brazeal *(CFO)*

Levlad, LLC   **(1)**
9200 Mason Ave, Chatsworth, CA 91311-6005   **(100%)**
Tel.: (818) 882-2951
Web Site: http://www.levlad.com
Sales Range: $25-49.9 Million
Cosmetics & Promotional Products Mfr
N.A.I.C.S.: 325620
Larsen Gaetos *(Controller-Plant)*

Neighborly, Inc.   **(1)**
1020 N University Parks Dr, Waco, TX 76707
Tel.: (800) 490-7501
Web Site: http://www.neighborlybrands.com
Nonfinancial Intangible Assets Lessor
N.A.I.C.S.: 533110
Mary Kennedy Thompson *(COO)*
Mike Bidwell *(Pres & CEO)*
Jon Shell *(CFO)*
Amer Waheed *(CTO)*
Lisa Zoellner *(CMO)*

Subsidiary (Domestic):

Lawn Pride Inc.   **(2)**
7320 Company Dr, Indianapolis, IN 46237
Tel.: (317) 882-3200
Web Site: http://www.lawnpride.com
Rev.: $5,000,000
Emp.: 30
Landscaping Services
N.A.I.C.S.: 561730
Andrew Neher *(Founder & Pres)*

Real Property Management   **(2)**
1455 W 2200 S Ste 300, Salt Lake City, UT 84119
Tel.: (801) 546-1770
Web Site: http://www.realpropertymgt.com
Residential Property Management Services
N.A.I.C.S.: 531210
Aaron Bracken *(Dir-IT)*
Jeff Pepperney *(Pres)*
Kent Frogley *(VP-Mktg)*
Valerie Krause *(VP-Franchise Dev)*
Tim Sedgwick *(Dir-Natl Accts)*
Stacy Brown *(Dir-Systems)*

PRO Unlimited, Inc.   **(1)**
1 Post St Ste 375, San Francisco, CA 94104
Tel.: (561) 995-5160
Web Site: http://www.prounlimited.com
Workforce Management Services
N.A.I.C.S.: 561499
Ben Barstow *(CFO)*
Michael Harvey *(Sr VP-Implementations)*
Teresa Golio *(Sr VP-Fin & Controller)*
Andrew Popler *(Exec VP-Bus Dev)*
Ted Sergott *(Exec VP-Product Dev)*
Allie Ben-Shlomo *(Exec VP-Strategy)*
Martin Schultz *(COO)*
James Cahalan *(Dir-Global Compliance)*
Mason Slaine *(Chm)*
Kevin Akeroyd *(CEO)*
Jessica Kane *(Chief Client Officer)*
Christian Barbato *(Sr Dir-Mktg)*
Mason Slaine *(Chm)*

Subsidiary (Non-US):

PRO Unlimited Global Japan (YK) Ltd.   **(2)**
Level 27 Shiroyama Trust Tower 4-3-1 Toranomon, Minato-ku, Tokyo, 105-0001, Japan

Tel.: (81) 3 5404 8462
Web Site: http://www.prounlimited.com
Workforce Management Services
N.A.I.C.S.: 561499

Packers Holdings, LLC (1)
3681 Prism Ln, Kieler, WI 53812
Tel.: (608) 568-3413
Janitorial Services
N.A.I.C.S.: 561720

Service Express, LLC (1)
3854 Broadmore Ave SE, Grand Rapids, MI 49512
Tel.: (616) 698-2221
Web Site: http://www.seiservice.com
Sales Range: $25-49.9 Million
Emp.: 270
Data Center Mainatenance Services
N.A.I.C.S.: 811210
Ron Alvesteffer *(Pres & CEO)*
Dwight Strayer *(COO)*
Mark Thomas *(Chief Revenue Officer)*
Eric Major *(Sr Acct Exec)*
John C. Madden *(CFO)*

Subsidiary (Domestic):

Compu-Fix, Inc. (2)
920 Thompson Run Rd, West Mifflin, PA 15122
Tel.: (412) 464-0275
Web Site: http://www.compu-fixinc.com
Sales Range: $1-9.9 Million
Emp.: 25
Office Machine Repair & Maintenance Services
N.A.I.C.S.: 811210
David Babcock *(Founder)*
Chris Harford *(Acct Mgr)*

Sherlock Services, Inc. (2)
440 4th St NW, Barberton, OH 44203
Web Site: http://www.sherlockservices.com
Sales Range: $1-9.9 Million
Emp.: 25
Information Technology Management Services
N.A.I.C.S.: 541512
Greg Brumbaugh *(VP)*

Trident Computer Resources, Inc. (2)
151 Industrial Way E A, Eatontown, NJ 07724
Tel.: (732) 544-9333
Web Site: http://www.tridentusa.com
Sales Range: $1-9.9 Million
Emp.: 55
Computer Integrated Systems Design, Nsk
N.A.I.C.S.: 541512

The Dwyer Group, Inc. (1)
1020 N University Parks Dr, Waco, TX 76707-3854
Tel.: (254) 745-2400
Web Site: http://www.dwyergroup.com
Service-Based Franchise Company Operator
N.A.I.C.S.: 561210
Mary Kennedy Thompson *(COO)*
Michael Bidwell *(Pres & CEO)*
Robert Tunmire *(Exec VP)*
Michael Gai *(VP-Ops-Dwyer Svc Solutions)*
Jon Shell *(CFO)*
Grayson Brown *(Gen Counsel)*
Lisa Zoellner *(Chief Strategy & Mktg Officer)*
Shayne Mehringer *(CIO)*
Jeff Meyers *(VP-Intl Ops)*
Mary Kay Liston *(Pres-Five Star Painting & Pro Tect Painters)*
Cody Pierce *(Sr VP-Mktg)*

Subsidiary (Domestic):

Aire Serv LLC (2)
5387 N State Hwy 6, Woodway, TX 76712
Tel.: (254) 300-8971
Web Site: http://www.aireserv.com
Heating, Ventilation & Air Conditioning Maintenance & Repair Services
N.A.I.C.S.: 238220
Steve Truett *(Pres)*

Subsidiary (Non-US):

Bright & Beautiful UK Limited (2)
Countrywide House Unit 11 Oak Green Earl

Road, Cheadle, SK8 6QL, Hulme, United Kingdom
Tel.: (44) 161 240 3700
Web Site: http://www.brightandbeautifulhome.com
Home Cleaning, Ironing & Laundry Services Franchisor
N.A.I.C.S.: 533110
Charmaine Nicolson *(Mng Dir)*

Subsidiary (Domestic):

Cumberland County Glass (2)
51 Pond Rd, Bowdoinham, ME 04008 (100%)
Tel.: (207) 666-3700
Web Site: http://www.cumberlandcountyglass.com
Commercial Glass Services
N.A.I.C.S.: 327211
Kenneth Soucher *(Pres)*
Louise Austin *(Project Mgr)*
Norman Boutin *(Project Mgr)*
Rena Saucier *(Office Mgr)*

Mr. Appliance LLC (2)
304 E Church Ave, Killeen, TX 76541
Tel.: (254) 613-2207
Web Site: http://www.mrappliance.com
Home & Business Appliance Repair Services
N.A.I.C.S.: 811412
Ron Shimek *(Pres)*

Mr. Electric LLC (2)
927 Enterprise Blvd, Hewitt, TX 76643
Tel.: (254) 304-7893
Web Site: http://www.mrelectric.com
Electrical Installation & Repair Services
N.A.I.C.S.: 811210
Joel Worthington *(Pres)*

Mr. Handyman International, LLC (2)
3948 Ranchero Dr, Ann Arbor, MI 48108
Web Site: http://www.mrhandyman.com
General Contracting Services Franchisor & Operator
N.A.I.C.S.: 236118
J. B. Sassano *(Pres)*

Mr. Rooter LLC (2)
3715 Franklin Ave, Waco, TX 76710
Tel.: (254) 340-1321
Web Site: http://www.mrrooter.com
Plumbing Services
N.A.I.C.S.: 238220
James Doyle *(Pres)*
Glenn Gallas *(VP-Ops)*

Rainbow International LLC (2)
1010 N University Parks Dr, Waco, TX 76707-3854
Tel.: (855) 724-6269
Web Site: http://www.rainbowintl.com
Home & Commercial Restoration & Carpet Cleaning Services
N.A.I.C.S.: 561740
Cary Fairless *(Pres)*

Synergistic International LLC (2)
133 N 1st St Ste 108, Hewitt, TX 76643
Tel.: (254) 230-9591
Web Site: http://www.glassdoctor.com
Residential, Commercial & Auto Glass Replacement, Repair & Services
N.A.I.C.S.: 811122
Brad Roberson *(Pres)*

Yellowstone Landscape Group, Inc. (1)
3235 North State St, Bunnell, FL 32110
Tel.: (386) 437-6211
Web Site: http://www.yellowstonelandscape.com
Landscape Design & Maintenance Services
N.A.I.C.S.: 541320
Tim Portland *(CEO)*
Jim Sivils *(Reg VP-Southeast Reg)*
Elise Johnson *(VP-HR)*
James Herth *(VP-Bus Dev)*
Chris Adornetti *(VP & Controller)*
Timo Sherman *(VP-Fin Planning & Analysis)*
Brian Wester *(Reg VP)*

HARVEST POWER INC.
1432 Main St Ste 240, Waltham, MA 02451
Tel.: (781) 314-9500

Web Site: http://www.harvestpower.com
Sales Range: $50-74.9 Million
Emp.: 300
Soil & Mulch Producer
N.A.I.C.S.: 424910
Michael J. Ahearn *(Chm)*
Brian Kura *(Sr VP-Consumer Products)*
Gary S. Aguinaga *(COO-Energy Bus)*
Mark Weidman *(CEO)*
Raja Bal *(CFO)*
Mike Connors *(Sr VP-Harvest Consumer Products)*
Bernard Fenner *(Sr VP-Sls & Dev-Global)*
Chris Mirick *(Gen Counsel & Sr VP)*

Subsidiaries:

Harvest Garden Pro, LLC (1)
1977 Bay Rd, Milford, DE 19963-6134
Tel.: (302) 732-6624
Web Site: http://www.coastalsupplyinc.com
Sales Range: $10-24.9 Million
Emp.: 20
Home & Garden Products Mfr
N.A.I.C.S.: 321999
Steve Liffers *(Co-Pres)*
David Hitchcock *(Sr VP-Corp Ops)*
Christian G. Kasper *(CEO)*
Brian Kura *(Sr VP-Consumer Products)*
Brandon Moffatt *(Sr VP-Energy)*

HARVEST SUPERMARKETS INC.
915 Jackson St, Anderson, IN 46016
Tel.: (765) 643-6415
Web Site: https://www.harvestsupermarkets.com
Rev.: $35,000,000
Emp.: 290
Owner & Operator of Supermarkets
N.A.I.C.S.: 445110
Donald Murphy *(Chief Admin Officer)*

HARVEST, INC.
3325 Emerson Ave, Parkersburg, WV 26104
Tel.: (304) 485-2016
Year Founded: 2004
Sales Range: $1-9.9 Million
Emp.: 15
Supermarkets & Other Grocery (except Convenience) Stores
N.A.I.C.S.: 445110
Brad Woodburn *(Pres)*

HARVESTERS - THE COMMUNITY FOOD NETWORK
3801 Topping Ave, Kansas City, MO 64129
Tel.: (816) 929-3000 MO
Web Site: https://www.harvesters.org
Year Founded: 1979
Sales Range: $75-99.9 Million
Emp.: 165
Hunger Relief Services
N.A.I.C.S.: 624210
Valerie Nicholson-Watson *(Pres & CEO)*
Joanna Sebelien *(Chief Resource Officer)*
Dan Crumb *(Treas)*
John George *(Sec)*
Russell S. Mosburg *(Chm)*
Steve Davis *(COO)*

HARVESTONE GROUP LLC
840 Crescent Ctr Dr Ste 540, Franklin, TN 37067
Tel.: (615) 716-1020
Web Site: http://www.harvestonegroup.com
Petroleum Distr
N.A.I.C.S.: 324191
Kevin Stewart *(CMO)*

Subsidiaries:

Gateway Terminals LLC (1)
177 3 Uppr Mississippi Riv 4 Pitzman Ave, Sauget, IL 62201
Tel.: (618) 215-7333
Web Site: http://www.gatewayterminalsllc.com
Sales Range: $25-49.9 Million
General Freight Transportation & Warehousing Services
N.A.I.C.S.: 493190

HARVEY & DAUGHTERS, INC./H&D BRANDING
952 Ridgebrook Rd Ste 1000, Sparks, MD 21152
Tel.: (410) 771-5566 MD
Web Site: http://www.harveyagency.com
Year Founded: 1986
Sales Range: $1-9.9 Million
Emp.: 39
Advertising Agencies
N.A.I.C.S.: 541810
Kathy Harvey *(Owner)*
Sue Baile *(Dir-Brand & Integration)*

HARVEY ALPERT & CO. INC.
2014 S Sepulveda Blvd Ste 200, Los Angeles, CA 90025
Tel.: (310) 689-6000
Web Site: http://www.harveyalpertco.com
Sales Range: $100-124.9 Million
Emp.: 5
Bond Brokers
N.A.I.C.S.: 424410
Harvey Alpert *(Pres)*

HARVEY CADILLAC
2600 28th St SE, Grand Rapids, MI 49512-1685
Tel.: (616) 949-1140
Web Site: https://www.harveycadillac.com
Year Founded: 1966
Sales Range: $25-49.9 Million
Emp.: 134
Car Whslr
N.A.I.C.S.: 441110
Eldon Grosvenor *(Gen Mgr)*
John M. Leese *(Pres)*

HARVEY CADILLAC COMPANY
2600 28th St SE, Grand Rapids, MI 49512-1685
Tel.: (616) 949-1140
Web Site: https://www.harveycadillac.com
Year Founded: 1966
Sales Range: $10-24.9 Million
Emp.: 65
Sales of Automobiles
N.A.I.C.S.: 441110
John M. Leese *(Owner & Pres)*
Eldon Grosvenor *(Gen Mgr)*

HARVEY CHEVROLET CORPORATION
1500 Tyler Ave, Radford, VA 24141
Tel.: (540) 639-3923
Web Site: https://www.harveysgm.com
Year Founded: 1959
Sales Range: $25-49.9 Million
Emp.: 65
Car Whslr
N.A.I.C.S.: 441110
George M. Harvey Jr. *(Pres)*

HARVEY FERTILIZER & GAS CO.
1291 Hwy 258 N, Kinston, NC 28504
Tel.: (252) 523-9090
Sales Range: $75-99.9 Million

Harvey Fertilizer & Gas Co.—(Continued)

Emp.: 30
Farm Supplies
N.A.I.C.S.: 424910
Herbert Rouse *(Pres)*
Frank Hill *(CFO)*
Linda Huggins *(Dir-Safety)*
Brian Jenkins *(Mgr-Warehouse)*

Subsidiaries:

L. Harvey & Son Co.   (1)
1291 Hwy 258 N, Kinston, NC 28504
Tel.: (252) 523-9090
Sales Range: $10-24.9 Million
Farm Machinery
N.A.I.C.S.: 459999
John O. McNairy *(Owner)*
Ed Cooper *(Treas & Sec)*

HARVEY INDUSTRIES, LLC.

17177 Laurel Park Dr Ste 243, Livo-
nia, MI 48152
Tel.: (734) 405-2430
Web Site: http://www.harvey-
industries.com
Year Founded: 1982
Sales Range: $100-124.9 Million
Emp.: 825
Aluminum Casting, Machining, As-
sembly, Testing & Polymer Injection
Molding Mfr
N.A.I.C.S.: 333248
Richard Levin *(Exec VP-Ops)*
Jerome Harvey *(Pres & CEO)*
Mark Stevens *(VP-Sls)*

HARVEY M. HARPER CO.

4800 US Hwy 101 N, Eureka, CA
95503
Tel.: (707) 443-7311
Web Site:
https://www.harpermotors.com
Sales Range: $10-24.9 Million
Emp.: 120
Automobiles, New & Used
N.A.I.C.S.: 441110
Rick Hrdina *(Controller)*

HARVEY PALLETS, INC.

13601 Western Ave, Blue Island, IL
60406
Tel.: (708) 293-1831
Web Site:
https://www.harveypallets.com
Year Founded: 1997
Sales Range: $10-24.9 Million
Emp.: 35
Wood Container & Pallet Mfr
N.A.I.C.S.: 321920
Manuel Tavarez *(Pres)*
Julia Tavarez *(VP)*
Johana Lopez *(Dir-Office & Acctg)*
Bernard Packo *(Dir-Sls & Mktg)*
Luichy Acevedo *(Dir-Pur & Outside
Logistics)*
Fernando Munoz *(Dir-Customer Svc
& Logistics)*

HARVEY SALT COMPANY INC

1325 Mohrs Ln, Baltimore, MD
21220-1488
Tel.: (410) 391-9100
Web Site:
https://www.harveysalt.com
Sales Range: $10-24.9 Million
Emp.: 40
Salt & Salt Products Mfr
N.A.I.C.S.: 424690
Al Prestilel *(VP-Sls)*
Sharon Davis *(VP)*
Michael Didominicus *(Treas)*
Bonnie Hammen *(Pres)*

HARWICK STANDARD DISTRI-
BUTION CORPORATION

60 S Seiberling St, Akron, OH 44305-
4217
Tel.: (330) 798-9300
Web Site: https://www.harwick.com
Year Founded: 1932
Supplier of Raw Materials to the Rub-
ber & Plastic Industries
N.A.I.C.S.: 424690
Ernest Pouttu *(Pres & CEO)*
Dan Davis *(Sr VP-Sls & CSO)*
Jim Houston *(CFO & Sr VP-Fin)*

HASC CENTER INC.

5601 1st Ave, Brooklyn, NY 11220
Tel.: (718) 745-7575   NY
Web Site: http://www.hasccenter.com
Year Founded: 1984
Sales Range: $25-49.9 Million
Emp.: 1,191
Developmental Disability Assistance
Services
N.A.I.C.S.: 624120
Samuel Kahn *(Exec Dir)*
Isaiah Levy *(Controller)*
Chaim Wakslak *(Dir-Clinical)*

HASCALL STEEL COMPANY
INC.

4165 Spartan Industrial Dr SW,
Grandville, MI 49418
Tel.: (616) 531-8600   MI
Web Site:
https://www.hascallsteel.com
Year Founded: 1971
Sales Range: $75-99.9 Million
Emp.: 150
Steel Product Mfr & Distr
N.A.I.C.S.: 423510
Dag Hascall *(CEO)*
Chris Vanwingerden *(Gen Mgr)*

Subsidiaries:

Hascall Steel Company Inc. - BEN-
TON PLANT   (1)
1325 River St, Benton, AR 72015
Tel.: (501) 778-1600
Rolled Steel Mfr
N.A.I.C.S.: 331221

Hascall Steel Company Inc. - NASH-
VILLE PLANT   (1)
407 Driftwood St, Nashville, TN 37210
Tel.: (615) 242-2074
Rolled Steel Mfr
N.A.I.C.S.: 331221

Hascall Steel Company Inc. -
STRONG STREET PLANT   (1)
6349 Strong St, Detroit, MI 48211
Tel.: (313) 262-5700
Rolled Steel Mfr
N.A.I.C.S.: 331221

Hascall Steel Company-Ecorse
Plant   (1)
64 Mill St, Ecorse, MI 48229-1449
Tel.: (313) 383-0800
Sales Range: $25-49.9 Million
Emp.: 73
Metal Processing Services
N.A.I.C.S.: 423510

HASCO OIL COMPANY, INC.

2800 Temple Ave, Long Beach, CA
90806
Tel.: (562) 595-8491
Web Site: https://www.hascooil.com
Rev.: $14,000,000
Emp.: 33
Whslr of Petroleum Products
N.A.I.C.S.: 424720
Renee Bjorklund *(Pres)*
Steve Edrich *(Mgr-Ops)*
Steve Hernandez *(Acct Mgr)*

HASE PETROLEUM WAX CO.
INC.

44 S Dunton Ave, Arlington Heights,
IL 60005

Tel.: (847) 259-2870
Web Site: https://www.hpwax.com
Rev.: $18,741,665
Emp.: 5
Reseller for Wax Producers
N.A.I.C.S.: 424690
Scott Hase *(Founder)*

HASELDEN CONSTRUCTION
LLC

6950 S Potomac St Ste 100, Centen-
nial, CO 80112
Tel.: (303) 751-1478
Web Site: https://www.haselden.com
Sales Range: $10-24.9 Million
Emp.: 300
Commercial & Office Building, New
Construction
N.A.I.C.S.: 236220
Ed J. Haselden *(CEO)*
Tracy Mathieu *(Dir-Corp Mktg)*
Bob Fox *(Dir-MEP Sys)*
David Lueders *(Chief Admin Officer &
Exec VP)*
Troy Schroeder *(CFO)*
Garrett Updike *(Dir-Talent Mgmt)*
Byron Haselden *(Pres)*
Derek Oliver *(Mgr-Haselden Wyo-
ming Constructors)*
Jarrod Fugate *(Mgr-On-Call)*
Mike Haselden *(Vice Chm & COO)*
Neil Sharples *(Mgr-Ops)*

HASKELL CORPORATION

1001 Meador Ave, Bellingham, WA
98229
Tel.: (360) 734-1200
Web Site:
https://www.haskellcorp.com
Sales Range: $10-24.9 Million
Emp.: 250
Nonresidential Construction
N.A.I.C.S.: 236220
Fred Haskell *(Chm & CEO)*
Jeff Jenkins *(CFO)*
Steve Macomber *(Mgr-Shop)*

HASKELL LEMON CON-
STRUCTION CO.

3800 SW 10th St, Oklahoma City, OK
73108
Tel.: (405) 947-6069
Web Site:
https://www.haskelllemon.com
Sales Range: $10-24.9 Million
Emp.: 142
Highway & Street Paving Contractor
N.A.I.C.S.: 237310
Kent Wert *(Sec & Treas)*
Jeff Burr *(Mgr-Sls)*
Robert Dawkins *(Plant Mgr)*

HASKINS ELECTRIC INC.

1414 N 25th Ave, Phoenix, AZ 85009
Tel.: (623) 937-3999
Web Site: https://www.haskins-
electric.com
Sales Range: $75-99.9 Million
Emp.: 500
General Electrical Contractor
N.A.I.C.S.: 238210
Byron Cannon *(CFO)*
Charles Haskins Jr. *(Pres)*

HASKINS STEEL CO., INC.

3613 E Main Ave, Spokane, WA
99202
Tel.: (509) 535-0657
Web Site:
https://www.haskinssteelinc.com
Year Founded: 1955
Sales Range: $10-24.9 Million
Emp.: 100
Metal Service Center & Other Re-
lated Metal Whslr
N.A.I.C.S.: 423510

Roy Haskins *(Co-Founder)*
Connie Haskins *(Co-Founder)*

HASKO TRADING INC.

9830 Bell Ranch Dr Ste 101, Santa
Fe Springs, CA 90670
Tel.: (562) 903-2626
Web Site:
http://www.haskotrading.com
Year Founded: 2014
Sales Range: $1-9.9 Million
Emp.: 22
Fashion Apparel & Accessory Mfr
N.A.I.C.S.: 315990
Kaya Gokhan *(CEO)*

HASLAM'S BOOK STORE,
INC.

2025 Central Ave, Saint Petersburg,
FL 33713
Tel.: (727) 822-8616
Web Site: https://www.haslams.com
Year Founded: 1933
Sales Range: $1-9.9 Million
Emp.: 10
Book Store Owner & Operator
N.A.I.C.S.: 459210
Raymond V. Hinst Jr. *(Pres)*

HASLER & COMPANY INCOR-
PORATED

6119 Studelui Ave, Norfolk, VA 23508
Tel.: (757) 625-3641
Web Site: http://www.hasler-
group.com
Year Founded: 1911
Sales Range: $10-24.9 Million
Emp.: 4
Freight Transportation Services
N.A.I.C.S.: 488510
Carl D. Parker III *(Pres & CEO)*

HASLER OIL COMPANY IN-
CORPORATED

45 E Mechanic St, Bloomfield, IN
47424
Tel.: (812) 384-8063
Sales Range: $10-24.9 Million
Emp.: 25
Gas, Oil & Automotive Tires Whslr
N.A.I.C.S.: 441340
Joe Chipman *(Pres)*

HASSELL & HUGHES LUM-
BER COMPANY, INC.

608 Hwy 13 S, Collinwood, TN 38450
Tel.: (931) 724-9191
Web Site:
http://www.greenwaypellets.com
Year Founded: 1929
Sales Range: $10-24.9 Million
Emp.: 210
Sawmill Services
N.A.I.C.S.: 321113
Darwin Rich *(Mgr-Mill & Quality Con-
trol)*
Ralph M. Hughes Jr. *(CEO)*

HASSETT AIR EXPRESS

18W100 22nd St te 109, Oakbrook
Terrace, IL 60181
Tel.: (630) 530-6515   IL
Web Site:
http://www.hassettexpress.com
Year Founded: 1975
Sales Range: $25-49.9 Million
Emp.: 300
Scheduled Air Transportation Ser-
vices
N.A.I.C.S.: 481112
Frank Borta *(VP-Sls)*
Dennis Cartwright *(VP-Ops)*
Don Prentice *(VP-Customer Rels)*

Subsidiaries:

Hassett Air Express **(1)**
2444 Forrest Park Rd Ste B, Atlanta, GA
30315 **(100%)**
Tel.: (404) 366-1448
Web Site: http://www.hassettexpress.com
Sales Range: $10-24.9 Million
Emp.: 10
Scheduled Air Transportation
N.A.I.C.S.: 488510

HASSINGER COMPANIES

320 W NW Hwy, Arlington Heights, IL
60004-5411
Tel.: (847) 590-0100 DE
Year Founded: 1949
Sales Range: $75-99.9 Million
Emp.: 5
Provider of Land Development &
Residential Construction Services
N.A.I.C.S.: 236220
Norman M. Hassinger Jr. (Pres, CEO
& COO)

HASSLEN CONSTRUCTION COMPANY

45 1st St SE, Ortonville, MN 56278
Tel.: (320) 839-2529
Web Site:
http://www.hasslenconstruction.com
Sales Range: $10-24.9 Million
Emp.: 48
Commercial & Office Building Con-
tractors
N.A.I.C.S.: 236220
Brent Haaslen (Pres)

HASTINGS + COHN REAL ES-TATE, LLC

423 Elmwood Ave, Buffalo, NY
14222-2209
Tel.: (716) 886-3325
Web Site:
https://www.hastingscohn.com
Commercial Real Estate Brokerage
Firm
N.A.I.C.S.: 531390
Dorothy Bennett (Office Mgr)

Subsidiaries:

HUNT Commercial Real Estate
Corp. **(1)**
403 Main St Ste 730, Buffalo, NY 14203
Tel.: (716) 854-5943
Web Site: http://www.huntcommercial.com
Real Estate Agent/Manager
N.A.I.C.S.: 531210
Clarke Thrasher (Dir-Corp Svcs)

HASTINGS CO-OP CREAMERY COMPANY

1701 Vermillion St, Hastings, MN
55033-3164
Tel.: (651) 437-9414 MN
Web Site:
https://www.hastingscreamery.com
Year Founded: 1914
Sales Range: $75-99.9 Million
Emp.: 35
Processor of Fluid Milk & Retail Dairy
Products
N.A.I.C.S.: 311511

HASTINGS DESIGN CO

PO Box 8813, Roanoke, VA 24014
Tel.: (540) 808-2233
Web Site:
http://www.hastingsdesign.com
Sales Range: Less than $1 Million
Emp.: 1
N.A.I.C.S.: 541810
Mary Hastings (Owner)

HASTINGS EQUITY PART-NERS, LLC

Lyondellbasell Twr 1221 McKinney St

Ste 3650, Needham, MA 77010
Tel.: (281) 407-4845 DE
Web Site:
http://www.hastingsequity.com
Year Founded: 2003
Investment Firm
N.A.I.C.S.: 523999
Ted Patton (CEO & Mng Dir)
Tanner Moran (Mng Dir-Bus Dev)
Katrina Starr-Frederick (CFO)
Chris Martin (VP)
Randy McMullen (Operating Partner)
Lauren Roberge (VP)
Marco Rodriguez (VP)
Joe Colon (Mng Dir)

Subsidiaries:

Celerity Consulting Group, Inc. **(1)**
2 Gough St Ste 300, San Francisco, CA
94103
Tel.: (415) 986-8850
Sales Range: $10-24.9 Million
Emp.: 35
Management Consulting Services
N.A.I.C.S.: 541618

Gridsource, Inc. **(1)**
8061 Pecue Ln, Baton Rouge, LA 70809
Tel.: (225) 752-2253
Web Site: http://www.cableworks.com
Rev.: $5,000,000
Emp.: 44
Wood Container & Pallet Mfr
N.A.I.C.S.: 321920

Subsidiary (Domestic):

Wise Connect, Inc. **(2)**
1117 Perimeter Ctr W Ste E306, Atlanta,
GA 30338
Tel.: (405) 708-6700
Web Site: http://www.wiseconnectinc.com
Engineeering Services
N.A.I.C.S.: 541330
Mickey Malkus (VP-Ops)

IMPACT! Chemical Technologies,
Inc. **(1)**
10501 E Hwy 80, Midland, TX 79702-7887
Tel.: (432) 458-3500
Web Site: http://www.impactchem.com
Chemical & Allied Products Merchant Whslr
N.A.I.C.S.: 424690
Brandon Martin (Pres)

Specialty Welding & Turnarounds
LLC **(1)**
40492 Cannon Rd, Gonzales, LA 70737
Tel.: (225) 644-1200
Web Site: https://www.swatservice.com
General Contracting Services
N.A.I.C.S.: 238290
Marcus Deal (CEO)

Subsidiary (Domestic):

Midwest Cooling Tower Services
Inc. **(2)**
8545 Hwy 105 N, Krotz Springs, LA 70750-
5215
Tel.: (337) 566-2233
Web Site: https://www.mwcts.com
Electrical Contractor
N.A.I.C.S.: 238210
Daniel Wiltz (Pres)

Subsidiary (Domestic):

Tower Performance, Inc. **(3)**
23 Vreeland Rd, Florham Park, NJ 07932
Tel.: (973) 966-1116
Web Site:
https://www.towerperformance.com
Sales Range: $1-9.9 Million
Emp.: 60
Cooling Towers Repair & Maintenance Ser-
vices
N.A.I.C.S.: 238990
Anthony Depalma (Pres)

HASTINGS TILE & BATH, INC.

711-8 Koehler Ave, Ronkonkoma, NY
11779
Tel.: (516) 379-3500 NY
Web Site:
https://www.hastingstilebath.com

Year Founded: 1944
Sales Range: $10-24.9 Million
Emp.: 60
Retailer of Ceramic Tiles & Bath Ac-
cessories
N.A.I.C.S.: 444180
Michael Homola (Pres & CEO)
Richard Kucera (CFO, Treas & Sec)

HATCH & BAILEY COMPANY

1 Meadow St Ext, Norwalk, CT 06854
Tel.: (203) 866-5515 CT
Web Site:
http://www.hatchandbailey.com
Year Founded: 1872
Sales Range: $25-49.9 Million
Emp.: 40
Supplier of Doors, Windows & Build-
ing Materials
N.A.I.C.S.: 423310
David Carpenter (Controller)

HATCH & KIRK, INC.

5111 Leary Ave NW, Seattle, WA
98107-4820
Tel.: (206) 783-2766 WA
Web Site: http://www.hatchkirk.com
Year Founded: 1947
Sales Range: $50-74.9 Million
Emp.: 365
Industrial Machinery & Equipment
Distr
N.A.I.C.S.: 423830
Michael Korotkin (Pres & CEO)
Martin Warfield (Mgr-Marine Diesel
Fuel Injection Shop)

Subsidiaries:

H.K. Castings, Inc. **(1)**
384 US Hwy 19 S, Weston, WV 26452-
9701
Tel.: (304) 269-7809
Sales Range: $10-24.9 Million
Emp.: 30
Metals Processing Services
N.A.I.C.S.: 423510

HATCH STAMPING COMPANY INC.

635 E Industrial Dr, Chelsea, MI
48118-1538
Tel.: (734) 475-8628 MI
Web Site:
https://www.hatchstamping.com
Year Founded: 1989
Sales Range: $200-249.9 Million
Emp.: 300
Automotive Stampings
N.A.I.C.S.: 336370
Ronald Hatch (CEO)
Chris Parrott (CFO & Exec VP)
Dan Craig (Pres & COO)
Todd Fyall (VP-Sls)
Steve Emmert (Mgr-Sls)

HATCHER CHEVROLET BUICK PONTIAC OLDS GMC INC.

2300 N Washington St, Brownsville,
TN 38012
Tel.: (731) 772-9082
Web Site: http://www.hatcher.com
Year Founded: 1986
Sales Range: $10-24.9 Million
Emp.: 35
New Car Whslr
N.A.I.C.S.: 441110
James D. Hatcher (Pres)
Beverly F. Hatcher (Treas & Sec)
Pat Moore (Office Mgr)

HATCHER CONSTRUCTION SERVICES LLC

2601 E Hwy 37, Tuttle, OK 73089
Tel.: (405) 381-9478
Web Site: http://www.hatcherconstruc
tionservices.com

Sales Range: $25-49.9 Million
Emp.: 25
Nonresidential Construction
N.A.I.C.S.: 236220

HATCO CORPORATION

635 S 28th St, Milwaukee, WI 53215
Tel.: (414) 671-6350
Web Site: https://www.hatcocorp.com
Sales Range: $10-24.9 Million
Emp.: 68
Commercial Cooking & Foodwarming
Equipment
N.A.I.C.S.: 333310
David Rolston (Pres & CEO)
Debra Kopczynski (Dir-Natl Accts)
Mike Whiteley (VP-Sls)
Gary Kramer (Mgr-Svc & Parts)

Subsidiaries:

American Range Corporation **(1)**
13592 Desmond St, Pacoima, CA 91331-
2315
Tel.: (818) 897-0808
Web Site: http://www.americanrange.com
Other Building Material Dealers
N.A.I.C.S.: 444180
Shane Demirjian (Founder & CEO)

Food Warming Equipment Co.,
Inc. **(1)**
7900 South Route 31, Crystal Lake, IL
60039
Tel.: (815) 459-7500
Web Site: http://www.fweco.com
Rev.: $6,666,666
Emp.: 80
Food Product Machinery Mfr
N.A.I.C.S.: 333241
Jonathan Vadnos (VP)
Linda Jackson (Mgr)
Mark Poultney (Dir-Sls)
Mathew Thomas (Mgr-Sls-Reg)
Richard Klemm (CEO & Chm)
Deron Lichte (Exec VP)

HATFIELD & COMPANY INC.

2475 Discovery Blvd, Rockwall, TX
75032
Tel.: (972) 285-0115 TX
Web Site:
http://www.hatfieldandcompany.com
Year Founded: 1958
Sales Range: $25-49.9 Million
Emp.: 73
Suppliers of Industrial Machinery &
Equipment
N.A.I.C.S.: 423830
Harvey Sparhawk (CIO)
George Boles (CFO)

HATHAWAY CONSTRUCTION COMPANY, INC.

5901-C Peachtree Dunwoody Rd Ste
125, Atlanta, GA 30328
Tel.: (770) 448-7047
Web Site:
http://www.hathawayconstruc
tion.com
Year Founded: 1990
Rev.: $150,600,000
Emp.: 39
Residential Construction
N.A.I.C.S.: 236116
James H. Booker III (Sr Project Mgr)
David S. Hathaway (CEO)
W. Michael Muggridge (COO)
Brandon Waters (VP-Ops)

HATHAWAY DEVELOPMENT CORP.

5901C Peachtree Dunwoody, Atlanta,
GA 30328
Tel.: (770) 448-7047
Web Site: http://www.hdcprop.com
Sales Range: $50-74.9 Million
Emp.: 18
Apartment Building Construction Ser-
vices
N.A.I.C.S.: 236117

Hathaway Development Corp.—(Continued)
Daniel Hathaway *(Pres)*
W. Michael Muggridge *(CEO)*
Tom Cook *(Project Mgr)*
Brandon Waters *(Project Mgr)*
Nick Hathaway *(Dir-Dev)*
Thomas Gunter *(Dir-Dev)*
Valorie Gutzman *(Controller)*

HATHAWAY DINWIDDIE CON-STRUCTION COMPANY
275 Battery St Ste 300, San Fran-cisco, CA 94111
Tel.: (415) 986-2718   CA
Web Site: http://www.hdcco.com
Year Founded: 1923
Sales Range: $300-349.9 Million
Emp.: 25
Commercial & Office Building Con-tract Services
N.A.I.C.S.: 236220
Greg Cosko *(Pres & CEO)*
Stephen McCoid *(Exec VP)*

HATHAWAY INC.
347 S Oak Ln, Waynesboro, VA 22980
Tel.: (540) 949-8285
Web Site:
   https://www.hathawaypaper.com
Year Founded: 1981
Rev.: $16,624,849
Emp.: 38
Paper & Paper Products Whslr
N.A.I.C.S.: 424130
Curtis Hathaway *(Founder)*
Curtis Hathaway Jr. *(VP)*

HATHAWAY LLC
4205 Atlas Ct, Bakersfield, CA 93308
Tel.: (661) 393-2004
Web Site:
   https://www.hathawayllc.com
Year Founded: 2001
Sales Range: $1-9.9 Million
Emp.: 15
Acquires, Optimizes & Develops Oil & Gas Properties
N.A.I.C.S.: 213112
Chad Hathaway *(Founder)*
Mark Yarlot *(Mgr-Geology)*

HATTERAS PRESS INC.
56 Park Rd, Tinton Falls, NJ 07724-9715
Tel.: (732) 223-9888
Web Site:
   http://www.hatteraspress.com
Sales Range: $10-24.9 Million
Emp.: 120
Commercial Sheet-Fed Printing Ser-vices
N.A.I.C.S.: 323111
Charles F. Duerr *(Pres)*
Richard Selby *(Mgr-Production)*
Mark Cordova *(Sr VP)*
Andrea Morciglio *(Mgr-Production)*

HATTON POINT, INC.
2955 Inca St Suite 1A, Denver, CO 80202
Tel.: (303) 232-3840
Web Site: http://www.hattonpoint.com
Year Founded: 2005
Sales Range: $10-24.9 Million
Emp.: 50
Custom Software Consultancy
N.A.I.C.S.: 513210
Jesse Hormachea *(Project Mgr)*
Denton Crofts *(CEO)*
Bartek Flejterski *(Engr-Software Dev)*
Ann Stary *(Dir-Programs)*

HAUENSTEIN & BURMEISTER, INC.
3000 Washington Ave N, Minneapo-lis, MN 55411
Tel.: (612) 721-5031   MN
Web Site: https://www.handbinc.com
Year Founded: 1923
Sales Range: $50-74.9 Million
Emp.: 40
Elevator Cabs & Construction Ser-vices Mfr
N.A.I.C.S.: 333921
Jashan Eison *(Pres)*

HAUG IMPLEMENT CO. INC.
3593 Hwy 12 E, Willmar, MN 56201
Tel.: (320) 235-8115
Web Site: http://www.haug.com
Sales Range: $10-24.9 Million
Emp.: 41
Agricultural Machinery & Equipment Whslr
N.A.I.C.S.: 423820
Paul Haug *(VP)*

HAULMARK INDUSTRIES INC.
14054 County Rd 4, Bristol, IN 46507
Tel.: (574) 825-5867   IN
Web Site: http://www.haulmark.com
Year Founded: 1977
Sales Range: $10-24.9 Million
Emp.: 100
Demountable Cargo Containers Mfr
N.A.I.C.S.: 336212
Tom Frey *(Pres)*
Matthew Krawczak *(Mgr-Reg Sls)*

HAUN WELDING SUPPLY INC.
5921 Court St Rd, Syracuse, NY 13206
Tel.: (315) 463-5241
Web Site:
   https://www.haunweldingsupply.com
Rev.: $23,100,000
Emp.: 72
Welding Supplies
N.A.I.C.S.: 423840

HAUSNER HARD - CHROME, INC.
670 Greenleaf Ave, Elk Grove Vil-lage, IL 60007
Tel.: (847) 439-6010
Web Site:
   https://www.hausnerinc.com
Year Founded: 1969
Sales Range: $10-24.9 Million
Emp.: 125
Electroplating & Coloring Services
N.A.I.C.S.: 332813
Dave Hausner *(CEO)*
Jeff Hausner *(Pres)*

HAVANA AUTO PARTS INC.
901 S Havana St, Aurora, CO 80012
Tel.: (303) 341-2611
Web Site:
   http://www.autopartsaurora.net
Sales Range: $10-24.9 Million
Emp.: 150
Automotive Supplies & Parts Whslr
N.A.I.C.S.: 423120
Frank Welsh *(Owner)*
Daryl Ryan *(Gen Mgr)*

HAVCO WOOD PRODUCTS LLC
3200 E Outer Rd, Scott City, MO 63780
Tel.: (573) 334-6024
Web Site: http://www.havcowp.com
Rev.: $75,000,000
Emp.: 300
Hardwood Flooring Mfr
N.A.I.C.S.: 321918
Bruce Bader *(Pres & CEO)*
Larry Wiggs *(VP-Sls & Svc)*
John Carr *(VP-Sls & Mktg)*

HAVEN BANCORP, MHC
621 Washington St, Hoboken, NJ 07030
Tel.: (201) 659-3600
Web Site:
   https://www.havenbank.com
Year Founded: 2010
Mutual Holding Company
N.A.I.C.S.: 551112
John H. Wessling III *(Pres & CEO)*

Subsidiaries:

Haven Bancorp, Inc.   (1)
621 Washington St, Hoboken, NJ 07030
Tel.: (201) 659-3600
Web Site: http://www.havenbank.com
Bank Holding Company
N.A.I.C.S.: 551111

Subsidiary (Domestic):

Haven Savings Bank   (2)
621 Washington St, Hoboken, NJ 07030   (100%)
Tel.: (201) 659-3600
Web Site:
   http://www.havensavingsbank.com
Rev.: $26,847,000
Assets: $696,610,000
Liabilities: $607,698,000
Net Worth: $88,912,000
Earnings: $3,469,000
Emp.: 81
Fiscal Year-end: 12/31/2012
State Savings Bank
N.A.I.C.S.: 522110
Mary Elizabeth Perry *(Branch Mgr)*
Carolyn Scalia *(Sr VP & Dir-Internal Audit)*

HAVEN FOR HOPE OF BEXAR COUNTY
1 Haven For Hope Way, San Antonio, TX 78207
Tel.: (210) 220-2100   TX
Web Site:
   https://www.havenforhope.org
Year Founded: 2006
Sales Range: $10-24.9 Million
Emp.: 128
Housing Assistance Services
N.A.I.C.S.: 624229
Jacqueline Bush *(Controller)*
Kenny Wilson *(Pres & CEO)*
Patti Radle *(Vice Chm)*
William E. Greehey *(Chm & Treas)*

HAVENCREST CAPITAL MAN-AGEMENT, LLC
2100 McKinney Ave Ste 1760, Dallas, TX 75201
Tel.: (214) 420-3492
Web Site: http://havencrest.com
Year Founded: 2017
Venture Capital & Private Equity
N.A.I.C.S.: 523999
Robert A. Kline *(Operating Partner)*
Christopher W. Kersey *(Founding Mng Partner)*

Subsidiaries:

ThermoTek, Inc.   (1)
1200 Lakeside Pkwy Ste 200 Bldg 2, Flower Mound, TX 75028
Tel.: (972) 242-3232
Web Site: http://www.thermotekusa.com
Surgical & Medical Instrument Mfr
N.A.I.C.S.: 339112
Sam McSpadden *(CEO)*
Robert Nickell *(Chm)*
Tony Quisenberry *(Vice Chm & Dir-Bus Dev)*

HAVENWOOD-HERITAGE HEIGHTS RETIREMENT COM-MUNITY
33 Christian Ave, Concord, NH 03301
Tel.: (603) 224-5364
Web Site: https://www.hhhinfo.com
Year Founded: 1967
Sales Range: $10-24.9 Million

Emp.: 325
Retirement Hotel Operation
N.A.I.C.S.: 531110
Michael A. Palmieri *(Pres & CEO)*

HAVERFORD SYSTEMS
152 Robbins Rd, Downingtown, PA 19335
Tel.: (610) 518-2200
Web Site: https://www.haverford.com
Sales Range: $10-24.9 Million
Emp.: 25
Business System Integrations
N.A.I.C.S.: 423410
Hugh Richards *(Pres)*
Joe Mulcahy *(Dir-Ops)*
Richard Rauch *(Mgr-Svc)*

HAVERLAND CARTER LIFE-STYLE GROUP
10701 Montgomery Blvd NE Ste F, Albuquerque, NM 87111
Tel.: (505) 291-3294   NM
Web Site:
   https://www.haverlandcarter.com
Year Founded: 2010
Sales Range: Less than $1 Million
Emp.: 364
Elder Care Services
N.A.I.C.S.: 624120
Linda Givens *(Exec Dir)*
E. DeAnn Eaton *(CEO)*
Lynne Carlberg *(Dir-HR)*
Dave Walbright *(Dir-Sls & Mktg)*
Chrissy Akes *(Dir-Admin Svcs)*
Andre Hawkins *(CFO)*
Ann M. Fick *(Chm)*
Dan Chavez *(Dir-Dev & Plant Ops)*
Pamela Schneider *(Treas, Sec & Dir-Integration)*
Shelly L. Fritz *(Vice Chm)*

Subsidiaries:

Sommerset Assisted Living Resi-dence LLC   (1)
1601 SW 119th St, Oklahoma City, OK 73170-4902
Tel.: (405) 691-9221
Web Site:
   http://www.sommersetassistedliving.com
Assisted Living Facilities
N.A.I.C.S.: 623812
Connie Flowers *(Dir-Sls & Mktg)*

HAVILAND ENTERPRISES INC.
421 Ann St NW, Grand Rapids, MI 49504-2019
Tel.: (616) 361-6691   MI
Web Site:
   https://www.havilandusa.com
Year Founded: 1934
Sales Range: $100-124.9 Million
Emp.: 220
Chemical Products for Home & In-dustry Mfr & Distr
N.A.I.C.S.: 325998
Graham Torr *(Mgr-Sls & Mktg)*
Bob Mastbergen *(Dir-Process Engrg)*
Arthur F. Harre III *(Chief Sls Officer & Exec VP)*

Subsidiaries:

Haviland Consumer Products, Inc.   (1)
421 Ann St NW, Grand Rapids, MI 49504-2019   (100%)
Tel.: (616) 361-6691
Web Site: http://www.haviland.com
Sales Range: $25-49.9 Million
Emp.: 160
Private Labels & Pool & Spa Chemicals
N.A.I.C.S.: 424690

Haviland Products Company   (1)
421 Ann St NW, Grand Rapids, MI 49504-2019   (100%)
Tel.: (616) 361-6691
Web Site: http://www.havilandusa.com
Distr of Bulk Industrial Chemical Mfr

N.A.I.C.S.: 424690
Benjamin Gaeth *(Mgr-Engrg)*
Christine Olmeda *(Engr-Chemical Process)*

HAVILL-SPOERL FORD LINCOLN, INC.
1642 Janesville Ave, Fort Atkinson, WI 53538
Tel.: (920) 568-4444
Web Site:
http://www.havillspoerlford.net
Year Founded: 1989
Sales Range: $10-24.9 Million
Emp.: 63
Car Whslr
N.A.I.C.S.: 441110
Drayl Spoerl *(Pres)*

HAVILL-SPOERL MOTOR SALES, LTD.
1121 S Main St, Jefferson, WI 53549
Tel.: (920) 674-7070
Web Site:
http://www.havillspoerlmotor.com
Sales Range: $10-24.9 Million
Emp.: 42
Car Whslr
N.A.I.C.S.: 441110
Chris Havill *(VP)*

HAVIS, INC.
75 Jacksonville Rd, Warminster, PA 18974
Tel.: (215) 957-0720
Web Site:
http://www.customers.havis.com
Year Founded: 1928
Vehicle Technical & Communication Equipment Mfr
N.A.I.C.S.: 334290
Joe Bernert *(CEO)*

Subsidiaries:

Vanner, Inc. **(1)**
4282 Reynolds Dr, Hilliard, OH 43026-1260
Tel.: (614) 771-2718
Web Site: http://www.vanner.com
Sales Range: $50-74.9 Million
Emp.: 55
Commercial Vehicle Power Conversion & Power Transformation Systems & Components Mfr
N.A.I.C.S.: 336320
Bruce Beegle *(VP-Sls & Mktg)*
Doug Adams *(Head-Bus Market Dept)*
Chrys McCoy *(Head-Gen Inquiry Dept)*
Chris Collet *(VP-Heavy Duty Bus & Bus Electrification Markets)*
Carl Postiglione *(Mgr-Bus Dev-Revolution Tech)*

HAWAII CARPENTERS VACATION & HOLIDAY FUND
200 N Vineyard Blvd Ste 100, Honolulu, HI 96817
Tel.: (808) 841-7575
Year Founded: 1972
Sales Range: $10-24.9 Million
Carpenter Vacation Fund Provider
N.A.I.C.S.: 813930
Paul Sasaki *(Sec)*
Gerard Sakamoto *(Co-Chm)*
Kyle Chock *(Co-Chm)*

HAWAII EMPLOYERS' MUTUAL INSURANCE COMPANY, INC.
1100 Alakea St Ste 1400, Honolulu, HI 96813
Tel.: (808) 524-3642
Web Site: http://www.hemic.com
Year Founded: 1996
Sales Range: $10-24.9 Million
Emp.: 70
Reinsurance Products & Services
N.A.I.C.S.: 524130
Martin J. Welch *(CEO)*
Jason Yoshimi *(Pres & CFO)*

Tammy Teixeira *(Sr VP-Bus Dev)*
Faye Bueno *(VP-Admin)*
Regina Harris *(VP-Underwriting)*
Paul Naso *(Gen Counsel)*
Barry K. Taniguchi *(Chm)*

HAWAII HEALTH CONNECTOR
201 Merchant St Ste 1810, Honolulu, HI 96813
Tel.: (808) 312-4400
Web Site:
http://www.hawaiihealthconnector.com
Year Founded: 2011
Sales Range: $25-49.9 Million
Emp.: 20
Online Health Insurance Services
N.A.I.C.S.: 524114
Clifford Alakai *(Chm)*

HAWAII LIFE
4614 Kilauea Ave Ste 206, Honolulu, HI 96816
Tel.: (808) 346-7413
Web Site: http://www.hawaiilife.com
Year Founded: 2008
Sales Range: $10-24.9 Million
Emp.: 140
Real Estate Brokerage
N.A.I.C.S.: 531210
Matt Beall *(Co-Owner, CEO & Principal)*
Kahea Zietz *(Co-Owner & VP)*
Rhonda Hay *(Dir-Operations)*
Beth Thoma Robinson *(Dir-Conservation & Legacy Lands-Big Island)*
Cherie Tsukamoto *(Dir-Coaching & Mentorship)*
Anthony Arnold *(Creative Dir)*
Brad Haeger *(Ops Dir-Technical)*
Debi Rickert *(Mgr-Transaction)*
Yoshiko Kerkau *(Mgr-Transaction)*
Tara Malchiodi *(Mgr-Transaction)*
Sara Keesler *(Controller)*
Errol Llantos *(Dir-Human Resources)*
Dan MacDonnell *(Mgr-Property-Maui)*
Chiyoshi Hansen *(Mgr-Property & Sls Rep-Oahu)*
Lisa Pegg *(Mgr-Reservations & Property-Big Island)*
Robinette Sherman *(Mgr-Property)*
Eric Rafter *(Mgr-Property-Kauai)*
Jolanta Valencia *(Mgr-Property)*
Alysha Toyama *(Controller-Rentals)*
Meredith Zietz *(Mgr-Property-Kauai)*
Lyra Bowers *(Mgr-Property-Kauai)*
Lynn Taylor *(Mgr-Property-Maui)*
Andrea Doe *(Mgr-Property-Oahu)*
Katie Vogler *(Mgr-Property-Oahu)*
River Knapp *(Mgr-Property-Kauai)*
Lejandra Sabdul *(Mgr-Property-Oahu)*

Subsidiaries:

Maui Estates International, LLC **(1)**
272 S Ulukoa Pl, Lahaina, HI 96761-1973
Tel.: (808) 250-1583
Web Site:
http://www.mauiestatesinternational.com
Professional, Scientific & Technical Services
N.A.I.C.S.: 541990
Shannon Owsley *(Office Mgr)*

HAWAII LIFE REAL ESTATE BROKERS
PO Box 356, Hanalei, HI 96714
Web Site: http://www.hawaiilife.com
Year Founded: 2008
Sales Range: $25-49.9 Million
Real Estate Development Services
N.A.I.C.S.: 531390
Brad Haeger *(Dir-Customer Svcs)*
Matt Beall *(Co-Owner, CEO & Principal)*
Winston Welborn *(Co-Founder, Co-Owner & Chief Design Officer)*

HAWAII MEDICAL SERVICE ASSOCIATION
818 Keeaumoku St, Honolulu, HI 96814
Tel.: (808) 948-6111
Web Site: https://www.hmsa.com
Year Founded: 1938
Sales Range: $10-24.9 Million
Emp.: 1,500
Direct Health & Medical Insurance Services
N.A.I.C.S.: 524114
Elisa Yadao *(Chief Comm & Community Engagement Officer & Sr VP)*
Michael A. Gold *(CEO)*
Mike Wong *(VP-HR)*
Eytan Abarbanel *(Mgr-Solutions Delivery)*
Karey Kapoi *(Dir-Neighbor Island)*
David R. Herndon *(Chief Member Svcs Officer & Exec VP)*
John T. Komeiji *(Vice Chm, Chief Admin Officer & Gen Counsel)*
Gina L. Marting *(CFO & Sr VP)*
Janna L. S. Nakagawa *(Chief Governance Officer, Chief Corp Svcs Officer & Exec VP)*
Mark M. Mugiishi *(Pres & CEO)*

HAWAII NATIONAL BANCSHARES, INC.
45 N King St, Honolulu, HI 96817
Tel.: (808) 528-7711
Web Site:
http://www.hawaiinational.com
Year Founded: 1986
Sales Range: $200-249.9 Million
Emp.: 200
Bank Holding Company
N.A.I.C.S.: 551111
Warren K. K. Luke *(Chm, Pres & CEO)*
Michael K. Kawamoto *(Exec VP & Sr Loan Administrator)*
Bryan Luke *(Exec VP-Corp Strategy & Svcs)*

Subsidiaries:

Hawaii National Bank **(1)**
45 N King St, Honolulu, HI 96817
Tel.: (808) 528-7755
Web Site: http://www.hawaiinational.bank
Emp.: 150
Retail & Commercial Banking
N.A.I.C.S.: 522180
Warren K. K. Luke *(Chm & CEO)*
Bryan Luke *(Pres & COO)*
Craig Bode *(Officer-Loan-Kahului)*
Ricky Ching *(CFO & Sr VP)*
Amy Tsuchiya *(Mgr-Hilo)*
Royce Fukuroku *(Officer-Loan-Kihei)*
Gerald Terasako *(VP)*
Derick Tam *(VP)*
Warren Watanabe *(Mgr-Residential Mortgage Sls)*

HAWAII PETROLEUM INC.
16 Railroad Ave Ste 202, Hilo, HI 96720
Tel.: (808) 935-6641
Web Site:
https://www.hawaiipetroleum.com
Sales Range: $25-49.9 Million
Emp.: 35
Petroleum Products Mfr
N.A.I.C.S.: 424720
Lloyd Leong *(Gen Mgr)*

HAWAII PLANING MILL LTD.
Shipman Industrial Park 16-166 Melekahiwa St, Keaau, HI 96749-8016
Tel.: (808) 966-5466
Web Site: http://www.hpmhawaii.com
Year Founded: 1921
Sales Range: $25-49.9 Million
Emp.: 275
Lumber & Plywood Services
N.A.I.C.S.: 423310

Robert Fujimoto *(Chm)*
Jason R. Fujimoto *(Pres & CEO)*

Subsidiaries:

Miyake Concrete Accessories, Inc. **(1)**
250 Waiehu Bch Rd Ste N, Wailuku, HI 96793
Tel.: (808) 244-7988
Web Site: http://www.miyakeconcrete.com
Rev.: $12,933,853
Emp.: 17
Concrete Building Products
N.A.I.C.S.: 423320
Jocelyn Kanohokula *(Mgr-Bonding Dept)*
Dennis Barut *(Mgr-Doors Dept)*
Wayne Fujimoto *(Mgr-Home Plng Dept)*
Elesio Arreola *(Mgr-Kihei Branch)*
Daryl Shigeta *(Mgr-Lahaina Branch)*

HAWAII PRINCE HOTEL WAIKIKI
100 Holomoana St, Honolulu, HI 96815
Tel.: (808) 956-1111
Web Site:
https://www.princeresortshawaii.com
Sales Range: $10-24.9 Million
Emp.: 440
Resort Hotel
N.A.I.C.S.: 721110
Donn J. Takahashi *(Pres)*
Linda Leung *(Dir-Sls-Asia Pacific)*
Jason Higashi *(Dir-Loss Prevention)*
Wade Gesteuyala *(Gen Mgr)*
Casey Collado *(Mgr-Conference Svcs)*

HAWAII TRANSFER CO. LTD.
94-1420 Moaniani St, Waipahu, HI 96797-4632
Tel.: (808) 677-3111
Web Site:
https://www.hawaiitransfer.com
Sales Range: $10-24.9 Million
Emp.: 167
Transportation Services
N.A.I.C.S.: 484110
Gordon Okumura *(Pres)*
Dave Kanda *(Asst VP)*

HAWAIIAN CEMENT
99 1300 Halawa Valley St, Aiea, HI 96701-3289
Tel.: (808) 532-3400
Web Site:
https://www.hawaiiancement.com
Year Founded: 1985
Sales Range: $25-49.9 Million
Emp.: 175
Mfr of Cement & Concrete
N.A.I.C.S.: 327310
John Delong *(Pres)*
Keoni DeRego *(Mgr-Quarry)*
Jack Almanza *(Gen Mgr)*
Jim Gomes *(Supvr-Ops)*
Edwin McCary *(Mgr-Concrete)*
Twight Ho *(Mgr-Sls-Cement Div Ops)*

HAWAIIAN COOL WATER, LLC
2002 Homerule St, Honolulu, HI 96819-2247
Tel.: (808) 847-4461
Web Site:
http://www.coffeesystemshawaii.com
Year Founded: 1968
Sales Range: $1-9.9 Million
Commercial Coffee-Break Supplies Sales & Services
N.A.I.C.S.: 445298
Paula Meehan *(Owner)*

HAWAIIAN EXPRESS SERVICE INC.
3623 Munster Ave, Hayward, CA 94545
Tel.: (510) 783-6100

Hawaiian Express Service Inc.—(Continued)

Web Site:
http://www.hawaiianexpressinc.com
Sales Range: $10-24.9 Million
Emp.: 12
Freight Forwarding
N.A.I.C.S.: 488510
Jeff Graham (Pres)
Kathy Manus (VP)

HAWAIIAN FRUIT SPECIAL-TIES LLC
2-2741 Kaumualii Hwy Ste C, Kalaheo, HI 96741-0637
Tel.: (808) 332-9333
Web Site: http://www.kukuibrand.com
Sales Range: Less than $1 Million
Emp.: 3
Mfr of Tropical Fruit Preserves, Syrups & Sauces
N.A.I.C.S.: 311421
Robert Gunther (Pres)

HAWAIIAN HOST INC.
500 Alakawa St Ste 111, Honolulu, HI 96817
Tel.: (808) 848-0500
Web Site:
http://www.hawaiianhost.com
Year Founded: 1927
Sales Range: $25-49.9 Million
Emp.: 110
Chocolate Candy
N.A.I.C.S.: 311351
Keith Sakamoto (Pres)
Darryl Miki (Mgr-Sls)
Terence Walsh (Mgr-Sls)
David Nguyen (Mgr-Logistics)
Dane Otani (Asst Mgr-Sls)
Verna Wong (VP-HR)

Subsidiaries:

Mauna Loa Macadamia Nut
Corporation   (1)
16 701 Macadamia Rd, Keaau, HI 96749
Tel.: (888) 628-6256
Web Site: http://www.maunaloa.com
Macadamia Nuts & Candy Producer
N.A.I.C.S.: 111335

HAWAIIAN ISLAND CRE-ATIONS
348 Hahani St, Kailua, HI 96734
Tel.: (808) 266-7201   HI
Web Site: https://www.hicsurf.com
Year Founded: 1972
Sales Range: $10-24.9 Million
Emp.: 75
Sports Apparel
N.A.I.C.S.: 458110
James Tsukayama (Exec VP)

HAWAIIAN ISLES ENTER-PRISES, INC.
2864 Mokumoa St, Honolulu, HI 96819-4402
Tel.: (808) 839-3255
Web Site:
http://www.hawaiianisles.com
Year Founded: 1981
Sales Range: $10-24.9 Million
Emp.: 100
Tobacco & Tobacco Products Mfr
N.A.I.C.S.: 424940
Michael Boulware (Pres)

HAWAIIAN MACADAMIA NUT ORCHARDS, L.P.
688 Kinoole St Ste 207, Hilo, HI 96720
Tel.: (303) 339-0500
Web Site: http://www.rholp.com
Year Founded: 1986
Rev.: $32,195,000
Assets: $69,472,000
Liabilities: $11,390,000

Net Worth: $58,082,000
Earnings: $1,187,000
Emp.: 83
Fiscal Year-end: 12/31/17
Macadamia Nuts Grower
N.A.I.C.S.: 111335
Bradford C. Nelson (CEO)

Subsidiaries:

Royal Hawaiian Resources, Inc.   (1)
13140 Coit Rd Ste 307, Dallas, TX 75240
Tel.: (972) 235-5100
Emp.: 1
Oil & Gas Exploration Services
N.A.I.C.S.: 213112

HAWAIIAN PACIFIC RESTAU-RANT GROUP, INC.
6600 Kalanianaole Hwy, Honolulu, HI 96825
Tel.: (808) 396-7697   HI
Web Site: http://www.royshawaii.com
Year Founded: 1988
Sales Range: $10-24.9 Million
Emp.: 115
Full-Service Restaurants Owner & Operator
N.A.I.C.S.: 722511
Roy Yamaguchi (Pres & CEO)

HAWAIIAN SPRINGS, LLC
1632 S King St Ste 201, Honolulu, HI 96826
Tel.: (808) 483-0520   DE
Web Site:
http://www.hawaiianspring.com
Sales Range: $150-199.9 Million
Bottled Water Mfr
N.A.I.C.S.: 312112
Tom VanDixhorn (Pres)

HAWAIIAN SUN PRODUCTS INC.
259 Sand Island Access Rd, Honolulu, HI 96819
Tel.: (808) 845-3211
Web Site:
https://www.hawaiiansunproducts.com
Rev.: $21,500,000
Emp.: 98
Fruit Juices Mfr & Distr
N.A.I.C.S.: 311421
Bert Okura (Pres)

HAWK AUTO GROUP
6100 W 95th St, Oak Lawn, IL 60453
Tel.: (708) 599-6000
Web Site: http://www.hawkauto.com
Sales Range: $10-24.9 Million
New & Used Car Dealerships Owner & Operator
N.A.I.C.S.: 441110
John Crane (Owner)

Subsidiaries:

Incipe, LLC   (1)
6100 W 95th St, Oak Lawn, IL 60453
Tel.: (708) 599-6000
Web Site: http://www.hawkford.com
New & Used Car Dealer
N.A.I.C.S.: 441110
Donald Boros (Gen Sls Mgr)
Mark Gorokhovsky (Gen Mgr)
Joseph Storti (Dir-Fin)

Phelia, LLC   (1)
8200 S Harlem Ave, Bridgeview, IL 60455
Tel.: (708) 594-6400
Web Site: http://www.hawkchevy.com
Emp.: 50
New & Used Car Dealer
N.A.I.C.S.: 441110
John Crane (Principal)
Arthur Wierzbicki (Gen Mgr)
Jorge Soria (Mgr-Sls-New Cars)

Sponte Sales, Inc.   (1)
7911 W Roosevelt Rd, Forest Park, IL 60130

Tel.: (708) 689-1394
Web Site:
http://www.hawkchryslerdodgejeep.com
New & Used Car Dealer
N.A.I.C.S.: 441110
John Crane (Pres)

HAWK MANAGEMENT & FI-NANCIAL SERVICES INC.
13451 Briar Dr Ste 200, Leawood, KS 66209-3426
Tel.: (913) 345-1300   KS
Year Founded: 1991
Sales Range: $75-99.9 Million
Emp.: 90
Financial & Management Services
N.A.I.C.S.: 541611
Richard C. Hawk (Pres & CEO)
Alden K. Shields (Sec)

Subsidiaries:

HRS Education Services, Inc.   (1)
13451 Briar Dr. Ste 200, Leawood, KS 66209
Tel.: (913) 345-1300
Sales Range: $25-49.9 Million
Emp.: 50
Hospitality Services
N.A.I.C.S.: 531120

HAWK RIDGE SYSTEMS, LLC
575 Clyde Ave Ste 420, Mountain View, CA 94043
Tel.: (510) 482-6110   CA
Web Site: https://hawkridgesys.com
Year Founded: 1996
3D Design, Manufacturing & 3D Printing Services
N.A.I.C.S.: 323111
Jon Toews (Dir-Product Sls)
Gabriel Rapisardo (Chief Revenue Officer)
Dale Ford (Pres & CEO)

HAWK STREET ACQUISITION CORPORATION
9545 Wilshire Blvd Ste 612, Beverly Hills, CA 90212
Tel.: (310) 888-1870   DE
Year Founded: 2016
Sales Range: Less than $1 Million
Investment Services
N.A.I.C.S.: 523999
Bardia Rahimzadeh (Pres, CFO & Sec)

HAWKE MEDIA, LLC
1640 5th St Ste 107, Santa Monica, CA 90403
Tel.: (310) 451-7295
Web Site:
http://www.hawkemedia.com
Year Founded: 2013
Sales Range: $1-9.9 Million
Emp.: 75
Advertising Services
N.A.I.C.S.: 541810
Erik Huberman (CEO)

Subsidiaries:

Leverage Marketing, LLC   (1)
2301 W Anderson Ln Ste 102-62, Austin, TX 78757
Tel.: (203) 270-6699
Web Site: https://www.theleverageway.com
Services Related to Advertising
N.A.I.C.S.: 541890
Lewis Talbert (Owner)

HAWKER ENERGY, INC.
326 S Pacific Coast Hwy Ste 102, Redondo Beach, CA 90277
Tel.: (310) 438-7997   NV
Year Founded: 2006
Sales Range: Less than $1 Million
Oil & Gas Exploration & Production Services
N.A.I.C.S.: 211120

Darren Katic (Pres, CEO & CFO)

HAWKES MOTORS
9393 W Fairview Ave, Boise, ID 83704
Tel.: (208) 322-4849
Web Site:
http://www.hawkesmotors.com
Sales Range: $10-24.9 Million
Emp.: 7
Automobiles, Used Cars Only
N.A.I.C.S.: 441120
Andrea Grieve (Owner)

HAWKEYE DISTRIBUTION INC.
620 Floyd Blvd, Sioux City, IA 51101
Tel.: (712) 277-4001
Web Site:
http://www.hawkeyedistribution.com
Sales Range: $25-49.9 Million
Emp.: 20
Lumber, Plywood & Millwork
N.A.I.C.S.: 423310
William Engelen (Pres)

HAWKEYE FOREST PROD-UCTS INC.
305 W Bannock St, Boise, ID 83702
Tel.: (208) 344-8865
Web Site:
http://www.hawkeyeforest.com
Sales Range: $10-24.9 Million
Emp.: 6
Hardwood Lumber
N.A.I.C.S.: 423310
John Hawkinson (Pres)
Jennifer Geiger (Office Mgr)

HAWKEYE PROPERTIES, INC.
320 N Halstead St Ste 280, Pasadena, CA 91107
Tel.: (626) 685-9300   CA
Year Founded: 2010
Sales Range: $10-24.9 Million
Property Management Services
N.A.I.C.S.: 531390
Brenda Miller (Dir-Acctg)
Jessica G. Ray (Gen Mgr)
Gary S. Wilfert (CFO)
Jamie Hall (Sec)
John C. Hall (Pres)
Joan C. Hall Jr. (Treas & VP)

HAWKEYE STEEL PRODUCTS, INC.
609 Main St, Houghton, IA 52631
Tel.: (319) 469-4141   DE
Web Site:
https://www.hawkeyesteel.com
Year Founded: 1920
Sales Range: $75-99.9 Million
Emp.: 60
Livestock Feeders & Waterers, Poultry Equipment, Grain Bins
N.A.I.C.S.: 333111
Marvin Bricker (Co-Pres)
Tom Wenstrand (Owner & Co-Pres)

Subsidiaries:

Brower Equipment   (1)
Hwy 16 W, Houghton, IA 52631   (100%)
Tel.: (319) 469-4141
Web Site: http://www.browerequip.com
Sales Range: $10-24.9 Million
Emp.: 30
Livestock & Poultry Feeders & Waterers
N.A.I.C.S.: 333111
Thomas Wenstrand (Pres)
Cynthia A. Wellman (VP-Sls)

Hawkeye Steel Products, Inc. - Pride of the Farm Division   (1)
609 Main St, Houghton, IA 52631
Tel.: (319) 469-4141
Web Site: http://www.prideofthefarm.com
Livestock Feeding Equipment Mfr
N.A.I.C.S.: 333111

Hawkeye Steel Products, Inc. - Span-Tech Division **(1)**
609 Main St, Houghton, IA 52631
Web Site: http://www.span-techbuildings.com
Fabric Building Component Mfr
N.A.I.C.S.: 332311

HAWKEYE, INC.
2828 Routh St Ste 200, Dallas, TX 75201
Tel.: (214) 749-0080
Web Site:
  http://www.hawkeyeww.com
Year Founded: 1999
Sales Range: $75-99.9 Million
Emp.: 334
Advertising Agencies
N.A.I.C.S.: 541810
John L. Tedstrom *(Mng Dir-Insight & Strategy)*
Greg Osenga *(Mng Dir-CRM)*
Steven G. Dapper *(Founder & Chm)*
Wes Wright *(Mng Dir-Digital)*
Megan Talbott *(Dir-Insight & Strategy)*
Cecil Bellon *(Dir-User Experience)*
Amanda Dempsey *(Dir-Sports & Experiential)*
Dan Kinsey *(Sr Project Mgr-Interactive)*
Robert Menditto *(Sr Mgr-Interactive Project)*
Adam Reed *(Dir-Creative)*
Matt Voltoline *(Dir-Sports & Experimental)*
Melinda Gladitsch *(Mng Dir-Client Svcs)*

Subsidiaries:

hawkeye **(1)**
325 Arlington Ave Ste 700, Charlotte, NC 28203
Tel.: (704) 344-7900
Sales Range: $10-24.9 Million
Emp.: 40
N.A.I.C.S.: 541810
Greg Osenga *(Mng Dir-Customer Rels Mgmt)*
Scott Grissinger *(VP-Info Svcs)*
Richard Beanland *(CEO)*
John Hill *(Mng Dir-Creative)*

hawkeye FFWD **(1)**
8310 S Valley Hwy Ste 175, Englewood, CO 80112
Tel.: (303) 768-0169
Sales Range: $25-49.9 Million
Emp.: 10
Direct Marketing
N.A.I.C.S.: 541860

HAWKINS ASSOCIATES INC.
Ste 104 909 NE Loop 410, San Antonio, TX 78209-1315
Tel.: (210) 349-9911
Web Site:
  http://www.hawkinspersonnel.com
Sales Range: $10-24.9 Million
Emp.: 1,500
Temporary Help Service
N.A.I.C.S.: 561320
Sally Hawkins *(Pres)*

HAWKINS CHEVROLET INC.
1244 Montour Blvd, Danville, PA 17821
Tel.: (570) 275-0710
Web Site:
  http://www.hawkinschevrolet.com
Year Founded: 1967
Sales Range: $10-24.9 Million
Car Dealer
N.A.I.C.S.: 441110
Douglas D. Hawkins *(VP)*
Jim Hawkins *(Pres)*
Josh Hawkins *(Gen Mgr)*
Bob Hunter *(Sls Mgr)*

HAWKINS CONSTRUCTION COMPANY
2516 Deer Park Blvd, Omaha, NE 68105
Tel.: (402) 342-1607
Web Site: https://www.hawkins1.com
Sales Range: $100-124.9 Million
Emp.: 250
Buildings, Runways, Highways, Bridges Construction
N.A.I.C.S.: 236220
Kim Hawkins *(Pres)*
Jim Gregory *(Exec VP)*
Chris Hawkins *(COO)*
Matt Miller *(CFO & Exec VP)*
Fred Hawkins Jr. *(CEO)*

HAWKINS CONSTRUCTION, INC.
1430 L&R Industrial Blvd, Tarpon Springs, FL 34689
Tel.: (727) 938-9719
Web Site:
  https://www.hawkinsnet.com
Year Founded: 1975
Sales Range: $75-99.9 Million
Emp.: 110
Commercial & Institutional Building Construction
N.A.I.C.S.: 236220
John McCaugherty *(Pres)*
Mike Beausir *(Exec VP)*
Earle Cooper *(Exec VP)*
Don Ondrejcak *(Exec VP)*
Todd Mullins *(Sr VP)*
R. J. Walker *(Dir-Bus Dev-North & Central Florida)*
Jean Snyder *(CFO)*
Dale E. Scott *(Dir-MKtg-South Florida)*
Miguel Leyva *(Principal & Exec VP)*
Aaron Leech *(Mgr-Preconstruction)*

HAWKINS COUNTY GAS UTILITY DISTRICT
202 Park Blvd, Rogersville, TN 37857
Tel.: (423) 272-8841
Web Site:
  http://www.hawkinscountygas.com
Year Founded: 1950
Rev.: $13,099,062
Emp.: 45
Natural Gas Distr
N.A.I.C.S.: 221210
Jeff Barrett *(Dir-Pur)*
Patrick Lund *(Gen Mgr)*
Reed Matney *(Vice Chm)*
Fred Montgomery *(Chm)*
Kay Wilson *(Accountant)*

HAWKINSON NISSAN, LLC.
5513 Miller Cir Dr, Matteson, IL 60433
Tel.: (708) 720-8900
Web Site:
  http://www.hawkinsonnissan.com
Year Founded: 1961
Sales Range: $10-24.9 Million
Emp.: 40
New Car Retailer
N.A.I.C.S.: 441110
Bob Hawkinson *(Co-Owner & Co-Partner)*
Jim Hawkinson *(Co-Owner & Co-Partner)*
Tim Curran *(Mgr)*
Randy Cowley *(Mgr-Sls)*
T. J. Blough *(Dir-Nissan & Kia Svc)*
Paul Hart *(Asst Mgr-Parts)*
Ben Hawkinson *(Mgr-Sls)*
Kevin Stoll *(Dir-Parts)*
Craig Walters *(Office Mgr)*
Joe Ward *(CFO)*
Kendall Gardner *(Mgr-Sls)*
Audrey Mendoza *(Mgr-Internet Sls)*
Melissa Cialdella *(Sec)*

HAWKSTONE ASSOCIATES, INC.
9171 Dry Fork Rd, Harrison, OH 45030
Tel.: (513) 367-9900
Web Site:
  https://www.triumphenergy.com
Petroleum Marketing
N.A.I.C.S.: 424710
Ron Wittekind *(Pres)*
Jason Wittekind *(COO)*

HAWLEY, LLC
1181 S Lake Dr, Lexington, SC 29073
Tel.: (803) 359-3492
Web Site: http://www.hawleyusa.com
Year Founded: 1964
Bicycle Parts Mfr
N.A.I.C.S.: 336991
Ed Barrett *(Pres)*

HAWORTH MARKETING & MEDIA COMPANY
45 S 7th St Ste 2400, Minneapolis, MN 55402
Tel.: (612) 677-8900   MN
Web Site:
  https://www.haworthmedia.com
Year Founded: 1970
Sales Range: $75-99.9 Million
Emp.: 140
Media Buying Services
N.A.I.C.S.: 541830
Bruce P. Gasperlin *(CFO & VP)*
Claudia Eggan *(Dir-Brdcst)*
Marie Rodman *(Dir-Brdcst)*
Marcie Durkot *(Dir-Grp Media)*
Andrea Luhtanen *(Pres)*
Gary Tobey *(Chm & CEO)*
Catherine Marchio *(Dir-HR & Ops)*
Chris Dennehy *(Sr VP & Dir-Grp Media)*
Scott Slater *(VP & Dir-Media)*

Subsidiaries:

Haworth Marketing & Media Company **(1)**
10940 Wilshire Blvd Ste 2050, Los Angeles, CA 90024-3941
Tel.: (310) 824-7777
Web Site: http://www.haworthmedia.com
Emp.: 6
Media Buying Services
N.A.I.C.S.: 541830
Gary Tobey *(Chm & CEO)*

HAWORTH, INC.
1 Haworth Ctr, Holland, MI 49423-9576
Tel.: (616) 393-3000   MI
Web Site: https://www.haworth.com
Year Founded: 1948
Emp.: 7,500
Office Furniture (except Wood) Manufacturing
N.A.I.C.S.: 337214
Franco Bianchi *(Pres & CEO)*
Mabel Casey *(VP-Global Mktg)*
Matthew Haworth *(Chm)*

Subsidiaries:

Haworth France **(1)**
Immeuble 6eme Sens 186 Avenue Thiers, 69006, Lyon, France **(100%)**
Tel.: (33) 478602050
Sales Range: $25-49.9 Million
Emp.: 250
Office Furniture Mfr
N.A.I.C.S.: 337214
Francois Broumais *(CEO)*

Haworth GmbH **(1)**
Am Deisterbahnhof 6, 31848, Bad Munder am Deister, Germany **(100%)**
Tel.: (49) 5042 5010
Web Site: http://www.haworth.de

Sales Range: $25-49.9 Million
Emp.: 500
Office Seating Mfr
N.A.I.C.S.: 337214
Hemming Siegel *(Mng Dir)*

Subsidiary (Domestic):

Haworth Buroeinrichtungen GmbH **(2)**
Am Deisterbahnhof 6, 31848, Bad Munder am Deister, Germany **(100%)**
Tel.: (49) 5042501220
Web Site: http://www.haworth.de
Sales Range: $100-124.9 Million
Office Furniture Mfr
N.A.I.C.S.: 337214

Haworth Hong Kong Ltd. **(1)**
30 Fl MLC Tower, 248 Queens Rd East, Wanchai, China (Hong Kong) **(100%)**
Tel.: (852) 25735628
Web Site: http://www.haworth-asia.com
Sales Range: $10-24.9 Million
Emp.: 30
Office Furniture Mfr
N.A.I.C.S.: 337211

Haworth Ltd. **(1)**
112-222 5 Ave SW, Calgary, T2P 0L1, AB, Canada
Tel.: (403) 203-6000
Web Site: http://www.haworth.com
Sales Range: $10-24.9 Million
Emp.: 8
Office Furniture Distr
N.A.I.C.S.: 423210

Haworth Portugal **(1)**
Estrada Consiglieri Pedroso 68 Apartado 15, 2746 955, Queluz, Portugal **(100%)**
Tel.: (351) 214345000
Web Site: http://www.haworth.pt
Sales Range: $25-49.9 Million
Emp.: 246
Wood & Metal Furniture Mfr
N.A.I.C.S.: 337214
Jose Amaral *(Gen Mgr)*

Haworth U.K. Ltd. **(1)**
150 St John Street, London, EC1V4UD, United Kingdom **(100%)**
Tel.: (44) 2073241360
Web Site: http://www.haworth-europe.com
Sales Range: $10-24.9 Million
Emp.: 50
Office Systems Mfr & Distr
N.A.I.C.S.: 337214
Martin Evetts *(Mng Dir)*

Janus Et Cie **(1)**
8687 Melrose Ave Ste B193, West Hollywood, CA 90069
Tel.: (800) 245-2687
Web Site: http://www.janusetcie.com
Furniture Merchant Whslr
N.A.I.C.S.: 423210
Gizelle Goyco *(Coord-Acct)*
Sarah Lubeck *(Dir-Studio Creative)*
Nancy Firment *(Mgr-Client Svcs)*
Marie Guerrero *(Supvr-Client Svcs)*

Poltrona Frau S.p.A. **(1)**
Via Sandro Pertini 22, 62029, Tolentino, Italy **(58.6%)**
Tel.: (39) 07339091
Web Site: http://www.poltronafrau.com
Sales Range: $350-399.9 Million
Emp.: 889
Furniture Mfr
N.A.I.C.S.: 337121

Subsidiary (Domestic):

Cassina S.p.A. **(2)**
Via Durini 16, 20122, Milan, Italy **(100%)**
Tel.: (39) 027 6020745
Web Site: http://www.cassina.it
Sales Range: $100-124.9 Million
Contemporary Furniture & Accessories Mfr & Distr
N.A.I.C.S.: 337121

HAWS CORPORATION
1455 Kleppe Ln, Sparks, NV 89431
Tel.: (775) 359-4712   CA
Web Site: https://www.hawsco.com
Year Founded: 1909
Sales Range: $75-99.9 Million

Haws Corporation—(Continued)

Emp.: 250
Emergency Equipment; Drinking Fountains; Water Coolers
N.A.I.C.S.: 332999
Tim Henderson (VP-Fin)
Scot McLean (Pres-Intl Bus)
Thomas White (CEO)
Claude Sapp (COO)
Stephanie Kilroy (Exec VP)

Subsidiaries:

Haws AG   (1)
Bachweg 3, 3401, Burgdorf, Switzerland   (100%)
Tel.: (41) 344206000
Web Site: http://www.haws.ch
Sales Range: $10-24.9 Million
Emp.: 20
Drinking Fountains; Water Coolers
N.A.I.C.S.: 333415
Urs Weder (Mng Dir)

Haws Avlis do Brasil   (1)
Av Senador Teotonio Vilela 505, Itu, SP, Brazil
Tel.: (55) 11 4813 9977
Web Site: http://www.avlisvalvulas.com.br
Water Dispensing Equipment Distr
N.A.I.C.S.: 423740

Haws Manufacturing Pte. Ltd.   (1)
5 Woodlands Terrace 03-01, Singapore, 738430, Singapore
Tel.: (65) 65869180
Web Site: http://www.haws.sg
Sales Range: $10-24.9 Million
Emp.: 8
Medical Equipment Mfr
N.A.I.C.S.: 339115

HAWTHORNE AUTOMOBILE SALES CO.
1180 Goffle Rd, Hawthorne, NJ 07506
Tel.: (973) 427-1560
Web Site:
http://www.hawthornechevrolert.com
Sales Range: $10-24.9 Million
Emp.: 100
New & Used Car Dealers
N.A.I.C.S.: 441110
Steve Darna (CFO)
Debbie Smith (Controller)

HAWTHORNE DIRECT INC.
2280 W Tyler Avenue Ste 200, Fairfield, IA 52556-2604
Tel.: (641) 472-3800
Web Site:
http://www.hawthornedirect.com
Year Founded: 1986
Rev.: $103,000,000
Emp.: 75
Broadcast, Direct Marketing, Infomercials
N.A.I.C.S.: 711310
Timothy R. Hawthorne (Founder)
Mark Ratner (VP-Acct Svcs)
Eugene Silverman (VP-Mktg Svcs & Acct Mgmt)
Mary Papp (VP-Media Acct Mgmt & Acct Dir)
Jessica Hawthorne-Castro (CEO)
Kathi Moore (VP & Acct Dir)
George Leon (Sr VP-Media & Acct Mgmt)
John Pucci (Chief Mktg & Creative Officer)
Karla Crawford Kerr (Dir-Bus Dev & Corp Rels)
Steve Jurgensen (Dir-Fin & Ops)
Steve Kelly (VP-Data Science)

HAWTHORNE MACHINERY COMPANY
16945 Camino San Bernardo, San Diego, CA 92127
Tel.: (858) 674-7000   **CA**

Web Site:
http://www.hawthornecat.com
Year Founded: 1956
Heavy Equipment & Machinery Distr
N.A.I.C.S.: 423830
Paul Kessel (Sls Mgr-Corp Product Support)
Tina Ly (Mgr-Corp Credit)
Diana Faumuina (Mgr-Accts Payable)
Larry Boardman (Gen Mgr-Svc)
Dan Stone (Mgr-Parts)
Chad Johnson (Mgr-Field Svc)
David Ness (CEO)
Brian Verhoeven (CFO)
Ross Farmer (Mgr-Corp Machinery Sls & Rental)
Craig Baker (Ops Mgr-Sls)

Subsidiaries:

Hawthorne Power Systems   (1)
16945 Camino San Bernardo Bldg D, San Diego, CA 92127
Tel.: (858) 376-6800
Web Site: http://www.hawthornecat.com
Sales Range: $25-49.9 Million
Emp.: 40
Generators & Electrical Systems
N.A.I.C.S.: 333611
Kirk Fowkes (VP)

HAY ISLAND HOLDING CORPORATION
20 Thorndal Cir, Darien, CT 06820
Tel.: (203) 656-8000
Web Site: http://www.swishter.com
Sales Range: $25-49.9 Million
Emp.: 15
Holding Company
N.A.I.C.S.: 551112
Robert Britten (CFO)
William T. Ziegler (Chm & CEO)
Cynthia Z. Brighton (Pres & Treas)
Karl H. Ziegler (VP & Sec)

Subsidiaries:

Swisher International, Inc.   (1)
20 Thorndal Cir, Darien, CT 06820-5421
Tel.: (203) 656-8000
Web Site: http://www.swisher.com
Cigars & Smokeless Tobacco Mfr
N.A.I.C.S.: 312230
Cherie Boruff Lee (VP-Creative & Consumer Engagement)
Lou Caldropoli (COO)
John Haley (Sr VP-Sls & Mktg)
John J. Miller (Pres, Pres & CEO)

HAYDEN BUILDING MAINTENANCE CORP.
169 Western Hwy, West Nyack, NY 10994
Tel.: (845) 353-3400
Web Site: https://www.roofline.com
Sales Range: $10-24.9 Million
Emp.: 80
Roofing Contractors
N.A.I.C.S.: 238160
Michael McWeeney (Mgr-Warehouse)
Kevin Lyons (Pres-Slate Roofing Div)
Robert Hayden (VP)
Gregory P. Hayden (Founder & Pres)

HAYDEN HOMES INC.
7 The Pines Ct Ste A, Saint Louis, MO 63141-6076
Tel.: (314) 434-5820
Web Site:
http://www.haydenhomes.com
Year Founded: 1977
Sales Range: $10-24.9 Million
Emp.: 20
Builders & Developer of New Home Communities in the St. Louis Metropolitan Area
N.A.I.C.S.: 237210

Dennis Hayden (Pres)
Bob Peters (VP-Construction & Project Mgr)
Bev Sharamitaro (Mgr-Community-Sls)

HAYDOCY PONTIAC-GMC TRUCK INC.
3895 W Broad St, Columbus, OH 43228   **OH**
Tel.: (614) 279-8880
Web Site: http://www.haydocy.com
Year Founded: 1954
Sales Range: $25-49.9 Million
Emp.: 65
Sales of New & Used Automobiles
N.A.I.C.S.: 441110
Bob Park (Mgr-Sls)
Aaron Jones (Mgr-Fin)
Dan Lynch (Mgr-Used Car Sls)
Ed Gabel (Mgr-New Car Sls)
Chet Heim (Mgr-Parts)
Don Wright (Dir-Svc)

HAYDON BUILDING CORP.
4640 E Cotton Gin Loop, Phoenix, AZ 85040
Tel.: (602) 296-1496
Web Site: https://www.haydonbc.com
Rev.: $80,473,442
Emp.: 200
Industrial Buildings & Warehouses
N.A.I.C.S.: 236220
Gary Haydon (Owner)
Eddie Garcia (Mgr-IT)
Fritz Behrhorst (VP-Pre-Construction)

HAYES CHRYSLER PLYMOUTH, INC.
3115 Frontage Rd, Gainesville, GA 30504-8210
Tel.: (770) 535-2835
Sales Range: $25-49.9 Million
Emp.: 120
New Car Whslr
N.A.I.C.S.: 441110
Mike Stovall (Exec Mgr)

HAYES CITY CORPORATION
4906 Burleson Rd, Austin, TX 78744-1212
Tel.: (512) 444-1941   **TX**
Web Site: https://www.texconoil.com
Year Founded: 1939
Sales Range: $10-24.9 Million
Emp.: 30
Petroleum Products
N.A.I.C.S.: 424720
Tim Ramsey (CEO)
Joe Kohl (Gen Mgr-Wholesale)
Clay Johnson (Pres)

HAYES E-GOVERNMENT RESOURCES, INC.
2551 Welaunee Blvd, Tallahassee, FL 32308
Tel.: (850) 297-0551
Web Site: https://www.hcs.net
Rev.: $32,600,000
Emp.: 67
Computer System Design Services
N.A.I.C.S.: 541512
Marsha Pittman (Mgr-Pur)
Connie Williams (Mgr)
Danny Hayes (VP)
Ron Dulay (Bus Mgr)
Mary Jane Hayes (Mgr)

HAYES FORD - LINCOLN MERCURY
987 E Main St, Newport, VT 05855
Tel.: (802) 334-6587
Web Site: http://hayesford.com
Year Founded: 1971
Sales Range: $10-24.9 Million
Emp.: 36

Car Whslr
N.A.I.C.S.: 441110
Mark Hayes (VP)

HAYES LOCUMS LLC
6700 N Andrews Ave Ste 600, Fort Lauderdale, FL 33309
Web Site:
http://www.hayeslocums.com
Year Founded: 2012
Sales Range: $100-124.9 Million
Emp.: 500
Health Care Facility Services
N.A.I.C.S.: 621999
John Hayes (CEO)
Ryan Scharer (COO)
Amy Perry (CFO)
Karen Hayes (VP-Risk Mgmt)
Andy Mouser (VP-Sls)

HAYES MANAGEMENT CONSULTING
1320 Center St Ste 402, Newton Center, MA 02459
Tel.: (617) 559-0404
Web Site:
http://www.hayesmanagement.com
Year Founded: 1993
Rev.: $17,000,000
Emp.: 95
Computer System Design Services
N.A.I.C.S.: 541512
Andy Treanor (COO)
Tracy Welsh (VP-Vendor Platforms & IT Solutions)
Don Michaels (Sr VP)
John Cronin (Dir-IT Svcs)
George Andrew (VP-Software Solutions)
Peter J. Butler (Pres & CEO)
Shawn DeWane (Chief Revenue Officer)
Patty Griffin Kellicker (VP-Mktg & Comm)
Lorie Richardson (Dir-Acct Mgmt)
Anita Archer (Dir-Healthcare Regulatory Compliance)
Sondra Akrin (Dir-Revenue Cycle Transformation)
Nick Barnes (VP-Fin)
Jodi Narahara (VP-People Strategies)
Sharon Christoforakis (VP-Revenue Cycle Transformation)

HAYES PROPERTY MANAGEMENT CO.
4101 Turtle Creek Dr, Port Arthur, TX 77642-7002
Tel.: (409) 724-0089
Year Founded: 1933
Sales Range: $10-24.9 Million
Emp.: 11
Real Estate Brokerage Services
N.A.I.C.S.: 531210
Jeff Hayes (Principal)

HAYES PUMP, INC.
66 Old Powder Mill Rd, Concord, MA 01742
Tel.: (978) 986-4109
Web Site:
https://www.hayespump.com
Year Founded: 1898
Sales Range: $25-49.9 Million
Emp.: 80
Pumping Equipment Distr
N.A.I.C.S.: 423830
Eric W. Zadravec (Pres)

HAYES WELDING INC.
12522 Violet Rd, Adelanto, CA 92301
Tel.: (760) 246-4878
Web Site: http://www.valew.com
Sales Range: $25-49.9 Million
Emp.: 104
Welding Manufacture

N.A.I.C.S.: 811490
Roger Hayes *(CEO)*

HAYMAKER ACQUISITION CORP.
650 5th Ave FL 10, New York, NY 10019
Tel.: (212) 616-9600   DE
Year Founded: 2017
Rev.: $6,104,835
Assets: $336,985,369
Liabilities: $331,985,368
Net Worth: $5,000,001
Earnings: $397,028
Emp.: 3
Fiscal Year-end: 12/31/18
Investment Services
N.A.I.C.S.: 523999
Steven J. Heyer *(Chm & CEO)*
Christopher Bradley *(CFO)*

Subsidiaries:

Haymaker Acquisition Corp. II   **(1)**
650 Fifth Ave 10th Fl, New York, NY 10019
Tel.: (212) 616-9600
Special Purpose Acquisition Company
N.A.I.C.S.: 523999

Subsidiary (Non-US):

ARKO Holdings Ltd.   **(2)**
Shapir Street 7, Herzliya Pituach, Israel
Tel.: (972) 2748790
Rev.: $3,729,448,381
Assets: $1,812,738,796
Liabilities: $1,645,952,930
Net Worth: $166,785,866
Earnings: $73,613,749)
Fiscal Year-end: 12/31/2019
Holding Company
N.A.I.C.S.: 551112
Arie Kotler *(Chm, Pres & CEO)*
Don Bassell *(CFO)*

Subsidiary (US):

GPM Investments, LLC   **(3)**
8565 Magellan Pkwy Ste 400, Richmond, VA 23227-1172
Tel.: (804) 730-1568
Web Site: http://www.gpminvestments.com
Emp.: 4,200
Convenience Store Operator
N.A.I.C.S.: 445131
Mike Bloom *(Chief Mdsg & Mktg Officer & Exec VP)*
Ruth Ann Lilly *(VP-Mktg & Mdsg)*

Subsidiary (Domestic):

E.J. Pope & Son. Inc.   **(4)**
1092 N Breazeale Ave, Mount Olive, NC 28365-1106
Tel.: (919) 658-6566
Sales Range: $50-74.9 Million
Emp.: 585
Provider of Grocery & Gasoline Services
N.A.I.C.S.: 445131
E. J. Pope *(Pres & CEO)*
Eddie Guthrie *(Mgr)*
Tesa Dove *(Mgr)*

Empire Petroleum Partners, LLC   **(4)**
9055 Comprint Ct Ste 200, Gaithersburg, MD 20877
Tel.: (301) 921-9200
Web Site: http://www.empirepetroleum.com
Crude Petroleum & Natural Gas Extraction Services
N.A.I.C.S.: 211120
Travis E. Booth *(Gen Counsel)*
Nandit Gandhi *(Chm)*

Affiliate (Domestic):

Empire Petroleum Partners, LP   **(5)**
8350 N Central Expwy Ste M2185, Dallas, TX 75206
Tel.: (214) 750-9313
Oil & Gas Operations
N.A.I.C.S.: 213112
Henry J. Heithaus *(CEO)*
Jeffrey Goodwin *(COO)*
Travis E. Booth *(Gen Counsel, Sec & VP)*

Affiliate (Domestic):

GPM Petroleum LP   **(4)**
8565 Magellan Pkwy Ste 400, Richmond, VA 23227
Tel.: (804) 887-1980
Rev.: $1,011,672,000
Assets: $106,708,000
Liabilities: $87,265,000
Net Worth: $19,443,000
Earnings: $24,629,000
Fiscal Year-end: 12/31/2016
Petroleum Product Distr
N.A.I.C.S.: 424720
Arie Kotler *(Chm, Pres & CEO)*
Eyal Nuchamovitz *(Exec VP)*
Don Bassell *(CFO)*
Chris Giacobone *(COO)*
Maury Bricks *(Gen Counsel & Sec)*

Subsidiary (Domestic):

GPM Southeast, LLC   **(4)**
1410 Commonwealth Dr Ste 202, Wilmington, NC 28403
Tel.: (910) 395-5300
Web Site: http://www.gpmsoutheast.com
Convenience Store Operator
N.A.I.C.S.: 445131
Arie Kotler *(CEO)*

HAYMAN COMPANY
29100 Northwestern Hwy Ste 410, Southfield, MI 48034
Tel.: (248) 879-7777
Web Site: http://www.haymanco.com
Year Founded: 1965
Rev.: $12,600,000
Emp.: 127
Real Estate Managers
N.A.I.C.S.: 531210
Andrew E. Hayman *(Pres)*

HAYNEEDLE, INC.
9394 W Dodge Rd Ste 300, Omaha, NE 68114-3319
Web Site:
   http://www.hayneedleinc.com
Year Founded: 1999
Sales Range: $100-124.9 Million
Emp.: 369
Online Retailer
N.A.I.C.S.: 459999
Mark D. Hasebroock *(Co-Founder)*
Dana Coonce *(VP-HR)*
Don Raymond *(CFO)*
Rebecca Gray *(VP-Mdsg)*
Ryan Paulson *(VP-Tech)*
Jeremy Podliska *(VP-Mktg)*

HAYNES & BOONE LLP
2323 Victory Ave Ste 700, Dallas, TX 75219
Tel.: (214) 651-5000
Web Site:
   http://www.haynesboone.com
Year Founded: 1964
Sales Range: $250-299.9 Million
Emp.: 500
Law firm
N.A.I.C.S.: 541110
David W. O'Brien *(Partner)*
Jennifer T. Wisinski *(Partner-Merger & Acq)*
Chris Rogers *(Partner-Dallas)*
Thomas Kelton *(Partner)*
Jason P. Bloom *(Partner)*
Jackie Sarlo *(CMO)*
Kirsten Polyansky *(Partner)*
Kenya S. Woodruff *(Partner)*
Leann L. Chen *(Partner)*
Christina Marshall *(Partner-Merger & Acq Practice Grp)*
Scott Cunning *(Partner-Admin)*
John D. Fognani *(Partner)*
John W. Bateman *(Partner)*
Whitney Remily *(Partner)*
Neal M. Kaminsky *(Partner)*
Todd Cubbage *(Partner)*
Matthew L. Fry *(Partner)*

Gavin D. George *(Partner)*
Evan K. Hall *(Partner)*
Autumn D. Highsmith *(Partner)*
Monika Singh Sanford *(Partner)*
Adam H. Sencenbaugh *(Partner)*
Michael Threet *(Partner)*
Kristina L. Trauger *(Partner)*
Robert P. Ziemian *(Partner)*
Jennifer M. Lantz *(Partner)*
Keith N. Sambur *(Partner)*
Arthur A. Cohen *(Partner)*
Brian D. Barnard *(Partner)*
Dave Calabrese *(Partner)*
David A. Bell *(Partner)*
David Brack Bryant *(Partner)*
Deborah S. Coldwell *(Partner)*
Eli Columbus *(Partner)*
Matt Ferris *(Partner)*
Tom Ferns *(Partner)*
Nick Foss-Pedersen *(Partner)*
Tim Powers *(Mng Partner)*
Sakina Rasheed Foster *(Partner-Fin Practice Grp)*
Charles A. Beckham Jr. *(Partner)*
Thomas B. King *(Partner)*

HAYNES BROTHERS LUMBER CO. LTD. PARTNER
739 NW Broad St, Murfreesboro, TN 37129
Tel.: (615) 893-1515
Web Site:
   http://www.haynesbroslumber.com
Sales Range: $25-49.9 Million
Emp.: 125
Lumber & Other Building Materials
N.A.I.C.S.: 423310
Terry G. Haynes *(Partner)*
Larry Haynes *(Partner)*
Mike Sams *(Mgr-Installation & Warranty)*

HAYNES FURNITURE COMPANY INCORPORATED
5324 Virginia Beach Blvd, Virginia Beach, VA 23462-1828
Tel.: (757) 497-5833
Web Site:
   http://www.haynesfurniture.com
Year Founded: 1959
Sales Range: $50-74.9 Million
Emp.: 1,000
Home Furnishings
N.A.I.C.S.: 449110
Ellis J. Strelitz *(Pres & CEO)*
James Enochs *(Mgr-Store)*

Subsidiaries:

Haynes Furniture Company Inc.   **(1)**
5324 Virginia Beach Blvd, Virginia Beach, VA 23462-1828
Tel.: (757) 497-5833
Web Site: http://www.haynesfurniture.com
Sales Range: $100-124.9 Million
Provider of Advertising Services
N.A.I.C.S.: 541810

HAYNES MARKETING NETWORK, INC.
721-B Walnut St, Macon, GA 31201
Tel.: (478) 742-5266   GA
Web Site:
   http://www.haynesmarketing.com
Year Founded: 1976
Sales Range: Less than $1 Million
Emp.: 2
Automotive, Industrial
N.A.I.C.S.: 541810
Phil Haynes *(Pres)*
Amelia Haynes *(VP & Graphic Designer)*

HAYNES MECHANICAL SYSTEMS
R 5654 Greenwood Plz Blvd, Englewood, CO 80111

Tel.: (303) 779-0787
Web Site:
   http://www.haynesmechsys.com
Rev.: $13,000,000
Emp.: 120
Warm Air Heating & Air Conditioning
N.A.I.C.S.: 423730
Kraig Haynes *(Pres)*
Jon Donahue *(Mgr-Sls)*
Terry Koenig *(VP)*
Nick LaFortuna *(Gen Mgr-Phoenix)*
Grant Willemarck *(Gen Mgr-SoCo)*

HAYNES SECURITY INC.
1 New York Ave, Newark, NJ 07105
Tel.: (973) 817-8300
Web Site:
   http://www.haynessecurity.com
Sales Range: $25-49.9 Million
Emp.: 1,500
Security Guard Services
N.A.I.C.S.: 561612

HAYNES-EAGLIN-WATERS, LLP.
6448 E Highway 290 Ste D 10, Austin, TX 78723
Tel.: (512) 451-6600
Web Site: http://www.hewaustin.com
Year Founded: 1988
Sales Range: $10-24.9 Million
Emp.: 17
Commercial & Institutional Building Construction Services
N.A.I.C.S.: 236220
Cloteal Davis Haynes *(Owner)*
Kirk Waters *(Owner)*

HAYNIE INCORPORATED
8741 Mylander Ln # F, Towson, MD 21286-2102
Tel.: (410) 494-1133
Year Founded: 1975
Sales Range: $10-24.9 Million
Emp.: 14
Chemicals, Industrial & Heavy
N.A.I.C.S.: 424690

HAYS FOOD TOWN INC.
PO Box 550, Wynne, AR 72396
Tel.: (870) 238-2656
Sales Range: $25-49.9 Million
Emp.: 375
Grocery Stores, Chain
N.A.I.C.S.: 445110
Michael Jon King *(Pres & CEO)*
Jimmy Clark *(Mgr)*

Subsidiaries:

Hays Food Town   **(1)**
1018 Wall St, Jonesboro, AR 72401-3854
Tel.: (870) 935-9503
Web Site:
   http://www.hayssupermarkets.com
Sales Range: $25-49.9 Million
Emp.: 200
Provider of Grocery Services
N.A.I.C.S.: 445110

HAYS MEDICAL CENTER
2220 Canterbury Dr, Hays, KS 67601
Tel.: (785) 623-5000   KS
Web Site: https://www.haysmed.com
Year Founded: 1944
Sales Range: $200-249.9 Million
Emp.: 1,656
Health Care Srvices
N.A.I.C.S.: 622110
Larry Watts *(Chief Medical Officer)*
Bryce A. Young *(COO)*
D. Bruce Whittington *(VP-HR)*
George Harns *(CFO, CIO & Sr VP)*

HAYTER OIL COMPANY, INC.
253 Baileyton Rd, Greeneville, TN 37745
Tel.: (423) 639-7226

Hayter Oil Company, Inc.—(Continued)

Sales Range: $25-49.9 Million
Emp.: 20
Petroleum Bulk Stations
N.A.I.C.S.: 424710
Sonny W. Marsh (Owner)

HAYWOOD B. HYMAN JR. INC.
11670 Midlothian Tpke, Midlothian, VA 23113
Tel.: (804) 256-8373
Web Site:
　https://www.landroverrichmond.com
Sales Range: $75-99.9 Million
Emp.: 30
Automobiles, New & Used
N.A.I.C.S.: 441110
Ryland Craze (Controller)
Haywood B. Hyman Jr. (Pres)

HAYWOOD ELECTRIC MEMBERSHIP CORPORATION
376 Grindstone Rd, Waynesville, NC 28785
Tel.: (828) 452-2281
Web Site:
　https://www.haywoodemc.com
Year Founded: 1939
Rev.: $20,485,342
Emp.: 70
Electronic Services
N.A.I.C.S.: 221118
Tom Batchelor (Mgr-Ops & Engrg)
Steve Foster (Treas & Sec)

HAZEL'S HOT SHOT, INC.
1735 W Crosby Rd Ste 120, Carrollton, TX 75006-6625
Tel.: (972) 466-4626
Web Site:
　http://www.hazelshotshot.com
Used Household & Office Goods Moving
N.A.I.C.S.: 484210
Hazel Marshall (Owner)

HAZELDEN BETTY FORD FOUNDATION
15251 Pleasant Valley Rd, Center City, MN 55012
Tel.: (651) 213-4231　　MN
Web Site:
　https://www.hazeldenbettyford.org
Year Founded: 1949
Sales Range: $125-149.9 Million
Drug & Alcohol Abuse Rehabilitation Services Organization
N.A.I.C.S.: 813212
Susan Fox Gillis (Chm)
Mark G. Mishek (Pres & CEO)
James A. Blaha (CFO, Chief Admin Officer & VP)
John Driscoll (VP-Midwest Reg)
Nick Motu (VP-Mktg, Comm & Bus Dev)
William C. Moyers (VP-Pub Affairs & Community Rels)
Marvin D. Seppala (Chief Medical Officer)
Mark Sheets (Exec Dir-Plymouth & The Youth Continuum)
Valerie Slaymaker (VP-Education, Quality & Res)
Kevin Chandler (Dir-Legal Professionals Program)
Emily Piper (Exec Dir-Govt Rels & Contracting)
David Anderson (Dir-Bellevue)
Heidi Wallace (Exec Dir-Northwest)
Subsidiaries:

Hazelden　　　　　　　　　(1)
15251 Pleasant Vly Rd, Center City, MN 55012
Tel.: (651) 213-4200
Web Site: http://www.hazelden.org

Emp.: 100
Residential Drug & Alcohol Abuse Rehabilitation Facilities Operator
N.A.I.C.S.: 623220
Mark Mishek (Pres & CEO)
Sharon Birnbaum (Dir-HR)
James A. Blaha (CFO & VP-Fin & Admin)
Ann Bray (Gen Counsel & VP-Strategic Initiatives)
John Driscoll (Exec Dir-Adult Svcs-Center City)
Nick Moyu (Publr & VP-Mktg & Comm)
William C. Moyers (VP-Foundation Rels)
Jana Olslund (VP-Dev)
Marvin D. Seppala (Chief Medical Officer)
Valerie Slaymaker (Chief Academic Officer)

Subsidiary (Domestic):

Hazelden/New York　　　　　(2)
322 8th Ave 12th Fl, New York, NY, 10001,
Tel.: (212) 420-9520
Web Site: http://www.hazelden.org
Residential Drug & Alcohol Abuse Rehabilitation Facility Operator
N.A.I.C.S.: 623220
Sharon Birnbaum (Dir-HR)
Nick Motu (VP-Mktg & Comm)
Jana Olslund (VP-Dev)
Mark Sheets (Exec Dir-Reg & Recovery Svcs)
Mark Mishek (Pres & CEO)
James A. Blaha (CFO & VP-Fin & Admin)
Marvin D. Seppala (Chief Medical Officer)
William C. Moyers (VP-Foundation Rels)

The Betty Ford Center　　　　(1)
39000 Bob Hope Dr, Rancho Mirage, CA 92270
Tel.: (760) 773-4100
Web Site: http://www.hazeldenbettyford.org
Emp.: 370
Residential Drug & Alcohol Abuse Rehabilitation Facilities Operator
N.A.I.C.S.: 623220
Jerry Moe (VP & Dir-Natl Children's Programs)
Briar Geraci (VP-Compliance Office)
Desire Washington (Dir-Trng)
Michela Sands (Dir-Corp Bus Dev & Admissions)
Neil Lingle (Dir-Security)

HAZELNUT GROWERS OF OREGON
21260 Butteville Rd NE, Aurora, OR 97002
Tel.: (503) 648-4176
Web Site: https://www.hazelnut.com
Year Founded: 1983
Producer & Retailer of Assorted Nuts & Fruit Products
N.A.I.C.S.: 311911
Ryan Whitney (Mgr-Production Plng & Logistics)

HAZEN & SAWYER
498 7th Ave 11th Fl, New York, NY 10018-6798
Tel.: (212) 539-7000　　NY
Web Site:
　https://www.hazenandsawyer.com
Year Founded: 1951
Sales Range: $125-149.9 Million
Emp.: 700
Civil Engineering
N.A.I.C.S.: 541330
Michael Wang (VP)
Sue Melamud (Dir-Mktg)
Charlie Hawkin (Chm)
Roger Austin (VP-Denver & Mgr-Intermountain)

HAZEN MEMORIAL HOSPITAL ASSOCIATION
510 8th Ave NE, Hazen, ND 58545
Tel.: (701) 748-2225　　ND
Web Site:
　http://www.sakmedcenter.org
Year Founded: 1943
Sales Range: $10-24.9 Million
Emp.: 174
Health Care Srvices

N.A.I.C.S.: 622110
Renae Snyder (CFO)

HAZEN PAPER COMPANY
240 S Water St, Holyoke, MA 01040
Tel.: (413) 538-8204　　MA
Web Site: https://www.hazen.com
Year Founded: 1925
Sales Range: $100-124.9 Million
Emp.: 200
Decorative Packaging Materials & Specialty Papers Mfr
N.A.I.C.S.: 322220
John Hazen (Pres)

HAZLEHURST INVESTORS, INC.
22 S Tallahassee St, Hazlehurst, GA 31539
Tel.: (912) 375-4228　　GA
Web Site:
　https://www.bankofhazlehurst.com
Year Founded: 2002
Sales Range: $1-9.9 Million
Bank Holding Company
N.A.I.C.S.: 551111
Leonard H. Bateman (Pres)

Subsidiaries:

Bank of Hazlehurst　　　　　(1)
22 S Tallahassee St, Hazlehurst, GA 31539
Tel.: (912) 375-4228
Web Site: http://www.bankofhazlehurst.com
Commericial Banking
N.A.I.C.S.: 522110
Leonard H. Bateman (Pres)
Regina Barton (Sec-Loan)

HAZLETON STANDARD-SPEAKER INC.
21 N Wyoming St, Hazleton, PA 18201
Tel.: (570) 455-3636
Web Site:
　https://www.standardspeaker.com
Rev.: $12,200,000
Emp.: 125
Newspapers, Publishing & Printing
N.A.I.C.S.: 513110
John F. Tatton (Gen Mgr)

HAZMAT ENVIRONMENTAL GROUP, INC.
60 Commerce Dr, Buffalo, NY 14218-1040
Tel.: (716) 827-7200　　DE
Web Site:
　https://www.hazmatinc.com
Sales Range: $10-24.9 Million
Emp.: 257
Trucking Except Local
N.A.I.C.S.: 484121
Dennis Dintino (Pres)
Eric Hoxsie (CFO)
Ricky Wickham (Gen Mgr-Ops)
Jennifer Weremblewski (Dir-Bus Dev)
Lisa Lange (Asst Controller)
Ron McGrath (Mgr-Sls)
Vince Phillips (Mgr-Maintenance)

HAZMED INC.
1050 Connecticut Ave NW 10th Fl Ste 1000, Washington, DC 20036
Tel.: (202) 742-6521
Web Site: http://www.hazmed.com
Rev.: $4,000,000
Emp.: 60
Scientific & Technical Consulting Services
N.A.I.C.S.: 541690
Gregory A. Davis (Exec VP)
Jacqueline Sales (Pres)

HAZTEK, INC.
143 Medford-Mt Holly Rd, Medford, NJ 08055
Tel.: (609) 714-1003

Web Site: https://www.haztekinc.com
Year Founded: 1997
Sales Range: $1-9.9 Million
Emp.: 120
Occupational Health And Safety Consulting
N.A.I.C.S.: 541990
Bruce Henderson (Mng Partner)
Robin McNaughton-Buckingham (Office Mgr)

HB BOYS, LLC
2280 S Main St, Salt Lake City, UT 84115-2629
Tel.: (801) 486-6777
Year Founded: 1984
Sales Range: $50-74.9 Million
Emp.: 1,200
Managment Company
N.A.I.C.S.: 722513
Dave Williams (Pres)
Gary Moore (VP-Ops)

HB EQUITY PARTNERS, L.P.
420 Lexington Ave 24th Fl Ste 2446, New York, NY 10170
Tel.: (212) 980-5510　　DE
Web Site: http://www.hbequity.com
Privater Equity Firm
N.A.I.C.S.: 523999
Michael Bonnet (Partner)

HB MANAGEMENT GROUP, INC.
7100 Broadway Ste 6L, Denver, CO 80221
Tel.: (303) 428-1873
Web Site: https://www.hbmgmt.com
Year Founded: 2003
Manages Home Health Care Services
N.A.I.C.S.: 621610
Kathy Hughes (Chm, Co-Founder & CEO)
Brad Brandt (Pres)
Patrick Hughes (Co-Founder & Dir)
Rick LeForce (CFO)

HB MANAGEMENT LLC
1 Union Sq 600 University St Ste 2018, Seattle, WA 98101
Tel.: (206) 812-9129　　WA
Web Site:
　http://www.hbnorthwest.com
Real Estate Services
N.A.I.C.S.: 531210
Ed Hewson (Co-Founder & Principal Partner)
Jon Breiner (Co-Founder & Principal Partner)

HB&G BUILDING PRODUCTS, INC.
PO Box 589, Troy, AL 36081
Tel.: (334) 566-4133　　DE
Web Site:
　http://www.hbgcolumns.com
Sales Range: $25-49.9 Million
Emp.: 360
Millwork
N.A.I.C.S.: 321918
Nick Loflin (Plant Mgr)
Gabriel Anderson (Mgr-Pur)
Glenn Camp (Dir-HR)
Barbara Sitler (CIO)
Robert Lacey (Plant Mgr)

HBC ACQUISITION CORP.
3963 Maple Ave Ste 450, Dallas, TX 75219
Tel.: (214) 451-4640　　DE
Year Founded: 2011
Investment Services
N.A.I.C.S.: 523999
Katherine Winson (CFO)
James M. Hoak (Chm)
Peter S. Brodsky (Co-CEO)

Joseph Colonnetta *(Co-CEO)*
J. Hale Hoak *(Pres)*
Isaac W. Isom *(VP & Sec)*

HBD CONSTRUCTION, INC.
5517 Manchester Ave, Saint Louis,
MO 63110-1975
Tel.: (314) 781-8000
Web Site: http://www.hbdgc.com
Year Founded: 1922
Sales Range: $50-74.9 Million
Emp.: 125
General Contracting & Construction
Management Services
N.A.I.C.S.: 236220
Michael J. Perry *(Pres)*
Brian Kowert *(COO)*
Steve Meeks *(VP)*
Ken Kayes *(Project Mgr)*
Nathan Munie *(Engr-Pre-Construction)*

HBD INDUSTRIES, INC.
5200 Upper Metro Pl Ste 110, Dublin,
OH 43017
Tel.: (614) 526-7000   OH
Web Site:
https://www.hbdindustries.com
Year Founded: 1903
Sales Range: $400-449.9 Million
Emp.: 1,750
Automotive Hoses, Industrial & Air-
craft Hoses, Ducting & Industrial
Coated Fabrics, Belting, V-Belts,
Rubber Bands & Urethane Rolls
N.A.I.C.S.: 326220
Nelson K. Law *(Dir-Strategic Initia-
tives)*
David D. Cawthon *(Gen Mgr-
HBD/Thermoid, Inc.)*

Subsidiaries:

California Drop Forge, Inc.   (1)
1033 Alhambra Ave, Los Angeles, CA
90012
Tel.: (323) 221-1134
Web Site: http://www.californiadrop.com
Sales Range: $10-24.9 Million
Emp.: 100
Closed Die Forging Mfr
N.A.I.C.S.: 332111
Elvia Reynaga *(Mgr-HR)*
Minh Tang *(Mgr-Quality Assurance)*
Robert Galbraith *(Mgr-Safety-NDT Level III)*

Carolina Rubber Rolls   (1)
110 Thermoid Way, Salisbury, NC 28144
Tel.: (704) 636-0121
Web Site:
http://www.carolinarubberrolls.com
Sales Range: $10-24.9 Million
Emp.: 125
Rubber Roll Mfr
N.A.I.C.S.: 326299

HBD/Thermoid, Inc.   (1)
1301 W Sandusky Ave, Bellefontaine, OH
43311-1082
Tel.: (937) 593-5010
Web Site: http://www.thermoid.com
Sales Range: $25-49.9 Million
Emp.: 200
Industrial & Specialty Hose Mfr
N.A.I.C.S.: 332999

Hydro Carbide Inc.   (1)
4439 Rt 982 S, Latrobe, PA 15650
Tel.: (724) 539-9701
Web Site: http://www.hydrocarbide.com
Sales Range: $10-24.9 Million
Emp.: 80
Wear Parts
N.A.I.C.S.: 331511
Paul Kuhns *(Mgr-Pur)*

Plant (Domestic):

Hydro Carbide, Inc. - Gulfport
Facility   (2)
14115 Seaway Rd, Gulfport, MS 39503
Tel.: (228) 863-2245
Tungsten Carbide Powder Mfr
N.A.I.C.S.: 325180

Hydro Carbide, Inc. - Latrobe
Facility   (2)
4439 Route 982, Latrobe, PA 15650
Tel.: (724) 539-9701
Tungsten Carbide Powder Mfr
N.A.I.C.S.: 325180
Don Wright *(Asst Gen Mgr)*

Ohio Magnetics, Inc. - Stearns Mag-
netics Division   (1)
5400 Dunham Rd, Maple Heights, OH
44137-3687
Tel.: (216) 662-8484
Web Site: http://www.ohiomagnetics.com
Emp.: 35
Magnetic Separation Equipment Mfr
N.A.I.C.S.: 335999
Ken Richendollar *(Gen Mgr)*

Peerless Blowers   (1)
1 Madison Ave, Hot Springs, NC 28743-
0187
Tel.: (828) 622-7500
Web Site: http://www.peerlessblowers.com
Sales Range: $10-24.9 Million
Emp.: 37
Industrial Fans Mfr
N.A.I.C.S.: 333413
Mike Sprinkle *(Mgr-Sls)*

Peerless-Winsmith, Inc.   (1)
172 Eaton St, Springville, NY 14141
Tel.: (716) 592-9310
Web Site: http://www.winsmith.com
Speed Reducer Mfr
N.A.I.C.S.: 333612
David Duerr *(Engr-Mfg)*
Robert Holdsworth *(Mgr-Engrg)*
Steve Dunlap *(Mgr)*
Dennis Wolbert *(Controller)*

Subsidiary (Domestic):

Ohio Electric Motors Inc.   (2)
30 Paint Fork Rd, Barnardsville, NC 28709
Tel.: (828) 626-2901
Web Site:
http://www.ohioelectricmotors.com
Electric Motor Mfr
N.A.I.C.S.: 335312

Peerless Electric   (2)
1401 W Market St, Warren, OH 44485
Tel.: (330) 399-3651
Web Site: http://www.peerlesselectric.com
Electric Motor Mfr
N.A.I.C.S.: 335312

Perfection Gear, Inc.   (2)
9 N Bear Creek Rd, Asheville, NC 28806
Tel.: (828) 253-0000
Web Site: http://www.winsmith.com
Emp.: 30
Gear Mfr
N.A.I.C.S.: 333612
Carl Pietzsch *(Mgr-Territory-Eastern &
Western Canada)*

Powertec Industrial Motors   (2)
2606 Eden Ter, Rock Hill, SC 29730
Tel.: (803) 328-1888
Web Site: http://www.powertecmotors.com
Electric Motor Mfr
N.A.I.C.S.: 335312
James Shores *(Controller)*

HBE CORPORATION
11330 Olive Blvd, Saint Louis, MO
63141-7149
Tel.: (314) 567-9000   DE
Web Site: http://www.hbecorp.com
Year Founded: 1960
Sales Range: $650-699.9 Million
Emp.: 6,000
Design & Construction Services for
Hospitals, Medical Office Buildings &
Financial Facilities; Owner of Hotels
N.A.I.C.S.: 721110
Fred S. Kummer *(Founder & CEO)*
Stephen Dailey *(VP-Hospital Consult-
ing)*
Matthew T. Baldy *(Sr VP-West)*
Jeffrey Siwak *(Dir-Mktg)*

Subsidiaries:

HBE Adam's Rib   (1)

1094 Frost Creek Dr, Eagle, CO 81631
Tel.: (970) 328-2326
Web Site: http://www.forestcreek.com
Sales Range: $100-124.9 Million
Emp.: 40
Building Construction & Designing Services
N.A.I.C.S.: 721110
Fred S. Kummer *(Pres & CEO)*

Hospital Building & Equipment
Co.   (1)
11330 Olive Blvd, Saint Louis, MO
63141   (100%)
Tel.: (314) 567-9000
Web Site: http://www.hbecorp.com
Sales Range: $25-49.9 Million
Emp.: 200
Planning, Design, Engineering & Construc-
tion of Healthcare & Financial Facilities
N.A.I.C.S.: 237990

Hospital Designers, Inc.   (1)
11330 Olive St Rd, Saint Louis, MO 63124
Tel.: (314) 567-9000
Hospital Construction Services
N.A.I.C.S.: 236220

HBE LLP
7140 Stephanie Ln, Lincoln, NE
68542-3110
Tel.: (402) 423-4343
Web Site: https://hbecpa.com
Year Founded: 1974
Accounting & Management Advisory
Services
N.A.I.C.S.: 541211
Scott A. Becker *(Mng Partner)*
Lanelle E. Herink *(Partner)*
Michael J. Arens *(Mgr)*
Jennifer L. Doll *(Controller)*
Jacklyne Duggan *(Dir-IT)*
Allisa L. Lovitt *(Mgr-Mktg & Exec
Support)*
Cynthia R. Love *(Partner)*
Scott J. Scheef *(Mgr)*
Niki L. Stehlik *(Mgr)*
Grant W. Nuttelmann *(Mgr)*

Subsidiaries:

Fuhrman, Smolsky & Furey, Inc.   (1)
9802 Nicholas St Ste 395, Omaha, NE
68114-2168
Tel.: (402) 895-5050
Tax Preparation Services
N.A.I.C.S.: 541213

HBM HOLDINGS COMPANY
387 S Lindbergh Blvd Suite 160,
Saint Louis, MO 63127-1393
Tel.: (314) 543-6305
Web Site:
http://www.hbmholdings.com
Year Founded: 2012
Holding Company
N.A.I.C.S.: 551112
Donald Roberts *(CFO & Sr VP-Corp
Dev)*
Ryan Supple *(Dir-Deal Origination)*
Michael Chill *(VP-IT)*
Amy Fields *(Chief HR Officer & VP)*
Andrew Fulford *(VP-Corp Dev)*
C. Anderson Fincher *(CEO)*
Nathan Matt *(Controller)*

Subsidiaries:

Control Devices, LLC   (1)
1555 Larkin Williams Rd, Fenton, MO
63026
Tel.: (636) 660-7100
Web Site: http://www.cdivalve.com
Valves & Nozzles Mfr
N.A.I.C.S.: 332911
Emily Quinlan *(Mgr-HR)*
James Reuter *(CEO)*
Thomas Skelton *(Dir-Supply Chain-Global)*
Clark Pierce *(Mgr-Ops)*

Harper-Love Adhesives
Corporation   (1)
11101 Westlake Dr, Charlotte, NC 28273
Tel.: (704) 588-1350
Web Site: http://www.harperlove.com

Adhesive Mfr
N.A.I.C.S.: 325520
Alan Clark *(CEO)*
Thomas Evans *(CFO)*
Gates Gravely *(Dir-Sls & Mktg)*
Augusto Cavallini *(Reg Mgr)*
Tyler Haggard *(Reg Mgr)*
Don Wolfe *(Reg Mgr)*
Gary Rowland *(Reg Mgr)*
Rick Bird *(Ops Mgr)*

Mississippi Lime Company   (1)
3870 S Lindbergh Blvd Ste 200, Saint
Louis, MO 63127-1308
Tel.: (314) 543-6300
Web Site: http://www.mississippilime.com
Sales Range: $150-199.9 Million
Emp.: 500
Limestone Mining & Lime Mfr
N.A.I.C.S.: 327410
William A. Ayers *(Pres & CEO)*
Richard Perry *(Sls Mgr-Kansas City)*
Daniel Okenfuss *(Sls Mgr-Midwest)*
Terrence Zerr *(VP-Ops)*
Martin Gran *(Mgr-R&D)*
Tom McCoy *(Dir-Process Tech & Quality)*
David Venhaus *(VP-Sls & Mktg)*
Ted Frey *(Sls Mgr-Louisville)*
Joe Hatfield *(Dir-Pur)*
Michael Sheffield *(Gen Mgr)*
Ryan Seelke *(Dir-Safety)*

Subsidiary (Domestic):

Falco Lime Company   (2)
1543 Haining Rd, Vicksburg, MS 39183
Tel.: (601) 636-0932
Sales Range: $10-24.9 Million
Emp.: 65
Lime, Except Agricultural
N.A.I.C.S.: 327410
Mike Noble *(Plant Mgr)*

Division (Domestic):

Reagent and Technology
Services   (2)
1551 Cochrane Causeway, Mobile, AL
36602
Tel.: (314) 543-6300
Web Site:
http://www.reagenttechnologyservices.com
Coal Byproduct Mfr & Supplier
N.A.I.C.S.: 212312

Schafer Industries, Inc.   (1)
4701 Nimtz Pkwy, South Bend, IN 46628-
4116
Tel.: (574) 234-4116
Web Site: http://www.schaferindustries.com
Sales Range: $10-24.9 Million
Emp.: 350
Gears & Mechanized Parts Mfr
N.A.I.C.S.: 333612
Bipin Doshi *(Pres)*
Linda Doshi *(Sec)*
Ruth Cheek *(Asst Controller)*
Stan Blenke *(CFO & Exec VP)*
Paresh Shah *(Mgr-Ops)*
David Alley *(Mgr-Sls & Mktg)*
Matt McClain *(Controller)*
Georganna Geraghty *(Mgr-HR)*
Eric Van Rens *(CEO)*

Subsidiary (Domestic):

Schafer Driveline, LLC   (2)
6635 Taylor Rd, Blacklick, OH 43004
Tel.: (614) 864-1116
Web Site: http://www.schaferdriveline.com
Emp.: 25
Small Axles Mfr
N.A.I.C.S.: 332999
Christopher Whiteley *(Mgr-Quality Assur-
ance)*
Chuck Tate *(Gen Mgr)*

Schafer Gear Works Roscoe,
LLC   (2)
5466 E Rockton Rd, Roscoe, IL
61073   (100%)
Tel.: (815) 389-6065
Web Site: http://www.schafergear.com
Sales Range: $10-24.9 Million
Emp.: 39
Gear & Shaft Mfr
N.A.I.C.S.: 333612
Bipin Doshi *(Pres)*

HBP, INC.

HBP, Inc.—(Continued)

952 Frederick St, Hagerstown, MD 21740
Tel.: (301) 733-2000
Web Site: http://www.hbp.com
Printing Services
N.A.I.C.S.: 323113
John Snyder (Pres)

HBR CONSULTING LLC
311 S Wacker Dr Ste 2200, Chicago, IL 60606
Tel.: (312) 201-8400   **DE**
Web Site:
   http://www.hbrconsulting.com
Year Founded: 1991
Sales Range: $50-74.9 Million
Emp.: 300
Legal Industry Management Consulting Services
N.A.I.C.S.: 541611
Nicholas G. Quil (CEO)
Steve Falkin (Mng Dir)
Kevin P. McClean (Mng Dir)
Adam Stoklosa (Mng Dir)
Kevin Clem (Mng Dir)
Wafik Guirgis (Mng Dir)
Lauren Chung (Mng Dir)
Laurie Fischer (Mng Dir)
Lee Garbowitz (Mng Dir)
Kathryn Carr (CFO)
Lauryn Haake (Mng Dir)
Donna Terjesen (Mng Dir)
Matthew Gillis (VP-Product Solutions & Strategy)
Terry Coan (Mng Dir)
Evan Trent (COO)
Ken Kulawiak (VP-Info Security & Tech)
Andrew Baker (Sr Dir-Digital Svcs & Analytics Practices)

HBS SYSTEMS, INC.
275 W Campbell Rd Ste 500, Richardson, TX 75080
Tel.: (972) 234-4444
Web Site:
   http://www.hbssystems.com
Rev.: $12,800,000
Emp.: 45
Business Systems & Electronic Information Cataloging Services
N.A.I.C.S.: 423430
John Mathison (CFO)
Todd Stone (Mgr-R&D)
Scot Kirkegaard (Mgr-Trng & Education)
Lynn Reed (CTO)
Jeff Clark (Mgr-Sls-Reg)
Chad Stone (Pres & CEO)
Greg Bennett (Dir-Sls)

HC BRANDS
2021 Saint Augustine Rd E Ste 2, Jacksonville, FL 32207
Tel.: (904) 396-2291   **FL**
Web Site: https://www.hcbrands.com
Year Founded: 1954
Sales Range: $1-9.9 Million
Emp.: 17
Personalized Products Mfr
N.A.I.C.S.: 339940
Bryan Croft (Co-Owner & CEO)
Steven Fernandez (Co-Owner)

Subsidiaries:

Wallmonkeys, LLC   **(1)**
16021 Industrial Dr Ste 14, Gaithersburg, MD 20877
Tel.: (888) 369-9255
Web Site: http://www.wallmonkeys.com
Printing Services
N.A.I.C.S.: 323111

HC INTERNATIONAL

Graybar Bldg 420 Lexington Ave, New York, NY 10017
Tel.: (561) 245-5155
Web Site:
   http://www.hcinternational.net
Sales Range: Less than $1 Million
Emp.: 10
N.A.I.C.S.: 541810
Matthew Hayden (Pres)
John T. Mattio (Sr VP)
Scott Powell (VP-New York)
Ted Haberfield (Exec VP)

HC PRIVATE INVESTMENTS LLC
141 West Jackson Ste 1801, Chicago, IL 60604
Tel.: (312) 789-8492
Web Site:
   http://www.hcprivateinvest.com
Private Investment Firm
N.A.I.C.S.: 523999
John P. Kelly (Mng Partner)
Matthew J. Moran (Mng Partner)
Joseph Niciforo (Chm-Investment Committee)

Subsidiaries:

Kruger Plastic Products, LLC   **(1)**
2691 Mercantile Dr, Rancho Cordova, CA 95742
Tel.: (916) 853-0717
Web Site: http://www.springboardmfg.com
Plastics Product Mfr
N.A.I.C.S.: 326199
Doug Constable (CEO)

Prince Industries, LLC   **(1)**
745 N Gary Ave, Carol Stream, IL 60188
Tel.: (630) 588-0088
Web Site: https://www.princeind.com
Rev.: $1,400,000
Emp.: 22
Sheet Metal Work Mfg
N.A.I.C.S.: 332322
Nancy Miller (Pres)

Subsidiary (Domestic):

Bradford Machine Co   **(2)**
30 Bradford Dr, Brattleboro, VT 05301
Tel.: (802) 257-9253
Web Site: http://www.bradfordmachine.com
Rev.: $3,075,000
Emp.: 25
All Other Miscellaneous Fabricated Metal Product Mfr
N.A.I.C.S.: 332999

Precision Shapes, Inc.   **(2)**
8835 Grissom Pkwy, Titusville, FL 32780
Tel.: (321) 269-2555
Web Site: http://www.precisionshapes.net
Machine Shops
N.A.I.C.S.: 332710
Mark Johnson (Plant Mgr)
Aren Winebrenner (Engr-Quality)
Cheryl Cleveland (Co-Owner & VP)
Susan Palma (Co-Owner & Pres)

Vulcan Machine, Inc.   **(2)**
1217 Tech Blvd, Tampa, FL 33619
Tel.: (813) 664-0032
Web Site: http://www.vulcanmachine.com
Sales Range: $1-9.9 Million
Emp.: 29
Machine Shops
N.A.I.C.S.: 332710
Debbie Slavens (Office Mgr)
Mick Augustin (Engr-Mfg)
Jim Williams (Gen Mgr)

HC&B HEALTHCARE COMMUNICATIONS INC.
701 Brazos St Ste 1100, Austin, TX 78701-3232
Tel.: (512) 320-8511
Year Founded: 2001
Emp.: 20
Advetising Agency
N.A.I.C.S.: 541810
Kerry Hilton (Pres & CEO)
Nancy Beesley (Exec Vice Pres-Acct Svcs)

Lloyd Sheep (Sr VP & Chief Strategist)
Lori Lipscomb (Controller)
Erica Stevenson (Acct Exec)
Amy Smith (Acct Dir-Clinical Div)
Sarah Drake (Sr Acct Exec)
Mandy Buhler (Media Dir)
Darren Fuller (Acct Supvr)
Micheal Dumigan (Mng Dir)
Jessica Worrell (Art Dir)
Joe Doyle (Dir-Interactive Svcs)
Kim Carpenter (Acct Dir)
David Walker (Creative Dir)
Tina Ho (Art Dir)
Amy Chase (Project Mgr-Interactive)
Christina Folger (Project Mgr-Interactive)
Meg Swallow (Sr Acct Exec)
Susan Dore (Mgr-Print Production)
Marcus Rice (Project Mgr-Interactive)
Mark Gillmore (Copywriter)
Michele Evans (Designer)

Subsidiaries:

HCB Health Chicago   **(1)**
205 N Michigan Ave Ste 2315, Chicago, IL 60601
Tel.: (312) 645-0100
Web Site: http://www.hcbhealth.com
Medical Marketing Communication Services
N.A.I.C.S.: 541810
Kelly Staunton (Art Dir & Supvr-Creative)
Nancy Beesley (Pres)
Amy Dowell (Mng Dir)
James Hamilton (Creative Dir)
Amy Hansen (Exec Creative Dir)
Kim Carpenter (Mng Dir)
Michele Evans (Creative Dir)
Colin Foster (Chief Digital Officer)
Francesco Lucarelli (Exec VP-BioPharma Div)

HCAP PARTNERS, LLC
3636 Nobel Dr Ste 401, San Diego, CA 92122-1042
Tel.: (858) 259-7654   **DE**
Web Site: http://www.hcapllc.com
Year Founded: 2000
Holding Company
N.A.I.C.S.: 551112
Tim Bubnack (Mng Partner)
Frank Mora (Partner)
Hope Mago (Principal)
Bhairvee Shavdia (Principal)
George Gonczar (Dir-Climate Risk)
Rebecca Karason (Dir-Environmental Strategy & Sustainability)
Steve Steinour (Chm, Pres & CEO)

HCC SURETY GROUP
601 S Figueroa St Ste1600, Los Angeles, CA 90017
Tel.: (310) 649-0990
Web Site: http://www.hccsurety.com
Sales Range: $10-24.9 Million
Emp.: 170
Insurance Agents Brokers & Service
N.A.I.C.S.: 524126
Adam S. Pessin (Pres)
Kaz Yasui (CIO)
James Hoyas (VP & Dir-Atlanta)

HCC, INC.
1501 First Ave, Mendota, IL 61342-0952
Tel.: (815) 539-9371   **IL**
Web Site:
   http://www.hccincorporated.com
Year Founded: 1946
Sales Range: $250-299.9 Million
Emp.: 150
Agricultural Combine Components Mfr
N.A.I.C.S.: 333111

Subsidiaries:

Shaver Manufacturing Company **(1)**

103 S Washington Ave, Graettinger, IA 51342
Tel.: (712) 859-3293
Web Site: http://www.shavermfg.com
Sales Range: $75-99.9 Million
Emp.: 16
Feeding Equipment Mfr
N.A.I.C.S.: 333111
Terry Roberts (Gen Mgr)
Jodi Elbert (Mgr-Shipping)

Triple C, Inc.   **(1)**
902 Hwy K246, Sabetha, KS 66534
Tel.: (785) 284-3674
Web Site: http://www.triple-c-inc.com
Cattle Management Equipment Mfr
N.A.I.C.S.: 333111

HCG ENERGY CORPORATION
13619 Inwood Rd Ste 360, Dallas, TX 75244
Tel.: (972) 404-9386
Sales Range: $10-24.9 Million
Emp.: 50
Crude Petroleum Production
N.A.I.C.S.: 211120

HCG TECHNOLOGIES INC.
2400 Ctr Park W Dr Ste 100, West Palm Beach, FL 33409
Tel.: (561) 840-1800
Web Site:
   http://www.svmicrowave.com
Sales Range: $10-24.9 Million
Emp.: 150
Holding Company: Microwave Components
N.A.I.C.S.: 551112
C. J. Janney (Controller)

HCI CARE SERVICES
3000 Easton Boulevard, Des Moines, IA 50317
Tel.: (515) 274-3400   **IA**
Web Site:
   http://www.hospiceofcentraliowa.org
Year Founded: 1978
Sales Range: $10-24.9 Million
Emp.: 313
Health Care Srvices
N.A.I.C.S.: 622110
Tom Mouser (Chief Medical Officer)
Kelly Dennis (CFO)
Tray Wade (Pres & CEO)
Nicole Kock (Coord-Volunteer-Knoxville)

HCI CHEMTEC, INC.
310 S Bellis St, Wausau, WI 54403-6333
Tel.: (715) 845-7221
Web Site: http://www.hciinfo.com
Sales Range: $1-9.9 Million
Emp.: 20
Paints & Allied Products
N.A.I.C.S.: 325510
Darryl Cielinski (Pres)
Mike Zahn (Acct Mgr)
Brenda Cheyka (Mgr-Supply Chain)

HCI EQUITY MANAGEMENT, L.P.
1730 Pennsylvania Ave NW Ste 525, Washington, DC 20006
Tel.: (202) 371-0150   **DE**
Web Site: http://www.hciequity.com
Privater Equity Firm
N.A.I.C.S.: 523999
Daniel A. Rodrigues (Partner)
Doug McCormick (Mng Partner)
Scott Gibaratz (Mng Dir)
Daniel M. Dickinson (Mng Partner)
Dan Moorse (Mng Dir)
Carl Nelson (Mng Dir)
Kevin G. Cramton (Operating Partner)
Bob Hund (Operating Partner)

Subsidiaries:

AmerCareRoyal, LLC　　(1)
420 Clover Mill Rd, Exton, PA 19341
Web Site: http://www.amercareroyal.com
Sales Range: $1-9.9 Million
Disposable Products Mfr
N.A.I.C.S.: 322220
Scott Milberg (Pres)
Ty King (CEO)
Vince Mazzei (CFO)
Chip Oxendine (COO)

Subsidiary (Domestic):

Mat-Pac Inc.　　(2)
404 Candlewood Commons, Howell, NJ 07731
Tel.: (732) 364-8124
Web Site: http://www.matpac.com
Sales Range: $10-24.9 Million
Emp.: 4
Disposable Plates, Cups, Napkins & Eating Utensils
N.A.I.C.S.: 424130
Michael McGovern (Dir-Private Label Sls)

Subsidiary (Domestic):

Biltmore Trading Corporation　　(3)
404 Candlewood Commons, Howell, NJ 07731
Tel.: (732) 364-8124
Disposable Plates, Cups, Napkins & Eating Utensils
N.A.I.C.S.: 424130
Manny Jimenez (Pres & CEO)

CTW Transport Inc.　　(1)
10 Creek Brook Dr, Haverhill, MA 01960
Tel.: (978) 977-0081
Sales Range: $1-9.9 Million
Emp.: 16
General Freight Trucking, Long-Distance, Truckload
N.A.I.C.S.: 484121
Costas Flessas (Pres)

Commercial Foodservice Repair, Inc.　　(1)
410 E Washington St, Greenville, SC 29601-2158
Tel.: (864) 271-6522
Web Site: http://www.mytech24.com
Complete Services for Foodservice Equipment Sales
N.A.I.C.S.: 423840
Corey Harrison (Mgr-Natl Sls)
Dan Rodstrom (CEO)

Subsidiary (Domestic):

Foodservice Technologies, Inc.　　(2)
5256 Eisenhower Ave, Alexandria, VA 22304
Tel.: (703) 354-3835
Web Site: http://www.mytech24.com
Sales Range: $10-24.9 Million
Plumbing & Contracting Services
N.A.I.C.S.: 238990
J. C. Viteri (Mgr-Svc)
Rick White (Gen Mgr)

United Service Technologies, Inc.　　(2)
3164 E La Palma Ave Ste M, Anaheim, CA 92806-2811
Tel.: (714) 630-3569
Web Site: http://www.ustservice.com
Commercial Equipment Merchant Whslr
N.A.I.C.S.: 423440
Robert Heidkamp (Owner)

Herndon Products, Inc.　　(1)
3801 Lloyd King Dr, O'Fallon, MO 63368
Tel.: (314) 739-7400
Web Site: http://www.herndonproducts.com
Sales Range: $25-49.9 Million
Emp.: 100
Aircraft Electronic Component Distr
N.A.I.C.S.: 423860
Gerry Modglin (CFO)
Terry Huston (VP-Comml Sls)

Subsidiary (Domestic):

Intercoastal, Inc.　　(2)
22425 76th Ave S, Kent, WA 98032
Tel.: (253) 437-0300
Web Site: http://www.intercoastalonline.com

Emp.: 13
Aircraft Hardware Distr
N.A.I.C.S.: 423710
Craig Cadeell (Gen Mgr)

Highland Commercial Roofing　　(1)
5105 Heintz St, Baldwin Park, CA 91706
Tel.: (626) 856-2076
Web Site: http://www.highlandroof.com
Sales Range: $1-9.9 Million
Emp.: 30
Roofing Contractors
N.A.I.C.S.: 238160
Brett Maurer (CEO)
Adriel Sheridan (VP)
Rick Cunningham (Pres)

Subsidiary (Domestic):

Fidelity Roof Company　　(2)
1075 40th St, Emeryville, CA 94608-3691
Tel.: (510) 547-6330
Web Site: http://www.fidelityroof.com
Roofing Contractors
N.A.I.C.S.: 238160
Ken White (Pres)

JGB Enterprises Inc.　　(1)
115 Metropolitan Dr, Liverpool, NY 13088
Tel.: (315) 451-2770
Web Site: http://www.jgbhose.com
Sales Range: $125-149.9 Million
Emp.: 290
Rubber & Plastics Hose & Beltings
N.A.I.C.S.: 326220
Bob Doran (Mgr-Credit & Collections)
Janice Fetterly (Supvr-Accts Payable)
Martin Salanger (Dir-Military Sls)

Subsidiary (Domestic):

All Serv Industrial LLC.　　(2)
3221 Petro Dr, Sulphur, LA 70665
Tel.: (337) 882-5100
Web Site: http://www.allservindustrial.com
Sales Range: $1-9.9 Million
Emp.: 13
Synthetic Rubber Mfr
N.A.I.C.S.: 325212
Mike Kelley (Owner)
Jarid Johnson (Owner)
Nealon Marcantel (Owner)
Derest Thibodeaux (Owner)

K.P. McNamara Company, Inc.　　(1)
3972 Hamilton Ave, Cleveland, OH 44114
Tel.: (216) 361-8955
Web Site: http://www.kpmcnamara.com
Poly Container & Valve Mfr
N.A.I.C.S.: 332911
Kerry McNamara (Pres)

Subsidiary (Domestic):

K.P. McNamara of Georgia, Inc　　(2)
205 Lissner Ave, Savannah, GA 31408
Tel.: (800) 608-8587
Poly Container & Valve Mfr
N.A.I.C.S.: 332911

MSI Express, Inc.　　(1)
5900 Carlson Ave, Portage, IN 46368
Tel.: (219) 762-4636
Web Site: http://msiexpress.com
Packaging Services
N.A.I.C.S.: 561910
Charles Weinberg (CEO)

Subsidiary (Domestic):

Power Packaging, Inc.　　(2)
525 Dunham Rd, Saint Charles, IL 60174-1490
Tel.: (630) 377-3838
Web Site: http://www.powerpackaging.com
Rev.: $5,000,000
Emp.: 35
Contract Packaging
N.A.I.C.S.: 311423
Chuck Woods (Exec Dir)
Gordon Gruszka (Pres)

Naumann/Hobbs Material Handling, Inc.　　(1)
4335 E Wood St, Phoenix, AZ 85040-2045
Tel.: (602) 437-1331
Web Site: http://www.nhmh.com
Sales Range: $150-199.9 Million
Emp.: 350
Industrial Machinery & Equipment Rental & Whslr

N.A.I.C.S.: 423830
Rick Kwiatkowski (COO)
Steve Dountz (Gen Mgr-Sls)
Keith Jaeger (Mgr-Svc)

Subsidiary (Domestic):

Hawthorne Lift Systems　　(2)
1600 E Mission Rd, San Marcos, CA 92069
Tel.: (858) 207-2800
Web Site: http://www.hawthornelift.com
Sales Range: $25-49.9 Million
Emp.: 65
Lift Truck Sales & Rental
N.A.I.C.S.: 423830
Jim Venters (Gen Mgr)
Bryan Armstrong (Pres & CEO)

SouthernAG Carriers, Inc.　　(1)
3422 Sylvester Rd, Albany, GA 31703
Tel.: (229) 432-9696
Web Site: http://www.sou-ag.com
Truckload Transportation Services
N.A.I.C.S.: 488490
Henry H. Griffin (Chm & CEO)
Hugh H. Nall (Pres)
Todd Griffin (Dir-Ops)
Zane Smith (Mgr-Hull Div)
Brooke Johns (Dir-Admin & HR)

Strategic Delivery Solutions LLC　　(1)
136 Central Ave 2nd Fl, Clark, NJ 07066
Web Site: http://www.sds-rx.com
Delivery & Logistics Services
N.A.I.C.S.: 541614
Drew Kronick (Founder, Pres & Mng Partner)
Jeff Enck (VP-Ops)
Tom Stevenson (CFO)
Mike Ruccio (Exec VP-Customer Experience)

Subsidiary (Domestic):

Medical Delivery Services, Inc.　　(2)
5313 W Crenshaw St, Tampa, FL 33634-2406
Tel.: (813) 931-0107
Web Site:
　http://www.medicaldeliveryservicesinc.com
General Freight Trucking, Local
N.A.I.C.S.: 484110
D. Donovan Maclaszek (Mgr)

Suntron Corporation　　(1)
2401 W Grandview Rd, Phoenix, AZ 85023-3112
Tel.: (602) 282-5059
Web Site: http://www.suntroncorp.com
Sales Range: $300-349.9 Million
Electronic Manufacturing Services for Original Equipment Manufacturers; Joint Venture of Thayer Capital Partners L.P. & BLUM Capital Partners, L.P.
N.A.I.C.S.: 423690

Division (Domestic):

Suntron Gulf Coast Operations　　(2)
1113 Gillingham Ln, Sugar Land, TX 77478-2865
Tel.: (281) 243-5000
Web Site: http://www.suntroncorp.com
Sales Range: $25-49.9 Million
Electronics Mfr
N.A.I.C.S.: 334419

Suntron Northeast Express　　(2)
300 Griffin Brook Dr, Methuen, MA 01844-1873
Tel.: (603) 627-9556
Web Site: http://www.suntroncorp.com
Sales Range: $10-24.9 Million
Circuit Board Mfr
N.A.I.C.S.: 334412

Suntron Northeast Operations　　(2)
104 Glenn St, Lawrence, MA 01843-1022
Tel.: (978) 747-2000
Web Site: http://www.suntroncorp.com
Sales Range: Less than $1 Million
Emp.: 40
Printed Circuit Board Mfr
N.A.I.C.S.: 334412

Terra Drive Systems, Inc.　　(1)
9098 W 800 S, Brookston, IN 47923
Tel.: (219) 279-2801
Web Site: http://www.tdsdrive.com
Emp.: 100

Steerable Hydraulic Drive Systems Designer & Mfr
N.A.I.C.S.: 333996
Jeff Campbell (VP-Ops)
C. Phillip Joy (Pres & CEO)
Katie Kleinschnitz (VP-Global Customer Accts)
Jeffrey A. Kropfl (CFO)
Tom Marshall (Dir-HR)

The Delaney, Co.　　(1)
265 Castle Berry Indus Dr, Cumming, GA 30040
Tel.: (800) 952-4430
Web Site: http://www.delaneyinc.com
Sales Range: $1-9.9 Million
Hardware Merchant Whslr
N.A.I.C.S.: 423710

Wellborn Forest Products, Inc.　　(1)
2212 Airport Blvd, Alexander City, AL 35010-3386
Web Site: http://www.wellbornforest.com
Nonupholstered Wood Household Furniture Mfr
N.A.I.C.S.: 337122
Tammy Walker (Dir-HR)
David Gordon (Pres & CEO)
Tim Wellborn (CEO)

Subsidiary (Domestic):

De Pere Cabinet, Inc.　　(2)
1745 E Matthew Dr, De Pere, WI 54115
Tel.: (920) 337-2989
Web Site:
　http://www.countrysidecabinets.net
Wood Kitchen Cabinets
N.A.I.C.S.: 337110
Bradley Burkard (VP)
Kelly Marks (Supvr-Shipping)
Dan Dhuey (Plant Mgr)

Holding (Domestic):

Wellborn Cabinet, Inc.　　(2)
2212 Airport Blvd, Alexander City, AL 35010
Tel.: (800) 846-2562
Web Site: https://www.wfcabinetry.com
Custom Wood Kitchen & Bath Cabinets Manufacturer
N.A.I.C.S.: 321911
Wally Cisowski (CEO)

Subsidiary (Domestic):

Woodharbor Molding & Millworks, Inc.　　(3)
3277 9th St SW, Mason City, IA 50401
Tel.: (641) 423-0444
Web Site: http://www.woodharbor.com
Sales Range: $25-49.9 Million
Emp.: 475
Cabinetry & Other Millwork
N.A.I.C.S.: 337110
Curtis L. Lewerke (Founder)
Dennis Lewerke (VP)
Abby Crosby (Coord-Mktg)

HCK2 PARTNERS

16775 Addison Rd Ste 550, Addison, TX 75001
Tel.: (972) 716-0500
Web Site: http://www.hck2.com
Year Founded: 1998
Sales Range: $10-24.9 Million
Emp.: 30
N.A.I.C.S.: 541810
Heather Capps (Pres & CEO)
Elizabeth Browne Cornelius (VP-Acct Svc)
Erin Groover (Sr Acct Exec)
Zoe Tennesen (Dir-Creative Svcs)
Martin Eggert (Dir-Interactive Svcs)
Melissa Galitz (Dir-Art)
Michelle Lentz (Dir-Client Svcs)
Megan Sedahl (Acct Exec)
Elisa Voff (Office Mgr)
Virginia Boutwell (Acct Exec-Creative Svcs)
Meredith Lockhart (Sr Acct Exec)
Tae Sendelbach (Assoc Dir-Creative)
Christy French (Acct Exec)
Jordan LaMons (Dir-Tech)
Kerri Fulks (Acct Dir & Mgr-PR Ops)
Lauren Griffin (Acct Dir)

HCK2 Partners—(Continued)

Jaclyn Amend *(Dir-Dev)*
Warren McNeely *(Mgr-Interactive Svcs)*
Rachel McCormick *(Acct Coord)*
Kalyn Ballard *(Acct Exec)*
Katie Post *(Acct Coord)*
Leila Mustafa *(Acct Coord)*
Mike Crouch *(Acct Dir)*

HCM SYSTEMS, INC.
7150 S Madison St Ste 1, Willow-
brook, IL 60527-7985
Tel.: (630) 734-1093
Web Site:
http://www.hcmsystems.com
Year Founded: 1962
Sales Range: $10-24.9 Million
Emp.: 20
Industrial Machinery & Equipment
Whslr
N.A.I.C.S.: 423830
Charlie Hillebold *(Pres)*

HCPRO, INC
100 Winners Circle Ste 300, Brent-
wood, TN 37027
Tel.: (781) 639-1872   DE
Web Site: http://www.hcpro.com
Sales Range: $10-24.9 Million
Emp.: 160
Newsletter Publishing
N.A.I.C.S.: 513199
Monique Fayad *(Sr VP-Strategy & Corp Dev)*
Ian Belinsky *(CFO, Treas & Sr VP)*
Dan Oswald *(CEO)*

HCS HEAD START, INC.
30 Madison Ave, Springfield, MA
01105
Tel.: (413) 788-6522   MA
Web Site:
http://www.hcsheadstart.org
Year Founded: 1970
Sales Range: $10-24.9 Million
Emp.: 372
Community Care Services
N.A.I.C.S.: 624190
Janis Santos *(Exec Dir)*

HCSS, INC.
13151 W Airport Blvd, Sugar Land,
TX 77478
Tel.: (713) 270-4000
Web Site: https://www.hcss.com
Year Founded: 1986
Sales Range: $10-24.9 Million
Emp.: 115
Software Mfr
N.A.I.C.S.: 513210

HD AMERICAN ROAD LLC
3770 37th St, Orlando, FL 32805
Tel.: (407) 423-0346
Web Site:
https://www.orlandoharley.com
Year Founded: 2000
Sales Range: $25-49.9 Million
Emp.: 100
Sales & Services of Motorcycle Parts
& Accessories
N.A.I.C.S.: 441227
Steve Deli *(Owner & Pres)*

HD MEDIA COMPANY, LLC
946 5th Ave, Huntington, WV 25701
Tel.: (304) 526-2813   WV
Web Site: http://www.herald-
dispatch.com
Year Founded: 2013
Newspaper Publishers
N.A.I.C.S.: 513110

Douglas V. Reynolds *(Mng. Partner)*
Georgetta Thevenin *(Controller)*
Judi Reed *(Mgr-Acctg)*
Lee Davis *(Mgr-IT)*

Subsidiaries:

Lincoln Journal, Inc.   **(1)**
328 Walnut St, Hamlin, WV 25523
Tel.: (304) 824-5101
Web Site: http://www.lincolnjournal.com
Sales Range: $1-9.9 Million
Emp.: 16
Newspaper Publishers
N.A.I.C.S.: 513110
Patty Robinson *(Sec)*

The Herald-Dispatch   **(1)**
946 5th Ave, Huntington, WV 25701-2004
Tel.: (304) 526-4000
Web Site: http://www.herald-dispatch.com
Emp.: 200
Newspaper Publishers
N.A.I.C.S.: 513110
Georgetta Thezenin *(Controller)*
Dave Hamilton *(Dir-Production & Circula-
tion)*
Les Smith *(Editor)*
Georgetta Thevenin *(Controller)*
Chuck Jessup *(Dir-Adv)*

The Logan Banner   **(1)**
218 Dingess St, Logan, WV 25601
Tel.: (304) 752-6950
Web Site: http://www.loganbanner.com
Newspaper Publishers
N.A.I.C.S.: 513110
Paul Adkins *(Editor-Sports)*

The Southwest Times   **(1)**
34 5th St NE, Pulaski, VA 24301-4608
Tel.: (540) 980-5220
Web Site: http://www.southwesttimes.com
Internet Publishing & Broadcasting & Web
Search Portals
N.A.I.C.S.: 516210
Mike Williams *(Publr)*

Williamson Daily News   **(1)**
48 W Second Ave, Williamson, WV 25661
Tel.: (304) 235-4242
Web Site:
http://www.williamsondailynews.com
Newspaper Publishers
N.A.I.C.S.: 513110
Melissa Blair *(Mgr-Adv)*

HD VIEW 360, INC.
3550 E Glencoe St, Miami, FL 33133
Tel.: (786) 294-0559
Electronic Security Device Mfr & Distr
N.A.I.C.S.: 334419
Dennis Mancino *(Pres & CEO)*

HDI SOLUTIONS, INC.
1550 Pumphrey Ave, Auburn, AL
36832-0529
Tel.: (334) 466-3010
Web Site:
http://www.hdisolutions.com
Year Founded: 1981
Sales Range: $50-74.9 Million
Emp.: 150
Data Management Software Services
N.A.I.C.S.: 518210
Jim Wilkerson *(Exec VP)*
Rob Eibenedetto *(CEO)*
Jonathan Seifried *(Asst Dir-Bus Ops)*
Brandi Crawley *(Office Mgr)*
Patrick Manning *(Dir-Pub Safety &
Bus Dev)*
Joan Golden *(Mgr-Quality Control)*

Subsidiaries:

Health Information Designs, Inc.   **(1)**
1550 Pumphrey Ave, Auburn, AL 36832-
4302
Tel.: (334) 821-0947
Web Site: http://www.hidinc.com
Sales Range: $10-24.9 Million
Emp.: 80
Medication Information Services
N.A.I.C.S.: 518210
Robert DiBenedetto *(CEO)*
Susie McGuire *(Controller)*

Mary Boyle *(Dir-Product Mgmt)*
Scott Donald *(Dir-Clinical Svcs)*
Howard Drake *(COO)*
Jamie Friedrich *(CIO)*
Rhonda Grabow *(Dir-Client Strategy)*
Clay Jones *(CFO)*
Mike McGinnity *(VP-Sls)*
Kathleen Sabo *(Dir-Mktg & Comm)*

HDR, INC.
1917 S 67th Street, Omaha, NE
68106-2973
Tel.: (402) 399-1000
Web Site: http://www.hdrinc.com
Year Founded: 1917
Architectural Services
N.A.I.C.S.: 541310
Colleen Moore *(VP)*
Eric L. Keen *(Chm)*
Erin Slayton *(Dir-Transportation Pro-
gram Mgmt)*
David F. LeCureux *(Chief Strategy
Officer)*
John Henderson *(CEO)*
Neil Graff *(Pres & COO)*

Subsidiaries:

Calthorpe Associates, Inc.   **(1)**
2095 Rose St Ste 201, Berkeley, CA 94709
Architectural Services
N.A.I.C.S.: 541310

City Point Partners LLC   **(1)**
11 Elkins St, Boston, MA 02127-1627
Tel.: (617) 315-7832
Web Site: http://www.citypointpartners.com
Construction Services
N.A.I.C.S.: 237990
Jay Moskowitz *(Mgr-Mktg)*
Derek Bellucci *(Asst Project Mgr)*
Jillian Gallagher *(Mgr-Lead Document Con-
trol)*

HDR Architecture Inc.   **(1)**
8404 Indian Hills Dr, Omaha, NE 68114-
4049
Tel.: (402) 399-1000
Web Site: http://www.hdrinc.com
Sales Range: $25-49.9 Million
Emp.: 800
Provider of Engineering Services
N.A.I.C.S.: 541330
H. Michael Smith *(Dir-Education-Science-
Tech)*
Susana Andrade Erpestad *(Principal-
Healthcare)*

Subsidiary (Non-US):

Rice Daubney Pty Ltd   **(2)**
Level 1 110 Walker Street, Sydney, 2060,
NSW, Australia
Tel.: (61) 2 9956 2666
Web Site: http://www.ricedaubney.com.au
Emp.: 90
Construction Engineering Services
N.A.I.C.S.: 541330
Darren Tims *(Dir-Major Projects)*
Graeme Smith *(Principal)*
John Daubney *(Chm)*
Paul Reidy *(Principal & Dir-Design &
Comml)*
Roland Hicks *(Dir-Health)*
Stephen Auld *(Mng Dir)*
Susanne Pini *(Dir-Retail & Mixed Use)*
Jonathan Croft *(Dir-Defense)*
David Keenan *(Dir-Education Science &
Tech)*

**HDR Construction Control
Corporation**   **(1)**
5426 Bay Ctr Dr Ste 400, Tampa, FL 33609
Tel.: (813) 282-3300
Sales Range: $10-24.9 Million
Emp.: 130
Provider of Engineering Services
N.A.I.C.S.: 541330

HDR Engineering Inc.   **(1)**
8404 Indian Hills Dr, Omaha, NE
68114-4049   **(100%)**
Tel.: (402) 399-1000
Web Site: http://www.hdrinc.com
Sales Range: $25-49.9 Million
Emp.: 700
Provider of Engineering Services

N.A.I.C.S.: 541330
Dick Bell *(CEO)*
Eric L. Keen *(Pres)*
Steve Schnell *(Asst VP)*
Sabrina Drago *(Mgr-Transportation & Mktg-
Arizona & New Mexico)*
Jeff Schaefer *(Mgr-Environmental-Louisville)*
Scott Wood *(Mgr-Bridge Section-Idaho)*
Jeff Arms *(Principal-Orlando)*

HDR Engineering Inc.   **(1)**
1020 Northeast Loop 410 Ste 400, San An-
tonio, TX 78209-1520   **(100%)**
Tel.: (210) 828-2217
Web Site: http://www.hdrinc.com
Sales Range: $10-24.9 Million
Emp.: 50
Provider of Engineering Services
N.A.I.C.S.: 541330

Maintenance Design Group LLC   **(1)**
707 17th St, Denver, CO 80202
Tel.: (303) 820-5270
Web Site:
http://www.maintenancedesigngroup.com
Sales Range: $1-9.9 Million
Emp.: 40
Design & Planning Consulting Services
N.A.I.C.S.: 541611
Don Leidy *(Mng Principal)*

Salva Resources Pty Ltd   **(1)**
Level 11 82 Eagle Street, Brisbane, 4000,
QLD, Australia
Tel.: (61) 7 3211 9911
Web Site: http://www.hdrsalva.com
Mining Exploration Services
N.A.I.C.S.: 213114
Manish Garg *(Dir-Consulting)*

Subsidiary (Non-US):

Salva Resources Pvt Ltd   **(2)**
Block 2A 5th Floor Unit 502A Ecospace Ra-
jarhat New Town, Kolkata, 700 156, India
Tel.: (91) 33 4025 0928
Mining Exploration Services
N.A.I.C.S.: 213114

Stetson Engineering, Inc.   **(1)**
601 Metz Dr, Gillette, WY 82717-0457
Tel.: (307) 682-8936
Web Site:
http://www.stetsonengineeringinc.com
Emp.: 14
Construction & Engineering Services
N.A.I.C.S.: 541330

HDS MARKETING, INC.
633 Napor Blvd, Pittsburgh, PA
15205
Tel.: (412) 279-1600
Web Site: http://www.hdsideas.com
Year Founded: 1992
Sales Range: $10-24.9 Million
Emp.: 48
Marketing Consulting Services
N.A.I.C.S.: 541613
Howard Schwartz *(Founder & CEO)*
Mark Algeri *(VP-Sls)*
Joss Witzel *(Dir-Ops)*

HDTV SUPPLY, INC.
3835-R E Thousand Oaks Blvd Unit
295, Westlake Village, CA 91362
Tel.: (805) 277-1870
Web Site:
https://www.hdtvsupply.com
Sales Range: $10-24.9 Million
Emp.: 11
Radio & Electronic Product Whslr
N.A.I.C.S.: 441330
Kent Christian *(VP & Gen Mgr)*

HE SERVICES CO. INC.
1900 N Saginaw St, Flint, MI 48505-
4768
Tel.: (989) 753-9015   MI
Web Site:
http://www.heservices.co.uk
Year Founded: 1982
Sales Range: $25-49.9 Million
Emp.: 415
Engineering Services

N.A.I.C.S.: 541330

HEAD INJURY ASSOCIATION, INC.
300 Kennedy Dr, Hauppauge, NY 11788
Tel.: (631) 543-2245   NY
Web Site: http://www.headinjuryassociation.org
Year Founded: 1988
Sales Range: $10-24.9 Million
Emp.: 345
Disability Assistance Services
N.A.I.C.S.: 624120
Stuart Gleiber *(Pres)*
Leonard Feinstein *(VP)*
Liz Giordano *(CEO)*
David Newman *(Sec)*
Robert Yaffe *(Treas)*

HEADCO INDUSTRIES
2550 S 25th Ave, Broadview, IL 60155
Tel.: (708) 681-9090
Web Site: https://www.bearingheadquarters.com
Sales Range: $100-124.9 Million
Emp.: 300
Industrial Parts & Equipment
N.A.I.C.S.: 423840
James Timble *(Pres & CEO)*
Karen M. Skinner *(Treas)*

Subsidiaries:

Bearing Headquarters Co.   (1)
2550 S 25th Ave, Broadview, IL 60155-6267
Tel.: (708) 681-9090
Web Site: http://www.bearingheadquarters.com
Sales Range: $25-49.9 Million
Bearing & Power Transmission Distr
N.A.I.C.S.: 423840
Bob Wallace *(VP)*
Jim Kuebler *(VP)*
Brent Harting *(VP-Gen Markets-Central)*

Division (Domestic):

Gears & Sprocketts, Inc.   (2)
2625 W Parks Dr, Broadview, IL 60153
Tel.: (708) 344-6188
Web Site: http://www.gearsandsprockets.com
Sales Range: $25-49.9 Million
Emp.: 8
Bearing & Power Transmission Distr
N.A.I.C.S.: 332710
James N. Timble *(Pres)*

Highland Hydraulics, Inc.   (2)
9905 Express Dr, Highland, IN 46322-2667
Tel.: (219) 922-7100
Web Site: http://www.bearingheadquarters.com
Sales Range: $25-49.9 Million
Emp.: 8
Bearing & Power Transmission Distr
N.A.I.C.S.: 423830
Greg Kraus *(Mgr-Shop)*

Bronze Headquarters, Inc.   (1)
1022-30 Berea Rd, Cleveland, OH 44102
Tel.: (216) 651-3811
Web Site: http://www.headco.com
Sales Range: $10-24.9 Million
Emp.: 6
Mfr of Bushing, Sleeves & Flanges
N.A.I.C.S.: 423840
John Sekerak *(Gen Mgr)*

Gear Headquarters Inc.   (1)
3012 S 24th St, Kansas City, KS 66106-4707
Tel.: (913) 831-1700
Web Site: http://www.gearheadquarters.com
Sales Range: $10-24.9 Million
Emp.: 15
Mfr of Special Gears & Sprockets
N.A.I.C.S.: 332111
John Lewman *(Gen Mgr)*

Headco Machine Works, Inc.   (1)

2666 Kindustry Park Rd, Keokuk, IA 52632-0969
Tel.: (319) 524-1804
Web Site: http://www.headco.com
Sales Range: $10-24.9 Million
Emp.: 25
Mfr of Machine Parts
N.A.I.C.S.: 332710
Dennis Church *(Office Mgr)*

HEADCOUNT MANAGEMENT, INC.
17 High St, Norwalk, CT 06851
Web Site: https://www.headcountmgmt.com
Year Founded: 2005
Sales Range: $1-9.9 Million
Emp.: 500
Office Administrative Services
N.A.I.C.S.: 561110
Mark P. Arrow *(CEO)*

HEADER PRODUCTS INC.
11850 Wayne Rd, Romulus, MI 48174-1447
Tel.: (734) 941-2220   MI
Web Site: http://www.headerproducts.com
Year Founded: 1963
Sales Range: $10-24.9 Million
Emp.: 129
Mfr of Specialty Fasteners
N.A.I.C.S.: 332721
Robert H. Polzin *(Plant Mgr)*
J. Rodney Guest *(Treas & Controller)*
William J. Harahan IV *(Owner)*

HEADHAUL CAPITAL PARTNERS LLC
600 Mamaroneck Ave Ste 400, Harrison, NY 10528
Tel.: (914) 798-9975   DE
Web Site: http://www.headhaulcapital.com
Private Equity Investment Firm
N.A.I.C.S.: 523999
Seth Eliot Wilson *(Co-Founder & Mng Partner)*
Mindy Luxenberg-Grant *(Co-Founder, Mng Partner & CFO)*
Farrukh A. Bezar *(Operating Partner)*
Jason Grant *(Co-Founder & Mng Partner)*
Craig Decker *(Mng Dir)*

Subsidiaries:

Anderson Cargo Services, LLC   (1)
1045 Gemini Rd, Saint Paul, MN 55121
Tel.: (651) 556-3400
Web Site: http://www.andersoncargo.com
Sales Range: $1-9.9 Million
Emp.: 13
Freight Transportation Arrangement
N.A.I.C.S.: 488510
Robert Masters *(CEO)*

HEADQUARTER TOYOTA
5895 NW 167th St, Hialeah, FL 33015
Tel.: (305) 364-9888
Web Site: https://www.headquartertoyota.com
Sales Range: $150-199.9 Million
Car Dealership Owner & Operator
N.A.I.C.S.: 441110
John Lino *(Mgr-Svc)*

HEADQUARTERS ADVERTISING INC.
350 Kansas St, San Francisco, CA 94103-5130
Tel.: (415) 626-6200   CA
Year Founded: 1987
Rev.: $20,000,000
Emp.: 20
Full Service, Hispanic Marketing
N.A.I.C.S.: 541810

Horacio Gomes *(Pres & CEO)*
Michael Greaney *(Pres & Mng Dir)*
Digna Roque *(Exec Dir-Creative)*
Carol Polombo *(Dir-Media)*

HEADSETS.COM, INC.
1 Daniel Burnham Ct Ste 400C, San Francisco, CA 94109
Tel.: (415) 351-5897
Web Site: http://www.headsets.com
Year Founded: 1997
Sales Range: $25-49.9 Million
Emp.: 55
Corded, Wireless, Cellular & Computer Headsets
N.A.I.C.S.: 334310
Michael Faith *(Pres & CEO)*

HEADSPACE INC.
2415 Michigan Ave Santa Monica, Los Angeles, CA 90404
Tel.: (855) 432-3822
Web Site: http://www.headspace.com
Year Founded: 2010
Meditation App Developer
N.A.I.C.S.: 513210
Russell Glass *(CEO)*
Rich Pierson *(Co-founder)*
Andy Puddicombe *(Co-founder)*
Kaplan Zapata *(CMO)*
Krithika Swaminathan *(CTO)*

Subsidiaries:

Alpine, Inc.   (1)
845 Market St, San Francisco, CA 94109
Tel.: (855) 432-3822
Web Site: http://alpine.ai
Voice Experiences, NLP, Information Retrieval & Dialogue Management
N.A.I.C.S.: 517810
Debby Reed *(Sec)*

HEADSTART NURSERY INC.
4860 Monterey Rd, Gilroy, CA 95020
Tel.: (408) 842-3030
Web Site: https://www.headstartnursery.com
Year Founded: 1979
Rev.: $15,000,000
Emp.: 190
Plant Nursery & Vegetable Whslr
N.A.I.C.S.: 111419
Cole Iten *(Mgr-Production)*
Doug Iten *(Gen Mgr-Desert)*
Lisa Branco *(Mgr-Sls)*
Randy Costa *(VP)*
Steve Costa *(Pres)*
Chris Peck *(Gen Mgr)*
Helder Faria *(Mgr-Gilroy Shipping & Logistics)*
Jennifer Speno *(Acct Mgr)*
Jose Gonzalez *(Mgr-Maintenance)*
Melissa Campilli *(Mgr-Ornamental Customer Svcs)*

HEADSTREAM INC
5301 Limestone Rd Ste 204, New Castle, DE 19808
Tel.: (302) 356-0156
Web Site: http://www.HeadStreamInc.com
Year Founded: 2006
Sales Range: $1-9.9 Million
Emp.: 75
Software Design & Development
N.A.I.C.S.: 513210
Prathapagirhi Aravind *(Pres)*

HEADWALL PHOTONICS, INC.
601 River St, Fitchburg, MA 01420
Tel.: (978) 353-4100
Web Site: http://www.headwallphotonics.com
Rev.: $4,400,000
Emp.: 32
Other Electronic Component Mfr
N.A.I.C.S.: 334419

Mark C. Willingham *(CEO)*
Larry Barstow *(Co-Founder)*
Peter Clemens *(Dir-Engrg)*
Jim Gennari *(Dir-Fin)*
Tom Breen *(Dir-Global Sls)*
Christian Felsheim *(Acct Mgr-Bus Dev & OEM-Sls Team-Europe)*
Francesco Beccari *(Sls Mgr-Europe)*
Will Rock *(Product Mgr-Machine Vision)*
Michelle deCastro *(Mgr-Bus Dev-Optical Components & Assemblies)*

Subsidiaries:

Holographix LLC   (1)
577 Main St, Hudson, MA 01749
Tel.: (978) 562-4474
Web Site: http://www.holographix.com
Rev.: $1,600,000
Emp.: 100
Offices of Other Holding Companies
N.A.I.C.S.: 551112

HEADWAY CORPORATE RESOURCES INC.
1 Bank of America Plza 421 Fayetteville ST STe 1020, Raleigh, NC 27601
Tel.: (919) 376-4929   DE
Web Site: http://www.headwaycorp.com
Year Founded: 1992
Sales Range: $250-299.9 Million
Emp.: 309
Full-Line Staffing, Recruitment & Workforce Solutions
N.A.I.C.S.: 561320
Jean-Pierre Sakey *(Pres & CEO)*
Debra Brown *(Exec VP)*

Subsidiaries:

Headway Corporate Staffing Services of North Carolina Inc.   (1)
The Bank Of America Plz 421 Fayetteville St Mall, Raleigh, NC 27601
Tel.: (919) 376-4929
Web Site: http://www.headwaycorp.com
Sales Range: $10-24.9 Million
Emp.: 15
Employment Agency Services
N.A.I.C.S.: 561311

HEADWORKS INTERNATIONAL INC.
11000 Brittmoore Park Dr, Houston, TX 77041
Tel.: (713) 647-6667   TX
Web Site: https://www.headworksinternational.com
Year Founded: 1993
Sales Range: $1-9.9 Million
Emp.: 13
Wastewater Screening Equipment Mfr
N.A.I.C.S.: 333310
Michele Lanoue *(Pres & CEO)*
Gerald Seidl *(Sr VP-Sls & Engrg)*

HEALEY BROTHERS AUTOMOTIVE
5216 Route 17M, New Hampton, NY 10958
Tel.: (845) 360-9821
Web Site: https://www.healeybrothers.com
Sales Range: $25-49.9 Million
Emp.: 60
Automobile Sales
N.A.I.C.S.: 441110
Paul Healey *(Owner)*
Dwight Healy *(VP)*

HEALEY RAILROAD CORPORATION
PO Box 190, Midlothian, VA 23113
Tel.: (804) 379-3904
Web Site: http://www.railsource.com
Rev.: $32,000,000

Healey Railroad Corporation—(Continued)

Emp.: 400
Railroad & Railway Roadbed Construction
N.A.I.C.S.: 236210
Glenn V. Healey (CEO)

HEALTH ACCESS NETWORK
175 W Broadway, Lincoln, ME 04457
Tel.: (207) 794-6700   **ME**
Web Site: https://www.hanfqhc.org
Year Founded: 2002
Sales Range: $10-24.9 Million
Emp.: 140
Health Care Srvices
N.A.I.C.S.: 622110
William Diggins (CEO)
Sonia Maxwell (Dir-HR)
Jeff Kirsch (CFO)
Nicole Morrison (Dir-Ops)
Hal Cote (Chm)
Susan Bailey (Sec)
Penelope Kneeland (Vice Chm)
Richard Broderick Jr. (Treas)

HEALTH ADVOCATES NETWORK, INC.
20283 State Rd7 Ste 106, Boca Raton, FL 33498
Tel.: (561) 437-4880
Web Site: http://www.hanstaff.com
Staffing & Recruiting Services
N.A.I.C.S.: 561311
Kevin Little (Chm & CEO)
Eddie Albert (Dir-M&A)

Subsidiaries:

Primestaff, LLC   (1)
8840 E Chaparral Rd Ste 185, Scottsdale, AZ 85250-6650
Tel.: (480) 551-1311
Web Site:
   http://www.acclivityhealthcare.com
Employment Agencies
N.A.I.C.S.: 561311
Ted French (Co-Founder & Pres)
Cheri French (Co-Founder & CFO)

HEALTH AFFILIATES MAINE
PO Box 1150, Auburn, ME 04211
Tel.: (207) 333-3278
Web Site:
   http://www.healthaffiliatesmaine.com
Year Founded: 2009
Sales Range: $10-24.9 Million
Emp.: 230
Health Care Srvices
N.A.I.C.S.: 621498
Andrea Krebs (Exec Dir)
Kate Marble (Program Dir-Case Mgmt)
Melissa Bowker-Kinley (Dir-Medical)
Nina Bartlett (Dir-Operations)

HEALTH CARE AND REHABILITATION SERVICES
390 River St, Springfield, VT 05156
Tel.: (802) 886-4500   **VT**
Web Site: http://www.hcrs.org
Year Founded: 1967
Sales Range: $25-49.9 Million
Emp.: 646
Behavioral Healthcare Services
N.A.I.C.S.: 623220
George Karaeakis (CEO)
Jeff Acker (Treas)
Adam Pippin (Chm)
Michelle Bos-Lun (VP)
Phil Blackburn (Sec)
Rhett Sorensen (Dir-Quality Assurance & Compliance)
Edmund Hmoore IV (CFO)

HEALTH CARE CAPITAL CONSOLIDATED

2 Ravinia Dr Ste 1350, Atlanta, GA 30346
Tel.: (770) 393-3355
Rev.: $119,400,000
Emp.: 5
Mortgage Bankers & Loan Correspondents
N.A.I.C.S.: 522310
Marshall Gill (Owner & VP-Ops)

HEALTH CARE FOR THE HOMELESS
421 Fallsway, Baltimore, MD 21202
Tel.: (410) 837-5533   **MD**
Web Site: https://www.hchmd.org
Year Founded: 1988
Sales Range: $10-24.9 Million
Emp.: 151
Health Care Srvices
N.A.I.C.S.: 622110
Keiren Havens (Chief Strategy Officer)
Kevin Lindamood (Pres & CEO)

HEALTH CARE FOUNDATION OF GREATER KANSAS CITY
2700 E 18th St Ste 220, Kansas City, MO 64127
Tel.: (816) 241-7006   **MO**
Web Site: http://www.hcfgkc.org
Year Founded: 2003
Sales Range: $25-49.9 Million
Emp.: 18
Health Care Srvices
N.A.I.C.S.: 622110
Rhonda Holman (COO & VP)
Richard H. Zimmer (CFO)
Kenny Southwick (Chm)

HEALTH CARE SERVICE CORPORATION
300 E Randolph St, Chicago, IL 60601-5099
Tel.: (312) 653-6000   **IL**
Web Site: http://www.hcsc.com
Year Founded: 1936
Sales Range: $25-49.9 Billion
Emp.: 24,000
Holding Company; Health & Life Insurance Products & Services
N.A.I.C.S.: 551112
Maurice S. Smith (Vice Chm, Pres & CEO)
Milton Carroll (Chm)
Thomas Lubben (Chief Ethics, Compliance & Privacy Officer & Sr VP)
Opella Ernest (COO & Exec VP)
Monica Berner (Chief Clinical Officer)
James Gibbs (Chief HR Officer & Sr VP)
Catherine Nelson (Chief Legal Officer, Sec & Sr VP)
Arun Prasad (Chief Strategy Officer & Sr VP)
Maurice S. Smith (Pres, CEO & Vice Chm)
Jeffrey Tikkanen (Exec VP-Comml Markets)
Kevin M. Cassidy (Chief Growth Officer)
Stephen Harris (Pres-Medicaid)
Christine Kourouklis (Pres-Medicare)
Nathan Linsley (Sr VP-Govt Programs)
James Walsh (CFO & Sr VP)
Jill Wolowitz (Chief Admin Officer & Sr VP)

Subsidiaries:

Blue Cross & Blue Shield of Illinois   (1)
300 E Randolph St, Chicago, IL 60601-5099
Tel.: (312) 653-6000
Web Site: http://www.bcbsil.com

Sales Range: $1-4.9 Billion
Emp.: 7,000
Health & Medical Insurance Carrier
N.A.I.C.S.: 524114
Scott Sarran (Chief Medical Officer)

Blue Cross & Blue Shield of New Mexico   (1)
4373 Alexander Blvd NE, Albuquerque, NM-87107   (100%)
Tel.: (505) 291-3500
Web Site: http://www.bcbshm.com
Sales Range: $150-199.9 Million
Emp.: 900
Health & Medical Insurance Carrier
N.A.I.C.S.: 524114
Laurie Volkin (Dir-Comm & PR)

Blue Cross & Blue Shield of Texas, Inc.   (1)
1001 E Lookout Dr, Richardson, TX 75082
Tel.: (972) 766-6900
Web Site: http://www.bcbstx.com
Sales Range: $1-4.9 Billion
Emp.: 5,600
Health Insurance
N.A.I.C.S.: 524114
Jack Towsley (Sr VP-Health Care Delivery)
Darrell Beckett (Sr VP-Sls & Mktg)
Bert E. Marshall (Pres)
Robert Morrow (Pres-Southeast Texas)
Michelle Riddell (VP-Strategic Comm & Community Investment)
Paul Hain (Chief Medical Officer & Sr VP-Market Delivery)

Dearborn National Life Insurance Company   (1)
1020 31st St, Downers Grove, IL 60515
Web Site: http://www.dearbornnational.com
Sales Range: $800-899.9 Million
Emp.: 400
Life Insurance Carrier
N.A.I.C.S.: 524113
Greg S. Benesh (Pres & CEO)
Claire Burke (VP-Fin & Compliance Mgmt)
Scott M. Morgan (CIO & VP-Bus Dev & Tech)
Mike Witwer (Pres & CEO)
Eric Chandler (Gen Counsel & Sec)
John Schwegel (Chief Actuary)

Subsidiary (Domestic):

Preferred Financial Corporation   (2)
5990 Greenwood Plz Blvd Ste 325, Greenwood Village, CO 80111-4704
Tel.: (303) 220-8500
Web Site: http://www.dearbornnational.com
Sales Range: $1-4.9 Billion
Emp.: 60
Holding Company; Life Insurance Carrier
N.A.I.C.S.: 551112
Paul Gauthier (CFO, Treas & VP)

Dentemax, LLC   (1)
25925 Telegraph Rd Ste 400, Southfield, MI 48033
Tel.: (248) 352-5672
Web Site: http://www.dentemax.com
Health Care Insurance Services
N.A.I.C.S.: 524298

Group Health Service of Oklahoma, Inc.   (1)
1215 S Boulder Ave, Tulsa, OK 74119-2827
Tel.: (918) 560-3500
Web Site: http://www.bcbsok.com
Sales Range: $300-349.9 Million
Emp.: 1,500
Health & Medical Insurance Carrier
N.A.I.C.S.: 524114
Bert Marshall (Pres)

HCSC Insurance Services Company   (1)
300 E Randolph St, Chicago, IL 60601
Tel.: (312) 653-7844
Health Care Insurance Services
N.A.I.C.S.: 621999

MEDecision, Inc.   (1)
550 E Ste Swedesford Rd Ste 220, Wayne, PA 19087
Tel.: (610) 540-0202
Web Site: http://www.medecision.com
Sales Range: $25-49.9 Million
Emp.: 249
Medical Decision & Support Management Software Designer & Mfr

N.A.I.C.S.: 541511
Kenneth Young (Pres & CEO)
Ellen Donahue-Dalton (CMO & Exec VP)
Kathleen D'Amario (Sr VP)
William Gillespie (Chief Medical Officer & Exec VP-Population Health Mgmt)
John P. McGahey (Chief Revenue Officer & Exec VP)
Susan L. Newton (Chief People Officer & Exec VP)
Jennifer Ponski (Chief Admin Officer & Exec VP)
Larry Schor (Sr VP-Analytics)
Shelby Solomon (Sr VP-Corp Dev & Strategy)
Donald E. Casey (Chief Clinical Affairs Officer)
Ian Chuang (Chief Analytics Officer)
Anna Roche Clark (Chief Revenue Officer & Sr VP)
Tamara Cull (VP-Market Dev)
Dan Speicher (CTO)
Tal Weitzman (CIO)

Subsidiary (Domestic):

GSI Health, LLC   (2)
1735 Market St 53rd Fl, Philadelphia, PA 19103
Tel.: (888) 206-4237
Web Site: http://www.gsihealth.com
Sales Range: $10-24.9 Million
Emp.: 50
Health Care Srvices
N.A.I.C.S.: 621498
Leroy E. Jones (Founder, Pres & CEO)
Alan Horton (CTO)
Sean T. Kelly (Sr VP-Growth & Commercialization)
Amy Koizim (Sr VP-Client Solutions)
Parag More (Sr VP-Integrated Product Mgmt)

HEALTH CAROUSEL, LLC
3805 Edwards Rd Ste 700, Cincinnati, OH 45209
Tel.: (800) 580-8239
Web Site:
   https://www.healthcarousel.com
Year Founded: 2004
Healthcare Staffing & Workforce Solutions Services
N.A.I.C.S.: 561311
Tom Herbort (VP-Compensations & Benefits)
Andrew Simon (VP-Corp Dev & Transformation)
Jonathan Kukulski (Gen Counsel & VP-Bus Dev)
Jessica Griffith (Dir-HR)
Mike McKee (Dir-FP&A)
Scott Metcalf (Mgr-Recruiting)
Chris Lake (Dir-Credit & Collections)
Neil Okonak (Sr Dir-Transformation)
Elena Bowman (Mgr-Recruiting)
Sarah Swango (Mgr-Recruiting)
Ashleigh Taylor (Mgr-Recruiting)
Chris McGraw (Mgr-Recruiting)
Andy Hurley (Mgr-Recruiting)
Michael Crane (Dir-Bus Dev)
Jim Stilgenbauer (Dir-Transformation)
Sarah Haines (Controller)
Erik Schumann (Chief Sls Officer)
Matthew Disher (Dir-Talent Acq)
Kevin Armour (CIO & VP-Tech)
Earl Dalton (Chief Nursing Officer)
Matt Williams (VP-Tailored Healthcare Staffing)
Marijke Woodruff (Chief People Officer)
John Sebastian (CEO)
Katie Glaser (VP-Ops-Intl)
Stacey Stanley (Pres-Locum Network)
Winnie Culbert (VP-Next Medical Staffing)
Bob Brayer (VP-Medical Staffing Options)

Subsidiaries:

McDermott & Wiedemann, LLC   (1)

505 t Main St, Houston, TX 77006-2836
Tel.: (713) 227-4600
Web Site: http://www.vitruvianmedical.com
Temporary Help Service
N.A.I.C.S.: 561320
Patrick Mcdermott (Mgr)

Medical Staffing Options   (1)
9200 Worthington Rd Ste 101, Westerville,
OH 43082
Tel.: (614) 848-7726
Web Site:
    http://www.medicalstaffingoptions.com
Sales Range: $1-9.9 Million
Emp.: 200
Healtcare Services
N.A.I.C.S.: 621999
Bob Gammill (Pres)
Paul Conklin (Dir-Ops)
Joshua Barry (Dir-Ops)
Steve Grace (Partner)

Next Medical Staffing LLC   (1)
7625 Paragon Rd Ste C, Dayton, OH
45459-4063
Web Site:
    http://www.nextmedicalstaffing.com
Temporary Help Service
N.A.I.C.S.: 561320
Keith Meddock (Acct Mgr)

HEALTH DELIVERY INC.
501 Lapeer Ave, Saginaw, MI 48607
Tel.: (989) 759-6400
Web Site:
    http://www.healthdelivery.org
Rev.: $21,700,000
Emp.: 350
Offices of Physicians, Mental Health
Specialists
N.A.I.C.S.: 621112
Becky Demers (Dir-Dental Svcs)
Gina Llewellyn (Coord-Admin-Medical
Svcs)
Kathy Davenport (Dir-HR)
Michelle Echeverria (Coord-Referrals)
Bridget Sonntag (Coord-Dental Svcs)
Santiago Peregrino (Chm)
Kari Gulvas (Sec)
Timothy J. Zlomak (Vice Chm)
Albert Martenis III (Treas)

HEALTH DESIGNS, INC.
35 Executive Way Ste 110, Ponte
Vedra Beach, FL 32082
Tel.: (904) 285-2019
Web Site:
    https://www.healthdesigns.net
Year Founded: 1995
Sales Range: $1-9.9 Million
Emp.: 10
Health & Wellness Programs
N.A.I.C.S.: 923120
Ann Sabbag (Founder & CEO)
Anglea Lee (Project Mgr)
Kate Thilges (Bus Mgr)
Tom Grebnstein (VP-Ops)

HEALTH DIMENSIONS GROUP
12900 Whitewater Dr Ste 201, Minne-
apolis, MN 55343
Tel.: (763) 537-5700
Web Site:
    https://www.healthdimensionsgroup.com0017
Sales Range: $25-49.9 Million
Emp.: 90
Healthcare Management & Consult-
ing Services
N.A.I.C.S.: 541611
Sergei Shvetzoff (Chm & Principal)
Craig Abbott (CEO)
Colin Higgins (Dir-Analytics & Res)
Leah Lindgren (Exec VP-Consulting
Practice)
Pamela Klingfus (Mgr-Consulting
Svcs)
Kristina Guindon (Dir-Ops)
Erin Shvetzoff Hennessey (Co-CEO)
Steve Nelson (Exec VP-Fin)

Ann Robinson (Exec VP-Ops & Qual-
ity)
Amber Rogotzke (Exec VP-HR)
Darrin Hull (Sr VP-Consulting)

Subsidiaries:

Belmont Nursing & Rehabilitation
Center   (1)
110 Belmont Rd, Madison, WI 53714-3129
Tel.: (608) 249-7391
Web Site: http://www.belmontmadison.com
Sales Range: $25-49.9 Million
Nursing & Rehabilitation Services
N.A.I.C.S.: 623311
Megan Simpson (Gen Mgr)

HEALTH DIRECTIONS INC.
2 Mid America Plaza Ste 1050, Oak-
brook Terrace, IL 60181
Tel.: (312) 396-5400
Web Site:
    http://www.healthdirections.com
Year Founded: 1985
Sales Range: $10-24.9 Million
Emp.: 100
Health Care Consulting Services
N.A.I.C.S.: 541618
Daniel J. Marino (Exec VP)
William K. Faber (Chief Medical Offi-
cer)
Tina Wardrop (VP)
Lucy Zielinski (VP)
Sabrina Burnett (VP)
Michael Miyagi (Sr VP)
James Smith (Sr VP)
Mary Witt (Sr VP)
Tawnya Bosko (VP)
Graham Brown (VP)
Peggy Crabtree (VP)
Andy Edeburn (VP)
Kimberly Hartsfield (VP)
Panos Lykidis (VP)
Marc Mertz (VP)

HEALTH E SYSTEMS, LLC
5100 W Lemon St Ste 311, Tampa,
FL 33609
Tel.: (813) 769-1880
Web Site:
    http://www.healthesystems.com
Year Founded: 2002
Sales Range: $50-74.9 Million
Emp.: 278
Workers Compensation Insurance
N.A.I.C.S.: 524292
Ron Roma (CEO)
Daryl Corr (Pres)
Stephanie Narvades (CFO)
Laura Moore (Sr VP)
Robert L. Goldberg (CMO)
Todd Pisciotti (VP-Sls & Mktg)
Matt Hewitt (VP-Product Svcs)
Kristine Kennedy (VP-Product Mgmt)
Craig Hoss (CIO)
Chris Rucker (COO)
Jennifer Locklear (VP-HR)
Brett Luna (Co-CIO)

HEALTH ENTERPRISE PART-
NERS LLC
365 Fifth Ave 26th Fl, New York, NY
10017
Tel.: (212) 981-6901
Web Site: https://www.hepfund.com
Privater Equity Firm
N.A.I.C.S.: 523999
Richard H. Stowe (Partner)
Tracy A. South (Operating Partner)
Dan Cain (Partner)
Bob Schulz (Partner)
Dave Tamburri (Mng Partner)
Lynn Weld (Controller)
Ezra Mehlman (Mng Partner)
Kulmeet Singh (Operating Partner)

Subsidiaries:

The InterMed Group, Inc.   (1)

13301 US Highway 441, Alachua, FL 32615
Web Site: http://intermed1.com
Sales Range: $1-9.9 Million
Emp.: 25
Sells & Services New & Used Biomedical
Equipment
N.A.I.C.S.: 423450
Rick Staab (Pres)

Subsidiary (Domestic):

Horizon CSA LLC   (2)
265 Pitt Rd, Mooresville, NC 28115-6783
Tel.: (704) 799-8661
Web Site:
    http://www.horizonbiomedicalservices.com
All Other Miscellaneous Ambulatory Health
Care Services
N.A.I.C.S.: 621999
Mike Marrow (Owner)

InterMed Nuclear Medicine, Inc.   (2)
13351 Progress Blvd, Alachua, FL
32615   (100%)
Tel.: (386) 462-5220
Web Site: http://www.intermednucmed.com
Nuclear Medicine Machinery Parts & Ser-
vices
N.A.I.C.S.: 339112
Danny Hamm (VP-Sls)
Rick Staab (Pres)
Dave Bauerle (VP)
Dave Fox (COO)
Theresa Smith (Treas)
Don MacLaren (Mgr-Svc)
Yvette Graham (Mgr-Svc)

InterMed Ultrasound   (2)
13351 Progress Blvd, Alachua, FL
32615   (100%)
Tel.: (386) 462-5220
Web Site:
    http://www.intermedultrasound.com
Sales Range: $1-9.9 Million
Emp.: 70
Sales & Services of Ultrasound Machines
Parts & Services
N.A.I.C.S.: 339113
Rick Staab (Pres)
Don Fletcher (Controller-Quality)
Dave Fox (COO)
Theresa Smith (Controller)

InterMed X-Ray, Inc.   (2)
14000 NW 126th Ter, Alachua, FL 32615
Tel.: (386) 462-5220
Web Site: http://www.intermedxray.com
Sales Range: $1-9.9 Million
Emp.: 18
Medical Imaging Equipment
N.A.I.C.S.: 423450
David Bauerle (Pres)

Modern Biomedical Services,
Inc.   (2)
600 E John Carpenter Fwy Ste 284, Irving,
TX 75062
Tel.: (214) 217-3700
Web Site:
    http://www.modernbiomedical.com
Sales Range: $1-9.9 Million
Emp.: 100
Healthcare Technology Management Ser-
vices
N.A.I.C.S.: 541618
Randy Bullard (CEO)

HEALTH EVOLUTION PART-
NERS, LLC
1 Letterman Dr Ste D3700, San Fran-
cisco, CA 94129
Tel.: (415) 362-5800   DE
Web Site:
    http://www.healthevolutionpartners.com
Health Investment Funds
N.A.I.C.S.: 523999
Rolf A. Classon (Partner-Operating)
Braden R. Kelly (Partner)
Rolf A. Classon (Partner-Operating)
David J. Brailer (Founder & Chm)
Richard Schwartz (Pres)

HEALTH FACILITY SOLU-
TIONS CO., (HFS)
124 Oakwell Farms Pkwy, San Antonio, TX 78201

Tel.: (210) 881-9714
Web Site:
    http://www.hfscompany.com
Year Founded: 2003
Sales Range: $1-9.9 Million
Emp.: 68
Consulting Services for Capital Im-
provement Projects for Healthcare
Facilities
N.A.I.C.S.: 541618
Michele Pauli (Founder & Pres)

HEALTH FEDERATION OF
PHILADELPHIA
1211 Chestnut St Ste 801, Philadel-
phia, PA 19107
Tel.: (215) 567-8001   PA
Web Site:
    https://www.healthfederation.org
Year Founded: 1983
Sales Range: $10-24.9 Million
Emp.: 286
Health Care Srvices
N.A.I.C.S.: 622110
Natalie Levkovich (Exec Dir)

HEALTH IMPERATIVES, INC.
942 W Chestnut St, Brockton, MA
02301
Tel.: (508) 583-3005   MA
Web Site:
    http://www.healthimperatives.org
Year Founded: 1977
Sales Range: $10-24.9 Million
Emp.: 195
Healtcare Services
N.A.I.C.S.: 622110
Julia Kehoe (Pres & CEO)
Elizabeth Torrant (VP-Family Health
Svcs)

HEALTH INNOVATION TECH-
NOLOGIES INC.
6 Boulder Creek Cir, Madison, WI
53717
Web Site:
    http://www.revolutionehr.com
Year Founded: 2006
Sales Range: $1-9.9 Million
Emp.: 16
Electronic Health Record Software
N.A.I.C.S.: 513210
Scott Jens (CEO)

HEALTH MANAGEMENT AS-
SOCIATES, INC.
2501 Woodlake Cir Ste 100, Lansing,
MI 48864
Tel.: (517) 482-9236   MI
Web Site:
    http://www.healthmanagement.com
Year Founded: 1985
Management Consulting Services
N.A.I.C.S.: 541618
Jay Rosen (Founder, Chm & Pres)
Jonathan Freedman (Senior Regional
Vice President-California)
Kelly Johnson (Chief Admin Officer)
Kathleen Nolan (Senior Regional Vice
President-Oregon)
Tim Spillane (VP-Corp Dev)
Jeff Wink (CFO)
Beth Kidder (Mng Principal)
Doug Elwell (CEO)

Subsidiaries:

Lovell Communications Inc.   (1)
3212 W End Ave Ste 500, Nashville, TN
37203
Tel.: (615) 297-7766
Web Site: http://www.lovell.com
Support Services
N.A.I.C.S.: 561990
Susanne Powelson (VP)
Robin Embry (VP)

Npo Solutions   (1)

Health Management Associates, Inc.—(Continued)

4370 Tujunga Ave Ste 220, Studio City, CA 91604-2753
Tel.: (818) 766-8448
Web Site: http://www.nposolutions.org
Process, Physical Distribution & Logistics Consulting Services
N.A.I.C.S.: 541614
Warren Riley (Pres)

The Moran Company, LLC   (1)
1000 Wilson Blvd Ste 2500, Arlington, VA 22209
Tel.: (703) 841-8400
Web Site:
    http://www.themorancompany.com
Professional, Scientific & Technical Services
N.A.I.C.S.: 541990
Mark Desmarais (Principal)
Bill Moran (Founder)

Wilson Strategic Communications, Inc.   (1)
3500 188th St SW Ste 590, Lynnwood, WA 98037-4763
Tel.: (425) 361-2118
Web Site: http://www.wilsonstrategic.com
Public Relations Agencies
N.A.I.C.S.: 541820
D. J. Wilson (Founder, Pres & CEO)

HEALTH MANAGEMENT SERVICES INC.
9100 SW Fwy 114, Houston, TX 77074
Tel.: (713) 541-2727
Web Site: http://www.cpap.com
Sales Range: $10-24.9 Million
Emp.: 80
Medical Apparatus & Supplies
N.A.I.C.S.: 456199
John Goodman (Pres)
Jason Holzman (Gen Mgr)

HEALTH PARTNERS, INC.
8170 33rd Ave S, Bloomington, MN 55425
Tel.: (952) 883-6000
Web Site:
    https://www.healthpartners.com
Health Care Srvices
N.A.I.C.S.: 621999
Andrea Walsh (Pres & CEO)
Barbara Tretheway (Sr VP)
Charlie Fazio (Sr VP)
Nance A. McClure (COO)
Anahita Cameron (Chief HR Officer & Sr VP)
Jim Eppel (Chief Admin Officer & Exec VP)
Todd Hofheins (CFO & Sr VP)
James Malecha (Chm)
Laura Oberst (Vice Chm)

HEALTH PRODUCTS CORPORATION
1060 Nepperhan Ave, Yonkers, NY 10703-1432
Tel.: (914) 423-2900   NY
Web Site: http://www.hpc7.com
Year Founded: 1973
Sales Range: $150-199.9 Million
Emp.: 200
Beauty Aids, OTC Drugs & Vitamins Mfr & Distr
N.A.I.C.S.: 325411
Joseph Lewin (Pres)
Bob Feinstein (VP-Mktg)
John Mills (VP)

HEALTH PROFESSIONS EDUCATION FOUNDATION
400 R St Ste 460, Sacramento, CA 95833-6213
Tel.: (916) 326-3640   CA
Web Site: http://www.oshpd.ca.gov
Year Founded: 1987
Sales Range: $25-49.9 Million
Educational Support Services

N.A.I.C.S.: 611710
Scott Sillers (Pres)
Karen Isenhower (Dir-Programs)
Linda Onstad-Adkins (Exec Dir)
Nanci Timmins (Chief Fire & Life Safety Officer)

HEALTH QUEST SYSTEMS, INC.
45 Reade Pl, Poughkeepsie, NY 12601
Tel.: (845) 454-8500   NY
Web Site: http://www.health-quest.org
Year Founded: 1887
Sales Range: $550-599.9 Million
Emp.: 22,000
Hospital Management Services
N.A.I.C.S.: 622110
Mike Weber (Pres & CEO)
David Ping (VP-Strategic Plng & Bus Dev)
Maryann Kepple (CFO, Treas & VP-Fin)
Rick Thomas (VP-Legal Svcs)
Ann Armater (VP-Dev)
Pat Borek (VP-HR)
Ron Tatelbaum (Sr VP-Medical Affairs)
Bob Diamond (CIO & VP)
Robert R. Dyson (Vice Chm)
Steven V. Lant (Chm)
Timmian Massie (Sr VP-Pub Affairs & Govt Rels)
Cheryl Booth (Asst Sec)
Katherine Bacher (Interim CFO, Treas & Interim Sr VP)

Subsidiaries:

Riverside Management Services Inc.   (1)
45 Reade Pl, Poughkeepsie, NY 12601-3947   (100%)
Tel.: (845) 431-5624
Web Site: http://www.health-quest.org
Sales Range: $10-24.9 Million
Emp.: 10
Management Services-Hospital
N.A.I.C.S.: 541611

HEALTH RECOVERY SOLUTIONS INC.
50 Harrison St Ste 310, Hoboken, NJ 07030
Tel.: (347) 699-6477
Web Site:
    http://www.healthrecoverysolutions.com
Year Founded: 2012
Sales Range: $1-9.9 Million
Emp.: 46
Health Care Srvices
N.A.I.C.S.: 621610
Jarrett Bauer (Co-Founder)
Rohan Udeshi (Co-Founder)
Dan Priece (Co-Founder)
Melissa Humphrey (CMO)
Kimberly O'Loughlin (CEO)

HEALTH RESEARCH INC.
Riverview Ctr, Menands, NY 12204
Tel.: (518) 431-1200
Web Site:
    https://www.healthresearch.org
Year Founded: 1953
Sales Range: $75-99.9 Million
Emp.: 1,400
Non-Profit Organization Providing Funds For Researchers
N.A.I.C.S.: 541618
Cheryl Mattox (Controller)
Carol A. Bailey (Dir-HR)
Michelle Coyne (Dir-Sub Contract Unit)
Charles Cummins (Assoc Dir-Application Dev)

HEALTH RESOURCES NORTHWEST
1550 N 115th St Ste 180, Seattle, WA 98133
Tel.: (206) 368-3012   WA
Year Founded: 1981
Sales Range: $10-24.9 Million
Emp.: 7
Health Care Srvices
N.A.I.C.S.: 622110
Brian David (Controller)
Gayle Ward (Chief Nursing Officer & VP)
Bruce Ferguson (CFO, Treas, Sec & VP)
C. William Schneider (Pres & CEO)
Gregory Schroedl (Chief Medical Officer & VP)

HEALTH SCIENCES SOUTH CAROLINA
1320 Main St Ste 625, Columbia, SC 29201
Tel.: (803) 544-4772   SC
Web Site:
    http://www.healthsciencessc.org
Year Founded: 2004
Sales Range: $50-74.9 Million
Health Care Srvices
N.A.I.C.S.: 622110
Christine Turley (Chief Medical Officer)
Arik Bjorn (Mgr-Academic Program)
Susan Jones (Mgr-Fin)
R. Maynard Cain (Mgr-Program)

HEALTH SERVICES GROUP, INC.
601 SW 2nd Ave, Portland, OR 97204-3154
Tel.: (503) 228-6554   OR
Web Site:
    http://www.modahealth.com
Year Founded: 1955
Sales Range: $200-249.9 Million
Emp.: 1,000
Hospital & Medical Service Plans
N.A.I.C.S.: 524114
Robert G. Gootee (CEO)
William Johnson (Pres)
Robin Richardson (Sr VP)
Dave Evans (Sr VP)
Kraig Anderson (Sr VP)

Subsidiaries:

Northwest Dentists Insurance Company Inc.   (1)
10505 SE 17th Ave, Milwaukie, OR 97222   (100%)
Tel.: (800) 662-4075
Web Site: http://www.nordicins.com
Sales Range: $50-74.9 Million
Emp.: 82
Liability Insurance
N.A.I.C.S.: 524113
Christopher Verbiest (VP)
Melissa Moore Sanchez (Mgr-Sls & Mktg)
Diane Wenz (Mgr-Compliance & Ops)
Debra Wong (Supvr-Underwriting)
Robert Petty (Specialist-Claims)

ODS Health Plan Inc.   (1)
601 SW 2nd Ave, Portland, OR 97204-3154
Tel.: (503) 228-6554
Web Site: http://www.modahealth.com
Sales Range: $200-249.9 Million
Emp.: 700
Hospital & Medical Service Plans
N.A.I.C.S.: 524114
Robert G. Gootee (Pres & CEO)
Tracy Lambert (Coord-Benefit Configuration)
Cynthia Lacro (Mgr-Quality Improvement)

HEALTH SERVICES MANAGEMENT, INC.
206 Fortress Blvd, Murfreesboro, TN 37128

Tel.: (615) 896-1191   TN
Year Founded: 2000
Sales Range: $150-199.9 Million
Emp.: 3,384
Women Healthcare Services
N.A.I.C.S.: 621610
Preston Sweeney (Pres)
Brian Perine (VP-Ops)
William Neely (Sr VP)
Eric P. Sweeney (Sr VP)
Eric Bell (Sec & Exec VP)

HEALTH SHARE OF OREGON
2121 SW Broadway Ste 200, Portland, OR 97201
Tel.: (503) 416-1460   OR
Web Site:
    http://www.healthshareoregon.org
Year Founded: 2012
Sales Range: $600-649.9 Million
Emp.: 60
Community Health Care Services
N.A.I.C.S.: 621498
Janet L. Meyer (CEO)
Rachel Arnold (Mgr-Contracting & Provider Rels)
Deborah Friedman (COO)
Michael Anderson-Nathe (Chief Equity & Engagement Officer)
Jennifer Hendrickson (Project Mgr)
Graham Bouldin (Mgr-Quality Improvement)
John A. Sanders (CIO)
Florence Hurita (Mgr-Customer Svcs)

HEALTH SOLUTIONS, LLC
151 5th Ave SE Ste 500, Cedar Rapids, IA 52401
Tel.: (319) 362-2409
Web Site:
    http://www.healthywithhsi.com
Year Founded: 2004
Sales Range: $1-9.9 Million
Emp.: 20
Health & Wellness Programs Including Lifestyle Coaching Services
N.A.I.C.S.: 621399
Jennifer Musick (Owner)

HEALTH SYSTEMS COOPERATIVE LAUNDRIES
725 Minnehaha Ave E, Saint Paul, MN 55106-4441
Tel.: (651) 774-6645
Year Founded: 2007
Sales Range: $10-24.9 Million
Emp.: 280
Drycleaning & Laundry Services
N.A.I.C.S.: 812320
Brian Knapp (Pres)

HEALTH UNION, LLC
1218 Chestnut St 2nd Fl, Philadelphia, PA 19107
Tel.: (484) 985-9715
Web Site: http://www.health-union.com
Year Founded: 2010
Sales Range: $25-49.9 Million
Emp.: 126
Health Care Srvices
N.A.I.C.S.: 621610
Olivier Chateau (Co-Founder & CEO)
Tim Armand (Co-Founder & Pres)
Lauren Lawhon (COO)
Amrita Bhowmick (Chief Community Officer)
J. Blake Harris (Chief Experience Officer)

HEALTH-RIGHT DISCOVERIES, INC.
18851 NE 29th Ave Ste 700, Aventura, FL 33180
Tel.: (305) 705-3247   FL
Web Site: http://www.health-right.com

Year Founded: 2011
Rev.: $3,467,661
Assets: $7,911,682
Liabilities: $9,459,375
Net Worth: ($1,547,693)
Earnings: ($1,460,664)
Emp.: 8
Fiscal Year-end: 12/31/19
Nutritional Product Mfr & Distr
N.A.I.C.S.: 325412
David Hopkins (Founder, Pres & CEO)

HEALTHAXIS GROUP, LLC

5509 W Gray St Ste 200, Tampa, FL 33609
Tel.: (888) 974-2947   FL
Web Site: http://www.healthaxis.com
Year Founded: 2011
Health Care Software Solutions
N.A.I.C.S.: 518210
Matt Hughes (COO)
Karen Edwards (CFO)
Neal Reizer (CTO)
Jim Clark (Chief Growth Officer)
Robert Nolan (Chief Compliance Officer)
Angela Benmassaoud (Chief People Officer)
Candice McGee (Sr VP-Healthcare Ops)

Subsidiaries:

Analytics Partners, LLC   (1)
725 Peninsular Pl, Jacksonville, FL 32204
Tel.: (904) 322-7736
Web Site: http://www.analyticspartners.com
Computer System Design Services
N.A.I.C.S.: 541512

HEALTHCARE ASSOCIATES CREDIT UNION

1151 E Warrenville Rd, Naperville, IL 60563
Tel.: (630) 276-5555   IL
Web Site: https://www.hacu.org
Year Founded: 1979
Sales Range: $10-24.9 Million
Emp.: 87
Financial Services
N.A.I.C.S.: 523999
Kenneth J. Rojek (Chm)
Dayla L. Randolph (Vice Chm)
Jack A. Gilbert (Treas & Sec)
Joseph J. Kregul (Pres & CEO)

HEALTHCARE ASSOCIATION OF NEW YORK STATE

1 Empire Dr, Rensselaer, NY 12144
Tel.: (518) 431-7600   NY
Web Site: https://www.hanys.org
Year Founded: 1953
Sales Range: $10-24.9 Million
Emp.: 200
Health Care Association
N.A.I.C.S.: 813920
Kristine Cottom (CIO & VP)
Valerie Grey (Exec VP)
Daniel del Pozzo (CFO)
Jeffrey Gold (Sr VP-Insurance & Managed Care)
Kathleen Ciccone (VP-Quality Institute)
Mark Thomas (Gen Counsel)
Nicholas Henley (VP-Mem Rels)
Kevin Krawiecki (VP-Fiscal Policy)
Mary Ellen Hennessy (VP-Regulatory Affairs)
Michael Ilnicki (CEO)
Robin Frank (VP-Govt Affairs)
Ellen Wagner (Exec Dir)
Bea Grause (Pres)
Courtney Burke (COO)

HEALTHCARE GROWTH PARTNERS

105 S York St Ste 230, Elmhurst, IL 60126
Tel.: (312) 445-8750
Web Site: http://www.hgp.com
Year Founded: 2005
Sales Range: $1-9.9 Million
Emp.: 6
Investment Banking & Strategic Advisory Services
N.A.I.C.S.: 523150
Christopher McCord (Mng Dir & Partner)
Amit Aysola (VP)
Margaret Carlson (Office Mgr)

HEALTHCARE INFORMATION & MANAGEMENT SYSTEMS SOCIETY

33 W Monroe St Ste 1700, Chicago, IL 60603-5616
Tel.: (312) 664-4467   IL
Web Site: http://www.himss.org
Year Founded: 1993
Sales Range: $50-74.9 Million
Emp.: 243
Health Care Management Services Organization
N.A.I.C.S.: 813920
Harold Wolf III (Pres & CEO)

Subsidiaries:

Health 2.0, LLC   (1)
650 Delancey St Apt 221, San Francisco, CA 94107-2083
Web Site: http://www.health2con.com
Digital Health Media Company
N.A.I.C.S.: 518210
Matthew Holt (Co-Chm)
Indu Subaiya (Co-Chm & CEO)

HEALTHCARE NETWORK OF SOUTHWEST FLORIDA

1454 Madison Ave W, Immokalee, FL 34142
Tel.: (239) 658-3000
Web Site: https://www.healthcareswfl.org
Year Founded: 1977
Sales Range: $25-49.9 Million
Medical & Dental Facilities Operator
N.A.I.C.S.: 621111
Edward Olesky (Treas)
Elda I. Hernandez (Sec)
Mike Ellis (Pres & CEO)
Emily Ptaszek (COO)
Mario Dorestal (Vice Chm)
Elizabeth Orr (VP-Dental Svcs)
Stephen Wheeler (VP-Dev)
Maria Ramos (VP-HR)
Larry Allen (VP-IT)
Scott Needle (VP-Medical Staff Affairs)
Gregory Preston (Chief Medical Officer)

HEALTHCARE OF TODAY, INC

2219 W Olive Ave Ste 266, Burbank, CA 91506
Tel.: (818) 557-0165   CA
Web Site: http://www.healthcareoftoday.com
Year Founded: 2008
Sales Range: $50-74.9 Million
Emp.: 5
Holding Company; Nursing Home Services
N.A.I.C.S.: 551112
Robert Hipple (CFO & Gen Counsel)
Kelvin Pan (COO)
Peter Ondi (CIO)
Jim Gray (VP-Healthcare Svcs)
Stewart Simpson (VP-Education & Healthcare Facilities)
Lilly Ghahremani (VP-Mktg)
Michael Chon (VP-Vendor Mgmt Svcs)

Eric Agustin (VP-Bus Dev-East Coast)
Richard Yamakawa (VP-Insurance)
Jose Garcia (VP-Facilities Dev-East Coast)
Jeffrey Place (VP-Consumer Direct & Licensed Businesses)

HEALTHCARE PARTNERS INVESTMENTS LLC

14024 Quail Pointe Dr, Oklahoma City, OK 73134
Tel.: (405) 424-6677
Web Site: http://www.hpillc.org
Year Founded: 2004
Physician Health Care Services
N.A.I.C.S.: 621111
Edward P. Gray (Pres & CEO)
Carl Mikesh (CFO)
Ashley Tate (VP & Gen Counsel)
Stacy Scheffler (Chief Acctg Officer)
Thomas Fondren (VP-Practice Mgmt)

HEALTHCARE REGIONAL MARKETING (HRM)

4270 Ivy Pointe Blvd Ste 220, Cincinnati, OH 45245
Tel.: (513) 864-8900
Web Site: http://www.hrmexperts.com
Year Founded: 2007
Sales Range: $10-24.9 Million
Emp.: 45
Strategic Marketing & Deployment Services to Pharmaceutical Companies
N.A.I.C.S.: 541613
William Goldberg (CEO & Principal)
Jeffrey A. Spanbauer (COO & Principal)
Scott M. Weintraub (CMO & Principal)
Kim Palermo (Mng Dir)
Sam Lowe (Creative Dir)

HEALTHCARE RESOURCE NETWORK LLC

Ste 518 12154 Darnestown Rd, Gaithersburg, MD 20878
Tel.: (301) 926-7666
Web Site: https://www.healthcareresourcenetwork.com
Year Founded: 2004
Sales Range: $1-9.9 Million
Emp.: 135
Healthcare Staffing & Consulting
N.A.I.C.S.: 621999
Laura Bankeroff (Pres & CEO)
Joann Koutsioukis (Owner & VP)

HEALTHCARE STAFFING INC

7600 Osler Dr, Baltimore, MD 21204
Tel.: (410) 823-5474
Rev.: $2,400,000
Emp.: 50
Human Resources & Executive Search Consulting Services
N.A.I.C.S.: 541612
Theo Ocheda (Pres)

HEALTHCARE STRATEGY GROUP, LLC

9900 Corporate Campus Dr Ste 2000, Louisville, KY 40223
Tel.: (502) 814-1180
Web Site: http://www.healthcarestrategygroup.com
Sales Range: $1-9.9 Million
Emp.: 21
Health Care Srvices
N.A.I.C.S.: 621999
John E. Hill (Partner)
David W. Miller (Mng Dir)
M. Davis Creech (Sr Mgr)
Neal D. Barker (Partner)

Bobby J. Morin (Sr Mgr)
Martin Shehan (Mgr)
Travis Ansel (Sr Mgr)
Wade Thomas (Mgr)

HEALTHCARE SUPPORT STAFFING, INC.

101 Southhall Ln Ste 100, Maitland, FL 32751
Tel.: (407) 478-0332
Web Site: https://www.healthcaresupport.com
Year Founded: 2002
Sales Range: $10-24.9 Million
Emp.: 50
Healthcare Staffing Services
N.A.I.C.S.: 561311
Don Langmo (Founder & CEO)
Jennifer Socarras (Pres-South Florida)
Jon Heid (Acct Exec)

HEALTHCARE SYSTEMS & TECHNOLOGIES, LLC

3675 Mt Diablo Blvd Ste 100B, Lafayette, CA 94549
Web Site: http://www.hstpathways.com
Year Founded: 2005
Sales Range: $10-24.9 Million
Emp.: 73
Software Development Services
N.A.I.C.S.: 541511
Tom Hui (Founder & CEO)
Tom Scott (CFO)
Tara Vail (COO)
Jiunn Lim (CTO)
Karlene Ochoa (Sr VP-Ops)

HEALTHCHAMPION PARTNERS LLC

125 S Wacker Dr Ste 2080, Chicago, IL 60606
Tel.: (773) 570-1733
Web Site: http://www.myhealthchampion.com
Healthcare Monitoring System Services
N.A.I.C.S.: 621491
Terrence M. Ryan (Chm & CEO)

Subsidiaries:

Alligator Computer Systems, Inc. (1)
200 S Wacker Dr, Chicago, IL 60606
Tel.: (312) 509-4000
Web Site: http://www.alligatortek.com
Custom Computer Programming Services
N.A.I.C.S.: 541511

HEALTHCHANNELS, INC.

1200 E Las Olas Blvd Ste 201, Fort Lauderdale, FL 33301
Web Site: http://www.healthchannels.com
Year Founded: 2005
Sales Range: $1-9.9 Million
Health Care Srvices
N.A.I.C.S.: 621610
David P. King (Exec Chm)
Adam T. Feinstein (Pres)
Michael Murphy (Founder & CEO)
Tony Andrulonis (COO)
Jennifer Larsen (Exec VP-Mgmt)
Fabio Giraldo Montoya (Exec VP-Ops)
Mike Welch (CFO)
David King (Exec Chm)

HEALTHCOMMUNITIES.COM, INC.

136 W St, Northampton, MA 01060-3709
Tel.: (413) 587-0244
Web Site: http://www.healthcommunities.com
Year Founded: 1998

Healthcommunities.com, Inc.—(Continued)

Sales Range: $1-9.9 Million
Emp.: 18
Online Health Information
N.A.I.C.S.: 517810
Tom Lund *(VP-Ops & Bus Dev)*
Diane Domina *(Dir-Content)*

HEALTHCREST SURGICAL PARTNERS, LLC

3540 S Blvd Ste 225, Edmond, OK
73013
Tel.: (405) 697-2400
Web Site:
   https://www.healthcrest.com
Year Founded: 2016
Ambulatory Surgery Centers
N.A.I.C.S.: 621498
Thomas A. Newman *(CEO)*

HEALTHE GOODS

3140 Mercer Ave, Bellingham, WA
98225
Tel.: (360) 306-8749
Web Site:
   http://www.healthegoods.com
Year Founded: 2005
Sales Range: $1-9.9 Million
Emp.: 25
Online Retailer of Natural Products
N.A.I.C.S.: 456191
Adam Rustad *(CEO)*

HEALTHEDGE INVESTMENT PARTNERS, LLC

5550 W Executive Dr Ste 230,
Tampa, FL 33609
Tel.: (813) 490-7100   **DE**
Web Site:
   https://www.healthedgepartners.com
Year Founded: 2005
Healthcare Industry Private Equity
Firm
N.A.I.C.S.: 523999
Jeffery Scott Thompson *(Partner)*
Brian W. Anderson *(Mng Partner)*
Steve Karasick *(Operating Partner)*
Phillip S. Dingle *(Mng Partner)*
Phillip S. Dingle *(Mng Partner)*
Guy F. Bryant *(Operating Partner)*
Ralph Nelson *(Operating Partner)*
Sandie Spangler *(Office Mgr)*
Elizabeth Breslin *(VP-Bus Dev)*
Matt Dawson *(CFO & Principal)*
Josh Hamrick *(VP)*
Scott Heberlein *(Partner)*
Jon Boumstein *(Operating Partner)*
Terry Conrad *(Operating Partner)*
Bob Cunard *(Operating Partner)*
Winston Haydon *(Operating Partner)*
Cedric Ragsdale *(Operating Partner)*

Subsidiaries:

Intra-Op Monitoring Services,
LLC   **(1)**
76 Starbrush Cir, Covington, LA 70433
Tel.: (985) 871-6800
Web Site: http://www.iomservices.com
Intra-Operative Neurophysiological Monitor-
ing Services
N.A.I.C.S.: 621999

LifeSync Corporation   **(1)**
11705 NW 39th St, Coral Springs, FL 33065
Tel.: (954) 345-9800
Web Site: http://www.lifesync.com
Sales Range: $10-24.9 Million
Emp.: 50
Electrocardiogram Data Communication
Systems Developer & Marketer
N.A.I.C.S.: 334510

SOS Brands, Inc.   **(1)**
1100 Satellite Blvd, Suwanee, GA 30024
Tel.: (678) 684-1426
Web Site: http://www.enaltus.com

Sales Range: $10-24.9 Million
Skin Care Products Developer & Marketer
N.A.I.C.S.: 325412
Jeffery Scott Thompson *(Chm, Pres & CEO)*
Zubin Meshginpoosh *(COO & Exec VP-Pro)*
Martin Floreani *(CMO & Exec VP-Intl)*

Subsidiary (Domestic):

MedAltus, LLC   **(2)**
760 Canning Pkwy, Victor, NY 14564
Tel.: (585) 582-1310
Web Site: http://www.medaltus.com
Sales Range: $1-9.9 Million
Emp.: 20
Physician E-Commerce Site Development,
Management & Skin Care Product Order
Fulfillment Services
N.A.I.C.S.: 493110
Lee Jacobson *(COO)*

SmartBox, LLC   **(1)**
819 Mount Tabor Rd No 8, New Albany, IN
47150
Tel.: (888) 741-1413
Web Site:
   http://www.smartboxwebmarketing.com
Sales Range: $1-9.9 Million
Digital Marketing Services
N.A.I.C.S.: 541613
Colin Receveur *(Founder & CEO)*
Seth Grundhoefer *(Mgr-PR)*
Jason Hahn *(Mgr-Client Success)*
Sean Bailey *(Supvr-Video Team)*
Rebekah Carroll *(Supvr-Content Team)*
Amanda Dalton *(Mgr-Client Success)*
Candice Graves *(Mgr-Client Success)*
Alex Hall *(Dir-Digital Storytelling)*
Kristina Huber *(Supvr-Call Quality Analyst)*
Stacey Iseler *(Dir-Client Success)*
Clinton Kelley *(Mgr-Client Success)*
Keri Langner *(Mgr-Client Success)*
Christina Roth *(Editor-Digital Content)*
Julie Gable *(Controller)*
Robin Hendrich *(Mgr-Client Success)*
Tim Horst *(Mgr-Web Dev)*
Ed Post *(VP-Ops)*
Rachel Reeves *(Dir-Sls)*
Sam Smock *(Mgr-Digital Mktg)*
Teresa G. Stephenson *(Coord-Office)*
Matt Tungate *(Dir-Production)*
Gary Wilson *(Mgr-Compliance)*
Lori Woody *(Dir-Digital Mktg)*
Darrell Rhodes III *(Mgr-Client Success)*

The Corridor Group, Inc.   **(1)**
6405 Metcalf Ave Ste 108, Overland Park,
KS 66202
Tel.: (913) 362-0600
Web Site: http://www.corridorgroup.com
Sales Range: $1-9.9 Million
Emp.: 9
Home Health & Hospice Industry Consult-
ing, Executive Search, Professional Educa-
tion & Training Services
N.A.I.C.S.: 561499
Marsha Lambert *(VP)*
Des Varady *(Co-CEO)*
Kathy Dodd *(Founder)*
Robbin Boyatt *(VP-Revenue Mgmt Svcs)*
Nick Dobrzelecki *(VP-Coding Svcs)*
Donna Galluzzo *(Co-CEO)*
Steve Molinari *(VP-Sls & Mktg)*
Ralph Nelson *(CFO)*
Peggy Patton *(VP-Education Svcs)*

Subsidiary (Domestic):

HMS Healthcare Management Solu-
tions, Inc.   **(2)**
8 Research Pkwy, Wallingford, CT 06492-
1930
Tel.: (203) 269-4667
Web Site: http://www.hmsabc.com
Management Services
N.A.I.C.S.: 541513
Donna Galluzzo *(Pres & CEO)*

Westone Laboratories, Inc.   **(1)**
2235 Executive Cir, Colorado Springs, CO
80906
Tel.: (800) 525-5071
Web Site: http://www.westone.com
In-ear Monitors, Music, Earpieces, Medical
Supplies & Earphones Mfr
N.A.I.C.S.: 334310

itrac LLC   **(1)**

1160 Johnson Ferry Rd Ste 400, Sandy
Springs, GA 30342
Tel.: (541) 342-2958
Web Site: https://www.alatussolutions.com
Dental Practice Management Software De-
veloper & Publisher
N.A.I.C.S.: 513210
Steve Karasick *(CEO)*
Trent Arkema *(COO)*
Becky Meek *(CMO)*
Darrell Swope *(CTO)*

Subsidiary (Domestic):

Belvedere Marketing Group LLC   **(2)**
611 S Congress Ste 310, Austin, TX 78704
Tel.: (512) 628-9509
Web Site:
   http://www.localsearchfordentists.com
Sales Range: $1-9.9 Million
Dental Marketing Software & Services
N.A.I.C.S.: 513210
Graig Presti *(Founder & CEO)*

Dental Post, Inc.   **(2)**
3522 Ashford Dunwoody Rd NE Ste 152,
Atlanta, GA 30319-2002
Tel.: (678) 805-7820
Web Site: http://www.dentalpost.net
Sales Range: $1-9.9 Million
Emp.: 3
Recruitment Consulting Services
N.A.I.C.S.: 541612
Christopher Wilkenloh *(Co-Founder & CTO)*
Tonya Lanthier *(Founder & CEO)*

HEALTHFIRST BLUEGRASS

1736 Alexandria Dr, Lexington, KY
40504
Tel.: (859) 288-2425   **KY**
Web Site:
   http://www.healthfirstlex.com
Year Founded: 2011
Sales Range: $10-24.9 Million
Community Health Care Services
N.A.I.C.S.: 621498
Deborah D. Stanley *(Dir-Medical)*

HEALTHFIRST CORP.

11629 49th Pl W, Mukilteo, WA
98275
Web Site: https://www.healthfirst.com
Year Founded: 1971
Medical, Dental & Hospital Equipment
& Supplies Merchant Whslr
N.A.I.C.S.: 423450
Bryan Thurman *(Mgr-Product & Mktg)*

HEALTHFIRST NETWORK

719 N 3rd Ave, Wausau, WI 54401
Tel.: (715) 675-9859
Web Site:
   http://www.healthfirstnetwork.org
Year Founded: 1973
Health Care Srvices
N.A.I.C.S.: 622110
Jessica Scharfenberg *(Exec Dir)*

HEALTHFIRST, INC.

100 Church St 18th Fl, New York, NY
10007-2601
Tel.: (212) 801-6000   **NY**
Web Site: http://www.healthfirst.org
Year Founded: 1993
Sales Range: $25-49.9 Million
Health Insurance Services
N.A.I.C.S.: 524114
Sean Kane *(Chief HR Officer)*
Patricia J. Wang *(CEO)*
G. T. Sweeney *(CIO)*
Elizabeth Saint Clair *(Cheif Legal Of-
ficer & Gen Counsel)*

HEALTHFLEX HOME HEALTH SERVICES

303 Hegenberger Rd Ste 388, Oak-
land, CA 94621   **CA**
Web Site: http://www.healthflex.com
Year Founded: 2012
Sales Range: $10-24.9 Million
Emp.: 202

Health Care Srvices
N.A.I.C.S.: 621610
Sofia Koshevatsky *(Founder & CEO)*

HEALTHINSIGHT MANAGE-MENT CORPORATION

756 E Winchester St Ste 200, Salt
Lake City, UT 84107
Tel.: (801) 892-0155   **UT**
Web Site: http://www.comagine.org
Health Care Improvement Services
Organization
N.A.I.C.S.: 813920
Marc Bennett *(Pres & CEO)*
Dan Memmott *(CFO & Sr VP-Fin & Admin)*
Juliana Preston *(Sr VP-Systemwide Quality Improvement)*
Jason Owens *(CIO & Chief Info Se-
curity Officer)*
Mylia Christensen *(Sr VP-Leadership Engagement)*
Dan Lessler *(Sr VP-Clinical Leader-
ship)*
Marie Dunn *(Sr VP-Research & Inno-
vation)*
Hugh Straley *(Chm)*
Kim Bateman *(Vice Chm)*
Chris Bosse *(Sec & Treas)*

Subsidiaries:

HealthInsight New Mexico   **(1)**
5801 Osuna Rd NE Ste 200, Albuquerque,
NM 87109
Tel.: (505) 998-9898
Web Site: http://www.healthinsight.org
Health Care Consulting Services Organiza-
tion
N.A.I.C.S.: 813920
Margaret Wienbar *(Exec Dir)*

HealthInsight Oregon   **(1)**
2020 SW 4th Ave Ste 520, Portland, OR
97201-4960
Tel.: (503) 279-0100
Web Site: http://www.healthinsight.org
Health Care Consulting Services Organiza-
tion
N.A.I.C.S.: 813920
Bob Kaiser *(Mgr-IT)*
Judith Wilson *(Dir-Human & Admin Svcs)*
Neidra Evans *(VP-Integration)*
Stacy Moritz *(Dir-Medicare Quality Svcs)*
Greg Martin *(Dir-Comm & Pub Policy)*
Denise Phillips *(Mgr-Medicare Review)*
Mylia Christensen *(Exec Dir)*

HealthInsight Utah   **(1)**
756 E Winchester St Ste 200, Salt Lake
City, UT 84107
Tel.: (801) 892-0155
Web Site: http://www.healthinsight.org
Health Care Consulting Services Organiza-
tion
N.A.I.C.S.: 813920
Juliana Preston *(Exec Dir)*

HealthInsight of Nevada   **(1)**
6830 W Oquendo Rd Ste 102, Las Vegas,
NV 89118
Tel.: (702) 385-9933
Web Site: http://www.healthinsight.org
Health Care Consulting Services Organiza-
tion
N.A.I.C.S.: 813920
Kevin Kennedy *(Exec Dir)*

Qualis Health   **(1)**
10700 Meridian Ave N Ste 100, Seattle, WA
98133
Web Site: http://www.qualishealth.org
Health Care Consulting Services Organiza-
tion
N.A.I.C.S.: 813920
Evan Stults *(VP-Comm)*

HEALTHIX, INC.

40 Worth St 5th Fl, New York, NY
10013
Tel.: (877) 695-4749   **NY**
Web Site: http://www.healthix.org
Year Founded: 2007
Sales Range: $10-24.9 Million

Emp.: 17
Health Care Information Management Services
N.A.I.C.S.: 621999
Tom Moore (VP-Innovation)
Todd M. Rogow (CIO & Sr VP)
Vivienne Destefano (VP-External Affairs & Corp Comm)

HEALTHJUMP, INC.
PO Box 5074, Limerick, PA 19468
Web Site: http://www.healthjump.com
Medical Record & Healthcare Services
N.A.I.C.S.: 518210
Martin Aboitiz (Co-Founder & CEO)
Jim Rowland (Co-Founder, Chief Revenue Officer & Chief Sls & Mktg Officer)
Cliff Cavanaugh (Co-Founder & CTO)

HEALTHLINC, INC.
1001 Sturdy Rd, Valparaiso, IN 46383
Tel.: (219) 462-7173   IN
Web Site:
    https://www.healthlincchc.org
Year Founded: 2001
Sales Range: $10-24.9 Million
Emp.: 189
Health Care Srvices
N.A.I.C.S.: 622110
Deborah Hickman (COO)
Sophia Mendez-Bork (Chief HR Officer)
Beth Wrobel (CEO)
Joan Bondi (CFO)
J. Timothy Ames (Dir-Integrated Care)
Isaac Zeckel (Chief Dental Officer)
Melissa Mitchell (CIO)
Sofia Mendez (Chief HR Officer)
Mary Ann Livovich (Dir-Admin Support)
Rishi Sud (Chief Medical Officer)
Ruth Stevens (Dir-Quality Mgmt)
Dorian Bush (Sec)
Laureen M. Painter (Vice Chm)
Michelle Tatgenhorst (Treas)
Robert Franko (Chm)

HEALTHLINE NETWORKS, INC.
660 3rd St, San Francisco, CA 94107
Tel.: (415) 281-3100
Web Site: http://www.healthline.com
Sales Range: $10-24.9 Million
Emp.: 100
Health Information Web Services
N.A.I.C.S.: 519290
Dean Stephens (CEO)
David Kopp (Exec VP & Gen Mgr)
Ingrid Eberly (VP-Mktg-Direct Adv Sls)
Emma Venturini (Coord-Production)
Isabel Spahn (Sr Editor)
Jessica Perkowitz (Dir-Strategic Analytics)
Kevin Wrathall (Dir-Product)
Kevin Yoshiyama (Dir-Engrg)
Rachael Maier (Dir-Editorial)
Robert Hanson (Dir-Editorial)
Ryan Hutto (Dir-Partner Rels)
Shirley Lin (Dir-Medical Content)

HEALTHNET, INC.
3403 E Raymond St, Indianapolis, IN 46203
Tel.: (317) 957-2000   IN
Web Site:
    https://www.indyhealthnet.org
Year Founded: 1983
Sales Range: $50-74.9 Million
Emp.: 650
Health Care Srvices
N.A.I.C.S.: 622110

Rick Diaz (Pres & CEO)
Larry Flick (CFO)
Sheila Allen (Chief Compliance & Quality Officer)
Donald Trainor (Chief Medical Officer)
Sonja Bachus (COO)
Terri Garcia (Treas)
Kay Johnson (Chief Dev & Comm Officer)

HEALTHOME INC.
601 Genome Way NW Ste 2005, Huntsville, AL 35806
Tel.: (844) 646-6427
Web Site: https://healthome.com
Insurance Services
N.A.I.C.S.: 524298
Darren Rowe (CEO)

Subsidiaries:

Kailos Genetics, Inc.   (1)
601 Genome Way Ste 3005, Huntsville, AL 35806-2908
Tel.: (256) 327-9800
Web Site: http://www.kailosgenetics.com
Medical Laboratories
N.A.I.C.S.: 621511
Brian Pollock (Pres & Founder)

HEALTHPAC COMPUTER SYSTEMS, INC.
1010 E Victory Dr, Savannah, GA 31405
Tel.: (912) 341-7420
Web Site: http://www.healthpac.net
Year Founded: 1981
Rev.: $2,500,000
Emp.: 16
Data Processing, Hosting & Related Services
N.A.I.C.S.: 518210
Buddy Claborn (Pres & CEO)

HEALTHPARTNERS, INC.
8170 33rd Ave S, Bloomington, MN 55425
Tel.: (952) 883-6000
Web Site:
    http://www.healthpartners.com
Year Founded: 1957
Sales Range: $10-24.9 Million
Emp.: 9,200
Health Plan
N.A.I.C.S.: 524114
Brian H. Rank (Dir-Medical)
Thomas R. Brinsko (Treas)
James Malecha (Vice Chm)
Luz Frias (Sec)
Kathy Cooney (Chief Admin Officer & Exec VP)
Barb Tretheway (Sr VP)
Charles Fazio (Sr VP & Dir-Medical)
Nance McClure (COO)
Steven Connelly (Exec Dir-Medical)
Jim Schowalter (Sr VP-Provider Partnerships)
Teresa Tran-Lim (Sr Dir-Medical-Neurosciences)
Andrea M. Walsh (Pres & CEO)
Megan Schmidt (Sr VP-Health Solutions)
Ginger Kakacek (Chief Medical Officer-Health Plan)
Mohammad Suleiman (Sr VP-Comml Bus-Health Plan)
Jennifer Danielson (Chief Health Plan Officer)

HEALTHPOINT
955 Powell Ave SW, Renton, WA 98057-2908
Tel.: (425) 277-1311   WA
Web Site:
    https://www.healthpointchc.org
Year Founded: 1987
Sales Range: $25-49.9 Million
Emp.: 567

Healtcare Services
N.A.I.C.S.: 622110
Vicki Hammond (CFO)
Judy Featherstone (Chief Medical Officer)
Lisa Yohalem (Chief Strategy & Dev Officer)

HEALTHPOINTCAPITAL, LLC
505 Park Ave 17th Fl, New York, NY 10022
Tel.: (212) 935-7780   DE
Web Site:
    https://www.healthpointcapital.com
Year Founded: 2002
Rev.: $650,000,000
Emp.: 10
Healthcare Industry Private Equity Firm
N.A.I.C.S.: 523999
John H. Foster (Chm & Mng Dir)
Joseph A. Fitzpatrick (CFO)
Laing F. Rikkers (Mng Dir)
Mike Mogul (Mng Dir)
David L. Helfet (Mng Dir)
William Johnson (CFO & Mng Dir)
Milen Todorov (Mng Dir)

Subsidiaries:

Illuminoss Medical, Inc.   (1)
993 Waterman Ave, East Providence, RI 02914-1314
Tel.: (401) 714-0008
Web Site: http://www.illuminoss.com
Sales Range: $1-9.9 Million
Emp.: 13
Medical Device Mfr
N.A.I.C.S.: 339112
Robert A. Rabiner (Founder & CTO)
Manny Avila (CEO)
Tekla Capital (Mng Partner)

HEALTHREACH COMMUNITY HEALTH CENTERS
10 Water St Ste 305, Waterville, ME 04901
Tel.: (207) 872-5610   ME
Web Site:
    http://www.healthreachchc.org
Year Founded: 1975
Rev.: $27,887,460
Earnings: $1,134,397
Emp.: 271
Fiscal Year-end: 12/31/18
Community Health Care Services
N.A.I.C.S.: 621498
Constance Coggins (Pres & CEO)
John Opperman (Chm)
Terry Brann (Treas & Sec)
Bruce Harrington (Vice Chm)

HEALTHRIGHT 360
1563 Mission St, San Francisco, CA 94103
Tel.: (415) 762-3700   CA
Web Site:
    http://www.healthright360.org
Year Founded: 1969
Sales Range: $50-74.9 Million
Emp.: 800
Health Care Srvices
N.A.I.C.S.: 622110
Demetrius Andreas (VP-Aftercare Svcs)
Wayne Garcia (VP-Programs)
Mardell Gavriel (VP-Mental Health Svcs)
Vitka Eisen (CEO)

HEALTHSCOPE BENEFITS, INC.
27 Corporate Hill Dr, Little Rock, AR 72205
Tel.: (501) 225-1551
Web Site:
    https://www.healthscopebenefit.com
Year Founded: 1985

Sales Range: $50-74.9 Million
Emp.: 800
Health Insurance Services
N.A.I.C.S.: 524298
Joe Edwards (CEO)
Mary Catherine Person (Pres)
Carol Gaines (Reg VP-Acct Mgmt)
Ed Grooms (VP-Bus Sys)
Susan Johnson (Reg VP-Acct Mgmt)
Kevin Ryan (VP-Strategic Sls)
Paula Thompson (Reg VP-Acct Mgmt)
Scott Barnes (VP-Sls)
Mike Castleberry (Sr VP-Network Svcs & Bus Dev)
Cathleen Armstrong (VP-Claims Admin)
Darren Ashby (Sr VP-Ops)
Wesley Jones (VP-Sls)
Brett Edwards (Sr VP-Legal & Compliance)
Tim Beasley (CIO)
Todd Archer (Sr VP-Acct Mgmt)
Carol Montgomery R. N. (Sr VP-Continuous Improvement)

HEALTHSMART HOLDINGS, INC.
222 W Las Colinas Blvd Ste 500 N, Irving, TX 75039
Tel.: (214) 574-3546   NV
Web Site:
    https://www.healthsmart.com
Holding Company; Third Party Insurance & Health Benefits Administration Services
N.A.I.C.S.: 551112
William Dembereckyj (CFO & Sr VP)
Amy Willingham (VP-HR)
Daniel D. Crowley (Chm)
Mark Stadler (CMO)
Korinne J. Bigelsen (VP-Sls)
John Jackson (Sr VP-Sls)
Tom Mafale (Chief Sls Officer & Exec VP)
Phil Christianson (CEO)
Ron Wozny (VP-Mktg)

Subsidiaries:

HealthSmart Benefit Solutions, Inc.   (1)
222 W Las Colinas, Irving, TX 75039
Tel.: (214) 574-2375
Web Site: http://www.healthsmart.com
Third Party Benefit Administration Services
N.A.I.C.S.: 524292
James M. Pennington (Pres)

HealthSmart Casualty Claims Solutions   (1)
PO Box 3389, Charleston, WV 25333-3389
Tel.: (304) 556-1100
Web Site: http://www.healthsmart.com
Compensation & Benefits Planning Consultant
N.A.I.C.S.: 524292

HEALTHSOURCE
36901 American Way Ste 7, Avon, OH 44011
Tel.: (440) 934-5858
Web Site:
    https://www.healthsourcechiro.com
Sales Range: $1-9.9 Million
Emp.: 11
Chiropractic Services
N.A.I.C.S.: 621310
Chris Tomshack (Founder & CEO)
Kristen Wallace (Controller)
Jim Hoven (VP-Education & Compliance)
Jennifer Work (Project Mgr)

HEALTHSOURCE OF OHIO
5400 Dupont Cir Ste A, Milford, OH 45150-2770
Tel.: (513) 576-7700   OH

Healthsource of Ohio—(Continued)

Web Site: http://www.hsohio.com
Year Founded: 1976
Sales Range: $25-49.9 Million
Emp.: 314
Community Health Care Services
N.A.I.C.S.: 621498
Lisa Jackson (VP-Mktg & Dev)
Kim Patton (Pres & CEO)
James Tomaszewski (Vice Chm)
Sandra K. Mongold (Treas & Sec)
Kevin D. Lefler (Chm)
Heather McNichols (VP-HR)
Tom Ducro (CFO)
Bridget Fossett (VP-Clinical Ops)

**HEALTHSTAR COMMUNICA-
TIONS, INC.**
1000 Wyckoff Ave, Mahwah, NJ
07430
Tel.: (201) 560-5370
Web Site:
　http://www.healthstarcom.com
Year Founded: 2001
Advetising Agency
N.A.I.C.S.: 541810
Chris Sweeney (CEO)
Shannon Sweeney (VP-Strategic So-
lutions)
Joe Tardibuono (Exec VP)
Cira Montreys (Sr VP, Head-Medical
Affairs & Dir-Medical)

Subsidiaries:

Centron　　　　　　　　　　　　(1)
1745 Broadway, New York, NY 10019
Tel.: (646) 722-8900
Web Site: http://www.centroncom.com
Sales Range: $10-24.9 Million
Emp.: 80
N.A.I.C.S.: 541810
Marcia McLaughlin (CEO)
Gary Stamp (Exec VP & Dir-Creative)
Letty Albarran (Dir-Creative)
Madeleine Gold (Mng Dir)
Jennifer Samuels (Mng Dir)
Gary Stamps (Exec Dir-Creative)
Celine Vita (Pres-Adv)
David Stolzer (Sr VP-Digital Strategy & In-
novation)
Meredith Pugh (Chief Growth & Strategy
Officer)
Carolyn O'Neill (Chief Creative Officer)

Photosound Communications　　(1)
1000 Wyckoff Ave, Mahwah, NJ 08536
Tel.: (609) 514-5366
Web Site: http://www.photosound.com
Sales Range: $10-24.9 Million
Emp.: 30
Education, Event Marketing, Exhibit/Trade
Shows, Health Care, Interactive Agencies,
Internet/Web Design, Medical, Pharmaceuti-
cal, Production, Strategic
Planning/Research
N.A.I.C.S.: 541810

Branch (Non-US):

Photosound Communications　　(2)
Sion Park Stansted Rd, Birchanger, Bish-
op's Stortford, CM23 5PU, Herts, United
Kingdom
Tel.: (44) 1279 818400
Web Site: http://www.photosound.co.uk
N.A.I.C.S.: 541810

HEALTHTAP, INC.
101 University Ave Ste 100, Palo
Alto, CA 94301
Tel.: (650) 268-9806　　　　DE
Web Site: http://www.healthtap.com
Year Founded: 2010
Sales Range: $1-9.9 Million
Health Network Mobile Application
Software Developer, Directory & Data
Services
N.A.I.C.S.: 513210
Geoff Rutledge (Chief Medical Offi-
cer)
Sean K. Mehra (Founder & CEO)

Jay Wohlgemuth (Chief Healthcare
Officer)
Bill Gossman (CEO)

Subsidiaries:

Docphin, Inc.　　　　　　　　　(1)
2020 Walnut St Apt 19A, Philadelphia, PA
19103
Web Site: http://www.docphin.com
Software Publisher
N.A.I.C.S.: 513210
Jon Wear (Dir-IT)

HEALTHTIQUE GROUP LLC
46 3rd St NW, Hickory, NC 28601
Tel.: (828) 322-8171
Web Site:
　http://www.healthtiquegroup.com
Senior Living Facility Operator
N.A.I.C.S.: 623311
Michael Jones (CEO)

Subsidiaries:

Healthtique Durham LLC　　　　(1)
411 S LaSalle St, Durham, NC
27705-3799　　　　　　　　(100%)
Tel.: (919) 383-5521
Web Site: http://www.healthtiquegroup.com
Sales Range: $25-49.9 Million
Emp.: 100
Senior Living Facility Operator
N.A.I.C.S.: 623311

Healthtique Winston Salem LLC　(1)
1900 W 1st St, Winston Salem, NC
27104-4220　　　　　　　　(100%)
Tel.: (336) 724-2821
Sales Range: $50-74.9 Million
Emp.: 250
Senior Living Facility Operator
N.A.I.C.S.: 623311

Lake Park of Madison LLC　　　(1)
259 SW Captain Brown Rd, Madison, FL
32340
Tel.: (850) 973-8277
Sales Range: $1-9.9 Million
Emp.: 100
Senior Living Facility Operator
N.A.I.C.S.: 623311

HEALTHTRAX INC.
622 Hebron Ave Ste 200, Glaston-
bury, CT 06033
Tel.: (860) 652-7066
Web Site: https://www.healthtrax.com
Year Founded: 1979
Sales Range: $10-24.9 Million
Emp.: 900
Operator of Health & Wellness Clubs
N.A.I.C.S.: 713940
Kenneth F. Navarro (Co-Founder &
CEO)

Subsidiaries:

Dartmouth Club Properties Inc.　(1)
250 Faunce Corner Rd, Dartmouth, MA
02747
Tel.: (508) 999-2171
Web Site: http://www.healthtrax.com
Rev.: $1,000,000
Emp.: 20
Health Club
N.A.I.C.S.: 713940
Robert E. Stauble Jr. (Pres & CEO)

Enfield Healthtrax Fitness &
Wellness　　　　　　　　　　　(1)
3 Weymouth Rd, Enfield, CT 06082
Tel.: (860) 745-2408
Web Site: http://www.healthtrax.net
Rev.: $2,000,000
Emp.: 47
Membership Sports & Recreation Clubs
N.A.I.C.S.: 713940
Kenneth F. Navarro (Co-Founder & CEO)
Matthew Wright (Dir-Fitness & Coaching-
North Haven)

Healthtrax International Inc.　　(1)
20 E St, Hanover, MA 02339
Tel.: (781) 826-1300
Web Site: http://www.healthtrax.net
Rev.: $1,700,000

Emp.: 65
Health Club
N.A.I.C.S.: 713940

Newington Health & Wellness
Center　　　　　　　　　　　　(1)
375 E Cedar St, Newington, CT 06111
Tel.: (860) 666-8451
Web Site: http://www.healthtrax.net
Rev.: $2,300,000
Emp.: 68
Membership Sports & Recreation Clubs
N.A.I.C.S.: 713940
Jason Otash (Gen Mgr)

West Springfield Properties　　(1)
155 Ashley Ave, West Springfield, MA
01089
Tel.: (413) 781-0181
Web Site: http://www.healthtrax.net
Rev.: $1,700,000
Emp.: 70
Health Club
N.A.I.C.S.: 713940
Kenneth F. Navarro (Co-Founder, Pres &
CEO)

HEALTHTRIO, LLC
603 N Wilmot Rd, Tucson, AZ 85711
Tel.: (303) 397-3000
Web Site: http://www.healthtrio.com
Rev.: $11,000,000
Emp.: 100
Communications Platforms for
Healthcare Industry
N.A.I.C.S.: 541512
Malik M. Hasan (Founder & CEO)
Ritch Haynes (Exec VP)
Dominic Wallen (CEO)
Asma Hasan (Chief Legal Officer)

Subsidiaries:

Online Insight Inc.　　　　　　(1)
84 Walton St NW, Atlanta, GA 30303
Tel.: (404) 600-5221
Web Site: http://www.onlineinsight.com
Computer & Computer Peripheral Equip-
ment & Software Merchant Whslr
N.A.I.C.S.: 423430
Charlie Flowers (CTO)
David M. Fiacco (Pres)

**HEALTHWAY SHOPPING NET-
WORK, INC.**
1300 N Florida Mango Rd Ste 22,
West Palm Beach, FL 33409
Tel.: (866) 220-2226　　　　FL
Web Site:
　http://www.healthwayshoppingnet
　work.com
Year Founded: 2008
Sales Range: Less than $1 Million
Emp.: 2
Natural Products Internet & Television
Marketer
N.A.I.C.S.: 424210
Cleveland Gary (Pres, CEO, CFO &
Sec)

HEALTHWELL FOUNDATION
9801 Washingtonian Blvd Fl 9, Gaith-
ersburg, MD 20878-5355
Tel.: (240) 632-5311　　　　DC
Web Site:
　http://www.healthwellfoundation.org
Year Founded: 2003
Sales Range: $10-24.9 Million
Emp.: 11
Financial Assistance Services
N.A.I.C.S.: 624190
Alan Klein (Chief Dev Officer)
Krista Zodet (Pres)
Shela Halper (Dir-Strategic Dev &
Mktg)
Nancy Carteron (Vice Chm & Sec)
Stephen M. Weiner (Chm)
Jerri Scarzella (Treas & Vice Chm)

HEALTHWISE

3800 Happy Lane Ste A, Sacra-
mento, CA 95827
Tel.: (916) 463-0171
Web Site: http://www.hwhealth.com
Year Founded: 2004
Sales Range: $10-24.9 Million
Emp.: 15
Juicers, Blenders, Dehydrators & Re-
lated Healthy Lifestyle Products Distr
& Whslr
N.A.I.C.S.: 423620
Terry Callahan (Founder & CTO)

HEALTHWYSE, LLC
60 Concord St, Wilmington, MA
01887
Tel.: (877) 777-9973
Web Site: http://www.healthwyse.com
Year Founded: 1998
Electronic Medical Record Software
Developer
N.A.I.C.S.: 513210
Bob Anders (VP-Product)
Kelley Chapman (VP-Engrg)
Graham Barnes (CEO)
Brian Dwyer (Sr VP-Sls & Mktg)
Andrea Leblanc (VP-Client Svcs)

**HEALTHY COFFEE INTERNA-
TIONAL, INC.**
22343 La Palma Ave Ste 113, Yorba
Linda, CA 92887
Tel.: (714) 620-1100
Web Site:
　http://www.healthycoffee.com
Sales Range: $1-9.9 Million
Coffee Mfr
N.A.I.C.S.: 311920
Rick Aguiluz (CEO)

**HEALTHY NEIGHBORHOODS,
INC.**
2 E Read St, Baltimore, MD 21202
Tel.: (410) 332-0387　　　　MD
Web Site:
　http://www.healthyneighborhoods.org
Year Founded: 2004
Sales Range: $10-24.9 Million
Emp.: 8
Neighborhood Development Services
N.A.I.C.S.: 813319
Rahn Barnes (Mgr-Loan Pool)
Timothy Armbruster (Treas)
Mark Sissman (Pres)
Jon M. Laria (Vice Chm)

**HEALTHY PLANET PROD-
UCTS PUBLISHING, INC.**
51 Moraga Way Ste 4, Orinda, CA
94963
Tel.: (925) 253-9595　　　　DE
Web Site:
　http://www.healthyplanet.com
Year Founded: 1978
Sales Range: $1-9.9 Million
Emp.: 13
Greeting Cards, Gifts & Stationery
Marketer & Distr
N.A.I.C.S.: 513191
Gregory C. McPherson (Pres)

**HEART OF AMERICA BEVER-
AGE COMPANY**
2802 S Prigmore, Joplin, MO 64804
Tel.: (417) 623-8585
Web Site: http://www.hoabev.com
Sales Range: $10-24.9 Million
Emp.: 53
Beer & Ale Merchant Whslr
N.A.I.C.S.: 424810
Kathy Slaughter (Office Mgr)
Nancy E. Walkenhorst (Owner)
Robert W. Walkenhorst (Owner)

**HEART OF COMPASSION DIS-
TRIBUTION, INC.**

600 S Maple Ave, Montebello, CA 90640
Tel.: (323) 727-7997   CA
Web Site:
https://www.heartofcompassion.org
Year Founded: 2003
Sales Range: $25-49.9 Million
Poor & Needy People Assistance Services
N.A.I.C.S.: 813410
Eric Tietze *(Pres)*

HEART OF TEXAS ELECTRIC COOPERATIVE INC.
1111 Johnson Dr, McGregor, TX 76657
Tel.: (254) 840-2871   TX
Web Site: https://www.hotec.coop
Year Founded: 2007
Sales Range: $25-49.9 Million
Emp.: 60
Electric Power Distr
N.A.I.C.S.: 221122
Rick Haile *(CEO & Gen Mgr)*
Brandon Young *(Mgr-Admin Svcs)*
Bryan Chandler *(Mgr-Ops)*

HEART TO HEART INTERNATIONAL INC.
13250 West 98th St, Lenexa, KS 66215
Tel.: (913) 764-5200   KS
Web Site: http://www.hearttoheart.org
Year Founded: 1992
Sales Range: $75-99.9 Million
Emp.: 35
Health Care Srvices
N.A.I.C.S.: 622110
Dan Neal *(Dir-Global Logistics)*
Jim Mitchum *(CEO)*

HEART TRUSS & ENGINEERING
1830 N Grand River Ave, Lansing, MI 48908
Tel.: (517) 372-0850
Year Founded: 1963
Sales Range: $10-24.9 Million
Emp.: 100
Truss Mfr
N.A.I.C.S.: 321215
Curt Schaberg *(Owner)*
Joe Butcher *(Partner)*
Donald Butcher *(VP)*

HEARTBEAT DIGITAL
200 Hudson St 9th Fl, New York, NY 10013
Tel.: (212) 941-9041
Emp.: 100
Advertising, Media Buying Services, Media Planning, Search Engine Optimization, Viral/Buzz/Word of Mouth
N.A.I.C.S.: 541810
Bill Drummy *(CEO)*
Jonah Meyers *(CEO)*
Jennifer Campanaro *(Sr Dir-Interactive Mktg)*
James Talerico *(Sr VP & Exec Dir-Creative)*
Lee Slovit *(Dir-Media)*
Nash Dunlap *(Acct Dir)*
Janelle Starr *(VP-Mktg Solutions)*
Chris Whaites *(Dir-Creative)*

HEARTFELT CREATIONS
2147 Eisenhower Dr N, Goshen, IN 46526-8807
Web Site:
https://www.heartfeltcreations.us
Year Founded: 2007
Sales Range: $1-9.9 Million
Emp.: 35
Handicrafts Instruction Services
N.A.I.C.S.: 611610
Linda Bontrager *(Founder & CEO)*

HEARTHSTONE
6720 E Green Lake Way N, Seattle, WA 98103-5439
Tel.: (206) 525-9666   WA
Web Site:
https://www.hearthstone.org
Year Founded: 1961
Sales Range: $10-24.9 Million
Emp.: 255
Retirement Care Services
N.A.I.C.S.: 623311
Judy Chaney *(Sec)*
John Engber *(Vice Chm)*
Jim Mertz *(CEO)*

HEARTHSTONE ENTERPRISES, INC.
251 Industrial Park Dr, Boone, NC 28607
Tel.: (828) 264-0100
Web Site:
https://www.charlestonforge.com
Year Founded: 1984
Sales Range: $10-24.9 Million
Emp.: 30
Metal Household Furniture
N.A.I.C.S.: 337126
Arthur H. Barber *(Owner)*
Susan Barber *(Owner)*

HEARTHSTONE INC.
1630 E Hwy 25 70, Dandridge, TN 37725
Tel.: (865) 397-9425
Web Site:
http://www.hearthstonehomes.com
Sales Range: $10-24.9 Million
Emp.: 15
Log Cabins, Prefabricated, Wood
N.A.I.C.S.: 321992
Carmen Capril *(Pres)*

HEARTLAND AG INC.
407 W Depot Rd, Farmer City, IL 61842
Tel.: (309) 928-9491
Web Site:
https://www.heartlandaginc.com
Sales Range: $10-24.9 Million
Emp.: 15
Mfr of Agricultural Chemicals
N.A.I.C.S.: 424910
Lynn Phelps *(Mgr-Sls)*
Scott Kelley *(Mgr-Ops)*

HEARTLAND AMERICA, INC.
8085 Century Blvd, Chaska, MN 55318
Tel.: (952) 361-3640
Web Site:
https://www.heartlandamerica.com
Year Founded: 1985
Sales Range: $10-24.9 Million
Emp.: 250
Internet & Phone-Based Sales of General Merchandise
N.A.I.C.S.: 423710
Sarah Bode *(Mgr-Call Center)*
Thomas Bulver *(VP)*

HEARTLAND AUTOMOTIVE LLC.
300 S Warren Dr, Greencastle, IN 46135
Tel.: (765) 653-4263
Web Site: https://www.hauto.net
Sales Range: $1-4.9 Billion
Emp.: 600
Motor Vehicle Parts Mfr
N.A.I.C.S.: 336390
Jim Fekete *(Mgr)*
Louis Gudino *(Mgr-HR)*
Joe Hannan *(Mgr-Pur)*
Irma Murray *(Mgr-HR)*
Minoru Shiraishi *(VP-Sls)*
Lawrence Smith *(Mgr-Pur)*

HEARTLAND BLOOD CENTERS
1200 N Highland Ave, Aurora, IL 60506
Tel.: (630) 892-7055   IL
Web Site: http://www.heartlandbc.org
Year Founded: 1943
Sales Range: $25-49.9 Million
Emp.: 539
Blood Bank
N.A.I.C.S.: 621991
Kevin Konrad *(VP-Ops)*

HEARTLAND BUILDING CENTER INC.
2510 General Hays Rd, Hays, KS 67601
Tel.: (785) 625-6554
Web Site:
http://www.heartlandbuilding
center.com
Sales Range: $10-24.9 Million
Emp.: 75
Lumber & Other Building Materials
N.A.I.C.S.: 423310
Curt Pfannenstiel *(Pres)*

HEARTLAND BUSINESS SYSTEMS
1700 Stephen St, Little Chute, WI 54140
Tel.: (920) 788-7720
Web Site: https://www.hbs.net
Sales Range: $125-149.9 Million
Emp.: 500
Information Technology Consulting Services
N.A.I.C.S.: 541512
Carol Henning *(Controller)*
Ben C. Turner *(CEO)*
Scott Papador *(Gen Mgr-South)*
Steve Velner *(VP-Sls & Mktg)*

HEARTLAND CATFISH COMPANY, INC.
55001 Hwy 82 W, Itta Bena, MS 38941
Tel.: (662) 254-7100
Web Site: http://www.catfish.net
Year Founded: 1996
Rev.: $38,039,141
Emp.: 425
Fresh Or Frozen Packaged Fish
N.A.I.C.S.: 311710
Brad Garrard *(CFO & Controller)*
Jonathan Mills *(VP-Sls & Mktg)*
Joseph A. Walker *(Pres)*
Jimmy Killies Tackett *(VP)*

Subsidiaries:

Heartland Catfish - Greensboro   (1)
19518 Alabama Hwy 69 N, Greensboro, AL 36744
Tel.: (334) 624-4021
Sales Range: $50-74.9 Million
Emp.: 185
Fresh Or Frozen Packaged Fish
N.A.I.C.S.: 311710
Tim Milwood *(VP)*

HEARTLAND COMMUNITY GROUP INC
1003 Central Ave, Fort Dodge, IA 50501
Tel.: (515) 955-1600
Web Site:
https://www.hlipublishing.com
Year Founded: 1966
Sales Range: $10-24.9 Million
Emp.: 150
Trade Journals: Publishing & Printing
N.A.I.C.S.: 424920

Subsidiaries:

Heartland Communications
Group   (1)

1003 Central Ave, Fort Dodge, IA 50501
Tel.: (515) 955-1600
Web Site: http://www.hlipublishing.com
Sales Range: $10-24.9 Million
Emp.: 70
Newspaper Publishers
N.A.I.C.S.: 423860
Joseph W. Peed *(Chm)*
Susan Peed *(COO)*
Rick Thomas *(Publr)*
Barbara Benton *(Publr)*
Carol Harrison *(Publr)*
Ian Lumpp *(Publr)*
Franci Motz *(Publr)*
Virginia Rodriguez *(Publr)*

HEARTLAND COOPERATIVE
2829 Westown Pkwy Ste 350, West Des Moines, IA 50266
Tel.: (515) 225-1334   IA
Web Site:
http://www.heartlandcoop.com
Year Founded: 1930
Sales Range: $200-249.9 Million
Emp.: 300
Grain & Field Bean Distr
N.A.I.C.S.: 424510
Craig Orr *(Dir-Market Dev)*
Jason Danner *(Acct Mgr-Sls)*
Randy Sunderman *(VP-IT)*
Terry Frahm *(VP-Admin)*
Todd Phillips *(VP-Grain & Risk Mgmt)*
Brian Bailey *(CFO)*
Tom Hauschel *(CEO & Gen Mgr)*
Dave Coppess *(VP-Sls & Mktg)*

HEARTLAND COOPERATIVE SERVICES
100 Parkside Dr, Dorchester, WI 54425
Tel.: (715) 654-5134   WI
Web Site:
http://www.heartlandcooperative
services.com
Year Founded: 1998
Agricultural Products & Services
N.A.I.C.S.: 424910
Dennis Schultz *(CEO)*
Chris Beeman *(Branch Mgr)*
Sharon Noland *(Controller)*

HEARTLAND CREDIT UNION
4000 N Monroe, Hutchinson, KS 67502
Tel.: (620) 669-0177   KS
Web Site: https://www.hcu.coop
Year Founded: 1948
Sales Range: $10-24.9 Million
Emp.: 111
Credit Union
N.A.I.C.S.: 522130
Michelle Waln *(VP-HR & Retail Ops)*
Zack Clobes *(VP-Tech)*
Dan McFadden *(VP-Lending)*
Mya Wilson *(Mgr-Waco)*
Dan Springer *(Pres & CEO)*
Mark Woleslagel *(Chm)*
Joel Andrew *(CFO)*
Shawn Riley *(VP-Comml Lending)*

HEARTLAND DERMATOLOGY AND SKIN CANCER CENTER, P.A.
828 Elmhurst, Salina, KS 67401
Tel.: (785) 827-2500
Web Site: https://heartland-derm.com
Emp.: 100
Office Of Physician
N.A.I.C.S.: 621111

Subsidiaries:

Manhattan Dermatology PA   (1)
1640 Charles Pl Ste 103, Manhattan, KS 66502-2868
Tel.: (785) 539-4645
Web Site: http://www.manhattanderm.net
Offices of Physicians (except Mental Health Specialists)
N.A.I.C.S.: 621111
Byron Alexander *(Owner)*

Heartland Engineered Products, LLC—(Continued)

HEARTLAND ENGINEERED PRODUCTS, LLC
355 Industrial Dr, Harrison, OH
45030
Tel.: (513) 367-0080
Web Site:
http://www.heartlandengineered
products.com
Year Founded: 1975
Sales Range: $10-24.9 Million
Emp.: 100
Fabricated Structural Metal
N.A.I.C.S.: 332312
Tim Vehr (Mgr-Safety Product)

HEARTLAND EQUIPMENT, INC.
2100 N Falls Blvd, Wynne, AR 72396
Tel.: (870) 318-5002   AR
Web Site: http://www.usatractor.net
Sales Range: $25-49.9 Million
Emp.: 23
Farm & Construction Equipment
Dealer
N.A.I.C.S.: 423820
Jerry Underwood (Owner & Pres)

HEARTLAND EQUITY MANAGEMENT LLC
PO Box 906, Eau Claire, WI 54702-0906
Tel.: (612) 940-4427
Web Site: http://heartland.fund
Privater Equity Firm
N.A.I.C.S.: 523999
Tom Ahonen (Mng Dir)

Subsidiaries:

Cass Screw Machine Products
LLC   (1)
4800 N Lilac Dr, Brooklyn Center, MN
55429-5429
Tel.: (763) 535-0501
Web Site: http://www.csmp.com
Emp.: 127
Precisioned Machined Products Mfr
N.A.I.C.S.: 332721
Steve Wise (Pres & CEO)

HEARTLAND FAMILY SERVICE
2101 S 42nd St, Omaha, NE 68105
Tel.: (402) 553-3000   NE
Web Site:
https://www.heartlandfamily
service.org
Year Founded: 1875
Sales Range: $25-49.9 Million
Emp.: 534
Family & Child Care Services
N.A.I.C.S.: 624110

HEARTLAND FARMS INC.
907 3rd Ave, Hancock, WI 54943
Tel.: (715) 249-5555
Rev.: $25,400,000
Emp.: 130
Vegetable & Melon Farming
N.A.I.C.S.: 111219
Tim Stevenson (Dir-Mktg)
Jeremie Pavelski (Dir-IT & Coord-Safety)
Dave Knights (VP)
Richard Pavelski (Pres)

HEARTLAND FOOD SERVICES INC.
6340 Glenwood Ste 110, Overland
Park, KS 66202
Tel.: (913) 789-7776
Rev.: $10,000,000
Emp.: 5
Fast Food Restaurants
N.A.I.C.S.: 722513

HEARTLAND FOR CHILDREN

1239 E Main St, Bartow, FL 33830
Tel.: (863) 519-8900   FL
Web Site:
https://www.heartlandforchildren.org
Year Founded: 2002
Sales Range: $25-49.9 Million
Emp.: 87
Child Care & Development Services
N.A.I.C.S.: 624110
Vanessa McCottry (Dir-Ops)
Kim Daugherty (Chief Community
Rels Officer)
Bill Nunnally (Chief Quality & Performance Officer)
Jay Halferty (CFO)

HEARTLAND HOME SERVICES, INC.
4101 Sparks Dr Ste B, Grand Rapids,
MI 49546
Web Site:
https://www.heartlandhomeser
vices.com
Year Founded: 2017
Emp.: 100
Plumbing, Heating & Air-Conditioning
Services
N.A.I.C.S.: 238220
William Viveen (CEO)

Subsidiaries:

Faszold Service Company   (1)
103 N Service Rd, Saint Peters, MO 63376
Tel.: (636) 279-1237
Web Site: http://www.faszold.com
Sales Range: $1-9.9 Million
Emp.: 20
Plumbing, Heating & Air-Conditioning Contractors
N.A.I.C.S.: 238220
Kathy Faszold (Treas & Sec)

National Heating & Air Conditioning
Company   (1)
11981 Millstone Ct, Loveland, OH 45140
Tel.: (513) 621-4620
Web Site:
http://www.nationalheatingandac.com
Sales Range: $1-9.9 Million
Emp.: 13
Plumbing, Heating & Air-Conditioning Contractors
N.A.I.C.S.: 238220
Scott Braun (Pres)

HEARTLAND HOMECARE SERVICES, INC.
1025 N 3rd St, Lawrence, KS 66044
Tel.: (785) 331-0807
Web Site: http://www.heartlandrx.net
Rev.: $2,000,000
Emp.: 13
Drugs & Druggists' Sundries Merchant Whslr
N.A.I.C.S.: 424210
Beth Simpson (VP-Ops & Mktg)

Subsidiaries:

Buckner's Heating & Cooling Co. (1)
202 NW 72nd St, Gladstone, MO 64118
Tel.: (816) 436-1244
Web Site: http://www.bucknershc.com
Site Preparation Contractor
N.A.I.C.S.: 238910
Roger Buckner (Founder)

HEARTLAND HONDA
824 S 48th St, Springdale, AR 72762
Tel.: (479) 751-7022
Web Site:
https://www.heartlandhonda.com
Sales Range: $1-9.9 Million
Emp.: 38
Motorcycle Dealers
N.A.I.C.S.: 441227
Greg Donahoe (Gen Mgr)
Mark Donahoe (Asst Gen Mgr-Ops)
Jack Donahoe (Pres)

HEARTLAND HOTEL CORP.
101 3rd Ave SE Fl 4, Cedar Rapids,
IA 52404
Tel.: (319) 363-8613
Web Site:
http://www.heartlandhotel.com
Sales Range: $25-49.9 Million
Emp.: 750
Hotel Management
N.A.I.C.S.: 721110
Derick Rackham (Pres)
James R. Smith (VP)

HEARTLAND LABEL PRINTERS, INC.
1700 Stephen St, Little Chute, WI
54140
Tel.: (920) 788-7720
Web Site: http://www.hbs.net
Year Founded: 1990
Sales Range: $25-49.9 Million
Emp.: 400
Value Added Integration Services &
Networking Technologies
N.A.I.C.S.: 541512
Peter Helander (Pres)
Tracy Reich (Mgr-HR)
Carol Henning (Controller)

HEARTLAND MEAT CO. INC.
3461 Main St, Chula Vista, CA 91911
Tel.: (619) 407-3668   CA
Web Site:
https://www.heartlandmeat.com
Sales Range: $10-24.9 Million
Emp.: 75
Whslr of Meats & Meat Products
N.A.I.C.S.: 424470
Joseph E. Stidman (Owner & Pres)

HEARTLAND MEDIA, LLC
3282 Northside Pkwy Ste 275, Atlanta, GA 30327
Tel.: (470) 355-1944   DE
Web Site: http://www.heartlandtv.com
Holding Company; Television Stations
Owner & Operator
N.A.I.C.S.: 551112
Robert S. Prather Jr. (Pres & CEO)
Bill Wagner (CFO)
Lisa A. Bishop (Chief Digital Officer)
Robert H. Buckler (Exec VP)
Tom Bennett (VP-Engrg)
Michael Spiesman (VP-Sls & Mktg)

Subsidiaries:

St. Joseph TV, LLC   (1)
4000 Faraon St, Saint Joseph, MO 64506
Tel.: (816) 364-2222
Web Site: http://www.kq2.com
Television Broadcasting Station
N.A.I.C.S.: 516120
Dirk Allsbury (Sls Mgr-Local)
Steve Cline (Ops Mgr)
Andy House (Dir-House)
Greg Hurt (Mgr-Digital Media)

WKTV, LLC   (1)
5936 Smith Hill Rd, Utica, NY 13501
Tel.: (315) 733-0404
Web Site: http://www.wktv.com
Television Broadcasting Station
N.A.I.C.S.: 516120
David Streeter (Ops Mgr)
Michelle Liddy (Dir-Digital Sls)
Tom McNicholl (Dir-Engrg)
Steve McMurray (Gen Mgr)
Jeremy Ryan (Dir-News)
Spencer Davidson (Dir-Sports)

HEARTLAND PROPERTIES, INC.
2418 Crossroads Dr Ste 2000, Madison, WI 53718-2423
Tel.: (608) 310-6900
Web Site: https://www.heartland-properties.com
Real Estate Investment
N.A.I.C.S.: 525990

John Stoneman (Pres & Treas)
Dan Fosdick (Sec & VP)
Dick Simonsen (Mgr-Asset)

HEARTLAND PUBLICATIONS, LLC
1 W Main St, Clinton, CT 06413
Tel.: (860) 664-1075
Web Site:
http://www.heartlandpublication.com
Year Founded: 2004
Sales Range: $25-49.9 Million
Emp.: 600
Newspaper Publishers
N.A.I.C.S.: 513110
Michael Bush (Pres & CEO)
Gary Lawrence (COO)
John Adams (CFO)

Subsidiaries:

Point Pleasant Register   (1)
200 Main St, Point Pleasant, WV 25550
Tel.: (304) 675-1333
Web Site: http://www.mydailyregister.com
Sales Range: $10-24.9 Million
Emp.: 4
Newspaper Publishers
N.A.I.C.S.: 513110
Dan Goodrich (Publr)
Julia Schultz (Dir-Adv)

The Robesonian   (1)
2175 N Roberts Ave, Lumberton, NC 28358
Tel.: (910) 739-4322
Web Site: http://www.robesonian.com
Sales Range: $10-24.9 Million
Emp.: 65
Daily Newspaper
N.A.I.C.S.: 513110
Denise Ward (Publr)

The Sampson Independent, Inc. (1)
303 Elizabeth St, Clinton, NC 28328
Tel.: (910) 592-8137
Sales Range: $10-24.9 Million
Emp.: 20
Publishing Daily (Except Monday) Morning
Newspaper
N.A.I.C.S.: 513110
Sherry Matthews (Editor-in-Chief)
Brenda McCullen (Dir-Adv-Classified)
Jules Molenda (Publr)
Jules Melinda (Publr)

HEARTLAND RURAL ELECTRIC COOPERATIVE, INC.
110 N Enterprise Dr, Girard, KS
66743
Tel.: (800) 835-9586
Web Site: https://www.heartland-rec.com
Year Founded: 1996
Sales Range: $10-24.9 Million
Electronic Services
N.A.I.C.S.: 221118
Dale Coomes (CEO)
Dennis Peckman (Pres)
Angie Erickson (Dir-Fin & Admin)
Paul Norris (Mgr-Ops)
Robert Stainbrook (Chm)
Ron Graber (Dir-Member Svc &
Comm)

HEARTLAND SERVICES, INC.
14206 Overbrook, Leawood, KS
66224
Tel.: (913) 685-8855
Web Site: http://www.heartlandsi.com
Year Founded: 1987
Rev.: $15,000,000
Emp.: 100
Hardware & Electrical Services
N.A.I.C.S.: 811310
Jayson Cummins (Mgr-Ops)
Jim Harris (Mgr-Pro Svcs)
Shannon McHone (VP)
Patrick J. Cocherl Jr. (Pres)

HEARTLAND TANNING INC.

4251 NE Port Dr, Lees Summit, MO
64064
Tel.: (816) 795-1414
Web Site:
   http://www.heartlandtan.com
Sales Range: $10-24.9 Million
Emp.: 85
Tanning Salon Equipment & Supplies
N.A.I.C.S.: 423990
Greg Henson *(Pres & CEO)*
Denise Swisher *(Sr Mgr-Info Sys)*
Steve Benner *(Dir-Corp Bus Dev)*
Tiernie Darr *(Sr Mgr-HR Admin)*
John Fromme *(Gen Mgr-Sls-Georgia)*
Jon Marcum *(Sr Mgr-Mfg & Produc-
tion)*
Brad Henson *(Exec VP & Gen Mgr)*
Tammy Reed *(VP-Distr)*
Bill Straka *(CFO & VP)*
Jeff Valaska *(Gen Mgr-Parts & Svc-
Georgia)*
Kenny Shinneman *(Sr Mgr-OEM)*
Trish Robinette *(Controller)*

HEARTLAND, INC.
1005 N 19th St, Middlesboro, KY
40965
Tel.: (606) 248-7323   MD
Web Site:
   http://www.heartlandholdingsinc.com
Year Founded: 1999
Sales Range: $75-99.9 Million
Emp.: 230
Investment Services
N.A.I.C.S.: 523999
Thomas C. Miller *(Sec & VP)*
Terry L. Lee *(Chm, Pres & CEO)*
Mitchell L. Cox *(CFO)*

Subsidiaries:

Harris Oil Company Inc.   **(1)**
330 Oak Dr, Spencer, WV 25276
Tel.: (304) 927-2470
Web Site: http://www.harrisoil.com
Sales Range: $75-99.9 Million
Emp.: 49
Authorized Shell, Pennzoil & Quaker State
Motor Oil Products Distr
N.A.I.C.S.: 424720

Mound Technologies, Inc.   **(1)**
25 Mound Park Dr, Springboro, OH 45066
Tel.: (937) 748-2937
Web Site:
   http://www.moundtechnologies.com
Sales Range: $1-9.9 Million
Emp.: 50
Structural Steel Fabrication
N.A.I.C.S.: 332312
John Barger *(VP)*
Thomas Miller *(Pres)*

HEARTLINE FITNESS SYS-
TEMS
8041 Cessna Ave, Gaithersburg, MD
20879
Tel.: (301) 921-0661
Web Site:
   http://www.heartlinefitness.com
Year Founded: 1995
Rev.: $4,200,000
Emp.: 20
Sporting & Athletic Goods Mfr
N.A.I.C.S.: 339920
Tony Giulioni *(Coord-Metro DC Parts)*
Paul J. Coughlin Jr. *(Chm & Sec)*
Anthony L. Otten *(Treas)*
Robert F. Burgess Jr. *(Pres & CEO)*
Amanda Luksis *(Dir-HR)*
Charlie Amazeen *(Dir-Delivery Ops &
Logistics)*
Jim Kennedy *(Dir-Svc Field Ops)*
Mike Hess *(Dir-Quality Control)*
Bill Pugh *(Mgr-Sls-Southeast US)*
Dennis Boyer *(Coord-Parts-North
East)*
Geoff Vogel *(Mgr-Sls-Northeast US)*

James Shipman *(Mgr-IT Support &
Bus Sys)*
Jeff Shipman *(Pres)*
Zack Smith *(Coord-Warranty & Inven-
tory)*

HEARTWOOD PARTNERS,
LLC
301 Merritt 7, Norwalk, CT 06851
Tel.: (203) 625-0770   CT
Web Site:
   https://www.heartwoodpartners.com
Year Founded: 1982
Privater Equity Firm
N.A.I.C.S.: 523999
Brian D. Fitzgerald *(Founder & Chm)*
Wendy E. Diglio *(Controller-Fund)*
Mark D. Allsteadt *(Mng Partner)*
John C. Willert *(Mng Dir)*
James Sidwa *(Mng Dir)*
Edwin C. Tan *(Mng Dir)*
Robert S. Tucker *(Mng Partner)*
Anastasia Kowal *(CFO & Chief Com-
pliance Officer)*
John Newman *(Principal)*
Michelle Ryan *(CMO)*

Subsidiaries:

All American Label & Packaging   **(1)**
6958 Sierra Ct, Dublin, CA 94568
Tel.: (925) 803-5709
Web Site: http://www.allamericanlabel.net
Label & Packaging Services
N.A.I.C.S.: 561910
Brad C. Brown *(CEO)*

Subsidiary (Domestic):

Tags & Labels   **(2)**
290 27th St, Oakland, CA 94612
Tel.: (925) 803-5709
Sales Range: $1-9.9 Million
Emp.: 30
Converted Paper Product Mfr
N.A.I.C.S.: 322299

Western Shield Acquisitions LLC **(2)**
2146 E Gladwick St, Rancho Dominguez,
CA 90220
Tel.: (310) 527-6212
Web Site: http://www.westernshield.com
Sales Range: $1-9.9 Million
Emp.: 28
Commercial Gravure Printing Services
N.A.I.C.S.: 323111
Dan Stadler *(Dir-Bus Dev)*
Lee Baba *(Mgr-Graphics Prepress)*
Nizar Elias *(CEO)*

Subsidiary (Domestic):

The Label Smith LLC   **(3)**
904 Perla Rd, Pasadena, TX 77502-7502
Tel.: (713) 378-6599
Web Site: http://www.thelabelsmith.com
Printing & Writing Paper Whslr
N.A.I.C.S.: 424110

American Leather Operations,
LLC   **(1)**
4501 Mtn Creek Pkwy, Dallas, TX 75236
Tel.: (972) 590-9250
Web Site: http://www.americanleather.com
Sales Range: $10-24.9 Million
Emp.: 270
Custom-Made Leather Furniture Mfr
N.A.I.C.S.: 337121
Veronica Schnitzius *(Pres)*

Subsidiary (Domestic):

Brookline Furniture Co. LLC   **(2)**
4015 Cheyenne Dr, Archdale, NC 27263
Tel.: (336) 841-8503
Web Site: http://www.brooklinefurniture.com
Upholstered Furniture Mfr
N.A.I.C.S.: 337121
Kristin Phillips *(Dir-Sls Admin)*
Bill Cotter *(VP-Sls)*
Jessica Chapman *(Mgr-Customer Svc &
Transportation)*

Fintube, LLC   **(1)**
555 W 41st St, Tulsa, OK 74107-7012
Tel.: (918) 446-4561

Web Site: http://www.fintubellc.com
Sales Range: $50-74.9 Million
Emp.: 99
Industrial Heat Transfer Equipment & Heat
Exchanger Mfr & Whslr
N.A.I.C.S.: 332410
Joseph Unis *(CFO)*

Parkway Products, LLC   **(1)**
51 Cavalier Blvd Ste 200, Florence, KY
41042
Tel.: (859) 282-4700
Web Site: http://www.parkwayproducts.com
Emp.: 500
Plastics Product Mfr
N.A.I.C.S.: 326199
Michael Alfred *(COO)*

Plant (Domestic):

Parkway Products, LLC - Atlanta
Facility   **(2)**
5300 B Fulton Industrial Blvd, Atlanta, GA
30336
Tel.: (404) 344-2006
Web Site: http://parkwayproducts.com
Plastics Product Mfr
N.A.I.C.S.: 326199
Derek Risner *(Plant Mgr)*

Parkway Products, LLC - Loveland
Facility   **(2)**
4150 St Cloud Dr, Loveland, CO 80538
Tel.: (970) 593-0033
Web Site: http://www.parkwayproducts.com
Thermoplastic Molded Product Mfr
N.A.I.C.S.: 325211

Parkway Products, LLC - Marietta
Facility   **(2)**
1040 Cobb Industrial Dr, Marietta, GA
30066
Tel.: (770) 425-2704
Web Site: http://www.parkwayproducts.com
Plastics Product Mfr
N.A.I.C.S.: 326199

Plant (Non-US):

Parkway Products, LLC - Saltillo
Facility   **(2)**
Calle 17 3364 Parque Industrial Amistad,
25290, Saltillo, Coah, Mexico
Tel.: (52) 844 482 3365
Web Site: http://parkwayproducts.com
Thermoplastic Molded Product Mfr
N.A.I.C.S.: 325211

Plant (Domestic):

Parkway Products, LLC - Seneca
Facility   **(2)**
1642 Blue Ridge Blvd, Seneca, SC 29672
Tel.: (864) 882-5652
Web Site: http://www.parkwayproducts.com
Emp.: 85
Thermoplastic Molded Product Mfr
N.A.I.C.S.: 325211
Bill Dick *(Plant Mgr)*

Premier Performance, LLC   **(1)**
278 E Dividend Dr, Rexburg, ID 83440-
3559
Tel.: (208) 356-0106
Web Site: http://www.premierwd.com
Emp.: 200
Motor Vehicle Parts Wholesale Distr
N.A.I.C.S.: 423120
Trev Burt *(Mgr-Mdsg & Events)*
Bob Barra *(Exec VP-Sls & Mktg)*
Alan Miller *(Mgr-Bus Dev-East)*

Subsidiary (Domestic):

RallySport Direct, LLC   **(2)**
4870 W 2100 S Ste A, West Valley City, UT
84120
Tel.: (801) 748-4910
Web Site: http://www.rallysportdirect.com
Emp.: 100
Motor Vehicle Parts & Consumer Products
Whslr & Online Retailer
N.A.I.C.S.: 423120
Nick Widdison *(Pres)*

UST Corporation   **(1)**
855 N McCormick Way, Layton, UT 84041
Tel.: (801) 547-8052
Web Site: http://www.ustcorp.net

Sales Range: $1-9.9 Million
Emp.: 22
Dietary Supplements Mfr
N.A.I.C.S.: 325411
Wendy English *(VP-Strategic Bus Dev)*
Andrew Saunders *(CFO)*
Kent Skidmore *(VP-Ops)*
Ron Elinkowski *(Exec VP-Sls)*

HEARTWOOD STUDIOS, INC.
400 South El Camino Real Ste 580,
San Mateo, CA 94402-1406
Web Site: http://www.hwd3d.com
Year Founded: 2002
Sales Range: $1-9.9 Million
Emp.: 12
Graphic Design & Marketing Services
N.A.I.C.S.: 541430
Timo Wadhawan *(CFO)*
Raj Raheja *(Co-Founder, Chm &
CEO)*
Neil Wadhawan *(Co-Founder & VP-
Sls & Mktg)*
Tara Scarrow *(Dir-Production)*

HEAT & CONTROL, INC.
21121 Cabot Blvd, Hayward, CA
94545-1132
Tel.: (510) 259-0500   CA
Web Site:
   https://www.heatandcontrol.com
Sales Range: $75-99.9 Million
Emp.: 150
Heating Control Ovens & Equipment
for Food Industry
N.A.I.C.S.: 333241
Tony Caridis *(Pres)*

Subsidiaries:

Heat & Control Inc.   **(1)**
339 Commerce Way, Pembroke, NH
03275-3718
Tel.: (603) 225-5190
Web Site: http://www.heatandcontrol.com
Sales Range: $10-24.9 Million
Emp.: 40
Mfr of Heating Control Ovens & Equipment
for Food Industry
N.A.I.C.S.: 423440
Tony Caridis *(Pres)*
Ronald Ferrante *(Mgr-Ops)*

HEAT SEAL LLC
4580 E 71 St, Cleveland, OH 44125
Tel.: (216) 341-2022
Web Site: http://www.heatsealco.com
Year Founded: 1950
Rev.: $12,600,000
Emp.: 75
Packaging Machinery Mfr
N.A.I.C.S.: 333993
Mike Slivers *(Mgr-Equipment Sls-
West & Midwest)*
Rick Price *(Mgr-Food Svc Sls & Cus-
tomer Svc)*
Bryan Rakovec *(Mgr-Equipment
Sls-East)*

HEAT TREATING SERVICES
CORPORATION OF AMERICA
217 Central Ave, Pontiac, MI 48342
Tel.: (248) 858-2230
Web Site: https://www.htsmi.com
Rev.: $14,641,113
Emp.: 40
Metal Heat Treating
N.A.I.C.S.: 332811
Brad Hynes *(VP)*
Tim Anderson *(Plant Mgr)*
Tony Patterson *(Plant Mgr)*
John Lund *(VP-Sls)*
Franklin Shepard *(VP-Tech Svcs)*
Cody Nash *(Asst Mgr-Plant)*
Pat Vanderworp *(Asst Mgr-Plant)*

HEATEFLEX CORPORATION
405 E Santa Clara St, Arcadia, CA
91006

Heateflex Corporation—(Continued)

Tel.: (626) 599-8566
Web Site: http://www.heateflex.com
Year Founded: 1998
Rev.: $7,300,000
Emp.: 33
Measuring, Testing Electricity, Electrical Signals & Instrument Mfr
N.A.I.C.S.: 334515
Cathy Zhou (VP-Fin)
Jorge Ramirez (Pres & CEO)
George Johnson (Dir-Ops)
Steve Hausle (VP-Sls & Mktg)
Steve Eszeki (Mgr-Sls-SAFNA)
Hector Castaneda (VP-Engrg)
J. P. Rivera (VP-Engrg)

HEATER SPECIALISTS LLC
3171 N Toledo Ave, Tulsa, OK 74115
Tel.: (918) 835-3126
Web Site: https://www.hsi-llc.com
Sales Range: $10-24.9 Million
Emp.: 100
Cement, Clay Refractory
N.A.I.C.S.: 327120
Don Mellott (Owner)
Randy Light (CFO)

HEATH CONSULTANTS IN-CORPORATED
9030 Monroe Rd, Houston, TX 77061-5229
Tel.: (713) 844-1300 DE
Web Site: https://www.heathus.com
Year Founded: 1933
Sales Range: $150-199.9 Million
Emp.: 350
Consulting Service to Gas, Oil, Water & Telephone Industry; Contract Locating & Leak Detection
N.A.I.C.S.: 541330
Paul D. Wehnert (Sr VP-Sls & Mktg)
Carolyn Heath Haag (Pres)
Jeffrey M. Tuttle (CEO)
Jim Rutherford (Sr VP-Products Bus Unit)
Andrew Sitgreaves (CFO & VP)

Subsidiaries:

Heath Consultants (1)
30 Main Ave Ste 3, West Sacramento, CA 95691
Tel.: (916) 921-5198
Web Site: http://www.heathus.com
Sales Range: $10-24.9 Million
Emp.: 2
Utility Protection Services
N.A.I.C.S.: 541618
Graham Midgley (Pres & CEO)

Heath Consultants Inc. Damage Prevention Services (1)
9030 Monroe Rd, Houston, TX 77061-5229 (100%)
Tel.: (713) 844-1200
Web Site: http://www.heathus.com
Sales Range: $100-124.9 Million
Emp.: 200
Consulting Service to Gas, Oil, Water & Telephone Industry; Contract Locating & Leak Detection
N.A.I.C.S.: 333310

Heath Consultants Incorporated - CENTRAL DIVISON (1)
6200 Rothway Ste 160, Houston, TX 77040
Tel.: (713) 844-1204
Leak Detection Device Mfr
N.A.I.C.S.: 334519

Heath Consultants Incorporated - NORTHEAST DIVISON (1)
1051 Garden St, Greensburg, PA 15601
Tel.: (724) 836-7830
Leak Detection Device Mfr
N.A.I.C.S.: 334519

Heath Consultants Incorporated - SOUTHEAST DIVISION (1)
6727 Heritage Business Ct Ste 720, Chattanooga, TN 37421

Tel.: (423) 485-8112
Leak Detection Device Mfr
N.A.I.C.S.: 334519

Heath Consultants Incorporated - WESTERN DIVISION (1)
4100 S Freemont Ave Ste 150, Tucson, AZ 85714
Tel.: (520) 790-4971
Leak Detection Device Mfr
N.A.I.C.S.: 334519
Patsy Avila (Mgr-Admin Div)

Heath Consultants Incorporated, International Sales (1)
9030 Monroe Rd, Houston, TX 77061-5229
Tel.: (713) 844-1300
Web Site: http://www.heathus.com
Sales Range: $50-74.9 Million
Emp.: 150
N.A.I.C.S.: 333310
Timothy G. Brown (Dir-Intl Svcs)

Utility Protection Services-East (1)
Instrument Repair Ctr 119 N Water St, West Newton, PA 15089
Tel.: (724) 836-7830
Web Site: http://www.heathus.com
Sales Range: $25-49.9 Million
Emp.: 30
N.A.I.C.S.: 333310

HEATH VILLAGE RETIREMENT COMMUNITY
430 Schooley's Mountain Rd, Hackettstown, NJ 07840
Tel.: (908) 852-4801 NJ
Web Site:
https://www.heathvillage.com
Year Founded: 1962
Sales Range: $10-24.9 Million
Emp.: 300
Lifecare Retirement Community Operator
N.A.I.C.S.: 623311
Mary Ellen Bove (COO)

HEATHCOTE COMMUNICA-TIONS
345 Auburn Ave Ste 102, Winnetka, IL 60093-3603
Tel.: (847) 446-8764
Year Founded: 1983
Rev.: $12,500,000
Emp.: 16
Fiscal Year-end: 12/31/04
Advetising Agency
N.A.I.C.S.: 541810
Hanod Leear (Chm)
Murray Bloom (VP)
John Connor (VP)
William Stahl (Acct Dir)
Lynn Comfort (Mngmt Supvr)
Bob Porter (Acct Exec)
Rob Gibbs (Media Planner)
Sid Arck (Market Res Dir)
Bill Sails (VP & Media Dir)
Harold Leddy (Pres & CEO)
Sue Silkworth (Sr Acct Dir)
Marcella Baker (Sr Acct Dir)
Dottie Niffy (Production Mgr)
Karl Kaessler (Dir-Creative)
Mary Bell (Acct Supvr)
Mary Bell (Acct Supvr)

HEATHERWOOD CONSTRUC-TION COMPANY
8880 Terrence Ct, Bonita Springs, FL 34135
Tel.: (239) 949-6855
Web Site:
https://www.heatherwoodconstruction.com
Year Founded: 1980
Sales Range: $1-9.9 Million
Emp.: 11
Office, Retail & Industrial Structures Construction
N.A.I.C.S.: 236210

Scott Whiteleather (Sr Project Mgr)
Walter M. Crawford IV (Pres & CEO)

HEATING & PLUMBING ENGI-NEERS INC.
407 W Fillmore Pl, Colorado Springs, CO 80907
Tel.: (719) 633-5414
Web Site: https://www.hpeinc.com
Year Founded: 1947
Sales Range: $25-49.9 Million
Emp.: 500
Plumbing Contractor
N.A.I.C.S.: 238220
Bill Eustace (Pres & Co-Owner)
Kelly Eustace (Co-Owner)
Grant Willemarck (Mgr-Svc Ops)
Brooks Williams (Project Mgr)

HEAVEN HILL DISTILLERIES, INC.
1064 Loretto Rd, Bardstown, KY 40004-2229
Tel.: (502) 348-3921 KY
Web Site: http://www.heavenhill.com
Year Founded: 1934
Sales Range: $200-249.9 Million
Emp.: 500
Mfr & Distr of Distilled Spirits
N.A.I.C.S.: 424820
Max L. Shapira (Pres)
Kate Latts (VP-Mktg)
Susan Wahl (Brand Mgr)
Debbie Morris (VP-HR)
Joe Neal (Reg Mgr-Strategic Chain Acct)

HEAVENSTONE CORP.
17800 Castleton St Ste 300, City of Industry, CA 91748
Tel.: (626) 581-3335 NV
Year Founded: 2014
Single Family Housing Development & Construction
N.A.I.C.S.: 236115
Jack Jie Qin (Pres & CEO)
William E. Sluss (CFO, Treas & Sec)

HEAVY CONSTRUCTORS INC.
4101 N Deadwood Ave, Rapid City, SD 57702
Tel.: (605) 342-3152
Web Site:
http://www.heavyconstructors.com
Rev.: $50,000,000
Emp.: 300
Commercial & Office Building, New Construction
N.A.I.C.S.: 237310
David Gustafson (Pres)
Wayne Gustafson (CEO & Treas)
Johnny Ward (VP)

HEAVY MACHINES, INC.
3926 E Raines Rd, Memphis, TN 38118-6936
Tel.: (901) 260-2200 TN
Web Site:
http://www.heavymachinesinc.com
Year Founded: 1971
Sales Range: $25-49.9 Million
Emp.: 150
Wholesale & Service Heavy Equipment Machines & Parts; Rebuild Electric Motor & Armature Services
N.A.I.C.S.: 423810
Gus Wilson (CFO)
Richard O. Wilson Jr. (Pres & CEO)

Subsidiaries:

HMI Electric (1)
3980 Pilot Ave, Memphis, TN 38118-6928 (100%)
Tel.: (901) 260-2340
Web Site: http://www.hmielectric.com

Sales Range: $10-24.9 Million
Emp.: 40
Sales & Service of Electric Motors & Apparatus; Rebuild of Large Special Handling Equipment; Electric Motor Wholesale, Distribution & Repair
N.A.I.C.S.: 811310
Phil Burton (Gen Mgr)
Jay Nelson (VP)

Heavy Machines, Inc. - Finley LLC Division (1)
364 Bob Jobe Rd, Gray, TN 37615
Tel.: (423) 282-5462
Sales Range: $25-49.9 Million
Emp.: 5
Construction & Heavy Industrial Machinery Distr
N.A.I.C.S.: 423830

Manitowoc Debarking Technology (1)
3926 E Raines Rd, Memphis, TN 38118-6936
Tel.: (888) 875-3954
Sales Range: $25-49.9 Million
Emp.: 40
Mfr of Debarkers For Forest & Logging Industry
N.A.I.C.S.: 423810

HEAVYBAG MEDIA
11732 Dorothy St Apt 5, Los Angeles, CA 90049-5500
Tel.: (310) 472-9803
Year Founded: 2002
Sales Range: Less than $1 Million
Emp.: 10
Market Research, Print, Web (Banner Ads, Pop-ups, etc.)
N.A.I.C.S.: 541810
Dennis Peters (Owner)
Jackie Peters (Partner)

Subsidiaries:

Heavybag West (1)
12160 Montana Ave Ste 5, Los Angeles, CA 90049
Tel.: (310) 472-9803
N.A.I.C.S.: 541810
Jackie Peters (Chief Creative Officer)

HEBBERD KULOW ENTER-PRISES
33 E Malan St, Brawley, CA 92227
Tel.: (760) 344-9343 CA
Year Founded: 2006
Rev.: $20,000,000
Emp.: 11
Containers, Paper & Disposable Plastic
N.A.I.C.S.: 424130

HEBELER CORPORATION
2000 Military Rd, Tonawanda, NY 14150
Tel.: (716) 873-9300
Web Site: http://www.hebeler.com
Year Founded: 1929
Rev.: $50,000,000
Emp.: 150
Custom Machinery
N.A.I.C.S.: 333998
Ken Snyder (Pres)
Jim Briar (CFO)

Subsidiaries:

Hebeler Process Solutions, LLC (1)
750 E Ferry St, Buffalo, NY 14211
Tel.: (716) 895-2100
Web Site: http://buflovak.com
Industrial Rotating & Thermal Process Equipment Mfr
N.A.I.C.S.: 333994
Todd Murray (Product Dir)

HEBERT CANDIES
575 Hartford Tpke, Shrewsbury, MA 01545
Tel.: (508) 845-8051
Web Site:
http://www.hebertcandies.com
Sales Range: $10-24.9 Million

Emp.: 120
Candy & Other Confectionery Products
N.A.I.C.S.: 424490
Lisa Kent Smith (Dir-Product Dev)

HEBERT STEEL CO. INC.

39179 Hwy 74, Gonzales, LA 70737
Tel.: (225) 644-5316
Web Site:
https://www.hebertsteel.com
Year Founded: 1978
Sales Range: $10-24.9 Million
Emp.: 80
Nonresidential Construction
N.A.I.C.S.: 236220
Sterling J. Hebert Jr. (Owner & Pres)
Ronnie Hebert Sr. (VP)

HEBRON SAVINGS BANK

101 N Main St, Hebron, MD 21830
Tel.: (410) 749-1185
Web Site:
http://www.hebronsavingsbank.com
Sales Range: $10-24.9 Million
Emp.: 60
Provider of Banking Services
N.A.I.C.S.: 522110
Cathy D. Brinsfield (COO & Sr VP)
Constance L. Raynor (VP-Ops)
Deborah W. Lowe (Asst VP & Branch Mgr-Sharptown)
Deborah H. Nelson (VP-Branch Ops)
Michelle L. Bramble (Asst VP & Mgr-Salisbury Carroll Street)
Melodie E. Carter (VP-Bus Dev)
Geraldine M. Dolinger (Asst VP & Mgr-Cambridge Cedar Street)
Sue E. Greene (VP-Internal Audit)
Ellen P. Vandegrift (Sr VP)
Mark D. Sewell (VP-Bus Dev)
Robert Freeman (VP-Bus Dev)
Judy E. Shupe (Asst VP & Mgr-Hebron)
David H. Leonard (VP-Bus Dev)
Dawn J. Rayne (Officer-Bus Dev, VP & Branch Mgr)
Kimberly T. Thomas (CFO & Sr VP)
Lori W. Walker (VP-HR)
Lou Ann Brown (Asst VP & Branch Mgr-Crisfield)
Tina M. Banks (Asst VP & Branch Mgr-Bus Dev)
W. Trent Pusey (Chief Lending Officer & Exec VP)
Tim S. Boston (VP-Bus Dev)
Charles Smith III (Chm)
Ronald T. Evans Jr. (Chief Credit Officer & VP)
William R. Riggin Jr. (VP-IT)

HEBS DIGITAL

1601 Broadway 11th Fl, New York, NY 10019
Tel.: (212) 752-8186
Web Site: http://www.hebsdigital.com
Year Founded: 2001
Sales Range: $1-9.9 Million
Emp.: 70
Online Marketing Consulting Services
N.A.I.C.S.: 541613
Max Starkov (Pres & CEO)
Jason Price (Exec VP-Bus Dev)
Mariana Mechoso Safer (VP-Mktg)
Tara Rattigan (VP-Client Svc)

HECATE ENERGY, LLC

115 Rosa Parks Blvd, Nashville, TN 37203-3731
Tel.: (480) 239-5617
Web Site:
http://www.hecateenergy.com
Electric Power Generation
N.A.I.C.S.: 221114
David Tohir (Chm)

HECATE EXPLORATION

7582 Las Vegas Blvd S, Las Vegas, NV 89123
Tel.: (702) 516-7156   NV
Year Founded: 2010
Copper Mining Services
N.A.I.C.S.: 212230
David McNay (Pres, CEO & CFO)
Andrew McCalpine (Sec & Treas)

HECK ENTERPRISES INC.

5415 Choctaw Dr, Baton Rouge, LA 70805
Tel.: (225) 356-2481
Web Site:
https://www.heckindustries.com
Sales Range: $10-24.9 Million
Emp.: 100
Mfr of Ready-Mixed Concrete
N.A.I.C.S.: 327320
Wallace E. Heck Jr. (Pres)

HECKENKEMPER HOMES, LLC.

5314 S Yale Ave Ste 710, Tulsa, OK 74135
Tel.: (918) 628-1255
Year Founded: 1985
Sales Range: $10-24.9 Million
Emp.: 2
Real Estate Development Services
N.A.I.C.S.: 531190
Randy J. Heckenkemper (Owner)

HECNY TRANSPORTATION INC.

150 N Hill Dr Ste 1, Brisbane, CA 94005-1018
Tel.: (415) 468-0600
Web Site: http://www.hecnyusa.com
Rev.: $11,500,000
Emp.: 15
Freight Forwarding
N.A.I.C.S.: 488510
Charles Lee (Chm)

HEDAHLS INC.

100 E Broadway Ave, Bismarck, ND 58501
Tel.: (701) 223-8393   ND
Web Site: http://www.hedahl.com
Year Founded: 1942
Sales Range: $10-24.9 Million
Emp.: 200
Automotive Supplies & Parts Mfr
N.A.I.C.S.: 423120
Larry Lysengen (COO)

HEDDINGER BROKERAGE INC.

535 S 18th St, West Des Moines, IA 50265
Tel.: (515) 222-4458
Rev.: $25,000,000
Emp.: 12
Bond Brokers
N.A.I.C.S.: 424410
David Heddinger (VP)
Deb Sackett (Sec)

HEDERMAN BROTHERS, LLC

247 Industrial Dr N, Madison, MS 39110
Tel.: (601) 853-7300
Web Site: http://www.hederman.com
Commercial Lithographic Printing
N.A.I.C.S.: 323111
Raymond Blevins (Mgr-Pre-Press)
Jim McBrayer (CFO)

Subsidiaries:

Service Printers, Inc.   (1)
1014 N Flowood Dr, Flowood, MS 39232
Tel.: (601) 939-4910
Web Site: http://www.serviceprintersinc.com
Commercial Flexographic Printing
N.A.I.C.S.: 323111

Jay Hill (VP)
Jeff Wolf (Coord-Plant)
M. H. McGee (CEO)
Missie Parker (Coord-Office)

HEDGE CONNECTION INC.

82 Wall St Ste 1108, New York, NY 10005-3610
Tel.: (212) 537-6152
Web Site:
http://www.hedgeconnection.com
Year Founded: 2005
Financial Software Publisher
N.A.I.C.S.: 513210
Andrew Saunders (VP)
Lisa Vioni (CEO)

HEDGEBROOK

PO Box 1231, Freeland, WA 98249
Tel.: (360) 321-4786
Web Site: http://www.hedgebrook.org
Independent Artist Services
N.A.I.C.S.: 711510
Cathy Bruemmer (Mgr-Ops)

HEDGEYE RISK MANAGEMENT LLC

1 High Ridge Park, Stamford, CT 06905
Tel.: (203) 562-6500
Web Site:
http://www.app.hedgeye.com
Investment Research & Advisory Services; Online Financial Media
N.A.I.C.S.: 541910
Keith R. McCullough (Founder & CEO)
Brian McGough (Head-Retail Sector)
Todd Jordan (Head-Gaming, Lodging & Leisure Sector)
Howard Penney (Head-Restaurants Sector)
Tom Tobin (Head-Healthcare Sector)

Subsidiaries:

Hedgeye Potomac Research   (1)
600 New Hampshire Ave NW 10th Fl, Washington, DC 20037
Tel.: (202) 600-7150
Web Site: http://www.potomacresearch.com
Marketing Research Service
N.A.I.C.S.: 541910
James Taylor (Mng Dir & Chief Political Strategist)

HEDRICK BROTHERS CONSTRUCTION CO., INC.

2200 Centrepark W Dr Ste 100, West Palm Beach, FL 33409
Tel.: (561) 689-8880
Web Site:
http://www.hedrickbrothers.com
Year Founded: 1979
Sales Range: $25-49.9 Million
Emp.: 100
Construction Services
N.A.I.C.S.: 236220
Dale R. Hedrick (Pres)
Gene Parker (Exec VP-Residential & Palm Beach)
Eric Engstrom (CFO)
Jack Ullrich (VP-Education, Municipal & Indus)
Donald W. Jones (VP-Comml & Hospitality)
Robin Lunsford (Sr Project Mgr)
Joe Morin (Mgr-Residential Project)
Erik Himmel (VP)
Lisa Hendricks (Dir-HR)

HEDRICK INDUSTRIES INC.

120 1/2 N Church St, Salisbury, NC 28144
Tel.: (704) 633-5982
Web Site: http://www.hedrickind.com
Year Founded: 1924
Sales Range: $25-49.9 Million

Emp.: 280
Mfr of Sand & Gravel
N.A.I.C.S.: 212321
Anthony Arnold (VP)

Subsidiaries:

Southern Concrete Materials Inc.   (1)
35 Meadow Rd, Asheville, NC 28803-2651
Tel.: (828) 253-6421
Web Site: http://www.scmusa.com
Rev.: $45,000,000
Emp.: 2
Mixed Concrete Mfr
N.A.I.C.S.: 327320
David Williams (Sls Mgr)

HEELY-BROWN COMPANY INC.

1280 Chattahoochee Ave, Atlanta, GA 30318-3649
Tel.: (404) 352-0022   GA
Web Site:
https://www.heelybrown.com
Year Founded: 1947
Sales Range: $10-24.9 Million
Emp.: 78
Provider of Roofing, Siding & Insulation
N.A.I.C.S.: 423330
William H. Brown (Pres)

HEETCO INC.

PO Box 188, Lewistown, MO 63452
Tel.: (573) 215-2295
Web Site: http://www.heetco.net
Sales Range: $10-24.9 Million
Emp.: 17,000
Liquefied Petroleum Mfr
N.A.I.C.S.: 424720
Joe Murfin (Pres)

HEETER PRINTING CO., INC.

441 Technology Dr, Canonsburg, PA 15317
Tel.: (724) 746-8900
Web Site: http://heeter.com
Rev.: $2,333,333
Emp.: 80
Other Commercial Printing
N.A.I.C.S.: 323111
Tom Boyle (VP-Sls & Mktg)
Scott Heeter (Pres)
Jason Kestivo (VP-Procurement)
Kirk Schlecker (VP-Ops)
Tim Thomas (Exec VP-Ops)

Subsidiaries:

Duke Graphics, Inc.   (1)
33212 Lakeland Blvd, Willoughby, OH 44095
Tel.: (440) 946-0606
Web Site: http://www.dukeprint.com
Sales Range: $1-9.9 Million
Emp.: 33
Commercial Lithographic Printing
N.A.I.C.S.: 323111
Blake A. Leduc (Pres)
Chris Leduc (VP-Mfg)

HEFFERNAN INSURANCE BROKERS

1350 Carlback Ave Ste 200, Walnut Creek, CA 94596
Tel.: (925) 934-8500
Web Site: http://www.heffgroup.com
Rev.: $14,800,000
Emp.: 500
Insurance Brokerage Services
N.A.I.C.S.: 524210
Jennifer Mahoney (COO)
Elizabeth Bishop (Exec VP)
Brian Dantzig (Exec VP)
Tiffany Maggard (VP-Mideast)
Christopher Dewey (VP)
John Petersen (CIO)
Matthew Skarin (Asst VP)

Heffernan Insurance Brokers—(Continued)

Paul Matlock (Asst VP-Comml Lines Dept-Petaluma)
Allison Redding (Asst VP-Employee Benefits)
Michelle Van Aken (Asst VP-Benefits Dept-Menlo Park)
John Tallarida (Chief Carrier Officer)
Dallas Otter (Exec VP)
Matthew Pearson (VP)
Diana Van Horn (Sr VP-Portland & Mgr-Oregon)
Philip Mortimer (CFO)
Phaedra Starr (VP & Head-Marketplace)
F. Michael Heffernan III (Pres & CEO)

Subsidiaries:

Heffernan Network Insurance
Brokers   (1)
1350 Carlback Ave, Walnut Creek, CA 94596
Tel.: (925) 448-2600
Web Site: https://www.heffnetwork.com
Insurance Brokerage Services
N.A.I.C.S.: 524210

Subsidiary (Domestic):

Barbary Insurance Brokerage   (2)
230 California St Ste 700, San Francisco, CA 94111-4316
Web Site: http://www.barbaryinsurance.com
Insurance Agencies & Brokerages
N.A.I.C.S.: 524210
Jerry Becerra (Pres)

Sierra Insurance Associates Inc.   (1)
12242 Business Park Dr Ste 1, Truckee, CA 96161-3303
Tel.: (530) 550-0123
Web Site: http://www.sierrainsurance.com
Insurance Agencies & Brokerages
N.A.I.C.S.: 524210

Stitz & Associates, Inc.   (1)
1350 Carlback Ave, Walnut Creek, CA 94596
Tel.: (314) 821-1946
Web Site: http://www.stitzinsurance.com
Commercial & Institutional Building Construction
N.A.I.C.S.: 236220
Victor Stitz (Owner)

HEFREN-TILLOTSON, INC.
308 7th Ave, Pittsburgh, PA 15222
Tel.: (412) 434-0990
Web Site: http://www.hefren.com
Year Founded: 1948
Sales Range: $25-49.9 Million
Emp.: 130
Provider of Investment Advisory Services
N.A.I.C.S.: 523150
Kimberly Tillotson Fleming (Chm & CEO)
James G. Meredith (Exec VP)
Craig Tillotson (Vice Chm)
Lillian Brandimarti (VP-Admin)
Sherry Zakelyhidi (Dir-HR)
Alfred Vallano (Sr VP & Branch Mgr)
Larry Sebbens (Dir-Mktg)
Rachel Hawili (Dir-Corp Svcs)
Craig McRoberts (Exec VP)
Tyler Vallano (VP)
Dan Richmond (VP)
Brian J. Koble (Dir-Res)
Michael T. McGrath (Dir-Fin Plng)
Trevor McCance (Dir-Insurance)
Joseph Niesslein (CFO)
Kurt Carlson (Exec VP)
Ryan Larkin (VP)
Joseph Grunwald (VP)

HEHMEYER, LLC
601 S Lasalle St Ste 200, Chicago, IL 60605
Tel.: (312) 327-4000   DE
Web Site: http://www.htgcap.com

Emp.: 200
Private Investment Firm
N.A.I.C.S.: 523999
Chris Hehmeyer (CEO & Mgr)
William McNeill (Mng Dir-Trading)

HEI HOSPITALITY, LLC
101 Merritt 7 Corporate Park 1st Fl, Norwalk, CT 06851
Tel.: (203) 849-8844
Web Site: https://www.heihotels.com
Year Founded: 2002
Sales Range: $200-249.9 Million
Emp.: 3,200
Hotel Owner, Operator & Manager
N.A.I.C.S.: 721110
Anthony Rutledge (CEO & Mng Partner)
Theodore W. Darnall (CEO-HEI Hotels and Resorts Lodging and Technical Services Company)
Clark Hanrattie (CFO & Partner)
Nigel Hurst (Sr VP-HR)
Brian Mayer (Exec VP-Ops)
Randy Sumner (Sr VP-Design & Construction)
Tory Waterman (Exec VP-Hotel Fin)
Dan Walworth (Sr VP-Operational Plng)
Brian Russo (Sr VP-Corp Fin)
Charlie Colletta (Sr VP-Investment Analysis & Asset Mgmt)
Steen Petri (Sr VP-Investments)
Rob Willis (Sr VP-Design & Construction)

HEIDE & COOK MECHANICAL CONTRACTORS
1714 Kanakanui St, Honolulu, HI 96819-3223
Tel.: (808) 841-6161
Web Site: http://www.heide-cook.com
Year Founded: 1996
Sales Range: $25-49.9 Million
Emp.: 160
Holding Company; Mechanical & Project Contractors
N.A.I.C.S.: 551112
Todd Y. Williams (Pres)

Subsidiaries:

Heide & Cook, Ltd.   (1)
1714 Kanakanui St, Honolulu, HI 96819-3223   (100%)
Tel.: (808) 841-6161
Web Site: http://www.heide-cook.com
Sales Range: $25-49.9 Million
Emp.: 100
Mfr, Sale, Design, Installation & Service of Plumbing, Heating & Air-Conditioning Products
N.A.I.C.S.: 238220
Earle Matsuda (Pres & CEO)

Division (Domestic):

AirReps Hawaii   (2)
1734 Kanakanui St, Honolulu, HI 96819
Tel.: (808) 846-9270
Web Site: http://www.airreps-hi.com
Sales Range: $25-49.9 Million
Emp.: 100
Air Cooling Products & Water Coolers Service & Distr
N.A.I.C.S.: 423730
Earle Matsuda (Pres)

HEIDEBREICHT, INC.
64200 Van Dyke, Washington, MI 48095
Tel.: (586) 752-5900
Web Site: https://www.heidebreicht.com
Sales Range: $50-74.9 Million
Emp.: 53
Car Whslr
N.A.I.C.S.: 441110
Kurt W. Heidebreicht (Principal)

HEIDELBERG PASTRY SHOPPE, INC.
2150 N Culpeper St, Arlington, VA 22207-2007
Tel.: (703) 527-8394
Web Site:
    https://www.heidelbergbakery.com
Sales Range: $10-24.9 Million
Emp.: 45
Bakery Retailer
N.A.I.C.S.: 311811
Carla Buchler (Owner)

HEIDT DESIGN LLC
5904 Hampton Oaks Blvd Ste A, Tampa, FL 33610
Tel.: (813) 253-5311
Web Site:
    https://www.heidtdesign.com
Sales Range: $1-9.9 Million
Emp.: 40
Engineeering Services
N.A.I.C.S.: 541330
B. Patrick Gassaway (Pres)
Michael Tucker (Sr VP)
Timothy Plate (Sr VP)
Michael Holbrook (Dir-Plng & Landscape Architecture)

HEIDTMAN STEEL PRODUCTS, INC.
2401 Front St, Toledo, OH 43605-1145
Tel.: (419) 691-4646
Web Site: https://www.heidtman.com
Year Founded: 1954
Sales Range: $50-74.9 Million
Emp.: 406
Blast Furnaces & Steel Mills
N.A.I.C.S.: 331110
John C. Bates (Pres & CEO)

Subsidiaries:

National Galvanizing LP   (1)
1500 Telb Rd, Monroe, MI 48162-2572
Tel.: (734) 243-1882
Web Site:
    http://www.nationalgalvanizing.com
Sales Range: $10-24.9 Million
Emp.: 99
Steel Processing Plant
N.A.I.C.S.: 331110
Micheal D. Robinson (Gen Mgr)

HEIK HOLDING COMPANY INC.
2608 S Hume Ave, Marshfield, WI 54449-5551
Tel.: (715) 387-3414   WI
Web Site: https://www.hsmfgco.com
Year Founded: 1993
Sales Range: $10-24.9 Million
Emp.: 250
Farm Machinery & Equipment Mfr
N.A.I.C.S.: 333111
Chris Heikenen (Pres)

Subsidiaries:

H&S Manufacturing Co. Inc.   (1)
2608 S Hume Ave, Marshfield, WI 54449-5551   (100%)
Tel.: (715) 387-3414
Web Site: http://www.hsmfgco.com
Sales Range: $10-24.9 Million
Emp.: 105
Farm Machinery & Equipment Mfr
N.A.I.C.S.: 333111
Chris Heikenen (Founder & Pres)

Steinberg Mfg. Co. Inc.   (1)
11651 N State Rd 22, Clintonville, WI 54929
Tel.: (715) 823-3974
Sales Range: $10-24.9 Million
Emp.: 105
Farm Machinery & Equipment Mfr
N.A.I.C.S.: 333111

HEILBRICE

1 Corporate Plz, Newport Beach, CA 92660
Tel.: (949) 336-8800   CA
Web Site: https://www.heilbrice.com
Year Founded: 1987
Rev.: $80,000,000
Emp.: 40
Advertising Specialties, Consumer Marketing, Retail
N.A.I.C.S.: 541810
Hal Brice (Co-Founder & CEO)
Joni Brice (Co-CEO)
Jeff Morris (Pres)
Joni Parenti (Dir-Creative)

HEILIND ELECTRONICS, INC.
58 Jonspin Rd, Wilmington, MA 01887
Tel.: (978) 657-4870
Web Site: http://www.heilind.com
Year Founded: 1974
Rev.: $200,000,000
Emp.: 500
Electronic Parts & Equipment Distr
N.A.I.C.S.: 423690
Robert W. Clapp (Founder)

Subsidiaries:

D.B. Roberts Company   (1)
30 Upton Dr Ste 3, Wilmington, MA 01887
Tel.: (978) 988-5777
Web Site: http://www.dbroberts.com
Sales Range: $25-49.9 Million
Emp.: 60
Fastener Distr
N.A.I.C.S.: 423710

Interstate Connecting
Components   (1)
120 Mount Holly Bypass, Lumberton, NJ 08048-1112
Tel.: (856) 722-5535
Web Site: http://www.connecticc.com
Sales Range: $10-24.9 Million
Emp.: 80
Electronic Connectors, Fiber Optic Connectors & Connector Accessories Distr
N.A.I.C.S.: 423690
Donna Wanger (Acct Mgr)
Regina Worthy (Mgr-HR)
Lisa Evans (Product Mgr)
Tracey Renshaw (Mgr-Sls)

HEILMAN HOLDING COMPANY INC.
4120 E Truman Rd, Kansas City, MO 64127
Tel.: (816) 231-5737
Sales Range: $10-24.9 Million
Emp.: 125
Uniforms
N.A.I.C.S.: 812332

HEINEMANN'S BAKERIES L.L.C.
PO Box 558265, Chicago, IL 60655
Tel.: (616) 885-9094
Web Site:
    http://www.heinemanns.com
Rev.: $29,000,000
Emp.: 175
Bakery
N.A.I.C.S.: 311813
Jim Bersell (VP-Production & Quality Assurance)

HEINEN & ASSOCIATES LLC
9668 Westheimer Ste 200-49, Houston, TX 77063
Tel.: (713) 974-3278
Web Site:
    http://heinenandassociates.com
Real Estate Appraisal Services
N.A.I.C.S.: 531320
Scott Heinen (Owner)

HEINEN'S INC.
4540 Richmond Rd, Warrensville Heights, OH 44128

Tel.: (216) 475-2300   OH
Web Site: https://www.heinens.com
Year Founded: 1929
Sales Range: $500-549.9 Million
Emp.: 1,400
Retailer of Groceries
N.A.I.C.S.: 445110
Jeffrey Heinen *(CEO)*
Thomas J. Heinen *(COO)*
Tom Heinen *(Co-Pres)*
Gary Wilshire *(Dir-Facilities)*
Joe O'Connor *(Dir-Labor Rels)*
Mary Ann Correnti *(CFO)*
Todd Pesek *(Chief Medical Officer)*

HEINN CHAPMAN CORPORATION
5431 N 27th St, Milwaukee, WI
53209
Tel.: (414) 906-3060   WI
Web Site:
    https://www.heinnchapman.com
Year Founded: 1896
Rev.: $8,000,000
Emp.: 60
Looseleaf Binders & Indexes Mfr
N.A.I.C.S.: 323111
Charles Tuff *(Pres)*
Jim Bullock *(Mgr-Ops)*
Jeffrey Morgan *(VP-Sls)*

HEINRICH CHEVROLET
5775 S Transit Rd, Lockport, NY
14094
Tel.: (716) 434-6681
Web Site:
    http://www.heinrichchevy.com
Year Founded: 1965
Sales Range: $10-24.9 Million
Emp.: 90
Car Whslr
N.A.I.C.S.: 441110
Charles Heinrich *(Owner)*
Greg Fitch *(Gen Mgr-Sls)*
Paul Collins *(Controller)*

HEINRICH MARKETING
1350 Independence St, Denver, CO
80215
Tel.: (303) 233-8660   DE
Web Site: http://www.heinrich.com
Year Founded: 1977
Rev.: $18,000,000
Emp.: 55
Direct Marketing
N.A.I.C.S.: 541810
Laura Sonderup *(Mng Dir & Dir-Heinrich Hispanidad)*
Sandi McCann *(Sr VP-Fin Svcs)*
Kathie Williams *(Exec VP)*
John Schlagel *(Dir-Strategy)*
Cathy Peeper *(Sr VP & Dir-Acct)*
Erin Iwata *(Dir-Acct)*
Jeff Davis *(Acct Exec)*
Erika Lidster *(Sr Mgr-Print Production)*
Robert L. McPhee *(Dir-Creative)*
Linds Johnson *(Assoc Dir-Media)*

Subsidiaries:

Heinrich Hawaii   **(1)**
900 Fort St Mall Ste 860, Honolulu, HI
96813
Tel.: (808) 275-1021
Web Site: http://www.heinrichhawaii.com
Sales Range: $10-24.9 Million
Emp.: 20
N.A.I.C.S.: 541810
Marc Witter *(Mng Dir)*
Patrick Bullard *(Sr Dir)*
Katie Gallo *(Sr Acct Mgr)*
Pat Nohara Ho *(Mgr-Brand Media)*
Rob McPhee *(Dir-Creative)*

Heinrich Hispanidad   **(1)**
1350 Independence St, Denver, CO 80215-
4629
Tel.: (303) 233-8660

Web Site:
    http://www.heinrichhispanidad.com
Sales Range: $10-24.9 Million
Emp.: 25
N.A.I.C.S.: 541810
Laura Sonderup *(Mng Dir & Sr Strategist)*

HEINTZ AUTOMOTIVE
1234 Raintree Rd, Mankato, MN
56001-6860
Tel.: (507) 387-1148
Web Site:
    http://www.heintztoyota.com
Sales Range: $10-24.9 Million
Emp.: 39
Car Whslr
N.A.I.C.S.: 441110
Mike Drysdale *(Mgr)*
Henry Heinz *(Principal-Dealer)*

HEINZERLING FOUNDATION
1800 Heinzerling Dr, Columbus, OH
43223-3698
Tel.: (614) 272-8888   OH
Web Site: https://www.heinzerling.org
Year Founded: 1959
Sales Range: $10-24.9 Million
Emp.: 809
Developmental Disability Assistance
Services
N.A.I.C.S.: 623210
Midge Dunaway *(Dir-Volunteer Svcs)*
Vanessa M. Wright *(Dir-HR)*
Debbie Rogner *(Fin Dir)*
Robert E. Heinzerling *(Exec Dir)*

HEIRLOOM RESTAURANT GROUP
102 NUniversity Parkway, Provo, UT
84601
Tel.: (801) 373-8000
Web Site:
    http://www.heirloomrestaurant
group.com
Year Founded: 2007
Sales Range: $1-9.9 Million
Emp.: 53
Restaurant Management
N.A.I.C.S.: 722511
Colton Soelberg *(Co-Founder & Co-Owner)*

HEISER AUTOMOTIVE GROUP INC.
1700 W Silverspring Dr, Glendale, WI
53209
Tel.: (414) 577-1600   WI
Web Site: https://www.heiser.com
Year Founded: 1917
Sales Range: $125-149.9 Million
Emp.: 320
Auto Dealership
N.A.I.C.S.: 441110
Dan Kane *(Asst Mgr-Svc)*
Michael Finn *(Mgr-Sls)*
Mickie Lavanda *(Mgr-Parts Svc & Body Shop Acctg)*
Rhonda Rendon *(Mgr-Fin)*
Gene Vicari *(Mgr-IT & Mktg)*
Maureen Ferguson *(Mgr-Customer Rels)*

HEISER TOYOTA, INC.
1700 W Silver Spring Dr, Milwaukee,
WI 53209
Tel.: (262) 334-3858
Web Site: http://heisertoyota.com
Sales Range: $10-24.9 Million
Emp.: 72
Car Whslr
N.A.I.C.S.: 441110
Rick Nelson *(Mgr)*

HEISLER GORDON & ASSOCI-ATES

1643 N Milwaukee Ave, Chicago, IL
60647
Tel.: (773) 342-9900   IL
Web Site: http://www.hgadgroup.com
Year Founded: 1987
Rev.: $20,000,000
Emp.: 17
Fiscal Year-end: 03/31/05
Full Service
N.A.I.C.S.: 541810
Larry Heisler *(Mng Partner)*
Barb Nasby *(Controller)*
Jim Rednour *(VP-Pub Rels)*
Dale McWilliams *(VP & Assoc Dir-Creative)*

HEISTER HOUSE MILL-WORKS, INC.
1937 Troup Valley Rd, Mount Pleasant, PA 17853-8115
Tel.: (570) 539-2611
Web Site:
    https://www.hhmillworks.com
Year Founded: 1988
Sales Range: $1-9.9 Million
Emp.: 68
Wood Product & Accessory Mfr
N.A.I.C.S.: 423310
Brad Lauver *(Partner)*

HEITECH SERVICES, INC.
8201 Corporate Dr Ste 600,
Landover, MD 20785
Tel.: (301) 918-9500
Web Site:
    http://www.heitechservices.com
Year Founded: 1999
Rev.: $20,900,000
Emp.: 450
Computer Related Services
N.A.I.C.S.: 541512
Heidi W. Gerding *(Pres & CEO)*
James R. Clement *(Exec VP)*
Cami Jordan *(Controller)*

HEITMAN LLC
191 N Wacker Dr Ste 2500, Chicago,
IL 60606
Tel.: (312) 855-5700   DE
Web Site: http://www.heitman.com
Year Founded: 1966
Rev.: $39,000,000,000
Emp.: 360
Real Estate Investment Management
Services
N.A.I.C.S.: 531390
Maury R. Tognarelli *(Pres & CEO)*
Mary K. Ludgin *(Mng Dir/Head-Global Res)*
Lewis S. Ingall *(Sr Mng Dir-Client Svc & Mktg)*
James M. Bachner *(Exec VP-Acq-North America)*
Gregory Leadholm *(Sr Mng Dir/Co-Head-Real Estate Debt-North America)*
Thomas McCarthy *(Sr Mng Dir-Private Equity-Chicago-North America)*
Thomas Turpin *(COO)*
Anthony G. Stamato *(Chief Legal Officer)*
Edward Rieger *(Sr VP & Dir-Global Consultant Rels)*
Anne Westbrook *(Sr VP-Client Svc & Mktg-north America)*
Darrah Bixler *(Mng Dir-HR)*
David Maki *(Sr Mng Dir/Co-Head-Real Estate Debt-North America)*
Larry Christensen *(CFO)*
Tamara Solarich *(Sr VP & Dir-Mktg & Comm-Global)*
Brad Fu *(Sr VP-Hong Kong & Dir-Acq-Asia Pacific)*
Skip Schwartz *(Mng Dir-Real Estate Equity Grp-Asia Pacific)*
Jerome Claeys III *(Chm)*

HEITS BUILDING SERVICES, INC.
1 University Plaza Dr Ste 118, Hackensack, NJ 07601
Tel.: (201) 288-7708   NJ
Web Site: https://www.heits.com
Year Founded: 2003
Sales Range: $1-9.9 Million
Emp.: 50
Building Maintenance Services
N.A.I.C.S.: 561720
David Heitner *(Founder & CEO)*

HEKTOEN INSTITUTE, LLC.
2240 W Ogden Ave 2nd Fl, Chicago,
IL 60612-4220
Tel.: (312) 768-6000   IL
Web Site: http://www.hektoen.org
Year Founded: 1943
Sales Range: $25-49.9 Million
Emp.: 396
Medical Research Services
N.A.I.C.S.: 541715
George Dunea *(Pres & CEO)*

HELDENFELS ENTERPRISES INC.
5700 IH-35 S, San Marcos, TX
78666-9505
Tel.: (512) 396-2376
Web Site:
    https://www.heldenfels.com
Year Founded: 1995
Sales Range: $25-49.9 Million
Emp.: 175
Prestressed Concrete Structures
N.A.I.C.S.: 327390
Gil Heldenfels *(Gen Mgr-Bldg Sys)*
Fred W. Heldenfels IV *(Pres & CEO)*

HELEN GORDON INTERESTS LTD.
2601 Main St, Houston, TX 77002-
9223
Tel.: (713) 371-3600
Web Site:
    http://www.thegreensheet.com
Year Founded: 1970
Sales Range: $200-249.9 Million
Newspaper & Print Advertising Services
N.A.I.C.S.: 513110

HELEN ROSS MCNABB CENTER, INC.
201 W Springdale Ave, Knoxville, TN
37917
Tel.: (865) 637-9711   TN
Web Site:
    http://www.mcnabbcenter.org
Year Founded: 1953
Sales Range: $100-124.9 Million
Outpatient Mental Health & Substance Abuse Care Centers Operator
N.A.I.C.S.: 813212
Charles Finn *(Chm)*
Richard Maples *(Chm)*
Fran Leonard *(Sec)*
Randy Miller *(Treas)*

HELEN THOMPSON MEDIA
8035 Broadway, San Antonio, TX
78209-2628
Tel.: (210) 822-2158
Web Site:
    http://www.helentmedia.com
Year Founded: 1989
Sales Range: $10-24.9 Million
Emp.: 5
Media Buying Services
N.A.I.C.S.: 541830
Helen Thompson *(Pres)*
Brandon Thompson *(Media Planner)*

Helen Woodward Animal Center—(Continued)

HELEN WOODWARD ANIMAL CENTER
6461 El Apajo Rd, Rancho Santa Fe, CA 92067
Tel.: (858) 756-4117   CA
Web Site:
   https://www.animalcenter.org
Year Founded: 1972
Sales Range: $10-24.9 Million
Emp.: 204
Animal Care Services
N.A.I.C.S.: 813312
Wendy Papera (Mgr-HR)
Rita V. Truderung (CFO & VP-Operations)
Jessica Gercke (Mgr-PR)
Megan McCarty (Mgr-Volunteer & Retail Svcs)
Lon Jones (Mgr-Sys Programming)
Michael M. Arms (Pres & CEO)
Renee Resko (VP-Development)
Renee Simmons (VP-Finance)

HELENA LABORATORIES CORPORATION
1530 Lindbergh Dr, Beaumont, TX 77707
Tel.: (409) 842-3714   TX
Web Site: https://www.helena.com
Year Founded: 1967
Sales Range: $150-199.9 Million
Emp.: 800
Clinical & Diagnostic Equipment Mfr
N.A.I.C.S.: 339112
Charl Louw (Mgr-Sls-Republic of Scientific Group-South Africa)
Ros Rafel (Dir-Ops-Republic of Scientific Group-South Africa)

Subsidiaries:

Helena Laboratories (Australia) Pty. Ltd.   (1)
37 Ricketts Rd, PO Box 340, Mount Waverley, 3149, VIC, Australia
Tel.: (61) 395437299
Web Site: http://www.helena.com.au
Sales Range: $10-24.9 Million
Emp.: 15
Clinical & Diagnostic Equipment
N.A.I.C.S.: 334510

Helena Laboratories (UK) Limited   (1)
Unit B M361 Queensway South, Team Valley Trading Estate, Gateshead, NE11 0SD, Tyne and Wear, United Kingdom (100%)
Tel.: (44) 191 482 8440
Web Site: http://www.helena-biosciences.com
Sales Range: $10-24.9 Million
Emp.: 130
Clinical & Diagnostic Equipment Mfr
N.A.I.C.S.: 334510

Helena Plastics   (1)
3700 Lakeville Hwy Ste 200, Petaluma, CA 94954
Tel.: (707) 766-2100
Web Site: http://www.labcon.com
Sales Range: $25-49.9 Million
Emp.: 200
Mfr of Clinical & Diagnostic Equipment
N.A.I.C.S.: 921110
Jim Happ (Pres)

Kabushiki Kaisha Helena Kenkyujyo   (1)
9-21-19 Tokiya, Urawa-ku, Saitama, 330-0061, Japan   (100%)
Tel.: (81) 488333208
Web Site: http://www.helena.co.jp
Sales Range: $10-24.9 Million
Emp.: 32
Mfr & Distr of Clinical & Diagnostic Equipment
N.A.I.C.S.: 334510
Tokiya Nakazato (Gen Mgr)

HELENA MOTORS LLC.
3401 E US Hwy 12, Helena, MT 59601
Tel.: (406) 442-6310
Web Site:
   http://www.helenamotors.com
Sales Range: $25-49.9 Million
Emp.: 55
Car Whslr
N.A.I.C.S.: 441110
Jim Stanger (Principal)

HELFMAN DODGE CHRYSLER JEEP FIAT
7720 Katy Fwy, Houston, TX 77024
Tel.: (713) 533-6100
Web Site:
   http://www.helfmandodge.com
Year Founded: 2002
Sales Range: $25-49.9 Million
Emp.: 50
Car Whslr
N.A.I.C.S.: 441110
Steven Wolf (Gen Mgr)

HELFMAN ENTERPRISES INC.
4807 Kirby Dr, Houston, TX 77098-5005
Tel.: (713) 524-3801
Web Site:
   https://www.riveroakscars.com
Sales Range: $100-124.9 Million
Emp.: 400
New & Used Car Dealers
N.A.I.C.S.: 441110
Alan Helfman (Pres)
Mike Gross (Controller)

HELGET SAFETY SUPPLY INC.
4144 S 87th St, Omaha, NE 68127
Tel.: (402) 339-1066
Rev.: $12,000,000
Emp.: 19
Safety Equipment
N.A.I.C.S.: 423830
William Helget (Pres)
Paula Rosenthal (Office Mgr)

HELI-MART INC.
3184 Airway Ave Ste E, Costa Mesa, CA 92626
Tel.: (714) 755-2999
Web Site: http://www.heli-mart.com
Rev.: $15,180,196
Emp.: 9
Helicopter Parts Mfr
N.A.I.C.S.: 423860
Ed Brown (VP-Sls)
Melinda Cooper (Controller)

HELICOPTERS INC.
5000 Omega Dr, Cahokia, IL 62206
Tel.: (314) 351-1400
Web Site: http://www.heliinc.com
Helicopter Carrier
N.A.I.C.S.: 481111
Stephen C. Lieber (Pres)

HELINET AVIATION SERVICES LLC
16303 Waterman Dr, Van Nuys, CA 91406
Tel.: (818) 902-0229
Web Site: http://helinet.com
Year Founded: 1987
Sales Range: $75-99.9 Million
Emp.: 50
Helicopter Carrier Services
N.A.I.C.S.: 481219
Kathryn Purwin (CEO)
Kevin LaRosa II (VP-Aerial Film Production)

Subsidiaries:

SHOTOVER Systems Ltd.   (1)
5660 Airport Blvd Ste 101, Boulder, CO 80301
Tel.: (720) 744-3300

Aviations & Aerospace Services
N.A.I.C.S.: 334511
Tom Churchill (CEO)

Subsidiary (Domestic):

Churchill Navigation Inc.   (2)
5660 Airport Blvd Ste 101, Boulder, CO 80301-2596
Tel.: (720) 841-0314
Web Site:
   http://www.churchillnavigation.com
Aircraft Part & Auxiliary Equipment Mfr
N.A.I.C.S.: 336413
Erin Murphy (Dir-Sls)

SHOTOVER Camera Systems LP   (2)
5660 Airport Blvd Ste 101, Boulder, CO 80301
Tel.: (720) 744-3300
Web Site: http://www.shotover.com
Aviation & Aerospace Services
N.A.I.C.S.: 334511
Tom Churchill (CEO)
Brad Hurndell (Gen Mgr)

HELIO PRECISION PRODUCTS INC.
601 N Skokie Hwy, Lake Bluff, IL 60044
Tel.: (847) 473-1300
Web Site:
   http://www.helioprecision.com
Rev.: $17,000,000
Emp.: 200
Engine Valves Mfr
N.A.I.C.S.: 336310
Dean Friebus (Engr-Mfg)

HELIOS EDUCATION FOUNDATION
2415 E Camelback Rd Ste 500, Phoenix, AZ 85016-4288
Tel.: (602) 381-2260   AZ
Web Site: http://www.helios.org
Year Founded: 2004
Sales Range: $100-124.9 Million
Emp.: 26
Educational Support Services
N.A.I.C.S.: 611710
Barbara Ryan Thompson (COO & Exec VP)
Noel McClain (Dir-Human Capital & Workplace Ops)
Charles Hokanson (Chief Policy Officer & Sr VP-Community Engagement-Florida)
Vince Roig (Chm)
Paul Luna (Pres & CEO)
Vince Yanez (Sr VP-Community Engagement-Arizona)
Braulio Colon (VP-Florida Regional Student Success)
Michael Chesin (CFO & Sr VP)

HELIOS HR, LLC
1925 Isaac Newton Sq E Ste 200, Reston, VA 20190
Tel.: (703) 860-3882
Web Site: http://www.helioshr.com
Year Founded: 2001
Sales Range: $1-9.9 Million
Emp.: 175
Human Resources & Executive Search Consulting Services
N.A.I.C.S.: 541612
Ellyn Krause (VP-Fin)
Kathy Albarado (Pres & CEO)
Amy Stark (Dir-Talent Acq Practice)
Madelyne D'Angelo (Mng Dir)

HELIX ELECTRIC INC.
8260 Camino Santa Fe Ste A, San Diego, CA 92121-3255
Tel.: (858) 535-0505   CA
Web Site:
   http://www.helixelectric.com
Year Founded: 1985

Sales Range: $100-124.9 Million
Emp.: 1,000
Electrical Work
N.A.I.C.S.: 238210
Gary Shekhter (Pres & CEO)

HELIX LIMITED
100 N Walnut St, Itasca, IL 60143
Tel.: (312) 421-6000
Web Site:
   https://www.helixcamera.com
Sales Range: $10-24.9 Million
Emp.: 6
Photographic Equipment & Supplies
N.A.I.C.S.: 423410
Valerie Marose (Pres)

HELIX WATER DISTRICT
7811 University Ave, La Mesa, CA 91942
Tel.: (619) 466-0585
Web Site: https://www.hwd.com
Year Founded: 1885
Sales Range: $25-49.9 Million
Emp.: 150
Supplier of Water
N.A.I.C.S.: 221310
Carlos Lugo (Gen Mgr)
Chuck Muse (Pres)
Lisa Stoia (Dir-Admin Svcs)
Jim Tomasulo (Dir-Engrg)
Tristan Hayman (Dir-Ops)
Mark Umphres (Dir-Water Quality & Sys Ops)
Sandy Janzen (Sec)

HELLER AUTO GROUP
1717 Auto Pkwy S, Escondido, CA 92029
Tel.: (760) 745-3361
Year Founded: 1947
Sales Range: $50-74.9 Million
Emp.: 175
Car Whslr
N.A.I.C.S.: 441110
Tony Fodor (Gen Mgr-Ford)

HELLER BROS. PACKING CORP.
288 9th St 34787, Winter Garden, FL 34777
Tel.: (407) 656-2124   FL
Web Site: http://www.hellerbros.com
Year Founded: 1939
Sales Range: $100-124.9 Million
Emp.: 690
Harvester, Packer & Shipper of Citrus Fruits
N.A.I.C.S.: 111310
Harvey R. Heller (Pres)
Harry Heller Falk (Exec VP)
Jeff Mckinney (CFO)
Alex Heller (VP)
Kevin Koppelman (VP-Field Ops & Production)
Justin Ficken (Mgr-Maintenance)
Jim Fulton (Mgr-IT)
John Merck (Mgr-Harvesting)
Belinda Perales (Mgr-Receiving)
Billy Teal (Mgr-Production)
David Gutierrez (Mgr-Transportation & Logistics)

HELLER DISTRIBUTING CO. INC.
4920 Wilshire Ave N, Albuquerque, NM 87113
Tel.: (505) 797-1600
Web Site:
   http://www.coldfrontdist.com
Rev.: $27,000,000
Emp.: 50
Packaged Frozen Goods
N.A.I.C.S.: 424420
Tim Valdez (Pres)

HELLER INDUSTRIES INC.
4 Vreeland Rd Ste 1, Florham Park,
NJ 07932
Tel.: (973) 377-6800
Web Site:
   http://www.hellerindustries.com
Sales Range: $10-24.9 Million
Emp.: 30
Ovens Mfr
N.A.I.C.S.: 333998
Marc Peo (Pres-Sls)
Don Angelo (VP-Sls & Mktg)
Phil Martin (Dir-European Ops)

HELLER MOTORS, INC.
720 S Deerfield Rd, Pontiac, IL
61764
Tel.: (815) 842-1128   IL
Web Site:
   http://www.hellermotors.com
Sales Range: $25-49.9 Million
Emp.: 60
New & Used Car Dealer
N.A.I.C.S.: 441110
Daniel G. Heller (Owner & Pres)
Marty Heller (VP)
Greg Head (Mgr-Sls)

HELLMAN & FRIEDMAN LLC
415 Mission St Ste 5700, San Fran-
cisco, CA 94105
Tel.: (415) 788-5111   DE
Web Site: http://www.hf.com
Year Founded: 1984
Privater Equity Firm
N.A.I.C.S.: 523999
Jacob Best (Partner)
Allen R. Thorpe (Partner)
David R. Tunnell (Partner)
Arrie R. Park (Chief Legal Officer &
Partner)
Tarim Wasim (Partner)
Trevor R. Watt (Partner)
Benjamin A. Farkas (Partner)
Zita Saurel (Partner)
Stuart D. Banks (Partner & Gen
Counsel)
Judd Sher (CFO & Partner)
Brian D. Doyle (Partner)
Sameer Narang (Partner)
Deepak Advani (Partner)
Blake Kleinman (Partner)
Patrick Healy (CEO)
Susanna Daniels (Partner & Head-IR)
Jacob Best (Executives)
Matthew B. Eisen (Executives)
Annmarie Neal (Partner & Chief Tal-
ent Officer)
P. Hunter Philbrick (Partner)
Ted Akiskalos (Mng Dir)
Gary E Bischoping Jr. (Partner)
Tumi Akinlawon (Associate)
Casilda Aresti (Assoc Dir-Associate)
Julia Arnold (Dir-Partner Svcs)
Michael K. Attal (Principal)
Catie Barile (Principal)
Jackson Baur (Associate)
Caleb Carter (Associate)
Dionne Chen (Associate)
Elaine Chirls (Principal)
Simon Chiu (Executives)
Zach Cohen (Associate)
Ajay Desai (Associate)
Michael Dessau (Associate)
Brian Doyle (Partner)
Abbie Drobnick (Associate)
Stephen Ensley (Partner)
David Crichlow Jr. (Associate)
Zomo Fisher (Head-Sustainability,
Environment, Safety & Governance)
Joseph Ghobrial (Principal)
Stefan Goetz (Partner)
Josh Gold (Dir)
Whitney Ping (Executives)
Morgan O'Connor (Associate)
Will Packwood (Associate)

Alexis Orenstein (Dir)
Adam Halpern Leistner (Executives)
Alex McGregor (Principal)
Adrien Motte (Dir)
Sonal Singla (Executives)
John Yoshida (Dir)
Lauren Zachry (Senior Counsel)
Greg Why (Mng Dir)
Rachel Stock (Mng Dir)
Angelo Teles (Associate)
Nina Sola Sola (Associate)
Emily Riemer (Associate)
Courtney O'Brien (Associate)
Patrick Peladeau (Associate)
Toto Nguyen (Associate)
Jack Munns (Associate)
Daniel McGarvey (Associate)
Justin Lee (Associate)
Joann Kong (Associate)
Alec Hsing (Associate)
Daniel Hong (Associate)
Annmarie Neal (Partner & Chief Tal-
ent Officer)
Johannes Korp (Partner)
Quyen Le (Director of Finance)
Alannah Nisbet (Associate)
Brian Powers (Senior Advisor &
Chairman Emeritus)
Matthew Barger (Senior Advisor)
Jeffrey Goldstein (Advisor Emeritus)
Philip U. Hammarskjold (Exec Chm)

Subsidiaries:

ABRA Auto Body & Glass LP   (1)
7225 Northland Dr Ste 210, Brooklyn Park,
MN 55428
Tel.: (763) 561-7220
Web Site: http://www.abraauto.com
Holding Company; Automotive Body &
Glass Repair Shops Owner, Operator &
Franchisor
N.A.I.C.S.: 551112
Timothy R. Adelmann (Exec VP-Bus Dev)
Duane A. Rouse (Vice Chm)
Scott M. Krohn (Chief Process & Quality
Officer)
David Kuhl (Chief People Officer & Exec
VP)
Barbara Ducat (Sr VP-Acq Integrations)
Chris Pudenz (CFO & Exec VP)
Erik Ragatz (Chm)
Laurie Janu (VP-Natl Mktg)
Toan Nguyen (Chief Info & Strategy Officer)

Subsidiary (Domestic):

ABRA Automotive Systems LP   (2)
6601 Shingle Creek Pkwy, Brooklyn Center,
MN 55430
Tel.: (763) 561-7220
Web Site: http://www.abraauto.com
Rev.: $5,000,000
Emp.: 55
Automotive Body & Glass Repair Shops
Operator
N.A.I.C.S.: 811121

ABRA Franchise Services LP   (2)
6601 Shingle Creek Pkwy Ste 200, Brook-
lyn Center, MN 55430
Tel.: (763) 585-6315
Web Site: http://www.abraauto.com
Automotive Body & Glass Repair Shop
Franchisor
N.A.I.C.S.: 533110

Caliber Bodyworks of Texas, Inc.   (2)
401 E Corporate Dr Ste 150, Lewisville, TX
75057   (55%)
Tel.: (469) 948-9500
Web Site: http://www.calibercollision.com
Automotive Body, Paint & Interior Repair &
Maintenance Services
N.A.I.C.S.: 811121
Steve H. Grimshaw (Chm)
Mark Sanders (Pres & CEO)
Greg Nichols (Chief Admin Officer & Gen
Counsel)
Ron Davis (Chief Dev Officer)
Janet DeBerardinis (CIO)
Shawn Hezar (Sr VP-Strategic Accts)
Judd Nystrom (CFO)
Claudia Schaefer (Chief Experience Officer)

Subsidiary (Non-US):

MacGregor Golf Asia Ltd.   (3)

Unit E 6/F Yeung Yiu Chung 7 Industrial
Building 2 Fung Yip St, 77 Leighton Road,
Chai Wan, China (Hong Kong)
Tel.: (852) 28918222
Web Site: http://www.macgregor.com.hk
Sales Range: $25-49.9 Million
Emp.: 11
Golfing Equipment Mfr
N.A.I.C.S.: 339920

Subsidiary (Domestic):

The Greg Norman Collection   (3)
134 W 37th St 4th Fl, New York, NY 10018
Tel.: (646) 840-5200
Web Site: http://www.gnccorporate.com
Emp.: 50
Golf Apparel & Equipment Designer & Distr
N.A.I.C.S.: 315250
Michael J. Setola (Pres & CEO)

Allfunds Bank, S.A.   (1)
Calle de los Padres Dominicos 7, 28109,
Madrid, Spain
Tel.: (34) 912746400
Web Site: http://www.allfundsbank.com
Mutal Fund Distr
N.A.I.C.S.: 523150
Juan Alcaraz (CEO)
Borja Largo (Head-Fund Grps-Global)
Simon Shapland (Reg Mgr-UK & Ireland)
Gianluca Renzini (Chief Comml Officer &
Deputy Gen Mgr)
Juan Carlos Gallego (COO)
Alexis Fosler (Reg Mgr-Asia)
Sebastian Ochagavia (Head-Chile)
Luigi Lubelli (CFO)
Georges Yayrura (Chief Product Officer)
Jorge Calvino (Chief People Officer)

Applied Systems Inc.   (1)
200 Applied Pkwy, University Park, IL
60484-4110
Tel.: (708) 534-5575
Web Site: http://www.appliedsystems.com
Sales Range: $75-99.9 Million
Emp.: 1,100
Insurance Software
N.A.I.C.S.: 513210
Doug Johnston (VP-Partner Rels)
Ian Hoffman (CMO)
James R. White (Exec VP-Sls)
Kristin Hackney (Sr VP-Svcs)
Michael Howe (Sr VP-Product Mgmt)
Jeffrey D. Purdy (Sr VP-Ops-Intl)
Tim Sander (Sr VP-IT)
Gregory Shiple (Sr VP-Support)
David H. Whitley (Sr VP-Dev)
Paul Ramsey (Sr VP-HR)
Teresa Smith (Sr VP-Customer Advocacy)
Taylor Rhodes (CEO)
Graham Blackwell (CFO)

Associated Materials Group, Inc.   (1)
3773 State Rd, Cuyahoga Falls, OH
44223   (97%)
Tel.: (330) 929-1811
Web Site:
   http://www.associatedmaterials.com
Sales Range: $1-4.9 Billion
Emp.: 5
Holding Company; Steel, Aluminum & Vinyl
Siding, Aluminum Trim Coil & Vinyl Window
Mfr & Distr
N.A.I.C.S.: 551112
James T. Kenyon (Chief HR Officer & Sr
VP)
David L. King (Sr VP-Direct Sls)
Brian C. Strauss (Pres & CEO)
William L. Topper (Exec VP-Ops)
Kenneth James (Gen Counsel & Sec)

Subsidiary (Domestic):

Associated Materials, LLC   (2)
3773 State Rd, Cuyahoga Falls, OH 44223
Tel.: (330) 929-1811
Web Site:
   http://www.associatedmaterials.com
Rev.: $1,184,969,000
Assets: $1,082,013,000
Liabilities: $1,296,374,000
Net Worth: ($214,361,000)
Earnings: ($50,112,000)
Emp.: 3,000
Fiscal Year-end: 01/02/2016
Steel, Aluminum & Vinyl Siding, Aluminum
Trim Coil & Vinyl Window Mfr & Distr
N.A.I.C.S.: 326199

Brad S. Beard (Chief Comml Officer/Sr VP-
AMI Distr & Svcs)
James T. Kenyon (Chief HR Officer & Sr
VP)
David L. King (Chief Comml Officer/Sr VP-
Direct Sls)
Brian C. Strauss (Pres & CEO)
William L. Topper (Exec VP-Ops)
Dana A. Schindler (CMO & Sr VP)
Scott F. Stephens (CFO & Exec VP)
Kenneth James (Gen Counsel & Sec)

Division (Domestic):

Alside   (3)
3773 State Rd, Cuyahoga Falls, OH 44223-
2603
Tel.: (330) 929-1811
Web Site: http://www.alside.com
Sales Range: $25-49.9 Million
Emp.: 300
Vinyl Siding Door & Window Mfr
N.A.I.C.S.: 326199
Tom Chieffe (Pres & CEO)

Plant (Domestic):

Alside - Bothell Plant   (4)
19720 Bothell Everett Hwy, Bothell, WA
98012-7120
Tel.: (425) 481-7101
Web Site: http://www.alside.com
Vinyl Siding, Doors & Windows Mfr
N.A.I.C.S.: 326199

Subsidiary (Domestic):

Gentek Building Products, Inc.   (3)
3773 State Rd, Cuyahoga Falls, OH 44223
Tel.: (330) 929-1811
Web Site: http://www.gentekinc.com
Sales Range: $10-24.9 Million
Emp.: 20
Mfr of Exterior Building Products
N.A.I.C.S.: 332322

At Home Group Inc.   (1)
1600 E Plano Pkwy, Plano, TX 75074
Tel.: (972) 265-6227
Web Site: http://www.athome.com
Rev.: $1,737,063,000
Assets: $2,524,913,000
Liabilities: $2,040,753,000
Net Worth: $484,160,000
Earnings: ($149,729,000)
Emp.: 7,692
Fiscal Year-end: 01/30/2021
Home Furniture, Accessories, Crafts & Sea-
sonal Products Retailer
N.A.I.C.S.: 459999
Mary Jane Broussard (Chief Admin Officer,
Gen Counsel & Sec)
Peter S. G. Corsa (Pres)
Norman E. McLeod (Chief Dev Officer)
Ashley F. Sheetz (COO)
Sumit Anand (CIO & Head-Strategy)
Chad C. Stauffer (Chief Mdsg Officer)
Catherine Aslin (Chief HR Officer)
Lewis L. Bird III (CEO)

Subsidiary (Domestic):

At Home Properties LLC   (2)
3091 University Dr E 110, Bryan, TX 77802
Tel.: (979) 696-5357
Web Site: http://www.athomepm.com
Home Furniture Product Retailer
N.A.I.C.S.: 459999

AutoScout24 GmbH   (1)
Dingolfinger Strasse 1-15, 81673, Munich,
Germany   (100%)
Tel.: (49) 89 444 561 666
Web Site: http://www.autoscout24.de
Online Automotive Marketplace Search Por-
tal Developer & Operator
N.A.I.C.S.: 518210

Subsidiary (Domestic):

**FMPP Verwaltungsgesellschaft
mbH**   (2)
Rosenheimerstr 143b, 81671, Munich, Ger-
many
Tel.: (49) 89189690100
Web Site: http://www.financescout24.de
Online Services
N.A.I.C.S.: 541519

Edelman Financial Services, LLC (1)

Hellman & Friedman LLC—(Continued)

4000 Legato Rd 9th Fl, Fairfax, VA 22033-4055
Web Site:
http://www.edelmanfinancialengines.com
Investment Advisory & Asset Management Services
N.A.I.C.S.: 523940
Fredric M. Edelman (Founder & Exec Chm)
Rene Chaze (Chief Dev Officer)
James Mendelsohn (CMO)
Ryan Parker (CEO)

Subsidiary (Domestic):

Align Wealth Management, LLC (2)
13921 Quail Pointe Dr, Oklahoma City, OK 73134
Tel.: (405) 607-4820
Web Site: http://www.alignmywealth.com
Financial Investment Activities
N.A.I.C.S.: 523999
Darlene Eisel (Mgr-Client Svcs)

Edelman Financial Engines, LLC (2)
1050 Enterprise Way 3rd Fl, Sunnyvale, CA 94089
Tel.: (408) 498-6000
Web Site:
http://www.edelmanfinancialengines.com
Portfolio Management, Investment Advice, Retirement Assistance & Online Investing Services
N.A.I.C.S.: 523940
Christopher L. Jones (Chief Investment Officer & Exec VP-Investment Mgmt)
Jeffrey C. Grace (VP & Controller)
Kelly S. O'Donnell (Chief Admin Officer, Chief Risk Officer & Exec VP)
Lee Antone (Gen Counsel & Exec VP)
John B. Bunch (COO & Exec VP)
Gina M. Cruse (Exec VP-HR)

Subsidiary (Domestic):

Financial Engines Advisors L.L.C. (3)
1050 Enterprise Way 3rd Fl, Sunnyvale, CA 94089
Tel.: (408) 498-6000
Financial Investment Management Services
N.A.I.C.S.: 523999

New England Pension Plan Systems, LLC (2)
790 N Main St, Providence, RI 02904-5706
Tel.: (401) 274-5000
Web Site:
http://www.newenglandpension.com
Pension Funds
N.A.I.C.S.: 525110
Sergio Decurtis (Mgr)

Subsidiary (Domestic):

Erman Retirement Advisory, Inc. (2)
3020 Old Ranch Pkwy Ste 100, Seal Beach, CA 90740-2751
Tel.: (562) 546-6021
Web Site:
http://www.ermanretirementadvisory.com
All Other Support Services
N.A.I.C.S.: 561990
Howard Erman (Mgr-Client Svc)

Enverus, Inc. (1)
2901 Via Fortuna Dr Ste 200, Austin, TX 78746
Tel.: (512) 519-5509
Web Site: http://www.enverus.com
Energy SaaS & Data Analytics Company
N.A.I.C.S.: 541519
Allen Gilmer (Founder)
Colin Westmoreland (Chief Innovation Officer)
Dave Piazza (CFO)
Jeff Hughes (Pres & CEO)
Matt Wilcoxson (Chief Revenue Officer & Chief Growth Officer)
Jimmy Fortuna (Chief Product Officer)
Mark Szygenda (CTO)
Simon Crisp (Gen Mgr-Trading & Risk)
Chris Dinkler (Chief Revenue Officer)
Jim Jarrell (Co-Pres-Oil & Gas Analytics & Senior Executive Consultant)
Manuj Nikhanj (Co-Pres-Oil & Gas Analytics)
Alicia Recupero (VP-Mktg)

Bernadette Johnson (Sr VP-Power & Renewables)
Manuj Nikhanj (Chartered Financial Analyst & Financial Risk Manager)
Keri Brooke (CMO)
Meredith Glendell (Chief HR Officer)
Mike Mroz (Chief Sls Officer)
David Ranucci (Chief Sls Officer)

Subsidiary (Non-US):

Cortex Business Solutions Inc. (2)
Suite 130-115 Quarry Park Road SE, Calgary, T2C 5G9, AB, Canada
Tel.: (403) 219-2838
Web Site: http://www.cortex.net
Rev: $9,920,557
Assets: $9,897,129
Liabilities: $1,358,886
Net Worth: $8,538,243
Earnings: $3,458,686
Emp.: 61
Fiscal Year-end: 07/31/2018
Business Automation Solution Services
N.A.I.C.S.: 561990
John Gilkison (VP-Sls & Bus Dev)
Andrew Stewart (VP-Customer Experience)
Joel Leetzow (Pres & CEO)
Chris Lambert (VP-Tech & Product Mgmt)
Owen Temple (Dir-Technical Solutions)
Henry Pham (Controller)
Jason Baird (CFO & VP-Fin)
Scott Dunlop (Dir-Implementation & PMO)

Subsidiary (Domestic):

Cortex Business Solutions Ltd. (3)
3404 25 Street NE, Calgary, T1Y 6C1, AB, Canada
Tel.: (866) 716-6272
Emp.: 73
Business Software Development Services
N.A.I.C.S.: 541511

Subsidiary (Domestic):

Energy Acuity LLC (2)
1623 Blake St Ste 350, Denver, CO 80202
Tel.: (720) 235-1296
Web Site: http://www.energyacuity.com
Emp.: 30
Renewable & Clean Energy Markets Information Provider
N.A.I.C.S.: 519290
Jason Krantz (Co-Founder)
Brian Graff (Pres)

GlobalView Software, Inc. (2)
100 S Wacker Dr Ste 200, Chicago, IL 60606
Tel.: (312) 628-2900
Web Site: http://www.marketview.com
Sales Range: $1-9.9 Million
Energy & Commodity Data Management Software
N.A.I.C.S.: 513210
Anthony M. Lagona (CEO)
Bruce Weis (Exec VP-Product Dev & Data Integration)
Tom Mallon (VP-Strategy & Alliances)
Terry Donlan (Dir-Help Desk)
Chris Harrison (Chief Product Officer)
Eddie Tan (Mng Dir-APAC)
Jeff Vandeveer (CFO)
Mike McSpedon (Head-Sls-Global)
Paul A. Bhatt (Mng Dir-Europe & Africa)
Jaenneke Wolf (Dir-Mktg)

Midland Map Company, LLC (2)
106 N Marienfeld St, Midland, TX 79701
Tel.: (432) 682-1603
Web Site: https://www.enverus.com
Map Products Mfr
N.A.I.C.S.: 541370
Tim Canon (Mgr)

Oil-Law Records Corp. (2)
8 NW 65th St, Oklahoma City, OK 73116
Tel.: (405) 840-1631
Web Site: http://www.oil-law.com
Information Retrieval Services
N.A.I.C.S.: 517810
Paul Lamb (CTO)

RigData (2)
7001 Blvd 26 Ste 600, Fort Worth, TX 76180-8816
Tel.: (817) 285-9600
Web Site: http://www.rigdata.com
Oil & Gas Drilling Industry Data Publisher

N.A.I.C.S.: 513199

Transzap, Inc. (2)
633 17th St Ste 2000, Denver, CO 80202
Tel.: (303) 863-8600
Web Site: http://www.transzap.com
Sales Range: $10-24.9 Million
Oil & Gas Industry Cloud-Based Accounting Software & Services
N.A.I.C.S.: 541511
David A. Kempf (CFO)
Michael Weiss (CTO)
Christopher Dinkler (VP-Sls)
Michael Corbett (VP-Mktg)
Dave Donaldson (VP-Ops)
Craig Charlton (Pres & CEO)

Grocery Outlet Inc. (1)
5650 Hollis St, Emeryville, CA 94608
Tel.: (510) 845-1999
Web Site: http://www.groceryoutlet.com
Discount Grocery Store Operator
N.A.I.C.S.: 445110
MacGregor Read (Vice Chm)
Jeff Oki (Sr VP-New Markets)
Tom McMahon (Exec VP-Retail Ops)
Charles Bracher (CFO)
R. J. Sheedy (Pres)
Michael Thomas (VP-Supply Chain)
Steve Wilson (Sr VP-Pur)
Bill Coyle (VP-Real Estate)
Pamela Burke (Chief Admin Officer)
Brian McAndrews (Sr VP-Store Dev)
Eric J. Lindberg Jr. (CEO)

HUB International Limited (1)
300 N LaSalle St 17th Fl, Chicago, IL 60654
Tel.: (800) 432-2558
Web Site: http://www.hubinternational.com
Insurance Brokerage Services
N.A.I.C.S.: 524210
Richard A. Gulliver (Vice Chm)
Joseph C. Hyde (CFO)
Trey Biggs (Chief Sls Officer & Pres-US West)
John Albright (Chief Legal Officer)
Chad Robertson (Exec VP-Intl Bus & Growth Initiatives)
Marc I. Cohen (Pres & CEO)
Neil Hughes (Pres-Central)
Jay Virdi (Chief Sls Officer-Cannabis Insurance & Risk Svcs-US & Canada)
Geoff Hatfield (Chief Strategy Officer-Central)
Scott Web (Chief Sls Officer-Central)
Seth Hopkins (CMO)
Andy Prill (Pres-Mountain Northwest)
Lawrence J. Lineker (Exec VP)
Christopher Treanor (HUB President of Programs & Specialties)
Tina Osen (HUB International Canada)
John McGrath (Reg Pres-Pacific)
Neil Hughes (Reg Pres)
Charles J. Brophy III (Pres-East)
Michael S. Chapman (Reg Pres-South)
Andy Prill (Reg Pres-HUB Mountain-Northwest)
Grace van Til (Technology and Operations)

Subsidiary (Domestic):

A S Arbury & Sons, Inc. (2)
115 Jerome St, Midland, MI 48640
Tel.: (989) 631-1920
Web Site: https://arburyins.com
Sales Range: $1-9.9 Million
Emp.: 11
Insurance Agencies & Brokerages
N.A.I.C.S.: 524210

Asset Protection, Inc. (2)
14021 Charter Park Dr., Midlothian, VA 23114
Tel.: (804) 323-3854
Web Site: http://www.apgroupinc.com
Rev.: $1,800,000
Emp.: 15
Insurance Agencies & Brokerages
N.A.I.C.S.: 524210

Brady Risk Management, Inc. (2)
141 E Main St Ste 1, Huntington, NY 11743
Tel.: (631) 549-8561
Web Site: http://www.bradyrisk.com
Sales Range: $1-9.9 Million
Emp.: 11
Insurance Agencies & Brokerages
N.A.I.C.S.: 524210

Sean Brady (Pres)
Peri Rohme (VP)
Deborah L. Brady (Exec VP)
Kate Schmitz (Project Coord)
Eloise Viscuso (VP-Customer Svc)
Michael McKeown (Sr VP-Brokerage & Program Mgmt Svcs)
Tanaquea Rosario (Dir-Program Dev)
Michelle Kuffo (Sr Acct Exec)
John Harris (Mng Dir)

Capax Management & Insurance Services, Inc. (2)
4335 N Star Way Ste D, Modesto, CA 95356
Tel.: (209) 526-3110
Web Site: http://www.capax.com
Sales Range: $1-9.9 Million
Emp.: 70
Insurance Agencies & Brokerages
N.A.I.C.S.: 524210
Joel Geddes III (Pres & CEO)

Combined Benefits Administrators, LLC (2)
4704 W Jennifer Ave, Fresno, CA 93722
Tel.: (559) 275-3984
Web Site:
https://combinedbenefitsadministrators.com
Sales Range: $10-24.9 Million
Emp.: 10
Insurance Related Activities
N.A.I.C.S.: 524298
Gregory Cucullu (Pres)

Conover Insurance, Inc. (2)
155 108th Ave NE Ste 725, Bellevue, WA 98004
Tel.: (509) 965-2090
Web Site: http://www.conoverinsurance.com
Insurance Agencies & Brokerages
N.A.I.C.S.: 524210
Bradley Green (CEO)
Ed Ray (Pres)
Steve Hook (VP-Div)
Connie Morrow (COO)
Kerri Record (Sr VP)

Dale Barton Agency (2)
1100 E 6600 S Ste 400, Salt Lake City, UT 84121-7418
Tel.: (801) 288-1600
Web Site: http://www.dalebartonagency.com
Insurance & Surety Bond Services
N.A.I.C.S.: 524126
Samuel W. Clark Jr. (Pres)

Dwight W. Andrus Insurance Inc. (2)
500 Dover Blvd, Lafayette, LA 70503
Tel.: (337) 406-5614
Web Site: http://www.andrus.com
Emp.: 130
Insurance Agencies & Brokerages
N.A.I.C.S.: 524210
David W. Andrus (Sec)
Elizabeth Beckworth (Acct Mgr)
Michelle Guidry Melchior (Acct Mgr-Comml)
Jenny L. Hurst (Acct Mgr)
Sonya L. Gore (Acct Mgr)
Ty Hopkins (Mgr)
Becky Sarver Morgan (Acct Mgr)
Sandy Dartez (Mgr-Dept)
Angie Viator (Acct Mgr)
Ashley Andrus Babin (Acct Mgr)
Elise M. Hebert (Acct Mgr)
Jodie Scott (Acct Mgr)
Keith A. Breaux (Office Mgr)
Megan Breaux (Acct Mgr)
Monika Swearingen (Acct Mgr)
Peggy Sargent (VP-Mktg)
Reed Andrus (Treas)
Suzette B. Hebert (Mgr-Select Accts)
Tasha Bourque (Acct Mgr)
Brandt Etier (Asst VP-Property & Casualty Sls)
Dwight Andrus IV (Pres)

E-Insure Services, Inc. (2)
39 S Lasalle St Ste 1000, Chicago, IL 60603
Web Site: http://www.einsurance.com
Women's, Girls & Infants Cut & Sew Apparel Contractors
N.A.I.C.S.: 315210
David N. Thompson (Pres & CEO)

Division (Domestic):

Glacier Insurance of Libby, Inc. (2)

PO Box 1510, Libby, MT 59923
Tel.: (406) 293-6244
Web Site: http://www.glacierins.com
Insurance Agencies & Brokerages
N.A.I.C.S.: 524210

Subsidiary (Domestic):

HUB International Great Plains, LLC (2)
11516 Miracle Hills Dr Ste 100, Omaha, NE 68154
Tel.: (402) 964-5400
Web Site: https://www.hubinternational.com
Insurance Brokerage Services
N.A.I.C.S.: 524210
John P. Nelson (Chm)
John H. Nelson (Pres & CEO)
Todd Rogge (CFO & COO)

Hamman-Miller-Beauchamp-Deeble, Inc. (2)
3633 E Broadway Ste 200, Long Beach, CA 90803
Tel.: (562) 439-9731
Web Site: http://www.hmbd.com
Insurance Agencies & Brokerages
N.A.I.C.S.: 524210
Daniel J. Roddy (Pres)
Glenn B. Agoncillo (VP)
Ted Elink-Schuurman (VP)
Travis L. England (VP)
Todd G. Miller (VP)

Horizon Agency, Inc. (2)
11000 W 78th St Ste 300, Eden Prairie, MN 55344
Tel.: (952) 944-2929
Web Site: http://www.horizonagency.com
Sales Range: $1-9.9 Million
Emp.: 42
Insurance Agencies & Brokerages
N.A.I.C.S.: 524210
Daniel Scattarella (Founder & CEO)
Rob Martin (Mng Dir)
Jake Hoeschler (Principal)
Neal White (Pres)

Hub International Insurance Services, Inc. (2)
3390 University Ave Ste 300, Riverside, CA 92501
Tel.: (951) 788-8500
Web Site: http://www.hubinternational.com
Insurance Broker Services
N.A.I.C.S.: 524210
Kathy Quintana (Exec VP & COO-California)
Jim Vawter (Exec VP & Dir-Mktg-Northern California)
Amy Hecklinger (Dir-Client Svcs-Employee Benefits)
Adam Caster (Acct Exec-La Palma)
Steve Vicencia (Exec VP & Mgr-La Palma)
Lynn Greene (VP-Employee Benefits Practice)
Blanca Vega (Acct Mgr-Santa Barbara)

Hub International Midwest Limited (2)
55 E Jackson Blvd 14th Fl, Chicago, IL 60604
Tel.: (312) 922-5000
Web Site: http://www.hubinternational.com
Insurance Broker Services
N.A.I.C.S.: 524210
Mark Naumann (CFO & Exec VP)
Matthew Johnson (Mgr-Acct)
Edward W. McConnell (Sr VP)
Clint W. Anderson (Pres-Specialty Practices)
Lerone Sidberry (CEO)

Hub International Mountain States Limited (2)
3533 Gabel Rd, Billings, MT 59102
Tel.: (406) 652-9151
Web Site: http://www.hubinternational.com
Emp.: 300
Insurance Brokerage Services
N.A.I.C.S.: 524210
Rene LeVeaux (Pres)
Linda Roe (VP-Mktg)
Wayne Dauwen (COO)
Kyle Phipps (CFO)
Scott Rasor (CMO)
Gustin Martel (Chief Sls Officer)
Jack Patterson (VP-HR)
Jenny L. Bolt (VP-Sls)
Linda M. Pinder (VP-Personal Insurance)

Hub International New England, LLC (2)
299 Ballardvale St, Wilmington, MA 01887
Tel.: (978) 657-5100
Web Site: http://www.hubinternational.com
Emp.: 350
Insurance Services
N.A.I.C.S.: 524210
Marina Bevens (Mgr-HR)
Frank Venuto (Pres-Ops Association Div)
Christopher Taylor (Sr VP)
Melissa Provost (Acct Mgr-Personal Lines)
Timm Marini (Pres)
Monique Matz (Mgr-Comml Lines Svc)
Jennifer Robinson (Acct Mgr-Employee Benefits)
Aimee Goddard (VP & Mgr-Spencer)
Pamela Famulari (Acct Mgr-Personal Lines-Spencer)
Candy Donahue (Acct Mgr)
Michelle McCabe (Acct Mgr)
Melanie Geotis (Acct Mgr)

Hub International Northeast Limited (2)
5 Bryant Park 4th Fl, New York, NY 10018
Tel.: (212) 338-2000
Web Site: http://www.hubinternational.com
Sales Range: $125-149.9 Million
Emp.: 700
Holding Company; Insurance Brokerage, Underwriting & Related Activities
N.A.I.C.S.: 551112
Michael P. Sabanos (COO)
Patti Clement (First VP)
Ken Schreiber (Pres-Comml Lines)
Harsh Bhasin (CFO)
Andrea Miller (Asst VP)
Paul Collins (Pres & CEO)

Subsidiary (Non-US):

Hub International Ontario Limited (2)
2265 Upper Middle Road East Suite 700, Oakville, L6H 0G5, ON, Canada
Tel.: (905) 847-5500
Web Site: http://www.hubinternational.com
Emp.: 500
Insurance Services
N.A.I.C.S.: 524298
Sharlene Locke (Pres-Personal Insurance Practice-Ontario)
Robert Keilty (CEO)
Susan Murphy (Pres)

Hub International Quebec Limited (2)
8500 Decarie Boulevard 5th Floor, Montreal, H4P 2N2, QC, Canada
Tel.: (514) 374-9600
Web Site: http://quebec.hubinternational.com
Sales Range: $50-74.9 Million
Emp.: 150
Insurance Broker Services
N.A.I.C.S.: 524210

Subsidiary (Domestic):

Hub International Southeast Limited (2)
2430 Mall Dr Ste 280, Charleston, SC 29406
Tel.: (843) 529-5470
Web Site: http://www.hubinternational.com
Insurance Services
N.A.I.C.S.: 524210
Robin Easterlin (COO)
Carrie B. Cherveny (Chief Compliance Officer-Employee Benefits)

Hub International Texas, Inc. (2)
421 W 3rd St Ste 800, Fort Worth, TX 76102
Tel.: (817) 820-8100
Web Site: http://www.texas.hubinternational.com
Emp.: 270
Insurance Brokers & Consulting Services
N.A.I.C.S.: 524210
Martin Yung (Pres & CEO)
Natalie V. Perry (CMO & VP)

Insurance Management Company (2)
123 W. Ninth St., Erie, PA 16512-1133
Tel.: (814) 452-3200
Insurance & Risk Management Services
N.A.I.C.S.: 524298

Invensure Insurance Brokers, Inc. (2)
17912 Cowan, Irvine, CA 92614
Tel.: (949) 756-4100
Web Site: http://www.invensure.net
Insurance Risk Management Services
N.A.I.C.S.: 524298
Bob Parent (Principal)
Richard Sherman (Pres)

James L. Miniter Insurance Agency, Inc. (2)
400 Hingham St, Rockland, MA 02370
Tel.: (781) 982-3100
Web Site: http://www.miniter.com
Sales Range: $25-49.9 Million
Emp.: 80
Insurance Services
N.A.I.C.S.: 524210
Lisa Burrows (Dir-Mktg)
Julianne Donley (Pres & CEO)
Mark Pfeifer (VP-Sls-New Jersey)
Kelly Adams (VP-Ops & Tracking)

Johnston Lewis Associates, Inc. (2)
5600 New King Dr Ste 210, Troy, MI 48098
Tel.: (248) 528-2400
Web Site: https://www.jlains.com
Sales Range: $1-9.9 Million
Emp.: 17
Insurance Agencies & Brokerages
N.A.I.C.S.: 524210
Todd Lewis (Pres)
Nancy Beard (Gen Mgr)

Sale Insurance Agency, Inc. (2)
309 S Tennessee Ave, Lakeland, FL 33801
Tel.: (863) 682-0363
Web Site: https://www.saleinsurance.com
Sales Range: $1-9.9 Million
Emp.: 10
Insurance Agencies & Brokerages
N.A.I.C.S.: 524210
Allen Sale (VP)
Cathy Wyatt (Office Mgr)

Shinstrom & Norman, Inc. (2)
525 Kirkland Way, Kirkland, WA 98033
Tel.: (425) 827-6200
Web Site: http://www.shinstromnorman.com
Insurance Related Activities
N.A.I.C.S.: 524298

Specialty Program Group LLC (2)
180 River Rd, Summit, NJ 07901-1449
Tel.: (908) 790-6884
Web Site: http://www.specialtyprogramgroup.com
Underwriting & Insurance Services
N.A.I.C.S.: 524210
Maryellen Dolan (COO)
Christopher Treanor (CEO)
Jonah Lipin (Chief Product Officer)
Steven Pickert (Asst VP-Bus Dev)
Scott Hoy (Pres)

Division (Domestic):

Borisoff Insurance Services, Inc. (3)
2540 Foothill Blvd # 101, La Crescenta, CA 91214
Tel.: (818) 249-0100
Web Site: http://www.monarchexcess.com
Sales Range: $1-9.9 Million
Emp.: 50
Insurance Brokerage Services
N.A.I.C.S.: 524210
Derek Borisoff (CEO)

Subsidiary (Domestic):

Commonwealth Underwriters Ltd. (4)
1301 N Hamilton St, Richmond, VA 23230-3959
Tel.: (804) 359-4568
Web Site: http://www.commund.com
Insurance Services
N.A.I.C.S.: 524298
Barry Scott (CEO)

Subsidiary (Domestic):

Brokers' Service Marketing Group (3)
500 S Main St, Providence, RI 02903-2915
Tel.: (401) 751-9400
Web Site: http://www.bsmg.net
Insurance Related Activities
N.A.I.C.S.: 524298

Pam De Melim (Mgr)
Trish O'Donnell (Sr VP & Dir-Ops)
Jason Lea (Pres)
David Greenberg (CEO)
Timothy Moynihan (Sr VP & Dir-Risk Appraisal)
Eric Chartier (Controller)
Paul Sepe (Partner & Sr VP)
Corrie Freudenstein (Dir-Mktg & Comm)
Pam DeMelim (Chief Admin Officer)

Business Underwriters Associates, LLC (3)
4000 Embassy Pkwy Ste 100, Akron, OH 44333
Tel.: (330) 929-2225
Web Site: http://www.buaweb.com
Sales Range: $1-9.9 Million
Emp.: 19
Insurance Agents, Brokers, And Service, N
N.A.I.C.S.: 524210
Jonathan Wright (Principal & Mgr-Sls)

Squaremouth Inc. (3)
100 2nd Ave S Ste 1200, Saint Petersburg, FL 33701
Tel.: (727) 564-9203
Web Site: http://www.squaremouth.com
Sales Range: $10-24.9 Million
Emp.: 11
Travel Insurance
N.A.I.C.S.: 524128
Rupa Mehta (CEO)

The Mechanic Group, Inc. (3)
1 Blue Hill Plz Ste 530, Pearl River, NY 10965
Tel.: (845) 735-0700
Web Site: http://www.mechanicgroup.com
Insurance Agencies & Brokerages
N.A.I.C.S.: 524210

Subsidiary (Domestic):

T&T2 Inc (2)
1631 Main St, Hellertown, PA 18055
Tel.: (610) 838-7801
Web Site: https://www.weissschantz.com
Insurance Management Services
N.A.I.C.S.: 524298
Timothy W. Schantz (Pres)

The Wooditch Company Insurance Services, Inc. (2)
1 Park Plz Ste 400, Irvine, CA 92614
Tel.: (949) 553-9800
Web Site: http://www.wooditch.com
Sales Range: $1-9.9 Million
Emp.: 28
Insurance Agencies & Brokerages
N.A.I.C.S.: 524210
William S. Wooditch (Pres)
Gezelle Lopez (Acct Mgr)
Jennifer Kelley (Acct Mgr)

Subsidiary (Non-US):

Totten Insurance Group Inc. (2)
20 Dundas St W Suite 910, Toronto, M5G 2C2, ON, Canada
Web Site: https://www.tottengroup.com
Insurance Services
N.A.I.C.S.: 524210
Barb Dinan (VP)
John Rhuland (VP-Atlantic Reg)
Richard Belanger (VP-Quebec)
Denis Dei Cont (Pres)
Gregory Knowles (Chief Underwriting Officer)
Paul Meinschenk (COO)
Robert Strain (VP)
Andrew De Ruiter (VP)

Subsidiary (Domestic):

Canadian Resources Insurance Solutions Inc. (3)
238 Elm Street Suite 102, Sudbury, P3C 1V3, ON, Canada
Tel.: (705) 222-2747
Web Site: http://www.crisinsure.com
General Insurance Services
N.A.I.C.S.: 524210
Robert Strain (Pres)

Subsidiary (Domestic):

Washington Financial Group (2)
8300 Greensboro Dr Ste 700, 22102, McLean, VA

Hellman & Friedman LLC—(Continued)

Tel.: (703) 847-4500
Web Site: http://www.washfinancial.com
Investment Advice
N.A.I.C.S.: 523940
Steven W. Dorman (Founder & Partner)
Joseph F. Denoyior (Pres)
Jeffrey D. Hamblen (Exec VP)
Derek H. Coburn (Exec VP)

Wyatt Insurance Services, Inc. (2)
312 Prosperity Dr Ste 105, Knoxville, TN
37923
Tel.: (865) 470-9654
Web Site: http://www.wyattinsurance.com
Insurance Related Activities
N.A.I.C.S.: 524298
Roger Wyatt (Pres)

Wyoming Financial Insurance
Company (2)
400 E 1st St Ste 105, Casper, WY 82601
Tel.: (307) 473-3000
Web Site: http://www.wyomingfinancialinsu
rance.com
Sales Range: $1-9.9 Million
Insurance Agents
N.A.I.C.S.: 524210
Tara Scheffelmaer (Acct Mgr)
Lou Gaspers (Branch Mgr)
Michael Kretzer (CFO)

Hellman & Friedman Europe
Limited (1)
30th Floor Millbank Tower, 21 24 Millbank,
London, SW1P 4QP, United Kingdom
Tel.: (44) 2078395111
Web Site: http://www.hf.com
Privater Equity Firm
N.A.I.C.S.: 523999
Patrick J. Healy (Mng Dir & Head-London
Office)
Blake C. Kleinman (Mng Dir)
Stuart D. Banks (Gen Counsel-Europe)
Stefan Goetz (Mng Dir)
Johannes Korp (Principal)
Zita Saurel (Dir-Investment)
Philip R. Sternheimer (Dir-Investment)

Information Resources, Inc. (1)
150 N Clinton St, Chicago, IL 60661
Tel.: (312) 726-1221
Web Site: http://www.iriworldwide.com
Sales Range: $700-749.9 Million
Emp.: 4,000
Computer Based Systems & Services for
Collection & Analysis of Detailed Market
Information on Sales of Consumer Pack-
aged Goods
N.A.I.C.S.: 541910
Jane Altobelli (Exec VP-HR)
Robert I. Tomei (Pres-Consumer, Shopper
Mktg Core Content & Insights)
Jose Carlos Gonzalez-Hurtado (Pres-Intl)
Susan E. Bennett (Gen Counsel & Exec
VP)
Michael Rosenthal (Exec VP-Global Ops)
Ignacio Marinas Monsalve (VP-Strategy Intl)
Jeffrey P. Ansell (Chm)
Ash M. Patel (CIO)
Baljit Dail (Pres-Global)
Evan Swidler (Chief HR Officer)
Kirk L. Perry (Pres & CEO)
Cecilia Ogude (Sr VP-Diversity, Equity &
Inclusion)
Euan Jarvie (Pres-Europe, Middle East &
Africa)
Misty Muscatel Davis (CMO-Global)
Malli Vangala (Chief Strategy Officer)

Subsidiary (Domestic):

Retail Solutions, Inc. (2)
100 Century Cr Ct Ste 800, San Jose, CA
95112
Tel.: (650) 390-6100
Web Site: http://www.retailsolutions.com
Sales Range: $10-24.9 Million
Retail Execution Management Services
N.A.I.C.S.: 513210
Jonathan Golovin (Co-Founder & Chief
Strategy Officer)
Richard Swan (Co-Founder)
Cedric Guyot (Gen Mgr)
Karl Waldman (Sr VP-WW Customer Ops)
David Sun (Mng Dir-China)
Michael E. Lynch (Principal)
Bert Clement (CEO)

Jessica Tobey (Mgr-Indus Rels)
Amit Jain (CTO)
James Smits (VP-Retail Dev)
Stuart Careford (Chief Customer Officer)
John Neale (CFO)
Caitlyn Bordeaux (Mktg Mgr-Global)
Kirk W. Wheeler (Sr VP-Sls & Mktg-Global)
Patrick U. Di Chiro (Chief Mktg Officer)

Nets A/S (1)
Klausdalsbrovej 601, DK-2750, Ballerup,
Denmark
Tel.: (45) 44684468
Web Site: http://www.nets.eu
Rev.: $1,264,993,856
Assets: $4,521,658,722
Liabilities: $2,816,559,886
Net Worth: $1,705,098,836
Earnings: $36,059,492
Emp.: 2,460
Fiscal Year-end: 12/31/2019
Holding Company; Payment Solutions, In-
formation Services & Digital Security Solu-
tions
N.A.I.C.S.: 551112
Soren Winge (Head-Media)
Bo Nilsson (CEO)
Pia Jorgensen (CIO)
Klaus Pedersen (CFO)
Robert Hoffmann (CEO-Merchant Svcs)
Gianluca Ventura (Chief HR Officer)
Christian Lintner (Sr Mgr-Treasury)

Subsidiary (Domestic):

Nets Denmark A/S (2)
Lautrupbjerg 10, DK-2750, Ballerup, Den-
mark
Tel.: (45) 4468 4468
Web Site: http://www.nets.eu
Payment, Card & Information Services
N.A.I.C.S.: 522320
Nevena Duric (Officer-Press)
Mads Allingstrup (Officer-Press)

Subsidiary (Non-US):

Nets Norway AS (2)
Haavard Martinsensvei 54, 0978, Oslo,
Norway
Tel.: (47) 22898989
Web Site: http://www.nets.eu
Payment Solutions
N.A.I.C.S.: 522320
Stein-Arne Tjore (Mgr-Press)

Nets Sweden AB (2)
Lumaparksvagen 11, 120 31, Stockholm,
Sweden
Tel.: (46) 8609 9400
Web Site: http://www.nets.eu
Electronic Payment Systems
N.A.I.C.S.: 522320
Soren Winge (Mgr-Press)

Securitas Direct AB (1)
Kalendegatan 26, Malmo, 203 20, Sweden
Tel.: (46) 40254500
Web Site: http://www.securitas-direct.com
Security Solution & Monitoring Services
N.A.I.C.S.: 561621
Henrik Heslyk (Mgr-Human Capital)
Fredrik Ostman (CFO)
Dick Seger (Executives)

Subsidiary (Non-US):

Verisure (2)
Drammensveien 175, 0277, Oslo, Norway
Tel.: (47) 23 68 90 99
Web Site: http://www.verisure.no
Sales Range: $50-74.9 Million
Home Security Services
N.A.I.C.S.: 561621
Thomas Berg (Mgr-Ops)
Cecilie Knudsen (Mgr-HR)

TriSure Corporation (1)
4325 Lake Boone TRL Ste 200, Raleigh,
NC 27607-7510
Tel.: (919) 469-2473
Web Site: http://www.trisure.com
Sales Range: $1-9.9 Million
Emp.: 25
Insurance Brokerage Services
N.A.I.C.S.: 524210
Linda Folger (Partner)
Kate Hartley (Controller)

Cleve Folger (Pres & Partner)
John Cramer (CEO)
Dan Sanderson (Partner)

UKG Inc. (1)
200 Park Ave S 2nd Fl, New York, NY
10003
Web Site: http://www.ukg.com
Holding Company; Human Resource &
Workforce Management Software & Ser-
vices
N.A.I.C.S.: 551112
Aron J. Ain (Chm)
Chris Todd (Pres & CEO)
John Butler (CFO)
Jim Kizielewicz (COO)
Jody Kaminsky (CMO)
John Machado (CTO)
Dave Almeda (Chief People Officer)
Bob Hughes (Chief Customer Officer &
Chief Strategy Officer)
Mark Julien (Chief Admin Officer)
John O'Brien (Co-Chief Revenue Officer)
Greg Swick (Co-Chief Revenue Officer)
Jim Welch (Chief Product Officer)
Brian Reaves (Chief Belonging, Diversity &
Equity Officer)

Subsidiary (Domestic):

Ascentis Corporation (2)
11995 Singletree Ln Ste 400, Eden Prairie,
MN 55344
Tel.: (866) 616-2589
Web Site: http://www.ascentis.com
Cloud-Based Human Capital Management
Solutions Services
N.A.I.C.S.: 513210
Jeff Cronin (Chief Product Officer)
Stephen Byrnes (Chief Sls Officer)
Troy Thibodeau (CMO)

Subsidiary (Domestic):

Cincinnati Time Systems, Inc. (3)
23399 Commerce Dr Ste B3, Farmington
Hills, MI 48335
Tel.: (248) 615-8300
Cloud Based Workforce Management Solu-
tions
N.A.I.C.S.: 513210

NOVAtime Technology, Inc. (3)
9680 Haven Ave, Rancho Cucamonga, CA
91730
Tel.: (909) 895-8100
Web Site: http://www.novatime.com
Emp.: 100
Workforce Management Solutions Devel-
oper
N.A.I.C.S.: 513210

Subsidiary (Domestic):

Great Place To Work Institute,
Inc. (2)
169 11th St, San Francisco, CA 94103
Tel.: (415) 503-1234
Web Site: http://www.greatplacetowork.com
Sales Range: $1-9.9 Million
Emp.: 17
Management Consulting Services
N.A.I.C.S.: 541611
Harald Hansen (CFO)
Erin Bartulski (Dir-Best Companies)
Emily Bergman (Sr Mgr-Mktg)
Rosana Cerna (Dir-People & Culture)
Marcus Erb (Assoc VP-Svcs & Products)
Lizelle Festejo (Sr Mgr-Program & Event)
Sonya George (Assoc VP-Client Solution-
East)
Jacob Goldstein (Mgr-Product)
Jessica Gupta (Mgr-Client Solutions)
Michael C. Bush (CEO)

Interboro Systems Corporation (2)
206 San Jorge St, San Juan, PR 00912
Tel.: (787) 641-7777
Web Site: http://www.interboropr.com
Sales Range: $10-24.9 Million
Emp.: 105
Office Equipment
N.A.I.C.S.: 423420
Donald Blasky (Acct Mgr)

Kronos, Incorporated (2)
900 Chelmsford St, Lowell, MA 01851
Tel.: (978) 250-9800
Software & Hardware for Labor Management, Human Resources & Payroll Development

N.A.I.C.S.: 513210
Aron J. Ain (Chm & CEO)
James J. Kizielewicz (COO)
Mark Julien (Chief Admin Officer)
Christopher Todd (Pres)
David Almeda (Chief People Officer)
Bob Hughes (Chief Customer & Strategy
Officer)
John Butler (CFO)

Subsidiary (Domestic):

Digital Instinct LLC (3)
7450 Arroyo Crossing Pkwy Ste 170, Las
Vegas, NV 89113
Tel.: (702) 272-0555
Web Site: http://www.virtualroster.net
Electronics Stores
N.A.I.C.S.: 449210
Ross Sly (Partner)

Empower Software Solutions,
Inc. (3)
315 E Robinson St Ste 350, Orlando, FL
32801
Web Site: http://www.empowersoftware.com
Software Solutions
N.A.I.C.S.: 513210
Jim Hoefflin (Pres & CEO)

Financial Management Solutions,
Inc. (3)
1720 Windwood Concourse Ste 250, Al-
pharetta, GA 30005
Tel.: (770) 619-3443
Web Site: http://www.fmsi.com
Workforce Management Applications &
Consulting Services
N.A.I.C.S.: 541618

Kronos (US) Inc (3)
16938 US Hwy 19, Port Richey, FL 34667-
4319
Tel.: (727) 862-3032
Real Estate Property Lessors
N.A.I.C.S.: 531190

Subsidiary (Non-US):

Kronos Australia Pty Ltd (3)
Level 1 Ste 3 7 Eden Park Dr Macquarie
Pk, 2113, Pymble, NSW, Australia
Tel.: (61) 294182266
Web Site: http://www.kronos.com.au
Sales Range: $50-74.9 Million
Emp.: 100
Software Publisher
N.A.I.C.S.: 513210
Peter Harte (Mng Dir)

Kronos Singapore Pte. Ltd (3)
Level 31 Six Battery Road Raffles Place,
049909, Singapore, Singapore
Tel.: (65) 63218948
Web Site: http://www.kronos.com
Software Publisher
N.A.I.C.S.: 513210

Kronos Systems B.V. (3)
Weltevreden 2A, 3731 AL, De Bilt, Nether-
lands
Tel.: (31) 302205901
Web Site: http://www.kronosglobal.nl
Software Publisher
N.A.I.C.S.: 513210

Kronos Systems BVBA (3)
Research Park Z 1.70, 1731, Asse, Vlaams
Brabant, Belgium
Tel.: (32) 2 481 64 00
Web Site: http://www.kronosglobal.be
Emp.: 50
Administrative Management Services
N.A.I.C.S.: 541611
Vanleierde Wolf (Gen Mgr)

Kronos Systems India Private
Limited (3)
Tridib Level 2 Unit 1 Bagmane Tech Park, C
V Raman Nagar, 560 093, Bengaluru, India
Tel.: (91) 8043340500
Web Site: http://www.kronos.com
Sales Range: $50-74.9 Million
Emp.: 52
Software Publisher
N.A.I.C.S.: 513210
James Thomas (Mng Dir)

Kronos Systems Ltd (3)
Kronos House 2 Carey Road, Wokingham,

RG40 2NP, Berkshire, United
Kingdom **(100%)**
Tel.: (44) 1189789784
Web Site: http://www.kronos.com
Sales Range: $50-74.9 Million
Emp.: 100
Office Equipment Whslr
N.A.I.C.S.: 423420

Kronos de Mexico SA de CV **(3)**
Av Ejercito Nacional No 579 Mezzanine,
Colonia Granada, 11260, Mexico, Mexico
Tel.: (52) 5550025000
Web Site: http://www.kronos.com
Sales Range: $50-74.9 Million
Emp.: 30
Software Publisher
N.A.I.C.S.: 513210
Gabriel Albaledo (Country Mgr)

Group, (Domestic):

Kronos, Incorporated - Hiring Solu-
tions Group **(3)**
9525 SW Gemini Dr, Beaverton, OR 97008
Tel.: (503) 596-3100
Web Site: http://www.kronos.com
Electronic Hiring Management Systems
N.A.I.C.S.: 513210
Michele Glorie (Sr Dir-Corp Comm)

Kronos, Incorporated - TeleStaff Solu-
tions Group **(3)**
50 Corporate Park, Irvine, CA 92606
Tel.: (800) 850-7374
Workforce Management Software Devel-
oper
N.A.I.C.S.: 513210
Chris McCormack (VP-Dev)
Greg Ekstrom (CEO)
John Moore (CTO)
Marie Salcedo (Mgr-Mktg)

Kronos, Incorporated - iSeries Solu-
tions Group **(3)**
814 N Nolan River Rd, Cleburne, TX 76033
Tel.: (817) 645-3200
Workforce Management Services
N.A.I.C.S.: 541611

Subsidiary (Domestic):

Optimum Solutions Inc. **(3)**
210 25th Ave N Ste 700, Nashville, TN
37203
Tel.: (615) 329-2313
Software Publisher
N.A.I.C.S.: 513210

Time Link International Corp. **(3)**
2975 Westchester Ave, Purchase, NY
10577
Tel.: (914) 834-9301
Web Site: http://www.timelink.com
Sales Range: $10-24.9 Million
Emp.: 75
Workforce Management & Data Collection
Services
N.A.I.C.S.: 513210
Andrea Kayal (Dir-Mktg)
James Pasmantier (Dir-Pro Svcs)

Subsidiary (Domestic):

PeopleDoc, Incorporated **(2)**
200 Park Ave S 2nd Fl, New York, NY
10003
Web Site: http://www.people-doc.com
Human Resource & Employee Management
Software & Services
N.A.I.C.S.: 513210

The Ultimate Software Group,
Inc. **(2)**
2000 Ultimate Way, Weston, FL 33326
Tel.: (800) 432-1729
Web Site: http://www.ultimatesoftware.com
Sales Range: $1-9.9 Million
Web Based Payroll & Employee Manage-
ment Solutions
N.A.I.C.S.: 334610
Scott S. Scherr (Founder)

Joint Venture (Non-US):

The Ultimate Software Group of
Canada, Inc.
144 Bloor St. West Suite 400, Toronto, M5S
1M4, ON, Canada
Tel.: (416) 861-8530

Software Development Services
N.A.I.C.S.: 541511

Web Reservations International,
Ltd. **(1)**
Charlemont Exchange Charlemont Street,
Dublin, Ireland
Tel.: (353) 1 498 0700
Web Site: http://www.webresint.com
Marketing Consulting Services
N.A.I.C.S.: 541613
Richard Segal (Chm)

Zendesk, Inc. **(1)**
989 Market St, San Francisco, CA 94103
Tel.: (415) 418-7506
Web Site: http://www.zendesk.com
Rev.: $1,338,603,000
Assets: $2,451,279,000
Liabilities: $1,962,061,000
Net Worth: $489,218,000
Earnings: ($223,644,000)
Emp.: 5,860
Fiscal Year-end: 12/31/2021
Computer Software Publisher & Retailer
N.A.I.C.S.: 513210
Alexander Aghassipour (Founder & Chief
Product Officer)
Toke Nygaard (Chief Creative Officer)
Tom Eggemeier (CEO)
Norman Gennaro (Pres-Sls)
Adrian McDermott (CTO)
Colleen Berube (CIO & Sr VP-Ops)
Julie Swinney (Acting CFO)
Shelagh M. Glaser (Principal Acctg Officer)
Teresa Anania (Sr VP-Global Customer
Success, Renewals, and Customer Experi-
ence)

Subsidiary (Non-US):

Base spolka z ograniczona
odpowiedzialnoscia **(2)**
ul Parowcowa 4C, 02-445, Warsaw, Poland
Tel.: (48) 226145204
Web Site: http://www.base.waw.pl
Machine Tools Mfr
N.A.I.C.S.: 333517

We Are Cloud SAS **(2)**
1 Place Francis Ponge, Montpellier, 34000,
France
Tel.: (33) 467416064
Web Site: http://www.bimeanalytics.com
Software Development Services
N.A.I.C.S.: 541511

Zendesk APAC **(2)**
Level 1 482 Bourke Street, Melbourne,
3000, VIC, Australia
Tel.: (61) 3 9008 6775
Computer Software Publisher & Retailer
N.A.I.C.S.: 513210
Adam Clark (VP-Sls-Australia & New Zea-
land)
Paul Bichsel (Dir-Success)
Amy Foo (VP-Fin & Ops)

Zendesk EMEA **(2)**
30 Eastbourne Terrace Bishops Bridge,
London, W2 6LA, United Kingdom
Tel.: (44) 20 3355 7960
Computer Software Publisher & Retailer
N.A.I.C.S.: 513210

Zendesk Korea LLC **(2)**
373 Gangnam-daero Seocho-dong,
Seocho-gu, Seoul, Korea (South)
Tel.: (82) 50409200518
Software Development Services
N.A.I.C.S.: 541511

Zendesk Singapore PTE. LTD **(2)**
401 Commonwealth Drive Haw Par Techno-
centre 07-01, Singapore, 149598, Singa-
pore
Tel.: (65) 63379102
Web Site: http://www.zopim.com
Software Development Services
N.A.I.C.S.: 541511

athenahealth, Inc. **(1)**
311 Arsenal St, Watertown, MA 02472
Tel.: (617) 402-1000
Web Site: http://www.athenahealth.com
Sales Range: $1-4.9 Billion
Emp.: 5,156
Internet-Based Healthcare Records Man-
agement Services

N.A.I.C.S.: 561499
Robert E. Segert (Chm & CEO)
Marc A. Levine (Chief Acctg Officer, Treas &
Exec VP)
Stacy Simpson (CMO)
Jessica Collins (Sec)
David Young (Asst Treas)
Paul Brient (Chief Product Officer)
Caleb Anderson (Chief Sls Officer)
Rob Julavits (Exec Dir-External Comm)
George Hamilton (Chief Corp Strategy &
Dev Officer)

HELLMAN ASSOCIATES, INC.
1225 W 4th St PO Box 627, Water-
loo, IA 50704-0627
Tel.: (319) 234-7055
Web Site: http://www.hellman.com
Year Founded: 1967
Sales Range: $25-49.9 Million
Emp.: 35
Advertising Services
N.A.I.C.S.: 541810
Bob Hellman (Gen Mgr)

Subsidiaries:

Hellman **(1)**
Ste 250 The Gilbert Bldg 413 Wacouta
Street, Saint Paul, MN 55101
Tel.: (612) 375-9598
Sales Range: $10-24.9 Million
N.A.I.C.S.: 541810

HELLMUTH, OBATA & KASSA-
BAUM, INC.
10 S Broadway Ste 200, Saint Louis,
MO 63102-2711
Tel.: (314) 421-2000   DE
Web Site: http://www.hok.com
Year Founded: 1955
Sales Range: $400-449.9 Million
Emp.: 1,700
Architectural Design & Consulting
N.A.I.C.S.: 541310
Paul Woolford (Principal-Design-San
Francisco)
Angelo Arzano (Principal-Technical-
St. Louis Office)
Bill Hellmuth (Chm & CEO)
Lisa Green (Gen Counsel)
Jan Harmon (Dir-HR)
Tom Robson (COO)
Ken Young (CIO)
Ron Bateman (Dir-Interior Design-
Texas)
Nate Appleman (Dir-Sports, Recre-
ation & Entertainment)
Paul McKenzie (Mng Principal-On-
Site Svcs)
Peter Sloan (Dir-Interior Design-
Kansas City)
Randa Tukan (Dir-Interior Design)
Randy Kray (Dir-Lab Programming
Plng)
Robert Chicas (Dir-Aviation & Trans-
portation)
Robert Cull (Mng Principal-Los Ange-
les)
Tom Kaczkowski (Dir-Lighting Design)
Sean Quinn (Chm-Social Responsibil-
ity)
Kai Olsen (Principal & Dir-Design &
Interiors)

HELLO METRO
455 S 4th St, Louisville, KY 40202
Tel.: (502) 582-2212
Web Site: http://www.hellometro.com
Year Founded: 2000
Rev.: $4,700,000
Emp.: 13
Travel Agency
N.A.I.C.S.: 561510

HELLO!
1641 Ivar Ave, Los Angeles, CA
90028-6304
Tel.: (323) 465-9494   CA

Web Site:
http://www.helloandcompany.com
Year Founded: 1981
Sales Range: $10-24.9 Million
Emp.: 25
Motion Picture & Video Production
Services
N.A.I.C.S.: 512110
Graham Henman (Co-Founder, Pres
& Partner)
Michael Karbelnikoff (Co-Founder)
Chris Spanos (Coord-Comml)

HELLO! FLORIDA DESTINA-
TION MANAGEMENT, INC.
3840 Vineland Rd Ste 200, Orlando,
FL 32811
Tel.: (407) 425-5300
Web Site: https://www.hello-dmc.com
Sales Range: $75-99.9 Million
Emp.: 150
Meeting Planning Services
N.A.I.C.S.: 561920
Timothy L. Baker (CFO)
Douglas Kahler (Exec VP)
Eileen Fahey (VP-Corporate Partner-
ships)
Vic Laxson Jr. (Sr VP & Gen Mgr-
Central FL)
Paul S. Mears III (Co-Owner & Pres)

Subsidiaries:

Hello! California **(1)**
2635 Camino del Rio S Ste 200, San Di-
ego, CA 92108-3729
Tel.: (619) 785-5828
Web Site: http://www.hello-dmc.com
Convention & Trade Show Organizers
N.A.I.C.S.: 561920
Bill Yahres (Gen Mgr)

HELLO, INC.
2315 W Broad St, Richmond, VA
23220
Tel.: (804) 353-5566
Web Site: http://www.helloinc.com
Rev.: $926,055,936
Assets: $1,471,504,066
Liabilities: $614,717,742
Net Worth: $856,786,324
Earnings: ($684,301,127)
Emp.: 4,477
Fiscal Year-end: 12/31/20
Telephone Answering Services
N.A.I.C.S.: 561421
Charles R. Smith (Chm & Pres)

HELM BANK USA
999 Brickell Ave, Miami, FL 33131
Tel.: (305) 379-4356   FL
Web Site:
https://www.helmbankusa.com
Year Founded: 1989
Rev.: $40,148,000
Assets: $1,090,690,000
Liabilities: $1,025,821,000
Net Worth: $64,869,000
Earnings: $9,286,000
Emp.: 122
Fiscal Year-end: 12/31/22
Commercial Banking Services
N.A.I.C.S.: 522110
Mark Anthony Crisp (Pres & CEO)
Aimee De Guzman (COO & Sr VP)

HELM HOLDING COMPANY
47911 Halyard Dr Ste 200, Plymouth,
MI 48170
Tel.: (313) 865-5000
Web Site: https://www.helm.com
Sales Range: $50-74.9 Million
Emp.: 271
Holding Company
N.A.I.C.S.: 561910
Dennis Gusick (Pres)

HELMARK STEEL, INC.

Helmark Steel, Inc.—(Continued)

813 S Market St, Wilmington, DE
19801
Tel.: (302) 652-3341   DE
Web Site:
  http://www.helmarksteel.com
Sales Range: $25-49.9 Million
Emp.: 100
Fabricated Structural Metal
N.A.I.C.S.: 332312
Pat Gallo *(Office Mgr)*

HELMES INC.
11815 NE 113th St Ste 110, Vancouver, WA 98662-1631
Tel.: (360) 254-9225
Web Site:
  http://www.newtraditionhomes.com
Rev.: $25,624,895
Emp.: 43
Single-Family Housing Construction
N.A.I.C.S.: 236115
Chris Helmes *(Pres & Co-Owner)*
Kelly Helmes *(Exec VP & Co-Owner)*

HELMICK CORPORATION
998 Minor Ave, Fairmont, WV 26554-3682
Tel.: (304) 366-3520
Web Site:
  https://www.helmickcorp.com
Year Founded: 1868
Sales Range: $10-24.9 Million
Emp.: 20
Mfr of Boiler Tube Shields & Replacement Parts for Pulverized Coal & Ash Handling Systems for Electric Generating Stations
N.A.I.C.S.: 331529
David G. Helmick *(Pres)*
Bruce Gezon *(VP-Mktg)*
Darlene Earl *(Controller)*
Louis G. Helmick III *(Chm & CEO)*

HELMKAMP CONSTRUCTION CO.
707 Berkshire Blvd, East Alton, IL 62024
Tel.: (618) 251-2600   MO
Web Site:
  https://www.helmkamp.com
Year Founded: 1938
Sales Range: $25-49.9 Million
Emp.: 150
Civil Engineering & Construction Services
N.A.I.C.S.: 237990
Gary Bradstreet *(Sec & VP)*
Robert M. Johnes *(Owner & Pres)*

HELMSBRISCOE INC
20875 N 90th Pl Ste 210, Scottsdale, AZ 85255
Tel.: (480) 718-1111   AZ
Web Site:
  https://www.helmsbriscoe.com
Year Founded: 1992
Rev.: $72,100,000
Emp.: 20
Management Consulting Services
N.A.I.C.S.: 541611
Greg Malark *(COO)*
Gary White *(Exec VP)*
Peter Shelly *(Exec VP)*
Roger Helms *(Founder & CEO)*
Richard C. Harper *(Exec VP)*
Amy Clark *(Mng Dir)*
Dana King *(Mgr-Accounts-Global)*
Dave Chapman *(Sr VP)*
Gail Henkin *(VP)*

HELMSLEY ENTERPRISES, INC.
10169 Park Ave, New York, NY 10169
Tel.: (212) 953-2800

Sales Range: $1-4.9 Billion
Emp.: 2,800
Owner & Operator of Lodging, Restaurants, Food Service, Real Estate Development & Management
N.A.I.C.S.: 531120
George Barameda *(Dir-Mktg)*

Subsidiaries:

Helmsley-Noyes Co., LLC   **(1)**
230 Park Ave, New York, NY
10169   **(100%)**
Tel.: (212) 679-3600
Sales Range: $10-24.9 Million
Emp.: 10
Real Estate Brokerage
N.A.I.C.S.: 531210

The Helmsley Carlton House   **(1)**
680 Madison Ave, New York, NY 10021
Tel.: (212) 838-3000
Sales Range: $10-24.9 Million
Emp.: 100
Hotel
N.A.I.C.S.: 721199

The Helmsley Park Lane   **(1)**
36 Central Park S, New York, NY 10019
Tel.: (212) 371-4000
Web Site: http://www.helmsleyparklane.com
Sales Range: $10-24.9 Million
Emp.: 100
Hotel
N.A.I.C.S.: 459420

The Helmsley Sandcastle   **(1)**
1540 Ben Franklin Dr, Sarasota, FL 34236
Tel.: (941) 388-2181
Web Site:
  http://www.sandcastlelidobeach.com
Sales Range: $10-24.9 Million
Emp.: 95
Hotel
N.A.I.C.S.: 721110
Eddie Sipple *(Gen Mgr)*

HELMSLEY-SPEAR, LLC
599 Lexington Ave 44th Fl, New York, NY 10022
Tel.: (212) 396-8100
Web Site:
  http://www.helmsleyspear.com
Year Founded: 1866
Real Estate Management & Brokerage
N.A.I.C.S.: 531210
Kent M. Swig *(Pres & Owner)*

HELP - NEW MEXICO, INC.
5101 Copper Ave NE, Albuquerque, NM 87108
Tel.: (505) 265-3717   NM
Web Site: https://www.helpnm.com
Year Founded: 1965
Emp.: 216
Economic Development Services
N.A.I.C.S.: 541690
Gilbert Ulibarri *(Sec)*
Joey Herrera *(Treas)*
Michael I. Gutierrez *(CEO)*
Cheri Lujan *(Vice Chm)*
Carmela Martinez *(Sec)*
Benai Padilla *(Vice Chm)*
Joseph Griego *(Treas)*
Christopher Madrid *(Treas)*
Charlene Lujan *(Treas)*
Sandra Steckler *(CFO)*

HELP USA INC.
115 E 13th St, New York, NY 10003
Tel.: (212) 400-7000
Web Site: https://www.helpusa.org
Sales Range: $10-24.9 Million
Emp.: 50
Apartment Building Operator
N.A.I.C.S.: 531110
Joseph Gallo *(CFO)*
Thomas Hameline *(CEO)*
Susan Cahill *(VP-Grants Mgmt & Contract Compliance)*
Missy Flower *(Chief Admin Officer)*

Fred Goodhartz *(VP-Materials Mgmt)*
George Nashak *(Exec VP)*
Nancy Nunziata *(VP-Trng & Natl Social Svcs)*
Frances Pierre *(Sr VP-Family Svcs & Day Care Programs)*
Ronnie Silverman *(Sr VP-Program Dev & Govt Funding)*
Anthony Williams *(Vice Chm)*
David Cleghorn *(Chief Housing Officer)*
Maria Cuomo Cole *(Chm)*

Subsidiaries:

Help Philadelphia   **(1)**
4910 Wyalusing Ave, Philadelphia, PA 19131
Tel.: (215) 473-6454
Web Site: http://www3.villanova.edu
Rev.: $3,300,000
Emp.: 20
Nonresidential Construction
N.A.I.C.S.: 236220
Theresa Maybusher *(Exec Dir)*

HELPFUL ALLIANCE COMPANY
700 W Hillsboro Blvd Ste 1-100, Deerfield Beach, FL 33441
Tel.: (754) 227-5783   FL
Web Site:
  http://www.helpfulalliance.com
Year Founded: 2012
Sales Range: Less than $1 Million
Emp.: 11
Real Estate Construction Services
N.A.I.C.S.: 236220
Maxim Temnikov *(Co-Founder & Pres)*
Earl B. Hailston *(Co-Founder & Chm)*
Sergey Gurin *(Co-Founder, Interim CFO & VP)*
Jonathan Barker *(CEO)*

HELPING HAND CENTER
9649 W 55th St, Countryside, IL 60525
Tel.: (708) 352-3580   IL
Web Site: https://helpinghand-il.org
Year Founded: 1955
Sales Range: $10-24.9 Million
Emp.: 571
Disability Assistance Services
N.A.I.C.S.: 624120
Jason Shirk *(Pres)*
Karen A. Mitchell *(VP)*
Carolyn Kline *(Dir-Community Outreach)*
Jeanne Reilly *(Sec)*
Sally Wilson-Gamble *(Sr Dir-School for Children with Autism)*
Melissa Mackay *(Sr Dir-Adult Day Programming & Clinical Svcs)*
Jim Zale *(Dir-Info Tech)*
Ken Gaul *(CFO)*
Herbert A. Smyers *(Chm)*
Howard E. Habenicht *(Treas)*
Dawn Winters *(CFO)*
Amy Moran *(Chief Program Officer)*

HELPING HAND FOR RELIEF & DEVELOPMENT
21199 Hilltop St, Southfield, MI 48033
Tel.: (313) 279-5378   MI
Web Site: https://www1.hhrd.org
Year Founded: 1998
Sales Range: $25-49.9 Million
Emp.: 29
Community Support Services
N.A.I.C.S.: 624210
Farooq Haque *(CFO)*
Fareed Nawaz *(CIO)*
Mariya Nadeem *(CMO)*
Nuzhat Jawed *(Dir-HR)*
Javaid Siddiqi *(COO)*
Mohsin Ansari *(Chm)*

Mustafa White *(Treas)*
Ilyas Choudry *(VP & Dir-Programs)*
Raza Farrukh *(Pres & CEO)*

HELPING HANDS MINISTRIES, INC.
135 Main St, Tallulah Falls, GA 30573
Tel.: (706) 754-6884   GA
Web Site: https://www.hhmin.org
Year Founded: 1996
Sales Range: $10-24.9 Million
Emp.: 8
Christian Ministry Services
N.A.I.C.S.: 813110
Bryan Green *(Pres & CEO)*

HELPING RESTORE ABILITY
4300 Beltway Pl Ste 130, Arlington, TX 76018
Tel.: (817) 469-1977   TX
Web Site: https://www.hratexas.org
Year Founded: 1977
Sales Range: $10-24.9 Million
Emp.: 226
Disability Assistance Services
N.A.I.C.S.: 624120
Ross Robinson *(VP)*
Jake Hardin *(Treas)*
Antoinette Bone *(Pres)*

HELSER INDUSTRIES INC.
10750 SW Tualatin Rd, Tualatin, OR 97062
Tel.: (503) 692-6909
Web Site: https://www.helser.com
Rev.: $20,000,000
Emp.: 129
Fabricated Plate Mfr
N.A.I.C.S.: 332313
Max Helser *(Pres)*
Rick Thomsen *(Chief Engr)*
Nancy Milton *(Controller)*

HELVETICA CREATIVE
1752 Hyde St, San Francisco, CA 94109
Tel.: (310) 361-6809
Year Founded: 2008
Sales Range: Less than $1 Million
Emp.: 10
Advetising Agency
N.A.I.C.S.: 541810
Sultan Mirza *(Principal & Sr Dir-Creative)*
Jeff Kerrin *(Dir-Creative)*
Bill Wade *(Dir-Design)*

HELWIG CARBON PRODUCTS, INC.
8900 W Tower Ave, Milwaukee, WI 53224-2849
Tel.: (414) 354-2411   WI
Web Site: http://www.helwigcp.com
Year Founded: 1928
Sales Range: $100-124.9 Million
Emp.: 300
Mfr of Carbon Brushes, Mechanical Carbon Parts, Constant Pressure Brush Holders & Quick Disconnect Terminals
N.A.I.C.S.: 335991
Jeff D. Koenitzer *(Pres)*
Jay G. Koenitzer *(VP-Mktg)*
Joyce C. Koenitzer *(Treas)*
Paul Casper *(Gen Mgr)*
Douglas Koethny *(Mgr-Pur)*
Gale Knight *(Mgr-Acctg)*
Nitin Kulkarni *(VP-Bus Dev)*

Subsidiaries:

Helwig Carbon Products de Mexico, S. de R.L. de C.V.   **(1)**
Oficina Corporativa Puebla, Col Loma Encantada, CP 72497, Puebla, Mexico
Tel.: (52) 2228686347
Web Site: http://www.helwigcarbon.com

Sales Range: $10-24.9 Million
Emp.: 1
Carbon Products
N.A.I.C.S.: 335991

Helwig Carbon Products of Canada, Inc. **(1)**
15 Ditton Drive Unit 8, Hamilton, L8W 2E5, ON, Canada **(100%)**
Tel.: (905) 385-9112
Sales Range: $10-24.9 Million
Emp.: 3
Carbon Products
N.A.I.C.S.: 335991

HEM INC.
4065 S Main & Webb, Pryor, OK 74362
Tel.: (918) 825-1000
Web Site: https://www.hemsaw.com
Rev.: $12,400,000
Emp.: 151
Machine Tools, Metal Cutting Type
N.A.I.C.S.: 333517
Martha Swank *(Mgr-Sls)*

HEMBREE & ASSOCIATES, INC.
1335 2nd St, Sarasota, FL 34236
Tel.: (941) 951-1776
Web Site: http://www.hembreeco.com
Year Founded: 1985
Sales Range: $1-9.9 Million
Emp.: 8
Commercial Real Estate Brokerage & Management
N.A.I.C.S.: 531210
Joe R. Hembree *(Pres)*
Joe C. Hembree *(VP)*

HEMISPHERE MEDIA GROUP, INC.
4000 Ponce de Leon Blvd Ste 650, Coral Gables, FL 33146
Tel.: (305) 421-6364   DE
Web Site:
   http://www.hemispheretv.com
Year Founded: 2013
HMTV—(NASDAQ)
Rev.: $195,650,000
Assets: $599,911,000
Liabilities: $350,363,000
Net Worth: $249,548,000
Earnings: $11,063,000
Emp.: 363
Fiscal Year-end: 12/31/21
Media Holding Company
N.A.I.C.S.: 551112
Craig D. Fischer *(CFO)*
Alex Tolston *(Chief Legal Officer, Sec & Exec VP)*

Subsidiaries:

Cine Latino, Inc. **(1)**
2000 Ponce de Leon Blvd Ste 500, Coral Gables, FL 33134
Tel.: (305) 421-6399
Web Site: http://www.cinelatino.com
Television Broadcasting Services
N.A.I.C.S.: 516120
James M. McNamara *(Chm & Pres)*

HMTV TV Dominicana, LLC **(1)**
7291 NW 74th St, Medley, FL 33166
Tel.: (305) 777-1900
Web Site:
   http://www.televisiondominicana.tv
Television Broadcasting Services
N.A.I.C.S.: 516120

HMTV, LLC **(1)**
4000 Ponce de Blvd Ste 650, Coral Gables, FL 33146
Tel.: (305) 421-6364
Web Site: http://www.hemispheretv.com
Emp.: 30
Cable TV Operator
N.A.I.C.S.: 516120
Alan J. Sokol *(Pres & CEO)*

InterMedia Espanol, Inc. **(1)**
Metro Office Park, San Juan, PR 00936

Tel.: (787) 200-2696
Television Broadcasting Services
N.A.I.C.S.: 516120

Subsidiary (Domestic):

Televicentro of Puerto Rico, LLC **(2)**
Km 0 Hm 5 Rr 19, Guaynabo, PR 00966
Tel.: (787) 792-4444
Emp.: 290
Television Broadcasting Services
N.A.I.C.S.: 516120
Vanessa Rosado Torres *(Mgr-PR)*
Javier Maynulet *(COO-WAPA-TV)*

Snap Global, LLC **(1)**
651 S Sutton Rd Ste 283, Streamwood, IL 60107-2366
Tel.: (630) 847-3123
Web Site: http://www.snapglobalinc.com
Consulting & Logistics Solution Services
N.A.I.C.S.: 488510

WAPA America Inc. **(1)**
4 Richmond Sq, Providence, RI 02906
Tel.: (401) 454-2880
Web Site: http://www.wapa.tv
Television Broadcasting Services
N.A.I.C.S.: 516120
Jonathan Garcia *(VP-Sls & Mktg)*
Jimmy Arteaga *(Pres-Programming & Promo)*
Jose Guerra *(Dir-Engrg)*
Rafael Perez Subira *(Dir-Sls-Natl)*
Paco Vargas *(Mgr-Deport)*
Olga Bonnin *(VP-Admin & Fin)*
Rafael Lenin Lopez *(Dir-News)*
Maria Elena Crespo *(Dir-HR)*

HEMMING MORSE, INC.
160 Spear St Ste 1900, San Francisco, CA 94105
Tel.: (415) 836-4000
Web Site: http://www.hemming.com
Rev.: $11,178,428
Emp.: 82
Certified Public Accountants
N.A.I.C.S.: 541211
Paul Regan *(Chm)*
Carl Saba *(Partner)*
Rachel Hennessy *(Mgr-Forensic & Fin Consulting Svcs Grp)*
Jeffrey Klein *(Principal-Forensic & Fin Consulting Svcs Grp)*
David Callaghan *(Partner-Forensic & Fin Consulting Svcs Grp)*
Christian Tregillis *(Partner-Forensic & Fin Consulting Svcs Grp)*

HEMOPHILIA CENTER OF WESTERN NEW YORK, INC.
936 Delaware Ave Ste 300, Buffalo, NY 14209
Tel.: (716) 896-2470   NY
Web Site:
   http://www.hemophiliawny.com
Year Founded: 1969
Sales Range: $10-24.9 Million
Emp.: 18
Health Care Srvices
N.A.I.C.S.: 622110
Laurel Reger *(Exec Dir)*
Shilpa Jain *(Dir-Pediatric Medical)*
Karin Kubicki *(Treas)*
Mary Haggerty *(VP)*
Robert Long *(Chm)*
Marcia Gellin *(VP)*
Michael Cimato *(Sec)*
Thomas Long *(Pres)*

HEMOPHILIA SERVICES CONSORTIUM, INC.
525 E 68th St, New York, NY 10065
Tel.: (212) 297-4356   NY
Year Founded: 1995
Sales Range: $10-24.9 Million
Health Care Srvices
N.A.I.C.S.: 622110
Alejandro Baquero *(Pres)*

HEMPHILL CORPORATION

1350 N Louisville Ave, Tulsa, OK 74115
Tel.: (918) 834-2200
Web Site:
   http://www.hemphillbts.com
Year Founded: 1957
Sales Range: $10-24.9 Million
Emp.: 30
Provider of Consulting, Design & Engineering Services
N.A.I.C.S.: 238990
Elmer L. Hemphill *(Founder)*
Gary Connelly *(Dir-Tower Site Dev)*
Dave Morrison *(Dir-Mfg)*

HEMPSTEAD AUTO CO. INC.
732 Northern Blvd, Great Neck, NY 11021-5205
Tel.: (516) 482-5500   NY
Web Site:
   http://www.greatneckjaguar.com
Year Founded: 1938
Sales Range: $25-49.9 Million
Emp.: 50
Passenger Car Leasing
N.A.I.C.S.: 532112
Jerry Rubin *(Controller)*
Amir Jarrah *(VP)*
Jake Weidinger *(Pres)*

HEMPSTEAD FORD LINCOLN
301 N Franklin St, Hempstead, NY 11550-1311
Tel.: (516) 568-4072   NY
Web Site:
   https://www.hempsteadford.net
Year Founded: 1929
Sales Range: $10-24.9 Million
Emp.: 49
New & Used Car Dealership
N.A.I.C.S.: 441110
John Talt *(Mgr-Truck)*
John Billard *(Pres)*
Ken Beckendorf *(Dir-Parts & Svc)*

HEMPT BROTHERS, INC.
205 Creek Rd, Camp Hill, PA 17011-7418
Tel.: (717) 737-3411   PA
Web Site: http://www.hemptbros.com
Year Founded: 1926
Sales Range: $200-249.9 Million
Emp.: 400
Provider of Highway Construction Services
N.A.I.C.S.: 237310
Gerald L. Hempt *(Treas & Sec)*
Max J. Hempt *(Pres)*
Richard Wagner *(Coord-Construction)*

HEMSTREET DEVELOPMENT CORP.
16100 NW Cornell Rd Ste 100, Beaverton, OR 97006
Tel.: (503) 531-4000
Web Site: http://www.hemstreet.com
Year Founded: 1975
Sales Range: $10-24.9 Million
Emp.: 60
Commercial Real Estate Development & Property Management
N.A.I.C.S.: 721110
Greg Hemstreet *(Owner & Pres)*

HENA, INC.
660 Berriman St, Brooklyn, NY 11208-5304
Tel.: (718) 272-8237
Sales Range: $10-24.9 Million
Emp.: 17
Dried & Dehydrated Food Mfr
N.A.I.C.S.: 311423
Daniel Kopf *(Mgr-Sls)*
Scott Tauber *(VP-Fin)*

HENCH ENTERPRISES INC.

1340 W High St Ste E, Defiance, OH 43512-1323
Tel.: (419) 782-0950   OH
Web Site:
   http://www.chiefmarkets.com
Year Founded: 1984
Sales Range: $25-49.9 Million
Emp.: 900
Grocery Stores
N.A.I.C.S.: 445110
Harding Hwy *(Mgr-Store)*

HENDELS INCORPORATED
35 Great Neck Rd, Waterford, CT 06385-3337
Tel.: (860) 437-4648   CT
Year Founded: 1945
Sales Range: $25-49.9 Million
Emp.: 150
Fuel Oil Dealers
N.A.I.C.S.: 457210
Myron Hendel *(Owner)*
Jacob Greene *(Controller)*

HENDERSON BANCSHARES, INC.
1000 Hwy 231 S, Troy, AL 36081
Tel.: (334) 566-4000   AL
Web Site:
   http://www.troybankandtrust.com
Bank Holding Company
N.A.I.C.S.: 551111
Jeff Kervin *(Pres & CEO)*

Subsidiaries:

Troy Bank & Trust Company **(1)**
1000 US 231 S, Troy, AL 36081
Tel.: (334) 566-4000
Web Site: http://www.troybankandtrust.com
Sales Range: $25-49.9 Million
Emp.: 128
Commercial & Investment Banking, Trust Services, Lending Services & Real Estate Sales
N.A.I.C.S.: 522110
Sherry Bray *(VP)*
Jeff Bentley *(Mgr-Fin Svcs)*
Jeff Kervin *(Pres & CEO)*

HENDERSON COMBINED GROUP OF COMPANIES, INC.
1902 Brandon Dr Ste A, Tyler, TX 75703
Tel.: (903) 787-8905   TX
Web Site: http://www.1hcgc.com
Sales Range: $10-24.9 Million
Emp.: 10
Storage & Transportation
N.A.I.C.S.: 488510
Mitch Henderson *(Pres)*

HENDERSON ENGINEERS INC.
8325 Lenexa Dr, Lenexa, KS 66214-1695
Tel.: (913) 742-5000
Web Site: http://www.hei-eng.com
Year Founded: 1970
Rev.: $44,400,000
Emp.: 350
Engineering Design Firm
N.A.I.C.S.: 541330
Rick Lahm *(CFO)*
Mike McCluskey *(Sr VP)*
Paul Mejia *(Sr VP)*
Cindy Carlson *(VP)*
Chris Culp *(VP)*
John Kaloupek *(Sr VP)*
Omid Mottahed *(VP)*
Marcus Sanchez *(Dir-Phoenix Ops & Higher Ed Practice)*
Darrell Stein *(Sr VP & Dir-Fire Protection & Life Safety)*
John Varberg *(VP)*
Marc Feyh *(VP)*
Scott Jack *(VP)*
Duane Henderson *(Pres)*

Henderson Engineers Inc.—(Continued)

Dustin Schafer *(Sr VP & Dir-Engrg)*
Robin Broder *(CMO)*
Tiffany Arnold *(Gen Counsel)*
Jason Wollum *(Sr VP)*
Pablo Mejia *(Sr VP & Dir-Retail Practice)*
Kevin Lewis *(Sr VP & Dir-Sports Practice)*
Andrew Knight *(VP)*
Tony Welter *(VP & Dir-Refrigeration)*
Maggie Curcio *(Chief People Officer)*

HENDERSON IMPLEMENT CO. INC.
211 W Service Rd, Welsh, LA 70591
Tel.: (337) 734-2166
Web Site: http://www.hendersonimplement.com
Sales Range: $10-24.9 Million
Emp.: 72
Agricultural Machinery & Equipment
N.A.I.C.S.: 423820
Evelyn Cole *(Office Mgr)*
Dale Bercher *(Gen Mgr-Equipment)*
Charles Henderson Sr. *(Chm)*

HENDERSON PROPERTIES INC.
4389 Indian Trl Fairview Ste11, Indian Trail, NC 28079-9648
Tel.: (704) 462-8015
Web Site: http://www.hendersonproperties.com
Offices of Real Estate Agents & Brokers
N.A.I.C.S.: 531210
Phil Henderson *(Mgr)*
Brenda Meetze *(Mgr-Rental Div)*
Tom Borloglou *(Mgr-Community Associations)*
Erin Yarbro *(Mgr-Community Associations)*
Kelsey Mellor *(Mgr-Community Association)*
Ashley Puckett *(Asst Mgr-Property-Rentals)*
Ryan Freeland *(Mgr-Maintenance)*
Lauren Scheer *(Mgr-Association Div)*

Subsidiaries:

Harpe Realty **(1)**
4801 E Independence Blvd Ste 905, Charlotte, NC 28212-5495
Tel.: (704) 453-3401
Web Site: http://www.rentahomeincharlotte.com
Offices of Real Estate Agents & Brokers
N.A.I.C.S.: 531210
Vicki Harpe *(Pres)*

HENDERSON SERVICES LLC
4502 Poplar Level Rd, Louisville, KY 40213
Tel.: (502) 719-6615
Web Site: https://www.henderson-services.com
Sales Range: $10-24.9 Million
Emp.: 300
General Electrical Contractor
N.A.I.C.S.: 238210
Bruce Henderson *(Chm & CEO)*
Rich Masterson *(Dir-Estimating & Engrg)*
Cheryl Banks *(Project Mgr)*
David Gross *(Pres)*
Dwayne Rice *(Dir-Bus Dev)*

HENDERSON, FRANKLIN, STARNES & HOLT, P.A.
1715 Monroe St, Fort Myers, FL 33902
Tel.: (239) 344-1100
Web Site: https://www.henlaw.com
Year Founded: 1924
Emp.: 50

Law firm
N.A.I.C.S.: 541110
Denis H. Noah *(Mng Partner)*

HENDERSON, JOSEPH J. & SONS
4288 Old Grand Ave, Gurnee, IL 60031
Tel.: (847) 244-3222
Web Site: https://www.jjhenderson.com
Year Founded: 1984
Sales Range: $200-249.9 Million
Emp.: 130
Civil Engineering Services
N.A.I.C.S.: 237310
David Henderson *(Pres)*

HENDERSON-JOHNSON CO. INC.
918 Canal St, Syracuse, NY 13210
Tel.: (315) 479-5561
Web Site: https://www.hjcoinc.com
Sales Range: $10-24.9 Million
Emp.: 75
Drywall
N.A.I.C.S.: 238310
Thad Collum *(Pres)*
Bob Henderson *(Exec VP)*
Nora McLaughlin-Lantry *(Project Mgr-Mgmt)*
Todd Henderson *(VP)*

HENDERSONS PRINTING INC.
Green Ave & 9th St, Altoona, PA 16601
Tel.: (814) 944-0855
Web Site: http://www.hendersonsprinting.com
Sales Range: $10-24.9 Million
Emp.: 30
Offset Printing
N.A.I.C.S.: 323111
R. Thomas Henderson *(Chm)*

HENDRICK CHEVROLET CADILLAC
3112 W Hwy 74, Monroe, NC 28110-8437
Tel.: (704) 289-8444
Web Site: http://www.hendrickchevy.com
Year Founded: 2006
Sales Range: $10-24.9 Million
Emp.: 50
New Car Whslr
N.A.I.C.S.: 441110
Chris Boone *(Gen Mgr)*

HENDRICK CHRYSLER JEEP
543 N McPherson Church Rd, Fayetteville, NC 28303
Tel.: (910) 425-4200
Web Site: http://www.hendrickchryslerjeep.com
Sales Range: $10-24.9 Million
Emp.: 60
Car Whslr
N.A.I.C.S.: 441110
Dan D. Dederick *(Gen Mgr)*
Brad Walser *(Mgr-Collision Center)*
Derrick Cassidy *(Mgr-Pre-Owned)*

HENDRICK HEALTH SYSTEM
1900 Pine St, Abilene, TX 79601
Tel.: (325) 670-2000
Web Site: http://www.hendrickhealth.org
Year Founded: 1924
Hospital & Health Care Services Organization
N.A.I.C.S.: 813920
Brad D. Holland *(Pres & CEO)*

Subsidiaries:

Hendrick Cancer Center **(1)**

2000 Pine St, Abilene, TX 79601
Tel.: (325) 670-6340
Cancer Treatment Services
N.A.I.C.S.: 621111

Hendrick Provider Network **(1)**
1900 Pine St, Abilene, TX 79601
Tel.: (325) 670-2000
Web Site: http://www.hendrickhealth.org
Sales Range: $1-9.9 Million
Emp.: 3,000
HMO Medical Centers
N.A.I.C.S.: 621491
I. Tim Lancaster *(Pres & CEO)*

HENDRICK MANUFACTURING COMPANY
1 7th Ave, Carbondale, PA 18407-2203
Tel.: (570) 282-1010   **DE**
Web Site: https://www.hendrickcorp.com
Year Founded: 1876
Sales Range: $75-99.9 Million
Emp.: 150
Perforated Metal Screens, Perforated Grilles Mfr & Distr
N.A.I.C.S.: 332119
Alicia McHale *(VP & Controller)*
Tom Mosca *(VP-Mfg)*

Subsidiaries:

Hendrick Screen Co. **(1)**
3074 Medley Rd, Owensboro, KY 42301
Tel.: (270) 685-5138
Web Site: http://www.hendrickscreenco.com
Sales Range: $25-49.9 Million
Emp.: 40
Mfr of Wedge Wire & Wire Screens in Stainless Steel, Copper Nickel & Other Alloys
N.A.I.C.S.: 332618
Steve Lawson *(Product Mgr)*

HENDRICKS & PARTNERS, INC.
2525 E Camelback Rd Ste 1150, Phoenix, AZ 85016
Tel.: (602) 955-1122   **AZ**
Web Site: http://www.hpapts.com
Year Founded: 1995
Sales Range: $50-74.9 Million
Emp.: 200
Real Estate Broker; Apartment Investment & Advisory Services
N.A.I.C.S.: 531210
Forrest Bass *(VP)*

HENDRICKS HOLDING COMPANY, INC.
690 3rd St Ste 300, Beloit, WI 53511
Tel.: (608) 362-8000   **WI**
Web Site: http://www.hendricksholding.com
Year Founded: 2001
Holding Company
N.A.I.C.S.: 551112
Diane Hendricks *(Chm)*
Brent Fox *(CEO)*
Carla Swain *(Treas & Sec)*
Jon Coulter *(Mng Dir)*
Karl Leo *(Chief Legal Officer & VP)*
Michael Willms *(Pres)*
Ned Moser *(Mng Dir)*
Kim Bliss *(VP)*
David Erickson *(Office Mgr)*

Subsidiaries:

American Builders & Contractors Supply Co., Inc. **(1)**
1 ABC Pkwy, Beloit, WI 53511-4466
Tel.: (608) 362-7777
Web Site: http://www.abcsupply.com
Sales Range: Less than $1 Million
Emp.: 15,000
Roofing, Siding, Windows & Tools Distr
N.A.I.C.S.: 423330
Diane Hendricks *(Founder & Chm)*
Todd Buehl *(CFO)*
Keith Rozolis *(Pres & CEO)*

Kim Hendricks *(VP-Corp Dev)*
Brad Money *(VP-Div Ops)*
Lisa Indgjer *(VP-Assoc Svcs & HR)*
Mike Boggs *(Dir-Ops)*
Daniel Piche *(VP-Natl Bus Dev)*
Kathy Hendricks *(Exec Dir-Customer Connectivity)*
Tony Vaden *(CIO)*
Mike Jost *(COO)*
Chris Slusar *(Controller)*
Ronald Frantantoni *(Mng Partner)*
Joe Shaw *(Mgr-Belleville)*
Jim Boudreau *(Mng Partner)*
Tim Kuchan *(Mgr-Facility-Runnemede)*
Matt Cooper *(VP-West)*
Karl W. Leo *(Chief Legal Officer & VP)*
John Simonelli *(VP-Strategic Initiatives)*
Jim Welch *(VP-Midwest)*
Andy Morris *(Branch Mgr)*
Jeff Apple *(Mgr-Columbus)*
Dan Manning *(Mgr-Hartford)*
Ryan Rhoden *(Mgr-Memphis)*
Danny Duncan *(Mng Partner-Pineville)*
Kyle Fisher *(Mng Partner)*
Steve Albritton *(Mgr-Building Products Distr-Sudbury)*
Frank Marcoccio *(VP-Southeast)*
Jonathan Shepard *(VP-Southwest)*
Marc Kramer *(Dir-Corp Dev)*
Dan Wrobleski *(Mng Partner-New Hudson)*
Greg Stempniewski *(Mng Partner-Southfield)*

Subsidiary (Domestic):

Alliance Wholesale Supply, Inc. **(2)**
1581 Solomon Run Rd, Johnstown, PA 15904
Tel.: (814) 532-0990
Lumber, Plywood, Millwork & Wood Panel Merchant Whslr
N.A.I.C.S.: 423310

AmCraft Building Products Co., Inc. **(2)**
1195 Prince Hall Dr Ste B, Beloit, WI 53511
Tel.: (608) 362-1800
Web Site: http://www.amcraft.com
Rev.: $25,000,000
Emp.: 7
Provider Of Roofing, Siding & Insulation
N.A.I.C.S.: 423330
Caroline Kelly *(Dir-Mktg)*

American Slate Company **(2)**
1900 Olympic Blvd Ste 200, Walnut Creek, CA 94596
Tel.: (925) 977-4880
Web Site: http://www.americanslate.com
Slate & Other Cut Stone Products Mfr & Distr
N.A.I.C.S.: 327991

Bradco Supply Corporation **(2)**
34 Englehard Ave, Avenel, NJ 07001
Tel.: (732) 382-3400
Web Site: http://www.bradcosupply.com
Sales Range: $1-4.9 Billion
Emp.: 3,100
Roofing, Building Materials, Siding, Windows & Doors Distr
N.A.I.C.S.: 423330

Branch (Domestic):

Elite Home Supplies **(2)**
3838 Patterson Rd, Bay City, MI 48706
Tel.: (989) 684-7501
Web Site: http://www.elitehomesupplies.net
Emp.: 7
Home Center Operator
N.A.I.C.S.: 444110
Dine Hendricks *(Owner & CEO)*

Subsidiary (Domestic):

G & F Roof Supply Co. **(2)**
1225 E Cerritos Ave, Anaheim, CA 92805-6416
Tel.: (714) 399-0250
Web Site: http://www.gfroof.com
Roofing Installation Services
N.A.I.C.S.: 238160
Jon Wetherbee *(Gen Mgr)*

Homexterior Building Supply, Inc. **(2)**
221 N White Fox Rd, Webster City, IA 50595-7603
Tel.: (515) 832-5471

Web Site: http://www.homexterior.com
Rev.: $1,200,000
Emp.: 6
Whol Siding & Mfg Awnings
N.A.I.C.S.: 423330

L&W Supply Corporation (2)
303 W Irving Park Rd, Roselle, IL
60172 **(100%)**
Tel.: (630) 894-5200
Web Site: http://www.lwsupply.com
Building Materials Distr
N.A.I.C.S.: 444180
Dan Piche *(Pres)*
Jake Gress *(VP-Ops)*
Chad Cutlip *(District Mgr)*
Scott Stuckert *(Mgr-Bus Dev-Central)*
Kelly Kalauli *(Branch Mgr-Ogden-Utah)*

Subsidiary (Domestic):

Daico Supply Company (3)
1084 W Jackson Rd, Carrollton, TX 75006
Tel.: (972) 245-6000
Web Site: http://www.daicosupply.com
Sales Range: $10-24.9 Million
Emp.: 40
Distr of Drywall Products
N.A.I.C.S.: 423330
David Daly *(Gen Mgr)*

Delta Gypsum, LLC (3)
3640 Banks Rd, Raleigh, NC 27603
Tel.: (919) 263-7252
Web Site: http://deltagypsum.com
Drywall, Ceiling Systems, Steel Framing &
Other Building Materials Distr
N.A.I.C.S.: 423320
David Raleigh *(Branch Mgr)*

Merrimack Building Supply, Inc. (3)
260 Daniel Webster Hwy, Merrimack, NH
03054
Tel.: (603) 424-7001
Web Site:
   http://www.merrimackbuildingsupply.com
Sales Range: $1-9.9 Million
Emp.: 43
Brick, Stone & Related Construction Material Merchant Whslr
N.A.I.C.S.: 423320
William Donegan *(Pres)*

Old Fort Building Supply of South
Bend Inc (3)
1401 S Main St, South Bend, IN 46613
Tel.: (574) 289-5566
Web Site: http://www.oldfort.com
Rev.: $3,200,000
Emp.: 15
Brick, Stone & Related Construction Material Merchant Whslr
N.A.I.C.S.: 423320

Subsidiary (Domestic):

Landis Supply of New Jersey,
Inc. (2)
1590 N Main Rd, Vineland, NJ 08360
Tel.: (856) 691-8040
Lumber, Plywood, Millwork & Wood Panel
Merchant Whslr
N.A.I.C.S.: 423310

Mule-Hide Products Co., Inc. (2)
1195 Prince Hall Dr, Beloit, WI 53511-3964
Tel.: (608) 365-3111
Web Site: http://www.mulehide.com
Sales Range: $25-49.9 Million
Emp.: 66
Commercial Roofing
N.A.I.C.S.: 423330
Tony Kleeman *(Controller)*
Jonathan Shepard *(Pres)*
Dan Williams *(Mng Dir)*
Ken Schultz *(Dir-West & Midwest)*
Rob Keating *(Dir-Northeast)*
Mark Wessinger *(Mgr-Product Category-Liquid-Applied Sys)*
Kurt Fago *(Mgr-Product Category-Low-Slope Roofing Sys)*
Jeremy Grunewald *(Product Mgr-Natl)*
Chris Kuykendall *(Mgr-Fluid-Applied Segment)*

Branch (Domestic):

Rome Building Products Inc. (2)
18 Sherman St, Worcester, MA 01610
Tel.: (508) 754-1792

Sales Range: $1-9.9 Million
Exterior Building Products Distr
N.A.I.C.S.: 444180
Dave Porter *(Branch Mgr)*

Subsidiary (Domestic):

Sidewinder Supply, Inc. (2)
1011 N 16 Street, Show Low, AZ
85901-5134 **(100%)**
Tel.: (928) 532-3446
Rev.: $3,500,000
Emp.: 6
Distributes Roofing & Roofing-related Products
N.A.I.C.S.: 423330
Wayne Margeson *(Branch Mgr)*

Standard Roofings Inc. (2)
100 Park Rd, Tinton Falls, NJ 07724-9715
Tel.: (732) 542-3300
Sales Range: $10-24.9 Million
Roofing, Siding & Insulation Materials Distr
N.A.I.C.S.: 423330

Town & Country Industries (2)
400 W McNab Rd, Fort Lauderdale, FL
33309
Tel.: (954) 970-9999
Web Site: http://www.tc-alum.com
Sales Range: $50-74.9 Million
Emp.: 350
Aluminum & Building Products Mfr & Whslr
N.A.I.C.S.: 423510
Kurt M. Lackore *(Mng Dir)*

Subsidiary (Domestic):

Ace Aluminum Distributors, Inc. (3)
370 W Lemon Ln, Casselberry, FL
32707 **(100%)**
Tel.: (407) 834-6633
Web Site: http://www.ace-aluminum.com
Sales Range: $1-9.9 Million
Emp.: 21
Distributes & Supplies Pool & Patio Products
N.A.I.C.S.: 423390
Deborah Tincher *(Gen Mgr)*

Subsidiary (Domestic):

Vande Hey Raleigh Roof Tile Manu-
facturing, Inc. (2)
1665 Bohm Dr, Little Chute, WI 54140-2529
Tel.: (920) 766-0156
Web Site: http://www.vrmtile.com
Sales Range: $25-49.9 Million
Roofing Tile Mfr & Distr
N.A.I.C.S.: 327120

Wameling Drywall Corp. (2)
9204 State Rte 49, Maroy, NY 13403
Tel.: (315) 736-9333
Web Site: http://www.gilbertsupply.com
Sales Range: $1-9.9 Million
Wallboard & Insulation Distr
N.A.I.C.S.: 423330
Anthony J. Wameling *(Pres)*

Avid Pallet Services, LLC (1)
1401 Eddy Ave, Beloit, WI 53511 **(100%)**
Tel.: (608) 299-0029
Web Site: http://www.avidpallet.com
Sales Range: $25-49.9 Million
Emp.: 100
Wood Pallet & Crate Mfr, Refurbisher &
Distr
N.A.I.C.S.: 321920
Chuck Hoppe *(Pres)*

Blackhawk Transport Inc. (1)
3800 Gateway Blvd Ste 100, Beloit, WI
53511
Tel.: (608) 364-4040
Web Site:
   http://www.blackhawktransport.com
Sales Range: $10-24.9 Million
Local & Long-Distance General Freight
Trucking Services
N.A.I.C.S.: 484121
Kevin McGrath *(VP-Ops)*
Mark Carter *(Mgr-Ops)*
Mike Holloway *(Pres & CEO)*

Corporate Contractors Inc. (1)
3800 Gateway Blvd Ste 200, Beloit, WI
53511 **(100%)**
Tel.: (608) 362-2912
Web Site: http://www.cciwi.com

Sales Range: $75-99.9 Million
Commercial, Industrial & Institutional Contract Building Renovation & Construction
Services
N.A.I.C.S.: 238990
Terry Russell *(VP-Quarry Ops)*
Brad Austin *(Pres)*

Garick, LLC (1)
13600 Broadway Ave Ste 1, Cleveland, OH
44125-1963
Tel.: (216) 581-0100
Web Site: http://www.garick.com
Sales Range: $25-49.9 Million
Natural Resource Products Distr & Mfr
N.A.I.C.S.: 424910
Gary P. Trinetti *(Pres & CEO)*
Patrick W. Mahoney *(Exec VP)*
Robert Schanz *(COO)*
John C. Gundlach *(Sr VP-Ops & Bus Dev)*
Enrico Varricchio *(CFO)*

Unit (Domestic):

New Milford Farms (2)
60 Boardman Rd, New Milford, CT 06776
Tel.: (860) 210-0250
Web Site: http://www.newmilfordfarms.com
Fertilizer & Mulch Mfr
N.A.I.C.S.: 325314

Paygro (2)
11000 Huntington Rd, South Charleston,
OH 45368
Tel.: (937) 462-8350
Web Site: http://www.paygro.com
Sales Range: $10-24.9 Million
Fertilizer & Mulch Mfr
N.A.I.C.S.: 325314

Hendricks River Logistics, LLC (1)
3254 Mississippi River Rd, Keokuk, IA
52632 **(100%)**
Tel.: (319) 524-6841
Web Site: http://www.hendrickrl.com
Sales Range: $25-49.9 Million
Train to Barge Cargo Handling Services
N.A.I.C.S.: 488390
Shawn Duer *(Gen Mgr)*

Henry Technologies, Inc. (1)
655 3rd St Ste 100, Beloit, WI
53511 **(100%)**
Tel.: (608) 361-4400
Web Site: http://www.henrytech.com
Sales Range: $10-24.9 Million
Emp.: 250
Commercial & Industrial Heating, Ventilation, Air Conditioning & Refrigeration Valve
& Component Mfr & Distr
N.A.I.C.S.: 332911

Subsidiary (Domestic):

American Industrial Steel & Supply,
LLC (2)
520 N Parker Dr, Janesville, WI
53547 **(100%)**
Tel.: (608) 754-1000
Web Site: http://www.aissllc.com
Industrial Supplies Distr
N.A.I.C.S.: 423840

Plant (Domestic):

Henry Technologies - Chatham
Plant (2)
701 S Main St, Chatham, IL 62629
Tel.: (217) 483-2406
Web Site: http://www.henrytech.com
Emp.: 70
Commercial & Industrial Heating, Ventilation, Air Conditioning & Refrigeration Valve
& Component Mfr
N.A.I.C.S.: 332911
Sandy MacDonald *(Gen Mgr)*

Plant (Non-US):

Henry Technologies Canada (2)
36 Craig Street, PO Box 1385, Brantford,
N3T 5T6, ON, Canada
Tel.: (519) 759-3010
Web Site: https://www.ht-industrial.com
Emp.: 75
Chillers Condenser Pressure Vessels &
Heat Exchanger Mfr
N.A.I.C.S.: 333415
Alex Barclay *(Mng Dir)*
Nancy Wieland *(Fin Dir)*
Ross Hainer *(Mgr-HR)*
Jennifer Church *(Mgr-Ops)*

Subsidiary (Non-US):

Henry Technologies Limited (2)
Block 76 Mossland Rd, Hillington Pk, Glasgow, G52 4XZ, Scotland, United
Kingdom **(100%)**
Tel.: (44) 1418824621
Web Site: http://www.henrytech.co.uk
Emp.: 60
Commercial & Industrial Heating, Ventilation, Air Conditioning & Refrigeration Component Mfr
N.A.I.C.S.: 333415
Sandy MacDonald *(Mng Dir)*

Henry-Technologies GmbH (2)
Im Gewerbepark 11a, D-36457, Stadtlengsfeld, Germany
Tel.: (49) 369658000
Web Site: http://www.henry-technologies.de
Polyethylene Ball Valves & Vehicle Mud
Guards Mfr
N.A.I.C.S.: 326191

Subsidiary (Domestic):

Stainless Tank & Equipment Co.,
LLC (2)
801 4th St, Beloit, WI 53511
Tel.: (608) 368-9663
Web Site: http://www.stainlesstanker.com
Sales Range: $10-24.9 Million
Emp.: 120
Stainless Steel Tank Designer & Mfr
N.A.I.C.S.: 332420
Steven Mayse *(Pres)*

Humane Manufacturing Company,
LLC (1)
805 Moore St, Baraboo, WI 53913
Tel.: (608) 356-8336
Web Site: http://www.humanemfg.com
Fabricated Rubber Mat & Flooring Products
Mfr
N.A.I.C.S.: 326299

Insential, Inc. (1)
5601 Granite Pkwy Ste 240, Plano, TX
75024
Tel.: (888) 571-6160
Web Site: http://www.insential.com
Insurance Wholesale Brokerage, Consulting
& Underwriting Services
N.A.I.C.S.: 524210
Allan Hildebrand *(Pres)*
Terry Byrne *(Exec VP)*
Jack Byrnes *(Asst VP)*

Universal Recycling Technologies,
LLC (1)
2535 Beloit Ave, Janesville, WI 53546
Tel.: (608) 754-3400
Web Site: http://www.universalrecyclers.com
Sales Range: $25-49.9 Million
Electronic Waste Recycling Services
N.A.I.C.S.: 562920
Jim Cornwell *(Founder & Pres)*

HENDRICKSON TRUCKING, INC.

7080 Florin Perkins Rd, Sacramento,
CA 95828
Tel.: (916) 387-9614
Web Site:
   http://www.hendricksontrucking.com
Rev.: $27,600,000
Emp.: 300
General Freight Trucking, Long-Distance, Truckload
N.A.I.C.S.: 484121
William Hendrickson *(Chm)*
Alban Lang *(CFO)*
Desire Habr *(Office Mgr)*

HENDRIX BUSINESS SYSTEMS, INC.

2040 Independence Commerce Dr,
Ste A, Matthews, NC 28105
Tel.: (704) 574-4800
Web Site:
   https://www.hendrixbusiness.com
Year Founded: 1976
Rev.: $2,035,000
Emp.: 5
Office Supplies & Stationery Stores

Hendrix Business Systems, Inc.—(Continued)

N.A.I.C.S.: 459410
Roger Hendrix *(Pres & CEO)*

HENDRY ALUMINUM, INC.
5592 Lee St Unit 3, Lehigh Acres, FL 33971
Tel.: (239) 303-0099
Web Site:
   https://www.hendryaluminuminc.com
Year Founded: 1987
Sales Range: $1-9.9 Million
Emp.: 20
Aluminum Sheet, Plate & Foil Mfr
N.A.I.C.S.: 331315
Thomas Hendry *(Pres)*

HENIFF TRANSPORTATION SYSTEMS INC.
2015 Spring Rd Ste 780, Oak Brook, IL 60523
Tel.: (630) 230-2100
Web Site: http://www.heniff.com
Sales Range: $10-24.9 Million
Emp.: 600
Liquid Bulk Transportation Services
N.A.I.C.S.: 484121
Robert J. Heniff *(Pres & CEO)*
Scott Templeman *(Dir-Ops)*
Leon Lupina *(Dir-Safety)*
Marty Martinson *(CFO)*
Joe Neal *(Dir-IT)*
Frank Schaeffer *(Dir-Sls)*
Jim D'Amico *(Gen Counsel)*
Kevin Loudon *(Dir-Corp Fin)*
Ed Thompson *(Dir-Dispatch)*
Bruce Schauer *(Mgr-Fleet)*

Subsidiaries:

Horizon Tank Lines, Inc.   (1)
141 Old Fayetteville Rd, Leland, NC 28451
Tel.: (910) 383-0067
Web Site: http://www.horizontanklines.com
Emp.: 27
Liquid Bulk Transportation Services
N.A.I.C.S.: 484121
Charles Collie *(Pres)*

Superior Bulk Logistics, Inc.   (1)
711 Jorie Blvd, Oak Brook, IL 60523-4425
Tel.: (630) 573-2555
Web Site:
  http://www.superiorbulklogistics.com
Specialized Freight Trucking & Logistic Services
N.A.I.C.S.: 484230
Len F. Fletcher *(CEO)*
Wes Stone *(Pres & Chief Comml Officer)*

Division (Domestic):

Carry Transport Inc.   (2)
711 Jorie Blvd Ste 101 N, Oak Brook, IL 60523
Tel.: (800) 654-7707
Web Site: http://www.carrytransit.com
Food Grade Transportation Arrangement
N.A.I.C.S.: 488510

Subsidiary (Domestic):

Superior Carriers, Inc.   (2)
711 Jorie Blvd Ste 101 N, Oak Brook, IL 60523
Tel.: (630) 573-2555
Web Site: http://www.superior-carriers.com
Sales Range: $25-49.9 Million
Emp.: 80
Liquid & Dry Bulk Chemical Trucking Services
N.A.I.C.S.: 484230
Brian T. Nowak *(Pres)*

HENIG FURS INC.
4135 Carmichael Rd, Montgomery, AL 36106
Tel.: (334) 277-7610
Web Site: https://www.henigfurs.com
Year Founded: 1976
Sales Range: $10-24.9 Million
Emp.: 105

Fur Apparel
N.A.I.C.S.: 458110
Colin Jones *(VP)*

HENKEL CHRYSLER JEEP INC.
1275 W Dickman Rd, Battle Creek, MI 49037
Tel.: (269) 968-1171
Web Site:
   https://www.henkelauto.com
Sales Range: $10-24.9 Million
Emp.: 50
Sales of New & Used Automobiles
N.A.I.C.S.: 441110
Tom Henkle *(Gen Mgr)*

HENKEL CONSTRUCTION COMPANY
208 E State St, Mason City, IA 50401
Tel.: (641) 423-5674
Web Site:
   https://www.henkelconstruction.com
Year Founded: 1892
Sales Range: $25-49.9 Million
Emp.: 90
Commercial Building Construction Services
N.A.I.C.S.: 236220
Gary J. Schmit *(Pres)*
Kent A. Brcka *(Pres-Ops)*
Stephen M. Watson *(VP-Construction Svcs)*
Jason R. Knipp *(Branch Mgr)*
Timothy M. Sautter *(CFO)*
Katrina M. Moore *(Dir-HR)*

HENLEY ENTERPRISES, INC.
54 Jaconnet St, Newton Highlands, MA 02461
Tel.: (617) 243-0404
Web Site: http://www.vioc.com
Sales Range: $75-99.9 Million
Emp.: 1,800
Oil Change Franchise Owner
N.A.I.C.S.: 811191
Joe Ribeiro *(Mgr-Comm)*
Lisa Earley *(Mgr-Info Sys)*
Stan Wallace *(Mgr-Fleet Sls)*
Todd Nelson *(Pres & COO)*

HENLEY MANAGEMENT COMPANY
555 Skokie Blvd Ste 555, Northbrook, IL 60062
Tel.: (847) 480-4690
Year Founded: 1991
Holding Company
N.A.I.C.S.: 551112
Richard Colburn *(Chm)*

Subsidiaries:

Aalco Metals Ltd.   (1)
25 High Street, Cobham, KT11 3DH, Surrey, United Kingdom
Tel.: (44) 1932576820
Web Site: http://www.aalco.co.uk
Sales Range: $10-24.9 Million
Emp.: 12
Aluminum, Bronze, Copper & Steel Distr
N.A.I.C.S.: 423510
Anthony Shilling *(Mgr-Logistics)*
Barry King *(Dir-Fin)*
Andrew Robert *(Dir-Fin)*

Almet   (1)
ZAC des Chesnes Nord Rue des Combes, Satolas-et-Bonce, 38290, Isere, France
Tel.: (33) 474958180
Web Site: http://www.almet-metal.com
Sales Range: $50-74.9 Million
Emp.: 430
Aluminium Product Distr
N.A.I.C.S.: 423510

Subsidiary (Non-US):

Almet Nederland BV   (2)

Aluminiumstraat 1, 4823 AL, Breda,, Netherlands
Tel.: (31) 765480200
Web Site: http://www.almet.nl
Sales Range: $25-49.9 Million
Emp.: 50
Aluminum Service Center
N.A.I.C.S.: 423510
W. Heezan *(Asst Dir)*

Amari Austria GmbH   (1)
Industriestrasse 54, 5600, Saint Johann im Pongau, Austria
Tel.: (43) 64125001
Web Site: http://www.amari.at
Sales Range: $25-49.9 Million
Emp.: 175
Aluminum Component Mfr
N.A.I.C.S.: 331313

Subsidiary (Domestic):

Alari Austria GmbH   (2)
Slamastrasse 43, 1230, Vienna, Austria
Tel.: (43) 161046
Web Site: http://www.amari.at
Sales Range: $25-49.9 Million
Aluminum Component Mfr
N.A.I.C.S.: 331318
Josef Reiter *(Mng Dir)*
Walter Maeslinger *(Gen Mgr)*

Subsidiary (Non-US):

Amari Hungaria Kft.   (2)
Ipari Parc utca 3, Budapest, 1044, Hungary
Tel.: (36) 12323400
Web Site: http://www.amari.hu
Sales Range: $10-24.9 Million
Emp.: 30
Aluminum Component Mfr
N.A.I.C.S.: 331318
Hajdu Tamas *(Mng Dir)*

Amari Metals Iberica SLU   (1)
Riera Can Pahisa 24 A Poligono Industrial El Pla, Molins De Rei, 08750, Barcelona, Spain
Tel.: (34) 936802725
Web Site: http://www.amari.es
Sales Range: $10-24.9 Million
Emp.: 50
Engineered Aluminum Products
N.A.I.C.S.: 331313

HENNEBERRY HILL TECHNOLOGIES
4933 Jamesville Rd, Jamesville, NY 13078-9428
Tel.: (315) 445-9000
Web Site: https://www.summsoft.com
Sales Range: $10-24.9 Million
Emp.: 12
Computer Software Development & Applications
N.A.I.C.S.: 541511
William Fisher *(Chm)*

HENNEN FURNITURE
1995 State Highway 15, Saint Cloud, MN 56303
Tel.: (320) 252-8484
Web Site:
   https://www.hennenfurniture.com
Sales Range: $10-24.9 Million
Emp.: 150
Furniture Retailer
N.A.I.C.S.: 449110
Darla Hacker *(Mgr-Store)*

HENNEPIN HEALTHCARE SYSTEM, INC.
701 Park Ave, Minneapolis, MN 55404
Tel.: (612) 873-3000
Web Site:
   https://www.hennepinhealthcare.org
Hospital Operator
N.A.I.C.S.: 622110
Derrick Hollings *(CFO)*
Kathy Tunheim *(Co-Pres & Co-CEO)*
David Ybarra *(Co-Pres)*
Diana Michael Cooper Vance-Bryan *(Vice Chm)*

Subsidiaries:

Minneapolis Medical Research Foundation, Inc.   (1)
701 Park Ave Suite PP7 700, Minneapolis, MN 55415
Tel.: (612) 873-5300
Web Site: http://www.mmrf.org
Sales Range: $25-49.9 Million
Emp.: 300
Research Services
N.A.I.C.S.: 541715
Paul Pentel *(Pres)*
Mary Emmons Bergaas *(VP-Ops)*
Mike Krekelberg *(CFO)*
Gaylan Rockswold *(VP)*
Carla Erickson *(Dir-Clinical Trails Trng)*
Kim Miller *(Dir-Grants & Contracts)*
Anne Murray *(Treas & Sec)*
Cheryl Backowski *(Dir-HR)*
Danielle Hennen *(Dir-HR)*
Nancy Oakes *(Sr Mgr-Fin Sys)*
Mark Willmert *(CFO)*

HENNESSEY'S TAVERN, INC.
1845 S Elena Ave Ste 300, Redondo Beach, CA 90277
Tel.: (310) 540-2274
Web Site:
   https://www.hennesseystavern.com
Rev.: $14,891,726
Emp.: 9
Nightclub/Restaurant
N.A.I.C.S.: 722410
Paul Hennessey *(Pres)*
Nicole Fay *(Controller)*
Camille Shakkour *(Dir-Special Events)*

HENNESSY CADILLAC INC.
3377 Satellite Blvd, Duluth, GA 30096
Tel.: (770) 680-7000
Web Site:
   http://www.hennessycadillac.com
Sales Range: $25-49.9 Million
Emp.: 70
Automobiles, New & Used
N.A.I.C.S.: 441110
Mark W. Hennessy *(Pres)*

HENNESSY CONSTRUCTION SERVICES CORP.
2300 22nd St N, Saint Petersburg, FL 33713
Tel.: (727) 821-3223
Web Site: https://www.hcsfl.com
Year Founded: 1920
Sales Range: $10-24.9 Million
Emp.: 32
General Contractors
N.A.I.C.S.: 236220
Mark Stalker *(Pres)*
Ken Nielsen *(VP-Ops)*

HENNESSY LEXUS OF ATLANTA
5955 Peachtree Industrial Blvd, Atlanta, GA 30341
Tel.: (678) 367-0542
Web Site:
   https://www.lexusatlanta.com
Sales Range: $50-74.9 Million
Emp.: 90
New & Used Automobile Dealership
N.A.I.C.S.: 441110
Peter R. Hennessy *(Pres)*
Nancy Benedit *(Comptroller)*
Steve Burroughs *(Gen Mgr-Sls)*

HENNESSY'S RIVER VIEW FORD
2200 US Hwy 30, Oswego, IL 60543
Tel.: (630) 897-8900
Web Site:
   https://www.riverviewford.com
Year Founded: 1966
Sales Range: $50-74.9 Million
Emp.: 60

New Car Retailer
N.A.I.C.S.: 441110
John Hennessy *(Owner)*
Jack Daniels *(Gen Mgr)*
Paul Firlit *(Treas)*
Culver Watson *(Mgr-Sls)*
Tom Julian *(Mgr-Sls)*
John Drake *(Mgr-Parts)*

HENNING CONSTRUCTION COMPANY LLC

5800 Merle Hay Rd Ste 14, Johnston, IA 50131-1217
Tel.: (515) 253-0943   IA
Web Site:
http://www.henningconstruction.com
Year Founded: 1924
Sales Range: $10-24.9 Million
Emp.: 120
Nonresidential Construction
N.A.I.C.S.: 236220
Jeff Charlson *(Controller)*
Al Cook *(Pres)*
Jeff Henning *(Chm)*

HENNINGER MEDIA SERVICES INC.

1320 N Courthouse Rd Ste 130, Arlington, VA 22201-3817
Tel.: (703) 243-3444   VA
Web Site: https://www.henninger.com
Year Founded: 1983
Sales Range: $10-24.9 Million
Emp.: 100
Provider of Motion Picture Production Services
N.A.I.C.S.: 512191
Robert L. Henninger *(Pres & CEO)*
Fred Elliott *(Gen Mgr)*
Eric Hansen *(COO & Exec VP)*

Subsidiaries:

Henninger D.C., L.L.C.   (1)
1150 17th St NW Ste 401, Washington, DC 20036-4622   (100%)
Tel.: (202) 833-3444
Web Site: http://www.henninger.com
Sales Range: $10-24.9 Million
Emp.: 15
Provider of Motion Picture Production Services
N.A.I.C.S.: 512191

HENNINGSEN COLD STORAGE COMPANY

7965 NE Cherry Dr, Hillsboro, OR 97124
Tel.: (503) 531-5400
Web Site:
http://www.henningsen.com
Rev.: $10,000,000
Emp.: 250
Refrigerated Warehousing Services
N.A.I.C.S.: 493120
Michael E. Henningsen *(Chm & Pres)*
Christopher R. Henningsen *(VP-Svcs)*
Tony Lucarelli *(Exec VP-Sls & Mktg)*
Eric Mauss *(CFO & Sec)*
Paul G. Henningsen *(COO)*
Mike Henningsen *(Founder)*

HENRICKSEN & COMPANY INC.

1070 Ardmore Ave, Itasca, IL 60143-1304
Tel.: (630) 250-9090   IL
Web Site: http://www.henricksen.com
Year Founded: 1970
Sales Range: $100-124.9 Million
Emp.: 188
Furniture
N.A.I.C.S.: 423210
Emily Keon *(Dir-Business Development-Wisconsin)*

HENRIKSEN-BUTLER DESIGN GROUP

249 S 400 E, Salt Lake City, UT 84111
Tel.: (801) 363-5881
Web Site: https://www.hbdg.com
Year Founded: 1980
Rev.: $22,138,832
Emp.: 100
Office Furniture Whslr
N.A.I.C.S.: 423210
Tony Coda *(Pres-Svcs & Principal)*
Mark Hendrickson *(Gen Mgr)*
Mike Taylor *(CFO)*
Ian Anderson *(Pres & Principal)*
Dennis Hobb *(VP-Ops)*
Paige Wright *(Principal & Sr VP-Sls)*
David Colling *(Pres)*
Andrea Barlow *(VP-Mktg)*
Russ Rowberry *(Controller)*
Jason Symons *(Dir-Design & Project Mgmt)*
Ashley Dehaan *(Dir-Project Mgmt)*
Ramon Dondoy *(Mgr-Installation, Svc & Warranty)*
Eric Mattingley *(Mgr-IT)*
Zach Fronk *(VP & Gen Mgr-Idaho)*
Ginger Seaman *(VP-Bus Dev)*
Jeff Clarke *(VP-Bus Dev-Idaho)*
Galen Natt *(VP-Design)*
Heather Bressler *(VP-Nevada)*

HENRIQUEZ ELECTRIC CORP.

7713 Benjamin Rd, Tampa, FL 33634
Tel.: (813) 877-1104   FL
Web Site:
http://www.henriquezelectric.com
Year Founded: 1976
Sales Range: $1-9.9 Million
Emp.: 30
Electrical Contractor
N.A.I.C.S.: 238210
Kenneth Henriquez *(Pres)*
Connie Martinez *(Asst Mgr-Svc)*
Angel Guzman *(VP)*

HENRY AVOCADO CORP

2355 E Lincoln Ave, Escondido, CA 92027
Tel.: (760) 745-6632
Web Site:
http://www.henryavocado.com
Sales Range: $50-74.9 Million
Emp.: 70
Avocado Orchard
N.A.I.C.S.: 111339
Phillip Henry *(Pres)*
Vic Varvel *(VP)*

HENRY CARLSON COMPANY

1205 W Russell St, Sioux Falls, SD 57104
Tel.: (605) 336-2410   SD
Web Site:
https://www.henrycarlson.com
Year Founded: 1919
Sales Range: $10-24.9 Million
Emp.: 75
Nonresidential Construction
N.A.I.C.S.: 236220
Dave Derry *(Chm)*
Jerry Fromm *(Pres)*
Matt Breck *(CFO)*
Henry Carlson III *(Owner)*

Subsidiaries:

Asphalt Surfacing Company   (1)
1205 W Russell St, Sioux Falls, SD 57104-1324   (100%)
Tel.: (605) 338-4921
Web Site: http://www.henrycarlson.com
Sales Range: $10-24.9 Million
Emp.: 20
Highways, Streets & Parking Lots Construction, Maintenance & Repair
N.A.I.C.S.: 237310

Henry Carlson Jr. *(Chm)*
Pat Keleher *(Sec)*

HENRY COUNTY HOSPITAL

1600 E Riverview Ave, Napoleon, OH 43545
Tel.: (419) 592-4015   OH
Web Site:
http://www.henrycountyhospital.org
Year Founded: 1982
Sales Range: $25-49.9 Million
Emp.: 298
Health Care Srvices
N.A.I.C.S.: 622110
Patricia Frank *(Chief Nursing Officer)*

HENRY CROWN & COMPANY

225 Sumac Rd, Wheeling, IL 60090-6315
Tel.: (312) 236-6300
Investment Holding Company
N.A.I.C.S.: 551112
James S. Crown *(Chm & CEO)*
Bill Crown *(Pres & CEO)*

Subsidiaries:

Aspen Skiing Company, LLC   (1)
117 Aspen Business Ctr, Aspen, CO 81611
Tel.: (970) 925-1220
Web Site: http://www.aspensnowmass.com
Sales Range: $10-24.9 Million
Emp.: 3,500
Ski Resort Operator
N.A.I.C.S.: 721110
David Perry *(COO)*
Jeff Hanle *(VP-Comm)*
Mike Kaplan *(Pres & CEO)*

CC Industries, Inc.   (1)
222 N La Salle St Ste 1000, Chicago, IL 60601
Tel.: (312) 855-4000
Sales Range: $350-399.9 Million
Holding Company; Home Furnishings, Paper Products, Outdoor & Casual Furniture; Owns, Develops & Manages Real Estate
N.A.I.C.S.: 314120
William H. Crown *(Pres & CEO)*
Lester Crown *(Chm)*
Richard J. Nassau *(Pres-Real Estate)*

Subsidiary (Domestic):

Great Dane Trailers   (2)
131 Technology Cir, Savannah, GA 31407
Tel.: (912) 644-2100
Web Site: http://www.greatdanetrailers.com
Sales Range: $25-49.9 Million
Emp.: 150
Truck Trailer Mfr
N.A.I.C.S.: 336212
Brandie Fuller *(VP-Mktg)*
Dan McCormack *(Product Mgr)*
Sam Gupta *(Sr VP-Mfg)*
Scott Ashley *(Controller)*
Bill Crown *(CEO)*
Dean Engelage *(Pres)*
Chris Hammond *(Exec VP-Sls)*
Rob Ulsh *(VP-Dealer & Intl Sls)*
Cyndi Rogers *(Dir-Mktg Comms)*
David Grant *(Dir-Customer Experience Mgmt)*

Branch (Domestic):

Great Dane Trailers   (3)
602 E Lathrop Ave, Savannah, GA 31415
Tel.: (912) 644-2100
Web Site: http://www.greatdanetrailers.com
Emp.: 180
Truck Trailers
N.A.I.C.S.: 336212
Harold Breitkreutz *(Supvr-HR)*
Chris Hammond *(Gen Mgr)*

Great Dane Trailers Tennessee, Inc.   (3)
290 W Mallory Ave, Memphis, TN 38109
Tel.: (901) 774-5741
Web Site: http://www.greatdanetrailers.com
Sales Range: $25-49.9 Million
Emp.: 30
Truck Trailers
N.A.I.C.S.: 336212

Subsidiary (Domestic):

Johnson Truck Bodies, Inc.   (3)
215 E Allen St, Rice Lake, WI 54868
Tel.: (715) 234-7071
Web Site:
http://www.johnsontruckbodies.com
Sales Range: $100-124.9 Million
Specialty Fiberglass Truck Body Developer & Mfr
N.A.I.C.S.: 336211
Mayo Rude *(VP-Sls & Mktg)*
Rob Cherry *(Dir-Aftermarket)*
Tim Griffin *(Dir-Sls)*
Marty Levack *(Reg Mgr-Sls-South)*
Luke Chilson *(Reg Mgr-Sls-East)*
Eduardo Navarro *(Dir-Bus Dev)*
Dennis Peterson *(Reg Mgr-Sls-West)*

Subsidiary (Domestic):

J.L. Clark, Inc.   (2)
923 23rd Ave, Rockford, IL 61104
Tel.: (815) 962-8861
Web Site: http://www.jlclark.com
Emp.: 250
Metal Container Mfr
N.A.I.C.S.: 332431
Christine Albert *(CFO-Acctg & Fin Grp)*
Lori Mack *(Controller-Acctg Dept)*

Plant (Domestic):

J.L. Clark, Inc. - Lancaster   (3)
303 N Plum St, Lancaster, PA 17602-2401
Tel.: (717) 392-4125
Web Site: http://www.jlclark.com
Metal Container Mfr
N.A.I.C.S.: 332431
Mike Tolliver *(VP-Sls & Mktg)*

Subsidiary (Domestic):

Provisur Technologies, Inc.   (2)
222 N LaSalle St Ste 720, Chicago, IL 60601
Tel.: (312) 204-6042
Web Site: http://www.provisur.com
Emp.: 32
Food Processing Equipment Mfr
N.A.I.C.S.: 333241
Mel Cohen *(Pres & CEO)*
Brian Perkins *(Exec VP-Americas)*
Scott Scriven *(Exec VP)*
Bert Jan Hardenbol *(Exec VP-EMEA & Asia Pacific)*
Paul Heskens *(VP-Asia Pacific)*
Silva Kumar *(Mgr-Engineered Sys & Svc-Asia Pacific)*
Patrick Corcoran *(CFO & VP)*
Sri Sathyanathan *(VP-IT & Bus Ops)*
William Wight *(VP-R&D)*
Jeff Johnson *(VP-HR)*
Thomas Neher *(VP-Slicing-Europe, Asia Pacific, Middle East & Africa)*

Subsidiary (Domestic):

Beehive Inc.   (3)
11814 S Election Dr Ste 140, Draper, UT 84020
Tel.: (801) 561-4211
Sales Range: $25-49.9 Million
Heavy Duty Food Processing Equipment
N.A.I.C.S.: 333241
Marshall Smith *(Engr)*

Formax, Inc.   (3)
9150 W 191st St, Mokena, IL 60448-8727   (100%)
Tel.: (708) 479-3500
Sales Range: $100-124.9 Million
Food Processing System Mfr
N.A.I.C.S.: 333241
Paul Taylor *(Dir-Engrg)*
Tom Wolcott *(Dir-R&D)*

Subsidiary (Non-US):

Lutetia   (3)
7 Rue Du Colonel Driant, 95400, Arnouville Les Gonesse, Val D Oise, France
Tel.: (33) 139862839
N.A.I.C.S.: 333248

Subsidiary (Domestic):

Weiler & Company, Inc.   (3)
1116 E Main St, Whitewater, WI 53190-2022
Tel.: (262) 473-5254

Henry Crown & Company—(Continued)

Web Site: http://www.weilerinc.com
Sales Range: $10-24.9 Million
Heavy Duty Food Processing Equipment
N.A.I.C.S.: 333241
Bill Wight (VP-Product Dev & Engrg)

Subsidiary (Domestic):

Selig Sealing Products, Inc. (2)
342 E Wabash, Forrest, IL 61741
Tel.: (815) 785-2100
Web Site: http://www.seligsealing.com
Emp.: 50
Sealing Products Mfr
N.A.I.C.S.: 339991
Steve Cassidy (Pres & CEO)
Patrick Schellinger (CFO)

Subsidiary (Domestic):

Performance Systematix, Inc. (3)
5569 33rd St SE, Grand Rapids, MI 49512
Tel.: (616) 949-9090
Web Site: http://www.psix.com
Plastics Product Mfr
N.A.I.C.S.: 326199
John Grover (Mgr)
Glenn Dunn (Pres)

Subsidiary (Domestic):

Southern Towing Company (2)
1874 Thomas Rd, Memphis, TN 38134
Tel.: (901) 386-2644
Web Site: http://www.southerntowing.net
Port & Harbor Operations
N.A.I.C.S.: 488310
Bill Stegbauer (Pres)

Trail King Industries, Inc. (2)
300 E Norway, Mitchell, SD 57301
Tel.: (605) 995-3624
Web Site: http://www.trailking.com
Sales Range: $100-124.9 Million
Specialty Truck Bed & Trailer Mfr
N.A.I.C.S.: 336212
Bruce Yakley (CEO)
Joe Kolb (Pres)
Rick Farris (VP-Sls & Mktg)
Mike Heschke (Dir-Market Dev-Intl)

Subsidiary (Domestic):

Dakota Trailer Manufacturing,
Inc. (3)
1200 Gehl Dr, Yankton, SD 57078
Tel.: (605) 665-8415
Web Site: http://www.dakotatrailer.com
Truck Trailer Mfr
N.A.I.C.S.: 336212
Brian D. Strahl (Pres)

Crown Golf Properties, LP (1)
222 N LaSalle St Ste 1000, Chicago, IL
60601
Tel.: (312) 395-7701
Web Site: http://www.crowngolf.com
Sales Range: $75-99.9 Million
Golf Course & Golf Club Owner & Operator
N.A.I.C.S.: 713910
David W. Fairman (Pres & CEO)

HENRY DAY FORD, INC.
4091 W 3500 S, West Valley City, UT
84120-3201
Tel.: (801) 973-7030
Web Site:
https://www.henrydayford.com
Sales Range: $25-49.9 Million
Emp.: 100
Car Whslr
N.A.I.C.S.: 441110
Jeremy Day (Pres)

HENRY ESTATE WINERY
687 Hubbard Creek Rd, Umpqua, OR
97486
Tel.: (541) 459-5120
Web Site:
https://www.henryestate.com
Year Founded: 1972
Sales Range: $10-24.9 Million
Emp.: 12
Wine Mfr
N.A.I.C.S.: 312130

Calvin Scott Henry III (Founder &
Pres)
Syndi Henry Beavers (Office Mgr)

HENRY F. MICHELL COMPANY INC.
225 W Church Rd, King of Prussia,
PA 19406
Tel.: (610) 265-4200
Web Site: http://www.michells.com
Sales Range: $50-74.9 Million
Emp.: 120
Provider of Field, Garden & Flower
Seeds
N.A.I.C.S.: 111422
Rick Michell (Chm)

HENRY F. TEICHMANN INCORPORATED
3009 Washington Rd, McMurray, PA
15317
Tel.: (724) 941-9550
Web Site: https://www.hft.com
Rev.: $51,200,000
Emp.: 40
Industrial Buildings, New Construction
N.A.I.C.S.: 236210
Chris Yoest (Mgr-Sls Acct)
Daniel Chen (VP-Bus Dev)
William Cairns (Dir-Pur)
Kenneth Lemasters (VP-Fin)
Archie L. McIntyre (Chm)
Tracy Hawkins (Dir-Pur)
Dennis Weichel (Mgr-Construction)
Kevin Yung (VP-Ops)

HENRY FARMERS COOPERATIVE INC.
1211 W Wood St PO Box 1058,
Paris, TN 38242
Tel.: (731) 642-1385
Web Site:
http://henryfarmerscoop.stihl
dealer.net
Rev.: $10,438,224
Emp.: 22
Feed Distr
N.A.I.C.S.: 424910

HENRY FORD HEALTH SYSTEM
1 Ford Pl, Detroit, MI 48202
Tel.: (313) 874-6677 MI
Web Site: https://www.henryford.com
Year Founded: 1915
Sales Range: $1-4.9 Billion
Emp.: 30,000
Non-Profit Healthcare Organization
N.A.I.C.S.: 813920
Robert G. Riney (Pres & CEO)
William A. Conway (CEO-Henry Ford
Medical Grp & Exec VP)
Rose M. Glenn (Chief Experience
Officer & Sr VP-Comm)
Veronica Hall (Pres, Chief Nursing
Officer & CEO-Henry Ford Hospital)
Edith L. Eisenmann (Chief Governance Officer, Sec & VP)
Kimberlydawn Wisdom (Chief Wellness Officer & Sr VP-Community
Health & Equity)
William R. Schramm (Sr VP-Strategic
Bus Dev)
Susan S. Hawkins (Sr VP-Population
Health)
Thomas Nantais (COO-Henry Ford
Medical Grp)
John Popovich (Exec VP & Chief
Medical Officer)
Denise Brooks-Williams (CEO/Sr VP-
Market-North)
Spencer C. Hoover (VP/Exec Dir-
Henry Ford Cancer Institute & Cancer
Care Svcs)
Elizabeth Kutter (Mgr-State & Federal
Govt Affairs)

Marc R. Corriveau (VP-Corp Govt
Affairs)
Seth Frazier (Chief Strategy Officer &
Exec VP)
Michelle Johnson Tidjani (Gen Counsel)
Nina Ramsey (Chief HR Officer & Sr
VP)
Paul Browne (CIO & Sr VP)
Adnan Munkarah (Chief Clinical Officer & Exec VP)
Robin Damschroder (CFO & Exec
VP)
Steve Hathaway (Sr VP-Corp Revenue Cycle)
Henry W. Lim (Sr VP-Academic Affairs)
Michelle B. Schreiber (Chief Quality
Officer & Sr VP-Sys Clinical Transformation)
David Duvall (Chief Mktg, Comm &
Experience Officer & Sr VP)
David Breen (Chm)
Emily Moorhead (Pres-Jackson Hospital)

Subsidiaries:

Health Alliance Plan of Michigan (1)
2850 W Grand Boulevard, Detroit, MI
48202 (100%)
Tel.: (313) 872-8100
Web Site: http://www.hap.org
Sales Range: $1-9.9 Million
Emp.: 1,000
Regional Health Plans to Individuals &
Companies
N.A.I.C.S.: 524114
Derick Adams (VP-HR)
Dan E. Champney (Deputy Gen Counsel)
Michael Genord (Pres & CEO)
Todd Hutchison (Sr VP)
Annette Marcath (CIO & VP-IT)
Mike Treash (COO & Sr VP)
Richard Swift (CFO)
Lillian Dittrick (VP-Actuarial & Healthcare
Analytics)
Charles Bloom (Chief Medical Officer & Sr
VP)
Nike Otuyelu (Chief Compliance Officer)
Michele Gale (VP-Mktg & Consumer Experience)
Margaret Anderson (Chief Sls & Mktg Officer)

Subsidiary (Domestic):

Trusted Health Plan Michigan,
Inc. (2)
PO Box 441970, Detroit, MI 48244-1970
Tel.: (844) 427-2671
Web Site: http://www.trustedhpmi.com
Health Plan Services
N.A.I.C.S.: 524114
Jesse Thomas (CEO)

Henry Ford Allegiance Health (1)
205 N East Ave, Jackson, MI 49201-1753
Tel.: (517) 205-4800
Web Site: http://www.allegiancehealth.org
Emp.: 4,000
Health System & Hospitals
N.A.I.C.S.: 622110
Georgia Fojtasek (Pres & CEO)
Kenneth W. Empey (Gen Counsel)
Ondrea Bates (Sr VP-Ops & Continuum of
Care)
Wendy Boersma (Chief Nursing Officer &
VP)
Kevin Leonard (Co-CFO)
Sandra L. Maes (VP-Physician Integration &
Plng)
Aaron Wootton (CIO & VP-Health Info Sys)
Mark Smith (Chief Medical Officer, CEO-
Medical Grp & Sr VP-Medical Affairs)
Mike Grisdela (Co-CFO)
Tim Levy (CHm)
Martha Fuerstenau (Vice Chm)
Bradley Clark (Treas & Sec)

HENRY FORD MUSEUM AND GREENFIELD VILLAGE
20900 Oakwood Blvd, Dearborn, MI
48124-5029

Tel.: (313) 982-6001
Web Site:
https://www.thehenryford.org
Year Founded: 1929
Sales Range: $300-349.9 Million
Emp.: 1,000
Indoor/Outdoor Museum Complex
N.A.I.C.S.: 712110
Wendy Metros (Dir-Media & Film
Rels)
Patricia E. Mooradian (Pres & Sec)
Sheila Ford Hamp (Vice Chm)
Gerard M. Anderson (Vice Chm)
S. Evan Weiner (Chm)

HENRY FORD VILLAGE
15101 Ford Rd, Dearborn, MI 48126
Tel.: (313) 584-1000 MI
Web Site:
http://www.henryfordvillage.com
Year Founded: 1992
Sales Range: $25-49.9 Million
Emp.: 749
Continuing Care Retirement Community Operator
N.A.I.C.S.: 623311
Bob Mueller (Chm)

HENRY GILL COMMUNICATIONS
900 S Broadway Ste 300, Denver,
CO 80209
Tel.: (303) 296-4100 CO
Year Founded: 1977
Rev.: $36,542,000
Emp.: 16
Business-To-Business, Consumer
Marketing, Full Service
N.A.I.C.S.: 541810
David A. Henry (Pres)
Chris Rhodes (VP)
Doug Griffin (Mgmt Supvr)
Ron Hayes (Controller)

HENRY J. AUSTIN HEALTH CENTER, INC.
321 N Warren St, Trenton, NJ 08618
Tel.: (609) 278-5900 NJ
Web Site:
https://www.henryjaustin.org
Year Founded: 1986
Sales Range: $10-24.9 Million
Emp.: 149
Community Health Care Services
N.A.I.C.S.: 621498
Kemi Alli (CEO & Officer-Medical)
Rachael Evans (Assoc Chief Medical
Officer)
Alba Hernandez (Sec)
Beverly Ann Smith (Vice Chm)
Charles L. Davis II (Chm)

HENRY LEE WILLIS COMMUNITY CENTER INC
119 Forest St, Worcester, MA 01609
Tel.: (508) 799-0702 MA
Year Founded: 1991
Sales Range: $10-24.9 Million
Emp.: 246
Community Action Services
N.A.I.C.S.: 624190
Jay Mattier (Pres)

HENRY LUST REAL ESTATE CO., INC.
506 Route 17M, Middletown, NY
10940
Tel.: (845) 343-0841
Rev.: $15,000,000
Emp.: 13
Offices Real Estate Agents & Brokers
N.A.I.C.S.: 531210
Henry Lust Jr. (Pres)

HENRY M. JACKSON FOUNDATION FOR THE ADVANCE-

MENT OF MILITARY MEDI-CINE, INC.

6720A Rockledge Dr, Bethesda, MD 20817
Tel.: (240) 694-2000
Web Site: http://www.hjf.org
Year Founded: 1983
Rev.: $495,039,325
Assets: $224,661,438
Liabilities: $84,777,261
Net Worth: $139,884,177
Earnings: $139,884,177
Emp.: 2,272
Fiscal Year-end: 09/30/19
Non for Profit Organization
N.A.I.C.S.: 813319
Joseph Caravalho *(Pres & CEO)*
Elizabeth Folk *(COO & Exec VP)*

Subsidiaries:

CAMRIS International, LLC   (1)
3 Bethesda Metro Cntr 16th Fl, Bethesda, MD 20814
Tel.: (301) 770-6000
Web Site: http://www.camris.com
Sales Range: $25-49.9 Million
Emp.: 250
Technical Consulting Services
N.A.I.C.S.: 541690
Laurence M. Day *(Pres & CEO)*
William Pendley *(CFO)*

HENRY MODELL & COMPANY, INC.

498 7th Ave 20th Fl, New York, NY 10018
Tel.: (212) 822-1000   NY
Web Site: http://www.modells.com
Year Founded: 1889
Retailer of Men's, Women's & Children's Apparel, Footwear & Sporting Goods
N.A.I.C.S.: 459110
Mitchell B. Modell *(Owner & CEO)*

Subsidiaries:

Modell's Sporting Goods Inc.   (1)
498 7th Ave 20th Fl, New York, NY 10018
Tel.: (212) 822-1000
Web Site: http://www.modells.com
Sales Range: $10-24.9 Million
Sporting Goods
N.A.I.C.S.: 459110
Mitchell Modell *(CEO)*
Charles Castaneda *(Chief Mdsg Officer)*
Deborah Fine *(Chief Comml Officer)*
Jamal Evans *(Dir-Loss Prevention)*

HENRY MOTORS INCORPO-RADO

2037 Ave Las Americas, Ponce, PR 00717
Tel.: (787) 841-5226
Web Site:
http://www.henrymotorspr.com
Sales Range: $10-24.9 Million
Emp.: 30
New & Used Car Dealers
N.A.I.C.S.: 441110
Manuel E. Cardona *(Pres)*

HENRY OIL COMPANY INC.

2621 Whitehouse Rd, Jasper, AL 35501
Tel.: (205) 221-9427
Rev.: $10,544,771
Emp.: 8
Petroleum Bulk Stations
N.A.I.C.S.: 424710
Donald C. Henry Sr. *(CEO)*

HENRY PRODUCTION INCOR-PORATED

3440 Morningstar Dr, Farmington, NM 87401
Tel.: (505) 327-6138
Web Site: http://www.hpi1.com
Sales Range: $25-49.9 Million

Emp.: 50
Oil Well Machinery, Equipment & Supplies
N.A.I.C.S.: 423830
Sam Henry *(Pres)*

HENRY PRODUCTS INCORPO-RATED

302 S 23rd Ave, Phoenix, AZ 85009
Tel.: (602) 253-3191
Web Site:
https://www.henryproducts.com
Rev.: $13,200,000
Emp.: 42
Mfr of Styrofoam & Plastering Materials: Building Supply Company
N.A.I.C.S.: 423320
James R. Owen *(Pres)*
Mark Norgaard *(Gen Mgr)*
Teresa Opara *(Mgr-Acctg)*

HENRY QUENTZEL PLUMBING SUPPLY CO., INC.

379 Throop Ave, Brooklyn, NY 11221
Tel.: (718) 455-6600
Web Site: http://www.quentzel.com
Sales Range: $10-24.9 Million
Emp.: 50
Plumbing Fittings & Supplies
N.A.I.C.S.: 423720
Ann Quentzel *(Pres)*
Arnold Greenwalt *(VP)*

HENRY S. MILLER MANAGE-MENT CORP.

14001 Dallas Pkwy 11th Fl, Dallas, TX 75240
Tel.: (972) 419-4000   TX
Web Site:
http://www.henrysmiller.com
Year Founded: 1914
Sales Range: $100-124.9 Million
Emp.: 725
Holding Company; Real Estate Investment, Development, Brokerage & Property Management Services
N.A.I.C.S.: 551112
Gregory L. Miller *(Pres & CEO)*
Robert W. Dubois *(CFO)*
Dan Spika *(Exec VP-Indus-Dallas)*
Keith Coelho *(Principal-San Antonio)*
Shawn Ackerman *(Principal-Houston)*
Dan Arnold *(Pres & COO)*
Darrell Hurmis *(Exec VP-Investments-Dallas)*

Subsidiaries:

Henry S. Miller Realty Services, LLC   (1)
14001 Dallas Pkwy 11th Fl, Dallas, TX 75240
Tel.: (972) 419-4000
Web Site: http://www.henrysmiller.com
Real Estate Investment, Development, Brokerage & Property Management Services
N.A.I.C.S.: 237210
Sam G. Kartalis *(Pres & COO)*
Gregory L. Miller *(CEO)*
Robert W. Dubois *(CFO)*

Subsidiary (Domestic):

HSM Development, Inc.   (2)
14001 Dallas Pkwy 11th Fl, Dallas, TX 75240
Tel.: (972) 419-4000
Web Site: http://www.henrysmiller.com
Emp.: 65
Commercial & Residential Real Estate Development
N.A.I.C.S.: 237210
William Bush *(Mng Dir-Multifamily Dev)*

Henry S. Miller Brokerage, LLC   (2)
14001 Dallas Pkwy 11th Fl, Dallas, TX 75240
Tel.: (972) 419-4000
Web Site: http://www.henrysmiller.com
Real Estate Investment & Brokerage Services

N.A.I.C.S.: 531210
Gregory L. Miller *(Pres & CEO)*
Shawn Ackerman *(Principal-Retail-Houston)*
Dan Arnold *(Exec VP-Corp Svcs-Dallas)*
Lew Wood *(Exec VP-Strategic Advisory Grp)*
Dan Spika *(Exec VP-Indus-Dallas)*
Jim Turano *(Exec VP-Dallas Office)*
Craig Webb *(Sr VP-Corp Svcs-Dallas)*
Max Tsai *(VP-Retail-Dallas)*
Jerry Averyt *(Sr VP-Dallas Office)*
Elton Harwell *(Sr VP-Dallas Office)*
Bill Knopick *(Sr VP-Dallas)*
Darrell Hurmis *(Exec VP-Investments Div)*
Elizabeth Stricklin *(Sr VP-Investments-Dallas)*
Peter Kosley *(Sr VP-Retail-Dallas)*
Richard Polishuk *(Sr VP-Retail-Dallas)*
Kevin Frederick *(VP-Corp Svcs-Dallas)*
John Blackburn *(VP-Land)*
Lily Chang *(Sr VP)*
Bill Bledsoe *(VP)*
Paul W. Vernon *(Exec VP)*
Merrel Moore *(VP)*
Mike Bristol *(VP-Investments-Dallas)*
William Bush *(Mng Dir-Dev-Dallas)*
Ben Chien *(VP-Investments-Dallas)*
Parvez Malik *(VP-Investments-Dallas)*
Mark Porterfield *(Sr VP-Multi-Family-Dallas)*
Henry S. Miller IV *(Sr VP-Retail-Dallas)*

Affiliate (Domestic):

Henry S. Miller Commercial Austin, Inc.   (3)
9442 N Capital of Texas Hwy Bldg 1 Ste 500, Austin, TX 78759
Tel.: (512) 794-9400
Web Site: http://www.henrysmiller.com
Real Estate Investment, Brokerage & Property Management Services
N.A.I.C.S.: 531210
Sue D. Gravett *(Principal)*
Richard Gravett *(VP)*
Sean Gravett *(VP)*

Subsidiary (Domestic):

Henry S. Miller Consulting, LLC   (2)
14001 Dallas Pkwy 11th Fl, Dallas, TX 75240
Tel.: (972) 419-4000
Web Site: http://www.henrysmiller.com
Real Estate Appraisal & Consulting Services
N.A.I.C.S.: 541690
Mark O'Briant *(Pres)*
Tracy Smith Law *(Exec VP)*

Henry S. Miller Investment Services, LLC   (2)
14001 Dallas Pkwy 11th Fl, Dallas, TX 75240
Tel.: (972) 419-4000
Web Site: http://www.henrysmiller.com
Real Estate Debt & Equity Financing Services
N.A.I.C.S.: 523150
Roy G. Norwood Jr. *(Pres)*

Subsidiary (Domestic):

Henry S. Miller Funding Corporation   (3)
14001 Dallas Pkwy 11th Fl, Dallas, TX 75240
Tel.: (972) 419-4000
Real Estate Investment Financing Services
N.A.I.C.S.: 522299
James D. Johnson *(Mgr-Ops)*

Subsidiary (Domestic):

Henry S. Miller Realty Management, LLC   (2)
14001 Dallas Pkwy 11th Fl, Dallas, TX 75240
Tel.: (972) 419-4000
Web Site: http://www.henrysmiller.com
Property Management Services
N.A.I.C.S.: 531312
Greg Miller *(CEO)*

Miller Realty Investment Partners, Inc.   (1)
14001 Dallas Pkwy 11th Fl, Dallas, TX 75240
Tel.: (972) 419-4000
Web Site: http://www.henrysmiller.com

Real Estate Investment & Asset Management Services
N.A.I.C.S.: 531390
Robert W. Dubois *(CFO)*
John Downs *(VP)*

HENRY STREET SETTLEMENT

265 Henry St, New York, NY 10002
Tel.: (212) 766-9200   NY
Web Site: http://www.henrystreet.org
Year Founded: 1944
Sales Range: $25-49.9 Million
Emp.: 648
Health Care Srvices
N.A.I.C.S.: 621610
Josephine Lume *(CFO)*
Craig Peterson *(Dir-Artistic)*
David Garza *(Exec Dir)*

HENRY WURST INC.

1331 Saline St, Kansas City, MO 64116-4410
Tel.: (816) 842-3113   MO
Web Site: http://www.henrywurst.com
Year Founded: 1937
Sales Range: $75-99.9 Million
Emp.: 850
Lithographic Commercial Printing
N.A.I.C.S.: 323111
Michael S. Wurst *(Co-Pres)*
Amy Wurst *(VP)*
Mark Hanf *(Co-Pres)*

HENRY'S WRECKER SERVICE FAIRFAX COUNTY

44827 Old Ox Rd Ste D, Sterling, VA 20166
Tel.: (703) 471-0010
Web Site:
http://www.henryswrecker.com
Year Founded: 1989
Sales Range: $10-24.9 Million
Emp.: 250
Moving Services
N.A.I.C.S.: 488410

HENSCHEL STEINAU INC.

50 Commerce Dr, Allendale, NJ 07401
Tel.: (201) 760-4103
Web Site: https://www.hspop.com
Sales Range: $25-49.9 Million
Emp.: 53
Design, Commercial & Industrial
N.A.I.C.S.: 541420
Paul Kapoin *(Controller)*
Gary Forman *(CEO)*
Michael Luberto *(Pres)*
Michael DeSena *(VP-Creative Svcs)*

HENSEL PHELPS CONSTRUC-TION CO.

420 6th Ave, Greeley, CO 80631
Tel.: (970) 352-6565   DE
Web Site:
https://www.henselphelps.com
Year Founded: 1937
Sales Range: $75-99.9 Billion
Emp.: 3,000
Commercial & Institutional Building Construction
N.A.I.C.S.: 236220
Michael J. Choutka *(Pres & CEO)*
Bradley D. Winans *(VP & Mgr-Southwest District)*
Matt McCaulley *(Dir-Ops)*
Brad Lewis *(Dir-Supplier Diversity)*
Mary Pigao *(Coord-Mktg)*
Allan J. Bliesmer *(Exec VP)*
Thomas J. Diersbock *(VP & Mgr-Pacific District)*
Steve M. Grauer *(VP & Mgr-Western District)*
Laird B. Heikens *(Pres-Dev Grp)*
Jenny Scholz *(CFO & VP)*

Hensel Phelps Construction Co.—(Continued)

Will Thompson *(VP & Mgr-Mid Atlantic District)*
Richard G. Tucker *(Exec VP)*
David Brooke *(Mgr-Ops)*
Bradley A. Jeanneret *(Exec VP)*
Joel B. Douglass *(Pres, Pres-Hensel Phelps Services Grp & Dir-Ops)*
Damian J. Buessing *(District Mgr-Southern California & VP)*
Robert P. Majerus *(Gen Counsel & VP)*
Shannon Gustine *(VP & District Mgr-Northern California)*
Derek H. Hoffine *(VP & District Mgr-Plains)*
Scott Bills *(VP & District Mgr-Pacific Northwest)*
Justin Starnes *(VP & District Mgr-Southeast)*

Subsidiaries:

Hensel Phelps International LLC   **(1)**
3950 N Lewiston St Ste 102, Aurora, CO 80011
Tel.: (303) 539-3300
Sales Range: $25-49.9 Million
Emp.: 180
Industrial & Institutional Building Construction Services
N.A.I.C.S.: 236210

HENSLEY & CO.
4201 N 45th Ave, Phoenix, AZ 85031-2109
Tel.: (602) 264-1635   **AZ**
Web Site: https://www.hensley.com
Year Founded: 1955
Sales Range: $125-149.9 Million
Emp.: 700
Whslr of Beer
N.A.I.C.S.: 424810
Bob Delgado *(Pres & CEO)*
Jim Hensley *(Founder)*

Subsidiaries:

Premier Distributing Company   **(1)**
4321 Yale Blvd NE, Albuquerque, NM 87107-4141
Tel.: (505) 344-0287
Web Site:
    http://www.premierdistributing.com
Sales Range: $200-249.9 Million
Emp.: 350
Wholesale Distributor of Beer
N.A.I.C.S.: 424810
Edward Dobbs *(Pres & CEO)*
Reggie Hardway *(Exec VP)*

HENSON LUMBER LTD.
11900 CR 917, Cresson, TX 76035
Tel.: (817) 396-4321
Web Site:
    https://www.hensonlumber.com
Year Founded: 1973
Sales Range: $10-24.9 Million
Emp.: 50
General Warehousing & Storage Services
N.A.I.C.S.: 493110
Mike Rainwater *(Mgr-Sls)*
Betty Henson *(Pres)*
Casey Wallace *(Sr VP-Ops)*
Glenn Wilson *(Sr VP-Admin)*

HENSON MOTOR COMPANY INC.
105 S May, Madisonville, TX 77864
Tel.: (936) 348-3618
Web Site:
    http://www.hensonmotors.com
Sales Range: $50-74.9 Million
Emp.: 70
Automobiles, New & Used
N.A.I.C.S.: 441110
Fred Henson *(Pres)*

Subsidiaries:

Henson Ford Inc.   **(1)**
581 I-45 N, Madisonville, TX 77864
Tel.: (936) 348-9610
Web Site: http://www.hensonmotor.com
Emp.: 25
New & Used Car Dealership
N.A.I.C.S.: 441110
Brian Creighton *(Gen Mgr)*

HENTSCHELL & ASSOCIATES INC.
1436 S Union Ave, Tacoma, WA 98405-1925
Tel.: (253) 272-1151
Web Site: https://www.hentschell.com
Year Founded: 1988
Sales Range: $10-24.9 Million
Emp.: 22
Insurance Services
N.A.I.C.S.: 524210
Thomas Hentschell *(Pres)*
Jerry Hentschell *(Office Mgr)*
Karen Smith *(Acct Mgr)*
Vanita Hitchcock *(Acct Mgr)*
Leslie Parks *(Acct Mgr)*
Laura Wilson *(Acct Mgr)*
Karen Ingram *(Acct Mgr)*
Julie Craker *(Acct Mgr)*
Anne Cutting *(Acct Mgr)*
Janet Johnson Pudists *(Acct Mgr)*

HENTZEN COATINGS INC.
6937 W Mill Rd, Milwaukee, WI 53218-1225
Tel.: (414) 353-4200
Web Site: http://www.hentzen.com
Year Founded: 1923
Sales Range: $75-99.9 Million
Emp.: 200
Sales of Paints & Allied Products
N.A.I.C.S.: 325510
Bill Johnson *(CFO)*

HEP MATERIALS CORP.
446 Waterloo Geneva Rd, Waterloo, NY 13165
Tel.: (315) 789-4970
Web Site: https://www.hepsales.com
Rev.: $14,370,059
Emp.: 210
Hardware Stores
N.A.I.C.S.: 444140
John J. Krueger *(Pres & Gen Mgr)*

HEPAHOPE, INC.
30 Fairbanks Ste 110, Irvine, CA 92618
Tel.: (949) 421-3600
Year Founded: 1999
Sales Range: $1-9.9 Million
Emp.: 25
Life Saving Medical Technologies Developer, Mfr & Marketer
N.A.I.C.S.: 339112
Sung-Soo Park *(Chm & CEO)*

HER CAMPUS MEDIA, LLC
9 Lansdowne St Ste 2, Boston, MA 02215
Tel.: (617) 783-3800
Web Site: http://www.hercampus.com
Media Entertainment & Communication
N.A.I.C.S.: 517810
Stephanie Kaplan Lewis *(Founder & CEO)*

Subsidiaries:

Spoon Media, Inc   **(1)**
9 Lansdowne St Ste 2, Boston, MA 02215
Tel.: (617) 783-3800
Information System & Entertainment
N.A.I.C.S.: 516210
Stephanie Kaplan Lewis *(CEO)*

HERALD MEDIA INC.

70 Fargo St Ste 600 Seaport Ctr, Boston, MA 02210
Tel.: (617) 426-3000
Web Site:
    http://www.bostonherald.com
Sales Range: $75-99.9 Million
Emp.: 270
Commercial Newspaper Publisher & Printer
N.A.I.C.S.: 513110
Patrick J. Purcell *(Pres & Publr)*
Kathleen Rush *(Dir-New Bus Dev)*

HERALD OFFICE SUPPLY COMPANY
110 E Roosevelt St, Dillon, SC 29536
Tel.: (843) 774-5155
Web Site: https://www.hosnet.net
Sales Range: $10-24.9 Million
Emp.: 130
Office Forms & Supplies Distr
N.A.I.C.S.: 459410
Thomas Jordan *(VP-Sls & Ops)*
Ronnie Lee *(Pres)*
Arthur Jordan *(VP-Sls)*

HERB CHAMBERS OF SOMERVILLE, INC.
259 McGrath Hwy, Somerville, MA 02143
Tel.: (617) 666-4100   **MA**
Web Site:
    https://www.herbchambers.com
Year Founded: 1985
Sales Range: $1-4.9 Billion
Emp.: 2,400
Automobile Dealers
N.A.I.C.S.: 441110
Herb Chambers *(Pres & Treas)*
Jim Xaros *(VP)*
Jack Moran *(Mgr-Pre-Owned)*

Subsidiaries:

Herb Chambers Honda of Seekonk   **(1)**
185 Taunton Ave Route 44, Seekonk, MA 02771
Tel.: (508) 336-7100
Web Site: http://www.herbchambershondaof seekonk.com
Sales Range: $10-24.9 Million
Emp.: 60
New Car Dealers
N.A.I.C.S.: 441110
Scott Birtles *(Gen Mgr)*

Herb Chambers of Natick, Inc.   **(1)**
253 N Main St, Natick, MA 01760
Tel.: (508) 655-5350
Web Site: http://www.fmwest.com
Sales Range: $200-249.9 Million
Emp.: 350
Car Dealership
N.A.I.C.S.: 441110
Herbert G. Chambers *(Pres & Treas)*

HERB EASLEY MOTORS INC.
1125 Central Fwy, Wichita Falls, TX 76306-5944
Tel.: (940) 723-6631
Web Site: http://www.herbeasley.com
Year Founded: 1988
Sales Range: $25-49.9 Million
Emp.: 123
New & Used Car Dealer Services
N.A.I.C.S.: 441110
Herb Easley *(Pres)*
Brad Lawson *(Gen Mgr)*

HERB HALLMAN CHEVROLET INC.
800 Kietzke Ln, Reno, NV 89502
Tel.: (775) 786-3111
Web Site:
    https://www.championchevrolet reno.com
Rev.: $46,000,000
Emp.: 150

Automobiles, New & Used
N.A.I.C.S.: 441110
John P. Stanko *(Pres)*
Stan Bundick *(Controller)*
Jack Stanko Jr. *(VP)*

HERB JONES CHEVROLET, INC.
1605 Ring Rd, Elizabethtown, KY 42701
Tel.: (270) 765-2123
Web Site:
    http://www.herbjoneschevrolet.com
Year Founded: 1969
Sales Range: $10-24.9 Million
Emp.: 45
Car Whslr
N.A.I.C.S.: 441110
Mark Jones *(Pres)*

HERB PHILIPSON'S ARMY & NAVY
1899 Black River Blvd, Rome, NY 13440
Tel.: (315) 336-1300
Web Site:
    http://www.herbphilipsons.com
Sales Range: $10-24.9 Million
Emp.: 50
Family Clothing Stores
N.A.I.C.S.: 458110
Gary Philipson *(Pres)*
Samantha Jassak *(Mgr)*

HERBEIN + COMPANY, INC.
2763 Century Blvd, Reading, PA 19610
Tel.: (610) 378-1175
Web Site: https://www.herbein.com
Year Founded: 1972
Emp.: 121
Accounting & Tax Consulting Services
N.A.I.C.S.: 541219
David J. Breitegam *(Mgr)*
Carl D. Herbein *(CEO & Partner)*
John T. Pagerly *(CFO)*
Maria Stromple *(Partner & Dir-Firmwide Tax Svcs-Pittsburgh)*
Elizabeth Hassler *(Partner)*

Subsidiaries:

Creese, Smith, Hune & Co., LLC   **(1)**
8150 Perry Hwy Ste 105, Pittsburgh, PA 15237
Web Site: http://www.creesesmith.com
Accounting, Tax Management, Assurance & Advisory Services
N.A.I.C.S.: 541211
Wes Creese *(Pres)*

Michael L. Cross & Co Ltd.   **(1)**
1303 N Charlotte St, Pottstown, PA 19464-1903
Tel.: (610) 326-7325
Web Site: http://www.herrrr
Offices of Certified Public Accountants
N.A.I.C.S.: 541211
Michael L. Cross *(Pres)*

HERBERT C. HAYNES INC.
RR 2, Winn, ME 04495
Tel.: (207) 736-3412
Web Site: http://www.hchaynes.com
Sales Range: $100-124.9 Million
Emp.: 50
Pulpwood Contractors Engaged In Cutting
N.A.I.C.S.: 113310
Ginger C. Maxwell Jr. *(Treas)*

HERBERT YENTIS & COMPANY
7300 City Line Ave, Philadelphia, PA 19151
Tel.: (215) 878-7300
Web Site: https://www.yentis.com

Year Founded: 1926
Rev.: $23,000,000
Emp.: 19
Provider of Real Estate Services
N.A.I.C.S.: 531120
George R. Goldstone *(Chm)*
Jeffrey Goldstone *(Pres)*
Peggie Brennan *(Controller)*

HERBIE WILES INSURANCE, INC.
400 N Ponce De Leon Blvd, Saint Augustine, FL 32084
Tel.: (904) 829-2201   FL
Web Site:
  https://www.herbiewiles.com
Year Founded: 1961
Rev.: $10,000,000
Emp.: 22
Insurance Agents
N.A.I.C.S.: 524210
Douglass F. Wiles *(Pres)*
Letha O'Neil-Wiseman *(VP)*
Herbie Wiles *(Founder & CEO)*
Steve Jones *(VP-Sls & Mktg)*
Wayne E. Howell Jr. *(VP)*

HERC-U-LIFT, INC.
5655 Hwy 12 W, Maple Plain, MN 55359
Tel.: (763) 479-2501
Web Site: https://www.herculift.com
Year Founded: 1968
Sales Range: $25-49.9 Million
Emp.: 130
Sales & Service of Lift Trucks & Parts
N.A.I.C.S.: 423830
Lester Nielsen *(Chm & CEO)*
Brad Ellingson *(Treas & Controller)*

HERCULES CHEMICAL CO., INC.
111 South St, Passaic, NJ 07055-7901
Tel.: (973) 778-5000   DE
Web Site: http://www.herchem.com
Year Founded: 1915
Sales Range: $75-99.9 Million
Emp.: 100
Miscellaneous Chemical Mfr
N.A.I.C.S.: 325998
David Siegal *(Pres & CEO)*
Leonard A. Ruvolo *(CFO & VP-Admin)*
John Domanico *(Mgr-IS)*
Erastus Muchioki *(Mgr-Safety)*

Subsidiaries:

Hercules Cloroben Corp.   (1)
111 S St, Passaic, NJ 07055-7901
Tel.: (973) 778-5000
Rev.: $7,000,000
Mfr of Drain Cleaning Products
N.A.I.C.S.: 325998

HERCULES CLEAN TECHNOLOGY CAPITAL, INC.
400 Hamilton Ave Ste 310, Palo Alto, CA 94301
Tel.: (650) 289-3060   MD
Web Site: http://www.htgc.com
Year Founded: 2011
Sales Range: $25-49.9 Million
Emp.: 50
Investment Services
N.A.I.C.S.: 523999
H. Scott Harvey *(Chief Legal Officer, Chief Compliance Officer & Sec)*
Manuel A. Henriquez *(Chm, Pres & CEO)*

HERCULES ENGINE COMPONENTS LLC
2770 Erie St S, Massillon, OH 44646
Tel.: (330) 830-2498

Web Site:
  http://www.herculesengine.com
Year Founded: 1915
Sales Range: $10-24.9 Million
Emp.: 25
Gasoline & Diesel Engines Mfr
N.A.I.C.S.: 336340
Jack Dienes *(Pres)*
Bruce Weick *(VP)*

Subsidiaries:

Saco Lowell Parts LLC   (1)
1395 Triplett Blvd, Akron, OH
44306-3124   (100%)
Tel.: (864) 850-4400
Web Site: http://www.sacolowell.com
Sales Range: $10-24.9 Million
Emp.: 8
Textile Machinery Parts Mfr
N.A.I.C.S.: 332119

HERCULES FENCE
8580 Mission Rd, Jessup, MD 20794
Tel.: (410) 799-1555
Web Site:
  http://www.herculesfence.com
Year Founded: 1955
Sales Range: $10-24.9 Million
Emp.: 40
Fence Construction Services
N.A.I.C.S.: 238990
Jay M. Klebanoff *(CEO)*

HERCULES INDUSTRIES INC.
1310 W Evans Ave, Denver, CO 80223
Tel.: (303) 937-1000
Web Site:
  https://www.herculesindustries.com
Rev.: $40,000,000
Emp.: 303
Fabricated Pipe & Fittings; HVAC Material
N.A.I.C.S.: 332996
Paul Newland *(VP)*
Bill Redden *(Mgr-Counter Sls)*
Roxann Harris *(Dir-HR)*

HERCULES OFFSHORE, INC.
9 Greenway Plz Ste 2200, Houston, TX 77046
Tel.: (713) 350-5100   DE
Web Site:
  http://www.herculesoffshore.com
Sales Range: $900-999.9 Million
Emp.: 1,800
Shallow-Water Drilling & Liftboat Services to Oil & Natural Gas Producers
N.A.I.C.S.: 213111
Todd A. Pellegrin *(Sr VP-Worldwide Liftboat Ops)*
Beau M. Thompson *(Gen Counsel, Sec & Sr VP)*
Shannon P. Guidry *(VP-Worldwide Drilling Ops)*

Subsidiaries:

Hercules Drilling Company, LLC   (1)
9 Greenway Plz Ste 2200, Houston, TX 77046
Tel.: (713) 979-9300
Web Site: http://www.herculesoffshore.com
Sales Range: $100-124.9 Million
Emp.: 250
Oil & Gas Well Drilling & Support Services
N.A.I.C.S.: 213111
Terrell L. Carr *(VP-Ops-Worldwide)*

Hercules Offshore Labuan Corporation   (1)
ZI Labuan Trust Company Limited Unit Level 13 A Main Office Tower, Jalan Merdeka, Labuan, 87000, Malaysia
Tel.: (60) 87451688
Web Site: http://www.herculesoffshore.com
Emp.: 1
Oil & Gas Exploration & Development Services
N.A.I.C.S.: 213111
Beau Thompson *(Dir)*

Hercules Offshore UK Limited   (1)
Badentoy Avenue Badentoy Park, Portlethen, Aberdeen, AB12 4YB, United Kingdom
Tel.: (44) 1224784113
Natural Oil & Gas Extraction Services
N.A.I.C.S.: 213111

HERCULES STEEL COMPANY INC.
13 Charlton St, Everett, MA 02149
Tel.: (617) 387-0387   MA
Web Site:
  http://www.herculessteelco.com
Year Founded: 1988
Sales Range: $10-24.9 Million
Emp.: 600
Mfr of Fabricated Structural Metal Steel
N.A.I.C.S.: 238990

HERCULES TIRE SALES INC.
10130 E 51st St, Tulsa, OK 74146
Tel.: (918) 627-7353
Web Site:
  http://www.herculestiresales.com
Sales Range: $10-24.9 Million
Emp.: 40
Automobile Tires & Tubes
N.A.I.C.S.: 423130
Gary Sicka *(Pres)*
Mark Rudrow *(Mgr)*
Barbara Sicka *(Owner)*

HERCULES TRANSPORT INC.
3452 Hwy 145 N, Choudrant, LA 71227
Tel.: (318) 768-2534
Web Site:
  https://www.herculestransport.com
Year Founded: 1952
Sales Range: $10-24.9 Million
Emp.: 25
Liquid Petroleum Transport Services
N.A.I.C.S.: 484230
Jim Berry *(Controller)*
Tom O'Neal *(Pres)*
John O'Neal Jr. *(Chm)*

HERCULES WINDOW CLEANING CO.
999 Executive Pkwy Ste 100, Saint Louis, MO 63141
Tel.: (314) 965-1150   MO
Web Site:
  http://www.herculeswindowcleaning.com
Emp.: 25
Building Maintenance Services
N.A.I.C.S.: 561790
Andrew Spann *(Pres)*
Lisa Keaveny *(Bus Mgr)*
Mike Reynard *(Mgr-Ops)*

Subsidiaries:

Hawkins Building Services Of Saint Louis, LLC   (1)
11040 Lin Valle Dr, Saint Louis, MO 63123
Tel.: (314) 845-7000
Business Maintenance Services
N.A.I.C.S.: 561790

HERCULES WIRE ROPE & SLING CO., INC.
3404 Trotter Ct, Houma, LA 70363
Tel.: (985) 876-5511
Web Site:
  https://www.herculeswirerope.com
Sales Range: $10-24.9 Million
Emp.: 28
Transportation Equipment & Supplies Merchant Whslr
N.A.I.C.S.: 423860
James Lablanc *(Mgr-Sls)*
Barbara Guidroz *(Sec)*
Ernest J. Guidroz Jr. *(Pres & CFO)*

HERD ENTERPRISES INC.
3500 N 28th Ter, Hollywood, FL 33020
Tel.: (954) 920-9774
Web Site:
  https://www.browardfactory.com
Year Founded: 1967
Rev.: $22,699,477
Emp.: 30
Refrigeration Repair Services
N.A.I.C.S.: 811412
Crockett Herd *(Pres)*

HERDRICH PETROLEUM CORP.
210 E US Hwy 52 Ste E, Rushville, IN 46173
Tel.: (765) 932-3224
Web Site: https://www.herdrich.com
Year Founded: 1953
Sales Range: $25-49.9 Million
Emp.: 220
Gas Station & Convenience Store Chain Operator
N.A.I.C.S.: 457110
William J. Herdrich *(Pres)*

HERE MEDIA INC.
10990 Wilshire Blvd PH, Los Angeles, CA 90024
Tel.: (310) 806-4288   DE
Web Site: http://www.heremedia.com
Sales Range: $25-49.9 Million
Emp.: 156
Cable Network Operator; Book & Magazine Publisher
N.A.I.C.S.: 517111
Stephen P. Jarchow *(Chm)*
Paul A. Colichman *(CEO)*
Lucas Grindley *(Sr VP, Editor-in-Chief-The Advocate & Dir-Editorial)*
Diane Anderson-Minshall *(Dir-Editorial-Print Div-The Advocate)*
Neal Broverman *(Exec Editor-The Advocate)*

Subsidiaries:

PlanetOut, Inc.   (1)
Folsom St 1069, San Francisco, CA 94107-4226
Tel.: (415) 834-6500
Sales Range: $10-24.9 Million
Emp.: 95
Online Information & Publications for Lesbian, Gay, Bisexual & Transgender Individuals
N.A.I.C.S.: 519290

HERGERT MILLING INC.
1424 Ave B, Scottsbluff, NE 69361-3023
Tel.: (308) 632-2315
Sales Range: $10-24.9 Million
Emp.: 27
Animal Feed Mfr
N.A.I.C.S.: 311119
Clarence Hergert *(Dir-Mfg & Engrg)*

HERGO ERGONOMIC SUPPORT SYSTEMS, INC.
56-01 55th Ave, Maspeth, NY 11378-1104
Tel.: (718) 894-0639
Web Site: https://www.hergo.com
Sales Range: $10-24.9 Million
Emp.: 20
Mfr of Modular Furniture, Enclosures & Rack Systems
N.A.I.C.S.: 334118
Eli E. Hertz *(Pres & CEO)*
Kristen Speranza-Diamond *(VP)*

Subsidiaries:

Remote IT.com, Inc.   (1)
56 01 55th Ave, Maspeth, NY
11378-1104   (100%)
Tel.: (718) 894-0639
Web Site: http://www.remoteit.com

Hergo Ergonomic Support Systems, Inc.—(Continued)

Sales Range: $10-24.9 Million
Provider of Internet & Network Services
N.A.I.C.S.: 517810
Eli E. Hertz (Pres & CEO)
Barry Gold (Gen Mgr)

HERITAGE AUTOMOTIVE GROUP INC.
1001 N Riley Hwy, Shelbyville, IN 46176
Tel.: (317) 398-4238   IN
Web Site:
http://www.heritageshelbyville.com
Year Founded: 1987
Sales Range: $10-24.9 Million
Emp.: 17
Sales of New & Used Automobiles
N.A.I.C.S.: 441110
Adrian Scripture (Pres)
Cheryl Wilson (CFO)

HERITAGE BABY PRODUCTS LLC
91 New England Ave, Piscataway, NJ 08854
Tel.: (866) 468-6473
Web Site:
http://www.heritagebabyproducts.com
Year Founded: 2014
Wood Household Furniture, Cribs & Baby Beds Mfr & Whslr
N.A.I.C.S.: 337122
Bill Wagner (Exec VP & Gen Mgr-Munire)
Maria Lage (Mgr-Customer Svc-Munire)
Venkat Chinni (CEO)
Peter Chinni (Exec VP-Supply Chain)
Brian Moore (VP-Sls)
Robert Rusnack (VP-Fin)
George Zapf (Dir-Sls)
Brian Cook (Dir-Sls)
Jeff Parker (Dir-Sls)
Barbara Riggins (Dir-Compliance)
Jenny Brown (Dir-Mktg)
Dawn Slocum (Ops Mgr)
Jayesh Lad (Mgr-Shipping)
Javier Cueto (Mgr-Quality Control)
Lisa Valdes (Mgr-E-commerce)
Laurient Toal (Coord-Mktg)
Melissa Evans (Coord-Social Media)
Lorena Rojas (Coord-Pur)
Malisisha Vazquez (Coord-Shipping)
Maria Zapata (Coord-Pur)

HERITAGE BANCSHARES GROUP, INC.
110 South St W, Spicer, MN 56288
Tel.: (320) 796-0215   MN
Web Site:
http://www.heritagebankna.com
Year Founded: 1993
Sales Range: $10-24.9 Million
Emp.: 148
Bank Holding Company
N.A.I.C.S.: 551111
Thomas Geiger (Chm & CEO)
Gary Geiger (Chm)

Subsidiaries:

Heritage Bank N.A.   (1)
110SSt W, Spicer, MN 56288
Tel.: (320) 796-0215
Web Site: http://www.heritagebankna.com
Emp.: 8
Federal Savings Institutions
N.A.I.C.S.: 522180
Thomas Geiger (Chm & CEO)
Dave Henle (VP-Bus Banking)
Brian Zech (Mgr-Bus Relationship-Sioux City)

HERITAGE BANK INC.
456 Commonwealth Ave, Erlanger, KY 41018
Tel.: (859) 342-0920
Web Site: http://www.heritagebank-ky.com
Year Founded: 1990
Rev.: $11,791,000
Emp.: 25
State Commercial Banks
N.A.I.C.S.: 522110
Augie Kruza (Dir-IT)

HERITAGE BROADCASTING GROUP, INC.
1 Broadcast Way, Cadillac, MI 49601
Tel.: (231) 775-3478
Web Site:
http://www.9and10news.com
Television Broadcasting Services
N.A.I.C.S.: 516120

HERITAGE CADILLAC, INC.
303 W Roosevelt Rd, Lombard, IL 60148
Tel.: (630) 282-4150
Web Site:
https://www.heritagecadillac.com
Year Founded: 1967
Sales Range: $10-24.9 Million
Emp.: 75
New Car Dealers
N.A.I.C.S.: 441110
Daren Schaffert (Gen Mgr-Sls)
Kathy Clapper (Mgr-Customer Svc)
Mike Stamenkovich (Dir-Svc)

HERITAGE CAPITAL GROUP, INC.
4417 Beach Blvd Ste 302, Jacksonville, FL 32207
Tel.: (904) 354-9600   FL
Web Site:
http://www.heritagecapitalgroup.com
Year Founded: 1977
Sales Range: $1-9.9 Million
Emp.: 20
Investment Banking & Securities Dealing
N.A.I.C.S.: 523150
Donna Barker (Mgr-Mktg & Res)
K. C. Caldabaugh (Principal)
Asok K. Chaudhuri (Principal)
Mac Holley (Principal)
Matt Laffey (Principal)
Douglas M. Kravet (Principal)
C. Donald Wiggins (Pres & Principal)
Bill Prescott (Principal)
Bill Sorenson (Principal)
Mary Frosio (Principal)
John Pregulman (Principal)
Travis Larson (Controller)
Daren Pietsch (Principal)
Jerry Mallot (Dir-Corp Dev)
Scott McCaleb (Principal)

HERITAGE CHEVROLET INC.
350 W Dickman Rd, Battle Creek, MI 49037-8497
Tel.: (269) 964-9431
Web Site:
https://www.heritagechevy.com
Sales Range: $25-49.9 Million
Emp.: 65
Automobiles, New & Used
N.A.I.C.S.: 441110
Timothy J. Kool (Pres)

HERITAGE CHRISTIAN SERVICES, INC.
349 W Commercial St Ste 2795, East Rochester, NY 14445-2402
Tel.: (585) 340-2000   NY
Web Site:
http://www.heritagechristianservices.org
Year Founded: 1980

Sales Range: $50-74.9 Million
Emp.: 1,676
Developmental Disability Assistance Services
N.A.I.C.S.: 624120
Marisa Geitner (Pres & CEO)
Drew Bielemeier (Sr VP-Operations)
Chuck Collard (Reg VP)

HERITAGE CONSTRUCTION CO. INC.
5505 N Atlanta Ave Ste 115, Cocoa Beach, FL 32931
Tel.: (321) 799-4090
Sales Range: $25-49.9 Million
Emp.: 5
Multi-Family Dwellings, New Construction
N.A.I.C.S.: 236116
Jacqueline Mcphillips (Pres)

HERITAGE COOPERATIVE INC.
11177 Twp Rd 133, West Mansfield, OH 43358
Tel.: (937) 355-0003   OH
Web Site:
http://www.heritagecooperative.com
Year Founded: 1935
Sales Range: $125-149.9 Million
Emp.: 300
Grains, Livestock Feed & Fertilizers
N.A.I.C.S.: 424510
Ronald P. Angelilli (COO & Exec VP-Ops)
Travis Rowe (Chief Comml Officer & Exec VP-Mktg & Sls)
George F. Rellinger (Chm)
Lamar L. Liming (Vice Chm)
Kenneth J. Schilling (Sec)

HERITAGE DAIRY STORES INC.
376 Jessup Rd, Thorofare, NJ 08086
Tel.: (856) 845-2855   DE
Web Site: https://www.heritages.com
Year Founded: 1929
Sales Range: $25-49.9 Million
Emp.: 425
Supermarket
N.A.I.C.S.: 445110
Harold M. Heritage (Chm, Pres & CEO)
Justin Phifer (Mgr-Reg)

HERITAGE DEVELOPMENT GROUP INC.
465 Heritage Rd, Southbury, CT 06488
Tel.: (203) 264-8291   CT
Web Site:
http://www.heritagehills.com
Year Founded: 1970
Sales Range: $25-49.9 Million
Emp.: 150
Real Estate Agents & Managers
N.A.I.C.S.: 531210
Keith Sorensen (Pres)
Marc Brassard (VP)

HERITAGE DISTILLING HOLDING COMPANY, INC.
3207 57th St Ct NW, Gig Harbor, WA 98335
Tel.: (253) 300-5179   DE
Web Site:
https://heritagedistilling.com
Emp.: 100
Holding Company
N.A.I.C.S.: 551112

Subsidiaries:

Heritage Distilling Company, Inc.   (1)
3207 57th St Ct NW, Gig Harbor, WA 98335-7586
Tel.: (253) 509-0008

Web Site: http://www.heritagedistilling.com
Distilleries
N.A.I.C.S.: 312140
Justin Stiefel (Owner)

HERITAGE EQUIPMENT INC.
322 Dry Hill Rd, Beckley, WV 25801
Tel.: (304) 254-7827
Web Site:
http://www.heritageequipment.net
Rev.: $30,600,000
Emp.: 86
Automobile & Other Motor Vehicle Merchant Whslr
N.A.I.C.S.: 423110
Carl Hubbard (COO & VP)
Gary Kale (Pres & CEO)

HERITAGE FAMILY SPECIALTY FOODS, INC.
901 Santerre Dr, Grand Prairie, TX 75050
Tel.: (972) 660-6511
Web Site: http://www.hfsfoods.com
Year Founded: 1991
Sales Range: $10-24.9 Million
Emp.: 65
Frozen Food Mfr
N.A.I.C.S.: 311412
Daniel Brackeen (Founder)
Lee Keller (VP-Ops)

HERITAGE FEDERAL CREDIT UNION
8266 Bell Oaks Dr, Newburgh, IN 47630
Tel.: (812) 253-6928
Web Site: http://www.hfcu.info
Holding Company
N.A.I.C.S.: 551111
Tony Aylsworth (CEO)

HERITAGE FINANCIAL CONSULTANTS, LLC
307 International Cir Ste 390, Hunt Valley, MD 21030
Tel.: (410) 785-0033
Web Site:
https://www.heritageconsultants.com
Year Founded: 1999
Sales Range: $10-24.9 Million
Emp.: 67
Financial Planning, Estate Planning, Wealth Management & Insurance Services
N.A.I.C.S.: 525990
Brent Fuchs (Partner-Baltimore)
Jane Davis (Dir-Client Experience)
Jacob Fenlason (Jr Mgr-Client Relationship)
Artie McGonigal (Jr Mgr-Client Relationship)
Andrew Shaffer (Mgr-Client Relationship)
Michael Behrman (Mgr-Client Relationship)
Markus Richter (COO)
Eric Wyss (Dir-Fin Plng & Risk Mgmt)

HERITAGE FINANCIAL GROUP, INC.
120 W Lexington Ave, Elkhart, IN 46516
Tel.: (574) 522-8000   IN
Web Site: http://www.hfgnet.com
Year Founded: 1981
Emp.: 85
Investment & Portfolio Management Firm
N.A.I.C.S.: 523999
Chris Pollock (Pres)
Brian J. Smith (Co-CEO)
Bruno DeJesus (CFO)
John Green (Area Mgr)
Angie Pennington (Area Mgr-Sls)
Dan Morrison (Co-CEO)

Subsidiaries:

Royal Motors of Middlebury, Inc. (1)
311 N Main St, Middlebury, IN 46540-9003
Tel.: (574) 825-3388
Web Site: http://www.royalmotorautos.com
Sales Range: $1-9.9 Million
Emp.: 5
Used Car Dealers
N.A.I.C.S.: 441120

HERITAGE FORD INC.
2100 Sisk Rd, Modesto, CA 95350
Tel.: (209) 529-5110
Web Site:
    https://www.heritagefordmo
    desto.com
Sales Range: $50-74.9 Million
Emp.: 100
Automobiles, New & Used
N.A.I.C.S.: 441110
George Frahoud (Gen Mgr-Sls)

HERITAGE FS INC.
1381 S Crescent St, Gilman, IL
60938
Tel.: (815) 265-4751
Web Site: http://www.heritagefs.com
Sales Range: $100-124.9 Million
Emp.: 125
Fertilizer & Fertilizer Materials
N.A.I.C.S.: 424910
Mark Weilbacher (Controller)
Jeremy Scher (Plant Mgr)

HERITAGE GROUP
6320 Intech Way, Indianapolis, IN
46278
Tel.: (317) 872-6010
Web Site: http://www.thgrp.com
Year Founded: 1930
Emp.: 5,000
Safety & Industrial Hygiene Consulting
N.A.I.C.S.: 541420
Kip A. Frey (Exec VP-New Ventures)
John P. Vercruysse (Exec VP-Fin &
Admin)
David Rosen (Exec VP-Strategy &
M&A)
Betsy McCaw (Exec VP-People &
Org Capabilities)
Fred M. Fehsenfeld Jr. (Bd of Dirs &
Chm)
Amy M. Schumacher (CEO)

Subsidiaries:

Asphalt Materials Inc. (1)
8720 Robbins Rd, Indianapolis, IN 46268
Tel.: (317) 872-6010
Web Site: https://asphalt-materials.com
Asphalt & Asphaltic Paving Mixtures
N.A.I.C.S.: 324121
Bill Kohler (Plant Mgr)

Subsidiary (Domestic):

Henry G. Meigs, LLC (2)
1220 Superior St, Portage, WI 53901
Tel.: (608) 742-5354
Web Site: https://asphalt-materials.com
Asphalt & Pavement Preservation Products
Mfr
N.A.I.C.S.: 324121
Rachel Yates (Bus Ops)
Darin Wendt (Dir-Trucking Ops)
Diane Franseen (Asphalt Tech)
Dan Swiertz (Dir-Mix Design Laboratories)
Ken Schakelman (Sls Mgr)

Crystal Flash Energy (1)
1754 Alpine Ave NW, Grand Rapids, MI
49504
Tel.: (616) 363-4851
Web Site: http://www.crystalflash.com
Petroleum Product Whslr
N.A.I.C.S.: 424720
Tom Olive (Pres & CEO)
Ray Duimstra (Dir-Corp Dev & Strategic
Acq)

Crystal Flash Petroleum Corp. (1)

5221 Ivy Tech Dr, Indianapolis, IN
46268-1016   (100%)
Tel.: (317) 879-2849
Web Site: http://www.crystalflash.com
Sales Range: $50-74.9 Million
Emp.: 350
Gasoline Stations & Convenience Stores
Operator
N.A.I.C.S.: 457110

Monument Chemicals, Inc. (1)
6325 Digital Way Ste 460, Indianapolis, IN
46278
Tel.: (317) 223-2630
Web Site:
    http://www.monumentchemical.com
Holding Company; Solvent & Specialty
Chemical Mfr
N.A.I.C.S.: 551112
Amy M. Schumacher (Pres)
Paul C. Raymond III (CEO)

Subsidiary (Domestic):

Advanced Aromatics, LLC (2)
5501 W Baker Rd, Baytown, TX 77520
Tel.: (281) 424-4505
Web Site:
    http://www.advancedaromatics.com
Sales Range: $10-24.9 Million
Emp.: 50
Heavy-Aromatic Solvent Mfr
N.A.I.C.S.: 325998

Johann Haltermann Ltd. (2)
16717 Jacintoport Blvd, Houston, TX
77015-6544
Tel.: (281) 452-5951
Web Site:
    http://www.monumentchemical.com
Sales Range: $25-49.9 Million
Emp.: 100
Solvent & Specialty Chemical Mfr
N.A.I.C.S.: 325998
Wayne E. Petersen (Pres & Gen Mgr)
Mark H. Overaker (Dir-Mfg & Supply Chain)
Elisha Petersen (Mgr-Acct-Sls)
Josh Petersen (Mgr-Mktg & Natl Accts)

Subsidiary (Non-US):

Monument Chemical bvba (2)
Haven 1972 Ketenislaan 3, Kallo, 9130,
Belgium
Tel.: (32) 3570 2811
Web Site:
    http://www.monumentchemical.com
Emp.: 100
Solvent & Specialty Chemical Mfr
N.A.I.C.S.: 325998
Christophe Vergote (Mgr-Supply Chain)

Retriev Technologies, Inc. (1)
265 Quarry Rd SE, Lancaster, OH 43130
Tel.: (740) 653-6290
Web Site: http://www.retrievtech.com
Battery Recycling & Management
N.A.I.C.S.: 541620

Subsidiary (Domestic):

Battery Solutions, Inc. (2)
7266 Kensington Rd, Brighton, MI 48116
Tel.: (248) 446-3001
Sales Range: $1-9.9 Million
Emp.: 35
Hazardous Waste Treatment & Disposal
N.A.I.C.S.: 562211
Chris Sova (Pres)
Donald Lynch (VP-Ops)

U.S. Aggregates Inc. (1)
8720 Robbins Rd, Indianapolis, IN 46268
Tel.: (317) 434-4600
Web Site: http://www.usagg.com
Limestone Mining Services
N.A.I.C.S.: 212312
Mark LeFever (Area Mgr-Eastern Div)

Plant (Domestic):

**U.S. Aggregates Inc. - Francesville
Plant** (2)
14530 W 700 S, Francesville, IN 47946
Tel.: (219) 567-9155
Web Site: http://www.usagg.com
Sand & Gravel Mining Services
N.A.I.C.S.: 212321

**U.S. Aggregates Inc. - Lafayette
Plant** (2)

5070 Swisher Rd, West Lafayette, IN 47906
Tel.: (765) 567-7625
Limestone Mining Services
N.A.I.C.S.: 212312

**U.S. Aggregates Inc. - Lowell
Plant** (2)
9331 W 205 Ave, Lowell, IN 46356
Tel.: (219) 696-5467
Limestone Mining Services
N.A.I.C.S.: 212321

**U.S. Aggregates Inc. - Monon
Plant** (2)
6857 US 421 S, Monon, IN 47959
Tel.: (219) 253-6686
Emp.: 6
Stone & Gravel Mining Services
N.A.I.C.S.: 212321
Jesse Hollifield (Plant Mgr)

**U.S. Aggregates Inc. - Sand & Gravel
- Crawfordsville Plant** (2)
3607 US 231 N, Crawfordsville, IN 47933
Tel.: (765) 362-2500
Emp.: 8
Sand & Gravel Mining Services
N.A.I.C.S.: 212321

**U.S. Aggregates Inc. - Sand & Gravel
- Perkinsville Plant** (2)
3172 N State Rd 13, Noblesville, IN 46060
Tel.: (765) 734-1019
Web Site: http://www.usagg.com
Sand & Gravel Mining Services
N.A.I.C.S.: 212321
Jim Fehsenfeld (Owner)
John Smith (Pres)

**U.S. Aggregates Inc. - Sand & Gravel
- Richmond Plant** (2)
6340 SR 121, Richmond, IN 47374
Tel.: (765) 966-8155
Emp.: 5
Sand & Gravel Mining Services
N.A.I.C.S.: 212321

**U.S. Aggregates Inc. - Sand & Gravel
- Thorntown Plant** (2)
6990 N 875 W, Thorntown, IN 46071
Tel.: (765) 436-7665
Web Site: http://www.usagg.com
Emp.: 5
Sand & Gravel Mining Services
N.A.I.C.S.: 212321
Hope Bray (Mgr-HR)

**U.S. Aggregates Inc. - Stone Quarry -
Columbus Plant** (2)
3415 S 650 E, Columbus, IN 47203-9556
Tel.: (812) 579-5243
Stone Quarrying Services
N.A.I.C.S.: 212319

**U.S. Aggregates Inc. - Stone Quarry -
Delphi Plant** (2)
2195 W US 421 N, Delphi, IN 46923
Tel.: (765) 564-2580
Stone Quarrying Services
N.A.I.C.S.: 212319

**U.S. Aggregates Inc. - Stone Quarry -
Linn Grove Plant** (2)
6311 W SR 218-1, Bluffton, IN 46714
Tel.: (260) 334-5311
Stone Quarrying Services
N.A.I.C.S.: 212319

**U.S. Aggregates Inc. - Stone Quarry -
Pleasant Mills Plant** (2)
699 S 500 E, Decatur, IN 46733
Tel.: (260) 592-7211
Emp.: 7
Stone Quarrying Services
N.A.I.C.S.: 212319
Greg Landis (Mgr)

**U.S. Aggregates Inc. - Stone Quarry -
Portland Plant** (2)
2228 W 125 S, Portland, IN 47371
Tel.: (260) 726-7642
Web Site: http://www.usagg.com
Emp.: 10
Stone Quarrying Services
N.A.I.C.S.: 212319
Eric Reynllbs (Mgr)

**U.S. Aggregates Inc. - Stone Quarry -
Ridgeville Plant** (2)

1972 W R 28, Ridgeville, IN 47380
Tel.: (765) 857-2493
Emp.: 10
Stone Quarrying Services
N.A.I.C.S.: 212319

HERITAGE GROUP, INC.
1101 12th St, Aurora, NE 68818
Tel.: (402) 694-3136   NE
Web Site:
    https://www.bankonheritage.com
Year Founded: 1952
Sales Range: $50-74.9 Million
Emp.: 148
Bank Holding Company
N.A.I.C.S.: 522110
Sam L. Moyer (Chm, Pres & CEO)
Craig Moyer (Dir-Sls-Insurance & Re-
tail Investments & Mgr-Rels)

Subsidiaries:

HGI Realty, Inc. (1)
110 E 9th St, Wood River, NE 68883
Tel.: (308) 583-2262
Web Site: http://www.hgirealty.com
Emp.: 20
Real Estate Manangement Services
N.A.I.C.S.: 531390

Heritage Bank (1)
800 W 3rd St, Hastings, NE
68901-5054   (100%)
Tel.: (402) 463-6611
Web Site: http://www.bankonheritage.com
Sales Range: $25-49.9 Million
Emp.: 50
Full Service Bank
N.A.I.C.S.: 522110
Robert A. Morris (Pres)

HERITAGE GROUP, LLC
20 Burton Hills Blvd Ste 150, Nash-
ville, TN 37215
Tel.: (615) 665-8220
Web Site:
    https://www.heritagegroupusa.com
Year Founded: 1986
Emp.: 8
Investment & Advisory Firm
N.A.I.C.S.: 523999
Rick Morphis (Mng Dir)
David McClellan (Mng Dir)
Paul Wallace (Mng Dir)
Jesse Bland (Principal)
Florence Chassaignac (Dir-Ops)
Graham Hunter (Principal)
Michelle Anderson (VP-Fin)
Bryan Bui (Principal)
Lauren Brueggen (Principal)

**HERITAGE HEALTH AND
HOUSING**
416 W 127th St, New York, NY
10027
Tel.: (212) 866-2600   NY
Web Site: http://www.heritagenyc.org
Year Founded: 1969
Sales Range: $10-24.9 Million
Emp.: 332
Health Care Srvices
N.A.I.C.S.: 622110

**HERITAGE HEALTH CARE
SERVICES, INC.**
1009 Reservoir Ave, Cranston, RI
02910
Tel.: (401) 943-2584
Web Site:
    http://www.heritagehealthcare.com
Year Founded: 1989
Sales Range: $10-24.9 Million
Emp.: 315
Industrial Laundery Services
N.A.I.C.S.: 812332
Gerard Hainse (Pres)
Gregory Goings (Chm & CEO)

HERITAGE HOME GROUP, LLC

Heritage Home Group, LLC—(Continued)

1925 Eastchester Dr, High Point, NC 27265
Tel.: (336) 888-4900   DE
Web Site:
  http://www.heritagehome.com
Year Founded: 2013
Emp.: 250
Holding Company; Home Furniture Designer, Mfr & Whslr
N.A.I.C.S.: 551112
Mark Stephens (Sr VP-Sls)
Paul Peters (Sr VP-Mdsg)
Tod Phelps (CTO)
Pierre De Villemejane (Pres & CEO)
Regan Inglesia (Chief Merchandising Officer)
Blair Hawley (COO)
Beegee Tagliaferri (VP-Retail Opos)
Kevin Bowman (VP-Sls & Luxury Brands)

Subsidiaries:

Broyhill Furniture Industries, Inc.   (1)
815 Visionary St, Lenoir, NC
28645-0003   (100%)
Tel.: (828) 758-3111
Web Site: http://www.broyhillfurn.com
Bedroom, Dining Room & Occasional, Casual Furniture & Upholstery Mfr
N.A.I.C.S.: 337122
Mark E. Stephens (Pres)

HDM Retail, Inc.   (1)
222 Merchandise Mart Plz Ste 1865, Chicago, IL 60654
Tel.: (312) 464-1865
Furniture Retailer
N.A.I.C.S.: 449110

Henredon Furniture Industries, Inc.   (1)
400 Henredon Rd, Morganton, NC
28655   (100%)
Tel.: (341) 863-1100
Web Site: http://www.henredon.com
Sales Range: $750-799.9 Million
Household Furniture Mfr
N.A.I.C.S.: 337122
Jane Bender (Mgr-Adv)

Subsidiary (Domestic):

Henredon Designer Showrooms, Inc.   (2)
400 Henredon Rd, Morganton, NC
28655   (100%)
Tel.: (828) 437-5261
Web Site: http://www.henredon.com
Sales Range: $10-24.9 Million
Emp.: 35
Interior Design Services
N.A.I.C.S.: 541410

Hickory Chair Company   (1)
37 9th St SE, Hickory, NC 28602   (100%)
Tel.: (828) 328-1801
Web Site: http://www.hickorychair.com
Sales Range: $10-24.9 Million
Furniture Mfr
N.A.I.C.S.: 337121
Frank J. Reardon (Pres)
Laura Holland (Dir-Mktg Svcs)
Cathy Mitchell (VP-Mdsg)

Lane Furniture Industries   (1)
5380 Hwy 145, Tupelo, MS 38801   (100%)
Tel.: (662) 566-7211
Web Site: http://www.lanefurniture.com
Home Furnishing Mfr
N.A.I.C.S.: 337121
Dane Masters (Pres)

Subsidiary (Domestic):

Action Transport, Inc.   (2)
12 Service Dr, Tupelo, MS 38802   (100%)
Tel.: (866) 339-9032
Sales Range: $10-24.9 Million
Emp.: 375
Truck Operator
N.A.I.C.S.: 484121

Lane Home Furnishings Retail, Inc.   (2)
900 Loughborough Dr, Merced, CA 95348

Tel.: (209) 723-5263
Web Site: http://www.lanefurniture.com
Furniture Retailer
N.A.I.C.S.: 449110

Division (Domestic):

Laneventure   (2)
205 Workman St, Conover, NC 28601
Tel.: (828) 328-2352
Web Site: http://www.laneventure.com
Sales Range: $75-99.9 Million
Emp.: 100
Upholstered Furniture Mfr
N.A.I.C.S.: 337121
Gary McCray (Pres)
Mary Harris (Mgr-Media Rels)

Maitland-Smith Furniture Industries, Inc.   (1)
1925 Eastchester Dr, High Point, NC
27265   (100%)
Tel.: (336) 812-2400
Web Site: http://www.maitland-smith.com
Decorative Accessories, Lamps & Furniture Mfr
N.A.I.C.S.: 423220

Subsidiary (Non-US):

Maitland-Smith Cebu, Inc.   (2)
Philippines Export Zone Authority, MEPZ 1, Lapu-Lapu, Philippines   (100%)
Tel.: (63) 323400277
Web Site: http://www.maitland-smith.com
Emp.: 39
Furniture Mfr
N.A.I.C.S.: 337126
Abbie Young (Gen Mgr)

The Pearson Company   (1)
37 9th St Pl SE, Hickory, NC 28602
Tel.: (336) 882-8135
Web Site: http://www.pearsoncompany.com
Sales Range: $50-74.9 Million
Emp.: 200
Upholstered Furniture Mfr
N.A.I.C.S.: 337121
Mike Heath (Pres)

Thomasville Furniture Industries, Inc.   (1)
401 E Main St, Thomasville, NC
27360   (100%)
Tel.: (336) 472-4000
Web Site: http://www.thomasville.com
Furniture Mfr
N.A.I.C.S.: 337215
Terry Bargy (CIO & VP)
Kathy Veltri (Pres)

Division (Domestic):

Thomasville Home Furnishings of Arizona   (2)
601 N 44th Ave, Phoenix, AZ 85043
Tel.: (602) 278-3500
Web Site: http://www.thomasville.com
Sales Range: $10-24.9 Million
Emp.: 32
Furniture Whslr
N.A.I.C.S.: 449110
Tom Erickson (Gen Mgr)

HERITAGE HOMES INC.
456 S Hampton Rd, Westfield, MA
01085-1327
Tel.: (413) 568-8614   MA
Year Founded: 1955
Sales Range: $10-24.9 Million
Emp.: 6
Custom Manufactured, Personalized & Modular Homes, Custom Additions & Garages, Remodeling Services, Commercial & Light Industrial Building
N.A.I.C.S.: 236115
Linda Greskowicz (Office Mgr)
Robert T. Goyette Sr. (Treas)
Robert T. Goyette Jr. (Pres)

HERITAGE INTERIORS, INC.
2501 W Phelps Rd, Phoenix, AZ
85023
Tel.: (602) 943-8599

Web Site: http://www.isidc.com
Rev.: $20,968,978
Emp.: 80
Floor Covering Stores & Interior Design Services
N.A.I.C.S.: 449121
Dennis M. Crowley (Pres)
Randy Bafuf (VP)
Kellie Gatewood (Acct Exec)

HERITAGE LACE INC.
309 S St, Pella, IA 50219
Tel.: (641) 628-4949
Web Site:
  http://www.heritagelace.com
Year Founded: 1983
Sales Range: $75-99.9 Million
Emp.: 30
Mfr & Marketing & Import of Lace
N.A.I.C.S.: 423220
Dan Decook (Co-CEO)
Tim Heerema (Co-CEO)

HERITAGE MANAGEMENT CORP.
2605 SW 33rd St Ste 200, Ocala, FL
34471
Tel.: (352) 482-0777
Web Site:
  https://www.heritagemanagement.net
Year Founded: 1977
Sales Range: $50-74.9 Million
Emp.: 15
Commercial Real Estate Services
N.A.I.C.S.: 531312
Ken Kirkpatrick (Pres)
James Day (Head-Property Mgmt Div)
Paul Ayoub (Controller)

Subsidiaries:

Links at Spruce Creek South   (1)
18050 SE 102nd Terr, Summerfield, FL
34491
Tel.: (352) 347-6172
Web Site:
  http://www.linksatsprucecreek.com
Golf Club, Membership
N.A.I.C.S.: 713910
Darren J. Irwin (Dir-Ops)

HERITAGE PALMS GOLF & COUNTRY CLUB INC.
10420 Washingtonia Palm Way, Fort Myers, FL 33966
Tel.: (239) 278-9090
Web Site: https://www.hpgcc.com
Sales Range: $10-24.9 Million
Emp.: 200
Golf & Country Club
N.A.I.C.S.: 713910
Andrea McCarraher (Mgr)

HERITAGE PAPER COMPANY, INC.
4011 Morton St, Jacksonville, FL
32217
Tel.: (904) 737-6603   FL
Web Site:
  http://www.heritagepaperco.com
Year Founded: 1972
Sales Range: $10-24.9 Million
Emp.: 32
Industrial Paper Distr
N.A.I.C.S.: 424130
David Clevinger (Mgr)
Robert F. Purser Sr. (Chm & CEO)

HERITAGE PARTNERS, INC.
800 Boylston St Ste 1535, Boston, MA 02199-8036
Tel.: (617) 439-0688
Web Site:
  http://www.newheritagecapital.com
Year Founded: 1986
Sales Range: $25-49.9 Million

Emp.: 10
Privater Equity Firm
N.A.I.C.S.: 523999

Subsidiaries:

American Package Express   (1)
1501 S Loop 12, Irving, TX 75060
Tel.: (972) 579-3431
Package Delivery, Vehicular
N.A.I.C.S.: 488510

HERITAGE PETROLEUM
516 N 7th Ave, Evansville, IN 47710
Tel.: (812) 422-3251
Web Site:
  https://www.heritageoil.com
Rev.: $15,094,333
Emp.: 15
Petroleum Bulk Stations
N.A.I.C.S.: 424720
Rod Hunter (Dir-Safety)
Randy Brack (CFO)

HERITAGE SCHOOLS, INC.
5600 N Heritage School Dr, Provo, UT 84604
Tel.: (801) 226-4600   UT
Web Site: https://www.heritagertc.org
Year Founded: 1993
Sales Range: $10-24.9 Million
Emp.: 424
Recreation & Other Welfare Services
N.A.I.C.S.: 813410
Jason Wright (Dir-Academic)
Kevin Curtis (COO)
Robin Ellis (Dir-Medical)
George Ballew (Dir-Residential)
Pat Davis (Sec)
Jerry Spanos (Chm & CEO)
Keven Downs (Exec Dir)
Eugene Marshall (Dir-Clinical)
Kristi Naumann (Dir-Asst Residential)

HERITAGE SOUTH COMMUNITY CREDIT UNION
763 N Main St, Shelbyville, TN 37160
Tel.: (931) 684-3596   TN
Web Site:
  https://www.heritagesouth.org
Year Founded: 1957
Sales Range: $10-24.9 Million
Emp.: 66
Credit Union
N.A.I.C.S.: 522130
Laura Parham (CEO)

HERITAGE SPORTSWEAR, INC.
102 Reliance Dr, Hebron, OH 43025
Tel.: (740) 928-7771   SC
Web Site:
  http://www.heritagesportswear.com
Year Founded: 1982
Knit Women's Apparel, Knit Sweaters & Skirts Mfr & Marketer
N.A.I.C.S.: 315120
Tami Miller (Dir-Mktg)

HERITAGE TECHNOLOGIES, LLC.
1550 Research Way, Indianapolis, IN
46231-3350
Tel.: (317) 486-5880
Web Site: http://www.heritage-global.com
Sales Range: $10-24.9 Million
Emp.: 60
Animal Feed Mfr
N.A.I.C.S.: 311119
Kevin Perryman (Mgr-Mktg Dev)
Mary King (Mgr-Quality)
Brian Wilson (Mgr-Quality)
Liz Koutsos (Mgr-Animal Res & Tech Svc)
Carson Landers (Mgr-Safety)
Ted Moore (COO)
David Washburn (Controller)

Rhonda Luddington (Coord-Customer Svc)
Jeff Cohen (VP-Mktg & Sls)

HERITAGE WHOLESALERS INC.
185 Commercial St, Malden, MA 02148
Tel.: (781) 324-8100
Web Site:
http://www.hertiagewholesaler.com
Year Founded: 1970
Sales Range: $10-24.9 Million
Emp.: 30
Rubber Roofing Asphalt Shingles, Siding & Roofing Materials
N.A.I.C.S.: 423330
Steven Field (Pres)
Thomas Wright (VP-Fin)

HERITAGENERGY (NY) INC.
625 Sawkill Rd, Kingston, NY 12401
Tel.: (845) 336-2000
Web Site:
http://www.heritagenergy.com
Rev.: $31,539,482
Emp.: 70
Fuel Oil Dealers
N.A.I.C.S.: 457210
Steve Shultis (Mgr-LP)

HERKER INDUSTRIES INC.
N 57 W 13760 Carmen Ave, Menom-onee Falls, WI 53051-6144
Tel.: (262) 781-8270
Web Site: https://www.herker.com
Sales Range: $10-24.9 Million
Emp.: 180
Screw Machine Products
N.A.I.C.S.: 332721
Rick Schneider (Engr-Ops)
Sue Neal (Dir-HR)
Dennis Driscoll (Dir-Sls)
Rick Bosshard (Engr-Sls)

HERKY HAWK FINANCIAL CORP.
117 W 1st St, Monticello, IA 52310
Tel.: (319) 465-5921   IA
Web Site:
http://www.citizensstateonline.com
Year Founded: 1986
Bank Holding Company
N.A.I.C.S.: 551111
Audrey G. Savage (Pres & CEO)

Subsidiaries:

Citizens State Bank   (1)
117 W 1st St, Monticello, IA 52310
Tel.: (319) 465-5921
Web Site:
http://www.citizensstateonline.com
Sales Range: $10-24.9 Million
Emp.: 66
Commericial Banking
N.A.I.C.S.: 522110
Brent Boies (CFO)
Audrey G. Savage (Pres & CEO)

HERM HUGHES & SONS, INC.
900 N Redwood Rd, North Salt Lake, UT 84054-2627
Tel.: (801) 292-1411   UT
Web Site: https://www.hughesgc.com
Year Founded: 1964
Commercial & Industrial Builders; Civil Engineering
N.A.I.C.S.: 236220
Dan Pratt (Sr VP)
Kendall Smith (VP-Building Div)
Lynn Hinrichs (VP-Govt Projects)
Gene Madsen (VP-Southern Utah)
Travis Davis (VP-Private/Design Build)

HERMAN ASSOCIATES, INC.

261 Madison Ave Fl 11, New York, NY 10016-2303
Tel.: (212) 616-1190
Web Site:
http://www.hermanassociatesnewyork.com
Year Founded: 1973
Sales Range: $1-9.9 Million
Emp.: 9
Advetising Agency
N.A.I.C.S.: 541810
Paula Herman (CEO)
Mario Almonte (Partner-PR)

Subsidiaries:

Herman Associates Public Relations   (1)
729 Seventh Ave 9th Fl, New York, NY 10019
Tel.: (212) 616-1190
Web Site: http://www.hermanassociatesnewyork.com
Emp.: 6
Business Publications, Consumer Publica-tions, Financial, High Technology, Informa-tion Technology, Leisure, Newspaper, Public Relations, Publicity/Promotions, Strategic Planning, Travel & Tourism
N.A.I.C.S.: 541810
Stu Herman (Pres)

HERMAN CONSTRUCTION SERVICES, INC.
10291 NW 46th St, Sunrise, FL 33351
Tel.: (954) 749-1800
Web Site: http://www.herman-construction.com
Sales Range: $10-24.9 Million
Emp.: 70
Commercial & Office Building, New Construction
N.A.I.C.S.: 236220
Gene L. Herman (Founder & Pres)
Tom Herman (VP)

HERMAN COOK VOLKSWA-GEN
1435 Encinitas Blvd, Encinitas, CA 92024
Tel.: (760) 683-8202
Web Site: https://www.cookvw.com
Year Founded: 1967
Sales Range: $10-24.9 Million
Emp.: 25
Car Whslr
N.A.I.C.S.: 441110
Dennis Cook (Owner)
Steve Walsh (Mgr-Bus Dev)
Dan Daniels (Mgr-Leasing & Internet)

HERMAN ELECTRONICS, INC.
10110 USA Today Way, Miramar, FL 33025
Tel.: (305) 477-0063
Web Site:
http://www.hermanelectronics.com
Rev.: $14,900,000
Emp.: 60
Electronic Parts
N.A.I.C.S.: 423690
Arnold Wolf (Chm)
Jeffrey A. Wolf (Exec VP-Sls & Mktg)

HERMAN GOLDNER COM-PANY INC.
7777 Brewster Ave, Philadelphia, PA 19153-3210
Tel.: (215) 365-5400   PA
Web Site: https://www.goldner.com
Year Founded: 1887
Sales Range: $50-74.9 Million
Emp.: 350
Full Service Mechanical Construction Company
N.A.I.C.S.: 238220
Stephen J. Williams (Pres & COO)

HERMAN KAY BROMLEY INC.
463 7th Ave Fl 12, New York, NY 10018-7499
Tel.: (212) 239-2025   NY
Year Founded: 1940
Sales Range: $10-24.9 Million
Emp.: 75
Mfr of Womens & Misses Coats
N.A.I.C.S.: 315250
Richard Kay (Co-Pres)
Barry Kay (Co-Pres)
Cynthia Leigh Flynn (Dir-Design)

HERMAN R. EWELL INC.
4635 Division Hwy, East Earl, PA 17519
Tel.: (717) 354-4556
Web Site: http://www.hrewell.com
Sales Range: $1-9.9 Million
Emp.: 200
Trucking Except Local
N.A.I.C.S.: 484121
Calvin E. Ewell (Pres)
Jack Francella (CFO)
Donald Thomas (VP-Natl & Intl Sls)
Douglas Buch (Dir-Ops)
Susan Haverstick (Controller)
John Keagel (Dir-Safety & HR)
Scott Ewell (Dir-Maintenance & Equipment)
Gene Kieffer (Mgr-Facilities)

HERMAN SEEKAMP INC.
1120 W Fullerton Ave, Addison, IL 60101
Tel.: (630) 628-6555
Web Site:
https://www.clydesdonuts.com
Year Founded: 1920
Sales Range: $10-24.9 Million
Emp.: 115
Bakery Products Mfr
N.A.I.C.S.: 311812
Dave Bennett (Mgr-Natl Sls)
Dina Hertogs (Mgr-HR)

HERMAN STRAUSS INC.
35th McColloch St, Wheeling, WV 26003
Tel.: (304) 232-8770
Web Site: http://www.strauss-ind.com
Sales Range: $10-24.9 Million
Emp.: 30
Nonferrous Metals Scrap
N.A.I.C.S.: 423930
Carter Strauss (Pres & CEO)
Ken Burns (VP)

HERMANN COMPANIES INC.
7701 Forsyth Blvd 10 Fl, Saint Louis, MO 63105
Tel.: (314) 863-9200
Web Site:
http://www.anchorpackaging.com
Sales Range: $50-74.9 Million
Emp.: 5
Mfr of Plastic Food Packaging & Shipping Materials
N.A.I.C.S.: 326150
Robert Ringen Hermann Jr. (Chm, Pres & CEO)

HERMANN ENGELMANN GREENHOUSES INC.
2009 Marden Rd, Apopka, FL 32703-6928
Tel.: (407) 886-3434   FL
Web Site:
http://www.exoticangel.com
Year Founded: 1971
Sales Range: $10-24.9 Million
Emp.: 230
Ornamental Nursery Products Mfr
N.A.I.C.S.: 111421
Sandra Kitain (CFO)

HERMANN SERVICES INCOR-PORATED
83 Stults Rd, Dayton, NJ 08810
Tel.: (609) 860-5810
Web Site:
https://www.hermanntds.com
Year Founded: 1927
Sales Range: $25-49.9 Million
Emp.: 500
General Warehousing, Transportation & Truck Leasing
N.A.I.C.S.: 493110
Richard J. Hermann (Pres)
Dennis Hermann (Pres-Transportation)

HERMANOS LOPEZ INC.
388 W Calle Primera, San Ysidro, CA 92173
Tel.: (619) 662-3032
Sales Range: $10-24.9 Million
Emp.: 150
Retailer of Groceries
N.A.I.C.S.: 424410
Roberto Lopez (Co-Pres & Treas)
Ellena Trujillo (VP-Ops)
Ricardo Perez (Controller)
Gloria Lopez (Mgr-HR)
Carlos Lopez (Mgr-Ops)
Leopoldo Lopez Jr. (Co-Pres)
Leo Lopez III (Mgr-Pur)

HERMANOS SANTIAGO CASH & CARRY
Avenida Ave Bldg 1, Ponce, PR 00731
Tel.: (787) 848-5542
Sales Range: $25-49.9 Million
Emp.: 140
Groceries, General Line
N.A.I.C.S.: 424410
Jose Santiago (Pres)

HERNANDEZ CONSULTING
3221 Tulane Ave, New Orleans, LA 70119
Tel.: (504) 305-8571
Web Site:
http://www.hernandezconsulting.com
Year Founded: 2005
Sales Range: $1-9.9 Million
Emp.: 12
Project Management Consulting Ser-vices
N.A.I.C.S.: 541618
Alex Hernandez (Pres & Mng Part-ner)
Richard Albert (Principal)
Sam King (Mgr-Construction)
Steve Riley (Mgr-Construction)

HERNON MANUFACTURING, INC.
121 Tech Dr, Sanford, FL 32771
Tel.: (407) 322-4000   FL
Web Site: http://www.hernonmfg.com
Year Founded: 1978
Sales Range: $1-9.9 Million
Emp.: 55
Adhesives & Sealants Mfr
N.A.I.C.S.: 325520
Harry Arnon (Owner, Pres & CEO)
Edgardo Rodriguez (Dir-Sls & Mktg)
Garret Walker (Mgr-Mktg)
Karen Arnon (Exec VP)
Gustavo Domit (Dir-Automation Solu-tions)

HEROES, INC.
509 River Dr, North Sioux City, SD 57049
Tel.: (605) 422-4166   NE
Year Founded: 1980
Sales Range: $10-24.9 Million
Emp.: 300

Heroes, Inc.—(Continued)

Merchandising Machine Operators & Vending Company
N.A.I.C.S.: 445132
Cal Kathol (Pres)
Joe Richter (Chm & CEO)

Subsidiaries:

Park Jefferson Speedway Inc. (1)
48426 332nd St, North Sioux City, SD 57049
Tel.: (605) 966-5517
Rev.: $120,000
Emp.: 1
Racing, Including Track Operation
N.A.I.C.S.: 711212

HERON STREET ACQUISITION CORPORATION
9454 Wilshire Blvd Ste 612, Beverly Hills, CA 90212
Tel.: (310) 888-1870   DE
Year Founded: 2016
Investment Services
N.A.I.C.S.: 523999
James Cassidy (Pres & Sec)
James McKillop (VP)

HERR FOODS INC.
273 Baltimore Pke, Nottingham, PA 19362-9788
Tel.: (610) 932-9330   PA
Web Site: http://www.herrs.com
Year Founded: 1946
Sales Range: $100-124.9 Million
Emp.: 1,300
Snack Food Mfr
N.A.I.C.S.: 311919
James M. Herr (Chm & CEO)
Ed Herr (Pres)

HERR INDUSTRIAL INC.
610 E Oregon Rd, Lititz, PA 17543
Tel.: (717) 569-6619
Web Site:
   https://www.herrindustrial.com
Year Founded: 1972
Sales Range: $10-24.9 Million
Emp.: 80
Paint Finishing Systems, Air Pollution Control Services & Material Handling
N.A.I.C.S.: 333248
Thomas Herr (VP)
Chris Herr (Mgr-Sls)
Don Knauss (Mgr-Air Pollution Control Svcs Product Line Sls)

HERREGAN DISTRIBUTORS, INC.
3695 Kennebec Dr, Eagan, MN 55122-1002
Tel.: (651) 452-7200
Web Site: https://www.herregan.com
Year Founded: 1966
Sales Range: $10-24.9 Million
Emp.: 120
Distr of Luxury Designer Tiles
N.A.I.C.S.: 423220
Jim Burns (Mgr-Ops)
Tom Splinter (Exec VP)

HERRICK, FEINSTEIN LLP
2 Park Ave, New York, NY 10016
Tel.: (212) 592-1400   NY
Web Site: https://www.herrick.com
Year Founded: 1928
Sales Range: $100-124.9 Million
Emp.: 201
Legal Advisory Services
N.A.I.C.S.: 541110
Stephen D. Brodie (Partner)
Richard J. Brown (Partner)
Jonathan A. Adelsberg (Partner)
Sheldon Chanales (Partner)
Therese M. Doherty (Partner)
Susan T. Dwyer (Co-Partner)

Howard R. Elisofon (Partner)
Daniel A. Etna (Partner)
Harvey S. Feuerstein (Partner)
Jennifer Smith Finnegan (Gen Mgr)
William R. Fried (Partner)
Kevin E. Fullington (Partner)
Stephen Jacobs (Chm-Corp Dept & Partner)

HERRING BANCORP, INC.
2201 Civic Cir, Amarillo, TX 79109
Tel.: (806) 677-7000
Web Site:
   https://www.herringbank.com
Year Founded: 1983
Rev.: $394,986,000
Bank Holding Company
N.A.I.C.S.: 551111
C. Coney Burges (Chm)
Donna Stribling (Sec)

Subsidiaries:

Herring Bank (1)
2201 Civic Cir, Amarillo, TX 79109
Tel.: (806) 677-7000
Web Site: http://www.herringbank.com
Rev.: $18,000,000
Emp.: 147
National Commercial Banks
N.A.I.C.S.: 522180

HERRING FORD, INC.
820 Memorial Blvd, Picayune, MS 39466
Tel.: (601) 798-8682
Web Site: http://www.herringford.com
New & Used Car Dealers
N.A.I.C.S.: 441110
Mark Herring (Sls Mgr)
Justin Herring (Mgr-Used Car)
Vic Tortorich (Dir-Svc)
Hiram Smith (Fin Mgr)

HERRING GAS COMPANY INC.
33 Main St, Meadville, MS 39653
Tel.: (601) 384-5833
Web Site: http://www.herringgas.com
Rev.: $33,887,017
Emp.: 130
Propane Gas, Bottled
N.A.I.C.S.: 457210
Edward G. Herring (Chm)

HERRMAN & GOETZ INC.
225 S Lafayette Blvd, South Bend, IN 46601-2109
Tel.: (574) 282-2596
Web Site:
   https://www.hgservices.com
Year Founded: 1968
Sales Range: $25-49.9 Million
Emp.: 175
Plumbing, Heating & Air-Conditioning Services
N.A.I.C.S.: 238220
Tom Herrmann (Gen Mgr)
Charmaine Varga (Sec)
Jack Hudgens (Project Mgr)

Subsidiaries:

H&G Infotech Office (1)
225 S Lafayette Blvd, South Bend, IN 46601-1822   (100%)
Tel.: (574) 237-6762
Web Site: http://www.hgservices.com
Sales Range: $50-74.9 Million
Provider of Technical Services & Support
N.A.I.C.S.: 238220
Bill Suter (Project Mgr)

HERRMAN LUMBER COMPANY
1917 S State Hwy MM, Springfield, MO 65802-3173
Tel.: (417) 862-3737   MO
Web Site:
   https://www.herrmanlumber.com
Year Founded: 1961

Sales Range: $25-49.9 Million
Emp.: 150
Producer of Lumber & Related Products
N.A.I.C.S.: 423310
Edward Powell (Pres)
Mark Olan (CFO & Exec VP)
Danny Burke (COO)

HERRSCHNERS, INC.
2800 Hoover Rd, Stevens Point, WI 54481-7103
Tel.: (715) 341-4554
Web Site:
   https://www.herrschners.com
Year Founded: 1899
Sales Range: $100-124.9 Million
Emp.: 200
Needlework Hobbycrafts
N.A.I.C.S.: 459130
Ted Hesemann (CEO)
Tim Frane (VP-Fin)

HERSAM ACORN NEWSPAPERS LLC
16 Bailey Ave, Ridgefield, CT 06877
Tel.: (203) 438-6544
Web Site:
   http://www.hersamacorn.com
Sales Range: $1-9.9 Million
Emp.: 50
Newspaper Publishing & Printing
N.A.I.C.S.: 513110
Jessica Perlinski (Dir-Mktg)
Mary Anne Hersam (VP-Adv Sls)
Susan Kiernan (Controller)

Subsidiaries:

Hersam Acorn Newspapers (1)
1000 Bridgeport Ave, Shelton, CT 06484-4660
Tel.: (203) 926-2080
Web Site: http://www.hersamacorn.com
Newspaper Publishing
N.A.I.C.S.: 513110
Nancy Doniger (Mng Editor)

Unit (Domestic):

Bridgeport News (2)
1000 Bridgeport Ave, Shelton, CT 06484   (100%)
Tel.: (203) 926-2080
Publishers of Weekly Newspapers
N.A.I.C.S.: 513110

Trumbull Printing Inc. (1)
205 Spring Hill Rd, Trumbull, CT 06611-1327   (100%)
Tel.: (203) 261-2548
Web Site: http://www.trumbillprinting.com
Pre-Press, Press, Bindery, Inserting, Mailing & Shipping Services
N.A.I.C.S.: 323120
Gustave C. Semon (Gen Mgr)
William McCann (Gen Mgr)

HERSCHEND FAMILY ENTERTAINMENT CORP.
5445 Triangle Pkwy Ste 200, Peachtree Corners, GA 30092
Tel.: (678) 993-1940   MO
Web Site: http://www.hfecorp.com
Year Founded: 1950
Themed Amusement Parks, Water Parks & Campgrounds
N.A.I.C.S.: 713110
Peter Herschend (Co-Founder)
Jack Herschend (Co-Founder)
Jason Blain (VP-Strategic Alliances)
Todd F. Schurz (Vice Chm)

Subsidiaries:

Harlem Globetrotters International, Inc. (1)
400 E Van Buren St Ste 300, Phoenix, AZ 85004
Tel.: (602) 258-0000
Web Site:
   http://www.harlemglobetrotters.com

Emp.: 16
Sports Teams & Clubs
N.A.I.C.S.: 711211
Kurt Schneider (CEO)
Peter LaPointe (Sr VP-Partnership Mktg & Sls)
Brett Meister (Sr VP-Comm)
Monica Neal (Exec VP-Brand Mktg & Partnerships)

Pink Jeep Tours, Inc. (1)
204 N State Rte 89A, Sedona, AZ 86336
Tel.: (928) 282-9000
Web Site: http://www.pinkjeep.com
Tour Operator
N.A.I.C.S.: 561520
Shawn Wendell (Owner)

HERSCHMAN ARCHITECTS, INC.
25001 Emery Rd Ste 400, Cleveland, OH 44128
Tel.: (216) 223-3200   OH
Web Site:
   http://www.herschmanarchitects.com
Sales Range: $10-24.9 Million
Emp.: 68
Architectural Services
N.A.I.C.S.: 541310
Jerry Herschman (Chm)
Stacey O'Guinn (Project Mgr-Architect)
Amanda Romeo (Project Mgr)
Mike Crislip (Pres)
Dushan Bouchek (Dir-Ops)
Roman Gumieniak (Project Mgr)
Carole Sanderson (CFO)
Pete Fitzgerald (Dir-Engrg)
Fred Margulies (Dir-Retail Architecture)

HERSHA ENTERPRISES, LTD.
44 Hersha Dr, Harrisburg, PA 17102
Tel.: (717) 412-5500   PA
Year Founded: 1984
Holding Company; Hotel Property Investor, Developer, Owner & Operator
N.A.I.C.S.: 551112
Hasu P. Shah (Chm & Pres)

Subsidiaries:

Hersha Hospitality Management Co. (1)
44 Hersha Dr, Harrisburg, PA 17102
Tel.: (717) 412-5500
Web Site: https://www.hhmhospitality.com
Sales Range: $10-24.9 Million
Emp.: 200
Hotel Operator
N.A.I.C.S.: 721110
Naveen P. Kakarla (Pres & CEO)
Michael Murray (COO)
Gregory Ade (Exec VP-Ops)
Joann Weber (VP-HR)
Z. Steve Kovats (Sr VP-Ops)
Stephanie Esposito (Sr VP-Sls)
David McCaslin (Exec VP)
Joseph Klam (Exec VP-Fin Svcs)
Dani Elhachem (Sr VP-Ops)
Jason Shane (Sr Dir-IT)

HERSHEY ENTERTAINMENT & RESORTS COMPANY
27 W Chocolate Ave, Hershey, PA 17033-0860
Tel.: (717) 534-3131   PA
Web Site:
   https://www.hersheypa.com
Year Founded: 1927
Sales Range: $300-349.9 Million
Emp.: 2,000
Theme Parks, Hotels & Recreational Facilities
N.A.I.C.S.: 713110
David P. Lavery (CFO)
Nathan D. Douty (VP-HR)
Kevin Stumpf (VP-Sports & Attractions)
John K. Lawn (CEO)

Brian Bucciarelli *(Dir-Corp Sls)*
Jen Alviani *(Dir-Guest Svcs & Ticketing)*
Maria Stouffer *(Mgr-Bus Svcs)*
Josh Carter *(Mgr-Equipment)*
Rob Gordon *(Mgr-Food & Beverage)*
Janet Dise *(Mgr-Grp Sls)*
Rebecca Kavli *(Mgr-Mdse)*
Andy Longenberger *(Mgr-Mktg)*
Bob Ancharski *(Mgr-Season Ticket Sls)*
Doug Yingst *(Gen Mgr)*
Andrew Helmer *(VP-HR)*
Lessy Ferraro *(CMO & Exec VP)*
Wendy McClintock *(Treas & VP-Fin)*
Vikki Hultquist *(Gen Mgr-Attractions & Entertainment)*

HERSHMAN CAPITAL CORP.
45 NE Industrial Rd, Branford, CT 06405
Tel.: (203) 488-0887
Web Site: http://www.chrecycling.com
Sales Range: $125-149.9 Million
Emp.: 30
Waste Paper Solutions
N.A.I.C.S.: 423930
Ethan J. Hershman *(CEO)*

HERSHOCKS INC.
3501 N 6 St, Harrisburg, PA 17110
Tel.: (717) 238-7331
Web Site:
 https://www.hershocks.com
Rev.: $10,766,645
Emp.: 75
Glass & Glazing Work
N.A.I.C.S.: 238150
Barry Deaven *(Pres)*
Ron Candioto *(VP)*
Dwayne Weaver *(Controller)*

HERSMAN SERLES ALMOND PLLC
520 Kirkland Way Ste 300, Kirkland, WA 98033-6256
Tel.: (425) 822-6557
Web Site: http://www.cpahsa.com
Offices of Certified Public Accountants
N.A.I.C.S.: 541211
Debbie Yaros *(Mgr-Tax)*

Subsidiaries:

Coldstream Capital Management, Inc. **(1)**
1 100th Ave NE Ste 102, Bellevue, WA 98004
Tel.: (425) 283-1600
Web Site: http://www.coldstream.com
Sales Range: $1-9.9 Million
Emp.: 22
Investment Advice
N.A.I.C.S.: 523940
Roger C. Reynolds *(Co-Founder & Mgr-Relationship)*
Howard Coleman *(Chief Investment Officer & Gen Counsel)*
David Powers *(Portfolio Mgr)*
Nina Rose *(Mgr-Relationship & Portfolio)*
Peter Beeson *(Co-Founder)*
Kevin Fitzwilson *(Mng Shareholder & Mgr-Relationship)*
Phil Platt *(COO)*
Robert Smith *(COO)*
Donna Oricchio *(CFO)*

Subsidiary (Domestic):

Rosenbaum Financial, Inc. **(2)**
150 SW Harrison St Ste 300, Portland, OR 97201
Tel.: (503) 296-9190
Web Site:
 http://www.rosenbaumfinancial.com
Insurance Related Activities
N.A.I.C.S.: 524298
Mark Rosenbaum *(Pres & CEO)*

HERSRUD CO. INC.
2651 Whitewood Service Rd, Sturgis, SD 57785
Tel.: (605) 347-2566
Web Site: http://www.hersruds.com
Year Founded: 1976
Sales Range: $10-24.9 Million
Emp.: 30
Automobiles, New & Used
N.A.I.C.S.: 441110
David Hersud *(Pres)*
Arnold Luptak *(Treas)*

HERTRICH NISSAN JEEP EAGLE
1378 S Dupont Hwy, Dover, DE 19901
Tel.: (302) 678-4553
Web Site:
 https://www.hertrichnissan.com
Sales Range: $10-24.9 Million
Emp.: 50
Car Whslr
N.A.I.C.S.: 441110
Andrew Miller *(Gen Mgr)*

HERTZBERG-NEW METHOD INC.
617 E Vandalia Rd, Jacksonville, IL 62650
Tel.: (217) 243-5451
Web Site: https://www.perma-bound.com
Year Founded: 1954
Books, Periodicals & Newspapers
N.A.I.C.S.: 424920
Todd Young *(Treas & Sec)*

HERWALDT AUTOMOTIVE GROUP, INC.
5615 E Westover, Fresno, CA 93727
Tel.: (559) 292-2269
Web Site: http://www.herwaldt.com
Sales Range: $50-74.9 Million
Emp.: 20
Motorcycle Dealership Operator
N.A.I.C.S.: 441227
Dan Herwaldt *(Owner)*

HERZING, INC.
525 N 6th St, Milwaukee, WI 53203-2703
Tel.: (414) 271-8103
Web Site: http://www.herzing.edu
Year Founded: 1965
Sales Range: $75-99.9 Million
Emp.: 2,000
Data Processing Schools
N.A.I.C.S.: 611420
David Brzeczkowski *(Sec & Controller)*

HERZOG CONTRACTING CORP.
600 S Riverside Rd, Saint Joseph, MO 64507
Tel.: (816) 233-9001
Web Site: https://www.herzog.com
Sales Range: $100-124.9 Million
Emp.: 1,000
Railroad & Railway Roadbed Construction Services
N.A.I.C.S.: 236210

HERZOG MEIER VOLKSWAGEN
4275 SW 139th Way, Beaverton, OR 97005
Tel.: (503) 644-9121
Web Site: https://www.herzog-meiervw.com
Sales Range: $25-49.9 Million
Emp.: 125
New Car Retailer
N.A.I.C.S.: 441110
James Stafford *(Mgr-New Car)*
Richard Kim *(Mgr-Internet Sls)*

Sean Trimble *(Dir-Internet)*
Chris Long *(Mgr-Gen Sls)*
Mike Ross *(Mgr-Used Car)*
Jesse Glimpse *(Mgr-Volkswagen Sls)*

HERZOG TRUE VALUE HOME CENTER INC.
151 Plz Rd, Kingston, NY 12401
Tel.: (845) 338-6300
Web Site:
 http://www.herzogstruevalue.com
Sales Range: $10-24.9 Million
Emp.: 80
Paint Plumbing & Lumber
N.A.I.C.S.: 444120
Bradley Jordan *(Pres)*

HERZOG-MEIER INC.
4275 SW 139th Way, Beaverton, OR 97005-2302
Tel.: (503) 372-3279   OR
Web Site:
 https://www.herzogmeier.com
Year Founded: 1985
Sales Range: $25-49.9 Million
Emp.: 130
New & Used Car Dealers
N.A.I.C.S.: 441110
Jim Meier *(Owner)*

HESCHONG MAHONE GROUP, INC.
11211 Gold Country Blvd Ste 103, Gold River, CA 95670
Tel.: (916) 962-7001   CA
Web Site:
 http://www.trcsolutions.com
Year Founded: 1994
Sales Range: $10-24.9 Million
Emp.: 30
Energy Conservation Consulting Services
N.A.I.C.S.: 541690

HESCO INC.
6633 N Milwaukee Ave, Niles, IL 60714
Tel.: (847) 647-6700
Web Site: https://www.hescoinc.com
Rev.: $24,139,455
Emp.: 50
Janitors' Supplies
N.A.I.C.S.: 423850
Rory Gurson *(Pres)*
Paulette Krzankowski *(VP)*
Al Kenderick *(VP)*

HESCO PARTS CORPORATION
990 S 9th St, Louisville, KY 40210
Tel.: (502) 589-9600   KY
Web Site: http://www.hescoparts.com
Year Founded: 1946
Rev.: $45,000,000
Emp.: 155
Engines, Transmissions & Component Parts Mfr & Distr
N.A.I.C.S.: 336390
Larry Ensor *(VP)*

Subsidiaries:

All-State Ford Truck Sales **(1)**
1357 Gardiner Ln, Louisville, KY 40213-1912
Tel.: (502) 459-0550
Web Site: http://www.allstatetrucks.com
Retail Truck Dealership
N.A.I.C.S.: 441110
Howard Ensor *(Pres)*
Randy Harrison *(Gen Mgr)*
Chad Ensor *(Mgr-F&I)*
Mike Housley *(Mgr-Parts)*

Hesco Parts **(1)**
707 Commercial Dr, Carlstadt, NJ 07072-2908
Tel.: (201) 438-9393

Sales Range: $1-9.9 Million
Mfr of Carburetors, Brake Shoes, Generators, Starter Motors, Water Pumps, Distributors, Voltage Regulators & Transmissions
N.A.I.C.S.: 423120

HESS BROTHER'S FRUIT COMPANY
500 Becker Rd, Leola, PA 17540-9314
Tel.: (717) 656-2631
Web Site: http://www.hessbros.com
Sales Range: $25-49.9 Million
Emp.: 48
Postharvest Crop Activity Related Services
N.A.I.C.S.: 115114

HESS FINE ARTS, INC.
1131 4th St N, Saint Petersburg, FL 33701
Tel.: (727) 896-0622   FL
Web Site: http://www.hessfineart.com
Year Founded: 1984
Sales Range: $10-24.9 Million
Emp.: 43
Jewelry & Precious Stones Mfr
N.A.I.C.S.: 423940
Jeffrey P. Hess *(Owner)*
Katrina Hess *(Co-Owner & Pres)*

HESS INDUSTRIES, INC.
30257 Redfield Rd, Niles, MI 49120-9766
Tel.: (269) 683-4182   DE
Year Founded: 1977
Sales Range: $50-74.9 Million
Emp.: 240
Holding Company
N.A.I.C.S.: 333517
Roxanne Louer *(Pres)*

Subsidiaries:

Capital Technologies, Inc **(1)**
30277 Redfield St, Niles, MI 49120-5958 **(100%)**
Tel.: (219) 232-3311
Sales Range: $25-49.9 Million
Emp.: 155
Designer & Builder of Metal Forming & Processing Systems, Dies & Automation Equipment
N.A.I.C.S.: 333517

Hess Industries, Inc. **(1)**
Langfeldstrasse 88, CH 8500, Frauenfeld, Switzerland **(100%)**
Tel.: (41) 527280420
Web Site: http://www.hessindustries.com
Sales Range: $10-24.9 Million
Emp.: 8
Sales & Service
N.A.I.C.S.: 333517

X-Cel Steel Fabricating, Inc. **(1)**
1760 Foundation Dr, Niles, MI 49120-8987 **(100%)**
Tel.: (269) 695-4580
Web Site: http://www.xcel-steel.com
Sales Range: $10-24.9 Million
Emp.: 25
MfrOf Steel Fabricator
N.A.I.C.S.: 332313

HESSCO
2344 Hwy 33, Saukville, WI 53080
Tel.: (262) 284-7600
Web Site: http://www.hessco.com
Year Founded: 1960
Rev.: $10,500,000
Emp.: 22
Medical Equipment & Supplies Distr
N.A.I.C.S.: 423450

HESSCOR, INC.
5222 E Larkspur Dr, Scottsdale, AZ 85254
Tel.: (602) 996-8488   AZ
Year Founded: 1991

Hesscor, Inc.—(Continued)

Sales Range: $1-9.9 Million
Emp.: 23
Specialty Trade Contractors
N.A.I.C.S.: 238990
Steven Hess (Pres)

Subsidiaries:

Professional Playground (1)
1548 E Main St, Mesa, AZ 85203
Tel.: (480) 464-2700
Web Site: http://www.hesscor.com
Construction, Mining & Forestry Machinery
& Equipment Rental & Leasing
N.A.I.C.S.: 532412

HESSE INDUSTRIAL SALES INC.
3370 N Benzing Rd, Orchard Park, NY 14127
Tel.: (716) 827-4951
Web Site:
http://www.hessereynolds.com
Sales Range: $10-24.9 Million
Emp.: 30
Industrial Machinery & Equipment
N.A.I.C.S.: 423830
John J. Breen Jr. (Controller)

HESSEL HOLDING CO. INC.
1419 W Reno Ave, Oklahoma City, OK 73106
Tel.: (405) 236-5561
Web Site:
https://www.whittonsupply.com
Sales Range: $10-24.9 Million
Emp.: 32
Industrial Machinery & Equipment
N.A.I.C.S.: 423830
John Hessel (Pres)
Christy Clark (Office Mgr)

HESSER OLDSMOBILE PON-TIAC INC.
988 S Green Bay Rd, Neenah, WI 54956
Tel.: (920) 725-7051
Rev.: $22,000,000
Emp.: 35
Owner & Operator of Car Dealerships
N.A.I.C.S.: 441110

HESSLER'S, INC.
12551 Cleveland Ave, Fort Myers, FL 33907
Tel.: (239) 208-5118
Web Site:
https://www.hesslerfloors.com
Year Founded: 1951
Sales Range: $1-9.9 Million
Emp.: 50
Floor Covering Stores
N.A.I.C.S.: 449121
Carl Hessler (Pres)

HETRICK COMMUNICATIONS, INC.
201 S Capitol Ave Ste 800, Indianapolis, IN 46225-1092
Tel.: (317) 262-8080
Year Founded: 1994
Sales Range: $10-24.9 Million
Emp.: 15
Public Relations Agency
N.A.I.C.S.: 541820
Bruce Hetrick (Owner)
Amy S. Ahlersmeyer (Sr Mgr-Client Relationship)
Mary Keleher (CFO)

HEUCOTECH LTD.
99 Newbold Rd, Fairless Hills, PA 19030-4307
Tel.: (215) 736-0712
Web Site: http://www.heubach.de
Year Founded: 1988

Sales Range: $10-24.9 Million
Emp.: 65
Cyclic Crudes & Intermediates
N.A.I.C.S.: 325180
Rainer Martens (Mng Dir)
Robert W. Mihalyi (CFO)
Donald Mcbride (COO)
Henry Brooks (Pres)
Johann Heubach (Chm)

HEUS MANUFACTURING COMPANY, INC.
1604 Michigan Ave, New Holstein, WI 53061
Tel.: (920) 898-2100
Rev.: $11,200,000
Emp.: 160
Cutting Tool & Machine Tool Accessory Mfr
N.A.I.C.S.: 333515
Edward Jones (Pres)
Terry Jones (Production Mgr)
Dave Schmitz (Mgr-Quality)
Robert Hues (VP)

HEWS COMPANY LLC
190 Rumery St, South Portland, ME 04106
Tel.: (207) 767-2136
Web Site: https://www.hewsco.com
Sales Range: $10-24.9 Million
Emp.: 87
Truck Bodies
N.A.I.C.S.: 423110
Robert E. Hews (Pres)

HEYCO INC.
1800 Industrial Way, Toms River, NJ 08755
Tel.: (732) 286-4836
Web Site: https://www.heyco.com
Rev.: $100,000,000
Emp.: 155
Rolled or Drawn Shapes, Copper & Copper Alloy Mfr
N.A.I.C.S.: 331420
William H. Jemison (Chm)

HEYDE COMPANIES
345 Frenette Dr, Chippewa Falls, WI 54729
Tel.: (715) 726-9237
Web Site:
http://www.heydecompanies.com
Year Founded: 1979
Sales Range: $10-24.9 Million
Emp.: 500
Health Care, Travel & Hospitality Services
N.A.I.C.S.: 722511
Dennis L. Heyde (Co-Owner)
Jeff Rowan (CFO)

HEYER CORP.
642 Glacier Trl, Roselle, IL 60172-1035
Tel.: (630) 671-0049
Year Founded: 1903
Sales Range: Less than $1 Million
Emp.: 3
Digital Duplicators Supplies Whslr
N.A.I.C.S.: 423840
William Heyer (Pres)
Nancy Devlin (Mgr-Mktg)
Kathleen Heyer (Sec)

HEYL TRUCK LINES INC.
220 Norka Dr, Akron, IA 51001
Tel.: (712) 568-2451
Web Site: http://www.heyl.net
Year Founded: 1949
Sales Range: $25-49.9 Million
Emp.: 200
Provider of Trucking Services
N.A.I.C.S.: 484121
Andrea Rozell (Mgr-Recruiting)

Subsidiaries:

Heyl Logistics (1)
PO Box 90410, Sioux Falls, SD 57109-0410
Tel.: (605) 336-6898
Web Site: http://www.heyl.net
Sales Range: $25-49.9 Million
Provider of Trucking Services
N.A.I.C.S.: 488510

HEYMANN CONSTRUCTION COMPANY
PO Box 606, New Ulm, MN 56073-0606
Tel.: (507) 354-3174
Web Site:
http://www.heymannconstruction.com
Sales Range: $10-24.9 Million
Emp.: 40
Nonresidential Construction Services
N.A.I.C.S.: 236220
Jerry O'Brien (Pres)

HEYWOOD HOSPITAL
242 Green St, Gardner, MA 01440
Tel.: (978) 632-3420
Web Site: https://www.heywood.org
Year Founded: 1907
Sales Range: $100-124.9 Million
Emp.: 988
Acute Healthcare Services
N.A.I.C.S.: 622110
Rose Kavalchuck (Chief Quality Officer & VP-Clinical Svcs)
Robert Crosby (CFO & Sr VP)
Dawn Casavant (Chief Philanthropy Officer & VP-External Affairs)
Bruce K. Bertrand (Chief Medical Officer & VP-Medical Affairs)
Carol Roosa (COO & VP-Ops)

HF GROUP INC.
203 W Artesia Blvd, Compton, CA 90220-5550
Tel.: (310) 605-0755
Web Site:
http://www.houstonfearless.com
Year Founded: 1976
Sales Range: $50-74.9 Million
Emp.: 68
Remedial Environmental & Industrial Water Purification Equipment Mfr
N.A.I.C.S.: 333413
Virginia Clarke (CFO)

Subsidiaries:

HF Group Inc. - Houston Fearless 76 Division (1)
5801 C St, Beale AFB, CA 95903
Tel.: (530) 788-0288
Airborne Reconnaissance System Mfr
N.A.I.C.S.: 334511

HF MANUFACTURING CORP.
65 W 36th St 11th Fl, New York, NY 10018
Tel.: (212) 594-9142
Rev.: $17,626,057
Emp.: 8
Men's & Boys' Sportswear & Athletic Clothing
N.A.I.C.S.: 315250
Todd Tucker (Pres)

HFI INC.
2421 Mcgaw Rd, Columbus, OH 43207
Tel.: (614) 491-0700
Web Site: http://www.hfi-inc.com
Rev.: $70,000,000
Emp.: 150
Automotive Trimmings, Fabric
N.A.I.C.S.: 336360
Walter E. Dennis Jr. (Pres & CEO)

HGA INC

300 Marconi Blvd 3rd Fl, Columbus, OH 43215
Tel.: (614) 221-3343
Year Founded: 1997
Rev.: $25,000,000
Emp.: 23
Advetising Agency
N.A.I.C.S.: 541810
Rick Adams (Co-Owner)
Bill Gallagher (Co-Owner)
Susan Holcomb (Partner & Dir-Creative)

HGGC, LLC
1950 University Ave, Palo Alto, CA 94303
Tel.: (650) 321-4910
Web Site: https://www.hggc.com
Year Founded: 2007
Emp.: 69,000
Privater Equity Firm
N.A.I.C.S.: 523999
Richard Lawson Jr. (Co-Founder, Chm & CEO)
Gregory M. Benson (Co-Founder & Exec Dir)
Gary L. Crittenden (Exec Dir)
Robert C. Gay (Co-Founder & Exec Dir)
Stephen K. Young (Exec Dir)
Lindsey Press (Head-IR-Global)
David Chung (Partner & Co-Chief Investment Officer)
Neil White (Pres & Partner)
Steven Leistner (Partner & Co-Chief Investment Officer)
Harv Barenz (Partner & Head-Bus Dev)
Bill Conrad (Partner)
Pat Dugoni (Principal)
Phil Sampognaro (Principal)
Lance Taylor (Partner & CFO)
Fariha Mirza (VP-Fin)
Kurt Krieger (Chief Legal Officer)
Chad Clawson (Operating Partner)
Scott St Clair (Operating Partner-ORG)
Matt Roesch (Principal)
Colin Phinisey (Head-Debt Capital Markets)
Anna Ike (VP)
Rich Gros (Operating Partner-ORG)
Edward Bryant Jr. (Exec Dir/Dir-Bus Dev)
Nicole Ongko (Dir-Ops)
Hao Qin (VP)
Victor Rudo (VP)
Chris Schulze (VP)
Melody Yuan (Controller)
Siv Hok (Controller-Fund & Mgr-Acctg)
Louise Husin (Chief Talent Officer)
Leslie M. Brown Jr. (Partner)
David H. S Chung (Partner & Co-Chief Investment Officer)

Subsidiaries:

American Megatrends, Inc. (1)
5555 Oakbrook Pkwy, Norcross, GA 30093
Tel.: (770) 246-8645
Web Site: http://www.ami.com
Sales Range: $75-99.9 Million
Emp.: 160
Computer Software Services
N.A.I.C.S.: 541512
Subramonian Shankar (Founder)
Sanjoy Maity (CEO)

Subsidiary (Non-US):

American Megatrends India Pvt. Ltd. (2)
Kumaran Nagar Semmenchery Off Rajiv Gandhi Salai OMR, Chennai, 600 119, India
Tel.: (91) 4466540922
Web Site: http://www.amiindia.co.in
Computer Peripheral Equipment Mfr
N.A.I.C.S.: 334118

Venkatesan Balakrishnan *(Head-Projects Unit)*

American Megatrends Information Technology (Kunshan) Co., Ltd. (2)
Room 501 3 Building No 177 Chang Jiang Road, Kunshan, 215301, Jiang Su, China
Tel.: (86) 51257360204
Web Site: http://www.ami.com.cn
Information Technology Consulting Services
N.A.I.C.S.: 541512

American Megatrends International GmbH (2)
Truderinger Strasse 283, 81825, Munich, Germany
Tel.: (49) 89969995
Web Site: http://www.ami.de
Computer Peripheral Equipment Mfr
N.A.I.C.S.: 334118

Aventri, Inc. (1)
13 Marshall St, Norwalk, CT 06854
Tel.: (203) 403-9470
Web Site: http://www.etouches.com
Cloud-Based Event Software Development & Services
N.A.I.C.S.: 541511
Kathleen Roberge *(Chief Revenue Officer)*
Nicola Rossetti *(VP-Global Mktg)*
Matthew Fish *(CFO)*
Chalva Tchkotoua *(CMO)*
Mike Mason *(VP-Sourcing & Hospitality Solutions)*
Michael Burns *(Head-Sls & Mktg-Global)*
Brad Langley *(Partner-Mgmt & VP-Channel)*
Joe Plastina *(Sr VP-Corp Dev-Global)*
Miranda DeSantis *(Chief People Officer)*
Jim Sharpe *(CEO)*

Subsidiary (Domestic):

ITN International Inc. (2)
9696 S 500 W, Sandy, UT 84070
Tel.: (801) 676-7900
Web Site: http://www.itn-international.com
Sales Range: $1-9.9 Million
Emp.: 50
Registration, Attendee Tracking & Data Collection for Exhibitions & Conferences
N.A.I.C.S.: 541519
Ivan Lazarev *(Co-Founder)*
Mark Williams *(Dir-Project Mgmt)*
Neil Pickard *(CTO)*
Spencer Segura *(COO)*

Davies Group Limited (1)
Floor 7 1 Minster Court Mincing Lane, London, EC3R 7AA, United Kingdom
Tel.: (44) 1782339152
Web Site: http://www.davies-group.com
Operations Management & Consulting Services
N.A.I.C.S.: 541611
William McKechnie *(Chm & CEO)*
Dan Saulter *(Grp CEO)*
James Heath *(Grp Chief Risk Officer)*
Jeff Chang *(Gen Counsel)*
Matt Button *(CEO-Claims Solutions Bus-US & Head-M&A)*
Emma Wedderburn *(Grp Chief HR Officer)*

Subsidiary (Non-US):

Frontier Adjusters, Inc. (2)
Tel.: (800) 426-7228
Web Site: http://www.frontieradjusters.com
Claims Adjusting
N.A.I.C.S.: 524291
Ed Ferrie *(Acct Mgr)*
Jon Yauck *(Coord-Quality)*
Jose Bridges *(Dir-Ops)*
Kathy Zartman *(Mgr-Bookeeping)*
Walter Leddy *(CEO)*

Subsidiary (US):

Johns Eastern Company Inc. (2)
6015 Resource Ln, Bradenton, FL 34202
Tel.: (941) 907-3100
Web Site: http://www.johnseastern.com
Sales Range: $10-24.9 Million
Emp.: 150
Insurance Adjusters
N.A.I.C.S.: 524291
Norman A. Sensinger *(VP)*
Donald E. Lederer *(Pres)*
Brian Harlow *(Exec VP-Field Ops)*
Stuart E. Bayer *(Treas & Sec)*

Beverely Adkins *(Exec VP-Acct Svc)*
Frank Feldman *(Dir-Client Dev)*
Kenneth M. Johns III *(Chm)*

Northshore International Insurance Services Inc. (2)
199 Rosewood Dr, Danvers, MA 01923
Tel.: (978) 745-6655
Web Site: http://www.niis.com
Rev.: $5,000,000
Emp.: 30
All Other Insurance Related Activities
N.A.I.C.S.: 524298
Charles H. Betz *(VP)*
David W. Cpcu *(CEO)*
Mark E. Cpcu *(Pres)*
Stephen V. Murphy *(COO)*
Ellen V. Gariepy *(Asst VP)*
Joy Keener-Borresen *(Asst Sec)*
Lea M. Zurek *(Sec)*
Susan A. Arsenault *(VP)*

US-Reports, Inc. (2)
3528 Precision Dr Ste 200, Fort Collins, CO 80528
Tel.: (800) 223-2310
Web Site: http://www.us-reports.com
Management Consulting Services
N.A.I.C.S.: 541611
Laurel West *(Reg Mgr-Dev)*
Debbie Guthrie *(VP-Premium Audit)*
Nick Holdridge *(Reg VP)*
Ryan Parker *(Reg Dir)*
Jon Kovach *(Pres)*
Mark de Waal *(Pres)*

Help/Systems, LLC (1)
11095 Viking Dr Ste 100, Eden Prairie, MN 55344
Tel.: (952) 933-0609
Web Site: http://www.helpsystems.com
Prepackaged Software Distr
N.A.I.C.S.: 513210
Jim Cassens *(Pres)*
Tom Huntington *(Exec VP-Technical Solutions)*
Kate Bolseth *(CEO)*
Matt Bresnan *(VP-Res & Dev)*
Mike Devine *(CMO)*
Joanna Leach *(Chief People Officer)*
Christopher D. Heim *(Chm)*
Matt Reck *(CFO)*
Scott Cole *(Chief Acquisition Officer & Chief Renewal Officer)*
John Grancarich *(VP-Product Strategy)*
Chris Reffkin *(Chief Info Security Officer)*
Raghunandan Koushik *(Reg Dir-India & SAARC)*
David Land *(Mng Dir-Asia Pacific & Japan)*

Subsidiary (Domestic):

Alert Logic, Inc. (2)
1776 Yorktown 7th Fl, Houston, TX 77056
Tel.: (713) 484-8383
Web Site: http://www.alertlogic.com
Software Development Services
N.A.I.C.S.: 541511
Chris Noell *(Sr VP-Engrg)*
Misha Govshteyn *(Co-Founder & Chief Security Officer)*
Greg Davis *(Exec VP-Worldwide Sls)*
Marty McGuffin *(Sr VP-Security & Compliance Svcs)*
P. Blake Allen *(Gen Counsel & Sr VP)*
Fritz Maxwell *(VP-Sls-Worldwide)*
Tom Veronie *(CIO)*
John Whiteside *(VP-Global Mktg Programs)*
Sheila Flaherty *(Chief Legal Officer)*
Matt Selheimer *(Chief Mktg Officer)*
Sydna Kelley *(Sr VP-Customer Success & Tech Ops)*
Christopher Rajiah *(Sr VP-Alliances & Partnerships-Worldwide)*
John Post *(CEO)*
Jon Sachs *(CFO)*
Prabuddha Biswas *(CTO)*

Subsidiary (Domestic):

Achilles Guard, Inc. (3)
4201 Spring Valley Rd Ste 1400, Dallas, TX 75244
Tel.: (214) 623-5600
Web Site: http://www.criticalwatch.com
Sales Range: $10-24.9 Million
Emp.: 25
Security Technology Services
N.A.I.C.S.: 541512

Eva Bunker *(Pres)*

Subsidiary (Domestic):

Beyond Security, Inc. (2)
2267 Lava Ridge Ct Ste 100, Roseville, CA 95661
Tel.: (703) 286-7725
Web Site: http://www.beyondsecurity.com
Rev.: $5,000,000
Emp.: 20
Cyber Security Consulting Services
N.A.I.C.S.: 561621
Aviram Jenik *(CEO)*
Noam Rathaus *(CTO)*
Zvi Magnes *(Dir-Sls-EMEA)*
Brian Pearce *(COO & CMO)*

Digital Defense, Inc. (2)
9000 Tesoro Dr Ste100, San Antonio, TX 78217
Tel.: (210) 822-2645
Web Site: http://www.ddifrontline.com
Sales Range: $1-9.9 Million
Emp.: 30
Security System Services
N.A.I.C.S.: 561621
Larry Hurtado *(Pres & CEO)*
Mark Bell *(Exec VP-Ops)*
Meg Grant *(Sr VP-Mktg)*
Gordon MacKay *(CTO & Exec VP)*
Neil Butchart *(Sr VP-Global Sls)*

GlobalSCAPE Inc. (2)
4500 Lockhill Selma Ste 150, San Antonio, TX 78249
Tel.: (210) 366-3993
Web Site: http://www.globalscape.com
Secure File Management Software Developer
N.A.I.C.S.: 513210
Michael P. Canavan *(Exec VP-Sls & Mktg)*
David Christopher Mello *(Exec VP-Technical Svcs)*
Karen J. Young *(CFO)*
Mark C. Hood *(COO)*
Leah Web *(Head-Admin Svcs)*
Roberto Garcia *(VP-Product Strategy & Engrg)*

GroundWork Open Source, Inc. (2)
23332 Mill Creek Dr Ste 155, Laguna Hills, CA 92653   **(100%)**
Tel.: (415) 992-4500
Web Site: http://www.gwos.com
Unified Monitoring of Hybrid Cloud, Container, Application, Server, Network & Storage Data
N.A.I.C.S.: 541512
Thomas Stocking *(VP-Product Strategy)*
Hans Kriel *(VP-Tech)*
Richard Campbell *(CEO)*
Michael Hale *(COO)*
Laura Hurd *(Dir-Corp Sls)*

Tripwire, Inc. (2)
308 SW 2nd Ave Ste 400, Portland, OR 97204
Tel.: (503) 276-7500
Web Site: http://www.tripwire.com
IT Security & Compliance Automation Software Solutions
N.A.I.C.S.: 513210
David Meltzer *(CTO)*
Chris Williams *(Chief Comml Officer)*
Maria Crawford *(CMO)*
Subhajit Bagchi *(Pres)*
Tim Erlin *(VP-Product Mgmt & Strategy)*
Alex Bagwell *(VP-Channels-Global)*
Neil Harvey *(VP-EMEA)*
Stacie Otto *(VP-Fin & Admin)*
Andrew Wagner *(VP-Engineering)*
Phil Labas *(VP)*
Staci Schwartz *(VP-Human Resources)*
Chris Kearney *(VP-Sales)*
Steve Cumings *(VP)*
Jeanmarie Martinko *(Dir)*
Andrew Wagner *(VP-Engineering)*
Phil Labas *(VP)*
Staci Schwartz *(VP-Human Resources)*
Chris Kearney *(VP-Sales)*
Steve Cumings *(VP)*
Jeanmarie Martinko *(Dir)*

Subsidiary (Non-US):

Tripwire Asia-Pacific (3)
50 Raffles Place 37 00 Singapore Land Tower, Singapore, 48623, Singapore
Tel.: (65) 31580229

Web Site: http://www.tripwire.com
IT Security & Compliance Automation Software Solutions
N.A.I.C.S.: 513210

Subsidiary (Non-US):

Tripwire Japan KK (4)
85 90 Level 3 Marunouchi Nijubashi Building 3-2-2 Marunouch, Chiyoda-ku, Tokyo, 100-0005, Japan
Tel.: (81) 368379615
Web Site: http://www.tripwire.com
IT Security & Compliance Automation Software Solutions
N.A.I.C.S.: 513210

Subsidiary (Non-US):

Tripwire EMEA (3)
1 Grenfell Road, Maidenhead, SL6 1HN, Berkshire, United Kingdom
Tel.: (44) 1628775850
Web Site: http://www.tripwire.com
IT Security & Compliance Automation Software Solutions
N.A.I.C.S.: 513210

Idera, Inc. (1)
Brookhollow Central III 2950 N Loop Fwy W Ste 700, Houston, TX 77092
Tel.: (713) 523-4433
Web Site: http://www.ideracorp.com
Application Software Development Services
N.A.I.C.S.: 541511
Randall Jacops *(CEO)*
Christopher Smith *(COO)*
Trey Chambers *(CFO)*
Heidi Farris *(VP/Gen Mgr-Database Tools Bus)*
Neil Garrett *(CMO)*
Tyler Parramore *(VP-Bus Dev & Mergers & Acquisition)*
Atanas Popov *(Gen Mgr)*
Wilson Warmack *(Gen Mgr)*

Subsidiary (Domestic):

Assembla Inc. (2)
122 E Houston St, San Antonio, TX 78205
Tel.: (800) 405-4408
Web Site: http://www.assembla.com
Software Development & Cyber Security
N.A.I.C.S.: 513210
Sergiy Golub *(VP-Engrg)*
Mitch Holt *(VP-Mktg)*
David Romoff *(Dir-Sls)*

Embarcadero Technologies, Inc. (2)
10801 N Mopac Expwy Bldg 1 Ste 100, Austin, TX 78759
Tel.: (512) 226-8080
Web Site: http://www.embarcadero.com
Strategic Data Management Tools Developer
N.A.I.C.S.: 541512
Atanas Popov *(Gen Mgr-Application Dev Tools Bus)*

Subsidiary (Non-US):

Embarcadero Technologies Europe Ltd. (3)
First Floor Unit 2 Easthamstead Road, Bracknell, RG12 1NF, Berks, United Kingdom
Tel.: (44) 1628684400
Web Site: http://www.embarcadero.com
Strategic Data Management Tools Developer
N.A.I.C.S.: 541512

Subsidiary (Domestic):

Preemptive Solutions, LLC (2)
767 Beta Dr Ste A, Cleveland, OH 44143
Tel.: (216) 732-5895
Web Site: http://www.preemptive.com
Sales Range: $1-9.9 Million
Emp.: 30
Prepackaged Software
N.A.I.C.S.: 513210
Gabriel Torok *(Founder & CEO)*
Sebastian Holst *(Chief Strategy Officer)*

Qubole Inc. (2)
469 El Camino Real Ste 205, Santa Clara, CA 94040
Tel.: (650) 644-5018
Web Site: http://www.qubole.com
Software Publisher

HGGC, LLC—(Continued)
N.A.I.C.S.: 513210
Ashish Thusoo (*Co-Founder & CEO*)
Joydeep Sen Sarma (*Co-Founder & Head-Qubole India*)
Shrikanth Shankar (*VP-Engrg*)
Gil Allouche (*VP-Mktg*)
Jonathan Trail (*VP-Customer Success*)
Andrew Daniels (*VP-Security, Compliance & Privacy*)
George Chow (*CTO*)
David Hsieh (*Sr VP-Mktg*)
Ken Tamura (*VP-Fin*)

Sencha, Inc. (2)
10801 N Mopac Expresswy Bldg 1 Ste 100, Austin, TX 78759
Tel.: (650) 299-9550
Web Site: http://www.sencha.com
Software Publisher
N.A.I.C.S.: 513210
Atanas Popov (*Gen Mgr*)

Innovative Interfaces Inc. (1)
1900 Powell St Ste 400, Emeryville, CA 94608
Tel.: (510) 655-6200
Web Site: http://www.iii.com
Sales Range: $75-99.9 Million
Software Developer
N.A.I.C.S.: 513210
Hilary Newman (*Sr VP-Library Success*)
Marina Keating (*Sr VP-Customer Experience*)
Leif Pedersen (*Exec VP-Product*)
James Tallman (*CEO*)
Aaron Terrell (*VP-Engrg & IT*)
Akin Adekeye (*Gen Counsel & VP-Partnerships & Bus Dev*)
Chris Fields (*CTO*)
Kathryn Harhish (*Sr VP-Product Strategy*)
Amy Hayes (*Sr VP-Mktg*)
Shaheen Javadizadeh (*Exec VP-Sls-Global*)
Roger Leitner (*COO*)
Joe McMorris (*CIO*)
Don Schad (*CFO*)

Subsidiary (Domestic):

VTLS, Inc. (2)
1701 Kraft Dr, Blacksburg, VA 24060
Tel.: (540) 557-1200
Web Site: http://www.vtls.com
Emp.: 100
Project Management & Digital Imaging Solutions
N.A.I.C.S.: 513210

Monotype Imaging Holdings, Inc. (1)
600 Unicorn Park Dr, Woburn, MA 01801
Tel.: (781) 970-6000
Web Site: http://www.monotype.com
Rev.: $246,737,000
Assets: $507,656,000
Liabilities: $177,950,000
Net Worth: $329,706,000
Earnings: $12,273,000
Emp.: 696
Fiscal Year-end: 12/31/2018
Text Imaging Solutions
N.A.I.C.S.: 541511
Janet M. Dunlap (*Chief Admin Officer, Gen Counsel, Sec & Exec VP*)
Steven R. Martin (*CTO & Exec VP*)
Scott E. Landers (*Principal Acctg Officer*)
Ben Semmes (*Chief Revenue Officer*)
Brett Zucker (*Chief Mktg Officer & Exec VP*)
Christopher Brooks (*Interim CFO, Interim Treas & Sr VP-Fin*)

Subsidiary (Domestic):

FontShop International, Inc. (2)
149 9th St Ste 402, San Francisco, CA 94103
Tel.: (415) 252-1003
Electronic Store Operator
N.A.I.C.S.: 449210

Subsidiary (Non-US):

Mark Boulton Design Limited (2)
Studio 2 The Coach House, Stanwell Road, Penarth, CF643EU, United Kingdom
Tel.: (44) 2920020959
Web Site:
　http://www.markboultondesign.com
Custom Computer Programming Services
N.A.I.C.S.: 541511

Emma Boulton (*Dir-Res*)
Nathan Ford (*Dir-Creative*)
Mark Boulton (*Founder*)

Monotype GmbH (2)
Werner-Reimers-Strasse 2-4, 61352, Bad Homburg, Germany
Tel.: (49) 6172 484 423
Web Site: http://www.monotype.com
Emp.: 45
Typeface & Fonts Design & Technology
N.A.I.C.S.: 541519

Monotype Hong Kong Limited (2)
7A Yardley Commercial Building, 3 Connaught Road West, Sheung Wan, China (Hong Kong)
Tel.: (852) 25756789
Web Site: http://www.monotype.com.hk
Sales Range: $25-49.9 Million
Emp.: 12
Font & Imaging Software
N.A.I.C.S.: 541519
Ricky Chun (*Gen Mgr*)

Subsidiary (Domestic):

Monotype ITC Inc. (2)
500 Unicorn Park Dr, Woburn, MA 01801 (100%)
Tel.: (781) 970-6020
Web Site: http://www.fonts.com
N.A.I.C.S.: 459410

Monotype Imaging, Inc. (2)
600 Unicorn Park Dr, Woburn, MA 01801
Tel.: (781) 970-6000
Web Site: http://www.monotypeimaging.com
Sales Range: $25-49.9 Million
Emp.: 120
Text Imaging Solutions For Consumer Electronics Devices
N.A.I.C.S.: 541511

Subsidiary (Non-US):

Monotype KK (2)
8th floor Hikari Building 1-43-7 Yoyogi, Shibuya-ku, Tokyo, 151-0053, Japan
Tel.: (81) 353040920
Sales Range: $25-49.9 Million
Emp.: 5
Font & Imaging Software Provider
N.A.I.C.S.: 541511

Monotype Limited (2)
Unit 2 Perrywood Business Park, Salfords, Redhill, RH1 5DZ, Surrey, United Kingdom
Tel.: (44) 1737765959
Web Site: http://www.monotype.com
Emp.: 20
Text Imaging Solutions
N.A.I.C.S.: 541511

Monotype Solutions India Private Limited (2)
Fourth Floor Tower B GYS Universal, Plot A-3 & 4 & 5 Sector 125, Noida, 201301, Uttar Pradesh, India
Tel.: (91) 120 4524974
Typeface & Fonts Design & Technology
N.A.I.C.S.: 541519

Subsidiary (Domestic):

MyFonts, Inc. (2)
500 Nickerson Rd Ste 100, Marlborough, MA 01752-4695
Tel.: (617) 497-6222
Web Site: http://new.myfonts.com
Sales Range: $100-124.9 Million
Emp.: 70
Online Font Retailer
N.A.I.C.S.: 323111

Nutraceutical International Corporation (1)
222 S Main St 16th Fl, Salt Lake City, UT 84101
Tel.: (435) 655-6000
Web Site: https://www.betterbeing.com
Dietary Supplements & Pharmaceutical Preparations Mfr
N.A.I.C.S.: 325411

Subsidiary (Domestic):

Au Naturel Inc. (2)
222 S. Main St 16th Fl, Salt Lake City, UT 84101
Tel.: (435) 655-6000

Pharmaceutical Preparation Mfr
N.A.I.C.S.: 325412

Honey Gardens, Inc. (2)
1777 Sun Peak Dr, Park City, UT 84098
Tel.: (435) 655-6000
Web Site: https://www.honeygardens.com
Food Products Mfr
N.A.I.C.S.: 311999

Monarch Nutraceuticals, Inc. (2)
933 Wall Ave, Ogden, UT 84404
Tel.: (801) 334-3911
Web Site:
　http://www.monarchnutraceuticals.com
Pharmaceuticals Product Mfr
N.A.I.C.S.: 325412

Nutraceutical Corporation (2)
222 S Main St 16th Fl, Salt Lake City, UT 84101
Tel.: (435) 655-6000
Web Site: https://www.nutraceutical.com
Dietary Supplements & Pharmaceutical Preparations Mfr
N.A.I.C.S.: 325412

Organix South, Inc. (2)
222 S. Main St, Salt Lake City, UT 84101
Tel.: (800) 538-5888
Organic Personal Care Products Mfr
N.A.I.C.S.: 325620

RPX Corporation (1)
1 Market Plz Steuart Tower Ste 1100, San Francisco, CA 94105
Web Site: http://www.rpxcorp.com
Patent Risk Solutions & Advisory Services
N.A.I.C.S.: 541618
Lily Loh (*VP-Mktg*)
Mallun Yen (*Exec VP*)
Shelby W. Bonnie (*Chm*)
Daniel P. McCurdy (*CEO*)
David Anderson (*CFO*)
Robert Kingsley (*Sr VP-Insurance Ops*)
Eric Olsen (*Sr VP-Acq*)
Andy Block (*Sr VP*)
Neal Rubin (*Sr VP-Ops*)
Emily Gavin (*Gen Counsel & Sr VP*)
Max Straube (*Sr VP & Head-Client Svcs*)
Kathy Humphreys (*Sr VP-HR*)
Geoffrey T. Barker (*Co-Founder*)

Subsidiary (Domestic):

Inventus, LLC (2)
500 W Madison Ave Ste 1210, Chicago, IL 60661
Tel.: (312) 546-6580
Web Site: http://www.inventus.com
Litigation Support Services
N.A.I.C.S.: 561499
Melanie White (*Sr VP-Discovery Solutions*)
Noel Kilby (*CTO*)
Paul Mankoo (*Pres & CEO*)

Subsidiary (Non-US):

RPX Asia Corporation (2)
Marunouchi Building Suite 906, 2-4-1 Marunouchi Chiyoda-ku, Tokyo, 100-6309, Japan
Tel.: (81) 352206633
Web Site: http://www.rpxcorp.com
Emp.: 4
Patent Risk Solutions & Advisory Services
N.A.I.C.S.: 541618
Kyoichi Ideno (*Pres*)

Subsidiary (Domestic):

RPX Freedom Corporation (2)
1 Market Plz Ste Uartt, San Francisco, CA 94105-1101
Tel.: (415) 852-3121
Information Services
N.A.I.C.S.: 519290

Waverly Advisors, LLC (1)
600 University Park Pl Ste 501, Birmingham, AL 35209
Tel.: (205) 871-3334
Web Site: https://waverly-advisors.com
Emp.: 100
Investment Adviser; Investment Management & Wealth Planning
N.A.I.C.S.: 523940
Joshua L. Reidinger (*CEO & Partner*)

Subsidiary (Domestic):

Omni Wealth Advisors, LLC. (2)

110 S Hoover Blvd, Tampa, FL 33609
Tel.: (813) 281-0028
Web Site: http://www.omniadvisors.com
Rev.: $2,905,000
Emp.: 7
Portfolio Management
N.A.I.C.S.: 523940
Brian Hershberger (*Pres*)

Rainsberger Wealth Advisors, Inc. (2)
980 Pico Pt, Colorado Springs, CO 80905
Tel.: (719) 328-1944
Web Site: http://www.rwapartners.com
Miscellaneous Financial Investment Activities
N.A.I.C.S.: 523999
Ellis Rainsberger (*Pres*)

iQor, Inc. (1)
335 Madison Ave 27th Fl, New York, NY 10017
Tel.: (973) 630-2515
Web Site: http://www.iqor.com
Sales Range: $300-349.9 Million
Emp.: 11,000
Call Center & Collection Services
N.A.I.C.S.: 561440
Christopher Dorval (*CMO*)
Barry Grant (*CTO*)
Dan Olp (*Chief Security Officer & VP-Infrastructure*)
Andrew Wood (*VP-Sls-Canada*)
Chris Crowley (*Pres & CEO*)
Mason Argiropoulos (*Chief HR Officer*)
Kip Ferris (*Exec VP-Strategic Accts*)
David Pester (*Gen Counsel*)
Peter Sykora (*COO-Electronics & Infrastructure*)
Deepak Batheja (*Grp CIO & Chief Digital Officer*)
James McClenahan (*Chief Sls Officer*)
John Jacobi (*CFO*)
Robert Constantine (*Sr VP-Mktg & Comm*)
Fleurette Navarro (*Chief People Officer*)
Christopher Carrington (*Chm*)

HGH HARDWARE SUPPLY INC.
3912 2nd Ave S, Birmingham, AL 35222
Tel.: (205) 595-4655
Web Site:
　http://www.hghhardware.com
Sales Range: $10-24.9 Million
Emp.: 100
Builders' Hardware
N.A.I.C.S.: 423710
Raymond Holcombe (*Pres*)
Mike Holt (*Reg Mgr-Sls*)
Janice Davis (*Asst Mgr-Warehouse*)
Edwin R. Holcombe Sr. (*Founder*)

HGH INFRARED SYSTEMS INC.
1 Broadway 11th Fl, Cambridge, MA 02142-1100
Tel.: (617) 401-2196
Web Site: http://www.hgh-infrared.com
Semiconductor & Related Device Mfr
N.A.I.C.S.: 334413

Subsidiaries:

Electro-Optical Industries, LLC (1)
320 Storke Rd Ste 100, Santa Barbara, CA 93117
Tel.: (805) 964-6701
Web Site: http://www.electro-optical.com
Electro-Optical Test & Calibration Device Mfr
N.A.I.C.S.: 334513
Stephen Scopatz (*Gen Mgr*)

HGREG.COM
8505 NW 12th St, Doral, FL 33126
Tel.: (833) 253-6807
Web Site: http://www.hgreg.com
Car Dealer
N.A.I.C.S.: 441110
Chase Sattler (*VP*)
Gabriella B. (*Controller*)
John Hairabedian (*Pres*)

Subsidiaries:

AutoNation USA of Perrine, Inc. (1)
17305 S Dixie Hwy Palmetto Bay, Kendall, FL 33157
Tel.: (305) 707-0144
Web Site:
http://www.autonationnissankendall.com
Sales Range: $25-49.9 Million
Emp.: 45
Car & Commercial Vehicle Dealer
N.A.I.C.S.: 441227

HGreg Nissan Buena Park (1)
6501 Auto Ctr Dr, Buena Park, CA 90621-2901
Tel.: (714) 690-3100
Web Site: http://www.buenaparknissan.com
New Car Dealers
N.A.I.C.S.: 441110
Greg Brown (Owner)

Metro Infiniti, Inc. (1)
821 E Central Ave, Monrovia, CA 91016-4277
Tel.: (626) 303-1000
Web Site: http://www.metroinfiniti.com
New Car Dealers
N.A.I.C.S.: 441110
Harris Ruderman (Mgr)

HH FLUORESCENT PARTS INCORPORATED

104 Beecher Ave, Cheltenham, PA 19012
Tel.: (215) 379-2750
Web Site:
https://www.hhfluorescentparts.net
Year Founded: 1950
Sales Range: $10-24.9 Million
Emp.: 75
Electric Lamps & Parts for Generalized Applications Mfr
N.A.I.C.S.: 335139
Jerry Anderson (Gen Mgr)
Robert J. Hillen Jr. (VP)

HH HOLDINGS INC.

5901 Peachtree-Dunwoody Ste B450, Atlanta, GA 30328
Tel.: (770) 325-1300
Web Site:
https://www.huddlehouse.com
Sales Range: $250-299.9 Million
Emp.: 2,600
Restaurant Franchise
N.A.I.C.S.: 722511
Melissa Rothring (Gen Counsel)

HHHUNT PROPERTY MANAGEMENT, INC.

800 Hethwood Blvd, Blacksburg, VA 24060
Tel.: (540) 552-3515
Web Site: https://www.hhhunt.com
Year Founded: 1966
Sales Range: $10-24.9 Million
Emp.: 1,000
Residential Building Leasing Services
N.A.I.C.S.: 531110
Janet Riddlebarger (VP-Property Mgmt)
Tom Hudson (Mgr-Land Acq)
Robert Chappelle (VP-Dev & Construction)
Steve Brant (Treas & VP-Fin)
Cheryl Fulghum (Controller)
Katelyn Willis (Controller-HHHunt Homes)
Ashley Payne (Asst Controller)
Brian Myers (VP-Fin-Income Properties)
Craig Koller (VP-Fin-Income Properties)

HHJ HOLDINGS LIMITED

830 Kirts Blvd Ste 100, Troy, MI 48084
Tel.: (248) 244-3300

Web Site: http://www.ajaxpaving.com
Rev.: $42,400,000
Emp.: 10
Holding Company: Highway & Street Paving Contractor
N.A.I.C.S.: 551112
James Jacob (CEO)
James Friel (CFO)

Subsidiaries:

Ajax Paving Industries Inc. (1)
1 Ajax Dr, North Venice, FL 34275
Tel.: (941) 486-3600
Web Site: http://www.ajaxpaving.com
Surfacing & Paving
N.A.I.C.S.: 237310
Mike Horan (Pres)
Mark Minich (Exec VP)

HHMI CORP.

109 Holomua St, Hilo, HI 96720
Tel.: (808) 961-3415 HI
Year Founded: 1996
Emp.: 10
Consulting Electrical Engineering Services
N.A.I.C.S.: 541330
Hilton H. Unemori (Pres)

HHP INC.

14 Buxton Industrial Dr, Henniker, NH 03242
Tel.: (603) 428-3298
Web Site: https://www.hhp-inc.com
Year Founded: 1966
Rev.: $11,000,000
Emp.: 47
Lumber & Lumber Products Mfr & Distr
N.A.I.C.S.: 423310
Ross D'Elia (Pres)
Richard Carrier (Owner)

HI DEVELOPMENT CORPORATION

111 W Fortune St, Tampa, FL 33602-3206
Tel.: (813) 229-6686 FL
Web Site:
https://www.hidevelopment.com
Year Founded: 1959
Sales Range: $25-49.9 Million
Emp.: 350
Hotels & Motel Services
N.A.I.C.S.: 721110
Andre Callen (Pres)
David Clement (VP)

HI NABOR SUPERMARKET INC.

7201 Winbourne Ave, Baton Rouge, LA 70805-5536
Tel.: (225) 357-1448 LA
Web Site: https://www.hinabor.com
Year Founded: 1963
Sales Range: $10-24.9 Million
Emp.: 200
Retailer of Groceries
N.A.I.C.S.: 445110
Samuel J. Crifasi (Pres)
James Crifasi (VP)
Jan Crifasi (Treas)

HI TECH HONEYCOMB INC.

9355 Ruffin Ct, San Diego, CA 92123
Tel.: (858) 974-1600
Web Site:
http://www.hthoneycomb.com
Year Founded: 1989
Sales Range: $10-24.9 Million
Emp.: 93
Gas Turbine Engine Seal Mfr
N.A.I.C.S.: 332119
Lilia Casillas (Mgr-Customer Svc)
John Costa (Pres)
Graham Ball (VP-Mktg)

HI TECMETAL GROUP, INC.

1101 E 55th St, Cleveland, OH 44103-1046
Tel.: (216) 881-8100 OH
Web Site: http://www.htg.cc
Year Founded: 1943
Sales Range: $10-24.9 Million
Emp.: 95
Metal Heat Treating
N.A.I.C.S.: 332811
Terence C. Profughi (CEO)
Louise Bowen (Mgr-Acctg)
Greg Hercik (VP-Engrg)

Subsidiaries:

Thermal Treatment Center Inc. (1)
28910 Lakeland Blvd, Wickliffe, OH 44092-2321 (100%)
Tel.: (440) 943-4555
Web Site: http://www.htg.com
Sales Range: $10-24.9 Million
Emp.: 15
Metal Heat Treating Product Mfr
N.A.I.C.S.: 332811
Tom Jones (Gen Mgr)

HI TEMP INSULATION INC.

4700 Calle Alto, Camarillo, CA 93012-8489
Tel.: (805) 484-2774
Web Site: https://www.hi-tempinsulation.com
Year Founded: 1974
Sales Range: $25-49.9 Million
Emp.: 35
Provider of Space & Aircraft Insulation Products
N.A.I.C.S.: 327993
Sieg Borck (Founder & Pres)

Subsidiaries:

Sheets Manufacturing Co. Inc. (1)
4680 Calle Carga, Camarillo, CA 93012-8559
Tel.: (805) 383-6684
Web Site: http://www.sheetsmfg.com
Sales Range: $10-24.9 Million
Emp.: 50
Mfr of Aerospace Parts
N.A.I.C.S.: 332119
David Lind (Gen Mgr)

HI-BOY GROUP INC.

816 Hwy 41 S, Forsyth, GA 31029
Tel.: (478) 994-1324
Web Site: http://www.hi-boy-group-inck.fedvendor.com
Sales Range: $25-49.9 Million
Emp.: 125
Trucking Service
N.A.I.C.S.: 484121
Henry Hicks (Pres)
Clay Grant (Dir-Safety)

Subsidiaries:

American International Movers (1)
816 Hwy 41 S, Forsyth, GA 31029
Tel.: (478) 994-1324
Web Site: http://www.aimovers.com
Rev.: $4,774,483
Emp.: 27
Household Goods Transport
N.A.I.C.S.: 484210
Henry J. Hicks II (Pres)

Covenant Storage Inc. (1)
816 Hwy 41 S, Forsyth, GA 31029
Tel.: (478) 994-1324
Web Site: http://www.aimovers.com
Sales Range: Less than $1 Million
Emp.: 20
Moving Services
N.A.I.C.S.: 484210
Henry Hicks (Pres)

Georgia Perfect Packers (1)
816 Hwy 41 S, Forsyth, GA 31029
Tel.: (478) 994-1324
Rev.: $710,538
Emp.: 5
Packing Goods For Shipping
N.A.I.C.S.: 488991

L & L Van Lines Inc. (1)
816 Hwy 41 S, Forsyth, GA 31029
Tel.: (478) 994-1324
Web Site: http://www.aimovers.com
Rev.: $250,000
Emp.: 20
Household Goods Transport
N.A.I.C.S.: 484210
Henry J. Hicks II (Pres)

Macon Trading Post Inc. (1)
816 Hwy 41 S, Forsyth, GA 31029
Tel.: (478) 994-1324
Web Site: http://www.ourbank.com
Sales Range: $1-9.9 Million
Emp.: 115
Trucking Except Local
N.A.I.C.S.: 484121
Brannon Hicks (Pres)

Move-Pro USA Inc. (1)
816 Hwy 41 S, Forsyth, GA 31029
Tel.: (478) 994-1324
Web Site: http://www.aimovers.com
Rev.: $400,775
Emp.: 5
Moving Services
N.A.I.C.S.: 484210
Henry J. Hicks II (Pres)

TP of Macon, Inc. (1)
816 Hwy 41 S, Forsyth, GA 31029
Tel.: (478) 994-1324
Rev.: $750,475
Emp.: 20
Trucking Except Local
N.A.I.C.S.: 484121

HI-COUNTRY CHEVROLET INC.

404 W Chaco St, Aztec, NM 87410
Tel.: (505) 390-2052 NM
Web Site:
https://www.hicountrychevrolet.com
Year Founded: 1964
Sales Range: $25-49.9 Million
Emp.: 50
Sales of New & Used Automobiles
N.A.I.C.S.: 441110
Jeff Thomas (Pres)

HI-HEALTH SUPERMART CORPORATION

7428 E Karen Dr, Scottsdale, AZ 85260-2443
Tel.: (480) 951-9000 AZ
Web Site: http://www.hihealth.com
Year Founded: 1972
Sales Range: $50-74.9 Million
Emp.: 300
Food Services
N.A.I.C.S.: 456191
Mitchell A. Chalpin (Pres)
Vicki Crum (Mgr-Customer Svc)

Subsidiaries:

Hi-Health Supermart (1)
7428 E Karen Dr, Scottsdale, AZ 85260-2443
Tel.: (480) 951-9000
Sales Range: $25-49.9 Million
Emp.: 50
Provider of Food Services
N.A.I.C.S.: 456191
Mitch Chalpin (Pres)

HI-LINE COOPERATIVE INC.

203 S Perkins Ave, Elsie, NE 69134
Tel.: (308) 352-2800
Web Site: https://www.hilinecoop.com
Sales Range: $10-24.9 Million
Emp.: 49
Gasoline
N.A.I.C.S.: 424720
Roy Evans (Pres & Gen Mgr)
David Lampkee (Vice Chm)

HI-LINE MOVING SERVICES INC.

4500 N Star Blvd, Great Falls, MT 59405
Tel.: (406) 455-8610

Hi-Line Moving Services Inc.—(Continued)
Web Site: https://www.hi-line.org
Sales Range: $10-24.9 Million
Emp.: 35
Provider of Trucking Services
N.A.I.C.S.: 484210
Paul Lindstrom (Pres)
Art Groux (VP)
Greg Lindstrom (VP)
Sharon Lindstrom (Treas & Sec)

HI-LO INDUSTRIES INC.
908 West Chestnut, Chanute, KS
66720
Tel.: (620) 431-8200
Web Site:
  http://www.bridgewoodcabinets.com
Year Founded: 1976
Sales Range: $10-24.9 Million
Emp.: 250
Distr of Wood Household Cabinetry &
Tables
N.A.I.C.S.: 337122
James M. Caldwell (Pres)
Robin Bearrick (Mgr-Production)
Karen Clounch (Dir-HR)
Steve Ballard (Mgr-Sls & Mktg)

**HI-PLAINS COOPERATIVE AS-
SOCIATION**
405 E 4th St, Colby, KS 67701
Tel.: (785) 462-3351
Web Site: http://www.hi-
  plainscoop.com
Sales Range: $25-49.9 Million
Emp.: 30
Grain Elevators
N.A.I.C.S.: 424510
John Strecker (Pres)

HI-SEAS OF DULAC INC.
6570 Grand Caillou Rd, Dulac, LA
70353
Tel.: (985) 563-7662
Sales Range: $10-24.9 Million
Emp.: 8
Seafoods
N.A.I.C.S.: 424460
Raymond Authement (Pres)

**HI-TECH COMPONENT DIS-
TRIBUTORS**
9120 Woodman Ave, Arleta, CA
91331
Tel.: (818) 672-8855
Web Site: http://www.hitechcafe.com
Sales Range: $10-24.9 Million
Emp.: 23
Internet Sales of Computers & Acces-
sories
N.A.I.C.S.: 423430
Steve Zip (VP-Sls & Mktg)

**HI-TECH CONSTRUCTION
COMPANY**
2083 Terry Rd, South Charleston, WV
25309
Tel.: (304) 746-0050
Web Site:
  http://www.hitechconstruction.com
Sales Range: $10-24.9 Million
Emp.: 40
Land Reclamation
N.A.I.C.S.: 236210
Carl D. Runyon (Pres)
Kim Jones (Controller)
Mark Moss (VP-Ops)

HI-TECH ELECTRIC INC.
11116 W Little York Bldg 8, Houston,
TX 77041
Tel.: (214) 951-0001
Web Site:
  https://www.hitechelectric.com
Year Founded: 1985

Sales Range: $25-49.9 Million
Emp.: 220
Providers of Electrical Services
N.A.I.C.S.: 238210
Chase Canfield (Chm & Pres)
Ken Sauer (VP & Mgr-Div)
Jose Valle (Project Mgr)

**HI-TECH ELECTRONIC MANU-
FACTURING, INC.**
7420 Carroll Rd, San Diego, CA
92121
Tel.: (858) 657-0908
Web Site: http://www.hitem.com
Sales Range: $50-74.9 Million
Emp.: 80
Bare Printed Circuit Board Mfr
N.A.I.C.S.: 334412
Vinh Lam (Pres)
Thai Nguyen (CEO)

HI-TECH FABRICATION INC.
8900 Midway W Rd, Raleigh, NC
27617
Tel.: (919) 781-2552
Web Site: http://www.htfi.com
Sales Range: $75-99.9 Million
Emp.: 75
Stamping Metal For The Trade
N.A.I.C.S.: 332119
Joseph W. Barbee (Pres & CEO)
A. Tyler Toney (COO & VP-Ops)
Herbert Williams (Dir-Info Sys)
Tom Talley (Engr-Quality)
Sherrill McNair (Supvr-Facilities)
Corey Bowers (Supvr-Shipping)
Kevin Sook (CFO & VP-Fin)
William Kaiser (Mgr-Quality)

HI-TECH HEALTHCARE
1805 Shackleford Ct Ste 100, Nor-
cross, GA 30093
Tel.: (770) 449-6785
Web Site:
  http://www.hitechcares.com
Sales Range: $10-24.9 Million
Emp.: 108
Miscellaneous Product Whslr
N.A.I.C.S.: 456120

HI-TECH HOME
2565 Alluvial Ave Ste 122, Clovis, CA
93611
Tel.: (559) 521-1400
Web Site:
  https://www.hitechhome.net
Year Founded: 2003
Sales Range: $1-9.9 Million
Emp.: 12
Electronic System Distr
N.A.I.C.S.: 423690
Jay Cobb (Founder & Pres)

**HI-TECH MOLD & ENGINEER-
ING**
2775 Commerce Dr, Rochester Hills,
MI 48309
Tel.: (248) 852-6600
Web Site:
  https://www.hitechmold.com
Year Founded: 1982
Sales Range: $50-74.9 Million
Emp.: 200
Mfr of Molds for Foundry & Plastics
Working Machinery
N.A.I.C.S.: 333511
Shawn Karn (CFO & Exec VP)
Robert Schulte (Pres & CEO)
Michael Allen (Mgr-Engrg)
Bradley Lawrence (Mgr-
Environmental, Health & Safety)
Jeff Robinson (Mgr-Pur)
Tommie Hyder (Supvr-Night Shift)
Kevin Taverner (VP-Ops)
Paul Glowicki (Dir-Engrg)

Tom Liberati (Dir-Sls)
Don Finch (Engr-Maintenance)
Mike Suits (Gen Mgr)

HI-VAC CORPORATION
117 Industry Rd, Marietta, OH 45750-
9355
Tel.: (740) 374-2306
Web Site: https://www.hi-vac.com
Year Founded: 1969
Sales Range: $75-99.9 Million
Emp.: 100
Industrial Vacuum Cleaners Mfr
N.A.I.C.S.: 333310
Craig Primiani (VP-Sls & Mktg)
Dave Oman (Regional Mgr-
Contractor Sls)
Shawn Doolittle (Reg Mgr-Sls)

Subsidiaries:
Beijing Hi-Vac Environmental Protec-
tion Technology Co., Ltd.　　(1)
19 Gu Cheng Xi Jie, Shijingshan, Beijing,
100043, China
Tel.: (86) 68812390
Web Site: http://www.hi-vac.com.cn
Industrial Vacuum Cleaners
N.A.I.C.S.: 333310

HIADVANCE INC.
2880 Zanker Rd Ste 203, San Jose,
CA 95134
Tel.: (408) 432-7254
Web Site: http://www.hiadvance.com
Holding Company; Testing Laborato-
ries Operator
N.A.I.C.S.: 551112

Subsidiaries:
HiAdvance (Korea) Co., Ltd.　　(1)
402 Eagle Town 278-20 Seong-dong 2-Ga
Sungdong-gu, Seongdong-gu, Seoul, Korea
(South)
Tel.: (82) 77 872 4812
Testing Laboratory
N.A.I.C.S.: 541380
Meehee Suk (Mgr)

HiAdvance Philippines Inc.　　(1)
3rd Floor Maga Center San Antonio Street,
Paseo de Magallanes, 1232, Makati, Metro
Manila, Philippines
Tel.: (63) 28548365
Web Site: http://www.hiadvance.com
Testing Laboratory
N.A.I.C.S.: 541380
Annabelle Bangoy (Mgr-Bus Dev)

HIALEAH INCORPORATED
2200 E 4th Ave, Hialeah, FL 33010
Tel.: (305) 885-8000
Web Site:
  http://www.hialeahparkracing.com
Sales Range: $10-24.9 Million
Emp.: 71
Race Track & Casino Operations
N.A.I.C.S.: 711212
John J. Brunetti (Owner & Pres)

HIAS INC.
1300 Spring St Ste 500, Silver
Spring, MD 20910
Tel.: (301) 844-7300
Web Site: http://www.hias.org
Year Founded: 1954
Rev.: $50,167,033
Assets: $70,255,224
Liabilities: $21,085,050
Net Worth: $49,170,174
Earnings: ($664,916)
Emp.: 80
Fiscal Year-end: 12/31/18
Immigration Services
N.A.I.C.S.: 624190
Mark Hetfield (Pres & CEO)
Jeffrey Blattner (Vice Chm)
Robert D. Aronson (Chm)

HIATUS SPA & RETREAT

5560 W Lovers Ln Ste 250, Dallas,
TX 75209
Tel.: (214) 352-4111
Web Site: https://www.hiatusspa.com
Year Founded: 2006
Sales Range: $1-9.9 Million
Emp.: 64
Day Spa & Retreat Services
N.A.I.C.S.: 721199
Sheila Garrison (Mng Partner)
Kristin Peabody (Mng Partner)

**HIAWATHA COMMUNITY HOS-
PITAL**
300 Utah St, Hiawatha, KS 66434
Tel.: (785) 742-2131
Web Site: https://www.hch-ks.org
Year Founded: 1945
Sales Range: $25-49.9 Million
Emp.: 293
Health Care Srvices
N.A.I.C.S.: 622110
Greg Rodvelt (Pres)

HIAWATHA NATIONAL BANK
N1555 770th St, Hager City, WI
54014
Tel.: (715) 792-2101
Web Site: https://www.hnbank.com
Year Founded: 1917
Retail & Commercial Banking
N.A.I.C.S.: 522110
James W. Meisser (Pres & CEO)
Cyndy Tuttle (Sr Mng Dir)
Amy Roxas (Sr Mng Dir)
Elijah Wayne (Assoc Mng Dir)

HIAWATHA, INC.
681 E Johns Prairie Rd, Shelton, WA
98584
Tel.: (360) 426-4562
Web Site:
  https://www.hiawathacorp.com
Sales Range: $10-24.9 Million
Emp.: 900
Evergreen Shippers & Supplies Whslr
N.A.I.C.S.: 424930
Richard Pasalich (Pres)

**HIBBING CHRYSLER CENTER,
LLC.**
1321 E 39th St, Hibbing, MN 55746-
3674
Tel.: (218) 263-7700
Web Site:
  http://www.hibbingchryslercenter.net
Sales Range: $10-24.9 Million
Emp.: 43
Car Whslr
N.A.I.C.S.: 441110
David Clusiau (Owner)
Peter Jones (Owner)

**HIBBS-HALLMARK & COM-
PANY**
501 Shelley Dr, Tyler, TX 75701
Tel.: (903) 561-8484
Web Site:
  https://www.hibbshallmark.com
Sales Range: $1-9.9 Million
Emp.: 150
Provider of Insurance Services
N.A.I.C.S.: 524210
Robert P. Monaghan (Pres)
Brenda Thomas (Sr VP)
Gerald Barker (VP)
Lori Nelson (VP)
Andrew Bertrand (Acct Exec)
Brandy Muller (Mgr-Personal Lines)
Brenda Massey (Acct Exec)
D'Ann Miller (Acct Exec)
Michele Hall (Sr VP & Mgr-Comml
Lines Claims)
Pam Golsan (Sr VP & Mgr-Mktg)
Ariella Payne (Coord-Sls & Mktg)

HIBCO PLASTICS INCORPO-RATED

1820 US Hwy 601 S, Yadkinville, NC 27055
Tel.: (336) 463-2391
Web Site: https://www.hibco.com
Sales Range: $10-24.9 Million
Emp.: 40
Insulation Or Cushioning Material, Foamed Plastics
N.A.I.C.S.: 326150
Mark Pavlansky *(Pres)*
Dan Pavlansky *(Chm)*
Michael Russell *(Mgr-Pur)*
John Waddell *(Mgr-Production)*
Landon Hardy *(Mgr-HR & Quality)*

HICAPS, INC.

600 N Regional Rd, Greensboro, NC 27409
Tel.: (336) 665-1234
Web Site: https://www.hicaps.com
Year Founded: 1984
Sales Range: $1-9.9 Million
Emp.: 39
Construction Management, Building Diagnostics & Public Safety Telecommunications Services
N.A.I.C.S.: 541611

HICKEL INVESTMENT COMPANY INC.

939 W 5th Ave, Anchorage, AK 99501-2032
Tel.: (907) 276-6000   AK
Web Site:
   http://www.captioncrook.com
Year Founded: 1948
Sales Range: $25-49.9 Million
Emp.: 450
Owner of Hotels & Motels
N.A.I.C.S.: 721110
Bruce Eliason *(CFO, Treas & Sec)*
Nolan Estrada *(Mgr-Hickel Maintenance)*

HICKEY & ASSOCIATES, LLC.

333 Washington Ave N Ste 300, Minneapolis, MN 55401
Web Site:
   http://www.hickeyandassociates.com
Year Founded: 1986
Sales Range: $1-9.9 Million
Emp.: 50
Management Consulting Services
N.A.I.C.S.: 541611
Jason Hickey *(Pres)*

HICKINGBOTHAM INVESTMENTS, INC.

11300 N Rodney Parham Rd, Little Rock, AR 72212
Tel.: (501) 223-1000
Rev.: $1,400,000
Emp.: 15
Industrial Building Construction
N.A.I.C.S.: 236210
Gene Whisenhunt *(CFO)*
Jackie Chandler *(VP-Tax)*

Subsidiaries:

Old Fort Harley Davidson   (1)
6304 S 36th St, Fort Smith, AR 72908
Tel.: (479) 648-1666
Web Site:
   http://www.oldfortharleydavidson.com
Sales Range: $1-9.9 Million
Emp.: 35
Motorcycle Dealers
N.A.I.C.S.: 441227
Dan Fielder *(Mgr-Riding Specialist)*
Debbie Ortiz *(Owner)*
Michael Crouch *(Owner)*
Mike Freeland *(Mgr-Svc)*
Ryan Bailey *(Owner)*
Zack Dodd *(Mgr-Fin)*

HICKMAN INVESTMENTS INC.

1200 W Risinger Rd, Fort Worth, TX 76134
Tel.: (817) 293-5313
Sales Range: $10-24.9 Million
Emp.: 200
Automotive Supplies & Parts
N.A.I.C.S.: 423120
John Bills *(CFO)*

Subsidiaries:

SCS Frigette   (1)
1200 West Risinger Rd, Fort Worth, TX 76134
Tel.: (817) 293-5313
Web Site: http://www.scsfrigette.com
Acceleration Equipment, Motor Vehicle
N.A.I.C.S.: 336390

Victory Climate Systems   (1)
8912 S Freeway Ste C, Fort Worth, TX 76140
Tel.: (817) 293-3331
Web Site: http://www.scsfrigette.com
Sales Range: $10-24.9 Million
Emp.: 5
Air Conditioning & Refrigeration Controls
N.A.I.C.S.: 333415
Nita Pound *(Mgr-HR)*

HICKMAN, WILLIAMS & COMPANY

Chiquita Ctr 250 E 5th St Ste 300, Cincinnati, OH 45202
Tel.: (513) 621-1946   DE
Web Site: http://www.hicwilco.com
Year Founded: 1890
Sales Range: $75-99.9 Million
Emp.: 98
Brokers of Coal, Coke & Other Products Used by the Foundry Industry; Coke Processing Plants
N.A.I.C.S.: 423510
David H. Gelwicks *(Pres)*
Terry L. Meadors *(CFO)*
Sandra C. Hartman *(Mgr-Computer Ops)*

Subsidiaries:

Hickman, Williams & Company   (1)
3101 Alton Park Blvd, Chattanooga, TN 37410-1014   (100%)
Tel.: (423) 756-7188
Web Site: http://www.hicwilco.com
Sales Range: $10-24.9 Million
Emp.: 4
Supplier of Foundry Products
N.A.I.C.S.: 424690

Hickman, Williams & Company   (1)
2015 Spring Road Ste715, Oak Brook, IL 60523   (100%)
Tel.: (773) 468-9700
Web Site: http://www.hicwilco.com
Sales Range: $10-24.9 Million
Emp.: 5
Wholesale Distribution of Coal, Coke & Other Minerals & Ores
N.A.I.C.S.: 423510

Hickman, Williams Canada, Inc.   (1)
886 Langs Dr, Cambridge, N3H 5P6, ON, Canada   (100%)
Tel.: (519) 650-1910
Web Site: http://www.hicwill.co.com
Sales Range: $10-24.9 Million
Emp.: 4
Wholesale Distribution of Coal, Coke & Other Minerals & Ores
N.A.I.C.S.: 423520

HICKORY BRANDS, INC.

429 27th St NW, Hickory, NC 28601
Tel.: (800) 438-5777
Web Site:
   http://www.hickorybrands.com
Year Founded: 1923
Fabrics Mfr
N.A.I.C.S.: 314994
Richard Schaftlein *(VP)*

HICKORY CONSTRUCTION COMPANY

1728 9th Ave NW, Hickory, NC 28601-3367
Tel.: (828) 322-9234   NC
Web Site: http://www.hickory-construction.com
Year Founded: 1941
Sales Range: $100-124.9 Million
Emp.: 150
Provider of Contracting & Construction Services
N.A.I.C.S.: 236220
Mark Baucom *(Pres & CEO)*
Charles W. Moss Sr. *(Chm)*
Charles Moss Jr. *(VP)*

HICKORY CREEK NURSERY INC.

20601 S La Grange Rd, Frankfort, IL 60423
Tel.: (815) 469-2008
Web Site:
   http://www.alsipnursery.com
Year Founded: 1969
Sales Range: $25-49.9 Million
Emp.: 210
Owner & Operator of Retail Nurseries & Garden Stores
N.A.I.C.S.: 444240
Chris Sheppard *(Pres)*

HICKORY FOODS, INC.

4339 Roosevelt Blvd, Jacksonville, FL 32210
Tel.: (904) 482-1900
Web Site:
   http://www.bubbafoods.com
Meat Processed from Carcasses
N.A.I.C.S.: 311612
William Morris *(Pres)*
David West *(Engr-Maintenance)*
Elizabeth Cordell *(Mgr-Mktg)*
Travis Crouse *(VP-Ops)*

Subsidiaries:

Peterbrooke Chocolatier, Inc.   (1)
8823 San Jose Blvd, Jacksonville, FL 32217
Tel.: (904) 652-1162
Web Site: http://www.peterbrooke.com
Confectionary & Nut Stores
N.A.I.C.S.: 445292

HICKORY HERITAGE OF FALLING CREEK, INC.

3211b Falling Creek Rd, Hickory, NC 28601
Tel.: (828) 256-3068
Sales Range: $10-24.9 Million
Emp.: 22
Metal Window & Door Mfr
N.A.I.C.S.: 332321
John C. Debonis *(Pres & CEO)*

HICKORY POINT BANK & TRUST FSB

225 N Water St, Decatur, IL 62523
Tel.: (217) 875-3131
Web Site:
   http://www.hickorypointbank.com
Year Founded: 1979
Sales Range: $50-74.9 Million
Emp.: 170
Banking Services
N.A.I.C.S.: 522110
Christie Weemer *(Branch Mgr)*
Jenny Krell *(Asst VP-Retail Banking)*
Lora Sloan *(Branch Mgr)*
Tamela Kramer *(VP & Branch Mgr)*
Lori Shields *(Officer-Loan & Branch Mgr)*
Randy Weatherly *(Officer-Loan & Branch Mgr)*
Morgan Nessler *(VP-Retail)*
Dan Marker *(Officer-Loan)*

Mitch Wilson *(Officer-Loan)*
Nick Lamb *(Officer-Loan)*
Sherry Cool *(Officer-Loan)*
James W. Schroeder *(Sr VP)*
Bruce M. Huber *(Sr VP)*
Teresa McCool *(Officer-Trust)*
Dave Brandon *(Officer-Trust)*

HICKORY SPRINGS MANUFACTURING COMPANY

235 2nd Ave NW, Hickory, NC 28603
Tel.: (828) 328-2201   NC
Web Site:
   https://www.hickorysprings.com
Year Founded: 1944
Sales Range: $75-99.9 Million
Emp.: 1,000
Furniture & Bedding Component Mfr
N.A.I.C.S.: 326299
Dwayne Welch *(Chief Mktg & Innovation Officer & Exec VP)*

Subsidiaries:

Allen-Beck Industries Inc.   (1)
3305 Kellina Ln Hwy 321 N, Granite Falls, NC 28630
Tel.: (828) 328-1587
Sales Range: $10-24.9 Million
Emp.: 3
Mfr of Plastic Foam Products
N.A.I.C.S.: 326140

Carpet Cushion Co., Inc.   (1)
1001 Arthur Ave, Elk Grove Village, IL 60007
Tel.: (847) 364-6760
Mfr of Plastics Foam Products
N.A.I.C.S.: 423220

Hickory Springs Manufacturing
Company   (1)
235 2nd Ave NW, Hickory, NC 28603
Tel.: (828) 328-2201
Home Furnishing Mfr
N.A.I.C.S.: 326299

Hickory Springs Manufacturing
Company   (1)
234 CDF Blvd, Verona, MS 38879-0459
Tel.: (662) 566-2322
Web Site: http://www.hickorysprings.com
Foam And Fiber
N.A.I.C.S.: 326299

Hickory Springs of California,
Inc.   (1)
3900 NE 158th Ave, Portland, OR 97230-5002
Tel.: (503) 255-4650
Sales Range: $10-24.9 Million
Emp.: 70
Home Furnishing Mfr
N.A.I.C.S.: 326150

Highland Fabricators Inc.   (1)
237 Kettering Rd, High Point, NC 27263
Tel.: (828) 328-2201
Sales Range: $10-24.9 Million
Emp.: 40
Mfr of Mattresses & Bedsprings
N.A.I.C.S.: 337910
Lee Lunsford *(Mgr-Ops)*

Plastic Technology Inc.   (1)
1101 Farrington St SW Bldg 3, Conover, NC 28613   (100%)
Tel.: (828) 328-2201
Web Site:
   http://www.plastictechnologyinc.net
Sales Range: $10-24.9 Million
Emp.: 50
Unsupported Plastic Mfr
N.A.I.C.S.: 326121
Tim Schulvz *(Gen Mgr)*

The C.E. White Co.   (1)
417 N Kibler St, New Washington, OH 44854
Tel.: (419) 492-2157
Web Site: http://www.cewhite.com
Sales Range: $10-24.9 Million
Emp.: 60
Motor Vehicle Seating Equipment Mfr
N.A.I.C.S.: 336360

Hickory Springs Manufacturing
Company—(Continued)

Tony Everett *(Pres & CEO)*
Jerry Hiler *(Engr-Sls)*
Kathy Everett *(Dir-OEM Sls-US & Canada)*
Tracy Risner *(Mgr-Engrg)*

**Volunteer Foam and Supply
Corporation** (1)
509 E Cedar St, Livingston, TN
38570-1934 **(100%)**
Tel.: (931) 823-6494
Sales Range: $10-24.9 Million
Emp.: 37
Mfr of Plastics Foam Products
N.A.I.C.S.: 326150

HICKS & OTIS PRINTS INC.
9 Wilton Ave, Norwalk, CT 06851
Tel.: (203) 847-5866
Web Site: http://www.dorrie.com
Sales Range: $10-24.9 Million
Emp.: 70
Plastics Finished Products, Lami-
nated
N.A.I.C.S.: 326130

Subsidiaries:

Harold M. Kaplan *(Pres)*
Steve Crovatto *(Controller)*

HICKS HOLDINGS, LLC
100 Crescent Ct Ste 1200, Dallas, TX
75201
Tel.: (214) 615-2300
Web Site:
   http://www.hicksholdings.com
Year Founded: 2004
Sales Range: $25-49.9 Million
Emp.: 30
Holding Company
N.A.I.C.S.: 551112
Thomas O. Hicks Jr. *(VP)*
Mindee Haas *(Mgr-Acctg)*

Subsidiaries:

**H-D Advanced Manufacturing
Company** (1)
2418 Greens Rd, Houston, TX 77032
Tel.: (346) 219-0320
Web Site: http://www.h-dam.com
Holding Company
N.A.I.C.S.: 551112
Dale B. Mikus *(CFO & Sr VP)*
Michael Vincent *(Pres & CEO)*
Tom Hicks *(Chm)*

Holding (Domestic):

Firstmark Corp. (2)
2200 Georgetowne Dr Ste 300, Sewickley,
PA 15143
Tel.: (724) 759-2850
Web Site: http://www.firstmarkcorp.com
Mfr of Components & Sub-Assemblies for
Aerospace & Defense Applications
N.A.I.C.S.: 334511
William H. Coogan Jr. *(CEO)*

Subsidiary (Domestic):

Aircraft Belts, Inc. (3)
1176 Telecom Dr, Creedmoor, NC 27522-
8294
Tel.: (919) 956-4395
Web Site: http://www.aircraftbelts.com
Sales Range: $1-9.9 Million
Emp.: 21
Aircraft Safety Restraints Mfr
N.A.I.C.S.: 336413
Rick O'Quinn *(Sls Mgr)*

Centroid, Inc. (3)
111 E Ames Ct, Plainview, NY 11803
Tel.: (516) 349-0070
Web Site: http://www.centroidinc.com
Sales Range: $1-9.9 Million
Emp.: 24
Electronic Components Mfr
N.A.I.C.S.: 334419
Matt Isley *(Pres)*

Firstmark Aerospace Corporation (3)
1176 Telecom Dr, Creedmoor, NC 27522-
8294
Tel.: (919) 956-4200

Web Site:
   http://www.firstmarkaerospace.com
Precision Electronic, Electromagnetic & Me-
chanical Components & Systems Mfr
N.A.I.C.S.: 334419
Derek Ashcroft *(Program Mgr)*
David Devine *(Exec VP)*

Twin Commander Aircraft LLC (3)
1176 Telecom Dr, Creedmoor, NC 27522-
8294
Tel.: (919) 956-4300
Web Site: http://www.twincommander.com
Aircraft Original Equipment Parts Mfr & Re-
pair Services
N.A.I.C.S.: 336413
Allen Goad *(Pres)*

Holding (Domestic):

Overton Chicago Gear Inc. (2)
530 S Westgate Dr, Addison, IL 60101-
4525
Tel.: (630) 543-9570
Web Site: http://www.oc-gear.com
Engineering Components & Industrial Gear
Products Mfr
N.A.I.C.S.: 333612
Louis Ertel *(CEO)*
Kevin Walsh *(VP-Ops)*
Don Brown *(CEO)*

Sungear, Inc. (2)
8535-G Arjons Dr, San Diego, CA 92126
Tel.: (858) 549-3166
Web Site: http://www.sungearinc.com
Emp.: 50
Aerospace Gear Mfr
N.A.I.C.S.: 336413
John Gizicki *(Founder)*
James Wilson *(Dir-Mfg)*
Paul M. Scott *(Dir-Quality Assurance)*

Hicks Sports Group, LLC (1)
1000 Ballpark Way Ste 400, Arlington, TX
76011-5170
Tel.: (817) 273-5222
Web Site: http://www.texasrangers.com
Sales Range: $75-99.9 Million
Emp.: 390
Sports Holding Company
N.A.I.C.S.: 551112
Thomas O. Hicks Jr. *(VP)*

Subsidiary (Domestic):

Dallas Stars L.P. (2)
2601 Ave Of The Stars, Frisco, TX 75034
Tel.: (214) 387-5500
Web Site: http://www.dallasstars.com
Sales Range: $50-74.9 Million
Professional Hockey Team
N.A.I.C.S.: 711211
Robert Hutson *(CFO & Exec VP-Fin)*
Randy Locey *(Exec VP-Bus Ops)*
Jason Rademan *(Dir-Media Rels)*
Mark Janko *(Asst Gen Mgr-Hockey Ops)*
Tony Tavares *(Pres)*
Brad Alberts *(Exec VP-Corp Dev)*
Grady Raskin *(VP-Corp Partnerships)*
Jim Nill *(Gen Mgr)*
Les Jackson *(Gen Mgr-Hockey Ops)*
Scott White *(Asst Gen Mgr-Hockey Ops)*

HICKS LIGHTNING PROTEC-
TION, INC.
7420 FM 2449, Ponder, TX 76259
Tel.: (940) 479-2114   TX
Web Site: http://www.hickslp.com
Electrical Contractor
N.A.I.C.S.: 238210
Mark Hicks *(Pres)*
Jason Snider *(VP-Ops)*
Jeremy Bilbrey *(VP-Pre-Construction)*
Tad Riney *(Svc Mgr)*
Eileen Britz *(HR Mgr)*
Jim Beminio *(Safety Dir)*
Octavio Torres *(Design Mgr)*

Subsidiaries:

Tectoweld Inc. (1)
1450 W 228th St Ste 1, Torrance, CA
90501
Tel.: (310) 846-8042
Web Site: http://www.tectoweld.com
Welding & Soldering Equipment Mfr
N.A.I.C.S.: 333992

HICKS OIL-HICKS GAS, INC.
US 54 115, Roberts, IL 60962
Tel.: (217) 395-2281   IN
Sales Range: $200-249.9 Million
Emp.: 350
Petroleum Products Whslr
N.A.I.C.S.: 424710
Daniel Schmidt *(Treas, Sec & Con-
troller)*
Dan Camp *(Mgr-Special Projects)*
Debra Rexroat *(Mgr-HR)*
Thomas R. Coady Jr. *(Exec VP)*

Subsidiaries:

Rocket Supply Corp. (1)
404 N State Rte 115, Roberts, IL 60962
Tel.: (217) 395-2281
Web Site: http://www.rocketsupply.com
Sales Range: $25-49.9 Million
Emp.: 30
Remote Shut-Off Systems for Bulk Trucks &
Bulk Plants
N.A.I.C.S.: 457210
Todd Coady *(Pres & CEO)*
Shawn Coady *(VP)*

HIDALGO COUNTY CLINICAL
SERVICES INC.
2801 Via Fortuna, Austin, TX 78746-
7573
Tel.: (512) 899-3995   TX
Year Founded: 2006
Sales Range: $10-24.9 Million
Health Care Srvices
N.A.I.C.S.: 622110
Lawrence R. Gelman *(Treas)*
Joe Riley *(Pres)*
Maura Walsh *(Second VP)*
James A. Summersett III *(First VP)*
Lorenzo Olivarez Jr. *(Sec)*

HIDALGO INDUSTRIAL SER-
VICES, INC.
2535 Brennan Ave, Fort Worth, TX
76106
Tel.: (817) 625-8222
Web Site:
   http://www.hidalgoindustrial.com
Year Founded: 1999
Rev.: $31,000,000
Emp.: 210
Plumbing, Heating & Air-Conditioning
Contractors
N.A.I.C.S.: 238220
Susan Riesz *(Mgr-IT & Internet Sup-
port)*
Jim Schneider *(Exec VP)*
Lanny Mooney *(CEO)*

HIDDEN HARBOR CAPITAL
PARTNERS
4855 Technology Way Ste 500, Boca
Raton, FL
Tel.: (954) 400-1140   FL
Web Site: https://hh-cp.com
Year Founded: 2016
Privater Equity Firm
N.A.I.C.S.: 523940
David Block *(Mng Partner)*

Subsidiaries:

Industrial Laminates/Norplex,
Inc. (1)
665 Lybrand St, Postville, IA 52162
Tel.: (563) 864-7321
Web Site: http://www.norplex-micarta.com
Sales Range: $25-49.9 Million
Emp.: 200
Mfr of Industrial Laminates
N.A.I.C.S.: 326199

Subsidiary (Non-US):

IDI Thermoset Molding Compounds
Shenzhen Company, Ltd. (2)
2 Xingtang Road, Hi-Tech Development
Zone, Changzhou, 213127, China
Tel.: (86) 755 2988 1383
Web Site: http://www.norplex-micarta.com

Thermoset Molding Compounds Mfr
N.A.I.C.S.: 325991

HIDE-AWAY STORAGE SER-
VICES INC.
6791 28th St Cir E, Sarasota, FL
34243
Tel.: (941) 315-6523
Web Site:
   https://www.hideawaystorage.com
Year Founded: 1977
Sales Range: $1-9.9 Million
Emp.: 50
Self Storage Services
N.A.I.C.S.: 531130
Steve Wilson *(Chm & CEO)*
Paul Feikema *(VP-Facility Ops)*

HIDEF LIFESTYLE
6195 Allentown Blvd, Harrisburg, PA
17112
Tel.: (717) 914-1751
Web Site:
   https://www.hideflifestyle.com
Year Founded: 2004
Rev.: $2,800,000
Emp.: 15
Electronics Store Retailer
N.A.I.C.S.: 459999
Aaron Sholtis *(Pres)*

HIDY MOTORS, INC.
2300 Heller Dr, Beavercreek, OH
45434
Tel.: (937) 426-9564   OH
Web Site:
   http://www.germainhondaofbea
   vercreek.com
Sales Range: $25-49.9 Million
Emp.: 70
New & Used Car Dealerships Owner
& Operator
N.A.I.C.S.: 441110
Rita Mays *(Controller)*

HIGBEE & ASSOCIATES
1504 Brookhollow Dr Ste 112, Santa
Ana, CA 92705
Tel.: (714) 617-8300
Web Site:
   https://www.higbeeassociates.com
Year Founded: 2006
Sales Range: $1-9.9 Million
Emp.: 36
Legal Consulting Services
N.A.I.C.S.: 541199
Mathew K. Higbee *(Founder & Pres)*
Kelsey Zahner *(Acct Mgr)*
Alison Begg *(Mgr-HR, Fin & Ops)*

HIGDON FURNITURE CO.
130 N Virginia St, Quincy, FL 32351
Tel.: (850) 627-7564
Web Site:
   http://www.higdonfurniture.com
Sales Range: $10-24.9 Million
Emp.: 170
Wood Bedroom Furniture Sales
N.A.I.C.S.: 337122
J. Warren Higdon III *(Pres)*

HIGGERSON-BUCHANAN INC.
5300 Bainbridge Blvd, Chesapeake,
VA 23320-6712
Tel.: (757) 545-4665   VA
Web Site:
   http://www.higgersonbuchanan.com
Year Founded: 1946
Sales Range: $25-49.9 Million
Emp.: 145
Heavy Construction Services
N.A.I.C.S.: 236210
Harold L. Higgerson *(Pres)*

HIGGINBOTHAM BROS. & COMPANY

202 W Central Ave, Comanche, TX 76442
Tel.: (325) 356-3456
Web Site:
https://www.higginbothams.com
Rev.: $40,000,000
Emp.: 16
Hardware & Lumber Supplies
N.A.I.C.S.: 444110
Corby Biddle *(COO)*
Mike Harris *(Mgr-Pur)*
Jim Lensing *(Reg Mgr)*
Trevor Crozier *(Reg Mgr)*
Donna Coolbaugh *(Dir-HR)*
Tim Vanbibber *(Dir-IT)*
Steve Olson *(Dir-Mdsg)*
Curtis Ferguson *(Reg Dir)*
Tanner Woods *(Mgr-Accts Payable)*
Rufus H. Duncan Jr, *(CEO)*

Subsidiaries:

Higginbotham-Bartlett Company
Ltd.   (1)
PO Box 392, Comanche, TX 76442
Tel.: (325) 356-3456
Web Site: http://www.higginbothams.com
Sales Range: $25-49.9 Million
Emp.: 100
Retailer of Building Materials & Hardware;
Owner of General Merchandise Stores
N.A.I.C.S.: 423390
Jim L. Higginbotham Jr. *(Exec VP)*

HIGGINBOTHAM OIL CO. INC.

562 Cahaba Vly Rd, Pelham, AL 35124-1365
Tel.: (205) 403-0456
Year Founded: 1971
Sales Range: $10-24.9 Million
Emp.: 50
Gasoline Service Stations
N.A.I.C.S.: 457110

HIGGINS CHEVROLET INC.

911 S 3rd St, Ironton, OH 45638
Tel.: (740) 532-0405
Year Founded: 1927
Sales Range: $10-24.9 Million
Emp.: 38
Car Whslr
N.A.I.C.S.: 441110
Walter E. Higgins *(VP)*

HIGGINS DEVELOPMENT PARTNERS, LLC

101 E Erie St Ste 800, Chicago, IL 60611-2812
Tel.: (312) 943-4999   IL
Web Site:
http://www.higginsdevelopment.com
Year Founded: 1981
Sales Range: $25-49.9 Million
Emp.: 60
Subdividers & Developers
N.A.I.C.S.: 523999
John W. Higgins *(Chm & CEO)*

HIGGINS ELECTRIC, INC. OF DOTHAN

1350 Columbia Hwy, Dothan, AL 36301
Tel.: (334) 793-4859   AL
Web Site:
http://www.higginselectric.com
Year Founded: 1932
Sales Range: $1-9.9 Million
Emp.: 60
Industrial Electric Contractor
N.A.I.C.S.: 238210
Jim Knighton *(Pres)*
Randy Smith *(Comptroller)*
Gary Granger *(Mgr-Bus Dev)*
David Deese *(Mgr-Construction)*

HIGGINS ERECTORS & HAULERS INC

7715 Lockport Rd, Niagara Falls, NY 14304-1078
Tel.: (716) 821-8000
Web Site:
http://www.terminalofcommerce.com
Sales Range: $25-49.9 Million
Emp.: 100
Installing Building Equipment
N.A.I.C.S.: 238290
Jeffrey C. Higgins *(Pres)*

HIGH COUNTRY BEVERAGE CORP.

4200 Ronald Reagan Blvd, Johnstown, CO 80534
Tel.: (970) 622-8444
Web Site:
https://www.highcountrybeverage.com
Year Founded: 1996
Alcoholic Beverage Distr
N.A.I.C.S.: 445320
Kelli Casteel *(Area Sls Mgr)*
Kopperud Bryce *(Dir-Sls & Mktg)*

HIGH COUNTRY FUSION COMPANY, INC.

20 N Poly Fusion Pl, Fairfield, ID 83327
Tel.: (208) 764-2000
Web Site: http://www.hcfusion.com
Year Founded: 1994
Sales Range: $10-24.9 Million
Emp.: 49
Fabricated Pipe & Pipe Fitting Mfr
N.A.I.C.S.: 332996
Steve Wilson *(CEO)*
John Bjorkman *(VP-Sls)*
Todd Claiborn *(Controller)*
David Hanks *(Pres)*
Rose Helton *(Coord-Headquarters Shipping & Receiving)*
Alyssa Obland *(Mgr-HR)*
Bryan Obland *(Mgr-Equipment Sls, Rentals & Repairs)*
Steve Sabin *(Mgr-Inventory Control & Supvr-Shipping & Receiving)*
Bill Seig *(Mgr-Production Ops)*

HIGH COUNTRY INVESTOR, INC.

855 Broadway, Saugus, MA 01906-3208
Tel.: (781) 233-7700   CO
Year Founded: 1994
Sales Range: $50-74.9 Million
Emp.: 800
Meat & Fish Market Services
N.A.I.C.S.: 445240
Lenny Derosa *(VP)*
Dick Monford *(Pres)*
Dennis January *(CFO)*

HIGH COUNTRY LINENS INC.

5199 DAB Plz W Twr Fl 12, Jericho, NY 11753
Tel.: (516) 931-3188
Sales Range: $10-24.9 Million
Emp.: 10
Linens & Towels
N.A.I.C.S.: 423220

HIGH COUNTRY LUMBER INC.

444 S Main St, Bishop, CA 93514
Tel.: (760) 873-5874
Web Site:
https://www.highcountrylumber.com
Rev.: $11,100,000
Emp.: 46
Lumber & Plywood Distr
N.A.I.C.S.: 423310
Steven Joseph *(Co-Owner & Co-Pres)*

HIGH DESERT CAPITAL, LLC

6080 Surety Dr Ste 101, El Paso, TX 79905
Tel.: (915) 593-7111   TX
Web Site:
https://www.highdesertcap.com
Year Founded: 2006
Financial Services
N.A.I.C.S.: 523999
Edward Escudero *(Founder & Pres)*

HIGH DESERT HOLDING CORP.

865 Tahoe Blvd Ste 302, Incline Village, NV 89451
Tel.: (775) 298-2856   NV
Web Site:
http://www.highdesertholding
corp.com
Year Founded: 2013
Assets: $2,513
Liabilities: $171,509
Net Worth: ($168,996)
Earnings: ($32,469)
Emp.: 1
Fiscal Year-end: 12/31/18
Mineral Exploration & Mining Svcs
N.A.I.C.S.: 213115
Mark Kersey *(Chm, CEO, CFO, Chief Acctg Officer, Sec & Treas)*

HIGH DESERT PARTNERSHIP IN ACADEMIC EXCELLENCE FOUNDATION, INC.

17500 Mana Rd, Apple Valley, CA 92307
Tel.: (760) 946-5414   CA
Web Site: https://www.lewiscenter.org
Year Founded: 1992
Sales Range: $10-24.9 Million
Educational Research Services
N.A.I.C.S.: 611710
H. O. Biggs *(Chm)*
Richard Piercy II *(Founder)*

HIGH ENERGY INC.

6825 E Tennessee Ave Ste 445, Denver, CO 80224
Tel.: (303) 333-0280
Web Site:
http://www.highenergyinc.com
Year Founded: 1998
Sales Range: $1-9.9 Million
Emp.: 16
Performs Studies, Design & Analysis & Construction Support for Electric Power Systems
N.A.I.C.S.: 221122
Irina Merson *(Founder & Pres)*
Ruth A. Johnson *(Partner & VP-Engrg)*

HIGH FALLS OIL COMPANY INC.

1611 Hwy 22, Highfalls, NC 27259
Tel.: (910) 464-3101
Web Site:
http://www.highfalls.nc.phonepages
inc.com
Sales Range: $10-24.9 Million
Emp.: 40
Convenience Store
N.A.I.C.S.: 445131
Steve Majors *(Pres)*

HIGH GRADE BEVERAGE

891 Georges Rd, Monmouth Junction, NJ 08852
Tel.: (732) 821-7600
Web Site: https://www.hgbev.com
Sales Range: $75-99.9 Million
Emp.: 200
Beer & Other Fermented Malt Liquors
N.A.I.C.S.: 424810
Joseph DeMarco *(Chm)*
Elizabeth DeMarco *(Treas & Sec)*

Jeffrey Epstein *(Controller)*
George Policastro *(Exec VP)*
Guy Battaglia *(VP)*
Diana Battaglia *(Asst Sec)*
Anthony DeMarco *(Pres)*
Bill Calcagno *(Dir-HR)*
Robert Pellicane *(Dir-Sls & Mktg)*
Chris Metz *(Mgr-IT)*
John Morra *(Mgr-Ops)*
John Benvenuto *(Mgr-Sls)*
Hank Monaco *(Mgr-Sls-Soft Drink)*
Anthony De Joseph *(Mgr-Vehicle Maintenance)*
Herbert J. Schloss *(VP-Corp Fin)*

HIGH GRADE MATERIALS COMPANY

9266 Snows Lk Rd, Greenville, MI 48838
Tel.: (616) 754-9148
Web Site:
http://www.highgradematerial.com
Sales Range: $10-24.9 Million
Emp.: 120
Mfr of Ready-Mixed Concrete
N.A.I.C.S.: 327320

HIGH INDUSTRIES, INC.

1853 William Penn Way, Lancaster, PA 17605-0008
Tel.: (717) 293-4444   PA
Web Site: https://www.high.net
Year Founded: 1931
Sales Range: $400-449.9 Million
Emp.: 2,300
Holding Company; Steel Fabrication & Erection, Concrete; Real Estate Development; Food Service, Employee Services, Hospitality Services, Management Consulting & Development
N.A.I.C.S.: 332312
James Crowley *(CFO)*
Larry Brown *(VP-HR Svcs)*
Vincent Mizeras *(HR Dir)*
Cathy Cironna *(Cash Mgr)*
Mark Aho *(Exec VP-Affiliated Companies)*
Barclay Tucker *(Telecomm Mgr)*
Dan Spealman *(Info Sys Dir)*
Kathy Shivery *(Employee Benefits Mgr)*
David Nile *(Devel Mgr)*
Mark Vogel *(Corporate Mktg Support Mgr)*
Paula R. Crowley *(Chm)*

Subsidiaries:

High Concrete Group LLC   (1)
125 Denver Rd, Denver, PA 17517
Tel.: (717) 336-9300
Web Site: http://www.highconcrete.com
Sales Range: $25-49.9 Million
Emp.: 400
Precast Concrete Products Mfr
N.A.I.C.S.: 327390
John J. Seroky *(Pres)*
Jeff Good *(Dir-Pur)*
Rhonda Kurtz *(Dir-HR)*
Daniel Pietropola *(VP-Construction Svcs)*
Parker Jones *(Controller)*
Dave Schneider *(VP-Engrg)*
Phoenix Rann *(VP-Ops)*

High Concrete Technology LLC   (1)
95 Mound Park Dr, Springboro, OH 45066
Tel.: (937) 748-2412
Web Site: http://www.highconcrete.com
Sales Range: $25-49.9 Million
Emp.: 400
Architectural Concrete Products Mfr
N.A.I.C.S.: 327390
Parker Jones *(VP-Fin)*

High Steel Service Center LLC   (1)
400 Steel Way, Lancaster, PA 17601
Tel.: (717) 299-8989

High Industries, Inc.—(Continued)

Web Site:
http://www.highsteelservicecenter.com
Aluminum, Carbon & Stainless Steel Product Distr
N.A.I.C.S.: 423510
James Cunningham (VP-Sls & Mktg)
Michael Brenneman (Territory Mgr)
Mark Lukes (Territory Mgr)
Steve Savage (Territory Mgr)
Terry Weller (Territory Mgr)
Kennedy Watkins (Territory Mgr)
Tom Ruth (Mgr-Inside Sls)

High Steel Structures Inc.   (1)
1915 Old Philadelphia Pike, Lancaster, PA 17605-0008
Tel.: (717) 390-4270
Web Site: http://www.highsteel.com
Steel Fabrication Services
N.A.I.C.S.: 331110
Tom Wandzilak (Mgr-Bus Dev)
John O'Quinn (Pres)

HIGH PLAINS COMPUTING, INC.
143 Union Blvd Ste 300, Lakewood, CO 80228
Tel.: (303) 216-9270
Web Site: http://www.hpc-solutions.net
Year Founded: 1994
Sales Range: $1-9.9 Million
Emp.: 40
Consulting, Assessment, Financial Services, Logistics & Technology Services to Government Clients
N.A.I.C.S.: 921190
Linda Shugart (Founder & CEO)
Paul Shugart (CFO)

HIGH PLAINS COOPERATIVE
240 W Broadway, Plainview, MN 55964
Tel.: (507) 534-3111
Web Site:
http://www.highplainscoop.com
Sales Range: $10-24.9 Million
Emp.: 59
Fertilizer
N.A.I.C.S.: 444240
Shane Kelley (Mgr-Energy)

HIGH PLAINS POWER INC.
1775 E Monroe Ave, Riverton, WY 82501
Tel.: (307) 856-9426   **WY**
Web Site:
https://www.highplainspower.org
Year Founded: 1998
Sales Range: $25-49.9 Million
Emp.: 54
Provider of Electric Power Transmission
N.A.I.C.S.: 221121
Hearley Dockham (Sec)
Gary Gordon (Asst Sec)
Jim Miller (Treas)

HIGH POINT ENTERPRISE
213 Woodbine St, High Point, NC 27260
Tel.: (336) 888-3558
Web Site: https://www.hpenews.com
Sales Range: $10-24.9 Million
Emp.: 65
Commercial Printing & Newspaper Publishing Combined
N.A.I.C.S.: 513110
Nancy Baker (Controller)
David Packston (Pres)
Alison Temple (Mgr)

HIGH POINT FURNITURE INDUSTRIES
1104 Bedford St, High Point, NC 27263
Tel.: (336) 431-7101

Web Site: https://www.hpfi.com
Year Founded: 1958
Sales Range: $10-24.9 Million
Emp.: 120
Wood & Metal Office Furniture Mfr
N.A.I.C.S.: 337211
Spencer O'Meara (Vice Chm, Pres & CEO)
Sue Rogers (Dir-Pur)
Robert Janson (Dir-Quality)
Tom Carrigan (VP-Mktg)
Doug Gaines (VP-Sls)
Jerry Samet (VP-Ops & Bus Dev)

HIGH POINT OIL CO.
3950 Priority Way S Dr Ste 114, Indianapolis, IN 46240-3782
Tel.: (317) 844-8886   **IN**
Web Site:
http://www.highpointoil.com
Year Founded: 1943
Sales Range: $75-99.9 Million
Emp.: 5
Operator of Gas Stations
N.A.I.C.S.: 457120
Karl Kelb (Pres)

HIGH POINT SOLUTIONS, INC.
5 Gail Ct, Sparta, NJ 07871
Tel.: (973) 940-0040
Web Site: https://www.highpoint.com
Year Founded: 1996
Sales Range: $10-24.9 Million
Emp.: 49
Information Technology Services
N.A.I.C.S.: 541512
Michael T. Mendiburu (Co-Founder & Pres)
Thomas T. Mendiburu (Co-Founder)
Sandra Curran (CFO)

HIGH POINT TREATMENT CENTER
52 Oak St, Middleboro, MA 02346
Tel.: (774) 213-8400   **MA**
Web Site: http://www.hptc.org
Year Founded: 1996
Sales Range: $25-49.9 Million
Emp.: 1,215
Medical Treatment Services
N.A.I.C.S.: 813319
Daniel S. Mumbauer (Pres)
Walter M. Murphy (Treas)
Michael Iannessa (Dir-Medical)
James Hatch Jr. (CFO)

HIGH POWER TECHNICAL SERVICES
2230 Ampere Dr, Louisville, KY 40299
Tel.: (502) 254-0768
Web Site: https://www.hpts.tv
Year Founded: 1999
Sales Range: $10-24.9 Million
Emp.: 250
Satellite Installation Services & Sales
N.A.I.C.S.: 238210
Scott Weis (Founder, Pres & CEO)
Richard Waddle (Controller)
Daniel Strickland (Gen Mgr)
Denis Goomey (Dir-Ops)

HIGH REAL ESTATE GROUP LLC
1853 William Penn Way, Lancaster, PA 17601
Tel.: (717) 291-2284
Web Site: https://www.highrealestate group.com
Year Founded: 1931
Rev.: $207,800,000
Emp.: 654
Offices Other Holding Companies
N.A.I.C.S.: 551112

Robin D. Stauffer (Sec)
Mark C. Fitzgerald (Pres & COO)
Nevin D. Cooley (CEO)

HIGH ROAD CAPITAL PARTNERS, LLC
15 E Putnam Ave Ste 3110, Greenwich, CT 06830
Tel.: (212) 554-3265   **DE**
Web Site:
http://www.highroadcap.com
Year Founded: 2007
Sales Range: $75-99.9 Million
Privater Equity Firm
N.A.I.C.S.: 523999
Robert J. Fitzsimmons (Co-Founder & Mng Partner)
William C. Connell (Co-Founder & Partner)
William B. R. Hobbs (Operating Partner)
Jeffrey M. Goodrich (Co-Founder & Partner)
Kristin A. Newhall (Partner)
Subsidiaries:

BlueSpire, Inc.   (1)
7650 Edinborough Way Ste 500, Minneapolis, MN 55435
Web Site:
http://www.bluespiremarketing.com
Advetising Agency
N.A.I.C.S.: 541810
Kathryn Hammond (CEO)
Sara Montalto (VP-Sr Living)

Subsidiary (Non-US):

Ariad Custom Publishing Limited   (2)
15 John Street 7th Floor, Toronto, M5V 3G6, ON, Canada
Tel.: (416) 971-9294
Web Site: http://www.ariad.ca
Emp.: 86
Digital Marketing Agency
N.A.I.C.S.: 541810
Hugh R. Furneaux (Founder)
Mark Michaud (Sr VP)
Richard Marcil (Gen Mgr)
Dave Stevenson (Sr VP-Creative Dir)
Emma Lyndon (Chief Bus Intelligence Officer)

Branch (Domestic):

BlueSpire, Inc. - Montvale   (2)
110 Summit Ave, Montvale, NJ 07645
Tel.: (201) 740-6100
Web Site:
http://www.bluespiremarketing.com
Marketing Services
N.A.I.C.S.: 541890

Subsidiary (Domestic):

Martino & Binzer, Inc.   (2)
270 Farmington Ave Ste 128, Farmington, CT 06032
Tel.: (860) 678-4300
Web Site: http://www.goodbait.com
Advetising Agency
N.A.I.C.S.: 541810
Robin Deroe (Dir-Art)
Fran Palma (VP-Digital Svcs)
Jen Mackenzie (Sr Dir-Art)
Rich Denver (Creative Dir)
Jay Hibbard (Sr VP-Sr Svcs)
Amy LaGrant (Dir- Grp Accts & VP)

Cali Bamboo LLC   (1)
9365 Waples St Ste D, San Diego, CA 92121
Tel.: (858) 200-9540
Web Site: http://www.calibamboo.com
Sales Range: $10-24.9 Million
Bamboo Building Materials Mfr
N.A.I.C.S.: 321211
Jeff Goldberg (Co-Founder)
Tanner Haigwood (Co-Founder & Exec VP)
Doug Jackson (CEO)

Exponential Power, Inc.   (1)
N56 W16665 Ridgewood Dr, Menomonee Falls, WI 53051
Tel.: (262) 703-5800

Web Site:
https://www.exponentialpower.com
Storage Batteries Mfr
N.A.I.C.S.: 335910
Jake Walker (CEO)

Subsidiary (Domestic):

Nolan Power Group, LLC   (2)
21448 Marion Ln, Mandeville, LA 70471-7756
Tel.: (985) 801-5000
Web Site: http://www.nolanpower.com
Electrical Apparatus & Related Equipment Merchant Whslr
N.A.I.C.S.: 423610
Bobby Nolan (CEO)
Roger Turner (VP-Sls)
Bryan Dardar (Dir-Tech Svcs)
John Todora (Dir-Bus Dev)
Casey Willis (CFO)
Rocky Colombo (Dir-Central Sls)

Power Product Services, Inc.   (2)
18150 E 32nd Pl Unit D, Aurora, CO 80011
Tel.: (303) 468-8200
Web Site:
http://www.powerproductservices.com
Electrical Apparatus & Equipment, Wiring Supplies & Related Equipment Merchant Whslr
N.A.I.C.S.: 423610
Dean Laliberte (Owner & Principal)
Karl Hochmuth (Reg Mgr-Sls)
Kevin Patrick (Mgr-Natl Sls)
Tom Broschinsky (Owner & Principal)

Mid-West Wholesale Hardware Co.   (1)
1000 N. Century Ave, Kansas City, MO 64120
Tel.: (816) 241-5663
Web Site: http://www.bannersolutions.com
Commercial Door, Hardware & Other Construction Building Supplies Whslr
N.A.I.C.S.: 423710
Ben A. Schnakenberg (Partner)
Scott J. Rubino (Principal)
Nicholas W. Martino (Operating Partner)

Quality Standby Services, LLC   (1)
1649 Sands Pl SE Ste C, Marietta, GA 30067
Tel.: (770) 916-1747
Electrical Contractor
N.A.I.C.S.: 238210

York Wallcoverings, Inc.   (1)
750 Linden Ave, York, PA 17404-3364
Tel.: (717) 846-4456
Web Site: http://www.yorkwall.com
Emp.: 250
Wall Coverings & Borders Mfr
N.A.I.C.S.: 322220
Ronald Redding (VP-Design)
Carl J. Vizzi (Pres)
Joanne Berwager (Mktg Mgr)
Kristine Spillman (Asst Mgr-Customer Svc)
Carol Miller (Mktg Mgr)
Jeffrey Goodrich (Chm)
Brian Golden (CEO)

HIGH SEA SUGAR INC.
19 W Flagler St Ste 904, Miami, FL 33130-4407
Tel.: (305) 733-4058
Sales Range: $550-599.9 Million
Emp.: 9
Wet Corn Milling Services
N.A.I.C.S.: 311221
Newell L. Smith (Pres)
Mark Lumsden (VP)

HIGH STREET CAPITAL MANAGEMENT, INC.
150 N Wacker Dr Ste 2420, Chicago, IL 60606
Tel.: (312) 423-2650   **DE**
Web Site:
http://www.highstreetcapital.com
Privater Equity Firm
N.A.I.C.S.: 523999
Joseph R. Katcha (Principal)
Kent C. Haeger (Principal)
Richard D. McClain (Principal)

Robert S. France *(Principal)*
Chris Brewster *(CFO & VP)*
Timothy J. Kurth *(Partner)*

Subsidiaries:

Adams Magnetic Products Co.   (1)
888 Larch Ave, Elmhurst, IL 60126
Tel.: (630) 617-8880
Web Site: https://www.adamsmagnetic.com
Rev.: $18,000,000
Emp.: 80
Mfr & Distributor of Magnetic Products
N.A.I.C.S.: 332999
John Cosmas *(COO)*
Scott Lewis *(Pres)*
John Maisch *(Mgr-Bus Dev)*

Applied Process, Inc.   (1)
12202 Newburgh Rd, Livonia, MI 48150
Tel.: (734) 464-8000
Web Site: http://www.appliedprocess.com
Metal Heat Treating, Nsk
N.A.I.C.S.: 332811
Harold Karp *(Pres & CEO)*

ShoreMaster Inc.   (1)
1025 International Dr, Fergus Falls, MN
56537
Tel.: (218) 739-4641
Web Site: http://www.shoremaster.com
Sales Range: $50-74.9 Million
Emp.: 115
Waterfront Equipment Mfr
N.A.I.C.S.: 423860

Transport Labor
Contract/Leasing   (1)
6160 Summit Dr N Ste 500, Brooklyn Center, MN 55430
Tel.: (763) 585-7000
Web Site: http://www.tlccompanies.com
Professional Employer Organizations
N.A.I.C.S.: 561330

**HIGH TECH CRIME INSTITUTE
INC.**
7935 114th Ave Ste 1100, Largo, FL
33773-5028
Tel.: (813) 343-0766
Web Site: http://www.gohtci.com
Sales Range: $1-9.9 Million
Emp.: 13
Computer Crime Investigation &
Computer Forensics
N.A.I.C.S.: 561621
Stephen Pearson *(Mng Partner)*
Thomas Eskridge *(Partner)*
Stacey Glogowski *(VP-Admin Svcs)*

HIGH TECH IRRIGATION INC.
80975 Indio Blvd Bldg A, Indio, CA
92201
Tel.: (760) 347-4116
Web Site:
   https://www.hightechirrigation.com
Year Founded: 1985
Sales Range: $10-24.9 Million
Emp.: 40
Whslr of Irrigation Equipment
N.A.I.C.S.: 423820
John Dixon *(Owner)*

**HIGH TEMPERATURE SUPER-
CONDUCTORS, INC.**
320 North Nopal Street, Santa Barbara, CA 93103
Tel.: (805) 232-7176
Web Site:
   https://www.hitsuperconductors.com
Year Founded: 2020
Emp.: 100
Semiconductor Mfr
N.A.I.C.S.: 333242
Ray Karam *(Founder & CEO)*

Subsidiaries:

PVD Products   (1)
231 Andover St, Wilmington, MA 01887
Tel.: (978) 694-9455
Web Site: http://www.pvdproducts.com
Rev.: $3,897,000

Emp.: 9
Office Supplies & Stationery Stores
N.A.I.C.S.: 459410
Larry Bourget *(COO)*

HIGH TOUCH, INC.
110 S Main Ste 600, Wichita, KS
67202
Tel.: (316) 832-1611
Web Site:
   http://www.hightouchinc.com
Year Founded: 1984
Sales Range: $10-24.9 Million
Emp.: 200
Software & Hardware Services
N.A.I.C.S.: 334118
Kevin Colborn *(VP-Tech Solutions)*
Vernon Dolezal *(Treas & VP)*
Wayne Chambers *(Pres & CEO)*
Jason Mock *(VP-Ops)*
Lyle Jones *(Chm)*
Amy Mounts *(VP-Sls)*
Jana Davis *(CFO)*

Subsidiaries:

High Touch, Inc.   (1)
7425 S Peoria St Ste 200, Englewood, CO
80112
Tel.: (303) 790-7100
Sales Range: $1-9.9 Million
Emp.: 4
Information Technology Consulting Services
N.A.I.C.S.: 541690
Scott Sundby *(Branch Mgr)*
Caleb Amyot *(Sr Acct Exec)*

HIGH WEST ENERGY, INC.
6270 Country Rd 212, Pine Bluffs,
WY 82082
Tel.: (307) 245-3261
Web Site:
   http://www.highwestenergy.com
Sales Range: $10-24.9 Million
Emp.: 75
Electric Power Distr
N.A.I.C.S.: 221122
Brian Heithoff *(CEO & Gen Mgr)*
Konnie Keehnen *(Mgr-Energy Svcs)*
Lindsay Forepaugh *(CFO)*
Lloyd Sisson *(Mgr-Engrg)*

HIGH WIRE NETWORKS, INC.
7162 Shady Oak Rd, Eden Prairie,
MN 55344
Tel.: (952) 934-9080
Web Site:
   http://www.highwirenetworks.com
Rev.: $10,200,000
Emp.: 65
Telecommunication Servicesb
N.A.I.C.S.: 517111
Philip Burnett *(Chief Info & Security
Officer)*
Anthony Sparber *(Dir-Front Line
Maintenance)*
Charles Hughes *(COO)*
Mark W. Porter *(Pres & CEO)*
David Hand *(VP-Sys Integrators-
Global)*
Don Schmidt *(Exec VP)*

HIGH'S OF BALTIMORE INC.
7477 New Ridge Rd, Baltimore, MD
21076-3129
Tel.: (410) 859-3636   MD
Web Site:
   http://www.highsdairystores.com
Year Founded: 1974
Sales Range: $50-74.9 Million
Emp.: 968
Grocery Stores
N.A.I.C.S.: 445298
William F. Darnell *(Pres)*
Richard Sheffler *(Mgr-Store)*
Bill Williams *(Mgr-Store)*

HIGHBAR MANAGEMENT, LLC

545 Middlefield Rd Ste 175, Menlo
Park, CA 94025
Tel.: (650) 900-4330   DE
Web Site:
   http://www.highbarpartners.com
Year Founded: 1995
Private Investment Firm
N.A.I.C.S.: 523940
John Kim *(Co-founder & Mng Partner)*
Roy Thiele-Sardina *(Co-founder &
Mng Partner)*

Subsidiaries:

SS8 Networks, Inc.   (1)
750 Tasman Dr, Milpitas, CA 95035-7456
Tel.: (408) 944-0250
Web Site: http://www.ss8.com
Communication Signal Enhancement Network Services
N.A.I.C.S.: 517810
Cemal Dikmen *(Chief Tech & Security Officer)*
Faizel Lakhani *(Pres)*
Kevin McTiernan *(VP)*
Debbie Ziolkowski *(VP-Sls-Americas)*
James Mullins *(VP-Sls-EMEA & APAC)*
Keith Bhatia *(CEO)*
Jerry Su *(CFO)*
Alan Elliot *(Chief Comml Officer)*
Kevin Isacks *(Chief Dev Officer)*
Jeff Jones *(Sr VP-Global Sls)*
DeAnn Baker *(VP-Mktg)*

**HIGHBRIDGE ADVISORY
COUNCIL FAMILY SERVICES,
INC.**
880 River Ave Fl 2, Bronx, NY 10452
Tel.: (718) 992-1321   NY
Web Site:
   http://www.hacfamilyservices.org
Year Founded: 1968
Sales Range: $10-24.9 Million
Emp.: 304
Community Care Services
N.A.I.C.S.: 624190
Sherry Frazier *(Mgr-HR)*
Pearl Thompson *(Dir-Special Education Programs)*
James W. Nathaniel *(CEO)*

**HIGHER LEARNING COMMIS-
SION**
230 S LaSalle St Ste 7-500, Chicago,
IL 60604-1411
Tel.: (312) 263-0456   IL
Web Site:
   http://www.hlcommission.org
Year Founded: 1895
Sales Range: $10-24.9 Million
Emp.: 64
Educational Support Services
N.A.I.C.S.: 611710
Barbara Gellman-Danley *(Pres)*
Sarah Byrne *(Dir-HR & Ops)*
Heather Berg *(Dir-Comm)*
Cheryl Johnson-Odim *(Chm)*
Joanne M. Burrows *(Vice Chm)*
Michael Seuring *(CFO & VP)*
Jim Meyer *(CIO)*
Andrew Lootens-White *(COO & VP)*
Karen L. Solinski *(Exec VP-Legal &
Govt Affairs)*
Eric Martin *(VP)*

HIGHER LOGIC, LLC
1919 N Lynn St Ste 500, Arlington,
VA 22209
Tel.: (202) 360-4402
Web Site:
   https://www.higherlogic.com
Year Founded: 2007
Social Networking, Mobile Applications & Software Developer
N.A.I.C.S.: 513210
Rob Wenger *(Founder & Chm)*
Conor Sibley *(CTO)*
Hunter Montgomery *(CMO)*

Heather McNair *(Chief Community
Officer)*
Edward English *(Chief Product Officer)*
Ann Burns *(Chief HR Officer)*
Richard Henderson *(Chief Sls Officer)*
Kevin Boyce *(CEO)*
Bettina Fowler *(Sr VP-Client Ops)*
Tricia Benedix *(CFO)*

Subsidiaries:

Informz, LLC   (1)
19 Railroad Place Ste 301, Saratoga
Springs, NY 12866
Tel.: (518) 691-0071
Web Site: http://www.higherlogic.com
Professional Services; Email Marketing
N.A.I.C.S.: 541910
Joseph C. Tyler *(Pres & CEO)*

Real Magnet, LLC   (1)
4853 Cordell Ave, Bethesda, MD 20814
Tel.: (240) 743-2950
Information Technology & Services; Marketing Automation, Social Media Publishing & Analytics, Inbound Marketing & Email Marketing
N.A.I.C.S.: 513210
Michael Al-Megdad *(VP-Product Mktg)*
Mike Zimmerman *(Sales Director)*

Socious, Inc.   (1)
1201 S Alma School Rd Ste 11100, Mesa,
AZ 85210
Tel.: (855) 762-4687
Web Site: http://www.socious.com
Social Media Services
N.A.I.C.S.: 513210
Paul Schneider *(CEO)*
Scott Balthazor *(Chief Customer Officer)*
Steve Balthazor *(CTO)*
Joshua Paul *(VP-Mktg & Strategy)*
Lew Conner *(Sr VP-Specialty Svcs)*

**HIGHER POWER MARKETING
(HPM)**
2949 E Shady Spring Trail, Phoenix,
AZ 85024
Tel.: (888) 501-5544
Web Site:
   http://www.hpowermarketing.com
Year Founded: 1999
Sales Range: $1-9.9 Million
Emp.: 15
Interactive & Print Placements
N.A.I.C.S.: 541613
Peter Feinstein *(Founder, Pres &
CEO)*

**HIGHFIELDS CAPITAL MAN-
AGEMENT LP**
200 Clarendon St 59th Fl, Boston,
MA 02116
Tel.: (617) 850-7500
Web Site:
   https://www.highfieldscapital.com
Year Founded: 1998
Sales Range: $25-49.9 Million
Emp.: 65
Privater Equity Firm
N.A.I.C.S.: 523999
Daniel S. Farb *(Mng Dir & Partner-
Investment Team)*

HIGHGATE HOTELS, L.P.
870 7th Ave 2nd Fl, New York, NY
10019
Tel.: (212) 707-5031   DE
Web Site: http://www.highgate.com
Hospitality Investment Holding Company
N.A.I.C.S.: 551112
Steve Barick *(COO)*
Marianne Balfe *(VP-Sustainability)*

Subsidiaries:

CorePoint Lodging Inc.   (1)
125 E John Carpenter Fwy Ste 1650, Irving,
TX 75062
Tel.: (972) 893-3199

Highgate Hotels, L.P.—(Continued)

Web Site: http://www.corepoint.com
Rev.: $411,000,000
Assets: $1,766,000,000
Liabilities: $909,000,000
Net Worth: $857,000,000
Earnings: ($178,000,000)
Emp.: 32
Fiscal Year-end: 12/31/2020
Real Estate Investment Services
N.A.I.C.S.: 531210
Keith A. Cline (Pres & CEO)
Howard S. Garfield (Chief Acctg Officer, Treas & Sr VP)
Daniel E. Swanstrom II (CFO & Exec VP)

DoubleTree by Hilton Metropolitan-New York City (1)
569 Lexington Ave, New York, NY 10022
Tel.: (212) 752-7000
Web Site:
http://www.metropolitanhotelnyc.com
Sales Range: $1-9.9 Million
Hotel Operator
N.A.I.C.S.: 721110

HIGHLAND BANKSHARES INC.
701 Central Ave E, Saint Michael, MN 55376
Tel.: (763) 497-2131   **MN**
Web Site:
http://www.highlandbanks.com
Year Founded: 1978
Sales Range: $25-49.9 Million
Emp.: 75
Bank Holding Company
N.A.I.C.S.: 551111
Harold Orcutt (CFO & Sr VP)

Subsidiaries:

Boundary Waters Bank (1)
601 E Sheridan St, Ely, MN 55731
Tel.: (218) 365-6181
Web Site: http://www.mybwbank.com
Commericial Banking
N.A.I.C.S.: 522110
Tony Pecha (Pres)

Highland Bank (1)
701 Central Ave E, Saint Michael, MN 55376
Tel.: (763) 497-2131
Web Site: http://www.highland.bank
Retail & Commercial Banking
N.A.I.C.S.: 522110
Rick Wall (CEO)
Harold Orcutt (CFO & Exec VP)
Gary Moore (VP & Branch Mgr)
Troy Rosenbrook (Pres)
Melissa Johnston (Sr VP-Bus Banking)
Jim Horton (Sr VP)
David Esposito (Sr VP & Dir-Retail Banking)
Ryan Giesmann (Sr VP)
Kim Storey (Sr VP)
Andrew Dahlen (Sr VP & Dir-Sls)

HIGHLAND CAPITAL MANAGEMENT, L.P.
300 Crescent Ct Ste 700, Dallas, TX 75201
Tel.: (972) 628-4100   **DE**
Web Site:
http://www.highlandcapital.com
Year Founded: 1997
Rev.: $13,700,000,000
Investment Advisory & Management Services
N.A.I.C.S.: 523940
Mark Okada (Co-Founder & Co-Chief Investment Officer)
Trey Parker (Co-Chief Investment Officer)
Damon Krytzer (Mng Dir)
Jon Poglitsch (Head-Credit Res)
Andrew Parmentier (Chief Strategy Officer, Partner & Head-Thematic Investing)
Laurie Whetstone (Mng Dir-San Francisco)

Kieran Brennan (Dir-New York)
Joe Sowin (Co-Chief Investment Officer)

Subsidiaries:

3P Manufacturing, Inc. (1)
4201 S 119th St W, Wichita, KS 67215
Tel.: (316) 522-5426
Sales Range: $25-49.9 Million
Aerospace Machined Parts & Assemblies Mfr
N.A.I.C.S.: 336413
William McKenna (CEO)
Merlin Belnap (CFO)

Highland Acquisition Corporation (1)
300 Crescent Ct Ste 700, Dallas, TX 75201
Tel.: (972) 628-4100
Emp.: 4
Investment Holding Company
N.A.I.C.S.: 551112
Mark Okada (Exec VP)
Frank Waterhouse (CFO)
Thomas Surgent (Sec)

Highland Financial Trust (1)
300 Crescent Ct Ste 700, Dallas, TX 75201
Tel.: (972) 628-4100
Financial Investment
N.A.I.C.S.: 523999

NexPoint Advisors, L.P. (1)
300 Crescent Ct Ste 700, Dallas, TX 75201
Tel.: (972) 628-4100
Web Site: http://www.nexpointadvisors.com
Investment Advisory & Portfolio Management Services
N.A.I.C.S.: 523940
Brian Dale Mitts (COO)
James David Dondero (Executives)
Dustin Norris (Sec)
Frank Waterhouse (Treas)

Affiliate (Domestic):

NexPoint Capital, Inc. (2)
300 Crk Ct Ste 700, Dallas, TX 75201   (26.52%)
Tel.: (972) 628-4100
Web Site: https://www.nexpointcapital.com
Rev.: $3,332,223
Assets: $51,279,034
Liabilities: $1,469,508
Net Worth: $49,809,526
Earnings: $1,666,934
Fiscal Year-end: 12/31/2023
Closed-End Investment Fund
N.A.I.C.S.: 525990
James David Dondero (Pres)
Frank George Waterhouse (Principal Fin Officer, Principal Acctg Officer & Treas)

NexPoint Hospitality Trust, Inc. (2)
300 Crescent Ct Ste 700, Dallas, TX 75201
Tel.: (972) 419-2500
Web Site:
http://www.nexpointhospitality.com
Real Estate Investment Trust
N.A.I.C.S.: 525990
Brian Dale Mitts (CFO, COO, Treas, Treas, Sec & Exec VP/Exec VP-Fin)
James David Dondero (CEO)
Brian Mitts (CFO, Treas, Sec & Exec VP-Fin)
Jesse Blair (Exec VP & Head-Lodging)
Matthew McGraner (Chief Investment Officer-Real Estate)
Paul Richards (VP-Asset Mgmt)

NexPoint Multifamily Capital Trust, Inc. (2)
300 Crescent Ct Ste 700, Dallas, TX 75201
Tel.: (972) 628-4100
Web Site: http://www.nmcreit.com
Rev.: $3,884,000
Assets: $45,826,000
Liabilities: $39,182,000
Net Worth: $6,644,000
Earnings: ($1,503,000)
Fiscal Year-end: 12/31/2016
Real Estate Investment Trust
N.A.I.C.S.: 525990
Brian Dale Mitts (CFO, Treas & Exec VP-Fin)
Scott Ellington (Gen Counsel & Sec)
Matthew McGraner (Chief Investment Officer & Exec VP)
Matthew Goetz (VP-Investments & Asset Mgmt)

NexPoint Residential Trust, Inc. (2)
300 Crescent Ct Ste 700, Dallas, TX 75201
Tel.: (214) 276-6300
Web Site: https://nxrt.nexpoint.com
Rev.: $263,952,000
Assets: $2,225,337,000
Liabilities: $1,705,671,000
Net Worth: $519,666,000
Earnings: ($9,260,000)
Emp.: 3
Fiscal Year-end: 12/31/2022
Real Estate Investment Trust
N.A.I.C.S.: 525990
Brian Dale Mitts (Co-Founder, CFO, CFO, Treas, Sec & Exec VP/Exec VP-Fin)
James David Dondero (Chm & Pres)
Brian Mitts (Co-Founder, CFO, Sec & Exec VP-Fin)
Matt McGraner (Chief Investment Officer & Exec VP)
Dennis D.C. Sauter Jr. (Gen counsel)

HIGHLAND CAPITAL PARTNERS, LLC
1 Broadway 16th Fl, Cambridge, MA 02142
Tel.: (617) 401-4500
Web Site: http://www.hcp.com
Sales Range: $25-49.9 Million
Emp.: 50
Privater Equity Firm
N.A.I.C.S.: 523999
Craig Driscoll (Partner-Talent)
Bob Davis (Partner)
Manish Patel (Partner)
Alex Taussig (Partner)
Jessica Pelletier (CFO)
Dan Nova (Partner)
Paul Maeder (Founder, Chm & Gen Partner)
Corey Mulloy (Partner)
Freddie Martignetti (Principal)
Sean Judge (Principal)
Jessica Healey (CFO)
Dan Nova (Gen Partner)

Subsidiaries:

City Sports (1)
64 Industrial Way, Wilmington, MA 01887-3434
Tel.: (978) 253-5300
Web Site: http://www.citysports.com
Sales Range: $25-49.9 Million
Sports Apparel & Accessories
N.A.I.C.S.: 458110
Eric Martin (Co-Founder)
Marty Hanaka (CEO)

Highland Consumer Partners Management Company LLC (1)
20 William St Ste 115, Wellesley, MA 02481
Tel.: (781) 992-5600
Web Site:
http://www.highlandconsumer.com
Retail Industry Private Equity Firm
N.A.I.C.S.: 523999
Peter Cornetta (Mng Gen Partner)
Thomas G. Stemberg (Mng Gen Partner)
David Krauser (Partner)
Michael Cam-Phung (Principal)

Highland Europe (UK) LLP (1)
12 Golden Square, London, W1F 9JE, United Kingdom
Tel.: (44) 20 3137 6892
Investment Services
N.A.I.C.S.: 523999
David Blyghton (Principal)

HIGHLAND COMPUTER FORMS INC.
1025 W Main St, Hillsboro, OH 45133-8219
Tel.: (937) 393-4215   **OH**
Web Site: https://www.hcf.com
Year Founded: 1979
Sales Range: $25-49.9 Million
Emp.: 120
Manifold Business Forms
N.A.I.C.S.: 323111
Steve Patton (VP-Ops)

HIGHLAND CORPORATION
108 Mill St, Hohenwald, TN 38462
Tel.: (931) 796-2274
Web Site:
https://www.highlandcorp.com
Sales Range: $1-9.9 Million
Emp.: 100
Petroleum Bulk Stations
N.A.I.C.S.: 424710
David M. Adcox (Owner & Pres)
Bobby Page (COO & VP)
Connie Adcox (Co-Owner)
Seth Blanks (VP-Sls & Mktg)
Rhonda Bass (Asst Controller)
Sharon Greene (Mgr-Credit)
Jerry Sharp (Gen Mgr-Retail)
Lydia Spears (Mgr-Pricebook)

HIGHLAND FORWARDING, INC.
35 Constitution Dr Ste A, Bedford, NH 03110
Tel.: (603) 471-2800
Web Site:
https://www.highlandforwarding.com
Year Founded: 1999
Rev.: $8,900,000
Emp.: 18
Freight Transportation Arrangement Services
N.A.I.C.S.: 488510
Radek Maly (Pres)
Natalia Derkach (Dir-Bus Dev)

HIGHLAND HOMES LTD.
5601 Democracy Dr Ste 300, Plano, TX 75024-1529
Tel.: (972) 789-3500   **TX**
Web Site:
https://www.highlandhomes.com
Year Founded: 1982
Sales Range: $25-49.9 Million
Emp.: 200
Residential Construction
N.A.I.C.S.: 236115
Amy Kinney (Mgr-Ops)
Evin Philbrick (Project Mgr)
James Dalton (Mgr-Pur)
Jim Cable (Supvr-IT)
Roxanne Bowen (Mgr-Community Sls)

Subsidiaries:

Sanders & Associates Custom Builders Inc. (1)
5601 Democracy Dr Ste 300, Dallas, TX 75230-1529   (100%)
Tel.: (972) 713-8494
Web Site:
http://www.sanderscustomhomes.com
Sales Range: $10-24.9 Million
Emp.: 75
Single-Family House Construction Services
N.A.I.C.S.: 236115
Jean Ann Brock (VP)

HIGHLAND MILLS INC.
340 E 16th St, Charlotte, NC 28233
Tel.: (704) 375-3333
Web Site:
https://www.highlandmills.com
Year Founded: 1972
Hosiery Mfr
N.A.I.C.S.: 315120

HIGHLAND PRODUCTIONS, LLC
433 Central Ave 3rd Fl Loft, Saint Petersburg, FL 33701
Tel.: (727) 623-0916
Web Site:
http://www.highlandproductions llc.com
Holding Company; Advertising Agencies
N.A.I.C.S.: 551112
Jenn Greacen (Principal)

Subsidiaries:

Red Frog Marketing **(1)**
2401 W Bay Dr Bldg 100 Ste 101, Largo,
FL 33770
Tel.: (727) 489-2332
Web Site: http://www.getyourfrogon.com
Advetising Agency
N.A.I.C.S.: 541810

The CLEAR Agency **(1)**
2529 Central Ave, Saint Petersburg, FL
33713
Tel.: (727) 489-2332
Web Site: http://www.theclearagency.com
Sales Range: $1-9.9 Million
Emp.: 8
Advetising Agency
N.A.I.C.S.: 541810
Jenn Greacen (CEO & Exec Dir)
Joe Russo (Assoc Dir)

HIGHLAND ROOFING CO.
4310 Deer Creek Ln, Wilmington, NC
28405
Tel.: (910) 798-0155
Web Site:
   https://www.highlandroofingcom
   pany.com
Roofing Services
N.A.I.C.S.: 238160
Iain Fergusson (Owner)

Subsidiaries:

Hanover Iron Works, Inc. **(1)**
1851 Dawson St, Wilmington, NC 28403
Tel.: (910) 763-7318
Web Site: http://www.hanoverironworks.com
Emp.: 50
Roofing Contractors
N.A.I.C.S.: 238160
Horace T. King (Pres)

HIGHLAND SUGARWORKS, INCORPORATED
Wilson Industrial Park, Websterville,
VT 05678
Tel.: (802) 479-1747
Web Site:
   http://www.highlandsugarworks.com
Year Founded: 1986
Sales Range: $75-99.9 Million
Emp.: 100
Maple Sugar Syrup Mfr
N.A.I.C.S.: 311999
Deb Frimodig (COO)

HIGHLAND SUPPLY CORPO-RATION
1111 6th St, Highland, IL 62249-1408
Tel.: (618) 654-2161   IL
Web Site:
   http://www.highlandsupply.com
Year Founded: 1937
Rev.: $29,900,000
Emp.: 275
Metal Foil & Leaf
N.A.I.C.S.: 332999
Donald E. Weder (Pres)
John Kunkel (Controller)
Michael Gilkey (Dir-Transportation)

Subsidiaries:

Southern Steel & Wire Inc. **(1)**
100 Minich Rd, Madison, NC 27025
Tel.: (910) 654-2161
Web Site: http://www.highlandsupply.com
Sales Range: $10-24.9 Million
Emp.: 30
Special Dies Tools Jigs & Fixtures
N.A.I.C.S.: 333514
Doen Waiter (Pres)

HIGHLAND TANK & MANU-FACTURING CO.
1 Highland Rd, Stoystown, PA 15563
Tel.: (814) 893-5701
Web Site:
   http://www.highlandtank.com
Sales Range: $10-24.9 Million

Emp.: 125
Tanks, Standard Or Custom Fabri-
cated: Metal Plate
N.A.I.C.S.: 332420
John Jacob (Pres)

HIGHLAND TELEPHONE CO-OPERATIVE, INC.
7840 Morgan County Hwy, Sunbright,
TN 37872
Tel.: (423) 628-2121   TN
Web Site: https://www.highlandtel.net
Year Founded: 1954
Rev.: $16,518,951
Emp.: 79
Local Telephone Communications
N.A.I.C.S.: 517121
Steve Armes (Mgr-Acctg)
Mark Patterson (Gen Mgr)
Dave Crawford (Mgr-Access Svc)
Diann Stephens (Mgr-HR)

HIGHLAND TEXAS ENERGY CO
7557 Rambler Rd Ste 918, Dallas,
TX 75231
Tel.: (214) 369-2020
Energy Exploration Services
N.A.I.C.S.: 211120
David Brewer (Mgr-Geology)
Steven M. Burr (Mgr-Engrg)
Russell L. Harlow (Mgr-Land)
Truitt Matthews (Sr Geologist)

HIGHLAND VENTURES, LTD.
2500 Lehigh Ave, Glenview, IL 60026
Tel.: (847) 904-9000   IL
Web Site:
   http://www.highlandventuresltd.com
Year Founded: 1985
Holding Company; Consumer Prod-
ucts & Services; Commercial Prop-
erty Leasing Services
N.A.I.C.S.: 551112
Keith A. Hoogland (Pres)

Subsidiaries:

Family Video Movie Club Inc. **(1)**
2500 Lehigh Ave, Glenview, IL 60026
Tel.: (847) 904-9000
Web Site: http://www.familyvideo.com
Emp.: 7,000
Video & Videogame Disc Rental Services
N.A.I.C.S.: 532282
Keith A. Hoogland (Pres)

Division (Domestic):

Legacy Commercial Property **(2)**
2500 Lehigh Ave, Glenview, IL 60026
Tel.: (847) 904-9200
Web Site: http://www.legacypro.com
Commercial Properties Leasing & Sales
Services
N.A.I.C.S.: 531120
Keith A. Hoogland (Pres)

Marco's Pizza, Inc. **(1)**
5252 Monroe St, Toledo, OH 43623
Tel.: (419) 885-7000
Web Site: http://www.marcos.com
Pizzeria Restaurants Franchisor & Operator
N.A.I.C.S.: 722513
Don Vlcek (VP-Pur)
Jack Butorac (Chm & Co-CEO)
Shawn Chowdhary (VP-Admin)
Joseph Marcoguiseppe (Reg Dir-Mktg)
Jim Strachan (VP-Franchise Ops)
Tony Libardi (Pres & Co-CEO)
Charles Solomon (CFO)
Steve Seyferth (Chief Experience Officer)
Chris Tussing (CMO & Sr VP)
John King (Sr VP-Ops)
Gerardo Flores (Chief Dev Officer)
Shannon Iverson (VP-Franchise Sls)

HIGHLAND-EXCHANGE SER-VICE COOPERATIVE INC.
5916 State Rd 540, Waverly, FL
33877
Tel.: (863) 439-3661   FL

Web Site: http://www.hesco-fl.com
Year Founded: 1972
Sales Range: $10-24.9 Million
Emp.: 20
Industrial Machinery & Supplies
N.A.I.C.S.: 424130
Donna Barnes (Gen Mgr)
Gasper Kovach Jr. (CEO)

Subsidiaries:

Highland-Exchange Petroleum Supply
Co. Inc. **(1)**
5916 Waverly Rd, Waverly, FL
33877   **(100%)**
Tel.: (863) 439-3661
Web Site: http://www.hepsco-fl.com
Petroleum Products
N.A.I.C.S.: 424720
Donna Barnes (Bus Mgr-Unit)

HIGHLANDER PARTNERS, LP.
300 Crescent Ct Ste 550, Dallas, TX
75201
Tel.: (214) 245-5000   TX
Web Site: https://www.highlander-
   partners.com
Year Founded: 2004
Privater Equity Firm
Michael R. Nicolais (Vice Chm &
CEO)
Jeff L. Hull (Pres & Mng Partner)
Alex L. Guiva (Partner)
Stanley C. Bould (Partner-Alternative
Investments)
Robert A. Sussman (CFO)
Chris M. McRorie (Gen Counsel)
Mark A. Blanchat (Partner)
Charles C. Thomas (VP)
Dawid Walendowski (Mng Partner-
Central Europe)
Artur Dzagarow (Co-Mng Partner-
CEE-Poland)
Jeff Partridge (Mng Dir)
Stewart Baseley (Chm-CEE-Poland)
Doran E. Smith (Assoc Gen Counsel)
John Rabenhorst (Dir)
Ben R. Slater (Dir)
Nicholas E. Thicksten (VP)
Artur Zaniewski (Dir-Investment)
Laurence E. Hirsch (Chm)
Laurence E. Hirsch (Chm)

Subsidiaries:

AP Formulators **(1)**
1015 Georgia St, South Houston, TX
77587-3918
Tel.: (713) 946-1600
Web Site: http://www.apchemical.com
Car Washes
N.A.I.C.S.: 811192
Alan Palermo (Pres)

Bevolution Group **(1)**
4401 S Oakley Ave, Chicago, IL 60609
Tel.: (773) 579-1291
Web Site: http://www.bevolutiongroup.com
Sales Range: $25-49.9 Million
Juice & Beverage Concentrate Mfr & Distr
N.A.I.C.S.: 311411
Dennis Paldin (Reg Mgr)
Jim Harwood (Reg Mgr-Sls)
Jim Croci (VP-Fin)
Matt Martens (VP-Ops)
Lynn Mayers (VP-Mktg)
Melody Austin (Mgr-Fin)
Stephanie Buckner (Mgr-Mktg)
John Capozzoli (Mgr-Engrg)
John Collum (Reg Mgr-Sls)
Melissa Machowski (Supvr-Acctg)
Dan O'Brien (Reg Mgr-Sls)
Mark Schacht (VP-Bus Dev)
Kirk Reid (CEO)

Subsidiary (Domestic):

Dr Smoothie Brands **(2)**
1730 Raymer Ave, Fullerton, CA 92833
Tel.: (714) 449-9787
Web Site: http://www.drsmoothie.com

Sales Range: $1-9.9 Million
Emp.: 37
Mfg Flavor Extracts/Syrup
N.A.I.C.S.: 311999
Ashlee Gonigam (Mgr-Market)
Sam Ltief (CEO)

Direct Scaffold Supply, Inc. **(1)**
6059 South Loop East, Houston, TX 77087
Tel.: (713) 673-7701
Web Site: https://dss.net
Sales Range: $1-9.9 Million
Emp.: 28
Construction And Mining Machinery
N.A.I.C.S.: 423810
Bobby Frederick (Pres)

Fuerst Day Lawson Ltd. **(1)**
Devon House 58-60 St Katharine's Way,
London, E1W 1JP, United Kingdom
Tel.: (44) 20 7488 0777
Web Site: http://www.fdlworld.com
Food & Beverage Ingredient Whslr
N.A.I.C.S.: 424480
Guy Humphry-Baker (CFO)
Maurice Day Lawson (Chm)
Eric Beatty (CEO)

Subsidiary (Non-US):

FDL China **(2)**
20C Strength Plaza No 4 Lane 600 Tian-
shan Road, Shanghai, 200051, China
Tel.: (86) 2152896655
Web Site: http://www.fdlworld.com
Food & Beverage Ingredient Distr
N.A.I.C.S.: 424480

Highlander Partners Sp. z o.o. **(1)**
plac Marszalka Jozefa Pilsudskiego 1, 00
078, Warsaw, Poland
Tel.: (48) 22 445 0340
Web Site: http://www.highlander-
   partners.com
Privater Equity Firm
N.A.I.C.S.: 523999
Dawid Walendowski (Mng Partner)

Hillside Candy, LLC **(1)**
35 Hillside Ave, Hillside, NJ 07205
Tel.: (973) 926-2300
Web Site: http://www.hillsidecandy.com
Mfg Candy/Confectionery
N.A.I.C.S.: 311340
Ted Cohen (Pres & CEO)

Lemon-X Corporation **(1)**
168 Railroad St, Huntington Station, NY
11746
Tel.: (800) 220-1061
Web Site: http://www.lemon-x.com
Cocktail Mixes, Nonalcoholic & Alcoholic
Beverages Mfr & Distr
N.A.I.C.S.: 311999
Gabe Froehlich (Mgr-Sls)

Liteye Systems, Inc. **(1)**
7330 S Alton Way 12-C, Centennial, CO
80112
Tel.: (720) 974-1766
Web Site: http://www.liteye.com
Sales Range: $1-9.9 Million
Emp.: 10
Electronic Computers, Nsk
N.A.I.C.S.: 334111
Guy Nason (Dir-Ops)

Niteo Products, LLC **(1)**
5949 Sherry Ln Ste 540, Dallas, TX 75225
Tel.: (844) 696-4836
Chemical & Allied Products Merchant Whslr
N.A.I.C.S.: 424690

Division (Domestic):

Cyclo Industries, Inc. **(2)**
902 S US Hwy 1, Jupiter, FL 33477
Tel.: (561) 775-9600
Web Site: http://www.cyclo.com
Chemical & Allied Products Merchant Whslr
N.A.I.C.S.: 424690

Profile Custom Extrusion, LLC **(1)**
100 Anderson Rd SW, Rome, GA 30161
Tel.: (706) 234-7558
Web Site: http://www.profile-extrusion.com
Aluminum Extrusion Product Mfr
N.A.I.C.S.: 331318
David Newby (Gen Mgr)
Danny Thomas (Mgr-Engrg)
Mike Simpson (Mgr-Production)
Jeff Brown (Mgr-Sls)
Eileen Albaugh (Mgr-Sls)

Highlander Partners, LP.—(Continued)

Trans-Mate, Inc. (1)
13 Sterling Rd, North Billerica, MA 01862
Tel.: (978) 667-0100
Web Site: http://www.trans-mate.com
Nondurable Goods Merchant Wholesalers
N.A.I.C.S.: 424990
Stephen A. Stockman (Pres, Treas & Sec)

Twitchell Corporation (1)
4031 Ross Clark Cir, Dothan, AL 36303
Tel.: (334) 792-0002
Web Site: http://www.twitchellcorp.com
Plastic Awnings & Outdoor Furniture & Fabric Mfr
N.A.I.C.S.: 313210

HIGHLANDS HOSPITAL
401 E Murphy Ave, Connellsville, PA
15425
Tel.: (724) 628-1500　　　　PA
Web Site:
　https://www.highlandshospital.org
Year Founded: 1985
Sales Range: $25-49.9 Million
Emp.: 425
Behavioral Healthcare Services
N.A.I.C.S.: 623220
Denise McCloy (Chief Admin Officer)
John S. Andursky (CFO & Asst Treas)
Mary Jane Krosoff (Chief HR Officer)
Angela R. Danko (Asst Sec & Coord-Admin Svcs)
Floyd C. Huggin (Sec)
Michael A. Jordan (Vice Chm)

HIGHLANDS INSURANCE GROUP INC.
10370 Richmond Ave, Houston, TX
77042
Tel.: (713) 952-9555　　　　DE
Sales Range: $550-599.9 Million
Emp.: 629
Casualty, Property, Surety & Marine
Insurance Services
N.A.I.C.S.: 524126
Stephen L. Kibblehouse (CEO)

HIGHLANDS MUTUAL HOUSING CORPORATION, INC.
8001 Fruitridge Rd Ste A, Sacramento, CA 95820-6760
Tel.: (916) 453-8400　　　　CA
Year Founded: 2009
Sales Range: $1-9.9 Million
Housing Rental Services
N.A.I.C.S.: 624229
Mindy Romero (Pres)
Elizabeth Beigh (VP)
Jack I. Dyard (Sec)

HIGHLANDS RANCH COMMUNITY ASSOCIATION, INC.
9568 University Blvd, Highlands
Ranch, CO 80126
Tel.: (303) 471-8958　　　　CO
Web Site: https://hrcaonline.org
Year Founded: 1981
Sales Range: $10-24.9 Million
Emp.: 973
Community Action Services
N.A.I.C.S.: 624190
Mike Bailey (Dir-Community Improvement Svcs)

HIGHLANDS REIT, INC.
1 S Dearborn St 20th Fl, Chicago, IL
60603
Tel.: (312) 583-7990　　　　MD
Web Site:
　https://www.highlandsreit.com
Year Founded: 2015
HHDS—(OTCIQ)
Rev.: $31,356,000
Assets: $315,114,000
Liabilities: $74,757,000

Net Worth: $240,357,000
Earnings: ($7,662,000)
Emp.: 8
Fiscal Year-end: 12/31/22
Real Estate Investment Services
N.A.I.C.S.: 531120
Richard Vance (Pres & CEO)
Robert J. Lange (COO, Gen Counsel, Sec & Exec VP)
Kimberly A. Karas (Chief Acctg Officer, Principal Fin Officer, Treas, Sr VP & Controller)

Subsidiaries:

1620 Central LLC (1)
1620 Central St, Evanston, IL 60201
Tel.: (847) 424-0199
Web Site: https://www.1620central.com
Apartment Rental Services
N.A.I.C.S.: 531110

The Lafayette Denver, LLC (1)
1575 Lafayette St, Denver, CO 80218
Tel.: (303) 333-3773
Web Site:
　https://www.thelafayettedenver.com
Apartment Rental Services
N.A.I.C.S.: 531110

HIGHLIGHTS FOR CHILDREN, INC.
1800 Watermark Dr, Columbus, OH
43216
Tel.: (614) 486-0631　　　　DE
Web Site: https://www.highlights.com
Year Founded: 1946
Sales Range: $150-199.9 Million
Emp.: 584
Children Magazine Publisher
N.A.I.C.S.: 513120
Kent S. Johnson (CEO)

Subsidiaries:

Boyds Mills Press, Inc. (1)
815 Church St, Honesdale, PA 18431
Tel.: (570) 253-1164
Web Site: http://www.boydsmillspress.com
Sales Range: $10-24.9 Million
Emp.: 50
Children's Books
N.A.I.C.S.: 513130
Tim Gillner (Dir-Art)

Highlights for Children International, Inc. (1)
1800 Watermark Dr, Columbus, OH 43216-0269
Tel.: (888) 372-6433
Magazine & Book Distr
N.A.I.C.S.: 424920

Staff Development for Educators, Inc. (1)
10 Sharon Rd, Peterborough, NH 03458
Tel.: (800) 924-9621
Web Site: http://www.sde.com
Professional Development Services
N.A.I.C.S.: 611430
Kate Maggs (Mgr-Program Plng)

Stenhouse Publishers (1)
1 Monument Way Ste 250, Portland, ME
04101
Tel.: (207) 253-1600
Web Site: http://www.stenhouse.com
Sales Range: $10-24.9 Million
Emp.: 15
Text Books & Materials
N.A.I.C.S.: 513130
Elaine Cyr (Mgr-Ops & Customer Svc)
Chuck Lerch (Mgr-Mktg)
William Varner (Editor)
Dan Tobin (Pres)

Zaner-Bloser, Inc. (1)
1400 Goodale, Columbus, OH
43215　　　　　　　　(100%)
Tel.: (614) 486-0221
Web Site: http://www.zaner-bloser.com
Children's Educational Materials
N.A.I.C.S.: 424920
Robert Page (Pres)

HIGHLINE ELECTRIC ASSOCIATION

1300 S Interocean, Holyoke, CO
80734
Tel.: (970) 854-2236
Web Site: https://www.hea.coop
Sales Range: $10-24.9 Million
Emp.: 50
Electric Power Distr
N.A.I.C.S.: 221122
Mark Farnsworth (Gen Mgr)
Jim Lueck (VP)

HIGHMARK HEALTH
5th Ave Pl 120 5th Ave, Pittsburgh,
PA 15222-3099
Tel.: (412) 544-7000　　　　PA
Web Site:
　http://www.highmarkhealth.org
Year Founded: 2011
Sales Range: $15-24.9 Billion
Emp.: 35,000
Health Care Services & Insurance
Organization
N.A.I.C.S.: 813910
David L. Holmberg (Pres & CEO)
Daniel A. Onorato (Chief Corp Affairs Officer & Exec VP)
Joseph C. Guyaux (Chm)
Karen L. Hanlon (COO & Treas)
Cindy Donohoe (CMO & Exec VP)
Michael J. Bennett (Chief Strategy Officer, Chief Transformation Officer & Exec VP)
Tony G. Farah (Chief Medical & Clinical Transformation Officer & Exec VP)
Larry Kleinman (Chief HR Officer & Exec VP)
Melissa M. Anderson (Compliance Officer & Exec VP)
John Orner (Chief Investment Officer & Sr VP)
Carolyn Duronio (Chief Legal Officer & Sec)
Bruce A. Meyer (Pres-Western Pennsylvania & Exec VP)
Carl Daley (CFO & Exec VP)
Janine Colinear (Sr VP)
Ja'Ron Bridges (CFO/Sr VP-Highmark Health Plans)
Tom Doran (Pres-Highmark Health Plan)

Subsidiaries:

Highmark Inc. (1)
120 5th Ave, Pittsburgh, PA 15222
Tel.: (412) 544-7000
Web Site: http://www.highmarkbcbs.com
Managed Care & Indemnity Health Care
Coverage & Employee Benefits Products &
Services
N.A.I.C.S.: 524114
David L. Holmberg (Chm)
Daniel A. Onorato (Chief External Affairs & Comm Officer & Exec VP)
Elizabeth D. Bierbower (Executives)
Eric Hays (VP-Reg Sls)
Dana Garcia (VP-Corp Real Estate)
Deborah L. Rice-Johnson (Pres-Health Plan)
Tony Farah (Chief Medical & Clinical Transformation Officer & Exec VP)
Brian D. Setzer (COO)

Subsidiary (Domestic):

AllOne Health Resources, Inc. (2)
100 North Pennsylvania Ave, Wilkes Barre,
PA 18701
Tel.: (877) 720-7770
Web Site: http://www.allonehealth.com
Onsite Health Clinics, Wellness & Health
Promotion
N.A.I.C.S.: 621999
Anthony Matrisciano (Mgr)

Subsidiary (Domestic):

Reach EAP, LLC (3)
182 North Breiel Blvd Ste B, Middletown,
OH 45042
Tel.: (513) 423-3327

Web Site: http://allonehealth.com
Wellness Student Assistance Programs
N.A.I.C.S.: 923120
Angela D. Diver (Exec Dir)

Subsidiary (Domestic):

Empire Vision Ctr. Inc. (2)
2921 Erie Blvd E, Syracuse, NY 13224-1430
Tel.: (315) 446-3145
Web Site: http://www.empirevision.com
Sales Range: $25-49.9 Million
Emp.: 80
Optical Goods Stores
N.A.I.C.S.: 456130

Gateway Health Plan, Inc. (2)
444 Liberty Ave Ste 2100, Pittsburgh, PA
15222　　　　　　　　(100%)
Tel.: (412) 255-4640
Web Site:
　http://www.gatewayhealthplan.com
Provider of Hospital & Medical Service
Plans
N.A.I.C.S.: 524114
Cain A. Hayes (Pres & CEO)
Bret Bissey (Chief Compliance Officer & VP)
Eina Fishman (Chief Clinical Officer)
Heather Price (CFO-Interim & Treas)
Joe Walsh (CIO & VP)

HM Insurance Group, Inc. (2)
120 5th Ave, Pittsburgh, PA 15222-3099
Tel.: (814) 871-6793
Web Site: http://www.hmig.com
Insurance Product & Services
N.A.I.C.S.: 551112
Mark Vescovi (Dir-Insurance Solutions)

Subsidiary (Domestic):

HM Life Insurance Company (3)
120 5th Ave Pl, Pittsburgh, PA 15222-3099
Tel.: (412) 544-7000
Web Site: http://www.highmarkbcbs.com
Fire Insurance Services
N.A.I.C.S.: 524113
David Hoomburg (CEO)

Subsidiary (Domestic):

HealthGuard of Lancaster (2)
280 Granite Run Dr, Lancaster, PA
17601-6820　　　　　　(100%)
Tel.: (717) 560-9049
Web Site: http://www.hguard.com
Sales Range: $50-74.9 Million
Emp.: 170
A Health Maintenance Organization Serving
the Lancaster County Area of Pennsylvania
N.A.I.C.S.: 524114

**Highmark Blue Cross Blue Shield
Delaware** (2)
800 Delaware Ave Ste 900, Wilmington, DE
19801
Tel.: (302) 421-3000
Web Site: http://www.highmarkbcbsde.com
Sales Range: $50-74.9 Million
Emp.: 600
Health Insurance, Direct Health Care & Administrative Services
N.A.I.C.S.: 524114
Matthew Stehl (Mgr-Corp Comm)
Nicholas A. Moriello (Pres)
William E. Kirk III (VP & Sec)

**Highmark Blue Cross Blue Shield
West Virginia** (2)
614 Market St, Parkersburg, WV 26101
Tel.: (304) 424-7700
Web Site: http://www.highmarkbcbsw.com
Sales Range: $100-124.9 Million
Emp.: 900
Accident & Health Insurance Services
N.A.I.C.S.: 524114
Fred Earley (Pres)

Highmark Caring Place (2)
Downtown 620 Stanwix St, Pittsburgh, PA
15222
Web Site:
　http://www.highmarkcaringplace.com
Human Support, Counseling, Advisory &
Other Caring Related Services
N.A.I.C.S.: 624221
Daniel A. Onorato (Exec Dir)
Merril D. Hoge (Chm)

Highmark Senior Resources Inc. **(2)**
120 5th Ave Pl, Pittsburgh, PA 15222-3099
Tel.: (412) 544-7000
Web Site: http://www.highmarkbcbs.com
Health Care Insurance Services
N.A.I.C.S.: 524114
Michael Meadows (Sr Dir-Markets Mktg)
Randy Staggers (Sr VP-Admin Svcs & Fin Ops)
Sally Rich (Sr VP-Markets Ops)
Augusta Kairys (VP-Provider Tech & Strategic Partnerships)
Alexis Miller (VP-Provider Reimbursement)

Keystone Health Plan West, Inc. **(2)**
120 5th Ave, Pittsburgh, PA 15222
Tel.: (412) 544-7000
Web Site: http://www.highmark.com
Health Maintenance Organization Serving Western Pennsylvania
N.A.I.C.S.: 524114
Kenneth R. Melani (Pres & CEO)

Standard Property Corporation **(2)**
120 5th Ave Ste 2626, Pittsburgh, PA 15222 **(100%)**
Tel.: (412) 544-7000
Web Site: http://www.highmark.com
Sales Range: $10-24.9 Million
Emp.: 25
Real Estate
N.A.I.C.S.: 531120

United Concordia Companies Inc. **(2)**
4401 Deer Path Rd, Harrisburg, PA 17110-3983
Tel.: (717) 260-6801
Web Site: http://www.ucci.com
Sales Range: $100-124.9 Million
Emp.: 800
Provider of Insurance Services
N.A.I.C.S.: 524114
Theresa Jansen (Mgr)
Darron Wilt (Mgr-Producer Admin)
Robert Mitchell (Project Mgr)
Timothy J. Constantinewho (Pres & COO)

HIGHPOINT GLOBAL, LLC
300 N Meridian St Ste 190, Indianapolis, IN 46204
Tel.: (317) 576-4500
Web Site: http://www.highpointglobal.com
Management Consulting Services
N.A.I.C.S.: 541611
Christie Cox (Dir-Mktg)
Eric Anderson (Dir-Capture Mgmt)
Cynthia Karst (Dir-Customer Solutions)
MaryAnn Monroe (Dir-Customer Experience)
Ben Lanius (CEO)
Gary Stage (Chief Legal Officer)
Scott Willis (COO)
Gary Skorko (Sr VP-Bus Dev-IT Svcs)
Kristen Mullins (Chief HR Officer)
Andrea Garvey (Sr Dir-Health & Human Svcs-Herndon)
Jim Bottorff (CFO)
Debbie Granberry (VP-Bus Dev)
John Cyrus (Dir-IT Strategy & Bus Solutions)
Jay Jones (Chief Growth Officer)

Subsidiaries:

Primescape Solutions, Inc. **(1)**
510A Herndon Pkwy, Herndon, VA 20171
Tel.: (703) 650-1900
Web Site: http://www.highpointglobal.com
Software & Database Applications (for Government Agencies) Developer
N.A.I.C.S.: 541990
Bob Dacanay (Founder & Chm)
Robert Sharp (Owner)
Kathy Danner (VP)
Wayne Hull (Dir-Contracts)

HIGHPOINT HOLDINGS, LLC
2236 Cahaba Valley Dr Ste 100, Birmingham, AL 35242
Tel.: (205) 981-0021

Web Site: https://www.highpointholdings.com
Year Founded: 2002
Rev.: $300,000,000
Residential Real Estate Investment & Management
N.A.I.C.S.: 523999
Jeff Brooks (Founder & CEO)
Russell Taylor (Pres)
Patrick Sullivan (Dir-Fin & Admin)
Steve Bowie (Mng Dir)
Andrew Bowie (Mng Dir-Midsouth Reg)

HIGHPOINT SOLUTIONS, LLC
Parkview Tower 1150 1st Ave Ste 450, King of Prussia, PA 19406
Tel.: (610) 233-2700
Web Site: http://www.highpoint-solutions.com
Year Founded: 2001
Rev.: $51,400,000
Emp.: 350
Administrative Management & General Management Consulting Services
N.A.I.C.S.: 541611
Tracy Burns (Exec VP-Delivery Excellence)
Chris Colapietro (Exec VP-Tech & Mktg)
James Dandy (CFO)
John P. Seitz (CEO)

HIGHPOINT TECHNOLOGY SOLUTIONS, INC.
2332 Galiano St 2nd Floor, Coral Gables, FL 33134
Web Site: http://www.mhighpoint.com
Year Founded: 2006
Sales Range: $1-9.9 Million
Emp.: 20
Specialized Mobile Technology & Consulting Services
N.A.I.C.S.: 513210
George Amalor (Founder & CEO)

HIGHPOST CAPITAL, LLC
75 Rockefeller Plaza Suite 1600B, New York, NY 10019
Web Site: https://www.highpost.com
Emp.: 100
Private Equity.
N.A.I.C.S.: 523999
Kevin M. Mailender (Sr VP)
David Moross (Founder, Chm & CEO)
Shreya Kedia (VP)
David Weston (Mng Dir-Fund I)

Subsidiaries:

Inspire Fitness **(1)**
4945 E Hunter Ave, Anaheim, CA 92807-2058
Tel.: (714) 738-1729
Web Site: http://www.inspirefitness.net
Fitness & Recreational Sports Centers
N.A.I.C.S.: 713940

HIGHRADIUS CORPORATION
9801 Westheimer Rd, Houston, TX 77042
Tel.: (281) 968-4474
Web Site: http://www.highradius.com
Rev.: $2,400,000
Emp.: 35
Software Publisher
N.A.I.C.S.: 513210
Gregory McStravick (Dir-Revenue)
Sashidhar Narahari (Founder, Pres & CEO)
Mike Gilbert (VP-Sls)
Pankaj Jagtap (VP)
Kenneth A. Sidelinger (Gen Counsel)
Tara Gallagher (Sr Mgr-Mktg)
Mike Dignen (VP-Banking Solutions)
Taylor Bartlett (Coord-Mktg)

Jerry Morgan (VP-Sls-Mid Market)
Urvish Vashi (VP-Mktg-Global)
Sayid Shabeer (Chief Product Officer)
Jon Keating (VP/Gen Mgr-Europe, Middle East & African)
Ken Laversin (Chief Revenue Officer)
Scott Buxton (CFO)

Subsidiaries:

Cforia Software, LLC **(1)**
4333 Park Ter Dr Ste 201, Westlake Village, CA 91361-5656
Tel.: (818) 871-9687
Web Site: http://www.cforia.com
Computer Related Services
N.A.I.C.S.: 541519
Rick Lechusz (VP)
Karl Florida (CEO)

HIGHROAD SOLUTION
PO Box 915, Ashburn, VA 20146
Tel.: (703) 297-8886
Web Site: http://www.highroadsolution.com
Year Founded: 2005
Sales Range: $1-9.9 Million
Emp.: 10
Messaging & Promotional Services, Virtual Meetings & Mobile Text
N.A.I.C.S.: 517810
Ron McGrath (Co-Founder & CEO)
Sue Wood (CFO)
Suzanne Carawan (Chief Mktg Officer)
Erika Beshore (Mgr-Client Care)
Aaron Kapaun (Project Mgr)
Jenny Lassi (Dir-Ops)
Kate Fisher (Mgr-Acct)
Peter Amendola (Mgr-IT)
Rhon Rheid (Gen Counsel)
Dave Martin (COO)

HIGHT CHEVROLET BUICK GMC
29 Madison Ave, Skowhegan, ME 04976
Tel.: (207) 708-8044
Web Site: https://www.hightchev.com
Year Founded: 1911
Sales Range: $10-24.9 Million
Emp.: 50
New Car Dealers
N.A.I.C.S.: 441110
Walter H. Hight II (Pres)

HIGHT ENTERPRISES, LTD. INC.
2525 Arapahoe Ave, Boulder, CO 80302-6720
Tel.: (303) 443-1822   CO
Web Site: http://www.mcguckin.com
Year Founded: 1961
Sales Range: $25-49.9 Million
Emp.: 300
Hardware Stores
N.A.I.C.S.: 444140

HIGHTIMES HOLDING CORP.
10990 Wilshire Blvd Penthouse, Los Angeles, CA 90024
Tel.: (844) 933-3287   DE
Web Site: http://www.hightimes.com
Year Founded: 2016
Emp.: 23
Online Publishing Services
N.A.I.C.S.: 561990
Adam E. Levin (Chm)
David Peck (VP-Bus Dev)
David Newberg (CFO & VP-Fin)
Colin Conway (Sec)
Peter Horvath (CEO)

HIGHTOWER HOLDING LLC
200 W Madison St Ste 2500, Chicago, IL 60606
Tel.: (312) 962-3800

Web Site: http://www.hightoweradvisors.com
Year Founded: 2008
Sales Range: $25-49.9 Million
Emp.: 178
Holding Company; Financial Management Services
N.A.I.C.S.: 551112
Elliot S. Weissbluth (Founder & Chm)
Larry Koehler (Vice Chm & Chief Admin Officer)
Michael LaMena (Pres)
Daniel Lidawer (Mng Dir-Fin & Acctg)
Robert Pagliuco (Exec VP-Corp Fin)
Kimberly Pozza (Exec Dir-Facilities)
Klaris Tamazian (Dir-Corp Events)
Lee Majkrzak (Dir-Trading & Sls)
Pamela McDermid (Chief Talent Officer)
Tim Woods (Gen Counsel)
Kimberly Papedis (Mng Dir & Head-Natl Sls & Platform Strategy)
Sagar Kurada (CFO)
Lance Murray (Mng Dir & Chief Compliance Officer)
Doug Besso (Chief Tech & Ops Officer)
Bob Oros (CEO)

Subsidiaries:

Acacia Wealth Advisors, LLC. **(1)**
245 S Beverly Dr, Beverly Hills, CA 90212
Tel.: (310) 246-0560
Web Site: http://www.hightoweradvisors.com
Financial Planning Services
N.A.I.C.S.: 523940
Alev T. Lewis (Co-Founder, Mng Dir & Partner)
Meloni M. Hallock (Co-Founder, Mng Dir & Partner)

Archer Wealth Management LLC **(1)**
8860 Ladue Rd Ste 130, Saint Louis, MO 63124-2068
Tel.: (314) 726-2208
Web Site: http://www.archerwealth.com
Investment Advice Services
N.A.I.C.S.: 523940
Barbara Archer (Founder & Pres)

HighTower Advisors, LLC **(1)**
200 W Madison St Ste 2500, Chicago, IL 60606
Tel.: (312) 962-3843
Wealth Management Firm
N.A.I.C.S.: 523999
Steve Billimack (Mng Dir)

Holding (Domestic):

Investment Security Group Inc. **(2)**
4900 S Monaco St 300, Denver, CO 80237
Tel.: (303) 759-9808
Web Site: http://www.investsg.com
Rev.: $2,490,000
Emp.: 6
Portfolio Management
N.A.I.C.S.: 523940
Michael Dibala (Founder & Principal)
David Giocomo (Principal)
Mitch Powers (Principal)
Rich Rust (Principal)
Barbara Krause (Principal)

HIGHTOWERS PETROLEUM COMPANY
3577 Commerce Dr, Middletown, OH 45005
Tel.: (513) 423-4272
Web Site: https://www.hightowerspetroleum.com
Year Founded: 1984
Sales Range: $200-249.9 Million
Emp.: 35
Petroleum & Petroleum Products Distr
N.A.I.C.S.: 424720
Stephen L. Hightower (Pres & CEO)

HIGHVIEW CAPITAL, LLC
11755 Wilshire Blvd Ste 1400, Los Angeles, CA 90025

Highview Capital, LLC—(Continued)
Tel.: (310) 806-9780
Web Site: http://www.highviewcp.com
Year Founded: 2016
Private Equity Investment Firm
N.A.I.C.S.: 523999
Ryan McCarthy *(Founder & Sr Mgr-Portfolio)*
Brice Baradel *(Principal)*
Steve Russell *(Principal)*
P. J. Gilbert *(Mng Dir)*
Dan Picmann *(VP)*
Subsidiaries:

American Plastics, LLC (1)
11840 Westline Industrial Dr Ste 200, Saint Louis, MO 63146
Tel.: (800) 325-1051
Web Site:
http://www.americanplasticsllc.com
Holding Company; Commercial Cleaning & Storage Products Mfr & Whslr
N.A.I.C.S.: 551112
Brian G. Nichols *(Chief Bus Officer & VP)*
Robert L. Guerra *(Pres & CEO)*

Subsidiary (Domestic):

Centrex Plastics, LLC (2)
814 W Lima St, Findlay, OH 45840
Tel.: (419) 423-1213
Web Site: http://www.centrexplastics.com
Mfg Plastic Products
N.A.I.C.S.: 326199
Larry Ray *(Mgr-Production)*
Pamela Fennell *(Dir-HR)*
Eric Hummel *(Mgr-Tooling)*

Continental Commercial Products, LLC (2)
11840 Westline Industrial Dr, Saint Louis, MO 63146
Tel.: (800) 325-1051
Commercial Cleaning & Storage Products Mfr
N.A.I.C.S.: 326199
Timothy C. Haeffner *(VP-Sls & Mktg)*
Michael B. Smith *(VP-Mfg Svcs)*

Firstlight Media Ltd (1)
39 Madison Ave, Toronto, M5R 2S2, ON, Canada
Web Site: http://www.firstlight.ai
Software Mfr
N.A.I.C.S.: 513210
Andre Christensen *(CEO)*
Tim Alavathil *(CFO)*
Katie Back *(Chief Revenue Officer)*
Bal O'Neil *(VP-Solutions Engrg)*
Eric Goldstein *(Head-Bus Dev)*
John Ferrandino *(Head-Sls)*
Paul Pastor *(Founder & Chief Bus Officer)*
Anthony Busse *(Head-Sls-Americas)*

Subsidiary (Domestic):

Quickplay Media Inc. (2)
901 King St W Ste 200, Toronto, M5V 3H5, ON, Canada
Tel.: (416) 586-6200
Web Site: http://www.quickplay.com
Mobile TV & Video Services
N.A.I.C.S.: 517112
Wayne Purboo *(Co-Founder & CEO)*
Xavier Marle *(Reg Sls Dir-Southeast Asia & Australia & New Zealand)*
Paul Pastor *(Co-Founder & Chief Bus Officer)*
Jim Vinh *(Head-Sls-Asia-Pacific)*

Frontier Fire Protection Inc. (1)
2617 W Holden Pl, Denver, CO 80204
Tel.: (303) 629-0221
Web Site:
http://www.frontierfireprotection.com
Site Preparation Contractor
N.A.I.C.S.: 238910
Jason Haire *(Project Mgr)*

Good Source Solutions, Inc. (1)
3115 Melrose Dr Ste 160, Carlsbad, CA 92010
Tel.: (858) 455-4800
Web Site: http://www.goodsource.com
Acquires & Distributes Food Products for Schools, Institutions & Non-Profit Organizations

N.A.I.C.S.: 722310
Eric Shiring *(CFO)*
Laurie McCluskey *(VP-Tools for Schools & Northwest Distr)*
Jim Worrall *(VP-Client Solutions & Contract Sls)*
Rich Friedlen *(Pres & CEO)*
Stephanie McCart *(VP-Sls & Mktg)*
Brandon Marvin *(VP-Product Dev & Sourcing)*

Subsidiary (Domestic):

Fresno Produce, Inc. (2)
1415 B St, Fresno, CA 93706
Tel.: (559) 495-0143
Web Site: http://www.fresnoproduce.com
Fresh Fruit & Vegetable Merchant Whslr
N.A.I.C.S.: 424480

Gold Star Foods Inc. (2)
3781 E Airport Dr, Ontario, CA 91761-1761
Tel.: (909) 843-9600
Web Site: http://www.goldstarfoods.com
Nutritional Food Distr
N.A.I.C.S.: 541614
Dan Madsen *(CEO)*
Sean Leer *(Pres)*

Branch (Domestic):

Good Source Solutions (2)
3115 Melrose Dr Ste 160, Carlsbad, CA 92010
Tel.: (208) 365-1445
Web Site: http://www.goodsource.com
Acquires & Distributes Food Products for Schools & Institutions in Idaho, Utah, Washington & Oregon
N.A.I.C.S.: 722310
Laurie McCluskey *(VP-Tools For Schools & ID-Northwest Div)*

Subsidiary (Domestic):

Hayes Distributing, Inc. (2)
4945 Industrial Way, Benicia, CA 94510
Tel.: (707) 746-1660
Web Site: http://www.hayesdist.com
Confectionery & Nut Stores
N.A.I.C.S.: 445292

Pon Food Corp (2)
101 Industrial Park Blvd, Ponchatoula, LA 70454
Tel.: (985) 386-6941
Packaged Frozen Goods
N.A.I.C.S.: 424420

School Lunch Products, Inc. (2)
558 Central Ave, Shafter, CA 93263
Tel.: (661) 746-3136
Web Site: http://www.slpdelivers.com
Sales Range: $1-9.9 Million
Emp.: 10
Packaged Frozen Food Merchant Whslr
N.A.I.C.S.: 424420
Michael Fackler *(Pres)*

Tools For Schools, Inc. (2)
1525 Faraday Ave Ste 200, Carlsbad, CA 92008
Tel.: (858) 455-4800
Web Site: http://tfs.goodsource.com
Foodservice for Schools
N.A.I.C.S.: 722310
Katie Silva *(Mgr-Sls-San Diego)*
Laurie McCluskey *(VP-Idaho)*

Lamm Food Service, LLC (1)
3219 NW Evangeline Thruway, Lafayette, LA 70507-3537
Tel.: (337) 896-0331
Web Site: http://www.lammfoodservice.com
General Line Grocery Merchant Whslr
N.A.I.C.S.: 424410
Dale Lagan *(Dir-Pur & IT)*
Bruce Mattingly *(CEO)*

National Fire & Safety, Inc. (1)
6400 S Fiddlers Green Cir Ste 1180, Greenwood Village, CO 80111
Tel.: (720) 657-1221
Web Site: http://www.natfiresafety.com
Fire Protection & Life Safety Solutions Platform
N.A.I.C.S.: 922160
Chris Gannon *(CEO)*
P.J. Gilbert *(Chm)*

Subsidiary (Domestic):

Maxim Fire Systems LLC (2)
8930 Diplomacy Row, Dallas, TX 75247
Tel.: (972) 484-1222
Web Site: http://www.maximfiresystems.com
Electrical Apparatus & Related Equipment Merchant Whslr
N.A.I.C.S.: 423610
Jeff Brooks *(Founder)*
Joe Cuevas *(Co-Founder)*
Dawn Cuevas *(Co-Founder)*

Texas Fire & Safety (2)
1618 Exchange Park, Waco, TX 76712-6903
Tel.: (254) 420-2727
Web Site: http://www.texasfireandsafety.com
Air-Conditioning, Warm Air Heating Equipment & Commercial & Industrial Refrigeration Equipment Mfr
N.A.I.C.S.: 333415
John Restivo *(Co-Founder)*
Cathy Restivo *(Co-Founder)*
P.J. Gilbert *(Chm)*

Randall Foods, Inc. (1)
2905 E 50th St, Vernon, CA 90058
Tel.: (323) 307-4280
Web Site: http://www.randallfarms.com
Poultry & Poultry Products
N.A.I.C.S.: 424440
Ruben Quezada *(Dir-Product Dev)*
Scott Dineen *(Pres & CEO)*

HIGHWATER ETHANOL, LLC
Tel.: (507) 752-6160
Web Site:
https://www.highwaterethanol.com
HEOL—(OTCBB)
Rev.: $199,052,359
Assets: $101,038,556
Liabilities: $21,345,184
Net Worth: $79,693,372
Earnings: $16,739,304
Emp.: 43
Fiscal Year-end: 10/31/23
Methanol Mfr
N.A.I.C.S.: 325193
Brian D. Kletscher *(CEO & Gen Mgr)*
David G. Moldan *(Chm & Pres)*
George Michael Goblish *(Bd of Dirs, Executives)*
Ronald E. Jorgenson *(Vice Chm)*
David Eis *(Sec)*
Derek Schultz *(Mgr-Lab)*
Dillon Imker *(Mgr-Plant Production Ops)*
Kimberly Frank *(Supvr-Grain Acctg)*
Michael J. Landuyt *(Treas)*
Mandy Bosacker *(Mgr-Lab)*
Todd Horning *(Mgr-Maintenance)*
Mark Pankonin *(Treas)*

HIGHWAY EQUIPMENT & SUPPLY CO.
4500 Paxton St, Harrisburg, PA 17111
Tel.: (717) 564-3031
Web Site: https://www.hwyequip.com
Sales Range: $10-24.9 Million
Emp.: 30
Contracting, Mining, Municipal, Utility, Agricultural & Manufacturing Equipment Mfr
N.A.I.C.S.: 423810
William J. Flood *(Treas & Sec)*
H. Michael Liptak *(Pres)*
Joe Glowacki *(Mgr-Parts)*
John Seroskie *(Mgr-Sls)*
Judy Racho *(Mgr-Credit)*

HIGHWAY EQUIPMENT COMPANY
1330 76th Ave SW, Cedar Rapids, IA 52404
Tel.: (319) 363-8281
Web Site:
http://www.highwayequipment.com
Year Founded: 1939
Sales Range: $75-99.9 Million
Emp.: 106

Mfr of Road Maintenance Equipment & Agricultural Spreaders
N.A.I.C.S.: 333120
Cory Venable *(Dir-Bus Dev)*
Jerry Tracey *(Pres & CEO)*

Subsidiaries:

Scott-Gallaher, Inc. (1)
8071 Lee Hwy, Troutville, VA 24175
Tel.: (540) 353-6711
Web Site: http://www.scott-gallaher.com
Sales Range: $1-9.9 Million
Emp.: 18
Construction Machinery & Equipment Distr
N.A.I.C.S.: 423810
Ronald E. Scott Sr. *(CEO)*
Ronald E. Scott Jr. *(Pres)*

HIGHWAY EQUIPMENT COMPANY
22035 Perry Hwy, Zelienople, PA 16063
Tel.: (724) 452-7800
Web Site: http://www.highway-equipment.com
Sales Range: $75-99.9 Million
Emp.: 100
Tractors, Construction
N.A.I.C.S.: 423810
Thomas H. Reynolds *(Pres)*
John McNally *(Mgr-Sls)*

HIGHWAY MARINE SERVICE INC.
875 NW End Blvd, Quakertown, PA 18951
Tel.: (215) 536-4721
Web Site:
https://www.highwaymarine.com
Rev.: $10,000,000
Emp.: 30
Retailer of Boats & Marine Supplies
N.A.I.C.S.: 441222
Gary W. Wimmer *(Pres)*
Sarah M. Wimmer *(Treas & Sec)*
Wes Johnston *(Mgr-Brokerage)*
Rhoda Landis *(Office Mgr)*

HIGHWAY MOTORS INC.
3185 N Valley Pike, Harrisonburg, VA 22802
Tel.: (540) 434-6716
Web Site:
http://www.highwaymotors.biz
Sales Range: $10-24.9 Million
Emp.: 100
Trucks; Tractors & Trailers: New & Used
N.A.I.C.S.: 441110
Tom Mohr *(Pres)*

HIGHWAY SERVICE VENTURES INC.
100 Arbor Oak Dr Ste 206, Ashland, VA 23005-2261
Tel.: (804) 752-4966
Year Founded: 1984
Sales Range: $100-124.9 Million
Emp.: 1,000
Gasoline Service Stations & Truck Stops
N.A.I.C.S.: 457120
Roger Cole *(Pres)*
Bill Furr *(Dir-HR & Risk Svcs)*

HIGHWAY TO HEALTH, INC.
1 Radnor Corp Ctr 100 Matsonford Rd Ste 100, Radnor, PA 19087
Tel.: (610) 254-8700
Web Site:
http://www.hthworldwide.com,
Emp.: 1,000
Proprietary Online & Mobile Global Healthcare Services
N.A.I.C.S.: 621999
Andrew G. Conn *(COO & Gen Counsel)*

Gerald A. Schaafsma (Chief Investment Officer)
Donald D. Joseph (CFO)
Alex Wood (Chief of Staff)
Michael Hartung (Chief Product Officer)
Alan Krigstein (Chm)
Guillaume Deybach (Pres & CEO)

HIGHWAYS, INC.
1623 Galleria Blvd, Brentwood, TN 37027
Tel.: (615) 373-5445   TN
Web Site:
    http://www.highwaysinc.com
Year Founded: 1981
Sales Range: $10-24.9 Million
Emp.: 56
Highway & Street Construction Services
N.A.I.C.S.: 237310
Brent Linder (Asst VP-Sand Div)

HIGMAN MARINE INC.
1980 Post Oak Blvd, Houston, TX 77056-3899
Tel.: (281) 457-0012   TX
Web Site: http://www.higman.com
Year Founded: 1982
Sales Range: $25-49.9 Million
Emp.: 400
Towing & Tugboat Service
N.A.I.C.S.: 488330
George Thomas (Pres)

Subsidiaries:

Higman Barge Lines Inc.   (1)
1980 Post Oak Blvd Ste 1101, Houston, TX 77056-3899
Tel.: (713) 552-1101
Web Site: http://www.higman.com
Sales Range: $10-24.9 Million
Emp.: 15
Towing And Tugboat Service
N.A.I.C.S.: 488999

HIGUERA HARDWOODS LLC
26273 12 Trees Ln Ste D, Poulsbo, WA 98370
Tel.: (360) 779-4050
Web Site:
    http://www.higuerahardwoods.com
Year Founded: 2001
Rev.: $2,300,000
Emp.: 10
Home Furnishing Merchant Whslr
N.A.I.C.S.: 423220
Joe Gallegos (Owner & CEO)

HII INDUSTRIES, INC.
710 N Post Oak Rd Ste 400, Houston, TX 77024
Tel.: (713) 821-3157   DE
Year Founded: 1997
Sales Range: $25-49.9 Million
Emp.: 1
Holding Company
N.A.I.C.S.: 551112
Matthew C. Flemming (Chm, Pres & CEO)

HILBISH FORD
2600 S Cannon Blvd, Kannapolis, NC 28083-6914
Tel.: (704) 935-3314
Web Site:
    https://www.hilbishford.com
Year Founded: 1954
Sales Range: $10-24.9 Million
Emp.: 68
Car Whslr
N.A.I.C.S.: 441110
Timothy Vaughn (Gen Mgr)

HILCO ELECTRIC COOPERATIVE
115 E Main St, Itasca, TX 76055

Tel.: (254) 687-2331
Web Site: https://www.hilco.coop
Sales Range: $300-349.9 Million
Emp.: 78
Electric Power Distribution
N.A.I.C.S.: 221122
Margaret Hill (Treas)
Debbie Cole (CEO)
Paula Farquhar (Dir-Acctg)

HILCO INC.
12725 Century Dr, Alpharetta, GA 30009-8360
Tel.: (770) 667-5005   GA
Web Site: http://www.hilco-inc.com
Year Founded: 1975
Sales Range: $10-24.9 Million
Emp.: 18
Electronic Parts & Components Mfr
N.A.I.C.S.: 423690
Marisa Owens (Office Mgr)
Vernon A. Hill Jr. (Pres & CEO)

HILCO MERCHANT RESOURCES LLC
5 Revere Dr Ste 300, Northbrook, IL 60062
Tel.: (847) 509-1100
Web Site: http://www.hilcomerchantresources.com
Emp.: 58
Retail Asset Services
N.A.I.C.S.: 523999
Michael Keefe (Chm)
Jeffrey A. Paronto (Pres & COO)
Charles M. Jayson (Exec VP-Retail Bus Dev)
Ben Nortman (CEO)

HILCO TRADING, LLC
5 Revere Dr Ste 206, Northbrook, IL 60062
Tel.: (847) 509-1100   DE
Web Site: http://www.hilcoglobal.com
Holding Company; Equity Investment Services
N.A.I.C.S.: 551112
Eric W. Kaup (Gen Counsel & Exec VP)
Benjamin L. Nortman (Exec VP)
Mark A. Smiley (Exec VP)
Jeffrey B. Hecktman (Founder, Chm & CEO)
Michael Keefe (Chm-HMR)
Gary C. Epstein (CMO)
John P. Chen (Pres & COO)
Roberto Perez (CEO-Hilco Redevelopment Partners)
Jasmine E. Sessoms (Sr VP-Corp Affairs-Hilco Redevelopment Partners)
C. John Mostofi (Exec VP-Capital Solutions)
Betsy Ratto (Sr VP-Capital Solutions)
Sarah Baker (Deputy Gen Counsel)

Subsidiaries:

Hilco Trading Co., Inc.   (1)
5 Revere Dr Ste 206, Northbrook, IL 60062
Tel.: (847) 509-1100
Web Site: http://www.hilcoglobal.com
Sales Range: $50-74.9 Million
Equity Investment Services
N.A.I.C.S.: 523999
Jeffrey B. Hecktman (Chm & CEO)
Michael Keefe (Pres & COO)
Mark A. Smiley (CFO)
Joseph A. Malfitano (VP & Asst Gen Counsel)

Subsidiary (Domestic):

Fixture Finders (DE) LLC   (2)
5 Revere Dr Ste 206, Northbrook, IL 60062
Tel.: (847) 509-1100
Web Site: http://www.fixturefinders.com
Sales Range: $1-9.9 Million
Emp.: 40
Fixed Asset Disposition Services

N.A.I.C.S.: 423840
Scott Hoek (CEO)
Ed Stepp (Exec VP)

Hilco Appraisal Services, LLC   (2)
5 Revere Dr Ste 202, Northbrook, IL 60062
Tel.: (847) 509-1100
Web Site: http://www.hilcoappraisal.com
Sales Range: $25-49.9 Million
Business Asset Appraisal Services
N.A.I.C.S.: 561499
Arnold H. Dratt (Chm)
John JJ Jefferson (Exec VP-Natl Accts)
Thomas A. Greco (CEO)
Thomas McNeely (Sr VP-Enterprise Valuation Svcs Grp)
Ed Zimmerlin Jr. (Sr VP-Inventory Grp)

Subsidiary (Non-US):

Hilco Appraisal Limited   (3)
3 Saint Helens Place, London, EC3A 6AB, United Kingdom
Tel.: (44) 8453130140
Web Site: http://www.hilcoind.com
Sales Range: $10-24.9 Million
Emp.: 20
Business Appraisal Services
N.A.I.C.S.: 561499
John Boorman (Dir-Indus Machinery & Bus Asset)

Subsidiary (Domestic):

Hilco Consumer Capital, LLC   (2)
5 Revere Dr Ste 206, Northbrook, IL 60062
Tel.: (847) 509-1100
Web Site: http://www.hilcoglobal.com
Privater Equity Firm
N.A.I.C.S.: 523999
M. Jeffrey Branman (Sr Mng Dir)

Joint Venture (Domestic):

Fashionology Group LLC   (3)
575 7th Ave, New York, NY 10018
Tel.: (212) 515-5301
Sales Range: $100-124.9 Million
Men's, Women's & Children's Apparel Mfr; Owned by Windsong Allegiance Apparel Group, LLC, Hilco Trading, LLC & Radius Partners, LLC
N.A.I.C.S.: 424350
William Sweedler (Co-Chm)

Polaroid Corporation   (3)
4350 Baker Rd Ste 180, Minnetonka, MN 55343
Tel.: (952) 641-1020
Web Site: http://www.polaroid.com
Sales Range: $125-149.9 Million
Camera & Optical Instrument Mfr
N.A.I.C.S.: 333310

Subsidiary (Non-US):

Nippon Polaroid Kabushiki Kaisha   (4)
Toranomon Marine Building, 3-18-19 Toranomon, Minato-ku, Tokyo, 105 0001, Japan
Tel.: (81) 334388811
Photographic Cameras, Films, Light Polarizing Filters, Lenses & Diversified Chemical, Optical & Commercial Products Mfr
N.A.I.C.S.: 333310

Polaroid (Espana) S.A.   (4)
Camino de las Ceudas 2 bis, Ctra de La Coruna Km 22 300, 28230, Madrid, Spain
Tel.: (34) 91 636 3521
Sales Range: $1-9.9 Million
Emp.: 6
Photographic Cameras, Films, Light Polarizing Filters, Lenses & Diversified Chemical, Optical & Commercial Products Mfr
N.A.I.C.S.: 333310

Polaroid (U.K.) Limited   (4)
7th Floor Ziggurat 25 Grosvenor Road, AL1 3BW, Saint Albans, Hertfordshire, United Kingdom - England
Tel.: (44) 1727792250
Photographic Cameras, Films, Light Polarizing Filters, Lenses & Diversified Chemical, Optical & Commercial Products Mfr
N.A.I.C.S.: 333310

Polaroid GmbH   (4)
Robert Bosch Str 32, 63303, Dreieich, Sprendlingen, Germany
Tel.: (49) 6966901800

Web Site: http://www.polaroid.com
Sales Range: $25-49.9 Million
Emp.: 6
Photographic Cameras, Films, Light Polarizing Filters, Lenses & Diversified Chemical, Optical & Commercial Products Mfr
N.A.I.C.S.: 333310

Polaroid de Mexico S.A. de C.V.   (4)
Torre Presidente Reforma, Andres Bello 45 22nd Fl, 11550, Mexico, DF, Mexico
Tel.: (52) 5552795555
Sales Range: $25-49.9 Million
Emp.: 14
Photographic Cameras, Films, Light Polarizing Filters, Lenses & Diversified Chemical, Optical & Commercial Products Mfr
N.A.I.C.S.: 333310

Subsidiary (Domestic):

Hilco Corporate Finance, LLC   (2)
5 Rever Dr Ste 206, Northbrook, IL 60062
Tel.: (847) 509-1100
Web Site: http://www.hilcocf.com
Sales Range: $50-74.9 Million
Emp.: 2
Equity Investment Services
N.A.I.C.S.: 523999
Teri Stratton (Sr Mng Dir)
Stephen Wrobel (Mng Dir)
Dan Arnold (Sr Mng Dir-Enterprise Valuation Svcs)
Geoffrey Frankel (CEO)
Sheon Karol (Mng Dir-Corp Fin/Special Situations)
Heather Morgan (Dir-Capital Solutions)
Eric Jenkins (Mng Dir-Enterprise Valuation Svcs)
Scott Hadfield (Sr Mng Dir)
Kyle Herman (Sr Mng Dir)

Hilco Equity Management, LLC   (2)
5 Revere Dr Ste 300, Northbrook, IL 60062
Tel.: (847) 509-1100
Web Site: http://www.hilcoequity.com
Sales Range: $50-74.9 Million
Emp.: 35
Equity Investment Services
N.A.I.C.S.: 523999
John W. Tomes (Pres & Mng Dir)
Keith S. Freeman (Partner & Principal)
Ryan M. Bohr (Principal)

Hilco Industrial, LLC   (2)
31555 W 14 Mile Rd Ste 207, Farmington Hills, MI 48334
Tel.: (248) 254-9999
Web Site: http://www.hilcoind.com
Sales Range: $50-74.9 Million
Emp.: 20
Equity Investment Services
N.A.I.C.S.: 523999
Stephan Wolf (CEO)
John Sharpe (Mng Dir-Canada)
Bryan Courcier (Sr VP & Key Acct Mgr-Denver)

Subsidiary (Domestic):

Hilco Industrial Online, LLC   (3)
5 Revere Dr Ste 206, Northbrook, IL 60062
Tel.: (847) 509-1100
Web Site: http://www.hilcoindonline.com
Emp.: 5
Equity Investment Services
N.A.I.C.S.: 523999
John Magnuson (Co-COO)
Brent Bonham (Co-COO)
Bryan Courcier (Sr VP)
Thomas A. Greco (CEO)
Mark Reynolds (Exec VP)
Stephan Wolf (Mng Partner)

Subsidiary (Domestic):

Hilco Real Estate, LLC   (2)
5 Revere Dr Ste 320, Northbrook, IL 60062
Tel.: (847) 714-1288
Web Site: http://www.hilcorealestate.com
Sales Range: $50-74.9 Million
Real Estate Investment
N.A.I.C.S.: 523999
Gregory S. Apter (Pres)
Navin Nagrani (Exec VP)
Tom Davidson (Sr VP)
Neil Aaronson (CEO)
Jan Nocita (Dir-Project Mgmt)
Jamie Cote (VP-Asset Sls Grp)
Don Groft (Sr Mng Dir-Golf & Resort Advisory Grp)
Jeff Azuse (Exec VP)

Hilco Trading, LLC—(Continued)

Hilco Receivables LLC (2)
5 Revere Dr Ste 510, Northbrook, IL 60062
Tel.: (847) 509-7800
Web Site: http://www.hilcoreceivables.com
Equity Investment Services
N.A.I.C.S.: 523999

Subsidiary (Non-US):

Hilco Receivables Europe B.V. (3)
Pompmolenlaan 10, 3447 GK, Woerden,
Netherlands
Tel.: (31) 348750590
Web Site: http://www.hilcoreceivables.com
Sales Range: $50-74.9 Million
Emp.: 30
Equity Investment Services
N.A.I.C.S.: 523999

Subsidiary (Non-US):

Hilco UK Ltd. (2)
80 New Bond Street, London, W1S 1SB,
United Kingdom
Tel.: (44) 2073172050
Web Site: http://www.hilcocapital.com
Equity Investment Services
N.A.I.C.S.: 523999
Paul McGowan (Exec Chm)
Mark O'Neill (Mgr-Sr Investment)
Lewis McMenamin (Mgr-Investment)

Holding (Non-US):

HMV Canada, Inc. (3)
5401 Eglinton Avenue West, Etobicoke,
M9C 5K6, ON, Canada
Tel.: (416) 620-4470
Web Site: http://www.hmv.ca
Sales Range: $350-399.9 Million
Retailer of Music, Videos & Books
N.A.I.C.S.: 449210

Holding (Domestic):

Habitat UK Ltd. (3)
42-46 Princelet Street, London, E1 5LP,
United Kingdom
Tel.: (44) 2076145500
Web Site: http://www.habitat.co.uk
Sales Range: $50-74.9 Million
Home Furnishings Retailer
N.A.I.C.S.: 423220

Homebase Group Ltd. (3)
500 Witan Gate, Milton Keynes, MK9 1BA,
United Kingdom
Tel.: (44) 8450778888
Web Site: http://www.homebase.co.uk
Home Improvement Stores Owner & Operator; Household Appliances, Hardware,
Paints, Glass, Furniture, Lighting & Similar
Products
N.A.I.C.S.: 449129
William Frame (Gen Mgr)
Ian Penney (Dir-Bathstore)

Holding (Non-US):

Kraus Carpet Mills Limited (3)
65 Northfield Drive West, Waterloo, N2L
0A8, ON, Canada
Tel.: (519) 884-2310
Web Site: https://krausflooring.com
Sales Range: $150-199.9 Million
Broadloom Carpet Mfr &
Hardwood/Laminate Flooring Distr
N.A.I.C.S.: 314110
Mike Wagner (VP-Mfg)

Unit (US):

Kraus USA - Distribution Center (4)
160 Amsler Ave, Shippenville, PA 16254
Tel.: (814) 226-9300
Web Site: http://www.krausflooring.com
Sales Range: $25-49.9 Million
Carpets & Floor Coverings Distr
N.A.I.C.S.: 423990
Brad Vollrath (Pres, Treas & Sec)
Dave Mumford (Pres & Gen Mgr)

Holding (Non-US):

Xtra-Vision Limited (3)
Greenhills Retail Park Greenhills Road Tallaght, Dublin, 24, Ireland
Tel.: (353) 14527722
Web Site: http://www.xtra-vision.ie

Sales Range: $50-74.9 Million
Emp.: 1,100
Videos & DVDs Rental & Sales; Video Production Services
N.A.I.C.S.: 532282
Tony Keating (Deputy CEO)

Subsidiary (Domestic):

RG Steel Warren, Inc. (2)
999 Pine Ave SE, Warren, OH 44483-6528
Tel.: (330) 841-8000
Web Site: http://www.woisteel.com
Sales Range: $350-399.9 Million
Custom Flat-Rolled Steel Products Mfr
N.A.I.C.S.: 332111

SD Retail Consulting (2)
5 Rever Dr Ste 202, Northbrook, IL 60062
Tel.: (847) 418-2721
Web Site: http://www.sdretail.com
Sales Range: $25-49.9 Million
Retail Consulting Services
N.A.I.C.S.: 541618
Farla Efros (COO & Exec VP)

HILCO TRANSPORT INC.
7700 Kenmont Rd, Greensboro, NC
27409
Tel.: (336) 273-9441
Web Site:
   https://www.hilcotransport.com
Sales Range: $10-24.9 Million
Emp.: 200
Liquid Petroleum Transport
N.A.I.C.S.: 484230
Gurney Long (Pres)
Mark Brookshire (Mgr-Terminal Ops)
Stephanie Laughrun (Mgr-Safety)
Jeff Loudermilk (Asst Dir-
Maintenance)
Steven Maschi (Mgr-Petroleum Dispatch)
James Winecoff (Mgr-Pur)
Jonita Luck (Dir-HR)

HILCORP ALASKA LLC
3800 Centerpoint Dr Ste 1400, Anchorage, AK 99503
Tel.: (907) 777-8300
Web Site: http://www.hilcorp.com
Oil & Natural Gas Exploration & Production
N.A.I.C.S.: 211120
Jeffery D. Hildebrand (Exec Chm)
Greg Lalicker (CEO)

HILCORP ENERGY CO.
1111 Travis St, Houston, TX 77002
Tel.: (713) 209-2400
Web Site: http://www.hilcorp.com
Year Founded: 1989
Sales Range: $150-199.9 Million
Emp.: 1,106
Oil & Gas Exploration & Production
N.A.I.C.S.: 211120
Jeffery D. Hildebrand (Founder,
Owner & Chm)
Greg R. Lalicker (CEO)
David R. Buehring (Sr VP-Exploration
& Production)
John A. Barnes (Sr VP-Exploration &
Production-Alaska)
David S. Wilkins (Sr VP-Alaska)
Mike Brezina (Sr VP-HR)
Sean P. Kolassa (Pres-Harvest Midstream Company)
Shelbie DeZell (CFO & Sr VP)
Brian A. Wilbanks (Sr VP-Lower 48
East)
Jill H. Fisk (Sr VP-Lower 48 East)
Curtis D. Smith (Sr VP-Land)
Fred Muck (Sr VP-Mktg)
Luke D. Saugier (Sr VP-Acquisitions
& Divestitures)
Michael D. Fertitta (Gen Counsel &
Sr VP)

HILDEN AMERICA, INC.

1044 Commerce Ln, South Boston,
VA 24592
Tel.: (434) 572-3965
Web Site:
   http://www.hildenamerica.com
Other Household Textile Product Mills
N.A.I.C.S.: 314120

HILER INDUSTRIES
118 Koomler Dr, La Porte, IN 46350-
2546
Tel.: (219) 362-8531
Web Site:
   https://www.hilerindustries.com
Year Founded: 1946
Sales Range: $50-74.9 Million
Emp.: 400
Mfr of Castings
N.A.I.C.S.: 331523
Dan Luck (VP)
Dave Gribben (Mgr-Sls)
Roger Orcutt (Mgr-Logistics)

Subsidiaries:

Accurate Castings Inc. (1)
118 Koomler Dr, La Porte, IN 46350-2546
Tel.: (219) 362-8531
Sales Range: $10-24.9 Million
Emp.: 80
Mfr of Nonferrous Die-Castings
N.A.I.C.S.: 331523
Dan Luck (VP)

Aurora Metals Division LLC (1)
1995 Greenfield Rd, Montgomery, IL
60538-1140 (100%)
Tel.: (630) 844-4900
Web Site: http://www.aurorametals.com
Sales Range: $10-24.9 Million
Emp.: 130
Mfr of Precision Vacuum Die & Permanent
Mold Casting Products
N.A.I.C.S.: 331529
Elmer Schelling (Controller)

HILEY AUTO DEALERSHIPS, INC.
1400 Tech Centre Pkwy, Arlington,
TX 76014
Tel.: (817) 493-5000
Web Site:
   http://www.hileymazdavw.com
Rev.: $47,500,000
Emp.: 130
New Car Dealers
N.A.I.C.S.: 441110
James Freeman (Pres)
Jerry Freeman Jr. (Treas & Sec)
Randy Hiley (Owner)

HILL & COX CORPORATION
1820-A Higdon Ferry Rd, Hot
Springs, AR 71913
Tel.: (501) 525-8273
Web Site: http://www.hillandcox.com
Year Founded: 1989
Sales Range: $10-24.9 Million
Emp.: 20
Industrial Building Construction Services
N.A.I.C.S.: 236210
Randall Cox (Pres)
Robert Cox (Project Mgr)
Brian Hill (Project Mgr)
Harold L. Hill (VP)

HILL & GRIFFITH COMPANY
1085 Summer St, Cincinnati, OH
45204-2037
Tel.: (513) 921-1075   OH
Web Site:
   http://www.hillandgriffith.com
Year Founded: 1896
Sales Range: $10-24.9 Million
Emp.: 32
Mfr of Foundry Sand Additives & Release Agents for Concrete
N.A.I.C.S.: 327992

Mike Lawry (CEO)
Ryan Canfield (Pres)
Dale P. Welsh (VP-Fin)
Bob Waterloo (Mgr-Distr)
Donna Nijak (Plant Mgr-Indianapolis)
John Spindler (Mgr-Specialty Lubricants)

Subsidiaries:

HG Logistics, LLC (1)
1085 Summer St, Cincinnati, OH 45204
Tel.: (513) 244-3026
Web Site: http://www.hglogisticsllc.com
Emp.: 20
Transportation & Logistics Services
N.A.I.C.S.: 541614
Mike Lawry (Pres)
Ryan Canfield (CEO)
Doug Bierman (Gen Mgr)
Michelle Webster (Mgr-Dispatch)
Donna Nijak (Plant Mgr-Indianapolis)

HILL ASSOCIATES INC.
300 Corner Stone Dr Ste 305, Williston, VT 05495
Tel.: (802) 655-0940
Web Site: https://www.hill.com
Year Founded: 1981
Sales Range: $10-24.9 Million
Emp.: 9
Data Communication Services
N.A.I.C.S.: 517810
Starr L. Bouvier (Sr Fulfillment Coord)
Paul Whalen (Pres & CEO)
Rik Dayvie (Project Mgr-IT & Tech
Svcs)

HILL BROTHERS CHEMICAL COMPANY INC.
1675 N Main St, Orange, CA 92867-
3442
Tel.: (714) 998-8800   CA
Web Site: http://www.hillbrothers.com
Year Founded: 1923
Sales Range: $10-24.9 Million
Emp.: 130
Mfr of Chemicals & Allied Products
N.A.I.C.S.: 424690
Terry Milligan (Mgr-Operations)

Subsidiaries:

**Hill Brothers Chemical Company Inc.
- City of Industry** (1)
15017 E Clark Ave, City of Industry, CA
91745
Tel.: (626) 333-2251
Web Site: http://www.hillbrothers.com
Emp.: 25
All Other Miscellaneous Chemical Product
& Preparation Mfr
N.A.I.C.S.: 325998
Dave Hernandez (Mgr)
John Padilla Jr. (Reg Mgr-Sls)

**Hill Brothers Chemical Company Inc.
- Salt Lake City** (1)
75 N 640 W, North Salt Lake, UT 84054
Tel.: (801) 936-4100
Web Site: http://www.hillbrothers.com
Emp.: 7
Other Chemical & Allied Products Merchant
Whslr
N.A.I.C.S.: 424690
Mark Greenburg (Mgr)

HILL BROTHERS CONSTRUCTION & ENGINEERING CO.
20831 Hwy 15 N, Falkner, MS 38629
Tel.: (662) 837-3041
Web Site: http://www.hbconst.com
Year Founded: 1978
Sales Range: $50-74.9 Million
Emp.: 500
Construction & Civil Engineering Services
N.A.I.C.S.: 237310
Ken Drewery (Treas & Office Mgr)
Clyde Robertson (Sr VP)
Gerald Hill (Pres)

Jane Horton Childs *(Sec)*
Sterling D. Akers *(Head-Estimator & VP)*
Kenneth W. Hill *(Chm)*
Kenneth W. Hill Jr. *(CEO)*

HILL BROTHERS, INC.
7850 I St, Omaha, NE 68127-1830
Tel.: (402) 331-2503   NE
Web Site: http://www.hillbros.com
Year Founded: 1985
Sales Range: $25-49.9 Million
Emp.: 350
Provider of Trucking Services
N.A.I.C.S.: 484121
Cale Berry *(Acct Exec-Dallas)*
John Ashley Turner *(Mgr-Ops)*
John Brooks *(Mgr-Ops)*
Subsidiaries:

Hill Brothers Intermodal Logistics
Inc.   **(1)**
7878 I St, Omaha, NE 68127-1871 **(100%)**
Tel.: (402) 331-2503
Sales Range: $25-49.9 Million
Emp.: 300
Provider of Freight Transportation Arrangement Services
N.A.I.C.S.: 488510

HILL CADILLAC
3960 W Chester Pike, Newtown Square, PA 19073
Tel.: (610) 356-4900
Web Site: http://www.hillcadillac.com
Sales Range: $10-24.9 Million
Emp.: 50
Car Whslr
N.A.I.C.S.: 441110
Geoffrey J. Hill *(Principal)*

HILL CITY OIL COMPANY INC.
1 Terminal Cir, Vicksburg, MS 39180
Tel.: (601) 636-2523   MS
Year Founded: 1980
Sales Range: $50-74.9 Million
Emp.: 500
Sales of Petroleum & Food Products
N.A.I.C.S.: 457120
Herbert E. Stathes *(Pres)*
Eric Stathes *(Exec VP)*

HILL CITY WHOLESALE CO. INC.
1711 16th St, Lynchburg, VA 24501
Tel.: (434) 847-6641
Sales Range: $10-24.9 Million
Emp.: 30
Chewing Tobacco
N.A.I.C.S.: 424940
William S. Thomasson *(Pres)*

HILL CONSTRUCTION CORPORATION
482 Wando Park Blvd, Mount Pleasant, SC 29464
Tel.: (843) 884-6888
Web Site: http://www.hillcon.com
Year Founded: 1977
Sales Range: $10-24.9 Million
Emp.: 60
Nonresidential Construction Services
N.A.I.C.S.: 236220
Robert E. Dunn Jr. *(VP)*
E. Burrow Hill III *(Pres)*

HILL COUNTRY BAKERY
122 Stribling, San Antonio, TX 78204
Tel.: (210) 475-9981
Web Site:
   http://www.hillcountrybakery.com
Year Founded: 1997
Sales Range: $10-24.9 Million
Emp.: 250
Baked Goods Mfr
N.A.I.C.S.: 311811

David Nolan *(Mng Partner)*
Phil Butrum *(CFO)*
Steve O'Donnell *(Mng Partner)*
Liz Banks *(Dir-Procurement)*
Paul Gabrielson *(Dir-Natl Acct)*
Danny Jones *(Dir-New Bus Dev)*
Fred Bey *(Dir-Ops)*
Erika Butler *(Dir-Quality Assurance)*
Trinity Greer *(Mgr-Creative Projects)*
Albert Salinas *(Mgr-Logistics)*
Pat Moczygemba *(Mgr-Pur)*

HILL COUNTRY COMMUNITY ACTION ASSOCIATION, INC.
2905 W Wallace, San Saba, TX 76877
Tel.: (325) 372-5167   TX
Web Site: http://www.hccaa.com
Year Founded: 1966
Sales Range: $10-24.9 Million
Emp.: 330
Community Action Services
N.A.I.C.S.: 624190
Angela Miller *(Dir-Human Resources)*

HILL COUNTRY DAIRIES INC.
912 Kramer Ln, Austin, TX 78758
Tel.: (512) 836-6123
Web Site:
   https://www.hillcountrydairies.com
Rev.: $16,000,000
Emp.: 50
Dairy Products Mfr
N.A.I.C.S.: 424430
Carl Schoener *(Gen Mgr)*

HILL COUNTRY ENTERPRISES
550 Benson Dr, Kerrville, TX 78028
Tel.: (830) 257-6121
Sales Range: $25-49.9 Million
Emp.: 55
Car Whslr
N.A.I.C.S.: 441110
Cecil Atkission *(Pres)*

HILL CRAFT FURNITURE CO.
101 Industrial Dr, New Albany, MS 38652
Tel.: (662) 534-7426
Sales Range: $25-49.9 Million
Emp.: 280
Living Room Furniture
N.A.I.C.S.: 337121
Barry Weeden *(Pres)*

HILL CREST DEVELOPMENT
2424 Kennedy St NE, Minneapolis, MN 55413
Tel.: (612) 371-0123
Web Site:
   https://www.hillcrestdevelopment.com
Rev.: $10,500,000
Emp.: 30
Commercial & Industrial Building Operation
N.A.I.C.S.: 531120
Joe Klein *(Mgr-Leasing)*
Tim Yost *(Mgr-Ops)*
Scott Tankenoff *(Mng Partner)*

HILL DISTRIBUTING COMPANY
2555 Harrison Rd, Columbus, OH 43204
Tel.: (614) 276-6533   OH
Web Site:
   http://www.hilldistributing.com
Year Founded: 1933
Sales Range: $10-24.9 Million
Emp.: 60
Mfr of Beer & Other Fermented Malt Liquors
N.A.I.C.S.: 424810
Charles D. Hill Jr. *(Owner)*

HILL INTERNATIONAL TRUCKS LLC
47866 Y and O Rd, East Liverpool, OH 43920
Tel.: (330) 386-6440   OH
Web Site:
   http://www.hillintltrucks.com
Year Founded: 1890
Sales Range: $75-99.9 Million
Emp.: 200
Sales of New & Used Trucks, Tractors & Trailers
N.A.I.C.S.: 441110
Jack Hill *(Chm)*
Dan Hickman *(Controller)*

HILL NISSAN, INC.
6401 Cypress Gardens Blvd, Winter Haven, FL 33884-3576
Tel.: (863) 266-4117
Web Site: https://www.hillnissan.com
Year Founded: 1976
Sales Range: $10-24.9 Million
Emp.: 38
New Car Whslr
N.A.I.C.S.: 441110
Timothy J. Hill *(Mgr)*
James W. Hill *(Pres)*

HILL PETROLEUM INC.
132 Railroad Pl, Goodwater, AL 35072
Tel.: (256) 839-6331
Sales Range: $10-24.9 Million
Emp.: 50
Petroleum Products
N.A.I.C.S.: 424720

HILL PETROLEUM, INC.
6301 Ralston Rd, Arvada, CO 80002
Tel.: (303) 424-6262
Web Site: https://www.hillpet.com
Sales Range: $25-49.9 Million
Emp.: 40
Petroleum Products
N.A.I.C.S.: 424720
Troy Hill *(VP & Gen Mgr)*
Subsidiaries:

Hill Petroleum   **(1)**
555 E 8th St, Greeley, CO 80631
Tel.: (970) 352-9208
Petroleum Products Distribution
N.A.I.C.S.: 213112
Carolyn Slocum *(Mgr-Acctg)*

HILL TOP RESEARCH INC.
6088 Main & Mill Streets, Miamiville, OH 45147
Tel.: (513) 831-3114   OH
Web Site: http://www.hill-top.com
Year Founded: 1947
Sales Range: $10-24.9 Million
Emp.: 250
Laboratory Services
N.A.I.C.S.: 541380

HILL TRUCK SALES INC.
1011 W Sample St, South Bend, IN 46619
Tel.: (574) 289-4065
Web Site:
   http://www.hilltrucksales.com
Sales Range: $10-24.9 Million
Emp.: 80
Trucks, Commercial
N.A.I.C.S.: 423110
Allen P. Hill *(Chm)*
David Hill *(Pres)*
Dennis Ziolkowski *(Gen Mgr)*

HILL WARD HENDERSON
101 E Kennedy Blvd Ste 3700, Tampa, FL 33602
Tel.: (813) 221-3900
Web Site: https://www.hwhlaw.com
Year Founded: 1986

Sales Range: $10-24.9 Million
Emp.: 80
Law firm
N.A.I.C.S.: 541110
Marie Attaway Borland *(Atty)*
Gregory P. Brown *(Atty)*
Rocco Cafaro *(Atty)*
Patricia Bean *(COO)*
Jeanie M. Poley *(Chief Admin Officer)*
John C. Connery Jr. *(Atty)*
Benjamin H. Hill III *(Co-Founder & Atty)*
David E. Ward Jr. *(Co-Founder & Attny)*
Thomas N. Henderson III *(Co-Founder & Atty)*

HILL YORK CORPORATION
2125 S Andrews Ave, Fort Lauderdale, FL 33316
Tel.: (954) 525-4200
Web Site: https://www.hillyork.com
Sales Range: $50-74.9 Million
Emp.: 180
Warm Air Heating & Air Conditioning Contractor
N.A.I.C.S.: 238220
Robert W. Lafferty *(Pres & CEO)*
Mark Kerney *(Exec VP)*
Jeffrey Phillabaum *(Exec VP)*
Charles H. Ewing *(Exec VP)*
John Cancel *(VP-Engrg & Pre-Construction Svcs)*
Michael Senecal *(Exec VP)*
Robert S. Lafferty Jr. *(Chm)*

HILL'S SUPPLY CO.
186 W Athens St, Winder, GA 30680
Tel.: (770) 867-3925   GA
Web Site: https://www.hillsace.com
Year Founded: 1957
Sales Range: $25-49.9 Million
Emp.: 140
Lumber & Other Building Materials Distr
N.A.I.C.S.: 423310
Pam Hanson *(Sec)*
Frank Burkett III *(Pres & CEO)*

HILL, BARTH & KING LLC
6603 Summit Dr, Canfield, OH 44406
Tel.: (330) 758-8613   OH
Web Site: https://www.hbkcpa.com
Year Founded: 1949
Accounting, Tax & Advisory Services
N.A.I.C.S.: 541211
Phillip L. Wilson *(COO)*
Joshua J. Zarlenga *(Principal)*
William Gonda *(Mgr-Info Sys)*
Linda A. Evans *(Chief HR Officer)*
James G Fahey *(Chief Learning Officer)*
William J Heaven *(Sr Mgr)*
Leannah R. Hostetler *(CFO)*
Patricia A. Kimerer *(Dir-Comm)*
Robert W. Snell *(CIO)*
Frank L Balog Jr. *(Sr Mgr)*
Subsidiaries:

HBK CPAs & Consultants   **(1)**
653 Skippack Pike Ste 300, Blue Bell, PA 19422
Tel.: (215) 628-8080
Web Site: http://www.hbkcpa.com
Other Accounting Services
N.A.I.C.S.: 541219
Steven Resnick *(Sr Dir)*
Gary M. Loewenstern *(Principal)*
Michael R. Wolf *(Principal)*
Kevin McGinn *(Sr Mgr)*
Ira S Letofsky *(Sr Dir)*
Lynn Warszawski *(Sr Dir)*
Anthony B Borzillo III *(Principal-in-Charge)*

Unicorn Solutions Group Inc.   **(1)**
1091 Bristol Rd, Mountainside, NJ 07092
Tel.: (908) 654-0900

Hill, Barth & King LLC—(Continued)

Data Processing, Hosting & Related Services
N.A.I.C.S.: 518210

HILL-N-DALE ABSTRACTERS, INC.
PO Box 547, Goshen, NY 10924
Tel.: (845) 294-5110
Web Site:
http://www.hillndaleabstracters.com
Year Founded: 1950
Emp.: 10
Title Insurance Services
N.A.I.C.S.: 524127

Subsidiaries:

Hardenburgh Title Agency   (1)
12 Scotchtown Ave, Goshen, NY 10924-1610
Tel.: (845) 294-6909
Title Search & Insurance Services
N.A.I.C.S.: 524127
James V. Rinaldi *(Pres)*

HILLANDALE FARMS OF PA INC.
4001 Crooked Run Rd Ste 2, North Versailles, PA 15137
Tel.: (412) 672-9685
Web Site:
http://www.hillandalefarms.com
Rev.: $20,300,000
Emp.: 20
Eggs
N.A.I.C.S.: 424440
Orland Bethel *(Pres)*
Karen Dykes *(Office Mgr)*

HILLCREST
2705 Mountain View Dr, La Verne, CA 91750
Tel.: (909) 392-4111   **CA**
Web Site:
https://www.livingathillcrest.org
Year Founded: 1947
Sales Range: $10-24.9 Million
Emp.: 299
Elderly People Assistance Services
N.A.I.C.S.: 624120
Matthew Neeley *(Pres & CEO)*
Barbara Johnson *(Sec)*
Jim Irwin *(Treas)*
Mike Wolfsen *(Dir-Facilities Ops)*
Ryan Harrison *(Dir-Resident Life & Wellness)*
Mary Kay Ogden *(Chm)*
Curtis Frick *(Vice Chm)*
Winnie Dang *(CFO)*
Reginald K. Ingram Jr. *(Chief Dev Officer)*

HILLCREST AUTOMOTIVE SERVICES
3620 Old Silver Hill Rd, Suitland, MD 20746
Tel.: (301) 423-3780
Web Site: http://www.hillcrestcar.com
Sales Range: $10-24.9 Million
Emp.: 4
Automotive Repair Services
N.A.I.C.S.: 811198
Alfonso Munguia *(Owner)*

HILLCREST CAPITAL PARTNERS LP
225 South 6th St, Minneapolis, MN 55402
Tel.: (612) 333-9922
Sales Range: $25-49.9 Million
Emp.: 5
Holding Company
N.A.I.C.S.: 551112
John G. Turner *(Chm)*
Margaret Hill *(Office Mgr)*

Subsidiaries:

Rosemount Office Systems LLC   (1)
2015 Silver Bell Rd Ste 195, Eagan, MN 55122
Tel.: (651) 289-6200
Sales Range: $10-24.9 Million
Emp.: 70
Office Furniture Mfr
N.A.I.C.S.: 337214

HILLCREST DEVELOPMENT INC.
1315 Franklin Grove Rd Ste 110, Dixon, IL 61021-9194
Tel.: (815) 288-4663
Web Site: https://www.hdihotels.com
Sales Range: $10-24.9 Million
Emp.: 4
Commercial & Office Building, New Construction
N.A.I.C.S.: 236220
Wendy Steck *(Coord-Construction Draw)*
Deb Hopkins *(Controller)*

HILLCREST EDUCATIONAL CENTERS, INC.
788 South St, Pittsfield, MA 01201
Tel.: (413) 499-7924   **MA**
Web Site:
https://www.hillcresteducational
centers.org
Year Founded: 1985
Sales Range: $25-49.9 Million
Emp.: 636
Disabled Child Development Services
N.A.I.C.S.: 624120
Gerard E. Burke *(Pres & CEO)*
Mark Placido *(Treas)*
Paul Clark *(Chm)*
Michele Morin *(VP-HR & Workforce Dev)*
Shaun Cusson *(Exec Dir)*
Cheryl Richards *(Mgr-Workforce Learning)*
Michael Supranowicz *(Dir-Bus Dev)*
Dana Welts *(Dir-Info Svcs)*
Diane P. Parks *(Dir-Education)*
John J. Martin Jr. *(Vice Chm)*

HILLCREST FOODS INC.
50 Satellite Blvd NW G, Suwanee, GA 30024
Tel.: (770) 932-1137
Rev.: $28,132,843
Emp.: 7
Fast-Food Restaurant, Chain
N.A.I.C.S.: 722513

HILLDRUP TRANSFER & STORAGE, INC.
4022 Richmond Hwy, Stafford, VA 22554-4827
Tel.: (703) 454-5085   **VA**
Web Site: https://www.hilldrup.com
Year Founded: 1976
Sales Range: $25-49.9 Million
Emp.: 525
Trucking Service
N.A.I.C.S.: 484121
Hilton Marshall *(CFO)*
Charles W. McDaniel *(Pres)*
D. Barry Dodson *(Exec VP)*
Jason Studer *(VP-Bus Dev)*
Robert McKillips *(VP-Global Bus Dev-St. Louis)*

HILLEL: THE FOUNDATION FOR JEWISH CAMPUS LIFE
800 8th St NW, Washington, DC 20001-3724
Tel.: (202) 449-6500   **DC**
Web Site: https://www.hillel.org
Year Founded: 1984
Sales Range: $25-49.9 Million
Emp.: 1,591

Child & Youth Care Services
N.A.I.C.S.: 624110
Deborah Kallick *(Vice Chm)*

HILLER COMPANY INCORPORATED
635 Mill St, Marion, MA 02738-1675
Tel.: (508) 748-0019   **MA**
Web Site: http://www.hillerco.com
Year Founded: 1935
Sales Range: $10-24.9 Million
Emp.: 40
Sales of New & Used Automobiles
N.A.I.C.S.: 441110
Jay Hiller Jr. *(Pres)*

HILLER PLUMBING, HEATING & COOLING COMPANY
1510 Fort Negley Blvd, Nashville, TN 37203
Tel.: (615) 292-6110
Web Site:
http://www.hillerplumbing.com
Year Founded: 1990
Sales Range: $10-24.9 Million
Emp.: 95
Commercial & Residential Plumbing, Heating & Cooling Services
N.A.I.C.S.: 238220
James Hiller *(Owner & Pres)*

Subsidiaries:

McKinzie Mechanical Heating & Air Conditioning, L.L.C.   (1)
1617 Highway 31 W, Goodlettsville, TN 37072-9621   **(100%)**
Tel.: (615) 851-4066
Web Site:
http://www.mckinziemechanical.com
Sales Range: $1-9.9 Million
Emp.: 100
Plumbing, Heating & Air-Conditioning Contractor
N.A.I.C.S.: 238220
Jimmy Hiller *(Owner)*

HILLERICH & BRADSBY CO., INC.
800 W Main St, Louisville, KY 40202-2620
Tel.: (502) 585-5226   **KY**
Web Site: http://www.slugger.com
Year Founded: 1884
Sales Range: $100-124.9 Million
Emp.: 600
Baseball & Softball Gloves & Bats, Golf Clubs, Hockey Sticks Mfr
N.A.I.C.S.: 339920
Suzanne Bowman *(Dir-Legal Svcs & Intellectual Property)*
Andrea Davis *(Mgr-Grp Sls & Events)*
Lucy English *(Mgr-Mktg & Comm)*
William Stauter *(Dir-Wood Bat Ops)*

HILLERS INC
24359 Northwestern Hwy Ste 150, Southfield, MI 48075-6802
Tel.: (248) 344-1030
Web Site:
http://www.hillersmarkets.com
Year Founded: 1989
Sales Range: $50-74.9 Million
Emp.: 600
Grocery Store Services
N.A.I.C.S.: 445110
James Hiller *(CEO)*
Justin Hiller *(VP)*

HILLHOUSE NATURALS FARM, LTD.
1917 Hughes Rd, Wickliffe, KY 42087
Tel.: (270) 335-3585
Web Site:
https://www.hillhousenaturals.com
Year Founded: 1986
Sales Range: $1-9.9 Million
Emp.: 32

Home Fragrance Products Including Potpourri, Candles, Sachets, Oils, Fragrance Mist & Pillar Candles Mfr & Retailer
N.A.I.C.S.: 325620
Shelly Batts *(Pres)*

HILLIS-CARNES ENGINEERING ASSOCIATES, INC.
10975 Guilford Rd Ste A, Annapolis Junction, MD 20701
Tel.: (410) 880-4788
Web Site: https://www.hcea.com
Year Founded: 1989
Sales Range: $25-49.9 Million
Emp.: 175
Engineering Consulting Services
N.A.I.C.S.: 541330
Brenda Frank *(Mgr-HR)*
Matt Van Rensler *(Mgr-Philadelphia)*
Christopher Lesjak *(VP-Bus Dev)*
Venisri Nagulapati *(Mgr-Bus Dev)*
Cindy S. Shepeck *(VP & Mgr-Hagerstown)*
Grant K. Autry *(VP & Dir-Ops)*
Jerry H. Johnson *(VP & Mgr-Delmarva)*
Robert T. Skepton *(CFO & Sr VP)*
Sandy Henningsen *(VP-Bus Dev)*
Timothy B. Hill *(COO & Sr VP)*
William M. Carnes *(Pres & CEO)*

HILLMAN OYSTER COMPANY
10700 Hillman Dr, Dickinson, TX 77539
Tel.: (281) 339-1506
Web Site:
https://www.hillmanoysters.com
Rev.: $11,610,323
Emp.: 100
Shellfish Packaging Services
N.A.I.C.S.: 311710

HILLMER INC.
2300 Fall Hill Ave Ste 511, Fredericksburg, VA 22401
Tel.: (540) 834-2467
Web Site: http://hillmerinc.com
Year Founded: 2001
Sales Range: $1-9.9 Million
Emp.: 39
Communications, Government, Political & Public Affairs Production Services
N.A.I.C.S.: 541820
Linda Hillmer *(Pres & CEO)*

HILLS
4901 Hunt Rd, Cincinnati, OH 45242
Tel.: (513) 984-0300
Web Site: http://www.hillsinc.com
Year Founded: 1958
Sales Range: $150-199.9 Million
Emp.: 250
New Housing Operate Building Services
N.A.I.C.S.: 236117
Rusty Lykes *(Sr VP)*

HILLS ACE HARDWARE & LUMBER CENTER
186 W Athens St, Winder, GA 30680
Tel.: (770) 867-3925
Web Site: https://www.hillsace.com
Year Founded: 1918
Rev.: $30,057,480
Emp.: 140
Hardware & Building Material Retailer
N.A.I.C.S.: 444180
Jon Foster *(Mgr-Retail)*
Brian Fisk *(Mgr-Hardware)*
Addison Pharr *(Mgr-Lumber & Building Matl)*
Pam Hanson *(Mgr-Admin)*
Alex Hill *(Pres)*

HILLS AND DALES GENERAL HOSPITAL
4675 Hill St, Cass City, MI 48726
Tel.: (989) 872-2121　　　MI
Web Site: https://www.hdghmi.org
Year Founded: 1960
Sales Range: $10-24.9 Million
Emp.: 239
Health Care Srvices
N.A.I.C.S.: 622110
Danny Haag (Vice Chm)
Pat Curtis (Treas & Sec)
Jean Anthony (Pres & CEO)

HILLSBORO AREA HOSPITAL
1200 E Tremont St, Hillsboro, IL 62049
Tel.: (217) 532-6111　　　IL
Web Site: https://www.hillsboroareahospital.org
Year Founded: 1906
Sales Range: $10-24.9 Million
Emp.: 255
Health Care Srvices
N.A.I.C.S.: 622110
Sharon Clark (Dir-HR)
Terri Carroll (VP-Fin Svcs)
E. David Harrison (VP-Patient Care Svcs)
Chris Kester (Mgr-Plant Ops)
Brian Knodle (Chm)
Patricia Clarke (Sec)
Rex Brown (Pres & CEO)
Barbara Hewitt (Chm)
Dawn Mascher (Dir-Inpatient Svcs)

HILLSBORO BANK
509 W Alexander St, Plant City, FL 33563
Tel.: (813) 707-6506　　　FL
Web Site: http://www.hillsborobank.com
Year Founded: 1998
Sales Range: $1-9.9 Million
Emp.: 22
Commericial Banking
N.A.I.C.S.: 522110
Gary L. Boothe (Chm)
Kenneth D. Hawthorne (CFO & Sr VP)
Pamela C. Warnock (COO & Sr VP)
Mike Ward (Pres & CEO)
Brett Mueller (VP)
Jennifer Denney (Asst VP)
Taryn Elliot (Asst VP)

HILLSBORO EQUIPMENT INCORPORATED
E 18898 Hwy 33 E, Hillsboro, WI 54634
Tel.: (608) 489-2275
Web Site: https://www.hillsboroequipment.com
Year Founded: 1978
Sales Range: $10-24.9 Million
Emp.: 40
Farm Implements
N.A.I.C.S.: 423820
Donald Slama (Owner & Mgr-Sls)
James Taylor (Gen Mgr)

HILLSBORO TRANSPORTATION CO.
6256 United States Route 50, Hillsboro, OH 45133
Tel.: (937) 393-4213
Sales Range: $10-24.9 Million
Emp.: 10
Trucking Except Local
N.A.I.C.S.: 484121
Michael Duckwall (Pres)
Jeff Duckwall (VP)
Jim Duckwall (Controller)

HILLSBOROUGH COUNTY AVIATION AUTHORITY
4100 George J Bean Pkwy, Tampa, FL 33607
Tel.: (813) 870-8700
Web Site: https://www.tampaairport.com
Year Founded: 1945
Sales Range: $200-249.9 Million
Airport
N.A.I.C.S.: 488119
Joseph Lopano (CEO)
Robert I. Watkins (Chm)
Bob Buckhorn (Asst Sec & Asst Treasurer)
Victor D. Crist (Sec)
John Tiliacos (Exec VP-Ops & Customer Svc)
Janet Zink (Asst VP-Media & Govt Rels)
Christopher Minner (VP-Mktg)
Damian L. Brooke (VP-Fin & IT)
Al Illustrato (VP-Facilities & Admin)
Gary W. Harrod (Vice Chm)
Chip Diehl (Treas)
Michael Stephens (Gen Counsel)
Emily Nipps (Mgr-Comm)
Christine Osborn (Mgr-Comm)
Danny Valentine (Mgr-Comm)

HILLSBOROUGH TITLE INC.
1605 S Alexander St Ste 102, Plant City, FL 33563
Tel.: (813) 754-4440
Web Site: https://www.hillsboroughtitle.com
Year Founded: 1984
Sales Range: $25-49.9 Million
Emp.: 90
Title Abstract Services
N.A.I.C.S.: 541191
Aaron M. Davis (Owner)

HILLSDALE CO-OPERATIVE ELEVATOR CO.
107 Butzer St, Hillsdale, IL 61257
Tel.: (309) 658-2218
Web Site: https://www.hillsdaleelevator.com
Rev.: $30,307,518
Emp.: 8
Grains
N.A.I.C.S.: 424510

HILLSIDE PLASTICS CORPORATION
125 Long Ave, Hillside, NJ 07205-2350
Tel.: (973) 923-2700
Web Site: https://www.hillsideplasticscorp.com
Year Founded: 1994
Sales Range: $10-24.9 Million
Emp.: 60
Unsupported Plastics Film & Sheet Mfr
N.A.I.C.S.: 326113
Harold Kaufman (Owner & Pres)
Maria Silva (VP-Bus Dev)

HILLSPIRE LLC
1010 El Camino Real, Menlo Park, CA 94025
Tel.: (650) 461-8080
Web Site: http://www.hillspirellc.com
Emp.: 15
Investment Management Firm
N.A.I.C.S.: 523999
Teling Peterson (COO & Sec)
Chuck Chai (Pres & Chief Investment Officer)
Amber Caska (CFO)

HILLSTREET FUND LP
807 Lemeom St, Cincinnati, OH 45202

Tel.: (513) 651-0800
Sales Range: $10-24.9 Million
Emp.: 2
Investment
N.A.I.C.S.: 325199
Christian Meininger (Pres)
Caryl Simpson (Office Mgr)

HILLTOP AVIATION SERVICES
5777 W Century Blvd Ste 1095, Los Angeles, CA 90045
Tel.: (310) 646-0089
Rev.: $19,900,000
Emp.: 15
Airports, Flying Fields & Services
N.A.I.C.S.: 488119

HILLTOP BASIC RESOURCES, INC.
1 W 4th St Ste 1100, Cincinnati, OH 45202-3610
Tel.: (513) 651-5000　　　OH
Web Site: http://www.hilltopbasicresources.com
Year Founded: 1941
Sales Range: $25-49.9 Million
Emp.: 200
Producer of Construction Sand & Gravel
N.A.I.C.S.: 212321
Kevin Sheehan (Pres)
Brad Slabaugh (VP-Sls & Gen Mgr)
Sabrina Ferree (Dir-HR & IT)
John F. Steele Jr. (Chm & CEO)

HILLTOP BUICK GMC INC.
3230 Auto Plz, Richmond, CA 94806
Tel.: (510) 662-7148　　　DE
Web Site: http://www.gmautoplaza.com
Rev.: $14,300,000
Emp.: 40
New & Used Car Dealer
N.A.I.C.S.: 441110
Maryanne Hernandez (Mgr)
Leonard Nomura (Pres)
Alex Morales (Mgr-Sls)

HILLTOP PRIVATE CAPITAL, LLC
509 Madison Ave 14th Fl, New York, NY 10022
Tel.: (917) 301-0980　　　NY
Web Site: http://www.hilltopprivatecapital.com
Year Founded: 2016
Privater Equity Firm
N.A.I.C.S.: 523999
W. Andrew Shea (Mng Partner)
Katherine A. Lehman (Mng Partner)
Edwin A. Moss (Partner)
Neil A. Burns (Operating Partner)

Subsidiaries:

Spiral Binding LLC　　　(1)
1 Maltese Dr, Totowa, NJ 07511
Tel.: (973) 256-0666
Web Site: http://www.spiralbinding.com
Sales Range: $25-49.9 Million
Emp.: 260
Print Finishing, Graphic Arts & Presentation Products Mfr & Services
N.A.I.C.S.: 424120
Robert Matthew Roth (Pres & CEO)
Ann Marie Boggio (VP-Strategic Accts)
Doris Dytchel (Dir-HR)
Richard Christmas (Dir-Ops)
Bob Cooke (Gen Mgr-Larger Equipment Div)

HILLVIEW MOTORS
5309 State Rt 30, Greensburg, PA 15601
Tel.: (724) 834-8440
Web Site: http://www.hillviewmotors.com
Sales Range: $10-24.9 Million
Emp.: 47

Car Whslr
N.A.I.C.S.: 441110
Frank Schimizzi (Treas & Sec)

HILLWOOD COUNTRY CLUB
6201 Hickory Valley Rd, Nashville, TN 37205
Tel.: (615) 352-6591　　　TN
Web Site: https://www.hillwoodcc.org
Year Founded: 1953
Sales Range: $10-24.9 Million
Emp.: 292
Country Club Operator
N.A.I.C.S.: 713910
Brent Elsasser (Dir-Comm)
Melvin Stewart (Supvr-Maintenance)
Mary Thomas Kuffner (Dir-Membership)
Mike Lathrop (Head-Golf Pro)
Marcus Currie (Mgr-Clubhouse)
Rocky Adcox (Mgr-WhitworthFacility)
Susie Quertermous (CFO)
Brad Reese (Dir-Fitness)
Charles Batt (Dir-Tennis)
Jon Forsthoff (Mgr-Acct)
Lauren Momcilovich (Mgr-Events & Catering)
David Robertson (Superintendent-Golf Course)

HILLYARD, INC.
302 N 4th St, Saint Joseph, MO 64501-1720
Tel.: (816) 233-1321　　　MO
Web Site: http://www.hillyard.com
Year Founded: 1907
Sales Range: $100-124.9 Million
Emp.: 1,000
Floor Care Products, Maintenance Equipment & Cleaners Mfr
N.A.I.C.S.: 424690
James P. Carolus (Pres)

Subsidiaries:

Hillyard-Rovic　　　(1)
127 Park Ave, East Hartford, CT 06108
Tel.: (860) 646-3322
Web Site: http://www.hillyard-rovic.com
Sales Range: $10-24.9 Million
Emp.: 55
Janitorial Supplies Distr
N.A.I.C.S.: 424690
Dermot Pelletier (Gen Mgr)
Keith Laramee (Mgr-Ops)
Mary Ellen Claffey (Mgr-Mktg)
Kim Waters (Mgr-Pur)
Tom Murphy (Mgr-Sls)
Charlie Wieczorek (Mgr-Warehouse)
Paul Goodnight (Mgr)
Tom Norman (Mgr)

HILLYER'S MID CITY FORD INC.
3000 Hillyer Ln, Woodburn, OR 97071-2803
Tel.: (503) 981-4747
Web Site: https://www.hillyers.com
Sales Range: $10-24.9 Million
Emp.: 50
New Car Whslr
N.A.I.C.S.: 441110
Leo Hillyer (Pres)

HILMAN, INC.
12 Timber Ln, Marlboro, NJ 07746
Tel.: (732) 462-6277　　　NJ
Web Site: https://www.hilmanrollers.com
Year Founded: 1953
Sales Range: $75-99.9 Million
Emp.: 60
Mfr of Rollers & Rolling Systems for Moving Heavy Weights
N.A.I.C.S.: 333924
Susan Montgomery (Pres)

HILMAR CHEESE COMPANY
8901 N Lander Ave, Hilmar, CA 95324

Hilmar Cheese Company—(Continued)

Tel.: (209) 667-6076
Web Site: https://www.hilmar.com
Year Founded: 1984
Sales Range: Less than $1 Million
Emp.: 1,500
Cheese Manufacturing
N.A.I.C.S.: 311513
Jeremy Travis *(VP-Quality & Technical Svcs)*
Ron Weltmer *(VP-Ops & Engrg)*
Kevin Vogt *(Chief Acctg Officer)*
Tony Pallios *(VP & Gen Mgr-Ingredients)*
David Ahlem *(Pres, Pres, CEO & CEO)*
Kyle Jensen *(VP & Gen Mgr-Cheese)*

HILO MAINTENANCE SYSTEMS, INC.
845 S 1st St, Ronkonkoma, NY 11779
Tel.: (631) 253-2600   NY
Web Site: http://www.hilousa.com
Year Founded: 1977
Sales Range: $10-24.9 Million
Emp.: 50
Industrial Machinery & Equipment Merchant Whslr
N.A.I.C.S.: 423830
Cindy Eisele *(Controller)*
Les Gobler *(CEO)*
Steven LoPiccolo *(Pres)*
Joe Veltri *(Gen Mgr)*

HILO PRODUCTS INC.
41 Makaala St, Hilo, HI 96720
Tel.: (808) 935-1106
Rev.: $14,000,000
Emp.: 40
Fresh Fruit & Vegetable Merchant Whslr
N.A.I.C.S.: 424480
Craig S. Suzuki *(VP-Pur)*
Royden N. Suzuki *(VP-Pur, Ops & Production Mfg)*
Henry Y. Suzuki *(Pres-Admin, Fin, Ops & Production Mfg)*
Susan Matsuda *(Treas & Sec)*

HILSCHER-CLARKE ELECTRIC COMPANY
519 4th St NW, Canton, OH 44703
Tel.: (330) 452-9806   OH
Web Site: https://www.hilscher-clarke.com
Year Founded: 1945
Sales Range: $10-24.9 Million
Emp.: 250
General Electrical Contractor
N.A.I.C.S.: 238210
Ronald D. Becker *(Mgr-Construction Svcs & Sr Engr-Electrical)*
Barbara Zwick *(CFO & Treas)*
Scott Goodspeed *(Pres)*
John Fether *(VP-Ops)*
Steven Chumney *(VP-Comml Ops)*
Bill Habyan *(Mgr-Div-Indus)*
Chuck Dulcie *(Mgr-Special Projects & Data, Voice & Video)*
Todd Bergert *(Mgr-Akron/Wooster Comml Div)*
John Russ *(Mgr-Automation Div)*
Tony Fay *(Mgr-Coshocton Branch & Testing Div)*

HILSINGER MENDELSON PUBLIC RELATIONS
115 N Kings Rd, Los Angeles, CA 90048
Tel.: (323) 931-5335
Web Site: http://www.hilsingermendelson.com
Sales Range: $10-24.9 Million
Emp.: 2

Public Relations & Marketing
N.A.I.C.S.: 541820
Judy Hilsinger *(Co-Founder)*
Sandi Mendelson *(Co-Founder & CEO)*

Subsidiaries:

Hilsinger Mendelson Public Relations   (1)
226 5th Ave Fl 4, New York, NY 10016
Tel.: (212) 725-7707
Web Site: http://www.hilsinger-mendelson.com
Emp.: 5
Public Relations & Marketing
N.A.I.C.S.: 541820
Sandi Mendelson *(CEO)*

HIM CONNECTIONS, LLC
1976 Gadsden Hwy Ste 101, Birmingham, AL 35235
Tel.: (205) 413-8300
Web Site: http://www.himconnections.com
Emp.: 25
Staffing Services
N.A.I.C.S.: 561311
Kayce Dover *(Pres & CEO)*

HIMALAYA HOMES INC.
1003 Cleveland Ave, Mount Vernon, WA 98273
Tel.: (360) 755-3430
Web Site: https://www.hhi-rentals.com
Year Founded: 1979
Sales Range: $25-49.9 Million
Emp.: 12
Housing Construction Services
N.A.I.C.S.: 236117
Kami Albright *(Dir-Customer Care)*
Chitra Parpia *(Owner)*
Zak Parpia *(Owner)*

HIMEC INC.
1400 7th St NW, Rochester, MN 55901
Tel.: (507) 288-7713   MN
Web Site: http://www.himec.com
Year Founded: 1988
Sales Range: $200-249.9 Million
Emp.: 600
Plumbing, Heating & Air-Conditioning Services
N.A.I.C.S.: 238220
Greg Donley *(Pres)*
Joe Beckel *(VP)*

HINCHCLIFF PRODUCTS COMPANY
13550 Falling Water Rd, Strongsville, OH 44136
Tel.: (440) 238-5200   OH
Web Site: http://www.hinchclifflumber.com
Year Founded: 1947
Pallets & Wood Supplier
N.A.I.C.S.: 321920
Jay Phillips *(Pres)*
Scott Phillips *(Sls Mgr)*

HINCKLEY, ALLEN & SNYDER LLP
50 Kennedy Plz Ste 1500, Providence, RI 02903-2319
Tel.: (401) 274-2000
Web Site: http://www.hinckleyallen.com
Year Founded: 1906
Emp.: 146
Law firm
N.A.I.C.S.: 541110
John J. Bolton *(Partner)*
David D. Barricelli *(Partner)*
Stephen J. Carlotti *(Partner)*
E. Jerome Batty *(Partner)*
Christine Bush *(Partner)*

Craig Scott *(Partner)*
Kris A. Moussette *(Partner-Pub Fin Practice)*
Margaret D. Farrell *(Co-Partner)*
Brian Tierney *(Partner)*
Robert J. Anthony *(Partner-Health Care Practice-Hartford)*
Leon C. Boghossian III *(Partner)*
William J. Squires III *(Partner)*
Robert T. Ferguson Jr. *(Partner-Construction & Pub Contracts Grp)*

Subsidiaries:

Ferencik Libanoff Brandt Bustamante & Goldstein, P.A .   (1)
7901 SW 6th Ct Ste 300, Plantation, FL 33324
Tel.: (954) 474-8080
Web Site: https://www.constructionlitigators.com
Emp.: 10
Law firm
N.A.I.C.S.: 541110
Ira L. Libanoff *(Mng Partner)*
Nestor Bustamante III *(Atty)*
Alan C. Brandt Jr. *(Atty)*
Robert E. Ferencik Jr. *(Atty)*
Alexander J. Williams Jr. *(Atty)*

HINCKLEYS INCORPORATED
2345 S State St, Salt Lake City, UT 84115
Tel.: (801) 484-8755
Web Site: http://www.hinckleydcj.com
Rev.: $40,100,000
Emp.: 125
New & Used Automobiles
N.A.I.C.S.: 441110
Jim Hinckley *(CEO)*

HINDA, INC.
2440 W 34th St, Chicago, IL 60608-5128
Tel.: (773) 890-5900   IL
Web Site: https://www.hinda.com
Year Founded: 1970
Sales Range: $75-99.9 Million
Emp.: 110
Business Consulting Services
N.A.I.C.S.: 541618
Bill Termini *(VP)*

HINDLEY MANUFACTURING COMPANY, INC.
9 Havens St, Cumberland, RI 02864
Tel.: (401) 722-2550
Web Site: https://www.hindley.com
Year Founded: 1897
Sales Range: $1-9.9 Million
Emp.: 80
Wire Hardware, Cotter Pin & Plumbing Accessories, Special Wire Forms & Peg Hook Mfr
N.A.I.C.S.: 332722
Scott A. Hindley *(VP-Sls & Mktg)*
Charles Hindley *(Pres)*

Subsidiaries:

Baker Sales   (1)
2260 S Haven Ave Ste C, Ontario, CA 91761
Tel.: (909) 930-1029
Web Site: http://www.hindley.com
Hardware Products Distr
N.A.I.C.S.: 332618

HINDMAN MANUFACTURING CO.
2 Industrial Dr, Salem, IL 62881
Tel.: (618) 548-2800   DE
Web Site: http://www.americana.com
Year Founded: 1947
Residential & Commercial Construction Services
N.A.I.C.S.: 236220
Anthony Purcell *(VP-Sls)*

Subsidiaries:

L.A. Steelcraft Products Co.   (1)
2 Industrial Dr, Salem, IL 62881
Tel.: (866) 210-5329
Web Site: http://www.lasteelcraft.com
Playground Equipment Mfr
N.A.I.C.S.: 339920

HINDS COUNTY HUMAN RESOURCE AGENCY
258 Maddox Rd, Jackson, MS 39212
Tel.: (601) 923-3930   MS
Web Site: https://www.hchra.org
Year Founded: 1975
Sales Range: $10-24.9 Million
Emp.: 459
Community Action Services
N.A.I.C.S.: 624190
Kenn Cockrell *(Pres & CEO)*
Kathleen Williams-McGriggs *(Sr VP-Admin & Bd Svcs)*
Al Junior *(CFO)*
Ann Burton *(Chm)*
Andrea McDaniel *(Sec)*
Trent L. Walker *(Vice Chm)*
William Roy Brown *(Dir-Facilities & Field Svc)*
Shirley A. Gibbs *(Dir-Pur & Procurement)*
Tarsha Henderson *(Deputy CFO)*
David Knight *(COO & Exec VP)*
Angelique Rawls *(Dir-Comm & Dev)*
Harry J. Lane III *(VP-Property Mgmt & Accountability)*

HINDS INSTRUMENTS, INC.
7245 NW Evergreen Pkwy Ste 150, Hillsboro, OR 97124-7124
Tel.: (503) 690-2000
Web Site: https://www.hindsinstruments.com
Year Founded: 1971
Sales Range: $10-24.9 Million
Emp.: 29
Polarization Measurement Instrumentation Mfr
N.A.I.C.S.: 334513
Paul W. Hinds *(Pres)*
James Hinds *(VP-Mfg)*
Tom Hinds *(VP-Fin & Admin)*

Subsidiaries:

Columbia Weather Systems, Inc.   (1)
5285 NE Elam Young Pkwy Ste C100, Hillsboro, OR 97124
Tel.: (503) 629-0887
Web Site: http://www.columbiaweather.com
Emp.: 7
Weather Monitoring System Mfr
N.A.I.C.S.: 334290
Nader Khoury *(Pres)*

HINES CORPORATION
1218 E Pontaluna Rd Ste B, Spring Lake, MI 49456-9634
Tel.: (231) 799-6240   MI
Web Site: https://www.hinescorp.com
Year Founded: 1985
Sales Range: $75-99.9 Million
Emp.: 500
Holding Company; Industrial Equipment Mfr
N.A.I.C.S.: 551112
Larry W. Hines *(Pres)*
Gregory Longcore *(CFO & Exec VP)*
Michele Buckley *(Exec VP-HR)*
Spencer Hines *(VP)*
George Hendrick *(Mng Partner-Hines Capital Partners & Exec VP-Corp Dev)*
Tom Thompson *(Exec VP)*
Brian Dunkle *(VP-Ops-Hines Specialty Vehicle Grp)*
Lisa Hartong *(Mgr-HR-Hines Specialty Vehicle Grp)*
Jeffrey McCauley *(VP-IT)*
Kent Taylor *(VP)*

Subsidiaries:

Bennett Pump Company (1)
1218 E Pontaluna Rd, Spring Lake, MI 49456-9634
Tel.: (231) 798-1310
Web Site: http://www.bennettpump.com
Rev.: $11,000,000
Emp.: 70
Mechanical & Electronic Gasoline Pumps & Pump Components Mfr
N.A.I.C.S.: 333914
Spencer Hines (Pres)
Michael Pomerantz (Dir-Hydrogen, Compressed Natural Gas & Liquefied Natural Gas Sls)
James Collier (Sr VP)

Johnston Boiler Company Inc. (1)
300 Pine St, Ferrysburg, MI 49409 (100%)
Tel.: (616) 842-5050
Web Site: http://www.johnstonboiler.com
Rev.: $14,000,000
Emp.: 75
Boiler Systems Designer & Mfr
N.A.I.C.S.: 332410
Dave Reinink (Pres)
Thom Parker (Dir-Sls-Natl)
Rick Ewing (Sr VP-Ops)

Kimble Chassis Company (1)
3389 Crooked Run Rd NW, New Philadelphia, OH 44663
Tel.: (330) 339-2181
Web Site: http://www.kimblemixer.com
Sales Range: $1-9.9 Million
Emp.: 25
Chassis Design & Construction
N.A.I.C.S.: 336211
Mark Ward (Mgr-Chassis Engrg)

Kimble Manufacturing Company (1)
1951 Reiser Ave SE, New Philadelphia, OH 44663
Tel.: (330) 339-2357
Web Site: http://www.kimblemixer.com
Sales Range: $25-49.9 Million
Emp.: 76
Concrete Mixing Machinery Mfr
N.A.I.C.S.: 333120
Phil Raber (Dir-Continuous Improvement)
Randy Rollins (Pres & CEO)

Michigan Spring & Stamping LLC (1)
2700 Wickham Dr, Muskegon, MI 49441 (100%)
Tel.: (231) 755-1691
Web Site: http://www.msands.com
Sales Range: $25-49.9 Million
Emp.: 150
Metal Spring & Stamping Mfr
N.A.I.C.S.: 332613
Tim Zwit (Pres)

Pacific, Inc. (1)
2259 S Sheridan Dr, Muskegon, MI 49442-6252
Tel.: (231) 773-1330
Web Site: http://www.pacificfloorcare.com
Sales Range: $10-24.9 Million
Emp.: 17
Floor Maintenance Machinery Mfr
N.A.I.C.S.: 333310
Dave Nelson (Pres)

Plymouth Industries Inc. (1)
2601 Niagara Ln, Plymouth, MN 55447-4721
Tel.: (763) 553-1935
Web Site: http://www.cimline.com
Rev.: $8,300,000
Emp.: 60
Holding Company; Equipment Design, Manufacture & Distribution for Road Maintenance & Roofing Industries
N.A.I.C.S.: 551112

Subsidiary (Domestic):

Cimline Inc. (2)
2601 Niagara Ln N, Plymouth, MN 55447-4721
Tel.: (763) 557-1982
Web Site: http://www.cimline.com
Rev.: $1,800,000
Emp.: 50
Road Maintenance Equipment Mfr
N.A.I.C.S.: 333120

Subsidiary (Domestic):

Duraco Industries, Inc. (3)

2000 Old Whitfield Rd, Pearl, MS 39208
Tel.: (601) 932-2100
Web Site: http://www.durapatcher.com
Road Maintenance Services
N.A.I.C.S.: 237310

EQUIPT Manufacturing, Inc. (3)
2601 Niagara Ln, Plymouth, MN 55447
Tel.: (763) 694-2604
Web Site: http://www.equiptdirect.com
Emp.: 150
Seal Coating Equipment Distr
N.A.I.C.S.: 423830

Subsidiary (Domestic):

Garlock Chicago Inc. (2)
628 Thomas Dr, Bensenville, IL 60106-1262
Tel.: (630) 521-9645
Web Site: http://www.garlockchicago.com
Roofing & Siding Product Whlsr
N.A.I.C.S.: 423330

Garlock East Equipment Co (2)
51-35 34th St, Long Island City, NY 11101
Tel.: (718) 706-0094
Web Site:
   http://www.garlockeastequipment.com
Roofing & Siding Product Whlsr
N.A.I.C.S.: 423330

Garlock Equipment Company (2)
2601 Niagara Ln N, Plymouth, MN 55447
Tel.: (763) 694-2649
Web Site: http://www.garlockequip.com
Roofing & Siding Product Distr
N.A.I.C.S.: 423330

HINES GLOBAL REIT, INC.
2800 Post Oak Blvd Ste 5000, Houston, TX 77056-6118   MD
Web Site:
   http://www.hinessecurities.com
Year Founded: 2008
Rev.: $308,865,000
Assets: $2,499,711,000
Liabilities: $906,849,000
Net Worth: $1,592,862,000
Earnings: $454,782,000
Fiscal Year-end: 12/31/18
Real Estate Investment Services
N.A.I.C.S.: 525990
Jeffrey C. Hines (Chm)
Sherri W. Schugart (Pres & CEO)
J. Shea Morgenroth (Chief Accounting Officer & Treas)
Kevin L. McMeans (Asset Mgmt Officer)
David L. Steinbach (Chief Investment Officer)

Subsidiaries:

Fibersoft Limited (1)
Diomidous Street 10 Lefkosia, Nicosia, Cyprus
Tel.: (357) 22361600
Real Estate Investment Services
N.A.I.C.S.: 525990

Hines Global REIT Marlborough Campus I LLC (1)
250 Royall St, Canton, MA 02021
Tel.: (508) 303-6900
Emp.: 11
Real Estate Investment Services
N.A.I.C.S.: 525990

HINES INTERESTS LIMITED PARTNERSHIP
2800 Post Oak Blvd Ste 48 Fl, Houston, TX 77056-6118
Tel.: (713) 237-5600   DE
Web Site: https://www.hines.com
Year Founded: 1954
Sales Range: $100-124.9 Million
Emp.: 1,700
Real Estate Developers
N.A.I.C.S.: 531210
C. Hastings Johnson (Vice Chm & CIO)
Jeffrey C. Hines (Co-Owner & Pres)
Charles M. Baughn (CEO-Capital Markets & Exec VP)

Gerald D. Hines (Founder & Chm)
Michael J. G. Topham (Co-CEO-Europe & MENA Reg)
James C. Buie (CEO-West Reg & Exec VP)
Kay P. Forbes (Treas)
Ken Hubbard (Sr Mng Dir)
C. Kevin Shannahan (CEO-Midwest & Southeast)
George C. Lancaster (Sr VP-Corp Comm)
Mark Cover (CEO-Southwest Reg & Mexico)
Thomas Owens (Chief Risk Officer & Sr Mng Dir)
Jerry Lea (Exec VP-Conceptual Construction)
Jesse Carrillo (CIO & Sr VP)
Keith Montgomery (Sr VP & Controller)
Connor Tamlyn (Dir-Indus-Mexico & Southwest)

HINES PARK LINCOLN MERCURY
40601 Ann Arbor Rd E, Plymouth, MI 48170
Tel.: (734) 453-2424
Web Site:
   https://www.hinesparklincoln.com
Rev.: $45,300,000
Emp.: 100
Car Dealership
N.A.I.C.S.: 441110
Michael Kolb (Owner)
Jennifer Olson (Controller)
Rhonda Sabatini (Gen Mgr-Sls)
Tim Worthington (Dir-Svc)

HINES REAL ESTATE INVESTMENT TRUST, INC.
2800 Post Oak Blvd Ste 5000, Houston, TX 77056-6118
Tel.: (888) 220-6121   MD
Web Site:
   http://www.hinessecurities.com
Year Founded: 2003
Real Estate Investment Trust
N.A.I.C.S.: 525990
Sherri W. Schugart (Pres & CEO)
Ryan T. Sims (CFO & Sec)

HINES SECURITIES, INC.
2800 Post Oak Blvd Ste 4700, Houston, TX 77056
Tel.: (713) 621-8000   DE
Web Site:
   http://www.hinessecurities.com
Year Founded: 2003
Emp.: 50
Securities Broker & Dealer
N.A.I.C.S.: 523150
Debbie Prosperie (Sr Controller-Fin Ops)

HINGE, INCORPORATED
12030 Sunrise Valley Dr, Reston, VA 20191
Tel.: (703) 391-8870
Web Site:
   http://www.hingemarketing.com
Graphic Design Services
N.A.I.C.S.: 541430
Lee Frederiksen (Mng Partner)
Karl Feldman (Partner)
Elizabeth Harr (Partner)

HINIKER COMPANY
58766 240th St, Mankato, MN 56001
Tel.: (507) 625-6621   MN
Web Site: https://www.hiniker.com
Year Founded: 1967
Sales Range: $100-124.9 Million
Emp.: 251

Mfr of Farm Machinery & Equipment, Snow Plows, Water Purification Equipment & Electronic Controllers
N.A.I.C.S.: 333111
Vincent J. Tomlonovic (Gen Mgr)
Mark Miller (Mgr-Adv & Mktg)

Subsidiaries:

Hiniker Company - Coster Engineering Division (1)
PO Box 3407, Mankato, MN 56002-3407
Tel.: (507) 625-6621
Web Site: http://www.costereng.com
Water Treatment Equipment Mfr
N.A.I.C.S.: 333310
Pat Krenik (Gen Mgr-Sls)

HINKLE MANUFACTURING INC
348 5th St, Perrysburg, OH 43551
Tel.: (419) 666-5550
Web Site: http://www.hinklemfg.com
Sales Range: $10-24.9 Million
Emp.: 100
Packaging & Shipping Materials Foamed Plastics
N.A.I.C.S.: 326150
Taber Hinkle (Pres & Gen Mgr)
Jeffery Wolens (CFO)

HINKLE METALS & SUPPLY CO. INC.
3300 11th Ave N, Birmingham, AL 35234
Tel.: (205) 326-3300   AL
Year Founded: 1980
Sales Range: $10-24.9 Million
Emp.: 105
Provider of Metal Services & Supplies
N.A.I.C.S.: 423510
Shane Atkins (Mgr-Pur)
F. Hunter Hinkle Jr. (Pres)

HINKLE'S PHARMACY
261 Locust St, Columbia, PA 17512
Tel.: (717) 684-2551
Web Site:
   http://www.hinklespharmacy.com
Year Founded: 1893
Sales Range: $10-24.9 Million
Emp.: 62
Pharmacy & Drug Product Distr
N.A.I.C.S.: 456110
Tom Davis (Mgr-Store)

HINKLEY LIGHTING INC.
33000 Pin Oak Pkwy, Avon Lake, OH 44012
Tel.: (216) 671-3300   OH
Web Site:
   http://www.hinkleylighting.com
Year Founded: 1922
Sales Range: $75-99.9 Million
Emp.: 60
Lighting & Accessories for Commercial & Residential
N.A.I.C.S.: 335132
Tom Dicks (Mgr-Sls-Natl)
Jess Wiedemer (Pres & COO)
Carmen Popa (Mgr-Info Sys)

HINRICHS FLANAGAN FINANCIAL
S Park Twrs 6000 Fairview Rd Ste 400, Charlotte, NC 28210
Tel.: (704) 557-9600
Web Site:
   http://www.hinrichsflanagan.com
Year Founded: 1935
Sales Range: $75-99.9 Million
Emp.: 128
Insurance & Securities Brokerage, Asset Management, Financial Planning & Advisory Services
N.A.I.C.S.: 524210
Timothy Flanagan (Pres)

Hinshaw & Culbertson LLP—(Continued)

HINSHAW & CULBERTSON LLP
222 N LaSalle St Ste 300, Chicago, IL 60601
Tel.: (312) 704-3000   IL
Web Site:
    http://www.hinshawlaw.com
Year Founded: 1934
Sales Range: $200-249.9 Million
Emp.: 1,001
Legal Advisory Services
N.A.I.C.S.: 541110
Anthony E. Antognoli *(Partner)*
David J. Alfini *(Partner)*
Joel D. Bertocchi *(Partner)*
Sergio E. Acosta *(Partner)*
V. Brette Bensinger *(Partner)*
Donald L. Mrozek *(Chm-Consultants & Coaches-Profession Practice)*
Kevin Joseph Burke *(Chm-Chicago)*
Robert P. Johnson *(CFO)*
Dan L. Boho *(Partner)*
Steven R. Bonanno *(Partner)*
Roy M. Bossen *(Partner)*
Lisa M. Burman *(Partner)*
Matthew J. Canna *(Partner)*
Leonor M. Lagomasino *(Partner)*
Mark D. Greenberg *(Partner)*
Esperanza Segarra *(Partner)*
Adam R. Vaught *(Partner)*
Gretchen Harris Sperry *(Partner)*
Adam S. Guetzow *(Partner)*
Anne C. Couyoumjian *(Partner)*
Albert C. Angelo *(Partner)*
Daniel A. Prywes *(Partner)*
Brian R. Zeeck *(Partner)*
Michael Hatting *(Partner-Comml Transactions Practice-Minneapolis)*
Dean Parker *(Chm-Comml Transactions)*
Vaishali S. Rao *(Partner)*
Kenneth Yeadon *(Partner-White Collar Defense Practice)*
Andrew M. Gordon *(Partner)*
Adam Rucker *(Partner)*
Brandon Takahashi *(Partner)*
William D. Trimble *(Partner-Peoria)*
David Nightingale *(Partner)*
James H. Kallianis Jr. *(Partner)*

HINSON GALLERIES, INC.
1208 13th Ave, Columbus, GA 31901
Tel.: (706) 327-3671
Web Site:
    https://www.hinsongalleries.com
Year Founded: 1951
Sales Range: $10-24.9 Million
Emp.: 12
Furniture Retailer
N.A.I.C.S.: 449110
Robert Hinson III *(Pres)*

HINTO ENERGY, INC.
5350 S Roslyn St Ste 400, Greenwood Village, CO 80111
Tel.: (303) 647-4850   WY
Web Site:
    http://www.hintoenergy.com
Year Founded: 1997
Sales Range: Less than $1 Million
Emp.: 1
Oil & Gas Exploration
N.A.I.C.S.: 211120
Gary Herick *(Sec & VP-Fin)*
J. David Keller *(VP-Exploration & Dev)*

HINZE INC.
53 County Rd 2AB, Cody, WY 82414
Tel.: (307) 527-7575
Year Founded: 1988
Sales Range: $25-49.9 Million
Emp.: 100

Owner & Operator of Convenience Stores; Petroleum Products Whslr
N.A.I.C.S.: 445131
Dale Hinze *(Pres)*
Brian Hinze *(VP)*

HIRE POWER, INC.
5229 DTC Blvd Ste 720, Greenwood Village, CO 80111
Tel.: (303) 554-2000   CO
Web Site:
    http://www.innovargroup.com
Year Founded: 2000
Sales Range: $25-49.9 Million
Emp.: 35
IT Staffing Services
N.A.I.C.S.: 561311
Diane Pacheco *(CEO)*
Darryl Hoogstrate *(Co-Founder & CEO)*
Tami Gravina *(VP-Sls)*
Michelle Strother *(VP-Ops)*
Blake Crawford *(Dir-Bus Dev)*

HIRE VELOCITY, LLC
375 Northridge Rd Ste 270, Atlanta, GA 30350
Tel.: (678) 798-8634
Web Site:
    https://www.hirevelocity.com
Year Founded: 2004
Rev.: $2,500,000
Emp.: 26
Management Consulting Services
N.A.I.C.S.: 541618
Byron West *(Founder & Pres)*
Matt Dawson *(CFO & COO)*
Sara West *(Dir-Strategic Dev)*
Don Boone *(Mng Dir)*
Jennifer Beck *(CEO)*
Marques Smith *(VP-Fin)*
Susan Moffet *(Mng Dir-Ops)*

HIREAHELPER LLC
PO Box 5829, Oceanside, CA 92052
Web Site: http://www.hireahelper.com
Year Founded: 2007
Sales Range: $1-9.9 Million
Emp.: 12
Moving Labor Marketplace
N.A.I.C.S.: 484210
Mike Glanz *(CEO & Founder)*

HIREASE, INC.
340 Commerce Ave, Southern Pines, NC 28387
Tel.: (910) 693-1764
Web Site: http://www.hirease.com
Year Founded: 2002
Rev.: $3,000,000
Emp.: 26
Personal Services
N.A.I.C.S.: 812990
Erik H. Stromberg *(VP)*

HIRED HANDS, INC.
10 Commercial Blvd Ste 102, Novato, CA 94949
Tel.: (415) 884-4343   CA
Web Site:
    http://www.hiredhandshomecare.com
Year Founded: 1994
Sales Range: $1-9.9 Million
Emp.: 476
Non-Medical Home Care Services
N.A.I.C.S.: 561311
Lynn Winter *(CEO)*

HIREGY
11011 NW Shore Blvd, Tampa, FL 33607
Tel.: (813) 449-4800
Web Site: http://www.hiregy.com
Sales Range: $1-9.9 Million
Emp.: 10

Staffing Services
N.A.I.C.S.: 561311
Bill Fries *(CEO)*
Shaun Androff *(VP-Client Rels)*
Amy Garrison *(Mgr-Client Svcs)*
Brandi McNenney *(Dir-Ops)*
Michelle Loudon *(Mgr-Client Svcs)*
Bill Curtiss *(Mgr-Client Rels)*
Caitlin Thompson *(Dir-Client Rels-Orlando)*
Christy McDonald *(Dir-Client Svcs-Orlando)*
Charis Ortiz *(Mgr-Client Svcs-Orlando)*
Jil Russell *(Sr Mgr-Client Svcs)*
Lorie Bryce *(VP-Client Svcs)*
Stacy Stephens *(Mgr-Client Svcs)*
Victoria Helton *(Mgr-Client Svcs-Tampa)*

HIREMETHODS
10748 Deerwood Park Blvd, Jacksonville, FL 32256
Tel.: (904) 398-4133
Web Site: http://www.imethods.com
Year Founded: 2004
Rev.: $3,500,000
Emp.: 10
Human Resouce Services
N.A.I.C.S.: 541612
Clint Drawdy *(Co-Founder, Co-Owner & Co-Pres)*

HIRENETWORKS
8020 Arco Corporate Dr Ste 118, Raleigh, NC 27617
Tel.: (919) 981-6200
Web Site:
    http://www.hirenetworks.com
Year Founded: 2001
Sales Range: $1-9.9 Million
Emp.: 114
Recruitment Consulting Services
N.A.I.C.S.: 561320
Craig Stone *(CEO)*
Tina Cochrane *(VP-Client Dev)*
Michelle Coviello *(VP-Client Dev)*
Stephanie Gore *(VP-Fin & Ops)*
Stephanie Slade Stone *(VP-Mktg)*
Jennifer Frederick *(Office Mgr)*
Kendra Andrews *(Dir-Recruiting)*
Kate Lewis *(Dir-Consulting Svcs)*
Jessica Harrold *(Mgr-Ops)*

HIRERIGHT, LLC
3349 Michelson Dr Ste 150, Irvine, CA 92612
Web Site: http://www.hireright.com
Year Founded: 1966
Background Screening & Risk Management Services
N.A.I.C.S.: 541614
Guy Abramo *(CEO)*
Todd Baxter *(Chief Svcs Officer)*
Scott Collins *(Chief Revenue Officer)*
Brian Copple *(Gen Counsel)*
Jim Daxner *(Chief Digital Officer)*

HIREWELL
20 N Wacker Dr Ste 2420, Chicago, IL 60606
Tel.: (312) 496-7955
Web Site: http://www.hirewell.com
Year Founded: 2001
Sales Range: $1-9.9 Million
Emp.: 45
Human Resource Consulting Services
N.A.I.C.S.: 541612
Matt Massucci *(Founder & Partner)*
Mike Ehlers *(VP-Bus Dev)*

HIRNING PONTIAC BUICK GMC
509 Yellowstone Ave, Pocatello, ID 83201

Tel.: (208) 269-3597
Web Site:
    https://www.hirningauto.com
Year Founded: 1965
Sales Range: $25-49.9 Million
Emp.: 68
Car Whslr
N.A.I.C.S.: 441110
Kelly Hirning *(VP)*

HIRONS
185 E 18th Ave, Eugene, OR 97401
Tel.: (541) 344-4832
Web Site:
    https://www.hironsdrug.com
Sales Range: $10-24.9 Million
Emp.: 80
Pharmacy & Drug Product Distr
N.A.I.C.S.: 456110
John Hirons *(Pres)*
Steve Hirons *(VP)*

HIRONS & COMPANY
422 E New York St, Indianapolis, IN 46202
Tel.: (317) 977-2206   IN
Web Site: http://www.hirons.com
Year Founded: 1978
Rev.: $30,000,000
Emp.: 50
N.A.I.C.S.: 541810
Tom Hirons *(CEO)*
Jim Parham *(COO)*
Chris Williams *(VP & Dir-HR)*
Shelby Siurek *(VP & Dir-Media)*
Ann Kneifel *(CFO)*
Ana Kotchkoski *(Sr Acct Mgr)*
Jay Schemanske *(Sr VP-Strategic Comm & Acct Svcs)*

Subsidiaries:

Hirons & Company   (1)
555 N Morton St, Bloomington, IN 47404
Tel.: (812) 331-7500
Web Site: http://www.hirons.com
Full Service
N.A.I.C.S.: 541810
Tom Hirons *(Pres)*

HIRSCH INTERNATIONAL CORP.
50 Engineers Rd, Hauppauge, NY 11788
Tel.: (631) 436-7100   NY
Web Site:
    http://www.hirschinternational.com
Year Founded: 1970
Sales Range: $25-49.9 Million
Emp.: 138
Computerized Embroidery Equipment & Supplies Distr; Developer of Computer Software Programs & Lessor of Computerized Embroidery Equipment
N.A.I.C.S.: 423830
Paul Gallagher *(Pres, CEO & COO)*
Kristof Janowski *(Pres-Huntersville)*
Randy L. Florio *(Asst Controller)*
Rich Fleming *(Mgr-IT)*
Brian Rees *(CFO)*

Subsidiaries:

Hirsch Business Concepts, LLC   (1)
50 Engineers Rd, Hauppauge, NY 11788
Tel.: (631) 436-7100
Sales Range: $500-549.9 Million
Provider of Embroidery Machines
N.A.I.C.S.: 423830

Tajima USA, Inc.   (1)
550 Commerce St, Franklin Lakes, NJ 07417
Tel.: (201) 405-1201
Sales of Multi-Head Electronic Embroidery Machines & Related Equipment; Joint Venture of Hirsch International Corp. (55%) & Tajima Industries Ltd. (45%)

N.A.I.C.S.: 811210

Tajima-Hirsch Incorporated (1)
50 Engineers Rd, Hauppauge, NY 11788
Tel.: (631) 436-7100
Web Site: http://www.tajima-hirsch.com
Sales Range: $10-24.9 Million
Emp.: 120
Provider of Embroidery Machines
N.A.I.C.S.: 423830

HIRSCH METALS CORPORATION
PO Box 480785, Delray Beach, FL 33448
Tel.: (561) 994-6440
Web Site:
   http://www.hirschmetals.com
Rev.: $15,000,000
Emp.: 6
Solder: Wire, Bar, Acid Core & Rosin Core
N.A.I.C.S.: 331491
Ron Hirsch (Pres)

HIRSCH PIPE & SUPPLY CO., INC.
15025 Oxnard St Ste 100, Van Nuys, CA 91411-2611
Tel.: (818) 756-0900
Web Site: https://www.hirsch.com
Year Founded: 1933
Sales Range: $10-24.9 Million
Emp.: 125
Supplier of Plumbing Fixtures & Equipment
N.A.I.C.S.: 423720
Daniel Mariscal (Chm)
William Glockner (Pres & CEO)

HIRSCHBACH MOTOR LINES, INC.
2460 Kerper Blvd, Dubuque, IA 52001
Tel.: (402) 404-2000   IA
Web Site: https://hirschbach.com
Year Founded: 1961
Freight Trucking Services
N.A.I.C.S.: 484121
Brad Pinchuk (CEO)
Brad Pinchuk (CEO)
Richard Stocking (Pres)

HIRSCHLER FLEISCHER, A PROFESSIONAL CORPORATION
The Edgeworth Bldg 2100 E Cary St, Richmond, VA 23223-7078
Tel.: (804) 771-9500   VA
Web Site: http://www.hf-law.com
Year Founded: 1946
Emp.: 120
Law firm
N.A.I.C.S.: 541110
Paul H. Davenport (Atty)
James K. Cluverius (Partner)
Richard Duke (Exec Dir)
Kristen M. Chatterton (CMO)
Jennifer R. Lutz (Controller)
Ellen B. Purcell (Dir-HR)
Christopher J. Schenack (CIO)
James L. Weinberg (Pres)
S. Brian Farmer (Chm-Bus Section & Treas)
Andrew M. Lohmann (Partner & Chm-Mergers & Acq Practice Grp)
Courtney Moates Paulk (Chm-Litigation & Head-Hiring)
John F. McManus (Mng Partner-Fredericksburg)
Charles H. Rothenberg (Partner & Chm-Real Estate Section)
Michael H. Terry (Exec VP)
James W. Theobald (Chm)
Wayne G. Travell (Mng Partner-Tysons)
Charles F. Witthoefft (Gen Counsel)

Eric Martin (Dir-Billing Svcs)
Victor H. Nelson (Dir-Facilities & Office Svcs)
Myrna H. Rooks (Dir-Legal Recruiting & Events)
Justine Fitzgerald (Partner-Real Estate Grp)
Robert A. Cox Jr. (Atty)

HIRSH INDUSTRIES, INC.
11229 Aurora Ave, Urbandale, IA 50322-7906
Tel.: (515) 299-3200   IA
Web Site:
   http://www.hirshindustries.com
Year Founded: 1945
Sales Range: $150-199.9 Million
Emp.: 800
Metal Office Furniture & Shelving Mfr
N.A.I.C.S.: 337214
Sandie McVey (Mgr-Customer Service)

Subsidiaries:

Hirsh Industries Dover Division (1)
1525 McKee Rd, Dover, DE 19904
Tel.: (302) 678-3454
Sales Range: $25-49.9 Million
Emp.: 220
Mfr of Steel Office Furniture, Metal Selving Units & Steel Filing Cabinets
N.A.I.C.S.: 337214
Tom Apostolico (Plant Mgr)

Hirsh Industries LLC (1)
3636 Westown Pkwy Ste 100, West Des Moines, IA 50266
Tel.: (515) 299-3200
Sales Range: $10-24.9 Million
Emp.: 28
Office Furniture Mfr
N.A.I.C.S.: 337214
Meagan Patterson (VP-Mktg)

MEG (1)
502 S Green St, Cambridge City, IN 47327
Tel.: (765) 478-3141
Web Site: http://www.megfixtures.com
Sales Range: $25-49.9 Million
Emp.: 200
Store Fixture Mfr
N.A.I.C.S.: 337126

HIRSHFIELD'S INC.
725 2nd Ave N, Minneapolis, MN 55405-1601
Tel.: (612) 377-9970   MN
Web Site: https://www.hirshfields.com
Year Founded: 1894
Sales Range: $50-74.9 Million
Emp.: 405
Paints, Wallcoverings & Industrial Coatings Retailer
N.A.I.C.S.: 424950
Steve Boylan (Mgr-Store)

Subsidiaries:

Hirshfield's Paint Manufacturing
Inc. (1)
4450 Lyndale Ave N, Minneapolis, MN 55412-1437
Tel.: (612) 522-6621
Web Site: http://www.hirshfields.com
Sales Range: $10-24.9 Million
Emp.: 17
Paints & Allied Products Mfr
N.A.I.C.S.: 325510

HIRTLE CALLAGHAN & CO.
300 Barr Harbor Dr Ste 500, West Conshohocken, PA 19428
Tel.: (610) 828-7200
Web Site:
   http://www.hirtlecallaghan.com
Year Founded: 1988
Sales Range: $10-24.9 Million
Emp.: 100
Investment Advising Services
N.A.I.C.S.: 523940

Eileen Brazitis (Principal)
Brad Conger (Deputy Chief Investment Officer-Pub Mrkets)
Jonathan Hirtle (Founder & Chm)
Erica Evans (Head-Client Engagement)
Jim Morris (Sr Dir-Client Engagement)
Mark Hamilton (Chief Investment Officer)
Daniel McCollum (Deputy Chief Investment Officer)
Scott Jacobson (Dir-Risk Mgmt)
Stephen Vaccaro (Dir-Private Equity)
Kristofer T. Kelleher (Dir-Client Engagement)

HIRZEL CANNING CO & FARMS
411 Lemoyne Rd, Northwood, OH 43619
Tel.: (419) 693-0531
Web Site: http://www.hirzel.com
Year Founded: 1923
Sales Range: $10-24.9 Million
Emp.: 100
Canned Tomato & Vegetable Products Mfr
N.A.I.C.S.: 311421
Joe Pickett (Controller)
Steve Hirzel (Pres)
Jeff Unverferth (Mgr-Agricultural)

HIS EQUIPMENT MARKETING CO.
1310 48th St 3rd Fl, Brooklyn, NY 11219-3158
Tel.: (718) 435-2222
Web Site: https://www.hisemc.com
Year Founded: 1981
Sales Range: Less than $1 Million
Emp.: 15
Computer Rental & Leasing Services
N.A.I.C.S.: 532420
Harry Silber (Pres)

HISPANIC ASSOCIATION OF COLLEGES AND UNIVERSITIES
8415 Datapoint Dr Ste 400, San Antonio, TX 78229
Tel.: (210) 692-3805   TX
Web Site: http://www.hacu.net
Year Founded: 1986
Sales Range: $10-24.9 Million
Emp.: 50
Educational Support Services
N.A.I.C.S.: 611710
William V. Flores (Treas)
Antonio R. Flores (Pres & CEO)

HISPANIC BUSINESS INC.
5385 Hollister Ave 204, Santa Barbara, CA 93111
Tel.: (805) 964-4554
Web Site:
   http://www.hispanicbusiness.com
Year Founded: 1979
Sales Range: $10-24.9 Million
Emp.: 60
Business Magazine Publisher
N.A.I.C.S.: 513120
Jesus Chavarria (Pres, CEO & Publr)
Karen Stephens (Dir-HR)

Subsidiaries:

Hispanic Business Magazine (1)
475 Pine Ave, Santa Barbara, CA 93117-3709
Tel.: (805) 964-4554
Web Site: http://www.hispanicbusiness.com
Sales Range: $10-24.9 Million
Emp.: 20
Magazine
N.A.I.C.S.: 513120
Jesus Chavarria (CEO, Publr & Editor)

HISPANIC SCHOLARSHIP FUND
1411 W 190th St Ste 700, Gardena, CA 90248
Tel.: (310) 975-3700   DC
Web Site: http://www.hsf.net
Year Founded: 1975
Sales Range: $25-49.9 Million
Emp.: 79
Grantmaking Services
N.A.I.C.S.: 813211
Anahi Godinez (Dir-Alumni Engagement)
Victoria L. Hardy (Dir-Fin & Controller)
Marcela Bailey (CMO & CIO)
Fernando Almodovar (CFO)
Lisa Garcia Quiroz (Chm)
Gene Camarena (Vice Chm)
Anthony Salcido (Treas)
Margarita Flores (Sec)

HISSHO SUSHI
11949 Steele Creek Rd, Charlotte, NC 28273
Tel.: (704) 926-2200
Web Site:
   https://www.hisshosushi.com
Sales Range: $25-49.9 Million
Emp.: 267
Specialty Food Product Distr
N.A.I.C.S.: 424420
Philip Maung (Pres, CEO & Chief Culture Officer)
Penny Kirsch (Dir-HR)
Minn Zin Htaik (Mgr-Chef Partner Program)
Joanna Lee (Sr Mgr-Sls-Natl & Dir-Wildlife)

HISSONG GROUP INC.
2820 Brecksville Rd, Richfield, OH 44286
Tel.: (330) 659-3770
Web Site:
   http://www.hissonggroup.com
Sales Range: $75-99.9 Million
Emp.: 115
Trucks, Tractors & Trailers: New & Used
N.A.I.C.S.: 441110
Robert E. Hissong (CEO)
Alan Murrow (CFO)
Mike Grau (Mgr-Admin)
Jeff Reutter (Mgr-IT & Sls Admin)

HISTORIC HUDSON VALLEY
639 Bedford Rd, Tarrytown, NY 10591
Tel.: (914) 366-6900   NY
Web Site:
   https://www.hudsonvalley.org
Year Founded: 1951
Sales Range: $10-24.9 Million
Emp.: 214
Historical Site Preservation Services
N.A.I.C.S.: 712120
David Parsons (Fin Dir & Dir-Admin)
Karen Sharman (Dir-Programs)
Peter Pockriss (Dir-Dev)

HISTORIC PRESERVATION PARTNERS, INC.
1200 S Kansas Ave, Topeka, KS 66612-1375
Tel.: (785) 290-0072   KS
Web Site:
   https://www.yourhistoricpartner.com
Year Founded: 2008
Sales Range: $10-24.9 Million
Emp.: 3
Historical Preservation Services
N.A.I.C.S.: 541720

Historic Preservation Partners,
Inc.—(Continued)

John Appel (Asst Treas)
Richard D. Kready (Pres)
Ross Freeman (Chm)
Debra Ricks (Treas & Sec)

HISTORIC RESTORATION, INC.

812 Gravier St Ste 200, New Orleans, LA 70112
Tel.: (504) 566-0204
Web Site: http://www.hrihci.com
Year Founded: 1982
Sales Range: $10-24.9 Million
Emp.: 60
Property Management, Construction & Real Estate Development
N.A.I.C.S.: 237210
Tom Leonhard (Pres & COO)
David Abbenant (Pres-HRI Mgmt)
Pres Kabacoff (Co-Chm & CEO)
Eddie Boettner (Co-Chm & Chief Admin Officer)
Sidney J. Bartholemy (VP-Civic Affairs)
Ray Spadafora (Treas & Sec)
Selim Berkol (Sr VP-Middle East & Europe)
Hal Fairbanks (VP-Acq)
Honore G. Aschaffenburg (Pres-HRI Lodging)
Gary Meadows (Pres-HCI Design)
Ronald H. Silverman (Sr VP & Reg Mgr)
Josh Collen (VP-Dev)
Leroy Prout (CIO)
Lew Derbes (CFO)

Subsidiaries:

Historic Construction Inc.   (1)
909 Poydras Ste 3100, New Orleans, LA 70112-1884
Tel.: (504) 566-0204
Web Site: http://www.hriproperties.com
Residential Construction
N.A.I.C.S.: 236220
Tom Leonhard (Pres & CEO)
David Abbenant (Pres-HRI Mgmt)
Pres Kabacoff (Chm)
Ray T. Spadafora (Treas & Sec)
Josh Collen (VP-Dev)
Wayne Clement (VP-Construction)
Chris Connolly (VP-Fin)
Lew Derbes (CFO)
Hal Fairbanks (VP-Acq)
Dione M. Heusel (Sr VP-HR)
Steven Nance (VP-Investments)
Leroy Prout (CIO)

HISTORIC TOURS OF AMERICA INC.

201 Front St, Key West, FL 33040-8349
Tel.: (305) 293-7253
Web Site:
   https://www.historictours.com
Year Founded: 1988
Sales Range: $10-24.9 Million
Emp.: 600
Amusement & Recreation Services
N.A.I.C.S.: 713990
Christopher C. Belland (Co-Founder & CEO)
Benjamin N. McPherson (Treas)
Ryan Darrah (CIO)
Edwin O. Swift III (Co-Founder & Pres)

Subsidiaries:

Buggy Bus Inc.   (1)
122 Simonton St, Key West, FL 33040-6006
Tel.: (305) 296-3609
Web Site: http://www.historictours.com
Sales Range: $10-24.9 Million
Emp.: 45

Provider of Amusement & Recreation Services
N.A.I.C.S.: 713990
Christopher Belland (CEO)

Conch Tour Train   (1)
108 Sea Grove Main St, Saint Augustine, FL 32080   (100%)
Web Site: http://www.conchtourtrain.com
Sales Range: $10-24.9 Million
Emp.: 55
Provider of Amusement & Recreation Services
N.A.I.C.S.: 713990
Eva Conaway (Gen Mgr)

Deacon Transportation Inc.   (1)
380 Dorchester Ave, Boston, MA 02127-1315
Tel.: (617) 269-7150
Web Site: http://www.trolleytours.com
Sales Range: $10-24.9 Million
Emp.: 100
Provider of Bus Services
N.A.I.C.S.: 485510
John Welby (Gen Mgr)

Old Town Trolley Tours   (1)
380 Dorchester Ave, Boston, MA 02127-1110   (100%)
Tel.: (617) 269-7010
Web Site: http://www.historictours.com
Rev.: $569,995
Emp.: 100
Tour Services
N.A.I.C.S.: 485510
Chris Crompton (Gen Mgr-Boston Ops)

Old Town Trolley Tours of San Diego Inc   (1)
2115 Kurtz St, San Diego, CA 92110-2016
Tel.: (619) 298-8687
Web Site: http://www.trolleytours.com
Sales Range: $10-24.9 Million
Emp.: 80
Provider of Tour Services
N.A.I.C.S.: 561520
Chris Belland (Pres)

Old Town Trolley Tours of Savannah Inc.   (1)
1115 Louisville Rd, Savannah, GA 31415
Tel.: (912) 233-0083
Web Site: http://www.trolleytours.com
Sales Range: $10-24.9 Million
Emp.: 125
Provider of Tour Services
N.A.I.C.S.: 561520
Chris Belland (CEO)

Old Town Trolley Tours of Washington Inc.   (1)
2640 Reed St NE, Washington, DC 20018-1704
Tel.: (202) 832-9800
Web Site: http://www.historictours.com
Sales Range: $10-24.9 Million
Emp.: 80
Provider of Amusement & Recreation Services
N.A.I.C.S.: 713990
Ed Swist (CEO)

Tropical Shell & Gifts Inc   (1)
205 Simonton St, Key West, FL 33040
Tel.: (305) 296-4557
Web Site: http://www.historictours.com
Sales Range: $25-49.9 Million
Emp.: 185
Gift, Novelty & Souvenir Shopping Services
N.A.I.C.S.: 459420
Sandra Campbell (Mgr-HR)
Nelson Nodal (Gen Mgr)

HISTORICAL EMPORIUM, INC.

188 Stauffer Blvd, San Jose, CA 95125
Tel.: (408) 280-5855
Web Site:
   https://www.historicalemporium.com
Year Founded: 2003
Sales Range: $1-9.9 Million
Emp.: 10
Retails Reproduction Victorian, Edwardian & Old West Clothing & Accessories to Theatres, Performing Arts Groups, Museums & Individuals

N.A.I.C.S.: 458110
Christopher Allen (Co-Founder)
Alicia Allen (Co-Founder)

HISTORY ASSOCIATES INC.

300 N Stonestreet Ave, Rockville, MD 20850-1655
Tel.: (301) 279-9697
Web Site:
   https://www.historyassociates.com
Year Founded: 1981
Sales Range: $1-9.9 Million
Emp.: 80
Historical Research & Consulting Services
N.A.I.C.S.: 541720
Philip L. Cantelon (Co-Founder & CEO)
Rodney P. Carlisle (Co-Founder)
Richard G. Hewlett (Founder)
Robert C. Williams (Co-Founder)
Brian W. Martin (COO)
Donald Donoghue (Dir-Fin & Contracts)
Kenneth D. Durr (Exec VP-History Svcs)
Doris E. Miles (Dir-Personnel & Facilities)
Michael C. Reis (Sr VP)
Anne Strong (Dir-Mktg)
Darlene Wilt (Dir-IT)
Mark Evans (VP-Digital Archives & Info Resources Mgmt Svcs)
Jason H. Gart (VP-Litigation Res Svcs)
Andy Bart (Sr Dir-Ops)
Gail Mathews (Sec)
Beth Maser (Pres)

HISWAY PARTNERS, INC.

317 N Washington St, New Paris, OH 45347-1155
Tel.: (937) 437-2821
Web Site:
   http://www.hometowncomfort.com
Year Founded: 1965
Sales Range: $10-24.9 Million
Emp.: 35
Petroleum Bulk Stations & Terminal Services
N.A.I.C.S.: 424710
Loren Brubaker (Pres)

HIT PROMOTIONAL PRODUCTS INC.

7150 Bryan Dairy Rd, Largo, FL 33777
Tel.: (727) 541-5561
Web Site: http://www.hitpromo.net
Year Founded: 1981
Sales Range: $150-199.9 Million
Emp.: 1,300
Promotional & Marketing Products
N.A.I.C.S.: 541890
Chris Platt (Mgr-Sls)
Jake Gaines (VP-Mfg)
Kim Bulinsky (Coord-Sls)
Frank Capolongo (Mgr-Pur)
Melissa Mezerowski (Supvr-CS)
C. J. Schmidt (Pres)

HIT, INC.

1007 18th St NW, Mandan, ND 58554
Tel.: (701) 663-0379
Web Site: https://www.hitinc.org
Year Founded: 1979
Sales Range: $25-49.9 Million
Emp.: 819
Disability Assistance Services
N.A.I.C.S.: 624120
Curt Walth (Treas & Sec)
Jane Porter (Pres)
Jim Froelich (VP)
Jill Staudinger (VP-Infant Dev)

HITCH ENTERPRISES INC.

309 Northridge Cir, Guymon, OK 73942-2735
Tel.: (580) 338-8575
Web Site: http://www.hitchok.com
Year Founded: 1946
Sales Range: $25-49.9 Million
Emp.: 364
Provider of General Farm Services
N.A.I.C.S.: 111998
Jason Hitch (Chm & Co-CEO)
Chris Hitch (Pres)
Mike Yates (Mgr-IT)

Subsidiaries:

Hitch Feeders Inc.   (1)
Route 1, Hooker, OK 73945
Tel.: (580) 652-2494
Web Site: http://www.hitchok.com
Sales Range: $10-24.9 Million
Emp.: 40
Beef Cattle Feedlot Services
N.A.I.C.S.: 112112
Robert Bergner (Gen Mgr)

Hitch Pork Producers, Inc.   (1)
309 Northridge Cir, Guymon, OK 73949
Tel.: (580) 338-8575
Sales Range: $1-9.9 Million
Pork Production Services
N.A.I.C.S.: 112990
Mike Branbherm (Gen Mgr)

HITCHCOCK AUTOMOTIVE RESOURCES

17110 Gale Ave, City of Industry, CA 91748
Tel.: (626) 839-8400
Year Founded: 1980
Sales Range: $150-199.9 Million
Emp.: 500
New & Used Automobiles
N.A.I.C.S.: 541611
Barry Wasserman (CFO)
David Hall (Owner)
Howard Hakes (VP)
Frederick E. Hitchcock Jr. (Chm, Pres & CEO)

HITCHCOCK CHAIR COMPANY LTD.

13 Riverton Rd, Riverton, CT 06065
Tel.: (860) 738-9958
Web Site:
   https://www.hitchcockchair.com
Year Founded: 1818
Sales Range: $75-99.9 Million
Emp.: 20
Wooden Furniture Mfr
N.A.I.C.S.: 337122
Gary Hath (Owner)
Maryanne Hath (Owner)
Nancy Swenson (Owner)
Rick Swenson (Owner)

Subsidiaries:

Hitchcock Chair Company Ltd. - Still River Antiques Division   (1)
13 Riverton Rd, Riverton, CT 06065
Tel.: (860) 738-9958
Web Site: http://www.hitchcockchair.com
Emp.: 14
Furniture Retailer
N.A.I.C.S.: 449110
Richard Swenson (Mng Partner)

HITCHCOCK FLEMING & ASSOCIATES, INC.

500 Wolf Ledges Pkwy, Akron, OH 44311-1022
Tel.: (330) 376-2111
Web Site: http://www.teamhfa.com
Year Founded: 1940
Sales Range: $75-99.9 Million
Emp.: 87
Advertising Agencies
N.A.I.C.S.: 541810

Charles Abraham (CFO & Mng Partner)
Shirley L. Shriver (Partner-Strategy & Insights)
Kevin Kinsley (Partner-Client Dev)
Keith Busch (Partner-Client Dev)
Matt McCallum (VP-Talent Dev)
Ted Paynter (Dir-Client Svcs)
Tracy McCutcheon (Partner & Exec Dir-Creative)
Alyssa Trowbridge (Acct Mgr)

HITCHCOCK SHOES, INC.
225 Beal St, Hingham, MA 02043-1543
Tel.: (781) 749-3260
Web Site:
https://www.wideshoes.com
Year Founded: 1951
Sales Range: $75-99.9 Million
Emp.: 22
Men's Footwear Mail Order & Marketer
N.A.I.C.S.: 458210
Evelyn F. Hitchcock (Chm)
Thomas R. Bright (Pres)

HITCHINER MANUFACTURING COMPANY INC.
117 Old Wilson Rd, Milford, NH 03055
Tel.: (603) 673-1100   NH
Web Site: http://www.hitchiner.com
Year Founded: 1946
Sales Range: $150-199.9 Million
Emp.: 2,500
Ferrous & Nonferrous Investment Casting
N.A.I.C.S.: 331512
Randal J. Donovan (CFO, Treas, Sec & Exec VP-Fin)
Mark Damien (Pres & COO)
John H. Morison III (Chm & CEO)

Subsidiaries:

Hitchiner France   (1)
153 Rue Fourny Zi, PO Box 244, 78532, Buc, Cedex, France   (100%)
Tel.: (33) 00139200731
Web Site: http://www.hitchiner.com
Sales Range: Less than $1 Million
Emp.: 3
Ferrous & Nonferrous Casting Mfr
N.A.I.C.S.: 331529
Olivier Dromard (Dir-Sls-Europe)

Hitchiner Manufacturing Company Inc. - Ferrous Division   (1)
594 Elm St, Milford, NH 03055
Tel.: (603) 673-1100
Web Site: http://www.hitchiner.com
Emp.: 1,800
Motor & Generator Mfr
N.A.I.C.S.: 335312

Hitchiner Manufacturing Company de Mexico S. de R.L. de C.V.   (1)
Parque Industrial Tres Naciones Segunda, Electricidad 1255 Etapa Ave Co, San Luis Potosi, 78395, Mexico   (100%)
Tel.: (52) 4448241492
Sales Range: $25-49.9 Million
Emp.: 50
Ferrous & Nonferrous Casting
N.A.I.C.S.: 331529

Hitchiner S.A. de C.V.   (1)
Cruce De Las Carreteras Tenango Marquesa Y Tianguistenco Chalma S N, Santiago Tianguistenco, Mexico, 52000, Mexico
Tel.: (52) 713 36283
Ferrous & Nonferrous Casting
N.A.I.C.S.: 331529

HITCHING POST INC.
350 17th Ave N, Hopkins, MN 55343
Tel.: (952) 933-9649
Web Site: http://www.hponline.com
Year Founded: 1969
Sales Range: $10-24.9 Million
Emp.: 60

Retailer of Motorcycles
N.A.I.C.S.: 441227
Sheri Rosoff (Owner)

HITOPS INC.
21 Wiggins St, Princeton, NJ 08542
Tel.: (609) 683-5155   NJ
Web Site: http://www.hitops.org
Year Founded: 1987
Sales Range: $1-9.9 Million
Emp.: 100
Health Education & Advocacy Promoting Healthy Relationships & Supportive Connections for Teenagers
N.A.I.C.S.: 813319

HITS, INC
611 Lambert Pointe Dr., Hazelwood, MO 63042
Tel.: (314) 837-4000
Web Site: https://hitscorp.com
Year Founded: 1994
IT Services
N.A.I.C.S.: 518210
Michael Steinmann (CEO)

Subsidiaries:

Imagex, Inc.   (1)
1985 Isaac Newton Sq W, Reston, VA 20190
Tel.: (703) 883-2500
Web Site: http://www.imagexinc.com
Rev.: $3,000,000
Emp.: 19
Office Supplies & Stationery Stores
N.A.I.C.S.: 459410
Nancy Gretzinger (Pres)

HITT CONTRACTING, INC.
2900 Fairview Park Dr, Falls Church, VA 22042
Tel.: (703) 846-9000
Web Site: https://www.hitt.com
Year Founded: 1937
Emp.: 1,647
Commercial & Institutional Building Construction
N.A.I.C.S.: 236220
Brett Hitt (Co-Chm)
Carson Knizevski (Sr VP-Charleston)
John M. Britt (Exec VP)
John W. Kane (Sr VP)
Peter T. Lanfranchi (Sr VP-Hospitality)
James E. Millar (Co-Chm)
Jeremy Bardin (Exec VP)
Russell Hitt (Chm)
Sara Collins (VP-Healthcare)
Brian Kriz (Exec VP)
Kim Roy (CEO)
Peter Thaler (Sr VP-Law Firms)
Erik Kandler (VP-Atlanta)
Evan Antonides (VP-Tech)
Ashley Campbell (Dir-Mktg)
Bobby Surles (VP-Houston)
Chris Hines (Sr VP-Houston)
Christian Zazzali (VP-Interiors)
Clifford Chow (VP-New York)
David Stone (Dir-Virtual Construction)
Sheila Sears (Gen Counsel-Risk Mgmt)
Steve Ferrari (VP-Govt)
Steve Schoenefeldt (VP-Tech)
Paul Edwards (CFO)
Wes Knostman (Sr VP-Houston)
E. D. Miko (VP-Atlanta)
Michael Coon (VP-Atlanta)
Josh Foreso (VP-Base Building)
Mark Roy (VP-Base Building)
Josh Van Scoy (VP-Charleston)
Jerry Orr (VP-Comml Svcs)
Michael Miller (VP-Fin)
Lauren Bediako (VP-HR)
Blaise Ferrara (VP-New York)
Jeet Kharde (VP-Preconstruction & Virtual Construction)
Mike McCaffrey (VP-Safety)

Chris Michael (VP-Site Ops)
Coleby Cyrtmus (VP-Site Ops)
Jim Nirich (VP-Site Ops)
Ken Whetzel (VP-Site Ops)
Luke Kane (VP-Site Ops)
Phillip Crook (VP-Site Ops)
Rio Maldonado (VP-Site Ops)
Brian Kilpatrick (VP-South Florida)
James Fox (VP-South Florida)
John Fritz (VP-Tech)
Ross Rebraca (VP-Tech & Corp Responsibility)
Christian Peterson (VP)

Subsidiaries:

Trademark Construction, Inc.   (1)
9300 Bamboo Rd, Houston, TX 77041
Tel.: (713) 688-9496
Web Site: http://www.hitt.com
Rev.: $2,800,000
Emp.: 55
Full-Service Commercial Contractor
N.A.I.C.S.: 238110
Chris Hines (Principal & Reg Pres)

HIVELOCITY VENTURES CORP.
8010 Woodland Center Blvd Ste 700, Tampa, FL 33614
Tel.: (813) 471-0355   FL
Web Site: https://www.hivelocity.net
Year Founded: 2001
Sales Range: $1-9.9 Million
Emp.: 15
Internet Service Provider
N.A.I.C.S.: 518210
Rob Wright (Acct Mgr)
Steven Eschweiler (Dir-Ops)
Mike Architetto (Pres & CEO)

HIXARDT TECHNOLOGIES, INC.
119 W Intendencia St, Pensacola, FL 32502
Tel.: (850) 439-3282   FL
Web Site: https://www.hixardt.com
Year Founded: 2001
Sales Range: $1-9.9 Million
Emp.: 21
Information Technology Consulting Services
N.A.I.C.S.: 541512
Michael E. Hicks (Co-Founder)
Violet B. Hicks (Exec VP)

HIXSON AUTOPLEX OF ALEXANDRIA
2506 S Macarthur Dr, Alexandria, LA 71301-2917
Tel.: (318) 448-0871
Year Founded: 1977
Sales Range: $10-24.9 Million
Emp.: 110
Car Whslr
N.A.I.C.S.: 441110
Dallas Hixson (Pres)

HIXSON FORD MONROE
1201 Louisville Ave, Monroe, LA 71201
Tel.: (318) 388-3300
Web Site:
http://www.hixsonfordmonroe.com
Sales Range: $10-24.9 Million
Emp.: 100
New Car Retailer
N.A.I.C.S.: 441110
Shelley Bedenbender (Dir-Internet)
Frank Brussel (Mgr-Desk)
David Brown (Mgr-Floor Sls)
Dill Carter (Mgr-New Car)

HIXSON LUMBER SALES, INC.
1440 Hutton Dr, Carrollton, TX 75006
Tel.: (972) 446-9000

Web Site:
http://www.hixsonlumbersales.com
Rev.: $24,900,000
Emp.: 12
Lumber & Plywood Distr
N.A.I.C.S.: 423310
Robert L. Hixson Jr. (Chm)

HK GLOBAL TRADING LTD.
1210 Water St, Laredo, TX 78040-5701
Tel.: (956) 728-5180
Web Site: http://www.hktronics.com
Year Founded: 1991
Sales Range: $10-24.9 Million
Emp.: 60
Mfr of Electrical Appliances, Televisions & Radios
N.A.I.C.S.: 423620

HKF INC.
5983 Smithway St, Los Angeles, CA 90040
Tel.: (323) 721-1333
Rev.: $24,000,000
Emp.: 20
Industrial Furnaces & Ovens
N.A.I.C.S.: 333994
James P. Hartfield (Pres)

HKM INC.
222 N 32nd St Ste 700, Billings, MT 59101-1911
Tel.: (406) 656-6399
Web Site: http://www.hkminc.com
Year Founded: 1995
Rev.: $12,000,000
Emp.: 700
Engineeering Services
N.A.I.C.S.: 541330

HKN, INC.
1621 E 27th St, Los Angeles, CA 90011
Tel.: (323) 846-1200   CA
Web Site: http://www.acs-america.com
Year Founded: 1994
Rev.: $23,038,665
Emp.: 35
Clothes Hangers
N.A.I.C.S.: 424990

HKS ENTERPRISES INC.
205 County Rd 17, Elkhart, IN 46516
Tel.: (574) 295-5535
Web Site: http://www.ats-tools.com
Rev.: $15,500,000
Emp.: 30
Industrial Supplies
N.A.I.C.S.: 423840
Curt Heeg (Owner)

HKS, INC.
350 N Saint Paul St, Dallas, TX 75201
Tel.: (214) 969-5599   TX
Web Site: https://www.hksinc.com
Year Founded: 1955
Sales Range: $10-24.9 Million
Emp.: 1,400
Architectural Services
N.A.I.C.S.: 541310
Todd Gritch (Principal)
Billy Hinton (Principal & Dir-Architecture)
Kirk Krueger (Principal & Dir-Construction Svcs)
Richard Johnston (Principal & Project Mgr)
David Prusha (Principal)
Kirk Teske (COO & Principal)
Craig Beale (Principal)
Roy Gunsolus (Principal)
Rick Lee (Principal)
Craig Stockwell (Principal)

HKS, Inc.—(Continued)

Jason Schroer *(Principal & Dir-Office-Houston)*
Brian McFarlane *(Principal & Dir-Health Grp-Bus Dev)*
Mark Williams *(Principal)*
Sergio Saenz *(VP)*
Britney Gore *(VP)*
Angela Lee *(Mng Dir-Singapore Office & Principal)*
Anita Isaacson *(Principal)*
Brian Eason *(Principal)*
Jeff LaRue *(Principal & Dir-Construction Svcs Quality Mgmt)*
Mark Vander Voort *(Principal)*
Jeff Stouffer *(Exec VP & Dir-Health Grp)*
Jennifer M. Kolstad *(Dir-Interior Architecture)*
Bryan Trubey *(Exec VP)*
Teresa Hurd *(Principal & Sr VP)*
Doug Childers *(Principal & Sr VP)*
Rand Ekman *(Chief Sustainability Officer)*
Brent Sparks *(Principal & Dir-Office-Fort Worth)*
David Harper *(Principal & Dir-Higher Education)*
Don Harrier *(Principal & Dir-Office-San Francisco)*
Gaurav Chopra *(Mng Dir & Principal-India)*
Leslie Hanson *(Principal & Dir-Office-Richmond)*
Mike Vela *(Principal & Dir-Office-Salt Lake City)*
Mo Stein *(Principal & Dir-Office-Phoenix)*
Ricardo Rondon *(Mng Dir & Principal)*
Scott Hunter *(Principal & Dir-Office-Los Angeles)*
Barbara Blum *(VP)*
Sheba Ross *(VP)*
Travis Cowie *(Assoc Principal)*
Mark Hults *(Principal)*
Whitney Fuessel *(VP)*
Andrew McCune *(VP)*
Tom Sprinkle *(Principal & Sr VP)*
Jessica Sager *(Sr VP-San Francisco)*
Laura Walters *(Sr VP & Assoc Principal)*
Jayme Schutt *(Dir-Studio-Comml Interiors)*
Michael Brendle *(Principal & Dir-Design)*
Tyler Cline *(VP-Atlanta)*
Lucy Williams *(VP/Dir-Health Interiors-Southeast Reg Health Practice)*
Frank D. Kittredge Jr. *(Principal & Dir-Knox Advisors)*

HLA COMPANY INC.
902 Ravenwood Dr, Selma, AL 36701-6723
Tel.: (334) 874-9010   AL
Year Founded: 1982
Sales Range: $10-24.9 Million
Emp.: 300
Composite Insurance Company
N.A.I.C.S.: 332510
Tetsuru Komaki *(Pres)*
Dennis Moore *(Plant Mgr)*

HLAVINKA EQUIPMENT COMPANY
17405 Hwy 90A, East Bernard, TX 77435
Tel.: (979) 335-7528
Web Site: https://www.hlavinka.com
Year Founded: 1939
Sales Range: $25-49.9 Million
Emp.: 30
Supplier of Farm Equipment & Supplies

N.A.I.C.S.: 423310
Terry Hlavinka *(Gen Mgr)*
Steve Hlavinka *(Mgr-Parts)*
Joseph C. Hlavinka Jr. *(Pres)*

HLB USA, INC.
US Bancorp Ctr 800 Nicollet Mall Ste 1300, Minneapolis, MN 55402-7033
Tel.: (612) 253-6500
Web Site: http://www.hlbusa.com
Auditing & Accounting Services
N.A.I.C.S.: 541211
David Stene *(Chm)*

HLG HEALTH COMMUNICA-TIONS
1700 Market St Sixth Fl, Philadelphia, PA 19103-3913
Tel.: (215) 990-6848   PA
Web Site: http://www.hlg.com
Year Founded: 1967
Communications, Medical, Planning & Consultation
N.A.I.C.S.: 541810
David J. Winigrad *(Pres)*

HLM MANAGEMENT CO., INC.
800 South St Ste 200, Waltham, MA 02453
Tel.: (617) 266-0030   MA
Web Site: http://www.hlmvp.com
Year Founded: 1983
Sales Range: $10-24.9 Million
Emp.: 15
Investment Management Firm
N.A.I.C.S.: 523940
Peter J. Gruza *(Mng Partner)*
Enrico Picozza *(Partner)*

Subsidiaries:
HLM Management Co., LLC   (1)
800 South St Ste 200, Waltham, MA 02453
Tel.: (617) 266-0030
Web Site: https://hlmvp.com
Investment Management Firm
N.A.I.C.S.: 523940

HLTC INC
1200 Memorial Dr Whitfield, Dalton, GA 30722-1168
Tel.: (706) 278-4043   GA
Year Founded: 1997
Sales Range: $25-49.9 Million
Nursing Care Services
N.A.I.C.S.: 623110
Joseph L. McGuire *(CFO)*
G. Lamar Lyle *(Chm)*
Gary L. Howard *(Exec VP)*
J. Sherwood Jones *(Treas & Sec)*
Jeffrey D. Myers *(CEO)*

HLW INTERNATIONAL LLP
115 5th Ave, New York, NY 10003-1004
Tel.: (212) 353-4600   NY
Web Site: http://www.hlw.com
Year Founded: 1885
Sales Range: $100-124.9 Million
Emp.: 150
Architects, Engineers, Planners & Interiors
N.A.I.C.S.: 541310
John Mack *(Sr Partner)*
Mark Zwagerman *(Mng Dir & Principal)*
Debra Cole *(Assoc Principal)*
Cristen Colantoni *(Assoc Principal)*
Adam Strudwick *(Dir-Design-London & Assoc Principal)*
Louise Sharp *(Principal-Interiors-Los Angeles)*
Ed Shim *(Mng Dir)*
Joseph Montalbano *(Principal)*
Kimberly Sacramone *(Principal & Mng Dir-NJ)*
Bennet Dunkley *(Principal)*

Alexander Dunham *(Dir-Workplace)*
Peter Bacevice *(Dir-Res)*
Julia Belkin *(Principal)*
Jonce Walker *(Dir-Sustainability & Wellness)*
Lee Devore *(Assoc Principal)*

Subsidiaries:
HLW International LLP   (1)
115 5th Ave, New York, NY 10003-1004
Tel.: (212) 353-4600
Web Site: http://www.hlw.design
Sales Range: $25-49.9 Million
Emp.: 130
Designs & Builds Construction Management
N.A.I.C.S.: 541310
Patrick H. Kinzler *(CFO)*
Scott Herrick *(Partner)*
Mary Jane Beatty *(Dir-HR)*
John Gering *(Mng Partner)*
Susan Boyle *(Mng Partner)*
Richard Brennan *(Partner)*
Keith Hanadel *(Principal & Dir-Brdcst Design)*
Lisa Knip *(Principal & Dir-Studio)*
Sejal Sonani *(Principal)*

HLW International Ltd.   (1)
29/31 Cowper Street, London, EC2A 4AT, United Kingdom
Tel.: (44) 20 7566 6800
Web Site: http://www.hlw.com
Sales Range: $10-24.9 Million
Emp.: 20
Architectural Design Services
N.A.I.C.S.: 541310
Patrick H. Kinzler *(Mng Principal)*
John Gering *(Mng Partner)*
Keith Hanadel *(Principal & Dir-Brdcst Design)*
Leonard Milford *(Mng Dir & Principal-Shanghai)*
Lisa Knip *(Principal & Dir-Studio)*
Patrick Kinzler *(Mng Principal)*
Richard Brennan *(Partner)*
Scott Herrick *(Partner-Spark Lighting)*
Sejal Sonani *(Principal)*
Susan Boyle *(Mng Partner)*
Francesca Gernone *(Principal)*

HM ELECTRONICS INCORPO-RATED
14110 Stowe Dr, Poway, CA 92064
Tel.: (858) 535-6000
Web Site: http://www.hme.com
Year Founded: 1971
Sales Range: $10-24.9 Million
Emp.: 500
Intercommunication Systems, Electric
N.A.I.C.S.: 334290
Dave Snyder *(Sr Mgr-Mfg Tech)*
Michael Ogami *(Product Mgr)*

Subsidiaries:
Clear-Com, LLC   (1)
1301 Marina Vlg Pkwy Ste 105, Alameda, CA 94501
Tel.: (510) 337-6666
Web Site: http://www.clearcom.com
Voice Communications Systems & Equipment Mfr
N.A.I.C.S.: 334290
Mitzi Dominguez *(CEO)*
Marco Lopez *(VP-Engrg)*

JTECH Communications Inc.   (1)
1400 Northbrook Pkwy Ste 320, Suwanee, GA 30024
Tel.: (561) 997-0772
Web Site: http://www.jtech.com
Sales Range: $25-49.9 Million
Emp.: 100
Text Messaging & Paging Systems Applications Developer & Supplier
N.A.I.C.S.: 513210
Sal Veni *(VP-Ops)*

HM INTERNATIONAL
5810 East Skelly Dr Ste 1650, Tulsa, OK 74135
Tel.: (918) 664-1914   TX
Web Site: http://www.hmintl.com
Sales Range: $50-74.9 Million

Emp.: 5
Investment Company
N.A.I.C.S.: 541611
Peter Meinig *(Pres & CEO)*

Subsidiaries:
American Innovations, Ltd.   (1)
12211 Technology Blvd, Austin, TX 78727-6102   (100%)
Tel.: (512) 249-3489
Sales Range: $25-49.9 Million
Automated Meter-Reading Industry
N.A.I.C.S.: 334515

Subsidiary (Domestic):

Bass Engineering   (2)
3200 Brent Rd, Longview, TX 75604
Tel.: (903) 759-1633
Web Site: http://www.bass-eng.com
Sales Range: $25-49.9 Million
Professional Engineering Services
N.A.I.C.S.: 541330
Christopher Shawhan *(Reg Mgr-Sls)*
Steve Hamblin *(Dir-Sls)*
Clay Brelsford *(Pres)*

Parker PGI   (1)
16101 Vallen Dr, Houston, TX 77041
Tel.: (713) 466-0056
Web Site: http://www.pgiint.com
Hardware Whslr
N.A.I.C.S.: 423710
Horace Payne *(Mgr-Mfg Dept)*
Brian Cruickshank *(Mgr-Engrg Div)*
Thomas Goike *(Mgr-Lean Div)*
Tim Ramponi *(Dir-Quality)*

HM MANAGEMENT COMPANY INC
1798 Wilson Pkwy, Fayetteville, TN 37334-2736
Tel.: (931) 433-7702   TN
Year Founded: 1980
Sales Range: $75-99.9 Million
Emp.: 5
Property Management Services
N.A.I.C.S.: 531110

HM ROYAL INC.
689 Pennington Ave, Trenton, NJ 08618-3012
Tel.: (609) 396-9176   NJ
Web Site: http://www.hmroyal.com
Year Founded: 1925
Sales Range: $50-74.9 Million
Emp.: 48
Speciality Compounds Distr
N.A.I.C.S.: 423520
Joseph E. Royal *(Pres)*
Robert D'Andrea *(Mgr-Tech Sls)*
Terry Smith *(Dir-Ops)*
Jeff Dvorak *(VP & Gen Mgr-California)*
Jack Stanek *(Reg Mgr-Central)*

HMC ADVERTISING LLC
65 Millet St Ste 301, Richmond, VT 05477
Tel.: (802) 434-7141   VT
Year Founded: 1980
Sales Range: Less than $1 Million
Emp.: 20
Advetising Agency
N.A.I.C.S.: 541810
Jim Espey *(Dir-Art)*
Heather Fordham *(Media Buyer & Planner)*
Paula Bazluke *(Dir-Media)*
Cheryl Sartwell *(Controller)*
Nicole Seguljic *(Mgr-Production)*
April Hanley *(Office Mgr)*
Monique Gramas *(Copywriter)*
Nathan Dana *(Dir-Art)*
Tom Holmes *(Mng Dir-Mktg Svcs)*
Bill Patton *(Dir-Interactive)*

HMC CORP.

284 Maple St, Contoocook, NH
03229
Tel.: (603) 746-4691
Web Site: https://www.hmccorp.com
Rev.: $11,000,000
Emp.: 1
Sawmill Machines
N.A.I.C.S.: 333243

Subsidiaries:

HMC Corporation   (1)
284 Maple St, Contoocook, NH 03229
Tel.: (603) 746-4691
Web Site: http://www.hmccorp.com
Sawmill Machines
N.A.I.C.S.: 333243
Donna Taylor (Controller)

HMD TRANSPORT, INC.
111 E Wacker Dr Ste 400, Chicago,
IL 60601
Tel.: (312) 778-8777
Web Site:
 http://www.hmdtransport.com
Year Founded: 2004
Sales Range: $10-24.9 Million
Emp.: 30
Transport Consulting Services
N.A.I.C.S.: 541614
Jamie Cioe (CEO)
Sean Bergman (COO)

HMG GROUP
5100 N Federal Hwy Ste 408, Fort
Lauderdale, FL 33308-3842
Tel.: (954) 928-0000   FL
Web Site: http://www.hmg-group.com
Year Founded: 1946
Rev.: $325,000,000
Emp.: 31
N.A.I.C.S.: 541810
H. Marshall Golnick (Chm)

HMI BUYING GROUP INC.
3530 Manor Dr Ste 6, Vicksburg, MS
39180
Tel.: (601) 636-4707
Web Site: http://www.hmibg.com
Sales Range: $50-74.9 Million
Emp.: 20
Billing & Bookkeeping Service
N.A.I.C.S.: 541219
Jerome A. Hayes (Founder & Pres)
Shirlen Prescott (VP-Ops)
Diane John (Dir-Mktg)

HMI INDUSTRIES INC.
13325 Darice Pkwy Unit A, Strongs-
ville, OH 44149
Tel.: (440) 846-7800
Web Site: http://www.filterqueen.com
Year Founded: 1928
Filtration Portable Surface Cleaners,
Portable Room Air Cleaners & Cen-
tral Vacuum Cleaning Systems Mfr
N.A.I.C.S.: 335210
EJ Watson (COO & CFO)

Subsidiaries:

Filter Queen Inc.   (1)
13325 Darice Pkwy Unit A, Strongsville, OH
44149   (100%)
Tel.: (440) 846-7800
Web Site: http://www.filterqueen.com
Sales Range: $10-24.9 Million
Emp.: 70
Indoor Air Quality System Mfr
N.A.I.C.S.: 333415

HMJ INC.
212 W Colfax Ave, South Bend, IN
46601-1607
Tel.: (574) 232-3061
Web Site: http://www.travelmore.com
Year Founded: 1970
Sales Range: $50-74.9 Million
Emp.: 20
Travel Agency

N.A.I.C.S.: 561510
Robert Hamilton (CEO)
Gina Hamilton (Owner)

HMK ENTERPRISES, INC.
1 Cranberry Hill 750 Marrett Rd Ste
401, Lexington, MA 02141
Tel.: (781) 891-6660   DE
Year Founded: 1978
Investment Holding Company
N.A.I.C.S.: 551112
Steven E. Karol (Chm, Pres & CEO)
Timothy C. Eburne (VP & Sec)

Subsidiaries:

Watermill Ventures, Ltd.   (1)
1 Cranberry Hill 750 Marrett Rd Ste 401,
Lexington, MA 02421
Tel.: (781) 891-6660
Web Site: http://www.watermill.com
Sales Range: $75-99.9 Million
Privater Equity Firm
N.A.I.C.S.: 523999
Steven E. Karol (Founder & Mng Partner)
Robert W. Ackerman (Partner)
Tim Eburne (Partner)
Benjamin P. Procter (Sr Partner)
Dale S. Okonow (Partner)
Julia Karol (Pres & COO)
Matthias Bergin (Principal)
Sarah Bowen (Dir-Mktg)
John N. Carr (Principal)
Tracy Streckenbach (Partner)

Holding (Domestic):

Experi-Metal Inc.   (2)
6385 Wall St, Sterling Heights, MI 48312
Tel.: (586) 977-7800
Web Site: http://www.experi-metal.com
Metal Products & Stampings
N.A.I.C.S.: 332119
Al Sharp (VP-Sls)
Keith Maslowski (Controller)
Rocco Mistretta (Dir-Program Mgmt)
Dwight Closson (COO)

Quality Metalcraft, Inc.   (2)
28101 Schoolcraft Rd, Livonia, MI 48150-
1615
Tel.: (734) 261-6700
Web Site: http://www.qualitymetalcraft.com
Motor Vehicle Metal Stamping
N.A.I.C.S.: 336370
Mike Kenyon (Mgr-Maintenance & Facilities)
Kurt Saldana (CEO)
Ken Lerg (COO)
Scott Bain (CFO)
E.J. Long (VP-Engrg)
Gary Kasaczun (Dir-Sls & Mktg)
Mark Anderson (Dir-Engrg)
Mark Gorski (Dir-Engrg Ops)
Dave Rybski (Dir-Pur)
Paul Jensen (Dir-New Bus Dev)
Mike Lottinville (Dir-Comml Ops)
Eric Uram (Dir-Program Mgmt)
Ron Hassan (Mgr-Plant)
Brian Payne (Dir-Corp Quality)

HMN INC.
865 Bud Blvd, Fremont, NE 68025
Tel.: (402) 721-3020
Web Site: https://www.fcc-inc.com
Sales Range: $25-49.9 Million
Emp.: 105
Contract Truck Haulers
N.A.I.C.S.: 484121
Mike Herre (Pres & CEO)
Tim McCormick (COO)
Guy Mumford (Reg VP-Sls)
Rob Musson (Mgr-Flatbed Ops-
Midwest)

Subsidiaries:

Fremont Contract Carriers   (1)
PO Box 489, Fremont, NE 68026-0489
Tel.: (402) 721-3020
Web Site: http://www.fcc-inc.com
Sales Range: $10-24.9 Million
Emp.: 400
Contract Haulers
N.A.I.C.S.: 484121
Michael F. Herre (Pres & CEO)

HMR ACQUISITION COMPANY INC.
1501 N Ironwood Dr, South Bend, IN
46635-1841
Tel.: (574) 272-5922
Web Site:
 https://www.haciendafiesta.com
Year Founded: 1978
Sales Range: $10-24.9 Million
Emp.: 1,100
Restaurant
N.A.I.C.S.: 722511
Tamara Boetsma (CEO)

HMS ENTERPRISES INC.
207 N Weichert St, Girard, KS 66743
Tel.: (620) 395-2151
Web Site: http://www.hms-
enterprises.com
Sales Range: $10-24.9 Million
Emp.: 80
Floor Covering Stores
N.A.I.C.S.: 449121
Keith Hank Smith (Pres)

HMS GLOBAL MARITIME, INC.
115 E Market St, New Albany, IN
47150
Tel.: (812) 941-9990
Web Site: http://www.hmsgm.com
Sales Range: $25-49.9 Million
Emp.: 344
Marine Service
N.A.I.C.S.: 114119
John W. Waggoner (Pres & CEO)
Greg Dronkert (Pres & COO-HMS
Ferries)
John Sainsbury (Pres-Consulting &
Technical)
Bob Herre (Gen Counsel)
Timothy Loesch (Gen Mgr)

HMS PRODUCTS CO.
1200 E Big Beaver Rd, Troy, MI
48083
Tel.: (248) 689-8120
Web Site:
 https://www.hmsproducts.com
Year Founded: 1960
Sales Range: $10-24.9 Million
Emp.: 90
Sales of Conveyors & Conveying
Equipment
N.A.I.C.S.: 333922
Dave Sofy (Pres)
Mike VanDaele (Gen Mgr)
Pat Cullen (Mgr-Sls)
Nancy Negohosian (VP)

HMS SERVICE CO. INC.
3612 E Johnson Ave, Haines City, FL
33844
Tel.: (863) 422-4651
Web Site:
 http://www.hmsserviceco.com
Sales Range: $50-74.9 Million
Emp.: 8
Truck Equipment & Parts Distr
N.A.I.C.S.: 441330
Norman Mattew (Owner)

HMS TECHNOLOGIES, INC.
1 Discovery Pl, Martinsburg, WV
25403
Tel.: (304) 596-5583
Web Site: http://www.hmstech.com
Year Founded: 2003
Sales Range: $10-24.9 Million
Emp.: 112
Information Technology Integration,
Business & Federal Government Fo-
cus
N.A.I.C.S.: 541512
Harry M. Siegel (Pres)
William Kirkpatrick (CEO)
Elizabeth M. Andrews (CFO)

HMY YACHT SALES, INC.
817 NE 3rd St, Dania, FL 33004
Tel.: (954) 926-0400   FL
Web Site:
 http://www.hmyyachtsales.com
Year Founded: 1979
Sales Range: $10-24.9 Million
Emp.: 35
Sales of Yachts
N.A.I.C.S.: 541990
Larry Thomas (CFO & VP)
Laura Hogle (Office Mgr)
Steve Moynihan (Owner & Pres)

HNB NATIONAL BANK
100 N Main St, Hannibal, MO 63401
Tel.: (573) 221-0050   MO
Web Site: https://www.hnbbanks.com
Year Founded: 1888
Sales Range: $10-24.9 Million
Emp.: 128
Commericial Banking
N.A.I.C.S.: 522110
John D. Zimmer (Pres & CEO)

HNG STORAGE LP
1010 Lamar St Ste 1720, Houston,
TX 77002-6361
Tel.: (713) 781-4949
Sales Range: $10-24.9 Million
Emp.: 9
Storage Natural Gas
N.A.I.C.S.: 486210

HNM SYSTEMS, INC.
505 Lomas Santa Fe Dr Ste 150, So-
lana Beach, CA 92075
Web Site:
 http://www.hnmsystems.com
Year Founded: 2011
Sales Range: $1-9.9 Million
Emp.: 132
Staffing & Recruitment Services
N.A.I.C.S.: 541612
Heather Moyer (Pres & CEO)
Emily Howe (Head-People Ops)
Allyson Indihar (Sr Mgr-Fin Ops)
Caroline Mathis (Mgr-Lead Client So-
lutions)
Morgan Mcmahon (Mgr-Recruiting &
Delivery)

HNTB CORPORATION
715 Kirk Dr, Kansas City, MO 64105-
1310
Tel.: (816) 472-1201   DE
Web Site: http://www.hntb.com
Year Founded: 1914
Sales Range: $250-299.9 Million
Emp.: 2,600
Engineering, Architectural & Planning
Services
N.A.I.C.S.: 541330
Scott Butzen (Exec VP)
Patricia Mosher (Sr VP)
Paul Yarossi (Exec VP)
Robert J. Slimp (Chm & CEO)
Mike Hegarty (Sr VP)
Nick Antonucci (Sr VP)
Stephen Dilts (Sr VP)
Ananth Prasad (Sr VP)
Doug Woodbury (VP & Mgr-Sys)
Anil Sharma (VP)
Christopher Lester (Assoc VP)
Derwin Irvine (Dir-Recruiting)
Paul Griesemer (Assoc VP-
Architecture Practice-Central)
Tom Ellis (Pres-Central Div)
Thandav Murthy (Grp Dir-Federal
Svcs-North Texas)
Art Hadnett (Pres-West)
Juan Carlos Arteaga (Sr Dir-Aviation
Architecture Practice-Southeast)
Adam Sheets (VP-Columbus)
Carrie Rocha (VP)

HNTB Corporation—(Continued)

Kevin Nelson *(Chief Growth Officer & Sr VP)*
Dennis Henderson *(Sr Dir-Transit Plng)*
Robert Baughman *(VP & Sr Mgr-Program)*
Cherie Gibson *(Dir-Comm-Mid Atlantic)*
Scott Russell *(VP)*
Dina Potter *(VP & Mgr-District Sls)*
Emily Tapia-Lopez *(Dir-Strategic Initiatives-Chicago)*
Lillian Yan *(Assoc VP & Sr Project Mgr)*
Laura Imperiale *(Dir-Govt Rels-Northeast)*
Lori Katzman *(Sr Project Mgr-Rail Transit Grp)*
Tirzah Gregory *(Grp Dir-Metro Bridge)*
James Cobb *(Engr-Water Resources)*
Ronald Giamario *(VP & Mgr-Ops-New Jersey)*
Anteneh Yohannes *(Engr-Travel Demand Modeler)*
Kevin Haboian *(Chief Bus Dev Officer & Sr VP)*
Andres Ocon *(VP-Downtown Los Angeles)*
Bill Lebegern *(Assoc VP & Project Dir-Aviation-Charlotte)*
Gustavo Pego *(VP-Miami)*
Charlie Herndon *(Pres-Southeast)*
Ian Choudri *(Sr VP & Dir-Natl Rail & Transit Bus Dev)*
Phil Armstrong *(Sr VP)*
Ben Robinson *(Mgr-Intelligent Transportation Sys & Traffic Engrg Practice)*
Peter Bruno *(Sr Project Mgr-Transportation Plng-Atlanta)*
Jack Allen *(VP)*
Katherine Nees *(Sr VP)*
Diana Mendes *(Pres-Infrastructure & Mobility Equity)*
Kara Lentz *(Sr Mgr-Program-Dallas)*
Peter Ryan *(Architect)*
Mathew Hallett *(Assoc VP & Dir-Design)*
David Nolle *(Sr Project Mgr-Rail & Transit Sys-Dallas)*
Aaron Marx *(Project Mgr-Positive Train Control Sys)*
Loy Warren *(Sr VP)*
Darlene K. Gee *(VP)*
Sohail Khan *(VP)*
Thomas Grassi *(Sr Project Mgr-Infrastructure & Transportation Architecture-New Y)*
David Flanders *(VP & Project Dir-Transportation)*
Joseph Cahill *(Assoc VP-Boston)*
Gary Bua *(VP-Massachusetts)*
Michael Steffen *(Sr Project Mgr-Sys)*
Kevin Hoeflich *(Chm-Toll Svcs & Sr VP)*
Leslie Wade *(Dir-Comm)*
Gordon Clark *(Dir-Technical-Tunnels & Complex Underground Structures)*
Michael Powers *(Mgr-Rail Program)*
Hiep Bui *(Mgr-Engrg)*
Ronnie Smith *(VP)*
Tracey Friggle Logan *(VP)*
Peter Gertler *(Sr VP-Corp & National Strategic Bus Dev)*
Omar Merheb *(Dir-Transportation)*
Michael Rassias *(VP)*
Taiwo Jaiyeoba *(Mgr-Bus Dev-Charlotte)*
Anthony Gouveia *(VP)*
Carlos Lopez *(Sr VP)*
Mark Niles *(Assoc VP/Sr Project Mgr-Washington)*
Kary Witt *(VP-San Francisco)*

Timothy Bond *(VP & Sr Mgr-Aviation Program)*
Laddie Irion *(Sr VP)*
Samantha Soules *(Assoc VP-West)*
Frank O'Dea *(VP & Grp Dir-Engrg-Lake Mary)*
Phil Brake *(Pres-Northeast)*
Dale McDaniel *(VP/Sr Project Dir-Atlanta)*
David Dye *(VP & Sr Project Dir)*
Jeffrey Parker *(VP)*
Dan D'Antonio *(Mgr-Transportation Sys Mgmt & Ops Dept)*
Gay Knipper *(VP)*
Kia Gillette *(Project Mgr-Environmental)*
Patrick Allen *(Mgr-Vehicle & Rolling Stock Products-Natl Rail Sys-Boston)*
Robert Stone *(Project Dir)*
Craig Denson *(CFO)*
James Gregg *(Assoc VP)*
Mark Ramsey *(VP-Los Angeles & Mgr-Implementation-Program Mgmt Team)*
Sanja Zlatanic *(Chm-Tunnel Svcs Practice-Natl & Sr VP)*
James Thomson *(Sr VP)*
Matthew Price *(Assoc VP-Lake Mary)*
James Egnot *(Assoc VP-Lake Mary)*
Eric Berg *(Project Engr-Transportation-Allentown)*
Joseph Guzzi *(VP)*
Yvonne Bilshausen *(Principal-Aviation Architecture & VP)*
Gerardo Prado *(VP)*
Ryan Gedney *(VP & Natl Dir-Design-Architecture)*
Michael Trabold *(VP/Sr Project Mgr-Transit & Rail Practice-Empire State Building)*
Jennifer Carrier *(Assoc VP)*
Bart Sweeney *(Assoc VP/Sr Project Mgr-Rocky Hill)*
Chris Migneron *(VP)*
Andres Chacon *(Deputy Project Manager-Aviation-Tampa)*
William Jones *(Associate VP & Dir-Engrg Grp)*
Chris Lory *(VP)*
Kevin R. Collins *(VP)*
Mark Becherer *(VP-Chicago)*
Daniel Loftus *(Sr Project Mgr-Transit-Chicago)*
Sudhish Verma *(Mgr-Plng Dept-Northern California)*
Kimberly Demuth *(Assoc VP & Mgr-Environmental Dept)*
Murali Hariharan *(Sr Engr-Tunnel)*
Wayne Feuerborn *(Pres-West)*
Mathew Antonelli *(Project Dir-Inland Empire)*
Keith Hinkebein *(Pres-Design Build & Exec VP)*
Jim Ray *(Pres)*
E. Gregory Thorpe *(Assoc VP & Sr Project Mgr-Rail & Transit-Salt Lake City)*
Anna Barry *(VP/Program Mgr-Massachusetts)*
Tim Kassa *(Mgr-Transportation Plng Dept-Atlanta)*
Jack Buckingham *(VP-Program Delivery)*
Brad Guilmino *(VP)*
Mark Fricke *(Project Dir-Southern California)*
James Young *(VP/Sr Program Mgr-New York)*
Satya Lory *(VP-Lake Mary)*
Debbie Gies *(Sr Project Mgr-Program Mgmt-Boston)*
Kurt Krauss *(VP-Natl Strategic Initiatives-Natl Advisory Practice)*
Bobby Lewis *(VP-Advisory Practice-Natl)*

Sally Librera *(VP-Strategic Plng & Client Support)*
Sotirios Vardakos *(Assoc VP)*
Michelle Dippel *(Pres-West)*
Martha Bogle *(VP & Project Dir)*
James Starace *(VP & Project Dir)*
Frank Raha *(VP)*
Doug Mann *(Pres-Corp Dev)*
Juanita Tavares *(VP-Global Supply Chain Mgmt)*
Thomas J. Spearing III *(Sr VP)*
Thomas Cary Jr. *(VP)*

Subsidiaries:

HNTB　　　　　　　　　　　　**(1)**
111 N Canal St Ste 1250, Chicago, IL 60606-7206
Tel.: (816) 472-1201
Web Site: http://www.hntb.com
Sales Range: $25-49.9 Million
Emp.: 200
Provider of Engineering Services
N.A.I.C.S.: 541330
Pat Mosher *(VP)*
Sharif Abou-Sabh *(Sr VP)*
Kevin Campbell *(Assoc VP & Project Dir-Rail)*
Johnny Morcos *(Assoc VP & Program Mgr)*
Dave Crosson *(VP)*

HNTB Architecture　　　　　　**(1)**
1615 M St NW 7th Fl, Washington, DC 20036
Tel.: (202) 628-7525
Web Site: http://www.hntb.com
Sales Range: $125-149.9 Million
Emp.: 1,200
Provider of Engineering Services
N.A.I.C.S.: 541310

HNTB Corporation　　　　　　**(1)**
1628 John F Kennedy Blvd 8 Penn Ctr Fl 7, Philadelphia, PA 19103　　**(100%)**
Tel.: (215) 568-6500
Web Site: http://www.hntb.com
Sales Range: $10-24.9 Million
Emp.: 40
Provider of Engineering Services
N.A.I.C.S.: 541330
Yassmin Gramian *(VP)*
Lori Cole *(Sr Project Mgr-Transportation Plng)*
David Staplin *(Sr Project Dir-Railroad Grp)*
Gary Hullfish *(VP)*
Jeff Konrad *(VP-Rail)*
James McGee *(Assoc VP)*
Joe Guzzi *(VP)*
Ulysses Koutsogiannis *(Mgr-Structural)*
Greg May *(VP)*
Mark Moschella *(Sr Project Mgr-King of Prussia)*

HNTB Corporation　　　　　　**(1)**
401 W Main St Ste 601, Louisville, KY 40202　　　　　　　　　　**(100%)**
Tel.: (502) 581-0985
Web Site: http://www.hntb.com
Sales Range: $10-24.9 Million
Emp.: 18
Provider of Engineering Services
N.A.I.C.S.: 541330
Carolyn Deangelis *(Mgr-HR)*

HNTB Corporation　　　　　　**(1)**
1301 Fannin St Ste 1800, Houston, TX 77002
Tel.: (346) 352-5620
Web Site: http://www.hntb.com
Sales Range: $10-24.9 Million
Emp.: 37
Provider of Engineering Services
N.A.I.C.S.: 541330
Michael Voinis *(VP)*
Steve Roth *(Grp Dir-Engrg-Austin)*
Charles Beauvoir *(VP & Sr Program Mgr)*

HNTB Corporation - Parsippany　**(1)**
9 Entin Rd Ste 202, Parsippany, NJ 07054
Tel.: (973) 434-3100
Web Site: http://www.hntb.com
Civil Engineering Services
N.A.I.C.S.: 541330
Matthew Riegel *(Assoc VP-Geotechnical Svcs)*
Todd Rothermel *(VP)*
Kerri Tyerman *(Mgr-Transportation)*

HNTB Corporation, Santa Ana Branch　　　　　　　　　　**(1)**

200 E Sandpointe Ave Ste 200, Santa Ana, CA 92707-8797　　　　**(100%)**
Tel.: (714) 460-1600
Web Site: http://www.hntb.com
Sales Range: $10-24.9 Million
Emp.: 55
Provider of Engineering & Architecture Services
N.A.I.C.S.: 541330
Laura Mohr *(VP & Dir-Rail & Transit Grp)*
Kevin Haboian *(Chief Bus Dev Officer & Sr VP)*
Lucy Wu *(Sr Engr-Tunnel & Geotechnical)*
Andres Ocon *(VP)*
Anthony Lee *(Assoc VP-North California)*
Enrique Alonso *(Mgr-Construction Mgmt Program)*
Francesco Cantatore *(Sr Program Dir-Rail Sys)*
Jeffery Bingham *(Sr Program Mgr-Evninronmental)*
Michael Bogonovich *(Sr Project Engr-Sys)*
Michael Haverstick *(Project Engr-Sys)*
Helene Kornblatt *(Assoc VP & Sr Dir-Environmental Sciences & Plng)*

HNTB Michigan Inc　　　　　**(1)**
333 Albert Ave Ste 333, East Lansing, MI 48823　　　　　　　　**(100%)**
Tel.: (517) 333-3330
Web Site: http://www.hntb.com
Sales Range: $10-24.9 Million
Emp.: 20
Provider of Engineering Services
N.A.I.C.S.: 541330

HNTB-Arlington　　　　　　　**(1)**
2900 S Quincy St Ste 200, Arlington, VA 22206
Tel.: (703) 824-5100
Web Site: http://www.hntb.com
Sales Range: $25-49.9 Million
Emp.: 100
Provider of Engineering Agriculture & Aviation Services
N.A.I.C.S.: 541310
Kimberly Hudgins *(Assoc VP)*
Lisa Thompson *(Assoc VP)*
Mike Snare *(Dir-Program)*
Nick Antonucci *(Sr VP)*
Charlie Dodge *(Sr VP)*
Yunxiang Chen *(VP)*
Christopher Collins *(VP)*

HNTB-Atlanta　　　　　　　　**(1)**
3715 NorthSide Pkwy NW Ste 800, Atlanta, GA 30327
Tel.: (404) 946-5700
Web Site: http://www.hntb.com
Sales Range: $10-24.9 Million
Emp.: 90
Provider of Engineering Services
N.A.I.C.S.: 541330
Jess Parker *(Pres)*

HNTB-Austin　　　　　　　　**(1)**
701 Brazos Ste 450, Austin, TX 78701
Tel.: (512) 447-5590
Web Site: http://www.hntb.com
Sales Range: $10-24.9 Million
Emp.: 35
Provider of Engineering Services
N.A.I.C.S.: 541330
Kammy Horne *(VP & Grp Dir)*

HNTB-Baton Rouge　　　　　**(1)**
9100 Bluebonnet Centre Blvd Ste 301, Baton Rouge, LA 70809　　　**(100%)**
Tel.: (225) 368-2800
Web Site: http://www.hntb.com
Sales Range: $10-24.9 Million
Emp.: 45
Provider of Engineering Services
N.A.I.C.S.: 541330

HNTB-Boston　　　　　　　　**(1)**
31 St James Ave Ste 300, Boston, MA 02116
Tel.: (617) 542-6900
Sales Range: $25-49.9 Million
Emp.: 50
Provider of Engineering Services
N.A.I.C.S.: 541330

HNTB-Charlotte　　　　　　　**(1)**
121 W Trade St Ste 2050, Charlotte, NC 28202
Tel.: (704) 372-8020
Web Site: http://www.hntb.com
Sales Range: $10-24.9 Million
Emp.: 9

Provider Of Urban Designing And Planning Services
N.A.I.C.S.: 541330

HNTB-Columbia (1)
120 E Baltimore Ste 1810, Baltimore, MD 21202 (51%)
Tel.: (410) 454-0939
Web Site: http://www.hntb.com
Sales Range: $350-399.9 Million
Landscaping Architects And Provider Of Engineering Services
N.A.I.C.S.: 541330

HNTB-Dallas (1)
5910 W Plano Pkwy Ste 200, Plano, TX 75093-4638 (100%)
Tel.: (972) 661-5626
Web Site: http://www.hntb.com
Sales Range: $25-49.9 Million
Emp.: 140
Provider of Engineering Services
N.A.I.C.S.: 541330
Stephen Novosad (Sr Project Mgr-Intelligent Transportation Sys)

HNTB-Denver (1)
1700 Lincolen St Ste 2450, Denver, CO 80203 (100%)
Tel.: (303) 839-8300
Web Site: http://www.hntb.com
Sales Range: $10-24.9 Million
Emp.: 18
Engineering Services & Landscape Architecture
N.A.I.C.S.: 541330

HNTB-Detroit (1)
719 Griswold Ste 620, Detroit, MI 48226
Tel.: (313) 961-3330
Web Site: http://www.hntb.com
Sales Range: $10-24.9 Million
Emp.: 20
Provider of Engineering Services
N.A.I.C.S.: 541330

HNTB-Hartford (1)
55 Capital Blvd 4th Floor, Rocky Hill, CT 06067-1344
Tel.: (860) 257-7377
Web Site: http://www.hntb.com
Emp.: 30
Provider of Engineering Services
N.A.I.C.S.: 541330
Rob Slimp (CEO)

HNTB-Indiana (1)
111 Monument Cir Ste 1200, Indianapolis, IN 46204-5408
Tel.: (317) 636-4682
Web Site: http://www.hntb.com
Sales Range: $25-49.9 Million
Emp.: 150
Provider of Engineering Services
N.A.I.C.S.: 541330
Mark Urban (VP)

HNTB-Jacksonville (1)
7077 Bonneval Rd Ste 440, Jacksonville, FL 32216-4046
Tel.: (904) 296-0207
Web Site: http://www.hntb.com
Sales Range: $25-49.9 Million
Emp.: 10
Provider of Engineering Services
N.A.I.C.S.: 541330
David H. Evans (VP)
Terry Shaw (Mgr)

HNTB-Los Angeles (1)
1 Bunker Hill Bldg 601 W 5th St Ste 1000, Los Angeles, CA 90071 (100%)
Tel.: (213) 403-1000
Web Site: http://www.hntb.com
Sales Range: $10-24.9 Million
Emp.: 52
Provider of Engineering Services
N.A.I.C.S.: 541330

HNTB-Madison (1)
10 W Mifflin St Ste 300, Madison, WI 53703 (100%)
Tel.: (608) 294-5000
Web Site: http://www.hntb.com
Sales Range: $25-49.9 Million
Emp.: 21
Provider of Engineering Services
N.A.I.C.S.: 541330

HNTB-Miami (1)
161 N W 6th St Ste 1000, Miami, FL 33136

Tel.: (305) 551-8100
Web Site: http://www.hntb.com
Sales Range: $25-49.9 Million
Emp.: 71
Provider Airport Engineering Services
N.A.I.C.S.: 541330
Jose J. De Almagro (Sr VP)

HNTB-Milwaukee (1)
11414 W Park Pl Ste 300, Milwaukee, WI 53224-3500 (100%)
Tel.: (414) 359-2300
Web Site: http://www.hntb.com
Sales Range: $25-49.9 Million
Emp.: 120
Provider of Engineering Services
N.A.I.C.S.: 541330
Tom Carlson (Dir-Opers)
Matt Hintze (Sr VP)

HNTB-Minneapolis (1)
5500 Wayzata Blvd Ste-450, Minneapolis, MN 55416
Tel.: (952) 920-4668
Web Site: http://www.hntb.com
Sales Range: $25-49.9 Million
Emp.: 100
Provider of Engineering Services
N.A.I.C.S.: 541330
Greg Albjeret (VP)

HNTB-Morgantown (1)
30 Smithtown Rd Ste 15, Morgantown, WV 26508-3982
Tel.: (304) 292-6411
Sales Range: $10-24.9 Million
Emp.: 20
Engineeering Services
N.A.I.C.S.: 541330

HNTB-New York (1)
Empire State Bldg 350 5th Ave 57th Fl, New York, NY 10118 (100%)
Tel.: (212) 594-9717
Web Site: http://www.hntb.com
Sales Range: $350-399.9 Million
Provider of Engineering Services
N.A.I.C.S.: 541330

HNTB-Oakland (1)
1111 Broadway 94, Oakland, CA 94607
Tel.: (510) 208-4599
Sales Range: $25-49.9 Million
Emp.: 60
Provider of Engineering Services
N.A.I.C.S.: 541330
Mary Lucas (Office Mgr)
Michael Lee (Sr Mgr-Rail Sys)

HNTB-Ohio Inc (1)
1100 Superior Ave Ste 1701, Cleveland, OH 44114-1816 (100%)
Tel.: (216) 522-1140
Web Site: http://www.hntb.com
Sales Range: $10-24.9 Million
Emp.: 40
Provider of Engineering Services
N.A.I.C.S.: 541330

HNTB-Ohio,Inc (1)
330 West Spring St Ste 310, Columbus, OH 43215 (100%)
Tel.: (614) 436-2878
Web Site: http://www.hntb.com
Sales Range: $10-24.9 Million
Emp.: 5
Engineering Services
N.A.I.C.S.: 541330

HNTB-Orlando (1)
300 Primera Blvd Ste 200, Lake Mary, FL 32746
Tel.: (407) 859-8380
Web Site: http://www.hntb.com
Sales Range: $25-49.9 Million
Emp.: 70
Provider Of Engineering Services
N.A.I.C.S.: 541310
Erika Booker (Assoc VP)
Erik Lange (Assoc VP)
Pam Nagot (Assoc VP)
Tom Neyer (Assoc VP)

HNTB-Overland Park (1)
7400 W 129th St Ste 100, Overland Park, KS 66213
Tel.: (913) 491-9333
Web Site: http://www.hntb.com
Sales Range: $25-49.9 Million
Emp.: 75
Provider of Engineering Services

N.A.I.C.S.: 541330

HNTB-Plano (1)
5910 W Plano St Ste 200, Plano, TX 75093
Tel.: (713) 354-1500
Web Site: http://www.hntb.com
Sales Range: $25-49.9 Million
Emp.: 67
Provider of Engineering Services
N.A.I.C.S.: 541330

HNTB-Portland (1)
340 County Rd Ste 6C, Westbrook, ME 04092-3824
Tel.: (207) 774-5155
Web Site: http://www.hntb.com
Sales Range: $10-24.9 Million
Emp.: 30
Provider of Engineering Services
N.A.I.C.S.: 541330
Paul Godfrey (VP)

HNTB-Raleigh (1)
343 E 6 Forks Rd Ste 200, Raleigh, NC 27609-7888
Tel.: (919) 546-8997
Web Site: http://www.hntb.com
Sales Range: $10-24.9 Million
Emp.: 40
Engineeering Services
N.A.I.C.S.: 541330

HNTB-Saint Louis (1)
211 N Broadway, Saint Louis, MO 63102-1731
Tel.: (314) 241-2808
Web Site: http://www.hntb.com
Sales Range: $10-24.9 Million
Emp.: 22
Provider of Engineering Services
N.A.I.C.S.: 541330
Derwin Irvine (Dir-Recruiting)

HNTB-Salt Lake City (1)
257 East 200 South STe750, Salt Lake City, UT 84116-4800
Tel.: (801) 575-3420
Sales Range: $10-24.9 Million
Emp.: 16
Provider of Engineering Services
N.A.I.C.S.: 541330

HNTB-San Antonio (1)
85 NE Loop 410 Ste 304, San Antonio, TX 78216-5836 (100%)
Tel.: (210) 349-2277
Web Site: http://www.hntb.com
Sales Range: $10-24.9 Million
Emp.: 41
Provider of Engineering Services
N.A.I.C.S.: 541330

HNTB-San Bernardino (1)
1845 Business Ctr Dr Ste 208, San Bernardino, CA 92408-3447 (100%)
Tel.: (909) 890-0622
Sales Range: $10-24.9 Million
Emp.: 7
Provider of Engineering Services
N.A.I.C.S.: 541330

HNTB-San Jose (1)
1735 Technology Dr Ste 650, San Jose, CA 95110
Tel.: (408) 451-7300
Web Site: http://www.hntb.com
Sales Range: $10-24.9 Million
Emp.: 45
Provider of Engineering Services
N.A.I.C.S.: 541330
Darlene Gee (VP)
Laura Mohr (VP & Dir-Rail & Transit)

HNTB-Santa Ana (1)
200 E Sandpointe Ave Ste 200, Santa Ana, CA 92707-8797
Tel.: (714) 460-1600
Web Site: http://www.hntb.com
Sales Range: $10-24.9 Million
Emp.: 50
Provider of Engineering Services
N.A.I.C.S.: 541330

HNTB-Seattle (1)
600 108th Ave NE Ste 900, Bellevue, WA 98004-5110
Tel.: (425) 455-3555
Web Site: http://www.hntb.com
Sales Range: $25-49.9 Million
Emp.: 200
Provider of Engineering Services

N.A.I.C.S.: 541330

HNTB-Tampa (1)
201 N Franklin St Ste 550, Tampa, FL 33602
Tel.: (813) 402-4150
Web Site: http://www.hntb.com
Sales Range: $10-24.9 Million
Emp.: 70
Engineering Services
N.A.I.C.S.: 541330
James E. Drapp (VP & Gen Mgr)
Ken Hartmann (VP-Florida Dept of Transportation)
Alphonse Stewart (Sr Mgr-Transportation Project)

HNTB-Toledo (1)
1838 Frnt St, Toledo, OH 43605-1438
Tel.: (419) 698-2965
Sales Range: $10-24.9 Million
Emp.: 10
Provider of Engineering Services
N.A.I.C.S.: 541330

HO-RO TRUCKING COMPANY INC.
400 Markley St, Port Reading, NJ 07064
Tel.: (732) 726-1166
Web Site: https://www.ho-ro.com
Sales Range: $10-24.9 Million
Emp.: 13
Trucking & Freight Transportation
N.A.I.C.S.: 484230
Howard Teitelbaum (Owner)
Betty Bellanca (Office Mgr)

HOAG HOSPITAL FOUNDA-TION
330 Placentia Ave, Newport Beach, CA 92663
Tel.: (949) 764-7217
Web Site:
https://www.hoaghospitalfoundation.org
Year Founded: 1944
Health Care Srvices
N.A.I.C.S.: 621610

HOAK MOTORS INC.
4300 Southgate Dr, Sioux City, IA 51106
Tel.: (712) 255-0117
Web Site:
http://www.hoakmotors.com
Year Founded: 1985
Sales Range: $25-49.9 Million
Emp.: 40
Automobiles, New & Used
N.A.I.C.S.: 441110
Eric Hoak (Pres)
Richard Hoak (Pres)

HOAR CONSTRUCTION LLC
2 Metroplex Dr Ste 400, Birmingham, AL 35209
Tel.: (205) 803-2121   DE
Web Site: http://www.hoarllc.com
Year Founded: 1940
Sales Range: $200-249.9 Million
Emp.: 400
Construction (Commercial, Retail & Health Care Projects)
N.A.I.C.S.: 236220
Robert O. Burton (Pres & CEO)
Steve McCord (COO & Exec VP)
Jeremy DiPiazza (CFO & VP)
Joe Guillaume (Exec VP-Field Ops)
Matt Allen (Acct Exec)
James Hodge (Project Mgr-Safety)
Jimmy Bates (Sr Mgr-Preconstruction)
Joel Chiman (Sr Superintendent)
Coker Barton (Sr VP)
Mark Hendricks (VP-Healthcare-Alabama)
Turner Burton (VP-Comml-Alabama)
Eric Brown (Sr Project Mgr-Florida)

Hoar Construction LLC—(Continued)

Jordan Ross *(Mgr-Preconstruction-Florida)*
Jake Snyder *(Dir-Preconstruction-Austin)*
Howard Gutman *(Pres)*
Brandon Smith *(Sr Project Mgr-Orlando)*
Seth Sargent *(VP-Healthcare)*
Stephen Clay *(Dir-Ops-Houston)*
Mike McKinnon *(VP-Construction)*
Nikolas Fowler *(Dir-Ops)*
Jeff Light *(VP-Ops)*

HOB-LOB LIMITED PARTNER-SHIP
7707 SW 44th St, Oklahoma City, OK
73179-4808
Tel.: (405) 745-1100
Web Site:
http://www.hobbylobby.com
Sales Range: $1-4.9 Billion
Emp.: 13,000
Hobbies, Arts & Crafts Supplies Retailer
N.A.I.C.S.: 551112
David Green *(Founder & CEO)*
Steve Green *(Pres)*
Jon Cargill *(CFO)*
John Graham *(Asst Gen Counsel)*

Subsidiaries:

Crafts, Etc! Ltd.　　　　　　　　(1)
7717 SW 44th St, Oklahoma City, OK
73179
Tel.: (405) 745-1200
Web Site: http://www.craftsetc.com
Arts & Crafts Supplies Retailer
N.A.I.C.S.: 459130

Hobby Lobby Manufacturing　　(1)
7509 SW 44th St, Oklahoma City, OK
73179
Tel.: (405) 745-1993
Wood Display Fixtures Mfr
N.A.I.C.S.: 339999

Hobby Lobby Stores Inc.　　　　(1)
7707 SW 44th St, Oklahoma City, OK
73179
Tel.: (405) 745-1275
Web Site: https://www.hobbylobby.com
Sales Range: Less than $1 Million
Emp.: 4,300
Hobby, Toy & Game Retailers
N.A.I.C.S.: 459120
David Green *(CEO & CEO)*
John Schumacher *(Asst VP-Adv)*

HOBAN & ASSOCIATES, LLC
2829 Rucker Ave Ste 100, Everett,
WA 98201
Tel.: (425) 339-3638　　　　　WA
Year Founded: 1987
Rev.: $4,000,000,000
Offices of Real Estate Agents & Brokers
N.A.I.C.S.: 531210
Thomas Hoban *(Co-Founder & Chm)*
Shawn Hoban *(Co-Founder & CEO)*
Matt Shaffer *(Pres)*
John Maihofer *(COO)*
Susan Stratton *(Exec VP-Ops)*
Sherry C. Reed *(Sr VP-Western WA & ID)*
Michael Rourke *(VP-Comml Properties)*
Pete Chittenden *(VP-Eastern WA)*
Preston O'Malley *(Mgr-Property Acctg)*

Subsidiaries:

Quantum Management Services,
Inc.　　　　　　　　　　　　　　(1)
3810 196th St SW Ste 10, Lynnwood, WA
98036
Tel.: (425) 776-1294
Sales Range: $1-9.9 Million
Emp.: 32

Apartment Building Operator Real Estate
Agent/Manager
N.A.I.C.S.: 531110
Harry Matsumoto *(VP-Ops & Tech)*
Gaye Barrett *(VP)*

HOBBICO, INC.
2904 Research Rd, Champaign, IL
61822
Tel.: (217) 398-3630　　　　　IL
Web Site: http://www.hobbico.com
Year Founded: 1984
Sales Range: $50-74.9 Million
Emp.: 650
Hobby Goods & Supplies Mfr & Distr
N.A.I.C.S.: 423920
Bob Klecka *(Sr Mgr-Product Dev)*
Dan Landis *(Mgr-Mktg Outreach)*
Janet Gallivan *(Sr Mgr-Projects & Plng)*

Subsidiaries:

ARRMA-Durango Ltd.　　　　　(1)
Unit 7 Charter Point Way, Ashby de la
Zouch, LE65 1NF, Leicestershire, United
Kingdom
Tel.: (44) 1530412352
Web Site: http://www.arrma-durango.com
Radio Controlled Motor Vehicle Whslr
N.A.I.C.S.: 423110

Axial R/C, Inc.　　　　　　　　(1)
8 Goodyear Ste 125, Irvine, CA 92618
Tel.: (877) 642-9425
Web Site: http://www.axialracing.com
Radio Controlled Motor Vehicle Whslr
N.A.I.C.S.: 423110

Estes-Cox Corp.　　　　　　　　(1)
1295 H St, Penrose, CO 81240
Tel.: (719) 372-6565
Web Site: http://www.estesrockets.com
Sales Range: $10-24.9 Million
Radio-Controlled Model Aircraft Mfr
N.A.I.C.S.: 339930

Great Planes Model Manufacturing
Co　　　　　　　　　　　　　　(1)
706 W Bradley Ave, Urbana, IL 61801
Tel.: (217) 367-2707
Web Site: http://www.greatplanes.com
Radio Controlled Motor Vehicle Mfr
N.A.I.C.S.: 339999

Revell, Inc.　　　　　　　　　　(1)
1850 Howard St Unit A, Elk Grove Village,
IL 60007
Tel.: (847) 758-3200
Web Site: http://www.revell.com
Sales Range: $10-24.9 Million
Emp.: 75
Model Kits & Die-Cast Collectibles Mfr &
Distr
N.A.I.C.S.: 339930
Lou Aguilera *(VP & Gen Mgr-Revell &
United Model)*

HOBBS & CURRY FAMILY LIM-ITED PARTNERSHIP
4119 Massard Rd, Fort Smith, AR
72903
Tel.: (479) 785-0844　　　　　AR
Year Founded: 1995
Sales Range: $10-24.9 Million
Emp.: 5
Hotels & Motels Operator
N.A.I.C.S.: 721110
David Curry *(Pres)*

HOBBS INCORPORATED
27 Grove St, New Canaan, CT
06840-5324
Tel.: (203) 966-0726　　　　　CT
Web Site: https://www.hobbsinc.com
Year Founded: 1954
Sales Range: $10-24.9 Million
Emp.: 100
Residential Construction
N.A.I.C.S.: 236115
Scott Hobbs *(Pres)*
Jorge Nunes *(Project Mgr)*

**HOBBY TOWN UNLIMITED,
INC.**
1223 Libra Dr, Lincoln, NE 68512
Tel.: (402) 434-5050　　　　　NE
Web Site: http://www.hobbytown.com
Year Founded: 1980
Sales Range: $1-9.9 Million
Emp.: 50
Toy Store Owner & Franchisor
N.A.I.C.S.: 459120
Bill Graeve *(CFO & VP)*
Merlin Hayes *(Co-Founder)*
Thomas Walla *(Co-Founder)*
Tim Van Ert *(VP)*

HOBBYTYME DISTRIBUTORS
64C Oakland Ave, East Hartford, CT
06108
Tel.: (860) 528-9854
Web Site:
https://www.hobbytyme.com
Year Founded: 1980
Sales Range: $10-24.9 Million
Emp.: 33
Toy & Hobby Good Whslr
N.A.I.C.S.: 423920
Joe St. John *(Founder & Pres)*

**HOBE SOUND GOLF CLUB,
INC.**
11671 SE Plandome Dr, Hobe
Sound, FL 33455
Tel.: (772) 546-4600
Web Site:
https://www.hobesoundgolfclub.com
Sales Range: $1-9.9 Million
Emp.: 60
Golf Club Operations
N.A.I.C.S.: 713910
Brian Wooldridge *(Controller)*

HOBIE CAT COMPANY
4925 Oceanside Blvd, Oceanside, CA
92056-3044
Tel.: (760) 758-9100　　　　　MO
Web Site: http://www.hobiecat.com
Year Founded: 1968
Sales Range: $75-99.9 Million
Emp.: 200
Catamaran Sailboats, Kayaks, Parts
& Accessories Mfr
N.A.I.C.S.: 336612
Doug Skidmore *(Pres)*
Bill Baldwin *(VP-Fin)*
Hugh Greenwald *(VP-Ops)*
Ruth Triglia *(VP-Sls)*
Greg Ketterman *(VP-Engrg)*
Michel Corigliano *(Dir Gen-Europe)*

Subsidiaries:

Hobie Bag Company　　　　　　(1)
32921 Calle Perfecto B, San Juan Capistrano, CA 92675
Tel.: (949) 240-5105
Web Site: http://www.hobiebag.com
Emp.: 1
Bag Mfr & Whslr
N.A.I.C.S.: 316990

Hobie Cat Australasia Pty Ltd　(1)
11 Erina Rd, Huskisson, 2540, NSW, Australia
Tel.: (61) 2 4441 8400
Web Site: http://www.hobiecat.com.au
Boat & Yacht Whslr
N.A.I.C.S.: 423860

Hobie Kayak Europe BV　　　　(1)
Delta Industrieweg 40, 3251 LX, Stellendam, Netherlands
Tel.: (31) 187 499 440
Web Site: http://www.hobie-kayak.com
Emp.: 5
Boat Dealers
N.A.I.C.S.: 441222
Richard Barth *(Owner)*

HOBSON FABRICATING COR-PORATION

6428 Bus Way, Boise, ID 83716-5550
Tel.: (208) 343-5423
Web Site: https://www.hobsonfab.com
Year Founded: 1986
Sales Range: $25-49.9 Million
Emp.: 450
Provider of Plumbing, Heating & Air-Conditioning Services
N.A.I.C.S.: 238220
Randy Frisbee *(Pres)*
Ted Frisbee *(Treas & Sec)*

HOC INDUSTRIES INC.
3511 N Ohio St, Wichita, KS 67219
Tel.: (316) 838-4663
Web Site:
https://www.hocindustries.com
Sales Range: $10-24.9 Million
Emp.: 40
Petroleum Bulk Stations & Terminals
N.A.I.C.S.: 424710
William R. Nath *(Pres)*
Tom Olsen *(VP-Sls-Mktg)*

**HOCHHEIM PRAIRIE FARM
MUTUAL INSURANCE**
500 US Highway 77A S, Yoakum, TX
77995-1399
Tel.: (361) 293-5201
Web Site: https://www.hpfm.com
Sales Range: $75-99.9 Million
Emp.: 65
Fire, Marine & Casualty Insurance:
Mutual
N.A.I.C.S.: 524126
Lynn Brewer *(VP-Info Sys)*
Tim McCoy *(CFO)*
Pamela Lahodny *(VP-Underwriting)*

**HOCKENBERG EQUIPMENT &
SUPPLY CO., INC.**
14063 Cornhusker Rd, Omaha, NE
68138
Tel.: (402) 339-8900
Web Site:
https://www.hockenbergs.com
Rev.: $15,300,000
Emp.: 80
Restaurant Equipment & Supplies
N.A.I.C.S.: 423440
Tom Schrack Sr. *(Chm)*
Tom Schrack Jr. *(Pres)*

**HOCKEY WESTERN NEW
YORK, LLC**
First Niagara Center 1 Seymour H
Knox III Plaza, Buffalo, NY 14203
Tel.: (716) 855-4100　　　　　NY
Web Site: http://www.sabres.nhl.com
Year Founded: 1970
Sales Range: $50-74.9 Million
Emp.: 120
Professional Hockey Team
N.A.I.C.S.: 711211
John Sinclair *(VP-Tickets & Svcs)*
Mike Gilbert *(VP-Pub & Community
Rels)*
Mike Kaminska *(Dir-Mdsg)*
Christine Ivansitz *(Accountant-Special
Project)*
Chuck LaMattina *(Exec VP-Fin & Bus
Ops)*
Stan Makowski *(VP-Arena Ops)*
Brigid Haensel *(Mgr-Payroll)*
Tom Matheny *(Mgr-Database Mktg)*
Terrence M. Pegula *(Owner)*
Austin Dunne *(Coord-Amateur Scouting)*
Charlie Cannan *(Mgr-Event)*
Chrisanne Bellas *(VP-Broadcasting)*
Marc Brenner *(Dir-Security)*
Mark Blaszak *(Dir-Videography)*
Paul Barker *(Mgr-Box Office)*
Theresa Cerabone *(Mgr-Store)*
Jason Botterill *(Gen Mgr)*

HOCKING ATHENS PERRY COMMUNITY ACTION
3 Cardaras Dr, Glouster, OH 45732
Tel.: (740) 767-4500   OH
Web Site: https://www.hapcap.org
Year Founded: 1965
Sales Range: $10-24.9 Million
Emp.: 530
Community Action Services
N.A.I.C.S.: 624190
Kelley McGhee (Pres)
Kathy Hecht (Treas)
Doug Stanley (Exec Dir)
Keith Andrews (VP)

HOCKMAN-LEWIS LIMITED
200 Executive Dr Ste 160 Fl 1, West Orange, NJ 07052
Tel.: (973) 325-3838
Web Site: http://www.hockman-lewisltd.com
Rev.: $18,000,000
Emp.: 15
Industrial Machinery & Equipment
N.A.I.C.S.: 423830
Rosanne M. Dlugosz (Mgr-Admin)

HODESS CLEANROOM CONSTRUCTION, LLC
100 John L Dietsch Sq, Attleboro Falls, MA 02763
Tel.: (508) 695-1012
Web Site: http://www.hodess.com
Year Founded: 1971
Sales Range: $25-49.9 Million
Emp.: 100
Industrial Buildings & Warehouses
N.A.I.C.S.: 236220
Blake Hodess (Founder & CEO)
Timothy Ouellette (Project Mgr)

Subsidiaries:

Clean Rooms West, Inc.   (1)
1392 Industrial Dr, Tustin, CA 92780
Tel.: (714) 258-7700
Web Site: https://www.cleanroomswest.com
Rev.: $10,900,000
Emp.: 50
Industrial Supplies Merchant Whslr
N.A.I.C.S.: 423840
Steve Alley (CEO)
Sharron Lauterborn (VP)
Lois Wallace (CFO)
Tony Mesec (Project Coord)

HODGDON POWDER COMPANY
6430 Vista Dr, Shawnee Mission, KS 66218
Tel.: (913) 362-9455
Web Site: https://www.hodgdon.com
Rev.: $22,000,000
Emp.: 85
Mfr of Gunpowder
N.A.I.C.S.: 325920
Chris Hodgdon (Dir-Sls)
Aaron Oelger (Dir-Mktg & Sls)

HODGDON YACHTS, INC.
14 School St, East Boothbay, ME 04544
Tel.: (207) 633-4194
Web Site:
     http://www.hodgdonyachts.com
Emp.: 150
Boat Mfr
N.A.I.C.S.: 336612
Timothy Hodgdon (Pres & CEO)
Audrey Hodgdon (Dir-Sls & Mktg)

Subsidiaries:

Hodgdon Yacht Services, LLC   (1)
100 Ebenecook Rd, Southport, ME 04576
Tel.: (207) 633-2970
Web Site:
     http://www.hodgdonyachtservices.com
Emp.: 30
Marina & Ship Repair Services

N.A.I.C.S.: 713930
Matt Elder (Gen Mgr)
Eric Leslie (Dir-Sls)
Jim Logan (Dir-East Boothbay Shipyard Ops)
Caleb Easton (Mgr-Customer Support)
Nate Hopkins (Mgr-Svc)
Charles Lopez (Mgr-Svc)
John Vinal (Mgr-Svc)

HODGE SCHINDLER INTEGRATED COMMUNICATIONS
900 N Franklin Ste 505, Chicago, IL 60610
Tel.: (312) 666-6662
Sales Range: Less than $1 Million
Emp.: 10
N.A.I.C.S.: 541820
Sally Saville Hodge (Pres)
Chris Scott (Sr VP)

HODGEN CONSTRUCTION & DEVELOPMENT GROUP INC.
1555 Bonaventure Blve Ste 1016, Weston, FL 33326
Tel.: (954) 727-0333
Sales Range: $10-24.9 Million
Emp.: 13
Commercial & Institutional Building Construction
N.A.I.C.S.: 236220
Debbie Brown (Mgr)
Brad Hodgen (Pres)

HODGES BADGE COMPANY INC.
1170 E Main Rd St 1, Portsmouth, RI 02871
Tel.: (401) 682-2000
Web Site:
     https://www.hodgesbadge.com
Rev.: $10,099,784
Emp.: 110
Emblems, Badges & Insignia: From Purchased Materials
N.A.I.C.S.: 315990
Rick Hodges (Pres)
Jane Fusa (Chm)

HODGES SUPPLY COMPANY
1730 Highwood E, Pontiac, MI 48340
Tel.: (248) 858-2605   MI
Web Site:
     https://www.hodgessupply.com
Year Founded: 1947
Sales Range: $10-24.9 Million
Emp.: 37
Plumbing & Heating Equipment & Supplies Distr
N.A.I.C.S.: 423720
Richard N. Brown (Pres)
Kevin Golden (Mgr-Flint)

HODGSON RUSS LLP
1 Plz Ste 2000, Buffalo, NY 14203-2391
Tel.: (716) 856-4000   NY
Web Site:
     http://www.hodgsonruss.com
Year Founded: 1817
Sales Range: $25-49.9 Million
Emp.: 480
Law firm
N.A.I.C.S.: 541110
James M. Wadsworth (Partner)
Kathy Krieger-Erbes (CIO)
Daniel C. Oliverio (Chm)
Mary P. O'Hara (Partner)

HODGSON/MEYERS ADVERTISING, INC.
10210 NE Points Dr Ste 220, Kirkland, WA 98033-7872
Tel.: (425) 827-2506   WA
Web Site:
     http://www.hodgsonmeyers.com
Year Founded: 1994

Sales Range: $1-9.9 Million
Emp.: 23
Advertising Agencies
N.A.I.C.S.: 541810
Gary Meyers (Pres)
Tim Hodgson (Dir-Video & Motion Media)
John Kennedy (Mgr-Bus Dev)
Charlie Worcester (Assoc Dir-Creative)

HOEHN MOTORS
5556 Paseio Del N, Carlsbad, CA 92008
Tel.: (760) 438-9599
Web Site:
     http://www.hoehnacura.com
Rev.: $71,100,000
Emp.: 200
New & Used Automobiles Dealers & Financing Services
N.A.I.C.S.: 522220
J. P. Paynter (Gen Mgr)

HOEKSTRA TRUCK EQUIPMENT COMPANY INC.
260 36th Ste SE, Grand Rapids, MI 49548
Tel.: (616) 241-6664   MI
Web Site:
     http://www.hoekstratruck.com
Year Founded: 1962
Sales Range: Less than $1 Million
Emp.: 10
Provider of Motor Vehicle Supplies
N.A.I.C.S.: 423102
Ken Kuiper (Gen Mgr)
Karen Babiarz (Mgr-HR)
Jim Durham (Mgr-Sls)

HOETING INC.
6048 Bridgetown Rd, Cincinnati, OH 45248
Tel.: (513) 451-4800
Web Site: https://www.hoeting.com
Sales Range: $50-74.9 Million
Emp.: 40
Real Estate Agent, Residential
N.A.I.C.S.: 531210
Dan Grote (Founder, Partner & Gen Mgr-Sls)
Steve Florian (Founder, Partner & Gen Mgr)
Mike Rolfes (Controller)
Jack Hoeting (Founder & Partner)

HOF HAUS
2386 S Blue Island Ave, Chicago, IL 60608-4228
Tel.: (773) 847-0700
Web Site: https://www.hofhaus.com
Year Founded: 1947
Sales Range: $25-49.9 Million
Emp.: 80
Turkey & Pork Product Mfr
N.A.I.C.S.: 112330
Mark J. Rataj (VP-Sls)
Justo Sanchez (Engr-Plant)
Robert Bukala (VP)
Matthew Hofmeister (Mgr-Mktg)

HOF'S HUT RESTAURANTS INC.
2601 E Willow St, Signal Hill, CA 90755
Tel.: (562) 596-0200   CA
Web Site: https://www.hofshut.com
Year Founded: 1951
Sales Range: $25-49.9 Million
Emp.: 3,000
Eating Place
N.A.I.C.S.: 722511
Craig Hoffman (Pres & CEO)
Lourdes Serrano (Coord-Payroll)

HOFF COMPANIES INC.

1840 N Lakes Ave, Meridian, ID 83646-2951
Tel.: (208) 884-2002   ID
Web Site: http://www.hotc.com
Year Founded: 1910
Sales Range: $25-49.9 Million
Emp.: 150
Windows & Doors Whslr
N.A.I.C.S.: 321918
Todd Armstrong (CFO)

HOFF COMPANIES, INC
8220 Ocean Gate Way, Las Vegas, NV 89128-7462
Tel.: (702) 838-9410
Web Site: http://www.hoffc.com
Wired Telecommunications Carriers
N.A.I.C.S.: 517111
Andrea Borbely (Owner)

Subsidiaries:

Trimco Millwork   (1)
15000 E 39th Ave, Aurora, CO 80011-1241
Tel.: (303) 371-8888
Web Site: http://www.trimcomillwork.com
Lumber, Plywood, Millwork & Wood Panel Merchant Whslr
N.A.I.C.S.: 423310
Paul Peters (Mgr)

HOFF DIAMONDS & GEMS
3001 White Bear Ave N Ste 1043, Maplewood, MN 55109-1215
Tel.: (651) 773-3464
Web Site:
     http://www.hoffdiamonds.net
Rev.: $12,700,000
Emp.: 9
Gem & Jewelry Stores
N.A.I.C.S.: 458310
Steven Hoff (Pres & CEO)

HOFFER PLASTICS CORPORATION
500 N Collins St, South Elgin, IL 60177-1104
Tel.: (847) 741-5740   DE
Web Site:
     https://www.hofferplastics.com
Year Founded: 1953
Sales Range: $50-74.9 Million
Emp.: 350
Plastics Product Mfr
N.A.I.C.S.: 326199
Tom Devens (Mgr-Matls)
Patricia Gaffney (Mgr-Bus Dev)

HOFFINGER INDUSTRIES, INC.
6914 Autumn Oaks Dr Ste B, Olive Branch, MS 38654
Tel.: (662) 890-7930   DE
Web Site: http://www.hoffinger.com
Year Founded: 1946
Sales Range: $25-49.9 Million
Emp.: 400
Sale of Sporting & Athletic Goods
N.A.I.C.S.: 339999
Kathy Chisnall (Mgr-Matls)

HOFFMAN & HOFFMAN INC.
3816 Patterson St, Greensboro, NC 27407
Tel.: (336) 292-8777   NC
Web Site: https://www.hoffman-hoffman.com
Year Founded: 1947
Sales Range: $10-24.9 Million
Emp.: 100
Warm Air Heating & Air Conditioning Services
N.A.I.C.S.: 423730
Louis Hoffman (Pres)
Jim Martinson (Treas & Sec)

HOFFMAN & REED INC.
915 Shanklin St, Trenton, MO 64683

Hoffman & Reed Inc.—(Continued)

Tel.: (660) 359-2258
Web Site:
  http://www.hoffmanreed.com
Sales Range: $10-24.9 Million
Emp.: 39
Grains
N.A.I.C.S.: 424510
Charles D. Hoffman (Pres)
Phil Hoffman (Sec)

HOFFMAN ARCHITECTS, P.A.
29 W Orange St, Tarpon Springs, FL
34689
Tel.: (727) 938-2835
Web Site:
  https://www.hoffmanarchitects.net
Year Founded: 1982
Sales Range: $1-9.9 Million
Emp.: 7
Architectural Services
N.A.I.C.S.: 541310
Edward C. Hoffman Jr. (Founder)

HOFFMAN BROS AUTO ELEC-TRIC
1115 E Madison St, South Bend, IN
46617
Tel.: (574) 287-7946
Sales Range: $10-24.9 Million
Emp.: 52
Automotive Supplies & Parts
N.A.I.C.S.: 423120
James T. Walsh Jr. (Pres)

HOFFMAN CHRYSLER PLYM-OUTH JEEP
101 S Edgewood Dr, Hagerstown,
MD 21740-6687
Tel.: (301) 733-5000
Year Founded: 1925
Sales Range: $25-49.9 Million
Emp.: 100
Car Whslr
N.A.I.C.S.: 441110
Wendy Coy (Controller)
Jennifer Stahl (Office Mgr-Customer
Svc)

HOFFMAN CORPORATION
805 SW Broadway Ste 2100, Port-land, OR 97205-3361
Tel.: (503) 221-8811   **OR**
Web Site:
  https://www.hoffmancorp.com
Year Founded: 1922
Sales Range: $900-999.9 Million
Emp.: 1,000
Commercial & Institutional Building
Construction
N.A.I.C.S.: 236220
Eric Hoffman (Chm)
Wayne Drinkward (Pres)
Dan Harmon (Gen Counsel)
Richard L. Silliman (VP)
Bart Eberwein (VP)

Subsidiaries:

Hoffman Construction Company of
Washington   **(1)**
600 Stewart St, Seattle, WA 98101-3528
Tel.: (206) 286-6697
Web Site: http://www.hoffmancorp.com
Sales Range: $10-24.9 Million
Emp.: 40
Commercial Construction Operations
N.A.I.C.S.: 236115
Tom Peterson (VP)

Hoffman Mechanical Corporation   **(1)**
805 SW Broadway Ste 2100, Portland, OR
97205
Tel.: (503) 221-8811
Web Site: http://www.hoffmancorp.com
Engineering Consulting Services
N.A.I.C.S.: 541330
Jerry Rosette (Pres)

Hoffman Structures, Inc.   **(1)**
805 SW Broadway Ste 2100, Portland, OR
97205
Tel.: (503) 221-8811
Web Site: http://www.hoffmancorp.com
Sales Range: $10-24.9 Million
Emp.: 130
Construction Operations
N.A.I.C.S.: 238110

Ming Surveyors, Inc.   **(1)**
8025 NE Killingsworth St, Portland, OR
97218
Tel.: (503) 221-8905
Sales Range: $10-24.9 Million
Emp.: 15
Construction Layout
N.A.I.C.S.: 541330
Dan Harmon (VP)

Precision Construction Company   **(1)**
8025 NE Killingsworth St, Portland, OR
97218-4029   **(100%)**
Tel.: (503) 253-4827
Web Site: http://www.precision-construction-
  company.com
Sales Range: $10-24.9 Million
Emp.: 20
Construction Operations
N.A.I.C.S.: 236220
Troy Weller (Pres)

HOFFMAN ESTATES PARK DISTRICT
1685 W Higgins Rd, Hoffman Es-tates, IL 60169
Tel.: (847) 885-7500
Web Site: https://www.heparks.org
Sales Range: $10-24.9 Million
Emp.: 223
Recreational Services
N.A.I.C.S.: 713990
Dean Bostrom (Exec Dir)
Debbie Albig (Mgr-Community Cen-ters)
Craig Talsma (Dir-Fin & Admin)
Gary Buczkowski (Div Dir)
Mike Kies (Dir-Recreation & Facili-ties)
David Young (Mgr-Ice Ops)
Ron Evans (Asst Sec)
Brian Bechtold (Dir-Golf Ops)
Cathy Burnham (Gen Mgr-Ops)
Pat McGinn (VP)

HOFFMAN FORD SALES INC.
5200 Jonestown Rd, Harrisburg, PA
17112
Tel.: (717) 657-1600
Web Site:
  https://www.hoffmanford.com
Sales Range: $10-24.9 Million
Emp.: 90
Sales of New & Used Automobiles
N.A.I.C.S.: 441110
Norman Zoumas (Dir-Svc)
Michael Irvin (Mgr-Parts)
Earl B. Hoffman Sr. (Chm, Pres &
CEO)
Earl Hoffman Jr. (Pres)

HOFFMAN MILLS INC.
470 Park Ave S, New York, NY
10016-6819
Tel.: (212) 684-3700
Year Founded: 1926
Sales Range: $25-49.9 Million
Emp.: 600
Mfr of Textiles
N.A.I.C.S.: 313210
Joseph Leone (Controller)
Sandy McNeil (Dir-Product)

HOFFMAN PLANNING, DE-SIGN & CONSTRUCTION, INC.
122 E College Ave Ste 1G, Appleton,
WI 54911
Tel.: (920) 731-2322
Web Site: https://www.hoffman.net
Year Founded: 1892

Sales Range: $125-149.9 Million
Emp.: 80
Planners, Architects & Construction
Management; Nonresidential Con-struction
N.A.I.C.S.: 236220
Sam Statz (Owner)
Terry Ellenbecker (Owner & Dir-Field
Ops)
Miles Girouard (Pres)
Scott Pigeon (Dir-Mktg)
Kevin Madalinski (Sr Project Mgr)
Mark Hanson (Dir-Sustainable Svcs)
Pat Del Ponte (Owner & Dir-Plng
Svcs)
Randy Bremhorst (Owner & VP-
Design)

HOFFMAN PLASTIC COM-POUNDS, INC.
16616 Garfield Ave, Paramount, CA
90723-5305
Tel.: (323) 636-3346
Web Site:
  https://www.hoffmanplastic.com
Year Founded: 1970
Sales Range: $10-24.9 Million
Emp.: 65
Plastics Materials & Resins Mfr
N.A.I.C.S.: 325211
Ronald Hoffman (Pres)

HOFFMAN TRANSPORT INC.
485 Mason Dixon Rd, Greencastle,
PA 17225
Tel.: (717) 597-7117
Web Site:
  https://www.hoffmantransport.com
Year Founded: 1981
Sales Range: $10-24.9 Million
Emp.: 121
Trucking Services
N.A.I.C.S.: 484121
John Hoffman (Pres)
Tim Reitz (Mgr-Freight Ops)

HOFFMAN VACATION RENT-ALS LLC
1000 Lions Rdg Loop Ste 3A, Vail,
CO 81657
Tel.: (970) 477-1777
Web Site:
  http://www.rockymountainvacation
  rentals.com
Year Founded: 1998
Sales Range: $1-9.9 Million
Emp.: 24
Customized Vacations
N.A.I.C.S.: 561599
Tommy Z. Hoffman (Owner)

HOFFMAN WEBER CON-STRUCTION
3515 48th Ave N, Minneapolis, MN
55429
Tel.: (866) 970-1133
Web Site:
  http://www.hwconstruction.com
Year Founded: 2004
Sales Range: $10-24.9 Million
Emp.: 48
Remodeling & Construction Services
& Hail Damage Repair to Homeown-ers
N.A.I.C.S.: 236118
Joseph Hoffman (Pres)

HOFFMAN YORK, INC.
200 N Water St, Milwaukee, WI
53202
Tel.: (414) 289-9700   **WI**
Web Site:
  https://www.hoffmanyork.com
Year Founded: 1933
Advertising & Public Relations
Agency

N.A.I.C.S.: 541810
Troy Peterson (CEO)

HOFFMAN/LEWIS
353 Sacramento St Fl 21, San Fran-cisco, CA 94111
Tel.: (415) 434-8500   **CA**
Web Site:
  http://www.handlpartners.com
Year Founded: 1985
Sales Range: $100-124.9 Million
Emp.: 85
Advertising Agencies
N.A.I.C.S.: 541810
Josh Nichol (CEO & Partner)
Trey Curtola (Partner, Exec VP & Dir-
Acct)
Maribel Orozco (VP & Dir-
Multicultural Mktg)
Tyler Martin (Partner, VP & Dir-Client
Svcs)
Mark Manion (Partner, Sr VP & Cre-ative Dir)
Mark Schaeffer (Pres-Saint Louis &
Partner)

Subsidiaries:

Hoffman/Lewis   **(1)**
30 Maryland Plz, Saint Louis, MO 63108-
1526
Tel.: (314) 454-3400
Web Site: http://www.hoffmanlewis.com
Emp.: 25
Advertising Agencies
N.A.I.C.S.: 541810
Mark Schaeffer (Pres)
Tyler Martin (VP & Dir-Client Svcs)
Andrea Alfano (COO & Partner)
Rob Bagot (Chief Creative Officer & Part-
ner)
Trey Curtola (Partner, Exec VP & Dir-Acct)
Jacob Ford (Dir-Digital Creative)
Maribel Orozco (VP & Dir-Multicultural
Mktg)
Laurie Pocher (VP-Insights & Dir-Plng)
Michael Ramirez (VP & Dir-Media)
Sue Ream (Partner, Sr VP & Dir-Media)

HOFFMAN/NEW YORKER INC.
46 Clinton Pl, Hackensack, NJ
07601-4523
Tel.: (201) 488-1800
Web Site: http://www.hoffman-
  newyorker.com
Sales Range: $10-24.9 Million
Emp.: 50
Pressing Machines, Commercial
Laundry & Drycleaning
N.A.I.C.S.: 333510
Terry Rothlisberger (Controller)

HOFFMANN DIE CAST COR-PORATION
229 Kerth St, Saint Joseph, MI 49085
Tel.: (269) 983-1102
Web Site:
  https://www.handlnndc.com
Year Founded: 1986
Sales Range: $1-9.9 Million
Emp.: 170
Aluminum Casting Mfr
N.A.I.C.S.: 331523
Mike Oros (Co-Owner & Pres)

HOFFMEYER COMPANY INC.
1600 Factor Ave, San Leandro, CA
94577
Tel.: (510) 895-9955
Web Site:
  http://www.hoffmeyerco.com
Sales Range: $10-24.9 Million
Emp.: 20
Hose, Belting & Packing
N.A.I.C.S.: 423840
Frederick Oshay (Pres & Chm)

HOFMANN INDUSTRIES, INC.
3145 Shillington Rd, Sinking Spring,
PA 19608-0147

Tel.: (610) 678-8051   DE
Web Site: https://www.hofmann.com
Year Founded: 1922
Sales Range: $25-49.9 Million
Emp.: 250
Welded Steel Tubing Mfr
N.A.I.C.S.: 331210
Steve Owens (Pres & CEO)
Bob Hess (Treas & Controller)
Jeff Hills (VP-Sls)

Subsidiaries:

Hofmann Industries, Inc. - Eau Claire
Division   (1)
6405 Love Rd, Eau Claire, MI 49111
Tel.: (269) 461-3586
Steel Tube Mfr
N.A.I.C.S.: 331210

HOG SLAT INC.
206 Fayetteville St, Newton Grove,
NC 28366-8992
Tel.: (910) 594-0219
Web Site: https://www.hogslat.com
Year Founded: 1970
Sales Range: $75-99.9 Million
Emp.: 1,100
Swine Production Solutions
N.A.I.C.S.: 112210
Tommy Herring (Pres)
Kimberly Warren (Asst Controller &
Mgr-Acctg)
Michele J. Blanchard (Mgr-Acctg)
Fritz Richards (Mgr-Sls-Natl)
Lyn Hearne (Mgr-Concrete Div)
Tim Hawkins (Engr-Product)

HOGAN HOMES INC
400 Mann St Ste 1000, Corpus
Christi, TX 78401
Tel.: (361) 883-1550
Web Site:
http://www.hoganhomestexas.com
Sales Range: $10-24.9 Million
Emp.: 30
Speculative Builder, Single-Family
Houses
N.A.I.C.S.: 236115
Angela Nelson (VP-Trng, Sls Mgmt &
External Affairs)
Augustine Hogan III (Chm)

HOGAN MANUFACTURING INC.
1704 Coley St, Escalon, CA 95320
Tel.: (209) 838-7323
Web Site: http://www.hoganmfg.com
Rev.: $15,600,000
Emp.: 150
Wheelchair Lifts
N.A.I.C.S.: 332999
Zach Hogan (VP-Ops)

HOGAN MOTOR LEASING INC.
1000 N 14th St, Saint Louis, MO
63106
Tel.: (314) 231-0966
Web Site: https://www.hogan1.com
Rev.: $16,000,000
Emp.: 50
Truck Rental, Without Drivers
N.A.I.C.S.: 532120
Brian J. Hogan (Co-Pres)
Geri Zinn (CFO)
Carl Hogan (VP)
Greg Thoelke (VP-Mktg-Sls)
David Hogan (Co-Pres)

HOGAR CREA INC.
PO Box 547, Trujillo Alto, PR 00978
Tel.: (787) 761-0715   PR
Web Site:
http://www.hogarcreainc.org
Year Founded: 1968
Sales Range: $10-24.9 Million
Behavioral Healthcare Services
N.A.I.C.S.: 623220

Sabino Colon (VP)
Genaro Rodriguez (VP)
Luis Rodriguez (Asst Sec)
Hector L. Figueroa (Exec Dir)
Raquel Pizarro (Dir-HR)

HOGE LUMBER COMPANY
701 S Main St, New Knoxville, OH
45871
Tel.: (419) 753-2263
Web Site: https://www.hoge.com
Sales Range: $10-24.9 Million
Emp.: 40
Lumber, Hardwood Dimension
N.A.I.C.S.: 321992
John H. Hoge (Pres)
Clark Froning (VP)
Bruce L. Hoge (VP)

HOGG CONSTRUCTION INC.
2351 Freedom Way, York, PA 17402
Tel.: (717) 741-0839   PA
Web Site:
http://www.hoggconstruct.com
Year Founded: 1952
Sales Range: $25-49.9 Million
Emp.: 65
Commercial & Office Building Con-
struction Services
N.A.I.C.S.: 236220
Chuck Hill (Controller)
Roger Barber (VP)

HOGLUND BUS CO. INC.
116 E Oakwood Dr, Monticello, MN
55362
Tel.: (763) 295-5119
Web Site:
http://www.hoglundbusandtruck.com
Year Founded: 1947
Rev.: $31,188,466
Emp.: 45
Sales of New & Used Cars
N.A.I.C.S.: 441110
Jack Potter (Controller)

HOGUE & ASSOCIATES INC.
250 Montgomery St Ste 1500, San
Francisco, CA 94104-3409
Tel.: (415) 788-4888
Web Site: http://www.hoguesf.com
Rev.: $30,000,000
Emp.: 20
Office Furniture
N.A.I.C.S.: 423210
Jonathan Gaber (Pres)
David G. Boggs (CFO)

HOHL INDUSTRIAL SERVICES CO.
770 Riverview Blvd, Buffalo, NY
14150
Tel.: (716) 332-0466
Web Site: https://www.hohlind.com
Sales Range: $75-99.9 Million
Emp.: 70
Installation of Manufacturing Pro-
cesses
N.A.I.C.S.: 236220
David Hohl (Chm)
Tom Habdo (Pres & CEO)
Rick Wolney (Controller)
Christopher Macrides (Mgr-Field Ops)
John Regdos (Mgr-Field Svc)
Michael Reilly (VP-Ops)
Thomas Santulli (VP-Ops)

HOIST FITNESS SYSTEMS INC.
11900 Community Rd, Poway, CA
92064
Tel.: (858) 578-7676
Web Site:
https://www.hoistfitness.com
Rev.: $10,300,000
Emp.: 60

Exercise Equipment
N.A.I.C.S.: 339920
Diane Andersson (Mgr-HR)
Rachel Griffiths (Mgr-Sls)
Brian Williams (Reg Mgr-Sls)

HOJ ENGINEERING & SALES CO., LLC
862 W Fine Dr, Salt Lake City, UT
84119
Tel.: (801) 266-8881   UT
Web Site: https://www.hoj.net
Year Founded: 1964
Industrial Machinery & Equipment Mfr
N.A.I.C.S.: 423830
Brian Keeran (Sls Mgr-Hoj Forklift
Systems)
Vince Rotta (VP-Overhead Cranes)
Tim Hoj (CEO)
Peter Hoj (Pres)
Chuck Archer (COO)
Robert Lyon (VP-Innovations)
Stan Witt (Dir-Conveyor Innovations)
Mark Westover (Dir-Bus Dev)
Mark Strong (Sls Mgr)
Lisa Hales (Mgr-HR)
Paz Hazlett (Mgr-Acctg)

Subsidiaries:

Hesco Services Inc.   (1)
862 W Fine Dr, Salt Lake City, UT 84119
Tel.: (801) 269-1042
Web Site: http://www.hoj.net
Rev.: $1,500,000
Emp.: 150
Installing Building Equipment
N.A.I.C.S.: 238290

Hoj Forklift Systems   (1)
862 W Fine Dr, Salt Lake City, UT 84119
Tel.: (801) 386-7327
Web Site: http://www.hoj.net
Emp.: 120
New & Used Forklift Dealer
N.A.I.C.S.: 441227
Brian Keeran (Mgr-Sls)
Peter Hoj (Pres)

Idaho Material Handling Inc.   (1)
4655 Federal Way, Boise, ID 83716-5531
Tel.: (208) 336-4400
Web Site: http://www.imhboise.com
Sales Range: $50-74.9 Million
Emp.: 10
Sales of Material Handling Equipment
N.A.I.C.S.: 423830

Branch (Domestic):

Idaho Material Handling Inc.   (2)
4800 N Yellow Stone, Idaho Falls, ID 83401
Tel.: (208) 529-2322
Web Site: http://www.imhboise.com
Emp.: 20
Business to Business Electronic Markets
N.A.I.C.S.: 425120
Randy Smith (Gen Mgr)

HOKE INC.
5800 N Bayshore Rd Ste A 214, Mil-
waukee, WI 53217
Tel.: (414) 962-4530
Web Site: http://www.hoke-inc.com
Sales Range: $10-24.9 Million
Emp.: 6
Hydraulic Systems Equipment & Sup-
plies
N.A.I.C.S.: 423830
Rex Millheam (Pres)

HOL-MAC CORPORATION
160 Commerce Dr, Bay Springs, MS
39422
Tel.: (601) 764-4121
Web Site: http://www.e-pac-mac.com
Year Founded: 1963
Sales Range: $10-24.9 Million
Emp.: 300
Fluid Power Cylinders Mfr
N.A.I.C.S.: 333995

Michael Pace (Dir-IT)
Jamie Holder (Pres & COO)

HOLADAY-PARKS FABRICA-TORS INC.
4600 S 134th Pl, Tukwila, WA 98168-
3241
Tel.: (206) 248-9700
Web Site:
https://www.holadayparks.com
Year Founded: 1952
Sales Range: $25-49.9 Million
Emp.: 200
Plumbing, Heating & Air Conditioning
Services
N.A.I.C.S.: 238220
Dan Connell (VP-Design Build)

HOLBROOK & MANTER INC.
775 Yard St Ste 160, Marion, OH
43212
Tel.: (740) 387-8620
Web Site:
http://www.holbrookmanter.com
Rev.: $2,000,000
Emp.: 20
Other Accounting Services
N.A.I.C.S.: 541219
Jamie S. Harrison (Mgr)
Molly Pensyl (Mgr-Bus Dev)
Mark Welp (Principal)
Carmen M. George (Mgr)
Danielle L. Irvine (Mgr)
Stephen C. Smith (Principal)

HOLBROOK LUMBER COM-PANY
Northeastern Industrial Park Bldg Ste
11, Guilderland, NY 12009
Tel.: (518) 489-4708   NY
Web Site:
http://www.holbrooklumber.com
Year Founded: 1911
Sales Range: $10-24.9 Million
Emp.: 25
Lumber Whslr
N.A.I.C.S.: 423310
Peter P. Krihak (CEO)

HOLBROOK MFG., INC.
288 Holbrook Dr, Wheeling, IL 60090
Tel.: (847) 229-1999   IL
Web Site:
http://www.holbrookinc.com
Year Founded: 2001
Sales Range: $10-24.9 Million
Emp.: 100
Bolt, Nut, Screw & Other Fasteners
Mfr
N.A.I.C.S.: 332722
Don Kuhns (CEO)
Gary VanderPoel (Pres)
Bill Collopy (Exec VP-Ops)

HOLCOMB & HOKE MANU-FACTURING COMPANY, INC.
1545 Van Buren St, Indianapolis, IN
46203-4176
Tel.: (317) 784-2444   IN
Web Site: http://www.foldoor.com
Year Founded: 1913
Sales Range: $75-99.9 Million
Emp.: 62
Vinyl Covered & Wood Doors & Parti-
tions Mfr
N.A.I.C.S.: 326199

HOLCOMB ENTERPRISES
25108 Marguerite Pkwy Ste MSA-
206, Mission Viejo, CA 92692-2446
Tel.: (949) 458-0292
Web Site:
http://www.holcombenterprises.com
Year Founded: 1972

Holcomb Enterprises—(Continued)

Sales Range: $10-24.9 Million
Emp.: 15
Value Added Reseller & Systems Integrator
N.A.I.C.S.: 541512
Scott P. Holcomb (Founder & CEO)

HOLCOMBE USA INC.
440 S State Rd 7, Plantation, FL 33317
Tel.: (954) 479-4014
Web Site:
    https://www.autoshowflorida.com
Rev.: $20,000,000
Emp.: 38
Used Car Dealers
N.A.I.C.S.: 441120
Paul Rogers (Pres)

HOLD BROTHERS INC.
1177 Of The Americas Fl 2, New York, NY 10036-2714
Tel.: (201) 499-8700
Web Site:
    http://www.holdbrothers.com
Year Founded: 1994
Sales Range: $75-99.9 Million
Emp.: 100
Security Brokers & Dealers
N.A.I.C.S.: 523150
Steven J. Hold (Pres)

HOLDAHL INC.
1925 Annapolis Ln, Minneapolis, MN 55441
Tel.: (763) 231-3130
Web Site:
    https://www.holdahlcompany.com
Sales Range: $10-24.9 Million
Emp.: 75
Lumber, Plywood & Millwork
N.A.I.C.S.: 423310
Layne Holdahl (Pres)
Bill Stokke (VP)
Maggie Muschel (Mgr-Credit)

HOLDEN GRAPHIC SERVICES
607 Washington Ave N, Minneapolis, MN 55401-1220
Tel.: (612) 349-0400
Sales Range: $75-99.9 Million
Emp.: 500
Business Printing Services & Direct Marketing Services
N.A.I.C.S.: 323111
Gary Plager (CFO)

HOLDEN INDUSTRIES, INC.
500 Lake Cook Rd Ste 400, Deerfield, IL 60015
Tel.: (847) 940-1500
Web Site:
    https://www.holdenindustriesinc.com
Year Founded: 2003
Holding Company
N.A.I.C.S.: 551112
Joseph S. Haas (Pres & CEO)
Barbara Barkley (Dir-HR)
Dave Danielski (Controller)
Greg Hamilton (CFO)
JoAnne Williams (Gen Counsel)
Elena Black (Mgr-Strategic Planning & Analysis)

Subsidiaries:

Ladder Industries, Inc, (1)
1040 S Camino Oro Dr, Goodyear, AZ 85338
Tel.: (623) 932-5798
Web Site: http://www.ladderindustries.com
Metal Ladders & Stairways Mfr
N.A.I.C.S.: 332999

Nosco, Inc. (1)
651 S Martin Luther King Jr Ave, Waukegan, IL 60085

Tel.: (847) 336-4200
Web Site: http://www.nosco.com
Printed Packaging Services
N.A.I.C.S.: 323111
Russell S. Haraf (Pres)
Ed Hudson (Exec VP)
Michael Biesboer (CFO)
R. Craig Curran (VP-Sls & Mktg)
Sue Fowler (Dir-Customer Svc, Pre-Press & IT)
Dick Leach (Dir-Quality)
Richard D. Potochnik (Dir-Ops)
Bob Trumbo (Dir-HR)

Subsidiary (Domestic):

Gooding Co., Inc. (2)
5568 Davison Rd, Lockport, NY 14094
Tel.: (716) 434-5501
Web Site: http://www.nosco.com
Commercial Printing; Lithographic; Inserts, Outserts & Manual Guides Supplier
N.A.I.C.S.: 323111
Gerald Hace (Pres)

Division (Domestic):

Nosco, Inc. (2)
1100 Venture Ct Ste 100, Carrollton, TX 75006
Tel.: (972) 478-6400
Web Site: http://www.nosco.com
Sales Range: $1-9.9 Million
Printed Packaging Material Services
N.A.I.C.S.: 322220
Brad Elledge (Dir-Ops)

Nosco, Inc. (2)
2199 Delany Rd, Gurnee, IL 60031-1208
Tel.: (847) 336-4200
Web Site: http://www.nosco.com
Printed Packaging Services
N.A.I.C.S.: 561910
Bob Trumbo (Dir-People Ops)
Craig Curran (Sr VP-Sls & Mktg)
James Struhar (CFO)
John McKeough (Sr VP-Ops)
Russell Haraf (Pres)

Setco Sales Company (1)
5880 Hillside Ave, Cincinnati, OH 45233-1524
Tel.: (513) 941-5110 (100%)
Web Site: http://www.setcousa.com
Mfr of Machine Tool Components, Spindles & Slides
N.A.I.C.S.: 333517
Craig Rath (CFO)
Jeff Clark (Pres)

Joint Venture (Domestic):

SE Setco Service Company (2)
2402 Tech Ctr Pkwy Ste 200, Lawrenceville, GA 30043
Tel.: (770) 932-2353
Web Site: http://www.sesetco.com
Sales Range: $125-149.9 Million
Emp.: 20
Machine Tool & Component Mfr
N.A.I.C.S.: 333514
Paul Bange (Gen Mgr)

Division (Domestic):

Setco Great Lakes Service Center (2)
41129 Jo Dr, Novi, MI 48375
Tel.: (248) 888-8989
Web Site: http://www.setcousa.com
Sales Range: $50-74.9 Million
Emp.: 25
Spindle Repair Service
N.A.I.C.S.: 811210
Don Langhorn (Dir-Ops)

Setco Midwest Service Center (2)
5880 Hillside Ave, Cincinnati, OH 45233-1524
Tel.: (513) 941-5110
Web Site: http://www.setcousa.com
Sales Range: $25-49.9 Million
Machine Tool Components Repair Services
N.A.I.C.S.: 333517

Setco Western Service Center (2)
5572 Buckingham Dr, Huntington Beach, CA 92649
Tel.: (714) 372-3730
Web Site: http://www.setcousa.com

Emp.: 10
Component Repair Service
N.A.I.C.S.: 811310
Sue Williams (Gen Mgr)

Timesavers Inc. (1)
11123 89th Ave N, Maple Grove, MN 55369
Tel.: (763) 488-6600
Web Site: http://www.timesaversinc.com
Sales Range: $10-24.9 Million
Emp.: 55
Wide Abrasive Sanding & Grinding Machines Mfr
N.A.I.C.S.: 333517
Gregory K. Larson (Pres)
Gary Besonen (Mgr-Natl Woodworking Equipment Sls)
Martin Flory (Mgr-Facility & Pur)

Division (Non-US):

Timesavers International BV (2)
Fruitlaan 20-30, Goes, 4462 EP, Netherlands
Tel.: (31) 113238911
Web Site: http://www.timesaversint.com
Emp.: 90
Wide Abrasive Sanding & Grinding Machines Mfr
N.A.I.C.S.: 333517
Paul Hartendorp (Gen Mgr)

Vac-Con, Inc. (1)
969 Hall Park Rd, Green Cove Springs, FL 32043
Tel.: (904) 493-4969
Web Site: http://www.vac-con.com
Emp.: 300
Truck Mfr & Distr
N.A.I.C.S.: 333924
Floyd Wilson (Dir-Bus-Intl)
Todd Masley (Pres)

Vector Technologies Ltd. (1)
6820 N 43rd St, Milwaukee, WI 53209
Tel.: (414) 247-7100
Web Site: http://www.vector-vacuums.com
Vacuum Excavator Mfr
N.A.I.C.S.: 333120
Paul Christensen (Dir-Ops)

Wildeck, Inc. (1)
405 Commerce St, Waukesha, WI 53186
Tel.: (262) 549-4000
Web Site: http://www.wildeck.com
Steel Products Mfr
N.A.I.C.S.: 332323
Keith G. Pignolet (Chm)
Paul Mihelich (VP-Strategic Accounts & Installations)
David H. Milner (VP-Sls & Mktg)
Richard Day (CFO)
Dan Lorenz (Pres)
Steve Holland (VP-Ops)

HOLDER CONSTRUCTION COMPANY
3300 Riverwood Pkwy Ste 1200, Atlanta, GA 30339-3304
Tel.: (770) 988-3000
Web Site:
    https://www.holderconstruction.com
Year Founded: 1960
Sales Range: $200-249.9 Million
Emp.: 3,500
Commercial & Institutional Building Construction
N.A.I.C.S.: 236220
Michael Kenig (Vice Chm)
Greer Gallagher (Sr VP)

HOLDER ELECTRIC SUPPLY, INC.
431 N Pleasantburg Dr, Greenville, SC 29607
Tel.: (864) 271-7111
Web Site:
    https://www.holderelectric.com
Sales Range: $25-49.9 Million
Emp.: 50
Distr of Electrical Fittings & Construction Materials
N.A.I.C.S.: 423610
Edward P. Holder (Owner)

HOLDER HOSPITALITY GROUP INC.
5355 Kietzky Ln Ste 102, Reno, NV 89511
Tel.: (775) 825-7026
Year Founded: 1992
Rev.: $29,200,000
Emp.: 2
Holding Company
N.A.I.C.S.: 551112
Harold D. Holder Jr. (Owner & CEO)

HOLDIMAN MOTOR, INC.
242 Tower Park Dr, Waterloo, IA 50701-9002
Tel.: (319) 277-1210
Sales Range: $10-24.9 Million
Emp.: 65
Car Whslr
N.A.I.C.S.: 441110
Tom Holdiman (Pres)

HOLES, INC.
9911 Franklin Rd, Houston, TX 77070
Tel.: (281) 469-7070   TX
Web Site: https://www.holesinc.com
Year Founded: 1972
Sales Range: $10-24.9 Million
Emp.: 52
General Contracting Services
N.A.I.C.S.: 238110
Chris Meador (Supvr-Shop)

HOLIDAY AUTO & TRUCK INC.
321 N Rolling Meadows Dr, Fond Du Lac, WI 54937
Tel.: (920) 921-8898
Web Site:
    http://www.holidayautomotive.com
Sales Range: $50-74.9 Million
Emp.: 97
Automobiles, New & Used
N.A.I.C.S.: 441110
Michael Shannon (Pres)
Ted McCaller (Controller)

HOLIDAY BUILDERS INC.
2293 W Eau Gallie Blvd, Melbourne, FL 32935
Tel.: (321) 610-5180   FL
Web Site:
    https://www.holidaybuilders.com
Year Founded: 1983
Sales Range: $75-99.9 Million
Emp.: 340
Single-Family Housing Construction
N.A.I.C.S.: 236115
Richard Fadil (CFO)

HOLIDAY CARPET & FLOOR COVERINGS
16600 Sherman Way Ste 278, Van Nuys, CA 91406
Tel.: (818) 786-3200
Web Site:
    https://www.holidaycarpet.com
Rev.: $13,000,000
Emp.: 10
Floor Coverings
N.A.I.C.S.: 423220
Mark Cane (Pres)

HOLIDAY CHEVROLET, LLC
1001 E US Hwy 192, Saint Cloud, FL 34769
Tel.: (407) 892-5144   DE
Web Site:
    http://www.sterlingbuickgmc.com
Sales Range: $10-24.9 Million
Emp.: 55
New & Used Car Dealer
N.A.I.C.S.: 441110
Alan C. Starling (Pres)
Gregg Ticehurst (Treas & Sec)

HOLIDAY COMPANIES

4567 American Blvd W, Bloomington, MN 55437
Tel.: (952) 830-8700   MN
Web Site:
http://www.holidaystationstores.com
Year Founded: 1928
Sales Range: $1-4.9 Billion
Emp.: 4,200
Gas Station & Convenience Store Owner & Operator; Sporting Goods Retailer & Distr
N.A.I.C.S.: 457120
Gerald A. Erickson (Vice Chm)
Lynn Anderson (Gen Counsel & Exec VP)

HOLIDAY DIVER INC.
180 Gulf Stream Way, Dania, FL 33004-2151
Tel.: (954) 926-4455
Web Site:
http://www.diversdirect.com
Sales Range: $10-24.9 Million
Emp.: 35
Sales of Scuba Equipment & Supplies
N.A.I.C.S.: 459110
Kevin Senecal (Pres)
Robert Darmanin (Mgr-Online Svcs)

HOLIDAY EXPRESS CORPORATION
721 S 28th St, Estherville, IA 51334
Tel.: (712) 362-5812
Web Site:
http://www.holidayxpress.net
Year Founded: 1969
Sales Range: $10-24.9 Million
Emp.: 25
Refrigerated Products Transport Services
N.A.I.C.S.: 484230
Merle Johnson (VP)
Steve Olson (Mgr-Brokerage)
Doug Johnson (VP)

HOLIDAY FOODS & GROCERIES INC.
12 N Kringle Ste A, Santa Claus, IN 47579
Tel.: (812) 937-4428
Web Site:
http://www.holidayfoodeonline.com
Year Founded: 1969
Sales Range: $25-49.9 Million
Emp.: 300
Grocery Store Services
N.A.I.C.S.: 445110
Josh Winkler (CEO)

HOLIDAY HOMES INC.
1252 State Rte 28, Milford, OH 45150-2261
Tel.: (513) 575-0100   OH
Web Site: http://www.holiday-homes.com
Year Founded: 1972
Sales Range: $10-24.9 Million
Emp.: 65
Mobile Home Dealer Services
N.A.I.C.S.: 459930
Daniel Rolfes (Founder & CEO)
Paul Ritter (VP)
Joe Gallina (CFO)

HOLIDAY HOUSE, INC.
425 Madison Ave Fl 12, New York, NY 10017
Tel.: (212) 688-0085   NY
Web Site:
http://www.holidayhouse.com
Year Founded: 1955
Sales Range: $1-9.9 Million
Emp.: 15
Book Publishers
N.A.I.C.S.: 513130

John Briggs (Pres)
Raina Putter (Mng Editor)
Judy Varon (Production Mgr)

HOLIDAY IMAGE, INC.
760 1st St, Harrison, NJ 07029
Tel.: (718) 369-3212   NY
Web Site:
http://www.holidayimageinc.com
Year Founded: 2005
Sales Range: $1-9.9 Million
Emp.: 30
Custom Holiday Themed Props Mfr
N.A.I.C.S.: 541430
Matthew Schwam (Pres & CEO)

HOLIDAY ISLE RESORT & MARINA
84001 Overseas Hwy, Islamorada, FL 33036
Tel.: (305) 664-2321   FL
Web Site:
https://www.holidayisle.com
Year Founded: 1983
Sales Range: $1-9.9 Million
Emp.: 280
Resort Hotel
N.A.I.C.S.: 721110
Mary Celentano (Pres)

HOLIDAY PROPERTIES
3511 Greensburg Rd, North Canton, OH 44720-1468
Tel.: (330) 494-5282   OH
Year Founded: 1975
Sales Range: $10-24.9 Million
Emp.: 5
Holding Company
N.A.I.C.S.: 531120
Robert E. Rohr (Office Mgr)

HOLIDAY SUPPORT FACILITY 2099
6890 Shingle Creek Pkwy, Minneapolis, MN 55430-1413
Tel.: (763) 566-4100
Sales Range: $10-24.9 Million
Emp.: 140
Food Products Mfr
N.A.I.C.S.: 311999
Ronald Erickson (Pres)
Brant Blacky (CEO)
William Ehrich (Mgr-Production)

HOLIDAY WHOLESALE INC.
225 Pioneer Dr, Wisconsin Dells, WI 53965
Tel.: (608) 254-8321
Web Site:
https://www.holidaywholesale.com
Rev.: $111,400,000
Emp.: 150
General Line Grocery Merchant Whslr
N.A.I.C.S.: 424410
Pam Rudoll (VP-Fin)
Bernard E. Gussel (Pres)
Ed Wognicz (VP-Mktg)
Bill Bray (VP-HR)

HOLIDAY WORLD OF DALLAS LTD.
4630 I-30, Mesquite, TX 75150
Tel.: (214) 609-1901
Web Site: https://www.hwhrv.com
Sales Range: $25-49.9 Million
Emp.: 50
Recreational Vehicle Whslr
N.A.I.C.S.: 441210
Micheal Peay (Owner)

HOLIEN INC.
121 Airport Dr, Watertown, SD 57201-5227
Tel.: (605) 886-3889   SD
Web Site: http://www.anza.com

Year Founded: 1993
Sales Range: $75-99.9 Million
Emp.: 1,627
Producer of Signs & Advertising Specialties
N.A.I.C.S.: 339950
Greg Kulesa (CFO & Sec)

Subsidiaries:

Anza Inc.   (1)
312 9th Ave SE Ste B, Watertown, SD 57201   (100%)
Tel.: (605) 886-3889
Web Site: http://www.anza.com
Sales Range: $10-24.9 Million
Emp.: 9
Signs & Advertising Specialties
N.A.I.C.S.: 339950
Greg Kulesa (Pres)
Persona Inc.   (1)
700 21st St SW, Watertown, SD 57201-4035
Tel.: (605) 882-2244
Web Site: http://www.personasigns.com
Sales Range: $25-49.9 Million
Emp.: 240
Producer of Signs & Advertising Specialties
N.A.I.C.S.: 339950
Lyle Norton (VP-Process Dev)
Tom Ries (Project Mgr)
David Holien (Chm)
Mike Peterson (Pres)
Craig Horn (COO)
Dennis Holien (Founder)

HOLLADAY CORPORATION
3400 Idaho Ave NW Ste 500, Washington, DC 20016-3049
Tel.: (202) 362-2400   DC
Web Site:
https://www.holladaycorp.com
Year Founded: 1952
Sales Range: $50-74.9 Million
Emp.: 750
Residential Construction
N.A.I.C.S.: 236117
Wallace F. Holladay (Pres)
Colleen S. Chavez (Comptroller)
Rita J. Bamberger (Sr VP)

Subsidiaries:

Georgetown Retirement Residence   (1)
2512 Q St NW, Washington, DC 20007-4310
Tel.: (202) 338-6111
Web Site: http://www.thegeorgetown.com
Sales Range: $10-24.9 Million
Emp.: 100
Residential Services for the Retired
N.A.I.C.S.: 721310

HOLLAND & HART LLP
555 17th St Ste 3200, Denver, CO 80202
Tel.: (303) 295-8000
Web Site:
https://www.hollandhart.com
Year Founded: 1947
Sales Range: $150-199.9 Million
Emp.: 400
Law firm
N.A.I.C.S.: 541110
Katherine A. LeVoy (Partner)
Jason Prince (Partner)
Billi McCullough (Partner)
David Crandall (Partner)
Samuel Holland Edwards (Partner)
Betty Arkell (Partner)
Bradley T. Cave (Partner)
Jane Michaels (Partner)
Matthew Cavarra (Partner)
Christopher A. Gunlikson (Partner)
Emily Hobbs-Wright (Partner)
Teresa Burkett Buffington (Partner)
Wendy J. Pifher (Partner)
John Wilson (Partner)
Laura Dinan (Partner)
Stephanie Edinger (Partner)

Stephen Villano (Partner-Fin-Denver)
Steven Gutierrez (Partner)
Maureen Reidy Witt (Partner-Denver Tech Center)
Margot Summers Edwards (Partner)
Sean Hanlon (Partner)
Elizabeth Harding (Partner)
Thomas C. Jensen (Partner)
Thomas Chandler (Partner)
Dean Bennett (Partner-Admin-Boise)
Lucy Stark (Mng Partner)
Chris Balch (Chm)

HOLLAND & KNIGHT LLP
100 N Tampa St Ste 4100, Tampa, FL 33602
Tel.: (813) 227-8500
Web Site: http://www.hklaw.com
Sales Range: $600-649.9 Million
Emp.: 1,900
Law firm
N.A.I.C.S.: 541110
Anderson L. Baldy (Partner)
Rod Anderson (Partner)
Bernard Barton (Partner)
Chester E. Bacheller (Partner)
Stacy D. Blank (Partner)
Bradford Kimbro (Exec Partner)
Dominic Kouffman (Partner)
Anna Marie Hernandez (Partner)
Francisco J. Sanchez (Partner)
Laurie Webb Daniel (Partner)
Monica Vila Castro (Partner)
Eric Ray (Partner)
Maximillian Bodoin (Partner)
Antonia Tzinova (Partner)
William Levay (Partner)
Paul W. Smith (Partner)
Angelique Lehmann Waddell (Partner)
Michael D. Emerson (Partner)
Renee Covitt (Partner)
Samuel Spital (Partner)
Anthony E. DiResta (Partner)
Terry Davis (Chm-Investment Management Practice & Partner)
Mark S. Lange (Partner-Atlanta)
Debbie M. Orshefsky (Partner)
John A. Decker (Partner-Atlanta)
Lynne M. Halbrooks (Partner)
Kelly Franklin Bagnall (Partner-Dallas)
Sara Heskett (Exec Partner)
Scott Wallace (Partner)
Frank Stearns (Partner)
Larry Shackelford (Partner)
Mary Goodrich Nix (Partner)
Ethan Cohen (Partner)
Sean Leonard (Partner)
Bryan Jung (Partner)
Ying Geneve DuBois (Partner)
Katherine Joffe (Partner)
Rebecca Plasencia (Partner)
John Chapman (Partner)
Chelsea McCarthy (Partner)
Steven Jedlinski (Partner)
Paula Kirlin (Partner)
Nathan Leavitt (Partner)
Gregory Hallmark (Partner)
Rebecca Leon (Partner-Fin Svcs Practice Grp)
Joe Steinberg (Partner)
Stephen Ratliff (Partner)
Kenneth Noble (Partner)
Robert Lang (Partner)
Faith Bruins (Partner)
Robert Haight (Partner)
Wayne Chancellor (Partner)
Andrew Steif (Partner)
Robert Riva (Partner)
Joshua Roberts (Partner)
Merri Moken (Partner)
Nicole Elliott (Partner-Public Policy & Regulation Grp)

Holland & Knight LLP—(Continued)

Grace Pan (Partner)
David Fine (Partner-Litigation-Denver)
Seth Belzle (Partner-Denver & Houston)
John Hogan (Chm-Litigation)
Mark Churchill (Partner)
Scott Lashway (Partner)
Joseph Mamounas (Partner-Litigation Practice Grp)
Juan Alcala (Partner-Austin)
Marjorie Gannett (Partner-Washington)
Vivian de las Cuevas-Diaz (Partner-Miami)
David B. Allswang (Partner)
Elizabeth Smegal Andersen (Partner)
Glenn A. Adams (Partner)
Joaquin J. Alemany (Partner)
Martin J. Alexander (Partner)
Michael A. Abel (Partner)
Bob Mendenhall (Partner-Charlotte)
Lisa Prager (Partner)
Michael Abramson (Partner)
Courtney Groh (Partner)
Jessica Early (Partner)
Cheryl Feeley (Partner)
Janene Jackson (Partner)
Kimberly Caccavaro (Partner)
Joshua Spencer (Partner)
Sameer Patel (Partner)
Carrie Friesen-Meyers (Partner)
Colin Barnacle (Partner)
Joseph Donovan (Partner-Energy)
Michael Cavanaugh (Chm-Energy Practice)
Lindsay Dennis Swiger (Partner)
Edward Sarnowski (Partner)
Brian Cary (Partner-Charlotte)
David Jacobs (Partner-Charlotte)
Alan S. Cohen (Partner-New York)
Kendel Drew (Partner-Atlanta)
Chris Dillon (Partner-Atlanta)
Doug Gosden (Partner-Atlanta)
Cindy Brazell (Chm-Fin Svcs Practice)
Erez Tucner (Partner)
David Taylor (Partner)
Stephen Dietrich (Partner)
Stewart Kasner (Partner-Nationally Recognized Private Wealth Svcs Grp)
Danielle V. Garcia (Partner-Los Angeles)
Emil Infante (Partner)
Dane McKaughan (Partner-Austin)
Todd Kimbrough (Partner-Austin)
David Cannella (Partner-Orlando)
Alyson Pirio (Partner)
K. Alyse Latour (Partner)
Cynthia Gausvik (Partner-Tysons)
Matthew Zimmerman (Partner)
Annapoorni Sankaran (Partner)
Steven D. Lear (Partner/Head-Joint Venture Practice Team-Natl)
Loren Higgins (Partner-Real Estate Practice Grp-West Coast)
John Riley (Partner)
Paul Sarahan (Partner)
Tricia DeLeon (Partner)
Beth Rothenberg (Partner)
John Hoover (Partner-Aviation Fin-Washington)
Benjamin Robinson (Partner-Orlando)
Mark Melton (Partner-Dallas)
Patrick Chidnese (Partner)
Jason Havens (Partner)
Nicholas Sarokhanian (Partner)
James Voelker (Partner)
Theresa Wanat (Partner)
Derrick Mitchell (Partner-Natl Pub Fin Team)
Sara Bernard (Partner-Orlando)
Kevin Christmas (Partner)
Seth Entin (Partner-Private Wealth Svcs Grp)

Matthew Detzel (Partner)
Christian Nagel (Partner-Govt Contracts & Enforcement Defense Grp-Tysons)
Wes Strickland (Partner)
Henry Lowe (Atty)
Matthew Bielen (Partner-Miami)
David Barkus (Head-Natl)
Jeffrey Wool (Dir-Law & Policy-Intl)
Mark Sloan (VP-Practice & Ops Committee)
Steven Sonberg (Mng Partner)
Wade Kennedy (Partner-Chicago)
Nathan A. Adams IV (Partner)
James R. Paine Jr. (Partner)

Subsidiaries:

Thompson & Knight LLP   (1)
One Arts Plz 1722 Routh St Ste 1500, Dallas, TX 75201
Tel.: (214) 969-1700
Web Site: http://www.tklaw.com
Sales Range: $200-249.9 Million
Emp.: 501
Legal Advisory Services
N.A.I.C.S.: 541110
William L. Banowsky (Partner-Dallas)
Emily A. Parker (Partner)
Ted M. Benn (Partner-Dallas)
Becky S. Jackson (Chief Client Svcs Officer)
Marcie Y. Davis (Chief Dev Officer)
Tom Laughlin (CFO)
Diane M. Scheffler (COO)
Gregory D. Binns (Partner-Dallas)
Christopher L. Chauvin (Partner-Dallas)
Micah Prude (Partner)
Luis F. Gomar (Partner)
Todd Lowther (Partner)
Jesse E. Betts (Partner)
Rick Haan (Partner)
Michael H. Peskowitz (Partner)
Mitchell G. Mandell (Partner-New York)
Mark M. Sloan (Mng Partner)
Vivian M. Arias (Partner)
J. Dean Hinderliter (Partner)
Ashley W. Anderson (Partner-Dallas & Fort Worth)
Charles W. Shewmake (Partner)
Robert W. Ray (Partner)
Michele L. Gibbons (Partner-Corp & Securities Practice Grp-Houston)
Lauren Foreman (Mgr-Comm)
Kenneth P. Held (Partner-Trial Practice Grp-Houston)
Elizabeth G. Myers (Partner-Trial Practice Grp-Austin)
Robert D. Eickenroht (Partner-Corp & Securities Practice Grp-Houston)
Brandon L. Bloom (Partner)
Nichole Dotson-Olajuwon (Chief Diversity Officer)
John D. Barney (CIO)
Abbey Garber (Partner-Tax)
Alfredo Raul Ramos (Partner-Oil & Gas Practice Grp-Houston)
Keith R. Whitman (COO)

Waller Lansden Dortch & Davis LLP   (1)
Nashville City Ctr 511 Union St Ste 2700, Nashville, TN 37219-1760
Tel.: (615) 244-6380
Web Site: http://www.wallerlaw.com
Law firm
N.A.I.C.S.: 541110
James B. Bristol (Partner)
Robert E. Boston (Partner)
Stephen C. Baker (Partner)
Brent Bowman (Partner)
Richard Hills (Partner)
J. D. Thomas (Partner)
Jack Waddey (Partner)
Kristen Larremore (Partner)
Wes Scott (Partner)
Frances Fenelon (Partner)
Tyson Bickley (Partner)
Daniel Flournoy (Partner)
Jon Gaston (Partner)
Laura Merritt (Partner)
Lauran Sturm (Partner)
Christopher A. Wilson (Partner)
John Burns (Partner)
Jeff Parrish (Partner)
J. Bryan Echols (Partner)

Chanelle R. Acheson (Partner & Atty)
John Arnold (Atty)
Lindsey R. Arnold (Atty)
Taylor J. Askew (Atty)
Bahar Azhdari (Atty)
Patsy Bowers (Partner)
Richard Westling (Partner)
Catie Lane Bailey (Atty)
Cleveland R. Burke (Partner)
Christopher Driskill (Partner)
Ken Marlow (Chm-Healthcare)
Morgan Ribeiro (Chief Bus Dev Officer)
Matt Burnstein (Chm)
Paula Torch (Exec Dir-Healthcare)
David Garcia (Partner)
A. J. Bahou (Partner)
Stephen Page (Partner)
George W. Bishop III (Partner)

HOLLAND BANCORP, INC.
12 S Main St, Holland, NY 14080
Tel.: (716) 537-2264   NY
Web Site:
   https://www.bankofhollandny.com
Year Founded: 2000
Bank Holding Company
N.A.I.C.S.: 551111

Subsidiaries:

Bank of Holland   (1)
12 S Main St, Holland, NY 14080
Tel.: (716) 537-2264
Web Site: https://www.bankofhollandny.com
Sales Range: $1-9.9 Million
Emp.: 19
Commericial Banking
N.A.I.C.S.: 522110
Mark George (VP)
Don Musielak (Asst VP)
Mark Luderman (Pres)
Jeremy Satchell (VP-Comml Lending & Branch Admin)

HOLLAND CONSTRUCTION COMPANY, INC.
4495 N Illinois St, Swansea, IL 62226-1005
Tel.: (618) 277-8870   IL
Web Site: https://www.hollandcs.com
Year Founded: 1986
Sales Range: $25-49.9 Million
Emp.: 30
Provider of Nonresidential Construction Services
N.A.I.C.S.: 236220
Bruce Holland (CEO)
Doug Weber (Dir-Multi-Family Housing)
Mike Marchal (Pres)
Katie McCutchen (Controller)
Mike Arnett (Superintendent)
Jamie Foster (Dir-HR)
Jeremy Maddox (VP-Bus Dev)
Dave Birk (Exec VP)

HOLLAND CORPORATION INC.
9131 Noland Rd, Shawnee Mission, KS 66215
Tel.: (913) 888-5277   KS
Year Founded: 1952
Sales Range: $10-24.9 Million
Emp.: 35
Highway & Street Paving Contractor
N.A.I.C.S.: 237310
James Holland (Pres)
Mac Holland (VP)
Harold Holland (VP)

HOLLAND TRANSPORTATION MANAGEMENT INC.
2227 Salisbury Hwy, Statesville, NC 28677
Tel.: (704) 872-4269
Web Site:
   https://www.hollandtms.com
Year Founded: 2002
Sales Range: $1-9.9 Million
Emp.: 9

Transportation & Warehousing Logistics Services
N.A.I.C.S.: 488510
Jeff Harvey (Owner)
Dawn Foxx (Mgr-Sls)

HOLLANDIA DAIRY, INC.
622 E Mission Rd, San Marcos, CA 92069-1999
Tel.: (760) 744-3222
Web Site:
   https://www.hollandiadairy.com
Year Founded: 1949
Sales Range: $10-24.9 Million
Emp.: 200
Dairy Products Mfr
N.A.I.C.S.: 112120
Arie H. Dejong (Pres)
Pete De Jong (Exec VP)
Klaas De Haan (Treas)
Rudy De Jong (VP & Gen Mgr)
Lee Hodge (Gen Mgr)

HOLLAR & GREENE PRODUCE CO. INC.
PO Box 3500, Boone, NC 28607
Tel.: (828) 264-2177   NC
Web Site:
   http://www.hollarandgreene.com
Year Founded: 1962
Sales Range: $10-24.9 Million
Emp.: 82
Fresh Fruits & Vegetables
N.A.I.C.S.: 424480
Dale L. Greene (Pres)
Don Addis (Controller)

HOLLENBACH CONSTRUCTION, INC.
166 Holly Rd, Gilbertsville, PA 19525
Tel.: (610) 367-4200
Web Site:
   https://www.hollenbach.com
Year Founded: 1968
Sales Range: $10-24.9 Million
Emp.: 30
Industrial Building Construction
N.A.I.C.S.: 236210
Timothy Little (Pres)
James Hollenbach (Chm)
Stephanie Hollenbach (Treas & Sec)

HOLLER DRIVER'S MART
1970 State Rd 436, Winter Park, FL 32792
Tel.: (407) 645-1234   FL
Web Site:
   http://www.hollerdriversmart.com
Year Founded: 1938
Sales Range: $250-299.9 Million
Emp.: 225
Car & Truck Dealership
N.A.I.C.S.: 441110
Gavin Hutchinson (Gen Mgr)
Phil Collins (Asst Gen Mgr)
Richard Ilgenfritz (Mgr-Svc)
Jill Holler Rogers (VP)
Jennifer Mantia (Mgr-Fin)
Kyle Smith (Mgr-Fin)
Fred Helfrich (Mgr-Parts-Columbus)
Kamal Ghai (Mgr-Sls)
Patrick Pimentel (Mgr-Sls)

HOLLEWAY CAPITAL PARTNERS LLC
8000 Maryland Ave Ste 420, Saint Louis, MO 63105
Tel.: (314) 764-4876
Web Site: https://www.holleway.com
Privater Equity Firm
N.A.I.C.S.: 523940
Holly Huels (Co-Founder & Mng Dir)

Subsidiaries:

Braner USA, Inc.   (1)

9301 W Bernice St, Schiller Park, IL 60176-2301
Tel.: (847) 671-3448
Web Site: https://www.braner.com
Sales Range: $10-24.9 Million
Emp.: 50
Metalworking Machinery & Coil Processing Equipment
N.A.I.C.S.: 333519
Chuck Damore (VP)

HOLLI-TEX SUPPLY CO.
131 E Olive St, Holliday, TX 76366
Tel.: (940) 586-1271
Sales Range: $25-49.9 Million
Emp.: 14
Oil Well Machinery, Equipment & Supplies
N.A.I.C.S.: 423830
Vickie Johnston (Office Mgr)

HOLLIDAY GROUP, LLC
3906 Mockingbird Hill, Sarasota, FL 34231
Tel.: (941) 951-2699   FL
Web Site:
http://www.hollidaygroup.com
Year Founded: 1993
Sales Range: $1-9.9 Million
Construction Management Services
N.A.I.C.S.: 541611
Craig Holliday (Pres)
Dianna Graham (Office Mgr)

HOLLIDAY ROCK CO., INC.
1401 N Benson Ave, Upland, CA 91786-2166
Tel.: (909) 982-1553   CA
Web Site:
http://www.hollidayrock.com
Year Founded: 1964
Sales Range: $25-49.9 Million
Emp.: 120
Aggregate, Concrete & Asphalt Mfr
N.A.I.C.S.: 423320
Jarrod Nachreiner (Mgr-Operations)

HOLLIDAY'S GENERAL SERVICE CORP.
4841 Summer Ave, Memphis, TN 38122
Tel.: (901) 522-1983
Web Site:
http://www.hollidaysfashions.com
Sales Range: $10-24.9 Million
Emp.: 400
Women's Clothing Store
N.A.I.C.S.: 458110
Jeff Presley (Pres)

HOLLINGSWORTH OIL CO. INC.
1503 Meml Blvd, Springfield, TN 37172-3234
Tel.: (615) 242-8466   TN
Web Site: http://www.hoclubes.com
Year Founded: 1975
Sales Range: $200-249.9 Million
Emp.: 400
Petroleum & Petroleum Products Distr
N.A.I.C.S.: 424720
Ronnie Hollingsworth (Pres)
Carol Justice (Controller)
Karen Sweatt (Office Mgr)

Subsidiaries:

Hollingsworth Oil Co.   (1)
417 N 4th St, Bessemer, AL 35030
Tel.: (205) 424-5823
Sales Range: $25-49.9 Million
Emp.: 15
Petroleum Lubricating Oils & Specialty Products Distr
N.A.I.C.S.: 424720
Ronnie Hollingsworth (Pres)

HOLLINGSWORTH RICHARDS MAZDA
7787 Florida Blvd, Baton Rouge, LA 70806
Tel.: (225) 272-2900
Web Site:
http://www.hollingsworthrichards
mazda.com
Year Founded: 1989
Sales Range: $10-24.9 Million
Emp.: 58
New Car Whslr
N.A.I.C.S.: 441110
Mark Hollingsworth (Gen Mgr)
G. Michael Hollingsworth (Pres)
Josh Bourque (Gen Mgr)
Louis Lecoq (Mgr-Svc)

HOLLIS D. SEGUR INC.
156 Knotter Dr, Cheshire, CT 06410
Tel.: (203) 699-4500   CT
Web Site: http://www.hdsegur.com
Year Founded: 1890
Sales Range: $25-49.9 Million
Emp.: 80
Insurance Services
N.A.I.C.S.: 524210
Scott C. Sundberg (Partner)
Nancy Cosgrove (VP & Mgr-Municipal Risk Svc)
James M. Herlihy (VP & Mgr-Comml Lines)

HOLLISTER CONSTRUCTION SERVICES, LLC
339 Jefferson Rd, Parsippany, NJ 07054
Tel.: (201) 393-7500
Web Site: https://www.hollistercs.com
Year Founded: 2004
Sales Range: $25-49.9 Million
Emp.: 150
Construction Engineering Services
N.A.I.C.S.: 237990
Christopher A. Johnson (Founder & CEO)
Sam Perrotta (Controller)

HOLLISTER INCORPORATED
2000 Hollister Dr, Libertyville, IL 60048-3746
Tel.: (847) 680-1000   IL
Web Site: https://www.hollister.com
Year Founded: 1921
Sales Range: $10-24.9 Million
Emp.: 1,400
Healthcare Products
N.A.I.C.S.: 339113
Thomas Meier (Dir-Key Acct Grp Germany)
Carolin Archibald (VP-U.S. & Canada)
Mike Gresavage (VP-North America)
Joanne Gresavage (Dir-Corp Comm)

Subsidiaries:

Dansac & Hollister Danmark   (1)
slotsmarken 17 1st Floor, 2970, Horsholm, Denmark
Tel.: (45) 48465100
Web Site: http://www.hollister.com
Sales Range: $10-24.9 Million
Emp.: 14
Healthcare Products Mfr, Marketer & Developer
N.A.I.C.S.: 423450

Hollister   (1)
1 Place de la Pyramide, Tour Atlantique, 92911, Paris, France
Tel.: (33) 145193850
Web Site: http://www.hollister.com
Sales Range: $10-24.9 Million
Emp.: 30
Healthcare Products Mfr, Marketer & Developer
N.A.I.C.S.: 423450

Hollister Asia Incorporated   (1)
Sam-E Logistics 6th Floor, Sam-Dong Kwangju-Si Gyeonggi, Seoul, 464-040, Korea (South)
Tel.: (82) 313227866
Web Site: http://www.hollister.com
Healthcare Products Mfr, Marketer & Developer
N.A.I.C.S.: 423450

Hollister B.V.   (1)
PO Box 2662, 3800 GE, Amersfoort, Netherlands
Tel.: (31) 334501000
Web Site: http://www.hollister.com
Sales Range: $10-24.9 Million
Emp.: 15
Healthcare Products Mfr, Marketer & Developer
N.A.I.C.S.: 423450
Rene Zonderland (Mng Dir)

Hollister Belgium   (1)
52 Chaussee des Collines, 1300, Wavre, Belgium
Tel.: (32) 10230470
Sales Range: $10-24.9 Million
Emp.: 11
Healthcare Products Mfr, Marketer & Developer
N.A.I.C.S.: 423450
Mark Beauchanp (Mgr)

Hollister Co., Ltd.   (1)
Ohno Takanawa Building 7F 2-21-38 Takanawa, Minato-ku, Tokyo, 108-0074, Japan
Tel.: (81) 332806200
Web Site: http://www.hollister.com
Healthcare Products Mfr, Marketer & Developer
N.A.I.C.S.: 423450
Koji Takada (Pres)

Hollister Europe Limited   (1)
Rectory Court, 42 Broad Street, Wokingham, RG40 1AB, Berkshire, United Kingdom
Tel.: (44) 1189895063
Web Site: http://www.hollister.com
Healthcare Products Mfr, Marketer & Developer
N.A.I.C.S.: 423450

Hollister GmbH   (1)
Bergmillergasse 5/1/1, Vienna, 1140, Austria
Tel.: (43) 18770800
Web Site: http://www.hollister.com
Sales Range: $10-24.9 Million
Emp.: 12
Healthcare Products Mfr, Marketer & Developer
N.A.I.C.S.: 423450
Wilfried Peufel (Gen Mgr)

Hollister Greece Medical Products Commercial S.A.   (1)
308 Messogion Avenue, 155 62, Athens, Greece
Tel.: (30) 106561550
Web Site: http://www.hollister.com
Sales Range: $10-24.9 Million
Emp.: 25
Healthcare Products Mfr, Marketer & Developer
N.A.I.C.S.: 423450

Hollister Iberica, sa   (1)
Avenida Brucelles 13 2F D Alcovendas, 28108, Madrid, Spain
Tel.: (34) 913838727
Sales Range: $10-24.9 Million
Emp.: 40
Healthcare Products Mfr, Marketer & Developer
N.A.I.C.S.: 423450

Hollister Incorporated Niederlassung Deutschland   (1)
Ries Strasse 25, 80992, Munich, Germany
Tel.: (49) 899928860
Sales Range: $10-24.9 Million
Emp.: 60
Healthcare Products Mfr, Marketer & Developer
N.A.I.C.S.: 423450
Richard Zwirner (Gen Mgr)

Hollister Kft   (1)
Retkoz u 18, 1118, Budapest, Hungary
Tel.: (36) 165966

Web Site: http://www.hollister.com
Healthcare Products Mfr, Marketer & Developer
N.A.I.C.S.: 423450

Hollister Latin America   (1)
Rodriguez Pena 694 8vo D, CP C1020ADN, Buenos Aires, Argentina
Tel.: (54) 11 4373 0500
Web Site: http://www.hollister.com
Healthcare Products Mfr, Marketer & Developer
N.A.I.C.S.: 423450

Hollister Liberty Medical (Switzerland) AG   (1)
Abteilung Hollister, Postfach 227, Zurcherstrasse 20, CH 8952, Schlieren, Switzerland
Tel.: (41) 17304505
Web Site: http://www.hollister.com
Healthcare Products Mfr, Marketer & Developer
N.A.I.C.S.: 423450

Hollister Limited   (1)
95 Eric T Smith Way Unit 1, Aurora, L4G 0Z6, ON, Canada
Tel.: (905) 727-4344
Web Site: https://www.hollister.ca
Sales Range: $10-24.9 Million
Emp.: 40
Healthcare Products Mfr, Marketer & Developer
N.A.I.C.S.: 423450
Carol Robinson (Pres)

Hollister Limited   (1)
Unit 4045 Kingswood Rd Citywest Business Park, Tallaght, Dublin, 24, Ireland
Tel.: (353) 14041680
Web Site: http://www.hollister.com
Sales Range: $10-24.9 Million
Emp.: 6
Healthcare Products Mfr, Marketer & Developer
N.A.I.C.S.: 423450

Hollister Limited   (1)
Rectory Ct, 42 Broad St, Wokingham, RG40 1AB, Berkshire, United Kingdom
Tel.: (44) 1189895000
Web Site: http://www.hollister.com
Sales Range: $10-24.9 Million
Emp.: 50
Healthcare Products Mfr, Marketer & Developer
N.A.I.C.S.: 423450

Hollister Medical India Private Limited   (1)
Plot No 27 Sector 5 Phase II HSIIDC Growth Center, Bawal, Rewari, 123501, Haryana, India
Tel.: (91) 128 430 8900
Web Site: http://www.hollister.com
Medical Equipment Mfr
N.A.I.C.S.: 339113

Hollister Norge   (1)
PO Box 273, 1377, Billingstad, Norway
Tel.: (47) 66776650
Web Site: http://www.dansac.at
Healthcare Products Mfr, Marketer & Developer
N.A.I.C.S.: 423450

Hollister S.A. de C.V.   (1)
Prolongacion Paseo de la Reforma No 1015 Torre B Piso 3, Colonia Desarrollo, Santa Fe Cuajimalpa Ciudad de, Mexico, 05348, Mexico
Tel.: (52) 5568205024
Web Site: http://www.hollister.com.mx
Sales Range: $10-24.9 Million
Emp.: 16
Medical Product Mfr & Distr
N.A.I.C.S.: 339113

Hollister S.p.A.   (1)
Strada 4 Palazzo A/7 20090 Milanofiori, Assago, 20090, Italy
Tel.: (39) 028228181
Web Site: http://www.hollister.it
Emp.: 25
Healthcare Products Mfr, Marketer & Developer
N.A.I.C.S.: 423450
Isabel Escobar (Gen Mgr)

Hollister Scandinavia Inc., Suomen Sivuliike   (1)

Hollister Incorporated—(Continued)

Metsalamtee 20, Helsinki, 320, Finland
Tel.: (358) 108413040
Web Site: http://www.hollister.com
Sales Range: $10-24.9 Million
Emp.: 7
Healthcare Products Mfr, Marketer & Developer
N.A.I.C.S.: 423450
Tuija Sinkkonen (Gen Mgr)

Hollister South Africa (Pty) Ltd　(1)
Northlands Production Park Unit 15 Epsom Road, North Riding, Johannesburg, 2192, South Africa
Tel.: (27) 11 704 7420
Web Site: http://www.hollister.com
Sales Range: $10-24.9 Million
Emp.: 8
Healthcare Products Mfr, Marketer & Developer
N.A.I.C.S.: 423450
Mari Ellis (Mng Dir)

Hollister Sp. zo.o.　(1)
Ul Poleczki 47, 02 822, Warsaw, Poland
Tel.: (48) 223227581
Web Site: http://www.hollister.com
Healthcare Products Mfr, Marketer & Developer
N.A.I.C.S.: 423450

Hollister Sverige　(1)
Enhagsslingan 5, S 187 40, Taby, Sweden
Tel.: (46) 84464646
Web Site: http://www.hollister.com
Sales Range: $10-24.9 Million
Emp.: 8
Healthcare Products Mfr, Marketer & Developer
N.A.I.C.S.: 423450

Hollister ULC　(1)
Foxford Road Rehins, Ballina, Mayo, Ireland
Tel.: (353) 96 60600
Health Care Products Mfr
N.A.I.C.S.: 339113

Hollister do Brasil Ltda　(1)
Av Jabaquara 2958 7 andar, Brooklin Nova, 04046-500, Sao Paulo, Brazil
Tel.: (55) 1155959650
Web Site: http://www.hollister.com.br
Sales Range: $10-24.9 Million
Emp.: 15
Healthcare Products Mfr, Marketer & Developer
N.A.I.C.S.: 339112
Jose Domingues (Gen Mgr)

Hollister s.r.o　(1)
Ptasinskeho 10, 602 00, Brno, Czech Republic
Tel.: (420) 230470
Healthcare Products Mfr, Marketer & Developer
N.A.I.C.S.: 423450

Liberty Medical (Switzerland) AG　(1)
Abteilung Dansac, Postfach 122, Zurcherstrasse 20, CH 8952, Schlieren, Switzerland
Tel.: (41) 17305010
Web Site: http://www.hollister.com
Healthcare Products Mfr, Marketer & Developer
N.A.I.C.S.: 423450

Liberty Medical NZ Limited　(1)
58 Richard Pearse Airport Oaks, Auckland, New Zealand
Tel.: (64) 99683620
Web Site: http://www.libertymedical.com.au
Healthcare Products Mfr, Marketer & Developer
N.A.I.C.S.: 423450

Liberty Medical Pty. Ltd.　(1)
Unit 6 Citi Link Estate, 345 Ingels St, Port Melbourne, 3207, VIC, Australia
Tel.: (61) 396734300
Web Site: http://www.hollister.com.au
Sales Range: $10-24.9 Million
Emp.: 45
Healthcare Products Mfr, Marketer & Developer
N.A.I.C.S.: 423450

HOLLISTER SUPER INCORPORATED

301 The Alameda Ste 5b, San Juan Bautista, CA 95045
Tel.: (831) 623-2485
Rev.: $15,912,407
Emp.: 32
Independent Supermarket
N.A.I.C.S.: 445110

HOLLISTON, LLC
905 Holliston Mills Rd, Church Hill, TN 37642
Tel.: (423) 357-6141
Web Site: https://www.holliston.com
Year Founded: 1895
All Other Miscellaneous Textile Product Mills
N.A.I.C.S.: 314999
Billy Adkins (Ops Mgr)

HOLLMAN INC.
1825 W Walnut Hill Ln Ste 110, Irving, TX 75038
Tel.: (972) 815-4082
Web Site: https://www.hollman.com
Year Founded: 1976
Rev.: $31,061,908
Emp.: 75
Wood Lockers & Plastic Laminated & Panelized Court Systems Mfr
N.A.I.C.S.: 337212
Vi Ho (CFO)
Kim Leng (VP-Mfg)
Rajat Agarwal (Mgr-Ops)
Travis Hollman (Pres)

HOLLOMAN CORPORATION
333 N Sam Houston Pkwy E Ste 600, Houston, TX 77060
Tel.: (281) 878-2600
Web Site:
　https://www.hollomancorp.com
Rev.: $67,000,000
Emp.: 30
Construction Services
N.A.I.C.S.: 237120
Collin Young (Exec VP)
Rodney Schwarzlose (VP-Utilities)
Mark Ellis Stevenson (Pres)

HOLLON OIL COMPANY
1300 Davenport St, Weslaco, TX 78596-6538
Tel.: (956) 968-9581
Web Site: https://www.hollonoil.com
Rev.: $24,000,000
Emp.: 22
Petroleum Products
N.A.I.C.S.: 424720
Bill C. Hollon (Pres)

HOLLSTADT & ASSOCIATES, INC.
1333 Northland Dr Ste 220, Mendota Heights, MN 55120
Tel.: (952) 892-3660
Web Site: http://www.hollstadt.com
Year Founded: 1990
Management Consulting Services
N.A.I.C.S.: 541611
Molly Jungbauer (CEO)
Jim Jungbauer (Pres)
Maxine Thomas (Sr VP-Operations)
Grete Tiemeier (Vp-Client Svcs)
Billy Hanson (Vp-Bus Dev)
Kelly Jans (Acct Mgr)

HOLLY CITY DEVELOPMENT CORPORATION
1153 Holly Berry Lane, Millville, NJ 08332
Tel.: (856) 825-8860
Year Founded: 1998
Sales Range: $1-9.9 Million
Emp.: 90
Community Housing & Recreation Services
N.A.I.C.S.: 624110

Paul Dice (Exec Dir)
Mithcell Moore (CFO)
Heather Santoro (Dir-Programs)

HOLLY'S CUSTOM PRINT, INC.
1001 O'Neil Dr SE, Hebron, OH 43025　　　　　　　　　　OH
Tel.: (740) 928-2697
Web Site: https://hollysprint.com
Year Founded: 1982
Sales Range: $1-9.9 Million
Emp.: 20
Fiscal Year-end: 12/31/13
Commercial Printing, Lithographic
N.A.I.C.S.: 323111

HOLLYMATIC CORPORATION
600 E Plainfield Rd, Countryside, IL 60525-6914　　　　　　　　IL
Tel.: (708) 579-3700
Web Site: https://www.hollymatic.com
Year Founded: 1938
Sales Range: $50-74.9 Million
Emp.: 55
Food Processing Equipment Mfr
N.A.I.C.S.: 333241
James D. Azzar (Chm)
Gisela Metzgar (Mgr-Pur & Inventory Control)
Scott Ryder (Mgr-DP & Network Admin)
Stanley Skowronski (Mgr-Acctg)

HOLLYWOOD BRANDED INC.
110 Lomita St, El Segundo, CA 90245
Tel.: (310) 606-2030
Web Site:
　http://www.hollywoodbranded.com
Year Founded: 2007
Sales Range: $10-24.9 Million
Emp.: 10
N.A.I.C.S.: 541810
Stacy Jones (Exec VP)
Jake Stango (CFO)

HOLLYWOOD CHRYSLER PLYMOUTH INC.
2100 N State Rd 7, Hollywood, FL 33021-3805
Tel.: (954) 239-7493
Web Site:
　http://www.hollywoodchrysler jeep.com
Year Founded: 1987
Sales Range: $25-49.9 Million
Emp.: 100
New & Used Car Dealers
N.A.I.C.S.: 441110
Rene Ruiz (Dir-Used Car)
Ruel Forbes (Mgr-Bus Dev)
Ulysses Hines (Mgr-Get Ready)

HOLLYWOOD CLASSICS NETWORK, INC.
16520 Vintage St, North Hills, CA 91343
Tel.: (818) 832-1890
Web Site:
　http://www.hollywoodclassicsnet work.com
Sales Range: $1-4.9 Billion
Emp.: 6
Television Broadcast Network
N.A.I.C.S.: 516210
Paul Webb (Chm & CEO)

HOLLYWOOD ENTERTAINMENT EDU HOLDING, INC.
1875 Century Park E 6th Fl, Century City, CA 90067　　　　　　　DE
Tel.: (323) 998-7187
Year Founded: 2007
Emp.: 5
Holding Company
N.A.I.C.S.: 551112

Alan J. Bailey (CFO)
David Lau (CEO)
Hollis Liu (Pres & Sec)

HOLLYWOOD FOREIGN PRESS ASSOCIATION
646 N Robertson Blvd, West Hollywood, CA 90069
Tel.: (310) 657-1731　　　　　CA
Web Site: http://www.hfpa.org
Year Founded: 1982
Sales Range: $10-24.9 Million
Emp.: 66
Arts Promotion Services
N.A.I.C.S.: 711310
Chantal Dinnage (Mng Dir)
Gregory Goeckner (COO & Gen Counsel)
Ali Sar (Pres)
Anke Hofmann (VP)
Ruben Nepales (Sec)

HOLLYWOOD RENTALS PRODUCTION SERVICES LLC
12800 Soothill Blvd, Sylmar, CA 91342
Tel.: (818) 407-7800
Web Site:
　http://www.hollywoodrentals.com
Sales Range: $10-24.9 Million
Emp.: 100
Motion Picture Equipment Rental
N.A.I.C.S.: 532490
Kelly Koskella (Pres)
Victor Duran (Dir-Ops)

HOLLYWOOD SUPER MARKET INC.
2670 W Maple Rd, Troy, MI 48084
Tel.: (248) 643-6770
Web Site:
　https://www.hollywoodmarkets.com
Sales Range: $50-74.9 Million
Emp.: 400
Grocery Stores
N.A.I.C.S.: 424410
William D. Welch (Pres)
Kim Welch (Treas)
Denis Karolak (Mgr-Produce)

HOLLYWOOD TANNING SYSTEMS, INC.
11 Enterprise Ct, Sewell, NJ 08080-4112
Tel.: (856) 914-9090
Web Site:
　http://www.hollywoodtan.com
Sales Range: $10-24.9 Million
Emp.: 50
Tanning Salons
N.A.I.C.S.: 533110

HOLLYWOOD WOODWORK, INC.
1551 S 30th Ave, Hollywood, FL 33020
Tel.: (954) 920-5009　　　　　FL
Web Site:
　http://www.hollywoodwoodwork.com
Year Founded: 1967
Sales Range: $10-24.9 Million
Emp.: 170
Custom-Made Woodwork Products Mfr
N.A.I.C.S.: 321918
Yves Desmarais (Chm)

HOLM AUTOMOTIVE CENTER
2005 N Buckeye, Abilene, KS 67410
Tel.: (785) 347-5029
Web Site: https://www.holmauto.com
Sales Range: $10-24.9 Million
Emp.: 40
New Car Retailer
N.A.I.C.S.: 441110

Corey Neufeld (Mgr-Fin & Insurance)
Gary Hasselman (Dir-Fixed Ops)
Matt Holm (Gen Mgr-Sls)
Pat Magee (Mgr-Sls)
Darwin Alderson (Controller)
Brad Signer (Mgr-Parts Dept)
Eric Murk (Mgr-Collision Center)

HOLMAN AUTOMOTIVE GROUP, INC.
4001 Leadenhall Rd, Mount Laurel, NJ 08052
Tel.: (856) 663-5200　　　NJ
Web Site:
　http://www.holmanauto.com
Year Founded: 1924
Sales Range: $1-4.9 Billion
Emp.: 2,700
Holding Company; New & Used Car Dealerships Owner & Operator; Engine & Transmission Rebuilding Services; Automobile Rental & Truck Leasing Services; Vehicle Sales Financing
N.A.I.C.S.: 551112
Carl A. Ortell (Vice Chm)
Glenn A. Gardner (COO-Retail Ops Grp)
Laura Carlisle (CFO)
Matt Newell (Sr VP-Legal)
Petter Witt (Sr VP-After Sls)
Craig Neuber (Sr VP-Dealership Ops)
Rick Deeck (Sr VP-Mktg)
Rick Tousaw (CMO)
Craig Balfour (VP-Mktg)
Anthony Foursha (Exec VP-Sls & Svc Excellence)
Pete Dondlinger (Pres-Mfg & Distr)
Chris Conroy (CEO)
Bob White (Pres-Fleet & Mobility)
Jarrod Phipps (CIO & Exec VP)
Mindy Holman (Chm)
George Athan III (Sr VP-Dealership Ops)

Subsidiaries:

Auto Truck Group, LLC　　(1)
1420 Brewster Creek Blvd, Bartlett, IL 60103
Tel.: (630) 860-5600
Web Site: http://www.autotruck.com
Sales Range: $50-74.9 Million
Emp.: 500
Fiscal Year-end: 12/31/2014
Truck Bodies & Equipment
N.A.I.C.S.: 423830
E. James Dondlinger (Exec VP-Railroads)
Matt McGowan (Dir-Sls-Eastern Reg)
Jerry Cortese (Dir-Sls-Western Reg)
Sean Otterberg (Mgr-Special Projects)
Pete Dondlinger (Pres)
Brad Blanco (VP-IT, Fin & Admin)
Pam Bodzioch (Mgr-HR)
Jeff Mower (Dir-Railroad Sls)
Scott Walters (Mgr-Fleet Sls)
Corey Stanley (VP-Sls & Mktg)
Jeff Kinghoffer (Mgr-Fleet Sls-Midwest Territory)
Joe Foster (Dir-Natl Fleet Sls)
Moza Fay (Mgr-Vocational Fleet Sls)
Jim Looysen (Dir-Vocational Fleet Sls)
Rick Tousaw (Chief Comml Officer)

Automotive Rentals, Inc.　　(1)
4001 Leadenhall Rd, Mount Laurel, NJ 08054-1539
Tel.: (856) 778-1500
Web Site: http://www.arifleet.com
Sales Range: $100-124.9 Million
Emp.: 1,411
Fleet Leasing & Management Services
N.A.I.C.S.: 532120
Chris Conroy (Pres)
Frank Cardile (Sr VP-Ops & Supply Chain)
Marc Demoulin (Mng Dir-European Ops)
Gene Welsh (Sr VP-Sls & Mktg)
Gregory Raven (Mgr-Global Sls & Consultation)
Steve Haindl (CIO & Sr VP)
Bob White (COO & Exec VP)
Denise Wildish (Sr VP-Global Svc Excellence)

Subsidiary (Non-US):

ARI Financial Services, Inc.　　(2)
1270 Central Pkwy W Ste 500, Mississauga, L5C 4P4, ON, Canada　　(100%)
Tel.: (905) 803-8000
Web Site: http://www.arifleet.ca
Sales Range: $100-124.9 Million
Emp.: 250
Fleet Management Services
N.A.I.C.S.: 522320
Ben Cozza (Mgr-HR)

Holman Cadillac　　(1)
1200 Route 73 S, Mount Laurel, NJ 08054
Tel.: (856) 778-1000
Web Site: http://www.holmancadillac.com
Sales Range: $10-24.9 Million
Emp.: 90
New & Used Car Dealer
N.A.I.C.S.: 441110
Tom Murphy (Gen Mgr)

Kuni Enterprises, Inc.　　(1)
17800 SE Mill Plain Blvd Ste 190, Vancouver, WA 98683
Tel.: (360) 553-7350
Web Site: http://www.kuniauto.com
Emp.: 1,250
Holding Company; New & Used Auto Dealerships Owner & Operator
N.A.I.C.S.: 551112
Greg Goodwin (CEO)
Tony Harb (Gen Mgr)
Shawn Evans (Gen Mgr)
Kraig Quisenberry (Gen Mgr)
Jason Puga (Gen Mgr)
Gregg Stone (Gen Mgr)
Anthony Brownlee (Gen Mgr)
Ryan Watson (Gen Mgr)
Brian Nicholson (Gen Mgr)
Jamie Hampson (Gen Mgr)
Brad Castonguay (Gen Mgr)
John Coats (Gen Mgr)

Subsidiary (Domestic):

Kuni Denver Motors, LLC　　(2)
5150 S Quebec St, Greenwood Village, CO 80111
Tel.: (303) 798-9500
Web Site:
　http://www.kunilexusofgreenwoodvillage.com
New & Used Car Dealership
N.A.I.C.S.: 441110
Gregg Stone (Pres & Gen Mgr)
Jared Thaut (Dir-Fixed Ops)
Brian Sheridan (Mgr-Sls Experience)
Archer Goodman (Mgr-Fin Svcs)
Kelly Kennedy (Mgr-Svc)
Jeff Valley (Mgr-Svc Drive)
Ed Klap (Mgr-Parts)
Jared Heilmann (Mgr-Sls Experience)
Matthew Urland (Mgr-Sls Experience)
Chris Neira (Mgr-Sls & Inventory)
Anthony Banno (Gen Sls Mgr)

Kuni German Motors, LLC　　(2)
10999 SW Canyon Rd, Beaverton, OR 97005
Tel.: (503) 748-5400
Web Site: http://www.kunibmw.com
New & Used Car Dealer
N.A.I.C.S.: 441110
Jamie Hampson (Gen Mgr)
Lee Maclean (Gen Sls Mgr)
Jeff Cline (Mgr-Svc)
Jeff Harlan (Mgr-Parts)
Katy Baker (Controller)
Ryan Malone (Mgr-New BMW)
Willie Higgins (Mgr-Pre-Owned)
Danny Lucero (Sls Mgr)
Tyler Murdock (Sls Mgr)
Bryan Feely (Mgr-Sls Ops)
Shelby Preble (Dir-Fin)
Beni Jinar (Mgr-Fin)
Trevyn Ashley (Fin Mgr)
Jacob Ambert (Mgr-Fin)
Gary Mills (Mgr-Svc Dr)
Davion Blunt (Coord-Loaner)
Michael Dasso (Coord-Loaner)

Division (Domestic):

Kuni Auto Center　　(3)
3725 SW Cedar Hills Blvd, Beaverton, OR 97005
Tel.: (503) 928-5670

Web Site: http://www.kuniautocenter.com
New & Used Car Dealerships
N.A.I.C.S.: 441110
Ryon Johnson (Gen Sls Mgr)
Bryan Feely (Mgr-Sls Ops)
Marie Ashley (Mgr-Fin)

Subsidiary (Domestic):

Kuni Hubacher Motors, LLC　　(2)
2449 Fulton Ave, Sacramento, CA 95825
Tel.: (877) 591-4625
Web Site: http://www.kunichevycadillac.com
Retail New & Used Automobiles
N.A.I.C.S.: 441110
Brandi Armstrong (Mgr-Fin)

Leith Inc.　　(1)
5601 Capital Blvd, Raleigh, NC 27616
Tel.: (919) 876-5432
Web Site: http://www.leithcars.com
Sales Range: $50-74.9 Million
Emp.: 600
Car Dealership
N.A.I.C.S.: 441110
Michael J. Leith (Pres)
Linda Leith (CFO)
Jeff Cunningham (Controller)

HOLMAN DISTRIBUTION CENTER OF OREGON
2300 SE Beta St, Milwaukie, OR 97222
Tel.: (503) 652-1912
Web Site: http://www.holmanusa.com
Rev.: $10,234,485
Emp.: 600
General Warehousing
N.A.I.C.S.: 493110
Elizabeth Clark (Chm)
Robert Downie (Pres)

HOLMAN DISTRIBUTION CENTER OF WASHINGTON
22430 76th Ave S, Kent, WA 98032
Tel.: (253) 872-7140　　　WA
Web Site: http://www.holmandist.com
Year Founded: 1864
Sales Range: $10-24.9 Million
Emp.: 100
Operates General Warehousing
N.A.I.C.S.: 493110
Eric Ness (Controller)
Robert Downie Jr. (Pres)

HOLMAN'S INCORPORATED
6201 Jefferson St NE, Albuquerque, NM 87109
Tel.: (505) 343-0007
Web Site: https://www.holmans.com
Year Founded: 1955
Sales Range: $25-49.9 Million
Emp.: 60
Maps, Custom Maps, CAD/Surveying Supplies, Equipment, Drafting Supplies, Printer Media, Books & Scientific Calculators
N.A.I.C.S.: 459999
A.T. Trujillo (Pres)

HOLMES & ASSOCIATES LLC
126 W Sego Lily Dr Ste 250, Sandy, UT 84070
Tel.: (801) 572-6363
Web Site:
　http://www.holmeshomes.com
Sales Range: $10-24.9 Million
Emp.: 40
Single-Family Housing Construction
N.A.I.C.S.: 236115
Patrick Holmes (Pres)
Spencer Holmes (VP)

HOLMES BODY SHOP INC.
1095 E Colorado Blvd, Pasadena, CA 91106
Tel.: (626) 795-6447
Web Site:
　http://www.holmesbodyshop.com
Rev.: $26,850,000

Emp.: 70
Body Shop, Automotive
N.A.I.C.S.: 811121
Thomas V. Holmes (Owner)
Maxie Alwag (Gen Mgr)
Bruce Mott (Controller)
Stephanie Kelleher (Controller)

HOLMES COMPANY OF JACKSON
535 Old Hwy 49, Ridgeland, MS 39218
Tel.: (601) 932-1399
Rev.: $12,000,000
Emp.: 100
Trucking Except Local
N.A.I.C.S.: 484121
Martin E. Holmes (Pres)

HOLMES CONSTRUCTION CO. LP
7901 W 34th Ave, Amarillo, TX 79121
Tel.: (806) 356-8296
Web Site: http://www.holmes-construction.co.nz.com
Sales Range: $10-24.9 Million
Emp.: 100
Highway & Street Paving Contractor
N.A.I.C.S.: 237310
Jim Holmes (CEO)
Rory Farrar (VP)

HOLMES FOODS INC.
101 S Liberty Ave, Nixon, TX 78140
Tel.: (830) 582-1551
Web Site:
　http://www.holmesfoods.com
Rev.: $27,500,000
Emp.: 265
Poultry, Processed
N.A.I.C.S.: 311615
Becky Morris (Asst Controller)
Andrew Rodriguez (Asst Mgr)
Fred Barlow (Plant Mgr)
Paul Pettijohn (Mgr-Feed Mill Quality Assurance)
Rafael Romero (Asst Mgr-Hatchery)

HOLMES MOTORS, INC.
10651 Boney Ave, Biloxi, MS 39540
Tel.: (228) 392-4054
Web Site:
　http://www.holmesmotors.com
Rev.: $4,200,000
Emp.: 27
Used Car Dealers
N.A.I.C.S.: 441120

HOLMES MURPHY & ASSOCIATES, INC.
3001 Westown Pkwy, West Des Moines, IA 50266
Tel.: (515) 223-6800
Web Site:
　http://www.holmesmurphy.com
Sales Range: $25-49.9 Million
Emp.: 210
Insurance Services
N.A.I.C.S.: 524210
Gerald Johnson (Sr VP-Property Casualty)
Daniel T. Keough (Chm & CEO)
Dennis Bishop (Pres)
Craig E. Hansen (Sr VP-Bonds & Property Casualty)
Lori Wiederin (Sr VP-Employee Benefits)
Chris Boyd (Sr VP-Employee Benefits)
Wally Gomaa (Sr VP-Employee Benefits)
Doug Muth (Sr VP-Property Casualty)
Todd Bengford (Asst Exec-Surety)
Tim Jardine (Acct Exec)
Tom Stewart (Pres-Innovative Captive Strategies)
Charisse McCumber (Sr VP)

Holmes Murphy & Associates, Inc.—(Continued)

Jim Steinkamp (VP-Employee Benefits)
Brad Bierman (Sr VP-Employee Benefits)
Lauren Roth (VP-Avant)
Joe Tiernan (Acct Exec-Property Casualty)
Susan Hatten (Sr Mgr-Corp Community Engagement)
Travis Brashear (VP-Employee Benefits)
Shawn Quildon (Asst VP & Dir-Client Svc-Employee Benefits)
Steve Miller (Acct Exec-Employee Benefits)
Jim Holder (VP-Employee Benefits)
Don Harrison (VP-Bus Dev-South & Central Texas)
Quinton Leith (Chief Strategic Investment Officer)
Dave Ashton (CIO)
John A. Hurley II (Pres-Property Casualty Brokerage Svcs)

HOLMES OIL COMPANY INC.
100 Europa Dr Ste 550, Chapel Hill, NC 27517
Tel.: (919) 929-9979
Web Site: http://www.holmesoil.net
Sales Range: $25-49.9 Million
Emp.: 200
Convenience Stores, Independent
N.A.I.C.S.: 445131
Edward S. Holmes Jr. (Pres)
Rodney Reade Jr. (Sr VP)

HOLMGREN & ASSOCIATES
1900 Mountain Blvd, Oakland, CA 94611
Tel.: (510) 339-2121
Web Site: http://www.mortgageholmgren.com
Year Founded: 1989
Sales Range: Less than $1 Million
Emp.: 14
Mortgage Banker
N.A.I.C.S.: 522292
John K. Holmgren (Owner & Pres)

HOLMQUIST FEEDMILL INC.
232 N Main, Trenary, MI 49891
Tel.: (906) 446-3326
Year Founded: 1953
Wood Products Mfr
N.A.I.C.S.: 321999
Sharon Boyer (Owner)
Subsidiaries:

Trenary Wood Products (1)
232 N Main, Trenary, MI 49891
Tel.: (906) 446-3325
Web Site:
http://www.trenarywoodproducts.com
Wood Products Mfr
N.A.I.C.S.: 321999

HOLMQUIST LUMBER CO.
200 N Logan Ave, Oakland, NE 68045
Tel.: (402) 685-5641
Year Founded: 1883
Sales Range: $75-99.9 Million
Emp.: 4
Distr of Building Materials
N.A.I.C.S.: 444110
Cal Anderson (Co-Owner)
Tim Anderson (Co-Owner)

HOLOGENIX, LLC
1112 Montana Ave Suite 13, Santa Monica, CA 90403
Web Site: http://www.celliant.com
Year Founded: 2003
Sales Range: $1-9.9 Million
Emp.: 17

Develops Textile for Bedding, Clothing & Veterinary Products with Proprietary Ingredients to Enhance Tissue Oxygen Levels for Athletic Performance, Sleep & Wellness
N.A.I.C.S.: 314999
Seth Casden (CEO)
Bill Werlin (Chm)
David Horinek (Founder)

HOLOGRAM USA NETWORKS INC.
342 N Canon Dr, Beverly Hills, CA 90210
Web Site:
http://www.hologramusa.com
Year Founded: 2014
Sales Range: Less than $1 Million
Emp.: 10
Video Streaming Services
N.A.I.C.S.: 512120
Alki David (Founder, Chm & CEO)
Nick Kutovyy (CTO)
Manuel Nelson (Head-Legal Affairs)

HOLSTEIN ASSOCIATION USA, INC.
1 Holstein Pl, Brattleboro, VT 05302-0808
Tel.: (802) 254-4551
Web Site:
https://www.holsteinusa.com
Year Founded: 1885
Dairy Cattle Breed Association
N.A.I.C.S.: 813990
Barbara Casna (CFO)

HOLSTON ELECTRIC COOPERATIVE INC.
1200 W Main St, Rogersville, TN 37857-2444
Tel.: (423) 272-8821
Web Site:
https://www.holstonelectric.com
Year Founded: 1940
Sales Range: $50-74.9 Million
Emp.: 65
Provider of Electric Services
N.A.I.C.S.: 221122
Larry E. Elkins (Gen Mgr)
Otis Munsey (Pres)
Danny Cockreham (Treas & Sec)
James Sandlin (Gen Mgr)

HOLSTON GASES INC.
545 Baxter Ave, Knoxville, TN 37921
Tel.: (865) 573-1917
Web Site:
https://www.holstongases.com
Year Founded: 1958
Sales Range: $25-49.9 Million
Emp.: 250
Chemical & Industrial Machinery
N.A.I.C.S.: 424690
Robert Anders (CEO)
Tammy White (Controller)
Steve Bowyer (Dir-IS)
Eric Zumbrun (Mgr-Chattanooga)

HOLSTON UNITED METHODIST HOME FOR CHILDREN
404 Holston Dr, Greeneville, TN 37743
Tel.: (423) 638-4171
Web Site:
https://www.holstonhome.org
Year Founded: 1946
Sales Range: $10-24.9 Million
Emp.: 247
Child & Family Care Services
N.A.I.C.S.: 624190
Nancy P. Casson (Vice Chm)
Debra B. Oldenberg (Sec)
Jeffrey J. Monson (Treas)
Bryan A. Jackson (Vice Chm)

HOLT & BUGBEE COMPANY
1600 Shawsheen St, Tewksbury, MA 01876
Tel.: (978) 851-7201
Web Site:
https://www.holtandbugbee.com
Rev.: $44,778,532
Emp.: 122
Lumber: Rough, Dressed & Finished
N.A.I.C.S.: 423310

HOLT & HOLT, INC.
1286 Hawthorne Ave SE, Smyrna, GA 30080-2134
Tel.: (770) 432-9184
Sales Range: $10-24.9 Million
Emp.: 200
Plastering Services
N.A.I.C.S.: 238310
Elizabeth Kellogg (Controller)

HOLT CAT COMPANY OF TEXAS INC.
3302 SWW White Rd, San Antonio, TX 78222-4830
Tel.: (210) 648-1111
Web Site: http://www.holtcat.com
Year Founded: 1961
Sales Range: $100-124.9 Million
Emp.: 1,800
Construction & Mining Machinery
N.A.I.C.S.: 532412
Dave Harris (VP & Gen Mgr-Machine Sls)
Ron Craft (Gen Mgr-Svc-Machines)
John Meyer (Mgr-Sls-San Antonio)
J. K. Baxter (Mgr-Fin Mktg)
Guy Clumpner (VP-HR)
Corinna Holt Richter (Pres & Chief Admin Officer)
Peter John Holt (Exec VP & Gen Mgr)
Jim Campbell (Sr Dir-Pub Affairs)
David Reynolds (Mgr-Svc-Irving)
Gary Matheaus (Supvr-Field Svcs-San Antonio)
Larry Wright (Mgr-Technical Svcs-Irving)
Bert Fulgium (Sr VP-Product Support)

HOLT CONSTRUCTION CORP.
50 E Washington Ave, Pearl River, NY 10965
Tel.: (845) 735-4054
Web Site: https://www.holtcc.com
Year Founded: 1919
Sales Range: $10-24.9 Million
Emp.: 30
Industrial Buildings & Warehouses
N.A.I.C.S.: 236115
Terry Allerton (Pres)
Dennis Berg (CFO & VP)
Matt Anselmi (Controller)
Phil Stiller (VP)

HOLT ELECTRIC INC.
1515 Walnut Rdg Dr, Hartland, WI 53029
Tel.: (262) 369-7100
Web Site: http://www.holtelectric.com
Year Founded: 1892
Sales Range: $10-24.9 Million
Emp.: 100
Electrical Apparatus & Equipment Distr
N.A.I.C.S.: 423610
Tom Eisman (Pres)
Mark A. Martin (Acct Mgr)
Cary Kottke (Mgr-Automation)
Jim Lisicki (VP-Ops)

HOLT HOSIERY MILLS, INC.
733 Koury Dr, Burlington, NC 27215
Tel.: (336) 227-1431
Web Site: http://www.holthosiery.com
Year Founded: 1947

Sales Range: $75-99.9 Million
Emp.: 100
Womens Hosiery Mfr
N.A.I.C.S.: 315120
Rusty Holt (Pres)
Ken Bennett (Controller)

HOLT INTERNATIONAL CHILDREN'S SERVICES
250 Country Club Rd, Eugene, OR 97401
Tel.: (541) 687-2202
Web Site:
https://www.holtinternational.org
Year Founded: 1971
Sales Range: $10-24.9 Million
Emp.: 156
Child Care & Development Services
N.A.I.C.S.: 624110
Lisa Vertulfo (VP-Adoption Svcs)
Kevin Sweeney (VP-Fin)
Susan Soonkeum Cox (VP-Policy & Advocacy)
Daniel Smith (Pres & CEO)
Derek Parker (Chm)

HOLT LUMBER INC.
1916 S Cherry Ave, Fresno, CA 93721-1088
Tel.: (559) 233-3291
Web Site: http://www.holtlumber.com
Sales Range: $10-24.9 Million
Emp.: 32
Lumber & Other Building Materials
N.A.I.C.S.: 423310
Tom Powers (Sec)
Veronica Fernandez (CFO)
Jack Holt (Pres)

HOLT MOTOR INC.
245 Cokato St W, Cokato, MN 55321
Tel.: (320) 286-2176
Web Site: http://www.holtmotors.com
Year Founded: 1936
Rev.: $14,000,000
Emp.: 65
Owner & Operator of Car Dealerships
N.A.I.C.S.: 441110
Greg Holt (Owner)

HOLT MOTORS, INC.
245 Cokato St W, Cokato, MN 55321-4654
Tel.: (320) 204-5223
Web Site:
https://www.holtmotors.com
Sales Range: $10-24.9 Million
Emp.: 45
Car Whslr
N.A.I.C.S.: 441110
Greg Holt (Owner)

HOLT OF CALIFORNIA INC.
7310 Pacific Ave, Pleasant Grove, CA 95668
Tel.: (916) 991-8200
Web Site: http://www.holtca.com
Year Founded: 1931
Sales Range: $50-74.9 Million
Emp.: 450
Industrial Machinery & Equipment Mfr
N.A.I.C.S.: 423810
Ron Monroe (Exec VP-Earthmoving & Construction)

HOLT TEXAS, LTD.
9601 S IH 35 Frontage Rd, Austin, TX 78744
Tel.: (512) 282-2011
Web Site: http://www.holtcat.com
Industrial Machinery Sales & Rental Services
N.A.I.C.S.: 532490
Peter J. Holt (CEO)

Subsidiaries:

Sullair of Houston, Inc.   **(1)**
8640 Panair St, Houston, TX 77061
Tel.: (713) 941-2800
Web Site: http://www.sullairhouston.com
Rev.: $7,333,333
Emp.: 30
Air & Gas Compressor Mfr
N.A.I.C.S.: 333912
Brad Fish *(Pres)*
Steve Metcalf *(Mgr-Parts)*

HOLT'S CIGAR HOLDINGS, INC.
12270 Townsend Rd, Philadelphia, PA 19154-1203
Tel.: (215) 676-8778   **DE**
Web Site: https://www.holts.com
Sales Range: $25-49.9 Million
Emp.: 200
Wholesalers of Cigars
N.A.I.C.S.: 459991
Robert G. Levin *(Chm, Pres & CEO)*
Nadia Trowbridge *(CFO)*
Maryanne Pentz *(VP-Admin)*
Sathya Levin *(Sec & Exec VP)*

HOLTEC INTERNATIONAL
1 Holtec Blvd, Marlton, NJ 08104
Tel.: (856) 797-0900
Web Site:
   https://www.holtecinternational.com
Year Founded: 1986
Sales Range: $10-24.9 Million
Emp.: 60
Provider of Research & Development
N.A.I.C.S.: 541330
Kris P. Singh *(Pres & CEO)*

HOLTHOUSE CARLIN VAN TRIGT LLP
11444 W Olympic Blvd Fl 11, Los Angeles, CA 90064-1500
Tel.: (310) 566-1900
Web Site: http://www.hcvt.com
Sales Range: $10-24.9 Million
Emp.: 300
Certified Public Accountants
N.A.I.C.S.: 541211
Greggory J. Hutchins *(Partner-Tax)*
James S. Carlin *(Partner)*
Philip J. Holthouse *(Partner)*
Joshua Wilson *(Principal)*
David L. Bierhorst *(Partner)*
Benjamin H. Shiao *(Partner)*
David O. Erard *(Partner)*
Jason A. Flashberg *(Partner)*
Julie Miller *(Partner)*
Kevin Cordano *(Partner)*
Nicholas A. Vinolus *(Partner)*
Curt Giles *(Partner-Intl Tax)*
Michele Carter *(Partner-Intl Tax)*
Doris Yau *(Principal)*
Eda Marin *(Principal)*
Felix Shapiro *(Principal)*
Jared Maclean *(Principal)*
Eckhard Walter *(Partner)*
Kei Morita *(Principal)*
Yan Zhang *(Principal)*
David Nowak *(Principal)*
Matthew Diesenbruch *(Principal)*
Hans Gustafsson *(Partner-Tax)*
Kyle Sakamoto *(Principal)*
John Samtoy *(Principal)*
Morris Zlotowitz *(Partner)*
Mark S. Yamamoto *(Principal)*
Michael Korbekian *(Principal)*
Sam Bachstein *(Partner)*
Rosario Bobadilla Farias *(Principal)*
Christopher Gays *(Principal)*
Cindy A. Cooper *(Principal)*
Eniko Earley *(Principal)*
Gina A. Ballard *(Principal)*
Greg Altman *(Principal)*
Jayson Duhn *(Principal-Private Equity Indus Sector)*

Jeffrey Desgroseilliers *(Principal)*
Kimberly Hastings *(Principal)*
Tom Firestone *(Principal)*

HOLTON COMMUNITY HOSPITAL
1110 Columbine Dr, Holton, KS 66436
Tel.: (785) 364-2116   **KS**
Web Site:
   http://www.holtonhospital.com
Year Founded: 1997
Sales Range: $10-24.9 Million
Emp.: 179
Health Care Srvices
N.A.I.C.S.: 622110
Carrie Saia *(CEO)*
Richard Lake *(Vice Chm)*
Alex Gilliland *(Treas)*
Margaret Pagel *(Sec)*

HOLTON SENTIVAN + GURY
7 E Skippack Pike, Ambler, PA 19002
Tel.: (215) 619-7600   **PA**
Web Site: http://www.hsgadv.com
Year Founded: 1983
Rev.: $24,500,000
Emp.: 10
Advertising Services
N.A.I.C.S.: 541810
Jack Holton *(CEO)*
Glenn Gury *(Dir-Creative)*
Bob Peischel *(Assoc Dir-Creative)*
Drew Sentivan *(Head-Art & Interactive)*

HOLTZMAN OIL CORP.
5534 N Main St, Mount Jackson, VA 22842-9508
Tel.: (540) 477-3131   **VA**
Web Site:
   https://www.holtzmancorp.com
Year Founded: 1972
Sales Range: $10-24.9 Million
Emp.: 300
Petroleum Products
N.A.I.C.S.: 424720
William B. Holtzman *(Founder)*
Richard L. Koontz Jr. *(Pres)*

Subsidiaries:

Holtzman Propane LLC   **(1)**
5534 Main St, Mount Jackson, VA 22842   **(100%)**
Tel.: (540) 465-9200
Web Site: http://www.holtzman.com
Sales Range: $10-24.9 Million
Emp.: 30
Petroleum Products
N.A.I.C.S.: 457210
Todd Holtzman *(Mgr)*

Valley Ice, LLC   **(1)**
PO Box 41, Mount Jackson, VA 22842
Tel.: (540) 477-4447
Web Site: http://www.valleyice.net
Ice Mfr
N.A.I.C.S.: 312113
Willam Holtzman *(CEO)*

HOLY CROSS ENERGY
3799 Hwy 82, Glenwood Springs, CO 81602
Tel.: (970) 945-5491   **CO**
Web Site: https://www.holycross.com
Year Founded: 1939
Sales Range: $200-249.9 Million
Emp.: 175
Co-Op; Distribution of Electric Power
N.A.I.C.S.: 221122
Del Worley *(CEO)*

HOLY NAME MEDICAL CENTER
718 Teaneck Rd, Teaneck, NJ 07666
Tel.: (201) 833-3000   **NJ**
Web Site: https://www.holyname.org
Year Founded: 1958

Sales Range: $300-349.9 Million
Emp.: 2,694
Health Care Srvices
N.A.I.C.S.: 621610
Sheryl Slonim *(Chief Nursing Officer & Exec VP-Patient Care Svcs)*
Adam Jarrett *(Chief Medical Officer & Exec VP)*
Edwin H. Ruzinsky *(Treas)*
Ronald White *(Pres-Medical Staff)*
Joseph A. Frascino *(Vice Chm)*
John M. Geraghty *(Chm)*
Michael Maron *(Pres & CEO)*
Ryan Kennedy *(CFO & VP)*
Kristen L. Silberstein *(Chief Experience Officer & VP-Patient Engagement)*
Michael Skvarenina *(CIO & VP-IT)*
Sean O'Rourke *(VP-Admin)*
Celeste A. Oranchak *(VP-Dev)*
Steven L. Mosser *(VP-Facilities Mgmt)*
Richard Van Eerde *(VP-Fin)*
Manny Gonzalez *(VP-HR)*
Maryann Kicenuik *(VP-Legal Affairs)*
Deborah Zayas *(VP-Nursing)*
Catherine A. V. Yaxley *(VP-Plng & Govt Affairs)*

HOLYOKE GAS & ELECTRIC DEPARTMENT
99 Suffolk St, Holyoke, MA 01040-4457
Tel.: (413) 536-9300
Web Site: https://www.hged.com
Year Founded: 1902
Sales Range: $25-49.9 Million
Emp.: 141
Provider of Electric Services
N.A.I.C.S.: 221210
James Lavelle *(Mgr)*
James Sutter *(Commissioner)*
John Fitzpatrick *(Engr-Electrical)*

HOLYOKE NEWS CO. INC.
720 Main St, Holyoke, MA 01040
Tel.: (413) 534-4537
Web Site:
   https://www.bookprincipal.com
Sales Range: $10-24.9 Million
Emp.: 99
Magazines,Books & Newspapers Distr
N.A.I.C.S.: 424920
Amir Evan *(Pres)*
Michelle Nowak *(Dir-Ops)*
Dan Berry *(VP-Mktg)*

HOLZ MOTORS, INC.
5961 S 108th Pl, Hales Corners, WI 53130-2501
Tel.: (414) 425-2400   **WI**
Web Site: http://www.holzmotors.com
Year Founded: 1914
Sales Range: $125-149.9 Million
Emp.: 200
New & Used Automobile Dealership
N.A.I.C.S.: 441110
Douglas Nalbert *(VP & Gen Mgr)*
Pam Nerby *(Controller)*
Jake Polinski *(Dir-Comml)*
Jennifer Fliss *(Dir-F&I Dept)*
Darlene Loch *(Dir-New Vehicle Dept)*
Chad Kallies *(Dir-Parts Dept)*
Ken Marquardt *(Dir-Pre-Owned Dept)*
Kevin Drury *(Dir-Svc Dept)*
Don Byington *(Mgr-Bus)*
Allen Johnson *(Mgr-Bus)*
Naomi Rueda *(Mgr-Bus)*
Ted Powell *(Mgr-New Car Sls)*
Harry Diament *(Mgr-Pre-Owned Sls)*

HOLZER HEALTH SYSTEM
100 Jackson Pike, Gallipolis, OH 45631-1560
Tel.: (740) 446-5000   **OH**

Web Site: https://www.holzer.org
Year Founded: 1909
Sales Range: $50-74.9 Million
Healtcare Services
N.A.I.C.S.: 622110
Brent A. Saunders *(Chm)*
Michael R. Canady *(CEO)*

HOLZHAUER AUTO & TRUCK SALES, INC.
17933 Holzhauer Auto Mall Dr, Nashville, IL 62263
Tel.: (618) 327-8837
Web Site:
   https://www.holzhauers.com
Sales Range: $25-49.9 Million
Emp.: 60
Automobiles, New & Used
N.A.I.C.S.: 441110
Brad Holzhauer *(Co-Owner)*
Allen Holzhauer *(Co-Owner)*

HOM FURNITURE, INC.
10301 Woodcrest Dr NW, Minneapolis, MN 55433-6519
Tel.: (736) 767-3600   **MN**
Web Site:
   http://www.homfurniture.com
Year Founded: 1981
Sales Range: $150-199.9 Million
Emp.: 1,000
Furniture Stores Owner & Operator
N.A.I.C.S.: 449110
Rod Johansen *(Pres & CEO)*

Subsidiaries:

Gabberts Design Studio & Fine Furnishings   **(1)**
3105 Galleria, Minneapolis, MN 55435-2536
Tel.: (952) 927-1500
Web Site: http://www.gabberts.com
Sales Range: $50-74.9 Million
Emp.: 550
Retailer of Home Furnishings
N.A.I.C.S.: 449110
Becky Lepley *(Gen Mgr)*

Seasonal Concepts Inc.   **(1)**
10301 Woodcrest Dr NW, Coon Rapids, MN 55433
Tel.: (763) 767-3700
Web Site: http://www.homfurniture.com
Sales Range: $50-74.9 Million
Emp.: 350
Furniture & Christmas & Home Accessories
N.A.I.C.S.: 449110
Wayne Johansen *(Founder & Chm)*

HOMAC MANUFACTURING COMPANY INC.
12 Southland Rd, Ormond Beach, FL 32174-3002
Tel.: (386) 677-9110   **NJ**
Web Site: http://www.homac.com
Year Founded: 1963
Sales Range: $25-49.9 Million
Emp.: 618
Current-Carrying Wiring Devices Mfr
N.A.I.C.S.: 335931
Mark Hammer *(VP-Mktg & Sls)*
Andy Chaguaceda *(Intl Sls Mgr)*
Jim Vinciguerra *(Natl Sls Mgr-Construction)*
Gerhard Schwebler *(Natl Sls Mgr)*

HOMAN AUTO SALES, INC.
240 Gateway Dr, Waupun, WI 53963
Tel.: (920) 324-3585
Web Site:
   https://www.homanauto.com
Sales Range: $10-24.9 Million
Emp.: 22
Automobiles, New & Used
N.A.I.C.S.: 441110
Steve Homan *(Controller)*
Dan Giove *(Gen Mgr-Sls)*
Mark Homan *(Pres)*

Homan Lumber Mart, Inc.—(Continued)

HOMAN LUMBER MART, INC.
1650 W Lusher Ave, Elkhart, IN
46517-1420
Tel.: (574) 293-6695   IN
Web Site:
    https://www.homanlumber.com
Year Founded: 1951
Sales Range: $75-99.9 Million
Emp.: 50
Wholesale Distributor of Lumber &
Other Building Materials
N.A.I.C.S.: 423310
Rita Stephan (Controller)

HOMAX OIL SALES INC.
605 S Poplar St, Casper, WY 82601
Tel.: (307) 237-5800
Web Site: https://www.homaxoil.com
Rev.: $14,964,486
Emp.: 50
Gasoline
N.A.I.C.S.: 424720
Michael Dwyer (Mgr-Transportation)

HOME & GARDEN PARTY, LTD.
2938 Brown Rd, Marshall, TX 75672
Tel.: (903) 935-4197
Web Site:
    http://www.celebratinghome.com
Year Founded: 1974
Sales Range: $25-49.9 Million
Emp.: 350
Direct Selling Establishments
N.A.I.C.S.: 423220
Steve Carlile (Co-Founder & CEO)
Penny Carlile (Co-Founder & Pres)

HOME ACRES BUILDING SUP-PLY CO., LLC
5203 Division Ave S, Grand Rapids,
MI 49548-5605
Tel.: (616) 534-4903   MI
Web Site: http://www.homeacres.com
Year Founded: 1923
Sales Range: $50-74.9 Million
Drywall, Insulation & Other Construc-
tion Supplies Dealer
N.A.I.C.S.: 444180
Grant R. Ellis (CEO)
Jeff Serba (Mgr)
Jonker Jerry (Chm)
Kirby Thompson (VP-Sls)
Jordon Anderson (Reg Mgr-Sls)
Peter Boers (Mgr-IT)

HOME APPLIANCE MART INC.
2023 W Stadium Blvd, Ann Arbor, MI
48103
Tel.: (734) 665-8653   MI
Web Site: http://www.big-
    georges.com
Year Founded: 1959
Sales Range: $25-49.9 Million
Emp.: 70
Household Products Mfr
N.A.I.C.S.: 449210
Abbud Bishar (Pres)
Mark Bishar (VP)
Ramsey Bishar (CFO)

HOME ATTENDANT SERVICE OF HYDE PARK
1273 53rd St, Brooklyn, NY 11219
Tel.: (718) 972-5300   NY
Year Founded: 1981
Sales Range: $25-49.9 Million
Emp.: 1,151
Elder Care Services
N.A.I.C.S.: 624120
Jonathan Redner (Exec Dir)

HOME BANCGROUP, INC.

900 N Federal Hwy, Hallandale
Beach, FL 33009
Tel.: (954) 458-2626
Bank Holding Company
N.A.I.C.S.: 551111
Scott F. Rosenberg (CEO)

Subsidiaries:

Home Federal Bank of
Hollywood   (1)
900 N Federal Hwy, Hallandale, FL 33009
Tel.: (954) 929-2265
Web Site: http://www.homefed.bank
Sales Range: $1-9.9 Million
Emp.: 16
Commercial Banking Services
N.A.I.C.S.: 522110
Lana Perez (Branch Mgr)
Scott F. Rosenberg (CEO)

HOME BANK SB
59 W Washington St, Martinsville, IN
46151
Tel.: (765) 342-6695
Web Site:
    https://www.homebanksb.com
Year Founded: 1890
Sales Range: $10-24.9 Million
Emp.: 50
Savings & Loan Associations
N.A.I.C.S.: 522180
Lisa Arnold (COO)
Matthew Craney (Sr VP)
Scott Hines (VP)
Wade Phelps (VP & Mgr-SBA Lend-
ing)

HOME BUILDERS & SUPPLY CO. INC.
2000 Dickinson Ave, Greenville, NC
27834
Tel.: (252) 758-4151
Web Site:
    https://www.homebuildersnc.com
Sales Range: $10-24.9 Million
Emp.: 35
Lumber & Other Building Materials
N.A.I.C.S.: 423310
William G. Blount (Pres)
Penny Rasberry (Controller)

HOME CARE ASSISTANCE CORPORATION
148 Hawthorne Ave, Palo Alto, CA
94301
Tel.: (650) 462-6900
Web Site: http://www.homecareassis
tance.com
Year Founded: 2002
Sales Range: $25-49.9 Million
Emp.: 700
Women Healthcare Services
N.A.I.C.S.: 621610
Lily Sarafan (Founder & CEO)
Barbara Schuh (VP-Ops)
Debi Brown (Mgr-Employee Care-
Sacramento)
Ashley Mirone (VP-Bus Dev-Southern
California)
Megan Heinen (Dir-Mktg)
Matt Neal (VP-Corp Dev)
Grace Zavolock (Mgr-Mktg & Comm)
Michael Schantz (CFO)

HOME CARE CONNECT LLC
507 N New York Ave Ste 200, Winter
Park, FL 32789   FL
Web Site:
    http://www.homecareconnect.com
Year Founded: 2011
Sales Range: $25-49.9 Million
Emp.: 58
Health Care Srvices
N.A.I.C.S.: 621610
Teresa Williams (Co-Founder & CEO)
Vonesa Wenzel (Co-Founder & CMO)

Gail A. Kasmir (CFO)
Tim Rametta (CIO)
Cindy Hailey (Co-Founder & Exec
VP-Mktg)

HOME CARE SPECIALISTS, INC.
113 Neck Rd, Haverhill, MA 01835
Tel.: (978) 373-7771
Web Site: http://www.hcshme.com
Year Founded: 1979
Sales Range: $10-24.9 Million
Emp.: 92
Medical Equipment Rental
N.A.I.C.S.: 532283
William E. Desmarais (Owner)
Gary K. Rudis (Co-Owner)
Jason Morin (Mgr-Reimbursement)

HOME CENTER, INC.
300 Green Oaks Pkwy, Holly Springs,
NC 27540
Tel.: (919) 303-2406
Web Site:
    https://www.hchomecenter.com
Year Founded: 1974
Sales Range: $10-24.9 Million
Emp.: 50
Floor Coverings Whslr
N.A.I.C.S.: 449121
Johnie E. Deal (Pres)

HOME CITY ICE COMPANY INC.
6045 Bridgetown Rd, Cincinnati, OH
45248
Tel.: (513) 574-1800
Web Site:
    https://www.homecityice.com
Sales Range: $25-49.9 Million
Emp.: 20
Ice Cubes
N.A.I.C.S.: 312113
Tom Sedler (Pres)

HOME DECOR INNOVATIONS
9115 Harris Corners Pkwy Ste 350,
Charlotte, NC 28269
Tel.: (704) 421-7700
Sales Range: $125-149.9 Million
Emp.: 300
Hardware, Industrial Hardware, Hand
Tools, Door Operating Equip., Garage
Door Openers, Storage Systems Fas-
tening Tools & Fasteners, Entry &
Garage Doors, Industrial & Builders'
Products
N.A.I.C.S.: 449110

HOME DECOR LIQUIDATORS FURNITURE & FLOORING
4227 Pleasant Hill Rd, Johns Creek,
GA 30022
Tel.: (770) 381-6100
Web Site:
    http://www.homedecorliquida
tors.com
Year Founded: 1993
Sales Range: $10-24.9 Million
Emp.: 75
Other Home Furnishing Services
N.A.I.C.S.: 449129
Hilbert Margol (Dir-Adv)

HOME DESIGN OUTLET CEN-TER
400 County Ave, Secaucus, NJ
07094
Tel.: (201) 531-0502
Web Site:
    http://www.homedesignoutlet
center.com
Year Founded: 2004
Sales Range: $1-9.9 Million
Emp.: 13

Washroom Fixture & Furnishing Re-
tailer
N.A.I.C.S.: 449129
Volkan Agbas (Principal)
Tolga Akyatan (Mgr-Store)

HOME DESIGN STUDIO
714 NW County Rd 3, Byron, MN
55920
Tel.: (507) 424-1800
Web Site:
    http://www.homedesignstudio.com
Sales Range: $10-24.9 Million
Emp.: 50
Floor Covering Product Distr
N.A.I.C.S.: 449121
Kim Enerson (Gen Mgr)
Mike Thom (Mgr-Sls)

HOME ESSENTIALS & BE-YOND INC.
114 Pived Ln E, Edison, NJ 08837
Tel.: (732) 590-3600
Web Site:
    http://www.homeessentials.com
Sales Range: $25-49.9 Million
Emp.: 45
Manufacture & Seller Of Home Fur-
nishings
N.A.I.C.S.: 423220
Izidore Godinger (Pres)
Ruben Kenigsberg (CFO)
Timothy Young (Acct Mgr)
Jean Claude Ethier (Product Mgr)
Nancy Cabrey (Acct Mgr)

HOME ETC
4535 McEwen Rd, Dallas, TX 75244
Tel.: (972) 701-8802
Web Site: http://www.homeetc.net
Rev.: $15,000,000
Emp.: 25
Giftware & Home Decor Mfr & Distr
N.A.I.C.S.: 423220
Alex Tsao (COO)

HOME FEDERAL BANK OF TENNESSEE FSB
515 Market St, Knoxville, TN 37902
Tel.: (865) 546-0910
Web Site:
    http://www.homefederalbanktn.com
Year Founded: 1924
Sales Range: $75-99.9 Million
Emp.: 310
Federal Savings & Loan Associations
N.A.I.C.S.: 522180
David E. Sharp (Chm & CEO)
Dale A. Keasling (Pres)
Debra S. Smith (Sec & VP)
Terry Rowland (VP)
Cheryl Light (Sr VP)
Keith Akard (VP)
Jonathan Mayfield (Asst VP)
Patrick Abbott (VP)
Patrick Gass (VP)
Jason August (Asst VP-Loan Review)
Jodie Bull (Asst VP-Info Security)
Johnny Cliburn (Asst VP-IT)
Jason Cox (Asst VP-Concord)
Valerie Duncan (Asst VP-Comml
Banking)
Tracy Riggins (Asst VP-Internal Audit)
Bill Spierdowis (Asst VP-Comml
Banking)

HOME FOOD SERVICE OF PA
2092 Farragut Ave, Bristol, PA 19007
Tel.: (215) 788-3337
Web Site: http://www.foodgift.com
Sales Range: $10-24.9 Million
Emp.: 45
Frozen Food & Freezer Plans, Except
Meat
N.A.I.C.S.: 445110
A. John Passanante (Pres)

HOME FORWARD

135 SW Ash St, Portland, OR 97204-3540
Tel.: (503) 802-8300
Web Site:
https://www.homeforward.org
Year Founded: 1941
Sales Range: $25-49.9 Million
Emp.: 300
Housing Services
N.A.I.C.S.: 531110
Steven D. Rudman (Exec Dir)

HOME FRONT COMMUNICA-TIONS, LLC
1201 New York Ave NW Ste 900, Washington, DC 20005
Tel.: (202) 544-8400
Web Site:
https://www.teamsubjectmatter.com
Information Services
N.A.I.C.S.: 519290
Paul Frick (Partner)

Subsidiaries:

Elmendorf Strategies LLC   (1)
900 7th St NW Ste 750, Washington, DC 20001
Tel.: (202) 737-1010
Web Site: http://www.elmendorfryan.com
Specialty Trade Contractors
N.A.I.C.S.: 238990
Steve Elmendorf (Pres)

HOME FURNITURE COMPANY OF LAFAYETTE INC.
1351 Surrey St, Lafayette, LA 70501
Tel.: (337) 234-8578   LA
Web Site: https://www.homefurn.com
Year Founded: 1972
Sales Range: $10-24.9 Million
Emp.: 25
Furniture Retailer
N.A.I.C.S.: 449110
Randy Paul (Gen Mgr)
Lori Berwick (Controller)

Subsidiaries:

Home Furniture Co. of Lake Charles Inc.   (1)
1314 Ryan St, Lake Charles, LA 70601-5917
Tel.: (337) 243-4154
Web Site: http://www.homefurn.com
Sales Range: $10-24.9 Million
Furniture Retailer
N.A.I.C.S.: 449110
Doug Smith (CEO)

Home Furniture Company Inc.   (1)
909 W Pont Des Mouton, Lafayette, LA 70507
Tel.: (337) 291-7855
Web Site: http://www.homefurn.com
Furniture Retailer
N.A.I.C.S.: 449110
Larry Douming (Mgr)

HOME GROWN INDUSTRIES OF GEORGIA, INC.
5375 Drake Dr, Atlanta, GA 30336
Tel.: (404) 505-2801
Web Site:
http://www.mellowmushroom.com
Year Founded: 1974
Sales Range: $10-24.9 Million
Emp.: 55
Catering Services & Pizza Mfr
N.A.I.C.S.: 311991
David Danowitz (Dir-Ops)
Tammy Lucich (Mgr-Promos & Events)
Annica Kreider (VP-Brand Dev)
Richard Brasch (Pres & CEO)
Michael R. Nicholson (Pres)
Jeff Wiggins (CFO)
Mel O. Mushroom (Pres & CEO)

HOME HARDWARE CENTER

187 Sgt S Prentiss Dr, Natchez, MS 39120
Tel.: (601) 445-5352
Sales Range: $25-49.9 Million
Emp.: 200
Hardware Whslr
N.A.I.C.S.: 423710
Ann Kaiser (Office Mgr)

HOME HEALTH DEPOT, INC.
9245 N Meridian St Ste 200, Indianapolis, IN 46260
Tel.: (317) 333-6033
Web Site: http://www.hhdepot.com
Year Founded: 1998
Sales Range: $10-24.9 Million
Emp.: 119
Medical Equipment Distr
N.A.I.C.S.: 423450
David Hartley (Pres)
Kathleena Smith (CFO)
Jim Duncan (VP-Respiratory)
Retha Matthews (Mgr)

HOME HELPERS OF TAMPA
3902 Henderson Blvd Ste 202, Tampa, FL 33629
Tel.: (813) 412-7190
Web Site:
http://www.inhomecaretampafl.com
Year Founded: 2007
Sales Range: $10-24.9 Million
Emp.: 20
Women Healthcare Services
N.A.I.C.S.: 621610
Joe Wicker (Owner)

HOME INSTEAD SENIOR CARE
13323 California St, Omaha, NE 68154
Tel.: (402) 498-4466
Web Site:
http://www.homeinstead.com
Rev.: $10,600,000
Emp.: 105
Non-Medical Home Care Services for the Elderly
N.A.I.C.S.: 533110
Scott Dingfield (CMO)
Johnny Allen (Dir-Bus Dev)
Jeff Huber (CEO)
Jim Hood (Pres)

HOME INSTRUCTION FOR PARENTS OF PRESCHOOL YOUNGSTERS (HIPPY)
1221 Bishop St, Little Rock, AR 72202
Tel.: (501) 537-7726   NY
Web Site: http://www.hippyusa.org
Year Founded: 1991
Sales Range: $1-9.9 Million
Emp.: 200
Parenting Support Services
N.A.I.C.S.: 624190
Lia Lent (Exec Dir)
Teri Todd (Dir-Ops)
Linda Frank (Chm)
Mary Beth Salomone Testa (Vice Chm)
Matthew Bellew (Dir-Dev & Outreach)
John Gonzales (Founder)

HOME LINE FURNITURE IN-DUSTRIES INC.
2121 Wheatsheaf Ln, Philadelphia, PA 19137
Tel.: (215) 537-6400
Web Site:
http://www.homelinefurniture.com
Year Founded: 1964
Sales Range: $25-49.9 Million
Emp.: 360
Wholesale Distributor of Furniture
N.A.I.C.S.: 423210

HOME LOAN & INVESTMENT BANK
1 Home Loan Plz, Warwick, RI 02886-1764
Tel.: (401) 739-8800   RI
Web Site:
https://www.homeloanbank.com
Year Founded: 1977
Sales Range: $25-49.9 Million
Emp.: 75
State Commercial Banks
N.A.I.C.S.: 522180
John Murphy (Founder & Chm)
Brian Murphy (Pres)
Everett Barton (Mgr-Home Improvement Ops)
Chris Tibbetts (Acct Exec)
Mark McDonough (Mgr-Sls)

Subsidiaries:

Home Loan & Investment Bank FSB Inc.   (1)
1 Home Loan Plz, Warwick, RI 02886-1764
Tel.: (401) 739-8800
Web Site: http://www.homeloanbank.com
Sales Range: $50-74.9 Million
Emp.: 70
Federal Savings Institutions
N.A.I.C.S.: 522180
Brian Murphy (Pres)

HOME LUMBER & SUPPLY CO.
106 W 8th St, Ashland, KS 67831-0427
Tel.: (620) 635-2207
Web Site:
http://www.homelumbersupply.com
Year Founded: 1905
Sales Range: $10-24.9 Million
Emp.: 103
Lumber & Other Building Materials Distr
N.A.I.C.S.: 423310
John Humphreys (Pres & Gen Mgr)

HOME MARKET FOODS IN-CORPORATED
140 Morgan Dr, Norwood, MA 02062
Tel.: (781) 948-1500
Web Site:
https://www.homemarketfoods.com
Year Founded: 1957
Sales Range: $50-74.9 Million
Emp.: 150
Research & Development, Manufacture & Marketing of Retail Packaged Food & Meal Products
N.A.I.C.S.: 424420
Al DePoali (Dir-Quality Assurance)
Ryan Botelho (Coord-Parts)
Brian Corcoran (Dir-FP&A)
Corinne Schultz (Mgr-EHS)
Daniel Gunn (Mgr-Supply Chain)
Patty Carr (Mgr-Logistics)
Rebekah Mazur (Mgr-AR)
Hilary Simons (CFO)
Barry Southworth (Dir-Pur)
Sokly Saing (Engr-Indus)

Subsidiaries:

Freezer Queen Foods, Inc.   (1)
975 Fuhrmann Blvd, Buffalo, NY 14203
Tel.: (716) 826-2500
Sales Range: $50-74.9 Million
Frozen Prepared Foods Mfr
N.A.I.C.S.: 424420

HOME MEDICAL SERVICES LLC
555 S Washington St, Wichita, KS 67211
Tel.: (316) 265-4991
Web Site: http://www.via-christi.org
Rev.: $10,000,000
Emp.: 48

Provider of Medical Equipment Rental Services
N.A.I.C.S.: 621498

HOME NEWS ENTERPRISES, LLC
333 2nd St, Columbus, IN 47201
Tel.: (812) 379-5658   IN
Web Site: http://www.homenewsenter prises.com
Newspaper Publisher & Commercial Printing Services
N.A.I.C.S.: 513110
Jeffrey N. Brown (Pres)

Subsidiaries:

Brown County Democrat   (1)
147 E Main St, Nashville, IN 47448
Tel.: (812) 988-2221
Web Site: http://www.bcdemocrat.com
Sales Range: $1-9.9 Million
Emp.: 6
Newspaper Publishers
N.A.I.C.S.: 513110

Daily Journal   (1)
2575 N Morton St, Franklin, IN 46131
Tel.: (317) 736-2777
Web Site: http://www.dailyjournal.net
Newspaper Publishers
N.A.I.C.S.: 513110
Mike Brogdon (Mgr-IT)
Christina Cosner (Dir-Adv)
Steve Hood (Dir-Circulation)
Nicole Bingham (Coord-Ops)

Daily Reporter   (1)
22 W New Rd, Greenfield, IN 46140
Tel.: (317) 462-5528
Web Site: http://www.greenfieldreporter.com
Emp.: 150
Newspaper Publishers
N.A.I.C.S.: 513110
John Senger (Dir-Adv)
Andrea Mallory (Exec Dir)

The Republic   (1)
2980 N National Rd Ste A, Columbus, IN 47201
Tel.: (812) 372-7811
Web Site: http://www.therepublic.com
Newspaper Publishers
N.A.I.C.S.: 513110
Julie McClure (Editor)

The Tribune   (1)
100 Saint Louis Ave, Seymour, IN 47274
Tel.: (812) 522-4871
Web Site: http://www.tribtown.com
Sales Range: $10-24.9 Million
Emp.: 20
Newspaper Publishers
N.A.I.C.S.: 513110
Dondra Brown (Mgr-Creative Svcs)
Zach Spicer (Editor-Sports)
Melissa Missy Bane (Dir-Adv)
Gary McDonough (Mgr-Ops)
Paul Hart (Dir-Circulation)
Tammy Smith (Bus Mgr)

Times-Post   (1)
104 W High St, Pendleton, IN 46064
Tel.: (765) 778-2324
Web Site:
http://www.pendletontimespost.com
Newspaper Publishers
N.A.I.C.S.: 513110
Scott Slade (Editor)
Chuck Wells (Publr)
Karen Branham (Mgr-Circulation)
John Senger (Dir-Adv)

HOME NURSING AGENCY
201 Chestnut Ave, Altoona, PA 16601
Tel.: (814) 946-5411
Web Site:
https://www.homenursingagency.com
Year Founded: 1968
Rev.: $11,545,514
Emp.: 720
Visiting Nurse Services
N.A.I.C.S.: 561110
Pam Seasoltz (Dir-Dev)
Robert Packer (Pres & CEO)

Home of Economy Inc.—(Continued)

HOME OF ECONOMY INC.

1508 N Washington St, Grand Forks, ND 58203
Tel.: (701) 772-6611
Web Site:
  http://www.homeofeconomy.biz
Sales Range: $10-24.9 Million
Emp.: 150
Department Stores, Discount
N.A.I.C.S.: 455110
Wade Pearson (Pres)
Brian Cox (Controller)

HOME OF HOPE, INC

960 W Hope Rd, Vinita, OK 74301
Tel.: (918) 256-7825   OK
Web Site:
  http://www.homeofhope.com
Year Founded: 1968
Sales Range: $10-24.9 Million
Emp.: 587
Disability Assistance Services
N.A.I.C.S.: 624120
Dena Pitts (COO)
Ralph Richardson (CEO)

HOME OIL & GAS COMPANY INC.

300 Atkinson St, Henderson, KY 42420
Tel.: (270) 826-3925
Sales Range: $10-24.9 Million
Emp.: 20
Petroleum Bulk Stations
N.A.I.C.S.: 424710
Robert G. Crafton (VP)
James M. Crafton Jr. (Pres)

HOME OIL CO. INC.

5744 E US Hwy 84, Cowarts, AL 36321
Tel.: (334) 793-1544
Web Site:
  https://www.homeoilcompany.com
Rev.: $30,825,740
Emp.: 300
Operator of Convience Stores & Gasoline Stations
N.A.I.C.S.: 457120
Andy Shirley (VP)

HOME OIL COMPANY INCORPORATED

1515 River Rd S, Baton Rouge, LA 70802
Tel.: (225) 383-4445
Rev.: $10,500,000
Emp.: 13
Fuel Oil Dealers
N.A.I.C.S.: 457210
Prudence Bennett (Pres)

HOME PARAMOUNT PEST CONTROL COMPANIES

2011 Rockspring Rd, Forest Hill, MD 21050
Tel.: (410) 638-0800
Web Site:
  https://www.homeparamount.com
Rev.: $24,800,000
Emp.: 40
Pest Control Services
N.A.I.C.S.: 561710
Walter A. Tilley (Pres)

HOME PERFECT RESTORATION, INC.

PO Box 892105, Temecula, CA 92589
Tel.: (951) 303-1333
Web Site:
  http://www.homeperfectsocal.com
Year Founded: 2012
Sales Range: $1-9.9 Million
Commercial Cleaning Services

N.A.I.C.S.: 561720
Scott Peterson (Pres)

HOME RUN INN, INC.

1300 Internationale Pkwy, Woodridge, IL 60517
Tel.: (630) 783-9696
Web Site:
  http://www.homeruninnpizza.com
Year Founded: 1923
Sales Range: $10-24.9 Million
Emp.: 100
Frozen Specialty Food Mfr
N.A.I.C.S.: 311412
Jeanette Davila (VP-HR)
Mark Carlson (Pres)
Kevin Costello (VP-Sls & Fin)
George Hall (Mgr-Production)

HOME SERVICE OIL CO. INC.

6910 Front St, Barnhart, MO 63012-1508
Tel.: (636) 464-5266   MO
Web Site: https://www.hsoil.com
Year Founded: 1951
Sales Range: $25-49.9 Million
Emp.: 222
Heating Oil Dealer & Convenience Store Operator
N.A.I.C.S.: 457210
David E. Mangelsdorf (CEO)

Subsidiaries:

Home Service Oil Co. Inc. - Doniphan
Division   (1)
210 Frank St, Doniphan, MO 63621
Tel.: (573) 996-2155
Petroleum Product Distr
N.A.I.C.S.: 424720

Home Service Oil Co. Inc. - Poplar
Bluff Division   (1)
624 Ashcroft Rd, Poplar Bluff, MO 63901
Tel.: (573) 686-1171
Petroleum Product Distr
N.A.I.C.S.: 424720

Home Service Oil Co. Inc. - Reyno
Division   (1)
15236 Highway 67, Reyno, AR 72462
Tel.: (870) 769-2324
Petroleum Product Distr
N.A.I.C.S.: 424710

Mango Distributing Co. Inc.   (1)
6918 Front St, Barnhart, MO 63012-1508
Tel.: (636) 464-2121
Web Site: http://www.hsoil.com
Sales Range: $10-24.9 Million
Emp.: 12
Motor Vehicle Supplies & New Parts
N.A.I.C.S.: 423120
Tom Denman (Mgr)

HOME SERVICES SYSTEMS INC

27-40 Hoytt Ave S, Astoria, NY 11102
Tel.: (718) 396-5024   NY
Year Founded: 1977
Sales Range: Less than $1 Million
Emp.: 4
Hospice Care Services
N.A.I.C.S.: 621610
Georgianna Whyte (Dir-Patient Svcs)
Demetria Tsafaris (Sec)
Chris Pappas (VP)
Arthur Cheliotes (Treas)

HOME SOURCE INTERNATIONAL, INC.

1100 Westlake Pkwy SW, Atlanta, GA 30353
Tel.: (404) 682-9820
Web Site:
  http://www.homesourceinternational.com
Year Founded: 2000
Sales Range: $1-9.9 Million

Household Furnishing Distr, Retailer & Mfr
N.A.I.C.S.: 423220
Keith Sorgeloos (Founder, Pres & CEO)
Andrea Bruckner (VP-Sls)
Scott Sorgeloos (COO)
Mike Beard (CFO)
Christopher Bajenski (VP-e-Commerce)

HOME STATE BANCORP, INC.

40 Grant St, Crystal Lake, IL 60014
Tel.: (815) 459-2000   IL
Web Site: http://www.homestbk.com
Year Founded: 1983
Sales Range: $25-49.9 Million
Emp.: 167
Bank Holding Company
N.A.I.C.S.: 551111
Steven L. Slack (Pres & CEO)
Joseph J. Morrow (Chm)

Subsidiaries:

Home State Bank, N.A.   (1)
40 Grant St, Crystal Lake, IL 60014
Tel.: (815) 459-2000
Web Site: http://www.homestbk.com
Sales Range: $25-49.9 Million
Federal Savings Bank
N.A.I.C.S.: 522180
Steven L. Slack (Pres & CEO)
Joseph T. Morrow (Gen Counsel)
Robert L. Cormier Jr. (Sec)

HOME SWEET HOME HOLDINGS INC.

6111 S 228th St, Kent, WA 98032
Tel.: (253) 850-6111   NY
Web Site: http://www.petrohunt.com
Year Founded: 1986
Sales Range: $1-9.9 Million
Emp.: 100
Homefurnishings
N.A.I.C.S.: 551112

HOME TEAM SERVICES,LLC

PO Box 540671, Omaha, NE 68154
Tel.: (402) 505-3888   NE
Web Site:
  http://hometeamservicesllc.com
Emp.: 100
Holding Company
N.A.I.C.S.: 551112

HOME TELEPHONE COMPANY INC.

579 Stoney Landing Rd, Moncks Corner, SC 29461
Tel.: (843) 761-9101
Web Site: https://www.homesc.com
Sales Range: $10-24.9 Million
Emp.: 124
Telephone Communication, Except Radio
N.A.I.C.S.: 517121
Robert L. Helmly (Vice Chm & CEO)
Julie H. Forte (Dir-Customer Ops)
William S. Helmly (Pres & COO)
H. Keith Oliver (Sr VP-Corp Ops)
Patrick L. Archibald (Mgr-Info Svcs)
Judy S. Cronin (Dir-Sls & Bus Dev)
Denny V. Thompson (Dir-Admin Svcs)
Eddie McGriff (Dir-Plant Ops)
Gina T. Shuler (Dir-Mktg)
Luke Lapierre (Mgr-Bus Dev)
Thomas J. Higgins (Mgr-Installation & Repair)
Bernard D. Motte (Mgr-Plant Support)
Alan L. Smoak Jr. (Controller)
Robert P. Abbott Jr. (Dir-Engrg)
Victor L. Smith Jr. (Mgr-Installation & Repair)

HOME TOWN MORTGAGE INC.

1550 Audubon Rd, Chaska, MN 55318-9508
Tel.: (952) 368-7257   MN
Year Founded: 1995
Sales Range: $25-49.9 Million
Emp.: 125
Provider of Mortgage Services
N.A.I.C.S.: 522310

HOME TRENDS & DESIGN, INC.

3910 S Industrial Dr Ste 100, Austin, TX 78744
Tel.: (512) 804-5450
Web Site: http://www.htddirect.com
Year Founded: 2005
Sales Range: $1-9.9 Million
Emp.: 35
Designs, Manufactures & Imports Asian Furnishings
N.A.I.C.S.: 449110
Hank Cravey (Co-Founder & CEO)

Subsidiaries:

Cottonwood Trading, Inc.   (1)
9311 Broadway Ste 300, San Antonio, TX 78217
Tel.: (210) 805-0191
Sales Range: $1-9.9 Million
Emp.: 17
Furniture Retailer
N.A.I.C.S.: 449110
Peter Markwardt (Pres)

HOME-TECH CONSOLIDATED, INC.

6400 Techster Blvd, Fort Myers, FL 33966
Tel.: (239) 433-3344   FL
Web Site: https://www.home-tech.com
Year Founded: 1981
Sales Range: $10-24.9 Million
Emp.: 140
Plumbing, Heating & Air-Conditioning Contractor
N.A.I.C.S.: 238220
Kerri Bigelow (Mgr-Customer Svc)
Pam Marino (Mgr-Svc Ops)

HOME/LIFE SERVICES, INC.

1222 Avenue M Ste 306, Brooklyn, NY 11230
Tel.: (718) 257-6600   NY
Web Site:
  http://www.homelifeservices.org
Year Founded: 1995
Sales Range: $10-24.9 Million
Community Housing Services
N.A.I.C.S.: 624229
Susan Alter (Exec Dir)
Gerald Schreck (Exec Dir)
Riquelma Moreno (Reg Mgr)

HOMEBOY INDUSTRIES

130 W Bruno St, Los Angeles, CA 90012
Tel.: (323) 526-1254
Web Site: http://www.homeboy-industries.org
Year Founded: 2007
Retail Bakery Services
N.A.I.C.S.: 311811
S. J. Gregory Boyle (Founder & Exec Dir)
Thomas Vozzo (CEO)
Mary Ellen Burton (Dir-Program Svcs)
Shirley Torres (Chief Program Officer)
Maria Flores (Dir-Strategic Initiatives)

Subsidiaries:

Homeboy Electronics Recycling   (1)
1370 E 18th St, Los Angeles, CA 90021
Tel.: (323) 222-3322
Web Site: http://www.isidorerecycling.com
Nonhazardous Waste Treatment & Disposal
N.A.I.C.S.: 562219
Kabira Strokes (CEO)
Chris Zwicke (COO)

HOMEBRIDGE FINANCIAL SERVICES, INC.

194 Wood Ave S 9th Fl, Iselin, NJ 08830
Tel.: (732) 738-7100   NJ
Web Site:
   https://www.homebridge.com
Year Founded: 1989
Real Estate & Mortgage Loan Brokers
N.A.I.C.S.: 522310
Jamie Zeitz *(Mgr-Renovation Lending-Jacksonville South)*
Peter Norden *(CEO)*
Jeff Covin *(Branch Mgr-Birmingham)*
Brandy Whitmire *(Branch Mgr-Fin My Home)*
Christian Walsh *(Mgr-Market)*
David Wells *(Branch Mgr)*
Greg Walker *(Branch Mgr-Tampa)*
Scott Bowling *(Branch Mgr-Orlando)*
Steve Marshall *(Dir-Natl Renovation Bus Dev)*
Barbara Sica *(Mgr-East Divisional Reverse-Iselin Branch)*

Subsidiaries:

HomeBridge Financial Services, Inc.   (1)
6330 Sprint Pkwy Ste 450, Overland Park, KS 66211
Tel.: (913) 402-7232
Web Site: http://www.gocapwest.com
Mortgage Banker
N.A.I.C.S.: 522310

HomeBridge Financial Services, Inc. - Sherman Oaks   (1)
15301 Ventura Blvd Ste D210, Sherman Oaks, CA 91403
Tel.: (818) 306-5011
Web Site: http://www.homebridge.com
Mortgage Banker
N.A.I.C.S.: 522310

HOMECARE & HOSPICE OF THE VALLEY

1901 Grand Ave Ste 206, Glenwood Springs, CO 81601-4710
Tel.: (970) 930-6008   CO
Web Site: http://www.hchotv.org
Year Founded: 2008
Sales Range: $1-9.9 Million
Emp.: 111
Individual Support Services
N.A.I.C.S.: 624190
Kelly Locke *(Sr Dir-Medical)*
Hogan McWilliams *(Mgr-Private Duty)*
Chris McDowell *(Dir-Clinical)*
Steve Swanson *(CFO)*
John Quinn *(Dir-Dev)*
Mike Brown *(Vice Chm)*
Markey Butler *(Exec Dir)*
Peter Guy *(Chm)*
Laura Kornasiewicz *(Sec)*
Colleen Weiss Hanen *(Treas)*
Mike Brown *(Vice Chm)*
Peter Guy *(Chm)*
Laura Kornasiewicz *(Sec)*
Colleen Weiss Hanen *(Treas)*

HOMECARE PRODUCTS, INC.

700 Milwaukee Ave N, Algona, WA 98001-7408
Tel.: (253) 249-1108   WA
Web Site: http://www.ezaccess.com
Year Founded: 1984
Sales Range: $1-9.9 Million
Emp.: 90
Mobility Ramp & Vertical Platform Lift Manufacturers
N.A.I.C.S.: 333922

Subsidiaries:

Phillips Lift Systems, Inc.   (1)
103 Rushmore Dr, Pickens, SC 29671-9307
Web Site: http://www.toiletliftchair.com

Services for the Elderly & Persons with Disabilities
N.A.I.C.S.: 624120
Barry Phillips *(Owner)*

HOMECARE SOFTWARE SOLUTIONS LLC

130 W 42nd St 2nd Fl, New York, NY 11120
Tel.: (718) 407-4633
Web Site:
   http://www.hhaexchange.com
Year Founded: 2007
Sales Range: $1-9.9 Million
Emp.: 28
Information Technology Consulting Services
N.A.I.C.S.: 541512
Carl Queton *(Dir-Mktg & Comm)*
David Cole *(Dir-Bus Dev)*
Desmond Martinez *(Dir-Implementations & Sls)*
Diane DiMuria *(Officer-Compliance & Dir-Clinical Info)*
Ghaitrie Ganesh *(Controller)*
Scott Schwartz *(VP-Sls)*
Greg Strobel *(CEO)*

Subsidiaries:

Annkissam LLC   (1)
38 Chauncy St 10th Fl, Boston, MA 02142
Tel.: (617) 401-2480
Web Site: http://www.annkissam.com
Sales Range: $1-9.9 Million
Emp.: 45
Software Development Services
N.A.I.C.S.: 541511
Martha Anne Murphy *(Co-Founder)*
Gavin Kissam Murphy *(Co-Founder & Co-CEO)*
Kevin Palmer *(Co-CEO)*
Eric Sullivan *(CTO)*
Allison Dyer *(Project Mgr)*

HOMECREST OUTDOOR LIVING LLC

1250 Homecrest Ave, Wadena, MN 56482
Tel.: (218) 631-1000
Web Site: http://www.homecrest.com
Year Founded: 1953
Sales Range: $50-74.9 Million
Emp.: 100
Metal Lawn & Garden Furniture
N.A.I.C.S.: 337126
Kelly McComb *(Dir-Mktg Svcs)*
Stacy Brichacek *(Engr-Design)*
Eckman Janet *(Mgr-Sls & Svcs)*
Tim DeJong *(CEO)*
Nathan Peterson *(Dir-Comml Sls)*

HOMEDICS USA LLC

3000 N Pontiac Trl, Commerce Township, MI 48390-2720
Tel.: (248) 863-3000
Web Site: https://www.homedics.com
Year Founded: 1987
Personal Care Product Mfr
N.A.I.C.S.: 339112

HOMEEXCHANGE.COM INC.

45 Prospect St, Cambridge, MA 02139
Tel.: (888) 609-4660
Web Site:
   http://www.homeexchange.com
Year Founded: 1992
Vacation Alternatives Including Home Swapping in Other Countries
N.A.I.C.S.: 721199
Emmanuel Arnaud *(CEO)*

HOMEFIX CORPORATION

1506 Joh Ave Ste 188, Baltimore, MD 21227
Tel.: (410) 760-1777
Web Site:
   http://www.homefixcorporation.com

Sales Range: $10-24.9 Million
Emp.: 40
General Remodeling, Single-Family Houses
N.A.I.C.S.: 236118
Nick Roberts *(VP)*
Tony Prestandrea *(Gen Mgr)*
Justin Januszkiewicz *(Mgr-Sls)*

HOMEGROWN NATURAL FOODS INC.

580 Gateway Dr, Napa, CA 94558
Tel.: (707) 254-3700
Web Site:
   http://www.homegrownnatural foods.com
Rev.: $42,000,000
Emp.: 35
Peanut Oil, Cake Or Meal
N.A.I.C.S.: 311224

HOMELAND CREDIT UNION, INC.

25 Consumer Center Dr, Chillicothe, OH 45601
Tel.: (740) 775-3331   OH
Web Site:
   https://www.homelandcu.com
Year Founded: 1932
Sales Range: $10-24.9 Million
Emp.: 82
Credit Union
N.A.I.C.S.: 522130
Brad Purdum *(Treas)*
Don Thompson *(Sec)*
Dennis Michael Miller *(Vice Chm)*

HOMELAND ENERGY SOLUTIONS, LLC

2779 Hwy 24, Lawler, IA 52154
Tel.: (563) 238-5555
Web Site:
   http://www.homelandenergyso lutions.com
Year Founded: 2005
Rev.: $531,073,383
Assets: $195,963,473
Liabilities: $32,167,489
Net Worth: $163,795,984
Earnings: $87,673,429
Emp.: 62
Fiscal Year-end: 12/31/21
Methanol Mfr
N.A.I.C.S.: 325193
Mathew Driscoll *(Sec)*
Patrick C. Boyle *(Vice Chm)*
Katherine Balk *(VP-HR)*
Steven H. Core *(Chm)*
Beth Eiler *(CFO)*
Aristotelis Papasimakis *(Pres & CEO)*

HOMELAND HEALTHCARE, INC.

825 Market St Ste 300, Allen, TX 75013
Tel.: (214) 871-2118   TX
Web Site:
   http://www.homelandhealthcare.com
Year Founded: 1997
Sales Range: $25-49.9 Million
Emp.: 160
National Administrator of Healthcare Plans & Benefits
N.A.I.C.S.: 524114
Jennifer Casey *(COO)*
Ron Fields *(Pres & CEO)*
Christopher D. Carpino *(Mng Dir-Strategy-Worksite Benefits Div)*

HOMELAND SECURITY SOLUTIONS, INC. (HSSI)

3130A Nasa Dr, Hampton, VA 23666
Tel.: (757) 722-4726
Web Site:
   http://www.homelandsecurityinc.com

Year Founded: 2002
Sales Range: $500-549.9 Million
Emp.: 530
Professional Security Services & Mobile Training Courses to Law Enforcement Agencies & Military Groups
N.A.I.C.S.: 928110
Stephen Cameron *(Pres & CEO)*
Julia Byron *(CFO)*
Richard Neville *(Owner & COO)*

HOMER ELECTRIC ASSOCIATION, INC.

3977 Lake St, Homer, AK 99603
Tel.: (907) 235-8551   AK
Web Site:
   https://www.homerelectric.com
Sales Range: $75-99.9 Million
Electric Power Distr Cooperative
N.A.I.C.S.: 813990
Jon Cress *(Dir-Ops)*
David B. Thomas *(Treas & Sec)*
Dick Waisanen *(Pres)*
Dan Chay *(VP)*

HOMER SKELTON FORD, INC.

6950 Hanna Cove, Olive Branch, MS 38654
Tel.: (662) 333-5929
Web Site:
   https://www.homerskeltonford.com
Year Founded: 1989
Sales Range: $10-24.9 Million
Emp.: 100
New Car Retailer
N.A.I.C.S.: 441110
Brian Chapman *(Gen Mgr)*
Craig Crews *(Mgr-Sls)*
Ronnie Easley *(Mgr-Fleet)*
Tommy Foster *(Mgr-Parts)*
Richard Lewis *(Mgr-Fleet)*
Matt McCalmon *(Mgr-Inventory)*

HOMER T. HAYWARD LUMBER CO. INC.

10 Ragsdale Dr Ste 100, Monterey, CA 93940
Tel.: (831) 643-1900
Web Site:
   http://www.haywardlumber.com
Year Founded: 1919
Sales Range: $50-74.9 Million
Emp.: 450
Lumber & Other Building Materials Retailer
N.A.I.C.S.: 423310
William Hayward *(CEO)*

HOMER WARREN PROCTOR INC.

5225 Crooks Rd, Troy, MI 48098
Tel.: (248) 269-5700
Web Site: http://www.pfic.com
Rev.: $15,721,368
Emp.: 300
Insurance Agents
N.A.I.C.S.: 524210

HOMES & SON CONTRACTORS, INC.

77 E Thomas Rd Ste 210, Phoenix, AZ 85012-3109
Tel.: (602) 955-2998   AZ
Web Site:
   https://www.homesandson.com
Year Founded: 1946
Sales Range: $10-24.9 Million
Emp.: 15
Contracting & Construction Services
N.A.I.C.S.: 236220
R. G. Homes *(Pres)*

HOMES BY DAVID POWERS

702 S Peek Rd Ste 3, Katy, TX 77450-8825
Tel.: (281) 374-6637

Homes By David Powers—(Continued)

Web Site:
  http://www.homesbydavidpo
wers.com
Year Founded: 1993
Sales Range: $10-24.9 Million
Emp.: 15
New Construction of Single-Family
Houses
N.A.I.C.S.: 236115
David Powers *(Founder & Pres)*

HOMES BY JOHN C. FOWKE, INC.
1444 E Bloomingdale Ave, Valrico, FL
33596
Tel.: (813) 657-8866
Web Site:
  https://homesbyjcfowke.com
Sales Range: $1-9.9 Million
Residential Construction
N.A.I.C.S.: 236115
David Fowke *(VP)*

HOMES BY WESTBAY, LLC
4065 Crescent Park Dr, Riverview,
FL 33578
Tel.: (813) 938-1250
Web Site:
  http://www.westbaytampa.com
Year Founded: 2009
Sales Range: $50-74.9 Million
Emp.: 60
Residential Construction
N.A.I.C.S.: 236115
Willy Nunn *(Pres)*
Roger Gatewood *(Owner)*

HOMES BY WHITTAKER
3333-4 Rue Royale, Saint Charles,
MO 63301
Tel.: (636) 916-1511
Web Site:
  http://www.whittakerhomes.com
Rev.: $41,000,000
Emp.: 25
Developer of Single Family Housing
N.A.I.C.S.: 236115
Greg Whittaker *(CEO)*
Bill Wideman *(CFO)*

HOMES FOR AMERICA HOLD-INGS
86 Main St, Yonkers, NY 10701
Tel.: (914) 964-3000
Web Site:
  http://www.hfaholdings.com
Year Founded: 1996
Sales Range: $10-24.9 Million
Emp.: 80
Real Estate Investors
N.A.I.C.S.: 523999
Steven Richman *(CFO)*

HOMESIDE FINANCIAL, LLC
5950 Symphony Woods Rd Ste 305,
Columbia, MD 21044
Tel.: (443) 741-8180
Web Site:
  http://www.gohomeside.com
Year Founded: 2014
Sales Range: $50-74.9 Million
Emp.: 418
Mortgage Loan Services
N.A.I.C.S.: 522310
Mike Baynes *(Co-Founder & Mng
Partner)*
Dan Snyder *(Co-Founder & Mng
Partner)*
Grayson Hanes *(Co-Founder & Mng
Partner)*
Bob Tyson *(Co-Founder & Mng Part-
ner)*
Chris Miller *(Co-Founder & Mng
Partner)*

HOMESMART HOLDINGS, INC.
8388 E Hartford Dr Ste 100, Scotts-
dale, AZ 85255
Tel.: (602) 230-7600   DE
Year Founded: 2020
Rev.: $392,506,000
Assets: $24,885,000
Liabilities: $9,694,000
Net Worth: $15,191,000
Earnings: $9,205,000
Emp.: 268
Fiscal Year-end: 12/31/20
Holding Company
N.A.I.C.S.: 551112
Matthew Widdows *(CEO)*
Ashley Bowers *(Pres)*
Alan Goldman *(CFO)*
Michael Swope *(Chief Revenue
Officer)*

HOMESMART INTERNA-TIONAL LLC
8388 E Hartford Dr Ste 100, Scotts-
dale, AZ 85255
Tel.: (602) 230-7600
Web Site:
  http://www.homesmartinterna
tional.com
Year Founded: 1999
Sales Range: $50-74.9 Million
Emp.: 40
Residential Real Estate Sales & Ser-
vices
N.A.I.C.S.: 531210
Matt Widdows *(Founder & CEO)*
Carol Perry *(Chief Bus Dev Officer)*
Ashley Bowers *(Pres)*
Todd Sumney *(CMO)*
John Kloian *(CTO)*
Bryan Brooks *(VP-Franchise Sls)*
Jeannie Blancq *(VP-Mktg)*
Britton Sanchez *(Dir-Brokerage Ops)*
Jayme DeVary *(Dir-Human Capital)*
Stephanie Kaufman *(Branch Mgr)*
Wendy Forsythe *(COO)*
Alan Goldman *(CFO)*
Shawn Brown *(Chief Product Officer)*
Lorraine Murrietta *(Chief Compliance
& Treasury Officer)*

Subsidiaries:

PalmerHouse Properties, LLC.   **(1)**
2911 Piedmont Rd NE, Atlanta, GA 30305
Tel.: (404) 876-4901
Web Site:
  http://www.palmerhouseproperties.com
Sales Range: $1-9.9 Million
Emp.: 12
Residential & Commercial Real Estate Bro-
kerage Services
N.A.I.C.S.: 531210
Connie Papp *(CFO)*
Tom Ellicott *(Founder)*
Angie Mezza-Smith *(Sr VP)*
Tod Von Brinegar *(VP-Qualifying Broker)*
Mark Jefferson *(Mgr-Transaction)*
Jay Harris *(Mgr-Closing)*
Garrett Jones *(Mgr-Closing)*

Subsidiary (Domestic):

PalmerHouse Properties, LLC-
Duluth   **(2)**
3590 Peachtree Indus Blvd, Duluth, GA
30096
Tel.: (770) 623-8400
Web Site: http://palmerhouseproperties.com
Offices of Real Estate Agents & Brokers
N.A.I.C.S.: 531210

Solid Source Realty Inc.   **(1)**
10900 Crabapple Rd, Roswell, GA 30075
Tel.: (770) 475-1130
Web Site: http://www.solidsourcerealty.com
Sales Range: $25-49.9 Million
Emp.: 2,768
Real Estate Services
N.A.I.C.S.: 531210
Michele Velcheck *(CEO)*

HOMESQUARE HOLDINGS LLC
97 Montgomery Ave, Scarsdale, NY
10583
Tel.: (914) 670-8100
Web Site: https://www.homsqr.com
Year Founded: 2003
Holding Company
N.A.I.C.S.: 551112
George Liu *(Founder)*

Subsidiaries:

HomeSquare Pro, LLC   **(1)**
97 Montgomery Ave, Scarsdale, NY 10583
Tel.: (914) 670-8100
Web Site: http://www.homsqr.com
Home Maintenance, Repair & Renovation
Services
N.A.I.C.S.: 238990
George Liu *(Founder)*

HOMESTEAD ENTERPRISES INC.
PO Box 460, Newport, ME 04953-
0460
Tel.: (207) 368-2566
Web Site: http://www.hannaford.com
Year Founded: 1985
Sales Range: $25-49.9 Million
Emp.: 240
Grocery Services
N.A.I.C.S.: 445110
Dan Hill *(VP)*
Dean Homestead *(Pres)*

HOMESTEAD GARDENS INC.
743 W Central Ave, Davidsonville,
MD 21035
Tel.: (410) 867-6336
Web Site:
  https://www.homesteadgardens.com
Sales Range: $10-24.9 Million
Emp.: 250
Retail Nurseries
N.A.I.C.S.: 444240
Nathan Powers *(Coord-Educational)*

HOMESTEADERS LIFE CO. INC.
5700 Westown Pkwy, West Des
Moines, IA 50266
Tel.: (515) 440-7777   IA
Web Site:
  http://www.homesteadersslife.com
Year Founded: 1906
Sales Range: $25-49.9 Million
Emp.: 120
Life Insurance Services
N.A.I.C.S.: 524113
Graham J. Cook *(*)*
Marla G. Lacey *(Gen Counsel & Exec
VP)*
Steve W. Pick *(CFO, Treas & Exec
VP)*
Kristie Lynch *(Acct Exec)*
Eolo Nizzi *(Acct Exec)*
Steve Shaffer *(Chm, Pres & CEO)*
Jim Koher *(Chief Actuary & Exec VP)*
Judy Ralston-Hansen *(Exec VP-HR &
Admin)*
Lyndon Peterson *(Exec VP-Sls &
Mktg)*
Wade Comstock *(Exec VP-Ops)*
Dean Lambert *(Sr VP-Mktg & Comm)*
Krista Frank *(Sr VP-Customer Svcs)*
Wayne Huegerich *(Sr VP-Acctg)*
Jill Lazar *(Acct Exec)*
Dan Lodermeier *(VP-Field Sls)*
Doug Farrell *(Acct Exec)*
Terri Bordenkircher *(Dir-East)*
Nick Gerhart *(Chief Innovation Officer
& Exec VP)*
Patrick McGuire *(Acct Exec)*
Jon Lefrandt *(Sr VP-Consumer Expe-
rience)*
Tom Doruska *(Chief Actuary)*
Laurie Covington *(Sr VP-Enterprise
Strategic Plng)*

Subsidiaries:

Park Lawn Corporation   **(1)**
2 St Clair Ave E Suite 705, Toronto, M4T
2T5, ON, Canada
Tel.: (416) 231-1462
Web Site: https://www.parklawncorp.com
Rev.: $289,083,933
Assets: $1,394,782,625
Liabilities: $859,191,176
Net Worth: $535,591,450
Earnings: $241,829,198
Fiscal Year-end: 12/31/2021
Funeral Services
N.A.I.C.S.: 812210
Jim Price *(Sr VP-Industry Rels)*
Daniel Millett *(CFO)*
Jeff Parker *(CTO)*
Lorie Johnson *(VP-HR)*
Linda Gilbert *(VP-Fin & Admin)*
Clark Harlow *(Sr VP)*

Subsidiary (US):

Callaway Jones Funeral Home   **(2)**
3001 S College Ave, Bryan, TX 77801-2512
Tel.: (979) 822-3717
Web Site: http://www.callawayjones.com
Funeral Homes & Funeral Services
N.A.I.C.S.: 812210
Cody Jones *(Owner)*

Christy Smith Funeral Homes,
Inc.   **(2)**
1801 Morningside Ave, Sioux City, IA
51106-2402
Tel.: (712) 276-7319
Web Site: http://www.christysmith.com
Sales Range: $1-9.9 Million
Emp.: 10
Funeral Homes & Funeral Services
N.A.I.C.S.: 812210

Farris Funeral Service, Inc.   **(2)**
427 E Main, Abingdon, VA 24210-3407
Tel.: (276) 628-3394
Web Site:
  http://www.farrisfuneralservice.com
Funeral Homes & Funeral Services
N.A.I.C.S.: 812210

Integrity Funeral Care   **(2)**
3915 Dacoma St Ste E, Houston, TX 77092
Tel.: (713) 344-0764
Web Site: https://www.integrityfuneral.com
Funeral Homes & Funeral Services
N.A.I.C.S.: 812210
David Pena *(Founder & Pres)*

Memorial Park Cemetery Association
of Missouri, Inc.   **(2)**
8251 Hillcrest Rd, Kansas City, MO 64138
Tel.: (816) 523-2053
Web Site: http://www.parklawnfunerals.com
Sales Range: $1-9.9 Million
Emp.: 25
Funeral Homes & Funeral Services
N.A.I.C.S.: 812210
Henry W. De Vry *(Pres)*

Speaks Chapels LLC   **(2)**
1501 W Lexington Ave, Independence, MO
64052
Tel.: (816) 252-7900
Web Site: http://www.speakschapel.com
Sales Range: $1-9.9 Million
Emp.: 40
Funeral Homes & Funeral Services
N.A.I.C.S.: 812210
Robert Speaks *(Chm)*
Chuck Townsend *(Mgr-Funeral Home)*
Becky Williams *(Controller)*

The Baue Funeral Home Co.   **(2)**
620 Jefferson St, Saint Charles, MO 63301-
4419
Tel.: (636) 940-1000
Web Site: http://www.baue.com
Funeral Services
N.A.I.C.S.: 812210
Lisa Bowley *(Pres & CEO)*
John Baue Devaney *(VP)*

WFH, Inc   **(2)**
3715 Asheville Highway, Canton, NC 28716
Tel.: (828) 648-2371
Web Site: http://www.wellsfuneralhome.com
Funeral Homes & Funeral Services
N.A.I.C.S.: 812210

J. Wells Greeley (Dir-Emeritus and Funeral Service)
Don Cooper (Gen Mgr)

HOMESTRONGUSA
8711 Monroe Ct Ste A, Rancho Cucamonga, CA 91730
Tel.: (909) 758-8971   CA
Web Site:
https://www.homestrongusa.org
Year Founded: 1998
Sales Range: $50-74.9 Million
Emp.: 9
Community Housing Services
N.A.I.C.S.: 624229
Benjamin Stuelke (CFO)
Jed Davis (Pres & CEO)

HOMETOWN AMERICA MANAGEMENT CORP.
150 N Wacker Dr Ste 2800, Chicago, IL 60606
Tel.: (312) 604-7500   DE
Web Site:
http://www.hometownamerica.com
Year Founded: 1999
Owner & Operator of Manufactured Home Communities
N.A.I.C.S.: 531120
Stephen H. Braun (Co-Pres & COO)
Doug Minahan (VP)
Sylvia Flores (Supvr-Payroll)

HOMETOWN AUTO RETAILERS, INC.
1230 Main St, Watertown, CT 06795-3128
Tel.: (203) 756-1300   DE
Web Site:
http://www.hometownautoretailers.com
Year Founded: 1997
Sales Range: $200-249.9 Million
Emp.: 297
Car & Light Truck Dealerships
N.A.I.C.S.: 441110
Corey Shaker (Pres, CEO & COO)
William C. Muller (Reg VP South Division)
Steven Shaker (Regional VP-Northern Division)
Charles F. Schwartz (CFO)

HOMETOWN BANK
142 N Water St, Kent, OH 44240
Tel.: (330) 673-9827   OH
Web Site: https://www.ht.bank
Year Founded: 1898
Rev.: $3,900,000
Emp.: 35
Fiscal Year-end: 09/30/10
Savings Institutions
N.A.I.C.S.: 522180
Brian Bialik (VP-Comml)
Judy Cochran (Asst Sec)
Megan Reiners (Asst VP)
Michael Cone (Asst VP)
Patricia Buchanan (Asst VP)
Scott Mikula (Asst VP)
Barbara A. Gregory (Mgr-Ops)
Colin P. Boyle (CFO, Treas, Sec & Exec VP)
Deborah Crease (VP & Controller)
Donna Kovolyan (VP & Office Mgr-Ravenna)
John Ryan (Officer-Comml Loan & VP)
Matthew H. Carter (Asst VP)
Sarah R. Pastor (Asst VP & Office Mgr-Kent)
Stephen J. Deibel (Officer-Comml Loan & VP)
Vickie L. Reed (Asst VP & Office Mgr-Brimfield)

HOMETOWN BANK, NA-

TIONAL ASSOCIATION
1801 45th St, Galveston, TX 77550
Tel.: (409) 763-1271
Web Site: http://www.htbna.bank
Year Founded: 1966
Sales Range: $1-9.9 Million
Emp.: 80
National Commercial Banks
N.A.I.C.S.: 522110
A. Jimmy Rasmussen (Pres & CEO)
Scott Kusnerik (Exec VP)
Donna Rizzo (VP)
Bill Provenzano (Sr VP)
Marvin Langston (Exec VP)
Angela Brooks (Sr VP)
Candy Temple (Exec VP)
Diana Ramos (VP)
Jim Goebel (VP)
Kyle McFatridge (Sr VP)
Lulu Higgins (VP)
Martha Salinas (Sr VP)
Ray Rusk (Sr VP)
Rosie Garcia (Sr VP)
Sean P. Murphy (VP)
Sharon Hansen (Sr VP)
Stephany Cantu (VP)
Susan Bachus (VP)
Allan Rasmussen Jr. (Sr Exec VP)

HOMETOWN COMMUNITY BANCORP, INC.
721 W Jackson St, Morton, IL 61550
Tel.: (309) 266-5337   DE
Web Site:
http://www.hometowncommunitybancorp.com
Bank Holding Company
N.A.I.C.S.: 551111
Kenny Eathington (Partner)
Bruce Huber (Chief Admin Officer)
Dirk Roecker (CFO)
Elaina Moline (COO)
Glenda McGraw (Chief HR Officer)
Jean Ann Honegger (Co-CEO)
Jeff Boss (Exec VP)
Maria Warner (Chief Compliance Officer)
Mark Gamage (Chief Credit Officer)
Patrick E. Oberle (Mng Dir)

Subsidiaries:

Morton Community Bank   (1)
721 W Jackson St, Morton, IL 61550
Tel.: (309) 266-5337
Web Site: http://www.hometownbanks.com
Sales Range: $50-74.9 Million
Emp.: 200
Commercial Banking Services
N.A.I.C.S.: 522110
Jean Ann Honegger (Co-CEO & Pres-Grp)
Andrew Honegger (Co-Chm, Pres & Co-CEO)
Bob Dittmer (Chief Lending Officer)
Rich Sauder (Co-Chm)
Jeremy Knepp (Exec VP)
Ken Jones (Chief Credit Officer)
Bob Knepp (Exec VP)
Tim Dwyer (Chief Retail Lending Officer)
Gary Shawgo (Chief Audit Officer)
Andy Sparks (Exec VP)

HOMETOWN FINANCIAL GROUP, INC.
36 Main St, Easthampton, MA 01027
Tel.: (413) 527-4111   MA
Web Site: http://www.bankhfg.com
Year Founded: 2008
Multi-Bank Holding Company
N.A.I.C.S.: 551111
Michael R. Wheeler (COO)
Kevin M. Tierney Sr. (Pres)
Matthew S. Sosik (Pres & CEO)
Karen Yancik (Sr VP)

Subsidiaries:

Abington Bank   (1)
6 Harrison Ave, Abington, MA 02351
Tel.: (781) 878-0045

Web Site: http://www.abingtonbank.com
Federal Savings Bank
N.A.I.C.S.: 522180
David Gomes (CFO & Exec VP)

Subsidiary (Domestic):

North Shore Bank, a Co-operative
Bank   (2)
248 Andover St, Peabody, MA 01960
Tel.: (978) 573-1300
Web Site: http://www.northshore-bank.com
Sales Range: $25-49.9 Million
Savings Bank
N.A.I.C.S.: 522180
Michael R. Wheeler (Pres & COO)
Kevin M. Tierney Sr. (CEO)
George J. Sophinos (CFO & Exec VP)
Elizabeth A. White (VP & Mgr-Retail Sls)
Geoffrey T. Leahy (Asst VP & Mgr-Sls & Svc)
Megan Shea-Pereira (Branch Mgr)
Beth A. Tichy (Sr VP & Dir-HR)
Kathryn V. Carty (Sr VP & Sr Ops Officer)
Michael D. Brown (Chief Lending Officer & Exec VP)
William S. Beitler (Chief Risk Officer & Sr VP)

Easthampton Savings Bank   (1)
36 Main St, Easthampton, MA
01027   (100%)
Tel.: (413) 527-4111
Web Site: http://www.bankesb.com
Sales Range: $25-49.9 Million
Federal Savings Bank
N.A.I.C.S.: 522180
Matthew S. Sosik (Pres & CEO)
Nancy Lapointe (Sr VP-Branch Admin)
Maryann Geiger (Sr VP & Dir-Ops)
Michael Fitzgerald (Asst VP)
Emily Drapeau (Asst VP-Electronic Banking)
Karen DeMaio (Asst VP-IRA & Ops Risk Mgmt)
Brenna Breeding (Officer-Digital Mktg)
Jeff Stegenga (Mng Dir)
Charles Moore (Mng Dir-Restructuring-Turnaround)

Hometown Bank   (1)
31 Sutton Ave, Oxford, MA 01540
Tel.: (508) 987-1200
Web Site: http://www.hometowncoop.com
Savings Bank
N.A.I.C.S.: 522180
Kathryn Latour (VP & Security Officer)
Michael P. Mahlert (Exec VP & Sr Loan Officer)
Norma Collins (Sr VP-Ops & HR)
Matthew S. Sosik (Pres & CEO)
Shawn McNerney (Sr VP-Comml Lending)

Randolph Bancorp, Inc.   (1)
2 Batterymarch Park Ste 301, Quincy, MA 02169
Tel.: (781) 963-2100
Rev.: $56,036,000
Assets: $803,278,000
Liabilities: $702,375,000
Net Worth: $100,903,000
Earnings: $9,601,000
Emp.: 170
Fiscal Year-end: 12/31/2021
Bank Holding Company
N.A.I.C.S.: 551111

Subsidiary (Domestic):

Prime Title Services, Inc.   (2)
1175 SW Gatlin Blvd Ste 105, Port Saint Lucie, FL 34953
Tel.: (772) 621-2882
Web Site: http://www.primetitleservices.net
Title Insurance Services
N.A.I.C.S.: 524127
Judy Otano-Jurcak (Owner)

Randolph Savings Bank   (2)
129 N Main St, Randolph, MA 02368
Tel.: (781) 963-2100
Web Site: http://www.randolphsavings.com
Sales Range: $10-24.9 Million
Emp.: 100
State Savings Bank
N.A.I.C.S.: 522180
James P. McDonough (Pres & CEO)
Ryan J. Kirwin (Sr VP-Residential Lending)

HOMETOWN PLUMBING & HEATING CO.
13606 118th Ave, Davenport, IA 52804
Tel.: (563) 381-4800
Web Site:
https://hometownmechanical.com
Sales Range: $10-24.9 Million
Emp.: 80
Plumbing Services
N.A.I.C.S.: 238220
Kelley Little (Office Mgr)
Michael O'Day (Pres)

HOMETOWN REALTY SERVICES INC.
7240 Lee Davis Rd, Mechanicsville, VA 23111
Tel.: (804) 730-7195
Web Site:
https://www.hometownrealtyservices.com
Year Founded: 1988
Rev.: $99,000,000
Emp.: 300
Real Estate Brokers & Agents
N.A.I.C.S.: 531210
Mike Chenault (Pres)
Todd Rogers (VP)
Rodney Chenault (VP)

HOMETOWN TELECOM
9720 Wilshire Blvd Ste 600, Beverly Hills, CA 90212
Tel.: (714) 271-5500
Web Site:
http://www.hometowntelecom.com
Year Founded: 2006
Sales Range: $10-24.9 Million
Emp.: 6
International Telecommunications Carrier
N.A.I.C.S.: 517112
David Schofield (Pres)

HOMEVALET, INC.
1593 Spring Hill Rd Ste 400, Tysons Corner, VA 22182
Tel.: (415) 400-4214
Web Site: http://www.homevalet.co
Software Platform Services
N.A.I.C.S.: 518210
John Simms (Co-Founder & CEO)
Jack Simms (Co-Founder & COO)
Steve Yankovich (Chief Experience Officer)

Subsidiaries:

Envolve Engineering, LLC   (1)
421 E Sycamore St, Evansville, IN 47713
Tel.: (812) 492-4585
Web Site: http://www.envolve-engineering.com
Engineering Services
N.A.I.C.S.: 541330
Michael Stagg (Principal & Mgr-Engrg)

HOMEWETBAR
425 E Hill St, Oklahoma City, OK 73105
Web Site:
https://www.homewetbar.com
Year Founded: 2004
Sales Range: $1-9.9 Million
Emp.: 13
Specializes in Online Home Entertaining & One of A Kind Gifts
N.A.I.C.S.: 459999
Keith Winter (Founder & Pres)

HOMEWOOD CORPORATION
2700 E Dublin Granville Rd Ste 300, Columbus, OH 43231-4078
Tel.: (614) 898-7200   OH
Web Site: http://www.homewood-homes.com
Year Founded: 1963
Sales Range: $75-99.9 Million
Emp.: 165

Homewood Corporation—(Continued)

Builder of Single Family Houses, Multi-Family Dwellings & Apartment Buildings
N.A.I.C.S.: 236117
George A. Skestos (Founder)

HOMEWORKS INC.
7700 Northfield Rd, Walton Hills, OH 44146
Tel.: (440) 439-7700
Web Site: http://www.arhaus.com
Sales Range: $25-49.9 Million
Emp.: 300
Furniture Retailer
N.A.I.C.S.: 449110
Adrian Mitchelle (CEO)

HOMIER & SONS INC.
21133 State Rte 613, Continental, OH 45831
Tel.: (419) 596-3965
Web Site:
http://www.homierandsons.com
Sales Range: $10-24.9 Million
Emp.: 20
Sales of New & Used RV's
N.A.I.C.S.: 423820
Raymond L. Homier (Pres)

HOMIER DISTRIBUTING COMPANY
84 Commercial Rd, Huntington, IN 46750
Tel.: (260) 356-9477
Rev.: $20,400,000
Emp.: 270
Hardware Stores
N.A.I.C.S.: 444140
Chuck Homier (Pres & CEO)
David Switzer (VP)

HONC INDUSTRIES, INC.
10101 Mallory Pkwy E, Saint James City, FL 33956
Tel.: (239) 772-4662
Web Site: https://www.honc.com
Sales Range: $1-9.9 Million
Emp.: 75
Site Construction
N.A.I.C.S.: 238910
Daniel Honc (Pres & CEO)
Pete DiMatteo (Mgr-Trucking Div)
Steve Honc (VP)
Jake Herring (Treas & Project Engr)

HONC MARINE CONTRACTING, INC.
1130 Pondella Rd Ste 2, Cape Coral, FL 33909
Tel.: (239) 772-2378   FL
Web Site: http://www.honcmarine.net
Year Founded: 1955
Sales Range: $1-9.9 Million
Emp.: 42
Marine Construction
N.A.I.C.S.: 237990
David Mulicka (Pres)

HONDA AUTOMOBILES OF BARTLESVILLE
3210 SE Washington Blvd, Bartlesville, OK 74006
Tel.: (918) 333-5400
Web Site:
http://www.bartlesvillehonda.com
Sales Range: $25-49.9 Million
Emp.: 45
New & Used Automobile Dealer
N.A.I.C.S.: 441110
David Counterman (Gen Mgr-Sls)

HONDA CARS OF CORONA
1080 Pomona Rd, Corona, CA 92882
Tel.: (951) 734-8400

Web Site:
http://www.hondacarsofcorona.com
Sales Range: $25-49.9 Million
Emp.: 132
Car Whslr
N.A.I.C.S.: 441110
Tanal Hassoun (Principal)
Greg Fisher (Mgr-Sls)
Bretz Alexis (Mgr-Parts)

HONDA CARS OF ROCK HILL
686 Galleria Blvd, Rock Hill, SC 29730
Tel.: (803) 366-8161
Web Site:
https://www.hondacarsrockhill.com
Year Founded: 1984
Sales Range: $50-74.9 Million
Emp.: 50
Car Whslr
N.A.I.C.S.: 441110
Pam Oakes (Mgr-Website-BDC)
Joel Suggs (Gen Mgr)

HONDA MOTORS INC.
1400 W Main St, Alhambra, CA 91801
Tel.: (626) 576-1114
Web Site:
http://www.goudyhonda.com
Sales Range: $100-124.9 Million
Emp.: 156
Automobiles, New & Used
N.A.I.C.S.: 441110
Mike Deville (Gen Mgr-Sls)

HONDA OF ITHACA
315 Elmira Rd, Ithaca, NY 14850
Tel.: (607) 273-5080
Web Site:
http://www.hondaofithaca.com
Rev.: $24,000,000
Emp.: 40
Automobiles, New & Used
N.A.I.C.S.: 441110
Seth Cohen (Exec VP)
Char Rodriguez (Mgr-Svcs)

HONDA OF SALEM
750 Commercial St, Salem, OR 97301
Tel.: (503) 370-7990
Web Site:
http://www.hondaofsalem.com
Sales Range: $75-99.9 Million
Emp.: 265
New Car Whslr
N.A.I.C.S.: 441110
Gary Boxer (Gen Mgr)

HONDA OF STATEN ISLAND
250 Parkinson Ave, Staten Island, NY 10305
Tel.: (718) 720-0075
Web Site: http://www.sihonda.com
Rev.: $16,200,000
Emp.: 16
Automobiles, New & Used
N.A.I.C.S.: 441110
Rodney T. Eddy (Dir-Svc & Parts)
Angelo Sciascia (Gen Mgr)
Samantha DiMartino (Mgr-Lease Return)
Joe Deluca (Mgr-Parts)
Greg Samborski (Mgr-Sls)
Jeffrey Pasenkoff (Mgr-Svc)
Randy Milejski (Mgr-Used Car)
Faysel Tahseen (Mgr-Fin)
Keith Weinstein (Mgr-Fin)
Anthony Raucci (Mgr-Sls)

HONE OIL COMPANY INC.
3065 Washington Blvd, Ogden, UT 84401
Tel.: (801) 394-2649
Rev.: $16,520,408
Emp.: 60

Petroleum Bulk Stations
N.A.I.C.S.: 424710
John Richardson (Pres)
David Moesinger (Gen Mgr)

HONEY DEW ASSOCIATES, INC.
2 Taunton St, Plainville, MA 02762
Tel.: (508) 699-3900   MA
Web Site:
https://www.honeydewdonuts.com
Year Founded: 1973
Sales Range: $10-24.9 Million
Emp.: 20
Doughnut Shops Operator & Franchiser
N.A.I.C.S.: 722513
Richard J. Bowen (Founder & Pres)

HONEY FARMS INC.
505 Pleasant St, Worcester, MA 01609-1821
Tel.: (508) 753-7678   MA
Web Site: http://myhoneyfarms.com
Year Founded: 1968
Sales Range: $50-74.9 Million
Emp.: 350
Provider of Grocery Store Services
N.A.I.C.S.: 445131
Susan Reno (Dir-Loss Prevention)
Sheila Smith (VP-HR)
Guy Penrose (Mgr-Mdsg)
Karen Campbell (Dir-Mktg)
Larry Bonin (Mgr-IT)
Vern Johnson (VP-Ops)
Maggie Moraitis (Dir-Fin)

HONEY LAKE PLANTATION RESORT & SPA
1290 Honey Lake Rd, Greenville, FL 32331
Tel.: (850) 948-9911
Web Site:
http://www.honeylakeplantation.com
Sales Range: $25-49.9 Million
Emp.: 42
Resort & Spa
N.A.I.C.S.: 713990
Jon Williamson (Pres & COO)
Bob Williamson (Owner)

HONEY-CAN-DO INTERNATIONAL
5300 St Charles Rd, Berkeley, IL 60163
Tel.: (708) 240-8100
Web Site:
https://www.honeycando.com
Year Founded: 2008
Sales Range: $10-24.9 Million
Emp.: 45
Home Storage, Organization & Garment Care Solutions
N.A.I.C.S.: 493190

HONEYBAKED HAM CO. OF OHIO
11935 Mason Montgomery Rd Ste 200, Cincinnati, OH 45249-3703
Tel.: (513) 583-9700
Web Site:
http://www.honeybakedforyou.com
Year Founded: 1965
Sales Range: $200-249.9 Million
Emp.: 400
Ham Mfr
N.A.I.C.S.: 445240
Jennie Peters (Mgr-Pur)
Tommy Meyer (Dir-Ops)

HONEYVILLE GRAIN INC.
1080 N Main Ste 101, Brigham City, UT 84302-9736
Tel.: (435) 279-8197   UT

Web Site:
http://www.honeyvillegrain.com
Year Founded: 1954
Sales Range: $10-24.9 Million
Emp.: 120
Provider Of Agricultural Services
N.A.I.C.S.: 424510
Robert Anderson (Pres)
Garth Rollins (Mgr-Ops)
Kevin Toyn (Mgr-Quality Assurance)

HONG KONG MARKET PLACE INC.
2651 W Pioneer Pkwy, Grand Prairie, TX 75051
Tel.: (972) 988-8811
Web Site: https://www.hkmkt.com
Year Founded: 1994
Sales Range: $10-24.9 Million
Emp.: 90
Grocery Store Services
N.A.I.C.S.: 445110
Richard Loh (Pres)

HONG KONG SUPERMARKET INC.
37 11 Main St, Flushing, NY 11354
Tel.: (718) 539-6868
Web Site: http://www.hk-supermarket.com
Sales Range: $10-24.9 Million
Emp.: 100
Supermarket Operators
N.A.I.C.S.: 445110
Jeffery Wu (Owner)

HONIGMAN MILLER SCHWARTZ & COHN LLP
2290 1st National Bldg 660 Woodward Ave, Detroit, MI 48226-3506
Tel.: (313) 465-7000
Web Site: https://www.honigman.com
Year Founded: 1948
Sales Range: $150-199.9 Million
Emp.: 500
Law firm
N.A.I.C.S.: 541110
Alan S. Schwartz (Vice Chm & Partner)
David Foltyn (Chm & CEO)
Craig W. Hardtke (CIO)
Patrick Andonian (Dir-Ops)
Kineret A. Gable (Dir-Library Svcs)
Frederick J. Morsches (Chief Community Officer)
Julie K. Norris (Chief Atty Dev & Recruitment Officer)
Robert C. Weigel (Dir-Fin Svcs)
Carl W. Herstein (Partner)
J. Michael Huget (Chm-Litigation & Partner)
Donald J. Kunz (Partner & Chm-Corp Dept)
Lawrence D. McLaughlin (Partner & Chm-Real Estate)
Jonathan P. O'Brien (Chm-Intellectual Property & Partner)
Julie E. Robertson (Chm-Insurance & Partner)
William D. Sargent (Chm-Labor & Employment & Partner)
Joseph R. Sgroi (Partner)
Barbara A. Kaye (Vice Chm-Corp Dept & Partner)
Stephanie C. Miller (CMO)
Jill R. Pace (Chief HR Officer)
Lowell D. Salesin (Vice Chm-Real Estate Dept & Partner)
Tim Flory (Atty-Patent-Grand Rapids)
Peter Cummings (Atty-Patent-Grand Rapids)
Tracy Larsen (Mng Partner-Grand Rapids)
Alex L. Parrish (Partner)
Anessa Owen Kramer (Partner)

David N. Parsigian *(Mng Partner-Ann Arbor & Partner)*
Deborah Swedlow *(Mng Partner-Ann Arbor & Partner)*
Gabrielle L. Sims *(Partner)*
Ilan Napchan *(Partner)*
Joshua F. Opperer *(Partner)*
Karen R. Pifer *(Partner)*
Kenneth T. Brooks *(Mng Partner)*
Khalilah V. Spencer *(Partner)*
Michael D. Dubay *(Partner)*
Michael P. Hindelang *(Vice Chm-Litigation Department & Partner)*
Nick Gorga *(Vice Chm-Litigation Department & Partner)*
Phillip D. Torrence *(Partner)*
Rebecca L. Grove *(Partner)*
Steven J. Rypma *(Partner)*
Dennis J. Abdelnour *(Partner)*
Fernando Alberdi *(Partner)*
James G. Blackledge *(Officer-Operating Div)*
Jason R. Abel *(Partner)*
Joseph Aviv *(Mng Partner-Bloomfield Hills & Partner)*
Norman H. Beitner *(Partner)*
Sean F. Crotty *(Partner)*
Thomas J. Appledorn *(Mng Partner-Bloomfield Hills & Partner)*
Uma Reddy *(CFO)*
Chauncey C. Mayfield II *(Partner)*

Subsidiaries:

Honigman Miller Schwartz & Cohn LLP - Chicago   **(1)**
1 S Wacker Dr 28th Fl, Chicago, IL 60606-4617
Tel.: (312) 701-9300
Web Site: http://www.honigman.com
Emp.: 20
Law firm
N.A.I.C.S.: 541110
Steven A. Weiss *(Partner)*
Alex Plakas *(Partner-Private Equity Practice Grp)*
David Koropp *(Partner)*
Ilan Napchan *(Partner)*
Vikram Mathrani *(Partner-Intellectual Property Practice)*
Ron Sklar *(Partner-Intellectual Property Practice)*
Abby M. Stover *(Dir-Attorney Dev & Recruitment)*
Alan S. Schwartz *(Vice Chm & Partner)*
David Foltyn *(Chm & CEO)*
Kim Thomas *(Dir-Benefits & Strategic HR Initiatives)*
Patrick Andonian *(Dir-Ops)*
Robert C. Weigel *(Dir-Fin Svcs)*
Simeon Papacostas *(Partner)*
Susan Welsh *(Partner-Corp Dept)*
Sarah Iyer *(Partner-Corp Dept & Bus Immigration Grp)*
S. Tony Ling *(Partner-Employee Benefits Practice Grp)*
Norbert Knapke *(Partner-Corp Dept-Private Equity Practice Grp)*
Harris R. Eisenberg *(Partner-Corp Dept & Private Equity Practice)*

HONKAMP KRUEGER & CO., PC

2345 JFK Rd, Dubuque, IA 52004
Tel.: (563) 556-0123
Web Site: http://www.honkamp.com
Year Founded: 1947
Sales Range: $1-9.9 Million
Emp.: 130
Accounting, Tax & Consulting Services
N.A.I.C.S.: 541211
Alan Krueger *(Partner)*
Jon Thoms *(Partner)*
Renee Hesselman *(Mgr-Acctg)*
Greg Burbach *(Mng Partner)*
Adam Reisch *(Partner)*
Jennifer Daughetee *(Partner)*
Kerry Smith *(Partner)*
Kyle Kunz *(Partner)*

Heather Deininger Vetter *(Partner)*
Katie Thomas *(Partner)*
Stephanie Imhoff *(Partner)*

Subsidiaries:

Schowalter & Jabouri Computer Solutions, Inc.   **(1)**
11777 Gravois Rd, Saint Louis, MO 63127
Tel.: (314) 842-2929
Web Site: http://sjcpa.com
Sales Range: $1-9.9 Million
Emp.: 20
Computer System Design Services
N.A.I.C.S.: 541512
Dennis Schowalter *(Sec)*
Jamie Jabouri *(Pres)*

HONOLD & LA PAGE, INC.

1128 S 11th St, Sheboygan, WI 53081
Tel.: (920) 457-7755
Web Site: http://www.honoldlp.com
Rev.: $10,700,000
Emp.: 32
Plumbing & Heating Equipment & Supplies Merchant Whslr
N.A.I.C.S.: 423720
John Kuznacic *(VP)*
William P. Honold *(Pres)*
Kevin Kalk *(Asst Mgr-Plumbing & Heating)*

HONOLULU FREIGHT SERVICE INC.

1400 Date St, Montebello, CA 90640-6323
Tel.: (323) 887-6777   HI
Web Site: http://www.hfsnet.com
Year Founded: 1978
Sales Range: $10-24.9 Million
Emp.: 95
Freight Transportation Services
N.A.I.C.S.: 488510
Mike Beidleman *(Pres)*

HONOR CREDIT UNION

8385 Edgewood Rd, Berrien Springs, MI 49103
Tel.: (269) 983-6357   MI
Web Site: http://www.honorcu.com
Year Founded: 1934
Rev.: $59,300,537
Assets: $934,011,968
Liabilities: $828,752,043
Net Worth: $105,259,925
Earnings: $10,736,468
Emp.: 274
Fiscal Year-end: 12/31/18
Credit Union
N.A.I.C.S.: 522130
Mimi Elwell *(Chm)*
Brian Brown *(Sec)*
Mark Fry *(Treas)*
Georgia Gipson *(Asst VP-Community-Benton Harbor, St. Joseph & Bridgman)*
Carrie Muessig *(Assoc Dir)*
Stephen W. Smith *(Assoc Dir)*

HONOR STATE BANK

2254 Henry St, Honor, MI 49640
Tel.: (231) 639-1701   MI
Web Site:
   https://www.myhonorbank.com
Year Founded: 1917
Emp.: 200
Commericial Banking
N.A.I.C.S.: 522110
Jessica Gross *(Branch Mgr)*
Jason Surratt *(VP)*
Michael L. Worden *(Pres & CEO)*

HONORS CONTRACTORS, INC.

4015 Crestwood Blvd, New Port Richey, FL 34653
Tel.: (727) 264-8889

Web Site: http://www.honorsgc.com
Year Founded: 2002
Sales Range: $10-24.9 Million
Emp.: 12
Commercial & Institutional Building Construction Services
N.A.I.C.S.: 236220
Don Bowen *(Pres)*
Jeff Bowen *(VP)*
Sue Lewis *(Controller)*

HOOAH LLC

807 S Orlando Ave, Winter Park, FL 32789
Tel.: (407) 362-7715
Web Site: http://www.hooah.cc
Year Founded: 2003
Sales Range: $1-9.9 Million
Emp.: 15
Communication Service
N.A.I.C.S.: 517112
Jorge Suria *(Pres)*
Tanya Zeiher *(VP)*
Marisol Rivera *(Office Mgr)*

HOOBER INCORPORATED

3452 Old Philadelphia Pike, Intercourse, PA 17534
Tel.: (717) 768-8231
Web Site: https://www.hoober.com
Sales Range: $50-74.9 Million
Emp.: 196
Farm Equipment & Supplies
N.A.I.C.S.: 459999
Mark Reichlin *(Mgr-Sls)*
David Jones *(Mgr-Sls)*
Alan Quillen *(Mgr-Store & Parts-Seaford)*
Brad Backenstose *(Dir-Mktg)*
Brad Hoffer *(Dir-Fin)*
Dan Balint *(Mgr-Store & Parts-Middletown)*
Edward Good *(Dir-HR)*
Rod Lefever *(Partner & Bus Mgr)*
Scot Goodling *(Dir-IT)*
Scott Hoober *(Owner)*
Seth Norris *(Mgr-Store & Svc)*
Tim Brinton *(Mgr-Store & Sls-Intercourse)*
Tyler Ranck *(Dir-Parts-East Div)*
Will Brown *(Mgr-Store & Svc-Ashland)*
Charles B. Hoober Jr. *(Founder)*

HOOD CONTAINER CORPORATION

2727 Paces Ferry Rd SE Bldg 1 Ste 1850, Atlanta, GA 30339
Tel.: (855) 605-6317
Web Site: https://hoodcontainer.com
Year Founded: 2012
Packaging & Containers Manufacturing
N.A.I.C.S.: 322219
Charlie Hodges *(Pres & COO)*

Subsidiaries:

Sumter Packaging Corporation   **(1)**
2341 Corporate Way, Sumter, SC 29154
Tel.: (803) 481-2003
Web Site: http://www.sumterpackaging.com
Sales Range: $10-24.9 Million
Emp.: 150
Solid Fiber Box Mfr
N.A.I.C.S.: 322211
Mickey Fordham *(Mgr-Production)*
Tom Lawrence *(Mgr-Quality)*
Jimmy Ezell *(Mgr-Cust Svcs)*
Jim Baibak *(Mgr-Sls)*
Benjamin DeSollar *(CEO)*

HOOD INDUSTRIES INC.

15 Professional Pkwy, Hattiesburg, MS 39402
Tel.: (601) 264-2962   MS
Web Site:
   https://www.hoodindustries.com

Year Founded: 1983
Sales Range: $125-149.9 Million
Emp.: 1,150
Wood & Lumber Supplies
N.A.I.C.S.: 321212
Ben Crim *(Dir-Engrg)*
Christine Alford *(Mgr-Mfg Div HR)*
Terry Lawhead *(Dir-HR)*
Darrin Martin *(Dir-Sls & Mktg)*
Sam Newbill *(Mgr-Safety & Environmental)*
Steve Smith *(Mgr-Procurement)*
Nola Alexander *(Mgr-Safety & Environmental)*

Subsidiaries:

Hood Distribution   **(1)**
15 Professional Pkwy, Hattiesburg, MS 39402
Tel.: (601) 296-4826
Web Site: http://www.hooddistribution.com
Lumber Distr
N.A.I.C.S.: 423310
Bruce Kulzer *(VP)*

Division (Domestic):

Hood Distribution McEwen Group   **(2)**
5037 Prospect St, High Point, NC 27263
Tel.: (336) 472-1677
Web Site: http://www.hooddistribution.com
Lumber Distr
N.A.I.C.S.: 423310
Frank Nelson *(Branch Mgr)*

Packaging Unlimited LLC   **(1)**
1729 McCloskey Ave, Louisville, KY 40210-1755
Tel.: (502) 515-3900
Web Site:
   http://www.packagingunlimited.com
Provider of Corrugated & Fiber Box Mfr
N.A.I.C.S.: 322211
Jeff Workinger *(VP-Corrugated Sls)*
Carol Waid *(Acct Mgr)*
Patrick Broderick *(VP-Sls-Promotional Pkg Div)*
Scott Graves *(Mgr)*

HOOD NORTHLAKE

69020 Hwy 190 Service Rd, Covington, LA 70433-5180
Tel.: (985) 892-4663
Web Site:
   https://www.hoodchevy.com
Sales Range: $10-24.9 Million
Emp.: 67
Car Whslr
N.A.I.C.S.: 441110
Mike Scarle *(Gen Mgr-Sls)*

HOOD PACKAGING CORPORATION

25 Woodgreen Pl, Madison, MS 39110-9531
Tel.: (601) 853-7260   MS
Web Site:
   http://www.hoodpackaging.com
Year Founded: 1959
Sales Range: $50-74.9 Million
Emp.: 26
Supplier of Paper Bag Packaging
N.A.I.C.S.: 322220
Warren A. Hood Jr. *(Chm & CEO)*
John Smith *(VP-Corp Svcs)*
Karen McLaughlin *(Dir-Reg HR)*

Subsidiaries:

Hood Packaging Corporation - Graphics Facility   **(1)**
1400 Sentinel Dr, Anniston, AL 36207
Tel.: (256) 835-3707
Plastic Packaging Film Mfr
N.A.I.C.S.: 326112
Ricky Baldwin *(Plant Mgr)*

Hood Packaging Corporation - Plastic Packaging - Glopak Division   **(1)**
1800 Vincent Massey Drive, Cornwall, K6H 5R6, ON, Canada

Hood Packaging Corporation—(Continued)
Tel.: (514) 323-4510
Plastic Packaging Film Mfr
N.A.I.C.S.: 326112

HOOD RIVER DISTILLERS INC.
660 Riverside Dr, Hood River, OR 97031-1177
Tel.: (541) 386-1588　　OR
Web Site: http://www.hrdspirits.com
Year Founded: 1949
Sales Range: $10-24.9 Million
Emp.: 40
Mfr of Distilled & Blended Liquors
N.A.I.C.S.: 312140
Erica Mitchell (Mgr-Acctg)

HOOK'S CHEESE COMPANY, INC.
320 Commerce St, Mineral Point, WI 53565
Tel.: (608) 987-3259
Web Site: https://hookscheese.com
Sales Range: $10-24.9 Million
Emp.: 2
Cheese Mfr
N.A.I.C.S.: 311513
Tony Hook (Pres & Treas)
Julie Hook (VP)

HOOKED MEDIA, LLC
701 Brazos St, Austin, TX 78701
Tel.: (512) 669-5000
Web Site:
　　http://www.reviewpush.com
Year Founded: 2011
Sales Range: $1-9.9 Million
Software Services
N.A.I.C.S.: 513210
Lee McNiel (Founder & CEO)

HOOKER NATIONAL BANCSHARES, INC.
119 N Broadway, Hooker, OK 73945
Tel.: (580) 652-2448　　OK
Web Site:
　　http://www.hookerbank.com
Year Founded: 1986
Sales Range: $1-9.9 Million
Emp.: 25
Bank Holding Company
N.A.I.C.S.: 551111
Charles Butler (Pres)

Subsidiaries:

The First National Bank of
Hooker　　　　　　　　　　　(1)
119 N Broadway, Hooker, OK 73945
Tel.: (580) 652-2448
Web Site: http://www.hookerbank.com
Sales Range: $1-9.9 Million
Emp.: 26
Commericial Banking
N.A.I.C.S.: 522110
Shanon Butler (Sr VP)

HOOKSETT KAWASAKI, INC.
1354 Hooksett Rd, Hooksett, NH 03106
Tel.: (603) 668-4343
Web Site:
　　https://www.hkpowersports.com
Year Founded: 1976
Sales Range: $10-24.9 Million
Emp.: 40
Sales of Motorcycles & Snowmobiles
N.A.I.C.S.: 441227
Jim Whalley (CEO)

HOOLEON CORPORATION
304 W Denby Ave, Melrose, NM 88124
Tel.: (928) 634-7515　　AZ
Web Site: http://www.hooleon.com
Year Founded: 1982

Computer Keyboards & Accessories Mfr
N.A.I.C.S.: 334118
Joan Crozier (Co-Founder)
Bob Crozier (Co-Founder)

HOOPER CORPORATION
2030 Pennsylvania Ave, Madison, WI 53704-4746
Tel.: (608) 249-0451　　WI
Web Site:
　　http://www.hoopercorp.com
Year Founded: 1959
Sales Range: $350-399.9 Million
Emp.: 400
Provider of Utility Construction Services
N.A.I.C.S.: 237130
Robert Schaller (Controller)
Doug Smithback (Project Mgr)
Steve Lindley (Pres)

Subsidiaries:

General Heating & Air Conditioning
Inc.　　　　　　　　　　　　(1)
PO Box 259596, Madison, WI 53725-9596
Tel.: (608) 271-3900
Web Site: http://www.generalheating.com
Sales Range: $25-49.9 Million
Emp.: 300
Provider of Plumbing, Heating & Air Conditioning Services
N.A.I.C.S.: 238220
Brad Werlein (Pres)

HOOSIER CARE PROPERTIES, INC.
1600 Division St, Nashville, TN 37203
Tel.: (615) 252-2305　　IN
Year Founded: 2003
Sales Range: $10-24.9 Million
Elder Care Services
N.A.I.C.S.: 623312
John G. Foos (VP & Asst Sec)
Bruce Hutson (Pres)
John E. Gillmor (Sec & VP)
Stephen F. Wood Sr. (CEO, Treas & VP)

HOOSIER ENERGY RURAL ELECTRIC COOPERATIVE INC.
2501 S Cooperative Way, Bloomington, IN 47403
Tel.: (812) 876-2021　　IN
Web Site: http://hoosierenergy.com
Year Founded: 1935
Electric Generation & Transmission Cooperative
N.A.I.C.S.: 221118
Donna Walker (Pres & CEO)
Tom Van Paris (Exec VP-Member Engagement)
Rob Horton (COO)
Bob Richhart (CTO)
David Sandefur (VP-Ops)
Chris Blunk (VP-Corp Svcs)
R.M. Mike Rampley (Sr VP)
Chris Goffinet (Gen Counsel)
Tommy Roberts (Mgr-Engrg Svcs)
Matt Randall (Mgr-Pub Policy & Community Rels)

HOOSIER EQUIPMENT BROKERS, INC.
5604 Fortune Circle Dr S Ste Ad, Indianapolis, IN 46241
Tel.: (317) 788-6920
Web Site: https://www.hebusa.com
Sales Range: $10-24.9 Million
Emp.: 14
Electronic Equipment Whslr
N.A.I.C.S.: 423690
Patrick Sullivan (Pres)

HOOSIER HILLS CREDIT UNION
630 Lincoln Ave, Bedford, IN 47421
Tel.: (812) 279-6644　　IN
Web Site:
　　http://www.hoosierhillscu.org
Year Founded: 1933
Sales Range: $10-24.9 Million
Emp.: 177
Credit Union Operator
N.A.I.C.S.: 522130
Steven D. Hawkins (Chief Credit Officer & Sr VP)
George McNichols (Pres)
Joe Ward (CFO)
Nan Morrow (CMO)
Cole Watson (Controller)
Debbie Reynolds (VP-Comml Svcs)

HOOSIER INVESTMENT LLC
4101 Edison Lakes Pkwy Ste 350, 46545, Mishawaka, IN
Tel.: (574) 931-2989　　IN
Web Site:
　　https://www.hoosierinvestments.com
Year Founded: 2016
Emp.: 100
Holding Company
N.A.I.C.S.: 551112
Jay Wilkinson (Founder & CEO)

Subsidiaries:

Albion Staffing Solutions Inc.　　(1)
2520 NW 97th Ave 110, Doral, FL 33172
Tel.: (305) 406-1000
Web Site: http://www.albionstaffing.com
Administrative Management & General Management Consulting Service
N.A.I.C.S.: 541611
Peter Santangelo (Pres)
David Del Rio (Mgr-Content)
Yamila Llanez (Dir-First Impressions)

HOOSIER MAGNETICS INC.
110 Denny St, Ogdensburg, NY 13669
Tel.: (315) 393-2203
Web Site:
　　https://www.hoosiermagnetics.com
Year Founded: 1975
Sales Range: $10-24.9 Million
Emp.: 50
Mfr of Ferrite Magnetic Powder
N.A.I.C.S.: 327110

HOOSIER UPLANDS ECONOMIC DEVELOPMENT CORPORATION
500 W Main St, Mitchell, IN 47446
Tel.: (812) 849-4447　　IN
Web Site:
　　https://www.hoosieruplands.org
Year Founded: 1966
Sales Range: $10-24.9 Million
Emp.: 334
Economic Development Services
N.A.I.C.S.: 541720
Ginger Knight (Dir-Administrative Services & Coord-Program Scholarship)
Andrew Wolber (Dir-Information Technology)
David L. Miller (CEO)

HOOTEN'S, LLC.
1139 W Lennon Dr, Emory, TX 75440-3049
Tel.: (903) 473-8788
Web Site:
　　https://www.hootensteel.com
Year Founded: 1994
Sales Range: $10-24.9 Million
Emp.: 40
Hardware Whslr
N.A.I.C.S.: 423710
Lance Hooten (Pres)
Darren Renshaw (Mgr)

HOOTERS MANAGEMENT CORPORATION
107 Hampton Rd Ste 200, Clearwater, FL 33759
Tel.: (727) 725-2551　　FL
Web Site:
　　http://www.originalhooters.com
Year Founded: 1983
Sales Range: $75-99.9 Million
Emp.: 800
Restaurant Management
N.A.I.C.S.: 722511
Chuck Riley (VP-Pur)
Nathan Weatherilt (Controller)
Dan Babbitt (Dir-Admin)
Rachael Reidenbach (Dir-Recruiting)
Jack Wagner (Gen Mgr)
Daniel Linn (Mgr)
Bill Moore (VP)

HOOVER CHRYSLER JEEP INC.
195 Mary Meade Dr, Summerville, SC 29483
Tel.: (843) 873-1114
Web Site:
　　http://www.hooverthemover.com
Sales Range: $50-74.9 Million
Emp.: 85
Car Dealership
N.A.I.C.S.: 441110
Ronald E. Hoover (Pres)
Keith Robert (Gen Mgr)

HOOVER CONSTRUCTION COMPANY
PO Box 1007, Virginia, MN 55792
Tel.: (218) 741-3280
Web Site:
　　http://www.hooverconstruction.biz
Sales Range: $10-24.9 Million
Emp.: 108
Highway Construction Heavy
N.A.I.C.S.: 237310
Peter G. Johnson (Pres & CEO)
Mike Riley (Controller)

HOOVER DODGE JEEP CHRYSLER, INC.
2250 Savannah Hwy, Charleston, SC 29414
Tel.: (843) 763-0040
Year Founded: 1970
Sales Range: $25-49.9 Million
Emp.: 40
New Car Whslr
N.A.I.C.S.: 441110
Jadd Buchanan (Gen Mgr-Sls)
Margie M. Cook (Mgr)
Mark Hoover (Owner)
Ron E. Hoover (Pres & Principal)
Shawn Rustin (Gen Mgr)

HOOVER INC.
1205 Bridgestone Pkwy, La Vergne, TN 37086
Tel.: (615) 793-2600
Web Site: http://www.hoover-inc.com
Year Founded: 1955
Rev.: $19,100,000
Emp.: 58
Ready Mixed Concrete
N.A.I.C.S.: 327320

HOOVER WELLS, INC.
2011 Seaman St, Toledo, OH 43605
Tel.: (419) 691-9220　　OH
Web Site:
　　https://www.hooverwells.com
Year Founded: 1978
Sales Range: $10-24.9 Million
Emp.: 65
Floor Laying Services
N.A.I.C.S.: 238330

Barbara Corsini *(Sec)*
Barbara L. Corsini *(Sec)*
Margaret Hoover *(Pres)*
John Corsini *(VP)*

HOP INDUSTRIES CORPORATION

1251 Vly Brook Ave, Lyndhurst, NJ 07071
Tel.: (973) 458-1600
Web Site:
http://www.hopindustries.com
Year Founded: 1977
Sales Range: $50-74.9 Million
Emp.: 80
Mfr of Plastic Materials
N.A.I.C.S.: 424610
Maria Vieray *(CFO)*

HOPE GROUP CORPORATION

70 Barefoot Rd, Northborough, MA 01532
Tel.: (508) 393-7660
Web Site:
https://www.thehopegroup.com
Sales Range: $25-49.9 Million
Emp.: 122
Industrial Supplies
N.A.I.C.S.: 423840
Carey Rhoten *(CEO)*
Jim Levesque *(Mgr-Svcs)*
Brian Sanborn *(Gen Mgr-Sls)*

HOPE HOSPICE AND COMMUNITY SERVICES INC.

9470 HealthPark Cir, Fort Myers, FL 33908
Tel.: (239) 482-4673
Web Site: https://www.hopehcs.org
Year Founded: 1979
Sales Range: $125-149.9 Million
Emp.: 500
Women Healthcare Services
N.A.I.C.S.: 621610
Charlotte King *(Chief HR Officer)*
Jill Lampley *(CFO)*
Samira Kanaan Beckwith *(Pres & CEO)*

HOPE OF LIFE INTERNATIONAL

85 Whipple St, Providence, RI 02908
Tel.: (401) 421-9078   RI
Web Site:
http://www.hopeoflifeintl.org
Year Founded: 2008
Sales Range: $10-24.9 Million
Emp.: 6
Community Welfare Services
N.A.I.C.S.: 624190
Katie Arriaza *(Pres)*

HOPE RESTORATION MINISTRIES, INC.

101-01 Springfield Blvd, Queens Village, NY 11429
Tel.: (718) 217-4799   NY
Web Site:
https://www.hoperestoration.org
Year Founded: 1996
Sales Range: $10-24.9 Million
Poor & Needy People Assistance Services
N.A.I.C.S.: 624230
Reuben Chizor *(Pres)*

HOPE WORLDWIDE, LTD.

1285 Drummers Ln Ste 105, Wayne, PA 19087
Tel.: (610) 254-8800   PA
Web Site: http://www.hopeww.org
Year Founded: 1991
Sales Range: $10-24.9 Million
Emp.: 177
Community Action Services
N.A.I.C.S.: 624190

Gary Jacques *(VP-Health & Social Svcs)*
Walter Kotkowski *(VP-Procurement)*
Catherine Shump *(Dir-Development)*
Dan Liu *(Chm)*
Charles Ham *(Coord-Disaster Response Svcs)*
Ian Correa *(Dir-India)*
Marc Aguirre *(Dir-South Africa)*
Russ Hargrove *(Chief Dev Officer)*
Wil Horwood *(Dir-United Kingdom)*

HOPE'S WINDOWS, INC.

84 Hopkins Ave, Jamestown, NY 14702-0580
Tel.: (716) 665-5124   DE
Web Site:
https://www.hopeswindows.com
Year Founded: 1912
Sales Range: $10-24.9 Million
Emp.: 230
Mfr of Steel Custom Windows
N.A.I.C.S.: 332321
Mary Lausterer *(VP)*
Alicia Troutman *(Mgr-Accts Receivable)*

HOPEDALE MEDICAL FOUNDATION

107 Tremont St, Hopedale, IL 61747
Tel.: (309) 449-3321   IL
Web Site:
https://www.hopedalemc.com
Year Founded: 1961
Sales Range: $10-24.9 Million
Emp.: 443
Health Care Srvices
N.A.I.C.S.: 622110
Mark F. Rossi *(COO)*

HOPEHEALTH

765 Attucks Ln, Hyannis, MA 02601
Tel.: (508) 957-0200   MA
Web Site:
http://www.hopehealthco.org
Year Founded: 1980
Sales Range: $25-49.9 Million
Emp.: 299
Patient Safety & Health Care Improvement Services
N.A.I.C.S.: 813212

HOPEHEALTH, INC.

600 E Palmetto St, Florence, SC 29506
Tel.: (843) 667-9414   SC
Web Site: https://www.hope-health.org
Year Founded: 1991
Sales Range: $25-49.9 Million
Emp.: 321
Health Care Srvices
N.A.I.C.S.: 622110
Celeste Johnson *(Dir-HR)*
Deena Hilton *(COO)*
Mark Vinson *(CFO)*
Christine Gordon *(Dir-Site)*
Carl M. Humphries *(CEO)*
Jayson Grice *(Dir-Quality Improvement)*
Mulamba Lunda *(Dir-Program Svcs)*
Darryl Bridges *(Chm)*
Jeannette Glenn *(Co-Chm)*
Ken Burgess *(Chief Performance Officer)*

HOPEWELL HEALTH CENTERS INC.

1049 Western Ave, Chillicothe, OH 45601
Tel.: (740) 773-4366
Web Site:
http://www.hopewellhealth.org
Healtcare Services
N.A.I.C.S.: 621111

Mark Bridenbaugh *(CEO)*
Sherry Shamblin *(Head-Behavioral Health Ops)*
Brad Nelson *(CFO)*
David Schenkelberg *(Chief Clinical Officer)*
Douglas Carr *(Chief Medical Officer)*

Subsidiaries:

Athens Behavioral Health Clinic   (1)
90 Hospital Dr, Athens, OH 45701
Tel.: (740) 592-3091
Web Site: http://www.tcmhcs.org
Sales Range: $10-24.9 Million
Emp.: 234
Behavioral Health Services
N.A.I.C.S.: 623220
Amanda Putnam *(Dir-HR)*
Mark Bridenbaugh *(CEO)*
Brad Nelson *(CFO)*
David Schenkelberg *(Chief Clinical Officer)*

Hopewell Health Centers Inc.   (1)
90 Hospital Dr, Athens, OH 45701-2301
Tel.: (740) 592-3091
Sales Range: $1-9.9 Million
Emp.: 20
Substance Abuse & Counseling Services
N.A.I.C.S.: 621420
Kathy Koska *(Mgr-IT)*
Kendall Brown-Clovis *(Dir-HR)*

HOPEWELL INDUSTRIES INC.

637 Chestnut St, Coshocton, OH 43812
Tel.: (740) 622-3563   OH
Web Site:
http://www.hopewellindustries.org
Year Founded: 1972
Sales Range: Less than $1 Million
Emp.: 146
Developmental Disability Assistance Services
N.A.I.C.S.: 623210
Mary Thom Pson-Hufford *(CEO)*

HOPKINS AUTO SUPPLY INC.

620 NE Kelly Ave, Gresham, OR 97030
Tel.: (503) 661-1552
Web Site:
http://www.thriftyautosupply.com
Rev.: $12,000,000
Emp.: 10
Automotive Parts
N.A.I.C.S.: 441330
Steven J. Hopkins *(Pres)*

HOPKINS FINANCIAL CORPORATION

100 E Havens Ave, Mitchell, SD 57301
Tel.: (605) 996-7775
Web Site:
https://www.cortrustbank.com
Year Founded: 1980
Bank Holding Company
N.A.I.C.S.: 551111
Jack E. Hopkins *(Pres & CEO)*

Subsidiaries:

CorTrust Bank N.A.   (1)
100 E Havens & Main St, Mitchell, SD 57301
Tel.: (605) 996-7775
Web Site: http://www.cortrustbank.com
Federal Savings Bank
N.A.I.C.S.: 522180
Jeff Smith *(CFO)*
Jack E. Hopkins *(Pres & CEO)*
Terry Torgerson *(Sr VP & Branch Mgr-Mitchell Havens)*
Audrey Stahl *(VP)*
Jay Gikas *(Sr VP & Mgr-Twin Cities Market)*
Diane Guthmiller *(VP & Dir-CorClub)*
John Heisler *(Sr VP-Wealth Mgmt & Mgr-Svc Div)*
Vanessa Klemme *(Mgr-Client Rels)*
Laurie Knutson *(Mgr-Client Rels)*

Nicole Nelson *(Mgr-Trust Ops)*
Dan Korbel *(VP & Mgr-Woodbury)*
Lynette Clayton *(VP & Mgr-Blaine)*

HOPKINS FORD, INC.

1650 The Fairway, Jenkintown, PA 19046
Tel.: (215) 886-5900
Web Site:
https://fordofjenkintown.com
Sales Range: $75-99.9 Million
Emp.: 100
New Car Dealers
N.A.I.C.S.: 441110
Jim Kennedy *(Mgr-Used Car)*
Tony DePasque *(Dir-Fin)*
Steve Jenet *(Dir-Svc)*
Grant Goodhart *(Dir-Parts)*
Linda Kring *(Controller)*
Michael Zaneski *(Mgr-Collision Center)*
Paul Hennessey *(Mgr-Comml Truck)*
Marty Reid *(Mgr-Sls)*
Chris Kennedy *(Gen Mgr)*

HOPKINS PONTIAC-GMC TRUCKS

4909 Hwy 90, Marianna, FL 32446
Tel.: (850) 526-3456
Web Site:
http://www.hopkinsmarianna.com
Sales Range: $25-49.9 Million
Emp.: 10
New & Used Car Dealership
N.A.I.C.S.: 441110
William H. Hopkins *(Pres)*
Gail Young *(Controller)*

HOPKINSVILLE ELEVATOR COMPANY, INC.

1040 Skyline Dr, Hopkinsville, KY 42241-0767
Tel.: (270) 886-5191   KY
Web Site: http://www.hop-elevator.com
Year Founded: 1968
Sales Range: $75-99.9 Million
Emp.: 40
Agricultural Services
N.A.I.C.S.: 424510
James E. Doss *(Treas & Gen Mgr)*
David Spain *(Pres)*
Heather Montgomery *(Office Mgr)*

Subsidiaries:

Commonwealth Agri-Energy, LLC   (1)
4895 Pembroke Rd, Hopkinsville, KY 42241
Tel.: (270) 475-4415
Web Site:
http://www.commonwealthagrienergy.com
Emp.: 30
Methanol Mfr
N.A.I.C.S.: 325193
David Brame *(Chm)*
Mick Henderson *(Gen Mgr)*
Phillip Garnett *(Vice Chm)*
Wayne Hunt *(Sec)*

HOPKINSVILLE MILLING CO.

2001 S Walnut St, Hopkinsville, KY 42240-4660
Tel.: (270) 886-1231   KY
Web Site:
https://www.sunflourflour.com
Year Founded: 1874
Sales Range: $10-24.9 Million
Emp.: 20
Flour Milling
N.A.I.C.S.: 311211
G. N. Harper *(Chm)*
Robert Y. Harper *(Pres)*
John Redmond *(Mgr-Sls)*
Ray Clark *(Treas & Sec)*

HOPSON HOLDINGS INCORPORATED

Hopson Holdings Incorporated—(Continued)

3700 Murchison Rd, Fayetteville, NC 28311
Tel.: (910) 488-5594
Sales Range: $1-9.9 Million
Emp.: 327
Contract Truck Hauling Services
N.A.I.C.S.: 484110
Julian A. Hopson (Chm)
Allen C. Hopson (Pres)
W. Scott Hopson (VP)
Sara W. Hopson (Sec)

HOPSON OIL CO. INC.
1225 Whiterock Ave, Waukesha, WI 53186
Tel.: (262) 542-5343
Web Site: http://www.hopsonoil.com
Sales Range: $50-74.9 Million
Emp.: 32
Petroleum Bulk Wholesale & Retail, Heating & A/C Systems Maintenance & Installation
N.A.I.C.S.: 424710
Terry Nagel (Pres)
Tom Nagel (VP)

HORACE G. ILDERTON INC.
701-09 S Main St, High Point, NC 27260
Tel.: (336) 841-6100
Web Site: http://www.ilderton.com
Rev.: $48,838,383
Emp.: 80
Automobiles, New & Used
N.A.I.C.S.: 441110
Christine Dowdy (Controller)

HORAN CAPITAL MANAGEMENT, LLC
230 Schilling Cir Ste 234, Hunt Valley, MD 21031
Tel.: (410) 494-4380
Web Site: http://www.horancm.com
Year Founded: 1995
Sales Range: $1-9.9 Million
Financial & Investment Advisory Services
N.A.I.C.S.: 523940
Patrick J. Horan (Chm)
John G. Heinlein (CEO & Portfolio Mgr)
Paul J. Piccone (Dir-Ops & IT)
Matt M. Rockstroh (COO)

HORAN CONSTRUCTION
1720 W Chanute, Peoria, IL 61615
Tel.: (309) 691-3133
Web Site:
http://www.horanconstruction.com
Year Founded: 1948
Sales Range: $10-24.9 Million
Emp.: 14
Commercial & Institutional Building Construction
N.A.I.C.S.: 236220
Sue Arnholt (Pres)
Charles Kim (Project Mgr)
Katie Arnholt Kim (VP)
Wayne Palmer (VP)

HORATIO ALGER ASSOCIATION OF DISTINGUISHED AMERICANS, INC.
99 Canal Center Plz Ste 320, Alexandria, VA 22314
Tel.: (703) 684-9444
Web Site:
https://www.horatioalger.org
Year Founded: 1951
Sales Range: $10-24.9 Million
Emp.: 91
Grantmaking Services
N.A.I.C.S.: 813211

Margaret Slipek (Mgr-Editorial Svcs)
Julie Reames (Dir-Program Svcs)
Terrence J. Giroux (Exec Dir)

HORCHATA FROZEN DESSERT SANDWICH FARCHITECTURE BB, LLC
310 Washington Blvd, Culver City, CA 90232
Tel.: (310) 853-8995
Web Site: http://www.cool.haus
Year Founded: 2009
Sales Range: $10-24.9 Million
Emp.: 50
Ice Cream Product Mfr
N.A.I.C.S.: 311520
Natasha Case (Founder, CEO & Creative Dir)

HORD COPLAN MACHT, INC.
750 E Pratt St Ste 1100, Baltimore, MD 21202
Tel.: (410) 837-7311
Web Site: http://www.hcm2.com
Year Founded: 1998
Sales Range: $25-49.9 Million
Emp.: 100
Support Services
N.A.I.C.S.: 561499
Jim Albert (Principal)
Peter Winebrenner (VP)
Gary Prager (Principal)
Lyn Eller (Principal-Denver)
Joe Schneider (Mng Principal-DC Metro)
Michelle Horn (Principal/Dir-Interior Design-Denver)
Robyn Bartling (Principal/Dir-Landscape Architecture Studio-Denver)
Zack Shankman (Gen Counsel)
Lee Coplan (CEO)

HORD LIVESTOCK COMPANY, INC.
PO Box 808, Bucyrus, OH 44820
Tel.: (419) 562-5934
Web Site:
http://www.hordlivestock.com
Sales Range: $1-9.9 Million
Emp.: 66
Pig, Cow & Grain Farm Services
N.A.I.C.S.: 112210
Pat Hord (Pres & CEO)
Robin Davis (Chief People Officer)
Matt Davis (COO-Swine Div)
Jay Shawk (Dir-Risk Mgmt & Nutritional Svcs)
Janel Hord (Dir-Admin Svcs)
Rod Rowlinson (Dir-Crop Production)

Subsidiaries:

Hord Family Farms LLC   (1)
PO Box 808, Bucyrus, OH 44820
Tel.: (419) 562-5934
Web Site: https://www.hordlivestock.com
Pig, Cow & Grain Farm Services
N.A.I.C.S.: 112210

Subsidiary (Domestic):

New Horizon Farm LLP   (2)
319 N Hiawatha Ave, Pipestone, MN 56164
Tel.: (507) 825-5462
Web Site: http://www.newhorizonfarms.com
Farming
N.A.I.C.S.: 112112
Robert Taubert (Pres)

HORICH PARKS LEBOW ADVERTISING
101 Shilling Rd Ste 30, Hunt Valley, MD 21031
Tel.: (410) 329-1950
Year Founded: 1989
Rev.: $25,000,000
Emp.: 35

Advertising Agencies, Cable T.V., Consumer Marketing, Newspaper, Planning & Consultation, Radio, Retail, T.V.
N.A.I.C.S.: 541810
Charles Horich (Pres & CEO)
Ronald Katzen (VP-Finance)
Jon Parks (Owner & Exec VP)
Brenda Hanlon (VP-Media)
Chip Hector (Partner & VP-Ops)
Win Snyder (Dir-Art)
Brad Lebow (COO & Sr VP)

HORICON STATE BANK
326 E Lake St, Horicon, WI 53032
Tel.: (920) 485-3040
Web Site:
https://www.horiconbank.com
Year Founded: 1896
Sales Range: $10-24.9 Million
Emp.: 100
Banking Services
N.A.I.C.S.: 522110
Bryon Pysek (Sr VP)

HORIX MANUFACTURING COMPANY
1384 Island Ave, McKees Rocks, PA 15136-2518
Tel.: (412) 771-1111
Web Site: http://www.horixmfg.com
Year Founded: 1903
Sales Range: $50-74.9 Million
Emp.: 25
Packaging & Processing Machinery Mfr
N.A.I.C.S.: 333993
Rob Felten (Mgr-Production)

HORIZON BEVERAGE CO.
45 Commerce Way, Norton, MA 02766
Tel.: (508) 587-1110
Web Site:
https://www.horizonbeverage.com
Year Founded: 1932
Sales Range: $50-74.9 Million
Emp.: 400
Distr of Alcoholic Beverages
N.A.I.C.S.: 424810
George Wright (Mgr-Sls)
Jennifer Ouellette (Mgr-Sls)
Mark Morin (VP-Wine Sls-New Hampshire)
Tim Murphy (Mgr-Sls)

HORIZON BUSINESS SERVICES, INC.
801 Orchid Dr, Naples, FL 34102
Tel.: (239) 261-5828   FL
Web Site: https://www.caterease.com
Year Founded: 1973
Sales Range: $1-9.9 Million
Emp.: 50
Catering Software Developer
N.A.I.C.S.: 513210
Robin Hooper (Controller)
Joseph R. Biasella (Mgr-IT & Support)

HORIZON CREDIT UNION
PO Box 15128, Spokane Valley, WA 99215
Tel.: (509) 921-6729   WA
Web Site: https://www.hzcu.org
Year Founded: 1947
Sales Range: $25-49.9 Million
Emp.: 257
Credit Union
N.A.I.C.S.: 522130
Greg Robinson (VP)

HORIZON DEVELOPMENT GROUP, INC.
5201 E Terrace Dr Ste 300, Madison, WI 53718

Tel.: (608) 354-0900
Web Site:
https://www.horizondbm.com
Rev.: $121,400,000
Emp.: 70
Commercial & Institutional Building Construction
N.A.I.C.S.: 236220
C. J. Wessel (Dir-Leasing & Mktg)
Ryan Alvin (Principal)

HORIZON DISTRIBUTION, INC.
811 Summitview, Yakima, WA 98902
Tel.: (509) 453-3181
Web Site:
https://www.horizondistribution.com
Sales Range: $100-124.9 Million
Emp.: 68
Hardware Merchant Whslr
N.A.I.C.S.: 423710
Connie Alseth (Mgr-Adv)
Sabina Foster (Acct Mgr)
Kenneth R. Marble (Pres)
Dan Marples (COO)

HORIZON EQUIPMENT
402 6th St, Manning, IA 51455
Tel.: (712) 653-2574
Web Site:
http://www.horizonequip.com
Sales Range: $25-49.9 Million
Emp.: 88
Farm Implements Whslr
N.A.I.C.S.: 423820
Dale Reinke (VP-Parts Ops)

HORIZON FOOD GROUP, INC.
1 Bush Ste 650, San Francisco, CA 94104
Tel.: (415) 394-9700
Web Site:
http://www.horizonfoodgroup.com
Rev.: $103,800,000
Emp.: 250
Roasted Coffee
N.A.I.C.S.: 424490
Lee Rucker (CFO)
Phil Estes (Chief Admin Officer)
Robert Sharp (CEO)

Subsidiaries:

Horizon Snack Foods of Cal   (1)
7066 Las Positas Rd Ste G, Livermore, CA 94550
Tel.: (925) 373-7700
Rev.: $12,267,850
Emp.: 70
Pies, Bakery: Except Frozen
N.A.I.C.S.: 311812

HORIZON FOODS COMPANY
1021 Crown Park Cir, Winter Garden, FL 34787
Tel.: (407) 877-6944
Web Site:
https://www.horizonfoodbrokers.com
Sales Range: $1-9.9 Million
Emp.: 10
Bond Brokers
N.A.I.C.S.: 424410
John Brauner (Founder)

HORIZON FREIGHT SYSTEM INC.
6600 Bessemer Ave, Cleveland, OH 44127
Tel.: (216) 341-7410
Web Site:
http://www.horizonfreightsystem.com
Sales Range: $25-49.9 Million
Emp.: 150
Trucking, National
N.A.I.C.S.: 484121
David Ferrante (Pres)

Subsidiaries:

Horizon Freight System   (1)

351 Doremus Ave, Newark, NJ 07105
Tel.: (973) 491-9514
Web Site:
   http://www.horizonfreightsystem.com
Rev.: $97,000
Emp.: 2
Freight Terminal Services
N.A.I.C.S.: 484121

HORIZON GROUP USA INC.
76 Stirling Rd, Warren, NJ 07059
Tel.: (908) 810-1111
Web Site:
   http://www.horizongroupusa.com
Sales Range: $50-74.9 Million
Emp.: 25
Trimmings, Apparel
N.A.I.C.S.: 424310
Alexandra Meyer (Product Mgr)
Bruce Diamond (Mgr-Credit)
Diana Castellanos (Dir-Category)
Jennifer Abele (Sr Dir-Sourcing)
Janet Hsu (CEO)
Roshan Wijerama (Owner & Chm)

HORIZON HEALTH CARE, INC.
208 S Main St, Howard, SD 57349
Tel.: (605) 772-4525   SD
Web Site:
   https://www.horizonhealthcare.org
Year Founded: 1977
Emp.: 250
Medical & Dental Clinics
N.A.I.C.S.: 621111
John Mengenhausen (CEO)
Wade Erickson (CFO)
Scott Weatherill (CIO)
Christina Konechne (COO)
Lance Lim (Chief Medical Officer)
Michelle Scholtz (Chief Dental Officer)

HORIZON HEALTH SERVICES, INC.
3020 Bailey Ave, Buffalo, NY 14215
Tel.: (716) 831-1800   NY
Web Site: https://www.horizon-
health.org
Year Founded: 1975
Sales Range: $1-9.9 Million
Emp.: 43
Health Care Srvices
N.A.I.C.S.: 622110
Anne D. Constantino (Pres & CEO)
Donald J. Will (VP-Infrastructure & Resource Mgmt)
Erin E. Ryan (CFO & Exec VP)
Brenda John-Banach (VP-Mental Health Ops)
Michelle Curto (VP-Admin Ops)
Veronica A. Meldrum (VP-Employee Svcs)
Kevin D. Robinson (Vice Chm)
Karen Merkel (Sec)
Michael Maxwell (Chm)
Paige K. Prentice (VP-Ops)
Judith Tejada (VP-Clinical Svcs)
Jack Sieber (Vice Chm)
Jacob Haacker (Chief Security Officer)

HORIZON HEALTHCARE SERVICES, INC.
3 Penn Plz E, Newark, NJ 07105-2200
Tel.: (888) 765-7786
Web Site:
   http://www.horizonblue.com
Year Founded: 1932
Sales Range: $5-14.9 Billion
Emp.: 5,300
Medical Insurance Plans
N.A.I.C.S.: 524114
Robert A. Marino (CEO & Pres)
Christopher M. Lepre (Sr VP-Market Bus Units)

David R. Huber (CFO, Treas & Sr VP)
Douglas E. Blackwell (CIO & Sr VP)
Mark L. Barnard (Sr VP)
Kevin P. Conlin (COO & Exec VP)
Linda A. Willett (Gen Counsel, Sec & Sr VP)
Erhardt H. L. Preitauer (Sr VP-Govt Programs)
Allen J. Karp (Sr VP-Healthcare Mgmt)
William J. Castner (Sr VP-Corp & Regulatory Affairs)
Margaret M. Coons (Sr VP-HR)
Minalkumar A. Patel (Chief Strategy Officer & Sr VP)

HORIZON HOBBY DISTRIBUTORS
4105 Fieldstone Rd, Champaign, IL 61822
Tel.: (217) 352-1913
Web Site:
   http://www.horizonhobby.com
Sales Range: $10-24.9 Million
Emp.: 500
Hobby Goods
N.A.I.C.S.: 423920
Robert Peak (CFO)

HORIZON HOLDINGS LLC
1 Push St Ste 650, San Francisco, CA 94104-4412
Tel.: (415) 788-2000
Web Site:
   https://www.horizonholdings.com
Year Founded: 1989
Sales Range: $100-124.9 Million
Emp.: 4
Investor in & Holding Company of Manufacturers & Distributors of Food, Beverages, Recreational & Consumer Products
N.A.I.C.S.: 424490
Martha C. Parriott (Office Mgr)

Subsidiaries:

Coffee Partners LP   (1)
1 Bush St Ste 650, San Francisco, CA 94104
Tel.: (415) 788-2000
Web Site: http://www.horizonholdings.com
Rev.: $15,300,000
Emp.: 2
Coffee Products
N.A.I.C.S.: 424490
Phil S. Estes (Co-Chm)

HORIZON HOLDINGS, INC.
6101 S 58th St Ste B, Lincoln, NE 68516
Tel.: (402) 421-6400
Web Site:
   http://www.horizonholding.com
Sales Range: $10-24.9 Million
Emp.: 15
Fast-Food Restaurant, Chain
N.A.I.C.S.: 551112
Dennis Erickson (Pres)
Sherrie Tepe (CFO)

HORIZON HOSPICE AND PALLIATIVE CARE
833 W Chicago Ave, Chicago, IL 60642
Tel.: (312) 733-8900   IL
Web Site:
   http://www.horizonhospice.org
Year Founded: 1978
Sales Range: $10-24.9 Million
Emp.: 156
Hospice & Palliative Care Services
N.A.I.C.S.: 623110
Licia Chiazim (VP-Dev & Comm)
Joanna L. Martin (Dir-Medical)
Michael T. Kolbuk (CFO)
John Brodson (Treas)

William W. Wachs (Chm)
Ada F. Addington (Founder)
Carol Asher (Sec)
Sally L. Downey (Vice Chm)

HORIZON HOTELS LTD.
99 Corvett Way Ste 302, Eatontown, NJ 07724
Tel.: (732) 935-9553
Web Site:
   https://www.horizonhotels.com
Year Founded: 1976
Sales Range: $300-349.9 Million
Emp.: 4,000
Hotel & Motel Management Services
N.A.I.C.S.: 721110
Cynthia Cox Olcott (Pres)
Robert A. Sacco (CFO & Sr VP)
Diane Sacco (VP)
Donna Post (VP-Res)

HORIZON HOUSE
900 University St, Seattle, WA 98101
Tel.: (206) 624-3700   WA
Web Site:
   https://www.horizonhouse.org
Year Founded: 1960
Sales Range: $25-49.9 Million
Emp.: 406
Elderly People Assisted Living Services
N.A.I.C.S.: 623312
Ed Mawe (COO)
Mike Ostrem (CFO)
Sara McVey (CEO)
Cathleen McGaffigan (Dir-Mktg)

HORIZON HOUSE PUBLICATIONS INC.
685 Canton St, Norwood, MA 02062
Tel.: (781) 769-9750
Web Site:
   https://www.horizonhouse.com
Rev.: $25,000,000
Emp.: 75
Trade Journals Publishing
N.A.I.C.S.: 513120
William Bazzy (CEO & Chm)
Ivar Bazzy (Pres)
Jared Bazzy (VP)

HORIZON INVESTMENTS, LLC
13024 Ballantyne Corporate Pl Suite 225, Charlotte, NC 28277
Web Site:
   http://www.horizoninvestments.com
Year Founded: 1995
Sales Range: $1-9.9 Million
Emp.: 30
Financial Consulting, Advisory & Investment Management Services
N.A.I.C.S.: 541618
Robbie Cannon (CEO)
Josh Bartholomew (Dir-Natl Sls)
Dan O'Toole (Sr Mng Dir & Head-Sls-West)
Brian R. O'Toole (Chm)
John Drahzal (Head-Distr)
Scott Ladner (Chief Investment Officer)

HORIZON MEAT & SEAFOOD DISTRIBUTORS INC.
79 Express St Ste C, Plainview, NY 11803-2404
Tel.: (516) 937-1550   DE
Year Founded: 1981
Sales Range: $10-24.9 Million
Emp.: 75
Provider of Packaged Frozen Goods
N.A.I.C.S.: 424420
Michael D'Agostino (CEO)
Steve Carlin (Gen Mgr)
Dave Clutter (Mng Partner & Mgr-Sls-Atlanta)

Stephen Dean (Mng Partner & Mgr-Sls-Nashville)
Mark DosSantos (Mng Partner)
Chris Haley (Mng Partner & Mgr-Sls-Manchester)
Geoff Jackson (Mng Partner & Mgr-Sls-Dallas)
Lee Wood (Mgr-Sls-Albany Horizon Foods)
George Thomas (Mng Partner & Mgr-Sls-Middlesex)
Bill Smith (Mng Dir & Mng Partner-Baltimore)

Subsidiaries:

Horizon Meat & Seafood of Georgia Inc.   (1)
4451 S Atlanta Rd, Smyrna, GA 30045   (100%)
Tel.: (770) 436-7600
Web Site: http://www.horizonfood.com
Sales Range: $10-24.9 Million
Emp.: 15
Packaged Frozen Goods Distr
N.A.I.C.S.: 424420

HORIZON MEDIA, INC.
75 Varick St, New York, NY 10013
Tel.: (212) 220-5000   NY
Web Site:
   http://www.horizonmedia.com
Year Founded: 1989
Sales Range: $1-4.9 Billion
Emp.: 2,000
Media Buying Agency Services
N.A.I.C.S.: 541830
Bill Koenigsberg (Founder, Pres & CEO)
Gene Turner (Exec VP)
Eileen Benwitt (Chief Talent Officer)
Lauren Russo (Mng Dir-Audio & Promos & Sr VP)
Nancy Larkin (Mng Dir-Local Television & Sr VP)
Eva Kantrowitz (Chief Strategy Officer-Brand Dev)
Vinnie O'Toole (CFO & COO)
Taylor Valentine (Chief Learning & Invention Officer)
Molly Sugarman (Mng Dir-Treehouse & VP)
Stephen Hall (CMO)
Donald Williams (Chief Digital Officer)
Charlie Rutman (Mng Partner)
Karina Dobarro (Sr VP & Mng Dir-Multicultural)
Sarah Bachman (Sr VP)
Serena Duff (Exec VP & Gen Mgr-West)
Stan Fields (Chief Client Officer & Exec VP)
Rick Watrall (Chief Analytics Officer)
Kevin Kivi (Sr VP & Gen Mgr-Canada)
Steve Faske (Sr VP & Mng Dir-Bus & Legal Affairs)
Gordon Zellner (Mng Partner-Eden Road Trading)
Michael Neuman (Mng Partner-Scout Sports & Entertainment)
Jennifer Moore McCutcheon (Sr VP & Mng Dir-Trading-Eden Road)
Jon Venison (Partner-InsideOut Sports & Entertainment)
John Koenigsberg (Gen Mgr-Big)
Sandra Alfaro (Mng Partner-305 Worldwide & Exec VP)
Armando Christian Perez (Chief Creative Officer-305 Worldwide)
Randy Browning (Pres-Night Market)
Kimberly Chulis (VP-Data Science)
Coleen Kuehn (Chief Bus Solutions Officer & Exec VP)
Phil Mitchell (Mng Dir & Exec VP)
Latraviette Smith-Wilson (Chief Mktg & Equity Officer)

Horizon Media, Inc.—(Continued)

Subsidiaries:

Eurizon Media   (1)
Wilgenweg 28a, 1031 HV, Amsterdam,
Netherlands
Tel.: (31) 20 344 66 33
Web Site: http://www.eurizon.nl
Sales Range: $125-149.9 Million
Emp.: 5
N.A.I.C.S.: 541870

Horizon Direct   (1)
330 Madison Ave, New York, NY 10022
Tel.: (212) 916-3235
Sales Range: $10-24.9 Million
Emp.: 30
N.A.I.C.S.: 541613

Horizon Media, Inc. - Los
Angeles   (1)
1888 Century Park E, Los Angeles, CA
90067
Tel.: (310) 282-0909
Web Site: http://www.horizonmedia.com
Full Service, Media Buying Services
N.A.I.C.S.: 541830
Julie Levin *(Mng Partner-Client Svcs & Bus
Dev & Exec VP)*

Horizon Out-of-Home   (1)
75 Varick St, New York, NY 10013
Tel.: (212) 916-8600
Web Site: http://www.horizonmedia.com
Sales Range: $25-49.9 Million
Emp.: 100
Out-of-Home Media
N.A.I.C.S.: 541830

Horizon Print Services Group   (1)
75 Varick St, New York, NY 10017
Tel.: (212) 916-8600
Web Site: http://www.horizonmedia.com
Sales Range: $10-24.9 Million
Emp.: 7
Advertising Services
N.A.I.C.S.: 541830
Debbie Sklar *(Dir-Print Svcs)*
Stephen Hall *(Mng Dir)*
Bill Koenigsberg *(Founder, Pres & CEO)*
Aaron Cohen *(Chief Media Negotiating Offi-
cer)*
Eva Kantrowitz *(Mng Partner-Brand Strat-
egy)*

**HORIZON MORTGAGE COR-
PORATION**
200 S Washington Blvd Ste 8, Sara-
sota, FL 34236
Tel.: (941) 365-0450
Web Site:
   http://www.horizonmort.com
Sales Range: $75-99.9 Million
Emp.: 10
Mortgage Banking & Real Estate Bro-
kerage Services
N.A.I.C.S.: 522310
N.J. Olivieri *(Pres)*

HORIZON PAPER CO., INC.
100 1st Stamford Pl, Stamford, CT
06902-6740
Tel.: (203) 358-0855   **NY**
Web Site:
   http://www.horizonpaper.com
Year Founded: 1978
Sales Range: $75-99.9 Million
Emp.: 28
Printing Paper Mfr
N.A.I.C.S.: 424110
Robert B. Obernier *(Chm)*
W. Johnston *(Vice Chm)*
Jeffrey Hansen *(COO)*
Alan S. Guthrie *(Sr VP)*

HORIZON PARTNERS LTD.
3838 Tamiami Trl N Ste 408, Naples,
FL 34103
Tel.: (239) 261-0020
Web Site:
   https://www.horizonpartnersltd.com
Sales Range: $1-9.9 Million
Emp.: 3

William W. Wachel
Ada F. Additional
Scott Asher
Privater Equity Firm
N.A.I.C.S.: 523999
Robert M. Feerick *(Chm)*
William H. Schaar *(CFO)*
Ronni Reese *(Office Mgr)*

**HORIZON PROPERTIES OF
PENSACOLA**
1335 Creighton Rd, Pensacola, FL
32504-7138
Tel.: (850) 476-6000
Web Site:
   https://www.floridapropertyman
   ager.com
Sales Range: $50-74.9 Million
Emp.: 1,000
Brokers, Business: Buying & Selling
Business Enterprises
N.A.I.C.S.: 541990
Judy Schall *(Owner)*

HORIZON PUBLICATIONS INC.
1120 N Carbon St Ste 100, Marion,
IL 62959
Tel.: (618) 993-1711   **DE**
Web Site:
   http://www.horizonpublications
   inc.com
Rev.: $11,500,000
Emp.: 400
Newspaper Publishers
N.A.I.C.S.: 513110
Roland McBride *(VP)*
David Radler *(Pres)*
Leslie Carson *(Controller)*
Roger Harnack *(Publr-Colville & Deer
Park)*

Subsidiaries:

Appeal-Democrat   (1)
1530 Ellis Lake Dr, Marysville, CA 95901
Tel.: (530) 749-4700
Web Site: http://www.appeal-democrat.com
Emp.: 100
Newspaper Publishing Services
N.A.I.C.S.: 513110
Donna Blair *(Dir-HR)*

Daily Times Leader   (1)
221 E Main St, West Point, MS 39773-2926
Tel.: (662) 494-1422
Web Site: http://www.dailytimesleader.com
Sales Range: $10-24.9 Million
Emp.: 6
Commercial Printing & Newspaper Publish-
ing
N.A.I.C.S.: 513110
Don Norman *(Publr)*
Donna Harris *(Dir-Retail Adv)*

Horizon North Dakota Publications
Inc.   (1)
146 3rd St NE, Valley City, ND 58072-3047
Tel.: (701) 845-0463
Web Site: http://www.times-online.com
Sales Range: $10-24.9 Million
Newspaper Publishers
N.A.I.C.S.: 513110
J. Reed Anderson *(Publr)*
Tina Olson *(Mgr-Production)*
Brenda Tompt *(Office Mgr)*
Alysha Thompson *(Mgr-Circulation)*

Malvern Daily Record   (1)
219 Locust St, Malvern, AR 72104-3721
Tel.: (501) 337-7523
Web Site: http://www.malvern-online.com
Sales Range: $10-24.9 Million
Emp.: 15
Daily Newspaper Publisher
N.A.I.C.S.: 513110
Richard Folds *(Publr)*

Porterville Recorder   (1)
115 E Oak Ave, Porterville, CA 93257
Tel.: (559) 784-5000
Web Site: http://www.recorderonline.com
Sales Range: $10-24.9 Million
Emp.: 65
Newspaper Publishing Services
N.A.I.C.S.: 513110

Craig Dimmitt *(Bus Mgr)*
Josie Chapman *(Dir-Ops)*
Bill Parsons *(Publr)*

The Spirit Publishing Company   (1)
510 Pine St, Punxsutawney, PA 15767-
1404
Tel.: (814) 938-8740
Web Site:
   http://www.punxsutawneyspirit.com
Sales Range: $10-24.9 Million
Emp.: 30
Newspapers
N.A.I.C.S.: 513110
Tracy Smith *(Publr & Mgr-Adv)*

Yuma Sun   (1)
2055 Arizona Ave, Yuma, AZ 85364-6549
Tel.: (949) 253-2300
Web Site: http://www.yumasun.com
Sales Range: $25-49.9 Million
Emp.: 150
Newspaper Publishing
N.A.I.C.S.: 513110
Lisa Miller *(Dir-Adv)*
David Fornof *(Dir-Ops & Production)*
Bob Roeser *(Dir-Circulation)*
Randy Hoeft *(Editor-Photo)*

HORIZON RESOURCES
209 Washington Ave, Williston, ND
58801
Tel.: (701) 572-2171
Web Site:
   https://www.horizonresources.coop
Sales Range: $50-74.9 Million
Emp.: 100
Petroleum Products
N.A.I.C.S.: 424720
Jeff Wagner *(Pres & CEO)*
Jim Radtke *(CFO)*
Chris Quamme *(Mgr-Grain Div)*
Peggy Conlin *(Mgr-Credit)*

HORIZON ROOFING
2010 County Rd 137, Waite Park,
MN 56387-2081
Tel.: (320) 252-1608
Web Site:
   https://www.horizonroofinginc.com
Year Founded: 1976
Sales Range: $1-9.9 Million
Emp.: 36
Roofing Contractors
N.A.I.C.S.: 238160
Kurt Scepaniak *(Pres-Bus Dev)*
Robert Jodsaas *(Gen Mgr)*
Brad Kurr *(Mgr-Svc)*

HORIZON SALES, INC.
8525 Edinbrook Xing Ste 2, Brooklyn
Park, MN 55443-1900
Tel.: (763) 315-0553
Web Site:
   http://www.horizonsalesinc.com
Sales Range: $10-24.9 Million,
Emp.: 4
Meat Product Whslr
N.A.I.C.S.: 424470
Dean Uglem *(CEO)*
David Smith *(Mgr-Sls-Pittsburgh, Co-
lumbus, Dayton & Indianapolis)*

HORIZON SOLUTIONS CORP.
2005 Brighton Henrietta Town Line
Rd, Rochester, NY 14623-2509
Tel.: (585) 424-7376
Web Site: http://www.hs-e.com
Year Founded: 1982
Sales Range: $50-74.9 Million
Emp.: 225
Provider of Electrical Apparatus &
Equipment
N.A.I.C.S.: 423610
Mike Herrmann *(CFO)*
James Newton *(Co-Owner)*
Richard Wilson *(Co-Owner & Chm)*
Karen Baker *(COO)*
Kathy Biesecker *(Sr VP-HR)*
Don Harrington *(Exec VP-Ops & IT)*

David Hayes *(Exec VP-Sls & Mktg
Comm)*
Bruce France *(VP-Ops)*
John Kerkhove *(Pres & CEO)*
Doug Walo *(VP-Energy Svcs & Con-
struction Sls-East)*

HORIZON STAFFING INC.
650 Mount Zion Rd Ste D, Jones-
boro, GA 30236
Tel.: (770) 961-0751
Web Site:
   https://www.horizonstaffing.com
Sales Range: $10-24.9 Million
Emp.: 30
Temporary Help Service
N.A.I.C.S.: 561320
Ron Ramsey *(Pres)*
Mike Emmanuel *(VP)*
Becky Henslee *(Office Mgr)*
Stephenie Webb *(Branch Mgr)*

HORIZON STEEL COMPANY
350 Northgate Pkwy, Wheeling, IL
60090-2665
Tel.: (847) 291-0440   **IL**
Web Site:
   https://www.horizonsteel.com
Year Founded: 1983
Sales Range: $10-24.9 Million
Emp.: 65
Wholesale & Retail of Metals
N.A.I.C.S.: 423510
Mark Jacobs *(Chm)*

HORIZON STONE LLC
2515 E 43rd St, Chattanooga, TN
37407
Tel.: (423) 629-0801
Web Site: https://www.horizon-
   stone.com
Year Founded: 2003
Brick, Stone & Related Construction
Material Mfr & Whslr
N.A.I.C.S.: 423320
Brent Large *(CEO)*

Subsidiaries:

Majestic Stone, Inc.   (1)
6219 Ogden Rd, Dayton, TN 37321-6613
Tel.: (423) 775-1907
Web Site: http://majesticstone.com
Brick, Stone & Related Construction Mate-
rial Whslr
N.A.I.C.S.: 423320
John Bryant *(Project Mgr)*
Patrick Wells *(CEO)*

HORIZON SYSTEMS, INC.
1101 Horizon Dr, Lawrence, KS
66046
Tel.: (785) 842-1299
Web Site:
   http://www.horizonsystemsinc.com
Rev.: $2,300,000
Emp.: 30
Conveyor & Conveying Equipment
Mfr
N.A.I.C.S.: 333922
Todd Baker *(Dir-Tech)*
Steve Remmers *(VP-Sls)*

Subsidiaries:

Process Systems, Inc.   (1)
8082 County Road 112, Frisco, TX 75035
Tel.: (972) 529-9910
Sales Range: $1-9.9 Million
Emp.: 15
Plastics Product Mfr
N.A.I.C.S.: 326199
Doug Kirkpatrick *(Treas, Sec & VP)*

HORIZON TRANSPORT INC.
407 E Wabash Ave, Wakarusa, IN
46573
Tel.: (574) 862-2161
Web Site:
   http://www.horizontransport.com
Sales Range: $25-49.9 Million
Emp.: 30

Contract Haulers
N.A.I.C.S.: 484121
Marion Schrock *(Pres)*
Donna Throesch *(Mgr-Yard)*
Kyla Grass *(Coord-Compliance)*
Brent Freyenberger *(Mgr-Traffic)*
Dave Miller *(VP-Sls & Mktg)*
Dick Evans *(Mgr-Compliance)*

HORIZONS FOUNDATION
550 Montgomery St Ste 700, San
Francisco, CA 94111
Tel.: (415) 398-2333   CA
Web Site:
  http://www.horizonsfoundation.org
Year Founded: 1979
Sales Range: $10-24.9 Million
Emp.: 9
Philanthropic Services
N.A.I.C.S.: 813211
Francisco O. Buchting *(VP-Grants,
Programs & Strategic Initiatives)*
Roger Doughty *(Pres)*

HORIZONS INCORPORATED
18531 S Miles Rd, Cleveland, OH
44128
Tel.: (216) 475-0555
Web Site:
  https://www.horizonsisg.com
Sales Range: $10-24.9 Million
Emp.: 97
Plates, Photographic (Sensitized)
N.A.I.C.S.: 325992
Bridgid Lehane *(Supvr-Acctg)*
David Cozzi *(Dir-Corp Engrg)*
Krymowski Jay *(Dir-Tech)*
Scott Lehner *(Dir-Sls)*
Duignan Wayne *(Dir-Intl Sls)*
Randy Parrish *(Gen Mgr)*
Eric Covarrubias *(Dir-e-Commerce)*
Thomas Zbiegien *(CFO)*
Dan Burke *(Controller)*

HORIZONTAL INTEGRATION
1660 Hwy 100 S Ste 200, Saint Louis
Park, MN 55416
Tel.: (612) 392-7580
Web Site:
  http://www.horizontalintegration.com
Year Founded: 2003
Sales Range: $10-24.9 Million
Emp.: 500
It Consulting
N.A.I.C.S.: 541690
Jeremy Langevin *(Partner & Exec
VP-Staffing Agency)*
Sabin Ephrem *(Pres & CEO)*
Chris Staley *(Owner, Partner & Exec
VP-Digital Agency)*
Matt Fairchild *(VP-Tech)*
Reed Varner *(Mng Dir-Digital Agency)*
Jason Estes *(Mng Dir-Digital Agency-
Dallas)*

HORN PACKAGING CORPO-
RATION
580 Fort Pond Rd, Lancaster, MA
01523
Tel.: (978) 772-0290   MA
Web Site:
  http://www.hornpackaging.com
Year Founded: 1944
Sales Range: $75-99.9 Million
Emp.: 125
Mfr of Corrugated Paperboard Boxes
& Wooden Shipping Crates
N.A.I.C.S.: 322211
Peter Hamilton *(Pres)*
Michael Gill *(Controller)*
Scott Del Baugh *(Mgr-QA)*
James Tattan *(Sr Acct Mgr)*
Dan Bilek *(Sr Acct Mgr)*
Frank Trovato *(Mgr-Warehouse &
Distr)*

Subsidiaries:

Horn International Forwarding   **(1)**
580 Fort Pond Rd, Lancaster, MA 01523
Tel.: (978) 667-8797
Web Site: http://www.randwhitney.com
Sales Range: $25-49.9 Million
Deep Sea Foreign Transportation Of Freigh
N.A.I.C.S.: 483111
Nick Smith *(Pres)*
Mike Yost *(Mgr-Forwarding)*

Horn International Packaging   **(1)**
580 Fort Pond Rd, Lancaster, MA 01523
Tel.: (978) 667-8797
Web Site: http://www.safetytoday.com
Rev.: $5,000,000
Emp.: 40
Crates, Except Paper
N.A.I.C.S.: 423840
David R. Gomer *(Pres)*

HORNADY MANUFACTURING
COMPANY
3625 Old Potash Hwy, Grand Island,
NE 68803
Tel.: (308) 382-1390   NE
Web Site: https://www.hornady.com
Year Founded: 1949
Sales Range: $100-124.9 Million
Emp.: 175
Bullets Mfr; Premium Hunting &
Match Ammunition
N.A.I.C.S.: 332992
Steve Hornady *(Pres)*
Mark Kroeker *(Controller)*

HORNBECK OFFSHORE SER-
VICES, INC.
103 Northpark Blvd, Covington, LA
70433
Tel.: (985) 727-2000   DE
Web Site:
  http://www.hornbeckoffshore.com
Year Founded: 1997
Rev.: $225,662,000
Assets: $2,668,887,000
Liabilities: $1,496,442,000
Net Worth: $1,172,445,000
Earnings: ($138,814,000)
Emp.: 1,157
Fiscal Year-end: 12/31/19
Marine Transportation of Petroleum
Products & Oil Field Equipment &
Supplies
N.A.I.C.S.: 483211
Todd M. Hornbeck *(Chm, Pres &
CEO)*
Carl G. Annessa *(COO & Exec VP)*
Timothy P. McCarthy *(Chief HR Offi-
cer & Exec VP)*
James O. Harp Jr. *(CFO & Exec VP)*
Samuel A. Giberga *(Chief Compli-
ance Officer, Gen Counsel & Exec
VP)*
John S. Cook *(CIO, Chief Comml Of-
ficer & Exec VP)*
Peter Fortier *(VP-Sls)*
Randy Tredinich *(VP-Specialty Ops &
MPSV)*

Subsidiaries:

HOS Port, LLC   **(1)**
11 Norman Doucet Dr 3, Golden Meadow,
LA 70357
Tel.: (985) 396-2372
Web Site: http://www.hornbeckoffshore.com
Sales Range: $100-124.9 Million
Deep Sea Freight Transportation Services
N.A.I.C.S.: 483111
Andy Bruzdzinski *(Gen Mgr)*

Hornbeck Offshore Operators,
LLC   **(1)**
103 Northpark Blvd Ste 300, Covington, LA
70433
Tel.: (985) 727-2000
Web Site: http://www.hornbeckoffshore.com
Sales Range: $25-49.9 Million
Emp.: 100
Marine Cargo Transportation Services

N.A.I.C.S.: 488320
Hornbeck Offshore Services,
LLC   **(1)**
103 Northpark Blvd Ste 300, Covington, LA
70433
Tel.: (985) 727-3707
Web Site: http://www.hornbeckoffshore.com
Sales Range: $100-124.9 Million
Marine Cargo Transportation Services
N.A.I.C.S.: 488320

HORNBLOWER CRUISES &
EVENTS
Pier 3 The Embarcadero, San Fran-
cisco, CA 94111
Tel.: (415) 788-8866   CA
Web Site: http://www.hornblower.com
Year Founded: 1980
Emp.: 2,200
Provider of Yatch Transportation &
Cruises
N.A.I.C.S.: 487210
Terry MacRae *(Founder & Chm)*
Kevin M. Rabbitt *(CEO)*
Annabella Stagner *(VP-Sls & Mktg)*
Cindee Beechwood *(VP-Fin & Con-
troller)*
Cameron Clark *(VP & Gen Mgr-New
York)*
Jim Unger *(VP & Gen Mgr-San Di-
ego)*
Kevin Lorton *(VP & Gen Mgr-Los An-
geles)*
Michael Burke *(COO & VP-Statue
Cruises)*
Jill Benson *(Gen Mgr-Northern Cali-
fornia)*
Scott Thornton *(VP & Gen Mgr-Ops-
Alcatraz Cruises)*
Tara Hippensteel *(Natl Dir-Tourism)*
Paul Sanett *(Sr VP-Sls & Mktg)*
Isis Ruiz *(Chief Comml Officer-
American Queen Voyages)*
Patrick Hood *(Dir-Health & Safety,
Security, Quality & Environment-
American Queen Voyages)*
Cynthia D'Aoust *(Pres-American
Queen Voyages)*
Chris Tallent *(CEO-Journey Beyond)*

HORNE AUTO CENTER INC.
651 W Deuce of Clubs Ave, Show
Low, AZ 85901
Tel.: (928) 892-5529
Web Site: https://www.horneauto.com
Sales Range: $25-49.9 Million
Emp.: 30
Automobiles New & Used Service &
Parts
N.A.I.C.S.: 441110
Erin Horne *(CEO)*

HORNE BUILDING SPECIAL-
TIES
2120 Oak Industrial Dr, Grand Rap-
ids, MI 49505
Tel.: (616) 235-3600
Web Site:
  http://www.pellawestmichigan.com
Windows Mfr
N.A.I.C.S.: 423310
John Estabrook *(Owner)*

HORNE FORD INC.
1777 N Grand Ave, Nogales, AZ
85621
Tel.: (520) 281-1976
Web Site:
  https://www.hornefordaz.com
Sales Range: $10-24.9 Million
Emp.: 30
Automobiles, New & Used
N.A.I.C.S.: 441110
Robert Horne *(Pres)*

HORNE INTERNATIONAL, INC.

3975 University Dr Ste 100, Fairfax,
VA 22030
Tel.: (703) 641-1100
Web Site: http://www.horne.com
Year Founded: 1990
Sales Range: $1-9.9 Million
Emp.: 14
Engineeering Services
N.A.I.C.S.: 541330
Dallas Evans *(CEO)*
John E. Donahue *(CFO)*

HORNE LLP
1020 Highland Colony Pkwy Ste 400,
Ridgeland, MS 39157
Tel.: (601) 948-0940
Web Site: http://www.horne-llp.com
Sales Range: $10-24.9 Million
Emp.: 200
Certified Public Accountants
N.A.I.C.S.: 541211
Kade Moody *(Partner)*
Michael R. Sassano *(Partner)*
Vera M. Reed *(Partner)*
Jason Saulters *(Partner)*
Brad Aldridge *(Mgr-Cyber Solutions)*
Mike Skinner *(Partner)*
Richard Romero *(Dir-Healthcare
Valuation)*
Matt Akin *(Sr Mgr-Govt Svcs)*
Anna Stroble *(Partner-Govt Svcs)*
Bruce Walt *(Partner)*
Whitney Powell *(Mgr-Govt Svcs
Team)*
Lacy Lyons *(Sr Mgr-Govt Svcs Team)*
Caleb Ward *(Mgr-Govt Svcs Team)*
Niv Bulsara *(Mgr-Govt Svcs Team)*
Megan Hudson *(Mgr-Cyber Team)*
Chris Hayes *(Mgr-Fin Institutions
Team)*

HORNER INDUSTRIAL GROUP
1521 E Washington St, Indianapolis,
IN 46201
Tel.: (317) 639-4261
Web Site:
  http://www.hornerelectric.com
Year Founded: 1949
Sales Range: $25-49.9 Million
Emp.: 350
Relays & Industrial Control Mfr
N.A.I.C.S.: 335314
Alan Horner *(Co-Pres)*
Phil Horner *(Co-Pres)*
Gina Tuttle *(Mgr-Customer Svc)*

HORNER MILLWORK CORP.
1255 Grand Army Hwy, Somerset,
MA 02726-1203
Tel.: (508) 679-6479   MA
Web Site:
  https://www.hornermillwork.com
Year Founded: 1948
Sales Range: $50-74.9 Million
Emp.: 400
Lumber, Plywood & Millwork Services
N.A.I.C.S.: 423310
Peter Humphrey *(Pres & CEO)*

HORNER PONTIAC BUICK
INC.
1705 Lafayette Rd, Crawfordsville, IN
47933
Tel.: (765) 362-4000
Web Site:
  http://www.hornerautomotivesuper
store.com
Sales Range: $10-24.9 Million
Emp.: 25
Automobiles, New & Used
N.A.I.C.S.: 441110
Sam Horner *(Pres)*
Fred Lieske *(Gen Mgr)*
Pat Olinger *(CFO)*

HORNER-RAUSCH EAST, INC.

Horner-Rausch East, Inc.—(Continued)

968 Main St, Nashville, TN 37206-3614
Tel.: (615) 226-0251   **TN**
Web Site:
http://www.hornerrauschoptical.com
Year Founded: 1960
Sales Range: Less than $1 Million
Emp.: 4
Retailer of Optical Products
N.A.I.C.S.: 456130
Glenna Fenn (Owner)
Ann Harris (Sec)
Mark Severence (Dir-Mktg)

HORNETS BASKETBALL, LLC
333 E Trade St, Charlotte, NC 28202
Tel.: (704) 688-8600   **DE**
Web Site: http://www.bobcats.com
Year Founded: 2003
Professional Basketball Team
N.A.I.C.S.: 711211
Fred A. Whitfield (Pres & COO)
Pete Guelli (CMO, Chief Sls Officer & Exec VP)
Rod Higgins (Pres-Basketball Ops)
Seth Bennett (Sr VP-Mktg, Entertainment & Interactive Media)
Ronnie Bryant (Dir-IT)
Jim Dunlevy (Sr Dir-Fin)
Josh Kramer (VP-Mktg & Brand Dev)
Elizabeth Clagon (Sr Dir-Ops)
Flavil Hampsten (Sr VP-Partnership Mktg & Ticketing)
Curtis J. Polk (Vice Chm)
Rich Cho (Gen Mgr)
James R. Jordan (Exec VP-Ops)
Donna P. Julian (Sr VP-Arena & Event Ops)
Mike Cristaldi (VP-Comm)
Rhonda Curry (VP-HR)
Marlene Hendricks (VP-Guest Svcs & Event Staffing)
Joe Pierce (VP & Gen Counsel)
Andrew Shure (VP-Ticket Ops)
Josh Rosen (Dir-Comm)
Dan Fitzsimmons (Sr Dir-Partnership Sls)
Jacob Gallagher (Sr Dir-Client Svcs & Retention)
Mike Tanda (Sr Dir-Ticketing)
Gabe Plotkin (Co-Chm)
Rick Schnall (Co-Chm & Governor)

HORNWOOD INC.
766 Haileys Ferry Rd, Lilesville, NC 28091
Tel.: (704) 848-4121
Web Site:
https://www.hornwoodinc.com
Year Founded: 1946
Sales Range: $25-49.9 Million
Emp.: 350
Fabric Milling Services
N.A.I.C.S.: 313240
Wesley Horne (Pres)

Subsidiaries:

Hornwood Inc.   (1)
1400 Broadway, New York, NY 10018-5300
Tel.: (212) 354-1373
Sales Range: $25-49.9 Million
Emp.: 300
Mfr of Lace & Warp Knit Fabric Mills
N.A.I.C.S.: 424310

HOROVITZ, RUDOY & ROTEMAN, LLC
875 Greentree Rd 7 Pkwy Ctr Ste 1000, Pittsburgh, PA 15220
Tel.: (412) 391-2920
Web Site: https://www.h2rcpa.com
Emp.: 100
Accounting Services
N.A.I.C.S.: 541219

William H. Westland Jr. (Partner)
Mark R. Exler (Partner)
Steven M. Gregory (Partner)

Subsidiaries:

Exler & Company, Inc.   (1)
357 N Craig St Ste A, Pittsburgh, PA 15213-1209
Tel.: (412) 683-8800
Web Site: http://www.exler.com
Offices of Certified Public Accountants
N.A.I.C.S.: 541211

HORROCKS ENGINEERS, INC.
2162 W Grove Pkwy Ste 400, Pleasant Grove, UT 84062
Tel.: (801) 763-5100
Web Site: http://www.horrocks.com
Year Founded: 1968
Rev.: $13,566,973
Emp.: 200
Civil Engineering Services
N.A.I.C.S.: 541330

HORRY COUNTY SOLID WASTE AUTHORITY INC.
1886 Highway 90, Conway, SC 29528-1664
Tel.: (843) 347-1651
Web Site:
https://www.solidwasteauthority.org
Sales Range: $10-24.9 Million
Emp.: 100
Recycling, Waste Materials
N.A.I.C.S.: 562920
Danny Knight (Exec Dir)
Susie Wofford (Supvr-Acctg)
Jan Brtting (Dir-Fin & Admin)

HORRY ELECTRIC COOPERATIVE INC.
2774 Cultra Rd, Conway, SC 29526
Tel.: (843) 369-2211   **SC**
Web Site:
https://www.horryelectric.com
Year Founded: 1940
Sales Range: $25-49.9 Million
Emp.: 145
Electric Power Distr
N.A.I.C.S.: 221122
James P. Howle (CEO)
Danny Shelly (CFO)
Gail Morton (Supvr-Customer Svc)
Dale Johnson (Mgr-IT)
Reed Cooper (Mgr-Engrg)

HORSEMEN, INC.
16911 Algonquin St, Huntington Beach, CA 92649
Tel.: (714) 847-4243   **CA**
Web Site:
https://www.horsemeninc.com
Year Founded: 1995
Sales Range: $1-9.9 Million
Emp.: 120
Investigation Services
N.A.I.C.S.: 561611
Patrick Carroll (Pres)
Sam Martin (Mgr-Client Rels)
Ed Carpenter (Mgr)

HORSESHOE BAY RESORT LTD.
Horseshoe Bay Blvd, Horseshoe Bay, TX 78657
Tel.: (830) 598-2511
Web Site: http://www.hsbresort.com
Rev.: $25,000,000
Emp.: 475
Country Club Membership
N.A.I.C.S.: 713910
Douglas Jaffe (CEO)
Derrick Russian (Engr-Night)
Gary D. Parsons (Head-Golf Pro)
Steve Hatch (Dir-Golf)

HORST-ZIMMERMAN INC.
1740 5th Ave, Rock Island, IL 61201
Tel.: (309) 788-9304
Web Site:
http://www.zimmermancars.com
Rev.: $29,722,143
Emp.: 50
Automobiles, New & Used
N.A.I.C.S.: 441110
Mark Zimmerman (Owner-Dealership)
Doug Pearsall (Mgr-Inventory-Honda)
Alyssa Sanders (Mgr-HR)
Audrie Rea (Coord-Sls)
Blake Pelland (Bus Mgr)
Darwyn Buechler (Mgr-Used Car)
James Craig (Mgr-Bus Dev)
Jeff Dolan (Mgr-Fin)
R. C. Rogers (Gen Mgr)
Todd Dorathy (Controller)
Warren Nagel (Mgr-Parts)

HORTENSE & LOUIS RUBIN DIALYSIS CENTER, INC.
1850 Peoples Ave, Troy, NY 12180
Tel.: (518) 271-0702   **NY**
Web Site:
http://www.rubindialysis.org
Year Founded: 1985
Sales Range: $10-24.9 Million
Dialysis Services
N.A.I.C.S.: 621492
Wayne Evancoe (CEO)
Donna Roarke (Mgr-Nurse)
Leslie S. Goldstein (Dir-Medical)
Heidi Olsen (Mgr-Nurse)
Nicolle Bateman (Mgr-Nurse)
Christopher D. Hoy (Dir-Medical)
Page Salenger (Dir-Medical)
Helen Anne Endres (Sec)
Richard Iannello (Treas)
Neil Roberts (Pres)

HORTICA INSURANCE
1 Horticultural Ln, Edwardsville, IL 62025-0428
Tel.: (618) 656-4240   **IL**
Web Site: http://www.hortica-insurance.com
Year Founded: 1887
Sales Range: $50-74.9 Million
Emp.: 250
Insurance for the Floral & Horticultural Industry
N.A.I.C.S.: 524210
Kenneth J. Krieg (COO)
Peter H. Fornof (CIO & Sr VP-Admin)
Brent Bates (Sr VP & Dir-Claim)
Connie J. Turner (VP-HR)
John M. Hodapp (Sr VP-Agency Ops)
Mona Best Haberer (Pres & CEO)

HORTON INC.
2565 Walnut St, Roseville, MN 55113-2522
Tel.: (651) 361-6400
Web Site: https://www.hortonww.com
Year Founded: 1951
Sales Range: $25-49.9 Million
Emp.: 400
Provider of Motor Vehicle Parts & Accessories
N.A.I.C.S.: 336350
Mary Bolan (Mgr-Mktg)
Joe Herzog (VP-Engrg)
John Getter (VP-Mfg)

Subsidiaries:

Horton Inc   (1)
201 W Carmel Dr, Carmel, IN 46032   (100%)
Tel.: (317) 249-4001
Web Site: http://www.hortonww.com
Sales Range: $10-24.9 Million
Emp.: 125
Fan Blade Mfr
N.A.I.C.S.: 333413

Horton Mexico, S. de RL de CV   (1)
Las Rosas 204 B, Col La Florida Naucalpan Edo D, 53160, Mexico, Mexico   (100%)
Tel.: (52) 5553601506
Web Site: http://www.hortonww.com
Sales Range: $10-24.9 Million
Emp.: 6
Motor Vehicle Parts & Accessories Distr
N.A.I.C.S.: 336390
Jeff Wood (Acct Mgr-North America)

HORTON INDUSTRIES, INC.
101 Indus Blvd, Eatonton, GA 31024-7254
Tel.: (706) 485-8506   **GA**
Web Site:
http://www.hortonhomes.com
Sales Range: $300-349.9 Million
Emp.: 1,900
Mfr of Mobile Homes
N.A.I.C.S.: 321991
Rudy W. Hicks (VP-HR)
Maude H. Hicks (Treas & Sec)
N. D. Horton Jr. (Pres)

Subsidiaries:

Horton Homes, Inc.   (1)
101 Industrial Blvd, Eatonton, GA 31024-7254
Tel.: (706) 485-8506
Web Site: http://www.hortonhomes.com
Sales Range: $300-349.9 Million
Emp.: 100
Mfr of Mobiles Homes
N.A.I.C.S.: 321991
Steve Gregory (VP-Pur)
Rus Hicks (VP-Sls)
Steve Sinclair (CEO)

Weeks Supply   (1)
186 Industrial Blvd, Eatonton, GA 31024
Tel.: (706) 485-4525
Emp.: 3
Window & Door Whslr
N.A.I.C.S.: 423310

HORUS VISION, LLC
598 San Mateo Ave, San Bruno, CA 94066-3608
Tel.: (650) 588-8862
Web Site:
http://www.horusvision.com
Optical Instrument & Lens Mfr
N.A.I.C.S.: 333310
Art Kiesel (Dir-Sls)

HORWITZ NS/I INC.
4401 Quebec Ave N, New Hope, MN 55428
Tel.: (763) 533-1900
Web Site: http://www.nsihorwitz.com
Year Founded: 1918
Sales Range: $10-24.9 Million
Emp.: 110
Plumbing, Heating & Air-Conditioning Services
N.A.I.C.S.: 238220
William R. McKoskey (Pres)
Joseph P. O'Shaughnessy (VP)
P. Hlavachek (Sec & VP)

HOS BROTHERS CONSTRUCTION, INC.
7733 W Bostian Rd, Woodinville, WA 98072-1788
Tel.: (425) 481-5569
Web Site: https://www.hosbros.com
Sales Range: $25-49.9 Million
Emp.: 400
Highway, Street & Bridge Construction Services
N.A.I.C.S.: 237310
John W. Caunt (Pres)

HOSE & FITTINGS ETC.
1811 Enterprise Blvd, West Sacramento, CA 95691
Tel.: (916) 372-3888

Web Site: http://www.hfeweb.com
Sales Range: $10-24.9 Million
Emp.: 35
Plumbing Fittings & Supplies
N.A.I.C.S.: 423720
Scott Weyin (CEO)

HOSEA O. WEAVER AND SONS INC.
7450 Howells Ferry Rd, Mobile, AL 36618-3407
Tel.: (251) 342-3025   AL
Web Site:
   https://www.hoseaweaver.com
Year Founded: 1952
Sales Range: $25-49.9 Million
Emp.: 170
Highway & Street Construction Services
N.A.I.C.S.: 237310
Paul E. Weaver (Pres)

HOSELTON CHEVROLET IN-CORPORATED
909 Fairport Rd, East Rochester, NY 14445
Tel.: (585) 586-7373   NY
Web Site: http://www.hoselton.com
Year Founded: 1927
Sales Range: $25-49.9 Million
Emp.: 100
Sales of New & Used Automobiles
N.A.I.C.S.: 441110
Drew Hoselton (Pres)
Dennis Segrue (CFO & VP)

HOSKIN & MUIR, INC.
6611 Preston Ave Ste C, Livermore, CA 94550
Tel.: (925) 373-1135
Web Site: http://www.prohmi.com
Sales Range: $10-24.9 Million
Emp.: 20
All Materials Molding Mfr & Whslr
N.A.I.C.S.: 423310
Don Ross (Pres)

HOSLEY INTERNATIONAL TRADING CORPORATION
20530 Stoney Is Ave, Chicago Heights, IL 60411
Tel.: (708) 758-1000
Web Site: http://www.hosley.com
Rev.: $28,000,000
Emp.: 1,000
Homefurnishings
N.A.I.C.S.: 423220
Piush Kumar (CEO)
Peter Gerike (Mgr-Ops)

HOSPARUS INC.
3532 Ephraim McDowell Dr, Louisville, KY 40205-3224
Tel.: (502) 456-6200   KY
Web Site: http://www.hosparus.org
Year Founded: 1978
Sales Range: $50-74.9 Million
Emp.: 633
Hospice Care Services
N.A.I.C.S.: 621610
Phil Marshall (Pres & CEO)
Sharon Orman (CFO & Sr VP)
Terri Graham (Chief Clinical Officer & Sr VP-Clinical Svcs)
Cathy Zion (Chm)
Dustin Dillon (Assoc Dir-Medical)
Bob Mueller (VP-Dev)
Kevin Wardell (Sec)
Bethany Cox Snider (Chief Medical Officer & VP)
Tawanda Lewis Owsley (VP-Dev)

HOSPECO BRANDS GROUP
26301 Curtiss Wright Pkwy, Cleveland, Ohio 44143
Tel.: (800) 942-9199

Web Site: https://hospecobrands.com
Year Founded: 1919
Cleaning Products & Services Manufacturer
N.A.I.C.S.: 561499

Subsidiaries:

Bullen Midwest Inc.   (1)
900 E 103rd St Ste D, Chicago, IL 60628
Tel.: (773) 785-2300
Web Site: http://www.nuancesol.com
Sales Range: $50-74.9 Million
Emp.: 20
Soap Mfr
N.A.I.C.S.: 325611
John Flanagan (VP-Pur)
Neil Houtsma (Exec VP)
Matt Ahrens (VP-Industrial Sls)
Dan Racan (Mgr-IT Svcs)
Ken Johnson (Mgr-Tech & Customs Solutions)
James Flanagan (CEO)
Bob Ernst (Mgr-Ops)
Dave Racan (Mgr-Tech & Industrial Markets)
Beth Dunning (CFO)
Sean Hoffman (Pres)
Phillip A. Ricketts (VP-Bus Dev)

HOSPICE & COMMUNITY CARE
685 Good Dr, Lancaster, PA 17604-4125
Tel.: (717) 295-3900   PA
Web Site:
   https://www.hospiceandcommunity
   care.org
Year Founded: 1980
Sales Range: $25-49.9 Million
Emp.: 406
Community & Hospice Care Services
N.A.I.C.S.: 624190
Bonnie Jess Lopane (VP-Dev & Community Rels)
Brent Keener (VP-HR)
Krista Kae Hazen (CFO & VP)
Steven M. Knaub (Pres & CEO)
Joan Harrold (Chief Medical Officer & VP-Medical Svcs)

HOSPICE & PALLIATIVE CARECENTER
101 Hospice Ln, Winston Salem, NC 27103
Tel.: (336) 760-1114   NC
Web Site:
   http://www.hospicecarecenter.org
Year Founded: 1978
Sales Range: $25-49.9 Million
Emp.: 502
Hospice & Palliative Care Services
N.A.I.C.S.: 621610
Linda Darden (Pres & CEO)
Kristine Elliott (VP-HR)
Dave Shelton (CFO)
Michael Lalor (Chief Medical Officer)
Anita Ford (VP-Clinical Svcs)
Todd M. Clark (VP-Community Rels)
Ellen Coble (VP-Dev)
Dianne Linville (Officer-Compliance & Quality)
Melissa Perrell Phipps (Sec)
Tim Sechrest (Treas)
Sarah Serrano (VP-Clinical Svcs)

HOSPICE AND PALLIATIVE CARE CENTER OF ALAMANCE-CASWELL
914 Chapel Hill Rd, Burlington, NC 27215
Tel.: (336) 532-0100   NC
Web Site: http://www.hospiceac.org
Year Founded: 1980
Sales Range: $10-24.9 Million
Emp.: 290
Hospice Care Services
N.A.I.C.S.: 621610

Gayle Scott (Dir-Family Svcs)
Caroline Durham (CFO)
Kenneth Allred (Dir-IT)
Peter Barcus (Exec Dir)
Beth Hodges (Dir-Medical)
Manuela Espinosa (Dir-HR)
Sandra Gibson (Dir-Hospice)
Sharon Terrell (Dir-Facility Svcs)
Bruce Shields (Dir)
Lane A. Jones (Sec)
Patricia Philipps (Chm)

HOSPICE AT GREENSBORO, INC.
2500 Summit Ave, Greensboro, NC 27405
Tel.: (336) 621-2500   NC
Web Site: http://www.hospicegso.org
Year Founded: 1979
Sales Range: $25-49.9 Million
Emp.: 265
Hospice Care Services
N.A.I.C.S.: 621610
Juan-Carlos Monguilod (Chief Medical Officer)
Risa Hanau (VP-Organizational Optimization & Outcomes)
James Haigler (Asst Treas)
Lori Shaw (Asst Sec)

HOSPICE AUSTIN
4107 Spicewood Springs Rd Ste 100, Austin, TX 78759
Tel.: (512) 342-4700   TX
Web Site:
   https://www.hospiceaustin.org
Year Founded: 1981
Sales Range: $10-24.9 Million
Emp.: 325
Hospice Care Services
N.A.I.C.S.: 621610
Karen Norman (Dir-HR)
Christine Reis (CFO)
Robert Friedman (Chief Medical Officer)

HOSPICE BUFFALO
225 Como Park Blvd, Buffalo, NY 14227
Tel.: (716) 686-8077   NY
Web Site:
   https://www.hospicebuffalo.com
Year Founded: 1976
Sales Range: $25-49.9 Million
Emp.: 479
Hospice Care Services
N.A.I.C.S.: 621610
Joseph Bach (Chief Admin Officer)
Christopher Kerr (CEO-Interim & Chief Medical Officer)
Kelley Clem (VP-Clinical Education & Patient Advocacy)
Maureen Lehsten (CFO)
Timothy G. McEvoy (Sec)
Paul Duggan (Vice Chm)
Cary Sisti (Chief Clinical Ops Officer)
Roseann McAnulty (COO)
R. Buford Sears (Vice Chm)
Patrick Flynn (Pres)
Susan Herold (VP-HR)
E. J. Butler Jr. (Chm)

HOSPICE CARE OF SOUTHWEST MICHIGAN
222 N Kalamazoo Mall Ste 100, Kalamazoo, MI 49007
Tel.: (269) 345-0273   MI
Web Site:
   http://www.hospiceswmi.org
Year Founded: 1981
Sales Range: $10-24.9 Million
Emp.: 197
Community Health Care Services
N.A.I.C.S.: 621610

Jean Maile (CEO)
M. Raphelson (Dir-Medical)
Ronald Seagle (Assoc Dir-Medical)

HOSPICE EL PASO
1440 Miracle Way, El Paso, TX 79925
Tel.: (915) 532-5699   TX
Web Site:
   https://www.hospiceelpaso.org
Year Founded: 1980
Sales Range: $10-24.9 Million
Emp.: 160
Hospice Care Services
N.A.I.C.S.: 621610
James Paul (CEO)

HOSPICE HAWAII
860 Iwilei Rd, Honolulu, HI 96817
Tel.: (808) 924-9255   HI
Web Site:
   http://www.hospicehawaii.org
Year Founded: 1979
Sales Range: $10-24.9 Million
Emp.: 145
Health Care Srvices
N.A.I.C.S.: 622110
Tori Abe (Chief Strategy Officer)
Kim Hanson (Controller)
J. P. Sabbithi (Dir-Counseling Svcs)
Tammi Barboza (Dir-HR)
Brigitte McKale (Sec)
Jim Alberts (Vice Chm)
Kenneth L. Zeri (Pres)
Kim Sung (Treas)
Lance N. Tanaka (Chm)

HOSPICE INC.
313 S Market, Wichita, KS 67202
Tel.: (316) 265-9441   KS
Web Site:
   http://www.hynesmemorial.org
Year Founded: 1982
Sales Range: $10-24.9 Million
Emp.: 210
Elder Care Services
N.A.I.C.S.: 623312
Gerald Kerschen (Pres & CEO)
Gerard Brungardt (Dir-Medical)
Renee Farha Hahn (CFO)
Jarrod Hayes (Dir-Patient & Family Care Svcs)
Kristen Walker (Dir-Patient & Family Care Svcs)
Jerry Kerschen (Pres & CEO)
Sheila Shaw (Dir-Volunteers)

HOSPICE OF CENTRAL PENN-SYLVANIA
1320 Linglestown Rd, Harrisburg, PA 17110
Tel.: (717) 732-1000   PA
Web Site:
   https://www.hospiceofcentralpa.org
Year Founded: 1979
Sales Range: $10-24.9 Million
Emp.: 150
Hospice Care Services
N.A.I.C.S.: 623110
Gilbert Brown (CEO)

HOSPICE OF CHATTANOOGA, INC.
4411 Oakwood Dr, Chattanooga, TN 37416
Tel.: (423) 892-4289   TN
Web Site:
   https://www.hospiceofchatta
   nooga.org
Year Founded: 1981
Sales Range: $25-49.9 Million
Emp.: 250
Elder Care Services
N.A.I.C.S.: 623312
David Winchester (CFO)
Tracy Wood (Pres & CEO)

HOSPICE OF CLEVELAND COUNTY, INC.

Hospice of Cleveland County, Inc.—(Continued)

951 Wendover Heights Dr, Shelby,
NC 28150
Tel.: (704) 487-7018   **NC**
Web Site: http://www.hospicecares.cc
Year Founded: 1984
Sales Range: $10-24.9 Million
Emp.: 196
Family Advocacy Services
N.A.I.C.S.: 813319
Myra McGinnis (Pres & CEO)
Pam Benfield (Dir-Financial Services)

HOSPICE OF DAYTON, INC.
324 Wilmington Ave, Dayton, OH
45420
Tel.: (937) 256-4490
Web Site:
   https://www.hospiceofdayton.org
Rev.: $31,521,000
Emp.: 450
Women Healthcare Services
N.A.I.C.S.: 621610

HOSPICE OF EAST TEXAS
4111 University Blvd, Tyler, TX 75701
Tel.: (903) 266-3400   **TX**
Web Site:
   https://www.hospiceofeasttexas.org
Year Founded: 1982
Sales Range: $10-24.9 Million
Emp.: 284
Hospice Care Services
N.A.I.C.S.: 621610
Marjorie Ream (Pres & CEO)
Myanh Bui (VP-Fin)
Nancy Lamar (VP-Community Rels)
Kurt Lorenz (Dir-Pharmacy)
Cassie Ransom (Dir-Inpatient Care)
Jeb Jones (Chm)
Bob Roseman (Treas)
Jane Green (Sec)
Scott Myers (Vice Chm)
Craig Adams (Sec)
Christi Baggett (VP-Ops & Innova-
tion)
Robert Bailes (Treas)
Craig Boyd (Chm)
Shaune Martinez (VP-People)
Kristy Morris (VP-Clinical Affairs)
Linda Navarro (Officer-Compliance)

HOSPICE OF HOPE
909 Kenton Station Dr, Maysville, KY
41056
Tel.: (606) 759-4050   **KY**
Web Site:
   https://www.hospiceofhope.com
Year Founded: 1988
Sales Range: $10-24.9 Million
Emp.: 204
Behavioral Healthcare Services
N.A.I.C.S.: 623220
Paul F. Junker (Dir-Medical)
Betsy Miller (Coord-Patient Care)
Kavin Cartmell (Exec Dir)
Michael Parker (Dir-Dev & PR)
Pam Tribby (Dir-Contracted Svcs)
Shawn Flaugher (Mgr-Bus)

**HOSPICE OF LAURENS
COUNTY, INC.**
1304 Springdale Dr, Clinton, SC
29325
Tel.: (864) 833-6287
Web Site:
   https://www.hospiceoflaurens
   county.com
Year Founded: 1987
Hospice Care Services
N.A.I.C.S.: 621610

Subsidiaries:

Hospice & Palliative Care Charlotte
Region   (1)
7845 Little Ave, Charlotte, NC 28226

Tel.: (704) 375-0100
Web Site: http://www.hpccr.org
Palliative Care Services
N.A.I.C.S.: 622110
Peter A. Brunnick (Pres & CEO)
Michael S. Bolewitz (COO & VP)
Christy Gisinger (VP-Philanthropy)
Lisa H. Hood (VP-Corp Compliance & Qual-
ity Improvement)
Robert Smith (Dir-Medical)
Cynthia L. Tilley (VP-HR)
John A. Morrice (Sec)

**HOSPICE OF MARION
COUNTY**
3231 SW 34th Ave, Ocala, FL 34474
Tel.: (352) 873-7400   **FL**
Web Site:
   https://www.hospiceofmarion.com
Year Founded: 1981
Sales Range: $25-49.9 Million
Emp.: 513
Hospice Care Services
N.A.I.C.S.: 621610
Mary Ellen Poe (CEO)
Carol D. Alvey (Chm)
Drexel Brunson (Treas)
Nathan Vooys (Sec)
Kathryn M. Beecher (CFO)
Bruce Chancellor (Officer-Safety &
Dir-Facilities)
Mery Lossada (Chief Medical Officer)
Amy Meiers (Chief Clinical Ops Offi-
cer)
Debbie Ronaldo (Chief Compliance
Officer & Dir-QAPI)

HOSPICE OF MICHIGAN INC.
400 Mack Ave, Detroit, MI 48201-
2136
Tel.: (313) 578-5000   **MI**
Web Site: http://www.hom.org
Year Founded: 1980
Sales Range: $25-49.9 Million
Emp.: 725
Women Healthcare Services
N.A.I.C.S.: 623110
Robert Cahill (Pres & CEO)
Lee Ann Myers (VP-Fin)
Michael Jasperson (VP-Mktg & Bus
Dev)
Jane McNamara (Chm)
Mark Drumheller (Vice Chm)

**HOSPICE OF NORTHWEST
OHIO**
3000 E River Rd, Perrysburg, OH
43551
Tel.: (419) 661-4001   **OH**
Web Site:
   https://www.hospicenwo.org
Year Founded: 1979
Sales Range: $25-49.9 Million
Emp.: 492
Hospice Care Services
N.A.I.C.S.: 621610
Patty O'Toole (Dir-Ops)
Michelle Power (Dir-HR)
Marsha Paul (Dir-Medical)
Joel Jerger (Pres)
David Schlaudecker (VP)
Ann Baker (Sec)
Linda Hillstrom (Treas)

**HOSPICE OF RUTHERFORD
COUNTY, INC.**
374 Hudlow Rd, Forest City, NC
28043
Tel.: (828) 245-0095   **NC**
Web Site:
   http://www.hospiceofrutherford.org
Year Founded: 1982
Sales Range: $10-24.9 Million
Emp.: 184
Hospice Care Services
N.A.I.C.S.: 621610

Ronda Patton (Dir-Palliative Care)
Debbie Martin (Sec)
Rita R. Burch (Exec Dir)

**HOSPICE OF SOUTHERN ILLI-
NOIS, INC.**
305 S Illinois St, Belleville, IL 62220
Tel.: (618) 235-1703   **IL**
Web Site: https://www.hospice.org
Year Founded: 1981
Sales Range: $10-24.9 Million
Emp.: 218
Hospice Care Services
N.A.I.C.S.: 623110
Amy Richter (Pres & CEO)
Ellen Middendorf (Dir-Medical)
Jan Bowman-Marsh (Dir-Medical)
Karen Kunsemiller (Vice Chm)
Matthew Waters (Treas)
Jennifer Barbieri (Chm)

**HOSPICE OF THE BLUE-
GRASS**
2312 Alexandria Dr, Lexington, KY
40504
Tel.: (859) 276-5344   **KY**
Web Site: http://www.hospicebg.org
Year Founded: 1978
Sales Range: $50-74.9 Million
Emp.: 893
Hospice & Palliative Care Services
N.A.I.C.S.: 623110
Todd Cote (Chief Medical Officer)
Salli Whisman (Sr Dir-Medical)
Elizabeth Durst Fowler (Pres & CEO)
Shannon Bishop Arvin (Sec)
Eric J. Frankl (Chm)
Jen Shah (Treas)
Nana Mensah (Vice Chm)

**HOSPICE OF THE COM-
FORTER, INC.**
480 W Central Pkwy, Altamonte
Springs, FL 32714
Tel.: (407) 682-0808
Web Site:
   http://www.hospiceofthecom
   forter.org
Year Founded: 1989
Sales Range: $50-74.9 Million
Emp.: 350
Health Care Srvices
N.A.I.C.S.: 621610
Robert Wilson (Founder)
Flavia Cipollaro (Mgr-Bereavement)
Jeff White (Chief Compliance Officer)
Annette Carter (Chief Clinical Officer)
Bonnie Renfro (Chief Medical Officer)
Cathy Du Treil (Chief Compliance
Officer)
Claire Hogan (Officer-Dev)
Jennifer Kane (Dir-HR)
Tabitha Mendez (Dir-Clinical Svcs)
William Largo (Dir-Mission & Ministry)

HOSPICE OF THE PIEDMONT
675 Peter Jefferson Pkwy Ste 300,
Charlottesville, VA 22911
Tel.: (434) 817-6900   **VA**
Web Site: https://www.hopva.org
Year Founded: 1981
Sales Range: $10-24.9 Million
Emp.: 188
Community Care Services
N.A.I.C.S.: 624190
James A. Avery (CEO)
Angela Stiltner (Sr Dir-Medical)
Kent Hunter (Officer-HR)
John Healy (Dir-Advancement)
Lois Pearson (Dir-Project Mgmt)
Mariellen Hagy (Dir-Fin)
Patricia Bruton (Chief Clinical Officer)
Tony Maybury (Dir-Tech Svcs)

**HOSPICE OF THE PIEDMONT,
INC.**
1801 Westchester Dr, High Point, NC
27262-7009
Tel.: (336) 878-7200   **NC**
Web Site:
   https://www.hospiceofthepied
   mont.org
Year Founded: 1980
Care & Support Services
N.A.I.C.S.: 621498
William T. Cockerham (Pres & CEO)
Barry Leonard (CFO)
Homa Magsi (Chief Medical Officer &
VP-Medical Affairs)
Susan Cox (Officer-Chief Nursing Of-
ficer & Sr VP-Clinical Svcs)
David Caughron (VP-Community En-
gagement & Education)
Jennifer Duncan (VP-HR)
Mary Leslie English (VP-Public & Do-
nor Rels)
Kat Gibson (VP-Family Care Svcs)
Matt Harkness (VP-Bus Dev)
Jeff Miller (Chm)
Stephanie Johnson (Vice Chm)
Dean Sexton (Treas)
Stan Beck (Sec)
William Trent Cockerham (CEO)

**HOSPICE OF THE RED RIVER
VALLEY**
1701 38th St S Ste 101, Fargo, ND
58103
Tel.: (701) 356-1500   **ND**
Web Site: https://www.hrrv.org
Year Founded: 1978
Sales Range: $25-49.9 Million
Emp.: 255
Hospice Care Services
N.A.I.C.S.: 621610
Rebecca Svaleson (Dir-Clinical Ops)
Deb Gemar (Dir-Community Rels)
Sheila Klose (Dir-HR)
Steve Slabik (Dir-Fin)
Jeff Sandgren (Treas & Sec)
Roberta Young (Pres)
Tracee Capron (Exec Dir)

**HOSPICE OF THE SACRED
HEART**
600 Baltimore Dr, Wilkes Barre, PA
18702
Tel.: (570) 706-2400   **PA**
Web Site:
   http://www.hospicesacredheart.org
Year Founded: 2003
Sales Range: $10-24.9 Million
Emp.: 127
Hospice Care Services
N.A.I.C.S.: 621610
Michele Penetar (Dir-Patient Svcs)
Mary Alice Cosgrove (Dir-HR)
John Stapert (Dir-Fin)
Diane Baldi (CEO)
Linda Menichetti (COO)

HOSPICE OF THE VALLEY
4850 Union Ave, San Jose, CA
95124
Tel.: (408) 559-5600   **CA**
Web Site:
   https://www.hospicevalley.org
Year Founded: 1979
Sales Range: $10-24.9 Million
Emp.: 152
Hospice Healthcare Services
N.A.I.C.S.: 621610
Louisa Gampon (Dir)
Vince Evans (VP-Patient Svcs)
Victoria Emmons (VP-Dev & Comm)
Sally Adelus (Pres & CEO)
Neal Slatkin (Chief Medical Officer &
VP-Medical Svcs)
Kathy Phelan (VP-Dev & Comm)
Carolyn DeLeon (VP-HR & Org Dev)

Sylvia Katzman *(Pres)*
Rajeev Singh *(Sec)*
Nancy Wendling *(Treas)*

HOSPICE OF THE WESTERN RESERVE, INC.
17876 Saint Clair Ave, Cleveland, OH 44110-2602
Tel.: (216) 383-2222   OH
Web Site: https://www.hospicewr.org
Year Founded: 1978
Sales Range: $75-99.9 Million
Emp.: 1,021
Hospice Care Services
N.A.I.C.S.: 621610
William E. Finn *(Pres & CEO)*
Clem Hearey *(VP-HR)*
Laura K. Navin *(Sec)*
Dan DeMonica *(Treas)*
Victoria Varley *(Vice Chm)*
Charles V. Wellman *(Co-Chief Medical Officer)*
May Al-Abousi *(Co-Chief Medical Officer)*
Mary Kay Tyler *(VP-Quality)*
Kathy Gatto *(VP-Support Svcs)*
John E. Harvan Jr. *(CFO)*

HOSPICE OF WAKE COUNTY
250 Hospice Cir, Raleigh, NC 27607
Tel.: (919) 828-0890   NC
Web Site:
   http://www.transitionslifecare.com
Year Founded: 1979
Sales Range: $10-24.9 Million
Emp.: 356
Hospice Care Services
N.A.I.C.S.: 623110
Cooper Linton *(VP-Mktg & Bus Dev)*
Toni Messler *(VP-Fin & Ops)*

HOSPICE SAVANNAH, INC.
PO Box 13190, Savannah, GA 31416-0190
Tel.: (912) 355-2289   GA
Web Site:
   http://www.hospicesavannah.org
Year Founded: 1979
Sales Range: $10-24.9 Million
Emp.: 252
General Medical Services
N.A.I.C.S.: 622110
Jamey Espina *(VP-Svc Excellence)*
Philip Solomons Jr. *(Chm)*
Maura Sovchen Jr. *(Vice Chm)*

HOSPICIO Y HOME CARE SAN LUCAS
291 Calle Monterey, Ponce, PR 00732-7064
Tel.: (787) 843-4185   PR
Web Site: http://www.sanlucaspr.org
Year Founded: 1967
Sales Range: $25-49.9 Million
Health Care Srvices
N.A.I.C.S.: 622110
Isuanet Castillo *(COO)*
Emilia Morales Vega *(VP)*

HOSPITAL BILLING & COLLECTION SERVICE, LTD.
118 Lukens Dr, New Castle, DE 19720
Tel.: (302) 552-8000
Web Site: http://www.hbcs.org
Year Founded: 1984
Sales Range: $25-49.9 Million
Emp.: 500
Billing & Bookkeeping Services
N.A.I.C.S.: 561491
Kevin R. Haggerty *(CFO & VP-Admin)*
Robert Siensa *(VP-Mktg)*
Brian J. Wasilewski *(VP-Ops)*

HOSPITAL BUEN SAMARITANO, INC.
PO Box 4055, Aguadilla, PR 00605-4055
Tel.: (787) 658-0000   PR
Web Site: http://www.hbspr.org
Year Founded: 1999
Sales Range: $25-49.9 Million
Emp.: 545
Health Care Srvices
N.A.I.C.S.: 622110
Elyonel Pontn Cruz *(Exec Dir)*
Luis J. Torres Rodrguez *(Fin Dir)*

HOSPITAL CENTRAL SERVICES, INC.
2171 28th St SW, Allentown, PA 18103
Tel.: (610) 791-2222
Web Site: https://www.hcsc.org
Year Founded: 1967
Sales Range: $10-24.9 Million
Emp.: 300
Industrial Launderers
N.A.I.C.S.: 541611
D. Kip Kuttner *(VP & Dir-Medical)*
Mark G. Angeny *(VP-HR)*
Louise Dolan *(Mgr-Indus Health)*
John Willson *(VP-Fiscal Affairs)*
Marie Clemens *(Dir-Comm)*
John Haney *(Chm)*
Deborah Templeton *(Vice Chm)*
Daniel J. Marcante *(COO & VP)*
Shirley Frederick *(Co-Sec)*
P. Michael Paulsen *(VP-Ops)*

HOSPITAL CORPORATION OF AMERICA
36 Kevin Dr, Flanders, NJ 07836
Tel.: (973) 796-4216   NJ
Year Founded: 2008
Healthcare Business Services
N.A.I.C.S.: 561499
Gary Sekulski *(Pres & CEO)*
Joseph Drucker *(Sec & Corp Counsel)*
Jan Goldberg *(Exec VP-Admin)*

HOSPITAL DE LA CONCEPCION
Carr Ste 2 Km 1734, San German, PR 00683
Tel.: (787) 892-1860   PR
Web Site:
   http://www.hospitalconcepcion.net
Year Founded: 1956
Sales Range: $75-99.9 Million
Emp.: 676
Health Care Srvices
N.A.I.C.S.: 622110
Gustavo A. Almodovar *(Exec Dir)*
Lizmari Calderon Arce *(Dir-Fin)*
Alvarado Corrada Del Ro *(Pres)*
Gonzalo Daz Hernandez *(VP)*
Juanita Flores *(Treas)*

HOSPITAL FOR SPECIAL CARE
2150 Corbin Ave, New Britain, CT 06053
Tel.: (860) 223-2761   CT
Web Site: https://www.hfsc.org
Year Founded: 1941
Sales Range: $150-199.9 Million
Emp.: 1,190
Health Care Srvices
N.A.I.C.S.: 622110
Laurie Ann Whelan *(CFO, Treas & Sr VP-Fin)*
Paul Scalise *(Sr VP-Medical Affairs)*
Lynn A. Ricci *(Pres & CEO)*
Victoria Golab *(Chief Nursing Officer & VP)*
Donald Cyr *(VP-Facilities & Hospitality Svcs)*

Felicia Dedominicis *(Sec)*
Stanislaw Jankowski *(CIO & VP)*
Nancy M. Martone *(Chief Admin Officer & VP-HR)*
J. Kevin Shushtari *(Chief Medical Officer)*
Marcy Goldstein *(Dir-Medical-Cardiac Unit)*
Nathan Nartey *(Dir-Medical-Medical Rehabilitation Unit)*
Wendy DeAngelo *(VP-Dev & Comm)*

HOSPITAL LAUNDRY SERVICES
45 W Hintz Rd, Wheeling, IL 60090
Tel.: (847) 229-0900
Web Site: http://www.hlschicago.com
Rev.: $25,735,296
Emp.: 450
Industrial Launderers
N.A.I.C.S.: 812332
Nader Ghazaleh *(Chief Engr)*

HOSPITAL SAN CARLOS BORROMEO
550 Concepcion Vera Ayala, Moca, PR 00676
Tel.: (787) 877-8000   PR
Web Site: http://www.hscbpr.org
Year Founded: 1965
Sales Range: $25-49.9 Million
Emp.: 370
Health Care Srvices
N.A.I.C.S.: 622110
Irma Cabrera Figueroa *(Fin Dir)*
Rosaida M. Crespo Cordero *(Exec Dir)*
Migdalia Ortiz Mestre *(Dir-HR)*
Juan C. Soto Gonzalez *(Mgr-IS)*

HOSPITAL SISTERS HEALTH SYSTEM
4936 LaVerna Rd, Springfield, IL 62707-9431
Tel.: (217) 523-4747
Web Site: http://www.hshs.org
Year Founded: 1978
Emp.: 100
Non-Profit Hospital Management Organization
N.A.I.C.S.: 561110
Michael W. Cottrell *(CFO)*
Stephen J. Bochenek *(Chm)*
Bill Murray *(Vice Chm)*
Gertrude O'Connor *(Sec)*
David K. Beach *(Chief HR Officer)*
Marybeth Culnan *(Sr VP)*

Subsidiaries:

HSHS Medical Group Inc.   (1)
3051 Hollis Dr, Springfield, IL 62704
Tel.: (217) 321-9292
Medical Devices
N.A.I.C.S.: 423450
Craig Brace *(Dir-Div)*

St. John's Hospital of the Hospital Sisters of the Third Order of St. Francis-Springfield   (1)
800 E Carpenter St, Springfield, IL 62769
Tel.: (217) 544-6464
Web Site: http://www.st-johns.org
Sales Range: $350-399.9 Million
Hospital Services
N.A.I.C.S.: 622110

HOSPITAL SOLUTIONS, INC.
10700 N Freeway Ste 475, Houston, TX 77037
Tel.: (713) 350-9900   TX
Web Site:
   http://www.hospitalsolutionsinc.com
Year Founded: 1996
Sales Range: $1-9.9 Million
Emp.: 90
Medicaid/SSI Eligibility Services for Contracted Hospitals

N.A.I.C.S.: 561110
Philip D. Kryk *(Pres & CEO)*

HOSPITALISTS OF NORTHERN MICHIGAN
10850 E Traverse Hwy Ste 4400, Traverse City, MI 49684
Tel.: (231) 346-6800
Web Site:
   http://www.michiganhospitalist.com
Year Founded: 2001
Sales Range: $10-24.9 Million
Emp.: 55
Hospital Management Services
N.A.I.C.S.: 622110
Heidi Henry *(Dir-Physician Recruiting)*
James Levy *(VP-Personnel)*

HOSPITALITY INVESTMENTS LP
16114 East Indiana Ste 200, Spokane, WA 99216-1608
Tel.: (509) 928-3736
Web Site:
   http://www.hospitalityassociates.com
Year Founded: 1989
Sales Range: $100-124.9 Million
Emp.: 741
Hospitality Services
N.A.I.C.S.: 523999

HOSPITALITY MARKETING CONCEPTS, INC.
1201 Dove St Ste 370, Newport Beach, CA 92660
Tel.: (949) 833-8000   DE
Web Site: http://www.hmcloyalty.com
Year Founded: 1988
Sales Range: $150-199.9 Million
Emp.: 2,000
Membership Programs for Hotels
N.A.I.C.S.: 541613
Mokhtar Ramadan *(Co-Founder, Co-Pres & CEO)*
Sylvia Hu *(Treas & Controller)*
Abed Chawa *(CIO)*

Subsidiaries:

HMC Consulting (Shanghai) Co. Ltd   (1)
Block 3 Suite 201 D1 International Creative Building, No 909 Tian Yao Qiao Road, Shanghai, 200030, China
Tel.: (86) 21 6100 6900
Loyalty Program Operator
N.A.I.C.S.: 561990

Hospitality Marketing Concepts, (Asia Pacific) Inc   (1)
one Common wealth 0906 Bldg Common wealth, Bk B Unit no 01-28/29, Singapore, 149544, Singapore
Tel.: (65) 68870060
Web Site: http://www.clubhotel.com
Sales Range: $10-24.9 Million
Emp.: 20
Provider of Member Services
N.A.I.C.S.: 561499
Michelle Sandhu *(Dir-Mktg Svcs-Bus Dev)*
Octavio Gamarra *(Mng Dir & VP)*

Hospitality Marketing Concepts, Inc.   (1)
1045 Howe St Ste 925, Vancouver, V6E 1B5, BC, Canada   (100%)
Tel.: (604) 608-0482
Web Site: http://www.clubhotel.com
Sales Range: $10-24.9 Million
Emp.: 12
Marketing of Hotel Packages
N.A.I.C.S.: 721110

HOSPITALITY PARTNERS
Ste M025 3 Bethesda Metro Ctr, Bethesda, MD 20814-6343
Tel.: (301) 718-6161
Web Site: http://www.hospart.com
Rev.: $40,400,000
Emp.: 12
Hotel

Hospitality Partners—(Continued)

N.A.I.C.S.: 721110
Michael M. Dickens *(Founder)*
John Vernon *(Founder)*
Fred Palloni *(Founder)*
Michael James *(Pres & CEO)*

HOSPITALITY PURVEYOR INC.
5000 SW 75th Ave Ste 111, Miami,
FL 33155
Tel.: (305) 667-9725
Rev.: $37,000,000
Emp.: 42
Purchasing Service
N.A.I.C.S.: 561499
David Diffel *(Gen Mgr)*

HOSPITALITY SPECIALISTS, INC.
5 Shenadoah, Jacksonville, IL 62650
Tel.: (217) 245-2220
Web Site:
   https://www.hospitalityspecialists
   inc.com
Sales Range: $1-9.9 Million
Emp.: 16
Hotel Development & Management
Services
N.A.I.C.S.: 721110
John A. Mann *(Pres & CEO)*
James L. Mann *(CFO & VP)*
Angela Mann *(VP-Ops)*
Rae Richardson *(VP-Construction & Renovation)*
Mike Hrusovsky *(Dir-Revenue Mgmt)*
Robb Carter *(Dir-Property Support)*
Matthew Hughes *(Dir-Performance & Tech)*
Ed Willcome *(Dir-Maintenance & Facility Integrity)*

**HOSPITALITY USA INVEST-
MENT GROUP, INC.**
10001 Westheimer Rd, Houston, TX
77042
Tel.: (713) 977-1857   TX
Web Site:
   http://www.hospitalityusa.com
Year Founded: 1995
Sales Range: $50-74.9 Million
Emp.: 1,354
Restaurant Operators
N.A.I.C.S.: 722513
Edgar Carlson *(Sec)*
Larry Martin *(Pres)*

HOSPITALITY WEST LLC
745 S Garfield Ave Ste A, Traverse
City, MI 49686
Tel.: (231) 941-5052   MI
Web Site: http://www.hrgonline.net
Year Founded: 1998
Sales Range: $25-49.9 Million
Emp.: 500
Eating Place Services
N.A.I.C.S.: 722513
Diane Burns *(Controller)*

HOSS INDUSTRIAL LLC
3118 Metric Dr, Sulphur, LA 70665
Tel.: (337) 513-4049
Web Site:
   http://www.hossindustrial.com
Year Founded: 2014
Sales Range: $1-9.9 Million
Emp.: 21
Industrial Cleaning Services
N.A.I.C.S.: 561790
Desi Gauthreaux *(Partner & Mgr)*

HOSS VALUE CARS & TRUCKS INC.
766 Miamisburg Centerville Rd State
725, Dayton, OH 45459
Tel.: (937) 434-6014

Web Site: http://www.vossauto.com
Sales Range: $10-24.9 Million
Emp.: 500
Automobile Dealers
N.A.I.C.S.: 441110
John E. Voss *(Pres)*

**HOSS'S STEAK & SEA
HOUSE, INC.**
170 Patchway Rd, Duncansville, PA
16635
Tel.: (814) 695-7600   PA
Web Site: https://www.hosss.com
Year Founded: 1983
Restaurant Chain Operator
N.A.I.C.S.: 722511
Carl Raup *(CFO)*
Billy Jo Walls *(Dir-Mktg)*

HOSTDIME.COM, INC.
2603 Challenger Tech Ct Ste 140,
Orlando, FL 32826
Tel.: (407) 756-1126
Web Site: http://www.hostdime.com
Year Founded: 2003
Rev.: $6,600,000
Emp.: 71
Wired Telecommunications Carriers
N.A.I.C.S.: 517111
Emanuel Vivar *(Pres)*

**HOSTELLING INTERNATIONAL
USA**
8401 Colesdile Rd Ste 600, Silver
Spring, MD 20910
Tel.: (301) 495-1240
Web Site: http://www.hiusa.org
Sales Range: $10-24.9 Million
Emp.: 160
Hotel Operators
N.A.I.C.S.: 721199
Charles Hokanson *(Sec)*

**HOSTETLERS SALES & CON-
STRUCTION LLC**
210 Kelly Rd, Buffalo, MO 65622
Tel.: (417) 345-7418   MO
Year Founded: 1966
Sales Range: $10-24.9 Million
Emp.: 40
Truss Plates, Metal
N.A.I.C.S.: 332313
David Hostetler *(Gen Mgr)*

HOSTING.COM, INC.
900 S Broadway Ste 400, Denver,
CO 80209
Tel.: (720) 389-3800
Web Site: http://www.hosting.com
Year Founded: 1997
Sales Range: $50-74.9 Million
Emp.: 350
Web Hosting & Other Computer Re-
lated Services
N.A.I.C.S.: 518210
Art Zeile *(Co-Founder)*
Craig McLellan *(CTO)*
Bruce Greiner *(Exec VP-Sls & Mktg)*
Bill Santos *(Pres)*
Don Barlow *(COO)*
Andrew Schroepfer *(Chief Strategy Officer)*
Darrell Hyde *(CTO)*
Rob Daly *(Exec VP-Public Cloud Consulting)*
Paul Duvall *(Co-CTO)*

Subsidiaries:

Hostway Services, Inc.   (1)
501 Waller St, Austin, TX 78702
Tel.: (312) 238-0125
Web Site: http://www.hostway.com
Internet Hosting Services
N.A.I.C.S.: 518210
John Lee *(Sr VP-Small Bus Hosting)*
Mark D. Adolph *(CFO & Exec VP)*
Aaron Hollobaugh *(VP-Sls & Mktg)*

Bobby Boughton *(VP-Sls)*
Jim Potter *(VP-Product)*
Mike Robski *(VP-R&D)*
Jim Ciampaglio *(VP-Channel Partners)*
John Enright *(Sr VP & Gen Mgr-Web & Ap-
plication Svcs)*
Tony Savoy *(Sr VP & Gen Mgr-Managed
Hosting & Cloud Svcs)*
Bart H. J. De Maertelaere *(COO & Sr VP)*
David Newton *(VP-Svcs Ops)*
Eric Milhizer *(VP-Mktg)*
Michael Kaplan *(Chm)*
Steve Armond *(CFO)*
Johan Cho *(VP-Legal)*
Jay Newman *(Sr VP-Sls)*
Emil Sayegh *(Pres & CEO)*

**HOSTMARK HOSPITALITY
GROUP**
1300 E Woodfield Rd Ste 400,
Schaumburg, IL 60173
Tel.: (847) 517-9100   IL
Web Site: https://www.hostmark.com
Year Founded: 1965
Sales Range: $150-199.9 Million
Emp.: 4,100
Developer & Manager of Resorts &
Hotels
N.A.I.C.S.: 531312
C. A. Cataldo *(Chm)*
Robert J. Cataldo *(Vice Chm)*
Jerome F. Cataldo *(Pres & CEO)*
L. W. Hawkey *(Sr VP-Dev)*
Ronald L. Vlasic *(COO)*
William D. Gingrich II *(CFO & Exec
VP)*

Subsidiaries:

Green Oaks Hotel   (1)
17950 Preston Rd Ste 710, Dallas, TX
75252-5637
Tel.: (817) 738-7311
Web Site: http://www.greenoakshotel.com
Rev.: $6,000,000
Emp.: 125
Full Service Hotel Conference Center And
Resort
N.A.I.C.S.: 721110

HOSTMYSITE.COM
650 Pencader Dr, Newark, DE 19702
Tel.: (302) 731-4948
Web Site: http://www.hostmysite.com
Year Founded: 1997
Sales Range: $1-9.9 Million
Emp.: 260
Hosts Websites
N.A.I.C.S.: 518210
Bryan Longacre *(Engr-Software)*
Mona Sen *(Acct Mgr)*
Ryan Barr *(Engr-Server)*
William Baker *(CFO)*

HOSTVENTURES.COM, INC.
7923 Honeygo Blvd Ste 212, White
Marsh, MD 21236
Tel.: (800) 272-0019
Web Site:
   http://www.hostventures.com
Year Founded: 2002
Sales Range: $1-9.9 Million
Emp.: 40
Boutique IT Consulting Services Spe-
cialists in Critical Infrastructures
N.A.I.C.S.: 541690
Vadim Hiekin *(CEO)*
Jen Vogel *(Mgr-Ops)*
Alexander Chizhik *(COO & Gen
Counsel)*

HOT FROG PRINT MEDIA LLC
118 W Allen St, Mechanicsburg, PA
17055
Tel.: (717) 697-2204
Web Site:
   http://www.hotfrogprintmedia.com
Year Founded: 2010
Printing Services
N.A.I.C.S.: 323111

James A. Geedy *(Founder & CEO)*
Jennifer Snyder *(COO)*
Stephanie Bender *(Dir-Creative)*
Dewi Geedy *(Controller)*
Wayde Spangler *(Mgr-Ops)*
Josh Smith *(Mgr-Plant)*

Subsidiaries:

Perry Printing Co.   (1)
RD-1 Box 85, New Bloomfield, PA 17068-
9683
Tel.: (717) 582-2838
Printing Services
N.A.I.C.S.: 323120

HOT MAMA'S FOODS, INC.
134 Avocado St, Springfield, MA
01104
Tel.: (413) 737-6572
Web Site:
   http://www.hotmamasfoods.com
Sales Range: $25-49.9 Million
Emp.: 137
Perishable Prepared Food Mfr
N.A.I.C.S.: 311991
Matthew Morse *(Chm & CEO)*
William Kenealy *(CFO & Sec)*

HOT OFF THE PRESS, INC.
1250 NW 3rd Ave, Canby, OR 97013
Tel.: (503) 266-9102
Web Site:
   http://www.paperwishes.com
Year Founded: 1980
Sales Range: $10-24.9 Million
Emp.: 45
Craft Books & Supplies
N.A.I.C.S.: 513130
Paulette Jarvey *(Pres)*

HOT SHOT DELIVERY INC.
747 N Sheperd Ste 100, Houston, TX
77007-5352
Tel.: (713) 869-5525   TX
Web Site: http://www.hotshot-
   delivery.com
Year Founded: 1978
Sales Range: $50-74.9 Million
Emp.: 30
Delivery & Messenger Services
N.A.I.C.S.: 484110
Darrell Donaldson *(Chm)*

HOT SHOT EXPRESS INC.
654 Enterprise Dr, Limerick, PA
19468
Tel.: (610) 948-8020   CA
Web Site: http://www.jonesmotor.com
Year Founded: 1985
Sales Range: $10-24.9 Million
Emp.: 15
Trucking Services
N.A.I.C.S.: 561499
Mary Fry *(VP-IT)*
Tony Coccia *(Dir-Ops)*

HOT SOX COMPANY, INC.
95 Madison Ave Fl 15, New York, NY
10016-7801
Tel.: (212) 957-2000
Web Site: http://www.hotsox.com
Year Founded: 1971
Sales Range: $10-24.9 Million
Emp.: 50
Hosiery Mfr
N.A.I.C.S.: 315120
Gary Wolkowitz *(Pres)*

**HOT SPRINGS CONVENTION
& VISITORS BUREAU**
134 Convention Blvd, Hot Springs
National Park, AR 71901-4135
Tel.: (501) 321-2277
Web Site: https://www.hotsprings.org
Year Founded: 1974
Sales Range: $1-9.9 Million

Emp.: 70
Convention & Visitors Bureau
N.A.I.C.S.: 561591
Steve Arrison (CEO)

HOT SPRINGS COUNTY MEMORIAL HOSPITAL

150 E Arapahoe St, Thermopolis, WY 82443
Tel.: (307) 864-3121   WY
Web Site: http://www.hscmh.org
Year Founded: 1944
Sales Range: $10-24.9 Million
Emp.: 140
Health Care Srvices
N.A.I.C.S.: 622110
Bill Williams (Chm)
Brian Green (Vice Chm)

HOT STUDIO, INC.

585 Howard St 1st Fl, San Francisco, CA 94105
Tel.: (415) 284-7250
Web Site: https://www.hotstudio.com
Sales Range: $10-24.9 Million
Emp.: 37
Graphic Design Services
N.A.I.C.S.: 541430
Henrik Olsen (Exec Dir-Creative)
Clancy Nolan (Exec Dir)

HOTARD COACHES, INC.

2838 Touro St, New Orleans, LA 70122
Tel.: (504) 942-5700
Web Site: https://www.hotard.com
Year Founded: 1960
Sales Range: $10-24.9 Million
Emp.: 247
Scenic & Sightseeing Land Transportation Services
N.A.I.C.S.: 487110
Colleen Hotard (Pres)

HOTCHKISS INSURANCE AGENCY

4120 International Pkwy Ste 2000, Carrollton, TX 75007
Tel.: (972) 512-7700
Web Site: http://www.hiallc.com
Rev.: $60,000,000
Emp.: 150
Property & Casualty Insurance Agent
N.A.I.C.S.: 524210
Douglas Hotchkiss (Founder)
Greg Hotchkiss (CFO)
Ken Hotchkiss (COO)
Wes Weatherred (Partner & VP-Sls & Mktg)
Farrah Carlton (VP-Svc)
Brad Burnham (Partner & VP)
Hunter Ramsey (Partner & VP)
Pat Janosky (Partner & VP)
Ross Conner (Partner & VP)
Wayne Bishop (Partner & VP)
Heather Etheredge (VP-HR)

HOTEL & RESTAURANT SUPPLY

5020 Aurundel Rd, Meridian, MS 39307
Tel.: (601) 482-7127
Web Site: https://www.hnrsupply.com
Sales Range: $25-49.9 Million
Emp.: 100
Commercial Cooking & Food Service Equipment
N.A.I.C.S.: 423440
Jerry R. Greene (Pres)
William Wolfe (VP)
Kim Nelson (Controller)

HOTEL COMPANY INC.

1191 Lakewood Farmingdale, Howell, NJ 07731
Tel.: (732) 905-6399

Web Site: http://www.hcsales.com
Sales Range: $100-124.9 Million
Emp.: 60
Hotel Equipment & Supplies
N.A.I.C.S.: 423440

HOTEL CONSULTING SERVICES INC.

369 Willis Ave, Mineola, NY 11501
Tel.: (516) 248-8828
Web Site: http://www.hvs.com
Sales Range: $10-24.9 Million
Emp.: 23
Appraiser, Real Estate
N.A.I.C.S.: 561110
Stephen Rushmore (Pres)

HOTEL EQUITIES, INC.

41 Perimeter Ctr E Ste 510, Atlanta, GA 30346
Tel.: (678) 578-4444
Web Site:
http://www.hotelequities.com
Year Founded: 1989
Sales Range: $10-24.9 Million
Emp.: 20
Intermediation Services
N.A.I.C.S.: 523910
Frederick W. Cerrone (Founder & Chm)
Joe Reardon (Chief Dev Officer)
Brad Rahinsky (Pres & CEO)
Carlos F. Melgar (VP-Fin)
Jeff Shockley (VP-Acq & Fin Analysis)
Elizabeth Derby (VP-Talent & Performance Excellence)
Rob Cote (VP-Ops)
Dennis Meroney (Chief Investment Officer)
Stacey Morgan (Mgr-Corp Revenue)
Yanbo Zhu (Reg Mgr-Revenue)
Dominic Buompastore (VP-Ops-Full Svc & Resorts)
Barbara Soucia (Reg Dir-Revenue Mgmt)
Mischa Moore (Reg Mgr-Revenue)
Jackie Edmonds (Dir-Sls-Texas)
Phillip Bullard (Dir-Facilities)
Sommer Shiver (VP-Branding & Comm)
Andrew Salapka (Sr VP-Revenue Generation)
Amy Greenwood (Reg Mgr-Revenue)
Jessica Bryant (Coord-Admin & Ops)
Jim Holliday (Reg Dir-Sls)
Tucker Stallings (Coord-Bus Dev)
Jimmy Grover (Reg Dir-Ops)
Foster White (Asst Gen Mgr)
Arthur Holman (Gen Mgr-175-room Residence Inn Miami Beach & Surfside)
Marcie Pruitt (Controller)
Susan Greenberg (Dir-Sls-Texas)
Bryan DeCort (COO)
Toi Brown (Dir-HR)
Cesar Wurm (VP-Sls & Mktg)
Ryan McRae (Sr VP-Bus Dev)
Albert Smith (Pres-Hotel Ops)
Mark Williams (Sr VP-Bus Dev)
Lindsay Meadows (Dir-Procurement)
Amber Edwards (Gen Mgr-The Hamilton, a Curio Collection by Hilton)
Peter Tziahanas (Sr VP-Ops)
Tipton Corbin (Reg Dir-Bus Dev-West)
Brody Aarhaus (Mgr-Bus Dev)
James Hansen (Exec VP)

HOTEL GROUP INTERNATIONAL, INC.

201 5th Ave S Ste 200, Edmonds, WA 98020
Tel.: (425) 771-1788
Web Site:
https://www.thehotelgroup.com

Year Founded: 1984
Sales Range: $10-24.9 Million
Emp.: 1,600
Hotel Owner & Operator
N.A.I.C.S.: 721110
Edmond A. Lee (Founder, Chm & Principal)
Douglas N. Dreher (Pres, CEO & Principal)
Randy J. Meyer (CFO & Principal)
Lara R. Latture (COO & Principal)
Jake Fischer (VP-Real Estate & Bus Dev)
Katherine Steed (VP-Sls & Mktg)
Isabel Dreher (VP-HR)
Robert Avila (Reg VP-Ops)
Brian Latture (Reg VP-Ops)
Jeff Gouge (Reg VP-Ops)
Robin Koetje (Dir-IT)
Neil Taylor (Dir-Project Mgmt)
Lynne Dematteo (Mgr-Corp Recruiting)
Don Haggerty (VP-Sls & Mktg)

Subsidiaries:

DoubleTree by Hilton - South
Bend   (1)
123 N Saint Joseph St, South Bend, IN 46601-1624   (100%)
Tel.: (574) 234-2000
Web Site:
   http://www.doubletreebyhilton.com
Sales Range: $10-24.9 Million
Emp.: 120
Hotel
N.A.I.C.S.: 721110
Jim Wynn (Gen Mgr)

HOTEL MAX

620 Stewart St, Seattle, WA 98101
Tel.: (206) 728-6299
Web Site:
http://www.hotelmaxseattle.com
Year Founded: 2005
Sales Range: $50-74.9 Million
Emp.: 70
Hotel
N.A.I.C.S.: 721110
Angela Murphy (Dir-Sls)
Kevin Scott (Gen Mgr)

HOTEL MONTELEONE INC.

214 Rue Royal, New Orleans, LA 70130-2201
Tel.: (504) 523-3341
Web Site:
   https://www.hotelmonteleone.com
Sales Range: $25-49.9 Million
Emp.: 350
Hotel
N.A.I.C.S.: 561110
Kent Wasmuth (Dir-Sls & Mktg)

HOTEL VANITIES INTERNATIONAL, LLC

5514 Stockwell Ct, Indianapolis, IN 46237
Tel.: (317) 787-2330
Web Site:
   http://www.hotelvanities.com
Sales Range: $1-9.9 Million
Emp.: 11
Installer of Bathroom Furnishings
N.A.I.C.S.: 444180
Chris E. Dolne (Pres)
John F. Schroeder (VP-Sls)
Elizabeth Hatfield (Mgr-Logistics)

HOTLINE TELECOMMUNICATIONS

3000 Beverly Blvd, Los Angeles, CA 90057
Tel.: (213) 387-5930
Web Site:
   http://www.hotlinetelecom.com
Sales Range: $10-24.9 Million
Emp.: 2

Telephone & Telephone Equipment Installation
N.A.I.C.S.: 238210

HOTMIX ASPHALT EQUIPMENT CO.

12711 Townepark Way, Louisville, KY 40243
Tel.: (502) 245-1977
Web Site: https://www.stansteel.com
Rev.: $10,000,000
Emp.: 8
Sales of Heating Units & Devices
N.A.I.C.S.: 333994
Leonard Loesch (Owner & Pres)

HOTMIX PARTS

12711 Townepark Way, Louisville, KY 40243
Tel.: (502) 245-1977   KY
Web Site:
   https://www.hotmixparts.com
Year Founded: 1999
Asphalt Mfr
N.A.I.C.S.: 333994
John Griffin (Engr-Sls Support)
Steve Elam (Mgr-Ops)

HOTSCHEDULES

6504 Bridge Point Pkwy Ste 425, Austin, TX 78730
Tel.: (512) 904-4299
Web Site:
   http://www.hotschedules.com
Year Founded: 1999
Sales Range: $1-9.9 Million
Emp.: 180
Online Scheduling Services
N.A.I.C.S.: 519290
John W. Chidsey (Chm)
Ray Pawlikowski (COO)
David Cantu (Chief Revenue Officer)

HOU ELECTRONICS INC.

16815 E Johnson Dr, City of Industry, CA 91745
Tel.: (626) 968-2222
Year Founded: 1986
Sales Range: $10-24.9 Million
Emp.: 10
Computer Peripheral Equipment Whslr
N.A.I.C.S.: 423430

HOUCHENS INDUSTRIES, INC.

700 Church St, Bowling Green, KY 42101
Tel.: (270) 843-3252   KY
Web Site: https://houchens.com
Year Founded: 1917
Emp.: 19,000
Supermarkets & Other Grocery Retailers (except Convenience Retailers)
N.A.I.C.S.: 445110
Dion Houchins (Chm & CEO)

Subsidiaries:

Center of Insurance   (1)
1750 Scottsville Rd, Bowling Green, KY 42104   (100%)
Tel.: (270) 781-6200
Web Site: http://www.coiky.com
Sales Range: $25-49.9 Million
Emp.: 9
Insurance Agents
N.A.I.C.S.: 524210

Cohen's Fashion Optical Inc.   (1)
100 Quentin Roosevelt Blvd Ste 400, Garden City, NY 11530-1558
Tel.: (516) 599-5500
Web Site:
   http://www.cohensfashionoptical.com
Sales Range: $25-49.9 Million
Emp.: 100
Eyeglass Retailer Distr
N.A.I.C.S.: 456130
Karen Miller (VP)

Houchens Industries, Inc.—(Continued)

Curneal & Hignite Insurance, Inc. (1)
2905 Ring Rd, Elizabethtown, KY 42702-0807
Tel.: (270) 737-2828
Web Site: http://www.curnealhigniteins.com
Sales Range: $25-49.9 Million
Emp.: 25
Fire Insurance Services
N.A.I.C.S.: 524210
Judy Besser (Mgr-Comml Lines)
Vicky Games (Mgr-Claims)
Tom Major (Mgr-Life & Health)
Joe Stewart (Gen Mgr)

Feeders Supply Company Inc. (1)
315 Baxter Ave, Louisville, KY 40204
Tel.: (502) 583-3867
Web Site: http://www.feederssupply.com
Sales Range: $10-24.9 Million
Emp.: 200
Pet Food
N.A.I.C.S.: 459910
Pam Longwell (Pres & CEO)

Food Giant Supermarkets, Inc. (1)
120 Indus Dr, Sikeston, MO 63801-2701
Tel.: (573) 471-3500
Web Site: http://www.foodgiant.com
Sales Range: $75-99.9 Million
Emp.: 32
Owner & Operator of Food Store Chains
N.A.I.C.S.: 445110
Ronnie J. Watkins (Pres)
Steve Malone (Controller)

Four Seasons Sales & Service, Inc. (1)
2505 E Wood St, Paris, TN 38242
Tel.: (731) 642-0234
Web Site: http://www.fstanning.com
Indoor Tanning Supplies Distr
N.A.I.C.S.: 424690
Janet Lutz (Acct Mgr)
Jonathan Travis (Acct Mgr)
Luz Valentin (Acct Mgr)
Marcie Snyder (Acct Mgr)
Becky Cheek (Acct Mgr-Sls)
Nita Rushing (Acct Mgr-Sls)
Graeme Parsons (Dir-Art)
Virginia Brewer (Mgr-Sls)

Hitcents (1)
2425 Nashville Rd, Bowling Green, KY 42101
Tel.: (270) 796-5063
Web Site: http://www.hitcents.com
Sales Range: $1-9.9 Million
Emp.: 50
Online Marketing Services
N.A.I.C.S.: 541519
Emily Camp (Mgr-Acctg)
Robert Camp (Mgr-Tech)
Courtney Cheatwood (Mgr-Acct)
Laura Gay (Dir-Mktg)
Cheryl McGuire (Accountant)
Ed Mills (Co-Owner & CFO)
Ada Beth Oliver (Designer-Graphic)
Derek Sabiston (Designer-Graphic)
Aaron Spalding (Mgr-Network Svcs)
Stuart Westphal V (VP-Games & Interactive)

Houchens Markets (1)
700 Church St, Bowling Green, KY 42101-5112 (100%)
Tel.: (270) 843-3252
Web Site:
   http://www.houchensindustries.com
Sales Range: $25-49.9 Million
Emp.: 200
Grocery Stores
N.A.I.C.S.: 445110
Gordon Minter (Controller)

Insurance Specialists (1)
1750 Scottsville Rd Ste 4, Bowling Green, KY 42101
Tel.: (270) 793-0367
Web Site: http://www.isbgky.com
Emp.: 35
Employee Welfare Services
N.A.I.C.S.: 524210
Brian Wiseman (Pres)

J.J.B. Hilliard, W.L. Lyons, LLC (1)
500 W Jefferson St Ste 700, Louisville, KY 40202
Tel.: (502) 588-8400

Web Site: http://www.hilliard.com
Sales Range: $125-149.9 Million
Emp.: 400
Asset Management Services
N.A.I.C.S.: 523150
James R. Allen (Chm & CEO)
Carmella Miller (Chief Admin Officer & Exec VP)
Alan Newman (Exec VP & Dir-Private Client Grp)
Randy Bugh (Exec VP & Dir-Fin Svcs)
Nick Papachristou (CMO)
Michael Barnett (VP)
Jaleigh White (Exec VP & Dir-Wealth Svcs)
Gail Burke Tway Bride (Sr VP & Portfolio Mgr)
Bary Dedge (Exec VP & Dir-IT, Ops & Enterprise Project Mgmt Office)
Joe Cutsinger (Exec VP & Dir-Budget & Fin Analytics)
Mark Nickel (Chief Investment Officer)
Gary England (Chief Legal Officer)
Curtis McCubbin (Gen Counsel)
Andy Dytrych (VP & Dir-Enterprise Project Mgmt Office)
Terry Sanctis (Sr VP-Cranberry Township)
Shane Prier (VP)
Donald L. Asfahl (Pres-HLTC & Exec VP)
Thomas B. Kessinger III (Pres)

Jr. Food Stores, Inc. (1)
700 Church St, Bowling Green, KY 42101-5112 (100%)
Tel.: (270) 843-3252
Web Site:
   http://www.houchensindustries.com
Sales Range: $25-49.9 Million
Emp.: 120
Convenience Store Operator
N.A.I.C.S.: 457120

Pan-Oston Co. (1)
6944 Louisville Rd, Bowling Green, KY 42101
Tel.: (270) 783-3900
Web Site: http://www.panoston.com
Emp.: 150
Store Fixture & Display Case Mfr
N.A.I.C.S.: 337215
Steve Guess (CFO)
Kendra Sewell (Project Mgr)

Save-A-Lot (1)
600 31W Bypass, Bowling Green, KY 42101 (100%)
Tel.: (270) 782-1204
Web Site: http://www.savealot.com
Sales Range: $600-649.9 Million
Emp.: 65
Grocery Stores, Chain
N.A.I.C.S.: 445110
Steven Morand (Sr Mgr-Shrink Optimization)

Sheldon's Express Pharmacy (1)
843 Fairview Ave, Bowling Green, KY 42101
Tel.: (270) 842-4515
Web Site: http://www.sheldonsexpresspharmacy.com
Drug Store Operator
N.A.I.C.S.: 456110
Terri Sheldon (Co-Founder & Co-Owner)
Rick Matthews (Asst Mgr-Retail Pharmacist-Franklin)
Steve Sheldon (Co-Founder & Co-Owner)
Shaun Curtis (Asst Mgr-Retail-Pharm D)
Kevin Davis (Mgr-Rockport)
Sherri Dunning (Specialist-Compounding)
Daniel Emery (Asst Mgr-Buckhead Square-Pharm D)
Melissa Greathouse (Mgr-Buckhead Square-Pharm D)
Mollie Hodges (Asst Mgr-Franklin)
Ralph Mehling (Mgr-Jasper)
Ryan Sheldon (Mgr-Peachtree-Pharm D)
Ben Washam (Mgr-Peachtree-Pharm D)

Southern Recycling Inc. (1)
620 Clay St, Bowling Green, KY 42101-1844 (100%)
Tel.: (270) 843-9727
Web Site:
   http://www.metalmanagement.com
Sales Range: $10-24.9 Million
Emp.: 50
Scrap Metal Recycling
N.A.I.C.S.: 423930
John Fellonneau (VP)

Stewart-Richey Construction, Inc. (1)
2137 Glen Lily Rd, Bowling Green, KY 42101-9409 (100%)
Tel.: (270) 842-5184
Web Site: http://www.stewartrichey.com
Sales Range: $50-74.9 Million
Emp.: 400
Commercial & Residential Construction
N.A.I.C.S.: 236220
Rodney Rogers (Pres)

Tampico Beverages, Inc. (1)
3106 N Campbell Ave, Chicago, IL 60618
Tel.: (773) 296-0190
Web Site: http://www.tampico.com
Soft Drinks Mfr
N.A.I.C.S.: 312111
Jenny Haas (CEO)

Van Meter Insurance Group (1)
1240 Fairway St, Bowling Green, KY 42103
Tel.: (270) 781-2020
Web Site: http://www.vanmeterins.com
Sales Range: $50-74.9 Million
Emp.: 200
General Insurance Services
N.A.I.C.S.: 524210
Brian Sewell (Co-Pres)
Mike Baas (VP)
Mike Hostetter (Sr VP)
Christiaan Volkert (Sr VP)
Geoff Bosley (CFO)

HOUCHIN COMMUNITY BLOOD BANK

11515 Bolthouse Dr, Bakersfield, CA 93311   CA
Tel.: (661) 323-4222
Web Site: https://www.hcbb.com
Year Founded: 1951
Sales Range: $10-24.9 Million
Emp.: 136
Blood Bank
N.A.I.C.S.: 621991
Greg Gallion (Pres & CEO)
Joseph C. Engel (Chm)

HOUCK INDUSTRIES, INC.

814 E Randall St, Greensburg, IN 47240-2311   CA
Tel.: (812) 663-5675
Web Site: http://www.houckind.com
Year Founded: 1949
Sales Range: $1-9.9 Million
Emp.: 16
Cabinet Hardware Mfr
N.A.I.C.S.: 332510
Vicky Ostendorf (Owner, CFO & VP-Pur)

HOUFF TRANSFER INC.

46 Houff Rd, Weyers Cave, VA 24486
Tel.: (540) 234-9233
Web Site: https://www.houff.com
Sales Range: $10-24.9 Million
Emp.: 250
Trucking Services
N.A.I.C.S.: 484121
Zane M. Houff (VP-Ops)
Alan Caviness (Dir-Safety)
E. Grant Doyle (Treas & Sec)
Douglas Z. Houff (Pres)

HOUG SPECIAL SERVICES, INC.

5333 E 58th Ave, Commerce City, CO 80022
Tel.: (303) 564-3355
Web Site: http://www.houg.net
Sales Range: $25-49.9 Million
Emp.: 228
Trucking Except Local
N.A.I.C.S.: 484121
Paul Will (Chm & CEO)
Bobby Peavler (CFO, Treas & Exec VP)
Eric Meek (Pres & COO)
Ken Core (VP-Risk Mgmt)
Steve Russell (Founder)

HOUGEN MANUFACTURING INC.

3001 Hougen Dr, Swartz Creek, MI 48473-7935
Tel.: (810) 635-7111   MI
Web Site: http://www.hougen.com
Year Founded: 1959
Sales Range: $10-24.9 Million
Emp.: 125
Mfr of Cutting Tools, Drill Bits & Portable Holemaking Equipment
N.A.I.C.S.: 333515
Randall Hougen (Pres & CEO)
Jeff Miller (Mgr-Engrg)
Jim Kaiser (Mgr-Sls)

HOUGHTON CHEMICAL CORPORATION

52 Cambridge St, Allston, MA 02134-1850
Tel.: (617) 254-1010   MA
Web Site:
   http://www.houghtonchemical.com
Year Founded: 1927
Sales Range: $75-99.9 Million
Emp.: 85
Chemical Distr; Automotive Products Mfr; Water Treatment Services
N.A.I.C.S.: 424690
Bruce E. Houghton (Pres)
Charles McCarte (Plant Mgr)
Ronald McGilvray (VP-Fin)
Alfonso Sira (Mgr-Acct)
Patricia Hanna (Sr VP)

Subsidiaries:

Houghton Chemical (1)
30 Amor Ave, Carlstadt, NJ 07072-2103
Tel.: (201) 460-0400
Web Site: http://www.houghton.com
Sales Range: $25-49.9 Million
Emp.: 40
Automotive Chemicals Mfr
N.A.I.C.S.: 424690
Randy Hunter (Dir-Info Sys)
Patty Daly (Mgr-HR)
Brian Hughes (Mgr-Acct)
Bill Hunjo (Plant Mgr)
Joe Lima (VP-Ops)
Ron McGilvray (VP-Fin)
Marybeth Moore (Mgr-Acct)
Tom Murphy (Mgr-Lab)
Stephen Richardson (Mgr-Acct)
Leo Thompson (Mgr-Production)

Houghton Chemical Corporation - Allston Facility (1)
52 Cambridge St, Allston, MA 02134
Tel.: (617) 254-1010
Industrial Chemicals Mfr
N.A.I.C.S.: 325998

HOULTON REGIONAL HOSPITAL

20 Hartford St, Houlton, ME 04730
Tel.: (207) 532-2900   ME
Web Site:
   https://www.houltonregional.org
Year Founded: 1973
Sales Range: $25-49.9 Million
Emp.: 506
Health Care Srvices
N.A.I.C.S.: 622110
Thomas Moakler (CEO)
Cynthia Thompson (CFO)

HOUR MEDIA GROUP, LLC

5750 New King Dr Ste 100, Troy, MI 48098
Tel.: (248) 691-1800   MI
Emp.: 200
Holding Company; Periodical Publisher
N.A.I.C.S.: 551112
Stefan Wanczyk (CEO)
John Balardo (Pres)

Subsidiaries:

Greenspring Media LLC (1)

706 2nd Ave S Ste 1000, Minneapolis, MN 55402-3003
Tel.: (612) 371-5800
Web Site: http://www.greenspring.com
Periodical Publishers
N.A.I.C.S.: 513120
Cindy Marking (Mgr-Production Project)
Tammy Galvin (Exec Dir-Content)
Reed Fischer (Sr Editor)

Hour Media, LLC (1)
5750 New King Dr Ste 100, Troy, MI 48098
Tel.: (248) 691-1800
Web Site: http://www.hourmediallc.com
Periodical Publishers
N.A.I.C.S.: 513120
Dorothy Hernandez (Mng Editor)
Jason Hosko (Dir-Adv)
Carolyn Chin Watson (Creative Dir)

Los Angeles Magazine, LLC (1)
5900 Wilshire Blvd 10th Fl, Los Angeles, CA 90036
Tel.: (323) 801-0100
Web Site: http://www.lamag.com
Magazine Publisher
N.A.I.C.S.: 513120
Jean M. Greene (Mgr-Local Adv)
Marielle Wakim (Editor-Arts & Culture)
Joe Donatelli (Mng Editor-Digital)
Eric Mercado (Editor-Res)
Michael Petruncola (Assoc Publr)
Caitlin Cullen (Mgr-Digital Mktg)
Suzy Starling (Coord-Mktg Svcs)
Sammy Galen (Assoc Mgr-Mktg)

Orange Coast Magazine, LLC (1)
1124 Main St Ste A, Irvine, CA 92614
Tel.: (949) 862-1133
Web Site: http://www.orangecoast.com
Magazine Publisher
N.A.I.C.S.: 513120
Mindy Benham (Dir-Design)
Christopher Schulz (Pres & Publr)
Victoria Alvarez (Deputy Dir-Art)

Palm Beach Media Group Inc. (1)
PO Box 3344, Palm Beach, FL 33480
Tel.: (561) 659-0210
Web Site: http://www.palmbeachmedia.com
Magazine Publisher
N.A.I.C.S.: 513120
Michelle Farina (Mgr-Natl Acct)

Unit (Domestic):

Naples Illustrated (2)
3066 Tamiami Trl N Ste 102, Naples, FL 34103
Tel.: (239) 434-6966
Web Site: http://www.naplesillustrated.com
Magazine
N.A.I.C.S.: 424920
Shalyn Ormspy (Mgr-Mktg & Sls Integration)

Palm Beach Illustrated (2)
PO Box 3344, Palm Beach, FL 33480
Tel.: (561) 472-1910
Web Site: http://www.palmbeachillustrated.com
Magazine
N.A.I.C.S.: 513120
Terry Duffy (Publr)

HOUR PUBLISHING COMPANY
1 Selleck St, Norwalk, CT 06855
Tel.: (203) 846-3281
Web Site: http://www.wiltonvillager.com
Sales Range: $10-24.9 Million
Emp.: 70
Newspapers
N.A.I.C.S.: 513110
Brent Whitton (Pres)
Jim Reid (Chm-Events & Mgr-Adv Sls)
John G. Brosz Jr. (VP-Sls & Mktg)

HOURGLASS ANGEL
2239 S Laramie Ave, Cicero, IL 60804
Tel.: (708) 298-9094
Web Site: http://www.HourglassAngel.com
Year Founded: 2009

Sales Range: $1-9.9 Million
Emp.: 10
Shape Wear Garments
N.A.I.C.S.: 458110
Ruben Soto (CEO)

HOURIGAN CONSTRUCTION CORP.
4429 Bonney Rd Ste 200, Virginia Beach, VA 23462-3877
Tel.: (757) 499-3434
Web Site: http://www.houriganconstruction.com
Rev.: $60,000,000
Emp.: 50
Provider of Commercial & Office Building Construction Services
N.A.I.C.S.: 236220
Mark J. Hourigan (Pres)
Mark L. Greenwalt (VP-Preconstruction & Estimating)
Janie F. Smith (Sec)
Todd M. Donaldson (Pres)
Nathan Leonard (Mgr-Client Solutions)
David Auman (Exec VP)
H. Chris Brandt III (Exec VP)

Subsidiaries:

The Capstone Contracting Company (1)
4235 Innslake Dr Ste 110, Glen Allen, VA 23060-5505
Tel.: (804) 755-8045
Web Site: http://www.capstonecontracting.com
Commercial & Institutional Building Construction
N.A.I.C.S.: 236220
David R. Auman (Pres)

HOUSATONIC PARTNERS MANAGEMENT CO., INC.
1 Post St Ste 2600, San Francisco, CA 94104-5203
Tel.: (415) 955-9020   DE
Web Site: https://www.housatonicpartners.com
Year Founded: 1994
Emp.: 20
Privater Equity Firm
N.A.I.C.S.: 523999
Mark G. Hilderbrand (Mng Dir)
Joseph M. Niehaus (Mng Dir)
Barry D. Reynolds (Gen Partner)
Jill A. Raimondi (CFO)
Amy L. Laforteza (Controller)
William B. Kuntz (VP)
Kirsi Fontenot (Dir-Tax)
William F. Gagliasso (Asst Controller)
William N. Thorndike Jr. (Founder)

Subsidiaries:

Offsite Archive Storage & Integrated Services Limited (1)
Unit 15C Kinsealy Business Park, Kinsealy, Dublin, Ireland
Tel.: (353) 1 866 6317
Web Site: http://www.oasisgroup.eu
Emp.: 120
Holding Company; Records & Information Management Services
N.A.I.C.S.: 551112
Ronnie Carroll (Exec VP-Ops & Sls)
Brian Connolly (CEO)
Darren Walsh (VP-Ops)
Claire Gallagher (Exec VP-Admin)
Sarah Sweeney (CFO)

Subsidiary (Domestic):

Offsite Archive Storage & Integrated Services (Ireland) Limited (2)
Unit 15C Kinsealy Business Park, Kinsealy, Dublin, Ireland
Tel.: (353) 1 866 6317
Web Site: http://www.oasisgroup.eu
Record & Information Management Services

N.A.I.C.S.: 561990
Darren Walsh (VP-Ops)

HOUSE OF ANTIQUE HARDWARE
802 NE Davis St, Portland, OR 97232
Tel.: (503) 231-4089
Web Site: https://www.houseofantiquehardware.com
Year Founded: 1999
Rev.: $8,900,000
Emp.: 66
Hardware Stores
N.A.I.C.S.: 444140
Roy Prange (Pres)
Albert Little (Mgr-New Products)
Gary Frazier (Mgr-Customer Svc)
Tim Iburg (Dir-Ops)

HOUSE OF BODS FITNESS, INC.
3234 NW 29th Ave, Boca Raton, FL 33434
Tel.: (407) 221-4943   DE
Web Site: http://www.houseofbodsfitness.com
Year Founded: 2007
Sales Range: Less than $1 Million
Emp.: 1
Dance Fitness Centers
N.A.I.C.S.: 713940
Tammy Skalko (Pres & CEO)
James Beshara (CFO, Treas & Sec)

HOUSE OF BRIDES INC.
1184 Roosevelt Rd, Glen Ellyn, IL 60137
Tel.: (630) 629-4040
Web Site: http://www.houseofbrides.com
Year Founded: 1929
Clothing Rental Services
N.A.I.C.S.: 532281
Dale Buziecki (Pres)

HOUSE OF FLAVORS, INC.
110 N William St, Ludington, MI 49431-1674
Tel.: (231) 845-7369   MI
Web Site: http://www.houseofflavors.com
Year Founded: 1977
Sales Range: $10-24.9 Million
Emp.: 120
Ice Cream & Frozen Dessert Products Mfr
N.A.I.C.S.: 311520
Sarah Holmes (CFO)
Jill Walls (Coord-Sls)
Pat Calder (VP-Ops)

HOUSE OF HARLEY-DAVIDSON INC.
6221 W Layton Ave, Milwaukee, WI 53220
Tel.: (414) 282-2211
Web Site: http://www.houseofharley.com
Sales Range: $25-49.9 Million
Emp.: 65
Motorcycles
N.A.I.C.S.: 441227
Keith Lewis (Mgr-Svcs)
Linda Semo (Controller)
Tom Derrico (Gen Mgr)

HOUSE OF IMPORTS INC.
6862 Aotu Ctr Dr, Buena Park, CA 90621
Tel.: (714) 562-1100
Web Site: http://www.houseofimportsinc.com
Rev.: $70,400,000
Emp.: 193

Automobiles, New & Used
N.A.I.C.S.: 441110
Sean Davisson (Gen Mgr)

HOUSE OF KAIZEN LLC
21 W 46th St, New York, NY 10036
Tel.: (212) 981-2700
Web Site: https://www.houseofkaizen.com
Year Founded: 2001
Sales Range: $10-24.9 Million
Emp.: 65
Marketing Consulting Services
N.A.I.C.S.: 541613
Peter Figueredo (Head-Client Svcs)
Chris Kramer (Head-Ops)
Matt Cronin (Pres)

Subsidiaries:

The House of Kaizen Limited (1)
Hoffman Sq, 50 Buttesland St, London, N1 6BY, United Kingdom
Tel.: (44) 20 7253 4133
Emp.: 15
Advertising Agencies
N.A.I.C.S.: 541810
Alain Portman (Head-Media & Insights)
David Shiell (CEO & Partner)
Ivan Imhoff (Head-Conversion Rate Optimisation)

HOUSE OF PACKAGING INC.
2225 Via Cerro Rd Ste B, Riverside, CA 92509
Tel.: (626) 369-3371
Web Site: http://www.hopbox.com
Sales Range: $1-9.9 Million
Emp.: 9
Setup Paperboard Boxes
N.A.I.C.S.: 322219
John T. Franck Jr. (Pres & CEO)

HOUSE OF PERFECTION, INC.
131 W 33rd St, New York, NY 10001-2908
Tel.: (212) 239-9780   SC
Year Founded: 1940
Sales Range: $200-249.9 Million
Emp.: 650
Children's & Infants' Clothing Mfr
N.A.I.C.S.: 315250

HOUSE OF RAEFORD FARMS, INC.
520 E Central Ave, Raeford, NC 28376-3020
Tel.: (910) 875-5161   NC
Web Site: http://www.houseofraeford.com
Year Founded: 1962
Sales Range: $450-499.9 Million
Emp.: 2,000
Turkey & Chicken Products Mfr
N.A.I.C.S.: 311615
E. Marvin Johnson (Chm)
Robert B. Johnson (Vice Chm, Pres & CEO)
Don Taber (Pres & COO)
Harold Brock (Mgr-Commodity & Export)

HOUSE OF SPICES INDIA INC.
127-40 Willets Point Blvd, Flushing, NY 11368-1506
Tel.: (718) 507-4600
Web Site: http://www.hosindia.com
Year Founded: 1970
Sales Range: $10-24.9 Million
Emp.: 120
Retailer of Spices
N.A.I.C.S.: 424490

Subsidiaries:

Subzi-Mandi (1)
832 Newark Ave, Jersey City, NJ 07306-3809
Tel.: (201) 656-5677
Web Site: http://www.subzi-mandi.com

House of Spices India Inc.—(Continued)

Provider of Fruit & Vegetables
N.A.I.C.S.: 445230

HOUSE OF TOOLS & ENGINEERING

2021 Congressional Rd, Saint Louis, MO 63146
Tel.: (314) 731-4444
Web Site:
http://www.htetechnologies.com
Year Founded: 1959
Emp.: 200
Industrial Automation & Robotics Mfr
N.A.I.C.S.: 423830
Kim Shearburn (Pres)
Dave Alexander (VP-Performance Mgmt & Mktg)
Eddie Tumminia (Div Mgr)
Marvin Dixon (Div Mgr)
Marion Strickland (VP-Ops)

HOUSE OF WESLEY, INC.

1704 Morrissey Dr, Bloomington, IL 61704
Tel.: (309) 664-7334   IL
Web Site:
http://www.houseofwesley.com
Year Founded: 1954
Sales Range: $75-99.9 Million
Emp.: 75
Garden & Nursery Products Mail Order & E-Commerce
N.A.I.C.S.: 424930
Richard B. Owen (Pres)

HOUSE OF WYOMING VALLEY INC.

5754 State Rd 23, Spring Green, WI 53588
Tel.: (608) 935-3639
Web Site:
http://www.houseontherock.com
Sales Range: $10-24.9 Million
Emp.: 200
Tourist Attraction, Commercial
N.A.I.C.S.: 712190
Nancy Schaaf (Mgr-HR)

HOUSE PARTY, INC.

1 Bridge St Ste 3, Irvington, NY 10533
Tel.: (720) 496-2503
Web Site: http://www.houseparty.com
Year Founded: 2005
Sales Range: $10-24.9 Million
Emp.: 57
House Party Arrangement Services
N.A.I.C.S.: 812990
Chris Maher (CEO)
Kerry Lyons (Sr VP-Sls & Mktg)
Liz Cuccinello (Gen Counsel & Sr VP-Admin)
Pam Seiler (Sr VP-Sls)
Parker Reilly (Founder)
Barbara Farmer (Dir-Program Mgmt)
Joe Epner (Sr Dir-Sls)
Kathy Foley (Sr Dir-Acct)
Meera Ganesan (Mgr-Sls Dev)
Stephanie Howard (Dir-Program Mgmt)
Gene DeRose (Co-Founder & Vice Chm)
Jeff Samberg (Chm)

HOUSE RESEARCH INSTITUTE

2100 W 3rd St, Los Angeles, CA 90057
Tel.: (213) 483-4431   CA
Web Site: http://www.hei.org
Year Founded: 1946
Sales Range: $10-24.9 Million
Healtcare Services
N.A.I.C.S.: 622110

HOUSE-AUTRY MILLS INC.

7000 US-301 S, Four Oaks, NC 27524
Tel.: (919) 963-6200   NC
Web Site: http://www.house-autry.com
Year Founded: 1812
Corn Meal Mfr
N.A.I.C.S.: 311211
Cherie Niskala (Dir-Reporting)
Ken Rose (Mgr-Maintenance, Sanitation & Facilities)
William Paschka (Dir-IT)

HOUSE-HASSON HARDWARE COMPANY

3125 Water Plant Rd, Knoxville, TN 37914
Tel.: (865) 525-0471   TN
Web Site:
https://www.househasson.com
Year Founded: 1906
Sales Range: $150-199.9 Million
Emp.: 250
Hardware, Tools, Plumbing & Ventilation Components, Electrical Components, Paint, Housewares, Industrial Supplies, Lawn & Garden Supplies, Lumber & Other Building Materials Distr
N.A.I.C.S.: 423710
Don C. Hasson (Pres)
David Helfenberger (VP-Mktg)
Kim Gibbs (Mgr-Adv)
Steve Henry (Exec VP)
Jamey Merritt (Mgr-Alabama, Arkansas, Louisiana & Florida)

Subsidiaries:

House-Hasson Hardware
Company-Persinger   (1)
122 Prichard Industrial Park Rd, Prichard, WV 25555
Tel.: (304) 486-5401
Web Site: http://www.househasson.com
Sales Range: $75-99.9 Million
Emp.: 200
Hardware, Tools, Plumbing & Ventilation Components, Electrical Components, Paint, Housewares, Industrial Supplies, Lawn & Garden Supplies Distr
N.A.I.C.S.: 423710
Beverly Smith Perry (VP-Sls & Mdsg)

Long-Lewis Hardware Co.   (1)
430 N 9th St, Birmingham, AL 35203-2585
Tel.: (205) 322-2561
Web Site: http://www.long-lewis.com
Sales Range: $25-49.9 Million
Hardware Stores
N.A.I.C.S.: 444140
Doug Stanford (Gen Mgr)

HOUSEHOLDER GROUP INC.

8985 E Bell Rd, Scottsdale, AZ 85260
Tel.: (602) 604-0600   AZ
Web Site:
https://www.householdergroup.com
Year Founded: 1994
Sales Range: $10-24.9 Million
Emp.: 12
Investment Services
N.A.I.C.S.: 523940
Scott Householder (Founder & CEO)
Nadia Gulli (Sr Dir-Bus Dev)

HOUSER SHOES INCORPORATED

5418 Asheville Hwy, Hendersonville, NC 28791
Tel.: (828) 254-0054
Web Site:
https://www.housershoes.com
Year Founded: 1976
Sales Range: $25-49.9 Million
Emp.: 150
Shoe Stores

N.A.I.C.S.: 458210
Gary E. Houser (Owner & Pres)
Celeste McKinney (Controller)
Bradley Sanders (Asst Mgr-Warehouse)

HOUSEWORKS, LLC

500 Unicorn Park Dr Ste 105, Woburn, MA 01801
Tel.: (617) 928-1010
Web Site: http://www.houseworks.com
Year Founded: 1999
Home Health Services
N.A.I.C.S.: 621610
Michael Trigilio (CEO)

Subsidiaries:

Extended Family, LLC   (1)
34 Dover Point Rd Ste 201, Dover, NH 03820
Tel.: (603) 343-4434
Web Site: http://www.extended-family.net
Women Healthcare Services
N.A.I.C.S.: 621610
Barbara Trimble (Founder & CEO)

HOUSING ASSISTANCE COUNCIL

1025 Vermont Ave NW Ste 606, Washington, DC 20005
Tel.: (202) 842-8600   DC
Web Site: https://www.ruralhome.org
Year Founded: 1971
Sales Range: $10-24.9 Million
Emp.: 43
Housing Assistance Services
N.A.I.C.S.: 624229
Karin Klusmann (Dir-Loan Fund)
Lance George (Dir-Res & Info)
Jeff Mosley (Dir-Trng & Tech Assistance)
Peter Carey (Chm)
Andrew Bias (Pres)
Moises Loza (Exec Dir)
Maria Luisa Mercado (Sec)
Janaka Casper (Treas)
Swynice Hawkins (Vice Chm)

HOUSING AUTHORITY NEW ORLEANS (HANO)

4100 Touro St, New Orleans, LA 70122
Tel.: (504) 670-3300
Web Site: https://www.hano.org
Year Founded: 1937
Sales Range: $25-49.9 Million
Emp.: 1,000
Operator of Housing Authority
N.A.I.C.S.: 531390
Cynthia Wiggins (Pres & CEO)
Griek Faulkner (Dir-Housing Authority)

HOUSING AUTHORITY OF THE CITY OF CHARLOTTE

400 E Blvd, Charlotte, NC 28204
Tel.: (704) 336-5183
Web Site: http://www.cha-nc.org
Year Founded: 1939
Sales Range: $25-49.9 Million
Emp.: 200
Public Housing Assistance
N.A.I.C.S.: 531390
Fulton Meachem (CEO)

HOUSING AUTHORITY RISK RETENTION GROUP INC.

189 Commerce Ct, Cheshire, CT 06410-1253
Tel.: (203) 272-8220
Web Site:
http://www.housingcenter.com
Year Founded: 1987
Sales Range: $50-74.9 Million
Emp.: 189

Provider of Risk Insurance Services
N.A.I.C.S.: 524298
Courtney Rice (Mgr-Corp Comm & Branding)
Jerry Williams (Sr VP-Insurance Ops)

HOUSING HELPERS OF COLORADO, LLC

2865 Baseline Rd, Boulder, CO 80303
Tel.: (303) 545-6000
Web Site:
http://www.housinghelpers.com
Year Founded: 1987
Relocation Services
N.A.I.C.S.: 812990
Stephanie Iannone (Mng Partner)
John Elms (Pres & CEO)
Tom Orlando (Mgr-Re-Location)

HOUSING MART INC.

149 Hamilton Rd, Chehalis, WA 98532
Tel.: (360) 273-8812
Web Site:
http://www.housingmart.com
Sales Range: $10-24.9 Million
Emp.: 8
Retailer of Manufactured Housing
N.A.I.C.S.: 459930
Gary W. Stoskopf (Owner, Pres & CEO)
Neena Stoskopf (Treas, Sec, Co-Owner & VP)
Kyle Deskins (Gen Mgr)

HOUSING NETWORK OF HAMILTON COUNTY INC.

3030 W Fork Rd, Cincinnati, OH 45211
Tel.: (513) 389-7509   OH
Year Founded: 1992
Sales Range: $1-9.9 Million
Disability Housing Assistance Services
N.A.I.C.S.: 624229
Chris Bohn (CFO)
Jim Steffey (Exec Dir)
Patricia Burke (CEO)

HOUSING TRUST SILICON VALLEY

95 S Market St Ste 610, San Jose, CA 95113
Tel.: (408) 436-3450   CA
Web Site:
http://www.housingtrustsv.org
Year Founded: 2000
Sales Range: $10-24.9 Million
Emp.: 12
Community Housing Services
N.A.I.C.S.: 624229

HOUSLEY COMMUNICATIONS LIMITED

3550 S Bryant Blvd, San Angelo, TX 76903
Tel.: (325) 944-9905
Web Site: http://www.hc-inc.com
Sales Range: $50-74.9 Million
Emp.: 320
Telephone & Telephone Equipment Installation
N.A.I.C.S.: 238210
Robert D. Housley (Pres & CEO)
Ana A. Henderson (Controller)
David R. Meek (VP-Engrg)

HOUSTON AREA COMMUNITY SERVICES

2150 W 18th St, Houston, TX 77008
Tel.: (713) 426-0027   TX
Web Site: http://www.hacstxs.org
Year Founded: 1997
Sales Range: $10-24.9 Million

Emp.: 114
Community Health Care Services
N.A.I.C.S.: 621498
Juan L. Garza *(Chief Medical Officer)*
Mandy Nebeker Porter *(Mgr-Dev)*
Nicole T. Brock *(CFO)*
Christopher Cole *(Mgr-HR)*
Patrice M. Williams *(COO)*
Sonya Butts *(Sec)*
Atif Riaz *(VP)*
Joe C. Fuentes *(CEO)*

HOUSTON ARMATURE WORKS INC.
6100 Harrisburg, Houston, TX 77011
Tel.: (713) 928-2615
Web Site:
   https://www.houstonarmature.com
Rev.: $19,721,443
Emp.: 38
Motors, Electric
N.A.I.C.S.: 423610
James Woolley *(Pres)*

HOUSTON BALLET FOUNDATION INC.
601 Preston St, Houston, TX 77002-1605
Tel.: (713) 523-6300
Web Site:
   http://www.houstonballet.org
Rev.: $29,674,725
Assets: $142,190,570
Liabilities: $7,465,522
Net Worth: $134,725,048
Emp.: 250
Fiscal Year-end: 06/30/18
Ballet Production
N.A.I.C.S.: 711120
James Nelson *(Exec Dir)*
Shelly Power *(Dir-Academy)*
Diamantina Pena *(Mgr-Acct Payable)*
Cheryl Lynn Zane *(CFO)*
James M. Jordan *(Chm)*
Phoebe Tudor *(Pres)*
Margaret Alkek Williams *(Sec)*
Leticia Loya *(VP-Academy)*
James M. Nicklos *(VP-Fin)*
Tripp Carter *(VP-Dev)*
James J. Parr *(VP-Institutional Giving)*
Daniel M. McClure *(VP-Investment)*
Becca Cason Thrash *(VP-Special Events)*
Donald M. Graubart *(VP-Trustee Dev)*
Jennifer Steiner *(Gen Mgr)*
Margot L. Curry *(Controller)*
Lacey DeLaine Chance *(Mgr-HR)*
Garth Luther *(Mgr-Facilities)*
Angie Lane *(Chief Dev Officer)*
Alexandra Yates *(Dir-Special Events)*
Shannon Stricker *(Mgr-Special Events)*
Sarah Lam *(Mgr-PR)*
Jared Murphy *(Project Mgr-Web/Digital Media)*
Alexandra Di Nunzio *(Coord-Dev Ops)*
Ally Krebeck *(Mgr-Dev)*
Vicky Attard *(Dir-Academy)*

HOUSTON BASEBALL PART-NERS LLC
501 Crawford St, Houston, TX 77002
Tel.: (713) 259-8000   DE
Year Founded: 2011
Holding Company; Professional Baseball Club & Stadium Owner & Operator
N.A.I.C.S.: 551112
James R. Crane *(Chm-Houston Astros & Principal Owner)*
John Havens *(Principal)*
Bill Morgan *(Principal)*
Doug Bauer *(Principal)*
John Hauck *(Principal)*

Neil Kelley *(Principal)*
Will Galtney *(Principal)*
Jeff Hines *(Principal)*
Cary Patterson *(Principal)*
Milton Carroll *(Principal)*
John Eddie Williams Jr. *(Principal)*

Subsidiaries:

Houston Astros, LLC   (1)
Minute Maid Park 501 Crawford St, Houston, TX 77002-2113
Tel.: (713) 259-8800
Web Site:
   http://www.houston.astros.mlb.com
Sales Range: $10-24.9 Million
Emp.: 200
Professional Baseball Club Operator
N.A.I.C.S.: 711211
James R. Crane *(Owner)*
Marian Harper *(VP-Foundation Dev)*
Michael Kenny *(Dir-Guest Svcs)*
Clay Kowalski *(Dir-Premium Sls & Svc)*
Bobby Forrest *(VP-Stadium Ops)*
Monica Rusch *(Sr Dir-Risk Mgmt)*
Bill Cannon *(Dir-Box Office Ops)*
Doug Seckel *(VP-Fin)*
Matt Brand *(Sr VP-Corp Partnerships)*
Marcel Braithwaite *(Sr VP-Bus Ops)*
Jason Howard *(Sr VP-Ticket Sls & Strategy)*
Chris Hanz *(VP-IT)*
Giles Kibbe *(Gen Counsel)*
Vivian Mora *(VP-HR)*
Stephanie Stegall *(VP-Event Sls & Ops)*
Jason Wooden *(VP-Mktg)*
Dusty Baker *(Mgr)*
Paula M. Harris *(Sr VP-Community & Foundation & Exec Dir)*
Anita Sehgal *(Sr VP-Comm & Mktg)*

HOUSTON DISTRIBUTING COMPANY
7100 High Life Dr, Houston, TX 77066
Tel.: (281) 583-4800
Sales Range: $150-199.9 Million
Emp.: 399
Beer & Other Fermented Malt Liquors Distr
N.A.I.C.S.: 424810
Bo Huggins *(Pres)*
Richard Posadas *(Brand Mgr)*
Ray Modeland *(Dir-Chain Sls)*
Brian Purvis *(Dir-Import & Specialty)*
Jack Chambers *(Mgr-Sls)*
Tony Quartero *(Mgr-Sls-C-Store Div)*

HOUSTON FIRST CORPORA-TION
Partnership Tower 701 Avenida De Las Americas, Houston, TX 77010
Tel.: (713) 853-8100
Web Site:
   https://www.houstonfirst.com
Convention Center Operator
N.A.I.C.S.: 561591
Maureen Haley *(Dir-Strategic Tourism Initiatives)*
Cynthia Decker *(VP-Sls Revenue & Mktg Strategy)*
David Mincberg *(Chm)*
Desrye M. Morgan *(Vice Chm)*
Brenda Bazan *(Pres & CEO)*
Mike Waterman *(Chief Mktg Officer & Chief Sls Officer)*
Robert Jackson *(Chief Policy Officer)*
Frank F. Wilson *(CFO)*
Lisa Hargrove *(Gen Counsel)*
Peter McStravick *(Chief Dev Officer)*
Luther Villagomez *(COO-Convention Center & Houston First Theaters)*

Subsidiaries:

Greater Houston Convention & Visitors Bureau   (1)
4 Houston Ctr 1331 Lamar St Ste 700, Houston, TX 77010
Tel.: (713) 437-5200
Web Site: http://www.visithoustontexas.com

Sales Range: $10-24.9 Million
Emp.: 100
Convention & Visitors Bureau
N.A.I.C.S.: 561591
Rick Ferguson *(VP & Exec Dir-Film Commission)*
Karen Williams *(VP-Fin)*
Holly Clapham Rosenow *(CMO)*
John Solis *(Sr VP-Sls)*
A. J. Mistretta *(Sr Mgr-PR)*
Jorge Franz *(Sr VP-Tourism)*
Cherry Eno *(Exec Dir-Visitors Center)*
John Rolfe *(Chief Admin Officer)*
Terry Beutler *(Sr VP-Destination Svcs)*
Judi Quesonova *(VP-Destination Svcs)*
Lauren Baker *(Mgr-Adv & Mktg)*
Paul Beckman *(Mgr-Employee Comm)*
David Ellison *(Officer-Media Info)*
Dennis Johnston *(Officer-Media Info)*
David Solce *(Coord-Mktg & Comm)*
Vargo Williams *(Mgr-Mktg Brand)*
Carla Fiorito *(Mgr-Sls & Mktg-Intl)*

HOUSTON GOLF ASSOCIA-TION
5810 Wilson Rd Ste 112, Humble, TX 77396
Tel.: (281) 454-7000   TX
Web Site: http://www.hga.org
Year Founded: 1946
Sales Range: $10-24.9 Million
Emp.: 54
Golf Association
N.A.I.C.S.: 713910
Trey Jackson *(Mgr-Ops)*
Doug Earle *(Exec Dir)*
Amanda Hansen *(VP-Mktg & Comm)*
John D. Sorrentino *(VP-Bus Dev)*

HOUSTON GRAND OPERA AS-SOCIATION
510 Preston, Houston, TX 77002
Tel.: (713) 546-0200
Web Site:
   https://www.houstongrandopera.org
Rev.: $17,844,042
Emp.: 100
Opera Company
N.A.I.C.S.: 711110
James W. Crownover *(Chm)*
Lynn Wyatt *(Vice Chm)*
Diane Zola *(Dir-Artistic Admin)*
Ken Vaughn *(Dir-Info Sys)*
Lee Whatley *(Dir-Bus Analytics)*
Patrick Summers *(Dir-Artistic & Music)*
Tanya Lovetro *(Dir-Fin)*
Deborah Hirsch *(Sr Dir-Dev)*
Perryn Leech *(Mng Dir)*
Molly Dill *(Gen Mgr)*
Melissa Williford *(Dir-HR)*
Scott Ipsen *(Dir-Patron Svcs)*
Christine Lee *(Mgr-Comm)*
Joanna Torok *(Dir-Advancement Ops)*
Judith Kurnick *(Dir-Comm)*
Pattima Singhalaka *(Dir-Art)*
Dale Edwards *(Dir-Mktg)*

HOUSTON LIVESTOCK SHOW AND RODEO
3 NRG Park, Houston, TX 77054
Tel.: (832) 667-1073   TX
Web Site:
   https://www.rodeohouston.com
Year Founded: 1932
Rev.: $138,764,164
Earnings: $5,830,945
Emp.: 1,172
Fiscal Year-end: 08/31/18
Rodeo & Livestock Show Organizer
N.A.I.C.S.: 711310
Jill H. Clement *(Dir-Admin & Ticketing)*
Jennifer Hazelton *(CFO)*
Joel Cowley *(Pres & CEO)*
Dana Barton *(Mng Dir-Auctions & Donors)*

Chris Boleman *(Exec Dir-Agricultural Competitions & Exhibits)*
Juan Carlos *(Coord-Entertainment Suites)*
Brittany Cooke *(Mgr-Entertainment & Concert Production)*
Jerrad Darty *(Mgr-Mail Center)*
Jim Gadd *(Mgr-Mdse Ops)*
Ginger Gaskamp *(Sr Coord-Mdse & Carnival Presales)*
Katie Grahmann *(Exec Dir & Controller)*
Pam Green *(Dir-Accounts Receivable)*
Melissa Hernlund *(Mng Dir-Membership)*
Katherine Herrmann *(Mgr-Membership)*
Jason Kane *(Mng Dir-Entertainment & Concert Production)*
Karen Koepke *(Mgr-Accounts Payable)*
Carolyn LaRue *(Mng Dir-Fin Reporting)*
Jennifer Lindsay *(Dir-Wine Show)*
Denise McCoy *(Mng Dir-Acctg Ops)*
Dennis Moynihan *(Dir-Ticketing)*
Bridget O'Brien *(Coord-Auctions)*
Alicia Pierce *(Mgr-Ticket Bus Ops)*
Katelyn Scates *(Mgr-Grants)*
Catherine Schultz *(Mng Dir-Sports & Event Presentations)*
Andy Sloan *(CIO)*
Paula Urban *(Mng Dir-Ticketing)*
Angel Valdez *(Coord-Season Suites)*
Jim Winne *(Chm)*
Julie Wood *(Mng Dir-Mdse)*

HOUSTON MOTOR & CON-TROL, INC.
14400 Hollister St Ste 100, Houston, TX 77066
Tel.: (713) 464-3910   TX
Web Site: https://www.motor-hmc.com
Year Founded: 1979
Sales Range: $1-9.9 Million
Emp.: 15
Electronic Motors, Starters & Drives Distr
N.A.I.C.S.: 335312
Jeanne Jobe *(Pres)*
Brian Moers *(Mgr-Production)*

HOUSTON PILOTS
203 Deerwood Glen Dr, Deer Park, TX 77536-3270
Tel.: (713) 645-9620
Web Site: https://www.houston-pilots.com
Year Founded: 1919
Sales Range: $10-24.9 Million
Emp.: 40
Provider of Water Transportation Services
N.A.I.C.S.: 488330
Susie Ward *(Sec)*

HOUSTON PIZZA VENTURE LP
13131 Champions Dr Ste 110, Houston, TX 77069-3220
Tel.: (281) 580-6088
Web Site:
   http://www.papajohnshouston.com
Year Founded: 1994
Sales Range: $50-74.9 Million
Emp.: 1,400
Dining Services
N.A.I.C.S.: 722513
Keith Sullins *(Pres)*

HOUSTON PLANTS AND GAR-DEN WORLD

Houston Plants and Garden World—(Continued)

16726 Interstate 45 N, Houston, TX
77090
Tel.: (281) 443-3188
Web Site:
http://www.houstonplantsandgar
denworld.com
Sales Range: $1-9.9 Million
Emp.: 25
Nursery Stock Seeds & Bulbs
N.A.I.C.S.: 444240
Chenell Carterman (Office Mgr)

HOUSTON POST TENSION, INC.
7015 San Antonio Rd, Houston, TX
77040
Tel.: (713) 937-6990
Web Site:
https://www.houstonpostten
sion.com
Year Founded: 1987
Sales Range: $10-24.9 Million
Emp.: 75
Fabricated Wire Product Mfr
N.A.I.C.S.: 332618
Debbie Abney (Office Mgr)
Dave Cooney (Mgr-Sls)
Angela Jordy (VP-Sls & Mktg)
Juanita Temores (Mgr-Stressing)
Ricki Abney Sr. (Pres)

HOUSTON REGIONAL HIV/AIDS RESOURCE GROUP, INC.
500 Lovett Blvd Ste 100, Houston,
TX 77006
Tel.: (713) 526-1016   TX
Web Site:
http://www.hivresourcegroup.org
Year Founded: 1993
Sales Range: $10-24.9 Million
Emp.: 13
AIDS Affected People Welfare Ser-
vices
N.A.I.C.S.: 813319
Yvette Garvin (Exec Dir)

HOUSTON TEXANS, L.P.
2 Reliant Pk, Houston, TX 77054
Tel.: (832) 667-2000
Web Site:
http://www.houstontexans.com
Year Founded: 1999
Sales Range: $10-24.9 Million
Emp.: 130
Professional Football Franchise
N.A.I.C.S.: 711211
Fayez Shalaby Sarofim (Partner)
Jamey Rootes (Pres)
Suzie Thomas (Chief Admin Officer,
Gen Counsel & Exec VP)
John Schriever (Sr VP-Ticketing &
Event Mgmt)
Marilan Logan (Chief Acctg Officer &
VP)
Greg Watson (VP-Fin)
Kirbyjon H. Caldwell (Partner)
Kay M. Onstead (Partner)
Jeff Schmitz (VP-IT)
Glenda Morrison (Sr Dir-HR)
Greg Kondritz (VP & Assoc Gen
Counsel)
Brian Varnadoe (Sr Dir-Premium
Seating)
Greg Grissom (Sr VP-Corp Dev)
Chris Olsen (VP-Football Admin)
Sean Washington (Sr Dir-Player En-
gagement)
Jennifer Davenport (VP-Mktg & Com-
munity Dev)
Jon Carr (Dir-College Scouting)
Amy Palcic (Sr Dir-Corp Dev)
Daniel Velasco (Dir-Mktg)
Dustin Kadri (Asst Dir-Video Ops)

Emmett Baylor (VP-Security)
Eric Saninocencio (Dir-Digital Media)
Jackie Maldonado (Dir-Mktg)
Trey Young (Dir-Ticket Svcs)
Jon Southern (VP & Asst Treas)
Marc Vandermeer (VP-Brdcst)
Doug West (VP-Football Ops)
Jan Kelly (VP-Risk Mgmt)
Debra Strait (VP-Tax)
Nick Caserio (Gen Mgr)
Joseph W. Sutton (Partner)
Charles W. Duncan Jr. (Partner)
Harry Gee Jr. (Partner)

HOUSTON VENTURES
600 Travis Ste 3350, Houston, TX
77002
Tel.: (832) 529-2829
Web Site: https://www.houven.com
Venture Capital Firm
N.A.I.C.S.: 523999
Charles Davis (Mng Dir)
Stephanie Cummings (Office Mgr)

HOUSTON'S RESTAURANTS INC.
2710 E Camelback Rd Ste 200,
Phoenix, AZ 85016-4221
Tel.: (602) 957-9700   DE
Web Site: https://www.hillstone.com
Year Founded: 1977
Sales Range: $100-124.9 Million
Emp.: 4,100
Eating Place Services
N.A.I.C.S.: 722511
George Biel (Pres)

HOVDE GROUP, LLC
1629 Colonial Pkwy, Inverness, IL
60067
Tel.: (847) 991-6622
Web Site:
http://www.hovdegroup.com
Year Founded: 1987
Sales Range: $25-49.9 Million
Emp.: 25
Investment Banking & Advisory Ser-
vices
N.A.I.C.S.: 523150
Steven Donald Hovde (Co-Founder,
Chm & CEO)
David Magli (Pres & COO)
James D. Nuber (Mng Dir)
Jonathan Knauss (Mng Dir & Head-
Diversified Financials Grp)
Michael Hedrei (Mng Dir & Head-
Capital Markets)
Mark Wilson (Mng Dir)
Anthony Di John (CFO)
Gabe Duran (Chief Compliance Offi-
cer)
Bryce Rowe (Dir-Equity Res Grp)
Brett Rabatin (Head-Equity Res)

HOVDE PRIVATE EQUITY AD-VISORS LLC
7151 Columbia Gateway Dr Ste A,
Columbia, MD 21046
Tel.: (410) 427-3727   DE
Web Site:
http://www.hovdeprivateequity.com
Sales Range: $25-49.9 Million
Emp.: 4
Privater Equity Firm
N.A.I.C.S.: 523999
Steven Donald Hovde (Partner)
Eric Donald Hovde (CEO)
Richard J. Perry Jr. (Gen Counsel)

HOVE BUICK-NISSAN
1405 N Kinzie Dr, Bradley, IL 60915-
5130
Tel.: (815) 932-8600
Year Founded: 1993
Sales Range: $10-24.9 Million
Emp.: 30

New Car Whslr
N.A.I.C.S.: 441110
Wayne Hove (Pres)
Bradley Hove (Owner)

HOVERINK BIOTECHNOLO-GIES, INC.
1801 Century Park E 24th Fl, Los
Angeles, CA 90067   DE
Web Site:
http://www.hoverinkbiotech.yo
lasite.com
Year Founded: 2013
Emp.: 3
Biopharmaceutical Product Mfr &
Distr
N.A.I.C.S.: 325412
Debbie Mae Carter (CEO, CFO &
Treas)
Davidra Sajna (Chm & Pres)
Cyrus Sajna (COO & VP)

HOWARD BENTLEY BUICK GMC, INC.
1230 Huntsville Hwy, Fayetteville, TN
37334-3618
Tel.: (931) 433-1585
Web Site:
http://www.howardbentley.net
Sales Range: $10-24.9 Million
Emp.: 35
Car Whslr
N.A.I.C.S.: 441110
Rick Tate (Gen Mgr)
Daniel Vaughn (Owner)
Howard W. Bentley Jr. (VP)

HOWARD BROWN HEALTH CENTER
4025 N Sheridan Rd, Chicago, IL
60613
Tel.: (773) 388-1600   IL
Web Site:
https://www.howardbrown.org
Year Founded: 1976
Sales Range: $10-24.9 Million
Emp.: 249
Health Care Srvices
N.A.I.C.S.: 622110
Magda Houlberg (Chief Clinical Offi-
cer)
Michelle Wetzel (Sr VP-Policy, Strat-
egy & Bus Dev)
Bill Joure (Sr Dir-Retail Ops)
Kelly Ducheny (Dir-Behavioral Health)
Aisha Davis (Mgr-Policy & Advocacy-
Center for Education, Res & Advo-
cacy)

HOWARD BUILDING CORPO-RATION
707 Wilshire Blvd Ste 3750, Los An-
geles, CA 90017
Tel.: (213) 683-1850
Web Site:
https://www.howardbuilding.com
Year Founded: 1983
Sales Range: $10-24.9 Million
Emp.: 90
Construction Services
N.A.I.C.S.: 238990
Michael Howard (Founder)
Steve Segel (Project Mgr)
Adam Herig (Project Mgr)
Don Fraser (Sr VP)
Mark Fuller (Sr VP)

HOWARD FARMERS COOP ASSOCIATION
200 W Market St, Howard, SD 57349
Tel.: (605) 772-5568
Web Site:
http://www.howardcoop.com
Sales Range: $10-24.9 Million
Emp.: 20

Grains
N.A.I.C.S.: 424510
Donita Potter (Controller)
Mark Neises (Mgr-Seed & Feed)
Martin J. Connor (Pres)
Joe Bechen (VP)
Bruce Yanish (Gen Mgr)

HOWARD FERTILIZER COM-PANY INC.
8306 S Orange Ave, Orlando, FL
32809
Tel.: (407) 855-1841
Web Site:
http://www.howardfertilizer.com
Rev.: $20,600,000
Emp.: 68
Plant Foods, Mixed: From Plants
Making Phosphatic Fertilizer
N.A.I.C.S.: 325312
Robert Howard Jr. (Pres & CEO)

HOWARD FINISHING LLC
32565 Dequindre Rd, Madison
Heights, MI 48071
Tel.: (248) 588-9050
Web Site:
http://www.howardfinishing.com
Sales Range: $10-24.9 Million
Emp.: 250
Coating & Plating of Auto Parts
N.A.I.C.S.: 332322
Jim E. Grimes (Owner & Pres)
Mike Kazy (Mgr-Production)

Subsidiaries:

Unicote Corporation   (1)
33165 Groesbeck Hwy, Fraser, MI 48026
Tel.: (586) 296-0700
Web Site:
http://www.unicotecorporation.com
Sales Range: $10-24.9 Million
Emp.: 30
Coating Of Metals & Formed Products
N.A.I.C.S.: 332812

HOWARD FISCHER ASSOCI-ATES INTERNATIONAL
1800 Kennedy Blvd Ste 702, Phila-
delphia, PA 19103
Tel.: (215) 568-8363
Web Site: https://www.hfischer.com
Sales Range: $10-24.9 Million
Emp.: 20
Executive Placement
N.A.I.C.S.: 541612
Howard Fischer (Founder, Pres &
CEO)
Dennis Pfizenmayer (CFO)

HOWARD GROUP
215 Grand Blvd Ste 102, Miramar
Beach, FL 32550
Tel.: (850) 837-1886
Web Site: http://www.howardgrp.com
Year Founded: 1987
Sales Range: $10-24.9 Million
Emp.: 20
Real Estate Development & Other
Related Services
N.A.I.C.S.: 237210
Bill Bubel (VP-Ops)
Judith Williams (Dir-Dev)
Huw Jones (Dir-Fin)
Nicholas Bewes (CEO)

HOWARD INDUSTRIES
8855 Washington Blvd, Culver City,
CA 90232
Tel.: (310) 837-9191
Web Site: https://www.howind.com
Sales Range: $10-24.9 Million
Emp.: 52
Air Conditioning Equipment
N.A.I.C.S.: 423730
Jeff Winter (VP & Controller)

HOWARD INDUSTRIES INC.

1840 Progress Ave, Columbus, OH
43207
Tel.: (614) 444-9900
Web Site:
https://www.howardchem.com
Sales Range: $10-24.9 Million
Emp.: 45
Emulsifiers Except Food & Pharma-
ceutical
N.A.I.C.S.: 325613
Lisa Parsley *(Mgr-Shipping & Site
Coord)*
Robert Howard *(Pres)*

HOWARD INDUSTRIES, INC.
3225 Pendorff Rd, Laurel, MS 39440
Tel.: (601) 425-3151   MS
Web Site: http://www.howard.com
Year Founded: 1969
Sales Range: $250-299.9 Million
Emp.: 4,000
Power Distribution Services
N.A.I.C.S.: 335311
Billy Howard *(CEO)*

Subsidiaries:

Howard Industries   (1)
3225 Pendorff Rd, Laurel, MS
39440-5820   (100%)
Tel.: (601) 425-3151
Web Site: http://www.howard-ind.com
Sales Range: $250-299.9 Million
Emp.: 2,700
Mfr of Transformers
N.A.I.C.S.: 335311
Michael Howard *(Pres)*

Howard Lighting Products   (1)
PO Box 1590, Laurel, MS 39441
Tel.: (601) 422-0033
Web Site:
http://www.howardlightingproducts.com
Emp.: 200
Lighting Equipment Mfr
N.A.I.C.S.: 335139
Derral Ward *(VP-Sls & Mktg)*
Mike Mauldin *(Mgr-Customer Svc)*

Howard Technology Solutions,
Inc.   (1)
36 Howard Dr, Ellisville, MS 39437
Web Site: http://www.howardcomputers.com
Medical Equipment Distr
N.A.I.C.S.: 423450

Howard Transportation, Inc. (1)
107 Nehi Rd, Ellisville, MS 39437
Web Site:
http://www.howardtransportation.com
General Freight Trucking Services
N.A.I.C.S.: 484121

HOWARD JOHNSON'S ENTER-
PRISES INC.
700 W Virginia St Ste 222, Milwau-
kee, WI 53204-1549
Tel.: (414) 276-1505
Web Site: http://www.hjefertilizer.com
Year Founded: 1963
Sales Range: $25-49.9 Million
Emp.: 8,200
Fertilizers, Mixing Only
N.A.I.C.S.: 325314

HOWARD LEASING INC.
6302 Manatee Ave W Ste K, Braden-
ton, FL 34209
Tel.: (941) 761-7704
Web Site:
https://www.howardleasinginc.com
Sales Range: $1-9.9 Million
Emp.: 20
Professional Employer Organizations
N.A.I.C.S.: 561330
Charles Howard *(Pres & CEO)*
C. J. Howard *(CFO)*
Denise Voshell *(Mgr-Payroll)*

HOWARD LUMBER COMPANY
475 Columbia Industrial Blvd, Evans,
GA 30809
Tel.: (706) 868-8400
Web Site:
https://www.howardlumbercom
pany.com
Year Founded: 1946
Sales Range: $10-24.9 Million
Emp.: 39
Home Center Operator
N.A.I.C.S.: 444110
W. J. Badger *(Pres & Treas)*
Phillip Stroud *(Sec)*

HOWARD M. SCHWARTZ &
ASSOCIATES, INC.
One Marketing Ctr 19020 Emerald
Dr, Brookfield, WI 53045
Tel.: (262) 879-0165   WI
Year Founded: 1964
Rev.: $26,530,000
Emp.: 25
Full Service
N.A.I.C.S.: 541810
Howard M. Schwartz *(Pres)*
Jerrie Schwartz *(Treas & Exec Sec)*
Robert Jon Schwartz *(Dir-Art & Cre-
ative)*
Elsa Vandervent *(Dir-Creative)*
Marion Lovejoy *(Dir-Media)*
Andrea Beth Schwartz *(Mgr-
Production)*

HOWARD MEMORIAL HOSPI-
TAL
130 Medical Cir, Nashville, AR 71852
Tel.: (870) 845-4400   AR
Web Site:
https://www.howardmemorial.com
Year Founded: 1949
Sales Range: $10-24.9 Million
Emp.: 180
Acute Care Services
N.A.I.C.S.: 622110
Debra J. Wright *(CEO)*
Paula Mitchell *(Chief Nursing Officer)*
Bill Craig *(CFO)*

HOWARD MIDSTREAM PART-
NERS, LP
16211 La Cantera Pkwy Ste 202, San
Antonio, TX 78256
Tel.: (210) 298-2222   DE
Year Founded: 2016
Natural Gas Service Provider
N.A.I.C.S.: 211130
J. Michael Howard *(CEO)*

HOWARD MILLER COMPANY
860 E Main Ave, Zeeland, MI 49464
Tel.: (616) 772-7277   MI
Web Site:
http://www.howardmiller.com
Year Founded: 1926
Sales Range: $1-4.9 Billion
Emp.: 1,500
Holding Company; Furniture & Clock
Mfr
N.A.I.C.S.: 551112
Howard J. Miller *(Pres)*

Subsidiaries:

Hekman Furniture Company   (1)
1400 Buchanan Ave SW, Zeeland, MI
49464
Tel.: (616) 452-1411
Web Site: http://www.hekman.com
Sales Range: $10-24.9 Million
Emp.: 50
Wood Household Furniture Mfr & Whslr
N.A.I.C.S.: 337122

Ridgeway Furniture Company (1)
860 E Main Ave, Zeeland, MI
49464-1300   (100%)
Tel.: (616) 748-2650
Web Site: http://www.ridgewayclocks.com
Sales Range: $10-24.9 Million
Emp.: 100
Grandfather, Mantel & Wall Clock Mfr

N.A.I.C.S.: 334519
Howard J. Miller *(Pres & CEO)*

HOWARD P. FAIRFIELD, LLC
9 Green St, Skowhegan, ME 04976
Tel.: (207) 474-9836   ME
Web Site: https://www.hpfairfield.com
Year Founded: 1951
Sales Range: $10-24.9 Million
Emp.: 51
Road Construction & Maintenance
Machinery
N.A.I.C.S.: 423810
Rod Winter *(Pres)*

HOWARD SHEPPARD INC.
755 Waco Dr, Sandersville, GA
31082
Tel.: (478) 552-5127   GA
Web Site:
https://www.howardsheppard.com
Year Founded: 1947
Sales Range: $25-49.9 Million
Emp.: 300
Trucking Services
N.A.I.C.S.: 484121
Cliff Sheppard *(Pres & CEO)*
Terry Bertoch *(Mgr-Intermodal Ops)*
Tracy Giddens *(VP-OTR Div & Logis-
tics)*
Michael Rice *(VP-Fleet Ops)*

HOWARD SYSTEMS INTERNA-
TIONAL INC.
290 Howard Dr, Stamford, CT 06902
Tel.: (203) 324-4600   CT
Web Site:
http://www.howardsystems.com
Year Founded: 1975
Sales Range: $25-49.9 Million
Emp.: 480
Custom Computer Programming Ser-
vices
N.A.I.C.S.: 541511
Howard Persky *(Pres)*

HOWARD TERNES PACKAG-
ING CO.
35275 Industrial Rd, Livonia, MI
48150
Tel.: (313) 531-5867
Web Site:
http://www.ternespackaging.com
Year Founded: 1948
Emp.: 400
Packing Goods for Shipping
N.A.I.C.S.: 488991
Bonnie Verville *(Controller)*
Howard A. Ternes Jr. *(Chm & CEO)*

HOWARD'S APPLIANCES, INC.
901 East Imperial Hwy, La Habra, CA
90631
Tel.: (714) 871-5830
Web Site: http://www.howards.com
Home Appliances Mfr & Dstr
N.A.I.C.S.: 423620
Joy Banducci *(Chief Fin & Tech Offi-
cer)*
Daryl Massy *(Sr VP)*
Michelle Nein *(Pres)*
Stacy Leiker *(COO)*
Cody Browne *(VP-Mktg)*
Peter Boutros *(CEO)*
Kent Baker *(Chm)*

Subsidiaries:

Midway Appliance Center, Inc. (1)
14444 Atstar Dr, Victorville, CA 92395
Tel.: (760) 245-3731
Web Site: http://www.midwayappliance.com
Sales Range: $1-9.9 Million
Emp.: 40
Household Appliance Stores
N.A.I.C.S.: 449210
Donald Lager *(Pres)*

HOWARD'S TV & APPLI-
ANCES, INC.
901 E Imperial Hwy, La Habra, CA
90631
Tel.: (714) 871-2700   CA
Web Site: https://www.howards.com
Year Founded: 1946
Sales Range: $25-49.9 Million
Emp.: 200
Electric Household Appliances, Tele-
vision Sets & Video Equipment
N.A.I.C.S.: 449210

HOWARD, MERRELL & PART-
NERS, INC.
8521 Six Forks Rd 4th Fl, Raleigh,
NC 27615-5278
Tel.: (919) 848-2400   DE
Year Founded: 1976
Sales Range: $50-74.9 Million
Emp.: 45
Advetising Agency
N.A.I.C.S.: 541810
Jim Cobb *(Pres & CEO)*
Bruce D. Hall *(Sr VP-Res)*
Donna Mercer *(COO & Sr VP-Media
Assets)*
Joe Ivey *(VP-Creative & Sr Dir-Art)*
Scott Piggott *(Sr VP-Tech & Interac-
tive Svcs)*
Lisa Powell *(Mgmt Supvr)*
Stephanie Dunford *(Sr VP-PR & So-
cial Media)*
Joanne Yue *(Sr Media Buyer)*
Stephanie Styons *(Sr VP-PR & Social
Media)*
Billy Barnes *(Creative Dir)*
Denise Lingenfelser *(Mgr-Digital Pro-
duction)*
Laura Gross *(Mgr-Event Svcs & PR)*
Robin Rogers *(Mgr-Print Production)*
Jessica Redman *(Sr Acct Exec)*
Ashley Harrington-Andrews *(Assoc
Acct Exec)*
Julia Anglin *(Acct Exec)*
Anna Agnew *(Acct Exec)*
Elizabeth Romero *(Mgmt Supvr)*
Kristen Liebers *(Asst Acct Exec)*
Ellen Wayland *(Dir-Media)*
Maria Martinat *(Assoc Acct Exec)*
Craig Schreiber *(Sr Acct Supvr)*
Greg Harbinson *(Mgr-Social Media
Mktg)*
Chloe Seipel *(Assoc Acct Exec)*
Julie Orsini *(Acct Coord)*
Lindsay Glosson *(Acct Coord)*
Taylor Waddell *(Acct Coord)*

HOWCO METALS INC.
9611 Telge Rd, Houston, TX 77095-
5114
Tel.: (281) 649-8800   TX
Web Site:
https://www.howcogroup.com
Year Founded: 1982
Sales Range: $10-24.9 Million
Emp.: 60
Metals Services
N.A.I.C.S.: 423510
Meghan Shively *(Coord-Sales)*

HOWE BARNES INVEST-
MENTS, INC.
222 S Riverside Plz, Chicago, IL
60606
Tel.: (312) 655-3000
Web Site:
http://www.howebarnes.com
Sales Range: $25-49.9 Million
Emp.: 100

Howe Barnes Investments, Inc.—(Continued)

Brokers Security
N.A.I.C.S.: 523150
Dan Coughlin (Chm, Pres & CEO)
Dan Cardenas (Sr VP)
Ron Sirt (Sr VP & Mgr-Private Client Svcs Grp)
Thomas Mecredy (Mng Dir)
Charles L. Stubbs (VP)
John Schramm (Mng Dir)
Ken Segal (Sr VP & Dir-Asset Fin Svcs Div)
Paul Reese (Mng Dir)

HOWE ELECTRIC INC.
4682 E Olive Ave, Fresno, CA 93702
Tel.: (559) 255-8992
Web Site: https://www.howe-electric.com
Rev.: $26,609,475
Emp.: 30
General Electrical Contractor
N.A.I.C.S.: 238210
Mike Madruga (Project Mgr)

HOWELL & HOWELL CONTRACTORS, INC.
2603 Grassland Dr, Louisville, KY 40299
Tel.: (502) 491-7985
Web Site: https://www.howellandhowellinc.com
Year Founded: 1987
Sales Range: $10-24.9 Million
Emp.: 100
Residential Remodeling Services
N.A.I.C.S.: 236118
Mark McQuillen (Superintendent-General Contracting)
Margaret Hoffman (Controller)
Greg Mullins (Superintendent-Field)
S. Oden Howell Jr. (Pres)

HOWELL INSTRUMENTS INC.
8945 S Fwy, Fort Worth, TX 76140-5722
Tel.: (817) 336-7411
Web Site: https://www.howellinst.com
Year Founded: 1951
Sales Range: $25-49.9 Million
Emp.: 80
Aircraft Engine Test Systems, Airborne Monitors & Indicators, Test Cell Instrumentation Systems, Aircraft Industrial & Laboratory Test Equipment Mfr & Distr
N.A.I.C.S.: 334513
Shep Brown (CEO)

HOWELL-OREGON ELECTRIC COOPERATIVE, INC.
6327 US Hwy 63, West Plains, MO 65775
Tel.: (417) 256-2131
Web Site: https://www.hoecoop.org
Year Founded: 1939
Sales Range: $10-24.9 Million
Emp.: 94
Electric Power Distr
N.A.I.C.S.: 221122
Dan Singletary (CEO & Gen Mgr)
Tracy Brower (Mgr-Fin & Acctg)
Troy Hogsett (Mgr-Engrg)
Bill Temple (Mgr-Acct Receivable)

HOWLAND PUMP & SUPPLY CO. INC.
7611 State Hwy 68, Ogdensburg, NY 13669
Tel.: (315) 393-3791
Web Site: https://www.howlandpump.com
Sales Range: $10-24.9 Million
Emp.: 50
Wholesale Plumbing & Heating

N.A.I.C.S.: 423830
Steve Larose (Owner & CEO)

HOWLETT LUMBER CO. INC.
28 Trolley Crossing Rd, Charlton, MA 01507
Tel.: (508) 248-4346
Web Site: http://www.howlettlumber.com
Year Founded: 1985
Sales Range: $10-24.9 Million
Emp.: 25
Mfr of Lumber & Other Building Materials
N.A.I.C.S.: 423310
Oliver E. Howlett (Pres)

HOWROYD-WRIGHT EMPLOYMENT AGENCY INC.
327 W Broadway, Glendale, CA 91204
Tel.: (818) 240-8688
Web Site: http://www.appleone.com
Year Founded: 1964
Sales Range: $200-249.9 Million
Emp.: 1,400
Employment Agency
N.A.I.C.S.: 561311
Bernard Howroyd (Founder & Pres)
Marc Goldman (VP-Sls & Mktg)

HOWS MARKETS LLC
3035 Huntington Dr, Pasadena, CA 91107
Tel.: (626) 535-9091
Web Site: http://www.howsmarkets.com
Rev.: $32,300,000
Emp.: 250
Supermarket
N.A.I.C.S.: 445110
David Wolff (Mgr-Store)

HOYE'S PHARMACY
4330 S Manhattan Ave, Tampa, FL 33611
Tel.: (813) 839-8861
Web Site: http://www.hoyespharmacy.com
Sales Range: $1-9.9 Million
Emp.: 55
Compounding Pharmacy
N.A.I.C.S.: 446110
Robert S. Hoye (Owner & Pres)
Jay Hawkins (CFO & Dir-HR)
Kathy Hoye (VP-Mktg)
Sean Clark (Mgr-Ops & IT)

HOYNE FINANCIAL CORPORATION
4786 N Milwaukee Ave, Chicago, IL 60630-3693
Tel.: (773) 283-4100
Web Site: http://www.hoyne.com
Bank Holding Company
N.A.I.C.S.: 551111
Ralph C. Carstensen (Pres & CEO)

Subsidiaries:

Hoyne Savings Bank   **(1)**
4786 N Milwaukee Ave, Chicago, IL 60630
Tel.: (773) 283-4100
Web Site: http://www.hoyne.com
Sales Range: $1-9.9 Million
Emp.: 52
State-Chartered Savings Bank
N.A.I.C.S.: 522180
Ralph C. Carstensen (Pres & CEO)
Chip Corbet (VP)
James Derrig (CFO & Treas)

Subsidiary (Domestic):

Loomis Federal Savings & Loan Association   **(2)**
6350 W 63rd St, Chicago, IL 60638-5021
Tel.: (773) 586-6900

Sales Range: $1-9.9 Million
Emp.: 18
Savings Institutions
N.A.I.C.S.: 522180
Margaret Stachon (VP)

HOYOS CONSULTING LLC
PO Box 368, McFarland, WI 53558
Tel.: (608) 616-9950
Web Site: http://www.hoyosconsulting.com
Year Founded: 2010
Sales Range: $1-9.9 Million
Emp.: 7
Information Technology Consulting Services
N.A.I.C.S.: 541512
Andrew Hoyos (Founder & Owner)

HOYT BRUMM & LINK, INC.
1400 E 9 Mile, Ferndale, MI 48220
Tel.: (248) 548-3355
Year Founded: 1971
Sales Range: $10-24.9 Million
Emp.: 125
Plumbing Services
N.A.I.C.S.: 238220
Todd Hoyt (Pres)

HOYT, SHEPSTON & SCIARONI INC.
B 161A Starlite St, South San Francisco, CA 94080-6313
Tel.: (650) 952-6930
Web Site: http://www.hoyt-shepston.com
Year Founded: 1978
Sales Range: $10-24.9 Million
Emp.: 35
Freight Transportation Arrangement Services
N.A.I.C.S.: 488510
Lew Harper (Pres)

HOYTE DODGE LTD.
2300 N Sam Rayburn Fwy, Sherman, TX 75090
Tel.: (903) 893-0144
Web Site: http://www.hoytedodge.com
Sales Range: $10-24.9 Million
Emp.: 70
Automobiles New & Used
N.A.I.C.S.: 441110
Hoyte Ridlehuber (Pres)

HP INGREDIENTS
707 24th Ave W, Bradenton, FL 34205
Web Site: https://www.hpingredients.com
Sales Range: $1-9.9 Million
Emp.: 4
Nutraceutical Mfr
N.A.I.C.S.: 325412
Annie Eng (Pres)

HP INSPECTIONS, INC.
690 Sunol St Bldg H, San Jose, CA 95126-3751
Tel.: (408) 288-8460
Web Site: https://www.hpinspectionsinc.com
Building Construction & Inspection
N.A.I.C.S.: 541990
Dave Pinkham (Pres)
Jody Moore (Office Mgr)

HP PRODUCTS CORPORATION
4220 Saguaro Trl, Indianapolis, IN 46268-0310
Tel.: (317) 298-9957
Web Site: http://www.hpproducts.com
Year Founded: 1965
Sales Range: $25-49.9 Million
Emp.: 500

Service Establishment Maintenance Equipment
N.A.I.C.S.: 423850
Jan Horton (Controller)
Bridget Shuel-Walker (Pres & CEO)
Dale McGinty (VP-Key Accts & Segment Dev)
Mark Summers (VP-Sls)
Jim Smith (Exec VP-Sls)

Subsidiaries:

Renard Paper Company, Inc.   **(1)**
4465 Manchester Ave, Saint Louis, MO 63110
Tel.: (314) 371-4422
Sales Range: $10-24.9 Million
Emp.: 21
Industrial & Personal Service Paper Merchant Whslr
N.A.I.C.S.: 424130

HP RESOURCES INC.
1516 Lincoln Rd, Wickliffe, OH 44092
Tel.: (440) 585-0031
Web Site: http://www.horizonpersonnel.com
Year Founded: 1993
Sales Range: $1-9.9 Million
Emp.: 150
Permanent, Contract & Temporary Staffing Placement
N.A.I.C.S.: 561311
Daniel Schivitz (Pres)

HPC FOODS, LTD.
288 Libby St, Honolulu, HI 96819
Tel.: (808) 848-2431
Web Site: https://www.hpcfoods.com
Rev.: $17,600,000
Emp.: 175
Food Mfr & Distr
N.A.I.C.S.: 311999
Flora Samis (Supvr-Quality Assurance)
LeeAnn Butler (Mgr-Process Produce)

HPC INDUSTRIES LLC
10250 Constellation Blvd Ste 2820, Los Angeles, CA 90067
Tel.: (310) 473-7005
Holding Company; Plastic Bottle Recycling Services
N.A.I.C.S.: 551112
Leon Farahnik (Chm & CEO)

Subsidiaries:

CarbonLITE Industries LLC   **(1)**
10250 Constellation Blvd Ste 2820, Los Angeles, CA 90067
Tel.: (310) 473-7005
Web Site: http://www.carbonlitecycling.com
Emp.: 130
Plastic Bottle Recycling Services
N.A.I.C.S.: 562920
Leon Farahnik (Founder)

HPC SOLUTIONS
143 Union Blvd Suite 300, Lakewood, CO 80228
Tel.: (303) 216-9270
Web Site: http://www.hpc-solutions.net
Year Founded: 1994
Sales Range: $1-9.9 Million
Emp.: 20
Information Technology Solutions
N.A.I.C.S.: 519290
Paula Gee (Mgr-Customer Rels)

HPC WIRELESS SERVICES
22 Shelter Rock Ln Bldg C, Danbury, CT 06811
Tel.: (203) 797-1112
Web Site: http://www.hpcwireless.com

Year Founded: 2005
Construction, Site Development &
Professional Consulting Services
N.A.I.C.S.: 561499
Marc Anderson (Co-Founder & Partner)
Joseph Tassone (Co-Founder & CEO)
Brian Savva (Chief Strategy Officer)
Michael Jones (COO)
Edwin Garces (CFO)
David Wyman (Dir-Bus Ops)
Brian Wyman (Dir-Safety & Compliance)

HPI INTERNATIONAL INC.
140 58 St Unit 1C, Brooklyn, NY
11220
Tel.: (718) 768-8800   NY
Web Site: http://www.hpi.com
Year Founded: 1983
Sales Range: $10-24.9 Million
Emp.: 52
Provider of Photographic Equipment
& Supplies
N.A.I.C.S.: 423410
Jerrold Berger (Pres)
Amy Berger (Exec VP & Sec)
David Beck (CFO)

HPI, LLC.
15503 W Hardy Rd, Houston, TX
77060
Tel.: (713) 457-7500
Web Site: https://www.hpi-llc.com
Year Founded: 2002
Sales Range: $200-249.9 Million
Emp.: 153
Industrial Machinery Mfr & Distr
N.A.I.C.S.: 333248
Hal Pontez (Pres & CEO)
Jerry Wheelwright (VP-Operations)
Richard Armstrong (CFO)
Mike Cook (Mng Dir-Mechanical
Svcs)
Eduardo Inciarte (Gen Mgr-Latin
America)
Frank Berry (Dir-Technical)
Howard Morgan (Dir-Technical)
Jake Williamson (Dir-Technical)
Martin Marsh (Product Mgr & Mgr-
Manufacturing)
Pete Johnston (Mgr-Field Svc)
Jaime Thornton (Mgr-Operations-
Mechanical Svcs)
Juanita Perez (Mgr-Human Resources)
Kelly Schreiber (Controller-Finance)
Frankie Foster (Dir-Technical)
Hilario Becerra (Mgr-Engineering)

HPL STAMPINGS INC.
425 Enterprise Pkwy, Lake Zurich, IL
60047
Tel.: (847) 540-1400
Web Site:
    https://www.hplstampings.com
Rev.: $16,700,000
Emp.: 50
Metal Stamping Services
N.A.I.C.S.: 332119
Dave Euginfki (Controller)
Sarah Christensen (Mgr-Customer
Svc)
Roger E. Hedberg Jr. (Pres)

HPR, INC.
3771 Rio Rd Ste 111, Carmel, CA
93923-8671
Tel.: (831) 375-1747   CA
Web Site: http://www.hunter-pr.com
Year Founded: 1990
Sales Range: Less than $1 Million
Emp.: 7
Public Relations Agency
N.A.I.C.S.: 541820

Karen Moraghan (Pres)
Kristen Hunter (VP)
Ed Vyeda (Sr Acct Exec)
Kery Maveus (Mgr-Asset)
Corrin Sullivan (Mgr-Media Database)

Subsidiaries:

HPR, Inc.   (1)
11 W Fox Hill Rd, Long Valley, NJ 07853-
3025
Tel.: (908) 876-5100
Web Site: http://www.hunter-pr.com
Public Relations Agency
N.A.I.C.S.: 541820
Karen Moraghan (Pres)
Kristen Hunter (VP)
Kerry Maveus (Mgr-Asset)

HPS INVESTMENT PARTNERS, LLC
40 W 57th St 33rd Fl, New York, NY
10019
Tel.: (212) 287-6767   DE
Web Site:
    https://www.hpspartners.com
Year Founded: 2007
Investment Management Service
N.A.I.C.S.: 523940
Mark Rubenstein (Mng Dir)
Michael Dorenfeld (Mng Dir)
Peggy Nugent (Sr VP)
Andrew Eiler (CTO)
Scott Bancroft Kapnick (CEO)
Andersen Fisher (Mng Dir)
Christopher Gunther (Mng Dir)
David Frey (Mng Dir)
Jeffrey Fitts (Mng Dir)
Marcus Colwell (Mng Dir)
Scot French (Mng Dir)
Serge Adam (Mng Dir)
Vikas Keswani (Mng Dir)

Subsidiaries:

HPS Investment Partners (UK)
LLP   (1)
Devonshire House 1 Mayfair Place 4th
Floor, London, W1J 8AJ, United Kingdom
Tel.: (44) 2035786030
Web Site: http://www.hpspartners.com
Emp.: 320
Investment Management Service
N.A.I.C.S.: 523940

Marlin Business Services Corp.   (1)
300 Fellowship Rd, Mount Laurel, NJ 08054
Web Site:
    http://www.marlincapitalsolutions.com
Rev.: $117,139,000
Assets: $1,021,998,000
Liabilities: $825,633,000
Net Worth: $196,365,000
Earnings: $342,000
Emp.: 254
Fiscal Year-end: 12/31/2020
Small-Ticket Lease Financing Services
N.A.I.C.S.: 525990
Greg Sting (COO & Sr VP)
Bill Stephenson (CEO)
Amy Vetere (Chief Informational Officer)
Richard Irwin (CFO & Sr VP)
Jeff Nicholas (Chief Risk Officer)

Subsidiary (Domestic):

Horizon Keystone Financial LLC   (2)
300 Fellowship Rd, Mount Laurel, NJ
08054-2321
Web Site: http://www.horizonkeystone.com
Equipment Financing Services
N.A.I.C.S.: 522220
Bill Waddell (VP-Sls)

Marlin Business Bank   (2)
2795 E Cottonwood Pkwy Ste 120, Salt
Lake City, UT 84121
Tel.: (801) 453-1722
Web Site:
    http://www.marlincapitalsolutions.com
Commercial Banking Services
N.A.I.C.S.: 522110

Marlin Leasing Corporation   (2)
300 Fellowship Rd, Mount Laurel, NJ
08054-1201

Tel.: (856) 359-9111
Rev.: $49,700,000
Emp.: 201
Leasing Businesses Equipment Providers
Services
N.A.I.C.S.: 532490

Nucleus Financial Group plc   (1)
Greenside 12 Blenheim Place, Edinburgh,
EH7 5JH, United Kingdom
Tel.: (44) 1312269800
Web Site: http://www.nucleusfinancial.com
Rev.: $70,342,115
Assets: $49,368,057
Liabilities: $18,505,724
Net Worth: $30,862,333
Earnings: $4,314,834
Emp.: 245
Fiscal Year-end: 12/31/2020
Financial Investment Advisory Services
N.A.I.C.S.: 523940
David Ferguson (Founder & CEO)
Stuart Geard (CFO)
Andrew Smith (CTO)
Kirsty Lynagh (Chief People Officer)
Martin Ettles (Chief Risk Officer)

SGS International, Inc.   (1)
626 W Main St Ste 500, Louisville, KY
40202
Tel.: (502) 637-5443
Web Site: http://www.sgsintl.com
Emp.: 2,500
Prepress Printing & Packaging Services
N.A.I.C.S.: 323120
Dennis Wilcox (Reg VP)
Marriott W. Winchester Jr. (Sr VP)

Subsidiary (Domestic):

C.M. Jackson Associates, Inc.   (2)
133 Williams Dr, Ramsey, NJ 07446
Tel.: (201) 828-5000
Packaging & Graphic Design Services
N.A.I.C.S.: 561910

Southern Graphic Systems, Inc.   (2)
2781 Roberts Ave, Philadelphia, PA 19129
Tel.: (215) 843-2243
Web Site: http://www.sgsintl.com
Rev.: $15,000,000
Emp.: 110
Prepress Printing & Packaging Services
N.A.I.C.S.: 323120

Division (Domestic):

Southern Graphic Systems, Inc. -
Flexo Divison   (2)
3045 Chastain Meadows Pkwy Ste 200,
Marietta, GA 30066
Tel.: (404) 351-4620
Web Site:
    http://www.southerngraphicsystems.com
Sales Range: $50-74.9 Million
Emp.: 25
Rotogravure Printing Cylinders, Extruded &
Consumer Products & Packaging Mfr
N.A.I.C.S.: 323120

Southern Graphic Systems, Inc. -
Gravure Divison   (2)
1411 Chattahoochee Ave NW, Atlanta, GA
30318
Tel.: (404) 352-2342
Web Site: http://www.sgsintl.com
Sales Range: $25-49.9 Million
Emp.: 40
Rotogravure Printing Cylinders, Extruded &
Consumer Products & Packaging Mfr
N.A.I.C.S.: 323111

Subsidiary (Domestic):

Southern Graphic Systems, LLC   (2)
626 W Main St Ste 500, Louisville, KY
40202
Tel.: (502) 637-5443
Web Site: http://www.sgsco.com
Graphic Design Services
N.A.I.C.S.: 541430
Piyush Chaudhari (CEO)
Jim Bresingham (CFO)
Hoyoung Pak (COO)
Andrew Tidwell (Chief HR Officer)
Justin Schauer (Gen Counsel, VP & Sec)
Rob McCarthy (Pres-Design & Digital)
Hollie Gonzales (Pres-Americas)

Subsidiary (Non-US):

Vavinel SAS   (3)

49 boulevard du General Martial VALIN,
75015, Paris, France
Tel.: (33) 1 45 58 80 00
Web Site: http://www.sgsco.com
Advertising Design Services
N.A.I.C.S.: 541810

Subsidiary (US):

Diadeis New York, LLC   (4)
33 E 17th St, New York, NY 10003
Tel.: (212) 242-8787
Web Site: http://www.sgsco.com
Advertising Design Services
N.A.I.C.S.: 541810

Subsidiary (Domestic):

The Stevenson Color Company,
Inc.   (2)
535 Wilmer Ave, Cincinnati, OH 45226
Tel.: (513) 321-7500
Web Site: http://www.steven.com
Sales Range: $1-9.9 Million
Emp.: 150
Platemaking Services
N.A.I.C.S.: 323120
Karen Reed (Acct Mgr)
Ellen Jacob (Acct Mgr)

HPS MECHANICAL, INC.
3100 E Belle Ter, Bakersfield, CA
93307-6830
Tel.: (661) 426-2166
Web Site:
    https://www.hpsmechanical.com
Year Founded: 1959
Sales Range: $10-24.9 Million
Emp.: 130
Air Conditioning System Installation
Services
N.A.I.C.S.: 238220
Les Denherder (Pres)
Justice Gradowitz (Mgr-Credit)

HPS PLUMBING SERVICE, INC.
3100 E Belle Ter, Bakersfield, CA
93307-6830
Tel.: (661) 426-2166
Web Site:
    https://www.hpsmechanical.com
Sales Range: $10-24.9 Million
Emp.: 300
Construction Engineering Services
N.A.I.C.S.: 237310
Les Denherder (Pres)
Justice Gradowitz (Mgr-Credit)

HPS TECHNOLOGIES, INC.
5448 Kingsbridge Rd, Winston Salem, NC 27103-5994
Tel.: (336) 287-6220
Sales Range: $10-24.9 Million
Emp.: 3
Cleaning Supplies Mfr
N.A.I.C.S.: 325998
David C. Bradford (Pres)

HR AMERICA INC.
1833 Magnavox Way, Fort Wayne, IN
46804
Tel.: (260) 436-3878
Web Site: http://www.hramerica.net
Sales Range: $50-74.9 Million
Emp.: 2,000
Employee Leasing Services
N.A.I.C.S.: 561330
Doug Curtis (Founder & Chm)

HR CERTIFICATION INSTI-
TUTE
1725 Duke St Ste 700, Alexandria,
VA 22314
Tel.: (571) 551-6700   DC
Web Site: https://www.hrci.org
Year Founded: 1979
Sales Range: $10-24.9 Million
Emp.: 57

HR Certification Institute—(Continued)

Human Resource Management Services
N.A.I.C.S.: 541612
Linda K. Anguish *(Dir-Certification Products)*
Kerry Morgan *(CMO)*
Amy Schabacker Dufrane *(CEO)*
James Lewis *(Vice Chm)*
Jim Steele *(Treas & Sec)*
Dania Eter *(Chief Credentialing & Products Portfolio Officer)*
John Lunde *(Chief Bus Dev Officer)*
Becky Haight *(CFO)*
Amine Issa Jr. *(Dir-Client Rels)*
Gardiner Hempel Jr. *(Chm)*

HR FOCAL POINT, LLC
6860 N Dallas Parkway Suite 200, Plano, TX 75024
Web Site:
    http://www.hrfocalpoint.com
Year Founded: 2007
Sales Range: $1-9.9 Million
Emp.: 13
Specialists in the Implementation & Support of SAP Human Capital Management Software & Applications
N.A.I.C.S.: 513210
David Adams *(Co-Founder)*
Graham Wong *(Co-Founder)*
Jennifer Becker *(Dir-Bus Ops)*

HR MACHINERY INC.
3355 Edison Way, Fremont, CA 94538-6137
Tel.: (510) 657-8180   CA
Web Site:
    http://www.hrmachinery.com
Industrial Machinery & Equipment Mfr
N.A.I.C.S.: 423830
Jim Fahey *(Pres)*

HR PHARMACEUTICALS, INC.
221 W Philadelphia St Ste 17, York, PA 17401-2992
Web Site: http://www.hrpharma.com
Chemicals Mfr
N.A.I.C.S.: 325412
Jon P. Wiesman *(Pres & CEO)*

Subsidiaries:

Medical Technologies of Georgia, Inc.   (1)
15151 Prater Dr Ste D, Covington, GA 30014-4961
Tel.: (770) 788-0763
Web Site: http://www.medtechga.com
Surgical & Medical Instrument Mfr
N.A.I.C.S.: 339112
John Golden *(Founder)*

HR STRATEGIES COMPANY
415 Horizon Dr Bldg 200 Ste 200, Suwanee, GA 30024
Tel.: (770) 339-0000   GA
Web Site: https://www.hr-strategies.com
Year Founded: 1983
Sales Range: $25-49.9 Million
Emp.: 25
Professional Employer Organizations
N.A.I.C.S.: 561330
Jim Beesley *(CEO)*
Georgiana Britt *(VP-Ops)*
Russ Berkhan *(VP-Sales)*
Brandy Barden *(CFO)*

HR WORKS, INC.
200 WillowBrook Office Park, Fairport, NY 14450
Tel.: (585) 381-8340
Web Site: https://www.hrworks-inc.com
Sales Range: $1-9.9 Million
Emp.: 49

Human Resource Consulting Services
N.A.I.C.S.: 541612
Candace C. Walters *(Pres)*
Christopher Dickens *(CFO)*
Teresa Meechan *(Dir-Bus Dev)*
Ruth Illingsworth *(Mgr)*
Karen Lustyk *(Mgr-Outsourcing Svcs)*
Shannon Craig *(VP-Compliance Svcs)*
Jamie Von Bramer *(VP-Outsourcing)*
Anne Marie Pernov *(Mgr-HR)*
Jessica Slye *(Mgr-HR Consultant Svcs)*

HR, INC.
36474 Emerald Coast Pkwy Bldg B, Destin, FL 32541
Tel.: (850) 650-9935   FL
Web Site: https://www.simplehr.com
Year Founded: 2002
Sales Range: $125-149.9 Million
Emp.: 30
Professional Employer Organization; Human Resource, Payroll & Administrative Management Services
N.A.I.C.S.: 561330
Bobby Newman *(CEO)*

HRANSWERLINK
6601 Koll Center Parkway Suite 201, Pleasanton, CA 94566
Web Site:
    http://www.hranswerlink.com
Year Founded: 2001
Sales Range: $1-9.9 Million
Emp.: 25
Software-as-a-Service Modules That Feature On-Demand HR Products
N.A.I.C.S.: 513210
Dennis Abraham *(Founder & Chm)*
Nathan Christensen *(CEO)*
Tricia Christensen *(CFO & Dir-Ops)*
Alain Schotland *(Dir-Creative)*
Kerry Lear *(Dir-HR Content)*
Camie Calderon *(Dir-Sls)*
John Ratcliff *(Dir-Tech)*

HRD AERO SYSTEMS, INC.
25555 Ave Stanford, Valencia, CA 91355-1101
Tel.: (661) 295-0670
Web Site: https://www.hrd-aerosystems.com
Rev.: $10,000,000
Emp.: 57
Aircraft & Heavy Equipment Repair Services
N.A.I.C.S.: 811310
Tim McBride *(CFO)*
Albert Leon *(Dir-Mgmt Info Sys)*
Donna Schrey *(Dir-Quality Assurance)*
Joseph Schoonover *(Dir-Quality Control)*
Wilbur Burritt *(Mgr-Mfg)*
Tom Salamone *(Pres)*
Brian Omahen *(Exec VP)*

HRGM CORPORATION
2021 Shannon Pl SE, Washington, DC 20020
Tel.: (202) 889-8400
Web Site: https://www.hrgm.com
Sales Range: $10-24.9 Million
Emp.: 25
Roofing Contractors
N.A.I.C.S.: 238160
Hansa Butani *(Sec & VP)*
Ramesh Butani *(Pres)*

HRH CONSTRUCTION LLC
11 Martine Ave, White Plains, NY 10606
Tel.: (212) 616-3100   NY
Sales Range: $200-249.9 Million

Emp.: 900
Construction Management; Hi-Rise Residential, Commercial Office Buildings
N.A.I.C.S.: 236115
Gregory Cuneo *(Chm)*
Brad Singer *(Pres)*
Louis Esposito *(Sr VP-Pur)*
Jim Muscianesi *(Sr VP-Estimating)*
Frank Ross Sr. *(VP-Admin)*
Frank Ross Jr. *(Exec VP-Project Ops)*

HRH MEDIA
206 Cleveland Blvd, Fayetteville, NY 13066-1104
Tel.: (818) 867-4442
Year Founded: 2007
Sales Range: Less than $1 Million
Emp.: 10
Advetising Agency
N.A.I.C.S.: 541810
Heather Radigan *(Dir)*

HRM ENTERPRISES INC.
1015 Edison St NW, Hartville, OH 44632
Tel.: (330) 877-9353
Web Site:
    http://www.hartvillecollectibles.com
Year Founded: 1972
Sales Range: $10-24.9 Million
Emp.: 300
American Restaurant
N.A.I.C.S.: 722511
Vernon Sommers *(Pres)*
Scott Micale *(Dir-IT)*

HRO INC.
390 Diablo Rd Ste 210, Danville, CA 94526-3432
Tel.: (925) 831-1771   CA
Web Site: http://www.hamradio.com
Year Founded: 1971
Sales Range: $25-49.9 Million
Emp.: 106
Sales of Radios, Television & Electronics
N.A.I.C.S.: 449210
Robert Ferrero *(Pres)*

HRQ, INC.
2859 Umatilla St, Denver, CO 80211
Tel.: (303) 455-1118
Web Site: http://www.hrqinc.com
Year Founded: 1998
Sales Range: $10-24.9 Million
Emp.: 12
Business Consulting Services
N.A.I.C.S.: 561499
Molly McCoy *(Co-Founder & Chm)*
Kathy Rapp *(Pres)*
Anne Mounts *(Sr VP-Denver)*
Brent McCombs *(Mng Dir/VP-Houston)*
Jen Alessandra *(Sr VP-HR)*
Pam Brown *(Mng Dir & VP)*
Anna Clepper *(Mng Dir & VP)*
Brian Coffman *(VP-Delivery)*
Kevin Delaney *(Gen Counsel, Sec & Sr VP)*
Charlie Piscitello *(Chief People Officer & Sr VP)*
Gwen Schreffler *(VP-HR)*
Whitney Shelley *(VP)*
Jared Simon *(Co-Founder & COO)*
Katy Theroux *(Chief HR Officer)*
Chris Lawrence *(Mng Dir/VP-Atlanta)*

HRS ERASE INC.
200 NE Mulberry St 200, Lees Summit, MO 64086
Tel.: (816) 524-9477
Web Site: http://www.hrserase.com
Year Founded: 1998
Sales Range: $1-9.9 Million

Emp.: 100
Healthcare Reimbursement Services
N.A.I.C.S.: 812990
Kevin Murphy *(Founder & Pres)*

HRST, INC.
6557 City West Pkwy, Eden Prairie, MN 55344
Tel.: (952) 767-8100
Web Site: https://www.hrstinc.com
Year Founded: 1998
Rev.: $7,000,000
Emp.: 34
Engineeering Services
N.A.I.C.S.: 541330
Robert Krowech *(CEO)*
Patrick Walker *(Engr)*
Bryan Craig *(Mgr-Tech)*
Brenda Peterson *(Office Mgr)*

HS BRANDS INTERNATIONAL
500 Myles Standish Blvd, Taunton, MA 02780
Web Site: http://www.hsbrands.com
Year Founded: 1992
Sales Range: $1-9.9 Million
Emp.: 20
Loss Prevention & Quality Assurance Services
N.A.I.C.S.: 541618
Mike Mershimer *(COO)*
Sidney Strachan *(Dir-Bus Dev-The Bahamas & Caribbean)*
Sheila Rivera *(Controller-Fin-Global)*
Greg Keeley *(Dir-Loss Prevention Svcs)*
Raymond Esposito *(Pres-Loss Prevention & Compliance)*
Tom Mills Jr. *(CEO)*

HS DIE & ENGINEERING, INC.
215 Lake Michigan Dr, Grand Rapids, MI 49534
Tel.: (616) 453-5451   MI
Web Site: http://www.hsdie.com
Year Founded: 1969
Sales Range: $75-99.9 Million
Emp.: 200
Special Dies, Tools, Jigs & Fixtures Mfr
N.A.I.C.S.: 333514
Marcia Steele *(Founder & CEO)*
Kent Hanson *(Engr-Sls)*

HS HOLDINGS, LLC
2520 Glenda Ln, Dallas, TX 75229
Tel.: (214) 919-1698
Web Site:
    http://www.hsholdingsllc.com
Privater Equity Firm
N.A.I.C.S.: 551112
Neal Shah *(Principal)*
Manish Chhadua *(Principal)*

Subsidiaries:

Dawson & Associates, Inc.   (1)
2290 Springlake Rd Ste 100, Farmers Branch, TX 75234
Tel.: (214) 357-3222
Web Site:
    http://www.dawsonandassociates.com
Sales Range: $1-9.9 Million
Emp.: 18
Industrial Electric Heating Equipment Mfr & Whslr
N.A.I.C.S.: 423830
Ken Dawson *(Pres)*

HeatSource, Inc.   (1)
2290 Springlake Rd Ste 100, Farmers Branch, TX 75234
Tel.: (214) 353-0303
Web Site: http://www.heatsourceinc.com
Sales Range: $1-9.9 Million
Emp.: 14
Industrial Machinery & Equipment Merchant Whslr
N.A.I.C.S.: 423830

Harold R. Dawson (Pres)
Neal Shah (Owner)

HSA COMMERCIAL REAL ES-TATE
233 S Wacker Dr Ste 350, Chicago, IL 60606-6413
Tel.: (312) 332-3555
Sales Range: $10-24.9 Million
Emp.: 200
Land Subdividing Services
N.A.I.C.S.: 237210
Jack Schaffer (CEO)
Robert E. Smietana (CEO)
Craig Phillips (Exec VP)
Margaret Gaca (Sr Mgr-Property)
Timothy Blum (VP)

HSF ENTERPRISES INC.
2151 Route 70 W, Cherry Hill, NJ 08002
Tel.: (856) 663-3200
Web Site:
http://www.cherryhillmercedes
benz.com
Sales Range: $100-124.9 Million
Emp.: 120
Automobiles, New & Used
N.A.I.C.S.: 532111
Michael Hartung (Pres)

Subsidiaries:

Cherry Hill Imports Corp   (1)
2261 NJ-70, Cherry Hill, NJ 08002
Tel.: (856) 665-5370
Web Site: http://www.porschecherryhill.com
Automobiles, New & Used
N.A.I.C.S.: 441110

HSMC ORIZON LLC
16924 Frances St Ste 210, Omaha, NE 68130-2311
Tel.: (402) 330-7008
Web Site:
http://www.hsmcorizon.com
Certified Public Accountants
N.A.I.C.S.: 541211
Gene Brixey (Partner)
C. David Bruce (Partner)
Gene G. Garrelts (Partner)
Rosalie Newkirk (Partner)
Jodi L. Rinne (Partner)
Michael Bohning (Partner)
G. Randall Hansen (Principal)
Phillip L. Richardson (Principal)
John J. Roderique (Principal)
Tim M. Lens (Principal)
James V. Lessley (Mgr-CPA Client Svc)
Jan Robinson (Mgr-Acctg & Payroll Svcs)
Steve Welsh (Mgr-Client Svc)
Cole Frye (Mgr-Client Svc)

Subsidiaries:

IT21 Inc.   (1)
2007 E Prairie Cir, Olathe, KS 66062
Tel.: (913) 393-4821
Web Site: http://www.it21.com
Wired Telecommunications Carriers
N.A.I.C.S.: 517111
Rick A. Mentel (Pricipal Partner)

HSU DEVELOPMENT
1335 Rockville Pike, Rockville, MD 20852
Tel.: (301) 881-3500
Web Site:
http://www.hsubuilders.com
Sales Range: $10-24.9 Million
Emp.: 45
Provider of Constuction, Renovation & Land Development Services
N.A.I.C.S.: 236220
Walter Hsu (Founder & Pres)
Randy Fetter (VP-Ops)

HSUS GINSENG ENTER-PRISES, INC.
T6819 County Rd W, Wausau, WI 54403
Tel.: (715) 675-2325
Web Site:
http://www.hsuginseng.com
Sales Range: $10-24.9 Million
Emp.: 90
Grocery & Related Products Merchant Whslr
N.A.I.C.S.: 424490
Tony Guo (VP)
Paul C. Hsu (Pres & Treas)
Sharon Hsu (Sec & VP)
William Lin (Gen Mgr)

HT CONCEPTS, INCORPO-RATED
215 S Mill St, Botkins, OH 45306
Web Site: http://www.htconcepts.com
Year Founded: 2001
Sales Range: $1-9.9 Million
Home Theater Electronics Retailers
N.A.I.C.S.: 449210

HT WINDOW FASHIONS
770 S Epperson Dr, City of Industry, CA 91748
Tel.: (626) 839-8866
Web Site: http://www.richview.com
Rev.: $12,200,000
Emp.: 60
Window Blinds
N.A.I.C.S.: 337920
Greg Miles (VP-Sls & Mktg)

HTC GLOBAL SERVICES INC.
3270 W Big Beaver Rd, Troy, MI 48084-1840
Tel.: (248) 786-2500   MI
Web Site: http://www.htcinc.com
Year Founded: 1990
Sales Range: $25-49.9 Million
Emp.: 400
Computer Related Services
N.A.I.C.S.: 541512
Madhava Reddy (Founder & CEO)
Chary Mudumby (Exec VP)
Sutbir Randhawa (VP-IT Solutions)
Vikas Bhutada (Exec VP)
James Joseph (VP-Govt Svcs)
Vani Prasad (VP-Insurance Svcs)
Laurie Maria (Dir-Fin)
Venu Vaishya (Exec VP-Ops)
Girish Arora (VP-Fin Svcs)
Narayan Renga (VP-Strategic Accts)
Nitesh Bansal (Pres & COO)
Vinod Eswaran (CFO-Global)

Subsidiaries:

CMTSU Liquidation, Inc.   (1)
6363 S Fiddler's Green Cir Ste 1400, Greenwood Village, CO 80111
Tel.: (303) 220-0100
Web Site: http://www.ciber.com
Sales Range: $750-799.9 Million
Emp.: 6,000
Computer Consulting Services
N.A.I.C.S.: 541511
Robin Caputo (VP-Mktg & PR)
Garth Carter (VP-Bus Dev)
David Plisko (VP-Employee Svcs)
Michael J. Boustridge (Pres & CEO)
M. Sean Radcliffe (Gen Counsel, Sec & Sr VP)
Brian Haskett (VP & Head-Application Dev & Mgmt practice)
Mark Zavrel (Sr VP-North American Practices)
Tina Piermarini (Chief Admin Officer & Exec VP)
Henrik Rasmussen (Country Mgr-Ops & Sls)
Andree LaRiviere (Mgr-Delivery-West)
Mark A. Floyd (Chm)

Subsidiary (Non-US):

CIBER Danmark A/S   (2)

Ringager 4C, Brondby, 2605, Denmark   (100%)
Tel.: (45) 44662466
Web Site: http://www.ciber.com
Sales Range: $10-24.9 Million
Emp.: 31
N.A.I.C.S.: 541512

CIBER Holding GmbH   (2)
Alte Eppelheimer Strasse 8, 69115, Heidelberg, Germany
Tel.: (49) 622145020
Holding Company
N.A.I.C.S.: 551112
Andreas Kremer (Gen Mgr)

Subsidiary (Domestic):

CIBER AG   (3)
Speyerer Strasse 14, 69115, Heidelberg, Germany
Tel.: (49) 622145020
Web Site: http://www.ciber.com
Information Technology Consulting & Outsourcing Services
N.A.I.C.S.: 541519

Subsidiary (Domestic):

CIBER Managed Services GmbH   (4)
Fahnenbergplatz 1, 79098, Freiburg, Germany
Tel.: (49) 761217560
Web Site: http://www.ciber.com
Computer System Design Services
N.A.I.C.S.: 541512

Topcontracts GmbH   (4)
Speyerer Strasse 14, 69115, Heidelberg, Germany
Tel.: (49) 622145020
Computer System Design Services
N.A.I.C.S.: 541512

Subsidiary (Non-US):

CIBER France SAS   (3)
8a rue Icare, Entzheim, 67960, Strasbourg, France
Tel.: (33) 388684360
Software Development Services
N.A.I.C.S.: 541511
Jorg Dietmann (Pres)

Subsidiary (Non-US):

CIBER LLC   (2)
ul Detskaya 5A, Saint Petersburg, 199026, Russia
Tel.: (7) 8123347670
Web Site: http://www.ciber.ru
Computer System Design Services
N.A.I.C.S.: 541512

CIBER Pty Ltd.   (2)
Level 4 235 Albert Road, Melbourne, 3004, VIC, Australia
Tel.: (61) 399818750
Web Site: http://www.ciber.com.au
Computer Consulting Services
N.A.I.C.S.: 541511

CIBER UK Ltd.   (2)
35 Portman Square, London, W1H 6LR, United Kingdom
Tel.: (44) 2074874366
Web Site: http://www.ciber-uk.com
Sales Range: $10-24.9 Million
Emp.: 30
Information Technology Services
N.A.I.C.S.: 541512

Branch (Domestic):

CIBER UK   (3)
Apex House 2 Watling Dr, Hinckley, LE10 3EY, Leics, United Kingdom
Tel.: (44) 8700000204
Web Site: http://www.ciber-uk.com
Computer Software, Supplies & Services
N.A.I.C.S.: 541511
Gary Springall (Mng Dir)

HTC HOLDING COMPANY
213 S Main St, Waterloo, IL 62298
Tel.: (618) 939-6112
Web Site: http://www.htc.net
Rev.: $15,900,000
Emp.: 100

Telephone Communication, Except Radio
N.A.I.C.S.: 517121
H. R. Gentsch (Pres)

HTC INC.
3480 Hwy 701 N, Conway, SC 29526-5702
Tel.: (843) 369-7399   SC
Web Site: https://www.htcinc.net
Year Founded: 1952
Sales Range: $25-49.9 Million
Emp.: 700
Provider of Telephone Services
N.A.I.C.S.: 517121
Carol G. Cox (Sec)
Michael Hagg (CEO)

Subsidiaries:

Horry Telephone Long Distance   (1)
3480 Hwy 701 N, Conway, SC 29528-5702
Tel.: (843) 365-2154
Sales Range: $10-24.9 Million
Emp.: 30
Long Distance Telephone Services
N.A.I.C.S.: 517121

HTH CORPORATION
2490 Kalakaua Ave, Honolulu, HI 96815
Tel.: (808) 922-1233
Web Site: http://hthcorp.com
Year Founded: 1975
Sales Range: $200-249.9 Million
Emp.: 2,641
Hotel & Meeting Services
N.A.I.C.S.: 721110
Bradley Pang (Controller-Ops)

Subsidiaries:

Pacific Beach Hotel   (1)
2490 Kalakaua Ave, Honolulu, HI 96815-3241
Tel.: (808) 922-1233
Web Site: http://www.pacificbeachhotel.com
Sales Range: $10-24.9 Million
Emp.: 300
Hotel, Spa & Meeting Services
N.A.I.C.S.: 721110
Meaghan Nagaji (Mgr-Guest Svcs)

Queen's Enterprises Ltd. Inc.   (1)
2490 Kalakaua Ave, Honolulu, HI 96815-3241
Tel.: (808) 923-4511
Web Site: http://www.hthcorp.com
Sales Range: $50-74.9 Million
Emp.: 700
Provider of Lodging Services
N.A.I.C.S.: 531110

HTSS, INC.
860 Broad St Ste 111, Emmaus, PA 18049
Tel.: (610) 432-4161
Web Site: https://www.htss-inc.com
Year Founded: 1993
Sales Range: $1-9.9 Million
Emp.: 10
Temporary Help Service
N.A.I.C.S.: 561320
Patricia Howells (Pres)

HTT, INC.
1828 Oakland Ave, Sheboygan Falls, WI 53085
Tel.: (920) 453-5300
Web Site: http://www.htt-inc.com
Year Founded: 1985
Metal Stamping Services
N.A.I.C.S.: 332119
Greg Noble (Pres)
Neil Leland (VP-Fin & CFO)
Todd Wanek (Mgr)
Scott Lynch (Mgr-Matls)
Angie Radi (Mgr-HR)

HUB BUICK INC

Hub Buick Inc—(Continued)

19300 NW Freeway, Houston, TX
77065
Tel.: (281) 894-5200
Web Site:
http://www.hubhouston.com
Rev.: $30,000,000
Emp.: 80
Automobiles, New & Used
N.A.I.C.S.: 441110
Robert C. Cox (Pres)

HUB CITY FORD INC.
2909 NW Evangeline Trwy, Lafayette,
LA 70507
Tel.: (337) 233-4500
Web Site: http://www.hubcityford.com
Year Founded: 1943
Rev.: $106,716,947
Emp.: 170
Automobiles, New & Used
N.A.I.C.S.: 441110
Rachel Calais (Comptroller)

HUB CITY FORD, INC.
4060 S Ferdon Blvd, Crestview, FL
32536
Tel.: (850) 682-2721
Web Site: http://www.ehubcity.com
Emp.: 43
Automobiles, New & Used
N.A.I.C.S.: 441110
Christopher Daggs (VP)
Rebecca Kaufman (Controller)
Leon Daggs Jr. (Pres)

**HUB INTERNATIONAL TEXAS,
INC. - DALLAS**
2711 N Haskell Ave Ste 2050 LB16,
Dallas, TX 75204
Tel.: (214) 855-5600
Web Site:
http://texas.hubinternational.com
Sales Range: $1-9.9 Million
Emp.: 30
Insurance Agencies & Brokerages
N.A.I.C.S.: 524210
Mark Lautensack (Acct Mgr)
Carla A. Moradi (Exec VP-Ops &
Tech)

HUB TECHNICAL SERVICES
44 Norfolk Ave, South Easton, MA
02375
Tel.: (508) 238-9887
Web Site:
http://www.hubtechnical.com
Year Founded: 1992
Rev.: $10,500,000
Emp.: 32
Computer System Design Services
N.A.I.C.S.: 541512
Joe Lovetere (Pres)
Paul Shiff (VP-Sls)
Robert Germain (VP-Engrg)
Lori Slabine (Partner)

HUB TRUCK RENTAL CORP.
94 Gazza Blvd, Farmingdale, NY
11735
Tel.: (631) 391-1000
Web Site: https://www.hubtruck.com
Rev.: $22,835,444
Emp.: 130
Truck Leasing, Without Drivers
N.A.I.C.S.: 532120
Robert Slater (Owner)
Lynn Katz (Controller)
Donna Blanc (CFO)
Ken Tirone (VP-Ops)
Paul Lirosi (Dir-Maintenance)
Jennifer Gelber (Mgr-Insurance)
Ken Choisez (Mgr-Mgmt Info Sys)

**HUBBARD & DRAKE GEN-
ERAL CONTRACTOR**

1002 5th Ave SE, Decatur, AL 35601
Tel.: (256) 353-9244
Web Site:
http://www.hubbarddrake.com
Sales Range: $10-24.9 Million
Emp.: 68
Mechanical Contractor
N.A.I.C.S.: 238220
Jocelyn Hubbard (Controller)
Jeffrey D. Marksberry (VP-Risk Mgmt
& Bus Ops)

**HUBBARD BROADCASTING,
INC.**
3415 University Ave, Saint Paul, MN
55114-1019
Tel.: (651) 642-4656
Web Site:
http://www.hubbardbroadcas
ting.com
Year Founded: 1923
Holding Company; Television & Radio
Broadcasting Stations Owner & Op-
erator
N.A.I.C.S.: 551112
William Cress (Dir-IT)

Subsidiaries:

Hubbard Radio, LLC   (1)
3415 University Ave, Saint Paul, MN 55114
Tel.: (651) 642-4656
Web Site: http://www.hubbardradio.com
Radio Stations Administrator
N.A.I.C.S.: 561110
Ginny Morris (Chm & CEO)
Drew Horowitz (Pres & COO)
Dave Bestler (CFO & Exec VP)
Scott Mahalick (Mgr-Ops)
Jeremy Sinon (VP-Digital Strategy)
Steve SVP, Digital Sales Strategy (Sr VP-
Digital Sls Strategy)
Trip Reeb (VP-Phoenix & Seattle & Mgr-
Phoenix & Seattle)

Subsidiary (Domestic):

Hubbard Radio Cincinnati, LLC (2)
2060 Reading Rd, Cincinnati, OH 45202
Tel.: (513) 699-5100
Web Site:
http://www.corporate.hubbardradio.com
Sales Range: $1-9.9 Million
Emp.: 140
Radio Broadcasting Services
N.A.I.C.S.: 516110
Ginny Morris (Chm & CEO)
Mike Fredrick (VP)
Terry Dean (Mgr-New Bus Acct Dev)
Dave Bestler (CFO & Exec VP)
Greg Strassell (Sr VP-Programming)

Hubbard Radio St. Louis, LLC   (2)
11647 Olive Blvd, Saint Louis, MO 63141-
7001
Tel.: (314) 983-6000
Web Site:
http://www.corporate.hubbardradio.com
Radio Broadcasting Services
N.A.I.C.S.: 516110
Bruce T. Reese (Pres & CEO)
Charlie Quinn (Dir-Program)
Scott Roddy (Dir-Program-92.3 WIL)

Unit (Domestic):

KSHE-FM   (2)
11647 Olive Blvd, Saint Louis, MO 63141
Tel.: (314) 983-6000
Web Site: http://www.kshe95.com
Radio Broadcasting Services
N.A.I.C.S.: 516110

Subsidiary (Domestic):

KSTP-FM, LLC   (2)
3415 University Ave, Minneapolis, MN
55414   (100%)
Tel.: (651) 642-4141
Web Site: http://www.ks95.com
Sales Range: $25-49.9 Million
Emp.: 500
FM Radio Station
N.A.I.C.S.: 516110
Jeff Gonsales (Dir-Sls)

KAAL-TV LLC   (1)

1701 10th Pl NE, Austin, MN 55912
Tel.: (507) 437-6666
Web Site: http://www.kaaltv.com
Sales Range: $10-24.9 Million
Emp.: 100
Television Station
N.A.I.C.S.: 516120
David Harbert (Gen Mgr)

KOB-TV, Inc.   (1)
4 Broadcast Plz SW, Albuquerque, NM
87104-1000   (100%)
Tel.: (505) 243-4411
Web Site: http://www.kob.com
Sales Range: $25-49.9 Million
Emp.: 200
TV Station
N.A.I.C.S.: 516120
Robert W. Hubbard (Pres)
Michelle Donaldson (Gen Mgr)

KSAX-TV, Inc.   (1)
415 Fillmore St, Alexandria, MN 56308-
1320
Tel.: (320) 763-5729
Web Site: http://www.ksax.com
Sales Range: $10-24.9 Million
Emp.: 25
Television Station
N.A.I.C.S.: 516120

KSTC-TV, LLC   (1)
3415 University Ave W, Saint Paul, MN
55114-1019
Tel.: (651) 645-4500
Web Site: http://www.kstc45.com
Sales Range: $10-24.9 Million
Emp.: 25
Television Broadcaster
N.A.I.C.S.: 516120
Joe Johnston (Dir-Mktg)
Rob Hubbard (Pres & Gen Mgr)
Susan Wenz (Mgr-Station)
Monica Doyle (Dir-Ops)
Jo Ferguson (Mgr-Sls)
Ed Smith (Dir-Engrg)

KSTP-TV, LLC   (1)
3415 University Ave, Saint Paul, MN
55114-2099   (100%)
Tel.: (651) 646-5555
Web Site: http://www.kstp.com
Sales Range: $25-49.9 Million
Emp.: 220
Television Broadcaster
N.A.I.C.S.: 516120
Stanley S. Hubbard (Chm, Pres & CEO)
Robert W. Hubbard (Pres-TV)
Dixie Hansen (VP & Bus Mgr)
Suzanne Cook (VP-HR)
Paul Gaulke (Dir-Mktg)

WDIO-TV, LLC   (1)
10 Observation Rd, Duluth, MN 55811
Tel.: (218) 727-6864
Web Site: http://www.wdio.com
Sales Range: $10-24.9 Million
Emp.: 60
Television Broadcasting Station
N.A.I.C.S.: 516120
Dan Williamson (Dir-Sports)

WHEC-TV LLC   (1)
191 E Ave, Rochester, NY
14604-2605   (100%)
Tel.: (585) 546-5670
Web Site: http://www.whec.com
Sales Range: $10-24.9 Million
Emp.: 130
Television Station
N.A.I.C.S.: 517410
Lauren Burruto (Gen Mgr-Sls)
Shannon Steinber (Mgr-Digital Media)
Richard Reingold (VP & Gen Mgr)
Kevin Kalvitis (Dir-Mktg & Creative Svcs)

WNYT-TV   (1)
715 N Pearl St, Albany, NY 12204-1819
Tel.: (518) 436-4791
Web Site: http://www.wnyt.com
Sales Range: $10-24.9 Million
Emp.: 130
Television Broadcasting Station
N.A.I.C.S.: 516120
Stephen P. Baboulis (VP & Gen Mgr)
Tony McManus (Dir-Sls)
Steve Robbins (Dir-Ops & Digital Svcs)

HUBBARD CHEVROLET

2937 G St, Hubbard, OR 97032-9805
Tel.: (503) 981-9546
Web Site:
https://www.hubbardchevrolet.com
Sales Range: $10-24.9 Million
Emp.: 34
New Car Whslr
N.A.I.C.S.: 441110
Margie Buchholz (Office Mgr)

HUBBARD SUPPLY CO.
901 W 2nd St, Flint, MI 48503-2680
Tel.: (810) 234-8681
Web Site:
http://www.hubbardsupply.com
Year Founded: 1984
Sales Range: $10-24.9 Million
Emp.: 76
Industrial Supply Services
N.A.I.C.S.: 423840
Jeff Bigelow (CEO)
Tim Brooks (COO)
Bill Hohn (Mgr-Pur)
Dave Albee (Mgr-Sls)

HUBBARD-HALL, INC.
563 S Leonard St, Waterbury, CT
06708-4316
Tel.: (203) 756-5521
Web Site:
https://www.hubbardhall.com
Year Founded: 1849
Sales Range: $75-99.9 Million
Emp.: 121
Metal Finishing & Industrial Chemi-
cals, Semi-Conductor & Microelec-
tronic Chemicals; Specialty Chemi-
cals, Rust Inhibitors & Black Oxides
Mfr & Distr
N.A.I.C.S.: 424690

HUBBARDS
901 W Broadway St, Monticello, IN
47960
Tel.: (574) 583-7121
Sales Range: $10-24.9 Million
Emp.: 46
Car Whslr
N.A.I.C.S.: 441110
Dora Hubbard (COO)

HUBER & ASSOCIATES INC.
1400 Edgewood Dr, Jefferson City,
MO 65109
Tel.: (573) 634-5000
Web Site:
https://www.teamhuber.com
Rev.: $12,000,000
Emp.: 75
Computer Integrated Systems Design
N.A.I.C.S.: 541512
Jim Huber (Pres)
Elizabeth Huber (CEO)
Joan Rundle (Dir-Fin)

**HUBER INVESTMENT CORPO-
RATION**
5550 Huber Rd, Huber Heights, OH
45424
Tel.: (937) 233-1122
Rev.: $18,000,000
Emp.: 50
Residential Buildings
N.A.I.C.S.: 531110
Rich Williams (Controller)
Teresa J. Huber (CEO)
Jill Rarick (Office Mgr-Acctg)

HUBER SUPPLY CO. INC.
149 4th St SW, Mason City, IA 50401
Tel.: (641) 423-9115
Web Site:
https://www.hubersupply.com
Year Founded: 1939
Rev.: $7,900,000
Emp.: 18
Industrial Machinery & Equipment Mfr

N.A.I.C.S.: 423830
Doug Huber *(VP & Mgr)*
Loren P. Huber *(Pres & CEO)*

HUBER TIRE INC.
3215 Industrial Pkwy, Jeffersonville, IN 47130
Tel.: (812) 285-5400
Web Site: http://www.hubertire.com
Rev.: $11,200,000
Emp.: 38
Tire Dealers
N.A.I.C.S.: 441340
Thomas Sander *(Pres)*
Fred Ralston *(Treas & Sec)*

HUBERS INC.
4330 Crittenden Dr, Louisville, KY 40209
Tel.: (502) 366-3833
Sales Range: $50-74.9 Million
Emp.: 89
Sales & Rentals of New & Used Cars, Trucks, Tractors & Trailers
N.A.I.C.S.: 441110
Bob Iezzi *(Pres)*

HUBERT CONSTRUCTION
9055 Comprint Ct Ste 150, Gaithersburg, MD 20877
Tel.: (301) 721-9000
Web Site: https://www.hubertco.com
Year Founded: 1998
Sales Range: $50-74.9 Million
Emp.: 20
Construction Services
N.A.I.C.S.: 236220
Matt Shea *(Pres)*
Scott Hallam *(Exec VP)*
Chuck Clar *(VP-Bus Dev)*

HUBERT VESTER CHEVROLET
3717 Raleigh Rd Pkwy W, Wilson, NC 27896-9743
Tel.: (252) 360-1978
Year Founded: 2003
Sales Range: $10-24.9 Million
Emp.: 65
New Car Whslr
N.A.I.C.S.: 441110
Herb Nelson *(COO)*
Hubert Vester *(Pres)*
Kevin Schoen *(Gen Mgr)*

HUBERTY & ASSOCIATES, S.C.
145 S Marr St, Fond Du Lac, WI 54935
Tel.: (920) 923-8400
Web Site:
  http://www.hubertyandassociates.com
Year Founded: 1981
Sales Range: $1-9.9 Million
Emp.: 30
Accounting, Auditing & Bookkeeping
N.A.I.C.S.: 541211
Wayne N. Huberty *(Founder, Co-Owner & Pres)*
Ann Freund *(Co-Owner)*
Gary Born *(Co-Owner)*

HUBLER CHEVROLET INC.
8220 S US 31, Indianapolis, IN 46227-0991
Tel.: (317) 882-4389   IN
Web Site:
  https://www.hublerchevyauto.com
Year Founded: 1961
Sales Range: $125-149.9 Million
Emp.: 200
Provider of Automotive Sales & Service
N.A.I.C.S.: 441110
Brad Hubler *(Owner & Pres)*

HUBPER GROUP INC.
9454 Wilshire Blvd Ste 612, Los Angeles, CA 90212
Tel.: (310) 888-1870   DE
Year Founded: 2017
Investment Services
N.A.I.C.S.: 523999
James Cassidy *(Pres & Sec)*
James McKillop *(VP)*

HUBSHOUT, LLC
200 Little Falls St, Falls Church, VA 22046
Tel.: (888) 266-6432
Web Site: http://www.hubshout.com
Year Founded: 2008
Sales Range: $1-9.9 Million
Emp.: 25
Online Marketing Software & Services
N.A.I.C.S.: 541613
Chad Hill *(CEO)*
Adam Stetzer *(Co-Founder & Pres)*
Nicole Shein *(Editor-in-Chief)*
Renee Stetzer *(Mgr-PR)*

HUCKLE MEDIA, LLC.
514 Central Ave N, Faribault, MN 55021-4304
Tel.: (507) 333-3110
Emp.: 50
Newspaper Printing Services
N.A.I.C.S.: 513110
Julie Gehrig *(Mgr-Adv)*
Kevin Haekenkamp *(Controller)*
Liz Holt *(Mgr-Acctg & HR)*

HUDAK INSULATION, INC.
6200 Days Cove Rd Ste 5, White Marsh, MD 21162-1204
Tel.: (410) 238-2000
Web Site: https://www.hudaksco.com
Year Founded: 2007
Sales Range: $10-24.9 Million
Emp.: 92
Plastering Services
N.A.I.C.S.: 238310
James Hudak *(Owner)*

HUDDLE HOUSE, INC.
5901 Peachtree Dunwoody Ste 450, Atlanta, GA 30328
Tel.: (770) 325-1300   GA
Web Site:
  http://www.huddlehouse.com
Year Founded: 1964
Restaurant Operators
N.A.I.C.S.: 722511
Michael Abt *(CEO)*
Melissa Rothring *(Gen Counsel, Sec & Exec VP)*
Alison Delaney *(Chief Brand Officer)*

Subsidiaries:

Perkins LLC   (1)
6075 Poplar Ave Ste 800, Memphis, TN 38119
Tel.: (901) 766-6400
Web Site:
  http://www.perkinsrestaurants.com
Restaurant Franchise & Operation Services
N.A.I.C.S.: 722511
Jeffrey Warne *(Pres & CEO)*

HUDIBURG CHEVROLET BUICK GMC
6000 Tinker Diagonal, Midwest City, OK 73110
Tel.: (405) 737-6641
Year Founded: 1957
Sales Range: $10-24.9 Million
Emp.: 42
Car Whslr
N.A.I.C.S.: 441110

David Hudiburg *(Pres)*
Jim Patch *(Gen Mgr-Hudiburg Toyota)*
Jeff Robinson *(VP)*

HUDSON & KEYSE, LLC
Blackbrook Rd, Painesville, OH 44077
Tel.: (440) 354-6971
Year Founded: 1984
Sales Range: $10-24.9 Million
Emp.: 40
Debt Recovery Services
N.A.I.C.S.: 561440
Bob Deter *(Exec VP-Asset Mgmt)*
Bradley Shropshire *(VP-Collection Mgmt)*
Karen O'Neill *(Dir-Talent Acq & Dev & Retention)*
Francis A. Carroll *(CIO & VP)*
Nancy McMullin *(Mgr-Acq)*
Tim Novak *(Mgr-Debt Sls)*
Mary Tomaro *(Mgr-Credit Union Svc)*

HUDSON ADVISORS LLC
2711 N Haskell Ave Ste 1800, Dallas, TX 75204-2921
Tel.: (214) 754-8400
Web Site: https://www.hudson-advisors.com
Year Founded: 1995
Sales Range: $50-74.9 Million
Emp.: 150
Commericial Realty Company
N.A.I.C.S.: 523940
Jason Ziegler *(Asst VP-IT Infrastructure & Ops)*
Daniel Yanez *(VP)*
Miao Song *(VP-Fin Reporting)*
Shantay Warren *(Mgr-Bus Intelligence)*
Sheryl Smith *(Mgr-Projects)*
Dee Irish *(Asst Controller)*
Rebecca Williams *(Atty)*
Jose Cormane *(Mgr-Sys Engrg)*
Lisa M. Crutchfield *(Mng Principal)*

Subsidiaries:

Lake Jeanette Development Co   (1)
3987 N Elm St, Greensboro, NC 27455
Tel.: (336) 282-5253
Web Site: http://www.smithmarketinginc.com
Rev.: $10,000,000
Emp.: 17
Real Estate Agents & Managers
N.A.I.C.S.: 531210

HUDSON AUTO SOURCE
441 Blue River Pkwy, Silverthorne, CO 80498
Tel.: (970) 468-0391
Web Site:
  http://www.hudsonautosource.com
Year Founded: 1974
Sales Range: $10-24.9 Million
Emp.: 40
Car Whslr
N.A.I.C.S.: 441110
Lynne Hudson *(Principal)*
Marilyn Miller *(Comptroller)*

HUDSON BLVD. GROUP LLC
89 5th Ave Ste 308, New York, NY 10003
Tel.: (646) 360-1430   DE
Web Site:
  http://www.hudsonblvdgroup.com
Year Founded: 2016
Holding Company; Beauty Service
Brand Owner & Operator
N.A.I.C.S.: 551112
Robin Moraetes *(Founder & Pres)*

Subsidiaries:

Valley Nails LLC   (1)
198 Elizabeth St, New York, NY 10012
Tel.: (212) 274-8985

Web Site: http://www.valleynail.com
Nail Salons
N.A.I.C.S.: 812113

HUDSON CLEAN ENERGY PARTNERS
400 Frank W Burr Blvd Ste 37, Teaneck, NJ 07666
Tel.: (201) 287-4100
Web Site: http://www.hudsoncep.com
Year Founded: 2007
Rev.: $1,024,000,000
Emp.: 40
Privater Equity Firm
N.A.I.C.S.: 523999
Neil Z. Auerbach *(CEO & Mng Partner)*
Larry L. Henry *(Partner)*
Joseph E. Slamm *(Partner)*
Paul Ho *(Partner)*
Gabriel Miller *(Chief Scientific Officer)*
David Tuohy *(Partner-Operating)*
Wilson Chang *(Principal)*
Jonathan Lee *(VP)*
Jason Chen *(VP)*
Michael Kasper *(VP)*

HUDSON COMMUNITY ENTERPRISES
68-70 Tuers Ave, Jersey City, NJ 07306
Tel.: (201) 434-3303   NJ
Web Site:
  http://www.hudsoncommunity.org
Year Founded: 1957
Sales Range: $10-24.9 Million
Emp.: 877
Disability Assistance Services
N.A.I.C.S.: 624120
Joseph Brown *(Pres)*
Bernie Lane *(VP)*
Sal Coppola *(VP)*
Maureen Walliser *(VP)*

HUDSON CONSTRUCTION COMPANY
1615 Sholar Ave, Chattanooga, TN 37406
Tel.: (423) 624-2631
Web Site: https://www.hudsoncc.com
Sales Range: $50-74.9 Million
Emp.: 50
Commercial & Office Building, New Construction
N.A.I.C.S.: 236220
Mark Collins *(Sr Project Mgr-Comml)*

HUDSON FOOD STORES INCORPORATED
6150 NW 122nd Ln, Chiefland, FL 32626
Tel.: (352) 493-4292
Web Site:
  http://hudsonfoodstores.com
Sales Range: $10-24.9 Million
Emp.: 150
Convenience Store
N.A.I.C.S.: 445131
Jim Smith *(CFO)*
W. S. Smith *(Pres)*
Page Brookins *(Dir-Food Stores)*
Jim Smith *(CFO)*

HUDSON HEADWATERS HEALTH NETWORK
9 Carey Rd, Queensbury, NY 12804
Tel.: (518) 761-0300   NY
Web Site: http://www.hhhn.org
Year Founded: 1981
Sales Range: $50-74.9 Million
Emp.: 776
Community Health Care Services
N.A.I.C.S.: 621498
Christopher C. Tournier *(CFO & Exec VP-Fin)*

Hudson Headwaters Health Network—(Continued)

Edward J. Shannon (Chief Dev Officer)
John Rugge (Founder & CEO)
David Slingerland (Deputy CEO)
Cathy Moses (Sec)
Ike Wolgin (Vice Chm)
Eugene Arsenault (Treas)
Barbara Sweet (Chm)
John Sawyer (Chief Medical Officer)
Paul Bachman (Co-Chief Medical Officer)
Deborah Bardin (VP-Health Center Ops)
William Borgos (VP-Medical Staff Ops)
James Donnelly (VP-Pharmacy Svcs)
Lori Gravelle (Chief Compliance Officer & VP-Staff Dev & Risk Mgmt)
Daniel C. Larson (Co-Chief Medical Officer)
Cyndi Nassivera-Reynolds (VP-Transformation & Clinical Quality)
George Purdue (Chief Admin Officer & Exec VP)
Nick Rebmann (VP-Health Center Performance)
Angela Petrone (VP-Compliance, Provider Support & Risk)
John Dudla (CIO)
Amy Bloom (Exec VP-Network Strategy)
Rich Valmore (Dir-Info Technologies)
Stacy Smith (Dir-Integrated Svcs)
Maureen Poole (VP-Nursing)
Jill Guillet (Chief Compliance Officer & VP-Compliance)
Sue Corney (Exec VP-HR)

HUDSON HILL CAPITAL LLC
609 Greenwich St, New York, NY 10014
Tel.: (212) 551-4690
Web Site:
  https://www.hudsonhillcapital.com
Year Founded: 2015
Privater Equity Firm
N.A.I.C.S.: 523999
Eric J. Rosen (Mng Partner)
Alexander Stacy (Partner)
Jason Palmatary (Partner)
Becca Schneider (Dir-Ops)

Subsidiaries:

Fusion Transport, LLC   (1)
301 NJ-17, Rutherford, NJ 07070
Tel.: (800) 599-2977
Web Site: https://www.fusiontransport.com
Logistic Services
N.A.I.C.S.: 541614
Daniel Colonna (VP-Logistics)

Subsidiary (Domestic):

Am Trans Expedite, Inc.   (2)
710 W Belden Ave, Addison, IL 60101
Tel.: (847) 238-9999
Web Site: http://www.amtransexpedite.com
Logistics & Warehousing Services
N.A.I.C.S.: 484121

Global Transport Logistics, Inc.   (2)
208 Harristown Rd, Glen Rock, NJ 07452
Tel.: (201) 251-7333
Web Site: https://www.gtli.net
Freight Transportation Arrangement Services
N.A.I.C.S.: 484121

HUDSON HOME HEALTH CARE INC.
151 Rockwell Rd, Newington, CT 06111
Tel.: (860) 666-7500
Web Site:
  http://www.hudsonmobility.com
Sales Range: $10-24.9 Million
Emp.: 100

Medical Apparatus & Supplies
N.A.I.C.S.: 456199
Shirley Curley (Pres)
Ed Curley (Vp)

HUDSON HORIZONS, INC.
299 Market St 3rd Fl, Saddle Brook, NJ 07663
Tel.: (201) 845-8700
Web Site:
  http://www.hudsonhorizons.com
Sales Range: $1-9.9 Million
Emp.: 26
Website Development & Search Engine Optimization
N.A.I.C.S.: 541519
Daryl H. Bryant (Pres & CEO)
Matt Mayernik (VP-Tech)
Rania Eldekki (Mgr-Internet Mktg)
Jeff Matta (VP-Bus Dev)

HUDSON INC.
Hwy 11 S, Ellisville, MS 39437
Tel.: (601) 477-4951
Web Site:
  http://www.hudsonsalvage.com
Year Founded: 1938
Sales Range: $10-24.9 Million
Emp.: 50
Variety Stores
N.A.I.C.S.: 455219
Mickey Hudson (Pres)

HUDSON INDUSTRIES INC.
5250 Klockner Dr, Richmond, VA 23231
Tel.: (804) 226-1155
Web Site:
  http://www.hudsonindustries.com
Year Founded: 1976
Sales Range: $10-24.9 Million
Emp.: 120
Mfr of Plastic Foam Products
N.A.I.C.S.: 326150
Gary C. Hudson (Pres)

HUDSON MEDIA SERVICES LLC
232 Madison Ave Ste 605, New York, NY 10016
Tel.: (212) 448-9741
Web Site: http://www.hudson-media.com
Year Founded: 2009
Sales Range: $10-24.9 Million
Emp.: 2
Media Buying Services
N.A.I.C.S.: 541830
Ed Weiner (CEO)
Jeremy Weiner (VP)

HUDSON PONTIAC BUICK GMC TRUCK INC.
2023 South Rd, Poughkeepsie, NY 12601
Tel.: (845) 298-4700
Year Founded: 1995
Sales Range: $10-24.9 Million
Emp.: 35
Car Whslr
N.A.I.C.S.: 441110
Michael Mullaney (Pres)

HUDSON RIVER HEALTH-CARE, INC.
1200 Brown St, Peekskill, NY 10566
Tel.: (844) 474-2273   NY
Web Site: http://www.hrhcare.org
Year Founded: 1975
Sales Range: $100-124.9 Million
Emp.: 864
Health Care Srvices
N.A.I.C.S.: 622110
Carmen Chinea (Chief Medical Officer)
Anne Kauffman Nolon (Pres & CEO)

Jeanette Phillips (Exec VP-Community Dev)
Allison Dubois (COO)
Paul Kaye (Exec VP-Practice Transformation)
Luke Hilpert (Sec)
Norma Johnson (Vice Chm)
Alan Steiner (Chm)
Andrew S. Richter (Treas)
Clifford Hames (Chief Dental Officer, Chief Infection Control Officer & VP)
James D. Sinkoff (CFO & Exec VP-Bus & Informational Svcs)

Subsidiaries:

Brightpoint Health, Inc.   (1)
71 W 23rd St 8th Fl, New York, NY 10010
Tel.: (855) 681-8700
Web Site: http://www.brightpointhealth.org
Health Care Srvices
N.A.I.C.S.: 622110
Charlene Butterfield (Sec)
James D. Cameron (Treas)
John Russell (Chm)

HUDSON SALVAGE INC.
6892 US Hwy 49, Ellisville, MS 39402-9135
Tel.: (601) 268-7555   MS
Web Site:
  http://www.hudsonsalvage.com
Year Founded: 1991
Sales Range: $25-49.9 Million
Emp.: 900
Consumer Goods
N.A.I.C.S.: 455219
Bill C. Hudson (Pres)
Rich Preusch (CFO)

HUDSON TANK TERMINALS CORPORATION
173 Export St, Newark, NJ 07114
Tel.: (973) 465-1115
Rev.: $14,772,201
Emp.: 44
Equipment Rental & Leasing
N.A.I.C.S.: 532490
Albert F. Mogerley (Pres)
Liam Rogers (VP)

HUDSON TRAIL OUTFITTERS LTD.
8525 Atlas Dr, Gaithersburg, MD 20877
Tel.: (301) 840-0650
Web Site: http://www.hudsontrail.com
Sales Range: $10-24.9 Million
Emp.: 40
Sporting Goods & Bicycle Shops
N.A.I.C.S.: 459110
Susan Strain (CFO)

HUDSON VALLEY CREDIT UNION
Tel.: (845) 463-3011
Web Site: https://www.hvcu.org
Emp.: 100
Credit Union
N.A.I.C.S.: 522130

HUDSON VALLEY ECONOMIC DEVELOPMENT CORPORA-TION
42 Catharine St, Poughkeepsie, NY 12601
Tel.: (845) 220-2244
Web Site: https://www.hvedc.com
Year Founded: 2003
Business Relocation & Expansion Related Consulting Services Provider
N.A.I.C.S.: 541618
Mike Oates (Pres & CEO)
Brian Gates (Sr VP)

Subsidiaries:

Westchester County Association, Inc.   (1)
1133 Westchester Ave Ste S-217, White Plains, NY 10604
Tel.: (914) 948-6444
Web Site: http://www.westchester.org
Rev.: $1,757,388
Assets: $393,761
Liabilities: $280,537
Net Worth: $113,224
Earnings: ($1,817)
Emp.: 10
Fiscal Year-end: 12/31/2013
Community Development Services
N.A.I.C.S.: 624190
Monica Ortiz (Fin Mgr)
Amy Allen (VP)
Julia Emrick (Mng Dir-Ops & Events)
William Mooney Jr. (CEO)

HUDSONYARDS
80 Broad St 26th Fl, New York, NY 10004
Tel.: (212) 716-6600
Web Site: http://www.hynyc.com
Emp.: 200
Advetising Agency
N.A.I.C.S.: 541810
Diane Romano (Pres & CEO)
Mary Cluney (CFO & VP)
John A. Regina (Sr VP-Major Accts)
Mark Potter (Exec VP-Sls & Mktg)

HUEY STOCKSTILL, INC.
130 Huey Stockstill Rd, Picayune, MS 39466
Tel.: (601) 798-2981
Web Site:
  https://www.hueystockstill.com
Sales Range: $25-49.9 Million
Emp.: 180
Highway & Street Paving Contracting Services
N.A.I.C.S.: 237310
Richard Stockstill (Pres)
David Stockstill (Owner & Partner)

HUF NORTH AMERICA AUTO-MOTIVE PARTS MANUFAC-TURING CORP.
395 T Elmer Cox Rd, Greeneville, TN 37743-3034
Tel.: (423) 787-8500   TN
Web Site: http://www.huf-group.com
Year Founded: 1995
Sales Range: $25-49.9 Million
Emp.: 350
Motor Vehicle Parts & Accessories
N.A.I.C.S.: 336390
Laura Rosenberg (Engr-Logistics)
Jerry Waybright (Mgr-Engrg)
Shane Patterson (Mgr-Production)

HUFF PAPER COMPANY INC.
10 Creek Pkwy, Boothwyn, PA 19061-3146
Tel.: (610) 497-5100   PA
Web Site:
  http://www.huffunitedpaper.com
Year Founded: 1977
Sales Range: $10-24.9 Million
Emp.: 115
Industrial & Personal Paper Services
N.A.I.C.S.: 424100
Fred Hilbert (VP-Ops)

HUFFINES AUTO GROUP
4500 W Plano Pkwy, Plano, TX 75093
Tel.: (972) 867-6000   TX
Web Site: http://www.huffines.net
Year Founded: 1924
Sales Range: $600-649.9 Million
Emp.: 600

Holding Company; New & Used Automobile Dealerships Owner & Operator
N.A.I.C.S.: 551112
S. Ray Huffines *(Pres & CEO)*
Eric Harter *(CFO)*
Rebecca Baker *(Dir-HR)*

Subsidiaries:

Huffines Chevrolet Lewisville   **(1)**
1400 S Stemmons Fwy, Lewisville, TX 75067
Tel.: (972) 597-2005
Web Site:
    http://www.huffineschevylewisville.com
Sales Range: $125-149.9 Million
Emp.: 300
New Car Whslr
N.A.I.C.S.: 441110
Ray Huffines *(CEO)*
Fred Whitfield *(Mgr-Fleet & Bus Rels)*
Eric Tanner *(Mgr-Fin)*
Ray Belfakih *(Dir-Fin)*
Gary Benner *(Mgr-Parts)*
Allen Moore *(Dir-Svc)*

Huffines Chrysler Jeep Kia
Denton   **(1)**
5150 S Interstate 35 E, Denton, TX 76210
Tel.: (972) 434-3090
Web Site: http://www.huffineskiacorinth.com
Sales Range: $10-24.9 Million
Emp.: 60
Car Whslr
N.A.I.C.S.: 441110
Robert Goodwin *(Gen Mgr)*

Huffines Chrysler Plymouth, Inc.   **(1)**
909 Coit Rd, Plano, TX 75086
Tel.: (972) 867-5000
Sales Range: $25-49.9 Million
Emp.: 119
Car Whslr
N.A.I.C.S.: 441110
Ray Huffines *(Pres)*

Huffines Dodge Plano, L.P.   **(1)**
4500 W Plano Pkwy, Plano, TX 75093
Tel.: (972) 867-6000
Web Site:
    http://www.huffineschryslerjeepdodge
    ramplano.com
New & Used Care Dealer
N.A.I.C.S.: 441110
Scott Millsap *(Gen Mgr & Dir-Sls)*
Charlie H. Hale *(Mgr-PreOwned Sls)*
Stewart Cloer *(Dir-New Car Internet)*
Robert Cotton *(Mgr-New Car)*
Eddy Erangey *(Mgr-New Car)*
Tony Lee *(Mgr-Credit Union)*
Zach Stanley *(Mgr-Fin)*

Huffines Hyundai McKinney, LP   **(1)**
1301 N Central Expy, McKinney, TX 75070
Tel.: (469) 525-4300
Web Site:
    http://www.huffineshyundaimckinney.com
Sales Range: $1-9.9 Million
Emp.: 28
New & Used Car Dealer
N.A.I.C.S.: 441110
S. Ray Huffines *(Pres)*

HUFFMAN & WRIGHT LOGGING INC.
801 SE 3rd St, Canyonville, OR 97417
Tel.: (541) 839-4251
Web Site: http://www.huffman-wright.com
Rev.: $28,000,000
Emp.: 125
General Contractor, Highway & Street Construction
N.A.I.C.S.: 237310
Roger W. Wright *(Pres)*

HUFFMAN OIL CO., INC.
1021 Queen Ann St, Burlington, NC 27217-7040
Tel.: (336) 227-8881   NC
Web Site: http://www.huffmanoil.com
Year Founded: 1966
Sales Range: $50-74.9 Million

Emp.: 450
Provider of Petroleum Services
N.A.I.C.S.: 424720
Sharon Braxton *(VP-Fin)*

HUFFY CORPORATION
8877 Gander Creek Dr, Miamisburg, OH 45342
Tel.: (937) 865-2800   OH
Web Site: https://www.huffybikes.com
Year Founded: 1928
Sales Range: $400-449.9 Million
Emp.: 110
Bicycles, Basketball Equipment, Product Assembly Mfr & Merchandising & Inventory Services
N.A.I.C.S.: 339920
Nancy Michaud *(Gen Counsel, Sec & Sr VP)*
William A. Smith *(Pres & Gen Mgr)*
Steven D. Lipton *(CFO)*
Ray Thomson *(VP-Mktg)*

Subsidiaries:

Huffy Bicycle Company   **(1)**
6551 Centerville Business Pkwy, Centerville, OH 45459   **(100%)**
Tel.: (937) 865-2800
Web Site: http://www.huffy.com
Sales Range: $10-24.9 Million
Emp.: 60
Bicycle Mfr
N.A.I.C.S.: 336991

HUGG & HALL EQUIPMENT COMPANY
7201 Scott Hamilton Dr, Little Rock, AR 72209
Tel.: (501) 562-1262
Web Site: https://www.hugghall.com
Year Founded: 1970
Sales Range: $50-74.9 Million
Emp.: 500
Construction & Industrial Equipment Whslr; Rentals, Servicing & Parts Dealer
N.A.I.C.S.: 423830
John C. Hugg *(Co-Owner)*
Robert Hall *(Co-Owner)*
Kevin Keith *(Mgr-Sls-Heavy Construction)*
Tim Waychoff *(Mgr-Sls-Little Rock Sls)*
Chris Shields *(VP-Parts & Svc)*
Jim Hancock *(Mgr-Sls-Light Construction)*
Andy Mays *(Mgr-Sls-Houma Sls)*
Tom Mitchell *(Reg Dir-Parts)*

Subsidiaries:

Southern Material Handling Co.   **(1)**
8118 E 44th St, Tulsa, OK 74145
Tel.: (918) 622-7200
Web Site: http://www.southernmaterial.com
Sales Range: $10-24.9 Million
Emp.: 60
Equipment Rental & Leasing
N.A.I.C.S.: 423830
Mark Segress *(Pres & CEO)*
Mark Matthews *(Controller)*
Gayla Banes *(Office Mgr)*
Terry Milan *(Mgr-Allied Sls)*

HUGGER MUGGER YOGA PRODUCTS LLC
1190 S Pioneer Rd, Salt Lake City, UT 84104
Tel.: (801) 268-9642
Web Site:
    http://www.huggermugger.com
Rev.: $10,000,000
Emp.: 30
Yoga Products Including Clothing, Equipment & Related Accessories Mfr
N.A.I.C.S.: 339920
Tom Chamberlain *(Pres)*

HUGHES ENTERPRISES INC.

300 W N Ave, Lombard, IL 60148
Tel.: (630) 932-4700
Year Founded: 1958
Sales Range: $25-49.9 Million
Emp.: 136
Laundry Equipment & Supplies
N.A.I.C.S.: 423850
Gordon S. Hughes *(Pres)*

HUGHES FURNITURE INDUSTRIES INC.
952 Stout St, Randleman, NC 27317-0486
Tel.: (336) 498-8700   NC
Web Site:
    https://www.hughesfurniture.com
Year Founded: 1990
Sales Range: $25-49.9 Million
Emp.: 337
Upholstered Household Furniture Mfr
N.A.I.C.S.: 337121
Bruce Hughs *(CEO)*
Terri Lynn Brown *(Mgr-Credit)*

HUGHES GROUP LLC
3701 S Lawrence St, Tacoma, WA 98409
Tel.: (253) 588-2626
Web Site:
    http://www.hughesgroup.biz
Year Founded: 1999
Sales Range: $1-9.9 Million
Emp.: 213
Logistic Services
N.A.I.C.S.: 488510
Patrick Hughes *(CEO)*

HUGHES GROUP, INC.
6200 E Hwy 62 Bldg 2501 Ste 100, Jeffersonville, IN 47130
Tel.: (812) 282-4393   IN
General Contractor; Highway, Coal Mining, Asphalt
N.A.I.C.S.: 551112
Mark Burdick *(CFO)*

Subsidiaries:

American Contracting & Services Inc.   **(1)**
6200 E Hwy 62 Building 2503, Jeffersonville, IN 47130-3106
Tel.: (812) 280-4404
Web Site:
    http://www.americancontracting.com
Sales Range: $10-24.9 Million
Heavy Construction
N.A.I.C.S.: 237110
Mark Burrick *(CFO)*

Hydro Technologies, Inc.   **(1)**
6200 E Hwy 62 Ste 300 Bldg 2501, Jeffersonville, IN 47130   **(100%)**
Tel.: (812) 284-9376
Web Site:
    http://www.hydrotechnologies.com
Sales Range: $10-24.9 Million
Emp.: 30
Wrecking & Demolition Work
N.A.I.C.S.: 238910
Jeff Hughes *(Pres)*
Robin Rosenburger *(Controller)*

Modified Concrete Suppliers Inc.   **(1)**
140 Neal Ave, Indianapolis, IN 46222-4529
Tel.: (317) 634-5258
Sales Range: $10-24.9 Million
Emp.: 17
Brick, Stone & Related Material
N.A.I.C.S.: 423320

HUGHES HUBBARD & REED LLP
1 Battery Park Plz Fl 12, New York, NY 10004-1482
Tel.: (503) 597-7690
Web Site:
    https://www.hugheshubbard.com
Year Founded: 1925
Sales Range: $250-299.9 Million
Emp.: 300

Law firm
N.A.I.C.S.: 541199
Candace Krugman Beinecke *(Sr Partner)*
Gerard F. Cruse *(COO)*
Ned H. Bassen *(Partner)*
Andrew H. Braiterman *(Partner)*
William J. Kolasky *(Partner-Washington)*
James Dabney *(Partner)*
Stephen S. Rabinowitz *(Partner)*
James Boykin *(Partner)*
Melissa Duffy *(Partner)*
Robert B. Bell *(Partner-Washington)*
Dean Pinkert *(Partner-Intl Trade Grp-Washington)*
Ted Mayer *(Chm)*
Amanda DeBusk *(Chm-Trade Grp)*
Parker Taylor *(Partner-Trusts & Estates Practice Grp-Miami & New York)*
Joanne Osendarp *(Chm-Trade Practice-Intl)*

HUGHES LUMBER COMPANY
5611 Bird Creek Ave, Catoosa, OK 74015
Tel.: (918) 266-9100
Web Site:
    https://www.hugheslumber.net
Sales Range: $10-24.9 Million
Emp.: 90
Lumber & Other Building Materials
N.A.I.C.S.: 423310
Tammy Rubuen *(Controller)*
Robert Hughes *(Pres)*
Thomas J. Hughes III *(CEO)*

HUGHES MACHINERY COMPANY
14400 College Blvd, Lenexa, KS 66215-2063
Tel.: (913) 492-0355
Web Site:
    http://www.hughesmachinery.com
Rev.: $10,880,922
Emp.: 23
Boilers, Power (Industrial)
N.A.I.C.S.: 423720
Raymond Miller *(Plant Mgr-Fabrication)*

HUGHES MOTORS INC.
6841 Bulldog Dr, North Charleston, SC 29406
Tel.: (843) 553-6410
Web Site: http://www.volvotrucks.com
Rev.: $18,526,012
Emp.: 75
New & Used Car Dealers
N.A.I.C.S.: 441110
Julian Garris *(Mgr-Svcs)*
X. O. Bunch Jr. *(Chm)*

HUGHES OIL CO. INC.
177 Wells Ave, Newton Center, MA 02459
Tel.: (617) 327-4600   MA
Web Site: http://www.hughesoil.com
Year Founded: 1934
Sales Range: $10-24.9 Million
Emp.: 50
Fuel Oil Distr
N.A.I.C.S.: 457210
Diane Horan-Rodier *(VP-Admin)*
Richard T. Horan Jr. *(Pres)*

HUGHES POOLS INC.
658 N Eastern Blvd, Montgomery, AL 36117
Tel.: (334) 270-5800   AL
Web Site:
    https://www.hughespools.com
Year Founded: 1952
Sales Range: $10-24.9 Million

Hughes Pools Inc.—(Continued)

Emp.: 15
Provider of Swimming Pool Construction
N.A.I.C.S.: 238990
Carroll Hughes *(Pres)*

HUGHES RELOCATION SERVICE INC.

5900 N Cannon Ave, Lansdale, PA 19446
Tel.: (215) 345-0234
Web Site:
  https://www.hughesrelo.com
Year Founded: 1982
Rev.: $17,168,399
Emp.: 150
General Warehousing
N.A.I.C.S.: 484110
Robert Hughes *(Pres)*
Jim McCloskey *(Controller)*

HUGHES-ANDERSON HEAT EXCHANGERS

1001 N Fulton Ave, Tulsa, OK 74115
Tel.: (918) 836-1681
Web Site:
  https://www.hughesanderson.com
Year Founded: 1971
Sales Range: $10-24.9 Million
Emp.: 130
Heat Exchangers Coolers & Condensors
N.A.I.C.S.: 332410
Monte B. Stewart *(Pres)*
Jim Harrison *(VP-Engrg)*
Michael Kindschi *(Mgr-Thermal Engrg & DP)*
Mike Longo *(VP & Controller)*

HUGHESLEAHYKARLOVIC, INC.

1141 S 7th St, Saint Louis, MO 63104
Tel.: (314) 571-6300   MO
Web Site: https://www.hlkagency.com
Year Founded: 1977
Sales Range: $25-49.9 Million
Emp.: 50
Advertising Agencies
N.A.I.C.S.: 541810
Joe Leahy *(Chief Creative Officer)*

HUGHEY & PHILLIPS, LLC

240 W Twain Ave, Urbana, OH 43078
Tel.: (937) 652-3500   OH
Web Site:
  https://www.hugheyandphillips.com
Obsstruction Lighting Equipment & Airport Products Mfr
N.A.I.C.S.: 335139
James Sullivan *(VP-Sls & Mktg)*
Jeff Jacobs *(Dir-Technical Sls & Support)*
Dale E. Jessick *(Pres)*

Subsidiaries:

Manairco, Inc.   (1)
28 Mansfield Indus Pkwy, Mansfield, OH 44903
Tel.: (419) 524-2121
Web Site: http://www.manairco.com
Airfield Lighting Systems & Accessories Mfr
N.A.I.C.S.: 335139
Gayle Gorman Green *(Pres)*
Sheila Copeland *(Ops Mgr)*

TowerSentry LLC   (1)
2720 Industrial Park Dr, Lakeland, FL 33801
Tel.: (863) 667-1006
Web Site: http://www.towersentry.com
Sales Range: $1-9.9 Million
Emp.: 10
Tower Light Monitoring Services
N.A.I.C.S.: 541350
Rodger Roth *(Founder & CEO)*
Brian Roth *(Gen Mgr)*

HUGHSON NUT, INCORPORATED

1825 Verduga Rd, Hughson, CA 95326
Tel.: (209) 883-0403
Web Site:
  http://www.hughsonnut.com
Year Founded: 1985
Sales Range: $10-24.9 Million
Emp.: 300
Crop Harvesting & Farming Services
N.A.I.C.S.: 115113
Martin Pohl *(Owner)*
Barry Baker *(Owner)*
Byron Baker *(Owner)*
Ty Angle *(Owner)*

HUGO BOSCA COMPANY, INC.

1905 W Jefferson St, Springfield, OH 45506
Tel.: (937) 323-5523   OH
Web Site: https://www.bosca.com
Year Founded: 1911
Sales Range: $75-99.9 Million
Emp.: 35
Small Leather Goods Mfr
N.A.I.C.S.: 316990
Christopher Bosca *(Pres & CEO)*

HUGO DUNHILL MAILING LISTS, INC.

542 Main St 4th Fl, New Rochelle, NY 10801   DE
Web Site: http://www.hdml.com
Year Founded: 1975
Sales Range: $1-9.9 Million
Emp.: 25
Direct Mail Advertising Services
N.A.I.C.S.: 541860
Adam Dunhill *(Pres)*

HUGO NEU CORPORATION

120 5th Ave Ste 600, New York, NY 10011
Tel.: (646) 467-6700
Web Site: https://www.hugoneu.com
Year Founded: 1947
Sales Range: $10-24.9 Million
Emp.: 20
Provider of Metals Services
N.A.I.C.S.: 423510
Wendy Kelman Neu *(Chm & CEO)*
Vanessa Stoffels *(Asst Gen Counsel)*
Irma Redwood *(Mgr)*
Pete Kelman *(VP-Bus Dev)*
Steve Nislick *(CFO)*
Alan Ratner *(Pres-Recycling)*

Subsidiaries:

Hugo Neu-Proler Co.   (1)
901 New Dock St, San Pedro, CA 90731-7539
Tel.: (323) 775-6626
Scrap Metal Processors; Joint Venture Between Proler International Corp. & Hugo Neu & Sons, Inc.
N.A.I.C.S.: 423930

HUHOT MONGOLIAN GRILLS, LLC

223 E Main St, Missoula, MT 59802
Tel.: (406) 251-4303   MT
Web Site: https://www.huhot.com
Year Founded: 1999
Sales Range: $1-9.9 Million
Emp.: 2,400
Mongolian Style Barbecue Restaurants Operator & Franchisor
N.A.I.C.S.: 722511
Andrew Vap *(Founder, Pres & CEO)*

HUHTALA OIL & TEMPLETON GARAGE

198 Patriots Rd, East Templeton, MA 01438
Tel.: (978) 632-1221   MA

Web Site: https://www.huhtalaoil.com
Year Founded: 1945
Sales Range: $10-24.9 Million
Emp.: 50
Sellers of Fuel Oil
N.A.I.C.S.: 457210
David Huhtala *(Pres)*
Paul Huhtala *(VP & Controller)*

HUI HULIAU

PO Box 587, Waianae, HI 96792-3118
Tel.: (808) 216-4241
Web Site: http://www.huihuliau.com
Year Founded: 2011
Native Hawaiian Organization
N.A.I.C.S.: 813410
Adrian Nakea Silva *(Founder & Chm)*
Deryl Wright *(CEO)*
Terry Clark *(Pres)*
Jane Sharrock *(VP-Corp Ops)*
Mark Baines *(COO)*

Subsidiaries:

Advanced C4 Solutions, Inc.   (1)
4017 W Dr Martin Luther King Jr Blvd, Tampa, FL 33614
Tel.: (813) 282-3031
Web Site: http://www.ac4s.com
Converged IP & Cyber Services; Professional Services
N.A.I.C.S.: 541690
Hugh S. Campbell *(Co-Founder & Co-CEO)*
Norm Abdallah *(Co-Founder & Co-CEO)*
Pauline McPhail *(CFO & VP-Fin)*
William Savage *(VP-Ops)*
William H. Hogan *(Sr VP-Bus Dev)*

HUITT-ZOLLARS, INC.

1717 McKinney Ave Ste 1400, Dallas, TX 75202-1236
Tel.: (214) 871-3311   TX
Web Site: http://www.huitt-zollars.com
Year Founded: 1975
Sales Range: $350-399.9 Million
Emp.: 700
Engineering, Architecture, Planning & Construction Management Services
N.A.I.C.S.: 541330
Robert L. Zollars *(Chm)*
Robert J. McDermott *(Pres)*
Mark Gavan *(Principal & VP)*
Stephanie M. Stanford *(VP-Land Dev Practice)*
Joel S. Colwell *(VP & Natl Dir-Healthcare)*

Subsidiaries:

Gavan & Barker, Inc.   (1)
3030 N Central Ave Ste 1530, Phoenix, AZ 85012
Tel.: (602) 200-0031
Web Site: http://www.gavanbarker.com
Engineering & Landscape Architecture Services
N.A.I.C.S.: 541330
John Barker *(Co-Partner)*

Morris Architects, Inc.   (1)
1001 Fannin Ste 4040, Houston, TX 77002
Tel.: (713) 622-1180
Web Site: http://www.morrisarchitects.com
Sales Range: $50-74.9 Million
Emp.: 200
Architecture, Landscape Architecture, Planning & Interior Design Services
N.A.I.C.S.: 541310
James H. Pope *(Principal & Dir-Plng & Entertainment Studio)*

HUIXINJIA CAPITAL GROUP, INC.

244 5th Ave Ste 2, New York, NY 10001
Tel.: (718) 215-9277   NY
Year Founded: 2019
Emp.: 250
Financial Investment Services
N.A.I.C.S.: 523940

Liu Xia *(Pres)*

HUIZENGA HOLDINGS, INC.

7900 Glades Rd Ste 402, Boca Raton, FL 33434
Tel.: (954) 627-5000   FL
Year Founded: 1984
Sales Range: $25-49.9 Million
Emp.: 25
Investment Holding Company
N.A.I.C.S.: 551112
H. Wayne Huizenga *(Chm)*
Ed Borgert *(Mgr-Property)*
Robert Henninger *(Exec VP)*
H. Wayne Huizenga Jr. *(Pres)*
Richard L. Handley *(Sr VP)*

HUIZENGA MANUFACTURING GROUP, INC.

3755 36th St SE Ste 200, Grand Rapids, MI 49512
Tel.: (616) 957-0398   MI
Web Site:
  http://www.huizengagroup.com
Year Founded: 1985
Sales Range: $150-199.9 Million
Emp.: 1,000
Holding Company
N.A.I.C.S.: 551112
Michael J. Brom *(CFO)*
J. C. Huizenga *(Founder & Chm)*
Stephen J. Klotz *(Pres & CEO)*

Subsidiaries:

ASCOM-HG, LLC   (1)
11925 James St, Holland, MI 49425
Tel.: (616) 538-9850
Web Site: http://www.ascominc.com
Sales Range: $1-9.9 Million
Emp.: 45
Commercial & Institutional Facility Communications & Audio Equipment Installation Contractor
N.A.I.C.S.: 238210
Frederic Billin *(Pres)*

Bulldog Automation, LLC   (1)
25880 Commerce Dr, Madison Heights, MI 48071-4151
Tel.: (248) 541-3500
Web Site: https://www.santannatool.com
Conveyor & Conveying Equipment Mfr
N.A.I.C.S.: 333922
Joseph Newton *(Pres)*

Subsidiary (Domestic):

Spectrum Automation Company   (2)
34447 Schoolcraft Rd, Livonia, MI 48150
Tel.: (734) 522-2160
Web Site:
  http://www.spectrumautomation.com
Sales Range: $1-9.9 Million
Emp.: 20
Conveyors And Conveying Equipment, Nsk
N.A.I.C.S.: 333922

Datum Industries, LLC   (1)
4740 44th St SE, Grand Rapids, MI 49512
Tel.: (616) 977-1995
Web Site: http://www.datumindustries.com
Sales Range: $1-9.9 Million
Emp.: 100
Medium to Large Line Die & Tool Mfr
N.A.I.C.S.: 333514

Monroe, LLC   (1)
4490 44th St SE, Grand Rapids, MI 49512
Tel.: (616) 942-9820
Web Site: http://www.monroeproducts.com
Sales Range: $25-49.9 Million
Emp.: 300
Precision Molded Plastic Components Mfr
N.A.I.C.S.: 333514
Michael Plont *(Mgr-HR)*

Parkway Electric & Communications LLC   (1)
11952 James St, Holland, MI 49424
Tel.: (616) 392-2788
Web Site: http://www.parkwayelectric.com
Sales Range: $25-49.9 Million
Emp.: 100

Power, Communications & Controls Contractor
N.A.I.C.S.: 238210
Michael J. Brom (CFO)
Doug Mitchell (Pres)
Jennifer Breymeyer (Controller)
Jeff Pratt (Mgr-Ops)
Gary Zandstra (Mgr-Mktg)
Steve Driesenga (Mgr-Ops)

Sixarp LLC (1)
7650 Caterpillar Ct SW Ste D, Grand Rapids, MI 49548
Tel.: (616) 827-8525
Web Site: http://www.praxispackaging.com
Sales Range: $10-24.9 Million
Emp.: 250
Packaging Services
N.A.I.C.S.: 561910
Scott Hanner (Sr VP)

HULETT BANCORP
133 Main St, Hulett, WY 82720
Tel.: (307) 225-9175
Web Site:
https://www.modeeleven.com
Year Founded: 1984
Emp.: 100
Banking Services & Cryptocurrency
N.A.I.C.S.: 522110

Subsidiaries:

Summit National Bank (1)
133 Main St, Hulett, WY 82720
Tel.: (307) 467-5261
Web Site: http://www.summitnb.com
Rev.: $2,443,000
Emp.: 23
Commercial Banking
N.A.I.C.S.: 522110
Clarence Elkin (Pres)

HULL COOPERATIVE ASSOCIATION INC.
1206 RailRd St, Hull, IA 51239
Tel.: (712) 439-2831   IA
Web Site: http://www.hullcoop.com
Year Founded: 1925
Sales Range: $25-49.9 Million
Emp.: 30
Mfr of Feed
N.A.I.C.S.: 424910
Ed Westra (Gen Mgr)

HULL LIFT TRUCK INC.
28747 Old US Hwy 33, Elkhart, IN 46516-1681
Tel.: (574) 293-8651   IN
Web Site:
https://www.hulllifttruck.com
Year Founded: 1962
Sales Range: $10-24.9 Million
Emp.: 105
Industrial Machinery & Equipment Services
N.A.I.C.S.: 423830
Bob Hull (Pres)
Michael Cox (COO)

HULL STREET ENERGY, LLC
4747 Bethesda Ave Ste 1220, Bethesda, MD 20814
Tel.: (410) 685-7950
Web Site:
http://www.hullstreetenergy.com
Year Founded: 2014
Privater Equity Firm
N.A.I.C.S.: 523940
Sarah Wright (Founder & Mng Partner)

Subsidiaries:

Sungrid Solutions, Inc. (1)
2500 City W Blvd, Houston, TX 77042
Tel.: (888) 407-4743
Web Site: https://www.sungridsolutions.com
Battery Energy Storage Engineering & Construction
N.A.I.C.S.: 335910
Jeremy Goertz (CEO)

Subsidiary (Domestic):

Black Electric, Inc. (2)
766 Freedom Plains Rd, Poughkeepsie, NY 12603
Tel.: (845) 221-9698
Web Site: http://www.blackelectric.net
Sales Range: $1-9.9 Million
Emp.: 15
Electrical Contractor
N.A.I.C.S.: 238210
James Black (Pres, CEO & Mgr)

Ra Electric, Inc. (2)
120 Waverly Dr, Pasadena, CA 91105
Tel.: (626) 304-1156
Web Site: http://www.raelectric.net
Sales Range: $1-9.9 Million
Emp.: 20
Electrical Contractor
N.A.I.C.S.: 238210

Waterbury Generation LLC (1)
160 Washington Ave, Waterbury, CT 06708
Tel.: (860) 430-2113
Eletric Power Generation Services
N.A.I.C.S.: 221118

HULMAN & COMPANY
900 Wabash Ave, Terre Haute, IN 47807-3208
Tel.: (812) 232-9446   IN
Web Site: http://www.clabbergirl.com
Year Founded: 1850
Sales Range: $650-699.9 Million
Emp.: 750
Holding Company; Baking Powder, Corn Starch & Other Food Products Mfr & Distr; Motor Racetrack & Racing League Owner & Operator
N.A.I.C.S.: 551112
Jeffrey G. Belskus (Pres)
Tony George (Chm)
Mark D. Miles (CEO)
Gretchen Snelling (VP)

HULT FRITZ MATUSZAK
401 SW Water St Ste 601, Peoria, IL 61602-1586
Tel.: (309) 673-8191   IL
Year Founded: 1956
Rev.: $10,000,000
Emp.: 20
Business-To-Business
N.A.I.C.S.: 541810
James Flynn (Pres & CEO)
Roger Mulhern (VP)

HUMAN CAPITAL STAFFING, L.L.C.
6001 N Adams Rd Ste 208, Bloomfield Hills, MI 48304
Tel.: (248) 593-1950
Web Site: https://www.hcsteam.com
Year Founded: 1995
Sales Range: $10-24.9 Million
Emp.: 415
Temporary Help Service
N.A.I.C.S.: 561320
Dawn Carion (VP-Fin)
Mary Oxendine Adams (Pres)

HUMAN CARE SERVICES FOR FAMILIES AND CHILDREN, INC.
1042 38th St, Brooklyn, NY 11219
Tel.: (718) 854-2747   NY
Web Site:
http://www.humancareservices.org
Year Founded: 1996
Sales Range: $10-24.9 Million
Emp.: 830
Disability Assistance Services
N.A.I.C.S.: 623210
Sara Weiss (Assoc Dir)
Roni Beer (Dir-Residential)
Edward S. Kirshenbaum (CFO)

HUMAN DEVELOPMENT ASSOCIATION
12 Heyward St 4 Fl, Brooklyn, NY 11211
Tel.: (718) 422-4700   NY
Year Founded: 1980
Sales Range: $25-49.9 Million
Emp.: 1,191
Women Healthcare Services
N.A.I.C.S.: 621610
Hershel Berkowitz (Treas)
Naftali Ausch (Sec)

HUMAN DEVELOPMENT CENTER
1500 N 34th St Ste 100, Superior, WI 54880-4477
Tel.: (715) 392-8216   WI
Web Site: https://hdcnorth.org
Year Founded: 1938
Healthcare Provider
N.A.I.C.S.: 623220
Daniel Maddy (Pres)
Kevin Moiser (VP)
Brent Malvick (Treas)
Jean Olson (Sec)
Linda Deneen (Pres)
Ben Hatfield (CEO)
Cale Dickey (CFO)
Annette Gunter (COO)
Katie Onofrechuk (Chief Clinical Officer)
Steve Baurer (Dir-Medical)
Amy Lisdahl (Dir-Psychiatry)

HUMAN FACTORS INTERNATIONAL, INC.
1680 highway 1 STE 3600, Fairfield, IA 52556
Tel.: (641) 472-4480
Web Site:
http://www.humanfactors.com
Year Founded: 1981
Sales Range: $10-24.9 Million
Computer Related Consulting Services
N.A.I.C.S.: 541512
Eric Schaffer (Founder & CEO)
Nigel Grace (Mng Dir)
Hitesh Agrawal (Chief Business Officer)
Mark Soth (VP-Ops & HR)
Suann Wells (Controller)
Jay More (Pres)
Douglas Hughes (VP-Global Contracts)
Deepak Batreja (VP-Project Mgmt Office)

HUMAN KINETICS PUBLISHERS INC.
1607 N Market St, Champaign, IL 61820
Tel.: (217) 351-5076
Web Site:
https://www.humankinetics.com
Year Founded: 1974
Sales Range: $25-49.9 Million
Emp.: 250
Books Publishing
N.A.I.C.S.: 513130
Rainer Martens (Founder & Pres)
Julie Martens (Exec VP)
Brian Holding (CEO)
Kim L. Brown (Dir-Mktg)

Subsidiaries:

Human Kinetics Australia (1)
Torrens Park, PO Box 80, 57 A Price Ave, Mitcham, 5062, South Australia, Australia
Tel.: (61) 883720999
Web Site: http://www.humankinetics.com
Sales Range: $10-24.9 Million
Emp.: 8
Books, Publishing Only
N.A.I.C.S.: 513130

Human Kinetics Canada (1)
475 Devonshire Rd Unit 100, Windsor, N8Y 2L5, ON, Canada   (100%)
Tel.: (519) 971-9500
Web Site: https://canada.humankinetics.com
Sales Range: $10-24.9 Million
Emp.: 9
Books, Publishing Only
N.A.I.C.S.: 513130

Human Kinetics Europe (1)
107 Bradford Road, Stanningley, Leeds, LS28 6AT, United Kingdom   (100%)
Tel.: (44) 1132555665
Web Site: http://uk.humankinetics.com
Sales Range: $10-24.9 Million
Emp.: 15
Books Publishing Services
N.A.I.C.S.: 513130
Sara Cooper (Mng Dir)
Shyam Patridge (Mng Dir)

Human Kinetics New Zealand (1)
PO Box 300 226 Albany, North Shore City, Auckland, New Zealand
Tel.: (64) 883720999
Web Site: http://www.humankinetics.com
Sales Range: $10-24.9 Million
Emp.: 2
Publisher of Books Pertaining to Human Kinesiology
N.A.I.C.S.: 513130

HUMAN LONGEVITY, INC.
4570 Executive Dr, San Diego, CA 92121
Tel.: (858) 249-7500
Web Site:
http://www.humanlongevity.com
Year Founded: 2013
Emp.: 200
Genomics & Cell Therapy-Based Diagnostic & Therapeutic Services
N.A.I.C.S.: 541713
Robert Joseph Hariri (Co-Founder & Pres-Cellular Therapeutics)
Peter H. Diamandis (Co-Founder)
Wei-Wu He (Chm)
Kenneth J. Bloom (Pres)
Kurt Oreshack (Gen Counsel)
Yaron Turpaz (CIO)
Amalio Telenti (Chief Data Scientist & Head-HLI-X)
William Biggs (Head-Genomic Sequencing)
Fernanda Gandara Coelho (Chief Bus Dev Officer)
Tom Wamberg (Pres-Insurance & Corp Bus)
Sara Hall (Head-Privacy & Info Security)
Sally A. Howard (Head-Regulatory Affairs & Policy)
Chrisa Mott (Head-HR)
Jill Westman Mullen (Head-IR)
Travis Lacey (Chief Corp Dev Officer)
Dale Gordon (Chief Comml Officer)
Scott Sorensen (Interim COO & CTO)
Pamila Brar (Chief Mktg Officer)
David Karow (Interim CEO)
Noah Nasser (Chief Comml Officer)
C. Thomas Caskey (Chief Medical Officer)
Debbie Feinberg (VP-Mktg)

Subsidiaries:

LifebankUSA (1)
45 Horsehill Rd, Cedar Knolls, NJ 07927-2009
Tel.: (973) 267-8200
Web Site: http://www.lifebankusa.com
Emp.: 30
Discovers, Develops & Commercializes Applications for Human Stem Cells & Biotherapeutics
N.A.I.C.S.: 541715
Robert Joseph Hariri (Pres)

HUMAN RESOURCE STAFFING, LLC

Human Resource Staffing, LLC—(Continued)

1456-A Triad Center Dr, Saint Peters,
MO 63376
Tel.: (636) 477-8889
Web Site: https://www.hrstaffing.biz
Sales Range: $10-24.9 Million
Emp.: 30
Business, Staffing & Consulting Services
N.A.I.C.S.: 541611
Brian Green (Pres)
John Beauchamp (Pres)

HUMAN RESOURCES AGENCY OF NEW BRITAIN, INC.

180 Clinton St, New Britain, CT
06053
Tel.: (860) 225-8601   CT
Web Site: http://www.hranbct.org
Year Founded: 1964
Sales Range: $10-24.9 Million
Emp.: 380
Community Action Services
N.A.I.C.S.: 624190
Catherine R. Baratta (Pres)
Pauline B. Davis (VP)
Gladys Willis (Sec)
Kevin Nodell (Treas)
Rocco Richard Tricarico (Exec Dir)
Elizabeth Donnellan (Dir-Head Start)
Andrea Goodison (Mgr-HR)
Marlo Greponne (Dir-Plng & Programs)
Philip H. Gutt (Dir-Ops & Fin)
Janice Johnson (Dir-Toddler & Preschool Program)
Leticia Mangual (Dir-Youth Svcs Center)
Barbara Parsons (Dir-Community Svcs)
Frederick E. Smith (Dir-Health & Wellness Div)

Subsidiaries:

Bristol Community Organization,
Inc.   (1)
55 South St, Bristol, CT 06010
Tel.: (860) 584-2725
Community Welfare Services
N.A.I.C.S.: 624190

HUMAN RESOURCES INCORPORATED

10901 Corporate Cir N Ste D, Saint
Petersburg, FL 33716-3722
Tel.: (727) 895-4700
Web Site: https://www.hrinc.com
Sales Range: $10-24.9 Million
Emp.: 1,600
Employee Leasing Services
N.A.I.C.S.: 561330
Scott Buchanan (Pres & CEO)
Judy Malone (VP)

HUMAN RESOURCES RESEARCH ORGANIZATION

66 Canal Center Plz Ste 700, Alexandria, VA 22314-1578
Tel.: (703) 549-3611
Web Site: https://www.humrro.org
Year Founded: 1951
Sales Range: $10-24.9 Million
Emp.: 100
Educational Research
N.A.I.C.S.: 541720
Lauress Wise (Principal)
Deirdre Knapp (VP-Res & Consulting Ops)
Gina J. Medsker (Mgr-Program)
Paul J. Sticha (Mgr-Program)
Paul R. Sackett (Chm)
Charles L. McKay (Vice Chm)

HUMAN RIGHTS DEFENSE

1110 Sonora St, Glendale, CA 91201
Tel.: (818) 914-8283   CA
Web Site: http://www.usahrd.org
Year Founded: 2007
Sales Range: $1-9.9 Million
Human Rights Organizations
N.A.I.C.S.: 813311
Karo Karapetyan (Pres)

HUMAN RIGHTS FIRST

805 15th St NW Ste 900, Washington, DC 20005
Tel.: (202) 547-5692   DC
Web Site:
    http://www.humanrightsfirst.org
Year Founded: 1978
Sales Range: $10-24.9 Million
Emp.: 81
Social Advocacy Organization
N.A.I.C.S.: 813319
Zachary Silverstein (COO)
Susan Corke (Dir-Countering Anti-semitism & Extremism)
Michael Breen (Pres & CEO)
Tom Bernstein (Co-Chm)
Bill Zabel (Co-Chm)

HUMAN RIGHTS WATCH

350 5th Ave Fl 34, New York, NY
10118
Tel.: (212) 290-4700
Sales Range: $10-24.9 Million
Emp.: 140
Sociological Research
N.A.I.C.S.: 541720
Kenneth Roth (Exec Dir)
Bruce Rabb (Sec)
Dinah PoKempner (Gen Counsel)
Jasmine Herlt (Mng Dir-Dev & Outreach)
Janet Walsh (Dir-Acting-Women's Rights Div)
Jo Becker (Dir-Advocacy-Children's Rights Div)
Stephen Goose (Exec Dir-Arms Div)
Peter Bouckaert (Dir-Emergencies)
Michele Alexander (Deputy Exec Dir-Dev & Global Initiatives)
Pierre Bairin (Dir-MultiMedia)
Emma Daly (Dir-Comm)
Minky Worden (Dir-Global Initiatives)
Daniel Wilkinson (Mng Dir-Americas Div)

HUMAN SERVICES CENTER

130 W North St, New Castle, PA
16101
Tel.: (724) 652-9000   PA
Web Site:
    https://www.humanservicescenter.net
Year Founded: 1962
Sales Range: $10-24.9 Million
Emp.: 268
Behavioral Healthcare Services
N.A.I.C.S.: 623220
Roger Smith (Dir-Community Svcs)
Dennis W. Nebel (Exec Dir)
Jeffrey Stockdale (Dir-Fin)
Steve Plyler (Dir-Residential)

HUMAN TECHNOLOGIES, INC.

105 N Spring St Ste 200, Greenville,
SC 29601
Tel.: (864) 467-0330
Web Site: https://www.htijobs.com
Year Founded: 1999
Sales Range: $25-49.9 Million
Emp.: 75
Placement for the Manufacturing Industry
N.A.I.C.S.: 541612
Nat Banks (Dir-Sls)
Rob Johnson (Mgr-Training & Dev)
Herbert W. Dew III (Pres)

HUMAN TOUCH, LLC

3030 Walnut Ave, Long Beach, CA
90807
Tel.: (562) 426-8700   DE
Web Site:
    http://www.humantouch.com
Year Founded: 1971
Sales Range: $50-74.9 Million
Emp.: 54
Massage Chair Producer & Marketer
N.A.I.C.S.: 423210
David Wood (CEO)
Todd Bogart (Mgr-Sls-Natl)
Bruce MacCallum (CFO & VP-Ops)

HUMANCENTRIC

200 MacKenan Dr, Cary, NC 27511
Tel.: (919) 481-0565
Year Founded: 2000
Rev.: $5,800,000
Emp.: 25
Marketing Research & Public Opinion Polling
N.A.I.C.S.: 541910
Vince Bankoski (Gen Mgr)

HUMANCO LLC

888 7th Ave 27th Fl, New York, NY
10019
Tel.: (510) 410-0611
Web Site: http://www.humanco.com
Privater Equity Firm
N.A.I.C.S.: 523999
Jason H. Karp (Founder & CEO)

Subsidiaries:

Against the Grain Gourmet LLC   (1)
22 Browne Ct Unit 119, Brattleboro, VT
05301
Tel.: (802) 258-3838
Web Site:
    http://www.againstthegraingourmet.com
Mfr Frozen Gluten-Free Breads & Pizzas for
National Distribution
N.A.I.C.S.: 311824
Tom Cain (Co-Founder & Pres)
Nancy Cain (Co-Founder)

Bliss Unlimited LLC   (1)
525 E 11th Ave, Eugene, OR 97401-3606
Tel.: (541) 345-0020
Web Site: http://www.coconutbliss.com
Ice Cream & Frozen Dessert Mfr
N.A.I.C.S.: 311520
Larry Kaplowitz (Owner)

HUMANE SOCIETY CALUMET AREA

421 45th Ave, Munster, IN 46321
Tel.: (219) 922-3811   IN
Web Site: http://www.hscalumet.org
Year Founded: 1941
Sales Range: $10-24.9 Million
Emp.: 74
Animal Welfare Services
N.A.I.C.S.: 813312
Julie Feinstein (Treas)
Keith Magiera (VP)
Rachel Delaney (Exec Dir)
Judith Olen (Pres)
Kenneth Wilk (Sec)
Katy Dowling (Treas)

HUMANE SOCIETY OF MISSOURI

1201 Macklind Ave, Saint Louis, MO
63110
Tel.: (314) 647-8800   MO
Web Site: https://www.hsmo.org
Year Founded: 1870
Sales Range: $10-24.9 Million
Emp.: 289
Animal Welfare Services
N.A.I.C.S.: 812910
Kathryn Warnick (Pres)
Debbie Hill (Sr VP-Ops)

Anne Goeckner (CFO)
Jeane Jae (VP-Comm)
Jessica Arnold (Chief Dev Officer)

HUMANIM, INC.

6355 Woodside Ct, Columbia, MD
21046
Tel.: (410) 381-7171   MD
Web Site: http://www.humanim.com
Year Founded: 1970
Sales Range: $25-49.9 Million
Emp.: 780
Disability Assistance Services
N.A.I.C.S.: 624120
Henry Posko (Pres & CEO)
Lori Somerville (COO & Sr VP)
Cindy Plavier-Truitt (Chief Dev Officer & Sr VP)
Robert Causer (VP-HR)
Scott Deadrick (VP-Behavioral Support Svcs)
Eric Booth (CFO)
Diana Ellis (VP-Advancement)
Samuel Brunt (Mgr-Ops-Baltimore City Projects)

HUMANIX CORP.

15920 E Indiana Ave Ste 200, Spokane Valley, WA 99216
Tel.: (509) 467-0062
Web Site: http://www.humanix.com
Year Founded: 1986
Sales Range: $10-24.9 Million
Emp.: 570
Provider of Temporary Staffing Services
N.A.I.C.S.: 561320
Nancy J. Nelson (Pres)
Leesa Braun (Dir-Mktg)
Susan Clevenger (Dir-Recruiting)

HUMANKIND

150 Linden Ave, Lynchburg, VA
24503
Tel.: (434) 384-3131   VA
Web Site: http://www.humankind.org
Year Founded: 1902
Sales Range: $10-24.9 Million
Emp.: 257
Individual & Family Support Services
N.A.I.C.S.: 624190

HUMANSCALE CORPORATION

Grace Bldg 1114 Ave of the Americas
15th Fl, New York, NY 10036
Tel.: (212) 725-4749
Web Site:
    http://www.humanscale.com
Year Founded: 1983
Sales Range: $50-74.9 Million
Premier Ergonomic Work Tools Mfr
N.A.I.C.S.: 337211
Robert King (Founder & CEO)
Michelle Gerards (CFO)
Sheila Rogers Bowen (Controller)
June Smith Muranyi (Mgr-Sls-Mid South)
Bob Hallinan (Mng Dir)
Bruny Carlo (Dir-HR)
Sean Resch (Dir-Sls)
Jonathan Puleio (Dir-Consulting)
Krzysztof Sosniak (Engr-Design-IV)
Jane Abernethy (Chief Sustainability Officer)
Meg Bruce Conway (VP-Architecture & Design Sls)
Lisa Hubbs (VP-Retail Sls)
John Finken (VP-Govt Sls)

HUMANTOUCH, LLC

7918 Jones Branch Dr Ste 800,
McLean, VA 22102
Tel.: (703) 910-5090
Web Site:
    http://www.humantouchllc.com
Year Founded: 1998
Sales Range: $10-24.9 Million
Emp.: 110

Information Technology Services to Government Agencies & Corporate Clients
N.A.I.C.S.: 519290
Moe Jafari *(Pres & CEO)*
Robin Mugaas *(Mng Dir-HR)*
David Temeles *(Gen Counsel & Sr VP-Admin)*
Rick Hill *(Sr VP)*
Michelle Jafari *(Chief Admin Officer)*
Wendy K. Laduca *(Gen Counsel)*
Les Buday *(Dir-Cybersecurity)*
Jacques Fournier *(Dir-Sls-Health Markets)*
Sean O'Neill *(VP-Growth & Ops)*
Kelly Morrison *(Sr VP)*

Subsidiaries:

CorasWorks Corporation   (1)
7918 Jones Branch Dr Ste 800, McLean, VA 22102
Tel.: (703) 797-1881
Web Site: http://www.corasworks.net
Emp.: 65
Software Publisher
N.A.I.C.S.: 513210
James Benson *(COO)*
Dan Naselius *(CTO)*
Paul Legere *(VP-Sls-North America)*
Rodney Fickas *(Dir-Pro Svcs)*

HUMBLE ABODE, INC.
5621 Skylane Blvd, Santa Rosa, CA 95403
Tel.: (707) 568-5800
Web Site:
    http://www.humbleabode.com
Year Founded: 1999
Sales Range: $1-9.9 Million
Emp.: 10
Retail Home Furnishings Store
N.A.I.C.S.: 449110
James Wickersham *(Pres)*
William Waymack *(Mgr-Mdse)*

HUMBLE CONSTRUCTION CO.
1180 Carlisle St, Bellefontaine, OH 43311
Tel.: (937) 465-6035
Web Site:
    https://www.humbleconstruction.com
Sales Range: $10-24.9 Million
Emp.: 45
Provider of Building Contracts & Products
N.A.I.C.S.: 236220
Paul Humble *(Pres)*
Matt Hull *(Mgr-Bus Dev & Special Projects)*

HUMBOLDT MANUFACTUR-ING CO. INC.
3801 N 25th Ave, Schiller Park, IL 60176-2116
Tel.: (708) 456-6300
Web Site:
    http://www.humboldtmfg.com
Rev.: $14,875,802
Emp.: 38
Construction Materials Testing Equipment Mfr
N.A.I.C.S.: 334519
Dennis E. Burgess *(Pres)*

HUMBOLDT STATE UNIVER-SITY CENTER
Humboldt State University Ctr, Arcata, CA 95521
Tel.: (707) 826-4160
Web Site: http://www.humboldt.edu
Sales Range: $10-24.9 Million
Emp.: 60
Student Union
N.A.I.C.S.: 459210
Lisa Rossbacher *(Pres)*

HUMCAP LP

5401 Village Creek Dr, Plano, TX 75093
Tel.: (214) 520-0760
Web Site:
    https://www.humcapinc.com
Year Founded: 2001
Sales Range: $1-9.9 Million
Emp.: 20
Recruitment & Human Resource Services
N.A.I.C.S.: 561311

HUME BROPHY COMMUNICA-TIONS
295 Madison Ave 12th Fl, New York, NY 10017
Tel.: (718) 407-1980
Web Site:
    http://www.humebrophy.com
Investor Relations & Financial Advice
N.A.I.C.S.: 523940
Josh Nova *(Mng Dir)*
Edel Bach *(Mng Dir-20 Strong UK Bus)*

HUMILIS HOLDINGS CAPITAL MANAGEMENT COMPANY LLC
900 Camp St Ste 356, New Orleans, LA 70130
Tel.: (504) 430-3340   DE
Private Investment Firm
N.A.I.C.S.: 523999
Ron Bienvenu *(Mng Partner)*
Trevor Colhoun *(Mng Partner)*
Ernest C. Mysogland *(Mng Partner)*

HUMMELS OFFICE EQUIP-MENT CO.
25 Canal St, Mohawk, NY 13407
Tel.: (315) 574-8300
Web Site:
    https://www.hummelsop.com
Sales Range: $10-24.9 Million
Emp.: 90
Office Supplies
N.A.I.C.S.: 424120
Tim Hall *(VP-Comml Sls)*
Daniel Stalteri *(VP-Contract Furniture)*
Gwynn Hall *(VP-Customer Satisfaction & Pur)*
Justin R. Hummel *(CEO)*
Harrison J. Hummel III *(Chm)*

HUMMER WINBLAD OPERAT-ING CO., LLC
50 Francisco St Ste 450, San Francisco, CA 94133
Tel.: (415) 979-9600   DE
Web Site: https://www.hwvp.com
Year Founded: 1989
Holding Company
N.A.I.C.S.: 551112
Ingrid Chiavacci *(CFO)*

Subsidiaries:

Sonatype, Inc   (1)
12501 Prosperity Dr Ste 350, Silver Spring, MD 20904
Tel.: (650) 248-2919
Web Site: http://www.sonatype.com
Component Based Software Development Services
N.A.I.C.S.: 541511
Wayne Jackson *(CEO)*
Dave Miller *(CFO)*
Mike Hansen *(Sr VP-Products)*
Ryan Berg *(Chief Security Officer)*
Joshua Corman *(CTO)*
Paul Bosco *(Gen Counsel)*
David Rudolph *(VP-Customer Success)*
Karen Gardner *(VP-Ops)*
Brian Fox *(Founder & CTO)*
Bill Karpovich *(Sr VP-Strategy & Corp Dev)*
Megan Lueders *(CMO)*
Alex Berry *(Pres)*

HUMMERT INTERNATIONAL INC.
4500 Earth City Expy, Earth City, MO 63045
Tel.: (314) 506-4500
Web Site: https://www.hummert.com
Rev.: $17,400,000
Emp.: 84
Greenhouse Equipment & Supplies Mfr & Distr
N.A.I.C.S.: 424910
Kevin Kettler *(Mgr-Pur)*

HUMPERDINK'S TEXAS LLC.
2208 W New Hwy Ste 200, Dallas, TX 75220
Tel.: (214) 353-0500
Web Site:
    http://www.humperdinks.com
Sales Range: $10-24.9 Million
Emp.: 450
Office Administrative Services
N.A.I.C.S.: 561110
Norene Boyer *(Controller)*

HUMPHREY & ASSOCIATES INC.
11235 Shady Trl, Dallas, TX 75229
Tel.: (972) 620-1075
Web Site:
    http://www.teamhumphrey.com
Sales Range: $50-74.9 Million
Emp.: 300
General Electrical Contractor
N.A.I.C.S.: 238210
Steve Humphrey *(Pres)*
Jeff Wolfla *(Coord-Safety)*
Roy Kirkland *(VP)*
Tom McCormick *(Project Dir)*
Don Ezzell *(Project Dir)*
Gerald May *(Superintendent)*
Sam Stoker *(Mgr-Svcs)*

HUMPHREY COMPANIES LLC.
2851 Prairie St SW, Grandville, MI 49418
Tel.: (616) 530-1717
Web Site: http://www.hadley-products.com
Sales Range: $10-24.9 Million
Emp.: 175
Industrial Truck, Tractor, Trailer & Stacker Machinery Mfr
N.A.I.C.S.: 333924
John W. Humphrey *(Chm & Principal)*
James D. Green *(CFO & Mgr-Bus Dev)*

HUMPHREY LUMBER CORPO-RATION
2867 Zelda Rd, Montgomery, AL 36106
Tel.: (334) 271-2666
Web Site:
    http://www.humphreylumber.com
Sales Range: $25-49.9 Million
Emp.: 4
Hardwood Lumber, Dimension Furniture, Cabinets, Flooring Whslr
N.A.I.C.S.: 423310
Steve J. Humphrey *(Pres)*

HUMPHREY PRODUCTS COR-PORATION
5070 E N Ave, Kalamazoo, MI 49048
Tel.: (269) 381-5500   MI
Web Site: https://www.humphrey-products.com
Year Founded: 1901
Sales Range: $100-124.9 Million
Emp.: 200
Pneumatic Valves & Actuators Mfr
N.A.I.C.S.: 332912
Linda Rynd *(Mgr-HR)*

Subsidiaries:

Humphrey Automation   (1)
570 Alden Road Unit 10, Markham, L3R 8N5, ON, Canada   (100%)
Tel.: (905) 479-3633
Web Site: https://www.pneumation.ca
Sales Range: $10-24.9 Million
Emp.: 7
Distribution of Valves & Cylinders
N.A.I.C.S.: 332911
Moshe Haber *(COO)*

South Haven Coil Inc.   (1)
05585 Blue Star Hwy, South Haven, MI 49090   (100%)
Tel.: (269) 637-5201
Web Site: http://www.southhavencoil.com
Sales Range: $10-24.9 Million
Emp.: 35
Electrical Coils & Electronic Components Mfr
N.A.I.C.S.: 334416
Robert Humphrey *(Pres)*

HUMPHREYS & PARTNERS ARCHITECTS, L.P.
5339 Alpha Rd Ste 300, Dallas, TX 75240
Tel.: (972) 701-9636
Web Site:
    https://www.humphreys.com
Sales Range: $25-49.9 Million
Emp.: 125
Architectural, Interior Design, Landscaping & Civil Engineering Services
N.A.I.C.S.: 541310
Mark Humphreys *(Founder & Chm)*
Megan Dimmer *(CEO)*

HUMPHRIES & COMPANY, LLC.
4581 S Cobb Dr Ste 200, Smyrna, GA 30080
Tel.: (770) 434-1890
Web Site:
    https://www.humphriesandcompany.com
Sales Range: $10-24.9 Million
Emp.: 92
Nonresidential Construction Services
N.A.I.C.S.: 236220
Bryan Benedict *(Pres)*

HUNDLEY FARM INC.
25849 County Rd 880, Belle Glade, FL 33430
Tel.: (561) 996-5135   FL
Year Founded: 1969
Rev.: $11,900,000
Emp.: 60
Sugarcane Mills
N.A.I.C.S.: 311314
Krista Hundley *(VP)*
John L. Hundley *(Pres)*

HUNGERFORD & TERRY INC.
226 N Atlantic Ave, Clayton, NJ 08312-0650
Tel.: (856) 881-3200
Web Site:
    https://www.hungerfordterry.com
Sales Range: $10-24.9 Million
Emp.: 55
Water Treatment Equipment, Industrial
N.A.I.C.S.: 333310
Douglas Bateman *(Mgr-Cad Drafting)*
Frank Caligiuri *(VP-Sls)*
Thomas J. Carrocino *(Pres)*
Robert Lilley *(Mgr-Svc Dept)*

HUNGRY HOWIE'S PIZZA & SUBS INC.
30300 Stephenson Hwy, Madison Heights, MI 48071-1600
Tel.: (248) 414-3300   MI
Web Site:
    http://www.hungryhowies.com
Year Founded: 1973

Hungry Howie's Pizza & Subs Inc.—(Continued)

Sales Range: $10-24.9 Million
Emp.: 60
Fast-Food Restaurant Franchising Services
N.A.I.C.S.: 722513
Steven E. Jackson (Pres & CEO)
Jeff Inke (VP-Mktg)
Paul Pfeiffer (VP-Ops)
Steve Clough (Dir-Franchise Dev)

HUNGRY MAN LLC
106 7th Ave Fl 2, New York, NY 10011
Tel.: (212) 625-5600
Web Site:
   https://www.hungryman.com
Rev.: $30,863,600
Emp.: 22
Television Film Production
N.A.I.C.S.: 512110

HUNNIWELL LAKE VENTURES LLC
4 Palo Alto Sq Ste 200 3000 El Camino Real, Palo Alto, CA 94306
Web Site: http://hunniwell.com
Year Founded: 2019
Holding Company
N.A.I.C.S.: 551112
Daniel Teo (Mng Dir)

Subsidiaries:

SynCardia Systems LLC   (1)
1992 E Silverlake Rd, Tucson, AZ 85713
Tel.: (520) 545-1234
Web Site: http://www.syncardia.com
Artificial Heart Mfr
N.A.I.C.S.: 339113
Mary Pat Sloan (Sr VP-Global Certification & Logistics)
Bill Watson (VP-Mfg & Facilities)
Paul Zaman (VP-Fin)
Brian Brogie (VP-Mfg & Facilities)
Janelle Drumwright (Dir-Mktg)
Don Webber (CEO)
Markus Leinberger (Mng Dir)
Oliver Voigt (Mng Dir)
Peter Spadaro (Pres & Chief Comml Officer)

HUNT & SONS, INC.
5750 S Watt Ave, Sacramento, CA 95829-9349
Tel.: (916) 383-4868
Web Site:
   https://www.huntnsons.com
Year Founded: 1955
Sales Range: $125-149.9 Million
Emp.: 70
Provider of Gasoline Station Services
N.A.I.C.S.: 457120
Warren Hunt (VP)
Greg Areans (Controller)
Josh Hunt (Gen Mgr)

HUNT ADKINS
15 5th Street S 3rd Fl, Minneapolis, MN 55402
Tel.: (612) 339-8003
Web Site: http://www.huntadkins.com
Year Founded: 1991
Rev.: $25,000,000
Emp.: 20
Advertising, Brand Development & Integration, Graphic Design, Interactive, Internet/Web Design, Media Buying Services, Media Planning, Strategic Planning/Research
N.A.I.C.S.: 541810
Patrick Hunt (Pres & CEO)
Doug Adkins (VP & Chief Creative Officer)
Steve Mitchell (Partner & Grp Dir-Creative)
Leah Steig (Dir-Media Strategy)
Josh Smerick (Dir-Strategic Plng)
Seamus Culligan (Mgr-New Bus)

Kelly Kytola (Dir-Integrated Production)
Miles Marmo (Acct Mgr)
Anna Zuehlke (Asst Acct Exec)

HUNT BROADCASTING, LLC
1032 S Union Blvd, Lakewood, CO 80228
Tel.: (303) 989-3920   CO
Year Founded: 1992
Sales Range: $1-9.9 Million
Radio Broadcasting Stations Owner & Operator
N.A.I.C.S.: 516110
James G. Hunt (Owner)

Subsidiaries:

KCKK-AM/FM   (1)
1032 S Union Blvd, Lakewood, CO 80228
Tel.: (303) 989-3920
Web Site: http://www.937therock.com
Radio Broadcasting Stations
N.A.I.C.S.: 516110
Janice Hunt (Gen Mgr)

HUNT COMPANIES, INC.
4401 N Mesa St, El Paso, TX 79902-1107
Tel.: (915) 533-1122   DE
Web Site:
   http://www.huntcompanies.com
Sales Range: $15-24.9 Billion
Emp.: 1,010
Holding Company; Real Estate Investment, Development & Management Services
N.A.I.C.S.: 551112
Woody Hunt (Chm)
Mike L. Hunt (Vice Chm)
Chris Hunt (CEO)
Joshua Hunt (Exec VP)
Kara Harchuck (Gen Counsel & Exec VP)
Brenda Christman (Sr VP-Corp Comm)
Clay Parker (CFO & Exec VP)
Dan Singer (Exec VP)
John Ehle (Pres)
Steve Colon (Pres-Dev-Hawaii)
Robin Vaughn (Pres-Pub Infrastructure & Capital Markets)
Sinclair Cooper (Pres-Pub Infrastructure & Dev)
Justin Chapman (Pres-Southwest Community Dev)
Stu Milam (Sr VP-Investor Acctg Svcs)
Mike Lam (Sr VP)
Alexandra Dosen (Asst Mgr-Asset-Dev Div-Hawaii)
Tammy Lee (Asst Mgr-Dev)
J. Bryan Hunt Jr. (Pres & CEO)

Subsidiaries:

CGL Management Group, LLC   (1)
801 Brickell Ave Ste 720, Miami, FL 33131
Tel.: (786) 409-7000
Web Site: http://www.cglcompanies.com
Commercial & Institutional Building Design & Construction Services
N.A.I.C.S.: 236220
Stephen A. Carter (Pres-Svcs Div)
Ken Ricci (Exec VP & Principal-Design)
Eli Gage (Chief Bus Dev Officer & Exec VP)
Elena Difiore (Mgr-Comm)
Chris Murphree (VP-Project Dev)

City Light & Power, Inc.   (1)
2961 Redondo Ave, Long Beach, CA 90806
Tel.: (562) 983-2000
Web Site: http://www.clpinc.com
Business Consulting Services
N.A.I.C.S.: 541690
William J. Simmons (Co-Pres)
Thomas P. Simmons (Co-Pres)

Hunt Building Company, Ltd.   (1)
4401 N Mesa St, El Paso, TX 79902-1107
Tel.: (915) 533-1122

Web Site: http://www.huntcompanies.com
Sales Range: $100-124.9 Million
Emp.: 400
Residential, Commercial & Institutional Building Construction Services
N.A.I.C.S.: 236116
Mike L. Hunt (Pres & CEO)
Tom Philley (Exec VP)
Robert Cabello (Sr VP & Dir-Estimating)
Rick Marshall (Sr VP)

Hunt Development Group, LLC   (1)
4401 N Mesa St, El Paso, TX 79902-1107
Tel.: (915) 533-1122
Web Site: http://www.huntcompanies.com
Emp.: 220
Real Estate Development, Asset Management & Financing Services
N.A.I.C.S.: 237210
Gary Sapp (Pres-Southwest Reg)
Jim Dobbie (Sr VP-Southwest Reg)
Juan Gonzalez-Garza (Sr VP)
Brion Georges (VP-Southwest Community Dev)
Kris Martin (VP)

Hunt Investment Management, LLC   (1)
161 Washington St Ste 900, Conshohocken, PA 19428
Tel.: (610) 729-7750
Web Site: http://www.huntcompanies.com
Real Estate Investment Services
N.A.I.C.S.: 531390
Steve DeBara (CFO)
Kara Harchuck (Gen Counsel & Exec VP)
Douglas A. Tibbetts (Chm)
Steve Janowiak (Sr VP)
Tom Duda (Exec VP)
Dominick J. Cristiano (Mng Dir)
Jim Dobbie (Sr VP)
Maryann Hermann (Chief Compliance Officer)
Jeffrey Rutishauser (Mng Dir-Capital Markets)

Hunt Military Communities Mgmt., LLC   (1)
4401 N Mesa St, El Paso, TX 79902-1150
Tel.: (915) 533-1122
Web Site: http://www.huntcompanies.com
Emp.: 200
Single-Family Military Housing Communities Management Services
N.A.I.C.S.: 531311
Joshua Hunt (Sr VP)
Steve Norman (Sr VP-Asset Mgmt)
Julie Strickland (VP-Asset Mgmt)

Hunt Mortgage Group, LLC   (1)
230 Park Ave 19th Fl, New York, NY 10169
Tel.: (212) 317-5700
Web Site:
   http://www.huntmortgagegroup.com
Commercial Real Estate Financing Services
N.A.I.C.S.: 522299
James P. Flynn (Pres & Chief Investment Officer)
Michael P. Larsen (CFO & COO)
William T. Hyman (Sr Mng Dir & Chief Production Officer)
Megan Goodfellow (Chief Credit Officer-Comml Real Estate)
Suzanne Cope (Sr VP-Affordable Housing & FHA Grp-Denver)
Paul Weissman (Sr Mng Dir)
Kathryn Burton Gray (Sr Mng Dir & Head-Health Care)
Owen Bouton (Dir-Proprietary Lending Grp-Charleston & Atlanta)
John Beam (Mng Dir)
Vic Clark (Sr Mng Dir)
Anthony Valenzuela (VP)
Jeff Payne (VP)
Kevin Chadwick (Mng Dir)

HUNT CONSOLIDATED, INC.
1900 N Akard St, Dallas, TX 75201-2300
Tel.: (214) 978-8000   DE
Web Site:
   https://www.huntconsolidated.com
Year Founded: 1934
Sales Range: $1-4.9 Billion
Emp.: 4,500
Offices of Other Holding Companies
N.A.I.C.S.: 551112

Harry Dombroski (Sr VP-Fin Admin)
Bruce Cope (Chief Acctg Officer & Sr VP)
Jim Savage (Sr VP-Security-Global)
Jeanne L. Phillips (Sr VP-Corp Affairs, Intl Rels, and Corp Engagement)
Karim Abuhamad (Sr VP)
Travis Armayor (Sr VP-Corp Fin & Bus Dev)
Adam Bishop (Sr VP-Exploration)
Michael Monroe (Gen Counsel, Sec & Sr VP)
Ken Topolinsky (Sr VP-Engrg & Applied Tech)

Subsidiaries:

Alabama Bulk Terminal Inc.   (1)
Blakely Is, Mobile, AL 36601
Tel.: (251) 438-9891
Sales Range: $10-24.9 Million
Emp.: 14
Provider of Warehousing & Storage Services
N.A.I.C.S.: 483211

Hoodoo Land And Cattle Company   (1)
1900 N Akard St, Dallas, TX 75201-2812
Tel.: (214) 978-8000
Web Site:
   http://www.hoodoolandandcattle.com
Sales Range: $10-24.9 Million
Emp.: 100
Crop Preparation Services
N.A.I.C.S.: 112111
Thomas E. Meurer (Pres)

Hunt Investment Group, L.P.   (1)
1900 N Akard St, Dallas, TX 75201-2300
Tel.: (214) 978-8690
Web Site: http://www.huntivvestment.com
Emp.: 500
Investment Services
N.A.I.C.S.: 523999
Mike Bierman (Pres)
Chris Kleinert (Pres & CEO)
Brian Jolly (VP)

Hunt Oil Company   (1)
1900 N Akard St, Dallas, TX 75201
Tel.: (214) 978-8000
Web Site: http://www.huntoil.com
Sales Range: $25-49.9 Million
Emp.: 2
Oil & Gas Exploration Services
N.A.I.C.S.: 211120
Paul Habenicht (Exec VP-North America)
Steve Suellentrop (Chm)
Michael Monroe (Gen Counsel, Sec & Sr VP-Legal)
Karim Abuhamad (Sr VP-Middle East Reg)
Travis Armayor (Sr VP-Corp Fin & Bus Dev)
Adam Bishop (Sr VP-Exploration)
Ken Topolinsky (Sr VP-Engrg & Applied Tech)

Subsidiary (Non-US):

Hunt Oil Company of Canada, Inc.   (2)
32700 255 5th Ave SW, Calgary, T2P 3G6, AB, Canada
Tel.: (403) 531-1530
Web Site: http://www.huntoil.com
Sales Range: $50-74.9 Million
Explorer & Distributor of Natural Gas
N.A.I.C.S.: 221210

Subsidiary (Domestic):

Hunt Refining Company Inc.   (2)
1855 Fairlawn Rd, Tuscaloosa, AL 35401
Tel.: (205) 391-3300
Web Site: http://www.huntrefining.com
Sales Range: $25-49.9 Million
Providers of Petroleum Refining Services
N.A.I.C.S.: 324110
Chris Contakos (CFO & VP)
David Carroll (Gen Counsel & Sr VP)
Michele Jarrell (Treas)
J. Mark Spencer (VP-HR)
Jay Junkin (Controller)
Steve Suellentrop (Chm)

Hunt Overseas Oil Company   (1)
1900 N Akard St, Dallas, TX 75201

Tel.: (214) 978-8000
Web Site: http://www.huntoil.com
Sales Range: $25-49.9 Million
Emp.: 8
Crude Petroleum & Natural Gas
N.A.I.C.S.: 211120

Hunt Realty Corporation (1)
1900 N Akard St, Dallas, TX 75201
Tel.: (214) 978-8000
Web Site: http://www.huntrealty.com
Sales Range: $25-49.9 Million
Emp.: 6
Investor & Real Estate Services
N.A.I.C.S.: 523999
Jeanne L. Phillips (Sr VP-Corp Engagement
& Intl Rels)

Jannah Hunt Oil Inc. (1)
1900N Akard St, Dallas, TX 75201
Tel.: (214) 978-8000
Web Site: http://www.huntoil.com
Sales Range: $25-49.9 Million
Emp.: 50
Oil & Gas Drilling Services
N.A.I.C.S.: 213111
Paul Hoffman (VP-HR)

Sharyland Utilities LP (1)
4600 W Military Hwy Ste 400, McAllen, TX
78503
Tel.: (956) 687-5600
Web Site: http://www.sharyland.com
Sales Range: $1-9.9 Million
Emp.: 7
Public Electric Utility
N.A.I.C.S.: 221122
Hunter L. Hunt (Chm & CEO)
Greg Boggs (Sr VP)
Greg Wilks (CFO)

Yemen Hunt Oil Company, Inc. (1)
1900 N Akard St, Dallas, TX 75201
Tel.: (214) 978-8000
Web Site: http://www.huntoil.com
Sales Range: $25-49.9 Million
Emp.: 5
Crude Petroleum & Natural Gas Supplier
N.A.I.C.S.: 211120

**HUNT COUNTRY FURNITURE
INC.**
19 Dog Tail Corners Rd, Wingdale,
NY 12594
Tel.: (845) 832-6601
Web Site:
http://www.huntcountryfurniture.com
Sales Range: $10-24.9 Million
Emp.: 110
Restaurant Furniture Mfr
N.A.I.C.S.: 337127
Caroline Williams (Pres)
Todd Gazzoli (Mgr-Plant)

**HUNT ELECTRIC SUPPLY
COMPANY INC.**
1213 Maple Ave, Burlington, NC
27215-6958
Tel.: (336) 229-5351
Web Site:
http://www.huntelectricsupply.com
Year Founded: 1971
Sales Range: $10-24.9 Million
Emp.: 70
Provider of Electrical Apparatus &
Equipment
N.A.I.C.S.: 423610
Victoria Hunt (CEO)
Rodney Sharp (VP-Sls)
Sam Hunt III (Chm)

**HUNT ENGINE INCORPO-
RATED**
14805 S Main St, Houston, TX 77035
Tel.: (713) 721-9400
Web Site:
https://www.huntengine.com
Year Founded: 1983
Sales Range: $10-24.9 Million
Emp.: 35
Engine Rebuilding, Parts & Services
N.A.I.C.S.: 423830

John Biggs (Treas)

HUNT ENTERPRISES INC.
4416 W 154th St, Lawndale, CA
90260
Tel.: (310) 675-3555
Web Site:
http://www.huntenterprises.net
Sales Range: $25-49.9 Million
Emp.: 25
Provider of Real Estate Services
N.A.I.C.S.: 531110
Donald G. Hunt (Owner & Pres)
Priscilla Hunt (Exec VP)
Tess David (Controller)
Scott Roecklein (Sr VP)

**HUNT FOREST PRODUCTS
INC.**
401 Reynolds Dr, Ruston, LA 71273-
1263
Tel.: (318) 255-2245
Web Site:
https://www.huntforpro.com
Rev.: $120,000,000
Emp.: 35
Softwood Veneer & Plywood
N.A.I.C.S.: 321212
Jim Huff (CFO)
Alex T. Hunt Jr. (Chm)

**HUNT INSURANCE GROUP,
LLC**
3606 Maclay Blvd S Ste 204, Talla-
hassee, FL 32312
Tel.: (850) 385-3636
Web Site: http://www.huntins.com
Year Founded: 1945
General Insurance Services
N.A.I.C.S.: 524210
Scott Hunt (Pres & CEO)
Chris Baker (CFO)
Tamara Volkert (Sr VP, Dir & Mgr-
Mktg-EB)
Stephen Blake (VP-P&C)
Jim Matheu (Mgr-Quality Control &
Compliance)
Gretchen Coon (Mgr-Employee Ben-
efits)
Erin Fields (Coord-Claims)
Patrice Brown (Acct Mgr-Employee
Benefits)
Tanesha Brown (Acct Mgr-Employee
Benefits)
Elizabeth Kienzle (Acct Mgr-
Employee Benefits)
Dan Lancaster (Acct Mgr-Inmate
Medical)
Laura Snider (Acct Mgr-P&C)
Sharon McGraw (Acct Mgr-P&C)
Angela Kersey (Coord-Eligibility)
John E. Hunt Jr. (Exec VP, Dir &
Mgr-Mktg-P&C)

**HUNT MIDWEST ENTER-
PRISES INC.**
8300 NE Underground Dr, Kansas
City, MO 64161
Tel.: (816) 455-2500
Web Site:
https://www.huntmidwest.com
Rev.: $20,400,000
Emp.: 55
Subdividers & Developers
N.A.I.C.S.: 237210
Dick Ringer (Asst Gen Mgr-Sls &
Leasing)
Don Hagan (CFO & VP)
Clayton Holder (Dir-Fin & Acctg)
Kim Smith (Dir-Fin & Acctg)
Doug Coleman (Gen Mgr-New Bus
Dev)
Aaron Schmidt (Asst Gen Mgr-Plng &
Construction)
Connie Kamps (Dir-Real Estate Ops)
Mike Bell (VP-Indus & Comml)

Brenner Holland (VP-Residential)
Chris Reasoner (Dir-Facilities)
Jenni Mann (Dir-Residential Mktg)
Ryan Tompkins (Mgr-Sls & Leasing)
Ora Reynolds (Pres & CEO)
Eric Ford (Mgr-Mktg Svcs)
Jeff Redhage (Mgr-Construction)
Jon Birkel (Dir-Dev)
Lee Derrough (Chm)
Terry Owens (Mgr-Residential Proj-
ects)
Wendy Padgett (Dir-Dev Svcs)
Michael Knight (Gen Mgr-Shared
Construction Svcs)
Matt Sobaski (Mgr-Construction-
Shared Construction Svcs Div)
Steven W. Caple (Chm)

**HUNT REAL ESTATE CORPO-
RATION**
430 Dick Rd, Depew, NY 14043
Tel.: (716) 633-9400   NY
Web Site:
https://www.huntrealestate.com
Year Founded: 1911
Sales Range: $10-24.9 Million
Emp.: 300
Real Estate Agency
N.A.I.C.S.: 531210
Charles F. Hunt (COO & Exec VP)
Dave Evans (Gen Mgr-Central &
Northern NY)
Peter Scarcello (Gen Mgr-Buffalo &
Rochester)
Sarah Klaiber (Mgr-Bus Dev-Buffalo)
Gregory Maher (CFO)
Carlos Pegado (CTO-Information
Svcs & VP)
Peter F. Hunt (Chm & CEO)
Gary Kenline (Sr VP-Residential Bro-
kerage)
Jennifer Maxian (Dir-Career Dev)

**HUNT, GUILLOT & ASSOCI-
ATES, LLC.**
603 E Reynolds Dr, Ruston, LA
71270
Tel.: (318) 255-6825
Web Site: https://www.hga-llc.com
Year Founded: 1997
Sales Range: $50-74.9 Million
Emp.: 360
Engineeering Services
N.A.I.C.S.: 541330
Mike Causey (VP-Sls)

HUNTAIR INC.
19855 SW 124th Ave, Tualatin, OR
97062
Tel.: (503) 639-0113   OR
Web Site: http://www.huntair.com
Year Founded: 1993
Sales Range: $10-24.9 Million
Emp.: 630
Refrigeration & Heating Equipment
N.A.I.C.S.: 333415
Russell Lilly (Mgr-Data Center Prod-
uct)
Mark Andersen (Mgr-Logistics)
Dave Benson (Founder)

HUNTER
204 Julie Dr, Parkesburg, PA 19365
Tel.: (610) 857-2977   PA
Web Site: http://www.rjhunter.com
Year Founded: 1986
Sales Range: $10-24.9 Million
Emp.: 3
Advertising Agencies
N.A.I.C.S.: 541810
John A. Willis (Pres)
Sallie Scripter (Exec VP-Americas)

**HUNTER & HARP HOLDINGS,
LLC**

311 E Jennings St, Tallahassee, FL
32301
Tel.: (850) 521-5821
Web Site:
http://www.hunterandharp.com
Sales Range: $25-49.9 Million
Emp.: 1,000
Privater Equity Firm
N.A.I.C.S.: 523999
J. T. Burnette (Principal)
Chad Kittrell (Principal)
Dennis Mason (Dir-Ops)
Steve Adams (Dir-Food & Beverage)

**HUNTER ASSOCIATES LABO-
RATORY**
11491 Sunset Hills Rd, Reston, VA
20190-5280
Tel.: (703) 471-6870
Web Site: https://www.hunterlab.com
Sales Range: $10-24.9 Million
Emp.: 65
Optical Test & Inspection Equipment
N.A.I.C.S.: 333310
Philip S. Hunter (Chm)
Eric Schaub (Dir-Mfg)

**HUNTER CHEVROLET COM-
PANY INC.**
2520 Asheville Hwy, Hendersonville,
NC 28791
Tel.: (828) 693-8661
Web Site:
https://www.hunterautogroup.com
Rev.: $48,491,346
Emp.: 85
New & Used Car Dealers
N.A.I.C.S.: 441110
Hal M. Hunter (Chm)
Tom Hunter (Pres & CFO)

**HUNTER CONTRACTING
COMPANY**
701 N Cooper Rd, Gilbert, AZ 85233-
3703
Tel.: (480) 892-0521   AZ
Web Site:
https://www.huntercontracting.com
Year Founded: 1961
Sales Range: $150-199.9 Million
Emp.: 225
Street & Highway Construction Ser-
vices
N.A.I.C.S.: 236210
Steve Padilla (CEO)
Gary Davis (Controller)
Allen E. Andrews (Sr VP)
Rob Padilla (Pres)
Samuel J. Napolitano (CFO)
Dig Karki (Mgr-Preconstruction)
Shauna Slevin (Controller-Ops)
Jesse Berry (Dir-IT)
Bob Carlson (VP-Estimating)

**HUNTER ENGINEERING COM-
PANY**
11250 Hunter Dr, Bridgeton, MO
63044-2306
Tel.: (314) 731-0000   MO
Web Site: https://www.hunter.com
Year Founded: 1946
Sales Range: $100-124.9 Million
Emp.: 300
Automotive Wheel Alignment Equip-
ment, Wheel Balancers, Brake
Lathes, Tire Changers, Lift Racks &
Brake Testers Mfr
N.A.I.C.S.: 336390
Kaleb Silver (Dir-Product Mgmt Sys
Tech)
Blackford F. Brauer (Pres)

Subsidiaries:

Hunter Canada (1)
4-240 Edward Street, Aurora, L4G 3S9,
ON, Canada

Hunter Engineering Company—(Continued)

Tel.: (905) 953-7799
Web Site: http://www.hunter.com
Sales Range: $10-24.9 Million
Emp.: 16
Transportation Equipment Mfr & Whslr
N.A.I.C.S.: 423860
John Peron (Dir-Southeast Reg)

Hunter Deutschland GmbH (1)
Beurerstrasse 25a, 86926, Greifenberg,
Germany
Tel.: (49) 8192 93399 0
Web Site: http://www.hunter-d.de
Sales Range: $10-24.9 Million
Emp.: 10
Automotive Service Equipment Mfr
N.A.I.C.S.: 336390

HUNTER GRAIN COMPANY
201 Main St, Hunter, ND 58048
Tel.: (701) 874-2112
Web Site:
http://www.huntergrain.com
Sales Range: $1-9.9 Million
Emp.: 18
Grain Elevators
N.A.I.C.S.: 424510
Paul Skarnagel (Gen Mgr)
Louis Rosenbau (Pres & Dir-Sls)
Tracy Bender (Office Mgr)

HUNTER INDUSTRIES INCOR-PORATED
1940 Diamond St, San Marcos, CA
92078-5120
Tel.: (760) 744-5240 DE
Web Site:
https://www.hunterindustries.com
Year Founded: 1981
Sales Range: $25-49.9 Million
Emp.: 850
Irrigation Systems Designer, Mfr &
Installation Services
N.A.I.C.S.: 332913
Stephanie Brownell (CFO)
Steve Abernethy (VP-Global Sls)

Subsidiaries:

Senninger Irrigation, Inc. (1)
16220 E Hwy 50, Clermont, FL
34711-6266 (100%)
Tel.: (407) 877-5655
Web Site: http://www.senninger.com
Sales Range: $1-9.9 Million
Emp.: 210
Agricultural Irrigation Systems & Services
N.A.I.C.S.: 221310

HUNTER INDUSTRIES LTD.
4501 Hunter Rd, San Marcos, TX
78666
Tel.: (512) 353-7757
Sales Range: $75-99.9 Million
Emp.: 650
General Contractor Services
N.A.I.C.S.: 237310
John R. Weisman (Owner)
Walter Ulbricht (Controller)
Gary Tackert (Project Mgr)

HUNTER OIL CO. INC.
801 W Main St, Cabool, MO 65689
Tel.: (417) 962-3757
Sales Range: $25-49.9 Million
Emp.: 25
Petroleum Bulk Stations
N.A.I.C.S.: 424710
Robert Beller (Pres)

HUNTER WARFIELD
4620 Woodland Corporate Blvd,
Tampa, FL 33614
Tel.: (813) 283-4500
Web Site:
http://www.hunterwarfield.com
Sales Range: $10-24.9 Million
Emp.: 130
Revenue Recovery Services

N.A.I.C.S.: 561440
Stephen Sobota (Founder & CEO)
Todd Wahl (Pres)
George Chambers (VP-IT)
Greg Duss (VP-Sls & Mktg)
Jonathan Juchnevics (VP-HR)
Warren Stoller (Gen Counsel)

HUNTERDON TRANSFORMER CO. INC.
75 Indus Dr, Alpha, NJ 08865
Tel.: (908) 454-2400
Web Site:
https://www.hunterdontransfor
mer.com
Year Founded: 1957
Sales Range: $10-24.9 Million
Emp.: 55
Electric Power Transformers
N.A.I.C.S.: 335311
Don MacMillan (VP-Engrg)

HUNTERS TRUCK SALES & SERVICE
480 Pittsburgh Rd, Butler, PA 16002
Tel.: (724) 791-2525
Web Site:
http://www.hunterstrucksales.com
Rev.: $140,000,000
Emp.: 70
Trucks, Commercial
N.A.I.C.S.: 423110
David Hunter (VP)
Robert L. Hunter (Chm)

HUNTING DOG CAPITAL CORP.
One Maritime Plz Ste 825, San Fran-
cisco, CA 94111 DE
Tel.: (415) 942-5316
Year Founded: 2015
Emp.: 5
Holding Company
N.A.I.C.S.: 551112
Christopher Allick (Chm & CEO)
Todd Blankfort (Pres)
Paul Clausing (CFO)

HUNTINGTON BANCSHARES INC.
208 US Hwy 69 S, Huntington, TX
75949-9145
Tel.: (936) 422-3000
Web Site: http://www.u.bank
Bank Holding Companies
N.A.I.C.S.: 551111

Subsidiaries:

UBank (1)
208 Hwy 69 S, Huntington, TX 75949
Tel.: (936) 422-3000
Web Site: http://www.u.bank
Sales Range: $10-24.9 Million
Commericial Banking
N.A.I.C.S.: 522110
Don Neill (CEO)
Chris Kelley (CFO)
Stacey Willmann (Dir-Mktg)

HUNTINGTON BUSINESS SYS-TEMS INC.
761-70 Coates Ave, Holbrook, NY
11741
Tel.: (631) 361-6820
Web Site: https://www.hbscorp.com
Rev.: $20,000,000
Emp.: 130
Computer Related Consulting Ser-
vices
N.A.I.C.S.: 541512
Allison Plank (Pres)
Frank Dianco (CFO)
Michael Cappiello (VP)

HUNTINGTON FEDERAL SAV-INGS BANK

1049 5th Ave, Huntington, WV 25701
Tel.: (304) 528-6200
Web Site:
http://www.huntingtonfederal.com
Year Founded: 1934
Sales Range: $25-49.9 Million
Emp.: 84
Federal Savings & Loan Associations
N.A.I.C.S.: 522120
J. Maurice Clark (Pres & CEO)
Mark A. Preston (VP)
Joseph M. Sullivan (VP)
Matthew M. Wagner (Chief Lending
Officer & VP)
Daniel D. Huron (VP),
Sandra H. Lockhart (VP)
Kerry E. Adkins (VP)
Lynn Barcus (VP)

HUNTINGTON FORD INC.
2890 S Rochester Rd, Rochester
Hills, MI 48307
Tel.: (248) 852-0400
Web Site:
http://www.huntingtonforddealer.com
Sales Range: $75-99.9 Million
Emp.: 100
Car Dealership
N.A.I.C.S.: 441110
Patrick Scoggin (Owner, Pres & Prin-
cipal)
Bradley Schiller (Gen Mgr)
Darryl Galka (Mgr-Svc)

HUNTINGTON HOMES INC.
344 Fassett Rd, East Montpelier, VT
05651
Tel.: (802) 479-3625
Web Site:
https://www.huntingtonhomesvt.com
Year Founded: 1978
Sales Range: $10-24.9 Million
Emp.: 100
Modular Home Manufacturers
N.A.I.C.S.: 321992
Duane Webster (Pres)
Richard Burnham (Mgr-Engrg & QC)

HUNTINGTON SANITARY BOARD
1217 Adams Ave, Huntington, WV
25704
Tel.: (304) 696-5564
Web Site:
http://www.huntingtonsb.com
Year Founded: 1935
Sales Range: $10-24.9 Million
Emp.: 75
Sewage Treatment Facility Services
N.A.I.C.S.: 221320
Mayor Steve Williams (Chm)
Gary Black (Vice Chm)
Lou Akers (Exec Dir)

HUNTINGTON SHEET METAL, INC.
1675 Riverfork Dr E, Huntington, IN
46750
Tel.: (260) 356-9011
Web Site: https://www.hsmetal.com
Year Founded: 1984
Sales Range: $10-24.9 Million
Emp.: 85
Sheet Metal Work Mfg
N.A.I.C.S.: 332322
Daniel M. Drummond (Pres)

HUNTINGTON STEEL & SUP-PLY CO.
100 3rd Ave, Huntington, WV 25701
Tel.: (304) 522-8218
Web Site:
https://www.huntingtonsteel.com
Rev.: $14,588,226
Emp.: 74
Steel

N.A.I.C.S.: 423510
Michael J. Emerson (Pres)
Mark Rutherford (VP)

HUNTLEIGH SECURITIES CORP.
7800 Forsyth Blvd, Saint Louis, MO
63105
Tel.: (314) 236-2400 MO
Web Site: https://www.hntlgh.com
Year Founded: 1977
Investment Firm General Brokerage
N.A.I.C.S.: 523150
Robert L. Chambers (Pres)
Karen Thomas (Dir-Ops)
Catherine Marshall (Chief Compli-
ance Officer)

HUNTLEY OIL & GAS COM-PANY
1370 Hwy 74 W, Wadesboro, NC
28170
Tel.: (704) 694-2144
Sales Range: $10-24.9 Million
Emp.: 15
Distr of Petroleum Products
N.A.I.C.S.: 424720
William K. Huntley (Pres)

HUNTMOUNTAIN RESOURCES LTD.
1611 N Molter Rd Ste 201, Liberty
Lake, WA 99019
Tel.: (509) 892-5287 NV
Web Site:
http://www.huntmountain.com
Sales Range: Less than $1 Million
Precious & Base Metals Mining Ser-
vices
N.A.I.C.S.: 713990
Tim Hunt (Chm, Pres & CEO)

HUNTMOUNTAIN RESOURCES LTD.
1611 N Molter Rd Ste 201, Liberty
Lake, WA 99019
Tel.: (509) 892-5287
Year Founded: 2005
Metal Mining Services
N.A.I.C.S.: 212290
Tim Hunt (Pres & CEO)

HUNTSINGER FARMS INC.
W 2394 State Rd 37, Eau Claire, WI
54701-9515
Tel.: (715) 832-9739 WI
Web Site:
http://www.huntsingerfarms.com
Year Founded: 1973
Sales Range: $25-49.9 Million
Emp.: 200
Pickles, Sauces & Salad Dressings
N.A.I.C.S.: 311941
Ken Traaseth (VP-Ag Ops)

Subsidiaries:

Silver Spring Foods, Inc. (1)
2424 Alpine Rd, Eau Claire, WI 54703-9515
Tel.: (715) 832-9739
Web Site: http://www.silverspringfoods.com
Sales Range: $25-49.9 Million
Emp.: 150
Retail of Pickles, Sauces & Salad Dressings
N.A.I.C.S.: 311941
Shawn Kapanke (VP-Ops)

HUNTSMAN FAMILY INVEST-MENTS, LLC
500 Huntsman Way, Salt Lake City,
UT 84108
Tel.: (801) 584-5921
Web Site:
https://www.huntsmanfamilyin
vestments.com
Equity Investment Firm
N.A.I.C.S.: 523999

Benjamin Wu *(Partner)*
Paul Huntsman *(Pres & CEO)*
Jon M. Huntsman Sr. *(Chm)*

Subsidiaries:

Huntsman Family Holdings Company LLC   **(1)**
500 Huntsman Way, Salt Lake City, UT 84108
Tel.: (801) 584-5921
Investment Holding Company
N.A.I.C.S.: 551112

TeleGuam Holdings, LLC   **(1)**
624 N Marine Corps Dr, Tamuning, GU 96913
Tel.: (671) 644-4482
Web Site: http://www.gta.net
Telecommunication Servicesb
N.A.I.C.S.: 517810

HUNTSVILLE EMERGENCY MEDICAL SERVICES INC

2700 6th Ave SW, Huntsville, AL 35805
Tel.: (256) 518-2242   **AL**
Web Site: https://www.hemsi.org
Year Founded: 1980
Sales Range: $10-24.9 Million
Emp.: 269
Ambulance Service Provider
N.A.I.C.S.: 621910
Don Webster *(COO)*
Sherrie Squyres *(Dir-Medical)*
Jon M. Howell *(CEO)*
Steven Werdehoff *(Sec)*
David Blair *(Treas)*
Melissa Musgrove *(VP)*

HUNTSVILLE HOUSING AUTHORITY

200 Washington St NE, Huntsville, AL 35801
Tel.: (256) 539-0774
Web Site:
   http://www.huntsvillehousing.org
Year Founded: 1941
Sales Range: $10-24.9 Million
Emp.: 100
Housing Authority Operator
N.A.I.C.S.: 531390
Carol J. Jones *(Dir-HR)*
Sandra Eddlemon *(CFO & Dir-Fin)*

HUNTSVILLE-MADISON COUNTY AIRPORT AUTHORITY

1000 Glenn Hearn Blvd, Huntsville, AL 35824
Tel.: (256) 772-9395
Web Site: http://www.hsvairport.org
Rev.: $24,600,000
Emp.: 115
Other Airport Operations
N.A.I.C.S.: 488119
Richard Tucker *(Exec Dir)*
Betty D. Fletcher *(Treas & Sec)*
Mark McDaniel *(Chm)*
William H. Johnston Jr. *(Vice Chm)*

HUNYADY AUCTION COMPANY

1440 Cowpath Rd, Hatfield, PA 19440
Tel.: (215) 361-9099
Web Site: https://www.hunyady.com
Rev.: $2,689,931
Emp.: 13
Fee-based Auction Services
N.A.I.C.S.: 561499
Michael J. Hunyady *(Founder, Owner & Pres)*
Richard M. Kriebel *(VP-Svcs)*
Timothy D. Dewey *(Mgr-Sls)*
Tim D. Schwer *(Exec VP)*

Subsidiaries:

Vilsmeier Auction Co.   **(1)**
1440 Cowpath Rd, Hatfield, PA 19440
Tel.: (215) 361-9204
Web Site: http://www.hunyady.com
Emp.: 10
Fee-Based Auction Services
N.A.I.C.S.: 561499
Sue Hunyady *(Office Mgr)*

HUNZICKER BROTHERS INC.

501 N Virginia Ave, Oklahoma City, OK 73106
Tel.: (405) 239-7771
Web Site: https://www.hunzicker.com
Rev.: $40,000,000
Emp.: 65
Electrical Supplies Sales
N.A.I.C.S.: 423610
Kim Louthan *(Branch Mgr)*
Louie Blough *(Mgr)*
Mike Lockard *(Pres & CEO)*
Scott Shepherd *(Branch Mgr)*
Travis Harrell *(Mgr-Sesco-Oklahoma City)*
Jack Henderson *(Exec VP)*
Elizabeth Brawner *(Controller)*
Linda Johnson *(Mgr-HR-Oklahoma)*
Brandi Guethle *(Mgr-Mktg-Oklahoma)*
Evan Smith *(Mgr-Ops)*
Stacey Loud *(Mgr-Pur-Oklahoma)*
Jerry Young *(VP-Sls-Oklahoma)*

HUNZINGER CONSTRUCTION COMPANY

21100 Enterprise Ave, Brookfield, WI 53045
Tel.: (262) 797-0797
Web Site: https://www.hunzinger.com
Rev.: $150,000,000
Emp.: 185
Commercial & Institutional Building Construction
N.A.I.C.S.: 236220
John C. Hunzinger *(Pres)*
Kevin P. O'Toole *(Exec VP)*
Jim Hunzinger *(Exec VP)*
Larry Palank *(VP-Preconstruction)*
Matt Hunzinger *(VP)*

HUPP ELECTRIC MOTORS INC.

275 33rd Ave SW, Cedar Rapids, IA 52404
Tel.: (319) 366-0761
Web Site: http://www.hupp-electric.com
Rev.: $15,000,000
Emp.: 175
Electrical Equipment Repair, High Voltage
N.A.I.C.S.: 423610
Sheri Kosman *(Acct Mgr)*
Terry Dolezal *(VP)*
Ignacio Mendieta *(Mgr-Engineered Products Div)*

HUPP REALTY ADVISORS, INC.

907 S Ft Harrison Ave Ste 102, Clearwater, FL 33756
Tel.: (727) 210-1900
Web Site: http://www.hupprealty.com
Year Founded: 1995
Sales Range: $1-9.9 Million
Emp.: 3
Real Estate Appraisal, Investment, Development & Management
N.A.I.C.S.: 531390
Andrew J. Hupp *(Owner & Pres)*
Rosalie Gallina *(Office Mgr)*

HURCKMAN MECHANICAL INDUSTRIES

1450 Velp Ave, Green Bay, WI 54303
Tel.: (920) 499-8771
Web Site: https://www.hurckman.com
Sales Range: $10-24.9 Million
Emp.: 100
Mechanical Contractor
N.A.I.C.S.: 238220
Bonnie Deschantz *(Dir-Mktg)*
Brad Franklin Hurckman *(Pres)*

HURLEY CHANDLER & CHAFFER

2757 Pawtucket Ave Ste 200, East Providence, RI 02914
Tel.: (401) 273-5530   **RI**
Year Founded: 1982
Sales Range: $10-24.9 Million
Emp.: 14
N.A.I.C.S.: 541810
Bob Hurley *(Partner & Acct Exec)*
Tom Chandler *(Partner & Dir-Creative)*
Kerry Chaffer *(Partner & Acct Mgr)*
Bill De Witt *(Partner & Mgr-Acct)*

HURLEY CHRYSLER PLYMOUTH

2173 S Woodland Blvd, Deland, FL 32720
Tel.: (386) 736-3000
Web Site: http://hurleycars.com
Year Founded: 1990
Sales Range: $10-24.9 Million
Emp.: 35
Car Whslr
N.A.I.C.S.: 441110
J. Brenday Hurley *(Pres)*

HURLEY LIMOUSINE INC.

820 Rte 15 S, Lake Hopatcong, NJ 07849
Tel.: (908) 654-9000
Web Site: http://www.hurleylimo.com
Rev.: $10,000,000
Emp.: 120
Limousine Service
N.A.I.C.S.: 485320
John Hurley *(Pres)*

HURON CAPITAL PARTNERS LLC

500 Griswold St Ste 2700, Detroit, MI 48226
Tel.: (313) 962-5800   **MI**
Web Site:
   http://www.huroncapital.com
Year Founded: 1999
Privater Equity Firm
N.A.I.C.S.: 523999
Brian A. Demkowicz *(Founder & Chm)*
Mike Beauregard *(Sr Partner)*
Peter E. Mogk *(Sr Partner)*
James Mahoney *(Mng Partner)*
Heather Madland *(Principal-Bus Dev)*
Matthew R. Hare *(Partner, CFO, COO & Chief Compliance Officer)*
Scott Hauncher *(Partner)*
Brian Rassel *(Partner)*
Michael Zukas *(Principal)*
Brian C. Walker *(Operating Partner)*
Tony Pulice *(Partner)*

Subsidiaries:

Absolute Coatings, Inc.   **(1)**
38 Portman Rd, New Rochelle, NY 10801
Tel.: (914) 636-0700
Web Site: http://www.absolutecoatings.com
Rev.: $9,459,676
Emp.: 40
Paint & Coating Mfr
N.A.I.C.S.: 325510
Jason Anagnostis *(VP & Gen Mgr-Automotive Div)*

Albireo Energy, LLC   **(1)**
3 Ethel Rd Ste 300, Edison, NJ 08817
Tel.: (732) 512-9100
Web Site: http://www.albireoenergy.com

Holding Company; Energy Products & Services
N.A.I.C.S.: 551112
George West *(Sr VP-Ops)*
Phil Rogers *(CEO)*
Jason Richards *(Pres & COO)*
James Mahoney *(Chm)*
James Denning *(CFO)*

Subsidiary (Domestic):

Advanced Automated Systems, Inc.   **(2)**
23691 Via Del Rio, Yorba Linda, CA 92887
Tel.: (714) 692-9003
Web Site:
   http://www.advancedautomated.com
Electrical Contractor
N.A.I.C.S.: 238210
Keith Voysey *(CTO)*

Electronic Control Systems, Inc.   **(2)**
12575 Kirkham Ct, Poway, CA 92064
Tel.: (858) 513-1911
Web Site: http://www.ecscontrols.com
Emp.: 50
Building Control Services
N.A.I.C.S.: 238210
Zbigniew Z. Cabaj *(Pres)*
Seth Schreiner *(VP)*
Jason McGehee *(Mgr-Tech)*
Walter Houle *(Acct Exec)*
Peter Trusewicz *(Project Mgr)*

Energy Management Control Corporation   **(2)**
4315 36th St, Long Island City, NY 11101
Tel.: (718) 786-7910
Electrical Apparatus & Equipment, Wiring Supplies & Related Equipment Merchant Whslr
N.A.I.C.S.: 423610

Energy Options, Inc.   **(2)**
3 Ethel Rd Ste 300, Edison, NJ 08817
Tel.: (732) 512-9100
Web Site: http://www.energy-options.com
Commercial Automation & Monitoring Equipment Installation & Maintenance Services
N.A.I.C.S.: 238210
Bradley Freeman *(Pres)*
Ed Bagonyi *(Mgr-Construction)*

Green Total Solutions, Inc.   **(2)**
Carmelo Dr, Camp Pendleton, CA 92058
Tel.: (858) 551-8190
Web Site:
   http://www.greentotalsolutions.com
Energy Technology Consulting Services
N.A.I.C.S.: 561210
Hector Lizarraga *(CEO)*

GxP Automation LLC.   **(2)**
121 Brick Kiln Rd Ste 100, Chelmsford, MA 01824
Tel.: (978) 710-3517
Web Site: http://www.gxpautomation.com
Process Control System Maintenance Services
N.A.I.C.S.: 811310
Jay Zaino *(Co-Founder & Pres)*
Mark Bryan *(VP)*
Jerome Kapferer *(Mgr-Ops)*

Quality Building Controls, Inc.   **(2)**
10011 Williams Rd, Tampa, FL 33624
Tel.: (813) 885-5005
Web Site:
   http://www.qualitybuildingcontrols.com
Sales Range: $1-9.9 Million
Emp.: 35
Building Automation Systems Supplier
N.A.I.C.S.: 423830
Gerald Dohse *(Pres)*

American Auto Auction Group, LLC   **(1)**
49 Archdale St Ste 100, Charleston, SC 29401
Tel.: (843) 579-2886
Web Site: http://www.xlerategroup.com
Emp.: 200
Holding Company; Used Car Auctioneer
N.A.I.C.S.: 551112
Cam Hitchcock *(CEO)*
Kelly McAllister *(Exec Dir-Digital Strategy)*
Pat Dudash *(Sr VP-Sls)*
Chuck Tapp *(Exec VP)*

Huron Capital Partners LLC—(Continued)

Subsidiary (Domestic):

Columbus Fair Auto Auction, Inc. (2)
4700 Groveport Rd, Columbus, OH 43207-5217
Tel.: (614) 497-2000
Web Site: http://www.cfaa.com
Wholesale Trade Agents & Brokers
N.A.I.C.S.: 425120

Corry Auto Dealers Exchange, Inc. (2)
12141 Rte 6, Corry, PA 16407-9542
Tel.: (814) 664-7721
Web Site: http://www.corryade.com
Automobile & Other Motor Vehicle Auction Whslr
N.A.I.C.S.: 423110
Merle E. Swift (Pres)

Grand Rapids Auto Auction (2)
2380 Port Sheldon Ct, Jenison, MI 49428-8188
Tel.: (616) 669-1050
Web Site: http://www.grandrapidsautoauction.com
Automobile Auction Services
N.A.I.C.S.: 425120
Mark Capel (Gen Mgr)
Deb Dotson (Chief Compliance Officer)

Texas Lone Star Auto Auction Lubbock (2)
2706 E Slaton Rd, Lubbock, TX 79404
Tel.: (806) 745-6606
Web Site: http://www.lsaalubbock.com
Automobile & Other Motor Vehicle Merchant Whslr
N.A.I.C.S.: 423110
Cory Wisdom (Mgr-Fleet/Lease)
Dale Martin (Gen Mgr)
Lorenzo Montoya (Mgr-Mobile Sls)
Stuart Willer (Mgr-Ops & Transportation)
Trevor Smith (Mgr-Sls)
Wade Kuykendall (Mgr-Collections)
Travis Hair (Mgr-Recon/Arbitration)
Robyn Casey (Mgr-Online Sls)
Diamond Gonzales (Head-HR & Admin Asst)

Your Auction, Inc. (2)
3010 Scherer Dr N, Saint Petersburg, FL 33716
Tel.: (727) 572-8800
Web Site: http://www.yourauctiontampabay.com
Sales Range: $1-9.9 Million
Used Car Auctioneer
N.A.I.C.S.: 425120
Marc Rickey (VP & Gen Mgr)
Pam Plummer (Controller)
Ryan Rickey (VP & Gen Mgr)
Kellie Kaser (Office Mgr)
Bill Lynes (Gen Mgr-Sls)
Mario Allmond (Asst Gen Mgr)
Alex Connors (Dir-Multi-Platform)
Justin Wold (Mgr-Ops)

Aquamar, Inc. (1)
10888 7th St, Rancho Cucamonga, CA 91730
Tel.: (909) 481-4700
Web Site: http://www.aquamar.net
Sales Range: $1-9.9 Million
Emp.: 40
Seafood Canning
N.A.I.C.S.: 311710
Martha Romo (Engr-Quality Assurance)

Dynamic Dental Partners Inc (1)
8620 S Tamiami Trl Ste N-P, Sarasota, FL 34238
Tel.: (941) 918-4300
Web Site: http://www.ddpfl.com
Dental Care Services
N.A.I.C.S.: 621210
Alex A. Giannini (CEO)
Armando J. Yanez (CFO)
George N. Strickland (Chief Clinical Officer)
Marvin Terrell (COO)
Lisa A. Woodman (Chief Admin Officer)
Maria Pia Giannini (Dir-Transitions)

Subsidiary (Domestic):

Comfortable Care Dental Group, Inc. (2)

5540 Bee Ridge Rd Ste 1, Sarasota, FL 34233
Tel.: (941) 220-0896
Web Site: http://www.comfortablecarebeeridge.com
Emp.: 75
Dental Care Services
N.A.I.C.S.: 621210
Alex Giannini (Pres)

Exigent Holdco LLC (1)
11921 Freedom Dr Ste 550, Reston, VA 20190
Tel.: (571) 205-4968
Web Site: https://exigentservices.com
Plumbing, Heating & Air-Conditioning Services
N.A.I.C.S.: 238220
Peter van Niekerk (CEO)

Subsidiary (Domestic):

Ambient Temperature Corp. (2)
14 Graf Rd, Newburyport, MA 01950
Tel.: (978) 646-0660
Web Site: http://www.ambienttemperature.com
Rev.: $2,920,000
Emp.: 20
Site Preparation Contractor
N.A.I.C.S.: 238910

JPG Plumbing and Mechanical Services, Inc. (2)
6700 Distribution Dr Ste 2, Beltsville, MD 20705-1436
Web Site: http://www.jpgplumbing.com
Plumbing, Heating & Air-Conditioning Contractors
N.A.I.C.S.: 238220

InterVision Systems, LLC (1)
2250 Walsh Ave, Santa Clara, CA 95050
Tel.: (408) 980-8550
Web Site: http://www.intervision.com
IT Infrastructure Solutions & Consulting
N.A.I.C.S.: 541512
Jonathan Lerner (Pres & CEO)
Jim Zaloudek (CFO & Interim COO)
Tony Bailey (Sr VP-Alliances)

Subsidiary (Domestic):

SyCom Technologies, L.L.C. (2)
1802 Bayberry Ct Ste 201, Richmond, VA 23226
Tel.: (804) 262-7100
Web Site: http://www.sycomtech.com
Sales Range: $50-74.9 Million
Emp.: 124
System Integration & Consulting Services
N.A.I.C.S.: 541512
Thomas J. Cricchi (Pres & CEO)
Renee L. Symons (VP-Strategic Ops)
Tom Carr (Sr VP-Sls & Emerging Markets)
Patrick Miller (VP-Tech)
John Schmohl (CFO)

Lab Crafters Inc. (1)
2085 5th Ave, Ronkonkoma, NY 11779-6903 (100%)
Tel.: (631) 471-7788
Web Site: http://www.lab-crafters.com
Laboratory Furniture & Fixtures Mfr
N.A.I.C.S.: 337127
Roberta DeLuca (Pres & CEO)

National Paint Industries, Inc. (1)
1999 Elizabeth St, North Brunswick, NJ 08902
Web Site: http://www.ipaint.us
Paints & Allied Products Mfr, Distr & Retailer
N.A.I.C.S.: 325510

Ronnoco Coffee, LLC (1)
4241 Sarpy Ave, Saint Louis, MO 63110
Tel.: (314) 371-5050
Web Site: http://www.ronnoco.com
Sales Range: $10-24.9 Million
Coffee, Tea & Other Brewing Products Mfr & Distr
N.A.I.C.S.: 311920
Dan Moloney (Pres)
Terry McDaniel (CEO)

Subsidiary (Domestic):

Henderson Coffee Corp (2)
3421 S 24th St W, Muskogee, OK 74401
Tel.: (918) 682-8751

Web Site: http://www.hendersoncoffee.com
Sales Range: $1-9.9 Million
Coffee Mfr & Distr
N.A.I.C.S.: 311920
Michael Dayan (Mgr-Bus Dev)

International Blends Coffee Co (2)
2204 Stone Hill Rd, Jefferson City, MO 65101
Tel.: (573) 636-2877
Web Site: http://www.internationalblends.net
Coffee Vending Machine Operator
N.A.I.C.S.: 445132

U.S. Roasterie, Inc. (2)
4100 Dixon St, Des Moines, IA 50313
Tel.: (515) 243-8805
Web Site: http://www.usroasterie.com
Sales Range: $1-9.9 Million
Emp.: 60
Coffee Mfr & Coffee Labels Mfr & Distr
N.A.I.C.S.: 311920
Howard Fischer (Pres)

Six Month Smiles, Inc. (1)
35 Main St, Scottsville, NY 14546
Tel.: (585) 594-0606
Web Site: http://www.6monthsmiles.com
Dental Care Services
N.A.I.C.S.: 621210
Michael Meehan (Pres & CEO)

Sock & Accessory Brands Global, Inc. (1)
Park Professional Ctr 5380 US Hwy 158 Ste 250, Advance, NC 27006
Tel.: (336) 751-0040
Web Site: http://www.wearsabg.com
Sales Range: $25-49.9 Million
Emp.: 33
Mfr & Distributor of Fashion, Casual & Athletic Socks
N.A.I.C.S.: 315120
Jeff Arnold (CEO)
Joe Amoruso (Sr VP-Sls)
Tom O'Riordan (CEO)
Brey Williams (VP-Sls-Strategic Accts)
Cindy Jones Dickson (Sr VP-Creative & Design)

Subsidiary (Domestic):

Twin City Knitting Co, Inc. (2)
PO Box 1179, Conover, NC 28613
Tel.: (828) 464-4830
Web Site: http://www.tcksports.com
Rev.: $9,500,000
Emp.: 195
Other Hosiery & Sock Mills
N.A.I.C.S.: 315120
Francis Davis (Pres)

Sunland Asphalt & Construction, LLC (1)
1625 E Northern Ave, Phoenix, AZ 85020
Tel.: (602) 323-2800
Web Site: http://www.sunlandasphalt.com
Highway & Street Construction
N.A.I.C.S.: 237310
Diana DeClusin (Treas)
Alex DeClusin (Mgr-Sls-Reg)
Craig Weems (COO)
Josh Phillips (Mgr-Div)
Tom Lawless (CFO)
Doug DeClusin (CEO)

Subsidiary (Domestic):

ACE Asphalt of Arizona, Inc. (2)
3030 S 7th St, Phoenix, AZ 85040
Tel.: (602) 243-4100
Web Site: http://www.aceasphalt.com
Parking Lot Construction & Maintenance
N.A.I.C.S.: 237310
John Drexler (Chm)
Scott Phillips (Pres)

Thermaserve, Inc. (1)
6695 Colray Ct Ste 301, Jacksonville, FL 32258
Tel.: (904) 260-8002
Web Site: http://thermaserve.com
Rev.: $1,898,000
Emp.: 12
Site Preparation Contractor
N.A.I.C.S.: 238910

W. W. Gay Fire & Integrated Systems, Inc. (1)
522 Stockton St, Jacksonville, FL 32204

Tel.: (904) 387-7973
Fire Protection & Security System Installation Services
N.A.I.C.S.: 238990

WSA Systems-Boca Inc. (1)
442 NW 35th St, Boca Raton, FL 33431-5708
Tel.: (561) 393-2933
Web Site: http://www.wsasystems.com
Sales Range: $1-9.9 Million
Emp.: 21
Fire Alarm System Whslr
N.A.I.C.S.: 423610
Golub A. Bradley (Pres)
Del Pizzo Joseph (VP)

HURON CASTING, INC.
7050 Hartley St, Pigeon, MI 48755
Tel.: (989) 453-3933
Web Site: https://www.huroncasting.com
Year Founded: 1976
Sales Range: $25-49.9 Million
Emp.: 450
Steel Foundry Services
N.A.I.C.S.: 331513
Leroy Wurst (Founder & CEO)
Steve Dubs (VP-Mfg)
Frank Kolar (Dir-Engrg & Estimation)

HURON DISTRIBUTORS INC.
509 Cavanaugh St, Alpena, MI 49707
Tel.: (989) 354-3450
Sales Range: $10-24.9 Million
Emp.: 25
Beer & Other Fermented Malt Liquors Distr
N.A.I.C.S.: 424810
James Johnson (Pres)

HURON SMITH OIL CO. INC.
204 Hays St, Batesville, MS 38606-4069
Tel.: (662) 563-9786 MS
Year Founded: 1950
Sales Range: $10-24.9 Million
Emp.: 20
Gas Jobber
N.A.I.C.S.: 457210
Donald Smith (Pres)

HURON VALLEY STEEL CORP.
1650 W Jefferson, Trenton, MI 48183
Tel.: (734) 479-3500 MI
Web Site: http://www.hvsc.net
Year Founded: 1961
Sales Range: $125-149.9 Million
Emp.: 250
Metal Recovery & Processing Services
N.A.I.C.S.: 423930

Subsidiaries:

Huron Valley Steel Corp. - Magnetics Division (1)
820 Ware St, Anniston, AL 36201
Tel.: (256) 238-1746
Emp.: 100
Metal Recovery Services
N.A.I.C.S.: 562920
Tom Bonds (Gen Mgr)

HURRICANE FOODS INC.
800 E Thompson Rd, Indianapolis, IN 46227
Tel.: (317) 789-4000
Sales Range: $10-24.9 Million
Emp.: 10
Fast-Food Restaurant, Chain
N.A.I.C.S.: 722513

HURRICANE SANDY NEW JERSEY RELIEF FUND INC.
906 Mount Kemble Ave 3rd Fl, Morristown, NJ 07960
Tel.: (973) 521-5820 NJ
Web Site: http://www.sandynjrelieffund.org

Year Founded: 2012
Sales Range: $10-24.9 Million
Emp.: 6
Fundraising Services
N.A.I.C.S.: 813211

HURRICANES HOLDINGS, LLC
1400 Edwards Mill Rd, Raleigh, NC
27607-3624
Tel.: (919) 467-7825   DE
Year Founded: 2011
Holding Company; Professional
Hockey Team & Sports Arena Owner
& Operator
N.A.I.C.S.: 551112
Thomas G. Dundon (CEO)
Peter Karmanos Jr. (Pres)

Subsidiaries:

Hurricanes Hockey Limited
Partnership   (1)
1400 Edwards Mill Rd, Raleigh, NC 27607-
3624
Tel.: (919) 467-7825
Web Site:
    http://www.carolinahurricanes.com
Professional Hockey Franchise
N.A.I.C.S.: 711211
Thomas G. Dundon (Governor & CEO)
Peter Karmanos Jr. (Alternate Governor)
Davin Olsen (VP & Gen Mgr-PNC Arena)
Jeff Vanderbilt (CFO)

HURST FARM SUPPLY INC.
Hwy 82 E, Lorenzo, TX 79343
Tel.: (806) 634-5717
Web Site: https://www.hurstfs.com
Year Founded: 1955
Sales Range: $10-24.9 Million
Emp.: 30
Farm Equipment & Supplies Sales
N.A.I.C.S.: 423820
Tim Hill (Mgr-Svc-Abernathy)

HURST HARVEY OIL INC.
1648 Waverly Ave, Kilmarnock, VA
22482
Tel.: (804) 435-2932
Web Site: http://www.getandzip.com
Rev.: $13,322,397
Emp.: 30
Convenience Stores, Independent
N.A.I.C.S.: 445131
Jean C. Lewis (Pres)
Melinda Lewis (Controller)

HURST STORES INCORPO-RATED
160 N Pluss, Saint George, UT
84770
Tel.: (435) 673-6141
Web Site: http://www.hurststores.com
Rev.: $11,100,000
Emp.: 75
Hardware Stores
N.A.I.C.S.: 444140
Dale Nuckles (Controller)
J. Ross Hurst (Owner & Pres)

HURTT FABRICATING CORP.
26707 E Scott Rd, Marceline, MO
64658
Tel.: (660) 376-3501
Web Site: https://www.hurttfab.com
Year Founded: 1966
Sales Range: $10-24.9 Million
Emp.: 13
Metal Fabricating Services
N.A.I.C.S.: 332999
Darren Buckner (Gen Mgr)
Alan Harman (Plant Mgr)
Craig Hengstenberg (Supvr-Engrg)
Robert J. Hurtt Sr. (Pres)

HURWITZ-MINTZ FINEST FUR-NITURE STORE SOUTH LLC
1751 Airline Dr, Metairie, LA 70001

Tel.: (504) 378-1000
Web Site:
    https://www.hurwitzmintz.com
Sales Range: $25-49.9 Million
Emp.: 150
Furniture Retailer
N.A.I.C.S.: 449110
Mitchell Mintz (Owner)
Susan Hibbs (Mgr-Credit)

HUSCH BLACKWELL LLP
4801 Main St Ste 1000, Kansas City,
MO 64112
Tel.: (816) 983-8000
Web Site:
    https://www.huschblackwell.com
Year Founded: 1916
Sales Range: $250-299.9 Million
Emp.: 1,001
Law firm
N.A.I.C.S.: 541110
Paul Haun (Sr Corp Counsel)
Thomas G. Dickson (Partner)
Mark G. Arnold (Partner-Saint Louis)
Melissa Z. Baris (Partner-Saint Louis)
Michael R. Annis (Partner-Saint
Louis)
Kyle C. Barry (Partner-Saint Louis)
Craig A. Adoor (Partner-Saint Louis)
James M. Ash (Partner)
Gary D. Barnes (Partner)
Mark T. Benedict (Partner)
John K. Brungardt (Partner)
Ryan C. Brunton (Partner)
Kirsten A. Byrd (Partner)
Curt J. Chase (Partner)
Jeffrey J. Simon (Partner)
Kevin H. Kelley (Partner)
Sonni Fort Nolan (Partner)
Jennifer Haynes (Partner)
Daniel L. Bray (Partner)
Eric A. Ess (Partner)
Benjamin J. Kelly (Partner)
Joe R. Thompson (Partner)
Thomas N. Molins (Partner)
Megan Scheiderer (Partner)
Sean Tassi (Partner)
John Sholar (Partner)
George Pavlik (Partner)
Amy Hammer (Partner)
Maurice Watson (Chm)
Jack Enea (Mng Partner-Milwaukee)
Mark Grider (Partner-Govt Compli-
ance, Investigations & Litigation-
Washington)
Elise Senti (Partner)
Ernesto Segura (Partner)
J. Andrew Crossett (Partner)
Cortney Morgan (Partner)
Jen Dlugosz (Partner)
Dominique Savinelli (Partner)
Megan Belcher (Partner-Food & Agri-
business Industry)
Joseph Lubinski (Partner-Real Estate,
Dev & Construction Indus Grp)
Vickie L. Driver (Partner)
Paul Eberle (CEO)
Angela Quinn (Chief Client Officer)
Kyle Gilster (Mng Partner-
Washington)
Samantha Lunn (Partner-
Chattanooga)
Nithya Nagarajan (Partner-Tech, Mfg
& Transportation Indus Grp-Intl Trade
Practice)
Stephen Brophy (Partner-Tech, Mfg &
Transportation Indus Grp-Intl Trade
Practice)
Joe Orlet (Head-TMT Grp)
Derek J. Taylor (Partner-Fin Svcs &
Capital Markets Indus Grp-Milwaukee
& Madison)
Tobias P. Moon (Partner-Dallas)
Stephanie Kaiser (Partner-Austin)
Jeffer Ali (Partner)
Daidre L. Burgess (Partner)

Subsidiaries:

Patterson Thuente Pedersen,
P.A.   (1)
4800 IDS Ctr 80 S 8th St, Minneapolis, MN
55402-2100
Tel.: (612) 349-5740
Web Site: http://www.ptslaw.com
Emp.: 23
Law firm
N.A.I.C.S.: 541110
Tye Biasco (Partner)
Aaron W. Davis (Partner)
Eric Hugh Chadwick (Partner, CFO & Atty)
Vadim Braginsky (Partner)
James Rieke (Partner)
Adam Szymanski (Atty-Intellectual Property
Litigation)
Christian Girtz (Partner)
Sarah Stensland (Partner)

HUSCO INTERNATIONAL, INC.
2239 Pewaukee Rd, Waukesha, WI
53188-1638
Tel.: (262) 513-4200   DE
Web Site: http://www.husco.com
Year Founded: 1947
Rev.: $143,000,000
Emp.: 600
Hydraulic & Electro-Hydraulic Con-
trols & Control Valves Mfr
N.A.I.C.S.: 332912
Agustin M. Ramirez (Pres & CEO)

Subsidiaries:

HUSCO Automotive Holdings,
LLC.   (1)
N19W24101 Riverwood Dr Ste 200,
Waukesha, WI 53188-1131
Tel.: (262) 953-1100
Hydraulic Control Valve Mfr
N.A.I.C.S.: 332912

HUSCO Hydraulics Private Ltd.   (1)
Plot A-4 Talegaon Floriculture Ind Estate
MIDC Village, Navlakh Umbre Talegaon,
Pune, 410507, India
Tel.: (91) 2114 305300
Sales Range: $25-49.9 Million
Emp.: 150
Hydraulic Control Valve Mfr
N.A.I.C.S.: 332912

HUSCO International, Ltd.   (1)
6 Rivington Road, Whitehouse Industrial
Estate, Runcorn, WA7 3DT, Cheshire,
United Kingdom   (100%)
Tel.: (44) 1928701888
Web Site: http://www.huscointl.com
Sales Range: $25-49.9 Million
Emp.: 175
Mfr of Hydraulic & Electro-Hydraulic Con-
trols & Control Valves For Off-Highway &
Automotive Applications
N.A.I.C.S.: 332911

HUSCO-KAYABA Hydraulics (Shang-
hai) Ltd.   (1)
No 235 Jiangtian Rd E Song Jiang Indus-
trial Zone, Shanghai, 201600,
China   (85%)
Tel.: (86) 2157746468
Web Site: http://www.huscointl.com
Sales Range: $25-49.9 Million
Emp.: 90
Mfr of Hydraulic & Electro-Hydraulic Con-
trols & Control Valves For Off-Highway &
Automotive Applications
N.A.I.C.S.: 332911

INCOVA Technologies, Inc.   (1)
1116 Universal Blvd, Whitewater, WI 53190
Tel.: (262) 472-7200
Web Site: http://www.incova.com
Sales Range: $10-24.9 Million
Emp.: 100
Design & Production of Systems & Compo-
nents for Automotive & Off-Highway Original
Equipment Manufacturers (OEM's)
N.A.I.C.S.: 332911
Austin M. Ramirez (CEO)

HUSEBY, LLC
1230 W Morehead St Ste 102, Charlotte, NC 28208-5210

Tel.: (704) 333-9889   DE
Web Site: http://www.huseby.com
Year Founded: 1928
Court Reporting & Litigation Support
Services
N.A.I.C.S.: 561492
Scott Huseby (Chm)
Mark Schaffner (Pres)
Jeff Barefoot (CFO)
Glenn Miller (CIO)
Brad Wickard (VP-Mktg)
Scott Klein (VP-Sls)
Doug Yarborough (Ops Mgr)

Subsidiaries:

Abextra, Inc.   (1)
8650 Buckhorn Plantation Rd, Sims, NC
27893
Tel.: (800) 333-2082
Translation & Interpretation Services
N.A.I.C.S.: 541930

Edwards Reporting Inc.   (1)
435 Katherine Dr Ste A, Flowood, MS
39232
Tel.: (601) 355-3376
Web Site: http://www.edwardsreporting.com
Court Reporting & Stenotype Services
N.A.I.C.S.: 561492

Maxene Weinberg Agency   (1)
1801 Century Park E 24th Fl, Los Angeles,
CA 90067
Tel.: (310) 552-0702
Web Site: http://www.mwadepos.net
Litigation Support Services
N.A.I.C.S.: 541199
Maxene Weinberg (CEO)
Stanley Weinberg (CFO)
Wes W. Kennedy (Exec VP)
Gus Serrano (Mgr-Production)
Sabrina DeRosa (Mgr-Client Svcs)
Jeanette Pasut (Mgr-Scheduling Svcs)
Suzette Tirado (Coord-Production & Video
Svcs)

HUSKER AG, LLC.
54048 Hwy 20, Plainview, NE 68769
Tel.: (402) 582-4446
Web Site: https://www.huskerag.com
Year Founded: 2000
Sales Range: $10-24.9 Million
Emp.: 48
Ethyl Alcohol Mfr
N.A.I.C.S.: 325193
Kristine Wacker (Controller)
Shaun Waldow (Plant Mgr)
Mike Wragge (Mgr-Production)
William Steffen (Mgr-Production)
Steve Mattern (Mgr-Utilities)
Kasey Richardson (Mgr-Maintenance)
Ross Wortman (Coord-CMMS)
Amy Greger (Mgr-Lab)
Seth Harder (Gen Mgr)

HUSKER COOP
1854 14th Ave, Columbus, NE 68601
Tel.: (402) 563-3636
Web Site:
    http://www.frontiercooperative.com
Sales Range: $25-49.9 Million
Emp.: 100
Grains
N.A.I.C.S.: 424510
Craig Franzen (Asst Gen Mgr)

HUSKY ADVERTISING, INC.
3933 Harca St, Eagle River, AK
99577-9709
Tel.: (907) 694-2977   AK
Year Founded: 1979
Sales Range: Less than $1 Million
Emp.: 1
Advetising Agency
N.A.I.C.S.: 541810
Chuck Talsky (Founder & Pres)

HUSKY ENVELOPE PROD-

HUSKY ENVELOPE PROD—(CONTINUED)

UCTS INCORPORATED
1225E W Maple Rd, Walled Lake, MI 48390
Tel.: (248) 624-7070
Web Site:
http://www.huskyenvelope.com
Rev.: $10,700,000
Emp.: 115
Envelopes Mfr
N.A.I.C.S.: 322230
William E. Settle (CEO)
Brian Tabaczka (VP & Mgr-Sls-Natl)
Dawn Reske (Pres)

HUSKY INTERNATIONAL TRUCKS INC.
13123 48th Ave S, Seattle, WA 98168-3306
Tel.: (206) 433-3466
Web Site:
http://www.huskytrucks.com
Year Founded: 1985
Sales Range: $25-49.9 Million
Emp.: 150
Automobiles Services
N.A.I.C.S.: 441110
Mike McDevitt (Pres)
Bill McJannet (Mgr)
Jodi Wilks (Mgr)
Tony Molina (Mgr-Sls)

HUSKY SPRING
5463 Mountain Iron Dr Ste 100, Virginia, MN 55792-3304
Tel.: (218) 741-4144
Web Site:
http://www.huskyspring.com
Year Founded: 1988
Sales Range: $1-9.9 Million
Emp.: 9
Nonwire Steel Springs Mfr
N.A.I.C.S.: 811114
Lee Anderson (Pres)
Mike Hamari (Gen Mgr)
John Kauppila (Mgr-Virgina)
Chad Decker (Mgr-Saint Cloud)
Mike Pavek (Mgr-Minneapolis)

HUSS BREWING CO. LLC
1520 W Mineral Rd Ste 102, Tempe, AZ 85283
Tel.: (480) 264-7611
Web Site:
https://www.hussbrewing.com
Brewery
N.A.I.C.S.: 312120
Jeff Huss (Co-Owner)
Leah Huss (Co-Owner)

Subsidiaries:

Papago Brewing Co. Inc.　　　　　(1)
7107 E McDowell Rd, Scottsdale, AZ 85257-3315
Tel.: (480) 425-7439
Web Site: http://www.papagobrewing.com
Restaurant
N.A.I.C.S.: 722511
Leah Huss (Mgr)

HUSSEY SEATING CO.
38 Dyer St Ext, North Berwick, ME 03906-6763
Tel.: (207) 676-2271　　　　ME
Web Site:
https://www.husseyseating.com
Year Founded: 1835
Sales Range: $50-74.9 Million
Emp.: 400
Mfr of Roll-out Gym Seats, Auditorium & Stadium Chairs, Telescopic Bleachers & Platforms
N.A.I.C.S.: 337127
Gary Merrill (Pres & CEO)

HUSSUNG MECHANICAL

CONTRACTORS, INC.
6913 Enterprise Dr, Louisville, KY 40214
Tel.: (502) 375-3500
Web Site: https://www.hussung.com
Year Founded: 1966
Sales Range: $25-49.9 Million
Emp.: 175
Plumbing Services
N.A.I.C.S.: 238220

HUSTON ELECTRIC INC.
1915 E N St, Kokomo, IN 46901
Tel.: (765) 457-9137　　　　IN
Web Site:
https://www.hustonelectric.com
Year Founded: 1939
Sales Range: $10-24.9 Million
Emp.: 20
Provider of General Electrical Contracts
N.A.I.C.S.: 238210
Jeff Cardwell (Pres & CEO)
Jason Huston (Exec VP)
Steve Huston (Exec VP)
Rick Cardwell (Mgr-Svc)
Samantha Milburn (Acct Exec)
Sarah Hill (Branch Mgr)
Robin Winter (Coord-Svc)
Kelsi Emery (Mgr-Pur)
Matt Boor (Pres-Sls & Svcs)
Paul Hayes (CFO)
Jon Huston (Pres)

HUSTON SUPPLY CO. INC.
2 Interhaven Ave, North Plainfield, NJ 07060
Tel.: (908) 439-6177
Web Site:
https://www.hustonlumber.com
Sales Range: $10-24.9 Million
Emp.: 75
Lumber & Other Building Materials Distr
N.A.I.C.S.: 423310
Nicholas J. Pietrone (Pres)
Paul Romano (Office Mgr)

HUTCHCRAFT VAN SERVICE, INC.
1614 N Lincoln Ave, Urbana, IL 61801
Tel.: (217) 328-3333
Web Site:
https://www.hutchcraftvanservice.com
Year Founded: 1946
Rev.: $3,000,000
Emp.: 34
Used Household & Office Goods Moving
N.A.I.C.S.: 484210
Orin J. Hutchcraft (Pres)
Jim Hutchcraft (VP)

HUTCHENS CHEVROLET
12920 Jefferson Ave, Newport News, VA 23608
Tel.: (757) 874-8111
Web Site:
http://www.hutchenschevrolet.com
Year Founded: 1921
Sales Range: $10-24.9 Million
Emp.: 77
New Car Dealers
N.A.I.C.S.: 441110
Kevin McLaughlin (Gen Mgr)

HUTCHENS INDUSTRIES INC.
215 N Patterson Ave, Springfield, MO 65802
Tel.: (417) 862-5012　　　　MO
Web Site:
https://www.hutchensindustries.com
Year Founded: 1950
Sales Range: $100-124.9 Million

Emp.: 300
Mfr of Suspension Systems & Sliding Subframes for Trailers & Trucks; Custom Steel Fabrication; Stampings & Castings
N.A.I.C.S.: 336390
Jeffrey C. Hutchens (Pres)
Brandon Covault (Mgr-Great Lakes Sls Territory)
Dan Cordier (VP-Sls)

Subsidiaries:

Mans-Steel Division　　　　　　　(1)
PO Box 137, Mansfield, MO 65704-0137
Tel.: (417) 924-3274
Steel Manufacturing
N.A.I.C.S.: 331513

Mans-Steel Foundry　　　　　　　(1)
898 E Comml St, Mansfield, MO 65704
Tel.: (417) 862-5012
Web Site:
http://www.hutchensindustries.com
Sales Range: $10-24.9 Million
Emp.: 50
Steel Manufacturing
N.A.I.C.S.: 331513
Jeff Hutchens (Pres & CEO)

HUTCHERSON TILE COMPANY
130 Mitchell Rd, Houston, TX 77037
Tel.: (281) 447-6354
Web Site:
http://hutchersontile.trustab.org
Sales Range: $10-24.9 Million
Emp.: 35
Tiles Mfr
N.A.I.C.S.: 423320
Mozelle Hutcherson (Pres)
Floyd Hall (Mgr)

HUTCHESON & COMPANY INC.
3017 W Leigh St, Richmond, VA 23230
Tel.: (804) 353-3144
Web Site:
http://www.hutchesonandcompany.com
Year Founded: 1973
Sales Range: $10-24.9 Million
Emp.: 7
Electrical Product Whslr
N.A.I.C.S.: 423610
Phillip Hutcheson (Pres)
Ed Hutcheson (Treas & Sec)
Jim Shannon (VP-Outside Sls)
Mark Horton (Mgr-Warehouse)

HUTCHINSON & BLOODGOOD LLP
550 N Brand Blvd Ste 14, Glendale, CA 91203
Tel.: (818) 637-5000
Web Site: https://www.hbllp.com
Sales Range: $10-24.9 Million
Emp.: 120
Accounting Services
N.A.I.C.S.: 541219
David Thompson (Partner-San Diego)
Steve Nessen (Partner)
Duane Sharp (Partner)
Richard Preciado (Mng Partner)
Kalena Rebollar (Controller)
Lauren Lee (Partner)
Bill Eckenrod (Partner)
Geri Wood (Partner)
Ed Cheeseman (COO)

HUTCHINSON HEALTH
1095 Highway 15 S, Hutchinson, MN 55350
Tel.: (320) 484-4438　　　　MN
Web Site:
http://www.hutchinsonhealthfoundation.org
Year Founded: 2007

Sales Range: $75-99.9 Million
Emp.: 720
Health Care Srvices
N.A.I.C.S.: 622110
Cary Linder (Dir-Foundation)

HUTCHINSON SHOCKEY ERLEY & CO.
222 W Adams St Ste 1700, Chicago, IL 60606
Tel.: (312) 443-1550
Web Site: http://www.hsemuni.com
Rev.: $19,525,690
Emp.: 20
Security Brokers & Dealers
N.A.I.C.S.: 523150
Douglas R. Fox (COO)
Tod Miles (Sr VP)
Bob Bergland (Sr VP)
Nancy Meier (CFO)
Paul M. Thompson (Exec VP-Pub Fin)

HUTCHISON INCORPORATED
7460 Hwy 85, Commerce City, CO 80022
Tel.: (303) 287-2826
Web Site: https://www.hutchison-inc.com
Sales Range: $25-49.9 Million
Emp.: 85
Farm & Ranch Products Whslr
N.A.I.C.S.: 423310
George G. Hutchison III (Pres)

HUTCO INC.
114 Park Ctr St, Broussard, LA 70518
Tel.: (337) 837-5594
Web Site: https://www.hutcoinc.com
Rev.: $13,000,000
Emp.: 8
Oil & Gas Company
N.A.I.C.S.: 561320
Yvonne Thomas (Supvr-Acctg)

HUTSON, INC.
306 Andrus Dr, Murray, KY 42071
Web Site: https://www.hutsoninc.com
Year Founded: 1928
Industrial Equipment Distr, Support & Services
N.A.I.C.S.: 423830
Dustin Adams (Mgr-HR)
Brandalyn Jared (Exec VP-HR)
Barry Carson (Pres)
Tracy Martin (CFO)
Doug Lawson (Exec VP-Svc & Parts)
Brian Hobbs (Mgr-Sls Strategy & Asset)
John Halcomb (Mgr-Strategic Initiatives)
Allen Besand (Mgr-Mktg)

Subsidiaries:

Hutson, Inc. - Jasper　　　　　　(1)
2951 N 600 W, Jasper, IN 47546
Tel.: (812) 634-1717
Web Site: http://hutsoninc.com
Farm Equipment Distr
N.A.I.C.S.: 423820
Randy Stemle (Reg Sls Mgr-Large AG)
Dennis Gress (Mgr-Svcs)
Elizabeth Barbero (Mgr-HR)
Greg Kyle (Asst Mgr-Svc)
Ryan Hopf (Mgr-Small AG)
Kenny Schum (Reg Mgr-Aftermarket)
David Main (Mgr-Parts)
Sarel Pretorius (Mgr-AG Svc)
Ivan Clark (Asst Mgr-Svc)
Greg Sermersheim (Mgr-Turf Svc)

HUTSONS AG EQUIPMENT INCORPORATED
1201 Fulton Rd, Mayfield, KY 42066
Tel.: (270) 247-0125　　　　KY
Web Site: http://www.hutsonsinc.com
Year Founded: 1990
Sales Range: $25-49.9 Million
Emp.: 35

Wholesalers of Agricultural Machinery & Equipment
N.A.I.C.S.: 423820
Barry Carson (Gen Mgr)

HUTTON CONSTRUCTION CORP.
2229 S West St, Wichita, KS 67213
Tel.: (316) 942-8855
Web Site:
  http://www.huttonbuilds.com
Year Founded: 1992
Emp.: 240
Construction Services
N.A.I.C.S.: 236220
Mark Hutton (Founder)
Josh Herrman (VP-Design)
Jim Keusler (Officer-Ops)
Benjamen M. Hutton (Chm & CEO)

HVAC DISTRIBUTORS, INC.
2 Old Market St, Mount Joy, PA 17552
Tel.: (717) 653-6674
Web Site: https://www.hvacdist.com
Year Founded: 1987
Sales Range: $25-49.9 Million
Emp.: 94
Construction Services
N.A.I.C.S.: 423730
David W. McIlwaine (Pres)

HVAC SALES AND SUPPLY CO. INC.
2015 Thomas Rd, Memphis, TN 38134-6316
Tel.: (901) 365-1137
Web Site:
  http://www.hvacsalesandsupply.com
Year Founded: 1982
Sales Range: $10-24.9 Million
Emp.: 35
Warm Air Heating Equipment & Supplies
N.A.I.C.S.: 423730
William D. Bomar (Pres)
Dale C. Smith (VP)

HVAC STORES
2900A NW 112th Ave, Doral, FL 33172
Web Site:
  http://www.acwholesalers.com
Year Founded: 2005
Sales Range: $10-24.9 Million
Emp.: 20
Operates a Network of e-Commerce Companies That Sell Climate Control Products & Services
N.A.I.C.S.: 333415
John Piquero (Pres & CEO)

HVAC TECHNOLOGIES, INC.
18 S Main St, Monroe, OH 45050
Tel.: (513) 793-6374   OH
Web Site:
  https://www.houshhomeenergy.com
Year Founded: 2006
Sales Range: $1-9.9 Million
Emp.: 25
Heating, Ventilation & Air Conditioning Contractor
N.A.I.C.S.: 238220
Larry Zimmer (VP)
Marty Boswell (Controller)
William M. Housh IV (Pres & CEO)

HVAC TECHNOLOGIES, INC.
142 S Iredell Industrial Park Rd, Mooresville, NC 28115
Tel.: (704) 878-9801
Web Site: http://www.hvac-technologies.com
Year Founded: 1994
Rev.: $2,300,000
Emp.: 19

Plumbing, Heating & Air-Conditioning Contractors
N.A.I.C.S.: 238220
Julie Turner (Acct Mgr)
Deborah P. Lankford (Exec VP)
B. D. Lankford Jr. (Pres)

HVH TRANSPORTATION INC.
181 E 56th Ave Ste 200, Denver, CO 80216
Tel.: (303) 292-3656   CO
Web Site:
  http://www.hvhtransportation.com
Year Founded: 1977
Sales Range: $25-49.9 Million
Emp.: 245
Provider of Trucking Services
N.A.I.C.S.: 484121
Bruce Holder (CEO)

HVL INC.
600 Boyce Rd, Pittsburgh, PA 15205
Tel.: (800) 245-4440   PA
Web Site:
  http://www.douglaslabs.com
Provider of Medicinal Products
N.A.I.C.S.: 325411

HW HOLDINGS, INC.
506 S Spring St Ste 13575, Los Angeles, CA 90013
Tel.: (213) 741-1920   NV
Web Site: http://www.thethiiird.com
Year Founded: 2006
Sales Range: Less than $1 Million
Emp.: 2
Clothing & Accessories
N.A.I.C.S.: 315990
Kerry Chung (Pres, CEO, Interim CFO, Treas & Sec)

HW MEDIA, LLC
433 E Las Colinas Blvd Ste 830, Irving, TX 75039
Tel.: (469) 893-1480
Web Site: http://www.hwmedia.co
Year Founded: 2016
Online Media; Digital Advertising & Content Marketing
N.A.I.C.S.: 541613
Clayton Collins (CEO)

Subsidiaries:

Real Trends, Inc.   (1)
7501 Village Square Dr Ste 200, Castle Rock, CO 80108
Tel.: (303) 741-1000
Web Site: http://www.realtrends.com
Residential Brokerage Communications & Consulting Services
N.A.I.C.S.: 531390
Doniece Welch (VP & Gen Mgr)
Daniele Stufft (Dir-Event Plng)
Alicia Vivian (CFO)

HW PUBLISHING, LLC
2701 Dallas Pkwy Ste 200, Irving, TX 75038
Tel.: (469) 893-1480
Web Site: http://www.hwpubs.com
Internet Publishing
N.A.I.C.S.: 541810
Paul Jackson (CEO)
James Kleimann (Mng Editor)

Subsidiaries:

HW Creative   (1)
1320 Greenway Dr Ste 870, Irving, TX 75038
Tel.: (469) 893-1480
Web Site: http://www.hwideas.com
Sales Range: $1-9.9 Million
Emp.: 22
Advetising Agency
N.A.I.C.S.: 541810
Paul Jackson (CEO)
Greg Lakloufi (Exec Dir-Creative)

Richard Bitner (Chief Revenue Officer)
Cory Davies (Dir-Brand Dev)
Roseangel DeMoreira (Dir-Art)

HWH CORP.
2096 Moscow Rd, Moscow, IA 52760-9603
Tel.: (563) 724-3396   MT
Web Site: http://www.hwhcorp.com
Year Founded: 1967
Sales Range: $10-24.9 Million
Emp.: 300
Motor Vehicle Parts & Accessories Services
N.A.I.C.S.: 336330
Paul E. Hanser (Pres)

HWH PUBLIC RELATIONS
1173A 2nd Ave #397, New York, NY 10065
Tel.: (212) 355-5049   NY
Web Site: http://www.hwhpr.com
Year Founded: 1977
Sales Range: $1-9.9 Million
Emp.: 30
Public Relations Agency
N.A.I.C.S.: 541820
Eliot Hess (Owner)

Subsidiaries:

HWH Public Relations   (1)
1000 S Pointe Dr, Miami Beach, FL 33139
Tel.: (917) 822-2591
Web Site: http://www.hwhpr.com
Emp.: 5
Public Relations Agency
N.A.I.C.S.: 541820

HWI PARTNERS, LLC
1000 NW St Ste 1200, Wilmington, DE 19801
Tel.: (302) 235-7117
Web Site:
  http://www.hwipartners.com
Sales Range: $10-24.9 Million
Emp.: 50
Privater Equity Firm
N.A.I.C.S.: 523999
Martin K. Hunt (Chm & Mng Dir)
Kenneth W. Hunt Jr. (Partner)

Subsidiaries:

Custom Cable Industries Inc.   (1)
3221 Cherry Palm Dr, Tampa, FL 33619   (100%)
Tel.: (813) 623-2232
Web Site: http://www.customcable.com
Sales Range: $50-74.9 Million
Electronic Cable Production & Installation Services
N.A.I.C.S.: 334419
Stewart Saad (Pres)

HY CITE CORPORATION
333 Holtzman Rd, Madison, WI 53713-2109
Tel.: (608) 273-3373   WI
Web Site: http://www.hycite.com
Year Founded: 1963
Sales Range: $25-49.9 Million
Emp.: 300
Provider of Household Goods
N.A.I.C.S.: 423220
Erik S. Johnson (Chm & CEO)
Arin Brost (CIO & Sr VP)
Dave Zimmerman (Sr VP-Treasury, Banking & Taxation)
Erick Jostad (Sr VP-Consumer Fin)
Glenn Johnston (CFO)
Jessica Marquez (Chief Compliance Officer & Gen Counsel)
Juan Carlos Franco (Sr VP-Sls-South America)
Miguel Angel Gonzalez (Sr VP-Sls & Mktg-North America)
Peter Johnson Jr. (Pres & COO)

Subsidiaries:

Royal Prestige of New York   (1)
10309 37th Ave, Flushing, NY 11368-1940
Web Site: http://www.royalprestige.com
Sales Range: $10-24.9 Million
Emp.: 6
Cookware Supplier
N.A.I.C.S.: 332215

HY LABONNE & SONS INC.
PO Box 448, Woodbury, CT 06798
Tel.: (203) 263-1940
Web Site: http://www.labonnes.com
Sales Range: $10-24.9 Million
Emp.: 250
Independent Grocery Store
N.A.I.C.S.: 445110
Robert H. Labonne Sr. (Owner & CEO)

HY-LINE INTERNATIONAL
1755 Westlakes Pkwy, West Des Moines, IA 50266-8228
Tel.: (515) 225-6030   IA
Web Site: http://www.hyline.com
Year Founded: 1978
Sales Range: $10-24.9 Million
Emp.: 180
Provider of Poultry Genetic Services
N.A.I.C.S.: 112340
Jonathan Cade (Pres)
Nigel Butcher (Mng Dir-Hy-Line-UK)
Olga Myasnikova (Mgr-Bus Dev-Hy-Line UK International Ltd.)
Daniel Valbuena (Mgr-Latin America)
Eduardo de Souza Pinto (Pres-Ops)
Danny Lubritz (Dir-R&D)

HY-TEST PACKAGING CORP.
515 E 41st St, Paterson, NJ 07504-1209
Tel.: (973) 754-7000   NJ
Web Site: http://www.hy-testpackaging.com
Year Founded: 1956
Sales Range: $1-9.9 Million
Emp.: 20
Custom Chemical Packaging
N.A.I.C.S.: 561910
John S. Smith (Chm, Pres & CEO)
Ted Smith (Vice Chm, CFO, Exec VP & Controller)

HY-VEE, INC.
5820 Westown Pkwy, West Des Moines, IA 50266-8223
Tel.: (515) 267-2800   IA
Web Site: https://www.hy-vee.com
Year Founded: 1930
Sales Range: $5-14.9 Billion
Emp.: 93,000
Supermarkets & Other Grocery Retailers (except Convenience Retailers)
N.A.I.C.S.: 445110
Randall Edeker (Chm)
Robert Wei (Mgr-Chinese Express-Asbury Plaza Hy-Vee)
Dan Wellinghoff (Dir-Store)
Travis Buysse (Dir-Store)
Jeremy Gosch (Bd of Dirs, Vice Chm, Vice Chm, Pres, Co/Co-CEO, COO & Pres/Pres-Retail Ops)
Georgia Van Gundy (Sr VP)
Jonathan Adashek (Chief Comm Officer)
Martin Schroeter (Sr VP-Global Markets)
Casey Decker (CIO)
Matt Ludwig (Chief Supply Chain Officer & Exec VP)
Aaron Wiese (Bd of Dirs, Vice Chm, Vice Chm, Co/Co-CEO & Pres/Pres-Subsidiaries & Supply Chain)

Hy-Vee, Inc.—(Continued)

Subsidiaries:

Amber Enterprises, Inc.   **(1)**
10004 S 152nd St, Omaha, NE 68138
Tel.: (402) 896-5000
Web Site: http://www.amberpharmacy.com
Sales Range: $1-9.9 Million
Emp.: 30
Pharmacies & Drug Stores
N.A.I.C.S.: 456110
Erin Harrell *(Dir-Sls)*
Michael Agostino *(Co-Pres)*
Peggy Tomes *(Sr VP-Reimbursement & Billing)*
Jo Ann Hyres *(Sr VP-Sls & Mktg)*
Julie Zatizabal *(Sr VP-Trade Rels)*
Kris Admire *(Mgr-Patient Education & Resources Program)*
Michael Caruso *(Mgr-Pharmacy-Philadelphia)*
Aaron Wiese *(Co-Pres)*
Micaila Ruiz *(Chief Pharmacy Officer)*
Kevin Combs *(Sr VP-Sls & Bus Dev)*

D&D Salads   **(1)**
9425 N 48th St, Omaha, NE 68152-1557
Tel.: (402) 571-4113
Sales Range: $10-24.9 Million
Emp.: 150
Grocery Stores
N.A.I.C.S.: 722511
Terri Damon *(Office Mgr)*

Florist Distributing, Inc.   **(1)**
2403 Bell Ave, Des Moines, IA 50321-1116
Tel.: (515) 243-5228
Web Site: http://www.fdionline.net
Sales Range: $10-24.9 Million
Emp.: 50
Flower Distribution Services
N.A.I.C.S.: 424930
Michael Jones *(VP-Acctg)*
Deb Riedel *(Pres)*

Hy-Vee Construction LLC   **(1)**
5605 NE 22nd St, Des Moines, IA 50313-5902
Tel.: (515) 645-2300
Web Site: http://www.hy-veeconstruction.com
Sales Range: $10-24.9 Million
Emp.: 75
General Contracting Services
N.A.I.C.S.: 236220

Hy-Vee Construction, L.C.   **(1)**
5605 NE 22nd St, Des Moines, IA 50313
Tel.: (515) 645-2300
Web Site: http://www.hy-veeconstruction.com
Emp.: 100
Construction Management Services
N.A.I.C.S.: 237990

Lomar Distributing   **(1)**
2500 Dixon St, Des Moines, IA 50316
Tel.: (515) 244-3105
Sales Range: $25-49.9 Million
Emp.: 120
Grocery Stores
N.A.I.C.S.: 424490
Katie Graham *(Sr VP)*
Tom Hobt *(Pres)*

Midwest Heritage Bank   **(1)**
1025 Braden Ave, Chariton, IA
50049-1714   **(100%)**
Tel.: (641) 774-8581
Web Site: http://www.mhbank.com
Rev.: $2,800,000
Emp.: 70
Savings & Loan Associations Not Federally Chartered
N.A.I.C.S.: 522180
Karen Minkoff *(Controller)*
Tony Kaska *(Pres & CEO)*
Mike Armstrong *(Branch Mgr)*

Perishable Distributors of IA   **(1)**
2741 SE PDI Pl, Ankeny, IA 50021 **(100%)**
Tel.: (515) 965-6300
Web Site: http://www.contactpdi.com
Sales Range: $50-74.9 Million
Emp.: 450
Retail Food & Drug Stores
N.A.I.C.S.: 424470
Andy Mccann *(CEO)*
Jason Farver *(Pres)*

Division (Domestic):

Sunrise Dairy   **(2)**
2741 SE PDI Pl, Ankeny, IA 50021 **(100%)**
Tel.: (515) 964-2281
Web Site: http://www.contactpdi.com
Sales Range: $75-99.9 Million
Emp.: 400
Retail Food & Drug Stores
N.A.I.C.S.: 424470

WJ Holding Company   **(1)**
1814 15th St NW, Rochester, MN 55901
Tel.: (507) 289-6047
Pharmacies & Drug Stores
N.A.I.C.S.: 456110

HYATT AUTOMOTIVE LLC
1887 Hwy 501, Myrtle Beach, SC
29577
Tel.: (843) 626-3657
Web Site:
    http://www.hyattbuickgmc.com
Sales Range: $150-199.9 Million
Emp.: 50
Automobiles, New & Used
N.A.I.C.S.: 441110
Polly Graham *(Controller)*

HYATT DIE CAST & ENGINEERING CORP.
4656 Lincoln Ave, Cypress, CA
90630
Tel.: (714) 826-7550
Web Site:
    https://www.hyattdiecast.com
Sales Range: $10-24.9 Million
Emp.: 113
Aluminum Die-Castings
N.A.I.C.S.: 331523
Walburga Meschuk *(Owner & CEO)*
Mark Miller *(Dir-Aerospace & Defense Products)*

HYATT REGENCY COLUMBUS
350 N High St, Columbus, OH 43215
Tel.: (614) 463-1234
Web Site:
    http://www.columbus.hyatt.com
Year Founded: 1980
Sales Range: $10-24.9 Million
Emp.: 325
Restaurant Operating Services
N.A.I.C.S.: 721110

HYBMM OVERSEAS, INC.
5635 Peachtree Pkwy Ste 150, Norcross, GA 30092
Tel.: (770) 242-8900
Sales Range: $10-24.9 Million
Emp.: 4
Computer Peripheral Equipment
Whslr
N.A.I.C.S.: 423430
H. Pamela Yao *(CFO & Sec)*

HYBRID TRANSIT SYSTEMS, INC.
818 Dows Rd SE, Cedar Rapids, IA
52403
Tel.: (319) 261-0749
Web Site: http://www.hybridtrans.com
Sales Range: $10-24.9 Million
Emp.: 21
Transportation & Freight Forwarding
Services
N.A.I.C.S.: 488999
Robert Helgens *(Founder & Partner)*
Gerald Moore *(COO)*
Cherie Wilson-White *(Mgr-Process & HR)*
Stephen Kossayian *(Mgr-Air Freight)*
Trisha Cornwell *(Controller)*
Angie Swartzendruber *(Dir-HR)*
Kendra Klooster *(Mgr-Ops)*
Melissa Chapman Pelley *(Mgr-Ops)*
Scott Wing *(Mgr-Ops)*
John Miller *(Pres & CEO)*

HYBRIDGE COMMERCIAL REAL ESTATE
119 N 11th St Ste 300 B, Tampa, FL
33602
Tel.: (813) 413-6700
Web Site:
    https://www.hybridgecre.com
Year Founded: 2014
Real Estate Broker
N.A.I.C.S.: 531210
Scott Dobbins *(Founder & Principal)*
David Cobb *(Principal)*
Chris Dowd *(Principal & Dir-Asset Mgmt)*
Justin Boudreau *(Principal & Dir-Brokerage Svcs)*
Janet Galvin *(Dir-Brokerage Svcs & Bus Dev)*
Donna Niles *(Comptroller)*

Subsidiaries:

The Inn on Fifth   **(1)**
699 5th Ave S, Naples, FL 34102
Tel.: (239) 403-8777
Web Site: http://www.innonfifth.com
Hotel
N.A.I.C.S.: 721110
Phil McCab *(Gen Mgr)*

HYCOMP, INC.
60 W 3800 N, Hyde Park, UT 84318
Tel.: (435) 563-3695
Web Site:
    https://www.hycompusa.com
Year Founded: 1969
Sales Range: $1-9.9 Million
Emp.: 40
Oil-Free Air & Gas Compressors Mfr
N.A.I.C.S.: 333912
Robert James *(Pres & CEO)*
Stacey Moss *(Mgr-Quality)*

HYDAC TECHNOLOGY CORPORATION
90 Southland Dr, Bethlehem, PA
18017
Tel.: (610) 266-0100
Web Site: http://www.hydac-na.com
Sales Range: $10-24.9 Million
Emp.: 9,000
Fluid-Power Products Mfr
N.A.I.C.S.: 333998
Matthias Mueller *(Exec VP)*
Doc Dieter *(Pres)*
Sharon Nash *(Dir-Customer Svc)*
Pam Munier *(Dir-HR)*

Subsidiaries:

Hydac Corporation, Accumulator
Division   **(1)**
2280 City Line Rd, Bethlehem, PA 18017
Tel.: (610) 264-9503
Web Site: http://www.hydacusa.com
Filter Elements, Fluid, Hydraulic Line
N.A.I.C.S.: 333995

Hydac Technology Corporation, Electronic Division   **(1)**
2260 City Line Rd, Bethlehem, PA 18017
Tel.: (610) 266-0100
Web Site: http://www.hydacusa.com
Filter Elements, Fluid, Hydraulic Line
N.A.I.C.S.: 333998
Matthias Mueller *(Pres)*

Hydac Technology Corporation, HYCON Division   **(1)**
2260 City Line Rd, Bethlehem, PA 18017
Tel.: (610) 266-0100
Web Site: http://www.hydacusa.com
Filter Elements, Fluid, Hydraulic Line
N.A.I.C.S.: 333998

Hydac Technology Corporation, Hydraulic Division   **(1)**
445 Windy Point Dr, Glendale Heights, IL
60139
Tel.: (630) 545-0800
Web Site: http://www.hydacusa.com
Filter Elements, Fluid, Hydraulic Line

N.A.I.C.S.: 423830

HYDE & HYDE INC.
300 El Sobrante Rd, Corona, CA
92879
Tel.: (951) 817-2300
Web Site:
    http://www.hydeandhyde.com
Rev.: $64,188,373
Emp.: 225
Candy & Salad
N.A.I.C.S.: 424450
Allen Hyde *(Chm)*
Charles Myberger *(Dir-Mfg)*
Gladys Wan *(Supvr-Quality Control)*
Thomas Stedman *(Mgr-Acctg)*

HYDE MANUFACTURING COMPANY
54 Eastford Rd, Southbridge, MA
01550-1875
Tel.: (508) 764-4344   MA
Web Site: https://www.hydetools.com
Year Founded: 1917
Sales Range: $75-99.9 Million
Emp.: 150
Hand Tools for the Paint, Drywall,
Flooring, Masonry & Industrial Knife
Markets Mfr & Distr
N.A.I.C.S.: 332216
Richard R. Clemence *(CEO)*
Robert Scoble *(Pres)*

Subsidiaries:

American Paint Paddle Co.   **(1)**
7240 Crosspark Dr, Charleston, SC
29418-8475   **(100%)**
Tel.: (843) 767-5229
Web Site:
    http://www.americanpaintpaddle.com
Sales Range: $10-24.9 Million
Emp.: 30
Wood Paint Paddles, Paint Can Openers &
Wood Yardsticks, Rulers, Wood Book Marks
N.A.I.C.S.: 321999
Jill Chamberlain *(Owner)*

Dexter-Russell Inc.   **(1)**
44 River St, Southbridge, MA
01550   **(100%)**
Tel.: (508) 765-0201
Web Site: http://www.dexter-russell.com
Sales Range: $25-49.9 Million
Mfr of Professional & Industrial Cutlery
N.A.I.C.S.: 332215
Jim Bellerose *(Mgr-Mktg)*
Kevin Clark *(VP-Sls)*
John Looney *(Mgr-HR)*

Wilson Machine Knife Co., Inc.   **(1)**
54 Eastford Rd, Southbridge, MA
01550   **(100%)**
Tel.: (508) 764-2184
Sales Range: $10-24.9 Million
Emp.: 4
Cutting Knives for Textile Industry Mfr
N.A.I.C.S.: 332216
Richard Clemence *(Pres)*

HYDE PARK CAPITAL PARTNERS, LLC
701 N Franklin St, Tampa, FL 33602
Tel.: (813) 383-0202   FL
Web Site:
    http://www.hydeparkcapital.com
Sales Range: $10-24.9 Million
Emp.: 10
Equity Investment Firm
N.A.I.C.S.: 523999
Keith W. Hodgdon *(Mng Dir)*
Greg Bosl *(VP)*
Jeffrey Hendricks *(VP-Bus Dev)*
Jami Gold *(VP-Bus Dev)*
Charlie Hendrick *(VP)*

John H. Hill Jr. *(Co-Founder & Sr Mng Dir)*
John M. McDonald III *(Co-Founder & Sr Mng Dir)*

HYDE PARK COMMUNICATIONS

1101 17th St NW Ste 508, Washington, DC 20036-4715
Tel.: (202) 872-4860
Sales Range: $10-24.9 Million
Emp.: 22
Public Relations Agency
N.A.I.C.S.: 541820
Jeffrey Sandman *(CEO)*

HYDE PARK HOLDINGS LLC

461 5th Ave, New York, NY 10017
Tel.: (212) 644-3450
Web Site: http://www.hphllc.com
Year Founded: 1986
Sales Range: $10-24.9 Million
Emp.: 2
Provider of Management Services
N.A.I.C.S.: 561110
Laurence S. Levy *(Chm)*

Subsidiaries:

NEPW Logistics, Inc.   (1)
309 Lewiston Rd, Mechanic Falls, ME 04256
Tel.: (207) 333-3345
Web Site: http://www.nepw.com
Warehousing & Outsourced Logistics Services
N.A.I.C.S.: 488510
Andrew Gilman *(Chm)*
Debra Roy *(VP-Transportation)*
George Graves *(VP-Supply Chain Dev)*

HYDE PARK INC.

3000 E 1st Ave Ste 243, Denver, CO 80206
Tel.: (303) 333-4446
Web Site:
    https://www.hydeparkjewelers.com
Sales Range: $10-24.9 Million
Emp.: 65
Jewelry Stores
N.A.I.C.S.: 458310
Shereen Pollak *(Pres)*

HYDE TOOLS, INC.

54 Eastford Rd, Southbridge, MA 01550-1875
Tel.: (508) 764-4344
Web Site: https://www.hydetools.com
Rev.: $41,900,000
Emp.: 135
Hand & Edge Tool Mfr
N.A.I.C.S.: 332216
Corey Talbot *(VP-Sls & Mktg)*
Robert Scoble *(COO & Exec VP)*
Richard M. Clemence *(Pres)*

HYDR-O-SEAL, INC.

1801 S Archibald Ave, Ontario, CA 91761-7677
Tel.: (949) 465-0555
Web Site: http://www.hydr-o-seal.com
Rev.: $18,800,000
Emp.: 37
Industrial Supplies Merchant Whslr
N.A.I.C.S.: 423840
Jason Van Driel *(CFO)*
Adam Burgener *(Pres)*

HYDRA-MATIC PACKING COMPANY

2992 Franks Rd, Huntingdon Valley, PA 19006
Tel.: (215) 676-2992
Web Site: http://www.hydra-maticinc.com
Rev.: $17,900,000
Emp.: 55
Fiberglass Building Materials

N.A.I.C.S.: 423330
Mark McKenna *(Pres)*
Kathy Tressue *(Office Mgr)*

HYDRA-POWER SYSTEMS INC.

5445 NE 122nd Ave, Portland, OR 97230
Tel.: (503) 777-3361
Web Site:
    http://www.hydrapowersystems.com
Year Founded: 1970
Rev.: $17,727,490
Emp.: 60
Hydraulic Systems Equipment & Supplies
N.A.I.C.S.: 423830
Dan Sowards *(VP)*
Jeff Stuart *(Pres)*
Andy Johnson *(Controller)*

HYDRAFLOW EQUIPMENT CO.

8125 Brentwood Industrial Dr, Saint Louis, MO 63144
Tel.: (314) 644-6677
Web Site:
    http://www.hydraflowequipment.com
Sales Range: $10-24.9 Million
Emp.: 25
Industrial Machinery & Equipment
N.A.I.C.S.: 423830
Steve Taylor *(VP)*
Kenneth A. Taylor Jr. *(Pres & Controller)*

HYDRAFLOW INC.

1881 W Malvern St, Fullerton, CA 92833
Tel.: (714) 773-2600
Web Site:
    http://www.hydraflowusa.com
Year Founded: 1961
Emp.: 250
Mfr of Aircraft Parts & Equipment
N.A.I.C.S.: 336413
Cindy Ayloush *(CFO & VP)*
Dennis Ullrich *(Pres)*
Paul Rodolf *(Mgr-Ops)*

HYDRAFORCE INC.

500 Barclay Blvd, Lincolnshire, IL 60069
Tel.: (847) 793-2300
Web Site:
    https://www.hydraforce.com
Sales Range: $10-24.9 Million
Emp.: 500
Control Valves, Fluid Power: Hydraulic & Pneumatic
N.A.I.C.S.: 332912
Peggy Bar *(Mgr-Customer Svc)*
Sam Bloodgood *(Mgr-Sls)*
Bill Fredrickson *(Engr-Mfg)*
Jacob Gricar *(Engr-Valve Design)*
Jomy Joseph *(Mgr-Incoming Quality)*
Wilson Klassen *(Reg Mgr-Sls)*
Edward Kretsch *(Mgr-Ops)*
Erik Lundstrom *(Engr-Hydraulic Manifold Process)*
Darren Miller *(Engr-Design)*
Dave Nolan *(Dir-Tax)*
Mark Otto *(Engr-Electronic)*
Michael Schneider *(Mgr-Assembly)*
Russ Schneidewind *(Mgr-Sls-OEM)*
Mara Shapiro *(Engr-Mfg)*
Arthur Smith *(VP-Intl Sls & Mktg)*
Scott Wickboldt *(Engr-Design)*
Girish Zaveri *(Mgr-Mfg Engrg)*
Tony Brown *(Dir-Global Operational Excellence)*

HYDRAULIC CONTROLS, INC.

4700 San Pablo Ave, Emeryville, CA 94608-3034
Tel.: (510) 658-8300   CA

Web Site: https://www.hydraulic-controls.com
Year Founded: 1966
Sales Range: $25-49.9 Million
Emp.: 164
Industrial Machinery & Equipment Services
N.A.I.C.S.: 423830

HYDRAULICS INTERNATIONAL, INC.

9201 Independence Ave, Chatsworth, CA 91311-5905
Tel.: (818) 998-1231   CA
Web Site: https://www.hiinet.com
Year Founded: 1976
Sales Range: $150-199.9 Million
Emp.: 341
Provider of Hydraulic Systems
N.A.I.C.S.: 334519
Larry Walker *(Mgr-Pur)*

Subsidiaries:

Flowmetrics, Inc   (1)
9201 Independence Ave, Chatsworth, CA 91311
Tel.: (818) 407-3420
Web Site: http://www.flowmetrics.com
Turbine Flow Meter & Rotameter Mfr
N.A.I.C.S.: 334513

Hydraulics International, Inc. - Pumps Division   (1)
9201 Independece Ave, Chatsworth, CA 91311
Tel.: (818) 407-3400
Web Site: http://www.hii-pumps.com
Hydraulic Equipment Mfr
N.A.I.C.S.: 333996

The Fitting Source, Inc.   (1)
19631 Prairie St, Northridge, CA 91324
Tel.: (818) 998-1528
Web Site: http://www.thefittingsource.com
Emp.: 12
Hose, Fittings & Valve Mfr
N.A.I.C.S.: 332912
Ben Griffith *(Gen Mgr)*

HYDRITE CHEMICAL COMPANY

300 N Patrick Blvd, Brookfield, WI 53045-5831
Tel.: (262) 792-1450   WI
Web Site: http://www.hydrite.com
Year Founded: 1929
Sales Range: $200-249.9 Million
Emp.: 560
Mfr & Producer of Chlorine, Metal Plating, Tanning, Phosphoric Acid & Custom Processing Chemicals
N.A.I.C.S.: 424690
John A. Honkamp *(Pres)*
Michael R. Honkamp *(VP-Admin)*
Paul F. Honkamp *(VP)*
Mark Minsky *(CFO)*
Kara Baldus *(Program Mgr-Food Safety)*

Subsidiaries:

Hydrite Chemical Company - Cottage Grove Plant   (1)
114 N Main St, Cottage Grove, WI 53527
Tel.: (608) 839-4571
Chemical Products Mfr
N.A.I.C.S.: 325998

Hydrite Chemical Company - LaCrosse Plant   (1)
701 Sumner St, La Crosse, WI 54603-2622
Tel.: (608) 784-0024
Chemical Products Mfr
N.A.I.C.S.: 325998

Hydrite Chemical Company - Milwaukee Plant   (1)
7300 W Bradley Rd, Milwaukee, WI 53223
Tel.: (414) 354-3750
Web Site: http://www.hydrite.com
Emp.: 125
Chemical Products Mfr
N.A.I.C.S.: 325998

John Honkmk *(Pres)*

Hydrite Chemical Company - Oshkosh Plant   (1)
191 W 28th Ave, Oshkosh, WI 54902
Tel.: (920) 233-8181
Chemical Products Mfr
N.A.I.C.S.: 325998

Hydrite Chemical Company - Terre Haute Plant   (1)
2400 S Erie Canal Rd, Terre Haute, IN 47802-3106
Tel.: (812) 232-5411
Web Site: http://www.hydrite.com
Emp.: 40
Chemical Products Mfr
N.A.I.C.S.: 325998
Adam Russell *(Mgr-Ops)*

Hydrite Chemical Company - Waterloo Plant   (1)
2815 WCF & N Dr, Waterloo, IA 50703
Tel.: (319) 232-9731
Chemical Products Mfr
N.A.I.C.S.: 325998

Hydrite Chemical Company - Wausau Plant   (1)
7400 Highland Dr, Wausau, WI 54401-9060
Tel.: (715) 848-1890
Web Site: http://www.hydrite.com
Chemical Products Mfr
N.A.I.C.S.: 325998

HYDRO CONSULTING & MAINTENANCE SERVICES, INC.

235 Rotonda Blvd N, Rotonda West, FL 33947
Tel.: (941) 276-2478
Web Site: http://www.hydro911.com
Year Founded: 2005
Sales Range: $10-24.9 Million
Emp.: 16
Management Consulting Services
N.A.I.C.S.: 541618
Ken Hostler *(Exec VP)*
Lorraine T. Krout *(CEO)*
Clyde E. Krout *(Pres)*
John Eppley *(Mgr-Bus Dev-West)*

HYDRO TUBE ENTERPRISES, INC.

137 Artino St, Oberlin, OH 44074-1205
Tel.: (440) 774-1022
Web Site: https://www.hydrotube.com
Year Founded: 1969
Sales Range: $10-24.9 Million
Emp.: 105
Fabricated Pipe & Pipe Fitting Mfr
N.A.I.C.S.: 332996
Tom Hamel *(VP-Sls)*
Richard Cook *(VP-Ops)*

HYDRO-LOGIC ASSOCIATES, INC.

1940 Soule Rd, Clearwater, FL 33759
Tel.: (727) 724-8337   FL
Web Site: http://www.hydro-logic.org
Year Founded: 1993
Sales Range: $1-9.9 Million
Emp.: 10
Environmental Consulting Services
N.A.I.C.S.: 541620
T. Jay McAllister *(Pres)*

HYDROGEN FUTURE CORPORATION

2525 Robinhood St Ste 1, Houston, TX 77005
Tel.: (514) 420-0333
Year Founded: 2006
Renewable Energy Services
N.A.I.C.S.: 221118

HYDROGEOPHYSICS, INC.

2302 N Forbes Blvd, Tucson, AZ 85745

hydroGEOPHYSICS, Inc.—(Continued)

Tel.: (520) 647-3315
Web Site: https://www.hgiworld.com
Year Founded: 1981
Scientific & Technical Consulting Services
N.A.I.C.S.: 541690
Marc Levitt (Sr Project Mgr)
Christopher Baldyga (Sr Project Mgr)
Bonnie Roripaugh (Office Mgr)
Dale Rucker (CTO)
Nigel Crook (Sr Project Mgr)
Gillian Noonan (Sr Engr)
Brian Cubbage (Project Mgr)
Joe Cain (Officer-Safety)

HYDROMAT INC.
11600 Adie Rd, Maryland Heights,
MO 63043
Tel.: (314) 432-4644
Web Site: http://www.hydromat.com
Sales Range: $100-124.9 Million
Emp.: 219
Metalworking Machinery
N.A.I.C.S.: 423830
Bruno Schmitter (Pres)
Mathias Walter (Chief Sls Officer)
Rodger Boswell (Dir-Sls)

HYDROMETRICS, INC.
3020 Bozeman Ave, Helena, MT
59601-1264
Tel.: (406) 443-4150
Web Site:
https://www.hydrometrics.com
Year Founded: 1979
Hydrological, Geological & Engineering Services
N.A.I.C.S.: 541620
Michael Wignot (Pres)
Bill Thompson (VP & Mgr-Sciences)
Michael Oelrich (Treas, Engr-Civil &
Coord-Environmental)
Marta Jourdonnais (Acctg Admin)

**HYDRONIC & STEAM EQUIP-
MENT CO., INC.**
8950 Bash St, Indianapolis, IN 46256
Tel.: (317) 577-8326   IN
Web Site: https://www.hydstm.com
Rev.: $13,000,000
Emp.: 30
Air Conditioning & Ventilation & Duct
Work Contractor
N.A.I.C.S.: 423730
Al Madden (Controller & Gen Mgr)
Dennis Kring (Pres)

**HYDROPHI TECHNOLOGIES
GROUP, INC.**
3404 Oakcliff Rd Ste C6, Doraville,
GA 30340
Tel.: (404) 974-9910   FL
Web Site: http://www.hydrophi.com
Year Founded: 2010
Sales Range: Less than $1 Million
Emp.: 8
Water-Based Hydrogen Fuel Production Systems Mfr
N.A.I.C.S.: 333995
Reid Meyer (COO)
Jonathan A. Goldman (CTO & VP-
Engrg)
Nikola Zaric (CEO)
Sagiv Israeli (COO)

**HYDROSCIENCE TECHNOLO-
GIES, INC.**
6100 Columbia Rd, Mineral Wells, TX
76067-9253
Tel.: (940) 325-8221   TX
Web Site: http://www.seamux.com
Year Founded: 1996
Sales Range: $1-9.9 Million
Emp.: 32

Oceanographic & Undersea Acoustic
Systems
N.A.I.C.S.: 334511
Fred G. Woodland (Pres & CEO)
Richard Allen (VP-Systems Devel)

HYDROTEX PARTNERS LTD.
12920 Senlac Dr, Farmers Branch,
TX 75234-9237
Tel.: (972) 389-8500
Web Site:
https://www.hydrotexlube.com
Year Founded: 1936
Sales Range: $10-24.9 Million
Emp.: 35
Lubricants & Fuel Improver Solutions
Mfr & Distr
N.A.I.C.S.: 324191
John Beasley (CEO)
John Cummins (VP-Product Tech)
William Link (VP-Sls, Food Process-
ing Market)

HYER INDUSTRIES INC.
91 Schoosett St, Pembroke, MA
02359
Tel.: (781) 826-8101   MA
Web Site:
http://www.thayerscale.com
Year Founded: 1949
Sales Range: $1-9.9 Million
Emp.: 50
Weight Belt, Loss-in-Weight Feeders,
Belt Scales, Bridge Breakers & Bin
Flow Aid Devices Mfr
N.A.I.C.S.: 333998
Frank S. Hyer (Chm & CEO)
Thomas Picone (VP-Sls & Mktg)
David Hyer (Pres)
Desmond Anantharaj (Sls Mgr-South
East Asia)

HYFN
1235 Hermosa Ave Suite 300, Her-
mosa Beach, CA 90254
Web Site: http://www.hyfn.com
Year Founded: 2000
Sales Range: $1-9.9 Million
Emp.: 30
Interactive Design Agency & Develop-
ment Services for iPhone & Android
Applications
N.A.I.C.S.: 541490
Morgan Harris (Founder & CEO)
Peter Pouliopoulos (Exec VP-Client
Partnerships & Mktg)
Adam Gerston (VP-Client Partner-
ships)

HYGEA HOLDINGS CORP.
9100 S Dadeland Blvd Ste 1500, Mi-
ami, FL 33156
Tel.: (786) 497-7718   NV
Year Founded: 2008
Sales Range: $1-9.9 Million
Emp.: 27
Medical Group Practices Operator
N.A.I.C.S.: 621399
Daniel T. McGowan (Chm)
Edward Moffly (CFO)
Martha Castillo (COO)
Lacy Loar (Compliance Officer)
Frank B. Olsen (Sr VP-Ops)

**HYGEN PHARMACEUTICALS,
INC.**
8635 154th Ave NE, Redmond, WA
98052
Tel.: (425) 451-9178
Web Site:
https://www.hygenpharma.com
Year Founded: 1993
Sales Range: $25-49.9 Million
Emp.: 16
Low-Priced Generic Drug Distr
N.A.I.C.S.: 424210

Nishit Mehta (CEO)

**HYGRADE ACQUISITION
METAL MOLDING**
1990 Highland Ave, Bethlehem, PA
18020
Tel.: (610) 866-2441
Web Site:
http://www.hygrademetal.com
Sales Range: $10-24.9 Million
Emp.: 70
Aluminum Pipe & Tube
N.A.I.C.S.: 331318
Vincent A. Pagano (Chm)

Subsidiaries:

Hygrade Metal Moulding Manufactur-
ing Corp.   **(1)**
1990 Highland Ave, Bethlehem, PA 18020-
9083
Tel.: (610) 866-2441
Web Site: http://www.hygrademetal.com
Sales Range: $10-24.9 Million
Emp.: 50
Roll Formed Metal Shapes, Spacer Tubing
Mfr for Insulated Glass
N.A.I.C.S.: 331318
Pat Eitner (Controller)
Doreen Murphy (Mgr-Customer Svc)
Mike Erb (Mgr-Matls)

**HYGRADE BUSINESS GROUP
INC.**
232 Entin Rd, Clifton, NJ 07014   NJ
Web Site:
http://www.hygradebusiness.com
Year Founded: 1981
Rev.: $30,000,000
Emp.: 110
Manifold Business Forms
N.A.I.C.S.: 323111
Jerry Rosenthal (CFO & VP)
Bob Isola (Sr VP-Strategic Accts)
Kelly Corless (VP-Sls)
Phil Masiello (VP-Sls)

Subsidiaries:

Hygrade Business Group   **(1)**
85 Tpke Dr, Waterbury, CT 06722
Tel.: (203) 758-8251
Web Site: http://www.hygradebusiness.com
Sales Range: $10-24.9 Million
Emp.: 15
Stationery & Office Supplies Distr
N.A.I.C.S.: 424120

**HYGRADE DISTRIBUTION &
DELIVERY SYSTEMS**
200 Seaview Dr, Secaucus, NJ
07094
Tel.: (201) 617-1800
Web Site:
http://www.homedelamerica.com
Year Founded: 1965
Rev.: $11,200,000
Emp.: 125
Local Trucking with Storage
N.A.I.C.S.: 484110
Richard Merians (Chm & CEO)
David Boyne (VP-Fin)
Kathy Hill (Dir-HR)

**HYLAN DATACOM & ELECTRI-
CAL, LLC**
101 Crawfords Corner Rd Bldg 2 Ste
2308, Holmdel, NJ 07733
Tel.: (732) 946-6000
Web Site: http://www.hylan.com
Year Founded: 1960
Electrical Repair Shops
N.A.I.C.S.: 811210
Robert DiLeo (Chm)
Scott Gindea (CFO)
Robert Bianco (VP-Bus Dev & Mktg)
Joe Cecin (CEO)
Mark Mickiewicz (Corp Counsel)
Jonathan Jones (Dir-Safety)
John Dileo Jr. (Vice Chm)

Subsidiaries:

Down Under Construction, LLC   **(1)**
10 Bryant Ct, Sterling, VA 20166
Tel.: (703) 709-2221
Web Site: http://www.downunderc.com
Underground Construction Services
N.A.I.C.S.: 237990
Daryl Dunbar (Pres)
David Kole (CFO)
Karen Rutherford (Mgr-Ops)

Western Utility Contractors, Inc.   **(1)**
2565 Palmer Ave, University Park, IL 60484
Tel.: (708) 235-1408
Web Site: http://www.westernutility.com
Emp.: 200
Utility Contractor
N.A.I.C.S.: 237130

Subsidiary (Domestic):

Western Utility LLC   **(2)**
2565 Palmer Ave, University Park, IL 60484
Tel.: (708) 235-1408
Web Site: http://www.westernutility.com
Engineering Services
N.A.I.C.S.: 541330

**HYLAN ELECTRICAL CON-
TRACTING**
950 Holmdel Rd, Holmdel, NJ 07733
Tel.: (732) 946-6000
Web Site: http://www.hylangroup.com
Rev.: $14,200,000
Emp.: 133
General Electrical Contractor
N.A.I.C.S.: 238210
John S. Di Leo Jr. (Pres)

HYLANT GROUP INC.
811 Madison Ave, Toledo, OH 43604
Tel.: (419) 255-1020
Web Site: https://www.hylant.com
Year Founded: 1935
Sales Range: $50-74.9 Million
Emp.: 650
Business Insurance Brokerage, Em-
ployee Benefits & Corporate Wealth
Management Services
N.A.I.C.S.: 524210
Patrick Hylant (Chm)
Richard C. Hylant (Pres-Sls & Inno-
vation)
Jon J. Strole (CFO & Sr VP)
Michael Hylant (CEO)
Kim Carpenter (VP)
Mark Holloway (VP)
Bill Nolan (VP & Mgr-Comml Lines &
Ops)
Jeff Lumpp (Pres-Grand Rapids)
Jim Stengle (Sr VP/Mgr-Employee
Benefits Bus Dev-Employee Benefits
Practice)
Lauren Rooney (Mgr-Personal Lines
Client Svc)
Andy Dale (COO & VP)
Steve Hylant (Exec VP-Detroit)
Patrick Sullivan (Exec VP-Fort
Wayne)
Bess Rumman (VP)
Jennifer Strole (VP)
Joe Wieligman (VP)
Bob Grigas (VP-Cincinnati)
Larry Johnson (VP-Cincinnati)
Steve Ligus (VP-Cleveland)
Todd Bennice (VP-Cleveland Office)
Todd Schreck (VP-Cleveland Office)
Errick Engert (VP-Columbus)
Mike McVey (VP-Columbus)
Steve Federer (VP-Columbus)
William Ley (VP-Detroit)
Guylaine Donavan (VP-Grand Rap-
ids)
John Maple (VP-Nashville)
Todd Harrison (VP-Nashville)

Brian Dinklage *(VP-Orlando)*
Tony Packo *(VP-Strategic Ops-Toledo-Corp Office)*
Deb Bubp *(VP-Talent Mgmt)*
Bob Miller *(VP-Toledo)*
Jeff Barnesky *(VP-Toledo)*
Jessica Xie *(VP-Toledo)*
Anne Marie Towle *(Sr VP)*

Subsidiaries:

Benefit Consulting Alliance, LLC (1)
8 Cadillac Dr Ste 230, Brentwood, TN 37027-5392
Tel.: (615) 724-0782
Employee Benefit Consulting & Brokerage Services
N.A.I.C.S.: 541612

Hylant (1)
250 International Pkwy Ste 330, Lake Mary, FL 32746
Tel.: (407) 740-5550
Web Site: http://www.hylant.com
Sales Range: $10-24.9 Million
Emp.: 10
Insurance Brokerage Services
N.A.I.C.S.: 524210
Lisa Hawker *(Pres-Employee Benefits)*
Michael Hylant *(CEO)*
Patrick Hylant *(Chm)*
William Pridgeon *(Pres)*
Jon Strole *(CFO & Sr VP)*
Brian Boone *(Pres)*
Craig Markos *(Pres-Property & Casualty)*
Richard Hylant *(Pres-Field Ops & Innovation)*

Hylant Group - Ann Arbor (1)
24 Frank Lloyd Wright Dr Ste J4100, Ann Arbor, MI 48105
Tel.: (734) 741-0044
Web Site: http://www.hylant.com
Sales Range: $150-199.9 Million
Emp.: 62
Business Insurance Brokerage, Employee Benefits & Corporate Wealth Management Services
N.A.I.C.S.: 524210
Matthew M. Hylant *(Pres)*
J. Paul Dixon *(Sr VP)*

Hylant Group - Indianapolis (1)
301 Pennsylvania Pkwy Ste 201, Indianapolis, IN 46280
Tel.: (317) 817-5000
Web Site: http://www.hylant.com
Sales Range: $150-199.9 Million
Emp.: 60
Business Insurance Brokerage, Employee Benefits & Corporate Wealth Management Services
N.A.I.C.S.: 524210
Katrina Lewis *(Mgr-Mktg Comm)*

HYLAS YACHTS INC.
2 Market Sq, Marblehead, MA 01945
Tel.: (781) 631-9499
Web Site:
http://www.hylasyachtusa.com
Sales Range: $10-24.9 Million
Emp.: 7
Yachts, Building & Repairing
N.A.I.C.S.: 336612
Richard D. Jachney *(Pres)*
Kyle Jachney *(VP)*

HYLETE, INC.
564 Stevens Ave, Solana Beach, CA 92075
Tel.: (858) 225-8998   DE
Web Site: http://www.hylete.com
Year Founded: 2012
Rev.: $11,689,200
Assets: $6,724,708
Liabilities: $18,267,868
Net Worth: ($11,543,160)
Earnings: ($5,652,192)
Emp.: 26
Fiscal Year-end: 12/31/18
Fitness Equipment Distr
N.A.I.C.S.: 423910
Matthew Paulson *(VP-Bus Dev)*
Pete Dirksing *(VP-Product)*

Jamie Wardlow *(VP-Mktg)*
Kate Nowlan *(VP-Experience)*
Scott Kennerly *(VP-Tech & Ops)*
Ron L. Wilson II *(Chm, Pres, CEO & Acting CFO)*

HYMAN BRICKLE & SON, INC.
235 Singleton St, Woonsocket, RI 02895-1832
Tel.: (401) 769-0189   RI
Web Site:
https://www.thebricklegroup.com
Year Founded: 1931
Sales Range: $10-24.9 Million
Emp.: 50
Scrap & Waste Materials
N.A.I.C.S.: 423930
Max Brickle *(Pres)*
Samuel Brickle *(CEO)*
Paulette Butler *(Dir-Sls & Mktg)*

Subsidiaries:

Bouckaert Industrial Textiles, Inc. (1)
235 Singleton St, Woonsocket, RI 02895
Web Site: http://www.bitfelt.com
Woolen Blanket Mfr
N.A.I.C.S.: 313230
Thomas Bouckaert *(Founder)*

Brickle Realty Group (1)
235 Singleton St, Woonsocket, RI 02895
Tel.: (401) 769-0189
Web Site: http://www.bricklerealty.com
Real Estate Manangement Services
N.A.I.C.S.: 531390

Subsidiary (Domestic):

J-Von Realty (2)
235 Singleton St, Woonsocket, RI 02895
Tel.: (401) 769-0189
Real Estate Manangement Services
N.A.I.C.S.: 531390

Sam-Man Realty, Inc. (2)
235 Singleton St, Woonsocket, RI 02895
Tel.: (401) 762-1130
Real Estate Manangement Services
N.A.I.C.S.: 531390

Hyman Brickle & Son, Inc. - Branch River Facility (1)
582 Great Rd, North Smithfield, RI 02896
Tel.: (401) 762-1130
Woolen Blanket Mfr
N.A.I.C.S.: 313230

Hyman Brickle & Son, Inc. - Brickle Fiber Trading Division (1)
235 Singleton St, Woonsocket, RI 02895
Tel.: (401) 769-0189
Web Site:
http://www.bricklefiberrecycling.com
Woolen Blanket Mfr
N.A.I.C.S.: 313230

Metcalf Brothers LLC (1)
235 Singleton St, Woonsocket, RI 02895
Tel.: (401) 766-0718
Web Site: http://www.metcalfbrothers.com
Woolen Fabric Mfr
N.A.I.C.S.: 313230
Bob Goralski *(Mgr)*

Northwest Woolen Mills (1)
235 Singleton St, Woonsocket, RI 02895   (100%)
Tel.: (401) 769-0189
Web Site: http://www.northwestwoolen.com
Woolen Blankets Retailer
N.A.I.C.S.: 423930

HYMAN LTD.
2310 Chaffee Dr, Saint Louis, MO 63146
Tel.: (314) 524-6000
Web Site: https://www.hymanltd.com
Year Founded: 1989
Sales Range: $1-9.9 Million
Emp.: 20
Antique & Classic Car Acquisition & Sales
N.A.I.C.S.: 441120
Mark Hyman *(Pres)*

HYPEMARKS, INC.
2591 Bryant St, San Francisco, CA 94110
Tel.: (213) 973-8468
Web Site: http://www.tintup.com
Year Founded: 2013
Software Publisher
N.A.I.C.S.: 513210
Tim Sae Koo *(Co-Founder & CEO)*
Nik Aitharaju *(Co-Founder & CTO)*
Ryo Chiba *(Co-Founder)*

Subsidiaries:

Vesta (1)
483 10th Ave Ste 500, New York, NY 10018
Tel.: (212) 302-0777
Web Site: https://www.vesta-go.com
Sales Range: $1-9.9 Million
Digital Advertising Services
N.A.I.C.S.: 541810
Susan Frech *(Founder & CEO)*
Rich Fetter *(VP-Client Ops)*
Jordan Ben *(VP-Product Mktg)*
James Yoo *(Dir-Product Mgmt)*
Kristi Alves *(Sr Dir-Bus Dev)*
Jennifer Lapso *(Dir-Bus Dev)*
Paula Nobiletti *(Dir-Bus Dev)*
Katie Takacs *(Coord-Mktg)*
Rebecca Cheatham *(Coord-Bus Dev)*
Dana Kappel *(Dir-Inside Sls)*
Keli Anaya *(Dir-Community Engagement)*
Stephanie Steup *(Acct Dir)*
Lexi Berkins *(Sr Mgr-Acct)*
Michael Torre *(Acct Mgr)*
Ivery Boston *(Mgr-Insights)*
Christian Bada *(Mgr-IT)*
Tripthi Shetty *(Engr-Software Quality Assurance)*
Mary Gilbert *(Dir-Bus Dev)*
Jim Sears *(VP-Strategy)*
Brad McEvilly *(VP-Tech)*
Caroline Sheppard *(Mgr-Community)*
Katrina Maughan *(Mgr-Community)*
Lauren Kessler *(Mgr-Community)*
Cindy Wu *(Mgr-Product)*
Brittany Meier *(Dir-Bus Dev)*
Joanna Sammartino Bailey *(COO)*

HYPER PET, LLC
3100 S Meridian, Wichita, KS 67217
Web Site: http://www.hyper-pet.com
Year Founded: 1983
Dog Toys & Accessories Mfr
N.A.I.C.S.: 459910
Tim Blurton *(CEO)*
Deborah Gallagher *(Chief Sls Officer)*
John Thaman *(VP-Treats & Consumables)*
Michael P. Ficke *(Mgr-Sls)*

Subsidiaries:

OurPet's Company (1)
1300 E St, Fairport Harbor, OH 44077
Tel.: (440) 354-6500
Web Site: http://www.ourpets.com
Rev.: $28,252,067
Assets: $18,166,716
Liabilities: $5,320,642
Net Worth: $12,846,074
Earnings: $1,748,753
Emp.: 48
Fiscal Year-end: 12/31/2017
Pet Product Mfr
N.A.I.C.S.: 311111
Steven Tsengas *(Chm, Pres & CEO)*

HYPERDRIVE
10034 Washington Ave, Loveland, OH 45140
Tel.: (513) 444-4000
Web Site: http://www.hyperdrivei.com
Year Founded: 2001
Sales Range: $1-9.9 Million
Emp.: 16
Online Marketing Services
N.A.I.C.S.: 541810
Ali Margello *(Acct Mgr-Mktg)*
Brian Essen *(Dir-Creative)*
Chris Timman *(VP-Client Svc)*
Dan Heimbrock *(CEO)*
Marc David Cohn *(Partner)*

Mark Lammers *(Acct Mgr)*
Lora Lietz *(Coord-Fulfillment)*
Megan Collins *(Mgr-Mktg Acct)*
Robin Wuest *(Project Coord)*

HYPERICE, INC.
15440 Laguna Canyon Rd Ste 230, Irvine, CA 92618
Tel.: (949) 565-4994
Web Site: http://www.hyperice.com
Year Founded: 2010
Sales Range: $1-9.9 Million
Athlete Recovery Device Distr
N.A.I.C.S.: 459110
Anthony Katz *(Founder)*
Jim Huether *(CEO)*
Robert Marton *(VP-Product Dev & Mfg)*
Joe Cannon *(Dir-Bus Dev)*
Margarita Martinez *(Accountant)*
Gilad Jacobs *(Chief Innovation Officer)*
Andy Miguel *(Head-Mktg)*

Subsidiaries:

NormaTec Industries, LP. (1)
480 Pleasant St, Watertown, MA 02459-2066
Tel.: (617) 928-3411
Web Site: http://www.normatecusa.com
Medical Equipment Whslr
N.A.I.C.S.: 423450

HYPERION ENERGY LP
12377 Merit Dr Ste 1200, Dallas, TX 75251
Tel.: (214) 750-3820
Web Site:
https://www.aethonenergy.com
Sales Range: $10-24.9 Million
Emp.: 100
Crude Petroleum Production
N.A.I.C.S.: 211120
Don McClure *(Controller)*

HYPERION PARTNERS LP
50 Charles Lindbergh Blvd, Uniondale, NY 11553
Tel.: (516) 745-6644
Rev.: $207,600,000
Emp.: 1
Investment Holding Companies
N.A.I.C.S.: 551112
Lewis Ranieri *(Chm)*

HYPERTHERM INC.
21 Great Hollow Rd, Hanover, NH 03755
Tel.: (603) 643-3441   NH
Web Site:
https://www.hypertherm.com
Year Founded: 1971
Sales Range: $75-99.9 Million
Emp.: 1,000
Tools Mfr
N.A.I.C.S.: 333517
Jeff Deckrow *(VP-Sls-North America)*
Evan Smith *(CEO)*

HYPEX INC.
1000 Industrial Blvd, Southampton, PA 18966
Tel.: (215) 322-0545
Web Site: http://www.hypex.com
Sales Range: $10-24.9 Million
Emp.: 34
Proprietary Custom Equipment, Assemblies & Parts Mfr
N.A.I.C.S.: 333515
Gerry Martin *(Mgr-Accts Payable)*
Billy McCarthy *(Mgr-Plng)*
Dave Hartman *(Mgr-Quality)*
George Pihonak *(Gen Mgr)*
Curtis Houle *(VP-Fin)*
Keith Berger *(Mgr-Acctg)*
Charlie Ehne *(Mgr)*
James E. Hasson *(Owner & Pres)*

HyPex Inc.—(Continued)

Subsidiaries:

Spadone-Hypex Inc   **(1)**
45 Banner Dr, Milford, CT 06460
Tel.: (203) 877-1041
Web Site: http://www.spadone.com
Sales Range: $10-24.9 Million
Emp.: 4
Mfr of Machinery for the Tire Industry
N.A.I.C.S.: 541420

HYPGEN INC.
1999 Avenue of the Stars Ste 1100,
Century City, CA 90067
Tel.: (424) 253-1210   NV
Year Founded: 2015
Assets: $1,481
Liabilities: $743,067
Net Worth: ($741,586)
Earnings: ($892,248)
Emp.: 3
Fiscal Year-end: 05/31/18
Biotechnology Research & Development Services
N.A.I.C.S.: 541714
McCoy L. Moretz (Chm, CEO, CFO &
Chief Medical Officer)

HYPHEN SOLUTIONS, LLC
1507 LBJ Fwy Ste 300, Dallas, TX
75234
Tel.: (877) 508-2547
Web Site:
  http://www.hyphensolutions.com
Year Founded: 1999
Electronics Stores
N.A.I.C.S.: 449210
Felix Vasquez (CEO)

HYPOWER FUEL, INC.
2711 Centerville Rd Ste 120, Wilmington, DE 19808
Tel.: (403) 601-8442
Web Site:
  http://www.hypowerfuel.com
Natural Gas Mfr
N.A.I.C.S.: 325120
Douglas Blender (Pres)

HYPOWER INC.
5913 NW 31st Ave, Fort Lauderdale,
FL 33309-2207
Tel.: (954) 978-9300   FL
Web Site:
  https://www.hypowerinc.com
Year Founded: 1991
Sales Range: $10-24.9 Million
Emp.: 60
Electrical Services
N.A.I.C.S.: 237110
Bernard Paul-Hus (Pres)
Eric Paul-Hus (VP)
Kevin Worrell (Controller)
David Weingarten (Dir-Risk Mgmt)

HYPRO INC.
600 S Jefferson St, Waterford, WI
53185-4218
Tel.: (262) 534-5141   WI
Web Site: http://www.hypro.com
Year Founded: 1969
Sales Range: $75-99.9 Million
Emp.: 200
Supply Industrial Commercial Markets
with Engineering Manufacturing Services
N.A.I.C.S.: 332710
Roy Nelson (CIO)
Ryan Paterson (Engr-Mfg)
Richard Brey (Plant Mgr)
Steve Waters (VP-Fin & Acctg)
Tedd Shellberg (Engr-Sls)
Mark Jessen (Plant Mgr)

HYSPAN PRECISION PRODUCTS, INC.
1685 Brandywine Ave, Chula Vista,
CA 91911-6020
Tel.: (619) 421-1355   CA
Web Site: https://www.hyspan.com
Year Founded: 1974
Sales Range: $100-124.9 Million
Emp.: 225
Steel Expansion Joints; Wire Braid &
Metal Hose
N.A.I.C.S.: 333613

Subsidiaries:

Universal Metal Hose   **(1)**
17111 Wallace St, South Holland, IL
60473   **(100%)**
Tel.: (773) 277-0700
Web Site:
  http://www.universalmetalhose.com
Sales Range: $10-24.9 Million
Emp.: 65
Metal Hose Mfr
N.A.I.C.S.: 332312
Don Heye (Pres)

HYSPECO INC.
1729 S Sabin St, Wichita, KS 67209
Tel.: (316) 943-0254
Web Site: http://www.hyspeco.com
Year Founded: 1969
Sales Range: $25-49.9 Million
Emp.: 90
Industrial Machinery & Equipment
Whslr
N.A.I.C.S.: 423830

HYTROL CONVEYOR CO., INC.
2020 Hytrol Dr, Jonesboro, AR
72401-6712
Tel.: (870) 935-3700   AR
Web Site: http://www.hytrol.com
Year Founded: 1947
Sales Range: $25-49.9 Million
Emp.: 500
Conveying Services
N.A.I.C.S.: 333922
David Peacock (Pres)
Chuck Waddle (VP-Business Development)
Mitch Smith (VP-Engrg)
Chris Brudos (Dir-Supply Chain
Mgmt)
Will Mangrum (Dir-Mfg Ops-Fort
Smith)

HYUNDAI OF WESLEY CHAPEL, LLC
27000 Wesley Chapel Blvd, Wesley
Chapel, FL 33544-8408
Tel.: (813) 279-7326
Web Site:
  https://www.hyundaiofwesley
  chapel.com
Sales Range: $25-49.9 Million
Emp.: 35
Car Whslr
N.A.I.C.S.: 441110
Scott Fink (Pres)
John Gauvey (Gen Mgr)
Michael Mullins (CFO)

I & E CONSTRUCTION, INC.
9550 SE Clackamas Rd, Clackamas,
OR 97015
Tel.: (503) 655-7933
Web Site:
  http://www.iandeconstruction.com
Year Founded: 1994
Sales Range: $10-24.9 Million
Emp.: 2
Roofing Installation Services
N.A.I.C.S.: 238390
Kiril Ivanov (Pres)

I & S GROUP, INC.

115 E Hickory St Ste 300, Mankato,
MN 56001
Tel.: (507) 387-6651
Web Site: http://www.is-grp.com
Year Founded: 1973
Emp.: 250
Engineering Services
N.A.I.C.S.: 541330
Chad Surprenant (Pres & CEO)
Lynn Bruns (Exec VP)
Brian Gjerde (Mng Partner)
Eric Eby (Dir-IT)
Samantha Boeck (Dir-Talent Engagement)
Tiffany Olson (Dir-Mktg)
Alec Pfeffer (Dir-Fin & Acctg)

Subsidiaries:

Martin Pevzner Engineering   **(1)**
8030 Old Cedar Ave S Ste 100, Bloomington, MN 55425
Tel.: (952) 854-1876
Web Site: http://www.martinpevzner.com
Engineeering Services
N.A.I.C.S.: 541330
Mohan Chettiar (Engr-Project)

I AM SMART TECHNOLOGY, INC.
1536 Wynkoop St Ste 5B, Denver,
CO 80202
Tel.: (303) 726-1211   CO
Year Founded: 2008
Sales Range: Less than $1 Million
Emp.: 1
Appliance Power Shut-Off Technology
N.A.I.C.S.: 335999
Michael L. Haynes (Chm & CEO)
Jason Bernal (CFO)
Derek Stephens (VP-Ops)
Daniel E. Muse (Sec & Corp Attorney)
Sylvester C. Maier Jr. (COO)

I BATT INC.
5850 Fayetteville Rd, Durham, NC
27713-6289
Tel.: (919) 361-7047
Web Site:
  http://www.panerabread.com
Sales Range: $10-24.9 Million
Emp.: 250
Baked Goods Mfr
N.A.I.C.S.: 311811
Ronald M. Shaich (Chm & Co-CEO)
William W. Moreton (Co-Pres & Co-CEO)

I L LONG CONSTRUCTION COMPANY, INC.
4117 Indiana Ave, Winston Salem,
NC 27105
Tel.: (336) 661-1887
Year Founded: 1936
Sales Range: $25-49.9 Million
Emp.: 140
Nonresidential Construction Services
N.A.I.C.S.: 236220
Edwin L. Welch (Pres)

I LOAN INC.
616 Corporate Way Ste 2-3523, Valley Cottage, NY 10989   DE
Year Founded: 2011
Online Consumer Loan Comparison
& Lead Services
N.A.I.C.S.: 522310
Rivka Ruth Yafe (Pres, CEO, CFO &
Treas)
Sergejs Petuhovs (Sec)

I PLAY, INC.
2000 Riverside Dr Ste 9, Asheville,
NC 28804
Tel.: (828) 254-9236
Web Site: http://www.iplaybaby.com

Sales Range: $1-9.9 Million
Emp.: 53
Baby Clothing & Accessory Retailer
N.A.I.C.S.: 458110
Becky Cannon (Founder)
Emi Kubota (VP)

I SQUARED CAPITAL ADVISORS (US) LLC
600 Brickell Ave Penthouse, Miami,
FL 33131
Tel.: (212) 339-5300   DE
Web Site:
  http://www.isquaredcapital.com
Year Founded: 2012
Emp.: 50
Infrastructure Investment Management Services
N.A.I.C.S.: 523940
Gautam Bhandari (Co-Founder &
Chief Investment Officer-Global)
Thomas Lefebvre (Partner)
Sadek Wahba (Co-Founder, Chm &
Mng Partner)
Adil Rahmathulla (Mng Partner)
Andreas Moon (Mng Dir & Head-IR)
Ronald Schweizer (CFO)
Harsh Agrawal (Partner)
Mohamed Adel El-Gazzar (Sr Partner)
Harsh Agrawal (Sr Partner)

Subsidiaries:

Aggreko plc   **(1)**
8th Floor 120 Bothwell Street, Glasgow, G2
7JS, Scotland, United Kingdom
Tel.: (44) 141 225 5900
Web Site: http://www.aggreko.com
Rev.: $2,115,610,800
Assets: $3,293,427,600
Liabilities: $1,510,963,200
Net Worth: $1,782,464,400
Earnings: $169,196,400
Emp.: 6,456
Fiscal Year-end: 12/31/2019
Power Generators, Temperature Control
Equipment & Compressed Air Systems Mfr
N.A.I.C.S.: 335312
Bruce Pool (Pres-Rental Solutions)
Chris Weston (CEO)
Stephen Beynon (Mng Dir-Power Solutions)
Heath Drewett (CFO)
Anna Filipopoulos (Dir-HR)
Dan Ibbetson (Mng Dir-Products & Tech-Global)
Grant Nairn (CIO)
Peter Kennerley (Sec & Dir-Legal)
Peter Kennerley (Sec & Dir-Legal)

Subsidiary (Non-US):

Aggreko (NZ) Limited   **(2)**
1048-1050 Great South Road, Mt Wellington, Auckland, 1060, New Zealand
Tel.: (64) 92597000
Motor & Generator Mfr
N.A.I.C.S.: 335312

Aggreko (Thailand) Limited   **(2)**
AIA Capital Center Building 7th Floor Unit
707 89 Ratchadaphisek Road, Din Daeng,
Bangkok, 10400, Thailand
Tel.: (66) 20263628
Motor & Generator Mfr
N.A.I.C.S.: 335312

Aggreko Angola Lda.   **(2)**
Edificio Bengo n 210, Belas, Luanda, Angola
Tel.: (244) 23482331
Motor & Generator Mfr
N.A.I.C.S.: 335312

Aggreko Canada Inc.   **(2)**
22-3500 Saprae Creek Trail, Fort McMurray, T9H 0H6, AB, Canada
Web Site: https://www.aggreko.com
Motor & Generator Mfr
N.A.I.C.S.: 335312

Aggreko Chile Limitada   **(2)**
Industrial Park Buenaventura, Quilicura,
Santiago, Chile
Tel.: (56) 24723902
Motor & Generator Mfr
N.A.I.C.S.: 335312

Aggreko Energy Rental Solutions Inc. (2)
Unit 1101 Picadilly Star Building 4th Avenue Corner 27th Street, Bonifacio Global City, Taguig, 1634, Philippines
Tel.: (63) 29898425
Motor & Generator Mfr
N.A.I.C.S.: 335312

Aggreko Energy Rental South Africa (Proprietary) Limited (2)
7 Stanley Street Richmond Hill, Port Elizabeth, South Africa
Tel.: (27) 861244735
Motor & Generator Mfr
N.A.I.C.S.: 335312

Aggreko Energy Rentals Panama SA (2)
Panama Pacifico Howard Boulevard De Las Americas Panamerica, PO Box 0823-03612, Corregimiento de Veracruz, Panama, Panama
Tel.: (507) 8000520526
Motor & Generator Mfr
N.A.I.C.S.: 335312

Aggreko Eurasia LLC (2)
16 Tverskaya St Bld 3 Office 10, Tyumen, 625014, Russia
Tel.: (7) 4956461782
Motor & Generator Mfr
N.A.I.C.S.: 335312

Aggreko Finland Oy (2)
Mannerheimintie 12 B, Helsinki, Finland
Tel.: (358) 102866320
Motor & Generator Mfr
N.A.I.C.S.: 335312

Aggreko Generator Rentals (PNG) Limited (2)
Gabaka Street, PO Box 107, Boroko, Port Moresby, Papua New Guinea
Tel.: (675) 3253825
Motor & Generator Mfr
N.A.I.C.S.: 335312

Subsidiary (Domestic):

Aggreko Holdings Ltd. (2)
121 W Regent St, Glasgow, G2 SD, United Kingdom
Tel.: (44) 412255900
Sales Range: $25-49.9 Million
Emp.: 30
Holding Company
N.A.I.C.S.: 551112

Subsidiary (Domestic):

Aggreko UK Ltd. (3)
121 W Rigent St, Glasgow, G2 SD, United Kingdom
Tel.: (44) 412255900
Supplier of Temporary Power, Temperature Control & Oil Free Compressed Air
N.A.I.C.S.: 334513

Subsidiary (US):

Aggreko Holdings, Inc. (2)
15600 JFK Blvd Ste 900, Houston, TX 77032
Web Site: http://www.aggreko.com
Holding Company; Regional Managing Office
N.A.I.C.S.: 551112
Bruce Pool (Mng Dir-North America)

Subsidiary (Domestic):

Aggreko, LLC (3)
15600 John F Kennedy Blvd Ste 600, Houston, TX 77032
Web Site: http://www.aggreko.com
Supplier of Temporary Power, Temperature Control & Oil Free Compressed Air
N.A.I.C.S.: 532490

Subsidiary (Domestic):

A Contact Electric Rentals, L.P. (4)
2217 Aldine Bender Rd, Houston, TX 77032
Tel.: (281) 442-7253
Web Site: http://www.acontact.net
Consumer Electronics & Appliances Rental
N.A.I.C.S.: 532210
Clay Jones (CEO)

DRYCO LLC (4)

5400 Janes Ave, Downers Grove, IL 60515
Tel.: (866) 672-4628
Web Site: http://www.drycogroup.com
Climate Control Equipment Rental Services
N.A.I.C.S.: 238220
Joe Schroeder (Founder & Pres)

Tuco Industrial Products, Inc. (4)
5223 180th St SW #4A-1, Lynnwood, WA 98037
Tel.: (425) 743-9533
Web Site: http://www.tucoheat.com
Warm Air Heating & Air-Conditioning Equipment & Supplies Merchant Whslr
N.A.I.C.S.: 423730

Subsidiary (Non-US):

Aggreko Iberia SA (2)
Pol Ind Can Salvatella Avgda Torre Mateu 35-37, Barbera Del Valles, Barcelona, 08210, Spain
Tel.: (34) 902221101
Motor & Generator Mfr
N.A.I.C.S.: 335312

Aggreko Italia S.R.L. (2)
Via A Einstein 29, 20090, Assago, MI, Italy
Tel.: (39) 024840491
Motor & Generator Mfr
N.A.I.C.S.: 335312

Aggreko Japan Limited (2)
1004 Aios Ginza 8-17-5 Ginza, Chuo-ku, Tokyo, 104-0061, Japan
Tel.: (81) 368108340
Motor & Generator Mfr
N.A.I.C.S.: 335312

Aggreko Kenya Energy Rentals Limited (2)
First Freight Lane JKIA Freight Terminal, Nairobi, Kenya
Tel.: (254) 707000888
Motor & Generator Mfr
N.A.I.C.S.: 335312

Aggreko Myanmar Co. Limited (2)
42 / A Pantra Street, Dagon Township, Yangon, 11191, Myanmar
Tel.: (95) 1378975
Motor & Generator Mfr
N.A.I.C.S.: 335312

Aggreko Namibia Energy Rentals (Pty) Ltd. (2)
Harbor Park Office no 7 B Second Street East, PO Box 5200, Walvis Bay, Namibia
Tel.: (264) 64227451
Motor & Generator Mfr
N.A.I.C.S.: 335312

Aggreko Norway AS (2)
Sorlandsveien 318, Egersund, 4379, Norway
Tel.: (47) 81000333
Motor & Generator Mfr
N.A.I.C.S.: 335312

Aggreko Polska Spolka Zorganiczana (2)
Ul Fort Ordona 6, Nowy Kazun, 05-152, Czosnow, Poland
Tel.: (48) 608608419
Motor & Generator Mfr
N.A.I.C.S.: 335312

Aggreko South East Europe S.R.L. (2)
36 Al I Cuza Tunari, Ilfov, 077180, Bucharest, Romania
Tel.: (40) 743151516
Motor & Generator Mfr
N.A.I.C.S.: 335312

Aggreko South Korea Limited (2)
101/2504 109 Mapo-Daero, Mapo-gu, Seoul, 04146, Korea (South)
Tel.: (82) 553430350
Motor & Generator Mfr
N.A.I.C.S.: 335312

Aggreko de Venezuela C.A. (2)
Av Venezuela Torre Lamaletto Piso 5, Oficina Unica Urbanizacion El Rosal, Caracas, 1060, Venezuela
Tel.: (58) 1148467403
Motor & Generator Mfr
N.A.I.C.S.: 335312

Subsidiary (Domestic):

Golden Triangle Generators Limited (2)

2 Voyager Drive Orbital Retail Center, Cannock, WS11 8XP, United Kingdom
Tel.: (44) 3458247365
Motor & Generator Mfr
N.A.I.C.S.: 335312

Subsidiary (Non-US):

Younicos GmbH (2)
Am Studio 16, 12489, Berlin, Germany
Tel.: (49) 30 818 79 9010
Energy Solutions; Mobile & Modular Power
N.A.I.C.S.: 457210

American Intermodal Management, LLC (1)
7320 E Butherus Dr Ste 201, Scottsdale, AZ 85260
Tel.: (602) 362-1153
Web Site: http://www.aimchassis.com
Logistic Services
N.A.I.C.S.: 541614
Nathaniel Seeds (CEO)
Ronald D. Widows (Chm)

Applus Services, S.A. (1)
Campus UAB Ronda de la Font del Carme s/n Bellaterra, 8193, Barcelona, Spain
Tel.: (34) 900103067
Web Site: https://www.applus.com
Rev.: $2,209,012,453
Assets: $2,619,887,292
Liabilities: $1,987,546,158
Net Worth: $632,341,134
Earnings: $42,348,648
Emp.: 26,770
Fiscal Year-end: 12/31/2023
Testing, Inspection, Certification & Technological Services
N.A.I.C.S.: 541990
Christopher Cole (Chm)
Joan Amigo I. Casas (CFO)
Jose Delfin Perez Fernandez (Sr VP-HR, Mktg & Comm)
Aitor Retes Aguado (Exec VP-Automotive Div)
Jordi Brufau Redondo (Exec VP-Laboratories Div)
Ramon Fernandez Armas (Exec VP-Energy & Industry Div)
Eva Argiles Malonda (Gen Counsel)
M. Teresa Sanfeliu (VP-Quality, H&S & Innovation)
Fernando Basabe Armijo (CEO)
Aston Swift (VP-IR)
Anna Diaz (Chief Compliance Officer)
Vicente Conde Vinuelas (Sec)
Javier Lopez Serrano (Sr VP-Corp Dev)

Subsidiary (Non-US):

3C Test Limited (2)
Unit 3 - Silverstone Technology Park, Silverstone Circuit, Northampton, NN12 8GX, Northamptonshire, United Kingdom
Tel.: (44) 1327857500
Web Site: https://www.3ctest.co.uk
Material Testing Services
N.A.I.C.S.: 541380
James Gordon (Founder)

A2M Industries, SAS (2)
ZA du Parc Secteur Gampille, 42490, Fraisses, France
Tel.: (33) 477401430
Web Site: https://www.a2m-industrie.fr
Material Testing Services
N.A.I.C.S.: 541380

Subsidiary (Domestic):

AC6 Metrologia, S.L. (2)
Poligono Comarca I Edificio Pasarela, 31160, Orkoien, Navarre, Spain
Tel.: (34) 948355300
Web Site: https://www.ac6m.com
Measurement Equipment Calibration Services
N.A.I.C.S.: 811210

Alpe Metrologia Industrial, S.L.U. (2)
Plz Donantes de Navarra 8 - trasera, Berriozar, 31013, Navarra, Spain
Tel.: (34) 948215858
Web Site: https://www.alpemetrologia.com
Industrial Calibration Services
N.A.I.C.S.: 541380

Subsidiary (Non-US):

Applus (Shangai) Quality inspection Co, Ltd. (2)

3999 Xiu Pu Rd - Building 23, Jucheng Industrial Park, Shanghai, 201315, Pudong, China
Tel.: (86) 2152370776
Testing Lab Services
N.A.I.C.S.: 541380

Applus Argentina, S.A. (2)
Reconquista 661 Piso 2, C1003ABM, Buenos Aires, Argentina
Tel.: (54) 1148931333
Automotive Inspection Services
N.A.I.C.S.: 811198

Applus Car Testing Service, Ltd. (2)
Lakedrive 3026 Citywest Business Campus Naas Road, Dublin, D24 RCRV, Ireland
Tel.: (353) 14135900
Web Site: https://www.ncts.ie
Automotive Inspection Services
N.A.I.C.S.: 811198

Applus Chile, S.A. (2)
Av Departamental 390, San Joaquin, Santiago, Chile
Tel.: (56) 232393670
Web Site: https://www.applusprt.cl
Automotive Inspection Services
N.A.I.C.S.: 811198

Applus Costa Rica, S.A. (2)
Paseo Ruben Dario s/n Panamerican Hwy Piso 2 San Pedro, Edificio Centro Hispanico, San Jose, Costa Rica
Tel.: (506) 2806890
Product Certification Services
N.A.I.C.S.: 541380

Applus Czech Republic, s.r.o. (2)
U Stadionu 89, 530 02, Pardubice, Czech Republic
Tel.: (420) 466530858
Web Site: https://www.applus.com
Testing Lab Services
N.A.I.C.S.: 541380

Applus Danmark, A/S (2)
Hoje Taastrup Boulevard 23 2 th, 2630, Taastrup, Denmark
Tel.: (45) 70131212
Web Site: https://www.applusbilsyn.dk
Automotive Inspection Services
N.A.I.C.S.: 811198

Applus Fomento de Control, S.A. (2)
1 Bd Chefchaouni Angle Avec Ancienne Routre De Rabat, Yassmine Business Center Etage 3 Bureau 26 Ain Sebaa, 21000, Casablanca, Morocco
Tel.: (212) 808625218
Web Site: https://www.applusfomentocontrole.com
Material Testing Services
N.A.I.C.S.: 541380

Applus II Meio Ambiente Portugal, Lda. (2)
Complexo Petroquimico Monte Feio Apartado 227-E C, Sines, 7521-903, Portugal
Tel.: (351) 269634325
Management Consulting Services
N.A.I.C.S.: 541611

Applus India Private Limited (2)
H No 1-11-254/255 Flat No 402 Vijaysri Nivas Street No 1 Prakash Nagar, Begumpet, Hyderabad, 500016, Telangana, India
Tel.: (91) 4029709499
Automotive Inspection Services
N.A.I.C.S.: 811198

Applus Ingenieria y Consultoria, SAS (2)
Calle 17 No 69-46, Montevideo industrial area, Bogota, Colombia
Tel.: (57) 17441133
Automotive Inspection Services
N.A.I.C.S.: 811198

Applus Italy, S.R.L. (2)
Via Cinquantenario 8, 24044, Dalmine, BG, Italy
Tel.: (39) 0351991131
Business Consulting Services
N.A.I.C.S.: 541611

Subsidiary (Domestic):

Applus Iteuve Galicia, S.L.U. (2)
Carretera Nacional VI Km 582, Sada, 15168, A Coruna, Spain

I Squared Capital Advisors (US) LLC—(Continued)
Tel.: (34) 981014500
Automotive Inspection Services
N.A.I.C.S.: 811198

Subsidiary (Non-US):

Applus Japan KK. (2)
Yamauchi Building 3F 3-24-8 Nishi Shim-
bashi, Minato-ku, Tokyo, 105-0003, Japan
Tel.: (81) 345773514
Automotive Inspection Services
N.A.I.C.S.: 811198

Subsidiary (US):

Applus K2 America, LLC (2)
7337 Empire Central Dr, Houston, TX
77031
Tel.: (281) 617-4021
Material Testing Services
N.A.I.C.S.: 541380

Subsidiary (Non-US):

Applus Kazakhstan LLC (2)
14 Kirov Square, 060000, Atyrau, Kazakh-
stan
Tel.: (7) 7017734141
Automotive Inspection Services
N.A.I.C.S.: 811198

Applus Laboratories, AS (2)
Tidemans gate 2, 3616, Kongsberg, Norway
Tel.: (47) 97471515
Testing Lab Services
N.A.I.C.S.: 541380

Applus Mexico, S.A. de C.V. (2)
Blvd Manuel Avila Camacho 184 Piso 4-B,
11650, Mexico, Mexico
Tel.: (52) 5591383838
Web Site: https://www.applus.com
Automotive Inspection Services
N.A.I.C.S.: 811198

Applus Mongolia, LLC (2)
The Landmark 7th Floor Chinggis Avenue -
13, Sukhbaatar District, Ulaanbaatar, Mon-
golia
Tel.: (976) 70119700
Web Site: http://applus-mongolia-
llc.business.site
Automotive Inspection Services
N.A.I.C.S.: 811198

**Applus Norcontrol Guatemala,
S.A.** (2)
Carretera a El Salvador Km 22 Ecoplaza
403 Oficina Applus, Guatemala, Guatemala
Tel.: (502) 30447507
Web Site: https://www.applus.com
Automotive Inspection Services
N.A.I.C.S.: 811198

Applus Norcontrol Peru, S.A.C. (2)
Av El Derby 254 Oficina 901 Edificio Lima
Central Tower, Santiago de Surco, 15023,
Lima, Peru
Tel.: (51) 12003830
Web Site: https://www.applus.com
Testing Lab Services
N.A.I.C.S.: 541380

**Applus Norcontrol Republica Domini-
cana, S.R.L.** (2)
Plaza El Avellano Calle Dr Jacinto Ignacio
Manon No 5 Local No 08, Primer Piso,
Santo Domingo, Dominican Republic
Tel.: (809) 2271285
Inspection & Technical Assistance Services
N.A.I.C.S.: 541990

Subsidiary (Domestic):

Applus Norcontrol, S.L. (2)
Carretera Nacional VI Km 582, Sada,
15168, A Coruna, Spain
Tel.: (34) 981014500
Laboratory Testing Services
N.A.I.C.S.: 541380

Subsidiary (Non-US):

Applus PNG Limited (2)
Unit 11 Section 53 Allotment 15 and 16
Ume Street 121, National Capital District,
Port Moresby, Papua New Guinea
Tel.: (675) 79998700
Web Site: https://www.applus.com
Automotive Inspection Services

Applus PTY, Ltd. (2)
94 Discovery Drive, Bibra Lake, 6163, WA,
Australia
Tel.: (61) 894109300
Testing Lab Services
N.A.I.C.S.: 541380

Applus Panama, S.A. (2)
Calle Jacinto Palacios Cobos Edificio No
223 piso 3 local Ay C, Ciudad del Saber,
0843-03081, Panama, Panamá
Tel.: (507) 2654150
Automotive Inspection Services
N.A.I.C.S.: 811198

Applus Portugal, Lda. (2)
Rua Joao de Rianho 33, Vila do Conde,
4480-195, Porto, Portugal
Tel.: (351) 252065227
Web Site: https://www.applus.com
Laboratory Testing Services
N.A.I.C.S.: 541380

**Applus Qualitec Servicos de Engenh-
aria, Ltda.** (2)
Av Marechal Floriano 45 - 10a Andar-
Centro, Rio de Janeiro, 20080-003, RJ,
Brazil
Tel.: (55) 213553183738
Web Site: https://www.applus.com
Laboratory Testing Services
N.A.I.C.S.: 541380

Applus RTD (2)
Delftweg 144, 3046 NC, Rotterdam, Nether-
lands
Tel.: (31) 107166000
Web Site: http://www.applus.com
Sales Range: $500-549.9 Million
Construction Inspection & Certification Ser-
vices
N.A.I.C.S.: 541350

Subsidiary (Non-US):

Applus UK Ltd (3)
Unit s 2c 2d West Mains Industrial Estate,
Grangemouth, Falkirk, FK3 8YE, United
Kingdom
Tel.: (44) 1324489785
Web Site: https://applustraining.co.uk
Construction Inspection & Certification Ser-
vices
N.A.I.C.S.: 541350

Subsidiary (US):

JanX Integrity Group, Inc. (3)
17 Kennedy Blvd, East Brunswick, NJ
08816-1250
Tel.: (732) 748-0220
Web Site: http://www.janx.net
Sales Range: $1-9.9 Million
Emp.: 50
Testing Laboratory
N.A.I.C.S.: 541715
Daniel Williams *(Gen Mgr)*

Quality Inspection Services, Inc. (3)
80 Lawrence Bill Dr, Williamsville, NY
14221
Tel.: (716) 853-2611
Web Site: http://www.applusrtd.com
Sales Range: $25-49.9 Million
Emp.: 15
Inspection, Testing & Engineering Services
N.A.I.C.S.: 541350
Greg Rossmiller *(Pres & CEO)*
Tim Loudenslager *(Gen Mgr)*

Subsidiary (Non-US):

**Applus RTD Deutschland inspektion-
sGesellschaft, Gmbh** (2)
Industriestrasse 34B, 44894, Bochum, Ger-
many
Tel.: (49) 234927980
Web Site: https://www.applus.com
Automotive Inspection Services
N.A.I.C.S.: 811198

Applus RTD PTE, Ltd. (2)
521 Bukit Batok St 23 Unit 05-E, Singapore,
659544, Singapore
Tel.: (65) 65457646
Automotive Inspection Services
N.A.I.C.S.: 811198

Subsidiary (US):

Applus RTD USA, Inc. (2)
3 Sugar Creek Ctr Blvd Ste 600, Sugar
Land, TX 77478
Tel.: (832) 295-5023
Automotive Inspection Services
N.A.I.C.S.: 811198

Subsidiary (Non-US):

Applus Singapore PTE Ltd. (2)
1 Corporation Drive 04-10, Singapore,
619775, Singapore
Tel.: (65) 65457646
Web Site: https://www.applus.com
Material Testing Services
N.A.I.C.S.: 541380

Applus Steel Test (Pty.) Ltd. (2)
28 Senator Rood Road, Vereeniging, 1939,
South Africa
Tel.: (27) 164224930
Laboratory Testing Services
N.A.I.C.S.: 541380

**Applus Turkey Gozetim Hizmetleri
Limited Sirketi** (2)
1042 Cadde 1319 Sokak No 9/5, Ovecler,
Ankara, Turkiye
Tel.: (90) 3124787992
Automotive Inspection Services
N.A.I.C.S.: 811198

Applus Uruguay, S.A. (2)
Br Artigas 220-Of 801, 11300, Montevideo,
Uruguay
Tel.: (598) 8001884
Web Site: https://www.applusitv.uy
Automotive Inspection Services
N.A.I.C.S.: 811198

Applus Velosi SA (Pty) Ltd. (2)
28 Senator Rood Road, Vereeniging, 1939,
Gauteng, South Africa
Tel.: (27) 164224930
Automotive Inspection Services
N.A.I.C.S.: 811198

**BK WerstofftechnikPrufstelle FUr
Werkstoffe, Gmbh** (2)
Zur Aumundswiese 2, 28279, Bremen, Ger-
many
Tel.: (49) 421438280
Web Site: https://www.bk-
werkstofftechnik.com
Material Testing Services
N.A.I.C.S.: 541380

Subsidiary (Domestic):

**CTAG-Idiada Safety Technology,
S.L.** (2)
Poligono A Granxa parcela 249 - 250,
36410, Porrino, Spain
Tel.: (34) 986900300
Automotive Engineering Services
N.A.I.C.S.: 541330

Subsidiary (Non-US):

Emilab, SRL. (2)
Via F Ili Solari 5/A, 33020, Amaro, UD, Italy
Tel.: (39) 0433468625
Web Site: http://en.emilab.it
Automotive Inspection Services
N.A.I.C.S.: 811198

Enertis Chile, SpA (2)
Nueva de Lyon 145 Oficina 503, Providen-
cia, Santiago, Chile
Tel.: (56) 224029642
Web Site: https://www.enertisapplus.com
Testing & Inspection Services
N.A.I.C.S.: 541350

Enertis Colombia S.A.S. (2)
Calle 93A no 13 - 24 Piso 5, 110221, Bo-
gota, Colombia
Tel.: (57) 16672590
Engineering Consulting Services
N.A.I.C.S.: 541330

Subsidiary (Domestic):

Enertis Solar, S.L.U. (2)
C/Campezo 1 Parque Empresarial Las Mer-
cedes, 28022, Madrid, Spain
Tel.: (34) 916517021
Web Site: https://www.enertisapplus.com
Information Technology Services

N.A.I.C.S.: 541511

Subsidiary (Non-US):

Enertis UK Limited (2)
51 Eastcheap, London, EC3M 1DT, United
Kingdom
Tel.: (44) 1928508858
Engineering Consulting Services
N.A.I.C.S.: 541330

Subsidiary (Domestic):

**IDIADA Automotive Technology,
S.A.** (2)
PO Box 20, Santa Oliva L'Albornar, 43710,
Tarragona, Spain
Tel.: (34) 977166000
Web Site: http://www.applusidiada.com
Emp.: 2,450
Automotive Engineering Services
N.A.I.C.S.: 541330

Subsidiary (Non-US):

IDIADA CZ, A.S. (2)
Prazska trida 320/8, 500 04, Hradec Kral-
ove, Czech Republic
Tel.: (420) 493654811
Web Site: https://www.idiada.cz
Emp.: 200
Automotive Engineering Services
N.A.I.C.S.: 541330

IDIADA Fahrzeugtechnik, GmbH (2)
Manchinger Str 97, 85053, Ingolstadt, Ger-
many
Tel.: (49) 841885380
Web Site: https://www.applusidiada.com
Automotive Testing Services
N.A.I.C.S.: 811198

**IMA Materialforschung und Anwend-
ungstechnik GmbH** (2)
Wilhelmine-Reichard-Ring 4, 01109, Dres-
den, Germany
Tel.: (49) 35188370
Web Site: https://www.ima-dresden.de
Emp.: 200
Software Product Development Services
N.A.I.C.S.: 541511

**Idiada Automotive Technology India
Pvt, Ltd.** (2)
Unit No 304 B wing 3rd floor Sai Radhe
Building, 100-101 Raja Bahadur Mill Road,
Pune, 411 001, India
Tel.: (91) 2066056800
Automotive Testing Services
N.A.I.C.S.: 811198

**Idiada Automotive Technology Mexico
S de RL de CV.** (2)
Carretera Lateral Mexico Puebla 7534,
72110, Puebla, Mexico
Tel.: (52) 12221078463
Automotive Testing Services
N.A.I.C.S.: 811198

**Idiada Automotive Technology Rus,
LLC** (2)
Lenina av 115 office 301, 603004, Nizhniy
Novgorod, Russia
Tel.: (7) 8312199183
Automotive Testing Services
N.A.I.C.S.: 811198

**Idiada Automotive Technology UK,
Ltd.** (2)
St Georges Way, Bermuda Industrial Estate,
Nuneaton, CV10 7JS, United Kingdom
Tel.: (44) 2476328083
Automotive Testing Services
N.A.I.C.S.: 811198

Subsidiary (Domestic):

Indoor Climate Management S.L. (2)
Av Via Augusta 15-25 Ed Sant Cugat Busi-
ness Park, 08174, Sant Cugat del Valles,
Spain
Tel.: (34) 931514559
Web Site: https://www.indoorclima.com
Air Conditioning Management Services
N.A.I.C.S.: 811412

Subsidiary (Non-US):

**Inspeccio Tecnica de vehicles i
serveis, S.A.** (2)
Carretera de Bixessarri s/n, Aixovall,

AD600, Sant Julia de Loria, Andorra
Tel.: (376) 741350
Web Site: http://www.itvserveis.ad
Automotive Inspection Services
N.A.I.C.S.: 811198

Subsidiary (Domestic):

Iteuve Canarias, S.L. (2)
Camino San Lazaro Los Rodeos, San Cristobal de La Laguna, 38206, Santa Cruz de Tenerife, Spain
Tel.: (34) 922100180
Web Site: https://www.iteuvecanarias.com
Automotive Engineering Services
N.A.I.C.S.: 541330

Subsidiary (Non-US):

K1 Kasastajat, OY (2)
Rieskalahteentie 76, 20300, Turku, Finland
Tel.: (358) 306100900
Web Site: http://www.k1katsastus.fi
Automotive Inspection Services
N.A.I.C.S.: 811198

Subsidiary (US):

Kiefner & Associates Inc. (2)
4480 Bridgeway Ave Ste D, Columbus, OH 43219
Tel.: (614) 888-8220
Web Site: http://www.kiefner.com
Sales Range: $1-9.9 Million
Emp.: 15
Engineering Consulting Services
N.A.I.C.S.: 541330

Subsidiary (Non-US):

LGAI Chile, S.A. (2)
Agustinas 640 piso 9 Santiago Centro, Providencia Metropolitana de Santiago, Santiago, Chile
Tel.: (56) 228187000
Testing Lab Services
N.A.I.C.S.: 541380

Subsidiary (Domestic):

LGAI Technological, Center, S.A. (2)
Campus UAB - Ronda de la Font del Carme s/n, Bellaterra, 08193, Barcelona, Spain
Tel.: (34) 935672000
Testing Lab Services
N.A.I.C.S.: 541380

Laboratorio de Ensayos Metrologicos, S.L. (2)
Avenida Can Sucarrats 110 nave 11, 08191, Rubi, Spain
Tel.: (34) 935862680
Web Site: http://www.lem-sl.com
Testing Lab Services
N.A.I.C.S.: 541380

Subsidiary (US):

Lightship Security USA, Inc. (2)
3600 O Donnell St Ste 2, Baltimore, MD 21224
Tel.: (512) 362-6594
Cyber Security Testing Services
N.A.I.C.S.: 541690

Subsidiary (Non-US):

Lightship Security, Inc. (2)
1101 - 150 Isabella Street, Ottawa, K1S 1V7, ON, Canada
Tel.: (613) 512-1070
Web Site: https://lightshipsec.com
Cyber Security Testing Services
N.A.I.C.S.: 541690

Liuzhou Reliable Auto Analysis Testing Ltd. (2)
No 12 Building 7 4th Floor Suite 417 Fuxin Road, Liuzhou, 545000, China
Tel.: (86) 7723605991
Testing Lab Services
N.A.I.C.S.: 541380

Subsidiary (US):

Matereality, LLC (2)
23 Dutch Mill Rd, Ithaca, NY 14850
Tel.: (607) 257-1784
Web Site: https://www.matereality.com
Software Development Services

N.A.I.C.S.: 541511

Subsidiary (Non-US):

NRAY Services, Inc. (2)
56A Head Street, Dundas, L9H 3H7, ON, Canada
Tel.: (905) 627-1302
Web Site: http://www.nray.ca
Radiographic Inspection Services
N.A.I.C.S.: 541380

Norcontrol Chile, S.A. (2)
Agustinas 640 Piso 9, Santiago Centro, Santiago, Chile
Tel.: (56) 225629000
Automotive Inspection Services
N.A.I.C.S.: 811198

Norcontrol Nicaragua, S.A. (2)
Colonia Los Robles Septima Etapa Casa 45, Managua, Nicaragua
Tel.: (505) 22935410
Automotive Inspection Services
N.A.I.C.S.: 811198

Subsidiary (Domestic):

Novotec Consultores, S.A., Sociedad Unipersonal (2)
Calle Campezo 1 edificio 3 Parque Empresarial Las Mercedes, 28022, Madrid, Spain
Tel.: (34) 912107900
Web Site: http://www.novotec.es
Consulting Services
N.A.I.C.S.: 541613

Subsidiary (US):

QPS America, Inc. (2)
Crown Ctr 5005 Rockside Rd Ste 600, Independence, OH 44131-6827
Tel.: (216) 377-3191
Web Site: http://www.qpsamerica.com
Product Testing & Certification Services
N.A.I.C.S.: 541380

Subsidiary (Non-US):

QPS Europe B.V. (2)
Berg en Dalseweg 122, 6522 BW, Nijmegen, Netherlands
Tel.: (31) 850030144
Web Site: http://www.qpscertification.eu
Product Certification Services
N.A.I.C.S.: 541380
Maurice Hoendervangers (Dir-Area)
Stanislav Christov (Specialist-Certification)

QPS Evaluation Services Inc. (2)
81 Kelfield St Unit 8, Toronto, M9W 5A3, ON, Canada
Tel.: (416) 241-8857
Web Site: http://www.qps.ca
Product Testing & Certification Services
N.A.I.C.S.: 541380

RITEVE SyC, S.A. (2)
Avenida Central Calles 8 y 10 puerta metalica segunda planta, Post Mail 65-3006, frente a MundoMagico, Alajuela, Costa Rica
Tel.: (506) 8007880000
Web Site: http://www.rtv.co.cr
Automotive Inspection Services
N.A.I.C.S.: 811198
Andres Muruais (Country Mgr)
Victor Rodriguez (Mgr-Admin)
Alexander Zamora (Ops Mgr)
Kenneth Lopez (Mgr-Technical)
Saray Piedra (Mgr-HR)

RTD Quality Services Nigeria Ltd. (2)
3A Alabi Street Off Toyin Street, Ikeja, Nigeria
Tel.: (234) 8033367195
Laboratory Testing Services
N.A.I.C.S.: 541380

Reliable Analysis (Shanghai) Inc. (2)
No 19 Lane 1365 Kang Qiao Road East, Shanghai, China
Tel.: (86) 2168183293
Web Site: https://ralab.com.cn
Automotive Raw Material Testing Services
N.A.I.C.S.: 541380

Revisiones Tecnicas Applus del Ecuador Applusiteuve, S.A. (2)
Avda Patria n E4-41 Interseccion Avda Amazonas edificio Patria, Piso 10 Oficina

01, Quito, Pichincha, Ecuador
Tel.: (593) 45005005
Web Site: http://www.applusrtv.ec
Automotive Inspection Services
N.A.I.C.S.: 811198

Rontgen Technische Dienst B.V. (2)
Delftweg 144, 3046 NC, Rotterdam, Netherlands
Tel.: (31) 107166505
Web Site: https://www.applus.com
Certification Services
N.A.I.C.S.: 541990

SKC Engineering Ltd. (2)
19165 94th Avenue, Surrey, V4N 3S4, BC, Canada
Tel.: (604) 882-1889
Web Site: https://www.skceng.com
Mfr Consultation Services
N.A.I.C.S.: 541614
Mathew Smith (Dir-Professional Svcs)
Ramin Abolghasemi (Engr-Consulting & Welding)

Shangai IDIADA Automotive Technology Services Co., Ltd. (2)
Jucheng Pioneer Park Building 23 3999 Xiu Pu Road, Nan Hui Pudong District, Shanghai, 201315, China
Tel.: (86) 2162100894
Automotive Testing Services
N.A.I.C.S.: 811198

Shanghai IDIADA Automotive Technology Services Co., Ltd. (2)
Jucheng Pioneer Park Building 23 3999 Xiu Pu Road Nan Hui, Kangqiao Town Pudong District, Shanghai, 201315, China
Tel.: (86) 2162100894
Laboratory Testing Services
N.A.I.C.S.: 541380

Subsidiary (US):

Talon Test Laboratories (Phoenix) Inc. (2)
5700 Crooks Rd Ste 450, Troy, MI 48089
Tel.: (602) 454-2500
Testing Lab Services
N.A.I.C.S.: 541380

Talon Test Laboratories Incorporated (2)
5700 Crooks Rd Ste 450, Troy, MI 48089
Tel.: (805) 987-7755
Web Site: http://www.talontestlabs.com
Testing Lab Services
N.A.I.C.S.: 541380

Subsidiary (Domestic):

Tunnel Safety Testing, S.A. (2)
Centro experimental San Pedro de Anes, 33189, Siero, Asturias, Spain
Tel.: (34) 985741645
Web Site: http://www.tunneltest.com
Ventilation Fan Testing Services
N.A.I.C.S.: 238220

Subsidiary (Non-US):

Velosi Bahrain WLL. (2)
Flat 11 Bldg 1033 Road 3721 Block 337, PO Box 5652, Umm al Hassam, Manama, Bahrain
Tel.: (973) 17180245
Automotive Inspection Services
N.A.I.C.S.: 811198

Velosi Engineering Management Consultancy (Shangai) Ltd Co. (2)
Room 1304 ShengKang LiaoShi Building No 738 Shang Cheng Rd, Pudong District, Shanghai, 200135, China
Tel.: (86) 2161650588
Business Management Consulting Services
N.A.I.C.S.: 541611

Velosi LLC (2)
Azadlyg Pr house 189 apt 61, Binagadi District, AZ1130, Baku, Azerbaijan
Tel.: (994) 124048998
Automotive Inspection Services
N.A.I.C.S.: 811198

Velosi Limited (2)
Walker House PO Box 72, 28-34 Hill Street, Saint Helier, JE4 8PN, Jersey
Web Site: http://www.velosi.com

Sales Range: $150-199.9 Million
Inspection, Quality Assurance, Certification & Testing Services
N.A.I.C.S.: 561499

Subsidiary (Non-US):

Applus+ Velosi (3)
Eli France Cafe Bldg Ramada Junction, PO Box 3408, Doha, Qatar
Tel.: (974) 4352850
Web Site: http://www.velosi.com
Sales Range: $200-249.9 Million
Emp.: 700
Inspection & Legislative Certification Services
N.A.I.C.S.: 926150

Kurtec Inspection Services Sdn Bhd (3)
No 46 Jalan PJS 11/20 Bandar Sunway, 46150, Petaling Jaya, Selangor Darul Ehsan, Malaysia
Tel.: (60) 356388689
Web Site: http://www.kurtec.com
Sales Range: $10-24.9 Million
Emp.: 16
Visual Inspection Services
N.A.I.C.S.: 926150

Plant Design Engineers Sdn Bhd (3)
C-17-5 Block C No 12 Megan Avenue II Jalan Yap Kwan Seng, 50450, Kuala Lumpur, Malaysia
Tel.: (60) 3 2168 8832
Sales Range: $25-49.9 Million
Emp.: 13
Software Solutions & 3D Laser Scanning Imaging for Oil & Gas Industries
N.A.I.C.S.: 334610

QA Management Services Pty Ltd. (3)
Ste 5 202 Hampden Rd, Nedlands, 6009, WA, Australia
Tel.: (61) 893865555
Web Site: http://www.qamanage.com.au
Sales Range: $200-249.9 Million
Emp.: 900
Quality Management Consulting & Inspection Services
N.A.I.C.S.: 541611
Philip Wilton (Mng Dir)

Steel Test (Proprietary) Ltd. (3)
28 Senator Rood Road Ext 1, Duncanville, Vereeniging, 1939, Gauteng, South Africa
Tel.: (27) 164224930
Web Site: http://www.steeltest.co.za
Sales Range: $50-74.9 Million
Emp.: 74
Pipe & Steel Testing Services
N.A.I.C.S.: 213112
Willie Maritz (Mgr-HR)

VCS Quality Services Pvt. Ltd (3)
505 5th Fl 360 Degree Bus Pk Next to R-Mall, LBS Marg Mulund West, Mumbai, 400080, Maharashtra, India
Tel.: (91) 2221649720
Web Site: https://www.vcsprojects.com
Sales Range: $75-99.9 Million
Emp.: 450
Certification Services
N.A.I.C.S.: 523150

Velosi (Ghana) Ltd. (3)
2nd Fl Design House Ring Rd E, PO Box OS 0854, Osu Dist, Accra, Ghana
Tel.: (233) 21 786828
Sales Range: $25-49.9 Million
Emp.: 10
Engineering Projects Inspection & Consulting Services
N.A.I.C.S.: 541330

Velosi (Vietnam) Co Ltd. (3)
Rm 250 Petro Tower 8 Hoang Dieu St Ward 1, Vung Tau, Ba Ria-Vung Tau, Vietnam
Tel.: (84) 646253222
Web Site: http://www.velosi.com
Sales Range: $25-49.9 Million
Emp.: 6
Project Inspection & Verification Services
N.A.I.C.S.: 541990
Chandra Shekhar (Reg Mgr)

Subsidiary (US):

Velosi America LLC (3)

I Squared Capital Advisors (US) LLC—(Continued)

222 Pennbright Dr Ste 230, Houston, TX 77090-5907
Tel.: (281) 872-3600
Emp.: 50
Quality Assurance & Inspection Services
N.A.I.C.S.: 926150

Subsidiary (Non-US):

Velosi Angola LDA (3)
Rua Marien Ngouabi N37 No 53, Maianga, Luanda, Angola
Tel.: (244) 923337622
Inspection & Manpower Supply Services
N.A.I.C.S.: 561320

Velosi CBL (M) Sdn Bhd (3)
No 2119 1st Fl Jln Yakin, 98000, Miri, Sarawak, Malaysia
Tel.: (60) 85425885
Web Site: http://www.vcbl.com.my
Sales Range: $25-49.9 Million
Emp.: 6
Third Party Survey & Certification Services
N.A.I.C.S.: 541380

Velosi Certification Bureau Limited (3)
Unit 18 Dawkins Road, Poole, BH15 4JY, Berkshire, United Kingdom
Tel.: (44) 1189207030
Sales Range: $10-24.9 Million
Emp.: 20
Inspection Services
N.A.I.C.S.: 926150
Martin Coles (Sec)

Velosi Certification Services L.L.C (3)
No 201 & 205 Block B Abu Dhabi Bus Hub ICAD-1, PO Box 427, Mussafah, Abu Dhabi, 114182, United Arab Emirates
Tel.: (971) 25502600
Web Site: http://www.velosi.com
Sales Range: $50-74.9 Million
Emp.: 200
Certification & Inspection Services
N.A.I.C.S.: 541380
Brian Dawes (Reg Mgr)

Velosi Certification W.L.L (3)
28 Bubyan Complex 1st Fl Dhajij, PO Box 1589, Farwaniya Salmiya Dist, 22016, Kuwait, Kuwait
Tel.: (965) 24346738
Web Site: http://www.velosi.com
Sales Range: $25-49.9 Million
Emp.: 15
Inspection & Certification Services
N.A.I.C.S.: 561110

Velosi Europe Limited (3)
Unit 18 Dawkins Road, Poole, BH15 4JY, Berkshire, United Kingdom
Tel.: (44) 1189207030
Web Site: http://www.velosi.com
Sales Range: $10-24.9 Million
Emp.: 30
Quality Assurance & Inspection Services
N.A.I.C.S.: 813910
Ben Upton (Mgr-Ops)
John Hepworth (Reg Mgr)
Adrian Payne (Mgr-Ops)

Velosi Industries Sdn Bhd (3)
No 152-3-18A Kompleks Malur, Jalan Jejaka Taman Maluri, 55100, Kuala Lumpur, Selangor, Malaysia
Tel.: (60) 60351914020
Web Site: http://www.velosi.com.my
Sales Range: $25-49.9 Million
Emp.: 20
Metal Wastes & Scrap Processing Services
N.A.I.C.S.: 331492

Velosi International Italy Srl (3)
Via Cinquantenario 8, 23807, Dalmine, Lecco, Italy
Tel.: (39) 0395983436
Web Site: http://www.applus.com
Sales Range: $10-24.9 Million
Emp.: 6
Certification & Inspection Services
N.A.I.C.S.: 926150

Velosi Quality Management International L.L.C. (3)
No 201 & 205 Block B Abu Dhabi Bus Hub

ICAD-1 Mussafah, PO Box 427, Abu Dhabi, United Arab Emirates
Tel.: (971) 25502600
Web Site: http://www.velosi.com
Sales Range: $25-49.9 Million
Emp.: 4
Certification & Inspection Services
N.A.I.C.S.: 523150
Hakim Genavdalla (Country Mgr)

Velosi Saudi Arabia Co Ltd. (3)
Buld No-7031 Additional No-2958 Sub of Amir Mohammed Bin Fahd Rd, PO Box 7114, Al-Qusur Dist, Dhahran, 34247, Saudi Arabia
Tel.: (966) 38315950
Sales Range: $25-49.9 Million
Emp.: 15
Engineering Projects Inspection & Consulting Services
N.A.I.C.S.: 541330

Velosi Thai Co., Ltd. (3)
217/27 Moo 12 Tumbol, Thungsukhla Amphoe, Si Racha, 20230, Chon Buri, Thailand
Tel.: (66) 38351660
Sales Range: $25-49.9 Million
Emp.: 2
Quality Assurance & Manpower & Inspection Services
N.A.I.C.S.: 561320

Subsidiary (Non-US):

Velosi PromService LLC (2)
Staropetrovsky passage Building 19 Office 7 7-a, 125130, Moscow, 125130, Russia
Tel.: (7) 4991108973
Corrosion Control Services
N.A.I.C.S.: 237120

Velosi Uganda Ltd. (3)
3rd Floor Rewenzori House 1 Lumumba Avenue, Kampala, Uganda
Tel.: (256) 417701000
Automotive Inspection Services
N.A.I.C.S.: 811198

WIAM GmbH (2)
Hermann-Reichelt-Str 3, 01109, Dresden, Germany
Tel.: (49) 35188376343
Web Site: https://www.wiam.de
Software Product Development Services
N.A.I.C.S.: 541511

Subsidiary (Domestic):

ZYX Metrology S.L.U. (2)
Avenida Torre de en Mateo no 29, Ripollet, 08291, Barcelona, Spain
Tel.: (34) 936917837
Web Site: http://www.zyx.es
Automotive Inspection Services
N.A.I.C.S.: 811198

Arriva plc (1)
Admiral Way, Doxford Intl Business Park, Sunderland, SR3 3XP, United Kingdom
Tel.: (44) 1915204000
Web Site: http://www.arriva.co.uk
Sales Range: $1-4.9 Billion
Emp.: 200
Bus, Train & Coach Transportation Services
N.A.I.C.S.: 485113
Martin Hibbert (CFO)
David Evans (Mng Dir-Mainland Europe)
Chris Burchell (Mng Dir-Trains)
Mike Cooper (CEO)
Kevin O'Connor (Mng Dir-UK Bus)
Stuart Cockburn (Dir-Strategy & Dev)
Liz Benison (Mng Dir-Mainland Europe)

Subsidiary (Non-US):

ARRIVA PORTUGAL - TRANSPORTES LDA (2)
Rua das Arcas - Edificio Arriva Pinheiro - Gmr, 4810-647, Guimaraes, Portugal
Tel.: (351) 253423500
Web Site: http://www.arriva.pt
Transportation Services
N.A.I.C.S.: 485113

Alpetour - Potovalna Agencija d.o.o. (2)
Ulica Mirka Vadnova 8, 4000, Kranj, Slovenia
Tel.: (386) 42013110
Web Site: http://www.alpetour.si

Car Rental & Tourism Services
N.A.I.C.S.: 532111
Bo Karlsson (Dir)
Andrej Susnik (Head-Transport Sector)
Damijana Marn (Head-Market Sector)
Tomaz Medja (Head-Information & Comm Technologies)
Irena Bertoncelj (Head-Controlling Svc)
Dusan Sinkovec (Head-Maintenance Sector)
Tomaz Kosir (Head-Jesenice Working Unit)
Vili Cimzar (Head-Kranj Work Unit)
Primoz Turk (Head-Radovljica Work Unit)
Boris Malensek (Head-Skofja Loka Work Unit)

Subsidiary (Domestic):

Integral AP Trzic dd (3)
Mlaka 4, 4290, Trzic, Slovenia
Tel.: (386) 45920940
Web Site: http://www.integral-ap.si
Sales Range: $50-74.9 Million
Emp.: 22
Tourism Services
N.A.I.C.S.: 713990

Integral Avto D.O.O. (3)
Cesta Marsala Tita 67, 4270, Jesenice, Slovenia
Tel.: (386) 45833350
Web Site: http://integral-avto.si
Sales Range: $25-49.9 Million
Vehicle Sales & Services
N.A.I.C.S.: 441227
Izidor Jekovec (Dir)

Kam-Bus dd (3)
Perovo 30, 1241, Kamnik, Slovenia
Tel.: (386) 18309400
Web Site: http://www.arriva.si
Sales Range: $25-49.9 Million
Emp.: 18
Passenger Transport Services
N.A.I.C.S.: 485999

Subsidiary (Domestic):

Arriva Bus & Coach Ltd. (2)
Lodge Garage Whitehall Rd W, Gomersal, Cleckheaton, BD19 4BJ, West Yorkshire, United Kingdom (100%)
Tel.: (44) 1274681144
Web Site: http://www.arrivabusandcoach.co.uk
Sales Range: $25-49.9 Million
Emp.: 60
Leasing & Distribution of Buses & Coaches
N.A.I.C.S.: 532411
David Brown (Mgr-Sls)

Arriva Croydon&North Surrey Limited (2)
Merstham Garage Station Road North, Merstham, Redhill, RH1 3ED, United Kingdom
Tel.: (44) 1737645600
Railway Freight Transportation Services
N.A.I.C.S.: 482111

Arriva East Herts & Essex Ltd (2)
Fourth Avenue, Harlow, CM20 1DU, Essex, United Kingdom
Tel.: (44) 8706082608
Logistics Consulting Servies
N.A.I.C.S.: 541614

Subsidiary (Non-US):

Arriva Holding Ceska Republika s.r.o (2)
Radlicka 3185/1c, Smichov, 150 00, Prague, Czech Republic
Tel.: (420) 251112111
Logistics Consulting Servies
N.A.I.C.S.: 541614

Arriva Hungary Zrt. (2)
Andor Utca 27-31, 1119, Budapest, Hungary
Tel.: (36) 22501478
Web Site: http://www.arrivahungary.hu
Transportation Services
N.A.I.C.S.: 488490

Arriva Insurance A/S (2)
Skojtevej 26, 2770, Kastrup, Denmark
Tel.: (45) 72302500
Web Site: http://www.arrivainsurance.dk
General Insurance Services
N.A.I.C.S.: 524210

Arriva Insurance Company (Gibraltar) Limited (2)
Suite 913 Europort, Gibraltar, Gibraltar
Tel.: (350) 20043882
Web Site: http://www.arriva.co.uk
General Insurance Services
N.A.I.C.S.: 524210

Arriva Italia s.r.l. (2)
Via Trebazio 1, 20145, Milan, Italy
Tel.: (39) 0234534110
Web Site: http://www.arriva.it
Railway Freight Transportation Services
N.A.I.C.S.: 482111
Luigi Roth (Chm-Mgmt Bd)
Angelo Costa (Mng Dir & Member-Mgmt Bd)
Ambrogio Benaglio (Member-Mgmt Bd)
Alberto Toneatto (Member-Mgmt Bd)
Luca Delbarba (Member-Mgmt Bd)
Giuseppe Proto (Member-Mgmt Bd)
Paolo Girino (Member-Mgmt Bd)
Alessandro Pampuri (Chm-Supervisory Bd)

Subsidiary (Domestic):

Arriva London Ltd (2)
16 Watsons Rd, Wood Green, London, N22 7TZ, United Kingdom (100%)
Tel.: (44) 2082710101
Web Site: http://www.arriva.co.uk
Sales Range: $100-124.9 Million
Bus Operator
N.A.I.C.S.: 485113
Mark Yexley (Mng Dir & Dir-Bus Ops)

Subsidiary (Non-US):

Arriva Michalovce, a.s. (2)
Lastomirska 1, 071 80, Michalovce, Slovakia
Tel.: (421) 566880312
Web Site: http://www.arrivami.sk
Transportation Services
N.A.I.C.S.: 488490
Jan Morvai (Mgr-Bus Dev)

Arriva Middle East FZE (2)
2 Floor Block B Office 238 Dubai International Airport, Dubai, United Arab Emirates
Tel.: (971) 42953747
Transportation Services
N.A.I.C.S.: 488490

Subsidiary (Domestic):

Arriva Midlands Limited (2)
Unit 5 Norman Rd, PO Box 613, Leicester, LE4 8EL, Leicestershire, United Kingdom (100%)
Tel.: (44) 1162640400
Web Site: http://www.arrivabus.co.uk
Sales Range: $100-124.9 Million
Bus Operator
N.A.I.C.S.: 485113

Subsidiary (Domestic):

Arriva Midlands North Limited (3)
Mot Bay The Garage, Spath, Uttoxeter, ST14 5AE, United Kingdom
Tel.: (44) 1889560381
Transportation Services
N.A.I.C.S.: 488490

Subsidiary (Non-US):

Arriva Nederland B.V. (2)
Trambaan 3, 8441 BH, Heerenveen, Netherlands (100%)
Tel.: (31) 513621421
Web Site: http://www.arriva.nl
Emp.: 5,500
Bus, Train & Coach Service Provider
N.A.I.C.S.: 485113

Arriva Nitra a.s (2)
Sturova 72, 949 01, Nitra, Slovakia
Tel.: (421) 376599224
Web Site: http://www.arriva.sk
Emp.: 1,000
Transportation Services
N.A.I.C.S.: 485113

Arriva Noroeste SL (2)
Paseo de la Estacion s/n, 15405, El Ferrol, Spain (100%)
Tel.: (34) 981330046
Web Site: http://www.arriva.es

Sales Range: $100-124.9 Million
Bus Operator
N.A.I.C.S.: 485113

Subsidiary (Domestic):

Arriva North East Limited (2)
Admiral Way, Doxford International Business, Sunderland, SR3 3XP, United Kingdom (100%)
Tel.: (44) 1915204000
Web Site: http://www.arrivabus.co.uk
Sales Range: $50-74.9 Million
Bus Operator
N.A.I.C.S.: 485113
Nigel Featham (Mng Dir)

Branch (Domestic):

Arriva North East - Newcastle upon Tyne (3)
33 Portland Ter, Jesmond, Newcastle upon Tyne, NE2 1QS, United Kingdom
Tel.: (44) 1912811313
Web Site: http://www.arriva.co.uk
Bus Operator
N.A.I.C.S.: 485113
Nigel Featham (Mng Dir)

Subsidiary (Domestic):

Arriva North West & Wales (2)
73 Ormskirk Rd, Aintree, Liverpool, L9 5AE, Merseyside, United Kingdom (100%)
Tel.: (44) 1515222800
Web Site: http://www.arriva.co.uk
Sales Range: $25-49.9 Million
Emp.: 50
Bus Operator
N.A.I.C.S.: 485113
Debra Mercer (Mgr-Mktg & Comm)

Subsidiary (Non-US):

Arriva Nove Zamky, a.s. (2)
Povazska 2, 940 14, Nove Zamky, Slovakia
Tel.: (421) 356424180
Web Site: http://www.arriva.sk
Emp.: 400
Transportation Services
N.A.I.C.S.: 485113

Arriva Ostgotapendeln AB (2)
Liljeholmsstranden 5, Stockholm, 117 43, Sweden
Tel.: (46) 841074474
Transportation Services
N.A.I.C.S.: 488490

Arriva Praha s.r.o. (2)
Krizikova 148/34, 186 00, Prague, 8, Czech Republic
Tel.: (420) 725100725
Web Site: http://www.arriva.cz
Passenger Transport Services Operator
N.A.I.C.S.: 485999

Arriva RP Sp. z o.o. (2)
Ul Dabrowskiego 8/24, 87-100, Torun, Poland
Tel.: (48) 566212222
Web Site: http://www.arriva.pl
Emp.: 47,000
Railway Freight Transportation Services
N.A.I.C.S.: 482111

Arriva Service s.r.o. (2)
Bratislavska cesta 1804, 945 01, Komarno, Slovakia
Tel.: (421) 357740004
Transportation Services
N.A.I.C.S.: 488490
Gabor Vago (Mgr-Compliance)

Subsidiary (Domestic):

Arriva Southern Counties (2)
1 Admiral Way Doxford International Business Park, Sunderland, SR3 3XP, United Kingdom (100%)
Tel.: (44) 191 520 4000
Web Site: http://www.arriva.co.uk
Sales Range: $50-74.9 Million
Emp.: 150
Bus & Tour Operations
N.A.I.C.S.: 485113

Subsidiary (Non-US):

Arriva Stajerska, druzba za prevoz potnikov, d.d. (2)

Meljska Cesta 97, 2000, Maribor, Slovenia
Tel.: (386) 23003360
Transportation Services
N.A.I.C.S.: 485113

Arriva Tag AB (2)
Adelgatan 2, Malmo, 211 22, Sweden
Tel.: (46) 107240510
Logistics Consulting Servies
N.A.I.C.S.: 541614

Arriva Teplice s.r.o (2)
Se Sidlem Emilie Dvorakove 70, 415 01, Teplice, Czech Republic
Tel.: (420) 417539443
Web Site: http://www.arriva-teplice.cz
Transportation Services
N.A.I.C.S.: 485113

Subsidiary (Domestic):

Arriva The Shires (2)
487 Dunstable Rd, Luton, LU4 8DS, United Kingdom (100%)
Tel.: (44) 1582587000
Web Site: http://www.arriva.co.uk
Sales Range: $100-124.9 Million
Bus Operator
N.A.I.C.S.: 485113
Heat Williams (Mng Dir)
Paul Adcock (Mng Dir)

Subsidiary (Non-US):

Arriva Tog A/S (2)
Drewsensvej 1, Silkeborg, 8600, Denmark
Tel.: (45) 70277482
Web Site: http://www.arriva.dk
Transportation Services
N.A.I.C.S.: 488490

Arriva Touring BV (2)
Bornholmstraat 60, 9723 AZ, Groningen, Netherlands
Tel.: (31) 505260268
Travel Operator
N.A.I.C.S.: 561510
Joop Spykstra (Mgr-Operational)

Subsidiary (Domestic):

Arriva Trains Wales/Trenau Arriva Cymru Limited (2)
St Mary's House 47 Penarth Road, Cardiff, CF10 5DJ, United Kingdom
Tel.: (44) 3457484950
Web Site: http://www.arrivatrainswales.co.uk
Railway Freight Transportation Services
N.A.I.C.S.: 482111
Mike Tapscott (Dir-Franchise)
Chris Burchell (Mng Dir-UK Trains)
Tom Joyner (Mng Dir)

Arriva Transport Solutions Limited (2)
Unit 5 Mount Pleasant Jackson Street, Oldham, OL4 1HH, United Kingdom
Tel.: (44) 7776356945
Transportation Services
N.A.I.C.S.: 488490

Subsidiary (Non-US):

Arriva Vychodni Cechy a.s. (2)
Na Ostrove 177, 537 01, Chrudim, Czech Republic
Tel.: (420) 469660811
Web Site: http://www.arriva.cz
Transportation Services
N.A.I.C.S.: 485113

Subsidiary (Domestic):

Arriva Yorkshire Ltd. (2)
24 Barnsley Rd, Wakefield, WF1 5JX, United Kingdom (100%)
Tel.: (44) 1924375521
Web Site: http://www.arriva.co.uk
Sales Range: $100-124.9 Million
Bus Operator
N.A.I.C.S.: 485113
Nigel Featham (Mng Dir)

Subsidiary (Domestic):

Arriva Yorkshire North Ltd (3)
Cotton Lane, Bury Saint Edmunds, IP33 1XT, United Kingdom
Tel.: (44) 1284772222
Transportation Services
N.A.I.C.S.: 485113

Arriva Yorkshire West Ltd (3)
Mill Street East, Dewsbury, WF12 9AG, West Yorkshire, United Kingdom
Tel.: (44) 1924461250
Transportation Services
N.A.I.C.S.: 485113
Anna Weeks (Gen Mgr)

Subsidiary (Domestic):

TGMGroup Limited (2)
Building 16300 MT2 Electra Avenue Heathrow Airport, Hounslow, London, TW6 2DN, United Kingdom
Tel.: (44) 2087574700
Web Site: http://www.tellingsgoldenmiller.co.uk
Transportation Distr
N.A.I.C.S.: 485113
Richard Telling (Mng Dir)

The Original London Sightseeing Tour Ltd. (2)
Jews Row, London, SW18 1TB, United Kingdom (100%)
Tel.: (44) 2088771722
Web Site: http://www.theoriginaltour.com
Sales Range: $50-74.9 Million
Emp.: 156
Sight-Seeing Bus Operator
N.A.I.C.S.: 485999

Atlantic Power Corporation (1)
3 Allied Dr Ste 155, Dedham, MA 02026
Tel.: (617) 977-2400
Web Site: http://www.atlanticpower.com
Rev.: $272,000,000
Assets: $847,200,000
Liabilities: $688,600,000
Net Worth: $158,600,000
Earnings: $74,200,000
Emp.: 261
Fiscal Year-end: 12/31/2020
Holding Company; Electric Power Generation & Distribution Services
N.A.I.C.S.: 551112
Terrence Ronan (CFO & Exec VP)
Joseph E. Cofelice (Exec VP-Comml Dev)
Jamie D'Angelo (Chief Admin Officer & Sr VP)
Nick Galotti (Sr VP-Ops)
Brian Dee (Treas & Sr VP-Fin)

Co-Headquarters (Non-US):

Atlantic Power Limited Partnership (2)
200 University Avenue Suite 1301, Toronto, M5H 4H1, ON, Canada
Tel.: (617) 977-2400
Holding Company; Electric Power Generation & Distr
N.A.I.C.S.: 551112

Subsidiary (US):

APDC, Inc. (3)
5047 Martin Luther King Freeway, Fort Worth, TX 76119
Tel.: (817) 395-0120
Web Site: http://www.apdc-inc.com
Pharmaceuticals Product Mfr
N.A.I.C.S.: 325412

Applied Energy LLC (3)
8835 Balboa Ave Ste D, San Diego, CA 92123
Tel.: (858) 492-5461
Web Site: http://www.phaseback.com
Emp.: 30
Electric Power Distribution Services
N.A.I.C.S.: 221122

Cadillac Renewable Energy LLC (3)
1524 Miltner, Cadillac, MI 49601 (100%)
Tel.: (231) 779-8609
Web Site: http://www.michiganbiomass.com
Emp.: 22
Wood & Wood Waste Fueled Electric Power Plant Operator
N.A.I.C.S.: 221118

Curtis/Palmer Hydroelectric Company LP (3)
15 Pine St, Corinth, NY 12822-1319
Tel.: (518) 654-6297
Hydroelectric Power Power Generating Activities
N.A.I.C.S.: 221111

EF Kenilworth LLC (3)
2000 Galloping Hill Rd, Kenilworth, NJ 07033
Tel.: (908) 245-7734
Eletric Power Generation Services
N.A.I.C.S.: 221122

EF Oxnard LLC (3)
550 Diaz Ave, Oxnard, CA 93030-7205
Tel.: (805) 385-6375
Eletric Power Generation Services
N.A.I.C.S.: 221118

Gregory Partners, LLC (3)
2727 S Belt Hwy, Saint Joseph, MO 64503-1555
Tel.: (816) 232-2151
Legal Aid Services
N.A.I.C.S.: 541110

Orlando Cogen Limited, L.P. (3)
8300 Exchange Dr, Orlando, FL 32809-7652
Tel.: (407) 859-5141
Sales Range: Less than $1 Million
Trucking Except Local
N.A.I.C.S.: 484121

Rollcast Energy, Inc. (3)
301 S Tryon St Ste 1590, Charlotte, NC 28282 (60%)
Tel.: (704) 625-3475
Web Site: http://www.rollcastenergy.com
Renewable Energy Power Plant Developer & Operator
N.A.I.C.S.: 221118

Euclyde Data Centers SAS (1)
49 rue Emile Hugues, 06600, Antibes, France
Tel.: (33) 489848484
Web Site: http://www.euclyde.com
Information Technology Services
N.A.I.C.S.: 513210
Magdi Houry (CEO)

Division (Domestic):

Euclyde DC2 (2)
2 rue Albert Einstein, 25000, Besancon, France
Tel.: (33) 489848484
Data & Web Hosting
N.A.I.C.S.: 518210
Magdi Houry (CEO)

Subsidiary (Domestic):

NeoClyde SAS (3)
2 Rue Albert Einstein, 25000, Besancon, France
Tel.: (33) 368462000
Web Site: http://www.neoclyde.com
Data Processing Services
N.A.I.C.S.: 518210

Ezee Fiber Texas LLC (1)
14850 Woodham Dr, Houston, TX 77073
Tel.: (713) 255-7500
Digital Infrastructure Platform
N.A.I.C.S.: 513199
Scott Widham (CEO)

Subsidiary (Domestic):

Interfacing Company of Texas, LLC (2)
14850 Woodham, Houston, TX 77073
Tel.: (713) 895-0002
Web Site: http://www.ictxwavemedia.net
Power & Communication Line & Related Structures Construction
N.A.I.C.S.: 237130
Carl Merzi (Pres)

Orazul Energy Corporation (1)
c/o I Squared Capital - 410 Park Ave Ste 830, New York, NY 10022
Tel.: (212) 339-5300
Holding Company; Hydroelectric Power Plants, Natural Gas Processing & Distribution Plants Operator
N.A.I.C.S.: 551112
Adil Rahmathulla (Operating Partner)

Subsidiary (Non-US):

Electroquil, S.A. (2)
Km Route to the coast 19, PO Box 09-01-5896, Guayaquil, Ecuador
Tel.: (593) 42046006

I Squared Capital Advisors (US)
LLC—(Continued)

Web Site: http://www.electroquil.com
Electric Power Plant Operator & Transmission Services
N.A.I.C.S.: 221118
Gustavo Larrea (Gen Mgr)
Raul Espinoza (Pres)

Orazul Energy Egenor S. en C. por A.   (2)
Calle Dionisio Derteano Nro 144 piso 19,
San Isidro, Lima, 27, Peru
Tel.: (51) 1 615 4600
Web Site: http://www.orazul.pe
Hydroelectric Power, Natural Gas Processing & Distribution Plants Operator
N.A.I.C.S.: 221111
Raul Espinoza (Pres)

Orazul Energy Generating S.A.   (2)
Av LN N Alem 855 Piso 26, C1001AAD,
Buenos Aires, Argentina
Tel.: (54) 11 4875 0000
Web Site: http://www.orazul.com.ar
Hydroelectric & Thermoelectric Power Generation Services
N.A.I.C.S.: 221111
Mariana Schoua (Pres)

Subsidiary (Domestic):

Orazul Energy Cerros Colorados, S.A.   (3)
Avenida Leandro N Alem 855 Piso 26, Buenos Aires, 1001, Argentina
Tel.: (54) 1148750000
Web Site: http://www.orazul.com.ar
Electric & Gas Service Provider
N.A.I.C.S.: 221118
Mariana Schoua (Gen Mgr)

Orazul Energy International Southern Cone S.R.L.   (3)
Duke Energy International Southern Cone
SRL, C1001AAD, Buenos Aires, Argentina
Tel.: (54) 1148750000
Web Site: http://www.orazul.com.ar
Emp.: 40
Electricity & Natural Gas Generation Services
N.A.I.C.S.: 221113
Mariana Schoua (Pres)

Subsidiary (Non-US):

Orazul Energy Guatemala y Compania Sociedad en Comandita por Acciones   (2)
Europlaza World Business Center 5a Av
5-55 Z 14 Torre 3 Nivel 12, Guatemala,
Guatemala
Tel.: (502) 2327 7400
Web Site: http://www.orazul.gt
Power Plant Operator
N.A.I.C.S.: 221118
Hugo Ferrer (Pres)
Fernando Oroxom (Mgr-Comml)

Subsidiary (Non-US):

Orazul Energy El Salvador, S. en C. de C.V.   (3)
Avenida El Espino y Boulevard Sur Edificio
HOLCIM 3er Nivel, San Salvador, El Salvador
Tel.: (503) 25007600
Web Site: http://www.orazul.gt
Fossil Fuel & Steam Power Plant Operator
N.A.I.C.S.: 221112
Carlos Polanco (Reg Dir-Comml & Dev)
Benjamin Mejia (Mgr-Mktg & Market Analysis)

Subsidiary (Non-US):

Orazul Energy International Chile C.P.A.   (2)
Cerro El Plomo 5630 piso 15 oficina 1502
Edificio de las Artes, Las Condes, 7561127,
Santiago, Chile
Tel.: (56) 226172701
Web Site: http://www.duke-energy.cl
Hydroelectric & Thermal Power Generation & Transmission Services
N.A.I.C.S.: 221111
Diego Hollweck (Pres)

Priority Power Management, LLC (1)

2201 E Lamar Blvd Ste 275, 76006, Arlington, TX
Web Site: http://www.prioritypower.net
Energy Management & Consulting Services
John J. Bick (Chm & Chief Comml Officer)
Danny Smedley (Mng Dir-Energy Sls)
Charlie Hewitt (Sr Mng Dir-Bus Process Ops)
Brandon Schwertner (CEO)
Katherine Graham (CTO)
Joe Loner (CFO)

Star Leasing Co.   (1)
4080 Business Park Dr, Columbus, OH
43204
Tel.: (614) 278-9999
Web Site: http://www.starleasing.com
Sales Range: $25-49.9 Million
Emp.: 180
Trailer Leasing
N.A.I.C.S.: 532120
Jeff Rosen (CFO & Sr VP)
Steve Jackson (Pres & CEO)
Robert D. Beaver (VP)
Jeff D. Egle (VP-Sls)
Linda S. Tulley (VP-Fin)
Bob Baker (Mgr-Svc)
Jim H. Goodwin (VP)

Viridian Group Ltd.   (1)
Greenwood House 64 Newforge Lane, Belfast, BT9 5NF, United Kingdom
Tel.: (44) 28 9038 3765
Web Site: http://www.viridiangroup.co.uk
Rev.: $2,106,246,144
Assets: $1,843,302,656
Liabilities: $1,571,724,800
Net Worth: $271,577,856
Earnings: ($117,103,616)
Emp.: 702
Fiscal Year-end: 03/31/2018
Electricity Generation & Distribution Services
N.A.I.C.S.: 221122
Ian Thom (CEO)
Siobhan Bailey (Dir-Fin)
Tom Gillen (Mng Dir-Energia Grp)
Stephen McCully (Mng Dir-Power NI)
Roy Foreman (Mng Dir-Power NI-Power Procurement Bus (PPB))

I WIRELESS
4135 NW Urbandale Dr, Urbandale,
IA 50322-7928
Tel.: (515) 258-7000   DE
Web Site: http://www.iwireless.com
Sales Range: $25-49.9 Million
Emp.: 300
Cellular Telephone Services
N.A.I.C.S.: 423610
Craven Shumaker (Pres & CEO)
David Frost (CFO)

I&E TIRE CORP.
195 Kings St, Brooklyn, NY 11231-
3809
Tel.: (718) 625-1300
Year Founded: 1961
Sales Range: $10-24.9 Million
Emp.: 12
Retailer of Tires & Tubes
N.A.I.C.S.: 423130
Edward Cohn (Pres)

Subsidiaries:

Northeast Wholesale Tire Corp. (1)
54 Winter St, Malden, MA 02148-1426
Tel.: (781) 322-5100
Web Site:
http://www.northeastwholesaletire.com
Sales Range: $10-24.9 Million
Emp.: 6
Retailer of Tires & Tubes
N.A.I.C.S.: 423130
Bob Bodnaruk (Gen Mgr)

I&I SLING INC.
2626 Market St, Aston, PA 19014
Tel.: (610) 485-8500
Web Site: http://www.slingmax.com
Sales Range: $50-74.9 Million
Emp.: 70
Provider of Wire & Rope

N.A.I.C.S.: 314994
Dennis St. Germain Sr. (Owner)

I&I SOFTWARE, INC.
2571 Baglyos Cir Ste B32, Bethlehem, PA 18020
Tel.: (610) 882-9699
Web Site: https://www.iandisoft.com
Year Founded: 2001
Sales Range: $1-9.9 Million
Emp.: 70
IT Consulting for Insurance Companies, Financial Firms, Medical Organizations, Online Companies & Utilities
N.A.I.C.S.: 541618
Betty Woodring (VP-HR)

I&MJ GROSS COMPANY
14300 Ridge Rd Ste 100, Cleveland,
OH 44133
Tel.: (440) 237-1681
Web Site:
http://www.grossbuilders.com
Sales Range: $10-24.9 Million
Emp.: 50
Multi-Family Dwellings, New Construction
N.A.I.C.S.: 236116
Gary Gross (Co-Pres)
Tom Miller (Controller)
Harley Gross (Co-Pres)

I-BANKERS SECURITIES, INC.
21550 Oxnard St 3rd Fl, Woodland
Hills, CA 91367
Tel.: (310) 907-5939
Web Site: http://www.i-bankers.net
Year Founded: 1996
Securities Brokerage Services
N.A.I.C.S.: 523150
Michael McCrory (Chm)
Shelley Leonard (Pres & CFO)

I-BUS CORPORATION
3350 Scott Blvd Ste 54, Santa Clara,
CA 95054
Tel.: (408) 450-7880   CA
Web Site: http://www.ibus.com
Year Founded: 1982
High Performance Computer & Power
Conditioning Products Developer &
Mfr
N.A.I.C.S.: 334419

I-K-I MANUFACTURING CO. INC.
116 Swift St, Edgerton, WI 53534
Tel.: (608) 884-3411
Web Site: https://www.ikimfg.com
Sales Range: $25-49.9 Million
Emp.: 10
Filling Pressure Containers
N.A.I.C.S.: 561990
Christopher Kaebisch (Mgr-Internal Logistics)

I-SITE, INC.
15 S Third St Ste 200, Philadelphia,
PA 19106-2801
Tel.: (215) 413-3135   PA
Web Site: http://www.i-site.com
Year Founded: 1996
Sales Range: $125-149.9 Million
Emp.: 13
N.A.I.C.S.: 541810
Ian Cross (CEO)

I-WIRELESS INC.
5755 Granger Rd Ste 750, Independence, OH 44131
Web Site:
http://www.thewirelesscenter.com
Year Founded: 2002
Sales Range: $25-49.9 Million
Emp.: 344
Verizon Wireless Retailer

N.A.I.C.S.: 517112
Ajmal Kazmi (Pres)

I. KEATING FURNITURE INC.
10 S Broadway, Minot, ND 58701
Tel.: (701) 852-3536
Web Site:
https://www.ikeatingfurniture.com
Year Founded: 1934
Rev.: $26,703,799
Emp.: 130
Furniture Retailer & Carpet & Rug
Dealer
N.A.I.C.S.: 423210
Matt Kramer (Treas)

I. OLA LAHUI INC.
1441 Kapiolani Blvd Ste 1802, Honolulu, HI 96814
Tel.: (808) 525-6255   HI
Web Site: http://www.iolalahui.org
Year Founded: 2007
Sales Range: $1-9.9 Million
Emp.: 28
Health Care Srvices
N.A.I.C.S.: 622110
Jill Oliveira Gray (Dir-Res & Evaluation)
A. Aukahi Austin (Exec Dir)

I. SCHUMANN & COMPANY
22500 Alexander Rd, Bedford, OH
44146
Tel.: (440) 439-2300
Web Site:
https://www.ischumann.com
Sales Range: $100-124.9 Million
Emp.: 160
Brass Smelting & Refining (Secondary)
N.A.I.C.S.: 331492
David Schumann (Exec VP)

I. SPIEWAK & SONS, INC.
463 7th Ave 1100, New York, NY
10018-7605
Tel.: (212) 695-1620   NY
Web Site: http://www.spiewak.com
Year Founded: 1903
Provider of Ladies', Men's, Young
Men's & Boys' Outerwear, Ski &
Sportswear, Insulated Clothing, Trappings, Uniforms & Industrial Jackets
& Parkas
N.A.I.C.S.: 315250
Roy Spiewak (Pres)

I.C. SYSTEM, INC.
444 Highway 96 E, Saint Paul, MN
55164-0378
Tel.: (651) 483-8201   MN
Web Site: https://www.icsystem.com
Year Founded: 1938
Sales Range: $350-399.9 Million
Emp.: 1,400
Accounts Receivable Management
N.A.I.C.S.: 561440
John A. Erickson (Pres & CEO)
Michelle Dove (Chief Compliance Officer & Corp Counsel)
Tom Emms (CIO & VP-Info Svcs)

Subsidiaries:

Adams, Cooper & Marks   (1)
5201 Congress Ave Ste 225, Boca Raton,
FL 33487   (100%)
Web Site: http://www.corpcollect.com
Sales Range: $10-24.9 Million
Emp.: 30
Provider of Commercial Collection Services
N.A.I.C.S.: 561440

I.C.E. SERVICE GROUP, INC.
192 Ohio River Blvd Ste 100, Ambridge, PA 15003-1214
Tel.: (724) 266-7580

Web Site:
http://www.iceservicegroup.com
Year Founded: 2007
Sales Range: $1-9.9 Million
Emp.: 10
Material Recycling Services
N.A.I.C.S.: 562920
Denise Rivas-Morgan *(Pres)*
Mark DelFratte *(Sr Program Mgr-Ops)*
Stephen Lipecky *(Sr Program Mgr-Equipment & Logistics)*
Gus Chirgott *(Sr Program Mgr-Estimating & Project Dev)*
Anthony Kindinis *(Sr Program Mgr-Field & Industrial Svcs)*
Dennis Morgan *(Sr Program Mgr-Special Projects)*

I.D. BOOTH INC.
620 William St, Elmira, NY 14902-0579
Tel.: (607) 733-9121
Web Site: https://www.idbooth.com
Sales Range: $10-24.9 Million
Emp.: 55
Plumbing & Hydronic Heating Supplies
N.A.I.C.S.: 423720
John Seeley Booth Jr. *(Pres)*

I.D. GRIFFITH, INC.
735 S Market St, Wilmington, DE 19899
Tel.: (302) 656-8253
Sales Range: $25-49.9 Million
Emp.: 85
Plumbing Services
N.A.I.C.S.: 238220
Rick Murphy *(Owner & CEO)*
David L. Zarrilli *(Pres)*

I.D. IMAGES LLC
2991 Interstate Pkwy, Brunswick, OH 44212
Tel.: (330) 220-7300
Web Site: http://www.idimages.com
Year Founded: 1995
Labels & Custom Label Solutions for Printing
N.A.I.C.S.: 323120
Jeffrey A. Fielkow *(Pres & CEO)*

Subsidiaries:

Kieran Label Corp.   (1)
2321 Siempre Viva Ct Ste 101, San Diego, CA 92154
Tel.: (619) 449-4457
Web Site: http://www.kieranlabel.com
Sales Range: $1-9.9 Million
Emp.: 46
Coated & Laminated Paper Mfr
N.A.I.C.S.: 322220
Denis Vanier *(CEO)*

I.G. BURTON & CO. INC.
793 Bay Rd, Milford, DE 19963-6122
Tel.: (302) 422-3041
Web Site:
https://www.igburtonchevymilford.com
Sales Range: $100-124.9 Million
Emp.: 215
Sales & Service Of Automobiles, New & Used
N.A.I.C.S.: 441110
Charles Burton *(Pres)*

I.H. CAFFEY DISTRIBUTING CO.
8749 W Market St, Greensboro, NC 27409
Tel.: (336) 668-0876
Web Site: http://www.ihcaffey.com
Rev.: $49,600,000
Emp.: 130
Beer & Other Fermented Malt Liquors
N.A.I.C.S.: 424810

Christopher Caffey *(Pres & CEO)*

I.O. INCORPORATED
2144 Franklin Dr NE, Palm Bay, FL 32905
Tel.: (321) 499-3819
Web Site: http://www.ioinc.us
Sales Range: $10-24.9 Million
Firearms Mfr
N.A.I.C.S.: 332994
Uli Wiegand *(Pres)*

I.P. CALLISON & SONS INC.
2400 Callison Rd NE, Lacey, WA 98516
Tel.: (360) 412-3340
Web Site: http://www.callison.com
Rev.: $25,000,000
Emp.: 50
Oils & Essential Oils
N.A.I.C.S.: 325998
Patricia Six *(Mgr-Flavor Applications)*

I.T. SOURCE
5670 Wilshire Blvd Ste 2300, Los Angeles, CA 90036
Tel.: (213) 550-4492
Year Founded: 2002
Sales Range: $1-9.9 Million
Emp.: 4
Credit Card Processing & Wholesale Telecom Services
N.A.I.C.S.: 561499
Andy Kim *(CEO)*

Subsidiaries:

Massive Telecom   (1)
5670 Wilshire Blvd Ste 2300, Los Angeles, CA 90036   **(100%)**
Tel.: (213) 550-4492
Web Site: http://www.massivetelecom.com
Wholesale Telecommunications Services
N.A.I.C.S.: 517112
Kim Chun *(CEO)*

Unlimited Merchant Services   (1)
3701 Wilshire Blvd Ste 409, Los Angeles, CA 90010   **(100%)**
Tel.: (877) 503-1117
Web Site:
http://www.unlimitedmerchant.com
Credit Card Processing Services
N.A.I.C.S.: 522299
Kim Chun *(CEO)*

I.T. WORKS RECRUITMENT INC.
4016 Flowers Rd Ste 440, Atlanta, GA 30360
Tel.: (678) 291-0081
Web Site: http://www.itworksrec.com
Year Founded: 2013
Sales Range: $10-24.9 Million
Emp.: 35
Recruitment Consulting Services
N.A.I.C.S.: 541612
Gary Dytor *(Founder & CEO)*
James Furness *(VP-Sls & Recruitment)*
Christina Woods *(Dir-Trng & Dev)*
Amanda Dytor *(Mgr-Operational Complaince)*
Kym Valdastri *(Office Mgr)*

I/D/E/A/ INC.
1 Idea Way, Caldwell, ID 83605
Tel.: (208) 459-6357   ID
Web Site:
http://www.ideaprinting.com
Year Founded: 1955
Sales Range: $10-24.9 Million
Emp.: 75
Mfr of Personalized Apparel & Mail-order Catalogs; Print Production
N.A.I.C.S.: 323111
Jane McConnell *(Mgr-Mktg)*

I/OMAGIC CORPORATION

20512 Crescent Bay Dr Ste 106, Lake Forest, CA 92630
Tel.: (949) 707-4800   NV
Web Site: http://www.iomagic.com
Sales Range: $1-9.9 Million
Emp.: 30
Data Storage, Digital Entertainment & Personal Computer & Peripheral Products Retailer
N.A.I.C.S.: 334112

I3LOGIC
408 South Lafayette Ave Ste 200, Royal Oak, MI 48067
Tel.: (248) 292-5100
Web Site: http://www.i3logic.net
Sales Range: $1-9.9 Million
Emp.: 30
Business Communication & Learning Software Development Services
N.A.I.C.S.: 541511
Peter Kelley *(Partner & Creative Dir)*
Tom Vasko *(VP-Innovative Technologies)*

I4DM
8227 Cloverleaf Dr Ste 312, Millersville, MD 21108
Tel.: (410) 729-7920
Web Site: https://www.i4dm.com
Year Founded: 2002
Sales Range: $1-9.9 Million
Emp.: 32
Information Technology Services
N.A.I.C.S.: 518210
Michael Peart *(Founder, Pres & CEO)*
Kurt Nordhoff *(Mgr-Bus Dev)*

I9 SPORTS CORPORATION
9410 Camden Field Pkwy, Riverview, FL 33578
Tel.: (800) 975-2937
Web Site: http://www.i9sports.com
Year Founded: 2002
Sales Range: $1-9.9 Million
Emp.: 100
Youth Sports Leagues Franchisor
N.A.I.C.S.: 711211
Frank Fiume *(Founder & Chm)*
Brian Sanders *(CEO)*
Kim Armellino *(VP-Fin & Admin)*
Steve Cox *(Program Dir)*
April Thomas *(Dir-Mktg)*
Charlie Carnahan *(Dir-Franchise Dev)*
Ryan Schalk *(Mgr-Franchise Dev)*
Roger Ewart *(VP-Ops)*

I95DEV
3 Bethesda Metro Ctr Ste 700, Bethesda, MD 20814
Tel.: (301) 760-7499
Web Site: http://www.i95dev.com
Year Founded: 2000
Sales Range: $1-9.9 Million
Emp.: 135
Software & IT Staffing
N.A.I.C.S.: 513210
Vanit Kumar *(CEO & Founder)*

IA ENERGY CORP.
1 World Trade Ctr Ste 130, Long Beach, CA 90831
Tel.: (310) 891-1959   WY
Web Site: http://www.iaenergy.com
Year Founded: 2016
Assets: $204
Liabilities: $324,231
Net Worth: ($324,027)
Earnings: ($44,883)
Emp.: 1
Fiscal Year-end: 12/31/22
Energy Research & Development Services
N.A.I.C.S.: 926110

IAB SOLUTIONS, LLC

233 Northern Blvd, Clarks Summit, PA 18411
Tel.: (570) 587-1000
Web Site: http://www.iabinc.com
Sales Range: $10-24.9 Million
Emp.: 85
Accounts Receivable Outsourcing Solutions
N.A.I.C.S.: 541211
Kenneth Green *(Pres)*
Michael Kowalski *(Controller)*

IAERO GROUP
5300 NW 36th St, Miami, FL 33166
Tel.: (305) 702-0410
Web Site: http://www.iaerogroup.com
Year Founded: 2018
Integrated Aviation Platform including Engine & Airframe MRO Provider & Services
N.A.I.C.S.: 333618
Robert Caputo *(CEO)*

Subsidiaries:

Swift Air Inc.   (1)
2717 W 6th St, Sioux Falls, SD 57104
Tel.: (800) 365-1573
Web Site: http://www.swiftairinc.com
Rev.: $1,200,000
Emp.: 12
Site Preparation Contractor
N.A.I.C.S.: 238910

IAF LTD.
13177 Foothill Blvd, Sylmar, CA 91342
Tel.: (818) 361-7724
Rev.: $28,800,000
Emp.: 17
Industrial Alcohol Mfr
N.A.I.C.S.: 325199

IAG HOLDINGS INC.
80 N 1400 W, Centerville, UT 84014
Tel.: (801) 393-1075
Web Site: http://www.armormax.com
Sales Range: $10-24.9 Million
Emp.: 30
Assembly Of Armored Cars
N.A.I.C.S.: 336110
Mark F. Burton *(Founder & CEO)*

Subsidiaries:

International Armoring Corp.   (1)
181 S 600 W 3A/5, Ogden, UT 84404
Tel.: (801) 393-1075
Web Site: http://www.armormax.com
Rev.: $3,000,000
Emp.: 20
Cars, Armored, Assembly Of
N.A.I.C.S.: 336110
Mark F. Burton *(Founder)*

IAN BLACK REAL ESTATE
1 One South School Ave, Sarasota, FL 34237
Tel.: (941) 906-8688
Web Site: http://www.ian-black.com
Year Founded: 2003
Sales Range: $25-49.9 Million
Emp.: 20
Real Estate Broker
N.A.I.C.S.: 531210
Marci Marsh *(COO)*
Cindy Jean *(Dir-Mktg)*
Diana Grandy *(Asst Mgr-Property)*

IAP WORLDWIDE SERVICES, INC.
413 Western Ln, Irmo, SC 29063
Tel.: (803) 798-1611
Web Site: http://www.iapws.com
Year Founded: 1989
Sales Range: $300-349.9 Million
Emp.: 5,000
Procurement Services for the U.S. Military
N.A.I.C.S.: 423440

IAP Worldwide Services, Inc.—(Continued)

Bob Phillips *(Pres)*
Terry DeRosa *(CFO & Exec VP)*
Christopher W. Parker *(Chm)*
Maureen P. Fitzgerald *(Dir-Comm & PR)*
Marcus Ward *(Dir-Ops)*
Amanda Brownfield *(CEO)*

Subsidiaries:

IAP World Services Inc. (1)
7315 N Atlantic Ave, Cape Canaveral, FL 32920 **(100%)**
Tel.: (321) 784-7100
Web Site: http://www.iapws.com
Facility Management Services to Military Bases, Space Centers & Other Large Complexes
N.A.I.C.S.: 488119
Robert Netolicka *(VP)*

IAPPSYS
505 Montgomery St Ste 1100, San Francisco, CA 94111
Web Site: https://www.iappsys.com
Year Founded: 2007
Sales Range: $1-9.9 Million
Emp.: 20
Full-Service Oracle Systems Services & Support
N.A.I.C.S.: 541519
Christine Wong *(Specialist-Sls & Support)*
Joe Young *(Dir-Oracle Solutions)*

IAS SERVICES GROUP LLC
1020 NE Loop 410 Ste 805, San Antonio, TX 78209
Tel.: (210) 804-1300
Web Site: https://www.iasclaims.com
Year Founded: 1984
Emp.: 30
Insurance Services
N.A.I.C.S.: 524298
Valerie Martinez *(Mgr-ClaimCare)*
Tony Scow *(Pres & COO)*
Walter Leddy *(CEO)*

Subsidiaries:

IAS Claim Services (1)
333 City Blvd W Ste 1410, Orange, CA 92868
Tel.: (714) 245-9544
Web Site: http://www.iasclaims.com
Sales Range: $1-9.9 Million
Emp.: 17
Claims Adjusting
N.A.I.C.S.: 524291
John Gomez *(VP)*
Walter Leddy *(CEO)*
Tony Scow *(Pres & COO)*

IASO BIOMED, INC.
7315 E Peakview Ave, Englewood, CO 80111
Tel.: (720) 389-0650   CO
Web Site:
   http://www.iasobiomedusa.com
Year Founded: 2015
Assets: $141,685
Liabilities: $744,204
Net Worth: ($602,519)
Earnings: ($1,637,237)
Emp.: 2
Fiscal Year-end: 12/31/18
Biotechnology Research & Development Services
N.A.I.C.S.: 541714
Richard M. Schell *(Founder, Chm, Pres & CEO)*
Duane C. Knight Jr. *(CFO)*

IAT REINSURANCE COMPANY, LTD.
2850 W Golf Rd Ste 900, Rolling Meadows, IL 60008-4053
Tel.: (847) 321-4800   BM

Web Site: http://www.iat-re.com
Holding Company; Reinsurance
N.A.I.C.S.: 551112
Peter R. Kellogg *(Principal)*

Subsidiaries:

Harco National Insurance Company, Inc. (1)
1701 Golf Rd Ste 600 Tower 1, Rolling Meadows, IL 60008-4241 **(100%)**
Tel.: (847) 321-4800
Web Site: http://www.iatinsurancegroup.com
Sales Range: $50-74.9 Million
Insurance Services
N.A.I.C.S.: 524126

IBA INC.
27 Providence St, Millbury, MA 01527
Tel.: (508) 865-6911   MA
Web Site: http://www.iba-usa.com
Year Founded: 1985
Sales Range: $10-24.9 Million
Emp.: 50
Farm Supplies Whslr
N.A.I.C.S.: 423820
Daniel Belsito *(Pres)*
Irwin Thomashow *(CFO & Controller)*

IBASE TECHNOLOGY (USA), INC.
1050 Stewart Dr, Sunnyvale, CA 94085
Tel.: (408) 992-0888   CA
Web Site: https://www.ibase-usa.com
Year Founded: 1986
Industrial Computer Systems & Components Designer, Mfr & Whslr
N.A.I.C.S.: 334111
C. S. Lin *(Pres)*

IBC ADVANCED TECHNOLOGIES, INC.
856 E Utah Valley Dr, American Fork, UT 84003
Tel.: (801) 763-8400
Web Site: https://www.ibcmrt.com
Year Founded: 1988
Sales Range: $10-24.9 Million
Emp.: 30
Chemical Product & Preparation Mfr
N.A.I.C.S.: 325998

IBC GROUP INC.
1000 NW 65th St Ste 103, Fort Lauderdale, FL 33309
Tel.: (954) 491-1002   DE
Year Founded: 1974
Sales Range: $100-124.9 Million
Emp.: 309
Mattresses & Bedsprings
N.A.I.C.S.: 337910
Jeff Maillet *(CEO)*
Bruce Miller *(VP-Logistics)*
Scott O'Bryant *(Mktg Mgr)*
Dave Dombar *(VP-Contract Div)*
Eric Johnson *(Sr VP-Mktg & Mdsg)*

Subsidiaries:

International Bedding Corp. (1)
400C Commerce Blvd, Cleburne, TX 76033-5060
Tel.: (817) 641-3777
Sales Range: $25-49.9 Million
Emp.: 60
Mattresses & Bedsprings Mfr
N.A.I.C.S.: 337910

International Bedding Corp. (1)
1214 Morea Rd, Barnesville, PA 18214
Tel.: (570) 773-1333
Sales Range: $25-49.9 Million
Emp.: 70
Mattresses & Bedsprings Mfr
N.A.I.C.S.: 337910

International Bedding Corp. (1)
8591 W Washington St, Tolleson, AZ 85353-3842
Tel.: (623) 478-7688

Sales Range: $25-49.9 Million
Emp.: 67
Mattresses & Bedsprings Mfr
N.A.I.C.S.: 337910

International Bedding Corp. (1)
15012 Edgerton Rd, New Haven, IN 46774
Tel.: (260) 749-6577
Sales Range: $25-49.9 Million
Emp.: 120
Mattresses & Bedsprings Mfr
N.A.I.C.S.: 337910

IBC MANAGEMENT, LLC
1700 Pacific Ave Ste 2740, Dallas, TX 75201
Tel.: (214) 722-6200
Web Site: http://www.ibcfund.com
General Management Consulting Services
N.A.I.C.S.: 541611
Margaret M. Taylor *(CFO)*

Subsidiaries:

Independent Rough Terrain Center LLC (1)
103 Guadalupe Dr Rd No 303, Cibolo, TX 78108
Tel.: (210) 599-6541
Web Site: http://www.irtc-tx.com
Container Handling Equipment Mfr
N.A.I.C.S.: 333923
Stephen Speakes *(Pres & CEO)*

IBC NORTH AMERICA INC.
4545 Clawson Tank Dr, Clarkston, MI 48346
Tel.: (248) 625-8700
Web Site:
   http://www.clawsoncontainer.com
Rev.: $22,300,000
Emp.: 50
Tanks, Storage
N.A.I.C.S.: 423830
Dick Harding *(Pres & CEO)*
Michael Harding *(VP)*
Jake Harding *(Gen Mgr)*

Subsidiaries:

Clean Tide Container, Inc. (1)
17270 Resnik Dr, Robertsdale, AL 36567
Tel.: (251) 947-3301
Web Site: http://www.cleantidecontainer.com
Sales Range: $10-24.9 Million
Emp.: 9
Container Reconditioning & Recycling Services
N.A.I.C.S.: 326199

IBERIA TILE CORP.
2975 NW 77th Ave, Miami, FL 33122
Tel.: (305) 591-3880
Web Site: http://www.iberiatiles.com
Year Founded: 1979
Rev.: $25,000,000
Emp.: 60
Tiles Mfr
N.A.I.C.S.: 327120
Rosa Sugranes Arimany *(Founder)*

IBERVILLE INSULATIONS INC.
11637 Sun Belt Ct, Baton Rouge, LA 70809
Tel.: (225) 752-2194
Web Site:
   http://www.ibervillecompanies.com
Sales Range: $10-24.9 Million
Emp.: 100
Insulation Of Pipes & Boilers
N.A.I.C.S.: 238990
Christopher Bonvillian *(Pres)*

IBETA QUALITY ASSURANCE LLC
2675 S Abilene St Ste 300, Aurora, CO 80014
Tel.: (303) 627-1110
Web Site: https://www.ibeta.com
Year Founded: 1999

Emp.: 100
Software Testing & Quality Assurance Services
N.A.I.C.S.: 541380
Glenn Kletzky *(Pres & CEO)*
Earl Wing *(CFO & VP)*
Gail Audette *(Mgr-Quality)*
Wick Gordon *(Dir-HR)*
Mike Stark *(Dir-Sls & Mktg)*

IBEX CONSTRUCTION COMPANY, LLC
1 Whitehall St, New York, NY 10004
Tel.: (646) 366-6200
Web Site:
   http://www.ibexconstruction.com
Commercial & Office Building Contractors
N.A.I.C.S.: 236220
Andy Frankl *(Pres)*
Neal Wegman *(CFO & Chief Admin Officer)*

IBEX IT BUSINESS EXPERTS, LLC
3295 River Exchange Dr Ste 550, Norcross, GA 30092
Tel.: (678) 752-7542
Web Site:
   http://www.ibexperts.com
Year Founded: 2012
Sales Range: $1-9.9 Million
Emp.: 80
Information Technology Consulting Services
N.A.I.C.S.: 541690
Tracey Grace *(CEO)*
Ray Schroeder *(VP-Ops)*

IBIS WEST PALM PARTNERS LP
8225 Ibis Blvd, West Palm Beach, FL 33412
Tel.: (561) 624-8000   DE
Web Site: https://www.clubatibis.com
Year Founded: 1995
Country Club Membership
N.A.I.C.S.: 713910

IBM SOUTHEAST EMPLOYEES' CREDIT UNION
PO Box 5090, Boca Raton, FL 33431-0990
Tel.: (800) 873-5100
Web Site: http://www.ibmsecu.org
Holding Company
N.A.I.C.S.: 523999
Mike Miller *(CEO)*

IBS PARTNERS LTD.
8100 SW 10th St Ste 4000, Fort Lauderdale, FL 33324
Tel.: (954) 581-0922
Web Site:
   http://www.nationalbeverage.com
Sales Range: $200-249.9 Million
Emp.: 1,600
Soft Drinks Mfr
N.A.I.C.S.: 312111

IBS&D CORP.
14641 Lee Hwy Ste 202, Centreville, VA 20121
Tel.: (703) 828-2345
Web Site: http://www.ibsdcorp.com
IT & Consulting Services
N.A.I.C.S.: 541618
Unmi Lee *(Pres & CEO)*
Shawn Kim *(Dir-Mktg)*
Peter Jin *(Dir-Mktg)*
Kevin Choi *(Gen Mgr)*

IBT MEDIA INC.
7 Hanover Sq 5th Fl, New York, NY 10004
Tel.: (646) 867-7100   NY

Web Site: http://www.ibtimes.com
Online News Magazine Publisher
N.A.I.C.S.: 513120
Etienne Uzac *(Co-Founder)*
Jonathan Davis *(Co-Founder & Chief Content Officer)*
Michael Lukac *(CTO)*
Dev Pragad *(CEO)*
David Kennedy *(Dir-Adv Ops)*
Peter S. Goodman *(Editor-in-Chief)*
Richard Pasqua *(Chief Experience Officer)*
Mitchell Caplan *(CMO)*
Marc Perton *(Dir-Editorial)*
Daniel Goodman *(VP & Dir-Mktg Ops)*
Alvaro Palacios *(COO)*
Emily Scheer *(Dir-PR)*
Dayan Candappa *(Global Editor-in-Chief)*
Madelin Bosakewich *(VP-Sls)*
Mohit Hira *(Pres & Head-India)*
Chandra Mohan *(Mng Dir-India)*
Alan Press *(Pres-Strategic)*

Subsidiaries:

Newsweek LLC   (1)
7 Hanover Sq 5th Fl, New York, NY 10004
Tel.: (212) 445-4000
Web Site: http://www.newsweek.com
Online Magazine Publisher
N.A.I.C.S.: 513120
Kira Bindrim *(Mng Editor)*
John Seeley *(Editor-Weekend)*
Cady Drell *(Editor-Culture)*
Matt McAllester *(Editor-in-Chief-Global)*
Kevin Dolak *(Exec Editor-Digital)*
Helen Russell *(Mgr-Production)*
Serena Kutchinsky *(Editor-Digital-Europe)*
Graham Smith *(Deputy Editor-Online News)*
Shaminder Dulai *(Dir-Photo)*
Mike Friel *(Dir-Art)*
Dev Pragad *(CEO)*
Nancy Cooper *(Acting Editor)*

IBT, INC.
9400 W 55th St, Merriam, KS 66203-2042
Tel.: (913) 428-2858   MO
Web Site: https://www.ibtinc.com
Year Founded: 1949
Sales Range: $200-249.9 Million
Emp.: 500
Industrial Parts & Supplies Distr
N.A.I.C.S.: 423840
Gary Hense *(Dir-Trng)*
Kevin Thompson *(Controller)*
Greg Drown *(VP-Fin)*

Subsidiaries:

IBT Central Distribution Center   (1)
9400 W 55th St, Merriam, KS 66203-1382   **(100%)**
Tel.: (913) 677-3151
Web Site: http://www.ibtinc.com
Sales Range: $25-49.9 Million
Emp.: 120
Industrial Supplies
N.A.I.C.S.: 423840

IBUYOFFICESUPPLY.COM
14940 28th Ave N, Plymouth, MN 55447
Web Site:
   http://www.iBuyOfficeSupply.com
Year Founded: 2005
Sales Range: $1-9.9 Million
Emp.: 8
Office Supply Distr
N.A.I.C.S.: 424120
Ron Weber *(Pres & CEO)*
Mark Melius *(VP-Sls & Mktg)*

IC GROUP
4080 S 500 W, Salt Lake City, UT 84123
Tel.: (801) 265-8100
Web Site: https://www.ic-group.net
Rev.: $12,800,000

Emp.: 180
Commercial Printing
N.A.I.C.S.: 323111
James L. MacFarlane *(Chm)*
David MacFarlane *(Pres)*
Ron Beynon *(Mgr-Matls)*

IC MECHANICAL, INC.
13925 Monroes Business Park, Tampa, FL 33635
Tel.: (813) 818-4889
Web Site: https://www.icmech.com
Year Founded: 1995
Sales Range: $10-24.9 Million
Emp.: 153
Engineering & Manufacturing Services
N.A.I.C.S.: 541330
Tom Szikszay *(Pres)*

IC REALTIME, LLC.
3050 N Andrews Ave Ext, Pompano Beach, FL 33064
Tel.: (954) 772-5327
Web Site: https://www.icrealtime.com
Year Founded: 2006
Sales Range: $10-24.9 Million
Emp.: 100
Security System Product Mfr
N.A.I.C.S.: 334290
Matt Sailor *(CEO)*
Frank Fishman *(Gen Mgr)*

IC SOLUTIONS, INC.
15 Holly St Ste 202, Scarborough, ME 04074
Tel.: (207) 883-8696
Sales Range: $75-99.9 Million
Emp.: 68
Multi-Disciplined Software Development
N.A.I.C.S.: 513210
Phil Grant *(Pres)*

ICAFE, INC.
W223N790 Saratoga Dr, Waukesha, WI 53186
Tel.: (262) 970-7153
Web Site: http://www.icafeinc.com
Year Founded: 1944
Sales Range: $10-24.9 Million
Emp.: 90
Industrial Supplies Merchant Whslr
N.A.I.C.S.: 423840
Jeff Treske *(Pres)*

Subsidiaries:

Dove Equipment   (1)
723 Sabrina Dr, East Peoria, IL 61611-3578
Tel.: (309) 694-6228
Web Site: http://www.doveequipment.com
Sales Range: $10-24.9 Million
Emp.: 20
Industrial Machinery & Equipment Distr
N.A.I.C.S.: 423830
Kenneth Hoosen *(Mgr-HR)*

ICAGEN, INC.
4222 Emperor Blvd Ste 350, Durham, NC 27703
Tel.: (919) 941-5206   DE
Web Site: http://www.icagen.com
Year Founded: 2003
Rev.: $13,583,218
Assets: $15,615,587
Liabilities: $34,973,296
Net Worth: ($19,357,709)
Earnings: ($13,039,313)
Emp.: 66
Fiscal Year-end: 12/31/18
Pharmaceutical Mfr, Researcher & Developer
N.A.I.C.S.: 325412
Douglas Krafte *(Chief Scientific Officer)*
Anil Nair *(VP-In Silico Drug Discovery)*

Paul August *(VP-Biology)*
Neil Castle *(VP-Res)*
Mark J. Korb *(CFO)*
Timothy C. Tyson *(Chm)*

Subsidiaries:

Icagen-T, Inc.   (1)
2090 E Innovation Pk Dr, Oro Valley, AZ 85755
Tel.: (520) 544-6800
Pharmaceuticals Product Mfr
N.A.I.C.S.: 325412

ICAN ENERGY CO.
4200 Stone Rd, Kilgore, TX 75662-6935
Tel.: (903) 983-1551   TX
Year Founded: 1980
Rev.: $36,992,920
Emp.: 75
Petroleum Products Mfr
N.A.I.C.S.: 424720

ICARE INDUSTRIES, INC.
4399 35th St N, Saint Petersburg, FL 33714-3717
Tel.: (727) 526-0501   FL
Web Site: https://www.icarelabs.com
Year Founded: 1968
Sales Range: $10-24.9 Million
Emp.: 100
Prescription Lenses & Diving Lenses Mfr
N.A.I.C.S.: 339115
J. Scott Payne *(CEO)*
J. T. Payne *(Pres)*
Greg Gerhig *(CFO)*

ICARE.COM LLC
401 E Las Olas Blvd Ste 2250, Fort Lauderdale, FL 33316
Tel.: (954) 616-5604
Web Site: http://www.icare.com
Year Founded: 2011
Sales Range: $10-24.9 Million
Emp.: 15
Electronic Health Record Solutions & Software
N.A.I.C.S.: 513210
Jim Riley *(Co-Founder & CEO)*
Don Cook *(Co-Founder & CMO)*

ICARUS WIND ENERGY, INC.
110 Greene St Ste 403, New York, NY 10012
Tel.: (315) 207-3222   NV
Year Founded: 2008
Small Wind Turbine Systems & Related Equipment Mfr
N.A.I.C.S.: 333611
Mohit Bhansali *(Pres & Sec)*

ICC FUNDING INC.
324 Datura St Ste 140, West Palm Beach, FL 33401
Tel.: (561) 515-8701
Rev.: $20,000,000
Emp.: 40
Telephone Equipment
N.A.I.C.S.: 423690

ICC INDUSTRIES, INC.
460 Park Ave, New York, NY 10022
Tel.: (212) 521-1700   NY
Web Site: http://www.iccchem.com
Year Founded: 1950
Sales Range: $1-4.9 Billion
Emp.: 1,700
Chemical Product Whslr
N.A.I.C.S.: 424690
John J. Farber *(Chm)*
Susan Abinder *(Treas & VP)*
James Miller *(Controller)*
Blaise Sarcone *(CFO & VP)*

Subsidiaries:

Dover Chemical Corporation   (1)

3676 Davis Rd NW, Dover, OH 44622-0040   **(100%)**
Tel.: (330) 343-7711
Web Site: http://www.doverchem.com
Sales Range: $100-124.9 Million
Emp.: 180
Chemicals Mfr
N.A.I.C.S.: 325180
Wendy Finch *(Mgr-Customer Svc & Coord-Mktg)*
Mark Harr *(Reg Mgr-Sls-Midwest)*
Marc Nolen *(Pres & VP-Ops)*
Michael Carr *(CFO)*
David Anderson *(VP-Sales & Marketing)*
Janette Murphy *(Mgr-Comml Support)*
Matt Fender *(Comml Dir-Global)*
Brad Barth *(Bus Mgr-Lubricants)*
Chris Ricklic *(Product Mgr-Polymer Additives)*
Mike Bonomo *(Reg Sls Mgr)*
Carlos Carpio *(Reg Sls Mgr)*
Shawn Cook *(Sls Mgr-Plastic Additives)*
Marshall Heard *(Mgr-Business Development)*
Doug Jewett *(Mgr-Strategic Accounts)*
Anju Singla *(Sls Mgr-MWF Lubricants & Fuel Additives)*
Ryan Wright *(Reg Sls Mgr)*

Division (Domestic):

Dover Chemical   (2)
3000 Sheffield Ave, Hammond, IN 46327-1013
Tel.: (219) 852-0042
Web Site: http://www.doverchem.com
Sales Range: $75-99.9 Million
Emp.: 85
Fuel Metalworking Additives; Flame Retardants
N.A.I.C.S.: 325110
Heath Colvin *(Mgr-Sls-Midwest)*
Wendy Finch *(Mgr-Customer Svc & Coord-Mktg)*
Mark Harr *(Mgr-Product-Metalworking Additives)*
Darren Schwede *(CFO)*
Jim Williamson *(Mgr-Sls-Northeast)*
Michimasa Yonekura *(Mgr-Mktg-Northeast Asia)*

Fallek Chemical Japan KK   (1)
PC Kanda Bldg 16-4 Uchikanda 1 chome, Chiyoda-ku, Tokyo, 10001, Japan   **(100%)**
Tel.: (81) 332912017
Sales Range: $25-49.9 Million
Emp.: 3
Trade & Distribution of Chemicals, Plastics & Pharmaceuticals
N.A.I.C.S.: 523160
Frank Nitsuyama *(Pres)*

Fallek Chemical S.A.   (1)
Hoogoorddrees 9, Amsterdam, 1101BA, Netherlands   **(100%)**
Tel.: (31) 206448888
Web Site: http://www.iccchem.com
Sales Range: $10-24.9 Million
Emp.: 3
Trading of Chemicals
N.A.I.C.S.: 424690
G. Roox *(Mng Dir)*

ICC (Hong Kong) Ltd.   (1)
Room 1007 10/F Tai Yau Building, 181 Johnston Road, Wanchai, China (Hong Kong)   **(100%)**
Tel.: (852) 23661678
Web Site: http://www.iccchem.com
Chemical Products Distr
N.A.I.C.S.: 424690

ICC Chemical (UK) Limited   (1)
Jubilee House Hill St, Saffron Walden, CB10 1EH, Essex, United Kingdom
Tel.: (44) 799520343
Sales Range: $25-49.9 Million
Emp.: 3
Trade & Distribution of Chemicals, Plastics & Pharmaceuticals
N.A.I.C.S.: 523160

ICC Chemical Corporation   (1)
460 Park Ave, New York, NY 10022
Tel.: (212) 521-1700
Web Site: http://www.iccchem.com
Emp.: 50
Industrial Chemical Distr
N.A.I.C.S.: 424690

ICC Industries, Inc.—(Continued)
Jim Muller (CFO & Exec VP)
John Budek (Mgr-Demurrage)
Jennifer N. Schongar (Product Mgr-Intl)
Dan Beldiman (Product Mgr)
Naveen Chandra (Pres)
Stephen Savard (Mgr-IT)

ICC Chemicals S.R.L. (1)
3-5 Splaiul Penes Curcanul, Timisoara,
300124, Romania
Tel.: (40) 256 490 433
Web Site: http://www.iccchem.com
Sales Range: $10-24.9 Million
Emp.: 7
Chemical Product Whslr
N.A.I.C.S.: 424690
Rafael Martin (Mgr)

ICC Chemicals UK Ltd. (1)
Jubilee House, 5-7 Hill Street, Saffron
Walden, CB10 1EH, Essex, United
Kingdom (100%)
Tel.: (44) 1799 520343
Web Site: http://www.iccchem.com
Sales Range: $10-24.9 Million
Emp.: 3
Chemical Products Distr
N.A.I.C.S.: 424690

ICC Handels AG (1)
Chamerstrasse 12C, 6304, Zug,
Switzerland (100%)
Tel.: (41) 417118044
Web Site: http://www.icchem.com
Sales Range: $10-24.9 Million
Emp.: 4
Trading of Chemicals & Plastics
N.A.I.C.S.: 424690
Eva Turi (Gen Mgr & Mgr-Fin)
Christoth Wimmer (Gen Mgr)

ICC Iberica S.A. (1)
Interlube SL, Rafael De La Hoz 10, 28022,
Madrid, Spain (100%)
Tel.: (34) 917419433
Sales Range: $25-49.9 Million
Emp.: 2
Trade & Distribution of Chemicals, Plastics
& Pharmaceuticals
N.A.I.C.S.: 523160

ICC Industries B.V. (1)
Kutuzovsky Pr 8 Kor 2 4th Floor, 121248,
Moscow, Russia
Tel.: (7) 495 723 7202
Sales Range: $10-24.9 Million
Emp.: 5
Chemical & Plastic Product Distr
N.A.I.C.S.: 424610
Konstantin Kuzmin (Country Mgr)

ICC Industries B.V. (1)
Amteldijk 166, PO Box 74700, Riverstate
7th Fl, 1079 LH, Amsterdam,
Netherlands (100%)
Tel.: (31) 206448888
Web Site: http://www.icchem.com
Sales Range: $10-24.9 Million
Emp.: 5
Trading of Chemicals
N.A.I.C.S.: 424690

ICC Italia S.R.L. (1)
Via G Cardano 8, 20124, Milan,
Italy (100%)
Tel.: (39) 02 670 1406
Web Site: http://www.icchem.com
Sales Range: $25-49.9 Million
Emp.: 2
Trade & Distribution of Chemicals, Plastics
& Pharmaceuticals
N.A.I.C.S.: 523160
Miner Vino (Mng Dir)

ICC Trading (Taiwan) Ltd. (1)
6th Fl. No. 8 Lane 22, 1369, Chi Lin Rd.,
Taipei, Taiwan (100%)
Tel.: (886) 2 5627131
Trade & Distribution of Chemicals, Plastics
& Pharmaceuticals
N.A.I.C.S.: 523160

ICC Trading, Inc. (1)
460 Park Ave, New York, NY
10022-1906 (100%)
Tel.: (212) 521-1700
Web Site: http://www.icchem.com
Sales Range: $50-74.9 Million
Emp.: 30

Trade & Distribution of Chemicals, Plastics
& Pharmaceuticals
N.A.I.C.S.: 523160
John Farber (Chm)

ICC-Chemol Kft. (1)
Pesti ut 237 Home Center 53/A, Budapest,
1173, Hungary
Tel.: (36) 1 883 8841
Web Site: http://www.iccchemol.hu
Emp.: 7
Chemical & Plastic Product Distr
N.A.I.C.S.: 424690
Laszlo Karpati (Gen Mgr)

Konsyl Pharmaceuticals Inc. (1)
8050 Industrial Park Rd, Easton, MD
21601-8602
Tel.: (410) 822-5192
Web Site: http://www.konsyl.com
Sales Range: $10-24.9 Million
Emp.: 70
Provider of Pharmaceutical Preparations
N.A.I.C.S.: 325412
John Flohr (COO & Exec VP)
Roger Giannico (VP-Sls & Mktg)
Blaise Sarcone (Pres)

**O'Neil Color & Compounding Corp. -
North Facility** (1)
61 River Dr, Garfield, NJ 07026
Tel.: (973) 777-8999
Web Site: http://www.oneilcolor.com
Color Concentrate & Plastic Additive Mfr
N.A.I.C.S.: 325998
Philip DeChard (VP)
Dave Sarkisian (Mgr-Sls-Natl)
Lee Pfaffle (Mgr-Product-Compounding)
Bob Anthony (Plant Mgr)

**O'Neil Color & Compounding Corp. -
South Facility** (1)
193 Commerce Pl, Jasper, TN 37347
Tel.: (423) 942-9195
Web Site: http://www.oneilcolor.com
Sales Range: $25-49.9 Million
Emp.: 100
Color Concentrate & Plastic Additive Mfr
N.A.I.C.S.: 325998
Gerd Radke (Plant Mgr)

Primex Plastics Corp. (1)
1235 N F St, Richmond, IN 47374 (100%)
Tel.: (765) 966-7774
Web Site: http://www.primexplastics.com
Sales Range: $25-49.9 Million
Emp.: 300
Mfr of Rigid Plastic Sheet
N.A.I.C.S.: 326199
Michael Cramer (Pres)
Tim Schultz (VP-Sls & Mktg)
Paul Uphaus (Mgr-Comml Dev)
Robert Stephens (Mgr-Central)
Gordon B. McFaul (Mgr-Bus-Quebec)
Allen Chamberlain (Mgr-Sls-West)
Cliff Brunson (Bus Mgr-Texas, Oklahoma &
Arkansas)
Travis Hopper (Sls Mgr-East)

Plant (Domestic):

Primex Plastics Corp. (2)
3435 Old Oakwood Rd, Oakwood, GA
30566-2908 (100%)
Tel.: (770) 534-0223
Web Site: http://www.primexplastics.com
Sales Range: $50-74.9 Million
Emp.: 150
Custom Sheet Extruder
N.A.I.C.S.: 326113

Subsidiary (Domestic):

Woodruff Corporation (3)
400 Industrial Pkwy, Richmond, IN 47374-
3727
Tel.: (765) 935-2990
Web Site: http://www.woodruffcorp.com
Sales Range: $25-49.9 Million
Emp.: 100
Corrugated Plastic & Foam Product Mfr
N.A.I.C.S.: 325211
Chris Helms (Mgr-Ops)

Subsidiary (Non-US):

Primex Plastics Limited (2)
Beaumont Way Aycliffe Industrial Park,
Newton Aycliffe, DL5 6SN, Durham, United
Kingdom

Tel.: (44) 1325 315 768
Web Site:
http://www.primexplasticslimited.com
Sales Range: $25-49.9 Million
Emp.: 50
Thermoplastic Sheet Mfr
N.A.I.C.S.: 325211
Alan Pollitt (Bus Mgr)
Andrea Hart (Mgr-Customer Svc)
Debbie Thompson (Head-Admin)
Gary Clement (Mgr-Mfr)

Rossi Comercial Imp. Exp. Ltda. (1)
Calçada Copos de Leite 45 Centro Comer-
cial de Alphaville, Barueri, 06453 047, SP,
Brazil (100%)
Tel.: (55) 1141958236
Web Site: http://www.icchem.com
Emp.: 1
Plastics Distr
N.A.I.C.S.: 424610
Marcio Rossi (Mng Dir)

SC AZUR SA (1)
Bulevardul Constructorilor Nr 1-3, Timi-
soara, 300571, Romania
Tel.: (40) 256 222139
Web Site: http://www.azur.ro
Paint & Coating Mfr
N.A.I.C.S.: 325510
Mihaela Kornis (Head-R&D Dept & Mgr-BU
Paints)
Rodica Gherdan (Mgr-Pur)

ICD GROUP INTERNATIONAL INC.

150 E 52nd St 25th Fl, New York, NY
10022-1615
Tel.: (212) 644-1500 NY
Web Site: https://www.icdgroup.com
Year Founded: 1952
Sales Range: $450-499.9 Million
Emp.: 1,100
International Trader of Chemicals,
Metals & Lumber
N.A.I.C.S.: 424690
Jacques Leviant (Chm)
Ed Ellenbogen (CFO)

Subsidiaries:

ICD Alloys and Metals, LLC (1)
3946 Westpoint Blvd, Winston Salem, NC
27103
Tel.: (336) 793-2222
Feroalloy Distr
N.A.I.C.S.: 423510
Scott Kirby (Mgr-Trading)

ICD America, LLC. (1)
145 Huguenot St Ste 106, New Rochelle,
NY 10801
Tel.: (914) 633-4200
Web Site: http://www.icdamerica.com
Synthetic Resin Distr
N.A.I.C.S.: 424610
Marianne Lundell (Mgr-Acctg)

ICD Metals, LLC. (1)
150 E 52nd St, New York, NY 10022
Tel.: (212) 644-1500
Web Site: http://www.icdmetals.com
Emp.: 15
Feroalloy Distr
N.A.I.C.S.: 423510
Kevin F. Kirby (Mgr-Intl Sls)

JRS International, LLC. (1)
1050 Wall St W Ste 660, Lyndhurst, NJ
07071
Web Site: http://www.jrschem.com
Emp.: 5
Food Additive & Preservative Whslr
N.A.I.C.S.: 424690

**United Mineral and Chemical
Corporation** (1)
160 Chubb Ave Ste 206, Lyndhurst, NJ
07071
Tel.: (201) 507-3300
Web Site: http://www.umccorp.com
Emp.: 18
Chemical Product Whslr
N.A.I.C.S.: 424690
Phil Befumo (Mgr-Specialty Pigments Div)
David J. Kotowski (Gen Mgr)
Michael Sansonetti Jr. (Pres)

ICD INSTITUTE FOR CAREER DEVELOPMENT

123 William St 5th Fl, New York, NY
10038
Tel.: (212) 585-6000 NY
Web Site: https://www.icdnyc.org
Year Founded: 1917
Sales Range: $1-9.9 Million
Emp.: 54
Vocational Rehabilitation Services
N.A.I.C.S.: 624310
Justin B. Wender (Chm)
Richard Weber (Vice Chm)
Christopher K. Wu (Vice Chm)
Martin Schneider (Sec)
Les Halpert (Pres & CEO)

ICE DELIVERY SYSTEMS INC.

2574 Seaboard Ave, San Jose, CA
95131
Tel.: (408) 965-2300
Web Site:
http://www.innercityexpress.com
Year Founded: 1987
Sales Range: $10-24.9 Million
Emp.: 50
Vehicular Delivery Services
N.A.I.C.S.: 484110
Michael S. Hubert (Founder)

ICE ENERGY INC.

3 E De La Guerra St, Santa Barbara,
CA 93101
Tel.: (877) 542-3232
Web Site: http://www.ice-energy.com
Year Founded: 2003
Sales Range: $10-24.9 Million
Emp.: 10
Air-Conditioning Equipment Mfr &
Distr
N.A.I.C.S.: 423730
Mike Hopkins (CEO)
Joe Draper (Co-Chm)
Chris Tillotson (CIO)
David Zezza (Co-Chm)
Charles Costenbader (CFO)
Brandon McNeil (Exec VP-Mfg &
Ops)
Greg Miller (Exec VP-Market Dev)
Joe Moyer (Treas & Controller)
Marcel Christians (CTO)

ICE INDUSTRIES INC.

3810 Herr Rd, Sylvania, OH 43560-
8925
Tel.: (419) 842-3600
Web Site:
https://www.iceindustries.com
Metal Stamping
N.A.I.C.S.: 332119
Howard Ice (Chm & CEO)
Paul Bishop (Pres & COO)
Lisa Horrell (Mgr-Acctg)
David McGranahan (CFO)

Subsidiaries:

Deerfield Manufacturing, Inc. (1)
320 Mason Montgomery Rd, Mason, OH
45040
Tel.: (513) 398-2010
Web Site: http://www.iceindustries.com
Sales Range: $25-49.9 Million
Emp.: 200
Mfr of Metal Stampings
N.A.I.C.S.: 332119
Ed Heller (Dir-IT)

ICE MILLER LLP

1 American Sq Ste 2900, Indianapo-
lis, IN 46282
Tel.: (317) 236-2100
Web Site: http://www.icemiller.com
Year Founded: 1910
Sales Range: $125-149.9 Million
Emp.: 230
Law firm

N.A.I.C.S.: 541110
Phillip L. Bayt *(Partner)*
Amy K. Fisher *(Partner)*
Angela P. Krahulik *(Partner)*
Lisa A. Lee *(Partner)*
Kevin M. Alerding *(Partner)*
Adam Arceneaux *(Partner-Comml Litigation)*
Holiday W. Banta *(Partner-Indianapolis)*
Jenifer M. Brown *(Partner)*
Brent W. Huber *(Partner)*
Mark Wilson Ford *(Partner-Indianapolis)*
Kristine J. Bouaichi *(Partner-Indianapolis)*
Christopher S. Sears *(Partner-Indianapolis)*
Patricia Batesole *(Chief Mktg & Bus Dev Officer)*
Mark R. Alson *(Partner)*
Joshua L. Christie *(Partner-Indianapolis)*
Aaron J. Dixon *(Partner-Indianapolis)*
George A. Gasper *(Partner-Indianapolis)*
Stephen E. Reynolds *(Partner & Co-Chm-Data Security & Privacy Practice Grp)*
David J. Carr *(Partner-Indianapolis)*
Gina M. Giacone *(Partner)*
Dustin S. DuBois *(Partner-Indianapolis)*
Jason A. McNiel *(Partner-Indianapolis)*
Marc W. Sciscoe *(Partner)*
Melissa Proffitt *(Partner-Indianapolis)*
Michael J. Lewinski *(Partner)*
Philip C. Genetos *(Partner-Chicago & Indianapolis)*
Rebecca J. Seamands *(Partner)*
Timothy E. Ochs *(Partner)*
Tyler J. Kalachnik *(Partner)*
Tory U. Cole *(Partner-Indianapolis)*
Robert J. Cochran *(Partner)*
Joseph M. Scimia *(Partner)*
Anthony P. Aaron *(Partner-Indianapolis)*
Paul L. Bittner *(Partner-Columbus)*
Randall S. Arndt *(Partner-Columbus)*
Robin Babbitt *(Partner-Indianapolis)*
William J. Barath *(Partner-Columbus)*
Susan Mayer Schonfeld *(Chief Talent Acq Officer & Dir-Strategic Plng-Washington)*
John Gregg *(Partner)*
Richard A. Barnhart *(Mng Partner)*
John David Burke *(Mng Partner)*
Mitchell E. Hopwood *(COO-Indianapolis)*
Carrie K. Houston *(Chief HR Officer)*
Samantha Lofton Moss *(Chief Risk & Info Governance Officer)*
Judy S. Okenfuss *(Mng Partner)*
Reena Bajowala *(Partner-Litigation & Data Security & Privacy Groups)*
Michael Chabraja *(Partner-Tax Exempt Grp)*
William Ellsworth *(Partner-Trusts & Estates Grp)*
Matthew Miller *(Partner-Municipal Fin Grp)*
Michael Perich *(Atty-Environmental & Insurance Recovery Practices)*
Jay Augustyn *(Partner-Real Estate Practice-Chicago)*
Justin Steffen *(Partner-Fin Svcs Practice Grp)*
Guillermo Christensen *(Partner-Data Privacy & Security & White Collar Defense Groups)*
Nicholas Merker *(Partner & Co-Chm-Data Security & Privacy Practice Grp)*

LaTonya Ellis *(Dir-Real Estate & Municipal Fin Practice Groups-Chicago)*
Jarrod Loadholt *(Partner-Pub Affairs)*
Wayne O. Adams III *(Partner)*

ICE SPECIALTY ENTERTAINMENT INC.
409 Santa Monica Blvd Ste E, Santa Monica, CA 90401
Tel.: (805) 520-7465
Web Site: https://www.iceoplex.com
Sales Range: $10-24.9 Million
Emp.: 10
Ice Skating Facilities
N.A.I.C.S.: 713940
Scott Slinger *(Pres)*

ICE TECHNOLOGIES, INC.
411 SE 9th St, Pella, IA 50219
Tel.: (641) 628-8724
Web Site:
   http://www.icetechnologies.com
Year Founded: 1990
Sales Range: $10-24.9 Million
Emp.: 36
Computer System Design Services
N.A.I.C.S.: 541512
Keith Van Donselaar *(Pres & CEO)*
Phil Stravers *(Partner & CMO)*
Isaac Roorda *(Engr-Sys)*
Mike VanBaale *(Engr-Sys)*
Loren Bogaards *(Dir-Client Svcs)*

Subsidiaries:

Computer Concepts of Iowa, Inc.   (1)
528 N Ct St, Carroll, IA 51401
Tel.: (712) 792-3565
Web Site:
   http://www.computerconceptsia.com
Rev.: $3,028,048
Emp.: 15
Computer System Design Services
N.A.I.C.S.: 541512
Adam Schweers *(Pres & CEO)*

ICF GROUP
19 Ohio Ave, Norwich, CT 06360
Tel.: (800) 237-1625
Sales Range: $50-74.9 Million
Emp.: 25
Holding Company; Furniture Mfr & Whslr
N.A.I.C.S.: 551112
James Kasschau *(Pres & CEO)*

Subsidiaries:

Nienkamper Furniture & Accessories Inc.   (1)
257 Finchdene Sq, Toronto, M1X 1B9, ON, Canada
Tel.: (416) 298-5700
Web Site: http://www.nienkamper.com
Sales Range: $25-49.9 Million
Office Furniture Designer, Mfr & Whslr
N.A.I.C.S.: 337211
Klaus Nienkamper *(Founder, Pres & CEO)*

ICF INDUSTRIES, INC.
617 S Main St, Pleasant Hill, MO 64080
Tel.: (816) 540-4200
Web Site: https://www.icfinc.com
Sales Range: $10-24.9 Million
Emp.: 90
Sheet Metal Work Mfg
N.A.I.C.S.: 332322
Robert Krug *(Pres & CEO)*
Kerri Myres *(Mgr-HR)*

ICG HOLLISTON HOLDINGS CORPORATION
905 Holliston Mills Rd, Church Hill, TN 37642
Tel.: (423) 357-6141   DE
Web Site: http://www.icgholliston.com
Year Founded: 1948
Sales Range: $50-74.9 Million
Emp.: 200

Holding Company
N.A.I.C.S.: 314999
Steve Lister *(CFO)*

Subsidiaries:

Industrial Coatings Group, Inc.   (1)
905 Holliston Mills Rd, Church Hill, TN 37642
Tel.: (423) 357-6141
Web Site: http://www.icgholliston.com
Industrial Fabrics & Polyethylene Films Mfr
N.A.I.C.S.: 314999
William Waldron III *(VP-Security Products)*

Division (Domestic):

ICG/Holliston   (2)
905 Holliston Mills Rd, Church Hill, TN 37642
Tel.: (423) 357-6141
Sales Range: $50-74.9 Million
Emp.: 180
Coated Fabrics, Not Rubberized
N.A.I.C.S.: 314999
Terry Queen *(Engr-Maintenance)*

ICI CONSTRUCTION INC.
24715 W Hardy Rd, Spring, TX 77373
Tel.: (281) 355-5151
Web Site: http://www.icidallas.com
Rev.: $98,375,584
Emp.: 20
Commercial & Office Building, New Construction
N.A.I.C.S.: 236220
Russell Cobb *(Pres)*
Janice Conway *(Controller)*
Darrell Irvin *(Mgr-Acctg)*

ICI MUTUAL INSURANCE COMPANY
126 College St Ste 400, Burlington, VT 05401-8456
Tel.: (802) 658-4600
Sales Range: $10-24.9 Million
Emp.: 3
Surety Insurance
N.A.I.C.S.: 524126
Marie Gaudette *(Program Mgr & VP)*

Subsidiaries:

ICI Mutual Insurance Brokers   (1)
1401 H St NW Ste 1000, Washington, DC 20005
Tel.: (202) 326-5464
Insurance Brokers
N.A.I.C.S.: 524210

ICIM Services Inc.   (1)
1401 H St NW Fl 10, Washington, DC 20005
Tel.: (202) 682-4150
Web Site: http://www.icimutual.com
Sales Range: $1-9.9 Million
Emp.: 23
Underwriters, Security
N.A.I.C.S.: 523150
Daniel Steiner *(Pres)*

ICIMS HOLDING CORP.
101 Crawfords Corner Rd Ste 3-100, Holmdel, NJ 07733   DE
Year Founded: 2000
Rev.: $251,283,000
Assets: $1,493,046,000
Liabilities: $761,708,000
Net Worth: $731,338,000
Earnings: ($48,170,000)
Emp.: 1,075
Fiscal Year-end: 12/31/20
Holding Company
N.A.I.C.S.: 551112
N. Steven Lucas *(CEO)*
Valerie Rainey *(CFO)*
Diane Fanelli *(COO)*
Patrick Bakey *(Chief Revenue Officer)*
Al Smith *(CTO)*
Michael Wilczak *(Chief Strategy Officer)*

Susan Vitale *(CMO)*
Jewell Parkinson *(Chief HR Officer)*
Kate Scavello *(Gen Counsel)*

ICIMS, INC.
101 Crawfords Corner Rd Ste 3-100, Holmdel, NJ 07733
Tel.: (732) 847-1941
Web Site: http://www.icims.com
Year Founded: 2000
Sales Range: $10-24.9 Million
Emp.: 100
Computer Software
N.A.I.C.S.: 334610
Len Carella *(VP-Infrastructure Shared Svcs)*
Adam Feigenbaum *(COO)*
Erinn Tarpey *(Dir-Mktg)*
Michael Wilczak *(Sr VP-Corp Dev)*
Russell Mikowski *(VP-Sls)*
Al Smith *(VP-Tech)*
Susan Vitale *(CMO)*
Irene DeNigris *(Chief People Officer)*
Clark Convery *(VP-Customer Success)*

Subsidiaries:

SkillSurvey, Inc.   (1)
1 Country View Rd Ste 102, Malvern, PA 19355
Tel.: (610) 947-6300
Web Site: http://www.skillsurvey.com
Computer Software Whslr
N.A.I.C.S.: 423430
Ray Bixler *(Pres & CEO)*
Cynthia Hedricks *(Chief Analytics Officer)*
Mark Norek *(CFO)*
Steve Heister *(Chief Product Officer)*
Burke Lashell *(CTO)*
John Routhier *(Chief Sls Officer)*
Keith Cook *(CMO)*
Brenda Dandrea *(Chief Client Rels Officer)*

ICLICK, INC.
3931 1st Ave S, Seattle, WA 98134
Web Site: https://www.iclick.com
Year Founded: 2001
Sales Range: $10-24.9 Million
Emp.: 45
Custom USB Flash Drives & USB Drive Duplication Services Mfr
N.A.I.C.S.: 513210
Mariah Wakeling *(Dir-Art)*

ICM HOLDINGS INC.
730 5th Ave, New York, NY 10019
Tel.: (212) 556-5600   DE
Web Site: http://www.icmtalent.com
Year Founded: 1975
Sales Range: $200-249.9 Million
Emp.: 400
Holding Company; Talent & Literary Agency
N.A.I.C.S.: 551112

ICON CAPITAL CORP.
3 Park Ave 36th Fl, New York, NY 10016
Tel.: (212) 418-4700   DE
Web Site:
   http://www.iconinvestments.com
Year Founded: 1985
Sales Range: $50-74.9 Million
Emp.: 100
Investment & Portfolio Management
N.A.I.C.S.: 523999
Michael A. Reisner *(Co-Pres & Co-CEO)*
Mark Gatto *(Co-Pres & Co-CEO)*
Harry Giovani *(Mng Dir & Chief Credit Officer)*
Gregory Schill *(Mng Dir)*
Nicholas A. Sinigaglia *(CFO & Chief Acctg Officer)*
Douglas Crossman *(Exec VP)*
Derek O'Leary *(Exec VP)*

ICON Capital Corp.—(Continued)

Keith S. Franz *(Mng Dir & CFO)*
Tobias Backer *(Mng Dir & Head-Shipping & Offshore)*

ICON CREDIT UNION

7615 W Riverside Dr, Boise, ID 83714
Tel.: (208) 344-7948   **ID**
Web Site:
   http://www.iconcreditunion.org
Year Founded: 1952
Sales Range: $10-24.9 Million
Emp.: 94
Credit Union Operator
N.A.I.C.S.: 522130
Connie Miller *(Pres & CEO)*
John Cotner *(Chief Lending Officer)*
Robert King *(VP-IT)*
Dee Carter *(Mgr-Mortgage Sls)*
Patricia Marler *(Chm)*
Michelle Wall *(COO)*
Glenda Fuller *(Sec)*
Rich Jackson *(Treas)*
Dan Eineichner *(Vice Chm)*

ICON ECI FUND FIFTEEN, L.P.

3 Park Ave 36th Fl, New York, NY 10016
Tel.: (212) 418-4700   **DE**
Web Site:
   http://www.iconinvestments.com
Year Founded: 2010
Sales Range: $10-24.9 Million
Investment Services
N.A.I.C.S.: 523999
Michael A. Reisner *(Co-Pres & Co-CEO)*
Mark Gatto *(Co-Pres & Co-CEO)*

ICON ECI FUND SIXTEEN

3 Park Ave 36th Fl, New York, NY 10016
Tel.: (212) 418-4700   **DE**
Web Site:
   http://www.iconinvestments.com
Year Founded: 2012
Investment Services
N.A.I.C.S.: 523999
Mark Gatto *(Co-Pres & Co-CEO)*
Michael A. Reisner *(Co-Pres & Co-CEO)*
Christine H. Yap *(Mng Dir)*

ICON HEALTH & FITNESS, INC.

1500 S 1000 W, Logan, UT 84321-8206
Tel.: (435) 750-5000   **DE**
Web Site: http://www.iconfitness.com
Year Founded: 1977
Sales Range: $350-399.9 Million
Emp.: 2,009
Home Fitness Equipment Mfr, Marketer & Distr
N.A.I.C.S.: 339920
S. Fred Beck *(CFO, Treas & VP)*
David J. Watterson *(Chm & CEO)*
Evertt Smith *(Gen Counsel)*
Matthew N. Allen *(Pres & Chief Mdsg Officer)*
Jace Jergensen *(Sr VP)*

ICON INFORMATION CONSULTANTS, L.P.

100 Waugh Dr Ste 300, Houston, TX 77007-5962
Tel.: (713) 438-0919
Web Site:
   https://www.iconconsultants.com
Sales Range: $75-99.9 Million
Emp.: 350

IT, Accounting & Finance Recruiting, Human Capital Solutions, Consulting, Payroll & Specialized Project Management Services
N.A.I.C.S.: 541612
Pamela O'Rourke *(Pres)*

ICON INTERNATIONAL INC.

107 Elm St 4 Stamford Plz, Stamford, CT 06902
Tel.: (203) 328-2300   **NY**
Web Site: http://www.icon-intl.com
Year Founded: 1986
Sales Range: $50-74.9 Million
Emp.: 250
Advetising Agency
N.A.I.C.S.: 541810
John P. Kramer *(CEO)*
Tom Bartholomew *(Exec VP-Media & Fulfillment)*
John Matluck *(Exec VP & Mng Dir-Sls)*
Peter M. Benassi *(Exec VP-Intl Ops)*
Brian Connally *(Mng Dir & Exec VP)*
Kathleen Chomienne *(Chief Credit Officer)*
Ryan J. Crosby *(CIO)*
Michael O'Hara *(Mng Dir & Exec VP)*
Dan Barutio *(VP-Bus Dev)*
Joshua Benig *(VP-Bus Dev)*
Bob Christman *(VP-Bus Dev)*
Jude DeCicco *(VP-Bus Dev)*
Jocelyn Egan *(Sr VP-Bus Dev)*
Mark Langer *(VP-Bus Dev)*
Ryan Masterson *(VP-Bus Dev)*
Michael J. Mazzeo *(VP-Bus Dev)*
Jerry Padilla *(Sr VP & Dir-Inside Sls)*
William L. Sullivan *(VP-Bus Dev)*
Jack Testani *(VP-New Bus Dev)*
James R. Tully *(VP-Real Estate)*
Cathy Yachouh *(Dir-Remarketing & Mdse Sls)*
Dawn Montelione *(Sr VP-HR)*
Kelly Emmert *(Exec VP & Mng Dir-Sls)*
Ed McCarrick *(Exec VP-Acct Mgmt & Media Partnerships)*
Bill Gaffney *(VP & Dir-Logistics)*
Evangeline Murray *(Sr VP & Acct Dir)*
Christine Childs *(VP & Acct Dir)*
Kevin McCarthy *(Sr VP & Acct Dir)*
Elizabeth Oakes *(VP & Acct Dir)*
Pamela Tramontano *(Sr VP & Acct Dir)*
Liz Blaine *(Mgr-HR)*
Jack Duffy *(Sr VP-Fin)*
Robert Carroll *(Controller)*
Dave Harrington *(Sr VP-Engrg)*
Peter Maniscalco *(Sr VP-Fin)*
Greg Caglione *(Exec VP-Retail Activation)*
Pierece Filippelli *(VP-Digital Strategy & Partnerships)*
Derek Lopez *(Sr VP & Mng Dir-Media Investment)*
Laura L. Mentekidis *(Sr VP & Dir-Direct Response)*
Jane Meyerson *(Sr VP & Dir-Local Media)*
Clarence V. Lee III *(CFO & Exec VP)*

ICON MECHANICAL CONSTRUCTION & ENGINEERING LLC.

1616 Cleveland Blvd, Granite City, IL 62040-4401
Tel.: (618) 452-0035
Web Site: https://www.iconmech.com
Year Founded: 1995
Sales Range: $10-24.9 Million
Emp.: 38
Specialty Trade Contractors
N.A.I.C.S.: 238910
Michael Bieg *(Pres)*
Tim Schaeffer *(VP)*
Jeff Smith *(Controller)*

ICON MEDICAL NETWORK LLC

8100 SW Nyberg Rd Ste 160, Tualatin, OR 97062-7062
Web Site:
   http://www.iconstaffingnetwork.com
Employment Placement Agencies
N.A.I.C.S.: 561311
Ashley Simpson *(Mng Partner)*

Subsidiaries:

Independence Anesthesia Services   **(1)**
3722 Atlanta Hwy Ste 1, Athens, GA 30606-1862
Tel.: (706) 425-8545
Web Site: http://www.imedservices.com
Employment Placement Agencies
N.A.I.C.S.: 561311

ICON UTILITY SERVICES, INC.

13771 Danielson St Ste K, Poway, CA 92064
Tel.: (858) 486-2929
Web Site: http://www.iconusinc.com
Year Founded: 2013
Sales Range: $10-24.9 Million
Emp.: 39
Building Materials Distr
N.A.I.C.S.: 444180
Paul Loska *(Principal)*
Carl Skaja *(Principal)*
Matthew Van Eck *(Principal)*
Douglas Maher *(Gen Mgr)*
Leonard Campos *(Mgr-Ops)*

ICONECTIV, LLC

100 Somerset Corporate Blvd, Bridgewater, NJ 08807
Tel.: (855) 685-9380
Web Site: https://iconectiv.com
Telecommunications Services
N.A.I.C.S.: 517410

Subsidiaries:

CSF, Inc.   **(1)**
270 Davidson Ave Ste 104, Somerset, NJ 08873
Tel.: (732) 302-0222
Sales Range: $1-9.9 Million
Emp.: 12
Computer System Design Services
N.A.I.C.S.: 541512
Clem Hergenhan *(CEO & Founder)*

ICONIC DEVELOPMENT LLC

820 Davis St Suite 420, Evanston, IL 60201
Tel.: (847) 869-2482
Web Site:
   http://www.iconicdevelopment.com
Year Founded: 2007
Sales Range: $10-24.9 Million
Emp.: 6
Real Estate Firm Specializing in Environmentally Friendly Development
N.A.I.C.S.: 531190
Bill Bennett *(Principal)*
Bo Parfet *(Principal)*

ICONIQ CAPITAL, LLC

394 Pacific Ave 2nd Fl, San Francisco, CA 94111
Tel.: (415) 967-7763   **DE**
Web Site:
   https://www.iconiqcapital.com
Year Founded: 2011
Rev.: $80,000,000,000
Investment & Portfolio Management Firm
N.A.I.C.S.: 523999
Jason Craig *(Chief Compliance Officer & Corp Counsel)*
Robert Bernshteyn *(Gen Partner)*

Subsidiaries:

IPI Partners, LLC   **(1)**

300 N LaSalle St Ste 1500, Chicago, IL 60654
Tel.: (312) 796-2200
Web Site: https://ipipartners.com
Digital Infrastructure Assets Investment Management Firm
N.A.I.C.S.: 523999
Matthew R. A'Hearn *(Partner)*

Holding (Domestic):

Stack Infrastructure, Inc.   **(2)**
1700 Broadway Ste 1750, Denver, CO 80290
Web Site: https://www.stackinfra.com
Holding Company; Data Center Leasing & Support Services
N.A.I.C.S.: 551112
Donough Roche *(Sr VP-Engrg & Client Svcs-EMEA)*
Ty Miller *(Chief Comml Officer)*
Andrew Gold *(Sr VP-Corp Dev & Chief Counsel)*
Jim Linkous *(Sr VP-Strategic Accts)*
Brian Cox *(CEO-Americas)*
Tim Hughes *(Chief Dev Officer-Americas)*

ICONIX ACQUISITION LLC

1900 Bausch & Lomb Pl, Rochester, NY 14604
Tel.: (585) 987-2820   **DE**
Investment Services
N.A.I.C.S.: 523999

Subsidiaries:

Iconix International Inc.   **(1)**
1450 Broadway 22nd Fl, New York, NY 10018
Tel.: (212) 730-0030
Web Site: https://www.iconixbrand.com
Rev.: $108,576,000
Assets: $412,736,000
Liabilities: $661,325,000
Net Worth: $248,589,000)
Earnings: ($7,336,000)
Emp.: 101
Fiscal Year-end: 12/31/2020
Women's & Girls' Casual & Fashion Footwear, Handbags, Clothing & Outerwear; Men's Underwear & Women's Intimates
N.A.I.C.S.: 424340

Subsidiary (Domestic):

Bright Star Footwear, Inc.   **(2)**
111 Howard Blvd Ste 206, Mount Arlington, NJ 07856-1315   **(100%)**
Tel.: (973) 398-2200
Sales Range: $50-74.9 Million
Emp.: 5
Whslr of Footwear
N.A.I.C.S.: 424340
Ron Parsons *(Pres)*

Danskin, Inc.   **(2)**
530 7th Ave Ste M1, New York, NY 10018
Tel.: (877) 443-2121
Web Site: http://www.danskin.com
Sales Range: $300-349.9 Million
Fitness, Dance & Yoga Apparel Mfr
N.A.I.C.S.: 315250

Plant (Domestic):

Danskin   **(3)**
3 Barker Ave Ste 575c, White Plains, NY 10601-1524
Tel.: (717) 852-6100
Web Site: http://www.danskin.com
Sales Range: $50-74.9 Million
Emp.: 30
Mfr of Exercise Wear
N.A.I.C.S.: 424350

Subsidiary (Domestic):

IP Holdings Unltd LLC   **(2)**
1450 Broadway 3rd Fl, New York, NY 10018
Tel.: (212) 730-0030
Web Site: http://www.iconixbrand.com
Fashion Apparels Mfr & Retailer
N.A.I.C.S.: 315990

IP Holdings and Management Corporation   **(2)**
103 Foulk Rd, Wilmington, DE 19803-3742
Tel.: (302) 691-6129

Commercial Lithographic Printing Services
N.A.I.C.S.: 323111

Icon NY Holdings LLC (2)
1450 Broadway, New York, NY 10018
Tel.: (212) 730-0030
Emp.: 120
Holding Company
N.A.I.C.S.: 551112
Christine Morena *(Mgr-HR)*

Subsidiary (Non-US):

Iconix China Limited (2)
Unit 602 6F Chuang Tower 30-32 Connaught Road Central, Hong Kong, China (Hong Kong)
Tel.: (852) 85228100883
Textile Products Mfr
N.A.I.C.S.: 313240
Karen Leung *(Office Mgr)*

Iconix Latin America LLC (2)
Torre Global Bank 36th floor Calle 50, Panama, Panama **(100%)**
Tel.: (507) 2137770
Web Site: http://www.uetainc.com
Emp.: 500
Consumer Goods Branding Services
N.A.I.C.S.: 533110

Subsidiary (Domestic):

Joe Boxer Company, LLC (2)
1450 Broadway Fl 3, New York, NY 10018
Tel.: (212) 730-0030
Web Site: http://www.joeboxer.com
Sales Range: $75-99.9 Million
Emp.: 100
Men's & Boys' Underwear & Nightwear
N.A.I.C.S.: 315250

Mossimo Holdings LLC (2)
103 Foulk Rd Ste 116, Wilmington, DE 19803-3742
Tel.: (302) 691-6413
Investment Management Service
N.A.I.C.S.: 551112

Subsidiary (Non-US):

Umbro Ltd. (2)
Umbro House, Cheadle, SK8 3GQ, Cheshire, United Kingdom
Tel.: (44) 01614922000
Web Site: http://www.umbro.com
Sales Range: $250-299.9 Million
Soccer Apparel, Footwear & Equipment
N.A.I.C.S.: 339920

Subsidiary (Domestic):

Unzipped Apparel LLC (2)
1450 Broadway 4th Fl, New York, NY 10018 **(100%)**
Tel.: (212) 730-0030
Sales Range: $100-124.9 Million
Emp.: 25
Markets Women's Clothing
N.A.I.C.S.: 458110
Howard Posner *(COO)*

Waverly Fabrics (2)
1450 Broadway 3rd Fl, New York, NY 10018
Tel.: (212) 730-0030
Web Site: http://www.waverly.com
Sales Range: $100-124.9 Million
Emp.: 80
Fabric & Wallcovering Mfr
N.A.I.C.S.: 424310

ICONMA, LLC.
850 Stephenson Hwy Ste 612, Troy, MI 48083
Tel.: (248) 583-1930
Web Site: https://www.iconma.com
Year Founded: 2000
Rev.: $40,500,000
Emp.: 450
Human Resources
N.A.I.C.S.: 561320
Claudine S. George *(Owner)*

ICONSOFT INC.
101 Cambridge St Ste 360, Burlington, MA 01803
Tel.: (781) 359-9333

Web Site: https://www.iconsoft.net
Year Founded: 1998
Sales Range: $10-24.9 Million
Emp.: 125
Mainframe, Client Server Computing Services
N.A.I.C.S.: 541511
Ravi Meruva *(Pres)*

ICONSTRUCTORS, LLC
2502 N Rocky Point Dr Ste 1000, Tampa, FL 33607
Tel.: (813) 287-9000
Web Site:
    http://www.iconstructors.com
Year Founded: 2009
Sales Range: $25-49.9 Million
Emp.: 40
General Contractors
N.A.I.C.S.: 236220
Robert W. Healy *(Pres)*
Kevin J. Murphy *(Exec VP-Building Div)*
Michael J. Montecalvo *(Exec VP-Interiors Div)*
Tracy L. Pritchard *(Controller)*
David T. Smith *(Founder & Chm)*
Mark D. Cooper *(VP-Interiors Div)*
Richard S. Katz *(VP-Building Div)*
Edward A. Smith III *(Exec VP-Fort Lauderdale)*

ICONTROL NETWORKS, INC.
555 Twin Dolphin Dr Ste 280, Redwood City, CA 94065
Tel.: (650) 592-2300
Web Site: http://www.icontrol.com
Information Technology Integration Software & Services
N.A.I.C.S.: 518210
Ken Hahn *(CFO)*
Steve Gribbon *(Sr VP-Sls-Worldwide)*
Letha McLaren *(CMO)*
Corey Gates *(CTO)*

ICOR PARTNERS, LLC
2200 Wilson Blvd Ste 102, Arlington, VA 22201-3324
Tel.: (703) 684-1840
Year Founded: 2002
Sales Range: $10-24.9 Million
Emp.: 59
Management Consulting Services
N.A.I.C.S.: 541618
Wayne Simmons *(Founder)*
Keary Crawford *(Chief Admin Officer & Partner)*
Heidi Ha *(Mng Dir & VP)*
Robert Kronzer *(Mng Dir & VP)*

ICR, LLC
761 Main Ave, Norwalk, CT 06851
Tel.: (203) 682-8200 DE
Web Site: http://www.icrinc.com
Year Founded: 1998
Public Relations & Corporate Advisory Services
N.A.I.C.S.: 541820
John Mills *(Mng Partner)*
Don Duffy *(Pres)*
Matthew Lindberg *(Partner)*
Alecia Pulman *(Partner)*
Anton Nicholas *(Mng Partner)*
Brendon Frey *(Partner)*
Jacques Cornet *(Partner)*
Jessica Liddell *(Partner)*
Stephen Swett *(Partner)*
Doug Donsky *(Mng Dir)*
Steve Parish *(Partner)*
Lee Stettner *(Partner)*
Thomas M. Ryan *(Founder & CEO)*
Tim Bishop *(Partner)*
Caitlin Burke *(Dir-Mktg)*
Michael Fox *(Chief Client Officer)*
Lindley Maglio *(Chief People Officer)*
John Sorensen *(Partner)*

Bobby Spezzano *(Partner)*
Matt Storms *(Sr Dir-IT)*
Reed Anderson *(Mng Dir)*
Matt Anthony *(Sr VP)*
Caldwell Bailey *(Sr VP)*
Patti Bank *(Mng Dir)*
Ujjal K. Basu Roy *(Sr VP)*
Eric Becker *(Sr VP)*
Adam Belmont *(Sr VP)*
Tim Bishop *(Partner)*
Michael Bowen *(Mng Dir)*
Bilun Boyner *(Sr VP)*
Dan Brennan *(Sr VP)*
Chris Brinzey *(Partner-Westwicke)*
Bradley Burgess *(Sr VP)*
Melissa Calandruccio *(Mng Dir)*
Michael Callahan *(Mng Dir)*
Stephanie Carrington *(Mng Dir)*
Mike Cavanaugh *(Mng Dir)*
Jason Chudoba *(Partner)*
Matthew Chudoba *(VP)*
Caitlin Churchill *(Sr VP)*
Terri Clevenger *(Partner-Westwicke)*
Brad D. Cohen *(Mng Partner)*
Mallory Cohen *(Acct Dir)*
Mark Corbae *(Mng Dir)*
Caroline Corner *(Partner)*
Kate Coyle *(Mng Dir)*
Katie Creaser *(Sr VP)*
Clay Crumbliss *(Mng Dir)*
Matt Dallas *(Sr VP)*

Subsidiaries:

Westwicke Partners, LLC (1)
2800 Quarry Lk Dr Ste 380, Baltimore, MD 21209
Tel.: (443) 213-0500
Web Site:
    http://www.westwickepartners.com
Financial Investment Services
N.A.I.C.S.: 523999
Patti Bank *(Mng Dir-San Francisco)*
Chris Brinzey *(Partner-Boston)*
Robert H. Uhl *(Mng Dir-San Diego)*
Bob East *(Co-Founder & Mng Partner)*
Mark Klausner *(Co-Founder & Mng Partner)*

ICS BUILDERS INC.
108 W 39th St 14th Fl, New York, NY 10018
Tel.: (212) 633-1300
Web Site:
    https://www.icsbuilders.com
Year Founded: 1980
Sales Range: $10-24.9 Million
Emp.: 18
Contractor of Commercial & Office Buildings
N.A.I.C.S.: 236220
John O'Rourke *(Pres)*
Ted O'Rourke *(VP)*

ICS CUSTOMS SERVICE INC.
1099 Morse Ave, Elk Grove Village, IL 60007
Tel.: (847) 718-9998
Web Site:
    https://www.icsworldwide.com
Emp.: 18
Freight Forwarding
N.A.I.C.S.: 488510
David Sharpe *(Owner)*
Bill Sharpe *(Pres)*

ICS LOGISTICS, INC.
2625 W 5th St, Jacksonville, FL 32254
Tel.: (904) 786-8038
Web Site: http://www.seaonus.com
Sales Range: $10-24.9 Million
Emp.: 100
Provider of Logistics Services
N.A.I.C.S.: 484230
Dennis Rhodes *(CIO)*

Subsidiaries:

Industrial Cold Storage Inc. (1)

2625 W 5th St, Jacksonville, FL 32254
Tel.: (904) 786-8038
Web Site: http://www.icslogistics.com
Rev.: $10,000,000
Emp.: 76
Warehousing, Cold Storage Or Refrigerated
N.A.I.C.S.: 493120

ICS NETT INC.
2650 Park Tower Dr 8th Fl, Vienna, VA 22180
Tel.: (703) 342-4260
Web Site: http://www.ics-nett.com
Year Founded: 2003
Sales Range: $10-24.9 Million
Emp.: 150
Business Solutions & Consulting
N.A.I.C.S.: 541513
Neal Conley *(Supvr-Field Electrical)*
Barbara Kelly *(Mgr-Contracts)*
Saadia Iqbal *(Dir-HR)*
Tim Stout *(VP-Client Rels)*
Ken Blount *(Exec VP-ICT & Bus Dev)*
Mike Poel *(CEO & COO)*

ICS PENETRON INTERNATIONAL LTD.
45 Research Way Ste 203, East Setauket, NY 11733
Tel.: (631) 941-9700
Web Site: http://www.penetron.com
Year Founded: 1978
Sales Range: $10-24.9 Million
Emp.: 67
Additive Preparation Mfr
N.A.I.C.S.: 325998
Robert Revera *(Pres & CEO)*
Jozef van Beeck *(Dir-Sls & Mktg-Intl)*
Christopher Chen *(Dir-Sls & Mktg-North America)*
John Read *(CFO)*
Florian Klouda *(Dir-Acct Coordination-Intl)*
Sue Yi *(Dir-Ops)*
Grant Urban *(Mgr-Sls-West Coast)*
Robert Lambermont *(Mgr-Specification-Intl)*
Alex Jauregui *(Acct Mgr-Mideast)*
Cassandra Gouws *(Mgr-Technical-North America)*

ICS, INC.
2500 State Mill Rd, Grand Forks, ND 58203-3158
Tel.: (701) 775-8480
Web Site: https://www.icsgf.com
Year Founded: 1991
Sales Range: $25-49.9 Million
Emp.: 75
Commercial & Institutional Building Construction Services
N.A.I.C.S.: 236220
Drew Molstad *(Pres)*

ICSN INC.
521 Princeland Ct, Corona, CA 92879
Tel.: (951) 687-2305
Web Site: https://www.icsngroup.com
Year Founded: 2000
Sales Range: $10-24.9 Million
Emp.: 20
Structural Metal Work Mfr
N.A.I.C.S.: 332312
Kenny Kim *(Mgr-Ops)*

ICT HOLDINGS INC.
271 E North Ave, Glendale Heights, IL 60139
Tel.: (630) 652-9000
Year Founded: 2007
Sales Range: $10-24.9 Million
Emp.: 35
Trucking Services & Freight Support
N.A.I.C.S.: 488510
Patrick Sacor *(Pres & CEO)*

ICV PARTNERS, LLC

ICV Partners, LLC—(Continued)

810 7th Ave 35th Fl, New York, NY
10019
Tel.: (212) 455-9600   DE
Web Site: http://www.icvpartners.com
Year Founded: 1998
Sales Range: $25-49.9 Million
Privater Equity Firm
N.A.I.C.S.: 523999
Lloyd E. Metz *(Mng Dir)*
Cory D. Mims *(Mng Dir)*
Zeena H. Rao *(Mng Dir)*
Ira L. Moreland *(Mng Dir)*
Qian W. Elmore *(Principal)*
Sheldon B. Howell *(Principal)*
Jermaine L. Warren *(Principal)*
Gregory J. Nolff *(CFO)*
John Wallace *(Mng Dir)*
Everett Hill *(Mng Dir-Atlanta)*
Willie E. Woods Jr. *(Pres & Mng Dir)*

Subsidiaries:

Diversified Restaurant Holdings,
Inc.   (1)
27680 Franklin Rd, Southfield, MI 48034
Tel.: (248) 223-9160
Web Site:
   http://www.diversifiedrestauranthold
   ings.com
Restaurant Owner, Operator & Franchisor
N.A.I.C.S.: 722511
Jason T. Curtis *(COO)*
Toni Werner *(Interim CFO & Controller)*

Subsidiary (Domestic):

AMC Burgers, Inc.   (2)
859 W Eisenhower Pkwy, Ann Arbor, MI
48103
Tel.: (734) 994-3283
Web Site: http://www.baggerdaves.com
Restaurant
N.A.I.C.S.: 722511

AMC Group, Inc.   (2)
21751 W 11 Mile Rd Ste 208, Southfield, MI
48076
Tel.: (248) 223-9160
Restaurant Management Services
N.A.I.C.S.: 722310
Gavin Pearce *(Mng Dir-AMC North America
& South America)*
Alvaro Munoz *(CEO)*
Greg Ogiba *(COO-AMC North America)*
Emmy Hume *(VP-Primary Production-AMC
North America)*
Casey Ison *(Dir-Sls-AMC North America)*

OneTouchPoint Corp.   (1)
1200 Harger Rd Ste 419, Oak Brook, IL
60523
Tel.: (800) 725-6310
Web Site: http://www.1touchpoint.com
Holding Company; Commercial Printing &
Digital Marketing Solutions
N.A.I.C.S.: 551112
Steve McConnell *(CFO)*
Joni Diderrich *(Pres-Midwest Div)*
Chris Greene *(Pres-Mountain States Div)*
Pam Sievers *(COO)*
David Holland *(CEO)*
Brian Frank *(Pres-East Div)*
Johnny Weaver *(Sr VP-Ops)*
Mike Fox *(CIO)*
Robert Gatz *(Pres-Southwest Div)*

Subsidiary (Domestic):

OneTouchPoint East Corp.   (2)
1441 Western Ave, Cincinnati, OH 45214
Tel.: (513) 421-1600
Web Site: http://www.1touchpoint.com
Commercial Printing Services
N.A.I.C.S.: 323111
Joe Bodner *(Project Coord)*
Matt Bethel *(Sr Acct Exec)*
Ben Griffith *(VP-Fin)*
Terry Gill *(Pres)*

OneTouchPoint MidWest Corp.   (2)
1225 Walnut Ridge Dr, Hartland, WI 53029
Tel.: (262) 369-6000
Web Site: http://www.1touchpoint.com
Commercial Printing, Material Distribution &
Digital Imaging Services
N.A.I.C.S.: 323111

Joni Diderrich *(Pres)*
Chris Greene *(Pres-Mountain States Div)*
Steve McConnell *(CFO)*
Brian Frank *(Pres-East Div)*
David Holland *(CEO)*
Johnny Weaver *(Sr VP-Ops)*
Mike Fox *(CIO)*
Robert Gatz *(Pres-Southwest Div)*

Branch (Domestic):

OneTouchPoint West Corp. - Tempe
Office   (3)
575 W Alameda Dr Ste 101, Tempe, AZ
85282
Tel.: (480) 966-4003
Web Site: http://www.1touchpoint.com
Commercial Printing, Material Distribution &
Digital Imaging Services
N.A.I.C.S.: 323111
Cris Rankin *(Gen Mgr)*

Security Alarm Financing Enterprises,
Inc.   (1)
2440 Camino Ramon Ste 200, San Ramon,
CA 94583
Tel.: (925) 830-4777
Web Site: http://www.safesecurity.com
Sales Range: $1-9.9 Million
Emp.: 70
Security System Services
N.A.I.C.S.: 561621
Paul F. Sargenti *(Pres & CEO)*
Gary Franklyn *(Sr VP-Dealer Sls)*

ICX GROUP INC.
76 S Laura St Ste 1700, Jacksonville,
FL 32202
Tel.: (904) 208-2200
Web Site: http://www.icxgroup.com
Sales Range: $1-9.9 Million
Emp.: 40
Business Professional Services In-
cluding Accounting, Finance, Recruit-
ing & IT
N.A.I.C.S.: 561499
Leonard Curry *(CEO)*
Todd Froats *(Pres)*

ID ADDITIVES, INC.
512 W Burlington Ave Ste 208, La
Grange, IL 60525
Tel.: (708) 588-0081
Web Site:
   https://www.idadditives.com
Year Founded: 2005
Sales Range: $1-9.9 Million
Emp.: 6
Additives for Plastics Mfr
N.A.I.C.S.: 325211
Lindsay Hosanna *(Office Mgr)*
Nick C. Sotos *(Pres)*
Lindsay Hosanna *(Office Mgr-Social
Media)*

ID GROUP, INC.
280 Trace Colony Park, Ridgeland,
MS 39157
Tel.: (601) 982-2651
Web Site: http://www.idgroup.net
Year Founded: 1976
Emp.: 20
Identity & Security Services
N.A.I.C.S.: 541519
Philip King *(Pres)*
Michael Byers *(VP-Ops)*
Brian Jackson *(VP-Bus Dev)*

Subsidiaries:

Addtronics Business Systems,
Inc.   (1)
4605 N Sewell Ave, Oklahoma City, OK
73118
Tel.: (405) 528-8881
Web Site: http://www.addtronics.net
Sales Range: $1-9.9 Million
Identification Software Mfr
N.A.I.C.S.: 513210
Casey Cook *(Pres)*

ID INSIGHT, INC.

635 Ninth St SE Ste 215, Minneapo-
lis, MN 55414
Web Site: http://www.idinsight.com
Year Founded: 2003
Sales Range: $1-9.9 Million
Emp.: 50
Information Technology Services
N.A.I.C.S.: 541519
Adam Elliott *(Founder & Pres)*

IDA CASON CALLAWAY FOUNDATION
17800 US Hwy 27, Pine Mountain,
GA 31822
Tel.: (706) 663-2281
Web Site:
   http://www.callowaygardens.com
Sales Range: $25-49.9 Million
Emp.: 700
Resort Hotel
N.A.I.C.S.: 721110
Rachel Crumbley *(Dir-Mktg)*
Edward C. Callaway *(Chm & CEO)*

IDA COUNTY, IOWA COMMU-NITY HOSPITAL
701 E 2nd St, Ida Grove, IA 51445
Tel.: (712) 364-3311   IA
Web Site:
   https://www.hornmemorialhos
   pital.org
Year Founded: 1966
Sales Range: $10-24.9 Million
Emp.: 212
Health Care Srvices
N.A.I.C.S.: 622110

IDA GROVE BANCSHARES, INC.
501 2nd St, Ida Grove, IA 51445
Tel.: (712) 364-3393   IA
Web Site: https://www.unitedbk.bank
Year Founded: 1981
Sales Range: $25-49.9 Million
Bank Holding Company
N.A.I.C.S.: 551111

Subsidiaries:

United Bank of Iowa   (1)
501 2nd St, Ida Grove, IA 51445
Tel.: (712) 364-3393
Web Site: http://www.unitedbk.com
Sales Range: $25-49.9 Million
Retail & Commercial Banking
N.A.I.C.S.: 522110
Owen C. Bolte *(Pres & CEO)*
Jeff Buehler *(Sr VP & Branch Mgr)*
Daniel Dotzler *(Exec VP-Ops & Control)*
Kenneth L. Van Kekerix *(Chm)*

IDAHO AGRICULTURAL CREDIT ASSOCIATION
188 W Judicial St, Blackfoot, ID
83221
Tel.: (208) 785-1510
Web Site:
   http://www.idahoagcredit.com
Year Founded: 1934
Sales Range: $25-49.9 Million
Emp.: 25
Agricultural Credit Association
N.A.I.C.S.: 522299
Jim Chase *(Treas & Sec)*

IDAHO ASPHALT SUPPLY INC.
2535 N 15th E, Idaho Falls, ID 83401
Tel.: (208) 524-5871
Web Site:
   https://www.idahoasphalt.com
Sales Range: $10-24.9 Million
Emp.: 80
Manufactures Asphalt Emulsion Prod-
ucts for Road Construct
N.A.I.C.S.: 324121
Kevin Maddox *(Mgr-Information Tech-
nology)*

Subsidiaries:

Western Emulsions, Inc.   (1)
PO Box 50538, Idaho Falls, ID 83405
Tel.: (520) 622-7203
Web Site: http://www.westernemulsions.com
Rev.: $5,800,000
Emp.: 27
Asphalt Paving Mixture & Block Mfr
N.A.I.C.S.: 324121
Robert Koleas *(Vice Chm)*
Kevin M. Trant *(CEO)*
Jeff Senkerik *(VP-Ops)*

IDAHO BEVERAGES INC.
2108 1st Ave N, Lewiston, ID 83501
Tel.: (208) 743-6535
Web Site:
   http://www.lewistonpepsi.com
Rev.: $10,400,000
Emp.: 55
Soft Drinks
N.A.I.C.S.: 424490
Gary D. Prasil *(Pres)*
Jason Dickerson *(VP-Sls Ops)*

IDAHO CENTRAL CREDIT UNION
4400 Central Way, Chubbuck, ID
83202
Tel.: (208) 478-3300   ID
Web Site: https://www.iccu.com
Year Founded: 1940
Sales Range: $75-99.9 Million
Emp.: 674
Financial Services
N.A.I.C.S.: 522130
Brenda Worrell *(Exec VP)*

IDAHO COMMUNITY FOUNDA-TION, INC.
210 W State St, Boise, ID 83702
Tel.: (208) 342-3535   ID
Web Site: http://www.idcomfdn.org
Year Founded: 1988
Sales Range: $10-24.9 Million
Emp.: 8
Grantmaking Services
N.A.I.C.S.: 813211
Holly Motes *(Controller)*
Jennifer Oxley *(Dir-Comm)*
Laura Swift *(Accountant)*
Lisa Bearg *(Program Mgr)*

IDAHO DEPARTMENT OF COMMERCE
700 W State St 2nd Fl, Boise, ID
83720-0093
Tel.: (208) 334-2470
Web Site: http://www.visitid.org
Year Founded: 1982
Sales Range: $50-74.9 Million
Emp.: 52
State Economic Development Admin-
istrative Services
N.A.I.C.S.: 926110
Melanie Bartolome *(CFO)*

Subsidiaries:

Idaho Division of Tourism
Development   (1)
700 W State St, Boise, ID 83720-0093
Tel.: (208) 334-2470
Web Site: http://www.visitidaho.org
Sales Range: $10-24.9 Million
Emp.: 7
Travel & Tour Operator
N.A.I.C.S.: 561520
Jeff Sayer *(Dir-Commerce)*

IDAHO FIRST BANK
475 E Deinhard Ln, McCall, ID
83638-4800
Tel.: (208) 634-1000
Web Site:
   http://www.idahofirstbank.com
Rev.: $10,681,269
Assets: $203,849,065

Liabilities: $185,774,114
Net Worth: $18,074,951
Earnings: $569,000
Fiscal Year-end: 12/31/18
Commericial Banking
N.A.I.C.S.: 522110
James Fletcher (Vice Chm)
Mark Miller (Chm)
David S. Dickey (Sr VP)
Shannon Stoeger (Chief Credit Officer & Exec VP)
Todd Cooper (Pres & CEO)
Stephen Speidel (CFO & Exec VP)
Bob Buersmeyer (Sr VP)
Aana Vannoy (Sr VP)
Morgan Poyser (Dir-IT)
Stacey Divine (CMO)
Chris Batt (Sr VP)
Steve Ferber (Sr VP)
Steve Zabel (Sr VP)
Spring Alexander (Officer-Compliance & Ops & VP)
Bryan Furlong (Chief Banking Officer & Exec VP)
Lupe Rodriguez (VP & Mgr-Mortgage Sls)

IDAHO FOREST GROUP, LLC

687 Canfield Ave Ste 100, Coeur D'Alene, ID 83815
Tel.: (208) 255-3200
Web Site: http://www.idfg.com
Year Founded: 2008
Sales Range: $25-49.9 Million
Emp.: 750
Wood Product Mfr & Distr
N.A.I.C.S.: 321113
Erol Deren (VP-Sls & Mktg)
Marc A. Brinkmeyer (Chm)
Alan Harper (Mgr-Resource)
Kevin Esser (CFO)
Bruce Brewer (Mgr-Residual)
Bill Higgins (Mgr-Resource)
Mike Henley (Mgr-Chilco, Laclede & Athol Mills)
Jesse Short (Mgr-Lewiston, Grangeville & St Regis Mills)
Chris Pease (Mgr-Moyie Springs Mill)
Tom Schultz (VP-Govt Affairs & Community Outreach)
Curtis Fryer (CTO)

Subsidiaries:

Laclede Mill   (1)
30 Riley Crk Park Dr, Laclede, ID 83841
Tel.: (208) 255-3220
Web Site: http://www.rileycreek.com
Sales Range: $25-49.9 Million
Emp.: 140
Sawmills
N.A.I.C.S.: 321113

IDAHO FRESH-PAK INC.

529 N 3500 E, Lewisville, ID 83431-5035
Tel.: (208) 754-4686   ID
Web Site: http://www.idahoan.com
Year Founded: 1960
Mfr of Dehydrated Fruits, Vegetables & Soups
N.A.I.C.S.: 311423
Drew Facer (Exec VP-Retail)
Dan Fitzgerald (Dir-Mktg)
Kerry Buck (CFO)
Gordan Lewis (Pres)

IDAHO NORTH RESOURCES CORP.

321 Spokane St, Richland, WA 99354
Tel.: (206) 790-3346
Web Site:
    http://www.idahonorthresources.com
Metal Mining Services
N.A.I.C.S.: 213114
Lane Griffin (Chm)

IDAHO PACIFIC LUMBER COMPANY INC.

7255 W Franklin Rd, Boise, ID 83709
Tel.: (208) 375-8052
Web Site: http://www.idapac.com
Year Founded: 1979
Sales Range: $10-24.9 Million
Emp.: 40
Lumber, Plywood & Millwork Services
N.A.I.C.S.: 423310
Eric Grenden (CFO)

IDAHO STEEL PRODUCTS INC.

255 E Anderson St, Idaho Falls, ID 83401
Tel.: (208) 522-1275
Web Site:
    https://www.idahosteel.com
Sales Range: $10-24.9 Million
Emp.: 150
Food Products Machinery
N.A.I.C.S.: 333241
Eric Call (Sr Acct Mgr)

IDAHO SUPREME POTATOES, INC.

614 E 800 N, Firth, ID 83236-0246
Tel.: (208) 346-6841   ID
Web Site:
    http://www.idahosupreme.com
Year Founded: 1966
Sales Range: $200-249.9 Million
Emp.: 350
Potato Processing Services
N.A.I.C.S.: 311423
Brad Chapman (Mgr-Adv)
Cindy Logan (Controller-Document)
Victor Guearra (Supvr-Pkg)

IDAHO TROUT PROCESSORS COMPANY

PO Box 72, Buhl, ID 83316-0072
Tel.: (208) 543-6444
Web Site: https://www.idahotrout.com
Year Founded: 1948
Rev.: $14,000,000
Emp.: 150
Processor of Fish
N.A.I.C.S.: 424460
Gregory Kaslo (VP)

IDAHO TRUST BANCORP

888 W Broad St, Boise, ID 83702
Tel.: (208) 373-6500   ID
Web Site: http://www.idahotrust.com
Year Founded: 1999
Bank Holding Company
N.A.I.C.S.: 551111
Thomas Prohaska (Co-Founder, Chm, Pres & CEO)

Subsidiaries:

Idaho Trust Bank   (1)
888 W Broad St, Boise, ID 83702
Tel.: (208) 373-6500
Web Site: http://www.idahotrust.com
Sales Range: $1-9.9 Million
Emp.: 45
Savings Bank
N.A.I.C.S.: 522180
Daniel Prohaska (Co-Founder)
Thomas Prohaska (Co-Founder, Chm, Pres & CEO)
Christopher Coyle (Chief Investment Officer)
Joel Hickman (Chief Banking Officer & Exec VP)
Desiree Prohaska (Chief Wealth Mgmt Officer & Exec VP)

IDAHO VENEER COMPANY

704 E 4th Ave, Post Falls, ID 83854
Tel.: (208) 773-4511
Web Site:
    https://www.idahoveneer.com
Year Founded: 1953
Sales Range: $25-49.9 Million

Emp.: 40
Softwood Veneer & Plywood Mills
N.A.I.C.S.: 321212
Terry Nuwcomb (CFO)

Subsidiaries:

Ceda-Pine Veneer Inc   (1)
26 Samuels Rd, Sandpoint, ID 83864
Tel.: (208) 263-7527
Veneer Stock, Softwood
N.A.I.C.S.: 321113

Idaho Veneer Co.   (1)
704 E 4th Ave, Post Falls, ID 83854
Tel.: (208) 773-4511
Web Site: http://www.idahoveneer.com
Rev.: $32,000,000
Softwood Veneer & Plywood
N.A.I.C.S.: 321212
John Malloy (Pres)
John Martinek (Mgr)

IDATA TECHNOLOGIES INC

1908 Mt Vernon Ave 2nd Fl, Alexandria, VA 22301
Web Site: https://www.idatainc.com
Year Founded: 2004
Sales Range: $1-9.9 Million
Emp.: 18
Technology Consulting & Software Services
N.A.I.C.S.: 541519
Brian S. Parish (Pres)

IDC TECHNOLOGIES, INC.

1851 McCarthy Blvd Ste 116, Milpitas, CA 95035
Tel.: (408) 376-0212
Web Site:
    http://www.idctechnologies.com
Year Founded: 2003
Sales Range: $25-49.9 Million
Emp.: 550
Staffing Services & Business Processing Outsourcing Services
N.A.I.C.S.: 561311
Samiran Das (Sr Mgr-Sls)
Prateek Gattani (Owner)
Suresh Menon (Head-Ops)

IDD AEROSPACE CORP.

18225 NE 76th St, Redmond, WA 98052
Tel.: (425) 885-4353
Web Site:
    http://www.iddaerospacecorp.com
Rev.: $17,000,000
Emp.: 160
Aircraft Parts & Auxiliary Equipment Mfr
N.A.I.C.S.: 336413
Beth de Young (VP-Sls-Mktg)

IDDINGS TRUCKING, INC.

741 Blue Knob Rd, Marietta, OH 45750
Tel.: (740) 568-1780
Web Site:
    http://www.iddingstrucking.com
Year Founded: 1966
Sales Range: $10-24.9 Million
Emp.: 105
Freight Transportation Services
N.A.I.C.S.: 484220
George C. Loeber (Pres)
Brad Loeber (Gen Mgr)

IDEA BANK MARKETING

701 W 2nd St, Hastings, NE 68901
Tel.: (402) 463-0588
Web Site:
    https://www.ideabankmarketing.com
Year Founded: 1982
Sales Range: $1-9.9 Million
Emp.: 13
Advertising Agencies
N.A.I.C.S.: 541810

Sherma Jones (Partner & Dir-Creative)
Ann Martin (Pres & Founding Partner)
Karen Stroebel (Office Mgr & Receptionist)
Julie Fahrlander (Project Mgr)

IDEA NUOVA INC.

302 5th Ave, New York, NY 10001
Tel.: (212) 643-0680
Web Site:
    https://www.ideanuova.com
Sales Range: $25-49.9 Million
Emp.: 60
Mfr of Recreational Accessories
N.A.I.C.S.: 424350
Nathan Accad (Co-Pres)
Benjamin Accad (Co-Pres)

IDEAL BOX CO.

4800 S Austin Ave, Chicago, IL 60638
Tel.: (708) 594-3100
Web Site: http://www.idealbox.com
Sales Range: $50-74.9 Million
Emp.: 250
Boxes Corrugated: Made From Purchased Materials
N.A.I.C.S.: 322211
Stephen Eisen (CEO)
Linda becker (Controller)

IDEAL CHEMICAL & SUPPLY COMPANY

4025 Air Park St, Memphis, TN 38118
Tel.: (901) 363-7720   TN
Web Site:
    http://www.idealchemical.com
Year Founded: 1932
Sales Range: $75-99.9 Million
Emp.: 115
Wholesale Distributor of Industrial Chemicals
N.A.I.C.S.: 424690
Dan Thompson (Mgr-Water Treatment)
Michael Blurton (Mgr-Ops)
Kelly McCabe (VP-Ops)
Sam Block Jr. (Pres)

IDEAL CLASSIC CARS LLC

2224 S Tamiami Trl, Venice, FL 34293
Tel.: (941) 966-1900
Web Site:
    https://www.idealclassiccars.net
Sales Range: $1-9.9 Million
Emp.: 15
Classic Car Dealership
N.A.I.C.S.: 441120
Michael Lombardo (Co-Owner)
Evelyn Lombardo (Co-Owner)

IDEAL CORP.

1143 W Flagler St, Miami, FL 33130
Tel.: (305) 548-3296
Web Site: http://www.idealbaby.com
Rev.: $10,000,000
Emp.: 50
Retailer of Children's Wear & Furniture
N.A.I.C.S.: 458110
Bernardino Rodriguez (Pres)
Marta Rodriguez (VP)

IDEAL CREDIT UNION

8499 Tamarack Rd, Woodbury, MN 55125
Tel.: (651) 770-7000
Web Site: http://www.idealcu.com
Year Founded: 1926
Financial Services
N.A.I.C.S.: 522320

Ideal Credit Union—(Continued)

Brian Sherrick *(Pres & CEO)*
Dennis Bauer *(CFO)*
Jeanine Swanson *(Sr VP-HR)*
Emily Kelly *(VP-Talent & Admin)*
Rachael Jones *(Branch Mgr-North St. Paul)*
Jill Robiller *(Asst VP-Payment Sys)*
Nash Shoker *(Branch Mgr-Stillwater)*
Hector Perez *(Branch Mgr-Inver Grove Heights)*
Jozsef Hegedus *(Branch Mgr-Hugo)*
Jay Hall *(Sr VP-Branch Ops)*
Jane Hennen *(VP-Mktg)*

IDEAL DEALS, LLC
3200 Parker Dr, Saint Augustine, FL 32084
Tel.: (386) 736-1700 **FL**
Web Site: https://www.ideal-ap.com
Year Founded: 2010
Sales Range: $10-24.9 Million
Emp.: 70
Designs & Manufactures Aluminum Fences, Railing & Gates
N.A.I.C.S.: 331318
Michael Siegel *(Co-Owner)*
Douglas J. Brady *(Co-Owner & CEO)*

IDEAL DISTRIBUTING CO. INC.
2059 Wilma Rudolph Blvd, Clarksville, TN 37040
Tel.: (931) 552-3300
Rev.: $23,400,000
Emp.: 65
Beer & Other Fermented Malt Liquors
N.A.I.C.S.: 424810
Charles W. Hand *(CEO)*
William Mosely *(CFO)*
Terry Griffen *(Dir-Sls)*

IDEAL ELECTRIC SUPPLY CORPORATION
2230 Adams Pl NE, Washington, DC 20018
Tel.: (202) 526-7500
Web Site:
http://www.idealelectric.com
Year Founded: 1991
Sales Range: $25-49.9 Million
Emp.: 25
Wholesale Distr of Electrical, Industrial & Telecommunications Infrastructure Products
N.A.I.C.S.: 423840
Cora H. Williams *(Co-Founder & Pres)*
Ken Rogers *(Co-Founder)*
Dennis Harris *(Sr VP & COO)*
Anil Chavan *(CFO & VP)*
Karl Pinkney *(Mgr-Warehouse Ops)*
Matthew Berry *(CFO)*

IDEAL FENCING CORP.
5795 Ideal Dr, Erie, CO 80516
Tel.: (303) 962-8100
Web Site:
http://www.idealfencingcorp.com
Year Founded: 2000
Sales Range: $1-9.9 Million
Emp.: 25
Highway, Street & Bridge Construction
N.A.I.C.S.: 237310
Steven McWilliams *(CEO)*

IDEAL INDUSTRIES INC
1 Becker Pl, Sycamore, IL 60178-2420
Tel.: (815) 895-5181 **DE**
Web Site:
http://www.idealindustries.com
Year Founded: 1916
Sales Range: $150-199.9 Million
Emp.: 600

Tools & Supplies for Electricians
N.A.I.C.S.: 334515
Jim James *(Chm)*
Vicki Slomka *(Sr VP)*
Carmelle Giblin *(Pres & Gen Mgr-Tool Grp)*
Jeffrey Burkhardt *(Pres & Gen Mgr)*
Douglas Sanford *(Pres & Gen Mgr-IDEAL Electrical Grp)*
Kevin Lamb *(CFO)*
Steve Henn *(CEO)*
Tony Randolph *(Acct Mgr-Natl)*

Subsidiaries:

Anderson Power Products **(1)**
13 Pratts Junction Rd, Sterling, MA 01564-2305
Tel.: (978) 422-3600
Web Site: http://www.andersonpower.com
Sales Range: $10-24.9 Million
Emp.: 50
Mfr & Distributor of Electrical Connectors
N.A.I.C.S.: 334519
Brian Davies *(Gen Mgr)*

Subsidiary (Non-US):

Anderson Power Products, Ltd. **(2)**
Unit 3 Europa Court Europa Boulevard, Westbrook, Warrington, WA5 7TN, Cheshire, United Kingdom
Tel.: (44) 1925 428390
Power Interconnect & Accessory Mfr & Distr
N.A.I.C.S.: 423690

Ideal Anderson Asia Pacific Ltd. **(2)**
4F-2 No 116 Dadun 20th St, Situn District, Taichung, 407, Taiwan
Tel.: (886) 4 2310 6451
Power Connector Mfr
N.A.I.C.S.: 335313

Ideal Anderson Technologies (Shenzhen) Ltd. **(2)**
Block A8 Tantou W Ind Park, Songgang Baoan District, Shenzhen, 518105, China
Tel.: (86) 755 2768 2118
Power Interconnect & Accessory Design & Mfr
N.A.I.C.S.: 334417

Ideal Industries (Canada) Corp. **(1)**
33 Fuller Road, Ajax, L1S 2E1, ON, Canada **(100%)**
Tel.: (905) 683-3400
Web Site: https://www.idealind.com
Sales Range: $10-24.9 Million
Emp.: 75
Industrial Products
N.A.I.C.S.: 334513
Rob Ackford *(Dir-Fin)*

Ideal Industries (U.K.) Limited **(1)**
225 Europa Boulevard, Gemini Business Park, Warrington, WA5 7TN, Cheshire, United Kingdom
Tel.: (44) 192544446
Industrial Products
N.A.I.C.S.: 334513

Ideal Industries Australia **(1)**
Level 6 75 85 Elizabeth St, Sydney, 2000, NSW, Australia
Tel.: (61) 405123100
Industrial Products
N.A.I.C.S.: 334513

Ideal Industries Brasil Ltda. **(1)**
America Business Park Av Marginal do Rio Pinheiros 5200-201/F, 05693-000, Sao Paulo, Brazil **(100%)**
Tel.: (55) 1137598777
Web Site: http://www.idealindustries.co.uk
Sales Range: $10-24.9 Million
Emp.: 2
Industrial Products
N.A.I.C.S.: 334513

Ideal Industries China L.L.C. **(1)**
Room 1702 City Champ Bldg 12 Taiyanggong Zhong Rd, Chaoyang Dist, Beijing, 100028, China
Tel.: (86) 1085183141
Web Site: http://www.idealindustries.com
Sales Range: $10-24.9 Million
Emp.: 14
Industrial Products
N.A.I.C.S.: 334513

Leo Chou *(Country Mgr-Shangai)*

Ideal Industries GmbH **(1)**
Gutenbergstr 10, 85737, Ismaning, Germany
Tel.: (49) 89996860
Web Site: http://www.idealindustries.de
Sales Range: $10-24.9 Million
Emp.: 20
Industrial Products
N.A.I.C.S.: 334513

Ideal Industries India Private Limited. **(1)**
229 - 230 Spazedge Tower B Sector 47 Sohna Road, Gurgaon, 122001, Haryana, India
Tel.: (91) 124 4495106
Web Site: http://www.idealind.com
Sales Range: $10-24.9 Million
Emp.: 8
Electrical Wiring Device Mfr & Whslr
N.A.I.C.S.: 423610
Ajay Agrawal *(Country Mgr)*

Ideal Industries Mexico **(1)**
Prol. Americas 1600 4to. Piso, Col. Country Club, Guadalajara, CP 44610, Jalisco, Mexico
Sales Range: $10-24.9 Million
Emp.: 2
Industrial Products
N.A.I.C.S.: 334513

Ideal Industries SAS. **(1)**
Route de Gisy ZA Burospace - Bat 7, Bievres, 91571, France
Tel.: (33) 1 69 35 54 70
Web Site: http://www.idealindustries.fr
Power Interconnect & Other Accessory Mfr & Distr
N.A.I.C.S.: 334417

Ideal Industries, Inc. - Casella Measurement Division **(1)**
Regent House Wolseley Road, Kempston, Bedford, MK42 7JY, United Kingdom
Tel.: (44) 1234 844 100
Web Site:
http://www.casellameasurement.com
Sales Range: $10-24.9 Million
Emp.: 45
Measuring Device & Controller Mfr
N.A.I.C.S.: 334513
Ben Henson *(Gen Mgr)*

Subsidiary (Non-US):

Casella Espana SA **(2)**
Belgrade 4B, Las Rozas, Madrid, 28230, Spain
Tel.: (34) 91 640 75 19
Web Site: http://www.casella-es.com
Emp.: 20
Instrument & Related Product Mfr
N.A.I.C.S.: 334513
Jose Carlos Guerra *(Gen Mgr)*

IDEAL INNOVATIONS, INC.
950 N Tlepe Rd Ste 800, Arlington, VA 22203
Tel.: (703) 528-9101
Web Site:
http://www.idealinnovations.com
Year Founded: 1998
Sales Range: $25-49.9 Million
Emp.: 210
Biometric Services
N.A.I.C.S.: 561621
Hope Farmer *(VP-HR)*
Bob Kocher *(Pres & CEO)*
Richard Syretz *(CFO)*
Craig M. Arridt *(CTO)*
Derrick Spearman *(VP-Security & Logistics)*
Ivan Quinn *(VP-Biometric Svcs)*
Rebecca Perlman *(Sr VP-Forensics)*
Donald Ross *(Chief Strategic Growth Officer)*

IDEAL INTEGRATIONS, INC.
501 Mosside Blvd, North Versailles, PA 15137
Tel.: (412) 349-6680

Web Site:
http://www.idealintegrations.net
Year Founded: 2003
Rev.: $5,200,000
Emp.: 45
Computer Related Services
N.A.I.C.S.: 541512
Michael Stratos *(Founder & CEO)*
Michael Castillo *(Dir-Network & Security)*
Joshua Sutton *(Engr-Cloud Svcs)*
Valerie Levanduski *(Mgr-Mktg)*
Ryan Romano *(Dir-Sls Engrg)*
Al Stasko *(CFO)*
Dennis Wheeler *(Engr-Sls)*
Carol Kirsch *(Dir-Quality Assurance)*
Christopher Fox *(Dir-Tech)*

IDEAL MACHINING & SUPPLY INC.
2537 Tyler Ave, El Monte, CA 91733
Tel.: (626) 444-7026
Web Site:
http://www.idealmachining.com
Rev.: $400,000
Emp.: 6
Machine Tools Mfr
N.A.I.C.S.: 333517

IDEAL RESTAURANT GROUP, INC.
277 North Ave Ste 200, New Rochelle, NY 10801
Tel.: (914) 774-8811 **FL**
Year Founded: 2011
Sales Range: $10-24.9 Million
Emp.: 3
Family Dining Restaurants
N.A.I.C.S.: 722511
Tessle Robinson *(VP)*
Rudolph Southwell Jr. *(Pres, CFO, Principal Acctg Officer & Sec)*

IDEAL SUPPLY CO.
445 Communipaw Ave, Jersey City, NJ 07304
Tel.: (201) 333-2600
Web Site: http://www.ideal-supply.com
Sales Range: $200-249.9 Million
Emp.: 65
Plumbing Fittings & Supplies
N.A.I.C.S.: 423720
Donald A. Strittmatter *(Pres)*

IDEAL WINDOW MANUFACTURING
100 W 7th St, Bayonne, NJ 07002
Tel.: (201) 437-4300
Web Site:
http://www.idealwindow.com
Sales Range: $25-49.9 Million
Emp.: 50
Plastic Window Mfr
N.A.I.C.S.: 326199
John Schack *(Gen Mgr)*

IDEALAB HOLDINGS, LLC
130 W Union St, Pasadena, CA 91103
Tel.: (626) 585-6900
Web Site: http://www.idealab.com
Sales Range: $25-49.9 Million
Holding Company
N.A.I.C.S.: 551112
William Gross *(Founder & Chm)*
Marcia Goodstein *(Pres & CEO)*
Craig Chrisney *(CFO)*
Allen Morgan *(Vice Chm)*
Debbie Chen *(Gen Counsel)*
Tom McGovern *(Mng Dir)*
Wes Ferrari *(VP-IT)*

Subsidiaries:

Idealab, Inc. **(1)**
130 W Union St, Pasadena, CA 91103

Tel.: (626) 585-6900
Web Site: http://www.idealab.com
Sales Range: $100-124.9 Million
Emp.: 100
Investments, Capital, Development Strategies, Financial Support, Network Infrastructure, Consulting, Marketing Advice & Branding for New Businesses
N.A.I.C.S.: 523999
William Gross (Co-Founder & Chm)
Marcia Goodstein (Pres & CEO)
Tom Hughes (Co-Founder)
Craig Chrisney (CFO)
Wes Ferrari (VP-IT)
Debbie Chen (Gen Counsel)
Alex Maleki (VP-Bus Dev)
Tom McGovern (Mng Dir)

Subsidiary (Domestic):

eSolar, Inc.   (2)
3355 W Empire Ave Ste 200, Burbank, CA 91504
Tel.: (818) 303-9500
Web Site: http://www.esolar.com
Sales Range: $50-74.9 Million
Emp.: 70
Solar Energy Solutions
N.A.I.C.S.: 221118
Dale Rogers (Exec VP-Projects)
Linda C. Heller (CFO)
Rick Huibregtse (Sr VP-Engrg)

IDEALEASE, INC.
430 N Rand Rd, North Barrington, IL 60010-5984
Tel.: (847) 304-6000   IL
Web Site: http://www.idealease.com
Year Founded: 1982
Sales Range: $25-49.9 Million
Emp.: 50
Commercial Truck Leasing & Rental Service Centers Operator & Franchisor
N.A.I.C.S.: 532120
Daniel J. Murphy (Pres & CEO)
Traci Royal (CFO)
Lance Bertram (VP-Mktg)
Zac Babenko (Engr-Sls)
Beth Scorzo (Mgr-HR)

Subsidiaries:

Idealease Risk Services, Inc.   (1)
430 N Rand Rd, North Barrington, IL 60010-5984
Tel.: (847) 304-6000
Risk Mitigation Services
N.A.I.C.S.: 541199
Daniel J. Murphy (Pres)
Dan Murphy (Pres)

Idealease Services, Inc.   (1)
430 N Rand Rd, North Barrington, IL 60010-5984
Tel.: (847) 304-6000
General Automotive Repair Shops
N.A.I.C.S.: 811198
Daniel J. Murphy (Pres)

Idealease de Mexico SA de CV   (1)
Avenida Jose Vasconcelos 640, Planta Baja Colonia Valle del Campestre, San Pedro Garza Garcia, CP 66225, Nuevo Leon, Mexico
Web Site: https://idealease.mx
Truck Rental & Leasing
N.A.I.C.S.: 532120

Idealease of Atlanta, L.L.C.   (1)
1902 Joy Lake Rd, Morrow, GA 30260
Tel.: (404) 608-0970
Web Site: https://idealeaseofatlanta.com
Rev.: $1,500,000
Emp.: 30
Truck, Utility Trailer & RV, Recreational Vehicle, Rental & Leasing
N.A.I.C.S.: 532120
Mario Delgado (Pres)

Idealease of Houston, L.L.C.   (1)
14201 Hempstead Rd, Houston, TX 77040
Tel.: (713) 690-3212
Web Site: https://www.idealease.com
Sales Range: $10-24.9 Million
Truck, Utility Trailer & RV (Recreational Vehicle) Rental & Leasing

N.A.I.C.S.: 532120
Lance Bertram (Sr VP-Sls, Mktg & Distr)

IDEAOVERTEN, LLC
3140 Tilghman St #128, Allentown, PA 18104
Tel.: (610) 437-4340
Web Site: http://www.ideaover10.com
Sales Range: $1-9.9 Million
Emp.: 22
Website Development, Marketing & Other Related Services
N.A.I.C.S.: 541519
Edward R. Kundahl (Pres)

IDEAS THAT DELIVER
4010 N Millwood Dr, Appleton, WI 54913-7110
Tel.: (920) 722-4014
Year Founded: 1987
Rev.: $15,000,000
Emp.: 25
Fiscal Year-end: 12/31/04
Business-To-Business, Consumer Marketing
N.A.I.C.S.: 541810
Mike Webb (Production Mgr)
Cindy Joslin (Bus Dir & Traffic Mgr)
Dick Van Driest (CEO)

IDEAS, INC.
1507 Boettler Rd, Uniontown, OH 44685
Tel.: (330) 896-8215
Web Site:
    http://www.ideasincweb.com
Year Founded: 1993
Sales Range: $25-49.9 Million
Emp.: 547
Product Design & Development Firm
N.A.I.C.S.: 334419
Brad Borne (CEO)

IDEASTREAM
1375 Euclid Ave, Cleveland, OH 44115-1835
Tel.: (216) 916-6100   OH
Web Site: http://www.ideastream.org
Year Founded: 2001
Sales Range: $25-49.9 Million
Emp.: 159
Public Broadcasting Services
N.A.I.C.S.: 516210
John Phillips (CFO)
Tom Furnas (Sr Dir-Tech)
Kevin McMullen (Chm)
Kathryn P. Jensen (COO)
Julie Adler Raskind (Sec)
Linda J. Williams (Sr Dir-Education)
Liesl Bonneau (Program Mgr-OGT)
Hali Breiner (Coord-Traffic & Sponsorship)
Jeff Carlton (Mgr-Radio Ops & Traffic)
Robin Carreon (Mgr-Membership)
Shelley Cochran (Coord-Admin Support)
Barbara Crouse (Acct Mgr-Underwriting)
John DeBarr (Mgr-IT)
Ella Fong (Mgr-Special Events & Projects)
Gail Grizzell (Mgr-Foundation Gifts)
Grace Heese (Acct Mgr-Underwriting)
Jerry Kest (Coord-Major Gifts)
Kim MacDonald (Dir-HR)
Lori Zoss Kraska (Dir-Support)
Jason Lapinski (Mgr-Budgets & Reporting)
John Ramicone (Dir-Distance Learning)
Gaye Ramstrom (Acct Mgr-Underwriting)
Traci Shaw (Mgr-Traffic)
Joseph Sheppa (Mgr-Digital Media)
Jan Silla (Mgr-Acctg)
Mike Vendeland (Mgr-Production)

Megan Wycuff (Mgr-Production-OGT)
Jean Zeller (Mgr-Membership Campaign)
Shadi Sabra (CTO)
Kevin Martin (Pres & CEO)
Todd Mesek (Chief Mktg & Dev Officer)
Daniel P. Walsh Jr. (Treas)

IDEASTREAM CONSUMER PRODUCTS, LLC
812 Huron Rd Ste 390, Cleveland, OH 44115
Tel.: (216) 459-2400
Web Site:
    http://www.ideastreamproducts.com
Year Founded: 2002
Rev.: $17,500,000
Emp.: 11
Graphic Design Services
N.A.I.C.S.: 541430
Anthony Decarlo (CEO)
Jim Mann (Dir-Fin & Ops)
Kristin Murphy (Acct Mgr-Natl)
Daniel V. Perella (Pres & COO)
Sean Williams (Acct Mgr-Natl)
Eric Klosky (Dir-Creative)
Vince Thomson (Co-Founder & Chief Mktg Officer)
Maureen McNea (Mgr-Logistics)
Ashlee Hietanen (Mgr-Mktg)
David Travis (VP-Sls)
Kelli Paugh (Designer-Graphic)

IDEAWORKS, INC.
301 W Main St, Plymouth, PA 18651
Tel.: (570) 779-9543
Web Site:
    http://www.ideaworksfoodmarketing.com
Year Founded: 1998
Advertising Agencies
N.A.I.C.S.: 541810
Peter Steve (Mng Partner)
Donna Hansbury (Pres)
Patty Pugh (VP-Ops)

IDEAWORKS, INC.
1110 N Palafox St, Pensacola, FL 32501-2608
Tel.: (850) 434-9095   FL
Web Site:
    http://www.ideaworksusa.com
Year Founded: 1995
Sales Range: $10-24.9 Million
Emp.: 7
Advertising Agencies
N.A.I.C.S.: 541810
Caron Sjoberg (Pres)

IDELIK FOOTWEAR, INC.
2610 Old S Dr, Jonesboro, GA 30236
Tel.: (404) 396-3581   GA
Web Site: http://www.shopidelik.com
Sales Range: $25-49.9 Million
Emp.: 4
Rubber Footwear Mfr & Distr
N.A.I.C.S.: 316210
David N. Golphin Jr. (CEO)
Allen N. Golphin III (VP)

IDENTCO IDENTIFICATION CORP.
28164 W Concrete Dr, Ingleside, IL 60041
Tel.: (815) 385-0011
Web Site: http://www.identco.com
Sales Range: $10-24.9 Million
Emp.: 35
Mfr of Labels
N.A.I.C.S.: 424310
Scott Lucas (Pres)

IDENTISYS, INC.
7630 Commerce Way, Eden Prairie, MN 55344

Tel.: (952) 294-1200   MN
Web Site: http://www.identisys.com
Year Founded: 1999
Electronic Components Mfr
N.A.I.C.S.: 334419
Joseph M. Wright (Exec VP-Sls)
Michael R. Shields (Founder & Chm)
Tony J. Dick (CFO)
Chris Sinnen (Exec VP-Svc)
David J. Richvalsky (Sr VP)
Michael R. Shields II (Pres & CEO)

IDENTITY
30700 Telegraph Rd Ste 1475, Bingham Farms, MI 48025-4590
Tel.: (248) 258-2333
Web Site: http://www.identitypr.com
Year Founded: 1998
Sales Range: $1-9.9 Million
Emp.: 25
Public Relations
N.A.I.C.S.: 541820
Oliver Higgs (Dir-Editorial)
Mark Winter (Mng Partner)
Brandon Chesnutt (Dir-Social Media)
Andrea Bogos Trapani (Mng Partner)

IDENTITY AUTOMATION, LP
7102 N Sam Houston Pkwy W Ste 300, Houston, TX 77064
Tel.: (281) 220-0021
Web Site:
    http://www.identityautomation.com
Software Product Distributor
N.A.I.C.S.: 513210
James Litton (CEO)
Michael Webb (CTO)

Subsidiaries:

2FA, Inc.   (1)
10713 N FM 620 Ste 201, Austin, TX 78726
Tel.: (512) 918-3200
Web Site: http://www.2fa.com
Cybersecurity Software Development
N.A.I.C.S.: 513210
Greg Salyards (Co-Founder, Pres & CEO)
Shaun Cuttill (Co-Founder & CTO)
Shiva Standifur (Project Mgr)

IDENTITY STRONGHOLD, LLC
565 Paul Morris Dr, Englewood, FL 34223
Web Site:
    http://www.idstronghold.com
Sales Range: $1-9.9 Million
Emp.: 13
Identity Theft Protection Sleeves & Wallets for Credit Cards, Debit Cards, Drivers' Licenses, Passports, ID Cards & Other Related Items
N.A.I.C.S.: 316990
Walt Augustinowicz (Founder & CEO)
Ted Whitaker (Exec VP-Sls & Mktg)

IDEO, LLC
154 Forest Ave, Palo Alto, CA 94301
Tel.: (650) 289-3400   CA
Web Site: http://www.ideo.com
Sales Range: $100-124.9 Million
Emp.: 600
Design Consultancy Services
N.A.I.C.S.: 541990
David Kelley (Founder)
Paul Bennett (Chief Creative Officer)
Dennis Boyle (Partner)
Duane Bray (Partner & Head-Talent-Global)
John Ravitch (Partner)
Lynda Deakin (Mng Dir & Partner)
Chris Domina (Partner)
Dana S. Cho (Mng Dir & Partner)
Amy Bonsall (Sr Dir-Design)
Ari Adler (Dir-Cambridge Studio)
Melanie Bell-Mayeda (Mng Dir & Assoc Partner)
Tom Eich (CTO & Partner)
Rebecca Hornbuckle (Mng Dir-Cambridge)

IDEO, LLC—(Continued)

Travis Lee *(Mng Dir-Chicago)*
Iain Roberts *(Mng Dir-Global & Partner)*
Clark Scheffy *(Mng Dir-San Francisco)*
Jen Panasik *(Mng Dir-San Francisco)*
Bryan Walker *(Partner & Mng Dir-San Francisco)*
Madison Mount *(Partner & Mng Dir-San Francisco)*
Sandy Speicher *(CEO)*
Detria Williamson *(CMO)*

IDEX MPT INC.
832 N Indus Dr, Elmhurst, IL 60126
Tel.: (630) 530-3333   DE
Web Site: http://www.fitzmill.com
Year Founded: 1988
Food Product Machinery Mfr
N.A.I.C.S.: 333241
Tony Divito *(Controller)*

IDISCOVERY SOLUTIONS, INC.
3000 K St NW Ste 330, Washington, DC 20007
Tel.: (202) 249-7860
Web Site:
   http://www.idiscoverysolutions.com
Year Founded: 2008
Sales Range: $10-24.9 Million
Emp.: 45
Information Technology Support Services
N.A.I.C.S.: 541512
Julian Ackert *(Mng Dir)*
Neal Lawson *(Pres)*
Louis J. Martin *(Sr Mgr-Solutions)*
Sharon A. O'Donnell *(VP-Admin Ops)*
Daniel Regard *(CEO)*
James Vaughn *(Mng Dir)*

IDLEWOOD ELECTRIC SUPPLY INC.
114 Skokie Valley Rd, Highland Park, IL 60035
Tel.: (847) 831-3600
Web Site:
   http://www.idlewoodelectric.com
Sales Range: $10-24.9 Million
Emp.: 100
Electrical Supplies Distr
N.A.I.C.S.: 423610
Barbara Lansing *(Owner)*
John Stonehouse *(Mgr-Electrical Supply Div)*
Karen Karen Kurschardt *(Mgr-Counter Sls & Warehouse)*
Kenneth Wimer *(Asst Mgr-Warehouse)*
Pat Bunting *(Mgr-Showroom)*

IDM HOME FURNISHINGS, INC.
40 SE 7th St, Boca Raton, FL 33432
Tel.: (561) 417-0040   FL
Web Site:
   http://www.idmhomefurnishings.com
Rev.: $15,000,000
Emp.: 5
Wood Household & Office Furniture Designer, Mfr & Distr
N.A.I.C.S.: 337122
W. Christian Buehl *(Pres)*

IDN INC.
2401 Mustang Dr Ste 100, Grapevine, TX 76051
Tel.: (817) 421-5470
Web Site: http://www.idn-inc.com
Rev.: $16,100,000
Emp.: 5
Equipment & Supplies
N.A.I.C.S.: 423850

Mike Groover *(Pres)*
Barry Johnson *(Pres)*

Subsidiaries:

Idn-Acme Inc.   (1)
1504 Justin Rd, Metairie, LA 70001
Tel.: (504) 837-7315
Web Site: http://www.idnacme.com
Sales Range: $1-9.9 Million
Locksmith Equipment & Supplies
N.A.I.C.S.: 423850

IDN-H.HOFFMAN INC.
7330 W Montrose Ave, Norridge, IL 60706
Tel.: (708) 456-9600
Web Site:
   http://www.idnhhoffman.com
Rev.: $16,500,000
Emp.: 35
Locksmith Equipment & Supplies
N.A.I.C.S.: 423850
Karen Hoffman-Kahl *(Pres)*
Danilo Lam *(Mgr-Inside Sls)*
Laura Larson *(Owner)*
Barb Welninski *(Mgr-Acctg)*

IDO SECURITY INC.
7875 SW 40th St Ste 224, Miami, FL 33155-3510
Tel.: (786) 603-5212   NV
Web Site: http://www.magshoe.info
Sales Range: Less than $1 Million
Emp.: 1
Security Device Mfr
N.A.I.C.S.: 561621
Magdiel Rodriguez *(Pres & CEO)*

IDS INTERNATIONAL GOVERNMENT SERVICES LLC
2500 Wilson Blvd Ste 200, Arlington, VA 22201
Tel.: (703) 875-2212
Web Site: http://idsinternational.net
Year Founded: 2006
Sales Range: $1-9.9 Million
Emp.: 70
National Security Consulting Services
N.A.I.C.S.: 928110
Nick Dowling *(Pres & CEO)*
Oron Strauss *(CFO & Sr VP)*

Subsidiaries:

DECO Inc.   (1)
2500 Wilson Blvd Ste 200, Arlington, VA 22201
Tel.: (703) 875-2212
Web Site: http://www.deco-inc.com
Military & Law Enforcement Training; Security Services
N.A.I.C.S.: 611519
Robert A. Dorr *(Co-Pres & CEO)*
Derek J. Dorr *(Co-Pres)*
Andrew C. Pierucki *(COO)*

IEA INCORPORATED
9625 55th St, Kenosha, WI 53144
Tel.: (262) 942-1414
Web Site: http://www.iearad.com
Year Founded: 1985
Sales Range: $10-24.9 Million
Emp.: 150
Engine Radiator Mfr
N.A.I.C.S.: 336390
Pat Frieman *(Controller)*
George Newell *(Owner)*
Jay Tench *(Mgr-Mgmt Info Sys)*

IENJOY HOME LLC
2021 Sunnydale Blvd Ste 130, Clearwater, FL 33765
Tel.: (727) 216-6754   FL
Web Site:
   http://www.ienjoyhome.com
Year Founded: 2011
Sales Range: $25-49.9 Million
Emp.: 88
Bed Sheet Distr

N.A.I.C.S.: 449129
Sean Noll *(CEO)*
Wendy Graffam *(CFO)*

IENTERTAINMENT NETWORK, INC.
206 Cherwell Dr, Cary, NC 27513-7400
Tel.: (919) 238-4090   NC
Web Site:
   http://www.imagicgames.com
Year Founded: 1982
Online Entertainment Sites, Gaming Content & Videogame Software Publisher
N.A.I.C.S.: 513210
J. W. Stealey *(CEO)*

IENTRY, INC.
851 Corporate Dr Ste 20, Lexington, KY 40503
Tel.: (859) 514-2720
Web Site: http://www.ientry.com
Year Founded: 1999
Wired Telecommunications Carriers
N.A.I.C.S.: 517111
Mike McDonald *(Dir-Ops)*
Rich Ord *(Pres & CEO)*
Susan Coppersmith *(Dir-Sls)*

IEX GROUP, INC.
4 World Trade Ctr 44th Fl, New York, NY 10007
Tel.: (646) 343-2000   DE
Web Site: http://www.iextrading.com
Emp.: 70
Holding Company; Alternative Trading System & Securities Exchange Operator
N.A.I.C.S.: 551112
Ronan Ryan *(Pres)*
Brad Katsuyama *(Founder & CEO)*
John Schwall *(COO)*
Rob Park *(CTO)*
Claudia Crowley *(Chief Regulatory Officer)*
John Ramsay *(Chief Market Policy Officer)*
Ben Smith *(Chief Info Security Officer)*
Sophia Lee *(Gen Counsel)*
Paul Bauccio *(Head-Market Ops)*
Adrian Facini *(Head-Product Mgmt)*
Zoran Perkov *(Head-Tech Ops)*
Andrea Ledford *(Chief People Officer)*

Subsidiaries:

Investors' Exchange LLC   (1)
3 World Trade Ctr 58th Fl, New York, NY 10007   **(100%)**
Tel.: (646) 343-2000
Web Site: http://www.iextrading.com
Securities Exchange Operator
N.A.I.C.S.: 523210
Brad Katsuyama *(Chm & CEO)*
Ronan Ryan *(Pres)*
John Schwall *(COO)*
Robert Park *(CTO)*
Claudia Crowley *(Chief Regulatory Officer)*
John Ramsay *(Chief Market Policy Officer)*
Eric Stockland *(Chief Strategy Officer)*

IF IT'S PAPER (2) LLC
1801 Gervais St, Columbia, SC 29201
Tel.: (803) 252-3636   SC
Web Site:
   http://www.ifitspaperonline.com
Sales Range: $10-24.9 Million
Party Supplies Retailer
N.A.I.C.S.: 459420

Subsidiaries:

If It's Paper - Greenville   (1)
405 S Pleasantburg Dr, Greenville, SC 29607
Tel.: (864) 233-6438
Web Site: http://www.ifitspaperonline.com

Emp.: 5
Party Supplies Retailer
N.A.I.C.S.: 459420
Jeannie Looper *(Mgr)*

IFAX SOLUTIONS, INC.
1020 E Main St, Norristown, PA 19401-2778
Tel.: (215) 825-8700
Web Site: http://www.ifax.com
Year Founded: 2002
Sales Range: $1-9.9 Million
Emp.: 7
Corporate Fax Management Software
N.A.I.C.S.: 513210
Darren Nickerson *(Founder & Pres)*
Laurie Smith *(Mgr-HR)*

IFBYPHONE
300 W Adams, Chicago, IL 60606
Tel.: (877) 295-5100
Web Site: http://public.ifbyphone.com
Year Founded: 2005
Sales Range: $1-9.9 Million
Emp.: 100
Manages, Measures & Automates Voice Conversations
N.A.I.C.S.: 517810
Irv Shapiro *(CEO, Founder & CTO)*
Steve Brown *(VP-Sls)*
Jason Ferrara *(VP-Bus Dev)*
Steve Griffiths *(Dir-Mktg & Product Strategy)*
Steve Dimmitt *(Exec VP-Customer Experience)*
Tim Cunningham *(CFO)*

IFG COMPANIES
238 International Rd, Burlington, NC 27215
Tel.: (336) 586-2500
Web Site:
   http://www.burlingtoninsurance.com
Sales Range: $250-299.9 Million
Emp.: 300
Holding Company; Commercial Insurance Products & Services
N.A.I.C.S.: 551112
Robert Linton *(Chm)*
Christopher M. Lewis *(Grp Pres)*
Michael A. Fleischer *(Chief Underwriting Officer & Exec VP)*
Andrew P. Kempen *(Chief Actuary)*
Michael R. Denton *(Exec Mng Dir-Property)*
Brett M. Blumencranz *(Sr VP & Head-Sls & Mktg-Alpharetta)*
Manuel Almagro *(CFO)*
John W. Mahoney *(Chief Claim Officer/Sr VP-Hartford)*
Stephanie W. Yocum *(Chief People Officer & Sr VP)*

Subsidiaries:

Guilford Specialty Group, Inc.   (1)
100 Pearl St, Hartford, CT 06103
Tel.: (860) 723-4150
Web Site: http://www.guilfordspecialty.com
Rev.: $25,000,000
Emp.: 100
Underwriters, Security
N.A.I.C.S.: 523150
Allison M. Adams *(Mng Dir)*

The Burlington Insurance
Company   (1)
238 International Rd, Burlington, NC 27215
Tel.: (336) 586-2500
Web Site:
   http://www.burlingtoninsurance.com
Emp.: 150
Insurance Brokerage
N.A.I.C.S.: 524210
Lou Levinson *(Pres)*

IFG CORP.
1400 Broadway, New York, NY 10018-3304
Tel.: (212) 239-8615   NY

Web Site: http://www.adjmi.com
Year Founded: 1986
Sales Range: $10-24.9 Million
Emp.: 50
Childrens Apparel
N.A.I.C.S.: 458110
Ronald Adjmi (Pres)
Kim Dabah (VP)
Donna Falco (VP)

IFH GROUP INC.
3300 E Rock Falls Rd, Rock Falls, IL
61071
Tel.: (815) 626-1018
Web Site: http://www.ifhgroup.com
Sales Range: $10-24.9 Million
Emp.: 100
Mfr of Fluid Power Pumps
N.A.I.C.S.: 333996
John Nagy (CFO)
Keith Ellefsen (Pres)
James L. King Jr. (CEO)

IFIT HEALTH & FITNESS INC.
1500 S 1000 W, Logan, UT 84321
Tel.: (435) 786-5000   DE
Year Founded: 1999
Rev.: $1,745,056,000
Assets: $992,566,000
Liabilities: $322,407,000
Net Worth: $670,159,000
Earnings: ($516,706,000)
Emp.: 2,500
Fiscal Year-end: 05/31/20
Holding Company
N.A.I.C.S.: 551112
Scott R. Watterson (Founder & CEO)
David J. Watterson (Chief Strategy
Officer & Exec VP)
Steven J. Barr (CFO & Exec VP)
Everett Smith (Gen Counsel, Sec &
Sr VP)

IFLY HOLDINGS, LLC
31310 Alvarado Niles Rd, Union City,
CA 94587-2802
Tel.: (779) 368-4359
Web Site: http://www.iflyworld.com
Sports & Recreation Instruction
N.A.I.C.S.: 611620
Emiko Taylor (Mgr)
Christie Matheis (Gen Mgr)

IFP, INC.
2125 Airport Dr, Faribault, MN 55021
Tel.: (507) 334-2730
Web Site: http://www.ifpinc.biz
Year Founded: 1981
Sales Range: $10-24.9 Million
Emp.: 180
Medical & Sport Drink Powder Product Mfr
N.A.I.C.S.: 325411
Ephi Eyal (Pres & CEO)
Anna Batsakes (Dir-Mktg)
Carin Draper (VP-Fin)
Itzhak Reichman (Chm)
Craig Siefken (VP-Comml Ops)
William Solomon (VP-Mfg)

IFS HOLDINGS, LLC
1601 Anthony Rd, Burlington, NC
27215
Tel.: (336) 227-1130
Web Site: http://www.impactfs.com
Holding Company
N.A.I.C.S.: 551112

Subsidiaries:

Impact Fulfillment Services, LLC   (1)
1601 Anthony Rd, Burlington, NC 27215
Tel.: (336) 227-1130
Web Site: https://www.impactfs.com
Broom, Brush & Mop Mfr
N.A.I.C.S.: 339994

IFTHEN, LLC

20900 NE 30 Ave Ste 200, Miami, FL
33180
Tel.: (305) 690-4380
Web Site: http://www.ifthen.biz
Sales Range: $1-9.9 Million
Emp.: 10
Media Buying Services
N.A.I.C.S.: 541810
Peter Vechi (CTO)
Geli Campbell (Acct Mgr)

IGA, INC.
8745 W Higgins Rd, Chicago, IL
60631-2716
Tel.: (773) 693-4520   DE
Web Site: http://www.iga.com
Year Founded: 1926
Sales Range: $75-99.9 Million
Supermarkets Licenser & Franchisor
N.A.I.C.S.: 445110
Dave Bennett (Sr VP-Procurement &
Private Brands)
John Ross (Pres & CEO)

IGAS, INC.
842 5th Ave, New Kensington, PA
15068
Tel.: (724) 472-9701
Web Site: http://www.igas.com
Year Founded: 1929
Sales Range: $350-399.9 Million
Emp.: 1,000
Professional Handwriting Analysis &
Psychological Testing
N.A.I.C.S.: 561990
Greg Greco (Pres)

IGD INDUSTRIES INC.
4150 C St SW, Cedar Rapids, IA
52404-0122
Tel.: (319) 396-2222   IA
Web Site:
   http://www.igdindustries.com
Year Founded: 1946
Managed Solution Services
N.A.I.C.S.: 541611
Steve Dummermuth Sr. (Pres)

IGENII, INC.
40 Exchange Pl # 401, New York, NY
10005
Tel.: (212) 932-7483   DE
Web Site: http://www.igenii.com
Year Founded: 2008
Sales Range: Less than $1 Million
Emp.: 11
Interactive Website Designer & Developer & Internet Marketing & Advertising Consulting Services
N.A.I.C.S.: 518210
Ross Lavnikevich (Pres & CEO)
Rafael Abdurachmanov (CFO)

IGM CREATIVE GROUP
166 Main St Ste 202, Lincoln Park,
NJ 07035
Tel.: (973) 709-1126
Web Site:
   http://www.igmcreativegroup.com
Sales Range: $100-124.9 Million
Emp.: 12
Advertising, Marketing Strategy &
Web Development
N.A.I.C.S.: 541820
Jay Stack (Pres)

**IGNITE MEDIA SOLUTIONS
LLC**
1001 St Petersburg Dr W, Oldsmar,
FL 34677
Tel.: (813) 855-5800
Web Site:
   http://www.ignitemedia.com
Sales Range: $25-49.9 Million
Emp.: 60
Direct Response Marketing Services

N.A.I.C.S.: 541910
Michael Ferzacca (CEO)
Doug Winslow (Founder & Pres)

IGNITE SOCIAL MEDIA LLC
14600 Weston Pkwy Ste 100, Cary,
NC 27513
Tel.: (919) 653-2590
Web Site:
   http://www.ignitesocialmedia.com
Year Founded: 2007
Sales Range: $1-9.9 Million
Emp.: 73
Social Media Agency Services
N.A.I.C.S.: 541840
Jim Tobin (Founder & CEO)
Lisa Braziel (Sr VP)

IGNITED
2221 Park Pl, El Segundo, CA 90245
Tel.: (310) 773-3100
Year Founded: 1999
Rev.: $10,000,000
Emp.: 150
Graphic Design, Information Technology, Interactive, Internet/Web Design,
Technical Advertising
N.A.I.C.S.: 541810
Eric Johnson (Pres)
Bill Rosenthal (COO)
Paul Small (Dir-Bus Dev & Social
Strategy)
Megan Crowell (Assoc Dir-Media)
Kim Haskell (Exec VP)
David Martin (Sr VP-Media Svcs)
Bryan Duffy (Exec VP-Experiential
Mktg & Mng Dir-Ignited New York)
Jordan Atlas (Sr VP)
Troy Scarlott (Exec Dir-Creative)
L. J. Kobe (Grp Dir-Media)
Robb Hittner (Sr VP)
Terri Simon (Sr VP)
Jackie Stasi (Sr VP)
Eric Springer (Chief Creative Officer)

IGNITION BRANDING
2211 E 7th Ave, Tampa, FL 33605
Tel.: (813) 356-0556
Web Site:
   http://www.ignitionbranding.com
Sales Range: $1-9.9 Million
Advertising & Public Relations
Agency
N.A.I.C.S.: 541810
Jack Glasure (Pres)
Arthur Porter (Mng Dir-Intl Brands)
Steve Tillack (Mgr-Bus Dev & Market)
Michael Schriefer (Dir-Mktg-
Motorsports)

IGNITION PARTNERS LLC
350 106th Ave NE 1st Fl, Bellevue,
WA 98004
Tel.: (425) 709-0772
Web Site:
   http://www.ignitionpartners.com
Sales Range: $25-49.9 Million
Emp.: 24
Venture Capital Firm
N.A.I.C.S.: 523999
John G. Connors (Mng Partner)
Robert Headley (Partner)
Steve Hooper (Partner)
Cameron Myhrvold (Partner)
Jonathan Roberts (Founder & Partner)
Brad Silverberg (Founder & Partner)
Frank Artale (Mng Partner)
Ryan Baker (CFO)
Kumar Sreekanti (Founder & CEO)
Molly Goudy (Mgr-Fin)
Lesly Mohr (Mgr-Fund Acctg)
Magdalene Teo (Mgr-Fund Acctg)
Kenji Kawasaki (Mgr-Fund Tax)
Nick Sturiale (Mng Partner)
Kristina Bergman (Principal)

Rachel Chalmers (Principal)
Nick Triantos (Venture Partner-Los
Altos)
Scott Coleman (Partner-Bus Dev-Los
Altos)
Bob Kelly (Mng Partner)
Preeti Rathi (Partner)
Kellan Carter (Partner)

IGNITIONONE, INC.
1545 Peachtree St Ste 500, Atlanta,
GA 30309
Web Site: http://www.ignitionone.com
Year Founded: 2001
Emp.: 350
Marketing Services
N.A.I.C.S.: 541810
Will Margiloff (CEO)
Eric Bamberger (Sr VP-Hospitality)

Subsidiaries:

IgnitionOne, Inc. - Akron   (1)
526 S Main St Ste 705, Akron, OH 44311
Tel.: (800) 801-4194
Web Site: http://www.ignitionone.com
Marketing Software & Solutions
N.A.I.C.S.: 513210
William Landers (Exec VP-Data Mgmt Platform Dev)
Dutch Hollis (Gen Mgr-Client Success)

IGP INDUSTRIES, LLC
101 Mission St Ste 1500, San Francisco, CA 94105
Tel.: (415) 882-4550   CA
Web Site: https://igpequity.com
Year Founded: 1997
Privater Equity Firm
N.A.I.C.S.: 523999
R. Patrick Forster (Founder)
Jeffrey M. Webb (Partner)
Eric D. Heglie (Partner)
Brett Johnson (COO & Chief Compliance Officer)
Dave DiFranco (Partner)
Rob Austin (Partner)

Subsidiaries:

APCT, Inc.   (1)
3495 De La Cruz Blvd, Santa Clara, CA
95054
Tel.: (408) 727-6442
Web Site: http://www.apctinc.com
Printed Circuit Boards
N.A.I.C.S.: 334412
Steve Robinson (Pres & CEO)
Eric Schmidt (Sr VP-Ops)
Bruce McMaster (Sr VP-Ops)
Joe Gisch (CFO)

Subsidiary (Domestic):

Advanced Circuits, Inc.   (2)
21101 E 32nd Pkwy, Aurora, CO 80011
Tel.: (303) 576-6610
Web Site: https://www.4pcb.com
Printed Circuit Board Mfr
N.A.I.C.S.: 334412
John Yacoub (CEO)
Dan Chouinard (VP-Ops)
Jeff Yacoub (Pres)

Cartel Electronics, Inc.   (2)
1900 Petra Ln Ste C, Placentia, CA 92870
Tel.: (714) 993-0270
Web Site: http://www.apctinc.com
Bare Printed Circuit Board Mfr
N.A.I.C.S.: 334412
Paul Walker (Dir-Tech)
John Peters (Co-Owner)
Bruce McMaster (Co-Owner)
Joe Gisch (CFO)

Tech Circuits Inc.   (2)
340 Quinnipiac St, Wallingford, CT 06492
Tel.: (203) 284-5322
Web Site: http://www.techcircuits.com
Rev.: $7,470,000
Emp.: 50
Bare Printed Circuit Board Mfr
N.A.I.C.S.: 334412

IGP Industries, LLC—(Continued)

Philip Walton *(Owner)*
Mike Epting *(Mgr-Multilayer)*
Kimberly Johnson *(Dir-Sls-Natl)*

Process Insights Holdings LLC   **(1)**
5710 W Gate City Blvd Ste K 185, Greensboro, NC 27407
Tel.: (713) 947-9591
Web Site: http://www.process-insights.com
Holding Company; Process Monitoring, Analytics, Control & Safety Services
N.A.I.C.S.: 551112
Monte Hammouri *(CEO)*

Subsidiary (Domestic):

Guided Wave Inc.   **(2)**
3033 Gold Canal Dr, Rancho Cordova, CA 95670-6129
Tel.: (916) 638-4944
Web Site: http://www.guided-wave.com
Sales Range: $25-49.9 Million
Emp.: 20
Optical Measurement Instrument Mfr & Installation Services
N.A.I.C.S.: 334513
Susan Foulk *(Pres)*

Zedi Inc.   **(1)**
902 11th Avenue SW, Calgary, T2R 0E7, AB, Canada
Tel.: (403) 444-1100
Web Site: http://www.zedisolutions.com
Sales Range: $100-124.9 Million
Support Activities for Oil & Gas Exploration Services
N.A.I.C.S.: 213112

Subsidiary (US):

Southern Flow Companies, Inc.   **(2)**
132 Demanade Blvd, Lafayette, LA 70503   **(100%)**
Tel.: (337) 233-2066
Web Site: http://www.southernflow.com
Rev.: $1,500,000
Emp.: 30
Measurement, Calibration & Analytical Services for Gas & Oil Operations
N.A.I.C.S.: 213112
Gary Edwards *(Pres)*

IGS STORE FIXTURES INC.
58 Pulaski St, Peabody, MA 01961
Tel.: (978) 532-0010
Web Site: http://www.igsfixtures.com
Sales Range: $10-24.9 Million
Emp.: 80
Fixtures: Display, Office, Or Store: Except Wood
N.A.I.C.S.: 337126
Dominic Butera *(Pres)*
Robert Giovino *(Sr Acct Mgr)*
Justin Perry *(Dir-Sls & Dev)*
Joe Collins *(Sr VP-Ops)*
Mark Braun *(VP-Design & Dev)*

IGUANAMED LLC
344 W Huron St, Chicago, IL 60654
Tel.: (877) 344-8262
Web Site: http://www.iguanamed.com
Year Founded: 2005
Sales Range: $1-9.9 Million
Emp.: 5
Medical Apparel for Health Care Personnel
N.A.I.C.S.: 315990
Greg Lilien *(Pres)*

IGXGLOBAL, INC
50 Inwood Rd, Rocky Hill, CT 06067
Tel.: (860) 513-0112
Web Site: http://www.igxglobal.com
Sales Range: $10-24.9 Million
Emp.: 40
Information Technology Services & Solutions
N.A.I.C.S.: 541519
Thomas J. Duffy *(CEO)*
Barry Johnson *(Pres & CTO)*

IH MISSISSIPPI VALLEY CREDIT UNION
2121 47th St, Moline, IL 61265
Tel.: (309) 793-6200   IL
Web Site: http://www.ihmvcu.org
Year Founded: 1934
Sales Range: $25-49.9 Million
Emp.: 345
Credit Union
N.A.I.C.S.: 522130
Barbara Reed *(VP-Reg Ops)*
Timothy Stecker *(VP-Bus)*
Josh Peterson *(Officer-Comml Loan)*
Laurie Burkholder *(Officer-Comml Loan Workout)*
Larry Makoben *(Officer-Bus Dev)*
Chris Ryner *(Officer-Bus Dev)*
Justin Johnson *(Officer-Comml Loan)*

IHA HEALTH SERVICES CORPORATION
24 Frank Lloyd Wright Dr Ste J2000, Ann Arbor, MI 48106-0446
Tel.: (734) 995-2950   MI
Web Site: http://www.ihacares.com
Year Founded: 2010
Sales Range: $150-199.9 Million
Emp.: 1,193
Health Care Srvices
N.A.I.C.S.: 622110
Lowell M. Sprague *(CFO & VP)*
Cindy Elliott *(COO & Exec VP)*
Amy Middleton *(Dir-Mktg)*
Martin Murray *(VP-Primary Care Ops)*
Linda MacEllven *(VP-HR & Customer Svc)*

IHC GROUP, INC.
1500 Executive Dr, Elgin, IL 60123
Tel.: (847) 742-1516   DE
Web Site: http://www.ihcgroup.com
Year Founded: 1906
Sales Range: $125-149.9 Million
Emp.: 240
Provider of General Contracting & Design Services
N.A.I.C.S.: 237110
Thomas S. Rakow *(Chm)*
David Rock *(Pres)*
Alan Orosz *(CFO)*

IHEALTHCARE, INC.
3901 NW 28th St 2nd Fl, Miami, FL 33142
Tel.: (305) 751-2327   DE
Web Site: http://www.ihealthcaresystems.com
Year Founded: 2014
Sales Range: Less than $1 Million
Emp.: 2
Healthcare Product Distr
N.A.I.C.S.: 423450
Noel Mijares *(Chm, Pres & CEO)*
David A. Bingaman *(CFO, COO, Chief Acctg Officer, Sec & VP)*

IHEARTRAVES, LLC
240 S Loara St, Anaheim, CA 92802
Web Site: http://www.iheartraves.com
Year Founded: 2010
Sales Range: $25-49.9 Million
Emp.: 70
Clothing Distr
N.A.I.C.S.: 458110
Brian Lim *(Founder & CEO)*
Wall Street *(Pres & COO)*
Matt Marchione *(Dir-Apparel)*
D. A. Coda *(Project Mgr-Technical)*
Matt Powell *(Mgr-Warehouse)*

IHLO SALES & IMPORT CO.
406 Payne St, Center, TX 75935
Tel.: (936) 598-2491
Web Site: http://www.ihlo.com
Sales Range: $10-24.9 Million
Emp.: 10

Lumber, Plywood & Millwork
N.A.I.C.S.: 423310
Danny Foster *(VP)*
Roy Blackshear *(Pres & CEO)*

IHP CAPITAL PARTNERS INC.
100 Bay View Circ Ste 200, Newport Beach, CA 92660
Tel.: (949) 851-2121
Web Site: http://www.ihpinc.com
Year Founded: 1992
Rev.: $100,000,000
Emp.: 30
Real Estate Brokers & Agents
N.A.I.C.S.: 531210
Douglas C. Neff *(Pres & Partner)*
Susan I. Pickle *(Sr VP)*
Jay W. Pruitt *(Principal & Sr VP)*
Renee P. McDonnell *(Sr VP)*
Peter Bridges *(Sr VP)*
Jennifer Dudley *(Sr VP)*

IHP INDUSTRIAL INC.
1701 S 8th St, Saint Joseph, MO 64503
Tel.: (816) 364-1581
Web Site:
   http://www.ihpindustrial.com
Rev.: $32,519,893
Emp.: 30
Mechanical Contractor
N.A.I.C.S.: 238220
Brian Pillippe *(Project Mgr)*
Danny Young *(Project Mgr)*
David Gillson *(Project Mgr)*
Greg Simpson *(Project Mgr)*
John Roster *(Project Mgr)*
Jon Vega *(Project Mgr)*
Ross Harmon *(Mgr-Safety)*

IHRIE SUPPLY CO. INC.
1605 Cargill Ave S, Wilson, NC 27893
Tel.: (252) 291-5521
Web Site: http://www.ihriesupply.com
Sales Range: $10-24.9 Million
Emp.: 55
Plumbing & Hydronic Heating Supplies
N.A.I.C.S.: 423720
Edward Ihrie *(CEO)*

IHS DISTRIBUTING CO. INC.
1800 Douglas Ave, Kalamazoo, MI 49007
Tel.: (269) 382-1111
Web Site: http://www.ihsdist.com
Sales Range: $25-49.9 Million
Emp.: 35
Provider of Beer & Other Fermented Malt Liquors
N.A.I.C.S.: 424810
Jay Scott Levene *(Pres)*
Kirk Schieman *(Mgr-Sls)*

IITS LLC
159 Overland Rd, Waltham, MA 02451
Tel.: (781) 272-1754
Web Site: http://www.integratedit.com
Sales Range: $10-24.9 Million
Emp.: 45
Electronic Computers & Networking
N.A.I.C.S.: 449210
Amy Connell *(Mgr-Mktg)*
Arthur Ataie *(CEO)*
Frank Vincentelli *(CTO)*
Jay Patterson *(VP)*
Nasser Khadjenoori *(COO)*

IJET INTERNATIONAL, INC.
185 Admiral Cochrane Dr, Annapolis, MD 21401-3091
Tel.: (443) 716-2419
Web Site: http://www.ijet.com

Intelligence-Driven Risk Management Services
N.A.I.C.S.: 541618
Bruce McIndoe *(Founder & Pres)*
John Rose *(COO)*
Charlie Terry *(Sr VP-Product Mgmt & Mktg)*
Mike Briskey *(CFO)*
Stephen D. Foley *(Sr VP-Sls-Global)*
Nuno Pereira *(CTO)*
Theresa M. Thomas *(Sr VP-Powered by iJET Bus Unit)*
Mark V. Donohue *(Sr VP-Customer Success)*
Barbara Cheek *(Dir-HR)*
Ellen Ryan *(Gen Counsel & Sec)*
Benjamin Allen *(CEO)*
Jim Simmons *(Chm)*
Maureen French *(Sr VP-Direct Sls-Americas)*

Subsidiaries:

red24 Limited   **(1)**
28 Lime Street, London, EC3M 7HR, United Kingdom
Tel.: (44) 200 500 0242
Web Site: http://www.red24.com
Risk Management Consulting Services
N.A.I.C.S.: 541611
Maldwyn Worsley-Tonks *(CEO)*
Neil Thompson *(Head-Crisis Response)*
Sarah Spolander *(Dir-Crisis Response Mgmt Centre)*
Jack Cloonan *(Head-Special Risks)*
Eric Smith *(Head-Food Safety & Product Recall)*
Nick Powis *(Head-Ops)*
Claire Harris *(Head-Travel Svcs & Bus Support)*
Michael Haughey *(Head-Asia Pacific & Corp Investigations)*
Nayana Bharti *(Head-Comm & Asst Sec)*

Subsidiary (Non-US):

red24 CRM (Pty) Limited   **(2)**
Block A The Terraces Steenberg Office Park, Westlake, Cape Town, 7945, South Africa
Tel.: (27) 217003800
Web Site: http://www.red24.com
Security Consulting Services
N.A.I.C.S.: 541618

IKANO COMMUNICATIONS, INC.
9221 Corbin Ave-Ste 260, Northridge, CA 91324
Tel.: (801) 924-0900   UT
Web Site: http://www.ikano.com
Year Founded: 1998
Sales Range: $10-24.9 Million
Emp.: 200
Enabler of Private-Label Internet Services & IP Solutions
N.A.I.C.S.: 518210
George Mitsopoulos *(COO)*
Jim Murphy *(CEO)*
Sam Ghahremanpour *(Pres)*

Subsidiaries:

Ikano Communications Inc.   **(1)**
171 W Main St S Unit 4, Newmarket, L3Y 3Y9, ON, Canada
Tel.: (905) 836-5479
Sales Range: $10-24.9 Million
Emp.: 50
Full Service Provider of Internet Networking Infrastructure & Private-Label Internet Services
N.A.I.C.S.: 517121

IKASYSTEMS CORPORATION
134 Turnpike Rd, Southborough, MA 01772
Tel.: (508) 229-0600   DE
Web Site: http://www.ikasystems.com
Year Founded: 1999
Management Consulting Services
N.A.I.C.S.: 541618

IKE BEHAR APPAREL & DE-SIGN LTD.
760 W 84th St, Hialeah, FL 33014-3126
Tel.: (305) 557-5212   FL
Web Site: http://www.ikebehar.com
Year Founded: 1975
Sales Range: $25-49.9 Million
Emp.: 200
Providers of Mens & Boys Clothing
N.A.I.C.S.: 424350
Isaac Behar *(Pres)*
Richarto Suarzo *(CFO)*

IKE GAMING, INC.
600 Fremont St, Las Vegas, NV 89101
Tel.: (702) 385-5200   NV
Web Site: http://www.ecvegas.com
Year Founded: 1963
Sales Range: $25-49.9 Million
Emp.: 650
Casino Hotel Owner & Operator
N.A.I.C.S.: 721120
Mike Nolan *(Gen Mgr)*
Alan Joseph Woody *(CFO)*
Kenneth Epstein *(Owner)*
Ike Lawrence Epstein *(Pres)*

IKE TRADING CO. LTD. INC.
8905 SW Nimbus Ave Ste 475 A, Beaverton, OR 97008-7136
Tel.: (503) 643-6688   OR
Web Site: http://www.iketrading.com
Year Founded: 1965
Sales Range: $50-74.9 Million
Emp.: 15
Lumber, Plywood & Millwork
N.A.I.C.S.: 423310

Subsidiaries:

Ike International Corporation   **(1)**
500 E Maple St, Stanley, WI 54768-1285
Tel.: (715) 644-5777
Sales Range: $10-24.9 Million
Emp.: 7
Softwood Veneer & Plywood
N.A.I.C.S.: 321212
Ted Fischer *(Pres)*

IKEDDI ENTERPRISES INC.
1407 Broadway Ste 1805, New York, NY 10018
Tel.: (212) 302-7644
Web Site: http://www.ikeddi.com
Sales Range: $10-24.9 Million
Emp.: 30
Women's Sportswear Mfr
N.A.I.C.S.: 315250
Peter Raymond *(Pres)*
David Hirsch *(VP-Sls)*
Maggie Lee *(Coord-Production)*

IKON FINANCIAL GROUP
1022 Carolina Blvd, Isle of Palms, SC 29451
Tel.: (843) 256-5100
Web Site: http://www.ikonfg.com
Year Founded: 2008
Sales Range: $1-9.9 Million
Emp.: 70
Financial Services Specializing in Residential & Commercial Lending
N.A.I.C.S.: 522291
Chris Barker *(Dir-Natl Sls)*
Chris Young *(Co-Owner & Principal)*
Jason Myers *(Co-Owner)*
Mick Jewell *(VP & Branch Mgr)*

IKONIX GROUP, INC.
28105 N Keith Dr, Lake Forest, IL 60045
Tel.: (847) 367-4671
Web Site:
   http://www.ikonixgroup.com
Sales Range: $25-49.9 Million
Emp.: 5

High Technology Investment Company
N.A.I.C.S.: 551112
Michael R. Braverman *(Pres)*
Adam Mikos *(Mgr-Intl Sls)*
David Larsson *(Mgr-Intl)*

Subsidiaries:

Associated Research Inc.   **(1)**
13860 W Laurel Dr, Lake Forest, IL 60045-4531
Tel.: (847) 367-4077
Web Site: http://www.arisafety.com
Sales Range: $10-24.9 Million
Emp.: 50
Designer of Electrical Testing Instrument Mfr
N.A.I.C.S.: 334515
Michael R. Braverman *(Pres)*
Adam Mikos *(Mgr-Sls-Intl)*
Pete Stevens *(Mgr-Domestic Sls)*

ILD CORP.
5000 Sawgrass Village Cir Ste 30, Ponte Vedra Beach, FL 32082
Tel.: (800) 637-4009   FL
Web Site:
   http://www.ildteleservices.com
Year Founded: 1995
Sales Range: $150-199.9 Million
Emp.: 400
Telecommunication & Billing Services
N.A.I.C.S.: 517121
Michael F. Lewis *(Chm & CEO)*
Dennis J. Stoutenburgh *(Pres & COO)*
Frederick W. Loyd *(Sr VP)*

Subsidiaries:

ILD Corp.   **(1)**
14180 Dallas Pkwy Ste 300, Dallas, TX 75254
Tel.: (972) 267-0100
Web Site: http://www.ildtelecom.com
Sales Range: $10-24.9 Million
Emp.: 10
Telephone Answering Services
N.A.I.C.S.: 561421
Dennis Stoutenburg *(Pres & COO)*
Mike Lewis *(CEO)*
Eddie Brooks *(CFO)*
Mike Cumpton *(Controller)*

ILIGHT TECHNOLOGIES
118 S Clinton Ste 370, Chicago, IL 60661
Tel.: (312) 876-8630
Web Site: http://www.ilight-tech.com
Year Founded: 2000
Sales Range: $10-24.9 Million
Emp.: 65
Accent Lighting Solutions
N.A.I.C.S.: 335132
Mark Cleaver *(Founder & Chm)*

ILINK SYSTEMS, INC.
10545 Willows Rd Ste 110, Redmond, WA 98052
Tel.: (425) 869-8104
Web Site: http://www.ilink-systems.com
Year Founded: 2002
Sales Range: $10-24.9 Million
Emp.: 500
Software Product Development Services
N.A.I.C.S.: 541511
Vishwenath Kizhapandal *(COO)*

ILION CAPITAL PARTNERS
, New York, NY
Tel.: (929) 333-6756
Web Site:
   https://www.ilioncapital.com
Investment Management
N.A.I.C.S.: 523999

Subsidiaries:

Magneto Equipment, Inc.   **(1)**

402 Hazel St, Jefferson, OR 97352
Tel.: (541) 327-3362
Web Site: http://www.amequipment.com
Rev.: $5,457,000
Emp.: 17
All Other Motor Vehicle Parts Mfr
N.A.I.C.S.: 336390
Paul Olesh *(CEO)*

Subsidiary (Domestic):

Dumore Corporation   **(2)**
1030 Veterans St, Mauston, WI 53948-9314
Tel.: (608) 847-6420
Web Site: https://www.dumorecorp.com
Sales Range: $75-99.9 Million
Emp.: 70
Automatic Drills, Portable Machinery, Custom Designed OEM Motors & Industrial Tools Mfr
N.A.I.C.S.: 335312
Dave Messer *(Gen Mgr)*

Unit (Domestic):

Dumore Corporation - Dumore Motors Unit   **(3)**
1030 Veterans St, Mauston, WI 53948
Tel.: (608) 847-6420
Web Site: http://www.dumoremotors.com
Sales Range: $10-24.9 Million
Emp.: 60
Motor Product Mfr
N.A.I.C.S.: 335312

ILITCH HOLDINGS, INC.
2211 Woodward Ave, Detroit, MI 48201-3469
Tel.: (313) 983-6000   MI
Web Site:
   http://www.ilitchholdings.com
Year Founded: 1959
Sales Range: $1-4.9 Billion
Emp.: 7,500
Holding Company
N.A.I.C.S.: 551112
Michael Ilitch *(Chm)*
Christopher Ilitch *(Pres & CEO)*
Marian Ilitch *(Vice Chm)*
Scott Fisher *(CFO)*
John Kotlar *(VP-Tax Affairs)*
Michael McLauchlan *(VP-Govt Rels)*
Michael Edicola *(VP-HR)*
Rick Fenton *(VP-Security)*
Stan Berenbaum *(Gen Counsel & VP)*
Chris Granger *(Grp Pres-Sports & Entertainment)*

Subsidiaries:

Champion Foods, L.L.C.   **(1)**
23900 Bell Rd, New Boston, MI 48164
Tel.: (734) 753-3663
Web Site: http://www.championfoods.com
Sales Range: $10-24.9 Million
Emp.: 70
Private Label & Branded Food Products Mfr
N.A.I.C.S.: 311999

Detroit Entertainment, LLC   **(1)**
2901 Grand River Ave, Detroit, MI 48201
Tel.: (866) 782-9622
Web Site: http://www.motorcitycasino.com
Casino & Entertainment Groups Management
N.A.I.C.S.: 721120
Jacci Woods *(VP-PR)*
Debbie Moffatt *(VP-HR)*
John Policicchio *(Sr VP-Mktg)*
James Flynn *(Dir-Pur)*
Philip Trofibio *(Sr VP-Gaming Ops)*
Bruce Dall *(Pres)*
Bradley Bailey *(Controller)*

Detroit Red Wings, Inc.   **(1)**
Joe Louis Arena 600 Civic Ctr Dr, Detroit, MI 48226
Tel.: (313) 396-7000
Sales Range: $75-99.9 Million
Emp.: 1,000
Professional Hockey Team
N.A.I.C.S.: 339920
Christopher Ilitch *(VP)*
Robert E. Carr *(Gen Counsel & Alternate Governor)*

Paul MacDonald *(VP-Fin)*
Mike Bayoff *(New Media & Alumni Rels)*
Ryan Martin *(Dir-Hockey Admin)*
Shawn Horcoff *(Dir-Player Dev)*

Detroit Tigers Baseball Club, Inc.   **(1)**
2100 Woodward Ave, Detroit, MI 48201-3474
Tel.: (313) 471-2000
Web Site: http://www.tigers.mlb.com
Sales Range: $25-49.9 Million
Emp.: 320
Professional Baseball Club
N.A.I.C.S.: 711211
Michael Ilitch *(Owner)*
Stephen Quinn *(CFO & VP-Fin & Admin)*
Elaine Lewis *(VP-Community & Pub Affairs)*
Ellen Hill Zeringue *(VP-Mktg)*
John Westhoff *(Gen Counsel, VP & Asst Gen Mgr)*
Duane McLean *(Exec VP-Bus Ops)*
Steve Harms *(VP-Corp Partnerships)*
Scot Pett *(VP-Ticket & Suite Sls)*
Michael Healy *(VP-Park Ops)*
Ron Colangelo *(VP-Comm)*
Mike Smith *(Dir-Baseball Ops)*
Tom Moore *(Dir-Intl Ops)*
Dan Lunetta *(Dir-Minor League Ops)*
David Chadd *(VP & Asst Gen Mgr)*
Cheryl Evans *(Dir-Minor League & Scouting Admin)*
Kelli Kollman *(Sr Dir-Fin)*
DeAndre Berry *(Dir-Pur & Supplier Diversity)*
Karen Gruca *(Sr Dir-HR)*
Maureen Kraatz *(Dir-Payroll)*
Ron Wade *(Dir-Mktg)*
Eli Bayless *(Dir-Promos & Special Events)*
Brian Britten *(Dir-Team Travel)*
Ed Goward *(Sr Mgr-Park Ops)*
Allan Carisse *(Mgr-Park Ops)*
Jill Baran *(Mgr-Event & Guest Svcs)*
Sam Abrams *(Mgr-Player Rels & Youth Sports Programs)*
Alexandra Thrubis *(Mgr-Community Affairs)*
Jordan Field *(Dir-Detroit Tigers Foundation)*
Steve Fox *(Dir-Ticket Sls)*
Dwain Lewis *(Dir-Fantasy Camps)*
Dan Griesbaum *(Mgr-Suite Sls & Svcs Acct)*
Jeff Lutz *(Asst Dir-Ticket Sls)*
Manny Crespo *(Dir-Latin American Player Dev)*
Miguel Garcia *(Dir-Latin American Ops)*
Ramon Perez *(Dir-Dominican Republic Ops)*
Dave Owen *(Dir-Player Dev)*
Robert Frutchey *(Mgr-Minor League Clubhouse)*
Steve Cleary *(Dir-Corp Sls)*
Kurt Buhler *(Sr Dir & Mgr-Corp Sls)*
Soula Burns *(Mgr-Corp Sls)*
Jim Darrow *(Dir-IT)*
Stan Fracker *(Dir-Brdcst & In-Game Entertainment)*
Aileen Villarreal *(Dir-Baseball Media Rels)*
Chad Crunk *(Dir-Baseball Media Rels)*
Brian Skipinski *(Dir-Park Ops)*
Gary Dobrowolski *(Mgr-Security)*
Jerry Conners *(Dir-Security)*
Grant Anderson *(Sr Dir-Ticket Svcs)*
Adam Klein *(Mgr-Ticket Svcs)*
Marc Himelstein *(Dir-Authentics)*
Stephanie Jenkins *(Coord-Payroll)*
Jessica Langolf *(Coord-Sponsorship Svcs)*
Kelsey Shuck *(Coord-HR)*
Debra Sword *(Coord-Acct Payable)*
Ellyn Yurgalite *(Coord-Sponsorship Svcs)*
Scott Harris *(Pres-Baseball Ops)*
Christopher Ilitch *(Chm & CEO)*

Little Caesar Enterprises, Inc.   **(1)**
2211 Woodward Ave Office Ctr, Detroit, MI 48201
Tel.: (313) 983-6000
Web Site: http://www.littlecaesars.com
Fast Food Restaurant Operator
N.A.I.C.S.: 722513
Ann Schaffer Greenough *(Coord-Architecture New Store)*
Paul Novachoff *(Coord-Computer Ops)*
Binaim Yohannes *(Coord-GIS Dev)*
Nancy Bartlett *(Dir-Franchise Fin)*
Christopher Hatty *(Mgr-Franchise Zone)*
Christine Snyder *(Mgr-Mktg Comm-Natl)*

Ilitch Holdings, Inc.—(Continued)

Jeffrey Drozdowski *(Mgr-Natl Trng)*
Ken Paczas *(Mgr-West Zone)*
Robert Karwan *(Sr Dir-Real Estate)*
Darrell Snygg *(Sr VP-Fin, Acctg & Admin)*
Syd Workman *(Dir-Loss Prevention-Southwest)*
Paul Isaacson *(Dir-Loss Prevention-Midwest)*
Brad Piros *(Dir-Loss Prevention-Natl)*

Little Caesars Enterprises, Inc. (1)
2211 Woodward Ave, Detroit, MI 48201
Tel.: (313) 983-6000
Web Site: http://www.littlecaesars.com
Sales Range: $400-449.9 Million
Carry-Out Pizza Restaurant Operator &
Franchiser
N.A.I.C.S.: 722513
David Scrivano *(Pres & CEO)*
Jeremy Vitaro *(Chief Dev Officer)*
Greg Hamilton *(CMO)*

Division (Domestic):

Blue Line Distributing (2)
24120 Haggerty Rd, Farmington Hills, MI
48335-2645
Tel.: (248) 478-6200
Web Site: http://www.bluelinedist.com
Sales Range: $25-49.9 Million
Emp.: 100
Distr of Little Caesars Products to Franchised & Company-Owned Locations
N.A.I.C.S.: 423440
David Scrivano *(CEO)*

Olympia Entertainment, Inc. (1)
2211 Woodward Ave, Detroit, MI 48201-3467
Tel.: (313) 471-3099
Web Site:
http://www.olympiaentertainment.com
Sales Range: $25-49.9 Million
Emp.: 500
Performing Arts, Sports & Special Exhibits
Promoter
N.A.I.C.S.: 711310
Tom Wilson *(Pres & CEO)*

ILLINI FS INC.
1509 E University Ave, Urbana, IL
61802
Tel.: (217) 384-8300
Web Site: http://www.illinifs.com
Year Founded: 1963
Rev.: $66,528,569
Emp.: 200
Distr of Farm Supplies
N.A.I.C.S.: 424910
Dan Kelley *(Chm)*
Mark Schluter *(Mgr-Info Svcs)*
Gala Alwood *(Supvr-Logistics)*

ILLINOIS ACTION FOR CHILDREN
4753 N Broadway St 1st Fl, Chicago,
IL 60608
Tel.: (312) 823-1100
Web Site:
http://www.actforchildren.org
Year Founded: 1971
Sales Range: $25-49.9 Million
Emp.: 528
Child Care Services
N.A.I.C.S.: 624110
April Janney *(Sr VP-Programs)*
Julie Gray *(COO)*
James A. Alexander *(Sr VP-Plng &
Execution)*
Joel Carp *(Treas)*
Maria Whelan *(Pres & CEO)*
Monica Moss *(Chm)*
Sandy Matthews *(Sr VP-Org Advancement)*
Laci Gatewood *(VP-Family & Community Svcs)*
Jeffrey Gawel *(CIO)*
Theresa Hawley *(Sr VP-Policy & Innovation)*
Jacqueline M. Zanders *(CFO)*
Bryan Stokes II *(VP-Early Learning
Programs)*

ILLINOIS ASSOCIATION OF SCHOOL BOARDS
2921 Baker Dr, Springfield, IL 62703-5929
Tel.: (217) 528-9688
Web Site: http://www.iasb.com
Year Founded: 1913
Sales Range: $10-24.9 Million
Emp.: 81
Educational Support Services
N.A.I.C.S.: 611710
Patrick Shea *(Asst Mgr-Tech)*
Susan Hilton *(Dir-Govt Rels)*
Tom Bertrand *(Exec Dir)*

ILLINOIS AUTO ELECTRIC CO.
700 Enterprise St, Aurora, IL 60504
Tel.: (630) 862-3300
Web Site:
http://www.illinoisautoelectric.com
Year Founded: 1915
Sales Range: $250-299.9 Million
Emp.: 250
Diesel Fuel Injection Rebuilding; Air-Cooled Engines & Parts; Transport
Refrigeration Sales & Service; Truck
Equipment Parts & Service
N.A.I.C.S.: 423830
H. Bruce Sirotek *(Chm & CEO)*
William M. Fritz *(Pres & COO)*
R. Gordon Sirotek *(Vice Chm & Dir-Strategic Dev)*
Kevin B. Sirotek *(VP-Sls & Mktg)*

Subsidiaries:

Illinois Auto Central Division (1)
4750 S Central Ave, Chicago, IL
60638-1531 (100%)
Tel.: (708) 563-2700
Sales Range: $10-24.9 Million
Emp.: 30
Refrigeration Repair Service; Truck Engine
Repair, Except Industrial
N.A.I.C.S.: 811210
Andy Marco *(Gen Mgr)*

Illinois Auto Electric Co. - Midwest
Engine Warehouse Division (1)
700 Enterprise St, Aurora, IL 60504-2042
Tel.: (630) 862-3300
Sales Range: $25-49.9 Million
Emp.: 80
Distr of Air Cooled Engines & Parts
N.A.I.C.S.: 423830

ILLINOIS FIBER RESOURCES GROUP
PO Box 755, Sycamore, IL 60178
Tel.: (815) 753-8113
Web Site: http://www.ifiber.org
Year Founded: 2011
Sales Range: $10-24.9 Million
Internet Service Provider
N.A.I.C.S.: 517111
William Tonne *(Treas)*
Glenn Trommels *(Vice Chm)*
Nora Fesco-Ballerine *(Sec)*
John L. Lewis *(Chm)*

ILLINOIS FOUNDATION SEEDS INC.
1083 County Rd 900 N, Tolono, IL
61880
Tel.: (217) 485-6260
Web Site: http://www.ifsi.com
Sales Range: $10-24.9 Million
Emp.: 35
Seeds: Dried, Dehydrated, Salted Or
Roasted
N.A.I.C.S.: 311911
John Hiser *(CEO)*
George Terry *(CFO)*
Rex Phipps *(Dir-Biotechnology &
Mgr-Station)*

ILLINOIS GAS CO.
1927 Miller Dr, Olney, IL 62450
Tel.: (618) 395-8588

Web Site: http://www.icc.illinois.gov
Rev.: $12,361,097
Emp.: 12
Natural Gas Distr
N.A.I.C.S.: 221210
Lloyd Morain *(Chm)*

ILLINOIS HEALTH & SCIENCE
2300 N Edward St, Decatur, IL 62526
Tel.: (217) 876-8121
Web Site: http://www.ihsholdings.org
Holding Company
N.A.I.C.S.: 551112
Ken Smithmier *(CEO)*
Al Naqvi *(Exec VP & CFO)*
Kevin Horath *(VP-HR)*

ILLINOIS HIGH SCHOOL ASSOCIATION
2715 McGraw Dr, Bloomington, IL
61704
Tel.: (309) 663-6377
Web Site: http://www.ihsa.org
Year Founded: 1940
Sales Range: $10-24.9 Million
Emp.: 23
Educational Support Services
N.A.I.C.S.: 611710
Marty Hickman *(Exec Dir)*
B. Kent Jones *(Sec)*
Chuck Nagel *(VP)*
Dan Klett *(Pres)*
Greg Bradley *(Treas)*
Tina Brown *(Office Mgr)*
Neil Hamon *(Dir-Activities)*
Eric Chrostoski *(Dir-Vocal)*
Kayode Adegoke *(Coord-Special Programs)*
Jeff Wardle *(Principal)*

ILLINOIS INDUSTRIAL TOOL INC.
530b W North Frontage Rd, Bolingbrook, IL 60440
Tel.: (708) 597-6000
Web Site: http://www.iittool.com
Rev.: $17,900,000
Emp.: 100
Hardware Merchant Whslr
N.A.I.C.S.: 423710
George Zahora *(Mgr-IT)*
Lance Ericson *(Pres)*

ILLINOIS INSURANCE GUARANTY FUND
150 S Wacker Dr Ste 2970, Chicago,
IL 60606
Tel.: (312) 422-9700
Web Site: http://www.iigf.ncigf.org
Year Founded: 1971
Sales Range: $25-49.9 Million
Emp.: 17
Risk Managemeng Srvices
N.A.I.C.S.: 524126
Tim Schotke *(Exec Dir)*
Gregory P. Jankowski *(Dir-Claims,
Liability & Property)*
Valerie McGregor *(Dir-Claims &
Workers Compensation)*
Brad Roeber *(Chm)*

ILLINOIS J. LIVINGSTON COMPANY
850 Lee St, Elk Grove Village, IL
60007
Tel.: (847) 439-5770
Sales Range: $10-24.9 Million
Emp.: 20
General Electrical Contracting Services
N.A.I.C.S.: 238210
Robert H. Rathmann *(Chm)*

ILLINOIS LIFE & HEALTH INSURANCE GUARANTY ASSOCIATION

1520 Kensington Rd Ste 112, Oak
Brook, IL 60523-2140
Tel.: (773) 714-8050
Web Site: http://www.ilhiga.org
Year Founded: 1980
Sales Range: $1-9.9 Million
Emp.: 4
Business Associations
N.A.I.C.S.: 813910
Barbara Adams *(Chief Acctg Officer)*
Janis Potter *(Exec Dir)*

ILLINOIS MUTUAL LIFE INSURANCE COMPANY
300 SW Adams St, Peoria, IL 61634-0001
Tel.: (309) 674-8255
Web Site:
http://www.illinoismutual.com
Year Founded: 1910
Sales Range: $10-24.9 Million
Emp.: 200
Life Insurance, Reinsurance, Property
& Casualty Insurance Products &
Services
N.A.I.C.S.: 524113
Susan M. Reitz *(Chief Actuary & VP)*

ILLINOIS ROAD CONTRACTORS
520 N Webster Ave, Jacksonville, IL
62650
Tel.: (217) 245-6181
Web Site: http://www.ircgrp.com
Sales Range: $50-74.9 Million
Emp.: 60
Highway & Street Maintenance
N.A.I.C.S.: 237310
P. Devon Davidsmeyer *(CEO)*

ILLINOIS RURAL ELECTRIC COOPERATIVE
2 S Main St, Winchester, IL 62694
Tel.: (217) 742-3128
Web Site: http://www.e-co-op.com
Rev.: $13,382,595
Emp.: 55
Electric Power Distr
N.A.I.C.S.: 221122
Robert A. Brown *(Pres)*
Bruce Giffin *(Gen Mgr)*
Shawn Rennecker *(Dir-Economic
Dev)*
Jenissa Ezard *(Dir-Mktg)*
Sean Middleton *(Mgr-Engrg & IT)*

ILLINOIS VALLEY COMMUNITY HOSPITAL
925 West St, Peru, IL 61354
Tel.: (815) 223-3300
Web Site: http://www.ivch.org
Year Founded: 1978
Sales Range: $75-99.9 Million
Emp.: 741
Community Hospital Support Services
N.A.I.C.S.: 541611
Tommy Hobbs *(CEO)*
Jim Schaefer *(VP-Ops & Physician
Svcs)*
Nancy McDonnell *(CIO)*
Wilma Hart-Flynn *(Co-Chief Nursing
Officer)*
Patricia Rogers *(Co-Chief Nursing
Officer)*
Robert Fortney *(Chief Nursing Officer)*
Lisa Lynch *(CFO)*
Joan Fernandez *(Dir-Community Rels
& Mktg)*
Jennifer Sines *(Dir-Pharmacy)*

ILLUMINATE OPERATIONS LLC
198 Van Buren St Ste 200, Herndon,
VA 20170
Tel.: (703) 659-9965

Web Site: https://oneilluminate.com
Emp.: 100
Cyber Security Solutions, Data Analytics & Law Enforcement Services
N.A.I.C.S.: 561621
Tameika Hollis *(CEO)*

ILLUMINATI STUDIOS INC.
Andrew Jackson Bldg 8100 Oak Ln Ste 202, Miami Lakes, FL 33016
Tel.: (305) 851-8112
Web Site:
    http://www.illuminatistudios.com
Year Founded: 2000
Sales Range: $1-9.9 Million
Emp.: 10
Internet Marketing & Advertising
N.A.I.C.S.: 541613
Aaron Lee *(Pres & Dir-Creative)*
Jamie Cundiff *(Dir-Ops)*
Ernie Millares *(Dir-Tech)*
Alexandra Lange *(Dir-Art)*

ILLUMIS, INC.
94 Bowery, New York, NY 10002
Tel.: (347) 941-2523   DE
Web Site: http://www.illumis.com
Year Founded: 2015
Emp.: 50
Information Service Provider
N.A.I.C.S.: 518210
Mike Phillips *(Founder & CEO)*
Jacob Perkins *(CTO)*
Taylor Lemmons *(Dir-Bus Dev)*

ILMO PRODUCTS COMPANY
7 Eastgate Dr, Jacksonville, IL 62650
Tel.: (217) 245-2183
Web Site:
    http://www.ilmoproducts.com
Sales Range: $10-24.9 Million
Emp.: 75
Distr of Welding Machinery & Equipment
N.A.I.C.S.: 423830
Linda Standley *(CEO)*
Brad Floreth *(Pres)*
Anthony McLaughlin *(Mgr-Sls)*

ILPEA INC.
3333 S Zero St, Fort Smith, AR 72908
Tel.: (479) 646-4535
Web Site: http://www.ilpea.com
Sales Range: $25-49.9 Million
Emp.: 110
Plastics Materials & Resins
N.A.I.C.S.: 325211
Paolo Cittadini *(Owner)*

Subsidiaries:

Ilpea Industries, Inc.   (1)
745 S Gardner St, Scottsburg, IN 47170
Tel.: (812) 752-2526
Web Site: http://www.ilpeaindustries.com
Sales Range: $75-99.9 Million
Mfr of Vinyl & Magnetic Profile Extrusions
N.A.I.C.S.: 339991
Wayne Heverly *(Pres)*

Subsidiary (Non-US):

Holm KK Extrusions Pvt. Ltd.   (2)
Plot No D 106 MIDC Ranjan Gaon Pune Nagar Rd, Pune, 412209, India
Tel.: (91) 2225930940
Web Site: http://www.kkliddlegiant.com
Sales Range: $25-49.9 Million
Emp.: 30
Mfr of Plastic Products for Appliance, Commercial Refrigeration, Industrial & Automotive Uses
N.A.I.C.S.: 326199

ILSI AMERICA LLC
5458 Louie Ln, Reno, NV 89511
Tel.: (775) 851-8880   NV
Web Site: http://www.ilsiamerica.com

Radio & Television Broadcasting & Wireless Communications Equipment Mfr
N.A.I.C.S.: 334220

Subsidiaries:

Ecliptek, LLC   (1)
5458 Louie Ln, Reno, NV 89511
Tel.: (714) 433-1200
Web Site: http://www.ecliptek.com
Electronic Components Mfr
N.A.I.C.S.: 334419

ILWU CREDIT UNION
PO BOX 445, Wilmington, CA 90748-0445
Tel.: (310) 834-6411   CA
Web Site: http://www.ilwucu.org
Year Founded: 1972
Sales Range: $10-24.9 Million
Emp.: 46
Credit Union Operator
N.A.I.C.S.: 522130
Pete Koeppen *(VP)*
Ralph Ruiz *(Treas)*
Kim Thomas *(Exec VP)*
Pete Ciaramitaro *(Chm)*
Victor Gallardo *(Sec)*
Robert Brooks *(Vice Chm)*
Devric Thomas *(VP-Fin)*

IMA FINANCIAL GROUP, INC.
1705 17th St Ste 100, Denver, CO 80202
Tel.: (303) 534-4567   KS
Web Site: http://www.imacorp.com
Year Founded: 1974
Sales Range: $450-499.9 Million
Emp.: 325
Insurance Agents
N.A.I.C.S.: 524210
Ruth Rohs *(Sr VP-Comm)*
Anna Ewing *(COO-Denver)*
Luke Proctor *(Pres)*
SueAnn Schultz *(Chief Admin Officer)*
Eric Pauly *(Gen Counsel)*
Jessica Burey *(Exec VP-Bus Consulting)*
Michelle Vercellino *(CIO)*
Steve Brockmeyer *(Pres-California Div)*
Brock Lewark *(VP-Exec Risk Solutions)*
Bobbi McPherson *(Chief People Officer)*
Ricky Bryan *(Exec VP)*
Joey Dryden *(Sr VP-Bus Dev)*
Donna MacConnell *(Mng Dir-Claims & Sr VP)*
Jordyn Arons Rosen *(Natl Dir-Private Equity & M&A Practice)*

Subsidiaries:

Bolton & Company   (1)
3475 E Footbill Blvd Ste 100, Pasadena, CA 91107
Tel.: (626) 799-7000
Web Site: http://www.boltonco.com
Insurance Agents
N.A.I.C.S.: 524210
Ronald Wanglin *(Chm)*
Julie Bowman *(CFO)*
Steven Brockmeyer *(Pres & CEO)*
Mike Morey *(COO)*
Matthew Chase *(Exec VP- Construction Practice Grp)*
Ryan Fridborg *(Exec VP)*
John Guthrie *(Exec VP)*
Richard B. Hagemeier *(Exec VP)*
Paul Palkovic *(VP)*
Robert Kral *(Exec VP)*
Brian Metcalfe *(Exec VP)*
Kenneth R. Turknette *(Exec VP)*
Jeff Whitaker *(Asst VP)*
Corey Tobin *(Asst VP)*
Jonathan Schreter *(Exec VP)*
Jacqueline S. Roth *(Exec VP)*
Brad Reaume *(Exec VP)*
Brett L. Moisa *(VP)*

David G. Miller *(Sr VP)*
Cheryl McDowell *(VP)*
Mike Martin *(Sr VP)*
Todd Jackson *(VP)*
Lyeng Ia *(Asst VP)*
Don Gutierrez *(Mng Dir)*
Rick Gombar *(Exec VP)*
Jamie Gershon *(Exec VP)*
John C. Garner *(Chief Compliance Officer)*
Greg M. Doherty *(Mng Dir-Dietary Supplement/Nutraceutical Grp & Exec VP)*
Jeannie DeLaura *(Sr VP)*
Esther Ceballos *(Sr VP)*
Andrew Agress *(Exec VP)*
Erin Powell *(VP-Property & Casualty)*
Avery Armani *(Dir-Fin)*
Lisa Markus *(VP-CX)*
Kim Sautter-Ramos *(Assoc VP)*
Jane Medel *(Mgr-Construction Practice Grp)*
Tony Reed *(Mgr-Construction Risk)*
David Kuo *(Mgr-Client)*
Alisa Lopez *(Assoc Mgr-Client)*
Tom Polenzani *(Dir-Employee Benefits)*
Scott Morsch *(Sr VP-Employee Benefits Practice)*
Greg Toumassian *(Mgr-Client Experience Comm)*

Subsidiary (Domestic):

Polenzani Benefits & Insurance Services, LLC   (2)
3452 E Foothill Blvd Ste 514, Pasadena, CA 91107
Tel.: (626) 792-4219
Web Site: http://www.polenzani.com
Emp.: 10
General Insurance & Employee Benefits Services
N.A.I.C.S.: 524298
Peggy L. Henderson *(Sr VP)*
Robert T. Hawkes *(VP)*
Traci Zycha *(Sr Acct Mgr)*
Kelly A. Beatty-Magee *(Acct Mgr)*
Tom G. Polenzani *(Pres)*
Natondra Knox *(Mgr-Acct)*

ESS Nextier Insurance Group, LLC   (1)
316 1st Ave Fl 3, Kittanning, PA 16201
Tel.: (724) 548-5178
Web Site: http://www.essnextier.com
Emp.: 35
Insurance Agency & Brokerage Services
N.A.I.C.S.: 524210
Donald J. Scalzott *(Partner)*
Holly M. Ardeno *(Acct Mgr)*
Stephanie L. Faykosh *(Acct Mgr)*
Nancy E. Greenawalt *(Acct Mgr)*
Linda G. Kindoll *(Acct Mgr)*
Meghann M. Peters *(Acct Mgr)*
George J. Polarinakis *(Acct Mgr)*
Jacqueline Romeo *(Acct Mgr)*
Wendy L. Ruffner *(Acct Mgr)*
Heather M. Rullo *(Acct Mgr)*
Mitzi A. Stull *(Acct Mgr)*

IMA Inc.   (1)
Centura Tower 14185 Dallas Pkwy Ste 800, Dallas, TX 75254
Tel.: (972) 581-4400
Insurance Brokerage Services
N.A.I.C.S.: 524210
Rick Dingman *(Dir-Enterprise Risk Mgmt-Denver)*
Jim Schaefer *(VP-Employee Benefits)*
Rene Velazquez *(Dir-Compensation Solutions)*
Jeff Stemper *(VP-Sls)*
Adam Sack *(Acct Exec-Energy Practice)*
Michael Campo *(Exec VP)*
Bob Reiter *(Pres)*
Maria Terry *(VP)*

IMA of Colorado Inc.   (1)
1550 17th St Ste 600, Denver, CO 80202
Tel.: (303) 534-4567
Web Site: http://www.imacorp.com
Sales Range: $50-74.9 Million
Insurance Brokerage
N.A.I.C.S.: 524210

IMA of Topeka Inc.   (1)
2820 SW Mission Woods Dr Ste 150, Topeka, KS 66614
Tel.: (785) 232-2202
Web Site: http://www.imacorp.com
Sales Range: $10-24.9 Million
Emp.: 31
Insurance Brokers

N.A.I.C.S.: 541618
Rhonda Keegan *(Mgr-Ops)*

IMA, Kansas Inc.   (1)
8200 E 32nd St N, Wichita, KS 67226
Tel.: (316) 267-9221
Web Site: http://www.imacorp.com
Sales Range: $50-74.9 Million
Emp.: 190
Commercial Insurance
N.A.I.C.S.: 524210

KPD Insurance, Inc.   (1)
1111 Gateway Loop, Springfield, OR 97477
Tel.: (541) 741-0550
Web Site: http://www.kpdinsurance.com
Insurance Agencies & Brokerages
N.A.I.C.S.: 524210
Jim Ginger *(Pres)*
Kelsea Meier *(Coord-Client Svcs)*
Ken Price *(COO & VP)*
LeighAnne Youngblood *(Acct Mgr-Property & Casualty)*
Tami Sanford *(Acct Mgr-Property & Casualty-Portland)*
Carlye Irwin *(Asst Dir-Property & Casualty-Portland)*
Paula Britton *(Acct Mgr-Employee Benefits-Portland)*

LTC Performance Strategies, Inc.   (1)
28001 Smyth Dr Ste 103, Valencia, CA 91355
Tel.: (661) 294-2929
Web Site: http://www.ltcperformance.com
Compensation & Performance Consulting Services
N.A.I.C.S.: 541612
Terry Lauter Comp *(Founder & Principal)*
Larry Comp *(Pres)*
Steve Smith *(Dir-Client Solutions)*

Parker, Smith & Feek, Inc.   (1)
2233 112th Ave NE, Bellevue, WA 98004
Tel.: (425) 709-3600
Web Site: http://www.psfinc.com
Sales Range: $10-24.9 Million
Emp.: 150
Insurance Agents & Brokers
N.A.I.C.S.: 524210
Greg Collins *(CEO & Principal)*
Sharon L. Hall *(VP)*
Guy P. Armfield *(VP)*
John L. Brassell *(VP & Acct Exec)*
Sally E. Borte *(VP & Acct Exec)*
Sarah J. Bactad *(VP & Acct Exec)*
Chad Kincaid *(CFO & VP)*
Jim Sorte *(VP)*
Linda Zook *(VP & Dir-Carrier Rels)*
Jennifer Stankovich *(VP & Dir-HR)*
Angela Samarel *(VP & Mgr-Acct)*
Cheryl Fischer *(VP & Mgr-Acct)*
Geoffrey Jolly *(VP & Mgr-Acct)*
Christin Hubble *(VP & Sr Mgr-Acct)*
Melissa Willhite *(VP-Mktg & Dir-Comm)*

Subsidiary (Domestic):

Professional Benefit Services, Inc.   (2)
771 Vly St Ste 301, Seattle, WA 98109-4300
Tel.: (336) 202-8621
Web Site:
    http://www.professionalbenefitservices.net
Insurance Agencies & Brokerages
N.A.I.C.S.: 524210

Riskpoint Insurance Advisors, LLC   (1)
700 NE Multnomah Ste 450, Portland, OR 97232
Tel.: (503) 327-8145
Web Site: http://www.riskpointins.com
Insurance Agencies & Brokerages
N.A.I.C.S.: 524210
Blake Schellenberg *(Pres & CEO)*
Tim Deggendorfer *(Mng Principal)*

Towerstone, Inc.   (1)
14185 Dallas Pkwy Ste 1000, Dallas, TX 75254
Tel.: (972) 725-2100
Web Site: http://www.towerstonecorp.com
Emp.: 50
Insurance Brokerage Services
N.A.I.C.S.: 524210
Steven Patrick Ashcraft *(Pres)*
Kim Hansard *(VP)*

IMA Financial Group, Inc.—(Continued)

Braden Brown *(VP & Dir-Special Casualty Practice)*
Jason Catron *(Asst VP)*
Candace Duke *(VP)*
Melissa Scott *(VP & Mgr-Ops)*
Chris Scott *(Asst VP)*
Chris Rohrer *(Asst VP)*
Jeffrey Hubbard *(Dir-Environmental Practice)*
George Schneller *(Exec VP)*
Joy Keller *(VP & Dir-Small Comml)*

Subsidiary (Domestic):

Professional Lines Underwriting Specialists, Inc.   **(2)**
716 Congress Ave Ste 100, Austin, TX 78701
Tel.: (512) 474-0404
Web Site: http://www.prolines.com
Sales Range: $1-9.9 Million
Emp.: 11
Insurance Related Activities
N.A.I.C.S.: 524298
Steve Sprowls *(Pres)*
Garrett Sprowls *(Gen Counsel)*
Judy Sprowls *(VP-Mgmt & HR)*

TrueNorth, Inc.   **(1)**
8200 E 32nd St N, Wichita, KS 67226
Tel.: (316) 266-6574
Web Site: http://www.truenorthcorp.com
Emp.: 10
Investment Advisory Services
N.A.I.C.S.: 523940
Margaret E. Hornbeck *(COO, Chief Compliance Officer & Mgr-Sls)*
Christine Mies *(Sr VP & Mgr-Ops)*
R. Kevin Taylor *(VP & Portfolio Mgr)*
Susan L. Pool *(Sr VP-Mktg & Mgr-Client Relationship)*
Brian D. Heinke *(Sr VP-Retirement Plan Specialist)*
Samantha K. Jenkins *(Sr VP-Retirement Plan Specialist)*
Heather M. Haines *(VP & Mgr-Retirement Plan)*
C. Weston Cooper *(Pres)*
Sean Spencer *(VP & Portfolio Mgr)*

Wallace Welch & Willingham, Inc.   **(1)**
300 1st Ave S 5th Fl, Saint Petersburg, FL 33701
Tel.: (727) 522-7777
Web Site: http://www.w3ins.com
Sales Range: $25-49.9 Million
Emp.: 115
Insurance & Benefits
N.A.I.C.S.: 524210
Connie Ferret *(Chief Admin Officer)*
Cheryl Gleaton *(Sr VP & Mgr-HR)*
Jeremy Miller *(Mgr-Comml Insurance)*
Scott B. Gramling *(CEO)*
Keith W. Gramling *(Pres)*
Jonathan Hammond *(COO)*

IMA GROUP MANAGEMENT COMPANY, LLC
660 White Plains Rd Ste 630, Tarrytown, NY 10591
Tel.: (914) 323-0300
Web Site:
    http://www.theimagroup.com
Year Founded: 1990
Technology-enabled Provider for Medical & Psychological Screening & Evaluation Services
N.A.I.C.S.: 524298
Dana Poff *(Exec VP-Clinical Res Div)*
Mark Weinberger *(Pres & CEO)*
Rob Snow *(Sr VP-Mktg & Sls)*
Sara Mulick *(Sr VP-Sls)*

Subsidiaries:

Albuquerque Neuroscience, Inc.   **(1)**
101 Hospital Loop NE Ste 209, Albuquerque, NM 87109-2128
Tel.: (505) 848-3773
Web Site: http://www.albneuro.com
Offices of Physicians (except Mental Health Specialists)
N.A.I.C.S.: 621111

Mireya Medina *(Office Mgr)*
Geraldine Dempsey *(Co-Founder)*

Clinical Trials of America, Inc.   **(1)**
1730 N Center St, Hickory, NC 28601
Tel.: (828) 322-3222
Web Site: http://www.ctamerica.net
Research & Development in Biotechnology
N.A.I.C.S.: 541714
Jeb Andrews *(Pres)*

Diagnostics Research Group, LLC   **(1)**
4410 Medical Dr Ste 360, San Antonio, TX 78229-3749
Tel.: (210) 692-7157
Web Site: http://www.dxrg.com
Clinical Research Services
N.A.I.C.S.: 621111
Charles P. Andrews *(Exec Dir)*

IMA WORLD HEALTH
500 Main St Bldg Old Main, New Windsor, MD 21776
Tel.: (410) 635-8720   **MD**
Web Site:
    http://www.imaworldhealth.org
Year Founded: 1960
Sales Range: $100-124.9 Million
Emp.: 40
Healtcare Services
N.A.I.C.S.: 622110
Richard L. Santos *(Pres & CEO)*
Laura A. Shahi *(Sr Dir-Bus Dev)*
Dragana Veskov *(VP-Intl Pub Health Programs)*
Sarah Newhall *(Co-Sec)*
Lisa Rothenberger *(Chm)*
William Clarke *(Treas)*
Cydney Bunn *(Sr Dir-HR)*
Susan Y. Duberstein *(Sr Dir-Technical Programs)*
Tracey Stevens *(CFO)*
Sonya Funna Evelyn *(Co-Sec)*

IMAG GROUP, INC.
144 Woodside Ct, Safety Harbor, FL 34695
Tel.: (727) 736-4724   **FL**
Year Founded: 2009
Aircraft Mfr
N.A.I.C.S.: 336411
Alvin Ayers *(CFO & Sec)*
Edwin B. Salmon *(Chm & CEO)*

IMAGE ADVERTISING, INC.
2828 Kraft Ave SE, Grand Rapids, MI 49512-2076
Tel.: (616) 957-1010   **DE**
Web Site: http://www.imagetours.com
Year Founded: 1985
Sales Range: $1-9.9 Million
Emp.: 30
Advetising Agency
N.A.I.C.S.: 541810
Daral Smalligan *(Dir-Mktg)*

IMAGE API INC.
2670 Exec Ctr Cir W, Tallahassee, FL 32301
Tel.: (850) 222-1400
Web Site: http://www.imageapi.com
Sales Range: $10-24.9 Million
Emp.: 125
Data Processing & Preparation
N.A.I.C.S.: 518210
Richard Griffith *(Founder)*
Kristine Davis *(CFO)*
Stefanie Voss *(Project Mgr)*
Patrick Menjor *(CIO)*
Becky Green *(Dir-HR)*
Jason Mosley *(Mgr-Tech Support)*
Greg Kracik *(VP-Sls)*

IMAGE APPAREL FOR BUSINESS INC.
1618 E Edinger Ave, Santa Ana, CA 92705

Tel.: (800) 445-2929   **CA**
Web Site: http://www.ia4biz.com
Industrial Uniform Supplier
N.A.I.C.S.: 812332

IMAGE BUSINESS INTERIORS
332 N Great Neck Rd, Virginia Beach, VA 23454-4062
Tel.: (757) 962-9810
Web Site: http://www.ibiva.com
Sales Range: $1-9.9 Million
Emp.: 14
Furniture Retailer
N.A.I.C.S.: 449110
Carrie Setliff *(Mng Partner)*
Deborah McDonald *(Partner-Sls)*
Bob Kraly *(Partner-Sls)*
Shawn Salony *(Project Mgr)*

IMAGE COMICS INC.
2701 NW Vaughn St Ste 780, Portland, OR 97210
Tel.: (510) 644-4980   **CA**
Web Site:
    http://www.imagecomics.com
Year Founded: 1993
Sales Range: $10-24.9 Million
Emp.: 10
Comic Books & Related Items Publisher & Mfr
N.A.I.C.S.: 513120
Eric Stephenson *(Publr)*

IMAGE DESIGN, INC.
2100 Riveredge Pkwy Ste 1200, Atlanta, GA 30328
Tel.: (770) 952-7171
Web Site:
    http://www.imagedesign.com
Sales Range: $1-9.9 Million
Emp.: 25
Interior Design & Facility Planning
N.A.I.C.S.: 541410
Linda Blair *(CEO)*

IMAGE FIRST PROFESSIONAL AP
42 Lukens Dr, New Castle, DE 19720
Tel.: (302) 656-2774
Web Site:
    http://www.myimagefirst.com
Sales Range: $10-24.9 Million
Emp.: 40
Men's & Boys' Clothing Mfr
N.A.I.C.S.: 424350
Brian Beere *(Owner)*

IMAGE HOLDINGS CORPORATION
27500 SW Parkway Ave, Wilsonville, OR 97070-9296
Tel.: (503) 685-8888
Holding Company
N.A.I.C.S.: 551112
John Lap Shun Hui *(Owner)*

Subsidiaries:

InFocus Corporation   **(1)**
13190 SW 68th Pkwy Ste 200, Portland, OR 97223-8368
Tel.: (503) 207-4700
Web Site: http://www.infocus.com
Sales Range: $250-299.9 Million
Emp.: 200
Networking Video Communications Products Mfr
N.A.I.C.S.: 334118
Bruce I. Berkoff *(VP-Product Line Mgmt)*
Jim Reddy *(VP-Sls-Presentation Solutions-US, Canada & Mexico)*
Mark Housley *(CEO)*
Dave Litwak *(Sr VP-Sls-Worldwide)*
Brady O. Bruce *(CMO)*
Glenn Jystad *(Dir-Product Mktg)*
Pippa Edelen *(Dir-PR & Social Media)*
Randy Arnold *(VP-Ops)*
Surendra Arora *(VP-Collaboration Products)*

Mike Driscoll *(VP-Sls-Collaborative Visualization Solutions-US, Canada & EMEA)*
Daniel LeCour *(VP-Sls-Collaborative Visualization Solutions-Latin America & APAC)*

IMAGE IV SYSTEMS INC.
512 S Varney St, Burbank, CA 91502
Tel.: (818) 841-0756
Web Site: http://www.imageiv.com
Year Founded: 1980
Rev.: $20,000,000
Emp.: 97
Supplier of Photocopy Machines
N.A.I.C.S.: 423420
Ronald Warren *(Pres)*
Armando Castellanos *(Mgr-Parts Dept)*
Jose Martinez *(Mgr-Svcs)*

IMAGE LOCATIONS INC.
2404 Wilshire Blvd Ste 4F, Los Angeles, CA 90057
Tel.: (310) 871-8004
Web Site:
    http://www.imagelocations.com
Year Founded: 2002
Sales Range: $1-9.9 Million
Emp.: 20
Luxury, Privately Owned Locations for Use in the Entertainment Industry
N.A.I.C.S.: 531120
Paul Kim *(Founder)*

IMAGE MICROSYSTEMS, INC.
9800 Metric Blvd Ste 300, Austin, TX 78757
Tel.: (512) 623-5621
Web Site:
    http://www.imagemicro.com
Year Founded: 1992
Sales Range: $10-24.9 Million
Emp.: 300
Logistics, Technology Restoration, Recycling & Asset Recovery Services
N.A.I.C.S.: 334111
Ken Findley *(VP-Bus Dev)*
Lennie Myers *(CMO)*
Alex Abadi *(CEO & Founder)*
Brian Buhro *(CIO)*

Subsidiaries:

Image Microsystems - Commerce   **(1)**
6301 Chalet Dr, Commerce, CA 90040
Tel.: (562) 776-3333
Web Site:
    http://www.imagemicrosystems.com
e-Waste Recycling & Asset Recovery Services
N.A.I.C.S.: 541620
Alex Abadi *(CEO)*

IMAGE ONE CORP.
13201 Capital, Oak Park, MI 48237
Tel.: (248) 414-9955
Web Site:
    http://www.imageoneway.com
Year Founded: 1991
Sales Range: $10-24.9 Million
Emp.: 57
Printer & Equipment Maintenance Services
N.A.I.C.S.: 333310
Robert Dube *(Co-Owner & Pres)*
Joel Pearlman *(Co-Owner)*
Marvin Simpson *(Mgr-Warehouse)*

IMAGE PROJECT, INC.
2451 River Tree Cir, Sanford, FL 32771
Tel.: (407) 380-1600   **FL**
Web Site:
    https://www.websitepulse.com
Year Founded: 1998
Sales Range: $1-9.9 Million
Emp.: 19
Website & Web Server Monitoring
N.A.I.C.S.: 541519

Iavor M. Marinoff *(CEO)*
George Tudor *(CTO)*
Andrew Gordon *(Chief Admin Officer)*
Mark Johnson *(Dir-Web Dev)*
Peter Porter *(Dir-Technical Support)*

IMAGE PROJECTIONS WEST, INC.

14135 E 42nd Ave Ste 40, Denver, CO 80239
Tel.: (303) 576-9477
Web Site: http://www.ipwusa.com
Year Founded: 1996
Sales Range: $10-24.9 Million
Emp.: 140
Advance Technology Imaging Supplies Mfr
N.A.I.C.S.: 333248
Kedar Morarka *(Co-Founder & Pres)*
Keith Arnold *(Co-Founder & Exec VP)*
Brian Gradey *(Controller)*

IMAGE SOLUTIONS APPAREL, INC.

10819 Hamilton Ave, Torrance, CA 90502
Tel.: (310) 464-8991
Web Site:
   http://www.eimagesolutions.com
Year Founded: 1998
Sales Range: $10-24.9 Million
Emp.: 30
Uniform Design & Sales for Restaurants & Grocery Store Chains
N.A.I.C.S.: 315250
Christopher Kelley *(Pres)*
Jenivee Vu *(Supvr-Acctg)*

IMAGE WATCHES, INC.

2099 S Atlantic Blvd Unit H, Monterey Park, CA 91754
Tel.: (323) 264-3686
Web Site:
   http://www.imagewatch.com
Year Founded: 1989
Sales Range: Less than $1 Million
Emp.: 12
Promotional Watches
N.A.I.C.S.: 423940
William Chien *(Pres)*

IMAGEFIRST HEALTHCARE LAUNDRY SPECIALISTS

900 E 8th Ave Ste 300, King of Prussia, PA 19406
Tel.: (484) 253-7200
Web Site: http://www.imagefirst.com
Sales Range: $10-24.9 Million
Emp.: 300
Medical-Oriented Laundry Services
N.A.I.C.S.: 812320
Joe Geraghty *(COO)*
David Burnette *(VP-Bus Dev)*
Jennifer Yanczak *(Mgr-Mktg)*
Jim Malandra *(CFO)*

IMAGEHAUS

12 S 6th St Ste 614, Minneapolis, MN 55402-1506
Tel.: (612) 377-8700
Web Site: http://www.imagehaus.net
Sales Range: Less than $1 Million
Emp.: 6
Full Service
N.A.I.C.S.: 541810
Jay Miller *(Pres & Dir-Creative)*
Colleen Meyer *(Designer)*

IMAGEMARK BUSINESS SERVICES

3145 Northwest Blvd, Gastonia, NC 28052
Tel.: (704) 478-8988
Web Site:
   http://www.imagemarkonline.com
Sales Range: $10-24.9 Million

Emp.: 45
Other Commercial Printing Services
N.A.I.C.S.: 323111
Walter Payne *(Pres)*
Karen Kaufman *(Exec VP)*

Subsidiaries:

Imperial Printing Products Co., Inc.   **(1)**
481 Vandell Way, Campbell, CA 95008
Tel.: (408) 378-1606
Web Site: http://www.imperialprint.com
Sales Range: $10-24.9 Million
Emp.: 60
Commercial Lithographic Printing Mfr
N.A.I.C.S.: 323111
Walter Payne *(Pres)*

IMAGEMARK, INC.

12 Godfrey Pl 3rd Fl, Wilton, CT 06897
Tel.: (203) 761-0025
Year Founded: 1996
Sales Range: $10-24.9 Million
Emp.: 7
Brand Development & Integration, Digital/Interactive
N.A.I.C.S.: 541810
Adam Pemberten *(Mng Dir)*
Sharon Peck *(Dir-Production)*
Troy Santi *(Sr Art Dir)*
Antonio Martins *(Dir-Art)*
Peter Baker *(Dir-Creative)*
Polly Akers *(Acct Dir)*

IMAGENET, LLC

6411 S 216th St, Kent, WA 98032
Web Site:
   http://www.imagenetllc.com
Sales Range: $10-24.9 Million
Image & Data Repository, Records Management & Platform Services
N.A.I.C.S.: 518210
Steve Strawn *(CEO)*

IMAGES USA

1320 Ellsworth Industrial Blvd, Atlanta, GA 30318
Tel.: (404) 892-2931   GA
Web Site: http://www.imagesusa.net
Year Founded: 1989
Rev.: $62,000,000
Emp.: 47
Advetising Agency
N.A.I.C.S.: 541810
Hank Ernest *(Dir-PR)*
Robert L. McNeil Jr. *(Pres & CEO)*

IMAGESTOCKHOUSE INC.

PO Box 711087, Salt Lake City, UT 84171
Tel.: (801) 550-8727
Web Site:
   http://www.imagestockhouse.com
Year Founded: 1999
Sales Range: $1-9.9 Million
Emp.: 5
Advetising Agency
N.A.I.C.S.: 541810
David A. Sherman *(Pres & CEO)*
Jerome Soller *(CTO & Exec VP)*

IMAGETEC L.P.

4509 Prime Pkwy, McHenry, IL 60050
Tel.: (815) 759-6000
Web Site: http://www.imagetec.com
Sales Range: $10-24.9 Million
Emp.: 130
Office Equipment
N.A.I.C.S.: 811210
Richard Cucco *(Gen Partner)*
James Cook *(Partner)*

IMAGETREND, INC.

20855 Kensington Blvd, Lakeville, MN 55044
Tel.: (952) 469-1589   MN
Web Site: http://www.imagetrend.com
Year Founded: 1998
Sales Range: $10-24.9 Million
Emp.: 100
Web-Based Data Collection Software
N.A.I.C.S.: 541511
Michael J. McBrady *(Pres & CEO)*
Joe Graw *(COO)*
Todd York *(Sr Acct Exec)*
Rosanna Roedder *(Dir-Mktg & Sls)*
Amanda Hiley *(Product Mgr)*
Toby Ritt *(Mgr-Sls)*
Dan Vanorny *(VP-EMS & Fire)*
Dave Zaiman *(Mgr-Bus Dev)*
Michael Wilcox *(Dir-Medical)*

IMAGINARY FORCES LLC

2254 S Sepulveda Blvd, Los Angeles, CA 90064
Tel.: (323) 957-6868
Web Site:
   http://www.imaginaryforces.com
Sales Range: $10-24.9 Million
Emp.: 100
Television Film Production
N.A.I.C.S.: 512110
Peter Frankford *(Co-Founder & Co-Mng Dir)*
Chip Houghton *(Co-Founder & Co-Mng Dir)*
Charles Khoury *(Dir-Creative)*

IMAGINATION PUBLISHING, LLC

600 W Fulton Ste 600, Chicago, IL 60661
Tel.: (312) 887-1000
Web Site:
   http://www.imaginepub.com
Sales Range: $10-24.9 Million
Emp.: 90
Periodical Publishers
N.A.I.C.S.: 513120
Andrew Schultz *(COO)*
Todd Cywinski *(Sr VP-Client Relationships)*
Andrea Scott *(VP)*
Kim Caviness *(Chief Content Officer & Exec VP)*
Marissa Wold Uhrina *(Dir-Production)*

IMAGINATION SPECIALTIES, INC.

230 Great Cir Rd Ste 248, Nashville, TN 37228
Tel.: (615) 255-5688
Web Site:
   http://www.imaginationbranding.com
Year Founded: 1989
Sales Range: $1-9.9 Million
Emp.: 30
Promotional Marketing Services
N.A.I.C.S.: 541613
Jan Nathanson *(Pres)*

IMAGINE ENTERTAINMENT

150 Camino Dr, Beverly Hills, CA 90212
Tel.: (310) 858-2000   CA
Web Site: http://www.imagine-
   entertainment.com
Year Founded: 1963
Sales Range: $50-74.9 Million
Emp.: 43
Motion Picture & Television Production
N.A.I.C.S.: 512110
Brian Grazer *(Co-Founder & Co-Chm)*
Ron Howard *(Co-Founder & Co-Chm)*
Erica Huggins *(Pres)*
Charlie Corwin *(CEO)*
Gary C. Parks *(CFO, Treas & Sec)*

IMAGINE NATION BOOKS, LTD.

282 Century Pl Ste 2000, Louisville, CO 80027
Tel.: (303) 516-3400
Web Site:
   http://www.booksarefun.com
Year Founded: 2004
Sales Range: $25-49.9 Million
Emp.: 100
Book Fairs & Display Marketing
N.A.I.C.S.: 424920
Earl Kaplan *(Founder & CEO)*

IMAGINE SOFTWARE INC.

233 Broadway FL 17, New York, NY 10279
Tel.: (212) 317-7600
Web Site: http://www.derivatives.com
Sales Range: $10-24.9 Million
Emp.: 70
Development Of Computer Software
N.A.I.C.S.: 541511
Cary Dorsei *(CFO)*
Neville Rosemin *(Controller)*
Brendan Quinn *(Dir-Sls)*
Debra Douglas *(Dir-Mktg)*

IMAGINE STAFFING TECHNOLOGY, INC.

892 Main St, Buffalo, NY 14202
Tel.: (716) 218-7819
Web Site:
   http://www.imaginestaffing.net
Year Founded: 2009
Sales Range: $10-24.9 Million
Recruitment Consulting Services
N.A.I.C.S.: 541612
Brian Manley *(Pres)*
Pete Smykowski *(Mgr-Recruiting)*

Subsidiaries:

Mary Kraft and Associates Inc.   **(1)**
1447 York Rd, Lutherville, MD 21093-1093
Tel.: (410) 296-0655
Web Site: http://www.marykraft.com
Employment Placement Agencies
N.A.I.C.S.: 561311
Lisa Benson *(Pres & CEO)*

IMAGINE SWIMMING, INC.

41 Union Sq W Ste 1528, New York, NY 10003
Tel.: (212) 253-9650
Web Site:
   http://www.imagineswimming.com
Sales Range: $1-9.9 Million
Emp.: 80
Swimming Training Center Operator
N.A.I.C.S.: 713940
Casey Barrett *(Co-Founder)*
Lars Merseburg *(Co-Founder)*
Emily Holstead *(Assoc Dir)*
Kaitlin Krause *(COO)*

IMAGINE THIS, INC.

1277 S Lyon St Ste 501, Santa Ana, CA 92705
Tel.: (714) 384-3838
Web Site:
   http://www.imaginethispromo.com
Year Founded: 1999
Sales Range: $25-49.9 Million
Emp.: 32
N.A.I.C.S.: 541810
Patrick Papaccio *(Pres)*

IMAGINEEASY SOLUTIONS, LLC

PO Box 4668 #38315, New York, NY 10163-4668
Tel.: (212) 675-6738

ImagineEasy Solutions, LLC—(Continued)

Web Site:
http://www.imagineeasy.com
Year Founded: 2001
Sales Range: $1-9.9 Million
Emp.: 19
Software Products Offering Research,
Citations & Customizable Products
for Schools & Individuals
N.A.I.C.S.: 513210
Neal Taparia *(Co-Founder & Co-CEO)*
Darshan Somashekar *(Co-Founder & Co-CEO)*
Maya Stevenson *(Dir-Sls)*

IMAGING ALLIANCE GROUP, LLC
2601 Minnehaha Ave, Minneapolis,
MN 55406
Tel.: (612) 588-9944
Web Site:
http://www.imagingpath.com
Year Founded: 1997
Sales Range: $10-24.9 Million
Emp.: 72
Office Equipment & Supplies
N.A.I.C.S.: 423420
Corey Tansom *(Pres & CEO)*

IMAGING ASSOCIATES INC.
11110 Westlake Dr, Charlotte, NC
28273
Tel.: (704) 522-8094
Web Site: http://www.imaginga.com
Sales Range: $25-49.9 Million
Emp.: 28
Medical & Hospital Equipment
N.A.I.C.S.: 423450
Michael Masterman *(Pres & CEO)*
Sandy Masterman *(Mgr-Website)*
Connie Duncan *(Controller)*

IMAGING BUSINESS MACHINES LLC
2750 Crestwood Blvd, Birmingham,
AL 35210-1227
Tel.: (205) 314-1800
Web Site: http://www.ibml.com
Sales Range: $10-24.9 Million
Emp.: 140
Paper Handling Machines
N.A.I.C.S.: 333310
Robert Sbrissa *(Exec VP-Sls)*
Duane Smith *(VP-Mfg)*
Tara Cola *(Mgr-Trng)*

IMAGING SUPPLIES & EQUIPMENT
9791 La Tierra Cir, Fountain Valley,
CA 92708-3529
Tel.: (310) 223-0500
Web Site: http://www.iseimc.com
Sales Range: $10-24.9 Million
Emp.: 60
Art Goods, Graphic Art Supplies
N.A.I.C.S.: 424990

IMANAGE LLC
540 W Madison St Ste 300, Chicago,
IL 60661
Tel.: (312) 667-7000
Web Site: http://www.imanage.com
Year Founded: 2015
Financial Services
N.A.I.C.S.: 523999
Neil Araujo *(CEO)*

Subsidiaries:

Elegrity, Inc.   (1)
160 Pine St Ste 720, San Francisco, CA
94111
Tel.: (855) 353-4462
Web Site: http://www.elegrity.com

Sales Range: $1-9.9 Million
Emp.: 15
Business Consulting Services
N.A.I.C.S.: 541690
Joy E. Spicer *(Pres & CEO)*
Kandace Donovan *(VP-Sls & Mktg)*
Timothy J. Conlon *(Sec)*
Jeffrey Wolk *(Treas)*

IMARC LLC
21 Water St, Amesbury, MA 01913
Tel.: (978) 462-8848
Web Site: http://www.imarc.net
Sales Range: $1-9.9 Million
Emp.: 22
Web & Online Application Design
Services
N.A.I.C.S.: 541511
Nick Grant *(CEO & Mng Partner)*
Judi Crofts *(Controller)*
Jeff Turcotte *(Dir-Engrg)*
Patrick McPhail *(CQO & Partner)*
Katie Desmond *(Chief Bus Dev Officer & Partner)*
Dave Tufts *(CTO & Mng Partner)*
Jared Laham *(Dir-Creative)*
Thomas Saraceno *(Dir-Experience)*
Kerri Cranwell *(Engr-Web)*
Victoria Andersen *(Office Mgr)*
Jessica Plance *(Office Mgr)*

IMARK INTEGRATED MARKETING SERVICES
6647 Green Dr, Trussville, AL 35173
Tel.: (205) 655-9000
Web Site:
http://www.imarkservices.com
Sales Range: Less than $1 Million
Emp.: 2
Brand Development, Electronic Media, Graphic Design, Industrial,
Internet/Web Design, Planning &
Consultation, Real Estate
N.A.I.C.S.: 541810
Joellen Seay *(Pres)*

IMB PARTNERS
7201 Wisconsin Ave, Bethesda, MD
20814
Tel.: (240) 507-1660
Web Site:
http://www.imbpartners.com
Privater Equity Firm
N.A.I.C.S.: 551112
Tarrus Richardson *(CEO)*
Farrah Holder *(Mng Dir)*
Derrick Weatherspoon *(Mng Dir)*

Subsidiaries:

Ashburn Consulting LLC   (1)
43848 Goshen Farm Ct, Leesburg, VA
20176
Tel.: (703) 652-9120
Web Site:
http://www.ashburnconsulting.com
Information Technology Consulting Services
N.A.I.C.S.: 541512
James Burris *(Pres)*
Sung Lewe *(Founder & CEO)*
Amante Bustamante *(CTO)*
Yong Kim *(VP)*

IMC CONSULTING
10529 Old Ct Rd, Woodstock, MD
21163
Tel.: (410) 505-4666
Web Site: http://www.consultimc.com
Sales Range: $1-9.9 Million
Emp.: 14
Business Management & Information
Technology Consulting Services
N.A.I.C.S.: 541611
Ellen G. Sweeney *(Mng Partner)*
John McCarvill *(CTO)*
Teresa Walton *(Sr Mgr)*
Michael P. Kelleher *(Partner)*

IMC HOLDING, LLC

3150 Lenox Park Ste 309, Memphis,
TN 38115
Tel.: (901) 312-2244
Web Site:
http://www.imccompanies.com
Trucking Service
N.A.I.C.S.: 484121
Mark H. George *(Chm)*
Joel Henry *(Pres)*
Katie George Hooser *(VP-Mktg & PR)*
Donna Lemm *(Exec VP)*

Subsidiaries:

Empire Truck Lines, Inc.   (1)
10043 Wallisville Rd, Houston, TX 77013-4615
Tel.: (713) 672-7403
Web Site: http://www.emtl.com
Sales Range: $25-49.9 Million
Emp.: 200
Provider of Trucking Services
N.A.I.C.S.: 484121
David Rex Acker *(Pres)*
Bill Acosta *(Pres-Empire Logistics)*
Dwight Jennings *(Dir-Safety)*
Judy Laird *(Dir-HR)*
Sharan Acker *(CEO)*
Craig Ward *(Gen Mgr-Sls)*

IMC HOLDINGS, INC.
12121 Jones Rd, Houston, TX 77070
Tel.: (858) 518-0447
Year Founded: 2005
Holding Company; Healthcare-Related Software Developer & Licensor
N.A.I.C.S.: 551112
Robert Zayas *(Chm, Pres, CEO, CFO & Sec)*

IMC INC.
140 Cuchrola Rd, Sterling, CO 80751
Tel.: (719) 561-1015
Rev.: $22,000,000
Emp.: 2
Mechanical Contractor
N.A.I.C.S.: 238220

IMCO CARBIDE TOOL INC.
28170 Cedar Park Blvd, Perrysburg,
OH 43551
Tel.: (419) 661-6313
Web Site: http://www.imcousa.com
Sales Range: $10-24.9 Million
Emp.: 75
Machine Tool Accessories
N.A.I.C.S.: 333515
Perry Osburn *(Pres & CEO)*
Tom Hammond *(Controller)*
Erich Wester *(Mgr-Quality)*
Jon Jacomet *(Mgr-IT)*
Tim Elfreich *(Mgr-Sls)*
Deanna Jackson-Roth *(Coord-HR)*

IMCORP
50 Utopia Rd, Manchester, CT
06042-2191
Tel.: (860) 427-7620
Web Site: http://www.imcorptech.com
Year Founded: 1995
Rev.: $5,300,000
Emp.: 24
Electrical Contractor
N.A.I.C.S.: 238210
Matthew Mashikian *(Founder)*
Ben Lanz *(Mgr-Applications Engrg)*
Bruce Broussard *(Pres & COO)*
Betty Tse *(Office Mgr)*

IMEDICAL EQUIPMENT & SERVICES LLC
2028 Virginia Beach Blvd Ste 105,
Virginia Beach, VA 23454
Tel.: (948) 888-5809
Web Site:
https://imedicalequipment.net
Emp.: 100

Health Care Srvices
N.A.I.C.S.: 621999
John Taylor *(CEO)*

Subsidiaries:

Bed Techs, Inc.   (1)
7080 Chartom Cir, Aurora, IN 47001
Tel.: (812) 926-0296
Web Site: http://bedtechs.com
Rev.: $4,700,000
Emp.: 35
Medical, Dental & Hospital Equipment &
Supplies Merchant Whslr
N.A.I.C.S.: 423450
Timothy Brandes *(Treas)*
Michael Wilson *(Pres)*

IMEDX, INC.
3424 Peachtree Rd NE Ste 2200,
Atlanta, GA 30326
Tel.: (404) 418-0096   DE
Web Site: http://www.imedx.com
Year Founded: 2002
Medical Transcription Software &
Services
N.A.I.C.S.: 513210
Christopher Foley *(Chm & CEO)*

Subsidiaries:

Amphion Medical Solutions, LLC   (1)
8301 Excelsior Dr Ste 402, Madison, WI
53717
Tel.: (608) 227-0560
Web Site: http://www.amphionmedical.com
Sales Range: $1-9.9 Million
Emp.: 600
Medical Documentation & Coding Services
N.A.I.C.S.: 561410
Cindy Barker *(Pres-Transcription Div)*
Karen Clay *(VP-Ops)*
Minnette Terlep *(Chief Compliance Officer & VP-Bus Dev)*
Peter Zopf *(CIO)*
Subbu Ravi *(COO)*
Betty Schulte *(Pres-Coding, Compliance & Quality)*
Emmy Johnson *(Exec VP)*
Jen Trost *(Dir-Technical Svcs)*
Lisa Boyer *(Mgr-Physician Svcs)*
Martha Taylor *(Mgr-Coding)*
Michael King *(Dir-Client Implementation)*
Monica Mayer *(Mgr-Coding)*
Rachel Jorgensen *(Mgr-Coding Support)*
Robin Romig *(Mgr-Coding)*
Shane Fetters *(CTO-Dev Div)*

IMEG CORP.
623 26th Ave, Rock Island, IL 61201
Tel.: (309) 788-0673
Web Site: http://www.imegcorp.com
Year Founded: 2015
Holding Company
N.A.I.C.S.: 551112
Paul VanDuyne *(Pres & CEO)*
Paul Parry *(VP-Engrg)*
Jeff Pratt *(VP-MEP & Market Sectors)*
Pat Eikenberry *(VP-Civil)*
Kelly Trilk *(CIO)*

IMETHODS, LLC
10748 Deerwood Park Blvd Ste 150,
Jacksonville, FL 32256
Tel.: (904) 306-2261
Web Site: http://www.imethods.com
Sales Range: $1-9.9 Million
Emp.: 25
IT Consulting & Staffing Services
N.A.I.C.S.: 541690
Chad Perce *(Co-Founder & CEO)*
Clint Drawdy *(Co-Founder, Pres & COO)*
Melissa Brannon *(VP-Strategic Partnerships)*
Dean Medley *(VP-HR & People Dev)*
Kim Bryant *(Dir-HR)*
Sulaiman H. Sulaiman *(CIO & Chief Consulting Officer)*
Tripp Drawdy *(VP-Client Results)*
Bryan Hassel *(VP-Fin & Strategic Initiatives)*

IMEX INTERNATIONAL CORP.
245 E Liberty St Ste 200, Reno, NV
89501   NV
Year Founded: 2009
Waste Conversion & Disposal Services
N.A.I.C.S.: 562219
Dennis Dalley *(Pres, CEO, CFO, Treas & Sec)*

IMEX INTERNATIONAL INC.
1519 Woodyard Rd, Elberton, GA
30635
Tel.: (706) 283-4417
Web Site:
   http://www.imexindustries.com
Sales Range: $10-24.9 Million
Emp.: 100
Diamond Related Services
N.A.I.C.S.: 423840
Masood Besharat *(Owner)*

IMH FINANCIAL CORPORATION
7001 N Scottsdale Rd Ste 2050,
Scottsdale, AZ 85253
Tel.: (480) 840-8400   DE
Web Site: http://www.imhfc.com
Rev.: $13,075,000
Assets: $139,608,000
Liabilities: $139,975,000
Net Worth: ($367,000)
Earnings: ($34,486,000)
Emp.: 149
Fiscal Year-end: 12/31/19
Mortgage Loans & Other Real Estate
Financial Services
N.A.I.C.S.: 522310
Denise Garcia *(Asst VP-Shareholder Svcs)*
Samuel J. Montes *(CFO)*
Jonathan T. Brohard *(Gen Counsel, Sec & Exec VP)*
Greg Hanss *(Exec VP-Hospitality)*
Chadwick S. Parson *(Chm & CEO)*
Joe Walsh *(VP-Dev)*
Paul Evans *(Sr VP-Fin & Controller)*
Cori Oles *(VP-Revenue Mgmt)*
Maggie Craft *(VP-Admin)*
Tina Littleman *(Sr VP-HR)*
Riky Serrano *(Mgr-IT Support)*
Will Moeller *(Mgr-Acctg)*
Annette Puhr *(Accountant)*
Martha Steinberg *(Accountant-Staff)*

Subsidiaries:

Carinos Properties, LLC   (1)
3519 E Shea Blvd Ste138, Phoenix, AZ
85028
Tel.: (602) 374-3372
Web Site: http://www.carinoproperties.com
Real Estate Services
N.A.I.C.S.: 531390

IMH Holdings, LLC   (1)
9725 Tidal Ct, Huntersville, NC 28078
Tel.: (828) 367-2789
Real Estate Financial Services
N.A.I.C.S.: 522310

LAuberge Newco, LLC   (1)
254 N State Route 89a, Sedona, AZ 86336
Tel.: (928) 282-2405
Real Estate Financial Services
N.A.I.C.S.: 522310

IMIN PARTNERS, L.P.
301 Commerce St Ste 3025, Fort
Worth, TX 76102
Tel.: (817) 336-8744   DE
Web Site:
   http://www.iminpartners.com
Sales Range: $25-49.9 Million
Emp.: 100
Privater Equity Firm
N.A.I.C.S.: 523999

Tom Chambers *(Co-Founder & Partner)*
Rankin Hobbs *(Co-Founder & Partner)*

Subsidiaries:

KaMin LLC   (1)
822 Huber Rd, Macon, GA 31217
Tel.: (478) 745-4751
Web Site: http://www.kaminllc.com
Sales Range: $150-199.9 Million
Hydrous & Calcined Kaolin Mining & Products Mfr
N.A.I.C.S.: 212323
Doug Carter *(VP-Tech & Bus Dev)*
C. Rankin Hobbs *(CEO)*
Gianluca Fedelini *(VP-Supply Chain)*
Mark Gillespie *(VP-Comml)*
Jason Maxwell *(VP-Ops)*
Roddy Wells *(CFO & VP)*

Subsidiary (Non-US):

CADAM S.A.   (2)
Vila Munguba s/n Jardim Limoeiro Monte
Dourado, Almeirim, 68240-000, Para, Brazil
Tel.: (55) 93 3736 6002
Kaolin Mining & Processing Services
N.A.I.C.S.: 212323
Rosalia Vieira *(Mgr)*

IMLACH MOVERS INC.
28349 Fort St, Trenton, MI 48183
Tel.: (734) 675-4500
Web Site:
   http://www.imlachgroup.com
Sales Range: $10-24.9 Million
Emp.: 200
Household Goods Transport
N.A.I.C.S.: 484210
Daniel W. Imlach *(Pres)*
Ken Imlach *(VP-Sls)*
Dave Bjerk *(Gen Mgr)*
Lorraine Holland *(Controller)*

IMLAY CITY FORD
1788 Van Dyke, Imlay City, MI 48444
Tel.: (810) 724-5900
Web Site:
   http://www.imlaycityford.com
Sales Range: $10-24.9 Million
Emp.: 51
Car Whslr
N.A.I.C.S.: 441110
Dustin Thammavongsa *(Mgr-Internet Net Sls)*

IMLERS POULTRY
187 Rte 764, Duncansville, PA 16635
Tel.: (814) 943-5563
Web Site:
   http://www.imlerspoultry.com
Sales Range: $50-74.9 Million
Emp.: 135
Poultry Processing Services
N.A.I.C.S.: 424440
Keith McQuillen *(Dir-Mktg)*
Missy Lovrich *(Controller)*
Nancy Boucher *(Dir-HR)*
Fred N. Imler Jr. *(Vice Chm)*

IMMEDIA, LLC
7661 E Gray Rd, Scottsdale, AZ
85260
Tel.: (480) 483-3399   AZ
Web Site:
   http://www.immediaavs.com
Year Founded: 2004
Sales Range: $1-9.9 Million
Emp.: 25
Audio Visual Services
N.A.I.C.S.: 334310
Jeff Emmons *(Owner & Pres)*
Matt Blair *(Gen Mgr)*
Jeff Pinter *(Controller)*

IMMEDIATE CARE, INC.
6311 DeBarr Rd Ste L, Anchorage,
AK 99504

Tel.: (907) 336-3365
Web Site:
   http://www.immediatecareak.com
Year Founded: 1999
Sales Range: $10-24.9 Million
Emp.: 570
In-Home Health Care Services
N.A.I.C.S.: 621610
Brian Richardson *(Pres)*
Candice Stewart *(Program Dir)*

IMMEDIENT CORPORATION
88 Centennial Ave, Piscataway, NJ
08854
Tel.: (732) 980-1800
Web Site: http://www.ins.com
Rev.: $56,024,000
Emp.: 120
Computer Related Consulting Services
N.A.I.C.S.: 541512

Subsidiaries:

Immedient Corporation   (1)
79001 Union Ave, Denver, CO 80237
Tel.: (303) 953-3400
Sales Range: $10-24.9 Million
Emp.: 30
Computer Integrated Systems Design
N.A.I.C.S.: 541512

IMMEDION LLC
78 Global Dr Ste 100, Greenville, SC
29607
Tel.: (864) 908-3000
Web Site: http://www.immedion.com
Year Founded: 2007
Sales Range: $1-9.9 Million
Emp.: 45
IT Consulting Services
N.A.I.C.S.: 541519
Frank Mobley *(Co-Founder & CEO)*
Rob Moser *(Co-Founder & COO)*
Ravi Sastry *(VP-Sls & Mktg)*
Steve Newman *(Gen Mgr-Greenville & Asheville)*
Kevin Phillips *(Acct Mgr)*

IMMIGRANT AND REFUGEE COMMUNITY ORGANIZATION
10301 NE Glisan St, Portland, OR
97220
Tel.: (503) 234-1541   OR
Web Site: http://www.irco.org
Year Founded: 1976
Sales Range: $25-49.9 Million
Emp.: 1,166
Refugee Welfare Services
N.A.I.C.S.: 624230
Trinh Tran *(VP)*
Ronault L. S. Catalani *(Sec)*
Claudia Burnett *(Treas)*
Lee Po Cha *(Exec Dir)*

IMMIGRANT LEGAL RESOURCE CENTER
1663 Mission St Ste 602, San Francisco, CA 94103
Tel.: (415) 255-9499   CA
Web Site: http://www.ilrc.org
Year Founded: 1979
Immigrant Legal Services
N.A.I.C.S.: 541199
Philip Garcia *(Office Mgr)*
Mark Silverman *(Atty)*
Jonathan Huang *(Mgr-IT)*
Ginny Wright *(Dir-Fin & Ops)*
Byron Spicer *(Coord-Fin)*
Linda Mogannam *(Mgr-Mktg)*
Melissa Rodgers *(Dir-Programs)*
Sharon Hing *(Dir-Special Projects-New Americans Campaign)*
Eric Cohen *(Exec Dir)*
Sara Feldman *(Dir-Ready California Project)*
Timothy Sheehan *(Coord-Publ & Program)*

Lisa Spiegel *(Chm)*
Bill Ong Hing *(Founder & Gen Counsel)*
Kemi Bello *(Comm Mgr)*
Ann Block *(Atty-Contract)*
Kathy Brady *(Atty)*
Allison Davenport *(Atty)*
Angie Junck *(Atty)*
Alison Kamhi *(Atty)*
Sally Kinoshita *(Deputy Dir)*
Sarah Letson *(Mgr-Best Practices-New Americans Campaign)*
Jose Magana Salgado *(Atty-Mng Policy)*
Deirdre O'Shea *(Mgr-Foundations Rels)*
Erin Quinn *(Atty)*
Gisel Ruiz *(Atty)*
Forest Thomas *(Controller)*
Araceli Amezquita *(Coord-Ready CA Program)*

IMMOBILIARE GLOBAL INVESTMENTS, INC.
13575 58th St N Ste 140, Clearwater,
FL 33760
Tel.: (602) 885-9792   FL
Year Founded: 2010
Sales Range: Less than $1 Million
Real Estate Investment
N.A.I.C.S.: 523999
Wayne Middleton *(Pres & CEO)*
Charles Irizarry *(Chm & VP)*
Bradford Margetts *(CFO)*

Subsidiaries:

Thomas Investment Holdings,
LLC   (1)
1163 Laird Ave, Salt Lake City, UT
84105   (100%)
Tel.: (801) 463-0366
Real Estate Investment
N.A.I.C.S.: 531390
Wayne Middleton *(CEO)*

IMMTECH PHARMACEUTICALS, INC.
1 N End Ave, New York, NY 10282
Tel.: (212) 791-2911   DE
Web Site:
   http://www.immtechpharma.com
Year Founded: 1984
Sales Range: $1-9.9 Million
Emp.: 11
Research & Development of Biopharmaceutical Drug Discoveries
N.A.I.C.S.: 325414
Gary C. Parks *(CFO, Treas & Sec)*
Cecilia Chan *(Vice Chm)*
Eric L. Sorkin *(Chm & CEO)*
Norman A. Abood *(Sr VP-Discovery Programs)*

IMMUNOCLIN CORPORATION
1800 Wyoming Ave NW 3rd Fl,
Washington, DC 20009
Tel.: (202) 450-3583
Year Founded: 2011
Health Care Srvices
N.A.I.C.S.: 621610

IMOCO, INC.
5130 Hendersonville Rd, Fletcher,
NC 28732-8615
Tel.: (828) 684-2000   NC
Web Site: http://www.imocoinc.net
Year Founded: 1964
Sales Range: $150-199.9 Million
Emp.: 110
Mechanical & Industrial Contractor
N.A.I.C.S.: 238220
Geoff Bagwell *(Gen Mgr)*

IMODERATE LLC
720 S Colorado Blvd Ste 500 N, Denver, CO 80246

iModerate LLC—(Continued)

Tel.: (303) 333-7880   NV
Web Site: http://www.imoderate.com
Year Founded: 2004
Sales Range: $1-9.9 Million
Emp.: 31
Marketing Research & Public Opinion Polling
N.A.I.C.S.: 541910
Joel Benenson (Co-Founder)
Scott Rossow (Gen Counsel)
Jen Mason Drolet (VP-Client & Moderating Svcs)
Adam Rossow (VP-Mktg)
Gary Zucker (VP)
Carl Rossow (Co-Founder)
Mike Israel (Sr VP-Sls)
Steve Lopez (VP-Bus Dev)
Michael Steinberg (Sr VP-Client Dev)
Steve Dodge (VP-Client Dev)

IMONEY TOOLS LLC
3451 N Triumph Blvd Garden Level, Lehi, UT 84043
Web Site: http://www.tranont.com
Year Founded: 2013
Sales Range: $10-24.9 Million
Dietary Supplement Distr
N.A.I.C.S.: 424210
Lorne Berry (Co-Founder & CEO)
Russ Losee (Co-Founder & COO)
Scott Bland (Pres)

IMORTGAGE SERVICES, LLC
2570 Boyce Plaza Rd Boyce Plz III Ste 210, Pittsburgh, PA 15241
Tel.: (412) 220-7330   PA
Web Site:
   http://www.imortgageservices.com
Year Founded: 2000
Sales Range: $25-49.9 Million
Emp.: 95
Outsourced Mortgage Services
N.A.I.C.S.: 522310
Brian Uffelman (Co-Owner & CEO)
Shawn McCall (Co-Owner & Pres)
Karen Bertini (VP & Dir-IT)
Sue Gambirasi (CFO)
Chris Porto (VP-Title Ops)

IMPACT ADVISORS LLC
400 E Diehl Rd Suite 190, Naperville, IL 60563
Web Site: http://www.impact-advisors.com
Year Founded: 2007
Sales Range: $25-49.9 Million
Emp.: 100
Consulting Services to the Health Care Industry
N.A.I.C.S.: 541618
Andrew Smith (Co-Founder & Pres)
Peter Smith (Founder, CEO & Mng Partner)
Todd Hollowell (COO)
Paula Elliott (VP)
Lydon Neumann (VP)
William Faust (VP)
Jenny McCaskey (VP)
Ted Reynolds (VP)
Michael Nutter (VP)
Matt Duncan (VP)
Kent Gray (VP)
Keith MacDonald (VP)
Joe Miccio (VP)
Scott Pillittere (VP)
John Stanley (VP)
Rob Faix (VP)
Mike Garzone (VP)
Susan Stewart (VP)
Amy Reid (VP-Recruiting)
Kim Reitter (VP)
Bruce Lemon (VP)
John Curin (VP)

Skip Lemon (VP)
John Lanari (VP)
Kristi Lanciotti (VP)

IMPACT BUSINESS GROUP INC.
3225 N Evergreen Dr, Grand Rapids, MI 49525
Tel.: (616) 254-8586
Web Site: http://www.impactbusiness group.com
Year Founded: 2004
Sales Range: $25-49.9 Million
Staffing Services
N.A.I.C.S.: 561311
Michael D. Trewhella (Co-Owner & Pres)
Matthew P. Peal (Co-Owner & VP)

IMPACT COAL SUBTRUST
333 W Vine St Ste 500, Lexington, KY 40507
Tel.: (859) 226-1700   KY
Year Founded: 1986
Sales Range: $25-49.9 Million
Health & Welfare Services
N.A.I.C.S.: 525120
David A. Gooch (Chm)

IMPACT CONFECTIONS, INC.
10822 W Toller Dr Ste 350, Littleton, CO 80127
Tel.: (303) 626-2222
Web Site:
   http://www.impactconfections.com
Year Founded: 1981
Sales Range: $25-49.9 Million
Emp.: 350
Candy & Confectionery Product Mfr
N.A.I.C.S.: 311340
Andy Telatnik (Dir-Mktg)
Jim Hanigan (VP-Sls)
Christine Fox (Dir-HR)
Barbara Klubertanz (Mgr-Quality Assurance-Melster Candies)

IMPACT GROUP INTERNATIONAL, LLC
12977 N Outer 40 Dr Ste 300, Saint Louis, MO 63141
Tel.: (314) 453-9002   MO
Web Site:
   http://www.impactgrouphr.com
Year Founded: 1988
Sales Range: $10-24.9 Million
Emp.: 100
Human Resources Consulting & Career Management Services
N.A.I.C.S.: 541612
Laura Herring (Founder & Chm)
Lauren Herring (CEO)
Max Barnett (CFO)
Ed Chaffin (Pres)
Marcia Mueller (VP-Global Leadership Dev)
Barrie Gilmour (Sr Dir-Global Sls)
Eric Breuer (Sr VP-Sls)

IMPACT INDUSTRIAL SUPPLIES INC.
7020 Anderson Rd, Tampa, FL 33634
Tel.: (813) 885-2343
Web Site:
   http://www.impactindustrialsup plies.com
Sales Range: $1-9.9 Million
Emp.: 19
Industrial Supplies Distr
N.A.I.C.S.: 423840
John Diaz (VP)
Rena Lewis (Mgr-Pur)

IMPACT LOGISTICS, INC.
3150 New Brunswick Rd, Memphis, TN 38133

Tel.: (901) 377-5298
Web Site:
   http://www.loadingservice.com
Year Founded: 1986
Sales Range: $10-24.9 Million
Emp.: 13
Freight Hauling Services
N.A.I.C.S.: 488510
David S. Hamilton (Founder & CEO)
Wayne D. Vandersteeg (CFO & Exec VP)
Angelina Dominguez (Dir-HR)
April Sinclair (Office Mgr)
Danny Soto (VP-Ops)
David Fultz (VP-Acctg)
Keny Hatley (Pres)

Subsidiaries:

Impact Human Resources   (1)
7200 Goodlett Farms Pkwy Ste 101, Cordova, TN 38016
Tel.: (901) 377-5298
Outsourced HR Management & Services
N.A.I.C.S.: 541611

Impact Staffing Solutions   (1)
7980 N Brother Blvd, Memphis, TN 38133
Tel.: (901) 377-5298
Staffing Services
N.A.I.C.S.: 561311

Impact Technology Solutions   (1)
7980 N Brother Blvd, Memphis, TN 38133
Tel.: (901) 377-5298
Web Site: http://www.loadingservice.com
IT & Systems Support Services
N.A.I.C.S.: 541513
Shawn Troxel (Pres & CIO)

IMPACT MAILING OF MINNESOTA, INC.
4600 Lyndale Ave N, Minneapolis, MN 55412
Tel.: (612) 521-6245   MN
Web Site:
   http://www.impactconnects.com
Year Founded: 1983
Direct Mail Ad Services, Data Processing & Fulfillment Services
N.A.I.C.S.: 541860
Bjorn Anderson (CFO & Exec VP)
Pete Studer (CEO)
Erik Anderson (Pres)
Jon Downing (CTO & Exec VP)
Rob Nordwall (Exec VP-Sls & Customer Experience)
Scott Williams (Gen Mgr-Ops)
Sy Vang (Mgr-Fulfillment Operations)
Mike Miller (Mgr-IT)
Jake Delk (Mgr-Mailing Operations)

Subsidiaries:

Infinity Direct, Inc.   (1)
10275 Wayzata Blvd Ste 200, Minnetonka, MN 55305
Tel.: (763) 559-1111
Web Site: http://www.infinitydirect.com
Direct Marketing Agency
N.A.I.C.S.: 541810
Bjorn Anderson (CFO)
David Greenblat (Pres)
Jake Bruhnding (CEO)
Katie Schmitz (VP-Integrated Services)
Jaime Strom (VP-Client Strategies)
Jim Engholm (VP-Data & Insights)
Derick Lapointe (COO)
Kathy Mays (VP-Client Svcs)

IMPACT MAKERS, INC.
1707 Summit Ave Suite 201, Richmond, VA 23230
Tel.: (804) 332-6383
Web Site:
   http://www.impactmakers.com
Year Founded: 2006
Sales Range: $1-9.9 Million
Emp.: 39
Management, Technology & Health Care IT Consultancy to Government & Multiple Industries

N.A.I.C.S.: 541618
Michael I. Pirron (CEO & Sec)
Carl Miller (Pres)
Rodney Willett (VP-Bus Strategy)
Ross Decker (Head-Client Solutions)

IMPACT MANAGEMENT SERVICES LLC
29792 Telegraph Rd Ste 150, Southfield, MI 48034
Tel.: (248) 262-5200
Web Site:
   http://www.theimpactanswer.com
Sales Range: $10-24.9 Million
Emp.: 350
Staff Management & Workforce Consulting Services
N.A.I.C.S.: 541612
Pete Davis (Pres & CEO)
Dennis Weist (Controller)
Oneil Franso (Dir-HR)
Joe Pomaranski (VP)

IMPACT NETWORKING, LLC.
953 Northpoint Blvd, Waukegan, IL 60085
Tel.: (847) 785-2250
Web Site:
   http://www.impactnetworking.com
Year Founded: 1999
Rev.: $25,000,000
Emp.: 155
Stationery & Office Supplies Merchant Whslr
N.A.I.C.S.: 424120
Nick Cosmano (COO)
Cory Carnes (Mgr-Chicago)
Dan Meyer (Pres & Partner)
Douglas Gamache (CIO)
Frank Cucco (CEO)
Terry Weilandt (VP-Warehouse & Ops)
Thomas Pieters (VP-Sls)
Tom Ferguson (Branch Mgr)
Bryan Beckner (CFO)
Don Duvall (VP-Bus Dev)
Frank DeGeorge (CTO)
Michael Borchew (CMO)
Patrick Layton (VP-Managed IT Svcs)
Scott Fujii (VP-Design & Mktg)

IMPACT TECHNOLOGIES, LLC
300 Canal View Blvd, Rochester, NY 14623
Tel.: (585) 424-1990
Web Site: http://www.impact-tek.com
Year Founded: 1999
Sales Range: $10-24.9 Million
Emp.: 125
Engineeering Services
N.A.I.C.S.: 541330
Joshua Koelle (Engr-Mechanical)

IMPACT UNLIMITED INC.
250 Ridge Rd, Dayton, NJ 08810
Tel.: (732) 274-2000
Web Site: http://www.impact-xm.com
Year Founded: 1973
Sales Range: $10-24.9 Million
Emp.: 150
Events, Exhibits & Meetings Solutions
N.A.I.C.S.: 541890
Ed Salge (Exec Dir-Ops-IT)
Kevin Padden (Exec Dir-Meeting & Comm Strategies)
Nat Rosen (Mgr-Creative Comm)
Krupali Desai (Dir-Mktg & Comm)

Subsidiaries:

Impact Unlimited Ltda.   (1)
Rua Albina Barbosa 210 U 14b, 01530 020, Sao Paulo, Brazil
Tel.: (55) 11 3586 7897
Web Site: http://www.impact-xm.com
Events, Exhibits & Meetings Solutions
N.A.I.C.S.: 541890
Eduardo Ishie (Mgr-Design Project)

IMPAXX, INC.
550 Burning Tree Rd, Fullerton, CA 92833-1400
Tel.: (714) 441-0700   DE
Web Site: http://www.label-aire.com
Sales Range: $1-4.9 Billion
Emp.: 1,200
Holding Company; Packaging & Labeling Products Mfr & Marketer
N.A.I.C.S.: 551112
Kenneth Phillips (CEO)

Subsidiaries:

Label-Aire, Inc.   (1)
550 Burning Tree Rd, Fullerton, CA 92833-1400
Tel.: (714) 449-5155
Web Site: http://www.label-aire.com
Sales Range: $10-24.9 Million
Emp.: 60
High-Speed Label Application Equipment Mfr
N.A.I.C.S.: 333993
Phil Wignall (Mgr-Technical Svcs)
Linda Grove (Mgr-HR)

Affiliate (Non-US):

Label-Aire A/S   (2)
Sjaellandsvej 27 A, Hobro, 9500, Denmark   (100%)
Tel.: (45) 96570063
Web Site: http://www.label-aire.com
Sales & Mfr of Labeling Equipment & Accessories
N.A.I.C.S.: 561910
George Allen (Mng Dir)
Michael Flanigan (Dir-European Sls)

IMPELSYS INC.
55 Broad St 16 Fl, New York, NY 10004
Tel.: (212) 239-4138
Web Site: http://www.impelsys.com
Rev.: $13,200,000
Emp.: 210
Engineering Services
N.A.I.C.S.: 541330
Sameer Shariff (Founder & CEO)
Deepak Kaushik (CFO)
Shyam Shetty (Exec VP-eLearning & Tech Svcs)

IMPERIAL BROWN INC.
2271 NE 194th, Portland, OR 97230
Tel.: (800) 238-4093
Web Site: http://imperialbrown.com
Walk-in Coolers & Freezers Mfr
N.A.I.C.S.: 333415
Justin Sandall (Pres)

Subsidiaries:

Artic Temp, Inc.   (1)
2115 W Main St, Prague, OK 74864
Tel.: (800) 238-4093
Web Site: http://www.artictemp.com
Air-Conditioning & Warm Air Heating Equipment & Commercial & Industrial Refrigeration Equipment Mfr
N.A.I.C.S.: 333415
Justin Sandall (CEO)

IMPERIAL CAPITAL GROUP, INC.
2000 Avenue of the Stars 9th Fl S Tower, Los Angeles, CA 90067
Tel.: (310) 246-3700   DE
Web Site:
http://www.imperialcapital.com
Sales Range: $75-99.9 Million
Emp.: 155
Investment Banking Services
N.A.I.C.S.: 523150
Mark C. Martis (COO)
Todd Wiench (Chief Compliance Officer & Gen Counsel)
Gayle Grant (Sr VP & Asst Gen Counsel)
Gregg Poillucci (Sr VP)
Jeff Zolkin (Mng Dir)

Don Ritucci (Mng Dir)
Todd Fasanella (Mng Dir)
Keith Grimaldi (Mng Dir)
Tom Corcoran (Pres)
Richard Genovese (VP & Controller)
Brian Robertson (Mng Dir)
Scott Marchakitus (Mng Dir)
Jonathan Glionna (Mng Dir)
Tom Champion (Mng Dir-Stamford)
James P. Kenney (Mng Dir-Convertible Credit Sls Grp-New York)
Kevin Cadden (Mng Dir-Convertible Credit Sls Grp-New York)
Kevin Andrews (Mng Dir/Head-Energy Investment Banking-Houston)
Daniel DeSnyder (Mng Dir-Investment Banking Energy-Houston)
Lenny Bianco (Sr VP-Investment Banking Energy-Houston)
Chris Lang (VP-Investment Banking Energy-Houston)
Jason Wangler (Mng Dir-Institutional Res Grp-Houston)
Irene Haas (Mng Dir-Houston)
Christopher Shepard (Exec VP & Head-Investment Banking)

IMPERIAL COMMODITIES CORP.
17 Battery Pl Ste 636, New York, NY 10004-1101
Tel.: (212) 837-9400   CA
Commodities Whslr
N.A.I.C.S.: 424990
John M. Morley (Pres & CEO)

IMPERIAL CRANE SERVICES INC.
7500 Imperial Dr 9735 S Industrial Dr, Bridgeview, IL 60455
Tel.: (708) 598-2300
Web Site:
http://www.imperialcrane.com
Sales Range: $10-24.9 Million
Emp.: 100
Cranes & Aerial Lift Equipment Rental & Leasing Services
N.A.I.C.S.: 532412
B. John Bohne (Owner & Pres)
Bill Tierney (VP)
Larry Eckardt (Mgr-Svc)
Laurie Wagner (Office Mgr)

IMPERIAL DISTRIBUTORS, INC.
150 Blackstone River Rd, Worcester, MA 01607-1455
Tel.: (508) 756-5156   MA
Web Site:
http://www.imperialdistributors.com
Year Founded: 1939
Sales Range: $50-74.9 Million
Emp.: 650
Health, Beauth Aids & Sundries
N.A.I.C.S.: 424210
Michael D. Sleeper (CEO)
Tony Germano (VP-Strategy & Bus Dev)
Joe Kirby (VP-Retailer Sls & Category Mgmt)

IMPERIAL HARDWARE COMPANY INC.
355 Olive St, El Centro, CA 92243
Tel.: (760) 353-1120   CA
Web Site:
http://www.imperialstores.com
Year Founded: 1908
Sales Range: $25-49.9 Million
Emp.: 300
Furniture Sales
N.A.I.C.S.: 449110
Phillip Heald (Pres)

IMPERIAL INVESTMENT COMPANY INC.
4800 Wisconsin Ave NW, Washington, DC 20016
Tel.: (202) 537-3000
Web Site:
http://www.martenscars.com
Rev.: $28,000,000
Emp.: 90
Owner & Operator of Car Dealerships
N.A.I.C.S.: 441110
Harry Martens (Pres)

IMPERIAL IRRIGATION SUPPLY, INC.
350 Mission Rd Escondido, Anaheim, CA 92807
Tel.: (760) 738-8301
Web Site:
http://www.imperialsprinkler.com
Sales Range: $10-24.9 Million
Emp.: 31
Sprinkler Systems
N.A.I.C.S.: 423850
John Thomason (Gen Mgr)

IMPERIAL PLASTICS, INC.
21320 Hamburg Ave, Lakeville, MN 55044
Tel.: (952) 469-4951   DE
Web Site:
http://www.imperialplastics.com
Year Founded: 1968
Sales Range: $50-74.9 Million
Emp.: 320
Plastic Component Mfr
N.A.I.C.S.: 326199
Bob Petersen (Acct Mgr-IT)
Tess Howard (Coord-Sls & Engrg)
Pauline Durand (Coord-Quality)
Bob Johnson (Engr-Maintenance)
Dave Sage (Mgr-Acctg)

Subsidiaries:

Engineered Polymers Corporation   (1)
1020 E Maple Ave, Mora, MN 55051-1217
Tel.: (320) 679-3232
Web Site: http://www.epcmolding.com
Sales Range: $25-49.9 Million
Emp.: 250
Plastic Injection Moldings & Structural Foam Plastics
N.A.I.C.S.: 326199
Ken Fackler (Pres)
Jeff Fackler (CEO)

IMPERIAL POOLS, INC.
33 Wade Rd, Latham, NY 12110-2604
Tel.: (518) 786-1200   NY
Web Site:
http://www.imperialpools.com
Year Founded: 1959
Sales Range: $75-99.9 Million
Emp.: 150
Swimming Pools Mfr
N.A.I.C.S.: 339920
Bill Churchman (CEO)

IMPERIAL REALTY COMPANY INC.
4747 W Peterson Ave Ste 200, Chicago, IL 60646-5769
Tel.: (773) 736-4100   IL
Web Site:
http://www.imperialrealtyco.com
Year Founded: 1955
Sales Range: $10-24.9 Million
Emp.: 50
Nonresidential Building Operators
N.A.I.C.S.: 531120
Larry Klairmont (CEO)
Alfred Klairmont (Pres)
Bob Klairmont (VP)
Steve Freeman (CFO)
Louis Pretekin (Gen Counsel)

Ben Lockwood (VP & Dir-Property Mgmt)
Bill Norman (Dir-HR)
Susan Paras (Mgr-Acctg)
Jeff Berkowitz (Mgr-Property)
Nadia Crudele (Mgr-Property)
Richard Fernandez (Mgr-Property)
Jamar Johnson (Mgr-Property)
Olga Olszewski (Mgr-Property)
Annie Rarey (Mgr-Property)
Michael Silverstein (Mgr-Property)
Sheri Dressler (Sr Mgr-Property)

IMPERIAL TOY CORPORATION
16641 Roscoe Pl, North Hills, CA 91343
Tel.: (818) 536-6500
Web Site: http://www.imperialtoy.com
Year Founded: 1969
Sales Range: $10-24.9 Million
Emp.: 50
Mfr of Games, Toys & Childrens Vehicles
N.A.I.C.S.: 339930
Peter Tiger (Pres)
Lisa Castanon (VP-Ops)
Mari Fox (Product Mgr)
Leone Zion (Mgr-Pur)

IMPERIAL TRADING CO, INC.
4101 Oleander Dr, Wilmington, NC 28403
Tel.: (910) 392-2605
Web Site: http://www.rugsnc.com
Rev.: $1,700,000
Emp.: 100
Floor Covering Stores
N.A.I.C.S.: 449121
Fred Nasseri (VP)

Subsidiaries:

City Wholesale Inc.   (1)
300 Industrial Dr, Birmingham, AL 35211
Tel.: (205) 945-7120
Web Site: https://www.citywholesale.com
Sales Range: $75-99.9 Million
Emp.: 100
Tobacco & Tobacco Products
N.A.I.C.S.: 424940
Sandy Harris (Mgr-Mgmt Info Sys)

IMPERIAL VALLEY FOODS INC.
1961 Buchanan Ave, Calexico, CA 92231-4306
Tel.: (760) 203-1896
Sales Range: $10-24.9 Million
Emp.: 300
Frozen Fruit, Juice & Vegetable Production Services
N.A.I.C.S.: 311411
Gustavo Cabellero (CEO)
Edna Cabellero (Treas)
Fernando Cabellero (VP)

IMPERIAL WOODWORKING COMPANY
310 N Woodwork Ln, Palatine, IL 60067
Tel.: (847) 358-6920
Web Site:
http://www.imperialwoodworking.com
Rev.: $13,200,000
Emp.: 120
Store Fixtures, Wood
N.A.I.C.S.: 337212
Paul Garvin (VP)
Matt Riemenschneider (Mgr-Engrg)
Richard Stiers (Project Mgr)
Frank Huschitt Sr. (Chm)

IMPERIAL WOODWORKS, INC.
PO Box 7835, Waco, TX 76714-7835
Tel.: (866) 249-1037
Web Site: http://www.pews.com
Year Founded: 1960
Church Furniture Mfr

Imperial Woodworks, Inc.—(Continued)

N.A.I.C.S.: 337127
Steve Smith (Owner)
Kimberly Laningham (VP-Logistics)
Kevin Smith (VP)

IMPERIAL ZINC CORP.
1031 E 103rd St, Chicago, IL 60628-3007
Tel.: (773) 264-5900   IL
Web Site: http://www.imperialgp.com
Year Founded: 1994
Secondary Nonferrous Metals
N.A.I.C.S.: 331492
Eric Crabtree (Pres)

IMPERIAL, INC.
2020 Mingo Rd, Tulsa, OK 74116
Tel.: (918) 437-1300
Web Site: http://www.imperialco.com
Sales Range: $50-74.9 Million
Emp.: 500
Vending, Catering, Corporate Dining & Coffee Service
N.A.I.C.S.: 445132
Paul M. Tims (Founder)
Lance Whorton (Pres)
Jerry Kahl (Gen Mgr-Northwest Arkansas)
John Slaughter (Gen Mgr-Tulsa Metro & District Mgr-Ops-Southeast Oklahoma & Texas)
Steve Hunt (Gen Mgr-Southeast Oklahoma & Southwest Arkansas)

IMPERIAL-DELTAH, INC.
795 Waterman Ave, East Providence, RI 02914-1713
Tel.: (401) 434-2597   DE
Web Site:
http://www.imperialpearl.com
Year Founded: 1899
Sales Range: $75-99.9 Million
Emp.: 100
Gold Filled, 14K Gold, Pearl & Sterling Silver Jewelry Mfr
N.A.I.C.S.: 339910
Banice C. Bazar (Owner)
Kathy Grenier (Mgr-Mktg)

IMPERIUM PARTNERS GROUP, LLC
400 Madison Ave, New York, NY 10017
Tel.: (212) 433-1360
Web Site:
http://www.michaelsoncapital.com
Sales Range: $25-49.9 Million
Emp.: 5
Alternative Investment Products & Services
N.A.I.C.S.: 523999
John C. Michaelson (CEO)

Subsidiaries:

ESS Technology, Inc.   (1)
237 S Hillview Dr, Milpitas, CA 95035
Tel.: (408) 643-8800
Web Site: http://www.esstech.com
Sales Range: $50-74.9 Million
Analog & Audio Device Mfr & Distr
N.A.I.C.S.: 334413
Robert L. Blair (Pres & CEO)
John Marsh (CFO)
Robert Wong (VP-Sls & Mktg-Worldwide)
Dustin Forman (Mng Dir & Sr VP-Engrg)
Martin Mallinson (Sr VP)

Subsidiary (Non-US):

ESS Electronics Technology (Shenzhen) Co., Ltd.   (2)
Room 1508 40th Fl World Plaza Building Shennan Road Futain District, Shenzhen, 518 031, China
Tel.: (86) 75525878318
Web Site: http://www.esstech.com

Sales Range: $25-49.9 Million
Emp.: 30
Semiconductor Retailer
N.A.I.C.S.: 423690
Ricky Loeung (Gen Mgr)

ESS Technology International (Korea) Ltd.   (2)
2 Fl Samsung Life Insurance Bldg, Garak-Dong 8-2 Songpa-Ku, Seoul, 138 160, Korea (South)
Tel.: (82) 2 448 6900
Web Site: http://www.esstech.com
Sales Range: $25-49.9 Million
Semiconductor Retailer
N.A.I.C.S.: 423690

IMPERO ELECTRONICS, INC.
105 Prairie Lk Rd, East Dundee, IL 60118
Tel.: (224) 836-3900   IL
Year Founded: 2005
Sales Range: $10-24.9 Million
Holding Company; Cameras & Computer Enhancement Products Distr
N.A.I.C.S.: 551112
Anthony Graffia Sr. (CEO)

Subsidiaries:

Argus Camera Company, LLC   (1)
105 Prairie Lk Rd Unit D, East Dundee, IL 60118
Tel.: (224) 836-3900
Web Site: http://www.arguscamera.com
Digital Camera Distr
N.A.I.C.S.: 423410

VisionTek Products, LLC   (1)
105 Prairie Lk Rd, East Dundee, IL 60118
Tel.: (224) 836-3900
Web Site: http://www.visiontek.com
Computer Enhancement Products Distr
N.A.I.C.S.: 423430
Michael Innes (COO & Exec VP)

IMPEX SERVICES INC.
221 Main St Ste 500, San Francisco, CA 94105
Tel.: (415) 227-0896
Sales Range: $10-24.9 Million
Emp.: 10
Freight Forwarding Services
N.A.I.C.S.: 488510
Yas Furuya (Pres)
Joanne Ikeda (Pres)

IMPEX TECH LAB INC.
6287 Smith Ave, Newark, CA 94560
Tel.: (510) 509-5115
Web Site:
http://www.impextechlab.com
Software Development & IT Consulting Firm
N.A.I.C.S.: 541690
Nilam Khanijow (Pres)

Subsidiaries:

Keshav Manglam Impex Pvt Ltd.   (1)
NPX Urbtech Suite No 25-26 Plot C-1 4th Floor Sector 153, Noida, 201301, India
Tel.: (91) 120 6522207
Web Site: http://kmilab.com
Software Development & IT Consulting Services
N.A.I.C.S.: 541690

IMPLANT & GENERAL DENTISTRY OF NORTHERN COLORADO
2975 Ginnala Dr Ste 100, Loveland, CO 80538
Tel.: (970) 663-1000
Web Site: http://www.implantdds.com
Year Founded: 1985
Sales Range: $1-9.9 Million
Emp.: 20
General & Implant Dentistry
N.A.I.C.S.: 621210
Ted E. Mioduski (Founder)

IMPORT MOTORS INC.
1601 Iowa St, Bellingham, WA 98229
Tel.: (360) 255-5999
Web Site:
http://www.kingvolvobellingham.com
Rev.: $20,500,000
Emp.: 15
Car Dealership Owner & Operator
N.A.I.C.S.: 441110
Frank King (Owner)

IMPORT PRODUCTS CO. INC.
55 Scotland Blvd, Bridgewater, MA 02324
Tel.: (508) 279-2770
Web Site:
http://www.ipcglobalsolutions.com
Sales Range: $10-24.9 Million
Emp.: 50
Sales of Automotive Supplies & Parts
N.A.I.C.S.: 423120
Michael Bowden (Pres)

IMPORT WAREHOUSE INC.
11029 Harry Hines Blvd Bldg A, Dallas, TX 75229
Tel.: (214) 389-7064
Web Site:
http://www.importwarehouseinc.com
Year Founded: 1982
Sales Range: $100-124.9 Million
Emp.: 52
Grocery Stores Products Whslr
N.A.I.C.S.: 424410
Ravi Bhatia (Pres)

IMPORT-IO CORPORATION
1999 S Bascon Ave, Campbell, CA 95008
Tel.: (408) 879-6253
Web Site: http://www.import.io
Custom Computer Programming Services
N.A.I.C.S.: 541511
Gary Read (Chm & CEO)
Matthew Painter (Co-Founder & CTO)
Carol Manchester (CFO)
Sunil Ramesh (VP-Product & Engrg)
Greg Leneveu (Chief Revenue Officer)
Matt Wilkinson (VP-Technical Svcs)
Gina Cerami (VP-Mktg)
Andrew Fogg (Co-Founder)
Kelly Scott (Dir-Software Engrg)

Subsidiaries:

Connotate, Inc.   (1)
317 George St Ste 320, New Brunswick, NJ 08901
Tel.: (732) 296-8844
Web Site: http://www.connotate.com
Sales Range: $10-24.9 Million
Emp.: 50
Social Media & Web Data Monitoring Software Developer
N.A.I.C.S.: 513210
Vincent Sgro (Founder)
Christian Giarretta (VP-Sls Engrg)
Frank Hunt (CFO)
Richard J. Kennelly (CEO)
Cheryl Galvin (Exec VP-Engrg, Ops & Tech Svcs)

IMPORTED CARS OF MARYLAND
9400 Baltimore Blvd, College Park, MD 20740
Tel.: (301) 441-2900
Web Site:
http://www.collegeparkhonda.com
Rev.: $53,527,116
Emp.: 65
Automobiles, New & Used
N.A.I.C.S.: 441110
Chris Scripture (Mgr-Svc)

IMPRES TECHNOLOGY SOLUTIONS, INC.
10330 Pioneer Blvd Ste 280, Santa Fe Springs, CA 90670
Tel.: (562) 298-4030
Web Site:
http://www.imprestechnology.com
Year Founded: 2001
Sales Range: $25-49.9 Million
Emp.: 17
Information Technology Consulting Services
N.A.I.C.S.: 541512
John Podolak (VP-Defense & Intelligence)

IMPRESS PUBLIC RELATIONS, INC.
777 W Roosevelt St Bldg 5, Phoenix, AZ 85007
Tel.: (602) 443-0030
Public Relations
N.A.I.C.S.: 541820
Martijn Pierik (Mng Dir)
Dave Richardson (Mng Dir)

Subsidiaries:

IMPRESS Public Relations, Inc.   (1)
632 Commercial St Ste 200, San Francisco, CA 94111
Tel.: (415) 992-7255
Public Relations
N.A.I.C.S.: 541820
Dave Richardson (Mng Partner)
Martijn Pierik (Mng Partner)
Amy Smith (Dir-Team-Semiconductor Lab)
Kelly Smith Bramlett (Dir-Creative Svc)
Francoise Von Trapp (Dir-Content Laboratory)

IMPRESS Public Relations, Inc.   (1)
50 Fairfield Dr, North Kingstown, RI 02852
Tel.: (401) 369-9266
Public Relations
N.A.I.C.S.: 541820
Amy Smith (Sr Dir-Accts)

IMPRESSIONS IN PRINT, INC.
753 Voyager Ct, Virginia Beach, VA 23452
Tel.: (757) 497-0671
Web Site:
http://www.impressionsinprint.com
Year Founded: 1994
Sales Range: $1-9.9 Million
Emp.: 15
Marketing Services
N.A.I.C.S.: 424310
Deborah Higgins (Pres)

IMPRESSIONS MARKETING GROUP INC
7951 Angleton Ct, Lorton, VA 22079
Tel.: (703) 550-2211
Web Site:
http://www.impressionsmkt.com
Rev.: $25,000,000
Emp.: 180
Store Fixtures; Wood
N.A.I.C.S.: 337212
Dennis Andrews (Dir-Design)
Duane Swogger (Mgr-Pur)
Jean Meade (Mgr-HR)

IMPRESSIONS MEDIA SERVICES, INC.
1204B E Washington St, Greenville, SC 29601
Tel.: (864) 233-8338
Web Site:
http://www.impressionsmedia.com
Year Founded: 1988
Sales Range: $1-9.9 Million
Emp.: 7
Media Buying Services
N.A.I.C.S.: 541810
Joe Thaler (CEO)
Suzy Roberts (Dir-Media)

Kate Eriksson *(VP-Bus Dev)*
Jeannie Grizzle *(Media Buyer)*
Kate Nichols *(Pres)*
Nina Gossett *(Acct Mgr)*
Walt Lafferty *(Gen Mgr & Dir-Bus Dev)*

IMPRESSIONS PRINTING & COPYING SERVICES

2241 W I-44 Service Rd, Oklahoma City, OK 73112
Tel.: (405) 524-2800
Web Site:
http://www.impressionsprinting.com
Year Founded: 1996
Rev.: $3,900,000
Emp.: 38
Quick Printing & Photocopying Services
N.A.I.C.S.: 323111
Jason McWilliams *(VP)*
Jeff Summerford *(Chm & CEO)*
John Braaten *(Pres)*

IMPRESSIONS-A.B.A. INDUSTRIES, INC.

393 Jericho Tpk St 200, Mineola, NY 11501
Tel.: (516) 739-3210
Web Site:
http://www.impressionsaba.com
Year Founded: 1971
Emp.: 30
Advertising Agencies
N.A.I.C.S.: 541810
Anthony M. Schettino *(Founder & Pres)*
LouAnn Pugliese *(Acct Supvr)*
Barbara Kerbel *(VP-Creative)*
Jeff Thurau *(Sr Dir-Art & Dir-IT)*

IMPRIMIS GROUP

4835 LBJ Fwy Ste 1000, Dallas, TX 75244
Tel.: (972) 419-1700
Web Site: http://www.imprimis.com
Year Founded: 1982
Sales Range: $10-24.9 Million
Emp.: 80
Temporary Help Service
N.A.I.C.S.: 561320
Valerie Freeman *(Founder & CEO)*
Kevin Beattie *(CFO)*
Sonia Bous *(VP)*

IMPRINT ENTERPRISES INC.

555 N Commons Dr, Aurora, IL 60504-4112
Tel.: (630) 505-1700
Web Site: http://www.imprint-e.com
Sales Range: $10-24.9 Million
Emp.: 40
Bar Code (Magnetic Ink) Printers
N.A.I.C.S.: 334118

IMPROVED CONSTRUCTION METHODS INC.

1040 N Redmond Rd, Jacksonville, AR 72076
Tel.: (501) 982-7715
Web Site:
http://www.improvedconstruction
methods.com
Year Founded: 1970
Sales Range: $10-24.9 Million
Emp.: 50
Mfr & Sales of General Construction Machinery & Equipment
N.A.I.C.S.: 423810
Bruce McFadden *(Pres)*

IMPROVEIT

40 W 1st Ave, Columbus, OH 43201
Tel.: (614) 291-5400
Web Site:
http://www.improveitusa.com

Year Founded: 1989
Sales Range: $10-24.9 Million
Emp.: 145
Building Construction & Remodeling Services
N.A.I.C.S.: 236118
Seth Cammeyer *(Pres & CEO)*
Jeffry Collignon *(COO)*
Brian Leader *(VP)*

IMPULSE NOVELTIES INC.

8 Mindy Ct, Locust Valley, NY 11560-1017
Tel.: (516) 609-2636
Sales Range: $10-24.9 Million
Emp.: 25
Novelties, Durable
N.A.I.C.S.: 423990
Noorullah Virani *(Pres)*

IMQUEST BIOSCIENCES INC.

7340 Executive Way Ste R, Frederick, MD 21704
Tel.: (301) 696-0274
Web Site: http://www.imquestbio.com
Year Founded: 2004
Sales Range: $1-9.9 Million
Emp.: 15
Pharmaceutical Researcher, Developer & Mfr
N.A.I.C.S.: 325412
Tracy Hartman *(Dir-Anti-Infective Svcs)*
Karen Buckheit *(Dir-Topical Microbicide & Microbiology Svcs)*
Anthony Ham *(Dir-Formulation Science)*
Christian Furlan-Freguia *(Dir-Immunology & Vaccines)*
Daniel R. Caffoe *(Co-Founder & Chm)*
Robert W. Buckheit Jr. *(Founder & Pres)*

IMRE, LLC

210 W Pennsylvania Ave, 7th Fl., Baltimore, MD 21204
Tel.: (410) 821-8220   MD
Web Site: http://www.imre.com
Year Founded: 1993
Public Relations Agency
N.A.I.C.S.: 541820
Dave Imre *(Chm)*
Mark Eber *(Board Member)*
Stephanie Friess *(Exec VP-Earned)*
Hui Tang *(Head-Mktg Analytics)*
Kristine Wobschall *(VP-Cient Experience)*
Sonal Adhav *(Sr Dir-Medical)*
Anna Kotis *(Pres)*

Subsidiaries:

JMPR, Inc.   (1)
5850 Canoga Ave Ste 300, Woodland Hills, CA 91367
Tel.: (818) 992-4353
Public Relations Agency
N.A.I.C.S.: 541820

IMRICOR MEDICAL SYSTEMS, INC.

400 Gateway Blvd, Burnsville, MN 55337
Tel.: (952) 818-8400
Web Site: https://www.imricor.com
Year Founded: 2006
Sales Range: Less than $1 Million
Emp.: 15
Electromedical & Electrotherapeutic Apparatus Mfr
N.A.I.C.S.: 334510
Steven Wedan *(Chm & CEO)*
Dan Sunnarborg *(VP-Engrg)*
Gregg Stenzel *(VP-Ops)*
Lori Milbrandt *(CFO)*
Tom Lloyd *(VP-Res)*

IMS CONSULTING & EXPERT SERVICES

4400 Bayou Blvd Ste 6, Pensacola, FL 32503
Tel.: (877) 838-8464
Web Site:
http://www.expertservices.com
Year Founded: 1992
Law firm
N.A.I.C.S.: 922130
James Crane *(CEO)*

Subsidiaries:

Litigation Insights, Inc.   (1)
9393 W 110th St St #400, Overland Park, KS 66210
Tel.: (913) 339-9885
Web Site: http://www.litigationinsights.com
Armored Car Services
N.A.I.C.S.: 561613
Merrie Jo Pitera *(CEO)*

IMS INTERNET MEDIA SERVICES, INC.

1441 Brickell Ave Ste 1530, Miami, FL 33131
Tel.: (305) 379-8222
Web Site:
https://www.imscorporate.com
Year Founded: 2005
Sales Range: $50-74.9 Million
Emp.: 129
Media Marketing Consulting Services
N.A.I.C.S.: 541613
Gaston Taratuta *(Founder & CEO)*
Ignacio Vidaguren *(COO & Co-Partner)*
Bruno Libonatti *(Partner & VP-Office Media)*
Patricia Molina *(Mng Dir-Mexico & Co-Partner)*
Jaime Guerra *(Mng Dir-Social)*
Daniel Alonso *(VP-Bus Dev)*
Juan Manuel Ruiz *(Sr VP-Fin & Admin)*
Manuela Mantilla *(Dir-Grp Client)*
Christopher Neary *(Mng Dir-IMS Chile)*
Mariana Krym *(VP-IMS Mobile)*
Enor Paiano *(Sr VP & Mgr-Brasil)*
Julian Coulter *(VP-Intl Ops)*
Tomas Heguy *(VP-Product & Tech)*

IMS RECYCLING SERVICE INC.

2697 Main St, San Diego, CA 92113-3612
Tel.: (619) 231-2521   CA
Web Site:
http://www.imsrecyclingservices.com
Year Founded: 1954
Sales Range: $25-49.9 Million
Emp.: 200
Scrap & Waste Materials
N.A.I.C.S.: 423930
Robert M. Davis *(Pres)*
Teddy Davis *(VP)*
Debra Odle *(Gen Mgr)*

Subsidiaries:

C-P Manufacturing, Inc.   (1)
6795 Calle De Linea, San Diego, CA 92154
Tel.: (619) 477-3175
Web Site:
http://www.cpglobalcompanies.com
Rev.: $9,431,876
Emp.: 65
Mfr of Special Industry Machinery
N.A.I.C.S.: 333998
Terry Schneider *(CEO)*

Recycling Services International   (1)
2697 Main St, San Diego, CA 00092
Tel.: (619) 231-2521
Rev.: $500,000
Emp.: 5
Provider of Scrap & Waste Materials
N.A.I.C.S.: 423930

IMS TECHNOLOGY SERVICES

3055 McCann Farm Dr, Garnet Valley, PA 19060
Tel.: (610) 361-1870
Web Site:
http://www.imstechnologyser-
vices.com
Year Founded: 1994
Sales Range: $10-24.9 Million
Emp.: 55
Audiovisual Systems Integration, Event Staging, Project Management & AV Managed Services
N.A.I.C.S.: 541618
John H. Renninger *(Principal)*
Jill Savoy Renninger *(Pres)*
Michael B. Shinn *(Mgr-Ops & Sys Integration)*
Keith Moss *(Mgr-Sys Engrg)*
Jason Cataldi *(VP-Sls, Mktg & Event Staging)*
Kip Myers *(Mgr-Ops-Event Staging)*
Patrick Britton *(VP-Sls & Mktg & Sys Integration)*
Anthony P. Grassia Jr. *(Dir-Production Mgmt-Event Staging)*

IMT INSURANCE COMPANY

4445 Corporate Dr, West Des Moines, IA 50266
Tel.: (515) 327-2777   IA
Web Site: http://www.theimtins.com
Year Founded: 1884
Sales Range: $100-124.9 Million
Emp.: 260
Property & Casualty Insurance Services
N.A.I.C.S.: 524126
Dennis G. Patterson *(Sr VP-Info Sys)*
Richard C. Keith *(Chm)*
Sean Kennedy *(Pres)*

IMTC, INC.

2028 Houston River Rd, Westlake, LA 70669-3642
Tel.: (337) 436-3788   LA
Year Founded: 1982
Sales Range: $1-9.9 Million
Emp.: 700
Heavy Construction
N.A.I.C.S.: 237990
Leo Thibodeaux *(Pres & VP)*
Ron Redkey *(VP)*
Dubby Fontenot *(Mgr-Construction)*

IMTRA CORPORATION

30 Samuel Barnet Blvd, New Bedford, MA 02745
Tel.: (508) 995-7000   MA
Web Site: http://www.imtra.com
Year Founded: 1962
Sales Range: $10-24.9 Million
Emp.: 40
Marine Crafts & Supplies Distr
N.A.I.C.S.: 423860
Eric Braitmayer *(Pres & CEO)*
Christopher Barnes *(Mgr-Sls-Southeast)*
Jeff Vancura *(CFO)*
Alex Larsen *(VP-Comml Sls)*
Peter Kilgore *(Pres-Maximum Weather & VP-Mktg)*
Chip Farnham *(VP-Sls)*
William H. Farnham Jr. *(Chm)*

IMULUS, LLC

3005 Sterling Cir Ste 201, Boulder, CO 80301
Tel.: (303) 247-0550
Web Site: http://www.imulus.com
Sales Range: $1-9.9 Million
Emp.: 16
Digital Advertising Services
N.A.I.C.S.: 541810

IMVU INC.

IMVU Inc.—(Continued)
164 Hamilton Ave, Palo Alto, CA
94301
Tel.: (650) 321-8334
Web Site: http://www.imvu.com
Year Founded: 2004
Sales Range: $25-49.9 Million
Emp.: 90
Social Network
N.A.I.C.S.: 517810
Matt Danzig (Founder)
Pamela Kelly (Sr VP-Mktg)
Kevin Henshaw (Sr VP-Bus Dev)
Peter Reeves (VP-Engrg)
Mike Smith (VP-People & Talent)
Jon Watte (VP-Tech)
Daren Tsui (CEO)
Lauren Bigelow (Chief Product Officer)
Victor Zaud (Sr VP-Mktg)
John Burris (Chief Dev Officer)
Lomit Patel (VP-Growth)

IMWAVE, INC.
1201 Tottenham Ct, Reston, VA
20194
Tel.: (703) 430-0422
Web Site: http://www.imwave.com
Year Founded: 2001
Sales Range: $1-9.9 Million
Emp.: 8
Search Engine Marketing Agency
N.A.I.C.S.: 541613
Adam Viener (Founder & Chm)
Tony Pantano (CEO)

IMWOO TECHNOLOGIES, LLC
4101 Redwood Ave, Los Angeles, CA
90066
Tel.: (310) 392-3555
Web Site: http://www.zefr.com
Year Founded: 2008
Sales Range: $75-99.9 Million
Advertising & Marketing Services
N.A.I.C.S.: 541810
Rich Raddon (Co-Founder & Co-CEO)
Zach James (Co-Founder & Co-CEO)
Oded Noy (CTO)
Jen Robinson (Exec VP-Product & Tech)
Toby Byrne (Pres)

IN BLOOM, INC.
627 Valley Brook Rd, Scottdale, GA
30079
Tel.: (404) 373-0023 DE
Web Site:
http://www.inbloomlandscaping.com
Year Founded: 2012
Sales Range: $1-9.9 Million
Emp.: 36
Landscape Maintenance Services
N.A.I.C.S.: 541320
Gene Wilhoit (Co-Chm)
Michele Cahill (Sec)
Bob Wise (Co-Chm)
Iwan Streichenberger (CEO)
Giani Casachi (Dir-Partnerships)
Adam Gaber (VP-Comm)
Jatinder Pannu (Sr VP-Pro Svcs)
Sharon Bates (Chief Product Officer)
Amelia Fox (COO)
Jason Hoekstra (Dir-Developer Engagement)
Garrett Suhm (CTO)

IN DYNE INC.
11800 Sunrise Valley Dr Ste 250,
Reston, VA 20191
Tel.: (703) 903-6900 MD
Web Site: http://www.indyneinc.com
Year Founded: 1984
Sales Range: $75-99.9 Million
Emp.: 1,500

Provider of Computer Integrated Systems Design Services
N.A.I.C.S.: 561210
C. Donald Bishop (Pres)
Candace Solomon (Mgr-Bus Dev)
Margaret James (Dir-HR)

IN MOCEAN GROUP LLC
463 7th Ave 21st Fl, New York, NY
10018
Tel.: (212) 944-0317
Web Site: http://www.inmocean.net
Sales Range: $10-24.9 Million
Emp.: 55
Swimwear Mfr & Distr
N.A.I.C.S.: 339920
Zvi Ben-Haim (Pres)
Debbie Walters (Mgr-Shipping)
Kathleen McAndrews (Mgr-Import)
Jerry Harary (Pres)
Roger Gordon (Sr VP)
Greg Kaplan (Controller)

IN SYNC BEMIS BALKIND
6135 Wilshire Blvd, Los Angeles, CA
90048
Tel.: (323) 965-4810
Web Site:
http://www.insyncbemisbalkind.com
Sales Range: $10-24.9 Million
Emp.: 60
Advetising Agency
N.A.I.C.S.: 541810
Robert Smith (CEO)
Peter Bemis (Co-Pres)
Aubrey Balkind (Co-Pres)

IN THE KNOW EXPERIENCES
37 W 20th St Suite 310, New York,
NY 10011
Tel.: (866) 634-9658
Web Site:
http://intheknowexperiences.com
Year Founded: 2007
Sales Range: $1-9.9 Million
Emp.: 25
Luxury & Lifestyle Travel Events
N.A.I.C.S.: 561510
Seth Kaplan (Co-Owner)
Lia Batkin (Co-Owner)

IN THE KNOW, INC.
4324 S Alston Ave Ste 204, Durham,
NC 27713-6102
Tel.: (919) 403-8979
Web Site:
http://www.knowingmore.com
Year Founded: 1998
Scientific & Technical Consulting Services
N.A.I.C.S.: 541690
Linda Leekley (Founder & Pres)

Subsidiaries:

Home Care Pulse LLC (1)
346 Grand Loop Ste 200, Rexburg, ID
83440-4952
Tel.: (208) 356-7880
Web Site: http://www.homecarepulse.com
Other Health & Personal Care Stores
N.A.I.C.S.: 456199
Erik Madsen (CEO)
Todd Austin (COO)
Kire Madsen (VP-Customer Success)
Jeralyn Petterson (Dir-Fin)
Jason Hamilton (Dir-IT)

IN ZONE, INC.
2859 Paces Ferry Rd SE Ste 2100,
Atlanta, GA 30339
Web Site: http://www.in-zone.com
Year Founded: 1995
Sales Range: $10-24.9 Million
Emp.: 50
Mfr of Beverageware, Coffee Tumblers & Soft-Sided Lunch Kits & Coolers

N.A.I.C.S.: 326199

IN-N-OUT BURGERS, INC.
4199 Campus Dr Ste 900, Irvine, CA
92612
Tel.: (949) 509-6200 CA
Web Site: http://www.innout.com
Year Founded: 1948
Sales Range: $300-349.9 Million
Emp.: 4,000
Hamburger Chain Restaurants
N.A.I.C.S.: 722513
Michelle Guzman (Dir-Mktg)

IN-PACT, INC.
12300 Marshall St, Crown Point, IN
46307
Tel.: (219) 662-1905 IN
Web Site: http://www.in-pact.org
Year Founded: 1980
Sales Range: $10-24.9 Million
Emp.: 472
Developmental Disability Assistance
Services
N.A.I.C.S.: 624120
Ray Giacomin (CFO)
Herbert Grulke (Exec Dir)

IN-Q-TEL, INC.
PO Box 749, Arlington, VA 22216
Tel.: (703) 248-3000 DE
Web Site: http://www.iqt.org
Year Founded: 1999
Sales Range: $125-149.9 Million
Emp.: 107
Venture Capital Investment Services
N.A.I.C.S.: 523910
Steve Bowsher (Pres & CEO)
Bob Gleichauf (Exec VP)
Lisbeth Poulos (Exec VP)
William Strecker (CTO & Exec VP)
Matthew Strottman (CFO & Exec VP)
Bruce A. Adams (Gen Counsel & Exec VP)
Michael M. Crow (Chm)
Judith A. Miscik (Vice Chm)

Subsidiaries:

Sonatype, Inc. (1)
12501 Prosperity Dr Ste 350, Silver Spring,
MD 20904
Tel.: (650) 248-2919
Web Site: http://www.sonatype.com
Component Based Software Development
Services
N.A.I.C.S.: 541511
Wayne Jackson (CEO)
Dave Miller (CFO)
Mike Hansen (Sr VP-Products)
Ryan Berg (Chief Security Officer)
Joshua Corman (CTO)
Paul Bosco (Gen Counsel)
David Rudolph (VP-Customer Success)
Karen Gardner (VP-Ops)
Brian Fox (Founder & CTO)
Bill Karpovich (Sr VP-Strategy & Corp Dev)
Megan Lueders (CMO)
Alex Berry (Pres)

IN-REL PROPERTIES, INC.
200 Lake Ave 2nd Fl, Lake Worth, FL
33460
Tel.: (561) 533-0344 FL
Web Site: http://www.in-rel.com
Year Founded: 1984
Sales Range: $1-9.9 Million
Emp.: 48
Nonresidential Property Owner &
Manager
N.A.I.C.S.: 531312
Dennis Udwin (Co-Founder & Principal)
Mukang Cho (CEO & Principal)
Ted Fischer (Principal)
Charles Stein (Co-Founder & Principal)
Kirk Cypel (CEO)
Paul Catalano (VP-Fin)

IN-SITU, INC.
221 E Lincoln Ave, Fort Collins, CO
80524
Tel.: (970) 498-1500 WY
Web Site: http://www.in-situ.com
Year Founded: 1976
Sales Range: $1-9.9 Million
Emp.: 65
Instruments & Related Products Mfr
for Measuring, Displaying & Controlling Industrial Process Variables
N.A.I.C.S.: 334513

Subsidiaries:

Ajax Environmental & Safety Supply,
Inc. (1)
10801 Hammerly Blvd #148, Houston, TX
77043
Tel.: (713) 789-4149
Web Site: http://www.ajaxrentals.com
Research & Development in Biotechnology
N.A.I.C.S.: 541714
Judd Johnson (Owner)

INACOMP TECHNICAL SERVICES GROUP
17250 W 12 Mile Rd, Southfield, MI
48076
Tel.: (248) 559-5700
Web Site: http://www.inacomp.net
Year Founded: 1982
Sales Range: $10-24.9 Million
Emp.: 50
IT Services
N.A.I.C.S.: 541519
Michael Kanan (Pres & CEO)

INBENTA TECHNOLOGIES INC.
1065 E Hillsdale Blvd Ste 425, Foster
City, CA 94404
Tel.: (408) 213-8771
Web Site: http://www.inbenta.com
Year Founded: 2005
Sales Range: $10-24.9 Million
Emp.: 165
Information Technology Consulting
Services
N.A.I.C.S.: 541512
Jordi Torras (Founder & CEO)
Ferran Saurina (COO)
Jordi Prats (CTO)
Sofia Gimeno (VP-Fin)
Genis Urena (Chief Info Security
Officer)

INCAPITAL LLC
200 S Wacker Dr Ste 3700, Chicago,
IL 60606
Tel.: (561) 361-1100
Web Site: http://www.incapital.com
Sales Range: $10-24.9 Million
Emp.: 35
Securities Dealing & Investment
Banking Services
N.A.I.C.S.: 523150
Tom Ricketts (Founder & Chm)
Thomas Belka (CFO)
Phillip Johnson (Pres)
Hugh McHaffie (Mng Dir & Head-Wealth Mgmt Solutions)
A. Brad Busscher (Chief Admin Officer)
Fred Lucier (Mng Dir-Fixed Income)
Sara Wehmeyer (Mng Dir-HR)
Laura Elliott (Mng Dir-Natl Accts)
Chris O'Connor (Mng Dir-Fixed Income)
Tom O'Neill (Vice Chm-Capital Markets)
David Connelly (Mng Dir/Mgr-Capital
Markets)
Sean McKenna (Mng Dir-Capital
Markets-New York)
Paul Steinborn (Sr VP-Capital
Markets-New York)

Patty Cohen *(VP-Market-Linked Products Origination)*
Steve Giles *(COO)*
Ted Kellerman *(Sr VP & Mgr-Market-Linked Products Origination)*
Tim Piatek *(VP-Market-Linked Products Trading)*
Paul Rothschild *(Sr VP-Market-Linked Products Trading)*
Nick Whiteley *(VP-Market-Linked Products Trading & Hybrid Sls)*
George Holstead *(Co-Head-Fixed Income-Boca Raton)*
Laura Elliot *(Co-Head-Fixed Income)*
Matthew Reilly *(Mng Dir-Market-Linked Products Trading & Origination)*
William White *(Mng Dir-Comml Mortgage-Backed Securities)*
John D. DesPrez III *(CEO)*

INCE DISTRIBUTING INCORPORATED
2233 N W Loop 410, San Antonio, TX 78230
Tel.: (210) 341-7161
Web Site: http://www.incedist.com
Sales Range: $25-49.9 Million
Emp.: 115
Air Conditioning Equipment Mfr
N.A.I.C.S.: 423730
Alan William *(Controller)*
Raymond B. Ince Sr. *(CEO)*

INCEDO, INC.
2350 Mission College Blvd Ste 246, Santa Clara, CA 95054
Tel.: (408) 531-6040
Web Site: http://www.incedoinc.com
Year Founded: 2011
Emp.: 1,500
Information Technology Services & Software Developer
N.A.I.C.S.: 513210
Robert E. Bartels Jr. *(Partner)*
Saurabh Mittal *(Chm)*
Tejinderpal Singh Miglani *(Founder)*
Ashish Choudhary *(Co-Founder & Head-Life Sciences)*
Anupam Wahi *(Head-Comm Engrg & Media)*
Nitin Seth *(CEO)*
Pratul Chopra *(Sr VP & Head-Digital & Analytics)*
Shubhasheesh Anand *(Sr VP & Head-Analytics Products)*
Vikram Chandna *(Head-Fin Svcs)*
Vishal Gauri *(Chief Strategy Officer)*
Krishna Rupanagunta *(Pres & Chief Customer Success Officer)*
Paresh Huria *(Chief Delivery Officer & Exec VP)*

INCENDIA PARTNERS, INC.
161 Worcester Rd Ste 400, Framingham, MA 01701-5300
Tel.: (508) 507-3555
Web Site: http://www.incendia.com
Year Founded: 2002
Sales Range: $1-9.9 Million
Emp.: 15
Information Technology & Software Engineering Staffing
N.A.I.C.S.: 561311
Robert Recchia *(Mng Partner)*
Brian Aldrich *(Founder & Partner)*
David Kerr *(Head-Recruiting)*

INCENTER, LLC
129 W Trade St 9th Fl, Charlotte, NC 28202
Tel.: (651) 412-2020
Web Site: http://www.incenterms.com
Financial Services
N.A.I.C.S.: 523999

Jeremy Prahm *(Mng Dir)*
Charles Macintosh *(Mng Dir)*
Pete Mahon *(VP)*
Bruno Pasceri *(Pres)*

Subsidiaries:

Boston National Title Agency, LLC **(1)**
129 W Trade St Fl 9, Charlotte, NC 28202-2143
Web Site: http://www.bostonnationaltitle.com
Title Abstract & Settlement Offices
N.A.I.C.S.: 541191
Jeffrey Valdez *(Branch Mgr)*
Lisa Vogel *(Sr VP-Comml Div-Natl)*
Nicole Wolosoff *(Pres-New York)*

Campus Door Holdings Inc. **(1)**
1415 Ritner Hwy, Carlisle, PA 17013
Tel.: (717) 249-8800
Web Site: http://www.campusdoor.com
Nondepository Credit Intermediation
N.A.I.C.S.: 522299
Steve Winnie *(CEO)*
Peter Zandvoort *(CTO)*
Ed Piccolo *(VP)*
Dave Knutelsky *(SR VP-Contact Center)*
Sara Parrish *(Sr VP-Client & Product Mgmt)*
Ryan Arndt *(VP-Governance)*

INCENTIVE SOLUTIONS
2299 Perimeter Park Dr Ste 130, Atlanta, GA 30341
Web Site: http://www.incentivesolutions.com
Year Founded: 1994
Sales Range: $10-24.9 Million
Emp.: 50
Business Incentive Products, Online Reward Programs, Channel Sales Incentives & Meeting/Event Planning
N.A.I.C.S.: 541613
Mark Herbert *(Pres & CEO)*
Kelly Held *(VP-IT)*
Alexis Oubre *(Mgr-Acct)*
Deven Crane *(Dir-Travel Svcs)*
Ebony Williams *(Coord-Mktg)*
Nazia Ali *(Coord-Participant Svcs)*
Jim Costello *(Exec VP)*
Nancy Piepho *(VP-Client Solutions-North America)*
Michael Heldebrandt *(Chief Revenue Officer)*

INCEPTION MEDIA GROUP, LLC
13412 Ventura Blvd Ste 200, Sherman Oaks, CA 91423
Tel.: (310) 582-5948   CA
Web Site: http://www.inceptionmediagroup.com
Year Founded: 2009
Motion Picture & Other Filmed Entertainment Distribution Services
N.A.I.C.S.: 512120
David Borshell *(Co-Founder & Partner)*
Andy Reimer *(Co-Founder & Partner)*
Burgess Wilson *(COO)*
Steven DeMille *(CMO)*
Steve Saltman *(Pres-Television & Digital)*
Jim Harvey *(Exec VP-Sls & Distr-Inception Film Partners)*
Lisa Yedlin *(Sr. VP-Sls)*
Steve Coppel *(VP-Ops)*
Laurie McQuaid *(Dir-Sls-Natl Accts)*
Brett Lehman *(Dir-Digital Ops)*
Rana Ashuri *(Dir-Admin)*

INCERTEC PLATING CORP.
500 73rd Ave NE Ste 123, Fridley, MN 55432
Tel.: (763) 717-7016
Web Site: http://www.incertec.com
Rev.: $7,333,333
Emp.: 95

Electroplating, Plating, Polishing, Anodizing & Coloring
N.A.I.C.S.: 332813
Steve Forsythe *(Pres)*

Subsidiaries:

Circle City Heat Treating, Inc. **(1)**
2243 Massachusetts Ave, Indianapolis, IN 46218
Tel.: (317) 638-2252
Web Site:
http://www.circlecityheattreating.com
Rev.: $3,933,245
Emp.: 16
Metal Heat Treating
N.A.I.C.S.: 332811
Tom Dunn *(Pres)*
Marla Reel *(Office Mgr)*

INCHARGE INSTITUTE OF AMERICA, INC.
5750 Major Blvd Ste 300, Orlando, FL 32819
Tel.: (407) 291-7770
Web Site: http://www.incharge.org
Sales Range: $10-24.9 Million
Emp.: 250
Personal Finance Education & Credit Counseling
N.A.I.C.S.: 561450
Etta Money *(Pres)*
Chris Henningsen *(VP-Consumer Awareness & IT)*
Gina Tucker *(Project Mgr)*

INCHES FITNESS
4702 Cortez Rd, Bradenton, FL 34210
Tel.: (941) 896-8878
Web Site:
http://www.inchesfitness.com
Sales Range: $10-24.9 Million
Emp.: 15
Women's Fitness Center
N.A.I.C.S.: 713940
Maryellen Patterson *(Pres)*

INCIPIO, LLC
6001 Oak Canyon, Irvine, CA 92618
Tel.: (949) 250-4929   DE
Web Site: http://www.incipio.com
Year Founded: 2015
Emp.: 300
Holding Company; Consumer Technology Platform Solutions Developer & Publisher
N.A.I.C.S.: 551112
Andy Fathollahi *(Founder)*
Rusty Everett *(Exec VP-Sls)*
Stuart Noyes *(CEO)*

Subsidiaries:

Incipio Technologies, Inc. **(1)**
6001 Oak Canyon, Irvine, CA 92618
Tel.: (949) 250-4929
Web Site: http://www.incipio.com
Consumer Technology Platform Solutions Developer & Publisher
N.A.I.C.S.: 513210
Andrew Fathollahi *(Founder & CEO)*

Subsidiary (Domestic):

Griffin Technology, Inc. **(2)**
1930 Air Lane Dr, Nashville, TN 37210
Tel.: (615) 399-7000
Web Site: http://www.griffintechnology.com
Rev.: $3,754,000
Emp.: 25
Switchgear & Switchboard Apparatus Mfr
N.A.I.C.S.: 335313
Paul Griffin *(Founder & CEO)*

INCLINATOR COMPANY OF AMERICA, INC.
601 Gibson Blvd, Harrisburg, PA 17104
Tel.: (717) 939-8420   PA
Web Site: http://www.inclinator.com
Year Founded: 1923

Sales Range: $50-74.9 Million
Emp.: 50
Home Elevators, Residential & Commercial Dumbwaiters & Platform Wheelchair Lifts Mfr
N.A.I.C.S.: 333921
Cliff Warner *(Pres & CEO)*

INCLINE MGMT CORP.
EQT Plz Ste 2300 625 Liberty Ave, Pittsburgh, PA 15222
Tel.: (412) 315-7800   PA
Web Site:
http://www.inclineequity.com
Year Founded: 2011
Privater Equity Firm
N.A.I.C.S.: 523999
Jack C. Glover *(Mng Partner)*
Justin Bertram *(Sr Partner)*
Deanna B. Barry *(Partner, CFO & Chief Compliance Officer)*
Leon Rubinov *(Sr Partner)*
April Simile *(Partner & Mng Dir-Bus Dev & IR)*
John Morley *(Partner)*
Joe Choorapuzha *(Partner)*
Michael Antonelli *(Mng Dir)*
Brad Phillips *(Mng Dir)*
Jason O'Toole *(Principal & Controller)*

Subsidiaries:

GMES LLC **(1)**
1391 E Boone Industrial Blvd, Columbia, MO 65202
Tel.: (718) 210-3913
Web Site: http://www.gmesupply.com
Industrial Equipment & Truck Distr
N.A.I.C.S.: 423830
Beau Aero *(Pres & CEO)*

Subsidiary (Domestic):

Custom Tool Supply, LLC **(2)**
14309 E 35th Pl Ste 103, Aurora, CO 80011
Tel.: (303) 576-6335
Web Site: http://www.customtoolsupply.com
Ret Hardware
N.A.I.C.S.: 444140
Erik Lemaire *(Acct Mgr)*

Gearcor, Inc. **(2)**
1037 Powers Rd, Conklin, NY 13748-1412
Tel.: (200) 510-9880
Web Site: http://www.gearcor.com
Footwear Merchant Whslr
N.A.I.C.S.: 424340
Carol R. Yeager *(CEO)*

Jon-Don, LLC **(1)**
400 Medinah Road Roselle, Chicago, IL 60172
Tel.: (800) 400-9473
Web Site: http://www.jondon.com
Carpet & Rug Cleaning Equipment & Supplies, Commer
N.A.I.C.S.: 423850
John Paolella *(Founder)*
Jay Davisson *(CEO)*

Subsidiary (Domestic):

Factory Cleaning Equipment, Inc. **(2)**
1578A Beverly Ct, Aurora, IL 60502
Tel.: (630) 406-9911
Web Site: http://www.thesweeper.com
Cleaning Equipment Mfr
N.A.I.C.S.: 423830
Rick Schott *(Pres)*

Quest Building Products Inc. **(2)**
1129 N Patt St, Anaheim, CA 92801-2568
Tel.: (714) 738-6640
Commercial & Industrial Machinery & Equipment Rental & Leasing
N.A.I.C.S.: 532490

Mr. Magic Car Wash Inc. **(1)**
3800 Saw Mill Run Blvd, Pittsburgh, PA 15227
Tel.: (412) 881-5911
Web Site: http://www.mrmagiccarwash.com
Car Washes
N.A.I.C.S.: 811192
James Schaming *(Pres)*

Incline MGMT Corp.—(Continued)

NovaVision, Inc. (1)
524 E Woodland Cir, Bowling Green, OH 43402
Tel.: (419) 354-1427
Web Site: http://www.novavisioninc.com
Security Stickers, Mechanical Security
Seals & Hologram Labels Printing
N.A.I.C.S.: 323111
Mike Messmer *(VP & Gen Mgr)*
Mike Manahan *(Dir-New Products & Processes)*

Porcelain Industries, Inc. (1)
20 Sanker Rd, Dickson, TN 37055
Tel.: (615) 446-7400
Web Site: http://www.porcelain-industries.com
Sales Range: $75-99.9 Million
Porcelain Enamel Coating Services
N.A.I.C.S.: 332999
Mark Oldham *(Controller)*

RKD Group, LLC (1)
2701 N Dallas Pkwy Ste 650, Plano, TX 75093
Tel.: (800) 222-6070
Web Site: http://rkdgroup.com
Multichannel Marketing & Fundraising Solutions
N.A.I.C.S.: 541613
Tim Kersten *(Chm)*
Rebekah Cooksey *(CFO)*
Chris Pritcher *(CEO)*
Chris Joos *(CIO)*
Max Bunch *(Exec VP)*
Perry Moore *(Exec VP)*
Amanda Wasson *(Exec VP-Strategic Plng & Integration)*
Steve Caldwell *(Sr VP-Data & Analytics Solutions)*
Ann Dunn *(Sr VP)*
Thalamus Hill *(Sr VP-Advanced Analytics)*
Emily Creonte *(VP-HR)*
Billy Vaudry *(Sr VP-Creative Services)*

Subsidiary (Domestic):

Data Best Practices, LLC (2)
6211 Shoal Creek Trl, Garland, TX 75044-5044
Tel.: (410) 963-3515
Web Site: http://www.databestpractices.com
Data Integration & Governance
N.A.I.C.S.: 513210

Data-Mail, Inc. (2)
160 Stone St, Stoneville, NC 27048
Tel.: (336) 573-5000
Rev.: $1,400,000
Emp.: 30
Data Processing, Hosting & Related Services
N.A.I.C.S.: 518210
James Strasbourger *(Pres)*

The Faucet-Queens, Inc. (1)
650 Forest Edge Dr, Vernon Hills, IL 60061
Tel.: (847) 478-2800
Sales Range: $50-74.9 Million
Distr of Hand Tools & Home Repair Products
N.A.I.C.S.: 423710

Unified Power, LLC (1)
217 Metro Dr, Terrell, TX 75160
Tel.: (972) 524-6050
Web Site: http://www.unifiedpowerusa.com
Inverter Sales & Maintenance Services
N.A.I.C.S.: 423610
Charles Cantrell *(Mgr-Natl Battery & Safety)*
Chui Muro *(Mgr-Svc-North Central)*
Jennifer Kotajarvi *(Coord-Svc)*
Carolyn Zello *(Mgr-Customer Care)*
Toriene Johnson *(Mgr-Customer Care)*
Justin McClung *(VP-Natl Ops)*

Subsidiary (Domestic):

24/7 Technology Inc. (2)
1349 Old 41 Hwy NW Ste 135, Marietta, GA 30060-7931 (100%)
Tel.: (770) 971-8480
Web Site: http://www.247technology.com
Emp.: 115
Critical Power Solutions
N.A.I.C.S.: 221122
Jim Weydman *(Pres & CEO)*

Computer Power Systems Inc. (2)

3421 State Rd 419, Winter Springs, FL 32708
Tel.: (407) 327-7373
Web Site: http://www.cpsfl.com
Commercial & Institutional Building Construction
N.A.I.C.S.: 236220

Power Protection Unlimited (2)
9351 Philadelphia Rd Ste A-B, Baltimore, MD 21237
Tel.: (410) 391-4222
Web Site: http://www.unifiedpowerusa.com
Inverter Sales & Maintenance Services
N.A.I.C.S.: 423610

Weaver Automotive, Inc. (1)
480 New Bethel Rd, Carnesville, GA 30521
Tel.: (706) 384-4422
Web Site: http://www.weaverparts.com
Rev.: $6,300,000
Emp.: 50
Motor Vehicle Supplies & New Parts Merchant Whslr
N.A.I.C.S.: 423120
Adrian Graby *(Mgr)*

Wholesale Supplies Plus, LLC (1)
10035 Broadview Rd, Broadview Heights, OH 44147
Tel.: (440) 526-5903
Web Site: http://www.wholesalesuppliesplus.com
Sales Range: $1-9.9 Million
Emp.: 45
Mfg Misc Products
N.A.I.C.S.: 339999
David May *(Co-Owner)*
Debbie May *(Co-Owner)*

Subsidiary (Domestic):

Rustic Escentuals (2)
7820 East Pleasant Valley Rd, Independence, OH 44131
Tel.: (216) 503-9395
Web Site: http://www.rusticescentuals.com
Home, Fragrances & Soap Products Mfr
N.A.I.C.S.: 325611
Amy Pascoe *(Owner)*

iWave Information Systems Inc. (1)
2nd Level, Confederation Court Mall 134
Kent Street, Charlottetown, C1A 8R8, PE, Canada
Tel.: (800) 655-7729
Web Site: http://www.iwave.com
Prospect Research Software Developer
N.A.I.C.S.: 513210
Gerry Lawless *(CTO)*
Ross Beattie *(Pres & CEO)*
Collin Paddington *(CFO)*
Jill McCarville *(VP-Mktg)*
Jordan Richards *(Chm)*

INCODE TECHNOLOGIES, INC.
221 Main St. Ste 520, San Francisco, CA 94105
Tel.: (650) 446-3444
Web Site: https://incode.com
Year Founded: 2015
Software Publisher
N.A.I.C.S.: 513210
Ricardo Amper *(Founder & CEO)*

Subsidiaries:

Metamap, Inc. (1)
3720 Willow Rdg Rd, Lexington, KY 40514-1562
Tel.: (859) 223-7651
Web Site: https://www.metamap.com
Software Publisher
N.A.I.C.S.: 513210
Meghna Mann *(CEO)*

INCODE TELECOM GROUP, INC.
1081 Camino Del Rio S Ste 102, San Diego, CA 92108
Tel.: (858) 550-1170 DE
Web Site: http://www.incodetel.com
Year Founded: 1998
Sales Range: $10-24.9 Million
Emp.: 400
Wireless Business & Technology
Consulting Services

N.A.I.C.S.: 541690
Todd Crick *(Pres & CEO)*
Jorge Funezalida *(VP-Strategy & Tech Grp)*
Rob Prudhomme *(VP-Practice Dev & Thought Leadership)*

Subsidiaries:

inCode Telecom Group (1)
3155 Royal Dr Ste 100, Alpharetta, GA 30022-2430
Tel.: (770) 751-8331
Web Site: http://www.incodetel.com
Sales Range: $10-24.9 Million
Emp.: 50
Wireless Business & Technology Consulting Services
N.A.I.C.S.: 541690

INCOE CORPORATION
1740 E Maple Rd, Troy, MI 48083-4209
Tel.: (248) 616-0220 MI
Web Site: http://www.incoe.com
Year Founded: 1963
Sales Range: $10-24.9 Million
Emp.: 125
Mfr of Fabricated Metal Products
N.A.I.C.S.: 332919
Joel Adkins *(Mgr-Design Engrg)*
Jim Bott *(Mgr-Sls & Mktg-North America)*

INCOMPASS LLC
11123 89th Ave N, Maple Grove, MN 55369
Tel.: (763) 488-6600
Web Site: https://manufacturedgrowthsolutions.com
Emp.: 100
Other Industrial Machinery Mfr
N.A.I.C.S.: 333248

Subsidiaries:

JLY Investments, Inc. (1)
507 Jackson St, Greensboro, NC 27403
Tel.: (336) 273-8261
Web Site: http://www.newmanwhitney.com
Sales Range: $50-74.9 Million
Emp.: 100
Woodworking Machinery
N.A.I.C.S.: 333243

INCONEN CORPORATION
6133 Bristol Pkwy Ste 232, Culver City, CA 90230
Tel.: (310) 410-1931
Web Site: http://www.inconen.com
Rev.: $17,000,000
Emp.: 125
Temporary Help Service
N.A.I.C.S.: 561320
Cathy O'Neil *(Mgr-Ops-Recruiter)*
Bordon Ross *(CFO)*

INCORP HOLDINGS, LLC
3020 Diego Dr, Evansville, IN 47715
Tel.: (812) 485-0035
Pipes & Boilers Insulation Services
N.A.I.C.S.: 238990
Ryan Schenk *(CFO)*

Subsidiaries:

East Coast Rigging & Contracting Company, Inc. (1)
8221 Main St, Laurel, MD 20724
Tel.: (301) 362-8801
Web Site: http://www.eastcoastrigging.com
Rev.: $1,830,000
Emp.: 10
Consumer Electronics & Appliances Rental
N.A.I.C.S.: 532210
Mark Kerner *(Owner)*

INCORPORATE MASSAGE CO.
10808 S River Front Pkwy, South Jordan, UT 84095

Web Site: http://www.incorporatemassage.com
Year Founded: 2014
Sales Range: $1-9.9 Million
Emp.: 1,024
Corporate Massage Services
N.A.I.C.S.: 611519
Amelia Wilcox *(Founder & CEO)*
Paul Shin *(Chief Revenue Officer)*
Melissa Johnson *(Dir-Ops)*
Shawn Stringham *(Mng Dir-Strategic Alliances)*
Stefanie Larson *(Mgr-HR)*

INCORPORATING SERVICES, LTD
3500 S Dupont Hwy, Dover, DE 19901
Tel.: (302) 531-0855
Web Site: http://www.incserv.com
Year Founded: 1972
Rev.: $3,300,000
Emp.: 35
Business Support Services
N.A.I.C.S.: 561499
Joshua Twilley *(Pres)*

INCREASE VISIBILITY, INC.
15 Enterprise Ste 150, Aliso Viejo, CA 92656
Tel.: (949) 600-9885
Web Site: http://www.increasevisibility.com
Sales Range: $1-9.9 Million
Emp.: 15
Internet Marketing, Adverting & Consulting Services
N.A.I.C.S.: 541613
James Lisi *(Pres)*

INCREDIBLE TECHNOLOGIES, INC.
200 Corporate Woods Pkwy, Vernon Hills, IL 60061
Tel.: (847) 870-7027
Web Site: http://www.itsgames.com
Year Founded: 1985
Sales Range: $100-124.9 Million
Emp.: 240
Video Game Machine Mfr
N.A.I.C.S.: 334610
Elaine Hodgson *(Pres & CEO)*
Richard Ditton *(Exec VP)*
Jim Dore *(COO)*
Gene Cherner *(VP-Fin)*
Daymon Ruttenberg *(Gen Counsel & VP-Regulatory Affairs)*

INDACO METALS, LLC.
3 American Way, Shawnee, OK 74804
Tel.: (405) 273-9200
Web Site: http://www.indacometals.com
Year Founded: 1995
Sales Range: $10-24.9 Million
Emp.: 53
Prefabricated Metal Building & Component Mfr
N.A.I.C.S.: 332311
Josh Inda *(CEO)*
Steve Moore *(COO)*

INDAK MANUFACTURING CORP.
1915 Techny Rd, Northbrook, IL 60062
Tel.: (847) 272-0343
Web Site: http://www.indak.com
Rev.: $46,000,000
Emp.: 184
Electric Power Switches Mfr
N.A.I.C.S.: 335314
David Frowes *(Pres)*
Al Shafie *(Mgr-Mfg Engrg)*

INDECK POWER EQUIPMENT COMPANY

1111 Willis Ave, Wheeling, IL 60090-5816
Tel.: (847) 541-8300   IL
Web Site: http://www.indeck.com
Year Founded: 1960
Sales Range: $75-99.9 Million
Emp.: 97
Power Plant Machinery Distr
N.A.I.C.S.: 423830
Gerald R. Forsythe *(Chm & CEO)*
Steve Page *(VP)*

Subsidiaries:

Indeck Energy Services, Inc.   (1)
1111 Willis Ave, Wheeling, IL
60090   (100%)
Tel.: (847) 541-8300
Web Site: http://www.indeck.com
Sales Range: $25-49.9 Million
Emp.: 55
Electronic Services
N.A.I.C.S.: 221122
Gerald R. Forsythe *(Chm & CEO)*

Subsidiary (Domestic):

Indeck Energy Services of Ilion
Inc.   (2)
11 Remington Ave, Ilion, NY 13357-1817
Tel.: (315) 894-1000
Web Site: http://www.indeckenergy.com
Sales Range: $50-74.9 Million
Emp.: 7
Electronic Services
N.A.I.C.S.: 221118

Indeck Energy Services of Olean
Inc.   (2)
140 Moore Ave, Olean, NY 14760-1123
Tel.: (716) 373-4705
Sales Range: $50-74.9 Million
Emp.: 12
Electronic Services
N.A.I.C.S.: 221118
Gerald R. Forsythe *(Chm)*
Todd Dobmeier *(Plant Mgr)*

Indeck Energy Services of Oswego
Inc.   (2)
600 N Buffalo Grove Rd, Buffalo Grove, IL
60089-2432
Tel.: (847) 520-3212
Web Site: http://www.indeck-energy.com
Sales Range: $50-74.9 Million
Emp.: 10
Electronic Services
N.A.I.C.S.: 221122
Joseph M. Oskorep *(VP & Controller)*

Indeck Energy Services of Silver
Springs Inc.   (2)
1 Indeck Dr, Silver Springs, NY 14550-9780
Tel.: (585) 493-2700
Web Site: http://www.indeck-energy.com
Sales Range: $25-49.9 Million
Emp.: 15
Engineeering Services
N.A.I.C.S.: 541330

Indeck-Corinth Limited
Partnership   (2)
24 White St, Corinth, NY 12822-1301
Tel.: (518) 654-7895
Sales Range: $50-74.9 Million
Emp.: 14
Electronic Services
N.A.I.C.S.: 221118
Gerald R. Forsythe *(Chm & CEO)*
Michael Minnolera *(Plant Mgr)*

Indeck-Yerkes Energy Services
Inc.   (2)
600 N Buffalo Grove Rd, Buffalo Grove, IL
60089-2432
Tel.: (847) 520-3212
Sales Range: $50-74.9 Million
Emp.: 26
Electronic Services
N.A.I.C.S.: 221118

INDECON INC.
Ste 1310 115 W Washington St, Indianapolis, IN 46204-3419
Tel.: (708) 449-4040
Web Site: http://www.indecon-consulting.com

Year Founded: 1966
Sales Range: $10-24.9 Million
Emp.: 250
Custom Computer Programming Services
N.A.I.C.S.: 518210

INDEL, INC.
10 Indel Ave, Rancocas, NJ 08073
Tel.: (609) 267-9000   NJ
Web Site:
    http://www.inductotherm.com
Year Founded: 1954
Sales Range: $700-749.9 Million
Emp.: 5,000
Holding Company; Induction Melting
& Heating Products
N.A.I.C.S.: 551112

Subsidiaries:

Alpha 1 Induction Service Center   (1)
1525 Old Alum Creek Dr, Columbus, OH
43209-2712
Tel.: (614) 253-8900
Web Site: http://www.alpha1induction.com
Rev.: $8,722,990
Emp.: 35
Industrial Process Furnace & Oven Mfr
N.A.I.C.S.: 333994
Sean Buechner *(VP & Gen Mgr)*
Gil Traverse *(Reg Mgr-Sls)*
A. J. Clemons *(Dir-Svc & Sls)*
Amy Lesser *(Mgr-Spare Parts & Exports)*
Joe Grabauskas *(Engr-Project)*
Jim Dyer *(Pres & CEO)*

Consarc Engineering Limited   (1)
9 Woodside, Eurocentral, Holytown, ML1
4XL, United Kingdom
Tel.: (44) 1698730430
Web Site: http://www.consarceng.com
Emp.: 52
Design & Manufacture of Vacuum Furnaces
& Controlled Atmosphere Furnaces for Processing of Metals
N.A.I.C.S.: 333994
Eric Rennie *(Mng Dir)*

Electric Melting Services Company,
Ltd.   (1)
Lovell Street, Sheffield, S4 7WN, United
Kingdom
Tel.: (44) 1142738700
Web Site: http://www.emscouk.com
Emp.: 15
Repair of Induction Furnaces, Coils, Water
Cooled Leads & Associated Systems
N.A.I.C.S.: 811310
Steven Hill *(Mng Dir)*

Inductoheat, Inc.   (1)
32251 N Avis Dr, Madison Heights, MI
48071
Tel.: (248) 585-9393
Web Site: http://www.inductoheat.com
Sales Range: $25-49.9 Million
Emp.: 145
Designer & Mfr of Induction Heating Equipment
N.A.I.C.S.: 333248
Douglas Brown *(Pres & COO)*
Gary Doyon *(Chm & Grp VP)*

Inductotherm Corp.   (1)
10 Indel Ave, Rancocas, NJ
08073-0157   (100%)
Tel.: (609) 267-9000
Web Site: http://www.inductotherm.com
Sales Range: $25-49.9 Million
Emp.: 150
Mfr of Induction Melting Systems; Electric
Resistance Melting Furnaces, Automatic
Metal Pouring Systems
N.A.I.C.S.: 333994
Tom Mukalian *(Engr-Automation)*

Inductotherm Europe Limited   (1)
The Furlong, Droitwich, WR9 9AH, Worcs,
United Kingdom
Tel.: (44) 1905795100
Web Site: http://www.inductotherm.co.uk
Sales Range: $10-24.9 Million
Emp.: 100
Mfr of Induction Melting Systems; Electric
Resistance Melting Furnaces, Automatic
Metal Pouring Systems

N.A.I.C.S.: 333994
David Heavey *(Mgr-Sls)*

Inductotherm Group Brasil Ltda   (1)
Rue Herminio de Mello 526, Distrito Industrial, Indaiatuba, 13347 330, SP, Brazil
Tel.: (55) 1938856800
Web Site:
    http://www.inductothermgroup.com.br
Sales Range: $25-49.9 Million
Emp.: 150
Induction Melting System Electric Resistance Melting Furnace Automatic Metal
Pouring System Mfr
N.A.I.C.S.: 333994

Inductotherm Group Canada Ltd.   (1)
165 Crown Court, Whitby, L1N 7B1, ON,
Canada
Tel.: (905) 576-8665
Web Site: http://www.inductotherm.ca
Sales Range: $10-24.9 Million
Emp.: 10
Sales of Induction Melting Systems; Electric
Resistance Melting Furnaces, Automatic
Metal Pouring Systems
N.A.I.C.S.: 423830

Inductotherm Group France   (1)
Immeuble Le River 9 Boulevard Georges
Melies, F 94356, Villiers-sur-Marne, CEDEX, France
Tel.: (33) 149307240
Web Site:
    http://www.inductothermgroup.com
Induction Melting Systems Mfr
N.A.I.C.S.: 333994

Inductotherm Heating & Welding
Technologies Ltd   (1)
Thermatool House, Crockford Lane, Basingstoke, RG24 8NA, Hampshire, United Kingdom
Tel.: (44) 1256335533
Web Site: http://www.inductothermhw.com
Sales Range: $25-49.9 Million
Emp.: 70
Mfr & Whslr of Induction Heating & Welding
Products
N.A.I.C.S.: 333248
John Taylor *(Gen Mgr)*

Inductotherm Pty., Ltd.   (1)
62 Bardia Ave, PO Box 171, Seaford, 3198,
VIC, Australia   (100%)
Tel.: (61) 397866000
Web Site: http://www.inductotherm.com.au
Sales Range: $10-24.9 Million
Emp.: 60
Mfr of Melting & Heating Equipment
N.A.I.C.S.: 333994
Wally A. Koscielecki *(Mng Dir)*
Peter Hearn *(Mgr-Customer Svcs)*
Jes Bouod *(CFO)*

Lepel Corporation   (1)
200 G Executive Dr, Edgewood, NY
11717-8365   (100%)
Tel.: (631) 586-3300
Web Site: http://www.lepel.com
Sales Range: $10-24.9 Million
Emp.: 13
Specialty Induction Heating & Processing
Equipment For Bottle Cap Sealing, Sputtering, Film Treating
N.A.I.C.S.: 333994

Magnetic Metals Corp.   (1)
1900 Hayes Ave, Camden, NJ
08105   (100%)
Tel.: (856) 964-7842
Web Site: http://www.magmet.com
Sales Range: $25-49.9 Million
Emp.: 400
Magnetic Component Mfr & Distr
N.A.I.C.S.: 335999
Henry M. Rowan *(Chm)*
Frank A. Raneiro *(Pres)*
Kurt Haley *(Mgr-Sls & Mktg)*

Radyne Corporation   (1)
211 W Boden St, Milwaukee, WI 53207
Tel.: (414) 481-8360
Web Site: http://www.radyne.com
Emp.: 70
Design, Manufacture & Sales of Advanced
Induction Power Supplies, Coils & Machine
Automation for Industrial Heating Applications
N.A.I.C.S.: 334416

Justin Mortimer *(Pres)*
Robert Kandetzke *(Mgr-Ops)*

Telegenix Inc.   (1)
1930 Olney Ave, Cherry Hill, NJ 08003-2016
Tel.: (856) 424-5200
Web Site: http://www.telegenix.com
Sales Range: $25-49.9 Million
Emp.: 75
Data Communication, Traffic Control & Telemetry Systems Mfr
N.A.I.C.S.: 334290

INDEPENDENCE
BANCSHARES, INC.
231 1st St E, Independence, IA
50644
Tel.: (319) 334-7035   IA
Web Site: http://www.banknsb.com
Year Founded: 1981
Sales Range: $10-24.9 Million
Bank Holding Company
N.A.I.C.S.: 551111
Gary F. Short *(Pres & CEO)*

Subsidiaries:

Northeast Security Bank   (1)
108 N Carpenter St, Sumner, IA 50674-1434
Tel.: (563) 578-3251
Web Site:
    http://www.northeastsecuritybank.com
Sales Range: $10-24.9 Million
Emp.: 43
Commericial Banking
N.A.I.C.S.: 522110
Marcy Bergman *(Exec VP)*

INDEPENDENCE BANK
435 3rd St, Havre, MT 59501
Tel.: (406) 265-1241
Web Site: http://www.ibyourbank.com
Sales Range: $50-74.9 Million
Emp.: 77
State Commercial Banks
N.A.I.C.S.: 522110
Bill Keller *(VP-Lending)*
Debbie Hedstrom *(VP-Lending)*
Miles Hamilton *(Pres)*
Juan Vassallo *(Pres-Market-Louisville)*
Erin Clark *(Portfolio Mgr)*
Ronald Jolly *(VP)*
Megan Ueltschy Scheps *(VP)*
John Shaver *(Sr VP-Private & Comml
Banking)*

INDEPENDENCE CAPITAL
COMPANY
5579 Pearl Rd Ste 100, Cleveland,
OH 44129-2555
Tel.: (440) 888-7000
Web Site: http://www.indcap.com
Emp.: 70
Financial Advisory & Investment Management Services
N.A.I.C.S.: 523150
Thomas Scheiman *(Pres)*

INDEPENDENCE CAPITAL
PARTNERS, LLC
2400 Market St, Philadelphia, PA
19103
Tel.: (215) 399-4710   PA
Web Site: http://www.icpartners.com
Year Founded: 1997
Private Equity Holding Company
N.A.I.C.S.: 551112
R. Eric Emrich *(CFO)*
Michelle W. Vaughn *(Chief Compliance Officer)*
Joe Muto *(CIO)*

Subsidiaries:

LBC Credit Partners, Inc.   (1)
Cira Ctr 2929 Arch St, Philadelphia, PA
19104-2868
Tel.: (215) 972-8900

Independence Capital Partners, LLC—(Continued)

Web Site: http://www.lbccredit.com
Emp.: 30
Corporate Financing & Equity Investment Services
N.A.I.C.S.: 525990
Ira M. Lubert (Partner)
John J. Brignola (Mng Partner)
Christopher J. Calabrese (Partner)
Nathaniel R. Cohen (Partner)
Homyar Choksi (Partner)
David E. Fraimow (Sr Mng Dir)
John Capperella (Mng Dir)
John T. Jadach (Mng Dir)
Allan Allweiss (Sr Mng Dir)
Jonathan Schor (VP)
Matthew Alles (VP)
Michael Hertz (VP)
Andrew Thornton (VP)
Kari Shumaker (Mgr-Acctg)
Joe Elsabee (VP)
Stephen Krawchuk (Mng Dir & Head-West)

LEM Capital, L.P. (1)
Cira Ctr 2929 Arch St, Philadelphia, PA 19104-2868
Tel.: (215) 557-9600
Web Site: http://www.lemcapital.com
Rev.: $450,000,000
Emp.: 15
Commercial Real Estate Investment & Property Management Services
N.A.I.C.S.: 531390
Ira M. Lubert (Partner)
Jay J. Eisner (Partner)
David M. Lazarus (Partner)
W. Marcus Duley (Sr VP-Investment Transaction Execution & Portfolio Mgmt Functions)
Brad A. Nemzer (CFO)
Joseph D. Stewart (Controller)
Michelle Vaughn (Chief Compliance Officer)
Chris T. Potavin (Sr VP-Acquisitions)
Joshua N. Grossman (Sr VP-Acquisitions)
Herbert L. Miller Jr. (Partner)

LLR Partners, Inc. (1)
Cira Ctr 2929 Arch St Ste 2700, Philadelphia, PA 19104-2868
Tel.: (215) 717-2900
Web Site: http://www.llrpartners.com
Sales Range: $1-4.9 Billion
Emp.: 38
Privater Equity Firm
N.A.I.C.S.: 523999
Ira M. Lubert (Partner)
Howard D. Ross (Co-Founder & Partner)
David J. Reuter (Partner)
Scott A. Perricelli (Partner)
Mitchell L. Hollin (Partner)
Todd Morrissey (Partner)
David A. Stienes (Partner)
Seth Lehr (Co-Founder & Partner)
Christian Bullitt (Principal-Bus Dev)
David Siegel (Dir-Bus Dev-Washington)
Jason Jerista (Mgr-IR)
Sasank Aleti (VP)
Michael Levenberg (VP)
Larry Coble (VP-Ops Excellence)
Andrew Capone (Accountant)
Elizabeth Campbell (VP)
Dennis Nguyen (Accountant)
Michael Pantilione (Partner)
Noah Becker (CFO)
Kristen Chang (VP-Talent Mgmt)
Kristy DelMuto (Dir-Bus Dev)
Jack Slye (Partner)
Geoff Baird (Sr Mng Dir-Value Creation Team)
Ryan Goldenberg (Partner)
Zack Sigal (Partner)

Holding (Domestic):

Celero Commerce LLC (2)
100 Westwood Pl Ste 200, Brentwood, TN 37027
Tel.: (844) 423-5376
Web Site: http://celerocommerce.com
Business Management Software & Payment Processing Services
N.A.I.C.S.: 522320
Kevin Jones (CEO)
Jeff Brown (COO)
Scott Farace (CMO)
Jim Harris (VP-Partnership Channel)
Abigail Lucier (VP-Corp Dev)

Troy Wilkerson (CFO)
Charlie Berard (CTO)
Kevin Brolan (Exec VP-Sls)
Jae Haas (Pres-Direct Channel)
Deidra Parsons (Sr VP-HR)

Subsidiary (Domestic):

FlashBanc, LLC (3)
185 NW Spanish River Bl Ste 204, Boca Raton, FL 33431-4230
Tel.: (561) 278-8888
Web Site: http://www.flashbanc.com
Data Processing, Hosting & Related Services
N.A.I.C.S.: 518210
Michael Gross (CEO)

Omega Processing Solutions, LLC (3)
1538 Alexandria Pike Ste 12, Fort Thomas, KY 41075
Tel.: (859) 442-8100
Web Site: http://www.omegap.com
Sales Range: $1-9.9 Million
Emp.: 19
Electronic Payment Processing Services
N.A.I.C.S.: 522320
Todd McHugh (Pres)
Jeff Cotrell (VP-Sls)
Zachary Hurtt (VP-Sls)
Daena Sprafka (COO)

RazorSync, LLC (3)
7725 Washington Ave S, Minneapolis, MN 55439
Tel.: (612) 617-6200
Web Site: http://www.razorsync.com
Emp.: 10
Mobile Field Service Software Publisher
N.A.I.C.S.: 513210
Christopher Rywelski (Founder & Pres)

Tandem Innovative Payment Solutions LLC (3)
728 N Pleasantburg Dr Ste 22, Greenville, SC 29607
Tel.: (844) 423-5376
Payment Processing Services
N.A.I.C.S.: 522320

Joint Venture (Domestic):

DaySmart Software, Inc. (2)
3520 Green Ct Ste 250, Brighton, MI 48105
Tel.: (800) 604-2040
Web Site: http://www.daysmart.com
Software Services
N.A.I.C.S.: 513210
Patrick Shanahan (CEO)
Cristi Tobelmann (VP-HR)

Subsidiary (Domestic):

StormSource LLC (3)
15300 N 90th St Suite 100, Scottsdale, AZ 85260
Tel.: (800) 988-0061
Web Site: http://www.appointment-plus.com
Sales Range: $1-9.9 Million
Emp.: 100
Online Appointment Scheduling Software Mfr
N.A.I.C.S.: 513210
Bob La Loggia (Founder & CEO)
Steve Booze (COO)
Kendall Matthews (VP-Global Mktg & Comm)
Brad Senff (Dir-IT Ops)
Derrick Disharoom (Dir-Quality Assurance)

Holding (Domestic):

Eye Health America (2)
10 Mansell Ct E, Alpharetta, GA 30009
Tel.: (470) 582-0316
Web Site: http://www.eyehealthamerica.com
Holding Company; Ophthalmology Care Services
N.A.I.C.S.: 551112
Joseph C. Parisi Jr. (Officer-Medical)
John Swencki (Co-CEO)
Mary Lou Parisi (Co-CEO)
Cathleen McCabe (Chief Medical Officer)
Philip Isham (Chief Dev Officer)
Ellen Grasso (Sr VP-Revenue Cycle)
Tara Matthews (Controller)
Chris Pivik (Dir-Fin)

Subsidiary (Domestic):

Clemson Eye, P.A. (3)

360 Pelham Rd, Greenville, SC 29615
Tel.: (864) 268-1000
Web Site: http://www.clemsoneye.com
Ophthalmology Care Services
N.A.I.C.S.: 621399
Jason Barden (CIO)
Corey Gareri (Mgr-Outreach)
Victoria Gaston (Mgr-Vision Correction)
Julie Hall (Mgr-Revenue Cycle)
Jennifer Johnson (Controller)
Kim Maciejewski (Mgr-Optical)
Sherri Mann (Mgr-Contact Center)
Courtney Mitchell (Dir-Mktg)
Lisa Moore (Dir-Clinical)
Holly Wildman (Dir-Quality Ops)
Molly Gleeton (Dir-HR)

Holding (Domestic):

Geoforce, Inc. (2)
5830 Granite Pkwy Ste 1200, Plano, TX 75024
Tel.: (972) 546-3878
Web Site: http://www.geoforce.com
Software Publisher
N.A.I.C.S.: 513210
Kyle L. Bowker (Chief Revenue Officer)
James MacLean III (CEO)
Vincent Hsieh (CFO)
Chris Gardner (CTO)

Paragon Technology Group, Inc. (2)
8229 Boone Blvd Ste 700, Vienna, VA 22182
Tel.: (703) 734-1102
Web Site: http://www.paragontech.net
Sales Range: $50-74.9 Million
Custom Computer Programming Services
N.A.I.C.S.: 541511
Bruce Card (Pres & CEO)
Scott Friedlander (Chm)
Marc Tommer (CFO)
Carl Weiss (VP-Logistics)

Joint Venture (Non-US):

Strategic Distribution, Inc. (2)
Tel.: (215) 633-1900
Web Site: https://www.sdi.com
Sales Range: $400-449.9 Million
Holding Company; Supply Chain Services
N.A.I.C.S.: 551112
Veronica Abarca (VP-Pur)
Scott Doyle (VP-Application Dev)
Ron Fijalkowski (CIO & Exec VP-Tech)
Chris Moore (Pres & CEO)
Jeremy Jordan (COO)
Neil Clover (CTO)
Adrian Mantini (CFO & Sr VP)
Lorraine Serva (Chief People Officer)
Jerome Blanc (Sr VP-Transformation)
Vee Browne (Dir-Operational Compliance)
Haitham Khudayri (VP-Operations)
Blaze Kurz (VP-Finance)
Chuck Doherty (VP-Operations)
Brian Harmon (VP-Procurement)

Subsidiary (Domestic):

SDI, Inc. (3)
1414 Radcliffe StSte300, Bristol, PA 19007
Tel.: (215) 633-1900
Web Site: https://www.sdi.com
Sales Range: $25-49.9 Million
Digital Supply Chain Management Services
N.A.I.C.S.: 541614
Sharon Malcolm (Office Mgr)
Scott Morehouse (VP-Bus Dev)
Kelley Ferguson (VP-MRO Supply Chain Solutions)
Jim Owens (Sr VP-Bus Dev)
Glenn Pierce (VP-Ops)
Chris Moore (Pres & CEO)

Subsidiary (Non-US):

Strategic Distribution Marketing de Mexico, S.A. de C.V. (3)
Ave Hermanos Escobar 7046-4, Col Partido Diaz, C.P. 32310, Ciudad Juarez, Chihuahua, Mexico
Tel.: (52) 6566270457
Sales Range: Less than $1 Million
Supply Chain Solutions
N.A.I.C.S.: 561499

Strategic Distribution Services de Mexico, S.A. de C.V. (3)
Ave Hermanos Escobar 7046-4, Col Partido

Diaz, 32310, Ciudad Juarez, Chihuahua, Mexico
Tel.: (52) 6566270415
Sales Range: Less than $1 Million
Industrial Supplies Whslr
N.A.I.C.S.: 423840
William Robert Berkley (Chm)

Holding (Domestic):

Stratix Corporation (2)
4920 Avalon Ridge Pkwy, Norcross, GA 30071
Tel.: (770) 326-7580
Web Site: http://www.stratixcorp.com
Emp.: 200
Enterprise Mobile Software & Solutions Services
N.A.I.C.S.: 541511
Gary Lee (Chief Solutions Officer)
Chris Koterski (CTO)
Marco Nielsen (VP-Managed Mobility Svcs)
Chris Hale (VP-Mktg)
Ross Homans (VP-Ops)
Darren P. Barnes (Sr VP-Sls & Mktg)
Jim Morgan (CFO)
Louis M. Alterman (CEO)
Elizabeth Klingseisen (Sr VP-Mktg)
Barry Schnur (CIO & Chief Svcs Officer)

Lubert-Adler Partners, L.P. (1)
171 17th St Ste 1575, Atlanta, GA 30363
Tel.: (404) 965-1000
Web Site: http://www.lubertadler.com
Real Estate Equity Investment & Asset Management Services
N.A.I.C.S.: 531390
Ira M. Lubert (Founder & Chm)
R. Eric Emrich (CFO, Treas & VP)
Gerald Andrew Ronon (Pres & COO)
Dean S. Adler (CEO)
Leonard M. Klehr (Vice Chm)
Stuart Margulies (Mng Principal & Head-Asset Mgmt)
Dan Nasser (Mng Principal-Acq & Disposition Strategies)
Michael Trachtenberg (Mng Principal-Acq & Asset Mgmt)
Ryan Forry (Sr VP-Portfolio & Asset Mgmt)
Mark S. Kripke (Sr VP-Fin)
Robert Morgan (VP-Acq & Asset Mgmt)
Jay Slovin (Sr VP-Asset Mgmt & New Acq Sourcing/Underwriting)
Neill B. Faucett (Mng Principal)
Vinod Paidipalli (Mng Principal)
Michael Phillips (Mng Principal-Acq & Asset Mgmt)
Jane M. Smith (Sr VP-Acq & Asset Mgmt)

Subsidiary (Domestic):

Lubert-Adler Management, LLC (2)
Cira Ct 2929 Arch St, Philadelphia, PA 19104
Tel.: (215) 972-2200
Web Site: http://www.lubertadler.com
Real Estate Asset Management Services
N.A.I.C.S.: 531312
Gerald Andrew Ronon (Pres & COO)

Patriot Financial Partners, L.P. (1)
Circa Centre 2929 Arch St, Philadelphia, PA 19104-2868
Tel.: (215) 399-4650
Web Site: http://www.patriotfp.com
Sales Range: $75-99.9 Million
Emp.: 12
Privater Equity Firm
N.A.I.C.S.: 523999
James J. Lynch (Mng Partner)
Stephanie Langer (Mng Dir & Head-IR)
James F. Deutsch (Mng Dir)
Michael Barley High (Partner)
Kevin J. Kooman (Principal)
Walter Kirk Wycoff (Mng Partner)

Joint Venture (Domestic):

Georgia Banking Company (2)
6190 Powers Ferry Rd NW 150, Sandy Springs, GA 30339
Tel.: (770) 690-9100
Web Site: http://www.geobanking.com
Banking Services

N.A.I.C.S.: 522110
S. Trezevant Moore Jr. *(Mng Dir)*
Elliott Miller *(Pres)*
Thomas Rockwood *(VP-Comml Lending)*
Joy Beam-Burns *(VP-Bus Dev & Warehouse Lending)*
Bartow Morgan Jr. *(CEO)*
James R. Lientz Jr. *(Chm)*

Quaker Partners Management, L.P. **(1)**
150 Monument Rd Ste 207, Bala Cynwyd, PA 19004
Tel.: (215) 988-6800
Web Site: http://www.quakerpartners.com
Rev.: $700,000,000
Emp.: 12
Healthcare Equity Investment Firm
N.A.I.C.S.: 523999
Ira M. Lubert *(Partner)*
Adele Cirone Oliva *(Partner)*
Richard S. Kollender *(Partner)*
P. Sherrill Neff *(Partner)*

Rubenstein Partners, L.P. **(1)**
Cira Ctr 2929 Arch St 28th Fl, Philadelphia, PA 19104-2868
Tel.: (215) 399-4624
Web Site:
   http://www.rubensteinpartners.com
Commercial & Institutional Real Estate Investment Management & Advisory Services
N.A.I.C.S.: 531390
Stephen A. Card *(Dir-Mid-Atlantic)*
Devon Cheshire *(VP-Dev & Construction)*
Salvatore Dragone *(Dir-Property Mgmt)*
Brandon Huffman *(Dir-IR & Midwest)*
Jeffery T. Kusumi *(Chief Compliance Officer)*
David B. Rubenstein *(Founder & Sr Mng Partner)*
Eric G. Schiela *(COO & Mng Principal)*
Craig G. Zolot *(Dir-Asset Mgmt)*
Rick Furches *(Dir-Dev)*
Scott Whittle *(Dir-Financings)*
Mike Daugard *(VP-Washington)*
Deke Schultze *(Reg Dir-New England)*
Jeremiah Kane *(Reg Dir-New York City)*
Stephen Evans *(Reg Dir-Washington)*
Taylor Smith *(Reg Dir-Southeast)*
Mark Turner *(Assoc Gen Counsel)*
R. Bruce Balderson Jr. *(Gen Counsel)*

Versa Capital Management, LLC **(1)**
Cira Centre 2929 Arch St, Philadelphia, PA 19104-7324
Tel.: (215) 609-3400
Web Site: http://www.versa.com
Sales Range: $100-124.9 Million
Emp.: 85
Privater Equity Firm
N.A.I.C.S.: 523999
Raymond C. French *(COO)*
Paul Halpern *(Chief Investment Officer)*
William R. Quinn *(Mng Dir-Investments)*
Gregory L. Segall *(Chm & CEO)*
David S. Lorry *(Mng Dir-Transaction Execution)*
Lewis H. Aronson *(Principal-Ops)*
Stephen E. Dorman *(Principal-Ops)*
Matthew S. Levitties *(Mng Dir)*
Randall R. Schultz *(Co-CFO & Mng Dir-Portfolio Ops)*
Aaron H. Headley *(Principal)*
Thomas A. Kennedy *(Chief Compliance Officer & Gen Counsel)*
Kamal Advani *(Mng Dir & Head-Portfolio Ops)*
Michael Fram *(Mng Dir-Ops)*
Patricia Graver *(Principal-Investments)*
Paul A. Guarino *(Principal-Investments)*
Matthew Raymon *(Principal-Investments)*
Rick Schreiber *(Mng Dir-Transaction Dev)*
Kenneth E. Kummerer Jr. *(Co-CFO)*

Holding (Domestic):

Alex Apparel Group, Inc. **(2)**
1407 Broadway Fl 15, New York, NY 10018
Tel.: (212) 730-1533
Web Site: http://www.alexevenings.com
Sales Range: $1-9.9 Million
Emp.: 45
Women's, Children's & Infants' Clothing & Accessories Merchant Whslr
N.A.I.C.S.: 424350
Jeanne Brizel *(VP)*
Karen Schneider *(Mgr-Ops)*
Colleen Kelly *(CEO)*

Holding (Non-US):

Allen-Vanguard Corporation **(2)**
2405 St Laurent Blvd Suite K, Ottawa, K1G 5B4, ON, Canada
Tel.: (613) 739-9646
Web Site: https://www.allenvanguard.com
Sales Range: $200-249.9 Million
Explosive, Hazardous Devices & Materials Device Security Equipment
N.A.I.C.S.: 561621

Subsidiary (Non-US):

Allen-Vanguard Limited **(3)**
Allen House, Alexandra Way Ashchurch Busin, Tewkesbury, GL20 8TD, United Kingdom
Tel.: (44) 1684851111
Web Site: http://www.allenvanguard.com
Sales Range: $10-24.9 Million
Emp.: 100
Security Products & Services
N.A.I.C.S.: 561621

Holding (Domestic):

Avenue Stores, LLC **(2)**
365 W Passaic St Ste 230, Rochelle Park, NJ 07662 **(100%)**
Tel.: (201) 845-0880
Web Site: http://www.avenue.com
Large-Size Women's Apparel & Accessories Specialty Retailer
N.A.I.C.S.: 458110
David D. English *(VP-Store Plng, Construction, Pur & Risk Mgmt)*
Kelly Ann Harbert *(VP-Sls-Midatlantic & Southeast Reg)*
Terence Puffer *(VP-Production Svcs)*
Gregory L. Segall *(Chm)*
Nancy Toth Viall *(Chief Mdsg Officer)*
Stephen Silbaugh *(Chief Mktg Officer)*
Scott Hampson *(COO)*
David Rhoads *(CFO)*
Mark Walsh *(CEO)*

BridgeStreet Worldwide Inc. **(2)**
485 Springpark Pl Ste 200, Herndon, VA 20170-5260
Tel.: (571) 481-2700
Web Site: http://www.bridgestreet.com
Sales Range: $125-149.9 Million
Corporate Apartment Rental Services
N.A.I.C.S.: 721199
Sean Worker *(Pres & CEO)*
Jeff Dunn *(Sr VP-Fin)*
Kelly Murphy *(VP-Mktg)*
Shaun Hinds *(Mng Dir-Ops-Intl)*
Ryan Rosenberg *(VP-Ops & Quality Assurance)*
John Janco *(Dir-Sls-Midwest)*
Mandy Ramzan *(Gen Mgr-New York)*
Paula Holloway *(Dir-Global Relocation Accts)*
Greg Kavanagh *(VP-Sls Ops-Paris & Washington)*
Kevin Toomer *(Dir-Sls-New York)*
C. A. Anderson *(Sr VP-Global Dev & Real Estate)*
Brian Proctor *(COO)*
Michael Snapkoski *(Sr VP-Revenue Generation)*
Keith Haas *(CFO)*
Jon Hile *(Chief Revenue Officer)*
Walter F. Dembiec Jr. *(Mng Dir-Ops & Brand Support Svcs)*

Subsidiary (Non-US):

Bridgestreet Accommodations London Ltd. **(3)**
1st Floor 8 Harewood Row, London, NW1 6SE, United Kingdom
Tel.: (44) 20 7792 2222
Web Site: http://www.bridgestreet.com
Corporate Apartment Services
N.A.I.C.S.: 721199
Samantha Thorne *(VP-Corp Client Rels)*

Holding (Domestic):

Brite-Line Technologies, Inc. **(2)**
10660 E 51st Ave, Denver, CO 80239
Tel.: (303) 375-1293
Web Site: http://www.brite-line.com
Emp.: 30
Highway Stripe Tape Mfr
N.A.I.C.S.: 325520
Fred Housewright *(VP-Ops)*

Civitas Media, LLC **(2)**
130 Harbour Place Dr Ste 300, Davidson, NC 28036
Tel.: (704) 897-6020
Web Site: http://www.civitasmedia.com
Emp.: 1,200
Newspaper Publishers
N.A.I.C.S.: 513110
Joe Pepe *(Sr VP-Newspapers)*

Unit (Domestic):

The (Alton) Telegraph **(3)**
111 E Broadway, Alton, IL 62002-6218
Tel.: (618) 463-2500
Web Site: http://www.thetelegraph.com
Sales Range: $10-24.9 Million
Emp.: 140
Newspaper Publishers
N.A.I.C.S.: 513110
Rick Thompson *(Bus Mgr)*
Bob Strickley *(Editor)*
Warren Watson *(Exec Editor)*
Bonnie Markham *(Sls Mgr-Adv)*

The Journal-Courier **(3)**
235 W State St, Jacksonville, IL 62650
Tel.: (217) 245-6121
Web Site: http://www.myjournalcourier.com
Newspapers
N.A.I.C.S.: 513110
David Bauer *(Editor)*
Daniel Cronin *(Mgr-Circulation)*
Vicki Selby *(Dir-Adv)*

The Lima News **(3)**
3515 Elida Rd, Lima, OH 45807
Tel.: (419) 223-1010
Web Site: http://www.limaohio.com
Newspapers
N.A.I.C.S.: 513110
Bill Clinger *(Dir-Mktg)*
Travis L. Sibold *(Mgr-Web Production & Tech)*
Jim Krumel *(Editor)*
Natalie Buzzard *(Mgr-Local Display)*
Doug Olsson *(Publr)*
Jose Nogueras *(Editor-Sports)*

The Sedalia Democrat **(3)**
700 S Massachusetts, Sedalia, MO 65301
Tel.: (660) 826-1000
Web Site: http://www.sedaliademocrat.com
Newspaper Publishers
N.A.I.C.S.: 513110
Eddie Crouch *(Mgr-Advertising)*
Nikki Monsees *(Mgr-Circulation)*
Mike Pace *(Mgr-District)*
Shane Allen *(Publr)*

Subsidiary (Domestic):

Wilkes-Barre Publishing Company, Inc. **(3)**
15 N Main St, Wilkes Barre, PA 18711
Tel.: (570) 829-7101
Web Site: http://www.timesleader.com
Sales Range: $25-49.9 Million
Emp.: 200
Newspaper Publishers
N.A.I.C.S.: 513110
Richard L. Connor *(Pres)*

Unit (Domestic):

Wilkes-Barre Times Leader **(4)**
15 N Main St, Wilkes Barre, PA 18711
Tel.: (570) 829-7101
Web Site: http://www.timesleader.com
Sales Range: $25-49.9 Million
Emp.: 225
Newspaper Publishers
N.A.I.C.S.: 513110
Brian Dudick *(Dir-IT)*
Michael Prazma *(VP-Circulation)*

Holding (Domestic):

Culberson Construction, LLC **(2)**
4500 Colony Rd, Granbury, TX 76048
Tel.: (817) 573-3079
Web Site: http://www.ccincservices.com
Oil & Gas Services
N.A.I.C.S.: 237120
Justin Culberson *(CEO)*
Brad Culberson *(Pres)*

Subsidiary (Domestic):

Nicholas Consulting Group, Inc. **(3)**
600 N Marienfeld St, Midland, TX 79701
Tel.: (432) 570-8093
Web Site: http://www.thencg.com
Sales Range: $1-9.9 Million
Emp.: 42
Engineeering Services
N.A.I.C.S.: 541330
Mark Nicholas *(Pres-Admin)*
Ramon Valles *(VP)*

Holding (Domestic):

Ohio Cummunity Media LLC **(2)**
4500 Lyons Rd, Miamisburg, OH 45342
Tel.: (937) 247-2700
Newspaper Publishers
N.A.I.C.S.: 513110
Bob Sample *(Dir-Production & IT)*

Subsidiary (Domestic):

Troy Daily News **(3)**
224 S Market St, Troy, OH 45373-3327
Tel.: (937) 335-5634
Web Site: http://www.troydailynews.com
Sales Range: $10-24.9 Million
Emp.: 25
Community Newspaper
N.A.I.C.S.: 513110
Joshua Byers *(Publr)*

Holding (Domestic):

Republic Storage Systems, LLC **(2)**
1038 Belden Ave NE, Canton, OH 44705-1459
Tel.: (330) 438-5800
Web Site: http://www.republicstorage.com
Sales Range: $50-74.9 Million
Lockers, Shelving, Metal Cabinets & Storage Racks Mfr
N.A.I.C.S.: 337215
Cathy Maxin *(Dir-Mktg)*

Silver Airways, LLC **(2)**
1100 Lee Wagener Blvd Ste 201, Fort Lauderdale, FL 33315
Tel.: (801) 401-9100
Web Site: http://www.silverairways.com
Airline Operations
N.A.I.C.S.: 481111
Jason Bewley *(Pres & CFO)*

Simplexity, LLC **(2)**
10790 Parkridge Blvd Ste 200, Reston, VA 20191
Tel.: (703) 657-4600
Web Site: http://www.simplexity.com
Sales Range: $75-99.9 Million
Online Cell Phone Retailer
N.A.I.C.S.: 449210
Frank C. Bennett III *(CEO)*

Branch (Domestic):

Simplexity Technology & Operations Center **(3)**
9301 Peppercorn Pl, Largo, MD 20774
Tel.: (301) 883-0040
Web Site: http://www.libertywireless.com
Cellular Phone Services
N.A.I.C.S.: 488510

Holding (Domestic):

The Wet Seal, LLC **(2)**
7555 Irvine Ctr Dr, Irvine, CA 92618
Tel.: (949) 699-3900
Web Site: http://www.wetseal.com
Sales Range: $500-549.9 Million
Emp.: 3,000
Contemporary Apparel & Accessories Retailer
N.A.I.C.S.: 458110
Melanie Cox *(CEO)*
Rachael Page *(Sr VP-Stores & Ops)*

Vestis Retail Group, LLC **(2)**
160 Corporate Ct, Meriden, CT 06450-8313
Tel.: (203) 235-5775
Holding Company; Apparel, Footwear & Related Products Retailer
N.A.I.C.S.: 551112
Mark T. Walsh *(Chm)*
Susan J. Riley *(Executives)*

Subsidiary (Domestic):

Sport Chalet, Inc. **(3)**
1 Sports Chalet Dr, La Canada, CA 91011
Tel.: (818) 949-5300

Independence Capital Partners,
LLC—(Continued)

Web Site: http://www.sportchalet.com
Rev.: $343,506,000
Assets: $123,516,000
Liabilities: $118,176,000
Net Worth: $5,340,000
Earnings: ($10,139,000)
Emp.: 1,200
Fiscal Year-end: 03/30/2014
Full Service Sporting Goods Stores
N.A.I.C.S.: 459110
Tim Anderson (Exec VP-Retail Ops, Loss Prevention & Specialty Svcs)
Tom Tennyson (Chief Mdsg Officer & Exec VP)
Brad Morton (Sr. VP-Sls)

INDEPENDENCE CARE SYSTEM
257 Park Ave S 2nd Fl, New York, NY 10010-7304
Tel.: (212) 584-2500　　　　**NY**
Web Site: http://www.icsny.org
Year Founded: 1999
Sales Range: $125-149.9 Million
Emp.: 354
Disability Assistance Services
N.A.I.C.S.: 624120
Mark T. Corcoran (CFO)
Jean Minkel (Sr VP-Rehabilitation Svcs)
Lisa M. Feliciano (Sr VP-HR)
Regina Martinez-Estela (COO)
Loreen Loonie (Sr VP-Mktg & Comm)

INDEPENDENCE EXCAVATING, INC.
5720 E Schaaf Rd, Cleveland, OH 44131-1308
Tel.: (216) 524-1700　　　　**OH**
Web Site: http://www.indexc.com
Year Founded: 1962
Sales Range: $10-24.9 Million
Emp.: 400
Excavation Work
N.A.I.C.S.: 238910
Victor DiGeronimo Sr. (Chm)

Subsidiaries:

Independence Recycling Division　(1)
9800 Recycle Ctr Rd, Orlando, FL 32824-8150
Tel.: (407) 240-1664
Web Site: http://www.indexc.com
Sales Range: $10-24.9 Million
Emp.: 6
Wrecking & Demolition Work
N.A.I.C.S.: 238910
Greg Moro (Mgr-Ops)

INDEPENDENCE FISH COMPANY
661 W Germantown Pike, Plymouth Meeting, PA 19462
Tel.: (610) 940-9227　　　　**PA**
Web Site: http://www.independencefish.com
Year Founded: 1997
Sales Range: $10-24.9 Million
Emp.: 3
Seafood Importer & Exporter
N.A.I.C.S.: 424460
Jonathon Goldstein (Pres)

INDEPENDENCE FUND, INC.
330 Coosaw Way Ste 1, Ridgeland, SC 29936
Tel.: (434) 409-0506　　　　**NC**
Web Site: http://www.independencefund.org
Year Founded: 2007
Sales Range: $10-24.9 Million
Veteran Support Services
N.A.I.C.S.: 813410
Steve Danyluk (Founder)

INDEPENDENCE MORTGAGE TRUST, INC.
Cira Centre 2929 Arch St 17th Fl, Philadelphia, PA 19103
Tel.: (215) 243-9000　　　　**MD**
Web Site: http://www.rait.com
Year Founded: 2011
Emp.: 200
Real Estate Investment Services
N.A.I.C.S.: 525990
Scott F. Schaeffer (Chm & CEO)
Matthew Anzideo (Sr VP-Underwriting)
James J. Sebra (CFO & Treas)

INDEPENDENCE REALTY, LLC
2315 Market Pl SW Ste E, Huntsville, AL 35801
Tel.: (256) 650-6262　　　　**AL**
Web Site: http://www.renthuntsvilleala bama.com
Real Estate Agency
N.A.I.C.S.: 531210
Robert Taylor (Owner)

INDEPENDENCE RESIDENCES, INC.
93-22 Jamaica Ave 2nd Fl, Woodhaven, NY 11421
Tel.: (718) 805-6796　　　　**NY**
Web Site: http://www.in-res.org
Year Founded: 1988
Sales Range: $10-24.9 Million
Emp.: 482
Developmental Disability Assistance Services
N.A.I.C.S.: 624120
Raymond J. DeNatale (Exec Dir)

INDEPENDENCEFIRST
540 S 1st St, Milwaukee, WI 53204-1516
Tel.: (414) 291-7520　　　　**WI**
Web Site: http://www.independencefirst.org
Year Founded: 1979
Sales Range: $25-49.9 Million
Emp.: 2,302
Developmental Disability Assistance Services
N.A.I.C.S.: 624120
Beth L. Schumacher (Vice Chm)
John Lauber (Treas)
Starlet Hayes (Dir-Fund Dev & Comm)
Brenda Duke (VP-HR)
Mike Lipscomb (Chm)
Deb Langham (VP-Independent Living)

INDEPENDENT BANCORP., LIMITED
206 E Main St, Little Chute, WI 54140
Tel.: (920) 788-4141　　　　**WI**
Web Site: http://www.blccb.com
Year Founded: 1996
Sales Range: $1-9.9 Million
Emp.: 27
Bank Holding Company
N.A.I.C.S.: 551111
Gary L. Vanden Heuvel (Pres)

Subsidiaries:

BLC Community Bank　(1)
206 E Main St, Little Chute, WI 54140
Tel.: (920) 788-4141
Web Site: http://www.blccb.com
Emp.: 30
Commericial Banking
N.A.I.C.S.: 522110
Gary L. Vanden Heuvel (Pres)
Vicki Running (Asst VP)

INDEPENDENT BANCSHARES, INC.
200 4th Ave SW, Red Bay, AL 35582
Tel.: (256) 356-4445　　　　**AL**
Web Site: http://www.communityspiritbank.com
Year Founded: 1981
Sales Range: $1-9.9 Million
Emp.: 38
Bank Holding Company
N.A.I.C.S.: 551111
Billy M. Bolton (Chm, Pres & CEO)
Patricia A. Nelson (Vice Chm & Exec VP)
Brad M. Bolton (Pres/CEO-Community Spirit Bank)

Subsidiaries:

Community Spirit Bank　(1)
200 4th Ave SW, Red Bay, AL 35582
Tel.: (256) 356-4445
Web Site: http://www.communityspiritbank.com
Sales Range: $1-9.9 Million
Commericial Banking
N.A.I.C.S.: 522110
Billy M. Bolton (Chm)
Patricia A. Nelson (Vice Chm & Exec VP)
Brad Bolton (Pres & CEO)
Tammy B. Montgomery (COO, Exec VP & Dir-HR)
Donna Purser (CFO & VP-Info Sys & Mgr-IT)
Rhonda Hardin (VP-Consumer Lending)
Emily Mays (VP & Sr Dir-Mktg)

INDEPENDENT BANK
5050 Poplar Ave Ste 112, Memphis, TN 38157
Tel.: (901) 844-0400
Web Site: http://www.i-bankonline.com
Year Founded: 1998
Sales Range: $25-49.9 Million
Emp.: 125
Commercial Bank
N.A.I.C.S.: 522110
Jessica Henderson (Mgr-Collection)

Subsidiaries:

Goodman Factors, Inc.　(1)
3010 LBJ Freeway Ste 140, Dallas, TX 75234
Tel.: (972) 241-3297
Web Site: http://www.goodmanfactors.com
Sales Range: $1-9.9 Million
Emp.: 18
Nondepository Credit Intermediation
N.A.I.C.S.: 522299
Keith Reid (Pres)
Jessie Valdivia (VP)
Alejandro Galindo (VP)
Bret Schuch (Partner & Sr VP)
Paul Ellenbogen (VP-Credit & Collections)
Alexandra Scoggin (VP-West Coast)
Dan Shepherd (VP-Denver)
Steven Sussman (VP-New Jersey)

INDEPENDENT BANKERS FINANCIAL CORPORATION
11701 Luna Rd, Farmers Branch, TX 75234
Tel.: (972) 650-6000　　　　**TX**
Web Site: http://www.mybankersbank.com
Year Founded: 1983
Bank Holding Company
N.A.I.C.S.: 551111
Michael G. O'Rourke (Pres & CEO)

Subsidiaries:

TIB The Independent BankersBank, National Association　(1)
11701 Luna Rd, Farmers Branch, TX 75234
Tel.: (972) 650-6000
Web Site: http://www.mybankersbank.com
Sales Range: $50-74.9 Million
Emp.: 350
Savings Bank
N.A.I.C.S.: 522180

Terri Bacot (Sr VP & Controller)
Patricia Blackshear (Exec VP-HR)
Lyle Walden (Sr VP & Dir-Ops & IT)
Greg Todd (VP & Dir-Comm)
Michael G. O'Rourke (Pres & CEO)
Scott Kelley (Sr VP & Dir-Card Svcs-Bus Dev)
David A. Linaburg (Exec VP-Mortgage & Capital Markets)
R. Kevin Drew (Chief Lending Officer & Exec VP)
T. Patrick Gray (COO & Exec VP)
Alicia Garrison (Sr VP)

INDEPENDENT BEVERAGE COMPANY, LLC
3936 Corporation Cir, Charlotte, NC 28216
Tel.: (704) 399-2504
Web Site: http://www.independentbever age.com
Year Founded: 1992
Bottled & Canned Soft Drinks
N.A.I.C.S.: 312111

INDEPENDENT CAN COMPANY
1300 Brass Mill Rd, Belcamp, MD 21017-1211
Tel.: (410) 272-0090　　　　**MD**
Web Site: http://www.independentcan.com
Year Founded: 1929
Sales Range: $100-124.9 Million
Emp.: 200
Decorative & Various Specialty Cans Mfr
N.A.I.C.S.: 332431
Douglas Huether (Chm)
Rick Huether (Pres & CEO)
George R. McClelland (VP-Admin)
Neil Defrancisco (VP-Sls & Mktg)
Ryan Huether (VP-Bus Dev)
Bryan Powell (VP-Engrg)

Subsidiaries:

Independent Can Company - Distribution Div　(1)
2040 S Lynx Ave, Ontario, CA 91761-8010　(100%)
Tel.: (909) 923-6150
Web Site: http://www.independentcan.com
Sales Range: $10-24.9 Million
Emp.: 10
Packaging Cans, Industrial & Promotional, Glass, Plastic & Paper Distr
N.A.I.C.S.: 423840
Brian Schuler (Reg Mgr)

INDEPENDENT CAPITAL MANAGEMENT
240 Calle Campesino, San Clemente, CA 92672
Tel.: (949) 366-0761
Web Site: http://www.icmfinancial.com
Sales Range: $200-249.9 Million
Emp.: 5
Investment Counselors
N.A.I.C.S.: 523940
Drew Marloe (Pres & CEO)
Lance Stanley (CFO)

INDEPENDENT CHEMICAL CORP.
7951 Cooper Ave, Glendale, NY 11385
Tel.: (718) 894-0700
Web Site: http://www.independentchemical.com
Sales Range: $25-49.9 Million
Emp.: 30
Industrial Chemicals
N.A.I.C.S.: 424690
Jonathan Spielman (Pres)
Jim Gregus (Mgr-Pur)
Erika Sheahan (Mgr-Customer Svc)
Ruby Tsaousis (Mgr)

INDEPENDENT COMMUNITY

BANKERS OF AMERICA
1615 L St NW Ste 900, Washington, DC 20036
Tel.: (202) 659-8111
Web Site: http://www.icba.org
Sales Range: $25-49.9 Million
Emp.: 140
Professional Organizations
N.A.I.C.S.: 813920
Camden R. Fine (Pres & CEO)
Terry Jorde (Sr Exec VP)
Mark A. Raitor (COO & Sr Exec VP)
Karen M. Thomas (Sr Exec VP-Govt Rels & Pub Policy)
Chris Lorence (Exec VP-Member Engagement & Strategy Grp)
Paul G. Merski (Exec VP-Congressional Rels & Strategy Grp)
Viveca Y. Ware (Exec VP-Regulatory Policy Grp)
Brenda Melvin (Chief HR Officer & Exec VP)
Julie Kulzer (Dir-Conferences & Meetings)
Brian Gimbel (VP-Fin & Budget)
Kris Winter (Asst VP-Acctg Svcs)
Adam Mahone (Asst VP-Vendor Rels)
Mary Smolenski (Asst VP-Online Svcs)
LuAnne Roelike (VP-Member Data)
Sandy Zehrer (Dir-Conferences & Meetings)
Jeanie Klasen (Dir-Member Engagement)
Scott Heitkamp (Chm)
Kevin Tweddle (Grp Exec VP-Innovation & Fin Tech-ICBA Svcs Network)
Prabhash Shrestha (Chief Digital Strategy Officer & Exec VP)
Christopher Jordan (Sec)
Derek B. Williams (Treas)
Preston L. Kennedy (Vice Chm)
Patricia Hopkins (CFO, COO & Sr Exec VP)
David Haithcock (Exec VP)
John McNair (Exec VP-Member Rels)
Aaron Stetter (Exec VP-Policy & Political Ops)
Mark K. Scanlan (Sr VP-Agriculture & Rural Policy)
Jim Mastey (Sr VP-Conventions & Meetings)
Aleis Stokes (Sr VP-Media & PR)
David Moore (Sr VP-Southeast Reg)
Joe Schneider (Sr VP-State Rels)
Caroline Prado Johnson (VP)
Jana Jurukovska (VP & Dir-Mktg & Creative)
Linda Heinze (VP-Acctg)
Kianga Lee (VP-Admin Ops)
Eric Hallman (VP-Central Plains Reg)
George Jenkins (VP-Information Sys)
Pam Wolbeck (VP-IT Sys)
Chip Lynch (VP-Southwest)

INDEPENDENT ELECTRIC SUPPLY
41 Innerbelt Rd Ste 2, Somerville, MA 02143
Tel.: (617) 625-5155
Web Site: http://www.iesbuy.com
Sales Range: $25-49.9 Million
Emp.: 60
Electrical Apparatus & Equipment
N.A.I.C.S.: 423610
William L. Gray (CEO)
Daniel Gray (Pres)

INDEPENDENT ELECTRICAL CONTRACTORS, INC.
4401 Ford Ave Ste 1100, Alexandria, VA 22302
Tel.: (703) 549-7351 VA

Web Site: http://www.ieci.org
Year Founded: 1962
Sales Range: $1-9.9 Million
Emp.: 18
Electrical Contractor Association
N.A.I.C.S.: 813920
Bruce Seilhammer (Treas)
Candy Branham (Dir-Midwest Reg)
Gary Golka (VP)
Janet Martin (Dir-Mountain West Reg)
Joseph Hovanec (Pres)
Bruce Seilhammer (Treas)
Candy Branham (Dir-Midwest Reg)
Gary Golka (VP)
Janet Martin (Dir-Mountain West Reg)
Joseph Hovanec (Pres)
Lloyd Quinney (Sec)
Steve Struble (Dir-Midwest Reg)
Thayer Long (CEO & Exec VP)
Troy Corrigan (Dir-Midwest Reg)

INDEPENDENT FINANCIAL AGENTS
14 Walnut Ave, Clark, NJ 07066
Tel.: (732) 815-1201
Web Site: http://www.ifaauto.com
Year Founded: 1972
Sales Range: $10-24.9 Million
Emp.: 35
Mutual Benefit Associations
N.A.I.C.S.: 522291
David Walsh (Pres)

INDEPENDENT FINANCIAL GROUP, LLC
12671 High Bluff Dr Ste 200, San Diego, CA 92130
Tel.: (858) 436-3180
Web Site: http://www.ifgsd.com
Sales Range: $25-49.9 Million
Emp.: 65
Investment Advisory Services
N.A.I.C.S.: 523940
Scott Heising (CFO & Mng Dir)
Joe H. Miller (CEO & Mng Dir)
David A. Fischer (Mng Dir)
Kian Rafia (Sr VP-Wealth Mgmt)

INDEPENDENT FINANCIAL PARTNERS
3030 N Rocky Point Dr W Ste 700, Tampa, FL 33607-7200
Tel.: (813) 341-0960
Web Site: http://www.ifpartners.com
Year Founded: 2000
Rev.: $2,800,000,000
Emp.: 400
Financial Advisory Services
N.A.I.C.S.: 523940
William E. Hamm (CEO)
Aaron Gilman (Chief Investment Officer)
Richard Richmond (Dir-Advisor Rels)
Jayne Alford (Mng Dir-Insurance Grp)
John Whisenant (Chief Compliance Officer)
Sarah Taylor (Dir-Examinations-Eastern)
W. Chris Hamm (Exec VP)
Trent Gain (Dir-Advisor Rels)
Sean Brennan (Dir-Mktg)
Jay Bloom (Dir-Bus Dev)
Kimberly Shaw Elliott (Pres-Plan Advisors)
Ned Van Riper (Dir-Recruiting)
Mark Duran (Dir-Res)
Peter Nunley (Dir-Asset Mgmt)
Scott Kaszyk (Dir-IT)
Michael Cadenhead (Mgr-Advisor Compensation)

INDEPENDENT FINANCIAL SYSTEMS, INC.

25541 Commercentre Dr Ste 100, Lake Forest, CA 92630
Tel.: (949) 789-6200
Web Site:
http://www.ifs.portfolioco.com
Year Founded: 1990
Sales Range: $1-9.9 Million
Emp.: 25
Formulates & Manages Professional Reinsurance Programs for Automotive Dealers
N.A.I.C.S.: 524130
Steve Burke (Mgr)

INDEPENDENT GROUP HOME LIVING PROGRAM INC.
221 N Sunrise Service Rd, Manorville, NY 11949
Tel.: (631) 878-8900 NY
Web Site: http://www.ighl.org
Year Founded: 1978
Sales Range: $50-74.9 Million
Emp.: 1,346
Disability Assistance Services
N.A.I.C.S.: 624120
Walter W. Stockton (CEO)
Paul Pontieri (Chm)
Chris McCann (Vice Chm)
Joseph Morris (Sec)
Janet Fernandez (Treas)

INDEPENDENT II, LLC
7825 National Tpke, Louisville, KY 40214-4901
Tel.: (502) 315-2525
Web Site:
http://www.independent2.com
Sales Range: $10-24.9 Million
Emp.: 66
Corrugated & Fiber Box Mfr
N.A.I.C.S.: 322211
Neil MacDonald (CEO)
Ken Walsh (Mgr-Pkg & Sls)
Linda Rogers (Mgr-Customer Svc)
Vern Jennings (Mgr-Production)

INDEPENDENT INSURANCE AGENTS & BROKERS OF AMERICA, INC.
127 S Peyton St, Alexandria, VA 22314-2803
Web Site:
http://www.independentagent.com
Year Founded: 1896
Sales Range: $50-74.9 Million
Emp.: 70
Insurance Providing Services
N.A.I.C.S.: 524210
Steve Cocke (CFO)

Subsidiaries:

Big I Advantage, Inc. (1)
127 S Peyton St Fl 3, Alexandria, VA 22314
Tel.: (703) 683-4422
Insurance Brokerage Services
N.A.I.C.S.: 524210
Blake Pierson (Asst VP)
Paul Buse (Pres)

IIAA Agency Administrative Services, Inc. (1)
127 S Peyton St, Alexandria, VA 22314
Tel.: (703) 683-4422
Web Site: http://www.independentagent.com
Insurance Brokerage Services
N.A.I.C.S.: 524210
Ines Hoyle (Office Mgr)

IIAA Membership Services, Inc. (1)
127 S Peyton St, Alexandria, VA 22314
Tel.: (703) 706-5366
Sales Range: $50-74.9 Million
General Insurance Services
N.A.I.C.S.: 524210

Insurance Brokers & Agents of the West (1)
7041 Koll Centre Pkwy Ste 290, Pleasanton, CA 94566
Tel.: (925) 426-3300

Sales Range: $10-24.9 Million
Emp.: 25
Insurance & Related Services Offered by Independent Insurance Brokers & Agents in California, Alaska, Oregon & Washington
N.A.I.C.S.: 524210
David Benesh (VP-Mktg & Comm)
Constance Cohrs (Mgr-Member Svcs)
Steve Young (Gen Counsel & Sr VP)
Clark Payan (CEO)
Jim Cross (VP-Fin Ops)
Jennifer Pouey (VP-Member Svcs)
Michael Orrick (VP-Member R&D)
Pauline Nakadachi (Mgr-Member Svcs)

Trusted Choice, Inc. (1)
127 S Peyton St, Alexandria, VA 22314
Tel.: (703) 299-4207
Web Site: http://www.trustedchoice.com
Insurance Brokerage Services
N.A.I.C.S.: 524210

INDEPENDENT INSURANCE CENTER, INC.
1739 Citadel Plz, San Antonio, TX 78209
Tel.: (210) 821-5080
Web Site: http://www.iicsa.com
Year Founded: 1983
Sales Range: $10-24.9 Million
Emp.: 50
Insurance Services
N.A.I.C.S.: 524210
Pat Quirk (Pres)
Bonnie Campa (Mgr-Fin)
Daniel M. Carmody (Owner)
Don Glasscock (VP)

INDEPENDENT LIVING SYSTEMS, LLC.
52100 Blue Lagoon Dr Ste 270, Miami, FL 33126
Tel.: (305) 262-1292 FL
Web Site:
http://www.ilshealthservices.com
Year Founded: 2001
Elderly Managed Long-Term Healthcare & Nutritional Support Services
N.A.I.C.S.: 624120
Nestor Plana (Founder, Chm & CEO)
Josefina Carbonell (Sr VP-Long Term Care & Nutrition)
Celia Nuno (Sr VP-Admin)
Evan Willette (CFO)
Peter McCann (Chief Revenue Officer)
David Gutwald (Sr VP-Ops)
Manjinder Singh (CIO)
Mariela Fermin (Chief Strategy Officer)
Maureen Lillis (COO)
Mari Netto (VP-Mktg)
Stuart Williams (Gen Counsel)
David Rogers (Pres)
Carol Gormley (VP-Govt Affairs)

Subsidiaries:

Royal Health Care of Long Island, LLC (1)
810 7th Ave Ste 801, New York, NY 10019
Tel.: (212) 808-4775
Web Site: http://www.royalhc.com
Emp.: 225
Managed Care Industry Business & Information Technology Support Services
N.A.I.C.S.: 524292
Ronald R. Arfin (CFO)
Edward Cotes (COO)
Mohammad A. Jangda (CIO)

INDEPENDENT LIVING, INC.
5 Washington Ter, Newburgh, NY 12550
Tel.: (845) 565-1162 NY
Web Site:
http://www.myindependentliving.org
Year Founded: 1987
Sales Range: $10-24.9 Million
Emp.: 632

Independent Living, Inc.—(Continued)

Disability Assistance Services
N.A.I.C.S.: 624120
Douglas J. Hovey *(Pres & CEO)*
Beth Abarca *(Dir-HR)*
Criss Ittermann *(Sec)*
Sean Soliva *(Treas)*
Jeffrey Sculley *(Sec)*
Andrew Weyant *(VP)*
Emily Robisch *(CFO)*
Charles Walwyn III *(Pres)*

INDEPENDENT MEDIA
3000 Olympic Blvd Bldg 5 Ste 1201,
Santa Monica, CA 90404
Tel.: (310) 659-3503   CA
Web Site:
http://www.independentmedia.com
Year Founded: 2000
Sales Range: $1-9.9 Million
Emp.: 14
Motion Picture & Video Production
N.A.I.C.S.: 512110
Susanne Preissler *(Pres)*
Iqbal Surve *(Chm)*
Aneez Salie *(Grp Editor)*
Sizwe Dlamini *(Editor-Special Investigations Unit)*

INDEPENDENT NEWSPAPERS, INC.
110 Galaxy Dr, Dover, DE 19901
Tel.: (302) 674-3600
Web Site: http://www.newszap.com
Sales Range: $25-49.9 Million
Emp.: 300
Newspaper Publishers
N.A.I.C.S.: 513110
Michelle Vinson *(Mgr-IT Production Sys)*
Wanda Ford-Waring *(Dir-Payroll & Benefit)*
Tony Howard *(Deputy Chm)*

Subsidiaries:

Caloosa Belle   (1)
22 Ft Thompson Ave, Labelle, FL 33975
Tel.: (863) 675-2541
Web Site: http://www.newszap.com
Sales Range: $10-24.9 Million
Emp.: 3
Newspaper Publishing
N.A.I.C.S.: 516210
Joe Smith *(Pres)*

Clewiston News   (1)
820 W Sugarland Hwy Ste 5, Clewiston, FL
33440
Tel.: (863) 983-9148
Web Site: http://www.newszap.com
Sales Range: $10-24.9 Million
Emp.: 7
Newspaper Publishing
N.A.I.C.S.: 513110

Crisfield Times   (1)
914 W Main St, Crisfield, MD 21817
Tel.: (410) 968-1188
Web Site: http://www.csctimes.com
Sales Range: $10-24.9 Million
Emp.: 2
Newspaper Publishing
N.A.I.C.S.: 513110
Ed Dulin *(Pres)*

Delaware Printing Company
110 Galaxy Dr, Dover, DE 19901
Tel.: (302) 741-8245
Web Site: http://www.newszap.com
Newspaper Publishers
N.A.I.C.S.: 513110
Jaclyn Fuller *(Sls Mgr)*
Thomas Bugbee *(Gen Mgr)*

Delaware State News   (1)
PO Box 737, Dover, DE 19903
Tel.: (302) 629-5505
Newspaper Publishing
N.A.I.C.S.: 513110
Andy West *(Editor)*
Tonda Parks *(VP-Adv Dev)*
Darel LaPrade *(Publr)*
Marty Valania *(Dir-Adv)*

Delmarva Real Estate   (1)
110 Galaxy Dr, Dover, DE 19901
Tel.: (302) 629-5505
Web Site: http://www.newszap.com
Sales Range: $10-24.9 Million
Emp.: 8
Newspaper Publishing
N.A.I.C.S.: 531210

Dorchester Banner   (1)
103 Cedar St, Cambridge, MD 21613
Tel.: (410) 228-3131
Web Site: http://www.newszap.com
Sales Range: $10-24.9 Million
Emp.: 12
Newspaper Publishing
N.A.I.C.S.: 513110
Michael Pelrine *(Editorial Mgr)*
Darel La Prade *(Publr)*

Frostproof News   (1)
14 W Wall St, Frostproof, FL 33843-2042
Tel.: (863) 635-2171
Sales Range: $10-24.9 Million
Emp.: 1
Newspaper Publishing
N.A.I.C.S.: 541840

Glades County Democrat   (1)
820 W Sugarland Hwy Ste 5, Clewiston, FL
33440
Tel.: (863) 983-9148
Sales Range: $10-24.9 Million
Emp.: 10
Newspaper Publishing
N.A.I.C.S.: 513110

Immokalee Bulletin   (1)
22 Fort Thompson Ave, Labelle, FL 33935
Tel.: (863) 675-2541
Web Site: http://www.newszap.com
Emp.: 3
Newspaper Publishing
N.A.I.C.S.: 513110
Katrina Elsken *(Publr)*

Independent Newspapers, Inc.
Arizona   (1)
23043 N 16th Ln, Phoenix, AZ 85027
Tel.: (623) 445-2800
Web Site: http://www.newszap.com
Sales Range: $100-124.9 Million
Regional Managing Office; Newspaper Publisher
N.A.I.C.S.: 551114
Ed Dulin *(CEO)*
Brad McKeand *(Pres)*

Unit (Domestic):

Apache Junction Independent   (2)
2066 W Apache Trl Ste 110, Apache Junction, AZ 85120
Tel.: (480) 982-7799
Web Site:
http://www.apachejunctionindependent.com
Sales Range: $10-24.9 Million
Emp.: 8
Newspaper Publishing
N.A.I.C.S.: 513110
Greg Tock *(Publr)*

Arrowhead Ranch Independent   (2)
17220 N Boswell Blvd, Sun City, AZ 85373
Tel.: (623) 972-6101
Web Site: http://www.newszap.com
Sales Range: $10-24.9 Million
Emp.: 10
Newspaper Publishing
N.A.I.C.S.: 513110

East Mesa Independent   (2)
2066 W Apache Trl Ste 110, Apache Junction, AZ 85120
Tel.: (480) 982-7799
Web Site: http://www.arizona.newszap.com
Sales Range: $10-24.9 Million
Emp.: 10
Newspaper Publishing
N.A.I.C.S.: 459420
Bret McKeand *(Publr)*

North Scottsdale Independent   (2)
23043 N 16th Ln, Phoenix, AZ 85027
Tel.: (623) 445-2777
Web Site:
http://www.scottsdaleindependent.com
Sales Range: $10-24.9 Million
Emp.: 40
Newspaper Publishing

N.A.I.C.S.: 813920
Bret McKeand *(Gen Mgr & VP)*

Peoria Independent   (2)
17220 N Boswell Blvd Ste L101, Sun City,
AZ 85373
Tel.: (623) 972-6101
Web Site: http://www.newszap.com
Sales Range: $10-24.9 Million
Emp.: 12
Newspaper Publishing
N.A.I.C.S.: 513110
Bret McKeand *(Pres)*
Charlene Bison *(Publr)*

Sun Cities Independent   (2)
17220 N Boswell Blvd Ste L101, Sun City,
AZ 85373
Tel.: (623) 972-6101
Web Site: http://www.arizona.newszap.com
Sales Range: $10-24.9 Million
Emp.: 10
Newspaper Publishing
N.A.I.C.S.: 513110
Ed Dulin *(CEO)*

Surprise Independent   (2)
17220 N Boswell Blvd Ste 101, Sun City,
AZ 85373
Tel.: (623) 972-6101
Web Site: http://www.arizona.newszap.com
Sales Range: $10-24.9 Million
Emp.: 12
Newspaper Publishing
N.A.I.C.S.: 513110
Joe Smith *(CEO)*
Joe Smith *(CEO)*

Town of Paradise Valley
Independent   (2)
23043 N 16th Ln, Phoenix, AZ 85027
Tel.: (623) 445-2777
Web Site: http://arizona.newszap.com
Sales Range: $10-24.9 Million
Emp.: 20
Newspaper Publishers
N.A.I.C.S.: 513110
Bret McKeanz *(VP & Gen Mgr)*

Valley Newspapers   (2)
23043 N 16th Ln, Phoenix, AZ 85027
Tel.: (623) 445-2800
Web Site: http://www.valleynewspapers.org
Sales Range: $10-24.9 Million
Emp.: 20
Newspaper Publishing
N.A.I.C.S.: 513110
Mike Jacobs *(Mgr-Customer Svc & Printing)*

Lake Okeechobee Real Estate
Magazine   (1)
107 SW 17th St, Okeechobee, FL 34974
Tel.: (863) 763-3134
Web Site: http://www.newszap.com
Sales Range: $25-49.9 Million
Emp.: 25
Newspaper Publishing
N.A.I.C.S.: 524210
Joe Smyth *(CEO)*

Milford Chronicle   (1)
37A N Walnut St, Milford, DE 19963
Tel.: (302) 422-1200
Web Site: http://www.milfordchronicle.net
Sales Range: $10-24.9 Million
Emp.: 10
Newspaper Publishing
N.A.I.C.S.: 513110
Darel Laprade *(Gen Mgr)*

Sunshine Newpaper Printing   (1)
3109 Old SR 8, Lake Placid, FL 33852
Tel.: (863) 465-4213
Sales Range: $10-24.9 Million
Emp.: 23
Newspaper Publishing
N.A.I.C.S.: 513110

Sussex Post   (1)
37A N Walnut St, Milford, DE 19963
Tel.: (302) 629-5505
Web Site:
http://www.delaware.newszap.com
Sales Range: $10-24.9 Million
Emp.: 15
Newspaper Publishing
N.A.I.C.S.: 513110

The Okeechobee News   (1)
107 SW 17th Ste D, Okeechobee, FL
34974

Tel.: (863) 763-3134
Web Site: http://www.newszap.com
Sales Range: $10-24.9 Million
Emp.: 20
Newspaper Publishing
N.A.I.C.S.: 513110
Tom Byrd *(Mgr-Admin)*
Katrina Elsken *(Mgr-Admin)*

The Sun   (1)
820 W Sugarland Hwy Ste 5, Clewiston, FL
33440
Tel.: (863) 983-9148
Sales Range: $10-24.9 Million
Emp.: 7
Newspaper Publishing
N.A.I.C.S.: 513110
Debra Miller *(Editor)*

INDEPENDENT OIL & COAL COMPANY
23 Devereaux St, Natchez, MS
39120
Tel.: (601) 442-2824
Sales Range: $10-24.9 Million
Emp.: 60
Convenience Stores, Independent
N.A.I.C.S.: 445131
Louise Finley *(Office Mgr)*
Charles Zuccora *(VP)*

INDEPENDENT PAPERBOARD MARKETING INC.
19950 Overseas Hwy, Summerland
Key, FL 33042-0228
Tel.: (305) 745-1116   FL
Web Site:
http://www.independentpaperboard.com
Year Founded: 1994
Sales Range: $75-99.9 Million
Emp.: 40
Paper Brokerage Firm
N.A.I.C.S.: 424130
Mike Greene *(Pres)*

INDEPENDENT PIPE & SUPPLY CORPORATION
6 Whitman Rd, Canton, MA 02021
Tel.: (781) 828-8500   MA
Web Site: http://www.indpipe.com
Year Founded: 1960
Rev.: $20,300,000
Emp.: 45
Heating Equipment (Hydronic)
N.A.I.C.S.: 423720
Edward J. Nierman *(Co-Chm)*
Jeffrey H. Nierman *(Pres & CEO)*
Sheldon Nierman *(Co-Chm & CFO)*
Sharon Norton *(Treas)*
Eric Kessler *(VP)*
Larry Perigel *(VP-Sls)*
Alan Mirson *(Exec VP)*
Brad Carstensen *(Mgr-Bridgeport)*
Kevin MacKenzie *(Mgr-Distr)*
Albert Connolly *(Mgr-Inside Sls & Transportation)*
Chris Larkin *(Mgr-Inventory & Receiving)*
Michael Levin *(Mgr-Sls)*
Cheryl Zajdel *(Supvr-Accts Payable)*
Steven Goldie Goldstein *(Supvr-Equipment Sls)*

INDEPENDENT PLASTIC INC.
6611 Petropark Dr, Houston, TX
77041
Tel.: (713) 329-9955
Web Site:
http://www.independentplastic.com
Year Founded: 1979
Sales Range: $10-24.9 Million
Emp.: 17
Plastic Pellets Whslr
N.A.I.C.S.: 423840
David Ressler *(Pres)*
Neal Scott *(VP-Sls)*

INDEPENDENT PRINTING

COMPANY, INC.
3930 Pacheco Blvd, Martinez, CA
94553
Tel.: (925) 229-5050   **CA**
Web Site:
http://www.ipcoprinting.com
Year Founded: 1955
Sales Range: $1-9.9 Million
Emp.: 40
Commercial Printing, Lithographic
N.A.I.C.S.: 323111
Kurt Brombacher (Owner)

Subsidiaries:

Independent Printing Co., Inc.   **(1)**
640 Tolman Creek Rd, Ashland, OR 97520
Tel.: (541) 482-4711
Web Site: http://www.ipcoprinting.com
Rev.: $3,333,333
Emp.: 30
Other Commercial Printing
N.A.I.C.S.: 323111
Kurt Brombacher (Pres)
Rick Marshall (Mgr-Pre-Press)

INDEPENDENT PROTECTION COMPANY
1607 S Main St, Goshen, IN 46526
Tel.: (574) 533-4116
Web Site: http://www.ipclp.com
Sales Range: $10-24.9 Million
Emp.: 200
Lighting Protection Mfr
N.A.I.C.S.: 335931
Robert E. Cripe Jr. (Exec VP & Gen Mgr)

INDEPENDENT PUBLICA-TIONS, INC.
945 E Haverford Rd, Bryn Mawr, PA
19010-3814
Tel.: (610) 527-6330   **PA**
Web Site:
http://www.independentpublica
tionsinc.com
Year Founded: 1975
Sales Range: $50-74.9 Million
Emp.: 500
Newspaper Publishing; Distribution
Service
N.A.I.C.S.: 513110
Charles E. Catherwood (Treas & VP)
Andrew T. Bickford (Pres & CEO)
Sal Favazza (Controller)
William L. McLean III (Chm)

Subsidiaries:

Nashua Telegraph   **(1)**
110 Main St Ste 1, Nashua, NH
03060   **(100%)**
Tel.: (603) 882-2741
Web Site: http://www.nashuatelegraph.com
Sales Range: $25-49.9 Million
Emp.: 150
Newspaper Publishing Services
N.A.I.C.S.: 513110

INDEPENDENT RESOURCES, INC.
5010 N Nebraska Ave, Tampa, FL
33603
Tel.: (813) 237-0945   **FL**
Web Site: http://www.independentre
sources.com
Year Founded: 1977
Sales Range: $1-9.9 Million
Emp.: 25
Commercial Printing, Direct Mail &
Promotional Products
N.A.I.C.S.: 323111
David J. Curbelo (Pres)
Rosanna Vasquez (Acct Exec)
David Gooveo (Supvr-Ops & Mfg)

INDEPENDENT SOUTHERN BANCSHARES, INC.
111 S Washington, Brownsville, TN
38012
Tel.: (731) 772-1201   **TN**
Web Site: http://www.insouth.com
Year Founded: 1983
Rev.: $22,543,000
Emp.: 12
Bank Holding Company
N.A.I.C.S.: 551111
Nick Nichols (Pres)

Subsidiaries:

INSOUTH Bank   **(1)**
111 S Washington Ave, Brownsville, TN
38012
Tel.: (731) 772-1201
Web Site: http://www.insouth.com
Rev.: $57,656,000
Emp.: 53
State Commercial Banks
N.A.I.C.S.: 522110
Rodney Spicer (Sr VP)
Jo Finn (VP)
Sandy McNeal (Mgr-Residential Lending)

INDEPENDENT SUPPORT SERVICES INC.
20 Cyrstal St 2nd Fl, Monticello, NY
12701
Tel.: (845) 794-5218   **NY**
Web Site: http://www.issny.org
Year Founded: 2003
Sales Range: $25-49.9 Million
Emp.: 1,500
Developmental Disabled People Resi-
dential Care Services
N.A.I.C.S.: 623210
Alan Kulchinsky (Exec Dir)
Louis Sharoff (Sec)
Matt Lennon (VP)
Marvin Shabus (Pres & Treas)

INDEPENDENT TELECOM SYSTEMS
4079 Park E Ct, Grand Rapids, MI
49546
Tel.: (616) 242-5300
Web Site:
http://www.itscommunications.com
Rev.: $10,118,080
Emp.: 50
System Integration Services
N.A.I.C.S.: 541512
Robert Sweezie (Pres)

INDEPENDENT TELEVISION NETWORK
747 3rd Ave FL 5, New York, NY
10017
Tel.: (212) 572-9200
Web Site:
http://www.itnnetworks.com
Rev.: $200,000,000
Emp.: 150
Television Broadcasting Services
N.A.I.C.S.: 516120
Thilaka Jayasundara (Chm)

INDEPENDENT TRUST COM-PANY OF AMERICA, LLC
1301 W Omaha St Ste 203, Rapid
City, SD 57701
Tel.: (605) 737-5100
Web Site:
http://www.independenttrust.com
Year Founded: 1997
Sales Range: $1-9.9 Million
Emp.: 28
Financial Consulting Services
N.A.I.C.S.: 523940
Geoff Madsen (Chm & CEO)

INDEPENDENT TUBULAR CORP.
4951 S Mingo Rd Ste C, Tulsa, OK
74146
Tel.: (918) 496-2476

Web Site: http://www.itcpipe.com
Sales Range: $25-49.9 Million
Emp.: 4
Pipe & Tubing, Steel
N.A.I.C.S.: 423510
Michael L. Allred (Pres)
Brenda Christ (Office Mgr)

INDEX EXCHANGE, INC.
20 W 22nd St Ste 1101, New York,
NY 10010
Tel.: (212) 647-7575
Web Site:
http://www.indexexchange.com
Year Founded: 2011
Sales Range: $125-149.9 Million
Advertising & Marketing Services
N.A.I.C.S.: 541810
Andrew Casale (Pres & CEO)
Joe Casale (Chm & Mng Dir)
Neil Dorken (CFO)
Alex Gardner (Chief Revenue Officer)
Marc Staveley (CTO)

INDEX NOTION COMPANY INC.
887 W Carmel Dr, Carmel, IN 46032
Tel.: (317) 573-3990
Rev.: $17,074,486
Emp.: 10
Greeting Cards
N.A.I.C.S.: 459420
James G. Sinclair (Pres)

INDEXCOMPUTER.COM
3981 SW 30th Ave, Fort Lauderdale,
FL 33312
Tel.: (954) 321-7885
Web Site:
http://www.indexworldwide.com
Sales Range: $10-24.9 Million
Emp.: 20
Computer & Computer Peripheral
Equipment & Software Merchant
Whslr
N.A.I.C.S.: 423430
Jorge Gil (VP)
Craig Schembri (Pres, Treas & Sec)

INDIA IMPORTS INC.
3940 Barron St, Metairie, LA 70002
Tel.: (504) 888-8832
Sales Range: $10-24.9 Million
Emp.: 5
Tobacco & Tobacco Products; Whole-
sale
N.A.I.C.S.: 424940
Hiren Shah (Pres)

INDIAN COUNTRY INC.
597 Airport Rd, Deposit, NY 13754
Tel.: (607) 467-3801
Web Site:
http://www.indiancountryinc.com
Year Founded: 1972
Sales Range: $25-49.9 Million
Emp.: 200
Reconstituted Wood Products
N.A.I.C.S.: 321219

Subsidiaries:

Indian Country Bluestone, LLC   **(1)**
597 Airport Rd, Deposit, NY 13754
Tel.: (607) 467-2000
Web Site:
http://www.indiancountrybluestone.com
Sales Range: $25-49.9 Million
Emp.: 10
Quarriers of Bluestone
N.A.I.C.S.: 238140
Harold Hubbell (Owner)

INDIAN ELECTRIC COOPERA-TIVE
US Hwy 64, Cleveland, OK 74020
Tel.: (918) 295-9500
Web Site: http://www.iecok.com

Sales Range: $10-24.9 Million
Emp.: 150
Distribution, Electric Power
N.A.I.C.S.: 221122
David Wilson (Mgr-Cust Svcs)
Karen Davis (Mgr-Cust Svcs)

INDIAN HEAD INDUSTRIES, INC.
6200 W WT Harris Technology Blvd,
Charlotte, NC 28269-9786
Tel.: (704) 547-7411   **NC**
Web Site:
http://www.indianheadindustries.com
Year Founded: 1984
Sales Range: $50-74.9 Million
Emp.: 30
Heavy Duty Truck Spring Brakes Mfr
N.A.I.C.S.: 336340
Rebecca Phillips-Parker (VP-Comm &
Bus Dev)
Bryan Schrandt (Sr VP-Worldwide Sls
& Mktg)

Subsidiaries:

MGM Brakes Division   **(1)**
6200 Harris Technology Blvd, Charlotte, NC
28269-9786   **(100%)**
Tel.: (704) 547-7411
Web Site: http://www.mgmbrakes.com
Heavy Duty Truck & Bus Spring Brakes Mfr
N.A.I.C.S.: 336340
Jackie Edwards (Supvr-Mktg Comm)

INDIAN HEALTH COUNCIL, INC.
50100 Golsh Rd, Valley Center, CA
92082
Tel.: (760) 749-1410   **CA**
Web Site:
http://www.indianhealth.com
Year Founded: 1970
Sales Range: $10-24.9 Million
Emp.: 205
Health Care Srvices
N.A.I.C.S.: 622110
Orvin Hanson (COO)
Caroline Lambert (Dir-Dental)
Daniel J. Calac (Chief Medical Offi-
cer)
William Gallagher (CFO)

INDIAN JEWELERS SUPPLY CO.
601 E Coal Ave, Gallup, NM 87301
Tel.: (505) 722-4451
Web Site: http://www.ijsinc.com
Rev.: $14,000,000
Emp.: 60
Jewelry Supply
N.A.I.C.S.: 423940
David Vining (Pres & CEO)
Jack Dill (Pres & CEO)

INDIAN RIVER TRANSPORT CO.
2580 Executive Rd, Winter Haven, FL
33884-1163
Tel.: (863) 324-2430   **FL**
Web Site:
http://www.indianrivertransport.com
Year Founded: 1974
Sales Range: $150-199.9 Million
Emp.: 700
Trucking Company
N.A.I.C.S.: 484230
John Harned (Owner)
Steve Furguson (Dir-Safety & Re-
cruiting)

INDIAN SUMMER CARPET MILLS, INC.
601 Callahan Rd SE, Dalton, GA
30721
Tel.: (706) 277-6277   **GA**

Indian Summer Carpet Mills,
Inc.—(Continued)

Web Site:
http://www.cherokeecarpet.com
Sales Range: $25-49.9 Million
Emp.: 300
Residential & Commercial Carpeting
Mfr
N.A.I.C.S.: 314110
Ann Eaton (Pres)

INDIAN SUMMER CO-OP, INC.
3958 W Chauvez Rd, Ludington, MI
49431-8200
Tel.: (231) 845-6248   MI
Year Founded: 1973
Sales Range: $25-49.9 Million
Emp.: 200
Fresh & Processed Fruit
N.A.I.C.S.: 311421
Roy D. Hackert (Pres & Gen Mgr)
Roy Hackard (CEO)
Laurie Bogner (Controller)

INDIANA COMPREHENSIVE HEALTH INSURANCE ASSOCIATION
9465 Counselors Row Ste 200, Indianapolis, IN 46240
Tel.: (317) 877-5376   IN
Year Founded: 1981
Sales Range: $125-149.9 Million
Emp.: 1
Health Insurance Services
N.A.I.C.S.: 524114
Douglas Stratton (Exec Dir)

INDIANA DONOR NETWORK
3760 Guion Rd, Indianapolis, IN
46222
Tel.: (317) 685-0389   IN
Web Site:
http://www.indianadonornetwork.org
Year Founded: 1987
Sales Range: $25-49.9 Million
Emp.: 139
Organ & Tissue Donation Services
N.A.I.C.S.: 621991
Matt Wadsworth (Mgr-Organ Svcs)
Cindy Alexander (Mgr-Family Svcs)
Kellie Hanner (Pres & CEO)
Steve Johnson (COO)
Kristi Winegarden (Chief Admin Officer)
Wade Lange (Chm)
Miranda Welch (Dir-Vital Link Donation)
Andrea Farmer (Dir-External Engagement & Govt Affairs)
Mark Back (Mgr-Mktg & Comm)
David Roe (Chief Medical Officer)
Eliott Stubblefield (Coord-Multicultural Community Dev)
Amy Pruitt (Mgr-Tissue Svcs)
Bradley Wiseman (Mgr-Hospital Svcs)
Chris Wright (VP-Fin & Admin)

INDIANA ENDOWMENT FUND, INC.
11 WMP Dr, Evansville, IN 47711
Tel.: (812) 491-9373
Sales Range: $25-49.9 Million
Grantmaking Services
N.A.I.C.S.: 813219
Sonja Williams (VP)
Tony Wiliams (Pres)

INDIANA FARM BUREAU INC.
225 S E St, Indianapolis, IN 46202
Tel.: (317) 692-7200
Web Site:
http://www.infarmbureau.com
Sales Range: $25-49.9 Million
Emp.: 500

Insurance Provider
N.A.I.C.S.: 813910
Mark Miske (CFO, Treas & Sr VP)
Joe Martin (CEO & Exec VP)
Greg Clancy (CIO & Sr VP)
Rick Kuster (CMO & Sr VP-Mktg)
Kristin Keltner (Gen Counsel, Sec & Sr VP)
Kevin Murphy (Sr VP-Property & Casualty)
Tom Bower (Sr VP-Life)
Patrick Williams (Mgr-Health Plans)

Subsidiaries:

Indiana Farm Bureau Insurance   (1)
225 SE St, Indianapolis, IN 46202-4058
Tel.: (317) 692-7200
Web Site: http://www.infarmbureau.com
Multiple Line Insurance Provider
N.A.I.C.S.: 524113
Lynn B. Jongleux (Gen Counsel, Sec & Sr VP)
Carl Shepherd (Sr VP)
Rick Kuster (CMO & Sr VP-Mktg)
Kevin Murphy (CEO & Exec VP)
Jeff McDonald (Sr VP-Property & Casualty Companies)

INDIANA FIRST SAVINGS BANK
935 Philadelphia St, Indiana, PA
15701
Tel.: (724) 349-2810
Web Site: http://www.infirstbank.com
Sales Range: $10-24.9 Million
Emp.: 70
Federal Savings Bank
N.A.I.C.S.: 522180
Timothy J. Kronenwetter (Pres & CEO)
Robert Nagel (Sr VP-Wealth Mgmt)
Ann Marie Riscinto (Asst VP-Loan Svcs)
George M. Evans (Chm)

INDIANA FURNITURE INDUSTRIES, INC.
1224 Mill St, Jasper, IN 47546-2852
Tel.: (812) 482-5727
Web Site:
http://www.indianafurniture.com
Year Founded: 1905
Sales Range: $10-24.9 Million
Emp.: 300
Desks, Tables & Chairs Mfr
N.A.I.C.S.: 337211
Bernie Kreilein (CFO, Sec, Treas & VP-Fin)
Paula Schmidt (Dir-Mktg)
Ashley Fair (VP-HR, Safety & Environmental)

INDIANA HISTORICAL SOCIETY
450 W Ohio St, Indianapolis, IN
46202
Tel.: (317) 232-1882   IN
Web Site:
http://www.indianahistory.org
Year Founded: 1831
Sales Range: $10-24.9 Million
Emp.: 140
Historical Preservation Services
N.A.I.C.S.: 813219
Patricia D. Curran (Sec)
David S. Evans (Chm)
Charles A. Liles (Treas)
Jody Blankenship (Pres & CEO)

INDIANA MASONIC HOME, INC.
690 State St, Franklin, IN 46131
Tel.: (317) 736-6141   IN
Web Site:
http://www.indianamasonichome.org
Year Founded: 2003
Sales Range: $25-49.9 Million

Emp.: 348
Continuing Care Retirement Community Operator
N.A.I.C.S.: 623311
Mike Spencer (Exec Dir)
James Barkdull (Exec Dir)
Richard J. Elman (Sec)
Robert R. Stevens (VP)

INDIANA MEMBERS CREDIT UNION
PO Box 47769, Indianapolis, IN
46247
Tel.: (317) 248-8556   IN
Web Site: http://www.imcu.org
Year Founded: 1956
Sales Range: $50-74.9 Million
Financial Services
N.A.I.C.S.: 522130
Robert Martin (Chm)
Nicholas Kellum (Vice Chm)
Margaret Miller (Sec)
Michael Ney (Treas)
Madonna Hasty (Chm)

Subsidiaries:

First Light Bancorp   (1)
7312 Eagle Crest Blvd, Evansville, IN
47715
Tel.: (812) 492-1800
Web Site:
http://www.bankwithcommerce.com
Bank Holding Company
N.A.I.C.S.: 551111
Luke Yaeger (Pres & CEO)
John Schenk (CFO & Exec VP)
Barbara Bond (Sec & Controller)

Subsidiary (Domestic):

The Commerce Bank   (2)
7312 Eagle Crest Blvd, Evansville, IN
47715
Tel.: (812) 492-1800
Web Site:
http://www.bankwithcommerce.com
Sales Range: $1-9.9 Million
Commercial Banking
N.A.I.C.S.: 522110
Michael Sutton (Sr VP-Comml Lending)
Luke Yaeger (Pres & CEO)
John Schenk (CFO & Exec VP)
Bill White (Pres-Clarksville Market)
Barbara Bond (Sec & Controller)
Diana Couch (Sr VP-Mortgage Lending)
Diane Tabor (Sr VP-Deposit Ops)
Alex Wahl (Sr VP-Credit & Mgr-Compliance)
Stephen Witting (Sr VP-Comml Banking)
Brian J. Woods (Sr VP-Comml Banking)
Michael Killen (Sr VP-Comml Lending-Clarksville)
Mallory Idleman (VP-Treasury Mgmt Sls-Houston)

INDIANA MILLS & MANUFACTURING, INC.
18881 Immi way, Westfield, IN 46074
Tel.: (317) 896-9531
Web Site: https://www.imminet.com
Year Founded: 1961
Rev.: $39,300,000
Emp.: 665
Belting & Belt Products
N.A.I.C.S.: 314999
Tom Anthony (Pres)
Larry Gray (CEO)
Scott Caudill (COO)
Norm Gould (CFO)
Julie Cooley (VP-Corp & Marketing Communications)
Mark Campbell (Sr VP-Global Ops)
Jon Tice (VP-Global HR)
Dan Veselsky (VP-Sales & Business Development)
Matt King (Gen Counsel)
Tom Braden (VP-Information Technology)

Subsidiaries:

Syn Tec Seating Solutions, LLC   (1)

200 Swathmore Ave, High Point, NC 27263
Web Site: http://www.syntecseating.com
Wood Window & Door Mfr
N.A.I.C.S.: 321911
Larry Bannon (VP-New Bus Dev)
Chad Blankenship (Gen Mgr)

INDIANA MUNICIPAL POWER AGENCY
11610 N College Ave, Carmel, IN
46032
Tel.: (317) 573-9955
Web Site: http://www.impa.com
Year Founded: 1983
Rev.: $461,116,000
Assets: $1,885,522,000
Liabilities: $1,524,929,000
Net Worth: $360,593,000
Earnings: $37,577,000
Fiscal Year-end: 12/31/18
Electric Power Distr
N.A.I.C.S.: 221122
Jack Alvey (COO & Exec VP)
Carolyn Wright (VP-Govt Rels)
Chris Rettig (CFO & Sr VP)
Niki Dick (Dir-Mktg Comm)
Frank Smardo (Exec VP-Energy Solutions)
Larry Brown (VP-Plng & Rates)
Brian Markley (Mgr-Combustion Turbine)
Jane Hemmerlein (VP-HR)
John Lloyd (Mgr-Market Ops)
Peter Prettyman (Gen Counsel & Sr VP)
Mel Denton (Asst Mgr-Combustion Turbine)

INDIANA OXYGEN COMPANY INCORPORATED
6099 Corporate Way, Indianapolis, IN
46278
Tel.: (317) 290-0003
Web Site:
http://www.indianaoxygen.com
Sales Range: $10-24.9 Million
Emp.: 83
Industrial Gases
N.A.I.C.S.: 424690
Walter L. Brant (Pres)

INDIANA PRINTING & PUBLISHING CO., INC.
899 Water St, Indiana, PA 15701-1705
Tel.: (724) 465-5555   DE
Web Site:
http://www.indianagazette.net
Year Founded: 1946
Sales Range: $25-49.9 Million
Emp.: 250
Commercial Printing, Lithographic
N.A.I.C.S.: 323111
Michael J. Donnelly (Pres)
Joseph Geary (VP & Gen Mgr)

INDIANA RECORDS MANAGERS, INC.
9325 Uptown Dr Ste 800, Indianapolis, IN 46256
Tel.: (317) 842-5580   IN
Web Site:
http://www.indianarecords.com
Year Founded: 1976
Sales Range: $75-99.9 Million
Emp.: 20
Office Equipment, Supplies & Systems Distr
N.A.I.C.S.: 424120
Jan Brown (Office Mgr)

Subsidiaries:

Productive Business Interiors   (1)
126 W Columbia St Ste 400, Fort Wayne,
IN 46802-1719   (100%)
Tel.: (260) 423-3482
Web Site: http://www.pbiftwayne.com

Sales Range: $10-24.9 Million
Emp.: 11
Ret Office Furniture
N.A.I.C.S.: 423210
Doug Mcphail *(Owner & Pres)*
Cheryl Sanders *(Mgr-Fin)*

INDIANA REGIONAL MEDICAL CENTER

835 Hospital Rd, Indiana, PA 15701-0788
Tel.: (724) 357-7000   PA
Web Site: http://www.indianarmc.org
Year Founded: 1944
Sales Range: $125-149.9 Million
Emp.: 1,459
Health Care Srvices
N.A.I.C.S.: 622110
Anne White *(Chm)*

INDIANA SOYBEAN ALLIANCE

8425 Keystone Crossing Ste 200, Indianapolis, IN 46240
Tel.: (317) 347-3620   IN
Web Site:
   http://www.indianasoybean.com
Year Founded: 1997
Sales Range: $10-24.9 Million
Emp.: 20
Social Welfare Services
N.A.I.C.S.: 813319
Andy Tauer *(Dir-Livestock)*
Megan Kuhn *(Sr Dir-Mktg & Comm)*
Joseph Steinkamp *(Pres & Dir-ASA)*
Jane Ade Stevens *(CEO)*
Dave Rodibaugh *(Treas)*
Joe Tuholski *(Vice Chm)*
Elaine Gillis *(Sec)*
Dennis Henry *(Mgr-Acct & Compliance)*
Ken Parrent *(Dir-Biofuels)*
Melanie Batalis *(Mgr-Mktg Program)*

INDIANA STATE TEACHERS ASSOCIATION

150 W Market St, Indianapolis, IN 46204
Tel.: (317) 263-3400   IN
Web Site: http://www.ista-in.org
Year Founded: 1968
Sales Range: $10-24.9 Million
Emp.: 65
Teacher Welfare Association
N.A.I.C.S.: 813920
Craig Blume *(Mgr-Unifed Svc & Organizing)*
Jennifer Clutter *(CFO)*

INDIANA STEEL FABRICATING INC.

4545 W Bradbury Ave, Indianapolis, IN 46241
Tel.: (317) 247-4545
Web Site:
   http://www.indianasteelfab.com
Sales Range: $10-24.9 Million
Emp.: 31
Fabricated Structural Metal
N.A.I.C.S.: 332312
Stephen Porter *(Pres)*
Steve Dowden *(VP)*
Linda Dilks *(Office Mgr)*
Norm Lindley *(Dir-Reinforcing Steel)*
James Bennett *(Mgr-Primary Checker)*

INDIANA SUGARS, INC.

911 Virginia St, Gary, IN 46401-2705
Tel.: (219) 886-9151   IN
Web Site: http://www.sugars.com
Year Founded: 1935
Sales Range: $100-124.9 Million
Emp.: 200
Wholesale of Food Additives
N.A.I.C.S.: 424490

John Witt *(Mgr-HR)*
John Yonover *(Pres & COO)*
Scott Sievers *(VP-Sls & Mktg)*

INDIANA VENEERS CORP.

1121 East 24th St, Indianapolis, IN 46205
Tel.: (317) 926-2458
Web Site:
   http://www.indianaveneers.com
Year Founded: 1892
Sales Range: $10-24.9 Million
Emp.: 100
Provider of Veneer
N.A.I.C.S.: 321211
Werner Lorenz *(Pres)*
Peter Lorenz *(VP)*
Sheryl Rooney *(Controller)*
Jim Shobe *(Mgr-Sls)*

INDIANA WESTERN EXPRESS INC.

2750 N Barnes Ave, Springfield, MO 65803-4921
Tel.: (417) 873-1000   IN
Web Site: http://www.iwxmf.com
Year Founded: 1990
Sales Range: $25-49.9 Million
Emp.: 940
Trucking Services
N.A.I.C.S.: 484121
Norman Bodine *(Controller)*
Steven Schloss *(Mng Dir)*

INDIANAPOLIS AIRPORT AUTHORITY

7800 Col H Weir Cook Memorial Dr, Indianapolis, IN 46241
Tel.: (317) 487-7243
Web Site:
   http://www.indianapolisairport.com
Year Founded: 1962
Sales Range: $100-124.9 Million
Emp.: 600
Airport Services
N.A.I.C.S.: 926120
Michael W. Wells *(Pres)*
Robert Duncan *(Deputy Exec Dir)*
Mario Rodriguez *(Exec Dir)*
Alfred R. Bennett *(Sec)*

INDIANAPOLIS CHAMBER ORCHESTRA

4603 Clarendon Rd Ste 36, Indianapolis, IN 46208
Tel.: (317) 940-9607   IN
Web Site: http://www.icomusic.org
Year Founded: 1984
Sales Range: $1-9.9 Million
Emp.: 110
Orchestra Organizer
N.A.I.C.S.: 711130
Daniel Golando *(Mgr-Personnel)*
Amylou Porter *(Mgr-Ops)*
Joshua Christie *(Sec)*
Nancy Knight *(Treas)*
Elaine F. Eckhart *(Exec Dir)*

INDIANAPOLIS COLTS, INC.

7001 W 56th St, Indianapolis, IN 46254-9725
Tel.: (317) 297-2658   IN
Web Site: http://www.colts.com
Year Founded: 1953
Sales Range: $50-74.9 Million
Emp.: 100
Professional Football Franchise
N.A.I.C.S.: 711211
James Irsay *(Owner & CEO)*
Pete Ward *(COO)*
Kurt Humphrey *(CFO)*
Larry Hall *(VP-Ticket Ops & Guest Svcs)*
Greg Hylton *(VP-Premium Seating & Ticket Sls)*
Robert Parenteau *(Dir-Ticket Ops)*

Brad Beery *(Mgr-Corp Partnership)*
Brian Healey *(Mgr-Corp Partnership)*
Jon Scott *(VP-Equipment Ops)*
Sean Sullivan *(Mgr-Equipment)*
Stacy Johns *(VP-Fin & HR)*
Ryan Lobsiger *(Dir-Corp Partnerships)*
Ryan Fannin *(Dir-Football Info Sys)*
Dan Emerson *(Chief Legal Officer)*
Kip Brownfield *(Sr Dir-Ticket Sls)*
Carlie Irsay-Gordon *(Owner & Vice Chm)*
Casey Foyt *(Owner & Vice Chm)*
Mike Bluem *(Dir-Football Admin)*
Avis Roper *(Sr Dir-Comm)*
Matt Conti *(Asst Dir-Comm)*
Troy Glendenning *(Dir-Facilities & Grounds)*
T. J. McCreight *(Dir-College Scouting)*
Morocco Brown *(Dir-College Scouting)*
Kyle Childress *(Coord-College Scouting)*
Ed Dodds *(VP-Player Personnel)*
Rex Hogan *(VP-Player Personnel)*
Brian A.D. Richardson *(Dir-Diversity, Equity & Inclusion)*
Jimmy Raye III *(VP-Football Ops)*

INDIANAPOLIS ELECTRIC COMPANY, INC.

241 S State Ave, Indianapolis, IN 46201
Tel.: (317) 636-3391
Web Site:
   http://www.indplselectric.com
Year Founded: 1956
Sales Range: $10-24.9 Million
Emp.: 50
Electronic Services
N.A.I.C.S.: 238210
Linville D. Coner *(Co-Owner & Mgr-Contract)*
Robert W. Coner *(Co-Owner & Mgr-Ops)*
J. Larry Thompson *(VP & Project Mgr)*
David B. Coner *(VP)*
Garry D. Elder *(VP-Special Acct)*

INDIANAPOLIS JEWISH HOME, INC.

7001 Hoover Rd, Indianapolis, IN 46260
Tel.: (317) 251-2261   IN
Web Site: http://www.hooverwood.org
Year Founded: 1968
Sales Range: $10-24.9 Million
Emp.: 264
Nursing Care Services
N.A.I.C.S.: 623110
Diana Wysocki *(CFO)*
Marc S. Penner *(Exec Dir)*

INDIANAPOLIS MUSEUM OF ART

4000 Michigan Rd, Indianapolis, IN 46208-3326
Tel.: (317) 923-1331   IN
Web Site: http://www.imamuseum.org
Year Founded: 1883
Sales Range: $10-24.9 Million
Emp.: 431
Art Museum Operator
N.A.I.C.S.: 712110
Jerry Wise *(CFO)*
Ersal Ozdemir *(Sec)*
Matthew Gutwein *(Vice Chm)*
Thomas Andrew Hiatt *(Chm)*
Gary Stoppelman *(Deputy Dir-Mktg & External Affairs)*
Kathryn Haigh *(COO)*
Peter A. Morse Jr. *(Treas)*

INDIANHEAD COMMUNITY AC-

TION AGENCY, INC.

1000 College Ave W, Ladysmith, WI 54848
Tel.: (715) 532-4222   WI
Web Site:
   http://www.indianheadcaa.org
Year Founded: 1966
Sales Range: $10-24.9 Million
Emp.: 659
Community Action Services
N.A.I.C.S.: 624190
Tammy Peacock *(Dir-Nurses)*
Jennifer Shearer *(CEO)*

INDICAR OF DAYTONA INC.

510 N Nova Rd, Daytona Beach, FL 32114
Tel.: (386) 252-7000
Web Site:
   http://www.daytonamitsu.com
Sales Range: $10-24.9 Million
Emp.: 35
Automobiles, New & Used
N.A.I.C.S.: 441110
Craig Conway *(Pres)*
Elaine Gorski *(Controller)*

INDICON CORP.

6417 Ctr Dr Ste 110, Sterling Heights, MI 48312
Tel.: (586) 274-0505
Web Site: http://www.indicon.com
Rev.: $35,000,000
Emp.: 80
Control Panels, Electric
N.A.I.C.S.: 335313
Ron Brown *(Engr-Control)*
Dave Kiras *(Project Mgr)*

INDIGO PARTNERS LLC

2525 East Camelback Rd, Phoenix, AZ 85016
Tel.: (602) 224-1500
Privater Equity Firm
N.A.I.C.S.: 523999
William A. Franke *(Co-Founder & Mng Partner)*
John Wilson *(Principal)*
William A. Franke *(Co-Founder & Mng Partner)*

Subsidiaries:

Frontier Airlines, Inc.   **(1)**
4545 Airport Way, Denver, CO 80239
Tel.: (720) 374-4200
Web Site: https://www.flyfrontier.com
Sales Range: $900-999.9 Million
Emp.: 4,000
Passenger Air Transportation Services
N.A.I.C.S.: 481111
Barry L. Biffle *(CEO)*
Mark C. Mitchell *(CFO & Exec VP)*
James G. Dempsey *(Pres)*
Mark C. Mitchell *(CFO & Exec VP)*

INDIGO SOUTH CAPITAL, INC.

1721 Atlantic Blvd Ste 200, Jacksonville, FL 32207
Tel.: (904) 559-2605
Web Site:
   https://indigosouthcapital.com
Privater Equity Firm
N.A.I.C.S.: 523999

Subsidiaries:

Chancey Metals, LLC   **(1)**
5130 Sunbeam Rd, Jacksonville, FL 32257
Tel.: (904) 260-6880
Web Site: https://chanceymetals.com
Metal Fabrication & Installation Services
N.A.I.C.S.: 238290

Subsidiary (Domestic):

Exact, Inc.   **(2)**
5285 Ramona Blvd, Jacksonville, FL 32210
Tel.: (904) 783-6640
Web Site: https://www.exactinc.com

Indigo South Capital, Inc.—(Continued)
Sales Range: $10-24.9 Million
Emp.: 115
Sheet Metal Work Mfg.
N.A.I.C.S.: 332322
William Allen IV (Pres)

INDINERO INC.
340 S Lemon Ave Ste 4637, Walnut,
CA 81620
Tel.: (407) 996-9999
Web Site:
http://www.beavercreeklodge.net
Electronics Stores
N.A.I.C.S.: 449210
Jessica Mah (CEO)

Subsidiaries:

mAccounting, LLC   (1)
9311 N Meridian St Ste 100, Indianapolis,
IN 46260
Tel.: (317) 581-1820
Web Site: http://www.maccounting.com
Sales Range: $1-9.9 Million
Financial, Advisory & Business Services
N.A.I.C.S.: 541611

INDIQUE HAIR, LLC.
13 Highland Cir Ste A, Needham
Heights, MA 02494-3031
Tel.: (617) 379-1280
Web Site: http://www.indiquehair.com
Year Founded: 2007
Sales Range: $1-9.9 Million
Emp.: 16
Hair Stylist Services
N.A.I.C.S.: 812111
Krishan Jhalani (Owner)
Ericka Dotson (Co-Founder & Dir-
Creative)

INDISOFT LLC
5550 Sterrett Pl Ste 311, Columbia,
MD 21044
Tel.: (410) 730-0667
Web Site: http://www.indisoft.us
Year Founded: 2005
Sales Range: $1-9.9 Million
Emp.: 15
Software for the Financial Services
Industry
N.A.I.C.S.: 423430
Sanjeev Dahiwadkar (Founder &
Chm)
Camillo Melchiorre (Pres)
Hans Rusli (CEO)
Steven Usserey (VP-Regulatory
Compliance)
Kenneth M. Goins Jr. (CFO)

INDIUM CORPORATION OF AMERICA
PO Box 269, Utica, NY 13503
Tel.: (315) 853-4900   **NY**
Web Site: http://www.indium.com
Year Founded: 1934
Sales Range: $10-24.9 Million
Emp.: 240
Mfr of Specialty Solders & Specialty
Chemicals
N.A.I.C.S.: 331491
Leo M. Devine (Mgr-Sls-Northeastern
United States & Eastern Canada)
Ivan Castellanos (Mgr-Tech Svcs-
Latin America)
Eric Bastow (Asst Mgr-Technical-
America)
Jordan Ross (Sr Mgr-Bus Dev)
Tim Jensen (Product Mgr-Engineered
Solders Matls)
Sehar Samiappan (Mgr-Northern
California)
Donna Vareha-Walsh (Dir-Metals
Bus)
Anita Brown (Sr Mgr-Mktg Comm)
Carol Gowans (Product Mgr)
Ed Briggs (Engr-Technical Support)

Jeff Anweiler (Mgr-Bus Dev-Precious
Metals Products)
Joe Bahou (Engr-Technical Sls
Support-West Coast)

INDIVIDUAL CENTRICITY CORPORATION
2603 Camino Ramon Ste 200, San
Ramon, CA 94583
Tel.: (925) 210-2524
Web Site:
https://individualcentricity.com
Health Care Srvices
N.A.I.C.S.: 621610

INDIVIDUALIZED APPAREL GROUP
641 Lexington Ave 19th Fl, New York,
NY 10022
Tel.: (212) 581-6968
Web Site: http://www.iagapparel.com
Sales Range: $200-249.9 Million
Emp.: 2,000
Holding Company; Clothing Manufac-
turing & Retailing
N.A.I.C.S.: 523999
Joe Blair (Pres)

Subsidiaries:

Coppley, Inc.   (1)
107 MacNab Street North, PO Box 2024,
Hamilton, L8R 2L9, ON, Canada
Tel.: (905) 529-1112
Web Site: https://www.coppley.com
Sales Range: $200-249.9 Million
Emp.: 600
Men's Tailored Apparel Mfr & Distr
N.A.I.C.S.: 315250

The Brown & Church Company   (1)
118 Marimorre Dr, Pilot Mountain, NC
27041
Tel.: (336) 368-5502
Web Site:
http://www.brownandchurchco.com
Rev: $2,000,000
Emp.: 40
Neckties Mfr
N.A.I.C.S.: 315250
Larry Marshall (CEO)

Tom James Company   (1)
263 Seaboard Ln, Franklin, TN 37067
Tel.: (615) 771-1122
Web Site: http://www.tomjamesco.com
Sales Range: $125-149.9 Million
Mfr & Retailer of Men's & Women's Cloth-
ing
N.A.I.C.S.: 458110
Todd Browne (Chm & Pres)

Subsidiary (Domestic):

Kenneth Gordon/IAG, Inc.   (2)
1209 Distributors Rd, New Orleans, LA
70123
Tel.: (504) 734-1433
Sales Range: $25-49.9 Million
Emp.: 150
Garments Mfr
N.A.I.C.S.: 424350

The Hubbard Company   (2)
208 Lurgan Ave, Shippensburg, PA
17257   (100%)
Tel.: (717) 532-4146
Sales Range: $25-49.9 Million
Emp.: 150
Mfr of Men's Pants
N.A.I.C.S.: 315120

Tom James of Atlanta, Inc.   (2)
2800 Century Pkwy NE Ste 100, Atlanta,
GA 30345
Tel.: (404) 479-9100
Web Site: http://www.tomjames.com
Rev: $2,000,000
Emp.: 34
Retailer of Men & Women Clothing Distr
N.A.I.C.S.: 458110
Todd Browne (Chm, Pres & CEO)
Brant Taylor (Mgr-Sls)

INDON INTERNATIONAL, LLC

306 Prairie View Dr, West Point, MS
39773
Tel.: (662) 494-6474
Web Site:
http://www.indoninternational.com
Sales Range: $10-24.9 Million
Emp.: 15
Hotel Furniture Mfr
N.A.I.C.S.: 423440
Butch Crouse (VP-Customer Rels)

INDONESIAN IMPORTS, INC.
4040 Alabama St, San Francisco, CA
94110
Tel.: (415) 486-1200   **DE**
Web Site: http://www.thesak.com
Sales Range: $25-49.9 Million
Emp.: 75
Women's Handbags Designer, Mfr &
Distr
N.A.I.C.S.: 316990
Mark Talucci (CEO)
Lorae Russo (Dir-Creative-The Sak &
Elliot Lucca)

Subsidiaries:

Elliott Lucca   (1)
339 5th Ave 2nd Fl, New York, NY 10016
Tel.: (888) 800-5899
Web Site: http://www.elliottlucca.com
Women's Handbags Designer & Whslr
N.A.I.C.S.: 424350

The Sak   (1)
2346 E Pacifica Pl, Rancho Dominguez, CA
90220
Tel.: (323) 325-9846
Web Site: http://www.thesak.com
Women's Handbags Designer & Whslr
N.A.I.C.S.: 424350

INDOTRONIX INTERNATIONAL CORPORATION
331 Main St Ste 108, Poughkeepsie,
NY 12601-3145
Tel.: (845) 473-1137   **DE**
Web Site: http://www.iic.com
Year Founded: 1986
Sales Range: $50-74.9 Million
Emp.: 500
Computer Related Services
N.A.I.C.S.: 541512
Rami Fakhoury (Gen Counsel)
Courtney Luther (Mgr-HR)

Subsidiaries:

Apollo Consulting Services
Corporation   (1)
331 Main St, Poughkeepsie, NY
12601-3104   (100%)
Tel.: (845) 473-1137
Rev: $26,000,000
Emp.: 50
IT Consulting Services
N.A.I.C.S.: 541512

INDSOFT, INC.
3755 E Main St Ste 180, Saint
Charles, IL 60174
Tel.: (630) 324-0006
Web Site: http://www.indsoft.com
Year Founded: 1998
Sales Range: $1-9.9 Million
Emp.: 83
Technical Consulting Services
N.A.I.C.S.: 541690
Vinoz Chanamolu (Pres)
Edward A. Batko (Sr VP-Sls & Mktg)
Sam Veera (Dir-Ops)

INDTAI INC.
21525 Ridgetop Cir Ste 280, Sterling,
VA 20166
Tel.: (703) 373-3188
Web Site: http://www.indtai.com
Year Founded: 1996
Rev: $10,200,000
Emp.: 150
Individual & Family Services

N.A.I.C.S.: 624190
Hsien W. Huang (Founder, Pres &
CEO)
Sunil Bala (Exec Dir)

INDUCTORS INC.
5 Technology Dr, Irvine, CA 92618
Tel.: (949) 623-2460
Web Site: http://www.inductor.com
Year Founded: 1991
Sales Range: $10-24.9 Million
Emp.: 50
Inductive Components Distr Special-
izing in Power & RF Products
N.A.I.C.S.: 423610
John Thompson (Gen Mgr)
George Klimek (Owner)
Mayra Montoto (Engr-Sls)
Heenle Vyas (Mgr-HR)

INDUS TECHNOLOGY, INC.
2243 San Diego Ave, San Diego, CA
92110
Tel.: (619) 299-2555
Web Site:
http://www.industechnology.com
Year Founded: 1991
Rev: $27,000,000
Emp.: 230
Computer Systems Design & Related
Services
N.A.I.C.S.: 541511
James B. Lasswell (Pres & CEO)
Ron File (VP-Bus Dev)
Jon Wakefield (VP)

INDUSTRIAL ASSETS CORP.
11426 Ventura Blvd 2nd Fl, Studio
City, CA 91604
Tel.: (818) 508-7034   **CA**
Web Site:
http://www.industrialassets.com
Year Founded: 1990
Auctioneers, Liquidators & Appraisers
N.A.I.C.S.: 423830
Tali Khoshbin (Sr Project Mgr)

Subsidiaries:

Midwest Paper Group   (1)
540 Prospect St, Combined Locks, WI
54113
Tel.: (800) 663-2259
Paper Mfr
N.A.I.C.S.: 322120
Doug Osterberg (Head-Strategy)
Jim Bird (Mgr-Product Dev)

INDUSTRIAL AUTOMATION CONTROLS
3150 I A C Dr, Memphis, TN 38186
Tel.: (901) 345-7000
Web Site: http://www.iacsupply.com
Sales Range: $10-24.9 Million
Emp.: 31
Electrical Apparatus & Equipment
N.A.I.C.S.: 423610

INDUSTRIAL BATTERY & CHARGER, INC.
5831 Orr Rd, Charlotte, NC 28213
Tel.: (704) 597-7330   **NC**
Web Site: http://www.ibciplusone.com
Year Founded: 1977
Sales Range: $10-24.9 Million
Emp.: 95
Storage Batteries, Industrial
N.A.I.C.S.: 423610
Terry K. Earnhardt (Pres & CEO)
Linda Earnhardt (Exec VP)
Tim Earnhardt (Exec VP)
Keith Earnhardt (Exec VP)

INDUSTRIAL BELTING & TRANSMISSION, INC.
4061 McCollum Ct, Louisville, KY
40218
Tel.: (502) 456-6100   **KY**

Web Site: http://www.indbelt.com
Sales Range: $10-24.9 Million
Emp.: 15
Industrial Conveyor Components &
Equipment Whslr
N.A.I.C.S.: 423830
Mark Deich (Pres)

INDUSTRIAL CASTER & WHEEL CO.

2200 Carden St, San Leandro, CA
94577
Tel.: (510) 569-8303
Web Site: http://www.icwco.com
Rev.: $12,908,003
Emp.: 40
Casters & Glides
N.A.I.C.S.: 423710
Bob Bingaman (Owner & Pres)

INDUSTRIAL CHEMICALS CORP.

4631 W 58th Ave, Arvada, CO 80002
Tel.: (303) 427-2727
Web Site:
http://www.industrialchemcorp.com
Rev.: $18,163,608
Emp.: 30
Industrial Chemicals
N.A.I.C.S.: 424690
Bob Wilson (Pres)

INDUSTRIAL CHEMICALS INC.

2042 Montreat Dr, Vestavia Hills, AL
35216-4002
Tel.: (205) 823-7330   AL
Web Site:
http://www.industrialchem.com
Year Founded: 1970
Sales Range: $10-24.9 Million
Emp.: 125
Chemicals & Allied Products Mfr
N.A.I.C.S.: 424690

Subsidiaries:

Industrial Chemicals Inc   (1)
1020 Sams Ave, Harahan, LA 70123
Tel.: (504) 733-6600
Sales Range: $10-24.9 Million
Emp.: 5
Industrial Chemicals Mfr & Distr
N.A.I.C.S.: 424690

INDUSTRIAL COMMUNICATIONS AND ELECTRONICS, INC.

40 Lone St, Marshfield, MA 02050
Tel.: (781) 319-1111
Web Site: http://www.induscom.com
Year Founded: 1974
Sales Range: $10-24.9 Million
Emp.: 105
Radiotelephone Communication
N.A.I.C.S.: 517112
Mike Umano (CFO & VP)

INDUSTRIAL COMPONENTS INC.

2250 NW 102nd Ave, Miami, FL
33172-2218
Tel.: (305) 477-0387   FL
Web Site:
http://www.icassemblies.com
Year Founded: 1981
Sales Range: $10-24.9 Million
Emp.: 5
Contract Manufacturing Services
N.A.I.C.S.: 339999
Albert Gomez (Co-Founder)
Lucy Gomez (Co-Founder)

INDUSTRIAL CONSTRUCTION COMPANY, INC.

10060 Brecksville Rd, Brecksville, OH
44141
Tel.: (440) 746-9200   OH

Year Founded: 1942
Sales Range: $25-49.9 Million
Emp.: 200
Renovations, Remodeling & Repairs
N.A.I.C.S.: 236220
Walter P. Kerr (Pres & CEO)
Rich Kreal (VP)
Hans Kern (VP)
Michael Kerr (Dir-Pur)

INDUSTRIAL CONSTRUCTORS/MANAGERS, INC.

1432 Stockyard Rd, Pueblo, CO
81001
Tel.: (719) 545-0296
Web Site: http://www.icmpueblo.com
Year Founded: 1972
Sales Range: $10-24.9 Million
Emp.: 60
Commercial & Institutional Building
Construction Services
N.A.I.C.S.: 236220
Burnell Zercher (Pres)
Sharon Tafoya (Controller)
Pamela Zercher (Treas)

INDUSTRIAL CONTAINER & SUPPLY

1845 S 5200 W, Salt Lake City, UT
84104-4706
Tel.: (801) 972-1561
Web Site:
http://www.industrialcontainer.com
Year Founded: 1962
Sales Range: $10-24.9 Million
Emp.: 50
Plastic Bottles & Related Products
Mfr
N.A.I.C.S.: 423840
Robert L. Hall (Gen Mgr)
J. Mitchell Hill (VP-Sls)

INDUSTRIAL CONTROL REPAIR, INC.

28601 Lorna Ave, Warren, MI 48092
Tel.: (586) 751-3335
Web Site: http://www.industrialcontrol
repair.com
Year Founded: 1992
Sales Range: $25-49.9 Million
Emp.: 135
Consumer Services
N.A.I.C.S.: 811210
Paul Gutierrez (Pres)
Glenn Dantes (VP)

INDUSTRIAL CUSTOM PRODUCTS, INC.

2801 37th Ave NE, Minneapolis, MN
55421
Tel.: (612) 781-2255   MN
Web Site:
http://www.industrialcustom.com
Year Founded: 1955
Sales Range: $50-74.9 Million
Emp.: 75
Custom Plastic Parts & Products Mfr;
Specialty Die-Cutting, Drape Forming,
Plastic Fabrication, Vacuum Forming
& Pressure Forming Services
N.A.I.C.S.: 326199
Herb Houndt (Pres)
Kerry Fritze (Gen Mgr)

Subsidiaries:

Industrial Custom Products, Inc. - Roseville Plant   (1)
2801 37th Ave NE, Minneapolis, MN 55421-
4217
Tel.: (612) 781-2255
Plastics Product Mfr
N.A.I.C.S.: 326199

INDUSTRIAL DESIGN & CONSTRUCTION, INC.

14061 Hwy 73, Prairieville, LA 70769
Tel.: (225) 673-4455   LA
Web Site: http://www.idcconst.com
Year Founded: 1988
Sales Range: $10-24.9 Million
Emp.: 30
Chemical Plant & Refinery Construc-
tion
N.A.I.C.S.: 237990
Donald Barden (Pres)
Donald McDowell Jr. (VP)

INDUSTRIAL DIELECTRICS HOLDINGS, INC.

407 S 7th St, Noblesville, IN 46060
Tel.: (317) 773-1766   IN
Web Site:
http://www.idicomposites.com
Year Founded: 1966
Sales Range: $125-149.9 Million
Emp.: 100
Holding Company; Electrical Insula-
tors & Insulation Materials Mfr
N.A.I.C.S.: 551112
William Funke (VP-Global Sls &
Tech)
Tom Flood (VP & Gen Mgr)
Alex DeSantis (VP-Personnel)

Subsidiaries:

IDI Fabrication, Inc.   (1)
1385 101st St Ste C, Lemont, IL 60439
Tel.: (630) 783-2246
Web Site: http://www.idifabrication.com
Sales Range: $10-24.9 Million
Emp.: 30
Fabrication of Parts From Insulating Plastic
Materials & Film
N.A.I.C.S.: 326199
Peter Jarosz (Office Mgr)

Subsidiary (Non-US):

Saturno de Mexico, SA de CV   (2)
Avenida Ind de Sta Catarina 169, Fracc Ind
de Sta Catarina, 66360, Nuevo Leon,
Mexico   (100%)
Tel.: (52) 8183906020
Web Site: http://www.saturnodemexico.com
Sales Range: $10-24.9 Million
Emp.: 18
Slitting, Sheeting, Stamping & Fabrication of
Parts
N.A.I.C.S.: 332315

Industrial Dielectrics, Inc.   (1)
407 S 7th St, Noblesville, IN 46060
Tel.: (317) 773-1766
Web Site: http://www.idicomposites.com
Sales Range: $10-24.9 Million
Emp.: 200
Thermoset Molding Compounds Mfr
N.A.I.C.S.: 327212
Thomas Flood (VP & Gen Mgr-North
America)
Jeffry Schumm (Dir-Sls-North America)

Subsidiary (Domestic):

IDI Caribe, Inc.   (2)
PO Box 400 Rd #3 KM 151 8, Aguirre, PR
00704
Tel.: (787) 853-2186
Web Site: http://www.idicomposites.com
Sales Range: $10-24.9 Million
Emp.: 40
Bulk Molding Compounds
N.A.I.C.S.: 335932

Subsidiary (Non-US):

IDI Composite Material (Shanghai)
Co., Ltd   (2)
918 Jinbai Road Jinshan Industrial Park,
Jinshan, 201506, Shanghai, PRC, China
Tel.: (86) 21 572 77688
Web Site: http://www.idichina.com
Thermoset Molding Compounds Mfr
N.A.I.C.S.: 333511

IDI Composites International Europe
(FR) SAS   (2)
Rue Laennec, Zone Industrielle, Vineuil,
41353, France
Tel.: (33) 254555554

Web Site: http://www.idicomposites.fr
Door & Sheet Molded Compound Mfr
N.A.I.C.S.: 327212
Magnaug Hemri (Gen Mgr)

Industrial Dielectrics (UK) Ltd.   (2)
Tat Bank Road, PO Box 10132, Oldbury,
B69 4WE, West Midlands, United
Kingdom   (100%)
Tel.: (44) 1215507611
Sales Range: $10-24.9 Million
Emp.: 28
Bulk Molding Compounds
N.A.I.C.S.: 325991
Peter Garland (Mng Dir)

INDUSTRIAL DIESEL INC.

8705 Harmon Rd, Fort Worth, TX
76177
Tel.: (817) 232-1071
Web Site:
http://www.industrialdiesel.net
Sales Range: $10-24.9 Million
Emp.: 26
Engines & Parts, Diesel
N.A.I.C.S.: 423830
Sam Bonar (VP-Sls)
Mike Smith (Mgr-Sls)

INDUSTRIAL DISPOSAL SUPPLY COMPANY

1106 Paulsun St, San Antonio, TX
78219
Tel.: (210) 227-3441
Web Site: http://www.idsequip.com
Sales Range: $10-24.9 Million
Emp.: 30
Industrial Machinery & Equipment
Whslr
N.A.I.C.S.: 423830
Darryl Fischbeck (VP)
Jeanie Mays (Mgr-Accts Payable)
Silvia Rodriguez (Mgr-Accts Receiv-
able)

INDUSTRIAL DISTRIBUTION RESOURCES, LLC

7255 E 46th St, Tulsa, OK 74145-
5901
Tel.: (918) 627-5639   OK
Web Site:
http://www.industrialdist.com
Year Founded: 1998
Sales Range: $75-99.9 Million
Emp.: 12
Industrial Supplies
N.A.I.C.S.: 423830
Steven E. Moellers (Pres & CEO)
Jeannie Dorsey (Mgr-Acctg)
Katy Small (Mgr-Mktg)

Subsidiaries:

Parts Services International LLC   (1)
251 Union St, Westfield, MA 01086-0845
Tel.: (413) 562-2324
Web Site: http://www.psiparts.com
Sales Range: $25-49.9 Million
Compressor Replacement Parts & Air Sys-
tems Accessories
N.A.I.C.S.: 423730

The Condit Company Inc.   (1)
7255 E 46th St, Tulsa, OK 74147-0146
Tel.: (918) 663-5310
Web Site: http://www.conditcompany.com
Industrial Machinery & Equipment
N.A.I.C.S.: 423830
Steve Moors (Pres)

INDUSTRIAL DOOR CO. INC.

360 Coon Rapids Blvd, Minneapolis,
MN 55433
Tel.: (763) 786-4730
Web Site: http://www.idc-
automatic.com
Sales Range: $10-24.9 Million
Emp.: 75
Sash Balances, Spring
N.A.I.C.S.: 332613

Industrial Door Co. Inc.—(Continued)

Jeremy Sizer *(Co-Owner)*
Jodi Boldenow *(Co-Owner)*

INDUSTRIAL DYNAMICS CO. LTD.

3100 Fujita St, Torrance, CA 90505
Tel.: (310) 325-5633
Web Site: http://www.filtec.com
Year Founded: 1958
Screening Equipment, Electric
N.A.I.C.S.: 333248

INDUSTRIAL ELECTRIC WIRE & CABLE INC.

5001 S Towne Dr, New Berlin, WI 53151-7956
Tel.: (262) 782-2323   WI
Web Site: http://www.iewc.com
Year Founded: 1963
Sales Range: $25-49.9 Million
Emp.: 200
Distr of Electrical Apparatus & Equipment
N.A.I.C.S.: 423610
David Nestingen *(Pres)*
Pat Rislov *(VP-Supply Chain)*
Lanny Million *(Chief Supply Chain Officer)*

Subsidiaries:

Delco Wire and Cable Limited   (1)
1 Saramia Cres, Concord, L4K 3S6, ON, Canada
Tel.: (905) 669-2476
Web Site: http://www.delcowire.com
Wire & Electric Cable Whslr
N.A.I.C.S.: 423610

IEWC Brazil   (1)
Avenida Independencia No 1544, Bairro Do Eden, Sorocaba, 18087-101, Brazil
Tel.: (55) 15 3218 1347
Wire & Electric Cable Whslr
N.A.I.C.S.: 423610

IEWC Germany GmbH   (1)
Rudolf-Braas-Strasse 2, Koeppern Nordost, 61381, Friedrichsdorf, Germany
Tel.: (49) 6175 79791 0
Web Site: http://www.iewc.de
Wire & Electric Cable Whslr
N.A.I.C.S.: 423610

IEWC Mexico, S. de R.L. de C.V.   (1)
Muebleros 232, Parque Ind Chichimeco, Aguascalientes, 20900, Mexico
Tel.: (52) 449 922 1200
Web Site: http://www.iewc.com
Emp.: 40
Wire & Electric Cable Whslr
N.A.I.C.S.: 423610
Ricardo Garcia *(Gen Mgr)*

IEWC Ontario   (1)
224 Don Hillock Dr Units 3-4, Aurora, L4G 0G9, ON, Canada
Tel.: (866) 303-6598
Web Site: http://www.iewc.ca
Emp.: 13
Wire & Electric Cable Whslr
N.A.I.C.S.: 423610
Andrew Robinson *(Gen Mgr)*

IEWC Suzhou   (1)
B2-9 Weiting Town Industrial-Workshop A No 9 Weixin Road, Suzhou Industrial Park, Suzhou, 215122, Jiangsu, China
Tel.: (86) 512 6275 6668
Web Site: http://www.iewc.com
Emp.: 35
Wire & Electric Cable Whslr
N.A.I.C.S.: 423610
David Nestingen *(Gen Mgr)*

IEWC UK & Ireland Ltd.   (1)
Unit 61 Gazelle Rd, Weston Industrial Estate, Weston-super-Mare, BS24 9ES, North Somerset, United Kingdom
Tel.: (44) 870 609 1257
Web Site: http://www.iewc.co.uk
Wire & Electric Cable Whslr
N.A.I.C.S.: 423610

Industrial Electric Wire & Cable Northwest   (1)
4020 Nelson Ave Ste 200, Concord, CA 94520
Tel.: (925) 939-3600
Web Site: http://www.iewc.com
Sales Range: $25-49.9 Million
Emp.: 21
Wire & Cable Products
N.A.I.C.S.: 423610

INDUSTRIAL ELECTRONIC ENGINEERS, INC.

7723 Kester Ave, Van Nuys, CA 91405-1105
Tel.: (818) 787-0311   CA
Web Site: http://www.ieeinc.com
Year Founded: 1946
Sales Range: $50-74.9 Million
Emp.: 50
Multi-Platform Graphic Displays, Point-of-Sale Pole Displays & Rugged & Military Display Panels Mfr
N.A.I.C.S.: 334118
Jodie Bennett *(Mgr-Sls)*
Michael Tubbs *(Dir-Ops)*

INDUSTRIAL ELECTRONIC SUPPLY

2321 Texas Ave, Shreveport, LA 71103
Tel.: (318) 222-9459
Web Site: http://www.goies.com
Sales Range: $10-24.9 Million
Emp.: 30
Electronic Parts
N.A.I.C.S.: 423690
David R. Doyal *(Owner & Pres)*
Ron Green *(Mgr-Automation Sls)*
Shannon Stanley *(Branch Mgr)*

INDUSTRIAL ENGINEERING & EQUIPMENT CO. INC.

425 Hanley Industrial Ct, Saint Louis, MO 63144-1511
Tel.: (314) 644-4300   MO
Web Site: http://www.indeeco.com
Year Founded: 1929
Industrial Furnaces & Ovens
N.A.I.C.S.: 333994
Dave Smith *(CEO)*

INDUSTRIAL ENGRAVING & MANUFACTURING CORP.

5324 Kunesh Rd, Pulaski, WI 54162
Tel.: (920) 865-7304
Web Site: http://www.industrial-engraving.com
Sales Range: $10-24.9 Million
Emp.: 27
Paper Industries Machinery
N.A.I.C.S.: 333243
Joe Kaufmann *(Pres)*

INDUSTRIAL EQUIPMENT CO. OF HOUSTON

6039 S Loop E, Houston, TX 77033
Tel.: (713) 928-3181
Web Site: http://www.indeco-tx.com
Sales Range: $10-24.9 Million
Emp.: 57
Electronic Parts & Equipment
N.A.I.C.S.: 423830
Larry Davis *(Pres)*
Carole Cook *(CEO)*

INDUSTRIAL FABRICATORS, INC.

4328 S York Rd, Gastonia, NC 28052
Tel.: (704) 864-3032
Web Site: http://www.ifabrication.com
Year Founded: 1994
Sales Range: $50-74.9 Million
Emp.: 210
Fabricated Structural Metal Mfr
N.A.I.C.S.: 332312

Roger Bingham *(Pres)*
Mike Resendez *(Plant Mgr)*
Pamela Parsons *(Mgr-Accts Receivable)*
Craig Pettit *(VP)*
Tammy Adams *(Mgr-HR & Payroll)*

INDUSTRIAL FIBERGLASS CORP.

10509 Business Dr, Fontana, CA 92337
Tel.: (909) 574-7433
Web Site: http://www.industrialinsulations.com
Sales Range: $10-24.9 Million
Emp.: 15
Fiberglass Insulation Services
N.A.I.C.S.: 423330
Terry Grill *(Owner)*
Eduardo Gomez *(CFO)*

INDUSTRIAL FILTER PUMP MANUFACTURING CO

2680 Us Hwy 1, Mims, FL 32754
Tel.: (708) 656-7800
Web Site: http://www.industrialfilter.com
Sales Range: $10-24.9 Million
Emp.: 26
Filters, General Line: Industrial
N.A.I.C.S.: 333998
Paul Eggerstedt *(Pres)*

INDUSTRIAL FINISHES & SYSTEMS INC.

3455 W 1st Ave, Eugene, OR 97402-0322
Tel.: (541) 485-1503   OR
Web Site: http://www.industrialfinishes.com
Year Founded: 1958
Sales Range: $50-74.9 Million
Emp.: 400
Paint Supplies Mfr
N.A.I.C.S.: 423840
Glen Duckworth *(Pres)*
Pfaff Ray *(Dir-Ops)*
Gay Brown *(Vice Chm)*
Stuart Barr *(Chm)*

INDUSTRIAL FIRST INC.

25840 Miles Rd Ste 2, Bedford, OH 44146-1426
Tel.: (216) 991-8600
Web Site: http://www.industrialfirst.com
Sales Range: $100-124.9 Million
Emp.: 136
Masonry & Other Stonework
N.A.I.C.S.: 238140
Dave Stanton *(CFO & Controller)*
Tom Niemiec *(Project Mgr)*
Doug Schwind *(Project Mgr)*

INDUSTRIAL GASKET INC.

9325 Southwest Ridder Rd Ste 410, Wilsonville, OR 97070
Tel.: (503) 682-3057
Web Site: http://www.cutparts.com
Sales Range: $10-24.9 Million
Emp.: 60
Gaskets & Sealing Devices
N.A.I.C.S.: 339991
Mike Smith *(Pres)*

INDUSTRIAL HARNESS COMPANY

100 Outlook Ln, Shippensburg, PA 17257
Tel.: (717) 477-0100
Sales Range: $10-24.9 Million
Emp.: 70
Provider of Automotive Wiring Harness Sets
N.A.I.C.S.: 336320

Jeffrey Lundeen *(Pres)*
Alicia Riggins *(Mgr-Acctg)*

INDUSTRIAL HEAT TRANSFER INC.

300 Old Mill Rd, Coon Valley, WI 54623
Tel.: (608) 452-3103
Web Site: http://www.iht-inc.com
Rev.: $12,186,420
Emp.: 50
Mfr of Heat Exchangers
N.A.I.C.S.: 332410
Jason Thomas *(Pres)*

INDUSTRIAL HUMAN CAPITAL, INC.

501 Brickell Key Dr Ste 300, Miami, FL 33135-3250   DE
Year Founded: 2021
Investment Services
N.A.I.C.S.: 523999
Scott W. Absher *(Chm & CEO)*
Mark A. Absher *(Gen Counsel & Sec)*
Scott W. Absher *(Chm & CEO)*
Manuel Rivera *(CFO & Treas)*

INDUSTRIAL INNOVATIONS, INC.

2650 Thornwood, Wyoming, MI 49519
Tel.: (616) 249-1525
Web Site: http://www.industrialinnovations.com
Year Founded: 1980
Sales Range: $1-9.9 Million
Emp.: 10
Machine Tool (Metal Forming Types) Mfr
N.A.I.C.S.: 333517
Troy W. Turnbull *(Pres)*

Subsidiaries:

Advance Products Corporation   (1)
2527 N M 63, Benton Harbor, MI 49022
Tel.: (269) 849-1000
Web Site: http://www.advanceproductscorp.com
Sales Range: $10-24.9 Million
Emp.: 20
Industrial Machinery Mfr & Whslr
N.A.I.C.S.: 333248
Zachary Boff *(Coord-Production & Inventory)*

INDUSTRIAL LADDER & SUPPLY CO.

245 E Adele Ct, Villa Park, IL 60181
Tel.: (630) 530-7580
Web Site: http://www.industrialladder.com
Year Founded: 1977
Sales Range: $10-24.9 Million
Emp.: 60
Ladders
N.A.I.C.S.: 423810
William A. Fuller *(Pres)*

INDUSTRIAL MACHINE & TOOL COMPANY INC.

88 Polk Ave, Nashville, TN 37210
Tel.: (615) 242-2596
Web Site: http://www.chiltonimtc.com
Rev.: $14,799,598
Emp.: 35
Machinery & Equipment
N.A.I.C.S.: 423820
Robert H. Chilton III *(Pres)*

INDUSTRIAL MACHINING SERVICES, INC.

700 Tower Dr, Fort Loramie, OH 45845
Tel.: (937) 295-2022   OH
Web Site: http://www.ims-spi.com
Year Founded: 1996

Sales Range: $1-9.9 Million
Emp.: 30
Mfg Dies/Tools/Jigs/Fixtures
N.A.I.C.S.: 333514
Brian Brackman (Plant Mgr)

Subsidiaries:

AIRAM Press Co. Ltd (1)
2065 Industrial Ct, Covington, OH 45318
Tel.: (937) 473-5672
Web Site: https://www.airam.com
Sales Range: $1-9.9 Million
Emp.: 24
Iron Foundries
N.A.I.C.S.: 331511
Tina Wright (Office Mgr)

Concept Machine & Tool Inc. (1)
2065 Industrial Ct, Covington, OH 45318
Tel.: (937) 473-3334
Web Site: http://www.conceptmach.com
Rev.: $3,075,000
Emp.: 25
All Other Miscellaneous Fabricated Metal Product Mfr
N.A.I.C.S.: 332999
Fred Ratermann (Production Mgr)

INDUSTRIAL MAINTENANCE CONTRACTORS, INC.
2301 Garden City Hwy, Midland, TX 79701
Tel.: (432) 682-3745
Web Site: http://www.imconinc.net
Year Founded: 1966
Sales Range: $10-24.9 Million
Emp.: 125
Painting & Wall Covering Contracting Services
N.A.I.C.S.: 238320
Jerry Bushman (Pres)
David Lesco (VP)
Kathy Oglesby (Sec)

INDUSTRIAL MAINTENANCE, WELDING & MACHINING CO, INC.
2nd & Hupp Rd, Kingsbury, IN 46345
Tel.: (219) 393-5531
Web Site: http://www.imwnet.com
Sales Range: $10-24.9 Million
Emp.: 120
Assembly Machines, Non-Metalworking
N.A.I.C.S.: 333998
Gene Berchem (Pres)
Matthew Sularski (VP)

INDUSTRIAL METAL PRODUCTS CORP.
3417 W Saint Joseph St, Lansing, MI 48917
Tel.: (517) 484-9411
Web Site: http://www.impco.com
Sales Range: $10-24.9 Million
Emp.: 50
Grinding, Polishing, Buffing, Lapping & Honing Machine Tools
N.A.I.C.S.: 333517
Patrick Cebelak (Pres)

INDUSTRIAL METAL SUPPLY COMPANY
8300 San Fernando Rd, Sun Valley, CA 91352-3222
Tel.: (818) 729-3333 CA
Web Site: http://www.imsmetals.com
Year Founded: 1948
Sales Range: $10-24.9 Million
Emp.: 100
Provider of Metals Services
N.A.I.C.S.: 423510
Eric Steihauer (Vice Chm)
Dave Berkey (CFO)
Neil Sherman (Owner & Chm)
David Pace (Pres)
David Cohen (COO)

Subsidiaries:

Campbell Tool & Metal Supply, Inc. (1)
569 Charcot Ave, San Jose, CA 95131
Tel.: (408) 432-4890
Web Site: http://campbellmetal.com
Sales Range: $1-9.9 Million
Emp.: 20
Metal Service Centers & Other Metal Merchant Whslr
N.A.I.C.S.: 423510
Joseph Herr (Pres)
Thuy Tau (Mgr)

INDUSTRIAL MILL & MAINTENANCE SUPPLY INC.
4401 Waco St, Texarkana, TX 75501
Tel.: (903) 832-3581
Web Site: http://www.industrialmill.com
Rev.: $10,157,133
Emp.: 24
Valves & Fittings
N.A.I.C.S.: 423830
Bobby Brannan (Mgr-IT)

INDUSTRIAL MOTOR POWER COPORATION
350 N Glenoaks Blvd Ste 200, Los Angeles, CA 91502-2915
Tel.: (323) 268-3380
Web Site: http://www.impcorporation.com
Year Founded: 2001
Sales Range: $25-49.9 Million
Emp.: 18
Industrial Equipment Distr
N.A.I.C.S.: 423830
Nicholas Nadjarian (CEO)
Javier Barahona (Dir-Intl Sls)

INDUSTRIAL OPPORTUNITY PARTNERS, LLC
1603 Orrington Ave Ste 700, Evanston, IL 60201
Tel.: (847) 556-3460 DE
Web Site: http://www.iopfund.com
Year Founded: 2005
Sales Range: $25-49.9 Million
Emp.: 14
Privater Equity Firm
N.A.I.C.S.: 523999
Kenneth Tallering (Sr Mng Dir)
Adam Gottlieb (Founder)
Robert Vedra (Sr Mng Dir)
Michael Hering (CFO & Chief Compliance Officer)
John Colaianne (Principal)
Nicholas Galambos (Principal)
Thomas Paisley (Principal-Operating)
James Todd (Operating Partner)
Andrew Weller (Operating Partner)
David Dorfman (VP)
Michael Hnatysko (Controller)
Ann Costello (Office Mgr)
Justin Livingston (VP-Ops)
Phil Fioravante (Operating Principal)

Subsidiaries:

AAA Sales & Engineering Inc. (1)
1120 W Northbranch Dr, Oak Creek, WI 53154-1433
Tel.: (414) 764-2700
Web Site: http://www.aaase.com
Sales Range: $10-24.9 Million
Emp.: 200
Precision Machining Services
N.A.I.C.S.: 332710
Jeff Barbian (Mgr-Sls)
Chuck Hyttel (VP & Gen Mgr)
John Colaianne (Chm)
Bradley Long (Pres)

Plant (Domestic):

AAA Sales & Engineering, Inc. - Angola (2)
1411 Wohlert St, Angola, IN 46703
Tel.: (260) 665-8441

Web Site: http://www.aaase.com
Rev.: $14,300,000
Emp.: 175
Drivetrain Related Products Mfr
N.A.I.C.S.: 336390

Creative Foam Corporation (1)
300 N Alloy Dr, Fenton, MI 48430-2648
Tel.: (810) 629-4149
Web Site: http://www.creativefoam.com
Sales Range: $100-124.9 Million
Emp.: 600
Plastic Foam Product Mfr
N.A.I.C.S.: 326150
Bruce Graham (CFO)
Terri Kovarik (Controller)
Phil Fioravante (Chm)

Subsidiary (Domestic):

Aetna Felt Corp. (2)
2401 W Emmaus Ave, Allentown, PA 18103
Tel.: (610) 791-0900
Web Site: http://www.aetnafelt.com
Nonwoven Fabric Mills
N.A.I.C.S.: 313230
James Weppler (VP)
Dennis Montalbano (Dir-Pur)

Bremen Corporation (2)
405 Industrial Dr, Bremen, IN 46506-2111 (100%)
Tel.: (574) 546-4238
Web Site: http://www.creativefoammedical systems.com
Sales Range: $10-24.9 Million
Emp.: 40
Mfr of Vinyl Coated Foam Products
N.A.I.C.S.: 326150
Paul Jonik (Controller)

GT Technologies, Inc. (1)
5859 Executive Dr, Westland, MI 48185-1932
Tel.: (734) 467-8371
Web Site: http://www.gttechnologies.com
Cam Follower Rollers & Other Precision Hardened, Ground Engine Components Mfr
N.A.I.C.S.: 336390
Paul Schwarzbaum (Pres & CEO)
Daniel Brinker (Sr VP-Sls, Mktg & Engrg)
Ryan Stacker (Plant Mgr)

N B Handy & Co Inc. (1)
4840 Brookside Ct, Norfolk, VA 23502
Tel.: (757) 857-8300
Web Site: http://www.nbhandy.com
Rev.: $8,670,000
Emp.: 17
Warm Air Heating & Air-Conditioning Equipment & Supplies Merchant Whslr
N.A.I.C.S.: 423730

Subsidiary (Domestic):

4M Metals, Inc. (2)
201 Red Oaks Way, Ridgeland, SC 29936
Tel.: (843) 208-2433
Web Site: http://www.4mmetals.com
Offices of All Other Miscellaneous Health Practitioners
N.A.I.C.S.: 621399
Chad J. Michael (Pres)

PolyVision Corporation (1)
10700 Abbotts Bridge Rd Ste 100, Johns Creek, GA 30097
Tel.: (678) 542-3100
Web Site: http://www.polyvision.com
Sales Range: $150-199.9 Million
Emp.: 65
Office Communication Products Mfr
N.A.I.C.S.: 337127
Peter Lewchanin (Pres & CEO)

Subsidiary (Domestic):

Marsh Industries, Inc. (2)
2301 E High Avenue, New Philadelphia, OH 44663
Web Site: http://www.marsh-ind.com
Sales Range: $1-9.9 Million
Emp.: 25
Visual Display Board Mfr
N.A.I.C.S.: 423840
Brian W. Marsh (CEO)

Branch (Domestic):

PolyVision Corporation-Beaverton (2)

14523 SW Millikan Way Ste 130, Beaverton, OR 97005
Tel.: (503) 626-5014
Web Site: http://www.polyvision.com
Sales Range: $10-24.9 Million
Emp.: 50
Display Systems Mfr
N.A.I.C.S.: 337214

Trantech Radiator Products, Inc. (1)
1 Trantor Dr, Edgefield, SC 29824
Tel.: (803) 637-3166
Web Site: http://www.trantechradiators.com
Sales Range: $25-49.9 Million
Fabricated Plate Radiator Designer & Mfr
N.A.I.C.S.: 333414
Steve Blane (VP-Sls & Mktg)

Wing Enterprises, Incorporated (1)
1198 Spring Creek Pl, Springville, UT 84663-3039
Tel.: (801) 489-3684
Web Site: http://www.littlegiantladders.com
Plastics Product Mfr
N.A.I.C.S.: 326199
Robert Lewis (CFO)

INDUSTRIAL PACKAGING CORP.
3060 11 Mile Rd, Berkley, MI 48072
Tel.: (313) 835-0930
Rev.: $10,000,000
Emp.: 10
Pallets, Wood
N.A.I.C.S.: 321920
John B. Mager (CEO)

INDUSTRIAL PALLET CORPORATION
4 N New York St, Remington, IN 47977
Tel.: (219) 261-3586 IN
Web Site: http://www.ind-pallet-corp.com
Year Founded: 1986
Sales Range: $25-49.9 Million
Emp.: 165
Pallet Mfr
N.A.I.C.S.: 321920
Rob Meister (Co-Owner, Pres & CEO)
Jay Wiegand (Co-Owner & COO)

Subsidiaries:

Industrial Pallet Corporation (1)
11349 US 52 S, Clarks Hill, IN 47930
Tel.: (765) 523-2298
Web Site: http://www.ind-pallet-corp.com
Sales Range: $25-49.9 Million
Emp.: 100
Wood Container & Pallet Mfr
N.A.I.C.S.: 321920
Rob R. Meister (Co-Owner, Pres & CEO)

INDUSTRIAL PARTS DEPOT INC.
23231 S Normandie Ave, Torrance, CA 90501
Tel.: (310) 530-1900 CA
Web Site: http://www.ipdparts.com
Year Founded: 1955
Sales Range: $10-24.9 Million
Emp.: 70
Diesel & Gas Engine Parts Mfr & Distr
N.A.I.C.S.: 333618
Guy E. Marge (CEO)
Michael Sweicher (Controller)
Michael Clogg (Pres & COO)
Steve Scott (Dir-Product Dev & Tech Support)
Gary Wilfert (CFO)

INDUSTRIAL PIPING SPECIALISTS INC.
606 N 145th E Ave, Tulsa, OK 74116
Tel.: (918) 437-9100
Web Site: http://www.ipipes.com
Year Founded: 1986
Rev.: $45,629,951

Industrial Piping Specialists Inc.—(Continued)

Emp.: 300
Steel Pipe & Tubing Distr
N.A.I.C.S.: 423510
Robert H. Westfield *(Pres)*
Paula Oonk *(Controller)*
Paul Mullins *(CFO)*

INDUSTRIAL POWER & LIGHTING CORP.

701 Seneca St Fl 5, Buffalo, NY 14210
Tel.: (716) 854-1811
Web Site: http://www.iplcorp.com
Rev.: $17,100,000
Emp.: 25
General Electrical Contractor
N.A.I.C.S.: 238210
George R. Schlemmer *(CEO)*
Richard Lombard *(Pres)*
Paul Rautenstrauch *(CFO)*

INDUSTRIAL POWER SYSTEMS INCORPORATED

146 Dixie Hwy, Rockford, OH 43460
Tel.: (419) 531-3121
Web Site:
   http://www.ipscontractor.com
Year Founded: 1985
Sales Range: $25-49.9 Million
Emp.: 150
Contractor of Mechanical, Electrical Systems & Millwrighting
N.A.I.C.S.: 238220
Kevin Gray *(CEO)*
Scott Horner *(VP-Petrochemical & Power)*
Beth Carr *(Mgr-Bus Dev)*

INDUSTRIAL PRODUCTS ENTERPISES LLC

Fl 16 119 W 40th St, New York, NY 10018-2516
Tel.: (973) 815-1880
Rev.: $20,000,000
Emp.: 60
Cleaning & Maintenance Equipment & Supplies
N.A.I.C.S.: 423850

INDUSTRIAL REALTY SOLUTIONS, INC.

PO Box 1485, Safety Harbor, FL 34695-1485
Tel.: (727) 724-3300
Web Site:
   http://www.industrialrealtysolutions.com
Year Founded: 1999
Sales Range: $1-9.9 Million
Industrial Real Estate Services
N.A.I.C.S.: 531210
Deron Thomas *(Owner & Pres)*

INDUSTRIAL REVOLUTION, INC.

5835 Segale Park Dr C, Tukwila, WA 98188
Tel.: (425) 883-6600
Web Site:
   http://www.industrialrev.com
Year Founded: 1974
Sales Range: $1-9.9 Million
Emp.: 17
Camping Gear & Cooking Equipment & Accessories Mfr
N.A.I.C.S.: 332510
Keith Jackson *(Owner & CEO)*
Graeme Esarey *(Pres)*
Peter Pontano *(Mgr-Product Dev)*
Anita Rodgers *(VP-Fin)*
Steve Llorente *(VP-Bus Dev)*
Addison Nanney *(Coord-Mktg)*

INDUSTRIAL SALES COMPANY INC.

1200 W Hamburg St, Baltimore, MD 21230-1913
Tel.: (410) 727-0665
Web Site:
   http://www.induscowirerope.com
Year Founded: 1939
Sales Range: $25-49.9 Million
Emp.: 190
Metals Service Centers & offices
N.A.I.C.S.: 423510
Keith Dennis *(Mgr-Sls & Svc)*

Subsidiaries:

J. Henry Holland Corporation **(1)**
5931 Thurston Ave, Virginia Beach, VA 23455-3308 **(100%)**
Tel.: (757) 460-3300
Web Site: http://www.jhenryholland.com
Sales Range: $10-24.9 Million
Emp.: 26
Retailer of Industrial Supplies
N.A.I.C.S.: 423840
Larry Lusk *(Gen Mgr)*

INDUSTRIAL SALES COMPANY INC.

1150 W Marley Rd, Olathe, KS 66061
Tel.: (913) 782-0473
Web Site:
   http://www.industrialsales.us
Year Founded: 1973
Sales Range: $10-24.9 Million
Emp.: 30
Plumbing & Hydronic Heating Supplies
N.A.I.C.S.: 423720
Ron Downing *(Mgr-Sls & Svcs)*
Roger Galloway *(Mgr-Ops)*
Ron Morford *(Branch Mgr)*
Jake J. Cooper III *(Pres)*

INDUSTRIAL SOLUTIONS, INC.

9120 Antares Ave, Columbus, OH 43240
Tel.: (614) 431-0170
Web Site: http://www.isi-controlpanels.com
Year Founded: 1988
Sales Range: $10-24.9 Million
Emp.: 24
Wiring & Fabrication of Electrical Enclosures for Industrial Control Systems
N.A.I.C.S.: 335313
James D. Cooke *(Pres)*

INDUSTRIAL SPECIALITY CONTRACTOR LLC

20480 Highland Rd, Baton Rouge, LA 70817-7347
Tel.: (225) 756-8001
Web Site: http://www.iscgrp.com
Year Founded: 1996
Sales Range: $100-124.9 Million
Emp.: 1,722
Provider of Electrical Work Services
N.A.I.C.S.: 238210
Glen J. Gulino *(Reg Mgr)*

Subsidiaries:

Industrial Specialty Contractors Inc. **(1)**
20480 Highland Rd, Baton Rouge, LA 70817-7347
Tel.: (225) 756-8001
Web Site: http://www.iscgrp.com
Sales Range: $100-124.9 Million
Emp.: 1,000
Instrumentation & Electrical Contractor
N.A.I.C.S.: 238210
Jerry Rispone *(Owner)*

INDUSTRIAL STAFFING SERVICES, INC.

557 Cranbury Rd Ste 22, East Brunswick, NJ 08816
Tel.: (732) 390-7100
Web Site: http://www.industrial-staffing.com
Year Founded: 1991
Sales Range: $75-99.9 Million
Emp.: 16
Professional, Technical, Administrative & Industrial Staffing
N.A.I.C.S.: 561320
Linda Block *(Pres)*
Marilyn Heiberger *(CFO)*
Bradley Block *(VP-Bus Dev & Project Mgr)*

INDUSTRIAL STEEL & WIRE COMPANY

1901 N Narragansett Ave, Chicago, IL 60639-3829
Tel.: (773) 804-0404   DE
Web Site: http://www.springsteel.com
Year Founded: 1986
Sales Range: $75-99.9 Million
Emp.: 50
Metal Service Centers for the Marketing of Metal
N.A.I.C.S.: 423510
Dave Ritter *(Mgr-New Products Dev)*

INDUSTRIAL STEEL INC.

3561 Industrial Rd, Titusville, FL 32796
Tel.: (321) 267-2341
Web Site: http://www.industrial-steel.com
Sales Range: $10-24.9 Million
Emp.: 60
Structural Steel & Precast Concrete Contractors
N.A.I.C.S.: 238120
Elsie Wilson *(Owner)*
Linda Townsend *(Comptroller)*
Randall Harris *(Gen Mgr)*
Jennifer Wilson *(Office Mgr-Acctg)*
Vickie Batz *(Coord-Document Control & Estimating)*
David Phillips *(Mgr-Production Control)*
Clint Rubianes *(Mgr-Production Control)*
John Sammarco *(Project Mgr)*
Alex Parham *(Project Mgr)*
Jocelyn Shinabarger *(Office Mgr-Quality)*
Gary Hood *(Mgr-Sls)*
Fred A. Wilson Jr. *(Pres & Project Mgr)*

INDUSTRIAL SUPPLY COMPANY INC.

1635 S 300 W, Salt Lake City, UT 84115
Tel.: (801) 484-8644
Web Site: http://www.indsupply.com
Sales Range: $200-249.9 Million
Emp.: 150
Large & Small Tools & Paint
N.A.I.C.S.: 423830
Jessica Polychronis *(VP-Procurement & Mktg)*
Ruben Mendez *(VP-Ops & Customer Svc)*
Chris Bateman *(CEO)*
Michelle Lakin *(VP-Fin)*

INDUSTRIAL SUPPLY EXPORT CORPORATION

11441 Interchange Cir S, Miramar, FL 33025-6009
Tel.: (954) 431-7787   FL
Year Founded: 1983
Industrial Supplies Wholesale Distr
N.A.I.C.S.: 425120
Fernando J. Maldonado *(Pres)*

INDUSTRIAL SUPPLY SOLUTIONS, INC.

804 Julian Rd, Salisbury, NC 28147
Tel.: (704) 636-4241
Web Site: http://www.issimro.com
Year Founded: 1946
Sales Range: $50-74.9 Million
Emp.: 150
Industrial Machinery & Equipment
N.A.I.C.S.: 423830
Frank Carmazzi *(Pres & CEO)*
Bill Hesse *(CFO)*
Rick Tankersley *(VP)*

Subsidiaries:

Industrial Supply Solutions, Inc. **(1)**
520 Elizabeth St, Charleston, WV 25311-2106 **(100%)**
Tel.: (304) 346-5341
Web Site: http://www.issimro.com
Sales Range: $10-24.9 Million
Emp.: 16
Retail Distributor of Industrial Supplies
N.A.I.C.S.: 423830
Frank Carmazzi *(Pres & CEO)*
Jim Daniel *(Gen Mgr)*

INDUSTRIAL TECHNOLOGIES INC.

2240 E I25 Frontage Rd, Erie, CO 80516
Tel.: (303) 828-5106
Web Site:
   http://www.industrialtechnology.com
Sales Range: $1-9.9 Million
Emp.: 18
Structural Steel & Precast Concrete Contractors
N.A.I.C.S.: 238120
Phillip Erby *(Owner & Pres)*
Karen Erby *(Mgr-Acctg)*
Eli Gabriella *(Mgr-Procurement)*

INDUSTRIAL THREADED PRODUCTS INC.

515 N Puente St, Brea, CA 92821-2805
Tel.: (562) 802-4626
Web Site: http://www.itpbolt.com
Sales Range: $10-24.9 Million
Emp.: 28
Industrial Fastener Sales
N.A.I.C.S.: 423710
Wally Gross *(Pres)*

INDUSTRIAL TOWEL & UNIFORM

2700 S 160th St, New Berlin, WI 53151-3602
Tel.: (262) 782-1950   WI
Web Site:
   http://www.industrialtowel.com
Year Founded: 1930
Sales Range: $25-49.9 Million
Emp.: 400
Supplier of Towels, Uniforms & Janitors' Supplies
N.A.I.C.S.: 812332
Paul Schoessow *(Dir-Mktg)*

Subsidiaries:

AbsorbTech, LLC **(1)**
3900 W William Richardson Dr, South Bend, IN 46628
Tel.: (800) 767-2487
Industrial Laundering Services
N.A.I.C.S.: 812332

Industrial Towel & Uniform - Neenah Plant **(1)**
945 Apple Blossom Dr, Neenah, WI 54956-4511
Tel.: (888) 729-4884
Laundry Services
N.A.I.C.S.: 812332
Kurt Meyer *(Dir-HR)*

INDUSTRIAL TUBE & STEEL CORPORATION

4658 Crystal Pkwy, Kent, OH 44240

Tel.: (330) 474-5530
Web Site:
    http://www.industrialtube.com
Sales Range: $10-24.9 Million
Emp.: 100
Industrial Products Mfr
N.A.I.C.S.: 423510
Richard B. Siess (Pres)

INDUSTRIAL TURNAROUND CORPORATION

13141 N Enon Church Rd, Chester, VA 23836
Tel.: (804) 414-1100   VA
Web Site: http://www.itac.us.com
Year Founded: 1988
Industrial Building Construction Services
N.A.I.C.S.: 236210
John Whitty (Dir-Specialty Svcs)
John Moody (VP-Engrg, Project Mgmt & Tech)
Jeff Stotesberry (Mgr-CSA Dept)
Teresa Meade (Mgr-Employee Svcs)
Mike Jones (Mgr-Electrical & Controls Dept)
Scot Garner (Mgr-Electrical & Controls Dept)
Jon Loftis (Pres)
Greg Sweeney (Sr Project Mgr)
Richard Starnes (Sr VP)
Sidney Harrison Jr. (CEO)

INDUSTRIAL VALUE PARTNERS, LLC

33 Market Point Dr, Greenville, SC 29607
Tel.: (864) 616-9937
Web Site:
    http://www.industrialvaluepartners.com
Investment Services
N.A.I.C.S.: 523940
Rod Grandy (Mng Dir)
Sam McEntyre (Partner)
Charles Runge (Mng Partner)

Subsidiaries:

South Carolina Elastic   (1)
201 S Carolina Elastic Rd, Landrum, SC 29356-0369   (100%)
Tel.: (864) 457-3388
Web Site: http://www.scelastic.com
Sales Range: $25-49.9 Million
Emp.: 175
Mfr Knit, Woven & Braided Elastic & Non-Elastic Narrow Fabrics & Cords
N.A.I.C.S.: 313220

INDUSTRIAL VALVE SALES & SERVICE

5310 Hwy 45, Eight Mile, AL 36613
Tel.: (251) 675-5282
Web Site: http://www.indvalve.com
Year Founded: 1975
Sales Range: $10-24.9 Million
Emp.: 200
Valve Repair, Industrial
N.A.I.C.S.: 811210
Donald F. Williams (Pres)
Jimmy Harrell (VP)
Donnie Lisenby (Mgr-Acct)

INDUSTRIAL VENTILATION INC.

W6395 Speciality Dr, Greenville, WI 54942
Tel.: (920) 757-6001
Web Site: http://www.ivinc.com
Sales Range: $10-24.9 Million
Emp.: 150
Plumbing Heating & Air Conditioning Contractors
N.A.I.C.S.: 238220
Gerald T. Auler (CEO)
James C. Hanegraaf (Pres)

INDUSTRIAL VENTILATION, INC.

723 E Karcher Rd, Nampa, ID 83687
Tel.: (208) 463-6305
Web Site: http://www.ivi-air.com
Sales Range: $10-24.9 Million
Emp.: 35
Metal Ventilating Fans
N.A.I.C.S.: 332322
Frank H. Bushman (Pres & CEO)
Jerry Bartels (CFO)

Subsidiaries:

Lineal Veneer Inc.   (1)
1704 Industrial Way, Caldwell, ID 83605
Tel.: (208) 454-1337
Sales Range: $10-24.9 Million
Whslr of Veneer Products
N.A.I.C.S.: 423310

INDUSTRIAL VIDEO & CONTROL CO.

330 Nevada St, Newton, MA 02460
Tel.: (617) 467-3059
Web Site: http://www.ivcco.com
Year Founded: 2001
Sales Range: $10-24.9 Million
Emp.: 25
Cameras & Camera Management Software Services
N.A.I.C.S.: 423690
Norman Fast (Pres)
Bill Richards (VP-Engrg)

INDUSTRIAL VIDEO CORPORATION

14885 Sprague Rd, Cleveland, OH 44136-1769
Tel.: (440) 891-9440
Web Site: http://www.ivideo.com
Year Founded: 1968
Sales Range: $10-24.9 Million
Emp.: 40
Distr of Electronic Video Equipment
N.A.I.C.S.: 423690
David Walters (Mgr-Sls)
Ron McGlothlin (Dir-Svcs)
Michael Sparke (Reg Mgr-Sls)

INDUSTRIAL WELDING SUPPLY INC.

1995 Commercial St NE, Salem, OR 97303
Tel.: (503) 581-6131   OR
Web Site:
    http://www.industrialwelding.net
Sales Range: $10-24.9 Million
Emp.: 60
Whslr & Retailer of Welding Machinery & Equipment
N.A.I.C.S.: 423830
Guy Worden (Pres)
Robert Bender (Mgr-Sls)

INDUSTRIAL-IRRIGATION SERVICES

221 E J St, Hastings, NE 68901
Tel.: (402) 463-1377
Web Site: http://www.industrial-irrigation.com
Sales Range: $10-24.9 Million
Emp.: 24
Engines & Transportation Equipment
N.A.I.C.S.: 423830
John C. Osborne (CEO)

INDUSTRIOUS NATIONAL MANAGEMENT COMPANY LLC

215 Park Ave S, 10003, New York, NY
Tel.: (929) 283-6780
Web Site:
    http://www.industriousoffice.com
Year Founded: 2013
Workspace Provider & Services

N.A.I.C.S.: 561210
Jamie Hodari (Founder & CEO)
Michael Robson (COO)

INDUSTRY DATA EXCHANGE ASSOCIATION, INC.

1300 17th St. N, Ste.900, Arlington, VA 22209
Tel.: (703) 562-4600
Web Site: https://idea4industry.com
Year Founded: 1998
Emp.: 100
IT Services
N.A.I.C.S.: 519290
David Oldfather (Pres & CEO)
Denise Keating (Pres-Customer Success)
Angela Baraks (Dir-Data Quality & Standards)
Brett Anderson (Dir-Bus Dev)

Subsidiaries:

Datagility, Inc.   (1)
3230 Sycamore Rd Ste 233, DeKalb, IL 60115
Tel.: (815) 981-4922
Web Site: http://www.datagility.com
Computer System Design Services
N.A.I.C.S.: 541512
Stacie Braffet (Program Dir-Mgmt)

INDUSTRY IDS, INC.

203 N Lasalle St Ste 2100, Chicago, IL 60601
Web Site: http://www.industryids.com
Sales Range: $1-9.9 Million
Marketing Related Software
N.A.I.C.S.: 513210
Sachin Ganglani (Pres)

Subsidiaries:

Industry IDS, Inc.   (1)
2/9 80 ft Road RMV Extension, 2nd Block 2nd Phase, Bengaluru, 560 094, India
Tel.: (91) 80 41748034
Marketing Related Software
N.A.I.C.S.: 513210

INDUSTRY-RAILWAY SUPPLIERS, INC.

811 Golf Ln, Bensenville, IL 60106
Tel.: (630) 766-5708   IL
Web Site:
    http://www.industryrailway.com
Year Founded: 1988
Sales Range: $25-49.9 Million
Emp.: 20
Railroad Equipment & Supplies Distr
N.A.I.C.S.: 423860
Scott Commo (Pres)

INDY CONNECTION ELECTRICAL CONTRACTORS, INC.

4625 W 86th St Ste 800, Indianapolis, IN 46268
Tel.: (317) 468-9170
Web Site:
    http://www.mrquikhomeservice.com
Year Founded: 2001
Sales Range: $10-24.9 Million
Emp.: 70
Heating & Air Conditioning Equipment Maintenance Services
N.A.I.C.S.: 811412
Brad Huff (Owner)

INDY ROHR MOTORS INC.

8455 US 31 S, Indianapolis, IN 46227
Tel.: (317) 887-0800
Web Site: http://www.indyhonda.com
Rev.: $65,000,000
Emp.: 93
New Car Dealers
N.A.I.C.S.: 441110

Robert V. Rohrman (Pres)
Linda Rohrman (Treas & Sec)
Amy Harbert (Dir-HR)

INDY TIRE CENTERS, INC.

9302 E 30th St, Indianapolis, IN 46229-1078
Tel.: (317) 541-2452   IN
Web Site: http://www.indytire.com
Year Founded: 1986
Sales Range: $1-9.9 Million
Emp.: 100
Tire Dealers
N.A.I.C.S.: 441340
Dennis Dickson (Co-Founder)
Paul Zurcher (Co-Founder)
Ray Monteith (Co-Founder)

Subsidiaries:

Riley Park Tire Services   (1)
801 E Main St, Greenfield, IN 46140-2698
Web Site: http://www.rileyparktire.com
Tire & Tube Merchant Whslr
N.A.I.C.S.: 423130

INDY WALLS & CEILINGS INCORPORATED

1740 Wales Ave, Indianapolis, IN 46218-4592
Tel.: (317) 352-9215   IN
Rev.: $10,200,000
Emp.: 75
Drywall & Insulation Contractors
N.A.I.C.S.: 238310
Rebecca Underwood (Pres)
Mary A. Pruitt (Treas & Sec)
Steve Pruitt (Owner)

INDYNE INC.

11800 Sunrise Vly Dr Ste 250, Reston, VA 20191
Tel.: (703) 903-6900
Web Site: http://www.indyneinc.com
Year Founded: 1984
Sales Range: $250-299.9 Million
Emp.: 1,900
System Integration Design Services
N.A.I.C.S.: 541512
Margaret James (Dir-HR)
C. Donald Bishop (Pres & CEO)
Jeffrey Riemer (COO)

INE, INC.

107 Spring St, Seattle, WA 98104
Tel.: (775) 826-4344
Web Site: http://www.ine.com
Year Founded: 2003
Sales Range: $1-9.9 Million
Emp.: 7
IT Certification Boot Camps, Classes, Workbooks & Self-Paced Training Solutions
N.A.I.C.S.: 611420
Brian Dennis (Owner)

INERGETICS, INC.

550 Broad St Ste 1212, Newark, NJ 07102
Tel.: (908) 604-2500   DE
Web Site: http://www.inergetics.com
Year Founded: 2000
Sales Range: $1-9.9 Million
Emp.: 9
Nutritional Supplement Mfr & Distr
N.A.I.C.S.: 325411
Scott Zitiello (VP-Natl Sls)
James E. Kras (Pres & CMO)
Alexis Graf (Assoc Dir-Creative)
Stacey Eng (Dir-Ops)

INERGEX INC.

Key Towers 50 Fountain Plz Ste 700, Buffalo, NY 14202
Tel.: (716) 829-1000
Web Site: http://www.inergex.com
Year Founded: 2000

Inergex Inc.—(Continued)
Sales Range: $10-24.9 Million
Emp.: 140
Information Technology Consulting Services
N.A.I.C.S.: 541512
Bob Clerici (VP-Sls & Mktg)
Karin Glazier (Dir-Mktg)
Mark Brownschidle (Mng Partner-IT Svc Mgmt)
Terry Courtney (VP-Professional Svcs)
Tim Frank (Pres & CEO)
Paul DeSarra (Dir-Bus Intelligence)
Cheri Petrus (Dir-HR)
Rick Muller (Chief Strategy Officer)
Mike Burgio (VP-Managed Svcs Ops)
Dan Bardwell (Dir-Svc Mgmt)
Mark Lundquist (Dir-Project Mgmt)
John Elie (Dir-Healthcare Svcs)
Shawn Claybolt (Controller)
Ryan Mecca (Dir-Managed Svc)
Geannine French (Mgr-Recruitment)
Richard Dynas (Mgr-Service Desk)
Shawn Willson (Dir-Sls)
Jon Gordon (Chm)
Patrice Bennett (Mgr-HR & Benefits)

INETICO, INC.
400 N Ashley Dr Suite 1550, Tampa, FL 33602
Tel.: (813) 258-2200
Web Site: http://www.inetico.com
Year Founded: 2004
Sales Range: $1-9.9 Million
Emp.: 41
Health Care Cost Containment Services
N.A.I.C.S.: 524114
Joseph C. W. Hodges (Pres & CEO)
Robert E. Pierce (CFO)
Maureen Becotte (VP-Fin)
Janet L. Koch (Dir-Clinical Care Mgmt)
Laura A. Conte (Gen Counsel)
Nancy Young (VP-Sls & Acct Mgmt)

INEX CORP.
727 S Cortez St, New Orleans, LA 70119
Tel.: (504) 484-6613
Rev.: $24,900,000
Emp.: 66
Building Materials, Interior
N.A.I.C.S.: 423310
James Geary (Pres)

INEX CORPORATION INC.
9229 Olean Rd, Holland, NY 14080
Tel.: (716) 537-2270
Web Site: http://www.inexinc.net
Emp.: 10
Composite Radiant Tube Mfr
N.A.I.C.S.: 322219
Michael Kasprzyk (Pres)

INFAITH
145 John Robert Dr, Exton, PA 19341
Tel.: (610) 527-4439 PA
Web Site: http://www.infaith.org
Year Founded: 1790
Rev.: $8,313,147
Assets: $13,664,597
Liabilities: $9,105,716
Net Worth: $4,558,881
Emp.: 327
Fiscal Year-end: 02/28/18
Christian Ministry Services
N.A.I.C.S.: 813110
Andrea Graver (Sr Dir-Innovation)
Buffy Bowman (Sr Dir-HR)
Dan Sheldon (CFO)
Ridge Burns (CEO & Exec Dir)
Gerald D. Wisneski (Chm)

INFAITH COMMUNITY FOUN-DATION
625 4th Ave S Ste 1500, Minneapolis, MN 55415
Tel.: (612) 844-4110 MN
Web Site: http://www.infaithfound.org
Year Founded: 1995
Fundraising Services
N.A.I.C.S.: 813211
David Meier (Mgr-Tech & Web Comm)
Lori Anderson (Mgr-Mktg Comm)
Chris Andersen (Pres & CEO)
Tom Peterson (Dir-Fin Svcs & Admin)
Roberta Groening (Mgr-Admin Svcs)
Mandy Tuong (Gen Counsel & Sr Dir-Donor Svcs)
Greg Shamey (Dir-Charitable Giving & Donor Svcs)
Kim Borton (Dir-Grants & Donor Svcs)
Kurt Senske (Chm)

INFANTE ASSOCIATES INC.
9 Robinson Ln, Ridgewood, NJ 07450
Tel.: (201) 447-0700
Year Founded: 1971
Sales Range: $10-24.9 Million
Emp.: 14
Industrial Buildings & Warehouses
N.A.I.C.S.: 236220
Louis R. Infante (Pres)
Geri Reynolds (Mgr-Property)

INFECTIOUS DISEASES SOCI-ETY OF AMERICA
1300 Wilson Blvd Ste 300, Arlington, VA 22209
Tel.: (703) 299-0200 DC
Web Site: http://www.idsociety.org
Year Founded: 1970
Sales Range: $10-24.9 Million
Emp.: 55
Disease Prevention Services
N.A.I.C.S.: 622110
Helen W. Boucher (Treas)
Johan S. Bakken (Pres)
Paul G. Auwaerter (VP)
Christopher D. Busky (CEO)
Thomas M. File (VP)

INFERNO LLC
505 Tennessee St Ste 108, Memphis, TN 38103
Tel.: (901) 278-3773
Web Site: http://www.creativeinferno.com
Year Founded: 1999
Sales Range: $10-24.9 Million
Emp.: 30
Advertising Agencies
N.A.I.C.S.: 541810
Dan O'Brien (Partner)
Michael Overton (Dir-Creative & Designer-Skillionaire)
Liza Routh (Acct Mgr)
Ryan Knoll (Acct Mgr)
Tarryn Sanchez (Project Mgr-Accts & Sr Acct Exec)
Anna Yarbo (Acct Exec)
Lane Cross (Acct Exec)
Kristin Wescott (Acct Exec)
Jennifer Johnson (Dir-Art)
Derrick Alston (Sr Dir-Art)
Natalie Clynes (Project Coord-PR)
Caitlin Berry (Acct Exec-PR)
Lauren Berry (Acct Coord-PR)
Alex Kenner (Acct Exec)
Kelly Supernaw (Acct Exec)
Jesse Wilcox (Jr Acct Exec)

INFINCOM, INC.
2720 S Hardy Dr Ste 1, Tempe, AZ 85282
Tel.: (602) 648-3000

Web Site: http://www.infincom.com
Year Founded: 2006
Sales Range: $1-9.9 Million
Emp.: 38
Office Products Distr
N.A.I.C.S.: 423420
Jeff Bucher (Branch Mgr)
Tiffany Bucher (Pres)
Kyle Hancock (VP-Svc Ops)

INFINEDI PARTNERS LP
E 55th St, New York, NY 10022
Tel.: (917) 596-4593
Web Site: https://www.infinedi.com
Year Founded: 2018
Privater Equity Firm
N.A.I.C.S.: 523999
Jay Hegenbart (Founder)

Subsidiaries:

BWG Strategy LLC (1)
25 Commerce Dr, Cranford, NJ 07016
Tel.: (908) 679-8933
Web Site: https://bwgstrategy.com
Market Research Services
N.A.I.C.S.: 541910
Anil Prahlad (Co-CEO)
Greg Irwin (Co-Founder & Co-CEO)
Bill Williams (Co-Founder)

Subsidiary (Domestic):

OTR Global LLC (2)
1 Manhattanville Rd, Purchase, NY 10577-2100
Tel.: (914) 460-4044
Web Site: http://www.otrglobal.com
Sales Range: $50-74.9 Million
Emp.: 150
Security Brokers & Dealers
N.A.I.C.S.: 523150
Brad Whitt (Dir-Software Res)
Mark Conley (Pres)
John F. O'Donoghue (Dir-Equities)
Kevin Heneghan (Chm)
Thomas Hickey (COO & Chief Compliance Officer)
Allison Malone (Dir-Custom Res Svcs)
Olya Klimiashvili (Dir-Res Ops)
Irene Neumansky (Dir-Tech)

INFINEX FINANCIAL HOLD-INGS, INC.
538 Preston Ave, Meriden, CT 06450
Web Site: http://www.infinexgroup.com
Holding Company; Investment, Insurance & Wealth Management Services
N.A.I.C.S.: 551112
Christine M. Strickland (VP-Lead Generation Div)
Stephen P. Amarante (Pres & CEO)
William F. Cummings (COO, Gen Counsel & Sr Exec VP)
Margaret C. Goz (CFO, Treas & Sr VP)
Scott Davis (Chief Relationship Officer & Exec VP)
John Cooney (Chief Compliance Officer & Sr VP)
Al Dabiri (Sr VP & Chief of Staff)
Anthony M. Santaniello (CTO & Sr VP)
W. Jere Colcer (Sr VP-Bus Dev)
Ida L. Viglione (Sr VP-Lead Generation Div)
Kevin Mancini (VP & Dir-Ops)
Michael B. Cook (VP & Mgr-Fixed Income)
Alexander L. Rosten (VP & Sr Portfolio Mgr)
John F. Martin Jr. (VP & Dir-Advisory Compliance)

Subsidiaries:

Infinex Investments, Inc. (1)
538 Preston Ave, Meriden, CT 06450
Web Site: http://www.infinexgroup.com
Investment, Insurance & Wealth Management Services

N.A.I.C.S.: 523150
Stephen P. Amarante (Pres & CEO)
Margaret C. Goz (CFO, Treas & Sr VP)
William F. Cummings (COO, Gen Counsel & Sr Exec VP)
John Cooney (Chief Compliance Officer & Sr VP)
Anthony M. Santaniello (CTO & Sr VP)
Scott Davis (Chief Relationship Officer & Exec VP)
W. Jere Colcer (Sr VP-Bus Dev)
Al Dabiri (Sr VP & Chief of Staff)
Ida L. Viglione (Sr VP-Lead Generation Div)
Kevin Mancini (VP & Dir-Ops)
Alexander L. Rosten (VP & Sr Portfolio Mgr)
Michael B. Cook (VP & Mgr-Fixed Income)
Christine M. Strickland (VP-Lead Generation Div)
John F. Martin Jr. (VP & Dir-Advisory Compliance)

INFINIDAT INC.
35 Highland Circle S304, Needham, MA 02494
Web Site: http://www.infinidat.com
Year Founded: 2011
Emp.: 200
Computer Data Storage Solutions
N.A.I.C.S.: 334118
Moshe Yanai (Founder)
Steve Sullivan (Pres-Sls-North America)
Avi Shillo (VP-Sls-Asia Pacific)
Randy Arseneau (CMO)
Adrian Flores-Serafin (Gen Mgr-Latin America)
Greg Scorziello (Mgr-UK)
Mitch Diodato (Dir-Channel Sls-North America)
Hayden Sadler (Mgr-South Africa)
Eugene Beauzec (Head-Solutions Architecture-South Africa)
Shahar Bar-Or (Chief Product Officer/Gen Mgr-Israel)
Boaz Chalamish (Chm)
Sapna Capoor (Dir-Global Comm)
Phil Bullinger (CEO)
Alon Rozenshein (CFO)
James Lewis (Dir-Channel-Europe, Middle East & Africa & Asia Pacific & Japan)
Richard Bradbury (Sr VP-Europe, Middle East & Africa & Asia Pacific & Japan)
Richard Connolly (Reg Dir-UKI & DACH)
Hitachi Vantara (Sls Dir-Global)

INFINIGY ENGINEERING
1033 Watervliet Shaker Rd, Albany, NY 12205
Tel.: (518) 690-0790
Web Site: http://www.infinigy.com
Year Founded: 2001
Sales Range: $10-24.9 Million
Emp.: 50
Wireless Networks Designer
N.A.I.C.S.: 541512
John Stevens (Pres & CEO)
Steve Gosnell (COO)

INFINISOURCE
13024 Ballantyne Corporate Pl Ste 400, Charlotte, NC 28277
Tel.: (517) 278-6384
Web Site: http://www.infinisource.com
Year Founded: 1986
Sales Range: $25-49.9 Million
Emp.: 211
Human Capital Management Services
N.A.I.C.S.: 541612
Kim Harrison-Clark (Dir-Tax)
Dave Dawson (CEO)

INFINITE BLUE PLATFORM LLC

399 Arcola Rd, Collegeville, PA 19426
Tel.: (267) 930-0700
Web Site: http://www.infiniteblue.com
Year Founded: 2012
Sales Range: $1-9.9 Million
Emp.: 50
Software Development Services
N.A.I.C.S.: 541511
Frank Shultz *(Chm & CEO)*
Vince Willis *(COO)*
Jennifer Kurtz *(CTO)*
Stephanie Marjoram *(VP-Strategic Accounts)*
Courtney Eiceman *(VP-Mktg)*
Jason Jackson *(VP-Customer Experience)*

INFINITE ENERGY INC.
7001 SW 24th Ave, Gainesville, FL 32607-3704
Tel.: (352) 331-1654   FL
Web Site:
http://www.infiniteenergy.com
Year Founded: 1994
Sales Range: $450-499.9 Million
Emp.: 300
Provider of Gas & Other Services
N.A.I.C.S.: 221122
Darin Cook *(Pres)*
Bill Wagner *(Dir-Sls)*
Michael Sallustio *(Project Mgr)*

INFINITE NETWORKS CORPORATION
3445 Lawrence Ave, Oceanside, NY 11572
Tel.: (646) 768-8417
Year Founded: 1996
Telecommunication Servicesb
N.A.I.C.S.: 517810
David Lazar *(CEO)*

INFINITE POOL FINISHES, LLC
16880 Gator Rd Ste 210, Fort Myers, FL 33912
Tel.: (239) 466-7665
Web Site:
http://www.infinitepoolfinishes.com
Year Founded: 2014
Sales Range: $10-24.9 Million
Emp.: 200
Swimming Pool Refinishing Services
N.A.I.C.S.: 561790
Christie Martino *(Ops Mgr)*

INFINITE REALTY
1455 W Highland Ave Ste 105, San Bernardino, CA 92411-1341
Tel.: (909) 880-6100
Web Site: http://www.infiniterealty.net
Offices of Real Estate Agents & Brokers
N.A.I.C.S.: 531210
Carlos A. Salazar *(Pres)*

Subsidiaries:

ReKTGlobal, Inc.   (1)
80 State St, Albany, NY 12207
Tel.: (833) 367-7358
Web Site: http://www.rektglobal.com
Holiding Company; Esports Conglomerate
N.A.I.C.S.: 551112
Dave Bialek *(CEO)*

Subsidiary (Domestic):

Fearless Media, LLC   (2)
10 Times Sq, New York, NY 10036
Tel.: (646) 856-6782
Web Site: http://www.fearlessmedia.com
Information Services
N.A.I.C.S.: 519290
Lisa Kirlick *(Supvr-Integrated Media)*
Cara Scharf *(Founder)*

INFINITE TECHNOLOGY GROUP LTD.

28C Jefryn Blvd, Deer Park, NY 11729
Tel.: (631) 392-0962
Web Site: http://www.itgl.net
Sales Range: $25-49.9 Million
Emp.: 17
Software Programming Applications On Hardware
N.A.I.C.S.: 541511
Diana Calvet *(Controller)*

INFINITI HR, LLC.
3905 National Dr Ste 400, Burtonsville, MD 20866
Tel.: (301) 841-6380
Web Site: http://www.infinitihr.com
Year Founded: 2008
Sales Range: $125-149.9 Million
Emp.: 17,000
Human Resource Consulting Services
N.A.I.C.S.: 541612
Scott Smrkovski *(CEO)*
Mark Schwaiger *(Mng Partner)*
Sheldon Altschuler *(VP-Risk Mgmt)*
Daniel Mormino *(Sr VP)*
Jeremy McNamara *(Sr VP-Sls)*

INFINITI NORTH SHORE
6030 N Green Bay Rd, Glendale, WI 53209
Tel.: (414) 351-3000
Web Site:
http://www.infinitinorthshore.com
Year Founded: 2005
Sales Range: $10-24.9 Million
Emp.: 50
Car Whslr
N.A.I.C.S.: 441110

INFINITI OF ARDMORE, INC.
1265 Wilmington Pike, West Chester, PA 19382-4976
Tel.: (610) 896-4400   PA
Web Site:
http://www.infinitiofardmore.com
Rev.: $25,373,846
Emp.: 40
New & Used Car Dealer
N.A.I.C.S.: 441110
Joe Bush *(Owner & Gen Mgr)*

INFINITI OF COCONUT CREEK INC.
5501 W Sample Rd, Coconut Creek, FL 33073
Tel.: (954) 861-6100
Web Site: http://www.877infiniti.com
Rev.: $19,500,000
Emp.: 100
New Car Dealers
N.A.I.C.S.: 441110
Bob Duggan *(Mgr-Sls)*
John Shirley *(Mgr-Fin)*
Micheal Crowley *(Gen Mgr & Owner)*

INFINITI OF HONOLULU
2845 Kilihau St, Honolulu, HI 96819
Tel.: (808) 836-0848
Web Site:
http://www.infinitiofhonolulu.com
Sales Range: $25-49.9 Million
Emp.: 51
New & Used Car Dealer
N.A.I.C.S.: 441110
David Kim *(Mgr-Fin)*

INFINITI OF NORWOOD
866 Providence Hwy, Norwood, MA 02062
Tel.: (781) 329-3040
Web Site:
http://www.infinitiofnorwood.com
Year Founded: 1994
Sales Range: $10-24.9 Million
Emp.: 50

Car Whslr
N.A.I.C.S.: 441110
Nigel D'Souza *(Mgr-Svc)*
George Albrecht Jr. *(Gen Mgr)*

INFINITI ON CAMELBACK
1250 E Camleback Rd, Phoenix, AZ 85014
Tel.: (602) 264-2332
Web Site:
http://www.infiniticamelback.com
Year Founded: 2009
Sales Range: $10-24.9 Million
Emp.: 64
Car Whslr
N.A.I.C.S.: 441110
Curt Kasik *(Gen Mgr)*

INFINITI SYSTEMS GROUP, INC.
6980 S Edgerton Rd, Brecksville, OH 44141-3184
Tel.: (440) 546-9440   OH
Year Founded: 1995
Sales Range: $1-9.9 Million
Emp.: 45
Information Technology Consulting Services
N.A.I.C.S.: 541690
Holly Bianco *(Owner)*
Bruce Veness *(VP)*
Joe Kirby *(Dir-IT)*

INFINITUM ELECTRIC, INC.
106 E Old Settlers Blvd Bldg D Ste 106, Round Rock, TX 78664
Tel.: (512) 588-5530   DE
Web Site: https://www.goinfinitum.com
Electric Motor Mfr
N.A.I.C.S.: 334418
Ben Schuler *(CEO & Founder)*

Subsidiaries:

Circuit Connect, Inc.   (1)
4 State St, Nashua, NH 03063
Tel.: (603) 880-7447
Web Site: http://www.circuit-connect.com
Bare Printed Circuit Board Mfr
N.A.I.C.S.: 334412
Richard Clutz *(CEO)*
Marsha Matzkin *(VP-Fin)*

INFINITY ASSOCIATES LLC
655 Redwood Hwy, Mill Valley, CA 94941
Tel.: (415) 380-0510
Web Site:
http://www.infinityassociates.net
Private Investment Firm
N.A.I.C.S.: 523999
David Maddocks *(Mng Dir)*

INFINITY CLASSICS INTERNATIONAL
1227 W St Georges Ave, Linden, NJ 07036
Tel.: (718) 851-2577
Rev.: $17,600,000
Emp.: 350
Hosiery Mfr
N.A.I.C.S.: 315120
Joe Steinberg *(CEO)*

INFINITY COMPUTER SOLUTIONS LLC
9270 Bay Plaza Blvd Ste 612, Tampa, FL 33619
Tel.: (813) 319-3704
Web Site:
http://www.solutionsbyics.com
Year Founded: 2004
Sales Range: $1-9.9 Million
Emp.: 6
IT Support & Related Services
N.A.I.C.S.: 541519
R. Grant Baxley *(Owner & Pres)*

INFINITY DISTRIBUTION, INC.
3311 S Rainbow Blvd Ste 135, Las Vegas, NV 89146
Tel.: (702) 881-5208   NV
Web Site:
http://www.infinitydistributioninc.com
Year Founded: 2015
Assets: $10,389
Liabilities: $716,545
Net Worth: ($706,156)
Earnings: ($373,407)
Fiscal Year-end: 05/31/18
Export Trade Support Services
N.A.I.C.S.: 561499
Raul Mansueto *(Chm, Pres & CEO)*
Josefa Gerona *(CFO, Treas, Sec & VP)*

INFINITY GROUP MANAGEMENT SERVICES, INC.
20550 S LaGrange Rd Ste 300, Frankfort, IL 60423
Tel.: (708) 390-0855   IL
Web Site: http://www.infgroup.com
Sales Range: $25-49.9 Million
Emp.: 10
Cargo Loading & Unloading Services
N.A.I.C.S.: 484121
Paul Goss *(Pres & CEO)*
Nate Lawson *(VP-Freight Svcs & Ops)*

INFINITY HOME SERVICES
18500 W Corporate Dr 250, Brookfield, WI 53045
Tel.: (262) 235-5171
Web Site:
https://www.infinityhomeservice.com
Year Founded: 1997
Residential Roofing & Exterior Remodeling Services
N.A.I.C.S.: 236118
Josh Sparks *(CEO)*

Subsidiaries:

Carpenters Roofing & Sheet Metal, Inc.   (1)
500 Flamingo Dr, West Palm Beach, FL 33401
Tel.: (561) 833-0341
Web Site: http://www.carpentersroofing.com
Sales Range: $1-9.9 Million
Emp.: 40
Roofing Contractors
N.A.I.C.S.: 238160
Joe Hart *(VP)*
Jason Lovelady *(Pres)*

INFINITY NETWORK SOLUTIONS, INC.
93 Gateway Dr, Macon, GA 31210
Tel.: (478) 475-9500
Web Site:
http://www.infinitynetworks.net
Year Founded: 2000
Rev.: $5,200,000
Emp.: 40
Integrated Systems Design
N.A.I.C.S.: 541512
Robert C. Betzel *(Founder, CEO & Partner)*
Harvey Logan *(Coord-Pur)*
Amy Anderson *(VP-Ops)*
Charlie Waters *(VP-Svc)*

INFINITY RESOURCES, INC.
900 N Rohlwing Rd, Itasca, IL 60143-1341
Tel.: (630) 775-3300
Web Site:
http://www.infinityresourcesinc.com
Year Founded: 2000
Sales Range: $150-199.9 Million
Emp.: 600
Direct Marketing Services; Movies & Music Print & Online Catalog Whslr
N.A.I.C.S.: 541613

Infinity Resources, Inc.—(Continued)

Frank Collazo *(Acct Coord-Payable)*
Karen Randle *(Mgr-Mdsg)*

Subsidiaries:

Critics' Choice Video, Inc.   (1)
900 N Rohlwing Rd, Itasca, IL 60143
Tel.: (630) 775-3300
Web Site: http://www.ccvideo.com
Sales Range: $25-49.9 Million
Emp.: 150
Movies Online Catalog Whslr
N.A.I.C.S.: 532282
Jeff Walker *(Pres)*

INFINITY SYSTEMS ENGI-NEERING, LLC

13560 Northgate Estates Dr, Colorado Springs, CO 80921
Tel.: (719) 548-9712
Web Site: http://www.infinity.aero
Year Founded: 1996
Sales Range: $10-24.9 Million
Emp.: 71
Computer & Engineering Services
N.A.I.C.S.: 541511
Andreas Wilfong *(Principal)*
Cheryll Hoggatt *(Mgr-HR)*
Brad Michelson *(VP)*

INFINITY TECHNOLOGY, INC.

430 Wynn Dr, Huntsville, AL 35805
Tel.: (256) 430-1484
Web Site: http://www.infitech.com
Year Founded: 1989
Sales Range: $10-24.9 Million
Emp.: 140
Aerospace Avionics Engineering,
Software Application Development,
Document Imaging Management &
Fabrication Manufacturing Services
N.A.I.C.S.: 334511
Cindy Calvert *(Mgr-Proposal)*

INFINITY TRADING & SOLUTIONS

450 E Elliot Rd, Chandler, AZ 85225
Tel.: (480) 940-1037
Web Site: http://www.itsparts.com
Sales Range: $10-24.9 Million
Emp.: 13
Sales of Aircraft Spare Parts to FAA-Certified Facilities
N.A.I.C.S.: 336413
Scott Tinker *(Mng Partner)*
Ryan Kohnke *(Mng Partner)*
Linn Shaw *(Controller)*

INFLECTION LLC

555 Twin Dolphin Dr Ste 200, Redwood City, CA 94065
Web Site: http://www.inflection.com
Year Founded: 2006
Sales Range: $50-74.9 Million
Emp.: 110
Background Check Software
N.A.I.C.S.: 513210
Matthew Monahan *(Co-Founder & CEO)*
Brian Monahan *(Co-Founder)*
Jeremy Wood *(VP-Fin)*

INFLIGHT SALES GROUP INC.

750 3rd Ave, New York, NY 10017
Tel.: (212) 527-7588
Rev.: $25,000,000
Emp.: 85
Infight Duty Free Shopping
N.A.I.C.S.: 455219
Ivan Giovanni Tassaro *(Acct Dir-Hong Kong)*
Karen Durban-Villeval *(Dir-Europe & Africa)*

INFLUENCE GRAPHICS

1105 44th Rd, Long Island City, NY 11101
Tel.: (212) 354-6123
Web Site: http://www.influencegraphics.com
Year Founded: 2001
Sales Range: $1-9.9 Million
Emp.: 25
Graphic Design Services
N.A.I.C.S.: 541430
Vincent G. Lobdell *(Partner)*
Ronald Sizemore *(Owner)*
Paul Gonzalez *(Mgr-Production)*

INFO RETAIL COMPANY

120 Interstate N Pkwy E Ste 226, Atlanta, GA 30339
Tel.: (770) 953-1500
Web Site: http://www.inreality.com
Year Founded: 1995
Sales Range: $10-24.9 Million
Emp.: 33
All Other Professional, Scientific & Technical Services
N.A.I.C.S.: 541990
Ryan McLaughlin *(Project Mgr)*
Gary Lee *(Pres & CEO)*
Melissa Lassiter *(Dir-Project Mgmt)*
Kevin Greer *(Assoc Dir-Creative)*
Chloe Kelsch *(Acct Mgr)*
Carl Davis *(VP-Ops)*
Florian Vollmer *(Chief Experience Officer & Principal)*

INFOAXIS INC

300 Rte 17 S, Mahwah, NJ 07430
Tel.: (201) 236-3000
Web Site: http://www.infoaxis.com
Year Founded: 1999
Sales Range: $10-24.9 Million
Emp.: 35
Technology Solutions
N.A.I.C.S.: 541690
Mickey McGraw *(CEO)*
Lauryn Laga *(Mgr-Mktg)*
Lindsey Schlossman *(Mgr-Acctg)*
Mike Hendrick *(Sr Acct Exec)*

INFOCISION MANAGEMENT CORP.

325 Springside Dr, Akron, OH 44333
Tel.: (330) 668-1400
Web Site: http://www.infocision.com
Rev.: $91,280,967
Emp.: 4,000
Telemarketing Services
N.A.I.C.S.: 561422
Mike Langenfeld *(COO)*
Dave Hamrick *(CFO)*
Mike Stokes *(Sr VP-Comml Ops)*
Craig Taylor *(CEO)*
Karen Taylor *(Chm)*
Michael Van Scyoc *(Chief Strategy Officer)*
Michael White *(CTO)*

INFOCORE, INC.

5973 Avenida Encinas Ste 218, Carlsbad, CA 92008
Tel.: (760) 607-2500   DE
Web Site: http://www.infocore.com
Year Founded: 1992
Sales Range: $1-9.9 Million
Emp.: 15
List Brokerage & Management Services
N.A.I.C.S.: 513140
Peter A. Jupp *(Co-Owner & CEO)*
Elizabeth Stewart *(Co-Owner)*
Amy MacNabb *(VP-List Brokerage)*
Denise Covington *(Mktg Dir)*
Craig W. Branigan *(Chm)*

INFOCUS PARTNERS

5950 Grand Ave Ste 100, West Des Moines, IA 50266

Tel.: (515) 223-2685
Sales Range: $10-24.9 Million
Emp.: 596
Professional Employment Services
N.A.I.C.S.: 561311
Charles Ganske *(Pres)*

INFOJINI INC

10015 Old Columbia Rd Ste B215, Columbia, MD 21046
Tel.: (410) 312-5458
Web Site: http://www.infojiniconsulting.com
Year Founded: 2006
Sales Range: $1-9.9 Million
Emp.: 25
It Consulting
N.A.I.C.S.: 541690
Amol Salunkhe *(Mgr-Talent Acq)*
Abby Mahadik *(Mgr-Talent Acq)*
Kajal Joshi *(Mgr-Recruiting)*

INFOLAB INC.

17400 Hwy 61 N, Lyon, MS 38645
Tel.: (662) 627-2283
Web Site: http://www.infolabinc.com
Year Founded: 1967
Rev.: $54,000,000
Emp.: 66
Medical & Hospital Equipment
N.A.I.C.S.: 423450
I. Dean Spradling *(Pres)*

INFOLOB SOLUTIONS, INC.

909 Lk Carolyn Pkwy Ste 300, Irving, TX 75039
Tel.: (972) 535-5559
Web Site: http://www.infolob.com
Year Founded: 2009
Sales Range: $10-24.9 Million
Emp.: 200
Information Technology Support Services
N.A.I.C.S.: 541512
Vijay Cherukuri *(Chm)*
Dirgesh Patel *(CEO)*
Varma Buddharaju *(COO & Head-Digital Bus Unit)*

INFOLYNX SERVICES, INC.

325 Danbury Rd, New Milford, CT 06776
Tel.: (860) 210-1203
Web Site: http://www.infolynx.com
Sales Range: $10-24.9 Million
Emp.: 200
Computer Related Services
N.A.I.C.S.: 541519

INFOMATICS, INC

31313 Northwestern Hwy Ste 219, Farmington Hills, MI 48334
Tel.: (248) 865-0300
Web Site: http://www.infomatinc.com
Year Founded: 1998
Sales Range: $1-9.9 Million
Emp.: 110
IT Consulting & Staffing Services
N.A.I.C.S.: 541618
Rajan Raghunathan *(Founder)*
Radha Rangarajan *(Dir-Chennai)*

Subsidiaries:

Infomatics Software Solutions
India   (1)
15/8 1st Floor MG Road, Shastri Nagar Adyar, Chennai, 600020, Tamil Nadu,
India   (100%)
Tel.: (91) 44 4351 1203
Web Site: http://www.infomatinc.com
IT Consulting & Software Solutions
N.A.I.C.S.: 513210

INFOMEDIA GROUP INC

11835 Ih 10 W, San Antonio, TX 78230
Tel.: (210) 475-7100

Web Site: http://www.callcarenet.com
Rev.: $1,400,000
Emp.: 30
Temporary Help Service
N.A.I.C.S.: 561320
John W. Erwin *(CEO)*
Rick Scheel *(VP-Sls)*
Frank Schilling *(VP-Member Svcs)*
Jane Binzak *(VP-People Svcs)*
Kristin Blasko *(VP-Product Dev)*
Larry Reyes *(VP-Talent Dev & Corp Culture)*
Linda Raileanu *(VP-Clinical Svcs)*
Marie James *(Dir-Clinical Svcs)*
Rick Hineline *(VP-Bus Process Mgmt)*
Scott Schawe *(Chief Fin & HR Officer)*
Stacie Stoner *(VP-Customer Experience)*
Vikie Spulak *(COO)*
Yvonne Daugherty *(Sr VP-Mktg)*

Subsidiaries:

Stericycle Communication Solutions,
Inc.   (1)
4010 Commercial Ave, Northbrook, IL 60062
Web Site:
   http://stericyclecommunications.com
Call Management Communication Solutions
for Healthcare Industry
N.A.I.C.S.: 517810
Charles A. Alutto *(Pres)*

INFOMEDIA INC

1151 Eagle Dr Ste 325, Loveland, CO 80537
Tel.: (970) 278-0011
Web Site:
   http://www.infomediainc.com
Year Founded: 1995
Rev.: $3,500,000
Emp.: 26
Data Processing, Hosting & Related Services
N.A.I.C.S.: 518210
Joel Comm *(CEO)*

INFOOBJECTS INC

2041 Mission College Blvd Ste 280, Santa Clara, CA 95054
Tel.: (408) 988-2000
Web Site: http://www.infoobjects.com
Year Founded: 2005
Sales Range: $1-9.9 Million
Emp.: 60
Custom Software Development
N.A.I.C.S.: 513210
Rishi Yadav *(Pres & CEO)*
Sudhir Jangir *(CTO)*
Utkarsh Panwar *(VP-Enterprise Solutions)*
Bart Hickenlooper *(Sr VP-Bus Dev & Client Svcs)*

INFORM PRODUCT DEVELOPMENT, INC.

700 Wilburn Rd, Sun Prairie, WI 53590
Tel.: (608) 825-4700
Web Site: http://www.in-form.com
Year Founded: 1995
Sales Range: $1-9.9 Million
Emp.: 28
Engineeering Services
N.A.I.C.S.: 541330
Edward Raleigh *(Pres)*
Steve Roberts *(Mgr-Prototype)*
Terri Karls *(Office Mgr)*

INFORM, INC.

415 1st Ave NW, Hickory, NC 28601
Tel.: (828) 322-7766
Web Site: http://www.informinc.net
Year Founded: 1967
Sales Range: $1-9.9 Million

Advetising Agency
N.A.I.C.S.: 541810
Charlene Nelson (Sls Mgr)
Brent Childers (Acct Mgr)
Denise Hatcher (Dir-Mktg)
J. Johnson (Dir-Art)
Paul Fogleman Jr. (Pres)

INFORMATICS GROUP
3800 S Tamiami Trail Ste 317, Sarasota, FL 34239
Tel.: (855) 544-2333
Web Site:
http://www.theinformaticsgroup.com
Year Founded: 2006
Sales Range: $1-9.9 Million
Electronic Medical & Health Records
Support Services
N.A.I.C.S.: 513210
Krystal Koppes (Pres)
Brett Koppes (VP)

INFORMATION & COMPUTING SERVICES, INC.
1650 Prudential Dr Ste 300, Jacksonville, FL 32207-8149
Tel.: (904) 399-8500   FL
Web Site: http://www.icsfl.com
Year Founded: 1982
Sales Range: $10-24.9 Million
Emp.: 145
Computer Software Development
N.A.I.C.S.: 541511
Jorge F. Morales (Founder, Chm & Pres)
Holli Anderson (Dir-Mktg)

INFORMATION CONTROL CORPORATION
2500 Corporate Exchange Dr Ste 310, Columbus, OH 43231
Tel.: (614) 523-3070
Web Site:
http://www.icctechnlogies.com
Year Founded: 1979
Sales Range: $25-49.9 Million
Emp.: 405
Information Technology Services
N.A.I.C.S.: 541512
Myke Taylor (Project Mgr)

INFORMATION EXPERTS, INC.
22978 Lois Ln, Ashburn, VA 20148
Tel.: (703) 787-9100
Web Site:
http://www.informationexperts.com
Year Founded: 1995
Rev.: $6,800,000
Emp.: 25
Management Consulting Services
N.A.I.C.S.: 541618
Adam Levin (Exec VP)
Marissa Levin (Pres & CEO)

INFORMATION MANAGEMENT RESOURCES, INC.
85 Argonaut Ste 200, Aliso Viejo, CA 92656
Tel.: (949) 215-8889
Web Site: http://www.imri.com
Sales Range: $1-9.9 Million
Emp.: 35
Engineering & Information Technology Consulting Services
N.A.I.C.S.: 541330
Martha Daniel (Pres & CEO)
Brenda Taylor (CTO & Exec VP-Bus Dev)
Maronya C. Schar (COO)
Vonnie Craig-Parker (Reg Dir)
Satwant Atwal (VP-Cyber Security)
Brian Berger (Exec VP-Comml Cybersecurity)
Kamran Khan (Sr VP-Federal Programs)
Christopher Powell III (VP-Bus Dev)

INFORMATION MANAGEMENT SERVICES
12501 Prosperity Dr Ste 200, Silver Spring, MD 20904
Tel.: (301) 680-9770
Web Site: http://www.imsweb.com
Sales Range: $100-124.9 Million
Emp.: 150
Computer Related Consulting Services
N.A.I.C.S.: 541512
Kevin Meagher (VP)
Janis Beach (Dir-IT)
Olivia Leonard (Dir-Mktg)

INFORMATION SYSTEMS AUDIT & CONTROL ASSOCIATION, INC.
3701 Algonquin Rd Ste 1010, Rolling Meadows, IL 60008
Tel.: (847) 253-1545   IL
Web Site: http://www.isaca.org
Year Founded: 1969
Sales Range: $50-74.9 Million
Emp.: 199
Technology Development Services
N.A.I.C.S.: 813920
Naimish Anarkat (Pres)
Adnan Dakhwe (VP & Dir-Res)
Brijen M. Joshi (Sec)
Anisha G. Tekwani (Treas)
Muralidharan Chandrasekhran (Dir-Membership)

INFORMATION SYSTEMS EXPERTS, LLC
615 W Carmel Dr Ste 130, Carmel, IN 46032
Tel.: (317) 814-1035
Web Site: http://www.ise-indy.com
Year Founded: 1993
Rev.: $3,700,000
Emp.: 28
Computer Related Services
N.A.I.C.S.: 541512
Rakesh Kapur (Dir-Bus Unit)

INFORMATION SYSTEMS MANAGEMENT, INC.
6400 SE Lk Rd Ste 210, Portland, OR 97222
Tel.: (503) 496-5350
Web Site: http://www.goism.com
Year Founded: 2000
Sales Range: $10-24.9 Million
Emp.: 20
IT Application, Design & Consulting Services
N.A.I.C.S.: 541690
B. J. O'Reilly (Pres)

INFORMATION SYSTEMS SOLUTIONS, INC.
51 Monroe St Ste 1609, Rockville, MD 20850-2498
Tel.: (301) 251-5101
Web Site: http://www.issits.com
Year Founded: 1990
Sales Range: $1-9.9 Million
Emp.: 32
Information Technology Services
N.A.I.C.S.: 541512
Linda Houk (CEO)
Matt Vross (Engr-Software)

INFORMATION TECHNOLOGY EXPERTS, INC.
2120 S College Ave, Fort Collins, CO 80525
Tel.: (970) 282-7333
Web Site: http://www.itxfc.com
Year Founded: 1996
Sales Range: $10-24.9 Million
Emp.: 130
Computer Related Services

N.A.I.C.S.: 541512
Bruce Hottman (VP-Govt Ops)
Mai A. Tran (Pres & CEO)

INFORMATION TODAY INC.
143 Old Marlton Pike, Medford, NJ 08055-8750
Tel.: (609) 654-6266
Web Site: http://www.infotoday.com
Sales Range: $25-49.9 Million
Emp.: 114
Book, Periodical & Internet Publisher & Business Services
N.A.I.C.S.: 513120
Thomas H. Hogan (Pres)
Roger R. Bilboul (Chm)
John C. Yersak (VP-Admin)
Sue Hogan (Dir-HR)
William C. Spence (VP-IT)
John B. Bryans (Editor-Library & Book Trade Almanac)
Janeen Welsh (Mgr-Circulation)
Joe Menendez (Mgr-Mktg)
Kathy Bayer (Sr Mgr-Event)
Monica Gray (Coord-Event)
Sheila Willison (Dir-Mktg, Conferences & Events)
Adrienne Snyder (Dir-Sls-East Coast & Midwest)
DawnEl Harris (Dir-Web Events)
Dennis Sullivan (Dir-Sls-West)
Owen O'Donnell (Dir-Reference)
Thomas H. Hogan Jr. (VP-Mktg & Bus Dev)

Subsidiaries:

CRM Media, LLC   (1)
237 W 35th St 8th Fl Ste 806, New York, NY 10001
Tel.: (212) 251-0608
Web Site: http://www.destinationcrm.com
Sales Range: $10-24.9 Million
Emp.: 4
Periodicals
N.A.I.C.S.: 513120
Bob Fernekees (Publr)
Dennis Sullivan (Acct Dir)
David Myron (Dir-Editorial)

Faulkner Information Services   (1)
116 Cooper Ctr 7905 Browning Rd Ste 212, Pennsauken, NJ 08109
Tel.: (856) 662-2070
Web Site: http://www.faulkner.com
Sales Range: $10-24.9 Million
Emp.: 10
Technical Manual Publisher
N.A.I.C.S.: 513140

ITI Reference Group - FL   (1)
3980 Tampa Rd Ste 207, Oldsmar, FL 34677
Tel.: (813) 855-4635
Web Site: http://www.infotoday.com
Book, Periodical & Internet Publisher & Business Services
N.A.I.C.S.: 513130
Debra James (Mgr-Editorial Ops)

ITI Reference Group - NJ   (1)
630 Central Ave, New Providence, NJ 07974
Tel.: (908) 219-0279
Web Site: http://www.infotoday.com
Sales Range: $25-49.9 Million
Emp.: 9
Book, Periodical & Internet Publisher & Business Services
N.A.I.C.S.: 513120
Lauri Weiss-Rimler (Mgr-Natl Product Sls)

Information Today, Ltd   (1)
Unit F 78 Cumnor Road Boars Hill, Oxford, OX1 5JP, United Kingdom
Tel.: (44) 1865 327813
Web Site: http://www.infotoday.eu
Emp.: 5
Magazine Publisher
N.A.I.C.S.: 513120
Kat Allen (Dir-Bus Dev)

KMWorld   (1)
22 Bayview St, Camden, ME 04843
Tel.: (207) 236-8524

Web Site: http://www.kmworld.com
Sales Range: $10-24.9 Million
Emp.: 5
Periodicals
N.A.I.C.S.: 513120
Hugh McKellar (Editor-in-Chief)
Andy Moore (Publr)

Online   (1)
143 Old Marlton Pike, Medford, NJ 08055-8750
Tel.: (609) 654-6266
Web Site: http://www.onlineinc.com
Product Reviews, Case Studies, Electronic, Industry & Online Databases Periodicals
N.A.I.C.S.: 513120

Speech Technology Media   (1)
2628 Wilhite Ct Ste 100, Lexington, KY 40503
Tel.: (859) 278-2223
Web Site: http://www.speechtechmag.com
Magazine Publisher
N.A.I.C.S.: 513120

Streaming Media, Inc.   (1)
143 Old Marlton Pike, Medford, NJ 08055-8750
Tel.: (203) 761-1466
Web Site: http://www.streamingmedia.com
Media Services
N.A.I.C.S.: 517810
Joel Unickow (Publr & VP)

INFORMATION VISUALIZATION AND INNOVATIVE RESEARCH INC.
1626 Barber Rd Ste A, Sarasota, FL 34240
Tel.: (941) 377-6329
Web Site: http://www.ivirinc.com
Year Founded: 2008
Sales Range: $1-9.9 Million
Education, Medical Education, Modeling & Simulation Researcher & Developer
N.A.I.C.S.: 541715
Catherine Strayhorn (Pres & CEO)
Emily Burns (VP-Bus Dev)
Ray Shuford (VP-Ops)
John J. Anton (Chm & CTO)

INFORMATIVE RESEARCH INC.
13030 Euclid St Ste 209, Garden Grove, CA 92843
Tel.: (714) 638-2855
Web Site:
http://www.informativeresearch.com
Year Founded: 1946
Sales Range: $10-24.9 Million
Emp.: 100
Credit Reporting Services
N.A.I.C.S.: 561450
Sean Buckner (Pres & CEO)
Tony D'Eccliss (Sr VP-Sls)
Brandy Randy (Pres, CFO & COO)
Stan Baldwin (COO)
Jane House (Dir-Portfolio Solutions)
Renae Sherman (VP-Bus Dev & Innovation)

INFORMED FAMILY FINANCIAL SERVICES, INC.
2570 Blvd of the Generals Ste 223, Norristown, PA 19403
Tel.: (610) 630-4495   PA
Web Site:
https://www.informedfamily.com
Year Founded: 1994
Financial Planning & Wealth Management Services
N.A.I.C.S.: 541618
Jeffrey E. Bush (CEO & CFO)

Subsidiaries:

Strategic Wealth Advisory LLC   (1)
180 Sunset Manor Dr, Birdsboro, PA 19508-1018
Tel.: (610) 404-3014

Informed Family Financial Services,
Inc.—(Continued)

Web Site:
http://www.strategicwealthadvisory.net
Sales Range: $10-24.9 Million
Investment Advice
N.A.I.C.S.: 523940
Earl Schultz *(Owner & Pres)*

INFORONICS, LLC
25 Porter Rd, Littleton, MA 01460
Tel.: (978) 698-7300
Web Site: http://www.inforonics.com
Year Founded: 1962
Sales Range: $10-24.9 Million
Emp.: 380
Technical, Application Management &
Infrastructure Services
N.A.I.C.S.: 541512
Bruce Mills *(Pres)*

INFORTAL ASSOCIATES
900 E Hamilton Ave Ste 100, Camp-
bell, CA 95008
Tel.: (408) 298-9700
Web Site: https://www.infortal.com
Year Founded: 1985
Investigation Services
N.A.I.C.S.: 561611
Candice Tal *(CEO)*

INFOSEMANTICS
2605 Sagebrush Dr Ste 207, Flower
Mound, TX 75028
Tel.: (469) 941-0266
Web Site:
http://www.infosemantics.com
Year Founded: 2001
Sales Range: $1-9.9 Million
Emp.: 50
Software Development & Information
Technology Consulting Services
N.A.I.C.S.: 541511
Naren Thota *(Founder & Pres)*
Susan Behn *(VP-Oracle Practise)*
Sunil Vaddadi *(VP-Staffing & Ops)*
Kishore Thota *(VP-Offshore Svc)*

INFOSMART SYSTEMS, INC.
5850 Town & Country Blvd Ste 1102,
Frisco, TX 75034
Tel.: (972) 267-5900
Web Site:
http://www.infosmartsys.com
Year Founded: 2004
Sales Range: $1-9.9 Million
Emp.: 70
Global IT Solutions
N.A.I.C.S.: 519290
Murali Killari Chandrasekar *(Mgr-HR)*

INFOSPECTRUM, INC.
30497 Canwood St Ste 104, Agoura
Hills, CA 91301
Tel.: (818) 874-9226   CA
Web Site: http://www.info-
spectrum.com
Year Founded: 1992
Sales Range: $100-124.9 Million
Software Developer
N.A.I.C.S.: 513210
Suresh Radhakrishnan *(Pres)*

Subsidiaries:

Hetrogenous, Inc.   **(1)**
30497 Canwood Street Ste 104, Agoura
Hills, CA 91301
Tel.: (818) 874-9226
Web Site: http://www.hetrogenous.com
Sales Range: $1-9.9 Million
Emp.: 20
Asset Tracking Software Publisher
N.A.I.C.S.: 513210

INFOSTRETCH CORPORATION
3200 Patrick Henry Dr, Santa Clara,
CA 95054

Tel.: (408) 727-1100   CA
Web Site: http://www.infostretch.com
Year Founded: 2004
Sales Range: $1-9.9 Million
Emp.: 240
Computer System Design Services
N.A.I.C.S.: 541512
Rutesh Shah *(Co-Founder & CEO)*
Manish Mistry *(VP-Mobile Svcs)*
Manish Mathuria *(Co-Founder &
CTO)*
Sivakumar Anna *(Dir-Enterprise Svcs)*
Rishabh Mishra *(Head-Corp Dev)*

INFOSURV, INC.
980 Hammond Dr Ste 720, Atlanta,
GA 30328
Tel.: (404) 745-9255
Web Site: http://www.infosurv.com
Year Founded: 1998
Sales Range: $10-24.9 Million
Marketing Research Service
N.A.I.C.S.: 541910
Carl Fusco *(Mng Dir & VP)*
Kyle Burnam *(VP-Intengo)*
Lenni Moore *(Dir-Client Svc)*

INFOSYNC SERVICES LLC
1938 N Woodlawn St Ste 110,
Wichita, KS 67208
Tel.: (316) 685-1622
Web Site: http://www.issvc.com
Year Founded: 2001
Sales Range: $10-24.9 Million
Emp.: 500
Outsourced Accounting, Payroll &
Reporting Services
N.A.I.C.S.: 541219
David Oden *(Pres)*
Bruce Smith *(Controller)*
Mark Roberson *(VP-Tech)*
Debby Haskell *(VP-Ops)*
Steve Davis *(Dir-Transitions)*
Rachel Range *(Controller)*
Denise Christian *(Dir-HR)*
Dale Hoyer *(CEO)*
Bob Robison *(CFO)*
Charlie Debbrecht *(Dir-Acctg)*
Chris Devore *(Dir-Acctg)*
Virginia Nash *(Dir-Payroll)*
Randy Wicklund *(Dir-Payroll)*
Karen Martinez *(Dir-Tax)*
Lisa Hoy *(Dir-Transitions)*
Joshua Bartel *(VP-Web Dev)*

INFOSYS INTERNATIONAL, INC.
110 Terminal Dr, Plainview, NY 11803
Tel.: (516) 576-9494   NY
Web Site:
http://www.infosysinternational.com
Year Founded: 1986
Sales Range: $1-9.9 Million
Emp.: 65
Information Technology Solutions &
Services to Federal, State & Local
Government Clients
N.A.I.C.S.: 921190

INFOTECH PRISM, LLC
5865 N Point Pkwy Ste 200, Al-
pharetta, GA 30022
Tel.: (770) 573-0666
Web Site: http://www.cirruslabs.io
Year Founded: 2005
Sales Range: $10-24.9 Million
Emp.: 144
Information Technology Management
Services
N.A.I.C.S.: 541512
Zia Rahman *(Founder & CEO)*
Courtney Courtney *(COO)*
Shiboo Varughese *(CTO)*
Kailash Lala *(Exec VP)*
Saulo Bomfim *(Exec VP-Cloud Mgmt
Svcs)*

INFOTREE SERVICE INC.
215 Ann Arbor Rd Ste 304, Plymouth,
MI 48170
Tel.: (734) 927-3145
Web Site:
http://www.infotreeservice.com
Year Founded: 2003
Sales Range: $25-49.9 Million
Emp.: 78
Engineering Services
N.A.I.C.S.: 541330
Carol Kulinski *(Mgr-Ops)*
Sanjay Dahiya *(Acct Mgr)*

INFOTRIEVE INC.
20 Westport Rd Ste 105, Wilton, CT
06897
Tel.: (203) 423-2130
Web Site: http://www.infotrieve.com
Rev.: $23,000,000
Emp.: 65
Business Service Solutions & Con-
sulting for Information Centers
N.A.I.C.S.: 541910
Kenneth J. Benvenuto *(Pres & CEO)*
Eileen Green *(Controller)*
Mary Ging *(Mng Dir-EMEA & Exec
Dir-Publr Rels)*

INFOTRUST GROUP, INC.
17671 Cowan Ave Ste 200, Irvine,
CA 92614-6078
Tel.: (949) 474-4200
Web Site:
http://www.infotrustgroup.com
Information Technology Consulting
Services
N.A.I.C.S.: 541690
Nancy Brodsky *(VP-HR)*
Geoffrey Godet *(Pres & CEO)*

Subsidiaries:

Flatirons Solutions, Inc.   **(1)**
17671 Cowan Ste 200, Irvine, CA 92614-
6078
Tel.: (949) 474-4200
Web Site: http://www.flatironssolutions.com
Emp.: 200
Information Technology Consulting Ser-
vices, Software Development & Program
Management Services
N.A.I.C.S.: 541519
Geoffrey Godet *(Pres)*
Bill Francis *(CFO & Sr VP-Corp Shared
Svcs)*
Nancy Brodsky *(VP-HR)*
Greg Beserra *(COO)*
Joe Mihalik *(VP-Bus Dev)*
Brandon Batt *(Sec)*
Jean-Daniel Sillion *(CEO)*

Subsidiary (Domestic):

Beach Street Consulting, Inc.   **(2)**
2 Wisconsin Cir Ste 700, Chevy Chase, MD
20815
Tel.: (240) 242-5375
Web Site: http://www.beachstreet.net
Information Technology Solutions & Con-
sulting Services
N.A.I.C.S.: 541690
John Burns *(Pres)*
Tom Shanley *(COO)*
Johnny Gee *(CTO)*
Tim Schwedes *(VP-Technical Sls)*

INFOVISION CONSULTANTS, INC.
800 E Campbell Rd Ste 388, Rich-
ardson, TX 75081
Tel.: (972) 234-0058
Web Site: http://www.infovision.com
Year Founded: 1995
Rev.: $9,300,000
Emp.: 200
IT & Engineering Services
N.A.I.C.S.: 541330
Sean Yalamanchi *(Pres)*
Namita Premnath *(Mgr-HR & Immi-
gration)*
Raj Vemula *(Dir-Resource Dev)*
Vinay Vattikuti *(Mgr-Resource Dev)*

INFOVISION TECHNOLOGIES INC.
2550 US Hwy No 1, North Brunswick,
NJ 08902
Tel.: (732) 398-1000
Web Site:
http://www.infovisiontech.com
Year Founded: 2005
Sales Range: $10-24.9 Million
Emp.: 150
Functional & Technical Software Ser-
vices
N.A.I.C.S.: 513210
Krishna Lakamsani *(CEO)*

Subsidiaries:

Infovision Technologies   **(1)**
First Canadian Place 100 King St West Ste
5700, Toronto, M5X 1K7, ON,
Canada   **(100%)**
Tel.: (888) 248-5627
Web Site: http://www.infovisiontech.com
Software Services
N.A.I.C.S.: 513210

Infovision Technologies   **(1)**
Sai Residency Ste No 101 Road No 4, Ban-
jara Hills, Hyderabad, 500034,
India   **(100%)**
Tel.: (91) 4066635353
Web Site: http://www.infovisiontech.com
Outsourcing Operations
N.A.I.C.S.: 561499

Infovision Technologies   **(1)**
1225 Franklin Ave Ste 325, Garden City,
NY 11530   **(100%)**
Tel.: (516) 345-4456
Web Site: http://www.infovisiontech.com
Outsourcing Services
N.A.I.C.S.: 561499

INFOWAY SOFTWARE
388 Washington Rd Ste A, Sayreville,
NJ 08872
Tel.: (732) 238-2122
Web Site:
http://www.infowaysoftware.com
Year Founded: 2005
Sales Range: $1-9.9 Million
Emp.: 37
IT & Software Development Services
N.A.I.C.S.: 334610
Dan Nandan *(Sr Mgr-IT)*
Sravan Karnati *(Mgr-HR)*
Aarti Thakkar *(Asst Mgr-Sls)*

INFOYOGI LLC
2320 Walsh Ave Ste A, Santa Clara,
CA 95051
Tel.: (408) 850-1700   CA
Web Site: http://www.infoyogi.com
Year Founded: 2004
Sales Range: $1-9.9 Million
Emp.: 50
Developer of Custom Software Appli-
cations
N.A.I.C.S.: 541512
Rao Tallapragada *(Founder & Pres)*
Jyothsna T. V. N. *(Mgr-Fin)*
Deepali Bargat *(Mgr-Recruitment)*
Sudhakar Saladi *(Mgr-HR & Admin)*
Sanjay Sharma *(Mgr-Tech Mgmt)*

INFRANET TECHNOLOGIES GROUP, INC.
235 Government Ctr Dr Ste 200,
Wilmington, NC 28403-6252
Tel.: (910) 392-0944
Web Site:
http://www.infranetgroup.com
Year Founded: 1998
Computer System Design Services
N.A.I.C.S.: 541512
John W. Livesay *(Chief Sls Officer &
VP)*
Michael Chittum *(CEO)*

INFRASAFE, INC.

1707 Orlando Central Pkwy, Orlando, FL 32809
Tel.: (407) 859-3350   FL
Web Site: http://www.infrasafe.com
Year Founded: 2002
Sales Range: $1-9.9 Million
Emp.: 60
Security System Services
N.A.I.C.S.: 561621
Bob Cetina *(Mgr)*

INFRASTRUCTURE ALTERNA-TIVES, INC.
7888 Childsdale Ave NE, Rockford, MI 49341-7487
Tel.: (616) 866-1600
Web Site: http://www.infrastructurealternatives.com
Year Founded: 2000
Sales Range: $10-24.9 Million
Emp.: 69
Fence Installation Services
N.A.I.C.S.: 238990
Kirk Foley *(Project Mgr)*
Dana Trierweiler *(Pres & CEO)*
Michelle Rioux *(Mgr-Bus Dev)*

INFRASTRUCTURE SERVICES INC.
5215 Fidelity St, Houston, TX 77029-3566
Tel.: (281) 233-8000
Web Site: http://www.infrastructure-inc.com
Sales Range: $10-24.9 Million
Emp.: 155
Highway & Street Paving Contractor
N.A.I.C.S.: 237310
Andy Gutierrez *(Mgr-Construction Div)*
Jhon Betancur *(Asst Controller)*
Subsidiaries:
Infrastructure Services Inc.   (1)
5215 Fidelity St, Houston, TX 77029-3566
Tel.: (281) 233-8000
Web Site: http://www.infrastructure-inc.com
Rev.: $19,097,000
Emp.: 147
Highway & Street Paving Contractor
N.A.I.C.S.: 237310
Timothy H. Herbert *(Chm)*

INFUSE MEDICAL
3369 W Mayflower Ave Ste 100, Lehi, UT 84043
Tel.: (801) 331-8610
Web Site: http://www.infusemed.com
Year Founded: 2007
Sales Range: $1-9.9 Million
Emp.: 42
Specialized Training & Education to Medical Device Mfr
N.A.I.C.S.: 339112
Jordan Erickson *(Co-Founder & Partner)*
James Norton *(Co-Founder & Partner)*
Steve Deverall *(Co-Founder & Partner)*
Brook Harker *(Co-Founder & Partner)*

INFUSERVE AMERICA, INC.
11880 28th St N, Saint Petersburg, FL 33716
Tel.: (727) 573-7847
Web Site: http://www.infuserveamerica.com
Sales Range: $1-9.9 Million
Emp.: 18
In-Home Infusion Medications, Equipment & Supplies
N.A.I.C.S.: 621610
David Kazarian *(Owner & CEO)*
Randy Breton *(Pres)*

Elena Gustin *(Dir-Ops)*
Jolaine Pedalino *(Dir-Case Mgmt)*
John Goettsche *(Dir-Pur & Warehouse)*

INFUSION DEVELOPMENT CORPORATION
599 Broadway 5th Fl, New York, NY 10012
Tel.: (212) 732-6100
Web Site: http://www.infusion.com
Year Founded: 1998
Sales Range: $50-74.9 Million
Emp.: 432
Software Product Development Services
N.A.I.C.S.: 541511
Bryan Shiffman *(VP & Gen Mgr-Ops & Bus Support Svcs-North America)*

INFUSIONSOFT, INC.
1260 S Spectrum Blvd, Chandler, AZ 85286
Tel.: (480) 807-0644
Web Site: http://www.infusionsoft.com
Year Founded: 2001
Sales Range: $25-49.9 Million
Emp.: 190
Sales & Marketing Software
N.A.I.C.S.: 513210
Clate Mask *(Co-Founder & CEO)*
Scott Martineau *(Co-Founder)*
Hal Halladay *(Chief People Officer)*
Jeff Mask *(VP-Bus Dev)*
Curtis Smith *(CFO)*
Terry Hicks *(COO)*
Keith Reed *(Chief Revenue Officer)*
Tom Romary *(VP-Partners & Bus Dev)*

INFUSYSTEMS HOLDINGS, INC.
3851 W Hamlin Rd, Rochester Hills, MI 48309
Web Site: https://www.infusystem.com
Year Founded: 2005
Healtcare Services
N.A.I.C.S.: 621999
Richard Dilorio *(Pres & CEO)*
Carrie Lachance *(COO)*
Barry Steele *(CFO & Exec VP)*
Addam Chupa *(CIO & Exec VP)*
Jerod Funke *(Chief HR Officer & Exec VP)*
Scott Shuda *(Chm)*

INFUTOR DATA SOLUTIONS, INC.
One Lincoln Centre 18W140 Butterfield Rd Ste 1020, Oakbrook Terrace, IL 60181
Tel.: (312) 348-7900
Web Site: http://www.infutor.com
Year Founded: 2003
Sales Range: $10-24.9 Million
Emp.: 53
Database Information Retrieval Services
N.A.I.C.S.: 518210
Gary V. Walter *(CEO)*
Don Coons *(Sr VP-Sls)*
Mary Jo Yafchak *(Sr VP-Product Dev)*
Brian Burke *(VP-Integration & Verification Products)*
Brian Wool *(Exec VP-Sls)*
John Payne *(VP-Bus Dev)*
Michelle Tilton *(Dir-Mktg & Comm)*
Lynn Rovelstad *(VP-Client Success)*
Dave Dague *(CMO)*
Kevin Dean *(COO)*
Drew Thomas *(CFO)*

Rachel Calomeni *(Sr VP-Sls)*
Todd Schoenherr *(VP-Strategy)*
Zora Senat *(Sr VP-Mktg & Partnerships)*

ING SOLUTIONS LLC
2035 NE 151 St, North Miami Beach, FL 33162
Tel.: (786) 866-9344
Year Founded: 2006
Sales Range: $25-49.9 Million
Emp.: 15
Auctions Cars, Motorcycles & Boats to Dealerships & Consumers
N.A.I.C.S.: 811114
Bob Martinez *(VP-Mktg)*

INGAGE NETWORKS, INC.
2210 Vanderbilt Beach Rd, Naples, FL 34109
Tel.: (239) 513-0092   DE
Web Site: http://www.ingagenetworks.com
Year Founded: 1999
Sales Range: $25-49.9 Million
Emp.: 65
Computer System Design Services
N.A.I.C.S.: 541512
Christine Richards *(Exec VP-Sls & Mktg)*
Tony Lynn *(VP-Tech & Product Dev)*
Lori Bacon *(Sr Dir-Admin)*
Don J. Gunther *(Chm)*

INGENESIS, INC.
10231 Kotzebue Dr, San Antonio, TX 78217
Tel.: (210) 366-0033
Web Site: http://www.ingenesis.org
Year Founded: 1998
Sales Range: $50-74.9 Million
Emp.: 304
Healthcare Industry
N.A.I.C.S.: 456199
Veronica Ann Edwards *(Founder & Pres)*
Rosie Franks *(Dir-Compliance)*
Norma Donahue *(COO)*

INGENIUM
2255 Barham Dr Ste A, Escondido, CA 92029
Tel.: (760) 745-8780
Web Site: http://www.pureingenium.com
Sales Range: $1-9.9 Million
Emp.: 28
Waste Management Services
N.A.I.C.S.: 562998
Heather Dody *(Dir-Sls)*
Mike Johnson *(Dir-Ops)*
Scott Rendleman *(Chief Compliance Officer)*
Gary Lundstedt *(Exec Dir)*

INGENIUM PROFESSIONAL SERVICES INC
136 S Illinois Ave Ste 202, Oak Ridge, TN 37830
Tel.: (865) 272-3213
Web Site: http://www.ingenium-services.com
Year Founded: 2006
Sales Range: $1-9.9 Million
Emp.: 30
Engineering & Design
N.A.I.C.S.: 541330
Diana West *(Project Mgr)*

INGENIUS, LLC
50 Mitchell Dr Ste 104, New Haven, CT 06511
Web Site: http://www.ingeniusprep.com
Year Founded: 2013
Sales Range: $1-9.9 Million

Emp.: 120
Educational Support Services
N.A.I.C.S.: 611710
Joel Butterly *(Co-Founder & CEO)*
David Mainiero *(Co-Founder & Chief Strategy Officer)*
Yosepha Greenfield *(Co-Founder & COO)*
Erin Gu *(Chief Education Officer)*
Nikola Champlin *(Dir-Curriculum Dev)*

INGENIUX CORP.
1601 2nd Ave 10th Fl, Seattle, WA 98101
Tel.: (206) 788-4300   WA
Web Site: http://www.ingeniux.com
Year Founded: 1999
Sales Range: $1-9.9 Million
Emp.: 25
Website Content Management Software
N.A.I.C.S.: 513210
James Edmunds *(Pres & CEO)*
Nathan Eggen *(Dir-Dev)*
Keith Osiewicz *(VP-Bus Dev)*

INGENUITY ASSOCIATES, LLC
783 Old Hickory Blvd Ste 300 E, Brentwood, TN 37027
Tel.: (615) 371-6607
Web Site: http://www.ingenuityassociates.com
Year Founded: 2003
Sales Range: $1-9.9 Million
Emp.: 15
IT Management Consulting
N.A.I.C.S.: 541618
Brian Prentice *(Sr Partner & Head-IT)*
David Adams *(Sr Partner & Head-Healthcare IT)*
Eric Enos *(Sr Partner & Head-Infrastructure & Security)*
Eric Parish *(Exec VP-Sls, Mktg, Alliances & Svcs)*

INGENUITY, INC.
8137 Helena Rd, Pelham, AL 35124
Tel.: (205) 263-1560   AL
Web Site: http://www.teamingenuity.com
Year Founded: 2001
Sales Range: $1-9.9 Million
Emp.: 12
Information Technology Consulting Services
N.A.I.C.S.: 541512
Rick Hayes *(Pres)*
Kirk Browne *(VP-Ops)*

INGLE-BARR INC.
20 Plyleys Ln, Chillicothe, OH 45601
Tel.: (740) 702-6117
Web Site: http://www.4ibi.com
Rev.: $10,198,825
Emp.: 150
General Remodeling, Single-Family Houses
N.A.I.C.S.: 236118
Wilbur B. Poole *(Pres)*
Rodney Poole *(VP)*
Jeff Poole *(VP)*

INGLENOOK AT BRIGHTON
2195 E Egbert St, Brighton, CO 80601
Tel.: (303) 659-4148
Web Site: http://www.inglenookatbrighton.com
Year Founded: 1980
Sales Range: $1-9.9 Million
Emp.: 65
Residential Building Leasing Services
N.A.I.C.S.: 531110
Sue Herzog *(Dir-Mktg)*

Ingleside at Rock Creek—(Continued)

INGLESIDE AT ROCK CREEK
3050 Military Rd NW, Washington, DC 20015
Tel.: (202) 407-9672   DC
Web Site: http://www.ircdc.org
Year Founded: 1906
Sales Range: $10-24.9 Million
Emp.: 283
Continuing Care Retirement Community Operator
N.A.I.C.S.: 623311
A. J. Mostafa (Dir-IT)
Kristin Shanks (Dir-Sls & Mktg)
Theresa Nwagu (Dir-Nursing)
Catherine Scott (Exec Dir)
Amanda Babineau (Dir-Resident Svcs)
Lynn O'Connor (Exec Dir)
Timothy Tivvis (Dir-Dining Svcs)

INGLETT & STUBBS, LLC
5200 Riverview Rd SE, Mableton, GA 30126-2953
Tel.: (404) 881-1199
Web Site: http://www.inglett-stubbs.com
Year Founded: 1955
Sales Range: $25-49.9 Million
Emp.: 60
Electrical Wiring Services
N.A.I.C.S.: 238210
Chris Williams (CFO)
Jeff Giglio (Chm)

INGLEWOOD IMAGING CENTER LLC
211 N Prairie Ste E, Inglewood, CA 90301
Tel.: (310) 672-9729
Web Site: http://www.inglewoodimaging.com
Year Founded: 2007
Sales Range: $1-9.9 Million
Emp.: 10
Diagnostic Radiology Center
N.A.I.C.S.: 621512
Bradley Schmidt (Founder & CEO)
Jaime Gomez (Mgr-Accts & Coord-Aeducation)

INGLEWOOD PARK CEMETERY INC.
720 E Florence Ave, Inglewood, CA 90301
Tel.: (310) 412-6500
Web Site: http://www.inglewoodparkcemetery.org
Year Founded: 1905
Sales Range: $10-24.9 Million
Emp.: 160
Cemetery, Mortuary & Cremation Services
N.A.I.C.S.: 812220
Art Allen (VP-Pre-Need Sls)

Subsidiaries:

Park Lawn Cemetery Inc.   (1)
6555 E Gage Ave, City of Commerce, CA 90040
Tel.: (562) 806-0660
Web Site: http://www.parklawncemetery.net
Rev.: $240,000
Emp.: 8
Cemeteries, Real Estate Operation
N.A.I.C.S.: 812220
Rick J. Miller (CEO & Gen Mgr)
Mary Guzman (CFO)

INGOMAR PACKING
9950 S Ingomar Grade, Los Banos, CA 93635
Tel.: (209) 826-9494

Web Site: http://www.ingomarpacking.com
Rev.: $51,400,000
Emp.: 250
Tomato Paste: Packaged In Cans, Jars, Etc.
N.A.I.C.S.: 311421
Larry Narbaitz (COO)

INGRAIN CONSTRUCTION, LLC
735 Lafayette St, Lancaster, PA 17603
Tel.: (717) 205-1475
Web Site: http://www.ingrainconstruction.com
Year Founded: 2012
Sales Range: $1-9.9 Million
Emp.: 9
Commercial Building Construction Services
N.A.I.C.S.: 236220
J. P. Bachman (Pres, CEO & Principal)
Dave Reinertsen (VP-Ops & Principal)
Tom Grab (Principal)

INGRAM ENTERPRISES INC.
3010 N Ingram Ave, Springfield, MO 65803
Tel.: (417) 862-1931
Web Site: http://www.fireworkssupermarket.com
Rev.: $13,000,000
Emp.: 10
Fireworks Retailer
N.A.I.C.S.: 423920
Michael Ingram (Pres)
Kim Deluce (Controller)

INGRAM ENTERTAINMENT INC.
2 Ingram Blvd, La Vergne, TN 37089
Tel.: (615) 287-4000   TN
Web Site: http://www.ingramentertainment.com
Year Founded: 1980
Sales Range: $1-4.9 Billion
Emp.: 600
Home Entertainment Products Distr
N.A.I.C.S.: 512120
David B. Ingram (Chm & CEO)
W. Donnie Daniel (Vice Chm)
Mark D. Ramer (Pres)

Subsidiaries:

Ingram Entertainment Inc. - Indianapolis   (1)
201 S Indiana St, Mooresville, IN 46158-1778
Web Site: http://www.ingramentertainment.com
Rev.: $266,000,000
Emp.: 260
Home Entertainment Products Distr
N.A.I.C.S.: 512120

INGRAM EQUIPMENT COMPANY, LLC.
11 Monroe Dr, Pelham, AL 35124
Tel.: (205) 663-3946
Web Site: http://www.ingramequipment.net
Year Founded: 1979
Sales Range: $10-24.9 Million
Emp.: 12
Automobile & Motor Vehicle Merchant Whslr
N.A.I.C.S.: 423110
Joe H. King Jr. (Pres)

INGRAM INDUSTRIES, INC.
4400 Harding Pike, Nashville, TN 37205
Tel.: (615) 298-8200   TN

Web Site: https://www.ingrambarge.com
Year Founded: 1962
Sales Range: Less than $1 Million
Emp.: 5,000
Offices of Other Holding Companies
N.A.I.C.S.: 551112
Orrin H. Ingram II (Pres & CEO)
Dan Mecklenborg (Chief Legal Officer & Sec)
Crystal Taylor (CFO)
David Sehrt (Sr VP & Chief Enrg Officer)
David Houghton (VP & CIO)
Jenny Butler (Chief People Officer)
Chuck Arnold (Sr VP-Dry Cargo)
John Roberts (Pres)

Subsidiaries:

Book Network International Limited   (1)
10 Thornbury Rd, Plymouth, PL6 7PP, United Kingdom
Tel.: (44) 1752 202301
Web Site: http://distribution.nbni.co.uk
Book Distr
N.A.I.C.S.: 424920
Ian Wordsworth (Head-Ops)
David Eagle (Mgr-IT & Digital Svcs)
Neil Tallis (Mgr-Warehouse)
Juliette Teague (Mgr-Client & Customer Svcs)
Tony Woodley (Mgr-Fin)
David Taylor (Mng Dir)

Ingram Barge Company   (1)
4400 Harding Rd, Nashville, TN 37205
Tel.: (615) 298-8200
Web Site: http://www.ingrambarge.com
Sales Range: $25-49.9 Million
Emp.: 235
Marine Barge Towing, Inland Marine Transportation
N.A.I.C.S.: 483211
Orrin H. Ingram II (Chm & CEO)
Dale A. Heller (Sr VP-Plng & Analysis)
Joe Johnson (Asst VP-Coal)
Scott Noble (Sr VP-Shore-Based Ops & Svcs)
Crystal Taylor (Sr VP & Controller)
Robert Barker (CIO & Sr VP)
David M. O'Loughlin (Pres & CEO)

Ingram Content Group Inc.   (1)
1 Ingram Blvd, La Vergne, TN 37086
Tel.: (615) 793-5000
Web Site: http://www.ingramcontent.com
Publishing Services
N.A.I.C.S.: 513130
John Ingram (Chm)
Shawn Morin (Pres & COO)
Brian Dauphin (CFO)
Shawn Everson (Chief Comml Officer)
Wayne Keegan (Chief HR Officer)
Phil Ollila (Chief Content Officer)
David Roland (Chief Venture Capital Officer)
John Secrest (Chief Logistics Officer)
Kent Freeman (Chief Strategy & Dev Officer)
Donald Roseman (VP-Retail Sls)
Robin Erwin (Mgr-Digital Retail Sls)
Alison Lewis (Sr Mgr-Content Acq)
Pamela Smith (VP & Gen Mgr-Ingram Library Svcs)
Nancy Morgan Stosik (Sr Mgr-Content Acq)
V. Valliappan (CEO)
Kurt Hettler (Dir-Ingram Academic)
Deanna Steele (CIO)
Kelly Arnold (Chief Legal Officer)

Subsidiary (Domestic):

Ingram Book Group Inc.   (2)
1 Ingram Blvd, La Vergne, TN 37086-3610
Tel.: (615) 793-5000
Web Site: http://www.ingramcontent.com
General Trade Books; Textbooks
N.A.I.C.S.: 424920

Subsidiary (Domestic):

Ingram Book Company   (3)
7315 Innovation Blvd, Fort Wayne, IN 46818
Tel.: (260) 489-2022

Web Site: http://www.ingrambook.com
Book Publishers
N.A.I.C.S.: 513130
Marshall Manoloff (Sr Mgr-Ops)

Ingram Customer Systems Inc.   (3)
1 Ingram Blvd, La Vergne, TN 37086-3629
Tel.: (615) 793-5000
Web Site: http://www.ingrambook.com
Sales Range: $50-74.9 Million
Emp.: 800
Books & CDs Distr
N.A.I.C.S.: 423990

Ingram Periodicals Inc.   (3)
18 Ingram Blvd, La Vergne, TN 37086-7000
Tel.: (615) 793-5000
Sales Range: $50-74.9 Million
Emp.: 500
Periodicals Distr
N.A.I.C.S.: 424920
Jeff Myrick (VP-Mgmt Info Sys)

Spring Arbor Distributors Inc.   (3)
1 Ingram Blvd, La Vergne, TN 37086-3629
Tel.: (615) 793-5000
Web Site: http://www.springarbor.com
Rev.: $230,000,000
Emp.: 250
Wholesale Distribution of Books
N.A.I.C.S.: 424920

Tennessee Book Company LLC   (3)
1550 Heil Quaker Blvd, La Vergne, TN 37086-9962
Tel.: (615) 793-5040
Web Site: http://www.tennesseebook.com
Sales Range: $10-24.9 Million
Emp.: 35
Textbook & Workbook Depository
N.A.I.C.S.: 424920
Mandy Bolin (Dir-Fin & Ops)
Kellie Dumas (Mgr-Customer Rels)
William P. Jones (Mgr-Warehouse)
Carol Anne Brown (Mgr-Product & Publr-Rels)
Phet Khamvongsa (Asst Mgr-Warehouse)
Todd Svec (VP & Gen Mgr)

Subsidiary (Domestic):

Lightning Source, Inc.   (2)
1246 Heil Quaker Blvd, La Vergne, TN 37086-3515
Tel.: (615) 213-5815
Web Site: http://www.lightningsource.com
Books Printing
N.A.I.C.S.: 323117
David Taylor (Sr VP-Content Acq-Intl)
John F. Secrest (Sr VP-Global Ops)
Linda Dickert (Gen Counsel & Sr VP)
Dave Piper (Mng Dir)

Vital Source Technologies Inc.   (2)
227 Fayetteville St Ste 400, Raleigh, NC 27601
Tel.: (919) 755-8100
Web Site: http://www.get.vitalsource.com
E-learning & Digital Textbook Solution Services
N.A.I.C.S.: 513199
Al Issa (CTO)
William Chesser (VP-Bus Dev)
Michael Hale (VP-Education-North America)
Rick Johnson (VP-Product Strategy)
Pep Carrera (Pres)
John Donovan (Editor-in-Chief)
Brian Hogue (Chief Product Officer)
Alice Duijser (Mng Dir-Europe, Middle East, Africa & Asia Pacific)

Subsidiary (Domestic):

Akademos, Inc.   (3)
200 Connecticut Ave, Norwalk, CT 06854
Tel.: (203) 866-0190
Web Site: https://www.akademos.com
Online Bookstore Management Solutions
N.A.I.C.S.: 513210
Bob Breunig (CFO)
Geoffrey Katz (VP-Program Mgmt)
Daniel Rubin (VP-Tech)

Intrepid Learning, Inc.   (3)
411 1st Ave S Ste 400, Seattle, WA 98104
Tel.: (206) 518-9870
Web Site: http://www.intrepidlearning.com

Consulting & Training Services
N.A.I.C.S.: 611430
Jo Surbrugg *(VP-Planning & Ops)*
Sam Herring *(VP & Gen Mgr)*
Justin Garrett *(VP-Tech)*
Thom Robbins *(Dir-Mktg)*
Colin Gause *(Dir-Product Management)*

Ingram Distribution Group Inc. **(1)**
1 Ingram Blvd, La Vergne, TN 37086-3610
Tel.: (615) 793-5000
Web Site: http://www.ingramcontent.com
Sales Range: $400-449.9 Million
Emp.: 900
General Trade Books & Textbooks; Micro-computer Software; Prerecorded Video Cassette Products
N.A.I.C.S.: 424920
John R. Ingram *(Chm & CEO)*

Ingram Marine Group **(1)**
4400 Harding Pike, Nashville, TN 37205-2290
Tel.: (615) 298-8200
Web Site:
    http://www.ingrammarinegroup.com
Sales Range: $25-49.9 Million
Emp.: 200
Provider of Water Freight Transportation
N.A.I.C.S.: 423430
David M. O'Loughlin *(Vice Chm)*
John Roberts *(Pres & CEO)*

Ingram Materials Co. **(1)**
1030 Visco Dr, Nashville, TN 37210
Tel.: (615) 256-0263
Web Site: http://www.ingrammaterials.com
Sales Range: $25-49.9 Million
Emp.: 15
Water Transportation & Wholesale Sand
N.A.I.C.S.: 212321
Daniel P. Mecklenborg *(Chief Legal Officer & Sr VP)*
Dale A. Heller *(CIO & Sr VP)*
David M. O'Loughlin *(VP)*
David G. Sehrt *(COO & Sr VP)*
Allen Oldham *(Sr VP & Controller)*
Steve Alley *(Dir-Sls)*

INGRAM READYMIX, INC.
3580 FM 482, New Braunfels, TX 78132
Tel.: (830) 625-9156   TX
Web Site:
    http://www.ingramreadymixinc.com
Year Founded: 1957
Sales Range: $25-49.9 Million
Emp.: 500
Ready-Mix Concrete Mfr & Aggregate Operations
N.A.I.C.S.: 327320
Gary Johnson *(VP)*
Earl Ingram *(Pres)*

INGREDIENTS SOLUTIONS INC.
631 Moosehead Trl, Waldo, ME 04915
Tel.: (207) 722-4172
Web Site:
    http://www.ingredientssolutions.com
Sales Range: $25-49.9 Million
Emp.: 10
Food Ingredients
N.A.I.C.S.: 424490
Scott Ranguf *(CEO)*
Janine Mehuren *(Controller)*
Debbie Hills *(Sec)*
Kevin Johndro *(VP-R&D)*

INGRETEC, LTD.
1500 Lehman St, Lebanon, PA 17046
Tel.: (717) 273-0711
Web Site: http://www.ingretec.com
Sales Range: $10-24.9 Million
Emp.: 25
Cheese Mfr
N.A.I.C.S.: 311513
Philippe Jallon *(Pres)*
Valerie Crouse *(VP)*
Greg Hehman *(Mgr-Natl Sls)*

INHIBRX, INC.
11025 N Torrey Pines Rd Ste 140, La Jolla, CA 92037
Tel.: (858) 795-4220   DE
Web Site: https://www.inhibrx.com
Year Founded: 2017
INBX—(NASDAQ)
Rev.: $2,192,000
Assets: $290,875,000
Liabilities: $232,818,000
Net Worth: $58,057,000
Earnings: ($145,226,000)
Emp.: 132
Fiscal Year-end: 12/31/22
Biotechnology Research & Develop-ment Services
N.A.I.C.S.: 541714
Michael J. Tolpa *(Treas)*
Stephen Kalinchak *(Asst Sec)*
Kelly Deck *(CFO & Exec VP)*
Carlos Bais *(Exec VP-Translational Sciences)*
Josep Garcia *(Chief Clinical Dev Offi-cer & Exec VP)*
Bonne Adams *(VP-Operations)*
Robert Boothroyd *(VP-Medical Affairs & Business Development)*
Dana Ebbets-Reed *(VP-Quality As-surance)*
Brian Lobo *(VP-Formulation Dev & Drug Product Mfg)*
Melissa Masterson *(VP-Value, Ac-cess, and Distribution)*
Shahram Alek-Ardakani *(VP-Res)*

INHOME THERAPY INC.
234 Mall Blvd Ste G-50, King of Prus-sia, PA 19406
Tel.: (866) 573-2556
Web Site:
    https://www.inhometherapy.com
Outsourced Therapy Solutions
N.A.I.C.S.: 621340
Rick Anglin *(Chief Corp Dev Officer)*

Subsidiaries:

Remedy Therapy Staffing PLLC **(1)**
320 N Main St, Buda, TX 78610-3314
Tel.: (512) 981-9573
Web Site:
    http://www.remedytherapystaffing.com
Offices of Other Health Practitioners
N.A.I.C.S.: 621340
Gwendi Ling *(Office Mgr)*

INITIALS, INC.
583 Grant St Ste G, Clarkesville, GA 30523
Tel.: (706) 754-0485
Web Site: http://www.initials-inc.com
Year Founded: 2005
Sales Range: $1-9.9 Million
Emp.: 32
Markets & Sells Personalized Hand-bags & Accessories Through Inde-pendent Direct Sellers & Host Parties
N.A.I.C.S.: 316990
Britney C. Vickery *(Co-Founder & Pres)*
Ivy C. Hall *(Co-Founder & Exec VP)*
Darren Vickery *(COO)*
James York *(CFO)*
Laurie Langill *(VP-Trng & Field Dev)*
Cindy Carpenter *(Dir-Field Dev)*

INITIO, INC.
212 3rd Ave N Ste 510, Minneapolis, MN 55401-1440
Tel.: (612) 339-7195   MN
Web Site:
    http://www.initioadvertising.com
Year Founded: 1991
Rev.: $15,000,000
Emp.: 15
Advetising Agency
N.A.I.C.S.: 541810

Geoffrey J. Grassle *(Pres & Partner)*
Paul Chapin *(Owner)*
Scott Sample *(Founding Partner & Exec Dir-Creative)*
Cindee Daugs *(Mgr-Traffic)*
Lee Ericksen *(Controller-Admin)*
Wade Weidner *(Media Planner & Buyer)*
Mary Murphy *(Dir-Media)*
Tamara Parrilli *(Acct Mgr)*
Tom Chapman *(Dir-Client Svcs)*
Jeremy Piller *(Electronic Production Artist)*

INJECTION MOLDERS SUP-PLY COMPANY
10373 Stafford Rd, Chagrin Falls, OH 44023
Tel.: (440) 543-1615
Web Site:
    http://www.imscompany.com
Rev.: $21,000,000
Emp.: 60
Industrial Machinery & Equipment
N.A.I.C.S.: 423830
Brad Morse *(Owner)*
Doug Bartlett *(Dir-Product Safety & Mgr-Chemical Products)*

INJECTRON CORPORATION
1000 S 2nd St, Plainfield, NJ 07063-1306
Tel.: (908) 753-1990   NJ
Web Site: http://www.injectron.com
Year Founded: 1959
Sales Range: $100-124.9 Million
Emp.: 300
Mfr of Custom Injection Moldings
N.A.I.C.S.: 326199
John Salerno *(Mgr-Pur & Matl)*
Hugo Douglas *(Mgr-Traffic & Ware-house)*
Al Hanzl *(Gen Mgr)*
Tony Cirello *(Mgr-Tech Sls)*

Subsidiaries:

Eagle Affiliates, Inc. **(1)**
1000 S 2nd St, Plainfield, NJ 07063
Tel.: (908) 753-1990
Sales Range: $25-49.9 Million
Emp.: 145
Plastic Household Product Mfr
N.A.I.C.S.: 326199
Eric Neumann *(Pres)*

INJECTRONICS INC.
1 Union St, Clinton, MA 01510-2916
Tel.: (978) 368-8701
Web Site: http://www.injectronics.com
Year Founded: 1967
Sales Range: $10-24.9 Million
Emp.: 85
Thermo Plastic Injection Molded Components & Assemblies Mfr
N.A.I.C.S.: 326199
Paul Nazzaro *(Pres & CEO)*
Mike Simmons *(VP-Engrg)*
Scott Nickerson *(Gen Mgr)*
Jeremiah O'Connor Jr. *(Dir-Sls & Mktg)*

INJURED GADGETS LLC
6141 Crooked Creek Rd, Norcross, GA 30092
Tel.: (770) 674-1150   GA
Web Site:
    http://www.injuredgadgets.com
Year Founded: 2009
Sales Range: $10-24.9 Million
Emp.: 34
Cellular Phone Parts Distr
N.A.I.C.S.: 423690
Aakshay Kripalani *(CEO)*

INJURED WORKERS' INSUR-ANCE FUND
8722 Loch Raven Blvd, Towson, MD 21286-2226
Tel.: (410) 494-2000
Year Founded: 1914
Sales Range: $10-24.9 Million
Emp.: 370
Direct Property & Casualty Insurance Services
N.A.I.C.S.: 524126
Tom Phelan *(Pres & CEO)*

INK
38 Discovery Ste 100, Irvine, CA 92618
Tel.: (949) 596-4500
Web Site: http://www.inkagency.com
Year Founded: 2007
Sales Range: $1-9.9 Million
Emp.: 25
Develops Integrated Marketing Cam-paigns
N.A.I.C.S.: 541820
Kelly Ward *(Brand Dir)*
Peter Watkins *(Exec Dir-Acct Svcs)*

INK SYSTEMS INC.
2311 S Eastern Ave, Los Angeles, CA 90040
Tel.: (323) 720-4000
Web Site:
    http://www.inksystemsinc.com
Sales Range: $25-49.9 Million
Emp.: 200
Printing Inks Mfr
N.A.I.C.S.: 325910
Dale Good *(VP)*
Mark Pannell *(Product Mgr)*
Urban S. Hirsch III *(CEO)*
Tim Van Scoy Jr. *(Mgr-Tech Svc & Trng)*

INK, INC. PR
511 Delaware St Ste 200, Kansas City, MO 64105
Tel.: (816) 753-6222
Web Site: http://www.inkincpr.com
Year Founded: 1997
Sales Range: $1-9.9 Million
Emp.: 30
Collateral, Crisis Communications, Event Planning & Marketing, Investor Relations, Media Relations, Media Training, Public Relations
N.A.I.C.S.: 541820
Richard Grove *(CEO)*
Cindy West *(VP & Dir-Ops)*
Ryan Gerding *(VP & Dir-Client Svcs)*

INKJET INC.
11111 Inkjet Way, Willis, TX 77378
Tel.: (936) 856-6600
Web Site: http://www.inkjetinc.com
Rev.: $10,000,000
Emp.: 5
Ink & Writing Fluid Mfr & Distr
N.A.I.C.S.: 325998
Curt Gladney *(Mgr-EHS & Quality Assurance)*

INKJET INTERNATIONAL, LTD.
4443 Simonton Rd, Dallas, TX 75244
Tel.: (972) 991-4577   TX
Web Site: http://www.inkjetintl.com
Year Founded: 1995
Fiscal Year-end: 04/30/15
Billboards, Banners, Posters & Other Large-Format Digital Printing
N.A.I.C.S.: 323111
Jeff Teasley *(Owner)*

INKJETMADNESS.COM, INC.
2205 1st St Ste 103, Simi Valley, CA 93065
Tel.: (805) 583-7755
Web Site: http://www.inkgrab.com
Year Founded: 2002

InkjetMadness.com, Inc.—(Continued)

Sales Range: $1-9.9 Million
Emp.: 23
Online Retailer of Toners, Inkjets, Ribbons & Office Accessories
N.A.I.C.S.: 325910
Brandon Timar (Mgr-Affiliate)
Keith Ramirez (Founder)

INKO'S TEA, LLC
650 Executive Dr, Willowbrook, IL 60527
Tel.: (630) 861-0422
Web Site: http://www.inkostea.com
Year Founded: 2002
Organic Tea Mfr, Sales & Marketer
N.A.I.C.S.: 445298
Andy Schamisso (Founder & Pres)

INKSOLUTIONS, LLC
800 Estes Ave, Elk Grove Village, IL 60007
Tel.: (847) 593-5200
Web Site: http://www.inksolutions.us
Year Founded: 2001
Ink, Varnish & Paint Mfr
N.A.I.C.S.: 325910

INKSTONE FEIBO ACQUISITION CORPORATION
221 W 9th St PMB 235, Wilmington, DE 19801
Tel.: (425) 365-2933   DE
Year Founded: 2022
Investment Services
N.A.I.C.S.: 523999
I-Fa Chang (CEO & Chm)
Xuedong Tian (CFO)

INKTEL DIRECT INC.
13975 NW 58th Ct, Miami Lakes, FL 33014-3114
Tel.: (305) 523-1100   FL
Web Site: http://www.inktel.com
Year Founded: 1997
Sales Range: $150-199.9 Million
Emp.: 400
Fulfillment & Telemarketing Center
Database Management
N.A.I.C.S.: 561422
J. Ricky Arriola (CEO)
Jason Schlenker (Sr VP-Bus Dev)
Ken Mark (CIO)
Summer Dennis (Pres & COO)
Christine Guzman (Controller-Fin)
Kyla Starks (VP-Client Svcs)
Michelle Roza (Dir-Quality Assurance & Trng Excellence)
Mindy Dunn (Dir-Client Svcs)

Subsidiaries:

Inktel Chicago   (1)
1269 N Wood Dale Rd, Wood Dale, IL 60191-1160
Tel.: (630) 694-7200
Web Site: http://www.inktel.com
Sales Range: $10-24.9 Million
Emp.: 100
Fulfillment & Telemarketing Center
N.A.I.C.S.: 541910
Dan Arriola (Exec VP)
Ricky Arriola (CEO)

iD Commerce + Logistics   (1)
80 Intl Blvd Unit A, Glendale Heights, IL 60139   (100%)
Tel.: (630) 694-7200
Web Site: http://www.idcomlog.com
Emp.: 100
Product & Promotional Fulfillments & Enterprise Solutions
N.A.I.C.S.: 541614
Mark Pell (Gen Mgr)
Dan Arriola (CEO)
David Drayton (Sr VP-Solutions)
Timmethy Mastrino (Specialist-Talent Acq)

INKWELL GLOBAL MARKETING
600 Madison Ave, Manalapan, NJ 07726
Tel.: (732) 167-3500
Web Site: http://www.inkwellusa.com
Year Founded: 1986
Full Service Promotional Merchandise Agency
N.A.I.C.S.: 541890
Steven Marder (Pres & CEO)

INLAND AMERICAN COMMUNITIES GROUP INC.
3890 W NW Hwy Ste 601, Dallas, TX 75220-8109
Tel.: (214) 739-8141   TX
Web Site: http://www.inlandac.com
Year Founded: 1978
Sales Range: $200-249.9 Million
Emp.: 450
Real Estate Investment & Development Services
N.A.I.C.S.: 531120
Alfred Scheer (Dir-Design Dev)
J. R. Thulin (Mgr-Construction)
Kristen Penrod (Mgr-Dev)
Joel Burton (Reg Mgr-Leasing)
Jennifer Wall (Mgr-Benefits)
Luca Finocchiaro (Reg Dir)

INLAND ASSOCIATES, INC.
18965 W 158th St, Olathe, KS 66062-9309
Tel.: (913) 764-7977   KS
Web Site:
    http://www.inlandassoc.com
Year Founded: 1971
Sales Range: $75-99.9 Million
Emp.: 10
Computer Peripherals Distr
N.A.I.C.S.: 423430
Chuck Floyd (Controller)
Theresa Johnson (Coord-Customer Svc)

INLAND CHEVROLET
400 Carriage Cir, Hemet, CA 92545
Tel.: (951) 216-3486
Web Site:
    http://www.inlandchevy.com
Sales Range: $10-24.9 Million
Emp.: 70
New Car Retailer
N.A.I.C.S.: 441110
Eric Gosch (Owner)
Israel Mora (Gen Mgr-Sls)
Phil Gilchrist (Gen Mgr-Sls)

INLAND COMPANIES, INC.
833 E Michigan St Ste 500, Milwaukee, WI 53202
Tel.: (414) 276-9500   WI
Web Site:
    http://www.inlandcompanies.com
Year Founded: 1977
Sales Range: $10-24.9 Million
Emp.: 100
Commercial & Industrial Building Operation
N.A.I.C.S.: 236115
Scott Welsh (Owner)

INLAND CONSTRUCTION COMPANY
120 W Cataldo Ave Ste 100, Spokane, WA 99201
Tel.: (509) 891-5162   WA
Web Site:
    http://www.inlandconstruction.com
Year Founded: 1975
Sales Range: $50-74.9 Million
Emp.: 50
Construction Services
N.A.I.C.S.: 236220

Thomas E. Clemson (Founder & Chm)

INLAND EMPIRE UTILITIES AGENCY
6075 Kimball Ave, Chino, CA 91709
Tel.: (909) 357-0241
Web Site: http://www.ieua.org
Year Founded: 1950
Sales Range: $50-74.9 Million
Emp.: 250
Water Supply
N.A.I.C.S.: 221310
Christina Valencia (CFO & Asst Gen Mgr)
Jasmin A. Hall (Treas & Sec)

INLAND IMAGING ASSOCIATES, P.S.
801 S Stevens St N3, Spokane, WA 99204
Tel.: (509) 455-4455
Web Site:
    http://www.inlandimaging.com
Office Of Physician
N.A.I.C.S.: 621111
Tavi Lohman (Founder)

Subsidiaries:

Missoula Radiology, P.C.   (1)
2827 Fort Missoula Rd, Missoula, MT 59804
Tel.: (406) 721-4906
Offices of All Other Miscellaneous Health Practitioners
N.A.I.C.S.: 621399

INLAND INDUSTRIES, INC.
19841, Lenexa, KS 66215-2014
Tel.: (913) 492-9050   KS
Year Founded: 1910
Sales Range: $25-49.9 Million
Emp.: 100
Holding Company
N.A.I.C.S.: 551112
Brian D. Murray (Chm, Pres & CEO)
Ann Campbell (VP-Ops)
Catherine Kenney (Controller)

Subsidiaries:

Inland Media Company   (1)
112 E Broadway, Fairfield, IA 52556
Tel.: (641) 472-4129
Web Site:
    http://www.goldentrianglenewspapers.com
Sales Range: $10-24.9 Million
Emp.: 15
Newspaper Publishers
N.A.I.C.S.: 513110
Darwin K. Sherman (Pres)
Andy Hallman (Editor-News-Fairfield Daily Ledger)
Amy Sparby (Publr-Fairfield Daily Ledger)

Unit (Domestic):

Mt. Pleasant News   (2)
215 W Monroe St, Mount Pleasant, IA 52641
Tel.: (866) 757-4489
Web Site:
    http://www.goldentrianglenewspapers.com
Sales Range: $10-24.9 Million
Newspaper Publishers
N.A.I.C.S.: 513110

The Washington Evening Journal   (2)
111 N Marion Ave, Washington, IA 52353
Tel.: (319) 653-2191
Web Site: http://www.washjrnl.com
Sales Range: $10-24.9 Million
Emp.: 30
Newspaper Publishers
N.A.I.C.S.: 513110
Darwin K. Sherman (Pres & Publr)

INLAND LABEL & MARKETING SERVICES, LLC
2009 W Ave S, La Crosse, WI 54601-6207
Tel.: (608) 788-5800   WI

Web Site:
    http://www.inlandpackaging.com
Year Founded: 1944
Sales Range: $100-124.9 Million
Emp.: 215
Label Supplier for the Beverage Food & Consumer Product Market Services
N.A.I.C.S.: 561910
Mark Glendenning (Owner & CEO)
Roman Artz (VP-Sls & Mktg)
Jackie Kuehlmann (Mgr-Mktg)
Tricia Sime (Dir-R&D)

Subsidiaries:

Inland Label & Marketing Services, LLC - In*Tech Division   (1)
2009W Ave S, La Crosse, WI 54601
Tel.: (888) 783-5207
Web Site: http://www.intechims.com
Emp.: 50
Marketing Services
N.A.I.C.S.: 541613
Marcia Bruha (Mgr-Fin & Inventory)

Plant (Domestic):

Inland Label & Marketing Services, LLC - La Crosse Facility   (2)
672 Breezy Point Rd, La Crosse, WI 54603
Tel.: (608) 783-4700
Web Site: http://www.intechims.com
Marketing Services
N.A.I.C.S.: 541613
Mark Wemette (Pres)

Inland Label & Marketing Services, LLC - Winona Facility   (2)
163 E 2nd St, Winona, MN 55987
Tel.: (507) 452-2658
Marketing Services
N.A.I.C.S.: 541613

INLAND LAKES MANAGEMENT INC.
561 E Western Ave, Muskegon, MI 49442
Tel.: (989) 354-2232
Web Site: http://www.andrie.com
Sales Range: $10-24.9 Million
Emp.: 110
Provider of Freight Transportation Services
N.A.I.C.S.: 483113
Stan Andrie (Pres)

INLAND MARINE SERVICES, LLC
1959 Woodchase Blvd, Baton Rouge, LA 70808
Tel.: (225) 241-0700
Web Site: http://www.inland-marine.us
Year Founded: 2005
Sales Range: $10-24.9 Million
Emp.: 25
Heavy & Civil Engineering Construction Services
N.A.I.C.S.: 237990
Stephen Loupe (Pres)

INLAND NEWSPAPER MACHINERY LLC
2298 W Layton Dr, Olathe, KS 66061
Tel.: (913) 492-9050
Web Site: http://www.inlandnews.com
Year Founded: 1946
Printing Machinery & Equipment Mfr
N.A.I.C.S.: 333248
Beau Campbell (Pres)

INLAND NORTHWEST HEALTH SERVICES
601 W 1st Ave, Spokane, WA 99201
Tel.: (509) 232-8100   WA
Web Site: http://www.inhs.info
Year Founded: 1994
Sales Range: $100-124.9 Million
Emp.: 1,230
Community Health Care Services

N.A.I.C.S.: 621498
Elaine Couture (CEO)
Patrick Clarry (Chief HR Officer)
Nancy Vorhees (Chief Admin Officer)
Helen Andrus (CFO)
Gary A. Livingston (Vice Chm)
Ron Wells (Chm)

INLAND OIL COMPANY INC.
747 Basin St NW, Ephrata, WA
98823
Tel.: (509) 754-4606
Rev.: $41,000,000
Emp.: 80
Gasoline Sales
N.A.I.C.S.: 457110
Gerry Ramm (Pres)
Skip Gregorie (Treas & Sec)

INLAND POWER & LIGHT COMPANY INC.
10110 W Hallet RD, Spokane, WA
99224
Tel.: (509) 747-7151
Web Site:
http://www.inlandpower.com
Year Founded: 1937
Rev.: $74,719,000
Assets: $305,985,000
Liabilities: $200,826,000
Net Worth: $105,159,000
Earnings: $6,256,000
Emp.: 86
Fiscal Year-end: 12/31/18
Provider of Electric Services
N.A.I.C.S.: 221122
Danny Lee (Sec)
Dick Ziehnert (Treas)
Garry Rosman (VP)
Brian Slaybaugh (Pres)

INLAND POWER GROUP, INC.
13015 W Custer Ave, Butler, WI
53007-1113
Tel.: (262) 781-7100
Diesel & Gas Engines & Turbine
Generating Equipment
N.A.I.C.S.: 336310
Mike Grinwald (Controller)
Angela Radosevich (Mgr-Credit)
Jim Morrison (Mgr-Ops)
Richard Hrabak (Mgr-Support Product)

INLAND REGIONAL CENTER
1365 S Waterman Ave, San Bernardino, CA 92408
Tel.: (909) 890-3000   CA
Web Site: http://www.inlandrc.org
Year Founded: 1971
Sales Range: $300-349.9 Million
Emp.: 630
Developmental Disability Assistance
Services
N.A.I.C.S.: 624120
Keith J. Nelson (Chm)
Marybeth Feild (Pres)

INLAND SEAFOOD
1651 Montreal Cir, Atlanta, GA 30084
Tel.: (404) 350-5850   GA
Web Site:
http://www.inlandseafood.com
Year Founded: 1977
Sales Range: $25-49.9 Million
Emp.: 600
Full-Line Processor & Distr of Fresh,
Frozen, Smoked & Specialty Seafood
Products
N.A.I.C.S.: 311710
Joel Knox (Founder & CEO)
Bill Demmond (COO)
Eric Sussman (Controller)
Chris Rosenberger (Pres)
Stephen Hall (Exec VP-Sls)
Robert Novotny (Exec VP)

Subsidiaries:

Inland Seafood   (1)
2700 Ave D, Birmingham, AL 35218
Tel.: (205) 252-0344
Web Site: http://www.inlandseafood.com
Sales Range: $10-24.9 Million
Emp.: 55
Distr of Fresh, Frozen, Smoked & Specialty
Seafood Items
N.A.I.C.S.: 424460
Joel Knox (Founder & CEO)
Dale Borne (Mgr-Credit)
Bill Demmond (COO)
Mike Hulsey (Mgr-Retail Sls)
Robert Novotny (Exec VP)
Brent Schilb (Gen Mgr)
Jerry Staines (VP-Corp Ops)
Eric Sussman (Controller)
Patricia Washington (Mgr-Safety)
Jennifer West (Mgr-HR)
Stephen T. Musser Jr. (Exec VP)

Inland Seafood   (1)
2527 Perdido St, New Orleans, LA
70119   (100%)
Tel.: (504) 704-1070
Web Site: http://www.inlandseafood.com
Sales Range: $25-49.9 Million
Emp.: 25
Seafood Distr
N.A.I.C.S.: 311710
Robby Hare (Gen Mgr)
Benjamin Plesic (Mgr-Quality Assurance)
Chris Hyver (Acct Exec-Retail)

Inland Seafood-Charlotte   (1)
3725 N Davidson St, Charlotte, NC
28205   (100%)
Tel.: (704) 332-3474
Web Site: http://www.inlandseafood.com
Sales Range: $25-49.9 Million
Emp.: 30
Seafood Distr
N.A.I.C.S.: 311710
Brent Schilb (Gen Mgr)

INLAND STAR DISTRIBUTION CENTERS
3146 S Chestnut Ave, Fresno, CA
93725
Tel.: (559) 237-2052
Web Site: http://www.inlandstar.com
Rev.: $13,956,368
Emp.: 125
General Warehousing & Storage
N.A.I.C.S.: 493110
Michael Kelton (Co-Founder, Chm &
CEO)
John Neale (Dir-Mktg)

INLAND SUPPLY CO., INC.
2820 Mill St, Reno, NV 89502
Tel.: (775) 323-8605
Web Site:
https://www.inlandsupplyco.com
Year Founded: 1946
Sales Range: $1-9.9 Million
Emp.: 100
Janitorial & Maintenance Equipment
Distr
N.A.I.C.S.: 423850
T. J. Elliott (Pres)

Subsidiaries:

A-1 Chemical, Inc.   (1)
1197 Greg St, Sparks, NV 89431
Tel.: (775) 331-7627
Web Site: http://www.a-1online.com
Sales Range: $1-9.9 Million
Emp.: 100
Service Establishment Equipment & Supplies Merchant Whslr
N.A.I.C.S.: 423850
Jeff Goodman (Ops Manager)

INLAND TRUCK PARTS COMPANY
4400 College Blvd Ste 145, Overland
Park, KS 66211
Tel.: (913) 345-9664
Web Site: http://www.inlandtruck.com
Sales Range: $75-99.9 Million

Emp.: 500
Truck Parts & Accessories
N.A.I.C.S.: 423120
Greg Klein (Pres)

INLIGN CAPITAL PARTNERS, LLC
4189 W Milky Way Unit 3, Chandler,
AZ 85226
Tel.: (480) 993-0464
Web Site:
http://www.inligncapital.com
Privater Equity Firm
N.A.I.C.S.: 523999
David Holthe (Pres)
Mark Feldman (Mng Partner)
Christopher Ko (Principal)

INLINE ELECTRIC SUPPLY CO., INC.
2880 Bob Wallace Ave SW, Huntsville, AL 35805
Tel.: (256) 533-2851
Web Site: http://www.inlineelectric.com
Year Founded: 1988
Sales Range: $10-24.9 Million
Emp.: 184
Electrical Supply Whslr
N.A.I.C.S.: 423610
Doug Halbrooks (Mgr-Sls-
Specification)
Steven Davis (Mgr-Birmingham)

Subsidiaries:

Inline Electric Supply Co., Inc.   (1)
2600 2nd Ave S, Birmingham, AL 35233
Tel.: (205) 322-2600
Web Site: http://www.inlineelectric.com
Sales Range: $1-9.9 Million
Emp.: 20
Electrical Apparatus & Equipment, Wiring
Supplies & Related Equipment Whslr
N.A.I.C.S.: 423610
Steven Davis (Branch Mgr)

Inline Electric Supply Co., Inc.   (1)
217 Broadway Dr, Cullman, AL 35055
Tel.: (256) 734-5670
Web Site: http://www.inlineelectric.com
Emp.: 5
Electrical Supplies Whslr
N.A.I.C.S.: 423610
Mike Stewart (Mgr)

INLINE PLASTICS CORP.
42 Canal St, Shelton, CT 06484-3223
Tel.: (203) 924-5933   CT
Web Site:
http://www.inlineplastics.com
Year Founded: 1968
Sales Range: $25-49.9 Million
Emp.: 283
Plastic Food Containers Mfr
N.A.I.C.S.: 326199
Thomas Orkisz (Pres)
Augie Lanzetta (VP-Sls)
Kevin McGuane (CFO)
Dan Landan (VP-Engrg)
Pam Corba (Mgr-Mktg)

Subsidiaries:

Inline Plastics Corp. - Shur-Lock
Division   (1)
42 Canal St, Shelton, CT 06484
Tel.: (203) 924-5933
Web Site: http://www.inlineplastics.com
Sales Range: $25-49.9 Million
Emp.: 275
Plastic Food Containers Mfr
N.A.I.C.S.: 326199
Thomas Orkisz (Pres)

Inline Poland Sp. z o.o.   (1)
Ul Polna 40, 62-095, Poznan,
Poland   (100%)
Tel.: (48) 612224100
Web Site: http://www.inline.com.pl
Sales Range: $25-49.9 Million
Emp.: 250
Plastics Product Mfr

N.A.I.C.S.: 326199

INLINE SERVICES, INC.
27731 Commercial Park Ln, Tomball,
TX 77375-6532
Tel.: (281) 401-8142
Web Site:
http://www.inlineservices.com
Sales Range: $10-24.9 Million
Emp.: 10
Pipeline Pigs, Pigging & Equipment
Mfr
N.A.I.C.S.: 423830
Harvey Diehl (VP)
Gary Smith (Pres)
Cathy Silhan (Controller)
Brian Todd (Gen Mgr)
Jessica Nichols (Mgr-Sls)

INMAN HOLDING CO. INC.
300 Park Rd, Inman, SC 29349
Tel.: (864) 472-2121   SC
Web Site: http://www.inmanmills.com
Year Founded: 1902
Sales Range: $25-49.9 Million
Emp.: 525
Holding Company; Broadwoven Fabric Mills
N.A.I.C.S.: 551112
Norman H. Chapman (Pres)
Robert H. Chapman III (Chm & CEO)
James Pace (CFO)

Subsidiaries:

Eastbank Textiles, LLC   (1)
3312 Northside Dr, Macon, GA 31210
Tel.: (478) 745-4040
Web Site: http://www.eastbanktextiles.com
Broadwoven Fabric Mfr
N.A.I.C.S.: 313210
Jackie Harwell (VP-Sls)
John Fry (VP-Sls)

Inman Mills Inc.   (1)
300 Park Rd, Inman, SC
29349-1754   (100%)
Tel.: (864) 472-2121
Web Site: http://www.inmanmills.com
Sales Range: $10-24.9 Million
Emp.: 100
Broadwoven Fabric Mills, Cotton
N.A.I.C.S.: 313210
Norman H. Chapman (Pres & Co-CEO)
Robert H. Chapman III (Chm, Co-CEO &
Treas)

INMARKET MEDIA LLC
1350 Abbott Kinney Bvld Ste 203,
Venice, CA 90291
Tel.: (310) 392-0500
Web Site: http://www.inmarket.com
Year Founded: 2010
Digital Advertising Services
N.A.I.C.S.: 541890
Todd Dipaola (Founder & CEO)
Michael Fordyce (Chief Bus Officer)
David Staas (Chief Product Officer)
Todd Morris (Pres)

Subsidiaries:

Mobestream Media, Inc.   (1)
3100 Carlisle St Ste 208, Dallas, TX 75204
Tel.: (214) 647-1389
Mobile Application Development Services
N.A.I.C.S.: 541511
Chris Fagan (Founder)

NinthDecimal, Inc.   (1)
150 Post St Ste 500, San Francisco, CA
94108
Tel.: (415) 821-8600
Web Site: http://www.ninthdecimal.com
Advertising Services
N.A.I.C.S.: 541810
Amy Caplan (Sr VP-Strategic Partnerships)
Brian Slitt (Sr VP-Partner Revenue)
David Staas (Pres)
Jeff Stephens (CFO)
Naftali Goldsmith (VP-Product Solutions)
Michael Fordyce (Chief Bus Officer)

inMarket Media LLC—(Continued)

INMED PARTNERSHIPS FOR CHILDREN
20110 Ashbrook Pl Ste 260, Ashburn, VA 20147
Tel.: (703) 729-4951   NY
Web Site: http://www.inmed.org
Year Founded: 1986
Sales Range: $10-24.9 Million
Emp.: 29
Child Rescue Services
N.A.I.C.S.: 624110
Linda Pfeiffer (Pres)
Wendy Balter (Sec)
James R. Rutherford (Treas)
Paul C. Bosland (Chm)
Cecilia Capece (Exec Dir)

INMUSIC, LLC
200 Scenic View Dr, Cumberland, RI 02864
Tel.: (401) 658-3131   FL
Web Site:
http://www.inmusicbrands.com
Holding Company; Audio Technologies Developer & Mfr
N.A.I.C.S.: 551112
Jack O'Donnell (Owner & CEO)

Subsidiaries:

AKAI Professional, L.P.   (1)
200 Scenic View Dr Ste 201, Cumberland, RI 02864
Tel.: (401) 658-4032
Web Site: http://www.akaipro.com
Digital Music Production Equipment Designer & Mfr
N.A.I.C.S.: 335999

Alesis, L.P.   (1)
200 Scenic View Dr, Cumberland, RI 02864
Tel.: (401) 658-5760
Web Site: http://www.alesis.com
Sales Range: $10-24.9 Million
Emp.: 100
Audio & Musical Instrument Products Mfr
N.A.I.C.S.: 334310

Subsidiary (Non-US):

inMusic GmbH   (2)
Harkortstrasse 12-32, 40880, Ratingen, Germany
Tel.: (49) 2102 74 02 0
Web Site: http://www.alesis.de
Semiconductor & Sound Software Mfr
N.A.I.C.S.: 334413
John O'Donnell (Mng Dir)

ION Audio, LLC   (1)
200 Scenic View Dr Ste 201, Cumberland, RI 02864
Tel.: (401) 658-3743
Web Site: http://www.ionaudio.com
Digital Audio & Video Conversion Technologies Developer & Mfr
N.A.I.C.S.: 334310
Fred Galpern (Brand Mgr)

Moog Music Inc.   (1)
160 Broadway St, Asheville, NC 28801
Tel.: (828) 251-0090
Web Site: http://www.moogmusic.com
Sales Range: $1-9.9 Million
Emp.: 40
Music Dealers
N.A.I.C.S.: 459140
Mike Adams (Owner & Pres)

Numark Industries, L.P.   (1)
200 Scenic View Dr, Cumberland, RI 02864
Tel.: (401) 658-3131
Web Site: http://www.numark.com
Sales Range: $75-99.9 Million
Audio Equipment Mfr
N.A.I.C.S.: 334310
Jack O'Donnell (Pres)

INN OF LAKE CITY INC.
US Hwy 90 & I 75, Lake City, FL 32055
Tel.: (386) 752-3901
Sales Range: $10-24.9 Million

Emp.: 100
Hotel
N.A.I.C.S.: 721110

INN OF NAPLES, LLC
4055 Tamiami Trl N, Naples, FL 34103
Tel.: (239) 649-5500
Web Site:
http://www.innofnaples.com
Sales Range: $1-9.9 Million
Emp.: 25
Hotel Operations
N.A.I.C.S.: 721110
Sara Booker (Mgr-Sls)
Jerry Nerad (Owner)
Susan Soldan (Gen Mgr)

INNER TRADITIONS INTERNATIONAL
1 Park St, Rochester, VT 05767
Tel.: (802) 767-3174
Web Site:
http://www.innertraditions.com
Year Founded: 1975
Sales Range: $1-9.9 Million
Emp.: 40
Publisher of Books
N.A.I.C.S.: 513130
Ehud Sperling (Founder)

INNERCEPT MANAGEMENT CORPORATION
7900 Nova Dr Ste 102, Davie, FL 33324
Tel.: (954) 472-2291   FL
Sales Range: $1-9.9 Million
Emp.: 500
Entertainment Group
N.A.I.C.S.: 711190
William Collins Jr. (Owner, Pres & CEO)

INNERFAX INC.
1117 S Milwaukee Ave D9, Libertyville, IL 60048
Tel.: (224) 207-4040
Rev.: $15,600,000
Emp.: 220
Internet Service Provider
N.A.I.C.S.: 517610
J. J. Barker (Pres)

INNERPLAN
7001 Innerplan Dr, North Little Rock, AR 72113
Tel.: (501) 371-0300
Web Site: http://www.innerplan.com
Sales Range: $10-24.9 Million
Emp.: 28
Furniture & Related Product Distr
N.A.I.C.S.: 449110
Tim McMennamy (Pres & COO)
Marsha Joyner (Acct Exec)
Jessica Lasley (Acct Exec)
Timmy Dammann (Mgr-Installation)
Rodney Dennis (Mgr-Logistics)
Laura Fletcher (Mgr-CAD Design)
Deborah Knutson (Project Coord)
Mark Phillips (VP-Sls)
JoAnn Pinter (Acct Exec)

INNEX, INC.
16622 E Johnson Dr, City of Industry, CA 91745
Tel.: (626) 638-7955
Web Site: http://www.innexinc.com
Year Founded: 2004
Rev.: $11,800,000
Emp.: 30
Toy, Hobby Goods & Supplies Merchant Whslr
N.A.I.C.S.: 423920

Titi Ngoy (Owner)
Mark Tabal (Dir-Ops)
Michael Carrico (Mgr-Ops)
Ron Pang (VP-Bus Dev)

INNIS ARDEN GOLF CLUB
120 Tomac Ave, Old Greenwich, CT 06870
Tel.: (203) 637-6900   CT
Web Site:
http://www.innisardengolfclub.com
Year Founded: 1899
Sales Range: $10-24.9 Million
Emp.: 217
Golf Club
N.A.I.C.S.: 713910
Daniel Jones (Asst Mgr)
Bonnie Bocchino (Gen Mgr)
Brett Palmer (Mgr-Clubhouse)

INNIS MAGGIORE GROUP, INC.
4715 Whipple Ave NW, Canton, OH 44718-2651
Tel.: (330) 492-5500
Web Site:
http://www.innismaggiore.com
Year Founded: 1974
Sales Range: $10-24.9 Million
Emp.: 32
Advetising Agency
N.A.I.C.S.: 541810
Dick Maggiore (Pres & CEO)
Kathi Maggiore (Principal-Admin)
Jeff Monter (Principal-Creative Svcs)
Lorraine Kessler (Principal-Strategy & Client Svcs)
Mark Vandegrift (COO & Principal)
Scott Edwards (Exec Dir-Creative)
Justin Allen (Dir-Creative-Web)
Jack Wollitz (Sr Dir-Digital Content)
Lee-Ann DeMeo (Assoc Dir-Creative)
Casey Schandel (Dir-Media Svcs)
Dave Collins (Principal-Web Dev)
Tony Bell (Dir-Client Svcs)

INNISFREE HOTELS, INC.
113 Bay Bridge Dr, Gulf Breeze, FL 32561
Tel.: (850) 934-3609
Web Site: http://www.innisfree.com
Year Founded: 1985
Sales Range: $1-9.9 Million
Emp.: 30
Home Management Services
N.A.I.C.S.: 721110
Carol Ruben (VP-HR & Admin)
Jill Thomas (CMO)
Rich Chism (Dir-Dev)
Brooks Moore (CFO)
Julian B. MacQueen (Founder)
Gabe DiCianni (Reg Dir-Ops)
George Coolbaugh (Reg Dir-Ops)
Jack Guillebeaux (Dir-Corp Culture)
Larisa Burnett (Reg Dir-Ops)
Mike Cosse (Dir-Food & Beverage Corp)
Rhiannon Reynolds (VP-Ops)
Ted Ent (Pres & CEO)

INNKEEPERS USA TRUST
340 Royal Poinciana Way Ste 306, Palm Beach, FL 33480
Tel.: (561) 835-1800   MD
Web Site:
http://www.innkeepersusa.com
Year Founded: 1994
Sales Range: $250-299.9 Million
Emp.: 36
Hotel Real Estate Investment Trust
N.A.I.C.S.: 525990
Mark A. Murphy (Gen Counsel & Sec)
Linda K. Price (VP & Controller)
Richard F. Fenton (VP-Fin Plng & Analysis)

Tim Walker (Pres & CEO)
Bob Martin (VP-Construction & Renovation)
Nathan Cook (CFO)

INNO-PAK, LLC
1932 Pittsburgh Dr, Delaware, OH 43015
Tel.: (740) 363-0090
Web Site: http://www.innopak.com
Rev.: $45,500,000
Emp.: 24
Rubber & Plastic Product Mfr
N.A.I.C.S.: 322220
Jonathan Sill (Founder)

INNOCEAN AMERICAS WORLDWIDE
4 Park Plz Ste 950, Irvine, CA 92614
Tel.: (949) 440-2100
Emp.: 100
N.A.I.C.S.: 541810
Jim Sanfilippo (COO & Exec VP)
Jeffrey Lee (CFO)
William Lee (CEO)
Doug James (Dir-Creative)
Frauke Tiemann (Dir-Art)
Greg Collins (Copywriter)
Robert Prins (Dir-Creative)
Greg Braun (Exec Dir-Creative)
Kathleen Kindle (Dir-Plng-Hyundai Motor America)
Sanjay Rana (VP-Digital Strategy)

INNOMAX CORPORATION
530 W Elk Pl, Denver, CO 80216
Tel.: (303) 296-9530
Web Site: http://www.innomax.com
Year Founded: 1975
Sales Range: $10-24.9 Million
Emp.: 35
Furniture Merchant Whslr
N.A.I.C.S.: 423210
R. Irvin Saathoff (Mgr-Mktg Svcs)
Dave Chandler (Gen Mgr)

INNOPATH SOFTWARE, INC.
1195 W Fremont Ave Ste 100, Sunnyvale, CA 94087-3832
Tel.: (408) 962-9200
Web Site: http://www.innopath.com
Year Founded: 1999
Sales Range: $25-49.9 Million
Emp.: 175
Mobile Phone Software Systems
N.A.I.C.S.: 513210
John Fazio (Pres & CEO)
Dave McCroskey (VP-Global Ops)
Chantal Rankowicz (CFO)

INNOTEC, CORP.
441 E Roosevelt Ave Ste 200, Zeeland, MI 49464
Tel.: (616) 772-5959
Web Site:
http://www.innotecgroup.com
Year Founded: 1992
Sales Range: $10-24.9 Million
Emp.: 90
Metal Stamping Services
N.A.I.C.S.: 332119
Rajamannar Ramaswamy (Grp Mng Dir)
Ian Kuipers (Engr-Mechanical)
Judy Cody (Controller)
Kevin Nienhuis (Engr-Mfg)
Mario Veldhuijzen (Project Mgr)
Robert Vance (VP)
Nick DeVries (CFO)
Chris Dattels (Controller)
Jeff Vroegindewey (Controller)
Tom Veenstra (Dir-Product Dev)
Kevin Henderson (Engr-Controls Div)
Preston Phillips (Engr-Mechanical)

Jon Lubbers *(Engr-Mfg)*
Ron Gunter *(Engr-Plastics)*
Phil DeJonge *(Engr-Mfg)*

INNOTEK CORPORATION
9140 Zachary Ln N, Maple Grove, MN 55369
Tel.: (763) 488-9910
Web Site: http://www.innotek-ep.com
Year Founded: 1959
Sales Range: $25-49.9 Million
Emp.: 70
Fluid Power Products Mfr & Distr
N.A.I.C.S.: 333996
Dennis Burns *(Chm)*

INNOTION ENTERPRISES, INC.
260 Cedar Ln SE Ste A, Vienna, VA 22180
Tel.: (703) 351-8151
Web Site: http://www.innotion.com
Year Founded: 1997
Sales Range: $25-49.9 Million
Emp.: 43
REO Property Management, Marketing & Sales
N.A.I.C.S.: 531390
Al Espinoza *(CEO)*
Ryan Gesinski *(Controller)*
Anna Buglaeva *(Mgr-Mktg)*

INNOV8 SOLUTIONS USA LLC
1500 W 47 Ave, Denver, CO 80211
Tel.: (303) 328-8888
Web Site: http://www.innov8solutionsusa.com
Rev.: $12,000,000
Emp.: 7
Telephone Communication, Except Radio
N.A.I.C.S.: 424120
Ronald E. Montoya *(Owner)*

INNOVANCE, INC.
505 W Front St, Albert Lea, MN 56007
Tel.: (507) 377-8910
Web Site: http://www.innovance.com
Holding Company
N.A.I.C.S.: 551112
Mike Larson *(CEO)*

Subsidiaries:

Almco, Inc.　(1)
507 W Front St, Albert Lea, MN 56007
Tel.: (507) 377-2102
Web Site: http://www.almco.com
Emp.: 60
Industrial Machinery Mfr
N.A.I.C.S.: 333248

Jorgensen Conveyors, Inc.　(1)
10303 N Baehr Rd, Mequon, WI 53092
Tel.: (262) 242-3089
Web Site: http://www.jorgensenconveyors.com
Rev.: $11,900,000
Emp.: 85
Conveyor & Conveying Equipment Mfr
N.A.I.C.S.: 333922
Greg Anzia *(Engr-Sls)*

Lou-Rich, Inc.　(1)
505 W Front St, Albert Lea, MN 56007-2751
Tel.: (507) 377-8910
Web Site: http://www.lou-rich.com
Sales Range: $75-99.9 Million
Emp.: 320
Provider of Assembly, Machining, Welding, Stamping, Tooling & Painting Services
N.A.I.C.S.: 332710
Mike Larson *(Pres & CEO)*
Mark Sipple *(Engr-Quality)*

Mass Finishing, Inc.　(1)
1060 Commerce Blvd, Howard Lake, MN 55349
Tel.: (320) 543-3222
Web Site: http://www.massfin.com

Emp.: 8
Industrial Machinery Mfr
N.A.I.C.S.: 333248
Mike Mathisen *(Co-Founder)*
Tom Mathisen *(Co-Founder)*

Midland Technologies, Inc.　(1)
14800 James Rd, Rogers, MN 55374
Tel.: (763) 428-4229
Web Site: http://www.midlandtechnologies.com
Plastic Pipe Fitting Mfr
N.A.I.C.S.: 326122

INNOVAR ENVIRONMENTAL, INC.
2795 S Shoshone Unit D, Englewood, CO 80110
Tel.: (303) 703-4674
Web Site: http://www.innovar-env.com
Year Founded: 2000
Sales Range: $10-24.9 Million
Emp.: 75
Environmental Consulting & Construction Services
N.A.I.C.S.: 541320
Anne Detten *(Controller)*
Lisa Gard *(Dir-Mktg & Program Mgr-Environment)*

INNOVARO, INC.
2109 Palm Ave, Tampa, FL 33605-3931
Tel.: (813) 754-4330　DE
Web Site: http://www.innovaro.com
Year Founded: 1997
Sales Range: Less than $1 Million
Emp.: 7
Software Publisher; Technology Consulting Services
N.A.I.C.S.: 513210
Asa W. Lanum *(Chm & CEO)*

Subsidiaries:

TechEx　(1)
2109 E Palm Ave Ste 300, Tampa, FL 33605-3931
Tel.: (813) 754-4330
Web Site: http://www.techex.com
Operator of an Internet-based Exchange for the Buying & Selling of Biomedical Technology
N.A.I.C.S.: 541512

UTEK Europe Ltd.　(1)
Harby House, Nose Bridge Rd, Berkhamsted, HP4 1EF, Hertfordshire, United Kingdom　(100%)
Tel.: (44) 442873456
Web Site: http://www.utek.co.uk
Provider of Technology Transfer Services to International Businesses
N.A.I.C.S.: 561499

INNOVATEMAP LLC
1002 Broad Ripple Ave Ste 201, Indianapolis, IN 46220
Tel.: (317) 456-5447　IN
Web Site: http://www.innovatemap.com
Year Founded: 2014
Sales Range: $1-9.9 Million
Emp.: 21
Digital Advertising Services
N.A.I.C.S.: 541850
Mike Reynolds *(CEO)*

INNOVATION ADS, INC.
233 Broadway 21st Fl, New York, NY 10279
Tel.: (212) 509-5218
Year Founded: 2002
Sales Range: $25-49.9 Million
Emp.: 70
Advetising Agency
N.A.I.C.S.: 541810
Patrick Sutton *(Dir-Mktg, Content & Press)*

Subsidiaries:

Innovation Ads, Inc.　(1)
433 Plaza Real Dr Ste 365, Boca Raton, FL 33432
Tel.: (561) 394-1600
Emp.: 30
Advetising Agency
N.A.I.C.S.: 541810

INNOVATION GRAPHICS
13710 Edith Hite Dr, Fountain, FL 32438
Tel.: (850) 319-2452　CA
Web Site: http://www.graphicsinnovation.com
Year Founded: 1950
Sales Range: $75-99.9 Million
Emp.: 96
Distribution Of Photographic Cameras Projectors Digital Equipment And Supplies
N.A.I.C.S.: 424990
Hiro Tada *(Pres)*
Jim Clark *(VP-Ops)*

INNOVATION TECHNOLOGY GROUP
945 Stewart Dr, Sunnyvale, CA 94085
Tel.: (408) 212-2700
Sales Range: Less than $1 Million
Emp.: 3
Holding Company
N.A.I.C.S.: 551112
JoMei Chang *(Dir)*

Subsidiaries:

Vitria Technology, Inc.　(1)
945 Stewart Dr Ste 200, Sunnyvale, CA 94085
Tel.: (408) 212-2700
Web Site: http://www.vitria.com
Prepackaged Software Mfr
N.A.I.C.S.: 334610
Mike Rossi *(Sr VP-Sls)*

Subsidiary (Non-US):

QiLinSoft, LLC　(2)
16th Floor E1 Oriental Plaza, Beijing, 100738, China
Tel.: (86) 10 8518 5728
Web Site: http://www.qilinsoft.com.cn
Business Software
N.A.I.C.S.: 513210
JoMei Chang *(CEO)*

INNOVATION VENTURES LLC
38955 Hills Tech Dr, Farmington Hills, MI 48331
Tel.: (248) 960-1700
Web Site: http://www.5hourenergy.com
Year Founded: 2000
Sales Range: $550-599.9 Million
Emp.: 400
Energy Supplement Mfr
N.A.I.C.S.: 311999
Manoj Bhargava *(Founder & CEO)*
Shawn McCue *(CFO)*
Vince Bodiford *(Head-Comm)*

INNOVATIONS FOR POVERTY ACTION
101 Whitney Ave, New Haven, CT 06510
Tel.: (203) 772-2216　NJ
Web Site: http://www.poverty-action.org
Year Founded: 2002
Sales Range: $50-74.9 Million
Emp.: 214
Anti-Poverty Advocacy Services
N.A.I.C.S.: 813319
Jessica Kiessel *(Asst Dir-Health Systems Solutions)*
Sarah de Tournemire *(Sr Dir-External Rels)*

Vivian Brady-Jones *(CFO)*
Annie Duflo *(Exec Dir)*
Thoai Ngo *(Sr Dir-Res Methods & Knowledge Mgmt)*
Burkina Faso *(Partner)*
John D. *(Partner)*
Universidad Cayetano Heredia *(Partner)*
Abdul Latif Jameel *(Partner)*
Asociacion Dominicana *(Partner)*
Ife M. Osaga-Ondondo *(Gen Counsel)*
Marie Stopes *(Partner)*

INNOVATIVE ADVERTISING, LLC.
4250 Hwy 22 Ste 7, Mandeville, LA 70471
Tel.: (985) 809-1975
Web Site: http://www.peoplewhothink.com
Year Founded: 1999
Sales Range: $10-24.9 Million
Emp.: 30
Advertising Services
N.A.I.C.S.: 541810
Meredith Nolan *(Acct Coord)*

INNOVATIVE AG SERVICES CO.
2010 S Main St, Monticello, IA 52310
Tel.: (319) 465-6896　IA
Web Site: http://www.innovativeag.com
Year Founded: 2005
Farm Raw Materials, Supplies, Lumber & Livestock Whslr
N.A.I.C.S.: 424590
Brenda Hoefler *(CFO)*
Mike Duncomb *(VP-Feed)*
Brian Kramer *(VP-Ops)*
Ron Barkema *(VP-Grain)*
Tim Krausman *(VP-Agronomy)*
Randy Swenson *(VP-Energy)*
Richard Vaughan *(CEO)*
Carla Elliott *(VP-HR)*
Loren Manternach *(Sec)*
Kevin Babcock *(VP-Innovative Building Supply)*
Randy Blake *(Pres)*

INNOVATIVE ANALYTICS INC.
Haymarket Five & Six 161 E Michigan Ave, Kalamazoo, MI 49007
Tel.: (269) 488-3200
Web Site: http://www.ianalytics.biz
Sales Range: $1-9.9 Million
Emp.: 24
Biotechnology Research & Development
N.A.I.C.S.: 541714
Patricia L. Ruppel *(Co-Founder, Pres & CEO)*
Kimberly T. Perry *(Dir-Clinical Statistics)*
Karen M. Tindall *(Dir-Clinical Data Mgmt)*
Lillian Neff *(Exec Dir-Medical Writing)*
Thomas H. Oliphant *(Exec Dir-Clinical Statistics)*
Gregory D. Elfring *(Exec Dir-SAS Programming)*
James M. Dancy *(Co-Founder, COO & VP)*

INNOVATIVE BUILDING SYSTEMS LLC
4900 Ritter Rd Ste 130, Mechanicsburg, PA 17055-6929
Tel.: (717) 458-1400　DE
Web Site: http://www.innovativebuildingsystems.com
Year Founded: 2010

Innovative Building Systems LLC—(Continued)

Holding Company; Modular Housing Construction
N.A.I.C.S.: 551112
Phil Hickman *(Pres-Ops)*
Jolene Myers *(Pres & CFO)*
Jeffrey Samson *(Co-Owner & Mng Dir)*
Steve Scheinkman *(Co-Owner & Mng Dir)*

Subsidiaries:

All American Homes, LLC   **(1)**
1418 S 13 St, Decatur, IN 46733-0451
Tel.: (260) 724-9171
Web Site:
   http://www.allamericanhomes.com
Sales Range: $10-24.9 Million
Emp.: 100
Modular Housing Construction
N.A.I.C.S.: 321992
Phil Hickman *(Pres)*
Chad Marchand *(VP & Gen Mgr)*
Jay Beplay *(Gen Sls Mgr)*

Subsidiary (Domestic):

All American Homes of Iowa,
LLC   **(2)**
1551 15th Ave SE, Dyersville, IA 52040-2373   **(100%)**
Tel.: (563) 875-2421
Web Site:
   http://www.allamericanhomes.com
Modular Housing Construction
N.A.I.C.S.: 321992
Douglas Stimpson *(VP & Gen Mgr)*

Excel Homes Group, LLC   **(1)**
10642 S Susquehanna Trl, Liverpool, PA 17045
Tel.: (717) 444-3395
Web Site: http://www.excelhomes.com
Holding Company; Modular Housing Construction
N.A.I.C.S.: 551112
Phil Hickman *(Pres)*

Subsidiary (Domestic):

EHI Modular Company, Inc.   **(2)**
10642 S Susquehanna Trail, Liverpool, PA 17045
Tel.: (717) 444-3395
Web Site: http://www.excelhomes.com
Sales Range: $25-49.9 Million
Emp.: 600
Modular Housing Construction
N.A.I.C.S.: 321992

Handcrafted Homes, LLC   **(2)**
101 Eastern Minerals Rd, Henderson, NC 27537
Tel.: (252) 436-0001
Web Site:
   http://www.handcraftedhomes.com
Custom Modular Homes Mfr
N.A.I.C.S.: 321992
Len Fairfield *(Principal & Gen Mgr)*

INNOVATIVE COLLABORA-TION, INC.
7307 Sandscove Ct Ste 11, Winter Park, FL 32792
Tel.: (407) 988-1240
Web Site: http://www.icavn.com
Year Founded: 2014
Sales Range: $1-9.9 Million
Emp.: 15
Telecommunication Servicesb
N.A.I.C.S.: 517810
Al Sheppard *(Co-Owner & Pres)*
William Holcomb *(Co-Owner & VP)*

INNOVATIVE COMMUNICA-TION CONCEPTS, INC.
519 8th Ave 4th Fl, New York, NY 10018
Tel.: (212) 629-3366
Web Site: http://www.icctel.com
Year Founded: 1987
Rev.: $16,228,592
Emp.: 50

Provider of Technology-Based, Integrated Communications Solutions
N.A.I.C.S.: 423690
L. Penzenbeck *(Pres)*
Bill Wenzel *(CEO)*
Frank Sussingham *(VP-Sls)*

INNOVATIVE COMMUNICA-TIONS
4611 Tutu Park Mall Ste 200, Saint Thomas, VI 00820
Tel.: (340) 777-7700
Web Site: http://www.innovativevi.net
Rev.: $11,700,000
Emp.: 3
Radiotelephone Communication
N.A.I.C.S.: 517112
Dennis J. Kanai *(CFO)*

INNOVATIVE COMPUTING & APPLIED TECHNOLOGY LLC
1900 Campus Commons Dr Ste 410, Reston, VA 20191
Tel.: (703) 391-1600
Web Site: http://www.incatech-corp.com
Year Founded: 2007
Sales Range: $1-9.9 Million
Emp.: 34
Information Technology Services
N.A.I.C.S.: 541512
Liliana Freedman *(Pres & CEO)*
Bruce Freedman *(VP-Corp Dev)*
Wayne Staub *(VP-Fin Ops)*

INNOVATIVE COMPUTING SYSTEMS, INC.
1960 E Grand Ave Ste 870, El Segundo, CA 90245
Tel.: (310) 265-7320   CA
Web Site:
   http://www.innovativecomp.com
Year Founded: 1989
Sales Range: $1-9.9 Million
Emp.: 24
Information Technology Services
N.A.I.C.S.: 541512
Michael Kemps *(CEO)*
Michael Paul *(CTO)*
Rob Meadows *(Engr-Sys)*
Timothy Sheehan *(Dir-Pro Svcs)*

INNOVATIVE CONCEPT GROUP
13521 Prestige Pl, Tampa, FL 33635
Tel.: (813) 282-0200
Web Site:
   http://www.innovativeconcept.com
Rev.: $34,400,000
Emp.: 65
Bond Brokers
N.A.I.C.S.: 424410
Josie Belizaire *(Mgr-Computer)*
Marc Preininger *(Exec VP)*

INNOVATIVE CONSTRUCTION & ROOFING
10850 Baur Blvd, Saint Louis, MO 63132
Tel.: (314) 546-4047
Web Site:
   http://www.innovativeroofs.com
Year Founded: 2008
Sales Range: $10-24.9 Million
Emp.: 17
Commercial & Residential Roofing, Gutters & Insurance Restoration Services
N.A.I.C.S.: 238160
Patrick McNichols *(Co-Owner)*
Brian Ben *(Co-Owner)*

INNOVATIVE CONTROL SYS-TEMS LP
10801 N 24th Ave, Phoenix, AZ 85029

Tel.: (602) 861-6984
Web Site: http://www.icsaero.com
Year Founded: 1990
Sales Range: $1-9.9 Million
Emp.: 10
Aviation Training Products Supplier
N.A.I.C.S.: 423490
Kevin Jacobson *(Founder, Pres & Gen Mgr)*

INNOVATIVE COURIER SOLU-TIONS INC.
3482 Keith Bridge Rd Ste 236, Cumming, GA 30041
Tel.: (404) 245-2322
Sales Range: $10-24.9 Million
Emp.: 55
Courier Service
N.A.I.C.S.: 492110
Mark E. Rykowski *(CEO & CFO)*
Judith A. Rykowski *(Sec)*

INNOVATIVE DIVERSIFIED TECHNOLOGIES INC.
14 Chrysler Dr, Irvine, CA 92618
Tel.: (949) 455-1701
Web Site:
   http://www.idtmediagroup.com
Year Founded: 1996
Sales Range: $1-9.9 Million
Emp.: 28
Holding Company
N.A.I.C.S.: 551112
Ben Abadi *(Pres & CEO)*

Subsidiaries:

DiskFaktory.com   **(1)**
14 Chrysler Dr, Irvine, CA 92618
Tel.: (949) 455-1701
Web Site: http://www.diskfaktory.com
Sales Range: $1-9.9 Million
Emp.: 21
CD, DVD & Data Disk Producer
N.A.I.C.S.: 334610

INNOVATIVE FOODS, INC.
330 Ballardvale St, Wilmington, MA 01887
Tel.: (781) 596-0070
Web Site:
   http://www.progressivegourmet.com
Year Founded: 1979
Sales Range: $10-24.9 Million
Emp.: 140
Frozen Specialty Food Mfr
N.A.I.C.S.: 311412
Vincent Pretola *(Plant Mgr)*

INNOVATIVE HESS PROD-UCTS, LLC.
2605 S Clearbrook Dr, Arlington Heights, IL 60005
Tel.: (847) 676-3260
Web Site: http://www.milmour.com
Year Founded: 1956
Sales Range: $10-24.9 Million
Emp.: 406
Plastic Material & Resin Mfr
N.A.I.C.S.: 325211
Scott Fohram *(Pres)*

INNOVATIVE IDM LLC
1625 Wallace Dr Ste 110, Carrollton, TX 75006
Tel.: (214) 574-9500   TX
Web Site:
   http://www.innovativeidm.com
Year Founded: 2000
Sales Range: $10-24.9 Million
Emp.: 120
Designs & Implements Production Automation Systems for Manufacturing Companies
N.A.I.C.S.: 333248
Eugene Gray *(Founder, Pres & CEO)*
Adam Ring *(Founder & Mgr-Engrg)*
Todd Mueller *(Founder & Dir-Ops)*

Subsidiaries:

Sunbelt Power Controls Inc.   **(1)**
2412 Richland Ave, Farmers Branch, TX 75234
Tel.: (972) 620-2950
Web Site:
   http://www.sunbeltpowercontrol.com
Emp.: 10
Pumps, Motors & Fans Mfr
N.A.I.C.S.: 333914
Richard Kreekon *(Owner)*

INNOVATIVE INFORMATION SOLUTIONS
61 Interstate Ln, Waterbury, CT 06705
Tel.: (203) 756-4243
Web Site:
   http://www.innovativeis.com
Sales Range: $10-24.9 Million
Emp.: 20
Computer & Software Stores
N.A.I.C.S.: 449210
Evan Walters *(Pres & CEO)*
Ingrid Naumann *(Coord-Mktg & Sls Support)*
Russ Sackowitz *(Dir-Software Sls)*

INNOVATIVE INTEGRATION, INC.
8902 Vincennes Cir Ste B, Indianapolis, IN 46268
Tel.: (317) 664-7600
Web Site: http://www.innovativeii.com
Year Founded: 2005
Sales Range: $1-9.9 Million
Emp.: 17
Data Processing, Hosting & Related Services
N.A.I.C.S.: 518210
Nicholas Hatch *(Pres)*
Terri Carson *(Acct Mgr)*
Scott Clements *(Dir-Client Support)*
Tony Johnson *(VP)*

INNOVATIVE LIGHTING, INC.
109 Progressive Ave, Roland, IA 50236
Tel.: (515) 388-1011
Web Site:
   http://www.innovativelight.com
Sales Range: $1-9.9 Million
Emp.: 100
Light-Emitting Diodes Mfr for Interior & Exterior Lighting in RVs, Trucks, Trailers & Boats
N.A.I.C.S.: 336320
Jerry Handsaker *(CEO)*
Anne L. Peterson *(Dir-HR)*
Jim Johnson *(Dir-Molding)*
Brian Flynn *(Dir-Mktg)*
Craig Van Gundy *(Coord-Sls)*

INNOVATIVE MANUFACTUR-ING SOLUTIONS CORP.
1 Innovation Dr, Des Plaines, IL 60016
Tel.: (847) 391-8100
Web Site: http://www.imsmfg.com
Year Founded: 1998
Sales Range: $25-49.9 Million
Emp.: 150
Metal Stamping Parts Mfr
N.A.I.C.S.: 332119
Mark Simanton *(CEO)*
Mike Chester *(Pres)*

Subsidiaries:

Electrol Co.   **(1)**
N77 W30924 Hartman Ct, Hartland, WI 53029
Tel.: (262) 966-3741
Web Site: http://www.imsmfg.com
Metal Stamping Mfr
N.A.I.C.S.: 336370

Global Gear & Machining   **(1)**

2500 Curtiss St, Downers Grove, IL 60515
Tel.: (630) 969-9400
Web Site: http://www.globalgearllc.com
Gear Mfr
N.A.I.C.S.: 333517

IMS Buhrke-Olson (1)
511 W Algonquin Rd, Arlington Heights, IL 60005
Tel.: (847) 981-7550
Web Site: http://www.metalstamper.com
Sales Range: $75-99.9 Million
Metal Stamping Services
N.A.I.C.S.: 332119
Robert J. Nellemann (Dir-Mktg-Bus Dev)
Keith Krutz (Pres)

INNOVATIVE OFFICE SOLUTIONS LLC
151 East Cliff Rd, Burnsville, MN 55337
Tel.: (952) 808-9900
Web Site:
   http://www.innovativeos.com
Year Founded: 2001
Rev.: $16,200,000
Emp.: 200
Stationery & Office Supplies Merchant Whlslr
N.A.I.C.S.: 424120
Jennifer Smith (Founder & CEO)
Jason Player (CIO & CMO)
Brooks Smith (CFO & Gen Counsel)

Subsidiaries:

Northern Business Products, Inc. (1)
2326 W Superior St, Duluth, MN 55806
Tel.: (218) 726-0167
Web Site: http://www.nbpoffice.com
Sales Range: $1-9.9 Million
Emp.: 60
Office Supplies & Stationery Stores
N.A.I.C.S.: 459410
Jim Farrell (Pres)
Brett Breimon (Mgr)
Dan Eggen (Mgr-Sls)

INNOVATIVE PICKING TECHNOLOGIES, INC.
W1236 Industrial Dr, Ixonia, WI 53036
Tel.: (262) 567-6525 WI
Web Site: http://www.ipti.net
Year Founded: 1994
Sales Range: $1-9.9 Million
Emp.: 37
Designs & Manufactures Paperless Order Fulfillment Systems for Warehouses & Distribution Centers
N.A.I.C.S.: 541512
Danielle Ireland (VP)
Darin Danelski (Pres)
Craig Kracht (Engr-Software Dev)
Kurt Cappelli (Project Mgr)

INNOVATIVE POWER PRODUCTS, INC.
1170 Lincoln Ave Unit 7, Holbrook, NY 11741
Tel.: (631) 563-0088
Web Site:
   http://www.innovativepp.com
Year Founded: 2006
Sales Range: $1-9.9 Million
Emp.: 22
Manufactures & Sells Passive Components for the Microwave & Radio Frequency Communications Industries
N.A.I.C.S.: 334220
Thomas Passaro (Pres)

INNOVATIVE SERVICES, INC.
445 S Madison St, Green Bay, WI 54301
Tel.: (920) 431-0962 WI
Web Site:
   http://www.myinnovativeser
   vices.com

Year Founded: 2003
Sales Range: $10-24.9 Million
Emp.: 1,539
Developmental Disability Assistance Services
N.A.I.C.S.: 623210
M. Scott Spear (Asst Sec)
Scott Jaeger (Sec)
T. Gerald Walker (Chm & Pres)

INNOVATIVE SOLUTION SYSTEMS
1 Woodbridge Ctr Ste 435, Woodbridge, NJ 07095
Tel.: (732) 596-0300
Sales Range: $10-24.9 Million
Emp.: 55
Computer Software Systems Analysis & Design
N.A.I.C.S.: 541511
Milan Awon (Pres & CEO)

INNOVATIVE SOLUTIONS INSURANCE SERVICES, LLC.
200 N Sepulveda Blvd Ste 900, El Segundo, CA 90245-4340
Tel.: (310) 851-8222
Web Site: http://www.isislife.com
Sales Range: $10-24.9 Million
Emp.: 40
Insurance Agencies & Brokerage Services
N.A.I.C.S.: 524210
Lynne Rosenberg (Pres)
Dave Costanza (VP-Underwriting)
Lisa Dibugnara (Dir-Ops & Mktg Strategy)
Veronica Luna (Dir-New Bus)

INNOVATIVE SOLUTIONS UNLIMITED, LLC
1862 Shyville Rd, Piketon, OH 45661
Tel.: (740) 289-3282
Web Site: http://www.insolves.com
Year Founded: 1993
Sales Range: $1-9.9 Million
Emp.: 118
Energy Services
N.A.I.C.S.: 541690
Steve Barbarits (Project Mgr)
Angela Stuart (Mgr-Contracts)

INNOVATIVE STAFFING, INC.
859 W S Jordan Pkwy Ste 77, South Jordan, UT 84095
Tel.: (801) 984-0252
Web Site:
   http://www.innovativestaffing.com
Year Founded: 1999
Sales Range: $100-124.9 Million
Emp.: 20
Human Resouce Services
N.A.I.C.S.: 541612
John Farnsworth (Pres)

INNOVATIVE SURFACES, LLC
4707 W 138th St, Crestwood, IL 60445
Tel.: (708) 389-7300 AL
Web Site:
   http://www.innovativesurfacesllc.com
Year Founded: 2004
Emp.: 10
Building Materials, Flooring & Supplies Whslr & Distr
N.A.I.C.S.: 444180
Mitch Hires (Principal)
Patrick Carney (Pres)

INNOVATIVE SYSTEMS GROUP INC.
799 Roosevelt Rd, Glen Ellyn, IL 60137
Tel.: (630) 858-8500

Web Site:
   http://www.innovativesys.com
Sales Range: $10-24.9 Million
Emp.: 150
Custom Computer Programming Services
N.A.I.C.S.: 541511
Joselito C. Salas (Founder, Pres & CEO)
Lisa Gorman (Dir-Enterprise Svcs)
Jamie Hogue (Acct Mgr)

INNOVATIVE TECHNOLOGY PARTNERSHIPS, LLC
4604 Columbine Ave NE, Albuquerque, NM 87113-2236
Tel.: (505) 796-0996 NM
Web Site: http://www.itpnm.com
Year Founded: 1997
Sales Range: $10-24.9 Million
Emp.: 146
Strategic Planning Software Consulting Services
N.A.I.C.S.: 541512
Jerry L. Greene (Co-Founder)
John P. Jekowski (Co-Founder)
Xenophon T. James (Co-Founder)

INNOVATIVE USA, INC.
50 Washington St Ste 201, Norwalk, CT 06854-2202
Tel.: (203) 838-6400
Web Site:
   http://www.innovativekids.com
Year Founded: 1989
Sales Range: $25-49.9 Million
Emp.: 25
Educational Toys Retailer; Children's Books Publisher
N.A.I.C.S.: 423920
Shari Kaufman (Pres)
Michael Levins (Owner)

INNOVATIVE, INC.
13332 Pennsylvania Ave, Hagerstown, MD 21742
Tel.: (301) 739-7414
Web Site:
   http://www.innovativeinc.net
Year Founded: 2001
Specialty Trade Contractors
N.A.I.C.S.: 238990
Jason Rappaport (Pres & CEO)

Subsidiaries:

Commlink Systems (1)
20021 Leitersburg Pike, Hagerstown, MD 21742-1448
Tel.: (301) 733-6000
Web Site: http://www.innovativeinc.net
Electronics Stores
N.A.I.C.S.: 449210

INNOVATUS CAPITAL PARTNERS LLC
777 3rd Ave 25th Fl, New York, NY 10017
Tel.: (212) 698-4580
Web Site:
   http://www.innovatuscp.com
Privater Equity Firm
N.A.I.C.S.: 523999
Andrew W. Hobson (Partner & CFO)
David Schiff (Co-Founder & CEO)
Andrew Dym (Co-Founder)

Subsidiaries:

Meet The People LLC (1)
777 3rd Ave 25th Fl, New York, NY 10017
Tel.: (212) 806-6647
Web Site: https://www.meet-the-people.com
Marketing & Advertising Services
N.A.I.C.S.: 541810
Tim Ringel (Founder & CEO)

Subsidiary (Domestic):

Saltwater Collective LLC (2)

40 Congress St Fl 5, Portsmouth, NH 03801
Tel.: (603) 964-1100
Web Site: http://www.saltwaterco.com
Sales Range: $1-9.9 Million
Emp.: 33
Digital Marketing Services
N.A.I.C.S.: 541810
Mike Carella (Co-Founder)
Christopher Griffin (Co-Founder)
Allison Potter (COO & Principal)
Mike Sullivan (VP & Dir-Creative Svcs)
Brendan Flavin (VP & Dir-Digital Mktg)

VSA Partners, Inc. (1)
600 W Chicago Ave Ste 250, Chicago, IL 60654
Tel.: (312) 427-6413
Web Site: http://www.vsapartners.com
Emp.: 20
Advetising Agency
N.A.I.C.S.: 541613
William Rosen (CEO)
Curt Schreiber (Pres & Chief Design Officer)
Dana Arnett (Founder, Vice Chm & Partner)
Bob Winter (Partner & Exec Creative Dir)
Jeff Walker (Sr Partner)
Heather Torreggiani (CMO)
Tracy Richards (VP-Talent Acq)
Morgan Waller (Dir-Comm & PR)
Cheri DeMong Hubbard (COO)
Jim Milligan (CFO)
Cory Clarke (Partner)
Claudine Litman (Partner)
Dave Ritter (Partner)
Jim Toth (Partner & Dir-Creative)
Patrick Palmer (Partner)
Eric Martinez (Partner)
Anne-Marie Rosser (Partner)
Andrea Spiegel (Partner-Client Engagement)
Sol Sender (Partner-Client Engagement)
Carolyn Frazier (Partner)
Andy Blankenburg (Partner)
Ariadna Navarro (Partner & Exec Dir-Strategy)
Bob Silverman (Co-CFO)
Michael Moroney (Partner-Tech Lead)

Branch (Domestic):

VSA Partners, Inc. (2)
322 First Ave N., #300, Minneapolis, MN 55401
Tel.: (612) 339-2920
Advertising Agencies
N.A.I.C.S.: 541810

VSA Partners, Inc. (2)
106 7th Ave 2nd Fl, New York, NY 10011
Tel.: (212) 869-1188
Advertising Agencies
N.A.I.C.S.: 541810
Avery Gross (Assoc Partner & Exec Creative Dir)

INNOVATUS LIFE SCIENCES ACQUISITION CORP.
777 3rd Ave 25th Fl, New York, NY 10017
Tel.: (212) 698-4580 DE
Year Founded: 2021
Investment Services
N.A.I.C.S.: 523999
Andrew W. Hobson (CFO)
David Schiff (Chm & CEO)
Claes Ekstrom (Chief Bus Officer)

INNOVETIVE PETCARE HOLDINGS LLC
1464 E Whitestone Blvd Ste 1703, Cedar Park, TX 78613
Tel.: (512) 969-6933 DE
Web Site:
   http://www.innovetivepetcare.com
Year Founded: 2015
Sales Range: $25-49.9 Million
Emp.: 302
Pet Care Services
N.A.I.C.S.: 541940
Mark Ziller (Pres & CEO)
Paul Covill (Chief Dev Officer & Exec VP)
Andrea Sharma (CFO)
Brittany Lopez (Controller)
Elizabeth Gibson (Dir-Bus Dev)

Innovim LLC—(Continued)

INNOVIM LLC
7474 Greenway Center Dr Ste 800,
Greenbelt, MD 20770
Tel.: (240) 542-0200
Web Site: http://www.innovim.com
Year Founded: 2002
Rev.: $3,600,000
Emp.: 100
Office Administrative Services
N.A.I.C.S.: 561110
Shahin Samadi (Co-Founder & CTO)
Sammy Samadi (Co-Founder & Partner)
Arnold Kravitz (Pres-INNOVIM Defense Solutions)
William J. Harris (VP-Bus Dev)
Philip Ardanuy (Chief Science Officer)

INNOVISION MEDIA GROUP
2417 E Rancho Del Amo Place, Rancho Dominguez, CA 90220
Tel.: (562) 961-3610
Web Site:
    http://www.innovisionmg.com
Year Founded: 1993
Sales Range: $25-49.9 Million
Emp.: 10
Media Buying Services
N.A.I.C.S.: 541830
Darren Moffett (Pres & Partner)

INNOVO INC.
172 Yacht Harbor Dr, Osprey, FL
34229
Tel.: (941) 587-3973   FL
Year Founded: 2010
Charitable Fundraising Services
N.A.I.C.S.: 525990
John J. Geldi Jr. (Pres, CEO, CFO, Treas & Sec)

INNOWAVE MARKETING GROUP, LLC
533 Airport Blvd Ste 400, Burlingame, CA 94010
Tel.: (650) 454-4952
Web Site:
    http://www.innowavemarketing.com
Year Founded: 2012
Sales Range: $1-9.9 Million
Emp.: 21
Consumer Goods Distr
N.A.I.C.S.: 423620
Stu Birger (Founder & CEO)

INNS OF AMERICA
755 Raintree Dr Ste 200, Carlsbad, CA 92011
Tel.: (760) 438-6661
Web Site:
    http://www.innsofamerica.com
Sales Range: $10-24.9 Million
Emp.: 300
Hotel
N.A.I.C.S.: 721110
Cassie Carter (Dir-Sls)

INNVENTURES INC.
500 108th Ave NE Ste 2050, Bellevue, WA 98004
Tel.: (206) 431-8000
Web Site:
    http://www.innventures.com
Rev.: $10,384,789
Emp.: 20
Hotel
N.A.I.C.S.: 237210
Larry Culver (Pres)
Greg Wasson (Founder)

INO.COM
Discovery Vlg 4800 Atwell Rd, Shady Side, MD 20764
Tel.: (410) 867-2100
Web Site: http://www.ino.com

Year Founded: 1995
Sales Range: $1-9.9 Million
Emp.: 20
Market Trade Internet Information
N.A.I.C.S.: 541611
J. Adam Hewison (Pres)
David Maher (Founder & Tech Dir)
Bob Fladung (Dir-Adv)

INOLEX GROUP INC.
Jackson & Swanson St, Philadelphia, PA 19148
Tel.: (215) 271-0800   PA
Web Site: http://www.inolex.com
Year Founded: 1892
Sales Range: $10-24.9 Million
Emp.: 100
Plastic Material & Resin Mfr
N.A.I.C.S.: 325211
Puja Agarwal (Bus Dir-Asia)
Jennie Creech (Acct Mgr-Technical-East)
Doreen Bailey (Mgr-Customer Experience)
Julia Benson (Acct Mgr-Technical-UK)

Subsidiaries:

Inolex Chemical Company   (1)
2101 S Swanson St, Philadelphia, PA 19148
Tel.: (215) 271-0800
Web Site: http://www.inolex.com
Sales Range: $10-24.9 Million
Emp.: 90
Raw Materials to Industrial & Cosmetic Applications
N.A.I.C.S.: 325211
Raymond Thomas (CFO)

INOLIFE TECHNOLOGIES INC.
300 Spectrum Ctr Dr #400, Irvine, CA 92618
Tel.: (866) 834-3777   NY
Web Site: http://www.inolifetech.com
Year Founded: 1998
Sales Range: Less than $1 Million
Drug Delivery Devices, Technologies & Products Developer & Marketer
N.A.I.C.S.: 339112
John Oda (Pres & CEO)
Janice Gray (Interim CFO, & VP-Fin)

INOVA HEALTH SYSTEM
8110 Gatehouse Rd, Falls Church, VA 22042
Tel.: (703) 289-2000   VA
Web Site: http://www.inova.org
Year Founded: 1956
Sales Range: $1-4.9 Billion
Emp.: 12,963
Hospital & Healthcare Services
N.A.I.C.S.: 622110
Richard Magenheimer (CFO & Asst Treas)
Mark Stauder (Pres)
Loring Flint (Chief Medical Officer & Exec VP)
John Gaul (Gen Counsel & Sr VP)
Jennifer Siciliano (VP-Govt Rels)
Patrick Christiansen (Exec VP)
John Fitzgerald (VP)
Tony Raker (Dir-Pub Rels)
Connie M. Pilot (CIO & Exec VP)
Amit Rastogi (Sr VP-Strategy, Growth & Innovation)
J. Stephen Jones (CEO)
Ben Frank (COO)
Sage Bolte (Pres & Chief Philanthropy Officer)
Terri Feely (Chief People Officer)
Paul Harbolick Jr. (Treas)

Subsidiaries:

INTotal Health   (1)
4425 Corporation Ln, Virginia Beach, VA 23462
Tel.: (855) 323-5588

Web Site: http://www.amerigroupcorp.com
Sales Range: $25-49.9 Million
Emp.: 33
Public Managed Healthcare
N.A.I.C.S.: 524114
Renee Maccannon (CEO)

Inova Alexandria Hospital   (1)
4320 Seminary Rd, Alexandria, VA 22304
Tel.: (703) 504-3000
Web Site: http://www.inova.org
Hospital Services
N.A.I.C.S.: 622110
Richard Kennedy (Asst VP & Dir-HR)
Martin Brown (Chm-Emergency Medicine Dept)
Christina Hortman (Coord-Clinical)
Alma Allen (Dir-Case Mgmt)
Thorrenna Lewis (Dir-Case Mgmt)
John Grinkley (Dir-Fin)
Carlos Artiles (Dir-Neuroradiolgy & MRI)
Lesley Chauncey (Dir-Patient Care)
Carol Feike (Dir-Patient Care & Critical Care)
Elaine Alexander (Dir-Patient Care-NICU & FCC)
Michelle Le (Dir-Pharmacy)
Joanne Gucciardo (Dir-Pro Practice)
David Reamy (Dir-Supply Chain Mgmt)
Vanessa McCain Johnson (Mgr-Emergency Dept)

INOVA HEALTH SYSTEM FOUNDATION
8095 Innovation Park Dr, Fairfax, VA 22031
Tel.: (703) 289-2072
Web Site: https://www.inova.org
Health Care Srvices
N.A.I.C.S.: 621610

INOVA PAYROLL, INC.
636 Grassmere Park Ste 110, Nashville, TN 37211
Tel.: (615) 921-0600
Web Site:
    http://www.inovapayroll.com
Year Founded: 2011
Payroll Services
N.A.I.C.S.: 541214
Joe Schweppe (Pres & CEO)
Coray Grove (Chief Revenue Officer)
Melanie Crow (Sr VP-Sales Enablement)
Jordan Rush (Sr VP-Sls)
Farsheed Ferdowsi (Founder & Chm)
Mary Leveridge (Exec VP-HRExperts)
Anthony Myers (Sr VP-Inova Benefits)
Charlie Wood (COO)
Kathey Palmer (Chief Growth Officer)
Matthew Higgins (CFO)

INOVEX INDUSTRIES INC.
45681 Oakbrook Ct Ste 102, Sterling, VA 20166
Tel.: (703) 421-9778
Web Site: http://www.ride-on.com
Year Founded: 1995
Sales Range: $25-49.9 Million
Emp.: 10
Adhesive Mfr
N.A.I.C.S.: 325520
Mark Farkhan (CEO)

INOVEX INFORMATION SYSTEMS, INC.
175 Admiral Cochrane Dr Ste 300, Hanover, MD 21076
Tel.: (443) 756-7197
Web Site: http://www.inovexcorp.com
Year Founded: 2006
Sales Range: $10-24.9 Million
Emp.: 52
Information Technology Consulting Services
N.A.I.C.S.: 541512
Gary Daigle (Pres)
Dennis Carey (Engr-Software)
Garvin Steele (Engr-Sys)
Ryan Kohl (Principal-Engrg)

INOVIS EMPLOYMENT SERVICE
4501 Circle 75 Pkwy SE, Atlanta, GA 30339-3025
Tel.: (770) 541-7500
Year Founded: 1994
Sales Range: $10-24.9 Million
Emp.: 47
Provider of Business Consulting Services
N.A.I.C.S.: 541618
Angel Babb (Asst Controller)

INPATIENT MEDICAL SERVICES, INC.
4040 Embassy Pkwy Ste 400, Akron, OH 44333
Tel.: (330) 576-0500   OH
Web Site:
    http://www.imshospitalist.com
Outsourced Hospitalist Physician Program Services
N.A.I.C.S.: 812199
Mark Foster (Pres & COO)
Greg Ferner (Reg Dir-Medical)
Dawn Murray (Reg Dir-Ops)
Mitch Cohen (Dir-Recruitment)

INPELLIS, INC.
300 Rosewood Dr Ste 103, Danvers, MA 01923
Tel.: (978) 750-0090   DE
Web Site: http://www.inpellisrx.com
Year Founded: 2012
Emp.: 6
Biopharmaceutical Product Mfr
N.A.I.C.S.: 325412
Patrick T. Mooney (Pres & CEO)
David R. Staskin (Chief Strategy Officer & Sec)
Frank A. Manguso (CFO & Treas)
John J. Clarke Jr. (Chm)

INPOWER LLC
8311 Green Meadows Dr, Lewis Center, OH 43035
Tel.: (740) 548-0965
Web Site:
    http://www.inpowerdirect.com
Year Founded: 2002
Sales Range: $1-9.9 Million
Emp.: 15
Electronic Components for the Transportation Industry Mfr
N.A.I.C.S.: 336330
John Melvin (VP)
Chuck Bennett (VP-Mktg)
Robert LaDow (Mgr-Natl Sls)
Karen Sullivan (Partner)

INPRIA CORPORATION
2001 NW Monroe Ave Ste 203, Corvallis, OR 97330
Tel.: (541) 250-0275
Web Site: http://www.inpria.com
Electrical Equipment & Component Mfr
N.A.I.C.S.: 335999
Andrew Grenville (CEO)

INPRO CORPORATION
S80 W18766 Apollo Dr, Muskego, WI 53150
Tel.: (262) 679-9010
Web Site: http://www.inprocorp.com
Rev.: $66,000,000
Emp.: 375
Unlaminated Plastics Film & Sheet Mfr
N.A.I.C.S.: 326113
Betsy Lewandowski (Mgr-Natl Accts)
Steve Baumgautner (VP-IT)
Matt Bennett (VP-Prod Dev)
Andy Ciesielski (CFO)
Glenn Kennedy (COO)

Laurie Oloughlin (*VP-HR*)
Susan Seghers (*Reg Dir-Sls Staff*)
Sean McCormick (*Dir-Sls*)

Subsidiaries:

Webbshade, Inc.   **(1)**
522 Front St, El Cajon, CA 92020
Tel.: (800) 262-9322
Blind & Shade Mfr
N.A.I.C.S.: 337920

INQUEST MARKETING

9249 Ward Pkwy, Kansas City, MO
64114-3335
Tel.: (913) 341-1966
Year Founded: 1986
Rev.: $17,000,000
Emp.: 12
N.A.I.C.S.: 541810
David E. Wilson (*Owner*)
Dennis Michael (*Production Mgr*)
Marian Shear (*Controller*)
Jody Hanson (*Acct Exec-PR*)
Jill Olson (*Dir-Interactive*)
Brian Olseon (*Partner*)

INRHYTHM

494 8th Ave Ste 1700, New York, NY
10001
Web Site: http://www.inrhythm.com
Year Founded: 2002
Sales Range: $1-9.9 Million
Emp.: 27
It Consulting
N.A.I.C.S.: 541690
Gunjan Doshi (*Founder & CEO*)
Georgie Ariano (*VP-Bus Dev*)

INRIX, INC.

10210 NE Points Dr Ste 400, Kirk-
land, WA 98033
Tel.: (425) 284-3800
Web Site: http://www.inrix.com
Year Founded: 2005
Sales Range: $10-24.9 Million
Emp.: 100
Traffic Data Services
N.A.I.C.S.: 519290

INSALA, LLC

2005 NE Green Oaks Blvd, Arlington,
TX 76006
Tel.: (817) 355-0939
Web Site: http://www.insala.com
Year Founded: 1996
Sales Range: $10-24.9 Million
Emp.: 17
Developer of Web-Based Applications
for Career Management
N.A.I.C.S.: 513210
Phillip Roark (*Pres & CEO*)
Matt Adams (*VP*)
Doug Maxwell (*CTO*)
Stephen Grindrod (*Dir-Global Mktg*)
Christine De Cock (*VP-Client Svcs-*
Europe)
Kathleen Brown (*VP-Career Transi-*
tion Svcs)
Rick Huntley (*VP-HR*)
Pamela Johnson (*Pres*)
Len Martinez (*CFO & VP-Admin*)
Len Rishkofski (*CEO*)

INSCERCO MANUFACTURING
INC.

4621 W 138th St, Crestwood, IL
60418
Tel.: (708) 597-8777
Web Site: http://www.inscerco.com
Year Founded: 1968
Sales Range: $10-24.9 Million
Emp.: 20
Mfr of Mail Inserters
N.A.I.C.S.: 333310
Anna M. Kruk (*Treas & Sec*)
Robert R. Kruk Sr. (*Pres*)

INSCO DISTRIBUTING, INC.

12501 Network Blvd, San Antonio, TX
78249
Tel.: (210) 690-8400
Web Site:
   http://www.inscodistributing.com
Rev.: $22,300,000
Emp.: 240
Commercial Refrigeration Equipment
N.A.I.C.S.: 423740
Rudy Trevino (*Pres*)
Bonnie Gossett (*Project Mgr & Mgr-*
Ops)
Kay Ford (*Mgr-HR*)
Mark Lehmann (*Mgr-IT*)
Jim Stone (*Mgr-Sls Support*)
Adolfo Perez (*Reg Mgr*)
Pat Patton (*Reg Mgr*)

INSCO, INC.

17 Powder Hill Rd, Lincoln, RI 02865-
4407
Tel.: (401) 334-6870   RI
Web Site: http://www.inscogroup.com
Year Founded: 1954
Sales Range: $10-24.9 Million
Emp.: 86
Industrial Machinery & Equipment
N.A.I.C.S.: 423830
Colin O'Sullivan (*VP-Sls*)
Tom Fitzgerald (*VP*)
Dennis Nelson (*VP-Bus Dev*)
Henry F. McManus (*Treas, Sec & VP*)
Edmund M. Mauro III (*Pres*)

Subsidiaries:

D.L. Thurrott Inc.   **(1)**
17 Powder Hill Rd, Lincoln, RI
02865-4407   **(100%)**
Tel.: (401) 334-6880
Web Site: http://www.dlthurrott.com
Sales Range: $10-24.9 Million
Emp.: 15
Wholesale Distributors of Industrial Pumps
N.A.I.C.S.: 423830

Niantic Seal Inc.   **(1)**
17 Powder Hill Rd, Lincoln, RI 02865-4407
Tel.: (401) 334-6870
Web Site: http://www.nianticseal.com
Sales Range: $10-24.9 Million
Emp.: 11
Sealing Products Mfr & Distr
N.A.I.C.S.: 339991
Peter Divoll (*VP-Sls*)

The Chisholm Corporation   **(1)**
17 Powder Hill Rd, Lincoln, RI 02865-4407
Tel.: (401) 334-6850
Web Site: http://www.thechisholmcorp.com
Filtration Products Mfr & Services
N.A.I.C.S.: 334514

INSEARCH WORLDWIDE COR-
PORATION

1 Landmark Sq Fl 1, Stamford, CT
06901
Tel.: (203) 355-3000   CT
Web Site:
   http://www.insearchworldwide.com
Rev.: $15,000,000
Emp.: 30
Executive Placement
N.A.I.C.S.: 541612
Randolph S. Gulian (*Founder, Pres &*
Mng Dir)
Philip M. Thawley (*Mng Dir & Sr VP*)
Eve Charny (*VP*)

INSEEV INTERACTIVE INC.

3565 Del Rey St Ste 202, San Diego,
CA 92109
Tel.: (619) 330-7510   CA
Web Site: http://www.inseev.com
Year Founded: 2013
Sales Range: $1-9.9 Million
Emp.: 20
Digital Marketing Services
N.A.I.C.S.: 541810

Jimmy Page (*Founder & CEO*)
Wesley Flippo (*VP*)
Sandra Page (*Dir-People & Culture*)
Sam Wheeler (*Dir-Global Partner-*
ship)
Sterling Morales (*Office Mgr*)

INSERO & CO. CPAS, LLP

Crossroads Bldg 2 State St Ste 300,
Rochester, NY 14614
Tel.: (585) 454-6996   NY
Web Site: http://www.inserocpa.com
Emp.: 125
Accounting, Auditing, Tax & Consult-
ing Services
N.A.I.C.S.: 541211
Frank A. Insero (*Co-Founder*)
Frederick J. Ciaschi (*Co-Founder*)
Nancy E. Catarisano (*Mng Partner-*
Rochester)
John H. Dietershagen (*Mng Partner-*
Ithaca Office)
David J. Mandrycky (*Dir-HR*)

INSERRA SUPERMARKETS,
INC.

20 Ridge Rd, Mahwah, NJ 07430-
2021
Tel.: (201) 529-5900   NJ
Web Site: http://www.shoprite.com
Year Founded: 1933
Sales Range: $1-4.9 Billion
Emp.: 4,000
Supermarket Operations
N.A.I.C.S.: 445110
Lawrence R. Inserra Jr. (*Chm, Pres &*
CEO)
Richard Chamberlain (*Controller*)
Ron Onorato (*Pres & COO*)
Jim Dorey (*Sr VP*)

INSERSO CORPORATION

1900 Gallows Rd Ste 750, Vienna,
VA 22182
Tel.: (703) 642-9598   VA
Web Site: http://www.inserso.com
Year Founded: 1994
Rev.: $3,700,000
Emp.: 30
Computer Programming Services
N.A.I.C.S.: 541511
Derrick Tam (*VP*)
Hamid Moinamin (*Founder, Pres &*
CEO)

INSERTECH, LLC.

711 Industrial Dr, Cary, IL 60013
Tel.: (847) 516-6184
Web Site: http://www.insertech.net
Sales Range: $10-24.9 Million
Emp.: 170
Plastics Product Mfr
N.A.I.C.S.: 326199
David Butt (*Pres & Founder*)

INSERVICE AMERICA INCOR-
PORATED

129 Vista Centre Dr, Forest, VA
24551
Tel.: (434) 316-7400
Web Site:
   http://www.inserviceamerica.com
Sales Range: $10-24.9 Million
Emp.: 399
Telemarketing Services
N.A.I.C.S.: 561422
Carl Townsend (*Pres*)
Tim Johnston (*Mgr-IT*)

INSIDE OUT COMMUNICA-
TIONS

24 Water St, Holliston, MA 01746
Tel.: (508) 429-8184
Web Site: http://www.iocomm.com
Year Founded: 1987
Sales Range: $10-24.9 Million

Emp.: 12
N.A.I.C.S.: 541810
Alicia Frick Laguarda (*Pres*)
Maria Stearns (*VP-Client Svcs*)
Rebecca Palmer (*Dir-Ops*)
Matt Lynch (*Dir-Creative*)

INSIDE SOURCE INC.

985 Industrial Rd Ste 101, San Car-
los, CA 94070
Tel.: (650) 508-9101
Web Site:
   http://www.insidesource.com
Sales Range: $25-49.9 Million
Emp.: 30
Office & Public Building Furniture
N.A.I.C.S.: 423210
David Denny (*Pres*)
Allison Crafts (*Project Mgr*)
Diane Walsh (*Project Mgr*)
Linda Wilson (*Mgr-Bus Dev*)
Stephanie Neutz (*Project Mgr*)
Gary Young (*Sr VP*)
Steve Haren (*Supvr-Acct*)
Robin Sedor (*Supvr-Acct*)
Tina Fong (*VP-Acct Dev*)
Lesley Duckworth (*VP-Acct Mgmt*)
Nancy Kusich (*VP-Market Dev*)
David Lombardi (*VP-Sls*)
Kristen Haren (*COO*)
Danielle Cogliati (*Coord-Acct*)

INSIDESALES.COM, INC.

34 E 1700 S Ste A113, Provo, UT
84606
Tel.: (801) 853-4090
Web Site: http://www.insidesales.com
Year Founded: 2004
Sales Range: $1-9.9 Million
Emp.: 170
Software Publisher & Marketing Con-
sulting Services
N.A.I.C.S.: 513210
David Elkington (*Co-Founder & CEO*)
Kenneth Krogue (*Co-Founder & Pres*)
Lindsey Armstrong (*COO*)
Tema Laussen (*Dir-Do Good Founda-*
tion)
Steve Brain (*Sr VP-Engrg*)
Jason Brickley (*VP-Talent Accelera-*
tion)
Martin Moran (*Sr VP-EMEA & Gen*
Mgr)
Chris Harrington (*COO*)

INSIDETRACK, INC.

150 Spear St Ste 900, San Fran-
cisco, CA 94105
Tel.: (415) 243-4440
Web Site: http://www.insidetrack.com
Year Founded: 2000
Sales Range: $10-24.9 Million
Emp.: 147
Success Coaching for College Stu-
dents
N.A.I.C.S.: 611710
Kai Drekmeier (*Co-Founder & Pres*)
Elena Wealty (*Controller*)
Chuck Kleiner (*Sr VP-Program Dev*)

INSIGHT EDITIONS, LP

800 A St, San Rafael, CA 94901
Tel.: (415) 526-1370   CA
Web Site: http://insighteditions.com
Book, Periodicals & Magazine Pub-
lisher
N.A.I.C.S.: 513130
Raoul Goff (*CEO*)
Michael Madden (*COO*)

Subsidiaries:

Weldon Owen, Inc.   **(1)**
814 Montgomery St, San Francisco, CA
94133
Tel.: (415) 291-0100
Web Site: http://www.weldonowen.com

Insight Editions, LP—(Continued)
Sales Range: $1-9.9 Million
Emp.: 40
Book Publishers
N.A.I.C.S.: 513130
Chris Hemesath (Dir-Production)
Terry Newell (CEO-US)
Roger Shaw (Pres & Publr)

INSIGHT EQUITY HOLDINGS LLC
1400 Civic Pl Ste 250, Southlake, TX 76092-7641
Tel.: (817) 488-7775　　　　　　**TX**
Web Site:
　http://www.insightequity.com
Sales Range: $1-4.9 Billion
Emp.: 27
Private Equity Firm
N.A.I.C.S.: 523999
Victor L. Vescovo (COO & Mng Partner)
Kevin Slaton (CFO)
Theodore W. Beneski (CEO & Mng Partner)
Warren B. Bonham (Partner)
Andrew Boisseau (Principal)
Jack Waterstreet (Partner)
Chris White (Dir-IR)
Dan Davidson (Sr VP-New York)
Lark Rayburn (Coord-Private Equity)
Alison Grimes (Controller)
Eliot E. Kerlin Jr. (Partner)

Subsidiaries:

A.P. Plasman, Inc.　　　　　　　　(1)
5245 Burke Street, Oldcastle, Windsor, N9G 0B9, ON, Canada
Tel.: (519) 737-6984
Web Site: https://plasman.com
Sales Range: $150-199.9 Million
Emp.: 1,000
Mfr of Exterior Trim & Plastic Injection Molding Parts for Automotive Industry
N.A.I.C.S.: 326199
Niklas Berntsson (Pres)
Tim Berezowski (VP)
Manuel Alejo (CFO)
Darrell Whitney (Chief HR Officer)
Tony Romanello (VP)
William Trapani (VP)
Peter Andersson (VP)
Stefan Jensen (VP)
Kristina Korsgren (VP)
Fredrik Olsson (VP)
Ole Tjeldflat (VP)
Anna Widerberg (VP)
Carl Roth (VP)

Subsidiary (Non-US):

Plastal Industri AB　　　　　　　　(2)
Lindholmspiren 9, S-417 56, Gothenburg, Sweden
Tel.: (46) 317617200
Web Site: http://www.plastal.com
Motor Vehicle Bumper System Mfr
N.A.I.C.S.: 336211
Thomas Comstedt (Dir-Pur)

Dustex LLC　　　　　　　　　　　(1)
60 Chastian Centre Blvd Ste 60, Kennesaw, GA 30144
Tel.: (770) 429-5575
Web Site: http://www.dustex.com
Sales Range: $10-24.9 Million
Emp.: 38
Air Purification Equipment
N.A.I.C.S.: 333413
Patrick Paul (Pres)

Subsidiary (Domestic):

Western Pneumatics, Inc.　　　　　(2)
110 N Seneca Rd, Eugene, OR 97402
Tel.: (541) 461-2600
Web Site: http://www.westernp.com
Sales Range: $10-24.9 Million
Emp.: 240
Air Pollution Control Equipment Mfr
N.A.I.C.S.: 333922
Bob Marshall (CEO)

Eddy Packing Co., Inc.　　　　　　(1)

404 Airport Rd, Yoakum, TX 77995
Tel.: (361) 293-2361
Web Site: http://www.eddypacking.com
Sales Range: $75-99.9 Million
Emp.: 200
Meat Product Production & Distribution Services
N.A.I.C.S.: 424470
Pauline Bosby (Dir-Customer Svc)
Linda Dolezal (Dir-Acctg)
Jerry Hollman (Plant Mgr)
Pete Ryholt (CFO)
Jim Reed (CEO)

MB Westfield, Inc.　　　　　　　　(1)
109 Apremont Way, Westfield, MA 01085-1303
Tel.: (413) 568-8676
Web Site:
　http://www.precisionholdingsllc.com
Sales Range: $100-124.9 Million
Emp.: 250
Mfr of Aircraft Components & Provider of Precision Machining Services
N.A.I.C.S.: 336412

Subsidiary (Domestic):

CalRAM, Inc.　　　　　　　　　　(2)
829 Via Alondra, Camarillo, CA 93012
Tel.: (805) 987-6205
Web Site: http://www.calraminc.com
Powder Metallurgy Part Mfr
N.A.I.C.S.: 332117
Duane Pekar (CEO)
Sean Treacy (VP-Sls & Mktg)
Shane Collins (Dir-Additive Mfg Programs)

Mid-State Machine Products, Inc.　(2)
83 Verti Dr, Winslow, ME 04901
Tel.: (207) 873-6136
Web Site: http://www.midstateusa.com
Sales Range: $25-49.9 Million
Emp.: 200
Mfr of Components & Assemblies
N.A.I.C.S.: 332710

Meadow Valley Corporation　　　　(1)
4602 E Thomas Rd, Phoenix, AZ 85018
Tel.: (602) 437-5400
Web Site: http://www.meadowvalley.com
Sales Range: $75-99.9 Million
Emp.: 100
Heavy Construction Contractor That Specializes In Structural Concrete Construction of Highway Bridges, Overpasses & Paving of Airport Runways; Construction Materials Supplier
N.A.I.C.S.: 237310
Kenneth D. Nelson (Chief Admin Officer)
Nicole R. Smith (Controller)
Grant E. Larson (VP-Bus Dev)
Norm Watkins (Dir-Safety)
Russ Versteeg (Dir-Info Svcs)
Ryan Evans (CFO)

Subsidiary (Domestic):

Meadow Valley Contractors Inc.　　(2)
4602 E Thomas Rd, Phoenix, AZ 85018
Tel.: (602) 437-5400
Web Site: http://www.meadowvalley.com
Roads, Bridges, Urban Freeways, Airport Runways & Other Transportation-Related Construction
N.A.I.C.S.: 237310

New Star Metals, Inc.　　　　　　(1)
835 McClintock Dr Ste 100, Burr Ridge, IL 60527
Tel.: (888) 603-1553
Web Site: http://www.newstarmetals.com
Emp.: 10
Steel Products Processing & Distr
N.A.I.C.S.: 332999
Patrick J. Murley (CEO)
Michael E. Noble (Chief Comml Officer & VP)
Alexi G. Touloumis (Dir-IT)
James L. Todd (Dir-Fin)

Panolam Industries International, Inc.　　　　　　　　　　　　　　(1)
20 Progress Dr, Shelton, CT 06484-6216
Tel.: (877) 726-6526
Web Site: http://www.panolam.com
Thermally Fused Melamine & HPL Mfr & Distr
N.A.I.C.S.: 321219

Jeff M. Muller (Chief Revenue Officer & Exec VP)
Nevin Caldwell (COO)
Peter Jones (CEO)

Saiia Construction, LLC　　　　　(1)
324 Commons Dr, Birmingham, AL 35209
Tel.: (205) 290-0400
Web Site: http://www.saiia.com
Sales Range: $100-124.9 Million
Emp.: 450
Excavation & Industrial Maintenance Services
N.A.I.C.S.: 238910
Joseph Saiia (Pres)

Virtex Enterprises LP　　　　　　(1)
12234 N IH-35 Bldg A, Austin, TX 78753
Tel.: (512) 835-6772
Web Site: http://www.virtex.us
Sales Range: $10-24.9 Million
Emp.: 100
Electronics Contract Manufacturing Services
N.A.I.C.S.: 334412
Brad Heath (CEO)
Jason Runge (Sr VP-Bus Dev)
Jeff Wanago (CFO)
Upinder Signh (Exec VP)
Eric Wichman (Gen Mgr)
Mike Montano (Gen Mgr)
Will Oliver (VP-Bus Dev Westren Region)
Rick Pelletier (VP & Gen Mgr-England)
Heidi Jackson (VP-Northeast Bus Dev)
Dana Pittman (Exec VP)
Dwayne Waller (Gen Mgr)

Subsidiary (Domestic):

MTI Electronics Inc.　　　　　　　(2)
W133 N5139 Campbell Dr, Menomonee Falls, WI 53051
Tel.: (262) 783-6080
Web Site: http://www.mtielectronics.com
Sales Range: $150-199.9 Million
Emp.: 175
Printed Circuit Boards
N.A.I.C.S.: 334412
Brad Heath (Pres & CEO)

PPI/Time Zero Inc.　　　　　　　(2)
11 Madison Rd, Fairfield, NJ 07004
Tel.: (973) 278-6500
Web Site: http://www.ppi-timezero.com
Sales Range: $10-24.9 Million
Emp.: 130
Printed Circuit Boards
N.A.I.C.S.: 334412
Dana Pittman (Pres & CEO)

Subsidiary (Domestic):

New Age Technologies, Inc.　　　(3)
527 Pleasent St Unit A, Attleboro, MA 02703
Tel.: (508) 226-6090
Web Site: http://www.newageems.com
Other Communication & Energy Wire Mfr
N.A.I.C.S.: 335929
Dan Amiralian (Gen Mgr)

Subsidiary (Domestic):

Precision Technology Inc.　　　　(2)
3601 E Plano Pkwy Ste 200, Plano, TX 75074
Tel.: (214) 343-0131
Web Site: http://www.ptiassembly.com
Electronic Design & Assembly
N.A.I.C.S.: 334419
Atul Patel (CFO)
Ketan Patel (Engr-Electronics)
Tim Poulin (Dir-Sls)
Gary Davis (VP-Sls)
Jay Clardy (Mgr-Pur)
Nick Robison (Engr-Test)
Chetan Gabani (Engr-Electronics)

INSIGHT HUMAN SERVICES
665 W 4th St, Winston Salem, NC 27101
Tel.: (336) 725-8389　　　　　　**NC**
Web Site: http://www.insightnc.org
Year Founded: 1974
Substance Abuse Rehabilitation Services
N.A.I.C.S.: 623220
James Harner (Dir-Clinical)
David Daggett (Chm)

Timothy P. Ronan (Sec)
Robin Lindner (VP-Comm)
Jeff Matkins (CEO)
Terri Fowler (VP-Prevention Svcs)
Michael Gray (VP-Justice Svcs)
John Reynolds (CFO)
Carleen Wood (VP-Justoce Svcs)
Selbert M. Wood Jr. (Chief Quality Control Officer)

INSIGHT INVESTMENTS LLC
611 Anton Blvd 7th Fl, Costa Mesa, CA 92626
Tel.: (714) 939-2300
Web Site:
　http://www.insightinvestments.com
Year Founded: 1987
Sales Range: $150-199.9 Million
Emp.: 264
Builds, Deploys & Manages Technology Systems for Data Management & Security Clients
N.A.I.C.S.: 519290
Richard Heard (Pres)
Dena Jurcik (Mgr-Comml Credit, IT & Medical Equipment Leasing)
Scott Sullivan (Exec VP)
Michael Dundon (VP-Bus Dev-Vendor Fin-Insight Fin Svcs)
Marc Pautz (Dir-Client)
Serkan Bektas (Head-Client Solutions Grp)
Sheryn Murray (COO)
Christopher Czaja (Pres)

INSIGHT MERCHANDISING, INC.
1000 Nolen Dr Ste 100, Grapevine, TX 76051
Tel.: (817) 424-9000
Web Site:
　http://www.insightmerchandising.com
Year Founded: 1996
Sales Range: $25-49.9 Million
Emp.: 125
Custom Store Fixtures & Displays
N.A.I.C.S.: 337215
Peter Rozes (Co-Owner & Pres)
Cody Phillips (Creative Dir)
Jeff Jones (Co-Owner)

INSIGHT OPTICAL MANUFACTURING CO.
285 W 74th Pl, Hialeah, FL 33014
Tel.: (305) 557-9004
Web Site: http://www.foreyes.com
Rev.: $27,800,000
Emp.: 700
Ophthalmic Goods
N.A.I.C.S.: 423460
Phillip Wolman (Pres)
Jeffrey Martin (VP)
Lauren Macleod (Chief Mktg Officer)
Andrea Kane (VP-Store Ops)

INSIGHT RESOURCE GROUP
3 Altarinda Rd Ste 301, Orinda, CA 94563
Tel.: (925) 254-4114　　　　　　**CA**
Web Site:
　http://www.insightresourcegroup.com
Year Founded: 2004
Sales Range: $1-9.9 Million
Emp.: 16
Brand Recognition & Market Share Services
N.A.I.C.S.: 561499
Christi Hutchison (Project Mgr)
Valerie Sison (Acct Mgr)
Eduardo Guardarramas (Project Mgr)

INSIGHT SOFTWARE, LLC
3050 Universal Blvd Ste 120, Weston, FL 33331-3528

Web Site:
   http://www.myvisionexpress.com
Year Founded: 2004
Sales Range: $1-9.9 Million
Emp.: 30
Software Designer & Developer for
The Eye Care Industry
N.A.I.C.S.: 513210
Vipul Katyal *(Pres)*
Jorge Torres *(Mgr-Sls & Mktg)*
Eduardo Martinez *(Mgr-Software Dev)*

INSIGHT SOURCING GROUP, INC.

5555 Triangle Pkwy Ste 310, Norcross, GA 30092
Tel.: (770) 446-9890
Web Site:
   http://www.insightsourcing.com
Year Founded: 2002
Rev.: $3,900,000
Emp.: 18
Business Support Services
N.A.I.C.S.: 561499
Brent Eiland *(Exec VP)*
Brian Houpt *(Sr VP)*
Jake Wojcik *(VP)*
Tom Beaty *(Founder & CEO)*

INSIGHT VENTURE MANAGEMENT, LLC

1114 Ave of the Americas 36th Fl,
New York, NY 10036
Tel.: (212) 230-9200   DE
Web Site:
   http://www.insightpartners.com
Year Founded: 1995
Equity Investment Firm
N.A.I.C.S.: 523999
Blair Flicker *(Gen Counsel & Mng Dir)*
Steve Rabin *(CTO)*
Hilary Gosher *(Mng Dir)*
Nikitas Koutoupes *(Mng Dir)*
Cian Cotter *(Mng Dir)*
Mark Lessing *(CFO & Mng Dir)*
Jeffrey Lieberman *(Mng Dir)*
Peter Sobiloff *(Mng Dir)*
Anika Agarwal *(Mng Dir)*
Matt Gatto *(Mng Dir)*
Rachel Geller *(Mng Dir)*
Kevin Hurth *(Mng Dir)*
Ian Sandler *(COO & Mng Dir)*
Michael Triplett *(Mng Dir)*
Lonne Jaffe *(Mng Dir)*
Peter Segall *(Mng Dir)*
Stu Phillips *(Mng Dir)*
Jason Ewell *(Operating Partner)*
Jenna Sigman *(Exec VP-Strategy)*
Ryan Hinkle *(Mng Dir)*
Adam Berger *(Mng Dir)*
Richard M. Wells *(Mng Dir)*
Justin Harrison *(Mng Partner)*
Jason Kustka *(Mng Dir)*
Deven Parekh *(Mng Dir)*
Deven Parekh *(Mng Dir)*

Subsidiaries:

Alteryx, Inc.   **(1)**
3347 Michelson Dr Ste 400, Irvine, CA 92612
Web Site: https://www.alteryx.com
Rev.: $970,000,000
Assets: $1,912,000,000
Liabilities: $1,722,000,000
Net Worth: $190,000,000
Earnings: ($179,000,000)
Emp.: 2,300
Fiscal Year-end: 12/31/2023
Data Analytics Software Developer
N.A.I.C.S.: 513210
Christopher Natali *(Interim CFO)*
Deven Parekh *(Partner-Insight)*
Boris Treskunov *(Partner-Insight)*
Amir Ravandoust *(Partner-Insight)*
Mark Anderson *(CEO)*
Edward P. Harding Jr. *(Founder)*

Subsidiary (Non-US):

Alteryx Czech Republic s.r.o.   **(2)**
Havlickova 1029/3, 110 00, Prague, Czech Republic
Tel.: (420) 777571433
Data Analytics & Software Publisher
N.A.I.C.S.: 513210

Alteryx GmbH   **(2)**
Tel.: (49) 8992561966
Web Site: http://www.alteryx.com
Data Analytics & Software Publisher
N.A.I.C.S.: 513210

Subsidiary (Domestic):

Lore IO, Inc.   **(2)**
100 S Murphy Ave Ste 200, Sunnyvale, CA 94086
Tel.: (408) 256-1521
Web Site: https://www.getlore.io
Computer Programming Services
N.A.I.C.S.: 541511
Digvijay Lamba *(CEO & Founder)*
Bill Chickering *(CTO)*
Steven Dozen *(Head-Marketing)*
Praveen Dua *(Head)*
Maurin Lenglart *(Head)*

Subsidiary (Non-US):

Trifacta GmbH   **(2)**
Neue Grunstrasse 17-18, 10179, Berlin, Germany
Tel.: (49) 22168943009
Software Services
N.A.I.C.S.: 541511

Subsidiary (Domestic):

Trifacta, Inc.   **(2)**
575 Market St 11th Fl, San Francisco, CA 94105
Tel.: (415) 226-4252
Web Site: https://www.trifacta.com
Data Processing Services
N.A.I.C.S.: 518210

Amber Road, Inc.   **(1)**
1 Meadowlands Plz, East Rutherford, NJ 07073
Tel.: (201) 935-8588
Web Site: http://www.amberroad.com
Rev.: $85,166,053
Assets: $100,102,977
Liabilities: $70,325,422
Net Worth: $29,777,555
Earnings: ($13,602,520)
Emp.: 699
Fiscal Year-end: 12/31/2018
Cloud-based Global Trade Management Services
N.A.I.C.S.: 541614
James W. Preuninger *(CEO)*
Stephanie J. Miles *(Sr VP-Comml Svcs)*
Nathan Pieri *(Chief Product Officer)*
Ty Bordner *(Sr VP-Mktg & Bus Dev)*
William J. Jackowski *(VP-Professional Svcs)*
Glenn T. Gorman *(CIO)*
Thomas E. Conway *(CFO)*
Kae-Por F. Chang *(Mng Dir-China)*
Claude Correll *(VP-Engrg-Global)*
Brad Holmstrom *(Gen Counsel)*
Albert C. Cooke III *(Sr VP & Mng Dir-EMEA)*

Subsidiary (Non-US):

Amber Road China, Ltd.   **(2)**
2/F Building 2 350 Xianxia Road, Shanghai, 200336, China
Tel.: (86) 2152896777
Web Site: http://www.cn.amberroad.com
Emp.: 55
Information Technology Services
N.A.I.C.S.: 519290
Kae-Por Chang *(Mng Dir)*

Amber Road Limited   **(2)**
Unit 1701-9 17/F Tower 1 Millennium City 1 388 Kwun Tong Road, Kwun Tong, China (Hong Kong)
Tel.: (852) 27881010
Software Development Services
N.A.I.C.S.: 541511

Amber Road Software Private, Ltd.   **(2)**
5th Floor 135 RMZ Titanium HAL Airport

Road, Varthur Hobli, Bengaluru, 560 017, Karnataka, India
Tel.: (91) 8067334000
Web Site: http://www.amber.com
Emp.: 300
Information Technology Services
N.A.I.C.S.: 519290
Sourabh Chandra *(Mng Dir)*

Branch (Domestic):

Amber Road, Inc.   **(2)**
701 Corporate Ctr Dr Ste 325, Raleigh, NC 27607
Tel.: (919) 468-3400
Web Site: http://www.amberroad.com
Sales Range: $10-24.9 Million
Emp.: 10
Global Multimode Supply Chain Visibility Solutions
N.A.I.C.S.: 541511
Michael Harrell *(Dir-Ops)*

Subsidiary (Non-US):

Japan ecVision Co., Ltd.   **(2)**
Shinagawa East One Tower 4F, 2-16-1 Konan Minato-ku, Tokyo, 108-0075, Japan
Tel.: (81) 368908240
Business Management Consulting Services
N.A.I.C.S.: 541611

ecVision (Shenzhen) Co. Ltd.   **(2)**
Unit 806-08 8/F Changhong Science & Tech Building, Keji South 12 Road Shenzhen High-Tech Industrial Park, Shenzhen, 518057, GuangDong, China
Tel.: (86) 75526995010
Business Management Consulting Services
N.A.I.C.S.: 541611
Emily Pan *(Engr-Software)*

Anaqua, Inc.   **(1)**
31 St James Ave Ste 1100, Boston, MA 02116
Tel.: (617) 375-6173
Web Site: http://www.anaqua.com
Software & Technology Development Services
N.A.I.C.S.: 513210
Vincent Brault *(VP-Sls-US)*
Jack A. Morgan *(Sr VP-Client Svcs)*
Denise Cheung *(VP-Product Mgmt)*
Steve Preston *(Sr VP-Mktg)*
Robert Romeo *(CEO)*
Justin Crotty *(COO)*
Gerard Borin *(Pres-ANAQUA Svcs)*
Jonathan Newcombe *(VP-Sls-Europe)*
Karen Taylor *(Gen Mgr-Asia Pacific)*
Amanda Hollis *(Mgr-PR)*
Dan Anderson *(VP & Gen Mgr)*

Subsidiary (Domestic):

Lecorpio, LLC   **(2)**
39300 Civic Ctr Dr Ste 390, Fremont, CA 94538
Tel.: (866) 841-4744
Web Site: http://www.lecorpio.com
Intellectual Property Management Software Developer, Publisher & Whslr
N.A.I.C.S.: 513210

SeeUnity Inc.   **(2)**
5255 Ronald Reagan Blvd Ste 100, Johnstown, CO 80534
Tel.: (970) 776-8300
Web Site: http://www.seeunity.com
Custom Computer Programming Services
N.A.I.C.S.: 541511
Ryan Bond *(Dir-Pro Svcs)*

Bullhorn, Inc.   **(1)**
100 Summer St 17th Fl, Boston, MA 02110
Tel.: (617) 478-9100
Web Site: http://www.bullhorn.com
Staffing & Recruiting Software Developer
N.A.I.C.S.: 541511
Arthur Papas *(Founder & CEO)*
Matt Fischer *(Pres & CTO)*
Gordon Burnes *(CMO)*
Brian Sylvester *(CFO)*
Jonathan Novich *(Sr VP-Product & Salesforce)*
Ryan Murphy *(Exec VP-Enterprise & Salesforce)*
Mike Restivo *(Chief Revenue Officer)*
Nina Eigerman *(Sr VP-Alliances & Bus Dev)*
J. R. Stricker *(Sr VP-Svcs & Support)*
Peter Linas *(Exec VP-Corp Dev-Intl)*

Kristin Machacek-Leary *(Chief People Officer)*
Richard Harrison *(Sr VP-Product-Executive Search)*
Anthony Meo *(Sr VP-Global Svcs)*
Jason Heilman *(Sr VP-Product-Automation & AI)*

Subsidiary (Domestic):

Jobscience, Inc.   **(2)**
160 Spear St Ste 1220, San Francisco, CA 94105
Tel.: (415) 777-1017
Cloud Based Software Services
N.A.I.C.S.: 541511

Sendouts LLC   **(2)**
200 S Hanley Rd Ste 710, Saint Louis, MO 63105
Tel.: (314) 862-6883
Web Site: http://www.sendouts.com
Sales Range: $25-49.9 Million
Emp.: 20
Staffing & Recruiting Software Developer
N.A.I.C.S.: 513210

CivicPlus, LLC   **(1)**
302 S 4th St Ste 500, Manhattan, KS 66502
Tel.: (888) 228-2233
Web Site: http://www.civicplus.com
Computer Programming Services
N.A.I.C.S.: 541511
William Eric Grant *(VP & Gen Mgr)*

Subsidiary (Domestic):

SeeClickFix, Inc.   **(2)**
770 Chapel St Fl 3, New Haven, CT 06510
Tel.: (203) 254-0777
Web Site: http://www.seeclickfix.com
Computer System Design Services
N.A.I.C.S.: 541512

CommerceHub, Inc.   **(1)**
201 Fuller Rd 6th Fl, Albany, NY 12203
Tel.: (518) 810-0700
Web Site: http://www.commercehub.com
Rev.: $111,121,000
Assets: $85,119,000
Liabilities: $30,572,000
Net Worth: $54,547,000
Earnings: $9,858,000
Emp.: 323
Fiscal Year-end: 12/31/2017
Holding Company; Commerce Network Software Publisher
N.A.I.C.S.: 551112
Francis Poore *(CEO)*
Richard Jones *(CTO)*
Michael Trimarchi *(CFO & Chief Comml Officer)*
John Hinkle *(CIO & Exec VP-Technical Ops)*
Douglas Wolfson *(Gen Counsel & Sec)*
Kathleen Conley *(Sr VP-Ops)*
Todd Johnson *(Pres)*
Ranjit Mulgaonkar *(VP & Gen Mgr-Marketplace & Adv Svcs)*

Subsidiary (Domestic):

ChannelAdvisor Corporation   **(2)**
3025 Carrington Mill Blvd, Morrisville, NC 27560
Tel.: (919) 228-4700
Web Site: http://www.channeladvisor.com
Rev.: $129,497,000
Assets: $239,972,000
Liabilities: $51,774,000
Net Worth: $188,198,000
Earnings: $47,215,000
Emp.: 846
Fiscal Year-end: 12/31/2021
E-Commerce Software
N.A.I.C.S.: 513210
Simon Clarkson *(Mng Dir-APAC)*
Steve Frechette *(VP-Product Mgmt)*
Randi Seran *(VP-Human Resources)*
Amy Rumford *(VP-Svcs-Global)*
Vladi Shlesman *(Mng Dir-EMEA)*
Jeremy Allen *(VP-FP&A & Ops)*
Kathy Twiddy *(Gen Counsel & Gen Counsel)*
Stephanie Levin *(VP-Human Resources)*

Subsidiary (Domestic):

CA Washington, LLC   **(3)**
2505 2nd Ave Ste 520, Seattle, WA 98121

Insight Venture Management, LLC—(Continued)

Tel.: (206) 654-4913
Software Design Services
N.A.I.C.S.: 541511

Subsidiary (Non-US):

ChannelAdvisor (AU) Pty Limited　(3)
Level 1 2 Stawell Street, Richmond, 3121,
VIC, Australia
Tel.: (61) 1300887239
Web Site: http://www.channeladvisor.com.au
Software Design Services
N.A.I.C.S.: 541511

**ChannelAdvisor (Shanghai) Informa-
tion Technology Co., Limited　(3)**
Room 1901 19/F Shanghai Times Square
Office Bldg 93 Huai Hai Zhong Rd, Shang-
hai, 200021, China
Tel.: (86) 21 6391 0887
Software Design Services
N.A.I.C.S.: 541511

ChannelAdvisor Asia-Pacific　(3)
Level 1 2 Stawell Street, Richmond, 3121,
VIC, Australia
Tel.: (61) 1300 887 239
Web Site: http://www.channeladvisor.com.au
E-Commerce Software
N.A.I.C.S.: 513210

**ChannelAdvisor Brasil Tecnologia
Ltda.　(3)**
R Porto Martins 546 &ar 2 Sala 3 Brooklin
Paulista, Sao Paulo, 04570-140, SP, Brazil
Tel.: (55) 1138868977
Software Design Services
N.A.I.C.S.: 541511

ChannelAdvisor EMEA　(3)
33 Kingsway, London, WC2B 6UF, United
Kingdom
Tel.: (44) 203 014 2700
Web Site: http://www.channeladvisor.co.uk
E-Commerce Software
N.A.I.C.S.: 513210

Division (Non-US):

ChannelAdvisor Germany　(4)
Kurfurstendamm 170, 10707, Berlin, Ger-
many
Tel.: (49) 30700173253
Web Site: http://www.channeladvisor.de
E-Commerce Software
N.A.I.C.S.: 513210

ChannelAdvisor Ireland　(4)
Block 1 International Science Centre Na-
tional Technology Park, Limerick, V94
C61W, Ireland
Tel.: (353) 61 261300
Web Site: http://www.channeladvisor.com
Emp.: 25
E-Commerce Software
N.A.I.C.S.: 513210

Subsidiary (Non-US):

ChannelAdvisor France　(3)
82 Rue d'Hauteville, 75010, Paris, France
Tel.: (33) 17 639 0221
Software Development Services
N.A.I.C.S.: 541511

ChannelAdvisor Ireland Limited　(3)
Block 1 International Science Centre Na-
tional Technology Park, Limerick, V94
C61W, Ireland
Tel.: (353) 61261300
Web Site: http://www.channeladvisor.com
Software Design Services
N.A.I.C.S.: 541511

ChannelAdvisor Spain S.L.　(3)
Paseo de la Castellana 95 Planta 8 Ed
Torre Europa, 28046, Madrid, Spain
Tel.: (34) 917498000
E Commerce Website Development Ser-
vices
N.A.I.C.S.: 541511

ChannelAdvisor UK Limited　(3)
33 Kingsway, London, WC2B 6UF, United
Kingdom
Tel.: (44) 203 014 2700
Web Site: http://www.channeladvisor.co.uk
Software Design Services
N.A.I.C.S.: 541511

Subsidiary (Domestic):

Commerce Technologies, LLC　(2)
201 Fuller Rd 6th Fl, Albany, NY 12203
Tel.: (518) 810-0700
Web Site: http://www.commercehub.com
Commerce Network Software Publisher
N.A.I.C.S.: 513210
Francis Poore (Co-Founder & CEO)
Richard Jones (Co-Founder & CTO)
John Hinkle (CIO & Exec VP-Technical
Ops)
Michael Trimarchi (CFO & Chief Comml Of-
ficer)
Douglas Wolfson (Gen Counsel & Sec)
Kathleen Conley (Sr VP-Ops)

Community Brands HoldCo, LLC　(1)
9620 Executive Ctr Dr N Ste 200, Saint Pe-
tersburg, FL 33702
Tel.: (727) 827-0046
Web Site: http://www.communitybrands.com
Holding Company
N.A.I.C.S.: 551112
Lars Powers (CTO)

Subsidiary (Domestic):

Abila, Inc.　(2)
10800 Pecan Park Blvd Ste 400, Austin, TX
78750
Tel.: (800) 647-3863
Web Site: http://www.abila.com
Management Software Solutions
N.A.I.C.S.: 513210

American Checked, LLC　(2)
601 S Boulder Ave 16th Fl, Tulsa, OK
74119
Tel.: (800) 975-9876
Web Site: http://www.americanchecked.com
Employment Agency
N.A.I.C.S.: 561311

Aptify　(2)
7900 Westpark Dr 5th Fl, Tysons Corner,
VA 22102
Tel.: (202) 223-2600
Web Site: http://www.aptify.com
Sales Range: $10-24.9 Million
Emp.: 100
Enterprise & E-Commerce Software Mfr
N.A.I.C.S.: 513210
Amith Nagarajan (Chm & CEO)
Andrew Crispino (Dir-R&D)
Robert Barnes (Dir-Aptify Australasia)
Kevin Friel (CFO)
Jennifer Barrell (Dir-Mktg)
Sandeep Shouche (Dir-R&D)
Mark Patterson (COO & Exec VP)
David Frick (Sr VP-Engagement)

Attendee Interactive, LLC　(2)
9620 Executive Ctr Dr N Ste 200, Saint Pe-
tersburg, FL 33702
Tel.: (888) 480-2031
Web Site:
http://www.attendeeinteractive.com
Custom Computer Programming Services
N.A.I.C.S.: 541511
J. Michael Tydings (Founder & Pres)

MobileCause, Inc.　(2)
27001 Agoura Rd Ste 350A, Calabasas, CA
91301
Tel.: (888) 661-8804
Web Site: http://www.mobilecause.com
Sales Range: $1-9.9 Million
Emp.: 69
Fundraising Software Development Ser-
vices
N.A.I.C.S.: 541511
Sean MacNeill (CEO)

Pathable, Inc.　(2)
4065 4th Ave NE, Seattle, WA 98105
Tel.: (503) 847-2753
Web Site: http://www.pathable.com
Software Publisher
N.A.I.C.S.: 513210
Peter Brown (CTO)
Matt Hodge (VP-Sls)
Jordan Schwartz (CEO)

YourMembership Inc.　(2)
9620 Executive Center Dr N Ste 200, Saint
Petersburg, FL 33702
Tel.: (727) 827-0046
Web Site: http://www.yourmembership.com

Sales Range: $1-9.9 Million
Emp.: 70
Membership & Association Software Pub-
lisher
N.A.I.C.S.: 513210
Greg T. Apple (CFO)
Chad M. Slager (Sr Dir-Bus Dev-YM Media
Div)
J. P. Guilbault (Pres & CEO)
Alastair Watson (VP-Revenue Ops)
Erlina Edwards (VP-HR & Org Dev)
Melea Blaskovich (VP-Strategic Partner-
ships & Market Dev)
Jim Cook (Dir-Career Svcs)
Vanessa Correa (Dir-Creative)
Blakley Echeverry (Dir-Bus Dev)
Matt Lee (Sr Dir-Product Mgmt)
David Mallinder (Dir-Sls-UK)
Tricia Noble (Dir-Talent Mgmt & HR)
Tara Pawlak (Dir-Customer Mktg)
Rick Rutherford (Dir-Indus Resource)
Christina Sansonetti (Dir-Channel Pro-
grams)
Pia Simeoni (Dir-Mktg-Demand Generation)
Patrice Cunningham (VP-Mktg)

Subsidiary (Domestic):

Affiniscape, Inc.　(3)
6200 Bridge Point Pkwy, Austin, TX 78730
Tel.: (512) 366-7100
Web Site: http://www.affiniscape.com
Data Processing, Technology & Marketing
Solutions
N.A.I.C.S.: 518210

CoreLogic, Inc.　(1)
40 Pacifica, Irvine, CA 92618
Tel.: (949) 214-1000
Web Site: http://www.corelogic.com
Rev.: $1,642,375,000
Assets: $4,283,222,000
Liabilities: $3,559,960,000
Net Worth: $723,262,000
Earnings: $301,355,000
Emp.: 5,300
Fiscal Year-end: 12/31/2020
Consumer, Financial & Property Information
Services
N.A.I.C.S.: 519290
James L. Balas (CFO)
Patrick L. Dodd (Pres, CEO, COO & Chief
Growth Officer)
Bob Frosell (CIO)
Aaron Henry (Chief Legal Officer & Sec)
Devi Mateti (Pres-Enterprise Entity Solu-
tions)
Waqas Cheema (Chief Transformation Offi-
cer)
Lisa Claes (Mng Dir-Intl)
WeiLing Jang (CMO)

Subsidiary (Non-US):

ACN 108 719 197 PTY LTD　(2)
L 1 1100 Waymouth St, Adelaide, 5000, SA,
Australia
Tel.: (61) 413491415
Emp.: 4
Real Estate Services
N.A.I.C.S.: 237210

ADL SOFTWARE PTY LTD　(2)
PO Box 364, Wilston, Brisbane, 4051, QLD,
Australia
Tel.: (61) 733671982
Web Site: http://www.adlsoftware.com
Software Development Services
N.A.I.C.S.: 541512

Subsidiary (Domestic):

Breakaway Holdings, LLC　(2)
14100 Parke-Long Ct Ste G, Chantilly, VA
20151
Tel.: (703) 953-3866
Web Site: http://www.homevisit.com
Marketing Services
N.A.I.C.S.: 541613
Greg Trzaska (Founder)

CDS Business Mapping, LLC　(2)
100 Riverview Ctr Ste 150, Middletown, CT
06457
Tel.: (617) 737-4444
Web Site: http://www.riskmeter.com
Digital Mapping Sales & Solutions
N.A.I.C.S.: 541370

Subsidiary (Non-US):

CORELOGIC NZ LIMITED　(2)

Level 2 275 Cuba St, Wellington, 6011,
New Zealand
Tel.: (64) 49156000
Web Site: http://www.corelogic.co.nz
Property Information & Geospatial Solution
Provider
N.A.I.C.S.: 531390
Nick Goodall (Head-Res)
Tom Coad (Head-Product)
Paul White (Head-SME)

Subsidiary (Domestic):

Closingcorp, Inc.　(2)
7817 Ivanhoe Ave, La Jolla, CA 92037
Tel.: (858) 551-1500
Web Site: http://www.closingcorp.com
Rev.: $2,900,000
Emp.: 37
Wired Telecommunications Carriers
N.A.I.C.S.: 517111
Anthony T. Farwell (Founder & Vice Chm)
James Bolger (CFO)
Kristin Henke (Sr Dir-Ops)
Debbie Day (COO)
Staffan Encrantz (Chm)
Matthew Lichtner (VP-Sls & Strategic Rela-
tionships)
Pat Carney (Chief Innovation Officer)
Bob Jennings (CEO)
Craig Austin (Sr VP-Sls & Bus Dev)
Dan Mugge (CTO)

Subsidiary (Non-US):

Cordell Information Pty Ltd　(2)
Level 10 10 Help Street, Chatswood, 2067,
NSW, Australia
Tel.: (61) 299345555
Web Site: http://www.cordellconnect.com.au
Emp.: 160
Engineeering Services
N.A.I.C.S.: 541330

Subsidiary (Domestic):

**CoreLogic Background Data,
LLC　(2)**
3001 Hackberry Rd, Irving, TX 75063
Tel.: (866) 234-4455
Real Estate Services
N.A.I.C.S.: 531390

CoreLogic Credco LLC　(2)
12395 1st American Way, Poway, CA
92064
Tel.: (619) 938-7012
Web Site: http://www.credco.com
Sales Range: $25-49.9 Million
Emp.: 100
Credit Reporting Services
N.A.I.C.S.: 561450

CoreLogic Flood Services, LLC　(2)
11902 Burnet Rd, Austin, TX 78758
Tel.: (512) 834-9595
Web Site: http://www.floodcert.com
Sales Range: $100-124.9 Million
Emp.: 400
Flood Insurance Coverage
N.A.I.C.S.: 524298

**CoreLogic National Background Data,
LLC　(2)**
PO Box 772277, Ocala, FL 34477-2277
Tel.: (352) 629-9904
Web Site:
http://www.nationalbackgrounddata.com
Sales Range: $50-74.9 Million
Criminal History Database Information Ser-
vices
N.A.I.C.S.: 513140

**CoreLogic REO Asset
Management　(2)**
40 Pacifica Ste 900, Irvine, CA 92618
Tel.: (949) 214-1000
Web Site: http://www.corelogic.com
Sales Range: $300-349.9 Million
Asset Disposition & Real Estate Manage-
ment Services
N.A.I.C.S.: 531210

**CoreLogic Rental Property Solutions,
LLC　(2)**
PO Box 509124, San Diego, CA 92150
Tel.: (888) 333-2413
Real Estate Services
N.A.I.C.S.: 531390

Subsidiary (Non-US):

CoreLogic SARL (2)
7 Rue Drouot, 75009, Paris, France
Tel.: (33) 144790101
Software Development Services
N.A.I.C.S.: 541512
Michel Voronkoff *(Mgr-Europe Modelling)*

Subsidiary (Domestic):

CoreLogic SafeRent, LLC (2)
11140 Rockville Pike, Rockville, MD 20852-3106
Tel.: (301) 881-3400
Web Site: http://www.fadvsaferent.com
Sales Range: $25-49.9 Million
Emp.: 100
Multifamily Housing Resident Screening Services
N.A.I.C.S.: 561611

Division (Domestic):

Jenark Business Systems, Inc. (3)
7300 Westmore Rd Ste 3, Rockville, MD 20850
Tel.: (301) 840-6292
Web Site: http://www.jenark.com
Sales Range: $100-124.9 Million
Property Management Software Developer
N.A.I.C.S.: 513210

Subsidiary (Non-US):

CoreLogic Solutions Limited (2)
6th Floor South Tower 26 Elmfield Road, Bromley, BR1 1WA, Kent, United Kingdom
Tel.: (44) 2082281288
Web Site:
http://www.corelogicsolutions.co.uk
Sales Range: Less than $1 Million
Emp.: 10
Automated Real Estate Valuation Products
N.A.I.C.S.: 531390

Subsidiary (Domestic):

CoreLogic Solutions, LLC (2)
40 Pacifica Ste 900, Irvine, CA 92618
Tel.: (949) 214-1000
Web Site: http://www.corelogic.com
Real Estate Investment Services
N.A.I.C.S.: 525990

CoreLogic Tax Collection Services, LLC (2)
1 CoreLogic Dr Bldg 4, Westlake, TX 76262
Tel.: (877) 442-2797
Real Estate Services
N.A.I.C.S.: 237210

CoreLogic Transportation Services (2)
94 Acoma Blvd S Ste 101, Lake Havasu City, AZ 86403
Tel.: (928) 680-9449
Web Site: http://www.fadvtransportation.com
Sales Range: $900-999.9 Million
Trucking Industry Credit Information Services
N.A.I.C.S.: 519290

Subsidiary (Non-US):

CoreLogic UK Limited (2)
Fore 2 2 Husklsson Way, Shirley, Solihull, B90 4SS, United Kingdom
Tel.: (44) 3331231414
Web Site: http://www.corelogic.uk
Residential Estate Management Services
N.A.I.C.S.: 531390
Jim Driver *(Mng Dir)*
David Driver *(Comml Dir)*
Mark Blackwell *(COO)*

Subsidiary (Domestic):

CoreLogic Valuation Services, LLC (2)
12395 1st American Way, Poway, CA 92064
Tel.: (619) 938-7078
Web Site: http://www.appraisals.com
Sales Range: $150-199.9 Million
Emp.: 185
Electronic Valuation Solutions for the Real Estate Industry
N.A.I.C.S.: 531320

CoreLogic Valuation Solutions, Inc. (2)
3256 Shetland Rd, Beavercreek, OH 45434
Tel.: (937) 671-1745
Real Estate Services
N.A.I.C.S.: 531390

DataQuick Information Systems, Inc. (2)
9530 Towne Centre Dr, San Diego, CA 92121
Tel.: (858) 597-3100
Web Site: http://www.dataquick.com
Real Estate Information Services
N.A.I.C.S.: 519290

Subsidiary (Domestic):

DataQuick Title LLC (3)
5700 Smetana Dr Ste 300, Minnetonka, MN 55343
Tel.: (952) 933-8804
Web Site: http://www.dataquicktitle.com
Title Insurance Products & Services
N.A.I.C.S.: 524127

Subsidiary (Non-US):

ECMK Limited (2)
Fore 2 2 Husklsson Way, Shirley, Solihull, B90 4SS, United Kingdom
Tel.: (44) 3331231418
Web Site: http://www.ecmk.co.uk
Accreditation Training Services
N.A.I.C.S.: 611519
Joe Mellon *(Dir-Comml)*
Stephen Farrow *(Mgr-Accreditation Scheme)*
Rob Cartwright *(Product Dir-Energy Solutions)*

Subsidiary (Domestic):

FNC, Inc. (2)
1214 Ofc Park Dr, Oxford, MS 38655
Tel.: (662) 236-2020
Web Site: http://www.fncinc.com
Real Estate Collateral Information Software Publisher
N.A.I.C.S.: 513210
Greg Dennis *(Exec VP-Ops)*
Michael Mitchell *(Chief Strategy Officer & Dir-Bus Dev)*
Kimberly Taylor *(Dir-Support Ops)*
Gwen Knight *(Mgr-Customer Support)*
Pat Brown *(Mgr-Contracts & Reporting)*
Bethany Cooper *(Partner-HR Bus & Coord-Corp Recruitment & Talent)*

Finiti Group, LLC (2)
7090 Samuel Morse Dr, Columbia, MD 21046-3442
Tel.: (443) 259-1000
Real Estate Investment Services
N.A.I.C.S.: 525990

Subsidiary (Non-US):

Intersect (2)
30 Adelaide St E, Toronto, M5C 3G8, ON, Canada
Tel.: (416) 924-2784
Web Site: http://www.weareintersect.com
Mobile Application Development Services
N.A.I.C.S.: 541511

Subsidiary (Domestic):

Location Inc. Group Corporation (2)
120 Front St Ste 420, Worcester, MA 01608
Tel.: (508) 753-8029
Web Site: http://locationinc.com
Risk Management Software Development Services
N.A.I.C.S.: 541511
Andrew Schiller *(Chm & CEO)*
Andy Couture *(VP-Sls)*
Chris Kokkinos *(VP-Product Dev)*
Paul Gallagher *(Dir-Mktg)*

Marshall & Swift/Boeckh, LLC (2)
10001 W Innovation Dr Ste 102, Milwaukee, WI 53226
Tel.: (262) 780-2800
Web Site: http://www.msbinfo.com
Sales Range: $25-49.9 Million
Emp.: 350
Residential & Commercial Property Valuation Products & Services
N.A.I.C.S.: 531390

Mercury Network, LLC (2)
501D NE 122nd St, Oklahoma City, OK 73114
Tel.: (405) 300-1450
Web Site: http://www.mercuryvmp.com
Management Software Provider
N.A.I.C.S.: 513210

Subsidiary (Domestic):

Platinum Data Solutions, Inc. (3)
12 Journey Ste 200, Aliso Viejo, CA 92656-5335
Tel.: (888) 794-0455
Web Site: http://www.platdata.com
Business Services Technology Providers
N.A.I.C.S.: 561499

Subsidiary (Domestic):

National Tax Search, LLC (2)
130 S Jefferson St Ste 300, Chicago, IL 60601
Tel.: (800) 426-7466
Web Site: http://www.nationaltaxsearch.com
Real Estate Consulting Service
N.A.I.C.S.: 531210

Next Gear Solutions, LLC (2)
304 Heritage Dr Ste 2, Oxford, MS 38655
Tel.: (866) 769-7855
Web Site: http://www.nextgearsolutions.com
Restoration Company Consulting Services & Management Software
N.A.I.C.S.: 513210

Subsidiary (Domestic):

Accurence, Inc. (3)
305 S Arthur Ave, Louisville, CO 80027
Tel.: (303) 500-5799
Web Site: http://www.accurence.com
Smart Property Insurance Services
N.A.I.C.S.: 513210

Subsidiary (Non-US):

REALTOR.COM.AU PTY LTD (2)
L 21 2 Market St, Sydney, 2000, NSW, Australia
Tel.: (61) 731149999
Web Site: http://www.corelogic.com.au
Emp.: 300
Real Estate Services
N.A.I.C.S.: 531210

Subsidiary (Domestic):

RELS, LLC (2)
8009 34th Ave S Ste 1300, Minneapolis, MN 55425
Tel.: (952) 933-8804
Real Estate Asset Valuation & Appraisal Services
N.A.I.C.S.: 531320

RES Direct, LLC (2)
8009 34th Ave S Ste 500, Bloomington, MN 55425-1616
Tel.: (952) 876-4300
Real Estate Investment Services
N.A.I.C.S.: 525990

Subsidiary (Non-US):

RP DATA NEW ZEALAND LIMITED (2)
Level 2 275 Cuba Street, PO Box 4072, Wellington, 6140, New Zealand
Tel.: (64) 800355355
Web Site: http://www.rpnz.co.nz
Real Estate Information Provider
N.A.I.C.S.: 531390

RP DATA VALUATION SERVICES PTY LTD (2)
Burwood Road 529, Hawthorn East, Melbourne, 3122, VIC, Australia
Tel.: (61) 388033199
Information Management Services
N.A.I.C.S.: 513199

RP Data Limited (2)
6 Eagleview Place, Eagle Farm, 4009, QLD, Australia
Tel.: (61) 731149999
Web Site: http://www.rpdata.com
Sales Range: $50-74.9 Million
Emp.: 350
Online Real Estate Information Services
N.A.I.C.S.: 531390

Subsidiary (Domestic):

Symbility Solutions Corp. (2)
Ste 200 100 Country Club Dr, Hendersonville, TN 37075
Risk Management Software Development Services
N.A.I.C.S.: 541511
Jeff Brinkman *(Sr VP-Client Dev)*

Subsidiary (Non-US):

Symbility Solutions GmbH (2)
Stammheimer Strasse 10, 70806, Kornwestheim, Germany
Tel.: (49) 621232010
Risk Management Software Development Services
N.A.I.C.S.: 541511

Symbility Solutions Limited (2)
The Old Stables Home Farm Cams Hall Estate, Fareham, PO16 8UT, Hampshire, United Kingdom
Tel.: (44) 3303801282
Risk Management Software Development Services
N.A.I.C.S.: 541511
Michael Porter *(Sr VP-Intl Markets)*

Symbility Solutions, Inc. (2)
30 Adelaide St E Ste 500, Toronto, M5C 3G8, ON, Canada
Tel.: (647) 775-8600
Web Site:
https://www.symbilitysolutions.com
Rev.: $25,513,981
Assets: $30,247,319
Liabilities: $6,846,691
Net Worth: $23,400,628
Earnings: ($76,473)
Emp.: 174
Fiscal Year-end: 12/31/2017
Software Development Services
N.A.I.C.S.: 513210

Subsidiary (Domestic):

Automated Benefits Inc. (3)
111 Peter Street Suite 901, Toronto, M5V 2H1, ON, Canada
Tel.: (416) 359-9339
Web Site: http://www.adjudicare.com
Health & Dental Claim Software Development Services
N.A.I.C.S.: 541511

Symbility Solutions Inc. (3)
30 Adelaide E Suite 500, Toronto, M5C 3G8, ON, Canada
Tel.: (866) 796-2454
Web Site: http://www.symbilitysolutions.com
Insurance Software Development Services
N.A.I.C.S.: 541511

Subsidiary (Domestic):

a la mode, Inc. (2)
3705 West Memorial 402, Salt Lake City, UT 73134
Tel.: (405) 359-6587
Web Site: http://www.alamode.com
Real Estate Software
N.A.I.C.S.: 513210

Subsidiary (Non-US):

eTech Solutions Limited (2)
Fore 2 2 Husklsson Way Shirley, Solihull, B90 4SS, United Kingdom
Tel.: (44) 3331231414
Web Site: http://www.etech.net
Emp.: 120
Real Estate Services
N.A.I.C.S.: 531390

Diligent Corporation (1)
1385 Broadway 19th Fl, New York, NY 10018
Tel.: (212) 741-8181
Web Site: http://www.diligent.com
Sales Range: $75-99.9 Million
Emp.: 500
Online Software Application Development Services
N.A.I.C.S.: 513210
Alessandro Sodi *(Founder, Chief Product Strategy Officer & Exec Dir)*
Al Percival *(Mng Dir-Australia & New Zealand)*
Charlie Horrell *(Mng Dir-EMEA)*

Insight Venture Management, LLC—(Continued)

Jeffrey Hilk *(Chief Revenue Officer)*
Brian Stafford *(CEO)*
Michael Stanton *(CFO)*
Amanda Carty *(CMO)*
Avigail Dadone *(Chief People Officer)*
Jack Van Arsdale *(VP-Legal)*
Marco Morsella *(Sr VP-Product Design)*
Ken Surdan *(Chief Product Officer)*
Matthew DiGuiseppe *(VP-Res & ESG)*
Ricardo Moreno *(Sr VP-Partnerships-Worldwide)*
Michael Flickman *(CTO)*
Nithya B. Das *(Chief Legal Officer & Chief Admin Officer)*

Subsidiary (Non-US):

ACL Services Ltd.   **(2)**
Suite 1500 980 Howe St, Vancouver, V6Z
0C8, BC, Canada
Tel.: (604) 669-4225
Web Site: http://www.wegalvanize.com
Software Services
N.A.I.C.S.: 513210
Laurie Schultz *(Pres & CEO)*
Keith Cerny *(CTO)*
Sean Zuberbier *(Chief Revenue Officer)*
Dan Zitting *(Chief Product Officer)*
Stephen Thurley *(Mng Dir-Asia-Pacific)*
Anthony Fernandez *(Dir-Data Driven GRC Consulting)*
Ian Halliday-Pegg *(Mng Dir-EMEA)*

Dotmatics, Inc   **(1)**
225 Franklin St 26th fl, Boston, MA 02110.
Tel.: (858) 552-8900
Web Site: https://www.dotmatics.com
Emp.: 405
Software Devolopment
N.A.I.C.S.: 513210
Thomas Swalla *(CEO)*

Subsidiary (Domestic):

SoftGenetics, LLC   **(2)**
100 Oakwood Ave Ste 350, State College,
PA 16803
Tel.: (814) 237-9340
Web Site: http://www.softgenetics.com
Software Publisher
N.A.I.C.S.: 513210
Jonathan Liu *(VP-Dev)*

E2open Parent Holdings, Inc.   **(1)**
9600 Great Hills Trl Ste 300E, Austin, TX
78759
Tel.: (512) 343-8727
Web Site: http://www.e2open.com
Rev.: $652,215,000
Assets: $4,400,175,000
Liabilities: $1,673,255,000
Net Worth: $2,726,920,000
Earnings: ($648,703,000)
Emp.: 4,017
Fiscal Year-end: 02/28/2023
Computer Software Services; Supply Chain
Management
N.A.I.C.S.: 541512
Ronald P. Kubera *(Pres-Distr)*
Andrew M. Appel *(CEO)*
Jennifer S. Grafton *(Gen Counsel, Sec & Exec VP)*
David J. Kenneson *(Pres-Mfg)*
Greg Randolph *(Chief Comml Officer)*
Marje Armstrong *(CFO)*
Kristin Seigworth *(VP-Comm)*
Greg Randolph *(Chief Comml Officer)*
Chinh Chu *(Chm)*

Subsidiary (Non-US):

E2open AG   **(2)**
An der Raumfabrik 31a, 76227, Karlsruhe,
Germany
Tel.: (49) 721 7900 8700
Web Site: http://www.e2open.com
Software Publisher
N.A.I.C.S.: 513210
Michael Lindner *(VP & Gen Mgr-EMEA)*

E2open China   **(2)**
12F Platinum Building 233 Tai Cang Road,
Shanghai, 200020, China
Tel.: (86) 21 5175 7788
Web Site: http://www.e2open.com
Software Publisher
N.A.I.C.S.: 513210

E2open Ltd.   **(2)**

Merlin House Brunel Road, Theale, Reading, RG7 4AB, United Kingdom
Tel.: (44) 118 902 6985
Web Site: http://www.e2open.com
Software Publisher
N.A.I.C.S.: 513210
Michael Sarkis *(CEO)*

E2open Malaysia   **(2)**
Level 17 Faber Imperial Court, Jalan Sultan
Ismail, Kuala Lumpur, 50250, Malaysia
Tel.: (60) 3 2025 6300
Web Site: http://www.e2open.com
Software Publisher
N.A.I.C.S.: 513210

Subsidiary (Domestic):

E2open, LLC   **(2)**
9600 Great Hills Trl Ste 300E, Austin, TX
78759
Tel.: (512) 425-3500
Web Site: http://www.e2open.com
Software Publisher
N.A.I.C.S.: 513210
Stephen Maurice Ward Jr. *(Co-Founder)*
Michael Farlekas *(CEO)*
Santosh Nanda *(Gen Mgr-Logistics Svc Providers Bus Unit)*
Joe Olson *(Exec VP)*
Pawan Joshi *(Exec VP-Product Mgmt & Strategy)*
Debbie Smith *(Exec VP-HR & Training)*
Jarett Janik *(CFO)*
Mike Verdeyen *(Exec VP-Product Dev & Infractructure)*
Laura L. Fese *(Gen Counsel & Exec VP)*
Michael Lindner *(Gen Mgr-Intl Bus Unit)*
Ron Kubera *(Gen Mgr-Discrete Indus Bus Unit)*
Bill Jackowski *(Gen Mgr-Process Indus Bus Unit)*
Azza Hararah *(Sr VP-Field Ops)*
Shane Martin *(Gen Mgr-CDOC & Cloud Logistics Bus Unit)*
Jeffrey K. Stouder *(VP & Controller-Global)*
Kari Janavitz *(CMO)*
Diane Mitchell *(VP-Mktg)*

Entomo, Inc.   **(2)**
9600 Great Hills Trl Ste 300E, Austin, TX
78759
Tel.: (512) 425-3500
Software Publisher
N.A.I.C.S.: 513210

INTTRA, Inc.   **(2)**
1 Upper Pond Rd, Parsippany, NJ 07054
Tel.: (973) 263-5100
Web Site: http://www.inttra.com
Rev.: $37,504,000
Shipping Management & Logistics Software
Developer
N.A.I.C.S.: 513210
Jeffrey E. Ganek *(Chm)*
Paul Mullins *(Sr VP-Global Sls)*
Bill Schwebel *(Pres-Data)*
Peter Ludvigsen *(Sr VP-European Bus Dev)*
Jeff White *(CFO & Head-Strategy)*
Philly Teixeira *(Pres-EMEA)*
Vijay Minocha *(Pres-Asia Pacific)*
Andrew Porter *(Gen Counsel & Sr VP)*

Orchestro Inc.   **(2)**
4330 E West Highway Suite 1120A,
Bethesda, MD 20814   **(100%)**
Tel.: (703) 640-3300
Web Site: http://www.orchestro.com
Sales Range: $1-9.9 Million
Emp.: 200
Offers Demand Execution Management
Software in Consumer-Driven Supply Chain
Systems
N.A.I.C.S.: 541511
Kevin McCurdy *(Co-Founder & VP-Strategic Accts)*
P. V. Boccasam *(CEO)*
Anuj Agrawal *(VP-Mktg)*
Manoj Joshi *(VP-Data Platform)*
Pranav Mundi *(VP-India Product Ops)*

EPiServer Group AB   **(1)**
Regeringsgatan 67, PO Box 7007, Stockholm, 103 86, Sweden
Tel.: (46) 855582700
Web Site: http://www.episerver.com
Web Content Management Services
N.A.I.C.S.: 513210
Alex Atzberger *(CEO)*
Myles Johnson *(CFO & Exec VP)*

Chad Wolf *(Chief Customer & Sls Officer)*
Jessica Fardin *(CMO & Sr VP)*
Fredrik Tjarnberg *(Sr VP-Engrg)*
Cliff Hill *(Sr VP-EMEA & APAC Sls)*
Dean Read *(Sr VP-America Sls)*
Justin Anovick *(Chief Product Officer)*
Peter Yeung *(VP & Gen Counsel)*
Sue Bergamo *(CIO, Chief Security Officer & VP)*
Laura Thiele *(Chief People Officer)*

Subsidiary (US):

EPiServer Inc.   **(2)**
542 Amherst St, Nashua, NH 03063
Tel.: (603) 594-0249
Web Site: http://www.episerver.com
Sales Range: $25-49.9 Million
Emp.: 270
Web Content Management Software & Services
N.A.I.C.S.: 518210
Adam Berger *(Chm)*
Myles Johnson *(CFO & Exec VP)*
Chad Wolf *(Chief Customer & Sls Officer & Exec VP)*
Virginia Frazer *(Chief People Officer & VP)*
Jessica Fardin *(Chief Mktg Officer & Sr VP)*
Dean Read *(Sr VP-Sls)*
Fredrik Tjarnberg *(Sr VP-Engrg)*
Sue Bergamo *(CIO, Chief Security Officer & VP)*
Kirsten Allegri Williams *(CMO)*

Subsidiary (Non-US):

EPiServer Pty. Ltd.   **(2)**
Suite 703 Level 7 No 1 Pacific Highway,
North Sydney, 2060, NSW, Australia
Tel.: (61) 2 9248 7222
Web Site: http://www.episerver.com
Emp.: 9
Holding Company; Web Content Management Software & Services
N.A.I.C.S.: 551112

Subsidiary (Domestic):

EPiServer Australia Pty. Ltd.   **(3)**
Suite 703 Level 7 No 1 Pacific Highway,
North Sydney, 2060, Australia
Tel.: (61) 2 9248 7222
Web Site: http://www.episerver.com
Emp.: 10
Web Content Management Software & Services
N.A.I.C.S.: 518210
Natalia Gamarra *(Gen Mgr)*

Subsidiary (US):

Insite Software Solutions, Inc.   **(2)**
110 N 5th St, Minneapolis, MN 55403
Shipping Solutions Software Publisher
N.A.I.C.S.: 513210

Optimizely, Inc.   **(2)**
631 Howard St Ste 100, San Francisco, CA
94105
Tel.: (415) 495-6546
Web Site: http://www.optimizely.com
Wired Telecommunications Carriers
N.A.I.C.S.: 517111
Pete Koomen *(Co-Founder)*
Jay Larson *(CEO)*
Dan Siroker *(Co-Founder & Chm)*
Carl Tsukahara *(CMO)*
Eric Anderson *(Chief Revenue Officer)*
Jo Ann Sanders *(VP-Product Mktg)*

Subsidiary (Domestic):

NewsCred, Inc.   **(3)**
386 Park Ave S 6, New York, NY 10016
Tel.: (212) 989-4100
Content Marketing & Syndication Services
N.A.I.C.S.: 513199

EveryAction, Inc.   **(1)**
1445 New York Ave NW, Washington, DC
20005
Tel.: (202) 686-9330
Web Site: http://www.everyaction.com
Sales Range: $25-49.9 Million
Software Development Services
N.A.I.C.S.: 541511
Stu Trevelyan *(CEO)*
Aaron Levine *(CFO)*
Amy Kim *(Chief Revenue Officer)*
John Lee *(CTO)*
Melissa Wyers *(Exec Dir)*

Subsidiary (Domestic):

GiveGab Inc.   **(2)**
401 E State St Ste 100, Ithaca, NY 14850
Tel.: (570) 313-6724
Web Site: http://www.givegab.com
Computer Software Publisher
N.A.I.C.S.: 513210
Charlie Mulligan *(CEO)*

Salsa Labs, Inc.   **(2)**
7920 Norfolk Ave #550, Bethesda, MD
20814
Tel.: (202) 318-2402
Web Site: http://www.salsalabs.com
Software Publisher
N.A.I.C.S.: 513210
Bill Donnelly *(Pres)*

FireMon LLC   **(1)**
8400 W 110th St Ste 500, Overland Park,
KS 66210
Tel.: (913) 948-9570
Web Site: http://www.firemon.com
Enterprise Security Management Solutions
N.A.I.C.S.: 513210
Donald Klumb *(CFO)*
Satin H. Mirchandani *(Pres)*
Jim Weakley *(Sr VP-Global Svcs)*
Andrew Warren *(VP-Global Channel Sls)*
Charles Gold *(CMO)*
Jim Birmingham *(Sr VP-Engrg)*
Brian Keets *(Chief Revenue Officer)*
Nicole Stavroff *(VP-Worldwide Channels)*
Jody Brazil *(CEO)*

Subsidiary (Domestic):

Lumeta Corp.   **(2)**
220 Davidson Ave Fl 4, Somerset, NJ
08873
Tel.: (732) 357-3500
Network Security
N.A.I.C.S.: 541519
Reggie Best *(Pres)*

Kaseya LLC   **(1)**
160 Spear St Ste 1220, San Francisco, CA
94105-1546
Tel.: (415) 694-5700
Web Site: http://www.kaseya.com
Custom Computer Programming Services
N.A.I.C.S.: 541511
Alex Cuevas *(Chief Customer Officer)*

Subsidiary (Domestic):

Datto Holding Corp.   **(2)**
101 Merritt 7 7th Fl, Norwalk, CT 06851
Web Site: https://www.datto.com
Rev.: $618,657,000
Assets: $1,962,191,000
Liabilities: $150,249,000
Net Worth: $1,811,942,000
Earnings: $51,434,000
Emp.: 2,089
Fiscal Year-end: 12/31/2021
Holding Company
N.A.I.C.S.: 551112
Sanjay Singh *(Chief Revenue Officer)*
John Abbot *(CFO)*
Bill Severance *(Chief Acctg Officer)*
Mark Clayton *(VP-Asia Pacific)*

Subsidiary (Domestic):

Backupify, Inc.   **(3)**
50 Milk St Fl 13, Boston, MA 02110
Tel.: (475) 288-1818
Web Site: https://www.backupify.com
Data Backup & Storage Services
N.A.I.C.S.: 518210

Subsidiary (Non-US):

Datto AsiaPac Pty. Ltd.   **(3)**
Level 25 161 Sussex Street, Sydney, 2000,
NSW, Australia
Tel.: (61) 296968190
IT Services
N.A.I.C.S.: 541519

Datto Canada Enterprises, Inc.   **(3)**
300 Town Centre Blvd 100, Markham, L3R
5Z6, ON, Canada
IT Services
N.A.I.C.S.: 541519

Datto GmbH   **(3)**
Landwehrstrasse 61, 80336, Munich, Germany

Tel.: (49) 8938036700
IT Services
N.A.I.C.S.: 541519

Datto Nederland B.V. (3)
101 Barbara Strozzilaan 101, 1083 HN, Amsterdam, Netherlands
Tel.: (31) 208886100
IT Services
N.A.I.C.S.: 541519

Datto Singapore Pte. Ltd. (3)
Suite 08-121 9 Battery Road, Singapore, 049910, Singapore
Tel.: (65) 31586291
IT Services
N.A.I.C.S.: 541519

Subsidiary (Non-US):

ITG Software Inc. (2)
700 128 West Pender St, Vancouver, V6B 1R8, BC, Canada
Tel.: (604) 449-2240
Computer Software Services
N.A.I.C.S.: 541512
Nadir Merchant *(CTO & Gen Mgr)*
Alex Ford *(VP)*
Amanda Luong *(VP)*

Subsidiary (US):

TruMethods, LLC (3)
66 E Main St Ste H, Moorestown, NJ 08057
Tel.: (856) 316-4900
Web Site: http://www.trumethods.com
Information Technology Consulting Services
N.A.I.C.S.: 541512
Susan Pica *(VP-Ops)*
Bob Penland *(CTO)*
Tim Fitzpatrick *(Dir-Bus Dev)*
Gary Pica *(Founder & Pres)*

Subsidiary (Domestic):

Zyrion, Inc. (3)
440 N Wolfe Rd, Sunnyvale, CA 94085
Tel.: (408) 524-7424
Web Site: http://www.zyrion.com
Sales Range: $25-49.9 Million
Emp.: 20
Cloud & IT Infrastructure Monitoring Software Developer
N.A.I.C.S.: 513210

Logistyx Technologies, LLC (1)
1701 Golf Rd Ste 1-1100, Rolling Meadows, IL 60008
Tel.: (877) 755-2374
Web Site: http://www.logistyx.com
Logistics & Supply Chain
N.A.I.C.S.: 541614
Geoffrey Finlay *(CEO)*
Ken Fleming *(Pres & Chief Sls Officer)*
John Berg *(VP-Strategic Alliances)*
Alain Breillatt *(VP-Product Mktg)*
Paul Homer *(Sls Mgr-UK & Ireland)*
Dipti Gupta *(COO)*
Jit Kulkarni *(CFO)*

Resolve Systems, LLC (1)
2302 Martin St Ste 300, Irvine, CA 92612
Tel.: (949) 325-0120
Web Site: http://www.resolvesystems.com
IT Process Automation Software Developer
N.A.I.C.S.: 513210
Scott Brown *(VP-Pro Svcs & Support-Worldwide)*
Larry Lien *(Chief Product Officer)*
Paul Gibson *(Gen Counsel)*
Peter Biber *(Sr VP-Customer Success)*
Philip Vorobeychik *(VP)*
Tammy Amini *(VP-Fin)*
Tim Simeonov *(VP-Engrg)*
Zahi Yaari *(VP-Sls-Worldwide)*
Vijay Kurkal *(CEO)*
Marin Sakhri *(VP-Mktg)*
Natalie Padula *(VP-Sls)*
Emmet B. Keeffe III *(Partner-Venture)*

S R Labs, LLC (1)
11 Broadway Ste 732, New York, NY 10004
Tel.: (917) 478-1243
Web Site: http://www.srtechlabs.com
Electronic Trading Services for Financial Industry
N.A.I.C.S.: 519290
Aaron Wald *(CTO)*
Jennifer Nayar *(CEO)*

Rob Lane *(Head-Sls & Bus Dev & Gen Mgr-London)*
Ian McIntyre *(COO)*
Christopher Nagy *(CFO)*
Mehul Shaha *(CTO)*

Subsidiary (Domestic):

Wombat Financial Software, Inc. (2)
55 Broad St 13th Fl, New York, NY 10004
Tel.: (212) 461-3222
Emp.: 175
Developer of Stock Market Data Software
N.A.I.C.S.: 513210
Dave Augenstein *(Head-Pro Svcs)*

Unitrends, Inc. (1)
7 Technology Cir Ste 100, Columbia, SC 29203
Tel.: (803) 454-0300
Web Site: http://www.unitrends.com
Sales Range: $25-49.9 Million
Emp.: 230
Data Protection & Recovery Systems
N.A.I.C.S.: 541519
Mark Campbell *(CTO)*
Joe Balazs *(VP-Engrg & Mfg)*
Bradley T. Miller *(CFO)*
Dave LeClair *(VP-Product Mktg)*
Steve Muddiman *(CMO)*
Stacey Comito *(Dir-Mktg Comm)*
Paul Brady *(CEO)*
Mike Dalton *(Sr VP-Worldwide Channels & Intl Field Ops)*

Veeam Software Group GmbH (1)
Linden Park Lindenstr 16, Baar, 6340, Switzerland
Tel.: (41) 766 71 31
Web Site: http://www.veeam.com
Sales Range: $125-149.9 Million
Emp.: 1,000
Backup, Replication & Virtualization Management Solutions
N.A.I.C.S.: 513210
Ratmir Timashev *(Co-Founder & Exec VP-Sls & Mktg)*
William H. Largent *(Chm)*
Kevin Rooney *(VP-Channel Sls-North America)*
Claude Schuck *(Mgr-Middle East & Central Africa)*
Gregg Petersen *(VP-Sls-Middle East & Africa)*
Jim Tedesco *(Sr VP-Sls-North America)*
Heidi Monroe Kroft *(Dir-PR)*
Andrei Baronov *(Co-Founder)*
Shaun McLagan *(Sr VP-Asia Pacific & Japan)*
Gary Mitchell *(VP-Australia & New Zealand)*
Sandeep Bhambure *(Mng Dir/VP-India & SAARC)*
Dave Russell *(VP-Enterprise Strategy)*
Kate Mollett *(Mgr-South Africa)*
Amarish Karnik *(Dir-Channel-India & SAARC)*
Belinda Jurisic *(Dir-Channel-Asia Pacific & Japan)*
Shiva Pillay *(VP-Sls & Field Ops-Australia & New Zealand)*
Jim Kruger *(CMO)*
Danny Allan *(CTO & Sr VP-Product Strategy)*
Gil Vega *(Chief Info Security Officer)*
Anand Eswaran *(CEO)*
John Jester *(Chief Revenue Officer)*

Subsidiary (Non-US):

Alcion Group (2)
67 Boulevard Bessieres, 75017, Paris, France
Tel.: (33) 146274510
Rev.: $13,600,000
Emp.: 35
N.A.I.C.S.: 541611
Eric Treguer *(Dir-Sls)*
Nathalie Maille *(Personnel Dir)*
Salomon Levy *(Dir & Fin)*

WorkForce Software, Inc. (1)
38705 Seven Mile Rd Ste 300, Livonia, MI 48152
Tel.: (734) 542-4100
Web Site:
   http://www.workforcesoftware.com
Sales Range: $10-24.9 Million
Prepackaged Software
N.A.I.C.S.: 513210

Kevin Choksi *(Founder)*
Leslie Tarnacki *(VP-HR & Gen Mgr)*
Mark Kurowski *(VP-Global Svcs)*
Michael Jepsen *(Sr VP-Sls)*
Travis Burke *(VP-Global Growth & Alliances)*
Ron Lev *(VP-Global Strategy)*
Ken Olsen *(VP-Product Dev)*
Paul Kramer *(Dir-Compliance)*
Robert E. Feller *(CFO)*
David Farquhar *(COO)*
Michael Morini *(CEO)*
Christopher Herter *(Gen Counsel & VP)*

Subsidiary (Non-US):

Workplace Systems International Limited (2)
Precedent Drive, Rooksley, Milton Keynes, MK13 8PP, Bucks, United Kingdom
Tel.: (44) 1908242042
Web Site:
   http://www.workforcesoftware.com
Labor & Workplace Management Software Services
N.A.I.C.S.: 513210
Tony Knight *(VP-Sls EMEA-Acct Relationship)*

Subsidiary (Domestic):

WorkForce Software Ltd (3)
Precedent Drive, Rooksley, Milton Keynes, MK13 8PP, Buckinghamshire, United Kingdom
Tel.: (44) 1908242042
Web Site:
   http://www.workforcesoftware.com
Workforce Management Software Development Services
N.A.I.C.S.: 541511
David Vonk *(Chief Revenue Officer)*
Mike Morini *(CEO)*

iParadigms, LLC (1)
1111 Broadway 3rd Fl, Oakland, CA 94607
Tel.: (510) 764-7600
Web Site: http://www.turnitin.com
Sales Range: $10-24.9 Million
Emp.: 225
Plagiarism Detection & Content Verification Software Developer
N.A.I.C.S.: 513210

INSIGHTSNOW, INC.
2101 NE Jack London S, Corvallis, OR 97330
Tel.: (541) 757-1404
Web Site:
   http://www.insightsnow.com
Year Founded: 2003
Rev.: $9,000,000
Emp.: 30
Advertising & Marketing
N.A.I.C.S.: 541810
Dave Lundahl *(Pres & CEO)*
Greg Stucky *(Chief Res Officer)*
Mark Turim *(COO & Mng Dir)*
Brent White *(Sr Dir-Client Svcs Dev)*
Dolores Oreskovich *(VP-Sensory & Consumer Insights)*
Jim Smith *(CFO)*
Kristen Dale *(VP-Client Partnerships)*
Sridhar Kankarla *(VP-Ops)*
Kristin Wright *(VP-Res & Insights)*

INSIGNIA CAPITAL GROUP, L.P.
1333 N California Blvd Ste 520, Walnut Creek, CA 94596
Tel.: (925) 399-8900   DE
Web Site: http://www.insigniacap.com
Privater Equity Firm
N.A.I.C.S.: 523999
David L. Lowe *(Co-Founder, CEO & Partner)*
Anthony L. Broglio *(Co-Founder & Partner)*
David L. Lowe *(CEO & Partner)*
Tony Broglio *(Co-Founder & Partner)*
Mel Deane *(Co-Founder & Partner)*
Jeremy Thatcher *(CFO)*
Sean Kelly *(VP-Bus Dev)*
Nick DeTrempe *(VP)*

Subsidiaries:

Century Snacks, LLC (1)
5560 E Slauson Ave, Commerce, CA 90040
Tel.: (323) 278-9578
Web Site: http://www.centurysnacks.com
Sales Range: $1-9.9 Million
Emp.: 50
Snack Food Mfr
N.A.I.C.S.: 311919
David L. Lowe *(Chm)*

Subsidiary (Domestic):

Snak Club, Inc. (2)
5560 E Slauson Ave, Commerce, CA 90040
Tel.: (310) 322-4400
Web Site: http://www.centurysnacks.com
Emp.: 60
Roasted Nuts & Peanut Butter Mfr
N.A.I.C.S.: 311911
Russell Riggs *(VP-Sls)*

NexGen RxMarketing LLC (1)
3220 Tillman Dr Ste 500, Bensalem, PA 19020
Web Site: http://www.mngdirect.com
Health Care Product Marketing Services
N.A.I.C.S.: 541870
Chris Wiltshire *(CEO)*

Tillamook Country Smoker Inc. (1)
8335 N Hwy 101, Bay City, OR 97107
Tel.: (503) 377-2222
Web Site: http://www.tcsjerky.com
Jerky, Meat Sticks & Similar Meat Snack Products Mfr
N.A.I.C.S.: 424470
David L. Lowe *(Chm)*

INSIGNIA REAL ESTATE COMPANIES, LLC
70 Gansett Ave, Cranston, RI 02910
Tel.: (401) 521-3553
Web Site: http://www.insigniare.com
Sales Range: $1-9.9 Million
Real Estate & Fund Investment Management Services
N.A.I.C.S.: 531390
William Davis *(Mgr-Property)*
Colleen Lewis *(Mgr-Property)*
John Zizzo *(Mgr-Property)*
Mayra Vazquez *(Controller)*
Anthony L. Emma Jr. *(CEO & Mng Partner)*

INSIGNIA TECHNOLOGY SERVICES, LLC
610 Thimble Shoals Blvd Bldg 6, Newport News, VA 23606
Tel.: (757) 591-2111
Web Site:
   http://www.insigniatechnology.com
Year Founded: 2006
Sales Range: $1-9.9 Million
Emp.: 70
IT Services & Solutions to Department of Defense & Commercial Customers
N.A.I.C.S.: 519290
Fred O'Brien *(Mng Partner)*
David LaClair *(Co-Founder & Pres)*
Chip LaClair *(Co-Founder & Mgr-Programs)*

INSILICA, INC.
3945 Freedom Cir, Santa Clara, CA 95054-1223
Tel.: (408) 327-4645
Year Founded: 2003
Sales Range: $1-9.9 Million
Emp.: 20
Fabless Semi-Conductor, ASIC & System-on-Chip Solutions
N.A.I.C.S.: 333242
Balaji Baktha *(Pres & CEO)*
David Lemberger *(Corp Controller & Dir-Fin)*
Sunil Baliga *(VP-Sls-Worldwide)*

Insilica, Inc.—(Continued)

INSOURCE SOFTWARE SOLUTIONS LLC
11321 Business Ctr Dr, Richmond, VA 23236
Tel.: (804) 378-8981
Web Site: http://www.insourcess.com
Sales Range: $10-24.9 Million
Emp.: 70
Prepackaged Software
N.A.I.C.S.: 513210
A. Dunn Dillard (CFO & Exec VP)
Thomas J. Barczak (CIO & VP)
Ann P. Croom (Pres)
Julie Joyce (VP-Client & Employee Experience)
Rob Bansek (VP-Sls)

INSPEC TECH, INC.
46 Inspec Dr, Valley Head, AL 35989
Tel.: (256) 635-6458 **AL**
Web Site: http://www.inspectech.us
Year Founded: 1992
Sales Range: $1-9.9 Million
Emp.: 23
Manufactures Labels, Barcoded Tags & RFID Devices
N.A.I.C.S.: 323111
Matt Freeman (VP)
J. Fowler (Mgr-Pur)
Tracy Tomlin (Dir-Quality)

INSPIRA MARKETING GROUP
50 Washington St, Norwalk, CT 06854
Tel.: (203) 939-1300
Web Site:
http://www.inspiramarketing.com
Year Founded: 2008
Sales Range: $1-9.9 Million
Emp.: 40
Advertising Agency Services
N.A.I.C.S.: 541810
Jeff Snyder (Chief Inspiration Officer)
Ralph Failla (Acct Dir)
Carter Thorson (VP-Client Leadership)
Bob Petrosino (Sr VP-Brand Strategy & Dev)
Brooke Stein (Acct Dir)
Clayton Samaroo (CFO)
Kendyl Wright (Dir-Activation)
Toby Trygg (Dir-Creative)
Jessica Branson (Chief Relationship Officer & Head-Client Svc)
Steve Winkel (VP-People & Culture)

INSPIRATA, INC.
1 N Dale Mabry Hwy Ste 600, Tampa, FL 33609
Tel.: (813) 570-9900
Web Site: http://www.inspirata.com
Year Founded: 2014
Medical Technology & Testing Services
N.A.I.C.S.: 541714
Satish Sanan (Chm & CEO)
Mark Lloyd (Founder & Exec VP)
Suhas Gudihal (Sr VP-Tech & Innovation Advisory)
Andrew Chomos (Sr VP-Gen Mgr Digital Pathology)
Oenone Duroe (Gen Mgr-Inspirata Europe)
Michael Gillen (CFO)
Stephen Keresztes (VP & Head-Oncology Informatics Bus)
Emil Mladenov (VP-Corp & Digital Mktg)

INSPIRATION SOFTWARE, INC.
9400 SW Beaverton-Hillsdale Hwy Ste 300, Beaverton, OR 97005
Tel.: (503) 297-3004

Web Site: http://www.inspiration.com
Year Founded: 1982
Sales Range: $10-24.9 Million
Emp.: 55
Publisher of Visual-Learning Software
N.A.I.C.S.: 541511
Mona Westhaver (Co-Founder & Pres)
Donald Helfgott (Co-Founder & CEO)
Richard Stone (VP-Ops)
Pam Judge (Dir-Mktg)

INSPIRE CREATIVE STUDIOS
6622 Gordon Rd Ste C, Wilmington, NC 28411-8415
Tel.: (910) 395-0200
Year Founded: 2005
Sales Range: Less than $1 Million
Emp.: 5
N.A.I.C.S.: 541810
Curtis Thieman (Dir-Creative)
Jonathan Medford (Dir-PR)
Craig Thieman (Dir-Production)
Michael Moody (Dir-Tech)

INSPIRE DEVELOPMENT CENTERS
105 S 6th St Ste B, Sunnyside, WA 98944
Tel.: (509) 837-2225 **WA**
Web Site: http://www.inspire-centers.org
Year Founded: 1983
Sales Range: $25-49.9 Million
Emp.: 1,168
Community Support Services
N.A.I.C.S.: 624190
Barbara Martinez-Griego (Treas)
Isabel Bedolla-Roos (Chm)
Rodolfo M. Mendoza (Vice Chm)
Sonia Olivera (Sec)

INSPIRED BEAUTY BRANDS INC.
277 Northern Blvd, Great Neck, NY 11021-4703
Tel.: (516) 466-0660 **NY**
Web Site:
http://www.inspiredbeauty.com
Year Founded: 1979
Sales Range: $10-24.9 Million
Emp.: 25
Shampoo, Hair Spray, Conditioner, Gels, Mousse, Relaxers & Other Hair Care Products Mfr
N.A.I.C.S.: 325620
Jeffrey Siegel (CFO)
Sam Maniaci (CEO)
Youyi Zan (Mgr-AP)

Subsidiaries:

Hask Toiletries **(1)**
277 Northern Blvd, Great Neck, NY 11021-4703
Tel.: (516) 466-0660
Web Site:
http://www.alleghanypharmacal.com
Mfr of Toiletries
N.A.I.C.S.: 325620

INSPIRICA, INC.
141 Franklin St, Stamford, CT 06901
Tel.: (203) 388-0100 **CT**
Web Site: http://www.inspiricact.org
Year Founded: 1987
Sales Range: $10-24.9 Million
Emp.: 108
Homelessness Ending Services
N.A.I.C.S.: 624229
Anahaita N. Kotval (COO)
Jason T. Shaplen (CEO)
Cyndy Goldberg (Chief Program Officer-Residential Svcs)
Anahaita N. Kotval (COO)
Melvin Osario (Chief Maintenance Officer)

INSPIRIX TECHNOLOGIES LLC
1270 Jungermann Rd Ste B, Saint Peters, MO 63376
Tel.: (636) 422-0068
Web Site: http://www.inspirixtek.com
Year Founded: 2007
Sales Range: $1-9.9 Million
Emp.: 34
Software Development Services
N.A.I.C.S.: 541511
Vamsi Malgireddy (Pres)

INSPIRUS CREDIT UNION
5200 Southcenter Blvd, Seattle, WA 98188
Tel.: (206) 628-4010 **WA**
Web Site: http://www.inspiruscu.org
Year Founded: 1936
Sales Range: $25-49.9 Million
Credit Union Operator
N.A.I.C.S.: 522130
Kristina Hanson (VP-IT)
Sherie Lotze (VP-Mktg)
Richard Rutkowski (Chm)
Scott Adkins (Pres)
Lesly Fox (CFO)

INSTALLER SALES & SERVICE INCORPORATED
5501 Thelin St, Fort Worth, TX 76115
Tel.: (817) 632-3900
Web Site:
http://www.wmautomotive.com
Rev.: $14,986,859
Emp.: 275
Motor Vehicle Supplies & New Parts
N.A.I.C.S.: 423120
Wilson McMillion (Owner)

Subsidiaries:

Jobbers Service of San Angelo **(1)**
208 Penland St, Fort Worth, TX 76111
Tel.: (817) 834-5559
Web Site: http://www.mautomotive.com
Rev.: $5,022,723
Emp.: 18
Motor Vehicle Supplies & New Parts
N.A.I.C.S.: 423120
Wilson Mcmillion (Pres)

INSTANATURAL, LLC
12001 Research Pkwy Ste 244, Orlando, FL 32826
Tel.: (800) 290-6932
Web Site:
http://www.instanatural.com
Year Founded: 2013
Consumer Goods & Skincare Products Mfr
N.A.I.C.S.: 325620
Heather Wilson (Dir-Brand Dev)

INSTANT TECHNOLOGY, LLC
200 W Adams St Ste 1440, Chicago, IL 60606-5226
Tel.: (312) 546-5300
Web Site:
http://www.instanttechnology.com
Year Founded: 2001
Rev.: $17,000,000
Emp.: 35
Employment Placement Agencies
N.A.I.C.S.: 561311
Rona Borre (Pres & CEO)

INSTANTRON CO., INC.
3712 Pawtucket Ave, Riverside, RI 02915-5105
Tel.: (401) 433-6800
Web Site: http://www.instantron.com
Year Founded: 1880
Sales Range: $1-9.9 Million
Emp.: 5
Electrolysis Epilators for Permanent Hair Removal Mfr & Retailer
N.A.I.C.S.: 335210

Harold C. Mahler Jr. (Pres)

INSTANTWHIP FOODS, INC.
2200 Cardigan Ave, Columbus, OH 43215-1092
Tel.: (614) 488-2536 **OH**
Web Site: http://www.instantwhip.com
Year Founded: 1933
Sales Range: $25-49.9 Million
Emp.: 146
Patent Leasing Services
N.A.I.C.S.: 533110
Douglas A. Smith (Pres)
G. Fred Smith (VP)
Tom Michaelides (Controller)

Subsidiaries:

Auburn Dairy Products, Inc. **(1)**
2200 Cardigan Ave, Columbus, OH 43215-1092
Tel.: (614) 488-0307
Web Site: http://www.instantwhipfoods.com
Sales Range: $10-24.9 Million
Emp.: 25
Fluid Milk Producer
N.A.I.C.S.: 311511

Instantwhip of Pennsylvania, Inc. **(1)**
302 June Ave, Blandon, PA 19510
Tel.: (610) 926-6655
Web Site: http://www.instantwhip.com
Sales Range: $10-24.9 Million
Emp.: 10
Warehousing of Dairy Products
N.A.I.C.S.: 424430

Instantwhip-Akron, Inc. **(1)**
4870 Hudson Dr, Stow, OH 44224
Tel.: (330) 688-8826
Dairy Products Distr
N.A.I.C.S.: 424430
Mike Bennett (Mgr-Fleet & Safety)

Instantwhip-Baltimore, Inc. **(1)**
3129 Penrisy Dr, Hyattsville, MD 20785
Tel.: (301) 583-8404
Emp.: 40
Dairy Products Distr
N.A.I.C.S.: 424430
Jeryl Schwartz (Office Mgr)

Instantwhip-Buffalo, Inc. **(1)**
2117 Genesee St, Buffalo, NY 14211
Tel.: (716) 892-7031
Web Site: http://www.instantwhip.com
Dairy Products Distr
N.A.I.C.S.: 424430

Instantwhip-Chicago, Inc. **(1)**
1535 N Cicero Ave, Chicago, IL 60651
Tel.: (773) 235-5588
Dairy Products Distr
N.A.I.C.S.: 424430

Instantwhip-Connecticut, Inc. **(1)**
49 N Plains Industrial Rd, Wallingford, CT 06492
Tel.: (203) 265-6636
Web Site: http://www.instantwhip.com
Dairy Products Distr
N.A.I.C.S.: 424430

Instantwhip-Eastern New York, Inc. **(1)**
3106 Wayne St, Endwell, NY 13760
Tel.: (607) 748-4343
Dairy Products Distr
N.A.I.C.S.: 424430

Instantwhip-Indianapolis, Inc. **(1)**
9125 Burk Rd9125, Indianapolis, IN 46229
Tel.: (317) 899-1533
Web Site: http://www.instantwhip.com
Emp.: 10
Dairy Products Distr
N.A.I.C.S.: 424430
Dave Kaufman (CEO)

Instantwhip-Minneapolis, Inc. **(1)**
2850 Anthony Ln S, Saint Anthony, MN 55418
Tel.: (612) 721-6905
Dairy Product Mfr & Distr
N.A.I.C.S.: 311511

Instantwhip-Rochester, Inc. **(1)**
88 Weicher St, Rochester, NY 14606
Tel.: (585) 279-0920

Web Site: http://www.instantwhip.com
Dairy Products Distr
N.A.I.C.S.: 424430

Ohio Processors, Inc. (1)
244 E 1st St, London, OH 43140
Tel.: (740) 852-9243
Web Site: http://www.instantwhip.com
Sales Range: $10-24.9 Million
Emp.: 5
Producers of Fluid Milk
N.A.I.C.S.: 311511
Sal Tallarico (Engr-Maintenance)

INSTITUTE FOR BETTER EDUCATION
911 S Craycroft Rd, Tucson, AZ
85711
Tel.: (520) 512-5438   AZ
Web Site:
   http://www.ibescholarships.org
Year Founded: 1971
Sales Range: $10-24.9 Million
Emp.: 8
Educational Support Services
N.A.I.C.S.: 611710
Dawn Parker (Pres)
Charlotte Beecher (Exec Dir)
Karen Yanes (Sec)

INSTITUTE FOR BUILDING TECHNOLOGY AND SAFETY
45207 Research Pl, Ashburn, VA
20147
Tel.: (703) 481-2000   VA
Web Site: http://www.ibts.org
Year Founded: 1997
Sales Range: $10-24.9 Million
Emp.: 178
Economic Development Services
N.A.I.C.S.: 926110
Ashok Goswami (Co-Founder & CEO)
Shyam Choudhary (Co-Founder & Pres)
Craig Thurmond (Chm)
Steven R. Sarkozy (Sec)
Hugh Hyman (Sr Mgr-Compliance & Fin Reporting)
Blake Ratcliff (Dir-Economic Dev & Disaster Recovery)
Dion Rudnicki (COO)
Chris Fennell (Chief Mktg & Dev Officer)

INSTITUTE FOR COMMUNITY LIVING
125 Broad St 3rd Fl, New York, NY
10004
Tel.: (212) 385-3030   NY
Web Site: http://www.iclinc.net
Year Founded: 1986
Sales Range: $75-99.9 Million
Emp.: 1,401
Disability Assistance Services
N.A.I.C.S.: 623210
Dewey H. Howard (CFO)
Chris Copeland (COO)
Frantz Lubin (Chief Medical Officer)
David Woodlock (Pres & CEO)

INSTITUTE FOR CORPORATE PRODUCTIVITY, INC.
411 1st Ave S Ste 403, Seattle, WA
98104
Tel.: (206) 624-6565
Web Site: http://www.i4cp.com
Year Founded: 2007
Sales Range: $1-9.9 Million
Emp.: 30
People Management Services
N.A.I.C.S.: 561311
Kevin Oakes (CEO)
Jay Jamrog (Sr VP-Res)
Erik Samdahl (Dir-Mktg)
Kevin Martin (Chief Res Officer)

Amy Armitage (Dir-Member Res Programs)
Kevin Copestick (Dir-Member Exchange Programs)
Lorrie Lykins (VP-Res & Mng Editor)
Patrick Murray (VP-Surveys & Assessments)
Mark Walker (VP-Member Svcs)
Jennifer Arlem Molina (Coord-Mktg)
Cher Murphy (Chief Talent Officer)
Kurt Fischer (Chm & Chief HR Officer)
Joseph Santana (Chm & Chief Diversity Officer)

INSTITUTE FOR HEALTHCARE COMMUNICATION, INC.
171 Orange St 2R, New Haven, CT
06510-3111
Tel.: (203) 772-8280
Web Site:
   http://www.healthcarecomm.org
Year Founded: 1987
Sales Range: $1-9.9 Million
Emp.: 5
Health Care Communications Services
N.A.I.C.S.: 611519
Kathleen Bonvicini (CEO)
Robert Levine (Chm)
Laurie Mansfield (Coord-Education)

INSTITUTE FOR PHYSICAL SCIENCE, INC.
1365 Beverly Rd Ste 300, Mclean,
VA 22101
Tel.: (703) 760-9889   NM
Year Founded: 1994
Sales Range: $10-24.9 Million
Emp.: 46
Scientific Research Services
N.A.I.C.S.: 541715
Mark Michalowski (Dir-Bus)
Karen Parsons (Dir-Analysis)
Sarah Dimonte (Dir-HR)
Curtis Hastings (Dir-Dev)

INSTITUTE FOR POPULATION HEALTH
1400 Woodbridge St, Detroit, MI
48207
Tel.: (313) 309-9300   MI
Web Site: http://www.ipophealth.net
Year Founded: 2012
Sales Range: $25-49.9 Million
Emp.: 200
Public Health Care Services
N.A.I.C.S.: 621498
Loretta V. Davis (Pres & CEO)

INSTITUTE FOR SUPPLY MANAGMENT
2055 E Centennial Cir, Tempe, AZ
85284
Tel.: (480) 752-6276
Web Site:
   http://www.instituteforsupplyman
   agement.org
Year Founded: 1915
Emp.: 100
Educational Training, Research & Leadership to Supply Management Professionals
N.A.I.C.S.: 611699
Tom Derry (CEO)
Bradley J. Holcomb (Chm)
James E. Martin (VP-IT)
Riley Conover (Specialist-Mktg & PR)

INSTITUTE FOR TRANSPORTATION & DEVELOPMENT POLICY
9 E 19th St Fl 7, New York, NY
10003
Tel.: (212) 629-8001   DC

Web Site: http://www.itdp.org
Year Founded: 1985
Sales Range: $10-24.9 Million
Emp.: 25
Community Transportation Support Services
N.A.I.C.S.: 485210
Melinda Eisenmann (COO)
Aimee Gauthier (Chief Program Officer)
Kathleen Letchford (Dir-Dev)
Ramon Cruz (Program Mgr-International Policy)
Michael Kodransky (Mgr-Global Res)
Enrique Penalosa (Pres)
Joseph Ryan (VP)
Bob Hambrecht (Treas)
Jules Flynn (Sec)
Heather Thompson (CEO)

INSTITUTE OF COMMUNITY SERVICES, INC.
160 W Valley Ave, Holly Springs, MS
38635
Tel.: (662) 252-1582   MS
Web Site: http://www.ics-hs.com
Year Founded: 1968
Sales Range: $25-49.9 Million
Emp.: 1,003
Child Day Care Services
N.A.I.C.S.: 624410
Willie Green (Dir-Acctg)
Norma Strickland (Dir-Education)
Fannie Lampley (Dir-PR)
Frances Young (Dir-Fiscal)

INSTITUTE OF ELECTRICAL AND ELECTRONICS ENGINEERS, INC.
3 Park Ave 17th Fl, New York, NY
10016-5997
Tel.: (212) 419-7900
Web Site: http://www.ieee.org
Year Founded: 1884
Emp.: 800
Technical Professional Information Organization
N.A.I.C.S.: 813920
Gerry Grenier (Sr Dir-Pub Tech)
Wendy McCarville (Mgr-Academic Acct-West)
Michael Petro (Mgr-Govt & Corp Accts-Natl)
Barry Holquist (Mgr-Academic Acct-Central)
Sharon Nadler (Dir-Bus Plng & Admin)
Peter Tuohy (Dir-Periodicals Production Svcs)
Joe Vaitkus (Mgr-Academic Acct-East)
Jose M. F. Moura (Pres)
Karen Bartleson (Pres & CEO)
Stephen Welby (COO)

Subsidiaries:

IEEE GlobalSpec, Inc. (1)
201 Fuller Rd Ste 202, Albany, NY 12203
Tel.: (518) 880-0200
Web Site: http://www.globalspec.com
Online Advertising & Marketing Services
N.A.I.C.S.: 541890
Amber Cooleen (Dir-Mktg)
Cheri A. Warren (Chm)
Patrick D. Mahoney (Pres & CEO)
Nicolette Emmino (Mng Dir-New York)
Nancy Ordman (Contributing Editor)
Marie Donlon (Editor)
Peter Brown (Editor-Silicon Valley)
Tony Pallone (Editor)
Roger Pink (Contributing Editor)
Shawn Martin (Contributing Editor)
Eric Olson (Contributing Editor)
Gary Kardys (Engr)
Abe Michelen (Contributing Editor)
David Wagman (Dir-Editorial-Denver)
Jonathan Fuller (Contributing Editor)

INSTITUTE OF FOOD TECHNOLOGISTS
525 W Van Buren St Ste 1000, Chicago, IL 60607
Tel.: (312) 782-8424   IL
Web Site: http://www.ift.org
Year Founded: 1939
Sales Range: $10-24.9 Million
Hunger Relief Services
N.A.I.C.S.: 624210
Robert Gravani (Treas)
Christie Tarantino-Dean (CEO)
John Neil Coupland (Pres)
Mark Barenie (CFO & Sr VP)
William Fisher (VP-Science & Policy Initiatives)
Jerry Bowman (VP-Comm & Media Rels)
Kelly McCohen (Mgr-Exec Offices)
Brandon Davis (Mgr-Certification)
Susan Young (Dir-Sls & Bus Partnerships)
Juliette Fry (Acct Mgr-Strategic-Midwest)
Anna Ylijoki (Mgr-Component Rels)
Rosetta Newsome (Dir-Science & Policy Initiatives)
Tejas Bhatt (Dir-Global Food Traceability Center)
George Miller (Dir-KLE)
Kelly M. Fox (Sr VP-Meetings & Business Partnerships)
Jean M. Heis (Dir-Meetings)
Iwona Kossak (Dir-Fin)
Lev Kaytsner (Dir-IT)
Bob Swientek (Dir-Publ)
Leslie Pappas (Dir-Publ Production)
Mindy Weinstein (Dir-Media Rels)
Jennifer London (Dir-Mktg)
Eric Schneider (Sr VP-Strategic & Comm)
Nancy Ukpe Gargula (Dir-Diversity & Inclusion)
Bryan Hitchcock (Chief Science & Tech Officer)

INSTITUTE OF NUCLEAR POWER OPERATIONS
700 Galleria Pkwy, Atlanta, GA 30339
Tel.: (770) 644-8000
Year Founded: 1979
Sales Range: $50-74.9 Million
Emp.: 400
Professional Services; Nuclear Consultant
N.A.I.C.S.: 541990
James Scarola (Sr Mgr-Nuclear Plant)
Jeffery Wheelock (Dir-HR)
Philip McCullough (VP-Trng Accreditation)
Kris Straw (Treas)

INSTITUTE OF SCRAP RECYCLING INDUSTRIES, INC.
1615 L St NW Ste 600, Washington,
DC 20036
Tel.: (202) 662-8500   DE
Web Site: http://www.isri.org
Year Founded: 1987
Sales Range: $10-24.9 Million
Emp.: 41
Recycling Services
N.A.I.C.S.: 325998
Thomas Casey (Gen Counsel)
Joe Bateman (Dir-Safety Outreach)
Mark Carpenter (Dir-Media Rels & Online Comm)
Chuck Carr (VP-Member Svcs & Meetings)
Terry Cirone (VP-Safety)
Robin K. Wiener (Pres)
Crag Boswell (Dir-Electronics Div)
Jim Levine (Dir-Electronics Div)
Christopher Bedell (Dir-Ferrous Div)

Institute of Scrap Recycling Industries, Inc.—(Continued)

Brian Halloran *(Dir-Ferrous Div)*
Kevin Lamar *(Dir-Nonferrous Div)*
Andy Wahl *(Dir-Nonferrous Div)*
Myles Cohen *(Dir-Paper Div)*
Don Majka *(Dir-Paper Div)*
Scott Saunders *(Dir-Plastics Div)*
Kip Vincent *(Dir-Tire & Rubber)*

INSTITUTION FOR SAVINGS IN NEWBURYPORT & ITS VICINITY

93 State St, Newburyport, MA 01950
Tel.: (978) 462-3106   **MA**
Web Site:
   http://www.institutionforsavings.com
Year Founded: 1820
Sales Range: $50-74.9 Million
Emp.: 170
Commericial Banking
N.A.I.C.S.: 522110
Kimberly A. Rock *(COO & Exec VP)*
Rebecca L. Conary *(VP-Retail & Branch Ops)*
Anna L. Makos *(Sr VP-Residential Lending)*
Caroline M. Meagher *(VP-Electronic Banking, Retail & Branch Ops)*
Melissa W. LeBel *(VP-Branch Admin, Trng, Retail & Branch Ops)*
Thomas M. Hopp *(CIO & Sr VP-IT)*
Rebecca L. Collins *(VP-Fin)*
Robert C. LeGallo *(CFO & Sr VP-Fin)*
Mary Anne Clancy *(VP-Comm & Admin)*
David E. Boudreau *(Sr VP-Comml Lending)*
Stephen P. Cote *(Treas, Sr VP & Controller-Fin)*
Lawrence R. Hunter *(Sr VP-Residential Lending)*
Tammy A. Roeger *(Sr VP-Retail Banking & Branch Ops)*
Karl R. Wilson *(Sr VP-Comml Lending)*
Christine N. Allen *(VP-IT)*
Nancy J. Taylor *(VP-Residential Lending)*
Kathleen M. Ferreira *(VP-HR & Admin)*
Amy L. Smith *(Asst VP-Fin & Asst Treas)*
Dian M. Dastous *(Asst VP-Loan Servicing & Residential Lending)*
Katrina P. Cutts *(Sr VP-Comml Lending)*
Kerry A. Hamel-Pope *(VP-Residential Lending & Mgr-Lending Appraisal)*
Lori G. Rostkowski *(VP-Comml Lending)*
Bruce P. Macdonald *(VP-Admin, Retail & Branch Ops)*
Marcia C. LaTorre *(Sr VP-Credit Admin)*
Hanson M. Webster *(VP-Info Security & IT)*
John A. LeBlanc *(VP-Loan Ops & Residential Lending)*
Christopher R. Sullivan *(VP-Residential Lending)*
Wesley R. Barry *(VP-Retail Banking & Branch Ops)*
David Collins *(Officer-Mortgage)*
Ellin M. McSweeney *(Officer-Mortgage)*
Jeffrey J. Salerno *(Officer-Mortgage)*
Rachel R. Lachance *(Officer-Community Reinvestment Act & VP-Lending Compliance)*
Sahag A. Kavlakian *(Officer-Mortgage)*
Isaac Raymond Webster II *(Asst VP-Facilities)*

INSTITUTIONAL CAPITAL NETWORK, INC.

60 E 42nd St, New York, NY 10165
Tel.: (212) 994-7400   **DE**
Web Site:
   http://www.icapitalnetwork.com
Year Founded: 2013
Emp.: 393
Fund Management Services
N.A.I.C.S.: 523940
Lawrence Calcano *(Chm & CEO)*
Jennifer Ashley *(Co-Mng Dir & Chief People Officer)*
Marco Bizzozero *(Co-Mng Dir & Head-Intl)*
Dan Vene *(Founder, Mng Partner & Head-Client Solutions)*
Michael Kushner *(Mng Partner & CFO)*

INSTITUTIONAL CASEWORK INC.

1865 N Market St, Paris, TN 38242
Tel.: (731) 642-4251
Web Site: http://www.iciscientific.com
Year Founded: 2006
Other Nonhazardous Waste Treatment & Disposal
N.A.I.C.S.: 562219
Jim Arthurs *(Pres & CEO)*
Mike Hodge *(Dir-HR)*

INSTITUTIONAL VENTURE PARTNERS

3000 Sand Hill Rd Bldg 2 Ste 250, Menlo Park, CA 94025
Tel.: (650) 854-0132
Web Site: http://www.ivp.com
Year Founded: 1980
Privater Equity Firm
N.A.I.C.S.: 523999
Todd C. Chaffee *(Gen Partner)*
Steve Harrick *(Gen Partner)*
Sandy Miller *(Gen Partner)*
Dennis Phelps *(Gen Partner)*
Jules A. Maltz *(Gen Partner)*
Somesh Dash *(Gen Partner)*
Eric Liaw *(Gen Partner)*
James Newell *(VP)*
Saydeah E. Howard *(Gen Partner)*
Christopher Esqueda *(VP-Fin)*
Gina Bauman *(Sr VP-Mktg & IR)*
Tracy Hogan *(CFO)*
Roseanne Wincek *(VP)*
Alex Lim *(VP)*
Louisa Xu *(VP)*
Cack Wilhelm *(Partner)*
Ajay Vashee *(Gen Partner)*

INSTREAM, LLC

240 Great Cir Rd Ste 342, Nashville, TN 37228-1759
Tel.: (615) 415-6000
Web Site: http://www.instreamllc.com
Year Founded: 2004
Computer Software & Programming Services
N.A.I.C.S.: 541511
Vincent Sessoms *(Mgr-Bus Dev)*
Mark Hinson *(Pres & CEO)*
Chad Streeter *(Dir-IT)*
Meredith Williams *(Sr Dir-Project Mgmt)*

Subsidiaries:

Tallega Software, LLC   **(1)**
15635 Alton Pkwy Ste 475, Irvine, CA 92618-7361
Tel.: (949) 367-9860
Web Site: http://www.tallega.com
Software Developer
N.A.I.C.S.: 513210
Richard Brown *(Dir-Pro Svcs)*
David Gerber *(CEO)*

INSTRUMART

35 Green Mountain Dr, South Burlington, VT 05403
Tel.: (802) 863-0085
Web Site: http://www.instrumart.com
Year Founded: 1988
Sales Range: $10-24.9 Million
Emp.: 50
Industrial Instruments Distr
N.A.I.C.S.: 423830
Robert M. Berman *(Pres)*
Brian Leffler *(VP)*
J. Arnoldy *(Engr-Application)*
Ron Pouliot *(Mgr-Warehouse)*

INSTRUMENT ASSOCIATES INC.

4839 W 128th Pl, Alsip, IL 60803
Tel.: (708) 597-9880   **DE**
Web Site:
   http://www.instrumentassociates.com
Year Founded: 1953
Sales Range: $10-24.9 Million
Emp.: 35
Valves & Fittings Distr
N.A.I.C.S.: 423830
Jay P. Fregeau *(Pres & CEO)*
John Yarmoska *(Bus Mgr)*

INSTRUMENT SALES AND SERVICE

16427 NE Airport Way, Portland, OR 97230
Tel.: (503) 239-0754
Web Site:
   http://www.instrumentsales.com
Sales Range: $10-24.9 Million
Emp.: 100
Automotive Supplies & Parts
N.A.I.C.S.: 423120
Jake DePew *(Engr-Mechanical)*
Kathy Wilson *(Acct Mgr)*
Noel Allen *(Supvr-Customer Svc)*
Rick Ashmore *(Mgr-Ops)*
Brian Clark *(Engr-Quality)*
Ron Freeman *(Pres & CEO)*
Sean Kelly *(Owner)*
Gary Jacobs *(Chm)*

INSULA COMPANIES

240 S Pineapple Ave Ste 400, Sarasota, FL 34236
Tel.: (941) 960-7000
Web Site:
   http://www.insulacompanies.com
Sales Range: $10-24.9 Million
Emp.: 70
Residential Real Estate Investor, Operator & Manager
N.A.I.C.S.: 531390
Frederick D. Cochran *(Mng Partner)*
Larry Fox *(Mng Partner)*
John F. Wilkins *(Principal)*
Jeff Talbot *(Principal)*
Kimberly H. Henderson *(Gen Counsel)*
Tammy K. Knowles *(VP-Property Mgmt)*
Brian W. Fortney *(Dir-MIS)*
Martin Hilliard *(Dir-Fin)*

INSULA PROPERTIES, LLC

1343 Main St Ste 201, Sarasota, FL 34236
Tel.: (941) 952-9055
Web Site:
   http://www.westwindmgt.com
Sales Range: $10-24.9 Million
Emp.: 120
Property Management
N.A.I.C.S.: 531311
Kimberly M. McAllister *(Gen Counsel)*
Casey McDaniel *(Controller)*
Richard S. Wakeley *(VP & Reg Mgr-Property)*
Brian W. Fortney *(Dir-MIS)*
Tammy M. Knowles *(Reg Mgr-Property)*

INSULATING SERVICES INC.

10709 Granite St Ste H, Charlotte, NC 28273
Tel.: (704) 588-7814
Web Site:
   http://www.insulatingservices.com
Year Founded: 1973
Sales Range: $25-49.9 Million
Emp.: 250
Insulation, Buildings
N.A.I.C.S.: 238990
Charles E. McKissick *(Pres)*
Kevin Beste *(Controller)*
Mike Carroll *(VP)*
Linda Emser *(Coord-HR, Genist & Safety)*
Steve Hinson *(Project Mgr)*
Russell Hyatt *(Project Mgr)*
Rick Robinson *(Project Mgr)*

INSULATION DEALERS & SUPPLY CO.

8710 N Pioneer Rd, Peoria, IL 61615
Tel.: (309) 693-8900
Rev.: $10,000,000
Emp.: 30
Roofing; Siding; & Insulation
N.A.I.C.S.: 423330
Dave Brush *(VP-Ops)*

INSULATION SUPPLY COMPANY INC.

1400 W Commerce St, Dallas, TX 75208-1403
Tel.: (214) 827-2000
Web Site: http://www.iscbm.com
Year Founded: 1972
Sales Range: $10-24.9 Million
Emp.: 85
Supplier of Acoustical Materials & Drywall
N.A.I.C.S.: 423310
Allan L. Burns *(Pres)*
Dell Street *(Controller)*
Allen Fisher *(Branch Mgr-Texas)*
Butch Yarborough *(Branch Mgr)*

INSULATIONS INCORPORATED

1101 Edwards Ave, Harahan, LA 70123
Tel.: (504) 733-5033
Web Site:
   http://www.insulationsinc.com
Year Founded: 1970
Sales Range: $50-74.9 Million
Emp.: 940
Insulation Of Pipes & Boilers
N.A.I.C.S.: 238990
David T. Branton *(Pres)*
Jack Biven *(Treas, Sec & Controller)*

INSULECTRO

20362 Windrow Dr, Lake Forest, CA 92630
Tel.: (949) 587-3200   **CA**
Web Site: http://www.insulectro.com
Year Founded: 1991
Sales Range: $25-49.9 Million
Emp.: 225
Electronic Parts & Equipment
N.A.I.C.S.: 423690
Brad Biddle *(CFO)*
Timothy P. Redfern *(Pres & CEO)*
Jason Marsh *(VP-Product Mgmt)*
Ken Parent *(VP-Sls)*
Patrick Redfern *(Pres)*

INSURANCE APPLICATIONS GROUP, LLC

250 Commonwealth Dr, Greenville, SC 29615
Tel.: (864) 527-0474
Web Site: http://www.iagbenefits.com
Year Founded: 1999
Rev.: $3,400,000

Emp.: 17
Insurance Agencies & Brokerages
N.A.I.C.S.: 524210
J. Marshall Dye III *(Pres & CEO)*
Aaron Lesher *(Exec VP)*

INSURANCE ASSOCIATES INC.

21 Church St Ste 100, Rockville, MD 20850
Tel.: (301) 838-9400
Web Site: http://www.insassoc.com
Year Founded: 1956
Sales Range: $450-499.9 Million
Emp.: 53
Insurance Agents
N.A.I.C.S.: 524210
Stephen A. Spencer *(Pres)*
Michael W. Howell *(VP-VA Office)*
Paul M. Troeschel *(Sr VP)*
Aldo Pasquariello *(Exec VP)*
MaryAnn Wood *(VP & Mgr-Underwriting)*

INSURANCE BROKERS WEST INC.

233 E High St Ste 200, Moorpark, CA 93021
Tel.: (805) 299-2150
Web Site: http://www.ibwins.com
Year Founded: 2008
Sales Range: $1-9.9 Million
Emp.: 9
Insurance Broker Services
N.A.I.C.S.: 524210
Daniel Groff *(Pres & CEO)*

INSURANCE CARE DIRECT INC

1002 E Newport Ctr Dr Ste 200, Deerfield Beach, FL 33442
Tel.: (954) 671-4920
Year Founded: 2006
Sales Range: $25-49.9 Million
Emp.: 45
Life, Health & Auto Insurance
N.A.I.C.S.: 524292
Arnold Cohen *(Pres)*
David Corsaut *(Chief Strategy Officer)*
John Doak *(COO)*
Christa Rapoport *(Chief Compliance Officer & Gen Counsel)*
Seth Cohen *(Chm)*
E. Benjamin Nelson *(CEO)*

INSURANCE CENTER, INC.

120 W Central Ave, El Dorado, KS 67042
Tel.: (316) 321-5600   KS
Web Site: http://www.ici.insurance
Year Founded: 1885
Insurance Services
N.A.I.C.S.: 524210
Ryan T. Murry *(Pres)*
Lonnie Currier *(VP-Risk Mgmt)*
Dustin J. Davis *(VP)*

INSURANCE HOUSE

1904 Leland Dr, Marietta, GA 30067
Tel.: (770) 952-0080
Web Site:
   http://www.insurancehouse.com
Sales Range: $50-74.9 Million
Emp.: 200
Property Damage & Casualty Insurance Services
N.A.I.C.S.: 524113
Rebecca J. Bittinger *(Chief Admin Officer)*
Jacqueline M. Schaendorf *(Pres & CEO)*
Arvind Kaushal *(CFO)*

Subsidiaries:

Southern General Insurance Co.   (1)

1902 Leland Dr, Marietta, GA 30067
Tel.: (770) 952-0080
Web Site: http://www.insurancehouse.com
Sales Range: $50-74.9 Million
Emp.: 110
Property Damage & Casualty Insurance Services
N.A.I.C.S.: 524126
Jacqueline M. Schaendorf *(Pres)*
Kenneth Widvoor *(Dir-Claims)*
Rebecca Bittinger *(Chief Admin Officer)*
Arvind Kaushal *(CFO)*

INSURANCE INSTITUTE FOR HIGHWAY SAFETY

1005 N Glebe Rd Ste 800, Arlington, VA 22201
Tel.: (703) 247-1500   DC
Web Site: http://www.iihs.org
Year Founded: 1959
Sales Range: $10-24.9 Million
Emp.: 94
Accident Prevention Services
N.A.I.C.S.: 813319
Brenda O'Donnell *(VP-Insurer Rels)*
Shelley M. Shelton *(Mgr-Consumer Ratings)*
Floyd M. Yager *(Chm)*
Angela Sparks *(Vice Chm)*

INSURANCE MARKETING AGENCIES, INC.

306 Main St, Worcester, MA 01608
Tel.: (508) 753-7233
Web Site: http://www.imaagency.com
Year Founded: 1924
Sales Range: $25-49.9 Million
Emp.: 60
Provider of Insurance Brokerage & Risk Management Services
N.A.I.C.S.: 524126
Peter H. Herman *(Pres)*
Laura Herman-Strohecker *(CEO)*
George Thorogood *(VP-Sls)*
Kenneth W. Eddy *(VP-Sls)*
Bill Wilcox *(VP-Admin & Fin)*
Dawn Lineberry *(VP-Ops)*

INSURANCE NETWORK OF TEXAS, INC.

143 E Austin St, Giddings, TX 78942
Tel.: (979) 542-3666   TX
Web Site: http://www.intonline.com
Rev.: $37,000,000
Emp.: 130
Insurance Agents
N.A.I.C.S.: 524210
Robert James Nitsche *(Chm & CEO)*
Jen Dietderich *(Coord-Claims)*
Patricia Short-Garcia *(Acct Mgr-Comml Lines)*
Brigette Burttschell *(Coord-Mktg)*
Jimmy Cobb *(Dir-Sls)*
Pam Machac *(Mgr-Agency Ops)*
Candy Martinez *(Mgr-Client)*
Rhonda Janak *(VP)*

INSURANCE OF AMERICA AGENCY

16775 Addison Rd Ste 410, Dallas, TX 75001
Tel.: (972) 991-2313
Web Site:
   http://www.insuranceofamerica.com
Rev.: $11,800,000
Emp.: 12
Insurance Agents
N.A.I.C.S.: 524210
Anita Beaty *(CFO)*
Pat Archibald *(Pres)*

INSURANCE OFFICE OF AMERICA, INC.

1855 W State Rd 434, Longwood, FL 32750
Tel.: (407) 788-3000
Web Site: http://www.ioausa.com

Year Founded: 1988
Sales Range: $100-124.9 Million
Emp.: 550
Insurance Services
N.A.I.C.S.: 524210
John Ritenour *(Chm)*
Jeff Lagos *(Pres)*
Heath Ritenour *(CEO)*
David Burr *(VP)*
John Shahinian *(VP-CPCU)*
David Hendrick *(Partner & VP)*
Herman Peery *(Sr VP)*
Bruce Johnson *(VP)*
Bryan Yoho *(VP-Risk Mgmt & Insurance Svcs)*
James Powell *(VP)*
Greg Masters *(CFO)*
Jon Thurman *(Exec VP)*
Michael Oliver *(Mgr-Comml Insurance Risk-West)*
Steve Thompson *(Sr VP-Enterprise Initiatives)*

INSURANCE OVERLOAD SERVICES, INC.

5220 Spring Valley Rd Ste 125, Dallas, TX 75240-1306
Tel.: (972) 991-9596   DE
Web Site: http://www.iosstaffing.com
Year Founded: 1983
Sales Range: $10-24.9 Million
Emp.: 14
Insurance Industry Employee Search & Screening Services
N.A.I.C.S.: 561311
Scott Hartman *(Pres)*

INSURANCE RESOURCE BROKERAGE GROUP

Ste 350 1 International Blvd, Mahwah, NJ 07495-0025
Tel.: (201) 236-9800
Web Site:
   http://www.capcoverage.com
Rev.: $35,000,000
Emp.: 45
Insurance Agents
N.A.I.C.S.: 524210
Robert G. Lull *(Pres & CEO)*
Ron Bergstein *(Exec VP)*
Laura DiPiazza *(VP-ACS)*
Deb Ezra *(VP-ACS)*
Carl A. Gerson *(COO)*
Dominic Morelli *(Pres-Capacity Benefits)*
Walter Wynn *(Pres-Capacity Marine)*
Jon Ziman *(VP-Mktg)*
Mark Weinraub *(Chm)*
Gary Maier *(Sr Exec VP)*

Subsidiaries:

Capacity Coverage Co.   (1)
1 International Blvd Fl 3, Mahwah, NJ 07495
Tel.: (201) 236-9800
Web Site: http://www.capcoverage.com
Insurance Brokers
N.A.I.C.S.: 524210
Gary S. Maier *(Mng Principal)*
Jay Bergstein *(Mng Principal)*

INSURANCE SERVICES GROUP

6521 Burnet Ln, Austin, TX 78757-2848
Insurance Agencies & Brokerages
N.A.I.C.S.: 524210
Gerald Collins *(Owner)*

INSURANCE.COM, INC.

29000 Aurora Rd, Solon, OH 44139
Tel.: (440) 498-0971
Web Site: http://www.insurance.com
Sales Range: $50-74.9 Million
Emp.: 175
Auto Insurance Seller
N.A.I.C.S.: 524298

Chris Kissell *(Mng Editor)*

INSURANCEAGENTS.COM

309 S 4th St Ste 212, Columbus, OH 43215
Year Founded: 2003
Sales Range: $10-24.9 Million
Emp.: 35
Online Insurance Services
N.A.I.C.S.: 524210
Lev Barinskiy *(Co-Founder & Pres)*
Seth Kravitz *(Co-Founder & CEO)*

INSURAPRISE INC.

12116 Jekel Cir, Austin, TX 78727-6111
Tel.: (512) 524-3330
Web Site:
   http://www.medigap360.com
Year Founded: 2006
Sales Range: $1-9.9 Million
Emp.: 43
Health Insurance Brokerage
N.A.I.C.S.: 524298
Brandon Todd *(CEO)*
Casey Hughes *(VP-Market Dev)*

INSURCOMM CONSTRUCTION, INC.

3510 Lafayette Rd Ste 4, Portsmouth, NH 03801
Tel.: (603) 430-7701
Web Site: http://www.insurcomm.com
Year Founded: 1996
Sales Range: $1-9.9 Million
Emp.: 14
Residential Remodeler
N.A.I.C.S.: 236118
Mike Brown *(VP)*
Josh Cote *(Project Mgr-Construction)*
Neil Robbins *(Pres)*

Subsidiaries:

Soil-Away Cleaning & Restoration Services   (1)
5 Eastpoint Dr Ste 16, Hooksett, NH 03106
Tel.: (603) 641-6555
Web Site: http://www.soilaway.com
Other Services to Buildings & Dwellings
N.A.I.C.S.: 561790
Rich Shaw *(Dir-Ops)*

INSUREON

30 N LaSalle Ste 2500, Chicago, IL 60602
Web Site: http://www.insureon.com
Online Insurance Services
N.A.I.C.S.: 524210
Ted Devine *(CEO)*
Yuri Ter-Saakyants *(CTO)*
Belen Tokarski *(Chief Admin Officer)*
Andrei Utkin *(CMO)*
Brandon Hickey *(Pres-Brokerage)*
Ralph Blust *(Pres)*
Jared Kaplan *(Co-Founder)*
Ted Devine *(Co-Founder)*
Jeff Somers *(Head-Retail)*

Subsidiaries:

InsuranceNoodle LLC   (1)
30 N. LaSalle St Ste 2500, Chicago, IL 60602
Tel.: (888) 466-8868
Web Site: http://www.insurancenoodle.com
Sales Range: $25-49.9 Million
Emp.: 50
Online Insurance Services
N.A.I.C.S.: 513199
Brian Dunn *(Mgr-Bus Dev)*

INSURICA, INC.

5100 N Classen Blvd Ste 400, Oklahoma City, OK 73118
Tel.: (405) 523-2100
Web Site: https://insurica.com
Insurance Related Activities
N.A.I.C.S.: 524298

Insurica, Inc.—(Continued)

Mike Ross *(Pres & CEO)*
Ed Young *(CFO & COO)*
Dillon Rosenhamer *(Chief Sls Officer & Sr VP)*

INSURMARK, INC.

820 Gessner Ste 970, Houston, TX 77024
Tel.: (713) 973-7575   TX
Web Site: http://www.insurmark.net
Year Founded: 1983
Sales Range: $10-24.9 Million
Emp.: 34
Business Consultants
N.A.I.C.S.: 561499
Steve Kerns *(Founder & CEO)*
Carolyn Luby *(Pres)*
Jeff Maxey *(VP)*
Tony Sifuentes *(Sr VP & Dir-Sls)*
Randy Yost *(VP)*
Darieke Hemphill *(Sr VP-Ops & Admin)*
Nicole Nguyen *(Dir-Sls-Life Insurance)*
Frank Lozano *(VP)*
Pamela Parks *(VP & Mgr-Annuity Case)*

INSYGHT

11900 W Olympic Blvd Ste 500, Los Angeles, CA 90064
Tel.: (310) 247-3840
Web Site: http://www.insyght.com
Sales Range: $10-24.9 Million
Emp.: 60
Continuing Medical Education Programs, Advisory Boards & Congresses
N.A.I.C.S.: 923110
Rina Yasuda *(Pres)*
Donato Crowley *(Coord-Event)*

INSYS THERAPEUTICS, INC.

1333 S Spectrum Blvd Ste 100, Chandler, AZ 85286
Tel.: (480) 500-3127   DE
Web Site: http://www.insysrx.com
Year Founded: 1990
Rev: $82,080,000
Assets: $192,527,000
Liabilities: $235,627,000
Net Worth: ($43,100,000)
Earnings: ($124,507,000)
Emp.: 226
Fiscal Year-end: 12/31/18
Cancer Treatment Drug Developer
N.A.I.C.S.: 325412
Venkat R. Goskonda *(Chief Scientific Officer)*
Steven J. Meyer *(Chm)*
B. Sanga Emmanuel *(Chief Compliance Officer & VP)*
Mark E. Nance *(Chief Legal Officer & Gen Counsel)*
Andrece Housley *(CFO)*

Subsidiaries:

Insys Manufacturing, LLC   (1)
2700 Oakmont Dr, Round Rock, TX 78665
Tel.: (512) 583-6974
Pharmaceuticals Product Mfr
N.A.I.C.S.: 325412

Insys Pharma, Inc.   (1)
444 S Ellis St, Chandler, AZ 85224
Tel.: (602) 910-2617
Emp.: 18
Pharmaceuticals Product Mfr
N.A.I.C.S.: 325412

INSZONE INSURANCE SERVICES, LLC

2721 Citrus Rd Ste A, Rancho Cordova, CA 95742
Tel.: (833) 819-5009

Web Site: http://www.inszoneinsurance.com
Year Founded: 2002
Insurance Provider
N.A.I.C.S.: 524298
Norm Hudson *(Chm)*
Chris Walters *(CEO)*
Pat Grignon *(Chief Revenue Officer)*
Rich Lemon *(Chief Integration Officer)*
Lisa Hermann *(VP-Carrier Rels)*
Kari Thies *(Exec VP-Benefits Dept)*
Kathleen Kozlowski *(VP-Carrier Rels)*

Subsidiaries:

Agape Insurance Services   (1)
2021 E 4th St Ste 122, Santa Ana, CA 92705-3912
Tel.: (503) 650-4325
Web Site: https://www.loveagape.com
Insurance Agencies & Brokerages
N.A.I.C.S.: 524210

Alliance Business & Commercial Insurance Services   (1)
163 Yorba St, Tustin, CA 92780-2924
Tel.: (714) 832-8192
Web Site:
    http://www.alliancebusinessinsurance.com
Insurance Agencies & Brokerages
N.A.I.C.S.: 524210

American Heritage Agency Inc.   (1)
1401 Main St Ste A, Hays, KS 67601-3772
Tel.: (785) 562-2820
Web Site: http://www.americanheritageinsurance.com
Insurance Agencies & Brokerages
N.A.I.C.S.: 524210

Appling Insurance Agency   (1)
5680 State Farm Dr Ste 104, Rohnert Park, CA 94928-1643
Tel.: (707) 585-1955
Web Site: http://www.applinginsurance.com
Insurance Agencies & Brokerages
N.A.I.C.S.: 524210

Brinch Agency, LLC   (1)
18200 13 Mile Rd, Roseville, MI 48066
Tel.: (586) 415-4214
Web Site: http://www.brinchagency.com
Insurance Related Activities
N.A.I.C.S.: 524298
Chris Brinch *(Owner)*

Brumfield & Peters Insurance Services, Inc.   (1)
16203 Clark Ave Ste B, Bellflower, CA 90706-4500
Tel.: (562) 461-8008
Web Site:
    http://www.brumfieldpetersinsurance.com
Insurance Agencies & Brokerages
N.A.I.C.S.: 524210
Herman O. Peters *(Owner)*

Cameo Insurance Services, Inc.   (1)
614 W Manchester Blvd Ste 202, Inglewood, CA 90306
Tel.: (310) 677-8199
Web Site: http://www.cameoinsurance.com
Insurance Agencies & Brokerages
N.A.I.C.S.: 524210

Capizzi Insurance Agency   (1)
11455 Paramount Blvd Ste C, Downey, CA 90241-4595
Tel.: (562) 869-3016
Web Site: http://www.capizziinsurance.com
Insurance Agencies & Brokerages
N.A.I.C.S.: 524210

Carmichael Associates, Inc.   (1)
2535 Townsgate Rd Ste 213, Westlake Village, CA 91361-5978
Tel.: (805) 379-1585
Web Site:
    http://www.carmichaelassociates.com
Insurance Agencies & Brokerages
N.A.I.C.S.: 524210
Stanley Carmichael *(CEO)*

Cascade Insurance Center LLC   (1)
336 SW Cyber Dr Ste 104, Bend, OR 97702-1682
Tel.: (541) 382-7772
Web Site: http://www.cascadeinsure.com

Insurance Agencies & Brokerages
N.A.I.C.S.: 524210

Desert Cornerstone Insurance Service, Inc.   (1)
81-557 Dr Carreon Blvd Ste B-8, Indio, CA 92201
Tel.: (760) 230-0777
Web Site:
    http://www.desertcornerstoneins.com
Insurance Services
N.A.I.C.S.: 524298
Sanae Martin *(Mgr-Acct-Comml Lines)*
Crystal Martin *(Mgr-Mktg)*
Josie Johnson *(CFO-Surety Bonds)*
Matthew List *(Pres)*

Financial Arts Inc.   (1)
921 S Halleck St, Demotte, IN 46310
Tel.: (219) 987-4438
Web Site: http://www.financialartsinc.com
Insurance Agencies & Brokerages
N.A.I.C.S.: 524210
John Fagen *(Pres)*

Frank Vitale Insurance Agency   (1)
4067 Cory St Ste 1, Soquel, CA 95073-2097
Tel.: (831) 462-9222
Web Site:
    http://www.frankvitaleinsurance.com
Insurance Agencies & Brokerages
N.A.I.C.S.: 524210

Huntington Pacific Insurance Agency, Inc.   (1)
22940 Lyons Ave, Newhall, CA 91321-2718
Tel.: (714) 841-6283
Web Site:
    http://www.huntpacificinsurance.com
Insurance Agencies & Brokerages
N.A.I.C.S.: 524210
Mark Heberden *(Mgr)*

Jones-Wilson Insurance & Investments, Inc.   (1)
700 W 4th St, Benson, AZ 85602
Tel.: (520) 586-2226
Web Site:
    http://www.joneswilsoninsurance.com
Insurance Related Activities
N.A.I.C.S.: 524298

Kelly, Naney Insurance Agency, Inc.   (1)
445 W Dakota Ave, Fresno, CA 93705
Tel.: (559) 224-7164
Web Site: http://www.kellynaney.com
Sales Range: $1-9.9 Million
Emp.: 10
Insurance Agents, Brokers, And Service, N
N.A.I.C.S.: 524210
Lisa Naney *(Principal)*

LPL Insurance Agency, Inc.   (1)
844 Steel Dr, Brea, CA 92821
Tel.: (714) 572-9700
Sales Range: $1-9.9 Million
Emp.: 100
Insurance Agents, Brokers, And Service, N
N.A.I.C.S.: 524210
Bud Laughlin *(Pres)*
Owen Lambourne *(Sr Mgr-Risk)*

Larry Fu Insurance Agency Inc   (1)
1801 Grand St., Alameda, CA 94501
Tel.: (510) 268-0888
Web Site: http://www.fuinsurance.com
Insurance Agencies & Brokerages
N.A.I.C.S.: 524210
Larry Fu *(Owner)*

Marshall Pierson, Inc.   (1)
209 Pajaro St, Salinas, CA 93901-3419
Tel.: (831) 758-8222
Web Site: http://www.piersonusa.com
Direct Health & Medical Insurance Carriers
N.A.I.C.S.: 524114
B. Randall Pierson *(Pres)*

Mattis Insurance Agency   (1)
4553 Hwy 6 N, Houston, TX 07753-3630
Tel.: (732) 212-0061
Web Site:
    http://www.theclaimsmanager.com
Insurance Agencies & Brokerages
N.A.I.C.S.: 524210
Derrik Mattis *(Owner)*

Maurice Taylor Insurance Brokers Inc.   (1)

PO Box 29127, Los Angeles, CA 90029-0127
Tel.: (323) 662-9110
Web Site:
    http://www.mauricetaylorinsurance.com
Insurance Agencies & Brokerages
N.A.I.C.S.: 524210
Maurice Taylor *(Founder)*

Mosaic Insurance Alliance, LLC   (1)
2122 164th St SW Ste 301, Lynnwood, WA 98087
Tel.: (425) 320-4280
Web Site: http://www.mosaicia.com
Insurance Related Activities
N.A.I.C.S.: 524298
Tom Dilley *(Sr VP & Head-Fin Institutions)*

NAIS, Inc   (1)
10722 Arrow Route Ste 116, Rancho Cucamonga, CA 91730-4809
Web Site: http://www.nugeninsurance.com
Insurance Agencies & Brokerages
N.A.I.C.S.: 524210
Bart Nugen *(Owner)*

Pacific Redwood Insurance Agency, Inc.   (1)
80 Eureka Sq Ste 219, Pacifica, CA 94044-2678
Tel.: (650) 359-0655
Web Site:
    http://www.pacificredwoodinsurance.com
Insurance Agencies & Brokerages
N.A.I.C.S.: 524210

Risco Insurance Services, Inc.   (1)
8534-B Long Beach Blvd, South Gate, CA 90280
Tel.: (323) 587-6326
Web Site: http://www.riscoins.com
Insurance Related Activities
N.A.I.C.S.: 524298
Javier Rodriguez *(Founder)*

Sanfilippo & Sons Insurance Services LLC   (1)
888 N 1st St Ste D, San Jose, CA 95112-6346
Web Site: http://www.sanfilippoins.com
Insurance Agencies & Brokerages
N.A.I.C.S.: 524210

Schaefer Agency, Inc.   (1)
707 N Nevada Ave, Colorado Springs, CO 80903-1088
Tel.: (620) 241-2200
Web Site: http://www.schaeferagency.com
Insurance Agencies & Brokerages
N.A.I.C.S.: 524210
John Schaefer *(Pres)*

Specialty Contractor's Insurance Services   (1)
4420 Tya Ln, Placerville, CA 95667-9288
Tel.: (530) 621-4433
Web Site: http://www.scisinc.net
Insurance Agencies & Brokerages
N.A.I.C.S.: 524210
Michelle Masters *(Pres)*

Speck Insurance & Financial Services PLLC   (1)
5130 Academy St, Houston, TX 77005-1002
Tel.: (713) 524-4303
Insurance Agencies & Brokerages
N.A.I.C.S.: 524210
Paeder Hoovestol *(Partner)*

Texstar Insurance Services, Inc.   (1)
14350 Northbrook Dr Ste 100, San Antonio, TX 78232
Tel.: (210) 402-0498
Web Site: http://www.texstarinsurance.com
Insurance Related Activities
N.A.I.C.S.: 524298
John Rusk *(Owner)*

Vaught Wright & Bond, Inc.   (1)
533 Main St, Placerville, CA 95667
Tel.: (530) 622-1835
Web Site: http://www.vwbins.com
Insurance Management Services
N.A.I.C.S.: 524298
Bruce Dezzani *(Pres & Dir-Ops)*
Candy Johnson *(Mgr-Personal Lines)*
Jenny LaShell *(Acct Mgr-Personal Lines)*
Debbie Barr *(Acct Mgr-Comml & Health)*
Martha Ash *(Mgr-Comml Lines)*

Williams Insurance Services, Inc. (1)
6259 Adobe Rd, Twentynine Palms, CA 92277-2649
Tel.: (760) 367-7542
Web Site: http://www.wisservice.com
Insurance Agencies & Brokerages
N.A.I.C.S.: 524210
Dee Richhart (Owner)

Willow Glen Insurance Agency, Inc. (1)
1500 E Hamilton Ave, Campbell, CA 95008
Tel.: (408) 371-9721
Sales Range: $1-9.9 Million
Emp.: 10
Insurance Agencies & Brokerages
N.A.I.C.S.: 524210
Pat Herron (Mgr-Admin)

INTACT INFO SOLUTIONS LLC
1370 Vly Vista Dr Ste 265, Diamond Bar, CA 91765
Tel.: (909) 396-9200
Web Site: http://www.intactinfo.com
Year Founded: 2005
Sales Range: $1-9.9 Million
Emp.: 20
Customized Search Engine Optimization
N.A.I.C.S.: 541810
Sodi Hundal (CEO)
Jon Lightfoot (Pres)
Leslee Detillo (Dir-Social Media & Digital Mktg)
Ricardo Flores (Mgr-Technical)
Michelle Vasquez (Mgr-Digital Mktg)
Roshni Taylor (Mgr-Technical Project)
Roberto Bustamante (Dir-Content)

INTACT TECHNOLOGY, INC.
9111 Edmonston Rd Ste 300, Greenbelt, MD 20770
Tel.: (301) 429-1923
Web Site: http://www.intact-tech.com
Year Founded: 1994
Sales Range: $10-24.9 Million
Emp.: 85
Custom Computer Programming Services
N.A.I.C.S.: 541511
Jesse White (CEO)
Randall Fulk (CFO)
Vincent Viola (VP-Product & Innovation)
Jason Hampel (Pres)
Danelle Prezioso (Dir-Strategic Comm)
Nicole Wise (Comm Mgr)
Brian Crosby (Chief Growth Officer)
Bahar Niakan (Mng Dir-HR Modernization)

INTALIO, INC.
644 Emerson St Ste 200, Palo Alto, CA 94301
Tel.: (650) 596-1800
Web Site: http://www.intalio.com
Year Founded: 1999
Sales Range: $1-9.9 Million
Emp.: 25
Software Publisher
N.A.I.C.S.: 513210
Mark Tolliver (Chm)
Raj Jain (CEO)
Stuart Finn (Sr VP-Sls-Worldwide)
Abdullah Daoud (VP-Products)
Bechara Wakim (Founder & Chm)
Firas Raouf (CEO)

Subsidiaries:

Intalio APAC (1)
2 Shenton Way 18-01 SGX Tower 1, Chye Sing Building, Singapore, 068804, Singapore
Tel.: (65) 6513 2655
Software Publisher
N.A.I.C.S.: 513210

Intalio EMEA (1)

Schwanthalerstrasse 5, 80336, Munich, Germany
Tel.: (49) 89 3801 2829
Software Publisher
N.A.I.C.S.: 513210

Intalio India (1)
No 4 1st Floor First Phase BTM Layout, Bengaluru, 560076, India
Tel.: (91) 80 41205826
Software Publisher
N.A.I.C.S.: 513210

Intalio Latin America (1)
Bouchard 644 7th Floor Suite C, Buenos Aires, Argentina
Tel.: (54) 11 5031 2809
Web Site: http://www.intalio.com
Software Publisher
N.A.I.C.S.: 513210

INTANDEM CAPITAL PARTNERS, LLC
One Vanderbilt Av Ste 2400, New York, NY 10017
Tel.: (646) 930-1530
Web Site:
http://www.intandemcapital.com
Private Equity Investment Firm
N.A.I.C.S.: 523940
Elliot S. Cooperstone (Executives)
Elliot Cooperstone (Mng Partner)
Bob Patricelli (Partner)
Todd Squilanti (Mng Dir)
Steven Cohen (Mng Dir)
Brad Coppens (Sr Mng Dir)
Chris Reef (Operating Partner)

Subsidiaries:

Pediatric Home Respiratory Services, LLC (1)
2800 Cleveland Ave N, Roseville, MN 55113
Tel.: (651) 642-1825
Web Site:
http://www.pediatrichomeservice.com
Independent Pediatric Home Care Company
N.A.I.C.S.: 621610
Rebecca Long (VP-Ops-MN, WI & IA)
Rick Mueller (Sr Dir-IT)
Adam Nielsen (CEO)
Cameo Zehnder (Chief Admin Officer)
Drue Pounds (CFO)
Chad Svihel (Chief Supply Chain Officer)
Donna Filar (Exec VP-Market Outreach)
Glenn Galloway (Exec VP-IT)
Joyce Bulman (VP-Quality & Compliance)
Rick Mueller (Sr Dir-IT)
Dana Johnson (Sr Dir-Mktg)
Sean Balke (Pres-Private Duty Nursing)
John Reed (VP-Ops-OH, KY & IN)
Joe Rodriguez (VP-Ops-TX)

Subsidiary (Domestic):

Apple Homecare Medical Supply, LLC (2)
1400 S Sherman St Ste 124, Richardson, TX 75081
Web Site: http://www.applehms.com
Surgical Appliance & Supplies Mfr
N.A.I.C.S.: 339113
Jimmy Shankle (Mgr-Ops)

INTARCIA THERAPEUTICS, INC.
24650 Industrial Blvd, Hayward, CA 94545
Tel.: (510) 782-7800   DE
Web Site: http://www.intarcia.com
Sales Range: $10-24.9 Million
Emp.: 69
Cancer Treatment Therapeutic Pharmaceutical Products Developer & Mfr
N.A.I.C.S.: 325412
Thomas R. Alessi (VP-Dev & Mfg)
Michelle Baron (Chief Medical Officer & VP-Clinical Res)
Raymond T. Keane (Chief Legal Officer, Gen Counsel & VP)
Jay Smith (Head-Customer Experience & Outcomes)

Sunita Zalani (VP & Global Head-Regulatory Affairs & Quality)
James P. Brady (VP-HR)
John Yee (VP & Head-Global Medical Affairs, Safety & Ops)
Anthony Hurley (VP-Global Comml Mfg & Ops)
Michael Williams (COO)
Paul Feldman (Head-Discovery & Translational Medicine)
David Franklin (VP-Alliance Mgmt & Advocacy)

INTCOMEX, INC.
3505 NW 107th Ave, Miami, FL 33178
Tel.: (305) 477-6230   DE
Web Site: http://www.intcomex.com
Year Founded: 1989
Sales Range: $1-4.9 Billion
Emp.: 1,728
Computer Software Wholesale Distr
N.A.I.C.S.: 425120
Anthony Shalom (Chm)
Michael Shalom (Pres & CEO)
Jose Biton (CFO)
Danny Schachtel (Chief Comml Officer)
Alejandra Molina (Gen Mgr-Chile y Uruguay)
Camilo Borda (Gen Mgr-Colombia)
Ariel Engelsztajn (Gen Mgr-Costa Rica)
Paul Bergmann (Gen Mgr-Ecuador)
Helfido Juarez (Gen Mgr-Guatemala)
Jerry Pelosi (Gen Mgr-Miami)
Eric Hachmann (Gen Mgr-Peru)
Mauro Butelmann (Pres-Chile)
Joseph Bouhadana (VP-Corp IT)

Subsidiaries:

Software Brokers of America, Inc. (1)
3505 NW 107th Ave, Miami, FL 33178
Tel.: (305) 477-6230
Web Site: http://www.intcomex.com
Rev.: $213,029,248
Emp.: 200
Computer Services
N.A.I.C.S.: 423430
Anthony Shalom (Chm & CEO)

INTEC COMPANY, INC.
3495 Viaduct St SW, Grandville, MI 49418
Tel.: (616) 257-1200   MI
Year Founded: 1966
Sales Range: $10-24.9 Million
Emp.: 45
Fire Detection & Burglar Systems
N.A.I.C.S.: 561621
Edward Butzer (Pres & Chm)

INTEC LLC
10306 Eaton Pl Ste 520, Fairfax, VA 22030
Tel.: (703) 255-1524
Web Site: http://www.intecllc.net
Year Founded: 2005
Sales Range: $10-24.9 Million
Emp.: 40
IT Services to the Federal Government & Departments of Defense & Homeland Security
N.A.I.C.S.: 921190
Bruce Donaldson (Founder & Pres)
Robbie Donaldson (VP-Ops)
Nate Copeland (COO & Sr VP)

INTEC SYSTEMS, INC.
3910 FM 1960 W, Houston, TX 77068-3002
Tel.: (281) 444-5566   TX
Year Founded: 1984
Sales Range: $50-74.9 Million
Emp.: 70

Computer Integrated Systems Design Services
N.A.I.C.S.: 541512
Paul Fisher (Controller)
Ming Chung (Pres)

INTECARE, INC.
8604 Allisonville Rd Ste 325, Indianapolis, IN 46250
Tel.: (317) 237-5770   IN
Web Site: http://www.intecare.org
Year Founded: 1998
Sales Range: $50-74.9 Million
Emp.: 11
Behavioral Healthcare Services
N.A.I.C.S.: 622110
Geoffrey E. Buck (CEO)
Stacy Veach (Dir-Clinical)
Venita J. Moore (CFO)
Allen Brown (Pres)

INTECH INVESTMENT MANAGEMENT LLC
250 S Australian Ave Ste 1800, West Palm Beach, FL 33401
Tel.: (561) 775-1100   DE
Web Site:
http://www.intechinvestments.com
Year Founded: 1987
Emp.: 100
Investment Advisory Services
N.A.I.C.S.: 523999
Churchill G. Franklin (Exec Chm)
Adrian Banner (Chief Investment Officer & Exec Dir)
John F. Brown (Exec VP & Head-Global Client Dev)
Jian Tang (Portfolio Mgr)
Andre Prawoto (CMO)
Ryan Stever (Deputy Chief Investment Officer & Exec VP)
Katherine Hardenbergh (Sr VP & Dir-Res)

INTECH PRINTING & DIRECT MAIL
4408 Corporate Sq, Naples, FL 34104
Tel.: (239) 643-3430   FL
Web Site:
http://www.intechprinting.com
Year Founded: 1987
Commercial Printing, Lithographic
N.A.I.C.S.: 323111
Dan Fitzgerald (Acct Exec)
Steve Bello (Mgr-Direct Mail)
Sue Lampitt (Dir-Sls & Mktg)
Rodney Held (CEO)
John Licari (Production Mgr)

Subsidiaries:

Coastal Printing, Inc. (1)
1730 Independence Blvd, Sarasota, FL 34234
Tel.: (941) 351-1515
Web Site: http://www.coastalprint.com
Commercial Lithographic Printing
N.A.I.C.S.: 323111
Rodney Held (Pres & CEO)

INTECH TRAILERS, INC.
1940 W Market St, Nappanee, IN 46550
Tel.: (574) 773-9536
Web Site:
http://www.intechtrailers.com
Year Founded: 2010
Sales Range: $25-49.9 Million
Emp.: 138
Automotive Aluminum Trailer Mfr
N.A.I.C.S.: 336212
Adam Maxwell (Owner)

INTEGRA BUSINESS CENTER INC.

Integra Business Center Inc.—(Continued)

7248 Tilghman St Ste 120, Allentown, PA 18106
Tel.: (484) 223-3480   PA
Web Site: http://www.integraone.com
Year Founded: 1990
Information Technology Solutions Services
N.A.I.C.S.: 518210
Duy Nguyen (Mgr-Svc)
Marty Andrefski (Pres)
Mary Brooks (Controller)
Anoure Fenstermaker (Mktg Dir)
Jim Bedics (Dir-Server)
Paul Eschbach (VP-Svc Ops)
Kyle Knecht (Dir-Managed Svcs)
Brad Rightmyer (Mgr-Network & Security Practice)
Chris Satterly (VP-Sls Ops)

Subsidiaries:

Lightspeed Technologies, Inc.   (1)
451 Third Ave, Kingston, PA 18704
Tel.: (570) 714-5005
Data Processing, Hosting & Related Services
N.A.I.C.S.: 518210
Denise Balkan (Office Mgr)

INTEGRA CONSULTING & COMPUTER SERVICES
1490 N Clinton Ave, Bay Shore, NY 11706
Tel.: (631) 969-2600
Web Site:
   http://www.integraservices.com
Sales Range: $10-24.9 Million
Emp.: 21
Custom Computer Programming Services
N.A.I.C.S.: 541511
David Antar (Pres)

INTEGRA ENCLOSURES, INC.
7716 Tyler Blvd, Mentor, OH 44060
Tel.: (440) 269-4966
Web Site:
   http://www.integraenclosures.com
Year Founded: 1993
Sales Range: $1-9.9 Million
Emp.: 19
Enclosures for Electrical Devices
N.A.I.C.S.: 335999
Jim McWilliams (Pres)

INTEGRA NETWORKS INC.
745 Albany Shaker Rd, Latham, NY 12110
Web Site:
   http://www.integranetworks.net
Year Founded: 2007
Sales Range: $10-24.9 Million
Emp.: 30
Fiber Optic Equipment
N.A.I.C.S.: 335921
David J. Prescott (Pres, CEO & CTO)

INTEGRA PARTNERS LLC
1701 Utica Ave, New York, NY 10005
Tel.: (718) 369-0012
Web Site: http://accessintegra.com
Year Founded: 2005
Sales Range: $25-49.9 Million
Emp.: 20
Offers Streamlined Access to Health Plans & Patients to Suppliers of Medical Equipment & Orthotic & Prosthetic Services
N.A.I.C.S.: 621610
Andrew Saltoun (Pres & CEO)
Bianca Flikweert (VP-Sls)

INTEGRA REALTY RESOURCES, INC.
11 Times Sq 640 8th Ave 15th Fl Ste A, New York, NY 10036

Tel.: (212) 255-7858   FL
Web Site: http://www.irr.com
Year Founded: 1999
Sales Range: $100-124.9 Million
Emp.: 860
Commercial Real Estate Valuation, Counseling & Advisory Services
N.A.I.C.S.: 531320
George Ward (VP)
Michael S. Miller (CIO)
Raymond Cirz (Sr Mng Dir)
Paul D. Griffith (Vice Chm, Pres & Sr Mng Dir-Pittsburgh)
Anthony M. Graziano (Chm & Sr Mng Dir-Miami & Palm Beach)
Anthony Sanna (Sr Mng Dir-Detroit)
Paul A. Waters (COO)
Matthew Krauser (Sr Mng Dir-Northern New Jersey & New York)
Scott Beebe (Sr Mng Dir-Sacramento)
Michael Silverman (Mng Dir-Philadelphia)
Matthew Albigese (Sr Mng Dir-Atlanta)
John D. Scott Jr. (Mng Dir-Charlotte)

INTEGRA STAFFING & SEARCH
201 W Morehead St, Charlotte, NC 28202
Tel.: (704) 527-9191
Web Site:
   http://www.integrastaffing.com
Year Founded: 2002
Rev.: $8,800,000
Emp.: 300
Help Supply & Executive Placement Services
N.A.I.C.S.: 561320
Katie Bendall (Dir-Admin)
Stephen Swanick (Mgr-Acctg)

INTEGRA TECHNOLOGIES LLC
3450 N Rock Rd Bldg 100, Wichita, KS 67226-1327
Tel.: (316) 630-6800   KS
Web Site: http://www.integra-tech.com
Sales Range: $10-24.9 Million
Emp.: 100
Semiconductors Testing, Qualification & Related Technical Services
N.A.I.C.S.: 541990
David Goss (Mgr-Acct)
Kent Wade (VP-Sls)
Suja Ramnath (Pres & CEO)

INTEGRA TECHNOLOGY CONSULTING CORPORATION
400 Fifth Ave Ste 100, Waltham, MA 02451
Tel.: (781) 890-0070
Web Site: http://www.integratc.com
Year Founded: 2000
Rev.: $8,400,000
Emp.: 32
Computer System Design Services
N.A.I.C.S.: 541512
Ted Bartlett (Acct Mgr)
David Teplow (Founder, Pres & CEO)

INTEGRACLICK, LLC
IntegraClick Professional Pk E Bldg Ste 220 5901 N Honore Ave, Sarasota, FL 34243-2632
Tel.: (941) 584-6543
Web Site: http://www.integraclick.com
Year Founded: 2002
Online Advertising & Marketing
N.A.I.C.S.: 541890

INTEGRACORE, INC.
1000 Hemphill Ave, Atlanta, GA 30318

Tel.: (404) 961-1000
Web Site: http://www.broadriver.com
Sales Range: $25-49.9 Million
Emp.: 5
Holding Company
N.A.I.C.S.: 551112
Kevin Beebe (VP & Gen Mgr)

Subsidiaries:

BroadRiver Communications
Corporation   (1)
1000 Hemphill Ave, Atlanta, GA 30318
Tel.: (404) 961-1000
Web Site: http://www.broadriver.com
Sales Range: $10-24.9 Million
Voice Over IP Web Hosting
N.A.I.C.S.: 517810
Kevin Beebe (Gen Mgr)

LecStar Telecom, Inc.   (1)
2 Ravinia Dr Ste 1300, Atlanta, GA 30346
Tel.: (770) 989-9800
Web Site: http://www.lecstar.com
Sales Range: $10-24.9 Million
Integrated Communication Services
N.A.I.C.S.: 334220

INTEGRAL GROUP, INC.
427 13th St, Oakland, CA 94612
Tel.: (510) 663-2070   CA
Web Site:
   http://www.integralgroup.com
Year Founded: 1996
Sales Range: $1-9.9 Million
Emp.: 250
Engineeering Services
N.A.I.C.S.: 541330
Kevin Hydes (Pres & CEO)
Stet Sanborn (Engr-HVAC Project)
Fe Reyes Deyhim (Mgr-Acctg)
Mike Kimsal (Mng Dir)
Ted van der Linden (Principal-Performance Engrg)
Brenden McEneaney (Principal-Urban Innovation-Oakland)

INTEGRAL MARKETING, INC.
2139 Espey Ct Ste 7, Crofton, MD 21114
Tel.: (410) 721-0645   MD
Web Site:
   http://www.integralmkting.com
Year Founded: 1994
Sales Range: $10-24.9 Million
Emp.: 6
Marketing Consulting Services
N.A.I.C.S.: 541613
Ronald J. Johnson (Pres, VP & Gen Mgr)

INTEGRAL MEDIA COMPANY
350 Highway 7 Ste 140, Excelsior, MN 55331-3160
Tel.: (952) 470-5254
Web Site:
   http://www.integralprintmedia.com
Year Founded: 1989
Sales Range: $10-24.9 Million
Emp.: 7
Media Buying Services
N.A.I.C.S.: 541830
Brenda Vasnosdahl (Dir-Client Plng & Relations)
Willi Abbott (Dir-Sls & Mktg)
Eric Sims (Founder)

INTEGRAL QUALITY CARE
4630 Woodland Corporate Blvd, Tampa, FL 33614
Tel.: (866) 258-4326   FL
Web Site:
   http://www.integralqualitycare.com
Year Founded: 2009
Sales Range: $25-49.9 Million
Medicaid Provider
N.A.I.C.S.: 524114

James Young (CEO)
Elizabeth Day (Dir-Medical Mgmt)
Patricia Simpson (Mgr-Compliance)
Fred Hill (CMO)

INTEGRAND INSURANCE COMPANY
369 Calle Ensenada, San Juan, PR 00920
Tel.: (787) 781-0707
Web Site: http://www.integrand-pr.com
Rev.: $75,205,128
Emp.: 239
Fire, Marine & Casualty Insurance
N.A.I.C.S.: 524126
Victor J. Salgado Jr. (Pres)

INTEGRANT, INC.
5405 Oberlin Dr, San Diego, CA 92121
Tel.: (858) 731-8700   CA
Web Site: http://www.integrant.com
Sales Range: $1-9.9 Million
Emp.: 97
Custom Computer Programming Services
N.A.I.C.S.: 541511
Yousef Awad (CEO)
Rami Awad (VP-Intl Bus)
Julie Pacheco (VP-Mktg & Delivery)
Darcy Fant (Mgr-Fin)
Karleen Wise Andersen (Mgr-Mktg)
Cheryle Ehmke (Mgr-Bus Dev)
Salah Ahmad (Mgr-Technical Acct)
Raed Al-Jawad (Mgr-Technical Acct)
Adham Fathallah (Mgr-Technical Acct)
Deidre Harwelll (Office Mgr)
Peter Sobhy (Principal)

INTEGRATED ACCESS CORP.
421 Woodland Ave, Wayne, PA 19087-3424
Tel.: (610) 886-4200
Web Site: http://www.goiac.com
Management Consulting Services
N.A.I.C.S.: 541618
Steve Sparkes (Pres)

INTEGRATED AIRLINE SERVICES, INC.
3980 Quebec St Ste 111, Denver, CO 80207
Tel.: (303) 398-2416
Web Site: http://www.iasair.com
Sales Range: $50-74.9 Million
Emp.: 1,800
Air Freight Handling At Airports
N.A.I.C.S.: 488119
Tom Wheeling (VP-Sls & Mktg)
Julio E. Feliciano (VP)
Michael V. LaBarbera (CFO)
Harry B. Combs Jr. (Chm & CEO)

INTEGRATED ARCHIVE SYSTEMS INC.
1121 N San Antonio Rd Ste D100, Palo Alto, CA 94303-4325
Tel.: (650) 390-9995   CA
Web Site: http://www.iarchive.com
Year Founded: 1994
Sales Range: $75-99.9 Million
Emp.: 75
Computer Integrated Systems Design
N.A.I.C.S.: 541512
Amy Rao (Founder & CEO)
Karin Napier (VP-Sls)
Anna Borden (CFO)

INTEGRATED ASSET SERVICES, LLC
4600 S Syracuse St, Denver, CO 80237
Tel.: (303) 770-1976
Web Site: http://www.iasreo.com

Year Founded: 1995
Sales Range: $25-49.9 Million
Emp.: 271
Default Mortgage Services
N.A.I.C.S.: 522310
John Burnett (COO)
Ryan Tomazin (Pres)

INTEGRATED BEHAVIORAL HEALTH, INC.

2 Park Plz Ste 1200, Irvine, CA
92614-2562
Tel.: (714) 442-4150   CA
Web Site: http://www.ibhcorp.com
Year Founded: 1999
Digitally-enabled Employee Assistance Programs & Behavioral Health Services
N.A.I.C.S.: 621498
Edward Bosanac (Sec)
David Sockel (Chief Comml Officer)
Dan Clark (CEO)

Subsidiaries:

Claremont Behavioral Services, Inc.   (1)
1050 Marina Village Pkwy, Alameda, CA 94501
Tel.: (510) 337-8844
Web Site: http://www.claremonteap.com
Vocational Rehabilitation Services
N.A.I.C.S.: 624310
Tom Farris (Pres)

Inflexxion, Inc.   (1)
890 Winter St Ste 235, Waltham, MA 02451
Tel.: (617) 332-6028
Web Site: http://www.ibhsolutions.com
Administrative Management & General Management Consulting Service
N.A.I.C.S.: 541611
Kevin Zacharoff (VP-Medical Affairs)
Albert Villapiano (VP-Clinical Dev)
Stephen Butler (Chief Science Officer & Sr VP)
John J. Regazzi (Chm)

INTEGRATED BUSINESS SYSTEMS, INC.

81 2 Bridges Rd Bldg 1, Fairfield, NJ 07004
Tel.: (973) 575-4950   NJ
Web Site: http://www.ibsre.com
Year Founded: 1979
Sales Range: $10-24.9 Million
Emp.: 85
Real Estate Automation Software Developer & Publisher
N.A.I.C.S.: 513210

INTEGRATED CIRCUIT PACKAGING CORPORATION

1602 Tacoma Way, Redwood City, CA 94063
Tel.: (650) 591-8300
Web Site:
http://www.coastalcircuits.net
Year Founded: 1967
Sales Range: $10-24.9 Million
Emp.: 40
Printed Circuit Boards Mfr
N.A.I.C.S.: 334412
Laura Boozer (COO)

INTEGRATED COMMUNICATIONS CORP.

5 Sylvan Way, Parsippany, NJ 07054
Tel.: (973) 984-2755
Sales Range: $125-149.9 Million
Emp.: 250
N.A.I.C.S.: 541810
Steve Viviano (Pres & CEO)
Sal Perreca (CEO)
Frank Galella (CFO & COO-Lowe Healthcare)
Chet Moss (Chief Creative Officer & Exec VP)

Stacy Patterson (Exec VP & Dir-Medical Affairs)
Christian Curry (VP & Dir-HR)

Subsidiaries:

Darwin-Grey Communications   (1)
5th Fl Lynton House 7-12 Tavistock Sq, London, WC1H 9LT, United Kingdom
Tel.: (44) 203 037 3600
N.A.I.C.S.: 541810
Sophie Berry (Mgr)

Darwin-Grey Communications Ltd.   (1)
Sterling House Oxford Road, Kingston, OX13 5AP, Oxfordshire, United Kingdom
Tel.: (44) 1865 822 555
Sales Range: Less than $1 Million
N.A.I.C.S.: 541810
Janet Walsh (Dir-Ops)
Richard Evans (Mng Dir)
Amanda Aiken (Dir-Fin)

Interlink Healthcare Communication   (1)
Princeton Pike Corp Ctr 989 Lenox Dr Ste 300, Lawrenceville, NJ 08648
Tel.: (609) 620-4201
Emp.: 100
Pharmaceuticals
N.A.I.C.S.: 541810
Dave Renner (Exec VP & Dir-Creative)

Pace, Inc.   (1)
35 Waterview Blvd, Parsippany, NJ 07054
Tel.: (973) 658-1200
Emp.: 75
N.A.I.C.S.: 541810
Dainus Jaras (Sr VP & Dir-Creative)
Cheryl Mervine (VP & Dir-Creative-Consumer)
Neil Drucker (Exec VP-New Bus Dev)

INTEGRATED COMMUNITY SOLUTIONS, INC.

2605 S Oneida St Ste 106, Green Bay, WI 54304
Tel.: (920) 498-3737   WI
Web Site: http://www.ics-gb.org
Year Founded: 1989
Sales Range: $10-24.9 Million
Emp.: 34
Social Advocacy Services
N.A.I.C.S.: 813319
Matt Roberts (Exec Dir-Ops)
Lori Degrave (Dir-HR)
Randall Gast (Chm)

INTEGRATED CONSTRUCTION, LLC

14827 Mandarin Rd, Jacksonville, FL 32223
Tel.: (904) 356-6715
Web Site: http://www.integratedfl.com
Year Founded: 2007
Sales Range: $25-49.9 Million
Commercial & Residential Construction
N.A.I.C.S.: 236220
Gregg Munn (CEO)
Tod Zona (COO)
Sean McCarthy (Project Mgr-Hospitality)

INTEGRATED CONTROL SYSTEMS INC.

4020 Vassar Dr NE Ste H, Albuquerque, NM 87107
Tel.: (505) 884-3503
Web Site: http://www.icsicontrols.com
Sales Range: $10-24.9 Million
Emp.: 160
Environmental Control & Facility Management Systems Mfr
N.A.I.C.S.: 334512
Steve Chavez (Pres)
Eric Eckles (VP)
Raymond Gonzales (CFO)

Subsidiaries:

Integrated Control Systems Inc.   (1)
4615 S 33rd Pl, Phoenix, AZ 85040
Tel.: (602) 454-0681
Environmental Control & Facility Management Systems Mfr
N.A.I.C.S.: 334512

Integrated Control Systems Inc.   (1)
10500 E 54th Ave Unit C, Denver, CO 80239
Tel.: (303) 277-0708
Web Site: http://www.icsicontrols.com
Emp.: 8
Environmental Control & Facility Management Systems Mfr
N.A.I.C.S.: 334512
Mohammed Sadaoui (Gen Mgr)
John Nitcher (Mgr-Ops)

INTEGRATED DATA STORAGE, LLC

11011 W 22st Ste 510, Chicago, IL 60523
Tel.: (312) 334-6400
Web Site:
http://www.integrateddatastorage.com
Year Founded: 2002
Sales Range: $25-49.9 Million
Emp.: 35
Computer System Design Services
N.A.I.C.S.: 541512
Matt Masick (CEO)
Justin Mescher (CTO)
Vince Buscareno (VP-Sls & Ops)
William Loupakos (VP-Pro Svcs)
Amy Lamboley (Controller)
Michelangelo Scalera (Dir-Sls Ops)
Jake Massick (Mgr-Cloud Svcs)
Zach Hinson (Mgr-Sls)

INTEGRATED DEICING SERVICES, LLC

175 Ammon Dr, Manchester, NH 03103
Web Site:
http://www.deicingsolutions.com
Sales Range: $25-49.9 Million
Emp.: 733
Transportation Services
N.A.I.C.S.: 488190
Mike Grantz (VP-Ops)
Salvatore Calvino (Pres)
Karen Fortin (Sr VP-Fin)
Patrick Brown (VP-Sls-Customer Rels)
Chad Knupp (Reg Mgr)
Ken Seth (Gen Mgr)
Ray Kristinsson (Gen Mgr)
John Kunkel (Dir-Ops)
Jonathan Savage (Gen Mgr)
Joseph Savage (Gen Mgr)
Al Greene (Gen Mgr)
Andy Hook (Gen Mgr)
Brian Buck (Dir-Safety & Quality Assurance)
Daniel Young (Dir-Sls & Mktg)
Gil Schuckman (Mng Dir)
James Alexander (Gen Mgr)
Jerry Tissera (Dir-Ops & Airport Rels)
Joe Davis (Dir-Maintenance)
Scott Cummings (Gen Mgr)
Roger Langille (Co-Pres & CEO)

INTEGRATED DERMATOLOGY GROUP

902 Clint Moore Rd Ste 226, Boca Raton, FL 33487
Tel.: (561) 314-2000
Web Site:
http://www.mydermgroup.com
Dermatology Practice Support Services
N.A.I.C.S.: 621999
Jeff Queen (Pres)

Subsidiaries:

Integrated Dermatology of Hickory PLLC   (1)
1870 N Ctr St, Hickory, NC 28601-1853
Tel.: (828) 322-7546
Web Site: http://www.reedderm.com
Freestanding Ambulatory Surgical & Emergency Centers
N.A.I.C.S.: 621493
Eileen Rogers (Mgr)
Charles N. Reed (Dir-Medical)

Integrated Dermatology of Ponchatoula LLC   (1)
180 N 5th St, Ponchatoula, LA 70454
Tel.: (985) 370-7546
Web Site: http://www.bensonderm.com
Health Practitioners
N.A.I.C.S.: 621399
Robert W. Benson (Dir-Medical)

INTEGRATED DESIGN, INC.

3768 Plaza Dr, Ann Arbor, MI 48108
Tel.: (734) 665-8470   MI
Web Site: http://www.idesign.com
Year Founded: 1985
Sales Range: $1-9.9 Million
Emp.: 33
Data System Integration Developer
N.A.I.C.S.: 541511
Kit Dickinson (Pres)

INTEGRATED DISTRIBUTION & LOGISTICS DIRECT LLC

2429 S 51st Ave St 10, Phoenix, AZ 85043
Tel.: (520) 573-1100
Web Site: http://www.spexpress.com
N.A.I.C.S.:
Michael K. Bayley (Founder, CEO & Pres)
Scott Guilmette (Exec VP-Ops)
Robert Castaldo (VP-Ops)

Subsidiaries:

Marketing Support Solutions, Inc.   (1)
110 Vista Centre Dr, Forest, VA 24551
Tel.: (434) 385-1900
Web Site: http://www.mssfulfillment.com
Emp.: 25
Marketin Support Services
N.A.I.C.S.: 541611
Dina Crowder (Pres)

INTEGRATED FINANCE & ACCOUNTING SOLUTIONS, LLC.

4500 Pond Way Ste 270, Woodbridge, VA 22192
Tel.: (703) 583-4327
Web Site: http://www.ifas-llc.com
Year Founded: 2007
Sales Range: $1-9.9 Million
Emp.: 35
Financial Software Development Services
N.A.I.C.S.: 541511
Tabatha Turman (Founder, Pres & CEO)
Wayne Porter (Chief Growth & Delivery Officer)

INTEGRATED FINANCIAL SETTLEMENTS, INC.

5613 DTC Pkwy Ste 700, Greenwood Village, CO 80111
Tel.: (303) 337-0400   DE
Web Site: http://ifscompanies.com
Financial Services
N.A.I.C.S.: 523999
Robert Lee (CEO)
Jeff Bowers (Pres)
Christopher Diamantis (Chm)
Sean J. Coleman (COO)
John McCulloch (VP)
Duong Nguyen (Dir-Acctg)

Integrated Financial Settlements, Inc.—(Continued)

Bennie Covington *(Chief People Officer)*
Denise Schumacher *(Dir-Product)*
Jonathan Stevens *(Dir-Software Engrg)*

INTEGRATED FREIGHT CORPORATION
42 Lake Ave Ext 208, Danbury, CT 06811
Tel.: (203) 628-7142 **FL**
Sales Range: $10-24.9 Million
Emp.: 22
Freight Transportation Services
N.A.I.C.S.: 484121
Henry P. Hoffman *(Pres & COO)*
Jackson L. Morris *(Sec)*
David N. Fuselier *(Chm & CEO)*

INTEGRATED IT SOLUTIONS, INC.
159 Overland Rd, Waltham, MA 02451
Tel.: (781) 453-5100 **MA**
Web Site: http://www.thinkmate.com
Year Founded: 1986
Rev.: $21,843,027
Emp.: 10
Computer & Software Stores
N.A.I.C.S.: 449210
Amy Connell *(Mgr-Mktg)*
Frank Vincentelli *(CTO)*
Michael Lovasco *(Project Mgr)*
Daryoosh Rajabi *(Sr Acct Exec)*
Nasser Khadjenoori *(VP-Ops)*

INTEGRATED LAB SYSTEMS INC.
1 Park Dr Ste 200, Research Triangle Park, NC 27709
Tel.: (919) 544-5857
Web Site: http://www.ils-inc.com
Year Founded: 1985
Sales Range: $10-24.9 Million
Emp.: 140
Environmental Research
N.A.I.C.S.: 541715
Thomas K. Rao *(Founder & Chm)*
Jason Shannon *(Dir-HR)*
Brad Blackard *(VP-Bus Mgmt)*
Leslie Recio *(VP-R&D)*
Mary Mulleady *(Dir-Bus Mgmt & Federal Bus Dev)*
Barbara Vinesett *(Dir-Fin)*
Sam C. Tetlow *(Chief Bus Officer & Gen Mgr)*
Kevin Causey *(VP-Comml Bus Dev)*
David Allen *(VP-Science & Strategy)*

INTEGRATED MAGNETICS
11250 Playa Ct, Culver City, CA 90230
Tel.: (310) 391-7213
Web Site: http://www.intemag.com
Rev.: $12,300,000
Emp.: 133
Miscellaneous Fabricated Metal Product Mfr
N.A.I.C.S.: 332999
Anil Nanji *(Pres & CEO)*
Dave Culp *(Supvr-QA)*
Gus Rivera *(Supvr-Quality Assurance)*

INTEGRATED MANAGEMENT RESOURCES GROUP INC.
4640 Forbes Blvd Ste 200, Lanham, MD 20706
Tel.: (301) 306-0502
Web Site: http://www.imrg2000.com
Rev.: $13,100,000
Emp.: 230

Administrative Management & General Management Consulting Services
N.A.I.C.S.: 541611
Myrna Cooks *(Pres)*

INTEGRATED MANAGEMENT SERVICES, PA
126 E Amite St, Jackson, MS 39201
Tel.: (601) 968-9194
Web Site: http://www.imsengineers.com
Year Founded: 1996
Sales Range: $10-24.9 Million
Emp.: 250
Infrastructure Construction & Management Services
N.A.I.C.S.: 237310
John D. Calhoun *(Co-Founder & CEO)*
Rod L. Hill *(Co-Founder, Pres & COO)*
John May *(Chief Fiscal Officer)*

Subsidiaries:

IMS Engineers, PA **(1)**
126 E Amite St, Jackson, MS 39201
Tel.: (901) 543-0416
Web Site: http://www.imsengineers.com
Sales Range: $10-24.9 Million
Emp.: 50
Infrastructure Construction & Management Services
N.A.I.C.S.: 237310

INTEGRATED MARKETING GROUP
237 Keamy St Ste 200, San Francisco, CA 94108
Web Site: http://www.imgdirectmarketing.com
Year Founded: 2008
Sales Range: $1-9.9 Million
Emp.: 12
Marketing Consulting Services
N.A.I.C.S.: 541613
Amy Townsend *(Mktg Mgr)*

INTEGRATED MARKETING SERVICES
279 Wall St Research Park, Princeton, NJ 08540-1519
Tel.: (609) 683-9055
Web Site: http://www.imsworld.com
Year Founded: 1981
Rev.: $11,000,000
Emp.: 50
Public Relations Agency
N.A.I.C.S.: 541820
Lois Kaufman *(Pres)*
Anthony Casale *(CEO)*

INTEGRATED MARKETING WORKS
3190 Airport Loop Dr Bldg K, Costa Mesa, CA 92626
Tel.: (714) 557-7100
Web Site: http://www.imwagency.com
Year Founded: 1990
Sales Range: $1-9.9 Million
Emp.: 14
Advetising Agency
N.A.I.C.S.: 541810
Kari Bretschger *(Co-Pres & CEO)*
Peter Bretschger *(Co-Pres & CMO)*
Marcie Gonzalez *(Assoc Dir-Creative)*

INTEGRATED MEDIA SOLUTIONS
500 Craig Rd Ste 101, Manalapan, NJ 07726
Tel.: (732) 303-0551
Web Site:
http://www.dentalproductshopper.com
Year Founded: 2007

Sales Range: $1-9.9 Million
Emp.: 30
Publisher of Dental Product Shopper & Online Supplier of Dental Products & Seminars
N.A.I.C.S.: 339114
Dave Branch *(CEO)*
Chris Donahower *(COO)*
Tim Schmitt *(VP-Sls & Mktg)*
Deborah Thalor *(Office Mgr)*
Michael Molfetto *(Mgr-Production)*
Veronica Gasper *(Coord-Sls & Mktg)*
Jeff Ginsberg *(Dir-Content)*
Mike Hubert *(Dir-Creative)*
Dana Perrotta *(Dir-Promotional Sls)*
Adam Rutkowski *(Mgr-Sls-Eastern)*
Amy Cochran *(Mgr-Western)*
Brian Donahue *(Mng Editor)*
Jennifer Klein *(Sr Acct Mgr)*
Joseph Riley *(Sr Dir-Ops)*

INTEGRATED MEDIA TECHNOLOGIES, INC.
5200 Lankershim Blvd Ste 700, North Hollywood, CA 91601
Tel.: (818) 761-9770
Web Site:
http://www.imtglobalinc.com
Year Founded: 2007
Sales Range: $25-49.9 Million
Emp.: 27
Design, Construction & Consulting Services
N.A.I.C.S.: 541618
Jason Kranitz *(VP-Sls)*
Dave Evans *(Sr Dir-Advanced Consulting Svcs & IT Strategy)*
Dave Fischetti *(Sr Acct Exec)*

INTEGRATED MEDICAL SOLUTIONS, LLC
99 Regency Pkwy Ste 307, Mansfield, TX 76063
Web Site: http://www.imsi-usa.com
Year Founded: 1999
Sales Range: $10-24.9 Million
Emp.: 18
Medical Solutions Providers
N.A.I.C.S.: 621610
Jerry B. Heftler *(Pres & CEO)*
Gail H. Wilhelm *(VP)*
Alison K. Landin *(CFO & VP)*

INTEGRATED PACKAGING CORP.
122 Quentin Ave, New Brunswick, NJ 08901
Tel.: (732) 247-5200
Web Site: http://www.ipcboxes.com
Sales Range: $10-24.9 Million
Emp.: 102
Corrugated & Solid Fiber Boxes Mfr
N.A.I.C.S.: 424130

INTEGRATED PARTNERS, INC.
99 Pine St, Albany, NY 12207
Tel.: (518) 433-1210
Year Founded: 1996
Sales Range: $1-9.9 Million
Emp.: 25
Computer System Design Services
N.A.I.C.S.: 541512
Stephen Vespia *(Pres & CEO)*

INTEGRATED PETROLEUM TECHNOLOGIES, INC.
1707 Cole Blvd Ste 200, Golden, CO 80401
Tel.: (303) 216-0703 **CO**
Web Site:
http://www.iptenergyservices.com
Year Founded: 1991
Sales Range: $1-9.9 Million
Emp.: 150
Support Activities for Oil & Gas Operations

N.A.I.C.S.: 213112
Todd Poulson *(Pres)*
Richard Burns *(VP-Production & Reservoir Engrg)*
Andrew Peterson *(VP)*

Subsidiaries:

Peterson Energy **(1)**
2154 W Eisenhower Blvd, Loveland, CO 80537
Tel.: (970) 669-7411
Web Site: http://www.petersonenergy.com
Emp.: 7
Support Activities for Oil & Gas Operations
N.A.I.C.S.: 213112
Andy Peterson *(Founder & Pres)*
Tim Sherwood *(Mgr-Completions)*
Tom Majors *(Mgr-Ops)*

INTEGRATED PROCESS TECHNOLOGIES, INC.
8 Charlestown St, Devens, MA 01434
Tel.: (978) 487-1000
Year Founded: 2000
Sales Range: $1-9.9 Million
Emp.: 45
Engineeering Services
N.A.I.C.S.: 541330
James V. Banks *(Co-Founder & Pres)*

Subsidiaries:

Integrated Process Technologies, Inc. **(1)**
8 Charlestown, Devens, MA 01434
Tel.: (978) 487-1100
High-Purity Process System Installation Services
N.A.I.C.S.: 541330

INTEGRATED PROCUREMENT TECHNOLOGIES, INC.
7230 Hollister Ave, Goleta, CA 93117
Tel.: (805) 682-0842
Web Site: http://www.iptsb.com
Sales Range: $75-99.9 Million
Emp.: 50
Transportation Equipment & Supplies Merchant Whslr
N.A.I.C.S.: 423860
Etty Yenni *(Pres)*
Christian Sorenson *(Acct Supvr-OEM)*
Ricardo Flores *(Mgr-Bus Dev-Intl)*

INTEGRATED PROJECT MANAGEMENT COMPANY, INC.
200 S Frontage Rd Ste 220, Burr Ridge, IL 60527
Tel.: (630) 789-8600
Web Site: http://www.ipmcinc.com
Year Founded: 1988
Sales Range: $10-24.9 Million
Onsite Project Management Services
N.A.I.C.S.: 541618
C. Richard Panico *(Founder, Pres & CEO)*

Subsidiaries:

Integrated Project Management Co., Inc. **(1)**
200 S Frontage Rd ,Ste 220, Burr Ridge, IL 60527 **(100%)**
Tel.: (636) 728-0476
Web Site: http://www.ipmcinc.com
Sales Range: $10-24.9 Million
Emp.: 80
Onsite Project Management Solutions
N.A.I.C.S.: 541618

Integrated Project Management Co., Inc. **(1)**
400 Oyster Point Blvd Ste 405, South San Francisco, CA 94080-1920 **(100%)**
Tel.: (650) 244-9981
Web Site: http://www.ipmcinc.com
Sales Range: $10-24.9 Million
Emp.: 30
Onsite Project Management Services
N.A.I.C.S.: 541618
Harry Georgiades *(Mng Dir)*

Integrated Project Management Co., Inc. (1)
One Broadway 14th Fl, Cambridge, MA 02142 (100%)
Tel.: (617) 401-2325
Web Site: http://www.ipmcinc.com
Sales Range: $10-24.9 Million
Emp.: 11
Onsite Project Management Services
N.A.I.C.S.: 541618

INTEGRATED PROPERTY SYSTEMS
15 Thornwood Dr, Ithaca, NY 14850
Tel.: (607) 257-5050   NY
Year Founded: 1987
Sales Range: $10-24.9 Million
Emp.: 12
Single-Family Home Remodeling, Additions & Repairs
N.A.I.C.S.: 236118
Timothy Colbert (Pres & Partner)

INTEGRATED REGIONAL LABORATORIES
5361 NW 33rd Ave, Fort Lauderdale, FL 33309
Tel.: (954) 777-0018
Web Site: http://www.irlfl.com
Rev.: $38,200,000
Emp.: 800
Medical Laboratories
N.A.I.C.S.: 621511
Joanne M. Trout (CEO)
Barbara Toth (Supvr-Laboratory Tech)
Alim Ali (Supvr-Laboratory)

INTEGRATED RESOURCES, INC.
4 Ethel Rd, Edison, NJ 08817-2841
Tel.: (732) 549-2030
Web Site: http://www.irionline.com
Year Founded: 1996
Sales Range: $1-9.9 Million
Emp.: 64
Consulting & Staffing Services
N.A.I.C.S.: 561311
Andy Kadiwar (Pres)

INTEGRATED SECURE, LLC
9595 6 Pines Dr Ste 8210, The Woodlands, TX 77380
Tel.: (281) 465-9414
Web Site:
   http://www.integratedsecure.com
Year Founded: 2004
Sales Range: $1-9.9 Million
Emp.: 33
IT Solutions
N.A.I.C.S.: 519290
Nathan Reeves (Dir-Tech)

INTEGRATED SOFTWARE SOLUTIONS, INC.
1 North Bacton Hill Rd Ste 203, Frazer, PA 19355
Tel.: (610) 560-4300
Web Site: http://www.issinfo.com
Financial Software Soultion Services
N.A.I.C.S.: 513210
Kathy Witman (VP)

Subsidiaries:

Ellen Philip Associates, Inc. (1)
134 W 26th St Fl 5, New York, NY 10001
Tel.: (212) 461-4328
Web Site: http://www.ellenphilip.com
Data Processing, Hosting & Related Services
N.A.I.C.S.: 518210
Barry Shapiro (Treas)

INTEGRATED SOLUTIONS GROUP, INC.
1632 E 23rd Ave, Hutchinson, KS 67502-4705
Tel.: (620) 662-5796   KS

Web Site: http://www.isg-inc.net
Year Founded: 1995
Sales Range: $10-24.9 Million
Emp.: 40
Provider of Strategic Consulting, Project Management, Development & Integration Services
N.A.I.C.S.: 449210
Gary Hobbs (Dir-Mktg)

Subsidiaries:

AgTrax Technologies (1)
1632 E 23rd, Hutchinson, KS 67502
Tel.: (620) 662-5796
Web Site: http://www.agtrax.com
Rev.: $16,524,423
Emp.: 30
Provider of Computer Systems to Agribusiness
N.A.I.C.S.: 513210

Data Strategies, Inc. (1)
13475 Danielson St, Poway, CA 92064
Tel.: (858) 514-0300
Sales Range: $10-24.9 Million
Emp.: 20
Computer & Computer Peripheral Equipment & Software Merchant Whslr
N.A.I.C.S.: 423430

INTEGRATED SYSTEMS ANALYSTS, INC.
Ste 600 2001 N Beauregard St, Alexandria, VA 22311-1722
Tel.: (703) 824-0700   VA
Year Founded: 1980
Sales Range: $150-199.9 Million
Emp.: 650
Systems Engineering; Information Systems Services, Corrosion Engineering; Computer & Network Maintenance, Repair & Installation
N.A.I.C.S.: 541512
C. Michael Gooden (Chm & CEO)
Ben Sazinis (Controller)
Kerry Kidd (Controller)

Subsidiaries:

ISA Information Systems Services (1)
2001 N Beauregard St Ste 600, Alexandria, VA 22311 (100%)
Tel.: (703) 824-0700
Sales Range: $25-49.9 Million
Emp.: 350
Computer Maintenance & nstallation
N.A.I.C.S.: 541512
Adrienne Geis (VP-Admin)
C. Michael Gooden (Chm & CEO)
Chris Wilson (VP-Ops)

Division (Domestic):

ISA Installation & Deployment Center (2)
15403 S Commerce Dr, Dearborn, MI 48120-1274 (100%)
Tel.: (313) 317-5000
Sales Range: $25-49.9 Million
Emp.: 25
Computer Services
N.A.I.C.S.: 541512

INTEGRATED TECHNICAL SYSTEMS, INC.
8 Capital Dr, Wallingford, CT 06492
Tel.: (203) 265-8100
Web Site: https://www.integrated-tec.com
Year Founded: 1969
Sales Range: $50-74.9 Million
Emp.: 70
Signaling Equipment, Electrical
N.A.I.C.S.: 423610

INTEGRATED TELEMANAGEMENT SERVICES, INC.
4100 Guardian St Ste 110, Simi Valley, CA 93063
Tel.: (805) 520-7020
Web Site: http://www.itstelecom.com

Year Founded: 1990
Sales Range: $1-9.9 Million
Emp.: 20
Computer Programming Services
N.A.I.C.S.: 541511
Sharon L. Woods (Pres & CEO)
Kim Konigsberg (Dir-Ops)
Daryl Frame (Dir-Info Sys)
Lisa Atwood (Exec Dir-Mktg)

INTEGRATED WASTE SOLUTIONS GROUP, LLC
, Austin, TX 73301
Tel.: (904) 704-6249
Web Site: http://www.iwsgusa.com
Year Founded: 2017
Integrated Solid Waste Collection & Disposal Operations
N.A.I.C.S.: 562111
Charlie Appleby (Co-Founder & Chm)
Chris Beall (Co-Founder)

Subsidiaries:

Central Texas Refuse, Inc. (1)
9316 Fm 812, Austin, TX 78719
Tel.: (512) 243-2833
Web Site:
   http://www.centraltexasrefuse.com
Nonhazardous Waste Treatment & Disposal
N.A.I.C.S.: 562219

INTEGRATED WEALTH CONCEPTS, LLC
200 Fifth Ave Ste 4010, Waltham, MA 02451
Tel.: (703) 840-4282
Web Site: https://integrated-partners.com
Year Founded: 1996
Investment Advice & Financial Services
N.A.I.C.S.: 523940
Paul Saganey (Founder & Pres)
Rob Sandrew (Chief Growth Officer)

Subsidiaries:

Integrated Financial Partners, Inc. (1)
4000 Legato Rd Ste 410, Fairfax, VA 22033
Tel.: (703) 840-4282
Web Site: https://www.ifp-nova.com
Fee-Based Financial Planning & Retirement Planning Services
N.A.I.C.S.: 523940
Jim Littleton (Dir-Client Operations)

Subsidiary (Domestic):

Wagner Resource Group, Inc. (2)
7601 Lewinsville Rd Ste 302, McLean, VA 22102-2835
Tel.: (703) 748-1474
Web Site: http://www.invest-taxfree.com
Investment Advice
N.A.I.C.S.: 523940
Phylyp Wagner (Owner)

Laurel Wealth Advisors, Inc. (1)
155 N Cawston Ave, Hemet, CA 92545-5278
Tel.: (951) 658-6200
Web Site: http://www.laurelwa.com
Investment Advice
N.A.I.C.S.: 523940
Michael Huerta (Mgr)

INTEGRATED, LLC
1426 Sadlier Cir W Dr, Indianapolis, IN 46239
Tel.: (317) 454-0454
Web Site:
   http://www.integratedvideoup ply.com
Sales Range: $10-24.9 Million
Emp.: 3
Digital Video Surveillance Solutions Distr
N.A.I.C.S.: 561621

Subsidiaries:

Integrated Video Supply (1)
1426 Sadlier Cir W Dr, Indianapolis, IN 46239
Web Site:
   http://www.integratedvideosupply.com
Digital Video-Surveillance Equipment Mfr & Distr
N.A.I.C.S.: 561621

INTEGRATION INNOVATION, INC.
689 Discovery Dr Bldg 1 5th Fl, Huntsville, AL 35806
Tel.: (256) 513-5179
Web Site: http://www.i3-corps.com
Year Founded: 2007
Sales Range: $25-49.9 Million
Emp.: 202
Engineeering Services
N.A.I.C.S.: 541330
Joseph Summers (Exec VP-Corp Dev)
Walter Strankman (COO)
Adam Harper (Exec VP-Strategic Programs & Capture)
Richard Kretzschmar (CEO)

INTEGRATION TECHNOLOGIES GROUP, INC.
2745 Hartland Rd Fl 2nd, Falls Church, VA 22043
Tel.: (703) 698-8282
Web Site: http://www.itgonline.com
Year Founded: 1984
Sales Range: $10-24.9 Million
Emp.: 110
System Integration, Computer Maintenance & Repair
N.A.I.C.S.: 811210
Giovanni Canobbio (Founder)
Regina Hwang (Controller)
Burl Williams (Pres)
Markus Darby (Exec VP & Gen Mgr)

INTEGRATION TECHNOLOGIES, INC.
745 Fort St Ste 600, Honolulu, HI 96813
Tel.: (808) 596-9500
Web Site: http://www.intech-hawaii.com
Year Founded: 1991
Sales Range: $1-9.9 Million
Emp.: 18
IT Support Services
N.A.I.C.S.: 541512
Sam Gridley (Co-Owner)
Paul Ventura (Co-Owner)
Jordan Silva (Dir-Ops)
Aubrey Holt (Mgr-Pur & Bus Dev)
Branden Baker (Pres)

INTEGRATIVE SYSTEMS, INC.
900 N Arlington Heights Rd, Itasca, IL 60143
Web Site:
   http://www.integrativesystems.com
Year Founded: 2001
Sales Range: $1-9.9 Million
Emp.: 200
Software Development Services
N.A.I.C.S.: 541511
Rajesh Rajan (Founder & CEO)
Joshua Saxe (Mgr-Client Svcs)
Meghna Wani (Mktg Mgr)
Nikhil Sheth (Mgr-HR)
Peter Grigg (Dir-Microsoft Technologies)

INTEGRATOUCH, LLC

IntegraTouch, LLC—(Continued)

300 Main St Ste 4-202, East Rochester, NY 14445
Tel.: (585) 750-6877
Web Site:
   http://www.symphonybilling.com
Year Founded: 2002
Sales Range: $1-9.9 Million
Emp.: 200
Software Development Services
N.A.I.C.S.: 541511
Kevin Maag *(Founder & CEO)*
Carlos Moreno *(VP-Intl Sls)*
Dave Slavny *(VP-Bus Dev)*
Jennifer Maag *(Mng Partner & Dir-Operating)*
Douglas Montevecchio *(VP-Engrg)*

INTEGREON GLOBAL
551 Raritan Center Pkwy, Edison, NJ 08837
Tel.: (732) 346-9200   NJ
Web Site: http://www.tcpreliable.com
Year Founded: 1990
Holding Company; Temperature Controlled Packaging, Temperature Monitoring & Polystyrene Resin Products Mfr & Whslr
N.A.I.C.S.: 551112
Maurice Barakat *(Pres & CEO)*

Subsidiaries:

DDL, Inc.   (1)
10200 Valley View Rd Ste 101, Eden Prairie, MN 55344
Tel.: (952) 941-9226
Web Site: http://www.testedandproven.com
Packaging Product & Material Testing Services
N.A.I.C.S.: 541380
Eric Borchardt *(Mgr-Facilities)*
Chad O'Fallon *(Mgr-IT)*
Amy Peterson *(Ops Mgr)*
Christopher Murphy *(Mgr-Mktg)*
Tamera Presler *(Gen Mgr)*

NexKemia Petrochemicals Inc.   (1)
24 rue Bellevue, PO Box 240, Mansonville, J0E 1X0, QC, Canada
Tel.: (450) 292-3333
Web Site: http://www.nexkemia.com
Emp.: 40
Expandable Polystyrene Resins Mfr
N.A.I.C.S.: 326140

TCP Reliable Manufacturing, Inc.   (1)
551 Raritan Ctr Pkwy, Edison, NJ 08837
Tel.: (732) 346-9200
Web Site: http://www.cryopak.com
Temperature Controlled Packaging & Temperature Monitoring Products Mfr & Whslr
N.A.I.C.S.: 339999
Saak Dertadian *(Gen Mgr-Cryopak Verification Tech)*
Maurice Barakat *(Pres & CEO)*
Amanda J. Riemer *(Coord-Mktg-Cryopak)*

Subsidiary (Domestic):

Cryopack Verification Technologies, Inc.   (2)
120 Pkwy Dr, Buchanan, VA 24066
Tel.: (540) 254-1433
Web Site: http://www.cryopak.com
Emp.: 10
Temperature Monitoring Products Mfr & Whslr
N.A.I.C.S.: 334513
Christopher Smith *(Mgr-Site & Quality Mgmt Sys)*

Plant (Non-US):

Cryopak Canada - Vancouver Plant   (2)
110-1081 Cliveden Ave, Delta, V3M 5V1, BC, Canada
Tel.: (604) 515-7977
Web Site: https://www.cryopak.com
Sales Range: $10-24.9 Million
Emp.: 40
Temperature Controlled Packaging Products Mfr & Whslr
N.A.I.C.S.: 339999

INTEGRIS HEALTH, INC.
3300 NW Expy, Oklahoma City, OK 73112
Tel.: (405) 951-2277   OK
Web Site: http://www.integrisok.com
Year Founded: 1983
Sales Range: $900-999.9 Million
Emp.: 9,600
Wealth Management Services
N.A.I.C.S.: 541511
Timothy Pehrson *(CEO)*
Peter B. Delaney *(Chm)*
Chris Hammes *(COO & Exec VP)*
Mike Hatch *(Chief Strategy & Transformation Officer & Exec VP)*

Subsidiaries:

INTEGRIS Bass Baptist Health Center   (1)
600 S Monroe, Enid, OK 73701
Tel.: (580) 233-2300
Web Site: http://www.integrisok.com
Hospital Operator
N.A.I.C.S.: 622110
Finny Mathew *(Pres-Enid)*

INTEGRIS Cardiovascular Physicians LLC   (1)
3545 NW 58th St Ste 450, Oklahoma City, OK 73112
Tel.: (405) 948-4040
Health Care Srvices
N.A.I.C.S.: 621999
Paul Szymanski *(VP)*

INTEGRIS Jim Thorpe Rehabilitation Center   (1)
4219 S Western Ave, Oklahoma City, OK 73109
Tel.: (405) 644-5200
Web Site: http://integrisok.com
Sales Range: $1-9.9 Million
Emp.: 300
Outpatient Care Centers
N.A.I.C.S.: 621498
Phil Lance *(VP)*
Brent Tipton *(Dir-Medical)*

INTEGRIS Realty Corporation   (1)
3300 NW Expwy, Oklahoma City, OK 73112
Tel.: (405) 949-3011
Real Estate Manangement Services
N.A.I.C.S.: 531390

INTEGRIS Rural Healthcare of Oklahoma, Inc.   (1)
3366 NW Expy Ste 800, Oklahoma City, OK 73112
Tel.: (405) 951-2616
Web Site: http://www.integrisok.com
Sales Range: $200-249.9 Million
Hospital & Health Services
N.A.I.C.S.: 622110

INTEGRIS Southwest Medical Center   (1)
4401 S Western Ave, Oklahoma City, OK 73109
Tel.: (405) 636-7000
Web Site: http://integrisok.com
Emp.: 10,000
Offices And Clinics Of Medical Doctors, N
N.A.I.C.S.: 621111
Michael Morgan *(Dir)*

Lakeside Women's Hospital   (1)
11200 N Portland Ave, Oklahoma City, OK 73102
Tel.: (405) 936-1500
Web Site: http://www.lakeside-wh.com
Emp.: 9
Women's Hospital & Medical Center
N.A.I.C.S.: 622110
Kelley Brewer *(Pres)*

INTEGRITEK LLC
1101 South Capital of Texas Highway Bldg B Ste 100, Austin, TX 78746
Tel.: (512) 535-0908
Web Site: http://www.iwsit.com
IT Services
N.A.I.C.S.: 519290
Lauren Paver *(Pres & COO)*
David Raymes *(Exec VP-Corp Dev)*

Subsidiaries:

Acutech Network Services Inc   (1)
2328 N Batavia St, Orange, CA 92865
Tel.: (714) 279-3901
Web Site: http://www.acutech.net
Sales Range: $1-9.9 Million
Computer & Office Machine Repair & Maintenance
N.A.I.C.S.: 811210
Paul Messier *(Gen Mgr)*

INTEGRITY CARGO SOLUTIONS, INC.
17315 Studebaker Rd Unit 300D, Cerritos, CA 90703
Tel.: (562) 375-6500
Web Site:
   http://www.shipintegrity.com
Year Founded: 2012
Sales Range: $1-9.9 Million
Emp.: 5
Freight Transportation Services
N.A.I.C.S.: 488510
Ferdie Patam *(Founder & Partner)*

INTEGRITY COAL SALES INC.
905 Marconi Ave, Ronkonkoma, NY 11779-7211
Tel.: (631) 467-6969   NY
Web Site:
   http://www.integritycoal.com
Year Founded: 1990
Sales Range: $75-99.9 Million
Emp.: 9
Sales of Minerals & Ores
N.A.I.C.S.: 423520
Robert Edouard *(Dir-Metallurgical Mktg)*
Ivan Stumbo *(Mgr-Field-Kentucky)*
Tony Bezanson *(Mgr-Field-Norfolk Virginia)*
Bill Clawges *(Mgr-Field-Pennsylvania)*
Tom Nordberg *(Mgr-Field-West Virginia)*
Kevin McEvoy *(Gen Mgr)*
Brian Palmer *(Mgr-Export)*
Gregg Licata *(Pres)*
Stacey Manning *(Treas)*

Subsidiaries:

Integrity Coal Sales International, Inc.   (1)
905 Marconi Ave, Ronkonkoma, NY 11779-7211
Tel.: (631) 467-6969
Web Site: http://www.integritycoal.com
Emp.: 8
Coal Mining Services
N.A.I.C.S.: 212114
Greg Licata *(Pres)*

Integrity International Corp.   (1)
905 Marconi Ave, Ronkonkoma, NY 11779
Tel.: (631) 467-6969
Web Site: http://www.integritycoal.com
Sales Range: $10-24.9 Million
Coal, Minerals & Ores
N.A.I.C.S.: 423520
Kevin McEvoy *(Office Mgr)*

INTEGRITY COMMUNICATIONS
5711 Grant Ave, Cleveland, OH 44105
Tel.: (216) 420-9700
Web Site: http://www.integrity-communications.com
Year Founded: 2002
Sales Range: $1-9.9 Million
Emp.: 50
Telecommunication Sales
N.A.I.C.S.: 517810
Mike Naughton *(CEO)*

INTEGRITY DATA SOLUTIONS INC.
4100 E Brdwy Rd Ste 140, Phoenix, AZ 85040

Tel.: (480) 458-0490
Web Site: http://www.accessids.com
Custom Computer Programming Services
N.A.I.C.S.: 541511
John Tavis *(Founder)*

INTEGRITY ELECTRONICS INC.
63 Flushing Ave Unit 285, Brooklyn, NY 11205
Tel.: (718) 858-9060
Sales Range: $25-49.9 Million
Emp.: 34
Television & Radio Electrical Appliances
N.A.I.C.S.: 423620
Avi Elkayam *(Pres)*

INTEGRITY EMPLOYEE LEASING, INC.
128 W Charlotte Ave, Punta Gorda, FL 33950
Tel.: (941) 625-0623
Web Site:
   http://www.integrityemployeeleasing.com
Year Founded: 2004
Sales Range: $100-124.9 Million
Emp.: 30
Professional Employer Organizations
N.A.I.C.S.: 561330
Tom Natoli *(CEO)*
Toby L. Starr *(Pres)*
Kaye Sessions *(Exec VP)*
Cathi Dryburgh *(Mgr-Acctg)*

INTEGRITY ENGINEERING & DESIGN SOLUTIONS
7150 E Camelback Rd Ste 444, Scottsdale, AZ 85251
Web Site: http://www.integrity-eds.com
Year Founded: 2002
Sales Range: $1-9.9 Million
Emp.: 41
Project Management & Engineering Support Services
N.A.I.C.S.: 541330
Joseph Machain *(Sec, Dir-Eng & Principal)*
Shereena Smith *(Controller)*
Art Bejarano Jr. *(Pres, CEO & Dir-Bus Dev)*

INTEGRITY EXPRESS LOGISTICS
4370 Malsbary Rd, Blue Ash, OH 45242
Web Site: http://www.intxlog.com
Year Founded: 2007
Sales Range: $10-24.9 Million
Emp.: 52
International Logistics & Trucking Carriers
N.A.I.C.S.: 488510
Pete Ventura *(Dir-Bus Dev)*
James Steger *(Mgr-Ops)*
Matt Ventura *(Dir-Sls)*
Jenna Slee *(Dir-HR)*

INTEGRITY FEEDS
2920 Fairview Dr, Owensboro, KY 42302
Tel.: (270) 689-0919
Web Site:
   http://www.integrityfeeds.com
Sales Range: $1-9.9 Million
Emp.: 35
Farm Supplies Whslr
N.A.I.C.S.: 424910
Dolores Aull *(Office Mgr)*

INTEGRITY FIRST FINANCIAL GROUP INC.

6333 Greenwich Ave Ste 280, San
Diego, CA 92122
Web Site:
http://www.integritydirectmort
gage.com
Year Founded: 2006
Sales Range: $1-9.9 Million
Emp.: 30
Mortgage Lending Services
N.A.I.C.S.: 522310
Alex Barnett (Pres)

INTEGRITY FUNDING, LLC
6003 Honore Ave Ste 101, Sarasota,
FL 34238
Tel.: (941) 684-0500
Web Site:
http://www.integrityfunding.com
Sales Range: $10-24.9 Million
Emp.: 15
Financial & Investment Services
N.A.I.C.S.: 525990
Gregory Roper (Pres)

INTEGRITY HOUSE, INC.
103 Lincoln Park, Newark, NJ 07102
Tel.: (973) 623-0600   NJ
Web Site:
http://www.integrityhouse.org
Year Founded: 1968
Sales Range: $10-24.9 Million
Emp.: 322
Substance Abuse Prevention Ser-
vices
N.A.I.C.S.: 623220
David G. Kostinas (Vice Chm)
Geoffrey S. Perselay (Chm)
Rebecca Cornell (Dir-Short Term
Residential)
Kathleen Dedrick (CFO)
Johanna Stroever (Dir-Dev)
Maribel Nunez (Dir-Women's Resi-
dential Programs-Newark)
Robert J. Budsock Jr. (Pres & CEO)

INTEGRITY JANITORIAL SER-
VICES, INC.
15025 Monroe St, Miami, FL 33176
Tel.: (305) 233-6089
Web Site:
http://www.integrityjanitorial
corp.com
Rev.: $400,000
Emp.: 5
Janitorial Services
N.A.I.C.S.: 561720
Donald James (Pres)

INTEGRITY MANAGEMENT
CONSULTING, INC.
7900 Westpark Dr A470, Tysons Cor-
ner, VA 22102
Tel.: (703) 349-3394
Web Site:
http://www.consultwithintegrity.com
Year Founded: 2006
Sales Range: $1-9.9 Million
Emp.: 56
Acquisition Management, Capital
Planning & Investment Services to
Government Agencies
N.A.I.C.S.: 921190
Christopher Romani (Co-Founder &
CE)
Mary Beth Romani (Co-Founder &
Chief Strategy Officer)
Marc Klein (CFO)
Mark Kulungowski (VP-Ops)

Subsidiaries:

MHM Innovations, Inc.   (1)
3975 University Dr Ste 310, Fairfax, VA
22030-2520
Tel.: (703) 877-1314
Web Site: http://www.mhminnovations.com
General Management Consulting Services
N.A.I.C.S.: 541611

Joseph L. Musella (Pres)

INTEGRITY MARKETING
GROUP LLC
1445 Ross Ave 22nd Fl, Dallas, TX
75202
Tel.: (866) 650-1857
Web Site:
https://www.integritymarketing.com
Year Founded: 2006
Emp.: 1,000
Life Insurance Sales
N.A.I.C.S.: 524298
Jess Carrasquillo (Mng Partner)
Michael Wilhelm (Mng Partner)
Jacob Knorpp (Mng Partner)
Dennis Hovis (Mng Partner)
Bryan W. Adams (Co-Founder &
CEO)
Mike White (Mng Partner)
Tom Schueth (Co-Founder & Mng
Partner)
Jacque Huggins (Mng Partner)
Steve Young (Chm)
Doug Price (Mng Partner)
Robert McMichael (Mng Partner)
Christina Sears (Mng Partner)
Dave Martens (Partner)
Dave Thesing (Partner)
Todd Villeneuve (Mng Partner)
Bryan Neary (Mng Partner)
Doug Feekin (Mng Partner)
Bob Berg (Mng Partner)
Keith Berg (Mng Partner)
Jace Rosenbluth (Mng Partner)
Mark Williams (Mng Partner)
George Dippel (Mng Partner)
Tim Brousseau (Mng Partner)
Randy Herman (Mng Partner)
Dan Freier (Mng Partner)
Rich Hamer (Mng Partner)
Todd Stewart (Mng Partner)
Dan Oberlin (Mng Partner)
Dustin Oberlin (Mng Partner)
Chris Shields (Mng Partner)
Bob Carter (Mng Partner)
Jim Cahill (Mng Partner)
Melinda Wilhelm (Mng Partner)
Kevin Hovis (Mng Partner)
Sandra Carrasquillo, (Mng Partner)

Subsidiaries:

ASPECT Management, LLC   (1)
405 Oakbrook Dr, Columbia, SC 29223-
8121
Tel.: (803) 736-1788
Web Site: http://www.aspectmgmt.org
Insurance Agencies & Brokerages
N.A.I.C.S.: 524210
Graham Miller (Pres)

American Independent Marketing,
Inc.   (1)
511 W A St, Yakima, WA 98902
Tel.: (509) 575-0290
Web Site: http://www.whyaim.com
Insurance Agencies & Brokerages
N.A.I.C.S.: 524210
Dale Moore (Mgr-IT)
David Wane (Gen Mgr)
Tiffani Karnes (Ops Mgr)

American Senior Benefits, LLC   (1)
12722 S Blackbob Rd, Olathe, KS 66062
Tel.: (913) 815-3475
Web Site:
http://www.americanseniorbenefits.com
Insurance Agencies & Brokerages
N.A.I.C.S.: 524210
Venae Jewett (COO)
Clayton LeGeyt (Co-Founder & Mng Gen
Partner)
Albert Hawks (Exec VP)
Greg Gelineau (Exec VP)
James Sweeney (Co-Founder & Mng Gen
Partner)

Brokers International, Ltd.   (1)
4135 NW Ubandale Dr, Urbandale, IA
50322

Web Site: http://www.biltd.com
Rev.: $6,500,000
Emp.: 82
Insurance Agent/Broker
N.A.I.C.S.: 524210
Roger Haines (Mgr)
Mark Williams (Pres & CEO)

CSG Actuarial, LLC   (1)
11011 Q St Ste 101B, Omaha, NE 68137
Tel.: (402) 502-7747
Web Site: http://www.csgactuarial.com
Insurance Services
N.A.I.C.S.: 524298
Shawn Everidge (Mgr-Database)
Bryan R. Neary (Principal)
Doug Feekin (Principal)
Matt Neal (Dir-Mktg)
Kellie Herrmann (Mgr-Ops)

Connexion Point LLC   (1)
9490 S 300 W Ste 400, Sandy, UT 84070
Tel.: (801) 216-3400
Web Site: http://www.connexionpoint.com
Sales Range: $10-24.9 Million
Emp.: 1,215
Database Management Software Develop-
ment Services
N.A.I.C.S.: 541511
Rachel Hartgrove (Mgr-Site)
Darren Wesemann (CTO & Chief Product
Officer)

Deft Research, LLC   (1)
333 S 7th St Ste 2150, Minneapolis, MN
55402-2433
Tel.: (612) 436-8300
Web Site: http://www.deftresearch.com
Customer & Market Data Sevices
N.A.I.C.S.: 524298
George Dippel (Sr VP-Client Svcs)

Easy Street Insurance, LLC   (1)
8000 S Meridian St., Indianapolis, IN 46217
Tel.: (317) 882-9602
Web Site: http://www.easystreetins.com
Insurance Agencies & Brokerages
N.A.I.C.S.: 524210
Jess Carrasquillo (Owner)

Heartland Financial Group, Inc   (1)
1600 NE Coronado Dr,, Blue Springs, MO
64014
Tel.: (800) 537-5445
Web Site: https://www.hfgagents.com
Rev.: $2,075,000
Emp.: 5
Insurance Marketing Agency
N.A.I.C.S.: 524298
Chris Lubbers (Owner)

Hovis & Associates   (1)
998 E Gannon Dr #240, Festus, MO 63020
Tel.: (636) 586-9233
Web Site: https://hovisandassociates.com
Insurance Agencies & Brokerages
N.A.I.C.S.: 524210
Dennis Hovis (Pres & CEO)
Kevin Hovis (VP-Medicare Sls)

IFC National Marketing Inc.   (1)
1307 Albion Ave Ste 101, Fairmont, MN
56031
Tel.: (507) 238-9993
Web Site:
http://www.ifcnationalmarketing.com
Financial Investment Activities
N.A.I.C.S.: 523999
Todd Villeneuve (Pres)
Dave Martens (COO)
Dave Thesing (CFO)

Insurance Administrative Solutions,
LLC   (1)
17757 US Hwy 19 N Ste 660, Clearwater,
FL 33764
Tel.: (727) 584-0007
Web Site: http://www.iasadmin.com
Sales Range: $50-74.9 Million
Emp.: 200
Third Party Insurance Administration
N.A.I.C.S.: 524292
Darcey Shaffer (Dir-Corp Rels)
David Carpenter (VP-Info Tech Applications)
Tim Grooms (Dir-Fin)
Mark Postove (Exec VP)
Howard Brethauer (Supvr-Commission
Acctg)
Rick A. Gordon (CFO)
Gary Cannaday (Dir-IT Sys)
Doug Price (CEO)

Insurance Marketing Group, LLC   (1)
53 W Main St, Clinton, CT 06413
Tel.: (860) 664-3662
Web Site: http://www.img-sis.com
Marketing Consulting Services
N.A.I.C.S.: 541613
Steven Bugg (Mgr-Agency)

J. Berg & Associates, Inc.   (1)
1023 Executive Pkwy Ste 12, Saint Louis,
MO 63141
Tel.: (314) 878-0081
Web Site: http://www.jbergassociates.com
Insurance Agencies & Brokerage Services
N.A.I.C.S.: 524210

Lion Street Inc.   (1)
515 Congress Ave, Austin, TX 78701-3509
Tel.: (512) 776-8400
Web Site: http://www.lionstreet.com
Investment Advice
N.A.I.C.S.: 523940
Karyn Hamilton (VP-Mktg)

McNerney Management Group,
Inc.   (1)
801 Gray Oak Dr, Columbia, MO 65201
Tel.: (573) 443-5007
Web Site: http://www.gowithmmg.com
Insurance Agencies & Brokerages
N.A.I.C.S.: 524210
Chris Kiley (VP)
Dan Mangus (VP-Sls)
Dan McNerney (Founder)
Mary Seyer (Officer-Compliance & VP-Corp
Rels)
JoAnn Wray (Pres)

Medicare Advantage Specialists,
LLC   (1)
1550 Woods Of Riverchase Dr Ste 310,
Hoover, AL 35244-2930
Tel.: (205) 263-8400
Web Site:
http://www.medicareadvantagespecia
lists.com
Insurance Agencies & Brokerages
N.A.I.C.S.: 524210
Shana Clark (VP-Ops)

Merit Insurance Services, Inc.   (1)
639 Prospect Ave, Hartford, CT 06105
Tel.: (860) 233-3626
Web Site: http://www.meritins.com
Administrative Management & General
Management Consulting Service
N.A.I.C.S.: 541611
Jace Rosenbluth (Pres)
Addison Rosenbluth (VP)

Modern Insurance Marketing,
Inc.   (1)
29174 SW Town Ctr Loop W 102, Wilson-
ville, OR 97070
Tel.: (503) 682-3323
Web Site: http://www.moderninsurance.com
Insurance Agencies & Brokerages
N.A.I.C.S.: 524210
Greg Osborne (Principal)

National Agents Alliance   (1)
1214 Turrentine St, Burlington, NC 27215
Tel.: (336) 212-2041
Web Site:
http://www.nationalagentsalliance.com
Insurance Agencies & Brokerages
N.A.I.C.S.: 524210
Andy Albright (Pres & CEO)

Neat Management Group   (1)
9433 Bee Caves Rd Bldg II Ste 110, Austin,
TX 78733
Tel.: (800) 451-9143
Web Site: http://www.neatmgmt.com
Insurance Agencies & Brokerages
N.A.I.C.S.: 524210
Tim J McCoy (Pres & CEO)
Anita Dixon (VP)
Shea McCoy (Exec VP)
Melissa Sifuentes (Supvr-Contract & Lis-
censing)

New Horizons Insurance Marketing
Inc.   (1)
122 W Prairie Ave Ste 200, Decatur, IL
62523-1275
Tel.: (217) 233-8000
Web Site: http://www.newhorizonsmktg.com
Insurance Agencies & Brokerages
N.A.I.C.S.: 524210
Jeffrey Sams (CEO)
John Hockaday (COO)

Integrity Marketing Group LLC—(Continued)

Oberlin Marketing Co., Inc. (1)
6417 Georgetown N Blvd, Fort Wayne, IN 46815-7007
Tel.: (260) 486-9739
Web Site: http://www.oberlinmarketing.com
Insurance Related Activities
N.A.I.C.S.: 524298
Daniel Oberlin *(Pres)*
Dustin Oberlin *(Exec VP)*
Justin Reinig *(Exec Dir)*

One Resource Group, LLC (1)
13548 Zubrick Rd, Roanoke, IN 46783
Tel.: (260) 423-6161
Web Site: http://www.orgcorp.com
Insurance Agencies & Brokerages
N.A.I.C.S.: 524210
Andrea Baume *(Principal)*
Adam Beckett *(Dir-Field Sls)*
Dustin Johnson *(Dir-Mktg)*
Aaron Baack *(VP-Underwriting)*
Christopher Wesner *(Exec VP-Sls)*
Todd Stewart *(Pres)*
Tony Wilson *(VP-Sls)*
Dustan Mohr *(Reg VP)*
Kathy Koch *(Sr Mgr-Case)*

Penn Global Marketing, LLC (1)
5109 Hollyridge Dr Ste 104, Raleigh, NC 27612-3146
Tel.: (919) 984-9161
Web Site: http://www.pennglobal.biz
Marketing Consulting Services
N.A.I.C.S.: 541613

Scott Riddle Agency (1)
200 W State Hwy 6 Ste 430, Woodway, TX 76712
Tel.: (800) 722-5157
Web Site: http://scottriddleagency.com
Accident/Health Insurance Carrier
N.A.I.C.S.: 524114
Jacque Huggins *(Pres)*
Scott Riddle *(Founder)*
Karie Huggins *(Ops Mgr)*

Senior Insurance Specialists (1)
204 E. 7th St. In, Joplin, MO 64801
Tel.: (417) 624-6464
Web Site:
https://seniorinsurancespecialists.com
Insurance Agencies & Brokerages
N.A.I.C.S.: 524210

Shields Brokerage LLC (1)
21 Hampton Rd Ste 101, Exeter, NH 03833
Tel.: (603) 772-6700
Web Site: http://www.shieldsbrokerage.com
Sales Range: $1-9.9 Million
Emp.: 12
Insurance Agencies & Brokerages
N.A.I.C.S.: 524210

The Pinnacle Benefits Group, LLC. (1)
601 W 4th St Ste 110, Winston Salem, NC 27101
Tel.: (336) 759-3959
Insurance Agencies & Brokerages
N.A.I.C.S.: 524210

ThomasArts Holding, Inc. (1)
240 S 200 W, Farmington, UT 84025
Tel.: (801) 451-5365
Web Site: http://www.thomasarts.com
Advetising Agency
N.A.I.C.S.: 541810
Dave Thomas *(CEO & Principal)*
Troy Thomas *(Pres, Chief Creative Officer & Principal)*
Russ Nelson *(CFO)*
Sharon Rask *(COO & Principal)*
Tom Scandaliato *(Mng Dir & Principal)*
Matt Thomas *(Principal & Dir-Film & Motion)*
Anne Wood *(Pres, CMO & Principal)*

Tidewater Management Group (1)
7100 6 Forks Rd Ste 201, Raleigh, NC 27615
Tel.: (919) 841-0527
Web Site: http://www.tidewatermg.com
Insurance Agencies & Brokerages
N.A.I.C.S.: 524210
Todd Fincher *(Pres)*
Chad Wilkerson *(VP)*

Trusted Senior Specialists (1)

10998 S Wilcrest Dr, Houston, TX 77099-3564
Web Site:
http://www.trustedseniorspecialists.com
Insurance Agencies & Brokerages
N.A.I.C.S.: 524210

INTEGRITY NETWORKING SYSTEMS
Ste 9 51 W Wetmore Rd, Tucson, AZ 85705-2082
Tel.: (520) 293-6430
Web Site: http://www.integrityns.com
Sales Range: $10-24.9 Million
Emp.: 25
Local Area Network (Lan) Systems Integrator
N.A.I.C.S.: 541512
Deborah Valenzuela Baxter *(Pres)*

INTEGRITY STAFFING SOLUTIONS
750 Shipyard Dr Ste 300, Wilmington, DE 19801-5128
Tel.: (302) 661-8770
Web Site:
http://www.integritystaffing.com
Year Founded: 1997
Sales Range: $100-124.9 Million
Emp.: 30,000
Temporary Staffing Services
N.A.I.C.S.: 561320
Todd Bavol *(Founder, Pres & CEO)*
Jaime Donnelly *(Chief Risk Officer)*
Deborah R. Pierce *(Gen Counsel & VP)*
Christine M. Hahn-Proffitt *(VP-Sls & Ops)*

INTEGRITY TEXTILES INC.
65 W Street Rd, Warminster, PA 18974-2821
Tel.: (215) 957-3339
Web Site:
http://www.integritytextilesinc.com
Sales Range: $10-24.9 Million
Emp.: 2
Woolen & Worsted Piece Goods
N.A.I.C.S.: 424310
Larry Targan *(Pres)*

INTEGRO BUILDERS LLC
5312 S Cornell Ave Unit 2, Chicago, IL 60615
Tel.: (773) 295-1827
Web Site: http://www.integro-builders.com
General Contractors
N.A.I.C.S.: 238990
Allyson Case Anderson *(Founder & CEO)*

INTEGWARE, INC.
1612 Specht Point Dr Ste 101, Fort Collins, CO 80525
Tel.: (970) 282-0400
Web Site: http://www.integware.com
Year Founded: 1993
Sales Range: $1-9.9 Million
Emp.: 25
Custom Computer Programming Services
N.A.I.C.S.: 541511

INTEK PLASTICS INC.
1000 Pico Blvd, Hastings, MN 55033
Tel.: (651) 437-7700
Web Site:
http://www.intekplastics.com
Year Founded: 1961
Sales Range: $50-74.9 Million
Emp.: 200
Engineered Thermoplastic Extrusions Mfr
N.A.I.C.S.: 326199
Jill Hesselroth *(CEO)*
Steve Glienke *(CFO)*

INTEKRAS, INC.
21515 Ridgetop Cir Ste 260, Sterling, VA 20166
Tel.: (703) 547-3500
Web Site: http://www.intekras.com
Year Founded: 2004
Rev.: $6,700,000
Emp.: 55
Computer System Design Services
N.A.I.C.S.: 541512
Charles Williams *(Pres & Partner)*
Darrell Green *(Founder, Chm & Partner)*
Peter Wilmot *(Co-Founder, Partner & VP-Support Svcs)*

INTELECT CORPORATION
4000 Dillon St, Baltimore, MD 21224
Tel.: (410) 327-0020
Web Site:
http://www.intelectcorp.com
Year Founded: 1995
Sales Range: $10-24.9 Million
Emp.: 80
Engineeering Services
N.A.I.C.S.: 541330
Rohit Patel *(Founder)*
Ron Brunt *(Project Mgr)*
Tanisia Wright *(Project Coord)*
Todd Davis *(Mgr-Electrical)*

INTELEPEER, INC.
2855 Campus Dr Ste 200, San Mateo, CA 94403
Tel.: (650) 525-9200   DE
Web Site: http://www.intelepeer.com
Year Founded: 2002
Sales Range: $100-124.9 Million
Emp.: 115
VoIP Managed-Services Supplier;
Software Publisher
N.A.I.C.S.: 517810
Frank Fawzi *(Pres & CEO)*
Andre Simone *(CFO)*
Lawrence R. Irving *(Chm)*
Mike Jerich *(Chief Comml Officer)*
Matt Edic *(Chief Experience Officer)*
Alison Haynes *(VP-Partner Programs & Mktg)*
Nicolas Dourassoff *(Chief Strategy Officer & Gen Mgr)*
Frank Lauria *(Sr VP-Bus Dev)*
Brian Gilman *(CMO)*
Ujjval Karihaloo *(Chief Product Officer)*
Geoff Chretien *(Sr VP-Channels)*

INTELETRAVEL.COM
1625 S Congress Ave Ste 100, Delray Beach, FL 33445
Tel.: (800) 873-5353
Web Site:
https://www2.inteletravel.com
Year Founded: 1991
Emp.: 100
Travel Agencies
N.A.I.C.S.: 561510
Joseph Traina *(Co-Founder & Chm)*

Subsidiaries:

McVeigh Global Meetings & Events, LLC (1)
209 W 40th St Ste 201, New York, NY 10018
Tel.: (212) 316-0052
Web Site: http://www.mcveigh.com
Holding Company; Events Services
N.A.I.C.S.: 551112
Jeff Guberman *(CEO)*
Carvie Gillikin *(Chief Revenue Officer)*
Manny Lesmes *(CFO)*
Renee Jacobs *(Exec VP)*
Ellen Montuori-Graziano *(Exec VP)*
Steve Casley *(Exec VP-Bus Dev)*
Douglas Hunt *(Sr VP-Mktg)*
Elliott Elsner *(Dir-Bus Dev)*
Brent Taylor *(Dir-Bus Dev)*
Karen Townsend *(Dir-Bus Dev)*

Subsidiary (Domestic):

Fourth Wall Events, Inc. (2)
209 W 40th St Ste 201, New York, NY 10018-1672
Tel.: (212) 316-0052
Web Site: http://www.fourthwallevents.com
Emp.: 100
Event Management Services
N.A.I.C.S.: 561920
Jeff Guberman *(CEO)*

McVeigh Associates Ltd. (2)
275 Dixon Ave, Amityville, NY 11701
Tel.: (631) 789-8833
Web Site: http://www.mcveigh.com
Strategic Meeting Management
N.A.I.C.S.: 541618
Frank McVeigh *(Pres & CEO)*
Robert G. LeValley *(Exec VP & Mng Partner)*
Ellen Montuori Graziano *(Exec VP & Mng Partner)*

WorldTEK Events, LLC (2)
PO Box 1022, Glastonbury, CT 06033
Tel.: (203) 563-8168
Web Site: http://worldtekevents.com
Events Services
N.A.I.C.S.: 711310
Steven G. Casley *(CEO & Partner)*
Renee C. Jacobs *(COO & Partner)*
David Rosen *(Partner & VP-Bus Dev)*
Jill Schaefer *(Sr Mgr-Meeting & Events)*
Michael Huntington *(Dir-Sponsorship & Exhibitions)*
Sandro Francini *(Dir-Sls, Sponsorship & Exhibitions)*

INTELICA COMMERCIAL REAL ESTATE COMPANY
600 Emerson Rd Ste 210, Creve Coeur, MO 63141
Tel.: (314) 270-5991   MO
Web Site: http://www.intelicacre.com
Commercial Real Estate Advisory Services
N.A.I.C.S.: 531390
Dan Dokovic *(CEO & Principal)*

Subsidiaries:

James Real Estate Services, Inc. (1)
90 Madison St Ste 403, Denver, CO 80206-5413
Tel.: (303) 388-1100
Web Site: http://www.jres.com
Real Estate Services
N.A.I.C.S.: 531320
Ann Del Nigro *(Dir-Residential Brokerage Svcs & Office Mgr)*
Bill James *(Founder)*

INTELISHIFT TECHNOLOGIES
9893 Georgetown Pike Ste 808, Great Falls, VA 22066-0000
Tel.: (410) 690-4100
Year Founded: 2010
IT Services & Consulting
N.A.I.C.S.: 513210

Subsidiaries:

Data Canopy Colocation LLC (1)
10500 Little Patuxent Pkwy Ste 303, Columbia, MD 21044
Tel.: (703) 504-5200
Web Site: http://www.datacanopy.com
Sales Range: $1-9.9 Million
Emp.: 8
Information Technology Development Services
N.A.I.C.S.: 541512
Ryan Barbera *(CEO)*
Jen Herson *(Pres)*
Andrew Iwamoto *(CTO)*
Adam Thomas *(Exec VP)*

INTELIUS, INC.
500 108th Ave NE Ste 1600, Bellevue, WA 98004
Tel.: (425) 974-6100   DE

Web Site: http://www.intelius.com
Year Founded: 2003
Cloud-Based Public Data Research
Services
N.A.I.C.S.: 518210
Naveen K. Jain (CEO)
Paul T. Cook (CFO)
William H. Beaver (Gen Counsel)
Edward Petersen (VP-Corp Dev)
Gregory L. Anderson (Chief Corp Officer)
Jay Caldwell (CFO)
William Arthur Owens (Chm)

Subsidiaries:

US Search.com Inc.   (1)
PO Box 4145, Bellevue, WA 98009-4145
Tel.: (310) 302-6300
Web Site: http://www.ussearch.com
Cloud-Based Public Data Research Services
N.A.I.C.S.: 518210

INTELLECT NEUROSCIENCES, INC.

550 Sylvan Ave, Englewood Cliffs, NJ
07632
Tel.: (201) 608-5101   DE
Web Site: http://www.intellectns.com
Year Founded: 2005
Biopharmaceutical Researcher & Mfr
N.A.I.C.S.: 325412

INTELLECT RESOURCES, INC.

3824 N Elm St Suite 102, Greensboro, NC 27455
Web Site:
    http://www.intellectresources.com
Year Founded: 1999
Sales Range: $1-9.9 Million
Emp.: 20
Consulting, Hiring & Recruiting Services for Health Professionals
N.A.I.C.S.: 561311
Tiffany Crenshaw (Pres & CEO)
Jennifer Anderson (VP-Client Svcs Delivery)

INTELLECT TECHNICAL SOLUTIONS, INC.

5404 Cypress Center Dr Ste 150,
Clearwater, FL 33609
Tel.: (813) 676-6400
Web Site:
    http://www.intellectcorp.com
Year Founded: 1998
Sales Range: $1-9.9 Million
Emp.: 12
Computer Programming Services;
Technical Staffing & Solutions
N.A.I.C.S.: 541511
James Barge (Co-Founder, Pres & CEO)
Rhonda Dabney (Ops Mgr)

INTELLI CENTRICS INC.

1420 Lakeside Pkwy Ste 110, Flower
Mound, TX 75028-4035
Tel.: (817) 732-3873
Web Site:
    http://www.intellicentrics.com
Security System Services
N.A.I.C.S.: 561621
Michael Sheehan (Co-Founder & CEO)
Julian Lin (Co-Founder & Chm)
David Taylor (Chief Innovation Officer)
Michael McDonald (COO)
Alpha Chen (CFO)

Subsidiaries:

Who Are You Ltd.   (1)
Devonshire Business Centre Works Road,
Letchworth Garden City, Hertford, SG6
1GJ, United Kingdom
Tel.: (44) 1462488369

Web Site: http://www.whoareyoultd.com
Credential Checking Services
N.A.I.C.S.: 621999

INTELLI-MARK TECHNOLO-GIES, INC.

909 Aviation Pkwy Ste 900, Morrisville, NC 27560
Tel.: (919) 201-3616   DE
Web Site: http://www.etix.com
Year Founded: 2000
Emp.: 100
Computer & Computer Peripheral
Equipment Distr
N.A.I.C.S.: 423430
Travis Janovich (Founder & CEO)
Paxton Badham (Pres)
Aaron Bare (CMO)

Subsidiaries:

TicketBiscuit, LLC   (1)
1550 Woods of Riverchase Dr Ste 330, Birmingham, AL 35244
Web Site: http://www.ticketbiscuit.com
Software Publisher
N.A.I.C.S.: 513210
Jamey Taylor (CTO)
Tom Bowen (VP-Sls)

TicketForce, LLC   (1)
313 N Gilbert Rd Ste 200, Gilbert, AZ
85234
Tel.: (866) 726-3581
Travel Arrangement & Reservation Services
N.A.I.C.S.: 561599

Tickets Plus, Inc.   (1)
620 Century Ave SW Ste 300, Grand Rapids, MI 49503
Tel.: (616) 222-4000
Ticketing Services
N.A.I.C.S.: 323120

INTELLIBRIGHT CORPORA-TION

3310 N Capital of Texas Hwy 2nd Fl,
Austin, TX 78746
Web Site: http://www.intellibright.com
Year Founded: 2009
Sales Range: $1-9.9 Million
Emp.: 10
Advertising Agency Services
N.A.I.C.S.: 541810
Ron Browning (Founder & CEO)

Subsidiaries:

MD Connect, Inc.   (1)
70 Walnut St Suite 102, Wellesley, MA
02481
Tel.: (888) 623-4443
Web Site: http://www.mdconnectinc.com
Sales Range: $1-9.9 Million
Emp.: 10
Digital Marketing Agency
N.A.I.C.S.: 541810
Ben Joslin (VP-Mktg)
Nick Snow (Sr Mgr-Online Mktg)

INTELLICENTS INC.

100 N Broadway Ave, Albert Lea, MN
56007
Tel.: (507) 377-2919   MN
Web Site:
    http://www.intellicentsinc.com
Year Founded: 1974
Employee Benefits Consulting & Administration Services
N.A.I.C.S.: 524292
Bradley K. Arends (Co-Founder & CEO)
Grant S. Arends (Co-Founder & Pres-Consulting Svcs)
Tom Singsank (CFO)
Kevin Dulitz (VP-Employee Benefits)
Matt Twedt (Pres-Personal Fin Mgmt)

INTELLICORP, INC.

2900 Lakeside Dr Ste 221, Santa
Clara, CA 95054-2817
Tel.: (650) 965-5500   DE

Web Site: http://www.intellicorp.com
Year Founded: 1980
Sales Range: $10-24.9 Million
Emp.: 60
Developing & Marketing Software
Products & Solutions for Enterprise
Resource Planning Customers
N.A.I.C.S.: 541511
Jerome Klajbor (CEO)
Christopher Trueman (CTO)

INTELLIDYN CORPORATION

175 Derby St Unit 40, Hingham, MA
02043
Tel.: (781) 741-5503
Year Founded: 1998
Sales Range: $10-24.9 Million
Emp.: 12
Data Integration, Warehousing, Analytics, Modeling Channel Integration &
Performance Assessment Services
N.A.I.C.S.: 518210
Peter Harvey (Founder, Pres & CEO)
Brian Balzarini (CFO)
Rajeev Kumar (CTO)
Dmitri Kuznetsov (VP & Dir-Analytics)

INTELLIGENCER PRINTING COMPANY INC.

330 Eden Rd, Lancaster, PA 17601-4218
Tel.: (717) 291-3100   PA
Web Site:
    http://www.intellprinting.com
Year Founded: 1839
Sales Range: $25-49.9 Million
Emp.: 160
Fiscal Year-end: 12/31/14
Commercial Printing, Lithographic
N.A.I.C.S.: 323111
Dean Baker (VP-Sls & Mktg-Mid-Atlantic Reg)
Kevin Hoover (Mgr-IT)
George Crognale (Mgr-Credit)
Kim Swope (Mgr-Customer Svcs)
Joseph Schott (VP-Ops)
Karen Peiffer (VP-Client Svc)
Margie Leddy (Mgr-Production-Intelligencer Mailing & Fulfillment)
Toby Ahnert (Dir-Digital Svcs)
Todd Foster (VP-Bus Dev)
Amy Popp (Bus Mgr)

INTELLIGENT AUDIT

365 W Passaic St Ste 235, Rochelle
Park, NJ 07662
Tel.: (201) 880-1110
Web Site:
    http://www.intelligentaudit.com
Year Founded: 1997
Sales Range: $125-149.9 Million
Emp.: 37
Logistics & Transportation Services
N.A.I.C.S.: 541614
Yosie Lebovich (CEO)

INTELLIGENT BEAUTY, LLC

2301 Rosecrans Ave Ste 5100, El
Segundo, CA 90245
Tel.: (310) 683-0940
Web Site: http://www.ibinc.com
Year Founded: 2006
Sales Range: $450-499.9 Million
Emp.: 175
Marketing & Brand Management
N.A.I.C.S.: 541613
Bob Johnson (Co-Founder)
Adam Goldenberg (Co-Founder & Co-CEO)
Don Ressler (Co-Founder & Co-CEO)
Scott Whittier (Chief Scientific Officer)
Dane Pescaia (CTO)
Matt Lueders (Gen Counsel)

INTELLIGENT CONTENT CORP.

20283 State Rd 7 Ste 400, Boca Raton, FL 33498
Tel.: (561) 237-2940
Web Site: http://www.petplace.com
Year Founded: 1999
Sales Range: $1-9.9 Million
Emp.: 12
Website with Articles about Pet
Health & Well Being
N.A.I.C.S.: 812910
Jon Rappaport (Founder, Chm & CEO)
Diego Saenz (Pres)

INTELLIGENT DIGITAL AVA-TARS, INC.

1341 W Mequon Rd Ste 210, Mequon, WI 53092-3223
Tel.: (262) 643-4740
Web Site: http://www.idavatars.com
Computer Related Services
N.A.I.C.S.: 541519
Norrie Daroga (Founder & CEO)
Neil Lemoureux (CTO)
Karen Dagerman (VP-Client Svcs)

INTELLIGENT HEARING SYS-TEMS CORP.

6860 SW 81 St, Miami, FL 33143-7708
Tel.: (305) 668-6102
Web Site: http://www.ihsys.com
Year Founded: 1983
Sales Range: $25-49.9 Million
Emp.: 22
Hearing Diagnostic Equipment Mfr
N.A.I.C.S.: 339112
Jerome Cohen (Owner)
Edward Miskiel (Pres)
Rafael Delgato (Exec VP)
Carlos Lopez (CFO)
Octavio Garrastacho (Product Mgr)
Marra Lashbrook (VP-Mktg)

INTELLIGENT INSTRUMENTA-TION, INC.

3529 N Williams Ave, Portland, OR
97227
Tel.: (503) 928-3188
Web Site: http://www.instrument.com
PC Instrumentation
N.A.I.C.S.: 334513
Vincent LaVecchia (COO)
Justin Lewis (CEO)
JD Hooge (Chief Compliance Officer)
Coryna Sorin (VP-Account Svcs)
Amie Pascal (Exec Dir)
Phong Ho (VP-Technology)
Marshall King (CFO)
Kara Place (Exec Dir)
Chris Larson (Dir-Creative)
Zech Bard (Dir-Writing)
Andrio Abero (Dir-Creative)
Jessie White (Dir-Creative)
Paul Welch (Exec Dir)
Thomas Reynolds (Dir-Technical)
Tim Kamerer (Dir-Design)
Rocky Puntney (Exec Dir)
Dave Mikush (Dir-Creative)
Kirsten Blair (Exec Dir)
John Brown (Dir-Technical)
Jered Cuenco (Dir-Technical)
Dan Schechter (Dir-Creative)
Moira Losch (Dir-Recruiting)
Paul Farning (Dir-Technical)
Justin Levinsohn (Dir-Technical)
Erin Kirby (Mgr-Studio)
Lisa Koluvek (Coord-Ops)
Mike Guss (Dir-Assoc. Design)
Jordan Lessler (Dir-Assoc. Design)
Stephen Bardwell (Dir-Assoc. Design)
Justin Holbrook (Dir-Design)
Jordan Sowers (Dir-Assoc. Creative)
Liz Luce (Mgr-Recruiting)
Eryka Gonzalez (Studio Coord)
Ravi Mongia (Dir-Strategy)

Intelligent Instrumentation, Inc.—(Continued)

Chip Truex *(Dir-Assoc. Creative)*
Jason King *(Dir-Strategy)*
Tessa Baston *(Mgr-Human Dev)*
Thomas Charlet *(Dir-Design)*
Alicia Fairclough-Buford *(Dir-Assoc. Design)*
Sean Klassen *(Dir-Assoc. Design)*
Jack De Caluwe *(Dir-Assoc. Creative)*
Darshan Phillips *(Dir-Assoc. Design)*
Michael Novia *(Dir-Assoc. Design)*
August Heffner *(Dir-Creative)*
Emily Griffith *(Mgr-Assoc. Human Dev)*
Chris Bright *(Dir-Writing)*
Adam Garcia *(Dir-Assoc. Creative)*
Leon Anderson *(Mgr-Product)*
Chris Piuggi *(Dir-Technical)*
Kristen Minarik *(Dir-Assoc. Design)*
Laureen Feeny *(Dir-Exec. Creative)*
Nishat Akhtar *(Dir-Assoc. Creative)*
David Brewer *(Dir-Assoc. Technical)*
Steve Mahn *(Dir-Design)*
Brent Mills *(Coord-IT)*
Kelsey Moede *(Coord-Acctg)*

INTELLIGENT INTEGRATION SYSTEMS, INC.
Ten Post Ofc Sq 8th Fl, Boston, MA 02109
Tel.: (617) 314-7872
Web Site: http://www.intelligent-isi.com
Year Founded: 2006
Sales Range: $10-24.9 Million
Emp.: 5
Wired Telecommunication Services
N.A.I.C.S.: 517111
Marshall R. Peterson *(Co-Founder & Chm)*
Rich Zimmerman *(Co-Founder, Pres & CTO)*
Paul Davis *(CEO)*

INTELLIGENT INTERIORS INC.
16837 Addison Rd Ste 500, Addison, TX 75001
Tel.: (972) 716-9979
Web Site: http://www.intelligentinteriors.net
Year Founded: 1996
Rev.: $8,200,000
Emp.: 35
Furniture Merchant Whslr
N.A.I.C.S.: 423210
Kraig Wellshear *(VP)*
Mindy Casas *(Owner)*

INTELLIGENT MICRO PATTERNING, LLC
9790 16th St N, Saint Petersburg, FL 33716
Tel.: (727) 522-0334
Web Site: http://www.intelligentmp.com
Year Founded: 2001
Sales Range: $1-9.9 Million
Emp.: 10
Smart Filter Technology
N.A.I.C.S.: 541715
Jay Sasserath *(CEO)*

INTELLIGENT MOBILE SOLUTIONS, INC.
1801 SW 3rd Ave 3rd Fl, Miami, FL 33129
Tel.: (786) 866-8050   FL
Sales Range: $25-49.9 Million
Emp.: 390
Integrated Internet Media & Solutions Company for Spanish & Portuguese-Speaking Audiences
N.A.I.C.S.: 517810

Gerardo Von Zehmen *(CTO)*
Eduardo Kawas *(Pres & CEO)*
Amaury Bonatto *(CFO)*
Jose Maria Carosella *(Sr VP-Product Dev)*

INTELLIGENT SOLUTIONS, INC.
9930 W 190th St Ste L, Mokena, IL 60448-5610
Tel.: (708) 479-6532
Web Site: http://www.intelligentsolutions.net
Year Founded: 1990
Sales Range: $1-9.9 Million
Emp.: 21
Information Technology Services
N.A.I.C.S.: 519290
Rich Fugett *(Owner & Pres)*

INTELLIGENT VAR TECHNOLOGY INC.
1652 Yeager Ave, La Verne, CA 91750
Tel.: (909) 394-5188
Web Site: http://www.intelli-tech.com
Year Founded: 1992
Sales Range: $25-49.9 Million
Emp.: 30
Technology Solutions & Computer Equipment Distr
N.A.I.C.S.: 541690
Cynthia Johnson *(Co-Founder & Owner)*
Darrell Johnson *(Co-Founder)*

INTELLIGERE
10000 Hwy 55 Ste 400, Plymouth, MN 55441
Web Site: http://www.intelligeresolutions.com
Year Founded: 1979
Translation & Interpretation Services
N.A.I.C.S.: 541930
Sharon Stein *(CEO)*
Ana Gregg *(Dir-Interpreter Management)*
Luis Lugo *(VP-Svc Ops)*

INTELLIGRAPHICS INC.
1401 N Central Exwpy Ste 320, Richardson, TX 75080
Tel.: (972) 479-1770
Web Site: http://www.intelligraphics.com
Year Founded: 1992
Sales Range: $10-24.9 Million
Emp.: 75
Professional Device Drivers & System Level Software Development Services to Hardware Mfrs & Software Development Companies
N.A.I.C.S.: 541511
Scott Lawson *(Pres)*
Candy Crawford *(Mgr-Ops)*

Subsidiaries:

Intelligent Software Solutions   (1)
1401 N Central Expy Ste 320, Richardson, TX 75080
Tel.: (972) 479-1770
Web Site: http://www.intelligraphics.com
Rev.: $600,000
Sales of Prepackaged Software
N.A.I.C.S.: 513210

INTELLIMAR, INC.
7560 Main St, Sykesville, MD 21784
Tel.: (410) 552-9940
Web Site: http://www.intellimar.com
Sales Range: $1-9.9 Million
Emp.: 16
Concrete Barriers, Guard Booths & Bomb-Resistant Trash Cans Mfr & Sales
N.A.I.C.S.: 561621

Mark O. Oakes *(Pres & CEO)*
Jan Grossnickle *(Comptroller)*

INTELLISITE CORPORATION
1141 Kansas Ave, Modesto, CA 95351-1525
Tel.: (209) 408-8140
Web Site: http://www.qpcs.net
Computer & Office Machine Repair & Maintenance
N.A.I.C.S.: 811210
Mario Campos *(Owner)*

Subsidiaries:

Broad Sky Networks, LLC   (1)
750 NW Charbonneau St No 201, Bend, OR 97703
Tel.: (877) 291-9575
Web Site: http://www.broadskynetworks.net
Sales Range: $1-9.9 Million
Emp.: 13
Wireless Network Services
N.A.I.C.S.: 517112
Mike Mudd *(Pres)*

INTELLISWIFT SOFTWARE INC.
2201 Walnut Ave 1st Fl Ste 180, Fremont, CA 94538
Tel.: (510) 490-9240
Web Site: http://www.intelliswift.com
Year Founded: 2001
Rev.: $148,000,000
Emp.: 187
Computer System Design Services
N.A.I.C.S.: 541512
Pat Patel *(VP)*
Sumit De Bhaumik *(Mgr-HR)*
Bob Patel *(CEO)*

Subsidiaries:

Global Infotech Corp.   (1)
2890 Zanker Rd Ste 202, San Jose, CA 95134
Tel.: (408) 567-0600
Web Site: http://www.global-infotech.com
Sales Range: $1-9.9 Million
Emp.: 75
Business Consulting Services
N.A.I.C.S.: 541690
Atul Sharma *(Pres)*

INTEPLAST GROUP, LTD.
9 Peach Tree Hill Rd, Livingston, NJ 07039-5702
Tel.: (973) 994-8000   NJ
Web Site: http://www.inteplast.com
Year Founded: 1991
Plastics Product Mfr
N.A.I.C.S.: 326113
Vinod Ghumwala *(Mgr-Product Dev)*
Serene Lee *(Mgr-Mgmt Analysis)*
Matthew Buckhannon *(Mgr-Bus Dev)*
Jennifer Stoll *(Mgr-Customer Svc)*
Janine Paley *(Sr Mgr-Mktg)*

Subsidiaries:

AmTopp Corporation   (1)
101 Inteplast Blvd, Lolita, TX 77971
Tel.: (361) 874-3000
Web Site: http://www.inteplast.com
Plastic Film & Sheet Mfr
N.A.I.C.S.: 326112
Brenda Wilson *(Dir-HR)*

Danafilms Corporation   (1)
5 Otis St, Westborough, MA 01581
Tel.: (508) 366-8884
Web Site: http://www.danafilms.com
Emp.: 70
Blown Plastic Films Mfr
N.A.I.C.S.: 326112
Adam Furtado *(Coord-Mktg & Sls)*

Inteplast Group, Ltd. - Integrated Bagging Systems   (1)
9 Peach Tree Hill Rd, Livingston, NJ 07039
Tel.: (973) 994-8000
Web Site: http://www.ibsbags.com
Plastic Bag & Liner Mfr
N.A.I.C.S.: 326111

Subsidiary (Domestic):

Niaflex Corporation   (2)
7549 Brokerage Dr, Orlando, FL 32809
Tel.: (407) 851-6620
Web Site: http://www.niaflex.com
Plastic Packaging Film Mfr
N.A.I.C.S.: 326112

Inteplast Group, Ltd. - World-Pak   (1)
9 Peach Tree Hill Rd, Livingston, NJ 07039-5702
Tel.: (973) 994-8000
Sales Range: $25-49.9 Million
Emp.: 160
Plastic Film & Sheet Mfr
N.A.I.C.S.: 326113

INTEPROD LLC
2583 Industry Ln, Eagleville, PA 19403
Tel.: (610) 650-9002
Web Site: http://www.inteprod.com
Sales Range: $1-9.9 Million
Emp.: 30
Medical Equipment Whslr
N.A.I.C.S.: 423450
Patricia L. Murphy *(VP-QA & RA)*
Dennis Verhagen *(Engr-Mechanical)*

INTEPROS CONSULTING INC
750 Marrett Rd, Lexington, MA 02421
Tel.: (781) 761-1140
Web Site: http://www.intepros.com
Rev.: $21,484,187
Emp.: 350
Labor Resource Services
N.A.I.C.S.: 561320
Ken Hull *(VP-Philadelphia TriState Reg)*
John Kovalcik Jr. *(CEO)*

INTER AMERICAN COSMETICS INC.
300 1 Ste 3 Rte 17S, Lodi, NJ 07644
Tel.: (973) 614-0700
Web Site: http://www.iawholesale.com
Sales Range: $25-49.9 Million
Emp.: 8
Cosmetics Perfumes & Hair Products
N.A.I.C.S.: 424210
Kevin Schlussel *(Pres)*

INTER CITY TIRE & AUTO CENTER
777 Dowd Ave, Elizabeth, NJ 07201
Tel.: (908) 354-1200
Web Site: http://www.intercitytire.biz
Rev.: $18,000,000
Emp.: 300
Automotive Tires
N.A.I.C.S.: 441340
Morris Erbesh *(Pres)*
Neil Erbesh *(VP)*

INTER TECHNOLOGIES CORPORATION (ITC)
1605 N Home St, Mishawaka, IN 46545
Tel.: (574) 271-8085
Web Site: http://www.intertech.tv
Year Founded: 2000
Sales Range: $10-24.9 Million
Emp.: 30
Designs & Installs A/V Equipment & Networks
N.A.I.C.S.: 334310
Tadz Juszczak *(VP-Ops)*
Jeff Bazow *(Dir-Client Svcs)*
William Brewster *(CEO)*

INTER TRIBAL COUNCIL OF ARIZONA, INC.
2214 N Central Ave Ste 100, Phoenix, AZ 85004
Tel.: (602) 258-4822   AZ
Web Site: http://www.itcaonline.com

Year Founded: 1975
Sales Range: $10-24.9 Million
Emp.: 66
Tribal Support Services
N.A.I.C.S.: 813410
Thomas Beauty *(Pres)*
Verna Monenerkit *(Office Mgr)*
Cynthia Freeman *(Coord-AAA Program)*
Tom Mike *(Dir-Acctg)*
Gwenda Gorman *(Dir-Health & Human Svcs)*
Alida Montiel *(Dir-Health Sys)*
Mindy Jossefides *(Dir-Special Supplemental Nutrition Program for Women & Infants)*
Jamie Ritchey *(Dir-Tribal Epidemiology Center)*
Maria Dadgar *(Exec Dir)*
Verna Johnson *(Mgr-Health Program)*
Scott Svatora *(Mgr-IT)*
Brandy Warwick-Thier *(Mgr-Nutrition)*
Esther Corbett *(Project Mgr)*

INTER-AMERICAN DEVELOPMENT BANK

1300 New York Ave NW, Washington, DC 20577
Tel.: (202) 623-1000   DC
Web Site: http://www.iadb.org
Year Founded: 1959
Rev.: $3,057,000,000
Assets: $129,459,000,000
Liabilities: $96,530,000,000
Net Worth: $32,929,000,000
Emp.: 2,000
Fiscal Year-end: 12/31/18
International Financial Institution
N.A.I.C.S.: 522299
Gina Montiel *(Exec Dir)*
Claudia Bock-Valotta *(VP-Fin & Admin)*
Ana Maria Rodriguez-Ortiz *(VP-Sectors & Knowledge)*
Jose Agustin Aguerre *(Mgr-Infrastructure & Energy Sector)*
Alexandre Meira da Rosa *(VP-Countries)*
Jose Luis Lupo Flores *(Mgr-Southern Cone Country Dept)*
Gustavo De Rosa *(CFO & Gen Mgr-Fin Dept)*
Marcelo Cabrol *(Mgr-Social Sector)*
Bernardo Guillamon *(Mgr-Outreach & Partnerships Office)*
Juan Bosco Marti Ascencio *(Exec Dir)*
Carola Alvarez *(Gen Mgr-Andean Strategic Plng & Dev Effectiveness)*
Nuria Simo Vila *(CIO & Gen Mgr-IT Dept)*
Federico C. Basanes *(Mgr-Knowledge, Innovation & Comm Sector)*
Therese Turner-Jones *(Gen Mgr-Caribbean Country Dept)*
Federico Galizia *(Chief Risk Officer)*
Juan Pablo Bonilla *(Mgr-Climate Change & Sustainable Dev Sector)*
John Scott *(Gen Counsel & Exec VP)*
Brian O'Neill *(Exec VP)*
Mauricio J Claver-Carone *(Pres)*
Marlon Tabora Munoz *(VP-Fin & Admin AI)*
Guillermo Alberto Francos *(Exec Dir)*
Leonardo Roberto Puppetto *(Exec Dir)*
Ranse Brian Mark Langrin *(Exec Dir)*
Christiane Elisabeth Bogemann-Hagedorn *(Exec Dir)*
Francisco Jose Mayorga Balladares *(Exec Dir)*
German Hugo Rojas Irigoyen *(Exec Dir)*
Jose Guilherme Almeida dos Reis *(Exec Dir)*
Donald John Bobiash *(Exec Dir)*

Alex Foxley *(Exec Dir)*
Sergio Diaz Granados *(Exec Dir)*
Shigeo Shimizu *(Exec Dir)*
Mario Alejandro Gaytan Gonzalez *(Exec Dir)*
Eliot Pedrosa *(Exec Dir)*
Jose Jorge Seligmann Silva *(Exec VP)*
Alberto Rivera-Fournier *(Officer-Ethics)*
Hugo R. Florez Timoran *(Office Mgr-Strategic Plng & Dev Effectiveness)*
Tomas Bermudez *(Mgr-Andean Country Grp)*
Eric Parrado Herrera *(Gen Mgr-Res Dept)*
Moises J. Schwartz *(Mgr-Institutions-Dev)*
Fabrizio Opertti *(Mgr-Integration & Trade Sector)*
Carolina Serra *(Gen Mgr-HR Dept)*
Diego Murguiondo *(Gen Mgr-Budget & Admin Svcs Dept)*
Diego Buchara *(Gen Counsel & Gen Mgr-Legal Dept)*

Subsidiaries:

Inter-American Investment Corporation   (1)
1350 New York Ave NW, Washington, DC 20577
Tel.: (202) 623-3900
Web Site: http://www.iic.org
Financial Support Services
N.A.I.C.S.: 525990
Carl Munana *(Gen Mgr)*
Orlando Ferreira *(COO)*
Sarah Fandell *(Gen Counsel)*

INTER-AMERICAN OIL WORKS INC.

2416 N FM 1936, Odessa, TX 79763
Tel.: (432) 381-5265
Web Site: http://www.oilworksinc.com
Rev.: $16,000,000
Emp.: 40
Oil Well Machinery, Equipment & Supplies
N.A.I.C.S.: 423830
Johnny C. Kidd *(Founder)*

INTER-COMMERCIAL BUSINESS SYSTEMS

601 Century Pkwy, Allen, TX 75013
Tel.: (972) 649-4949
Web Site: http://www.icbsrepair.com
Rev.: $15,400,000
Emp.: 50
Electronic Parts & Equipment
N.A.I.C.S.: 423690
Tom Lacey *(Pres)*

INTER-CON SECURITY SYSTEMS, INC.

210 S De Lacey Ave, Pasadena, CA 91105
Tel.: (626) 535-2200
Web Site: http://www.icsecurity.com
Year Founded: 1973
Sales Range: $250-299.9 Million
Emp.: 4,550
Security Guard Services & Security Consulting, Investigations & Training
N.A.I.C.S.: 561612
Neil Martau *(CFO & VP)*
Robin Simpson *(CFO)*
Enrique Hernandez Jr. *(Exec Chm)*

INTER-COUNTY BAKERS, INC.

1095 Long Island Ave, Lindenhurst, NY 11757
Tel.: (631) 957-1350
Web Site: http://www.icbakers.com
Rev.: $62,000,000
Emp.: 100
Grocery & Related Products Merchant Whslr

N.A.I.C.S.: 424490
Theodore P. Heim Sr. *(CEO)*
Anthony E. Lotito Sr. *(Dir-Bus Dev)*

INTER-COUNTY ELECTRIC COOP ASSOCIATION

102 Maple Ave, Licking, MO 65542
Tel.: (573) 674-2211
Web Site: http://www.ieca.coop
Sales Range: $25-49.9 Million
Emp.: 110
Distribution, Electric Power
N.A.I.C.S.: 221122
Brian Nelson *(Dir-Engrg)*
Jack Rinne *(Mgr-Ops & Maintenance)*
Sarah Akers *(Dir-Acctg)*
Dan Sisco *(Dir-IT)*
Karen McNew *(Dir-Member Svcs & Member Accounts)*
Doug Lane *(Dir-Safety & Facilities)*
Denna Tune *(Dir-HR)*

INTER-COUNTY ENERGY COOP CORP.

1009 Houstonville Rd, Danville, KY 40423
Tel.: (859) 236-4561
Web Site:
   http://www.intercountyenergy.net
Rev.: $22,868,965
Emp.: 62
Distribution, Electric Power
N.A.I.C.S.: 221122
James L. Jacobus *(Pres & CEO)*
Kevin J. Preston *(Treas & Sec)*
Joseph H. Spalding *(Vice Chm)*
Sheree H. Gilliam *(Sr VP-Fin & Admin)*
David Phelps *(VP-Ops)*
Jason E. Todd *(Vice Chm)*

INTER-INDUSTRY CONFERENCE ON AUTO COLLISION REPAIR

5125 Trillium Blvd, Hoffman Estates, IL 60192
Tel.: (847) 590-1198   IL
Web Site: http://www.i-car.com
Year Founded: 1979
Sales Range: $10-24.9 Million
Emp.: 568
Business Associations
N.A.I.C.S.: 813910
Jason Bartanen *(Dir-Indus Tech Rels)*
Margaret Knell *(Dir-Coorp Admin)*
Joshua McFarlin *(Dir-Curriculam & Product Dev)*
Nick Notte *(Dir-Fin & Ops)*
Lori Barrington *(Dir-Project Mgmt Officer)*
John Bosin *(Dir-Segment Dev)*
Bill Stage *(Dir-Segment Dev & Edu)*
John S. Van Alstyne *(Pres & CEO)*
Jeff Peevy *(VP-Technical Products, Programs & Svcs)*

INTER-LAKES COMMUNITY ACTION PARTNERSHIP

111 N Van Eps Ave, Madison, SD 57042
Tel.: (605) 256-6518   SD
Web Site:
   http://www.interlakescap.com
Year Founded: 1966
Sales Range: $10-24.9 Million
Emp.: 220
Community Support Services
N.A.I.C.S.: 624190
Steph Lebeda *(Dir-Child Dev)*
Kimberly McCoy *(Dir-Fiscal)*
Eric Kunzweiler *(Dir-Plng)*
Cindy Dannenbring *(Exec Dir)*
Scott Finck *(Dir-Weatherization Program)*

INTER-PACIFIC CORPORATION

2257 Colby Ave, Los Angeles, CA 90064
Tel.: (310) 473-7591
Year Founded: 1957
Sales Range: $100-124.9 Million
Emp.: 30
Footwear
N.A.I.C.S.: 424340
Frank G. Arnstein *(Owner)*
Nancy Richards *(Mgr-HR)*
Eddy Karyadi *(Mgr-Import Ops)*
Jeff Brager *(VP)*

INTER-POWER /AHLCON PARTNERS LP

254 Interpower Dr, Colver, PA 15927-4305
Tel.: (724) 933-7647
Sales Range: $50-74.9 Million
Emp.: 5
Electronic Services
N.A.I.C.S.: 221118
John S. Hall *(CFO)*

INTER-STATE FORD TRUCK SALES, INC.

45 Brainard Rd, Hartford, CT 06114
Tel.: (860) 706-0950
Web Site:
   http://www.interfordtruck.com
Year Founded: 1980
Sales Range: $10-24.9 Million
Emp.: 30
Truck Dealership
N.A.I.C.S.: 423110
John Breslin *(Mgr-Svc)*
Dave Damaschi *(Mgr-Parts)*

INTER-STATE HARDWOODS COMPANY, INC.

Rte 250/92, Bartow, WV 24920
Tel.: (304) 456-4597
Web Site: http://www.inter-statehardwoods.com
Rev.: $31,200,000
Emp.: 180
Hardwood Dimension, Floor Mill Sawmill & Planing Mill
N.A.I.C.S.: 321918
Barry Frazee *(VP)*
Gene Frazee *(CEO)*
Bryan Vernon *(Pres)*
Donnie Nottingham *(Mgr-Mill)*
Allen Sisler *(Mgr-Ops)*
Rob Walthour *(Mgr-District Sls)*

INTER-TRACK PARTNERS LLC

8600 W N Ave, Melrose Park, IL 60160
Tel.: (708) 615-1200
Web Site: http://www.illinoisotb.com
Sales Range: $25-49.9 Million
Emp.: 1,200
Off-Track Betting Services
N.A.I.C.S.: 713290

INTER-WIRE PRODUCTS INC.

355 Main St Ste 2, Armonk, NY 10504
Tel.: (914) 273-6633
Web Site:
   http://www.interwiregroup.com
Year Founded: 1981
Sales Range: $100-124.9 Million
Emp.: 200
Wire
N.A.I.C.S.: 423510
Frank Cardile *(Chm)*
Debbie Cardile *(Vice Chm)*
Mario Gallo *(VP)*
Sergio Gallo *(VP)*

INTERACT FOR HEALTH

Interact for Health—(Continued)

3805 Edwards Rd Ste 500, Cincinnati, OH 45209-1948
Tel.: (513) 458-6600   OH
Web Site:
http://www.interactforhealth.org
Year Founded: 1978
Sales Range: $25-49.9 Million
Emp.: 35
Health Promotion Services
N.A.I.C.S.: 813212
Cliff Hastings (Dir-IT)
Kelly Firesheets (Officer-Program)
Christine Bennett (Dir-Mgmt Svcs)
O'Dell M. Owens (Pres & CEO)
Jeanne Marie Tapke (Chm)

INTERACT INCORPORATED
1225 L St Ste 600, Lincoln, NE 68508
Tel.: (402) 476-8786
Web Site: http://www.iivip.com
Rev.: $10,600,000
Emp.: 40
Communications Equipment
N.A.I.C.S.: 423690
Greg Gissler (Founder)

INTERACT PUBLIC SAFETY SYSTEMS
102 W 3rd St Ste 750, Winston Salem, NC 27101
Tel.: (336) 397-5300
Web Site: http://www.interact911.com
Sales Range: $10-24.9 Million
Emp.: 35
Public Safety Software Developer
N.A.I.C.S.: 513210
Andrew J. Filipowski (Chm)
J. Evans Wroten (CIO)
Mark Fetherolf (CTO)
Matthew G. Roszak (Sr VP-Corp Dev)
Paul Tatro (Pres-Intl Ops)
Steven J. McDowall (Sr VP-Engrg)
Doug Laux (CFO)
Ken Souza (COO)
John E. McNulty (Pres & CEO)
James Cape (Sr VP-Corp Mktg)
Terry Turner (Sr VP & Chief Sls Officer)
Tim Bigwood (Sr VP-Ops)
Mike McGarry (Sr VP & Gen Mgr-InterAct Products)

INTERACTIVATION HEALTH NETWORKS LLC
115 East 57th Street, Ste 1101, New York, NY 10022
Tel.: (888) 219-4678   DE
Web Site:
http://www.interactivation.com
Year Founded: 2008
Health Industry Cable Television & Video-On-Demand Broadcasting Services
N.A.I.C.S.: 517111
Joe Covey (Co-Owner)
Matthew Davidge (Co-Owner)

Subsidiaries:

Interactivation Health Networks LLC -
Operations Office   (1)
N16 W22419 Watertown Rd, Waukesha, WI 53186
Tel.: (262) 574-8518
Web Site: http://www.thewellnessnetwork.tv
Health Industry Cable Television & Video-On-Demand Broadcasting Services
N.A.I.C.S.: 517111

Unit (Domestic):

HealthStyle Press   (2)
W175 N11117 Stonewood Dr Ste 110, Germantown, WI 53022
Tel.: (262) 532-4000
Web Site: http://www.healthstylepress.com

Sales Range: $1-9.9 Million
Emp.: 5
Health Education Booklet Publisher
N.A.I.C.S.: 513130
Dan Schultz (Mgr-Sls)
Trudie Gauerke (Mgr-Production)
Christina Jester (Mgr-Fin)
Jayne Ruelle (Coord-Mktg)
Kim Wilkins (Mgr-Health Education solutions)
Julie Wonders (Mgr-Member Health Solutions)

Subsidiary (Domestic):

LOGICARE Corporation   (2)
2620 Stein Blvd, Eau Claire, WI 54701
Tel.: (715) 839-0700
Web Site: http://www.logicare.com
Sales Range: $1-9.9 Million
Emp.: 25
Hospital Patient Education & Management Software Developer, Publisher & Whslr
N.A.I.C.S.: 513210
Jean Fisher (Dir-Ops)
Rachel Zacho (Office Mgr)

Milner-Fenwick, Inc.   (1)
119 Lk Frnt Dr, Hunt Valley, MD 21030
Tel.: (800) 432-8433
Web Site: http://www.milner-fenwick.com
Motion Picture & Video Production
N.A.I.C.S.: 512110

INTERACTIVE COMMUNICATIONS INC
250 Williams St Ste M 100, Atlanta, GA 30303
Tel.: (770) 240-6100
Web Site: http://www.incomm.com
Year Founded: 1992
Sales Range: $100-124.9 Million
Emp.: 1,700
Holding Company; Phone Cards, ISPs & Telecommunications Services; Switch-Based Carrier
N.A.I.C.S.: 561421
M. Brooks Smith (Pres & CEO)
Phil Graves (Exec VP)
Daniel M. Kahrs (Exec VP-Ops)
Brenda Agee (VP-Admin & Fin)
Edward Vargo (Mgr-Mktg Svcs)
Frank Squilla (Exec VP-Indus & Trade Rels)
Scott Meyerhoff (CFO & COO)

Subsidiaries:

Hallmark Business Connections, Inc.   (1)
121 S 8th St 7th Fl, Minneapolis, MN 55402
Tel.: (612) 672-8600
Web Site:
http://www.hallmarkbusinessconnections.com
Business Management Consulting Services
N.A.I.C.S.: 541611
Gus Thompson (Chief Client Dev Officer)
Tressa Angell (Pres)
Daryl Person (VP-Brand & Dir-Creative)
Kyle Korzenowski (CIO)

InComm Canada LLC   (1)
2050 Derry Road West Suite 100, Mississauga, L5N 0B9, ON, Canada
Tel.: (905) 567-5040
Information Technology Consulting Services
N.A.I.C.S.: 541512

InComm Europe Limited   (1)
1638 Parkway Solent Business Park, Whiteley, PO15 7AH, Hants, United Kingdom
Tel.: (44) 1489 556700
Web Site: http://www.incomm-europe.com
Information Technology Consulting Services
N.A.I.C.S.: 541512

InComm Japan KK   (1)
Shinjuku Center Building 41F 1-25-1 Nishi Shinjuku, Shinjuku-ku, Tokyo, 163-0610, Japan
Tel.: (81) 3 6279 4881
Information Technology Consulting Services
N.A.I.C.S.: 541512

InComm Ltd.   (1)
11th Fl POSCO Center Bldg West Wing

892 Daechi 4-dong, Gangnam-gu, Seoul, 135-777, Korea (South)
Tel.: (82) 2 559 0715
Information Technology Consulting Services
N.A.I.C.S.: 541512

Incomm Mexico, LLC   (1)
Shakespeare 30 10th Fl, Mexico, 11590, Mexico
Tel.: (52) 55 5202 2811
Information Technology Consulting Services
N.A.I.C.S.: 541512

Incomm Puerto Rico LLC   (1)
107 Ortegon Ave Ste 101, Guaynabo, PR 00966
Tel.: (787) 781-2600
Information Technology Consulting Services
N.A.I.C.S.: 541512

INTERACTIVE FINANCIAL CORPORATION
3250 W Big Beaver Rd Ste 300, Troy, MI 48084
Tel.: (248) 283-5400
Year Founded: 1993
Rev.: $10,100,000
Emp.: 462
Securities Brokerage
N.A.I.C.S.: 523150
Hunt Gersin (Pres & Principal)

INTERACTIVE INNOVATION GROUP, INC.
1640 5th St #226, Santa Monica, CA 90401
Tel.: (424) 272-0291
Web Site: http://www.panjo.com
Year Founded: 2011
Online Retailer & Marketer
N.A.I.C.S.: 541519
Chad Billmyer (Co-Founder & CEO)
Tom Gerken (Co-Founder & CTO)
Gary Shikhelman (Head-Design)
Juan Vasconez (Co-Founder & Product Mgr)
Todd Simmons (Head-Mktg)
Huy Nguyen (Engr)
Brian Lee (Mgr-Community)

INTERACTIVE LIQUID, LLC
9999 Hamilton Blvd One Tek Park Ste 130, Breinigsville, PA 18031
Tel.: (484) 397-4171
Web Site: http://www.liquidint.com
Year Founded: 2006
Sales Range: $1-9.9 Million
Emp.: 39
Interactive Marketing Services; Digital Strategy, Analytics & Metrics
N.A.I.C.S.: 541512
James Ludlow (Pres & Founder)
Doug Mancini (Exec VP)
Lawrence Wolfe (CTO & Dir-Mobility)
Brian Noreika (Dir-Photography)

INTERACTIVE MARKETING SERVICES, INC.
2 N Maple Ave, Ridgely, MD 21660
Tel.: (410) 634-2060
Rev.: $17,600,000
Emp.: 170
Promotional Fulfillment Services
N.A.I.C.S.: 493190

INTERACTIVE MEDIA GROUP INCORPORATED
12536 Beatrice St, Los Angeles, CA 90066
Tel.: (310) 301-4190
Rev.: $23,400,000
Emp.: 100
Computer Peripheral Equipment
N.A.I.C.S.: 449210
Richard Dorfman (Pres)

INTERACTIVE RESPONSE TECHNOLOGIES

4400 N State Rd 7, Fort Lauderdale, FL 33319
Tel.: (954) 484-4973
Web Site: http://www.callcenter.com
Year Founded: 1993
Sales Range: $75-99.9 Million
Emp.: 2,200
Telemarketing & Call Center Services
N.A.I.C.S.: 561422

Subsidiaries:

IRT of Texas   (1)
600 Jefferson St Fl 4, Houston, TX 77002-7363
Tel.: (713) 289-8300
Web Site: http://www.cccinteractive.com
Sales Range: $25-49.9 Million
Emp.: 700
Telemarketing & Call Center Services
N.A.I.C.S.: 561422

INTERACTIVE SERVICES NETWORK, INC.
1035 NE 125th St Ste 200, Miami, FL 33161
Tel.: (305) 573-5300
Year Founded: 1995
Sales Range: $1-9.9 Million
Emp.: 68
Telecommunications Resellers
N.A.I.C.S.: 517121
Damian Zhmielewski (VP)

Subsidiaries:

Kapp Communications, Inc.   (1)
8100 Ohio River Blvd, Pittsburgh, PA 15202
Tel.: (412) 761-7700
Web Site: http://www.kappcom.com
Rev.: $3,200,000
Emp.: 16
Radio, Television & Other Electronics Stores
N.A.I.C.S.: 449210
James Kapp (CEO)
James Blick (VP & Mgr-Field Ops)
Robert Kapp (Pres & Mgr-Ops)

INTERACTIVE SOLUTIONS, INC.
3860 Forest Hill Irene Rd Ste 101, Memphis, TN 38125
Tel.: (901) 866-1474
Web Site: http://www.isitn.com
Year Founded: 1996
Sales Range: $10-24.9 Million
Emp.: 60
Videoconferencing Systems Sales & Support
N.A.I.C.S.: 517810
Derek Plummer (VP-Design & Engrg)
Jay Myers (Founder & CEO)
Pooven Naidoo (Mgr-Software Dev)

INTERACTIVE SOLUTIONS, LLC
100 Tournament Dr, Horsham, PA 19044
Tel.: (215) 675-1400
Web Site:
http://www.ispartnersllc.com
Year Founded: 2005
Sales Range: $10-24.9 Million
Emp.: 25
Accounting Services
N.A.I.C.S.: 541219
John DeCesare (Pres)

INTERACTIVE STUDY SYSTEMS, INC.
3985 Gateway Center Blvd N Ste 200, Pinellas Park, FL 33782
Tel.: (727) 450-0476
Web Site:
http://www.careersaver.com
Year Founded: 2003
Sales Range: $1-9.9 Million
Emp.: 40
Interactive IT Training

N.A.I.C.S.: 611420
Jason Bortz (Pres)
Dave Barnesky (Dir-Bus Dev)

INTERACTYX LIMITED
3461 Bonita Bay Blvd Ste 207, Bonita
Springs, FL 34134
Web Site: http://www.interactyx.com
Year Founded: 1995
eLearning Software Developer
N.A.I.C.S.: 513210
Jodi Harrison (VP-Bus Dev)
Jeffrey A. Roth (VP-Mktg & Comm)
Thomas G. Rennie (Chm)

Subsidiaries:

Interactyx Limited   (1)
100 Union Street, Aberdeen, AB10 1QR,
United Kingdom
Tel.: (44) 2070846244
eLearning Software Developer
N.A.I.C.S.: 513210

INTERAMERICAN BANK FSB
9190 SW 24th St, Miami, FL 33165
Tel.: (305) 223-1434
Web Site:
    http://www.interamericanbank.com
Sales Range: $10-24.9 Million
Emp.: 80
Federal Savings Bank
N.A.I.C.S.: 522180
Agustin F. Velasco (CEO)
Giorgina Ruiz (Sr VP)

INTERBIT DATA, INC.
235 W Central St, Natick, MA 01760
Tel.: (508) 647-0013
Web Site: http://www.interbitdata.com
Year Founded: 1997
Rev.: $2,200,000
Emp.: 12
Custom Computer Programming Ser-
vices
N.A.I.C.S.: 541511
Sarah Bloom (Acct Mgr-Existing
Accts)
Arthur Young (Founder & Pres)
Edward Norton (VP)
Ken Hoffman (Partner)

INTERBOROUGH DEVELOP-
MENTAL AND CONSULTATION
CENTER
1623 Kings Hwy, Brooklyn, NY 11229
Tel.: (718) 375-1200   NY
Web Site:
    http://www.interborough.org
Year Founded: 1974
Sales Range: $10-24.9 Million
Emp.: 295
Behavioral Healthcare Services
N.A.I.C.S.: 621420
Geraldine Abelson (Dir-Clinical)
Leon Gersten (CEO)
Mikhael Pilmon (Dir-Medical)
Stephen Gersten (COO)

INTERCEL TELECOMS
GROUP, INC.
3914 Centreville Rd Ste 200, Chan-
tilly, VA 20151
Tel.: (703) 773-3500
Sales Range: $1-9.9 Million
Emp.: 12
VoIP Products & Services
N.A.I.C.S.: 334220
Joseph F. Gatt (Chm & CEO)

INTERCEPT CORPORATION
1700 42nd St S Ste 2000, Fargo, ND
58103
Tel.: (701) 241-7832
Web Site: http://www.intercepteft.com
Year Founded: 1993
Sales Range: $10-24.9 Million

Emp.: 32
Financial Transactions Processing,
Reserve & Clearinghouse Activities
N.A.I.C.S.: 522320
Craig Dresser (CEO)
Chad Schornack (CIO)
Christy Stock (COO)
Bryan Smith (Pres)
Jim Haug (Mgr-Sls-Natl)
Connie Mosier (VP-Risk Mgmt)

INTERCHEM CORPORATION
120 Rte 17 N, Paramus, NJ 07653-
1579
Tel.: (201) 261-7333
Web Site: http://www.interchem.com
Year Founded: 1981
Sales Range: $10-24.9 Million
Emp.: 50
Supplier of Fine Chemicals, Interme-
diates & Bulk Actives
N.A.I.C.S.: 424210
Joseph M. Pizza (Pres & CEO)
Theresa Kelly (Sr VP)
Ron Mannino (Owner)

INTERCITY TRANSIT
526 Pattison St SE, Olympia, WA
98501
Tel.: (360) 786-8585
Web Site:
    http://www.intercitytransit.com
Year Founded: 1981
Sales Range: $25-49.9 Million
Emp.: 285
Interurban & Rural Bus Transporta-
tion Services
N.A.I.C.S.: 485210
Ann Freeman (Gen Mgr)
Lee Peterson (Coord-Vanpool)

INTERCOASTAL MEDICAL
GROUP, INC.
943 S Beneva Rd Ste 306, Sarasota,
FL 34232
Tel.: (941) 955-1108   FL
Web Site:
    http://www.intercoastalmedical
    grp.com
Year Founded: 1993
Sales Range: $25-49.9 Million
Emp.: 100
Medical Office
N.A.I.C.S.: 621111
John M. Steele (Pres)
Mark A. Rehder (Dir-Fin)

INTERCOASTAL MORTGAGE,
LLC
4100 Monument Corner Dr, Fairfax,
VA 22030
Tel.: (703) 449-6800
Web Site: http://www.icmtg.com
Rev.: $12,074,122
Emp.: 67
Mortgage Bankers & Loan Corre-
spondents Services
N.A.I.C.S.: 522292
Keith A. Brown (VP)
Todd Marumoto (Officer-Loan & VP)
Steve R. Draper (VP)
Fred Bowers (VP)
Tom Pyne (Pres & CEO)
Dave W. Hollopeter (Exec VP)
Larry F. Mazza (Founder)
Josh Cilman (Exec VP)

Subsidiaries:

Potomac Mortgage Group, Inc.   (1)
4035 Ridge Top Rd Ste 100, Fairfax, VA
22030
Tel.: (571) 266-6500
Web Site: http://www.icmtg.com
Mortgage Lending Services
N.A.I.C.S.: 525990
Ed Dean (Pres & CEO)
Peter Cameron (Exec VP)

INTERCOMMUNICATIONS INC.
620 Newport Center Dr Ste 600,
Newport Beach, CA 92660-6400
Tel.: (949) 644-7520   CA
Web Site:
    http://www.intercommunication.com
Year Founded: 1984
Sales Range: $25-49.9 Million
Emp.: 45
N.A.I.C.S.: 541810
Toni Alexander (Pres & Creative Dir)
Pat Cherpeski (Sr VP)
Bill Strateman (Mktg Dir-Relationship)
Barbara Landa (Supvr-Production)
Richard Darner (Exec Dir-Art)
Steve Sandborg (Sr VP)
Carolyn Merek (Media Dir)
Jeffrey Mercer (Dir-Art)
Deidre Michalski (VP-Client Svcs)
Mel Newhoff (VP & Dir-Creative
Svcs)
Marinella Georgino (Designer)
Robert Barritt (Dir-MIS)
Katherine Estrada (Acct Mgr)

INTERCOMP U.S.A., INC.
275 Commercial Blvd, Lauderdale by
the Sea, FL 33308
Tel.: (954) 493-6461
Web Site: http://www.intercomp.com
Year Founded: 1990
Sales Range: $10-24.9 Million
Emp.: 20
Electronic Components Distr
N.A.I.C.S.: 423690
Alberto Menacho (Dir-ISO)

INTERCON INC.
635 N Billy Mitchell Rd Ste B, Salt
Lake City, UT 84116
Tel.: (801) 364-2504
Web Site: http://www.intercon-
furniture.com
Sales Range: $10-24.9 Million
Emp.: 30
Household Furniture
N.A.I.C.S.: 337122
Jim Jones (Mgr-Pur-Intl)

INTERCON SOLUTIONS, INC.
1001 Washington Ave, Chicago
Heights, IL 60411
Tel.: (708) 756-9838
Web Site:
    http://www.interconrecycling.com
Year Founded: 1987
Sales Range: $1-9.9 Million
Emp.: 15
Electronic Waste Recycling Services
N.A.I.C.S.: 562920

INTERCONN RESOURCES,
LLC
2000A Southbridge Pkwy Ste 330,
Birmingham, AL 35209-1334
Tel.: (205) 969-1047
Web Site:
    http://www.interconnresources.com
Sales Range: $75-99.9 Million
Emp.: 20
Natural Gas Distr
N.A.I.C.S.: 221210
Kevin R. Stump (Pres & CEO)
Joseph McLean (VP-Sls & Mktg)
Tad Templeton (Sr VP-Ops)

INTERCONNECT CABLE
TECHNOLOGIES CORP.
16090 Flight Path Dr, Brooksville, FL
34604
Tel.: (352) 796-1716
Web Site: http://www.ictcusa.com
Year Founded: 1988
Sales Range: $50-74.9 Million
Emp.: 65

Cable Assemblies Used In Electron-
ics
N.A.I.C.S.: 334419
Rick Osgood (VP)
Sareet Majumdar (Pres)

Subsidiaries:

Interconnect Cable Technologies
Corp. - Asia   (1)
78 De Zheng Middle Road 4th Floor, Chang
An Town, Dongguan, 523850, China
Tel.: (86) 769 8539 1645
Emp.: 30
Cable Assemblies Used In Electronics
N.A.I.C.S.: 334419
William Wen (Mgr)

INTERCONNECT SERVICES
GROUP
155 Willowbrook Blvd, Wayne, NJ
07470
Tel.: (973) 638-2111
Web Site: http://www.isgcom.com
Year Founded: 1984
Rev.: $10,300,000
Emp.: 50
Digital Telephone Systems, Interac-
tive Voice Response Applications,
Video Conferencing & Long Distance
Network Products
N.A.I.C.S.: 517121
Jon Kaufman (Pres & CEO)
Jack Quinn (Controller)

INTERCONNECT SOLUTIONS
INC.
1651 E St Andrew Pl, Santa Ana, CA
92705
Tel.: (714) 258-0200
Web Site: http://www.isiconnect.com
Year Founded: 2001
Sales Range: $10-24.9 Million
Emp.: 150
Aluminum Rolling & Drawing Services
N.A.I.C.S.: 331318
Eric Shumway (Sr VP-Sls & Bus Dev)
Michael Engler (CEO)

INTERCONTINENTAL CHEMI-
CAL CORP
4660 Spring Grove Ave, Cincinnati,
OH 45232
Tel.: (513) 541-7100   OH
Web Site: http://www.icc-
chemicals.com
Year Founded: 1964
Emulsions & Stencils Removers;
Tapes; Polishes & Adhesives; Screen
Printing Industry & Ink Removal
N.A.I.C.S.: 333248
Cameron W Cord (Pres)

INTERCONTINENTAL EXPORT
IMPORT INC.
8815 Centre Park Dr Ste 400, Colum-
bia, MD 21045
Tel.: (410) 674-5600
Web Site: http://www.ieiplastics.com
Year Founded: 1987
Rev.: $15,300,000
Emp.: 70
Plastics Recycling Industry
N.A.I.C.S.: 325991
Saurabh Naik (Pres)

INTERCONTINENTAL TERMI-
NALS COMPANY
1943 Indepence Pkwy, La Porte, TX
77571
Tel.: (281) 884-0300
Web Site: http://www.iterm.com
Rev.: $10,500,000
Emp.: 25
Petroleum & Chemical Bulk Stations
& Terminals For Hire
N.A.I.C.S.: 493190

Intercontinental Terminals
Company—(Continued)

Richard C. Merz *(Sr VP-Sls & Mktg)*
John Everett *(Mgr-Sls & Customer Svc)*
Bob P. Pennacchi *(COO)*
Bernt A. Netland *(Pres & CEO)*
Mark P. Jeansonne *(CFO & Chief Compliance Officer)*

INTERCORE, INC.
1615 S Congress Ave Ste 103, Delray Beach, FL 33445
Tel.: (561) 900-3709   DE
Web Site: http://intercoreenergy.com
Year Founded: 2010
Sales Range: Less than $1 Million
Emp.: 27
Investment Services
N.A.I.C.S.: 523999
James F. Groelinger *(Pres & CEO)*
Frederick Larcombe *(CFO)*

INTERCOSMOS MEDIA GROUP, INC.
3409 16th St, Metairie, LA 70002-3495
Tel.: (504) 679-5170
Web Site: http://www.directnic.com
Year Founded: 1999
Sales Range: $10-24.9 Million
Emp.: 40
Internet Hosting & Domain Name Registration Services
N.A.I.C.S.: 541512
Sigmund Solares *(CEO)*
Butch Decossas *(CFO)*
Vivian Cahill *(Owner-Restaurant)*

INTERCOUNTY ELECTRIC CO-OPERATIVE
102 Maple Ave, Licking, MO 65542-0209
Tel.: (573) 674-2211
Web Site: http://www.ieca.coop
Year Founded: 1936
Sales Range: $10-24.9 Million
Emp.: 118
Eletric Power Generation Services
N.A.I.C.S.: 221118
Dan Sisco *(Dir-IT)*
Terry Lewis *(Engr-Staking-Rolla Saint James)*
Brian Nelson *(Mgr-Engrg)*
Jack Rinne *(Mgr-Ops & Maintenance)*
Karen McNew *(Mgr-Member Svcs)*
Doug Lane *(Mgr-Safety & Facilities)*
Sarah Akers *(Mgr-Acctg)*
Denna Tune *(Officer-HR)*
Billy Cordsmeyer *(Supvr-Right-of-Way)*

INTERCOUNTY SUPPLY INC.
255 S Regent St, Port Chester, NY 10573
Tel.: (914) 939-4350
Web Site:
http://www.intercountysupply.com
Rev.: $13,900,000
Emp.: 24
Plumbing & Heating Supplies Whslr
N.A.I.C.S.: 423720
Stanley Scarduzio *(Mgr)*

INTERCREDIT BANK, N.A.
6400 SW 8th St, Miami, FL 33144
Tel.: (305) 375-8442
Web Site:
http://www.intercreditbank.com
Year Founded: 1992
Sales Range: $25-49.9 Million
Emp.: 78
Commericial Banking
N.A.I.C.S.: 522110
Simon Cruz *(Pres)*

INTEREVCO, LTD.
143 W 29th St Fl 4, New York, NY 10001-5195
Tel.: (212) 696-5893
Year Founded: 2000
Rev.: $4,300,000
Emp.: 24
Telecommunication Servicesb
N.A.I.C.S.: 517111
Paul Debraccio *(CEO)*
Joan Gugliotta *(VP)*

INTEREXPO COMMUNICA-TIONS
3309 Bennington Ct, Winter Park, FL 32792-6221
Tel.: (407) 310-4168   FL
Year Founded: 1998
Rev.: $11,000,000
Emp.: 6
Advetising Agency
N.A.I.C.S.: 541810
Richard A. Brunsman *(Dir-Mktg)*
Richard M. Brunsman *(Pres)*
Steven J. Kuehl *(Sec & VP)*
James W. Limotta *(Chm & CEO)*
Michael A. Brunsman *(Mgr-Show Ops)*

INTERFAB INC.
3050 S Alvernon Way, Tucson, AZ 85713
Tel.: (520) 790-7040
Web Site: http://www.inter-fab.com
Rev.: $10,173,687
Emp.: 50
Water Sports Equipment
N.A.I.C.S.: 339920
Michael Haggerty *(Pres)*
Julie Menard *(Mgr-Customer Svc)*

INTERFACE CABLE ASSEM-BLIES & SERVICES CORP.
4219 23rd Ave, Long Island City, NY 11105
Tel.: (718) 278-1100
Web Site: http://www.icascorp.com
Sales Range: $10-24.9 Million
Emp.: 35
Fiber Optic Cable Installation Services
N.A.I.C.S.: 238210
Matthew Bonfitto *(Pres)*
Pio Bonfitto *(VP)*

INTERFACE SECURITY SYS-TEMS, LLC
3773 Corporate Center Dr, Earth City, MO 63045
Tel.: (314) 595-0100   LA
Web Site:
http://www.interfacesystems.com
Year Founded: 1983
Sales Range: $10-24.9 Million
Emp.: 65
Electronic Security Systems
N.A.I.C.S.: 561621
Michael Shaw *(Founder & CEO)*
Ken Obermeyer *(CFO)*
Charles H. Moeling *(Chief Mktg Officer & Exec VP-Sls & Acct Mgmt)*
Brent Duncan *(Pres & COO)*

INTERFAITH HOUSING FOUN-DATION
2169 E Francisco Blvd Ste B, San Rafael, CA 94901
Tel.: (415) 250-1800   CA
Year Founded: 1971
Rev.: $301,942
Assets: $9,831,424
Liabilities: $15,990
Net Worth: $9,815,434
Earnings: ($1,244,463)
Fiscal Year-end: 12/31/14
Housing Services

N.A.I.C.S.: 624229
Alvin Bonnett *(VP)*
Laura Hall *(Treas)*
Mary Murtagh *(Pres)*

INTERFAITH MEDICAL CEN-TER
1545 Atlantic Ave, Brooklyn, NY 11213
Tel.: (718) 613-4000   NY
Web Site:
http://www.interfaithmedical.com
Year Founded: 1984
Emp.: 1,850
Health Care Srvices
N.A.I.C.S.: 622110
Mohammed El-Dakkak *(Dir-Orthopedics)*
LaRay Brown *(Pres & CEO)*

INTERFOODS OF AMERICA, INC.
9500 S Dadeland Blvd Ste 800, Miami, FL 33156
Tel.: (305) 670-0746   NV
Sales Range: $200-249.9 Million
Emp.: 600
Holding Company; Franchised Fast-Food Restaurants Owner & Operator
N.A.I.C.S.: 551112
Robert S. Berg *(Co-Owner, Chm & CEO)*
Steven M. Wemple *(Co-Owner, Pres & COO)*

Subsidiaries:

Sailormen Inc.   (1)
9500 S Dadeland Blvd Ste 800, Miami, FL 33156
Tel.: (305) 670-0746
Rev.: $47,000,000
Emp.: 10
Franchise Fast-Food Restaurants Operator
N.A.I.C.S.: 722513
Robert S. Berg *(Chm & CEO)*
Steven M. Wemple *(Pres & COO)*

INTERFORM
22 S 1400 W, Centerville, UT 84014
Tel.: (801) 292-7971
Web Site: http://www.interform.net
Year Founded: 1986
Rev.: $20,000,000
Emp.: 100
Fiscal Year-end: 12/31/15
Advertising Agencies
N.A.I.C.S.: 541810
Jerry Quick *(Owner)*

INTERFRESH INC.
1619 E Chapman Ave, Fullerton, CA 92831
Tel.: (714) 449-1669
Web Site:
http://www.getinterfresh.com
Year Founded: 1987
Sales Range: $10-24.9 Million
Emp.: 50
Sales & Distribution of Avocados & Citrus
N.A.I.C.S.: 424410
Chris Puentes *(Pres)*

INTERGALACTIC INC.
1135 N Jones Blvd, Tucson, AZ 85716
Tel.: (520) 881-1744
Web Site: http://www.bookmans.com
Rev.: $15,037,913
Emp.: 18
Book Stores, Secondhand
N.A.I.C.S.: 459510
Robert Schlesinger *(Pres)*

INTERGENERATIONAL LIVING AND HEALTH CARE, INC.

1107 Hazeltine Blvd No 200, Chaska, MN 55318
Tel.: (952) 361-8000   MN
Web Site:
http://www.intergenerationalliving andhealthcare.org
Year Founded: 1996
Sales Range: $25-49.9 Million
Emp.: 670
Elderly & Child Care Services
N.A.I.C.S.: 624110
Mary Yaeger *(Exec Dir)*
Dona King *(Exec Dir)*

INTERGLASS CORP.
8150 NW 64th St, Miami, FL 33166
Tel.: (305) 887-2200
Web Site:
http://www.interglasscorp.com
Year Founded: 2004
Sales Range: $25-49.9 Million
Emp.: 72
Glass Mfr
N.A.I.C.S.: 327215
Miguel Juliao *(Fin Dir)*

INTERGROUP INTERNA-TIONAL, LTD.
1111 E 200th St, Euclid, OH 44117
Tel.: (216) 862-9289
Web Site:
http://www.intergroupinterna tional.com
Year Founded: 1999
Sales Range: $1-9.9 Million
Emp.: 50
Sustainable Plastic Scrap Recycling, Processing & Recovery Operations
N.A.I.C.S.: 325211
Neil Gloger *(Owner)*
Threse Novotny *(Supvr-Acctg)*
Tim Carter *(Sls Mgr-Natl)*

INTERIM HEALTHCARE OF HARTFORD, INC.
231 Farmington Ave Ste 3, Farmington, CT 06032
Tel.: (860) 677-0005   CT
Web Site:
http://www.interimhealthcare.com
Year Founded: 1970
Medical Staffing & Home Health Care Services
N.A.I.C.S.: 561320
Sue Palmisano *(Dir-Client Svcs, Homecare & Personal Care & Support Svcs)*

INTERIM PHYSICIANS, LLC
12140 Woodcrest Executive Dr Ste 310, Saint Louis, MO 63141
Web Site:
http://www.interimphysicians.com
Year Founded: 1979
Sales Range: $25-49.9 Million
Emp.: 40
Physician Staffing Services to HMO's, Clinics, Hospitals & Medical Groups
N.A.I.C.S.: 561311
Tim Hand *(CEO)*
Tim Sarlone *(Controller)*

INTERIM SOLUTIONS FOR GOVERNMENT, LLC
2224 NW 50th St Ste 293 W, Oklahoma City, OK 73112
Tel.: (405) 286-0915
Web Site: http://www.isgovt.com
Year Founded: 2001
Sales Range: $10-24.9 Million
Emp.: 175
Air Traffic Training & Support Services to the FAA
N.A.I.C.S.: 488111
Gerald Williams *(Pres)*
Richard Rodine *(Exec VP-Strategy, Trng, Fin & Consulting)*
Robert Igo *(VP-Aviation Svcs)*

INTERIOR ARCHITECTS, INC.
350 California St, San Francisco, CA
94104-1402
Tel.: (415) 434-3305   **CA**
Web Site:
   http://www.interiorarchitects.com
Year Founded: 1984
Sales Range: $10-24.9 Million
Emp.: 150
Business Services
N.A.I.C.S.: 541310
David Mourning *(Pres)*
Don Lam *(Project Mgr)*
Mary Lee Duff *(Principal)*
Mick McCullough *(Mng Principal)*

Subsidiaries:

Interior Architects, Inc .   **(1)**
205 W Wacker Dr Ste 1500, Chicago, IL
60606-1443   **(100%)**
Tel.: (312) 553-2155
Web Site: http://www.interiorarchitects.com
Sales Range: $10-24.9 Million
Emp.: 40
Interior Architectural Services
N.A.I.C.S.: 541410

INTERIOR CRAFTS INC.
2513 W Cullerton St, Chicago, IL
60608
Tel.: (773) 376-8160
Web Site:
   http://www.interiorcraftsinc.com
Sales Range: $10-24.9 Million
Emp.: 180
Upholstered Household Furniture
N.A.I.C.S.: 337121
Vito Ursini *(CEO)*

INTERIOR DESIGN & ARCHITECTURE, INC.
1700 S 5th St, Louisville, KY 40208
Tel.: (502) 562-9255
Web Site: http://www.id-a.com
Year Founded: 1981
Rev.: $16,206,661
Emp.: 30
Furniture & Household Distr
N.A.I.C.S.: 449110
D. A. Kamer *(Treas)*
Jessica Hardin *(VP-Sls)*

INTERIOR DESIGN SERVICES, INC.
4020 Armory Oaks Dr, Nashville, TN
37204
Tel.: (615) 376-1200
Web Site: http://www.ids-tn.com
Rev.: $30,000,000
Emp.: 100
Office Furniture Whslr
N.A.I.C.S.: 423210
Daryl Dunn *(VP-Healthcare)*
Daniel Meek *(Dir-Client Svcs)*
Kelley Lyle *(Acct Mgr)*

INTERIOR DISTRIBUTORS INC.
1105 New Hope Rd, Raleigh, NC
27610-1415
Tel.: (919) 231-6355   **NC**
Web Site:
   http://www.alliedbuliding.com
Year Founded: 1969
Sales Range: $10-24.9 Million
Emp.: 25
Lumber, Plywood & Millwork Services
N.A.I.C.S.: 423310
Gene Mack *(Reg Mgr)*
Craig Maynor *(Mgr-Ops)*

INTERIOR DYNAMICS INC.
1742 Crooks Rd, Troy, MI 48084
Tel.: (248) 244-8910
Web Site:
   http://www.interiordynamics.com
Sales Range: $25-49.9 Million

Emp.: 65
Sales of Office Furniture
N.A.I.C.S.: 423210
Ronald E. Waring *(Pres)*

INTERIOR ENVIRONMENTS, INC.
3450 4th Ave S, Seattle, WA 98134
Tel.: (206) 432-8800   **WA**
Web Site: http://www.iecustom.com
Year Founded: 1987
Sales Range: $1-9.9 Million
Emp.: 35
Custom Furniture, Cabinetry & Interior Trim Designer & Mfr
N.A.I.C.S.: 337212
David Brzusek *(Pres)*

Subsidiaries:

IE CONNECT LLC   **(1)**
1755 Blake St Ste 125, Denver, CO 80202
Tel.: (303) 292-0437
Web Site: http://ieoffices.com
Office Furniture Whslr
N.A.I.C.S.: 423210
Kimberly Zeller *(Dir-Design)*
Lori Hager *(Mgr-Office & Acctg)*

INTERIOR FUSION, LLC
8380 Bay Pines Blvd, Saint Petersburg, FL 33709-4004
Tel.: (813) 281-5632
Web Site: http://www.ifsdv.com
Furniture Merchant Whslr
N.A.I.C.S.: 423210
Richard Fendley *(Pres & CEO)*

Subsidiaries:

Office Furniture Depot, Inc.   **(1)**
2440 US Highway 98 N, Lakeland, FL
33805
Tel.: (863) 682-3450
Web Site:
   http://www.officefurnituredepot.com
Sales Range: $1-9.9 Million
Emp.: 18
Furniture Merchant Whslr
N.A.I.C.S.: 423210
David K. Boles *(Pres)*
Joanne Boles *(CEO)*

INTERIOR INVESTMENTS LLC
550 Bond St, Lincolnshire, IL 60069
Tel.: (847) 325-1000
Web Site:
   http://www.interiorinvestments.com
Year Founded: 1994
Sales Range: $100-124.9 Million
Emp.: 75
Office & Public Building Furniture
N.A.I.C.S.: 423210
Donald Shannon *(Co-Founder)*
Michael Greenberg *(Co-Founder)*

INTERIOR SPECIALTIES INC.
947 Josaine Ct Ste 1010, Altamonte
Springs, FL 32701
Tel.: (407) 539-1303
Web Site:
   http://www.windowinteriors.com
Window Treatment Contractor
N.A.I.C.S.: 238990
Dave Riley *(Pres)*

INTERIOR SYSTEMS INC.
6667 Hwy 211 E, West End, NC
27376
Tel.: (910) 673-0633
Web Site:
   http://www.interiorsystemsinc.com
Year Founded: 1978
Sales Range: $10-24.9 Million
Emp.: 20
Furniture Sales
N.A.I.C.S.: 423210
Mark E. Goudy *(COO)*
Karen Goudy *(Treas & Sec)*

INTERIOR SYSTEMS INC.
525 Rolling Meadows Dr, Fond Du
Lac, WI 54937
Tel.: (920) 923-4313
Web Site: http://www.isiamerica.com
Rev.: $11,431,562
Emp.: 200
Restaurant Furniture, Wood Or Metal
N.A.I.C.S.: 541410
Lindsey S. Bovinet *(Founder & Chm)*
Alan Patti *(Mgr-Market-West Coast Reg)*
Tony Lutz *(Pres & CEO)*
Sandy Bee *(Reg Market Mgr-Ohio Valley Region)*
Richard Best *(Brand Mgr-Natl)*
Brett Rutledge *(Sr Mgr-Brand-Restaurants)*
Stanya LeMay *(Brand Mgr-Natl Education)*
Lee Lenox *(Sr Mgr-Brand-Restaurants)*
Jim Zielinski *(Sr Mgr-Brand-Restaurants)*
Tony Pagliuca *(Dir-Creative)*
Jon Paul Ruelle *(Supvr-Field Svc)*
Mark Huck *(VP-Fulfillment)*

INTERIOR SYSTEMS INC.
5446 W State St, Boise, ID 83703
Tel.: (208) 853-2233
Web Site: http://www.isiperforms.com
Rev.: $19,457,929
Emp.: 200
Wall & Ceiling Contracting Services
N.A.I.C.S.: 238310
Harvey L. Neef *(Owner)*

INTERIOR WORKPLACE SOLUTIONS LLC
6765 Ambassador Dr, Allentown, PA
18106
Tel.: (610) 391-0733
Web Site:
   http://www.interiorworkplace.com
Interior Design Services
N.A.I.C.S.: 541410
Gary Clewell *(Pres)*
Susan Phillips *(Controller)*
Michael Schultz *(Dir-Ops)*
David Torrence *(VP & Gen Mgr)*

Subsidiaries:

Creative Business Interiors, Inc.   **(1)**
145 Stewart Rd, Wilkes Barre, PA 18706
Tel.: (570) 288-7211
Web Site: http://www.cbiltd.com
Emp.: 15
Interior Design Services
N.A.I.C.S.: 541410
Valerie Flaim *(Project Mgr)*
Mike Cherubini *(Dir-Construction Svcs)*

INTERIORS OF WINTER PARK, INC.
919 Orange Ave Ste 100, Winter
Park, FL 32789
Tel.: (407) 629-7756
Web Site:
   http://www.beasleyandhenley.com
Year Founded: 1993
Sales Range: $1-9.9 Million
Emp.: 10
Interior Design Services
N.A.I.C.S.: 541410
Troy Beasley *(Principal)*
Stephanie Henley *(Principal)*

INTERLAB SUPPLY
26018 Budde Rd, Spring, TX 77380
Tel.: (281) 298-9410   **TX**
Web Site: http://www.polyseed.com
Biological Based Products for Environmental Tests
N.A.I.C.S.: 621511

INTERLAKEN CAPITAL, INC.

475 Steamboat Rd, Greenwich, CT
06830-7144
Tel.: (203) 629-8750   **DE**
Web Site:
   http://www.interlakencapital.com
Year Founded: 1980
Sales Range: $10-24.9 Million
Emp.: 10
Holding Company
N.A.I.C.S.: 523940
Joshua A. Polan *(Mng Dir)*
James M. Vitti *(Controller)*
William L. Mahone *(VP-Legal)*
William Robert Berkley *(Chm)*

INTERLEX COMMUNICATIONS INC
4005 Broadway Ste B, San Antonio,
TX 78209-6311
Tel.: (210) 930-3339
Web Site: http://www.interlexusa.com
Year Founded: 1995
Sales Range: $25-49.9 Million
Emp.: 40
Advetising Agency
N.A.I.C.S.: 541810
Rudy Ruiz *(Co-Founder, Pres & Chief Creative Officer)*
Heather Kristina Ruiz *(Co-Founder & Dir-Creative)*
Thomas Schlenker *(Dir-Medical)*

INTERLINC MORTGAGE SERVICES, LLC
10613 W Sam Houston Pkwy N Ste
200, Houston, TX 77064
Tel.: (281) 367-9595
Web Site:
   http://www.interlincmortgage.com
Emp.: 300
N.A.I.C.S.:
David Scheiderich *(CFO & Exec VP)*
Brennan Holland *(Gen Counsel & Exec VP)*
Melody Warren *(Dir-Mktg)*
Ana LeBlanc *(Dir-HR)*
Gene F. Thompson III *(Pres & CEO)*

INTERLOCK INDUSTRIES, INC.
545 S 3rd St Ste 310, Louisville, KY
40202-6100
Tel.: (502) 569-2007   **KY**
Web Site:
   http://www.interlockindustries.com
Year Founded: 1982
Sales Range: $150-199.9 Million
Emp.: 2,047
Holding Company
N.A.I.C.S.: 332322
Craig Mackin *(Chm, Pres & CEO)*

Subsidiaries:

Louisville Transportation   **(1)**
1601 S Preston St, Louisville, KY 40217-
1038
Tel.: (502) 637-6511
Sales Range: $25-49.9 Million
Emp.: 500
Yellow Cab, Yellow Ambulance
N.A.I.C.S.: 485310

Subsidiary (Domestic):

Gateway Ambulance Service
LLC   **(2)**
1530 Fairview Ave, Saint Louis, MO 63132
Tel.: (314) 351-5599
Web Site: http://gatewayambulance.com
Sales Range: $25-49.9 Million
Emp.: 130
Ambulance Service
N.A.I.C.S.: 621910

Metal Sales Manufacturing
Corporation   **(1)**
545 S 3rd St Ste 200, Louisville, KY 40202
Tel.: (502) 855-4300
Web Site: http://www.interlockindustries.com

Interlock Industries, Inc.—(Continued)

Sales Range: $10-24.9 Million
Emp.: 100
Mfr of Steel Siding, Roofing Components &
Related Accessories
N.A.I.C.S.: 332322
Craig Mackin (CFO)
David Stermer (Dir-Engrg)

Ohio Valley Aluminum Company LLC (1)
1100 Brooks Industrial Rd, Shelbyville, KY 40065-9178
Tel.: (502) 633-2783
Web Site: http://www.ovaco.com
Sales Range: $10-24.9 Million
Emp.: 100
Mfr of Aluminum Extrusions; Scrap Recycler
N.A.I.C.S.: 331314

Procarent (1)
1601 S Preston St, Louisville, KY 40217
Tel.: (502) 637-6511
Web Site: http://www.procarent.com
Taxi Service Operator
N.A.I.C.S.: 485310
Allison Porter (Dir-HR)
Deborah Thompson (Mgr-Billing)
Erick Franco (Dir-IT)
Lisa Hudgins (Mgr-Benefits & Wellness)
Mike Gilbert (Dir-Care Ambulance)
Jamie Hardin (Dir-Yellow Ambulance Owensboro)
Kent Mayrose (Dir-Gateway Ambulance)

INTERLUDE HOME, INC.
25 Trefoil Dr, Trumbull, CT 06611
Tel.: (203) 445-7617
Web Site:
    http://www.interludehome.com
Sales Range: $25-49.9 Million
Emp.: 35
Designer, Importer & Distr of Home Accessories & Furniture
N.A.I.C.S.: 337121
Carl Philips (CEO)
Jessica Allen Soubotin (VP-Product Dev)
Rachel Bergini (Dir-Hospitality Sls)

Subsidiaries:

Weiman (1)
135 Warren St, Christiansburg, VA 24073-0670 **(100%)**
Tel.: (540) 381-7745
Web Site: http://www.weiman-preview.com
Upholstered Furniture Mfr
N.A.I.C.S.: 337121
Carl Philips (Pres & CEO)

INTERMARINE, INC.
2900 N Loop W Ste 1100, Houston, TX 77092
Tel.: (281) 885-3500
Web Site:
    http://www.intermarineusa.com
Sales Range: $75-99.9 Million
Emp.: 200
Ocean Transport, Terminal & Inland Heavy-Haul Services
N.A.I.C.S.: 483111
Will Terrill (Pres)
Richard Seeg (VP-Americas)
Andre Grikitis (CEO)
Bill Curtin (CIO & VP)
Frank Fischer (Mng Dir-Tonnage Procurement)
Alejandro Pla (Mgr-Mexico)
Mark Bowden (Production Mgr)

Subsidiaries:

Industrial Terminals, L.P. (1)
14035 Industrial Rd, Houston, TX 77015
Tel.: (713) 450-7770
Web Site: http://www.intermarineusa.com
Sales Range: $10-24.9 Million
Emp.: 2
Deep Water Ocean Terminal Services
N.A.I.C.S.: 488320
Brian Powney (VP-Marine Tech Svcs)

Intermarine Denmark ApS (1)

Vestre Kaj 6, 4700, Naestved, Denmark
Tel.: (45) 5572 2000
Marine Freight Transportation Services
N.A.I.C.S.: 483211
Panos Patsadas (Mgr-Chartering)
Esben F. Noergaard (Dir-Sls)
Martin Juul (Dir-Chartering)
Lars Bonnesen (Mng Dir)
Daghan Mgr (Mgr-Chartering)
Jacob T. Jacobsen (Dir-Ops)
Rene Olsen (Mgr-Ops)
Soeren Peter Wibholm (Controller)
Soeren Steffensen (Mgr-Ops)
Jan Jensen (Mgr-Ops)

Intermarine Project Services S.L. (1)
Paseo de la Castellana 8-1 Dcha, 28046, Madrid, Spain
Tel.: (34) 91 423 00 30
Marine Freight Transportation Services
N.A.I.C.S.: 483211
Tero Valtonen (Mgr-Chartering & Sls)

INTERMARK FOODS, INC.
1351 NW 97th Ave, Miami, FL 33172
Tel.: (305) 718-8754   FL
Web Site:
    http://www.intermarkfoods.com
Year Founded: 2002
Sales Range: $1-9.9 Million
Emp.: 22
Refrigerated & Frozen Foods
N.A.I.C.S.: 424420
Maria Elena Ibanez (Founder & Pres)

INTERMARK GROUP, INC.
101 25th St N, Birmingham, AL 35203
Tel.: (205) 803-0000   AL
Web Site:
    http://www.intermarkgroup.com
Year Founded: 1977
Sales Range: $100-124.9 Million
Emp.: 180
Advertising Agency Services
N.A.I.C.S.: 541810
Jake McKenzie (CEO)
Bill Dinan (Mgr-Acct)
Matt McKenzie (Pres-Alloy)
Randy Milhalchik (Pres-Vazda)

INTERMARKET CORP.
7286 SW 48th St, Miami, FL 33155
Tel.: (305) 663-9400   FL
Web Site:
    http://www.intermarketcorp.com
Year Founded: 1987
Sales Range: $25-49.9 Million
Emp.: 28
Industrial Machinery Whslr
N.A.I.C.S.: 423830
Manuel A. Alvarez (CEO)
Patricia M. Alvarez (Pres)
Mario Vallejo (Dir-Sls & Mktg)
Sandra Garcia (Dir-Ops & Supply Chain)

INTERMARKETS, INC.
11911 Freedom Dr Ste 1140, Reston, VA 20190
Tel.: (703) 242-7878
Web Site: http://www.intermarkets.net
Sales Range: $10-24.9 Million
Emp.: 25
Advertising Sales Management Services
N.A.I.C.S.: 541613
Michael Snow (Chief Bus Dev Officer)
William L. Trommelen (COO)
Erik Requidan (Dir-Sls)

INTERMAT TRADING CORP.
666 Old Country Rd Ste 711, Garden City, NY 11530
Tel.: (516) 622-6600
Web Site:
    http://www.intermatusa.com
Sales Range: $25-49.9 Million

Emp.: 7
Paper & Board Export Services
N.A.I.C.S.: 523150
Mitchell A. Tamkin (Pres)

INTERMATIC, INC.
7777 Winn Rd, Spring Grove, IL 60081-7801
Tel.: (815) 675-2321   DE
Web Site: http://www.intermatic.com
Year Founded: 1891
Sales Range: $650-699.9 Million
Emp.: 102
Low-Voltage Outdoor Lighting; Consumer & Industrial Timers; Pool & Spa Controls; Surge Suppressors Mfr
N.A.I.C.S.: 335131
Cindy Nichols (Mgr-Electrical Distr-Northern Reg)
Steven French (Dir-Electrical Distr)
Michael Bartindale (Dir-Municipality, Utility & Co-Ops)

INTERMEDIA ADVISORS, LLC
405 Lexington Ave 48th Fl, New York, NY 10174
Tel.: (212) 503-2850   DE
Web Site:
    http://www.intermediaadvisors.com
Year Founded: 1988
Emp.: 20
Privater Equity Firm
N.A.I.C.S.: 523999
Leo J. Hindery Jr. (Mng Partner)
Peter M. Kern (Mng Partner)

Subsidiaries:

InterMedia Partners, L.P. (1)
405 Lexington Ave 48th Fl, New York, NY 10174
Tel.: (212) 503-2850
Web Site:
    http://www.intermediaadvisors.com
Private Equity Fund
N.A.I.C.S.: 523999
Leo J. Hindery Jr. (Mng Partner)

Holding (Domestic):

InterMedia Outdoors, Inc. (2)
512 7th Ave 11th Fl, New York, NY 10018
Tel.: (212) 852-6600
Web Site: http://www.imoutdoorsmedia.com
Hunting, Fishing & Shooting Sports Magazine Publisher
N.A.I.C.S.: 513120
Ted Gramkow (VP-Strategic Sls & Mktg)
David Grant (VP-Digital Sls)
Jim McConville (Mgr-Natl Sls)
Kevin Donley (Mgr-Strategic Acct)

Unit (Domestic):

Bowhunter Magazine (3)
6385 Flank Dr Ste 800, Harrisburg, PA 17112-2784
Tel.: (717) 657-9555
Web Site: http://www.bowhunter.com
Sales Range: $25-49.9 Million
Magazine Publisher
N.A.I.C.S.: 513120

In-Fisherman (3)
7819 Highland Scenic Rd, Baxter, MN 56425
Tel.: (218) 829-1648
Web Site: http://www.in-fisherman.com
Sales Range: $10-24.9 Million
Magazine & Book Publisher
N.A.I.C.S.: 513120
Doug Stange (Editor-in-Chief)
Mike Pentler (Coord-Production)
Thomas Allen (Mgr-Digital Content)

Shotgun News (3)
2 News Plz, Peoria, IL 61614
Tel.: (309) 679-5071
Web Site: http://www.shotgunnews.com
Sales Range: $10-24.9 Million
Emp.: 12
Magazine Publisher
N.A.I.C.S.: 513120
Chris Agnus (Publr)

Holding (Domestic):

The Sportsman Channel, Inc. (2)
2855 S James Dr Ste 101, New Berlin, WI 53151
Tel.: (262) 432-9100
Web Site:
    http://www.thesportsmanchannel.com
Hunting, Fishing & Other Outdoor Sports Cable Programming
N.A.I.C.S.: 516210
Graig Hale (VP-Bus Dev)
Brian Moyer (Sr Digital Svcs)
Jeff Brown (VP-Western Reg)
Lisa Swan (Dir-Partnership Mktg)
Maura Fried (VP-Sls & Ops)
Mitch Petrie (VP-Programming)
Craig Bobula (Acct Exec)
Andi Leston (Mgr-Pricing & Plng)
Steve Shepherd (Acct Exec)

Joint Venture (Domestic):

World Championship Sports Network, Inc. (2)
12100 Wilshire Blvd, Los Angeles, CA 90025
Tel.: (310) 921-7001
Sports Cable Network
N.A.I.C.S.: 516210

INTERMETRO COMMUNICATIONS, INC.
2685 Park Center Dr Bldg A, Simi Valley, CA 93065
Tel.: (805) 433-8000   NV
Web Site: https://www.intermetro.net
IMTO—(OTCBB)
Sales Range: $10-24.9 Million
Emp.: 24
Enhanced Voice & Data Services
N.A.I.C.S.: 517810
Charles Rice (Chm, Pres & CEO)
Jon DeOng (CIO)

INTERMODAL CARTAGE CO., INC.
5707 E Holmes Rd, Memphis, TN 38141
Tel.: (901) 363-0050   TN
Web Site: http://www.imcg.com
Year Founded: 1982
Trucking Service
N.A.I.C.S.: 484121
Michael Baker (CFO)
Joel Henry (Pres)
Rob Carpenter (Sr VP-Sls)

INTERMODAL SALES CORPORATION
8650 Macon Rd, Cordova, TN 38018-1640
Tel.: (901) 753-2500   TN
Web Site:
    http://www.intermodalsales.com
Year Founded: 1985
Sales Range: $10-24.9 Million
Emp.: 50
Freight Transportation Arrangement
N.A.I.C.S.: 488510
Troy D. Stubbs (Pres)
Michael Stubbs (VP)
Steven Stubbs (CFO)

INTERMOUNTAIN CONCRETE SPCECIALTY
425 W 1700 S, Salt Lake City, UT 84115
Tel.: (801) 486-5311
Web Site: http://www.ics50.com
Sales Range: $10-24.9 Million
Emp.: 26
Concrete Building Products
N.A.I.C.S.: 423320
Tony Frasier (CEO)
Mark Brewer (VP-Mktg)
Sharon Rupp (Mgr-Fin)
Bob Honeycutt (VP-Pur)

INTERMOUNTAIN DONOR SERVICES

230 S 500 E Ste 490, Salt Lake City, UT 84102
Tel.: (801) 521-1755   UT
Web Site: http://www.idslife.org
Year Founded: 1987
Sales Range: $10-24.9 Million
Emp.: 100
Organ Donation Services
N.A.I.C.S.: 621991
Karen Hannahs *(Dir-Donor Family Svcs)*
Melissa Lloyd *(CFO)*
Chuck Zollinger *(Dir-Admin-Organ Recovery)*
Woody Marshall *(Mgr-Hospital Svcs)*

INTERMOUNTAIN ELECTRIC SERVICE INC.

701 S Federal Blvd, Riverton, WY 82501
Tel.: (307) 856-7321
Web Site:
http://www.intermountainelectric.com
Rev.: $14,400,000
Emp.: 90
Electrical Contractor
N.A.I.C.S.: 238210
Thale Ellison *(VP)*
Don Larson *(Pres)*
Bonny Medow *(CFO)*

INTERMOUNTAIN ELECTRIC, INC.

PO Box 3384, Spokane, WA 99220-3384
Tel.: (509) 536-7522   WA
Web Site:
http://www.intermountainelectric.net
Year Founded: 1968
Sales Range: $10-24.9 Million
Emp.: 35
Electrical Contracting Services
N.A.I.C.S.: 238210

INTERMOUNTAIN FARMERS ASSOCIATION

1147 W 2100 S, Salt Lake City, UT 84119-1533
Tel.: (801) 972-2122   UT
Web Site: http://www.ifa-coop.com
Year Founded: 1923
Sales Range: $200-249.9 Million
Emp.: 400
Feed & Farm Supplies Whslr; Farming Community Retail Stores Owner & Operator
N.A.I.C.S.: 424910
Dan Allen *(Chm)*
Robert McMullin *(Vice Chm)*
Layne B. Anderson *(Pres & CEO)*
Bryan Coulter *(VP-IFA Country Stores Ops)*
W. Brad Camp *(VP-Mktg)*
Andrea Van Hazelen *(Sec)*

Subsidiaries:

Intermountain Farmers Association - Draper Feed Mill   (1)
1071 E Pioneer Rd, Draper, UT 84020
Tel.: (801) 571-0125
Agriculture & Farm Supplies Whslr
N.A.I.C.S.: 424910
Jim Brown *(Mgr)*

Intermountain Farmers Association - North Region Feed Mill   (1)
1750 E Center St, Lewiston, UT 84320
Tel.: (435) 258-0522
Agriculture & Farm Supplies Whslr
N.A.I.C.S.: 424910
Marty Short *(Gen Mgr)*
Dale Clark *(Mgr-Production)*

Intermountain Farmers Association - South Region Feed Mill   (1)

2979 W 6300 S, Nephi, UT 84648
Tel.: (435) 623-1949
Emp.: 20
Agriculture & Farm Supplies Whslr
N.A.I.C.S.: 424910
Dan Lovingier *(Gen Mgr)*
Ray Miller *(Mgr-Sls)*

INTERMOUNTAIN HEALTH-CARE INC.

36 S State St, Salt Lake City, UT 84111
Tel.: (801) 442-2000   UT
Web Site: http://www.ihc.com
Year Founded: 1975
Sales Range: $1-4.9 Billion
Emp.: 39,000
Health Care Facilities; Health Care Plans
N.A.I.C.S.: 622110
Janet Frank *(Mgr-Media)*
Robert Allen *(COO)*
Shannon Connor Phillips *(Chief Patient Safety & Experience Officer)*
Dan Liljenquist *(Chief Strategy Officer & Sr VP)*
Bert Zimmerli *(CFO & Exec VP)*
Allison Corry *(Chief Supply Chain Officer & VP-Supply Chain Org)*
Tiffany Capeles *(Chief Equity Officer)*
Mikelle Moore *(Chief Community Health Officer & Sr VP)*
Craig Richardville *(CIO & Chief Digital Officer)*
Mike Leavitt *(Chm)*
Michele Arnold *(Chief Medical Officer & VP)*
Ann Gantzer *(Chief Nursing Officer)*
Rob Allen *(Pres & CEO)*

Subsidiaries:

Sisters of Charity of Leavenworth Health System   (1)
9801 Renner Blvd Ste 100, Lenexa, KS 66219-9745
Tel.: (913) 895-2800
Web Site: http://www.sclhsc.org
Sales Range: $75-99.9 Million
Emp.: 1,200
Owns & Operates Hospitals & Clinics
N.A.I.C.S.: 622110
Judith Jackson *(VP-Sponsorship)*
Edward L. Barker *(Gen Counsel & Sr VP)*
Robert Boysen *(CIO & VP-Info Svcs)*
Sharon Owens *(VP-Fin Ops)*
Irma C. Napoli *(VP-HR)*
William M. Murray *(Pres & CEO)*
Robert W. Ladenburger *(Pres)*

INTERMOUNTAIN INDUS-TRIES, INC.

960 Broadway Ave, Boise, ID 83706
Tel.: (208) 685-7600   ID
Web Site:
http://www.intermountainindustries.com
Year Founded: 1977
Sales Range: $150-199.9 Million
Holding Company; Natural Gas Exploration, Development, Extraction, Processing & Distr
N.A.I.C.S.: 551112
Richard N. Hokin *(Chm)*
William C. Glynn *(Pres)*
Michael E. Rich *(CFO, Sec & Exec VP)*
Marshall Murrin *(Treas & VP)*

Subsidiaries:

III Exploration Company   (1)
960 Broadway Ave, Boise, ID 83706   (100%)
Tel.: (208) 685-7600
Holding Company; Petroleum & Natural Gas Exploration & Development
N.A.I.C.S.: 551112
Richard N. Hokin *(Chm)*

Subsidiary (Domestic):
Petroglyph Energy, Inc.   (2)
960 Broadway Ave Ste 500, Boise, ID 83706   (100%)
Tel.: (208) 685-7600
Web Site:
http://www.intermountainindustries.com
Sales Range: $75-99.9 Million
Emp.: 50
Petroleum & Natural Gas Development, Production & Whslr
N.A.I.C.S.: 211120
Richard N. Hokin *(Chm)*
William C. Glynn *(Pres)*
Paul R. Powell *(CFO & Exec VP-Fin/Investments)*
Marshall Murrin *(Treas & VP)*

INTERMOUNTAIN POWER AGENCY

10653 S River Front Pkwy Ste 120, South Jordan, UT 84095
Tel.: (801) 938-1333
Web Site: http://www.ipautah.com
Sales Range: $600-649.9 Million
Emp.: 10
Electric Power Generation Facility Financing & Development Services
N.A.I.C.S.: 921130
R. Dan Eldredge *(Asst Gen Mgr)*
James A. Hewlett *(Gen Mgr)*
Blaine Haacke *(Vice Chm)*
Eric Larsen *(Treas)*
Cameron Cowan *(Mgr-Treasury)*
Linford E. Jensen *(Mgr-Acctg)*
Vance K. Huntley *(Mgr-Audit)*

INTERMOUNTAIN RURAL ELECTRIC ASSOCIATION

5496 N United States Hwy 85, Sedalia, CO 80135
Tel.: (303) 688-3100
Web Site: http://www.intermountain-rea.com
Sales Range: $75-99.9 Million
Emp.: 200
Electronic Services
N.A.I.C.S.: 221118
Timothy L. White *(Pres)*
Ann Bennett *(Controller)*
Stanley R. Lewandowski *(Gen Mgr)*
John Pope *(Asst Gen Mgr-Ops & En-grg)*
Jeff Baudier *(CEO)*

INTERMOUNTAIN WEST COM-MUNICATIONS COMPANY

1500 Foremaster Ln, Las Vegas, NV 89101-1103
Tel.: (702) 642-3333   NV
Year Founded: 1987
Sales Range: $75-99.9 Million
Emp.: 200
Holding Company; Television Broadcasting Stations Owner & Operator
N.A.I.C.S.: 551112
James E. Rogers *(Founder, Owner & Chm)*
Lisa Howfield *(Pres & COO)*
Tim Yock *(CFO, Treas & VP)*

Subsidiaries:

Sierra Broadcasting Company   (1)
1790 Vassar St, Reno, NV 89502-2721
Tel.: (775) 322-4444
Web Site: http://www.krnv.com
Sales Range: $10-24.9 Million
Emp.: 110
Television Broadcasting Station
N.A.I.C.S.: 516120
Marybeth Sewald *(Gen Mgr)*

INTERMOUNTAIN WOOD PRODUCTS INC.

1948 SW Temple, Salt Lake City, UT 84165
Tel.: (801) 486-5414   UT

Web Site:
http://www.intermountainwood.com
Year Founded: 1961
Sales Range: $10-24.9 Million
Emp.: 100
Lumber, Plywood & Millwork Services
N.A.I.C.S.: 423310
Ben Banks *(Pres)*
Scott Miles *(Controller)*
Al Harrison *(VP-Indus Div)*
Kent Baker *(Reg Mgr-Credit)*
Dustin Perrin *(COO)*
Thadius Oldridge *(VP-Flooring)*

INTERNAL ENGINE PARTS GROUP INC.

100 Virginia Dr, Meridian, MS 39302
Tel.: (601) 693-8282
Web Site:
http://www.internalengineparts.com
Year Founded: 1974
Sales Range: $10-24.9 Million
Emp.: 50
Automotive Supplies & Parts
N.A.I.C.S.: 423120
John Gartrell *(Pres)*

INTERNAP HOLDING LLC

5051 Peachtree Corners Cir Ste 200, Norcross, GA 30092
Tel.: (404) 302-9700   DE
Web Site: https://www.horizoniq.com
Year Founded: 1996
INAPQ—(OTCIQ)
Rev.: $291,505,000
Assets: $599,354,000
Liabilities: $732,176,000
Net Worth: ($132,822,000)
Earnings: ($138,250,000)
Emp.: 540
Fiscal Year-end: 12/31/19
Holding Company; High-Speed Computer Networking & Internet Solutions
N.A.I.C.S.: 551112
Ali Marashi *(CTO)*
Kevin Bostick *(CFO)*
John Scanlon *(Pres & CEO)*
Marisa Canez *(VP-Sls & Customer Success)*
Sameer Aghera *(Head-Product & Mktg)*
Jim Grady *(VP-Bus Ops)*

Subsidiaries:

Internap Connectivity LLC   (1)
1 Ravinia Dr Ste 1300, Atlanta, GA 30346
Tel.: (404) 861-2260
Internet Broadcasting Services
N.A.I.C.S.: 518210

Internap Japan Co., Ltd.   (1)
3-3-12 Kanda Kaji-Cho 7th Floor Kanda Kaji-Cho Chitose Building, Chiyoda-ku, Tokyo, 101-0045, Japan   (51%)
Tel.: (81) 352092222
Web Site: http://www.internap.co.jp
Sales Range: $10-24.9 Million
Emp.: 30
Telecommunication Servicesb
N.A.I.C.S.: 517810
Masaki Okuno *(CEO)*

Internap Network Services (Australia) Ltd.   (1)
L 3 2 Bulletin Pl, Sydney, 2000, NSW, Australia
Tel.: (61) 292472227
Data Processing Hosting & Related Services
N.A.I.C.S.: 518210
David Robinson *(Mgr-HR)*

Internap Network Services UK Ltd.   (1)
10 5th Street 3rd Floor, London, W1D3 JF, United Kingdom
Tel.: (44) 2074782360
Web Site: http://www.internap.com
Sales Range: $10-24.9 Million
Emp.: 10
Telecommunication Servicesb
N.A.I.C.S.: 517810

Internap Holding LLC—(Continued)

Ubersmith, Inc. (1)
1460 Broadway 5th Fl, New York, NY 10036
Tel.: (646) 216-7554
Web Site: http://www.ubersmith.com
Data Processing Hosting & Related Services
N.A.I.C.S.: 518210
Michael Styne (Dir-Ops)
Boo Van Alstyne (VP-Product)
Kurt Daniel (CEO)
Dominique Archambault (CTO)
Christy Joo (Dir-Mktg)
Rob Kuczynski (Dir-Svcs)
Sebastien Plourde (Dir-Engrg)
Akash Krishnani (VP-Sls & Partnerships)

Voxel Dot Net, Inc. (1)
29 Broadway, New York, NY 12180
Tel.: (212) 812-4190
Web Site: http://www.voxel.net
Sales Range: $1-9.9 Million
Emp.: 33
Virtual & Dedicated Servers & Hosting Services
N.A.I.C.S.: 517810

iWeb Group Inc. (1)
20 Place du Commerce, Nuns' Island, Montreal, H3E 1Z6, QC, Canada
Tel.: (514) 286-4242
Web Site: http://www.iweb.com
Website Hosting Services
N.A.I.C.S.: 518210

Subsidiary (Domestic):

iWeb Technologies Inc. (2)
14 Place du Commerce Suite 500 Nuns Island, Montreal, H3E 1T5, QC, Canada
Tel.: (514) 286-4242
Web Site: http://www.iweb.com
Web Hosting Services
N.A.I.C.S.: 518210

INTERNATIONAL AIR CONSOLIDATORS
10700 Richmond Ste 225, Houston, TX 77042
Tel.: (713) 952-3904
Web Site: http://www.iacfares.com
Rev.: $32,000,000
Emp.: 26
Airline Services
N.A.I.C.S.: 488190
Josephi Karkab (Pres)

INTERNATIONAL ASSOCIATION FOR K-12 ONLINE LEARNING
1934 Old Gallows Rd Ste 350, Vienna, VA 22182-4040
Tel.: (703) 752-6216   DE
Web Site: http://www.inacol.org
Year Founded: 2003
Sales Range: $1-9.9 Million
Emp.: 115
Online, Blended & Competency Services for K-12 Education
N.A.I.C.S.: 611710
Dale Frost (Dir-State Policy)
Jim Benson (Dir-Ops)
Andrew Schwartz (VP-IT & Digital Strategy)
Maria Worthen (VP-Federal & State Policy)
Susan Patrick (Pres & CEO)
Bruce Friend (COO)
Tracy Breithaupt (Sr Mgr-Events)

INTERNATIONAL ASSOCIATION OF AMUSEMENT PARKS & ATTRACTIONS
1448 Duke St, Alexandria, VA 22314
Tel.: (703) 836-4800   DE
Web Site: http://www.iaapa.org
Year Founded: 1918
Sales Range: $1-9.9 Million
Emp.: 38
Business Associations

N.A.I.C.S.: 813910
Molly Fernandes (Dir-Mktg)
Victor Danau (Dir-Education Programs & Svcs)
Colleen Mangone (Dir-Media Rels)
David Mandt (Sr VP-Mktg & Comm)
Ivan Hicks (Mgr-Office)
Jeroen Verrezen (Mgr-Mktg)
Jessica Gelsinon (Mgr-Sponsorships)
Karen Staley (Sr VP-Europe, Middle East & Africa)
Liderby Gladden (Mgr-Education)
Julie Sullivan (Mgr-Exhibition Sls)
Ken Troshinsky (Sr VP)
Gerardo Arteaga Cerda (Co-Chm)
Greg Hale (Co-Chm)
Hal McEvoy (Pres & CEO)
John Hallenbeck (VP-North America)
Josh Powers (CFO & Exec VP)

INTERNATIONAL ASSOCIATION OF BRIDGE, STRUCTURAL, ORNAMENTAL, AND REINFORCING IRON WORKERS
1750 New York Ave, NW Lowr Lobby, Washington, DC 20006
Tel.: (202) 383-4800   DC
Web Site: http://www.ironworkers.org
Year Founded: 1896
Sales Range: $25-49.9 Million
Emp.: 114
Employees' associations for improvement
N.A.I.C.S.: 813930
Walter W. Wise (Gen Pres)
Eric Dean (Gen Sec)
John F. Hurley (VP)
Marvin Ragsdale (VP)
Darrell LaBoucan (Eighth Gen VP)
Ron Piksa (VP)

INTERNATIONAL ASSOCIATION OF CHIEFS OF POLICE
44 Canal Center Plz Ste 200, Alexandria, VA 22314
Tel.: (703) 836-6767   DC
Web Site: http://www.theiacp.org
Year Founded: 1893
Sales Range: $25-49.9 Million
Emp.: 124
Professional Organizations
N.A.I.C.S.: 813910
Paul Santiago (Dir-Intl Policing Div)
John Firman (Dir-Res Programs & Pro Svcs)
Vincent Talucci (Exec Dir)
Noirin O'Sullivan (Dir-Strategic Partnerships-Europe)

INTERNATIONAL ASSOCIATION OF FIRE FIGHTERS
1750 New York Ave NW, Washington, DC 20006
Tel.: (202) 737-8484   DC
Web Site: http://www.iaff.org
Year Founded: 1918
Sales Range: $50-74.9 Million
Emp.: 168
Firefighter Association
N.A.I.C.S.: 813319
Ryan Weber (Dir-Acctg)
Dawn Iacino (Dir-Conference & Event Plng)
Matt Vinci (Dir-Education)
Barry Kasinitz (Dir-Govt Affairs)
Harold Schaitberger (Pres)
Thomas H. Miller (Treas & Sec)
James T. Ferguson (VP)
Paul Hufnagel (VP)
James B. Johnson (VP)
Roy L. McGhee (VP)
Larry F. Osborne (VP)
William V. Taylor (VP)
Danny Todd (VP)

Mark S. Woolbright (VP)
William Romaka (VP)
David Burry (VP)
Fred Leblanc (VP)
Lorne West (VP)
Ray R. Rahne (VP)
Michele Shaffer (Dir-Labor Issues & Collective Bargaining)
Kelly Fox (VP)
Carrie Tucker (COO)
David Billy (Dir-Political)
Jim Brinkley (Dir-Occupational Health & Safety)
Juliet Mason (Dir-Membership)
Thomas Woodley (Gen Counsel)
Warren May (Acting COO)
Thomas Hill (Deputy Dir-HazMat/WMD Trng)
Phil Gauer (Deputy Dir-HazMat Grants)
Andy LaVigne (Deputy Dir-Political)
Shannon Meissner (Deputy Dir-Govt Affairs)
Larry Petrick (Deputy Dir-Occupational Health & Safety)
Rick Swan (Dir-Wildland Fire Fighting Safety & Response)
Matthew Szlapak (Dir-HR)
Jane Blume (Dir-Comm)
Carmen Gloukhoff (Dir-Database Admin)
Mark Treglio (Dir-Strategic Campaigns & Media Rels)
Thomas Breyer (Dir-Fire & EMS/GIS Ops)
Ron Saathoff (Dir-Pension Dept)
Jim Tate (Dir-Labor Issues & Collective Bargaining)
Jay Colbert (VP)
Thomas Thornberg (VP)

INTERNATIONAL AUTOMATED SYSTEMS, INC.
4325 Pheasant Rdg Dr Ste 603, Blaine, MN 55449
Tel.: (763) 717-9066   UT
Web Site: https://www.iasmn.com
Year Founded: 1987
IAUS—(OTCBB)
Sales Range: Less than $1 Million
Software Publisher
N.A.I.C.S.: 513210

INTERNATIONAL AUTOPARTS, INC.
4351 Seminole Trail, Charlottesville, VA 22906
Tel.: (434) 974-7118
Web Site: http://www.international-auto.com
Year Founded: 1971
Sales Range: $10-24.9 Million
Emp.: 75
Automotive Parts & Accessories Retailer
N.A.I.C.S.: 441330
Paul Opiela (Pres)
Mark Davis (VP-Mktg & Mdsg)

INTERNATIONAL BACCALAUREATE
7501 Wisconsin Ave Ste 200 W, Bethesda, MD 20814
Tel.: (301) 202-3000   SD
Web Site: http://www.ibo.org
Year Founded: 1968
Sales Range: $150-199.9 Million
Emp.: 146
Educational Support Services
N.A.I.C.S.: 611710
David Hawley (Chief Academic Officer)
John Bader (Chief External Academic Relations Officer)

Andrew MacDonald (Chief Schools Officer)
Carolyn Adams (Dir-Strategy Dev & Execution)

INTERNATIONAL BANCSHARES OF OKLAHOMA, INC.
400 W Main St, Yukon, OK 73099
Tel.: (405) 354-5281   OK
Web Site: http://www.ynbok.com
Year Founded: 1982
Sales Range: $10-24.9 Million
Bank Holding Company
N.A.I.C.S.: 551111
Randy Wright (Chm, Pres & CEO)

Subsidiaries:

YNB (1)
400 W Main St, Yukon, OK 73099
Tel.: (405) 354-5281
Web Site: http://www.ynbok.com
Sales Range: $10-24.9 Million
Emp.: 73
Commericial Banking
N.A.I.C.S.: 522110
Kent Hess (Exec VP)
Lisa LaRose (Asst VP)
Becky Day (VP)
Carson Wright (Sr VP)
David Goodwin (Exec VP)
Donna Kline (Officer-Loan & Branch Mgr)
Eddie Burns (VP)
Joe Horn (VP)
Robert Dyer (Sr VP)

INTERNATIONAL BONDED COURIERS INC.
152-01 Rockaway Blvd, Jamaica, NY 11434
Tel.: (718) 526-5300
Web Site: http://www.ibcinc.com
Sales Range: $25-49.9 Million
Emp.: 300
Shipping
N.A.I.C.S.: 492110
Roberto Moreno (VP-Bus Dev)

INTERNATIONAL BROTHERHOOD OF ELECTRICAL WORKERS
900 7th St NW, Washington, DC 20001
Tel.: (202) 833-7000
Web Site: https://www.ibew.org
Sales Range: $1-9.9 Million
Emp.: 40
Labor Unions & Similar Labor Organizations
N.A.I.C.S.: 813930
Angela Carpenter (Sec)

INTERNATIONAL BROTHERHOOD OF TEAMSTERS
25 Louisiana Ave NW, Washington, DC 20001
Tel.: (225) 924-3886
Web Site: https://www.teamster.org
Year Founded: 1903
Labor Organization Services
N.A.I.C.S.: 813930

INTERNATIONAL BUILDING MATERIALS LLC
14421 SE 98th Ct, Clackamas, OR 97015
Tel.: (503) 650-9663
Web Site: http://www.iwpllc.com
Rev.: $13,600,000
Emp.: 45
Lumber: Rough, Dressed & Finished
N.A.I.C.S.: 423310
Terry Hargian (Pres)

INTERNATIONAL BUSINESS COMMUNICATIONS INC.

1981 Marcus Ave Ste C105, Lake Success, NY 11042-1032
Tel.: (516) 352-4505   NY
Web Site: http://www.ibcshell.com
Year Founded: 1980
Sales Range: $25-49.9 Million
Emp.: 300
Plastics Foam Products
N.A.I.C.S.: 326150
Norman Kay *(CEO & Chief Creative Officer-IBC Shell Pkg & Chm-Intl Bus Comm)*
Margaret Maher-Healion *(CFO)*

Subsidiaries:

IBC Shell Containers Inc.   (1)
1981 Marcus Ave Ste C105, New Hyde Park, NY 11042-1032
Tel.: (516) 352-4505
Web Site: http://www.ibcshell.com
Sales Range: $10-24.9 Million
Emp.: 30
Plastics Foam Products
N.A.I.C.S.: 326150

INTERNATIONAL BUSINESS EXCHANGE CORPORATION
14205 Burnet Rd Ste 640, Austin, TX 78728
Tel.: (512) 310-2966
Web Site:
  http://www.ibexbeyond.com
Year Founded: 1979
Business Services
N.A.I.C.S.: 561499
Dylan Harvey *(Mgr-Mktg)*

INTERNATIONAL CARS LTD.
382 Newbury St, Danvers, MA 01923
Tel.: (978) 777-2550
Web Site: http://www.iclautos.com
Sales Range: $200-249.9 Million
Emp.: 80
New & Used Car Dealers
N.A.I.C.S.: 441110
Marshall Jespersen *(Owner & Pres)*
Richard Collins *(CEO)*
Eric Adams *(Mgr-Parts)*
Bruce Sellar *(Mgr)*
Bryan Laskis *(Mgr-Sls)*
Erica Nicholas *(Controller)*
Paul Desrosier *(Gen Mgr-Sls-Honda North)*
Joseph Hajjar *(Gen Mgr-Honda North)*

INTERNATIONAL CASINGS GROUP, INC.
4420 S Wolcott Ave, Chicago, IL 60609
Tel.: (773) 376-9200   IL
Web Site: http://www.casings.com
Sales Range: $25-49.9 Million
Emp.: 40
Sausage Casings, Natural
N.A.I.C.S.: 311612
John Chovanec *(Mgr-Sls)*
Eric Svendsen *(VP)*
Bryan Sholtz *(CFO)*

INTERNATIONAL CENTER FOR ENTREPRENEURIAL DEVELOPMENT, INC.
12715 Telge Rd, Cypress, TX 77429-2164
Tel.: (281) 256-4100   TX
Web Site: http://www.iced.net
Year Founded: 1967
Sales Range: $125-149.9 Million
Emp.: 175
Franchiser of Instant Printing, Thermography, Pack & Ship & Computer Education Centers
N.A.I.C.S.: 533110
Steve Hammerstein *(Pres & CEO)*
Perry Hillegeist *(COO & VP)*

INTERNATIONAL CENTER FOR ENVIROMENTAL ARTS
519 Karen Dr, Berea, OH 44017
Tel.: (440) 891-8376   OH
Web Site: http://www.theicea.com
Year Founded: 1994
Sales Range: $10-24.9 Million
Art Education Program Services
N.A.I.C.S.: 923120
Renate Jakupca *(Pres)*
Patrick Cahill *(Treas)*
David Jakupca *(Pres)*
Priscilla Reagan *(VP-External Affairs)*

INTERNATIONAL CENTER FOR JOURNALISTS
2000 M St NW Ste 250, Washington, DC 20036
Tel.: (202) 737-3700   MA
Web Site: http://www.icfj.org
Year Founded: 1984
Sales Range: $10-24.9 Million
Emp.: 48
Journalist Professional Organization
N.A.I.C.S.: 813920
Vjollca Shtylla *(VP-Dev)*
Patrick Butler *(VP-Programs)*
Sharon Moshavi *(Sr VP-New Initiatives)*
Raju Narisetti *(Vice Chm)*
Michael Golden *(Chm)*
Jason Wright *(Chm-Dev)*
Joyce Barnathan *(Pres)*
John Maxwell Hamilton *(Treas)*
Pamela Howard *(Vice Chm)*
Matthew Winkler *(Vice Chm)*
Nancy Frye *(Dir-HR)*
Ben Colmery *(Dir-Knight Intl Journalism Fellowships)*
Jerri Eddings *(Sr Dir-Program)*
Johanna Carrillo *(Sr Dir-Program)*
Zainab Imam *(Mgr-Program)*
Emily Schult *(Sr Dir-Program)*
Jacqueline Strzemp *(Mgr-Program)*
Robert Tinsley *(Dir-Proposal Dev)*
Luis Botello *(Sr Dir-Special Projects Program)*
Mario Scherhaufer *(VP-Fin)*
James F. Hoge Jr. *(Vice Chm)*

INTERNATIONAL CENTER FOR NOT-FOR-PROFIT LAW
1126 16th St NW Ste 400, Washington, DC 20036
Tel.: (202) 452-8600   DE
Web Site: http://www.icnl.org
Year Founded: 1992
Sales Range: $10-24.9 Million
Emp.: 27
Bar Association
N.A.I.C.S.: 813920
Sylvia Staggs *(Mgr-Office)*
Darla Mecham *(VP-Fin)*
Marina Korsakova *(Controller)*
Nilda Bullain *(VP-Ops)*
Catherine Shea *(VP-Programs)*
Natalia Bourjaily *(VP)*
David Moore *(VP-Legal affairs)*

INTERNATIONAL CERAMIC CONSTRUCTION, LLC
5260 Pkwy Plaza Blvd Ste 170, Charlotte, NC 28217
Tel.: (704) 504-5544
Web Site: http://www.icc-tileconstruction.com
Year Founded: 2005
Sales Range: $25-49.9 Million
Emp.: 75
Commercial Building Construction Services
N.A.I.C.S.: 236220
Frank Muller *(Pres)*

INTERNATIONAL CHECKOUT, INC.
7950 Woodley Ave Ste C, Van Nuys, CA 91406-1261
Tel.: (310) 601-8196
Web Site:
  http://www.internationalcheckout.com
Year Founded: 2002
Sales Range: $1-9.9 Million
Emp.: 19
Freight Transportation Arrangement
N.A.I.C.S.: 488510
Saskia Strick *(CEO)*
Kathy Beteta *(Dir-Bus Dev)*

INTERNATIONAL CHEMICAL COMPANY
1887 E 71st St, Tulsa, OK 74136
Tel.: (918) 496-7711   OK
Web Site: http://www.ictulsa.com
Year Founded: 1976
Sales Range: $150-199.9 Million
Emp.: 50
Fertilizer Trading Company & Coal Supplier, Wholesale Distr
N.A.I.C.S.: 424910
John R. Arend *(Founder & Chm)*
John Mayfield *(Mgr-Intl Ops)*

Subsidiaries:

Ozark Steel, LLC.   (1)
908 W 41st St, Tulsa, OK 74107
Tel.: (918) 234-1212
Sales Range: $1-9.9 Million
Fabricated Structural Metal Mfr
N.A.I.C.S.: 332312
Lindsey Yates *(Mgr-Sls & Mktg)*

INTERNATIONAL CHEMICAL CORP.
55 Woodridge Dr, Amherst, NY 14228
Tel.: (716) 689-4600
Rev.: $18,600,000
Emp.: 80
Industrial Inorganic Chemicals
N.A.I.C.S.: 325180

INTERNATIONAL CITY/COUNTY MANAGEMENT ASSOCIATION
777 N Capitol St NE Ste 500, Washington, DC 20002-4201
Tel.: (202) 962-3680   DE
Web Site: http://www.icma.org
Year Founded: 1972
Sales Range: $200-249.9 Million
Emp.: 100
Community Welfare Services
N.A.I.C.S.: 624190
Uma Ramesh *(COO)*
Mark Ott *(Exec Dir)*

INTERNATIONAL CMA RETIREMENT CORP.
777 N Capitol St NE, Washington, DC 20002
Tel.: (202) 962-4600   DC
Web Site: http://www.icmarc.org
Year Founded: 1979
Sales Range: $100-124.9 Million
Emp.: 500
Pension & Retirement Plans
N.A.I.C.S.: 524298
Rich Whitty *(Controller)*

INTERNATIONAL CODE COUNCIL, INC.
500 New Jersey Ave NW 6th FL, Washington, DC 20001
Tel.: (202) 370-1800
Web Site: http://www.iccsafe.org
ePeriodicals, Technical Manuals on Building & Safety Codes Regulations
N.A.I.C.S.: 513199
John Belcik *(CFO & COO)*
Dominic Sims *(CEO)*

Michael P. Wich *(Pres)*
Stuart D. Tom *(VP)*
David Spencer *(Treas & Sec)*

Subsidiaries:

ICC Chicago   (1)
4051 W Flossmoor Rd, Country Club Hills, IL 60478   (100%)
Tel.: (888) 422-7233
Web Site: http://www.iccsafe.org
Code Books & Reference Guides Publishers
N.A.I.C.S.: 513120
John Belcik *(CFO)*
Annie Martinez *(Mgr-Client Svcs & Trng)*

ICC Evaluation Service   (1)
900 Montclair Rd, Birmingham, AL 35213   (100%)
Tel.: (888) 423-6587
Web Site: http://www.iccsafe.org
Construction Codes Publishers
N.A.I.C.S.: 513120
Gary Nichols *(VP-Engrg)*
John Battles *(VP-Architectural & Engrg Svcs)*
Steve Daggers *(VP-Comm)*
Laurence Genest *(VP-Sls Mktg)*
Carolina Khoury *(Sr Mgr-Admin)*
Margi Leddin *(VP-Publ & Multimedia)*
Hamid Naderi *(Sr VP-Product Dev)*
David Pereg *(Dir-Quality Sys)*
Dominic Sims *(CEO)*
Steve Thorsell *(Dir-Environmental Program)*
Sara Yerkes *(Sr VP-Governmental Rels)*

ICC Evaluation Service   (1)
5360 Workman Mill Rd, Whittier, CA 90601   (100%)
Tel.: (562) 699-0541
Web Site: http://www.icc-es.org
Code Books & Certification /Training Manuals Publisher
N.A.I.C.S.: 513120
Shahin Moinian *(Pres)*
Maribel Campos *(Dir-Standards)*
Michael Temesvary *(Dir-Sls)*

NTA, LLC   (1)
305 North Oakland Ave, Nappanee, IN 46550
Tel.: (574) 773-7975
Web Site: http://www.ntainc.com
Engineeering Services
N.A.I.C.S.: 541330
David Tompos *(Pres & CEO)*
Eric Tompos *(VP & Dir-Compliance)*
David R. Tompos *(Founder, VP & Dir-Sls)*
Phil Jones *(VP-Ops)*
Mike Luna *(Sr Dir-Bldg Products)*
Eric Bozzo *(Dir-Engrg & CAD Svcs)*
Robert Lee *(Dir-Inspection Svcs)*
Jessica Ott *(Dir-Admin Svcs)*
Chuck Osterday *(Dir-Modular Svcs)*
Harry Odum *(Dir-Dapia Svcs)*
David A. Tompos *(Pres & CEO)*

INTERNATIONAL COMMUNITY HEALTH SERVICES
720 8th Ave S 2nd Fl, Seattle, WA 98104
Tel.: (206) 788-3650   WA
Web Site: http://www.ichs.com
Year Founded: 1973
Sales Range: $10-24.9 Million
Emp.: 295
Community Health Care Services
N.A.I.C.S.: 621498
Kimo Hirayama *(Asst Dir-Medical)*
Hermes Shahbazian *(CFO)*
Teresita Batayola *(CEO)*
Ji Choi *(Dir-Dental)*
Ron Chew *(Dir-Foundation)*
Charles Hayashi *(Dir-Compliance)*
Michael McKee *(Dir-Health Svcs & Community Partnership)*
Sherman Lohn *(Dir-Ops)*
Gildas Cheung *(Chm)*
Rachel Koh *(COO)*
Richard Mellon *(Treas)*
Hiroshi Nakano *(Sec)*
Rayburn Lewis *(Chief Medical Officer)*
Samantha Lee-Chiu *(Interim Chief Dental Officer)*

International Components Corporation—(Continued)

INTERNATIONAL COMPO-NENTS CORPORATION
215 Mccormick Dr, Bohemia, NY 11716
Tel.: (631) 952-9595   NY
Web Site: http://www.icc107.com
Year Founded: 1970
Sales Range: $50-74.9 Million
Emp.: 65
Electronic Parts & Equipment Mfr
N.A.I.C.S.: 334416
Irwin Friedman (Pres)
Fredric Grossman (VP-Mktg & Sls)
Joanne Hanley (Controller)

INTERNATIONAL COMPUTER MARKETING CORPORATION (ICM)
4025 Steve Reynolds Blvd Ste 120, Norcross, GA 30093
Tel.: (770) 381-2947
Web Site: http://www.icmcorp.com
Year Founded: 1985
Sales Range: $25-49.9 Million
Emp.: 50
Field & Sales Force Automation
Value Added Integrator
N.A.I.C.S.: 541512
Jim Simpson (Co-Founder & Pres)

INTERNATIONAL COMPUTER SOLUTIONS INC.
15201 Diamondback Dr Ste 125, Rockville, MD 20850-3695
Tel.: (301) 795-1275
Rev.: $4,100,000
Emp.: 60
Computer System Design Services
N.A.I.C.S.: 541512
John Azhdam (Mgr)
Vaibhav Bhatnagar (VP)
Aparna Challu (VP)
Mike Goldberg (Mgr)
Sanjay Govil (Pres)
Mike Mortazavi (Mgr)
Joseph Pedano (Mgr)
Ashoka Tankala (VP-Fin)

INTERNATIONAL CONSTRUC-TION EQUIPMENT
301 Warehouse Dr, Matthews, NC 28104
Tel.: (704) 821-8200
Web Site: http://www.iceusa.com
Year Founded: 1974
Sales Range: $10-24.9 Million
Emp.: 100
Vibrators For Concrete Construction
N.A.I.C.S.: 333120
Christian Cunningham (Owner)
Rick Sadler (Mgr-Sls)
Jim Ziemer (Mgr-Sls-Intl)

INTERNATIONAL CONTRACT FURNITURE
19 Ohio Ave, Norwich, CT 06360-1536
Tel.: (860) 886-1700
Web Site: http://www.icfsource.com
Sales Range: $25-49.9 Million
Emp.: 15
Household Furniture
N.A.I.C.S.: 423210
James H. Kasschau (Pres & CEO)

INTERNATIONAL CONTROLS & MEASUREMENTS CORP.
7313 William Barry Blvd, North Syracuse, NY 13212
Tel.: (315) 233-5266   NY
Web Site:
   http://www.icmcontrols.com
Year Founded: 1984
Sales Range: $10-24.9 Million

Emp.: 350
Mfr of Industrial Timers, Controls, Motor Starters Designed for the Heating, Ventilating, Air Conditioning & Refrigeration (HVACR) Market
N.A.I.C.S.: 335314
Laurie Kadah (Treas)
Andrew Kadah (Pres)

INTERNATIONAL COOPERAT-ING MINISTRIES
1901 N Armistead Ave, Hampton, VA 23666-4311
Tel.: (757) 827-6704   VA
Web Site: http://www.icm.org
Year Founded: 1986
Sales Range: $10-24.9 Million
Emp.: 43
Christian Ministry Services
N.A.I.C.S.: 813110
Jan Stringer (COO & Sr VP)
Don Douglas (Sr VP-Ministry Programs)
Anh Lam (Mgr-IT)
Janice Rosser Allen (Chm & CEO)
Keith Pivik (Dir-Dev)
Mattie Wezah (Dir-Donor Correspondence)
Kimberly Hansin (Officer-Dev)
Dois I. Rosser Jr. (Founder)

INTERNATIONAL CRYSTAL MANUFACTURING, INC.
10 North Lee St, Oklahoma City, OK 73102
Tel.: (405) 236-3741
Web Site: http://www.icmfg.com
Year Founded: 1951
Sales Range: $250-299.9 Million
Emp.: 55
Quartz Crystal Mfr & Broker
N.A.I.C.S.: 334419
Royden Freeland (Founder & CEO)

INTERNATIONAL DELIGHTS, LLC.
230 Brighton Rd, Clifton, NJ 07012
Tel.: (973) 928-5582
Web Site: http://www.intdelights.com
Year Founded: 1986
Sales Range: $10-24.9 Million
Emp.: 130
Bakery Products Mfr
N.A.I.C.S.: 311812
Nick Sayegh (Pres)
Hamid Chowdhury (Office Mgr)

INTERNATIONAL DELIVERY SOLUTIONS
7340 S Howell Ave, Oak Creek, WI 53154
Tel.: (414) 856-1188
Web Site: http://www.idstrac.com
Year Founded: 1999
Rev.: $25,000,000
Emp.: 25
Mailing & Printing Services
N.A.I.C.S.: 492110
Margaret Schneider (COO)
Jim Winterle (Pres)
Greg Sniadach (Dir-Ops)
Rich Phillips (Dir-Ops & Logistics)

INTERNATIONAL DEVELOP-MENT, LLC
899 Henrietta Creek Rd, Roanoke, TX 76262-6309
Tel.: (817) 251-6999   DE
Web Site:
   http://www.westinghousesolar lights.com
Sales Range: $25-49.9 Million
Emp.: 60
Electrical Apparatus & Equipment
N.A.I.C.S.: 423610

INTERNATIONAL DIRECT SELLING TECHNOLOGY CORP.
1208 E Kennedy Blvd Ste 222, Tampa, FL 33602
Tel.: (813) 277-0625
Web Site: http://www.idsto.com
Year Founded: 2001
Sales Range: $10-24.9 Million
Emp.: 22
Management Software, Website Design, Multimedia Design & Sales Force Tools
N.A.I.C.S.: 513210
Ian Cordell (CEO)
Curtis Wiggins (VP-Sys Engrg)
Valerie Cordell (Mgr-Acctg)
Danielle Williams (Mgr-Bus Dev)
Justin Tetreault (Project Mgr-Enterprise)
Brent Fernandez (Project Mgr)
Eric Flasterstein (Project Mgr)
Anthony Calo (Sr Mgr-Application Dev)
Eric Flsterstein (Project Mgr)

INTERNATIONAL ELECTRICAL SALES CORPORATION
7540 NW 66th St, Miami, FL 33166
Tel.: (305) 591-8390
Web Site: http://www.iescomia.com
Sales Range: $10-24.9 Million
Emp.: 35
Electrical Products Distr
N.A.I.C.S.: 423610
Robert Bernstein (Pres)

INTERNATIONAL ENERGY SERVICES, INC.
800 Gassner Ste 210, Houston, TX 77024
Tel.: (713) 571-0688
Sales Range: $10-24.9 Million
Emp.: 10
Heating Services
N.A.I.C.S.: 213112

INTERNATIONAL EXHIBI-TIONS, INC.
1635 W Alabama St, Houston, TX 77006
Tel.: (713) 529-1616   TX
Year Founded: 1992
Sales Range: $1-9.9 Million
Emp.: 29
Database & Directory Publishers
N.A.I.C.S.: 513140
Brion Palmer (Pres)
Gina Mayfield (Mgr-Bus Dev)

Subsidiaries:

Atlantic Communications-Houston
Office   (1)
1635 W Alabama St, Houston, TX 77006-4101
Tel.: (713) 831-1768
Web Site: http://www.oilonline.com
Publishers of Magazines & Directories
N.A.I.C.S.: 513199

INTERNATIONAL EXTRU-SIONS, INC.
5800 Venoy Rd, Garden City, MI 48135
Tel.: (734) 427-8700   MI
Web Site: http://www.extrusion.net
Sales Range: $25-49.9 Million
Emp.: 199
Aluminum Extruded Products
N.A.I.C.S.: 331318
Nicholas Noecker (Pres)
Marshall V. Noecker (Chm)
George Gazepis (CFO)
Alecia Schneider (Controller)

INTERNATIONAL FALLS ME-

MORIAL HOSPITAL ASSOCIA-TION
1400 Highway 71, International Falls, MN 56649
Tel.: (218) 283-4481   MN
Web Site:
   http://www.rainylakemedical.com
Year Founded: 1945
Sales Range: $10-24.9 Million
Emp.: 202
Health Care Srvices
N.A.I.C.S.: 622110
Kris Foss (Exec Dir-Ancillary Svcs)
Donita Ettestad (Chief Nursing Officer)
Melissa Marcotte (CFO)
Dan Odegaard (CEO)
Brian Briggs (Sec)
Jon Talsness (Vice Chm)
Susan Congrave (Chm)
Don Billig (Treas)
David Monson (Exec Dir-HR)
Dave Monson (Chief HR Officer)
Rosalind Snyder (Co-Chief Nursing Officer)

INTERNATIONAL FASHION CONCEPTS, INC.
519 8th Ave, New York, NY 10018
Tel.: (212) 967-2990   NY
Web Site: http://www.barami.com
Women's Apparel Mfr
N.A.I.C.S.: 458110
Bahram Hakakian (CEO)

INTERNATIONAL FERTILIZER DEVELOPMENT CENTER
PO Box 2040, Muscle Shoals, AL 35662
Tel.: (256) 381-6600   AL
Web Site: http://www.ifdc.org
Year Founded: 1974
Rev.: $46,299,000
Assets: $17,126,000
Liabilities: $19,991,000
Net Worth: ($2,865,000)
Earnings: ($1,471,000)
Emp.: 4,000
Fiscal Year-end: 12/31/18
Agricultural Develpment Services
N.A.I.C.S.: 813910
Scott Hudson (CFO & Dir-Ops)
Albin Hubscher (Pres & CEO)
Jeremy Crow (Head-Legal)
J. J. Groot (Dir-Bus Dev & Strategic Partnerships)
Jose Ramon Lazo de la Vega (Head-Engrg & Pilot Plant Svcs)
Andy Thigpen (Head-Comm)
Upendra Singh (Deputy Dir-Headquarters Res)
Jimmy Cheek (Chm)
Rudy Rabbinge (Vice Chm)

INTERNATIONAL FIDELITY IN-SURANCE COMPANY
1 Newark Ctr Fl 20, Newark, NJ 07102
Tel.: (973) 624-7200
Web Site: http://www.ific.com
Sales Range: $100-124.9 Million
Emp.: 190
Insurance Services
N.A.I.C.S.: 524126
Mark Riccordela (CFO)

INTERNATIONAL FOOD POLICY RESEARCH INSTI-TUTE
2033 K St NW, Washington, DC 20006-1002
Tel.: (202) 862-5600   DC
Web Site: http://www.ifpri.org
Year Founded: 1975
Sales Range: $125-149.9 Million

Emp.: 262
Hunger Relief Services
N.A.I.C.S.: 624210
Roby Jacob (Controller)
Mark Rosegrant (Dir-Div)
Marie Ruel (Dir-Div)
Maximo Torero (Dir-Div)

INTERNATIONAL FOOD-SOURCE LLC.
52 Richboynton Rd, Dover, NJ 07801
Tel.: (973) 361-7044
Web Site: http://valuednaturals.com
Year Founded: 2004
Sales Range: $10-24.9 Million
Emp.: 90
Snack & Nut Mfr
N.A.I.C.S.: 311919
David Lipson (Co-Owner, Pres & Dir-Ops)
Dan Baron (Co-Owner, CEO & Dir-Pur & Sls)
Tiffany Bender (Mgr-Quality)

INTERNATIONAL FOUNDA-TION FOR ELECTION SYS-TEMS
1850 K St NW 5th Fl, Washington, DC 20006
Tel.: (202) 350-6700   DC
Web Site: http://www.ifes.org
Year Founded: 1987
Sales Range: $75-99.9 Million
Emp.: 193
Civic & Social Organization
N.A.I.C.S.: 813410
Anchal Gupta (Dir-HR & Admin)
Michael Svetlik (VP-Programs)
Donald R. Sweitzer (Co-Chm)
Staffan Darnolf (Dir-Program Dev & Innovation)
Thomas A. Devine (Sec)
William J. Hybl (Vice Chm)
Daniela Colaiacovo (Dir-Comm & Advocacy)
Juliette Schmidt (Deputy Dir-Asia-Pacific)
Richard Twigg (Dir-IT)
Rushdi Nackerdien (Dir-Africa Reg)
Susan Kupperstein (Deputy Dir-Africa)
Vasu Mohan (Dir-Asia-Pacific Reg)
June Langston Dehart (Treas)
Fernando Barragan (CFO)

INTERNATIONAL FOUNDA-TION OF EMPLOYEE BENEFIT PLANS
18700 W Bluemound Rd, Brookfield, WI 53045
Tel.: (262) 786-6700   WI
Web Site: http://www.ifebp.org
Year Founded: 1954
Sales Range: $25-49.9 Million
Emp.: 146
Employee Benefit Services
N.A.I.C.S.: 525120
Paul Hackleman (Sec)
Gene H. Price (Treas)
Terence Davidson (CEO)
Wendell W. Young IV (Co-Sec)

INTERNATIONAL FRAGRANCE & TECHNOLOGY
210 Hickory Springs Ind Dr, Canton, GA 30115-7962
Tel.: (770) 345-3079
Web Site:
     http://www.iftfragrances.com
Year Founded: 1991
Sales Range: $10-24.9 Million
Emp.: 90
Mfr & Sales of Perfumes
N.A.I.C.S.: 325199
Deepak Shah (Pres)

INTERNATIONAL FREIGHT FORWARDING, INC.
302 International Blvd, Laredo, TX 78045
Tel.: (956) 718-7100   TX
Sales Range: $10-24.9 Million
Emp.: 130
Freight Forwarding
N.A.I.C.S.: 488510
Ruben Bazan Jr. (Pres)

INTERNATIONAL FREIGHT SYSTEMS LLC.
1200 S 192nd St Ste 100, Seatac, WA 98148-2345
Tel.: (206) 433-2614
Web Site: http://www.intfreight.com
Year Founded: 1995
Sales Range: $10-24.9 Million
Emp.: 13
Motor Vehicle Transit System Services
N.A.I.C.S.: 485113
Shelley Moine (Pres)

INTERNATIONAL FUND FOR ANIMAL WELFARE
290 Summer St, Yarmouth Port, MA 02675
Tel.: (508) 744-2000   MA
Web Site: https://www.ifaw.org
Year Founded: 1998
Sales Range: $10-24.9 Million
Emp.: 165
Animal Welfare Services
N.A.I.C.S.: 112990
Azzedine Downes (Pres & CEO)
Ian Robinson (VP-Programs & Intl Ops)
Kevin McGinnis (Dir-HR)
Thomas Maul (CFO)
Erica Martin (VP-Comm)
Philip Milburn (VP-Philanthropy)
Phyllis Bayer (Dir-IT Ops & Facilities)
Cynthia Milburn (Dir-Animal Welfare Outreach & Education)
Kevin M. Shields (VP-Programs)
Ann L. Noble (Dir-Dev)
Kelvin Alie (Exec VP-Washington)
Sonja Van Tichelen (VP-Ops-Intl)
Joyce C. Doria (Chm)

INTERNATIONAL GAMCO INC.
9335 N 48th St, Omaha, NE 68152
Tel.: (402) 571-2449
Web Site: http://www.intlgamco.com
Sales Range: $10-24.9 Million
Emp.: 135
Commercial Printing Services
N.A.I.C.S.: 323111
Steve Edie (VP-Ops)
Mark Stevens (VP-Sls & Mktg)

INTERNATIONAL GOURMET FOODS INC.
7520 Fullerton Rd, Springfield, VA 22153
Tel.: (703) 569-4520
Web Site: http://www.igf-inc.com
Year Founded: 1987
Rev.: $20,000,000
Emp.: 78
Sales of Groceries
N.A.I.C.S.: 424410
Maurizio Dibenigno (Founder)

Subsidiaries:

Dolce Europa   (1)
7520 Fullerton Rd, Springfield, VA 22153
Tel.: (703) 451-9501
Sales Range: $1-9.9 Million
Emp.: 20
Groceries, General Line
N.A.I.C.S.: 424410

INTERNATIONAL GRANITE & MARBLE
2038 83rd St, North Bergen, NJ 07047
Tel.: (201) 869-5200
Web Site: http://www.igmcorp.com
Sales Range: $25-49.9 Million
Emp.: 26
Granite Building Stone
N.A.I.C.S.: 423320
John Weiss (Pres)
Tom Gibb (Exec VP)
Jane Hagaden (CFO)
Robert Weiss (VP-Foreign Sls-Brazil)
Steven Weiss (VP-Imports-Exports)

INTERNATIONAL HARDCOAT, INC.
12400 Burt Rd, Detroit, MI 48228
Tel.: (313) 535-3210
Web Site: http://www.ihccorp.com
Year Founded: 1962
Sales Range: $10-24.9 Million
Emp.: 115
Anodizing Metal Services
N.A.I.C.S.: 332813
Jeff Pernick (Pres)

INTERNATIONAL HARVESTER EMPLOYEE CREDIT UNION, INC.
5000 Urbana Rd, Springfield, OH 45502-9539
Tel.: (937) 390-1800   OH
Web Site: http://www.ihecu.com
Year Founded: 1934
Sales Range: $10-24.9 Million
Emp.: 45
Financial Services
N.A.I.C.S.: 523999
Robb White (CFO)

INTERNATIONAL HOUSE
2299 Piedmont Ave, Berkeley, CA 94720-2320
Tel.: (510) 643-8315   CA
Web Site: https://ihouse.berkeley.edu
Year Founded: 1929
Sales Range: $10-24.9 Million
Student Housing & Residential Services
N.A.I.C.S.: 721310

INTERNATIONAL HOUSE PHILADELPHIA
3701 Chestnut St, Philadelphia, PA 19104
Tel.: (215) 387-5125   PA
Web Site: http://www.ihousephilly.org
Year Founded: 1970
Sales Range: $1-9.9 Million
Emp.: 100
Multicultural Residential Center for International Students
N.A.I.C.S.: 624190
Glenn Martin (COO)
Ludo C. P. Scheffer (Chm)
Clara Fomich (Office Mgr)
James M. Papada III (Pres-Interim & CEO-Interim)
Giacomo F. Cesareo III (Sec)

INTERNATIONAL IMPACT BUILDING PRODUCTS, LLC.
5900 Australian Ave Ste 3, West Palm Beach, FL 33407
Tel.: (561) 578-5450
Web Site: http://www.intl-impact.com
Year Founded: 1960
Sales Range: $10-24.9 Million
Emp.: 30
Metal Window & Door Mfr
N.A.I.C.S.: 332321

Michael J. Fry (Owner & CEO)
Randy Stowell (VP)
Julie Bugaj (Office Mgr)

INTERNATIONAL INDUSTRIES, INC.
96 MacCorkle Ave SW, South Charleston, WV 25303
Tel.: (304) 746-6021   WV
Year Founded: 1947
Sales Range: $150-199.9 Million
Emp.: 575
Coal Mining Services
N.A.I.C.S.: 213113
James H. Harless (Founder & Chm)

Subsidiaries:

Gilco Lumber, Inc.   (1)
Rt 52, Roderfield, WV 24881   (100%)
Tel.: (304) 436-2125
Sales Range: $1-9.9 Million
Emp.: 30
Sawmills & Planing Mills
N.A.I.C.S.: 321999
Ed Weiner (Gen Mgr)

Leader Trailer, Inc.   (1)
1569 Steele Hill Rd NW, New Philadelphia, OH 44663-6503
Tel.: (330) 339-3877
Rev.: $5,100,000
Emp.: 25
Automobiles & Other Motor Vehicles
N.A.I.C.S.: 423110

Logan & Kanawha Coal Company, Inc.   (1)
96 Maccorkle Ave SW, South Charleston, WV 25303-1412
Tel.: (304) 746-2980
Sales Range: $10-24.9 Million
Emp.: 10
Coal & Other Minerals & Ores
N.A.I.C.S.: 423520
Brian Varney (Mgr-Traffic & Distr)
Steve Melton (Dir-Utility-Indus Sls)
Mike Poole (Controller)

INTERNATIONAL INFORMA-TION SYSTEMS CONSORTIUM INC.
311 Park Place Blvd Ste 400, Clearwater, FL 33759
Tel.: (727) 785-0189   MA
Web Site: http://www.isc2.org
Year Founded: 1989
Sales Range: $1-9.9 Million
Emp.: 23
Information Security Consulting & Training Services
N.A.I.C.S.: 541690
Debra Taylor (CFO)
Elise Yacobellis (Dir-Bus Dev-Americas)
Jennifer Minella (Vice Chm)
Wesley Simpson (COO)
Graham Jackson (Gen Counsel)
Brian Correia (Dir-Bus Dev-North America)
Dan Waddell (Mng Dir-North America)
John McCumber (Dir-Cybersecurity Advocacy-North America)
Jarred LeFebvre (Sr Mgr-Corp Comm)
Casey Marks (Chief Product Officer & VP)
Brian Alberti (Mgr-PR)
Greg Thompson (Treas)
Kevin Charest (Chm)
Mirtha Collin (Dir-Education)
Timothy Campo (Dir-Applications, Architecture & Security)
Sommer Hess (Dir-Project Mgmt, Software Quality Assurance & IT Trng)
Mat Young (VP-Advocacy-Global)
Clar Rosso (CEO)
Amy Eubanks (Exec VP-Strategy & Pro Dev)

International Information Systems Consortium
Inc.—(Continued)

Subsidiaries:

ISC2 Asia-Pacific **(1)**
25 Canton Road Tsim Sha Tsui Unit 807 8th
Floor Tower 1 The Gateway, Harbour City,
Kowloon, China (Hong Kong)
Tel.: (852) 2850 6951
Information Security Consulting & Training
Services
N.A.I.C.S.: 541690
Tony Vizza *(Dir-Cybersecurity Advocacy)*
Clayton Jones *(Reg Mng Dir)*

ISC2 EMEA **(1)**
3 More London Riverside Office No 173,
London, SE1 2RE, United Kingdom
Tel.: (44) 2039607800
Information Security Consulting & Training
Services
N.A.I.C.S.: 541690
Deshini Newman *(Reg Mng Dir)*
Mark Johnson *(Dir-Cybersecurity Advocacy)*

ISC2 Japan **(1)**
Hirakawa-cho Mori Tower 2-16-1 Hirakawa-
cho, Chiyoda-ku, Tokyo, 102-0093, Japan
Tel.: (81) 3 6757 0138
Information Security Consulting & Training
N.A.I.C.S.: 541690

INTERNATIONAL INGREDIENT CORP.
150 Larkin Williams Industrial Ct,
Saint Louis, MO 63026
Tel.: (636) 343-4111
Web Site: http://www.iicag.com
Rev.: $36,000,000
Emp.: 265
Livestock Feeds
N.A.I.C.S.: 311119
Kevin Halpin *(VP)*
Mike Trotter *(Mgr-Nutrition & Quality
Assurance)*

INTERNATIONAL INSPIRA-TIONS
362 5th Ave, New York, NY 10001
Tel.: (212) 465-8500
Web Site: http://www.international-
inspirations.com
Year Founded: 2005
Sales Range: $10-24.9 Million
Emp.: 35
Costume Jewelry Design
N.A.I.C.S.: 339910
Shaya Reiter *(Owner)*
Gabrielle Teta *(Mgr-Production)*
Tarkan Boke *(Mgr-Ops)*

INTERNATIONAL INSTITUTE FOR LEARNING, INC.
110 E 59th St, New York, NY 10022-
1380
Tel.: (212) 758-0177
Web Site: http://www.iil.com
Sales Range: $10-24.9 Million
Emp.: 200
Corporate Training Services
N.A.I.C.S.: 611430
E. LaVerne Johnson *(Pres & CEO)*
Rodolfo Ambriz *(Mng Dir)*
Cathryn Chee *(Mng Dir)*
Cristina Garcia de la Santa *(Mng Dir)*
Jennifer Sabine *(Mng Dir)*
Barry Schnell *(Exec VP)*
Steve Osborn *(Mgr-Ops-Global)*
Wilma Driessler *(Mng Dir)*
Cristina Garcia *(Mng Dir)*

INTERNATIONAL INSTITUTE FOR TRAUMA AND ADDIC-TION PROFESSIONALS
PO Box 2112, Carefree, AZ 85377
Tel.: (480) 575-6853
Web Site: http://www.iitap.com

Training & Educational Resources for
Practitioners Who Treat People With
Addictive & Compulsive Sexual Be-
haviors
N.A.I.C.S.: 611430
Patrick J. Carnes *(Founder)*
Stefanie Carnes *(Pres)*

Subsidiaries:

Gentle Path Press **(1)**
PO Box 2112, Carefree, AZ 85377
Tel.: (480) 488-0150
Web Site: http://www.gentlepath.com
Addiction-Oriented Books, Videos & CDs
Publisher
N.A.I.C.S.: 513130
Patrick J. Carnes *(Founder)*

INTERNATIONAL INTEGRATED SOLUTIONS, LTD.
137 Commercial St Ste 100, Plain-
view, NY 11803
Tel.: (516) 396-6700
Web Site: http://www.iisl.com
Year Founded: 1990
Sales Range: $25-49.9 Million
Emp.: 35
IT Solutions
N.A.I.C.S.: 541519
John Iacone *(CEO)*
Jay Singh *(Mgr-Practice)*

INTERNATIONAL INTIMATES, INC.
180 Madison Ave 7th Fl, New York,
NY 10016-5267
Tel.: (212) 213-4848   **DE**
Web Site: http://www.renerofe.com
Year Founded: 1986
Sales Range: $10-24.9 Million
Emp.: 250
Womens Clothing Designer & Mfr
N.A.I.C.S.: 424350
Alexandra Eloriaga *(Coord-Design &
Product Dev)*
Andy Leffler *(Asst Controller)*
Paul Coraggio *(Gen Mgr)*
Susan Lee *(Mgr-Production)*
Vijay Kamra *(Mgr-Sls & Ops)*
Michele Goetz *(Coord-Pre-
Production)*
Leslie Mario *(Mgr-Production)*
Michael Roslin *(Dir-Sls & Mktg)*

INTERNATIONAL JUSTICE MISSION
PO Box 58147, Washington, DC
20037
Tel.: (703) 465-5495   **VA**
Web Site: http://www.ijm.org
Year Founded: 1994
Sales Range: $25-49.9 Million
Emp.: 194
Human Rights Protection Services
N.A.I.C.S.: 813311
Gary Haugen *(Pres & CEO)*
Gary Veurink *(Exec VP)*
Sean Litton *(Sr VP-Justice Ops)*
Rebecca Chan *(Sec)*
Lauren Weaver *(Treas & VP-Fin)*
Katy Akester *(VP-Advancement)*
Blair Burns *(Sr VP-Justice Ops)*
Kim Kerley *(Chief People Officer)*
Philip Langford *(VP-Intl Advance-
ment)*
Melissa Russell *(Sr VP-
Advancement-Global)*
Christa Hayden Sharpe *(VP-
Southeast Asia)*
Jeremy Steffens *(VP-Brand-Global &
Comm)*
Pablo Villeda *(VP-Ops-Latin America)*

INTERNATIONAL LIFE SCI-ENCES LLC

3200 West End Ave Ste 500, Nash-
ville, TN 37203
Tel.: (615) 783-1712
Medical Implants Mfr
N.A.I.C.S.: 339112
Jim Tyson *(VP-Sls & Mktg)*
Aaron C. Smith *(CEO)*
Mark Cohen *(Chm)*

INTERNATIONAL LONG-SHOREMEN'S ASSOCIATION, AFL-CIO
5000 W Side Ave, North Bergen, NJ
07047
Tel.: (212) 425-1200   **NJ**
Web Site: http://www.ilaunion.org
Year Founded: 1892
Sales Range: $10-24.9 Million
Emp.: 78
Family Support Services
N.A.I.C.S.: 624190
Virgil Maldonado *(VP)*

INTERNATIONAL MANAGE-MENT CONSULTANTS INC.
3 Great Vly Pkwy Ste 200, Malvern,
PA 19335-2551
Tel.: (610) 889-3600
Web Site:
http://www.imcconstruction.com
Year Founded: 1974
Sales Range: $10-24.9 Million
Emp.: 46
Provider of Nonresidential Construc-
tion Services
N.A.I.C.S.: 236220
Robert Cottone *(Pres & CEO)*
Michael Ryan *(VP-Preconstruction)*
Rick Reinhard *(Dir-Preconstruction)*

Subsidiaries:

IMC Inc. **(1)**
3 Great Valley Pkwy Ste 200, Malvern, PA
19355
Tel.: (610) 889-3600
Sales Range: $10-24.9 Million
Emp.: 100
Management Consulting Services
N.A.I.C.S.: 236220

INTERNATIONAL MANAGE-MENT CONSULTING INC.
590 Herndon Pkwy Ste 300, Hern-
don, VA 20170
Tel.: (703) 467-2970
Web Site: http://www.imci.net
Sales Range: $10-24.9 Million
Emp.: 65
Computer Integrated Systems Ser-
vices
N.A.I.C.S.: 541512
Mohammad Feizipour *(VP-
Technology)*
Roy A. Gross *(VP-Mktg & Bus Dev)*

INTERNATIONAL MANAGE-MENT SERVICES COMPANY
3633 Wheeler Rd Ste 350, Augusta,
GA 30909
Tel.: (706) 855-1014
Web Site: http://www.imsco.com
Year Founded: 1974
Sales Range: $100-124.9 Million
Emp.: 2,600
Transportation & Logistic Service
N.A.I.C.S.: 561330
L. M. Hall III *(Founder)*

Subsidiaries:

TFE Group Inc. **(1)**
3633 Wheeler Rd Ste 350, Augusta, GA
30909-6552
Tel.: (706) 855-1014
Web Site: http://www.tfegroup.com
Emp.: 7
Logistics Company
N.A.I.C.S.: 561330

Bob Cunningham *(Gen Counsel)*

INTERNATIONAL MANAGE-MENT SERVICES GROUP, INC.
725 Kapiolani Blvd Ste C103, Hono-
lulu, HI 96813
Tel.: (808) 566-7000   **HI**
Year Founded: 1972
Sales Range: $75-99.9 Million
Emp.: 5
Travel Agencies
N.A.I.C.S.: 561510
Raymond I. Miyashiro *(Pres)*

Subsidiaries:

Regal Travel, Inc. **(1)**
725 Kapiolani Blvd Ste C103, Honolulu, HI
96813
Tel.: (808) 566-7620
Web Site: http://www.regaltravel.com
Sales Range: $25-49.9 Million
Travel Agencies
N.A.I.C.S.: 561510

Rendezvous Tours, Inc. **(1)**
725 Kapiolani Blvd Ste C103, Honolulu, HI
96814
Tel.: (808) 593-2119
Web Site: http://www.rendezvoustours.com
Tour Operator
N.A.I.C.S.: 561520

INTERNATIONAL MARCH OF THE LIVING
2 W 45th St Ste 1500, New York, NY
10036
Tel.: (212) 869-6800   **NY**
Web Site: http://www.motl.org
Year Founded: 1993
Sales Range: $10-24.9 Million
Emp.: 3
Civic & Social Organization
N.A.I.C.S.: 813410
David Machlis *(Vice Chm)*
Eli Rubenstein *(Dir-Education)*

INTERNATIONAL MARINA GROUP, LP
11226 Indian Trl, Dallas, TX 75229
Tel.: (972) 488-1314   **TX**
Web Site: http://www.marinasintl.com
Year Founded: 2001
Sales Range: $1-9.9 Million
Emp.: 58
Marinas
N.A.I.C.S.: 713930
Marshall Funk *(Co-Founder)*
Stan Johnson *(Co-Founder)*
Jo Wilsmann *(Controller)*
John Swick *(VP-Field Ops)*
Gregg Kenney *(VP-Southeast)*
Jeff Rose *(VP-South)*
Layne Wilson *(Mgr-District Ops)*
Robert Faflik *(VP-Midwest)*
Andrew Barksdale *(VP-Field Ops)*
Baxter Underwood *(CEO)*
Courtenay Milliron *(VP-HR)*
Gavin McClintock *(Exec VP)*
Jack Brewer *(Co-Founder)*
James Phyfe *(Sr VP)*
Jason Hogg *(Sr VP-Investments)*
Meagan Thompson *(VP-Acctg)*
Rives Potts *(COO)*
Stephen Kurtz *(CTO)*

Subsidiaries:

Harborage Marina, LLC **(1)**
1110 3rd St S, Saint Petersburg, FL 33701
Tel.: (727) 821-6347
Web Site: http://www.harboragemarina.com
Marinas
N.A.I.C.S.: 713930
Brian Sweeney *(Gen Mgr)*

INTERNATIONAL MASONRY INSTITUTE

17101 Science Dr, Bowie, MD 20715
Tel.: (301) 291-2124   MD
Web Site: http://www.imiweb.org
Year Founded: 1970
Sales Range: $10-24.9 Million
Emp.: 118
Fundraising Services
N.A.I.C.S.: 813219
Eva Miller (Office Mgr)
Maria Viteri (Dir-Sustainability & Program Dev-Central Pennsylvania)
Dawn Lafey (Mgr-Mktg)
Brian E. Trimble (Dir-Pittsburgh)
Bob Arnold (Dir-Apprenticeship & Trng-Natl)
Bob Campbell (Dir-Missouri, Kansas & Nebraska)
David Collins (Dir-Indiana & Kentucky)
David Sovinski (Dir-Indus Dev-Natl)
John Bachenski (Dir-New York City)
Jonas Elmore (Dir-Natl Job Corps)
Keith Lashway (Dir-New York State)
Ken McKinney (Dir-Oregon)
Pat Conway (Dir-Wisconsin)
Rick Filloramo (Dir-Connecticut & Rhode Island)
Steve Bolognese (Dir-New England)
Theresa Indelli (Coord-Mktg)

INTERNATIONAL MATERIALS INC.

327 Plaza Real Ste 320, Boca Raton, FL 33432
Tel.: (610) 520-1980   PA
Web Site: http://www.inius.com
Year Founded: 1987
Sales Range: $10-24.9 Million
Emp.: 15
Brick, Stone & Related Materials Mfr
N.A.I.C.S.: 423320

INTERNATIONAL MEDIA PARTNERS, INC.

103 118th Ave SE Ste 100, Bellevue, WA 98005-3753
Tel.: (425) 455-5900   WA
Web Site:
  http://www.intlmediapartners.com
Year Founded: 1985
Sales Range: $10-24.9 Million
Emp.: 10
Media Buying Services
N.A.I.C.S.: 541810
Gordon D. Bryson (Pres)
Betsy J. Moseley (Exec VP)
Shirley Eclipse (Dir-Client Svcs)

INTERNATIONAL MEDICAL EQUIPMENT COLLABORATIVE

1620 Osgood St, North Andover, MA 01845
Tel.: (978) 557-5510   MA
Web Site:
  http://www.imecamerica.org
Year Founded: 1995
Sales Range: $25-49.9 Million
Medical Equipment Supply Services
N.A.I.C.S.: 423450
Thomas Keefe (Pres)
Phillip Haughey (Chm)
John Gould (Vice Chm)

INTERNATIONAL METALS & CHEMICALS GROUP

1 Pitcairn Pl Ste 1200, Jenkintown, PA 19046
Tel.: (215) 517-6000
Web Site: http://www.imc-group.com
Year Founded: 1983
Sales Range: $50-74.9 Million
Emp.: 150
Nonferrous Metals & Metallic Salts for Electroplating Industries Distr
N.A.I.C.S.: 334513
David Verlen (Exec VP)

INTERNATIONAL METALS EKCO LTD.

2777 E Washington Blvd, Los Angeles, CA 90023
Tel.: (323) 264-1615
Web Site:
  http://www.ekcometals.com
Year Founded: 1962
Sales Range: $10-24.9 Million
Emp.: 50
Nonferrous Scrap Metals Whslr
N.A.I.C.S.: 423930
Ely Keenberg (Pres)

INTERNATIONAL MISSING PERSONS FOUNDATION

23016 Lake Forest Dr, Laguna Hills, CA 92653
Tel.: (949) 429-8271
Sales Range: $10-24.9 Million
Community Support Services
N.A.I.C.S.: 561990
Donald Smith (Pres)
Doug Suchesk (CFO & VP)
Craig Bogard (Sec)

INTERNATIONAL MOTOR CARS

5000 Auth Way, Suitland, MD 20746
Tel.: (301) 423-8400
Web Site: http://www.motorcars-intl.com
Sales Range: $50-74.9 Million
Emp.: 150
New & Used Car Dealers
N.A.I.C.S.: 441110
Everett Hellmuth (Pres)

INTERNATIONAL OCD FOUNDATION

18 Tremont St Ste 308, Boston, MA 02108
Tel.: (617) 973-5801   MA
Web Site: http://www.iocdf.org
Year Founded: 1987
Sales Range: $1-9.9 Million
Emp.: 9
Health Care Srvices
N.A.I.C.S.: 621111
Jeff Szymanski (Exec Dir)
Pamela Lowy (Dir-Ops)
Marissa Keegan (Program Dir)
Jeff Smith (Dir-Dev)
Denise Egan Stack (Pres)
Susan B. Dailey (VP)
Michael J. Stack (Treas)
Shannon A. Shy (Sec)

INTERNATIONAL OFFICE SUPPLY

301 E Calton Rd, Laredo, TX 78041
Tel.: (956) 723-2332   TX
Web Site: http://www.patria.com
Year Founded: 1984
Rev.: $11,573,518
Emp.: 21
Office Forms & Supplies
N.A.I.C.S.: 459410
Jorge Gonzalez Sr. (Pres)

INTERNATIONAL PACKAGING CORP.

517 Mineral Spring Ave, Pawtucket, RI 02860
Tel.: (401) 724-1600
Web Site: http://www.presbox.com
Sales Range: $25-49.9 Million
Emp.: 600
Metal Boxes for Packing & Shipping Mfr
N.A.I.C.S.: 332439
Gordon Smith (Sr Mgr-Accts)
Gus Vale (Gen Mgr)
Frank Duffy (VP)
Jared Fogel (Acct Mgr)
John Lopez (Gen Mgr)

INTERNATIONAL PARTNERSHIP FOR HUMAN DEVELOPMENT

722 E Market St Ste 100, Leesburg, VA 20176
Tel.: (703) 443-1691   VA
Web Site: http://www.iphd.org
Year Founded: 1984
Sales Range: $25-49.9 Million
Emp.: 7
Community Care Services
N.A.I.C.S.: 624190
Alicia C. Payne (Accountant)
Michael E. Pruzensky (Mgr-Shipping)
Susan Langley (Coord-Program)
Traian Patru (Mgr-Program)
Daniel E. Shaughnessy (Treas)

INTERNATIONAL PICTURES CORP.

19528 Ventura Blvd 371, Tarzana, CA 91356
Tel.: (818) 725-7621
Rev.: $116,677,511
Emp.: 6
Motion Picture Production & Distr
N.A.I.C.S.: 512110

INTERNATIONAL PLANNING ALLIANCE, LLC

300 Broadacres Dr Ste 175, Bloomfield, NJ 07003-3153
Tel.: (973) 244-4420
Web Site:
  http://www.planningalliance.com
Sales Range: $10-24.9 Million
Emp.: 100
Provider of Financial Services
N.A.I.C.S.: 524210
David R. Alter (CEO)
Gerald J. Clericuzio (Chm)
Linda Bellofatto (Dir-Ops)
Anthony P. Campanile (Mgr-Sls)
Steven Cucinelli (Mgr-Sls)
Meta DiPietro (Dir-Mktg)
Mark D. Lowe (Sr VP-Investment)
Donna Matelski (Assoc Dir-New Bus)
Howard A. Udoff (Sr VP-Brokerage)
Melanie A. Werling (Officer-Compliance)

INTERNATIONAL PLANT NUTRITION INSTITUTE

3500 Pkwy Ln Ste 550, Peachtree Corners, GA 30092-2844
Tel.: (770) 447-0335   DE
Web Site: http://www.ipni.net
Year Founded: 1935
Sales Range: $10-24.9 Million
Emp.: 16
Health Care Information Management Services
N.A.I.C.S.: 621999
Svetlana Ivanova (VP)
Steven J. Couch (VP & Asst Sec)
Adrian M. Johnston (VP)
Paul E. Fixen (Sr VP)

INTERNATIONAL PORT SERVICES, INC.

2115 NW 115 Ave, Miami, FL 33172
Tel.: (305) 418-4070   FL
Web Site:
  http://www.interportservices
  miami.com
Year Founded: 2000
Sales Range: $1-9.9 Million
Emp.: 500
Freight Transportation Arrangement
N.A.I.C.S.: 488510
Anthony Pupo (VP)
Esteban Szalay (Pres)

INTERNATIONAL PRECIOUS METALS INCORPORATED

64040 Harvest Moon Rd, Desert Hot Springs, CA 92240
Tel.: (760) 799-9462   NV
Year Founded: 2013
Precious Metals Exporter
N.A.I.C.S.: 423940
Roger J. Robertson (Pres, CEO, CFO,Chief Acctg Officer, Treas & Sec)

INTERNATIONAL PRECISION COMPONENTS CORPORATION

28468 N Ballard Dr, Lake Forest, IL 60045
Tel.: (847) 234-1111
Web Site:
  http://www.ipcclakeforest.com
Year Founded: 1984
Sales Range: $25-49.9 Million
Emp.: 320
Plastics Pipe & Pipe Fitting Mfr
N.A.I.C.S.: 326122
Rene Velasquez (VP-Sls & Mktg)

INTERNATIONAL PRODUCT DEVELOPMENT CO., INC.

11744 NE Ainsworth Cir, Portland, OR 97220
Tel.: (503) 257-7500
Web Site: http://www.ipdusa.com
Year Founded: 1963
Sales Range: $1-9.9 Million
Emp.: 26
All Other Motor Vehicle Parts Mfr
N.A.I.C.S.: 336390
Michael Bernardi (Mgr-Pur)
Bryan Cottrell (Mgr-Mktg)
Bud Cowgill (Mgr-Logistics)
Kevin Rutledge (Dir-Tech & Inventory)
Andrew Carlson (Mgr-Returns)
Chris Delano (VP)
Stuart Hockman (Pres)

INTERNATIONAL PURCHASE SYSTEMS, INC.

534 Furnace Dock Rd, Cortlandt Manor, NY 10567
Tel.: (914) 788-5400   NY
Web Site:
  http://www.internationalpurchase
  systems.com
Rev.: $10,000,000
Emp.: 5
General Merchandise
N.A.I.C.S.: 424990
Michael Brooks (Pres)

INTERNATIONAL READING ASSOCIATION, INC.

800 Barksdale Rd, Newark, DE 19714-8139
Tel.: (302) 731-1600
Web Site: http://www.reading.org
Year Founded: 1956
Sales Range: $1-9.9 Million
Educational Support Services
N.A.I.C.S.: 611710
Marcie Craig Post (Exec Dir)
Diane Barone (Chm)
William Teale (Vice Chm)
Stephen Sye (Assoc Exec Dir)
Christine Heesters (Dir-Bus Solutions)
Shannon Fortner (Dir-Educational Resources)
Dan Mangan (Dir-Public Affairs)
Linda Martson (Dir-Fin)

INTERNATIONAL RESCUE COMMITTEE, INC.

International Rescue Committee, Inc.—(Continued)

Tel.: (212) 551-3000 NY
Web Site: https://www.rescue.org
Year Founded: 1933
Sales Range: $700-749.9 Million
Emp.: 1,454
Rescue Services
N.A.I.C.S.: 624190
Patricia Long (VP)
Carrie Simon (Gen Counsel)
John Keys (Dir-Great Lakes Reg)
David Miliband (Pres & CEO)
David M. Johnson (CFO)
Katherine Farley (Co-Chm)
Tracy R. Wolstencroft (Co-Chm)
Glenda Burkhart (Sec)
Gordon Smith (Treas)
Ciaran Donnelly (Sr VP-Intl Programs)
Jodi Nelson (Sr VP-Policy & Practice)
Madlin Sadler (Sr VP-Ops & Strategy)
Amanda Seller (Sr VP-Revenue)
Jennifer Sime (Sr VP-United States Programs)
Dana Freyer (Interim Gen Counsel)
Jane Waterman (Sr VP-Europe)
Alyoscia D'Onofrio (Sr Dir-Technical-Governance)
Amanya Michael Ebye (Reg Dir-Democratic Republic of Congo)
Bob Kitchen (Dir-Emergency Preparedness & Response Unit)
Bre Jefferson (VP-Awards Mgmt Unit)
Chris Honsberger (Chief Global Supply Chain Officer)
Colleen Ryan (VP-Comm)
Danusia Dzierzbinski (Controller)
Debi Wheeler (Reg Dir-Atlantic)
Eleanor Dougood (Deputy Exec Dir-United Kingdom)
Ellen Beattie (Sr Dir-Program Quality-United States Programs)
Em Fackler (CIO)
Emmanuel D'Harcourt (Sr Dir-Health)
Giselle Holloway (Dir-Dev)
Hans Van de Weerd (VP-United States Programs)
Jeannie Annan (Sr Dir-Res Evaluation & Learning)
Jelle Boot (Acting Chief HR Officer)
Judson Flanagan (VP-Ops-Intl)
Kate Phillips-Barasso (Dir-Policy & Advocacy)
Kurt Tjossem (Reg Dir-Horn, East Africa & Zimbabwe)
Mania Boyder (VP-Dev)
Mark Schnellbaecher (Reg Dir-Syria Reg Response)
Mireille Cronin Mather (Reg Dir-Pacific)
Nazanin Ash (VP-Public Policy & Advocacy)
Nicole Behnam (Sr Dir-Technical-Violence Prevention & Response Technical Unit)
Pamela Kournetas (Sr Dir-Fin Plng & Analysis)
Paul Taylor (Reg Dir-West Africa, Sahel, Central African Republic & Haiti)
Radha Rajkotia (Sr Dir-Technical-Economic Recovery & Dev)
Ravi Gurumurthy (Chief Innovation Officer)
Robin Dunn Marcos (Sr Dir-Resettlement & Processing)
Sanjayan Srikanthan (Dir-Policy & Practice-United Kingdom)
Sanna Johnson (Reg Dir-Asia, Caucasus & Middle East)
Sarah Smith (Sr Dir-Technical-Education)
Tineke Ceelen (Exec Dir)

INTERNATIONAL RESEARCH

AND EXCHANGES BOARD
1275 K St NW Ste 600, Washington, DC 20005
Tel.: (202) 628-8188 NJ
Web Site: http://www.irex.org
Year Founded: 1991
Sales Range: $50-74.9 Million
Emp.: 170
Community Development Services
N.A.I.C.S.: 624190
Rebecca Bell Meszaros (Assoc VP-Education)
Kristin M. Lord (Pres)
Kevin Rubio (Exec VP-Strategy & Dev)
Mike Graham (CFO)

INTERNATIONAL RESTAU-RANT DISTRIBUTORS, INC.
150 Semoran Commerce Pl, Apopka, FL 32703
Tel.: (407) 886-6691 FL
Web Site:
http://www.irdequipment.com
Sales Range: $10-24.9 Million
Emp.: 15
Restaurant Equipment & Supplies
N.A.I.C.S.: 423440
Michael Schutz (CEO)

INTERNATIONAL RESTAU-RANT SERVICES
Amelia Dist Ctr 23 Ema St, Guaynabo, PR 00968
Tel.: (787) 273-3131
Web Site: http://www.chilispr.com
Sales Range: $10-24.9 Million
Emp.: 30
Restaurant Owner & Operator
N.A.I.C.S.: 722410
Arthur Jotic (Pres)

INTERNATIONAL REVOLVING DOOR COMPANY
2138 N 6th Ave, Evansville, IN 47710-2814
Tel.: (812) 425-3311
Web Site:
http://www.internationalrevolving
doors.com
Sales Range: $1-9.9 Million
Emp.: 40
Revolving & Swing Doors Mfr
N.A.I.C.S.: 332321
Steve Lowe (Controller)
Mel Vinson (Mgr-Estimating)
Jim Kratochvil (Gen Mgr)

INTERNATIONAL ROBOTICS, INC.
2001 Palmer Ave Ste LL1, Larchmont, NY 10538
Tel.: (914) 630-1060
Web Site:
http://www.internationalrobotics.com
Year Founded: 1972
Sales Range: $10-24.9 Million
Emp.: 4
Social Robotics Communications Tools for Special Needs Individuals Mfr
N.A.I.C.S.: 541720
Robert Doornick (Pres & CEO)
Marie Modica (Comptroller)

INTERNATIONAL ROLLFORMS INC.
8 International Ave, Sewell, NJ 08080
Tel.: (856) 228-7100 NJ
Web Site:
http://www.internationalrollform.com
Year Founded: 1970
Sales Range: $10-24.9 Million
Emp.: 80
Mfr of Nonferrous Rolling & Drawing

N.A.I.C.S.: 331491
Jack Vosbikian (Pres)

INTERNATIONAL SEAWAY TRADING CORPORATION
851 Broken Sound Pkwy NW, Boca Raton, FL 33487
Tel.: (561) 447-4433 OH
Web Site: http://www.seaway-trading.com
Year Founded: 1956
Sales Range: $25-49.9 Million
Emp.: 10
Importer of Athletic Footwear, Cold Weather Footwear & Leather & Synthetic Sandals
N.A.I.C.S.: 424340
Harvey K. Gerdy (CEO)

INTERNATIONAL SOCIETY FOR PHARMACEUTICAL ENGINEERING INC.
7200 Wisconsin Ave Stte 305, Bethesda, MD 20814
Tel.: (301) 364-9201 FL
Web Site: http://www.ispe.org
Year Founded: 1980
Sales Range: $10-24.9 Million
Pharmaceutical Engineering Association
N.A.I.C.S.: 813920
David Everett (Dir-IT-North America)
Wendy Perez (Sr Dir-HR)
Mark Hernick (CFO & VP-Admin)
Wendy Sturley (VP-Mktg, Comm & Membership)
Meredith Pritchett (Mgr-Acctg-North America)
Julie Amburn (Coord-Acctg-North America)
Susan Obarski (Dir-Project Mgmt Office-North America)
Debbie W. Miller (Coord-Admin-North America)
Diane Munda (Mgr-Sls Ops, Exhibits & Sponsorships-North America)
Robin Lane (Coord-Sls, Exhibits & Sponsorships-North America)
John Donaldson (Dir-Continuing Education-North America)
Marianne Bock (Dir-Continuing Education)
Rameeza Shaikh (Program Mgr-Continuing Education)
Jennifer Bayne (Coord-Continuing Education-North America)
Kindra Bess (Dir-Event Ops)
Barbara Tyler (Coord-Event Ops-North America)
Carol Winfield (Dir-Regulatory Ops-North America)
Maria Robertson (Sr Dir-Mktg Comm)
Renee Smith (Assoc Dir-Mktg Comm)
Jessica Bleess (Mgr-Digital Strategy & Web Content-North America)
Lynda Goldbach (Mgr-Guidance Documents-North America)
Amy Loerch (Mgr-Publ-North America)
Alicia Montes (Sr Dir-Trng-North America)
Brenda Kendrick (Coord-Pub Trng-North America)
Barbara Peck (Mgr-Community & Indus Recognition-North America)
Ciara Durkan (Sr Dir-Member & Component Rels)
Alain Van Damme (Mgr-Member Svcs-North America)
Linda Walls (Mgr-Data Production & Analysis-North America)
Thomas Zimmer (VP-European Ops)
Tammy Belcher (Coord-Acctg-North America)
James A. Breen (Chm)

Joanne R. Barrick (Sec)
Thomas B. Hartman (Pres & CEO)
Frances M. Zipp (Vice Chm)
Amy Henry (Mgr-Mktg Comm)

INTERNATIONAL SOCIETY FOR THE STUDY OF XENOBI-OTICS
2025 M St Nw Ste 800, Washington, DC 20036
Tel.: (202) 367-1160 NJ
Web Site: http://www.issx.org
Year Founded: 1981
Sales Range: $1-9.9 Million
Medical Professional Association
N.A.I.C.S.: 813920
Steve Kemp (Exec Dir)
Bill Smith (Pres)
John O. Miners (Sec)
Charles Crespi (Treas)

INTERNATIONAL SOCIETY OF AUTOMATION
67 T W Alexander Dr, Research Triangle Park, NC 27709
Tel.: (919) 549-8411 NC
Web Site: http://www.isa.org
Year Founded: 1945
Sales Range: $10-24.9 Million
Emp.: 54
Engineering & Technology Standard Accrediation Services
N.A.I.C.S.: 561990
Brian J. Curtis (Member-Exec Bd & Sec)
Nicholas P. Sands (Member-Exec Bd)
Shari L. S. Worthington (Member-Exec Bd)
Thomas Devine (Treas)
Brad Carlberg (Member-Exec Bd)
Eric C. Cosman (Member-Exec Bd)
William Walsh (Member-Exec Bd)
Patrick J. Gouhin (CEO & Exec Dir)
Steven W. Pflantz (Pres & Member-Exec Bd)
Mary Ramsey (Exec Dir)

INTERNATIONAL SOCIETY ON THROMBOSIS AND HAEMOS-TASIS, INC.
610 Jones Ferry Rd Ste 205, Carrboro, NC 27510
Tel.: (919) 929-3807 NC
Web Site: http://www.isth.org
Year Founded: 1991
Sales Range: $10-24.9 Million
Emp.: 10
Disease Research Services
N.A.I.C.S.: 813212
Thomas Reiser (Exec Dir)
Louise M. Bannon (Dir-Mktg & Membership)
Lisa Astorga (Dir-Meetings)
Cary Clark (Mgr-Program & Education)

INTERNATIONAL SOFTWARE SYSTEMS, INC.
7337 Hanover Pky Ste A, Greenbelt, MD 20770
Tel.: (301) 982-9700
Web Site: http://www.issi-software.com
Year Founded: 1995
Sales Range: $1-9.9 Million
Emp.: 48
Computer System Design Services
N.A.I.C.S.: 541512
Bhaskar Ganti (Pres & CEO)
Mark Anderson (VP-Tech)
Soma Sundaram Pappu (Project Mgr)
Seema Raj (Mgr-Bus Dev)
Zeeshan Muhammad (Engr-Software)
V. C. Sekhar Parepalli (Product Mgr)

INTERNATIONAL SOLUTIONS GROUP, INC.
1110 Elden St Ste 201, Herndon, VA 20170
Tel.: (703) 766-8800
Web Site: http://www.isgit.com
Year Founded: 2002
Sales Range: $10-24.9 Million
Emp.: 140
Information Technology Solutions & Services
N.A.I.C.S.: 541519
Ravi Puli (Pres & CEO)

INTERNATIONAL SPECIAL RISKS
50 Salem St Bldg B 3rd Fl, Lynnfield, MA 01940
Tel.: (781) 295-0270
Web Site: http://www.isr-insurance.com
Sales Range: $10-24.9 Million
Emp.: 17
Insurance Services, Dealing Mostly with Marine Equipment
N.A.I.C.S.: 524210
Steve Macquarrie (Pres)
Bonnie Levine (Sr VP)
Ansley Martin (Mgr-Claims)
Wendi Corcoran (Sr VP)

INTERNATIONAL STEEL SERVICES, INC.
Foster Plz 7 661 Andersen Dr, Pittsburgh, PA 15220
Tel.: (412) 922-9100   PA
Web Site: http://www.issi-amrox-usa.com
Year Founded: 1989
Sales Range: $10-24.9 Million
Emp.: 159
Design, Construction & Operation of Hydrochloric Acid Recycling Centers; Production & Marketing of Iron Oxide
N.A.I.C.S.: 541330
Michael Sieckmann (VP-Mktg)
Edgar Robert (Dir-Special Projects)
Andrew Roth (Engr-Process Automation)
Satish Wadhawan (Exec VP)
George Grachen (Mgr-Civil Dept)
John Kelman (Vice Chm)
Malvin Sander (Gen Counsel & Sr VP)

Subsidiaries:

Magnetics International, Inc.   (1)
1111 N State Rd 149, Burns Harbor, IN 46304   **(100%)**
Tel.: (219) 763-1199
Sales Range: $10-24.9 Million
Emp.: 20
Mfr of Iron Oxide Powder; Acid Recycling Facility
N.A.I.C.S.: 325180
Don Kuschel (Dir-Ops)

INTERNATIONAL STUDENT VOLUNTEERS
4848 Lakeview Ave Ste 100-A, Yorba Linda, CA 92886
Tel.: (714) 779-7392   CA
Web Site: http://www.isvolunteers.org
Year Founded: 1983
Sales Range: $10-24.9 Million
Emp.: 41
Educational Support Services
N.A.I.C.S.: 611710
Narelle Webber (Co-Founder & Program Dir)
Deanna Mathewson (Dir-Education-Intl)
John R. Sykes (Exec Dir)
Randy Sykes (Co-Founder)
Rick Webb (Dir-Tours-Intl)

INTERNATIONAL STUDIES ABROAD, INC.
1112 W Ben White Blvd, Austin, TX 78704
Tel.: (512) 480-8522
Web Site: http://studiesabroad.com
Year Founded: 1987
Educational Programs
N.A.I.C.S.: 611710
Rafael Hoyle (Mng Dir & Sr VP)
Arturo Artaza (Sr VP-University Rels & Mktg)
Jennifer Acosta (Sr VP-Enrollment Mgmt)
Angel Eguiluz Pacheco (Sr VP-Global Ops)
Gustavo Artaza (Sr VP-Strategic Initiatives)
Susan Farley (VP-Institutional Agreements & Fin Affairs)
Deborah Morrison (VP-Australia Programs & Strategic Initiatives)
Mark Gallovic (VP-Strategic Partnerships)
Lisette Montoto (VP-Academic Affairs)
Laura Reyez Ruiz (Assoc VP-Italian, South Africa & Pacific Ops)
Jimmy Brazelton (Assoc VP-Asia Programs & Strategic Initiatives)
Dominick Luciano (Assoc VP-University Rels & Mktg)
Laura Pierce Weldon (Assoc VP-Custom Programs)
Ivan Lopez (Assoc VP-High School Programs)
Alonso De La Fuente (Assoc VP-Academic Records)
Mark Mackintosh (Assoc Dir-Academic Resources)
David Puente (Reg VP-Academic Affairs & Global Mobility)
Rebecca Anderson (Dir-Enrollment Mgmt)

INTERNATIONAL TEFL ACADEMY, INC.
916 W Diversey Pkwy, Chicago, IL 60614
Tel.: (773) 634-9900
Web Site:
    http://www.internationalteflacademy.com
Year Founded: 2010
Sales Range: $1-9.9 Million
Emp.: 40
Educational Support Services
N.A.I.C.S.: 611710
Bruce Jones (Co-Founder & Pres)
Karen Crone (Co-Founder & Dir-Student Affairs & Ops)
Havvah Holl (Mgr-Student Affairs)
John Bentley (Dir-Content Dev)
Jessie Smith (Mktg Mgr)

INTERNATIONAL THERMAL SYSTEMS, LLC
4697 W Greenfield Ave, Milwaukee, WI 53214
Tel.: (414) 672-7700
Web Site: http://www.itsllcusa.com
Rev.: $13,600,000
Emp.: 126
Industrial Process Furnace & Oven Mfr
N.A.I.C.S.: 333994
Mike Hintze (COO)
Chris Johnson (Mgr-Engrg)
Doug Haberlein (Mgr-Sls)
Joe Zhao (Mgr-R&D)
Keith Skadahl (Plant Mgr & Mgr-Mfg)
Larry Peters (Engr-Field Svcs)
Linda Wood (Coord-HR & Payroll)
Pam Kniess (Coord-Traffic)
Matthew Zea (Engr-Applications)
Mikel Blaauw (Engr-Electrical)

INTERNATIONAL TOOL MANUFACTURING
7108 51st Ave, Woodside, NY 11377
Tel.: (718) 446-0711   NY
Web Site: http://www.itmtools.com
Year Founded: 1987
Sales Range: $25-49.9 Million
Emp.: 17
Drill Bits Mfr
N.A.I.C.S.: 423830
Berardo Paradiso (Pres)

INTERNATIONAL TOOLING SOLUTIONS LLC
731 Broadway Ave NW, Grand Rapids, MI 49504-5247
Tel.: (616) 459-8285
Web Site: http://www.its-mtc.com
Sales Range: $25-49.9 Million
Emp.: 120
Metal Stamping Dies, Jigs & Fixtures Mfr
N.A.I.C.S.: 561499

Subsidiaries:

ITS Maghielse LLC   (1)
731 Broadway Ave NW, Grand Rapids, MI 49504
Tel.: (616) 459-8285
Web Site: http://www.its-mtc.com
Sales Range: $10-24.9 Million
Emp.: 93
Mfr of Metal Stamping Dies, Jigs & Fixtures
N.A.I.C.S.: 561499

INTERNATIONAL TRANSPORTATION CORP.
3204 E Platte Ave, Colorado Springs, CO 80909
Tel.: (719) 570-1122
Web Site:
    http://www.intermountaincoach.com
Rev.: $30,000,000
Emp.: 25
Bus Distr
N.A.I.C.S.: 423110
Dan Meyer (CEO)
Steve Francom (Pres)

INTERNATIONAL TRUCKS OF HOUSTON
8900 North Loop E, Houston, TX 77029
Tel.: (713) 674-3444
Web Site:
    http://www.internationaltrucksofhouston.com
Rev.: $67,400,000
Emp.: 100
Trucks, Tractors & Trailers: New & Used
N.A.I.C.S.: 441110
Edward A. Kyrish (Chm & Pres)
Rose Miller (Treas & Sec)
Dwayne Kyrish (VP)

INTERNATIONAL TURF INVESTMENT CO., INC.
3001 Street Rd, Bensalem, PA 19020
Tel.: (215) 639-9000   DE
Investment Holding Company
N.A.I.C.S.: 551112
Watche A. Manoukian (Owner)

Subsidiaries:

Greenwood Racing Inc.   (1)
3001 St Rd, Bensalem, PA 19020 **(78.96%)**
Tel.: (215) 639-9000
Web Site: http://www.parxracing.com
Sales Range: $550-599.9 Million
Holding Company; Racetrack & Casino Operator
N.A.I.C.S.: 551112
Robert W. Green (Chm)
William E. Hogwood (Deputy Chm)
Eric Hausler (CEO)

Subsidiary (Domestic):

Bensalem Racing Association, Inc.   (2)
2999 St Rd, Bensalem, PA 19020 **(100%)**
Tel.: (215) 639-9000
Web Site: http://www.parxcasino.com
Sales Range: $100-124.9 Million
Emp.: 1,000
Horse Racing Association
N.A.I.C.S.: 813910
Robert W. Green (Chm)
Joseph Wilson (COO)

Greenwood Gaming & Entertainment, Inc.   (2)
3001 Street Rd, Bensalem, PA 19020 **(100%)**
Tel.: (215) 639-9000
Web Site: http://www.parxcasino.com
Sales Range: $350-399.9 Million
Emp.: 1,500
Casino Operator; Gambling & Entertainment Services
N.A.I.C.S.: 713210
Robert W. Green (Chm)
Carrie Nork Minelli (Dir-Adv & PR)
Anthony Faranca (Gen Mgr)

Keystone Turf Club, Inc.   (2)
3001 St Rd, Bensalem, PA 19020 **(100%)**
Tel.: (215) 639-9000
Web Site: http://www.parxracing.com
Rev.: $44,900,000
Racetrack Operator
N.A.I.C.S.: 711212

INTERNATIONAL UNION OF PAINTERS AND ALLIED TRADES
7234 Pkwy Dr, Hanover, MD 21076
Tel.: (410) 564-5900
Web Site: https://www.iupat.org
Year Founded: 1887
Emp.: 140,000
Professional Development Training Services
N.A.I.C.S.: 611430

INTERNATIONAL VIDEOCONFERENCING, INC.
180 Adams Ave Ste 100, Hauppauge, NY 11788
Tel.: (631) 273-5800
Web Site: http://www.ivci.com
Sales Range: $10-24.9 Million
Emp.: 95
Tele Conferencing Services
N.A.I.C.S.: 561499
Robert Swing (CEO)
Charles Macli (Pres)
Tim Hennen (Sr VP-Sys)
Karen Cantalupo (VP)

INTERNATIONAL VOYAGER HOLDINGS, INC.
Overlook at Great Notch 150 Clove Rd, Little Falls, NJ 07424-0410
Tel.: (973) 256-3234
Web Site:
    http://www.internationalvoyager.com
Year Founded: 2001
Sales Range: $1-9.9 Million
Emp.: 16
Holding Company: Collection of Six Unique Travel Companies Assisting with Travel-Related Information
N.A.I.C.S.: 551112
John Maguire (Pres & CEO)
Lea Nielsen (Dir-Corp Dev)

INTERNATIONAL WATERJET PARTS, INC.
1145 85th Ave SE, Tumwater, WA 98501
Tel.: (360) 338-4920   ID
Web Site: http://www.iwpwaterjet.com
Ultra-High Pressure Waterjet Cutting Machine Component Distr
N.A.I.C.S.: 423810

International Waterjet Parts, Inc.—(Continued)

Chris Goodson (Mgr-Sls-Global)

INTERNATIONAL WHOLESALE SUPPLY, INC.

2265 Swanson Ste B, Lake Havasu City, AZ 86403
Tel.: (928) 764-7777
Web Site: http://www.shopiws.com
Sales Range: $10-24.9 Million
Emp.: 6
Durable Goods Whslr
N.A.I.C.S.: 423990
Linda Nash (Pres)

INTERNATIONAL WINE & SPIRITS OF LOUISIANA, INC.

4927 Bloomfield St, Jefferson, LA 70121-1004
Tel.: (504) 736-9577
Web Site: http://www.iwsla.com
Sales Range: $10-24.9 Million
Emp.: 10
Wine Mfr
N.A.I.C.S.: 312130
Floriano Taviani (VP)

INTERNATIONAL YOUTH FOUNDATION

1 E Pratt St Ste 701, Baltimore, MD 21202
Tel.: (410) 951-1500   IL
Web Site: http://www.iyfnet.org
Year Founded: 1990
Sales Range: $25-49.9 Million
Emp.: 94
Youth Care Services
N.A.I.C.S.: 624110
Samantha Barbee (CFO & Exec VP-Fin, Admin & IT)
Peter Shiras (Exec VP-Bus Dev)
Jim Peirce (VP-Strategic Plng & Outreach)
Karen Conklin (Controller)

INTERNET CORPORATION FOR ASSIGNED NAMES & NUMBERS

12025 Waterfront Dr Ste 300, Los Angeles, CA 90094
Tel.: (310) 823-9358
Web Site: http://www.icann.org
Year Founded: 1998
Sales Range: $1-9.9 Million
Emp.: 100
Internet Services
N.A.I.C.S.: 541512
Daniel P. Halloran (Deputy Gen Counsel)
Denise Michel (VP-Policy Dev)
Tanzanica S. King (Mgr)
Thomas Spiller (VP-Europe)
Francisco Arias (Dir-Technical Svcs)
Indra Dosanjh (Dir-Sys Integration)
Jacqui Cook (Dir-Product Mgmt)
Kim Lerch (Dir-Customer Svc)
Mary Wong (Sr Dir-Policy-US)
Megan Bishop (Coord-Bd Ops)
Michelle Bright (Sr Mgr-Bd Content)
Scott Swedorski (Founder)
Susanna Bennett (COO & Sr VP)
Goran Marby (Pres & CEO)
Cyrus Namazi (Sr VP-Global)
Michael Goldstein (Dir-Brand Mgmt)
Michael Goldstein (Dir-Brand Mgmt)

INTERNET COWBOY VENTURES LLC

3518 Fremont Ave N Ste 598, Seattle, WA 98103
Web Site:
http://www.internetcowboy.com
Year Founded: 2005
Investment Company
N.A.I.C.S.: 523999

Vivek Bhaskaran (Mng Partner)

Subsidiaries:

Making Sense LLC   (1)
17806 IH-10 W Ste 300, San Antonio, TX 78257
Web Site: http://www.makingsense.com
Software Design Services
N.A.I.C.S.: 513210
Cesar Donofrio (Principal)
Damian Donofrio (Co-Founder & Pres)
Nacho Caldentey (CPO)
Sergio Marchetti (COO)
Juan Fazzini (CTO)

INTERNET FOR CONTINUING EDUCATION INC.

2088 Highway 130 N, Monmouth Junction, NJ 08852
Tel.: (732) 821-7800
Rev.: $14,677,097
Emp.: 44
Convention & Show Services
N.A.I.C.S.: 524210

INTERNET PRODUCTION INC.

1080 W County Rd E, Saint Paul, MN 55126
Tel.: (651) 717-4300   MN
Web Site: http://www.iproduction.com
Year Founded: 1991
Sales Range: $1-9.9 Million
Emp.: 20
Publishing Software & Website Hosting
N.A.I.C.S.: 513210
Steve Laliberte (Pres)

INTERNET SCIENCES, INC.

667 Madison Ave 5th Fl, New York, NY 10065
Tel.: (212) 823-6272   DE
Web Site:
http://www.internetsciences.co
Year Founded: 2016
Liabilities: $182,828
Net Worth: ($182,828)
Earnings: ($72,857)
Fiscal Year-end: 12/31/22
Information & Communication Technology Services
N.A.I.C.S.: 541512
Lynda Chervil (Chm, Pres, CEO, CFO, Treas & Sec)
Matthew Liotine (Sr Mng Dir & CTO)
Christopher Morris (Sr Mng Dir & CFO)
Gregory Scott Buczynski (Sr Mng Dir & CFO)

INTERNET SERVICES CORPORATION

1300 Altura Rd, Fort Mill, SC 29715
Tel.: (803) 547-9100
Web Site: http://www.internet-services.com
Sales Range: $50-74.9 Million
Emp.: 300
Cassettes Recording
N.A.I.C.S.: 423690
Jeff Yager (Pres)
Gary Baker (Project Mgr-Audio & Video)
Danny Brady (Mgr-Global Media Dev)
Daniel Brown (Mgr-Tax)

INTERNET TRUCKSTOP GROUP, LLC

222 N Plymouth Ave, New Plymouth, ID 83655
Tel.: (888) 364-1189   DE
Web Site: http://truckstop.com
Transportation Technology & Freight Matching Solutions
N.A.I.C.S.: 488999
Paris Cole (CEO)

Subsidiaries:

Registry Monitoring Insurance Services, Inc.   (1)
5703 Corsa Ave 1st fl, Westlake Village, CA 91362
Tel.: (818) 933-6350
Web Site: http://www.registrymonitoring.com
Sales Range: $1-9.9 Million
Emp.: 160
Insurance Agencies & Brokerages
N.A.I.C.S.: 524210
David Chang (Mgr-Customer Svc)
Greg Sadikoff (Controller)
Nick Anderson (VP-Sls)

INTERNETFITNESS.COM, INC.

780 5th Ave Ste 200, King of Prussia, PA 19406
Tel.: (484) 751-0794   DE
Sales Range: $25-49.9 Million
Emp.: 52
Fitness Equipment Whslr & Online Retailer
N.A.I.C.S.: 423910
William Olson (Pres & CEO)

Subsidiaries:

Smooth Fitness   (1)
780 5th Ave Ste 200, King of Prussia, PA 19406
Tel.: (484) 751-0794
Web Site: http://www.smoothfitness.com
Sales Range: $10-24.9 Million
Emp.: 34
Online Fitness Equipment Retailer
N.A.I.C.S.: 459110
Richard Hebert (Pres & CEO)

INTERNEWS NETWORK

PO Box 4448, Arcata, CA 95518-4448
Tel.: (707) 826-2030   CA
Web Site: http://www.internews.org
Year Founded: 1986
Sales Range: $50-74.9 Million
Emp.: 110
News Publishing Services
N.A.I.C.S.: 513110
Jennifer Cobb (VP-Comm & Outreach)
Erica Feldkamp (VP-Admin)
Kathleen Reen (VP-ICT Policy & Programs)
Shannon England (VP-Global Dev)

INTERNEWS NETWORK

1133 15th St NW Ste 350, Washington, DC 20005
Tel.: (202) 833-5740
Web Site: http://www.internews.org
Year Founded: 1982
Sales Range: $25-49.9 Million
Emp.: 600
Broadcasting Network Services
N.A.I.C.S.: 516120
Simone Otus Coxe (Chm)
Jeanne Bourgault (Pres & CEO)
Marjorie Rouse (Sr VP-Programs)
Erica Feldkamp (VP-Admin)
Jennifer Cobb (VP-Comm & Outreach)
Kat Duffy (VP-Tech Programs-Global)
Mark Frohardt (Sr VP-Strategic Practice)
Shannon England (VP-Dev-Global)

INTEROCEANIC CORPORATION

7 Renaissance Sq, White Plains, NY 10601
Tel.: (914) 762-7800   NY
Web Site: http://www.ioccorp.com
Year Founded: 1983
Bulk Chemical Fertilizer Distr
N.A.I.C.S.: 424690
Elio A. Mazzella (Pres & CEO)

INTEROP TECHNOLOGIES, LLC

13500 Powers Ct Ste 200, Fort Myers, FL 33912
Tel.: (239) 425-3000
Web Site:
http://www.interoptechnologies.com
Year Founded: 2002
Sales Range: $10-24.9 Million
Emp.: 100
Wireless Telecommunications & Software Applications
N.A.I.C.S.: 517112
John Dwyer (Pres & CEO)
Patricia M. Heath (CFO)
Stephen J. Zitnik (CTO & Exec VP)
Margaret M. Dwyer (Gen Counsel)
John Bickford (Sr VP)
Jim Dwyer III (VP-Strategic Dev)

INTERPACIFIC GROUP INC.

576 Beale St, San Francisco, CA 94105-2019
Tel.: (415) 781-7767   CA
Year Founded: 1986
Equity Investments & Retail Holdings Firm
N.A.I.C.S.: 523999
Dave Smith (Pres)

INTERPACIFIC INVESTORS SERVICES, INC.

119 Cedar St, Seattle, WA 98121-1231
Tel.: (206) 269-5050   WA
Web Site: http://www.iisbonds.com
Year Founded: 1970
Sales Range: $150-199.9 Million
Emp.: 25
Retail Brokerage of Bonds, Mutual Funds & Stocks
N.A.I.C.S.: 523150
Gary Lundgren (Principal)
Brian Kline (Exec VP-Trading Dept)
Tiffany Hodkin (Acctg Mgr)

INTERPARK LLC

200 N LaSalle St Ste 1400, Chicago, IL 60601
Tel.: (312) 935-2800   DE
Web Site:
http://www.interparkholdings.com
Year Founded: 1997
Parking Lots & Garages Investor & Operator
N.A.I.C.S.: 812930
J. Marshall Peck (Founder & Pres)
Michael Prussian (Chief Investment Officer)
Andrew Runge (CFO)
Frith C. Crandall (Gen Counsel & Sec)
Robert Higgins (Sr VP-HR)
Andrew R. McLaughlin (Sr VP-Acq)
John Pjescich (VP-Acq & Asset Mgmt)
David Nelson (VP-IT)
Chad Wells (VP-Fin & Real Estate)
James Mueller (COO)

Subsidiaries:

PreFlight LLC   (1)
200 N LaSalle St Ste 1400, Chicago, IL 60601   (100%)
Tel.: (800) 332-7275
Web Site:
http://www.preflightairportparking.com
Airport Parking Lots & Garages Operator
N.A.I.C.S.: 812930

INTERPLASTIC CORPORATION

1225 Willow Lk Blvd, Saint Paul, MN 55110-5145
Tel.: (651) 481-6860   MN
Web Site: http://www.interplastic.com

Year Founded: 1959
Sales Range: $150-199.9 Million
Emp.: 500
Synthetic Resins & Companion Items;
Sheet Molding Compound Mfr &
Sales
N.A.I.C.S.: 325211
Steve Wetzel *(Mgr-Natl Sls)*
Daryl Francis *(Bus Mgr)*
David Herzog *(Dir-Res & Bus Dev)*
Lou Ross *(Dir-Tech Transfer &
Product/Process Optimization)*
Peter Surmak *(Bus Mgr-Vinyl Esters
& Engineered Resins)*

Subsidiaries:

Interplastic Corporation   (1)
2015 NE BoardWay, Minneapolis, MN
55413   **(100%)**
Tel.: (651) 481-6860
Web Site: http://www.interplastic.com
Sales Range: $10-24.9 Million
Emp.: 55
Synthetic Resin Mfr
N.A.I.C.S.: 325211
Bob DeRoma *(Sr VP)*

Interplastic Corporation   (1)
5019 Hunt St Mid America Industrial Pk,
Pryor, OK 74361   **(100%)**
Tel.: (918) 825-2756
Web Site: http://www.interplastic.com
Sales Range: $10-24.9 Million
Emp.: 53
Mfr of Plastic Resins
N.A.I.C.S.: 325211

Interplastic Corporation Molding Prod-
ucts Div.   (1)
1545 S Olive St, South Bend, IN
46619-4295   **(100%)**
Tel.: (574) 234-1105
Web Site: http://www.interplastic.com
Sales Range: $10-24.9 Million
Emp.: 50
Bulk & Sheet Molding Compound
N.A.I.C.S.: 326299
Troy Wade *(Gen Mgr)*

North American Composites   (1)
300 Apollo Dr, Circle Pines, MN
55014   **(100%)**
Tel.: (651) 766-6892
Web Site: http://www.nacomposites.com
Sales Range: $10-24.9 Million
Emp.: 22
Distr of Products To Reinforce Fiberglass
Industry
N.A.I.C.S.: 325211
Richard Rodriguez *(VP & Mgr-Bus-East)*

Silmar Resins   (1)
3535 Latonia Ave, Frankfort, KY
41015   **(100%)**
Tel.: (859) 292-7400
Sales Range: $25-49.9 Million
Emp.: 55
Synthetic Resins
N.A.I.C.S.: 424690

INTERPLAY LEARNING INC.
1717 W 6th St #405, Austin 78703
Tel.: (855) 980-2525
Web Site:
    https://www.interplaylearning.com
Year Founded: 2016
Industrial Training Services
N.A.I.C.S.: 611430
Doug Donovan *(CEO)*

Subsidiaries:

Industrial Training International,
Inc.   (1)
9428 Old Pacific Hwy, Woodland, WA
98674
Web Site: http://www.iti.com
Sales Range: $1-9.9 Million
Emp.: 200
Industrial Training Services
N.A.I.C.S.: 611430
Billie Snow *(VP-Fin & Human Capital)*
Zack Parnell *(Pres & CEO)*
Darlene Parnell *(Founder & CFO)*
Jonathan Parnell *(Sr VP-Product Dev)*
Amanda Long *(VP-Sls)*

INTERPOWER CORPORATION
100 Interpower Ave, Oskaloosa, IA
52577
Tel.: (641) 673-5000
Web Site: http://www.interpower.com
Year Founded: 1975
Sales Range: $10-24.9 Million
Emp.: 83
Whslr of Electrical Apparatus &
Equipment
N.A.I.C.S.: 335931
Robert D. Wersen *(Pres)*
Dave Krutzfeldt *(Owner)*
Ralph Bright *(Mgr-Mktg)*
Pat Moore *(Mgr-Sls)*

INTERPRETERS UNLIMITED, INC.
11199 Sorrento Valley Rd Ste 203,
San Diego, CA 92121
Tel.: (800) 726-9891
Web Site:
    http://www.interpretersunlimited.com
Year Founded: 1970
Sales Range: $10-24.9 Million
Translation & Interpretation Services
N.A.I.C.S.: 541930
Shamus Ali Sayed *(VP-Sls & Mktg)*
Sayed Ali *(VP-Sls & Mktg)*
Summer Sayed *(Mgr-Ops)*

Subsidiaries:

Albors & Associates, Inc.   (1)
2789 Wrights Rd, Oviedo, FL 32765
Tel.: (407) 678-8634
Web Site: http://www.alborsalnet.com
Emp.: 10
Translation & Interpretation Services; Medi-
cal Transportation Services
N.A.I.C.S.: 541930
Kim Glassco *(Mgr)*

INTERPRINT INC.
7111 Hayvenhurst Ave, Van Nuys, CA
91406
Tel.: (818) 989-3600
Web Site:
    http://www.interprintusa.com
Sales Range: $10-24.9 Million
Emp.: 100
Commercial Printing Services
N.A.I.C.S.: 323111
Micheal Jacobs *(Owner)*

INTERPRISE/SOUTHWEST IN-TERIOR & SPACE DESIGN, INC.
5080 Spectrum Dr, Addison, TX
75001
Tel.: (972) 385-3991   TX
Web Site:
    http://www.interprisedesign.com
Year Founded: 1981
Sales Range: $10-24.9 Million
Emp.: 40
Interior Design Services
N.A.I.C.S.: 541410
Katherine C. Berg *(Chm & CEO)*

INTERPROSE INC.
2635 Steeplechase Dr, Reston, VA
20191
Tel.: (703) 860-0577
Web Site:
    http://www.interprosepr.com
Sales Range: $50-74.9 Million
Emp.: 20
Public Relations Agency
N.A.I.C.S.: 541820
Vivian Kelly *(Founder & CEO)*
Cathy Palmen *(Pres)*
Becky Obbema *(Acct Dir)*
Renee Ayer *(Acct Mgr)*

INTERRA CREDIT UNION
300 W Lincoln Ave, Goshen, IN
46526
Tel.: (574) 534-2506   IN
Web Site: http://www.interracu.com
Year Founded: 1932
Sales Range: $25-49.9 Million
Emp.: 247
Credit Union
N.A.I.C.S.: 522130
Andrew Gangwer *(Chief Admin Offi-
cer)*
David Birky *(Chief Strategy Officer)*
Rex Hochstedler *(CFO)*
Tim Yoder *(Chm)*
Andy Marshall *(COO)*
Kelly Gast *(VP-HR)*
Darrin McLaughlin *(Sr VP-Tech)*
Blair Juarez *(Asst VP-Project Mgmt)*
Phil Wiens *(Chief Lending Officer &
Sr VP)*
Angela Pletcher *(Sr VP-Enterprise
Risk Mgmt)*
Joel Richard *(Sr VP-Member Experi-
ence)*
Amy Sink *(CEO)*
Ron Cannon *(VP-Mortgage Lending)*
Stephanie Weldy *(Sls Mgr-Residential
Mortgage)*
Tara Hudson *(Asst VP-Member Solu-
tions)*

INTERRA HEALTH, INC.
1675 N Barker Rd Ste 200, Brook-
field, WI 53045
Tel.: (414) 755-4898
Web Site:
    http://www.interrahealth.com
Year Founded: 2001
Rev.: $2,000,000
Emp.: 30
Health & Allied Services
N.A.I.C.S.: 621999
Derek Boyce *(Pres)*
Dana Skinner *(Dir-Wellness Svcs)*
Ryan Sommers *(Principal & VP-Bus
Dev)*
Laura Collins *(Acct Mgr)*

INTERREL CONSULTING PARTNERS
1000 Ballpark Way Ste 304, Arling-
ton, TX 76011
Tel.: (972) 735-8716
Web Site: http://www.interrel.com
Year Founded: 1996
Sales Range: $1-9.9 Million
Emp.: 30
IT Services & Solutions
N.A.I.C.S.: 519290
Edward Roske *(CEO)*
Gwen Coyle *(Pres)*
Ali Flint *(CFO)*
Ron Guadagno *(VP-Sls)*

INTERSCHOLASTIC TRADING COMPANY LLC
1004A O'Reilly Ave 3rd Fl, San Fran-
cisco, CA 94129
Tel.: (415) 563-4100
Web Site: http://www.interschola.com
Year Founded: 2004
Sales Range: $1-9.9 Million
Emp.: 11
Sales of Surplus Goods & School
Supplies
N.A.I.C.S.: 423990

INTERSEA FISHERIES LTD.
777 Ter Ave Ste 509, Hasbrouck
Heights, NJ 07604
Tel.: (201) 692-9000
Web Site: http://www.intersea-
fish.com
Sales Range: $10-24.9 Million
Emp.: 7
Fish, Fresh

N.A.I.C.S.: 424460
Walter J. Enders *(Controller)*
William Gilman *(Pres)*

INTERSECT GROUP
10 Glenlake Pkwy Ste 300 S, Atlanta,
GA 30328
Tel.: (770) 500-3636
Web Site:
    http://www.theintersectgroup.com
Year Founded: 2006
Sales Range: $10-24.9 Million
Emp.: 213
Consulting, Staffing & Advisory Firm
N.A.I.C.S.: 541618
Keith Ordan *(Partner)*
Rebecca Rogers Tijerino *(CEO)*
Edwin Miller *(CEO)*
Matt Beyer *(Dir-Bus Analytics)*

INTERSOCIETAL ACCREDITA-TION COMMISSION
6021 University Blvd Ste 500, Ellicott
City, MD 21043
Tel.: (443) 973-3239   MD
Web Site: http://www.intersocietal.org
Year Founded: 1996
Sales Range: $10-24.9 Million
Emp.: 55
Medical Laboratory Operator
N.A.I.C.S.: 621511
Bonnie Miller *(CFO & Chief Admin
Officer)*
Tammie Sloper *(Dir-Mktg & Comm)*
Kenneth Kirby *(CIO)*
Erin Riggleman *(Coord-Admin)*
Julie Kincaid *(Mgr-Comm)*
Mary Lally *(Deputy CEO & Dir-
Accreditation)*
Mike Ralph *(Dir-IT Svcs)*
David Sacks *(Treas & Sec)*

INTERSOUTH PARTNERS
102 City Hall Plz Ste 200, Durham,
NC 27701
Tel.: (919) 493-6640
Web Site: http://www.intersouth.com
Year Founded: 1985
Rev.: $780,000,000
Venture Capital
N.A.I.C.S.: 523999
Dennis J. Dougherty *(Mng Gen Part-
ner)*

INTERSPIRO INC.
10225 82nd Ave, Pleasant Prairie, WI
53158-5800
Tel.: (262) 947-9901   CT
Web Site: http://www.interspiro.com
Sales Range: $75-99.9 Million
Emp.: 25
Mfr of Breathing Apparatus; Diving
Equipment
N.A.I.C.S.: 423850
Mike Brookman *(Pres)*

INTERSTAR MARKETING & PUBLIC RELATIONS
610 Grove St, Fort Worth, TX 76102-
5555
Tel.: (817) 332-6522   TX
Web Site:
    http://www.interstargroup.com
Year Founded: 1975
Sales Range: $1-9.9 Million
Emp.: 10
Public Relations Agency
N.A.I.C.S.: 541820
Jane E. Schlansker *(Pres & CEO)*
Catherine Whittington *(Acct Exec)*
Jane Cohen *(Acct Exec)*
Kathy Korge Albergate *(Sr VP)*

INTERSTATE BATTERY SYS-TEM OF AMERICA INC.

Interstate Battery System of America
Inc.—(Continued)

12770 Merit Dr Ste 400; Dallas, TX
75251-1296
Tel.: (972) 991-1444   **TX**
Web Site:
http://www.interstatebatteries.com
Year Founded: 1991
Sales Range: $10-24.9 Million
Emp.: 800
Electrical Batteries Distr
N.A.I.C.S.: 335910
Norm Miller *(Chm)*
Chris Willis *(VP-HR)*

Subsidiaries:

Interstate Battery System of America
Inc.
12770 Merit Dr Ste 400, Dallas, TX 75251-
1296
Tel.: (972) 991-1444
Web Site: http://www.interstatebattery.com
Rev.: $63,400,000
Emp.: 720
Electrical Batteries
N.A.I.C.S.: 423120
Mitch Lee *(Reg Mgr)*

Interstate Battery System of Hawaii
Inc.   **(1)**
94 1037 Leokane St, Waipahu, HI 96797-
2209
Tel.: (808) 676-6000
Web Site: http://www.corporate.interstatebat
teries.com
Sales Range: $10-24.9 Million
Battery Distr
N.A.I.C.S.: 423120

INTERSTATE CATERERS

2101 Parker Ave, South Plainfield, NJ
07080
Tel.: (908) 822-0500
Web Site:
http://www.interstatecaterers.com
Year Founded: 1987
Sales Range: $10-24.9 Million
Emp.: 44
General Line Grocery Whslr
N.A.I.C.S.: 424410
Augy Fernandes *(Owner)*

INTERSTATE CHEMICAL CO., INC.

2797 Freedland Rd, Hermitage, PA
16148-9027
Tel.: (724) 981-3771
Web Site:
http://www.interstatechemical.com
Year Founded: 1968
Sales Range: $25-49.9 Million
Emp.: 300
Markets & Distributes Chemicals
N.A.I.C.S.: 424690
Albert R. Puntureri *(Chm & Pres)*

Subsidiaries:

Interstate Chemical   **(1)**
23247 W Eames St, Channahon, IL 60410-
3150
Tel.: (815) 467-1777
Web Site: http://www.interstatechemical.com
Sales Range: $25-49.9 Million
Emp.: 60
Distribution of Specialty Chemicals
N.A.I.C.S.: 424690

United Erie   **(1)**
1432 Chestnut St, Erie, PA 16502-1741
Tel.: (814) 456-7561
Web Site: http://www.unitederie.com
Sales Range: $25-49.9 Million
Emp.: 18
Allied Product Mfr
N.A.I.C.S.: 424690
Rich Sorillo *(Dir-Mktg)*

INTERSTATE COMMODITIES INC.

7 Madison St, Troy, NY 12180-4929

Tel.: (518) 272-7212   **NY**
Web Site: http://www.icigrain.com
Year Founded: 1947
Sales Range: $1-4.9 Billion
Emp.: 12
Producer & Retailer of Feed Ingredi-
ents & Grains
N.A.I.C.S.: 424510

Subsidiaries:

RM Railcars LLC   **(1)**
7 Madison St, Troy, NY 12180
Tel.: (800) 833-3636
Web Site: http://www.icigrain.com
Passenger Car Leasing Services
N.A.I.C.S.: 532112
Kelly Doris *(Controller)*

INTERSTATE COMPANIES, INC.

21568 Highview Ave, Lakeville, MN
55044
Tel.: (952) 854-2044
Web Site: http://www.istate.com
Year Founded: 1957
Rev.: $152,000,000
Emp.: 1,100
Engines, Transportation, Power Gen-
eration Equipment & Bearing System
Mfr
N.A.I.C.S.: 423610
Bob Woodward *(Exec VP-Ops Mgmt)*
Carl Brown *(VP-Ops-East Reg)*
Larry Schwartz *(CFO)*
Travis Penrod *(CEO)*
Chris Dacus *(VP-Ops-East Reg)*
John Hartleib *(VP-Ops-West Reg)*
Russ Dreyer *(VP-Ops-Assembly Sys)*
Michael Masters *(Pres-Interstate
Power Sys)*

Subsidiaries:

I-State Truck Center   **(1)**
11152 Courthouse Blvd, Inver Grove
Heights, MN 55077
Tel.: (651) 455-9775
Web Site: http://www.istatetruck.com
Rev.: $27,757,466
Emp.: 61
Truck Distr
N.A.I.C.S.: 441110
Mike Thomas *(Mgr-Fin)*
Adam Clarey *(Mgr-Fin)*

Subsidiary (Domestic):

I State Truck Center   **(2)**
3615 Ulm N Frontage Rd, Great Falls, MT
59404
Tel.: (406) 454-1311
Web Site: http://www.istatetruck.com
Sales Range: $10-24.9 Million
Emp.: 20
Freight Trucks & Other Motor Vehicles
Sales & Services
N.A.I.C.S.: 423110
Herb Wyatt *(Mgr-Parts)*

The Rocky Mountain Truck
Center   **(2)**
310 Alaska Frntage Rd, Belgrade, MT
59714
Tel.: (406) 388-1505
Web Site: http://www.billingstruckcenter.com
Sales Range: $10-24.9 Million
Emp.: 25
Retailer of Trucks
N.A.I.C.S.: 333998

INTERSTATE CONSTRUCTION CO.

3511 Farm Bank Way, Grove City,
OH 43123
Tel.: (614) 539-1188
Rev.: $15,000,000
Emp.: 25
Multi-Family Dwellings, New Con-
struction
N.A.I.C.S.: 236116
Dwight D. Kincaid *(Pres)*

INTERSTATE DIESEL SER-VICE, INC.

4901 Lakeside Ave, Cleveland, OH
44114
Tel.: (216) 881-0015   **OH**
Web Site: http://www.interstate-
mcbee.com
Year Founded: 1947
Sales Range: $10-24.9 Million
Emp.: 100
Fuel System Repair, Motor Vehicle
N.A.I.C.S.: 336310
Alfred J. Buescher *(Pres)*
Brad Buescher *(VP)*
Bruce Bollinger *(Controller)*

INTERSTATE ELECTRIC COM-PANY INCORPORATED

2240 Yates Ave, Los Angeles, CA
90040
Tel.: (323) 724-0420
Web Site: http://www.iecdelivers.com
Sales Range: $10-24.9 Million
Emp.: 95
Signs, Electrical
N.A.I.C.S.: 423440
Ed Urlik *(Pres)*
Rebekah Hogan *(Mgr-Mktg)*

INTERSTATE ELECTRICAL SERVICES CORP.

70 Treble Cove Rd, North Billerica,
MA 01862
Tel.: (978) 667-5200
Web Site: http://www.iesc1.com
Rev.: $53,058,772
Emp.: 600
Electronic Controls Installation
N.A.I.C.S.: 238210
Erik Richman *(Dir-Safety)*
Carl Brand *(Exec VP)*
James Alibrandi *(Pres)*
John Sloane *(VP)*
Gary Eason *(Dir-Fin)*
Brian Lewis *(VP)*
Luiza Mills *(Dir-HR)*
Michael D. Gould *(Dir-Sls & Mktg)*
Peter Cicolini *(VP)*

INTERSTATE ELECTRICAL SUPPLY, INC.

2300 2nd Ave, Columbus, GA 31901
Tel.: (706) 324-1000
Web Site: http://www.interstate-
electrical.com
Year Founded: 1973
Sales Range: $10-24.9 Million
Emp.: 80
Electrical Products Distr
N.A.I.C.S.: 423610

INTERSTATE ENERGY LLC

PO Box 16108, Duluth, MN 55816-
2619
Tel.: (218) 834-2666   **MN**
Web Site:
http://www.comooilandpropane.com
Year Founded: 1946
Sales Range: $25-49.9 Million
Emp.: 115
Fuel Oil Dealers
N.A.I.C.S.: 457210
Joe Stariha *(Pres & CFO)*
Will Norman *(Co-Pres & COO)*

Subsidiaries:

Como Oil & Propane   **(1)**
2 Hwy 61 E, Grand Marais, MN 55604
Tel.: (218) 387-1165
Rev.: $450,000
Emp.: 6
Liquefied Petroleum Gas Dealers
N.A.I.C.S.: 424720
Rich Palmer *(Asst Mgr)*

INTERSTATE ENGINEERING CORP.

193 Jefferson Ave, Salem, MA 01970
Tel.: (978) 744-8883   **MA**
Year Founded: 1973
Sales Range: $10-24.9 Million
Emp.: 20
Mechanical Contracts
N.A.I.C.S.: 238220
Arnold Pike *(Pres)*

INTERSTATE EQUIPMENT COMPANY

1604 Salisbury Rd, Statesville, NC
28677
Tel.: (704) 873-9048
Sales Range: $10-24.9 Million
Emp.: 3
Road Construction & Maintenance
Machinery
N.A.I.C.S.: 423810
Franklin H. Eller *(Pres)*

INTERSTATE FUEL SYSTEMS, INC.

8221 Alpine Ave, Sacramento, CA
95826-4708
Tel.: (916) 457-6572
Web Site:
http://www.interstateoil.com
Year Founded: 1986
Sales Range: $10-24.9 Million
Emp.: 100
Petroleum Product Whslr
N.A.I.C.S.: 424720
Dominic Dacay *(Mgr)*

INTERSTATE GAS SUPPLY INC.

6100 Emerald Pkwy, Dublin, OH
43016
Tel.: (614) 923-1000
Web Site: http://www.igsenergy.com
Rev.: $219,757,788
Emp.: 40
Natural Gas Distr
N.A.I.C.S.: 221210
Scott L. White *(Pres)*

Subsidiaries:

DPL Energy Resources, Inc.   **(1)**
1065 Woodman Dr, Dayton, OH 45432
Tel.: (937) 224-6000
Web Site:
http://www.daytonohioelectricsupply.com
Sales Range: $350-399.9 Million
Retail Electric Energy Marketer
N.A.I.C.S.: 221122

INTERSTATE GROUP HOLD-INGS, INC.

5801 Rolling Rd, Springfield, VA
22152
Tel.: (703) 569-2121   **VA**
Web Site:
http://www.moveinterstate.com
Year Founded: 1998
Holding Company; Moving & Logis-
tics Services
N.A.I.C.S.: 551112
Mark Lundgren *(VP/Gen Mgr-
Interstate Van Lines)*
Arthur E. Morrissette IV *(CEO)*
Margie Malloy *(Exec VP-Quality &
Customer Svc)*
Albert Greene *(VP-Economics & Bus
Analysis)*
Ron Granville *(VP & Gen Mgr-
Residential & Comml Svcs)*
Mark Lundgren *(VP & Gen Mgr-
Interstate Van Lines & Inc.)*
Dave Roe *(Controller)*
Jude J. Covas *(Chm)*
Arthur E. Morrissette IV *(CEO)*
Kenneth Morrissette Jr. *(Corp Coun-
sel & VP)*

Subsidiaries:

Ambassador Worldwide Moving,
Inc.   (1)
22455 Powers Ct, Sterling, VA
20166   **(100%)**
Tel.: (703) 260-0100
Sales Range: $25-49.9 Million
Emp.: 50
Moving & Relocation Services
N.A.I.C.S.: 484110

American Red Ball Transit Co.
Inc.   (1)
1335 Sadlier Cir E Dr, Indianapolis, IN
46239-1051
Tel.: (800) 733-8139
Web Site: http://www.redball.com
Moving Services
N.A.I.C.S.: 484210
Katrina Blackwell *(Partner)*

Interstate International, Inc.   (1)
5801 Rolling Rd, Springfield, VA 22152
Tel.: (703) 569-2121
International Relocation Services
N.A.I.C.S.: 484210
Ruth Moritz *(VP & Gen Mgr)*

Interstate Moving Systems, Inc.   (1)
5801 Rolling Rd, Springfield, VA
22152-1064   **(100%)**
Tel.: (703) 569-2121
Web Site: http://www.interstatevanlines.com
Sales Range: $25-49.9 Million
Emp.: 50
Provide Moving Services
N.A.I.C.S.: 488510
Arthur E. Morrissette *(Pres & CEO)*
Ron Gallier *(VP-Quality Control & HR)*

Interstate Relocation Services,
Inc.   (1)
5801 Rolling Rd, Springfield, VA 22152
Tel.: (703) 923-1600
Web Site: http://www.invan.com
Emp.: 100
Provider of Full Service Relocation Management Services
N.A.I.C.S.: 488510
Bud Morrissette *(Pres)*

Interstate Van Lines, Inc.   (1)
5801 Rolling Rd, Springfield, VA 22152-
1064
Tel.: (703) 569-2121
Web Site: http://www.moveinterstate.com
Sales Range: $100-124.9 Million
Emp.: 300
Local, Interstate, Long Distance & International Household Goods Carrier; Storage Facilities
N.A.I.C.S.: 488510
Mark Lundgren *(VP & Gen Mgr)*
Arthur E. Morrissette IV *(CEO)*
Mark Lundgren *(VP & Gen Mgr)*
Jude J. Covas *(Chm)*
Sang Han *(CFO & Exec VP)*
Ron Granville *(VP & Gen Mgr-Residential & Comml Svcs)*

INTERSTATE HIGHWAY CONSTRUCTION
7135 S Tucson Way, Englewood, CO
80112
Tel.: (303) 790-9100
Web Site: http://www.ihcquality.com
Rev.: $130,000,000
Emp.: 240
Highway & Street Paving Contractor
N.A.I.C.S.: 237310
J. Kenyon Schaeffer *(CEO)*
Calvin K. Thomas *(VP & Mgr-Corp Equipment)*
John L. Edwards *(VP-Bus Dev)*
Martin L. Holt *(Mgr-Quality Control)*
Tony Maccioli *(Dir-Safety & Environmental)*
Matt Randall *(Project Mgr)*
John D. Medberry *(VP-Admin)*

INTERSTATE HIGHWAY SIGN CORP
7415 Lindsey Rd, Little Rock, AR
72206-3829

Tel.: (501) 490-4242   AR
Web Site:
    http://www.interstatesigns.com
Year Founded: 1959
Sales Range: $10-24.9 Million
Emp.: 140
Mfr of Reflective Highway Directional Signs Used by the U.S. Interstate Highway System
N.A.I.C.S.: 339950
Bobby Brown *(Pres)*
Cathie Hamilton *(Sls Mgr)*
David Smallwood *(Mgr-Engrg)*

INTERSTATE HOME LOAN CENTER
535 Broadhollow Rd Ste A2, Melville,
NY 11747-3701
Tel.: (516) 938-0022   NY
Web Site:
    http://www.myequityloan.com
Year Founded: 1994
Sales Range: $25-49.9 Million
Emp.: 22
Mortgage Banker
N.A.I.C.S.: 522292
Alex J. Niven *(Pres)*
Nicholas Bucco *(Mgr-Sls)*
Robert Haufler *(Dir-Mktg Bus Dev)*
Colin Nupp *(Acct Exec)*

INTERSTATE INTERNATIONAL, INC.
Tel.: (775) 685-6000   DE
Year Founded: 1974
Holding Company
N.A.I.C.S.: 551112

Subsidiaries:

Interstate Truck Center, LLC   (1)
2110 S Sinclair Ave, Stockton, CA 95215-
1169
Tel.: (209) 944-5821
Web Site: https://www.itctrucks.com
Sales Range: $75-99.9 Million
Emp.: 163
Commercial Truck Rental, Sales & Service
N.A.I.C.S.: 423110
David T. Morganson *(Principal)*
Rickey Coslett *(Controller)*

Silver State International   (1)
2255 Larkin Cir, Sparks, NV 89431-6503
Tel.: (775) 685-6000
Web Site: https://ssitrucks.com
Sales Range: $25-49.9 Million
Emp.: 68
Commercial Truck & Bus Whslr
N.A.I.C.S.: 423110
Katie Brecke *(Mgr-Rental)*
Shasta Botts *(Controller)*
Kory Krug *(Mgr-Body Shop)*

INTERSTATE LOGISTICS GROUP, INC.
324 1st Ave N, Saint Petersburg, FL
33701
Tel.: (727) 822-9999
Web Site: http://www.interstatelg.com
Emp.: 50
Logistics & Transportation Services
N.A.I.C.S.: 541614
Tim Higham *(Pres & CEO)*

INTERSTATE LUMBER & MILL CORP.
184 S Water St, Greenwich, CT
06830
Tel.: (203) 531-8050
Web Site:
    http://www.interstatelumber.com
Rev.: $12,900,000
Emp.: 100
Lumber & Other Building Materials
N.A.I.C.S.: 444110
Sheldon Kahan *(Pres)*
Gary Schneidman *(CFO)*

INTERSTATE MECHANICAL CONTRACTORS, INC.
3200 Henson Rd, Knoxville, TN
37921
Tel.: (865) 588-0180
Web Site:
    http://www.interstatemechanics.com
Year Founded: 1982
Sales Range: $10-24.9 Million
Emp.: 150
Plumbing, Heating & Air-Conditioning Services
N.A.I.C.S.: 238220
Terry L. Self *(Pres & Owner)*
Robin G. Self *(Owner & Sec)*
Joe R. Webb *(COO)*
Amanda C. Yearwood *(CFO)*

INTERSTATE MOTOR TRUCKS INC.
1900 Sorenson Rd, Albert Lea, MN
56007
Tel.: (507) 373-0653
Web Site: http://www.imtrucks.com
Sales Range: $25-49.9 Million
Emp.: 30
Trucks, Tractors & Trailers: New & Used
N.A.I.C.S.: 441110
Terrance Kvenvold *(Pres)*
Michael Jacobs *(VP)*

INTERSTATE OIL COMPANY
8221 Alpine Ave, Sacramento, CA
95826
Tel.: (916) 457-6572
Web Site:
    http://www.interstateoil.com
Rev.: $15,400,000
Emp.: 30
Distr of Lubricating Oils & Greases
N.A.I.C.S.: 424720
Terrance W. Andrews *(Pres)*

INTERSTATE PERSONNEL SERVICES, INC.
3443 US Hwy 641 S, Murray, KY
42071
Tel.: (270) 753-1717   KY
Web Site: http://www.ptl-inc.com
Sales Range: $150-199.9 Million
Emp.: 825
Trucking
N.A.I.C.S.: 484121

INTERSTATE PRODUCTS, INC.
8260 Vico Ct, Sarasota, FL 34240
Tel.: (941) 377-8610   FL
Web Site:
    http://www.interstateproducts.com
Year Founded: 1996
Sales Range: $1-9.9 Million
Emp.: 6
Industrial Products Merchant Whslr
N.A.I.C.S.: 423840
Richard Eisenberg *(Pres)*
Scott Sagalow *(Owner)*
Melissa Jenkins *(Supvr-Admin)*

INTERSTATE REALTY MANAGEMENT CO.
3 E Stow Rd, Marlton, NJ 08053
Tel.: (856) 596-0500
Web Site: http://www.irmmgmt.com
Rev.: $22,600,000
Emp.: 700
Real Estate Managers
N.A.I.C.S.: 531210
Mark Morgan *(Pres)*
William Geddes *(Controller & Mgr-Risk)*
Andrea Babcock *(Mgr-Site)*
Sandy Cipollone *(Sr VP)*

INTERSTATE RESOURCES, INC.

1300 Wilson Blvd Ste 1075, Arlington,
VA 22209
Tel.: (703) 243-3355   DE
Web Site:
    http://www.interstateresources.com
Year Founded: 1982
Sales Range: $50-74.9 Million
Emp.: 850
Kraft Linerboard, Medium Board & Corrugated Shipping Containers Mfr
N.A.I.C.S.: 322130
Ramez G. Skaff *(Treas)*
Antonie Frem *(Chm & CEO)*
Pierre Khattar *(CFO)*
Jim Morgan *(Pres)*

Subsidiaries:

Interstate Container   (1)
501 Finnegan Ln, North Brunswick, NJ
08902-3458
Tel.: (732) 821-8100
Web Site:
    http://www.interstatecontainer.com
Emp.: 40
Mfr of Corrugated & Solid Fiber Boxes
N.A.I.C.S.: 322211

Interstate Container - Cambridge   (1)
903 Woods Rd, Cambridge, MD
21613-9469   **(100%)**
Tel.: (410) 221-7777
Web Site: http://www.iripaper.com
Sales Range: $10-24.9 Million
Emp.: 100
Waxed Containers
N.A.I.C.S.: 322211
Jeff Cormier *(Mgr-Sls)*
Pete Bugas *(Gen Mgr)*

Interstate Container Lowell, LLC   (1)
240 Industrial Ave E, Lowell, MA 01852
Tel.: (978) 458-4555
Web Site: http://www.iclowell.com
Sales Range: $10-24.9 Million
Emp.: 120
Corrugated Shipping Containers
N.A.I.C.S.: 322211
Mark Surprenant *(Gen Mgr)*
Kim Lodge *(Mgr-Customer Svcs)*

Interstate Container Reading
LLC   (1)
100 Grace St, Reading, PA 19611   **(100%)**
Tel.: (610) 376-7123
Sales Range: $25-49.9 Million
Emp.: 200
Corrugated Shipping Containers
N.A.I.C.S.: 322120
Brett Penhollow *(Mgr-HR)*

Interstate Paper LLC   (1)
2366 Interstate Rd, Riceboro, GA 31323
Tel.: (912) 884-3371
Web Site: http://www.interstatepaper.com
Sales Range: $25-49.9 Million
Emp.: 200
Mfr of Kraft Linerboard
N.A.I.C.S.: 322130
Amelia Milligan *(Coord-Traffic-Customer Svc)*
Meta Willis *(Mgr-Quality)*

Newport Timber LLC   (1)
2366 2 Interstate Rd, Riceboro, GA
31323-3900   **(100%)**
Tel.: (912) 884-3386
Web Site: http://www.iripaper.com
Sales Range: $10-24.9 Million
Emp.: 9
Timber Buying Agent, Chip Mill
N.A.I.C.S.: 423990
Pat Reddish *(Mgr-Wood Procurement)*
Tom Norris *(Gen Mgr)*

United Corrstack LLC   (1)
720 Laurel St, Reading, PA 19602-2718
Tel.: (610) 374-3000
Web Site: http://www.unitedcorrstack.com
Sales Range: $10-24.9 Million
Emp.: 80
Corrugating Medium
N.A.I.C.S.: 322130
Ken Day *(Mgr-Engrg & Maintenance)*

INTERSTATE RESTORATION GROUP, INC.

Interstate Restoration Group, Inc.—(Continued)

3401 Quorum Dr Ste 300, Fort
Worth, TX 76137
Tel.: (817) 293-0035   TX
Web Site:
  http://www.interstaterestoration.com
Year Founded: 1998
Emp.: 100
Emergency Response Restoration &
Reconstruction Services
N.A.I.C.S.: 562910
Stacy Mazur (CEO & Pres)

Subsidiaries:

Interstate Restoration Hawaii
LLC   (1)
94-1388 Moaniani St Unit #220, Waipahu,
HI 96797-6997
Tel.: (808) 484-4095
Web Site:
  http://www.interstaterestoration.com
Disaster Response Restoration & Recon-
struction Services
N.A.I.C.S.: 562910
David Heard (Dir-Mktg)
Raymond Gould (Pres)

Restorx of Texas, Ltd.   (1)
13717 Beta Rd, Dallas, TX 75244
Tel.: (972) 417-1111
Web Site: http://www.restorxtexas.com
Sales Range: $1-9.9 Million
Emp.: 35
Masonry Contractors
N.A.I.C.S.: 238140
Harley Jeanise (Pres & Gen Mgr)

INTERSTATE ROCK PROD-
UCTS INC.
42 S 850 W Ste 201, Hurricane, UT
84737
Tel.: (435) 635-2628
Web Site:
  http://www.interstaterockpro
  ducts.com
Sales Range: $10-24.9 Million
Emp.: 200
General Contracts Including Highway
& Street Construction
N.A.I.C.S.: 237310
Donald Stratton (Pres)
Craig Stratton (CFO)
Brian Stratton (VP)

INTERSTATE TELECOM CO-
OPERATIVE, INC.
312 4th St W, Clear Lake, SD 57226
Tel.: (605) 874-2181
Web Site: http://www.itc-web.com
Year Founded: 1954
Rev.: $33,421,054
Assets: $120,088,236
Liabilities: $42,561,288
Net Worth: $77,526,948
Earnings: $8,477,469
Emp.: 65
Fiscal Year-end: 03/31/19
Local Telephone Communications
N.A.I.C.S.: 517121

INTERSTATE WAREHOUSING
INC.
9009 Coldwater Rd, Fort Wayne, IN
46825-2072
Tel.: (260) 490-3000
Web Site:
  http://www.tippmanngroup.com
Year Founded: 1997
Sales Range: $10-24.9 Million
Emp.: 300
Provider of Refrigerated Warehousing
& Storage Services
N.A.I.C.S.: 493120
John V. Tippmann Sr. (Chm)

INTERSTATE WASTE SER-
VICES, INC.

300 Frank W Burr Blvd Ste 39, Tean-
eck, NJ 07666
Web Site:
  http://www.interstatewaste.com
Year Founded: 1998
Nonhazardous Waste Management
Disposal Services
N.A.I.C.S.: 562219
Michael DiBella (CEO)
Brian Giambagno (CFO)

Subsidiaries:

Action Carting Environmental Ser-
vices, Inc.   (1)
300 Frank W Burr Blvd Ste 39, Teaneck, NJ
07666
Web Site: http://www.actioncarting.com
Repair Services, Nec, Nsk
N.A.I.C.S.: 562910
Michael DiBella (CEO)

Kohler Waste Services Inc.   (1)
PO Box 354, Berkeley Heights, NJ 07922
Tel.: (908) 790-1100
Web Site:
  http://www.kohlerwasteservices.com
Waste Management Services
N.A.I.C.S.: 562998
Lynne Kohler (Pres)

Pequannock Disposal, Inc.   (1)
70 Riverdale Rd, Riverdale, NJ 07457
Tel.: (973) 835-3367
Web Site:
  http://www.pequannockdisposal.com
Sales Range: $1-9.9 Million
Emp.: 20
Nonhazardous Waste Treatment & Disposal
Services
N.A.I.C.S.: 562219
John DiMarco (VP)

INTERSTEEL INC.
3837 Fitzgerald Rd, Louisville, KY
40216
Tel.: (502) 778-9800
Web Site: http://www.interysteelinc.net
Rev.: $15,000,000
Emp.: 20
Commercial & Office Building Con-
struction Services
N.A.I.C.S.: 236220
Stanley Jsa (Pres)
Jeff Dowell (VP)

INTERSYSTEMS CORPORA-
TION
1 Memorial Dr, Cambridge, MA
02142
Tel.: (617) 621-0600
Web Site:
  http://www.intersystems.com
Year Founded: 1978
Sales Range: $350-399.9 Million
Emp.: 500
Computer Software Development
N.A.I.C.S.: 513210
Phillip T. Ragon (Founder, Owner &
CEO)
Paul Grabscheid (VP-Strategic Plng)
Matthew J. Nee (VP-Sls-North
America)
Susan M. Ragon (VP-Fin, Admin &
Recruitment)
John Paladino (VP-Client Svcs)
Christine Chapman (VP)
Steve Garrington (VP-Bus-Intl)
Jim Rose (VP-Mktg)

Subsidiaries:

InterSystems Australia Pty
Limited   (1)
Level 12 383 Kent Street, Sydney, 2000,
NSW, Australia
Tel.: (61) 2 9380 7111
Web Site: http://www.intersystems.com
Emp.: 114
Computer Software Development
N.A.I.C.S.: 513210
Kerry Stratton (Mng Dir)

InterSystems Australia Pty
Limited   (1)
Unit 11 663 Victoria Street, Abbotsford,
3067, VIC, Australia
Tel.: (61) 3 8416 9500
Web Site: http://www.intersystems.com.au
Emp.: 2
Computer Software Development
N.A.I.C.S.: 513210
Goeff Doherty (Reg Dir)

InterSystems B.V.   (1)
Regus Utrecht Papendorp Papendorpseweg
1000, Utrecht, 3528 BJ, Netherlands
Tel.: (31) 30 7991013
Web Site:
  http://www.intersystemsbenelux.com
Emp.: 13
Computer Software Development
N.A.I.C.S.: 513210
Thomas Leitner (Mng Dir)

Branch (Non-US):

InterSystems B.V. - Belgium
Branch   (2)
Medialaan 32/1, 1800, Vilvoorde, Belgium
Tel.: (32) 2 464 97 20
Web Site:
  http://www.intersystemsbenelux.com
Emp.: 1
Computer Software Development
N.A.I.C.S.: 513210
Thomas Leitner (Mng Dir)

InterSystems B.V. - Czech Republic
Branch   (2)
Slepa 1007/15 Praha 4, Lhotka, 142 00,
Prague, Czech Republic
Tel.: (420) 244 466 773
Web Site: http://www.intersystems.cz
Emp.: 6
Computer Software Development
N.A.I.C.S.: 513210
Martin Zubek (Mng Dir)

InterSystems B.V. - Finland
Branch   (2)
Kone Building Keilasatama 3, FIN-02150,
Espoo, Finland
Tel.: (358) 9 2510 7151
Web Site: http://www.intersystems.fi
Computer Software Development
N.A.I.C.S.: 513210

InterSystems B.V. - Israel
Branch   (2)
Herzelia Business Park Building G 9th
Floor, 85 Medinat HaYehudim Street,
46766, Herzliyya, Israel
Tel.: (972) 9 950 6664
Computer Software Development
N.A.I.C.S.: 513210

InterSystems B.V. - Saudi Arabia
Branch   (2)
Centria Mall Office Tower 4th Floor Suite
404, PO Box 9629, 11423, Riyadh, Saudi
Arabia
Tel.: (966) 1 288 5400
Computer Software Development
N.A.I.C.S.: 513210

InterSystems Chile   (1)
Edificio Technologico CORFO 3rd Floor Tu-
pungato 3850, Curauma, Valparaiso, Chile
Tel.: (56) 32 257 0188
Web Site: http://www.intersystemschile.cl
Computer Software Development
N.A.I.C.S.: 513210

InterSystems Chile   (1)
Avenida del Valle N 890 6 piso Ciudad Em-
presarial, Huechuraba, Santiago, Chile
Tel.: (56) 2 8926000
Web Site: http://www.intersystemschile.cl
Computer Software Development
N.A.I.C.S.: 513210
Carlos Noguera (Gen Mgr)

InterSystems Corporation - New
York   (1)
1330 6th Ave Fl 11 Ste 1102, New York, NY
10019
Tel.: (212) 661-1709
Web Site: http://www.intersystems.com
Rev.: $2,300,000
Emp.: 1,600
Administrative Management & General
Management Consulting Service

N.A.I.C.S.: 541611
Ceci DeJesus (Acct Mgr)

InterSystems Dubai   (1)
Suite 502 Block A Ibn Sina Building 27
Dubai Healthcare City, PO Box 505012,
Dubai, 505012, United Arab Emirates
Tel.: (971) 4 457 5700
Web Site: http://www.InterSystems.com
Emp.: 34
Computer Software Development
N.A.I.C.S.: 513210
Michel Amous (Country Mgr-Middle East)

InterSystems GmbH   (1)
Hilpertstrasse 20a, 64295, Darmstadt, Ger-
many
Tel.: (49) 6151 17 47 0
Web Site: http://www.intersystems.de
Emp.: 45
Computer Software Development
N.A.I.C.S.: 513210
Elina Lencler (Country Mgr)

InterSystems Iberia, S.L.   (1)
Parque Empresarial La Moraleja Avda Eu-
ropa 12, Edificio Monaco Alcobendas,
28108, Madrid, Spain
Tel.: (34) 914841880
Web Site: http://www.intersystems.com
Emp.: 30
Computer Software Development
N.A.I.C.S.: 513210
Gordi Calavera (Gen Mgr)

InterSystems Iberia, S.L.   (1)
Avda de les Corts Catalanes 5-7 Sant Cu-
gat del Valles, Barcelona, 08173, Spain
Tel.: (34) 93 504 1050
Web Site: http://www.intersystems.com
Computer Software Development
N.A.I.C.S.: 513210

InterSystems Italia s.r.l.   (1)
Piazzale Biancamano 8, 20121, Milan, Italy
Tel.: (39) 02 62 03 22 00
Web Site: http://www.intersystemsitalia.it
Computer Software Development
N.A.I.C.S.: 513210

InterSystems Italia s.r.l.   (1)
Corte Don Giuliano Botticelli 11, 47023,
Cesena, Italy
Tel.: (39) 0547 368211
Computer Software Development
N.A.I.C.S.: 513210

InterSystems Japan KK   (1)
Nittochi Nishi-shinjuku Building 17th Floor
6-10-1 Nishishinjuku, Shinjuku-ku, Tokyo,
160-0023, Japan
Tel.: (81) 3 5321 6200
Web Site: http://www.intersystems.co.jp
Computer Software Development
N.A.I.C.S.: 513210

InterSystems Japan KK   (1)
4F Keihan Dojima Bldg, 2-1-31 Dojima Kita-
ku, Osaka, 530-0003, Japan
Tel.: (81) 6 4797 3388
Web Site: http://www.intersystems.co.jp
Computer Software Development
N.A.I.C.S.: 513210

InterSystems Korea   (1)
30th Floor ASSEM Tower Samsung-1dong,
Gangnam-Gu, Seoul, 135-798, Korea
(South)
Tel.: (82) 2 6001 3505
Computer Software Development
N.A.I.C.S.: 513210

InterSystems Russia   (1)
WTC-2 Office 609, 12 Krasnopresnenskaya
Nab, 123610, Moscow, Russia
Tel.: (7) 495 967 0088
Web Site: http://www.intersystems.ru
Emp.: 25
Computer Software Development
N.A.I.C.S.: 513210
Nick Krechetov (Head-Moscow)

InterSystems SA   (1)
Ground Floor Block B Cullinan Place Culli-
nan Close, Morningside, 2196, Sandton,
South Africa
Tel.: (27) 11 324 1800
Web Site: http://www.intersystems.co.za
Emp.: 1
Computer Software Development
N.A.I.C.S.: 513210

R. K. Dalmia (Gen Mgr)

InterSystems SAS (1)
Tour EuroPlaza La Defense 4 20 Avenue
Andre Prothin, 92400, Courbevoie, France
Tel.: (33) 1 77 49 16 00
Web Site: http://www.intersystems.com
Emp.: 70
Computer Software Development
N.A.I.C.S.: 513210
Thomas Leitner (Mng Dir)

InterSystems Shanghai (1)
Suite 13 47th Floor, Hong Kong New World
Tower, 300 Huaihai Zhong Road, Shanghai,
200021, China
Tel.: (86) 21 51162887
Web Site: http://www.intersystems.cn
Computer Software Development
N.A.I.C.S.: 513210

**InterSystems Software (Beijing) Co.,
Ltd.** (1)
10th Floor Twin Towers East B12 Jian-
guomenwai Avenue, Chaoyang District, Bei-
jing, 100022, China
Tel.: (86) 10 5123 5152
Web Site: http://www.intersystems.cn
Computer Software Development
N.A.I.C.S.: 513210

**InterSystems Software (Thailand)
Ltd.** (1)
14th Floor Thanapoom Tower Makkasan,
Ratthawi, Bangkok, 10400, Thailand
Tel.: (66) 2 652 8770
Computer Software Development
N.A.I.C.S.: 513210

InterSystems UK (1)
InterSystems House 70 Tangier Lane, Eton,
Windsor, SL4 6BB, Berkshire, United King-
dom
Tel.: (44) 1753 855450
Web Site: http://www.intersystems.co.uk
Computer Software Development Services
N.A.I.C.S.: 513210

InterSystems UK (1)
Holyrood Park House 106 Holyrood Road,
Edinburgh, EH8 8AS, Scotland, United
Kingdom
Tel.: (44) 131 52 45 500
Web Site: http://www.intersystems.com
Emp.: 20
Computer Software Development
N.A.I.C.S.: 513210
Laura Martin (Office Mgr)

InterSystems do Brasil Ltda. (1)
Praca Professor Jose Lannes 40 11th Fl
Andar Edificio Berrini 500, Brooklin Novo,
0457-1100, Sao Paulo, Brazil
Tel.: (55) 11 3014 7000
Web Site: http://www.intersystems.com.br
Emp.: 15
Computer Software Development
N.A.I.C.S.: 513210
Fabano Sanches (Mgr)

InterSystems do Brasil Ltda. (1)
Setor Hoteleiro Sul Quadra 6 conjunto A
Bloco E, Brasil XXI sala 1212, Brasilia, Bra-
zil
Tel.: (55) 61 3033 5101
Web Site: http://www.intersystems.com.br
Computer Software Development
N.A.I.C.S.: 513210

**INTERTECH COMPUTER
PRODUCTS INC.**
5225 S 39th St, Phoenix, AZ 85040
Tel.: (602) 437-0035
Web Site:
http://www.itcomputers.com
Sales Range: $10-24.9 Million
Emp.: 61
Terminals; Computer; Cabling
N.A.I.C.S.: 423430
Mike Novotny (Pres & CEO)
Gordon Volden (Dir-Ops)

INTERTECH INC.
1575 Thomas Ctr Dr, Eagan, MN
55122
Tel.: (651) 288-7100
Web Site: http://www.intertech.com

Year Founded: 1991
Sales Range: $10-24.9 Million
Emp.: 60
Computer Software Publisher
N.A.I.C.S.: 513210
Tom Salonek (Founder & CEO)
David Brenner (Partner & Dir-Fin &
Acctg)

INTERTECH SECURITY, LLC
1501 Preble Ave, Pittsburgh, PA
15233
Tel.: (412) 246-1200
Web Site: http://www.intertechci.com
Year Founded: 2000
Technology & Software Integration
Services
N.A.I.C.S.: 541519
Ronald Petnuch (Pres & CEO)
Bob Markovich (Controller)
Christopher J. Wetzel (Founder &
Exec VP)

**INTERTECH WORLDWIDE
CORPORATION**
4400 N Federal Hwy Ste 400, Boca
Raton, FL 33431-5183
Tel.: (561) 395-5441
Web Site:
http://www.intertechworldwide.com
Year Founded: 1977
Sales Range: $10-24.9 Million
Emp.: 8
Supplier of Industrial Machinery &
Equipment
N.A.I.C.S.: 333515
David A. Igdanoff (Owner)

**INTERTEX GENERAL CON-
TRACTORS, INC.**
28338 Constellation Rd 900, Valen-
cia, CA 91355
Tel.: (661) 702-2222 CA
Web Site: http://www.intertexlv.com
Year Founded: 1982
Commercial & Office Building, New
Construction
N.A.I.C.S.: 236220
Dale R. Donohoe (CEO)
Bob Lyon (Pres)
Bill Fitzpatrick (VP)
Greg Lazarek (VP)
Danny Cato (CFO)
Joe Lopez (Dir-Sls & Mktg)

**INTERTRADE INDUSTRIES
LTD.**
14600 Hoover St, Westminster, CA
92683
Tel.: (714) 894-5566 CA
Thermoforming Plastics Mfr
N.A.I.C.S.: 326199

**INTERTREND COMMUNICA-
TIONS, INC.**
555 E Ocean Blvd, Long Beach, CA
90802-5003
Tel.: (562) 733-1888 CA
Web Site: http://www.intertrend.com
Year Founded: 1991
Rev.: $70,000,000
Emp.: 50
Advetising Agency
N.A.I.C.S.: 541810
Julia Y. Huang (CEO)
Rita Cheng (VP)
Susanna Jue (CFO)

INTERVALA, LLC
700 Braddock Ave E, Pittsburgh, PA
15112
Tel.: (412) 829-4807
Web Site: http://www.intervala.com

High-Performance Printed Circuit
Board Assemblies, Electromechanical
Systems & Cable & Harness Assem-
blies
N.A.I.C.S.: 334418
James D. Bell Jr. (VP & Gen Mgr)
Teresa Huber (Pres & CEO)
Sara Fenimore (Corp Dir-Supply
Chain)
William Hib (Mgr-Pur)
Laura Bradbury (Mgr-Pur)

Subsidiaries:

E P E Corp. (1)
540 N Commercial St, Manchester, NH
03101
Tel.: (603) 669-9181
Web Site: http://www.epecorp.com
Sales Range: $1-9.9 Million
Emp.: 70
Electronic Components Mfr
N.A.I.C.S.: 334419
Chuck Thistle (Exec VP-Bus Dev)

Princeton Technology Corp. (1)
33 Constitution Dr, Hudson, NH 03051
Tel.: (603) 595-1987
Web Site: http://www.princetontech.com
Sales Range: $1-9.9 Million
Emp.: 41
Mfg Printed Circuit Boards Mfg Electronic
Components
N.A.I.C.S.: 334412
Craig Norton (VP)
Maureen Abbott (Supvr-Pur)

INTERVALE CAPITAL, LLC
20 University Rd Ste 360, Cam-
bridge, MA 02138
Tel.: (617) 497-8282 DE
Web Site:
http://www.intervalecapital.com
Rev.: $280,000,000
Emp.: 25
Privater Equity Firm
N.A.I.C.S.: 523999
Charles Cherington (Mng Partner)
Tuan Tran (VP)
Christine Smoragiewicz (CFO)
Jason Turowsky (Partner)
Patrick Connelly (Partner)
Jason Arnoldy (VP)
Patrick Conroy (VP)
Melissa Rocco (Controller)

Subsidiaries:

Aegis Chemical Solutions, LLC (1)
1095 Evergreen Cir Ste 200, The Wood-
lands, TX 77380
Tel.: (713) 299-1617
Production Chemicals Services
N.A.I.C.S.: 325998

Allied Oil & Gas Services LLC (1)
950 E State Hwy 114, Southlake, TX 76092
Tel.: (817) 546-3358
Web Site: http://www.alliedservices.com
Cementing & Acidizing Services
N.A.I.C.S.: 327310

**Antelope Oil Tool & Manufacturing
Company** (1)
912 Hood St, Mineral Wells, TX 76067
Tel.: (940) 325-8989
Web Site: http://www.antelopeoiltool.com
Casing & Cementation Products Mfr
N.A.I.C.S.: 423810
Bill Kelley (CEO)

Benchmark Completions, LLC (1)
6614 Gant Rd, Houston, TX 77066
Tel.: (281) 537-8483
Emp.: 30
Cementing Equipment
N.A.I.C.S.: 327310

**Innovex Downhole Solutions,
Inc.** (1)
4310 N Sam Houston Pkwy E, Houston, TX
77032
Tel.: (281) 602-7815
Web Site: http://innovexdownhole.com
Downhole Products & Technology
N.A.I.C.S.: 213112

Adam Anderson (CEO)
Nichola Alexander (Mktg Dir)
Elizabeth Johnson (Mktg Mgr)

Subsidiary (Domestic):

Quick Connectors, Inc. (2)
5226 Brittmoore Rd, Houston, TX 77429
Tel.: (713) 984-1800
Web Site: http://www.quickconnectors.com
Electrical Apparatus & Equipment, Wiring
Supplies & Related Equipment Merchant
Whslr
N.A.I.C.S.: 423610
Peter Lawson (Pres & COO)

**Rubicon Oilfield International
Limited** (2)
10613 W Sam Houston Pkwy N Ste 600,
Houston, TX 77064
Tel.: (832) 386-2500
Web Site: http://www.rubicon-oilfield.com
Oil & Gas Exploration Services
N.A.I.C.S.: 213112
Mike Reeves (Founder, Pres & CEO)
John B. Griggs (CFO)
Jayme Sperring (Chief Comml Officer)
Scott Watson (COO)
Richard Rodriguez (Chief Production Offi-
cer)
Cory Roclawski (VP-HR)
Tom Holloway (Co-CFO)

Intervale Capital, LLC - Houston (1)
2800 Post Oak Blvd Ste 2000, Houston, TX
77056
Tel.: (713) 961-0118
Web Site: http://www.impactfluids.net
Privater Equity Firm
N.A.I.C.S.: 523999

TEAM Oil Tools LP (1)
1400 Woodlock Forrest Dr Ste 400, The
Woodlands, TX 77380
Tel.: (281) 602-7815
Web Site: http://www.teamoiltools.com
Oil Field Tools & Equipment Mfr
N.A.I.C.S.: 333132
Byron Cowart (Chm)
David Fleming (CFO)
Steve Chauffe (VP-Tech & Bus Dev)
Adam Anderson (CEO)
Justin Kellner (VP-Engrg)

Subsidiary (Domestic):

Odessa Packer Service, Inc. (2)
213 N 57th St, Odessa, TX 79764
Tel.: (432) 368-9285
Sales Range: $1-9.9 Million
Construction, Mining & Forestry Machinery
& Equipment Rental & Leasing
N.A.I.C.S.: 532412
Steve Hughes (Pres)
Leonard Neatherlin (VP-Ops)

Schlehuber Oil Tools, LLC (2)
2902 Quail Ridge Rd, Denver City, TX
79323
Tel.: (806) 592-5045
Web Site: http://www.schlehuberoiltools.com
Emp.: 28
Oil Well Machinery Mfr
N.A.I.C.S.: 333132
Rob Schlehuber (Gen Mgr)

Top Notch Energy Services, Inc. (2)
5025 Leopard St, Corpus Christi, TX
78408-2514 (100%)
Tel.: (361) 225-0447
Web Site: http://www.topnotchcc.com
Emp.: 100
Oil Site Preparation Services
N.A.I.C.S.: 238910
Terry Bennetsen (Mgr-Sls)
Robert Winstead Jr. (VP)

Taurex Drill Bits LLC (1)
2601 Venture Dr, Norman, OK 73069
Tel.: (405) 321-8850
Web Site: http://www.taurexbits.com
Drill Bits, PDC Bits And Roller Cones Mfr
N.A.I.C.S.: 333991
Warren Dyer (Pres & CEO)

Subsidiary (Domestic):

PDC Logic, LLC (2)
2601 Venture Dr, Norman, OK
73069 (60%)
Tel.: (405) 321-8850

Intervale Capital, LLC—(Continued)

Web Site: http://www.pdclogic.com
Oil & Gas Drill Bit Designer, Mfr & Whslr
N.A.I.C.S.: 333132
Ronnie Thompson (Pres)

INTERVALZERO INC.
400 5th Ave 4 Fl, Waltham, MA
02451-8706
Tel.: (781) 996-4481
Web Site:
http://www.intervalzero.com
Year Founded: 1980
Sales Range: $10-24.9 Million
Emp.: 25
Embedded Computing Software Developer
N.A.I.C.S.: 513210
Jeffrey D. Hibbard (CEO)
Bryan Levey (VP-Engrg)
Mark Van Vranken (CFO)
Fabrice Boisset (Gen Mgr-Europe, Middle East & Africa)
Brian Calder (VP-Sls-NA & APAC)
Terri Hawker (VP-Product Mgmt)
Alex Hung (VP-Sls-APAC)
Dipesh Mukerji (VP-Mktg & Strategy)
Daron Underwood (CTO & VP-R&D)

INTERVIEWING SERVICE OF AMERICA
15400 Sherman Way 4th Fl, Van Nuys, CA 91406
Tel.: (818) 989-1044
Web Site: http://www.isacorp.com
Year Founded: 1982
Sales Range: $10-24.9 Million
Emp.: 680
Market Analysis, Business & Economic Research Services
N.A.I.C.S.: 541910
Michael Halberstam (Chm)
Gregg Stickeler (Sr VP-Client Svcs)
John Fitzpatrick (VP-Information Sys & Tech)
Anthony Kretzmer (Pres)

Subsidiaries:

SoapBoxSample   (1)
15400 Sherman Way 4th Fl, Van Nuys, CA 91406
Tel.: (818) 989-1044
Web Site: http://www.soapboxsample.com
Data Collection & Research
N.A.I.C.S.: 518210
Jacqueline Rosales (COO)

Subsidiary (Domestic):

Sentient Services   (2)
6604 Toolwrich Ln, Austin, TX 78739
Tel.: (512) 498-3830
Web Site: http://www.sentientservices.com
Marketing Research & Public Opinion Polling
N.A.I.C.S.: 541910
Paul Janowitz (Founder & CEO)

INTERVISE CONSULTANTS INC.
120110 Molecular Dr, Rockville, MD 20850
Tel.: (240) 364-9500
Web Site: http://www.intervise.com
Sales Range: $10-24.9 Million
Emp.: 150
Computer Related Consulting Services
N.A.I.C.S.: 541512
Michael D. Priddy (Pres & CEO)

INTERWEST CONSTRUCTION, INC.
609 N Hill Blvd, Burlington, WA 98233
Tel.: (360) 757-7574

Web Site:
http://www.interwestconstruction
inc.com
Year Founded: 1987
Water & Sewer Line & Related Structures Construction
N.A.I.C.S.: 237110
Kip Twaddle (Superintendent)
Izaak Fox (Project Mgr)

INTERWEST CORPORATION
35 N Redwood Rd, North Salt Lake, UT 84054
Tel.: (801) 936-6200   UT
Web Site:
http://www.interwestconst.com
Sales Range: $25-49.9 Million
Emp.: 20
Holding Company; Commercial & Institutional Building Construction
N.A.I.C.S.: 551112
Kenneth R. Cutler (Chm)
Max D. Griffin (Pres & CEO)
Roger Cox (Treas)
Evelyn Herzog (Sec)
Mark L. Brown (Pres/CEO-Interwest Construction)

Subsidiaries:

Interwest Construction Company, Inc.   (1)
35 N Redwood Rd, North Salt Lake, UT 84054
Tel.: (801) 936-6200
Web Site: http://www.interwestconst.com
Sales Range: $25-49.9 Million
Commercial & Institutional Building Construction
N.A.I.C.S.: 236220

INTERWEST INSURANCE SERVICES, INC.
8950 Bldg 3 2n Fl Ste 200, Sacramento, CA 95826
Tel.: (916) 679-2960   CA
Web Site:
http://www.infosourcecafe.com
Sales Range: $10-24.9 Million
Emp.: 400
Insurance Brokers
N.A.I.C.S.: 524210
Keith Schuler (Pres & CEO)
Don Pollard (CFO)
Jeff Keena (Dir-Alternative Markets)
Rob Oates (Dir-Carrier Rels)

INTERWEST SAFETY SUPPLY INC.
724 E 1860 S, Provo, UT 84606
Tel.: (801) 375-6321
Web Site:
http://www.interwestsafety.com
Rev.: $10,000,000
Emp.: 50
Sign Mfr
N.A.I.C.S.: 339950
Lora Sorenson (VP)

INTERWORKS, INC.
1425 S Sangre Rd, Stillwater, OK 74074
Tel.: (405) 624-3214   OK
Web Site: http://www.interworks.com
Year Founded: 1996
Sales Range: $1-9.9 Million
Emp.: 57
IT Outsourcing & Business Solutions
N.A.I.C.S.: 541512
Behfar Jahanshahi (CEO)
Dan Murray (COO)
Staci Bejcek (VP-Ops)

INTETICS CO.
809 Ridge Rd Ste 205, Wilmette, IL 60091
Tel.: (847) 512-4272
Web Site: http://www.intetics.com

Year Founded: 2003
Rev.: $5,500,000
Emp.: 175
Custom Computer Programming Services
N.A.I.C.S.: 541511
Alla Liokumovich (Mgr-IT)
Oleg Ridchenko (VP & Dir-Intetics Belarus)
Serge Stepantsov (VP-Bus Dev)
Sergei Terekhov (Dir-Quality Assurance)
Eugene Lanetski (Dir-Intetics-Ukraine)
Janos Orosz (CTO)
Nadezhda Gagauz (Dir-HR)
Yoshio Sugano (Reg Dir)
Yuri Piskunovich (VP-Tech & Dir-Delivery)
Natalia Sidorenko (VP-HR & Ops-Europe)

INTEX ENVIRONMENTAL GROUP, INC.
6907A Easton Rd, Pipersville, PA 18947-9709
Tel.: (215) 766-7230
Web Site: http://www.intexenv.com
Environmental Consulting
N.A.I.C.S.: 541690
Daniel Fitzgerald (Pres)

INTEX RECREATION CORP.
PO Box 1440, Long Beach, CA 90801-1440
Tel.: (310) 549-5400   CA
Web Site: http://www.intexcorp.com
Rev.: $97,800,000
Emp.: 600
Distribution of Water Beds Inflatables Diecast Toy Fiberglass Product & Sporting Good Distr
N.A.I.C.S.: 423210
Alex Yang (Mgr-Sls & Admin)
Fatima Echavez (Supvr-Sls & Admin)
Mike Chiu (Asst Controller)
Robert Koenig (Asst Gen Mgr)
Wayne Farmer (Mgr-Mgmt Info Sys)
Phil Mimaki (Dir-Creative)
Chip Whalen (Dir-Risk Mgmt)
Gerald Margolis (Asst Gen Counsel)

Subsidiaries:

Intex Development Company Ltd.   (1)
9/F Dah Sing Financial Centre 108 Gloucester Road, Wanchai, China (Hong Kong)
Tel.: (852) 2827 0000
Web Site: http://www.intexdevelopment.com
Emp.: 140
Swimming & Recreational Goods Distr
N.A.I.C.S.: 423910
Tony Zee (Dir)

Subsidiary (Non-US):

Intex Trading B. V.   (2)
Venneveld 9, 4705 RR, Roosendaal, Netherlands
Tel.: (31) 165 593920
Web Site: http://www.intexcorp.nl
Swimming & Recreational Goods Distr
N.A.I.C.S.: 423910

Intex Trading s.r.o.   (2)
Benesovska 23, Prague, 10100, Czech Republic
Tel.: (420) 267 312 645
Emp.: 5
Swimming & Recreational Goods Distr
N.A.I.C.S.: 423910
Michaela Perinova (CEO)

INTEZYNE TECHNOLOGIES, INC.
3720 Spectrum Blvd Ste 104, Tampa, FL 33612
Tel.: (813) 910-2120
Web Site: http://www.intezyne.com
Year Founded: 2004

Sales Range: $1-9.9 Million
Emp.: 8
Cancer Pharmaceutical Researcher, Developer & Mfr
N.A.I.C.S.: 325412
Habib Skaff (Co-Founder)
Daniel J. Devers (Chief Bus Officer)
Carolyn M. Paradise (Acting Chief Medical Officer)
E. Russell McAllister (Pres & CEO)
Glenn Walthall (Chm)

INTHINC
4225 W Lake Park Blvd Ste 100, West Valley City, UT 84120
Tel.: (801) 886-2255
Web Site: http://www.inthinc.com
Year Founded: 1997
Rev.: $71,600,000
Emp.: 412
Industrial Machinery Mfr
N.A.I.C.S.: 333248
Todd W. Follmer (CEO)

INTHINC TECHNOLOGY SOLUTIONS, INC
4225 W Lk Park Blvd Ste 100, Salt Lake City, UT 84120
Tel.: (801) 886-2255
Web Site: http://www.inthinc.com
Sales Range: $25-49.9 Million
Emp.: 85
Safety Consulting Services
N.A.I.C.S.: 541690
Todd W. Follmer (CEO)
Jeffrey M. Harvey (Chief Admin Officer & Exec VP)
Corey Catten (CTO)
Vivek Chaturvedi (CFO)
Carleton Watkins (VP-R&D)
David Muse (Pres)
Mason Vincent (CIO)

INTIGRAL INC
7850 Northfield Rd, Walton Hills, OH 44146
Tel.: (440) 439-0980   OH
Web Site: http://www.intigral.com
Sales Range: $10-24.9 Million
Emp.: 200
Insulating Glass Mfr
N.A.I.C.S.: 327215
Mark Hutchinson (Mgr-Tech & Sls Support)
DeAnna Negron (VP)
Jason Thomas (Pres)
Don Smith (Plant Mgr)
Tom Calcei (Mgr-Sls)
Henri Holm (CFO)
Ben Kinealy (CEO)
Holly Mostardi (Coord-Sls Integration)

INTIMO INC.
143 W 29th St Fl 5, New York, NY 10001
Tel.: (212) 868-6888
Web Site: http://www.intimo.com
Rev.: $15,000,000
Emp.: 15
Men's & Boy's Clothing
N.A.I.C.S.: 424350
Bruce Ostrow (Pres-Women's Apparel)
Debra Mitchell (Sr Acct Exec)
Randy Devivo (VP-Mfg)

INTIVA INC.
773 Cherry Creek N Dr Ste 575, Denver, CO 80209
Tel.: (800) 815-2071
Web Site: http://www.intiva.us
Holding Company; Invests in Plant Science Industry
N.A.I.C.S.: 551112
Jeffrey Friedland (Chm & CEO)
Evan Wasoff (CFO)
Richard Greenberg (Exec VP)

Subsidiaries:

Nexien BioPharma Inc.   **(1)**
4340 E Kentucky Ave Ste 206, Glendale,
CO 80246   **(88.07%)**
Tel.: (303) 495-7583
Web Site:
   https://www.nexienbiopharma.com
Assets: $43,127
Liabilities: $295,134
Net Worth: ($252,007)
Earnings: ($361,902)
Emp.: 6
Fiscal Year-end: 06/30/2023
Investment Services
N.A.I.C.S.: 523999
Richard S. Greenberg (Chm & CEO)
Robert I. Goldfarb (COO)
Evan Wasoff (CFO)

INTLX SOLUTIONS, LLC
1 Edgewater Dr Ste 110, Norwood,
MA 02062
Tel.: (781) 352-0377
Web Site:
   http://www.intlxsolutions.com
Year Founded: 2015
Sales Range: $1-9.9 Million
Telecommunication Servicesb
N.A.I.C.S.: 517810
Kenny Pearl (Co-Founder & Pres)
Jim Monopoli (Co-Founder & CEO)

INTO METAL INC.
3340 N 33rd St, Lincoln, NE 68504
Tel.: (402) 466-2571
Web Site: http://www.intometal.com
Sales Range: $10-24.9 Million
Emp.: 50
Distribution & Manufacturing Machine
Parts Metal
N.A.I.C.S.: 332119

INTONE NETWORKS INC.
10 Austin Ave, Iselin, NJ 08830
Tel.: (732) 721-3002
Web Site:
   http://www.intonenetworks.com
Year Founded: 2003
Sales Range: $10-24.9 Million
Emp.: 100
It Consulting
N.A.I.C.S.: 541519
Prathima Devulapally (Sr Mgr-Sls)
Prabhakar Reddy (CEO)

INTOUCH CREDIT UNION
5640 Democracy Dr, Plano, TX
75024
Tel.: (214) 291-1776   **TX**
Web Site: http://www.itcu.org
Year Founded: 1974
Rev.: $39,299,820
Assets: $907,799,272
Liabilities: $838,283,286
Net Worth: $69,515,986
Earnings: ($4,301,464)
Emp.: 313
Fiscal Year-end: 12/31/18
Credit Union Operator
N.A.I.C.S.: 522130
J. Diane Gerstner (Exec VP)
Kent L. Lugrand (Pres & CEO)
Sammie Cantrell (Chief Admin Officer
& Sr VP)
Nancy Pressel (Chm)
Robert McDonald (CFO & Sr VP)
Jodie Robinson (Sec)
Tom Condos (CIO & Sr VP)
Kristen Schmieg (VP-Retail Ops)
Bridger Robinson (VP-Member Expe-
rience)

INTOUCH TECHNOLOGIES, INC.
7402 Hollister Ave, Santa Barbara,
CA 93117
Tel.: (805) 562-8686   **DE**

Web Site:
   http://www.intouchhealth.com
Year Founded: 2002
Telemedicine Machinery Mfr
N.A.I.C.S.: 333998
Yulun Wang (Founder, Chm & Chief
Innovation Officer)
Greg Brallier (VP-Solution Analysis &
Design)
Stephen L. Wilson (Chief Admin Offi-
cer)
Steve Jordan (VP-Tech)
Michael Chan (Exec VP-Mktg & Gen
Mgr-Intl Markets)
Andy Puterbaugh (Exec VP & Gen
Mgr-United States Markets)
Tim Wright (Chief Strategy Officer)
Joseph M. DeVivo (CEO)
Steve DeGennaro (CFO)
Gary Douville (COO)
Ole Eichhorn (CTO)
Karen M. Deli (Sr VP & Gen Mgr-
Physician Capacity Mgmt)
Chris Joslin (VP-Strategic Accnts)

INTOXIMETERS INC.
2081 Craig Rd, Saint Louis, MO
63146
Tel.: (314) 429-4000
Web Site: http://www.intox.com
Sales Range: $10-24.9 Million
Emp.: 44
Distribution Of Breathalyzers
N.A.I.C.S.: 334519
Tim Brewer (Reg Mgr-Sls)
Debbie Mandell (Mgr-Inside Sls)
Bryan Heaven (Mgr-Matls)
Steve Kendrick (Dir-Tech)

INTRA, CORP.
885 Manufacturers Dr, Westland, MI
48186
Tel.: (734) 326-7030   **MI**
Web Site: http://www.intra-corp.net
Year Founded: 1977
Sales Range: $1-9.9 Million
Emp.: 105
Cutting Tool & Machine Tool Acces-
sory Mfr
N.A.I.C.S.: 333515
John Battista (CEO)
Jeff Harrison (Mgr-Engrg)
Kristen Headrick (Mgr-HR)
David Kruszewski (Sr Mgr)
Rob Sayig (VP-Sls)

INTRACORP COMPANIES
419 Occidental Ave S Ste 300, Se-
attle, WA 98104-2886
Tel.: (206) 625-9226
Web Site:
   http://www.intracorpcompanies.com
Sales Range: $75-99.9 Million
Emp.: 60
Real Estate Investment
N.A.I.C.S.: 525990
Michael Miller (Chm & CEO)
Daniel Miller (VP-Capital Intracorp
Companies)

INTRADECO, INC.
9500 NW 108 Ave, Miami, FL 33178
Tel.: (305) 264-8888   **FL**
Web Site:
   http://intradecoapparel.com
Casual Clothing & Thermal Garments
Mfr
N.A.I.C.S.: 424350
Luis Marquina (COO)

Subsidiaries:

Intradeco Apparel, Inc.   **(1)**
N Walton Blvd Ste 1, Bentonville, AR 72712
Tel.: (479) 471-8488
Web Site: http://www.intradecoapparel.com
Men's & Boys' Clothing & Furnishings Mer-
chant Whslr

N.A.I.C.S.: 424350
Nicole Engleman (Mgr-Site)

Division (Domestic):

Indera Mills Company   **(2)**
350 W Maple St, Yadkinville, NC 27055
Tel.: (336) 679-4440
Web Site: http://www.inderamills.com
Sales Range: $75-99.9 Million
Emp.: 88
Knitted & Thermal Garments Mfr
N.A.I.C.S.: 315250
John Willingham (Pres)

INTRALOGIC SOLUTIONS INC.
504 Hicksville Rd, Massapequa, NY
11758
Tel.: (516) 799-7061
Web Site: http://www.ilsny.com
Year Founded: 2004
Sales Range: $1-9.9 Million
Emp.: 26
Security & Surveillance
N.A.I.C.S.: 561621
Matt Carrique (COO)
Lee Mandel (CEO)
Michael Nirenberg (Mgr-Support)

INTRANSIT INC.
3525 Excel Dr, Medford, OR 97504
Tel.: (541) 773-3993
Web Site: http://www.utits.com
Sales Range: $50-74.9 Million
Emp.: 100
Brokers, Shipping
N.A.I.C.S.: 488510
Don Farthing (Pres)
Marion Harp (Controller)

INTREORG SYSTEMS, INC.
2600 E Southlake Blvd Ste 120-366,
Southlake, TX 76092
Tel.: (817) 491-8611   **TX**
Web Site: http://www.intreorg.com
Year Founded: 2003
Assets: $100
Liabilities: $3,181,189
Net Worth: ($3,181,089)
Earnings: ($330,257)
Emp.: 1
Fiscal Year-end: 12/31/17
Information Technology Consulting
Services
N.A.I.C.S.: 541690

INTREPID CAPITAL MANAGE-MENT, INC.
1400 Marsh Landing Pkwy Ste 106,
Jacksonville Beach, FL 32250
Tel.: (904) 246-3433
Web Site:
   http://www.intrepidcapital.net
Year Founded: 1994
Sales Range: $1-9.9 Million
Emp.: 18
Portfolio Management
N.A.I.C.S.: 523940
Chris Pilinko (VP)
Beth Holbrook (Chief Compliance
Officer-Client Svcs)
Donald White (CFO-Admin)
Sam Solem (Coord-Ops)
Erick J. Lucera (Founder)

INTREPID ENTERPRISES, INC.
1848 Indus Blvd, Harvey, LA 70058-
2314
Tel.: (504) 348-2861   **LA**
Web Site:
   http://www.intrepidstone.com
Year Founded: 1973
Sales Range: $125-149.9 Million
Emp.: 20
Provider of Masonry Contracting Ser-
vices
N.A.I.C.S.: 238140

Kevin Prestenberg (Pres)
Harold Prestenberg Jr. (CEO)

INTREPID SOUTHEAST INC.
805 NE 3rd St, Dania, FL 33004
Tel.: (954) 922-7544
Web Site:
   http://www.intrepidboats.com
Rev.: $21,200,000
Emp.: 220
Sporting & Recreational Goods &
Supplies Merchant Whslr
N.A.I.C.S.: 423910
Michael Obolsky (Sr VP)
Ken Clinton (Pres)

INTRI-PLEX TECHNOLOGIES INC.
751 S Kellogg Ave, Santa Barbara,
CA 93117
Tel.: (805) 683-3414
Web Site: http://www.intriplex.com
Year Founded: 1987
Rev.: $35,748,750
Emp.: 70
Stamping Metal For The Trade
N.A.I.C.S.: 332119
Lawney Falloon (Pres & CEO)
John Sullivan (Executives)
Gordon Booth (Dir-Quality Assurance)
Sherri Pastorino (Dir-HR)
Ryan Schmidt (VP-Product Eng)
Dale Schudel (Sr Gen Mgr-Thailand)
Dave Swabash (Dir-Strategic Accts)
Ernest Swayney (Dir-Thermal Pro-
cessing)
Paul W. Smith (Dir-R&D)
Sal Penza (Sr Dir-Fin)
Tanee Maneenut (Dir-Quality-
Thailand)
Tong Ho (Sr Mng Dir)

INTRIDEA INC.
1020 16th St NW 7th Fl, Washington,
DC 20006
Web Site: http://www.intridea.com
Sales Range: $1-9.9 Million
Emp.: 34
Website Design Provider
N.A.I.C.S.: 518210
Marc Garrett (Chief Strategy Officer)
Andy Wang (Sr Engr)
Kathryn Ottinger (Dir-Mktg)
Mike Tierney (Dir-UI Engrg)

INTRINIUM, INC.
4418 E 8th Ave, Spokane Valley, WA
99212
Web Site: http://www.intrinium.com
Year Founded: 2007
Sales Range: $1-9.9 Million
Emp.: 50
Information Technology Consulting
Services
N.A.I.C.S.: 541512
Nolan Garrett (CEO)
Pat Atwal (COO)
Bobbie McIntyre (Fin Dir)
Stephen Heath (Chief Information
Security Officer)

INTRINSIC MEDICINE, INC.
500 Yale Ave N, Seattle, WA 98109
Tel.: (206) 426-3624   **DE**
Web Site:
   https://www.intrinsicmedicine.com
Year Founded: 2018
Assets: $3,763,000
Liabilities: $17,767,000
Net Worth: ($14,004,000)
Earnings: ($11,953,000)
Emp.: 8
Fiscal Year-end: 12/31/21
Biotechnology Research & Develop-
ment Services

Intrinsic Medicine, Inc.—(Continued)

N.A.I.C.S.: 541714
Alexander Martinez (CEO & Chm)
Jason Ferrone (Pres & COO)
Emil Chuang (Chief Medical Officer)
Dustin Crawford (Sec, VP-Corporate Development & Gen Counsel)
David Donahue (VP)

INTRUST FINANCIAL CORPORATION
105 N Main St, Wichita, KS 67202
Tel.: (316) 383-1111   KS
Web Site: http://www.intrustbank.com
Year Founded: 1971
Sales Range: $150-199.9 Million
Emp.: 1,100
Bank Holding Company
N.A.I.C.S.: 551111
Charles Q. Chandler IV (Chm, Pres & CEO)
Jay L. Smith (Vice Chm)
Rick Beach (Vice Chm)
J. V. Lentell (Vice Chm)
Brian Sullivan (Gen Counsel & Sr VP)

Subsidiaries:

Intrust Bank, N.A.   (1)
105 N Main St, Wichita, KS
67202-1412   (100%)
Tel.: (316) 383-1234
Web Site: http://www.intrustbank.com
Emp.: 100
National Commercial Banks
N.A.I.C.S.: 522110
Charles Q. Chandler IV (Chm & CEO)
Doug Gaumer (Pres)
Michele Ballard (Mgr-Bus Dev Relationship)
Russell Dunn (Portfolio Mgr)
Shawn Eidson (Sr Mgr-Comml Relationship)
Kelvin Liebelt (Sr Mgr-Credit)
Jeff Brownlee (Portfolio Mgr)
Keenan Bender (Sr Mgr-Consumer Lending)
Matt Davis (Mgr-Comml Real Estate Relationship)
Diane Iseman (Mgr-Comm & PR)
Matt Fuhrman (Mgr-Comml Relationship)

INTUEOR CONSULTING INC.
7700 Irvine Ctr Dr Ste 470, Irvine, CA 92618
Tel.: (949) 753-9010
Web Site: http://www.intueor.com
Year Founded: 2005
Sales Range: $1-9.9 Million
Emp.: 26
Business Consultants
N.A.I.C.S.: 541618
Vijay Mididaddi (Founder & Mng Principal)

INTUITIVE RESEARCH & TECHNOLOGY CORPORATION
5030 Bradford Dr Bldg 2 Ste 205, Huntsville, AL 35805
Tel.: (256) 922-9300
Web Site: http://www.irtc-hq.com
Sales Range: $1-9.9 Million
Emp.: 150
Management & Technical Services to Government & Commercial Customers
N.A.I.C.S.: 541618
A. R. Almodovar (Co-Founder & CEO)
Donna Meadows (VP)
Joshua Hasty (Engr-Reliability)
Harold Brewer (Pres)

INTUITIVE TECHNOLOGY GROUP LLC
1650 W 82nd St Ste 650, Bloomington, MN 55431
Tel.: (952) 854-1663
Web Site: http://www.intuitivetg.com

Year Founded: 2006
Sales Range: $10-24.9 Million
Emp.: 130
It Consulting
N.A.I.C.S.: 541519
Justin Ware (Pres)
Jason Livingston (Mng Dir)
Michael Dionne (Mgr-IBM Incident)

INTUITIVE WEB SOLUTIONS, L.L.C.
509 W Olive Ste 101, Springfield, MO 65806
Tel.: (417) 851-1289
Web Site: http://www.iws-web.com
Year Founded: 2004
Sales Range: $1-9.9 Million
Emp.: 27
Software Solutions Provider
N.A.I.C.S.: 334610
Chris Reynolds (Pres-Bus Dev)
Phil Reynolds (Pres-Products)

INVACARE CORPORATION
1 Invacare Way, Elyria, OH 44035-4190
Tel.: (440) 329-6000   OH
Web Site: https://global.invacare.com
Year Founded: 1979
IVC—(OTCIQ)
Rev.: $741,733,000
Assets: $770,969,000
Liabilities: $689,877,000
Net Worth: $81,092,000
Earnings: ($101,071,000)
Emp.: 2,800
Fiscal Year-end: 12/31/22
Non-Acute Health Care Products for Home Health Care, Retail & Extended Care Markets Mfr & Distr
N.A.I.C.S.: 339112
Geoffrey P. Purtill (Pres & CEO)
Anthony C. LaPlaca (Chief Admin Officer, Gen Counsel, Sec & Sr VP)
Samuel Brill (Chm)
Kai Zhu (CFO & Sr VP)
Brad Duff (Chief Comml Officer)
Eric Regis (VP-Supply Chain, Operations, and R&D Global)
Magda Stepniewicz (VP-Global Mktg)
Paul Lavin (VP-Rehab North America)
Regis Opfermann (VP-Comml Ops)
Madeleine Gloy (VP-Quality & Regulatory Global)
Scott Hughes (VP-Lifestyles Bus Unit)

Subsidiaries:

Adaptive Switch Laboratories, Inc.   (1)
125 Spur 191 Ste C, Spicewood, TX 78669
Tel.: (830) 798-0005
Web Site: https://www.asl-inc.com
Sales Range: $1-9.9 Million
Emp.: 15
Home Health Care Products
N.A.I.C.S.: 334510
Codie Ealey (Office Mgr)
Chris Moses (Production Mgr)
James Pham (Engr)

Alber GmbH   (1)
Vor dem Weissen Stein 14, Tailfingen, 72461, Albstadt, Germany
Tel.: (49) 74 322 0060
Web Site: https://www.alber.de
Electronic Components Mfr
N.A.I.C.S.: 334419

Alber USA, LLC   (1)
1005 International Dr, Oakdale, PA 15071
Tel.: (724) 695-7822
Web Site: https://www.alber-usa.com
Metal Household Furniture Mfr
N.A.I.C.S.: 337126

Aquatec Operations GmbH   (1)
Alemannstr 10, 88316, Isny, Baden-Wurttemberg, Germany

Tel.: (49) 75627000
Web Site: http://www.invacare.com
Emp.: 260
Medical Equipment Mfr & Distr
N.A.I.C.S.: 334510
Marc Bender (CEO)

Carroll Healthcare, Inc.   (1)
994 Hargrieve Rd, London, N6E 1P5, ON, Canada
Tel.: (519) 659-1395
Web Site: http://www.carrollhealthcare.com
Beds & Furniture Mfr for Healthcare Industry
N.A.I.C.S.: 337127

Dolomite AB   (1)
Vaxjovagen 303, 343 71, Dio, Kronobergs lan, Sweden
Tel.: (46) 476 53500
Web Site: http://www.dolomite.biz
Emp.: 1
Medical Equipment Mfr
N.A.I.C.S.: 334510

Dynamic Europe Ltd.   (1)
Unit 7 Finepoint Way, Kidderminster, DY11 7FB, Worcestershire, United Kingdom
Tel.: (44) 1562826600
Web Site: https://www.dynamiccontrols.com
Sales Range: $25-49.9 Million
Emp.: 20
Electronic Components Mfr
N.A.I.C.S.: 334419

Dynamic Medical Systems, Inc.   (1)
2811 E Ana St, Rancho Dominguez, CA 90221
Tel.: (310) 928-0251
Web Site: http://www.godynamic.com
Sales Range: $50-74.9 Million
Emp.: 40
Medical Equipment Distr, Clinical Consulting & Educational Training Services
N.A.I.C.S.: 423450

Family Medical Supply LLC   (1)
2300 E 61st St N, Park City, KS 67219-1930
Tel.: (316) 744-1261
Medical Equipment Mfr
N.A.I.C.S.: 334510

Freedom Designs, Inc.   (1)
2241 N Madera Rd, Simi Valley, CA 93065
Tel.: (805) 582-0077
Web Site: https://www.freedomdesigns.com
Surgical Appliance Mfr
N.A.I.C.S.: 339113

Invacare (Portugal) II-Material Ortopedico, Lda.   (1)
Rua Estrada Velha n 949 Leca do Balio, 4465-784, Porto, Portugal
Tel.: (351) 225193360
Web Site: https://www.invacare.pt
Emp.: 125
Hospital Furniture Whslr
N.A.I.C.S.: 423450
Matthew E. Monaghan (Pres & CEO)

Invacare A/S   (1)
Sdr Ringvej 37, 2605, Brondby, Denmark
Tel.: (45) 3 690 0000
Web Site: https://www.invacare.dk
Emp.: 50
Medical Equipment Mfr & Distr
N.A.I.C.S.: 334510

Invacare AG   (1)
Benkenstrasse 260, 4108, Witterswil, Switzerland
Tel.: (41) 61 487 7080
Web Site: https://www.invacare.ch
Sales Range: $10-24.9 Million
Emp.: 9
Medical Equipment Mfr & Distr
N.A.I.C.S.: 334510

Invacare Australia Pty Limited   (1)
Unit 18/12 Stanton Road, Seven Hills, 2147, NSW, Australia   (100%)
Tel.: (61) 288395300
Web Site: https://www.invacare.com.au
Sales Range: $75-99.9 Million
Emp.: 80
Home Medical Products
N.A.I.C.S.: 621610
Geoffrey P. Purtill (Mng Dir)

Invacare Austria GmbH   (1)

Herzog-Odilo-Strasse 101, Tiefgraben, 5310, Mondsee, Austria
Tel.: (43) 62 325 5350
Web Site: https://www.invacare.at
Sales Range: $10-24.9 Million
Emp.: 6
Medical Equipment Mfr & Distr
N.A.I.C.S.: 334510

Invacare B.V.   (1)
Galvanistraat 14-3, 6716 AE, Ede, Netherlands   (100%)
Tel.: (31) 31 869 5757
Web Site: https://www.invacare.nl
Sales Range: $10-24.9 Million
Emp.: 40
Home Medical Products
N.A.I.C.S.: 621610

Invacare Canada LP   (1)
570 Matheson Blvd East Unit 8, Mississauga, L4Z 4G4, ON, Canada   (100%)
Tel.: (905) 890-8300
Web Site: http://pro.invacare.ca
Sales Range: $10-24.9 Million
Emp.: 80
Home Medical Products
N.A.I.C.S.: 621610

Invacare Canadian Holdings, Inc.   (1)
1 Invacare Way, Elyria, OH 44035
Tel.: (440) 329-6000
Investment Management Service
N.A.I.C.S.: 551112

Invacare Continuing Care, Inc.   (1)
1 Invacare Way, Elyria, OH 44035-4190
Tel.: (800) 333-6900
Web Site: http://www.invacare.com
Motorized & Manual Beds, Patient Room Furniture (For Hospitals & Other Health Care Facilities) Mfr
N.A.I.C.S.: 339113

Invacare Deutschland GmbH   (1)
Am Achener Hof 8, PO Box 13 15, 88316, Isny, Germany   (100%)
Tel.: (49) 756270038
Web Site: http://www.invacare.de
Sales Range: $100-124.9 Million
Emp.: 200
Hospital Equipment Whslr
N.A.I.C.S.: 423450

Invacare Dolomite AB   (1)
Fagerstagatan 9, 163 91, Spanga, Sweden
Tel.: (46) 87617090
Web Site: https://www.invacare.se
Medical Equipment Mfr & Distr
N.A.I.C.S.: 334510

Invacare EC-Hong A/S   (1)
Ostergade 3, Hong, 4270, Kalundborg, Denmark
Tel.: (45) 58852722
Medical Equipment Mfr & Distr
N.A.I.C.S.: 334510

Invacare France   (1)
Route de Saint Roch, 37230, Fondettes, France   (100%)
Tel.: (33) 247626400
Web Site: http://www.invacare.fr
Sales Range: $125-149.9 Million
Emp.: 400
Mfr of Home Healthcare Supplies
N.A.I.C.S.: 456199

Invacare France Operations SAS   (1)
Route de Saint Roch, 37230, Fondettes, France
Tel.: (33) 247626466
Web Site: http://www.invacare.fr
Surgical Instrument Mfr
N.A.I.C.S.: 339113

Invacare Germany Holding GmbH   (1)
Alemannstr 10, 88316, Isny, Baden-Wurttemberg, Germany
Tel.: (49) 756270099
Web Site: http://www.invacare.com
Investment Management Service
N.A.I.C.S.: 551112

Invacare GmbH   (1)
Am Achener Hof 8, Isny im Allgau, 88316, Isny, Germany
Tel.: (49) 75 627 0038
Web Site: https://www.invacare.de
Emp.: 200

Medical Equipment Mfr & Distr
N.A.I.C.S.: 334510

Invacare Holding Two AB (1)
PO Box 66, 163 91, Spanga, Sweden
Tel.: (46) 87617090
Web Site: http://www.invacare.se
Surgical & Medical Instrument Whslr
N.A.I.C.S.: 423450

Invacare Holdings AS (1)
Brynsveien 16, 0667, Oslo, Norway
Tel.: (47) 22579500
Web Site: https://www.invacare.no
Emp.: 50
Investment Management Service
N.A.I.C.S.: 551112

Invacare Holdings C.V. (1)
Celsiusstraat 46, 6716BZ, Ede, Netherlands
Tel.: (31) 318695757
Investment Management Service
N.A.I.C.S.: 551112

Invacare International SARL (1)
Benkenstrasse 260, 4108, Witterswil, Switzerland
Tel.: (41) 61 487 7070
Web Site: https://www.invacare.eu.com
Sales Range: $25-49.9 Million
Emp.: 30
Medical Equipment Mfr & Distr
N.A.I.C.S.: 334510
Matt Monaghan (CEO)

Invacare Ireland Ltd. (1)
Unit 5 Seatown Business Campus Seatown Road, Swords, K67 K271, Dublin, Ireland
Tel.: (353) 1 810 7084
Web Site: https://www.invacare.ie
Emp.: 8
Medical Equipment Mfr & Distr
N.A.I.C.S.: 334510

Invacare Lda. (1)
Rua da Estrada Velha 949, Leca do Balio, 4465-784, Porto, Portugal (100%)
Tel.: (351) 225193360
Web Site: https://www.invacare.pt
Sales Range: $50-74.9 Million
Emp.: 100
Home Medical Products
N.A.I.C.S.: 621610

Invacare Ltd. (1)
Unit 4 Pencoed Technology Park, Bridgend, CF35 5AQ, United Kingdom (100%)
Tel.: (44) 165 677 6222
Web Site: https://www.invacare.co.uk
Sales Range: $25-49.9 Million
Emp.: 200
Wheelchair Mfr
N.A.I.C.S.: 339113

Invacare NV (1)
Autobaan 22, 8210, Loppem, Belgium (100%)
Tel.: (32) 5 083 1010
Web Site: https://www.invacare.be
Sales Range: $1-9.9 Million
Emp.: 15
Home Medical Products
N.A.I.C.S.: 621610

Invacare Outcomes Management LLC (1)
7564 Market Pl Dr, Eden Prairie, MN 55344
Tel.: (612) 210-5717
Sales Range: $10-24.9 Million
Emp.: 10
Medical Equipment Mfr & Distr
N.A.I.C.S.: 334510

Invacare Poirier SAS (1)
Route de Saint Roch, 37230, Fondettes, France
Tel.: (33) 247626923
Web Site: http://www.invacare.fr
Non-Acute Health Care Products Mfr & Distr
N.A.I.C.S.: 423450

Invacare Rea AB (1)
Vaxjovagen 303 Dio, Box 66, 163 91, Spanga, Sweden
Tel.: (46) 8 761 7090
Web Site: https://www.invacare.se
Medical Equipment Mfr & Distr
N.A.I.C.S.: 334510

Invacare Verwaltungs GmbH (1)

Kleiststr 49, 32457, Porta Westfalica, Nordrhein-Westfalen, Germany
Tel.: (49) 57317540
Web Site: http://www.invacare.de
Emp.: 200
Surgical Instrument Mfr
N.A.I.C.S.: 339113
Mark Binder (Mng Dir)

Invacare, S.A. (1)
Avenida del Oeste N 50 11a, 46001, Valencia, Spain
Tel.: (34) 97 249 3214
Web Site: https://www.invacare.es
Emp.: 29
Medical Equipment Mfr & Distr
N.A.I.C.S.: 334510

Kuschall AG (1)
Benkenstrasse 260, 4108, Witterswil, Switzerland
Tel.: (41) 614877070
Web Site: http://www.kuschall.com
Medical Equipment Mfr & Distr
N.A.I.C.S.: 334510

Medbloc, Inc. (1)
700 Ensminger Rd Ste 112, Tonawanda, NY 14150
Tel.: (716) 447-0050
Web Site: https://www.motionconcepts.com
Surgical Appliance Mfr
N.A.I.C.S.: 339113

Motion Concepts, L.P. (1)
84 Citation Drive Unit 1, Concord, L4K 3C1, ON, Canada
Tel.: (905) 695-0134
Web Site: https://www.motionconcepts.com
Sales Range: $25-49.9 Million
Emp.: 80
Electronic Control Design & Mfr
N.A.I.C.S.: 339113

Perpetual Motion Enterprises Limited (1)
3520 Pharmacy Avenue Unit 9, Toronto, M1W 2T8, ON, Canada
Tel.: (416) 756-2517
Web Site: https://www.pmeltd.com
Emp.: 19
Electronic Control Design & Mfr
N.A.I.C.S.: 339113

The Aftermarket Group, Inc. (1)
39400 Taylor Pkwy, North Ridgeville, OH 44039
Web Site: http://www.aftermarketgroup.com
Medical & Surgical Equipment Repair & Maintenance Services
N.A.I.C.S.: 811210

INVENDA CORPORATION
7315 Wisconsin Ave Ste 400W, Bethesda, MD 20814
Tel.: (240) 333-6100   DE
Web Site: http://www.invenda.com
Year Founded: 1996
Sales Range: $10-24.9 Million
Emp.: 42
Digital Marketing & Promotional Services
N.A.I.C.S.: 541890
Kamran Amjadi (Co-Founder, Chm & CEO)
Peter Friedli (Co-Founder)

Subsidiaries:

ConsumerREVIEW, Inc. (1)
100 Marine Pkwy Ste 550, Redwood Shores, CA 94065
Tel.: (650) 264-4800
Web Site: http://www.consumerreview.com
Sales Range: $1-9.9 Million
Emp.: 30
Consumer Product Information Services
N.A.I.C.S.: 513199
Francis Cebedo (Founder & Gen Mgr)
Jim Thomas (Mgr-Sls)
Forrest Arakawa (Mgr-Sls)

E-centives, Inc. (1)
100 Marine Hwy Ste 550, Redwood Shores, CA 94065
Tel.: (650) 264-4800
Computer Programming Services
N.A.I.C.S.: 541511

INVENIO SOLUTIONS
2201 Donley Dr Ste 200, Austin, TX 78758
Tel.: (512) 990-2000
Web Site:
  http://www.inveniomarketing.com
Year Founded: 1994
Sales Range: $25-49.9 Million
Emp.: 450
Full Service Sales & Marketing Solutions
N.A.I.C.S.: 541613
John Grady (CEO)
Frank Reeves (Pres-Div)
Wasif Khan (Pres)
Billy Wilkinson (COO)
Michelle McDonald (Exec VP-Sls)

INVENIOS, INC.
320 N Nopal St, Santa Barbara, CA 93103-3225
Tel.: (805) 962-3333
Web Site: http://www.invenios.com
Sales Range: $10-24.9 Million
Emp.: 55
Nano Positioning Equipment Mfr
N.A.I.C.S.: 333242
Ray Karam (Pres & CEO)
Berkeley Johnson (COO & Exec VP)
George Roussos (VP & Dir-Engrg)

INVENT NOW, INC.
3701 Highland Park NW, North Canton, OH 44720
Tel.: (330) 849-6889   OH
Web Site: http://www.invent.org
Year Founded: 1987
Sales Range: $10-24.9 Million
Emp.: 118
Educational Support Services
N.A.I.C.S.: 611710
Shawn Loman (VP-Project Mgmt)
Vincent Greczanik (VP-Facilities & Technical Production)
David Clare (Co-Sec)

INVENT VENTURES, INC.
3651 Lindell Rd Ste D 146, Las Vegas, NV 89103
Tel.: (702) 943-0320   NV
Web Site: http://www.invent.vc
Sales Range: Less than $1 Million
Emp.: 5
Computer Related Investment Services
N.A.I.C.S.: 541519
Timothy Symington (CEO, CFO & Chief Investment Officer)

INVENTABIOTECH INC.
3463 Magic Dr Ste 120, San Antonio, TX 78229
Tel.: (210) 767-2727   CO
Year Founded: 2007
INVB— (OTCBB)
Investment Services
N.A.I.C.S.: 523999

INVENTORY LIQUIDATORS CORP.
8999 Palmer St, River Grove, IL 60171
Tel.: (708) 583-1000   IL
Web Site:
  http://www.regentproducts.com
Year Founded: 1985
Sales Range: $25-49.9 Million
Emp.: 200
Whslr of Home Furnishings
N.A.I.C.S.: 423220
Michael Depaul (Founder & Pres)
Pat Bratek (Mgr-Credit)
Ken Soens (Mgr-Sls)

INVENTORY SALES CO., INC.

9777 Reavis Rd, Saint Louis, MO 63123-1436
Tel.: (314) 776-6200
Web Site:
  http://www.inventorysales.com
Year Founded: 1972
Sales Range: $10-24.9 Million
Emp.: 99
Fastener Whslr
N.A.I.C.S.: 423710
Bryan Reinisch (Mgr-Sls)

INVERNESS MANAGEMENT, LLC
21 Locust Ave Ste 1D, New Canaan, CT 06840
Tel.: (203) 966-4177
Web Site:
  http://www.invernessmanagement.com
Year Founded: 1975
Sales Range: $25-49.9 Million
Emp.: 6
Private Equity Investment Firm
N.A.I.C.S.: 523999
Dean Anderson (Mng Dir)
James C. Comis III (Mng Gen Partner)
Robert N. Sheehy Jr. (Mng Dir)

INVESHARE INC.
777 3rd Ave 20th Fl, New York, NY 10017
Tel.: (212) 433-2370   DE
Web Site: http://www.inveshare.com
Year Founded: 2009
Shareholder Communications Market Services
N.A.I.C.S.: 561499
Davidi Gilo (CEO)
Richard Reinemann (COO)
Leonard Belvedere (Chief Compliance Officer & Sr VP-Ops & Relationship Mgmt)
Terry Shine (VP-Sls)

INVEST WEST FINANCIAL CORPORATION
1700 Red Hill 92614, Santa Barbara, CA 93109
Tel.: (805) 957-0095   CA
Web Site: http://www.investwest.net
Sales Range: $10-24.9 Million
Commercial Real Estate Investment & Development
N.A.I.C.S.: 531390
Dale J. Marquis (Founder & Chm)
Matthew D. Marquis (Pres & CEO)
Thomas J. Gamble (Gen Counsel & VP)
Adam Marquis (Exec VP)

Subsidiaries:

Pacifica Hotel Company (1)
1933 Cliff Dr Ste 1, Santa Barbara, CA 93109 (100%)
Tel.: (805) 957-0095
Web Site: http://www.pacificahotelco.com
Hotel Management
N.A.I.C.S.: 531210
Dale J. Marquis (Chm)

Subsidiary (Domestic):

IWF San Simeon Pines, L.P. (2)
7200 Moonstone Beach Dr, Cambria, CA 93428-1824
Tel.: (805) 927-4648
Web Site: http://www.sansimeonpines.com
Hotels & Resort Operator
N.A.I.C.S.: 721110

INVESTAR HOLDINGS INC.
3500 Financial Plz, Tallahassee, FL 32312
Tel.: (404) 851-1700
Rev.: $10,000,000
Emp.: 5
Insurance Agents, Brokers & Service

Investar Holdings Inc.—(Continued)

N.A.I.C.S.: 524210

INVESTMENT ENTERPRISES INC.

8240 Haskell Ave, Van Nuys, CA 91406
Tel.: (818) 988-0011
Sales Range: $10-24.9 Million
Emp.: 100
Magazine Printing
N.A.I.C.S.: 323111
Michael Warner (Pres)

INVESTMENT PARTNERS GROUP, INC.

10 Station Pl, Metuchen, NJ 08840
Tel.: (732) 205-0391   DE
Web Site:
    http://www.investmentpartners.com
Holding Company; Investment Advisory & Asset Management Services
N.A.I.C.S.: 551112
Gregg T. Abella (Principal & Portfolio Mgr)
Frank J. Abella Jr. (Founder, Pres & CEO)
Frank J. Abella III (VP & Portfolio Mgr)

Subsidiaries:

Investment Partners Asset Management, Inc.   (1)
10 Station Rd, Metuchen, NJ 08840
Tel.: (732) 205-0391
Web Site:
    http://www.investmentpartners.com
Emp.: 6
Investment Advisory & Asset Management Services
N.A.I.C.S.: 523940
Thomas W. Shepherd (VP)

INVESTMENT PROPERTIES CORPORATION

3838 Tamiami Trl N Ste 402, Naples, FL 34103
Tel.: (239) 261-3400
Web Site: http://www.ipcnaples.com
Year Founded: 1976
Sales Range: $1-9.9 Million
Emp.: 10
Commercial Real Estate Brokerage Services
N.A.I.C.S.: 531210
Craig D. Timmons (Principal)
David J. Stevens (Principal)
William V. Gonnering (Principal)
Clint L. Sherwood (Principal)

INVESTMENT RARITIES INCORPORATED

7850 Metro Pkwy, Minneapolis, MN 55425-1521
Tel.: (952) 853-0700
Web Site:
    http://www.investmentrarities.com
Year Founded: 1973
Sales Range: $25-49.9 Million
Emp.: 65
Retailer of Miscellaneous Products
N.A.I.C.S.: 459999
James R. Cook (Pres & Treas)
Tom Stock (Controller)

INVESTMENT SEMINARS, INC.

The Githler Ctr 1258 N Palm Ave, Sarasota, FL 34236
Tel.: (941) 955-0323
Web Site:
    http://www.moenyshow.com
Year Founded: 1978
Sales Range: $10-24.9 Million
Emp.: 65

Conference (Trade Show) Producer for Individual Investors, Active Traders & Financial Advisors
N.A.I.C.S.: 561920
Aaron West (Sr VP-Media & Platform Relationships-US)
Kim Githler (Pres & CEO)
Mecheal Res (CFO)
Jennifer Bruce (Mgr-Adv)

INVESTMENT TRUST COMPANY

3200 Cherry Creek S Dr Ste 730, Denver, CO 80209-3247
Tel.: (303) 778-6800   CO
Web Site:
    http://www.investmenttrust.com
Year Founded: 1983
Sales Range: $150-199.9 Million
Emp.: 7
Asset Management
N.A.I.C.S.: 523940
John S. Benson (Co-Founder & Chm)
Thomas L. Herrington (Pres & Principal)
Cynthia Payseur (Sr VP & Dir-Fiduciary Svcs)

INVESTOR SOLUTIONS INC.

2665 S Bayshore Dr Ste 230, Miami, FL 33133
Tel.: (305) 443-3339
Web Site:
    http://www.investorsolutions.com
Year Founded: 1993
Rev.: $500,000,000
Emp.: 12
Portfolio Management & Investment Advisory Services
N.A.I.C.S.: 523940
David Seiglie (Chief Compliance Officer & Mgr-Ops)
Frank Armstrong (Founder & CEO)
Richard Feldman (Mng Partner)

INVESTORCOM INC.

65 Locust Ave Ste 300, New Canaan, CT 06840-4753
Tel.: (203) 972-9300
Web Site: http://www.investor-com.com
Year Founded: 2000
Sales Range: $1-9.9 Million
Emp.: 10
Corporate Communications, Financial, Media Relations
N.A.I.C.S.: 541820
John Glenn Grau (Pres)

INVESTORS CORPORATION OF VERMONT

30 Main St Ste 401, Burlington, VT 05401
Tel.: (802) 863-2311
Web Site: http://www.icv-vt.com
Year Founded: 1973
Sales Range: $25-49.9 Million
Emp.: 10
Investment Holding Companies, Except Banks
N.A.I.C.S.: 551112
Barbara Surprenant (Dir-Leasing)

Subsidiaries:

American International Distribution Corporation   (1)
50 Winter Sport Ln, Williston, VT 05495-0080
Tel.: (802) 862-0095
Web Site: http://www.aidcvt.com
Sales Range: $25-49.9 Million
Investment Holding Companies, Except Banks
N.A.I.C.S.: 424920
Michael Pelland (Mgr-Ops)

INVESTORS HERITAGE CAPITAL CORP.

200 Capital Ave, Frankfort, KY 40601
Tel.: (502) 223-2361   KY
Web Site:
    http://www.investorsheritage.com
Year Founded: 1960
Sales Range: $50-74.9 Million
Emp.: 76
Life Insurance Holding Company
N.A.I.C.S.: 524128
Raymond L. Carr (COO & Exec VP)
Harry Lee Waterfield II (Chm, Pres & CEO)
Robert M. Hardy Jr. (Gen Counsel & Exec VP)
Jane S. Jackson (Sec)
Larry Joe Johnson II (CFO & VP)

Subsidiaries:

Investors Heritage Life Insurance Company   (1)
200 Capital Ave, Frankfort, KY 40601   (100%)
Tel.: (502) 223-2361
Web Site: http://www.investorsheritage.com
Sales Range: $50-74.9 Million
Life Insurance Sales
N.A.I.C.S.: 524113
Harry Lee Waterfield II (Chm, Pres & CEO)

INVESTORS MANAGEMENT CORPORATION

801 N West St, Raleigh, NC 27603
Tel.: (919) 653-7499   NC
Web Site:
    http://www.investorsmanage
    ment.com
Year Founded: 1971
Sales Range: $550-599.9 Million
Emp.: 13
Investment Holding Company
N.A.I.C.S.: 551112
Sampson Starling (VP)
Dick Chase (VP-Special Dev)
Glen Kinkade (Dir-Ops-Real Estate)
Larry Weiland (Dir-Real Estate)
Easter A. Maynard (Chm & Exec Dir)
Richard A. Urquhart III (COO)
Jennifer K. Moses (CFO)

Subsidiaries:

Fleet Feet Sports, LLC   (1)
310 E Main St Ste 120, Carrboro, NC 27510
Tel.: (919) 968-3338
Web Site: http://www.fleetfeet.com
Emp.: 40
Athletic Sport Product Retailer Services
N.A.I.C.S.: 713940
Joey Pointer (Pres & CEO)
Robyn Goby (VP-Dev)
Brian Breedlove (Dir-Dev)
Tremayne Cryer (Dir-Art)
Jon Davis (Dir-Retail Ops)
Ellen Donahue (Sr Dir-Mktg)
Jason Jabaut (COO)
Frank Pitts (Sr Mgr-Retail Dev)
Matt Werder (Dir-Retail Experience)
Matt Zeiger (CFO)
Brent Hollowell (CMO)
Sarah Holden (Partner-HR Bus)

Golden Corral Corporation   (1)
5151 Glenwood Ave, Raleigh, NC 27612
Tel.: (919) 781-9310
Web Site: http://www.goldencorral.net
Emp.: 200
Family Buffet-Style Restaurants Operator & Franchisor
N.A.I.C.S.: 722514
Robert M. McDevitt (Sr VP-Franchising)
Judy Irwin (VP-HR & Trng)
Mary Bowen (Office Mgr-Svcs)
Sam Starling (VP)
Lance Trenary (Pres & CEO)
Paul Hanke (CMO)

KDI Capital Partners, LLC   (1)
4101 Lake Boone Trl Ste 218, Raleigh, NC 27607
Tel.: (919) 573-4124

Emp.: 7
Investment Advisory Services
N.A.I.C.S.: 523940
John Day (Mng Partner)
Beth Dalton (Office Mgr)

Morehead Capital Management LLC   (1)
1101 Haynes St Ste 108, Raleigh, NC 27604
Tel.: (919) 827-8803
Web Site: http://www.moreheadcapital.com
Investment Management Service
N.A.I.C.S.: 523940
Quinton Maynard (Mng Partner)
Nathan Edgerly (Partner)
Adam Daland (Partner)
Tom Donaldson (Gen Counsel & Partner)

INVESTORS MANAGEMENT TRUST REAL ESTATE GROUP INC.

15303 Ventura Blvd Ste 200, Sherman Oaks, CA 91403
Tel.: (818) 784-4700
Web Site:
    http://www.imtresidential.com
Sales Range: $10-24.9 Million
Emp.: 53
Property Management
N.A.I.C.S.: 531110
John M. Tesoriero (Pres)

INVESTORTOOLS INC.

2135 City Gate Ln Ste 340, Naperville, IL 60563
Tel.: (630) 553-0040   IL
Web Site: http://www.invtools.com
Year Founded: 1983
Custom Computer Programming Services
N.A.I.C.S.: 541511
Ronald Mattson (Mgr-Client Relationship)
Mike Green (COO)
Jon Anderson (Chief Product Officer & Head)
Jack Brothers Jr. (Mgr-Client Relationship)

Subsidiaries:

Merritt Research Services LLC   (1)
1212 Dina Ct, Hiawatha, IA 52233
Tel.: (319) 861-5400
Web Site: http://www.merrittresearch.com
Data Processing, Hosting & Related Services
N.A.I.C.S.: 518210
Troy A. Gerleman (COO & Exec VP)
Richard A. Ciccarone (Pres)
Carrie A. Benjamin (Sr VP & Dir-R&D)

INVETECH, LLC

10665 Richmond Ste 192, Houston, TX 77042-4910
Tel.: (713) 781-4749
Web Site: http://www.invetech.com
Year Founded: 1985
Engineered Product Laboratory Testing Services
N.A.I.C.S.: 541380
John E. Slater (Principal)

INVETEK, INC.

15415 Redhill Ave Ste A, Tustin, CA 92780
Tel.: (714) 259-8041
Web Site: http://www.invetek.com
Year Founded: 1995
Pharmaceuticals Product Mfr
N.A.I.C.S.: 325412
George Garcia (Mgr-Production)
Manoj Saraiya (Pres)

INVICTUS INTERNATIONAL CONSULTING, LLC

66 Canal Center Plz Ste 501, Alexandria, VA 22314
Tel.: (703) 214-1002
Web Site: http://www.invictusic.com

Year Founded: 2014
Sales Range: $25-49.9 Million
Emp.: 151
Cyber Security Consulting Services
N.A.I.C.S.: 541690
Jim Kelly *(Pres & CEO)*
Jamie Navarro *(COO)*
April Jackson *(VP-Admin)*
Sage Cesspooch *(VP-Growth)*

INVINCIBLE OFFICE FURNI-TURE
842 S 26th St, Manitowoc, WI 54220
Tel.: (920) 682-4601   WI
Web Site:
   http://www.invinciblefurniture.com
Year Founded: 1904
Sales Range: $50-74.9 Million
Emp.: 75
Steel Office Furniture Mfr
N.A.I.C.S.: 337214
James Leiser *(Pres & CEO)*

INVISIBLE CLOSE
PO Box 2407, La Jolla, CA 92038
Tel.: (646) 368-8210
Web Site:
   http://www.theinvisibleclose.com
Year Founded: 2007
Sales Range: $1-9.9 Million
Emp.: 10
Sales Training & Coaching
N.A.I.C.S.: 611430
Lisa Sasevich *(Owner)*

INVISION COMMUNICATIONS, INC.
1280 Civic Dr 3rd Fl, Walnut Creek, CA 94596
Tel.: (925) 944-1211
Web Site: http://www.iv.com
Sales Range: $10-24.9 Million
Emp.: 80
Marketing & Communications Services
N.A.I.C.S.: 541613
Rod Mickels *(Co-Founder & CEO)*
Drew Hagan *(Co-Founder & Exec Producer)*
Mike Hagan *(COO)*
Mike Burgess *(Dir-Client Svcs & Corp Mktg)*
Amy Lewis *(Dir-Production)*
Valerie Hill *(Dir-HR)*

Subsidiaries:

InVision Communications, Inc.   (1)
550 7th Ave 17th Fl, New York, NY 10018
Tel.: (212) 792-7800
Web Site: http://www.iv.com
Emp.: 25
Marketing & Communications Services
N.A.I.C.S.: 541613
Renee Miller *(Gen Mgr)*
Drew Hagen *(Co-Founder & Chief Culture Officer)*
Valerie Hill *(Dir-HR)*
Molly Hodge *(Dir-Creative)*
Spratley Kay *(Dir-Client Svcs-NY)*
Jennifer Lowery *(Dir-Ops)*
Rod Mickels *(Co-Founder & CEO)*
Kandiss Schulz *(Dir-Fin)*
Tracy Verrett *(Dir-Mktg & Brand Dev)*

InVision Communications, Inc. - Chicago   (1)
308 W Erie St Ste 302, Chicago, IL 60654
Tel.: (312) 429-1211
Web Site: http://www.iv.com
Emp.: 8
Marketing & Communications Services
N.A.I.C.S.: 541613
Ted Ergo *(Dir-Client Svcs & Bus Dev)*

INVITATION CONSULTANTS, INC.
12175 W Linebaugh Ave, Tampa, FL 33626-1732
Tel.: (813) 879-3748

Web Site:
   http://www.invitationconsultants.com
Year Founded: 1999
Rev.: $6,200,000
Emp.: 19
Direct Selling Establishments
N.A.I.C.S.: 424120
Audrey Martin *(Coord-Shipping)*
Lucy Teague *(Coord-Client Rels)*
Olivier De Meulder *(Owner)*

INVIZION, INC.
1650 Tyson's Blvd Ste 1580, McLean, VA 22102
Tel.: (703) 226-5000
Web Site: http://www.invizion.com
Year Founded: 2003
Sales Range: $25-49.9 Million
Emp.: 8
Management Consulting Services
N.A.I.C.S.: 541611
Steven A. Johnson *(Co-Founder, Chm & CEO)*
George E. Washington *(Co-Founder & Pres)*

INVNT, LLC
524 Broadway Fl 4, New York, NY 10012
Tel.: (212) 343-3415
Web Site: http://www.invnt.com
Year Founded: 2008
Meetings, Events, Brand Initiatives, Product Launches, Custom Training Programs, Environments, Exhibits, Film & Video Services
N.A.I.C.S.: 541890
Scott Cullather *(Founder & CEO)*

INVOLTA, LLC
PO Box 1986, Cedar Rapids, IA 52406
Tel.: (319) 364-3061
Web Site: http://www.involta.com
Year Founded: 2007
Sales Range: $1-9.9 Million
Emp.: 36
Full-Service Data Center Facilities & Critical Recovery Systems
N.A.I.C.S.: 519290
Bruce Lehrman *(Founder & Vice Chm)*
Ken Kremer *(COO)*
Jeff Thorsteinson *(VP-Compliance & Sec)*
Thomas Wilcox *(CTO)*
Jeffrey Szymanski *(VP-Strategic Markets)*
James Buie *(Pres & CEO)*

INVUE SECURITY PRODUCTS
15015 Lancaster Hwy, Charlotte, NC 28277
Tel.: (704) 752-6513
Web Site:
   http://www.invuesecurity.com
Sales Range: $75-99.9 Million
Emp.: 162
Electronic Security Product Mfr
N.A.I.C.S.: 334419
Jim Sankey *(Pres & CEO)*
Andy Moock *(Exec VP)*

INWARE TECHNOLOGIES, INC.
870 111th Ave N Ste 8, Naples, FL 34108
Tel.: (239) 384-9335   DE
Web Site:
   http://www.inwaretechnologies.com
Sales Range: Less than $1 Million
Emp.: 30
E-Mail Migration & Directory Synchronization Services
N.A.I.C.S.: 541519
John E. Baker *(CFO & Treas)*

INWOOD BANCSHARES INC.
7621 Inwood Rd, Dallas, TX 75209
Tel.: (214) 358-0294
Web Site:
   http://www.inwoodbank.com
Year Founded: 1985
Sales Range: $50-74.9 Million
Emp.: 125
Bank Holding Company
N.A.I.C.S.: 551111
Jerald W. Freeman Jr. *(Chm)*

Subsidiaries:

Inwood National Bank Inc.   (1)
7621 Inwood Rd, Dallas, TX 75209-4000
Tel.: (214) 358-5281
Web Site: http://www.inwoodbank.com
Sales Range: $50-74.9 Million
Emp.: 200
Banking Services
N.A.I.C.S.: 522110
Gary Tipton *(Pres & CEO)*
Dennis Lorch *(CFO)*
Elizabeth Weaver *(VP)*
Martin J. Noto Jr. *(Chief Lending Officer & Exec VP)*

INYX, INC.
825 3rd Ave 40th Fl, New York, NY 10022-9510
Tel.: (212) 838-1111
Pharmaceuticals Product Mfr
N.A.I.C.S.: 325412
Jack Kachkar *(Chm & CEO)*

IOCHEM CORPORATION
5801 Broadway Ext Ste 305, Oklahoma City, OK 73118
Tel.: (405) 848-8611
Web Site: http://www.iochem.net
Sales Range: $10-24.9 Million
Emp.: 6
Iodine Mfr
N.A.I.C.S.: 325199
Takeshi Kita *(Chm)*
Bruce Hamel *(VP-Sls & Mktg)*
Kathy Frame *(Office Mgr)*

IODINE SOFTWARE, LLC
6850 Austin Ctr Blvd Ste 350, Austin, TX 78731
Tel.: (512) 829-0600   TX
Web Site:
   http://www.iodinesoftware.com
Year Founded: 2010
Software Publisher
N.A.I.C.S.: 513210
William Chan *(CEO)*
Michael Lovell *(CFO)*
David Chao *(CTO)*
Steven J. Mason Jr. *(Exec VP)*

Subsidiaries:

ChartWise Medical Systems, Inc.   (1)
1174 Kingstown Rd, Wakefield, RI 02879
Web Site: http://www.chartwisemed.com
Software Publisher
N.A.I.C.S.: 513210
Kathy Luther *(Mgr-Clinical Product)*
Tom Emberson *(VP-Sls & Mktg)*
Mary Cooper *(Exec VP)*
Jon Elion *(Founder & CEO)*
Steven Mason *(Pres & COO)*

IOFFICE, LLC
5300 Memorial Ste 300, Houston, TX 77007
Tel.: (713) 526-1029
Web Site: http://www.iofficecorp.com
Year Founded: 2002
Sales Range: $1-9.9 Million
Emp.: 33
Facilities Management Software Development Services
N.A.I.C.S.: 541511
Don Traweek *(Pres & CEO)*
Elizabeth Dukes *(Founder & Chief Mktg Officer)*

Nathan Krichel *(Acct Mgr)*
Mike Petrusky *(Dir-Events & Growth Mktg)*

Subsidiaries:

ManagerPlus Solutions, LLC   (1)
9350 S 150 E Ste 650, Sandy, UT 84070
Tel.: (800) 730-9809
Web Site: http://www.managerplus.com
Software Publisher
N.A.I.C.S.: 513210

IOMEDIA
640 W 28th St, New York, NY 10001
Tel.: (212) 352-1115
Web Site: http://www.io-media.com
Year Founded: 1997
Sales Range: $25-49.9 Million
Emp.: 35
Advertising Agencies
N.A.I.C.S.: 541810
Peter Korian *(Founder & Pres)*
Steve Korian *(Exec VP)*
John Leone *(Sr VP-Strategy & Analytics)*
Eugene Carroll *(VP-Infrastructure & IT Svcs)*
Marc Porter *(Mng Dir-Healthcare)*

ION CORPORATION
7500 Equitable Dr, Eden Prairie, MN 55344-3673
Tel.: (952) 936-9490
Web Site: http://www.ioncorp.com
Sales Range: $10-24.9 Million
Emp.: 50
Aircraft Parts & Equipment
N.A.I.C.S.: 336413
Wendell Maddox *(Founder, Pres & CEO)*

ION FINANCIAL, MHC
PO Box 370, Naugatuck, CT 06770
Tel.: (203) 729-4442
Bank Holding Company
N.A.I.C.S.: 551111
Charles J. Boulier *(Chm)*

Subsidiaries:

Ion Bank   (1)
5 Minortown Rd, Woodbury, CT 06798-3007
Tel.: (203) 217-5767
Web Site:
   http://www.naugatucksavingsbank.com
Assets: $1,661,727,000
Liabilities: $1,530,248,000
Net Worth: $131,479,000
Emp.: 5,867
Fiscal Year-end: 12/31/2020
Commericial Banking
N.A.I.C.S.: 522110
David J. Rotatori *(Pres & CEO)*
Philip V. Vaz *(Reg Pres-New Jersey)*
Charles J. Boulier III *(Chm)*

Lincoln Park Bancorp   (1)
31 Boonton Turnpike, Lincoln Park, NJ 07035
Tel.: (973) 694-0330
Commercial Banking Services
N.A.I.C.S.: 522110
Stanford Stoller *(Chm)*

ION INTERACTIVE, INC.
200 E Palmetto Park Rd Ste 107, Boca Raton, FL 33432
Tel.: (561) 394-9484
Web Site:
   http://www.ioninteractive.com
Sales Range: $1-9.9 Million
Emp.: 30
Data Processing, Hosting & Related Services
N.A.I.C.S.: 518210
Justin Talerico *(CEO)*
Scott Brinker *(Co-Founder, Pres & CTO)*

ion interactive, inc.—(Continued)

Ann Talerico *(Co-Founder & Exec VP)*
Susan Deltz *(Dir-Enterprise Acct Dev)*
Audrey Ross *(Dir-Customer Success)*
Carla Mariotti *(Dir-Ops)*
Jason Palter *(Dir-User Experience)*
Mary Ward *(VP-Acct Svcs)*
Eric Amodio *(VP-Engrg)*

ION-3 CORPORATION
1460 NE 57th Ct, Fort Lauderdale, FL 33334
Tel.: (954) 684-0679 **FL**
Year Founded: 2012
Lithium Ion Battery Mfr
N.A.I.C.S.: 335910
Byron Ellison *(CEO)*
Shawn Durand *(CFO, Principal Acctg Officer, VP-Fin)*
Bruce J. Black *(Exec VP-Engrg)*
Jean-Marc Sellier *(VP-Legal)*

IONEX RESEARCH CORP.
1301 E Wind Dr, Lafayette, CO 80026
Tel.: (303) 666-5550
Web Site: http://www.ionexres.com
Sales Range: $10-24.9 Million
Emp.: 50
Blowers & Fans
N.A.I.C.S.: 333413
Tara Rickerson *(Project Mgr)*
Ellis Howard *(Mgr-Quality Assurance)*
Jeremy Ballew *(Coord-Safety)*

IONIC MEDIA
16501 Ventura Blvd Ste 500, Sherman Oaks, CA 91436
Tel.: (818) 849-3737
Web Site: http://www.ionicmedia.com
Year Founded: 2002
Sales Range: $100-124.9 Million
Emp.: 40
Advertising Agencies
N.A.I.C.S.: 541810
Michael Kubin *(Founder & Mng Dir)*

IONIDEA, INC.
3913 Old Lee Hwy Ste 33B, Fairfax, VA 22030
Tel.: (703) 691-0400 **VA**
Web Site: http://www.ionidea.com
Year Founded: 1994
Sales Range: $25-49.9 Million
Emp.: 450
Information Technology Solutions; Consulting & Turnkey Services
N.A.I.C.S.: 541512
Kisham Ananthram *(Chm & CEO)*
Alan Krishnan *(CFO & Exec VP)*
Amrit Yegnanarayan *(VP-Solutions Delivery)*

IONIQ SCIENCES, INC.
350 W 800 N Ste 214, Salt Lake City, UT 84103
Tel.: (801) 736-0729 **DE**
Web Site:
https://www.ioniqsciences.com
Year Founded: 2004
Assets: $534,569
Liabilities: $13,584,073
Net Worth: ($13,049,504)
Earnings: ($4,359,401)
Emp.: 9
Fiscal Year-end: 12/31/22
Medical Device Mfr
N.A.I.C.S.: 334510
Michael A. Garff *(COO)*
Rex Chin-Wei Yung *(Chief Medical Officer)*
Andy C. Robertson *(VP-Bus Dev)*
Jared B. Bauer *(CEO)*
Owen Brimhall *(Dir-R&D)*

IOSTUDIO
565 Marriott Dr Ste 100, Nashville, TN 37214
Tel.: (615) 256-6282
Web Site: http://www.iostudio.com
Sales Range: $25-49.9 Million
Emp.: 212
Advertising Agency Services
N.A.I.C.S.: 541810
Ed Brown *(CFO & Partner)*
Chris West *(COO & Partner)*
Claire Rogers *(Sr Acct Exec)*
Lindsey Schwalb *(Acct Supvr)*

IOWA 80 GROUP, INC.
515 Sterling Dr, Walcott, IA 52773
Tel.: (563) 284-6965 **IA**
Web Site:
http://www.iowa80group.com
Year Founded: 1965
Sales Range: $100-124.9 Million
Emp.: 1,300
Gasoline Service Stations
N.A.I.C.S.: 457120
Mike Dailing *(Mgr-Fleet Sls)*

Subsidiaries:

284 Fuel Supply, LLC (1)
515 Sterling Dr, Walcott, IA 52773
Tel.: (563) 284-6965
Web Site: http://www.284fuelsupply.com
Emp.: 3
Petroleum Product Whslr
N.A.I.C.S.: 424720
Ron Burmeister *(VP)*

CAT Scale Company (1)
PO Box 630, Walcott, IA 52773
Tel.: (563) 284-6668
Web Site: http://www.catscale.com
Truck Scale Mfr
N.A.I.C.S.: 333998
Delia Moon Meier *(Sr VP)*

Iowa 80 Truckstop (1)
755 W Iowa 80 Rd Interstate 80 Exit 284, Walcott, IA 52773
Tel.: (563) 284-6961
Web Site: http://www.iowa80truckstop.com
Truckstop Operator
N.A.I.C.S.: 457120
Mike Hutchison *(Gen Mgr)*

Iowa 80.Com Inc. (1)
515 Sterling Dr, Walcott, IA 52773
Tel.: (563) 284-6965
Web Site: http://www.iowa80.com
Emp.: 200
Automotive Parts Store Operator
N.A.I.C.S.: 441330

Joplin Petro (1)
4240 Hwy 43 I-44 Exit 4, Joplin, MO 64804
Tel.: (417) 624-3400
Web Site: http://www.joplin44.com
Sales Range: $10-24.9 Million
Emp.: 5
Gasoline Service Stations
N.A.I.C.S.: 457120
Joel Hamilton *(Gen Mgr)*

Oak Grove Petro Truckstop (1)
301 SW 1st St, Oak Grove, MO 64075-9102
Tel.: (816) 690-4455
Web Site: http://www.oakgrovepetro.com
Sales Range: $25-49.9 Million
Emp.: 175
Gasoline Service Stations
N.A.I.C.S.: 457120

Truckomat Corporation (1)
I 80 Exit 284, Walcott, IA 52773 (100%)
Tel.: (563) 284-6139
Web Site: http://www.truckomat.com
Sales Range: $10-24.9 Million
Emp.: 116
Truck & Fleet Wash Services
N.A.I.C.S.: 811192
Ron Crino *(Gen Mgr)*

IOWA BEER & BEVERAGE
1825 Edgewood Rd SW, Cedar Rapids, IA 52404
Tel.: (319) 396-8981

Year Founded: 1955
Sales Range: $10-24.9 Million
Emp.: 65
Beer & Other Fermented Malt Liquors Whslr
N.A.I.C.S.: 424810

IOWA BEVERAGE SYSTEMS INC.
2115 NE 58th Ave, Des Moines, IA 50313-1633
Tel.: (515) 266-2274 **IA**
Web Site: http://www.ibev.com
Beer, Wine & Liquor Stores
N.A.I.C.S.: 445320
Mike Brewington *(Pres)*

Subsidiaries:

Iowa Beer & Beverage Company (1)
11125 High Life Ct SW, Cedar Rapids, IA 52404
Tel.: (319) 848-8275
Beer & Ale Merchant Whslr
N.A.I.C.S.: 424810
Dudley Fleck *(Exec VP)*
Mike Schulte *(Sls Mgr)*

IOWA BRIDGE & CULVERT LLC
409 N Avenue B, Washington, IA 52353
Tel.: (319) 653-5436
Web Site: http://www.iowabridge.com
Sales Range: $10-24.9 Million
Emp.: 100
Bridge Construction
N.A.I.C.S.: 237310
Burge Hammond *(VP)*

IOWA COMPREHENSIVE HEALTH ASSOCIATION
2015 16th St, Great Bend, KS 67530
Tel.: (877) 793-6880 **IA**
Web Site: http://www.hipiowa.com
Year Founded: 1987
Sales Range: $10-24.9 Million
Health Insurance Benefit Services
N.A.I.C.S.: 524114
Joe Day *(Pres)*
Kevin Van Dyke *(Sec)*
Angela Burke Boston *(VP)*
Mark Willse *(Treas)*
Cecil D. Bykerk *(Exec Dir)*

IOWA DONOR NETWORK
550 Madison Ave, North Liberty, IA 52317
Tel.: (319) 665-3787 **IA**
Web Site:
http://www.iowadonornetwork.org
Year Founded: 1993
Sales Range: $10-24.9 Million
Emp.: 138
Organ Donor Services
N.A.I.C.S.: 621991
Tammi Erb *(Treas)*
Kim Burdakin *(Sec)*
Nancy Richardson *(Chm)*
Suzanne Conrad *(CEO)*
Christie Thomas *(Vice Chm)*
Sarah Fewell *(COO)*

IOWA FARM BUREAU FEDERATION
5400 University Ave, West Des Moines, IA 50266-5950
Tel.: (515) 225-5400 **IA**
Web Site: http://www.ifbf.org
Year Founded: 1921
Sales Range: $1-9.9 Million
Emp.: 1,971
Business Associations
N.A.I.C.S.: 813910

Jerry Downin *(Treas)*
David Miller *(Dir-Res)*
Steven Flug *(Mgr-Facility)*
Don McDowell *(Mgr-Grassroots Program)*

Subsidiaries:

FBL Financial Group, Inc. (1)
5400 University Ave, West Des Moines, IA 50266-5997 (61%)
Tel.: (515) 225-5400
Web Site: http://www.fblfinancial.com
Rev.: $732,265,000
Assets: $10,996,272,000
Liabilities: $9,304,156,000
Net Worth: $1,692,116,000
Earnings: $72,513,000
Emp.: 1,754
Fiscal Year-end: 12/31/2020
Insurance Holding Company
N.A.I.C.S.: 323113
Donald J. Seibel *(CFO & Treas)*
Anthony J. Aldridge *(Chief Acctg Officer)*
Lori K. Geadelmann *(Gen Counsel)*
Kelli A. Eddy *(COO-Life Companies)*
Jay W. Seiboldt *(COO-Property Casualty Companies)*
Jeffrey A. Whitehead *(Chief Investment Officer)*

Subsidiary (Domestic):

FBL Leasing Services, Inc. (2)
5400 University Ave, West Des Moines, IA 50266-5997
Tel.: (515) 225-4647
Office Equipment Rental Services
N.A.I.C.S.: 532310

FBL Marketing Services, L.L.C. (2)
5400 University Ave, West Des Moines, IA 50266-5997
Tel.: (515) 225-5400
Web Site: http://www.fbfs.com
Fire Insurance Services
N.A.I.C.S.: 524113

Farm Bureau Life Insurance Company (2)
5400 University Ave, West Des Moines, IA 50266 (100%)
Tel.: (515) 225-5400
Web Site: http://www.fblfinancial.com
Sales Range: $800-899.9 Million
Emp.: 1,100
Life Insurance
N.A.I.C.S.: 524113

Subsidiary (Domestic):

Utah Farm Bureau Financial Services (Inc.) (3)
9865 S State St, Sandy, UT 84070 (100%)
Tel.: (801) 233-3000
Web Site: http://www.fbff.com
Emp.: 13
Fire, Marine & Casualty Insurance
N.A.I.C.S.: 524126

Subsidiary (Domestic):

Farm Bureau Mutual Insurance Co. (2)
5400 University Ave, West Des Moines, IA 50266
Tel.: (515) 225-5400
Web Site: http://www.fbfs.com
Rev.: $460,227,456
Emp.: 1,920
Insurance Agents, Brokers & Service
N.A.I.C.S.: 524210

IOWA LABORERS DISTRICT COUNCIL HEALTH & WELFARE PLAN
2600 Grand Ave Ste 230, Des Moines, IA 50312
Tel.: (515) 243-2080 **IA**
Year Founded: 1969
Sales Range: $25-49.9 Million
Health Care Srvices
N.A.I.C.S.: 621610
James Piazza Jr. *(Treas & Sec)*

IOWA LAKES ELECTRIC COOPERATIVE

702 South 1st St, Estherville, IA 51334
Tel.: (712) 362-7870
Web Site: http://www.ilec.coop
Year Founded: 1989
Sales Range: $25-49.9 Million
Emp.: 32
Electronic Services
N.A.I.C.S.: 221118
Rick Olesen *(Pres & CEO)*
September L. Dau *(Sr VP-Fin)*
Alan Madden *(Treas)*
Shelly Tredway *(Mgr-Acctg)*
Tresa L. Hussong *(VP-Customer & Corp Rels)*
Ann Ingvall *(Mgr-Customer Care)*
Bob Emgarten *(Mgr-Engrg)*
Kristin Hanson *(Mgr-HR & Payroll)*
Al Zeitz *(Mgr-Renewable Energy Svcs)*
Pam Caboth *(VP-Admin Svcs)*
Aaron Ruschy *(VP-Ops & Engrg)*

IOWA LIMESTONE COMPANY

3301 106th Cir, Urbandale, IA 50322-4908
Tel.: (515) 243-8106   IA
Web Site:
    http://www.ilcresources.com
Year Founded: 1924
Sales Range: $10-24.9 Million
Emp.: 100
Feed-Grade Calcium Carbonate Mfr & Livestock Feed Ingredients Distr
N.A.I.C.S.: 424910
Frank Goode *(Pres & CEO)*

IOWA MANAGEMENT SYSTEMS INC.

2441 Coral Ct Ste 3, Coralville, IA 52241-2872
Tel.: (319) 545-7775
Year Founded: 1976
Sales Range: $10-24.9 Million
Emp.: 100
Provider of Management Consulting Services
N.A.I.C.S.: 541611
Lee Staak *(CEO)*

IOWA MUTUAL INSURANCE COMPANY

509 9th St, De Witt, IA 52742
Tel.: (563) 659-3231   IA
Web Site:
    http://www.iowamutual.com
Year Founded: 1900
Sales Range: $25-49.9 Million
Emp.: 96
Property & Casualty Insurance Products & Services
N.A.I.C.S.: 524126
Charles D. Stapleton *(COO)*
Georgia Puls *(Pres)*

IOWA NATURAL HERITAGE FOUNDATION

505 5th Ave Ste 444, Des Moines, IA 50309-2321
Tel.: (515) 288-1846   IA
Web Site: http://www.inhf.org
Year Founded: 1979
Sales Range: $10-24.9 Million
Emp.: 30
Wildlife Conservation Services
N.A.I.C.S.: 813312
Kari Walker *(Dir-Admin)*
Heather Jobst *(Sr Dir-Land Conservation)*
Lisa Hein *(Sr Dir-Conservation Programs)*
Don Beneke *(Sec)*
Joe McGovern *(Pres)*
Wendy Wiedner *(Treas)*
David Crouse *(Chm)*
Jodi Baker *(Fin Dir)*

Ross Baxter *(Dir-Land Projects)*
Andrea Boulton *(Dir-Trails & Greenways)*
Brian Fankhauser *(Dir-Blufflands)*
Cheri Grauer *(Dir-Donor Rels)*
Joe Jayjack *(Dir-Comm)*
Stacy Nelson *(Mgr-Donor svcs)*
Anita O'Gara *(VP)*
Ryan Schmidt *(Dir-Land Stewardship)*
Erin Van Waus *(Dir-Conservation Easement)*

IOWA NETWORK SERVICES INC.

7760 Office Plz Dr 7, West Des Moines, IA 50266
Tel.: (515) 830-0110   IA
Web Site:
    http://www.iowanetworkservice.com
Year Founded: 1986
Sales Range: $200-249.9 Million
Emp.: 600
Telephone Communication Services
N.A.I.C.S.: 517121
Ronald Keller *(Pres & CEO)*
Jeff Schill *(VP-Fin)*
Frank Hilton *(VP-Info Mgmt)*
Kristy McDermott *(VP-Products & Svcs)*

Subsidiaries:

Alliance Connect, LLC   (1)
4201 Corporate Dr, West Des Moines, IA 50266
Tel.: (877) 777-7128
Web Site: http://www.alliance-connect.com
Internet Service Provider
N.A.I.C.S.: 517810

Caleris, Inc.   (1)
1501 42nd St Ste 110, West Des Moines, IA 50266-1005
Tel.: (515) 331-0560
Web Site: http://www.caleris.com
Sales Range: $10-24.9 Million
Business Process Outsourcing
N.A.I.C.S.: 561499
Sheldon Ohringer *(Co-Founder & CEO)*
Rick Grewell *(Co-Founder & Pres)*
Jeremy Cooper *(COO)*

Merit Resources, Inc.   (1)
4410 114th St, Des Moines, IA 50322
Tel.: (515) 278-1931
Web Site: http://www.meritresources.com
Sales Range: $10-24.9 Million
Emp.: 100
Management Consulting Services
N.A.I.C.S.: 541618
Lisa Welshhons *(Pres-Senior Living)*
Sean Yolish *(VP-Insurance Ops)*
Melissa Ness *(VP-Fin & IT)*
Jeff Garrison *(Recruiting & Employer Svcs)*
Christy Smith *(VP-HR Ops)*
Cynde Cronin *(Dir-Bus Dev)*
Frank A. Accurso *(VP-Bus Dev)*
Janette Fiedler *(Dir-Bus Dev)*
Matt Nuetzman *(Dir-Bus Dev)*

Division (Domestic):

Merit Resources, Inc. - Merit Senior Living Division   (2)
7760 Ossice Plaza Dr W, Des Moines, IA 50266
Tel.: (800) 336-1931
Web Site:
    http://www.seniorliving.resources.com
Emp.: 80
Human Resource Management Services
N.A.I.C.S.: 541611

IOWA NORTHERN RAILWAY CO., INC.

201 Tower Park Dr Ste 300, Waterloo, IA 50701
Tel.: (319) 297-6000
Web Site:
    http://www.iowanorthern.com
Sales Range: $1-9.9 Million
Emp.: 38
Railroad Company

N.A.I.C.S.: 482111
Daniel R. Sabin *(Pres)*
Amy Homan *(Dir-Carload Mktg)*
William Rhodes *(Dir-Iowa Northern Reload)*
Beth Bilharz *(Asst Dir-Svc)*
Bob Geary *(Dir-Svc)*
Brad Sabin *(Project Mgr & Dir-Hazardous Matls)*
Dan Tegtmeier *(Project Engr)*
Joshua D. Sabin *(Dir-Admin)*
Lynne Edleman *(Mgr-Acctg)*
Lisa Grifin *(Mgr-HR)*
Matt Hoover *(Mgr-IT)*
Mark Vaughn *(Officer-Regulatory & Safety & Asst Gen Mgr)*
Matthew Walz *(Controller)*

IOWA PACIFIC HOLDINGS, LLC

118 S Clinton St Ste 400, Chicago, IL 60661-5772
Tel.: (312) 466-0900
Web Site: http://www.iowapacific.com
Sales Range: $25-49.9 Million
Emp.: 10
Holding Company; Railroad Investment & Management Services
N.A.I.C.S.: 525910
Ed E. Ellis *(Pres)*
Stephen Gregory *(VP-Mktg)*
Steven Butler *(Gen Mgr-Texas State Railroad)*

Subsidiaries:

Permian Basin Railways   (1)
118 S Clinton St Ste 400, Chicago, IL 60661
Tel.: (312) 466-0900
Web Site: http://www.iowapacific.com
Railroad Services
N.A.I.C.S.: 482111

Unit (Domestic):

Texas-New Mexico Railroad   (2)
821 West Broadway, Brownfield, TX 79316
Tel.: (806) 637-8323
Web Site: http://www.iowapacific.com
Sales Range: $10-24.9 Million
Provider of Short Line Railroad Services
N.A.I.C.S.: 482111
Ed E. Ellis *(Pres)*
Stephen Gregory *(VP-Mktg)*
Mike McConville *(VP-Ops)*
Howard W. Clark III *(VP-Fin)*

IOWA PACIFIC PROCESSORS INC.

2606 Sunset Rd, Des Moines, IA 50321
Tel.: (515) 288-5435
Web Site:
    http://www.iowapacificprocess.com
Year Founded: 1995
Sales Range: $10-24.9 Million
Emp.: 80
Processed Beef & Pork Mfr
N.A.I.C.S.: 311611
Michael K. Everett *(Pres)*
Todd Smith *(Mgr-Traffic)*

IOWA REGIONAL UTILITIES ASSOCIATION

1351 Iowa Speedway Dr, Newton, IA 50208
Tel.: (641) 792-7011   IA
Web Site: http://www.ciawa.com
Year Founded: 1977
Sales Range: $10-24.9 Million
Emp.: 65
Water Distribution Services
N.A.I.C.S.: 221310
Dan Brandt *(VP)*
Delwin Van Zante *(Sec)*
Ron Dunsbergen *(Pres)*
Janice Jontz *(Treas)*

IOWA RENEWABLE ENERGY, LLC

1701 E 7th St, Washington, IA 52353
Tel.: (319) 653-2890
Web Site:
    http://www.irebiodiesel.com
Sales Range: $10-24.9 Million
Emp.: 20
Soybean Oil Mfr
N.A.I.C.S.: 311224
Mark A. Cobb *(Vice Chm)*
Ron Lutovsky *(CFO & COO)*

IOWA RIVER BANCORP, INC.

2206 S Center St, Marshalltown, IA 50158
Tel.: (641) 752-2393
Web Site:
    http://www.bankpinnacle.us
Year Founded: 1927
Bank Holding Company
N.A.I.C.S.: 551111
David S. Burrell *(Pres & CEO)*

Subsidiaries:

Pinnacle Bank   (1)
2206 S Center St, Marshalltown, IA 50158-5961
Tel.: (641) 752-2393
Web Site: http://www.bankpinnacle.us
Sales Range: $1-9.9 Million
Emp.: 16
Retail & Commercial Banking
N.A.I.C.S.: 522110
David S. Burrell *(Pres & CEO)*
Craig V. McGarry *(Sr VP)*
Jane Heatwole *(VP-Ops)*
Laura Farrington *(VP-Comml Lending)*
Rose Duffy *(Asst VP-Customer Svc)*

IOWA SELECT FARMS, L.L.P.

811 S Oak St, Iowa Falls, IA 50126
Tel.: (641) 648-4479
Web Site: http://www.iowaselect.com
Year Founded: 1992
Sales Range: $10-24.9 Million
Emp.: 850
Hog & Pig Farming Services
N.A.I.C.S.: 112210
Jen Sorenson *(Dir-Comm)*

IOWA SPEEDWAY, LLC

3333 Rusty Wallace Dr, Newton, IA 50208
Tel.: (641) 791-8000
Web Site:
    http://www.iowaspeedway.com
Year Founded: 2013
Automobile Racetrack Operator
N.A.I.C.S.: 711212
Jimmy Small *(Pres)*
Casey Campbell *(Dir-Fin & Admin)*
Chuck Spicer *(VP-Sls & Mktg)*
Karen Baldon *(Dir-Corp Sls)*
Tami Hansen *(Dir-Mktg)*
Chris Baker *(Dir-Ticketing & Grp Sls)*
Luke Clement *(Dir-Track Svcs)*

IOWA STATE BANK

105 Albany Ave SE, Orange City, IA 51041
Tel.: (712) 737-4818
Web Site:
    http://www.iowastatebank.net
Year Founded: 1988
Sales Range: $300-349.9 Million
Emp.: 80
Commercial Banking Services
N.A.I.C.S.: 522110
Leroy Van Kekerix *(Pres & CEO)*
Duane Muecke *(CFO)*
Frank Vogel *(Chm)*
Drew Vogel *(Vice Chm)*
Wrede Vogel *(Vice Chm)*
Denny Van Oort *(Mgr-Ireton)*
Paul Struve *(Mgr-Paullina)*
Mike Broek *(Mgr-Hull)*

Iowa State Bank—(Continued)

IOWA STATE EDUCATION AS-SOCIATION
777 3rd St, Des Moines, IA 50309
Tel.: (515) 471-8000   IA
Web Site: http://www.isea.org
Year Founded: 1854
Sales Range: $10-24.9 Million
Emp.: 91
Educational Support Services
N.A.I.C.S.: 611710
Tammy Wawro (Pres)
Mary Jane Cobb (Exec Dir)
Mike Beranek (VP)
Tom McLaughlin (Treas)
Joshua Brown (Dir-NEA)
Roni Swift (Dir-Affiliate Svcs)
Corey Marquardt (Mgr-Network Ops)
Roberta Hass (Member-Exec Bd)
Susan Cahill (Member-Exec Bd)

IOWA STUDENT LOAN LI-QUIDITY CORPORATION
6775 Vista Dr, West Des Moines, IA
50266-9305
Tel.: (515) 273-7210   IA
Web Site: http://www.studentloan.org
Year Founded: 1979
Sales Range: $50-74.9 Million
Emp.: 303
Educational Support Services
N.A.I.C.S.: 611710
Cindy Bartz (CIO & VP-Project Mgmt)
Erin Lacey (Treas & Exec VP)
Steven W. McCullough (Pres)

IOWA TANKLINES INC.
PO Box 1217, Ankeny, IA 50021-1217
Tel.: (515) 963-8386
Web Site: http://www.ltltanklines.com
Sales Range: $10-24.9 Million
Emp.: 50
Bulk Liquid Hauling, Except Local
N.A.I.C.S.: 484121
Dick Sosalla (Controller)

IOWA TURKEY GROWERS CO-OPERATIVE
207 W 2nd St, West Liberty, IA
52776
Tel.: (319) 627-6000   IA
Rev.: $150,000,000
Emp.: 1,000
Holding Company; Turkey Production,
Processing & Food Products Distr
N.A.I.C.S.: 551112
Ed Garrett (Pres & CEO)
Paul Hill (Chm)

Subsidiaries:

West Liberty Foods, LLC   (1)
207 W 2nd St, West Liberty, IA 52776
Tel.: (319) 627-2126
Web Site: http://www.wlfoods.com
Turkey Production, Processing & Food
Products Distr
N.A.I.C.S.: 112330
Glenn Elzey (CFO & Sr VP)
Brandon Achen (Pres & CEO)
Paul Hill (Chm)

Plant (Domestic):

West Liberty Foods -
Bolingbrook   (2)
750 S Schmidt Rd, Bolingbrook, IL 60440
Tel.: (630) 679-2300
Portion Controlled Meats for Food Services
Mfr & Distr
N.A.I.C.S.: 311612
Frank Suss (Sls Mgr-Natl Accts)
Lucy Skowyra (Mgr-QA)
Brian Etten (Mgr-Safety)
Joseph Cangelosi (Plant Mgr)

IP COMMUNICATIONS LLC
1925 Vaughn Rd Ste 215, Kennesaw,
GA 30144
Tel.: (678) 460-1475
Web Site: http://www.ipcomms.net
Sales Range: $1-9.9 Million
Emp.: 12
Affordable Voice Communication Ser-
vices
N.A.I.C.S.: 517810
Donald Hansil (Pres)

IP NETWORKS, INC.
PO Box 2669, Sedona, AZ 86339
Tel.: (520) 762-0000
Web Site: http://www.ipnetworks-inc.com
Year Founded: 2003
Sales Range: $1-9.9 Million
Emp.: 5
Full Suite of Networking Solutions for
Businesses
N.A.I.C.S.: 513210
John Pearson (Owner & Founder)

IP PATHWAYS, LLC
3600 109th St, Urbandale, IA 50322
Tel.: (515) 422-9300
Web Site: http://www.ippathways.com
Year Founded: 2007
Sales Range: $10-24.9 Million
Emp.: 45
Computer Data Storage Services
N.A.I.C.S.: 518210
Joe Shields (Pres)
Sean Lair (Dir-Engrg & Consulting
Svcs)

Subsidiaries:

Sophisticated Systems Inc.   (1)
2191 Citygate Dr, Columbus, OH 43219
Tel.: (614) 418-4600
Web Site: http://www.ssicom.com
Rev.: $25,235,072
Emp.: 120
Computer Related Consulting Services
N.A.I.C.S.: 541512
Zach Evans (Mng Dir)
Dwight E. Smith (Founder)

IPACESETTERS, LLC
4115 S 100th E Ave, Tulsa, OK
74146
Tel.: (267) 530-6000   DE
Web Site:
http://www.ipacesetters.com
Year Founded: 1988
Sales Range: $75-99.9 Million
Emp.: 1,600
Data Management & Contact Center
Services
N.A.I.C.S.: 518210
Richard Sauter (CFO)
Greg Darr (Chief Client Officer)
Steve Eveland (COO)
Frank Pettinato (CEO)

Subsidiaries:

iPacesetters India   (1)
Plot B-9/A Green Boulevard Tower B Sixth
Floor Sector 62, Noida, 201301, India
Tel.: (91) 120 4549900
Data Management & Contact Center Ser-
vices
N.A.I.C.S.: 518210

IPC
3000 Lakeside Dr 105 N, Bannock-
burn, IL 60015
Tel.: (847) 615-7100   NY
Web Site: http://www.ipc.org
Year Founded: 1957
Sales Range: $10-24.9 Million
Emp.: 83
Business Associations
N.A.I.C.S.: 813910
David Bergman (VP-Intl Rels-India)
Brian Knier (CMO)
John Hasselmann (VP-Govt Rels)

Sanjay Huprikar (VP-Member Suc-
cess)
Ed Trackman (VP-Special Projects)
Shane Whiteside (Vice Chm)
Bob Neves (Treas & Sec)
John Mitchell (Pres & CEO)
Dave Hernandez (Sr Dir-Learning &
Pro Dev)
Mikel H. Williams (Chm)

IPCREATE INC.
426 Industrial Ave Ste 150, Williston,
VT 05495
Tel.: (802) 859-7800
Web Site: http://www.ipcreateinc.com
Year Founded: 2012
Product Research, Invention & Devel-
opment Services
N.A.I.C.S.: 541715
John Cronin (Founder)
Kate Lampron (Sr VP-Bus Dev &
Compliance)

IPEXPERT, INC.
3100 King Rd Ste B, China, MI
48054
Tel.: (810) 326-1444
Web Site: http://www.ipexpert.com
Year Founded: 2001
Rev.: $4,700,000
Emp.: 13
Miscellaneous Schools & Instruction
N.A.I.C.S.: 611699
Wayne A. Lawson II (Founder &
Pres)

IPFOLIO CORPORATION
350 Massachusetts Ave Ste 300, In-
dianapolis, IN 46204
Tel.: (510) 982-1421
Web Site: http://www.ipfolio.com
Year Founded: 2012
Sales Range: $1-9.9 Million
Emp.: 30
Software Development Services
N.A.I.C.S.: 541511
Rupert Mayer (Founder)
Heather Fleener (VP-Solution Deliv-
ery)
Kevin Nugent (VP-Customer Suc-
cess)

IPFS CORPORATION
301 W 11th St, Kansas City, MO
64105
Tel.: (816) 627-0500   MO
Web Site: http://www.ipfs.com
Year Founded: 1977
Secondary Market Financing Services
N.A.I.C.S.: 522299
Michael Gallagher (Pres)
Bryan Andres (CFO & Exec VP)
Herb Chirico (Sr VP)
Scott Marr (Chief Data Officer & Sr
VP)
Jack Merriman (Chief Growth Officer
& VP)
Josh Ellwanger (Gen Counsel)
Jason Sanders (VP & Mgr-Natl Ops)

Subsidiaries:

Imperial PFS   (1)
30 Montgomery St Ste 501, Jersey City, NJ
07302
Tel.: (877) 803-9252
Web Site: http://www.ipfs.com
Short-Term Loans for Property & Casualty
Insurance Coverage
N.A.I.C.S.: 525990

Premium Assignment
Corporation   (1)
3522 Thomasville Rd Ste 400, Tallahassee,
FL 32309
Tel.: (800) 342-0991
Web Site:
http://www.premiumassignment.com
Insurance Premium Services

N.A.I.C.S.: 524298
Paul Kugelman (Pres)
Naomi Harris (Dir-Mktg)

IPG
11605 Haynes Bridge Rd Ste 200,
Alpharetta, GA 30009
Tel.: (770) 753-0046
Web Site: http://www.ipg.com
Sales Range: $25-49.9 Million
Emp.: 85
Software Development Services
N.A.I.C.S.: 511511
Dennis Antinori (Chm)
Vince Coppola (Pres & CEO)
Kevin Smith (CMO)
Mary Rountree (VP-Fin)
Michael Stricklin (VP-HR)
Harry Evans (VP-Implementation &
Delivery)
C. J. Warner (VP-Manufacturer &
Physician Program Dev)
Kerry Lee Perry (VP-Mktg)
Nadine Drake (VP-Ops)
Winfred Tse (CIO)
Neepa Patel (Chief Growth Officer)
Brian Holt (Chief Innovation Officer)
Sherwin Krug (CFO)
Julie Roberts (COO)

IPI GRAMMTECH, INC.
16116 Unitery Oak, San Antonio, TX
78249
Tel.: (210) 694-4313
Year Founded: 1995
Sales Range: $10-24.9 Million
Emp.: 17
Retailer of Computers Peripherals &
Software
N.A.I.C.S.: 423430
Debbie Walters (Pres)

IPITEK
2320 Faraday Ave, Carlsbad, CA
92013
Tel.: (760) 438-1010
Web Site: http://www.ipitek.com
Year Founded: 1983
Sales Range: $10-24.9 Million
Emp.: 125
Fiber Optics Communications Equip-
ment & Sensor Applications
N.A.I.C.S.: 335921
Michael M. Salour (Chm, Founder &
CEO)
Bill Moore (Sr VP-Bus Dev)

IPLACEMENT, INC.
1516 E Colonial Dr Ste 303, Orlando,
FL 32803
Tel.: (407) 893-3711
Web Site: http://www.iplacement.com
Year Founded: 1999
Sales Range: $10-24.9 Million
Emp.: 325
Employment Services
N.A.I.C.S.: 561311
Randy Davis (Chm)
David Nuxol (Pres & CEO)
Sharon Ball (Sr VP-HR)
William J. Cooke (Dir-IT)
Gemma Filliben (Sr VP-Bus Dev)
Robert J. Byrne (Exec Chm)

IPM INTEGRATED PRESCRIP-TION MANAGEMENT
7815 N Palm Ave Ste 400, Fresno,
CA 93711
Tel.: (559) 476-8000
Web Site: http://www.rxipm.com
Year Founded: 2009
Sales Range: $50-74.9 Million
Emp.: 30
Prescription Management Services
N.A.I.C.S.: 541611

Ken Perrin *(Dir-Clinical Pharmacy Svcs)*

IPOWERWEB INC.
919 E Jefferson St, Phoenix, AZ 85034
Tel.: (888) 511-4678
Web Site: http://www.ipowerweb.com
Year Founded: 2001
Rev.: $29,100,000
Emp.: 158
Web Hosting
N.A.I.C.S.: 518210

IPS CORPORATION
455 W Victoria St, Compton, CA 90220
Tel.: (310) 898-3300
Web Site: http://www.ipscorp.com
Year Founded: 1954
Adhesives & Commercial Solvent Cements Mfr
N.A.I.C.S.: 325520
George C. Moore *(Exec Chm)*
Tracy Bilbrough *(CEO)*
Sharon Georgoulias *(Pres-Adhesives)*

Subsidiaries:

IPS Adhesives (Jiashan) Co., Ltd. (1)
1001 10th Floor C Building Guang Da Exhibition Center 70 Cao Bao Road, Xu Hui District, Shanghai, 200235, China
Tel.: (86) 21 64325990
Web Site: http://www.ipscorp.com
Adhesives & Solvent Cements Mfr
N.A.I.C.S.: 325520

IPSWICH SHELLFISH CO. INC.
8 Hayward St, Ipswich, MA 01938
Tel.: (978) 356-4371
Web Site:
  http://www.ipswichshellfish.com
Sales Range: $75-99.9 Million
Emp.: 100
Seafoods
N.A.I.C.S.: 424460
Chrissi Pappas *(Pres)*

IPT ASSOCIATES LLC.
700 Technology Park Dr Ste 204, Billerica, MA 01821
Tel.: (781) 271-0696
Web Site:
  http://www.iptassociates.com
Year Founded: 1992
Sales Range: $10-24.9 Million
Emp.: 105
Management Consulting Services
N.A.I.C.S.: 541611
Dan Beaulieu *(Sr Engr-Software)*
Bill Williams *(COO & VP)*

IQ CREDIT UNION
PO Box 1739, Vancouver, WA 98668
Tel.: (360) 695-3441   WA
Web Site: http://www.iqcu.com
Year Founded: 1940
Sales Range: $25-49.9 Million
Emp.: 242
Credit Union
N.A.I.C.S.: 522130
DeWayne Ledbetter *(CFO & Sr VP)*
Eric Petracca *(Chief Risk Officer & Sr VP)*
Kari Stansberry *(Sr VP-HR)*
Danette LaChapelle *(Chief Comm Officer & Sr VP)*
James Sork *(Chm)*
Ed Maxwell *(Treas)*
Jim Askey *(VP)*
Sharon Eastman *(Sec)*
Jim Church *(Vice Chm)*
Kelly Schrader *(Pres & CEO)*
Gayle Rust Gustafson *(Chief Lending Officer)*
Ali Migaki *(Sr VP-Retail Delivery)*

IQ OFFICE PRODUCTS LLC
5055 E Washington Ste 220, Phoenix, AZ 85034
Tel.: (480) 588-2670
Web Site:
  http://www.iqofficeproducts.com
Year Founded: 2007
Sales Range: $1-9.9 Million
Emp.: 15
Office Products, Furniture & Janitorial Supplies
N.A.I.C.S.: 561499
Katie Wilson *(Ops Mgr)*
Amanda Thomas *(Project Coord)*
Ryan Puccinelli *(Co-Founder)*
Bryan Freund *(Co-Founder)*

IQ PHYSICAL DIAMOND TRUST
800 Westchester Ave Ste N611, Rye Brook, NY 10573   NY
Investment Services
N.A.I.C.S.: 523150
Adam S. Patti *(CEO)*
David Fogel *(CFO & Exec VP)*

IQ PIPELINE
1550 Hotel Cir N Ste 270, San Diego, CA 92108
Tel.: (858) 483-7400
Web Site: http://www.iqpipeline.com
Year Founded: 2003
Rev.: $5,000,000
Emp.: 100
Temporary Help Service
N.A.I.C.S.: 561320
Angie Bisone *(Dir-Support Svcs)*

IQ SOLUTIONS
11300 Rockville Pk Ste 901, Rockville, MD 20852
Tel.: (301) 984-1471
Emp.: 275
E-Commerce, Health Care, Information Technology, Strategic Planning/Research, Web (Banner Ads, Pop-ups, etc.)
N.A.I.C.S.: 541810
Ileana Quintas *(CEO)*
Lisa Swanberg *(Sr VP)*
Michael Collins *(Sr VP)*
Tom Brackett *(CFO & COO)*
Lee Loman *(VP-Fin)*
Kim Callinan *(Sr VP-Comm & Social Mktg)*
Stephen Murphy *(Sr VP-Digital Strategy & Innovation)*
Bryan Daniels *(Chief Creative Officer)*
Stephanie Adams *(VP-Res-Mktg Analytics)*
Kim Barnes *(VP-Program Dev)*
Ruth Ann Speir *(VP-Info Svcs)*

IQNAVIGATOR, INC.
6465 Greenwood Plz Blvd Ste 800, Centennial, CO 80111
Tel.: (303) 563-1500
Web Site: http://www.iqnavigator.com
Sales Range: $50-74.9 Million
Emp.: 300
Expense Management Software & Services
N.A.I.C.S.: 513210
Joseph Juliano *(Pres & CEO)*
Sherri Hammons *(CTO)*
Eric Riddle *(Exec VP-Sls & Mktg)*
Barry Capoot *(CFO)*
Jeffrey Varon *(Chief Strategy Officer)*
Ron Wessel *(Gen Counsel)*

IR SPECIALTY FOAM, LLC
3500 20th St E Ste B, Fife, WA 98424-1700
Tel.: (253) 922-1148   WA
Web Site: http://www.irfoam.com
Year Founded: 1946

Sales Range: $10-24.9 Million
Emp.: 60
Specialty Foam Products Mfr
N.A.I.C.S.: 326150
Scott Smalling *(Chm)*
Todd Olstad *(Pres)*

IRA HIGDON GROCERY, INC.
150 I G A Way, Cairo, GA 39828
Tel.: (229) 377-1272   GA
Web Site:
  http://www.irahigdongc.com
Year Founded: 1909
Sales Range: $75-99.9 Million
Emp.: 95
Grocery Distr
N.A.I.C.S.: 424410
Lawrence Higdon *(Pres)*
Walt Sellars *(Mgr-DP)*

IRB MEDICAL EQUIPMENT, LLC
1432 Genesys Pkwy, Grand Blanc, MI 48439
Tel.: (810) 866-9435
Web Site: http://hartmedical.org
Medical Equipment & Supply Whslr
N.A.I.C.S.: 423450
Allen Hunt *(Pres)*

IRELAND GANNON ASSOCIATES INC.
6050 Northern Blvd, East Norwich, NY 11732
Tel.: (516) 922-4800
Web Site:
  http://www.irelandgannon.com
Rev.: $10,159,194
Emp.: 80
Landscape Contractors
N.A.I.C.S.: 561730
Anthony Rubino *(Project Mgr)*
Russell Ireland Jr. *(CEO)*

IRELL & MANELLA LLP
1800 Avenue of the Stars Ste 900, Los Angeles, CA 90067
Tel.: (310) 277-1010
Web Site: http://www.irell.com
Year Founded: 1941
Sales Range: $250-299.9 Million
Emp.: 185
Law firm
N.A.I.C.S.: 541110
Marc S. Maister *(Partner)*
Elliot N. Brown *(Partner)*
Ellisen Shelton Turner *(Mng Partner)*
Ian Wiener *(Partner-Transactional)*
Jason G. Sheasby *(Partner)*
Jeffrey M. Reisner *(Partner)*
Keith A. Orso *(Partner)*
Richard M. Birnholz *(Partner)*
David C. McPhie *(Partner)*
Morgan Chu *(Partner-Los Angeles)*
A. Matthew Ashley *(Partner)*
Alan J. Heinrich *(Partner)*
Andra B. Greene *(Partner)*
Ashok V. Mukhey *(Partner)*
Ben J. Yorks *(Partner)*
Bruce A. Wessel *(Partner)*
Craig I. Varnen *(Partner)*

IREX CORPORATION
120 N Lime St, Lancaster, PA 17602-2923
Tel.: (717) 397-3633   PA
Web Site:
  http://www.irexcontracting.com
Year Founded: 1969
Sales Range: $250-299.9 Million
Emp.: 2,500
Mechanical Insulation, Sheet Metal Lagging, Architectural Finishes, Passive Fire Protection, Asbestos, Lead-

Containing Materials, Mold & Other Hazardous Materials Removal & Abatement Services
N.A.I.C.S.: 238310
W. Kirk Liddell *(Chm)*
Lori A. Pickell *(Pres & CEO)*
James E. Hipolit *(Sec & Sr VP)*
John M. Levitski *(Mgr-Natl Bus Dev)*

Subsidiaries:

ADVANCED ENERGY SOLUTIONS LLC (1)
1825 Latrobe St, Parkersburg, WV 26102-1110
Tel.: (800) 846-9094
Web Site:
  http://www.advancedenergysolutions.com
Industrial Engineering Services
N.A.I.C.S.: 541330

ARGUS CONTRACTING, INC (1)
11807 E Smith Ave, Santa Fe Springs, CA 90670
Tel.: (562) 422-7370
Web Site: http://www.irexcontracting.com
Sales Range: $10-24.9 Million
Emp.: 50
Drywall & Insulation Contractor
N.A.I.C.S.: 238310

Advanced Energy Protection (1)
11111 Katy Fwy Ste 910, Houston, TX 77079
Tel.: (713) 973-5723
Web Site: http://www.advancedenergyprotection.com
Passive Fire Protection & Radiant Heat Shielding Services
N.A.I.C.S.: 237120

Advanced Industrial Services (1)
123 Oakdale Ave, Toledo, OH 43605
Tel.: (419) 661-8522
Web Site:
  http://www.advancedindustrialservices.com
Emp.: 15
Industrial Engineering Services
N.A.I.C.S.: 541330
Bradley Viers *(Branch Mgr)*

Advanced Nuclear (1)
120 N Lime St, Lancaster, PA 17602
Tel.: (717) 399-5213
Web Site: http://www.advancednuclear.com
Sales Range: $10-24.9 Million
Emp.: 8
Industrial Engineering Services
N.A.I.C.S.: 541330
James Petrides *(Gen Mgr)*

Advanced Specialty Contractors (1)
7020 Troy Hill Dr, Elkridge, MD 21075 (100%)
Tel.: (410) 540-4935
Web Site: http://www.advancedspecialtycontractors.com
Sales Range: $10-24.9 Million
Emp.: 6
Interior Space Contracting
N.A.I.C.S.: 238310

Altair Contracting (1)
9464 51st AVE NW, Edmonton, T6E 5A6, AB, Canada
Tel.: (780) 465-5363
Web Site: http://www.altaircontracting.ca
Sales Range: $10-24.9 Million
Emp.: 15
Insulation Contract Services
N.A.I.C.S.: 238310
Dean Seidler *(Gen Mgr)*

Atlantic Contracting & Specialties LLC (1)
925 Saw Mill River Rd, Yonkers, NY 10710
Tel.: (914) 226-8475
Web Site: http://www.atlanticcontracting.com
Sales Range: $25-49.9 Million
Emp.: 250
Mechanical Insulation Installation Services
N.A.I.C.S.: 238310
Bruce Schilling *(Gen Mgr)*

Cornerstone Services Group (1)
1809 Liberty St, Kansas City, MO 64102
Tel.: (816) 842-2990
Web Site:
  http://www.cornerstoneservicesgroup.com

Irex Corporation—(Continued)

Specialty Trade Contracting Services
N.A.I.C.S.: 238990

Enertech Specialty Contracting **(1)**
6956 Roper Rd, Edmonton, T6B 3H9, AB,
Canada
Tel.: (780) 424-0029
Web Site:
http://www.enertechspecialtycontrac
ting.ca
Sales Range: $10-24.9 Million
Emp.: 2
Interior Design Services
N.A.I.C.S.: 541410
Dave Powers *(Gen Mgr)*

Insulmax Construction Services **(1)**
2461 76th Avenue NW Unit 111, Edmonton,
T6P 1Y8, AB, Canada
Tel.: (780) 784-2408
Web Site:
http://www.insulmaxconstruction.ca
Insulation Contract Services
N.A.I.C.S.: 238310

New States Contracting **(1)**
2400 Main St Ext Ste 10, Sayreville, NJ
08872
Tel.: (732) 525-0100
Web Site:
http://www.newstatescontracting.com
Industrial Engineering Services
N.A.I.C.S.: 541330

SUMMIT CONTRACTING LLC **(1)**
2037 S 4130 W Ste E, Salt Lake City, UT
84104
Tel.: (801) 972-2116
Web Site:
http://www.summitcontractingllc.com
Industrial Construction & Maintenance Services
N.A.I.C.S.: 236210

Spacecon Solutions, LLC **(1)**
4915 Iris St, Wheat Ridge, CO 80033
Tel.: (720) 889-6424
Web Site: http://www.spacecon.com
Insulation Contract Services
N.A.I.C.S.: 238310
Robert Yelinski *(Pres)*

Spacecon Specialty Contractors
LLC **(1)**
PO Box 1268, Lancaster, PA 17608
Tel.: (888) 870-4870
Web Site:
http://www.spaceconspecialtycontrac
tors.com
Insulation Contract Services
N.A.I.C.S.: 238310

Spacecon, LLC **(1)**
292 New Churchmans Rd, New Castle, DE
19720-3110 **(100%)**
Tel.: (302) 322-9285
Web Site: http://www.spacecon.com
Interior Space Contracting
N.A.I.C.S.: 238310
W.K. Liddell *(Mng Dir)*

IRIS ID SYSTEMS INC.
Cedar Brook Corp Ctr 7 Clarke Dr,
Cranbury, NJ 08512
Tel.: (609) 819-4747
Web Site: http://www.irisid.com
Year Founded: 1997
Sales Range: $10-24.9 Million
Biometric Technologies Developer,
Mfr & Distr
N.A.I.C.S.: 334519
Charles Koo *(Pres & CEO)*
Moon Choi *(Exec VP)*

IRIS SOFTWARE, INC.
200 Metroplex Dr Ste 300, Edison,
NJ 08840
Tel.: (732) 393-0034
Web Site:
http://www.irissoftware.com
Sales Range: $10-24.9 Million
Emp.: 90
Provider of Software Development &
Consulting Services
N.A.I.C.S.: 541512

Sanjiv Khanna *(CEO)*

IRIS TECHNOLOGY CORPO-RATION
2811 McGaw Ave Ste A, Irvine, CA
92614
Tel.: (949) 975-8410 CA
Web Site:
http://www.iristechnology.com
Year Founded: 1986
Sales Range: $1-9.9 Million
Military Power Supply Systems &
Aerospace Technologies Developer,
Mfr & Whslr
N.A.I.C.S.: 423690
Edward J. O'Rourke *(Pres & CEO)*
Jeannette M. Morvan *(Co-Founder,
CFO & Sec)*
Carl S. Kirkconnell *(CTO)*
Sandra L. Thomson *(Chief Admin Of-
ficer)*
Michael J. Barthlow *(Chief Strategy
Officer & Exec VP)*

IRISE
2321 Rosecrans Ave, El Segundo,
CA 90245
Tel.: (310) 426-7800
Web Site: http://www.irise.com
Year Founded: 1996
Sales Range: $10-24.9 Million
Emp.: 150
Custom Computer Programming Ser-
vices
N.A.I.C.S.: 541511
Maurice Martin *(Founder & CEO)*
Stephen Brickley *(Exec VP-Customer
Success)*
Stuart Larking *(Exec VP-Engrg & IT)*
Bryan Lipson *(Exec VP-Product
Mgmt)*
Michael Loria *(VP-Bus Dev)*
Emmet B. Keeffe III *(Co-Founder)*

IRISH STUDIO, LLC
347 W 36th St Ste 1300, New York,
NY 10018
Tel.: (917) 532-7306 DE
Web Site: http://www.irishstudio.com
Magazine Publisher
N.A.I.C.S.: 513199
Katie Molony *(Co-CEO)*
Ciaran Casey *(Co-CEO)*
Liam Lynch *(Founder & Chm)*

Subsidiaries:

Irish Studio, LLC - Ireland Corporate
Office **(1)**
Drumcliffe House 47 Stephen's Place, Dub-
lin, D02 NX78, Ireland
Tel.: (353) 1 699 5400
Corporate Office
N.A.I.C.S.: 551114
Liam Lynch *(Founder & Chm)*
Ciaran Casey *(Grp Co-CEO-Ireland Ops)*

Subsidiary (US):

Palm Coast Data, LLC **(2)**
11 Commerce Blvd, Palm Coast, FL 32164
Tel.: (386) 445-4662
Web Site: http://www.palmcoastdata.com
Subscription Fulfillment
N.A.I.C.S.: 518210
Jim Bradley *(VP-Network & Telecom)*
Gary Blumenfeld *(VP-Sls & Mktg)*
Keith Macdonald *(VP-Client Svcs)*
Doug Kline *(VP-Contact Center Sls)*
Cheryl Anasagasti *(VP-Client Svcs)*

IRISH TIMES
3267 Motor Ave, Los Angeles, CA
90034-3709
Tel.: (310) 559-9648
Web Site: http://www.irishtimes.com
Full-Service Restaurants
N.A.I.C.S.: 722511
James McGurrin *(Owner)*
Pat Leahy *(Editor-Political)*

Kevin O'Sullivan *(Editor-Environment,
Agriculture & Science)*
Paul O'Neill *(Editor)*

Subsidiaries:

Landmark Media Enterprises,
LLC **(1)**
150 W Brambleton Ave, Norfolk, VA 23510-
2075
Tel.: (757) 446-2010
Sales Range: $1-4.9 Billion
Emp.: 11,750
Holding Company; Newspaper Publishing,
Television Broadcasting, Cable Program-
ming & Specialty Periodical Publishing
N.A.I.C.S.: 513110
David Mele *(Pres-Homes Media Solutions)*
Charlie Watkins *(Pres & CEO)*
Frank Batten Jr. *(Chm)*

Subsidiary (Domestic):

Capital Gazette Communications
Inc. **(2)**
2000 Capital Dr, Annapolis, MD 21401
Tel.: (410) 268-5000
Web Site:
http://www.hometownannapolis.com
Sales Range: $25-49.9 Million
Emp.: 150
Newspaper Publishers
N.A.I.C.S.: 513110
Rob Pryor *(Dir-Circulation)*
Doris Burgess *(Mgr-Circulation)*

Cynthiana Publishing Co. **(2)**
302 Webster Ave, Cynthiana, KY 41031-
1660
Tel.: (859) 234-1035
Web Site:
http://www.cynthianademocrat.com
Sales Range: $25-49.9 Million
Emp.: 40
Commercial Printing & Newspaper Pub-
lisher
N.A.I.C.S.: 513110
Patricia Jenkins *(Gen Mgr & Mgr-Adv)*
Becky Barnes *(Editor)*

Dominion Enterprises **(2)**
150 Granby St, Norfolk, VA 23510
Tel.: (757) 351-7000
Web Site:
http://www.dominionenterprises.com
Sales Range: $800-899.9 Million
Emp.: 6,600
Media & Information Services
N.A.I.C.S.: 561499
Guy R. Friddell III *(Gen Counsel & Exec
VP)*
Susan R. Blake *(Sr VP-HR)*
Charlie Watkins *(Pres & CEO)*
Dan Sykes *(Pres-Dominion Dealer Solu-
tions)*
Debra Bunn *(Chief Acctg Officer & Sr VP)*
Frank Batten Jr. *(Chm)*

Subsidiary (Domestic):

Autobase, Inc. **(3)**
201 W 103rd St Ste 600, Indianapolis, IN
46290
Tel.: (317) 842-4242
Web Site: http://www.autobase.net
Sales Range: $10-24.9 Million
Emp.: 140
Auto Industry Software Solutions & Services
N.A.I.C.S.: 513210
Randy Sill *(Dir-Dev)*
Anthony Sutherlin *(Mgr-Tech)*

Homes.com, Inc. **(3)**
5510 Morehouse Dr Ste 100, San Diego,
CA 92121
Tel.: (858) 535-9332
Web Site: http://www.homes.com
Sales Range: $50-74.9 Million
Emp.: 120
Online Real Estate & Home Services
N.A.I.C.S.: 531210
Jason Doyle *(VP)*

PowerSports Network, Inc. **(3)**
N 56 W 24660 N Corporate Cir, Sussex, WI
53089
Tel.: (262) 246-7900
Web Site:
http://www.powersportsnetwork.org

Sales Range: $1-9.9 Million
Emp.: 80
Power Sports & Marine Website Services
N.A.I.C.S.: 541512

United Advertising Publications,
Inc. **(3)**
2301 McDaniel Dr Ste 100, Carrollton, TX
75006-8355 **(100%)**
Tel.: (972) 280-0050
Rev.: $120,028,000
Emp.: 110
Publishing Services
N.A.I.C.S.: 513199

eNeighborhoods Inc. **(3)**
1 Park Pl Ste 500, Boca Raton, FL 33487
Tel.: (561) 981-9700
Web Site: http://www.eneighborhoods.com
Sales Range: $75-99.9 Million
Emp.: 225
Real Estate Marketing & Information Ser-
vices
N.A.I.C.S.: 541890
Melissa Crow *(Exec Dir-Technical Ops)*
Shawn Brown *(Exec Dir-Bus Ops)*
Michael Hayes *(Exec Dir-Enterprise Svcs)*

Subsidiary (Domestic):

Inside Business Inc. **(2)**
150 W Brambleton Ave, Norfolk, VA 23510
Tel.: (757) 222-5353
Web Site: http://www.insidebiz.com
Sales Range: $10-24.9 Million
Emp.: 12
Newspaper Publishing
N.A.I.C.S.: 513110
Rawles Magee *(Mgr-Legal Adv)*
Mike Herron *(Gen Mgr & Assoc Publr)*
Bill Blake *(Dir-Sls)*
Robin Simmons *(Sr Acct Exec)*
John Kinsley *(Sr Acct Exec)*
Butch Maier *(Editor)*

Landmark Community Newspapers,
LLC **(2)**
601 Taylorsville Rd, Shelbyville, KY
40066-0549 **(100%)**
Tel.: (502) 633-4334
Web Site: http://www.lcni.com
Sales Range: $10-24.9 Million
Emp.: 55
Publishers of Daily, Tri-Weekly, Semi-
Weekly, Weekly Newspapers & Specialty
Publications
N.A.I.C.S.: 323111
Michael Abernathy *(Pres)*
Vicky Noel *(Controller)*
Patty Bottom *(Dir-HR)*
Tony Martinette *(Dir-Adv)*

Unit (Domestic):

Carroll County Times **(3)**
201 Railroad Ave, Westminster, MD
21157 **(100%)**
Tel.: (410) 875-5400
Web Site: http://www.carrollcountytimes.com
Daily Newspaper
N.A.I.C.S.: 513110
Jerry Blizzard *(Dir-Homes Magazines &
Classified)*
Brian Patterson *(Editor-Night News)*
Wayne Carter *(Editor)*

Citrus County Chronicle **(3)**
1624 N Meadowcrest Blvd, Crystal River,
FL 34429-5760 **(100%)**
Tel.: (352) 563-6363
Web Site: http://www.chronicleonline.com
Emp.: 150
Newspapers
N.A.I.C.S.: 513110
Gerry Mulligan *(Publr)*
Trina Murphy *(Publr)*

The News-Enterprise **(3)**
408 W Dixie Ave, Elizabethtown, KY
42701-2455 **(100%)**
Tel.: (270) 769-1200
Web Site:
http://www.thenewsenterprise.com
Sales Range: $10-24.9 Million
Emp.: 80
Daily Newspaper
N.A.I.C.S.: 513110
Chris Ordway *(Publr)*
Lisa D'Alessio *(Bus Mgr)*
Erin Hahn *(Dir-Adv)*

Subsidiary (Domestic):

Landmark Education Services **(2)**
150 W Brambleton Ave, Norfolk, VA 23510-2018
Tel.: (757) 446-2799
Sales Range: $10-24.9 Million
Emp.: 10
Vocational Training
N.A.I.C.S.: 611430

Landmark Publishing **(2)**
150 W Brambleton Ave, Norfolk, VA 23510-2018
Tel.: (757) 446-2455
Web Site: http://www.pilotonline.com
Sales Range: $10-24.9 Million
Emp.: 29
Publishers of Guides
N.A.I.C.S.: 513120

Unit (Domestic):

Los Alamos Monitor **(3)**
256 DP Rd, Los Alamos, NM 87544-1268 **(100%)**
Tel.: (505) 662-4185
Web Site: http://www.lamonitor.com
Sales Range: $10-24.9 Million
Emp.: 25
Daily Newspaper
N.A.I.C.S.: 513110
Ben Carlson *(Publr)*

Subsidiary (Domestic):

News & Record **(2)**
200 E Market St, Greensboro, NC 27420-0848
Tel.: (336) 373-7000
Web Site: http://www.news-records.com
Sales Range: $75-99.9 Million
Emp.: 450
Daily Newspaper Publisher; Contract Printing
N.A.I.C.S.: 513110
Allen Johnson *(Editor-Editorial Page)*
Daniel Finnegan *(Publr & Exec Editor)*

Affiliate (Domestic):

News-Enterprise Corporation **(2)**
408 W Dixie Ave, Elizabethtown, KY 42701-2455
Tel.: (270) 769-1200
Web Site:
   http://www.newsenterpriseonline.com
Rev.: $9,000,000
Emp.: 130
Newspapers Publishing & Printing
N.A.I.C.S.: 513110
Debbie Crawford *(Adv Mgr)*
Chris Ordway *(Publr)*
Chuck Jones *(Editor-Sports)*
Ben Sheroan *(Editor)*

Subsidiary (Domestic):

Style Weekly Inc. **(2)**
1313 E Main St Ste 103, Richmond, VA 23219
Tel.: (804) 358-0825
Web Site: http://www.styleweekly.com
Rev.: $1,700,000
Emp.: 35
Newspaper Publishing
N.A.I.C.S.: 513110
Gordon Poindexter *(Editor-Copy)*
Dana Elmquist *(Mgr-Publ & New Media Dev)*
Lauren Moss *(Acct Exec)*
Melanie Roupas *(Mgr-Events & Mktg)*
Jack Cooksey *(Editor)*

The Roanoke Times **(2)**
201 Campbell Ave SW, Roanoke, VA 24011
Tel.: (540) 981-3100
Web Site: http://www.roanoke.com
Sales Range: $25-49.9 Million
Emp.: 400
Newspaper Publishers
N.A.I.C.S.: 513110
Lawrence McConnell *(Exec Editor)*
Lee Wolverton *(Mng Editor)*

IRISS, INC.
10306 Technology Ter, Bradenton, FL 34211
Tel.: (941) 907-9128

Web Site: http://www.iriss.com
Sales Range: $1-9.9 Million
Emp.: 25
Industrial-Grade Infrared Inspection Window Mfr
N.A.I.C.S.: 335999
Martin Robinson *(CEO)*

Subsidiaries:

IRISS, Ltd. **(1)**
Unit 2 Grafton Place Montrose Road, Chelmsford, CM2 6TG, Essex, United Kingdom
Tel.: (44) 1245 399 713
Web Site: http://www.iriss.com
Emp.: 4
Industrial-Grade Infrared Inspection Window Mfr
N.A.I.C.S.: 335999
Daniel Robinson *(Branch Mgr)*

IRISS-Asia Pty Ltd **(1)**
Unit 15 634-644 Mitcham Road, Mitcham, 3132, VIC, Australia
Tel.: (61) 3 9872 3000
Industrial-Grade Infrared Inspection Window Mfr
N.A.I.C.S.: 335999
Garry Ward *(Dir-Sls & Mktg)*

IRMA S. MANN, STRATEGIC MARKETING INC.
46 Waltham St, Boston, MA 02118
Tel.: (617) 353-1822 MA
Web Site: http://www.ismtravels.com
Year Founded: 1984
Sales Range: $1-9.9 Million
Emp.: 150
Advetising Agency
N.A.I.C.S.: 541810
Sal DeLuca *(CFO)*
Matt Kaiser *(Assoc Dir-Creative)*
Gary Leopold *(Pres & CEO)*

IRMSCHER INC.
1030 Osage St, Fort Wayne, IN 46808
Tel.: (260) 422-5572
Web Site:
   http://www.irmscherinc.com
Sales Range: $10-24.9 Million
Emp.: 15
Industrial Buildings, New Construction
N.A.I.C.S.: 236210
Thomas A. Irmscher *(Owner)*
Leo Kuntz *(VP)*
Richard Marx *(Treas)*

IROKO PHARMACEUTICALS INC.
One Kew Pl 150 Rouse Blvd, Philadelphia, PA 19112
Tel.: (267) 546-3003 VG
Web Site: http://www.iroko.com
Year Founded: 2007
Sales Range: $1-9.9 Million
Emp.: 71
Pharmaceuticals Mfr
N.A.I.C.S.: 325412
Louis J. Vollmer *(Pres & CEO)*
Osagie O. Imasogie *(Chm)*

IRON BOW TECHNOLOGIES LLC
2121 Cooperative Way Ste 500, Herndon, VA 20171
Tel.: (703) 279-3000
Web Site: http://www.ironbow.com
Custom Computer Programming Services
N.A.I.C.S.: 541511
John Hanifan *(Pres)*

Subsidiaries:

GuardSight, Inc. **(1)**
755 S Main St 4-137, Cedar City, UT 84720
Web Site: http://www.guardsight.com
Emp.: 100
Computer Related Services

N.A.I.C.S.: 541519
Brian O'Neil *(VP-Strategic Accts)*

IRON CITY INDUSTRIAL CLEANING CORP.
6640 Frankstown Ave, Pittsburgh, PA 15206
Tel.: (412) 661-2001 PA
Web Site:
   http://www.ironcityuniform.com
Year Founded: 1928
Sales Range: $10-24.9 Million
Emp.: 160
Rental & Direct Sale of Uniforms; Related Industrial Services
N.A.I.C.S.: 812332
Philip Sonnenklar *(Pres)*
Debra Zidell *(Treas)*
John Seliga *(Mgr-Svc)*

IRON HORSE ACQUISITION CORP.
875 Third Ave, New York, NY 10022
Tel.: (212) 891-2100 Ky
Year Founded: 2017
Emp.: 2
Investment Services
N.A.I.C.S.: 523999
Steven F. Mayer *(Chm & CEO)*
Chan W. Galbato *(Vice Chm)*
Mark W. Smith *(CFO)*

IRON MINING GROUP, INC.
295 Madison Ave 12th Fl, New York, NY 10017
Tel.: (646) 389-3070 FL
Sales Range: Less than $1 Million
Emp.: 11
Holding Company; Iron Mining
N.A.I.C.S.: 551112
Garrett K. Krause *(Chm & CEO)*
Michael R. Carney *(VP-Banking & Global Bus Dev)*
Conrad C. Chase *(VP-Ops)*

IRON PATH CAPITAL, L.P.
424 Church St, Ste 2240, Nashville, TN 37219
Tel.: (615) 953-7133
Web Site: https://ironpathcapital.com
Year Founded: 2021
Emp.: 100
Private Equity
N.A.I.C.S.: 523940
Rob Reistetter *(Mng Partner)*

Subsidiaries:

Capitol Pain Institute PA **(1)**
8015 Shoal Creek Blvd Ste 103, Austin, TX 78757
Tel.: (512) 467-7246
Web Site: https://capitolpain.com
Office Of Physician
N.A.I.C.S.: 621111

Subsidiary (Domestic):

Matthew F Mccarty M D PLLC **(2)**
4544 S Lamar Blvd, Austin, TX 78745-1575
Tel.: (512) 834-4141
Web Site: http://www.balconespain.com
Offices of Physicians (except Mental Health Specialists)
N.A.I.C.S.: 621111
Lisa Robinot *(Office Mgr)*

Gateway Chemicals, Ltd. **(1)**
221 Rochester St, Avon, NY 14414
Tel.: (585) 226-6177
Web Site: http://www.aldon-chem.com
Sales Range: $1-9.9 Million
Emp.: 35
Fiscal Year-end: 12/31/2013
Chemical & Allied Products Merchant Whslr
N.A.I.C.S.: 424690
Alex Molinich *(Pres)*

IRON PEDDLERS, INC.
3504 Rocky River Rd N, Monroe, NC 28110

Tel.: (704) 289-8591 NC
Web Site:
   http://www.ironpeddlers.com
Year Founded: 1974
Rev.: $21,800,000
Emp.: 33
General Construction Machinery & Equipment
N.A.I.C.S.: 423810
Anthony Broome *(Pres)*

IRON POINT PARTNERS, LLC
1133 Connecticut Ave NW Ste 800, Washington, DC 20036
Tel.: (202) 452-8400 DE
Web Site:
   http://www.ironpointpartners.com
Year Founded: 2007
Emp.: 20
Real Estate & Other Asset Investment Private Equity Firm
N.A.I.C.S.: 523999
Tom Lynch *(Founding Partner)*

Subsidiaries:

IPI Partners, LLC **(1)**
300 N LaSalle St Ste 1500, Chicago, IL 60654
Tel.: (312) 796-2200
Web Site: https://ipipartners.com
Digital Infrastructure Assets Investment Management Firm
N.A.I.C.S.: 523999
Matthew R. A'Hearn *(Partner)*

Holding (Domestic):

Stack Infrastructure, Inc. **(2)**
1700 Broadway Ste 1750, Denver, CO 80290
Web Site: https://www.stackinfra.com
Holding Company; Data Center Leasing & Support Services
N.A.I.C.S.: 551112
Donough Roche *(Sr VP-Engrg & Client Svcs-EMEA)*
Ty Miller *(Chief Comml Officer)*
Andrew Gold *(Sr VP-Corp Dev & Chief Counsel)*
Jim Linkous *(Sr VP-Strategic Accts)*
Brian Cox *(CEO-Americas)*
Tim Hughes *(Chief Dev Officer-Americas)*

IRON PONY MOTORSPORTS GROUP, INC.
5436 Westerville Rd, Westerville, OH 43081
Tel.: (614) 891-2461 OH
Web Site: http://www.ironpony.com
Year Founded: 1999
Sales Range: $1-9.9 Million
Emp.: 50
Motorcycle Dealers
N.A.I.C.S.: 441227
Christopher Jones *(Pres & CEO)*
Tammy Jones *(VP)*
Cory Atwood *(CFO)*
Frank Lark *(VP-Mktg & Mgr-Growth)*
Alan Schatz *(Mgr-Ops)*

Subsidiaries:

Mccune Cycle World, Inc. **(1)**
327 Ashland Rd, Mansfield, OH 44905
Tel.: (419) 524-2222
Web Site:
   http://www.mccunecycleworld.com
Sales Range: $1-9.9 Million
Emp.: 15
Motorcycle Dealers, Nsk
N.A.I.C.S.: 441227
Cynthia McCune *(VP)*
Kale McCune *(Mgr-Fin)*

IRON SPARK I INC.
125 N Cache St 2nd Fl, Jackson, WY 83001
Tel.: (307) 200-9007 DE
Web Site: https://www.ironspark.com
Emp.: 100

Iron Spark I Inc.—(Continued)

Investment Services
N.A.I.C.S.: 523999
Joshua L. Spear *(CEO)*

IRON TRADE IMPORTS, INC.
2590 Mercantile Dr Ste C, Rancho
Cordova, CA 95742
Tel.: (916) 638-5802
Web Site:
   http://www.viphomeandgarden.com
Year Founded: 2006
Sales Range: $1-9.9 Million
Emp.: 12
Importer & Whslr of Home & Garden
Decor Products
N.A.I.C.S.: 423220
Ty Maclure *(Mgr-Ops)*

IRONARCH TECHNOLOGY, LLC
1313 Dolley Madison Blvd Ste 404,
McLean, VA 22101
Tel.: (703) 942-8868
Web Site:
   http://www.ironarchtechnology.com
Year Founded: 2013
Sales Range: $1-9.9 Million
Emp.: 43
Information Technology Development
Services
N.A.I.C.S.: 541512
Joe Punaro *(Pres)*

IRONGATE REALTORS INC.
122 N Main St, Dayton, OH 45459
Tel.: (937) 433-3300
Web Site:
   http://www.irongaterealtors.com
Sales Range: $10-24.9 Million
Emp.: 400
Real Estate Brokers & Agents
N.A.I.C.S.: 531210
Steve Brown *(Owner & Pres)*
Bill Rogers *(Dir-Agent Dev)*
Scot Sutherland *(Mgr-Centerville)*

IRONMAN PARTS & SERVICES
2535 Anselmo Dr, Corona, CA 92879
Tel.: (951) 735-3710
Web Site:
   http://www.ironmanparts.com
Sales Range: $10-24.9 Million
Emp.: 120
Heavy-Duty Replacement Parts Distr
N.A.I.C.S.: 441330
Craig Phillips *(Pres)*
Angela Lin *(Controller)*
Joselyn Rendon *(Coord-Mktg)*
Anna Ballou *(Mgr-Mktg)*
Christina Ross *(Mgr-Svc)*
Celso Lontok *(Mgr-Parts)*

IRONRIDGE GLOBAL PARTNERS, LLC
1 Montgomery St Ste 2575, San
Francisco, CA 94104-4505
Tel.: (415) 658-9550
Web Site:
   http://www.ironridgeglobal.com
Sales Range: $1-9.9 Million
Investment Banking & Securities
Dealing
N.A.I.C.S.: 523150
John C. Kirkland *(Mng Dir)*

IRONTRAFFIC.COM
555 8th Ave Ste 1903, New York, NY
10018
Tel.: (646) 688-1033
Web Site: http://www.irontraffic.com
Year Founded: 2002
Rev.: $6,900,000
Emp.: 21
Marketing Research Public Opinion
Polling

N.A.I.C.S.: 541910
Assaf Malinick *(Pres)*

IRONWARE TECHNOLOGIES, LLC
6834 S University Blvd Ste 416, Centennial, CO 80122
Tel.: (303) 832-3970
Web Site: http://www.forcebi.com
Year Founded: 1996
Sales Range: $1-9.9 Million
Emp.: 21
Information Technology Consulting
Services
N.A.I.C.S.: 541690
Gregory Houston *(Founder & Pres)*
Lawrence Bickel *(VP-Dev)*

IRONWAVE TECHNOLOGIES LLC
7430 Merritt Park Dr, Manassas, VA
20109
Tel.: (860) 828-3332
Web Site: http://www.iwtllc.com
Year Founded: 2016
Holding Company
N.A.I.C.S.: 551112
Elio Scaccio *(VP-Bus Dev)*

Subsidiaries:

American Microwave Corporation **(1)**
7430 Merritt Park Dr Ste 140, Manassas,
VA 20109
Tel.: (301) 662-4700
Web Site: https://americanmic.com
Radio & Television Broadcasting & Wireless
Communications Equipment Mfr
N.A.I.C.S.: 334220

Mu-Del Electronics, Inc. **(1)**
8576 Wellington Rd, Manassas, VA 20109
Tel.: (703) 709-9400
Rev.: $1,300,000
Emp.: 15
Radio & Television Broadcasting & Wireless
Communications Equipment Mfr
N.A.I.C.S.: 334220
Sami Antrazi *(CEO)*

Subsidiary (Domestic):

Luff Research Inc. **(2)**
20 N Tyson Ave, Floral Park, NY 11001
Tel.: (516) 358-2880
Web Site: http://www.luffresearch.com
Radio, Television & Other Electronics
Stores
N.A.I.C.S.: 449210
Greta Gorder *(Pres)*

Syntonics LLC **(1)**
9160 Red Branch Rd, Columbia, MD 21045
Tel.: (410) 884-0500
Web Site: http://www.syntonicscorp.com
Rev.: $3,441,000
Emp.: 15
Radio & Television Broadcasting & Wireless
Communications Equipment Mfr
N.A.I.C.S.: 334220
Ed Connor *(Dir-Sls)*
Ed O'Malley *(VP-Fin & Admin)*
Gary Bruce *(Sr Dir-Ops)*
Steve Gemeny *(Dir-Bus Dev)*
Bruce G. Montgomery *(Pres)*
Doug Crowe *(Chief Engr)*
Ernest Keijzers *(Acct Mgr)*
Lukasz Miazgowski *(Mgr-Mktg)*
Martin Ryan *(Mng Dir)*

IRONWOOD CAPITAL MANAGEMENT LLC
45 Nod Road Ste 2, Avon, CT 06001-3819
Tel.: (860) 409-2100
Web Site: http://ironwoodcap.com
Rev.: $4,565,000
Emp.: 11
Portfolio Management
N.A.I.C.S.: 523940
Marc A. Reich *(Chm & CEO)*
Carolyn C. Galiette *(Pres & Chief Investment Officer)*

Subsidiaries:

Newbury Franklin Industrials LLC **(1)**
4 Inn St., Newburyport, 01950, MA
Tel.: (978) 225-0663
Web Site: https://www.newburyfranklin.com
Industrial Mfg.
N.A.I.C.S.: 333310

Subsidiary (Domestic):

Metaltech Service Center Inc. **(2)**
9915 Monroe Rd, Houston, TX 77075-2664
Tel.: (713) 991-5100
Web Site: http://www.metaltechsc.com
Industrial Valve Mfr
N.A.I.C.S.: 332911
Greg Rayburn *(Pres)*

IRONWOOD PARTNERS LLC
420 Lexington Ave Ste 2334, New
York, NY 10170
Tel.: (212) 682-7100
Web Site: http://www.ironwood-
   partners.com
Emp.: 6
Privater Equity Firm
N.A.I.C.S.: 523999
John A. Cosentino Jr. *(Partner)*
Paul F. Balser *(Founder)*

IRONWORKER MANAGEMENT PROGRESSIVE ACTION CO-OPERATIVE TRUST
1750 New York Ave Ste 400, Washington, DC 20006
Tel.: (202) 393-1147
Web Site: http://www.impact-net.org
Year Founded: 2003
Sales Range: $10-24.9 Million
Emp.: 9
Ironworker Job Opportunity Services
N.A.I.C.S.: 561311
Kevin Hilton *(CEO)*
Eric Dean *(Pres)*

IROQUOIS NURSING HOME, INC.
4600 Southwood Heights Dr, Jamesville, NY 13078
Tel.: (315) 469-1300
Web Site:
   http://www.iroquoisnursing.com
Year Founded: 1990
Sales Range: $10-24.9 Million
Emp.: 303
Nursing Care Services
N.A.I.C.S.: 623110
Penny Hefferon *(CFO)*
Sonya Moshier *(Pres)*

IROQUOIS PAVING CORPORATION
1889 E US Hwy 24, Watseka, IL
60970
Tel.: (815) 432-5211
Rev.: $13,720,691
Emp.: 25
Highway & Street Paving Contractor
N.A.I.C.S.: 237310
John D. Lynch *(Chm)*

IRR SUPPLY CENTERS INC.
908 Niagara Falls Blvd, North
Tonawanda, NY 14120-2019
Tel.: (716) 692-1600
Web Site: http://www.irrsupply.com
Year Founded: 1965
Sales Range: $50-74.9 Million
Emp.: 300
Plumbing Fixtures, Equipment & Supplies
N.A.I.C.S.: 423720
Michael P. Duffy *(Pres)*
Al Moskal *(Mgr-Credit)*
Jim Adamski *(Branch Mgr)*
Joe Perrelli *(Asst Mgr)*
John Newman *(Mgr-Credit)*

Subsidiaries:

L.A. Hazard & Sons Inc. **(1)**
1695 Overhead Rd, Derby, NY 14047
Tel.: (716) 627-2364
Web Site: http://www.lahazard.com
Sales Range: $10-24.9 Million
Emp.: 42
Plumbing & Hydronic Heating Supplies
N.A.I.C.S.: 423720
Micheal Dussy *(Pres)*

IRRADIANT PARTNERS, LP
2025 Guadalupe St., Ste 260, Austin,
TX 78705
Tel.: (512) 676-3535
Web Site:
   https://irradiantpartners.com
Year Founded: 2021
Investment Management
N.A.I.C.S.: 523999

Subsidiaries:

Franchise Group, Inc. **(1)**
109 Innovation Ct Ste J, Delaware, OH
43015
Tel.: (740) 363-2222
Web Site: https://www.franchisegrp.com
Rev.: $4,397,832,000
Assets: $3,630,412,000
Liabilities: $3,209,032,000
Net Worth: $421,380,000
Earnings: ($68,573,000)
Emp.: 8,575
Fiscal Year-end: 12/31/2022
Holding Company; Tax Preparation Services
N.A.I.C.S.: 551112
Andrew Kaminsky *(Chief Admin Officer &
Exec VP)*
Kenneth Todd Evans *(Chief Franchising Officer)*
Jason Mattes *(VP-Franchise Dev)*
Scott Harvey *(VP-Franchise Ops)*
Eric F. Seeton *(CFO)*
Tiffany McMillan-McWaters *(Gen Counsel,
Dir & Deputy Gen Counsel)*

Subsidiary (Domestic):

American Freight, LLC **(2)**
109 Innovation Ct Ste J, Delaware, OH
43015
Web Site: http://www.americanfreight.com
Freight Transportation Services
N.A.I.C.S.: 488510

Furniture Factory Outlet, LLC **(2)**
8819 Rogers Ave, Fort Smith, AR 72908
Tel.: (479) 452-2869
Web Site: http://www.ffohome.com
Furniture & Home Furnishings Retailer
N.A.I.C.S.: 449110
Keri Durkin *(COO)*
Jay Peters *(Chief Merchandising Officer &
Exec VP)*
Hank Mullany *(CEO)*

JTH Financial, LLC **(2)**
1716 Corporate Landing Pkwy, Virginia
Beach, VA 23454
Web Site: http://www.jthfinancialllc.com
Investment Advisory Services
N.A.I.C.S.: 523940

JTH Tax, Inc. **(2)**
1716 Corporate Landing Pkwy, Virginia
Beach, VA 23454-5681
Tel.: (757) 493-8855
Web Site: http://www.libertytax.com
Sales Range: $75-99.9 Million
Tax Preparation Services
N.A.I.C.S.: 541213

Liberty Tax Service Inc. **(2)**
1716 Corporate Landing Pkwy, Virginia
Beach, VA 23454
Tel.: (757) 493-8855
Web Site: http://www.libertytax.com
Investment Advisory Services
N.A.I.C.S.: 523940
Shaun York *(COO)*
Nicole Ossenfort *(Pres & CEO)*
John T. Hewitt *(Chm)*

Subsidiary (Domestic):

Vitamin Shoppe, Inc. **(3)**

300 Harmon Meadow Blvd, Secaucus, NJ 07094
Tel.: (201) 868-5959
Web Site: http://www.vitaminshoppe.com
Rev.: $1,114,160,000
Assets: $388,079,000
Liabilities: $199,738,000
Net Worth: $188,341,000
Earnings: ($3,752,000)
Emp.: 3,503
Fiscal Year-end: 12/29/2018
Holding Company; Vitamins & Other Health Supplements Retailer
N.A.I.C.S.: 551112
Teresa Orth (Chief People Officer & Exec VP)
Andrew Laudato (COO & Exec VP)
Neal Panza (Exec VP-Retail Sls, Ops & Svcs)
Muriel F. Gonzalez (Chief Mdsg & Mktg Officer & Exec VP)
Laura Coffey (CFO & Exec VP)
Sharon M. Leite (CEO)

Subsidiary (Domestic):

Betancourt Sports Nutrition, LLC (4)
14700 NW 60th Ave, Miami Lakes, FL 33014
Tel.: (305) 593-9296
Web Site:
http://www.betancourtnutrition.com
Bodybuilder Food Supplement Distr
N.A.I.C.S.: 456191

FDC Vitamins, Inc. (4)
14620 NW 60 Ave, Miami, FL 33014
Tel.: (305) 468-1600
Web Site: http://www.fdcvitamins.com
Sales Range: $1-9.9 Million
Emp.: 25
Drugs, Proprietaries, And Sundries
N.A.I.C.S.: 424210
Mike Beargall (CEO)

VS Direct Inc. (4)
2100 88th St F4, North Bergen, NJ 07047
Tel.: (201) 758-0404
Web Site: http://www.vitaminshoppe.com
Online Vitamin & Health Supplement Retailer
N.A.I.C.S.: 456191

VS Hercules LLC (4)
2101 91st St, North Bergen, NJ 07047
Tel.: (201) 868-5959
Pharmaceuticals Product Mfr
N.A.I.C.S.: 325412

Vitamin Shoppe Industries, Inc. (4)
2100 88th St F4, North Bergen, NJ 07047
Tel.: (201) 758-0404
Web Site: http://www.vitaminshoppe.com
Emp.: 200
Vitamin & Health Supplement Store Operator
N.A.I.C.S.: 456191
Richard L. Markee (Chm)

Subsidiary (Domestic):

PSP Stores LLC (2)
22710 Haggerty Ste 100, Farmington Hills, MI 48335
Tel.: (248) 348-7300
Pet Supplies Store
N.A.I.C.S.: 459910
Alex Roberts (VP-Franchising)
Dave Bolen (Pres & CEO)

Subsidiary (Domestic):

PSP Group, LLC (3)
29493 7 Mile Rd, Livonia, MI 48152-1909
Tel.: (248) 615-0039
Web Site: http://www.petsuppliesplus.com
Sales Range: $10-24.9 Million
Emp.: 16
Sales of Pet Food & Related Products
N.A.I.C.S.: 459910
Dan Boose (CFO)
Heidi Char (Sr VP-HR)
Derek T. Panfil (Sr VP-Merchandising-Marketing)
Christopher Rowland (CEO)
Jeff Suttle (Sr VP-Merchandising)
Dan McNamara (CFO)
Nick Russo (Sr VP)
Stan Mac (CIO-Information Technology & Sr VP-Information Technology)

Dan McNamara (CFO)
Nick Russo (Sr VP)
Stan Mac (CIO-Information Technology & Sr VP-Information Technology)
Kenneth Miles Tedder Jr. (COO)

Subsidiary (Domestic):

SiempreTax LLC (2)
1716 Corporate Landing Pkwy, Virginia Beach, VA 23454
Tel.: (800) 790-3863
Investment Advisory Services
N.A.I.C.S.: 523940

IRRIGATION SPECIALISTS INC.
2410 N 4th Ave, Pasco, WA 99301
Tel.: (509) 547-1761
Web Site: http://www.irrspec.com
Sales Range: $10-24.9 Million
Emp.: 45
Irrigation Equipment Distr
N.A.I.C.S.: 423820
Mike Engelhart (Gen Mgr)

IRRIGATION STATION LLP
11929 Windfern Rd, Houston, TX 77064
Tel.: (281) 890-6574
Web Site:
http://www.irrigationstation.com
Year Founded: 1987
Sales Range: $10-24.9 Million
Emp.: 20
Irrigation Equipment Distr
N.A.I.C.S.: 423820
George Burtch (Partner)

IRSIK & DOLL FEED SERVICES INC.
104 W Ave A, Cimarron, KS 67835
Tel.: (620) 855-3111
Web Site: http://www.irsikanddoll.com
Year Founded: 1961
Sales Range: $25-49.9 Million
Emp.: 200
Grain & Field Beans
N.A.I.C.S.: 424510
John M. Petz (Pres & CEO)

IRTH SOLUTIONS, INC.
5009 Horizons Dr, Columbus, OH 43220
Tel.: (614) 784-8000
Web Site:
http://www.irthsolutions.com
Year Founded: 1985
Management Software Solutions
N.A.I.C.S.: 513210
Joe Pardi (CFO)
Rod A. Ball (CTO)
Trent A. Peugh (Pres & CEO)

IRVINE ACCESS FLOORS INC.
9425 Washington Blvd N Ste YWW, Laurel, MD 20723-1378
Tel.: (301) 617-9333
Web Site:
http://www.irvineaccessfloors.com
Year Founded: 1961
Sales Range: $10-24.9 Million
Emp.: 31
Installing Building Equipment
N.A.I.C.S.: 238330
Larry Worthington (Pres)
Jim Radtke (VP)
Kenneth Carfine (Project Mgr)

IRVINE COMMUNITY LAND TRUST
1 Civic Center Plz 3rd Fl, Irvine, CA 92606-5207
Tel.: (949) 724-7388 CA
Web Site: http://www.irvineclt.org
Year Founded: 2006
Sales Range: $1-9.9 Million
Housing Assistance Services

N.A.I.C.S.: 624229
Mark Asturias (Exec Dir)
Kim Radding (Sec-Admin)
Mary Ann Gaido (Chm)
Christina Shea (Vice Chm)
Nancy Donnelly (Treas)
Beth Krom (Sec)

IRVINE MARKETING COMMUNICATIONS
960 Holmdel Rd, Holmdel, NJ 07733-2138
Tel.: (732) 332-0515
Web Site: http://www.imc-nj.com
Year Founded: 1983
Sales Range: $10-24.9 Million
Emp.: 15
Advetising Agency
N.A.I.C.S.: 541810
Robert Zick (Pres)
Steven Aronson (Partner-Integrated Mktg Comm & Strategy)
Stephen Norton (VP-Digital Mktg Svcs & CRM Strategy)

IRVINE RANCH WATER DISTRICT INC.
15600 Sand Canyon Ave, Irvine, CA 92618-3100
Tel.: (949) 453-5300 CA
Web Site: http://www.irwd.com
Year Founded: 1961
Sales Range: $75-99.9 Million
Emp.: 375
Water Supply Services
N.A.I.C.S.: 221310
Tony Mossbarger, (Dir-Admin Svcs)
Beth Beeman (Dir-Pub Affairs)
Paul A. Cook (Gen Mgr)

IRVING MATERIALS INC.
8032 N St Rd 9, Greenfield, IN 46140
Tel.: (317) 326-3101
Web Site: http://www.irvmat.com
Sales Range: $250-299.9 Million
Emp.: 2,500
Ready Mixed Concrete
N.A.I.C.S.: 327320
Brian Duncan (Mgr-Area)
Shawn Burgess (CFO)
Jeff McPherson (VP-Sls & Mktg)
Pete Irving (Chm)
Earl Brinker (CEO)

IRVING PLACE CAPITAL MANAGEMENT, L.P.
745 5th Ave, New York, NY 10151
Tel.: (212) 551-4500
Web Site:
http://www.irvingplacecapital.com
Year Founded: 1997
Privater Equity Firm
N.A.I.C.S.: 523999
John D. Howard (Co-Mng Partner)
Philip M. Carpenter III (Co-Mng Partner)
Devraj Roy (Partner)
Matthew J. Turner (Partner)
Keith E. Zadourian (Partner)
David Knoch (Partner & Head-Strategic Svcs)
Jim McDonough (Principal)
David Grochow (CFO & Principal)
Blake Austin (Principal-Strategic Svcs)
Bob Bode (Principal-Strategic Svcs)
Brian Blackman (VP-Finance & Ops)
David Choi (Principal)
Maritza Colon (Mgr-Accounts Payable, Fin & Ops)
Joshua Suchow (Mgr-Fin & Ops)
Joe El Chami (VP)
Adam Felsenthal (VP-Legal & Compliance)

Swen Kupferschmid-Rojas (Controller-Fin & Ops)
Phil Yates (Principal)

Subsidiaries:

Alpha Packaging LLC (1)
1555 Page Industrial Blvd, Saint Louis, MO 63132
Tel.: (314) 427-4300
Web Site: http://www.alphap.com
Plastic Container Mfr
N.A.I.C.S.: 326160
Jack Baily (Exec VP-Sls & Distr)

Subsidiary (Domestic):

Alpha Packaging LLC (2)
1236 Watson St, Ypsilanti, MI 48198
Tel.: (734) 481-1373
Web Site: http://www.alphap.com
Sales Range: $25-49.9 Million
Plastics Bottle Mfr
N.A.I.C.S.: 326160

Balducci's LLC (1)
12920 Cloverleaf Center Dr, Germantown, MD 20874-1173
Tel.: (240) 403-2440
Web Site: http://www.balduccis.com
Sales Range: $400-449.9 Million
Specialty Food Stores, Restaurants & Catering Services
N.A.I.C.S.: 445110
Allen Merken (VP-Engrg, Real Estate & Construction)
Kathe Benjamin (VP-HR & Labor Rels)
Sharon Bastianelli (VP-IT)
Joseph C. Parisi Jr. (COO)

Bendon, Inc. (1)
1840 Baney Rd, Ashland, OH 44805
Tel.: (419) 207-3600
Web Site: http://www.bendonpub.com
Emp.: 40
Children's Book Publishers
N.A.I.C.S.: 513130
Rick Littleton (Controller & VP-Fin)
Heather Robinson (VP-Creative)
Ben Ferguson (Pres & CEO)
David Swank (CFO)
Jeff Davis (VP-Ops)
Jenny Hastings (Exec VP & Gen Mgr)
Tim Walker (VP & Controller)

Subsidiary (Domestic):

Artistic Studios, LTD (2)
444 Spear St Ste 101, San Francisco, CA 94105-1693
Tel.: (415) 284-8256
Web Site: http://www.artistic-studios.com
Children's Specialty Books & Activity Products Mfr & Distr
N.A.I.C.S.: 611699

Dots, Inc. (1)
30300 Emerald Valley Pkwy, Solon, OH 44139
Tel.: (440) 349-7000
Web Site: http://www.dots.com
Sales Range: $125-149.9 Million
Women's Clothing Store Operator
N.A.I.C.S.: 458110

Dynojet Research, Inc. (1)
2191 Mendenhall Dr Ste 105, North Las Vegas, NV 89081
Tel.: (702) 399-1423
Web Site: http://www.dynojet.com
Emp.: 160
Dynamometer Instruments Mfr
N.A.I.C.S.: 334519
David Winiarczyk (CFO)
Danny Hourigan (Sr VP)

MC Shipping, Inc. (1)
Clarendon House 2 Church Street, Hamilton, HM 11, Bermuda
Tel.: (441) 2957933
Sales Range: $50-74.9 Million
Emp.: 9
Owner & Operator of Light General Cargo Vessels
N.A.I.C.S.: 483111

Subsidiary (Non-US):

MC Shipping S.A.M. (2)
Gildo Pastor Center, 7, rue du Gabian, MC

Irving Place Capital Management, L.P.—(Continued)

98000, Monaco, Monaco
Tel.: (377) 97974990
Sales Range: $100-124.9 Million
Emp.: 6
Ocean Freight Services
N.A.I.C.S.: 483111
Antony Crawford (CEO)
Giles Francis (CFO)
Anton Pardini (COO)

Subsidiary (Non-US):

MC Shipping Ltd. (3)
80 Cheapside, London, EC2V 6EE, United Kingdom
Tel.: (44) 2076265787
Sales Range: $10-24.9 Million
Emp.: 6
Ocean Freight Services
N.A.I.C.S.: 483111

MC Shipping Pte Ltd (3)
Cantonment Rd Room 0602 S Point, Singapore, 089763, Singapore
Tel.: (65) 64231045
Sales Range: $10-24.9 Million
Ocean Freight Services
N.A.I.C.S.: 483111

Mold-Rite Plastics LLC (1)
1 Plant St, Plattsburgh, NY 12901
Tel.: (518) 561-1812
Web Site: http://www.mrpcap.com
Sales Range: $75-99.9 Million
Plastic Packaging & Services
N.A.I.C.S.: 326112
Brian Bauerbach (Pres & CEO)
Phil Yates (Chm)

Subsidiary (Domestic):

Stull Technologies Inc. (2)
17 Veronica Ave, Somerset, NJ 08873-3448
Tel.: (732) 873-5000
Web Site: http://www.stulltech.com
Sales Range: $25-49.9 Million
Mfr, Designer & Developer of Injection-Molded Closures & Other Packaging Solutions
N.A.I.C.S.: 326199
Gene Stull (CEO)
Jason Stull (Mgr-Mktg Svcs)

New York & Company, Inc. (1)
330 W 34th St 9th Fl, New York, NY 10001
Tel.: (212) 884-2000
Web Site: https://www.nyandcompany.com
Rev.: $926,868,000
Assets: $302,956,000
Liabilities: $216,095,000
Net Worth: $86,861,000
Earnings: $5,675,000
Emp.: 1,547
Fiscal Year-end: 02/03/2018
Women's Clothing Store
N.A.I.C.S.: 458110
Gregory J. Scott (CEO)
Grace A. Nichols (Chm)
Michelle Pearlman (Chief Mktg Officer & Exec VP-ECommerce)
Faeth Bradley (Exec VP-HR)
Adam Ratner (Gen Counsel & VP)
John M. Worthington (Pres & COO)

Subsidiary (Domestic):

Lerner New York, Inc. (2)
450 W 33rd St 5th Fl, New York, NY 10001
Tel.: (212) 736-1222
Women's Clothing Retailer
N.A.I.C.S.: 458110

IRVINGTON ELEVATOR COMPANY
W Superior St, Irvington, IL 62848
Tel.: (618) 249-6206 DE
Sales Range: $10-24.9 Million
Emp.: 12
Grain Elevators
N.A.I.C.S.: 424510

IRWIN CONTRACTING INC.
671 Old Willets Path, Hauppauge, NY 11788
Tel.: (631) 434-8400

Web Site: http://www.irwincontractinginc.com
Year Founded: 1986
Sales Range: $10-24.9 Million
Emp.: 25
Residential Remodeling Services
N.A.I.C.S.: 236118
John C. Irwin (Pres)

IRWIN CORPORATION
958 Union Ave, Laconia, NH 03246
Tel.: (603) 524-6661 NH
Web Site: http://www.irwinmarine.com
Year Founded: 1919
Sales Range: $10-24.9 Million
Emp.: 45
Sales of Boats & Boating Products
N.A.I.C.S.: 441222
John P. Irwin (Pres)
Bruce Wright (Gen Mgr)
Jason D. Marceau (Mgr-Svc)
Bill Irwin (VP-Sls & Mktg)

IRWIN INTERNATIONAL, INC.
PO Box 4000, Corona, CA 92878-4000
Tel.: (951) 372-9555 CA
Web Site: http://www.aircraftspruce.com
Sales Range: $100-124.9 Million
Emp.: 160
Holding Company; Aircraft Parts Dealer
N.A.I.C.S.: 551112
James J. Irwin (Pres)

Subsidiaries:

Aircraft Spruce & Specialty Co. (1)
225 Airport Cir, Corona, CA 92880
Tel.: (951) 372-9555
Web Site: http://www.aircraftspruce.com
Sales Range: $75-99.9 Million
Emp.: 92
Aircraft Parts Dealer
N.A.I.C.S.: 423860
Jim Irwin (Pres)

IRWIN SEATING COMPANY INC.
3251 Fruit Rdg Ave NW, Grand Rapids, MI 49544
Tel.: (616) 574-7400 MI
Web Site: http://www.irwinseating.com
Year Founded: 1907
Sales Range: $25-49.9 Million
Emp.: 450
Public Seating Mfr & Retailer
N.A.I.C.S.: 337127
Earle S. Irwin (Chm)
Bruce Cohen (Sr VP-Sls & Mktg)
Ray Vander Kooi (CFO)
Graham Irwin (Pres & CEO)

Subsidiaries:

Irwin Telescopic Seating (1)
610 E Cumberland Rd, Altamont, IL 62411 (100%)
Tel.: (618) 483-6157
Web Site: http://www.irwintelescopicseating.com
Sales Range: $25-49.9 Million
Emp.: 160
Public Building & Related Furniture
N.A.I.C.S.: 337127
Eric Conrad (Pres)

IRWIN-HODSON COMPANY
2838 SE 9th Ave, Portland, OR 97202
Tel.: (503) 231-9990
Web Site: http://www.ihco.com
Sales Range: $10-24.9 Million
Emp.: 25
Commercial Printing, Lithographic
N.A.I.C.S.: 323111
Mark S. McDonald (VP)

IRX THERAPEUTICS, INC.
140 W 57th St Ste 3D, New York, NY 10019
Tel.: (212) 582-1199
Web Site: http://www.irxtherapeutics.com
Emp.: 25
Cancer Therapies Researcher & Developer
N.A.I.C.S.: 325412
Mark Leuchtenberger (Pres & CEO)
Monil Shah (COO)
David H. Deming (Chm)

ISA ADVERTISING
845 3rd Ave Fl 6, New York, NY 10022-6630
Tel.: (212) 295-9191 NY
Year Founded: 1989
Rev.: $34,000,000
Emp.: 15
N.A.I.C.S.: 541810
Iris Shokoff (Founder & CEO)
Alexandra Reuters (Sr VP & Dir-Media)
Bob Feinberg (Chief Creative Officer)
Jeff Bretl (Dir-Creative)
Suzanne Ghosh (Grp Acct Dir-Direct Mail Div)

ISAAC HEATING & AC
180 Charlotte St, Rochester, NY 14607
Tel.: (585) 546-1400
Web Site: http://www.isaacheating.com
Sales Range: $10-24.9 Million
Emp.: 250
Warm Air Heating & Air Conditioning Contractor
N.A.I.C.S.: 238220
Bill Isaac (Owner)
Ray Isaac (Pres)

ISAAC TIRE INC.
3525 Independence Dr, Fort Wayne, IN 46808
Tel.: (260) 482-9770
Sales Range: $10-24.9 Million
Emp.: 80
Rebuilding & Retreading Tires
N.A.I.C.S.: 326212
Jonee Dill (Pres)

ISAAC'S RESTAURANT & DELI INC.
354 N Prince St Ste 220, Lancaster, PA 17603
Tel.: (717) 394-0623
Web Site: http://www.isaacsdeli.com
Rev.: $18,000,000
Emp.: 12
Restaurant Operators
N.A.I.C.S.: 722511
Philip R. Wenger (Founder & Chm)
D. Michael Weaver (Pres & CEO)

ISAACS ENTERPRISES INC.
101 N Fairmont Ave, Morristown, TN 37814
Tel.: (423) 586-7090
Sales Range: $10-24.9 Million
Emp.: 270
Provider of Petroleum Bulk Stations
N.A.I.C.S.: 424710
Steve Isaacs (Pres)
Lonnie Johnson (Mgr-IT)

ISABEL BLOOM LLC
736 Federal St, Davenport, IA 52803
Tel.: (563) 333-2040
Web Site: http://www.ibloom.com
Sales Range: $10-24.9 Million
Emp.: 60
Fountains, Concrete
N.A.I.C.S.: 327390

Cathy Nevins (Owner)
Bill Barrett (Owner)
Lexi Brems (Asst Mgr)

ISABELLA STEWART GARDNER MUSEUM
25 Evans Way, Boston, MA 02115
Tel.: (617) 566-1401 MA
Web Site: http://www.gardnermuseum.org
Year Founded: 1936
Sales Range: $25-49.9 Million
Emp.: 241
Museums
N.A.I.C.S.: 712110
Amy Scheuerman Browning (Mgr-Digital Content)
David W. Scudder (Chm)
Faith Diver (Mgr-Creative Svcs)
Cynthia A. Hallenbeck (CFO & COO)

ISABELLE RIDGWAY CARE CENTER
1520 Hawthorne Ave, Columbus, OH 43203
Tel.: (614) 252-4931 OH
Web Site: http://www.isabelleridgway.com
Year Founded: 1916
Sales Range: $1-9.9 Million
Emp.: 212
Elder Care Services
N.A.I.C.S.: 624120
Patricia B. Mullins (Pres & CEO)
John E. Atala (Fin Dir)
Grant Timothy (Treas)
W. Sandra Moody (Chm)
Thomas Isabella (Sec)

ISACO INTERNATIONAL INC.
5980 Miami Lakes Dr, Miami Lakes, FL 33014
Tel.: (305) 594-4455
Web Site: http://www.isaco.com
Rev.: $32,400,000
Emp.: 250
Men's & Boy's Clothing
N.A.I.C.S.: 424350
Isaac Zelcer (Pres)
Dave Tanner (Controller)
Oscar Vera (Dir-Design)
Philip Goldberg (Dir-Sourcing)

ISAGENIX INTERNATIONAL, LLC
155 E Rivulon Blvd, Gilbert, AZ 85297
Tel.: (480) 889-5777 AZ
Web Site: http://www.isagenix.com
Year Founded: 2002
Sales Range: $200-249.9 Million
Emp.: 300
Health, Beauty & Pharmaceuticals Mfr
N.A.I.C.S.: 325412
John Anderson (Co-Founder)
James Coover (Co-Founder & Chm)
Kathy Coover (Co-Founder & Exec VP)
Scott Luther (COO)
Darren Fuji (CFO)
Travis Garza (Chief Sls Officer & Sr VP)
Patty Raphael (VP-Opportunity Solutions)
Richard Stagg (Gen Counsel & VP)
Justin Powell (Deputy Gen Counsel & Sr VP)
Tony Blodgett (CIO)
Amy Rushia (Mgr-Mktg & Sls Comm)
Lyndsay Clark (Mgr-Sls Support-North America)
Eli Rohlf (Mgr-Digital Mktg)
Devon Shaw (Mgr-Events Trng & Comm)

Jonas Hedberg *(Gen Mgr-Eurpoe)*
Sharron Walsh *(CEO)*
Mac Larsen *(Sr VP-Sls-Global)*

Subsidiaries:

Zija International, Inc.   **(1)**
3300 N Ashton Blvd Ste 100, Lehi, UT
84043
Tel.: (801) 494-2300
Web Site: http://www.zijainternational.com
Sales Range: $100-124.9 Million
Emp.: 158
Other Grocery & Related Product Whslr
N.A.I.C.S.: 424490
Kenneth Brailsford *(Founder & CEO)*
Ryan Palmer *(Pres)*
Whitney Davis *(VP-Mktg Comm)*
Jarom Dastrup *(Dir-North American Sls)*

ISAM MITCHELL & CO. INC.
362 Montello St, Brockton, MA 02301
Tel.: (508) 586-1271
Sales Range: $10-24.9 Million
Emp.: 20
Lumber: Rough, Dressed & Finished
N.A.I.C.S.: 423310
John R. Corcoran *(Pres)*
Michael Regan *(Controller)*

ISAMAX SNACKS, INC.
1 Commonwealth St, Gardiner, ME
04345
Tel.: (207) 582-0125
Web Site:
    http://www.wickedwhoopies.com
Year Founded: 1994
Sales Range: $1-9.9 Million
Emp.: 30
Bakery Goods
N.A.I.C.S.: 445291
Amy Bouchard *(Pres)*
David Bouchard *(VP)*

**ISBA MUTUAL INSURANCE
COMPANY**
20 South Clark St Ste 800, Chicago,
IL 60603
Tel.: (312) 379-2000
Web Site: http://www.isbamutual.com
Sales Range: $10-24.9 Million
Emp.: 18
Direct Property & Casualty Insurance
Carriers
N.A.I.C.S.: 524126
Kurt B. Bounds *(VP-Bus Dev & Svc)*
Jon W. DeMoss *(Pres & CEO)*
Melissa Kaplan *(VP-Clients & Under-
writing)*
Jack C. Carey *(VP)*

**ISBELL CONSTRUCTION CO.
LTD**
PO Box 434, Florence, TX 76527-
0434
Tel.: (254) 793-3603
Web Site:
    http://isbellconstructionltd.com
Year Founded: 1985
Rev.: $11,067,891
Emp.: 67
Telephone & Communication Line
Construction
N.A.I.C.S.: 237130
Alan Isbell *(Co-Founder, Co-Owner &
Co-Pres)*
Larry Parker *(Mgr)*
Randy Isbell *(Co-Founder, Co-Owner
& Co-Pres)*

ISC CONSTRUCTORS, LLC.
20480 Highland Rd, Baton Rouge, LA
70817
Tel.: (225) 756-8001
Web Site: http://www.iscgrp.com
Sales Range: $50-74.9 Million
Emp.: 1,722
Electrical Wiring Services

N.A.I.C.S.: 238210
Glen J. Gulino *(Reg Mgr)*

ISC CORP.
401 E E St, Casper, WY 82601
Tel.: (307) 473-8933
Web Site: http://www.isccorp.net
Sales Range: $25-49.9 Million
Emp.: 60
Computer System Design Services
N.A.I.C.S.: 541512
Win C. Farnsworth *(Founder & CEO)*
Larry Graham *(Treas)*
Jack Lenhart *(VP)*

ISCAN ONLINE, INC.
5600 Tennyson Pkwy Ste 380, Plano,
TX 75024
Tel.: (214) 276-1150
Web Site: http://www.iscanonline.com
Internet Application Development
Services
N.A.I.C.S.: 541511
Carl Banzhof *(Co-Founder & CEO)*
Billy Austin *(Co-Founder & Pres)*
David Raphael *(Dir-Engrg)*

**ISCO HOLDING COMPANY
INC.**
1078 S Jefferson Ave, Lebanon, MO
65536-3601
Tel.: (417) 588-4151   MO
Web Site:
    http://www.independentstavecom
    pany.com
Year Founded: 1912
Sales Range: $25-49.9 Million
Emp.: 860
Wood Containers
N.A.I.C.S.: 321920
Brad Boswell *(Pres)*
Tim Sexton *(Controller)*

Subsidiaries:

Independent Stave Co. Inc.   **(1)**
PO Box 104, Lebanon, MO 65536-0104
Tel.: (417) 588-4151
Web Site: http://www.independentstavecom
    pany.com
Sales Range: $25-49.9 Million
Emp.: 210
Mfr of Wood Containers
N.A.I.C.S.: 321920

Missouri Cooperage Co. Inc.   **(1)**
1078 S Jefferson Ave, Lebanon, MO 65536-
3601
Tel.: (417) 588-4151
Web Site: http://www.worldcooperage.com
Sales Range: $25-49.9 Million
Emp.: 200
Wood Container Mfr
N.A.I.C.S.: 321920
Jan Bishop *(Office Mgr)*

Stave Associates International,
Inc.   **(1)**
109 Orr St, Columbia, MO 65201
Tel.: (573) 442-5707
Web Site: http://www.staveassociatesinterna
    tional.com
Barrel Heading & Stave Mfr
N.A.I.C.S.: 321920

World Cooperage Company Inc.   **(1)**
2557 Napa Vly Corporate Way Ste D,
Napa, CA 94558
Tel.: (707) 255-5900
Web Site: http://www.worldcooperage.com
Rev.: $110,000
Emp.: 10
Wood Containers Distr
N.A.I.C.S.: 423840
Yuri DeLeon *(Acct Mgr)*
Gary Kroll *(Acct Mgr)*
Jason Stout *(Dir-Sls-Intl)*
Patrick Schwerdt *(Gen Mgr-Australia & New
Zealand)*

ISCO INDUSTRIES LLC
100 Witherspoon St 2 W, Louisville,
KY 40202

Tel.: (502) 583-6591
Web Site: http://www.isco-pipe.com
Sales Range: $25-49.9 Million
Emp.: 170
Valves & Fittings
N.A.I.C.S.: 423830
Jimmy Kirchdorfer *(Chm)*
Bryan Fletcher *(Reg Mgr-Sls)*
Rick Hart *(Reg Mgr-Sls)*
Vince Tyra *(CEO)*

ISCO INTERNATIONAL LLC
1450 Arthur Ave Ste A, Elk Grove
Village, IL 60007-5745
Tel.: (847) 391-9400   DE
Web Site: http://www.iscointl.com
Year Founded: 1989
Sales Range: $1-9.9 Million
Emp.: 35
Wireless Systems Solutions Mfr &
Distr
N.A.I.C.S.: 517112

ISE LIMITED
4520 Modern Ln, Laredo, TX 78041
Tel.: (956) 722-4611   TX
Year Founded: 1966
Sales Range: $25-49.9 Million
Emp.: 250
Electronics, Clothing & Shoes Distr
N.A.I.C.S.: 449210
Luis Lidsky *(CEO)*

ISEATZ INC.
643 Magazine St Ste 100, New Or-
leans, LA 70130
Tel.: (504) 525-1186   LA
Web Site: http://www.iseatz.com
Year Founded: 1999
Sales Range: $25-49.9 Million
Emp.: 20
Global Online Travel & Entertainment
Solutions
N.A.I.C.S.: 541512
Kenneth Purcell *(Founder & CEO)*
Michael Bauer *(Sr VP-Distr & Supply)*
Ed Silver *(CIO)*

ISEC INCORPORATED
33 Inverness Dr E, Englewood, CO
80112-5412
Tel.: (303) 790-1444   CO
Web Site: http://www.isecinc.com
Year Founded: 1967
Sales Range: $100-124.9 Million
Emp.: 1,200
Specialized Building Interiors &
Equipment
N.A.I.C.S.: 238350
Mark Lane *(Controller)*
Dusty Morgan *(Pres & CEO)*
David Herzel *(VP)*
John Davenport *(Mgr-Preconstruction
Svcs)*
Steve Lasik *(Mgr-Bus Dev)*
Kelly Martin *(VP)*
Tim McCoy *(Sr VP)*
Greg Timmerman *(Exec VP)*
Brent Paden *(Exec VP)*

**ISEMOTO CONTRACTING CO.
LTD.**
648 Pilani St, Hilo, HI 96720-4613
Tel.: (808) 935-7194   HI
Year Founded: 1926
Sales Range: $25-49.9 Million
Emp.: 210
Provider of Contracting & Construc-
tion Services
N.A.I.C.S.: 236210
Leslie Isemoto *(Pres)*
Jerry Egami *(Sr VP)*
Loren Tsugawa *(VP, Controller &
Treas)*

**ISENHOUR FURNITURE COM-
PANY**
486 S Center St, Taylorsville, NC
28681
Tel.: (828) 632-8849
Sales Range: $10-24.9 Million
Emp.: 20
Upholstered Household Furniture
N.A.I.C.S.: 337121

ISFEL COMPANY, INC.
110 W 34th St 5th FL, New York, NY
10001-2115
Tel.: (212) 736-6216   NY
Web Site: http://www.theisfelco.com
Year Founded: 1958
Sales Range: $50-74.9 Million
Emp.: 150
Childrens Clothing Mfr
N.A.I.C.S.: 315250
Joseph Feldman *(Pres & CEO)*
Donald Spitzner *(CFO)*

ISG TECHNOLOGY, INC.
127 N 7th St, Salina, KS 67401
Tel.: (785) 823-1555
Web Site: http://www.isgdirect.com
Year Founded: 1982
Sales Range: $25-49.9 Million
Emp.: 125
Information Technology Solutions
N.A.I.C.S.: 541512
Ben Foster *(Pres)*
Scott Cissna *(CFO)*
Kipp Adkins *(VP-Sls)*
Matt Brickey *(VP-Data Center Svcs)*
Scott Leitzel *(VP-Ops-Twin Valley
Telephone, Inc)*
Eric Tabor *(VP-Ops & Strategy)*
Mike Morrison *(CEO)*

ISGETT DISTRIBUTORS INC.
51 Highland Ctr Blvd, Asheville, NC
28806
Tel.: (828) 667-9846
Web Site:
    http://www.isgettdistributors.com
Sales Range: $10-24.9 Million
Emp.: 30
Lubricating Oils & Greases
N.A.I.C.S.: 424720
Scott Isgett *(VP-Sls)*
Mary Anne Rayburn *(VP)*
Susan Raines *(Mgr-Credit)*

ISHIR, INC.
17719 Misty Grove Dr, Dallas, TX
75287
Tel.: (214) 893-8755   TX
Web Site: http://www.ishir.com
Year Founded: 1999
Sales Range: $1-9.9 Million
Emp.: 200
IT Outsourcing Services
N.A.I.C.S.: 561499
Rishi Khanna *(Founder & CEO)*
Chetan Saxena *(Head-Search)*
Mike Collins *(VP)*
Anne Lacey Holmes *(Dir-Microsoft
Partner Alliance)*

**ISHPI INFORMATION TECH-
NOLOGIES, INC.**
496 Bramson Ct, Mount Pleasant, SC
29464
Tel.: (843) 329-4100
Web Site: http://www.ishpi.net
Sales Range: $1-9.9 Million
Emp.: 65
Information Technology Solution &
Services
N.A.I.C.S.: 519290
Noah T. Leask *(Co-Founder, Chm,
Pres & CEO)*
Michael Beadle *(COO & VP)*

Ishpi Information Technologies, Inc.—(Continued)

Earl D. Bowers *(Chief Strategy Officer & Pres)*
Claire Murchison *(Chief Admin Officer & VP)*

ISI ENVIRONMENTAL
215 S Laura, Wichita, KS 67211
Tel.: (316) 264-7050
Web Site:
   http://www.isienvironmental.com
Sales Range: $10-24.9 Million
Emp.: 159
Environmental Consulting & Facility Support Services
N.A.I.C.S.: 541620
Amanda Scheufler *(Project Mgr)*

ISIRONA, LLC
430 W 5th St Ste 800, Panama City, FL 32401
Tel.: (850) 303-0764
Web Site: http://www.isirona.com
Sales Range: $1-9.9 Million
Emp.: 105
Medical Management Software
N.A.I.C.S.: 513210

ISIS PARENTING, INC.
110 2nd Ave, Needham, MA 02494
Tel.: (781) 429-1500   DE
Web Site:
   http://www.isisparenting.com
Year Founded: 2003
Sales Range: $1-9.9 Million
Emp.: 160
Women's Clothing Store
N.A.I.C.S.: 458110
Heather Coughlin *(Pres & CEO)*
Nancy Holtzman *(VP-Programs & Svcs)*
Allison McCabe *(VP-Retail Mdsg)*
Heather Coughlin *(Pres & CEO)*
Allison McCabe *(VP-Mdsg & Center Experience)*
Nick Newlin *(VP-Mktg & Digital Experience)*
Nancy Holtzman *(VP-Clinical Content & Learning)*
Sandy Tierney *(VP-HR)*
Chris Just *(Exec Dir-Prenatal Education)*
Gregg Dionn *(Dir-Fin)*
Johanna Myers McChesney *(Founder)*

ISITE DESIGN INC.
2030 NW Pettygrove St, Portland, OR 97209
Tel.: (503) 221-9860
Web Site: http://www.isitedesign.com
Year Founded: 1998
Sales Range: $10-24.9 Million
Emp.: 56
Custom Computer Programming Services
N.A.I.C.S.: 541511
Jeff Cram *(Co-Founder, Chief Strategy Officer & Mng Dir-Boston)*
Andrew McLaughlin *(Dir-Client Svcs)*
Paul Williams *(Pres)*
Michelle Auchter *(VP-Bus Dev)*
Colin O'Neill *(VP-Experience Design)*
Erin Bell *(Acct Dir)*

ISLAMIC FOOD AND NUTRITION COUNCIL OF AMERICA
777 Busse Hwy, Park Ridge, IL 60068
Tel.: (847) 993-0034   IL
Web Site: http://www.ifanca.org
Year Founded: 1982
Sales Range: $10-24.9 Million
Emp.: 28
Community Food Services

N.A.I.C.S.: 624210
Muhammad Munir Chaudry *(Pres)*
Mohamed Sadek *(VP)*

ISLAMORADA FISH COMPANY LLC
81532 Overseas Hwy, Islamorada, FL 33036
Tel.: (305) 664-9271
Web Site:
   http://www.fishcompany.com
Rev.: $50,000,000
Emp.: 150
Seafoods
N.A.I.C.S.: 424460
Leon Williams *(Gen Mgr-Myrtle Beach)*
Patrick Cozad *(Gen Mgr-Fort Myers)*
Zeb King *(Gen Mgr-Garland)*
Brian Dolan *(Gen Mgr-Pearland)*
Mark Vigil *(Gen Mgr-San Antonio)*
Jeffery Richardson *(Gen Mgr-Ashland)*
Kathy Milano *(Gen Mgr-Bolingbrook)*
Jerry Bonner *(Gen Mgr-Denham Springs)*
Michelle Hobbs *(Gen Mgr-Portage)*
Greg Schaafsma *(Gen Mgr-Dania Beach)*
Jeremiah Hiser *(Gen Mgr-Denver)*
Keith Wolfe *(Gen Mgr-Rancho Cucamonga)*
Dave Kemmer *(Gen Mgr-Mesa)*
Stephen Fasanello *(Gen Mgr-Spanish Fort)*
J. R. Sutton *(Gen Mgr-Independence)*
Eric Harrell *(Gen Mgr-Prattville)*
Dave Holly *(Gen Mgr)*

ISLAND CAPITAL GROUP LLC
717 5th Ave Fl 18, New York, NY 10022
Tel.: (212) 705-5000   DE
Web Site: http://www.islecap.com
Year Founded: 2003
Real Estate & Investment Holding Company
N.A.I.C.S.: 551112
Marc W. Levy *(Exec Mng Dir)*
Mark Lande *(Sr Mng Dir)*
Robert C. Lieber *(Exec Mng Dir)*
Andrew L. Farkas *(Founder, Chm & CEO)*
George E. Carleton *(Exec Mng Dir)*
Jeffrey P. Cohen *(Pres & Exec Mng Dir)*
Lawrence S. Block *(Chief Compliance Officer)*

Subsidiaries:

C-III Capital Partners LLC   (1)
5221 N O'Connor Blvd Ste 600, Irving, TX 75039
Tel.: (972) 868-5300
Web Site: http://www.c3cp.com
Emp.: 300
Real Estate Investment, Brokerage & Private Equity Firm
N.A.I.C.S.: 531390
Robert C. Lieber *(Exec Mng Dir)*
Andrew L. Farkas *(Chm & CEO)*
George E. Carleton *(Exec Mng Dir)*
Jeffrey P. Cohen *(Exec Mng Dir)*
Rank M. Garrison *(Pres)*
James A. Aston *(CFO & Exec Mng Dir)*
Paul A. Hughson *(Exec Mng Dir)*

Holding (Domestic):

NAI Global, Inc.   (2)
186 Princeton Hightstown Rd Bldg 3 A Ste 7, Princeton, NJ 08540
Tel.: (609) 945-4000
Web Site: http://www.naiglobal.com
Sales Range: $10-24.9 Million
Emp.: 35
Commercial Real Estate Agents & Managers
N.A.I.C.S.: 531210

David Blanchard *(Exec VP-Member Svcs)*
Ted M. Parcel *(Exec VP-Corp Svcs)*
Bobbi Jean Formosa *(Sr VP-Ops)*
David Perry *(VP-EMEA)*
Jay Olshonsky *(Pres)*
Jim Crismale *(Sr VP-Fin)*
Simon Hartdell *(Sr VP-Client Svcs)*
Taylor Glaze *(Bus Dir-NAI Chase Commercial-Birmingham)*
Charlie Grelier Jr. *(Pres-NAI Chase Commercial)*

Subsidiary (Domestic):

Hiffman Shaffer Associates, Inc.   (3)
1 Oakbrook Terrace Ste 400, Oakbrook Terrace, IL 60181
Tel.: (630) 932-1234
Web Site: http://www.hiffman.com
Real Estate Services
N.A.I.C.S.: 531210
Bob Assoian *(Exec Mng Dir & Exec VP)*
Michael Flynn *(COO)*

NAI Excel   (3)
6064 S Durango Dr, Las Vegas, NV 89113
Tel.: (702) 383-3383
Web Site: https://excelcres.com
Commercial Real Estate Services
N.A.I.C.S.: 531390

Subsidiary (Domestic):

Rohde Ottmers Siegel Realty, Inc.   (4)
11503 NW Military Hwy Ste 330, San Antonio, TX 78231-1895
Tel.: (210) 366-1400
Web Site: http://www.rohderealty.com
Residential Property Managers
N.A.I.C.S.: 531210
Alfred W. Rohde III *(Pres)*
Bryan Ottmers *(Pres-Mgmt Div)*
Lori Rose-Alvarez *(Dir-Property Mgmt)*

Subsidiary (Domestic):

NAI Hunneman   (3)
303 Congress St, Boston, MA 02210
Tel.: (617) 457-3400
Web Site: http://www.naihunneman.com
Real Estate Agents & Managers
N.A.I.C.S.: 531210
Jonathon Aron *(Principal & Exec VP)*
Jeffrey Becker *(Sr VP)*
James Boudrot *(Exec VP)*
Carl Christie *(Principal & Exec VP)*
Stephen James *(Principal & Exec VP)*
Stuart W. Pratt *(Chm)*
Doug Potter *(Exec VP)*
David Ross *(Exec VP)*
Robert Tito *(Exec VP)*
Evan Gallagher *(Exec VP)*
David Slye *(Pres & CEO)*
Stephen Prozinski *(COO & Dir-Property Mgmt)*
Jim Nicoletti *(Exec VP)*
Tim Ervin *(Asst VP)*
Markell Blount *(Asst VP)*
Glenne Bachman *(Coord-Mktg)*
Gina Barroso *(Asst VP)*
Liz Berthelette *(Dir-Res)*
Cassie Dykes *(Coord-Mktg)*
David Finnegan *(VP-Mktg Svcs)*
Sharon Gazley *(CFO & VP)*
Andrew Kaeyer *(Exec VP)*
Emmet Logue *(Exec VP)*
Cathy Minnerly *(Exec VP)*
Amy Stewart *(Mgr-Graphics)*
Leeanne Rizzo *(Sr VP-Leasing & Advisory Svcs)*
Ned Halloran *(Sr VP-Leasing & Advisory Svcs)*
Christopher Curley *(Exec VP-Leasing & Advisory Svc Team)*

Holding (Domestic):

Resource America, Inc.   (2)
1845 Walnut St 18th Fl, Philadelphia, PA 19103
Tel.: (215) 546-5005
Web Site: http://www.resourceamerica.com
Sales Range: $75-99.9 Million
Specialty Finance Company Engaged in the Acquisition & Resolution of Commercial Real Estate Loans & Commercial Equipment Leasing
N.A.I.C.S.: 523999

Andrew L. Farkas *(Chm, Pres & CEO)*
Jeffrey P. Cohen *(Exec VP)*
Alan F. Feldman *(CEO-Resource Real Estate & Sr VP)*
David E. Bloom *(Sr VP & Head-Real Estate)*
Marshall P. Hayes *(Mng Dir)*
David J. Bryant *(CFO-Resource Capital Corp, Treas-Resource Capital Corp & Sr VP)*
Jeffrey D. Blomstrom *(Sr VP)*
Purvi Kamdar *(Dir-Mktg & IR)*
Darshan Patel *(Sr VP & Chief Compliance Officer)*
Kyle Geoghegan *(Mng Dir)*
Michael Magaldi *(Mng Dir)*
Yvana Rizzo *(Sr VP-Asset Mgmt)*
Michael Terwilliger *(Mng Dir & Portfolio Mgr-Global)*
John Snowden *(Mng Dir & Portfolio Mgr-Global)*
Thomas C. Elliott *(CFO & Exec VP)*

Subsidiary (Domestic):

LEAF Financial Corp.   (3)
One Commerce Square 2005 Market Street 15th Floor, Philadelphia, PA 19103
Tel.: (800) 819-5556
Web Site: http://www.leaf-financial.com
Commercial Finance & Asset Management Services
N.A.I.C.S.: 525990

Merit Capital Advance, LLC   (3)
20 Salem Church Rd, Newark, DE 19713
Tel.: (302) 737-3850
Investment Management Service
N.A.I.C.S.: 523940

Resource Real Estate, Inc.   (3)
1845 Walnut St 18th Fl, Philadelphia, PA 19103
Tel.: (215) 231-7050
Web Site: http://www.resourcealts.com
Emp.: 1,000
Real Estate Investment & Portfolio Management Services
N.A.I.C.S.: 531390
Alan F. Feldman *(CEO)*
Marshall P. Hayes *(Mng Dir)*
Steven Saltzman *(CFO)*
Shelle Weisbaum *(Gen Counsel & Exec VP)*
Peggy L. Gold *(Exec VP-Relationship Mgmt)*
Martin Caverly *(Chief Investment Officer)*
John Snowden *(Portfolio Mgr-Resource Real Estate Diversified Income Fund)*
Justin Milberg *(COO-Resource Liquid Alternatives)*
Michael Terwilliger *(Portfolio Mgr-Resource Credit Income Fund)*

Affiliate (Domestic):

Resource Innovation Office REIT, Inc.   (4)
1845 Walnut St 18th Fl, Philadelphia, PA 19103
Tel.: (215) 231-7050
Web Site: http://www.resourcealts.com
Sales Range: Less than $1 Million
Real Estate Investment Trust
N.A.I.C.S.: 525990
Alan F. Feldman *(CEO)*

Subsidiary (Domestic):

Resource Property Management, LLC   (4)
1845 Walnut St 18th Fl, Philadelphia, PA 19103
Tel.: (215) 231-7050
Real Estate Investment Management Services
N.A.I.C.S.: 531390

Affiliate (Domestic):

Resource Real Estate Opportunity REIT, Inc.   (4)
1845 Walnut St 18th Fl, Philadelphia, PA 19103
Tel.: (215) 231-7050
Web Site: http://www.resourcereit.com
Rev.: $135,545,000
Assets: $1,005,088,000
Liabilities: $822,273,000
Net Worth: $182,815,000

Earnings: ($1,747,000)
Fiscal Year-end: 12/31/2019
Real Estate Investment Trust
N.A.I.C.S.: 525990
George E. Carleton *(Pres & COO)*
Alan F. Feldman *(Chm & CEO)*
Steven R. Saltzman *(CFO, Treas & Sr VP)*
Shelle Weisbaum *(Chief Legal Officer, Sec & Sr VP)*

ISLAND COMPANY
312 Clematis St Ste 401, West Palm Beach, FL 33401
Tel.: (561) 833-8110
Web Site:
http://www.islandcompany.com
Year Founded: 2002
Sales Range: $1-9.9 Million
Emp.: 52
Cloth Store
N.A.I.C.S.: 458110
Spencer Antle *(Founder & Dir-Creative)*

ISLAND COMPUTER PRODUCTS, INC.
20 Clifton Ave, Staten Island, NY 10305-4912
Tel.: (718) 556-6700   NY
Web Site: http://www.icpcorp.com
Year Founded: 1989
Sales Range: $10-24.9 Million
Emp.: 100
Mfr of Computers, Peripherals & Software
N.A.I.C.S.: 423430
Michelle Fabozzi *(Co-Founder, Pres & CEO)*
Paul S. Fabozzi *(Co-Founder & CIO)*
Annette Fabozzi *(Co-Founder & Chief Admin & Dev Officer)*
Erik Lieberman *(Exec VP-Bus Dev & Sls)*

Subsidiaries:

ICP Inc.   (1)
20 Clifton Ave, Staten Island, NY 10305-4912
Tel.: (718) 556-6700
Web Site: http://www.icpcorp.com
Sales Range: $10-24.9 Million
Emp.: 4
Provider of Computer Related Services
N.A.I.C.S.: 541512
Louis Esposito *(CIO)*

ISLAND EQUIPMENT INC
91-238 Kalaeloa Blvd, Kapolei, HI 96707
Tel.: (808) 682-0447
Sales Range: $10-24.9 Million
Emp.: 46
Equipment Sales Rental
N.A.I.C.S.: 459999
Gordon Ogi *(Pres)*
Jeff Ashmoore *(Owner)*
Liz Yabes *(Accountant)*

ISLAND GROVE AG PRODUCTS
2600 SE 193rd Ave, Hawthorne, FL 32640
Tel.: (352) 481-5558
Web Site:
http://www.islandgroveagpro
  ducts.com
Sales Range: $1-9.9 Million
Emp.: 35
Blueberry Farming & Sales
N.A.I.C.S.: 111334
Ken Patterson *(Owner)*

ISLAND HOLDINGS, INC.
1022 Bethel St 4th Fl, Honolulu, HI 96813-4302
Tel.: (808) 531-1311   HI
Web Site:
http://www.islandinsurance.com

Year Founded: 1990
Sales Range: $75-99.9 Million
Emp.: 300
Holding Company; Property & Casualty Insurance Products & Services
N.A.I.C.S.: 551112
Colbert Masayuki Matsumoto *(Chm)*
Paul Iijama *(Controller)*

Subsidiaries:

Island Insurance Company, Ltd.   (1)
1022 Bethel St, Honolulu, HI 96806-1520   **(100%)**
Tel.: (808) 564-8200
Web Site: http://www.islandinsurance.com
Property & Casualty Insurance Products & Services
N.A.I.C.S.: 524126
Robert K. W. H. Nobriga *(Vice Chm)*
John Schapperle *(CEO)*
Sharon M. Lee *(VP-Admin Svcs)*
Michael A. Onofrietti *(Sr VP-Actuarial Svcs, Product Dev & Mgmt)*
Dawn Hirano *(Asst VP-HR)*
Beverly Ament *(Pres)*
Jeff Fabry *(CIO, Chief Security Officer & Sr VP)*
Lyle Harada *(VP-Claims)*
Lynne Nishiura *(VP-HR)*
Todd Yamanaka *(VP-Mktg)*
Tyler Tokioka *(Chm)*

Subsidiary (Domestic):

Tradewind Insurance Company, Ltd.   (2)
PO Box 1520, Honolulu, HI 96806-1520
Tel.: (808) 531-1311
Web Site: http://www.islandinsurance.com
Sales Range: Less than $1 Million
Emp.: 8
Insurance Agents, Brokers & Service
N.A.I.C.S.: 524210
Robert K. W. H. Nobriga *(VP)*

Island Premier Insurance Company, Ltd.   (1)
680 Iwilei Rd Ste 760, Honolulu, HI 96817
Tel.: (808) 532-2888
Insurance Management Services
N.A.I.C.S.: 524298

ISLAND HOSPITALITY MANAGEMENT, LLC
222 Lakeview Ave Ste 200, West Palm Beach, FL 33401
Tel.: (561) 655-9001   DE
Web Site:
http://www.islandhospitality.com
Year Founded: 1986
Home Management Services
N.A.I.C.S.: 561110
Jeffrey H. Fisher *(Founder, CEO & Principal)*
Roger Pollak *(Exec VP-Fin)*
Jeff Waldt *(Exec VP-Sls & Mktg)*
Gregg Forde *(Pres & COO)*
Drew Allison *(Sr VP-Ops)*
Barbara Bachman *(Sr VP-Acctg)*
Michele Mainelli *(Sr VP-Revenue Mgmt)*
John Marques *(Sr VP-Ops)*
Rob Auerbach *(VP-Pur)*
Jean Abou Ghannam *(VP-Bus Intelligence & Corp Strategy)*
Sam Logan *(VP-Risk Mgmt)*
Michelle Westbrook *(VP-Revenue Mgmt)*
Marc Winer *(VP-Corp Support & Hotel Tech)*
Mark R. George *(Sr VP-Sls & Mktg)*
Samantha Fisher *(Chief Investment Officer)*
Tonya Moore *(Sr VP-HR)*

ISLAND INN CO. INC.
3111 W Gulf Dr, Sanibel, FL 33957
Tel.: (239) 472-1561
Web Site:
http://www.islandinnsanibel.com
Sales Range: $1-9.9 Million

Emp.: 30
Hotel Operations
N.A.I.C.S.: 721110
Joe Orndorff *(Pres & CEO)*
Chris Davison *(Gen Mgr)*

ISLAND LINCOLN-MERCURY, INC.
1850 E Merritt Island Causeway, Merritt Island, FL 32952-2665
Tel.: (321) 452-9220   DE
Web Site:
http://www.islandlincoln.com
Year Founded: 1985
Sales Range: $125-149.9 Million
Emp.: 300
Retailer of New & Used Automobiles
N.A.I.C.S.: 441110
Renee Chaney *(Controller)*
James Cavanaugh *(Gen Mgr)*

ISLAND MOVERS INC.
3179 Koapaka St, Honolulu, HI 96819
Tel.: (808) 832-4000   HI
Web Site:
http://www.islandmovers.com
Year Founded: 1958
Sales Range: $10-24.9 Million
Emp.: 300
Moving Services
N.A.I.C.S.: 484210
Donald M. Takaki *(Chm & CEO)*

ISLAND OASIS FROZEN COCKTAIL CO.
141 Norfolk St, Walpole, MA 02081
Tel.: (508) 660-1176
Web Site: http://www.islandoasis.com
Sales Range: $50-74.9 Million
Emp.: 80
Fruit Juices, Frozen
N.A.I.C.S.: 424420
Robert Gorman *(Dir-Logistics)*

ISLAND OPERATING COMPANY INC.
108 Zachary Dr, Scott, LA 70583-5332
Tel.: (337) 233-9594
Web Site:
http://www.islandoperating.com
Year Founded: 1986
Sales Range: $75-99.9 Million
Emp.: 1,800
Management Services
N.A.I.C.S.: 561110

ISLAND PEER REVIEW ORGANIZATION, INC.
1979 Marcus Ave, Lake Success, NY 11042-1002
Tel.: (516) 326-7767   NY
Web Site: http://www.ipro.org
Year Founded: 1983
Sales Range: $50-74.9 Million
Emp.: 468
Health Care Srvices
N.A.I.C.S.: 622110
Harry M. Feder *(COO & Sr VP)*
Alan F. King *(CFO)*
Clare B. Bradley *(Chief Medical Officer & Sr VP)*
Richard A. Alfieri *(CIO)*
Theodore O. Will *(CEO)*
Edison A. Machado Jr. *(Chief Quality Officer & VP-Strategic Plng)*

ISLAND REALTY INC.
2213 Long Beach Blvd, Surf City, NJ 08008
Tel.: (609) 494-4091
Web Site:
http://www.islandrealtylbi.com
Rev.: $25,000,000
Emp.: 10

Real Estate Brokers & Agents
N.A.I.C.S.: 531210
Francis Hodgson *(Pres)*

ISLAND RECREATIONAL
1059 Hicksville Rd, Massapequa, NY 11758
Tel.: (516) 735-2225
Web Site:
http://www.islandrecreational.com
Rev.: $20,000,000
Emp.: 4
Swimming Pool Chemicals, Equipment & Supplies
N.A.I.C.S.: 459999

ISLAND REHABILITATION AND NURSING CENTER INC
5537 Expressway Dr N, Holtsville, NY 11742
Tel.: (631) 758-3336   NY
Web Site:
http://www.islandnursing.org
Year Founded: 1999
Sales Range: $10-24.9 Million
Emp.: 291
Nursing & Rehabilitation Services
N.A.I.C.S.: 624120
Kwang Jung *(Dir-Nursing)*
Catherine Fourquet *(CFO)*
David Fridkin *(CEO)*

ISLAND TENNIS LP
275 Old Indian Head Rd, Kings Park, NY 11754
Tel.: (631) 269-1055
Web Site: http://www.sportimeny.com
Sales Range: $10-24.9 Million
Emp.: 600
Tennis Club Membership
N.A.I.C.S.: 713940
Claude Okin *(Mng Partner)*
Chris Leahy *(Mgr-Retail)*
Jeffery Crowne *(Chief Admin Officer & Mng Dir-Bus Plng)*

Subsidiaries:

Long Island Tennis Time Inc.   (1)
175 Merrick Rd, Lynbrook, NY 11563
Tel.: (516) 887-1330
Web Site: http://www.sportimeny.com
Sales Range: Less than $1 Million
Emp.: 80
Outdoor/Indoor Tennis Courts
N.A.I.C.S.: 713940
Claude Oaken *(Principal)*

ISLAND TUG & BARGE CO.
3546 W Marginal Way SW, Seattle, WA 98106
Tel.: (206) 938-0403
Web Site: http://www.islandtug-barge.com
Sales Range: $10-24.9 Million
Emp.: 50
Towing & Tugboat Services
N.A.I.C.S.: 488999
Frank Ellefsen *(Pres)*
Marc Sprute *(Controller)*
Jon Anderson *(VP)*

ISLAND WATER SPORTS, INC.
1985 NE 2nd St, Deerfield Beach, FL 33441
Tel.: (954) 427-4929
Web Site:
http://www.islandwatersports.com
Year Founded: 1978
Sales Range: $10-24.9 Million
Emp.: 50
Sporting Goods Retailer
N.A.I.C.S.: 459110
M. L. Cottrell-Timoney *(Pres)*

ISLANDS HOSPICE, INC.
1301 Young St Ste 300, Honolulu, HI 96814
Tel.: (808) 550-2552   OK

Islands Hospice, Inc.—(Continued)

Web Site:
http://www.islandshospice.com
Year Founded: 2009
Sales Range: $10-24.9 Million
Emp.: 150
Hospice Care Services
N.A.I.C.S.: 621610
Kevin Web (CEO)

ISLANDS RESTAURANTS LP
5750 Fleet St Ste 120, Carlsbad, CA 92008
Tel.: (760) 268-1800
Web Site:
http://www.islandsrestaurants.com
Rev.: $78,788,000
Emp.: 25
Hamburger Stand
N.A.I.C.S.: 722513
John Ladd (Gen Mgr)
Michael Smith (Pres)

ISLET SCIENCES, INC.
8601 Six Forks Rd Ste 400, Raleigh, NC 27615
Tel.: (919) 480-1518 NV
Web Site:
http://www.isletsciences.com
Year Founded: 1994
Emp.: 3
Investment Holding Company
N.A.I.C.S.: 551112
David E. Wilder (CFO & COO)

ISN SOFTWARE CORP.
3232 McKinney Ave Ste 1500, Dallas, TX 75204
Tel.: (214) 303-4900
Web Site: http://www.isnetwork.com
Year Founded: 2000
Sales Range: $10-24.9 Million
Emp.: 85
Data Systems For Businesses
N.A.I.C.S.: 541519
Joseph Eastin (Pres)
William M. Addy (Chm & CEO)
Brian Callahan (Sr VP)

ISO NEW ENGLAND INC.
1 Sullivan Rd, Holyoke, MA 01040
Tel.: (413) 535-4000
Web Site: http://www.iso-ne.com
Year Founded: 1997
Sales Range: $50-74.9 Million
Emp.: 470
Regional Transmission Organization
N.A.I.C.S.: 237130
Gordan van Welie (Pres & CEO)
Vamsi Chadalavada (Sr VP & COO)
Jamshid A. Afnan (VP-IT)
Peter T. Brandien (VP-Sys Ops)
Janice S. Dickstein (VP-HR)
Robert Ethier (VP-Market Dev)
Anne C. George (VP-External Affairs & Corp Comm)
Raymond W. Hepper (VP, Gen Counsel & Corp Sec)
Robert C. Ludlow (VP, CFO & Chief Compliance Officer)
Stephen J. Rourke (VP-Sys Plng)
Philip Shapiro (Chm)
Jeffrey McDonald (VP-Market Monitoring)

ISOKINETICS, INC.
PO Box 21, De Queen, AR 71832
Tel.: (870) 386-2144
Web Site:
http://www.isokineticsinc.com
Year Founded: 1987
Sales Range: $10-24.9 Million
Emp.: 86
Distr of Physical Therapy & Rehabilitation Supplies to Homes & Clinics
N.A.I.C.S.: 423450

Sandy Polk (Office Mgr)
Terrel Bailey (Area Mgr-Sls)

ISOLITE CORPORATION
31 Waterloo Ave, Berwyn, PA 19312
Tel.: (610) 647-8200
Web Site: http://www.isolite.com
Year Founded: 1982
Rev.: $45,641,786
Emp.: 36
Emergency Lighting Products Mfr
N.A.I.C.S.: 335132
Richard Renzi (Mgr-Eastern Reg)
William Rowan (Dir-Regulatory Compliance)
Edward Silverthorn (CFO)
William Lynch (Pres)

ISOLVED HCM LLC
13024 Ballantyne Corp Pl Ste 400, Charlotte, NC 28277
Tel.: (800) 733-8839 DE
Web Site: http://www.isolvedhcm.com
Year Founded: 1986
Human Capital Management Solutions
N.A.I.C.S.: 541511
Dave Dawson (CEO)
Justin Raniszeski (Chief Comml Officer)
Shane Whittington (CFO)
Todd La Fever (Pres & COO)
Trish Stromberg (CMO)

Subsidiaries:

Simplified Business Solutions, Inc. (1)
10201 S 51st St Ste 100, Phoenix, AZ 85044
Tel.: (480) 763-5900
Web Site: http://www.amcheck.com
Sales Range: $25-49.9 Million
Emp.: 5,000
Employee Resource Services
N.A.I.C.S.: 561330

ISOMET CORPORATION
10342 Battleview Pkwy, Manassas, VA 20109
Tel.: (703) 321-8301 NJ
Web Site: https://www.isomet.com
Year Founded: 1956
Sales Range: $10-24.9 Million
Emp.: 23
Lasers, Scanners & Other Components Mfr
N.A.I.C.S.: 335999

Subsidiaries:

Isomet (UK) Ltd. (1)
18 John Baker Close, Llantarnam Park, Cwmbran, NP44 3AX, Torfaen, United Kingdom
Tel.: (44) 1633872721
Emp.: 6
Mfr of Acousto-Optic Laser Systems
N.A.I.C.S.: 334510
Michael Hillier (Mgr)

ISOTECH LABORATORIES, INC.
1308 Parkland Ct, Champaign, IL 61821
Tel.: (217) 398-3490
Web Site: http://www.isotechlabs.com
Year Founded: 1985
Rev.: $8,800,000
Emp.: 30
Testing Laboratories
N.A.I.C.S.: 541380
Steve Pelphrey (Gen Mgr)
Alan Langenfeld (Asst Mgr-Laboratory)
Kerry Riley (Co-Founder)
Dennis Coleman (Co-Founder)
Gavin Steele (Mgr-Product Dev)
Corben Rice (Mgr-Satellite Lab)

Sher Dixon (Project Mgr)
Jack Liu (Co-Founder)
Jerry Benson (Co-Founder)

ISOTECH PEST MANAGEMENT, INC.
12881 Ramona Blvd, Irwindale, CA 91706
Tel.: (909) 594-8939
Web Site:
http://www.isotechpest.com
Year Founded: 2004
Sales Range: $1-9.9 Million
Emp.: 75
Pest Management Services
N.A.I.C.S.: 561710
Mike Masterson (CEO)

ISOVERA, LLC
460 Totten Pond Rd Ste 200, Waltham, MA 02451
Tel.: (617) 621-8555
Web Site: http://www.isovera.com
Professional, Scientific & Technical Services
N.A.I.C.S.: 541990
Richard Jenkins (Dir-Creative)
Doug Sisko (Sr Dir-Ops)
Jason Pamental (Sr Dir-Design & Technical Strategy)
Stephen Sanzo (CEO)
Matt Naffah (Partner)

Subsidiaries:

The Boston Group, Inc. (1)
364 Boylston St Ste 301, Boston, MA 02116-3831
Tel.: (816) 540-3746
Web Site: http://www.bostongroup.com
Marketing Communication Services
N.A.I.C.S.: 541613
William Boston (Pres)

ISP SUPPLIES LLC
10770 Highway 30 Ste 200, College Station, TX 77845
Tel.: (855) 947-7776
Web Site: http://www.ispsupplies.com
N.A.I.C.S.:
Steve Discher (Founder & Owner)
Violeta Thompson (Dir-Mktg)
Jerrod Lane (Mgr-Bus Dev)

Subsidiaries:

Titan Wireless LLC (1)
3914 Gattis School Rd Ste 102, Round Rock, TX 78664-8021
Tel.: (512) 291-7605
Web Site:
http://www.titanwirelessonline.com
Custom Computer Programming Services
N.A.I.C.S.: 541511
Lisa Strong (Mgr)

ISPACE FURNITURE, INC.
811 Glenwood Ave, Minneapolis, MN 55405
Tel.: (612) 922-1300
Web Site:
http://www.ispacefurniture.com
Office Furniture Sales
N.A.I.C.S.: 423210
Joel Peterson (CEO)
Aaron Eggert (Pres)
Kathy Blake (Principal)
Amy Ayd (CFO)
Scott Clare (Dir-Ops)

ISPACE, INC.
2381 Rosecrans Ave Ste 110, El Segundo, CA 90245
Tel.: (310) 563-3800 CA
Web Site: http://www.ispace.com
Year Founded: 2000
Sales Range: $10-24.9 Million
Emp.: 130

Information Technology Staffing, Consulting & Outsourcing Services
N.A.I.C.S.: 541690
Jamie Gutierrez (Asst Controller)

ISPICE LLC
6450 Hwy 43, 36545, Jackson, AL
Tel.: (251) 246-8001
Web Site:
https://www.ispicefoods.com
Year Founded: 2016
Herbs & Spices Mfr
N.A.I.C.S.: 311999
Manouch Ilkhani (CEO)

Subsidiaries:

Spice Chain Corporation (1)
9 Elkins Rd, East Brunswick, NJ 08816
Tel.: (732) 518-1100
Web Site: http://www.spicechain.com
Spice & Extract Mfr
N.A.I.C.S.: 311942
Jennie Ann Reitemeyer (VP-Food Safety, Quality & Res)
Steve Silk (CEO)
Cindy Seal (VP-Sls)
Chad Silberman (Dir-Bus Dev)

ISPIRI
7779 Afton Rd, Woodbury, MN 55125
Tel.: (651) 578-0122
Web Site: http://www.ispiri.com
Year Founded: 2007
Sales Range: $1-9.9 Million
Emp.: 27
Commercial Building Remodeling Services
N.A.I.C.S.: 236118
Jason Fabio (Pres)
Scott Sample (Project Mgr)

ISPOT.TV, INC.
15831 NE 8th St Ste 100, Bellevue, WA 98008
Web Site: http://www.ispot.tv
TV Ad Data & Analytics Services
N.A.I.C.S.: 512191
Sean Muller (Founder & CEO)
Peter Daboll (Chief Strategy Officer)

Subsidiaries:

Ace Metrix, Inc. (1)
2115 Landings Dr, Mountain View, CA 94043
Tel.: (800) 279-7984
Web Site: http://www.acemetrix.com
Television Advertising Broadcasting Services
N.A.I.C.S.: 516120
Peter Daboll (CEO)
William Parducci (CTO & Chief Product Officer)
William Scharninghausen (CFO)

ISR GROUP, INC.
670 Industrial Rd, Savannah, TN 38372
Tel.: (731) 926-4188
Web Site: http://www.isrgroup.com
Year Founded: 2005
Sales Range: $25-49.9 Million
Emp.: 200
Systems & Technical Training for Unmanned Military Vehicles
N.A.I.C.S.: 921190
Michael Eakin (Mgr-Flight Ops)

ISRAEL A. ENGLANDER & CO., LLC
666 5th Ave, New York, NY 10103
Tel.: (212) 841-4500 DE
Web Site:
http://www.iaenglander.com
Year Founded: 1977
Emp.: 50
Derivatives Brokerage & Dealing Services
N.A.I.C.S.: 523150

Stephen Tobias *(Founder & Pres)*

Subsidiaries:

Dash Financial Services 2, LLC **(1)**
2712 S Midwest Blvd, Midwest, OK 73310
Tel.: (405) 794-0122
Emp.: 2
Derivatives Transaction Processing Services
N.A.I.C.S.: 522320
Anthony Dunphy *(Head-Sls-New York)*
David Karat *(CMO)*
Jennifier Green *(Office Mgr)*

ISRAEL ANDLER & SON INC.
376 3rd St, Everett, MA 02149
Tel.: (617) 387-5700
Web Site: http://www.andler.com
Sales Range: $25-49.9 Million
Emp.: 40
Specialty Packaging Products & Solutions
N.A.I.C.S.: 423840
Arnold E. Andler *(Pres)*

ISRAM WHOLESALE TOURS & TRAVEL LTD.
233 Park Ave S, New York, NY 10003
Tel.: (212) 661-1193   NY
Web Site: http://www.isram.com
Year Founded: 1967
Sales Range: $100-124.9 Million
Emp.: 200
Tour Operator; Travel Agency
N.A.I.C.S.: 561520
Ady Gelber *(Owner & CEO)*
Ilana Apelboim *(COO & Sr VP)*
Eileen Lowe Hart *(Sr VP-Mktg & Product Dev)*
Betty Van Dyke *(Sr VP-R&D)*

Subsidiaries:

Holy Lands Sun Tours **(1)**
Fl 10 233 Park Ave S, New York, NY 10003-1606
Tel.: (212) 867-7292
Web Site: http://www.holylandssuntours.com
Sales Range: $10-24.9 Million
Emp.: 5
Travel Agencies
N.A.I.C.S.: 561510

Orient Flexi-Pax Tours **(1)**
25 Broadway 9th Fl, New York, NY 10004
Tel.: (212) 692-9550
Web Site: http://www.isram.com
Sales Range: $10-24.9 Million
Emp.: 70
International Travel Tour Agencies
N.A.I.C.S.: 561510
Neomie Menahem *(Mng Dir)*

ISS GROUP, INC.
200 Woodport Rd Ste F, Sparta, NJ 07871
Tel.: (973) 729-0013
Web Site: http://www.issgroup.com
Year Founded: 1986
Sales Range: $10-24.9 Million
Emp.: 35
Low Cost Business Process Enhancement (BPE) Solutions
N.A.I.C.S.: 541512

ISSGR, INC.
6611 Portwest Dr Ste 190, Houston, TX 77024
Tel.: (713) 869-7700   TX
Web Site: http://www.imageset.com
Year Founded: 1985
Sales Range: $1-9.9 Million
Emp.: 17
Direct Marketing Services, Graphic Design & Digital Priniting Services
N.A.I.C.S.: 323111
Debra R. Briggs *(Pres)*
Rachel Shepherd *(Sr VP-Tech)*

ISSPRO INC.
2515 NE Riverside Way, Portland, OR 97211
Tel.: (503) 288-4488
Web Site: http://www.isspro.com
Sales Range: $10-24.9 Million
Emp.: 150
Motor Vehicle Instrument Board Mfr
N.A.I.C.S.: 336320
Bob Landgraf *(Mgr-OEM Sls)*
Curt Bourgoine *(Mgr-Sls)*
Michael Pliska *(Mgr-Engrg)*

ISSQUARED INC.
3623 Old Conejo Rd Ste 203, Newbury Park, CA 91320
Tel.: (805) 480-9300
Web Site:
   http://www.issquaredinc.com
Year Founded: 2010
Sales Range: $75-99.9 Million
Information Technology Consulting Services
N.A.I.C.S.: 541512
Bala Ramaiah *(Pres & CEO)*
Suchinth Kumar *(Chief Revenue Officer)*
John Charles *(Sr VP-Cloud Svcs)*
Jagan Jata *(Sr VP-Consulting Svcs)*
Ganesh Ramaiah *(Sr VP-Managed Svcs)*
Kirit Sarvaiya *(VP-Sls & Mktg)*

Subsidiaries:

Network Computing Architects, Inc. **(1)**
330 120th Ave NE Ste 210, Bellevue, WA 98005
Tel.: (425) 451-8995
Web Site: http://www.ncanet.com
Sales Range: $25-49.9 Million
Emp.: 35
Value-Added Resellers, Computer Systems
N.A.I.C.S.: 541512
Thomas Gobeille *(VP & Chief Evangelist)*
Susan Sison *(Dir-Mktg)*
Scott Hussey *(Mgr-Carrier & IP Solutions Div)*
Kevin Hagen *(Treas & Dir)*

ISSUE MEDIA GROUP, LLC
4470 2nd Ave, Detroit, MI 48201
Tel.: (313) 850-8616
Web Site:
   http://www.issuemediagroup.com
Year Founded: 2005
Sales Range: $1-9.9 Million
Emp.: 600
Online Publisher of Various Magazines
N.A.I.C.S.: 513120
Paul Schutt *(Co-CEO)*
Deepa Ramsinghani *(Partner)*
Brian Boyle *(Co-CEO)*

ISSUETRAK, INC.
249 Central Park Ave, Virginia Beach, VA 23462
Tel.: (757) 213-1300
Web Site: http://www.issuetrak.com
Year Founded: 1992
Sales Range: $10-24.9 Million
Emp.: 25
Web-Based Issue-Tracking Software
N.A.I.C.S.: 513210
Hank Luhring *(Co-Founder)*
Steve Anderson *(Co-Founder & Partner-Bus Dev)*
Dan Luhring *(CEO)*

IST MANAGEMENT SERVICES, INC.
934 Glenwood Ave Ste 250, Atlanta, GA 30316
Tel.: (404) 582-8850
Web Site:
   http://www.istmanagement.com

Year Founded: 1997
Rev.: $29,900,000
Emp.: 740
Facilities Support Services
N.A.I.C.S.: 561210
Craig Hamel *(Partner & Sr VP)*
Dale McKee *(VP-Fin)*
Dan Blechinger *(VP-Tech)*
Hal Blackman *(Pres)*
Joe Carroll *(VP-HR)*
Kim Oleniacz *(Partner & Sr VP)*
Lori Mitchum *(VP-Admin)*
Stuart Schwartz *(Partner & Sr VP)*
Tim Richardson *(VP-Ops & Implementations-Atlanta)*
Chris Eckl *(Partner & Sr VP)*
Robert Swan *(VP-Legal Tech)*

ISTONISH HOLDING COMPANY, INC.
6400 S Fiddlers Green Cir Ste 1750, Greenwood Village, CO 80111
Tel.: (303) 713-9700
Web Site: http://www.istonishhc.com
Year Founded: 2002
Sales Range: $25-49.9 Million
Emp.: 30
Holding Company
N.A.I.C.S.: 551112
Annette Quintana *(CEO)*
Jim Roberts *(CTO)*

Subsidiaries:

Istonish Inc. **(1)**
6400 S Fiddlers Green Cir Ste 1750, Greenwood Village, CO 80111
Tel.: (303) 771-1765
Web Site: http://www.istonish.com
Sales Range: $25-49.9 Million
Computer Related Consulting Services
N.A.I.C.S.: 541512
John J. LaMere *(Controller)*
Victoria Quintana *(Founder)*
Annette Quintana *(CEO)*
Rod Taylor *(COO)*

ISUBSCRIBED INC.
15 Network Dr, Burlington, MA 01803
Tel.: (617) 332-0291
Web Site: http://aura.com
Information Technology & Services
N.A.I.C.S.: 519290
Hari Ravichandran *(Founder & CEO)*

Subsidiaries:

WC SACD One, Inc. **(1)**
15 Network Dr, Burlington, MA 01803
Tel.: (617) 818-1887
Vehicle Company
N.A.I.C.S.: 523940

Subsidiary (Domestic):

Intersections Inc. **(2)**
2553 Dulles View Dr 4th Fl, Herndon, VA 20171
Tel.: (703) 488-6100
Web Site: http://www.auracompany.com
Identity Management Solutions
N.A.I.C.S.: 518210
Stephen Ruggieri *(VP-Partner Solutions)*

Subsidiary (Domestic):

American Background Services, Inc. **(3)**
629 Cedar Creek Grade Ste C, Winchester, VA 22601
Tel.: (540) 665-8056
Web Site:
   http://www.americanbackground.com
Sales Range: $100-124.9 Million
Background Screening
N.A.I.C.S.: 561611

Captira Analytical, LLC **(3)**
3 E Comm Sq 11 Pruyn St, Albany, NY 12207
Tel.: (518) 312-4163
Web Site: http://www.captira.com
Sales Range: $10-24.9 Million
Emp.: 20

Software & Automated Service Solutions for Bail Bond Industry
N.A.I.C.S.: 513210
Steven Alan Sjoblad *(Chm & CEO)*

Intersections Insurance Services Inc. **(3)**
315 W University Dr, Arlington Heights, IL 60004-1811
Tel.: (847) 797-8500
Web Site:
   http://www.intersectionsinsurance.com
Insurance Brokerage Services
N.A.I.C.S.: 524210

Net Enforcers, Inc. **(3)**
2633 E Indian School Rd Ste 270, Phoenix, AZ 85016
Tel.: (270) 721-5491
Web Site: http://www.netenforcers.com
Sales Range: $10-24.9 Million
Emp.: 25
Brand Protection Services
N.A.I.C.S.: 541519

i4c Innovations Inc. **(3)**
3800 Concorde Pkwy Ste 400, Chantilly, VA 20151
Tel.: (703) 961-6596
Web Site: http://www.voyce.com
Animal Production Services
N.A.I.C.S.: 112990

ISURE INSURANCE BROKERS
8700 W Flagler St Ste 270, Miami, FL 33174
Tel.: (305) 223-2533
Web Site: http://isurepro.com
Year Founded: 1984
Sales Range: $10-24.9 Million
Emp.: 10
Insurance Agency & Brokerage Services
N.A.I.C.S.: 524210
Javier A. Fernandez *(Principal)*

ISWILL ACQUISITION CORPORATION
533 Airport Blvd Ste 400, Burlingame, CA 94010
Tel.: (619) 736-6855   DE
Year Founded: 2018
Emp.: 3
Investment Services
N.A.I.C.S.: 523999
Rodney Rogers *(CEO)*
Kevin Reid *(Pres & COO)*
Michael Provenzano *(CFO & Sec)*

ISYS, INC.
801 W Mineral Ave Ste 105, Littleton, CO 80120
Tel.: (303) 290-8922
Web Site:
   http://www.isystechnologies.com
Year Founded: 1990
Sales Range: $10-24.9 Million
Emp.: 140
Engineering & Information Technology Services
N.A.I.C.S.: 541330
Teresa Porter *(Pres & CEO)*
Kurt Hotto *(Founder & VP-Special Projects)*

IT AMERICA INC.
100 Metroplex Dr Ste 207, Edison, NJ 08817
Tel.: (732) 985-5100
Web Site: http://www.itamerica.com
Sales Range: $10-24.9 Million
Emp.: 250
Information Technology Consulting Services
N.A.I.C.S.: 541990
Praveen T. *(Co-Founder & CEO)*
Zinnat Khan *(Mgr-HR)*

IT ASCENT, INC.

IT Ascent, Inc.—(Continued)

3000 Oak Rd Ste 200, Walnut Creek,
CA 94597
Tel.: (925) 627-4900
Web Site: http://www.itascent.com
Year Founded: 2000
Sales Range: $25-49.9 Million
Emp.: 426
Information Technology Recruiting
Services
N.A.I.C.S.: 561311
Joseph Nordlinger (Pres & CEO)

Subsidiaries:

IT Ascent, Inc.-Walnut Creek   (1)
3000 Oak Rd Ste 200, Walnut Creek, CA
94597
Tel.: (925) 627-4900
Web Site: http://www.ascentsg.com
Strategic Employment Solutions & Tactical
Services
N.A.I.C.S.: 561311
Joseph Nordlinger (Pres & CEO)

PharmAscent   (1)
5445 DTC Pkwy Penthouse #4, Greenwood
Village, CO 80111
Tel.: (303) 488-3415
Web Site: http://www.pharmascent.com
Strategic Employment Solutions & Tactical
Services
N.A.I.C.S.: 561311

IT FIRST SOURCE
4249 Rte 9 N Ste 2 Freeworld, Edi-
son, NJ 07728
Tel.: (732) 632-4661
Web Site: http://www.itfsinc.com
Year Founded: 2000
Sales Range: $10-24.9 Million
Emp.: 73
IT Services & Solutions
N.A.I.C.S.: 513210
Arvind Prakash (Pres)
Avijit Chakravarty (Mgr-Ops)

IT GIRL PUBLIC RELATIONS
3763 Eddingham Ave, Calabasas, CA
91302
Tel.: (310) 577-1122
Web Site:
   http://www.itgirlpublicrelations.com
Year Founded: 1998
Sales Range: Less than $1 Million
Emp.: 5
Public Relations
N.A.I.C.S.: 541820
Juliette Harris (CEO)

IT PEOPLE CORPORATION, INC.
1 Copley Pkwy Ste 216, Morrisville,
NC 27560
Tel.: (919) 806-3535
Web Site:
   http://www.itpeoplecorp.com
Year Founded: 1999
Computer System Design Services
N.A.I.C.S.: 541512
Sai Nidamarty (Co-Founder & CEO)
Sri Mudunuri (Co-Founder & Pres)
Mohan Venkataraman (CTO)
Sesha Agnihotram (VP-Managed
Svcs & Global Delivery)
Ozay Ertan (Officer)
Srini Gollapudi (COO-India)

IT PROPHETS, LLC
3030 Woodbridge Ln, Canton, GA
30114
Tel.: (770) 335-1410
Web Site: http://www.itprophets.com
Year Founded: 2003
Rev.: $4,500,000
Emp.: 11
Computer Related Services
N.A.I.C.S.: 541512

Jean Landmesser (Mng Partner)
Lee Cullom (Dir-Sls)
Niraj Tenany (Founder & CEO)

IT RESOURCES CORP.
11910 Race Track Rd, Tampa, FL
33626
Tel.: (813) 749-7538
Web Site:
   http://www.itresourcescorp.com
Sales Range: $1-9.9 Million
Emp.: 10
IT & Communications Staffing Ser-
vices
N.A.I.C.S.: 561311
Dan Jones (Pres)
Donna Springer (Office Mgr)
Kevin Trussler (Acct Mgr)

IT SOLUTIONS CONSULTING LLC
414 Commerce Dr Ste 150, Fort
Washington, PA 19034
Tel.: (215) 886-7166
Web Site: http://www.itsolutions-
   inc.com
Year Founded: 1994
Information Technology Services
N.A.I.C.S.: 541512
Garrett Graney (CEO)
Jim Higgins (Principal & VP-Sls &
Mktg)
Ted Swanson (Founder)
Justin Ozol (Principal & VP-Network
Services,)
Ben Greenberg (VP-Corp Dev)

Subsidiaries:

Acropolis Computers, Inc.   (1)
915 Whitelaw Ave, Wood River, IL 62095
Tel.: (618) 254-8733
Web Site: http://www.acropolistech.com
Rev.: $4,500,000
Emp.: 20
Computer & Office Machine Repair & Main-
tenance
N.A.I.C.S.: 811210
Sugi Rule (Controller)
Kevin Geiger (CIO)
Barton Olney (VP-Bus Dev)
Jim Sammons (Mgr-Svc)
Gary Hilligoss (VP)
Ryan Fairless (Acct Mgr)
Tracy Butler (CEO & Co-Founder)
Deanna Busby (Acct Mgr)

CHIPS Technology Group LLC   (1)
5 Aerial Way, Syosset, NY 11791
Tel.: (516) 377-6585
Web Site: http://chipstechnologygroup.com
Rev.: $2,243,400
Emp.: 10
Computer & Computer Peripheral Equip-
ment & Software Merchant Whslr
N.A.I.C.S.: 423430
Evan J. Leonard (Co-Founder & Pres)
Barbara Gouze (VP-Key Accts)
David Tan (Co-Founder & CTO)
Ken Indovino (Dir-Technical Svc)

SecurElement Infrastructure Solutions
LLC   (1)
7 Great Vly Pkwy Ste 110, Malvern, PA
19355
Tel.: (484) 323-1626
Computer Related Services
N.A.I.C.S.: 541519

Spade Technology Inc.   (1)
129 N Main St, Mansfield, MA 02048
Tel.: (508) 339-5163
Web Site: http://www.spadetechnology.com
Rev.: $1,900,000
Emp.: 21
Data Processing, Hosting & Related Ser-
vices
N.A.I.C.S.: 518210
Myles M. Keough (Pres)

The Network Pro, Inc.   (1)
1561 E Orangethorpe Ave Ste 120, Fullerton, CA 92831
Tel.: (714) 333-9620
Web Site: http://www.thenetworkpro.net

Sales Range: $1-9.9 Million
Emp.: 28
Information Technology Support Services
N.A.I.C.S.: 541512

IT SOLUTIONS, INC.
2000 Cornwall Rd Ste 220, Mon-
mouth Junction, NJ 08817
Tel.: (732) 985-5900
Web Site: http://www.itcsolutions.com
Year Founded: 1998
Sales Range: $10-24.9 Million
Emp.: 120
Computer Software Systems Analysis
& Design
N.A.I.C.S.: 541511
Ranga Gurrala (Pres & CEO)
Brian Armstrong (Dir-Bus Dev)

IT USA INC.
535 W 24th St Fl 4, New York, NY
10011-1140
Tel.: (212) 265-4166
Year Founded: 1996
Sales Range: $10-24.9 Million
Emp.: 18
Mens & Womens Clothing
N.A.I.C.S.: 424350
Enrico Dimuccio (CEO)
Alessandro Parladori (CFO)

IT WORKS! GLOBAL, INC.
5325 State Rd 64 E, Bradenton, FL
34208
Tel.: (941) 348-6650
Web Site: http://www.myitworks.com
Year Founded: 2001
Sales Range: $200-249.9 Million
Emp.: 58
Health, Skin Care & Supplement Di-
rect Marketer & Mfr
N.A.I.C.S.: 325620
Pam Sowder (Chief Networking Offi-
cer)
Chris Burns (CIO)
Timothy Seat (Gen Counsel)
Steve Neeson (VP-Bus Dev)

ITA INTERNATIONAL, LLC
111 Cybernetics Way Ste 112, York-
town, VA 23693-5642
Tel.: (757) 234-6949
Web Site: http://www.ITA-Intl.com
Year Founded: 2000
Sales Range: $10-24.9 Million
Emp.: 86
Government Services
N.A.I.C.S.: 921190
Mike Melo (Pres)
Kathy Melo (Exec VP-Corp Gover-
nance)
Mike Carlson (VP-Contracts)
Jack Federoff (VP-Ops)
John Altizer (CFO)
John J. Muldoon (COO)
Amy Landers (Dir-HR)
Jake Greever (Mgr-Proposal)

ITAC SOLUTIONS
700 Montgomery Hwy Ste 148, Bir-
mingham, AL 35216
Tel.: (205) 326-0004
Web Site:
   http://www.itacsolutions.com
Year Founded: 2000
Rev.: $10,600,000
Emp.: 21
Professional Recruiting Firm
N.A.I.C.S.: 541612
Brian Pitts (Founder)
J. G. Carver (Owner)
Jeff Hopkins (Mgr-Bus Dev)

ITAGROUP, INC.
4600 Westown Pkwy, West Des
Moines, IA 50266-6719

Tel.: (515) 326-3400   IA
Web Site: http://www.itagroup.com
Year Founded: 1963
Sales Range: $150-199.9 Million
Emp.: 420
Performance Marketing Programs
N.A.I.C.S.: 541612
Brent Vanderwaal (Pres & COO)
Carrie Valster (VP-Client Svcs)
Sarah Haines (VP-Event Mgmt)
Robert Danna (Sr VP-Sls & Mktg)
Thomas J. Mahoney Jr. (Chm &
CEO)

Subsidiaries:

ITAGroup, Inc.-Atlanta   (1)
4600 Westown Pkwy, West Des Moines, IA
50266
Web Site: http://www.itagroup.com
Sales Range: $25-49.9 Million
Emp.: 6
Full Service Marketing Company Specializ-
ing in Performance Marketing Programs
N.A.I.C.S.: 237210

ITAGroup, Inc.-Chicago   (1)
2800 W Higgins Rd Ste 695, Hoffman Es-
tates, IL 60169   (100%)
Tel.: (847) 397-2855
Web Site: http://www.itagroup.com
Sales Range: $10-24.9 Million
Emp.: 7
Full Service Marketing Company Specializ-
ing in Performance Marketing Programs
N.A.I.C.S.: 561520
Phil Brewster (Reg VP)

ITAGroup, Inc.-Dallas   (1)
222 W Las Colinas Blvd Ste 1650, Irving,
TX 75039-5403
Tel.: (972) 830-7387
Web Site: http://www.itagroup.com
Emp.: 2
Full Service Marketing Company Specializ-
ing in Performance Marketing Programs
N.A.I.C.S.: 541511
Tom Mahoney (Pres)

ITAGroup, Inc.-Indianapolis   (1)
8520 Allison Point Blvd Ste 220, Indianapo-
lis, IN 46250-1390
Tel.: (317) 713-2969
Web Site: http://www.itagroup.com
Sales Range: $10-24.9 Million
Emp.: 10
Full Service Marketing Company Specializ-
ing in Performance Marketing Programs
N.A.I.C.S.: 541820

ITAGroup, Inc.-Minneapolis   (1)
681 E Lk St Ste 253, Wayzata, MN
55391   (100%)
Tel.: (952) 476-5482
Web Site: http://www.itagroup.com
Management Consulting
N.A.I.C.S.: 541611

International Travel Associates
Corp.   (1)
4600 Westown Pkwy, West Des Moines, IA
50266-6719   (100%)
Tel.: (515) 326-3400
Sales Range: $25-49.9 Million
Emp.: 500
Travel Agency
N.A.I.C.S.: 561510
Thomas Mahoney (CEO)

PerFormance Awards Inc.   (1)
4800 Westown Pkwy Ste 100, West Des
Moines, IA 50266-6719   (100%)
Tel.: (515) 224-3400
Sales Range: $25-49.9 Million
Emp.: 360
Fulfills Merchandise Awards
N.A.I.C.S.: 541890

ITAL-AMERICAS FOODS CORP.
312 Calle Fortaleza Ste 312, San
Juan, PR 00901
Tel.: (787) 723-2627
Sales Range: $10-24.9 Million
Emp.: 15
Italian Restaurant
N.A.I.C.S.: 722511

Elisabeth Saldana Schmier *(Pres)*

ITALEE OPTICS INC.
2641 W Olympic Blvd, Los Angeles, CA 90006
Tel.: (213) 385-8805
Web Site: http://www.italee.com
Year Founded: 1959
Sales Range: $10-24.9 Million
Emp.: 50
Frames, Ophthalmic
N.A.I.C.S.: 423460
Amy Hahn *(VP-Acct Rels)*

ITALENT INC.
13610 Barrett Ofc Dr Ste 105, Manchester, MO 63021
Tel.: (314) 720-4402
Web Site: http://www.italentinc.com
Year Founded: 2004
Sales Range: $1-9.9 Million
Emp.: 26
It Consulting
N.A.I.C.S.: 541519
Madhu Hittuvalli *(CEO)*
Sridhar Srigiri *(Partner)*

ITALIAN CAST STONE
5418 W Ingraham St, Tampa, FL 33616
Tel.: (813) 902-8900
Web Site:
    http://www.italiancaststone.com
Sales Range: $1-9.9 Million
Emp.: 15
Precast Architectural Stone & Foam Mfr
N.A.I.C.S.: 327991
Rosy Conto *(Owner & Pres)*

ITALIAN TERRAZZO & TILE CO., OF BREVARD, INC.
432 S Babcock St, Melbourne, FL 32901
Tel.: (321) 723-0651   FL
Rev.: $20,000,000
Emp.: 12
Ceramic Floor Tile Installation
N.A.I.C.S.: 238330
Alexander Pezzimenti *(Pres)*

ITASCA BANCORP INC.
308 W Irving Park Rd, Itasca, IL 60143
Tel.: (630) 773-0350   DE
Web Site: http://www.itascabank.com
Bank Holding Company
N.A.I.C.S.: 551111
James R. Mensching *(Pres)*

Subsidiaries:

Itasca Bank & Trust Co.   (1)
308 W Irving Park Rd, Itasca, IL 60143
Tel.: (630) 773-0350
Web Site: http://www.itascabank.com
Sales Range: $10-24.9 Million
Emp.: 100
Commericial Banking
N.A.I.C.S.: 522110
Jack E. Mensching *(Chm)*
John Binneboese *(Officer-Bus Dev & Sr VP)*
James R. Mensching *(Pres)*
John Hunt *(Chief Loan Officer & Sr VP)*
Carrie Pazienza *(Sr VP-Ops)*
Dolores Little *(Officer-Bus Continuity & Sr VP-Compliance)*
Richard Barth *(Officer-Special Assets & VP)*
Cathy Brewer *(Officer-Comml Real Estate & VP)*
Mark Stelter *(Officer-Comml Loan & VP)*
John Mueller *(Officer-Comml Loan & VP)*
George Kearns *(Officer-Comml Loan & VP)*
Joseph Marzan *(Officer-Comml Loan & VP)*
Valerie DalPino *(Officer-Consumer Loan & VP)*
Connie Zak *(Officer-Loan Ops & VP)*
Elvira Zamudio *(Officer-Loan Credit & VP)*
Carol DiFiglio *(Officer-Ops & VP)*

RoseMary Ciolino *(Officer-Ops & VP)*
Sherrell Coutain *(Officer-Trust & VP)*
Gerald Wiel *(Officer-Trust & VP)*
Marc DeFauw *(CFO & Sr VP)*
John Paul Sweeney *(Chief Trust Officer & VP)*

ITC HOLDING COMPANY, LLC
1791 OG Skinner Dr Ste A, West Point, GA 31833
Tel.: (706) 645-9482   DE
Web Site: http://www.itchold.com
Year Founded: 1989
Sales Range: $125-149.9 Million
Emp.: 30
Holding Company; Owner & Operator of Real Estate Properties
N.A.I.C.S.: 551112
Timothy B. Knight *(CFO & Sr VP)*
Shirley K. Coker *(Dir-HR & Corp Svcs)*
Campbell B. Lanier III *(Chm)*

Subsidiaries:

Instawares, LLC   (1)
1305 Chastain Rd Bldg 100 Ste 500, Kennesaw, GA 30144
Tel.: (770) 517-1838
Web Site: http://www.instawares.com
Restaurant Equipment Online Retailer
N.A.I.C.S.: 449210

Kinetic Ventures, L.L.C.   (1)
2 Wisconsin Cir Ste 620, Chevy Chase, MD 20815-7046
Tel.: (301) 652-8066
Web Site: http://www.kineticventures.com
Emp.: 7
Investment Management Service
N.A.I.C.S.: 523940
William Heflin *(Mng Dir)*
Jake Tarr *(Mng Dir)*
Nelson Chu *(Mng Dir)*
Sydney Shepherd *(CFO)*

Realview TV, LLC   (1)
1954 Airport Rd Ste 202, Atlanta, GA 30341
Tel.: (678) 242-1400
Web Site: http://www.realviewtv.com
Video Streaming Services
N.A.I.C.S.: 518210

ITC LEARNING CORP.
1616 Anderson Rd Ste 208, McLean, VA 22102   MD
Web Site: http://www.itclearning.com
Year Founded: 1977
Sales Range: Less than $1 Million
Emp.: 10
Producer of Off-the-Shelf & Custom Computer-Based Interactive Training Programs; Full-Service Training Organization, Training Consulting & Services
N.A.I.C.S.: 611519
Bill Walton *(Founder)*

Subsidiaries:

ITC Australasia Pty Ltd   (1)
Level 1 272 Pacific Hwy, Crows Nest, 2065, NSW, Australia
Tel.: (61) 294382500
Web Site: http://www.itclearning.com.au
Emp.: 15
ITC Multimedia Training Products Distr
N.A.I.C.S.: 611420
Mark F. Roberts *(Mng Dir)*

ITE MANAGEMENT L.P.
200 Park Ave S Ste 1511, New York, NY 10003
Tel.: (212) 220-5802   DE
Web Site: http://www.itemgmt.com
Investment Services
N.A.I.C.S.: 523999
David Smilow *(Mng Partner)*
Jason Koenig *(Mng Partner)*
James Unger *(Mng Partner)*
Matthew Brand *(Dir-Structured Fin & Investments)*
Stephanie Leichter *(Dir-Credit & Res)*

Lisette Farah *(CFO)*
Dan Lee *(COO & Controller-Fund)*
Joseph Gervasi *(Office Mgr)*

Subsidiaries:

American Railcar Industries, Inc   (1)
100 Clark St, Saint Charles, MO 63301   (54%)
Tel.: (636) 940-6000
Web Site: http://www.americanrailcar.com
Rev.: $476,843,000
Assets: $1,473,426,000
Liabilities: $809,892,000
Net Worth: $663,534,000
Earnings: $142,177,000
Emp.: 1,932
Fiscal Year-end: 12/31/2017
Covered Hopper & Tank Railcars Mfr
N.A.I.C.S.: 336510
Yevgeny Fundler *(Gen Counsel, Sec & Sr VP)*

Subsidiary (Non-US):

ARI Fleet Services of Canada, Inc.   (2)
1000 Degurse Road, Sarnia, N7T 7H5, ON, Canada
Tel.: (519) 332-3739
Sales Range: $300-349.9 Million
Emp.: 32
Financial Investment Services
N.A.I.C.S.: 523999

Subsidiary (Domestic):

ARI Longtrain, Inc.   (2)
100 Clark St Ste 201, Saint Charles, MO 63301-2075
Tel.: (636) 940-6000
Railroad Rolling Stock Mfr
N.A.I.C.S.: 336510

Group (Domestic):

ARI-Industrial Products Group   (2)
100 Clark St, Saint Charles, MO 63301
Tel.: (636) 940-6059
Web Site: http://www.ari-ipg.com
Sales Range: $250-299.9 Million
Holding Company
N.A.I.C.S.: 551112
Thomo Rhoads *(Dir-Insurance & Customer Svc)*

Subsidiary (Domestic):

ARI Jackson Manufacturing   (3)
100 Clark St, Saint Charles, MO 63301
Tel.: (636) 940-6000
Web Site: http://www.ari-jackson.com
Sales Range: $10-24.9 Million
Emp.: 50
Steel Products Mfg Services
N.A.I.C.S.: 541330

Subsidiary (Domestic):

American Railcar Leasing, LLC   (2)
100 Clark St Ste 201, Saint Charles, MO 63301-2075
Tel.: (636) 940-5000
Web Site: http://www.arleasing.com
Railcar Leasing Services
N.A.I.C.S.: 532411
Stephen Johnson *(Sr VP-Sls)*

J&L Holding Company   (2)
650 N Main Ctr, Saint Charles, MO 63301-2186   (100%)
Tel.: (636) 410-3500
Web Site: http://www.corbittmfg.com
Sales Range: $75-99.9 Million
Engineeering Services
N.A.I.C.S.: 541330

ITECHART GROUP, INC.
575 Lexington Ave 14th Fl, New York, NY 10022
Tel.: (718) 374-5043
Web Site: http://www.itechart.com
Year Founded: 2002
Sales Range: $25-49.9 Million
Emp.: 5,000
Software Development Services
N.A.I.C.S.: 541511
Sergei Kovalenko *(CEO)*

ITELAGEN INC
3 Second St Ste 1204, Jersey City, NJ 07311
Tel.: (212) 999-7280
Web Site: http://www.itelagen.com
Sales Range: $1-9.9 Million
Emp.: 32
Data Processing, Hosting & Related Services
N.A.I.C.S.: 518210
John O'Keefe *(CEO)*
Robert Spadaro *(VP-Tech)*
Richard J. Bandoy *(VP-Healthcare Tech)*
Michael T. Fuller *(VP-Sls)*
Mike Frost *(Chm)*
David M. Ulrich *(Exec VP)*
Emile Ondrus *(VP)*
Jeremy Kirchner *(VP-Fin)*
Carmen Soto-Rodriguez *(VP-Pro Svcs)*

ITEN INDUSTRIES INC.
4602 Benefit Ave, Ashtabula, OH 44004-5455
Tel.: (440) 997-6134
Web Site:
    http://www.itenindustries.com
Year Founded: 1958
Sales Range: $25-49.9 Million
Emp.: 235
Plastics Product Mfr
N.A.I.C.S.: 326199
Peter D. Huggins *(Pres)*
Clint Jackson *(Mgr-Mktg)*
Bill Kain *(Pres)*
Terry Grabe *(Mgr-Mktg)*

ITG HOLDINGS LLC
13490 Old Livingston Rd, Naples, FL 34109
Tel.: (239) 514-4484
Web Site: http://www.itgholdings.com
Holding Company; Real Estate Services
N.A.I.C.S.: 551112
Daniel E. Carter *(Founder & Principal)*
Andrew E. Sanford *(Chief Investment Officer)*
Blaine E. Barton *(VP)*

Subsidiaries:

ITG Realty LLC   (1)
1455 S Wickham Rd, Melbourne, FL 32904
Tel.: (321) 622-2701
Web Site: http://www.itgrealty.com
Emp.: 7
Real Estate Broker
N.A.I.C.S.: 531210
Harold E. Melle *(Pres)*

ITHAKA
2 Rector St 18th Fl, New York, NY 10006
Tel.: (212) 500-2600   NY
Web Site: http://www.ithaka.org
Year Founded: 1995
Sales Range: $75-99.9 Million
Emp.: 339
Educational Support Services
N.A.I.C.S.: 611710
Jabin White *(VP-Content Mgmt)*
Laura Brown *(Exec VP)*
Heidi McGregor *(VP-Comm)*
Bruce Heterick *(VP-Outreach & Participation Svcs)*
LaChonne Walton *(VP-Work Life & Culture)*

ITI TRAILERS & TRUCK BODIES, INC.
8535 Mason Dixon Hwy, Meyersdale, PA 15552-7100
Tel.: (814) 634-0080   PA
Web Site: http://www.itimfg.com
Year Founded: 2007

ITI Trailers & Truck Bodies, Inc.—(Continued)

Motor Truck Trailers Mfr
N.A.I.C.S.: 336212
Michael Nicoletti *(COO)*
Mike Seganos *(Controller)*
Steve LaRue *(Mgr-Sls)*
Jan Firl *(Mgr-HR)*

ITM TWENTYFIRST, LLC
333 S 7th St Ste 300, Minneapolis,
MN 55402
Tel.: (612) 371-3008   DE
Web Site: http://www.itm21st.com
Year Founded: 1998
Sales Range: $1-9.9 Million
Life Insurance Settlement & Adminis-
tration Services
N.A.I.C.S.: 524292
Kurt Gearhart *(CEO)*
Ralph Medici *(Pres-Life Insurance
Svcs)*
Lori Austin *(Pres-Underwriting Div)*
Cory Cates *(CIO)*
Maureen Sheehan *(Chief Compliance
Officer & Gen Counsel)*
Kurt Niederloh *(CFO)*
John Bikus *(Pres-PBI Res Svcs)*

ITOWNSTORE LLC
45 Keebler Ave, Norwalk, CT 06854
Tel.: (203) 202-2929
Web Site: http://www.itownstore.com
Sales Range: $10-24.9 Million
Emp.: 4
Printed Media Services
N.A.I.C.S.: 323111
Brad Lareau *(Pres)*

ITR INDUSTRIES INC.
441 Saw Mill River Rd, Yonkers, NY
10701
Tel.: (914) 476-9000
Rev.: $52,500,000
Emp.: 200
Shower Stalls, Fiberglass & Plastics
N.A.I.C.S.: 551112

Subsidiaries:

Accurate Partitions Corp.   (1)
8000 Joliet Rd, McCook, IL 60525
Tel.: (708) 442-6800
Web Site: http://www.accuratepartitions.com
Rev.: $10,400,000
Emp.: 100
Mfr of Bathroom Partitions for Public Rest-
rooms
N.A.I.C.S.: 327110
Jim Povejsil *(Pres & Gen Mgr)*

Global Steel Products
Corporation   (1)
95 Marcus Blvd, Deer Park, NY 11729-4501
Tel.: (631) 586-3330
Web Site: http://www.globalpartitions.com
Sales Range: $25-49.9 Million
Emp.: 150
Mfr of Toilet Partitions, Dressing Booths,
Shower Stalls & Accessory Items
N.A.I.C.S.: 337126

TBS Specialties Direct Inc.   (1)
1312 B Colony Ct, Fort Worth, TX 76117
Tel.: (817) 831-0337
Web Site: http://www.tbs.specialties-
direct.com
Sales Range: $10-24.9 Million
Emp.: 11
Metal Doors, Sash & Trim
N.A.I.C.S.: 423310
Adrienne Rolla *(Pres)*
Ray Bean *(Mgr-Acctg)*

ITRADEFAIR.COM, INC.
601 S Washington Ste 196, Stillwa-
ter, OK 74074
Tel.: (405) 372-6200
Web Site: http://www.itradefair.com
Year Founded: 1999
Sales Range: $10-24.9 Million
Emp.: 10

Online Trade Shows, Job Fairs &
Exhibitions
N.A.I.C.S.: 513210
Ramesh Sharda *(Co-Founder & Pres)*
Ramesh Sambasivan *(Co-Founder)*

ITS PARTNERS, LLC
4079 Park E Ct, Grand Rapids, MI
49506
Tel.: (616) 242-5300
Web Site: http://www.itsdelivers.com
Year Founded: 1984
Sales Range: $10-24.9 Million
Emp.: 75
Software Products Whslr
N.A.I.C.S.: 541519
Robert Sweezie *(CEO)*
Wade Wyant *(Pres)*

ITSHOT.COM
2W 46th St Ste 602, New York, NY
10036
Tel.: (212) 398-3123
Web Site: http://www.itshot.com
Year Founded: 2004
Sales Range: $1-9.9 Million
Emp.: 6
Online Diamond Jewelry & Watch
Retailer
N.A.I.C.S.: 339910
Boris Barshevsky *(CEO)*
Denis Stepansky *(Founder & Owner)*

ITSOURCE TECHNOLOGY INC.
1401 Los Gamos Dr Ste 102, San
Rafael, CA 94903
Tel.: (415) 472-5700
Web Site: http://www.itsource.com
Year Founded: 2006
Sales Range: $1-9.9 Million
Emp.: 43
Information Technology Consulting
Services
N.A.I.C.S.: 541512
Brian M. Arellanes *(Chm & CEO)*
Nina Do *(COO)*
Matt Whitmarsh *(Exec VP)*
Sammuel Washington *(VP)*

ITT EDUCATIONAL SERVICES, INC.
13000 N Meridian St, Carmel, IN
46032-1404
Tel.: (317) 706-9200   DE
Web Site: http://www.ittesi.com
Year Founded: 1968
Sales Range: $800-899.9 Million
Emp.: 4,100
Business Schools & Technical Educa-
tion
N.A.I.C.S.: 611710
Glenn E. Tanner *(CMO & Exec VP)*
Angela K. Knowlton *(Treas, Sr VP &
Controller)*
Barry S. Simich *(Sr VP-Ops)*
David E. Catalano *(Sr VP-Bus Dev)*
Phillip B. Frank *(Gen Counsel, Sr VP
& Asst Sec)*
Ronald F. Hamm *(Exec VP)*
June M. McCormack *(Pres-Online Div
& Exec VP)*
Jill M. Minnick *(Sr VP-Mktg)*
John Montgomery *(Sr VP-Project
Mgmt Office)*
Nancy Brown *(Dir-Corp Rels)*
Shawn J. Crawford *(Chief Compli-
ance Officer & Sr VP)*
Rocco F. Tarasi III *(Exec VP)*

Subsidiaries:

Daniel Webster College, Inc.   (1)
20 University Dr, Nashua, NH 03063
Tel.: (603) 577-6600
Web Site: http://www.dwc.edu
Educational Institution Services
N.A.I.C.S.: 611310
Michael E. Diffily *(Pres)*

ITU ABSORBTECH, INC.
2700 S 160th St, New Berlin, WI
53151
Web Site:
http://www.ituabsorbtech.com
Year Founded: 1930
Laundry Services
N.A.I.C.S.: 812320
Jim Leef *(Pres)*

IUNLIMITED INC.
7801 Folsom Blvd Ste 100, Sacra-
mento, CA 95826
Web Site: http://www.iunlimited.net
Year Founded: 2004
Sales Range: $1-9.9 Million
Emp.: 50
Investigation Services
N.A.I.C.S.: 561611
Keith Jacobs *(Pres)*

IUPAT DISTRICT COUNCIL 21
2980 Southampton Rd, Philadelphia,
PA 19154
Tel.: (215) 677-7980
Web Site: https://www.dc21.org
Emp.: 6,000
Labor Organization Services
N.A.I.C.S.: 813930

IUPAT DISTRICT COUNCIL 9
45 W 14th St, New York, NY 10011
Tel.: (212) 255-2950
Web Site:
https://www.districtcouncil9.net
Year Founded: 1900
Labor Organization Services
N.A.I.C.S.: 813930

IUVO BIOSCIENCE, LLC
7500 W Henrietta Rd, Rush, NY
14543
Tel.: (585) 533-1672   NY
Web Site:
http://www.iuvobioscience.com
Year Founded: 2015
Sterilization Testing Services
N.A.I.C.S.: 541380
Ben Burton *(Pres & CEO)*
Mary Richardson *(Chief Scientific Of-
ficer & Exec VP)*
Donna Ventura *(Dir-Toxicology)*
Sanjeev Ganatra *(Chief Comml Offi-
cer)*
Daniel Spasic *(Chm)*
Robert McFall *(Dir-Fin)*

IVALUA, INC.
702 Marshall St Ste 520, Redwood
City, CA 94063
Tel.: (650) 930-9710
Web Site: http://www.ivalua.com
Year Founded: 2000
Sales Range: $50-74.9 Million
Emp.: 500
Software Development Services
N.A.I.C.S.: 513210
Laurence Mechali *(Sr VP-Pro Svcs)*
Dan Amzallag *(Founder & CEO)*
Jean-Manuel Bullukian *(VP-Indirect
Sls Channels & Sls Ops)*
Pascal Bensoussan *(Chief Product
Officer)*
Alex Saric *(CMO)*
Laura Smith *(VP-Sls-North America)*
Franck Lheureux *(Chief Revenue
Officer)*

IVAN DOVERSPIKE CO.
9501 Conner St, Detroit, MI 48213
Tel.: (313) 872-7000
Sales Range: $10-24.9 Million
Emp.: 50
Industrial Machinery & Equipment
N.A.I.C.S.: 423830

Robert Reno *(Controller)*
Gary Henninge *(VP)*
Craig Neal *(Pres)*
Todd Coulter *(Mgr-Engrg)*
Gary Ede *(Mgr-Tooling Svc)*
Gary Phillips *(Mgr-Aftermarket Parts
& Attachments)*
Mark Spresser *(Mgr-Natl Sls)*

IVAN GANDRUD CHEVROLET, INC.
919 Auto Plz Dr, Green Bay, WI
54302
Tel.: (920) 468-6800
Web Site:
http://www.gandrudchevrolet.com
Sales Range: $25-49.9 Million
Emp.: 250
Car Whslr
N.A.I.C.S.: 441110
Daniel Mangless *(Pres)*

IVAN H. STEWART INC.
1313 3rd St, International Falls, MN
56649
Tel.: (218) 283-8440
Web Site: http://www.s1foods.com
Sales Range: $10-24.9 Million
Emp.: 70
Grocery Stores
N.A.I.C.S.: 445110
Dave Stewart *(Owner)*
Ivan H. Stewart Jr. *(Pres)*

IVAN LEONARD CHEVROLET, INC.
1620 Montgomery Hwy, Hoover, AL
35216-4918
Year Founded: 1981
Sales Range: $50-74.9 Million
Emp.: 110
Car Whslr
N.A.I.C.S.: 441110
Matt Gettys *(Gen Mgr)*
Ivan J. Leonard Jr. *(Pres)*

IVAN SMITH FURNITURE, LLC
5434 Technology Dr, Shreveport, LA
71129
Tel.: (318) 688-1335   LA
Web Site: http://www.ivansmith.com
Year Founded: 1995
Sales Range: $25-49.9 Million
Emp.: 410
General Furniture, Appliances & Elec-
tronics Retailer
N.A.I.C.S.: 449110
Peyton Childs *(Dir-Adv)*
Marty Curtis *(Mgr-Store)*
Monique Moore *(Office Mgr)*

IVANHOE INDUSTRIES, INC.
818 William Leigh Dr Bldg H, Tully-
town, PA 19007-6306
Tel.: (215) 547-1200
Web Site:
http://www.ivanhoeindustries.com
Year Founded: 1983
Sales Range: $1-9.9 Million
Emp.: 7
Chemical & Allied Products Whslr
N.A.I.C.S.: 424690
Rafael Valle *(Co-owner & Mng Part-
ner)*

IVARS INC.
1001 Alaskian Way, Seattle, WA
98104
Tel.: (206) 587-6500
Web Site: http://www.ivars.net
Rev.: $10,400,000
Seafood Restaurants
N.A.I.C.S.: 722511

IVC-USA INC.

1551 Montgomery St, South Hill, VA 23970
Tel.: (434) 447-7100
Web Site: http://www.ivcusa.com
Sales Range: $10-24.9 Million
Emp.: 250
Holding Company; Hardwood Veneer Mfr
N.A.I.C.S.: 551112
Tyler Howerton *(Mgr-Export Sls)*
Brian Ellis *(Mgr-Mktg & Sls)*

Subsidiaries:

International Veneer Company   **(1)**
1551 Montgomery St, South Hill, VA 23970
Tel.: (434) 447-7100
Web Site: http://www.ivcusa.com
Sales Range: $10-24.9 Million
Emp.: 200
Veneer Stock, Hardwood
N.A.I.C.S.: 321211
Pitt Neukirchner *(Pres)*

IVCI, LLC

601 Old Willets Path Ste 100, Hauppauge, NY 11788
Tel.: (631) 273-5800
Web Site: http://www.ivci.com
Year Founded: 1995
Sales Range: $75-99.9 Million
Managed Conferencing Services
N.A.I.C.S.: 561499
Robert Swing *(Founder, Pres & CEO)*
Chris Bottger *(CTO)*
Tim Hennen *(CTO)*
Curtis Heath *(COO)*
Doug Lefko *(VP-Sls-Northeast)*
Jim Burke *(Chief Revenue Officer)*
Dawn Cagliano *(Sr VP-Ops)*
Adrian Bennett *(Sr Acct Mgr)*
Dave Ferlino *(Dir-Strategic Partnerships)*

IVDESK HOLDINGS, INC.

Baker Technology Pl 6121 Baker Rd Ste 101, Minnetonka, MN 55345
Tel.: (612) 605-5461   DE
Web Site: http://www.ivdesk.com
Year Founded: 2001
Cloud Computing Services
N.A.I.C.S.: 541511
James J. Polakowski *(Pres & COO)*
William E. Sorenson *(CTO)*
Larry D. Ingwersen *(Chm)*
Kris Tufto *(Chief Revenue Officer)*
Bill McDonald *(CFO & Controller)*
Don Bybee *(Dir-Procurement)*
Tom Riemann *(Exec VP-Sls & Mktg)*
Martin L. Dehen *(Sr VP-Shareholder Svcs)*
Jeremy Anderson *(VP-Customer Svc)*
Todd Copley *(VP-HR)*
Phil Wicke *(VP-Ops)*
Chuck Reese *(CEO)*

IVENTURE SOLUTIONS, INC.

5210 Belfort Rd Ste 140, Jacksonville, FL 32256
Tel.: (904) 332-8645
Web Site:
    http://www.iventuresolutions.com
Year Founded: 2000
Sales Range: $10-24.9 Million
Emp.: 50
Computer System Design Services
N.A.I.C.S.: 541512
Gray Mabry *(CEO)*
Mark Schnitzius *(Pres)*
Kory Martin *(Acct Mgr)*
Alan Schwartz *(Pres)*

Subsidiaries:

Gwanda, LLC   **(1)**
4900b Us Highway 1 N, Saint Augustine, FL 32095
Tel.: (904) 808-1386
Web Site: http://www.gwanda.com

Computer System Design Services
N.A.I.C.S.: 541512

IVERIFY US, INC.

150 Iverify Dr, Charlotte, NC 28217
Tel.: (704) 525-2701
Web Site:
    http://www.iverifysecurity.com
Year Founded: 2002
Sales Range: $10-24.9 Million
Emp.: 300
Video Monitoring Security Services
N.A.I.C.S.: 561621
Jose Chavarria *(CTO)*
James Fanella *(Co-CEO)*
Alex Froyo *(COO)*
Steve Martin *(CFO)*
Kimberly Soublet *(Chief People Officer)*
Kevin J. Thomas *(CMO)*

Subsidiaries:

Trans-Alarm, Inc.   **(1)**
500 E Travelers Trail, Burnsville, MN 55337
Tel.: (952) 894-1700
Web Site: http://www.transalarm.com
Sales Range: $1-9.9 Million
Emp.: 80
Security System Services
N.A.I.C.S.: 561621
J. C. Kiser *(Chm)*
Todd Sellner *(Dir-Tech & Trng)*
Paula A. Keimig *(Controller)*
Steve Champeau *(Pres)*

IVEY MECHANICAL COMPANY LLC

134 W Washington St, Kosciusko, MS 39090
Tel.: (662) 289-3646
Web Site:
    http://www.iveymechanical.com
Sales Range: $200-249.9 Million
Emp.: 64,700
Mechanical Contractor
N.A.I.C.S.: 238990
Larry Terrell *(Chm & CEO)*
Denny Terrell *(Pres)*
Bob Cooper *(VP-Corp)*
Nathan Upchurch *(VP-Bus Dev)*
Steve Barnhill *(VP-Fabrication Svcs)*

Subsidiaries:

OptiMech, LLC   **(1)**
Parkside Plz I 131 Mir Pkwy Ste 200, Hendersonville, TN 37075
Tel.: (615) 338-4044
Web Site: http://www.optimech.us
Sales Range: $10-24.9 Million
Engineeering Services
N.A.I.C.S.: 541330
Arch Hatfield *(Pres)*
Tim Page *(Exec VP)*
Mac Brown *(VP-Special Projects)*

IVEYS CONSTRUCTION INC.

4060 N Courtenay Pkwy, Merritt Island, FL 32953
Tel.: (321) 453-3812
Web Site:
    http://www.iveysconstruction.com
Sales Range: $10-24.9 Million
Emp.: 40
Commercial & Office Building, New Construction
N.A.I.C.S.: 236210
Wade Ivey *(Founder & Pres)*
Ellie Lucas *(Supvr-Payroll)*
Lori Mynheir *(Controller)*

IVGSTORES LLC

1806 N Flamingo Rd Ste 415, Pembroke Pines, FL 33028
Tel.: (954) 416-5000
Web Site: http://www.ivgstores.com
Year Founded: 2003
Sales Range: $25-49.9 Million
Emp.: 56

Furniture & Decor
N.A.I.C.S.: 423210
Jim Tyson *(Pres)*

IVINEX

533 W 2600 S Ste 312, Bountiful, UT 84010
Tel.: (801) 335-8390
Web Site: http://www.ivinex.com
Sales Range: $1-9.9 Million
CRM Software
N.A.I.C.S.: 513210
Derek Minor *(Pres)*

IVISION SCALE, LLC

1430 W Peachtree St, Atlanta, GA 30309
Tel.: (678) 999-3002
Web Site: http://www.ivision.com
Sales Range: $10-24.9 Million
Emp.: 75
Information Technology Services
N.A.I.C.S.: 518210
David Degitz *(CEO)*
Stewart Cartin *(CTO)*
Laura Melton *(CFO)*

Subsidiaries:

Carve Systems LLC   **(1)**
600 5th Ave 2nd Fl, New York, NY 10020
Tel.: (201) 632-3422
Web Site: http://www.carvesystems.com
Sales Range: $1-9.9 Million
Emp.: 50
Security System Services
N.A.I.C.S.: 561621
Jeremy Allen *(CTO)*
Mike Zusman *(CEO)*
Max Sobell *(COO)*

Plus Consulting LLC   **(1)**
505 Washington Ave, Carnegie, PA 15106
Tel.: (412) 206-0160
Web Site: http://www.plusconsulting.com
Information Technology & Services
N.A.I.C.S.: 541519

IVIZ GROUP, INC.

900 Tower Dr 4th Flr, Troy, MI 48098
Tel.: (248) 528-7160
Web Site:
    http://www.idashboards.com
Year Founded: 2000
Sales Range: $1-9.9 Million
Emp.: 80
Enterprise Dashboard Software
N.A.I.C.S.: 513210
Shadan Malik *(Founder & CEO)*
Matthias Glatschke *(Mgr-Germany)*
Marina Morris *(Acct Mgr-Channel)*

IVOICEIDEAS, INC.

Arboretum Great Hills 9600 Great Hills Trl, Austin, TX 78759
Tel.: (512) 637-1330   NV
Web Site: http://www.ivoiceideas.com
Year Founded: 2002
Sales Range: Less than $1 Million
Social Networking Website Focusing on Communication of New Ideas & Solutions to Problems
N.A.I.C.S.: 516210
Kathy Gilchrist *(CFO, Principal Acctg Officer & Sec)*

IVOLUTION MEDICAL SYSTEMS, INC.

129 Oser Ave, Hauppauge, NY 11788
Tel.: (631) 998-3495
Web Site: http://www.ivmedical.us
Software Publisher
N.A.I.C.S.: 513210
Daniel Frieling *(VP-New Bus Dev)*

IVORY HOMES

978 Woodoak Ln, Salt Lake City, UT 84117
Tel.: (801) 747-7000

Web Site:
    http://www.ivoryhomes.com
Sales Range: $50-74.9 Million
Emp.: 70
Single-Family Housing Construction
N.A.I.C.S.: 236115
John Cahoon *(Dir-Sls & Mktg)*
Danny Berg *(Superintendent-Construction)*
Dave Zollinger *(Area Mgr)*
David Wolfgramm *(CFO)*
Ann Hatch *(Coord-Mktg)*
Brian Apsley *(Mgr-Architectural Design)*
Bryon Prince *(Project Mgr)*
Ryan Little *(Superintendent-Warranty)*
Kevin Carlson *(Coord-Sls & Mktg)*

IVORY INTERNATIONAL, INC.

15400 NW 34th Ave, Opa-Locka, FL 33054-2461
Tel.: (305) 687-2244   FL
Year Founded: 1976
Sales Range: $100-124.9 Million
Emp.: 110
Women's & Girls' Outerwear Distr
N.A.I.C.S.: 424350
Will Hopper *(CFO)*
Sandy Lipson *(Pres)*
Joseph Carvajal *(Mgr-Compliance)*
Erwin Horwitz *(CIO)*
Jodi Weisman *(Dir-Imports)*
Robert J. Lodge *(Owner & CEO)*
Kathy McConville *(VP-Mdse & Design)*

IVOX SOLUTIONS, LLC

4485 SW Port Way, Palm City, FL 34990
Tel.: (772) 286-8183
Web Site:
    http://www.ivoxsolutions.com
Year Founded: 2003
Sales Range: $25-49.9 Million
Emp.: 500
Business Solutions
N.A.I.C.S.: 561439
Rob Newton *(CEO)*
Christopher Stapleton *(CFO)*
Karen Cullen *(Dir-Bus Solutions Center)*
Tom Gavin *(Dir-IT)*
Abigail Thompson *(Dir-HR)*

IVX HEALTH, INC.

214 Centerview Dr Ste 250, Brentwood, TN 37027
Tel.: (615) 510-6002
Web Site: http://www.ivxhealth.com
Healtcare Services
N.A.I.C.S.: 621610
Doug Ghertner *(CEO)*

Subsidiaries:

Precision Healthcare, Inc.   **(1)**
441 Donelson Pike Ste 395, Nashville, TN 37214
Tel.: (931) 375-1132
Web Site: http://www.precisionhc.com
Insurance Agencies & Brokerages
N.A.I.C.S.: 524210
Matt Roberts *(Dir-Ops)*
Brian Smith *(Pres)*
Jeff Piscadlo *(VP-Bus Dev)*

IVY CREDIT OPPORTUNITIES FUND

6300 Lamar Ave, Shawnee Mission, KS 66202-4200
Tel.: (913) 236-2000
Investment Services
N.A.I.C.S.: 523999
Joseph W. Kauten *(CFO, Principal Acctg Officer, Treas & VP)*
Henry John Herrmann *(Chm, Pres & CEO)*

Ivy Credit Opportunities Fund—(Continued)

IVY EXEC, INC.
6 E 39th St 11th Fl, New York, NY
10016
Tel.: (888) 551-3444
Web Site: http://www.ivyexec.com
Year Founded: 2006
Sales Range: $1-9.9 Million
Emp.: 30
Online, Membership-Based Executive
Employment Services
N.A.I.C.S.: 561330
Elena Bajic (Founder & CEO)
Alex Baranpuria (VP & Gen Mgr-Pro
Svcs)
Gayle Rigione (Chief Community Dev
Officer)
Anil Nain (Dir-Sls)

IVYSTONE GROUP, LLC
301 Commerce Dr, Exton, PA 19341
Tel.: (610) 524-6400
Web Site: http://www.Ivystone.com
Merchandise Sales & Marketing Ser-
vices
N.A.I.C.S.: 541613
Doug Cofiell (CEO)
Andy Bjork (VP-Strategy & Bus Dev)
Nancy Lee (VP-Mktg)
Jennifer Kohn (VP-Ops)
Mike Steidle (VP)
Christy Baum (Mgr-Sls-Midwest)
Julie Rutherford (Mgr-Sls-West)
Monica Loving (VP-Vendor Rels)
Susan Tirard (Mgr-Sls-Northeast)
Tracy Pettee (Mgr-Sls-Southeast)

Subsidiaries:

California Marketing Associates,
Inc.   (1)
110 E 9th St Ste A 669, Los Angeles, CA
90079
Tel.: (213) 452-7000
Web Site: http://www.cmagifts.com
Sales Range: $1-9.9 Million
Emp.: 2
Marketing Services
N.A.I.C.S.: 541613
Jackie Hoggan (VP-Sls)

Ivystone Group, LLC - Dallas   (1)
137 World Trade Ctr 2050 Stemmons Fwy,
Dallas, TX 75207
Tel.: (214) 231-4200
Sales Range: $50-74.9 Million
Emp.: 430
Merchandise Sales & Marketing Services
N.A.I.C.S.: 541613
Monica S. Loving (VP-Vendor Rels)

The Simblist Group Inc   (1)
230 Spring St Ste 1621, Atlanta, GA 30303
Tel.: (404) 524-2812
Web Site: http://www.simblistgroup.com
Emp.: 3
Merchandise Sales & Marketing Services
N.A.I.C.S.: 541613
Lee Farber (Pres)

IW GROUP, INC.
6300 Wilshire Blvd Ste 2150, Los An-
geles, CA 90048
Tel.: (213) 262-4090
Web Site: http://www.iwgroup.agency
Year Founded: 1990
Sales Range: $75-99.9 Million
Emp.: 64
Advetising Agency
N.A.I.C.S.: 541810
Bill Imada (Chief Connectivity Officer)
Martin Yang (Chief Prosperity Officer)
Nita Song (Chief Momentum Officer)
Dean DeMarchi (VP)
Sisi Zhang (Dir-Art)

Subsidiaries:

IW Group, Inc. - New York Office   (1)
1 Dag Hammarskjold Plz 885 2nd Ave 7th
Fl, New York, NY 10017

Tel.: (646) 865-3719
Web Site: http://www.iwgroupinc.com
Sales Range: $10-24.9 Million
Emp.: 4
Advetising Agency
N.A.I.C.S.: 541810
Hiroko Hatanaka (VP)
Bill Imada (Chm & CEO)

IW Group, Inc. - San Francisco
Office   (1)
33 New Montgomery St Ste 990, San Fran-
cisco, CA 94105
Tel.: (415) 905-0360
Web Site: http://www.iwgroupinc.com
Rev.: $50,000,000
Emp.: 10
Advetising Agency
N.A.I.C.S.: 541810
Matin Yung (Gen Mgr)

IWATA BOLT USA INC.
7131 Orangewood Ave, Garden
Grove, CA 92841
Tel.: (714) 897-0800
Web Site: http://www.iwatabolt.co.jp
Sales Range: $10-24.9 Million
Emp.: 80
Miscellaneous Fasteners
N.A.I.C.S.: 423710
Kiyotaka Iwata (Pres)

IWI INC.
1399 Rockefeller Rd, Wickliffe, OH
44092
Tel.: (440) 585-5900
Web Site: http://www.iwiinc.com
Sales Range: $10-24.9 Million
Emp.: 30
Materials Handling Machinery
N.A.I.C.S.: 423830
Jeffery Iacco (Pres)

IXL LEARNING, INC.
777 Mariners Is Blvd Ste 650, San
Mateo, CA 94404
Tel.: (650) 372-4040
Web Site: http://www.ixl.com
Year Founded: 1998
Course Learning Services
N.A.I.C.S.: 513210
Jennifer Gu (VP-Product Dev)
Paul Mishkin (CEO)

Subsidiaries:

Carson-Dellosa Publishing Group,
LLC   (1)
7027 Albert Pick Rd, Greensboro, NC
27409
Tel.: (336) 632-0084
Web Site: http://www.carsondellosa.com
Supplemental Educational Products Pub-
lishing & Sales
N.A.I.C.S.: 611710
Richard Lugo (VP-Ops)
Al Greco (CEO)

IXRF SYSTEMS, INC.
10421 Old Manchaca Rd Ste 620,
Austin, TX 78748
Tel.: (512) 386-6100
Web Site: http://www.ixrfsystems.com
Year Founded: 1993
Sales Range: $1-9.9 Million
Emp.: 10
Software & Hardware Designer & Mfr
of Microanalysis & X-Ray Fluores-
cence Products
N.A.I.C.S.: 513210
Ken Witherspoon (Owner & VP)
Per Sjoman (Pres & Engr)
Christina Roman (Mgr-Ops)

IZ TECHNOLOGIES, INC.
44081 Pipeline Plz Ste 220, Ashburn,
VA 20147-5891
Tel.: (703) 724-7500
Web Site:
http://www.iztechnologies.com
Year Founded: 2006

Sales Range: $10-24.9 Million
Emp.: 26
IT & Telecommunication Services to
Department of Defense Operations
N.A.I.C.S.: 921190
Donna Dacier (Pres)
Evin Planto (VP)

**IZZY'S FRANCHISE SYSTEMS
INC.**
PO Box 1689, Albany, OR 97321
Tel.: (541) 926-8693
Web Site: http://www.izzyspizza.com
Year Founded: 1979
Sales Range: $25-49.9 Million
Emp.: 1,040
Franchisor of Family Restaurants
N.A.I.C.S.: 485320
Fred Jansen (Co-Founder)

J & E PRECISION TOOL, LLC
107 Vly Rd, Southampton, MA 01073
Tel.: (413) 527-8778
Web Site: http://www.jeprecision.com
Rev.: $3,690,000
Emp.: 30
All Other Miscellaneous Fabricated
Metal Product Mfr
N.A.I.C.S.: 332999
Eugene Labrie (Gen Mgr)
Jim Lebrie (Owner)

Subsidiaries:

Alloy Specialties Inc.   (1)
110 Batson Dr, Manchester, CT 06042
Tel.: (860) 646-4587
Web Site: http://www.alloysp.com
Rev.: $2,300,000
Emp.: 17
All Other Miscellaneous General Purpose
Machinery Mfr
N.A.I.C.S.: 333998
Rich Ramondetta (Co-Owner)
Rose Sadosky (Mgr-Quality Sys)
Barry Zorda (Mgr-Quality)
Dennis DiMauro (Co-Owner)

Beranek, Inc.   (1)
2340 W 205th St, Torrance, CA 90501
Tel.: (310) 328-9094
Web Site: http://www.beranekinc.com
Sales Range: $1-9.9 Million
Emp.: 35
Machine Shops
N.A.I.C.S.: 332710
Jose Florez (Dir-Quality)
George Beranek (Pres)

**J & J EXTERMINATING CO.
INC.**
105 College St, Lafayette, LA 70503
Tel.: (337) 234-3929
Web Site: http://www.jjext.com
Rev.: $12,000,000
Emp.: 170
Exterminating & Pest Control Ser-
vices
N.A.I.C.S.: 561710
Charlie Duhon (Branch Mgr)
Robert L. John Sr. (Founder & VP)
Robert L. John Jr. (Pres)

**J & J IMPORTS & FABRICA-
TION, INC.**
180 Cumberland Park Dr, Saint Au-
gustine, FL 32095
Tel.: (904) 826-0602
Web Site: http://www.jandjcorp.com
Year Founded: 1999
Sales Range: $10-24.9 Million
Emp.: 90
Brick, Stone & Related Construction
Material Whslr
N.A.I.C.S.: 423320
Jeff Czyzewski (Pres)

J & J INDUSTRIES INC.
315 Howell Ave, Brooksville, FL
34601

Tel.: (352) 799-6872
Sales Range: $10-24.9 Million
Emp.: 250
Management Consulting Services
N.A.I.C.S.: 541618
Judy David (Treas & Sec)

J & J MARTS INC.
99 E Main St, Buckhannon, WV
26201
Tel.: (304) 472-1202
Rev.: $14,400,000
Emp.: 100
Gasoline Stations
N.A.I.C.S.: 457120
James D. Hinkle III (Pres)
Barbara Helmick (Treas & Sec)

J & L ENTERPRISES INC.
710 N Walnut St, Chaska, MN 55318
Tel.: (952) 448-2325
Sales Range: $10-24.9 Million
Emp.: 75
Grocery Stores, Independent
N.A.I.C.S.: 445110
Gary Cooper (Pres)
Sandra Cooper (VP)
Gary Dad (Owner)

J & L VENTURES LLC
3 Villa Dr, Rome, GA 30165
Tel.: (706) 232-2064
Web Site:
http://www.jandlventuresllc.com
Sales Range: $10-24.9 Million
Emp.: 56
Beer Distr
N.A.I.C.S.: 424810
Jean Stanley (Sr VP-Fin)
Lee J. Jackson (Co-Owner & Pres)
Donald M. Leebern III (Co-Owner &
Chm)

Subsidiaries:

Better Brands South Georgia
LLP   (1)
3900 Pecan Grove Ct, Albany, GA 31701
Tel.: (229) 888-2390
Rev.: $12,608,242
Emp.: 47
Alcoholic Beverage Distr
N.A.I.C.S.: 424810

J & M CHEVROLET, INC.
606 W Gannon Ave, Zebulon, NC
27597-2512
Tel.: (919) 269-7478
Web Site: http://www.jmchevy.com
Year Founded: 1927
Sales Range: $10-24.9 Million
Emp.: 34
Car Whslr
N.A.I.C.S.: 441110
Carlos Wheeler (Pres)

J & R SLAW, INC.
438 Riverview Rd, Lehighton, PA
18235
Tel.: (610) 852-2020
Web Site:
http://www.slawprecast.com
Year Founded: 1979
Sales Range: $10-24.9 Million
Emp.: 84
Precast Concrete Manufacturing
N.A.I.C.S.: 238120
Robert Slaw (Pres)

J & S MACHINE
W6009 490th Ave, Ellsworth, WI
54011
Tel.: (715) 273-3376
Web Site: http://www.jsmachine.com
Year Founded: 1998
Sales Range: $1-9.9 Million
Emp.: 4
Industrial Machinery

N.A.I.C.S.: 332710
Joe Seibel (Pres)

J FITZGIBBONS LLC
405 Lexington Ave The Chrysler Bldg
71st Fl, New York, NY 10174
Tel.: (212) 695-7376   **DE**
Investment Holding Company
N.A.I.C.S.: 551112
John B. Fitzgibbons (Founder, Chm & CEO)

Subsidiaries:

Basin Holdings US LLC   (1)
200 Park Ave Ste 5800, New York, NY 10166
Tel.: (212) 695-7376
Web Site: http://www.basinholdings.com
Emp.: 1,400
Holding Company; Integrated Oilfield Equipment Mfr, Distr & Services
N.A.I.C.S.: 551112
John B. Fitzgibbons (Founder, Chm & CEO)
Tyler Hassen (CFO & Pres-Fin)
Antonio Campo (Vice Chm)

Subsidiary (Domestic):

Basin Precision Machining LLC   (2)
211 Collins Rd, Jefferson, WI 53549
Tel.: (920) 674-6003
Web Site: http://www.basinprecision.com
Sales Range: $10-24.9 Million
Emp.: 150
Machined Components Mfr
N.A.I.C.S.: 332710
Erik Anderson (Pres)

Subsidiary (Non-US):

Basin Supply FZCO   (2)
Jafza View 19 Office 1105, PO Box 261057, Dubai, United Arab Emirates
Tel.: (971) 4 880 0203
Web Site: http://www.basinsupply.com
Emp.: 7
Oil & Gas Field Equipment & Supplies Distr
N.A.I.C.S.: 423830
Marc Allenby (Pres-Middle East & North Africa)
Ayman Khattab (Pres)

Subsidiary (US):

WB Supply LLC   (3)
111 N Naida St, Pampa, TX 79065
Tel.: (806) 669-1103
Web Site: http://www.shopoilsupplies.com
Sales Range: $25-49.9 Million
Emp.: 30
Oil & Gas Field Equipment & Supplies Distr
N.A.I.C.S.: 423830
Ronald G. Hess (Pres & COO)
Renae L. Hotz (VP-Sls)
Ray White (Dir-Pur)
Kay Swart (Controller)
Mark Bailey (Mgr-Tubular)

Subsidiary (Domestic):

Basin Tools, LP   (2)
405 Lexington Ave The Chrysler Bldg 71st Fl, New York, NY 10174
Tel.: (212) 695-7376
Web Site: http://www.basintools.com
Holding Company; Oil & Gas Field Equipment Mfr
N.A.I.C.S.: 551112
Leif Syversen (Pres)

Subsidiary (Domestic):

FHE USA LLC   (3)
1597 Cipolla Rd, Fruita, CO 81521
Tel.: (970) 243-0727
Web Site: http://www.builtbyfhe.com
Sales Range: $1-9.9 Million
Emp.: 70
Oil & Gas Field Equipment Mfr & Whslr
N.A.I.C.S.: 333132
Hannah Manley (Coord-Inventory Control)

Plant (Domestic):

FHE USA LLC - San Antonio   (4)
3400 Nacogdoches Rd Bldg 3, San Antonio, TX 78217
Tel.: (210) 236-5427

Web Site: http://www.builtbyfhe.com
Oil & Gas Field Equipment Mfr & Whslr
N.A.I.C.S.: 333132
Gary W. Bentsen (Area Mgr)

Subsidiary (Domestic):

OTS International, Inc.   (3)
2615 Industrial Ln, Conroe, TX 77301-7301
Tel.: (936) 539-0099
Web Site: http://www.otsintl.com
Oil & Gas Drilling Equipment Mfr
N.A.I.C.S.: 333132

Subsidiary (Non-US):

Wenzel Downhole Tools Ltd.   (3)
5920 Macleod Trail SW Suite 504, Calgary, T2H 0K2, AB, Canada
Tel.: (403) 262-3050
Web Site: http://www.downhole.com
Sales Range: $75-99.9 Million
Emp.: 3
Oil & Gas Drilling Equipment Mfr & Distr
N.A.I.C.S.: 333132
Jonathan Thiele (Chm-Mgmt Bd)
Rick Doiron (Gen Mgr)
Tyler Hassen (Pres)

Subsidiary (Non-US):

Wenzel Downhole Tools Europe GmbH   (4)
Grafftring 5, 29227, Celle, Germany
Tel.: (49) 5141 977 65 0
Web Site: http://www.downhole.com
Oil & Gas Drilling Equipment Mfr & Distr
N.A.I.C.S.: 333132
Dirk von Kittlitz (Mng Dir)

Subsidiary (US):

Wenzel Downhole Tools, U.S., Inc.   (4)
4205 FM 1485 Rd, Conroe, TX 77306
Tel.: (936) 441-1480
Web Site: http://www.downhole.com
Emp.: 21
Oil & Gas Drilling Equipment Mfr
N.A.I.C.S.: 333132

Subsidiary (Domestic):

Pinnacle Oilfield Services, Inc.   (2)
1469 Old Spanish Trail Hwy 182, Broussard, LA 70518
Tel.: (337) 365-8753
Web Site: http://www.pinnacle-oilfield.com
Oil & Gas Equipment Inspection, Technical Consulting, Procedural Training, Hardbanding & Other Related Services
N.A.I.C.S.: 213112
Ricky J. Suire (Founder & Pres)
Sully Tauzin (Mgr-Hardbanding)
Coty Laliberte (Mgr-Trnng & Consulting)

SteelTech Industrial Fabricating Corporation   (2)
240 S Meridian Rd, Mitchell, IN 47446
Tel.: (812) 849-0124
Web Site: http://www.steeltechcorp.com
Steel Component & Assembly Fabrication Services
N.A.I.C.S.: 332999
Mark Suvak (CEO)
Dan Brown (CFO)
Will Preston (VP-Bus Dev)

VCI, Inc.   (2)
1500 Progress St, Sturgis, MI 49091
Tel.: (269) 659-3676
Web Site: http://www.vciusa.com
Sales Range: $10-24.9 Million
Emp.: 190
Contract Fabricated Component & Material Handling Products Mfr
N.A.I.C.S.: 332999
Al Stimson (Dir-Sls)

J PUBLIC RELATIONS, INC.
1620 5th Ave 700, San Diego, CA 92101
Tel.: (619) 255-7069
Web Site:
http://www.jpublicrelations.com
Year Founded: 2004
Sales Range: $1-9.9 Million
Emp.: 22

Public Relations Services
N.A.I.C.S.: 541820
Jamie Lynn Sigler (Partner)
Ali Lundberg (VP)
Lindsey Back (CFO)
Amy Ogden (Dir-Mktg & Dev)
Heidi Baldwin (Acct Dir-California)
Tanya Scalisi (Dir-Acct)
Emma Hartland-Mahon (Dir-New York)
Marrissa Mallory (Acct Supvr)
Jillian Hunter (Acct Supvr)
Kevinie Woo (Acct Supvr-California)
Tom Dietz (Acct Dir)
Kristin Moller (Sr VP-New York)

J RUSSELL & ASSOCIATES LLC
1057 Baxter St, Athens, GA 30606
Tel.: (404) 277-3316
Web Site:
https://www.jrussellandassociates.com
Management Consulting Services
N.A.I.C.S.: 541618

J SQUARED INC.
2588 Jannetides Blvd, Greenfield, IN 46140
Tel.: (317) 631-5433
Web Site: http://www.uloft.com
Sales Range: $10-24.9 Million
Emp.: 42
Wood Office Furniture
N.A.I.C.S.: 337211
James Jannetides (Founder & CEO)

J SUPPLY CO.
88 Addington Dr NW, Rome, GA 30165
Tel.: (706) 235-3321   **GA**
Web Site: http://www.jsupply.com
Year Founded: 1973
Sales Range: $10-24.9 Million
Emp.: 30
Industrial Supplies Whslr
N.A.I.C.S.: 423840
Freeman Robbins (Pres)
Rhett Robbins (VP)
Jim Rogers (Chm)

J W R CONSTRUCTION SERVICES
1311 W Newport Center Dr Ste C, Deerfield Beach, FL 33442
Tel.: (954) 480-2800
Web Site:
http://www.jwrconstruction.cc
Year Founded: 1985
Sales Range: $10-24.9 Million
Emp.: 15
Commercial & Institutional Building Construction Services
N.A.I.C.S.: 236220
Jerry W. DuBois (Pres)
William J. Gallo (Exec VP)
Timothy M. Anderson (VP-Ops)

J WOOD REALTY, LLC
330 S Pineapple Ave Ste 113, Sarasota, FL 34236
Tel.: (941) 922-7600
Web Site: http://www.jwoodrealty.com
Sales Range: $10-24.9 Million
Emp.: 8
Real Estate Broker
N.A.I.C.S.: 531210

J&B GROUP, INC.
13200 43rd St NE, Saint Michael, MN 55376-8420
Tel.: (763) 497-3913   **MN**
Web Site: http://www.jbgroup.com
Year Founded: 1995
Sales Range: $150-199.9 Million
Emp.: 400

Holding Company Meat & Meat Product Processing Packaging & Distr
N.A.I.C.S.: 541820
Bob Hageman (CEO)
Mike Hageman (Pres)

Subsidiaries:

J&B Wholesale Distributing, Inc.   (1)
13200 43rd St NE, Saint Michael, MN 55376-8420   (100%)
Tel.: (763) 497-3913
Web Site: http://www.jbgroup.com
Frozen & Refrigerated Meat Distr
N.A.I.C.S.: 424470
Robert Hageman (Pres)

Midwest Pride Inc.   (1)
13200 43rd St NE, Saint Michael, MN 55376-8420
Tel.: (763) 497-3913
Web Site: http://www.mwpride.com
Sales Range: $50-74.9 Million
Provider of Meats & Meat Products
N.A.I.C.S.: 424470

No Name Steaks LLC   (1)
13200 43rd St NE, Saint Michael, MN 55376-8420
Tel.: (763) 497-3913
Web Site: http://www.nonamesteaks.com
Sales Range: $50-74.9 Million
Provider of Meats & Meat Products
N.A.I.C.S.: 424470

J&B IMPORTERS INC.
119 25 SW 128th St, Miami, FL 33182
Tel.: (305) 238-1866   **FL**
Web Site: http://www.jbimporters.com
Year Founded: 1971
Sales Range: $10-24.9 Million
Emp.: 85
Provider of Sporting & Recreation Goods
N.A.I.C.S.: 423910
Bill Tannen (VP)
Gary Mendenhall (Mgr-Customer Svc & Sls)

Subsidiaries:

J&B Importers Pacific Inc.   (1)
1725 Puyallup St Ste 300, Sumner, WA 98390
Tel.: (253) 395-0441
Web Site: http://www.jbi.bike
Rev.: $110,000
Emp.: 12
Provider of Sporting & Recreation Goods
N.A.I.C.S.: 423910

J&B RESTAURANT PARTNERS INC.
4000 Veterans Memorial Hwy, Bohemia, NY 11716
Tel.: (631) 218-9067
Web Site:
http://www.jbrestaurants.com
Sales Range: $50-74.9 Million
Emp.: 2,500
Owns & Operates Restaurants & Eating Places
N.A.I.C.S.: 722511
Joseph Vitrano (Pres)
Greg Alagna (Sr VP)
Kimberly Schuller (Mgr-Store)
Robert Radovanovich (Mgr)
Jerry Snearly (CFO)
Dawn Petite (COO)
Joseph Quinto (Dir-Construction Real Estate & Facilities)
Colleen Capone (Dir-HR)

J&B SAUSAGE COMPANY, INC.
100 Main St, Waelder, TX 78959
Tel.: (830) 788-7511
Web Site: http://www.jbfoods.com
Year Founded: 1960
Sales Range: $50-74.9 Million
Emp.: 350

J&B Sausage Company, Inc.—(Continued)

Mfr of U.S.D.A. Inspected Food Products
N.A.I.C.S.: 311611
Danny V. Janecka *(Pres)*

J&B SUPPLY, INC.
4915 Zero St, Fort Smith, AR 72903
Tel.: (479) 649-4915
Web Site: http://www.jbsupply.com
Year Founded: 1968
Sales Range: $10-24.9 Million
Emp.: 98
Suppliers of Warm Air Heating & Air Conditioning
N.A.I.C.S.: 423730
Barry S. Jones *(Pres)*

J&D PRODUCE, INC.
7310 N Expy 281, Edinburg, TX 78540
Tel.: (956) 380-0353
Web Site:
　http://www.littlebearproduce.com
Rev.: $96,600,000
Emp.: 50
Vegetable & Melon Farming
N.A.I.C.S.: 111219
James V. Bassetti *(Pres)*
Diane Bassetti *(VP)*
Yvonne Benavidez *(Dir-Admin)*
Matthew J. Bradley *(Mgr-Sls)*
Mike de Los Santos *(Mgr-Traffic)*
Trent Bishop *(VP-Sls)*

J&F ENTERPRISES INC.
1100 Meeting St, West Columbia, SC 29169
Tel.: (803) 794-5382
Web Site: http://www.jandfinc.com
Sales Range: $10-24.9 Million
Emp.: 7
Liquor Store Owner & Operator; Alcoholic Beverage Distr
N.A.I.C.S.: 445320
Rusty Johnson *(Pres)*

J&H ASSET PROPERTY MANAGEMENT INC.
22880 Savi Ranch Pkwy, Yorba Linda, CA 92887
Tel.: (714) 974-0397
Web Site: http://www.jandhmgt.com
Year Founded: 1986
Sales Range: $25-49.9 Million
Emp.: 30
Management Mobile Parks
N.A.I.C.S.: 531110
Jim Joffe *(Pres)*
William Hanks *(VP)*
Julie Hickenbottom *(Dir-Property Mgmt)*

J&H FOREST PRODUCTS
18 Saddleback CT, Danville, CA 94506
Tel.: (925) 743-0360
Rev.: $11,000,000
Lumber, Plywood & Millwork
N.A.I.C.S.: 423310

J&H OIL COMPANY INC.
1619 Chicago Dr SW, Wyoming, MI 49519
Tel.: (616) 245-1114　　MI
Web Site: http://www.jhoil.com
Year Founded: 1970
Sales Range: $200-249.9 Million
Emp.: 40
Provider of Petroleum Services
N.A.I.C.S.: 424710
Craig Hoppen *(Pres)*
Sandy Arrasmith *(VP)*

Subsidiaries:

Service Oil Company　　　　　　　(1)

604 E Water St, Cassopolis, MI 49031
Tel.: (269) 445-2441
Sales Range: $10-24.9 Million
Emp.: 9
Heating Oil Services
N.A.I.C.S.: 424720
John C. Loupee *(Gen Mgr)*

West Side Onestop　　　　　　　(1)
5 W Main Ave, Zeeland, MI 49464-1611
Tel.: (616) 772-9053
Sales Range: $10-24.9 Million
Emp.: 8
Groceries & Gasoline Sales
N.A.I.C.S.: 445131

J&H TRANSPORTATION INC.
1534 N Main St, Andover, KS 67002
Tel.: (316) 733-8200
Web Site: http://www.jhtrucking.com
Sales Range: $10-24.9 Million
Emp.: 30
Truck Transportation Brokers
N.A.I.C.S.: 488510
Scott Sanchez *(CFO)*

J&J AG PRODUCTS, INC.
1813 Davidson Rd, Clewiston, FL 33440
Tel.: (863) 983-2900　　　FL
Web Site:
　http://www.jjagproducts.com
Year Founded: 1994
Sales Range: $10-24.9 Million
Emp.: 60
Farming Services
N.A.I.C.S.: 111219
Alva Mickler *(Pres)*
Elena Mickler *(Sec)*

J&J CARDS INC.
1212 S Air Depot Blvd Ste 27, Oklahoma City, OK 73110
Tel.: (405) 733-9480
Year Founded: 1972
Sales Range: $10-24.9 Million
Emp.: 5
Gift Shop
N.A.I.C.S.: 459420
Jay Lynn Orr *(Pres)*

J&J DISTRIBUTING COMPANY
2721 E Sharon Rd, Cincinnati, OH 45241
Tel.: (513) 326-1120
Web Site: http://www.watsons.com
Sales Range: $10-24.9 Million
Emp.: 125
Swimming Pools, Above Ground
N.A.I.C.S.: 459999
Erik Mueller *(Pres & CEO)*

J&J FOODS INC.
1075 Jesse Jewell Pkwy SW, Gainesville, GA 30501
Tel.: (770) 536-6848
Web Site: http://www.jandjfoods.com
Sales Range: $25-49.9 Million
Emp.: 170
Grocery Stores, Independent
N.A.I.C.S.: 445110
Darrell Wiley *(Owner)*
Keddy Bolles *(Mgr-HR)*

J&J FURNITURE INCORPORATED
10 Walnut St, Middletown, MD 21769-8019
Tel.: (301) 473-9842
Web Site:
　http://www.gladhillfurniture.com
Rev.: $13,250,000
Emp.: 36
Furniture Retailer
N.A.I.C.S.: 449110

J&J STAFFING RESOURCES INC.

1814 Marlton Pike E, Cherry Hill, NJ 08003
Tel.: (856) 424-0199
Web Site: http://www.jjstaff.com
Sales Range: $25-49.9 Million
Emp.: 11
Temporary Help Service
N.A.I.C.S.: 561320
Jack E. Malady *(Founder & Pres)*

J&K NOVELTY, INC.
6581 43rd St Ste 1510, Pinellas Park, FL 33781-5949
Tel.: (727) 527-1816
Web Site: http://www.jknovelty.com
Year Founded: 1978
Sales Range: $1-9.9 Million
Emp.: 12
Miscellaneous Product Mfr
N.A.I.C.S.: 339999
Richard Renaud *(CFO & VP)*
Judy Renaud *(Pres)*

J&K PLUMBING AND HEATING CO.
24 Thorp St, Binghamton, NY 13905
Tel.: (607) 772-1666
Sales Range: $10-24.9 Million
Emp.: 50
Mechanical Contractor
N.A.I.C.S.: 238220
Allyn Jones *(Pres)*
Mark Larson *(VP-Fin)*

J&L BUILDING MATERIALS INC.
600 Lancaster Ave, Frazer, PA 19355-1810
Tel.: (610) 644-6311　　　PA
Web Site: http://www.jlbuilding.com
Year Founded: 1961
Sales Range: $10-24.9 Million
Emp.: 100
Building Material Supplier
N.A.I.C.S.: 423330
Robert Stewart *(Gen Mgr)*
David Feeley *(VP)*
Sue Nichols *(Mgr-Payroll)*
Jim Savant *(Mgr)*
Bill Sniegowski *(Mgr-Kitchen Div)*
Lester Stafford *(Branch Mgr-Ops)*
Rob Tyre *(Mgr-Warehouse)*

Subsidiaries:

Contractors Choice Equipment Rental Inc.　　　　　　　(1)
600 Lancaster Ave, Malvern, PA 19355-1810
Tel.: (610) 408-0195
Sales Range: $10-24.9 Million
Emp.: 5
Provider Of Equipment Rental & Leasing Services
N.A.I.C.S.: 532490

J&L Building Materials Of Delaware Inc.　　　　　　　(1)
59 Lukens Dr, New Castle, DE 19720　　　　　　　(100%)
Tel.: (302) 504-0350
Web Site: http://www.jlbuilding.com
Rev.: $4,200,000
Emp.: 16
Supplier of Building Materials
N.A.I.C.S.: 423330

J&L METROLOGY, INC.
280 Clinton St, Springfield, VT 05156
Tel.: (802) 885-7100
Web Site: http://www.jlmetrology.com
Optical Comparators
N.A.I.C.S.: 333310

J&M ADVERTISING & PRODUCTIONS
16122 Sherman Way, Van Nuys, CA 91406
Tel.: (818) 787-2170

Web Site: http://www.jmadv.com
Sales Range: $10-24.9 Million
Emp.: 20
Advetising Agency
N.A.I.C.S.: 541810
Sam Johnson *(Co-Founder & Co-Owner)*
Kevin Murphy *(Co-Founder & Co-Owner)*
Brian Hoffmann *(Designer)*
Russ Davis *(Head-Motion Graphics Animator)*

J&M ADVERTISING LLC
13618 W Hillsborough Ave, Tampa, FL 33635
Tel.: (727) 451-6510
Web Site:
　http://www.jmadvertising.com
Year Founded: 2008
Sales Range: $1-9.9 Million
Emp.: 5
Advetising Agency
N.A.I.C.S.: 541810
John P. Harp *(Pres)*

J&M DISTRIBUTING COMPANY, INC.
2500 N America Dr, West Seneca, NY 14224
Tel.: (716) 827-1133
Rev.: $60,300,000
Emp.: 200
Beer & Other Fermented Malt Liquors
N.A.I.C.S.: 424810
Peter I. Certo *(Pres)*
Mike Schott *(Acct Mgr-Chain)*
Randy Walker *(Supvr-Warehouse)*
Dennis Hartman *(COO & Gen Mgr)*
Robert Brooks *(CFO)*

J&M INDUSTRIES INC.
300 Ponchatoula Pkwy, Ponchatoula, LA 70454
Tel.: (985) 386-6000
Web Site: http://www.jm-ind.com
Sales Range: $10-24.9 Million
Emp.: 150
Textile Bags
N.A.I.C.S.: 314910
Maurice Gaudet III *(CEO)*

J&M MOBILE HOMES INC.
3418 Hwy 65 S, Pine Bluff, AR 71601
Tel.: (870) 535-1524
Web Site:
　http://www.jmhomespinebluff.com
Sales Range: $10-24.9 Million
Emp.: 4
Mobile Home Dealers
N.A.I.C.S.: 459930

J&M TANK LINES INC.
100 US Hwy 19 N, Americus, GA 31709-3443
Tel.: (229) 924-3663　　　GA
Web Site: http://www.jmtank.com
Year Founded: 1948
Provider of Trucking Services
N.A.I.C.S.: 484121
Peter Summerford *(Pres)*
Kyle Gailey *(VP-Ops)*
Chris Horner *(CFO)*
Billy Lollar *(VP-Maintenance)*
Dave Edmondson *(VP-Safety)*
Eric Hanson *(VP-HR Dev)*
Sherri Hill *(Mgr-HR)*
Keith Wisener *(Dir-Training & Orientation)*
Harold Summerford Jr. *(CEO)*

J&P FLASH INC.
304 e broadway, West Memphis, AR 72301
Tel.: (870) 735-3744

Web Site:
http://www.jandpflashmarket.com
Rev.: $40,630,810
Emp.: 14
Convenience Stores, Independent
N.A.I.C.S.: 445131
Dwayne Jones *(VP)*
Oscar Patterson *(Pres)*

J&P HOLDINGS, LLC
1900 Fand Road Ride, Chubbuck, ID
83202
Tel.: (208) 232-1062   ID
Web Site:
http://www.pocatellonissankia.com
Year Founded: 2010
Sales Range: $10-24.9 Million
New & Used Car Dealer
N.A.I.C.S.: 441110
Chris Russell *(Owner)*

**J&R FILM & MOVIOLA DIGI-
TAL CO.**
1135 N Mansfield Ave, Los Angeles,
CA 90038
Tel.: (323) 467-3107   CA
Web Site: http://www.moviola.com
Year Founded: 1963
Sales Range: $75-99.9 Million
Emp.: 50
Sales of Motion Picture Film Editing
Equipment & Supplies
N.A.I.C.S.: 449210
Michael Mostin *(VP-Rentals)*
Randy Paskal *(Mng Dir)*

J&R MUSIC WORLD
23 Park Row, New York, NY 10038-
2302
Tel.: (212) 732-8600
Web Site: http://www.jr.com
Sales Range: $100-124.9 Million
Emp.: 100
Music Stores
N.A.I.C.S.: 449210
Joe Friedman *(VP)*
Rachelle Friedman *(Pres)*
Pinny Safier *(Controller-AP)*

**J&R SCHUGEL TRUCKING
INC.**
2026 N Broadway St, New Ulm, MN
56073
Tel.: (507) 359-2037
Web Site: http://www.jrschugel.com
Rev.: $65,500,000
Emp.: 185
Trucking Except Local
N.A.I.C.S.: 484121
Rick Schugel *(Pres)*
Leah Shaver *(Dir-HR)*
Jeff Boettger *(Mgr-Fleet)*

J&S CAFETERIA INC.
110 Westover Dr, High Point, NC
27265
Tel.: (336) 884-0404
Web Site:
http://www.jandscafeteria.com
Sales Range: $10-24.9 Million
Emp.: 550
Cafeterias
N.A.I.C.S.: 722514
F. B. Nowlan *(Pres & CEO)*
Ana Ward *(Mgr-High Point)*
Lloyd Gaines *(Mgr-High Point)*
Robert Procter *(Mgr-Hickory)*
Ian Paul *(Mgr-Asheville)*
David Yontz *(Mgr-Fletcher)*
Gordon Norman *(Mgr-Fletcher)*
Colleen McCurry *(Mgr-Enka)*

**J&S CONSTRUCTION COM-
PANY INC**
1843 Foreman Dr, Cookeville, TN
38501

Tel.: (931) 528-7475
Web Site:
http://www.jsconstruction.com
Sales Range: $10-24.9 Million
Emp.: 100
Industrial Building Construction
N.A.I.C.S.: 236210
Johnny Stites *(CEO)*
Jennifer Guerrero *(Dir-HR)*

J&S MASONRY INC.
201 Sydney Ave N, North Bend, WA
98045
Tel.: (425) 888-0200
Web Site:
http://www.jandsmasonry.com
Rev.: $11,618,214
Emp.: 100
Masonry & Other Stonework
N.A.I.C.S.: 238140
Shayne Jackson *(Pres)*

J&T COINS, LLC
169 E Wisconsin Ave Ste E, Ocono-
mowoc, WI 53066
Tel.: (262) 354-3020
Year Founded: 2001
Sales Range: Less than $1 Million
Emp.: 2
Jewelry, Watch, Precious Stone &
Precious Metal Merchant Whslr
N.A.I.C.S.: 423940
Jim Orcholski *(Owner)*

J&T ENTERPRISES INC.
21 Ctr St, Weston, MA 02493
Tel.: (781) 894-0546
Web Site:
http://www.omnifoodssupermar
kets.com
Sales Range: $10-24.9 Million
Emp.: 90
Owner & Operator of Supermarkets
N.A.I.C.S.: 445110
Laura Conrad *(Office Mgr)*

J&W INC.
2406 Denny Ave, Pascagoula, MS
39567
Tel.: (228) 769-9608
Rev.: $13,800,000
Emp.: 4
Tobacco & Tobacco Products Mfr
N.A.I.C.S.: 459991

J-AD GRAPHICS INC.
1351 N M 43 Hwy, Hastings, MI
49058
Tel.: (269) 945-9554
Web Site: http://www.j-
adgraphics.com
Sales Range: $10-24.9 Million
Emp.: 85
Guides: Publishing & Printing
N.A.I.C.S.: 513199
Fred Jacobs *(VP)*

J-K CHEVROLET, INC.
1800 Hwy 69 N, Nederland, TX
77627
Tel.: (409) 722-0443
Web Site: http://www.jkchevrolet.com
Sales Range: $10-24.9 Million
Emp.: 89
Car Whslr
N.A.I.C.S.: 441110
Robert Turner *(Mgr-Fixed Ops)*
Daylyn Turner *(Mgr-Sls)*
Lee Dean *(Mgr-Sls)*

J-U CARTER, INC.
555 N El Camino Rel St A 462, San
Clemente, CA 92672
Tel.: (949) 852-5960
Web Site: http://www.j-u.com
Year Founded: 1991
Sales Range: Less than $1 Million

Emp.: 12
Advetising Agency
N.A.I.C.S.: 541810
Marianne Biedermann *(Dir-Media)*
Donna Carter *(Pres)*

J-W ENERGY COMPANY
15505 Wright Brothers Dr, Addison,
TX 75001
Tel.: (972) 233-8191
Web Site: http://www.jwenergy.com
Year Founded: 1960
Sales Range: $25-49.9 Million
Emp.: 700
Natural Gas Extraction Services
N.A.I.C.S.: 211130
Lindon H. Leners *(VP-Fin)*
Don G. Bizzell *(VP)*
Paul N. Stephenson *(VP-Mfg)*
David A. Miller *(Pres)*
Howard G. Westerman *(CEO)*

**J. A. MOSS CONSTRUCTION
CO. INC.**
1682 Hwy 49 S, Florence, MS 39073
Tel.: (601) 939-4141
Web Site:
http://www.jamossconstruction.com
Sales Range: $10-24.9 Million
Emp.: 30
Commercial & Office Building Con-
tractors
N.A.I.C.S.: 236220
Jim Moss *(Owner & Pres)*

**J. A. PETERSON ENTER-
PRISES**
10000 W 75th St Ste 100, Shawnee
Mission, KS 66204
Tel.: (913) 384-3800
Rev.: $51,239,719
Emp.: 200
Apartment Building Operator
N.A.I.C.S.: 531110
Gordon J. Peterson *(CEO)*
Ken Riedman *(Pres)*
Joyce Bournonville *(Office Mgr)*
Roger Siegrist Sr. *(Controller)*

**J. ARTHUR TRUDEAU MEMO-
RIAL CENTER**
3445 Post Rd, Warwick, RI 02886
Tel.: (401) 739-2700   RI
Web Site:
http://www.trudeaucenter.org
Year Founded: 1964
Sales Range: $25-49.9 Million
Emp.: 1,251
Disabled Child Care Services
N.A.I.C.S.: 624110
Judith A. Sullivan *(Pres & CEO)*
Jacqueline Ferreira *(Dir-Crayons)*
Roberta Ryan *(Dir-HBCS)*
Robert Burgess *(Dir-Facilities)*
William Bryan *(Co-Chm)*
Gloria Fairbanks *(Co-Chm)*
David Feeney *(Treas)*

J. BREED CLOTHING INC.
35 Pinelawn Rd Ste 212 E, Melville,
NY 11747
Tel.: (631) 694-9888
Rev.: $50,000,000
Emp.: 50
Sportswear, Women & Children's
N.A.I.C.S.: 424350
Kenneth Fang *(Chm)*

J. BRENLIN DESIGN, INC.
2054 Tandem Way, Norco, CA 92860
Tel.: (951) 549-1515   CA
Web Site:
http://www.jbrenlindesign.com
Year Founded: 1985
Sales Range: $1-9.9 Million
Emp.: 9

Advetising Agency
N.A.I.C.S.: 541810
Jane Brenlin *(Pres & Partner)*
Karyne Cooper *(Bus Mgr)*
Rick Haan *(Partner & VP)*

J. C. LEWIS FORD, LLC.
9505 Abercorn St, Savannah, GA
31406
Tel.: (912) 925-0234
Web Site: http://www.jclewisford.com
Year Founded: 1912
Sales Range: $25-49.9 Million
Emp.: 135
Car Whslr
N.A.I.C.S.: 441110
Walter Lewis *(VP)*
Mike Offer *(Gen Mgr)*

**J. CALNAN & ASSOCIATES,
INC.**
3 Battery March Park, Quincy, MA
02169
Tel.: (617) 801-0200
Web Site: http://www.jcalnan.com
Sales Range: $75-99.9 Million
Emp.: 60
Construction Management Services
N.A.I.C.S.: 236220
Jay Calnan *(CEO)*
Timothy Kelly *(CFO)*
Michael Crowther *(COO & Partner)*
Jim Cahill *(Pres & Partner)*
Karen Van Riper *(Dir-Acctg & Sr
Mgmt)*
Maureen Rystrom *(VP-Mktg)*
Mike Garrity *(Dir-Estimating)*
Michael Wilson *(Dir-Strategic Dev)*
Steve Robak *(Partner & Exec VP)*
Scott Trull *(VP)*

**J. CARL H. BANCORPORA-
TION**
122 Main St, Earling, IA 51530
Tel.: (712) 747-2000   IA
Web Site: http://www.ftnsbank.net
Year Founded: 1985
Sales Range: $1-9.9 Million
Bank Holding Company
N.A.I.C.S.: 551111
Todd M. Langenfeld *(Pres & CEO)*

Subsidiaries:

Farmers Trust & Savings Bank   (1)
122 Main St, Earling, IA 51530
Tel.: (712) 747-2000
Web Site: http://www.ftnsbank.net
Savings Bank
N.A.I.C.S.: 522180
Todd M. Langenfeld *(Pres & CEO)*

J. CINCO, INC.
1113 E Sarah Dewitt Dr, Gonzales,
TX 78629-3311
Tel.: (830) 672-9574
Web Site:
http://www.johnsonoilcompany.com
Year Founded: 1958
Sales Range: $10-24.9 Million
Emp.: 70
Gasoline Service Stations
N.A.I.C.S.: 424720
Jan Johnson *(VP)*

J. D. MELLBERG FINANCIAL
3067 W Ina Rd, Tucson, AZ 85741
Tel.: (520) 731-9000
Web Site: http://www.jdmellberg.com
Year Founded: 2004
Sales Range: $1-9.9 Million
Emp.: 28
Wealth Preservation Portfolios & Es-
tate Planning
N.A.I.C.S.: 523999
Joshua Mellberg *(Founder)*
Meetwith Josh *(Owner)*
Myrna Peterson *(Mgr-Fin)*

J. F. Johnson, Inc.—(Continued)

J. F. JOHNSON, INC.
225 Summerland Ave, Batesburg, SC
29006-1348
Tel.: (803) 532-6341
Web Site:
   http://www.jfjohnsoninc.com
Year Founded: 1947
Sales Range: $10-24.9 Million
Emp.: 32
Tobacco Products Whslr
N.A.I.C.S.: 424940
James F. Johnson (Pres)
Laurie Johnson Boozer (Dir-Pur)
Tony Martin (Mgr-Ops-Warehouse)
Jamie Johnson (Dir-Sls)

**J. FLETCHER CREAMER &
SON INC.**
101 E Broadway, Hackensack, NJ
07601-6851
Tel.: (201) 488-9800
Web Site: http://www.jfcson.com
Year Founded: 1923
Sales Range: $250-299.9 Million
Emp.: 1,164
Highway & Street Construction & Wa-
ter Main Rehabilitation Services
N.A.I.C.S.: 237310
J. Fletcher Creamer Jr. (CEO)

Subsidiaries:

J. Fletcher Creamer & Son, Inc.   (1)
1701 E Linden Ave, Linden, NJ
07036   (100%)
Tel.: (908) 925-3200
Web Site: http://www.jfcson.com
Contractors & Construction Projects
N.A.I.C.S.: 238190
J. Fletcher Creamer Jr. (CEO)

J. Fletcher Creamer & Son, Inc.   (1)
1219 Mays Landing Rd, Folsom, NJ
08037   (100%)
Tel.: (609) 561-2403
Web Site: http://www.jfcson.com
Emp.: 100
Contractors & Construction Management
Services
N.A.I.C.S.: 236220
J. Fletcher Creamer Jr. (CEO)

J. Fletcher Creamer & Son, Inc.   (1)
6720 Ammendale Rd, Beltsville, MD
20705   (100%)
Tel.: (301) 931-7400
Web Site: http://www.jfcson.com
Emp.: 200
Construction & Contractor Project Services
N.A.I.C.S.: 236220
J. Fletcher Creamer Jr. (CEO)

**J. G. TOWNSEND, JR. & COM-
PANY**
316 N Race St, Georgetown, DE
19947
Tel.: (302) 856-2525
Year Founded: 1987
Sales Range: $1-9.9 Million
Emp.: 15
Convenience Foods Mfr
N.A.I.C.S.: 311991
Paul G. Townsend (Pres)

**J. GIBSON MCILVAIN COM-
PANY**
10701 Philadelphia Rd, White Marsh,
MD 21162-1715
Tel.: (410) 335-9600
Web Site: http://www.mcilvain.com
Year Founded: 1798
Sales Range: $25-49.9 Million
Emp.: 75
Whslr of Lumber & Millwork
N.A.I.C.S.: 423310
Scott McAllister (VP & Controller)

J. HELLMAN PRODUCE, INC.

734 S Alameda St, Los Angeles, CA
90021
Tel.: (213) 627-1093
Web Site:
   http://www.jhellmanproduce.com
Year Founded: 1956
Sales Range: $75-99.9 Million
Emp.: 51
Fresh Vegetable Distr
N.A.I.C.S.: 424480

Subsidiaries:

J. Hellman Frozen, Inc.   (1)
1601 E Olympic Blvd Ste 200, Los Angeles,
CA 90021-1941
Tel.: (213) 243-9105
Wholesale Distributor of Frozen Fruits
N.A.I.C.S.: 424420

J. HILBURN
2601 W Mockingbird Ln, Dallas, TX
75235
Tel.: (214) 631-2601
Web Site: http://www.jhilburn.com
Year Founded: 2007
Sales Range: $10-24.9 Million
Emp.: 42
Luxury Men's Clothing
N.A.I.C.S.: 458110
Jennifer Birdwell (Founder)
Jill Kennedy (Founder)
Kim Barnes (Founder)
Michelle Williams (Sr Partner)
Monica Taylor (Sr Partner)

J. HUNTER ADVERTISING INC.
1111 Broadhollow Rd Ste 211,
Farmingdale, NY 11735
Tel.: (631) 777-3331
Year Founded: 1992
Sales Range: Less than $1 Million
Emp.: 5
Automotive, Legal Services, Real Es-
tate, Recruitment, Retail
N.A.I.C.S.: 541810
Jeffrey H. Slatkin (Founder & Pres)
Helen Bruntrop (VP)
Melody Rozsa (Sr Dir-Art)

J. JOSEPHSON, INC.
35 Horizon Blvd, South Hackensack,
NJ 07606-1804
Tel.: (201) 440-7000
Web Site: http://www.jjosephson.com
Sales Range: $100-124.9 Million
Emp.: 150
Mfr of Vinyl Wall Coverings
N.A.I.C.S.: 322220
Mark Goodman (Pres)
Gilbert Goodman (CEO)
Christina Bosco (Controller)

J. KNIPPER & COMPANY, INC.
1 Healthcare Way, Lakewood, NJ
08701
Tel.: (732) 905-7878
Web Site: http://www.knipper.com
Year Founded: 1986
Healthcare Marketing Solution Ser-
vices
N.A.I.C.S.: 541613
Jim Knipper (Founder)
Michael J. Laferrera (Pres & CEO)
Linda Hatt (Gen Counsel & Sr VP)
David Merkel (Sr VP-Bus Solutions)
Joe Schmadel (Chief Data Officer)
Eric Johnson (Chief Comml Growth
Officer)
Chris Dillon (Gen Mgr-3PL)
Adrian Drew (Gen Mgr-Mktg Solu-
tions & Sample Mgmt)
James Caruso (CFO)

Subsidiaries:

J. Knipper & Company, Inc.-
Somerset   (1)
270 Davidson Ave, Somerset, NJ 08873

Tel.: (732) 356-7200
Web Site: http://www.knipper.com
Sales Range: $25-49.9 Million
Emp.: 125
Management Consulting Services
N.A.I.C.S.: 541613
Jim Knipper (Founder & CEO)

**J. KOKOLAKIS CONTRACT-
ING, INC.**
202 E Center St, Tarpon Springs, FL
34689
Tel.: (727) 942-2211
Web Site: http://www.jkokolakis.com
Year Founded: 1972
Sales Range: $100-124.9 Million
Emp.: 112
Construction Services
N.A.I.C.S.: 236220
Nick Leo (Exec VP)
Joseph J. Kokolakis (Pres)
Roderick C. Voigt (VP)
Machell Baetens (Corp Treas)
Kathy Gallagher (Dir-Admin)
J. Ted Walker (Mng Dir)
Bill Athanasoulis (VP)
Jim Cummings (Dir-Preconstruction)
Paul Schnabl (Dir-Preconstruction)
Artie Gureck Jr. (VP-Ops)

**J. LOHR WINERY CORPORA-
TION**
1000 Lenzen Ave, San Jose, CA
95126
Tel.: (408) 288-5057
Web Site: http://www.jlohr.com
Year Founded: 1974
Sales Range: $25-49.9 Million
Emp.: 195
Winery
N.A.I.C.S.: 312130
Jerome J. Lohr (Founder & Owner)
Steve Peck (VP-Winemaking)
Ian Herdman (VP-Production)
Steve Lohr (Pres & CEO)

J. LORBER CO. INC.
2659 Bristol Pike, Bensalem, PA
19020
Tel.: (215) 638-2300
Web Site: http://www.jlorber.com
Year Founded: 1918
Sales Range: $10-24.9 Million
Emp.: 30
Provider of Power Resources
N.A.I.C.S.: 423720
Edwin Lorber (Pres)
Steven Lorber (VP)
Martin Lorber (VP)

**J. M. MARSCHUETZ CON-
STRUCTION, CO.**
15 Truitt Dr, Eureka, MO 63025
Tel.: (636) 938-3600
Web Site:
   http://www.marschuetz.com
Sales Range: $10-24.9 Million
Emp.: 12
Highway, Street & Bridge Construc-
tion Services
N.A.I.C.S.: 237310
Dennis Marschuetz (Owner & Pres)
Michael Marschuetz (VP)
Jason Marschuetz (VP)

J. MANN INC.
85A Galli Dr, Novato, CA 94949
Tel.: (415) 883-1085
Rev.: $10,074,082
Emp.: 45
Used Merchandise Stores
N.A.I.C.S.: 459510
Lisa Cecil (Mgr-Supply)

**J. MCGARVEY CONSTRUC-
TION COMPANY, INC.**

9260 Estero Park Commons Blvd Ste
101, Estero, FL 33928
Tel.: (239) 738-7800
Web Site:
   http://www.mcgarveydevelop
   ment.com
Year Founded: 1985
Sales Range: $25-49.9 Million
Emp.: 45
New Single-Family Housing & Com-
mercial Construction
N.A.I.C.S.: 236115
John Berry (VP-Comml Field Opera-
tion)
John S. McGarvey (Founder)
Jennifer McGarvey Burch (Project
Mgr-Residential)
David E. Childers (Sr Project Mgr)
Brett Backus (Dir-Sls & Mktg)
Diana L. Regal (Mgr-HR)
Jennifer McGarvey Burch (Mgr-
Residential Project)

J. MOORE & CO. INC.
118 Naylon Ave, Livingston, NJ
07039
Tel.: (973) 992-6970
Web Site: http://www.jmoore.com
Emp.: 13
Mechanical Contractor
N.A.I.C.S.: 238220
A. Michael Candido (Pres)
Mark E. Moore (VP)
Bruce Auriemma (Project Mgr)
Patrick Butler (Mgr-Pur)
Michael Kral (Project Mgr)
Jeanne Jameson (Mgr-Acctg)
John Walako (Project Mgr)
Joe Cosentini (Mgr-Svc-Columbus)
Robert Frank (Project Mgr)

J. P. MASCARO & SONS
2650 Audubon Rd, Audubon, PA
19403
Tel.: (215) 256-1900
Web Site: http://www.jpmascaro.com
Year Founded: 1964
Sales Range: $25-49.9 Million
Emp.: 700
Provider of Refuse Systems
N.A.I.C.S.: 562211
Pasquale Mascaro (Pres)
Robert Clark (Controller)
Diana Iskoskly (Coord-Education)
Justin Gagliardi (Mgr-Transportation
& Safety)
Dennis McVeigh (Dir-Transportation)

Subsidiaries:

Great Valley Recycling Inc.   (1)
315 W 6th St, Bridgeport, PA 19405
Tel.: (610) 272-7100
Sales Range: $10-24.9 Million
Emp.: 50
Provider of Refuse Systems
N.A.I.C.S.: 562920

White Pines Corporation   (1)
515 State Rte 442, Millville, PA
17846-9708   (100%)
Tel.: (570) 458-4602
Web Site: http://www.mascarosons.com
Sales Range: $10-24.9 Million
Emp.: 15
Provider of Refuse Systems
N.A.I.C.S.: 562212
Matt Meyer (Gen Mgr)

J. PAWLEY MOTORS, INC.
6200 S 36th St, Fort Smith, AR
72908-7514
Tel.: (479) 646-7800
Web Site:
   http://www.jpawleytoyota.com
Year Founded: 1991
Sales Range: $25-49.9 Million
Emp.: 35
New Car Whslr

N.A.I.C.S.: 441110
Becky Horne *(Office Mgr)*
Ronald Pawley Sr. *(Owner)*

J. PEREZ ASSOCIATES INC.

10833 Vly View St Ste 200, Cypress, CA 90630
Tel.: (562) 801-5397
Web Site: http://www.jperez.com
Rev.: $12,100,000
Emp.: 55
Sign Installation & Maintenance
N.A.I.C.S.: 238990
Craig Hammond *(CFO)*

J. RANCK ELECTRIC INC.

1993 Gover Pkwy, Mount Pleasant, MI 48858
Tel.: (989) 775-7393
Web Site: http://www.jranck.com
Year Founded: 1986
Rev.: $39,499,527
Emp.: 100
Provider of General Electrical Contracting Services
N.A.I.C.S.: 238210
James A. Ranck *(Pres & CEO)*
Matt Warren *(CFO & Controller)*
Angie Wood *(Dir-HR)*
Adam Gohs *(Project Mgr)*

J. RAYMOND CONSTRUCTION CORPORATION

465 W Warren Ave, Longwood, FL 32750
Tel.: (407) 862-6966
Web Site: http://www.jray.com
Sales Range: $100-124.9 Million
Emp.: 50
Civil Engineering Services
N.A.I.C.S.: 237310
John R. Sofarelli *(Pres, Treas & Sec)*
Claudia Garcia *(Superintendent)*
Tom Borgia *(CFO)*
Michael Gramblin *(Mgr-Bus Dev)*

J. RECKNER ASSOCIATES INC.

1600 Manor Dr, Montgomeryville, PA 18914
Tel.: (215) 822-6220
Web Site: http://www.reckner.com
Year Founded: 1978
Sales Range: $10-24.9 Million
Emp.: 130
Provider of Market Analysis & Research Services
N.A.I.C.S.: 541910
Ryan Ritter *(Mgr-Web Programming)*
Kevin Rohm *(Sr Mgr)*
Todd Weand *(Project Mgr)*

J. REYNOLDS & CO.

369 Sansom Blvd, Saginaw, TX 76179
Tel.: (817) 306-9596
Web Site: http://www.jreynolds.com
Year Founded: 2002
Sales Range: $10-24.9 Million
Emp.: 100
Roofing Contracting Services
N.A.I.C.S.: 238160
Matthew Skipper *(Pres)*

J. ROBERT SCOTT INC.

500 N Oak St, Inglewood, CA 90302
Tel.: (310) 680-4200
Web Site: http://www.jrobertscott.com
Rev.: $34,200,000
Emp.: 125
Furniture & Woven Textiles
N.A.I.C.S.: 424310
June Lockhart-Triolo *(Dir-Art & Mgr-Mktg)*

J. ROBERTS & COMPANY

2311 Santa Barbara Blvd Ste 111, Cape Coral, FL 33991
Tel.: (239) 244-8858
Web Site: http://www.jroberts.com
Sales Range: $10-24.9 Million
Emp.: 60
Real Estate Broker
N.A.I.C.S.: 531210
Jeremy Sposato *(Owner & CEO)*

J. SOSNICK & SON INC.

258 Littlefield Ave, South San Francisco, CA 94080-6922
Tel.: (650) 952-2226
Web Site:
http://www.sosnickcandy.com
Year Founded: 1906
Sales Range: $25-49.9 Million
Emp.: 85
Groceries & Related Products
N.A.I.C.S.: 424490
Martin Sosnick *(VP)*
Jeffrey Sosnick *(Pres)*
Print Cates *(VP-Product Dev)*

J. STEPHEN SCHERER INC.

2850 Commerce Dr, Rochester Hills, MI 48309
Tel.: (248) 852-8500
Sales Range: $10-24.9 Million
Emp.: 60
Manicure Preparations
N.A.I.C.S.: 325620

J. STOKES & ASSOCIATES, INC.

1444 N Main St, Walnut Creek, CA 94596-4605
Tel.: (925) 933-1624
Web Site: http://www.jstokes.com
Year Founded: 1974
Sales Range: $25-49.9 Million
Emp.: 25
Advetising Agency
N.A.I.C.S.: 541810
James A. Stokes *(Co-Founder)*
Dan Stokes *(Co-Founder)*
Christopher Kane *(Dir-Media Svcs)*

J. STRICKLAND & COMPANY

10420 Desoto Rd, Olive Branch, MS 38654-5301
Tel.: (662) 890-2306   TN
Web Site: http://www.jstrickland.net
Year Founded: 1936
Sales Range: $75-99.9 Million
Emp.: 65
Hair & Skin Care Products & Cosmetics Mfr
N.A.I.C.S.: 325620
Donald Baldock *(Coord-Adv)*
Linda Clifton *(Pres)*
Angie Percy *(Dir-PR & Personnel)*

J. SUPOR & SON TRUCKING & RIGGING CO., INC.

433 Bergen Ave, Kearny, NJ 07032
Tel.: (201) 299-1100
Web Site: http://www.jsupor.com
Year Founded: 1960
Rev.: $10,000,000
Emp.: 150
Trucking Services
N.A.I.C.S.: 484121
Mark Dmiszewicki *(Controller)*
Joseph Supor III *(Pres)*

J. SUSSMAN, INC.

109-10 180th St, Jamaica, NY 11433
Tel.: (718) 297-0228   NY
Web Site:
http://www.jsussmaninc.com
Year Founded: 1906
Sales Range: $1-9.9 Million
Emp.: 45
Metal Window & Door Mfr

N.A.I.C.S.: 332321
David Sussman *(Pres)*
Vadim Mergold *(Project Mgr)*

Subsidiaries:

Sunbilt Solar Products by Sussman, Inc.   (1)
109-10 180th St, Jamaica, NY 11433
Tel.: (718) 297-6040
Web Site: http://www.sunbilt.com
Prefabricated Metal Building & Component Mfr
N.A.I.C.S.: 332311
Steven Sussman *(Pres)*

J. TARRAN MARKETING INC.

1104 Lincoln Ave Ste 2, San Rafael, CA 94901
Tel.: (415) 448-5608
Web Site:
http://www.manifestemarketing.com
Sales Range: $1-9.9 Million
Emp.: 6
Direct Marketing & Advertising Serives
N.A.I.C.S.: 541613
Jeff Tarran *(Pres & CEO)*
Jim Chazer *(Dir-Production)*
Ken Brooks *(VP & Gen Mgr-OC)*
Nellie Newman *(VP & Acct Dir)*

J. TECH SALES, L.L.C.

6531 Park of Commerce Blvd Ste 170, Boca Raton, FL 33487
Tel.: (561) 995-0070
Web Site: http://www.jtechsales.com
Year Founded: 1997
Sales Range: $25-49.9 Million
Emp.: 10
Specialty Chemicals Distr
N.A.I.C.S.: 424690
Jesse Tanner *(Sr Mgr-Accts)*

J. THOMAS & CO. INC.

7231 Tylersvle Rd Ste 110, Dayton, OH 45424
Tel.: (937) 235-0021
Sales Range: $10-24.9 Million
Emp.: 850
Restaurant Services
N.A.I.C.S.: 722511
Judith Thomas *(Pres)*
Ruth Grubb *(Sec)*

J. VINTON SCHAFER & SONS, INC.

1309 A Continental Dr, Abingdon, MD 21009
Tel.: (410) 335-3000
Web Site: http://www.jvschafer.com
Sales Range: $25-49.9 Million
Emp.: 50
Commercial & Office Building, New Construction
N.A.I.C.S.: 236220
Ronald E. Knowles *(Pres)*
Warren Hamilton *(Sr VP & Dir-Mktg)*
Thomas Gnau *(VP-Construction)*
Deborah German *(Controller)*
Holly Edminster *(Project Mgr)*
Michael Hogan *(VP)*
Scott Elling *(Sr Project Mgr)*

J. WASSON ENTERPRISES INC.

6821 S 220th St, Kent, WA 98032-1921
Tel.: (425) 272-0707
Year Founded: 1970
Sales Range: $10-24.9 Million
Emp.: 4
Manufacturers Representative for Home Furnishings
N.A.I.C.S.: 423210
James W. Wasson *(Pres)*

J. WRIGHT BUILDING CENTER INC.

208 S Williams St, Murphysboro, IL 62966
Tel.: (618) 687-1702
Web Site: http://www.wrightdoit.com
Sales Range: $10-24.9 Million
Emp.: 80
Lumber & Other Building Materials
N.A.I.C.S.: 423310
Jerry Wright *(Pres)*

J..A. CROSON, L.L.C.

31550 County Rd 437, Sorrento, FL 32776
Tel.: (352) 729-7100
Web Site: http://www.jacroson.com
Year Founded: 1959
Sales Range: $25-49.9 Million
Emp.: 150
Plumbing, Heating & Air-Conditioning Contracting Services
N.A.I.C.S.: 238220
James A. Croson *(Chm)*
David Croson *(CEO)*
Paul Croson *(Pres)*
Taki Spinos *(VP)*
Joseph Harvard *(CFO)*
Bobby Hedrick *(Mgr-HVAC Div)*

J.A .TUCKER COMPANY

56 N Haddon Ave, Haddonfield, NJ 08033
Tel.: (856) 317-9600
Web Site: http://www.tuckerco.com
Sales Range: $10-24.9 Million
Emp.: 130
Transportation Agents & Brokers
N.A.I.C.S.: 488510
Jim Tucker *(Pres & COO)*
Jeff Tucker *(CEO)*

J.A. FRATE TRANSPORT SERVICES, INC.

1202 S IL Rte 31, McHenry, IL 60050
Tel.: (815) 459-0839   IL
Web Site: http://www.jafrate.com
Year Founded: 1971
Sales Range: $10-24.9 Million
Emp.: 88
Local Trucking & Delivery Services
N.A.I.C.S.: 484110
R. Douglas Jennings *(Founder)*
Chris Rosinski *(Mgr-Fleet Maintenance)*
Jill Jennings Dinsmore *(Pres)*

Subsidiaries:

J.A. Logistics, Inc.   (1)
3905 W Albany St, McHenry, IL 60050   (100%)
Tel.: (815) 363-5310
Web Site: http://www.jalogistics.com
Sales Range: $10-24.9 Million
Emp.: 8
Warehousing & Intermodal Services
N.A.I.C.S.: 493110
Jill Dinsmore *(Pres)*

J.A. KOERNER & COMPANY

PO Box 1477, Evanston, IL 60204
Tel.: (847) 392-5100
Web Site: http://www.jakoerner.com
Rev.: $30,000,000
Emp.: 5
Metal Service Centers & Other Metal Merchant Whslr
N.A.I.C.S.: 423510
Christopher P. Schenk *(Sec & VP)*

J.A. MOORE & SONS INC.

20408 Silver Lake Dr Unit 1, Rehoboth Beach, DE 19971
Tel.: (302) 226-8080
Web Site:
http://www.mbmproperty.com
Sales Range: $1-9.9 Million

J.A. Moore & Sons Inc.—(Continued)
Emp.: 3
General Remodeling & Home Improvements
N.A.I.C.S.: 236118
Ronald T. Moore (Mng Partner)
Maureen White (Controller)

J.A. RIGGS TRACTOR CO.
9125 Interstate 30, Little Rock, AR 72209-3731
Tel.: (501) 570-3100 AR
Web Site: http://www.riggscat.com
Year Founded: 1928
Sales Range: $125-149.9 Million
Emp.: 460
Wholesale Construction Equipment, Engines & Parts
N.A.I.C.S.: 423810
Denny Upton (Controller)

Subsidiaries:

Riggs Rental Services Inc. (1)
9125 Interstate 30, Little Rock, AR 72209-3731 (100%)
Tel.: (501) 570-3100
Web Site: http://www.riggs-cat.com
Equipment Rental & Leasing
N.A.I.C.S.: 423810
John Riggs IV (Pres)

J.A. STREET & ASSOCIATES, INC.
245 Birch St, Blountville, TN 37617
Tel.: (423) 323-8017
Web Site: http://www.jastreet.com
Year Founded: 1985
Sales Range: $25-49.9 Million
Emp.: 100
Commercial & Institutional Building Construction Services
N.A.I.C.S.: 236220
J. A. Street (Founder)

J.A.M SHELL BUILDERS, INC.
2930 NW 17th Ter, Oakland Park, FL 33311
Tel.: (954) 893-5900
Web Site:
http://www.jamshellbuilders.com
Sales Range: $10-24.9 Million
Emp.: 200
Construction Management Services
N.A.I.C.S.: 236115
Frank Mormando III (Project Mgr)

J.B. BOSTICK COMPANY
2870 E La Cresta Ave, Anaheim, CA 92806
Tel.: (714) 238-2121
Web Site: http://www.jbbpaving.com
Year Founded: 1969
Sales Range: $10-24.9 Million
Emp.: 70
Provider of Asphalt Paving & Maintenance Services
N.A.I.C.S.: 237310
James B. Bostick (Pres)
Jerry Hamlin (VP)
Carlene Smith (Treas)

J.B. CLARK OIL COMPANY INC.
PO Box 822, Dublin, GA 31040
Tel.: (478) 272-3413
Rev.: $11,200,000
Emp.: 10
Petroleum Bulk Stations
N.A.I.C.S.: 424710
Robert B. Clark (Pres)

J.B. COXWELL CONTRACTING, INC.
6741 Lloyd Rd W, Jacksonville, FL 32254-1249
Tel.: (904) 786-1120 FL

Web Site: http://www.jbcoxwell.com
Year Founded: 1983
Sales Range: $125-149.9 Million
Emp.: 150
Grading & Paving Contractor
N.A.I.C.S.: 237110
Chip Patterson (Dir-Coxwell Disaster Svcs Div)
Garland Chick (VP)
Raymond Pace (Gen Mgr-Whitehouse Recycling Facility)

J.B. DEWAR INC.
75 Prado Rd, San Luis Obispo, CA 93401
Tel.: (805) 543-0180
Web Site: http://www.jbdewar.com
Sales Range: $10-24.9 Million
Emp.: 60
Petroleum Bulk Stations
N.A.I.C.S.: 424710
Kenneth L. Dewar (Pres)
Paul Tucker (Mgr-Sls)
Jack Dewar (Owner)

J.B. DOLLAR STRETCHER MAGAZINE
3105 Farnham Rd, Richfield, OH 44286
Tel.: (330) 659-3590 OH
Year Founded: 1985
Sales Range: $10-24.9 Million
Emp.: 150
Magazine Publisher
N.A.I.C.S.: 513120
Robert J. Minchak (Owner)
Joan Minchak (Co-Owner & Co-Publisher)
Mark Kozer (Pres-Sls)

J.B. DUNN COMPANY INC.
3230 59th Dr E Ste 103, Bradenton, FL 34203
Tel.: (941) 727-3960
Sales Range: Less than $1 Million
Emp.: 3
Marine Supplies
N.A.I.C.S.: 423860
Chris Byal (Pres & CEO)
Mike Bugeski (Mgr-Territory)
Paul Perry (Mgr-Territory)

J.B. GOODWIN REAL ESTATE CO. INC.
3933 Steck Ave Ste 110, Austin, TX 78759-8670
Tel.: (512) 502-7800 TX
Web Site: http://www.jbgoodwin.com
Year Founded: 1972
Sales Range: $10-24.9 Million
Emp.: 200
Real Estate Agents & Managers
N.A.I.C.S.: 531210
J. B. Goodwin (CEO)
Byron Schilling (Pres)
Mary Castro (Sec)
Tammy Gardner (VP)

J.B. JAMES CONSTRUCTION, LLC.
1881 Wooddale Blvd, Baton Rouge, LA 70806
Tel.: (225) 927-3131
Web Site: http://www.jbjamesllc.com
Sales Range: $50-74.9 Million
Emp.: 230
Highway & Street Construction Services
N.A.I.C.S.: 237310
Jeffrey James (Owner)

J.B. KENEHAN, LLC
W238 N1700 Rockwood Dr, Waukesha, WI 53188
Tel.: (262) 523-8400 WI
Web Site: http://www.jbkenehan.com

Year Founded: 1984
Sales Range: $10-24.9 Million
Emp.: 150
Commercial Printing
N.A.I.C.S.: 323111
Tom Majdoch (Pres)

J.B. MARTIN COMPANY
645 5th Ave Ste 400, New York, NY 10022-5062
Tel.: (212) 421-2020 DE
Web Site: http://www.jbmartin.com
Year Founded: 1893
Sales Range: $150-199.9 Million
Emp.: 400
Mfr & Distributor of Velvet Material
N.A.I.C.S.: 313210
Robert Lachow (VP & Dir-Sls & Mktg)
Yaakov Shteiyer (Dir-Res)
Jean-Francois Changeux (Dir-Sls)
Michael Benjamin (Dir-Retail Sls)

J.B. MATHEWS COMPANY
2459 Clark st, Apopka, FL 32703
Tel.: (407) 656-1289
Web Site: http://www.jbmathews.com
Sales Range: $10-24.9 Million
Emp.: 30
Window & Door (Prefabricated) Installation
N.A.I.C.S.: 238130
Paul Hunt (Mgr-Ops)

J.B. PEARL SALES & SERVICE INC.
27425 W Hwy 24, Saint Marys, KS 66536-9700
Tel.: (785) 597-9909
Web Site: http://www.jbpearl.com
Year Founded: 1961
Rev.: $10,000,000
Emp.: 29
Nursery & Garden Centers
N.A.I.C.S.: 424910
Doyle Pearl (Pres)
James B. Pearl (Chm)
Laura Pearl (Treas)
Patty Pearl (Sec)

J.B. POINDEXTER & CO., INC.
600 Travis Ste 400, Houston, TX 77002-5218
Tel.: (713) 655-9800 DE
Web Site:
http://www.jbpoindexter.com
Year Founded: 1994
Sales Range: $700-749.9 Million
Emp.: 3,348
Motor Vehicle Body Mfr
N.A.I.C.S.: 336110
John B. Poindexter (Chm & CEO)
Phil Schull (VP-Risk Mgmt)
Vicki Baum (VP & Controller)
Ranjan Bhattacharjee (VP-Continuous Improvement & Bus Sys)
Matt Marthinson (VP-Supply Chain)
Raj Menon (Sr VP-Ops)
Woodie Perkins (VP-IT)

Subsidiaries:

EFP Corporation (1)
223 Middleton Run Rd, Elkhart, IN 46516
Tel.: (574) 295-4690
Web Site: http://www.efpcorp.com
Sales Range: $10-24.9 Million
Emp.: 100
Foam Products Mfr
N.A.I.C.S.: 326140

Eagle Coach Company (1)
3344 State Rte 132, Amelia, OH 45102
Tel.: (513) 797-4100
Web Site:
http://www.eaglecoachcompany.com
Sales Range: $10-24.9 Million
Emp.: 120
Funeral Vehicle Mfr
N.A.I.C.S.: 336110

Fred Wolfinger (Mgr-Sls-Eagle Brand)
Duane Toney (Mgr-Matls)
Tim Molony (Controller)
Sharry Banner (VP-HR)
Terry Campbell (Mgr-Ops)
Jerry Looney (Mgr-Sls & Mktg)
David Albers (VP-Engrg & R&D)
Jay Cook (Mgr-Production)
Nathan Mosier (Dir-Matls)
Kevin Klatte (Dir-Engrg)
Brad Smith (VP-Ops)
Tim Lautermilch Sr. (Pres)

Federal Coach Company (1)
3344 State Route 132, Amelia, OH 45102
Tel.: (513) 797-4100
Web Site: http://www.federalcoach.com
Emp.: 200
Specialty Vehicle Mfr
N.A.I.C.S.: 336110
Nathan Hurst (Mgr-Natl Sls)
Sherry Banner (Dir-HR)
Jay Cook (Mgr-Production)
Nathan Mosier (Dir-Matls)
Daniel MacCrindle (Pres & COO)

Federal Coach, LLC (1)
7400 S 28th St, Fort Smith, AR 72908
Tel.: (479) 646-6800
Web Site: http://www.federalcoach.com
Funeral Vehicle Mfr
N.A.I.C.S.: 336110

MIC Group (1)
325 Lockhaven Dr, Houston, TX 77073
Tel.: (281) 209-1177
Web Site: http://www.micgrp.com
Precision Contract Machining Services
N.A.I.C.S.: 332710

Morgan Corporation (1)
111 Morgan Way, Morgantown, PA 19543 (100%)
Tel.: (610) 286-5025
Web Site: http://www.morgancorp.com
Sales Range: $10-24.9 Million
Emp.: 100
Truck Body Mfr
N.A.I.C.S.: 336211
Norbert Markert (Pres & COO)
Elton E. Mountz (Founder)

Subsidiary (Non-US):

Commercial Babcock Inc. (2)
12 Chelsea Lane, Brampton, L6T 3V4, ON, Canada
Tel.: (905) 791-8100
Web Site:
http://www.commercialbabcock.com
Medium-Duty Truck Body Mfr
N.A.I.C.S.: 336120

Subsidiary (Domestic):

Morgan Truck Body, LLC (2)
111 Morgan Way, Morgantown, PA 19543
Tel.: (610) 286-5025
Web Site: http://www.morgancorp.com
Motor Vehicle Body Mfr
N.A.I.C.S.: 336211

Subsidiary (Non-US):

Multivans Inc. (3)
13289 Collin Dr, Bolton, L7E 3B6, ON, Canada
Tel.: (905) 857-3171
Web Site: http://www.multivans.com
Rev.: $14,644,787
Emp.: 140
Transportation Services
N.A.I.C.S.: 488999
Helen Rowley (Mgr-Warranty)
Steve Schafer (COO)
Rick Rovito (Mgr-Procurement & Facilities)
Peter Almeida (Mgr-Production)
Ray Doll (VP-Sls)
Dan Pavkov (VP-US)

Morgan Olson Corporation (1)
1801 S Nottawa St, Sturgis, MI 49091-8723
Tel.: (269) 659-0200
Web Site: http://www.morganolson.com
Sales Range: $25-49.9 Million
Emp.: 500
Commercial Walk-In Van Mfr
N.A.I.C.S.: 336211
Mike Ownbey (Pres)
Rich Tremmel (VP-Sls & Mktg)
Allan Young (Dir-Sls)

The Reading Group, LLC (1)
201 Hancock Blvd, Reading, PA 19611
Tel.: (610) 775-3301
Web Site: http://www.readingbody.com
Sales Range: $25-49.9 Million
Emp.: 450
Holding Company & Truck Body Mfr & Services
N.A.I.C.S.: 551112
Craig Bonham (VP-New Bus Dev)
Eric McNally (VP-Sls & Mktg)
Alan Farash (Pres & COO)

Subsidiary (Domestic):

General Body Manufacturing Company (2)
7110 Jensen Dr, Houston, TX 77093
Tel.: (713) 692-5177
Web Site: https://www.generalbody.com
Sales Range: $10-24.9 Million
Emp.: 95
Mfr of Vehicle Bodies
N.A.I.C.S.: 336211
Josh Paull (Pres)

Rayside Truck & Trailer Inc. (2)
2983 S Military Trl, West Palm Beach, FL 33415
Tel.: (561) 965-7950
Web Site: http://www.rayside.com
Rev.: $12,000,000
Emp.: 90
Motor Vehicle Supplies & New Parts Merchant Whslr
N.A.I.C.S.: 423120
Charles C. Rayside (Pres)

Reading Truck Body, Inc. (2)
201 Hancock Blvd, Reading, PA 19611
Tel.: (610) 775-3301
Web Site: http://www.readingbody.com
Sales Range: $25-49.9 Million
Truck Body & Related Parts & Accessory Mfr
N.A.I.C.S.: 336211
John Howley (VP-Engrg)
Ken Fpear (VP-Engrg)

Subsidiary (Domestic):

Action Fabrication & Truck Equipment, Inc. (3)
1476 L&R Industrial Blvd, Tarpon Springs, FL 34689
Tel.: (727) 572-6319
Web Site: http://www.actionfabrication.com
Rev.: $8,677,500
Emp.: 30
Motor Vehicle Body Mfr
N.A.I.C.S.: 336211
Jay Hudgens (Mgr-Sls)
Alishia Watts-Smith (Mgr-HR & Admin Ops)
Cody Carlbert (Mgr-Ops)
Ray Orban (Mgr-Pur)
Christina Ozturk (Office Mgr)
Jenny Yaman (Mgr-Receivables)
Rodney Coulton (Mgr-Shop)
Joanna Rivera (Mgr-Receivables)

Subsidiary (Domestic):

Semi Service, Inc. (2)
4285 W 1385 S, Salt Lake City, UT 84104
Tel.: (801) 521-0360
Web Site: http://www.semiservice.com
Trailer Repair
N.A.I.C.S.: 811114
Martin Seelos (Pres)
Mike Anderson (VP)

J.B. SULLIVAN INC.
425 1st St, Savanna, IL 61074-1535
Tel.: (815) 273-4511
Web Site:
http://www.sullivansfoods.net
Year Founded: 1967
Sales Range: $50-74.9 Million
Emp.: 780
Grocery Stores
N.A.I.C.S.: 445110
John B. Sullivan (CEO)
Kent Dauphin (Controller)
Tim Klein (Dir-Deli & Bakery)
Michelle Heister (Mgr-Bakery)

J.C. BILLION INC.

270 Automotive Ave, Bozeman, MT 59718
Tel.: (406) 582-7777   MT
Web Site: http://www.billiondeal.com
Year Founded: 1978
Sales Range: $10-24.9 Million
Emp.: 80
Dealer of New & Used Cars
N.A.I.C.S.: 441110
Joseph C. Billion (Pres)

J.C. CANNISTRARO, LLC.
80 Rosedale Rd, Watertown, MA 02471
Tel.: (617) 926-0092
Web Site: http://www.cannistraro.com
Year Founded: 1963
Sales Range: $25-49.9 Million
Emp.: 400
Plumbing Services
N.A.I.C.S.: 238220
John Cannistraro (Principal)

J.C. CHEEK CONTRACTORS, INC.
2087 Attala Rd 5257, Kosciusko, MS 39090
Tel.: (662) 289-1631
Web Site: http://www.jccheek.com
Year Founded: 1948
Rev.: $13,200,000
Emp.: 125
Landscape Architectural Services
N.A.I.C.S.: 541320
Hollis C. Cheek (Pres)
Randolph Cheek (VP)
Emma Ivester (Controller)

J.C. FLOWERS & CO. LLC
767 5th Ave 23rd Fl, New York, NY 10153
Tel.: (212) 404-6800   DE
Web Site: http://www.jcfco.com
Year Founded: 1998
Privater Equity Firm
N.A.I.C.S.: 523999
Eric C. Rahe (Mng Dir)
J. Christopher Flowers (CEO & Mng Dir)
Thomas Harding (Mng Dir)

Subsidiaries:

Affirmative Insurance Holdings, Inc. (1)
4450 Sojourn Dr Ste 500, Addison, TX 75001
Tel.: (800) 877-0226
Web Site: http://www.affirmative.com
Holding Company; Property & Casualty Insurance Products & Services
N.A.I.C.S.: 551112
Ursula Rentfro (VP-IT Support Svcs)
Jackie Debowski (VP-HR Ops)

Subsidiary (Domestic):

Affirmative Insurance Company (2)
PO Box 9041, Addison, TX 75001-9041
Tel.: (800) 333-5530
Sales Range: $10-24.9 Million
Emp.: 100
Auto Insurance
N.A.I.C.S.: 524210

Affirmative Premium Finance, Inc. (2)
4450 Sojourn Dr Ste 500, Addison, TX 75001
Tel.: (630) 560-7205
Web Site:
http://www.affirmativepremiumfinance.com
Insurance Brokerage Services
N.A.I.C.S.: 524210

Affirmative Property Holdings, Inc. (2)
4450 Sojourn Dr Ste 500, Addison, TX 75001-5094
Tel.: (972) 728-6300

Sales Range: $150-199.9 Million
Property Insurance Services
N.A.I.C.S.: 524126

USAgencies, LLC (2)
7163 Florida Blvd, Baton Rouge, LA 70806
Tel.: (225) 928-9000
Web Site: http://www.usagencies.com
Insurance Brokerage Services
N.A.I.C.S.: 524210

Subsidiary (Domestic):

USAgencies Casualty Insurance (3)
440 N 3 St Fl 8, Baton Rouge, LA 70802
Tel.: (225) 928-9000
Web Site: http://www.usagencies.com
Sales Range: $150-199.9 Million
Emp.: 200
Automobile Insurance
N.A.I.C.S.: 524210

Subsidiary (Domestic):

LIFCO, LLC (4)
7163 Florida Blvd, Baton Rouge, LA 70806-4549
Tel.: (225) 928-9000
Web Site: http://www.usagencies.com
Rev.: $11,428,453
Emp.: 200
Consumer Finance Companies
N.A.I.C.S.: 522291

USAgencies Management Services, Inc. (4)
7163 Florida Blvd, Baton Rouge, LA 70806
Tel.: (225) 928-9000
Web Site: http://www.usagencies.com
Rev.: $10,252,865
Emp.: 200
Management Services
N.A.I.C.S.: 541611

Crump Group, Inc. (1)
105 Eisenhower Pkwy, Roseland, NJ 07068
Tel.: (973) 461-2100
Web Site: http://www.crump.com
Sales Range: $450-499.9 Million
Emp.: 30
Holding Company; Insurance & Financial Retirement Services
N.A.I.C.S.: 551112

Hamburg Commercial Bank AG (34.96%)
Gerhart-Hauptmann Platz 50, 20095, Hamburg, Germany
Tel.: (49) 4033330
Web Site: http://www.hcob-bank.de
Rev.: $2,462,572,140
Assets: $53,430,760,320
Liabilities: $47,048,678,180
Net Worth: $6,382,082,140
Earnings: $13,438,320
Emp.: 1,482
Fiscal Year-end: 12/31/2019
Commericial Banking
N.A.I.C.S.: 522110
Stefan Ermisch (CEO & Member-Mgmt Bd)
Uwe-Jens Werner (Head-Savings Banks & Institutional Clients)
Judith Steinhoff (Head-HR)
Ralf Lowe (Head-Treasury)
Peter Axmann (Head-Real Estate-Global)
Barbara Himmel (Head-Legal & Taxes)
Oliver Waldeck (Head-Bus Origination)
Bernd Gabor (Head-Shipping-Europe & Americas)
Loukas Lagaras (Head-Shipping-Athens Branch)
Jutta Arlt (Head-Cash & Trade Svcs)
Ulrik Lackschewitz (Deputy CEO, Chief Risk Officer & Member-Mgmt Bd)
Michael Rothehuser (Head-Trade, Food, Commodities, Industry & Svcs)
Martin Jonas (Head-IR)
Franziska von Scholz (Head-Strategic Projects)
Stephan Otto (Head-Risk Mgmt)
Ian Banwell (CFO & Member-Mgmt Bd)
Nicolas Blanchard (Chief Clients & Products Officer & Member-Mgmt Bd)
Christopher Brody (Chief Investment Officer & Member-Mgmt Bd)
Thomas Jakob (Head-Corp Banking & Advisory)
Stephen Scheuer (Head-Corp Fin & Working Capital Solution)
Inka Klinger (Head-Infrastructure Project Fin-Global)

Jan-Philipp Rohr (Head-Shipping-Global)
Donald Banks (Head-Capital Markets)
Tilo Kraus (Head-Sls & Syndicate-Global)
Monika Feher (Head-Middle Office & Bus Dev)
Markus Best (Head-Transaction Banking)
Nicole Neumann (Head-Mktg & Digital Media)
Katrin Steinbacher (Head-Press)
Eileen Maschmann (Head-Corp & Securities Compliance)
Dirk von Thaden (Head-Acctg)
Jorg Reinicke (Head-Regulatory Reporting)
Henrik Stein (Head-Internal Auditing)
Svenja Neuhaus (Head-Law)
Juan Rodriguez Inciarte (Chm-Supervisory Bd)

Subsidiary (Domestic):

CAPCELLENCE Holding GmbH & Co. KG (2)
Gasstrasse 4, 22761, Hamburg, Germany
Tel.: (49) 40 30700700
Financial Management Services
N.A.I.C.S.: 551112

HSH Facility Management GmbH (2)
Rosenstr 11, Hamburg, 20095, Germany
Tel.: (49) 40 33330
Financial Management Services
N.A.I.C.S.: 551112

HSH Move+More GmbH (2)
Martensdamm 6, 24103, Kiel, Schleswig-Holstein, Germany
Tel.: (49) 43190001
Logistics Services & Consulting Services
N.A.I.C.S.: 541614

Subsidiary (US):

HSH N Financial Securities LLC (2)
230 Park Ave, New York, NY 10169
Tel.: (212) 407-6000
Financial Management Services
N.A.I.C.S.: 551112

Representative Office (Non-US):

HSH Nordbank AG (Luxembourg) (2)
2 rue Jean Monnet, L-2180, Luxembourg, Luxembourg
Tel.: (352) 424137
Web Site: http://www.hsh-nordbank.lu
Banking Services
N.A.I.C.S.: 522110

Subsidiary (Non-US):

HSH Nordbank Securities S.A. (2)
2 Rue Jean Monnet, Luxembourg, 2180, Luxembourg
Tel.: (352) 42414111
Web Site: http://www.hshn-securities.com
Sales Range: $100-124.9 Million
Emp.: 145
Private Banking Services
N.A.I.C.S.: 522320
Carsten Backer (Chm-Mgmt Bd, CFO & Chief Risk Officer)
Jan Luhrs-Behnke (Mng Dir & Head-Bus Unit)
Franz-Josef Glauben (Member-Mgmt Bd)

Subsidiary (Domestic):

Kontora Family Office GmbH (2)
Ballindamm 39, 20095, Hamburg, Germany
Tel.: (49) 4032908880
Web Site: http://www.kontora-advisory.com
Financial Management Services
N.A.I.C.S.: 551112

J.C. Flowers & Co. UK Ltd. (1)
125 Old Broad Street 24th Floor, London, EC2N 1AR, United Kingdom
Tel.: (44) 20 7710 0500
Web Site: http://www.jcfco.com
Emp.: 12
Privater Equity Firm
N.A.I.C.S.: 523999
Tim Hanford (Mng Dir)

Jefferson Capital Systems, LLC (1)
16 McLeland Rd, Saint Cloud, MN 56303
Tel.: (320) 229-8499
Web Site: http://www.jcap.com
Debt Collection & Credit Recovery Services

J.C. Flowers & Co. LLC—(Continued)

N.A.I.C.S.: 561440
David M. Burton *(Pres & CEO)*
Mark Zellmann *(Dir-Debt Collection Acq & Ops)*
Paul Dunn *(CFO)*
Matt Pfohl *(Gen Counsel & Sr VP)*
Tom Hofer *(Dir-Bankruptcy Acq & Servicing Ops)*
Joe Fejes *(Chief Compliance Officer)*
Mary Lewandowski *(Dir-HR)*

Kent Reliance Building Society   (1)
Reliance House, Sun Pier, Chatham, ME4 4ET, Kent, United Kingdom
Tel.: (44) 1634848944
Web Site: http://www.krbs.com
Sales Range: $100-124.9 Million
Emp.: 147
Financial Servicing
N.A.I.C.S.: 541611
Stephan Wilcke *(Chm)*
Andy Golding *(CEO)*

Subsidiary (Domestic):

Easioption Ltd.   (2)
Reliance House, Sun Pier, Chatham, ME4 4ET, Kent, United Kingdom
Tel.: (44) 1634835706
Sales Range: $25-49.9 Million
Emp.: 40
Management Services
N.A.I.C.S.: 551114

Subsidiary (Non-US):

EasiOption BPO Services Private Ltd.   (3)
SP Infocity SEZ Wing 4B 3rd Fl Pune Saswad Rd, Fursungi Hadapsar, Pune, 412 308, Maharashtra, India
Tel.: (91) 2040628000
Web Site: http://www.easioption.com
Business Process Outsourcing Solutions
N.A.I.C.S.: 561499

Subsidiary (Non-US):

Easiprocess Private Ltd.   (2)
Brigade Tech Park Block B Unit 134 1 Pattandur Agrahara Vlg, Whitefield Rd, Bengaluru, 560 066, Karnataka, India
Tel.: (91) 8066374701
Web Site: http://www.easiprocess.com
Sales Range: $25-49.9 Million
Emp.: 82
Business Process Outsourcing Services
N.A.I.C.S.: 518210
Irfan Khan *(Mng Dir)*

Subsidiary (Domestic):

Jersey Home Loans Limited   (2)
PO Box 387, Chatham, ME4 4WJ, Kent, United Kingdom
Tel.: (44) 1534877833
Web Site: http://www.jerseyhomeloans.com
Sales Range: $50-74.9 Million
Emp.: 4
Home Loan Mortgage Services
N.A.I.C.S.: 522310

Reliance Property Loans Limited   (2)
Reliance House Sun Pier Medway St, Chatham, ME4 4ET, Kent, United Kingdom
Tel.: (44) 1634848944
Web Site: http://www.krbs.com
Sales Range: $100-124.9 Million
Property Loan Services
N.A.I.C.S.: 522310

J.C. LEWIS PRIMARY HEALTH CARE CENTER INC.
125 Fahm St, Savannah, GA 31401-2391
Tel.: (912) 495-8887   **GA**
Web Site:
  http://www.jclewishealth.org
Year Founded: 2008
Sales Range: $1-9.9 Million
Emp.: 50
Health Care Association
N.A.I.C.S.: 813910
Rena Douse *(COO)*
Michael Adams *(Chief Medical Officer)*

LaVanda Brown *(Co-Chm)*
Jennifer Wright *(Co-Chm)*
Betty Jean Smalls *(Treas)*
Brandon J. Gaffney *(CEO)*
Gwendolyn Lowe *(CFO)*

J.C. MACELROY CO. INC.
91 Ethel Rd W, Piscataway, NJ 08854
Tel.: (732) 572-7100
Web Site: http://www.macelroy.com
Sales Range: $10-24.9 Million
Emp.: 40
Fabricated Structural Metal
N.A.I.C.S.: 332312
Scott Spota *(Pres)*
Jeff Spota *(VP)*
Marc Habel *(Project Mgr)*

J.C. MADIGAN INC.
450 Old Union Tpke, Lancaster, MA 01523
Tel.: (978) 772-2067
Web Site: http://www.jcmadigan.com
Sales Range: $25-49.9 Million
Emp.: 27
Truck Equipment & Parts
N.A.I.C.S.: 441330
Timothy Madigan *(Owner)*
Mark Staggerwood *(Controller)*
Rob Lockhart *(Mgr-Parts)*
Jessica Lazuka *(Mgr-Accts Receivables)*

J.C. NEWMAN CIGAR CO.
2701 N 16th St, Tampa, FL 33605
Tel.: (813) 248-2124   **FL**
Web Site: http://www.cigarfamily.com
Year Founded: 1953
Sales Range: $10-24.9 Million
Emp.: 208
Tobacco Product Mfr
N.A.I.C.S.: 312230
Eric Newman *(Pres)*
Scott Lewis *(Controller)*
Billie McGuirk *(Coord-Export)*
Shira Martin *(CFO)*
Terri Ryan *(Mgr-Inside Sls)*
Kara Guagliardo *(Coord-PR & Mktg)*

J.C. PALLET COMPANY, INC.
18427 New Kent Hwy, Barhamsville, VA 23011
Tel.: (757) 566-4834
Web Site: http://www.jcpallet.com
Year Founded: 1990
Pallets, Wood
N.A.I.C.S.: 321920
Larry Miller-Bopp *(Pres-Sls)*

J.C. PENNEY COMPANY, INC.
6501 Legacy Dr, Plano, TX 75024-3698
Tel.: (972) 431-1000   **DE**
Web Site: http://www.jcpenney.com
Year Founded: 2002
Rev.: $11,167,000,000
Assets: $7,989,000,000
Liabilities: $7,160,000,000
Net Worth: $829,000,000
Earnings: ($268,000,000)
Emp.: 90,000
Fiscal Year-end: 02/01/20
Holding Company; Department Stores & Catalog Sales
N.A.I.C.S.: 551112
Pam Mortensen *(Sr VP & Gen Mgr-Mdse-Fine Jewelry)*
Brynn Evanson *(Chief HR Officer & Exec VP)*
Val Harris *(Sr VP-Product Design & Dev-Apparel, Footwear & Handbags)*
Brandy L. Treadway *(Gen Counsel, Sec & Sr VP)*
Truett Horne *(Chief Transformation Officer & Sr VP)*

Michelle Wlazlo *(Chief Mdsg Officer & Exec VP)*
Mark Stinde *(Sr VP-Asset Protection)*
Jeff Useforge *(Sr VP & Gen Mgr-Mdse-Men's & Children's)*
James DePaul *(Exec VP-Stores)*
Stacey Shively *(Sr VP & Gen Mgr-Mdse-Home Div)*
Colin Dougherty *(Sr VP-Fin)*
Brooke Buchanan *(Sr VP-Comm)*
Victor Ejarque *(Sr VP-GMM, Women's Apparel, Footwear & Accessories)*
Laurene Gandolfo *(Sr VP-Product Dev, Design & Trend Home)*
Karl Walsh *(Chief Digital Officer & Sr VP)*
Laurie Wilson *(Sr VP-Pln, Allocation & Pricing)*
Stanley Shashoua *(Chm)*
Stephanie Plaines *(CFO)*
Marc Rosen *(CEO)*
John Aylward *(CMO)*
Steve Whaley *(Principal Acctg Officer, Sr VP & Controller)*
Steve Whaley *(Principal Acctg Officer, Sr VP & Controller)*

Subsidiaries:

J.C. Penney Corporation, Inc.   (1)
6501 Legacy Dr, Plano, TX 75024
Tel.: (972) 431-1000
Web Site: http://www.jcpenney.net
Sales Range: $10-24.9 Million
Departmental Store Operator
N.A.I.C.S.: 455110
Jerry Murray *(Sr VP-Fin)*

Subsidiary (Domestic):

J.C. Penney Properties, Inc.   (2)
6501 Legacy Dr, Plano, TX 75024   **(100%)**
Tel.: (972) 431-1000
Web Site: http://www.jcpenney.com
Real Estate Holding Company
N.A.I.C.S.: 531120

JCP Realty, Inc.   (2)
6501 Legacy Dr, Plano, TX 75024-3612   **(100%)**
Tel.: (972) 431-1000
Web Site: http://www.jcp.com
Emp.: 4,000
Development & Operation of Real Estate Through Participation in Joint Ventures, with Interests in about 70 Shopping Center Projects
N.A.I.C.S.: 237210

J.C. SMITH
345 Peat St, Syracuse, NY 13210
Tel.: (315) 428-9903
Web Site: http://www.jcsmithinc.com
Year Founded: 1976
Sales Range: $10-24.9 Million
Emp.: 53
Construction & Mining Machinery & Equipment Whslr
N.A.I.C.S.: 423810
Joanne S. Reed *(Co-Owner)*
Mary S. Smith *(Co-Owner)*
Jay C. Smith *(Co-Owner)*

J.C. SNAVELY & SONS INC.
150 Main St, Landisville, PA 17538
Tel.: (717) 898-2241
Web Site: http://www.jcsnavely.com
Sales Range: $25-49.9 Million
Emp.: 75
Lumber & Other Building Materials
N.A.I.C.S.: 423310
Steve Snavely *(VP-Ops)*
Rich Snavley *(VP-Admin)*
Charles B. Fessler Jr. *(Pres)*

J.C. VIRAMONTES INC.
12361 Montana Ave, El Paso, TX 79938
Tel.: (915) 857-4545

Web Site: http://www.jcv-igp.com
Rev.: $31,000,000
Emp.: 50
Garment Finishing & Processing Services
N.A.I.C.S.: 512110
Ceser Viramontes *(Pres)*

J.C. WHITNEY & CO.
111 E Wacker Dr, Chicago, IL 60601
Tel.: (312) 431-6000   **DE**
Web Site: http://www.jcwhitney.com
Year Founded: 1915
Automotive Supplies & Equipment
N.A.I.C.S.: 441330
Jerome Mascitti *(VP-Fin)*
Tom Iossi *(Mgr-Facilities)*
Jim Nelson *(Dir-Distr)*

J.CON SALON & SPA
5811 4th St N, Saint Petersburg, FL 33703
Tel.: (727) 525-9119
Web Site: http://www.jconsalon.com
Year Founded: 1978
Sales Range: $1-9.9 Million
Emp.: 70
Salon & Spa Operators
N.A.I.C.S.: 812112
Joe Connell *(Founder & Owner)*

J.D. & BILLY HINES TRUCKING, INC.
407 Hines Blvd, Prescott, AR 71857-0777
Tel.: (870) 887-6693
Web Site:
  http://www.hinestrucking.com
Year Founded: 1936
Sales Range: $10-24.9 Million
Emp.: 350
General Freight Trucking, Long-Distance & Truckload Services
N.A.I.C.S.: 484121
Bruce Olney *(Dir-Safety & Ops)*
Wayne Morrow *(Dir-Maintenance)*
Steve Brzeski *(Mgr-Svc)*
Bruce Teutsch *(Mgr-Svc)*
Danny Stewart *(Mgr-IT)*
David Jackson *(Mgr-Tire)*
Jeff McNeal *(Mgr-Dispatch)*
Laura Bradley *(Controller)*
Robert Denton *(Dir-HR)*
Vickie Hines *(Exec VP)*

J.D. DADDARIO CO. INC.
22 National Dr, Franklin, MA 02038
Tel.: (508) 528-0006   **MA**
Web Site: http://www.ferguson.com
Year Founded: 1937
Rev.: $31,808,569
Emp.: 180
Plumbing Fixtures, Equipment & Supplies
N.A.I.C.S.: 423720
John Carney *(Gen Mgr)*

J.D. DIFFENBAUGH, INC.
6865 Airport Dr, Riverside, CA 92504-1903
Tel.: (951) 351-6865   **CA**
Web Site:
  http://www.diffenbaugh.com
Year Founded: 1950
Sales Range: $75-99.9 Million
Emp.: 120
Commercial Construction Contractors
N.A.I.C.S.: 236210
Jack Hawkins *(CEO)*
Jim Whitaker *(Mgr-Facilities)*

Subsidiaries:

Inland Concrete Constructors   (1)
6869 Airport Dr Bldg 400, Riverside, CA 92504-1903   **(100%)**
Tel.: (951) 351-7770
Web Site: http://www.diffenbaugh.com

Sales Range: $10-24.9 Million
Emp.: 100
General Contractor & Concrete Services
N.A.I.C.S.: 238110

J.D. FIELDS & COMPANY INC.

15995 N Barkers Landing Rd Ste
230, Houston, TX 77079-2467
Tel.: (972) 869-3794   TX
Web Site: http://www.jdfields.com
Year Founded: 1985
Sales Range: $10-24.9 Million
Emp.: 42
Metals Service Centers & Offices
N.A.I.C.S.: 423510
Jerry D. Fields (Founder, Chm &
CEO)

Subsidiaries:

Alameda Pipe & Supply Co., Inc.   (1)
14500 S Avalon Blvd, Gardena, CA 90248
Tel.: (310) 532-7911
Web Site: http://www.alamedapipe.com
Sales Range: $1-9.9 Million
Emp.: 6
Steel Products Whslr
N.A.I.C.S.: 423510

J.D. HEISKELL & CO.

1939 Hillman St, Tulare, CA 93274-
5348
Tel.: (559) 685-6100   CA
Web Site: https://www.jdhco.com
Year Founded: 1886
Sales Range: $25-49.9 Million
Emp.: 615
Farm Supplies Merchant Wholesalers
N.A.I.C.S.: 424910
Scot Hillman (Chm)
Clark Jeary (VP-Protein Product Grp)
Aaron Reid (Sr VP)
Kimberly Brewer (Controller)
Timothy J. Regan (CFO & Exec VP)
Jefferson Hillman (Chm)

J.D. HONIGBERG INTERNA-
TIONAL, INC.

650 Dundee Rd Ste 150, Northbrook,
IL 60062-2753
Tel.: (847) 412-0200
Web Site: http://www.jdhintl.com
Sales Range: $10-24.9 Million
Emp.: 20
Hotel Equipment & Supplies
N.A.I.C.S.: 423440
Albert Elkaim (Sr VP)

J.D. MARTIN CO. INC.

1801 Royal Lane Ste 100, Dallas, TX
75229
Tel.: (972) 277-5600
Web Site: http://www.jdmartin.com
Year Founded: 1949
Emp.: 200
Electrical Fittings & Construction Ma-
terials
N.A.I.C.S.: 423610
Greg Baker (Pres)
Greg Rutch (Reg Mgr-Sls)
Cindy Page (Sls Mgr-Comml & Indus)

J.D. MURCHISON INTERESTS
INC.

7250 Dallas Pkwy Ste 1400, Plano,
TX 75024
Tel.: (972) 931-0700   TX
Web Site:
    http://www.murchisonoil.com
Year Founded: 1979
Sales Range: $25-49.9 Million
Emp.: 30
Provider of Crude Petroleum & Natu-
ral Gas
N.A.I.C.S.: 211120
J. D. Murchison (Pres)
Michael Thomann (CFO)

Subsidiaries:

Murchison Properties Inc.   (1)
1100 Mira Vista Blvd, Plano, TX 75093-
4698
Tel.: (972) 931-0700
Sales Range: $10-24.9 Million
Emp.: 15
Provider of Real Estate Services
N.A.I.C.S.: 236115
Branka Daravong (Office Mgr)

J.D. RIVET & CO., INC.

1635 Page Blvd, Springfield, MA
01104-1752
Tel.: (413) 543-5660
Web Site: http://www.rivetroofing.com
Year Founded: 1960
Sales Range: $10-24.9 Million
Emp.: 20
Roofing Installation Services
N.A.I.C.S.: 238390
James Trask (Pres)
Matthew Theberge (Project Mgr)

J.D. RUSH COMPANY INC.

5900 E Lerdo Hwy, Shafter, CA
93263-4023
Tel.: (661) 392-1900
Web Site: http://www.jdrush.com
Year Founded: 1957
Rev.: $33,700,000
Emp.: 105
Metals Service Centers & Offices
N.A.I.C.S.: 423510
Jim Warner (CEO)

Subsidiaries:

Tryad Service Corporation   (1)
5900 E Lerdo Hwy, Shafter, CA 93263
Tel.: (661) 392-1900
Web Site: http://www.jdrush.com
Sales Range: $1-9.9 Million
Industrial Supplies Whslr
N.A.I.C.S.: 423840
Danny Seely (VP)

West Coast Pipe Inspection & Main-
tenance Inc.   (1)
5900 E Lerdo Hwy, Shafter, CA 93263-
4023
Tel.: (661) 392-1900
Web Site: http://www.jdrush.com
Sales Range: $10-24.9 Million
Emp.: 40
Pipe Inspection & Maintenance
N.A.I.C.S.: 541990
Tony Curtis (VP)

Weststar Trucking Inc.   (1)
5760 E Lerdo Hwy, Shafter, CA 93263
Tel.: (661) 393-4453
Web Site: http://www.truckingweststar.com
Logistics Consulting Servies
N.A.I.C.S.: 541614
Matt Melnyk (Gen Mgr)
Jack Jennings (Mgr-Safety)

J.D. RUSSELL COMPANY

4075 N Hwy Dr, Tucson, AZ 85705
Tel.: (520) 742-6194
Web Site: http://www.jdrussellco.com
Sales Range: $10-24.9 Million
Emp.: 15
Concrete Building Products
N.A.I.C.S.: 423320
Nicholas H. Danna (Pres)

J.D. SMITH CUSTOM HOMES,
LLC

501 La Mesa Rd Ste E, Mount Pleas-
ant, SC 29464-8404
Tel.: (843) 881-8843   SC
Year Founded: 2010
Single-Family Housing
N.A.I.C.S.: 236115
James D. Smith (Owner)

J.D. STREETT & CO., INC.

144 Weldon Pkwy, Maryland Heights,
MO 63043-3102
Tel.: (314) 432-6600   MO
Web Site: http://www.jdstreett.com
Year Founded: 1884
Sales Range: $100-124.9 Million
Emp.: 225
Petroleum Products Producer & Re-
tailer
N.A.I.C.S.: 424710
Tommy Irwin (Mgr-Sls-Lube & Anti-
Freeze)
Chuck Whelehon (Mgr-Branded Sls)
William Starbuck (Gen Mgr-Gasoline
Ops)

Subsidiaries:

J.D. Streett & Co., Inc. - St. Louis
Park Plant   (1)
4055-67 Park Ave, Saint Louis, MO 63110
Tel.: (314) 771-7250
Petroleum Product Mfr & Whslr
N.A.I.C.S.: 424720

J.D. Streett & Co., Inc. - St. Louis
River Plant   (1)
1 River Rd, Saint Louis, MO 63125
Tel.: (314) 892-2958
Petroleum Product Mfr & Distr.
N.A.I.C.S.: 424720

J.E. BERKOWITZ, LP

1 Gateway Blvd, Pedricktown, NJ
08067
Tel.: (856) 456-7800   DE
Web Site: http://www.jeberkowitz.com
Year Founded: 1920
Sales Range: $100-124.9 Million
Emp.: 250
Distr & Fabricator of Flat Glass Prod-
ucts, Mirrors, Insulating & Tempered
Glass
N.A.I.C.S.: 327215
Robert Price (Dir-Sls)
Chris Frye (Project Coord-Specialty
Projects)
Diane Decembrino (Mgr-Credit)
Barry Blumenfeld (Mgr-Logistics)
Beverly Humenik (Mgr-HR)
Darrell Cherry (Mgr-Bus Dev)

Subsidiaries:

Renovate by Berkowitz LLC   (1)
1 Gateway Blvd, Pedricktown, NJ 08067
Tel.: (856) 456-7800
Glass Products Mfr
N.A.I.C.S.: 327215
Brian Larson (Mgr-Sls)

J.E. CARSTEN COMPANY

61 S Seiberling St, Akron, OH 44305
Tel.: (330) 794-9834
Sales Range: $10-24.9 Million
Emp.: 56
Cigarettes, Candy & Snacks Distr
N.A.I.C.S.: 424940
J. M. Carsten (Pres)

J.E. CHARLOTTE CONSTRUC-
TION CORP.

1500 E Venice Ave Ste 101, Venice,
FL 34292
Tel.: (941) 445-4045
Web Site: http://www.jecharlotte.com
Sales Range: $1-9.9 Million
Emp.: 5
Commercial Construction
N.A.I.C.S.: 236220
Jeff Charlotte (Pres & CEO)
Virginia Charlotte (VP)
Billie Jo VanGilder (Office Mgr)
Steven Franks (Asst Superintendent)
Thomas Whelan (Superintendent)

J.E. DUNN CONSTRUCTION
GROUP, INC.

1001 Locust St, Kansas City, MO
64106
Tel.: (816) 474-8600   MO
Web Site: https://www.jedunn.com

Year Founded: 1924
Sales Range: $1-4.9 Billion
Emp.: 4,000
Commercial & Institutional Building
Construction
N.A.I.C.S.: 236220
Stephen D. Dunn (Chm)
Casey S. Halsey (Chief Risk Officer
& Exec VP)
Beth Soukup (CFO)
Greg Nook (CMO & Exec VP)
Tom Whittaker (Chief Legal Officer &
Exec VP)
Patrick Oaks (VP)
Justin Davidson (Mgr-Mktg)
Josh McConaughey (VP & Mgr-
Comml)
Andy Elliott (Sr Superintendent)
Fred Tull (Mgr-Preconstruction Svcs)
Randall Reid (VP-Bus Dev-Tampa
Bay)
Brad Schenck (Sr VP)
John Jacobs (CIO)
Dan Kaufman (Pres-East)
Dirk Schafer (Pres-Midwest)
Amy Winterowd (Dir-Bus Dev)
Gary Morgan (Grp Mgr-Advanced
Industries Grp)
Greg Lorei (Pres-South Central)
Lesley Elwell (Chief People Officer)
Paul Neidlein (Pres-Midwest)
Rodd Merchant (Pres-West)
Dan Frazier (Sr Project Mgr-Tampa)
Drew Emerson (VP/Grp Mgr-
Nashville)
Glen Miller (Sr Mgr-Client Solutions)
Kenny Sommerkamp (Mgr-Client So-
lutions)
Mishaune Sawyer (Sr Mgr-Diversity,
Equity & Inclusion-East)
Randy Holt (VP)
Marques Lowe (Reg Dir-Safety-East
Reg)
Gordon Lansford (Pres)

Subsidiaries:

J.E. Dunn Construction Co.   (1)
800 Washington Ave N Ste 600, Minneapo-
lis, MN 55401
Tel.: (952) 830-9000
Sales Range: $25-49.9 Million
Emp.: 200
Provider of Contracting & Construction Ser-
vices
N.A.I.C.S.: 236220
Kenneth A. Styrlund (VP)

J.E. Dunn Construction Co.   (1)
424 NW 14th Ave, Portland, OR 97209
Tel.: (503) 978-0800
Web Site: http://www.jedunn-nw.com
Sales Range: $10-24.9 Million
Emp.: 120
General Contractors Non-Residential Build-
ings, Construction Management & Consult-
ing
N.A.I.C.S.: 236220
Terrence P. Dunn (Pres & CEO)
Jim Ray (VP-Preconstruction Svcs)
Matthew Braun (VP & Mgr-Ops)
Keith Knight (VP-Bus Dev)
Kyle Boehnlein (VP)

J.E. Dunn Construction Co.   (1)
10350 Richmond Ave Ste 900, Houston, TX
77042   (80%)
Tel.: (713) 521-4664
Web Site: http://www.jedunn.com
Sales Range: $25-49.9 Million
Emp.: 300
General Construction Services
N.A.I.C.S.: 236220
Juan Garza (Partner-Bus Dev & Commu-
nity)

J.E. Dunn Construction Co.   (1)
2555 Cumberland Pkwy SE, Atlanta, GA
30339
Tel.: (770) 551-8883
Web Site: http://www.jedunn.com
Sales Range: $50-74.9 Million
Emp.: 370

J.E. Dunn Construction Group, Inc.—(Continued)

General Contracting, Pre-Construction, Construction Management & Design/Build Services
N.A.I.C.S.: 236220
Tom Murray (Mgr-Scheduling-East)
Marty Laskey (Dir-Safety-East)
Jillian Levy Nahum (Mgr-Talent Acq-East)
Molly Hermreck (VP & Dir-Fin-East)

J.E. JOHNSON INC.
1550 E Virginia Dr, Midland, MI 48642
Tel.: (989) 835-6671
Web Site: http://www.jejohnson.com
Sales Range: $10-24.9 Million
Emp.: 115
Plumbing, Heating, Air-Conditioning
N.A.I.C.S.: 238220
James E. Johnson (Chm)
Cheryl Seigel (Sec)
Justin Trent (VP & Gen Mgr)

J.E. KINGHAM CONSTRUC-TION CO., INC.
312 Old Tyler Rd, Nacogdoches, TX 75961
Tel.: (936) 564-3329
Web Site: http://www.jek-net.com
Year Founded: 1895
Sales Range: $150-199.9 Million
Emp.: 45
Nonresidential Construction Services
N.A.I.C.S.: 236220
Janie Andress (Office Mgr)

J.E. ROBERT COMPANY
1650 Tysons Blvd Ste 1600, McLean, VA 22102
Tel.: (703) 714-8000
Web Site: http://www.jer.com
Rev.: $22,000,000
Emp.: 120
Real Estate & Asset Management
N.A.I.C.S.: 531210

Subsidiaries:

Longhouse Hospitality   (1)
502 S Broad St, Thomasville, GA 31792
Tel.: (404) 351-9700
Web Site:
   http://www.longhousehospitality.com
Emp.: 4
Hotels Holding Company
N.A.I.C.S.: 551112
Mike Shea (Chm & CEO)

Subsidiary (Domestic):

Park Management Group   (2)
4770 S Atlanta Rd, Smyrna, GA 30080
Tel.: (404) 350-9990
Web Site: http://www.pmghotels.com
Sales Range: $10-24.9 Million
Emp.: 45
Extended Stay & Limited Service Hotels
N.A.I.C.S.: 721110
Dan Burdakin (Pres)

Subsidiary (Domestic):

Jameson Inns, Inc.   (3)
4770 S Atlanta Rd, Smyrna, GA 30080
Tel.: (404) 350-9990
Web Site: http://www.jamesoninns.com
Economy & Mid-Scale Inns Owner, Operator & Franchisor
N.A.I.C.S.: 721191

J.E. SHEKELL INC.
424 W Tennessee St, Evansville, IN 47710
Tel.: (812) 425-9131
Web Site: http://www.shekell.com
Rev.: $16,617,725
Emp.: 105
Heat & Air Contractor; Electric; Plumbing; Refrigeration
N.A.I.C.S.: 238220
John E. Shekell (CEO)
Scott Watters (CFO)

Kevin E. Shekell (Pres)
Mark Unfried (VP & Mgr-Ops)
Jim Poag (Dir-Svcs)

J.F. AHERN CO.
855 Morris St, Fond Du Lac, WI 54935-5611
Tel.: (920) 921-9020   WI
Web Site: http://www.jfahern.com
Year Founded: 1880
Sales Range: $100-124.9 Million
Emp.: 250
Mechanical & Fire Protection Contractors
N.A.I.C.S.: 238220
John E. Ahern III (Co-Chm & Co-CEO)
Anthony J. Ahern (Pres & COO)
Robert J. Fischer (Exec VP-Ops-Milwaukee)
James R. Jarvis (Exec VP-Northern WI & Madison Reg)
Adam Wunderlin (CFO)
Jace Hierlmeier (Exec VP-Fire Protection)
Krista Ebbens (Gen Counsel, Sec & Exec VP-HR)
Tim Schneider (Exec VP-Milwaukee)
Tripp Ahern (Co-Chm & Co-CEO)

Subsidiaries:

Ahern Fire Protection   (1)
2111 N Sandra St, Appleton, WI 54911
Tel.: (920) 954-8242
Sales Range: $25-49.9 Million
Emp.: 60
Fire Protection Contractor
N.A.I.C.S.: 238220

Ahern Fire Protection   (1)
10301 S 152nd St Ste 2, Omaha, NE 68138-3867   (100%)
Tel.: (402) 894-1045
Web Site: http://www.ahernfire.com
Sales Range: $25-49.9 Million
Emp.: 1,500
Fire Protection Contractor
N.A.I.C.S.: 238220
Michael Mariam (VP)

Ahern Fire Protection   (1)
1364 Hamilton Pkwy, Itasca, IL 60143   (100%)
Tel.: (815) 633-9372
Web Site: http://www.ahernfire.com
Emp.: 15
Fire Protection Contractor
N.A.I.C.S.: 238990

Ahern Fire Protection   (1)
5555 W Pk Ave, Saint Louis, MO 63110-1852   (100%)
Tel.: (314) 535-4544
Web Site: http://www.ahernfire.com
Sales Range: $25-49.9 Million
Emp.: 25
Fire Protection Contractor
N.A.I.C.S.: 238220

Ahern Fire Protection   (1)
4247 Argosy Ct, Madison, WI 53714-3101
Tel.: (608) 216-0283
Web Site: http://www.ahern.com
Sales Range: $25-49.9 Million
Emp.: 20
Fire Protection Contractor
N.A.I.C.S.: 238220

J.F Ahern Co. - Industrial & Process Piping Division   (1)
3012 E Capital Dr Unit B, Appleton, WI 54911   (100%)
Tel.: (920) 954-8242
Web Site: http://www.jfahern.com
Sales Range: $25-49.9 Million
Emp.: 8
Fire Protection Contractor
N.A.I.C.S.: 238220

J.F. ALLEN COMPANY
US Rte 33 W, Buckhannon, WV 26201
Tel.: (304) 472-8890

Web Site: http://www.jfallenco.com
Rev.: $44,000,000
Emp.: 300
General Contractor, Highway & Street Construction
N.A.I.C.S.: 423320
Greg Hadjif (Pres)
Tony Closson (Mgr)
Jay Witt (VP)

J.F. BRENNAN CO., INC.
820 Bainbridge St, La Crosse, WI 54603
Tel.: (608) 784-7173
Web Site: http://www.jfbrennan.com
Rev.: $14,500,000
Emp.: 90
Industrial Building Construction
N.A.I.C.S.: 236210
Anthony Binsfeld (Pres)
Steven Becker (Gen Mgr-Lock & Dam & Indus Div)

J.F. JOHNSON LUMBER COMPANY
8200 Veterans Hwy, Millersville, MD 21108
Tel.: (410) 987-5200
Web Site:
   http://www.johnsonlumberco.biz
Sales Range: $10-24.9 Million
Emp.: 75
Lumber & Other Building Materials
N.A.I.C.S.: 423310
Terry Higdon (VP)
Frankie Johnson (Mgr-Store-Edgewater)
Steve Drumm (Mgr-Store-Millersville)

J.F. KIELY CONSTRUCTION CO.
700 McClellan St, Long Branch, NJ 07740
Tel.: (732) 222-4400
Web Site: http://www.jfkiely.com
Rev.: $35,000,000
Emp.: 170
Gas Main Construction
N.A.I.C.S.: 237990
Mark Schwartz (Gen Mgr)
John M. Kiely (Pres)
Robert A. Patterson (Sec & Sr VP)
Daniel I. Huber (VP)
Raymond Sexton (VP)
David J. Applegate (Sr VP-Water Resources)

J.F. LEHMAN & COMPANY, INC.
110 E 59th St 27th Fl, New York, NY 10022
Tel.: (212) 634-0100   DE
Web Site: http://www.jflpartners.com
Year Founded: 1992
Privater Equity Firm
N.A.I.C.S.: 523999
Stephen L. Brooks (Partner)
C. Alexander Harman (Partner)
George A. Sawyer (Member-Exec Bd)
Louis N. Mintz (Partner)
Thomas B. Fargo (Member-Exec Bd)
Michael V. Cuff (Member-Exec Bd)
David L. Rattner (Mng Dir-Legal & Compliance)
Glen Shor (Partner)
Thomas B. Fargo (Member-Exec Bd)
Donald Glickman (Founder & Partner)
James R. Baumgardner (Member-Exec Bd)
Michael J. Bayer (Member-Exec Bd)
Caroline R. Bibb (Member-Exec Bd)
General John F Campbell (Member-Exec Bd)
Allan Cook (Member-Exec Bd)
John D. W. Corley (Member-Exec Bd)

Thomas Michael Dyer (Member-Exec Bd)
Frederick J. Harris (Member-Exec Bd)
Stephanie Ng (Assoc Dir)
Karina Perelmuter (Dir-IR & Mktg)
Michael P. Leber (Dir-Acctg & Fin)
Dave Thomas (Mng Dir)

Subsidiaries:

Aircraft Appliances & Equipment Limited   (1)
150 East Drive, Brampton, L6T 1C1, ON, Canada
Tel.: (905) 791-1666
Web Site: http://www.aaeltd.com
Aircraft Equipment Design & Mfr
N.A.I.C.S.: 336413
Andrew Brand (Bus Unit Mgr-Marine Sls & Mktg)
Bruce Howe (Supvr-Mktg-Marine)

American Scaffold   (1)
3210 Commercial St, San Diego, CA 92113
Tel.: (619) 231-4898
Web Site: http://www.americanscaffold.com
Emp.: 300
Industrial & Maritime Scaffolding Systems & Environmental Containment Solutions
N.A.I.C.S.: 238990
Michael Olenoski (CFO)
Levi Diehl (Gen Mgr-Northwest & Hawaii)
Paul Zimmerman (Gen Mgr-Maritime)
Mick Ruis (Pres & CEO)

Atlas Air Worldwide Holdings, Inc.   (1)
2000 Westchester Ave, Purchase, NY 10577
Tel.: (914) 701-8000
Rev.: $4,549,104,000
Assets: $6,696,316,000
Liabilities: $3,631,540,000
Net Worth: $3,064,776,000
Earnings: $355,880,000
Emp.: 4,500
Fiscal Year-end: 12/31/2022
Holding Company; Airline Transportation Services
N.A.I.C.S.: 551112
Adam R. Kokas (Gen Counsel, Sec & Exec VP)
Michael T. Steen (CEO)
James A. Forbes (COO & Exec VP)
Spencer Schwartz (CFO & Exec VP)
Keith H. Mayer (Chief Acctg Officer, Sr VP & Controller)
Martin Drew (Chief Strategy & Transformation Officer)
Artem Gonopolskiy (CFO & Exec VP)
Patricia Goodwin-Peters (Sr VP-HR)
David Siegel (Chm)

Subsidiary (Domestic):

Atlas Air, Inc.   (2)
2000 Westchester Ave, Purchase, NY 10577-2543
Tel.: (914) 701-8000
Web Site: https://www.atlasair.com
Sales Range: $250-299.9 Million
Emp.: 450
Airport-to-Airport Cargo Transportation Services
N.A.I.C.S.: 481112

Polar Air Cargo Worldwide, Inc.   (2)
2000 Westchester Ave, Purchase, NY 10577   (51%)
Tel.: (914) 701-8000
Web Site: https://www.polaraircargo.com
Sales Range: $250-299.9 Million
Emp.: 500
Air Cargo Carriers Nonscheduled
N.A.I.C.S.: 481212
William J. Flynn (Pres & CEO)
Adam R. Kokas (Gen Counsel, Exec VP & Asst Sec)
Jeffrey Carlson (VP-Flight Ops)
Thomas Betenia (VP-Sales-Marketing-Americas)
Kersti Krepp (VP-Sls & Mktg-Asia-Pacific)
Sylvie Blondeel (CFO & Sr VP)
Abilash Kurien (VP-Marketing)
Carlton Llewellyn (VP-Quality-Worldwide)
Jon Olin (COO & Exec VP)
Ingrid Chariah (Sr Dir)

Drew McGee *(Sr Dir)*
Jon Olin *(COO & Exec VP)*
Ingrid Chariah *(Sr Dir)*
Drew McGee *(Sr Dir)*

Division (Domestic):

Polar Air Cargo Inc. (3)
5761 W Imperial Hwy Los Angeles International Airport, Los Angeles, CA 90045
Tel.: (310) 730-7112
Web Site: https://www.polaraircargo.com
Sales Range: $550-599.9 Million
Air Cargo Carriers Nonscheduled
N.A.I.C.S.: 481112
William J. Flynn *(Pres & CEO)*

Subsidiary (Domestic):

Worldwide Air Logistics Group, Inc. (2)
2000 Westchester Ave, Purchase, NY 10577 **(100%)**
Tel.: (914) 701-8000
Air Cargo Services
N.A.I.C.S.: 481112

CTS Engines, LLC (1)
3060 SW 2nd Ave, Fort Lauderdale, FL 33315-3310
Tel.: (954) 889-0600
Web Site: http://www.ctsengines.com
Emp.: 180
Engine Performance Restoration Services to Airlines
N.A.I.C.S.: 488190
Stephen L. Brooks *(Chm)*
Vesa Paukkeri *(CEO)*
Diane E. Cavuoto *(Sr VP-Supply Chain)*
Michael Ray *(CFO)*
Bill Kircher *(Vice Chm)*
Randy Mengel *(COO)*

CodeMettle, LLC (1)
6 Concourse Pkwy NE Ste 2500, Atlanta, GA 30328-6104
Tel.: (678) 336-8590
Web Site: http://www.codemettle.com
Custom Computer Programming Services
N.A.I.C.S.: 541511
Richard Graham *(Co-Founder & CEO)*

Corvus Airlines (1)
4700 Old International Airport Rd, Anchorage, AK 99502
Tel.: (907) 248-4422
Web Site: http://www.flyravn.com
Sales Range: $10-24.9 Million
Emp.: 100
Oil Transportation Services
N.A.I.C.S.: 481111
Bob Hajdukovich *(Pres)*
Wendy Yow *(Sr VP-HR)*
Dave Pflieger *(Pres & CEO)*
Derek Shanks *(Chief Comml Officer)*
Steve Jackson *(CFO)*
Len Sloper *(Sr VP-Airports, Cargo & Real Estate)*
George Nichols *(CIO)*
Deke Abbott *(Sr VP-Flight Ops)*
Mark Swearingin *(Sr VP-Technical Ops)*

Subsidiary (Domestic):

Peninsula Airways Inc. (2)
6100 Boeing Ave, Anchorage, AK 99502-1026
Tel.: (907) 771-2500
Web Site: http://www.penair.com
Air Transportation
N.A.I.C.S.: 481111
Scott Bloomquist *(Pres)*
Dave Hall *(COO)*
William Batman *(Dir-Flight Personnel)*
Lynette Schroeder-Einwiller *(Dir-HR)*
Nick Aderman *(Dir-Maintenance & Engrg)*
James McCormick *(Dir-Northeast US)*
Matt Macri *(Dir-Ops-Flight)*
Kristin Folmar *(Dir-Sls & Mktg)*
Al Orot *(VP-Cargo & Postal Svcs)*
Brian Whilden *(VP-Safety)*
Melissa Roberts *(VP-Sls & Mktg)*
Murphy Forner *(VP-Svcs)*

Defense Venture Group Ltd. (1)
793 Fort Mill Hwy, Fort Mill, SC 29707
Tel.: (803) 396-9600
Web Site: http://www.defenseventure.com
Armored Vehicle Mfr
N.A.I.C.S.: 336992

Subsidiary (Domestic):

Indigen Armor, Inc. (2)
793 Fort Mill Hwy, Fort Mill, SC 29707
Tel.: (803) 396-9600
Web Site: http://www.indigenarmor.com
Armored Vehicle Mfr
N.A.I.C.S.: 336992

ENTACT, LLC (1)
1 E Oakhill Dr Ste 102, Westmont, IL 60559
Tel.: (630) 986-2900
Web Site: http://www.entact.com
Emp.: 24
Environmental & Geotechnical Remediation & Construction Services
N.A.I.C.S.: 562910
Dean C. Pisani *(CEO)*

Subsidiary (Domestic):

USA Environment, L.P. (2)
10234 Lucore St, Houston, TX 77017
Tel.: (713) 425-6900
Web Site: http://www.usaenviro.com
Environmental Remediation Services
N.A.I.C.S.: 562910
Debbie Jorgensen *(Mgr-Acct)*
Tony Rose *(Dir-Project)*
Vince Barlock *(Mgr-Western)*
Sandra Larosa *(Mgr-Acct)*
Kevin Smarz *(Mgr-Northeast)*

White Lake Dock & Dredge, Inc. (2)
4927 Stariha Dr, Norton Shores, MI 49441
Tel.: (231) 894-2600
Web Site: http://www.wlddi.com
Sales Range: $1-9.9 Million
Emp.: 10
Ship Building & Repairing Services
N.A.I.C.S.: 336611
Bob Gezon *(Sr Mgr-Fin)*
Jeremy Bernhardt *(Sr Mgr-Ops)*
Devon Draper *(Sr Project Mgr)*

Global Marine Holdings Limited (1)
Ocean House 1 Winsford Way Boreham Interchange, Chelmsford, CM2 5PD, Essex, United Kingdom
Tel.: (44) 1245702000
Web Site: http://www.globalmarine.co.uk
Subsea Cable Installation & Underwater Services
N.A.I.C.S.: 237990
Mike Daniel *(Mng Dir-Global Offshore)*
Bruce Neilson-Watts *(Mng Dir-Global Marine)*
Gail Clark *(Dir-Mktg)*
Hamish Yates *(Dir-Corp Dev)*

Subsidiary (Domestic):

Global Marine Systems Limited (2)
Ocean House 1 Winsford Way Boreham Interchange, Chelmsford, CM2 5PD, Essex, United Kingdom
Tel.: (44) 1245702000
Web Site: http://www.globalmarine.co.uk
Submarine Cable Installation & Maintenance Services
N.A.I.C.S.: 237130
Dick H. Fagerstal *(Chm)*
Ian Douglas *(CEO)*
Mike Daniel *(Mng Dir-Offshore-Global)*
Bruce Neilson-Watts *(Mng Dir-Marine-Global)*
Ian Bryan *(Mng Dir-Ops)*

Subsidiary (US):

Global Marine Systems (Americas) Inc. (3)
100 Cummings Center Ste 435P, Beverly, MA 01915 **(100%)**
Tel.: (978) 922-7706
Web Site:
    http://www.globalmarinesystems.com
Sales Range: $50-74.9 Million
Installation of Submarine Fibre Optic Cables, Maintenance
N.A.I.C.S.: 331318

Heritage-Crystal Clean, Inc. (1)
2000 Ctr Dr Ste E C300, Hoffman Estates, IL 60192
Tel.: (847) 836-5670
Web Site: https://www.crystal-clean.com
Rev.: $515,334,000
Assets: $526,864,000
Liabilities: $184,808,000

Net Worth: $342,056,000
Earnings: $60,948,000
Emp.: 1,296
Fiscal Year-end: 01/01/2022
Parts Cleaning & Containerized Waste Services
N.A.I.C.S.: 562998
Brian J. Recatto *(Bd of Dirs, Executives)*
Glenn M. Shor *(Chm)*
Dennis Wolff *(Exec VP)*
Glenn Casbourne *(VP)*
Pierre Chalhoub *(VP)*
David Chameli *(Gen Counsel)*
Anita Decina *(VP)*
Chris Gordon *(VP)*
Ed Guglielmi *(VP)*
Matthew Munz *(VP)*
Mike Petkovich *(VP)*
Todd Rohde *(VP)*
Craig Rose *(CIO)*
Josh Teves *(VP)*

Subsidiary (Domestic):

Envirosafe Services Of Ohio, Inc. (2)
876 Otter Creek Rd, Oregon, OH 43616-1243
Tel.: (215) 659-2001
Web Site:
    http://www.envirosafeservices.com
Materials Recovery Facilities
N.A.I.C.S.: 562920
Doug Roberts *(Pres)*

International Petroleum Corporation of Delaware (2)
505 S Market St, Wilmington, DE 19801
Tel.: (302) 421-9306
Hazardous Waste Collection Services
N.A.I.C.S.: 562112

Mirachem, LLC (2)
4645 W McDowell Rd Unit 103, Phoenix, AZ 85035
Tel.: (602) 272-6066
Web Site: https://mirachem.com
Chemical Products Mfr
N.A.I.C.S.: 325998

Patriot Environmental Services, Inc. (2)
1900 W Anaheim St, Long Beach, CA 90813-1106
Web Site:
    http://www.patriotenvironmental.com
General Freight Trucking
N.A.I.C.S.: 484121

Subsidiary (Non-US):

Sav-Tech Solvent, Inc (2)
80 Cigas Rd, Courtice, L1E 2S9, ON, Canada
Tel.: (905) 438-7955
Web Site: https://www.sav-tech.com
Liquid Waste Collection & Disposal Services
N.A.I.C.S.: 562119

IMECO, Inc. (1)
1401 Carpenter Ave, Iron Mountain, MI 49801
Tel.: (906) 774-0202
Web Site: http://www.imeco.us
Emp.: 70
Fire Protection System Mfr
N.A.I.C.S.: 339999
Jim Laydon *(Dir-Production Svcs)*
Gary Schettler *(Pres)*
Gary Merrill *(VP)*

Inland Pipe Rehabilitation LLC (1)
1510 Klondike Rd Ste 400, Conyers, GA 30094
Tel.: (678) 374-8194
Web Site: http://www.teamipr.com
Pipe Repair & Maintenance Services
N.A.I.C.S.: 237110
Raymond Cuevas *(Dir-HR)*
Jim Baumgardner *(CEO)*
Glenn Roy *(Chm)*
Mick Fegan *(CEO)*
Patrick Maginn *(COO)*
Bob Muff *(CFO)*
Thomas Gottsegen *(Chief Legal Officer)*
James Michaud *(Exec VP-Fin)*
Fil Borroni *(Exec VP-Mktg & Sls)*
Jignesh Madhani *(Sr VP-Engrg & Technical)*
Christian Abels *(VP-Ops)*

Subsidiary (Domestic):

Inland Waters Pollution Control Inc. (2)
987 W Hurd Rd, Monroe, MI 48162 **(100%)**
Tel.: (313) 841-5800
Web Site: http://www.teaminland.com
Sales Range: $75-99.9 Million
Emp.: 70
Refuse System
N.A.I.C.S.: 562920
Alan Gordon *(Branch Mgr)*

Inliner Technologies, LLC (2)
1468 W Hospital Rd, Paoli, IN 47454
Tel.: (812) 723-0704
Web Site: http://www.inliner.com
Oil & Gas Pipeline Related Services
N.A.I.C.S.: 237120
Ken Thompson *(Mgr-Ops)*

Joseph Daiji Taylor Jr. Enterprises, LLC (2)
3523 Williams Street, Apt. A, Patterson, GA 31557-0477
Tel.: (912) 647-1377
Clay Building Material & Refractories Mfr
N.A.I.C.S.: 327120

Murphy Pipeline Contractors, LLC (2)
4700 N Pearl St, Jacksonville, FL 32206
Tel.: (904) 764-6887
Web Site: http://www.murphypipelines.com
Rev.: $8,620,700
Emp.: 12
Wood Container & Pallet Mfr
N.A.I.C.S.: 321920
Andy Mayer *(Pres)*

PM Construction (2)
131 N Richey, Pasadena, TX 77506
Tel.: (713) 921-2905
Web Site: http://www.teampr.com
Emp.: 200
Pipe Construction Services
N.A.I.C.S.: 237110
Bac Ong *(Gen Mgr)*

rePipe, Inc. (2)
7600 S Santa Fe Bldg E, Houston, TX 77061
Tel.: (713) 634-0489
Web Site: http://www.repipeinc.com
Rev.: $42,162,000
Pipeline Building & Rehabilitation Services
N.A.I.C.S.: 237110

Branch (Domestic):

rePipe-California (3)
5525 E Gibralter St, Ontario, CA 91764
Tel.: (909) 291-4050
Web Site: http://www.repipeinc.com
Pipeline Building & Rehabilitation Services
N.A.I.C.S.: 332996
Jacob Crowe *(Mgr-Bus Dev)*
Allyson Jones *(Mgr-Bus Dev)*
Collis Parrish *(Mgr-Bus Dev)*
Bob Serenko *(Mgr-Bus Dev)*

Integrated Global Services, Inc. (1)
7600 Whitepine Rd, Richmond, VA 23237
Tel.: (804) 794-1646
Web Site: http://www.integratedglobal.com
Metal Coatings Mfr
N.A.I.C.S.: 325510
Abe Evans *(Sr Mgr-Resource)*
Rich Crawford *(CEO)*
Nico Verwey *(Mng Dir)*
Takehiko Yoshikawa *(Dir)*
Michael R. Place *(Reg Mgr-Sls)*
Colin Bateman *(Mgr-Bus Dev-EMEA)*
Jeff Shelton *(VP-SCR Solutions)*
Tom Naughton *(Gen Mgr)*

Subsidiary (Domestic):

Cetek, Ltd. (2)
20600 Sheldon Rd, Brook Park, OH 44142
Tel.: (216) 362-3900
Web Site: http://www.ceteklimited.com
Ceramic Coating & Maintenance Services
N.A.I.C.S.: 325510

NorthStar Group Holdings, LLC (1)
7 Penn Plza 370 7th Ave Ste 1803, New York, NY 10001
Tel.: (212) 951-3660

J.F. Lehman & Company, Inc.—(Continued)

Web Site: http://www.northstar.com
Holding Company
N.A.I.C.S.: 551112
Subhas Khara (Pres)

Subsidiary (Domestic):

NorthStar Demolition & Remediation, LP (2)
404 N Berry St, Brea, CA 92821-3104
Tel.: (714) 672-3500
Web Site: http://www.northstar.com
Demolition & Remediation Services
N.A.I.C.S.: 562910
Scott Brady (Sr Project Mgr)
Eddie Vasquez (Project Mgr)

NorthStar Group Services, Inc. (2)
Seven Penn Plza 370 7th Ave Ste 1803,
New York, NY 10001
Tel.: (212) 951-3660
Web Site: http://www.northstar.com
Sales Range: $150-199.9 Million
Holding Company; Environmental Remediation, Deconstruction & Demolition, Nuclear Decommissioning, Emergency Response & Asset Recovery Management Services
N.A.I.C.S.: 551112
Scott E. State (CEO)
John M. Leonard (COO)
Jeffrey P. Adix (CFO & VP)
Gregory G. Dicarlo (Gen Counsel & VP)
Gary Thibodeaux (VP & Dir-Health & Safety)

Subsidiary (Domestic):

Entergy Nuclear Vermont Yankee, LLC (3)
185 Old Ferry Rd, Brattleboro, VT 05301-7002
Tel.: (802) 258-4181
Web Site: http://www.vermontyankee.com
Sales Range: $500-549.9 Million
Emp.: 600
Generator of Electricity by Nuclear Power
N.A.I.C.S.: 221113

Heneghan Wrecking & Excavating Co., Inc. (3)
1321 W Concord Pl, Chicago, IL 60642
Tel.: (773) 342-9009
Web Site:
http://www.heneghanwrecking.com
Site Preparation Contractor
N.A.I.C.S.: 238910
Greg Mlot (Project Mgr)

NorthStar Contracting Group, Inc. (3)
13320 Cambridge St, Santa Fe Springs, CA 90670
Tel.: (714) 639-7600
Web Site: http://www.northstar.com
Asbestos Removal & Encapsulation
N.A.I.C.S.: 812990
Don Earle (Mgr-Bus Dev)

NorthStar Contracting Group, Inc. (3)
4795 Quality Ct, Las Vegas, NV 89103
Tel.: (702) 220-4848
Web Site: http://www.northstar.com
Demolition, Buildings & Other Structures
N.A.I.C.S.: 238910
Mark Lory (Project Mgr)

NorthStar Demolition and Remediation, LP (3)
16421 Aldine Westfield Rd, Houston, TX 77032
Tel.: (281) 449-5911
Web Site: http://www.northstar.com
Asbestos Removal & Encapsulation
N.A.I.C.S.: 562910

Northstar Demolition & Remediation, Inc. (3)
120 Elmgrove, Rochester, NY 14624
Tel.: (585) 458-3570
Web Site: http://www.northstar.com
Environmental Remediation, Deconstruction & Demolition, Nuclear Decommissioning, Emergency Response & Asset Recovery Management Services
N.A.I.C.S.: 562910

Branch (Domestic):

NorthStar Contracting Group, Inc. (4)

621 E Wildwood Ave, Villa Park, IL 60181
Tel.: (630) 758-0202
Web Site: http://www.northstar.com
Asbestos Removal & Encapsulation
N.A.I.C.S.: 562910

NorthStar Contracting Group, Inc. (4)
2250 E Adams Ave, Philadelphia, PA 19124
Tel.: (215) 533-8890
Web Site: http://www.northstar.com
Asbestos Removal & Encapsulation
N.A.I.C.S.: 562910
Gary Bowman (Pres)

NorthStar Contracting Group, Inc. (4)
401 S 2nd St, Everett, MA 02149
Tel.: (617) 389-8880
Web Site: http://www.northstar.com
Asbestos Removal & Encapsulation
N.A.I.C.S.: 541620

NorthStar Demolition and Remediation, Inc. (4)
55 Progress Pl Unit, Jackson, NJ 08527
Tel.: (609) 371-7500
Web Site: http://www.northstar.com
Asbestos Removal & Encapsulation
N.A.I.C.S.: 562910

NorthStar Demolition and Remediation, Inc. (4)
5150 Fox St, Denver, CO 80216
Tel.: (303) 727-9205
Web Site: http://www.northstar.com
Asbestos Removal & Encapsulation
N.A.I.C.S.: 562910

NorthStar Demolition and Remediation, LP (4)
12 Oak Dr, Shawnee, OK 74801
Tel.: (405) 273-4800
Web Site: http://www.northstar.com
Decontamination Services
N.A.I.C.S.: 238990
Danny Childers (Branch Mgr)

Northstar Demolition and Remediation, LP (4)
2343 Lincoln Ave, Hayward, CA 94545
Tel.: (925) 307-1500
Web Site: http://www.northstar.com
Asbestos Removal & Encapsulation
N.A.I.C.S.: 562910

Trident Maritime Systems, LLC (1)
2011 Crystal Dr Ste 1102, Arlington, VA 22202
Tel.: (703) 236-1599
Web Site: https://tridentllc.com
Maritime Systems
N.A.I.C.S.: 713930

Subsidiary (Domestic):

Custom Alloys Corporation (2)
3 Washington Ave, High Bridge, NJ 08829-2108
Tel.: (908) 638-6200
Web Site: https://www.customalloy.us
Sales Range: $25-49.9 Million
Emp.: 170
Pipe & Pipe Fittings Mfr
N.A.I.C.S.: 332919

US Joiner, LLC (1)
Crozet Commons 5690 3 Notched Rd Ste 200, Crozet, VA 22932-3109
Tel.: (434) 220-8500
Web Site: http://www.usjoiner.com
Sales Range: $150-199.9 Million
Emp.: 500
Marine Interior Outfitting Solutions, Marine Furniture Mfr & Marine Joiner Subcontractor
N.A.I.C.S.: 336611
Jay Desai (VP-Shipyard Ops)
Joseph J. Mullen (Pres & COO)
David R. Rathburn (CEO)
David Madigan (Exec VP)
Louis V. Frank (VP-Mfg)

Subsidiary (Domestic):

Infinity Offshore Marine, LLC (2)
12775 Nimitz St, Houston, TX 77015
Tel.: (713) 330-1700
Web Site: http://www.infinitymarine.com
Marine Engineering Services
N.A.I.C.S.: 541330

JCI Metal Products, Inc. (2)
6540 Federal Blvd, Lemon Grove, CA 91945
Tel.: (619) 229-8206
Web Site: http://www.jcimetalproducts.com
Sales Range: $1-9.9 Million
Emp.: 57
Fabricated Structural Metal
N.A.I.C.S.: 332312

Robichaux Automation & Control, Inc. (2)
2840 Lausat St, Metairie, LA 70001
Tel.: (504) 834-1167
Web Site: http://www.tridentllc.com
Sales Range: $1-9.9 Million
Emp.: 30
Other Communications Equipment Mfr
N.A.I.C.S.: 334290
Dennis Robichaux (VP)
Trudy B. Robichaux (Pres)

Unit (Domestic):

USA Environmental, Inc. (3)
1024 Luoma St, Holiday, FL 34690
Tel.: (813) 349-3050

US Joiner LLC - Gulf Coast (2)
4007 Shortcut Rd, Pascagoula, MS 39581
Tel.: (228) 407-1200
Web Site: http://www.usjoiner.com
Emp.: 70
Marine Interior Outfitting Solutions, Marine Furniture Mfr & Marine Joiner Subcontractor
N.A.I.C.S.: 336611
Mike Miller (VP-Sls)

Waste Control Specialists LLC (1)
17101 Preston Rd Ste 115, Dallas, TX 75248
Tel.: (682) 503-0030
Web Site: http://www.wcstexas.com
Hazardous Waste Collection & Disposal Services
N.A.I.C.S.: 562211
Elicia Sanchez (Sr VP-Key Initiatives & Comm)
Dan Burns (Sr VP-Plng & Bus Dev)
Jay Britten (VP & Gen Mgr)
Ryan Williams (VP-Integration & Comm Svcs)
Scott State (CEO & Chief Nuclear Officer)
David Carlson (Pres & COO)
Jeff Adix (CFO)

J.F. LOMMA INC.
48 3rd St, Kearny, NJ 07032
Tel.: (973) 589-2000
Web Site: http://www.excursion-powered.com
Sales Range: $10-24.9 Million
Emp.: 81
Heavy Machinery Transport
N.A.I.C.S.: 484230
Phil Mascoll (Controller)
Andrew Durkin (Mgr-Dispatch)
April Majewski (Supvr-Billing)

J.F. MILLS/WORLDWIDE
6106 E Yale Ave, Denver, CO 80222
Tel.: (303) 639-6186
Web Site:
http://www.jfmillsworldwide.com
Year Founded: 1995
Sales Range: Less than $1 Million
Emp.: 7
Business & Communications Management
N.A.I.C.S.: 541820
James F. Mills (Principal)

J.F. MONTALVO CASH & CARRY INC.
Amelia Industrial Park Amelia St 46,
Guaynabo, PR 00968-8003
Tel.: (787) 781-2962   PR
Year Founded: 1968
Sales Range: $25-49.9 Million
Emp.: 846
Groceries, General Line
N.A.I.C.S.: 424410
Hector Diaz (Dir-Pur)

J.F. SHEA CO., INC.

655 Brea Canyon Rd, Walnut, CA 91789
Tel.: (909) 594-9500   CA
Web Site: http://www.jfshea.com
Year Founded: 1881
Sales Range: $1-4.9 Billion
Emp.: 3,299
Holding Company for Private Construction Services
N.A.I.C.S.: 236115
Peter O. Shea Jr. (Pres & CEO)
John F. Shea (Chm)
Jim Shontere (CFO & Sec)

Subsidiaries:

Bluestar Resort & Golf LLC (1)
8777 N Gainey Center Dr Ste 135, Scottsdale, AZ 85258
Tel.: (480) 348-6519
Web Site: http://www.bluestarresorts.com
Emp.: 20
Resort Operator
N.A.I.C.S.: 721110
Tim Steckbeck (Pres)
Kirk Kokoska (VP-Golf)
Ben Keilholtz (Dir-Mktg & Sls)
Brett Magnan (Gen Mgr)

J.F. Shea Construction, Inc. (1)
655 Brea Canyon Rd, Walnut, CA 91789
Tel.: (909) 594-9500
Construction Engineering Services
N.A.I.C.S.: 541330

Reed Manufacturing Company (1)
13822 Oaks Ave, Chino, CA 91710
Tel.: (909) 287-2100
Web Site: http://www.reedpumps.com
Emp.: 60
Industrial Equipment Whsr
N.A.I.C.S.: 423830
Jim Shea (Pres)

Shea Homes Limited Partnership (1)
655 Brea Canyon Rd, Walnut, CA 91789-3078
Tel.: (909) 594-9500
Web Site: http://www.sheahomes.com
Rev.: $1,140,606,000
Assets: $1,666,710,000
Liabilities: $1,111,852,000
Net Worth: $554,858,000
Earnings: $133,399,000
Emp.: 668
Fiscal Year-end: 12/31/2014
Construction Company
N.A.I.C.S.: 236115
Robb Pigg (VP-Ops)

Unit (Domestic):

Shea Homes Arizona (2)
8800 N Gainey Ctr Dr Ste 350, Scottsdale, AZ 85258-2124
Tel.: (480) 348-6000
Web Site: http://www.sheahomes.com
Sales Range: $25-49.9 Million
Emp.: 100
House Builder
N.A.I.C.S.: 236117
Buddy Satterfield (Pres)
Ken Peterson (VP-Sls & Mktg)

Shea Homes Northern California (2)
2630 Shea Center Dr, Livermore, CA 94550
Tel.: (925) 245-3600
Web Site: http://www.sheahomes.com
Sales Range: $25-49.9 Million
Emp.: 110
Home Builder Services
N.A.I.C.S.: 236117
Jeff McQueen (Pres)

Shea Homes San Diego (2)
9990 Mesa Rim Rd, San Diego, CA 92131-1039
Tel.: (858) 549-3156
Web Site: http://www.sheahomes.com
Sales Range: $25-49.9 Million
Emp.: 200
House Builder
N.A.I.C.S.: 236117

Shea Homes Southern California (2)
603 Valencia Ave, Brea, CA 92823-6346
Tel.: (714) 985-1300
Web Site: http://www.sheahomes.com

Sales Range: $25-49.9 Million
Emp.: 150
House Builder
N.A.I.C.S.: 236117

Shea Homes-Colorado (2)
1805 Shea Ctr Dr Ste 450, Highlands Ranch, CO 80129-2372
Tel.: (303) 791-8180
Web Site: http://www.sheahomes.com
Sales Range: $25-49.9 Million
Emp.: 70
House Builder
N.A.I.C.S.: 236117
Chetter Latcham (Pres)
Terri Kershisnik (Exec VP)

Shea Properties Inc. (1)
130 Vantis Ste 200, Aliso Viejo, CA 92656
Tel.: (949) 389-7000
Web Site: http://www.sheaproperties.com
Emp.: 100
Real Estate Manangement Services
N.A.I.C.S.: 531390
Colm Macken (Pres & CEO)
Bryan McGowan (CFO & COO)
Yunmi Martin (Sr VP-Shea Apartment Communities)

J.G. BOSWELL CO., INC.
101 W Walnut St, Pasadena, CA 91103-3636
Tel.: (626) 583-3000   CA
Year Founded: 1925
Sales Range: $10-24.9 Million
Emp.: 50
Cotton Production
N.A.I.C.S.: 111920
James W. Boswell (Chm)

Subsidiaries:

Boswell Properties Inc. (1)
101 W Walnut St, Pasadena, CA 91103   (100%)
Tel.: (626) 583-3000
Subdividers & Developers
N.A.I.C.S.: 237210

J.G. Boswell Co., Inc. (1)
26073 Santa Fe Ave, Corcoran, CA 93212
Tel.: (559) 992-5011
Sales Range: $10-24.9 Million
Emp.: 4
Irrigation Systems
N.A.I.C.S.: 112111

The Eastlake Company (1)
7777 Alvarado Rd Ste 115, La Mesa, CA 91942-8245   (100%)
Tel.: (858) 513-7800
Sales Range: $10-24.9 Million
Emp.: 20
Subdividers & Developers
N.A.I.C.S.: 237210

J.G. EDELEN CO. INC.
8901 Kelso Dr, Baltimore, MD 21221
Tel.: (410) 918-1200
Web Site: http://www.jgedelen.com
Year Founded: 1923
Rev.: $10,477,265
Emp.: 30
Furniture Hardware Specialists
N.A.I.C.S.: 423710
John Healy (Pres)
James G. Edelen Jr. (Chm)
Jim Edelen III (VP)

J.G. O'NEILL INC.
655 NE 6th Ave, Delray Beach, FL 33483
Tel.: (561) 265-0000
Web Site:
   http://www.delrayacura.com
Sales Range: $25-49.9 Million
Emp.: 50
Automobile Sales
N.A.I.C.S.: 441110
Dianna Calderone (Controller)
James G. O'Neill Jr. (Pres)

J.H. ALLEN INC.

409 W Central Ave, Asheboro, NC 27204
Tel.: (336) 672-1035   NC
Year Founded: 1963
Sales Range: $10-24.9 Million
Emp.: 80
Commercial & Institutional Building Construction Services
N.A.I.C.S.: 236220
Douglas M. Allen (Pres)

J.H. BARKAU & SONS INC.
200 N Stephenson St, Cedarville, IL 61013
Tel.: (815) 563-4812
Web Site: http://www.barkau.com
Year Founded: 1952
Sales Range: $10-24.9 Million
Emp.: 40
Owner & Operator of Car Dealerships
N.A.I.C.S.: 423110
Jim Barkau (Owner-Freeport)
Rick Barkau (Owner-Stockton)
Willie Barkau (Owner-Cedarville)
Kevin Martin (Gen Mgr-Sls-Cedarville)
Pat Gillespie (Co-Owner)
Chad Piefer (Mgr-F&I-Cedarville)
Louis Lorenz (Mgr-Sls-Freeport)

J.H. BAXTER & COMPANY
1700 S El Camino Real Ste 365, San Mateo, CA 94402-3073
Tel.: (650) 349-0201   CA
Web Site: http://www.jhbaxter.com
Year Founded: 1914
Sales Range: $25-49.9 Million
Emp.: 220
Pressure Treated Poles, Piling & Lumber Mfr
N.A.I.C.S.: 523940
Robert Stockton (VP-Fin)

J.H. BENNETT & COMPANY INC.
PO Box 8028, Novi, MI 48376-8028
Tel.: (248) 596-5100   MI
Web Site: http://www.jhbennett.com
Year Founded: 1975
Sales Range: $10-24.9 Million
Emp.: 100
Industrial Machinery & Equipment
N.A.I.C.S.: 423830
Dave Castle (VP)

J.H. BENNETT INC.
1951 Lehigh St, Allentown, PA 18103
Tel.: (610) 437-6711
Web Site:
   http://www.bennettcars.com
Rev.: $19,979,719
Emp.: 200
Sales & Service of New & Used Automobiles
N.A.I.C.S.: 441110
Robert Bennett (Pres & CEO)
Dolly Wolfe (Controller)

J.H. BERRA HOLDING CO., INC.
5091 Baumgartner Rd, Saint Louis, MO 63129-2821
Tel.: (314) 487-9400   MO
Web Site: http://www.jhberra.com
Year Founded: 1994
Sales Range: $125-149.9 Million
Emp.: 300
Holding Company; Engineering & Construction Services
N.A.I.C.S.: 551112
Rob Berra (CFO)
John H. Berra (Pres & CEO)

Subsidiaries:

J.H. Berra Construction Co., Inc. (1)

5091 Baumgartner Rd, Saint Louis, MO 63129-2821   (100%)
Tel.: (314) 487-5617
Web Site: http://www.jhberra.com
Sales Range: $50-74.9 Million
Emp.: 20
Highway & Street Construction
N.A.I.C.S.: 237310
Kevin Bielicki (Project Mgr)
Brian Pinkley (Project Mgr)
John H. Berra Jr. (Pres & CEO)

Division (Domestic):

J.H. Berra Construction Co., Inc. - Grading Division (2)
5091 New Baumgartner Rd, Saint Louis, MO 63129
Tel.: (314) 487-5617
Construction Engineering Services
N.A.I.C.S.: 541330

J.H. Berra Construction Co., Inc. - Land Development Division (2)
5091 New Baumgartner Rd, Saint Louis, MO 63129
Tel.: (314) 487-6717
Construction Engineering Services
N.A.I.C.S.: 541330

J.H. Berra Construction Co., Inc. - Utility Division (2)
5091 New Baumgartner Rd, Saint Louis, MO 63129
Tel.: (314) 487-5617
Construction Engineering Services
N.A.I.C.S.: 541330

Subsidiary (Domestic):

J.H. Berra Engineering & Surveying Co., Inc. (2)
5055 New Baumgartner Rd, Saint Louis, MO 63129
Tel.: (314) 487-0440
Web Site: http://www.sterling-eng-sur.com
Civil Engineering Services
N.A.I.C.S.: 541330
George J. Gower (VP)
Michael G. Boerding (VP-Engrg)
Rodney L. Arnold (Dir-Engrg)
Jamey A. Henson (Dir-Surveying)

J.H. Berra Paving Co., Inc. (2)
5091 New Baumgartner Rd, Saint Louis, MO 63129
Tel.: (314) 487-2588
Asphalt Paving Services
N.A.I.C.S.: 324121

J.H. BUHRMASTER COMPANY INC.
421 Sacandaga Rd, Scotia, NY 12302
Tel.: (518) 382-0260
Web Site: http://www.buhrmaster.com
Sales Range: $10-24.9 Million
Emp.: 25
Fuel Oil Dealers
N.A.I.C.S.: 457210
James R. Buhrmaster (Pres)

J.H. ELLWOOD & ASSOCIATES
33 W Monroe Ste 1000, Chicago, IL 60603
Tel.: (312) 782-5432
Web Site:
   http://www.ellwoodassociates.com
Year Founded: 1977
Financial Consultant
N.A.I.C.S.: 523999
Russell Hill (Chm & CEO)
Bradley Levandoski (COO)
Susan Toth (Pres)
Daniel George (Chief Investment Officer)

Subsidiaries:

Watershed Investment Consultants, Inc. (1)
5299 Dtc Blvd, Greenwood Village, CO 80111
Tel.: (303) 738-0300

Web Site: http://www.watershedinvest.com
Rev.: $2,490,000
Emp.: 6
Portfolio Management
N.A.I.C.S.: 523940
Dale Connors (CEO)
Terri Baldwin (Dir-Bus Dev)
Paul Schreder (Mng Dir)
Kevin Yoshida (Pres & Mng Dir)

J.H. EVANS INC.
4918 Taylor Ct, Turlock, CA 95382
Tel.: (209) 394-4000
Rev.: $20,567,213
Emp.: 40
Local & Long Distance Telephone Communications
N.A.I.C.S.: 449210
Delwyn Williams (CEO)

Subsidiaries:

Global Valley Networks (1)
515 Keystone Blvd, Patterson, CA 95363
Tel.: (209) 394-4000
Web Site: http://www.gvni.com
Sales Range: $10-24.9 Million
Cellular Telephone Services
N.A.I.C.S.: 517112

J.H. FAGAN COMPANY
1711 Pair Amount Ct, Waukesha, WI 53186
Tel.: (262) 786-9610
Web Site: http://www.jhfagan.com
Rev.: $24,400,000
Emp.: 23
Electrical & Electronic Appliance Television & Radio Set Merchant Whslr
N.A.I.C.S.: 423620
Linda Emerson (Branch Mgr-Minnesota)
Lamon Elrod (Pres)
John Chadwick (Branch Mgr)
Dana Bergh (Controller)

J.H. FINDORFF & SON, INC.
300 S Bedford St, Madison, WI 53703
Tel.: (608) 257-5321   WI
Web Site: http://www.findorff.com
Year Founded: 1890
Sales Range: $200-249.9 Million
Emp.: 600
Construction & Contracting Services
N.A.I.C.S.: 236220
Richard M. Lynch (Chm)
Tim Stadelman (CFO)
F. Curtis Hastings (Chm)
Eric Wynn (Gen Mgr-Southeast Wisconsin & Dir-Project Mgmt)
Jeff Garretson (Dir-Bus Dev)
Joe Schuchardt (Gen Mgr)
Jeff McLean (VP)

J.H. FLETCHER & CO.
402 High St, Huntington, WV 25705-1747
Tel.: (304) 525-7811   DE
Web Site: http://www.jhfletcher.com
Year Founded: 1937
Sales Range: $125-149.9 Million
Emp.: 175
Mfr of Underground Mine Equipment
N.A.I.C.S.: 423810
Gregory Hinshaw (CEO)
Ben Hardman (VP-Domestic Sls)
Steve McIntyre (Mgr-District Sls)
Bill Kendall (Mgr-Sls-Western District)
Gary Cline (Asst Mgr-Safety)
Dave Schneider (Asst Mgr-Safety)
Shizhong Han (Mgr-Bus Dev-EPC & End Users)
Dave Tate (Mgr-Sls-Midwester)
Tim Martin (Mgr-Sls-Southern)
Pat Damron (Mgr-Sls-Southern West Virginia)

J.H. Larson Electrical Company—(Continued)

J.H. LARSON ELECTRICAL COMPANY

10200 51st Ave N, Plymouth, MN
55442
Tel.: (763) 545-1717   **WI**
Web Site: http://www.jhlarson.com
Year Founded: 1931
Sales Range: $50-74.9 Million
Emp.: 225
Wholesale Distribution of Electrical &
Plumbing Supplies
N.A.I.C.S.: 423610
Greg Pahl (Pres & CEO)

Subsidiaries:

J.H. Larson Electrical Company   **(1)**
1022 51 Ave N, Plymouth, MN
55442   **(100%)**
Tel.: (763) 545-1717
Web Site: http://www.jhlarson.com
Sales Range: $25-49.9 Million
Emp.: 175
Wholesale Distribution of Electrical &
Plumbing Supplies
N.A.I.C.S.: 423610
Greg Miller (Branch Mgr)

J.H. Larson Electrical
Company-Hudson   **(1)**
901 Okeefe Rd, Hudson, WI 54016-0566
Tel.: (715) 386-2388
Web Site: http://www.jhlarson.com
Sales Range: $25-49.9 Million
Emp.: 40
Wholesale Distribution of Electrical &
Plumbing Distr
N.A.I.C.S.: 423720
Brad Schwartz (Branch Mgr)

J.H. LYNCH & SONS INC.

50 Lynch Pl, Cumberland, RI 02864-
5334
Tel.: (401) 333-4300   **RI**
Web Site: http://www.jhlynch.com
Year Founded: 1957
Sales Range: $25-49.9 Million
Emp.: 225
Highway & Street Construction
N.A.I.C.S.: 237310

Subsidiaries:

Granger-Lynch Corp.   **(1)**
18 McCracken Rd, Millbury, MA 01527-
1514
Tel.: (508) 756-6244
Web Site: http://www.jhlynch.com
Sales Range: $10-24.9 Million
Emp.: 21
Distr of Asphalt Paving Mixtures & Blocks
N.A.I.C.S.: 324121
Stephen P. Lynch (Pres)

Wescon Corp of Conn.   **(1)**
PO Box 296, Westerly, RI 02891
Tel.: (860) 599-2500
Web Site: http://www.wesconco.com
Readymix Concrete Mfr
N.A.I.C.S.: 327320

J.H. MCCORMICK, INC.

2507 W Empire Ave, Burbank, CA
91504-3320
Tel.: (818) 843-2010   **CA**
Web Site:
  http://www.mccormickconstruc
  tion.com
Year Founded: 1914
Sales Range: $75-99.9 Million
Emp.: 65
Provider of Construction & Contract-
ing Services
N.A.I.C.S.: 236220
Steven McCormick (VP)
Michael McCormick (Pres)

J.H. ROUTH PACKING CO.

4413 W Bogart Rd, Sandusky, OH
44870-9648
Tel.: (419) 626-2251   **OH**

Web Site:
  http://www.routhpacking.com
Year Founded: 1947
Sales Range: $125-149.9 Million
Emp.: 300
Packer of Pork Products
N.A.I.C.S.: 311611
Thomas M. Routh (Chm, Pres &
CEO)
David P. Stearns (VP)
Frank Moscioni (Controller)

J.H. RUDOLPH & CO. INC.

1251 N Stockwell Rd, Evansville, IN
47715-2210
Tel.: (812) 476-4921   **IN**
Web Site: http://www.jhrudolph.com
Year Founded: 1940
Sales Range: $1-9.9 Million
Emp.: 40
Highway & Street Construction
N.A.I.C.S.: 237310
Jeff Mulzer (Pres)
Tim Mulzer (Exec VP)
Tom Falkenstein (Controller)

J.H. WALKER INC.

11404 Hempstead Rd, Houston, TX
77092
Tel.: (713) 688-8400
Web Site:
  http://www.jhwalkertrucking.com
Sales Range: $10-24.9 Million
Emp.: 300
Trucking Service
N.A.I.C.S.: 484121
Johny Walker (CEO)

J.H. WHITNEY & CO., LLC

212 Elm St, 06840, New Canaan, CT
Tel.: (203) 716-6100
Web Site: http://www.whitney.com
Year Founded: 1946
Privater Equity Firm
N.A.I.C.S.: 523999
Robert M. Williams Jr. (Sr Mng Dir)
Kevin J. Curley (Chief Compliance
Officer)

Subsidiaries:

J.H. Whitney Capital Partners,
LLC   **(1)**
130 Main St, New Canaan, CT 06840
Tel.: (203) 716-6100
Web Site: http://www.whitney.com
Privater Equity Firm
N.A.I.C.S.: 523999
Kevin J. Curley (Chief Compliance Officer)

Holding (Non-US):

3B Scientific GmbH   **(2)**
Rudorffweg 8, 21031, Hamburg, Germany
Tel.: (49) 40 73966 0
Web Site: http://www.3bsclentific.com
Medical Device Mfr
N.A.I.C.S.: 339112
Todd Murray (CEO)

Subsidiary (US):

Excellus Technologies, Inc.   **(3)**
910 Bay Star Blvd, Webster, TX 77598
Tel.: (281) 488-5901
Web Site: http://www.cardionics.com
Auscultation Products & Services Mfr
N.A.I.C.S.: 339112
Keith Johnson (Mgr)
Andrew Strandell (COO)
Mark Bedar (Mgr-QA)

Wallcur, LLC   **(3)**
8525 Arjons Dr., Ste I, San Diego, CA
92126
Tel.: (858) 565-4366
Web Site: http://www.wallcur.com
All Other Schools & Instruction
N.A.I.C.S.: 611699
Wendy LaGrange (Mng Dir & VP)

Holding (Domestic):

C.J. Foods, Inc.   **(2)**
322 Main St, Bern, KS 66408
Tel.: (785) 336-6132
Web Site: http://cjfoodsinc.com
Pet Food Mfr
N.A.I.C.S.: 311119
Tod Morgan (Chm)
Brad Berentson (CFO)
Brian Lundquist (COO)
Elliott Haverlack (Pres)
Rand Schafer (Chief Revenue Officer)
David McLain (CEO)

Subsidiary (Domestic):

American Nutrition, Inc.   **(3)**
2890 Reeves Ave, Ogden, UT 84401-3552
Tel.: (801) 394-3477
Web Site: http://www.animanufacturing.com
Pet Food Mfr
N.A.I.C.S.: 311111
Bill Behnken (Pres & CEO)

Holding (Domestic):

FNF Construction Inc.   **(2)**
115 S 48th St, Tempe, AZ 85281
Tel.: (480) 784-2910
Web Site: http://www.fnfinc.com
Asphalt Production & Highway, Road &
Tunnel Construction Services
N.A.I.C.S.: 237310
Thomas Billings (VP-Crushing & Paving)
David James (CFO)
Tom Kennedy (VP-Texas Project Sponsor)
Jason Ruskey (VP-Rail)
Robert Bottcher (Pres & COO)
James Anderson Jr. (VP & Mgr-Equipment
Svcs)

Ignite Restaurant Group, Inc.   **(2)**
10555 Richmond Ave, Houston, TX 77042
Tel.: (713) 366-7500
Web Site: http://www.igniterestaurants.com
Sales Range: $450-499.9 Million
Restaurant Owner & Operator
N.A.I.C.S.: 722511
Paul R. Vigano (Chm)
Jonathan Tibus (CEO)
Steve Metzger (Gen Counsel & Sr VP)
Shauna R. King (Officer)

Subsidiary (Domestic):

BHTH Entertainment, Inc.   **(3)**
9900 Westpark Dr, Houston, TX 77063-
5277
Tel.: (713) 366-7521
Restaurant Operators
N.A.I.C.S.: 722511

Ignite Restaurants-New Jersey,
Inc.   **(3)**
2000 Clements Bridge Rd, Deptford, NJ
08096
Tel.: (856) 251-2314
Restaurant Operators
N.A.I.C.S.: 722511
Anthony Wrapps (Gen Mgr)

JCS Monmouth Mall-NJ, LLC   **(3)**
190 N J State Hwy 35, Eatontown, NJ
07724
Tel.: (732) 389-2116
Sales Range: $10-24.9 Million
Restaurant Operators
N.A.I.C.S.: 722511
Andrea Braxton (Gen Mgr)

Joe's Crab Shack   **(3)**
2288 N Garden St, Boise, ID 83706-2430
Tel.: (208) 336-9370
Web Site: http://www.joescrabshack.com
Eating Place
N.A.I.C.S.: 722511
Chris Moore (Gen Mgr)
Michael Nesloney (Mgr)

Joe's Crab Shack-Abingdon MD,
Inc.   **(3)**
3414 Merchant Blvd, Abingdon, MD 21009
Tel.: (410) 569-8343
Restaurant Operators
N.A.I.C.S.: 722511

Joe's Crab Shack-Alabama Private
Club Inc.   **(3)**

20 Meadow View Dr Hwy 280, Hoover, AL
35242
Tel.: (205) 981-2999
Restaurant Operators
N.A.I.C.S.: 722511

Joe's Crab Shack-Anne Arundel MD,
Inc.   **(3)**
7051 Arundel Mills Blvd, Hanover, MD
21075
Tel.: (410) 799-2155
Restaurant Operators
N.A.I.C.S.: 722511

Joe's Crab Shack-Hunt Valley MD,
Inc.   **(3)**
50 Shawan Rd, Cockeysville, MD 21030
Tel.: (410) 771-1259
Restaurant Operators
N.A.I.C.S.: 722511

Joe's Crab Shack-Kansas, Inc.   **(3)**
11965 S Strang Line Rd, Olathe, KS 66062
Tel.: (913) 393-2929
Web Site: http://www.joescrabshack.com
Emp.: 25
Restaurant Operators
N.A.I.C.S.: 722511
Alex Gonclaves (Gen Mgr)

Joe's Crab Shack-Maryland, Inc.   **(3)**
221 Rio Blvd, Gaithersburg, MD 20878
Tel.: (301) 947-4377
Restaurant Operators
N.A.I.C.S.: 722511

Joe's Crab Shack-Redondo Beach,
Inc.   **(3)**
230 Portofino Way, Redondo Beach, CA
90277
Tel.: (310) 406-1999
Web Site: http://www.joescrabshack.com
Restaurant Operators
N.A.I.C.S.: 722511
John Card (Gen Mgr)

Joe's Crab Shack-San Diego
Inc.   **(3)**
Rowing Club 525 E Harbor Dr, San Diego,
CA 92101
Tel.: (619) 233-7391
Restaurant Operators
N.A.I.C.S.: 722511
Sicily McCambridge (Dir-Sls & Field Mktg)

Joe's Crab Shack-Texas, Inc.   **(3)**
600 E Riverside Dr, Austin, TX 78704
Tel.: (512) 441-1010
Restaurant Operators
N.A.I.C.S.: 722511

J.H. WILLIAMS OIL COMPANY INC.

1237 E Twiggs St, Tampa, FL 33602
Tel.: (813) 228-7776   **IL**
Web Site: http://www.jhwoil.com
Year Founded: 1945
Sales Range: $350-399.9 Million
Emp.: 185
Petroleum Products Distr; Gas Sta-
tion Owner
N.A.I.C.S.: 424720
J. Hulon Williams III (Pres)

J.H. WRIGHT & ASSOCIATES INC.

27395 Pollard Rd, Daphne, AL 36526
Tel.: (251) 621-1491   **AL**
Web Site: http://www.jhwright.com
Year Founded: 1961
Sales Range: $10-24.9 Million
Emp.: 48
Provider of Industrial & Municipal
Pump Sales & Distribution
N.A.I.C.S.: 423830
Mark Wright (Pres)

J.I. GARCIA CONSTRUCTION CO.

5591 N Golden State Blvd #101,
Fresno, CA 93722
Tel.: (559) 276-7726
Web Site: http://www.jigarcia.com
Sales Range: $10-24.9 Million

Emp.: 25
General Contractors of Commercial &
Office Buildings
N.A.I.C.S.: 236220
Joseph V. Garcia *(Pres & Gen Mgr)*
Claudia Carlos *(Project Mgr)*
Jeanne Clason *(Controller)*

J.I. KISLAK INC.
7900 NW 154th St, Miami Lakes, FL
33016
Tel.: (305) 364-4100   NJ
Web Site: http://www.kislak.com
Year Founded: 1906
Sales Range: $450-499.9 Million
Emp.: 700
Holding Company; Real Estate, Insur-
ance & Banking Services
N.A.I.C.S.: 522292
Jay I. Kislak *(Chm)*
Thomas Bartelmo *(Pres & CEO)*

Subsidiaries:

Kislak Company   (1)
100 Woodbridge Center Dr, Woodbridge,
NJ 07095   (100%)
Tel.: (732) 750-3000
Web Site: http://www.kislakrealty.com
Sales Range: $10-24.9 Million
Emp.: 25
Real Estate Agency
N.A.I.C.S.: 531210
Doug Zastrow *(Sr VP & Controller)*
Francine Girimonte *(VP-HR)*
Jonathan Greenberg *(Sr VP)*
Robert Holland *(Pres)*
Jason Pucci *(COO)*
Joni Sweetwood *(Sr VP)*
Mathew Weilheimer *(Sr VP)*
Peter Wisniewski *(Exec VP-Comml Sls &
Leasing)*
Dorothy LaGreca *(Sr VP-Comml Sls &
Leasing)*
Jeffrey Wiener *(Sr VP)*
Barry Waisbrod *(Sr VP)*
Robert Squires *(Sr VP)*
Scott Davidovic *(Sr VP)*
Janet Bortz *(Sr VP)*
Jeff Squires *(Sr VP)*

Kislak National Bank   (1)
7900 Miami Lakes Dr, Miami, FL 33016
Tel.: (305) 364-4100
Web Site: http://www.bankonus.com
Sales Range: $50-74.9 Million
Emp.: 250
National Commercial Banks
N.A.I.C.S.: 522110

J.J. COLLINS SONS INC.
7125 Janes Ave Ste 200, Woodridge,
IL 60517
Tel.: (630) 960-2525
Web Site: http://www.jjcollins.com
Rev.: $25,643,075
Emp.: 30
Business Forms Printing Services
N.A.I.C.S.: 323111
James F. Collins Jr. *(Chm)*

J.J. GOUGE & SON OIL CO.
INC.
112 Greenwood Rd, Spruce Pine, NC
28777
Tel.: (828) 765-2371
Sales Range: $1-9.9 Million
Emp.: 15
Gasoline
N.A.I.C.S.: 424720
J. J. Gouge Jr. *(Pres)*

J.J. GUMBERG CO. INC.
1051 Brinton Rd, Pittsburgh, PA
15221-4599
Tel.: (412) 244-4000   PA
Web Site: http://www.jjgumberg.com
Year Founded: 1937
Sales Range: $50-74.9 Million
Emp.: 500
Apartment Building Operator

N.A.I.C.S.: 531311
Ira J. Gumberg *(Pres & CEO)*
Darla Burns *(Mgr-Credit & Collec-
tions)*
Robert Irr *(VP-Retail Leasing)*

J.J. HAINES & CO. INC.
6950 Aviation Blvd, Glen Burnie, MD
21061
Tel.: (410) 760-4040   MD
Web Site: http://www.jjhaines.com
Year Founded: 1874
Sales Range: $500-549.9 Million
Emp.: 750
Floor Covering Distr
N.A.I.C.S.: 449121
Pierce B. Dunn *(Chm)*
Brian Green *(Exec VP-Sls & Mktg)*
Hoy Lanning Jr. *(Pres & CEO)*

Subsidiaries:

CMH Space Flooring Products,
Inc.   (1)
2732 US Hwy 74 W, Wadesboro, NC 28170
Tel.: (704) 694-6213
Web Site: http://www.cmhspace.com
Sales Range: $25-49.9 Million
Emp.: 170
Flooring Product Distr
N.A.I.C.S.: 449121
Charlie Kerfoot *(Mgr-Hardwood Product)*
James Bailey *(Controller)*
Shelli Kelly *(Mgr-Comml Products)*
Art Layton *(VP-Mktg)*
John Capell *(VP & Treas)*

Branch (Domestic):

CMH Space Flooring   (2)
3500 Highlands Pkwy, Smyrna, GA 30082
Tel.: (770) 431-8222
Web Site: http://www.spaceflooring.com
Sales Range: $25-49.9 Million
Emp.: 120
Flooring Product Distr
N.A.I.C.S.: 449121
Rocky Thomas *(VP-Credit)*
Juan Martinez *(Supvr-Quality Control)*

J.J. KELLER & ASSOCIATES,
INC.
3003 Breezewood Ln, Neenah, WI
54956
Tel.: (920) 722-2848   WI
Web Site: http://www.jjkeller.com
Year Founded: 1953
Sales Range: $400-449.9 Million
Emp.: 1,200
Workplace Compliance Materials
Publisher
N.A.I.C.S.: 513199
Marne L. Keller-Krikava *(Pres &
CEO)*
Rustin R. Keller *(COO & Exec VP)*
Dana S. Gilman *(CFO)*
Charles T. Govin III *(VP-Field Sls)*

J.J. POWELL INC.
Presque Isle St, Philipsburg, PA
16866
Tel.: (814) 342-3190   PA
Web Site: http://www.jjpowell.com
Year Founded: 1952
Sales Range: $10-24.9 Million
Emp.: 35
Heating Oil Distr
N.A.I.C.S.: 424720
Keith Powell *(VP)*
Jeffrey S. Powell *(Pres)*
Jill Curtorillo *(Asst Controller)*

J.J. TAYLOR COMPANIES INC.
655 N A1A, Jupiter, FL 33477-4579
Tel.: (561) 354-2900
Web Site: http://www.jjtaylor.com
Year Founded: 1958
Sales Range: $150-199.9 Million
Emp.: 900
Beer Distributor

N.A.I.C.S.: 424810
Henri J. DesPlaines *(CFO & Exec
VP)*
Manuel E. Portuondo *(Vice Chm)*
David S. Miller *(VP-HR)*
Jay A. Martin *(COO & Exec VP)*
John J. Taylor Jr. *(Chm, Pres & CEO)*

Subsidiaries:

J.J. Taylor Distributing Company of
Minnesota, Inc.   (1)
701 Industrial Blvd NE, Minneapolis, MN
55413
Tel.: (651) 482-1133
Web Site: http://www.jjtaylor.com
Sales Range: $25-49.9 Million
Emp.: 300
Beer & Wine Distr
N.A.I.C.S.: 424810
Mike Bamonti *(Pres & Gen Mgr)*
Cal Anderson *(VP-Admin)*
Todd Teigen *(Gen Mgr-Sls)*
Doug Picht *(Dir-Sls-Off Premise)*
Jeff Ruprecht *(Dir-Delivery)*

J.J. Taylor Distributing of Florida,
Inc.   (1)
5102 S 16th Ave, Tampa, FL 33619
Tel.: (813) 247-4000
Web Site: http://www.jjtaylor.com
Sales Range: $50-74.9 Million
Emp.: 380
Beer Distr
N.A.I.C.S.: 424810
Peter Marer *(Pres & Gen Mgr)*

J.J. Taylor Distributing of Florida,
Inc.   (1)
2040 Park 82 Dr, Fort Myers, FL 33905
Tel.: (239) 267-1006
Web Site: http://www.jjtaylor.com
Sales Range: $25-49.9 Million
Emp.: 175
Beer Distr
N.A.I.C.S.: 424810
Jose Rivera *(VP-Admin)*

J.L. ANDERSON COMPANY
INC.
3501 Brick Yard Rd, Wallace, SC
29596
Tel.: (843) 537-7861
Web Site:
http://www.palmettobrick.com
Sales Range: $100-124.9 Million
Emp.: 50
Brick & Construction Products Mfr
N.A.I.C.S.: 327120
Robert Rogers *(Pres & Treas)*
Douglas Anderson *(Sec)*
Andy Rogers *(VP-Sls & Mktg)*
Mark Howle *(Branch Mgr)*

J.L. BAINBRIDGE AND COM-
PANY, INC.
1582 Main St, Sarasota, FL 34236
Tel.: (941) 365-3435
Web Site:
http://www.jlbainbridge.com
Year Founded: 1981
Sales Range: $10-24.9 Million
Emp.: 6
Investment Banking & Advisory Ser-
vices
N.A.I.C.S.: 523150
Jerry L. Bainbridge *(Pres)*
Kip David Schoonover *(Sr VP)*
Joel G. Oldham *(Sr VP)*
John Leeming *(Sr VP)*

J.L. BUCHANAN INC.
50 S 10th St Ste 440, Minneapolis,
MN 55403
Tel.: (612) 334-1710
Web Site: http://www.jlbuchanan.com
Sales Range: $75-99.9 Million
Emp.: 18
Variety Store Merchandise
N.A.I.C.S.: 424990

Jeff Buchanan *(Founder & Pres)*
Cindy Francis *(Dir-Compliance)*
Robin Harris *(Bus Mgr)*

J.L. BURKE CONTRACTING,
INC.
18927 Hickory Creek Dr, Mokena, IL
60448
Tel.: (708) 478-1546
Web Site: http://www.jlburke.com
Rev.: $13,000,000
Emp.: 15
Construction Services
N.A.I.C.S.: 236220
James L. Burke *(Pres)*
Michael Colliander *(VP)*

J.L. DAVIS COMPANIES
211 N Colorado, Midland, TX 79701
Tel.: (432) 682-6311
Web Site:
http://www.westtexasgas.com
Sales Range: $200-249.9 Million
Emp.: 800
Holding Company; Natural Gas Pro-
cessing & Distribution
N.A.I.C.S.: 551112
J. L. Davis *(Owner, Pres & CEO)*
Richard D. Hatchett *(CFO & VP)*

Subsidiaries:

Davis Gas Processing, Inc.   (1)
211 N Colorado St, Midland, TX 79701
Tel.: (432) 682-2370
Natural Gas Processing Services
N.A.I.C.S.: 213112

WTG Exploration, Inc.   (1)
401 W Wadley Ave, Midland, TX 79705
Tel.: (432) 682-4030
Natural Gas Mfr
N.A.I.C.S.: 211130

West Texas Gas, Inc.   (1)
211 N Colorado, Midland, TX
79701-4607   (100%)
Tel.: (432) 682-4349
Web Site: http://www.westtexasgas.com
Sales Range: $25-49.9 Million
Emp.: 80
Natural Gas Distr
N.A.I.C.S.: 221210
J. L. Davis *(Founder & Owner)*
Richard D. Hatchett *(Pres)*
J. J. King *(VP-Gas Mktg)*
Jan Thompson *(Mgr-Customer Svc)*
Bart Bean *(Mgr-Gas Ops)*
Bobby Roach *(Dir-Health Safety & Environ-
mental)*
Carson Watt *(Mgr-Gas Supply)*

J.L. GADDY ENTERPRISES
INC.
PO Box 277, Hickory Grove, SC
29717-0277
Tel.: (803) 925-2121   SC
Web Site: http://www.jlgaddy.com
Year Founded: 1980
Sales Range: $75-99.9 Million
Emp.: 39
Supplier of Tobacco Products
N.A.I.C.S.: 424940
Dudley S. Wilkerson *(Pres)*
Bill Wilkerson *(Controller)*
Eddie Mitchell *(Mgr-Sls)*

J.L. MAUPIN ENTERPRISES
INC.
8508 Rannie Rd, Houston, TX 77080
Tel.: (713) 460-2115
Rev.: $12,100,000
Emp.: 18
General Electrical Contractor
N.A.I.C.S.: 238210
James L. Maupin *(Pres)*
Ron Murray *(VP)*

J.L. ROTHROCK INC.
3111 S Brook Dr, Greensboro, NC
27406

J.L. Rothrock Inc.—(Continued)

Tel.: (336) 854-6050
Web Site: http://www.jlrothrock.com
Sales Range: $10-24.9 Million
Emp.: 70
Trucking Service
N.A.I.C.S.: 484121
W. D. Bondurant *(Pres)*
Jo Ellen McCormick *(Mgr-AR & Collection)*

J.L. TODD AUCTION CO.
28 Bale St, Rome, GA 30165-2842
Tel.: (706) 291-7007   GA
Web Site: http://www.jltodd.com
Year Founded: 1917
Sales Range: $75-99.9 Million
Emp.: 10
Auction Services
N.A.I.C.S.: 531210
Randy Land *(Exec VP)*
John Todd *(Exec VP)*
Doris Todd *(VP)*
Carolyn Prater *(Treas & Sec)*
Frank Coker *(Pres)*
Jerry Hammond *(Sr VP)*

J.L. WALLACE, INC.
9111 W College Pointe Dr, Fort Myers, FL 33919
Tel.: (239) 437-1111
Web Site:
   http://www.jlwallaceinc.com
Year Founded: 1997
Sales Range: $1-9.9 Million
Emp.: 12
General Contractors
N.A.I.C.S.: 236220
Jerry Wallace *(Pres)*
Jani Denison *(Controller)*
Ted Gadoury *(Project Mgr)*

J.LIEB FOODS, INC.
2550 23rd Ave Ste D, Forest Grove, OR 97116
Tel.: (503) 359-9279
Web Site: http://www.jliebfoods.com
Year Founded: 1992
Sales Range: $10-24.9 Million
Emp.: 80
Fruit & Vegetable Canning Services
N.A.I.C.S.: 311421
A. James Lieb *(Pres & CEO)*

J.LODGE, LLC
13130 Westlinks Ter Ste 5, Fort Myers, FL 33913
Tel.: (239) 220-5212
Web Site: http://www.jlodge.com
Year Founded: 1999
Sales Range: $1-9.9 Million
Emp.: 71
Call Monitoring & Call Center Operating Services
N.A.I.C.S.: 561421
Craig McElroy *(Dir-Database)*
Adam Smeigh *(Exec VP)*
Rodney A. Mason *(Dir-Internal Ops)*

J.M. DAVIDSON INC.
Fm 1069 Rd & Millsville Rd, Aransas Pass, TX 78336
Tel.: (361) 883-0983
Web Site:
   http://www.jmdavidson.com
Sales Range: $25-49.9 Million
Emp.: 250
Civil Engineering Services
N.A.I.C.S.: 237310
Johnny Davidson *(Owner)*

J.M. FAHEY CONSTRUCTION COMPANY
408 High Grove Rd, Grandview, MO 64030
Tel.: (816) 763-3010

Web Site: http://www.jmfahey.com
Year Founded: 1971
Sales Range: $10-24.9 Million
Highway & Street Construction Services
N.A.I.C.S.: 237310
Kevin F. Fahey *(Pres)*
Kevin Connell *(Mgr-Construction Div)*
Jim Easterday *(Controller)*
Bridget Fahey *(Office Mgr)*
Rick McCloud *(Mgr-Asphalt Div)*
Joe Fahey *(CEO)*

J.M. GRIMSTAD INC.
S84 W18887 Enterprise Dr, Muskego, WI 53150
Tel.: (414) 422-2300
Web Site: http://www.grimstad.com
Sales Range: $10-24.9 Million
Emp.: 49
Hydraulic Systems Equipment & Supplies
N.A.I.C.S.: 423830
Eric Grimstad *(Pres)*
Ron Poock *(VP & Gen Mgr-Minn & Iowa)*
Dan Macejkoviz *(VP-Bus Dev)*
Jim Weber *(VP-Manufacturing)*
Mark Godlewski *(Bus Mgr)*

J.M. HUBER CORPORATION
499 Thornall St 8th Fl, Edison, NJ 08837-2267
Tel.: (732) 549-8600   NJ
Web Site: https://www.huber.com
Year Founded: 1890
Sales Range: $1-4.9 Billion
Emp.: 4,900
Other Basic Inorganic Chemical Manufacturing
N.A.I.C.S.: 325180
Michael L. Marberry *(Pres, CEO, CFO & VP-Corp Strategy & New Bus Development)*
Jeff Vincent *(Chm)*
Carol Lynn Messer *(Gen Counsel & Exec VP)*
Don A. Young *(Exec VP-Environment, Health, Safety & Sustainability)*
Vivek Dhir *(Exec VP-Corp Strategy & Bus Dev)*
Lily Prost *(Chief HR Officer & Exec VP)*
Gretchen W. McClain *(Pres & CEO)*

Subsidiaries:

CP Kelco   **(1)**
3100 Cumberland Blvd Ste 600, Atlanta, GA 30339-2118
Tel.: (678) 247-7300
Web Site: http://www.cpkelco.com
Sales Range: $10-24.9 Million
Emp.: 40
Hydrocolloids Mfr
N.A.I.C.S.: 325998
Jennifer Aspen Mason *(Sr VP-Innovation-Global)*
Didier Viala *(Pres)*

Branch (Domestic):

CP Kelco   **(2)**
8225 Aero Dr, San Diego, CA 92123-1718
Tel.: (858) 292-4900
Web Site: http://www.cpkelco.com
Specialty Hydrocolloids Mfr
N.A.I.C.S.: 311999

Subsidiary (Non-US):

CP Kelco ApS   **(2)**
Ved Banen 16, 4623, Lille Skensved, 4623, Denmark
Tel.: (45) 56165616
Web Site: http://www.cpkelco.com
Producer of Pectin, Carrageenan & Refined Locust Bean Gum
N.A.I.C.S.: 311942
Jone Rn Stryger *(Plant Mgr)*

Branch (Non-US):

CP Kelco ApS   **(3)**
Bolshaya Ordynka str 44 1st Fl, Moscow, RU-119017, Russia
Tel.: (7) 495 937 36 47
Web Site: http://www.cpkelco.com
Sales Range: $50-74.9 Million
Emp.: 4
Chemical Products Mfr
N.A.I.C.S.: 325998
Jens Lykner *(Mgr-Maintenance & Reliability)*
Joern Stryger *(Plant Mgr)*

Subsidiary (Non-US):

CP Kelco Argentina S.A.   **(2)**
Bolivar 187-6th A, C1066AAC, Buenos Aires, Argentina
Tel.: (54) 1143318483
Web Site: http://www.cpkelco.com
Chemical Products Mfr
N.A.I.C.S.: 325998

CP Kelco B.V.   **(2)**
Kerkenbos 1057b, Postbus 31, 6500 AA, Nijmegen, Netherlands
Tel.: (31) 243719900
Chemical Products Mfr
N.A.I.C.S.: 325998

CP Kelco Belgium b.v.b.a.   **(2)**
Industrieweg 150, 3538, Beringen, Belgium
Tel.: (32) 11458656
Sales Range: $10-24.9 Million
Emp.: 2
Food Processing Machinery Mfr
N.A.I.C.S.: 333241
Jan Noben *(Mgr-Sls)*

CP Kelco Germany GmbH   **(2)**
Neuer Wall 63, 20354, Hamburg, Germany   **(100%)**
Tel.: (49) 403749920
Sales Range: $10-24.9 Million
Emp.: 5
Mfr of Pectin
N.A.I.C.S.: 311942

CP Kelco Japan ApS   **(2)**
Izumi Kamiyacho Bldg 8-1 Higashi-Azabu 1-chome, Minato-ku, Tokyo, 106-0044, Japan
Tel.: (81) 335607313
Chemical Products Mfr
N.A.I.C.S.: 325998

CP Kelco Oy   **(2)**
Kuhnamontie 2, Aanekoski, 44101, Finland
Tel.: (358) 145183000
Web Site: http://www.cpkelco.com
Chemical Products Mfr
N.A.I.C.S.: 325180
Sari Vertanen *(Mgr-HR)*

CP Kelco Poland Sp. Z.o.o.   **(2)**
ul Abpa A Baraniaka 88 C, Malta Office Park, 61-131, Poznan, Poland
Tel.: (48) 616258555
Chemical Products Mfr
N.A.I.C.S.: 325180

CP Kelco Singapore Pte., Ltd.   **(2)**
151 Lorong Chuan 04-01 A New Tech Park, Singapore, 556741, Singapore
Tel.: (65) 64919100
Web Site: http://www.cpkelco.com
Chemical Products Mfr
N.A.I.C.S.: 325998
Amy Wong *(Gen Mgr)*

CP Kelco UK Limited   **(2)**
Cleeve Court Cleeve Road, Leatherhead, KT22 7UD, Surrey, United Kingdom
Tel.: (44) 1372 369 400
Web Site: http://www.cpkelco.com
Emp.: 20
Chemical Products Mfr
N.A.I.C.S.: 325998

Huber Engineered Materials, LLC   **(1)**
3100 Cumberland Blvd Ste 600, Atlanta, GA 30339
Tel.: (678) 247-7300
Web Site: http://www.hubermaterials.com
Sales Range: $25-49.9 Million
Emp.: 120
Engineered Materials
N.A.I.C.S.: 325998

Craig Gentile *(Dir-Sls)*
Damon Boling *(Mgr-Quality Control)*
Ed Maxwell *(Reg Mgr-Sls)*
E. J. Evans *(Coord-Distr Sls)*
Con Mills *(Dir-Global Sls)*

Plant (Domestic):

Huber Engineered Materials, LLC - Havre de Grace   **(2)**
907 Revolution St, Havre de Grace, MD 21078-3700
Tel.: (410) 939-3500
Web Site: http://www.hubermaterials.com
Sales Range: $25-49.9 Million
Synthetic & Inorganic Pigments & Fillers
N.A.I.C.S.: 325180
Markley Ligon *(Mgr-Productivity)*

Huber Engineered Materials, LLC - Quincy   **(2)**
3150 Gardner Expy, Quincy, IL 62305-9378
Tel.: (217) 224-1100
Web Site: http://www.huber.com
Sales Range: $75-99.9 Million
Engineered Materials
N.A.I.C.S.: 212312

Joint Venture (Non-US):

Magnifin Magnesiaprodukte GmbH & Co KG   **(2)**
Magnesitstr 40, 8614, Breitenau, Austria   **(50%)**
Tel.: (43) 38662002
Web Site: http://www.magnifin.com
Sales Range: $25-49.9 Million
Emp.: 54
Magnesium Oxide, Hydroxide Powders & Special Sodium Silicates
N.A.I.C.S.: 325180
Christian Kienesberger *(Mng Dir-Breitenau)*

Huber Engineered Woods LLC   **(1)**
10925 David Taylor Dr Ste 300, Charlotte, NC 28262
Tel.: (704) 547-0671
Web Site: http://www.huberwood.com
Emp.: 70
Engineered Wood Products Mfr
N.A.I.C.S.: 113210
Michael L. Marberry *(Chm-Mgmt Bd)*
Brian Carlson *(Pres & Member-Mgmt Bd)*
Gary A. Acinapura *(Member-Mgmt Bd)*
Bryan Cecala *(Member-Mgmt Bd)*
Kurt Liebich *(Member-Mgmt Bd)*
Joseph G. May *(Member-Mgmt Bd)*
Carol Lynn Messer *(Member-Mgmt Bd)*
W. Andrew Trott *(Member-Mgmt Bd)*

Huber Resources Corporation   **(1)**
1141 Main St, Old Town, ME 04468-2022
Tel.: (207) 827-7195
Web Site: http://www.huberresources.com
Sales Range: $10-24.9 Million
Emp.: 20
Forest Management Services
N.A.I.C.S.: 115310
Pete Triandafillou *(VP)*
Christopher Washburn *(Dir-Fin)*
Trevor London *(Mgr-Mktg)*
Kenny E. Fergusson *(Mgr-Ops)*

Huber Specialty Hydrates, LLC   **(1)**
4701 Alcoa Rd, Benton, AR 72015
Tel.: (501) 326-6799
Chemical Products Mfr
N.A.I.C.S.: 325180

J.M. Huber (India) Pvt. Ltd.   **(1)**
504 Meadows Sahar Plaza J B Nagar Kurla Road, Andheri E, 400059, Mumbai, India
Tel.: (91) 2261415713
Sales Range: $10-24.9 Million
Emp.: 9
Chemical Products Mfr
N.A.I.C.S.: 325998

J.M. Huber Corp.-Natural Resources   **(1)**
11451 Katy Freeway, Houston, TX 77079   **(100%)**
Tel.: (713) 871-4400
Web Site: http://www.huber.com
Sales Range: $50-74.9 Million
Emp.: 350
Crude Oil; Natural Gas
N.A.I.C.S.: 561110

J.M. Huber Finland Oy   **(1)**

Telakkatie 5, 49460, Hamina,
Finland   **(100%)**
Tel.: (358) 20 791 3500
Web Site: http://www.hubermaterials.com
Sales Range: $25-49.9 Million
Emp.: 100
Silica Mfr
N.A.I.C.S.: 325130
Tom Steyaert (Controller)

J.M. Huber Investment (China)
Ltd   **(1)**
7F Xingyuan Tech Plaza No 418 Guiping
Road Cao He Jing Hi-Tech Park, Xuhui Dis-
trict, Shanghai, 200233, China
Tel.: (86) 2151758488
Web Site: http://www.cpkelco.co.jp
Investment Management Service
N.A.I.C.S.: 523999

Miller Chemical & Fertilizer, LLC   **(1)**
120 Radio Rd, Hanover, PA 17331-1139
Tel.: (717) 632-8921
Web Site: http://www.millerchemical.com
Sales Range: $10-24.9 Million
Emp.: 60
Non-Hazardous Crop Protection Adjuvants
& Nutritional Agrochemicals Mfr & Marketer
N.A.I.C.S.: 325320
Jackie Walker (Dir-Pur)
Andrew Smith (Plant Mgr)

J.M. HUTTON & CO., INC.
1501 S 8th St, Richmond, IN 47374
Tel.: (765) 962-3591
Web Site: http://www.jmhutton.com
Year Founded: 1845
Rev.: $16,000,000
Emp.: 83
Metal Stampings & Metal & Hard-
wood Caskets Mfr
N.A.I.C.S.: 339995
Rick Jeffers (Pres-Wood Div)
Steve Campbell (Plant Mgr)
Paul Faddis (Mgr-Ops)

J.M. JAYSON & CO., INC.
2350 N Forest Rd Ste 35B, Getzville,
NY 14068-1296
Tel.: (716) 636-9090   **NY**
Year Founded: 1968
Sales Range: $125-149.9 Million
Emp.: 250
Real Estate Investment Services
N.A.I.C.S.: 531210
Joseph M. Jayson (Pres & CEO)
Carol Platter (Dir-Property Mgmt)

J.M. MCCONKEY & CO. INC.
1615 Puyallup St, Sumner, WA
98390
Tel.: (253) 863-8111
Web Site:
   http://www.mcconkeyco.com
Rev.: $34,168,816
Emp.: 100
Horticulture Products & Systems for
Greenhouse Suppliers & Growers
Whslr
N.A.I.C.S.: 424910
Ed McConkey (Pres)

J.M. MCCORMICK COMPANY
INC.
521 S Enterprise Blvd, Lebanon, IN
46052
Tel.: (317) 874-4444
Web Site:
   http://www.jmmccormick.com
Year Founded: 1974
Sales Range: $25-49.9 Million
Emp.: 30
Lumber, Plywood & Millwork
N.A.I.C.S.: 423310
Ed Espey (CEO)
Greg Johnson (Pres)
Rod Forrest (Plant Mgr-Hardwood)
Diana Kenipe (Office Mgr)
Angie Daugherty (Comptroller)

J.M. MURRAY CENTER INC.
823 New York State Bicycle Rte 13,
Cortland, NY 13045
Tel.: (607) 756-9913
Web Site: http://www.jmmurray.com
Rev.: $16,006,831
Emp.: 400
Reupholstery & Furniture Repair
N.A.I.C.S.: 811420
Thomas Turck (Treas)
James Nichols (Sec)
Stephen Pearsall (Chm)
Stephen Compagni (Vice Chm)
Kathleen Hennessy (Chm)
Dale Davis (VP-Fin)
Ernest Dodge (Dir-Ops)
Karen Morgan (Dir-IT)
Floyd Moon (Pres)
Gerald Gebhard (VP-Ops & Sls)
Judy O'Brien (VP-Svcs)
Barbara Ackley (VP-HR & Compli-
ance)

Subsidiaries:

J. M. Murray Center inc   **(1)**
823 New York State Rte 13, Cortland, NY
13045
Tel.: (607) 756-9913
Web Site: http://www.jmmurray.com
Rev.: $15,059,055
Emp.: 200
Building Maintenance Services
N.A.I.C.S.: 561720

J.M. PERRONE CO., INC.
105 Research Rd, Hingham, MA
02043-4322
Tel.: (781) 741-2200   **MA**
Year Founded: 1981
Rev.: $18,000,000
Emp.: 120
Advertising Agencies, Collateral,
Communications, Consulting,
E-Commerce, Financial, Retail, Stra-
tegic Planning
N.A.I.C.S.: 541810
Tom Reed (Dir-Creative)
C. J. Floros (CEO)
Stuart Swanson (Sr Dir-Intergrated
Mktg)
Paul Barry (Pres)
Deborah Kerr (Dir-Sls & Strategic
Mktg)
Eric Henneman (VP-Ops)
Michele Fontaine (Dir-New Bus Dev)
Kelly Minichell (Dir-Bus Ops)
Jenny Patridge (Dir-Acct Svcs)
Steve van der Veen (CFO)

J.M. RODGERS CO., INC.
1975 Linden Blvd Ste 305, Elmont,
NY 11003
Tel.: (516) 872-5570
Web Site: http://www.jmrodgers.com
Year Founded: 1963
Sales Range: $10-24.9 Million
Emp.: 50
International Logistics Specialists
N.A.I.C.S.: 541990
Brian John Rodgers (Pres)
Kenny Chen (Treas)
Megan Wrynn (Coord-Import)
Donna Rogers (Coord-Ocean & Air
Import)
Colin Joyce (Mgr-Sls)
Arturo Guevara (Mgr-Import)

J.M. SMITH CORPORATION
101 W Saint John St Ste 305, Spar-
tanburg, SC 29306
Tel.: (864) 542-9419   **SC**
Web Site:
   http://www.jmsmithcorp.com
Year Founded: 1944
Sales Range: $1-4.9 Billion
Emp.: 960
Software & Technology Distr Services

N.A.I.C.S.: 541511
Kyle Waltz (VP-Corp Controller)
Kevin Welch (CTO)
Alan Turfe (Chm & CEO)
Philip Ryan III (CFO & Treas)

Subsidiaries:

Burlington Drug Company, Inc.   **(1)**
91 Catamount Dr, Milton, VT 05468-3236
Tel.: (802) 893-5105
Web Site: http://www.burlingtondrug.com
Pharmaceuticals, Health & Beauty Aids,
Makeup, Sundries & Specialties Distr
N.A.I.C.S.: 424210
Kathy Deavitt (Gen Mgr)
Aileen Wagner (Mgr-Ops)
David Fisher (Dir-Sls)

Integral Solutions, LLC   **(1)**
450 Wofford St, Spartanburg, SC 29301
Tel.: (864) 574-8161
Web Site: http://www.integralsg.com
Sales Range: $10-24.9 Million
Emp.: 30
Institutional Network & Cabling Integration
Services; Stock & Customized Printed
Healthcare Materials Distr
N.A.I.C.S.: 541512
Kimberly Mann (VP-Sls & Mktg)
Joe Strayer (Pres)

QS/1   **(1)**
201 W Saint John S, Spartanburg, SC
29306
Tel.: (864) 253-8600
Web Site: http://www.qs1.com
Sales Range: $75-99.9 Million
Emp.: 550
Healthcare Industry Software Publisher &
Custom Programming Services
N.A.I.C.S.: 513210
Rory Barzee (Dir-Bus Intelligence & Project
Mgmt)
Chris Lewis (Mgr-Sys Dev)
Tammy Devine (Pres)
Joey Parrish (VP-Customer Support)
Brent Thomasson (VP-Fin & Admin)
Ed Willett (VP-Natl Sls)

Division (Domestic):

QS/1 Governmental Solutions   **(2)**
201 W Saint John St, Spartanburg, SC
29306
Tel.: (864) 253-8650
Web Site: http://www.qs1.com
Sales Range: $75-99.9 Million
Emp.: 516
Government Administrative & Data Process-
ing Software Publisher
N.A.I.C.S.: 513210
Rich Muller (Dir-Ops)

Smith Drug Company   **(1)**
PO Box 1779, Spartanburg, SC 29304-
1779
Tel.: (864) 582-1218
Web Site: http://www.smithdrug.com
Sales Range: $10-24.9 Million
Emp.: 100
Drugs Whslr
N.A.I.C.S.: 424210
Brian Purscell (Sr VP-Pharmacy Solutions)
Jeff Schneider (VP-Long Term Care Phar-
macy Solutions)
Jeff Foreman (Pres)
Lena Jouran (VP-Fin)
Matthew Pike (Assoc VP-Strategy Indus
Rels)
Joe Willaman (Assoc VP-Strategic Accts)

J.N. WHITE ASSOCIATES, INC.
129 North Center St, Perry, NY
14530
Tel.: (585) 237-5191
Web Site: http://jnwhiteusa.com
Rev.: $8,420,000
Emp.: 115
Commercial Screen Printing
N.A.I.C.S.: 323113
Ken Boss (VP-Sls & Mktg)
Jason Aymerich (Pres)

Subsidiaries:

ECI Screen Print Inc.   **(1)**
15 Mountain View Dr, Watertown, CT 06795

Tel.: (860) 283-9849
Web Site: http://www.eciscreenprint.com
Sales Range: $1-9.9 Million
Emp.: 28
Electrical Products Mfr
N.A.I.C.S.: 335999
Edward Cook (Pres & CEO)

J.O. DELOTTO AND SONS,
INC.
924 E Busch Blvd, Tampa, FL 33612
Tel.: (813) 935-2191
Web Site: http://www.delotto.com
Year Founded: 1946
Sales Range: $10-24.9 Million
Emp.: 37
General Contractors
N.A.I.C.S.: 236210
Craig Lamberson (Pres)
Wayne Fernandez (Exec VP)
Doug Littrell (Exec VP)
Darrin Thomson (VP)

J.O. MORY INC.
7470 S State Rd 3, South Milford, IN
46786
Tel.: (260) 351-2221
Web Site: http://www.jomory.com
Sales Range: $10-24.9 Million
Emp.: 200
Mechanical Contractor
N.A.I.C.S.: 238220
Mike Rowe (Pres)
Shane M. Shanton (Mgr-Bus Dev)

J.O. WILLIAMS MOTORS, INC.
419 Broadway Ave, Gladewater, TX
75647-2449
Tel.: (903) 845-2222
Web Site:
   http://www.jowilliamsford.com
Sales Range: $10-24.9 Million
Emp.: 23
Car Whslr
N.A.I.C.S.: 441110
Michael Williams (Gen Mgr)

J.P. CULLEN & SONS INC.
330 E Delavan Dr, Janesville, WI
53546
Tel.: (608) 754-6601
Web Site: http://www.jpcullen.com
Sales Range: $350-399.9 Million
Emp.: 500
Commercial & Office Building, New
Construction
N.A.I.C.S.: 236210
Mark Cullen (Chm)
Daniel Swanson (VP-Estimating &
Work Procurement)
David Cullen (CEO)
Richard Cullen (VP-Field-Ops)
Larry Rocole (VP)
Steve Wisnefsky (CFO)
Ron Becher (Pres)
Pete Scharenbroch (Mgr-BIM & MEP)
Todd Christensen (Mgr-Concrete &
Masonry Div)
Jim Schumacher (Mgr-Epic Div)
Ryan Riemenschneider (Mgr-
Preconstruction & Estimating)
Mike Larue (Mgr-Prefabrication)
Chad Schakelman (VP-Indus Div)

J.P. HART LUMBER COMPANY
INC.
9810 Ball St, San Antonio, TX 78217
Tel.: (210) 337-6464
Web Site: http://www.hartlumber.com
Sales Range: $10-24.9 Million
Emp.: 100
Lumber: Rough, Dressed & Finished
N.A.I.C.S.: 423310
Greg Wright (Pres)
Bryan Arnold (Mgr-Window Dept)

J.P. Hunter Enterprises Inc.—(Continued)

J.P. HUNTER ENTERPRISES INC.
675 Elton St, Riverhead, NY 11901-2554
Tel.: (631) 283-4120
Sales Range: $10-24.9 Million
Emp.: 25
Roofing Contractors
N.A.I.C.S.: 238160
Kevin Borch (VP)
John P. Hunter Jr. (Pres)

J.P. KOTTS & CO.
3737 Willowick Rd, Houston, TX 77019-1115
Tel.: (713) 439-0996
Privater Equity Firm
N.A.I.C.S.: 523999
John P. Kotts (Owner)

Subsidiaries:

Pamarco Global Graphics   (1)
235 E 11th Ave, Roselle, NJ 07203-2015
Tel.: (908) 241-1200
Web Site: http://www.pamarco.com
Sales Range: $150-199.9 Million
Emp.: 700
Holding Company; Printing Industry Solutions
N.A.I.C.S.: 551112

Subsidiary (Domestic):

Pamarco Global Graphics (PGG)   (2)
11103 Indian Trl, Dallas, TX 75229
Tel.: (972) 484-6808
Web Site: http://www.pamarcoglobal.com
Sales Range: $25-49.9 Million
Emp.: 8
Mfr of Graphics & Offset Printing Equipment
N.A.I.C.S.: 423830

Pamarco, Incorporated   (2)
500 Wharton Cir SW, Atlanta, GA 30336
Tel.: (404) 691-1700
Web Site: http://www.pamarco.com
Printing Rollers & Other Printing Equipment Mfr & Distr
N.A.I.C.S.: 333248
Bill Ford (Pres)
John Burgess (Pres-Flexo Div)
Nick Walker (Gen Mgr-Flexo Div-UK)
John Meyer (VP-Sls-Offset)
Antony Whiteside (Pres-Engineered Products Div)
Allan Li (CEO)

J.P. MORGAN PHYSICAL COPPER TRUST
270 Park Ave, New York, NY 10017
Tel.: (212) 270-6000   DE
Year Founded: 2010
Copper Investment Services
N.A.I.C.S.: 523999
Daniel Hines (CEO)
David Connor (Exec Dir)
Nomar Morado (VP)
Zarko Cvetanovic (VP-TPM)

J.P. NOONAN TRANSPORTATION
415 W St PO Box 400, West Bridgewater, MA 02379
Tel.: (508) 583-2880
Web Site: http://www.jpnoonan.com
Rev.: $24,607,777
Emp.: 250
Trucking Services
N.A.I.C.S.: 484121
Paul Noonan (Mgr-Terminal)
Terry Chamberlain (Mgr-Terminal)
Bill Vieno (Office Mgr)

J.P. THIBODEAUX INC.
2511 Hwy 90 W, New Iberia, LA 70560-9446
Tel.: (337) 364-4126
Web Site:
http://www.jpthibodeaux.com

Sales Range: $75-99.9 Million
Emp.: 130
Automobile Sales & Service
N.A.I.C.S.: 441110
Joe Thibodeaux (Pres)

J.P.B. ENTERPRISES, INC.
8820 Columbia 100 Pkwy Ste 400, Columbia, MD 21045
Tel.: (410) 884-1960   FL
Web Site: http://www.jpbe.com
Year Founded: 1995
Sales Range: $10-24.9 Million
Emp.: 35
Holding Company; Private Equity & Real Estate Investment Services
N.A.I.C.S.: 551112
J. P. Bolduc (Chm & CEO)
Mary E. Glagola (Dir-Corp Comm)
Gayle A. Van Horn (VP-HR)
Michael J. Kalinock (Sr VP-Real Estate)
Mark Rohde (Mng Dir-JPB Capital Partners)
Matt Buckley (CFO)

Subsidiaries:

JPB Partners, LLC   (1)
8820 Columbia 100 Pkwy Ste 400, Columbia, MD 21045
Tel.: (410) 884-1960
Web Site: http://www.jpbe.com
Private Equity & Real Estate Investment Services
N.A.I.C.S.: 531210
J. P. Bolduc (Chm & CEO)
James R. Bolduc (Sr Mng Dir)
Gregory C. Carey (Mng Dir)
Jay Jang (VP)
Mark Rohde (Mng Dir)
Michael J. Kalinock (Sr VP-Real Estate)
Tom Cullen (CFO & Chief Compliance Officer)

Holding (Domestic):

Mulligan's Beach House Bar & Grill   (2)
1025 Beachland Blvd, Vero Beach, FL 32963-1610
Tel.: (772) 492-6744
Web Site:
    http://www.mulligansbeachhouse.com
Full-Service Restaurants
N.A.I.C.S.: 722511
George Hart (Founder & Pres)

J.R. ABBOTT CONSTRUCTION, INC.
3408 1st Ave S Ste 101, Seattle, WA 98134-1805
Tel.: (206) 467-8500   WA
Web Site: http://www.jrabbott.com
Year Founded: 1986
Sales Range: $75-99.9 Million
Emp.: 80
Provider of Commercial Building Construction Services
N.A.I.C.S.: 236220
John McGowan (Pres & CEO)
Mark Seaman (CFO)
Doug Klein (VP-Bus Dev)
Troy Stedman (COO)

J.R. COLE INDUSTRIES INC.
435 Minuet Ln, Charlotte, NC 28217
Tel.: (704) 523-6622
Web Site: http://www.jrcole.com
Sales Range: $10-24.9 Million
Emp.: 175
Packaging Materials Designer & Mfr
N.A.I.C.S.: 322299
Joe Richards (VP-Sls & Mktg)
Don Griffin (VP-Fin)
J. R. Cole Sr. (Pres & CEO)

Subsidiaries:

Carolina Prepress   (1)
235 W Tremont Ave, Charlotte, NC 28203

Tel.: (704) 342-0335
Rev.: $500,000
Emp.: 20
Printing Plates
N.A.I.C.S.: 333248
Jim Pruit (Gen Mgr)

Labeltec   (1)
435 Minuet Ln, Charlotte, NC 28217
Tel.: (704) 588-8881
Web Site: http://www.jrcole.com
Rev.: $6,000,000
Emp.: 56
Labels, Paper: Made From Purchased Material
N.A.I.C.S.: 322299

Southern Converters   (1)
1304 Berry Hill Rd, Charlotte, NC 28208
Tel.: (704) 393-5941
Web Site: http://www.jrcole.com
Rev.: $5,200,000
Emp.: 60
Folding Paperboard Boxes
N.A.I.C.S.: 322212
J. R. Cole Sr. (Pres)

J.R. KELLY COMPANY INC.
3450 Concord Rd, Lafayette, IN 47909
Tel.: (765) 772-3991
Web Site: http://www.jrkellyco.com
Rev.: $19,700,000
Emp.: 60
Industrial Building Construction
N.A.I.C.S.: 236210
Jeffery L. Mutzl (VP)
Elizabeth A. Spencer (Pres)
Alesa Dienhart (Controller)

J.R. MCDADE COMPANY, INC.
4317 E Broadway Rd, Phoenix, AZ 85040
Tel.: (602) 230-8800
Web Site: http://www.jrmcdade.com
Sales Range: $25-49.9 Million
Emp.: 150
Floor Laying Services
N.A.I.C.S.: 238330
Maryann Evans (Mgr-HR)

J.R. NAVARRO & ASSOCIATES INC.
12400 Wilshire Blvd Ste 240, Los Angeles, CA 90025-1040
Tel.: (310) 820-7676
Web Site: http://www.jrnavarro.com
Year Founded: 1977
Rev.: $12,000,000
Emp.: 17
N.A.I.C.S.: 541810
Mike Navarro (CEO)
John Navarro (Pres)
Omar Fish (Acct Exec)
Toby Navarro (VP-Acct Mngmt)
Paul McCarty (Graphic Designer & Art Dir)

J.R. PIERCE PLUMBING CO., INC.
14481 Wicks Blvd, San Leandro, CA 94577
Tel.: (510) 483-5473
Web Site:
    http://www.jrpierceplumbing.com
Year Founded: 1927
Sales Range: $10-24.9 Million
Emp.: 100
Plumbing, Heating & Air-Conditioning Contracting Services
N.A.I.C.S.: 238220
Richard Pierce (Owner & Pres)
Vanessa Aumua (Office Mgr)

J.R. SHORT MILLING COMPANY
1580 Grinnell Rd, Kankakee, IL 60901-8246
Tel.: (815) 937-2635
Web Site: http://www.shortmill.com

Sales Range: $25-49.9 Million
Emp.: 200
Flour Milling & Sales
N.A.I.C.S.: 311211
Janet Ibanic (VP-Acctg)
Craig R. Petray (CEO)
Tom Harris (Chm)

J.R. SIMPLOT COMPANY
1099 W Front St, Boise, ID 83702-9000
Tel.: (208) 336-2110   NV
Web Site: https://www.simplot.com
Year Founded: 1955
Sales Range: $1-4.9 Billion
Emp.: 13,000
Frozen Fruit, Juice & Vegetable Mfr
N.A.I.C.S.: 311411
Trish Arave (Mgr-Don Plant Phosphate Ops-Pocatello)
Doug Stone (Pres-Simplot AgriBusiness)
Garrett Lofto (Pres & CEO)
Richard Sunderland (VP-Supply Chain)
Darron Page (Sr VP-Global Solutions)
Scott R. Simplot (Chm)

Subsidiaries:

Dorman Brothers, LLC   (1)
19230 County Rd 55, Burlington, CO 80807
Tel.: (719) 346-7970
Sales Range: $10-24.9 Million
Emp.: 20
Farm Supplies Merchant Whslr
N.A.I.C.S.: 424910
Mike Dorman (Principal)

Hawaii Grower Products, Inc.   (1)
400 Lehuakona St, Kahului, HI 96732-3511
Tel.: (808) 877-6636
Web Site: http://www.simplot-hawaii.com
Farm Supplies
N.A.I.C.S.: 424910

J.R. Simplot Company   (1)
PO Box 27, Boise, ID 83707-0027
Tel.: (208) 336-2110
Sales Range: $50-74.9 Million
Emp.: 150
Agricultural Product Mfr & Distr
N.A.I.C.S.: 325320
Darrell Bateman (Dir)

J.R. Simplot Company - Land & Livestock   (1)
1301 Hwy 67, Grand View, ID 83624-9701   (100%)
Tel.: (208) 834-2231
Web Site: http://www.simplot.com
Sales Range: $100-124.9 Million
Emp.: 300
Beef Cattle Feedlots
N.A.I.C.S.: 112112

J.R. Simplot Company Food Group   (100%)
PO Box 9386, Boise, ID 83707
Tel.: (208) 384-8000
Web Site: http://www.simplotfoods.com
Sales Range: $125-149.9 Million
Emp.: 200
Frozen Potatoes, Fruits & Vegetables Mfr
N.A.I.C.S.: 311411

J.R. Simplot Company, Agri Business   (1)
999 Main St Ste 1300, Boise, ID 83702
Tel.: (208) 672-2700
Web Site: http://www.simplot.com
Sales Range: $100-124.9 Million
Emp.: 300
Superphosphate Fertilizer & Phosphoric Acid (Wet Process), Ammonium Phosphates Agricultural Chemicals Formulation
N.A.I.C.S.: 325312
Steve Gray (Dir-Risk Mgmt)
Joel Parker (VP & Controller-Agri Bus)

Subsidiary (Domestic):

J.R. Simplot Company Lathrop Plant   (2)

16777 Howland Rd, Lathrop, CA 95330-0198
Tel.: (209) 858-2511
Web Site: http://www.simplot.com
Emp.: 150
Fertilizer
N.A.I.C.S.: 325320
John Yanak (Plant Mgr)

Pacific Agricultural Sales & Services, Inc. (1)
91-262 Olai St, Kapolei, HI 96707
Tel.: (808) 682-5113
Web Site: http://www.simplot-hawaii.com
Nursery & Garden Products Distr
N.A.I.C.S.: 444240

Simplot Australia Pty. Ltd. (1)
Chifley Business Pk 2 Chifley Dr, Melbourne, 3194, VIC, Australia (100%)
Tel.: (61) 395883000
Web Site: http://www.simplot.com.au
Sales Range: $300-349.9 Million
Emp.: 400
Mfr & Distributor of Food Products
N.A.I.C.S.: 311423
Terry O'Brien (Mng Dir)
Sam Leycock (Gen Mgr)

Simplot Korea Inc. (1)
770-14 Yeoksam 2-dong, Gangnam-gu, 135-928, Seoul, Korea (South)
Tel.: (82) 25614787
Web Site: http://www.simplot.co.kr
Sales Range: $10-24.9 Million
Emp.: 15
Food Products Mfr
N.A.I.C.S.: 311999

Simplot Partners (1)
4107 Challenger Way, Caldwell, ID 83605
Tel.: (208) 454-6343
Web Site: http://www.simplot.com
Fertilizer, Turf Grass Seed & Chemical Products Distr
N.A.I.C.S.: 325312
Kristi Smith (Mgr-Mktg Solutions)

Simplot Phosphates, LLC (1)
515 S Hwy 430, Rock Springs, WY 82902
Tel.: (307) 382-1400
Web Site: http://www.simplot.com
Sales Range: $25-49.9 Million
Emp.: 275
Phosphatic Fertilizer Mfr
N.A.I.C.S.: 325312
Eric Schillie (Plant Mgr)

J.R. THOMPSON COMPANY, LLC

26970 Haggerty Rd Ste 100, Farmington Hills, MI 48331
Tel.: (248) 553-4566
Web Site: http://www.jrthompson.com
Year Founded: 1974
Sales Range: $50-74.9 Million
Emp.: 65
Automotive, Industrial, Marine
N.A.I.C.S.: 541810
Ruth Newman (Coord-Client Svc)
Jim Yetter (CMO)
Mark Bellissimo (CEO)

J.S. BLADE ADVERTISING AGENCY, INC.

1620 US Hwy 22 E, Union, NJ 07083-3414
Tel.: (908) 686-0022   DE
Web Site: http://www.jsblade.com
Year Founded: 1986
Sales Range: $10-24.9 Million
Emp.: 20
N.A.I.C.S.: 541810
Suzanne Firsichbaum (Pres & Co-Owner)
Joseph G. Ubil (Sr VP & Co-Owner)
James Paroline (CFO)
Kristen Keich (Art Dir)
Joan Filiaci (Acct Exec)
Laurie Firsichbaum (Acct Mgr)
John Introcaso (Acct Exec)
Daniela Biba (Acct Coord)

J.S. KARLTON COMPANY, INC.

2 Greenwich Office Park Ste 300, Greenwich, CT 06831
Tel.: (203) 629-5333
Web Site: http://www.jskarlton.com
Sales Range: $1-9.9 Million
Emp.: 35
Real Estate Management & Investment
N.A.I.C.S.: 531312
Stephen P. Lipkins (Exec VP)

J.S. MCCARTHY INC.

15 Darin Dr, Augusta, ME 04330
Tel.: (207) 622-6241
Web Site: http://www.jsmccarthy.com
Sales Range: $10-24.9 Million
Emp.: 180
Offset Printing
N.A.I.C.S.: 323111
Richard Tardiff (Pres)
Conrad L. Ayotte (Co-Owner, CFO, Treas & VP)

J.S. PALUCH CO. INC.

3708 River Rd Ste 400, Franklin Park, IL 60131
Tel.: (847) 678-9300   IL
Web Site: http://www.jspaluch.com
Year Founded: 1913
Pamphlets: Publishing & Printing
N.A.I.C.S.: 513130
William J. Rafferty (Pres)
Dolores Orzel (Creative Dir-NVAD)
Deb Johnston (Mgr-Production)
Lenice Levy (District Mgr)
Cristy Guzman (Dir-Parish Svcs)
Mary Lou Rafferty (Owner)
Kevin Royal (District Mgr-Eastern US Reg)
Vincent DiNicola (District Mgr-Western Pennsylvania)
Kirk Durham (District Mgr)
Daniel Radillo (District Sls Mgr)
Hector Brignoni (District Sls Mgr-Puerto Rico)
Anthony Brassil (District Mgr)
Heather Gaudet (District Mgr-Louisiana)
Justin Willis (District Mgr-Southern California)
Dean Hartwig (District Mgr-Northern California)

J.S. VENTURES, INC.

2400 N Woodlawn St, Wichita, KS 67220
Tel.: (316) 683-7799   KS
Web Site: http://www.jsvapplebees.com
Sales Range: $50-74.9 Million
Emp.: 1,800
Franchise Restaurants Owner & Operator
N.A.I.C.S.: 722511
James H. Stevens (Owner, Pres & CEO)

J.S. WEST & COMPANY

501 9th St, Modesto, CA 95354
Tel.: (209) 577-3221
Web Site: http://www.jswest.com
Sales Range: $25-49.9 Million
Emp.: 300
Propane; Animal Feed Retail; Hardware Retail; Furniture Retail
N.A.I.C.S.: 444140
Gary West (Owner)
Hank Easton (VP)

J.T. FENNELL CO. INC.

1104 N Front St, Chillicothe, IL 61523
Tel.: (309) 274-2145
Sales Range: $1-9.9 Million
Emp.: 80
Machine Shop, Jobbing & Repair
N.A.I.C.S.: 332710

Dan Coldwell (Mgr-Production)
Scott Meints (Mgr-IT)

J.T. LANEHART ELECTRIC CO. INC.

2033 Bingle Rd, Houston, TX 77055
Tel.: (713) 465-0477
Web Site: http://www.lanehart.com
Rev.: $10,800,000
Emp.: 50
General Electrical Contractor
N.A.I.C.S.: 238210
Bill Russell (Gen Mgr)
Mike Bouwman (Mktg Mgr)
Tigh Cundieff (Mktg Mgr)
Chad Denney (Mgr-Mktg)
James Edwards (Mktg Mgr)
Derek Kirby (Mgr-Mktg)
Jeff Knight (Mktg Mgr)
Mark McGarity (Mktg Mgr)
Chris Liston (Mktg Mgr)
Travis Willis (Mgr-Mktg)
John T. Lanehart Sr. (Pres)

J.T. MEGA MARKETING COMMUNICATIONS

4020 Minnetonka Blvd, Minneapolis, MN 55416-4100
Tel.: (952) 929-1370   MN
Web Site: http://www.jtmega.com
Year Founded: 1976
Rev.: $17,000,000
Emp.: 40
Brand Development, Business-To-Business, Exhibit/Trade Shows, Food Service, Industrial, Point of Purchase
N.A.I.C.S.: 541810
Philip Lee (Pres)
Sandri Dekker (VP-Production)
Mur Pulver (Media Dir & PR Dir)
Tim Glovatsky (Exec VP)
Bob Beach (VP-Creative Svcs)
Patrick DuPont (Sr Dir-Art)
Clarice Hallberg (VP, Mgmt Supvr)
Muriel Bartelme Kreske (VP & Exec Dir-Creative)
Don Mullen (VP & Dir-Media)
Ashley Kile (Dir-Res & Insights)

J.T. SHANNON LUMBER INC.

2200 Cole Rd, Horn Lake, MS 38637-2300
Tel.: (662) 393-3765   MS
Web Site: http://www.jtshannon.com
Year Founded: 1982
Sales Range: $50-74.9 Million
Emp.: 400
Provider of Lumber; Plywood & Millwork
N.A.I.C.S.: 423310
Jack Shannon (CEO)
Rick Chubb (Gen Mgr-Superior Hardwoods Lumber Co)
Mary Considine (Acting CEO)

Subsidiaries:

Shamrock Wood Industries Inc. (1)
2200 Cole Rd, Horn Lake, MS 38637-2300
Tel.: (662) 393-2125
Sales Range: $10-24.9 Million
Emp.: 50
Provider of Wood Products
N.A.I.C.S.: 321918

Superior Hardwoods Inc. (1)
4990 Crittenden Dr, Louisville, KY 40209-1704 (100%)
Tel.: (502) 361-7131
Sales Range: $10-24.9 Million
Emp.: 20
Provider Of Lumber & Wood Products
N.A.I.C.S.: 321912

J.T. TURNER CONSTRUCTION CO.

2250 E Victory Dr Ste 104, Savannah, GA 31414
Tel.: (912) 356-5611

Web Site: http://www.jttconst.com
Rev.: $18,000,000
Emp.: 70
Renovation & Repair of Commercial & Office Buildings
N.A.I.C.S.: 236220
Sandi Wubbena (Mgr-HR)
James T. Turner Jr. (Founder & Pres)

J.T. VAUGHN CONSTRUCTION COMPANY INCORPORATED

10355 Westpark Dr, Houston, TX 77042
Tel.: (713) 243-8300
Web Site: http://www.vaughnconstruction.com
Sales Range: $25-49.9 Million
Emp.: 290
Commercial & Office Building Construction Services
N.A.I.C.S.: 236220
Joe Vaughn (CEO)

J.T. WALKER INDUSTRIES, INC.

861 N Hercules Ave, Clearwater, FL 33765-1922
Tel.: (727) 461-0501   FL
Web Site: http://www.metalaire.com
Sales Range: $200-249.9 Million
Emp.: 200
Holding Company
N.A.I.C.S.: 332321
Jay K. Poppleton (Pres)
Janet Fasenmyer (VP-Fin)
Peter DeSoto (CEO)

Subsidiaries:

Metalaire, Inc. (1)
1985 Carroll St, Clearwater, FL 33765-1922
Tel.: (727) 441-2651
Web Site: http://www.metalindustriesinc.com
Sales Range: $25-49.9 Million
Emp.: 50
Mfr of Air Distribution Products
N.A.I.C.S.: 333415
Damian Macaluso (Pres)

Prefco, Inc. (1)
896 Rutherford Rd, Marion, NC 28752
Tel.: (828) 652-1424
Web Site: http://www.prefco-hvac.com
Emp.: 140
Fire & Smoke Damper Mfr
N.A.I.C.S.: 332322
Steve Brush (Mgr-Plant)

J.T. WIMSATT CONTRACTING CO., INC.

28064 Ave Stanford Ste B, Valencia, CA 91355
Tel.: (661) 775-8090
Web Site: http://www.jtwimsatt.com
Sales Range: $10-24.9 Million
Emp.: 155
Poured Concrete Foundation & Structure Services
N.A.I.C.S.: 238110
Edward Spurgeon (Mgr-Safety)
Christina Pack (Mgr-Bus Dev)
John Price (VP)

J.V. ROCKWELL PUBLISHING INC.

810 Missouri Ave, Corning, AR 72422
Tel.: (870) 857-3531
Web Site: http://www.jvrockwellpublishing.com
Rev.: $14,400,000
Emp.: 80
Magazine Publisher
N.A.I.C.S.: 513120
J. V. Rockwell (Pres)
Mark Rockwell (VP)
Lois Grooms (Supvr-Autos Dept)

J.W. BAILEY CONSTRUCTION COMPANY

2171

J.W. Bailey Construction Company—(Continued)

424 Olive St, Santa Barbara, CA
93101
Tel.: (805) 963-1855
Web Site: http://www.jwbailey.com
Sales Range: $10-24.9 Million
Emp.: 5
Nonresidential Construction
N.A.I.C.S.: 236220
William R. Bailey *(Pres)*

J.W. COLE FINANCIAL, INC.
4301 Anchor Plz Pkwy Ste 450,
Tampa, FL 33634
Tel.: (813) 935-6776   FL
Web Site: http://www.jw-cole.com
Year Founded: 2002
Sales Range: $600-649.9 Million
Emp.: 170
Investment Banking & Advisory Ser-
vices
N.A.I.C.S.: 523150
John R. Carlson *(Founder & Princi-
pal)*
Jason Card *(VP-Advisor Solutions)*
Craig Towle *(Exec VP)*

J.W. GRAND INC.
5940 Perkins Rd, Baton Rouge, LA
70808-4113
Tel.: (225) 767-3724   LA
Web Site: http://www.jwgrand.com
Year Founded: 1975
Sales Range: $25-49.9 Million
Emp.: 150
Industrial, Institutional & Commercial
Buildings & Warehouses
N.A.I.C.S.: 236210
John W. Grand *(Co-Owner & Pres)*
Patrick Hollier *(Project Mgr)*

J.W. JONES COMPANY, LLC
2468 State Rd 67 S, Paragon, IN
46166
Tel.: (765) 537-2279
Web Site:
   http://www.jwjonescompany.com
Year Founded: 1967
Sales Range: $10-24.9 Million
Emp.: 38
Mfr of Crushing & Screening Equip-
ment
N.A.I.C.S.: 333131
John W. Jones *(Pres)*

Subsidiaries:

Rock Equipment Inc.   (1)
2468 S State Rd 67, Paragon, IN 46166
Tel.: (765) 537-2279
Sales Range: $10-24.9 Million
Whslr of Construction Machinery & Equip-
ment
N.A.I.C.S.: 423810
John W. Jones *(Pres)*
Jessica Jones *(VP)*
Pete Hassett *(Controller)*

J.W. JUNG SEED COMPANY
335 S High St, Randolph, WI 53957-
0001
Tel.: (920) 326-3121   WI
Web Site: http://www.jungseed.com
Year Founded: 1907
Sales Range: $125-149.9 Million
Emp.: 150
Seeds, Plants, Shrubs & Bulbs Retail
& Mail Order
N.A.I.C.S.: 444240
Richard J. Zondag *(Pres & CEO)*
David Wild *(Controller)*
Aron Hill *(Mgr-Call Center)*

Subsidiaries:

McClure & Zimmerman   (1)
335 S High St, Randolph, WI
53956   **(100%)**
Tel.: (920) 326-3121

Web Site: http://www.mzbulb.com
Fall Planted Bulb Specialty Catalog
N.A.I.C.S.: 444240

J.W. KOEHLER ELECTRIC, INC.
2716 W Central Park Ave, Davenport,
IA 52804
Tel.: (563) 386-1800
Web Site: http://www.jwkoehler.com
Year Founded: 1969
Sales Range: $10-24.9 Million
Emp.: 150
Provider of Electrical Contracting &
Cabling Services
N.A.I.C.S.: 238210
Timothy W. Koehler *(Pres)*
Don Luth *(Exec VP)*

J.W. PEPPER & SON INC.
2480 Industrial Blvd, Paoli, PA 19301
Tel.: (610) 648-0500
Web Site: http://www.jwpepper.com
Sales Range: $25-49.9 Million
Emp.: 240
Sales of Musical Instruments
N.A.I.C.S.: 459140
Glenn Burtch *(Pres & CEO)*

J.W. PERRY INC.
707 S Ctr Ave, Merrill, WI 54452
Tel.: (715) 536-9465
Web Site: http://www.jwperry.com
Year Founded: 1938
Sales Range: $10-24.9 Million
Emp.: 250
Whslr of Flowers
N.A.I.C.S.: 424930
Leroy Brose *(Pres)*
Lynn Hansen *(Controller)*
Donivan Brose *(Pres)*
Mark Toburen *(Mgr-Shop)*

J.W. PIERSON COMPANY INC.
89 Dodd St, East Orange, NJ 07017
Tel.: (973) 673-5000
Web Site: http://www.jwpierson.com
Sales Range: $10-24.9 Million
Emp.: 33
Fuel Oil Dealers
N.A.I.C.S.: 457210

J.W. SPEAKER CORPORA-TION
N120 W19434 Freistadt Rd, German-
town, WI 53022-8211
Tel.: (262) 251-6660
Web Site: http://www.jwspeaker.com
Year Founded: 1935
Rev.: $130,000,000
Emp.: 200
Vehicle Lighting Equipment Mfr
N.A.I.C.S.: 336320

J.W. WINCO, INC.
2815 S Calhoun Rd, New Berlin, WI
53151
Tel.: (262) 786-8227
Web Site: http://www.jwwinco.com
Rev.: $11,400,000
Emp.: 40
Industrial Supplies Merchant Whslr
N.A.I.C.S.: 423840
Robert Winkler *(VP)*
John M. Winkler *(Chm)*
Mark Winkler *(CFO)*

J.W.E. INC.
180 Madison Ave 20th Fl, New York,
NY 10016
Tel.: (212) 704-2033
Web Site:
   http://www.jweconcepts.com
Sales Range: $10-24.9 Million
Emp.: 17
Men's & Women's Uniforms
N.A.I.C.S.: 424350

Joe Wei Zhang *(Pres & CEO)*

J.W.S. DELAVAU CO. INC.
10101 Roosevelt Blvd, Philadelphia,
PA 19154-2105
Tel.: (215) 671-1400   PA
Web Site: http://www.delavau.com
Year Founded: 1847
Sales Range: $125-149.9 Million
Emp.: 300
Pharmaceutical Preparations
N.A.I.C.S.: 325412
Stephen Bryan *(Pres)*

J.Y. LEGNER ASSOCIATES INC
340 N Evergreen Rd, Louisville, KY
40243
Tel.: (502) 585-9000
Web Site:
   http://www.powerstaffing.com
Year Founded: 1999
Rev.: $4,600,000
Emp.: 10
Professional Services
N.A.I.C.S.: 541330
Jozi Legner *(Pres & CEO)*
Matt Linvelle *(CFO)*

J/P HAITIAN RELIEF ORGANI-ZATION
6464 Sunset Ave Ste 1170, Los An-
geles, CA 90028
Tel.: (323) 934-4400   CA
Web Site: http://www.jphro.org
Year Founded: 2010
Sales Range: $10-24.9 Million
Emp.: 29
Community Development Services
N.A.I.C.S.: 624190

J2 ENGINEERING INC.
6921 Pistol Range Rd Ste 101,
Tampa, FL 33635
Tel.: (813) 888-8861
Web Site: http://www.j2-eng.com
Year Founded: 2001
Sales Range: $50-74.9 Million
Emp.: 50
Industrial & Commercial Construction
N.A.I.C.S.: 236210
Fred Portofe *(VP)*
Lori Johnson *(CFO)*

J2 SOLUTIONS, INC.
1515 Tamiami Trl S Ste 404, Venice,
FL 34285
Tel.: (941) 492-3266   FL
Web Site:
   http://www.j2solutionsinc.com
Sales Range: $1-9.9 Million
Emp.: 10
Industrial & Residential Building Con-
struction
N.A.I.C.S.: 236210
Jess Fronckowiak *(Pres)*
David Fouche *(VP-Ops)*

JA CARPENTRY, INC.
150 English St, Hackensack, NJ
07601
Tel.: (201) 498-1477
Web Site:
   http://www.jacarpentryinc.com
Sales Range: $10-24.9 Million
Emp.: 40
Commercial & Institutional Building
Construction Services
N.A.I.C.S.: 236220
James Agresta *(Pres)*
Robert Krzykowski *(VP)*

JA INTEGRATED THINKING
104 Continental Pl Ste 300, Brentwood, TN 37027-4645
Tel.: (615) 377-9111

Web Site: http://www.jathinking.com
Year Founded: 1956
Rev.: $46,000,000
Emp.: 65
Business-To-Business, Co-op Adver-
tising, Full Service, Media Buying
Services, Restaurant, Retail, Sports
Marketing
N.A.I.C.S.: 541810
Stephen Barry *(Pres)*
Melanie Corbett *(VP & Media Svc)*
Karen Smith *(Grp VP-KFC)*
Donna Steinkamp *(Mgr-Employee
Rel)*
Simone Marsalis *(VP-Taco Bell Grp)*
Peter Boswell *(Dir-Print)*
Jeannie Powell *(CFO)*
Leo Blumberg *(Dir-Strategic Info &
Plng)*
Mary Ingram *(Sr Acct Supvr)*
Amy Stepp *(Acct Exec)*
Leigh Grugett *(Supvr-Media)*
Kevin Endres *(Sr VP-Creative)*
Joe Harkins *(VP & Grp Dir)*
Bill Ralston *(VP-Mktg)*
Carter Toole *(VP-Digital Team)*
Paul Lassiter *(Chief Technologist)*

Subsidiaries:

JA Integrated Thinking   (1)
110 E Reynolds St Ste 808, Plant City, FL
33563
Tel.: (813) 659-8222
Web Site: http://www.jathinking.com
Sales Range: Less than $1 Million
Emp.: 1
N.A.I.C.S.: 541810
Jay Ritenbaugh *(Sr Acct Supvr)*

JA MARKETING CORP.
1 Mall Dr, Sunriver, OR 97707
Tel.: (541) 593-8113
Web Site: http://jamarketinginc.com
Rev.: $11,000,000
Emp.: 30
Grocery Stores
N.A.I.C.S.: 445110
Jay Audia *(Pres)*
Dave Schu *(Owner)*

JA-RU INC.
12901 Flagler Center Blvd, Jackson-
ville, FL 32258
Tel.: (904) 733-9311
Web Site: http://www.jaru.com
Year Founded: 1961
Sales Range: $10-24.9 Million
Emp.: 150
Toy Mfr
N.A.I.C.S.: 339930
Jack Selevan *(Pres)*
Bruce Connor *(Exec VP)*
Danny Bergman *(Dir-Sls & Mktg)*

Subsidiaries:

JA-RU Inc.   (1)
11/F Inter-Continental Plaza 94 Granville
Road, Tsim Sha Tsui East, Kowloon, China
(Hong Kong)
Tel.: (852) 3602 7000
Toy Mfr & Distr
N.A.I.C.S.: 339930

JAB WIRELESS, INC.
61 Inverness Dr E, Ste 250, Engle-
wood, CO 80112
Tel.: (303) 705-6522
Web Site:
   http://www.risebroadband.com
Wired Telecommunications Carriers
N.A.I.C.S.: 517111
Jeff Kohler *(Principal)*

Subsidiaries:

Telebeep Wireless   (1)
2404 Taylor Ave Ste 100, Norfolk, NE
68701
Tel.: (402) 371-2337

Data Processing, Hosting & Related Services
N.A.I.C.S.: 518210

JABIAN
1117 Perimeter Ctr W Ste N400, Atlanta, GA 30338
Web Site: http://www.jabian.com
Year Founded: 2006
Sales Range: $10-24.9 Million
Emp.: 73
Management & IT Consulting
N.A.I.C.S.: 541618
Brian Betkowski *(Co-Founder & Partner)*
Nigel Zelcer *(Co-Founder & Partner)*
Chris Reinking *(Co-Founder & Partner)*

JABO SUPPLY CORPORATION
5164 Braley Rd, Huntington, WV 25705
Tel.: (304) 736-8333   WV
Web Site: http://www.jabosupply.com
Year Founded: 1970
Sales Range: $10-24.9 Million
Emp.: 60
Steel Pipe & Tubing Distr
N.A.I.C.S.: 423510
Jack G. Bazemore *(Pres)*
Bob Bazemore *(Founder & Principal-Product Quality)*

JAC. VANDENBERG, INC.
100 Corporate Blvd, Yonkers, NY 10701-6807
Tel.: (914) 964-5900   NY
Web Site:
   http://www.jacvandenberg.com
Year Founded: 1940
Sales Range: $10-24.9 Million
Emp.: 40
Sales of Fresh Fruits & Vegetables
N.A.I.C.S.: 424480
David Schiro *(Pres)*
Ed Paap *(Controller)*
Craig Padover *(Acct Mgr)*

JACAM CHEMICAL COMPANY, INC.
205 S Broadway, Sterling, KS 67579
Tel.: (620) 278-3355
Web Site: http://www.jacam.com
Year Founded: 1982
Sales Range: $10-24.9 Million
Emp.: 150
Chemical Products Mfr
N.A.I.C.S.: 325998
Gene Zald *(Founder & CEO)*
Byron Owen *(VP-Down Hole Ops)*

JACC STUDIOS INC.
18124 Wedge Pkwy Ste 1050, Reno, NV 89511
Tel.: (778) 995-1267   NV
Web Site: http://www.jaccstudios.com
Year Founded: 2014
Assets: $16,581
Liabilities: $23,956
Net Worth: ($7,375)
Earnings: ($40,154)
Fiscal Year-end: 12/31/19
Online Game Development Services
N.A.I.C.S.: 541511
Jianhua Yu *(Pres, CEO, CFO, Chief Acctg Officer, Treas & Sec)*

JACER CORPORATION
10640 Page Ave, Fairfax, VA 22030
Tel.: (703) 352-1964
Web Site: http://www.jacer.com
Sales Range: $10-24.9 Million
Emp.: 15
IT Services
N.A.I.C.S.: 541519

Edgar Caburian *(CEO)*
Tom Cox *(COO)*

JACK & JILL OF AMERICA, INC.
1930 17th St NW, Washington, DC 20009
Tel.: (202) 667-7010   DC
Web Site:
   http://www.jackandjillinc.org
Year Founded: 1947
Sales Range: $10-24.9 Million
Emp.: 6
Youth Care Services
N.A.I.C.S.: 624110
Dyonicia Brown *(Exec Dir)*
Crystal Johnson-Turner *(Treas)*
Gladys Henderson *(Program Dir)*
Kimberley Goode *(Editor-Natl)*
Regina Page *(Sec-Recording-Natl)*
Tammy King *(Pres)*
Joli Cooper-Nelson *(VP-Natl)*
Kornisha McGill Brown *(Pres-Natl)*

JACK A. ALLEN INC.
2105 Old State Route 7, Steubenville, OH 43952
Tel.: (740) 282-4531
Rev.: $26,415,793
Emp.: 8
Gasoline
N.A.I.C.S.: 424720

JACK B. HENDERSON CONSTRUCTION CO. INC.
10100 Trumbull Ave SE, Albuquerque, NM 87123
Tel.: (505) 292-8955
Web Site:
   http://www.jbhenderson.com
Rev.: $45,604,989
Emp.: 650
Commercial & Office Building, New Construction
N.A.I.C.S.: 236220
Mark G. Henderson *(CEO)*
Dorian Atwater *(VP & Mgr)*
Linda Henderson *(Treas & Sec)*
John Robertson *(VP)*

JACK BECKER DISTRIBUTORS, INC.
6800 Suemac Pl, Jacksonville, FL 32254
Tel.: (800) 488-8411
Web Site: http://www.jackbecker.com
Rev.: $16,200,000
Emp.: 50
Petroleum Bulk Stations & Terminals
N.A.I.C.S.: 424710
Don Hudson *(VP-Admin)*
David Rowland *(Treas & Sec)*
Kathy Sharp *(Controller)*
Duane Rowland *(Pres)*

JACK BOWKER FORD LEASING COMPANY
2415 N 14th St, Ponca City, OK 74601
Tel.: (580) 765-5533
Web Site:
   http://www.jackbowkerford.com
Sales Range: $10-24.9 Million
Emp.: 43
New Car Dealers
N.A.I.C.S.: 441110
Jay Layman *(Gen Mgr-Sls)*

JACK BROWN PRODUCE, INC.
8035 Fruit Ridge Ave NW, Sparta, MI 49403
Tel.: (616) 887-9568
Web Site:
   http://www.jackbrownproduce.com
Sales Range: $10-24.9 Million

Emp.: 45
Fresh Fruit Distribution Services
N.A.I.C.S.: 424480
Tom Labbe *(Mgr-Sls)*
John Schaefer Jr. *(Pres)*

JACK BURFORD CHEVROLET-OLDSMOBILE-GEO, INC.
819 Eastern Byp, Richmond, KY 40475-2569
Tel.: (859) 623-3350
Web Site: http://www.jackburford.com
Sales Range: $10-24.9 Million
Emp.: 45
Car Whslr
N.A.I.C.S.: 441110
John Burford *(Mgr-Mktg)*

JACK BYRNE FORD & MERCURY, INC.
1003 Hudson River Rd, Mechanicville, NY 12118
Tel.: (888) 698-5382   NY
Web Site:
   http://www.jackbyrneford.net
Year Founded: 1965
Retailer of New & Used Automobiles
N.A.I.C.S.: 811111
Jack Byrne *(Pres)*

JACK CARUSO REGENCY DODGE INC.
10979 Atlantic Blvd, Jacksonville, FL 32225-2921
Tel.: (904) 642-5600   FL
Year Founded: 1969
Sales Range: $75-99.9 Million
Emp.: 55
Sales of Automobiles & Trucks
N.A.I.C.S.: 441110
John E. Caruso *(Pres)*
Deborah Caruso *(VP)*
John M. Caruso *(VP)*
Marisa Bunet *(Controller)*

JACK COOPER TRANSPORT CO., INC.
1100 Walnut St Ste 2400, Kansas City, MO 64106
Tel.: (816) 983-4000   DE
Web Site: http://www.jackcooper.com
Year Founded: 1928
Sales Range: $900-999.9 Million
Emp.: 4,000
Provider of Trucking Services
N.A.I.C.S.: 484230
Theo A. Ciupitu *(Gen Counsel, Sec & Exec VP)*
Kirk Hay *(CIO)*
Kyle Haulotte *(Co-CFO)*

Subsidiaries:

Axis Group, Inc.   (1)
2302 Parklake Dr NE, Atlanta, GA 30345
Tel.: (404) 370-0110
Web Site: http://www.axisgrp.com
Sales Range: $25-49.9 Million
Emp.: 200
Automotive Transport & Logistics Services
N.A.I.C.S.: 488510

Jack Cooper Transport-Team Auto
Processing Inc.   (1)
100 Walnut St Ste 2400, Kansas City, MO 64106   (100%)
Tel.: (816) 983-4000
Web Site: http://www.jackcooper.com
Sales Range: $10-24.9 Million
Emp.: 60
Provider of Transportation Services
N.A.I.C.S.: 484230

Pacific Motor Trucking Company
Inc.   (1)
1100 Walnut St 2400, Kansas City, MO 64106   (100%)
Tel.: (816) 983-4000
Web Site: http://www.jackcooper.com

Sales Range: $10-24.9 Million
Emp.: 70
Trucking Service
N.A.I.C.S.: 484121
Greg May *(Pres)*
Curtis Goodwin *(Sr VP-Labour Rels)*
Sarah Amico *(Head-M&A)*
Theo A. Ciupitu *(Gen Counsel & Exec VP)*
Don Herring *(Exec VP-Ops)*
Alex Meza *(Chief Comml Officer)*
Michael Riggs *(CEO)*
Michael S. Testman *(CFO)*
Brian Varano *(Chief Admin Officer)*

JACK DEMMER FORD, INC.
37300 Michigan Ave, Wayne, MI 48184-1165
Tel.: (734) 721-2600   MI
Web Site: http://www.demmer.com
Year Founded: 1957
Sales Range: $100-124.9 Million
Emp.: 140
Retailer of New & Used Automobiles
N.A.I.C.S.: 441110
John E. Demmer *(Chm & CEO)*
William J. Demmer *(Pres)*
John Engler *(Mgr-Fin)*

JACK DOHENY SUPPLIES, INC.
777 Doheny Dr, Northville, MI 48167
Tel.: (248) 349-0904
Web Site:
   http://www.dohenycompanies.com
Year Founded: 1973
Commercial Vehicles & Truck Rental Services
N.A.I.C.S.: 423110
Kay Doheny *(Pres & Owner)*

JACK EVANS CHEVROLET CADILLAC
125 S Royal Ave, Front Royal, VA 22630
Tel.: (540) 635-2153   VA
Web Site: http://www.jechevy.com
Year Founded: 1975
Sales Range: $10-24.9 Million
Emp.: 29
Sales of New & Used Automobiles
N.A.I.C.S.: 441110
Scott Burner *(Mgr-Parts)*
Glenn Murphy *(Gen Mgr-Sls)*
John W. Evans IV *(Owner)*

JACK GARRETT FORD, INC.
270 Ripley Rd, Spencer, WV 25276
Tel.: (304) 927-2490
Web Site:
   http://www.jackgarrettford.com
Rev.: $10,400,000
Emp.: 30
New Car Dealers
N.A.I.C.S.: 441110
Jack Garrett II *(Pres)*

JACK GIAMBALVO MOTOR CO., INC.
1390 Eden Rd, York, PA 17402
Tel.: (717) 846-1821   PA
Web Site: http://www.giambalvo.com
Year Founded: 1974
Car Dealer
N.A.I.C.S.: 441110
Don Dusich *(CFO)*
John W. Giambalvo *(Pres & CEO)*

JACK GOSCH FORD, INC.
150 Carriage Cir, Hemet, CA 92545
Tel.: (909) 658-3181   CA
Web Site: http://www.goschford.com
Rev.: $39,900,000
Emp.: 100
Automobiles, New & Used
N.A.I.C.S.: 441110
Kelly McMullen *(Gen Mgr)*
Tom Fuller *(Svc Mgr)*

Jack Gosch Ford, Inc.—(Continued)

JACK GRAHAM INC.
2 Marina Plz, Sarasota, FL 34236
Tel.: (941) 365-4232
Sales Range: $1-9.9 Million
Emp.: 120
Holding Company; Marina & Restaurant Owner
N.A.I.C.S.: 551112

Subsidiaries:

Marina Jack, Inc. (1)
2 Marina Plz, Sarasota, FL 34236
Tel.: (941) 955-9488
Web Site: http://www.marinajacks.com
Emp.: 15
Marinas
N.A.I.C.S.: 713930
Sam Chavers Jr. (Dir-Ops)

JACK GRAY TRANSPORT, INC.
4600 E 15th Ave, Gary, IN 46403-3639
Tel.: (219) 938-7020 IN
Web Site: http://www.jackgray.com
Year Founded: 1956
Sales Range: $75-99.9 Million
Emp.: 100
Provider of Long-Distance Trucking Services
N.A.I.C.S.: 488320
Carmen Mormino (Exec VP)
Diane R. Jones (Sec & Dir-Admin Svcs)
John S. Gray Sr. (Chm & Pres)

Subsidiaries:

Lakes & Rivers Transfer Div. (1)
4600 E 15th Ave, Gary, IN 46403-3639
Tel.: (219) 787-9280
Sales Range: $10-24.9 Million
Emp.: 50
Transportation of Bulk Commodities
N.A.I.C.S.: 488320

JACK GRIGGS INC.
1149 S Kaweah Ave, Exeter, CA 93221
Tel.: (559) 592-3154 CA
Web Site:
http://www.jackgriggsinc.com
Year Founded: 1933
Sales Range: $75-99.9 Million
Emp.: 40
Distr of Petroleum
N.A.I.C.S.: 424710
David Griggs (Pres, CEO, CFO & Treas)

JACK HOOD TRANSPORTATION INC.
10827 W County Rd 400 N, Michigan City, IN 46360
Tel.: (219) 874-2085
Rev.: $10,402,332
Emp.: 139
Trucking Except Local
N.A.I.C.S.: 484121
Jack Hood (Pres)
Scott Howard (Mgr)

JACK HORNER COMMUNICATIONS
671 Moore Rd Ste 100, King of Prussia, PA 19406
Tel.: (610) 768-3700
Web Site: http://www.jackhorner.com
Year Founded: 1992
Sales Range: $10-24.9 Million
Emp.: 22
Public Relations
N.A.I.C.S.: 541820
Jack Horner (Pres)

JACK JENNINGS & SONS, INC.
1030 Wilfred Dr, Orlando, FL 32803
Tel.: (407) 896-8181 FL
Web Site:
http://www.jackjennings.com
Year Founded: 1948
Sales Range: $1-9.9 Million
Emp.: 30
Commercial & Institutional Building Construction
N.A.I.C.S.: 236220
Jeffrey Jennings (Pres)
Toni Jennings (Chm)

JACK KAIN FORD, INC.
3405 Lexington Rd, Versailles, KY 40383
Tel.: (859) 873-6666
Web Site: http://www.kainford.com
Sales Range: $25-49.9 Million
Emp.: 45
New Car Dealers
N.A.I.C.S.: 441110
Bob Kain (Gen Mgr)
Vickie Kain Fister (Dir-Ops)
David Griggith (Gen Mgr-Sls)
Donna Sturgeon (Mgr-Mktg & Adv)

JACK KEY MOTOR COMPANY INC.
1840 N Main St, Las Cruces, NM 88001
Tel.: (505) 524-7741
Web Site: http://www.jackkey.com
Year Founded: 1987
Sales Range: $10-24.9 Million
Emp.: 60
Dealer of New & Used Automobiles
N.A.I.C.S.: 441110
Jack Key (Pres)
Derek Hagen (Gen Mgr-Sls)

JACK KISSEE FORD AGENCY, INC.
PO Box 40, Claremore, OK 74018-0040
Tel.: (918) 341-0101
Sales Range: $25-49.9 Million
Emp.: 40
Car Whslr
N.A.I.C.S.: 441110
Steve Kissee (Mgr)

JACK L. SLAGLE FIRE EQUIPMENT SUPPLY CO.
1100 Bill Tuck Hwy, South Boston, VA 24592
Tel.: (434) 575-7905
Web Site: http://www.slaglefire.com
Sales Range: $10-24.9 Million
Emp.: 35
Fire Trucks
N.A.I.C.S.: 423110
Jack L. Slagle (Chm)
Joe O'Malley (Comptroller & Coord-Special Projects)
Barry Slagle (Pres & Mgr-Sls)
Garry Slagle (Mgr-Svc)
Virgil Slagle (Exec VP & Mgr-Mktg & Sls-South Carolina)
John Teem (Mgr-Svc)

JACK M. BERRY INC.
3655 State Rd 80, Alva, FL 33920
Tel.: (863) 675-2769
Rev.: $10,000,000
Emp.: 200
Provider of Citrus Grove Management & Maintenance Services
N.A.I.C.S.: 115116
Jack Berry Jr. (Owner)

JACK MADDEN FORD SALES INC.
825 Providence Hwy, Norwood, MA 02062
Tel.: (781) 762-4200 MA
Web Site:
http://www.jackmaddenford.com
Year Founded: 1942
Sales Range: $25-49.9 Million
Emp.: 55
Sales of New & Used Automobiles
N.A.I.C.S.: 441110
Thomas Lucier (Mgr-Sls)
Eva Kraus (Mgr-IT)
John P. Madden Jr. (Pres)

JACK MARSHALL FOODS INC.
113 25th Ave E, Tuscaloosa, AL 35404
Tel.: (205) 553-8621
Web Site: http://www.jmfkfc.com
Sales Range: $10-24.9 Million
Emp.: 380
Franchise Owner of Fast-Food Restaurants
N.A.I.C.S.: 722513
Jack Marshall (Pres)

JACK MAXTON CHEVROLET INCORPORATED
700 E Granville Rd, Columbus, OH 43229
Tel.: (614) 885-5301 OH
Web Site:
http://www.jackmaxton.com
Year Founded: 1948
Sales Range: $125-149.9 Million
Emp.: 168
Sales of New & Used Automobiles
N.A.I.C.S.: 441110
Cheryl Fenner (Mgr-BDC)
Michael Craig (Mgr-Parts)
Tim Hall (Dir-Svc)
Heather Todd (Dir-Web Mktg)
Ron Taft (Mgr-Fleet & Comml Sls)
Phil Bruce (Mgr-Quick Svc)
Doug Lange (Mgr-Sls)

JACK MYERS REPORT
PO Box 660, Rhinebeck, NY 12572
Tel.: (201) 572-8675
Web Site: http://www.jackmyers.com
Year Founded: 1981
Sales Range: $10-24.9 Million
Emp.: 6
Advertising Agencies
N.A.I.C.S.: 541810
Maryann Teller (VP-Ops Res)
Jack Myers (CEO & Editor)

JACK NADEL INC.
8701 Bellanca Ave, Los Angeles, CA 90045
Tel.: (310) 815-2600 CA
Web Site: http://www.nadel.com
Year Founded: 1953
Sales Range: $50-74.9 Million
Emp.: 325
Direct Response Marketing
N.A.I.C.S.: 541890
Bob Kritzler (Mng Partner & CFO)
Craig Nadel (Pres)

Subsidiaries:

Jack Nadel Inc. - Southport Office (1)
107 John St 2nd Fl, Southport, CT 06890
Tel.: (203) 226-7733
Web Site: http://www.nadel.com
Sales Range: $10-24.9 Million
Emp.: 4
Advertising, Business-To-Business, Merchandising, Publicity/Promotions, Sales Promotion
N.A.I.C.S.: 541810
Lynne DuVivier (Partner & Acct Mgr)

JACK NEAL & SON, INC.
360 La Fata St, Saint Helena, CA 94574
Tel.: (707) 963-7303
Web Site:
http://www.jacknealandson.com
Year Founded: 1968
Sales Range: $10-24.9 Million
Emp.: 200
Vineyard Cultivation Services
N.A.I.C.S.: 115112
Mark Neal (Pres)

JACK POUST & COMPANY, INC.
420 Lexington Ave Ste 421, New York, NY 10170
Tel.: (212) 582-3330 NY
Web Site: http://www.jackpoust.com
Year Founded: 1945
Sales Range: $10-24.9 Million
Emp.: 5
Wine Importer
N.A.I.C.S.: 424820

JACK RICE INSURANCE, INC.
13080 S Belcher Rd Ste H, Largo, FL 33773
Tel.: (727) 530-0684 FL
Web Site:
http://www.jackriceinsurance.com
Year Founded: 1985
Sales Range: $25-49.9 Million
Emp.: 34
Insurance, Risk Management & Benefits Administration
N.A.I.C.S.: 524210
Cynthia M. Webster (Pres & CEO)

JACK RICH INCORPORATED
617 Altamont Blvd, Frackville, PA 17931
Tel.: (570) 874-3277 PA
Web Site: http://www.jackrich.com
Year Founded: 1963
Sales Range: $25-49.9 Million
Emp.: 60
Distr of Gasoline
N.A.I.C.S.: 424720
Brian Rich (Pres)

JACK RUBIN & SONS INC.
13103 S Alameda St, Compton, CA 90222
Tel.: (310) 635-5407
Web Site: http://www.wirerope.net
Sales Range: $10-24.9 Million
Emp.: 25
Distribution of Wire Rope, Cable, Rigging Hardware & the Manufacture of Slings, Lifting Devices & Cargo Handling Gear
N.A.I.C.S.: 423510
Bruce Rubin (Pres)
Sall Mandel (Controller)

JACK SCHMITT FORD INC.
1820 Vandalia St, Collinsville, IL 62234-4853
Tel.: (618) 344-5105
Web Site:
http://www.jackschmittford.com
Sales Range: $10-24.9 Million
Emp.: 40
Automobiles; New & Used
N.A.I.C.S.: 441110
Jack L. Schmitt (Pres)
Ben Firnkes (Mgr-Fin)

JACK SCHWARTZ SHOES, INC.
155 Avenue Of Americas 9th Fl, New York, NY 10013
Tel.: (212) 691-4700 NY
Web Site: http://www.lugz.com
Year Founded: 1936
Casual Footwear & Clothing Distr

N.A.I.C.S.: 424340
Ray Ricci (COO)
Jack Schwartz (Owner)
Rashaun Smith (VP-Mktg)

JACK VAN IMPE MINISTRIES INTERNATIONAL
1718 Northfield Dr, Rochester Hills, MI 48309
Tel.: (248) 852-2244   MI
Web Site: http://www.jvim.com
Year Founded: 1970
Sales Range: $10-24.9 Million
Emp.: 35
Christian Ministry Services
N.A.I.C.S.: 813110
Kenneth Vancil (Exec Dir)
Jack Van Impe (Pres)

JACK WALTERS & SONS CORP.
6600 Midland Ct, Allenton, WI 53002
Tel.: (262) 629-5521
Web Site:
   http://www.waltersbuildings.com
Year Founded: 1966
Sales Range: $10-24.9 Million
Emp.: 100
Prefabricated Metal Buildings
N.A.I.C.S.: 332311

JACK WILLIAMS TIRE CO. INC.
700 Rocky Glen Rd, Avoca, PA 18641
Tel.: (570) 457-5000   PA
Web Site:
   http://www.jackwilliams.com
Year Founded: 1929
Sales Range: $25-49.9 Million
Emp.: 310
Tire Sales & Service
N.A.I.C.S.: 441340
William C. Williams (Pres & CEO)
Jason Williams (Mgr-Mktg)
Bill Hamlin (VP-Mktg)
Dave Matriccino (Mgr-Wholesale Div)
Tim Franz (Engr-IT)
Michael J. Mellody (CFO)

JACK WINEGARDNER CHEV-ROLET, INC.
11001 Indian Head Hwy, Fort Washington, MD 20754
Tel.: (301) 292-6500
Web Site:
   http://www.jackwinegardner
   chevy.com
Sales Range: $10-24.9 Million
Emp.: 61
Auto Operator & Services
N.A.I.C.S.: 441110
Leroy Walker Jr. (Mgr-Sls)

JACK WOLF CADILLAC GMC
1855 N State St, Belvidere, IL 61008-2011
Tel.: (815) 544-3406
Web Site: http://www.jackwolf.com
Year Founded: 1984
Sales Range: $10-24.9 Million
Emp.: 90
Car Whslr
N.A.I.C.S.: 441110
Amy Wilcox (Mgr)
Jack Wolf (Pres)

JACK'S AQUARIUM & PETS
802 N Orchard Ln, Dayton, OH 45434
Tel.: (937) 320-4300
Web Site: http://www.jackspets.com
Rev.: $24,800,000
Emp.: 200
Pets & Supplies
N.A.I.C.S.: 459910

Phil Bresol (Controller)
Scott Brenner (Pres)

JACK'S BEAN COMPANY, LLC
402 N Interocean Ave, Holyoke, CO 80734-1000
Tel.: (970) 854-3702
Web Site: http://www.jacksbean.com
Year Founded: 1932
Sales Range: $75-99.9 Million
Emp.: 15
Domestic & International Dry Bean & Mexican Yellow Popcorn Pea & Bean Distr
N.A.I.C.S.: 111130
Tom Harmon (Gen Mgr)

JACK'S CAMERA INC.
200 Geiger Rd, Philadelphia, PA 19115
Tel.: (215) 677-1050   PA
Web Site:
   http://www.delawarecamera.com
Year Founded: 1951
Sales Range: $10-24.9 Million
Emp.: 30
Provider of Cameras
N.A.I.C.S.: 449210
Jim Contoudis (CEO)
Chris Contoudis (VP)

JACK'S FRUIT MARKET INC.
1511 W Center Rd, Essexville, MI 48732
Tel.: (989) 893-0591
Web Site: http://www.jacksmarket.net
Rev.: $33,000,000
Emp.: 150
Meat Markets, Including Freezer Provisioners
N.A.I.C.S.: 445240
Al McKenna (Asst Mgr)
Jack W. Stehle II (Pres)

JACK'S HEAVY EQUIPMENT INCORPORATED
6100 Douglas S Hwy, Gillette, WY 82718
Tel.: (307) 686-0608
Web Site: http://www.jacksinc.com
Rev.: $10,584,071
Emp.: 32
Construction & Mining Machinery
N.A.I.C.S.: 423810
Kevin Chafee (Pres)

JACK'S SURF & SPORT
101 Main St, Huntington Beach, CA 92647
Tel.: (714) 536-6567
Web Site: http://www.jacksurf.com
Rev.: $10,217,070
Emp.: 1,000
Men's & Boys' Clothing Stores
N.A.I.C.S.: 458110

JACK'S WHOLESALE WIN-DOWS AND DESIGN
2732 165th St, Hammond, IN 46323
Tel.: (219) 845-5367
Web Site:
   http://www.jackswholesalewin
   dows.com
Sales Range: $10-24.9 Million
Emp.: 60
Replacement Windows, Doors & Vinyl Siding
N.A.I.C.S.: 238170
Jack Tilka (Pres)

JACK-POST CORPORATION
800 E 3rd St, Buchanan, MI 49107
Tel.: (269) 695-7000
Web Site: http://www.jack-post.com
Rev.: $18,200,000
Emp.: 25

Metal Lawn & Garden Furniture
N.A.I.C.S.: 337126
John T. Bycraft (Pres)
Bob Bycraft (VP)
Dale Swihart (Controller)
Sarah Taylor (Mgr-Mktg & Sls)

JACKASS CREEK LAND & LIVESTOCK COMPANY
213 E Main St, Ennis, MT 59729
Tel.: (406) 682-4215   MT
Web Site:
   http://www.bankingonthefuture.com
Year Founded: 1967
Sales Range: $1-9.9 Million
Emp.: 46
Bank Holding Company
N.A.I.C.S.: 551111
Tim Combs (Chm, Pres & CEO)
C. Bruce Combs (Sec & VP)

Subsidiaries:

Madison Valley Bank   (1)
213 E Main St, Ennis, MT 59729
Tel.: (406) 682-4215
Web Site:
   http://www.bankingonthefuture.com
Sales Range: $1-9.9 Million
Commericial Banking
N.A.I.C.S.: 522110
Tim Combs (Chm, Pres & CEO)

JACKIE COOPER BMW MINI
14145 N Broadway Extn, Edmond, OK 73013
Tel.: (405) 755-3600
Web Site:
   http://www.cooperbmw.com
Sales Range: $25-49.9 Million
Emp.: 80
Automobiles, New & Used
N.A.I.C.S.: 532111
Ray Kyte (Mgr-Sls)
Alma Anguiano (Mgr-Fin)

JACKIE COOPER TIRE DIS-TRIBUTORS
4117 NW 63rd St, Oklahoma City, OK 73116
Tel.: (405) 848-8656
Web Site: http://www.jce.com
Sales Range: $10-24.9 Million
Emp.: 59
Automotive Tires
N.A.I.C.S.: 441340
Arlie Crase (Office Mgr)

JACKPOT JUNCTION CASINO HOTEL
39375 County Hwy 24, Morton, MN 56207
Tel.: (507) 697-8000
Web Site:
   http://www.jackpotjunction.com
Rev.: $71,019,316
Emp.: 900
Casino Hotels
N.A.I.C.S.: 721120
Brian Pendleton (Gen Mgr)
Jeanne Koehn (Mgr)
Jeff Stancer (Supvr-Table Games)
Theodora Boone (Coord-HR)

JACKRABBIT TECHNOLO-GIES, INC.
21333 Summerbrook Dr, Cornelius, NC 28031
Tel.: (704) 895-4034
Web Site:
   http://www.jackrabbitclass.com
Year Founded: 1986
Sales Range: $1-9.9 Million
Emp.: 15
Co-Founder & Pres
N.A.I.C.S.: 518210

Mark Mahoney (Co-Founder & Pres)
Jorine Jones (Mgr-Customer Support)
Tracey Chantry (Dir-HR)
Kristin Stoutz (Acct Mgr-Sls)

JACKSON & ASSOCIATES GENERAL CONTRACTORS, INC.
6254 Colan Pl, Sarasota, FL 34240
Tel.: (941) 377-9911   FL
Web Site:
   http://www.jacksonassociatesgc.com
Year Founded: 1991
Sales Range: $1-9.9 Million
Emp.: 20
General Contractors
N.A.I.C.S.: 236220
Nancee Jackson (VP)
Thomas A. Jackson (Pres)

JACKSON & BLANC
7929 Arjons Dr, San Diego, CA 92126
Tel.: (858) 831-7900
Web Site:
   http://www.jacksonandblanc.com
Year Founded: 1931
Sales Range: $10-24.9 Million
Emp.: 98
Provider of Mechanical, Heating & Air Conditioning Contracting Services
N.A.I.C.S.: 238220
Kirk I. Jackson (CEO)
Debbie Kainz-Brodie (Controller)

JACKSON & TULL
2705 Bladensburg Rd NE, Washington, DC 20018
Tel.: (202) 333-9100
Web Site: http://www.jnt.com
Rev.: $27,600,000
Emp.: 300
Computer System Design Services
N.A.I.C.S.: 541512
Knox W. Tull Jr. (Pres)

JACKSON ASSOCIATES, INC.
1140 Hammond Dr Ste H-8100, Atlanta, GA 30328
Tel.: (770) 394-8700
Web Site:
   http://www.jacksonassociates.
Telecommunication Servicesb
N.A.I.C.S.: 517810
Marisa Pope (Pres)
Melisa Gipson (Exec VP)
Kelly Gray (Dir-Res)

Subsidiaries:

Jackson Adept Research   (1)
345 Maple Dr Ste 325, Beverly Hills, CA 90210
Tel.: (310) 279-4600
Web Site: http://www.adeptresearch.com
Sales Range: $1-9.9 Million
Emp.: 50
Telecommunication Servicesb
N.A.I.C.S.: 541910
Angela Lorinchak (Pres)
Marisa Pope (Principal)

JACKSON AUTO GROUP
704 Ala Moana Blvd, Honolulu, HI 96813-5507
Tel.: (808) 836-2441
Sales Range: $25-49.9 Million
Emp.: 140
Car Dealership
N.A.I.C.S.: 441110
Jack Jackson (Pres)

JACKSON BUILDERS, INC.
1608 US Hwy 70 W, Goldsboro, NC 27530-1120
Tel.: (919) 734-5428
Web Site:
   http://www.jacksonbuilders.com

Jackson Builders, Inc.—(Continued)
Year Founded: 1974
Sales Range: $10-24.9 Million
Emp.: 25
Industrial Building Construction Services
N.A.I.C.S.: 236210
Tim Robbins (Pres)

JACKSON CLAYBORN, INC.
5800 W Plano Pkwy Ste 220, Plano, TX 75093-4690
Tel.: (972) 732-0051
Web Site:
http://www.jacksonclayborn.com
Sales Range: $10-24.9 Million
Emp.: 30
Real Estate Appraisering Services
N.A.I.C.S.: 531320
Jimmy Jackson (Owner)

JACKSON CORPORATION
330 5th Ave Fl 11, New York, NY 10001-3101
Tel.: (212) 239-4530
Web Site:
http://www.jacksonbags.com
Year Founded: 1931
Sales Range: $10-24.9 Million
Emp.: 15
Mfr & Wholesaler of Handbags
N.A.I.C.S.: 424350
Jackson Liao (Pres)
Annie Liao (VP)
Michelle Soon (Controller)

JACKSON COUNTY OIL CO. INC.
504 Linden St, Scottsboro, AL 35768
Tel.: (256) 574-5204
Rev.: $26,175,738
Emp.: 100
Petroleum Bulk Stations
N.A.I.C.S.: 424710

JACKSON COUNTY RURAL ELECTRIC MEMBERSHIP CORPORATION
274 E Base Rd, Brownstown, IN 47220
Tel.: (812) 358-4458
Web Site:
http://www.jacksonremc.com
Year Founded: 1937
Sales Range: $50-74.9 Million
Emp.: 74
Electric Transmission Services
N.A.I.C.S.: 221122
John Trinkle (Pres)
Jerry Kelley (Treas & Sec)
Earl Pottschmidt (VP)

JACKSON DEAN CONSTRUCTION
3414 S 116th St, Seattle, WA 98168
Tel.: (206) 832-2900
Web Site:
http://www.jacksondean.com
Year Founded: 1949
Sales Range: $75-99.9 Million
Emp.: 100
Provider of Home/Office Interiors Finishing Furnishing & Remodeling
N.A.I.C.S.: 238990
Miles Jackson (Pres & CEO)
Mark Lunsford (VP-Ops)
Mike Shapiro (CIO)
Joan Walters (Project Mgr)
Joe McInelly (Project Mgr)
Wayman Loughry (Project Mgr)
Bill Miller (Sr Project Mgr)
Jamie Martinez (Project Mgr)
Jerry Pollock (Project Mgr)
Ryan McCallen (Dir-Mktg & Bus Dev)

JACKSON DESIGN & REMODELING, INC.
4797 Mercury St, San Diego, CA 92111
Tel.: (619) 442-6125
Web Site:
http://www.jacksondesignandremodeling.com
Year Founded: 1989
Sales Range: $1-9.9 Million
Emp.: 36
Residential Building Remodeling Services
N.A.I.C.S.: 236118
Todd R. Jackson (CEO)

JACKSON ELECTRIC CO-OPERATIVE CORPORATION
8925 State Hwy 111 N, Ganado, TX 77962
Tel.: (361) 782-7193
Web Site: http://www.jecec.com
Sales Range: $10-24.9 Million
Emp.: 50
Electronic Services
N.A.I.C.S.: 221118
Cindy Bures (CFO)
Dick Koop (VP)
Roy D. Griffen (Gen Mgr)

JACKSON ELECTRIC MEMBERSHIP CORP.
850 Commerce Rd, Jefferson, GA 30549
Tel.: (706) 367-5281
Web Site:
http://www.jacksonemc.com
Sales Range: $200-249.9 Million
Emp.: 150
Electric Power Distr
N.A.I.C.S.: 221122
Lee Chapman (Dir-Comml & Indus Mktg)
Bonnie Jones (Dir-PR)

JACKSON ENERGY AUTHORITY
351 Doctor Martin Luther King, Jackson, TN 38301
Tel.: (731) 422-7500
Web Site: http://www.jaxenergy.com
Sales Range: $125-149.9 Million
Emp.: 375
Distr of Electric & Natural Gas; Supplier of Water
N.A.I.C.S.: 221118
Teresa Cobb (Gen Counsel)
Jim Ferrell (Pres & CEO)
Howard Bond (Vice Chm)
Barry Cross (VP-HR)
Ken Marston (Chm)
Aletza Boucher (Sec)
Ted Austin (VP-Customer Svc & Community Rels)
Rowland Fisher (VP-Engrg)
Mike Baughn (VP-IT)
Lara Coleman (VP-Ops)
Ben Lovins (Sr VP-Telecom Div)
Braxton Williams (Sr VP-Gas Div)
John Nanney (VP-Economic & Industrial Dev)
Monte Cooper (Sr VP-Electric Div)
Nancy Nanney (CFO & Sr VP)

JACKSON ENERGY COOPERATIVE
115 Jackson Energy Ln, McKee, KY 40447
Tel.: (606) 364-1000
Web Site:
http://www.jacksonenergy.com
Rev.: $52,373,726
Emp.: 100
Distribution, Electric Power
N.A.I.C.S.: 221122

Fred Callahan (Chm)
Edward Stamper (Treas & Sec)
Fred Brown (Vice Chm)

JACKSON FAMILY WINES, INC.
425 Aviation Blvd, Santa Rosa, CA 95403
Tel.: (707) 525-6244
Web Site:
http://www.jacksonfamilywines.com
Sales Range: $650-699.9 Million
Holding Company; Wineries
N.A.I.C.S.: 551112
Barbara Banke (Chm)
Peter Repole (Sr VP & Sls Mgr-Natl-Estates Div)
Cory Jones (Sr VP-Sls-Natl)
Donald Hartford (Vice Chm)
Rick Tigner (Pres & CEO)
Katie Jackson (Sr VP-Corp & Social Responsibility)
Gayle Bartscherer (Sr VP-Mktg & Dev-Intl)
Viviann Stapp (Gen Counsel & Sr VP)
Kristen Reitzell (VP-PR)
Jane Catelani Howard (Sr VP-Fin)

Subsidiaries:

Arrowood Vineyards & Winery (1)
14347 Sonoma Hwy, Glen Ellen, CA 95442
Tel.: (707) 935-2600
Web Site:
http://www.arrowoodvineyards.com
Sales Range: $1-9.9 Million
Emp.: 25
Winery & Grape Vineyards
N.A.I.C.S.: 312130
Grace Graham (Office Mgr)

Field Stone Winery & Vineyard, Inc. (1)
10075 Highway 128, Healdsburg, CA 95448
Tel.: (707) 433-7266
Web Site: http://www.fieldstonewinery.com
Sales Range: $10-24.9 Million
Winery & Vineyards
N.A.I.C.S.: 312130
Jason Robinson (Mgr-Estate)

Kendall-Jackson Wine Estates, Ltd. (1)
421 Aviation Blvd, Santa Rosa, CA 95403
Tel.: (707) 544-4000
Web Site: http://www.kj.com
Sales Range: $400-449.9 Million
Emp.: 1,200
Winemaker Services
N.A.I.C.S.: 312130
Barbara Banke (Chm)

Subsidiary (Domestic):

Kendall-Jackson (2)
1190 Kittyhawk Blvd, Santa Rosa, CA 95403-1013
Tel.: (707) 836-2000
Web Site: http://www.kj.com
Sales Range: $10-24.9 Million.
Emp.: 64
Wines, Brandy & Brandy Spirits
N.A.I.C.S.: 424820
Chuck Shea (Gen Mgr)

Regal & Royal Wine Co. (2)
1190 Kittyhawk Blvd, Santa Rosa, CA 95403-1013
Tel.: (707) 544-4000
Web Site: http://www.kj.com
Sales Range: $1-9.9 Million
Emp.: 50
Wines, Brandy & Brandy Spirits
N.A.I.C.S.: 424820
Rick Tigner (Pres)

La Crema, Inc. (1)
3575 Slusser Rd, Windsor, CA 95492
Tel.: (707) 525-6200
Web Site: http://www.lacrema.com
Winery
N.A.I.C.S.: 312130
Craig McAllister (Head-Winemaker)

Matanzas Creek Winery (1)

6097 Bennett Valley Rd, Santa Rosa, CA 95404
Tel.: (707) 528-6464
Web Site: http://www.matanzascreek.com
Sales Range: $1-9.9 Million
Emp.: 35
Winery
N.A.I.C.S.: 312130
Michelle Davis (Mgr-Wine Club)

Murphy-Goode Winery (1)
4001 Hwy 128, Geyserville, CA 95441
Tel.: (800) 499-7644
Web Site:
http://www.murphygoodewinery.com
Sales Range: $10-24.9 Million
Emp.: 34
Winery
N.A.I.C.S.: 312130
Dave Ready Jr. (Mgr-Winemaking)

Siduri Wines, LLC (1)
981 Airway Ct Ste E, Santa Rosa, CA 95403-2000
Tel.: (707) 578-3882
Web Site: http://www.siduri.com
Winery
N.A.I.C.S.: 312130
Adam Lee (Head-Winemaker)

Stonestreet Winery (1)
7111 Hwy 128, Healdsburg, CA 95448
Tel.: (800) 355-8008
Web Site: http://www.stonestreetwines.com
Sales Range: $1-9.9 Million
Emp.: 35
Winery & Grape Vineyards
N.A.I.C.S.: 312130
Gabriel Valencia (Mgr-Vineyards)
Lisa Valtenbergs (Head-Winemaker)

WillaKenzie Vineyards, Inc. (1)
19143 NE Laughlin Rd, Yamhill, OR 97148
Tel.: (503) 662-3280
Web Site: http://www.willakenzie.com
Grape Vineyards & Winery
N.A.I.C.S.: 111332
Sherry Simmons (Mgr-Tasting Room)
Wendy Henderlong (Asst Mgr-Tasting Room)
Molly McWhorter (Mgr-Cellar Club)
Jess Ferrentino (Coord-Hospitality & Events)

JACKSON FURNITURE INDUSTRIES
1910 King Edward Ave SE, Cleveland, TN 37311-3076
Tel.: (423) 476-8544
Web Site: http://www.catnapper.com
Year Founded: 1896
Sales Range: $350-399.9 Million
Emp.: 1,000
Upholstered Furniture Mfr
N.A.I.C.S.: 337121
Mark Lynn (Dir-Quality Control)
Matt Smith (Dir-Quality)
Susan Beals (Mgr-Credit & Billing)

Subsidiaries:

Cleveland Chair Company (1)
1910 King Edward Ave SE, Cleveland, TN 37311
Tel.: (423) 476-8544
Web Site: http://www.catnapper.com
Reclining Chairs Mfr
N.A.I.C.S.: 337121
W. Ronald Jackson (CEO)
Leo Matheny (VP)
Keith Jackson (Sr VP-Sls & Mktg)

JACKSON HEALTH SYSTEM
1611 NW 12th Ave, Miami, FL 33136
Tel.: (305) 585-1111
Web Site: http://www.jhsmiami.org
Year Founded: 1918
Sales Range: $1-4.9 Billion
Emp.: 9,000
Integrated Healthcare & Rehabilitation Hospital Services
N.A.I.C.S.: 621491
Carlos A. Migoya (Pres & CEO)
Marcos Jose Lapciuc (Treas)
Flavia Llizo (Chief Dev Officer & Exec VP)

JACKSON HEALTHCARE, LLC
2655 Northwinds Pkwy, Alpharetta, GA 30009-2280
Tel.: (770) 643-5500
Web Site:
   https://www.jacksonhealthcare.com
Year Founded: 2000
Emp.: 2,721
Human Resource Consulting Services
N.A.I.C.S.: 541612
Richard L. Jackson *(Chm & CEO)*
R. Shane Jackson *(Pres)*
Ryan Esparza *(CIO)*
Leslie Day-Harrell *(Sr VP-Corp Real Estate)*
Keith Jennings *(VP-Community Impact)*
Randall Mink *(Chief Risk Officer)*
Robyn Smith *(Chief HR Officer)*
Anne Patton *(VP-Mktg & Corp Comm)*
Leslie Kurtz *(CFO)*
Jay Mitchell *(Gen Counsel)*
Josh Berman *(VP-Corp Dev)*
Brad Chason *(Sr VP-IT)*

Subsidiaries:

Avant Healthcare Professionals, LLC   **(1)**
1211 State Rd 436 Blvd Ste 227, Casselberry, FL 32707
Tel.: (407) 681-2999
Web Site: http://www.avanthealthcare.com
Healthcare Staffing Services
N.A.I.C.S.: 561320
Shari Dingle Costantini *(Founder)*
Brian Hudson *(Sr VP-Sls & Mktg)*
Adam Kless *(VP-Clinical Ops)*
Lesley Hamilton-Powers *(Sr VP-Ops)*
Tony Hughes *(VP-IT)*
Arun Divakaruni *(CEO)*

Kirby Bates Associates, Inc.   **(1)**
1 Bala Ave 312, Bala Cynwyd, PA 19004
Tel.: (610) 667-1800
Web Site: http://www.kirbybates.com
Administrative Management & General Management Consulting Services
N.A.I.C.S.: 541611

Tyler & Co.   **(1)**
400 Northridge Rd Ste 1250, Atlanta, GA 30350
Tel.: (678) 916-9295
Web Site: http://www.tylerandco.com
Emp.: 20
Human Resources & Executive Search Consulting Services
N.A.I.C.S.: 561312
Kristen E. Sumner *(Dir-HR)*

JACKSON HEWITT TAX SERVICE INC.
3 Sylvan Way, Parsippany, NJ 07054
Tel.: (973) 630-1040   **DE**
Web Site:
   http://www.jacksonhewitt.com
Year Founded: 1985
Sales Range: $200-249.9 Million
Emp.: 305
Tax Preparation Services
N.A.I.C.S.: 541213
Mark Steber *(Chief Tax Officer)*
Dave Prokupek *(Co-CEO)*
Alan D. Ferber *(Co-CEO)*
Richard E. Thornburgh *(Chm)*

JACKSON HOLE MOUNTAIN RESORT
3395 W Cody Dr, Teton Village, WY 83025
Tel.: (307) 733-2292   **WY**
Web Site:
   http://www.jacksonhole.com
Year Founded: 1963
Sales Range: $75-99.9 Million
Emp.: 200
Mountain Resort Owner & Operator
N.A.I.C.S.: 713940

Jerry M. Blann *(Pres)*
Matt McCreedy *(CFO)*
Bill Lewkowitz *(Dir-Bus Dev)*
Shawn Daus *(Mgr-Sls)*
Spencer Long *(Mgr-Sls)*
Ty Hoath *(VP-HR)*

JACKSON HOSPITAL
1725 Pine St, Montgomery, AL 36106
Tel.: (334) 293-8000   **AL**
Web Site: http://www.jackson.org
Year Founded: 1894
Sales Range: $125-149.9 Million
Health Care Srvices
N.A.I.C.S.: 622110
Michael James *(COO & VP)*
Joe B. Riley *(Pres & CEO)*
Janet S. McQueen *(Co-Pres)*
Lemuel Gorden *(Chm)*
Sharon Goodison *(Chief Nursing Officer & VP)*
C. James Platt *(CEO)*
Kelly Connolly *(CFO)*
Jesse Roberts *(Asst Chief Nursing Officer)*

JACKSON HOUSE
705 Malvern Ave, Hot Springs National Park, AR 71901-5431
Tel.: (501) 623-4048
Web Site:
   http://www.jacksonhouse.org
Child & Youth Services
N.A.I.C.S.: 624110
June Smith *(Exec Dir)*
Jim Sechrist *(Pres-Ops-Reg)*

Subsidiaries:

Cameron Care, LLC   **(1)**
10011 SE Division St Ste 207, Portland, OR 97266-7266
Tel.: (503) 719-4784
Web Site: http://www.cameroncare.com
Residential Mental Health & Substance Abuse Facilities
N.A.I.C.S.: 623220
Andrew Sperry *(Mgr-HR)*
Corey Cameron *(Exec Dir)*

JACKSON HUNTER MORRIS & KNIGHT LLP
620 Newport Ctr Dr Ste 1100, Newport Beach, CA 92660
Year Founded: 2005
Sales Range: $1-9.9 Million
Emp.: 60
Debt Counseling, Restructuring & Collections
N.A.I.C.S.: 525990
John Legge *(Founder & Partner)*

JACKSON INTEGRATED
5804 Churchman Bypass, Indianapolis, IN 46203-6109
Tel.: (317) 791-9000   **IN**
Year Founded: 1961
Rev.: $18,500,000
Emp.: 50
Advetising Agency
N.A.I.C.S.: 541810
Kris Smith *(Dir-Media)*
Lee Ann Miller *(Sr Acct Mgr & New Bus Dev Leader)*
Jeff Costin *(VP & Acct Supvr)*

JACKSON KEARNEY GROUP
1555 Poydras St Ste 1600, New Orleans, LA 70112
Tel.: (504) 587-1100
Web Site: http://www.jkgroup.com
Sales Range: $25-49.9 Million
Emp.: 150
Stevedoring
N.A.I.C.S.: 488320
Daniel L. Haeuser *(Pres)*
David Wilkins *(Exec VP)*
Elisa Azze *(Controller)*

JACKSON KELLY PLLC
500 Lee St E Ste 1600, Charleston, WV 25301-3202
Tel.: (304) 340-1000
Web Site:
   http://www.jacksonkelly.com
Emp.: 202
Law firm
N.A.I.C.S.: 541110
Jennifer Cain *(Atty)*
Michelle Wooton *(Atty)*
Douglas Crouse *(Atty-Environmental)*
Sara Walker *(Dir-HR)*
Vinson Stephanie *(Mgr-Acctg)*
Louie Southworth *(Partner)*
Minued Janna *(Sec)*

Subsidiaries:

Jackson Kelly PLLC - Evansville   **(1)**
221 NW 5th St, Evansville, IN 47708
Tel.: (812) 422-9444
Web Site: http://www.jacksonkelly.com
Law firm
N.A.I.C.S.: 541110
Marc D. Fine *(Partner & Atty)*

JACKSON LEWIS LLP
44 S Broadway 14th Fl, White Plains, NY 10601
Tel.: (914) 328-0404
Web Site:
   http://www.jacksonlewis.com
Year Founded: 1958
Sales Range: $300-349.9 Million
Emp.: 700
Workplace Law
N.A.I.C.S.: 541199
Francis P. Alvarez *(Principal)*
Scott T. Baken *(Partner)*
Richard D. Landau *(Partner)*
Andrew A. Peterson *(Partner)*
Mary A. Smith *(Principal-White Plains)*
Thomas V. Walsh *(Principal-White Plains)*
Monique Warren *(Principal-White Plains)*
Vincent A. Cino *(Chm)*
Jeffrey A. Bernick *(Mng Principal-Phoenix)*
Matthew F. Nieman *(Principal-Washington & Office Mgr-Litigation)*
Stephanie M. Cerasano *(Principal-Phoenix & Office Mgr-Litigation)*
Michael J. DePonte *(Principal & Mgr-Office Litigation-Dallas)*
Daniel V. Duff *(Principal)*
Nadine T. Trinh *(Principal)*
Ashley Bryan Abel *(Principal)*
David S. Allen *(Principal)*
Gregory T. Alvarez *(Principal)*
Brett M. Anders *(Principal)*
Andrew L. Pepper *(Principal)*
Brooks R. Amiot *(Mng Principal-Baltimore)*
Gil A. Abramson *(Principal)*
Alyson Guyan *(Principal)*
Jeffrey L. Rudd *(Principal-Chicago)*
Victor Barkalov *(Chief Digital Officer)*
Brian T. Benkstein *(Principal)*
Adrienne L. Conrad *(Principal)*
Alison B. Crane *(Principal)*
Allan S. Friedland *(Principal)*
Beverly W. Garofalo *(Principal)*
Amy J. Gittler *(Principal)*
Brian P. Goldstein *(Principal)*
Barry Alan Johnsrud *(Principal)*
Andrew D. La Flura *(Principal)*
Brian E. Lewis *(Principal)*
Adriana R. Midence *(Principal)*
Benjamin F. Neidl *(Principal)*
Amy L. Peck *(Principal)*
Andrew C. Pickett *(Principal)*
Bradley M. Pryba *(Principal)*
Allan S. Rubin *(Principal)*
Andreas N. Satterfield *(Principal)*

Allison E. Serafin *(Principal)*
Ana C. Shields *(Principal)*
Adam Y. Siegel *(Principal)*
Ann H. Smith *(Principal)*
Alison Jacobs Wice *(Principal)*
Alissa M. Yohey *(Principal)*
Armen Zenjiryan *(Principal)*
Thomas P. Murphy *(Principal-Washington)*
Joseph A. Saccomano Jr. *(Mng Principal-White Plains)*
Charles F. Seemann III *(Principal-New Orleans)*
Alexander L. Betke II *(Principal)*

JACKSON LUMBER AND MILLWORK CO.
215-245 Market St, Lawrence, MA 01843
Tel.: (978) 686-4141
Web Site:
   http://www.jacksonlumber.com
Rev.: $40,579,804
Emp.: 150
Lumber & Other Building Materials
N.A.I.C.S.: 423310
Peter LeBlanc *(Asst Mgr)*

JACKSON MARKETING GROUP, INC.
1068 Holland Rd, Simpsonville, SC 29681
Tel.: (864) 272-3000
Web Site: http://www.jacksonmg.com
Year Founded: 1987
Sales Range: $10-24.9 Million
Emp.: 105
Advetising Agency
N.A.I.C.S.: 541810
Larry Jackson *(Chm)*
Darrell Jackson *(Pres & CEO)*
Kevin R. Johnson *(COO & Exec VP)*
David Madson *(CFO & Exec VP)*
David Jones *(Chief Mktg Officer & Exec VP)*
Frank DeAngelo *(Exec Dir-Motorsports)*
Scott Taylor *(Exec Dir-Client Financial Mgmt)*
Kristie D. GraySmith *(Dir-HR-Motorsports & Events)*
Richard De Leonardis *(VP-Creative Solutions)*
Andy Aparicio *(Dir-PR)*
Connor Cox *(Acct Coord-Motorsports)*

JACKSON MATTRESS COMPANY LLC
3154 Camden Rd, Fayetteville, NC 28306
Tel.: (910) 425-0131
Web Site: http://www.restonic.com
Rev.: $11,376,064
Emp.: 46
Mattresses & Bedsprings
N.A.I.C.S.: 337910
Randy Bancroft *(Pres)*

JACKSON MEDICAL MALL FOUNDATION
350 W Woodrow Wilson Dr Ste 501-B 1st Fl, Jackson, MS 39213
Tel.: (601) 709-5130   **MS**
Web Site:
   http://www.jacksonmedicalmall.org
Year Founded: 1996
Sales Range: $10-24.9 Million
Emp.: 142
Medical Support Services
N.A.I.C.S.: 622110
Primus Wheeler *(Exec Dir)*
Lori Greer *(Sr VP-Fin & Admin)*
Dionne Bibb *(VP-Facilities & Ops)*
James Bennett *(Mgr-Facility)*
Aaron Shirley *(Chm)*

Jackson Medical Mall Foundation—(Continued)

Shante Black *(VP-Support & Outreach Programs)*
Dana Profice *(VP-Leasing & Tenant Rels)*
Mahalia Wright *(VP-HR)*
Erica Reed *(Exec Dir)*
Juanita Davis *(Program Mgr)*
Beverly Wade Hogan *(Chm)*
Beverly Wade Hogan *(Chm)*

JACKSON METAL SERVICES INC.

1320 E Chester St, Jackson, TN 38301
Tel.: (731) 423-3297
Web Site: http://www.jmsmetal.com
Sales Range: $10-24.9 Million
Emp.: 40
Steel & Aluminum Products Distr
N.A.I.C.S.: 423510
Mickey Crum *(Gen Mgr)*
Brian R. Hedges *(Pres & CEO)*
Lesley Coleman *(Asst Sec & VP)*
Marion E. Britton *(CFO, Sec & Exec VP)*

JACKSON OIL & SOLVENTS INC.

1970 Kentucky Ave, Indianapolis, IN 46221
Tel.: (317) 636-4421
Web Site:
    http://www.jacksonoilsolvents.com
Year Founded: 1935
Sales Range: $10-24.9 Million
Emp.: 100
Gasoline
N.A.I.C.S.: 424720
Monica Heath *(Pres)*
Lou Carter *(VP)*
Ron Willis *(Gen Mgr-Ops)*

JACKSON OIL COMPANY, INC.

PO Box 968, Cheraw, SC 29520
Tel.: (843) 537-7080
Sales Range: $25-49.9 Million
Emp.: 190
Wholesale Distributor of Petroleum Products
N.A.I.C.S.: 424710
Charles R. Jackson Jr. *(Owner)*

JACKSON PAPER COMPANY

4400 Mangum Dr, Flowood, MS 39232
Tel.: (601) 352-0837   MS
Web Site:
    http://www.jacksonpaper.com
Year Founded: 1921
Sales Range: $10-24.9 Million
Emp.: 130
Mfr & Distributor of Fine Paper Products & Janitorial Supplies
N.A.I.C.S.: 424130
Ricky Martin *(Gen Mgr)*

Subsidiaries:

Harris Industrial Products & Packaging   (1)
4400-A Mangum Dr, Flowood, MS 39232
Tel.: (800) 543-5088
Emp.: 30
Packaging Products Mfr
N.A.I.C.S.: 326112
Ritchie Morton *(Gen Mgr)*

Newell Paper Co. of Gulfport   (1)
2513 Westgate Pkwy, Gautier, MS 39553-4423
Tel.: (228) 864-1770
Web Site: http://www.newell.com
Sales Range: $10-24.9 Million
Emp.: 6
Janitorial Paper Supplies Distr
N.A.I.C.S.: 424110

Newell Paper Co. of Hattiesburg   (1)

5192 Hwy 42, Hattiesburg, MS 39401-2252   **(100%)**
Tel.: (601) 582-3371
Web Site: http://www.newellpaper.com
Sales Range: $10-24.9 Million
Emp.: 25
Janitorial & Paper Supplies
N.A.I.C.S.: 424110
Bill Gates *(Pres & Controller)*

Newell Paper Co. of Meridian   (1)
1212 Grand Ave, Meridian, MS 39301-6509   **(100%)**
Tel.: (601) 693-1783
Web Site:
    http://www.meridian.newellpaper.com
Sales Range: $10-24.9 Million
Emp.: 50
Mfr & Distributor of Fine Paper Products & Janitorial Supplies
N.A.I.C.S.: 424110
Bill Allen *(Pres)*

JACKSON PROPERTIES INC.

5665 Power Inn Rd Ste 140, Sacramento, CA 95824
Tel.: (916) 381-8113
Web Site:
    http://www.jacksonprop.com
Sales Range: $10-24.9 Million
Emp.: 48
Industrial Buildings & Warehouses
N.A.I.C.S.: 236220
Gerlinde Bernd *(Mgr-Property)*
Dan Monical *(Project Mgr)*
Bernardo Hubbard *(Sr Mgr-Asset)*
Eric Edelmayer *(VP)*
Ben Smith *(Mgr-Asset)*
Trevor Johnson *(Mgr-Asset)*
Desiree Garcia *(Mgr-Corp Svcs)*
Tracy Kelly *(Mgr-Property)*
Gregg Mason *(VP-Mktg)*
John M. Jackson Jr. *(Owner & Pres)*

JACKSON SQUARE VENTURES, LLC

727 Sansome St Ste 300, San Francisco, CA 94111
Tel.: (415) 229-7100   DE
Web Site: http://www.jsv.com
Venture Capital Investment Firm
N.A.I.C.S.: 523999
Peter Solvik *(Mng Dir)*
Josh Breinlinger *(Mng Dir)*
John W. Otterson *(Partner-IR)*
Bob Spinner *(Mng Dir)*
Andrea Boyer *(CFO)*
Gregory C. Gretsch *(Mng Dir)*

JACKSON SUMNER & ASSOCIATES, INC.

491 George Wilson Rd, Boone, NC 28607-8611
Tel.: (828) 264-2787
Web Site: http://www.jsausa.com
Insurance Related Activities
N.A.I.C.S.: 524298
Wayne Sumner *(Owner)*

Subsidiaries:

Landers Underwriting Inc.   (1)
108 5th St SE, Charlottesville, VA 22902-5279
Tel.: (434) 984-6363
Web Site:
    http://www.landersunderwriting.com
Insurance Related Activities
N.A.I.C.S.: 524298

JACKSON SUPPLY COMPANY

6655 Roxburgh Dr Ste 100, Houston, TX 77041
Tel.: (713) 849-5865
Web Site:
    http://www.jacksonsupplycompany.com
Sales Range: $25-49.9 Million
Emp.: 100
Provider of Warm Air Heating Equipment & Supply Services

N.A.I.C.S.: 423730
Brande Greene *(Mgr-Credit)*

JACKSON SYSTEMS, LLC

5418 Elmwood Ave, Indianapolis, IN 46203-6025
Tel.: (317) 788-6800
Web Site:
    http://www.jacksonsystems.com
Year Founded: 1997
Sales Range: $1-9.9 Million
Emp.: 26
Direct-to-Contractor HVAC Zone-Control Equipment Mfr & Distr
N.A.I.C.S.: 334512
Ronald E. Jackson *(Co-Founder)*
Thomas W. Jackson *(Co-Founder)*
Phil Kimble *(Mgr-Product Dev)*
Joe Jackson *(VP-Custom Controls Div)*

JACKSON THORNTON & CO. PC

200 Commerce St, Montgomery, AL 36104
Tel.: (334) 834-7660
Web Site:
    http://www.jacksonthornton.com
Emp.: 225
Accounting, Tax & Consulting Services
N.A.I.C.S.: 541211
Ned F. Sheffield *(Pres & Mng Partner)*
Rusty J. Golden *(Principal)*

JACKSON TUBE SERVICE INC.

8210 Industry Pk Dr, Piqua, OH 45356
Tel.: (937) 773-8550
Web Site: http://www.jacksontube.com
Year Founded: 1972
Sales Range: $100-124.9 Million
Emp.: 160
Welded Steel Tubing Mfr
N.A.I.C.S.: 331210
Mark Sergy *(VP-Fin)*
David Hare *(VP-Sls & Mktg)*
Dennis Walker *(Dir-IS)*
Pamela Jackson-Crabtree *(Gen Mgr-Acctg)*

JACKSON WALKER LLP

2323 Ross Ave Ste 600, Dallas, TX 75201
Tel.: (214) 953-6000
Web Site: http://www.jw.com
Year Founded: 1887
Sales Range: $150-199.9 Million
Emp.: 550
Law firm
N.A.I.C.S.: 541110
David T. Moran *(Partner-Dallas)*
Alex Frutos *(Partner-Dallas)*
Brian A. Kilpatrick *(Partner-Dallas)*
W. Ross Forbes *(Partner-Dallas)*
Jay K. Wieser *(Partner-Fort Worth)*
Monica Pace Messick *(Partner)*
Chris Bankler *(Partner)*
S. Brad Brown *(Partner-Dallas)*
Debbie A. Robinowitz *(Partner-Dallas)*
Frank P. McEachern *(Partner-Dallas)*
Ronald D. Kerridge *(Partner-Dallas)*
Scott M. McElhaney *(Partner-Dallas)*
Stephanie Collett Sparks *(Partner-Dallas)*
Jorge A. Padilla *(Partner-Austin)*
Michelle Moore Smith *(Partner-Austin)*
Nathaniel St. Clair *(Partner-Dallas)*
Alden S. Crow *(Partner-Dallas)*
Brad Nitschke *(Partner-Dallas)*
Ashley J. Martzen *(Partner-Dallas)*
J. Scott Rose *(Partner-San Antonio)*

Lewis S. Kasner *(Partner)*
David W. Jones *(Partner-Houston)*
Thad H. Armstrong *(Partner)*
Alfie M. Meyerson *(Partner-Houston)*
David M. Robins *(Partner-Houston)*
Sean D. Jordan *(Partner)*
Kent C. Sullivan *(Chm-Appellate Practice Grp & Partner)*
Matthew J. Swantner *(Partner)*
Cale McDowell *(Partner)*
Brit Nelson *(Partner)*
Matt D. Cavenaugh *(Partner)*
Amanda Zimmerman *(Partner)*
Richard A. Howell *(Partner)*
Matt C. Acosta *(Partner)*
Sara K. Borrelli *(Partner)*
Wasif Qureshi *(Partner)*
Steven Dimitt *(Partner)*
Jordan Smith *(Partner)*
Ann Leafstedt *(Partner-San Antonio)*
Courtney Carlson *(Partner)*
Amanda Shaw-Castro *(Partner)*
Emilio Nicolas *(Partner)*
Pamela Madere *(Partner-Real Estate Practice)*
William Stowe *(Partner)*
Jamila Brinson *(Partner)*
Luke Gilman *(Partner)*
George Hinchey *(Partner)*
Scott Tuthill *(Partner)*
Kevin Kelley *(Partner)*
Cynthia Brotman Nelson *(Partner)*
Elizabeth Carol Freeman *(Partner-Bankruptcy Practice Grp-Houston)*
Larry Glasgow *(Partner)*
Richard Waggoner *(Partner)*
Brett Kutnick *(Partner)*
Dawn Holiday *(Partner-Trial & Appellate Litigation Practice)*
Greta Cowart *(Partner)*
Christian Triantaphyllis *(Partner-Land Use & Real Estate Practice)*
Kal Grant *(Partner)*
Jennifer Wertz *(Partner)*
Scott Weatherford *(Partner)*
David Snyder *(Partner)*
Kati Orso *(Partner)*
Andee Hartig *(Partner)*
Noah Galton *(Partner)*
William Dillard *(Partner)*
Collin Baker *(Partner)*
Edwin Buffmire *(Partner)*
G. Scott Fiddler *(Partner)*
Carey Hain *(Partner)*
Stephen Calhoun *(Partner)*
Lindsey Moorhead *(Partner)*
Julia Mann *(Mng Partner-San Antonio)*
Jennifer Caughey *(Partner)*
Jonathan Bull *(Partner-Environment & Natural Resources Practice)*
Kirk Tucker *(Partner-Corp & Securities Practice)*
R. Thomas Groves Jr. *(Partner)*
George Dunlap Jr. *(Partner)*

JACKSON WELDING SUPPLY CO., INC.

1421 W Carson St, Pittsburgh, PA 15219
Tel.: (412) 391-4500
Web Site:
    http://www.jacksonweldingsup.com
Rev.: $3,600,000
Emp.: 20
Other Chemical & Allied Products Merchant Whslr
N.A.I.C.S.: 424690
Diane Russell *(Sec)*
LeAnn Mazziotti *(Controller)*

Subsidiaries:

Delo Welding & Industrial Supply, Inc.   (1)
1729 Erie Blvd E, Syracuse, NY 13210
Tel.: (315) 478-2188

Web Site: http://delowelding.com
Sales Range: $1-9.9 Million
Emp.: 11
Industrial Supplies Merchant Whslr
N.A.I.C.S.: 423840
Charles W. Davoli (Pres)

JACKSON WHOLESALE HARDWARE
982 Lower Brownsville Rd, Jackson, TN 38301
Tel.: (731) 427-7725
Web Site: http://www.hcisupply.com
Rev.: $10,000,000
Emp.: 80
Hardware
N.A.I.C.S.: 423710
Bill Richardson (Pres)
Tommy Kelly (CFO)

JACKSON'S GARAGE INC.
1130 W Logan St, Celina, OH 45822
Tel.: (419) 586-1681
Web Site:
    http://www.jacksongarage.com
Rev.: $10,000,000
Emp.: 10
Retailer of Automotive Parts; Provider of Automotive Repair Services
N.A.I.C.S.: 441330
Mark Jackson (Pres)

JACKSONVILLE JAGUARS, LLC
1 Everbank Fields Dr, Jacksonville, FL 32202
Tel.: (904) 633-6000   DE
Web Site: http://www.jaguars.com
Year Founded: 1993
Sales Range: $10-24.9 Million
Emp.: 150
Professional Football Franchise
N.A.I.C.S.: 711211
Dan Edwards (Sr VP-Comm)
Tim Bishko (Dir-Ticket Ops)
Mike Perkins (Dir-Football Tech & Facilities)
Skip Richardson (Dir-Team Security)
Tim Walsh (Dir-Football Admin)
Mark Lamping (Pres)
Shahid R. Khan (Owner)
Hussain Naqi (Sr VP-Intl Dev)
Scott Massey (Sr VP-Corp Partnerships)
Chad Johnson (Sr VP)
Tony Khan (Sr VP-Football Admin & Tech)
David Caldwell (Gen Mgr)
Kelly Flanagan (CFO & Sr VP)
Joe DeCamillis (Coord-Special Teams)
Daniel Caudy (Partner-Rels & Mgr-Acct)
Jean Mitchell (Partner-Rels & Mgr-Acct)
Kathleen Dwulet (Partner-Rels & Mgr-Acct)
Megan Kerr (Partner-Rels & Mgr-Acct)
Mark Sirota (VP-Fin)
Mike Webb (VP-IT)
Steve Ziff (VP-Mktg & Digital Media)
Megha H. Parekh (Chief Legal Officer & Sr VP)

JACKSONVILLE JETPORT LLC
Cecil Airport 13365 Aeronautical Cir, Jacksonville, FL 32221
Tel.: (904) 317-6550
Web Site: http://www.jaxjetport.aero
Sales Range: $1-9.9 Million
Emp.: 30
Airport Operations
N.A.I.C.S.: 488119

Charles Morris (Pres)
Chuck Lawson (Dir-Ops)
Scott Chuck (Dir-Mktg)

JACKY JONES FORD LINCOLN
714 New Highway 68, Sweetwater, TN 37874
Tel.: (423) 337-5066
Web Site:
    http://www.jackyjonesflm.com
Year Founded: 2000
Sales Range: $10-24.9 Million
Emp.: 45
New Car Retailer
N.A.I.C.S.: 441110
David McMahan (Owner)
Steve Woody (Mgr-Sls)
Les Givens (Mgr-Parts)

JACMAR COMPANIES, INC.
2200 W Vly Blvd, Alhambra, CA 91803-1928
Tel.: (626) 576-0737   CA
Web Site: http://www.jacmar.com
Year Founded: 1973
Sales Range: $10-24.9 Million
Emp.: 900
Franchiser of Restaurants
N.A.I.C.S.: 424410
Robert R. Hill (Exec VP)
Cindy Staats (Dir-Mktg)
Randy Hill (Pres-Restaurant Div)

Subsidiaries:

Jacmar Food Service   (1)
300 N Baldwin Pk Blvd, City Of Industry, CA 91746   (100%)
Tel.: (626) 430-9082
Web Site:
    http://www.jacmarfoodservice.com
Sales Range: $10-24.9 Million
Emp.: 100
Food Service Distribution
N.A.I.C.S.: 541820
Bruce Harris (Controller)

Shakey's USA, Inc.   (1)
2200 W Vly Blvd, Alhambra, CA 91803
Tel.: (626) 576-0616
Web Site: http://www.shakeys.com
Sales Range: $10-24.9 Million
Emp.: 19
Franchise Restaurant Chain
N.A.I.C.S.: 722511
Sonia Barajas-Najera (VP-Franchise Admin)
Cindy Staats (VP-Mktg)
Randy Hill (VP-New Concept Dev)
Linda Bryant (Dir-Trng & Staffing)
Victor Santillan (VP-HR)
Michael Grundgeiger (VP-Ops)
Nick Mayer (Pres & CEO)
David Reid (CFO)

JACMEL GROWTH PARTNERS MANAGEMENT LLC
320 Park Ave, 26th Floor,, New York, NY 10022
Tel.: (646) 397-5699
Web Site: https://jacmelpartners.com
Year Founded: 2015
Private Equity
N.A.I.C.S.: 523940

Subsidiaries:

Virtual Technologies Group LLC   (1)
1605 Indian Wood Circle, Maumee, OH 43537
Tel.: (419) 255-9070
Web Site: https://vtgus.com
Software Publisher
N.A.I.C.S.: 513210

Subsidiary (Domestic):

Quotient Inc.   (2)
6310 Hillside Ct Ste 101, Columbia, MD 21046-3234
Tel.: (410) 309-9000
Web Site: https://www.quotient-inc.com
Custom Computer Programming Services

N.A.I.C.S.: 541511
Clark Lare (VP)

JACO ENVIRONMENTAL INC.
PO Box 14307, Mill Creek, WA 98082
Tel.: (425) 398-6200
Web Site: http://www.jacoinc.net
Rev.: $25,500,000
Emp.: 130
Industrial Machinery & Equipment Merchant Whslr
N.A.I.C.S.: 423830
Terry Jacobsen (Pres)
Michael Jacobsen (Controller)

JACO MANUFACTURING CO. INC.
468 Geiger St, Berea, OH 44017
Tel.: (440) 234-4000
Web Site: http://www.jacomfg.com
Year Founded: 1949
Sales Range: $10-24.9 Million
Emp.: 120
Plastics Product Mfr
N.A.I.C.S.: 326199
Stephen C. Campbell (Pres & CEO)
Bill Gareis (Mgr-Quality)

JACO OIL
3101 State Rd, Bakersfield, CA 93308
Tel.: (661) 393-7000
Web Site: http://www.fastrip.com
Rev.: $26,900,000
Emp.: 60
Owner & Operator of Convenience Stores
N.A.I.C.S.: 457120
Thomas J. Jamieson (Owner, Pres & CEO)

JACOB STERN & SONS, INC.
1464 E Vly Rd, Santa Barbara, CA 93108-1241
Tel.: (805) 565-1411   CA
Web Site: http://www.jacobstern.com
Year Founded: 1863
Sales Range: $10-24.9 Million
Emp.: 120
Mfr of Tallow, Grease, Vegetable Oils, Animal Feed, Fats & Fatty Acids
N.A.I.C.S.: 424990
Philip L. Bernstein (Chm)
E. Chip Hull (CFO)
Doug Shreves (CEO)
Steven Kulchin (VP-HR)

Subsidiaries:

Acme-Hardesty Co.   (1)
450 Sentry Pkwy E Ste 104, Blue Bell, PA 19422
Tel.: (215) 591-3610
Web Site: http://www.acme-hardesty.com
Marketer & Distributor of Vegetable & Animal Fat Oleochemicals
N.A.I.C.S.: 424690
Bill Herrera (Mgr-Sls-Southwestern Reg)
Jeff Kenton (Pres)

Jacob Stern & Sons, Inc. - Texas Division   (1)
2104 75th St, Houston, TX 77011
Tel.: (713) 926-8386
Agriculture Product Distr
N.A.I.C.S.: 424910
Marvin Pierson (Office Mgr)

JACOBI SALES INC.
425 Main St NE, Palmyra, IN 47164
Tel.: (812) 364-6141   IN
Web Site: http://www.jacobisales.com
Year Founded: 1972
Sales Range: Less than $1 Million
Emp.: 35
Sales of Agricultural Machinery & Equipment
N.A.I.C.S.: 423820
Brian Jacobi (Pres)
Jerry Uhl (Office Mgr)

Ed Henry (Mgr-Store)
Mark Bartman (Mgr-Sls)
Dave Heck (Mgr-Equipment Rental)

JACOBS & CLEVENGER, INC.
515 N State St Ste 1700, Chicago, IL 60654-4776
Tel.: (312) 894-3000   IL
Web Site:
    http://www.jacobsclevenger.com
Year Founded: 1982
Rev.: $30,000,000
Emp.: 30
Advetising Agency
N.A.I.C.S.: 541810
Ron Jacobs (Pres)
Penny Clevenger (CFO & VP)
Sheera Eby (VP & Dir-Strategic & Client Svcs)
Kim Redlin (VP & Dir-Creative)
Randy Mitchell (Assoc Dir-Creative)
Ellen Bakal (Mgr-Bus Dev)

JACOBS AGENCY, INC.
325 W Huron St, Chicago, IL 60654
Tel.: (312) 664-5000
Web Site:
    http://www.jacobsagency.com
Year Founded: 1997
Sales Range: $1-9.9 Million
Emp.: 25
Advetising Agency
N.A.I.C.S.: 541810
Tom Jacobs (Pres)
Bernie Pitzel (Grp Dir-Creative)
Joanna Mirowska (Dir-Art)
Valerie Sherpa (Mgr-Traffic & Production)

JACOBS AUTO ENTERPRISES INC.
69011 US Hwy 19, New Port Richey, FL 34652
Tel.: (727) 944-2886
Web Site:
    http://www.autoenterpriseonline.com
Emp.: 8
Used Car Dealership
N.A.I.C.S.: 441120
Daniel Jacobs (Owner)

JACOBS CAPITAL, LLC
307 W Barbee Chapel Rd, Chapel Hill, NC 27517
Tel.: (919) 428-4800   GA
Web Site:
    http://www.jacobscapital.net
Year Founded: 1998
Equity Investment Firm
N.A.I.C.S.: 523999
Michael Jacobs (Founder & CEO)
Mark Philips (Mng Dir)
Jason Layton (VP)
Elaine Leggett (Mgr-Bus Valuations Svcs)

JACOBS ENTERTAINMENT, INC.
17301 W Colfax Ave Ste 250, Golden, CO 80401
Tel.: (303) 215-5200   DE
Web Site:
    http://www.jacobsentertainment inc.com
Year Founded: 2001
Holding Company; Gaming & Pari-Mutuel Wagering Facilities Developer, Owner & Operator
N.A.I.C.S.: 551112
Jeffrey P. Jacobs (Chm & CEO)
Stephen R. Roark (Pres)
John East (COO)
Brett A. Kramer (CFO)
Stan Politano (Exec VP)

Jacobs Entertainment, Inc.—(Continued)

Subsidiaries:

Colonial Downs Holdings, Inc.   **(1)**
10515 Colonial Downs Pkwy, New Kent, VA 23124-2228
Tel.: (804) 966-7223
Web Site: http://www.colonialdowns.com
Sales Range: $10-24.9 Million
Emp.: 200
Owner & Operator of Racing Centers
N.A.I.C.S.: 711212
Aaron Gomes *(COO)*
John Marshall *(Sr VP & Gen Mgr)*

The Sands Regent, LLC   **(1)**
345 N Arlington Ave, Reno, NV 89501-1132
Tel.: (775) 348-2200
Web Site: http://www.sandsregency.com
Emp.: 1,239
Casino/Hotel Owner & Operator
N.A.I.C.S.: 713910
Lisa Miolini *(Mgr-Mktg & Sls)*

Division (Domestic):

Sands Regency Casino Hotel   **(2)**
345 N Arlington Ave, Reno, NV 89501-1132
Tel.: (775) 348-2200
Web Site: http://www.sandsregency.com
Emp.: 600
Casino/Hotel
N.A.I.C.S.: 721120
Wendy Durden *(Mgr-Lead Slot Shift)*

JACOBS FINANCIAL GROUP, INC.
179 Summers St Ste 307, Charleston, WV 25301
Tel.: (304) 343-8171   DE
Year Founded: 2005
Rev.: $2,869,316
Assets: $42,470,142
Liabilities: $44,938,919
Net Worth: ($2,468,777)
Earnings: ($1,007,197)
Emp.: 9
Fiscal Year-end: 05/30/17
Insurance Services
N.A.I.C.S.: 524298
John M. Jacobs *(Pres)*

JACOBS MECHANICAL CO.
1366 Hopple St, Cincinnati, OH 45225
Tel.: (513) 681-6800
Web Site:
http://www.jacobsmech.com
Sales Range: $10-24.9 Million
Emp.: 125
Plumbing Services
N.A.I.C.S.: 238220
John McDonald *(Pres)*

JACOBS TRADING, LLC
8090 Excelsior Blvd, Hopkins, MN 55343
Tel.: (763) 843-2000   MN
Web Site:
http://www.jacobstrading.com
Returns & Damaged Goods Whslr
N.A.I.C.S.: 423990
Scott Armstrong *(Gen Mgr)*

JACOBSEN CONSTRUCTION COMPANY, INC.
3131 W 2210 S, Salt Lake City, UT 84119-1267
Tel.: (801) 973-0500   UT
Web Site:
http://www.jacobsenconstruction.com
Year Founded: 1922
Nonresidential Construction
N.A.I.C.S.: 236220
Lonnie M. Bullard *(Chm)*
Douglas C. Welling *(CEO)*
John Furtuna *(COO)*
Gary Ellis *(Pres)*

Scott Braithwaite *(VP-Self-Performed Work)*
Dennis Cigana *(VP-Estimating)*
Matt Rich *(VP-Bus Dev & Mktg)*
Peggy Stone *(VP-HR)*
Jim Cavey *(VP-Public Market)*
Blake Court *(VP-Healthcare Market)*
Kirk Dickamore *(VP-Religious Market)*
Greg Fix *(VP-Private Market)*
Doug Hronek *(VP-Private Market)*
Steve Nelson *(VP-National Market)*
Reed Price *(VP-Private Market)*
Matt Radke *(VP-Healthcare Market)*
Jon Wight *(VP-Religous Market)*

JACOBSEN MANUFACTURING, INC.
600 Packard Ct, Safety Harbor, FL 34695-3001
Tel.: (727) 726-1138   FL
Web Site: http://www.jachomes.com
Year Founded: 1959
Sales Range: $25-49.9 Million
Emp.: 215
Mobile Home Mfr
N.A.I.C.S.: 321991
Janet Weis *(Dir-Mktg)*

JACOBSON & COMPANY, INC.
1079 E Grand St, Elizabeth, NJ 07207-0511
Tel.: (908) 355-5200
Web Site:
http://www.jacobsoncompany.com
Year Founded: 1989
Sales Range: $10-24.9 Million
Emp.: 150
Drywall & Insulation Contracting Services
N.A.I.C.S.: 238310
Thomas D. Jacobson *(Chm & CEO)*
David P. Norgard *(Pres)*
Patrick Oates *(Exec VP)*
Jonathan Burt *(Treas & Sec)*
Michael Pellicano *(Mgr-Pur)*

JACOBSON CAPITAL SERVICES INC.
150 Croton Ave, Cortlandt Manor, NY 10567
Tel.: (914) 736-0600
Web Site:
http://www.venusribbion.com
Sales Range: $10-24.9 Million
Emp.: 30
Commercial & Industrial Building Operation
N.A.I.C.S.: 531120
Seth Jacobson *(Pres)*
Patricia O'Neill *(Controller)*

JACOBSON FLORAL SUPPLY INC.
500 Albany St, Boston, MA 02118
Tel.: (617) 426-4287   MA
Web Site:
http://www.jacobsonfloral.com
Year Founded: 1943
Sales Range: $10-24.9 Million
Emp.: 70
Whslr of Florists' Supplies
N.A.I.C.S.: 424930
Michael Mattern *(Gen Mgr)*

JACOBSON HAT CO. INC.
1301 Rdg Row, Scranton, PA 18510
Tel.: (570) 342-7887
Web Site: http://www.jhats.com
Rev.: $12,100,000
Emp.: 50
Hat & Paper Novelty Mfr
N.A.I.C.S.: 315990
Jeff Jacobson *(VP)*

JACOBSON PARTNERS

595 Madison Ave 31st Fl, New York, NY 10022-1646
Tel.: (212) 758-4500
Web Site:
http://www.jacobsonpartners.com
Sales Range: $25-49.9 Million
Emp.: 10
Management Firm
N.A.I.C.S.: 523150
Benjamin R. Jacobson *(Mng Gen Partner)*
Jamie L. Goldberg *(Controller)*
James C. Morgan *(Gen Partner)*

Subsidiaries:

Swan Hose   **(1)**
1201 Delaware Ave, Marion, OH 43302-6419
Tel.: (419) 562-1011
Web Site: http://www.swanhose.com
Sales Range: $10-24.9 Million
Emp.: 100
Hose Mfr
N.A.I.C.S.: 326220

JACOBSON ROST
233 N Water St 6th Fl, Milwaukee, WI 53202
Tel.: (414) 220-4888   WI
Web Site:
http://www.jacobsonrost.com
Year Founded: 1956
Rev.: $64,000,000
Emp.: 50
N.A.I.C.S.: 541810
Jerry Flemma *(Pres & COO)*
Paula Switalski *(CFO, Exec VP & Partner)*
Steve Simoncic *(Partner & Chief Creative Officer)*
Kelley Prom *(Acct Coord)*

JACOBUS ENERGY, INC.
11815 W Bradley Rd, Milwaukee, WI 53224
Tel.: (414) 359-0700   WI
Web Site:
http://www.jacobusenergy.com
Year Founded: 1919
Sales Range: $50-74.9 Million
Emp.: 500
Heating Oil Dealer, Petroleum Products Whslr, Gas Station Refueling Services & Commercial Fuel Stations Owner & Operator
N.A.I.C.S.: 424710
Eugene T. Jacobus *(Pres)*
Charles D. Jacobus *(CEO)*

Subsidiaries:

Jacobus Energy - Quickflash Division   **(1)**
11815 W Bradley Rd, Milwaukee, WI 53224
Tel.: (414) 359-1100
Web Site: http://www.quickflash.com
Heating Oil Dealer; Heating & Air Conditioning Maintenance & Repair Services
N.A.I.C.S.: 457210
Eugene T. Jacobus *(Pres)*

Jacobus Petroleum Products, LLC   **(1)**
11815 W Bradley Rd, Milwaukee, WI 53224
Tel.: (414) 359-0700
Web Site: http://www.jacobusenergy.com
Petroleum Product Whslr
N.A.I.C.S.: 424720

Quick Fuel Fleet Services, LLC   **(1)**
11815 W Bradley Rd, Milwaukee, WI 53224
Tel.: (414) 359-0700
Web Site: http://www.quickfuel.com
Commercial Diesel Truck Fuel Stations Operator
N.A.I.C.S.: 457210

JACOBY & MEYERS, P.C.
10900 Wilshire Blvd 15th Fl, Los Angeles, CA 90024   CA

Web Site:
http://www.jacobyandmeyers.com
Year Founded: 1972
Legal Professional Organization
N.A.I.C.S.: 813920
Leonard Jacoby *(Founder & Partner)*
Gabriel Miller *(CEO & Gen Counsel)*

Subsidiaries:

Jacoby & Meyers Attorneys LLP   **(1)**
10900 Wilshire Blvd 15th Fl, Los Angeles, CA 90024
Web Site: http://www.jacobyandmeyers.com
Personal Injury Legal Services
N.A.I.C.S.: 541110
Michael Akiva *(Mng Partner)*

Jacoby & Meyers, LLC   **(1)**
300 N Foster St, Dothan, AL 36301
Web Site: http://www.jacobymeyers.com
Firm Office Administrative Services
N.A.I.C.S.: 561110

Jacoby & Meyers, LLP   **(1)**
1279 Route 300, Newburgh, NY 12550
Tel.: (887) 565-2993
Web Site: http://www.jmlawyer.com
Sales Range: $50-74.9 Million
Emp.: 36
Personal Injury Legal Services
N.A.I.C.S.: 541110
Michael Catuto *(CFO)*
Andrew G. Finkelstein *(Mng Partner)*

JACON AIRCRAFT SUPPLY CO. INC.
9539 Vassar Ave, Chatsworth, CA 91311
Tel.: (818) 700-2901
Web Site: http://www.jacon.com
Rev.: $10,650,936
Emp.: 37
Fasteners, Industrial: Nuts, Bolts, Screws
N.A.I.C.S.: 423840
Donald Wientjes *(Pres)*

JACQUES MORET, INC.
1411 Broadway, New York, NY 10018
Tel.: (212) 354-2400   NY
Web Site: http://www.moret.com
Year Founded: 1975
Sales Range: $10-24.9 Million
Emp.: 100
Bodywear & Activewear for Women & Children
N.A.I.C.S.: 424350
Joey Harary *(Pres)*
Jonah Goldschmidt *(VP-Real Estate Ops)*
Mark Lopiparo *(CFO)*
Malcolm Louis Adams *(Dir-Art)*
John Debease *(VP)*

JACQUES TORRES CHOCOLATE
66 Water St, Brooklyn, NY 11201
Tel.: (718) 875-9772
Web Site:
http://www.mrchocolate.com
Sales Range: $1-9.9 Million
Emp.: 18
Chocolate Products Mfr & Retailer
N.A.I.C.S.: 311351
Jacques Torres *(Owner)*
Keitaro Goto *(Owner)*
Linda Lee *(Mgr-Wholesale)*

JACSTEN HOLDINGS, LLC
759 N Milwaukee St Ste 200, Milwaukee, WI 53202
Tel.: (414) 755-5816
Web Site: http://www.jacsten.com
Investment Management Service
N.A.I.C.S.: 523940
Stephen Hansen *(Principal)*
Jake Hansen *(Principal)*

Subsidiaries:

CDM Tool & Manufacturing Co., Inc.   **(1)**
749 N Wacker Dr, Hartford, WI 53027
Tel.: (262) 673-5620

Web Site: http://www.cdmtool.com
Sales Range: $1-9.9 Million
Emp.: 48
Plastic Injection Mold Mfr
N.A.I.C.S.: 333511
Scott Kolkema (COO)

Stanek Tool Corp. (1)
2500 S Calhoun Rd, New Berlin, WI 53151
Tel.: (262) 786-0120
Web Site: http://www.stanektool.com
Rev.: $10,000,000
Emp.: 50
Special Die & Tool, Die Set, Jig & Fixture Mfr
N.A.I.C.S.: 333514
Don Novak (Mgr-Workholding Engrg)
Douglas Brockelman (VP-Mfg)
Mary Wehrheim (Pres)
Paul Bartkowiak (VP-Workholding)
Bracken Heiges (Mgr-Project & Quality Control)
William Hying (Mgr-Sls-Mold Div)

Vonco Products, LLC (1)
10826 250th Ave, Trevor, WI 53179
Tel.: (847) 356-2323
Web Site: http://www.vonco.com
Emp.: 100
Flexible Packaging Products Mfr
N.A.I.C.S.: 322220
Tim Murphy (VP-Sls & Mktg)
Robert Scarcelli (Dir-Ops)
Keith Smith (Pres & CEO)
Kyle Vlasak (Gen Mgr-Healthcare Div)

Subsidiary (Domestic):

Flex-Pak Packaging Products, Inc. (2)
651 N Raddant Rd, Batavia, IL 60510
Tel.: (630) 761-3335
Web Site: http://www.flex-pak.biz
Paper, except Newsprint, Mills
N.A.I.C.S.: 322120
William J. Reimann (Pres)

McFarlane Medical, Inc. (2)
2571 Kaneville Ct, Geneva, IL 60134
Tel.: (630) 208-8404
Web Site: http://www.mcfarlanemedical.com
Rev.: $1,500,000
Emp.: 10
Medical, Dental & Hospital Equipment & Supplies Merchant Whslr
N.A.I.C.S.: 423450
Matthew McFarlane (Pres)

JADE DESIGN, INC.
131 SE Parkway Ct, Franklin, TN 37064
Tel.: (615) 790-6754   TN
Web Site: http://www.jadedesign.com
Year Founded: 1983
Sales Range: $10-24.9 Million
Emp.: 50
Global Consumer Electronics Specializing in High Performance Consumer & Professional Audio Products & Services
N.A.I.C.S.: 541490
Dan Laufman (Pres & CEO)

Subsidiaries:

Emotiva Audio Corporation (1)
135 SE Pkwy Ct, Franklin, TN 37064
Tel.: (615) 790-6754
Web Site: http://www.emotiva.com
Sales Range: $1-9.9 Million
Emp.: 35
Designs & Sells Quality Home Theater & Stereo Products Directly to Consumers
N.A.I.C.S.: 334310
Catherine Laufman (Owner & VP-Ops)
Lonnie Vaughn (CTO & VP)
Walter Schofield (VP-Global Strategy)
Dan Laufman (Founder & Pres)

Emotiva Professional, LLC (1)
135 SE Pkwy Ct, Franklin, TN 37064   (100%)
Tel.: (615) 790-6754
Web Site: http://www.emotiva.com
Emp.: 25
Direct-Sale Marketer to the Professional Audio Industry Distr
N.A.I.C.S.: 449210

Dan Laufman (CEO)

Sherbourn Technologies, LLC (1)
131 SE Pkwy Ct, Franklin, TN 37064   (100%)
Tel.: (615) 791-4046
Web Site: http://www.sherbourn.com
Emp.: 30
Retailer of High-End Audiophile Home Theater & Custom Audio Brands
N.A.I.C.S.: 449210
Dan Laufman (Pres & CEO)

JADE EASTERN TRADING INC.
245 Moonachie Rd, Moonachie, NJ 07074
Tel.: (201) 440-8500
Web Site: http://www.marquisny.com
Rev.: $21,722,443
Emp.: 13
Trousers, Men's & Boys'
N.A.I.C.S.: 424350
Jade R. Lee (Pres)

JADE GLOBAL, INC.
1731 Technology Dr Ste 350, San Jose, CA 95110
Tel.: (408) 899-7200   DE
Web Site: http://www.jadeglobal.com
Year Founded: 2000
Emp.: 750
Information Technology Services
N.A.I.C.S.: 541512
Karan Yaramada (CEO)
Anant Soni (Exec VP-Delivery Excellence & Enterprise IT)
Harmeet Bhatia (Exec VP-Global Sls & Bus Dev)
Sudipta K. Bhattacharjee (Exec VP-Client Svcs)
Spiro Aronis (Reg Dir-UK)
Steve Vibhute (Reg VP-East Coast)
Arun Menon (Sr VP-Global Delivery Ops)

Subsidiaries:

Saturn Infotech, Inc. (1)
1120 Welsh Rd Ste 110, North Wales, PA 19454
Tel.: (267) 337-6779
Web Site: http://www.saturninfotech.com
Information Technology Consulting Services
N.A.I.C.S.: 541512
Ash Batra (Dir)

JADE STEEL GROUP, LTD.
26400 Richmond Rd, 26400 Richmond Rd Bedford Heights, OH 44146, Bedford Heights, OH 44146
Tel.: (330) 425-3141
Web Site:
    https://www.jadesteelgroup.com
Metals & Minerals Whslr
N.A.I.C.S.: 423510

Subsidiaries:

Precision Kidd Steel Co. Inc. (1)
1 Quality Way, Aliquippa, PA 15001-2459
Tel.: (724) 378-7670
Web Site: http://www.precisionkidd.com
Sales Range: $25-49.9 Million
Emp.: 70
Cold Finishing Steel Mfr
N.A.I.C.S.: 331221
Dom Lea (Pres)
Joel Ruckert (Mgr-Quality Sys)

JADE-STERLING STEEL CO. INC.
2300 E Aurora Rd, Twinsburg, OH 44087
Tel.: (330) 425-3141
Web Site:
    http://www.jadesterling.com
Sales Range: $25-49.9 Million
Emp.: 50
Steel
N.A.I.C.S.: 423510

Scott Herman (Pres)
Joann Groves (Mgr-Acctg)
Anh Luu (Mgr-IT)
Dwight Mosley (Mgr-Quality)
DeAnn Straus (Mgr-Traffic)
Derek Kreinbih (Dir-Metallurgy & Quality)
Howard Fertel (CEO)
Lori Rapo (Mgr-Inventory)

JADES SUPER FOOD
601 N Main St, Hamburg, AR 71646
Tel.: (870) 853-2521
Sales Range: $25-49.9 Million
Emp.: 60
Grocery Stores, Independent
N.A.I.C.S.: 445110
Joel Foote (Pres & CEO)

JAECKLE WHOLESALE INC.
4101 Owl Creek Dr, Madison, WI 53718
Tel.: (608) 838-5400   WI
Web Site:
    http://www.jaecklewholesale.com
Year Founded: 1958
Sales Range: $25-49.9 Million
Emp.: 135
Home Furnishings; Flooring; Counter top
N.A.I.C.S.: 423220
Michelle Wallace (VP-HR)
Torrey L. Jaeckle (VP-Madison)
Jeff Jaeckle (Pres)
Shawn Gagg (CIO & VP-Mktg & Sls)
Brad Simonson (CFO)

Subsidiaries:

Jaeckle Minnesota Inc. (1)
504 Malcolm Ave SE, Minneapolis, MN 55414-3341
Tel.: (612) 676-0388
Sales Range: $10-24.9 Million
Emp.: 20
Suppliers of Lumber Plywood & Millwork
N.A.I.C.S.: 423310

JAEGER LUMBER AND SUPPLY CO. INC.
2322 Morris Ave, Union, NJ 07083
Tel.: (908) 686-0070
Web Site:
    http://www.jaegerlumber.com
Sales Range: $25-49.9 Million
Emp.: 85
Lumber & Other Building Materials Sales
N.A.I.C.S.: 423310
Lowell E. Jaeger (Owner)
Brian Jaeger (Pres)

JAEGER, INC.
8981 Timberedge Dr, North Ridgeville, OH 44039
Tel.: (440) 243-8700   OH
Year Founded: 1972
Sales Range: Less than $1 Million
Emp.: 1
Advetising Agency
N.A.I.C.S.: 541810
Donald C. Auble (Owner)

JAENSCH IMMIGRATION LAW FIRM
2198 Main St, Sarasota, FL 34237
Tel.: (941) 366-9841
Web Site:
    http://www.visaamerica.com
Year Founded: 1984
Sales Range: $1-9.9 Million
Law firm
N.A.I.C.S.: 541110
Peter Jurgen Jaensch (Principal)
P. Christopher Jaensch (Principal)

JAFFARIAN AUTOMOTIVE GROUP
600 River St, Haverhill, MA 01832
Tel.: (978) 372-8551
Web Site: http://www.jaffarian.com
Sales Range: $25-49.9 Million
Emp.: 110
New Car Retailer
N.A.I.C.S.: 441110
Gary R. Jaffarian (Treas & Sec)

JAFFE TILCHIN INVESTMENT PARTNERS, LLC
15350 N Florida Ave, Tampa, FL 33613
Tel.: (813) 960-5293
Web Site: http://www.jaffetilchin.com
Year Founded: 2007
Rev.: $360,000,000
Emp.: 40
Investment Banking, Investment Advisory, Portfolio Management & Insurance Services
N.A.I.C.S.: 523150
Lou Tilchin (Mng Partner)
Scott Jaffe (Partner & Dir-Investment Mgmt)
Victor J. Mandia (Dir-Insurance Ops)
Scott Jones (Chief Compliance Officer)
Colleen Patterson (Mgr-Investment Ops)

JAFFE/BRAUNSTEIN FILMS, LTD.
12301 Wilshire Blvd Ste 110, Los Angeles, CA 90025
Tel.: (310) 207-6600
Sales Range: $10-24.9 Million
Emp.: 8
Film Production Services
N.A.I.C.S.: 512110
Howard Braunstein (Co-Founder & Partner)
Michael Jaffe (Co-Founder & Partner)

JAG CONSTRUCTION CO.
11257 109th Rd, Dodge City, KS 67801
Tel.: (620) 225-0061
Web Site: http://www.jagconst.com
Sales Range: $10-24.9 Million
Emp.: 80
Commercial & Office Building, New Construction
N.A.I.C.S.: 236220
James A. Coffin (Pres)
Mark Green (VP)
Scott Riederer (VP)

JAG SPECIALTY FOODS, LLC
115-05 15th Ave, College Point, NY 11356
Tel.: (718) 762-4466
Web Site: http://www.angonoa.com
Year Founded: 1897
Sales Range: $10-24.9 Million
Emp.: 110
Snack Food Mfr
N.A.I.C.S.: 311919
John Ferrante (VP-Mktg)
Andrew Zampieri (VP-Ops & Sls & R&D)
Gregg DeSantis (VP-Sls)
John Armao (Plant Mgr)
Christopher Desantis (Dir-Bus Dev)
Michael Kroczynski (Mgr-Special Projects)

JAGEMANN STAMPING COMPANY
5757 W Custer St, Manitowoc, WI 54221
Tel.: (920) 682-4633
Web Site: http://www.jagemann.com
Rev.: $12,800,000

Jagemann Stamping Company—(Continued)

Emp.: 160
Metal Stamping
N.A.I.C.S.: 332119
Thomas M. Jagemann *(Chm & CEO)*
John Ryan *(Acct Mgr)*
William P. Jagemann Sr. *(Founder)*
Mark Greenlund *(Dir-Ops)*

JAGGER BROWN, INC.
13428 Maxella Ave Ste 144, Marina
Del Rey, CA 90292
Tel.: (571) 921-4200   VA
Web Site: http://www.emaginos.com
Year Founded: 2008
Emp.: 2
Education Training & Support Ser-
vices
N.A.I.C.S.: 611710
Keith Larick *(Chief Education Officer)*
Jarom Heaps *(Pres, CEO, CFO &
Sec)*

JAGUAR FUELING SERVICES, LLC
8515 E North Belt, Humble, TX
77396
Web Site:
   http://www.jaguarfueling.com
Year Founded: 2014
Sales Range: $25-49.9 Million
Emp.: 33
Fuel Station Operator
N.A.I.C.S.: 423120
Rachel Dowdell *(CEO)*
Erika Curtis *(COO)*
Rachel Clark *(CFO)*
Amber Isaacks *(CMO)*
Pearl Tullos *(Coord-Billing)*

JAH ENTERPRISES, INC.
13340 Florida Blvd, Livingston, LA
70754
Tel.: (225) 686-2252   LA
Web Site:
   http://www.hendersonauctions.com
Year Founded: 1957
Sales Range: $75-99.9 Million
Emp.: 15
Holding Company
N.A.I.C.S.: 423810
Jeffrey Henderson *(Pres & CEO)*
Marvin Henderson *(Founder)*
Janet Henderson Cagley *(CFO)*

Subsidiaries:

Henderson Auctions   (1)
13340 Florida Blvd, Livingston, LA
70754   (100%)
Tel.: (225) 686-2252
Web Site:
   http://www.hendersonauctions.com
Sales Range: $25-49.9 Million
Auctioneering Service
N.A.I.C.S.: 423810
Jeffery A. Henderson *(Pres & CEO)*
Janet Henderson Cagley *(CFO)*
Jessica Cason *(Mgr-Website Mgmt & Mktg)*

JAHABOW INDUSTRIES INC.
1004 Indus Dr, Owensville, MO
65066
Tel.: (573) 437-4151
Web Site: http://www.jahabow.com
Rev.: $22,000,000
Emp.: 145
Cabinetry Mfr
N.A.I.C.S.: 337212
Hootie Decker *(Mgr-Pur & Logistics)*

JAINDL FAMILY FARMS LLC
3150 Coffeetown Rd, Orefield, PA
18069-2511
Tel.: (610) 395-3333
Web Site: http://www.jaindl.com
Turkey Farming, Real Estate Development & Soft Drink Mfr

N.A.I.C.S.: 112330
David M. Jaindl *(Owner & Pres)*

JAIR ELECTRONICS CORPO-RATION
2400 NW 92nd Ave, Miami, FL 33172
Tel.: (305) 594-7361
Web Site: http://www.jaircorp.com
Year Founded: 1978
Sales Range: $10-24.9 Million
Emp.: 50
Electrical & Electronic Appliance,
Television & Radio Set Whslr
N.A.I.C.S.: 423620
Alberto Pizano *(Dir-Mktg & Product
Dev)*
Leopoldo Garcia *(Acct Mgr)*

JAJO, INC.
200 N Broadway Ste 110, Wichita,
KS 67202
Tel.: (316) 267-6700
Year Founded: 2003
Sales Range: $10-24.9 Million
Emp.: 20
Advertising, Event Planning & Mar-
keting, Graphic Design, Identity Mar-
keting, Internet/Web Design, Logo &
Package Design, Market Research,
Media Buying Services, Print, Public
Relations, Radio, T.V.
N.A.I.C.S.: 541810
Amy Jabara *(Acct Exec)*
Steve Randa *(Mng Partner)*
Shawn Stuckey *(Mng Partner)*
Brian Weins *(Graphic Designer)*
Neil McDaniel *(Dir-Interactive)*
Jolynn Berk *(Dir-Acct Svcs)*
Kevin Gehrer *(Mgr-Bus)*
Mike Gangwere *(Assoc Dir-Creative)*
Andrew Stephens *(Art Dir)*
Ashley Devlin *(Brand Mgr)*
Eric Andreae *(Art Dir)*
Meg Foreman *(Coord-Brand)*
Aubrie Lockamy *(Dir-Art)*
Charlie Culella *(Assoc Dir-Creative)*

JAKE SWEENEY AUTOMO-TIVE INC.
33 W Kemper Rd, Cincinnati, OH
45246-2509
Tel.: (513) 782-2800   OH
Web Site:
   http://www.jakesweeney.com
Year Founded: 1971
Sales Range: $150-199.9 Million
Emp.: 1,500
New & Used Auto Sales & Service
N.A.I.C.S.: 541611
Gregory Sweeney *(VP)*
James Clark *(Dir-Adv)*
Fred Mangold *(Gen Mgr)*
Jacob B. Sweeney Jr. *(Pres)*

Subsidiaries:

Jake Sweeney Auto Leasing,
Inc.   (1)
7901 Vine St, Cincinnati, OH 45216
Tel.: (513) 489-5253
Sales Range: $25-49.9 Million
Emp.: 13
Retail & Leasing of Automobiles
N.A.I.C.S.: 532112

Jake Sweeney Chrysler Jeep Dodge,
Inc.   (1)
85 W Kemper Rd, Cincinnati, OH 45246
Tel.: (513) 782-1000
Web Site:
   http://www.jakesweeneychryslerjeep
   dodge.com
Sales Range: $10-24.9 Million
Emp.: 70
New Car Dealers
N.A.I.C.S.: 441110
Mike Sunderman *(Mgr-New Sls)*
Gary Allen *(Mgr-Fin)*
Zach Sweeney *(Gen Mgr)*

JAKOB MARKETING PART-NERS
4535 S 2300 E, Holladay, UT 84117
Tel.: (801) 930-5354
Web Site: http://www.jakobmp.com
Year Founded: 1999
Sales Range: $1-9.9 Million
Emp.: 15
Creative Development Consulting
Services
N.A.I.C.S.: 541618
Julie Jakob *(CEO)*
Lana Stoddard *(Dir-Graphics)*

JAKROO INC.
5906 Stoneridge Mall Rd, Pleasan-
ton, CA 94588   NV
Web Site: http://www.jakroo.com
Year Founded: 1996
Rev.: $10,975,325
Assets: $7,185,268
Liabilities: $2,712,491
Net Worth: $4,472,777
Earnings: $335,593
Emp.: 178
Fiscal Year-end: 12/31/18
Clothing Product Mfr & Distr
N.A.I.C.S.: 315250
Weidong Du *(Co-Founder, Chm, Pres
& CEO)*
Wei Tan *(Co-Founder & Treas)*
Derek Wiseman *(COO & Sec)*
Eric Peterson *(Sr Mgr-Production)*
Michael Hernandez *(Dir-Sls)*
Joseph Siwa *(Mgr-Acct)*
John Beriault *(Sr Mgr-Acct)*
Alex Chiu *(Mgr-Acct)*
Ben Jacques-Maynes *(Mgr-R&D &
Specialty Accts)*
Patrice Spyrka *(Sls Dir-Wholesale
Div)*
David Wang *(CFO)*

JAM ASSOCIATES LLC
9707 Waples St Ste 102, San Diego,
CA 92121
Tel.: (858) 457-4888   CA
Web Site: http://www.jhg.com
Year Founded: 1993
Rev.: $13,500,000
Emp.: 35
N.A.I.C.S.: 541810
Elizabeth Estes-Cooper *(Exec VP &
Chief Strategy Officer)*
Alex Benjamin *(Sr VP-Fin & Ops)*
Morgan Witt *(Dir-Digital Strategy)*
Jan Whitbeck *(Sr Acct Exec)*
Mary Fechtig *(Pres & CEO)*

JAMA SOFTWARE INC.
1060 NW 9th Ave, Portland, OR
97209
Tel.: (503) 922-1058
Web Site:
   http://www.jamasoftware.com
Year Founded: 2006
Sales Range: $1-9.9 Million
Emp.: 30
Mfr of Web Management Software
N.A.I.C.S.: 513210
Bruce Charles Rhine *(Chm)*
Eric Winquist *(Co-Founder, Chm &
Chief Strategy Officer)*
Keith Johnson *(VP-Product Solutions)*
Sean Tong *(Co-Founder)*
Jennifer Jaffe *(VP-Product & Strat-
egy)*
Susy Dunn *(VP-People)*
Barry Allen *(CFO)*
Ian Miller *(VP-Worldwide Sls)*
Scott Roth *(CEO)*
Jonathan Cogan *(VP-Sls)*
Clay Moore *(VP-Customer Success)*
John Gasper *(VP-Engrg)*
Rakesh Narasimhan *(COO)*
Laura Trotter *(VP-Mktg)*
Josh Turpen *(Chief Product Officer)*

JAMAICA BEARINGS CO. INC.
1700 Jericho Tpke, New Hyde Park,
NY 11040
Tel.: (516) 326-1350
Web Site:
   http://www.jamaicabearings.com
Rev.: $14,700,000
Emp.: 50
Bearings Mfr
N.A.I.C.S.: 423840
Peter F. Negri *(Pres)*
M chael Mayer *(VP-Sls & Corp Dev)*
Scott Carpenter *(VP-Sls)*

JAMAICA HOSPITAL MEDICAL CENTER
8900 Vanwyck Expy, Jamaica, NY
11418
Tel.: (718) 206-6000   NY
Web Site:
   http://www.jamaicahospital.org
Year Founded: 1934
Sales Range: $500-549.9 Million
Emp.: 3,621
Health Care Srvices
N.A.I.C.S.: 622110
Angelo Canedo *(VP)*
Bruce J. Flanz *(Pres & CEO)*
Sheila Garvey *(VP-HR)*
Manzar Sassani *(VP-Fin)*
William Lynch *(COO & Exec VP)*
Anthony Maffia *(VP-Psychotherapy)*
Fred Beekman *(VP-Ambulance Care)*
Geoffrey Doughlin *(Second VP)*
Anthony DiMaria *(Sec)*
Neil Foster Phillips *(Chm)*
Robert W. Koop *(First Vice Chm &
Treas)*

JAMCO INC.
1615 Clare Ave, West Palm Beach,
FL 33401
Tel.: (561) 655-3634
Web Site:
   http://www.themurphyco.com
Sales Range: $10-24.9 Million
Emp.: 50
Dams, Waterways, Docks & Other
Marine Construction
N.A. .C.S.: 236210
Victor Martinelli *(Treas)*
Marin E. Murphy Sr. *(Pres)*

Subsidiaries:

Cracker Boy Boat Works, Inc.   (1)
1124 Avenue C, Riviera Beach, FL 33404
Tel.: (561) 845-0357
Web Site:
   http://www.crackerboyboatworks.com
Sales Range: $1-9.9 Million
Emp.: 26
Marinas
N.A.I.C.S.: 713930
John Murphy *(VP)*
Martin E. Murphy Sr. *(Pres)*

JAMERSON & BAUWENS ELEC CONTRS
3160 Macarthur Blvd, Northbrook, IL
60062-1901
Tel.: (847) 291-2000
Web Site: http://www.jbelectric.com
Year Founded: 1989
Sales Range: $50-74.9 Million
Emp.: 200
Electrical Wiring Services
N.A.I.C.S.: 238210
Rick Jamerson *(Pres)*

JAMERSON-LEWIS CON-STRUCTION INC.
1306 Stephenson Ave, Lynchburg, VA
24501
Tel.: (434) 845-3468
Web Site:
   http://www.jamersonlewis.com
Sales Range: $50-74.9 Million

Emp.: 85
Commercial & Office Building Contractors
N.A.I.C.S.: 236220
Kevin Hooper *(VP)*
William Cook *(VP)*
S. Preston Craighill III *(Pres)*

JAMES & LUTHER, INC.
11520 Cedar Oak, El Paso, TX
79936
Tel.: (915) 591-2429   TX
Web Site:
   http://www.jamesandluther.com
Rev.: $24,000,000
Emp.: 180
Provider of Construction Services
N.A.I.C.S.: 236210
Neal Luther *(Pres)*

JAMES & SONS LTD.
112 US Hwy 41, Schererville, IN
46375-1204
Tel.: (708) 862-3800
Web Site:
   http://www.jamesandsons.com
Year Founded: 1964
Sales Range: $10-24.9 Million
Emp.: 25
Jewelry, Precious Stones & Precious
Metals
N.A.I.C.S.: 423940
Jim Sutherland *(Pres)*

JAMES & THOMAS, INC.
6N397 Corron Rd Ste 100, Saint
Charles, IL 60175-8420
Tel.: (630) 587-9901   IL
Year Founded: 1965
Sales Range: Less than $1 Million
Emp.: 4
Advetising Agency
N.A.I.C.S.: 541810
William Bloch *(Pres)*
Ann Bloch *(VP)*
David Bloch *(VP)*

JAMES A. ANDREW INC.
3315 Brady Ln, Lafayette, IN 47909
Tel.: (765) 474-1388
Web Site: http://www.henrypoor.com
Sales Range: $25-49.9 Million
Emp.: 75
Provider of Hardware Services &
Products
N.A.I.C.S.: 423310
James A. Andrew *(Pres)*

JAMES A. HALEY VETERANS'
HOSPITAL
13000 Bruce B Downs Blvd, Tampa,
FL 33612
Tel.: (813) 972-2000
Web Site: http://www.tampa.va.gov
Year Founded: 1972
Emp.: 4,240
Hospital Operations
N.A.I.C.S.: 622110
Kathleen R. Fogarty *(Dir)*
Laureen Doloresco *(Associate Dir-Patient Care & Nursing Svcs)*
Roy L. Hawkins Jr. *(Deputy Dir)*

JAMES A. JENNINGS CO. INC.
480 Mamaroneck Ave, Harrison, NY
10528-1621
Tel.: (914) 381-5300
Web Site: http://www.jajennings.com
Rev.: $51,632,033
Emp.: 10
Industrial Building Construction
N.A.I.C.S.: 236210
Marke Jennings *(Pres)*
James A. Jennings III *(Pres)*
James A. Jennings Jr. *(Chm & CEO)*

JAMES A. SCOTT & SON INC.
1301 Old Graves Mill Rd, Lynchburg,
VA 24502
Tel.: (434) 832-2100
Web Site: http://www.scottins.com
Year Founded: 1864
Sales Range: $10-24.9 Million
Emp.: 170
Fire, Marine & Casualty Insurance:
Mutual
N.A.I.C.S.: 524126
Craig K. Ryder *(CFO & COO)*
Joel A. Nichols *(Sr VP)*
Erik A. Koroneos *(Sr VP)*
Bret S. Grieves *(VP)*
Paul Huckfeldt *(CFO & Sr VP)*
W. Bolling Izard Jr. *(VP)*
James S. Redmond III *(VP)*

JAMES ALEXANDER CORPO-
RATION
845 State Rte 94, Blairstown, NJ
07825
Tel.: (908) 362-9266
Web Site: http://www.james-alexander.com
Year Founded: 1976
Sales Range: $1-9.9 Million
Emp.: 70
Fill & Seal Glass & Plastic Ampoules
N.A.I.C.S.: 561910
Francesca Fazzolari *(Pres)*
David Robinson *(VP & Gen Mgr)*
Alexander T. Davidson *(Owner)*
Carol Bottiglierie *(Mgr-Qualilty Assurance)*

JAMES AUSTIN CO.
115 Downieville Rd, Mars, PA 16046
Tel.: (724) 625-1535   PA
Web Site:
   http://www.austinsbleach.com
Year Founded: 1889
Sales Range: $75-99.9 Million
Emp.: 125
Household Cleaning Product Mfr &
Distr
N.A.I.C.S.: 325611
Henry G. Austin III *(Pres)*

Subsidiaries:

James Austin Co. - DeLand
Plant   (1)
1560 Lexington Ave, Deland, FL 32724
Tel.: (386) 734-6553
Emp.: 20
Cleaning Product Mfr
N.A.I.C.S.: 325998
Harry Austin *(CEO)*

James Austin Co. - Ludlow Plant   (1)
203 West Ave, Ludlow, MA 01056
Tel.: (413) 589-1600
Cleaning Product Mfr
N.A.I.C.S.: 325998

James Austin Co. - Statesville
Plant   (1)
124 Commerce Blvd, Statesville, NC 28625
Tel.: (704) 878-0980
Cleaning Product Mfr
N.A.I.C.S.: 325998

JAMES AVERY CRAFTSMAN
INC.
145 Avery Rd N, Kerrville, TX 78028
Tel.: (830) 895-1122
Web Site:
   http://www.jamesavery.com
Sales Range: $75-99.9 Million
Emp.: 2,000
Jewelry Mfr
N.A.I.C.S.: 339910
George Lee *(CFO)*
Andy Dolan *(Project Coord-IT)*
Chris M. Avery *(Chm)*

JAMES B. NUTTER & COM-
PANY
4153 Broadway St, Kansas City, MO
64111
Tel.: (816) 531-2345
Web Site:
   http://www.jamesbnutter.com
Rev.: $20,000,000
Emp.: 287
Mortgage Banker
N.A.I.C.S.: 522292
Keith Ward *(Controller)*
Russ Moore *(Dir-PR)*
Kerry Thomas *(VP)*
James B. Nutter Sr. *(Founder)*

JAMES BATMASIAN
215 N Federal Hwy Ste 1, Boca Raton, FL 33432
Tel.: (561) 392-8920
Web Site:
   http://www.investmentslimited.com
Sales Range: $25-49.9 Million
Emp.: 100
Residential Building Construction
N.A.I.C.S.: 531110
James Batmasian *(Owner & Pres)*

JAMES C. JENKINS INSUR-
ANCE
1390 Willow Pass Rd Ste 800, Concord, CA 94520
Tel.: (925) 798-3334
Web Site:
   http://www.epicbrokers.com
Sales Range: $10-24.9 Million
Emp.: 125
Insurance Agents, Brokers & Service
N.A.I.C.S.: 524210
Curt Perata *(VP-Ops)*
John Connell *(Sr VP)*

JAMES CAMPBELL CORPO-
RATION
1001 Kamokila Blvd, Kapolei, HI
96707
Tel.: (808) 674-6674
Web Site: http://www.kapolei.com
Sales Range: $150-199.9 Million
Emp.: 57
Real Property Lessor
N.A.I.C.S.: 531190

JAMES CHAPPEL
691 Hwy 70 E, Dickson, TN 37055
Tel.: (615) 441-3655
Rev.: $16,500,000
Emp.: 30
Grocery Store Operator
N.A.I.C.S.: 445110
Mike McGuire *(Pres)*

JAMES CONEY ISLAND INC.
1750 Stebbins Dr, Houston, TX
77043-2807
Tel.: (713) 932-1500
Web Site:
   http://www.jamesconeyisland.com
Sales Range: $10-24.9 Million
Emp.: 15
Hot Dog Stand
N.A.I.C.S.: 722513
Darrin Straughan *(Pres)*
Dave N. Tresch *(Controller)*
Paul Dondlinger *(Dir-Trng & HR)*
Rosy Tamayo *(Mgr-Catering)*
Wendy Medrano *(Coord-Events &
Catering)*
Alfonso Hernandez Jr. *(Vp-Ops)*

JAMES CRAFT AND SON INC.
2780 York Haven Rd, York Haven, PA
17370
Tel.: (717) 267-3114
Web Site:
   http://www.jamescraftson.com

Sales Range: $10-24.9 Million
Emp.: 200
Mechanical Contractor
N.A.I.C.S.: 238220
James L. Craft *(Pres)*
Vickie Kerns *(Treas & Sec)*
Robert Plumeri *(Mgr-Ops)*

JAMES D. MORRISSEY INC.
9119 Frankford Ave, Philadelphia, PA
19114-2854
Tel.: (215) 333-8000   PA
Web Site: http://www.jdm-inc.com
Year Founded: 1920
Sales Range: $25-49.9 Million
Emp.: 200
Highway & Street Construction
N.A.I.C.S.: 237310
James Furey *(Dir-Environmental
Safety)*
John Ehling *(Project Mgr)*
Rob Montgomery *(Controller)*
Scott Rainey *(Project Mgr)*

JAMES DORAN COMPANY
INC.
474 Wando Park Blvd, Mount Pleasant, SC 29464
Tel.: (843) 881-7550
Web Site:
   http://www.jamesdoranco.com
Rev.: $65,000,000
Emp.: 12
Real Estate Development Services
N.A.I.C.S.: 237210
Robert J. Doran Jr. *(CEO)*

JAMES DRURY PARTNERS,
LTD.
875 N Michigan Ave, Chicago, IL
60611-1803
Tel.: (312) 654-6708
Web Site:
   https://www.jdrurypartners.com
Year Founded: 2001
Rev.: $2,000,000
Emp.: 7
Employment Agencies
N.A.I.C.S.: 561311
James Drury *(Founder)*
Lizabeth P. Hancock *(Exec VP-
Administration)*
Matthew V. McGreal *(Mng Dir)*
Steven J. Lewis *(Sr Partner)*
Brian Waivada *(Sr Partner)*
Nancy M. Konieczki *(Partner)*
Abby C. Abruzzo *(Principal)*
James D. Pruett *(Principal)*
Casey M. Gober *(Principal)*
Kaitlyn B. O'Connor *(Principal)*
William S. C. Stanbrook *(Principal)*
Adam J. Zajac *(VP-Communications)*

JAMES E. BARNES ENTER-
PRISES INC.
2204 Government St, Mobile, AL
36606
Tel.: (251) 478-3223
Rev.: $10,700,000
Emp.: 3
Franchise Owner of Fast-Food Restaurants
N.A.I.C.S.: 722513
James E. Barnes *(Pres)*

JAMES F. KNOTT REALITY
GROUP
1 Texas Sta Ct Ste 200, Timonium,
MD 21093-8288
Tel.: (443) 689-8000   MD
Web Site: http://www.jfknott.com
Year Founded: 1969
Sales Range: $10-24.9 Million
Emp.: 40
Operative Builders, Construction
Building & Leasing

James F. Knott Reality Group—(Continued)

N.A.I.C.S.: 236117
Sue Palmer (Mgr-HR)

JAMES G. DAVIS CONSTRUCTION CORPORATION
12530 Parklawn Dr, Rockville, MD 20852-1762
Tel.: (301) 881-2990
Web Site:
   http://www.davisconstruction.com
Year Founded: 1966
Sales Range: $25-49.9 Million
Emp.: 300
Provider of Nonresidential Construction Services
N.A.I.C.S.: 236220
Dennis J. Cotter (Sr Exec VP)
William Moyer (Exec VP)
Carl Hirrlinger (Sr VP)
Mark Johnson (VP-Risk Mgmt)
Michael McCaffrey (VP-Safety)
Kevin Clark (VP)
Dominic Argentieri (VP-Construction Plng & Strategies)
Andrew Geisert (Sr Mgr-Safety)
Jason Kibler (Sr Mgr-Safety)
Rita Waltz (Sr Mgr-MEP)
David Wahler (Dir-Scheduling)
James G. Davis Jr. (Pres & CEO)

JAMES G. MURPHY CO. INC.
18226 68th Ave NE, Kenmore, WA 98028
Tel.: (425) 486-1246
Web Site:
   http://www.murphyauction.com
Year Founded: 1970
Rev.: $26,000,000
Emp.: 25
Commercial & Industrial Auctions
N.A.I.C.S.: 561990
Timothy Murphy (Pres)
Terry Moore (Mgr-Adv)
Bob Hensel (VP)

JAMES G. PARKER INSURANCE ASSOCIATES
1753 E Fir Ave, Fresno, CA 93720
Tel.: (559) 222-7722
Web Site: http://www.jgparker.com
Rev.: $10,900,000
Emp.: 73
Insurance Services
N.A.I.C.S.: 524210
Paul Thompson (VP)
Daniel Todd (VP)
Brad Shannon (VP)
Carrie Stubblefield (Mgr-Production & Acct Mgr)
John Cleveland (VP)
Leroy Berrett (VP)
James G. Parker III (Pres & CEO)

JAMES GROUP, INC.
3350 Riverhood Pkwy Ste GL25, Atlanta, GA 30339
Tel.: (770) 951-9653
Year Founded: 1987
Rev.: $19,947,399
Emp.: 10
Commercial & Residential Real Estate Development Services
N.A.I.C.S.: 238990
Rob Barfield (Co-Founder)
Brian Hosch (Co-Founder)

Subsidiaries:

Vision Construction Services of Atlanta   (1)
2060 Franklin Way Ste 1000, Marietta, GA 30067
Tel.: (770) 951-9653
Web Site: http://www.visioninv.com
Commercial & Residential Real Estate Development Services

N.A.I.C.S.: 236220

JAMES H. CROSS CO.
3602 W 23rd St, Erie, PA 16506
Tel.: (814) 833-1104
Web Site: http://www.jhctool.com
Sales Range: $10-24.9 Million
Emp.: 30
Machine Tools & Accessories
N.A.I.C.S.: 423830
Jeff Cross (Pres)

JAMES H. MALOY INC.
421 Albany Shaker Rd, Albany, NY 12211
Tel.: (518) 438-7881
Web Site: http://www.jhmaloy.com
Sales Range: $10-24.9 Million
Emp.: 30
General Contractor Highway & Street Construction
N.A.I.C.S.: 237310
Tom McClain (Project Mgr)

JAMES HAMILTON CONSTRUCTION CO.
17 Ridge Rd, Silver City, NM 88062
Tel.: (575) 388-1546
Web Site: http://www.dignpave.com
Year Founded: 1945
General Contractor, Highway & Street Construction
N.A.I.C.S.: 237310
Charles Hamilton (Pres)

JAMES J. ANDERSON CONSTRUCTION CO. INC.
6958 Torresdale Ave 200, Philadelphia, PA 19135-1932
Tel.: (215) 331-7150
Web Site:
   http://www.jjaconstruction.com
Year Founded: 1981
Sales Range: $10-24.9 Million
Emp.: 30
Highway & Street Construction
N.A.I.C.S.: 237310
Ed Dowd (Dir-Bus Dev & Equipment Rentals)
John M. Herbut (Superintendent-Equipment)
Robert Kermon (Dir-Safety)
Thomas H. Meehan (Project Mgr)
Peter Fanous (Project Mgr)

JAMES J. BOYLE & CO.
400 Oyster Point Blvd Ste 221, San Francisco, CA 94080
Tel.: (650) 871-6334
Web Site: http://www.jjboyle.com
Year Founded: 1964
Sales Range: $10-24.9 Million
Emp.: 100
Customhouse Broker; Provider of International Logistics
N.A.I.C.S.: 488510

JAMES J. WELCH & CO., INC.
27 Congress St, Salem, MA 01970
Tel.: (978) 744-9300
Web Site:
   http://www.jamesjwelch.com
Year Founded: 1949
Sales Range: $10-24.9 Million
Emp.: 50
Nonresidential Construction Services
N.A.I.C.S.: 236220
Maria Holtz (VP-Mktg)

JAMES L. MAHER CENTER
120 Hillside Ave, Newport, RI 02840
Tel.: (401) 846-0340
Web Site:
   http://www.mahercenter.org
Year Founded: 1953
Sales Range: $10-24.9 Million

Emp.: 629
Disability Assistance Services
N.A.I.C.S.: 624120
Rose Morton (Dir-HR)
Lori Scionti (Dir-Horticulture)
Maryoli Vargas (Dir-Residential Svcs)
Bill Rush (Dir-Fin)
Russle Struble (Dir-Bus Ops)
Sonia Ledo (Dir-Residential Svcs)
William Maraziti (Exec Dir)
Jennifer Murray (Dir-Transition & Employment Svcs)

JAMES L. TAYLOR MANUFACTURING CO.
108 Parker Ave, Poughkeepsie, NY 12601
Tel.: (845) 452-0691
Web Site:
   http://www.jamesltaylor.com
Year Founded: 1911
Woodworking Machinery Mfr
N.A.I.C.S.: 333243
Michael Burdis (Chm & Pres)

Subsidiaries:

JLT Clamps   (1)
108 Parker Ave, Poughkeepsie, NY 12601-1951
Tel.: (336) 375-3232
Web Site: http://www.jltclamps.com
Sales Range: $10-24.9 Million
Emp.: 12
Clamp Mfr
N.A.I.C.S.: 333243

JAMES LUMBER CO.
19801 Viking Ave NW, Poulsbo, WA 98370
Tel.: (360) 779-5571
Web Site:
   http://www.jameslumber.com
Year Founded: 1926
Sales Range: $10-24.9 Million
Emp.: 100
Construction Products Sales
N.A.I.C.S.: 423310
Mitch James (Owner)

JAMES M. PLEASANTS COMPANY INC.
603 Diamond Hill Ct, Greensboro, NC 27406
Tel.: (336) 378-9911
Web Site: http://www.jmpco.com
Year Founded: 1958
Sales Range: $10-24.9 Million
Emp.: 96
Warm Air Heating & Air Conditioning
N.A.I.C.S.: 423730
Chris Edmondson (Pres)
Chuck Moore (Mgr-Ops)
Jamie Edmondson (VP)

JAMES MACHINE WORKS, LLC
1521 Adams St, Monroe, LA 71201
Tel.: (318) 322-6104
Web Site: http://www.jmwinc.net
Year Founded: 1927
Emp.: 160
Metal Tank Mfr
N.A.I.C.S.: 332420
Paul M. McElroy (Pres)
Dale Harris (Dir-Vessels & Tanks)
Fred Korn (Project Mgr-Field Tank)
Joe K. Reljac (VP & Gen Mgr)
Ronnie Davidson (Mgr-Production-Vessel Shop)
Warren Wolleson (Mgr-Construction)
Marty Herlevic (Dir-Field Ops & Engr-Sls)
Susan M. Weaver (Treas & Sec)
Mark Pullin (Mgr-Estimating)
Don McManus (Dir-Quality Control)
Robert Mason (Dir-Safety)

JAMES MARINE INC.
4540 Clarks River Rd, Paducah, KY 42003
Tel.: (270) 898-7392
Web Site:
   http://www.jamesmarine.com
Year Founded: 1986
Rev.: $19,100,000
Emp.: 190
Provider of Barge Building & Repairing Services
N.A.I.C.S.: 336611
C. Ronald James (Pres & CEO)
Tom Freeman (Gen Mgr-Safety)
Kerry Amis (Engr-Safety)
Tim Culp (Mgr-Ops-Midstream Div)
Eric Haney (VP)
Lonnie Means (Gen Mgr-Wheel Shop)
Gordon Southern (Gen Mgr)
Jamie Hall (Gen Mgr)
Larry Perilloux (Gen Mgr)
Ron Greenlee (Mgr-Grocery)

JAMES MATTHEWS INC.
1101 N Baldwin Ave, Marion, IN 46952
Tel.: (765) 662-3831
Web Site:
   http://www.matthewsbuick.com
Sales Range: $25-49.9 Million
Emp.: 35
Sales of New & Used Automobiles
N.A.I.C.S.: 441110
Richard C. Harris (Owner & Pres)
Jeff Harris (Gen Mgr)

JAMES MCCULLAGH CO. INC.
75E Bethpage Rd, Plainview, NY 11803
Tel.: (516) 293-8800
Sales Range: $10-24.9 Million
Emp.: 5
Plumbing Contractor
N.A.I.C.S.: 238220
Bill Doremus (Pres & CEO)

JAMES MOORE & CO., P.L.
5931 NW 1st Pl, Gainesville, FL 32607
Tel.: (352) 378-1331
Web Site: http://www.jmco.com
Rev.: $10,138,113
Emp.: 65
Certified Public Accountants
N.A.I.C.S.: 541211
Bob Powell (Partner)
Carol Villemaire (Partner)
Donna Brown (Partner)
Erin Spiwak (Partner)
James Halleran (Partner)
Jay Hutto (Partner)
Ken Kurdziel (Partner)
Margo Cook (Partner)
Mark Payne (Partner)
Mary Walsh (Partner)
Mike Sibley (Partner)
Roger Swanger (Partner)
Suzanne Forbes (Partner)
Andrea Newman (Dir-Nonprofit Tax)
Nadia Batey (Sr Mgr)
Tiffany Edwards (Mgr)
Trey Long (Partner)
Varsha Mohinani (Mgr)
Zach Chalifour (Sr Mgr)

JAMES P. HILL DISTRIBUTORS
1031 Ward Chapel Rd, Farmerville, LA 71241
Tel.: (318) 368-3101
Web Site:
   http://www.hilloilcompany.com
Sales Range: $10-24.9 Million
Emp.: 43
Petroleum Bulk Stations

N.A.I.C.S.: 424710
G. Scott Hill *(VP)*
Terry D. Hill *(VP)*
Kerry D. Hill *(VP)*
Jess Brown *(CIO & VP)*
Larry Stoddard *(Pres & CEO)*
Paul Helton *(CFO)*

JAMES R. ROSENCRANTZ & SONS
184 S Rd, Kingston, NH 03833
Tel.: (603) 772-4414
Web Site:
    http://www.rosencrantztractor.com
Sales Range: $10-24.9 Million
Emp.: 60
Lawn & Garden Equipment
N.A.I.C.S.: 444230
Peter Poole *(Mgr-Parts)*

JAMES R. THOMPSON INC.
2626 Cole Ave Ste 700, Dallas, TX 75204-4070
Tel.: (713) 722-0222
Web Site:
    http://www.jrtconstruction.com
Year Founded: 1983
Sales Range: $10-24.9 Million
Emp.: 40
Nonresidential Construction Services
N.A.I.C.S.: 236220
Ryan Thompson *(Project Mgr)*

JAMES R. VANNOY & SONS CONSTRUCTION COMPANY INC.
1608 US Hwy 221 N, Jefferson, NC 28640-9304
Tel.: (336) 846-7191   NC
Web Site: http://www.jrvannoy.com
Year Founded: 1947
Sales Range: $25-49.9 Million
Emp.: 300
Nonresidential Construction Services
N.A.I.C.S.: 236220
William E. Vannoy *(Pres)*
Doug Moxley *(Project Mgr)*

JAMES RITTER LUMBER COMPANY
4796 Summer Shade Rd, Summer Shade, KY 42166
Tel.: (270) 428-5411
Web Site:
    http://www.jamesritterlumber.com
Sales Range: $10-24.9 Million
Emp.: 90
Rough, Dressed & Finished Lumber Mfr & Distr
N.A.I.C.S.: 423310
Suzanne Keele *(Mgr-Acctg & Admin)*
Jeff Ritter *(Pres & Mgr-Sls)*

JAMES RIVER COAL COMPANY
901 E Byrd St Ste 1600, Richmond, VA 23219
Tel.: (804) 780-3000   VA
Web Site:
    http://www.jamesrivercoal.com
Year Founded: 1982
Sales Range: $1-4.9 Billion
Emp.: 2,124
Bituminous Coal & Lignite-Surface Mining
N.A.I.C.S.: 212114
Peter T. Socha *(Chm, Pres & CEO)*
Michael E. Weber *(Chief Comml Officer & Sr VP)*
Elizabeth M. Cook *(Dir-IR)*
Richard L. Douthat *(VP-Risk Mgmt)*

Subsidiaries:

Bell County Coal Corporation   **(1)**
6340 W Cumberland Ave, Middlesboro, KY 40965-9093

Tel.: (606) 248-6404
Emp.: 60
Bituminous Coal Mining Services
N.A.I.C.S.: 212115
Tim Frasure *(VP)*

Bledsoe Coal Corporation   **(1)**
1374 Hwy 192 E, London, KY 40741
Tel.: (606) 878-7411
Rev.: $106,100,000
Emp.: 305
Bituminous Coal & Lignite-Surface Mining
N.A.I.C.S.: 212114

Bledsoe Coal Leasing Company   **(1)**
901 E Byrd St Ste 1600, Richmond, VA 23219
Tel.: (804) 780-3000
Bituminous Coal Mining Services
N.A.I.C.S.: 221121

James River Coal Sales Inc.   **(1)**
901 E Byrd St Ste 1600, Richmond, VA 23219
Tel.: (804) 780-3000
Web Site: http://www.jamesrivercoal.com
Rev.: $4,000,000
Coal
N.A.I.C.S.: 423520

James River Coal Service Co.   **(1)**
1374 Hwy 192 E, London, KY 40741
Tel.: (606) 878-7411
Web Site: http://www.jamesrivercoal.com
Rev.: $8,500,000
Emp.: 30
Bituminous Coal Underground Mining
N.A.I.C.S.: 212115

McCoy Elkhorn Coal Corporation   **(1)**
1148 Long Fork Rd, Kimper, KY 41539
Tel.: (606) 835-2233
Rev.: $10,900,000
Emp.: 320
Bituminous Coal Underground Mining
N.A.I.C.S.: 212115

Triad Mining Inc.   **(1)**
1524 Frederica St, Owensboro, KY 42301-4805
Tel.: (270) 683-4186
Sales Range: $150-199.9 Million
Emp.: 270
Bituminous Coal & Lignite Production
N.A.I.C.S.: 212114
Donald Aerosmith *(Pres)*

Triad Underground Mining, LLC   **(1)**
14972 E State Rd 58, Edwardsport, IN 47528
Tel.: (812) 328-2491
Bituminous Coal Mining Services
N.A.I.C.S.: 212114

JAMES RIVER EQUIPMENT INC.
11047 Leadbetter Rd, Ashland, VA 23005
Tel.: (804) 798-6001   VA
Web Site:
    http://www.jamesriverequipment.com
Year Founded: 1926
Industrial Machinery & Equipment Whslr
N.A.I.C.S.: 423830
Mark D. Romer *(Pres)*
Tucker LaForce *(Gen Mgr)*
Leslie Eliades *(Mgr-HR & Payroll)*

JAMES RIVER TRANSPORTATION
915 N Allen Ave, Richmond, VA 23220
Tel.: (804) 342-7300
Web Site:
    http://www.jamesrivertrans.com
Year Founded: 1928
Sales Range: $10-24.9 Million
Emp.: 200
Bus Transportation
N.A.I.C.S.: 485510
Laura Jaquez *(Mgr-Acctg)*

JAMES ROSS ADVERTISING

1180 SW 36th Ave Ste 101, Pompano Beach, FL 33069
Tel.: (954) 974-6640
Web Site:
    http://www.jamesrossadvertising.com
Year Founded: 2003
Rev.: $18,000,000
Emp.: 12
N.A.I.C.S.: 541810
Neil Ross *(Owner)*

JAMES SKINNER BAKING COMPANY
4651 F St, Omaha, NE 68117
Tel.: (402) 734-1672
Web Site:
    http://www.skinnerbaking.com
Sales Range: $25-49.9 Million
Emp.: 200
Frozen Baked Goods Mfr & Sales
N.A.I.C.S.: 311813
James G. Skinner *(Co-Founder)*
Mike Knott *(VP-Fin)*
Audie Keaton *(Pres)*
Gary Kyle *(Dir-Mktg)*

JAMES THOMPSON & CO. INC.
463 7th Ave, New York, NY 10018
Tel.: (212) 686-4242
Web Site:
    http://www.jamesthompson.com
Sales Range: $10-24.9 Million
Emp.: 9
Burlap, Jute
N.A.I.C.S.: 314999
Robert B. Judell *(Pres)*
Barry Garr *(Treas)*
Marc Bieler *(VP-Sls & Mktg)*

JAMES TRUSS COMPANY
2080 Mondo Ct, Las Vegas, NV 89123-1553
Tel.: (702) 642-7548   NV
Web Site: http://www.dialmfg.com
Rev.: $22,000,000
Emp.: 80
Roof Truss Mfr
N.A.I.C.S.: 321215

JAMES W. BELL CO. INC.
1755 I Ave NE, Cedar Rapids, IA 52402
Tel.: (319) 362-1151
Web Site: http://www.jwbell.biz
Sales Range: $10-24.9 Million
Emp.: 35
General Construction Machinery & Equipment
N.A.I.C.S.: 423810
Dennis McGiveren *(Treas & Sec)*
Keith McPhee *(Asst Mgr-Parts)*
Scott Cummings *(Pres)*

JAMESMARK BANCSHARES, INC.
3570 S National Ave, Springfield, MO 65807
Tel.: (417) 869-9000   MO
Web Site:
    http://www.oldmissouribank.com
Year Founded: 1998
Bank Holding Company
N.A.I.C.S.: 551111
Mark A. Harrington *(Pres & CEO)*

Subsidiaries:

Old Missouri Bank   **(1)**
3570 S National Ave, Springfield, MO 65807
Tel.: (417) 869-9000
Web Site: http://www.oldmissouribank.com
Sales Range: $1-9.9 Million
Emp.: 19
Commericial Banking
N.A.I.C.S.: 522110

Tammy Cunningham *(COO & VP)*
Mark A. Harrington *(Pres & CEO)*

JAMESON PUBLISHING INC.
Knowledge Park 5340 Fryling Rd Ste 300, Erie, PA 16510
Tel.: (814) 897-9000
Web Site:
    http://www.jamesonpublishing.com
Year Founded: 1980
Sales Range: $10-24.9 Million
Emp.: 70
Publisher of Trade Journals
N.A.I.C.S.: 513120
Terry C. Peterson *(Founder)*
John Howland *(VP-Sls & Mktg)*
Rick Peterson *(Co-Founder & Co-Owner)*

Subsidiaries:

VertMarkets, Inc.   **(1)**
101 Gibraltar Rd Ste 100, Horsham, PA 19044
Tel.: (215) 675-1800
Web Site: http://www.vermarkets.com
Sales Range: $25-49.9 Million
Emp.: 60
Provider of Online Sales & Marketing Services
N.A.I.C.S.: 449210
Tom Roberts *(Gen Mgr)*

Division (Domestic):

CareerMag.com   **(2)**
1060 First Ave Ste 100, King of Prussia, PA 19406
Tel.: (610) 878-2800
Web Site: http://www.careermag.com
Sales Range: $25-49.9 Million
Emp.: 30
Online Recruiting Agency
N.A.I.C.S.: 561311
Joe Smith *(Pres)*

JAMESTOWN CONTAINER CORPORATION
14 Deming Dr, Falconer, NY 14733
Tel.: (716) 665-4623   NY
Web Site:
    http://www.jamestowncontainer.com
Rev.: $70,000,000
Emp.: 110
Corrugated & Solid Fiber Boxes
N.A.I.C.S.: 322211
Richard Weimer *(Controller)*
Bruce Janowsky *(CFO & Gen Mgr)*

Subsidiaries:

Jamestown Container Corp.   **(1)**
8146 Bavaria Dr E, Macedonia, OH 44056-2248   **(100%)**
Tel.: (216) 831-3700
Web Site:
    http://www.jamestowncontainer.com
Sales Range: $25-49.9 Million
Emp.: 60
Mfr of Corrugated Boxes
N.A.I.C.S.: 322211
Joseph M. Palmeri *(Gen Mgr)*

Midwest Box Company, Inc.   **(1)**
9801 Walford Ave, Cleveland, OH 44102
Tel.: (216) 281-3980
Web Site: http://midwestboxco.com
Sales Range: $1-9.9 Million
Emp.: 19
Corrugated & Solid Fiber Box Mfr
N.A.I.C.S.: 322211
Suzy Hecht Remer *(CEO)*

JAMESTOWN DISTRIBUTORS
17 Peckham Dr, Bristol, RI 02809
Tel.: (401) 253-3840
Web Site:
    http://www.jamestowndistributors.com
Year Founded: 1977
Sales Range: $10-24.9 Million

Jamestown Distributors—(Continued)

Emp.: 45
Transportation Equipment & Supplies Whslr
N.A.I.C.S.: 423860
Mike Mills (Pres)
Barbara Smith (Mgr-Acctg & HR)
Melanie Curley (Mgr-Sls & Customer Svc)
Rui Fernandes (Mgr-Warehouse)
Ed Botelho (Mgr-Receiving)

JAMESTOWN ENTERTAIN-MENT
1206 Wisconsin Ave NW Ste 2000, Washington, DC 20007
Tel.: (202) 904-0040
Web Site:
http://www.jamestownentertainment.com
Sales Range: $1-9.9 Million
Emp.: 50
Event Production & Marketing Services
N.A.I.C.S.: 337215
Frederick Wyatt (Owner)
Ellen Silverberg (Coord-Event)

JAMESTOWN METAL MARINE SALES, INC.
4710 Boca Raton Blvd Ste 400, Boca Raton, FL 33431
Tel.: (561) 994-3900
Web Site:
http://www.jamestownmetal.com
Year Founded: 1973
Sales Range: $25-49.9 Million
Ship Building Services
N.A.I.C.S.: 336611
Richard Hazard (Pres)
Christina Dolomount (Mgr-Project)
Bob Browne (Mgr-Pur)

JAMESTOWN PLASTICS INC.
8806 Highland Ave PO Box U, Brocton, NY 14716
Tel.: (716) 792-4144
Web Site:
http://www.jamestownplastics.com
Sales Range: $10-24.9 Million
Emp.: 75
Plastic Container Mfr
N.A.I.C.S.: 326199
Jay Baker (Pres)
Dale Akin (Mgr-Tools)

JAMIE GIBBS & ASSOCIATES
120 W 73rd St, Indianapolis, IN 46260
Tel.: (917) 862-5313
Web Site:
http://www.jamiegibbsassociates.com
Sales Range: $10-24.9 Million
Emp.: 6
Interior Design & Landscape Architecture Services
N.A.I.C.S.: 541410
Jamie Gibbs (Owner)

JAMISON DOOR COMPANY
55 JV Jamison Dr, Hagerstown, MD 21740
Tel.: (301) 733-3100   MD
Web Site:
http://www.jamisondoor.com
Year Founded: 1906
Sales Range: $75-99.9 Million
Emp.: 165
Mfr of Cold Storage, Sound Reduction & Other Specialty Engineered Doors
N.A.I.C.S.: 332321
Curtis L. Berry (VP-Engrg)
John Williams (Chm, Pres & CEO)

Monte Lucas (Pres-Jamison RFID)
Matthew Wyskiel (Vice Chm)
Boyce Martin III (Gen Counsel & Exec VP)

Subsidiaries:
HCR, Inc.   (1)
Hwy 87 W, Lewistown, MT 59457
Tel.: (800) 326-7700
Web Site: http://www.hcr-inc.com
Emp.: 35
Air Conditioning Equipment Mfr
N.A.I.C.S.: 333415
Rebecca Jackson (Office Mgr)
Mel Jackson (Project Mgr)

JAMISON/MCKAY LLC
335 Powell St 14th Fl, San Francisco, CA 94102
Tel.: (415) 398-2848   IL
Web Site:
http://www.jamisonmckay.com
Year Founded: 1982
Rev.: $10,000,000
Emp.: 10
N.A.I.C.S.: 541810
David Jamison (CEO)
Caryn Weiss (Sr VP-Client Svcs)
Lori Zorr (Mgr-Fin)
Clarissa Klimek (Mgr-Media)

JAMPLAY LLC
1905 Woods Dr Ste 101, Beavercreek, OH 45432
Web Site: http://www.jamplay.com
Year Founded: 2006
Sales Range: $1-9.9 Million
Emp.: 30
Online Music Education
N.A.I.C.S.: 611710
Jeff Booth (Co-Founder)
Chris Dawson (Co-Founder)
Kevin Wimer (Co-Founder)

JAMS MEDIA LLC
PO Box 220, Lapeer, MI 48446
Tel.: (810) 245-9343
Web Site:
http://www.mihomepaper.com
Sales Range: $25-49.9 Million
Emp.: 45
Holding Company
N.A.I.C.S.: 551112
Dale Phillips (CFO)
Eric E. Burrough (Owner)

Subsidiaries:
Brown City Banner   (1)
4241 Main St, Brown City, MI 48416-0250
Tel.: (810) 346-2753
Web Site:
http://browncitybanner.mihomepaper.com
Sales Range: $10-24.9 Million
Emp.: 2
Newspaper Publishers
N.A.I.C.S.: 513110
Dawn Diller (Office Mgr)

Lapeer County Press   (1)
1521 Imlay City Rd, Lapeer, MI 48446-3175
Tel.: (810) 664-0811
Web Site: http://www.countypress.com
Sales Range: $10-24.9 Million
Newspaper Publishers
N.A.I.C.S.: 513110
Jeff Hogan (Editor)

Sherman Publications, Inc.   (1)
666 S Lapeer Rd, Oxford, MI 48371
Tel.: (248) 628-4801
Web Site: http://www.clarkstonnews.com
Sales Range: $1-9.9 Million
Emp.: 65
Newspaper & Publishing
N.A.I.C.S.: 513110
James A. Sherman (Publr)

JAMS, THE RESOLUTION EXPERTS
1920 Main St at Gillette Ave Ste 300, Irvine, CA 92614
Tel.: (949) 224-1810
Web Site: http://www.jamsadr.com
Sales Range: $50-74.9 Million
Emp.: 125
Dispute Resolution Services
N.A.I.C.S.: 523910
John Welsh (Gen Counsel & Exec VP)
Laura A. Martinez (VP-HR)
William Zauner (CIO & VP)
Brian Parmelee (VP-Corp Dev & Panel Rels)

JAN X-RAY SERVICES INCORPORATED
8550 E Michigan Ave, Parma, MI 49269
Tel.: (517) 531-8210
Web Site: http://www.janx.net
Year Founded: 1981
Sales Range: $10-24.9 Million
Emp.: 400
Pipeline & Power Line Inspection Services
N.A.I.C.S.: 541990
James Barrett (Mgr-Special Projects-New Jersey)

JANA PARTNERS, LLC
201 Post St Ste 1000, San Francisco, CA 94108
Tel.: (415) 989-7775
Web Site:
https://www.janapartners.com
Year Founded: 2001
Sales Range: $1-9.9 Million
Emp.: 22
Financial Vehicles
N.A.I.C.S.: 525990
Barry S. Rosenstein (Mng Partner)
Scott D. Ostfeld (Mng Partner & Portfolio Mgr)

JANCO ELECTRONICS INC.
50 Goodwin Rd, Rollinsford, NH 03869
Tel.: (603) 742-1581
Web Site: http://www.janco-electronics.com
Year Founded: 1959
Emp.: 200
Electronic Circuits Mfr
N.A.I.C.S.: 334419
Rollins L. Janetos (Pres & CEO)
David Trippett (COO)

JANCO FOODS, INC.
1216 Silber Rd, Houston, TX 77055
Tel.: (713) 237-8200
Web Site: http://www.jancofoods.com
Year Founded: 1955
Sales Range: $10-24.9 Million
Emp.: 20
Food Service Products Distr
N.A.I.C.S.: 424410
Peter Mousoudakis (Pres)

JANCO LTD.
34 Burgess Pl, Wayne, NJ 07470
Tel.: (973) 696-7700
Web Site: http://www.jancoltd.com
Year Founded: 1975
Entertainment Transportation Services
N.A.I.C.S.: 484121
Jan Mallow (Owner)

JANDD MOUNTAINEERING, INC.
2365 Marconi Ct Ste F, San Diego, CA 92154-7265
Tel.: (760) 597-9021   CA
Web Site: http://www.jandd.com
Year Founded: 1983

Sales Range: $10-24.9 Million
Emp.: 100
Outdoor Bags & Accessories Mfr
N.A.I.C.S.: 314910
Dave Sisson (Pres)
David Sisson (Pres)

JANE TODD CRAWFORD MEMORIAL HOSP., INC.
202-206 Milby St, Greensburg, KY 42743
Tel.: (270) 932-4211   KY
Year Founded: 2007
Sales Range: $10-24.9 Million
Emp.: 311
Healthcare Services
N.A.I.C.S.: 622110
Ruthie Shuffett (Chm)
Valerie Perkins (Sec)
Rusty Tungate (CEO)

JANELL INC.
6130 Cornell Rd, Cincinnati, OH 45242
Tel.: (513) 489-9111
Web Site: http://www.janell.com
Sales Range: $10-24.9 Million
Emp.: 55
General Construction Machinery & Equipment
N.A.I.C.S.: 423810
Wayne Hodge (Branch Mgr)

JANESVILLE SAND & GRAVEL CO
1110 Harding St, Janesville, WI 53545
Tel.: (608) 754-7701
Web Site: http://www.jsandg.com
Sales Range: $25-49.9 Million
Emp.: 30
Ready Mixed Concrete
N.A.I.C.S.: 327320
Wendy Facinger (Mgr-Credit)

JANGLE ADVERTISING
240 S Main St, Nazareth, PA 18064
Tel.: (610) 365-8383
Web Site:
http://www.jangleadvertising.com
Year Founded: 2003
Sales Range: $1-9.9 Million
Emp.: 7
Advertising, Branding & Marketing
N.A.I.C.S.: 541810
Dan Kleckner (Designer)
Jan Haley-Schwoyer (Principal & Creative Dir)
Gale Schmidt Hodavance (Principal & Dir-Acct Svcs)
Elaine Cobb (Office Mgr)
Scott Bazzett (Art Dir)

JANI-KING INTERNATIONAL, INC.
16885 Dallas Pkwy, Addison, TX 75001-5215
Tel.: (972) 991-0900   TX
Web Site: http://www.janiking.com
Year Founded: 1969
Sales Range: $100-124.9 Million
Emp.: 250
Janitorial Services
N.A.I.C.S.: 561720
Cindy Christian (Chief Nursing Officer)

Subsidiaries:
Jani King Franchising, Inc.   (1)
16885 Dallas Pkwy, Addison, TX 75001-5215
Tel.: (972) 991-0900
Web Site: http://www.janiking.com

Sales Range: $10-24.9 Million
Emp.: 85
Janitorial Maintenance Service
N.A.I.C.S.: 533110

Jani King Leasing Corp. **(1)**
16885 Dallas Pkwy, Addison, TX 75001-5215
Tel.: (972) 991-0900
Web Site: http://www.janiking.com
Sales Range: $25-49.9 Million
Emp.: 100
Janitorial Maintenance Service
N.A.I.C.S.: 533110
Jim Cavanaugh (Founder & CEO)
Jill Bean (VP)
Jerry Crawford (VP)

Jani King, Inc. **(1)**
16885 Dallas Pkwy, Addison, TX 75001-5215
Tel.: (972) 991-0900
Web Site: http://www.janiking.com
Sales Range: $25-49.9 Million.
Emp.: 100
Janitorial Maintenance Service
N.A.I.C.S.: 533110
Jerry Crawford (Pres)

Subsidiary (Domestic):

Jani King of California, Inc. **(2)**
500 N State College Ste 900, Orange, CA 92868
Tel.: (714) 990-2221
Web Site: http://www.janiking.com
Sales Range: $25-49.9 Million
Emp.: 70
Janitorial Services
N.A.I.C.S.: 561720
Gary Clark (Sr VP-Sls & Mktg)

Jani King of California, Inc. **(2)**
6170 Cornerstone Ste 330, San Diego, CA 92121 **(100%)**
Tel.: (619) 682-3400
Web Site: http://www.janiking.com
Sales Range: $25-49.9 Million
Provider of Commercial Maintenance
N.A.I.C.S.: 533110
Carlos Negron (Reg Dir)

Jani King of Cincinnati, Inc. **(2)**
3800 Red Bank Rd Ste A, Cincinnati, OH 45227-3476 **(100%)**
Tel.: (513) 771-8006
Web Site: http://www.janiking.com
Sales Range: $25-49.9 Million
Emp.: 12
Commercial Maintenance of Buildings
N.A.I.C.S.: 533110
James Dixon (Reg Pres)

Jani King of Cleveland, Inc. **(2)**
9075 Town Dr, Broadview Heights, OH 44147-3521
Tel.: (440) 546-0000
Web Site: http://www.janiking.com
Sales Range: $25-49.9 Million
Emp.: 17
Lessors of Nonfinancial Intangible Assets (except Copyrighted Works)
N.A.I.C.S.: 533110
Jim Cavanaugh (Chm & Pres)
Arlene Cavanaugh (Sec)
Pam Carollo (Office Mgr)
Joe Corollo (Pres)

Jani King of Colorado, Inc. **(2)**
12835 E Arapahoe Rd Tower 2 Ste 650, Centennial, CO 80112 **(100%)**
Tel.: (303) 294-0200
Sales Range: $25-49.9 Million
Emp.: 12
Lessors of Nonfinancial Intangible Assets (except Copyrighted Works)
N.A.I.C.S.: 533110

Jani King of Dallas **(2)**
4535 Sunbelt Dr, Addison, TX 75001-5204
Tel.: (972) 991-0900
Web Site: http://www.janiking.com
Sales Range: $25-49.9 Million
Emp.: 15
Commercial Cleaning Services
N.A.I.C.S.: 561720
Steve Tapken (Owner & Pres)
Andrew Espitia (COO)
Keath Hance (CFO)
Charles Oney (Exec VP)

Jani King of Florida, Inc. **(2)**
5700 St Augustine Rd, Jacksonville, FL 32207-4783
Tel.: (904) 346-3000
Web Site: http://www.janiking.com
Sales Range: $25-49.9 Million
Emp.: 10
Maintenance of Commercial Building Services
N.A.I.C.S.: 533110
Michael Kearns (Owner)

Jani King of Hartford, Inc. **(2)**
40 Cold Spring Rd, Rocky Hill, CT 06067 **(100%)**
Tel.: (860) 623-3888
Web Site: http://www.jani-king.com
Sales Range: $25-49.9 Million
Emp.: 10
Lessors of Nonfinancial Intangible Assets (except Copyrighted Works)
N.A.I.C.S.: 533110
Jim Cavanaugh (Founder & Pres)
Lisa Crow (Treas)

Jani King of Illinois, Inc. **(2)**
1100 E Woodfield Rd Ste 101, Schaumburg, IL 60173
Tel.: (847) 619-3800
Web Site: http://www.janiking.com
Sales Range: $25-49.9 Million
Emp.: 45
Janitorial Services
N.A.I.C.S.: 561720
Jim Cavanaugh (Founder)
Bob Limbach (VP-Sls)

Jani King of Miami, Inc. **(2)**
4000 Hollywood Blvd Ste 6950, Hollywood, FL 33021-6751
Tel.: (305) 944-1811
Web Site: http://www.janiking.com
Sales Range: $25-49.9 Million
Emp.: 16
Lessors of Nonfinancial Intangible Assets (except Copyrighted Works)
N.A.I.C.S.: 533110

Jani King of Michigan, Inc. **(2)**
31420 Northwestern Hwy Ste 125, Farmington Hills, MI 48334-8259
Tel.: (248) 936-0040
Web Site: http://www.janiking.com
Sales Range: $25-49.9 Million
Emp.: 6
Maintenance Services
N.A.I.C.S.: 533110
Jim Cavanaugh (Chm & Pres)
Arleen Cavanaugh (Sec)

Jani King of Minnesota, Inc. **(2)**
5930 Shingle Creek Pkwy, Brooklyn Center, MN 55430
Tel.: (763) 746-7333
Web Site: http://www.janiking.com
Sales Range: $25-49.9 Million
Emp.: 6
Commercial Training
N.A.I.C.S.: 561720
Helen Nelson (Office Mgr)

Jani King of Nashville, Inc. **(2)**
3343 Perimeter Hill Dr Ste 110, Nashville, TN 37211
Tel.: (615) 445-7979
Sales Range: $10-24.9 Million
Emp.: 10
Franchisee Sales
N.A.I.C.S.: 561720
Victor Barrios (Pres)

Jani King of New Jersey, Inc. **(2)**
30 2 Bridges Rd, Fairfield, NJ 07004 **(100%)**
Tel.: (973) 808-0909
Web Site: http://www.janiking.com
Sales Range: $25-49.9 Million
Emp.: 12
Lessors of Nonfinancial Intangible Assets (except Copyrighted Works)
N.A.I.C.S.: 533110

Jani King of Oklahoma, Inc. **(2)**
3535 NW 58th St Ste 200, Oklahoma City, OK 73112-4802
Tel.: (405) 943-5464
Web Site: http://www.jani-king.com
Sales Range: $25-49.9 Million
Emp.: 12
Commercial Cleaning Services

N.A.I.C.S.: 533110
Terri Newton (Office Mgr)

Jani King of Philadelphia, Inc. **(2)**
2500 Eisenhower Ave, Norristown, PA 19403 **(100%)**
Tel.: (610) 650-0355
Web Site: http://www.janiking.com
Sales Range: $25-49.9 Million
Emp.: 15
Building Cleaning Services
N.A.I.C.S.: 533110
Jim Cavanaugh (Founder)

Jani King of St. Louis, Inc. **(2)**
2337 Welding Pkwy, Maryland Heights, MO 63146 **(100%)**
Tel.: (314) 576-4330
Web Site: http://www.janiking.com
Sales Range: $25-49.9 Million
Emp.: 10
Maintenance & Commercial Cleaning Service
N.A.I.C.S.: 533110
Leslie Phillips (Mgr-Ops)

Jani King of Washington D.C., Inc. **(2)**
11351 Random Hills Rd, Fairfax, VA 22030 **(100%)**
Tel.: (703) 922-4300
Web Site: http://www.janiking.com
Sales Range: $25-49.9 Million
Emp.: 15
Lessors of Nonfinancial Intangible Assets (except Copyrighted Works)
N.A.I.C.S.: 533110

Jani-King of New York, Inc. **(2)**
1800 Walt Whitman Rd Ste 170, Melville, NY 11747
Tel.: (631) 773-5477
Web Site: http://www.janiking.com
Sales Range: $10-24.9 Million
Emp.: 12
Janitorial Services
N.A.I.C.S.: 561720

Jani-King of Phoenix **(2)**
7740 N 16th St Ste 110, Phoenix, AZ 85020
Tel.: (602) 433-0550
Web Site: http://www.janikingaz.com
Rev.: $16,129,150
Emp.: 20
Janitorial Service, Contract Basis
N.A.I.C.S.: 561720
Julie Robinson (CEO)
Bill Pearsall (Mgr-Ops)

JANITRONICS INC.
29 Sawyer Rd Ste 1, Waltham, MA 02453
Tel.: (781) 647-5570
Web Site: http://www.janitronics.com
Sales Range: $25-49.9 Million
Emp.: 2,200
Commercial Cleaning Services
N.A.I.C.S.: 561720
Donald Brecher (Pres)
Vince Long (CFO)
Dorrian Cohen Fragola (VP-Mktg & Bus Dev)

JANKLOW & NESBIT ASSOCIATES
445 Park Ave 13th Fl, New York, NY 10022
Tel.: (212) 421-1700
Web Site: http://www.janklow.com
Sales Range: $10-24.9 Million
Emp.: 43
Representation Services for Authors
N.A.I.C.S.: 711410
Jared Barron (Coord-Contracts)
Morton L. Janklow (Co-Founder)
Lynn Nesbit (Co-Founder)
Luke Janklow (Pres & Mng Dir)
Bennett Ashley (Gen Counsel & Head-Legal & Bus Affairs)
Anne Sibbald (Mng Dir & Partner)
Dmitri Chitov (CFO, CIO & Partner)
Michael Steger (Dir-Contracts, Bus & Legal Affairs)

JANKOVICH COMPANY
Berth 74, San Pedro, CA 90731
Tel.: (310) 547-3305   CA
Web Site:
http://www.thejankovichcompany.com
Sales Range: $25-49.9 Million
Emp.: 60
Petroleum Bulk Stations & Terminals
N.A.I.C.S.: 424710
Thomas J. Jankovich (Pres)
Patrick Wheat (Mgr-Ops)

JANKOWSKICO.
570 Kirts Blvd Ste 202, Troy, MI 48084
Tel.: (248) 404-9900
Web Site:
http://www.jankowskico.com
Year Founded: 1998
Sales Range: $10-24.9 Million
Emp.: 8
Advertising Agencies
N.A.I.C.S.: 541810
Roger Jankowski (Pres & Chief Creative Officer)
Alex Eve (Acct Exec)

JANLYNN CORPORATION
2070 W Dover Rd, Chicopee, MA 01022
Tel.: (413) 543-7500   MA
Web Site: http://www.janlynn.com
Year Founded: 1979
Sales Range: $75-99.9 Million
Emp.: 75
Crafts & Stitchery Kits Mfr
N.A.I.C.S.: 313310
John F. Kozub (Pres & CEO)
Andrew J. Goetsch (CFO)
Paul St. Jean (VP-Mfg)
Thomas J. Lonergan III (Exec VP)

JANNELL MOTORS, INC.
2000 Washington St Rte 53, Hanover, MA 02339
Tel.: (781) 982-4500
Web Site: http://www.jannellford.com
Year Founded: 1921
Sales Range: $10-24.9 Million
Emp.: 55
Car Whslr
N.A.I.C.S.: 441110
Joseph Clapp (VP)
William D. Roderick (Gen Mgr)

JANOTTA & HERNER, INC.
309 Monroe St, Monroeville, OH 44847-9406
Tel.: (419) 465-4611
Web Site:
http://www.janottaherner.com
Sales Range: $25-49.9 Million
Emp.: 165
Nonresidential Construction Services
N.A.I.C.S.: 236220
James Limbrid (Principal)

JANSEN COASTAL PROPERTIES GROUP
423 Mandalay Ave Ste 102, Clearwater Beach, FL 33767
Tel.: (727) 493-1555
Web Site: http://www.coastalpgi.com
Sales Range: $10-24.9 Million
Emp.: 20
Real Estate Broker
N.A.I.C.S.: 531210
Alexander Jansen (Co-Founder)
Laren Jansen (Co-Founder)
Michael W. Jansen (Mng Dir-South Beaches)

JANSEN VALK THOMPSON & REAHM PC

Jansen Valk Thompson & Reahm PC—(Continued)

7171 Stadium Dr, Kalamazoo, MI 49009
Tel.: (269) 381-7600
Web Site: http://www.jvtr.com
Offices of Certified Public Accountants
N.A.I.C.S.: 541211
Amanda Bobalik *(Processing Coord)*
Ashley Clum *(Mgr)*
Chris Wipper *(Dir-IT)*
Debra Pellerito *(Principal)*
Jim Valk *(Mng Principal)*

JANSONS ASSOCIATES, INC.
130 Mozart St, East Rutherford, NJ 07073
Tel.: (201) 438-5455
Web Site:
http://www.jansonsassociates.com
Year Founded: 1958
Sales Range: $10-24.9 Million
Construction Materials Whslr
N.A.I.C.S.: 423390
Robert Sumanis *(VP)*

JANUS DISPLAYS
12000 28th St N, Saint Petersburg, FL 33716
Tel.: (727) 531-4000
Web Site:
http://www.janusdisplays.com
Rev.: $7,500,000
Emp.: 48
Electronic Computer Mfr
N.A.I.C.S.: 334111
Sharon Morrow *(Pres)*
Jamie Saeger *(Dir-Mktg & Admin)*

JANUS HOTELS & RESORTS, INC.
2300 Corporate Blvd NW Ste 232, Boca Raton, FL 33431-8596
Tel.: (561) 997-2325
Web Site:
http://www.janushotels.com
Year Founded: 1997
Sales Range: $25-49.9 Million
Emp.: 30
Hospitality Property Manager & Operator
N.A.I.C.S.: 561110
Louis S. Beck *(Chm)*
Richard A. Tonges *(CFO)*
Michael Nanosky *(Pres & CEO)*
Greg Cappel *(VP-Sls & Mktg)*

JANZEN JOHNSTON & ROCKWELL EMERGENCY MEDICINE MANAGEMENT SERVICES, INC.
1700 E Walnut Ave Ste 250, El Segundo, CA 90245
Tel.: (310) 301-2030
Web Site: http://famouspotatoes.net
Sales Range: $10-24.9 Million
Provider of Billing & Bookkeeping Services for Medical ER Doctors
N.A.I.C.S.: 541219
Barry Staum *(Treas)*
Ed Buckley *(Pres)*
Brent Dupper *(VP-Fin)*

JAPAN SOCIETY, INC.
333 E 47th St, New York, NY 10017
Tel.: (212) 832-1155
Web Site:
http://www.japansociety.org
Year Founded: 1913
Sales Range: $10-24.9 Million
Emp.: 68
Sociological Development Services
N.A.I.C.S.: 541720

Lisa Bermudez *(VP-Fin & Admin)*
Jane Fenton *(Dir-HR)*
Betty Borden *(Dir-Policy Projects)*
Janet Fu *(Dir-Program Ops)*

JAPANESE WEEKEND INC.
222 Dore St, San Francisco, CA 94103
Tel.: (415) 621-0555
Web Site:
http://www.japaneseweekend.com
Sales Range: $10-24.9 Million
Emp.: 65
Maternity Clothes Mfr & Retailer
N.A.I.C.S.: 315250

JARBOE'S PLUMBING, HEATING & COOLING, INC.
3258 Ruckriegel Pkwy, Louisville, KY 40299
Tel.: (502) 225-9089
Web Site: http://www.jarboes.com
Year Founded: 1987
Sales Range: $1-9.9 Million
Emp.: 32
Plumbing Services
N.A.I.C.S.: 238220
Jacob Huck *(Pres)*

Subsidiaries:

Pacific Plumbing Co. **(1)**
2121 Reynolds Ln Unit A, Louisville, KY 40218
Tel.: (502) 587-0603
Web Site: http://www.pacificplumbingky.com
Plumbing, Heating & Air-Conditioning Contractors
N.A.I.C.S.: 238220

JARCHEM INDUSTRIES, INC.
414 Wilson Ave, Newark, NJ 07105
Tel.: (973) 344-0600
Web Site: http://www.jarchem.com
Year Founded: 1978
Sales Range: $50-74.9 Million
Emp.: 45
Pharmaceutical Preservatives & Acetate Salts for Food, Textile, Photographic & Chemical Processing Industry Mfr
N.A.I.C.S.: 325199
Arnold Stern *(Pres)*
Robert Honig *(VP)*
David Honig *(Controller)*
Arthur Hein *(VP-Specialty Chemical Div)*

JARDINIER ALTERNATIVE IRRIGATION SYSTEMS, INC.
16520 Harbor Blvd 3 Fl, Fountain Valley, CA 92704
Tel.: (714) 241-4200
Year Founded: 1988
Sales Range: $1-9.9 Million
Emp.: 10
Mfr of Sub Irrigation Growing Containers; Interior-Exterior Sub Irrigation Systems; Automated Systems
N.A.I.C.S.: 221310
Cher Kater *(Controller & Dir-Ops)*
Eugene Nalbandian *(CEO)*

JARDINIER CORP.
2840 W First St, Santa Ana, CA 92703
Tel.: (714) 241-4200
Home Appliance Distr
N.A.I.C.S.: 423620
Gene Nalbandian *(Pres & CEO)*

JARDIS INDUSTRIES INC.
1201 W Ardmore Ave, Itasca, IL 60143
Tel.: (630) 860-5959
Web Site: http://www.jardis.com
Year Founded: 1985

Sales Range: $10-24.9 Million
Printing Machinery Mfr
N.A.I.C.S.: 333248
Alan W. Jardis *(Pres)*

JARDON & HOWARD TECHNOLOGIES
2710 Discovery Dr Ste 100, Orlando, FL 32826
Tel.: (407) 381-7797
Web Site: http://www.jht.com
Rev.: $25,294,823
Emp.: 200
Custom Computer Programming Services
N.A.I.C.S.: 541511
James E. Jardon II *(Founder & CEO)*

JARMEL KIZEL ARCHITECTS & ENGINEERS, INC.
42 Okner Pkwy, Livingston, NJ 07039
Tel.: (973) 994-9669
Web Site: http://www.jarmelkizel.com
Year Founded: 1975
Sales Range: $25-49.9 Million
Emp.: 50
Architectural & Engineering Services
N.A.I.C.S.: 541310
Marvin Jarmel *(Principal)*
Richard A. Jarmel *(Principal)*
Matthew B. Jarmel *(Principal)*
Irwin H. Kizel *(Principal)*
Vladimir Ayzenberg *(Dir-MEP Engrg)*

JARRARD, NOWELL & RUSSELL, LLC
975 Morrison Dr, Charleston, SC 29403-4270
Tel.: (843) 723-2768
Web Site: http://www.jnrcpas.com
Year Founded: 2005
Accounting, Tax & Consulting Services
N.A.I.C.S.: 541211
William H. Jarrard *(Principal)*
Christopher C. Nowell *(Principal)*
William A. Russell III *(Principal)*

JARRETT LOGISTICS SYSTEMS, INC.
1347 N Main St, Orrville, OH 44667
Tel.: (330) 682-0099
Web Site:
http://www.jarrettlogistics.com
Sales Range: $10-24.9 Million
Emp.: 45
Transportation Management Services
N.A.I.C.S.: 541614
W. Michael Jarrett *(Pres)*
Matt Angell *(VP-Logistics Ops)*
Carol Bauman *(Supvr-Admin)*
Michael Rootes *(Dir-Bus Dev-Noblesville)*
Glenn Edgin *(Dir-Bus Dev-Oklahoma City)*
Tom Brenner *(Dir-Bus Dev-Orrville)*
Mike Frank *(Dir-Bus Dev-Orrville)*
Steven Dotterer *(Dir-Fin & Admin)*

JARROW INDUSTRIES INCORPORATED
12246 Hawkins St, Santa Fe Springs, CA 90670-3365
Tel.: (562) 906-1919
Web Site: http://www.jiimfg.com
Year Founded: 2000
Sales Range: $10-24.9 Million
Emp.: 200
Pharmaceutical Preparation Mfr
N.A.I.C.S.: 325412
Mohammed Khalid *(Pres)*

JARVIS CUTTING TOOLS
100 Jarvis Ave, Rochester, NH 03868
Tel.: (603) 332-9000

Web Site:
http://www.jarviscuttingtools.com
Rev.: $19,800,000
Emp.: 92
Machine Tools Mfr
N.A.I.C.S.: 333517
Cathy Brown *(Sr Acct Mgr)*
Ken Pickering *(VP-Mfg Tech)*

JARVIS DOWNING & EMCH INC.
200 G C & P Rd, Wheeling, WV 26003
Tel.: (304) 232-5000
Web Site: http://www.jde-inc.com
Sales Range: $10-24.9 Million
Emp.: 100
Industrial Buildings, New Construction,
N.A.I.C.S.: 236210
Kim Carfagna *(Pres & CEO)*
Mark Sampson *(VP)*
Mike Leo *(CFO)*

JARVIS METALS RECYCLING INC.
7825 Olive Ave, Lubbock, TX 79404
Tel.: (806) 744-7091
Web Site:
http://www.jarvismetals.com
Rev.: $29,700,000
Emp.: 52
Recyclable Material Merchant Whslr
N.A.I.C.S.: 423930
Gene Day II *(VP)*
Bob Jarvis *(CEO)*
John Shelby *(Treas & Sec)*
Deborah Vasquez *(Mgr)*

JAS FORWARDING INCORPORATED
6165 Barfield Rd, Atlanta, GA 30328-4309
Tel.: (770) 688-1206
Web Site: http://www.jas.com
Sales Range: $50-74.9 Million
Emp.: 4,000
Customhouse Brokers
N.A.I.C.S.: 488510
Marco Rebuffi *(Pres & CEO)*
Biagio Bruni *(Founder & Chm)*
Carol Kijac *(Chief Comml Officer)*
David Bang *(Exec VP-Pharma & Healthcare)*
Frank Cascante *(Sr VP-Global Sls, Pharma & Healthcare)*

Subsidiaries:

JAS Ocean Services Inc. **(1)**
22615 54th Ave S, Kent, WA 98032
Tel.: (253) 395-1906
Web Site: http://www.jasusa.com
Rev.: $100,000
Emp.: 7
Foreign Freight Forwarding
N.A.I.C.S.: 488510

JAS W. GLOVER LTD. INC.
248 Sand Island Access Rd, Honolulu, HI 96819-6012
Tel.: (808) 591-8977
Web Site: http://www.gloverltd.com
Year Founded: 1957
Sales Range: $25-49.9 Million
Emp.: 150
Highway & Street Construction Services
N.A.I.C.S.: 237310
Maile Romanowski *(Pres)*
John Romanowski *(VP)*

JAS WORLDWIDE, INC.
6195 Barfield Rd, Atlanta, GA 30328
Tel.: (770) 688-1240
Web Site: http://www.jas.com
Year Founded: 1978

Freight Forwarding & Logistics Provider
N.A.I.C.S.: 484121
Marco Rebuffi *(Pres-Global & CEO-Global)*
Vishal Bedi *(CIO)*

Subsidiaries:

Tigers Limited **(1)**
4A Kenning Industrial Building 19 Wang Hoi Road, Kowloon Bay, Kowloon, China (Hong Kong)
Tel.: (852) 2215 5500
Web Site: http://www.go2tigers.com
Logistics, Supply Chain Solutions & Freight Transportation Services
N.A.I.C.S.: 541614
Andrew Jillings *(Founder & CEO)*
Catherine Tam *(Dir-HR)*
Mark Gatenby *(CIO)*
Sara Cheung *(Dir-Admin)*

Subsidiary (Domestic):

Tigers (HK) Co., Ltd. **(2)**
4B Kenning Industrial Building 19 Wang Hoi Road, Kowloon Bay, Kowloon, China (Hong Kong)
Tel.: (852) 2799 8000
Web Site: http://www.go2tigers.com
Sales Range: $10-24.9 Million
Emp.: 60
Freight Forwarding & Logistics Consultation Services
N.A.I.C.S.: 488510

Subsidiary (US):

Tigers (USA) Global Logistics, Inc. **(2)**
2551 Allan Dr, Elk Grove Village, IL 60007
Tel.: (224) 653-2805
Web Site: http://www.go2tigers.com
Sales Range: $150-199.9 Million
Emp.: 353
Freight Forwarding & Logistics Consultation Services
N.A.I.C.S.: 488510

Subsidiary (Domestic):

Tigers Global Logistics **(3)**
1100 Thorndale Ave, Elk Grove Village, IL 60007
Tel.: (847) 860-8360
Sales Range: $75-99.9 Million
Freight Forwarding & Logistics Consultation Services
N.A.I.C.S.: 488510
Maureen Cervone *(Gen Mgr)*

Subsidiary (Non-US):

Tigers Global Logistics Pty Ltd **(2)**
Unit 4 2 Simblist Road, Port Botany, Sydney, 2036, NSW, Australia
Tel.: (61) 283242766
Web Site: http://www.go2tigers.com
Freight Forwarding & Logistics Consultation Services
N.A.I.C.S.: 488510

JASA TRANSIT, INC.
357 N Industrial Park Dr, Blair, NE 68008
Tel.: (402) 533-2300
Web Site: http://www.jasatransit.com
Sales Range: $1-9.9 Million
Emp.: 8
Bulk Trucking Services
N.A.I.C.S.: 484220
Linda Ingram Jasa *(Pres)*

JASCO INDUSTRIES INC.
1401 Lakeland Ave, Bohemia, NY 11716
Tel.: (631) 348-1772
Web Site:
    http://www.mgconcepts.com
Sales Range: $50-74.9 Million
Emp.: 150
Wood Display Fixtures
N.A.I.C.S.: 337212
Jay Austrian *(Pres)*

JASCO TOOLS INC.
195 St Paul St, Rochester, NY 14604
Tel.: (585) 254-7000
Web Site: http://www.jascotools.com
Rev.: $49,845,895
Emp.: 60
Metal Cutting Machinery Mfr
N.A.I.C.S.: 333517
Diane Simon *(CFO)*
Ken Marvald *(Gen Counsel & VP)*

Subsidiaries:

Burrell Colour Inc. **(1)**
1311 Merrillville Rd, Crown Point, IN 46307
Tel.: (219) 663-3210
Web Site: http://www.burrellprolabs.com
Photofinishing Laboratory Services
N.A.I.C.S.: 812921

Jasco Heat Treating Inc **(1)**
75 Macedon Center Rd, Fairport, NY 14450-8748
Tel.: (585) 388-1040
Metal Heat Treating Services
N.A.I.C.S.: 332811
Mike Veed *(Pres)*

Little Rock Tools Inc. **(1)**
11600 Arch St, Little Rock, AR 72206
Tel.: (501) 888-2457
Web Site: http://www.lrti.net
Sales Range: $1-9.9 Million
Metal Cutting Tool Mfr
N.A.I.C.S.: 333517
Mike Bomer *(Engr-Mfg)*

JASCULCA/TERMAN AND ASSOCIATES
730 N Franklin St Ste 510, Chicago, IL 60654
Tel.: (312) 337-7400
Web Site: http://www.jtpr.com
Year Founded: 1981
Sales Range: $1-9.9 Million
Emp.: 50
Public Relations Agency
N.A.I.C.S.: 541820
Richard J. Jasculca *(Chm & CEO)*
James L. Terman *(Founder, Pres & CFO)*
Mary Kelley Patrick *(Mng Partner)*
Holly Bartecki *(Sr VP-Creative & Strategic Dev)*
Febie Cabanlit *(Bus Mgr)*
Andrew Jasculca *(VP-Events Mgmt)*
Jennifer Hutchison *(VP)*
Bess Featherstone *(Acct Exec)*
Venita Griffin *(Dir-Digital Strategies & Engagement)*
Ryan Vejr *(Mgr-Info Sys)*
Nicole Johnson *(Office Mgr)*
Lauren Foley *(VP)*
Marci May *(VP)*
Jessica Thunberg *(VP-Bus Strategies)*

JASMINE VINEYARDS, INC.
33319 Pond Rd, Delano, CA 93215
Tel.: (661) 792-2141
Web Site:
    http://www.jasminevineyards.com
Year Founded: 1947
Sales Range: $10-24.9 Million
Emp.: 20
Grape Vineyard Services
N.A.I.C.S.: 111332
George Zaninovich *(Pres)*

JASON INDUSTRIAL, INC.
340 Kaplan Dr, Fairfield, NJ 07004-2511
Tel.: (973) 227-4904   NJ
Web Site:
    http://www.jasonindustrial.com
Year Founded: 1958
Sales Range: $25-49.9 Million
Emp.: 100
Provider of V Belting, Rubber & Plastic Hoses & Couplings

N.A.I.C.S.: 423840
Philip Cohenca *(Pres & CEO)*
Diane Fobert *(Controller)*
Thomas H. Tesoro *(VP-Sls & Mktg)*

JASON INDUSTRIES, INC.
833 E Michigan St Ste 900, Milwaukee, WI 53202
Tel.: (414) 277-9300   DE
Web Site: http://www.jasoninc.com
Year Founded: 2013
JASN—(OTCBB)
Rev.: $337,897,000
Assets: $387,101,000
Liabilities: $477,960,000
Net Worth: ($90,859,000)
Earnings: ($81,608,000)
Emp.: 1,940
Fiscal Year-end: 12/31/19
Holding Company
N.A.I.C.S.: 551112
Brian K. Kobylinski *(Chm, Pres & CEO)*

Subsidiaries:

Dronco France SARL **(1)**
Za Sud 6 Route De Bergheim, 67600, Selestat, France
Tel.: (33) 388583480
Industrial Machinery & Equipment Distr
N.A.I.C.S.: 423830

Dronco Scandinavia AB **(1)**
Ostanvindsg 17, 652 21, Karlstad, Varmland County, Sweden
Tel.: (46) 54688660
Industrial Machinery & Equipment Whslr
N.A.I.C.S.: 423830
Christian Branth *(CEO)*

Jason Incorporated **(1)**
833 East Michigan Street Suite 900, Milwaukee, WI 53202
Tel.: (414) 277-9300
Web Site: http://www.jasoninc.com
Sales Range: $700-749.9 Million
Emp.: 4,000
Nonwoven Fabric Mill Services
N.A.I.C.S.: 313230

Subsidiary (Non-US):

Dronco GmbH **(2)**
Wiesenmuhle 1, 95632, Wunsiedel, Germany
Tel.: (49) 92326090
Web Site: http://www.dronco.com
Emp.: 250
Abrasive Product Mfr
N.A.I.C.S.: 327910
Marc Stahlschmidt *(Mng Dir)*
Hans-Joachim Schneider *(Mng Dir)*

Subsidiary (Domestic):

Janesville Acoustics **(2)**
29200 Northwestern Hwy Ste 400, Southfield, MI 48034
Tel.: (248) 948-1811
Web Site:
    http://www.janesvilleacoustics.com
Acoustical & Thermal Fiber Insulation Mfr for the Automotive Industry
N.A.I.C.S.: 326150
Ken Ostrander *(VP-Fin)*
Fred Rheinlander *(VP-Sls, Bus Dev & Acoustics)*
Matt Oberski *(VP-Supply Chain-Acoustics)*
John Berghammer *(Dir-Mfg & Ops-North American)*

Subsidiary (Non-US):

Janesville de Mexico, S.A. de C.V. **(3)**
Privada de Encino No 243 Col Cororin Norte, Uruapan, 60120, Mexico
Tel.: (52) 452 519 8100
Web Site:
    http://www.janesvilleacoustics.com
Automotive Acoustic Product Mfr
N.A.I.C.S.: 336390

Plant (Domestic):

Janesville de Mexico, S.A. de C.V. - Celaya Plant **(4)**

Carretera Panamericana Federal Mexico-Guadalajara km, Ejido Ciudad de, 38110, Celaya, Guanajuato, Mexico
Tel.: (52) 4616110115
Automotive Acoustic Product Mfr
N.A.I.C.S.: 336390

Subsidiary (Non-US):

Jason Holding GmbH **(3)**
Eisenhammerstr. 9, 92237, Sulzbach, Germany
Tel.: (49) 96619040
Holding Company
N.A.I.C.S.: 551112

Plant (Domestic):

Jason Incorporated - Battle Creek Plant **(3)**
2500 Logistics Dr, Battle Creek, MI 49037
Tel.: (269) 275-4021
Automotive Acoustic Product Mfr
N.A.I.C.S.: 336390

Jason Incorporated - Columbus Plant **(3)**
221 Fabritek Dr, Columbus, MS 39702
Tel.: (662) 327-0756
Automotive Acoustic Product Mfr
N.A.I.C.S.: 336390

Jason Incorporated - Old Fort Plant **(3)**
157 Lackey Town Rd, Old Fort, NC 28762
Tel.: (828) 668-9251
Emp.: 230
Automotive Acoustic Product Mfr
N.A.I.C.S.: 336390
Brent Cook *(Mgr-HR)*
Spencer Clark *(Mgr-Reg Environmental Health & Safety)*
John Berghammer *(Gen Mgr)*

Subsidiary (Non-US):

Jason Holdings UK Limited **(2)**
Unit 10 Avenue West, Newhouse Farm Indus Estate, Chepstow, NP16 6UD, Monmouthshire, United Kingdom
Tel.: (44) 1291643200
Financial Holding Services
N.A.I.C.S.: 551112
Alison Yong *(Sec & Grp Controller-Fin)*

Subsidiary (Domestic):

Matchless Metal Polish Company **(2)**
840 West 49th Pl, Chicago, IL 60609
Tel.: (773) 924-1515
Web Site: http://www.matchlessmetal.com
Polish & Other Sanitation Good Mfr
N.A.I.C.S.: 325612

Milsco Manufacturing Company **(2)**
1301 W Canal St, Milwaukee, WI 53233
Tel.: (414) 354-0500
Web Site: http://www.milsco.com
Motor Vehicle Seating Mfr
N.A.I.C.S.: 336360

Subsidiary (Non-US):

Milsco Europe **(3)**
Harrington Way Bermuda Park Indust Estate, Nuneaton, CV10 7SH, United Kingdom
Tel.: (44) 247 658 0400
Emp.: 24
Automotive Seat Mfr
N.A.I.C.S.: 336360
Gary Prichard *(Mgr-European Program)*

Plant (Domestic):

Milsco Manufacturing Company - Jackson **(3)**
2313 Brooklyn Rd, Jackson, MI 49203
Tel.: (517) 787-3650
Web Site: http://www.milsco.com
Motor Vehicle Seating Mfr
N.A.I.C.S.: 336360

Subsidiary (Non-US):

Milsco de Mexico, S.A. de C.V. **(3)**
Tab Cat 2932 Carr A Dzibikak, 97390, Uman, Yucatan, Mexico
Tel.: (52) 988 951 9008
Automobile Seating Mfr
N.A.I.C.S.: 336360

Jason Industries, Inc.—(Continued)

David Patterson *(Gen Mgr)*

Subsidiary (Domestic):

Osborn International (2)
2350 Salisbury Rd N, Richmond, IN 47374
Tel.: (765) 965-5333
Web Site: http://www.osborn.com
Sales Range: $25-49.9 Million
Emp.: 150
Industrial Power Brushes, Paint Brushes, Idler Rollers, Industrial Aerosols, Grinding Wheels, Load Runners, Cut-off Wheels, Abrasive Specialties, Maintenance Brushes, Buffs & Compounds Mfr
N.A.I.C.S.: 339999

Subsidiary (Non-US):

Hsin Feng Buff Factory Co., Ltd. (3)
No 57 Heping Rd Lu-Chou Dist, Lu Chou Hsiang, New Taipei City, 247, Taiwan
Tel.: (886) 222817735
Web Site:
http://hsinfeng.en.taiwantrade.com
Emp.: 26
Buffing Compounds Mfr
N.A.I.C.S.: 325612

JacksonLea Polishing Materials Co. Ltd. (3)
No185 Dongsheng Road, Hi-Tech Industrial Development Zone, Jiangmen, 529080, Guangdong, China
Tel.: (86) 7503869588
Machine Tools Mfr
N.A.I.C.S.: 333517

JascksonLea de Mexico S.A, de C.V. (3)
Emilio Cardenas No 211 Centro Industrial, 54030, Tlalnepantla, Mexico
Tel.: (52) 5555659555
Machine Tools Mfr
N.A.I.C.S.: 333517

Subsidiary (Domestic):

Jason Ohio Corporation (3)
3440 Symmes Rd, Hamilton, OH 45015
Tel.: (513) 860-3400
Mfr of Buffing Wheels & Buffing Compounds
N.A.I.C.S.: 327910

Subsidiary (Non-US):

Osborn International AB (3)
Huskvarnavagen 105, Huskvarna, 561 32, Sweden
Tel.: (46) 36 38 92 00
Emp.: 35
Surface Treatment & Finishing Tool Distr
N.A.I.C.S.: 333517
Per Axelsson *(Gen Mgr)*

Osborn International GmbH (3)
Ringstrasse 10, 35099, Burgwald, Germany
Tel.: (49) 64515880
Surface Treatment & Conditioning Tools & Products Mfr
N.A.I.C.S.: 332813
Kay Hanselmann *(Mng Dir)*

Osborn International GmbH (3)
Ringstrasse 10, 35099, Burgwald, Germany
Tel.: (49) 6451 588 0
Surface Treatment & Finishing Tool Mfr
N.A.I.C.S.: 333991
Kai Voehl *(Mgr-Technical Advice)*
Torsten Hildebrandt *(Mgr-Export Sls)*

Osborn International Ltda (3)
Rua Lemos Torres 150 Sao Bernado do Campo, Sao Paulo, 09890-070, Brazil
Tel.: (55) 11 4391 6559
Power Brush Mfr
N.A.I.C.S.: 339999
Andre Baptista *(Gen Mgr)*

Osborn International SRL (3)
Bd Bucovina Nr 151, Suceava, 725300, Gura Humorului, Romania
Tel.: (40) 230 234 212
Surface Treatment & Finishing Tool Mfr
N.A.I.C.S.: 333991
Alfred Hrisca *(Gen Mgr)*
Constantan Florea *(Gen Mgr)*
Florea Constantin *(Gen Mgr)*

Osborn Lippert Pvt. Ltd. (3)
Plot No E-66 MIDC Waluj, Aurangabad, 431 136, India
Tel.: (91) 2402556538
Emp.: 80
Finishing-Product & Component Mfr
N.A.I.C.S.: 313310
Shirish Tambe *(Gen Mgr)*
Jaydeep Datar *(Mgr-Export Sls)*
Sudheendra Bellurkar *(Mgr-Prod)*

Osborn Singapore Pte Ltd. (3)
206 Tuas South Avenue 2 West Point Bi-zhub, Singapore, 637208, Singapore
Tel.: (65) 6863 0318
Web Site: http://www.osborn.com
Surface Treatment & Finishing Tool Distr
N.A.I.C.S.: 333517

Osborn Unipol (UK) Ltd. (3)
Newhouse Farm Industrial Estate, Chepstow, NP16 6UD, United Kingdom
Tel.: (44) 1291643200
Mfr of Surface Treatment & Conditioning Tools & Products
N.A.I.C.S.: 332813
Rhys Williams *(Mng Dir)*
Ashley Wood *(Gen Mgr)*

Osborn Unipol Lda. (3)
Rua Pardelhas, Brito, 4805-062, Guimaraes, Portugal
Tel.: (351) 253479550
Surface Treatment & Conditioning Tools & Products Mfr
N.A.I.C.S.: 332813
Florestan von Boxberg *(Gen Mgr)*

Osborn Unipol SAS (3)
Parc Mail - Batiment Orion 24B Avenue de la Demi-Lune, CS 80006, Roissy, 95735, Charles de Gaulle, Cedex, France
Tel.: (33) 1 34 45 06 00
Web Site: http://www.osborn.com
Surface Treatment & Finishing Tool Distr
N.A.I.C.S.: 333517
Nicolas Lapalu *(Gen Mgr)*

Osborn-Unipol SL (3)
C/ Ronda Norte 320, Poligono Industrial Apartado, 46470, Catarroja, Valencia, Spain
Tel.: (34) 96 1325876
Surface Treatment & Finishing Tool Distr
N.A.I.C.S.: 333517
Joaquim Piteira *(Gen Mgr)*

Shanghai JacksonLea Polishing Materials Co., Ltd. (3)
Room 2 No 168 Shenguang Road Xinqiao, Songjiang, Shanghai, 201612, China
Tel.: (86) 2164190744
Machine Tools Mfr
N.A.I.C.S.: 333517

Subsidiary (Domestic):

Sealeze (2)
8000 Whitepine Rd, North Chesterfield, VA 23237
Tel.: (804) 743-0982
Web Site: http://www.sealeze.com
Brushes & Brush Materials Mfr
N.A.I.C.S.: 339994

Jason Partners Holdings Inc. (1)
833 E Michigan St Ste 900, Milwaukee, WI 53202
Tel.: (414) 277-9300
Finishing-Product & Component Mfr
N.A.I.C.S.: 313310

Milsco de Mexico S. de R.L. de C.V. (1)
Tab Cat 2932 Carr A Dzibikak, Uman, Yucatan, Mexico
Tel.: (52) 9889519008
Automobile Mfr
N.A.I.C.S.: 336110
Roger Loria *(Controller)*

JASON'S HAULING, LLC.
1306 E 4th Ave, Tampa, FL 33605
Tel.: (813) 872-8440
Web Site:
http://www.jasonshauling.com
Sales Range: $10-24.9 Million
Emp.: 52
Specialized Freight Trucking Services
N.A.I.C.S.: 484220

Jason Freyre *(Pres & CEO)*
Isabel Morris *(Controller)*

JASPER CONTRACTORS INC
125 N Weinbach Ave, Evansville, IN 47711
Tel.: (812) 475-3450
Web Site: http://www.jasperroof.com
Year Founded: 2004
Sales Range: $25-49.9 Million
Emp.: 113
Roofing Installation Services
N.A.I.C.S.: 238160
Brian Wedding *(CEO)*
Daniel Milanovic *(VP)*
David Dickerson *(Gen Mgr-Denver)*

JASPER CORP.
530 Beacon Pkwy W Ste 700, Birmingham, AL 35209-3196
Tel.: (205) 942-9100
Year Founded: 1986
Sales Range: $50-74.9 Million
Emp.: 40
Mfr of Building Materials for Insulation, ISO, EPS & Dryvit
N.A.I.C.S.: 321219

JASPER ENGINE & TRANSMISSION EXCHANGE INC.
815 Wernsing Rd, Jasper, IN 47546
Tel.: (812) 482-1041
Web Site:
http://www.jasperengines.com
Year Founded: 1942
Sales Range: $200-249.9 Million
Emp.: 2,800
Engines, Transmissions, Differentials, Marine Engines, Stern Drives & Electric Motors Remanufacturer
N.A.I.C.S.: 336310
Alvin C. Ruxer *(Founder)*

Subsidiaries:

Indiana Tool & Die Co. Inc. (1)
815 Wernsing Rd, Jasper, IN 47546
Tel.: (812) 482-1041
Web Site: http://www.jasperengine.com
Sales Range: $100-124.9 Million
Emp.: 1,000
Motor Vehicle Transmission Components Mfr
N.A.I.C.S.: 336350
Mike Schwenk *(Exec VP-Production)*
Douglas A. Bawel *(Chm & CEO)*
Zachary W. Bawel *(Pres & COO)*

Jasper Electric Motors Inc. (1)
733 W Division Rd, Jasper, IN 47546
Tel.: (812) 482-1660
Web Site:
http://www.jasperelectricmotors.com
Sales Range: $10-24.9 Million
Emp.: 15
Industrial & Agricultural Electric Motor Repair & Maintenance Services
N.A.I.C.S.: 811310

Jasper Engine & Transmission Exchange Inc. - JASPER Alternate Fuels (1)
815 Wernsing Rd, Jasper, IN 47547-0650
Tel.: (800) 827-7455
Web Site: http://www.jasperengines.com
Sales Range: $50-74.9 Million
Emp.: 900
Alternative Fuel Engine Services
N.A.I.C.S.: 457210
Jason Nord *(Gen Mgr-HR)*

Jasper Engine Exchange Inc. (1)
815 Wernsing Rd, Jasper, IN 47546
Tel.: (812) 482-1041
Web Site: http://www.jasperengines.com
Emp.: 900
Motor Vehicle & Industrial Engine Remanufacturer
N.A.I.C.S.: 336310
Mike Schwenk *(Exec VP-Production)*
Douglas A. Bawel *(Chm & CEO)*
Ryan Dooley *(Mgr-Diesel Div)*
Alex Ernst *(Mgr-Quality)*

Jasper Engines & Transmissions, Inc. (1)
102 D St, South Charleston, WV 25303
Tel.: (304) 744-6378
Sales Range: $1-9.9 Million
Emp.: 10
Industrial Machinery & Equipment Merchant Whslr
N.A.I.C.S.: 423830
Zachary W. Bawel *(Pres, COO & VP-Sls)*
Matt Weinzapfel *(COO & Exec VP-Mfg)*
Jason Nord *(VP-People Svcs)*
Doug Bawel *(Chm & CEO)*
Zach Bawel *(Pres)*

JASPER ENGINEERING & EQUIPMENT CO.
3800 5th Ave W Ste 1, Hibbing, MN 55746
Tel.: (218) 262-3421
Web Site: http://www.jaspereng.com
Year Founded: 1958
Mining Machinery & Equipment; Except Petroleum
N.A.I.C.S.: 423810
Thomas Jamar *(CEO)*
Emil Hakomaki *(Mgr-Field Svcs)*

JASPER OIL COMPANY
719 Hwy 63 W, Jasper, TX 75951
Tel.: (409) 383-0555
Rev.: $68,079,170
Emp.: 15
Gasoline Sales
N.A.I.C.S.: 424720
Ed Few *(Pres)*
Missy Robinson *(Office Mgr)*

JASPER RUBBER PRODUCTS INC.
1010 1st Ave W, Jasper, IN 47546
Tel.: (812) 482-3242
Web Site:
http://www.jasperrubber.com
Sales Range: $50-74.9 Million
Emp.: 869
Mechanical Rubber Goods
N.A.I.C.S.: 326291
Doug Mathias *(Pres)*
Kyle Kuczynski *(CFO)*
Laura Mohr *(Mgr-Pur)*
Reva Baker *(VP-HR)*
Michael Hayden *(Exec VP-Ops)*

JASPER SEATING CO., INC.
225 Clay St, Jasper, IN 47546-2821
Tel.: (812) 482-3204
Web Site:
http://www.jaspergroup.us.com
Year Founded: 1929
Sales Range: $25-49.9 Million
Emp.: 500
Wooden Furniture Mfr
N.A.I.C.S.: 337211
Mike Elliot *(Pres & CEO)*

Subsidiaries:

Jasper Seating Co., Inc., JSI Division (1)
8084 W County Rd 25 S, French Lick, IN 47432
Tel.: (812) 936-9977
Web Site: http://www.jaspergroup.us.com
Rev.: $7,000,000
Emp.: 110
Mfr of Wood Office Furniture
N.A.I.C.S.: 337211
Ashley Werner *(Mgr-Mktg)*

Jasper Seating Company (1)
932 Mill St, Jasper, IN 47546 **(100%)**
Tel.: (812) 482-3204
Sales Range: $25-49.9 Million
Emp.: 300
Mfr of Wood Office Furniture
N.A.I.C.S.: 337211

JASPER WYMAN & SON
PO Box 100, Milbridge, ME 04658
Tel.: (207) 546-3800

Web Site: http://www.wymans.com
Rev.: $38,000,000
Emp.: 100
Grower & Processor of Wild Berries;
Processor of Frozen Berries & Berry,
Food & Beverage Products
N.A.I.C.S.: 311421
Edward Flanagan *(Pres)*
Kenny Fitzpatrick *(Dir-Logistics)*
Robert Stanley *(Dir-Engrg)*
Shannon Fickett *(Dir-Quality Assurance)*

JASTICON INC.
626 Gravelly Hollow Rd, Medford, NJ
08055
Tel.: (609) 953-0690
Web Site: http://www.jasticon.com
Sales Range: $10-24.9 Million
Emp.: 40
Concrete Work
N.A.I.C.S.: 238110
John C. Hotz *(Pres)*

JAT OIL & SUPPLY INC.
600 W Main, Chattanooga, TN 37402
Tel.: (423) 629-6611
Web Site: http://www.jatoil.com
Year Founded: 1975
Sales Range: $25-49.9 Million
Emp.: 20
Wholesale Distributor Petroleum
Products
N.A.I.C.S.: 424720
Bert Kaiser *(Mgr-Ops & Sls)*
Pat Conroy *(Pres & CEO)*

JATA LLC
11055 Excelsior Blvd, Hopkins, MN
55343
Tel.: (952) 931-2400
Rev.: $11,300,000
Computer Peripheral Equipment &
Software Wholesaler
N.A.I.C.S.: 423120
Gerald Theisen *(CFO)*

Subsidiaries:

Napco International, Inc.   (1)
11055 Excelsior Blvd, Hopkins, MN 55343-
3434
Tel.: (952) 931-2400
Web Site: http://www.napcointl.com
Emp.: 40
International Marketing of Defense-Related
Products
N.A.I.C.S.: 423120
Gerald Theisen *(CFO)*
Nick Wesenberg *(Mgr-Vehicle Spares)*
Kelly Goldbeck *(Mgr-Ops)*
Hamid Shirgir *(Dir-Quality Assurance)*
Jerry Campagnoli *(Mgr-Defense Electronics
Engrg)*
Tunus Botha *(Pres & CEO)*

JATON CORP.
47677 Lakeview Blvd, Fremont, CA
94538-6544
Tel.: (510) 933-8888
Web Site: http://www.jaton.com
Sales Range: $10-24.9 Million
Emp.: 10
Printed Circuit Boards
N.A.I.C.S.: 334412
George Cheng *(Mgr)*

JATRODIESEL, INC.
845 N Main St, Miamisburg, OH
45342
Tel.: (937) 847-8050
Web Site: http://www.jatrodiesel.com
Year Founded: 2004
Basic Organic Chemical Mfr
N.A.I.C.S.: 325199
Rajesh Mosali *(Co-Founder & CEO)*
Rahul Bobbili *(Co-Founder & CTO)*

JAVA CITY

1300 Del Paso Rd, Sacramento, CA
95834-1106
Tel.: (916) 565-5500   CA
Web Site: http://www.javacity.com
Year Founded: 1985
Coffee Shop Operator; Specialty Coffee Roaster & Wholesale Distr
N.A.I.C.S.: 311920
Chuck Van Vleet *(Exec VP)*
Frank Cardona *(Mgr-POS)*

JAVA CONNECTIONS LLC
17304 Preston Rd Ste 800, Dallas,
TX 75252
Web Site:
  http://www.laptopsanytime.com
Year Founded: 2008
Sales Range: $1-9.9 Million
Emp.: 8
Laptop Computers Mfr
N.A.I.C.S.: 334111
Matthew Buscher *(Co-Founder, Pres
& CEO)*
Jonathan Ruttenberg *(Co-Founder &
VP-Mktg & Ops)*

JAVAN TECHNOLOGY INC
8030 Old Cedar Ave Ste 225, Bloomington, MN 55425
Tel.: (952) 698-4454
Web Site:
  http://www.javentechnologies.com
Year Founded: 2003
Sales Range: $1-9.9 Million
Emp.: 50
IT Services
N.A.I.C.S.: 449210
Venkat Kota *(Gen Mgr)*

JAVELIN SOUTHEAST CORPORATION
1586 Howell Mill Rd, Atlanta, GA
30318
Tel.: (404) 355-2891
Web Site: http://www.javelintire.com
Sales Range: $10-24.9 Million
Emp.: 13
Tires & Tubes
N.A.I.C.S.: 423130
Mel Vukas *(Pres)*

JAVIC PROPERTY LLC
4263 Henderson Blvd, Tampa, FL
33629
Tel.: (813) 870-2838
Web Site: http://www.javichomes.com
Sales Range: $10-24.9 Million
Emp.: 10
Residential Construction
N.A.I.C.S.: 236115
Jon Solomon *(Owner)*
Adam Salhanick *(Mgr-Ops)*
Lana Bingham *(Mgr-Mktg)*
Nancy Vieira *(Mgr-Fin)*
Matt Merola *(Mgr-Construction)*

**JAVO BEVERAGE COMPANY,
INC.**
1311 Specialty Dr, Vista, CA 92081
Tel.: (760) 560-5286
Web Site:
  http://www.javobeverage.com
Sales Range: $1-9.9 Million
Emp.: 59
Coffee & Tea Products
N.A.I.C.S.: 311920
Dennis Riley *(Pres & CEO)*
Chris Johnson *(Exec VP)*
Brad Petersmeyer *(VP-Ops)*

JAWONIO
260 N Little Tor Rd, New City, NY
10956
Tel.: (845) 708-2000   NY
Web Site: http://www.jawonio.org
Year Founded: 1947

Sales Range: $25-49.9 Million
Emp.: 1,161
Disability Assistance Services
N.A.I.C.S.: 624120
Donna Ouimette *(Chief HR Officer)*
Diana Hess *(Chief Comm & Dev Officer)*
Joseph Bloss *(Chief Bus Officer)*
Matthew Shelley *(Chief Program Officer)*
Jill A. Warner *(CEO & Exec Dir)*
Cheryl L. Fuqua *(Dir-Admin)*

JAWOOD
32270 Telegraph Rd Ste 200, Bingham Farms, MI 48025
Tel.: (248) 833-8000
Web Site: http://www.jawood.com
Year Founded: 1989
Sales Range: $25-49.9 Million
Emp.: 299
Consulting Services
N.A.I.C.S.: 541618
Blaine Mallat *(COO & Sr VP)*
Sanjeev Vishwakarma *(Dir-IT)*

**JAWS WILDCAT ACQUISITION
CORPORATION**
1601 Washington Ave Ste 800, Miami
Beach, FL 33139
Tel.: (305) 695-5500   Ky
Year Founded: 2021
Investment Services
N.A.I.C.S.: 523999
Barry Stuart Sternlicht *(Founder &
Chm)*
Matthew Walters *(CEO)*
Michael Racich *(CFO)*

JAX ENTERPRISES INC.
32844 Hwy S 14 CNR 146, Gotham,
WI 53540
Tel.: (608) 583-7922
Rev.: $30,000,000
Emp.: 4
Convenience Store
N.A.I.C.S.: 445131

JAXON ENTERPRISES
1643 Tahoe Ct, Redding, CA 96003
Tel.: (530) 241-2112
Web Site:
  http://www.jaxonaggregates.com
Sales Range: $25-49.9 Million
Emp.: 50
Highway & Street Paving Contractor
N.A.I.C.S.: 237310
W. Jaxon Baker *(Pres)*

**JAY & SILENT BOB'S SECRET
STASH**
35 Broad St, Red Bank, NJ 07701
Tel.: (732) 275-0508
Web Site: http://jayandsilentbob.com
Comic Books, Toys, DVDs & Other
Related Merchandise Retailer & Mail
Order
N.A.I.C.S.: 459210
Kevin Smith *(Owner)*
Walt Flanagan *(Mgr-Store)*

JAY ADVERTISING, INC.
170 Linden Oaks, Rochester, NY
14625-2836
Tel.: (585) 264-3600   DE
Web Site: http://www.jayww.com
Year Founded: 1973
Sales Range: $75-99.9 Million
Emp.: 80
Advertising Agency Services
N.A.I.C.S.: 541810
Guy S. Smith *(Sr VP & Acct Exec-
Automotive)*

JAY CASHMAN INC.
549 South St, Quincy, MA 02169

Tel.: (617) 890-0600
Web Site:
  http://www.jaycashman.com
Sales Range: $125-149.9 Million
Emp.: 200
Marine Construction
N.A.I.C.S.: 236210
Jay Cashman *(Owner)*
Dale Pyatt *(Pres)*
Bruce Wood *(Sr VP)*
Bill Campbell *(Project Mgr)*

**JAY DEE CONTRACTORS,
INC.**
38881 Schoolcraft Rd, Livonia, MI
48150
Tel.: (734) 591-3400
Web Site:
  http://www.jaydeecontr.com
Year Founded: 1965
Sales Range: $10-24.9 Million
Emp.: 100
Site Preparation Contracting Services
N.A.I.C.S.: 238910
Diane Allred *(Office Mgr)*

JAY FRANCO & SONS INC.
295 5th Ave Ste 312, New York, NY
10016
Tel.: (212) 679-3022
Web Site: http://www.jfranco.com
Rev.: $25,000,000
Emp.: 20
Towels & Toweling, Cotton
N.A.I.C.S.: 313210
Nathan Franco *(Pres)*
Joe A. Franco *(VP)*
Barbara Romano *(Sr Dir-Licensing &
Mktg)*

JAY FULKROAD & SONS INC.
2736 Free Spring Church Rd, McAlisterville, PA 17049
Tel.: (717) 463-3701
Web Site: http://www.jayfulkroad.com
Sales Range: $10-24.9 Million
Emp.: 100
Bridge Construction
N.A.I.C.S.: 237310
Gerald Fulkroad *(Pres)*

**JAY HENGES ENTERPRISES
INC.**
4133 Shoreline Dr, Earth City, MO
63045
Tel.: (314) 291-6600   MO
Web Site: http://www.henges.com
Year Founded: 1932
Insulation Services
N.A.I.C.S.: 238310
Steve Schulte *(Pres, CEO & Owner)*

JAY INDUSTRIAL REPAIR, INC.
5300 E Lake Blvd, Birmingham, AL
35217-3548
Tel.: (205) 591-5566
Web Site: https://jayindustrial.com
Sales Range: $10-24.9 Million
Emp.: 200
Motors, Electric
N.A.I.C.S.: 459999
Joel McMahon *(Pres)*
Pat Gray *(Mgr-Sls)*
Gerald Sartain *(Mgr)*

Subsidiaries:

Precision Coil and Rotor   (1)
5300 East Lake Blvd, Burmingham, AL
35217
Tel.: (91) 2055915566
Web Site: https://pecoil.com
Emp.: 100
Rotating Electrical Equipment & Coil Mfr;
Rotor Services
N.A.I.C.S.: 335999

Jay Industrial Repair, Inc.—(Continued)

Subsidiary (Domestic):

Industrial Coil Inc.   (2)
4305 Beacon Dr, Oklahoma City, OK 73179
Web Site: http://www.industrialcoil.net
Electronic Parts & Equipment Merchant
Whslr
N.A.I.C.S.: 423690
Doug Kemp (Pres)

JAY INDUSTRIES INC.
150 Longview Ave E, Mansfield, OH
44903
Tel.: (419) 524-3778
Web Site: http://www.jayindinc.com
Sales Range: $200-249.9 Million
Emp.: 700
Injection Molding Of Plastics
N.A.I.C.S.: 326199
Roger Loch (CFO)
Rick R. Taylor (Pres)
Paul Boggs (Exec VP)

JAY JEMS INC.
590 5th Ave Ste 1801, New York, NY
10036
Tel.: (212) 751-2575   NY
Web Site:
   http://www.simplydiamondsusa.com
Jewelry Mfr & Whslr
N.A.I.C.S.: 339910
Siraj Shah (CEO)

Subsidiaries:

M.A. Reich & Co., Inc.   (1)
481 Franklin St, Buffalo, NY 14202
Tel.: (716) 856-4085
Web Site: http://www.mareich.com
Sales Range: $10-24.9 Million
Jewelry Mfr & Whslr
N.A.I.C.S.: 339910
Vinnie Davis (Pres)
William Reich (VP)

JAY KADOWAKI INC.
518 Ahui St, Honolulu, HI 96813
Tel.: (808) 596-7457
Sales Range: $10-24.9 Million
Emp.: 25
Commercial & Office Building Con-
tractors
N.A.I.C.S.: 236220
Jay Kadowaki (Pres)
Joel Choo (CFO)

JAY MAR INC.
2130 Jay Mar Rd, Plover, WI 54467
Tel.: (715) 341-3445
Web Site: http://www.jay-mar.com
Sales Range: $10-24.9 Million
Emp.: 16
Sales of Fertilizer & Fertilizer Materi-
als
N.A.I.C.S.: 115112
Dave Warner (Gen Mgr)

JAY N. NELSON INC.
5335 Hill 23 Dr, Flint, MI 48507
Tel.: (810) 767-7800   MI
Web Site:
   http://www.nelsontrane.com
Year Founded: 1929
Sales Range: $10-24.9 Million
Emp.: 55
Air Conditioning Equipment
N.A.I.C.S.: 423730
Parry R. Hughes (VP & Gen Mgr-
Comml Sys & Svcs Ingersoll Rand)
Matthew Krusniak (Mgr-Flint-Lansing
Sls)

JAY PETROLEUM, INC.
533 S 200 W, Portland, IN 47371
Tel.: (260) 726-9374   IN
Web Site: http://www.pakasak.com
Year Founded: 1948
Sales Range: $50-74.9 Million

Emp.: 400
Grocery Services
N.A.I.C.S.: 445110
Ron Freeman (Pres)

Subsidiaries:

Ottawa Oil Company   (1)
10305 US 224, Ottawa, OH 45875-9490
Tel.: (419) 523-6441
Web Site: http://www.ottawaoil.com
Sales Range: $50-74.9 Million
Emp.: 280
Gasoline Service Stations
N.A.I.C.S.: 457120
Janel Frazee (Gen Mgr)

JAY PLASTICS, INC.
325 N Jackson Ave, Mason City, IA
50401-2626
Tel.: (757) 247-5200   NY
Web Site: http://www.jayplastics.com
Year Founded: 1948
Sales Range: $75-99.9 Million
Emp.: 100
Advertising Specialties Including Wal-
let Inserts & Photo Album Pages
N.A.I.C.S.: 326199

JAY PONTIAC INC.
18800 Rockside Rd, Cleveland, OH
44146
Tel.: (440) 232-5000
Web Site:
   http://www.jaybuickgmc.com
Sales Range: $75-99.9 Million
Emp.: 50
Sales of New & Used Automobiles
N.A.I.C.S.: 441110
Marc Jacobson (Pres)

JAY R. SMITH MFG. CO.
2781 Gunter Park Dr E, Montgomery,
AL 36109-1405
Tel.: (334) 277-8520   AL
Web Site: http://www.jrsmith.com
Year Founded: 1926
Industrial Plumbing Supplies Mfr
N.A.I.C.S.: 332913
Thomas Dixon (Sls Mgr)

Subsidiaries:

J.R. Smith Manufacturing
Company   (1)
2781 Gunter Park Dr E, Montgomery, AL
36109-1409   (100%)
Tel.: (334) 277-8520
Web Site: http://www.jrsmith.com
Sales Range: $25-49.9 Million
Emp.: 360
Mfr of Roof & Floor Drains
N.A.I.C.S.: 332913

Potter Roemer Div.   (1)
17451 Hurley St, City of Industry, CA 91744
Tel.: (626) 366-3473
Web Site: http://www.potterroemer.com
Sales Range: $25-49.9 Million
Emp.: 160
Mfr of Fire Protection
N.A.I.C.S.: 423310

JAY WOLFE ACURA
1029 W 103rd St, Kansas City, MO
64114
Tel.: (816) 942-1550
Web Site:
   http://www.jaywolfeacura.com
Year Founded: 1954
Sales Range: $25-49.9 Million
Emp.: 42
New & Used Car Dealers
N.A.I.C.S.: 441110
Lee Hubbard (Mng Partner)
Jeff Johnson (Dir-Fin)

**JAY WOLFE TOYOTA OF
WEST COUNTY**
14700 Manchester Rd, Ballwin, MO
63011-3702

Tel.: (636) 207-3900
Web Site:
   http://www.toyotaofwestcounty.com
Year Founded: 1954
Sales Range: $50-74.9 Million
Emp.: 60
New Car Whslr
N.A.I.C.S.: 441110
Warren Rice (Controller)
Steve Maher (Gen Mgr)
Robert Feuerbacher (Gen Mgr-Sls)

**JAY'S SPORTING GOODS,
INC.**
8800 S Clare Ave, Clare, MI 48617
Tel.: (989) 386-3475
Web Site:
   http://www.jayssportinggoods.com
Year Founded: 1974
Sales Range: $25-49.9 Million
Emp.: 240
Retailer of Sporting Goods
N.A.I.C.S.: 459110
Jeff Poet (Pres)
Joe Murphy (Controller)
Mark Copeland (Mgr-Gaylord Store)

JAYA APPAREL
5175 S Soto St, Vernon, CA 90058
Tel.: (323) 584-3500
Sales Range: $100-124.9 Million
Emp.: 150
Women's Sportswear
N.A.I.C.S.: 315250
Don Lewis (CFO)
Alma Gonzalez (Mgr-Compliance &
EDI)
Maila Santos (Acct Supvr-Payable)
Jalal Elbasri (CEO)

JAYCO INTERNATIONAL
14433 Rue de Gascony Ct, Ballwin,
MO 63011
Tel.: (636) 220-8299
Year Founded: 1999
Sales Range: $10-24.9 Million
Emp.: 2
Valve, Pump & Drive-Train Sales to
the Department of Defense
N.A.I.C.S.: 423830
Stephen J. Walko (Pres & CEO)

JAYCOX IMPLEMENT INC.
403 S Market St, Lake Park, IA
51347
Tel.: (712) 832-3151   IA
Web Site:
   http://www.jaycoximplement.com
Year Founded: 1956
Sales Range: $10-24.9 Million
Emp.: 20
Whslr of Agricultural Machinery &
Equipment
N.A.I.C.S.: 423820
Chad Jaycox (Pres)

JAYEN INC.
4102 Hwy 59 N, Victoria, TX 77905
Tel.: (361) 575-1981
Rev.: $14,446,832
Emp.: 3
Convenience Store
N.A.I.C.S.: 445131
Virginia Furness (Controller)

JAYLYN SALES INC.
19 W 34th St Rm 905, New York, NY
10001
Tel.: (212) 947-0510
Sales Range: $10-24.9 Million
Emp.: 25
Lingerie
N.A.I.C.S.: 424350
Don Kreiss (Pres)
Dana Gilson (VP-Sls)

JAYNES CORPORATION
2906 Broadway Blvd NE, Albuquer-
que, NM 87101-1506
Tel.: (505) 345-8591   NM
Web Site: http://www.jaynescorp.com
Year Founded: 1954
Sales Range: $125-149.9 Million
Emp.: 200
General Contractors
N.A.I.C.S.: 236220
Shad James (VP-Project Mgmt)

JAYRAY ADS & PR, INC.
535 E Dock St Ste 205, Tacoma, WA
98402-4630
Tel.: (253) 627-9128   WA
Web Site: http://www.jayray.com
Year Founded: 1970
Advertising & Public Relations
Agency
N.A.I.C.S.: 541810
Jerry McLaughlin (Exec VP-Advisor
Pathfinder)
Kathleen Deakins (Pres-Counselor
Svc Superhero)
Barbie Pratt (Sr Creative Dir)
Jackie Zils (Acct Mgr)

**JAYSON OIL COMPANY IN-
CORPORATED**
2150 Stanley Ter, Union, NJ 07083
Tel.: (908) 688-1111   NJ
Web Site:
   http://www.jaysoncompany.com
Year Founded: 1936
Sales Range: $25-49.9 Million
Emp.: 75
Provider of Service, Renovations &
Installations to Families & Businesses
N.A.I.C.S.: 457210
Richard Jayson (Owner & Pres)
Joe Dibella (Dir-Sls & Mktg)

**JAZZ BASKETBALL INVES-
TORS, INC.**
301 W S Temple, Salt Lake City, UT
84101-1216
Tel.: (801) 325-2500   UT
Web Site: http://www.nba.com
Year Founded: 1979
Sales Range: $50-74.9 Million
Professional Basketball Team
N.A.I.C.S.: 711211
Kevin O'Connor (Exec VP-Basketball
Ops)
Chris Baum (Sr VP-Corp Partner-
ships)
Nathan Kenyon (VP-Fin)
Greg Tanner (VP-Corp Partnerships
& Bus Dev)
Richard Smith (Dir-Basketball Ops)
Amy Gunn (Mgr-Payroll)
Paul Welsh (VP-HR)
Linda Luchetti (VP-Comm)
Jonathan Rinehart (Dir-Comm)
Derek Garduno (Dir-Comm & Player
Rels)
Patti Balli (Dir-Community Rels)
Brian Devir (Dir-Sls)
Ted Roberts (VP-Events)
Mark Powell (VP-Events)
Jamie Galileo (VP-Facilities)
Dan Knight (Dir-Facilities Svcs)
Mark Stedman (Gen Mgr)
Clay Jensen (Sr VP-Tickets, Suites &
Clubs)
Jim Olson (COO-Miller Sports Prop-
erties)
Jim Bell (VP-Pub Safety)
Meikle LaHue (VP-Promos & Game
Ops)
Brendan Burke (VP-Mktg)
Rich Muirbrook (VP-Ticket Sls &
Svcs)
Bobbie Walker (VP-Ticket Ops)
Jeremy Castro (VP-Brdcst & Ops)

Randy Wright *(VP-Fin)*
Sue Wood *(Controller)*
McKay Smith *(Controller)*
Dave Goulding *(Mgr-Ops)*
Craig Sanders *(CMO)*
Mike Snarr *(VP & Dir-Sls)*
Jon Jacobsen *(Dir-Ticket Ops)*
Dustin Dehlin *(Mgr-Ticket Sls)*
Jared Geurts *(Sr Dir-Mktg Analytics)*
Trevor Haws *(Dir-Inside Sls)*
Bryan Jewkes *(Dir-Event Security)*
Marc Lowry *(VP & Dir-Asset & Inventory Mgmt)*
Rob Nish *(Dir-Mktg-Vivint Smart Home Arena)*
Bart Sharp *(Dir-Mktg-Vivint Smart Home Arena)*
Rich Sheubrooks *(Exec Dir-Pro & Global Scouting)*
Susan Truman *(Dir-Meetings & Banquets)*
Matthew Yessick *(Mgr-Mktg)*
Don Stirling *(Interim Pres)*
Danny Ainge *(CEO)*
Ryan Smith *(Owner)*

JAZZERCISE, INC.
2460 Impala Dr, Carlsbad, CA 92010
Tel.: (760) 476-1750   CA
Web Site: http://www.jazzercise.com
Year Founded: 1969
Sales Range: $10-24.9 Million
Emp.: 150
Exercise Program Franchisor; Dancewear & Diet Program Retailer
N.A.I.C.S.: 533110
Judi Sheppard Missett *(Founder & CEO)*
Shanna Missett Nelson *(Pres)*

Subsidiaries:

JM Digital Works   (1)
2460 Impala Dr, Carlsbad, CA
92010   (100%)
Tel: (760) 476-1750
Web Site: http://www.jmdigitalworks.com
Video Production, Post-Production & Duplication Company
N.A.I.C.S.: 533110
Jon Magnuson *(Gen Mgr)*

JB ALLOY CORPORATION
1050 Penner Crest St, Houston, TX
77055
Tel.: (713) 869-6000
Web Site: http://www.unibraze.com
Rev.: $10,000,000
Emp.: 20
Welding Supplies
N.A.I.C.S.: 423840
Larry Robinson *(Pres)*
Matt Shawver *(Mgr-Sls)*

JB CONTRACTING CORPORATION
2999 E 350th Rd, La Salle, IL 61301
Tel.: (815) 223-9800
Web Site:
   http://www.jbcontracting.com
Sales Range: $10-24.9 Million
Emp.: 130
Electrical Contracting Services
N.A.I.C.S.: 238210
Jim Brady *(Pres & Coord-Cost)*
Jeff Sloan *(Project Mgr)*
Tom Brady *(Project Mgr)*
Patrick Brady *(Project Mgr)*

JB HOWELL
7450 Griffin Rd Ste 210, Davie, FL
33314
Tel.: (954) 514-7880
Web Site: http://www.jbhowell.com
Sales Range: $1-9.9 Million
Real Estate Broker
N.A.I.C.S.: 531210
Adam Jacobson *(Pres)*

JB INDUSTRIES, INC.
601 N Farnsworth Ave, Aurora, IL
60505
Tel.: (630) 851-9444   DE
Web Site: http://www.jbind.com
Year Founded: 1967
HVAC Tools, Valves & Fittings Mfr
N.A.I.C.S.: 332913
Jeff Cherif *(Pres)*
Ron Hill Jr. *(Treas & Sec)*
Paul Dachota *(CEO)*
Oscar Lopez *(VP-Sls)*

Subsidiaries:

C&D Valve LLC   (1)
201 NW 67th St, Oklahoma City, OK 73116
Tel.: (800) 654-9233
Web Site: http://www.cdvalve.com
Refrigeration Equipment & Supplies Mfr
N.A.I.C.S.: 332919
Lance Gill *(Pres)*

JB MANAGEMENT INC.
3601 Eisenhower Ave Ste 400, Alexandria, VA 22304
Tel.: (703) 354-8884
Web Site: http://www.gojbm.com
Year Founded: 1990
Sales Range: $25-49.9 Million
Emp.: 214
Technical Services
N.A.I.C.S.: 541690
Harry Gibb *(Chm)*
Andrew L. Vonada *(Pres & CEO)*
Doug Coleman *(CFO)*
Nelson Slye *(Exec Dir)*

JB WHOLESALE ROOFING & BUILDING SUPPLIES
21544 Nordhoff St, Chatsworth, CA
91311
Tel.: (818) 998-0440
Web Site: http://www.jbroofing.com
Rev.: $30,520,164
Emp.: 70
Roofing & Building Supplies Sales
N.A.I.C.S.: 444110
W. Keith Jones *(Pres)*

JB&A AVIATION INC.
8620 W Monroe Rd Ste 230, Houston, TX 77061-3000
Tel.: (713) 850-9300
Web Site: http://www.jbaaviation.com
Sales Range: $75-99.9 Million
Emp.: 9
Transportation Equipment & Supplies
N.A.I.C.S.: 423860
Jerry Smith *(Pres)*
Jon Taylor *(VP)*
Toby Smith *(VP)*
Angelo Marasco *(Assoc Partner)*
Leslie Space *(Assoc Partner)*
Susan Doiron *(Dir-Ops)*

JBC HOLDING CO.
3601 S Banker St, Effingham, IL
62401
Tel.: (217) 347-7701   DE
Web Site: http://www.johnboos.com
Sales Range: $75-99.9 Million
Emp.: 160
Holding Company; Wood & Metal Furniture Mfr
N.A.I.C.S.: 551112
Louis W. Kenter *(Chm)*
Joseph A. Emmerich *(Pres)*

Subsidiaries:

Diversified Woodcrafts, Inc.   (1)
300 S Kruger St, Suring, WI 54174
Tel.: (920) 842-2136
Web Site:
   http://www.diversifiedwoodcrafts.com
Sales Range: $10-24.9 Million
Emp.: 100
Institutional & Laboratory Furniture Mfr
N.A.I.C.S.: 337127

Julie Ryno *(Mgr-Catalog Sls & Mktg)*
Greg McClure *(Mgr-Plant)*
Jim Gulbransen *(Sr Project Mgr)*
David Roland *(Mgr-Fin & Admin)*

John Boos & Co.   (1)
3601 S Banker St, Effingham, IL 62401
Tel.: (217) 347-7701
Web Site: http://www.johnboos.com
Sales Range: $25-49.9 Million
Emp.: 110
Wood Butcher Blocks, Counter Tops & Stainless Steel Kitchen Products Mfr
N.A.I.C.S.: 321999
Joseph A. Emmerich *(Pres)*
Patrick Wrigley *(Mgr-Network)*

JBC INC.
1414 E 20th St Ste 6, Scottsbluff, NE
69361
Tel.: (308) 635-0455
Web Site: http://www.jbc1.com
Year Founded: 1975
Sales Range: $25-49.9 Million
Emp.: 7
Petroleum Product Sales
N.A.I.C.S.: 424710
Elizabeth Stricker *(Controller)*
Robert Godinez *(Coord-Compliance & Safety)*
Jack Copsey *(Owner)*
Brian Copsey *(Pres)*

JBC TECHNOLOGIES, INC.
7887 Bliss Pkwy, North Ridgeville,
OH 44039
Tel.: (440) 327-4522
Web Site: http://www.jbc-tech.com
Year Founded: 1986
Sales Range: $1-9.9 Million
Emp.: 55
Mfg Metal Household Furniture Whol Industrial Equipment
N.A.I.C.S.: 337126
Denny Waggoner *(Mgr-Engrg)*

Subsidiaries:

HST Materials, Inc.   (1)
777 Dillon Dr, Wood Dale, IL 60191-1273
Tel.: (630) 766-3333
Rev.: $1,000,000
Emp.: 21
Electrical Apparatus & Equipment, Wiring Supplies & Related Equipment Merchant Whslr
N.A.I.C.S.: 423610
Kathryn Miller *(VP)*

JBG CORPORATION
1130 N Nimitz Hwy Ste A265, Honolulu, HI 96817-4579
Tel.: (808) 524-3255   HI
Web Site: http://www.mhrhawaii.com
Year Founded: 1971
Sales Range: $25-49.9 Million
Emp.: 340
Marine Cargo Handling
N.A.I.C.S.: 488320
Robert T. Guard *(Pres)*

Subsidiaries:

McCabe Hamilton & Renny Company
Ltd.   (1)
521 Ala Moana Blvd Ste M-311, Honolulu,
HI 96813
Tel.: (808) 524-3255
Sales Range: $25-49.9 Million
Emp.: 400
Marine Cargo Handling
N.A.I.C.S.: 488320
Matthew Guard *(Pres)*
Kim Hudson Chock *(CFO)*

JBG PROPERTIES
4445 Willard Ave Ste 400, Chevy
Chase, MD 20815
Tel.: (240) 333-3600
Web Site: http://www.jbgsmith.com
Sales Range: $50-74.9 Million
Emp.: 400

Land Subdividing Services
N.A.I.C.S.: 237210
Benjamin Jacobs *(CEO)*

JBI ELECTRICAL SYSTEMS INCORPORATED
5631 Stratum Dr, Fort Worth, TX
76137
Tel.: (817) 589-1545
Web Site: http://www.jbielectric.com
Sales Range: $25-49.9 Million
Emp.: 100
General Electrical Contractor
N.A.I.C.S.: 238210
Jacky D. Martin *(Owner & Pres)*
Troy Courville *(Project Mgr)*

JBI TECHNOLOGIES INC
312 3rd St 2nd Fl, Annapolis, MD
21403
Tel.: (443) 786-2700
Web Site: http://www.jbitec.com
Year Founded: 1995
Rev.: $5,000,000
Emp.: 36
Custom Computer Programming Services
N.A.I.C.S.: 541511
William R. Farmer *(CFO & Controller)*
Robert G. Bell *(VP-Corp Security)*
Jo A. Bell *(Pres & CEO)*

JBI, INC.
2650 E El Presidio St, Long Beach,
CA 90810
Tel.: (310) 537-8200
Web Site: http://www.jbi-interiors.com
Year Founded: 1968
Rev.: $20,000,000
Emp.: 175
Restaurant Furniture Mfr
N.A.I.C.S.: 337127
Michael Buchbinder *(Co-CEO)*
Jean Reeves *(Controller)*
Gregg Buchbinder *(Co-CEO)*

JBJ SALES & ASSOCIATES INC.
425 W Schrock Rd Ste 204, Westerville, OH 43081
Tel.: (614) 898-0155
Sales Range: $10-24.9 Million
Emp.: 6
Food Broker Services
N.A.I.C.S.: 424410
Jim Anthony *(Pres)*

JBK ASSOCIATES INTERNATIONAL, INC.
607 E Palisade Ave, Englewood
Cliffs, NJ 07631
Tel.: (201) 567-9070
Web Site:
   http://www.jbkassociates.net
Year Founded: 2003
Sales Range: $1-9.9 Million
Emp.: 15
Human Resource Consulting Services
N.A.I.C.S.: 541612
Julie B. Kampf *(CEO & Chief Possibilities Officer)*
Steve Prisco *(Principal-Mgmt & Bus Dev)*
Michael Lazar *(Principal)*
Timothy Hayes *(Mng Dir-Consumer & Leadership Svcs)*
Gregory Williamson *(Dir-Bus Dev)*
Kathryne Monier *(VP)*

JBL HAWAII, LTD.
905 Kokea St, Honolulu, HI 96817-
4528
Tel.: (808) 847-4021
Web Site: http://www.jblhawaii.com
Year Founded: 1968

JBL Hawaii, Ltd.—(Continued)
Sales Range: $10-24.9 Million
Emp.: 51
Hardware Distr
N.A.I.C.S.: 423710
Michelle Regn *(Controller & Asst Sec)*
Taylor Kaaina *(Asst VP & Gen Mgr)*

JBL RESOURCES
5250 B Northland Dr NE, Grand Rapids, MI 49525
Tel.: (616) 855-1146
Web Site:
http://www.JBLResources.com
Year Founded: 2003
Sales Range: $1-9.9 Million
Emp.: 52
Engineeering Services
N.A.I.C.S.: 541330
Ross Engelkes *(Founder)*

JBLH COMMUNICATIONS
160 E 88th St, New York, NY 10128
Tel.: (646) 248-7787
Year Founded: 2003
Sales Range: Less than $1 Million
Emp.: 8
Advetising Agency
N.A.I.C.S.: 541810
Jocelyn Brandeis *(Co-Founder)*

JBM INCORPORATED
2651 Scottish Pike, Knoxville, TN 37920
Tel.: (865) 573-9800
Web Site:
http://www.jbmincorporated.com
Year Founded: 1989
Sales Range: $10-24.9 Million
Emp.: 68
Sheet Metal Work Mfg
N.A.I.C.S.: 332322
Ray Pate *(Co-Owner)*
Mack Stiles *(Co-Owner)*
Paula Aethranis *(Office Mgr)*
Cathy Popham *(Mgr-Pur)*

JBM TECHNOLOGIES, INC.
60 Vincent Cir, Warminster, PA 18974
Tel.: (215) 672-8878
Web Site:
http://www.jbmtechnologies.com
Sales Range: $1-9.9 Million
Emp.: 16
Industrial Machinery & Equipment Whslr
N.A.I.C.S.: 423830
Deborah J. Miller *(Treas)*

JBNV HOLDING CORP.
4730 S Fort Apache Rd Ste 180, Las Vegas, NV 89147
Tel.: (702) 912-0700
Web Site:
http://www.kirkwoodbanknv.com
Year Founded: 2018
Bank Holding Company
N.A.I.C.S.: 551111
Jeffrey Berns *(Pres & CEO)*
John Dru *(Pres/CEO-Kirkwood Bank of Nevada)*

Subsidiaries:

Kirkwood Bank of Nevada   **(1)**
4730 S Fort Apache Rd Ste 180, Las Vegas, NV 89147
Tel.: (702) 912-0700
Web Site: http://www.kirkwoodbanknv.com
Sales Range: $1-9.9 Million
Emp.: 17
Commericial Banking
N.A.I.C.S.: 522110
John Dru *(Pres & CEO)*

JBO HOLDING COMPANY
Oswald Ctr 1100 Superior Ave Ste

1500, Cleveland, OH 44114-1715
Web Site:
https://unisonriskadvisors.com
Emp.: 100
Insurance Services
N.A.I.C.S.: 524210

Subsidiaries:

Riggs, Counselman, Michaels & Downes, Inc.   **(1)**
555 Fairmount Ave, Towson, MD 21286
Tel.: (804) 237-5900
Web Site: http://www.rcmd.com
Insurance Agencies & Brokerages
N.A.I.C.S.: 524210
Leroy Schmelz *(Sr VP)*
Linda E. Jones *(Sr VP)*
Debra Spade *(Sr VP)*
Albert R. Counselman *(Chm & CEO)*
Robert T. Cawley *(Pres)*

Subsidiary (Domestic):

Consolidated Insurance Center, Inc.   **(2)**
11403 Cronridge Dr Ste 270, Owings Mills, MD 21117
Tel.: (410) 356-9500
Web Site: http://www.clcinc.com
Sales Range: $1-9.9 Million
Emp.: 29
Insurance Agencies & Brokerage Services
N.A.I.C.S.: 524210
John Doetzer *(Principal)*

JBR INC.
1731 Aviation Blvd, Lincoln, CA 95648-9317
Tel.: (510) 638-1300
Web Site: http://www.o-coffee.com
Sales Range: $10-24.9 Million
Emp.: 85
Manufacture & Distribute Roasted Coffee
N.A.I.C.S.: 311920
Jon B. Rogers *(Pres)*

JBR MEDIA VENTURES LLC
2 Wisconsin Cir Ste 700, Chevy Chase, MD 20815
Tel.: (240) 235-5075
Web Site:
http://www.jbrmediacorp.com
Year Founded: 2003
Rev.: $19,000,000
Emp.: 18
Consumer Services
N.A.I.C.S.: 541990
Brenton Shaw *(CEO)*
Michael Dultz *(Controller)*

JBS LIMITED
1400 Broadway FL 17, New York, NY 10018
Tel.: (212) 764-4600
Sales Range: $10-24.9 Million
Emp.: 33
Clothing Mfr
N.A.I.C.S.: 315250
Shari Levine *(Pres)*
Denise Stein *(Controller)*

JBS LOGISTIC INC.
2043 Corporate Ln, Naperville, IL 60563
Tel.: (630) 924-2000
Web Site: http://www.jbstrans.com
Year Founded: 1986
Sales Range: $10-24.9 Million
Emp.: 39
Transportation & Warehousing Fulfillment Services; Transportaion Agents & Brokers
N.A.I.C.S.: 488510
Alec A. Gizzi *(Pres)*
Sam DiMaio *(Chm)*
Steve Chris *(Dir-Mktg)*

JBS PACKING COMPANY INC.

101 Houston Ave, Port Arthur, TX 77640
Tel.: (409) 982-3216
Rev.: $40,000,000
Emp.: 140
Fish & Seafoods
N.A.I.C.S.: 424460
Jack Hemmenway *(Owner)*
James Stringfellow *(Pres)*

JC MARKETING ASSOCIATES INC.
467 Main St, Wakefield, MA 01880-0589
Tel.: (781) 245-7070
Web Site:
http://www.jcmarketingassociates.com
Year Founded: 1964
Sales Range: Less than $1 Million
Emp.: 7
Advertising & Public Relation Agency Services
N.A.I.C.S.: 541820
Ann Hadley *(Pres)*

Subsidiaries:

JCM Events   **(1)**
PO Box 289, Wakefield, MA 01880-0589
Tel.: (781) 245-7070
Web Site:
http://www.jcmarketingassociates.com
Emp.: 4
Event Marketing
N.A.I.C.S.: 541820
Ann Hadley *(Pres)*
Jayne Donofrio *(VP)*

JC PUBLIC RELATIONS, INC.
1 Gatehall Dr Ste 107, Parsippany, NJ 07054
Tel.: (973) 850-7300
Web Site: http://www.jconnelly.com
Sales Range: $10-24.9 Million
Emp.: 12
Public Relations Agency
N.A.I.C.S.: 541820
Jennifer Connelly *(CEO)*
Carol Graumann *(Pres)*
Jami Schlicher *(VP)*
Leslie Billera *(VP-Mktg)*

JC RESTORATION INC.
3200 Squibb Ave, Rolling Meadows, IL 60008
Tel.: (630) 496-0220
Web Site:
http://www.jcrestoration.com
Year Founded: 1982
Sales Range: $10-24.9 Million
Emp.: 85
Disaster Restoration & Reconstruction
N.A.I.C.S.: 237990
Jose Cruz *(Founder)*
Efren Ortiz *(Dir-IT)*
Thomas Taff *(Exec Dir-Emergency Svcs)*

JC TECHNOLOGY, INC.
575 Lively Blvd, Elk Grove Village, IL 60007
Tel.: (847) 952-6900
Web Site:
http://www.acecomputers.com
Year Founded: 1983
Sales Range: $25-49.9 Million
Emp.: 30
IT Solutions
N.A.I.C.S.: 541512
Marianne Samborski *(Pres)*

JC TRADING INC.
1001 W Newport Ctr Dr, Deerfield Beach, FL 33442
Tel.: (954) 426-9001
Web Site: http://www.jctrading.net

Sales Range: $10-24.9 Million
Emp.: 8
Jewelry, Watch, Precious Stone & Precious Metal Merchant Whslr
N.A.I.C.S.: 423940
Eli Goldman *(VP)*
Albert Gozlan *(Pres)*
Simon Jeckell *(VP)*

JCAT GENERAL CONTRACTORS & MAINTENANCE
1519 Carroll Dr Ste 200, Atlanta, GA 30318
Tel.: (678) 797-1898
Web Site: http://www.jcatgcm.com
Year Founded: 2003
Sales Range: $1-9.9 Million.
Emp.: 25
Commercial Construction
N.A.I.C.S.: 236220
Brian Johnson *(Pres)*

JCC ASSOCIATION
520 8th Ave, New York, NY 10018
Tel.: (212) 532-4949   NY
Web Site: http://www.jcca.org
Year Founded: 1917
Sales Range: $10-24.9 Million
Emp.: 64
Social Welfare & Public Relation Services
N.A.I.C.S.: 813410
Bob Kimsal *(CFO & Sr VP)*
David E. Posner *(VP & Dir-Strategic Performance)*
Stephen Hazan Arnoff *(Pres & CEO)*
Robin Ballin *(Sr VP-Program Dev)*
Jcy Brand-Richardson *(VP)*
Alan S. Goldberg *(Sr VP-Ops)*
Jcanne Harmon *(VP-Mktg & Comm)*
Andrew C. Paller *(VP-Community Consultant)*
Arlene Swartz *(Sr VP-Fin Resource Dev)*

JCI INDUSTRIES INC.
1161 SE Hamblen Rd, Lees Summit, MO 64081
Tel.: (816) 525-3320
Web Site: http://www.jciind.com
Sales Range: $125-149.9 Million
Emp.: 150
Pumps & Pumping Equipment
N.A.I.C.S.: 423830
Bob Kopp *(CEO)*
Robert L. Toth *(Pres & CEO)*
M ke Davis *(Acct Mgr)*
Mark Swendrowski *(Acct Mgr)*
Ty Cooper *(Acct Mgr)*

Subsidiaries:

Technical Equipment Co., Inc.   **(1)**
810 NW Main St A, Lees Summit, MO 64086
Tel.: (816) 525-1350
Web Site: http://www.techequipment.com
Rev.: $4,720,000
Emp.: 5
Other Miscellaneous Durable Goods Merchant Whslr
N.A.I.C.S.: 423990
Paul Rohner *(Engr-Sls)*

JCI JONES CHEMICALS, INC.
1765 Ringling Blvd, Sarasota, FL 34236-6765
Tel.: (941) 330-1537   NY
Web Site: http://www.jcichem.com
Year Founded: 1930
Sales Range: $100-124.9 Million
Emp.: 250
Water Treatment Chemicals Mfr & Distr
N.A.I.C.S.: 424690
Jeffrey W. Jones *(Chm & CEO)*
Ryan C. Jones *(Pres & COO)*
Jeffrey R. W. Jones *(Pres & Treas)*

Susan Malloy Jones *(Chief Admin Officer)*
James Hartman *(Gen Counsel)*

Subsidiaries:

JCI Jones Chemicals, Inc.-CSC (1)
1500 Tar Heel Rd, Charlotte, NC 28208-1533 **(100%)**
Tel.: (704) 392-9767
Web Site: http://www.jcichem.com
Sales Range: $10-24.9 Million
Emp.: 30
N.A.I.C.S.: 325180
Jeff Jones *(CEO)*

JCI Jones Chemicals, Inc.-Corporate Financial Center (1)
100 Sunny Sol Blvd, Caledonia, NY 14423
Tel.: (941) 330-1537
Web Site: http://www.jcichem.com
N.A.I.C.S.: 325180
Tim Gaffney *(VP)*
Mike Croke *(Dir-Transportation-Charlotte & Branch Mgr)*
Debbie Stella *(Office Mgr)*

JCJ ARCHITECTURE
38 Prospect St, Hartford, CT 06103
Tel.: (860) 247-9226
Web Site: http://www.jcj.com
Architectural Services
N.A.I.C.S.: 541310
James LaPosta Jr. *(Chief Architectural Officer & Principal)*

Subsidiaries:

Randall/Baylon Architects, Inc. (1)
605 W Olympic Blvd Ste 840, Los Angeles, CA 90015
Tel.: (213) 623-9899
Web Site: http://www.randall-baylon.com
Architectural Design Services
N.A.I.C.S.: 541310
Donald Randall *(Co-Founder)*
Hector M. Baylon *(Co-Founder)*

JCL COMPANY LIMITED
7510 Jurupa Ave Ste 102, Riverside, CA 92504-1021
Tel.: (951) 359-8898
Web Site: http://www.jclcompany.com
Sales Range: $1-9.9 Million
Information Technology Products Whslr
N.A.I.C.S.: 423430
Eve Chang *(Pres)*

JCM PARTNERS, LLC
2151 Salvio St Ste 325, Concord, CA 94520-2451
Tel.: (925) 676-1966
Year Founded: 2000
Sales Range: $10-24.9 Million
Emp.: 200
Real Estate Broker
N.A.I.C.S.: 531210
Gayle M. Ing *(CEO)*
Brian S. Rein *(COO)*
Scott Fujihara *(CFO)*

JCMC, INC.
911 Golden Belt Blvd, Junction City, KS 66441-3963
Tel.: (785) 238-3141
Web Site: http://jcmc-inc-in-junction-city-ks.cityfos.com
Year Founded: 1981
Sales Range: $10-24.9 Million
Emp.: 51
New Car Whslr
N.A.I.C.S.: 441110
James Clark *(Pres)*
Willie Thornberg *(Gen Mgr)*
Debra Clark *(Treas)*
Sheryl D. Williams *(Sec)*

JCPE INVESTMENTS
2724 W Reservoir Blvd, Peoria, IL 61615

Tel.: (309) 685-6580   IL
Year Founded: 2001
Sales Range: $10-24.9 Million
Investment Management Service
N.A.I.C.S.: 523940
Donna Malone *(Pres, Sec & Asst Treas)*

JCW SEARCH LTD.
232 Madison Ave Ste 1600, New York, NY 10016
Tel.: (646) 934-8400
Web Site:
  http://www.jcwresourcing.com
Year Founded: 2011
Sales Range: $1-9.9 Million
Emp.: 55
Human Resource Consulting Services
N.A.I.C.S.: 541612
Jamie Woods *(CEO)*
Et Halstead *(Mng Dir & Chief Comml Officer)*
Simon Elsbury *(Dir-Global Fin)*
Daniel Evans *(Dir-Global Mktg)*
Kate Turner *(Dir-Global HR)*

JD BYRIDER AUTOMAX LLC
7776 N 76th St, Milwaukee, WI 53223
Tel.: (414) 371-4040
Web Site: http://www.jdbyrider.com
Sales Range: $10-24.9 Million
Emp.: 60
Car Dealership Owner & Operator
N.A.I.C.S.: 441120
Dan Duggan *(Gen Mgr-Sls)*

JD EQUIPMENT INC.
1660 United States Hwy 42 NE, London, OH 43140
Tel.: (614) 879-6620
Web Site:
  http://www.jdequipment.com
Sales Range: $25-49.9 Million
Emp.: 150
Farm Equipment & Supplies
N.A.I.C.S.: 459999
Norm Murphy *(CFO)*
Bob Gingerich *(Mgr-Svc)*
Brian Miller *(Mgr-Svc)*
Ed Smith *(VP)*
Dave Donohue *(Mgr-Mktg)*
John Griffith *(Owner)*
Ben Butcher *(Dir-Agricultural Sls)*
Arin Severt *(Dir-Turf & Utility Sls)*
Cody Kirkpatrick *(Dir-Aftermarket Sls)*
Peter Gallant *(Mgr-Aftermarket Sls)*
Peter Kibby *(Exec Dir-J.D. Power Systems & J.D. Power & Tool)*
Jeff Mitchell *(CEO)*

JD NORMAN INDUSTRIES, INC.
787 W Belden Ave, Addison, IL 60101-4942
Tel.: (630) 458-3700
Web Site: http://www.jdnorman.com
Year Founded: 2004
Metal Components & Systems Mfr
N.A.I.C.S.: 332999
Justin D. Norman *(Pres & CEO)*
Gary Wilhite *(VP-Fin)*
Alberto Hernadez *(Dir-Ops-North America)*
Thomas Schulte *(Dir-Ops-Europe)*
Patty Ryan Vincent *(Dir-HR-North America & UK)*

Subsidiaries:

Henman Engineering & Machine Inc. (1)
3301 W Mount Pleasant Blvd, Muncie, IN 47302
Tel.: (765) 288-8098
Web Site: http://www.henmaneng.com

OEM Mfr of Automobile Component Parts
N.A.I.C.S.: 336390
Steve Oliphant *(Plant Mgr)*

JD Norman Industries-Windsor Plant (1)
6845 Hawthorne Dr, Windsor, N8T 3B8, ON, Canada **(100%)**
Tel.: (519) 944-1439
Web Site: http://www.jdnorman.com
Sales Range: $10-24.9 Million
Emp.: 35
Original & Aftermarket Automotive Parts
N.A.I.C.S.: 336390
Jeff Wiles *(Plant Mgr)*

JD Norman Lydney Limited (1)
Tutnalls, Lydney, GL15 5PX, Gloucestershire, United Kingdom
Tel.: (44) 1 594 842 112
Web Site: http://www.jdnorman.com
Emp.: 170
Engine Camshaft Castings Mfr
N.A.I.C.S.: 333618
Susana Fernandez *(Plant Mgr)*

JD Norman de Mexico, S. de R.L. de C.V. (1)
Avenida El Sabinal 215, Sabinal Industrial Park, Apodaca, CP 66645, Nuevo Leon, Mexico
Tel.: (52) 81 1769 2059
Web Site: http://www.anvisgroup.com
Metal Components & Systems Mfr
N.A.I.C.S.: 332999
Guillermo Quesada *(Plant Mgr)*

JD RESEARCH INC.
1247 N Glassell St Ste 1, Orange, CA 92867
Tel.: (714) 282-3995
Web Site: http://www.jdresearch.com
Rev.: $10,000,000
Emp.: 7
Computers, Peripherals & Software
N.A.I.C.S.: 423430
Amy Wang *(Pres)*
Connie Wang *(CFO)*

JD RESTAURANTS INC.
136 W Jefferson St, Tipton, IN 46072
Tel.: (765) 675-7531
Web Site: http://www.jdrest.com
Sales Range: $10-24.9 Million
Emp.: 500
Family Restaurant Owner & Operator
N.A.I.C.S.: 722511
David Reasner *(Pres)*
Brent Reasner *(Exec VP)*

JD STEEL CO. INC.
2101 W Jackson St, Phoenix, AZ 85009
Tel.: (602) 254-8833
Web Site: http://www.jdsteel.com
Sales Range: $10-24.9 Million
Emp.: 100
Concrete Reinforcement Services
N.A.I.C.S.: 238190

JD2 INC.
450 Neveda St, Auburn, CA 95603-9500
Tel.: (530) 889-2979
Web Site: http://www.jd2inc.com
Year Founded: 1964
Sales Range: $25-49.9 Million
Emp.: 21
Builders of Industrial Buildings & Warehouses
N.A.I.C.S.: 236220
John L. Mayo *(Pres & CEO)*
Steve Knudsvig *(Sr Project Mgr)*
Ross Jeffrey *(COO)*
Steve Torrens *(Project Mgr)*
Todd Duke *(CFO)*
Mike Todd *(Project Mgr)*

Subsidiaries:

JD2 Inc. - Los Angeles (1)

960 N Amelia Ave Ste A, San Dimas, CA 91773
Tel.: (909) 599-9195
Web Site: http://www.jd2inc.com
Sales Range: $25-49.9 Million
Emp.: 4
Construction Company
N.A.I.C.S.: 238160
Tracy Cody *(Gen Mgr)*
Brad McGlothlin *(Gen Mgr)*

JD2 Inc. - San Diego (1)
135 W Mission Ave Ste 200, Escondido, CA 92025
Tel.: (760) 480-1820
Web Site: http://www.jd2inc.com
Sales Range: $25-49.9 Million
Construction Company
N.A.I.C.S.: 236220
Charlie Brill Codilla *(Project Coordinator)*
George Oosterwijk *(Gen Mgr-Los Angeles & San Diego)*

JDB INC.
811 N 1st St, Silverton, OR 97381
Tel.: (503) 874-3000
Web Site: http://www.brucepac.com
Year Founded: 1949
Rev.: $57,500,000
Emp.: 135
Meat Packing Services
N.A.I.C.S.: 311613
Larry Bruce *(Pres)*

JDH CAPITAL HOLDINGS, L.P.
1111 Travis St, Houston, TX 77002
Tel.: (713) 209-2495
Holding Company
N.A.I.C.S.: 551112
Ryan Connelly *(Mng Dir)*

JDH PACIFIC, INC.
15301 Blackburn Ave, Norwalk, CA 90650
Tel.: (562) 926-8088
Web Site: http://www.jdhpacific.com
Year Founded: 1989
Sales Range: $10-24.9 Million
Emp.: 120
Iron Foundry Services
N.A.I.C.S.: 331511
Nellie Liu *(Coord-Logistics)*
Jeff Russo *(Mgr-Ops, Warehouse & Facilities)*
Tim Bradley *(Coord-Shipping)*

JDL CASTLE CORPORATION
301 N Main St Ste 2300, Winston Salem, NC 27101
Tel.: (336) 722-2033
Web Site:
  http://www.jdlcastlecorp.com
Sales Range: $10-24.9 Million
Emp.: 20
Industrial Buildings: Renovation, Remodeling & Repairs
N.A.I.C.S.: 531130
David Shannon *(Pres)*
Craig Longhurst *(Dir-Property Mgmt)*

JDL DEVELOPMENT CORP.
908 N Halsted St, Chicago, IL 60642
Tel.: (312) 642-9797
Web Site: http://www.jdlcorp.com
Year Founded: 1994
Sales Range: $1-9.9 Million
Emp.: 15
Land Subdivision; Family Housing Construction
N.A.I.C.S.: 237210
James Letchinger *(Pres)*

JDM MATERIALS COMPANY INCORPORATED
851 County Line Rd, Huntingdon Valley, PA 19006
Tel.: (215) 333-8000
Web Site: http://www.jdm-inc.com
Rev.: $19,300,000

JDM Materials Company Incorporated—(Continued)

Emp.: 65
Ready Mixed Concrete
N.A.I.C.S.: 327320
Scott Bercuski (Treas)
James D. Morrissey Jr. (Pres)

JDR MICRODEVICES INC.
1850 S 10th St, Mountain View, CA
94043
Tel.: (408) 494-1400
Web Site: http://www.jdr.com
Year Founded: 1979
Sales Range: $10-24.9 Million
Emp.: 35
Direct Marketer of Electronic Components
N.A.I.C.S.: 423690
Jeffrey D. Rose (Founder & Pres)

JDS CAPITAL MANAGEMENT, INC.
1091 Boston Post Rd, Rye, NY
10580
Tel.: (914) 921-3030
Private Equity Investment Firm
N.A.I.C.S.: 523999
Daniel Stein (Pres)
Joseph D. Samberg (CEO)

Subsidiaries:

Dimensional Associates, LLC   (1)
1091 Boston Post Rd, Rye, NY 10580
Tel.: (914) 921-3060
Digital Media Private Equity Holdings
N.A.I.C.S.: 523999

Subsidiary (Domestic):

1091 Media   (2)
1091 Boston Rd, Rye, NY 10580
Tel.: (914) 921-3060
Digital Media Private Equity Holdings
N.A.I.C.S.: 541840

Subsidiary (Domestic):

The Orchard Media, Inc.   (3)
23 E 4th St 3rd Fl, New York, NY 10003
Tel.: (212) 201-9280
Web Site: http://www.theorchard.com
Music, Video & Game Licensing
N.A.I.C.S.: 512230
Richard Gottehrer (Co-Founder)
Scott Cohen (Co-Founder)
Prashant Bahadur (Sr VP-Strategy)
JP Lester (CTO)
Colleen Theis (COO)
Jessica Phelps (Gen Mgr-Nashville)
Tim Pithouse (Head-Artist & Label Svcs-Global)

Dimensional Music Publishing, LLC   (1)
100 Park Ave 17th Fl, New York, NY
10017   (100%)
Tel.: (212) 300-2811
Private Equity Firm; Music Publisher
N.A.I.C.S.: 551112

JDW MANAGEMENT CO.
2674 Raymond Ave, Signal Hill, CA
90755
Tel.: (562) 997-2920
Web Site: http://www.montroy.com
Sales Range: $25-49.9 Million
Emp.: 18
Electrical Apparatus & Equipment
N.A.I.C.S.: 423610
James D. Wilson (Pres)

Subsidiaries:

Montroy Sign & Graphic
Products   (1)
2674 Raymond Ave, Signal Hill, CA 90755
Tel.: (562) 997-2920
Web Site: http://www.montroy.com
Rev.: $18,800,000
Emp.: 10
Signs, LED Lighting, Neon Supplies, Equipment & Graphic Products
N.A.I.C.S.: 339950

James D. Wilson Jr. (Pres)

JDW WRAP UP, INC.
1620 N Tuckahoe St, Bellwood, PA
16617
Tel.: (814) 742-4380   PA
Year Founded: 1902
Furniture Retailer
N.A.I.C.S.: 449110
Eugene Stoltz (Pres)

JEA
21 W Church St, Jacksonville, FL
32202-3139
Tel.: (904) 665-6000   FL
Web Site: http://www.jea.com
Year Founded: 1895
Sales Range: $1-4.9 Billion
Electric Power, Water & Sewer Services
N.A.I.C.S.: 221122
Mike Hightower (Chief Pub Affairs Officer)
Mike Brost (VP & Gen Mgr-Electric Sys)
Ted Hobson (Chief Compliance Officer)
Brian Roche (VP & Gen Mgr-Water & Wastewater Sys)
Angelia Hiers (Chief HR Officer)
Melissa Dykes (CFO)
Delores Kesler (Sec)
Edward Burr (Vice Chm)
Jody Brooks (Chief Legal Officer)
Paul Cosgrave (CIO)
G. Alan Howard (Chm)
Aaron Zahn (Interim CEO)

JEAD AUTO SUPPLY INC.
1810 E Tremont Ave, Bronx, NY
10460
Tel.: (718) 792-7113   NY
Web Site: http://www.jeadauto.com
Year Founded: 1978
Sales Range: $10-24.9 Million
Emp.: 47
Sales of Automotive Supplies & Parts
N.A.I.C.S.: 423120
David Barbag (Pres & Mgr-Sls)
Bill Fisher (Mgr-Ops)

JEAN SIMPSON PERSONNEL SERVICES, INC.
1318 Shreveport Barksdale, Shreveport, LA 71105
Tel.: (318) 869-3494
Web Site:
   http://www.jeansimpson.com
Sales Range: $10-24.9 Million
Emp.: 49
Temporary Help Service
N.A.I.C.S.: 561320
Sandra J. Braddock (CFO)

JEANNE B. MCCOY COMMUNITY CENTER FOR THE ARTS
100 W Dublin Granville Rd, New Albany, OH 43054
Tel.: (614) 245-4701   OH
Web Site:
   http://www.mccoycenter.org
Year Founded: 2007
Sales Range: $10-24.9 Million
Emp.: 100
Arts Promotion Services
N.A.I.C.S.: 711310
Chad Palmer (Treas)
Thomas Hill (Vice Chm)
Jill Beckett-Hill (Co-Chm)
Linda Taylor (Sec)

JEANS WAREHOUSE, INC.
2612 Waiwai Loop, Honolulu, HI
96819
Tel.: (808) 839-2421

Web Site:
   http://www.jeanswarehousehawaii.com
Year Founded: 1978
Sales Range: $25-49.9 Million
Emp.: 240
Women's Clothing Retailer
N.A.I.C.S.: 458110
William Estill (CEO)

JEANS.COM INC.
Km 29 Hm 4 RR 2, Vega Alta, PR
00692
Tel.: (787) 270-2210
Web Site: http://www.jeanspr.com
Sales Range: $10-24.9 Million
Emp.: 3
Operator of Men's & Boys' Clothing Stores
N.A.I.C.S.: 458110
Felix Fanti (Pres)
Mike Silba (VP)
Johnny Torres (Controller)

JEBCO VENTURES, INC.
202 N Tamiami Trl, Sarasota, FL
34236
Tel.: (941) 363-0979
Web Site:
   http://www.jebcoventuresinc.com
Year Founded: 1975
Sales Range: $1-9.9 Million
Emp.: 3
Real Estate Development & Investment Services
N.A.I.C.S.: 237210
Jim Bridges (CEO)

JEBCOMMERCE LLC
610 W Hubbard Ave Ste 124, Coeur
D'Alene, ID 83814
Web Site:
   http://www.jebcommerce.com
Year Founded: 2004
Marketing Consulting Services
N.A.I.C.S.: 541613
Jamie Birch (Co-Founder & CEO)
Sarah Birch (Co-Founder)
Jon Goodwin (Dir-Accounts)
Gabe Ripley (Dir-Creative Svcs)
Louann Schneidmiller (CFO)

Subsidiaries:

Sixth Man Marketing   (1)
542 W Cataldo Ave, Spokane, WA 99201-4916
Tel.: (509) 624-5580
Web Site:
   http://www.sixthmanmarketing.com
Marketing Consulting Services
N.A.I.C.S.: 541613
Ed Reese (Principal)

JEEP CHRYSLER DODGE OF ONTARIO
1202 Auto Center Dr, Ontario, CA
91761
Tel.: (909) 390-9898
Web Site:
   http://www.jeepchryslerofontario.com
Year Founded: 1965
Sales Range: $25-49.9 Million
Emp.: 95
New Car Whslr
N.A.I.C.S.: 441110
Doug Verk (Mgr-Fin & Insurance)
Kirk Irvine (Mgr-Svc)

JEEVY COMPUTING, LLC
450 S Tamiami Trl, Osprey, FL 34229
Tel.: (941) 918-0000
Web Site:
   http://www.jeevycomputing.com
Sales Range: $1-9.9 Million
IT Consulting Services
N.A.I.C.S.: 541690

Ven Konuru (Founder & Pres)

JEFF BELZER'S CHEVROLET DODGE KIA
21111 Cedar Ave, Lakeville, MN
55044-9089
Tel.: (952) 469-4444
Web Site: http://www.jeffbelzer.com
Sales Range: $25-49.9 Million
Emp.: 130
New Car Whslr
N.A.I.C.S.: 441110
Jeff Belzer (Owner)

JEFF D'AMBROSIO AUTO GROUP
1221 E Lancaster Ave, Downingtown,
PA 19335
Tel.: (610) 269-9500
Web Site: http://www.gojeffauto.com
Year Founded: 1983
Sales Range: $25-49.9 Million
Emp.: 200
Dealer of New & Used Automobiles
N.A.I.C.S.: 441110
Allan Glasschroeder (Mgr-Bus Dev)

JEFF DAVIS BANCSHARES, INC.
1611 Elton Rd, Jennings, LA 70546
Tel.: (337) 824-1422   LA
Web Site: http://www.jdbank.com
Year Founded: 1990
Sales Range: $25-49.9 Million
Emp.: 100
Bank Holding Company
N.A.I.C.S.: 551111
Carly Leonards (Chief Banking Officer & Sr Exec VP)
Boyd R. Boudreaux (Pres & CEO)
George Shafer (Chief Compliance Officer & Sr VP)
Dan L. Donald Jr. (Chm)

Subsidiaries:

Jeff Davis Bank & Trust
Company   (1)
1611 Elton Rd, Jennings, LA 70546
Tel.: (337) 824-1422
Web Site: http://www.jdbank.com
Emp.: 40
Savings, Commercial Banking & Trust Services
N.A.I.C.S.: 522180
Carly Leonards (CEO)
Judy Duhon (VP & HR Officer)

JEFF HUNTER MOTORS, INC.
1440 W Loop 340, Waco, TX 76712
Tel.: (254) 662-6644
Web Site:
   http://www.jeffhuntertoyota.com
Sales Range: $10-24.9 Million
Emp.: 59
Car Whslr
N.A.I.C.S.: 441110
Jeff Hunter (Owner)

JEFF KERBER POOL PLASTERING, INC.
10735 Kadota Ave, Montclair, CA
91763
Tel.: (909) 465-0677
Web Site: http://www.jeffkerber.com
Year Founded: 1989
Sales Range: $25-49.9 Million
Emp.: 260
Specialty Trade Contracting Services
N.A.I.C.S.: 238990
Jeff Kerber (Owner)

JEFF LUNGREN CHEVROLET, INC.
801 E 3rd St, Grove, OK 74344
Tel.: (918) 786-4477
Web Site:
   http://www.jefflungrenchevrolet.com

Sales Range: $10-24.9 Million
Emp.: 25
Car Whlslr
N.A.I.C.S.: 441110
Jeff Lungren *(Owner & Pres)*
Brian Schwartz *(Gen Mgr-Sls)*
Steve Lungren *(Gen Mgr-Sls)*

JEFF SCHMITT AUTO GROUP
1001 N Broad St, Fairborn, OH 45324
Tel.: (937) 878-3471
Web Site: http://www.jeffdeals.com
Sales Range: $25-49.9 Million
Emp.: 110
Car Whlslr
N.A.I.C.S.: 441110
Adam Kopans *(Mgr-Sls)*
Mark Skiba *(Project Mgr)*

JEFF WYLER AUTOMOTIVE FAMILY, INC.
101 Milford Pkwy, Milford, OH 45150
Tel.: (513) 752-7450   OH
Web Site: http://www.wyler.com
Year Founded: 1973
Sales Range: $350-399.9 Million
Emp.: 1,000
Holding Company; Automobile Dealerships, Repair Shops & Insurance Agencies Owner & Operator
N.A.I.C.S.: 551112
Jeff Wyler *(Pres)*
Jim Simon *(Dir-Mktg)*

Subsidiaries:

Jeff Wyler Alexandria, Inc.   (1)
1154 Burlington Pike, Florence, KY 41042-1249
Tel.: (859) 952-8001
Web Site:
    http://www.jeffwylerflorencebuickgmc.com
New & Used Car Dealer
N.A.I.C.S.: 441110
Noah Brauer *(Gen Mgr)*

Jeff Wyler Eastgate, Inc.   (1)
1117 State Rte 32, Batavia, OH 45103
Tel.: (513) 752-3447
Web Site: http://www.wylereastgate.com
Sales Range: $25-49.9 Million
Emp.: 100
New & Used Car Distr
N.A.I.C.S.: 441110
Jeff Schaeper *(Gen Mgr)*

Jeff Wyler Fairfield, Inc.   (1)
5815 Dixie Hwy, Fairfield, OH 45014-3008
Tel.: (513) 682-2500
Web Site: http://www.jeffwylerfairfield.com
Sales Range: $25-49.9 Million
Emp.: 70
New & Used Car Dealer
N.A.I.C.S.: 441110
Dave Meinert *(Gen Mgr)*

Jeff Wyler Florence, Inc.   (1)
949 Burlington Pike, Florence, KY 41042
Tel.: (859) 479-2319
Web Site:
    http://www.jeffwylerflorencehonda.com
Sales Range: $10-24.9 Million
Emp.: 105
New & Used Car Dealer
N.A.I.C.S.: 441110
Kathryn Collier *(Mgr-Internet Sls)*
David Barnhart *(Mgr-Fin)*
Michael Donnellon *(Mgr-Used Car Sls)*
Jay Deaton *(Dir-Fixed Ops)*

Jeff Wyler Frankfort, Inc.   (1)
1440 Versailles Rd, Frankfort, KY 40601
Tel.: (502) 695-6100
Sales Range: $10-24.9 Million
Emp.: 37
New & Used Car Dealer
N.A.I.C.S.: 441110
Julie W. Bristow *(Treas)*
Dustin Maynard *(Mgr-Sls)*

Jeff Wyler Ft. Thomas, Inc.   (1)
100 Alexandria Pike, Fort Thomas, KY 41075
Tel.: (859) 605-9596

Web Site: http://www.jeffwylerfortthomas.net
Sales Range: $10-24.9 Million
Emp.: 43
New & Used Car Dealer
N.A.I.C.S.: 441110
Jeffrey L. Wyler *(Pres)*

Jeff Wyler Louisville II, Inc.   (1)
5340 Dixie Hwy, Louisville, KY 40216
Tel.: (502) 448-2820
Web Site: http://jeffwylerdixiechevrolet.com
Sales Range: $10-24.9 Million
New & Used Car Dealer
N.A.I.C.S.: 441110
Rodney Carter *(Exec Mgr)*

Jeff Wyler Springfield, Inc.   (1)
1501 Hillcrest Ave, Springfield, OH 45504
Tel.: (937) 783-7030
Web Site:
    http://www.jeffwylerspringfield.com
Sales Range: $50-74.9 Million
Emp.: 110
New & Used Car Dealer
N.A.I.C.S.: 441110
Jeff Wyler *(Pres)*

JEFFCO FIBRES, INC.
12 Park St, Webster, MA 01570
Tel.: (508) 987-6600
Web Site: http://www.jeffcofibres.com
Rev.: $25,000,000
Emp.: 50
Supplier of Textiles
N.A.I.C.S.: 424310
Blanche Lonstein *(Pres)*
Jeff Lonstein *(VP)*
Catherine Cyr *(Mgr-Customer Svc)*
Don Clayton *(VP-Mfg & Ops)*
Jerry Katz *(Mgr-Sls-Retail Div)*
Mark Lorusso *(VP)*
Hugh Oxnard *(CFO & Dir-E-Commerce)*

JEFFCO LEASING COMPANY INC.
1700 Kosciusko Rd, Saint Louis, MO 63104
Tel.: (314) 385-2545
Web Site:
    http://www.Jeffcotrucking.com
Year Founded: 1989
Sales Range: $10-24.9 Million
Emp.: 80
Trucking Transportation
N.A.I.C.S.: 484121
Ryan Abeln *(Pres)*
Ed Wisniewski *(Mgr-Ops)*

JEFFER MANGELS BUTLER & MITCHELL LLP
1900 Ave of the Stars 7th Fl, Los Angeles, CA 90067
Tel.: (310) 203-8080   CA
Web Site: http://www.jmbm.com
Year Founded: 1981
Sales Range: $100-124.9 Million
Emp.: 201
Legal Advisory Services
N.A.I.C.S.: 541110
Joel J. Berman *(Partner)*
Sheri L. Bonstelle *(Partner)*
Rod S. Berman *(Chm-Intellectual Property Dept)*
Susan Allison *(Partner)*
Kenneth C. Bovard *(Partner)*
Robert E. Braun *(Partner)*
R. Scott Brink *(Partner)*
Jessica Bromall Sparkman *(Partner)*
Barry L. Burten *(Partner)*
Joel David Deutsch *(Partner)*
Neil C. Erickson *(Partner)*
Marta M. Fernandez *(Partner)*
Barry V. Freeman *(Partner)*
Bernard R. Gans *(Partner)*
Bridget McInerney Harris *(Partner)*
Brennan C. Swain *(Partner)*
Bennett G. Young *(Partner)*
Carol James *(Dir-Mktg & Bus Dev)*

David M. Poitras *(Partner)*
Jacklyn Krikorian *(Dir-HR)*
Seth Weissman *(Partner)*
Terri Wind *(CFO)*
Sophia Ho *(Sec)*
Jeffrey T. Myers *(Partner-Global Hospitality GroupÂ® & Real Estate Dept)*

JEFFERDS CORPORATION
652 Winfield Rd, Saint Albans, WV 25177
Tel.: (304) 755-8111   WV
Web Site: http://www.jefferds.com
Year Founded: 1947
Sales Range: $50-74.9 Million
Emp.: 220
Industrial Machinery & Equipment
N.A.I.C.S.: 423830
K. Richard C. Sinclair *(Pres & CEO)*
Rod Brown *(Controller)*
Mike Jarrett *(Branch Mgr)*
Mike Milhoan *(Mgr-Mktg)*
Linda Vermillion *(Mgr-Acctg)*
Terri Patton *(Mgr-Personnel)*

JEFFERS, INC.
310 W Saunders Rd, Dothan, AL 36301
Tel.: (334) 793-6257   AL
Web Site: http://www.jefferspet.com
Year Founded: 1975
Sales Range: $125-149.9 Million
Emp.: 300
Animal & Human Health Supplies
N.A.I.C.S.: 424210
Dorothy Jeffers *(Pres & CEO)*

Subsidiaries:

JeffersPet.com   (1)
310 W Saunders Rd, Dothan, AL 36301-8622
Tel.: (334) 793-6257
Web Site: http://www.jefferspet.com
Sales Range: $25-49.9 Million
Emp.: 250
Animal & Human Health Supplies
N.A.I.C.S.: 424210
Ruth Jeffers *(Pres & CEO)*

JEFFERSON ASPHALT PRODUCTS COMPANY
175 John J Thomas Way, Charles Town, WV 25414
Tel.: (304) 725-2539
Web Site:
    http://www.jeffersonasphalt.net
Sales Range: $750-799.9 Million
Emp.: 60
Highway, Street & Bridge Construction
N.A.I.C.S.: 237310
James Thomas *(Pres)*
Beverly Thomas *(Treas)*
David McCauley *(Controller & VP)*
John J. Thomas Jr. *(Sec)*

JEFFERSON BANK OF FLORIDA
3711 Tampa Rd, Oldsmar, FL 34677
Tel.: (727) 781-7500
Web Site:
    http://www.jeffersonbankfl.com
Year Founded: 2007
Sales Range: $1-9.9 Million
Emp.: 45
Commericial Banking
N.A.I.C.S.: 522110
Robert B. McGivney *(Chm & CEO)*
James P. Nelson *(Pres & COO)*
Jeffrey P. Seligsohn *(CFO & Exec VP)*

JEFFERSON CHEVROLET CO.
2130 E Jefferson Ave, Detroit, MI 48207
Tel.: (313) 259-1200

Web Site:
    http://www.jeffersonchevrolet.com
New & Used Automobile & Truck Retailer
N.A.I.C.S.: 441110
Brian Tellier *(Gen Mgr)*
Robert Prater *(Mgr-New Car)*
Mario Puglise *(Mgr-Used Car)*
Eddie Freeman *(Mgr-Svc)*
Dave Higgins *(Mgr-Parts)*
Mike Beydoun *(Mgr-Collision)*
Kirsten Abbott *(Mgr-Customer Care)*

JEFFERSON CITY COCA-COLA BOTTLING CO.
604 Jefferson St, Jefferson City, MO 65101
Tel.: (573) 636-6165   MO
Web Site: https://jccoke.com
Sales Range: $10-24.9 Million
Emp.: 50
Soft Drinks: Packaged In Cans & Bottles
N.A.I.C.S.: 312111
Carl Vogel *(Chm)*
Jacob L. Vogel *(Pres & CEO)*

JEFFERSON CITY OIL CO. INC.
1601 Christy Dr, Jefferson City, MO 65101
Tel.: (573) 634-2025
Web Site: http://www.jcoil.com
Sales Range: $25-49.9 Million
Emp.: 50
Petroleum Bulk Stations
N.A.I.C.S.: 424710
John Kolb *(Pres)*
Tom Kolb *(VP)*

JEFFERSON ENERGY COOP-ERATIVE
3077 Hwy 17 N, Wrens, GA 30833
Tel.: (706) 547-2167
Web Site:
    http://www.jeffersonenergy.com
Sales Range: $25-49.9 Million
Emp.: 102
Distribution, Electric Power
N.A.I.C.S.: 221122
Kenneth Cook *(Pres & CEO)*
Cynthia Anderson *(Sr VP-Corp Svcs)*
Kim Sharpe *(Mgr-Acctg)*

JEFFERSON FINANCIAL CREDIT UNION
7701 Airline Dr, Metairie, LA 70003
Tel.: (504) 348-2424   LA
Web Site:
    http://www.jeffersonfinancial.org
Year Founded: 1966
Sales Range: $10-24.9 Million
Emp.: 183
Credit Union
N.A.I.C.S.: 522130
Casey Grimes *(VP-Fin)*
Rob Crowley *(CTO)*
Kristin Morrison *(VP-Ops)*
Carie Lopez *(VP-Lending)*
Mark E. Rosa *(Pres & CEO)*
Joann Tassin *(Sec)*
Sharon Wegner *(Treas)*
Susan Bloom *(Co-Chm)*
Feliciano Feliciano Jr. *(Co-Chm)*

JEFFERSON HEALTH SYS-TEM, INC.
259 N Radnor-Chester Rd Ste 290, Radnor, PA 19087-5299
Tel.: (610) 225-6200
Web Site:
    http://www.jeffersonhealth.org
Year Founded: 1995
Network Health System Operator
N.A.I.C.S.: 622110

Jefferson Health System, Inc.—(Continued)

Kirk E. Gorman *(CFO & Sr VP)*
Austin Chiang *(Chief Medical Social Media Officer)*

JEFFERSON HOMEBUILDERS INC.

501 N Main St, Culpeper, VA 22701
Tel.: (540) 825-5898
Web Site:
  http://www.culpeperwood.com
Year Founded: 1972
Rev.: $157,530,774
Emp.: 163
Wood Preserving
N.A.I.C.S.: 321114
Joseph R. Daniel *(CEO)*
Doris Batiste *(Treas & Sec)*

JEFFERSON INDUSTRIES CORPORATION

6670 State Rte 29, West Jefferson, OH 43162
Tel.: (614) 879-5300
Rev.: $177,176,044
Emp.: 700
Automobile Parts Mfr
N.A.I.C.S.: 336110
Larry McDonald *(Asst Mgr-Safety)*
David Sullenberger *(Asst Mgr-Info Svcs)*
Geoffrey Barth *(Coord-Stamping Quality)*
Jason Becker *(Asst Mgr-Sls)*
Kevin Tackett *(Coord-Ops)*

JEFFERSON MANOR HEALTH CENTER

417 Rte 28, Brookville, PA 15825
Tel.: (814) 849-8026   PA
Web Site:
  http://www.jeffersonmanor.net
Year Founded: 1985
Sales Range: $10-24.9 Million
Emp.: 281
Community Health Care Services
N.A.I.C.S.: 621498
Rick Graham *(CFO)*
Heather Lasher *(Dir-Mktg & Admissions)*
Carrie Park *(Dir-Rehabilitation)*

JEFFERSON PUBLIC RADIO

1250 Siskiyou Blvd, Ashland, OR 97520
Tel.: (541) 552-6301
Web Site: http://www.ijpr.org
Media Communications Services
N.A.I.C.S.: 517810
Mitchell Christian *(Dir-Fin)*
Paul Westhelle *(Exec Dir)*

Subsidiaries:

Ashland Home Net   (1)
485 E Main St Ste 1, Ashland, OR 97520
Tel.: (541) 488-9207
Web Site: http://www.ashlandhome.net
Computer & Office Machine Repair & Maintenance
N.A.I.C.S.: 811210
Jim Teece *(Owner)*

JEFFERSON REGIONAL MEDICAL CENTER

1600 W 40th Ave, Pine Bluff, AR 71603
Tel.: (870) 541-7100   AR
Web Site: http://www.jrmc.org
Year Founded: 1959
Sales Range: $150-199.9 Million
Emp.: 2,188
Healthcare Services
N.A.I.C.S.: 622110
Thomas Harbuck *(Exec VP)*
Louise Hickman *(VP-Patient Care Svcs)*

Brian Thomas *(Interim CEO)*
Bryan Jackson *(CFO & VP)*
Chuck Morgan *(Vice Chm)*
Scott Pittillo *(Sec)*
Annette Kline *(Treas)*

JEFFERSON SECURITY BANK

105 E Washington St, Shepherdstown, WV 25443
Tel.: (304) 876-9000
Web Site:
  http://www.jeffersonsecurity
  bank.com
Rev.: $10,250,489
Emp.: 75
Banking Services
N.A.I.C.S.: 522110
Cinthia A. Kitner *(Pres & CEO)*
Karl J. Keller *(Exec VP-Lending)*
Patti Snyder *(Asst VP & Officer-Loan)*
Brenda Painter *(Officer-Loan & VP)*
Don Jacot *(VP-Comml Loans)*
Joe Hronesz *(Sr VP)*
Dustin T. Branner *(Sr VP-Martinsburg)*
Frederick K. Parsons *(Chm)*
Eric J. Lewis *(Vice Chm)*
Sara Wasson *(Dir-Mktg & Community Rels)*
Mike Chapman *(VP-Ops & Innovation)*

JEFFERSON VINEYARDS

1353 Thomas Jefferson Pkwy, Charlottesville, VA 22902
Tel.: (434) 977-3042
Web Site:
  http://www.jeffersonvineyards.com
Year Founded: 1981
Sales Range: $10-24.9 Million
Emp.: 25
Vineyard & Wine Mfr
N.A.I.C.S.: 111332
Amanda Charette *(Asst Gen Mgr)*

JEFFERSON YARNS

27 Valley St, Pulaski, VA 24301-5613
Tel.: (540) 980-1530   VA
Web Site:
  http://www.jeffersonyarns.com
Year Founded: 1898
Sales Range: $10-24.9 Million
Emp.: 80
Yarn Texturizing Services
N.A.I.C.S.: 313110
Marc Bishop *(Pres & CEO)*
Charles R. Ibach III *(VP-Mktg)*

JEFFERSON-COCKE COUNTY UTILITY DISTRICT

122 Hwy 25 E, Newport, TN 37821
Tel.: (423) 623-3069
Web Site: http://www.jccud.com
Sales Range: $10-24.9 Million
Emp.: 50
Natural Gas Distr
N.A.I.C.S.: 221210
Carolyn Ramsey *(Mgr-Bus Svcs)*

JEFFORDS STEEL & SPECIALTY CO.

4398 Rte 22, Plattsburgh, NY 12901
Tel.: (518) 561-4061
Web Site:
  http://www.jeffordssteel.com
Sales Range: $10-24.9 Million
Emp.: 65
Steel Products Mfr
N.A.I.C.S.: 423510
Larry W. Jeffords *(Co-Founder)*
James Favreau *(CFO & VP)*

JEFFREY AUTOMOTIVE GROUP

30800 Gratiot Ave, Roseville, MI 48066-1751

Tel.: (586) 296-1300   MI
Web Site: http://www.jeffreyauto.com
Year Founded: 1983
Sales Range: $100-124.9 Million
Emp.: 120
Sales of Automobiles
N.A.I.C.S.: 441110
Jeffrey L. Tamaroff *(Pres)*
Susan Hauss *(Treas & Sec)*

Subsidiaries:

Jeffrey Buick-Nissan   (1)
30800 Gratiot Ave, Roseville, MI 48066
Tel.: (586) 296-1300
Web Site: http://www.jeffreyacura.com
Sales Range: $25-49.9 Million
New Car Dealers
N.A.I.C.S.: 441110
Michael Scenga *(Gen Mgr-Sls)*
Daniel Kern *(Coord-Special Fin)*
Todd Thompson *(Mgr-Acura Bus)*
William Edwards *(Mgr-Acura Parts)*
Jeffrey Emmons *(Mgr-Acura Body Shop)*

JEFFREY FABRICS INC.

261 5th Ave Rm 2001, New York, NY 10016
Tel.: (212) 447-7333
Sales Range: $10-24.9 Million
Emp.: 17
Sales of Piece Goods & Other Fabrics
N.A.I.C.S.: 424310
Jeffery Ardhine *(VP)*
Dan Cacella *(VP-Sls)*
Jenny Capuozzo *(Mgr-Production)*
Francesca Cortes *(VP-Ops)*

Subsidiaries:

Heritage House Fabrics Inc.   (1)
261 5th Ave Fl 20, New York, NY 10016
Tel.: (212) 685-5556
Rev.: $2,000,000
Emp.: 9
Textile Converters
N.A.I.C.S.: 314999

JEFFREY M. BROWN ASSOCIATES

2337 Philmont Ave, Huntingdon Valley, PA 19006
Tel.: (215) 938-5000
Web Site:
  http://www.jmbassociates.com
Rev.: $134,030,777
Emp.: 30
Commercial & Office Building, New Construction
N.A.I.C.S.: 236220
Jeffrey M. Brown *(CEO)*
Gregory R. Hill *(Pres)*
Joah Schleinkofer *(Office Mgr)*

JEFFREY M. CONSULTING LLC

10900 NE 4th St, Bellevue, WA 98004
Tel.: (425) 885-3071
Web Site: http://www.jeffreym.com
Year Founded: 2006
Sales Range: $1-9.9 Million
Emp.: 75
Project & Program Management, Strategic Consulting, Marketing, Business Intelligence & Commercial Services
N.A.I.C.S.: 541613
Jeffrey McCannon *(Owner & Pres)*
Christina Steele *(Mgr-Engagement & Mktg)*

JEFFREY SCOTT AGENCY, INC.

1544 Fulton St, Fresno, CA 93721-2704
Tel.: (559) 268-9741
Web Site: http://www.jsaweb.com
Year Founded: 1976

Full Service Advertising Agency
N.A.I.C.S.: 541810
Lauren Ruh *(Coord-Pub Rels/Acct)*
Alejandra Garcia *(Mgr-Social Media)*
Cynthia Fidel *(Dir-Client & Digital Svcs)*

JEFFRIES BROTHERS, INC.

750 Hwy 46, Wasco, CA 93280
Tel.: (661) 387-0592
Web Site: http://www.jeffriesbros.com
Sales Range: $10-24.9 Million
Emp.: 10
Petroleum Products Distr
N.A.I.C.S.: 424720
Don A. Jeffries *(Pres)*

JEK CARPET INC.

3550 NW 77th Ct, Miami, FL 33122
Tel.: (305) 591-4141   FL
Web Site:
  http://www.dolphincarpet.com
Year Founded: 1978
Sales Range: $10-24.9 Million
Emp.: 150
Retailer of Carpets
N.A.I.C.S.: 423220
Jeffrey Katz *(Owner & Pres)*
Randy Grossman *(Controller)*
Cary Cass *(Gen Mgr)*

JELEC, INC.

16901 Park Row, Houston, TX 77084-7161
Tel.: (713) 977-6500
Web Site: http://www.jelec.com
Year Founded: 1996
Rev.: $27,800,000
Emp.: 27
Electrical Contractor
N.A.I.C.S.: 238210
Jean-Jacques Paufiques *(Pres)*

JELINEK HARDWARE CO.

1704 W 3rd St, Grand Island, NE 68803
Tel.: (308) 382-0897
Web Site:
  http://www.aceistheplace.com
Rev.: $12,321,912
Emp.: 60
Hardware Stores
N.A.I.C.S.: 444140
Randall Jelinek *(Pres)*

JELLIFF CORPORATION

354 Pequot Ave, Southport, CT 06890
Tel.: (203) 259-1615   CT
Web Site: http://www.jelliff.net
Year Founded: 1880
Sales Range: $50-74.9 Million
Emp.: 100
Wire, Wire Cloth, Fabricated-Mesh Products & Electrical Resistance Wire Mfr
N.A.I.C.S.: 332618
Gelff Wheele *(Pres)*

Subsidiaries:

Jelliff Corporation - Florida
Facility   (1)
1351 NE 51st St, Pompano Beach, FL 33064
Tel.: (954) 427-9300
Electrical Wire Mfr
N.A.I.C.S.: 332618

JELLY BELLY CANDY COMPANY

1 Jelly Belly Ln, Fairfield, CA 94533
Tel.: (707) 428-2800   DE
Web Site: http://www.jellybelly.com
Year Founded: 1869
Sales Range: $50-74.9 Million
Emp.: 455
Jelly Beans & Other Candies Mfr

N.A.I.C.S.: 811340
Andrew Joffer *(VP-Sls)*
John Pola *(VP-Specialty Sls)*
Lisa Brasher *(Pres & CEO)*
Jeff Brown *(Exec VP-Ops & Distr-Global)*
Herman G. Rowland Sr. *(Chm)*

JELMAR COMPANY
5550 Touhy Ave Ste 200, Skokie, IL
60077
Tel.: (847) 675-8400
Web Site: http://www.jelmar.com
Year Founded: 1949
Sales Range: $10-24.9 Million
Emp.: 14
Mfr of Tarnish Remover
N.A.I.C.S.: 424690
Arthur Gutterman *(Chm)*
Fredrick Edmonds *(COO)*
Alison Gutterman *(Pres)*
Adrienne Czech *(Dir-Mktg)*

**JEMEZ MOUNTAIN ELECTRIC
CO-OP**
19365 State Rd 84-285, Hernandez,
NM 87537
Tel.: (505) 753-2105
Web Site: http://www.jemezcoop.org
Sales Range: $10-24.9 Million
Emp.: 100
Electric Power Distr
N.A.I.C.S.: 221122
Joseph Sanchez *(Gen Mgr)*

JEMI INC.
20 Stern Ave, Springfield, NJ 07081-
2905
Tel.: (925) 254-7840
Service Establishment Equipment &
Supplies Merchant Whslr
N.A.I.C.S.: 423850
Ron Hill *(Owner)*

JEMISON-DEMSEY METALS
3800 Colonnade Pkwy Ste 350, Bir-
mingham, AL 35243
Tel.: (205) 428-9949
Web Site:
   http://www.jemisondemsey.com
Sales Range: $10-24.9 Million
Emp.: 120
Steel Service Center
N.A.I.C.S.: 423510
Craig Wyatt *(VP-Sls)*

Subsidiaries:

Jemison-Demsey Metals   (1)
Sumter Industrial Park 1255 N Gate Dr,
Sumter, SC 29154
Tel.: (803) 481-0707
Web Site: http://www.jemisondemsey.com
Sales Range: $10-24.9 Million
Emp.: 25
Blast Furnaces & Steel Mills
N.A.I.C.S.: 423510
Marian Pitts *(Plant Mgr)*
Pete Heinke *(CEO)*
Craig Mathiason *(Exec VP-Comml)*
Dave Pratt *(Exec VP-Matls & Ops)*
Randy Richards *(VP-Ops)*
Christopher Sweet *(Exec VP-Bus Dev)*

JEN PARTNERS, LLC
551 Madison Ave Ste 300, New York,
NY 10022-3212
Tel.: (212) 755-4300
Web Site: http://www.jenpartners.com
Year Founded: 2005
Sales Range: $25-49.9 Million
Emp.: 10
Real Estate Investment Services
N.A.I.C.S.: 523999
Reuben S. Leibowitz *(Mng Dir)*
Allen J. Anderson *(Mng Dir)*
Ethan Leibowitz *(VP)*

JENCO PRODUCTIONS INC.

401 S J St, San Bernardino, CA
92410
Tel.: (909) 381-9453
Web Site: http://www.jencoprod.com
Sales Range: $10-24.9 Million
Emp.: 200
Packaging & Labeling Services
N.A.I.C.S.: 561910
John Imbriani *(Controller & Mgr-
Production)*
Hazel Walters *(CFO)*
Nelson Escobar *(Mgr-Shipping)*

**JENKINS & WYNNE FORD
INC.**
2655 Trenton Rd, Clarksville, TN
37040
Tel.: (931) 647-3353
Web Site:
   http://www.jenkinsandwynne.com
Sales Range: $50-74.9 Million
Emp.: 170
New & Used Car Dealers Service &
Parts
N.A.I.C.S.: 441110
Don Jenkins *(Owner)*

**JENKINS DIESEL POWER,
INC.**
1845 E Blaine St, Springfield, MO
65803-4504
Tel.: (417) 862-7021
Web Site:
   http://www.jenkinsdiesel.com
Year Founded: 1956
Sales Range: $10-24.9 Million
Emp.: 64
New Car Retailer
N.A.I.C.S.: 441110
Chris Fredrick *(Principal)*

JENKINS ELECTRIC CO.
5933 Brookshire Blvd, Charlotte, NC
28216
Tel.: (704) 392-7371
Web Site: http://www.jenkins.com
Rev.: $6,200,000
Emp.: 45
Other Electronic Component Mfr
N.A.I.C.S.: 334419
Ian E. Jenkins *(VP)*

Subsidiaries:

Wheeler Industries, Inc.   (1)
7261 Investment Dr, North Charleston, SC
29418
Tel.: (843) 552-1251
Web Site:
   http://www.wheelerfluidfilmbearings.com
Sales Range: $1-9.9 Million
Emp.: 30
Mechanical Power Transmission Equipment
Mfr
N.A.I.C.S.: 333613
Tom M. Tighe *(Mng Dir)*

**JENKINS FORD/MERCURY
INC.**
1 Billingsley Dr, Buckhannon, WV
26201
Tel.: (304) 472-1700
Web Site: http://jenkinsford.com
Sales Range: $10-24.9 Million
Emp.: 45
Sales of New & Used Automobiles
N.A.I.C.S.: 441110
Joey Jenkins *(Gen Mgr)*
Susie Miller *(Office Mgr & Controller)*
Ronald Snyder *(Mgr-Parts)*

JENKINS GROUP, INC.
1129 Woodmere Dr Ste B, Traverse
City, MI 49686
Tel.: (231) 933-0445
Web Site:
   http://www.bookpublishing.com
Year Founded: 1988

Sales Range: $10-24.9 Million
Emp.: 10
Publishing & Promotional Services
N.A.I.C.S.: 513120
Jerrold Jenkins *(Owner)*
James J. Kalajian *(Pres & COO)*

Subsidiaries:

Independent Publisher Online   (1)
1129 Woodmere Ave Ste B, Traverse City,
MI 49686-4275
Tel.: (231) 933-0445
Web Site:
   http://www.independentpublisher.com
Sales Range: $10-24.9 Million
Publishing News Service
N.A.I.C.S.: 513120

Printellectual   (1)
1129 Woodmere Ave Ste B, Traverse City,
MI 49686-4275
Tel.: (231) 933-0445
Web Site: http://www.printellectual.com
Sales Range: $10-24.9 Million
Emp.: 8
Book Printing Quote Network
N.A.I.C.S.: 531120

JENKINS HYUNDAI
1602 SW College Rd, Ocala, FL
34471-1644
Tel.: (352) 620-2264
Web Site:
   http://www.jenkinshyundai.com
Year Founded: 1998
Sales Range: $10-24.9 Million
Emp.: 55
New Car Whslr
N.A.I.C.S.: 441110
Donald Jenkins *(Owner)*
Ryan Baroni *(Mgr-Sls)*
Jay Blake *(VP)*

JENKINS OIL COMPANY INC.
1100 W Indus Rd, Cedar City, UT
84721
Tel.: (435) 586-6931
Web Site: http://www.jenkins-oil.com
Sales Range: $1-9.9 Million
Emp.: 19
Gasoline
N.A.I.C.S.: 424720
Jordan Jenkins *(Controller-Fin)*

**JENKINS SECURITY CONSUL-
TANTS, INC.**
2001 Bunker Hill Rd NE, Washington,
DC 20018
Tel.: (202) 398-1225
Web Site:
   http://www.jenkinssecurityconsul
   tants.com
Year Founded: 1994
Sales Range: $10-24.9 Million
Emp.: 450
Security System Services
N.A.I.C.S.: 561621
Robert Jenkins *(Pres)*
Carl Profater *(Dir-Ops)*
Shahnaz Ariff *(Mgr-Acctg)*
Donna Ford *(Project Mgr)*
Nate Wood *(Area Mgr)*

JENKINS-ESSEX COMPANY
136 Howell Dr, Elizabethtown, KY
42701
Tel.: (270) 765-6113
Web Site:
   http://www.jenkinsessex.com
Rev.: $12,000,000
Emp.: 10
Commercial & Office Building, New
Construction
N.A.I.C.S.: 236220
Robert Gregory Jenkins *(Pres)*

JENNER & BLOCK LLP

353 N Clark St, Chicago, IL 60654-
3456
Tel.: (312) 222-9350
Web Site: http://www.jenner.com
Sales Range: $350-399.9 Million
Emp.: 433
Legal Advisory Services
N.A.I.C.S.: 541199
Charlotte L. Wager *(Chief Talent Offi-
cer)*
Angela M. Allen *(Partner)*
G. Thomas Stromberg *(Partner)*
Steven Siros *(Partner)*
Brian R. Boch *(Chm-Securities Prac-
tice)*
Elizabeth Coleman *(Partner)*
Jeremy M. Creelan *(Partner)*
Richard F. Ziegler *(Partner)*
Anna Margasinska *(Atty)*
Erin R. Schrantz *(Partner)*
Kristen Boike *(Partner)*
E. Lynn Grayson *(Partner)*
Adam Petravicius *(Partner)*
Megan Poetzel *(Partner)*
Michelle McAtee *(Partner)*
Terri Mascherin *(Partner)*
Jack Henry *(Partner)*
Jason D. Osborn *(Partner)*
Damon Y. Smith *(Partner-
Washington)*
William Pericak *(Partner)*
Neil Cummings *(Partner-Los Angeles)*
Gayle E. Littleton *(Partner)*
Craig C. Martin *(Chm)*
Randall E. Mehrberg *(Co-Mng Part-
ner)*
Michael McNamara *(Partner-Los An-
geles)*
Kirsten Hick Spira *(Partner-Los Ange-
les)*
Almuhtada Smith *(Atty)*
Olga A. Loy *(Partner)*
Rebekah Preston Goodheart
*(Partner-Comm, Internet & Tech
Practice)*
George Pain *(Partner)*
Jason Yardley *(Partner-London)*
Charlie Lightfoot *(Chm-Intl Arbitration
Practice & Mng Partner-London)*
David M. Lynn *(Chm-Securities Prac-
tice & Partner-Washington)*
William L. Tolbert *(Chm-Securities
Practice)*
Howard J. Symons *(Partner-Comm,
Internet & Tech Practice-Washington)*
Samuel L. Feder *(Co-Chm-Comm,
Internet & Tech Practice)*
John L. Flynn *(Co-Chm-Comm, Inter-
net & Tech Practice)*
Suedeen Kelly *(Partner-Washington)*
Emily Petrovic Li *(Partner)*
Patrick W. Pearsall *(Chm-Pub Intl
Law Practice)*
Michael J. Nelson *(Partner)*
Max J. Minzner *(Partner)*
Jeffery S. Dennis *(Partner)*
David W. DeBruin *(Partner)*
Matthew E. Price *(Partner)*
Michael T. Wolf *(Partner-Chicago)*
Joseph P. Gromacki *(Chm-Firmwide
Corp Practice)*
Sam Hirsch *(Partner-Washington)*
Thomas J. Perrelli *(Chm-Govt Con-
troversies & Pub Policy Litigation
Practice)*
Emily Loeb *(Partner-Washington)*
Devi Rao *(Partner-Washington)*
Brent E. Kidwell *(Chief Information
Security Officer)*
Dina Panfil *(CFO)*
Peter B. Pope *(Chm-Investigations,
Compliance & Defense Practice-
London)*
Christine Braamskamp *(Partner/Chm-
Investigations, Compliance & De-
fense Practice-London)*

Jenner & Block LLP—(Continued)

Lizzie Shimmin (Partner)
Melida Hodgson (Partner-Intl Arbitration Practice-New York)
Laurie Edelstein (Partner-San Francisco)
Ann O'Leary (Partner)
Katya Jestin (Co-Mng Partner)
Reid Schar (Mng Partner-San Francisco)

JENNER EQUIPMENT CO.
3200 Deadwood Ave, Rapid City, SD 57702
Tel.: (605) 343-6682
Web Site:
http://www.jennerequipment.com
Sales Range: $10-24.9 Million
Emp.: 24
Farm & Garden Machinery Equipment Whslr
N.A.I.C.S.: 423820
Jerry Severson (Mgr-Parts)

JENNER'S POND
2000 Greenbriar Ln, West Grove, PA 19390
Tel.: (610) 869-8600
Web Site:
http://www.jennerspond.org
Year Founded: 1997
Sales Range: $10-24.9 Million
Emp.: 426
Continuing Care Retirement Community Operator
N.A.I.C.S.: 623311
Diane Dutko (Dir-Bus Svcs)
Nadine O'Neil (Dir-Health & Wellness)
Daryl Hertsenberg (Dir-Facilities & Construction)
Linda Wilmont (Exec Dir)

JENNIE M. MELHAM MEMORIAL MEDICAL CENTER
145 Memorial Dr, Broken Bow, NE 68822
Tel.: (308) 872-4100
Web Site: http://www.melham.org
Year Founded: 1962
Sales Range: $10-24.9 Million
Emp.: 224
Health Care Srvices
N.A.I.C.S.: 622110
Jim Scott (Treas)
Michael J. Steckler (Pres & CEO)

JENNINGS AMERICAN LEGION HOSPITAL
1634 Elton Rd, Jennings, LA 70546
Tel.: (337) 616-7000
Web Site: http://www.jalh.com
Year Founded: 1952
Sales Range: $25-49.9 Million
Emp.: 400
Healtcare Services
N.A.I.C.S.: 622110
Dana D. Williams (CEO)

JENNINGS ANDERSON FORD SALES
31480 I10 W, Boerne, TX 78006
Tel.: (210) 698-3456
Web Site:
http://www.jenningsandersonford.com
Sales Range: $75-99.9 Million
Emp.: 116
New & Used Automobiles, Sales Service Bodywork
N.A.I.C.S.: 441110
Scott Wilson (Principal)
Steve Pollack (Gen Mgr)
Scott Miller (Gen Mgr-Sls)

JENNINGS CENTER FOR OLDER ADULTS
10204 Granger Rd, Garfield Heights, OH 44125
Tel.: (216) 581-2900
Web Site:
http://www.jenningscenter.org
Year Founded: 1941
Sales Range: $10-24.9 Million
Emp.: 435
Elder Care Services
N.A.I.C.S.: 624120
Lisa Brazytis (Dir-Mktg & Outreach)
Sara Adamo (Dir-Dev)
Allison Q. Salopeck (Pres & CEO)

JENNINGS CHEVROLET, INC.
241 Waukegan Rd, Glenview, IL 60025-5158
Tel.: (847) 729-1000
Web Site:
http://www.jenningschevrolet.com
Year Founded: 1958
Sales Range: $25-49.9 Million
Emp.: 118
New Car Whslr
N.A.I.C.S.: 441110
James R. Jennings (Owner)
John P. Jennings (Treas & Sec)
James M. Walsh (Gen Mgr)

JENNINGS TIRE COMPANY INC.
805 NW Broad St, Murfreesboro, TN 37129
Tel.: (615) 890-0100
Web Site: http://www.american-tire.com
Rev.: $36,600,000
Emp.: 40
Tires & Tubes
N.A.I.C.S.: 441340
Herman B. Willis Jr. (CEO)

JENNINGS VALUE CENTER
1005 Lincoln Way W, Chambersburg, PA 17202
Tel.: (717) 263-4191
Rev.: $17,200,000
Emp.: 49
New & Used Car Dealers
N.A.I.C.S.: 441110
Allan E. Jennings Jr. (Pres)

JENNINGS VOLKSWAGEN INC.
201 Waukegan Rd, Glenview, IL 60025
Tel.: (847) 729-3500
Web Site: http://www.jennings-vw.com
Rev.: $11,100,000
Emp.: 40
New Car Dealers
N.A.I.C.S.: 441110
Ken Lyon (Gen Mgr-Sls)
Andrew Low (Mgr-Sls)

JENNINGS-DILL, INC.
PO Box 6066, Greenville, SC 29606
Tel.: (864) 235-2518
Web Site: http://www.jennings-dill.com
Year Founded: 1947
Sales Range: $10-24.9 Million
Emp.: 175
Plumbing, Heating & Air-Conditioning Contracting Services
N.A.I.C.S.: 238220
Kenny Dunaway (Mgr-Svc)
Ralph Bailey (VP-Pre-Construction Svcs)

JENNINGS-GOMER EQUITY INC.

3798 W Lincoln Hwy, Gomer, OH 45809
Tel.: (419) 642-3191
Web Site:
http://www.jenningsgomer.com
Sales Range: $10-24.9 Million
Emp.: 15
Grains & Chemicals Distr
N.A.I.C.S.: 424510
Gary Kruse (Gen Mgr)

JENNY CORPORATION OF OHIO
101 Chardin Dr, Nokomis, FL 34275
Tel.: (941) 966-5684
Sales Range: $10-24.9 Million
Emp.: 15
General Line Grocery Merchant Whslr
N.A.I.C.S.: 424410
Peter J. Rowan (VP)
Jennifer Rowan (Mgr)
Roberta Rowan (Pres)

JENNY MARAGHY TEAM, INC.
4917 Grove Ave, Richmond, VA 23226
Tel.: (804) 405-7337
Web Site:
http://www.jennymaraghyteam.com
Year Founded: 2011
Sales Range: $1-9.9 Million
Emp.: 25
Real Estate Consulting Service
N.A.I.C.S.: 531210
Dany Srour (Dir-Ops)
Darby Chastain (Mng Dir)
Mari Kotze (Mgr-Transaction)

JENNY PRODUCTS, INC.
850 N Pleasant Ave, Somerset, PA 15501
Tel.: (814) 445-3400
Web Site:
http://www.steamjenny.com
Year Founded: 1927
Sales Range: Less than $1 Million
Emp.: 50
Steam Cleaners, Pressure Washers, Car Washers & Cleaning Chemicals Mfr
N.A.I.C.S.: 333310
Peter Leiss (Pres)
Daniel Leiss (VP)
Jodell Antram (Mgr-Acctg)

JENSEN & PILEGARD
1739 E Terrace Ave, Fresno, CA 93703
Tel.: (559) 268-9221
Web Site:
http://www.jensenandpilegard.com
Rev.: $14,000,000
Emp.: 25
Lawn & Garden Equipment Parts & Supplies
N.A.I.C.S.: 423820
Cris Pilegard (Owner)

JENSEN AUDIO VISUAL
210 E Cota St, Santa Barbara, CA 93101
Tel.: (805) 962-0110
Web Site: http://www.jensenav.com
Year Founded: 1997
Sales Range: $10-24.9 Million
Emp.: 14
Audio Visual Equipment Sales & Services
N.A.I.C.S.: 459999
Kelly Magne (Pres & CEO)
Cindy Fairbanks (Office Mgr)
Eric Kalpakoff (Mgr-Ops)
Rob Butson (Mgr-Rentals)

JENSEN BRIDGE & SUPPLY COMPANY
400 Stoney Creek Dr, Sandusky, MI 48471
Tel.: (810) 648-3000
Web Site:
http://www.jensenbridge.com
Sales Range: $10-24.9 Million
Emp.: 65
Sheet Metal Products Mfr
N.A.I.C.S.: 332322
Roger Loding (Chm & Pres)
Marcie Kolakovich (Controller)
Dale Chambers (Mgr-Sls)

JENSEN ENTERPRISES INC.
825 Sterni Way, Sparks, NV 89431
Tel.: (775) 352-2700
Web Site:
http://www.jensenprecast.com
Year Founded: 1968
Sales Range: $10-24.9 Million
Emp.: 110
Concrete Products, Precast
N.A.I.C.S.: 327390
Don Jensen (CEO)
Tony Shanks (Pres)
Rusty Stever (VP)
Tamara Buckner (Asst Controller)
Wally Hahne (Sr VP-Bus Dev)
Bevin Eagle (Dir-HR)
Anthony Bosco (Gen Mgr)
Eric Jensen (COO)
Kurt Jensen (Pres-Jensen Precast Sparks)
Josh Ballew (Controller)
Brett Patterson (Dir-IT)
Tyrus Cobb (Gen Counsel & Dir-Govt Affairs)
Holly McVicker (Mgr-Acctg)
Kellen Easter (Mgr-Inventory Control)
Leonard Smith (VP-Mfg)

JENSEN FORD INC.
2805 S Ctr St, Marshalltown, IA 50158
Tel.: (641) 753-5501
Web Site: http://www.jensenford.com
Sales Range: $10-24.9 Million
Emp.: 50
New Car Retailer
N.A.I.C.S.: 441110
Joe Hobson (Mgr-Bus)
Brad Hood (Gen Mgr)
Kevin Jensen (Co-Owner)
Kendall Jensen (Co-Owner)

JENSEN INFORMATION TECHNOLOGIES INC
1689 Elk Blvd, Des Plaines, IL 60016
Tel.: (847) 803-0044
Web Site: http://www.jensenit.com
Year Founded: 1991
Sales Range: $1-9.9 Million
Emp.: 12
Network Solutions & Data Storage
N.A.I.C.S.: 334112
Jay Jensen (Pres & CEO)

JENSEN INTERNATIONAL INC.
1004 W 14th St, Coffeyville, KS 67337
Tel.: (620) 251-5700
Web Site: http://www.jencast.com
Sales Range: $10-24.9 Million
Emp.: 120
Gray & Ductile Iron Foundries
N.A.I.C.S.: 331511
Diana Knisley (Controller)
Mike Emery (Dir-Ops)

JENSEN JEWELERS OF IDAHO LLC
133 Shoshone St N, Twin Falls, ID 83301-6150
Tel.: (208) 734-7920

Web Site: http://www.jensen-jewelers.com
Sales Range: $10-24.9 Million
Emp.: 125
Jewelry Stores
N.A.I.C.S.: 458310
Tony Pranter *(CFO & VP)*

JENSEN METAL PRODUCTS INC.
7800 Northwestern Ave, Racine, WI 53406
Tel.: (262) 886-9318
Web Site:
http://www.jensenmetal.com
Year Founded: 1920
Sales Range: $50-74.9 Million
Emp.: 50
Mfr of Ventless Fireplaces; Metal Fabrication
N.A.I.C.S.: 333414
Geeta Jensen *(Pres)*
Seth Jensen *(CFO & VP)*

JENSEN TIRE & AUTO CO.
10609 I St, Omaha, NE 68127
Tel.: (402) 339-2917
Web Site: http://www.jensentire.com
Rev.: $10,800,000
Emp.: 25
General Automotive Repair Shops
N.A.I.C.S.: 811111
Matthew Jensen *(Pres)*
Allen Harry *(Controller)*

JENSEN UNDERGROUND UTILITIES, INC.
5585 Taylor Rd, Naples, FL 34109-1842
Tel.: (239) 597-0060
Web Site:
http://www.jensenunderground.com
Sales Range: $10-24.9 Million
Emp.: 110
Construction Engineering Services
N.A.I.C.S.: 237310
Kevin Jensen *(Pres)*
Tim Schlief *(Project Coord)*
Tom Mitchell *(Project Mgr)*

JENSENS COMPLETE SHOP-PING
27264 Hwy 189, Blue Jay, CA 92317
Tel.: (909) 337-8484
Web Site:
http://www.jensensfoods.com
Rev.: $37,700,000
Emp.: 500
Grocery Stores, Independent
N.A.I.C.S.: 445110
Jack Meyer *(Mgr)*
Matt Zack *(VP)*
Mary Cass *(Dir-Floral)*
Lila Fulton *(Treas, Sec & Dir-Gift Basket)*
Karen McMullen *(Dir-HR)*
Gene A. Fulton *(Pres)*
Cindy Slayton *(Mgr-Acctg)*
Eric Lee *(Mgr)*
Frank Dorame *(Dir-Meat & Seafood Buyer Svc Delivery)*
Mike Zack *(Dir-Buying & Mdsg)*
Ricardo Parra *(Mgr)*
Rick Cronk *(Mgr)*
Steve Buxton *(Mgr)*
Todd Hodges *(Mgr)*
Tom Guffey *(Mgr)*
Wes Worley *(Mgr)*

JENZABAR, INC.
101 Huntington Ave Ste 2205, Boston, MA 02199
Tel.: (617) 492-9099
Web Site: http://www.jenzabar.com
Year Founded: 1998
Sales Range: $25-49.9 Million

Emp.: 250
Provider of Internet Connectivity Services
N.A.I.C.S.: 517810
Ling Chai *(Pres & COO)*
Jayne W. Edge *(VP-Mktg)*
Robert A. Maginn Jr. *(Chm & CEO)*

Subsidiaries:

RJM Systems Inc. (1)
Reservoir Office Pk 1449 Old Waterbury Rd Ste 204, Southbury, CT 06488
Tel.: (203) 262-2310
Web Site: http://www.sonis.com
Hosting & Data Processing Services
N.A.I.C.S.: 518210
Reece J. Schuler *(Pres)*
Joanne E. Milburn *(CEO)*

Spark451 Inc. (1)
865 Merrick Ave., Suite 451, Westbury, NY 11590
Tel.: (516) 442-4650
Web Site: http://www.spark451.com
Advertising Agencies
N.A.I.C.S.: 541810

JEP MANAGEMENT, INC.
101H Cherry Ln, Wynnewood, PA 19096
Tel.: (610) 658-0888
Sales Range: $10-24.9 Million
Emp.: 8
Management Services
N.A.I.C.S.: 541611
Jeffrey E. Perelman *(CEO)*
Robin Gall *(Dir-Fin)*
Vickie Waitsman *(Gen Counsel & VP)*

Subsidiaries:

General Machine Corporation (1)
301 S 4th St, Emmaus, PA 18049-3854
Tel.: (610) 462-5987
Web Site: http://www.genmachcorp.com
Sales Range: $10-24.9 Million
Seal Rings Mfr
N.A.I.C.S.: 332119

JER HR GROUP LLC
36 W 44 St Ste 77A, New York, NY 10036
Tel.: (646) 453-7560 NY
Web Site: https://jerhrgroup.com
Sales Range: $1-9.9 Million
Human Resource Consulting Services
N.A.I.C.S.: 541612
Mahesh Kumar *(Mng Dir)*

Subsidiaries:

Human Resources Plus Inc. (1)
1443 S Washington St, Denver, CO 80210-2242
Tel.: (303) 733-3933
Web Site: http://www.hrplusinc.com
Human Resource Consulting Services
N.A.I.C.S.: 541612
Erin Osbourne *(Founder)*

JER INVESTORS TRUST INC.
1650 Tysons Blvd Ste 1600, McLean, VA 22101
Tel.: (212) 705-5034 MD
Web Site:
http://www.jerinvestorstrust.com
Year Founded: 2004
JERT—(OTCBB)
Sales Range: $600-649.9 Million
Real Estate Investment Trust
N.A.I.C.S.: 525990
Joseph E. Robert Jr. *(Chm)*
Keith W. Belcher *(Exec VP)*
J. Michael McGillis *(CFO)*

JERAL CONSTRUCTION SER-VICES
320 Belleville Ave, Bloomfield, NJ 07003
Tel.: (973) 748-6400

Web Site:
http://www.jeralconstruction.com
Sales Range: $10-24.9 Million
Emp.: 18
Commercial & Institutional Building Construction Services
N.A.I.C.S.: 236220
Pierre Ibanez *(Dir-Ops)*

JERDON CONSTRUCTION SERVICES LLC
5925 Tilghman St Ste 20, Allentown, PA 18104
Tel.: (610) 530-2430
Web Site: http://www.jerdoncs.com
Year Founded: 2011
Sales Range: $1-9.9 Million
Emp.: 18
General Contracting, Renovations & Expansions
N.A.I.C.S.: 238120
Ron Jerdon *(Pres)*

JERDON STYLE LLC
1820 N Glenville Dr Ste 124, Richardson, TX 75081-7201
Tel.: (800) 223-3571
Web Site: http://www.jerdonstyle.com
Year Founded: 1977
Personal Care Products & Accessories Mfr
N.A.I.C.S.: 423620

JERGENS INC.
15700 S Waterloo Rd, Cleveland, OH 44110-3814
Tel.: (216) 486-5540 OH
Web Site: http://www.jergensinc.com
Year Founded: 1942
Sales Range: $100-124.9 Million
Emp.: 250
Fixturing & Tooling Product Mfr
N.A.I.C.S.: 333514
Bob Rubenstahl *(Gen Mgr)*

Subsidiaries:

ASG Jergens Inc. (1)
Jergens Way 15700 S Waterloo Rd, Cleveland, OH 44110-3898
Tel.: (216) 486-6163
Web Site: http://www.asg-jergens.com
Industrial Machine Tool Product Mfr
N.A.I.C.S.: 333515
Bryon Shafer *(Gen Mgr)*

Acme Industrial Company (1)
441 Maple Ave, Carpentersville, IL 60110 (100%)
Tel.: (847) 428-3911
Web Site: http://www.acmeindustrial.com
Sales Range: $10-24.9 Million
Emp.: 95
Mfr of Tooling Components
N.A.I.C.S.: 333515
John Evans *(Pres)*
George Margelos *(Gen Mgr)*
Megan Evans *(Mgr-Order Fulfillment)*

JIS Distribution LLC (1)
15700 S Waterloo Rd, Cleveland, OH 44110
Tel.: (216) 486-2100
Web Site: http://www.jis.com
Metalworking Equipment Distr
N.A.I.C.S.: 423830
Leanna Rummes *(Mktg Mgr)*
Mat Schron *(Gen Mgr)*

Subsidiary (Domestic):

Erie Tool & Supply Co. (2)
304 N Westwood Ave, Toledo, OH 43635-2707
Tel.: (419) 531-2811
Web Site: http://www.erietool.com
Industrial Supply Whslr
N.A.I.C.S.: 423840
Robert Seeman *(Pres)*

Jergens India Private, Ltd. (1)
307 A Wing 3rd Floor Hermes Atrium Plot No 57 Sector 11 Cbd Belapur, Navi Mumbai, Mumbai, India

Tel.: (91) 22 4123 8039
Web Site: http://www.jergensindia.com
Sales Range: $10-24.9 Million
Emp.: 5
Machine Tooling Equipment Distr
N.A.I.C.S.: 423830
Joseph P. Killukan *(Mng Dir)*
Premkumar M. *(Mgr-Dev)*
Karthikeyan Dhananbal *(Engr-Resident Application & Bus Dev)*
Vishwesh Kulkarni *(Engr-Resident Application & Bus Dev)*

JERICOL MINING INC.
549 Londonderry Rd, Cumberland Gap, TN 37724
Tel.: (423) 869-4755
Rev.: $35,600,000
Emp.: 3
Bituminous Coal Underground Mining
N.A.I.C.S.: 212115
James Sigmon *(Pres)*

JERNIGAN CAPITAL, INC.
6410 Poplar Ave Ste 650, Memphis, TN 38119
Tel.: (901) 567-9510 MD
Web Site:
http://www.jernigancapital.com
Year Founded: 2014
Rev.: $45,093,000
Assets: $812,777,000
Liabilities: $223,903,000
Net Worth: $588,874,000
Earnings: $23,928,000
Emp.: 16
Fiscal Year-end: 12/31/19
Real Estate Investment Trust
N.A.I.C.S.: 525990
Dean Jernigan *(Founder)*
Kelly P. Luttrell *(CFO, Treas, Sec & Sr VP)*
William Q. Perry *(Sr VP-Investment Mgmt)*
John A. Good *(CEO)*
Jonathan L. Perry *(Pres & Chief Investment Officer)*
David Corak *(Sr VP-Fin)*

JERNIGAN OIL CO. INC.
415 E Main St, Ahoskie, NC 27910
Tel.: (252) 332-2131
Web Site: http://www.jerniganoil.com
Sales Range: $25-49.9 Million
Emp.: 175
Petroleum Bulk Stations
N.A.I.C.S.: 424710
Donna Hill *(Controller)*
James Michael Harrell Jr. *(Owner)*

JEROME HOME
975 Corbin Ave, New Britain, CT 06052
Tel.: (860) 229-3707 CT
Web Site:
http://www.jeromehome.org
Year Founded: 1932
Sales Range: $10-24.9 Million
Emp.: 317
Elderly People Assisted Living Services
N.A.I.C.S.: 623312
Lori Toombs *(Exec Dir)*
Susann Pavano *(Dir-Nurses)*
Nicole Archambault-Benson *(Dir-Admissions)*
Sue Kuchman *(Dir-HR)*
Crisla Ryan *(Program Mgr-Rehab)*

JEROME'S FURNITURE WAREHOUSE
780 Los Vallecitos Blvd, San Marcos, CA 92069
Tel.: (760) 744-4851
Web Site: http://www.jeromes.com
Year Founded: 1955
Sales Range: $50-74.9 Million
Emp.: 400

Jerome's Furniture Warehouse—(Continued)

Furniture Whslr
N.A.I.C.S.: 449110
Dave Evans (Mgr)
Kevin Bligh (COO)
Brian Woods (CEO)

JERRS PLUS INC.
1235 Broadway FL 4, New York, NY 10001
Tel.: (212) 889-9630
Rev.: $14,019,361
Emp.: 25
Jewelry
N.A.I.C.S.: 423940
David Saad (Pres)

Subsidiaries:

DB Plus Inc. (1)
1235 Broadway Fl 4, New York, NY 10001
Tel.: (212) 889-9630
Rev.: $13,188,394
Emp.: 13
Apparel Belts, Women's & Children's
N.A.I.C.S.: 424350

JERRY BIGGERS CHEVROLET - ISUZU INC.
1385 E Chicago St, Elgin, IL 60120
Tel.: (847) 742-9000
Web Site:
    http://www.biggerschevy.com
Year Founded: 1970
Sales Range: $25-49.9 Million
Emp.: 125
New & Used Car Dealer & Services
N.A.I.C.S.: 441110
James Leichter (Principal-Dealer)
Bob Colwell (VP)
Bruce Westphal (Mgr-Parts)
Diego Montes (Mgr-Sls)
Fred Paolilli (Mgr-Sls-Used Car)
Jose Velasquez (Mgr-Sls)
Mike Dacheff (Mgr-Fleet)
Stephen Reiter (Dir-Fin)

JERRY BRUCKHEIMER FILMS INC.
1631 10th St, Santa Monica, CA 90404
Tel.: (310) 664-6260
Web Site: http://www.jbfilms.com
Sales Range: $10-24.9 Million
Emp.: 25
Motion Picture & Television Producer & Distr
N.A.I.C.S.: 512110
Jerry Bruckheimer (Pres)

JERRY CHEN
3795 Sierra Rd, San Jose, CA 95132
Tel.: (408) 238-4492
Web Site: http://www.lionestates.com
Sales Range: $10-24.9 Million
Emp.: 1
Land Subdividers & Developers, Commercial
N.A.I.C.S.: 237210

JERRY ERWIN ASSOCIATES INC.
5101 NE 82nd Ave Ste 200, Vancouver, WA 98662
Tel.: (360) 254-9442
Web Site:
    http://www.jeaseniorliving.com
Year Founded: 1985
Rev.: $25,000,000
Emp.: 11
Subdividers & Developers
N.A.I.C.S.: 237210
Jerry Erwin (Pres)
Codey Erwin (Pres)

JERRY FERGUSON BUICK-GMC TRUCK LLC

1601 N Elm Pl, Broken Arrow, OK 74012
Tel.: (918) 258-1800
Web Site:
    http://www.fergusondeal.com
Sales Range: $10-24.9 Million
Emp.: 80
Automobiles, New & Used
N.A.I.C.S.: 441110
Jerry Ferguson (Owner)
Angel Ingle (Controller)
Stewart Brown (Gen Mgr)
Ryan Ferguson (Exec Mgr)

JERRY HAAG MOTORS INC.
1475 N High St, Hillsboro, OH 45133
Tel.: (937) 393-1981
Web Site:
    http://www.jerryhaagmotors.com
Sales Range: $10-24.9 Million
Emp.: 30
Automobiles, New & Used
N.A.I.C.S.: 441110
Steven R. Haag (Pres)

JERRY HAMM CHEVROLET INC.
3494 Phillips Hwy, Jacksonville, FL 32207
Tel.: (904) 398-3036
Web Site: http://www.jerryhamm.com
Year Founded: 1952
Sales Range: $100-124.9 Million
Emp.: 60
Sales of New & Used Cars
N.A.I.C.S.: 441110
Damon Ferguson (Gen Mgr)

JERRY HEFLIN COURTESY CHEVROLET
3161 Madison Rd, Cincinnati, OH 45209
Tel.: (513) 871-3161
Web Site: http://www.gocourtesy.com
Sales Range: $10-24.9 Million
Emp.: 25
Car Dealership
N.A.I.C.S.: 441110

JERRY LAWLEY INCORPORATED
205 W 9th St, Tishomingo, OK 73460
Tel.: (580) 371-2126
Sales Range: $25-49.9 Million
Emp.: 5
Distr of Petroleum Products
N.A.I.C.S.: 424710
Jerry Lawley (Pres)

JERRY LEE'S GROCERY, INC.
1417 Hwy 90, Gautier, MS 39553-5444
Tel.: (228) 497-2730
Web Site: http://www.jerrylees.net
Year Founded: 1958
Sales Range: $25-49.9 Million
Emp.: 300
Grocery Store Operator
N.A.I.C.S.: 445110
Susan Lee (Mgr)

JERRY PATE TURF & IRRIGATION INC
301 Schubert Dr, Pensacola, FL 32504
Tel.: (850) 479-4653
Web Site: http://www.jerrypate.com
Rev.: $23,000,000
Emp.: 140
Lawn Machinery & Equipment
N.A.I.C.S.: 423820
Joe Brown (Dir-Golf Irrigation Sls)

JERRY SEINER CHEVROLET, INC.

1530 South 500 West, Salt Lake City, UT 84115
Tel.: (385) 212-3155
Web Site:
    http://www.seinerchevy.com
Sales Range: $10-24.9 Million
Emp.: 70
Car Whslr
N.A.I.C.S.: 441110
Mary Ann Moyle (Controller & Office Mgr)
Dustin Hartung (Dir-Svc)
Marcy Hartung (Principal)
Chris Hemmersmeier (VP)
Ty Johnson (Mgr-Store)
Jennifer Newman (Mgr-Customer Rels)
Brandon Kempff (Mgr-Svc)

Subsidiaries:

Jerry Seiner Salt Lake (1)
1530 S 500 W, Salt Lake City, UT 84115
Tel.: (801) 952-5700
Web Site: http://www.jerryseinerslc.com
New Car Retailer
N.A.I.C.S.: 441110
Jerry Seiner (Founder)
Marcy Hartung (Mgr-HR)
Chris Hemmersmeier (Pres & CEO)

JERRY SMITH CHEVROLET
12484 Reservation Rd, Anacortes, WA 98221
Tel.: (360) 293-5166
Web Site:
    http://www.jerrysmithchevrolet.com
Sales Range: $10-24.9 Million
Emp.: 50
New Car Dealers
N.A.I.C.S.: 441110
Jerry Smith (Pres)

JERRY ULM DODGE, INC.
2966 N Dale Mabry Hwy, Tampa, FL 33607
Tel.: (813) 872-6645
Web Site:
    http://www.jerryulmdodgechrysler
    jeepram.com
Year Founded: 1990
Sales Range: $100-124.9 Million
Emp.: 180
Car Dealership
N.A.I.C.S.: 441110
Gerald H. Ulm (Pres)
Rob Brenneke (Dir-Svc & Parts)
Mike Martinez (Mgr-Svc)
Angie Fleming (Mgr-Svc Lane)

JERRY W. BAILEY TRUCKING, INC.
12609 Indianapolis Rd, Indianapolis, IN 46798-9733
Tel.: (260) 747-3511
Year Founded: 1981
Sales Range: $10-24.9 Million
Emp.: 60
General Freight Services
N.A.I.C.S.: 484121
Jerry Bailey (Pres)

JERRY'S ENTERPRISES INC.
5101 Vernon Ave S, Edina, MN 55436
Tel.: (952) 922-8335
Web Site: http://www.jerrysfoods.com
Year Founded: 1947
Sales Range: $550-599.9 Million
Emp.: 3,500
Owner & Operator of Grocery Stores
N.A.I.C.S.: 445110
Robert Shadduck (Pres)
Kent Dixon (VP-Fin)
Molly Mitch (VP-HR)

JERRY'S FAMOUS DELI, INC.

12711 Ventura Blvd Ste 400, Studio City, CA 91604
Tel.: (818) 766-8311
Web Site:
    http://www.jerrysfamousdeli.com
Year Founded: 1978
Sales Range: $150-199.9 Million
Emp.: 1,200
Owner & Operator of New York Deli-Style Restaurants
N.A.I.C.S.: 722511
Guy Starkman (Pres)

JERRY'S FORD SALES INC.
6510 Little River Tpke, Annandale, VA 22312
Tel.: (703) 256-5000
Web Site: http://www.jerrysauto.com
Rev.: $48,600,000
Emp.: 137
Automobiles, New & Used
N.A.I.C.S.: 441110
Jerry C. Cohen (Pres & Gen Mgr)
Bill Hall (Mgr-Fleet Sls)

JERRY'S HOMES INC.
3301 106th Cir, Urbandale, IA 50322
Tel.: (515) 278-5992
Web Site:
    http://www.jerryshomes.com
Sales Range: $25-49.9 Million
Emp.: 30
Speculative Builder; Multi-Family Dwellings
N.A.I.C.S.: 236116
Ronald R. Grubb (Pres)
Brent Kouba (CFO)

JERRY'S SPORTS CENTER, INC.
100 Capital Rd, Jenkins Township, PA 18640
Tel.: (570) 785-9400
Web Site:
    http://www.jerryssportscenter.com
Year Founded: 1950
Sales Range: $150-199.9 Million
Emp.: 375
Sports Equipment Whslr
N.A.I.C.S.: 423910
Bernard Ziomek (Chm)
Andrew Kupchik (Mgr-Outside Sls-Bus Dev & Mgr-Inside Sls)

JERRY'S SUPERMARKET INC.
532 W Jefferson Blvd, Dallas, TX 75208
Tel.: (214) 941-8110
Web Site:
    http://www.supermarket.com
Rev.: $26,900,000
Emp.: 70
Supermarkets, Chain
N.A.I.C.S.: 445110
James R. Westmoreland (Pres)

JERSEY CONSTRUCTION INCORPORATED
838 Piney Hollow Rd, Hammonton, NJ 08037
Tel.: (609) 704-0005
Web Site:
    http://www.jerseyconstruction.com
Sales Range: $10-24.9 Million
Emp.: 30
Highway & Street Construction
N.A.I.C.S.: 237310
Theodore J. Whitmyer (Pres)
Anna Marie Whitmyer (Sec)

JERSEY HEALTH CONNECT
782 Alexander Rd 2nd Fl, Princeton, NJ 08543
Tel.: (609) 945-1183
Web Site:
    http://www.jerseyhealthconnect.org
Year Founded: 2010
Sales Range: $1-9.9 Million

Health Care Srvices
N.A.I.C.S.: 622110
Linda Reed *(Chm)*
Dave Dyer *(Vice Chm)*
Neal Ganguly *(Vice Chm)*
Judy Comitto *(Sec)*

JERSEY MIKE'S FRANCHISE SYSTEMS, INC.
2251 Landmark Pl, Manasquan, NJ 08736
Tel.: (732) 223-4044   NJ
Web Site:
http://www.jerseymikes.com
Year Founded: 1956
Sales Range: $200-249.9 Million
Restaurant Owner & Franchisor
N.A.I.C.S.: 722513
Peter Cancro *(Founder & CEO)*
Phil Holcomb *(Dir-Graphic Svcs)*
Brian O'Hagan *(VP-Sls)*

JERSEY SHORE HOSPITAL
1020 Thompson St, Jersey Shore, PA 17740
Tel.: (570) 398-0100   PA
Web Site: http://www.jsh.org
Year Founded: 1922
Sales Range: $25-49.9 Million
Emp.: 352
Health Care Srvices
N.A.I.C.S.: 622110
Samantha Weaver *(Chief Quality Officer)*
Mark Rice *(CFO)*
Christine E. Haas *(CIO)*
Paulette Nish *(Chief Nursing Officer)*

JERSEY SHORE STEEL CO.
70 Maryland Ave, Jersey Shore, PA 17740
Tel.: (570) 398-0220
Web Site: http://www.jssteel.com
Sales Range: $50-74.9 Million
Emp.: 130
Steel Products Mfr
N.A.I.C.S.: 331110
John C. Schultz *(Chm)*
Terri Fry *(Plant Mgr)*
Thomas Tillman *(Mgr-Sls)*

JERYCO INDUSTRIES INC.
8401 Ambassador Row PO Box 560187, Dallas, TX 75247
Tel.: (214) 631-6510
Sales Range: $10-24.9 Million
Emp.: 145
Sheet Metalwork
N.A.I.C.S.: 332322
Jerry Green *(Pres)*

JES CONSTRUCTION, LLC
1741 Corporate Landing Pkwy, Virginia Beach, VA 23454
Tel.: (866) 370-4816
Web Site: http://www.jeswork.com
Year Founded: 1993
Sales Range: $25-49.9 Million
Emp.: 350
Foundation Repair & Basement Waterproofing Services
N.A.I.C.S.: 238190
Jesse Waltz *(Co-Owner)*
Matt Malone *(Co-Owner & CEO)*
Stella Waltz *(Co-Owner)*
Mike Irby *(Pres)*
Cary McGuckin *(CMO)*
Kim McDonald *(CTO)*
Stephen Frey *(CFO)*
George Frates *(Pres-Ops)*
Guy Stello *(Sr VP-Fin)*

Subsidiaries:

Tar Heel Basement Systems LLC   (1)
2910 Griffith Rd, Winston Salem, NC 27103

Tel.: (336) 916-2150
Web Site:
http://www.tarheelbasementsystems.com
Emp.: 80
Basement, Foundation & Crawl Space Waterproofing & Repair
N.A.I.C.S.: 238390
Pete Burgess *(Founder & CEO)*
Andy Krause *(Mgr-Production)*
Phil Mandel *(Asst Mgr-Production)*
Garrett Atkinson *(Mgr-Sls)*
Geoff Keller *(Asst Mgr-Sls)*
Ryan Austin *(Dir-Trng)*
Anthony Cass *(Dir-Svc & Technical)*
Jackie Hoffman *(Dir-Mktg)*

JESCO CONSTRUCTION CORPORATION
46 Flint Creek Rd, Wiggins, MS 39577
Tel.: (601) 928-2323
Web Site:
http://www.jescoconstruction.com
Rev.: $17,000,000
Emp.: 15
Dredging Contractor
N.A.I.C.S.: 236210
John E. Shavers *(Founder & Pres)*

JESCO INC.
118 Saint Nicholas Ave, South Plainfield, NJ 07080
Tel.: (908) 753-8080
Web Site: http://www.jesco.us
Sales Range: $50-74.9 Million
Emp.: 60
Excavating Machinery & Equipment
N.A.I.C.S.: 423810
Anthony Falzarano *(VP-Sls)*
Cris Robustelli *(Mgr-IT)*
Greg Blaszka *(CFO)*
Lee Grover *(Mgr-Svcs)*
Doug Pritchard *(Coord-Rental)*
Colby Hyduke *(Mgr-Comml Worksite Products-Territory)*

JESCO LIGHTING GROUP, LLC.
15 Harbor Park Dr, Port Washington, NY 11050
Tel.: (718) 366-3211
Web Site:
http://www.jescolighting.com
Year Founded: 1998
Sales Range: $10-24.9 Million
Emp.: 40
Electrical Apparatus & Equipment, Wiring Supplier & Whslr
N.A.I.C.S.: 423610
Richard Kurtz *(Pres & CEO)*
Jeffrey L. Sessler *(Mgr-Sls-West)*

JESCO WHOLESALE ELECTRICAL SUPPLIES INC.
950 N Main Ave, Sioux Center, IA 51250
Tel.: (712) 722-3737
Web Site: http://www.jescousa.com
Sales Range: $25-49.9 Million
Emp.: 12
Electrical Apparatus & Equipment
N.A.I.C.S.: 423610
Mitch Lane *(CEO)*

JESON ENTERPRISES INC.
504 NE 5th Ave, Camas, WA 98607
Tel.: (360) 834-7728
Web Site:
http://www.craftwarehouse.com
Rev.: $32,600,000
Emp.: 550
Arts & Crafts Supplies
N.A.I.C.S.: 459120
Jerry Williams *(Pres)*
Becca Web *(Office Mgr)*

JESS HOWARD ELECTRIC COMPANY

6630 Taylor Rd, Blacklick, OH 43004
Tel.: (614) 861-1300
Web Site:
http://www.jesshoward.com
Year Founded: 1945
Sales Range: $300-349.9 Million
Emp.: 120
Electrical Wiring Services
N.A.I.C.S.: 238210
Jonathan Howard *(Pres)*

JESS SMITH & SONS COTTON
2905 F St, Bakersfield, CA 93301-1819
Tel.: (661) 325-7231
Web Site: http://www.jesssmith.com
Year Founded: 1943
Sales Range: $10-24.9 Million
Emp.: 45
Agricultural Services
N.A.I.C.S.: 424590
Ernst D. Schroeder Sr. *(Chm)*
Ernst D. Schroeder Jr. *(CEO)*

JESS3
1707 L St NW, Washington, DC 20036
Tel.: (571) 213-4308
Web Site: http://www.jess3.com
Year Founded: 2008
Sales Range: $1-9.9 Million
Emp.: 20
Advetising Agency
N.A.I.C.S.: 541810
Jesse Thomas *(Founder & CEO)*

JESSE ENGINEERING COMPANY
1840 Marine View Dr, Tacoma, WA 98422-4106
Tel.: (253) 922-7433
Web Site:
http://www.jesseengineering.com
Rev.: $22,730,525
Emp.: 130
Fabricated Structural Metal
N.A.I.C.S.: 332312
Darrell Jesse *(Owner)*
Jeff Gellert *(Pres)*
Gust Erickson *(Mgr-Sls)*
Phil Jesse *(Chief Engr)*

JESSIE TRICE COMMUNITY HEALTH CENTER, INC.
5607 NW 27th Ave, Miami, FL 33142
Tel.: (305) 805-1700   FL
Web Site: http://www.jtchc.org
Year Founded: 1967
Sales Range: $10-24.9 Million
Emp.: 265
Community Health Care Services
N.A.I.C.S.: 621498
Irene Taylor-Wooten *(Vice Chm)*
Annie R. Neasman *(Pres & CEO)*
Deborah George *(Chief Clinical Officer & Exec VP)*
Deborah Rice-Lamar *(Chief HR Officer & VP)*
Fabian Thurston *(COO & Exec VP)*
Luckner Denord *(Chief Strategy Officer & Sr VP)*
Sammy King *(CFO)*

JESSUP AUTO PLAZA
68 111 E Palm Canyon Dr, Cathedral City, CA 92234
Tel.: (760) 904-0525
Web Site:
http://www.jessupautoplaza.com
Year Founded: 1938
Sales Range: $25-49.9 Million
Emp.: 100
New Car Retailer
N.A.I.C.S.: 441110

Andrew T. Jessup *(Chm)*
Andy Jessup *(Pres)*
Dan Jessup *(Gen Mgr)*

JESSUP MANUFACTURING COMPANY, INC.
2815 W Route 120, McHenry, IL 60051
Tel.: (815) 385-6650
Web Site: http://www.jessupmfg.com
Year Founded: 1956
Sales Range: $10-24.9 Million
Emp.: 50
Non-Slip Material & Film Mfr
N.A.I.C.S.: 325992
Robert A. Jessup *(Pres)*

JESUP FURNITURE OUTLET INC.
167 SE Broad St, Jesup, GA 31546
Tel.: (912) 427-7727
Web Site:
http://www.jesupfurnitureoutlet.com
Rev.: $10,500,517
Emp.: 22
Furniture Retailer
N.A.I.C.S.: 449110
Roy Davis *(Partner)*

JET ADVERTISING
100 N Sepulveda Blvd Ste 1700, El Segundo, CA 90245
Tel.: (310) 649-3820
Web Site:
http://www.ymtvacations.com
Year Founded: 1967
Sales Range: $1-9.9 Million
Emp.: 10
In House Advertising Agency
N.A.I.C.S.: 541810
Oliver Milton *(Gen Mgr & Media Planner)*

JET BOX CO., INC.
1822 Thunderbird Dr, Troy, MI 48084-5479
Tel.: (248) 362-1260
Sales Range: $10-24.9 Million
Emp.: 26
Corrugated & Solid Fiber Box Mfr
N.A.I.C.S.: 322211
Kathryn L. Woch *(Pres)*
Wayne Davidson *(Gen Mgr)*
Mickey Dejonghe *(Mgr)*
Robert L. Zardus *(VP)*

JET EDGE INTERNATIONAL LLC
16700C Roscoe Blvd, Van Nuys, CA 91406
Tel.: (818) 442-0096
Web Site: http://www.flyjetedge.com
Year Founded: 2011
N.A.I.C.S.:
Bill Papariella *(CEO)*
Michael Sanders *(CFO)*

Subsidiaries:

JetSelect, LLC   (1)
4130 E 5th Ave, Columbus, OH 43219
Tel.: (614) 338-4380
Web Site: http://www.jetselectaviation.com
Nonscheduled Air Transportation Services
N.A.I.C.S.: 481219

JET EXPRESS INC.
4518 Webster St, Dayton, OH 45414
Tel.: (937) 274-7033
Web Site:
http://www.jetexpressinc.com
Sales Range: $25-49.9 Million
Emp.: 60
Trucking Service
N.A.I.C.S.: 484110

Jet Express Inc.—(Continued)

Kevin W. Burch (Pres)
Archie Crawford (Dir-Ops)
Roger Atkinson (VP)

JET FOOD STORES OF GEORGIA INC
1106 S Harris St, Sandersville, GA 31082
Tel.: (478) 552-2588
Web Site:
http://www.jetfoodstores.com
Rev.: $32,300,000
Emp.: 550
Convenience Store
N.A.I.C.S.: 445131
Charles E. Turner (Pres)
Mike Beckworth (Controller)
Chuck Hancock (VP)

JET GAS CORPORATION
1808 Hwy 16, Houghton, IA 52631
Tel.: (319) 469-4321
Web Site: http://www.interl.net
Year Founded: 1952
Sales Range: $25-49.9 Million
Emp.: 40
Petroleum Products Sales
N.A.I.C.S.: 424710
Rob Phipps (Supvr-Store)
Laurie Riddle (Asst Mgr)

JET INC.
1500 Center Cir Dr, Downers Grove, IL 60515
Tel.: (630) 932-9000
Web Site: http://www.imaginejet.net
Sales Range: $25-49.9 Million
Emp.: 212
Color Lithography
N.A.I.C.S.: 323111
George Bogdanovic (CEO)

JET INTERNATIONAL CO., LLC
1811 Elmdale Ave, Glenview, IL 60026
Tel.: (847) 657-8666
Web Site:
http://www.jetinternational.com
Rev.: $14,000,000
Emp.: 15
Aircraft Parts Distr
N.A.I.C.S.: 423860
Alexander Farrell (VP-Airline Sls)
Neal Mehlman (CFO)
Jeff Crosby (VP-Trading)

JET SPECIALTY, INC.
211 Market Ave, Boerne, TX 78006
Tel.: (210) 408-0905
Web Site: http://www.jetspecialty.com
Rev.: $61,500,000
Emp.: 116
Operate Oil Field Supply Houses
N.A.I.C.S.: 213112
Ted Williams (CFO)

JET STAR INC.
10825 Andrade Dr, Zionsville, IN 46077
Tel.: (317) 873-4222
Web Site: http://www.jetstarinc.com
Sales Range: $10-24.9 Million
Emp.: 120
Jet Fuel Transport Services
N.A.I.C.S.: 484220
Greg Patchett (CFO-Risk Mgmt)
Ray Rothenberger (CIO)

JET STREAM INTERNATIONAL
931 Summit Ave, Niles, OH 44446
Tel.: (330) 505-9988
Web Site: http://www.jetstr.com
Year Founded: 2002
Sales Range: $10-24.9 Million

Emp.: 38
Hanging & Supporting Components for Plumbing & Electrical Systems
N.A.I.C.S.: 335999
Jim Constas (Mgr-Ops)

JET-PEP INC.
9481 Hwy 278 E, Holly Pond, AL 35083
Tel.: (256) 796-2237
Year Founded: 1981
Gasoline Stations with Convenience Stores Owner & Operator
N.A.I.C.S.: 457110
Robert G. Norris (Pres)
Casey Hellums (Engr)
Kris Pierce (Engr)

JETAVIVA
2800 28th St Ste 306, Santa Monica, CA 90405
Tel.: (310) 907-5099
Web Site: http://www.jetaviva.com
Year Founded: 2006
Sales Range: $1-9.9 Million
Emp.: 15
Aircraft Dealers
N.A.I.C.S.: 441227
David Lee (VP-Pilatus PC-12)
Marcio Lucchese (Mgr-Phenom Acceptance & Delivery)
Brian Singer (Controller)
Dustin Cordier (Mng Partner)
Robin Eissler (COO)

JETPOOL, LLC
4690 First Flight Dr, Charlotte, NC 28208
Tel.: (704) 359-4674
Web Site: http://www.flyjetpool.com
Sales Range: $1-9.9 Million
Emp.: 14
Air Charter Services
N.A.I.C.S.: 481219
Scott Voglesonger (Dir-Safety)
Ryan Stone (Chm)
Paul Sameit (Pres & CFO)
Ronald Dietz (Dir-Maintenance)
Julie Layne (Dir-Charter)
Rick Wade (Mgr-Scheduling)

JETRO CASH & CARRY ENTERPRISES, LLC
15-24 132nd St, College Point, NY 11356-2440
Tel.: (718) 762-8700   DE
Web Site: http://www.jetro.com
Year Founded: 1996
Sales Range: $75-99.9 Million
Emp.: 100
Grocery Store & Food Service Supplies Whslr
N.A.I.C.S.: 424410
Richard Kirschner (COO & VP)

Subsidiaries:

Jetro Cash & Carry   (1)
2041 NW 12th Ave, Miami, FL 33127-4505   (100%)
Tel.: (305) 324-4414
Web Site: http://www.jetro.com
Wholesale Grocers; Foodservice Suppliers
N.A.I.C.S.: 424470
Robert Acevedo (Gen Mgr)

Jetro Cash & Carry   (1)
700 Pattison Ave, Philadelphia, PA 19148-5313
Tel.: (215) 334-2100
Web Site: http://www.jetroord.com
Sales Range: $25-49.9 Million
Wholesale Grocers, Foodservice Suppliers
N.A.I.C.S.: 424470
Stanley Fleishman (CEO)

Jetro Cash & Carry   (1)
2300 E 60th St, Long Beach, CA 90805   (100%)

Tel.: (562) 634-6771
Web Site: http://www.jetro.com
Sales Range: $25-49.9 Million
Emp.: 80
Wholesale Grocers; Foodservice Suppliers
N.A.I.C.S.: 424470
Adrian Padilla (Gen Mgr)

Restaurant Depot, LLC   (1)
15-24 132nd St, College Point, NY 11356-2440
Tel.: (718) 939-6400
Web Site: http://www.restaurantdepot.com
Sales Range: $50-74.9 Million
Restaurant Food & Supplies Whslr
N.A.I.C.S.: 424410
Stanley Fleishman (CEO)
Brian Emmert (CFO)

JETS MRO, LLC
5555 Apollo Dr., Dallas, TX 5237
Tel.: (214) 305-9247
Web Site: https://jetsmro.com
Transportation Services
N.A.I.C.S.: 481219

Subsidiaries:

Britt Metal Processing, Inc.   (1)
15800 NW 49th Ave, Hialeah, FL 33014
Tel.: (305) 621-5200
Web Site: http://www.brittmetal.com
Sales Range: $1-9.9 Million
Emp.: 35
Electronic & Precision Equipment Repair & Maintenance
N.A.I.C.S.: 811210

JETSON TV & APPLIANCE CENTERS
4145 S Federal Hwy, Fort Pierce, FL 34982
Tel.: (772) 464-7050
Web Site:
http://www.jetsonline.com
Sales Range: $25-49.9 Million
Emp.: 122
Household Appliance Stores
N.A.I.C.S.: 449210
John T. Jetson (CEO)
Betty Flynn (CFO & Treas)
John E. Thofner (Pres)

JETT MECHANICAL INC.
9031 Euclid Ave, Manassas, VA 20110-5345
Tel.: (703) 256-4884
Web Site:
http://www.jettmechanical.com
Sales Range: $10-24.9 Million
Emp.: 15
Plumbing Contractor
N.A.I.C.S.: 238220
David Jett (Pres & CEO)

JETTA CORPORATION
425 Centennial Blvd, Edmond, OK 73013
Tel.: (405) 340-6661
Web Site: http://www.jettacorp.com
Sales Range: $10-24.9 Million
Emp.: 50
Plastic Bath & Laundry Tub Mfr
N.A.I.C.S.: 326191
Scott Kraddict (CFO)
Lea Sevier (Mgr-Mktg & Customer Support)

JETTA PRODUCTION COMPANY, INC.
777 Taylor St P1-D Fort Worth Club Tower, Fort Worth, TX 76102-4919
Tel.: (817) 335-1179
Web Site:
http://www.jettaoperating.com
Sales Range: $25-49.9 Million
Emp.: 130
Oil & Gas Production
N.A.I.C.S.: 213112

Gregory A. Bird (Pres & CEO)
Catherine V. Severin (VP-Admin & Corp Comm)
Gordon Roberts (Sr VP-Eastern US)
John T. Jarrett (CFO & VP)
Kurt Pizalate (VP-Drilling Ops)
Marsha Davee (VP-HR)
Michael S. McKee (VP-Geology)
Michael F. Richardson (Exec VP)
Shannon Nichols (VP-Land)

JETTON ELECTRIC INC.
1211 Carroll Rd, Paragould, AR 72450-3883
Tel.: (870) 240-8008
Web Site: http://www.jettoncon.com
Year Founded: 1972
Sales Range: $10-24.9 Million
Emp.: 55
Electrical Wiring Services
N.A.I.C.S.: 238210
Andrew Berner (Owner)

JEUNESSE GLOBAL LLC
650 Douglas Ave, Altamonte Springs, FL 32714-2593
Tel.: (407) 788-3614
Web Site:
http://www.jeunesseglobal.com
Cosmetic & Nutritional Product Mfr
N.A.I.C.S.: 325411
Randy Ray (Co-Founder & CEO)
Wendy Lewis (Co-Founder & COO)
Rob Dawson (Chief Legal Officer)
Scott A. Lewis (Chief Visionary Officer)
Ryan Ogden (CFO)
Mark Patterson (CMO)
Dennis Windsor (Chief Dev Officer)
A. K. Khalil (Pres-Field Dev-Global)

JEUNIQUE INTERNATIONAL INC.
1875 Century Park E Ste 1970, Los Angeles, CA 90067-2520
Tel.: (909) 598-8598
Year Founded: 1959
Rev.: $23,800,000
Emp.: 75
Health & Beauty Products
N.A.I.C.S.: 325411
Mulford J. Nobbs (Pres)
Theresa Goodwin (Controller)
Phyills Kruckenberg (VP)

JEWELERS INC.
2400 Western Ave, Las Vegas, NV 89102
Tel.: (702) 382-7411
Web Site:
http://www.thejewelers.com
Sales Range: $25-49.9 Million
Emp.: 60
Jewelry, Precious Stones & Precious Metals
N.A.I.C.S.: 458310
Mordichai Yerushalmi (Pres)
Benjamin Yerushalmi (CFO)

JEWELERS MUTUAL INSURANCE COMPANY
24 Jewelers Park Dr, Neenah, WI 54956-3702
Tel.: (920) 725-4326   WI
Web Site:
http://www.jewelersmutual.com
Year Founded: 1913
Sales Range: $25-49.9 Million
Emp.: 180
Jewelry Insurance Services
N.A.I.C.S.: 524126
Darwin Copeman (CEO)
Chris Hartrich (VP-HR & Org Dev)
Nancee A. James (Chm)
Mike Alexander (Sr VP-Comml Lines)

Kathryn Sieman *(CFO & Treas)*
Scott Murphy *(Pres & CEO)*
Larry Spicer *(VP-Loss Prevention & Risk Mgmt Svcs)*

JEWELL GRAIN COMPANY
8049 Independence Rd, Jewell, OH 43530
Tel.: (419) 497-2101
Web Site: http://www.jewellgrain.com
Sales Range: $10-24.9 Million
Emp.: 13
Provider of Farm Supplies
N.A.I.C.S.: 424510
Brent Petersen *(Gen Mgr)*

JEWELL INSTRUMENTS, LLC
850 Perimeter Rd, Manchester, NH 03103
Tel.: (603) 669-6400   DE
Web Site:
http://www.jewellinstruments.com
Panel Meters, Avionics Components, Inertial Sensors & Precision Solenoids Mfr & Distr
N.A.I.C.S.: 335313
Carlo Carluccio *(CEO)*
Steve Morin *(Controller & CFO)*

JEWELRY REPAIR ENTER-PRISES, INC.
1515 S Center Hwy Ste 412, Delray Beach, FL 33432
Tel.: (561) 330-6060
Web Site:
http://www.fastfixfranchise.com
Year Founded: 1984
Sales Range: $50-74.9 Million
Emp.: 825
Jewelry & Watch Repairs Franchisor
N.A.I.C.S.: 533110
Yvette Rivera *(Dir-Franchise Rels)*
Pia Terol *(Dir-Mktg)*
Mark Fineman *(Dir-Design & Construction)*
Jerry Weper *(CEO)*

JEWELRY TO YOUR DOOR-STEP
1747 Canyon Dr, Los Angeles, CA 90028
Tel.: (323) 461-4528
Web Site:
http://www.jewelrytoyourdoor step.com
Rev.: $10,100,000
Emp.: 93
Jewelry Stores
N.A.I.C.S.: 458310
Jim Mangiamele *(VP)*
Karen Mangiamele *(Pres)*

JEWETT CITY SAVINGS BANK
111 Main St, Jewett City, CT 06351
Tel.: (860) 376-4444
Web Site: http://www.jcsbank.com
Year Founded: 1873
Rev.: $11,843,000
Assets: $283,805,000
Liabilities: $236,918,000
Net Worth: $46,887,000
Earnings: $1,816,000
Fiscal Year-end: 12/31/18
Banking Services
N.A.I.C.S.: 522180
Diana L. Rose *(COO, Sec & Sr VP)*
Ernest Muccio *(Chief Credit Officer & Sr VP)*
Louis J. Demicco *(Chm)*
Gary W. Peloquin *(Vice Chm)*
James A. McDonald *(CFO & Sr VP)*
Sandra Y. Boucher *(Officer-Retail Banking & VP)*
Peter Cannon *(Officer-BSA & VP-Compliance & Security)*

Dianne Chiavarini *(Officer-Bus Dev, Asst VP & Branch Mgr-Plainfield)*
Jenny M. Driscoll *(Asst VP & Mgr-Loan Originations)*
Kevin J. Goyen *(VP & Dir-IT)*
Tomasz E. Kosek *(VP)*
Lisa Legler *(Asst VP & Branch Mgr-Dayville)*
Katherine E. Quackenbush *(VP & Dir-HR)*
Terrill A. Sabourin *(Officer-eBanking & VP-Ops)*
Jane M. Watson *(Asst VP & Mgr-Acctg)*
Melissa Waite *(Officer-Trng, Asst VP & Branch Mgr)*
William Couture *(Officer-Bus Loan & VP)*
Michael Alberts *(Officer-Comml Loan & VP)*
Karen Brodeur *(Asst VP)*

JEWETT ORTHOPAEDIC CLINIC, P.A.
1285 Orange Ave, Winter Park, FL 32789
Tel.: (407) 647-2287
Web Site: http://www.jewettortho.com
Sales Range: $1-9.9 Million
Emp.: 99
Orthopaedic Services
N.A.I.C.S.: 621111
Jeanetta Lawrence *(COO)*
T. J. Black *(Dir-IT)*
C. Chad Wiggins *(CEO)*

JEWISH CHILD & FAMILY SER-VICES
216 W Jackson Blvd Ste 800, Chicago, IL 60606
Tel.: (312) 357-4800   IL
Web Site: http://www.jcfs.org
Year Founded: 1893
Sales Range: $25-49.9 Million
Emp.: 498
Child & Family Care Services
N.A.I.C.S.: 624190
Susan Schulman *(Sec)*
Toby Bernstein *(Vice Chm)*
Linda Kellough *(Vice Chm)*
Neil Posner *(Chm)*
Karen Levine *(Vice Chm)*
Milton Zimmerman *(Chm)*
Alan Alport *(Treas)*
Elizabeth Taggart *(Dir-Mktg & Comm)*
Michelle Jackson *(VP & Officer-HR)*
Vincent Everson *(CFO & VP)*
Stacey Shor *(Chief Dev Officer & VP)*
Howard Sitron *(Pres & CEO)*

JEWISH COMMUNITY CENTER OF SAN FRANCISCO
3200 California St, San Francisco, CA 94118
Tel.: (415) 292-1200   CA
Web Site: http://www.jccsf.org
Year Founded: 1877
Sales Range: $25-49.9 Million
Emp.: 687
Community Welfare Services
N.A.I.C.S.: 624190
Craig Salgado *(COO)*
Adrian Breitfeld *(CFO)*
Susan Lowenberg *(Treas)*
Samuel Klein *(Chief Jewish Officer)*

JEWISH COMMUNITY CEN-TERS OF GREATER BOSTON, INC.
333 Nahanton St, Newton, MA 02459
Tel.: (617) 558-6522   MA
Web Site: http://www.bostonjcc.org
Year Founded: 1972
Sales Range: $10-24.9 Million
Emp.: 1,121

Jewish Community Services
N.A.I.C.S.: 624190
Betsy Jacobs *(COO & VP)*
Louis J. Grossman *(Treas)*
Mark Sokoll *(Pres)*

JEWISH COMMUNITY FOUN-DATION OF GREATER KAN-SAS CITY
5801 W 115th St Ste 104, Overland Park, KS 66211
Tel.: (913) 327-8245   KS
Web Site: http://www.jcfkc.org
Year Founded: 1959
Sales Range: $10-24.9 Million
Emp.: 8
Grantmaking Services
N.A.I.C.S.: 813211
Lauren Mattleman Hoopes *(Exec Dir)*
Alice Jacks Achtenberg *(VP)*
Edward Goldstein *(VP)*
David R. Goodman *(VP)*
Linda B. Lyon *(VP)*
Robert V. Palan *(Treas)*
Frank W. Lipsman *(VP)*
James M. Klein *(VP)*
Irvin V. Belzer *(Pres)*
Beatrice Fine *(Dir-Funder Svcs)*
Brooke Hardy *(Dir-Comm)*
Joshua Stein *(Dir-Fund Dev)*
Kevin Taylor *(CFO)*

JEWISH COMMUNITY FOUN-DATION OF SAN DIEGO
4950 Murphy Canyon Rd, San Diego, CA 92123
Tel.: (858) 279-2740   CA
Web Site: http://www.jcfsandiego.org
Year Founded: 1967
Sales Range: $75-99.9 Million
Emp.: 16
Grantmaking Services
N.A.I.C.S.: 813211
Josie Arellano *(Accountant)*
Jeremy Pearl *(CFO & Exec VP)*
Eli Landau *(Controller)*
Traci Serrano *(Dir-Donor Svcs & Mgr-HR)*
Beth Sirull *(Pres & CEO)*
Sharleen Wollach *(VP-Ops)*
Bryan Pepper *(VP-Philanthropy & Social Impact)*

JEWISH COMMUNITY SER-VICES
5750 Park Heights Ave, Baltimore, MD 21215
Tel.: (410) 466-9200   MD
Web Site: http://www.jcsbaltimore.org
Year Founded: 1942
Sales Range: $10-24.9 Million
Emp.: 265
Community Support Services
N.A.I.C.S.: 624190
Joseph Honsberger *(Sr Mgr-Therapy Svcs)*
Jacki Post Ashkin *(Sr Mgr-Mktg & Dev)*
Ruth Klein *(Dir-Behavioral Health Svcs & Compliance)*
Joan Roth *(Chief Admin Officer-Budget & Admin)*
Alison J. Magat *(VP)*
Jonathan N. Davidov *(First VP)*
Michael S. Saxon *(Treas)*
Joan Grayson Cohen *(Exec Dir)*
Elaine Kitt *(Sr Mgr-Svc Coordination)*

JEWISH COUNCIL FOR YOUTH SERVICES
180 W Washington St Ste 1100, Chicago, IL 60602
Tel.: (312) 726-8891   IL
Web Site: http://www.jcys.org
Year Founded: 1907

Sales Range: $10-24.9 Million
Emp.: 597
Child & Youth Care Services
N.A.I.C.S.: 624110
Kevin Faulkner *(Dir-Property Mgmt)*
Molly Harlow Hill *(Dir-Dev)*
Sid Singer *(COO)*

JEWISH FAMILY & CHIL-DREN'S SERVICE
1430 Main St, Waltham, MA 02451
Tel.: (781) 647-5327   MA
Web Site: http://www.jfcsboston.org
Year Founded: 1922
Sales Range: $25-49.9 Million
Emp.: 897
Jewish Community Services
N.A.I.C.S.: 624190
Alan Jacobson *(Sr VP-Programs)*
Bruce Haskin *(CFO)*
Donna Magnasco *(Sr VP-HR)*
Ira Schor *(Sr VP-Ops)*
Beth Wynne *(Assoc Exec Dir)*
Marla Meyers *(Exec Dir)*
Laura Robbins *(Chief Dev Officer)*
Miriam Seidenfeld *(CEO)*

JEWISH FAMILY AND CHIL-DREN'S SERVICES OF SAN FRANCISCO, THE PENIN-SULA, MARIN AND SONOMA COUNTIES
2150 Post St, San Francisco, CA 94115
Tel.: (415) 449-1200   CA
Web Site: http://www.jfcs.org
Year Founded: 1904
Sales Range: $25-49.9 Million
Emp.: 781
Child & Family Welfare Services
N.A.I.C.S.: 624190
Laura Jamieson *(CFO)*
Barbara Farber *(Dir-Dev)*
Richard Segal *(Treas)*
Scott C. Kay *(VP)*
Tammy Crown *(Sec)*
Ian Altman *(VP)*
James Shapiro *(VP)*
Luba Troyanovsky *(VP)*
Marina Tikhman *(Pres)*
Christine Coleman *(Dir-Mktg & Comm)*
Diana Klein *(Dir-Sonoma County Reg)*
Greg Murphy *(Dir-Facilities)*
Michael Berke *(Dir-Cleanerific)*
Nancy Masters *(Assoc Exec Dir)*
Traci Dobronravova *(Dir-Seniors At Home)*

JEWISH FAMILY SERVICE AS-SOCIATION OF CLEVELAND
The PDC Bldg 3659 S Green Rd Ste 322, Beachwood, OH 44122
Tel.: (216) 292-3999   OH
Web Site: http://www.jfsa-cleveland.org
Year Founded: 1907
Sales Range: $10-24.9 Million
Emp.: 628
Disability Assistance Services
N.A.I.C.S.: 624120
David Hlavac *(CFO & VP)*
Thomas Petersen *(Controller & Dir-Fin)*
Robert Bologa *(Sr Dir-HR)*

JEWISH FAMILY SERVICE OF LOS ANGELES
3580 Wilshire Blvd Ste 700l, Los Angeles, CA 90010
Tel.: (323) 761-8800   CA
Web Site: http://www.jfsla.org
Year Founded: 1854
Rev.: $47,076,146
Assets: $50,663,479
Liabilities: $6,383,839

Jewish Family Service of Los Angeles—(Continued)

Net Worth: $44,279,640
Earnings: $9,244,819
Emp.: 300
Fiscal Year-end: 06/30/19
Family Welfare Services
N.A.I.C.S.: 624190
Susie Forer Dehrey (Exec VP)
Josh Passman (Vice Chm-Resource Dev)
Tami Kupetz Stapf (Vice Chm-Resource Dev)
Stanley Kandel (Vice Chm-Programs)
Randy A. Magnin (Chm)
Colette Ament (Sec)
Amanda Bender (Dir-Grant Dev)
Michael Sidman (Dir-Comm)
Nancy Volpert (Dir-Pub Policy & Strategic Initiatives)
Joyce Williams (Dir-Volunteer Svcs & Trng)
Eli Veitzer (Pres & CEO)
Susie Forer-Dehrey (Exec VP)
David Felman (CFO)
Sylvia LaMalfa (Chief Program Officer & Sr VP-Programs & Svcs)
Dawn Wallace (Dir-HR)
Margaret Avineri (Sr Dir-Integrated Clinical Svcs & Quality Mgmt)
Karen Rosenthal (Sr Dir-Children & Family Svcs)
Fred Summers (Sr Dir-Nutrition, Transportation & SOVA Programs)
Meri Barkinskaya (Dir-IT)
Carol Bar-Or (Dir-Resource Dev)
Remy Bender (Dir-Resource Dev)
Susan Belgrade (Dir-Senior & Multipurpose Centers)

JEWISH FOUNDATION FOR GROUP HOMES
1500 E Jefferson St, Rockville, MD 20852
Tel.: (240) 283-6000   MD
Web Site: http://www.jfgh.org
Year Founded: 1983
Sales Range: $10-24.9 Million
Emp.: 215
Developmental Disability Assistance Services
N.A.I.C.S.: 623210
Deborah M. Fisher (Chief Initiatives Officer)
Vivian G. Bass (CEO)
Keith J. Danos (CFO)
Michele Lizear (Office Mgr)
LeyAna Crumpton (Dir-Svcs)
Denise Gomez (Dir-Programs)
Lew Fontek (Chief Dev Officer)
Samuel Kaplan (VP-Dev)
Carol West (VP-Programs)

JEWISH FUNDERS NETWORK
150 W 30th St Ste 900, New York, NY 10001
Tel.: (212) 726-0177   NY
Web Site: http://www.jfunders.org
Year Founded: 1994
Sales Range: $10-24.9 Million
Emp.: 14
Philanthropic Services
N.A.I.C.S.: 813211
Andres Spokoiny (Pres & CEO)
Judy Mann (COO)
Samantha Anderson (Sr Dir-Member Svcs)
Scott Casper (Office Mgr)
Angelica Berrie (Co-Chm)
Beth Klarman (Vice Chm)
Dorothy Tananbaum (Sec)
Douglas Bitonti Stewart (Treas)
Georgette Bennett (Co-Chm)
Larry Moses (Vice Chm)
Briana Holtzman (Dir-Teen Funders Network)

David Ezer (Sr Dir-Programs)
Elizabeth Gerber (Dir-Fin)
Emily Friedman-Novak (Program Mgr-Israel)
Maya Natan (Mgr-Projects & Activities-Israel)
Merav Fine (Mgr-Program & Member-to-Member Svcs)
Seth Chalmer (Mgr-Strategic & Digital Comm)

JEWISH HEALTHCARE CENTER
629 Salisbury St, Worcester, MA 01609
Tel.: (508) 798-8653   MA
Web Site: http://www.jewishhealthcarecenter.com
Year Founded: 1916
Sales Range: $10-24.9 Million
Emp.: 512
Medical Care Services
N.A.I.C.S.: 621511
Alan Yaffe (Pres)
Joel Greenberg (Treas)
Peter Herman (VP)
Philip Shwachman (Sec)
Steve Willens (CEO)

JEWISH HEALTHCARE FOUNDATION
650 Smithfield St Ste 2400, Pittsburgh, PA 15222
Tel.: (412) 594-2550   PA
Web Site: http://www.jhf.org
Year Founded: 1990
Sales Range: $10-24.9 Million
Emp.: 35
Grantmaking Services
N.A.I.C.S.: 813211
Louis Plung (Treas)
Debra L. Caplan (Sec)
Nancy L. Rackoff (Chm)
David Ehrenwerth (Vice Chm)
Karen Wolk Feinstein (Pres & CEO)

JEWISH HOME LIFECARE
120 W 106th St, New York, NY 10025
Tel.: (212) 870-5000
Web Site: http://www.jewishhome.org
Sales Range: $75-99.9 Million
Emp.: 900
Geriatric, Rehabilitative & Home Health Services
N.A.I.C.S.: 623312
Audrey Wathen (Sr VP-HR)
Elliot Hagler (CFO)
Tammy Marshall (Chief Experience Officer)
Jacob Victory (COO)
Gabrielle Genauer (Gen Counsel & VP)
Bruce Nathanson (Sr VP)
Elena Quevedo (Sr VP-Advancement)
Regina Melly (Sr VP-Bus Dev)
Elizabeth Weingast (VP-Clinical Excellence)
Nancy Stoddard (VP-IT)
Svetlana DeBellis (VP-Managed Care)

JEWISH HOME OF CINCINNATI
5467 Cedar Village Dr, Mason, OH 45040
Tel.: (513) 754-3100   OH
Web Site: http://www.cedarvillage.org
Year Founded: 1997
Sales Range: $10-24.9 Million
Emp.: 560
Lifecare Retirement Community Services
N.A.I.C.S.: 623311

Terron Cruey (Dir-HR)
Barb Reed (Chm)
Bob Applebaum (Asst Sec)
Debi Tyler (Dir-Rehabilitation)
Gail Davis (Dir-Health Care Admissions)
Gary Blachman (Chm)
Jim Ellis (Treas)
Karen Raitt (Dir-Facilities Svcs)
Mike Kriner (Sec)
Mike Mobley (COO)
Patti Heldman (Vice Chm)
Oscar Jarnicki (Pres & CEO)

JEWISH MUSEUM
1109 5th Ave 92nd St, New York, NY 10128
Tel.: (212) 423-3200   NY
Web Site: https://www.thejewishmuseum.org
Year Founded: 1952
Sales Range: $10-24.9 Million
Emp.: 215
Art Support Services
N.A.I.C.S.: 711310
Al Lazarte (Dir-Ops)
Linda Padawer (Dir-Special Events)
Robert A. Pruzan (Chm)
Ruth K. Beesch (Deputy Dir-Program Admin)
Jens Hoffmann (Dir-Special Exhibitions & Pub Programs)
Joseph Rorech (Deputy Dir-Fin & Admin)
Claudia Gould (Dir-Helen Goldsmith Menschel)
Cindy Caplan (Chief Counsel & Talent Officer)

JEWISH RENAISSANCE MEDICAL CENTER INC.
275 Hobart St, Perth Amboy, NJ 08861
Tel.: (732) 376-9333   NJ
Web Site: http://www.jrmc.us
Year Founded: 2001
Sales Range: $10-24.9 Million
Emp.: 188
Community Health Care Services
N.A.I.C.S.: 621498
Tonya Cook (Chief Dental Officer)
Nancy Tham (Chief Medical Officer)
Paul McCloud (CFO)
Janet White-Hunt (COO)
Mark Roberts (CEO)
Jaime Rivello (Dir-HR)

JEWISH SENIOR SERVICES OF FAIRFIELD COUNTY INC.
4200 Park Ave, Bridgeport, CT 06604
Tel.: (203) 365-6400   CT
Web Site: http://www.jseniors.org
Year Founded: 1967
Sales Range: $25-49.9 Million
Emp.: 933
Elder Care Services
N.A.I.C.S.: 623312
Kenneth I. Wirfel (Vice Chm)
Russell Beitman (Treas)
Jeffrey Radler (Chm)
Alan Phillips (Sec)
Andrew H. Banoff (Pres & CEO)
Larry Condon (Sr VP)
Linda Ciszkowski (Chief Admin Officer & VP)
Marge Nicolia (VP-Nursing Svcs)

JEWISH VOCATIONAL SERVICE AND EMPLOYMENT CENTER
216 W Jackson Blvd Ste 700, Chicago, IL 60606
Tel.: (312) 673-3400   IL
Web Site: http://www.jvschicago.org
Year Founded: 1910

Sales Range: $10-24.9 Million
Emp.: 163
Employment & Placement Services
N.A.I.C.S.: 561311
Howard Sitron (Exec Dir)
Janice Kaufman (Chief Dev Officer)
Vince Everson (CFO)

JEWISHCOLORADO
300 S Dahlia St Ste 300, Denver, CO 80246
Tel.: (303) 321-3399   CO
Web Site: http://www.jewishcolorado.org
Year Founded: 2005
Sales Range: $10-24.9 Million
Emp.: 37
Philanthropic Services
N.A.I.C.S.: 813211
Amy Toltz-Miller (Chm)
Carl Boymel (Dir-IT & Facilities)
David Fellows (CFO)
Dirk Bird (Chief Dev Officer)

JEZOWSKI & MARKEL CONTRACTORS INC.
749 N Poplar St, Orange, CA 92868
Tel.: (714) 978-2222
Web Site: http://www.jmcontractors.com
Year Founded: 1953
Sales Range: $10-24.9 Million
Emp.: 100
Concrete Work
N.A.I.C.S.: 238110
Leonard Michael Barth (CEO)
Dorothy DeStefano (Controller)

JFD ADVERTISING & PUBLIC RELATIONS, INC.
7402 N 56th St Ste 375, Tampa, FL 33617
Tel.: (813) 223-4545
Web Site: http://www.jfdadvertising.com
Year Founded: 2003
Sales Range: $1-9.9 Million
Advertising & Public Relations
N.A.I.C.S.: 541810
Karin Arden (Principal)

JG BLACK BOOK OF TRAVEL
350 7th Ave Ste 1104, New York, NY 10001
Tel.: (212) 967-5895
Web Site: http://www.jgblackbook.com
Year Founded: 2002
Rev.: $2,100,000
Emp.: 18
Marketing, Public Relations & Sales Services
N.A.I.C.S.: 541910
Cathy Courtney (Dir-Comm & Branding)
Jena Gardner (Pres & CEO)
Andrew Martell (Dir-Mktg)
David Corke (Dir-Indus Rels)
Jackie Cittone Magid (Exec Dir-The Bodhi Tree Foundation)
Karen Morris (Dir-Indus Rels-Aus)
Malcom MacFarlane (Mgr-Sls-UK)
Maureen Kim (VP-Indus Rels)
Richard Butler (Mgr-Sls-Australia)
Tania Popovic (Dir-Indus Rels-Latin America)
Tyler LaMont (Sr Dir-Indus Rels)
Whitney McCasland (Mgr-Sls)
Alexandra Avila (VP-Industry & Media Rels)
Yvette De Vries (Mng Dir)

JG MACLELLAN CONCRETE CO.
180 Phoenix Ave, Lowell, MA 01852

Tel.: (978) 458-1223
Rev.: $12,100,000
Emp.: 60
Ready Mixed Concrete
N.A.I.C.S.: 327320
David Pina (Asst Dir-Quality Control)
John G. Maclellan III (Pres)

JG MANAGEMENT SYSTEMS, INC.
336 Main St Ste 207, Grand Junction, CO 81501
Tel.: (970) 254-1354
Web Site: http://www.jgmsinc.com
Year Founded: 2001
Sales Range: $10-24.9 Million
Emp.: 50
Engineering Services for Government Agencies
N.A.I.C.S.: 541330
Jerome Gonzales (Pres & CEO)

JG SERVICE COMPANY
15632 El Prado Rd, Chino, CA 91710
Tel.: (909) 993-9393
Web Site: http://www.jgserviceco.com
Sales Range: $10-24.9 Million
Emp.: 65
Construction Engineering Services
N.A.I.C.S.: 541330
Jack Grothe (Pres)

JG TAX GROUP
1430 S Federal Hwy, Deerfield Beach, FL 33441
Tel.: (954) 531-1864
Web Site: http://www.jgtaxgroup.com
Year Founded: 2008
Sales Range: $1-9.9 Million
Emp.: 50
Tax Resolution Firm
N.A.I.C.S.: 523999
Jeffrey Galante (Co-Founder)
Marcia Hamm (Co-Founder)
Raymond Loo (Co-Founder)
Barbara Galante (Co-Founder)

JGB INDUSTRIES, INC.
1310 Rosemeath, Richmond, VA 23230-4516
Tel.: (804) 358-0481
Web Site:
    http://www.bakerequipment.com
Year Founded: 1918
Sales Range: $25-49.9 Million
Emp.: 150
Holding Company; Truck & Bus Hydraulics
N.A.I.C.S.: 441330
Ann Dodd (CFO)
Joseph Glen Baker Jr. (Chm)

JGB VENTURES INC.
3100 Monticello Ave Ste 600, Dallas, TX 75205
Tel.: (214) 515-7000
Sales Range: $25-49.9 Million
Emp.: 60
Real Estate Agents & Managers
N.A.I.C.S.: 531210
Joseph G. Beard (Pres)
Ken Carlson (CFO)

Subsidiaries:

Westdale Asset Management Inc.   (1)
3100 Monticello Ave, Dallas, TX 75205
Tel.: (214) 515-7000
Web Site: http://www.westdale.com
Sales Range: $25-49.9 Million
Emp.: 100
Real Estate Agents & Managers
N.A.I.C.S.: 531210
Joseph G. Beard (Founder, Pres & CEO)
Evan Griffiths (COO)
Cindi Scoggins (Exec VP-Multifamily)
Jeff Allen (Exec VP-Comml)

Kevin Jennings (Mng Principal-Multifamily Acquisitions)
Frank Aevoet (Mng Principal-Distressed Debt Acquisitions)
Andrew Schmeltekopf (Mng Principal-Distressed Debt Acquisitions)

JGEAR
653 Triangle Rd, Fond Du Lac, WI 54935
Web Site:
    http://www.onlinebootstore.com
Year Founded: 1997
Sales Range: $1-9.9 Million
Emp.: 15
Footwear Retailer
N.A.I.C.S.: 458210
Shane Baganz (Owner)

JGS SUPERMARKETS INC.
10538 Rockaway Beach Blvd, Rockaway Park, NY 11694
Tel.: (845) 446-0061
Rev.: $28,000,000
Emp.: 7
Supermarkets, Chain
N.A.I.C.S.: 445110

JH BIOTECH, INC.
4951 Olivas Park Dr, Ventura, CA 93003
Tel.: (805) 650-8933
Web Site: http://www.jhbiotech.com
Year Founded: 1987
Sales Range: $10-24.9 Million
Emp.: 62
Fertilizer Mfr
N.A.I.C.S.: 325314
Monica Cheng (Office Mgr)

JH GLOBAL SERVICES, INC.
378 Neely Ferry Rd, Simpsonville, SC 29680
Tel.: (864) 297-8833
Web Site: http://www.starev.com
Year Founded: 2003
Sales Range: $10-24.9 Million
Emp.: 31
Transportation Equipment Supplier
N.A.I.C.S.: 423860
Jane Zhang (CEO)
Jun Hu (Pres)
Bob Weist (VP-Mfg & Technical Support)
Joe Wallington (VP-Sls & Mktg)
Michael Alexander (Sr VP-Market Engagement-Global)

JH KELLY LLC
821 3rd Ave, Longview, WA 98632
Tel.: (360) 423-5510
Web Site: http://www.jhkelly.com
Year Founded: 1923
Sales Range: $250-299.9 Million
Emp.: 1,000
General Mechanical & Industrial Contractors
N.A.I.C.S.: 238220
Mason Evans (Pres)
Dan Evans (Chm)
Terry Major (Sr VP)
Robert Harris (VP)
Lisa Ulrich (VP)
Craig Yabui (VP)
Paul Furth (CFO & VP)
Willy McOmie (VP & Dir-Safety)

Subsidiaries:

Seven Sisters Inc.   (1)
613 Sunset Park Dr, Sedro Woolley, WA 98284
Tel.: (360) 856-0842
Web Site: http://www.sevensisters.com
Rev.: $11,800,000
Emp.: 75
Electrical Contractor
N.A.I.C.S.: 238210

Nancy K. Williams (Pres)
Christine Thompson (VP)
Robert C. Stuart (Project Mgr)

JH PARTNERS LLC
451 Jackson St, San Francisco, CA 94111-1615
Tel.: (415) 364-0300
Web Site: http://www.jhpartners.com
Year Founded: 1986
Sales Range: $25-49.9 Million
Emp.: 9
Private Equity Investment Firm
N.A.I.C.S.: 523999
John C. Hansen (Pres)
Michael J. John (Partner)

Subsidiaries:

AmeriMark Direct, LLC   (1)
6864 Engle Rd, Cleveland, OH 44130
Tel.: (847) 748-2201
Web Site: https://www.amerimark.com
Sales Range: $50-74.9 Million
Direct Marketing; Women's Apparel; Cosmetics & Fragrances; Jewelry, Watches & Accessories; Health Related Merchandise
N.A.I.C.S.: 541860
Gareth Giesler (Chm & CEO)
Louis Giesler (Pres)
Diane Huzar (Exec VP)

Subsidiary (Domestic):

Harriet Carter Gifts, Inc.   (2)
425 Stump Rd, North Wales, PA 19454
Tel.: (215) 361-5100
Web Site: http://www.harrietcarter.com
Household Accessories & Gifts Mail Order
N.A.I.C.S.: 459420
George Feenie (Dir-Ops)
Lowell Bergey (CTO & CIO)
Mary Norton (Mgr-Mail List)

Chef's Catalogue, Inc.   (1)
5070 Centennial Blvd, Colorado Springs, CO 80919-2402
Tel.: (719) 272-2700
Web Site: http://www.chefscatalog.com
Sales Range: $25-49.9 Million
Online & Mail Order Kitchen Equipment
N.A.I.C.S.: 423620

JH ROSE LOGISTICS INC.
4950 Avenida creel, Santa Teresa, NM 92882-1642
Tel.: (915) 581-7300
Web Site: http://www.jhrose.com
Specialized Freight Trucking; Long-Distance
N.A.I.C.S.: 484230
Dean Genova (Mgr)

Subsidiaries:

Stagecoach Cartage & Distribution, LLC.   (1)
7167 Chino Dr, El Paso, TX 79915
Tel.: (915) 779-8315
Web Site:
    http://www.stagecoachcartage.com
Freight Forwarding
N.A.I.C.S.: 488510
Scott Mclaughlin (Pres)
Manny Roman (Mgr-Safety)

JH SERVICES INC.
1401 Hwy 82 W, Tifton, GA 31793
Tel.: (229) 382-6021
Sales Range: $10-24.9 Million
Emp.: 7
Family Restaurant Chain
N.A.I.C.S.: 722511
Dallas Hunt (CEO)

JH TECHNOLOGIES INC.
213 Hammond Ave, Fremont, CA 94539
Tel.: (408) 436-6336
Web Site:
    http://www.jhtechnologies.com
Sales Range: $10-24.9 Million
Emp.: 20

Radio & Television Equipment & Parts
N.A.I.C.S.: 423490
John Hubacz (Pres & CEO)
Shawn Evans (Acct Mgr)

JH&A ADVERTISING INC.
2312 Western Trl Ste 303C, Austin, TX 78745
Tel.: (512) 444-0716   TX
Web Site:
    http://www.jhaadvertising.com
Sales Range: $10-24.9 Million
Emp.: 15
Advetising Agency
N.A.I.C.S.: 541810
John Hamm (Owner & Pres)
Patrick Cline (VP-Austin)

JHB INC.
608 Adams St NE, Albuquerque, NM 87110
Tel.: (505) 268-4123
Rev.: $11,300,000
Emp.: 6
Independent Supermarket
N.A.I.C.S.: 445110

JHC STRUCTURES CORPORATION
Carr 1 Km 33.3, Caguas, PR 00725
Tel.: (787) 653-3010
Rev.: $11,026,747
Emp.: 31
Single-Family Housing Design & Construction Services
N.A.I.C.S.: 236115
Jose Hernandez Castroded (Pres)

JHM ENTERPRISES INC.
60 Pointe Cir, Greenville, SC 29615
Tel.: (864) 232-9944
Web Site: http://www.jhmhotels.com
Year Founded: 1973
Sales Range: $50-74.9 Million
Emp.: 800
Motel, Franchised
N.A.I.C.S.: 721110
Jayanti P. Rama (Vice Chm)
Manhar P. Rama (Principal)
Dharmendra J. Rama (Pres)
Hasmukh P. Rama (Chm & CEO)
Heather Meadors (Dir-Community Rels)
Jason Hope (Dir-Integrated Mktg)
Daniel Hart (Dir-Legal Svcs)
Donald J. Curotto (Gen Counsel)
Marie Ennabili (Reg Dir-Sls)
Tim Morrey (VP & Controller)
Jay Burnett (VP-Real Estate)
Michael Smith (VP-Sls & Mktg)
Luke W. Finlay III (CFO)

JHM FINANCIAL GROUP, LLC
1266 E Main St Ste 601, Stamford, CT 06902
Tel.: (203) 348-2644   CT
Web Site: https://groupjhm.com
Year Founded: 1997
Real Estate Investment, Development & Construction Services
N.A.I.C.S.: 541990
John H. McClutchy Jr. (Owner & Pres)
Todd McClutchy (Gen Mgr)

JHM RESEARCH & DEVELOPMENT INC.
1110 Bonifant St Ste 500, Silver Spring, MD 20910
Tel.: (301) 589-4000
Web Site: http://www.jhmrad.com
Year Founded: 1987
Sales Range: $75-99.9 Million
Emp.: 130

JHM Research & Development Inc.—(Continued)
Data Management, Document Conversion & IT Services
N.A.I.C.S.: 541513
Elizabeth Goodwill *(Dir-IT)*
Marvin Senter *(VP-Bus Dev)*
John H. Macklin *(Owner & Pres)*

JHNA, INC.
2111 Eisenhower Ave Ste 201, Alexandria, VA 22314
Tel.: (571) 388-2810
Web Site: http://www.jhna.com
Year Founded: 2001
Technical Consulting Services
N.A.I.C.S.: 541690
Ian Northrop *(CEO)*

Subsidiaries:

Technology Security Associates, Inc. (1)
22685 3 Notch Rd Ste E, California, MD 20619-3045
Tel.: (301) 866-0295
Web Site: http://www.thetsateam.com
Engineeering Services
N.A.I.C.S.: 541330
Thomas H. Jarboe *(Pres & CEO)*

JHOC INC.
323 Cash Memorial Blvd, Forest Park, GA 30297-2667
Tel.: (404) 675-1950
Web Site:
http://www.premiertransportation.com
Year Founded: 1991
Sales Range: $10-24.9 Million
Emp.: 85
Trucking Service
N.A.I.C.S.: 484121
Joseph T. Hughes *(Chm & CEO)*
Tom Rowan *(Controller)*

JHS INC.
7 Schiber Ct, Maryville, IL 62062
Tel.: (618) 288-7982
Web Site:
http://www.jansadvantage.com
Sales Range: $1-9.9 Million
Emp.: 125
Greeting Cards
N.A.I.C.S.: 459420
Don L. Tschannen Jr. *(Pres)*

JHT, INC.
2710 Discovery Dr Ste 100, Orlando, FL 32826
Tel.: (407) 381-7797
Web Site: http://www.jht.com
Year Founded: 1990
Sales Range: $10-24.9 Million
Emp.: 250
Interactive Training Services
N.A.I.C.S.: 611430
Carla Holoman *(COO)*
Millie Roman *(VP-Pur)*
Tiffany Sanders *(Chief Mktg Officer)*
Matt Robinson *(Sr VP-Bus Dev)*
James E. Jardon II *(CEO)*

JIANGSU ROYAL HOME USA, INC.
13451 S Point Blvd, Charlotte, NC 28273
Tel.: (704) 542-2304
Sales Range: $10-24.9 Million
Emp.: 8
Home Furnishing Whslr
N.A.I.C.S.: 423220
Lei Huang *(Pres)*
Kathy O. Dayvault *(Pres)*
Joey Plummer *(Dir-Supply Chain)*

JILCO EQUIPMENT LEASING CO., INC.
377 Half Acre Rd, Cranbury, NJ 08512
Tel.: (609) 655-5001
Web Site: http://www.jilco.com
Rev.: $10,000,000
Emp.: 25
Whslr & Leasing of Truck Trailers
N.A.I.C.S.: 423110
Steve G. Pavone *(Pres)*
Dawn Pavone *(Treas & Sec)*

JILL S. SCHWARTZ & ASSOCIATES, P.A.
655 W Morse Blvd Ste 212, Winter Park, FL 32789
Tel.: (407) 647-8911
Web Site:
http://www.schwartzlawfirm.net
Sales Range: $1-9.9 Million
Emp.: 17
Law firm
N.A.I.C.S.: 541110
Jill S. Schwartz *(Pres)*

JILL STUART INTERNATIONAL LLC
550 7th Ave, New York, NY 10018
Tel.: (212) 921-2600
Web Site: http://www.jillstuart.com
Sales Range: $1-9.9 Million
Emp.: 20
Women's Clothing Store Operations
N.A.I.C.S.: 458110
Ronald Curtis *(Pres)*

JIM BAIER FORD LINCOLN MERCURY DODGE CHRYSLER JEEP
5601 Avenue O, Fort Madison, IA 52627
Tel.: (319) 372-1253
Web Site: http://www.jimbaier.com
Year Founded: 1971
Sales Range: $10-24.9 Million
Emp.: 62
Car Whslr
N.A.I.C.S.: 441110
Jamie Baier *(Pres)*

JIM BALL PONTIAC-BUICK-GMC, INC.
3475 Southwestern Blvd, Orchard Park, NY 14127
Tel.: (716) 667-2000
Year Founded: 1966
Sales Range: $50-74.9 Million
Emp.: 190
Car Whslr
N.A.I.C.S.: 441110
Robert Basil *(Pres)*

JIM BARNARD CHEVROLET, INC.
7101 Buffalo Rd, Churchville, NY 14428
Tel.: (585) 293-2120
Web Site:
http://www.barnardchevy.com
Year Founded: 1972
Sales Range: $25-49.9 Million
Emp.: 50
New Car Retailer
N.A.I.C.S.: 441110
Allyn Barnard *(Principal)*

JIM BROWN CHEVROLET INC.
6877 Center St, Mentor, OH 44060
Tel.: (440) 255-5511
Web Site:
http://www.classicchevy.com
Rev.: $74,000,000
Emp.: 175
Automobiles, New & Used
N.A.I.C.S.: 441110
James Brown *(Pres)*

JIM BURKE AUTOMOTIVE INC.
1301 5th Ave N, Birmingham, AL 35203
Tel.: (205) 324-3371
Web Site: http://www.jimburke.com
Rev.: $117,613,368
Emp.: 200
Automobiles, New & Used
N.A.I.C.S.: 441110
Mark Levins *(CEO)*
Jim Burke Jr. *(Owner)*

JIM BUTLER AUTO GROUP, LLC
11157 Lindberg Bus Ctr, Saint Louis, MO 63123
Tel.: (314) 892-9600 MO
Web Site:
http://jimbutlerbodyshop.com
Year Founded: 1990
Sales Range: $100-124.9 Million
Emp.: 35
New & Used Car Dealers
N.A.I.C.S.: 441110
Don Barker *(Comptroller)*
James J. Butler Jr. *(Pres)*

JIM CAREY DISTRIBUTING COMPANY
726 W 26th Ave, Covington, LA 70433
Tel.: (985) 892-1234
Sales Range: $10-24.9 Million
Emp.: 49
Beer & Other Fermented Malt Liquors
N.A.I.C.S.: 424810
James C. Carey *(Pres)*

JIM CAUSLEY, INC.
38111 Gratiot Ave, Clinton Township, MI 48036-3592
Tel.: (586) 465-1281 DE
Web Site: http://www.jimcausley.com
Year Founded: 1957
Sales Range: $100-124.9 Million
Emp.: 117
Sales of Automobiles & Trucks
N.A.I.C.S.: 441110
Robert Causley *(Pres)*
Dan Weis *(Treas)*
Mike Elliott *(Mgr-Sls)*
David Gray *(Mgr-Ops)*

JIM CLICK, INC.
780 W Competition Rd, Tucson, AZ 85705
Tel.: (520) 884-4100
Web Site: http://www.jimclick.com
Sales Range: $150-199.9 Million
Emp.: 75
Sales of New & Used Cars
N.A.I.C.S.: 441110
Richard Nolen *(Controller)*
Susan Artav *(CFO)*
James H. Click Jr. *(Owner & Pres)*

Subsidiaries:

Jim Click Collision Center Eastside (1)
1441 S Wilmot Rd, Tucson, AZ 85711-6051
Tel.: (520) 747-2000
Web Site: http://www.jimclick.com
Sales Range: $100-124.9 Million
Auto Repair
N.A.I.C.S.: 811198
Sam Khayat *(Exec VP)*
Louis Serrano *(Gen Mgr)*
James H. Click Jr. *(Owner)*

Jim Click Ford, Lincoln-Mercury, Inc. (1)
1030 W Duval Mine Rd, Green Valley, AZ 85614-4900
Tel.: (520) 625-8262
Sales Range: $10-24.9 Million
Emp.: 43
Car Whslr
N.A.I.C.S.: 441110

Mo Hindash *(Gen Mgr)*
James H. Click Jr. *(Owner)*

JIM COLEMAN COMPANY
5842 W 34th St, Houston, TX 77092
Tel.: (713) 683-9878
Web Site:
http://www.jcolemanco.com
Year Founded: 1966
Sales Range: $25-49.9 Million
Emp.: 300
Mfr of Car Wash Equipment & Franchisor of Car Washes
N.A.I.C.S.: 333310

JIM CRIVELLI CHEVROLET, INC.
108 McKees Rocks Plz, McKees Rocks, PA 15136
Tel.: (412) 331-0120
Web Site: http://www.jimcrivelli.com
Sales Range: $10-24.9 Million
Emp.: 53
Car Whslr
N.A.I.C.S.: 441110
James Crivelli *(Owner)*

JIM CURLEY DEALERSHIP
US Hwy 9, Lakewood, NJ 08701
Tel.: (732) 363-7400
Web Site: http://www.jimcurley.com
Sales Range: $10-24.9 Million
Emp.: 40
Car Whslr
N.A.I.C.S.: 441110
Anthony Luongo *(Head-Sls)*

JIM DOYLE FORD
3330 Delaware Ave, Kenmore, NY 14217
Tel.: (716) 875-6100
Year Founded: 1989
Sales Range: $10-24.9 Million
Emp.: 77
Car Whslr
N.A.I.C.S.: 441110
James J. Doyle *(Owner & Pres)*

JIM DUNWORTH INC.
8927 International St, San Antonio, TX 78216
Tel.: (210) 930-3449
Rev.: $14,011,782
Emp.: 25
Rent-A-Car Service
N.A.I.C.S.: 532111
James F. Dunworth *(CEO)*

JIM ELLIS ATLANTA INC.
5901 Peachtree Indus Blvd S, Atlanta, GA 30341
Tel.: (770) 458-6811
Web Site: http://www.jimellis.com
Rev.: $98,157,999
Emp.: 1,200
Automobiles, New & Used
N.A.I.C.S.: 441110
Robert Schofield *(Controller)*
Rodney Woods *(Gen Mgr)*
James W. Ellis Jr. *(Pres)*

JIM FOREMAN PONTIAC INC.
242 E Columbia St, Springfield, OH 45503
Tel.: (937) 324-5571
Web Site:
http://www.foremanblair.com
Year Founded: 1970
Sales Range: $25-49.9 Million
Emp.: 60
Car Dealership
N.A.I.C.S.: 441110
Judith Papenbrock *(Sec & Comptroller)*
Dean Blair *(VP)*
James M. Foreman *(Pres & Treas)*

JIM FUOCO MOTOR CO.
741 N 1st St, Grand Junction, CO 81501
Tel.: (970) 242-1571
Web Site:
http://www.fuocomotors.com
Sales Range: $50-74.9 Million
Emp.: 85
Sales & Service of New & Used Automobiles
N.A.I.C.S.: 441110
Robert Fuoco (Pres)
Ed Nielsen (Gen Mgr)
Tony Fuoco (VP)

JIM GILMAN EXCAVATING INC.
3099 Grand Ave, Butte, MT 59701
Tel.: (406) 723-6349
Sales Range: $10-24.9 Million
Emp.: 50
General Contractor, Highway & Street Construction
N.A.I.C.S.: 237310
Paul Thompson (Controller)
James C. Gilman Sr. (Pres)
James C. Gilman Jr. (VP)

JIM GLOVER CHEVROLET ISUZU
PO Box 4940, Tulsa, OK 74159-4940
Tel.: (918) 663-2300
Web Site:
http://www.jimgloverchevy.com
Sales Range: $50-74.9 Million
Emp.: 200
Car Whslr
N.A.I.C.S.: 441110
Bailley Caperton (Gen Mgr)

JIM HAWK GROUP INC.
3119 S 9th St, Council Bluffs, IA 51501
Tel.: (712) 366-2241
Web Site: http://www.jhtt.com
Rev.: $78,800,000
Emp.: 275
Automobile & Other Motor Vehicle Merchant Whslr
N.A.I.C.S.: 423110
Charles O'Hollearn (VP)
James V. Hawk (Pres)
Lanny Goetzinger (Treas & Sec)

JIM HERRICK MOTORS INC.
4215 Liberty Ave, Vermilion, OH 44089
Tel.: (440) 967-6191
Web Site: http://www.libertyford.com
Sales Range: $10-24.9 Million
Emp.: 70
Automobiles, New & Used
N.A.I.C.S.: 441110
James R. Herrick (Pres)
Dustin Peugeot (Gen Mgr)
Monica Simon (Mgr-Customer Rels)

Subsidiaries:

Liberty Ford Lincoln Mercury   (1)
4215 Liberty Ave, Vermilion, OH 44089
Tel.: (440) 967-6191
Web Site: http://www.libertyford.com
Rev.: $35,600,000
Emp.: 55
Automobiles, New & Used
N.A.I.C.S.: 441110
James R. Herrick (Pres)

JIM HICKS & COMPANY INC.
565 Mercury Ln, Brea, CA 92821-4831
Tel.: (714) 671-2153   CA
Web Site:
http://www.jhasoftware.com
Year Founded: 1982
Sales Range: $100-124.9 Million
Emp.: 20

Farm Supplies
N.A.I.C.S.: 424910
James P. Hicks (Pres & CEO)

JIM HINTON OIL COMPANY INC.
204 NE Haines St, Live Oak, FL 32064
Tel.: (386) 362-2935
Sales Range: $10-24.9 Million
Emp.: 15
Distr of Petroleum Products
N.A.I.C.S.: 424710
Judy Hinton (Treas)
Stephanie Hinton (Pres)

JIM HUDSON AUTOMOTIVE GROUP
4035 Kaiser Hill Rd, Columbia, SC 29203
Tel.: (803) 783-0110   SC
Web Site: http://www.jimhudson.com
Sales Range: $100-124.9 Million
Emp.: 78
Retailer of New & Used Automobiles & Trucks
N.A.I.C.S.: 441110
Jim Hudson (Founder & CEO)
Keith Hudson (Pres)
Don Dese (Controller)
Randy Alexander (Mgr-Svc)
Mel Musgrove (Mgr-Parts)
Todd Fisher (Mgr-Sls)
Chris Friedah (Dir-Fin)
Matt Hickey (Mgr-Svc)

JIM KERAS CHEVROLET MEMPHIS
2000 Covington Pike, Memphis, TN 38128-6982
Tel.: (901) 387-2000   TN
Web Site: http://www.jimkeras.com
Sales Range: $25-49.9 Million
Emp.: 100
New & Used Automobile Dealership
N.A.I.C.S.: 441110
Jay Keras (Gen Mgr)
George Gully (Mgr-Sls)
Jim Largue (Dir-Fixed Ops)

JIM KERAS SUBARU
2080 Covington Pike, Memphis, TN 38128
Tel.: (901) 373-2700
Web Site:
http://www.subarumemphis.com
Year Founded: 1949
Sales Range: $10-24.9 Million
Emp.: 60
New Car Whslr
N.A.I.C.S.: 441110
Mark Jordan (Dir-Internet Sls)
Vinny Girard (Gen Mgr)
Rick McCollum (Mgr-Bus)
Joe Matthews (Mgr-Detail)
David Fleming (Mgr-Fin)
Tyler Benitone (Mgr-Gen Sls)
Dave Ellison (Mgr-Internet)
Jim Gaskins (Mgr-Parts-Columbus)

JIM KRANTZ ASSOCIATES INC.
228 E 45th St 12th Fl, New York, NY 10017
Tel.: (212) 286-0325
Web Site:
http://www.krantzsecure.com
Sales Range: $10-24.9 Million
Emp.: 25
Local Area Network (Lan) Systems Integrator
N.A.I.C.S.: 541512
James Krantz (Pres)

JIM L. SHETAKIS DISTRIBUTING CO. INC.
3840-A N Civic Center Dr, Las Vegas, NV 89030
Tel.: (702) 735-8985   NV
Web Site: http://www.shetakis.com
Year Founded: 1959
Sales Range: $10-24.9 Million
Emp.: 80
Food Services & Distr
N.A.I.C.S.: 424410
Lloyd Meher (Pres & CEO)

JIM MARSH AMERICAN CORP.
8555 W Centennial Pkwy, Las Vegas, NV 89149
Tel.: (702) 946-1000
Web Site:
http://www.jimmarshkia.com
Sales Range: $10-24.9 Million
Emp.: 30
Used Car Sales
N.A.I.C.S.: 441110
James R. Marsh (Pres)

JIM MCKAY CHEVROLET INC.
3509 University Dr, Fairfax, VA 22030
Tel.: (703) 591-4800
Web Site:
http://www.jimmckaychevrolet.com
Sales Range: $10-24.9 Million
Emp.: 65
Automobiles, New & Used
N.A.I.C.S.: 441110
Justin Crawford (Dir-Comm & Mktg)
Kathleen McKay (Owner)

JIM MURPHY BUICK GMC, INC.
3000 Walden Ave, Depew, NY 14043
Tel.: (716) 684-8900
Web Site:
http://www.jimmurphycars.com
Sales Range: $10-24.9 Million
Emp.: 35
New Car Retailer
N.A.I.C.S.: 441110
James A. Murphy (Pres)

JIM PALMER TRUCKING INC.
9730 Derby Dr, Missoula, MT 59808-9422
Tel.: (406) 721-5151   MT
Web Site:
http://www.jimpalmertrucking.com
Year Founded: 1967
Sales Range: $25-49.9 Million
Emp.: 400
Trucking Service
N.A.I.C.S.: 484121
Rachel Leisle (Dir-HR)

JIM RAYSIK INC.
1500 E Harisson Rd, Clinton, MO 64735
Tel.: (660) 885-3355
Web Site: http://www.jimraysik.net
Year Founded: 1988
Sales Range: $10-24.9 Million
Emp.: 30
New Car Dealers
N.A.I.C.S.: 441110
Jim Raysik (Owner)

JIM RIEHL'S FRIENDLY BUICK HONDA HUMMER
18900 Hall Rd, Clinton Township, MI 48038
Tel.: (586) 412-9600
Web Site: http://www.jimriehl.com
Year Founded: 1945
Sales Range: $10-24.9 Million
Emp.: 60
Car Whslr
N.A.I.C.S.: 441110
James Riehl (Pres)

JIM ROBINSON INC.
95 Robinson Dr, Triadelphia, WV 26059
Tel.: (304) 232-2400
Web Site:
http://www.jimrobinsonford.com
Sales Range: $10-24.9 Million
Emp.: 42
Car Whslr
N.A.I.C.S.: 441110
Theresa Johnston (Treas & Sec)
James Robinson (Pres)

JIM RYAN CHEVROLET INC.
1800 S Broadway, Minot, ND 58701
Tel.: (701) 852-3571
Web Site:
http://www.ryanchevrolet.com
Sales Range: $25-49.9 Million
Emp.: 80
New Car Whslr
N.A.I.C.S.: 441110
Kathleen Gaddie (Pres)
Mary Prough (Gen Mgr)

JIM SCHMIDT CHEVROLET-OLDSMOBILE, INC.
575 W High St, Hicksville, OH 43526
Tel.: (419) 542-7731
Sales Range: $25-49.9 Million
Emp.: 39
Car Whslr
N.A.I.C.S.: 441110
James P. Schmidt (Pres)

JIM SKINNER FORD
9924 Pkwy E, Birmingham, AL 35215
Tel.: (205) 854-2222
Web Site:
http://www.jimskinnerford.com
Year Founded: 1958
Sales Range: $25-49.9 Million
Emp.: 80
New Car Dealers
N.A.I.C.S.: 441110
Bobby Skinner (Owner)
James Skinner (VP)
Tracy Duckworth (Mgr-Internet Sls)
Bob Skinner (Partner)
Ricky Argo (Mgr-Parts)
Christopher Coats (Asst Mgr-Bodyshop)
Shannon Dickinson (Mgr-Fleet & Delivery)
Stan Dickinson (Mgr-Special Fin)
Charles Freind (Mgr-BHPH)
Mario Hicks (Mgr-Fin)
Tom Kelly (Mgr-Svc)
Latarsha Mack (Controller)
Charlie Martin (Mgr-Sls & Leasing)
Myron Miller (Mgr-Sls)
Tyrone Trimuel (Mgr-Used Car)
Fred Whitworth (Mgr-Bodyshop)
Terry Kurth (Mgr-Fin)

JIM SKINNER HONDA
3823 Ross Clark Cir, Dothan, AL 36303
Tel.: (334) 671-8100
Web Site:
http://www.jimskinnerhonda.com
Year Founded: 1992
Sales Range: $10-24.9 Million
Emp.: 31
New Car Retailer
N.A.I.C.S.: 441110
Clay Pelland (Dir-Internet)
Garnett Rigsby (VP & Gen Mgr)
Tim Rigsby (Gen Mgr)
Robert M. Skinner (Pres)
James H. Skinner Jr. (VP)

JIM SMITH BOATS, INC.
4396 SE Commerce Ave, Stuart, FL 34997
Tel.: (772) 286-1172   FL

Jim Smith Boats, Inc.—(Continued)
Web Site:
http://www.jimsmithboats.net
Year Founded: 1981
Sales Range: $1-9.9 Million
Emp.: 19
Boat Building
N.A.I.C.S.: 336612
John A. Vance (Pres)

JIM SMITH CONTRACTING CO. LLC
1108 Dover Rd, Grand Rivers, KY 42045
Tel.: (270) 362-8661
Web Site:
http://www.jimsmithcontracting.com
Sales Range: $10-24.9 Million
Emp.: 75
Highway & Street Construction
N.A.I.C.S.: 237310
Lori Martin (Mgr-HR)

JIM TAYLOR CHEVROLET, LLC.
139 Grimshaw, Rayville, LA 71269
Tel.: (318) 728-6550
Web Site:
http://www.jimtaylorchevy.com
Sales Range: $50-74.9 Million
Emp.: 45
Car Whslr
N.A.I.C.S.: 441110
Steve Lawrence (Mgr-Svcs)
Felicia Lively (Acct Mgr)
Buddy Smitherman (Mgr-Customer Rels)
Jim Taylor (Owner)

JIM THORP LUMBER PRODUCTS, INC.
PO Box 103, Yoncalla, OR 97499
Tel.: (541) 849-2452
Sales Range: $10-24.9 Million
Emp.: 42
Lumber Mfr
N.A.I.C.S.: 321912
Harold J. Thorp (Pres)
Dee A. Thorp (Sec)

JIM TRENARY CHEVROLET INC.
501 Auto Mall Dr, O'Fallon, MO 63368
Tel.: (636) 946-6300
Web Site:
http://www.jimtrenarychev.com
Sales Range: $50-74.9 Million
Emp.: 60
New & Used Car Dealers
N.A.I.C.S.: 441110
James W. Trenary (Pres)
Jeff Winheim (Dir-Internet Sls)

JIM VREELAND FORD
340 E Hwy 246, Buellton, CA 93427
Tel.: (805) 688-7760
Web Site:
http://www.jimvreelandford.com
Sales Range: $10-24.9 Million
Emp.: 40
New Car Retailer
N.A.I.C.S.: 441110
Blaine Hewitt (Mgr-Sls-Used Car)
Michael Gamboian (Mgr-Sls)
Dan Vreeland (Mgr-New Vehicle Sls)
Derek Frazier (Mgr-Fin)
Michael Dawson (Mgr-Parts)
Tony Hernandez (Mgr-Detail Shop)
Lori Hopkins (Office Mgr)
Tom Madden (Dir-Parts)
Jim Vreeland Jr. (Gen Mgr)

JIM WHITE LUMBER SALES INC.

5225 Hampton Pl, Saginaw, MI 48604
Tel.: (989) 790-6500
Web Site:
http://www.jimwhitegroup.com
Year Founded: 1987
Sales Range: $100-124.9 Million
Emp.: 50
Lumber, Plywood & Millwork
N.A.I.C.S.: 423310
Fred Cook (Pres & CEO)
Jeff Roscoe (Gen Mgr)

JIM WILSON & ASSOCIATES, INC.
Ste 100 2660 Eastchase Ln, Montgomery, AL 36117-7024
Tel.: (334) 260-2500
Web Site: http://www.jwamalls.com
Year Founded: 1975
Sales Range: $75-99.9 Million
Emp.: 35
Property Manager & Developer
N.A.I.C.S.: 531210
Will Wilson (Pres)
Carl Bartlett (Exec VP)
Woody Rush (Sr VP-Leasing)
Doug Jeffords (VP-Construction)
Evan Conder (Dir-Dev)

JIM WINTER BUICK-GMC TRUCK-NISSAN INC.
3303 W Michigan Ave, Jackson, MI 49202
Tel.: (517) 787-5100
Web Site:
http://www.jimwinterauto.com
Rev.: $17,000,000
Emp.: 40
New Car Dealers
N.A.I.C.S.: 441110
Richard Walicki (Pres & Gen Mgr)

JIM WRIGHT ASSOCIATES
30 E Kensington Ave, Salt Lake City, UT 84115
Tel.: (801) 487-4820
Year Founded: 1984
Sales Range: $1-9.9 Million
Advetising Agency
N.A.I.C.S.: 541810

JIM'S CONCRETE OF BREVARD INC.
6760 Greenland Ind Blvd, Jacksonville, FL 32258
Tel.: (904) 886-4743
Web Site:
http://www.jimsconcrete.com
Sales Range: $10-24.9 Million
Emp.: 90
Concrete Contracting Services
N.A.I.C.S.: 238110
Fran Roe (Office Mgr)
Shawn McNeely (Pres)

JIM'S FORMAL WEAR CO.
1 Tuxedo Park, Trenton, IL 62293
Tel.: (618) 224-9211
Web Site: http://www.jimsfw.com
Sales Range: $25-49.9 Million
Emp.: 400
Tuxedo Rental
N.A.I.C.S.: 532281
Tom Barnett (Sr VP-Ops & Admin)
Glenn Dorries (Project Mgr)
Aaron Lovitt (Coord-Production)
Jennifer Roesener (Mgr-Accts Receivable)
Art Schulte (Mgr-Missouri Acct)
Barry Brody (Coord-Chain Store)

JIM'S SUPPLY CO. INC.
3530 Buck Owens Blvd, Bakersfield, CA 93308
Tel.: (661) 324-6514

Web Site: http://www.jimssupply.com
Sales Range: $25-49.9 Million
Emp.: 100
Mfr & Sales of Steel Products
N.A.I.C.S.: 423510
Bryan Boylan (CFO)
Dan Drake (VP)

JIMARI INTERNATIONAL, INC.
9454 Wilshire Blvd Ste 612, Beverly Hills, CA 90212
Tel.: (310) 888-1870
Year Founded: 2016
Investment Services
N.A.I.C.S.: 523999
James Cassidy (Pres & Sec)
James McKillop (VP)

JIMCO MAINTENANCE, INC.
710 Commerce Dr Unit 107, Venice, FL 34292
Tel.: (941) 485-5985
Web Site: http://www.jimcos.com
Year Founded: 1967
Sales Range: $1-9.9 Million
Emp.: 80
Shopping Cart Maintenance & Repair
N.A.I.C.S.: 811310
Lynn Moseley (Co-Owner & Pres)
Lee Radefeld (Sr VP)
Joe Kurecki (Mgr-Ops)
Paul Moseley (Co-Owner & CEO)

JIMCOR AGENCY INC.
60 Craig Rd, Montvale, NJ 07645
Tel.: (201) 573-8200
Web Site: http://www.jimcor.com
Year Founded: 1986
Sales Range: $10-24.9 Million
Emp.: 43
Insurance Agents
N.A.I.C.S.: 524210
Francis J. Mastowski (Pres)
Ellen Mastowski (Sec & VP)
David J. Laquidara (CFO)
Coryn Thalmann (CEO & COO)

JIMENEZ CUSTOM PAINTING, INC.
5937 Lemona Ave, Van Nuys, CA 91411
Tel.: (818) 908-9937
Web Site: http://www.jcp-inc.net
Year Founded: 2000
Sales Range: $1-9.9 Million
Emp.: 36
Residential Painting, Plastering & Wood Finishing
N.A.I.C.S.: 238320
Jorge G. Jimenez (Pres)

JIMLAR CORPORATION
350 5th Ave Empire State Bldg, New York, NY 10118
Tel.: (516) 829-1717
Web Site: http://www.jimlar.com
Year Founded: 1956
Sales Range: $100-124.9 Million
Emp.: 150
Importer & Whslr of Shoes
N.A.I.C.S.: 424340
Lawrence Tarica (Pres & COO)
James Tarica (Chm & CEO)
Frank Vignola (CFO & VP)
John Castello (VP-Sourcing)
Vincent DeStefano (Sr VP)

Subsidiaries:

The Frye Company (1)
160 Great Neck Rd, Great Neck, NY 11021-3304
Tel.: (516) 829-1717
Web Site: http://www.fryeboots.com
Sales Range: $10-24.9 Million
Emp.: 70
Shoes & Boots Whslr
N.A.I.C.S.: 424340

JIMMIE CROWDER EXCAVATING INC.
901 Geddie Rd, Tallahassee, FL 32304
Tel.: (850) 576-7176
Web Site:
http://www.crowderexcavating.com
Rev.: $20,457,006
Emp.: 75
Excavation & Grading, Building Construction
N.A.I.C.S.: 238910
Tina Crowder (Pres)

JIMMIE VICKERS
545 E Merritt Island Causeway, Merritt Island, FL 32952-3504
Tel.: (321) 453-2660
Web Site:
http://www.jimmievickers.com
Sales Range: $10-24.9 Million
Emp.: 35
Car Whslr
N.A.I.C.S.: 441110
Terry Bryan (Mgr-Svc)
Thomas Schlegal (Mgr-Svc)
Buddy Vickers (Gen Mgr)
Charles A. Vickers (Pres)

JIMMY BEANS WOOL
4850 Joule St Ste A1, Reno, NV 89502
Tel.: (775) 827-9276
Web Site:
http://www.jimmybeanswool.com
Year Founded: 2002
Sales Range: $1-9.9 Million
Emp.: 36
Yarn & Knitting Supplies
N.A..C.S.: 459130
Laura Zander (Owner)

JIMMY JONES TOYOTA OF ORANGEBURG
3237 St Matthews Rd, Orangeburg, SC 29118-8221
Tel.: (803) 536-4512
Web Site:
http://www.jimmyjonestoyota.com
Car Whslr
N.A.I.C.S.: 441110
Lorenzo Anderson (Gen Mgr-Sls)
LaJaeric Miller (Sls Mgr)
Jimmy Jones (Owner & Gen Mgr)
Faye Menefee (Bus Mgr)
Morris Rhodes (Mgr-Fin)
Shalanda Levy (Mgr-Svc)
April Ridgeway (Office Mgr)

JIMMY SALES NECKWEAR CORP
243 44th St, Brooklyn, NY 11232
Tel.: (718) 768-8484
Web Site: http://www.jimmysales.com
Sales Range: $10-24.9 Million
Emp.: 59
Men's & Boys' Neckties & Bow Ties
N.A.I.C.S.: 315990
David Azizo (Controller & Gen Mgr)

JIMMY WHITTINGTON LUMBER CO.
3637 Jackson Ave, Memphis, TN 38108
Tel.: (901) 386-2800
Web Site:
http://www.whittingtonlumber.com
Sales Range: $10-24.9 Million
Emp.: 25
Lumber & Other Building Materials
N.A.I.C.S.: 423310
Danny Clarke (VP)
Jimmy Whittington Jr. (Pres)

JINNY BEAUTY SUPPLY CO. INC.

3587 Oakcliff Rd, Doraville, GA 30340
Tel.: (770) 734-9222
Web Site: http://www.jinny.com
Sales Range: $10-24.9 Million
Emp.: 35
Ethnic Beauty Supply Whslr & Distr
N.A.I.C.S.: 424210
Eddie Jhin (Pres)

JINX, INC.
13465 Gregg St, Poway, CA 92064
Tel.: (858) 457-5469
Web Site: http://www.jinx.com
Year Founded: 2004
Sales Range: $1-9.9 Million
Emp.: 70
Retail Miscellaneous Apparel & Accessories
N.A.I.C.S.: 458110
Sean Gailey (Pres & CEO)

JIREH METAL PRODUCTS, INC.
3635 Nardin St SW, Grandville, MI 49418
Tel.: (616) 531-7581   MI
Web Site: http://www.jirehmetal.com
Year Founded: 2000
Sales Range: $10-24.9 Million
Emp.: 100
Contract Metal Products & Assemblies Mfr
N.A.I.C.S.: 332999
Michael S. Davenport (Pres & CEO)

JIT CORPORATION
1610 Commerce Way, Paso Robles, CA 93446-3699
Tel.: (714) 256-9100
Web Site: http://www.jitmfg.com
Sales Range: $25-49.9 Million
Emp.: 50
Mfr & Sales of Electronic Parts
N.A.I.C.S.: 423690

JITCO GROUP LIMITED
30 N Raymond Ave, Pasadena, CA 91103
Tel.: (626) 666-3366
Web Site: http://www.jitco.com
Sales Range: $10-24.9 Million
Emp.: 3
Industrial Products & Consumer Goods
N.A.I.C.S.: 423620
Ravinder S. Sethi (Pres & CEO)

JJ DETWEILER ENTERPRISES INC.
2814 Edison St NW, Uniontown, OH 44685
Tel.: (330) 699-2741
Rev.: $11,314,047
Emp.: 3
Land Subdividers & Developers, Residential
N.A.I.C.S.: 237210
Joseph Detweiler (Pres)
Thomas Schmidt (CEO)

JJ FERGUSON SAND & GRAVEL
4510 Hwy 82 E, Greenwood, MS 38930
Tel.: (662) 453-5451
Sales Range: $10-24.9 Million
Emp.: 180
Construction Materials Sales
N.A.I.C.S.: 444180
Rocky Steen (Pres)
Jerry Steen Jr. (Owner & Pres)

JJ OPPORTUNITY CORP.
1 Broadway 14th Fl, Cambridge, MA 02142

Tel.: (978) 295-1858   DE
Year Founded: 2021
Investment Services
N.A.I.C.S.: 523999
Junhui Zhang (CEO & Chm)
Shangyong Zhang (CFO)
Hamish Allan Raw (COO)

JJ WADE & ASSOCIATES, INC.
212 S Main St, Davidson, NC 28036
Tel.: (704) 892-9297
Web Site:
    http://www.jjwadeinsurance.com
Year Founded: 1992
Insurance & Risk Management Advisory Services
N.A.I.C.S.: 524210
Jim Roberts (Pres)
Carolyn Roberts (VP)
Wendy Garner (Sec & Treas)
JJ Wade III (CEO)

JJ&H LTD.
30 W Manroe, Chicago, IL 60603
Tel.: (312) 726-1578
Web Site:
    http://www.jacobsononline.com
Rev.: $10,000,000
Emp.: 70
Placement Agencies
N.A.I.C.S.: 561311
Rick Jacobson (CEO)

JJF MANAGEMENT SERVICES, INC.
11411 Rockville Pike, Rockville, MD 20852
Tel.: (301) 881-4000
Web Site: http://www.fitzgerald.com
Year Founded: 2005
Sales Range: Less than $1 Million
Emp.: 2
Management & Investment Services
N.A.I.C.S.: 541611
Jack Fitzgerald (Pres)
Ron Jaffe (Controller)

Subsidiaries:

Rent-A-Wreck of America, Inc.   (1)
105 Main St, Laurel, MD 20707
Tel.: (240) 581-1350
Web Site: http://www.rent-a-wreck.com
Rental & Leasing of New & Used Cars, Trucks & Vans; Franchise Services
N.A.I.C.S.: 532120
Jason Manelli (VP-Mktg-Comm)
Dale Tripp (Mgr-Franchise Dev)

Subsidiary (Domestic):

Bundy American Corporation   (2)
99 Main St, Laurel, MD 20707-4303
Tel.: (410) 581-5755
Franchisor of Rental Cars
N.A.I.C.S.: 532111

JJJ FLOOR COVERING INC.
4831 Passons Blvd A, Pico Rivera, CA 90660
Tel.: (562) 692-9008
Web Site:
    http://www.jjjfloorcovering.com
Rev.: $26,065,818
Emp.: 150
Carpets
N.A.I.C.S.: 423220
Bud Lillard (Controller)
Maria Guiterrez (CEO)
Jimmy O'Quinn (Project Mgr)
Kevin Copeland (Project Mgr)
Jim Lank (Project Mgr)
Yolanda Escobar (Office Mgr)

JJLA LLC
3780 Wilshire Blvd 601, Los Angeles, CA 90028
Tel.: (213) 248-1225
Web Site: http://www.jj-la.com

Year Founded: 2009
Sales Range: $1-9.9 Million
Emp.: 50
Event Management Services
N.A.I.C.S.: 711310
Jeff Consoletti (Founder & CEO)
Luke Przybylski (VP & Head-Production)
Lee Doud (Head-Events)
Artie Kenney (Head-Talent Rels)
Abby Borden (Dir-Event & Design)

JJR ENTERPRISES INC.
10491 Old Placerville Rd Ste 150, Sacramento, CA 95827
Tel.: (916) 363-2666
Web Site: http://www.caltronics.net
Sales Range: $25-49.9 Million
Emp.: 100
Office Equipment
N.A.I.C.S.: 423420
Barry Crider (Mgr-Svcs)
Dan Reilly (Pres)
Tony Riehl (Mgr-Ops)
Mike Phipps (Reg Mgr-Sls)

JK ASSOCIATES, INC.
The Boiler House 1010 Spring Mill Ave Ste 300, Conshohocken, PA 19428-2391
Tel.: (484) 434-2800
Web Site: http://www.jkmed.com
Sales Range: $1-9.9 Million
Emp.: 38
Developer & Implementer of Scientific Education Programs for Physicians
N.A.I.C.S.: 541611
John Czekanski (Pres-US Ops)
Kevin Pawley (COO-Ops-United States)

JK FOODS INC.
300 W 11th St, Williston, ND 58801
Tel.: (701) 572-2927
Web Site: http://www.dia.net
Sales Range: $10-24.9 Million
Emp.: 149
Grocery Store Operator
N.A.I.C.S.: 445110
Michael D. Kraft (CEO)
Mike Steffan (CFO)
Nigel Parrott (Head-Tiger Tiger)

JK JEWELRY INC.
1500 Brighton Henrietta Town Line Rd, Rochester, NY 14623
Tel.: (585) 292-0770
Web Site: http://www.jkfindings.com
Year Founded: 1975
Sales Range: $10-24.9 Million
Emp.: 45
Mfr, Whslr & Importer of Jewelry & Precious Metals
N.A.I.C.S.: 423940
John S. Kaupp (Pres)

Subsidiaries:

JK Findings USA   (1)
1500 Brighton Henrietta Town Line Rd, Rochester, NY 14623
Tel.: (585) 346-3464
Web Site: http://www.jkfindings.com
Supplier of Precious Metal Findings to the Jewelry Industry
N.A.I.C.S.: 423940
Joni Lucas (COO)
Daniel Pabrinkis (Mgr-Sls)

JK MOVING & STORAGE INC.
44112 Mercure Cir, Sterling, VA 20166
Tel.: (703) 260-4282
Web Site: http://www.jkmoving.com
Sales Range: $25-49.9 Million
Emp.: 302
Special Warehousing & Storage
N.A.I.C.S.: 493190

Charles Sanford Kuhn (Founder, Pres & CEO)
David Harris (CFO)
Tom Grass (Gen Mgr-Maryland)
David Cox (Exec VP-Residential Svcs)
David Macpherson (Sr VP-Intl Div)
Paul McCullough (CIO)

Subsidiaries:

Capital Relocation Services LLC   (1)
44112 Mercure Cir, Sterling, VA 20166
Tel.: (703) 260-3006
Web Site: http://www.caprelo.com
Rev.: $1,900,000
Emp.: 50
Relocation Services
N.A.I.C.S.: 493190
Mickey Williams (Pres, CEO & Partner)
Tamara Bianchi (Dir-Admin & Comm)
Keela Shumard (Dir-Client Dev)
Matt Tandy (Dir-Client Dev)
Rebecca Chanin (Dir-Mktg)
Wesam Sarsour (Dir-Bus Sys)
Angela Palange (Dir-Global Bus Dev)
Heather Hudnall (Dir-Global Svc Delivery)
Cindy Klammer (Dir-Operational Excellence)
Chris Owens (Dir-Global Supply Chain)
Angela Tan (Dir-Client Dev)

JKAISER WORKSPACES, LLC
20 E Congress Ste 10, Tucson, AZ 85701
Tel.: (520) 647-2121
Web Site: http://www.jkaiser.com
Year Founded: 2014
Sales Range: $1-9.9 Million
Emp.: 3
Architectural & Interior Design Services
N.A.I.C.S.: 541410
Jessica Kaiser (CEO)
Janina Copp (Chief Project Officer)

JKC TRUCKING INC.
5450 S Ctr Ave, Summit Argo, IL 60501
Tel.: (708) 496-3636
Web Site: http://www.jkctrucking.com
Rev.: $18,389,968
Emp.: 200
Refrigerated Products Transport
N.A.I.C.S.: 484230
Bryan Korda (Mgr-Sls)
Mark McKee (VP-Sls)

JKMILNE ASSET MANAGEMENT
1520 Royal Palm Sq Blvd Ste 210, Fort Myers, FL 33919
Tel.: (239) 936-3430
Web Site: http://www.jkmilne.com
Year Founded: 2004
Sales Range: $1-9.9 Million
Emp.: 10
Asset Management Fixed Income Adviser
N.A.I.C.S.: 523940
John K. Milne (CEO & Chief Investment Officer)
H. Gregory Moore (Principal & Strategist)
Brian Borneman (Portfolio Mgr-Asset Mgmt)
David Milne (Portfolio Mgr)

JL FOODS CO., INC.
1498 Broadway, Camden, NJ 08104
Tel.: (856) 963-3250
Sales Range: $10-24.9 Million
Emp.: 150
Poultry & Poultry Products Whslr
N.A.I.C.S.: 424440

JL FURNISHINGS LLC

JL Furnishings LLC—(Continued)

19007 S Reyes Ave, Rancho Dominguez, CA 90221
Tel.: (310) 605-6600
Web Site:
http://www.jlfurnishings.com
Rev.: $10,000,000
Emp.: 90
Factory Furniture & Fixtures
N.A.I.C.S.: 337127
Jeffrey Lazar (Owner)

JL MEDIA, INC.
1600 Rte 22 E, Union, NJ 07083-3415
Tel.: (908) 687-8700   NJ
Web Site: http://www.jlmedia.com
Year Founded: 1981
Sales Range: $550-599.9 Million
Emp.: 60
Media Buying Services
N.A.I.C.S.: 541830
Jerry Levy (CEO)
Paula Brooks (Dir-Client Svcs)
Rich Russo (Dir-Radio Brdcst Svcs)
Susan Ringel (VP-Client Svcs)
Marc Gross (Dir-Acct Svcs)
Matt Feinberg (Exec VP)
William Paladini (Mng Partner)
Chris Robbie (Exec VP)

JLC FOOD SYSTEMS INC.
2480 Superior Dr NW, Rochester, MN 55901
Tel.: (507) 282-3090
Sales Range: $10-24.9 Million
Emp.: 6
Family Restaurant Operator
N.A.I.C.S.: 722511
Dave Hanson (Pres)

JLE INDUSTRIES, LLC
119 ICMI Rd Ste 210, Dunbar, PA 15431
Tel.: (724) 603-2228
Web Site:
http://www.jleindustries.com
Year Founded: 2012
Sales Range: $25-49.9 Million
Emp.: 500
Logistic & Transportation Services
N.A.I.C.S.: 488510
Raymond Gamrat (VP-Admin & Gen Mgr)

JLE MANUFACTURING, INC.
3346 W Guadalupe Rd, Apache Junction, AZ 85120
Tel.: (480) 632-1421   AZ
Year Founded: 1998
Sales Range: $1-9.9 Million
Emp.: 34
Constructs & Installs Architectural Millwork, Store Fixtures & Cabinetry
N.A.I.C.S.: 337212
Rob Dodge (Mgr-Engrg)

JLL INCOME PROPERTY TRUST, INC.
333 W Wacker Dr, Chicago, IL 60606
Tel.: (312) 897-4000
Web Site: https://www.jllipt.com
Rev.: $337,188,000
Assets: $5,154,218,000
Liabilities: $2,971,458,000
Net Worth: $2,182,760,000
Earnings: ($42,551,000)
Fiscal Year-end: 12/31/22
Real Estate Investment Trust
N.A.I.C.S.: 525990
C. Allan Swaringen (Pres & CEO)
Lucas Kimmel (Portfolio Mgr)
Peter Bucher (Dir-Acctg)

JLL PARTNERS, LLC

245 Park Ave Ste 1601, New York, NY 10167
Tel.: (212) 286-8600   DE
Web Site: http://www.jllpartners.com
Year Founded: 1988
Private Equity Investment Firm
N.A.I.C.S.: 523999
Frank J. Rodriguez (Mng Dir)
Eugene Hahn (Mng Dir)
Daniel Agroskin (Mng Dir)
Derrick M. Preston (Principal)
Brooks Powlen (Principal)
Daniel Di Piazza (Principal)
Vikas Mouli (Principal)
William Miles (Mng Dir)
Johanna Doherty (Principal)
Daren Schneider (CFO & Chief Compliance Officer)
Paul S. Levy (Mng Dir)

Subsidiaries:

ACE Cash Express, Inc.   (1)
1231 Greenway Dr Ste 600, Irving, TX 75038-9904
Tel.: (972) 550-5000
Web Site: http://www.acecashexpress.com
Sales Range: $300-349.9 Million
Emp.: 500
Check Cashing, Bill Payment & Short-Term Consumer Loan Services
N.A.I.C.S.: 522130
Jay B. Shipowitz (Pres & CEO)
Eric C. Norrington (Sr VP-Pub Affairs)
Susan S. Pressler (CFO & Exec VP)
Victor Faszczuk (VP-Sls)
Allen J. Klose (CMO)
Ted M. Eades (COO & Exec VP)
David Sternblitz (VP-Cash Mgmt)
R. B. Ramsey (Gen Counsel, Sec & Sr VP)
Laurie Goodine Hill (Chief Compliance Officer & Sr VP)

Subsidiary (Domestic):

Q.C.& G. Financial, Inc.   (2)
1160 E Van Buren St, Phoenix, AZ 85006   (100%)
Tel.: (602) 252-2853
Retail Financial Services
N.A.I.C.S.: 522390

American Dental Partners, Inc.   (1)
401 Edgewater Pl Ste 430, Wakefield, MA 01880-6225
Tel.: (781) 224-0880
Web Site: http://www.amdpi.com
Sales Range: $250-299.9 Million
Management Services for Dentists
N.A.I.C.S.: 339116
Gregory A. Serrao (Founder & Chm)
Michael J. Vaughan (COO & Exec VP)
Michael J. Kenneally (Sr VP-Reg Ops)
Kevin Trexler (CEO)
Patricia E. Duncan (VP-Org Dev)
Michael W. Hoyt (VP-Info Svcs)
David M. Nelsen (VP & Controller)
Timothy C. Rodenberger (Gen Counsel, Sec & VP)
Nancy M. Schiaparelli (CFO, Treas & VP)
Jesley C. Ruff (Sr VP)

Aviation Technical Services Inc.   (1)
3121 109th St SW, Everett, WA 98204
Tel.: (425) 347-3030
Web Site: http://www.atsmro.com
Aircraft Maintenance, Repair & Overhaul Services
N.A.I.C.S.: 488190
David Lagger (Dir-New Bus Dev)
Matt Yerbic (CEO)
Paul Dolan (Pres-Airframe Svcs)
Gabe Doleac (CFO)
Clark Graves (VP-IT)
David Keimig (Gen Mgr-Engrg Solutions)
Darek Schiesser (VP-Airframe Programs)
Brian Olsen (Pres-Component & Engrg Solutions)
Dayna Eden (Chief People Officer)
Nima Seyedali (Gen Counsel & VP)
Carla Bowman (VP-Op Ex, Quality & EH&S)

Subsidiary (Domestic):

American Cooler Service, LLC   (2)
919 W Mayfield Rd, Arlington, TX 76015

Tel.: (817) 419-8008
Web Site: http://www.americancooler.us
Commercial & Industrial Machinery & Equipment Repair & Maintenance Services
N.A.I.C.S.: 811310
Steve Dellinger (Sls Dir-Natl)
Stan Greenleaf (Dir-Bus Dev)
Brady McGuinness (Dir-Bus Dev)
Rob Tilson (VP-Sls & Mktg)
Phil Fields (VP-Airframe & Engrg Sls)
Mark Thomas (Dir-Bus-Sls)
Nick Holbeck (Dir-Bus Dev)
Michael Fleck (Dir-Bus Dev)
Jeramie Handran (Mgr-Bus Dev)
Jeff Cornell (Sr Dir-Quality)

Ranger Air Aviation Ltd.   (2)
2670 Edmonds Ln Ste 200, Lewisville, TX 75067-6732
Tel.: (972) 245-6699
Web Site: http://www.rangeraav.com
Aircraft Goods & Services
N.A.I.C.S.: 336412
Mark Perlioni (Owner)

Texas Air Composites, Inc.   (2)
15050 Trinity Blvd, Fort Worth, TX 76155
Tel.: (972) 709-2866
Web Site:
http://www.texasaircomposites.com
Airplane Component Repair Services
N.A.I.C.S.: 336413
Jason Dickson (Mgr-Engrg)
Brady McGuinness (Dir-Sls & Mktg)

Texas Pneumatic Systems, Inc.   (2)
2404 Superior Dr, Arlington, TX 76013   (100%)
Tel.: (817) 794-0068
Web Site: http://www.txps.com
Sales Range: $1-9.9 Million
Emp.: 56
Repair & Overhaul Services for Commercial Airlines
N.A.I.C.S.: 336413
Richard Simmons (Mgr-Ops)
Bernard E. Rookey (Pres & CEO)

Definitive Media Corp.   (1)
2000 Centregreen Way Ste 300, Cary, NC 27513
Tel.: (866) 392-4788
Web Site: http://www.threadresearch.com
Technology & Service Provider
N.A.I.C.S.: 541990
John Reites (CEO)

Subsidiary (Domestic):

inVibe Labs, LLC   (2)
2900 Bristol D201, Costa Mesa, CA 92626
Tel.: (949) 438-4836
Web Site: http://www.invibe.co
Pharmaceutical Product Mfr & Distr
N.A.I.C.S.: 325412
Fabio Gratton (Co-Founder & CEO)
Jeremy Franz (Co-Founder & CTO)
Stephanie Huminski (Assoc Dir-Research)
Sunny Shah (Head-Strategy)
Adam Kleger (Head-Client Solutions)

Education Affiliates Inc.   (1)
5026 Campbell Blvd Ste D, Baltimore, MD 21236
Tel.: (410) 633-2929
Web Site: http://www.edaff.com
Holding Company; Post-Secondary Educational Institution Operator
N.A.I.C.S.: 551112
Phil Blessington (Controller)
Duncan M. Anderson (Pres & CEO)
Stephen J. Budosh (CFO)

Subsidiary (Domestic):

All-State Career, Inc.   (2)
2200 Broening Hwy Ste 160, Baltimore, MD 21224
Tel.: (410) 631-1818
Web Site: http://www.allstatecareer.edu
Trade Schools Operator
N.A.I.C.S.: 611519

Fortis College   (2)
7757 W Flagler St Ste 230, Miami, FL 33144
Tel.: (305) 261-5511
Web Site: http://www.fortis.edu
Sales Range: $1-9.9 Million
Trade School Operator
N.A.I.C.S.: 611519

Eversana Life Science Services, LLC   (1)
190 N Milwaukee St, Milwaukee, WI 53202
Tel.: (414) 299-4900
Web Site: http://www.eversana.com
Pharmaceuticals Mfr
N.A.I.C.S.: 325412
Jim Lang (CEO)

Subsidiary (Domestic):

Alamo Pharma Services, Inc.   (2)
77 N Broad St, Doylestown, PA 18901
Tel.: (215) 489-9500
Web Site:
http://www.alamopharmaservices.com
Pharmaceutical Product Whslr
N.A.I.C.S.: 424210
Amanda DaSilva (Project Mgr)
Amy Peek (Dir-Employee Rels & Recruiting)
Joelle Novak (Project Mgr)
Kevin Horak (Dir-HR)
Melissa Hayes (Project Mgr)
Peter Marchesini (Pres)
Denise Fullowan (Exec Dir-Trng & Dev)
Leora Haas (Mgr-Employee Engagement & Retention)
Susan Pike (Mgr-Talent Acq)

HVH Precision Analytics LLC   (2)
1255 Drummers Ln Ste 100, Wayne, PA 19087
Web Site: http://www.hvhprecision.com
Information Technology Support Services
N.A.I.C.S.: 541512
Steve Costalas (CEO)
Pierantonio Russo (Sr VP-Medical Affairs)
Jennifer Furniss (Sr Dir-Fin)
Oodaye Shukla (Chief Data & Analytics Officer)

Triplefin LLC   (2)
11333 Cornell Pk Dr, Cincinnati, OH 45242
Tel.: (513) 794-9870
Web Site: http://www.triplefin.com
Order to Cash Solutions to Healthcare & Pharmaceutical Companies
N.A.I.C.S.: 541613

Heads Up Technologies, Inc.   (1)
2033 Chenault Dr Ste 100, Carrollton, TX 75006
Tel.: (972) 980-4890
Web Site: http://www.heads-up.com
Voice & Data Systems, LED Lighting, Cabin Management Systems
N.A.I.C.S.: 336320
Dennis Beal (CFO & Exec VP)
Jim Newby (Dir-Engrg)
Robert Harshaw (Pres & CEO)

Jonathan Engineered Solutions, Corp.   (1)
410 Exchange Rd Ste 200, Irvine, CA 92602
Tel.: (714) 665-4400
Web Site: http://www.jonathanengr.com
Sales Range: $75-99.9 Million
Precision Ball Bearing Slide Mechanisms & Sheet Metal Fabrications
N.A.I.C.S.: 332991
Christine Suarez (Controller)
Marco Haminez (Mgr-Quality Assurance)

Medical Card System, Inc.   (1)
MCS Plz 255 Ave Ponce de León Ste 1600, Hato Rey, PR 00918-5644
Tel.: (787) 758-2500
Web Site: http://www.mcs.com.pr
Sales Range: $1-4.9 Billion
Emp.: 1,600
Holding Company; Health & Life Insurance Products & Services
N.A.I.C.S.: 551112
Jose Duran (Pres)
Richard Luna (Sr VP-Membership)
Carmen Molina (Sr VP-Customer Svc)
Ines Hernandez (Chief Medical Officer)
Jim O'Drobinak (Co-CEO)
Maritza I. Munich (Chief Legal Officer & Gen Counsel)
Maite Morales Martinez (Chief Compliance Officer)
Jose Aponte Amador (CFO)
Raymond Ortiz Marty (CTO)
Gladys Y. Flores Maldonado (Sr VP-Ops)
Ixel Rivera (VP-Clinical Affairs Ops)
Camalis Flores (VP-Comml Sls)
Un Tian See (VP)
Linda Lee (VP-Quality Improvement)
Gretchen Muniz (VP-HR)

Subsidiary (Domestic):

MCS Advantage, Inc. (2)
MCS Plz 255 Ave Ponce de Leon Ste 203,
Hato Rey, PR 00918-1919
Tel.: (787) 758-2500
Web Site: http://www.mcsclassicare.com
Sales Range: $800-899.9 Million
Health Insurance Products & Services
N.A.I.C.S.: 524114
David Scanavino (Pres)
Jose Aponte (CFO)

MCS Health Management Options, Inc. (2)
MCS Plz 255 Ave Ponce de Leon Ste 203,
Hato Rey, PR 00918-1919
Tel.: (787) 758-2500
Sales Range: $500-549.9 Million
Medicaid Sponsored Health Insurance
Products & Services
N.A.I.C.S.: 524114
David P. Schaffer (CFO)

MCS Life Insurance Co. (2)
MCS Plz 255 Ave Ponce de Leon Ste 900,
Hato Rey, PR 00902-3547
Tel.: (787) 758-2500
Sales Range: $150-199.9 Million
Life Insurance Products & Services
N.A.I.C.S.: 524113
Jose Duran (Pres)

Point Blank Enterprises, Inc. (1)
2102 SW 2nd St, Pompano Beach, FL
33069
Tel.: (954) 630-0900
Web Site:
　http://www.pointblankenterprises.com
Holding Company; Bulletproof Vest Mfr
N.A.I.C.S.: 551112
Daniel Gaston (CEO)
Hoyt Schmidt (Sr VP-Law Enforcement Sls)
Michael Foreman (Exec VP-Intl Bus Dev,
Federal Sls & Mktg)
Walter Kreidell (Dir-Correctional Sls & Product Mgmt)
Kevin Beary (Dir-Bus Dev)
Ulrich Grandt (Dir-Sls-European)
Mark Edwards (Exec VP-Military Sls & Bus Dev)

Subsidiary (Domestic):

Gould & Goodrich Leather, Inc. (2)
709 E McNeill St, Lillington, NC 27546
Tel.: (910) 893-2071
Web Site: http://www.gouldusa.com
Sales Range: $1-9.9 Million
All Other Leather Good Mfr
N.A.I.C.S.: 316990
Scott Nelson (Pres)

Point Blank Body Armor Inc. (2)
2102 SW 2nd St, Pompano Beach, FL
33069-4671　　　　　　　　　　(100%)
Tel.: (954) 630-0900
Web Site:
　http://www.pointblankenterprises.com
Body Armor Mfr
N.A.I.C.S.: 339113
Hoyt Schmidt (Exec VP-Comml Bus)
Michael Foreman (Exec VP-Intl Bus Dev,
Federal Sls & Mktg)
Walter Kreidell (Dir-Correctional Sls & Product Mgmt)
Daniel Gaston (CEO)

**Protective Apparel Corporation of
America** (2)
2102 SW 2nd St, Pompano Beach, FL
33069　　　　　　　　　　　　　(100%)
Tel.: (954) 630-0900
Web Site:
　http://www.pointblankenterprises.com
Body Armor Mfr
N.A.I.C.S.: 339113
Kevin Beary (Dir-Bus Dev)
Hoyt Schmidt (Sr VP-Law Enforcement Sls)
Michael Foreman (Exec VP-Int Bus Dev,
Federal Sls & Mktg)
Walter Kreidell (Dir-Correctional Sls & Product Mgmt)
Ulrich Grandt (Dir-Sls-European)
Daniel Gaston (Pres)

Repario (1)
112 W 34th St Ofc 18001, New York, NY
10120
Tel.: (816) 809-2892

Web Site: https://repariodata.com
Law firm
N.A.I.C.S.: 541199
Jim Urdanick (CFO)

Subsidiary (Domestic):

Modus eDiscovery, Inc. (2)
92 Cornerstone Dr Ste 403, Cary, NC
27519
Tel.: (202) 332-5500
Web Site: http://www.discovermodus.com
Sales Range: $1-9.9 Million
Emp.: 30
Litigation Support Services
N.A.I.C.S.: 561499
Steven Horan (Chm & CEO)
John Crites (CIO)

Ross Education, LLC (1)
22800 Hall Rd Ste 800, Clinton Township,
MI 48036
Tel.: (810) 637-6100
Web Site: http://www.rosseducation.edu
Trade School Operator for Health Services
N.A.I.C.S.: 611519
Anthony Iaquinto (CFO & Treas)
George Grayeb (Pres)

The J.G. Wentworth Company (1)
201 King of Prussia Rd Ste 501, Radnor,
PA 19087
Tel.: (484) 434-2300
Web Site: http://www.jgw.com
Rev.: $324,672,000
Assets: $4,992,907,000
Liabilities: $5,033,315,000
Net Worth: ($40,408,000)
Earnings: ($46,857,000)
Emp.: 600
Fiscal Year-end: 12/31/2016
Holding Company
N.A.I.C.S.: 551112
Randi Sellari (CEO)
William Schwartz (Chief HR Officer)
Dwight Perry (CFO)
Lori Lasher (Chief Compliance Officer, Chief
Legal Officer & Gen Counsel)
Brian Lawlor (VP-Pur)
Shannan Colangelo (VP-Pur & Customer
Support)
Joe Kelly (VP-Pur Ops)
Mark Haslam (VP-Capital Markets)
Mike Roakes (VP-Tax)
Richard Connelly (VP)
Lauren Crilley (VP)
Doreen Ghusar (VP-Compliance)
Kim Banks (Chief Acctg Officer)

Subsidiary (Domestic):

J.G. Wentworth SSC, L.P. (2)
40 Morris Ave, Bryn Mawr, PA 19010
Tel.: (215) 567-7660
Sales Range: $125-149.9 Million
Annuity & Structured Settlement Deferred
Payment Purchasing & Lending Services
N.A.I.C.S.: 525990
Randy Parker (Pres-Annuity & Structured
Settlement Payments)
Steven Sigman (Sr VP-Enterprise Transformation & Admin)
Stewart A. Stockdale (CEO)

Xcellence, Inc. (1)
5800 Foxridge Dr Ste 406, Shawnee Mission, KS 66202
Tel.: (913) 362-8662
Web Site: http://www.xactdatadiscovery.com
Data Management & Hosting Services
N.A.I.C.S.: 518210
Robert Polus (Founder & CEO)
Nick Reizen (VP-eDiscovery)
David Moran (Pres & COO)
Kate Mortensen (Chief Legal Officer)
Bob Lorum (VP-Mktg, Branding, Lead Generation & Inside Sls)
Bill Millican (VP-Admin)
Bill Anderson (Regional VP-eDiscovery
Svcs)
Liz Letak (Mng Dir-Orange Res Grp)
Scott Polus (Regional VP-Forensic Svcs)
Keri Grimmet (Corp Controller-Fin)
Roshan Simon (VP-IT)
David Sundwall (Sr Dir-Mgr Review Svcs)
T.J. Stamerro (Regional VP-eDiscovery Sls-
East)

Subsidiary (Domestic):

Lexolution, LLC (2)

75 Broad St Ste 610, New York, NY 10004
Tel.: (212) 370-9400
Web Site: http://www.lexolution.net
Sales Range: $1-9.9 Million
Emp.: 20
Human Resources & Executive Search
Consulting Services
N.A.I.C.S.: 541612
Scott Krowitz (Principal)

QDiscovery, LLC (2)
125 Eugene O'Neill Dr Ste 140, New London, CT 06320
Tel.: (860) 271-7080
Web Site: http://www.qdiscovery.com
Electronic Data & Document Management
Solutions
N.A.I.C.S.: 561439
Brian Dillon (Dir)

Subsidiary (Domestic):

Preferred Imaging, Inc. (3)
1402 Sadlier Cir W Dr, Indianapolis, IN
46239
Tel.: (317) 354-0680
Web Site: http://www.preferredimaging.com
Sales Range: $10-24.9 Million
Emp.: 15
Litigation Support Document Management
Consulting & Solutions
N.A.I.C.S.: 561439
Katie Nading (Dir-Production)
Bret Crist (Pres)

Subsidiary (Domestic):

RVM Enterprises, Inc. (2)
525 Washington Blvd 25th Fl, Jersey City,
NJ 07310
Tel.: (212) 693-1525
Web Site: http://www.rvminc.com
Corporate Consulting Services
N.A.I.C.S.: 541611
Vincent Brunetti (CEO)
Sean King (COO)
Geoffrey Sherman (CTO)
Salvatore Mancuso (Mng Dir)

Subsidiary (Domestic):

The Oliver Group LLC (3)
595 Greenhaven Rd, Pawcatuck, CT
06379-2055
Tel.: (860) 599-9760
Web Site: http://www.the-olivergroup.com
Data Acquisition & Litigation Support Services
N.A.I.C.S.: 561990
Ken Oliver (Partner)
Brian Oliver (Founder & Mng Partner)

JLM INDUSTRIES, INC.
106 S Tampania Ave Ste 200, Tampa,
FL 33609-3248
Tel.: (813) 632-3300　　　　　DE
Year Founded: 1986
Sales Range: $200-249.9 Million
Emp.: 163
Mfr, Marketer & Distr of Chemicals
N.A.I.C.S.: 424690
John L. MacDonald (Founder, Chm,
Pres & CEO)
Sean D. MacDonald (COO, VP-Sls &
Mktg)
Michael Molina (CFO & VP)
Linda L. Sato (Treas & VP)
Louis Conte (Controller)
Michael Jeffers (VP-Sls-JLM Mktg)

JLMOORE, INC.
27102 Royalton Rd, Columbia Station, OH 44028
Tel.: (440) 236-3589
Web Site: http://www.jlmooreinc.com
Year Founded: 1994
Rev.: $11,100,000
Emp.: 24
Commercial & Office Building Construction
N.A.I.C.S.: 236220
Patti A. Moore (CFO)
Steven W. Moore (CEO)
J. Ernie Mejia (Project Mgr)

JLS GROUP INC.
320 W 57th St Fl 2, New York, NY
10019-3705
Tel.: (212) 682-6700
Sales Range: $50-74.9 Million
Emp.: 35
Insurance Brokers
N.A.I.C.S.: 524210
Howard Bagdorf (Chm)
Frank Pearl (Pres)

JLS INVESTMENT GROUP LLC
4101 County Rd M, Middleton, WI
53562
Tel.: (608) 355-4570
Sales Range: $100-124.9 Million
Investment Services
N.A.I.C.S.: 523999
Jay L. Smith (Pres)

Subsidiaries:

Teel Plastics Inc. (1)
1060 Teel Ct, Baraboo, WI 53913
Tel.: (608) 355-3080
Web Site: http://www.teel.com
Rev.: $30,200,000
Emp.: 205
Thermoformed Finished Plastics Products
N.A.I.C.S.: 326199
Steve Schick (Dir-New Product Dev)
Randy Thomas (Dir-Sls & Mktg)
Fred Roeder (Engr-New Product & Process
Dev)
Bill Cannady (Dir-Mfg & Logistics)
DeeAnna Deane (Mgr-HR)
Brian Kelley (Mgr-Extrusion Shift)

JLS INVESTMENT REALTY
4111 Land O Lakes Blvd Ste 303BC,
Land O Lakes, FL 34639
Tel.: (813) 506-8212
Web Site:
　http://www.jlsinvestmentrealty.com
Sales Range: $1-9.9 Million
Real Estate Services
N.A.I.C.S.: 531210
Sandy Stepanek (Partner)

JM COX RESOURCES LP
400 W Wall St, Midland, TX 79701
Tel.: (432) 682-9435
Sales Range: $25-49.9 Million
Emp.: 30
Crude Petroleum Production
N.A.I.C.S.: 211120
Kelly Cox (Owner)

**JM EQUIPMENT COMPANY
INC.**
321 Spreckles Dr, Manteca, CA
95336
Tel.: (209) 522-3271
Web Site:
　http://www.jmequipment.com
Rev.: $40,861,575
Emp.: 170
Equipment Rental & Leasing Services
N.A.I.C.S.: 532490
Ray Azevedo (CEO)
Dave Baiocchi (VP)
Audie Burgan (Pres)
Vincent Victorine (CFO)

**JM FAMILY ENTERPRISES
INC.**
100 Jim Moran Blvd, Deerfield
Beach, FL 33442-1702
Tel.: (954) 429-2000　　　　　FL
Web Site: https://www.jmfamily.com
Year Founded: 1968
Sales Range: $5-14.9 Billion
Emp.: 5,037
Automobile & Other Motor Vehicle
Merchant Wholesalers
N.A.I.C.S.: 423110
Ed Sheehy (Exec VP)
Forrest Heathcott (Exec VP)
Brent Burns (Pres & CEO)

JM Family Enterprises Inc.—(Continued)

Colin Brown *(Chm)*
Carmen S. Johnson *(Exec VP-HR & Legal)*
Ken Yerves *(Chief Admin Officer & Exec VP)*
Jim Moran *(Founder)*
Dan Chait *(Exec VP)*
Chad Couch *(CIO & Sr VP)*
Eric Gebhard *(Interim CFO, Treas & Grp VP)*

Subsidiaries:

Home Franchise Concepts, Inc. (1)
19000 MacArthur Blvd Ste 100, Irvine, CA 92612
Tel.: (714) 637-2100
Web Site:
  http://www.homefranchiseconcepts.com
Emp.: 90
Window Coverings Mfr
N.A.I.C.S.: 449122
Gayle Milling *(CMO)*
Shirin Behzadi *(CEO)*
Adele Nasr *(VP-Digital Mktg)*
Faisal Khan *(CIO)*

Subsidiary (Domestic):

Budget Blinds, Inc. (2)
19000 MacArthur Blvd Ste 100, Irvine, CA 92612
Tel.: (714) 637-2100
Web Site: http://www.budgetblinds.com
Sales Range: $25-49.9 Million
Emp.: 100
Window Treatment Mfr & Franchising Services
N.A.I.C.S.: 449122
Brent Hallock *(Founder)*

InspectMyRide LLC (1)
30600 Aurora Rd Ste 180, Solon, OH 44139
Tel.: (877) 917-3767
Web Site: http://www.inspectmyride.com
Vehicle Inspection Services
N.A.I.C.S.: 561990

JM Lexus (1)
5350 W Sample Rd, Margate, FL 33073
Tel.: (954) 496-9220
Web Site: http://www.jmlexus.com
Sales of Automobiles
N.A.I.C.S.: 441110
Carlos Nunez *(Asst Mgr-Svc)*
Karen Reiner *(Sr Mgr-Svc)*
Keegan Potter *(Mgr-Client Care Center)*
Conrad Backer *(Sr Mgr-Svc)*
Robert Collins *(Fin Dir)*
Donald Cook *(Mgr-Customer Rels)*
Greg Zeigler *(Gen Mgr-Sls)*

JM&A Group (1)
100 Jim Moran Blvd, Deerfield Beach, FL 33442-1702
Tel.: (954) 429-2000
Web Site: http://www.jmfamily.com
Sales Range: $125-149.9 Million
Emp.: 1,200
Provider of Insurance & Warranty Products & Services
N.A.I.C.S.: 441110
Forrest Heathcott *(Pres)*
Robert Haeffner *(CFO & VP)*
Maria Guttuso *(Gen Counsel & VP)*

Subsidiary (Domestic):

Fidelity Warranty Services, Inc. (2)
500 Jim Moran Blvd, Deerfield Beach, FL 33442
Tel.: (800) 327-5172
Web Site:
  http://www.fidelitywarrantyservices.com
Automobile Repair & Maintenance Services
N.A.I.C.S.: 811111

Southeast Toyota Distributors, LLC (1)
100 Jim Moran Blvd, Deerfield Beach, FL 33442-1702
Tel.: (954) 429-2000
Web Site: http://www.jmfamily.com
Sales Range: $350-399.9 Million
Emp.: 2,500

Distr of Vehicles & Automotive Parts & Accessories
N.A.I.C.S.: 423110
Ed Sheehy *(Pres)*
Craig Pollock *(Grp VP & Asst Gen Mgr)*
Kevin Fleeger *(VP-Fixed Ops)*
Al Green *(VP-Vehicle Processing)*
Hank Grooms *(VP-Mktg & Field Ops)*
David Vincent *(VP-Market Representation & Bus Mgmt)*
Ray Natour *(VP-Field Ops)*
Andy Eccher *(VP-Distr & Accessories)*
Mike Stark *(VP-Sls Plng & Admin)*
Billy Hayes *(VP-Sls Ops)*
Robert D. Johnson *(CFO & VP-Fin)*
Todd Clarke *(Gen Counsel & VP)*
Myra Adams *(VP-Mktg)*
Jose Curtis *(VP-IT)*

World Omni Financial Corp. (1)
100 Jim Moran Blvd, Deerfield Beach, FL 33442-1702
Tel.: (954) 429-2000
Web Site: http://www.worldomni.com
Sales Range: $250-299.9 Million
Emp.: 2,000
Automobile Financing Services
N.A.I.C.S.: 522220
Dan Chait *(Pres)*
Michael Hollis *(VP-Ops)*

Subsidiary (Domestic):

CenterOne Financial Services, LLC (2)
190 Jim Moran Blvd, Deerfield Beach, FL 33442
Tel.: (888) 982-9800
Web Site:
  http://www.centeronefinancial.com
Financial Lending Services
N.A.I.C.S.: 522220

DataScan Holdings LLC (2)
100 Jim Moran Blvd, Deerfield Beach, FL 33442-1702
Tel.: (954) 429-2200
Investment Management Service
N.A.I.C.S.: 523940
Chris Atmore *(Dir-Bus Dev)*
Ed Brown *(Pres)*

Subsidiary (Domestic):

DataScan Field Services, LLC (3)
5925 Cabot Pkwy, Alpharetta, GA 30005
Tel.: (770) 521-6500
Web Site: http://www.dsfs.com
Automotive Inventory Verification & Vehicle Inspection Services
N.A.I.C.S.: 561499
David Lodigensky *(VP)*
Ann Cammarata *(Dir-Client Rels)*
Don Fowler *(Dir-Bus Dev)*

DataScan Technologies LLC (3)
5925 Cabot Pkwy, Alpharetta, GA 30005
Tel.: (770) 521-6500
Web Site: http://www.datascantech.com
Accounting & Risk Management Software Publisher
N.A.I.C.S.: 513210

Subsidiary (Domestic):

Southeast Toyota Finance (2)
401 Market St, Mobile, AL 36691-8817
Tel.: (800) 686-3494
Web Site: http://www.setf.com
Automobile Financing Services
N.A.I.C.S.: 522220
Brent Sergot *(Grp VP)*

JM INDUSTRIES INC.
26300 Bunert Rd, Warren, MI 48089
Tel.: (586) 771-7800
Web Site:
  http://www.jmindustries.com
Rev.: $20,000,000
Emp.: 40
Shipping Supplies
N.A.I.C.S.: 424130
Kristopher Moulds *(Pres)*

JM OIL COMPANY INC.
1222 Kuhn Dr, Saint Cloud, MN 56301
Tel.: (320) 251-2082

Year Founded: 1977
Sales Range: $10-24.9 Million
Emp.: 150
Sales Of Petroleum Products
N.A.I.C.S.: 424710
Brian Laudenbach *(Gen Mgr)*

JM PROCESS SYSTEMS INC.
15507 S 70th Ct, Orland Park, IL 60462-5105
Tel.: (708) 429-3040   **IL**
Web Site: http://www.jmprocess.com
Year Founded: 1981
Sales Range: $75-99.9 Million
Emp.: 3
Environmental Controls & Instrumentation Distr
N.A.I.C.S.: 423830
Marie McDermott *(Treas & Sec)*

Subsidiaries:

Aquatrol Corporation (1)
15507 S 70th Ct, Orland Park, IL 60462-5105
Tel.: (708) 429-3040
Industrial Products Mfr
N.A.I.C.S.: 332919

JM WALKER LP
3733 Flory St, Fort Worth, TX 76180
Tel.: (817) 595-1121
Sales Range: $10-24.9 Million
Emp.: 20
Hospital Construction & General Commercial Contractors
N.A.I.C.S.: 236220
Joe Walker *(Pres)*
Chip Walker *(Controller)*

Subsidiaries:

Advantage Steel Service, Inc. (1)
3700 Flory St, Fort Worth, TX 76180
Tel.: (817) 284-1693
Web Site:
  http://www.advantagesteelservice.com
Emp.: 35
Iron & Steel Forgings
N.A.I.C.S.: 332111
Tom Church *(Pres)*

JMA INFORMATION TECHNOLOGY
10551 Barkley Ste 400, Overland Park, KS 66212
Tel.: (913) 722-3252
Web Site: http://www.jmait.com
Year Founded: 1994
Sales Range: $50-74.9 Million
Emp.: 375
Information Technology Consulting Services
N.A.I.C.S.: 541512
Joseph Melookaran *(Pres)*
David Brown *(COO & Exec VP)*
Raqib Huq *(VP-Integrated Solutions)*
Maria Will *(VP-Tech Solutions Div)*

JMA PROPERTIES LLC
205 SE Spokane St Ste 300, Portland, OR 97202
Web Site:
  http://www.jmaproperties.com
Year Founded: 2008
Sales Range: $1-9.9 Million
Emp.: 40
Real Estate Broker
N.A.I.C.S.: 531210
Gerry Mains *(Founder)*

JMA SOLUTIONS
600 Maryland Ave SW Ste 900 W, Washington, DC 20024
Tel.: (202) 863-2680
Web Site: http://www.jma-solutions.com
Year Founded: 2005
Sales Range: $1-9.9 Million

Emp.: 40
Traffic Flow Management Services
N.A.I.C.S.: 928110
Jan Adams *(Pres & CEO)*

JMA VENTURES, LLC
460 Bush St, San Francisco, CA 94108
Tel.: (415) 728-0794   **CA**
Web Site:
  http://www.jmaventuresllc.com
Year Founded: 2002
Sales Range: $1-9.9 Million
Emp.: 30
Real Estate Investment & Development Firm
N.A.I.C.S.: 531390
Art Chapman *(Founder & Chm)*
David Tirman *(Exec VP)*
Todd Chapman *(Pres & CEO)*
Anthony Demelo *(Controller)*
Belinda Silva *(Controller)*
Michael McManus *(Principal)*
Paul Faries *(VP)*
Kevin Morgan *(VP-Acq & Fin)*
Kathy Chan *(VP-HR)*
Chris Heinrich *(VP-Resort Dev)*
Jose Luis Martinez *(CFO)*

Subsidiaries:

Homewood Mountain Resort (1)
5145 Westlake Blvd, Homewood, CA 96141
Tel.: (530) 525-2992
Web Site: http://www.skihomewood.com
Rev.: $1,200,000
Fiscal Year-end: 12/31/2006
Ski Resort
N.A.I.C.S.: 713920

JMAC INC.
150 E Wilson Bridge Rd, Worthington, OH 43085-2328
Tel.: (614) 436-2418   **OH**
Year Founded: 1980
Sales Range: $200-249.9 Million
Emp.: 2,500
Mfr of Steel Products
N.A.I.C.S.: 331513
Kim Sievers *(VP & Controller)*

Subsidiaries:

Hughes Parker Industries LLC (1)
1604 Mahr Ave, Lawrenceburg, TN 38464-2202
Tel.: (931) 762-9403
Web Site: http://www.hughesparker.com
Sales Range: $10-24.9 Million
Emp.: 100
Provider of Metal Stamping Services
N.A.I.C.S.: 332119
William L. Hillis *(Dir-Quality & Process Engrg)*

RPI of Indiana Inc. (1)
8339 County Rd 245, Holmesville, OH 44633-9724
Tel.: (330) 279-2411
Sales Range: $10-24.9 Million
Emp.: 20
Mfr of Metal Products
N.A.I.C.S.: 332313

JMAR, LLC
10905 Technology Pl, San Diego, CA 92127
Tel.: (858) 946-6800   **DE**
Sales Range: Less than $1 Million
Emp.: 16
Laser & X-Ray Technologies Developer & Mfr
N.A.I.C.S.: 339112

Subsidiaries:

JMAR Research, Inc. (1)
3956 Sorrento Vly Blvd, San Diego, CA 92121-1427
Tel.: (858) 535-1706
Provider of Semiconductor Research Services
N.A.I.C.S.: 541715

JSI Microelectronics (1)
4235 Forcum Ave, McClellan, CA 95652
Tel.: (916) 648-2088
Web Site: http://www.jsi-micro.com
N.A.I.C.S.: 334413

JMARK BUSINESS SOLUTIONS, INC.

601 N National Ave Ste 102, Springfield, MO 65802
Tel.: (417) 863-1700   MO
Web Site: http://www.jmark.com
Year Founded: 2001
Sales Range: $1-9.9 Million
Emp.: 50
Computer & Software Sales
N.A.I.C.S.: 449210
Thomas Douglas (Pres & CEO)
Jeff Bendure (Dir-Acct Mgmt)
Brandon Walker (Mgr-Backup)
Christy Cravens (Coord-HR)
Daniel Strader (Engr-Network)
Doug Deetz (Partner & Sr VP-Sls)
Jason Stewart (Chief Compliance Officer)
Russell Wall (Mgr-RMM)
Todd Nielsen (Chief Strategy Officer)
Chris Huels (Chief Svc Officer)
Kevin Graves (COO)

JMB REALTY CORPORATION

900 N Michigan Ave Ste 1500, Chicago, IL 60611-1542
Tel.: (312) 440-4800   IL
Sales Range: $1-4.9 Billion
Emp.: 1,000
Real Estate Investment Firm, Syndicator & Developer
N.A.I.C.S.: 523999
Neil G. Bluhm (Co-Founder & Pres)
Ron Godsey (Controller)
Judd Malkin (Co-Founder & Chm)
Rigel Barbec (COO)
Steve Lovelett (CFO)

Subsidiaries:

JMB/245 Park Avenue Associates, Ltd. (1)
900 N Michigan Ave, Chicago, IL 60611
Tel.: (312) 915-1987
Rev.: $11,435,979
Earnings: $10,982,721
Fiscal Year-end: 11/27/2017
Commercial Property Management Services
N.A.I.C.S.: 531120
Patrick J. Meara (Pres & CEO)

JMC CAPITAL PARTNERS LLC

53 State St Ste 2303, Boston, MA 02109
Tel.: (617) 338-1144
Web Site: http://www.jmccp.com
Year Founded: 1999
Privater Equity Firm
N.A.I.C.S.: 523999
Michael A. D'Amelio (Co-Founder & Mng Partner)
G. Lawrence Bero (Co-Founder & Partner)
Bill Tamul (Operating Partner)
Todd Rainville (Partner)
Greg Dunne (Partner-Ops)
Gerry Burns (Operating Partner)
David Logan (Operating Partner)
Chris Moore (CFO)
Greg Schultz (VP)
Nicole Verderame (Acct Mgr)

Subsidiaries:

CIVIQ Smartscapes LLC (1)
430 Fortune Blvd, Milford, MA 01757
Tel.: (508) 381-2900
Web Site: http://www.civiqsmartscapes.com
Interactive Digital Signage & Kiosk Systems Designer & Mfr
N.A.I.C.S.: 541511
Brad Gleeson (Chief Comml Officer)
Joshua Berglund (Mgr-Engrg Program)

Scott Plesh (Mgr-Bus Dev)
Brian Dusho (Pres-Digital Out-of-Home)
Joanne Mavroides (VP-Ops)
Ilan Rozenblat (CTO)
Gerry Burns (Pres)
Brian Diver (Chief Revenue Officer)

Branch (Domestic):

CIVIQ Smartscapes (2)
200 S Michigan Ave Ste 1305, Chicago, IL 60604
Tel.: (312) 300-4776
Web Site: http://www.elevatedigital.com
Emp.: 20
Digital Advertising Software Developer
N.A.I.C.S.: 513210
George Burciaga (CEO)
Tony Filko (CFO)
Erwin Rezelman (Pres)

Mansfield Sales Partners, LLC (1)
100 Brickstone Sq Ste 205, Andover, MA 01810
Tel.: (781) 460-2100
Web Site: http://www.mansfieldsp.com
Sales Outsourcing Service
N.A.I.C.S.: 541613
Greg Dunne (CEO)
Jennifer Hunt (VP)
Eileen Sciarra (Dir-Client Svcs)

Phoenix Products Company, Inc. (1)
8711 W Port Ave, Milwaukee, WI 53224-3429
Tel.: (414) 973-3300
Web Site: http://www.phoenixproducts.com
Special Purpose Lighting Fixtures & Ovens Mfr
N.A.I.C.S.: 335132
George J. Wordingham (Pres)
Scott Fredrick (CEO)
Yazi Fletcher (VP-Engrg)
Tom Feldhusen (Mgr-Natl Acct)

Subsidiary (Domestic):

Phoenix International, Inc. (2)
8711 W Port Ave, Milwaukee, WI 53224
Tel.: (414) 973-3400
Web Site: http://www.phx-international.com
Sales Range: $10-24.9 Million
Electrode & Flux Ovens Mfr
N.A.I.C.S.: 333994
Nate Klieve (Gen Mgr)

Pro-Vision Inc. (1)
8625 B Byron Commerce Dr SW, Byron Center, MI 49315
Tel.: (616) 583-1520
Web Site: http://www.seeingissafety.com
Sales Range: $1-9.9 Million
Emp.: 26
Rear Vision Video Recording Systems for Vehicles
N.A.I.C.S.: 334310
Sam Lehnert (Mgr-Mktg)
Michael Finn (Pres)

Subsidiary (Domestic):

Zone Defense, LLC (2)
2135 13th Ave N, Saint Petersburg, FL 33713
Tel.: (866) 672-1212
Web Site: http://www.zonedefensetruck.com
Sales Range: $10-24.9 Million
Emp.: 19
Video & Photographic Equipment Mfr
N.A.I.C.S.: 334310
James Markus (Pres)
Josh Markus (Reg Mgr-Sls)
Dan Camm (Reg Mgr-Sls)
Gabriela Aviles (Mgr-Sls-Intl)
Doug Mesler (Controller)
Mark Vosler (Officer Mgr)
Elaine Ferguson (Officer Mgr)
Teresa Prisbrey (Mgr-Mktg)

JMC COMMUNITIES, INC.

2201 4th St N Ste 200, Saint Petersburg, FL 33704
Tel.: (727) 823-0022   FL
Web Site:
http://www.jmccommunities.com
Year Founded: 1978
Sales Range: $10-24.9 Million
Emp.: 30

Condominium Developer
N.A.I.C.S.: 237210
J. Michael Cheezem (Founder & CEO)
John Michael Cheezem (CEO)
Claudia Emery (VP-Sls & Mktg)
Gail Cooper (Mgr-Admin)
John P. Hobach (COO)
Jim Baar (Controller)
Michael Green (Mgr-Construction)
Gil St.Clair (Mng Dir)

JMC EQUIPMENT LLC

340C Central Ave, Bohemia, NY 11716
Web Site:
http://www.jmcautomotiveequipment.com
Year Founded: 2012
Sales Range: $1-9.9 Million
Emp.: 8
Automotive Equipment & Tool Distr
N.A.I.C.S.: 423120
Juan E. Chavez (CEO)

JMD COMMUNICATIONS

760 Calle Bolivar, San Juan, PR 00909
Tel.: (787) 728-3030
Web Site: http://www.jmdcom.com
Year Founded: 1996
Rev.: $25,000,000
Emp.: 35
Full Service
N.A.I.C.S.: 541810
Joey Jimenez (Pres)
Carlos Davila Rinaldi (Creative Dir)

JME INCORPORATED

527 Park Ave, San Fernando, CA 91340
Tel.: (818) 899-8818
Web Site: http://www.tmb.com
Rev.: $20,000,000
Emp.: 45
Lighting Fittings & Accessories
N.A.I.C.S.: 423610
Colin Waters (CEO)

JMG REALTY, INC.

5605 Glenridge Dr Ste 1010, Atlanta, GA 30342
Tel.: (404) 995-1111
Web Site: http://www.jmgrealty.com
Year Founded: 1989
Sales Range: $200-249.9 Million
Emp.: 500
Real Estate Investment, Management & Development
N.A.I.C.S.: 523999
Karlton Jackson (CEO)
Tim Brock (Pres)
LuAnne Acton-Ross (Partner & Exec VP)
Charles F. Coburn (Exec VP)
Lorraine B. Johnson (Partner & Exec VP)
Cynthia G. Kelley (COO)
Thomas H. Staten (CFO)
Bonnie B. Smetzer (Partner & Exec VP)
Jean Woodworth (Partner & Exec VP)

JMGT STUDIOS SATELLITE TELEVISION NETWORK, LLC

7485 SVL Box, Victorville, CA 92395
Tel.: (760) 671-0014   CA
Year Founded: 2005
Sales Range: $10-24.9 Million
Emp.: 1
3D Television
N.A.I.C.S.: 334220
JayCee James (CEO & Gen Mgr)

JMH CAPITAL

155 Federal St Ste 502, Boston, MA 02110
Tel.: (617) 910-2602
Web Site: http://www.jmhcapital.com
Sales Range: $25-49.9 Million
Emp.: 10
Equity Investment Firm
N.A.I.C.S.: 523999
John A. Nies (Mng Dir)
Scott D. Steele (Mng Dir)
Kim Menegoni (CFO)
Tate Bevis (Mng Dir)
Michael Stanek (Mng Partner)

Subsidiaries:

Berean Christian Stores (1)
1183 Smiley Ave, Cincinnati, OH 45240
Tel.: (513) 671-0300
Web Site: http://www.berean.com
Sales Range: $25-49.9 Million
Religious Retail Bookstores
N.A.I.C.S.: 459210

Carlisle Wide Plank Floors, Inc. (1)
1676 Rte 9, Stoddard, NH 03464
Tel.: (603) 239-2350
Web Site: http://www.wideplankflooring.com
Sales Range: $1-9.9 Million
Wooden Plank Flooring Mfr & Retailer
N.A.I.C.S.: 444110
David Ashton (Coord-Comml Dev)

JMI SERVICES, INC.

12265 El Camino Real Ste 150, San Diego, CA 92130
Tel.: (858) 350-4800   TX
Web Site: http://www.jmi-inc.com
Year Founded: 1992
Sales Range: $50-74.9 Million
Emp.: 15
Investment Holding Company
N.A.I.C.S.: 551112
John Moores (Founder, Chm & CEO)

Subsidiaries:

JMI Equity (1)
2 Hamill Rd Ste 272, Baltimore, MD 21210
Tel.: (410) 951-0200
Web Site: http://www.jmi.com
Sales Range: $50-74.9 Million
Equity Investment Firm
N.A.I.C.S.: 523999
Harry S. Gruner (Co-Founder & Mng Gen Partner)
Jit Sinha (Gen Partner)
Beth Hicks Thorpe (Office Mgr)
Randy Guttman (Gen Partner)
Bob Nye (Gen Partner)
Matt Emery (Gen Partner)
Brian Hersman (Gen Partner-San Diego)
Paul Barber (Chm)
David Greenberg (Gen Partner)
Kathy Fields (Gen Partner, Chief Compliance Officer & Gen Counsel)
Krishna Potarazu (Partner)
Suken Vakil (Gen Partner)
Chris Rhodes (VP)
Maggie Schmitt (Partner & CFO)
Vincent Prajka (Partner)
Sureel Sheth (VP)
Jackie Coombe (VP-IR & Mktg)
Peter Arrowsmith (Mng Gen Partner)
Katie Frisch (Asst Controller)
Melissa Caslin Guttman (VP-Talent)
Larry Contrella (Principal)
Paul Chang (VP)
Tyler Duke (VP-San Diego)
Meredith Keller (Dir-Portfolio Talent-San Diego)

Joint Venture (Domestic):

Applied Systems Inc. (2)
200 Applied Pkwy, University Park, IL 60484-4110
Tel.: (708) 534-5575
Web Site: http://www.appliedsystems.com
Sales Range: $75-99.9 Million
Emp.: 1,100
Insurance Software
N.A.I.C.S.: 513210
Doug Johnston (VP-Partner Rels)
Ian Hoffman (CMO)
James R. White (Exec VP-Sls)

JMI Services, Inc.—(Continued)

Kristin Hackney *(Sr VP-Svcs)*
Michael Howe *(Sr VP-Product Mgmt)*
Jeffrey D. Purdy *(Sr VP-Ops-Intl)*
Tim Sander *(Sr VP-IT)*
Gregory Shiple *(Sr VP-Support)*
David H. Whitley *(Sr VP-Dev)*
Paul Ramsey *(Sr VP-HR)*
Teresa Smith *(Sr VP-Customer Advocacy)*
Taylor Rhodes *(CEO)*
Graham Blackwell *(CFO)*

Innovative Interfaces Inc.   (2)
1900 Powell St Ste 400, Emeryville, CA
94608
Tel.: (510) 655-6200
Web Site: http://www.iii.com
Sales Range: $75-99.9 Million
Software Developer
N.A.I.C.S.: 513210
Hilary Newman *(Sr VP-Library Success)*
Marina Keating *(Sr VP-Customer Experience)*
Leif Pedersen *(Exec VP-Product)*
James Tallman *(CEO)*
Aaron Terrell *(VP-Engrg & IT)*
Akin Adekeye *(Gen Counsel & VP-Partnerships & Bus Dev)*
Chris Fields *(CTO)*
Kathryn Harnish *(Sr VP-Product Strategy)*
Amy Hayes *(Sr VP-Mktg)*
Shaheen Javadizadeh *(Exec VP-Sls-Global)*
Roger Leitner *(COO)*
Joe McMorris *(CIO)*
Don Schad *(CFO)*

Subsidiary (Domestic):

VTLS, Inc.   (3)
1701 Kraft Dr, Blacksburg, VA 24060
Tel.: (540) 557-1200
Web Site: http://www.vtls.com
Emp.: 100
Project Management & Digital Imaging Solutions
N.A.I.C.S.: 513210

Branch (Domestic):

JMI Equity   (2)
7776 Ivanhoe Ave Ste 200, La Jolla, CA
92037
Tel.: (858) 362-9880
Web Site: http://www.jmiequity.com
Sales Range: $75-99.9 Million
Emp.: 12
Equity Investment Firm
N.A.I.C.S.: 523999
Paul V. Barber *(Mng Gen Partner)*

Joint Venture (Non-US):

Paradigm B.V.   (2)
WTC A Tower 7th Floor Strawinskylaan 717,
1077 XX, Amsterdam, Netherlands
Tel.: (31) 203337570
Web Site: http://www.pdgm.com
Sales Range: $125-149.9 Million
Emp.: 7
Software Solutions for Oil & Gas Exploration
N.A.I.C.S.: 541511

Subsidiary (Non-US):

Paradigm FZ-LLC   (3)
Building 2 Office 101, PO Box 500148,
Dubai Internet City, Dubai, United Arab
Emirates
Tel.: (971) 43910673
Web Site: http://www.pdgm.com
Sales Range: $10-24.9 Million
Software Services for Oil & Gas Production
Industry
N.A.I.C.S.: 513210

Paradigm Geophysical (UK)
Limited   (3)
Dukes Court Bldg C 3rd Flr, Dukes Street,
Woking, GU21 5BH, Surrey, United Kingdom
Tel.: (44) 1483758000
Web Site: http://www.pdgm.com
Sales Range: $10-24.9 Million
Software Services for Oil & Gas Production
Industry
N.A.I.C.S.: 513210

Paradigm Geophysical Canada
Limited   (3)

125 9th Avenue SE Suite 2110, Calgary,
T2G 0P6, AB, Canada
Tel.: (403) 571-1555
Web Site: http://www.pdgm.com
Sales Range: $10-24.9 Million
Software Services for Oil & Gas Production
Industry
N.A.I.C.S.: 513210

Subsidiary (US):

Paradigm Geophysical Corp.   (3)
2 Memorial Plz 820 Gessner Rd Ste 400,
Houston, TX 77024
Tel.: (713) 393-4800
Web Site: http://www.pdgm.com
Sales Range: $25-49.9 Million
Oil & Natural Gas Software Systems
N.A.I.C.S.: 513210
Samhita Shah *(Dir-Mktg Comm)*
Morris Hasting *(VP-Strategic Accts)*
Chris Chaffin *(Chief Compliance Officer,
Gen Counsel & Sec)*
Indy Chakrabarti *(Sr VP-Product Mgmt &
Strategy)*

Subsidiary (Non-US):

Paradigm Geophysical LLC   (3)
Dubininskaya Street 53 Building 5, Moscow,
Russia
Tel.: (7) 4959334440
Web Site: http://www.pdgm.com
Sales Range: $10-24.9 Million
Software Services for Oil & Gas Production
Industry
N.A.I.C.S.: 513210
Mikhail Porechenkov *(Gen Dir)*

Paradigm Geophysical S.A.   (3)
Carlos Pellegrini 713 Piso 9, Buenos Aires,
C1009ABO, Argentina
Tel.: (54) 1143225735
Web Site: http://www.pdgm.com
Sales Range: $10-24.9 Million
Software Services for Oil & Gas Production
Industry
N.A.I.C.S.: 513210

Paradigm Geophysical Sdn Bhd   (3)
Level 12 Tower 1 Etiqa Twins 11 Jalan
Pinang, 11 Jalan Pinang, Kuala Lumpur,
50450, Malaysia
Tel.: (60) 321638111
Web Site: http://www.pdgm.com
Sales Range: $10-24.9 Million
Software Services for Oil & Gas Production
Industry
N.A.I.C.S.: 513210
Jonathan Ling *(Reg VP-Asia Pacific)*

Paradigm Technology (Beijing) Co.,
Ltd.   (3)
1803 Capital Mansion No 6 Xin Yan South
Road, Chao Yang District, Beijing, 100004,
China
Tel.: (86) 1064654870
Web Site: http://www.pdgm.com
Sales Range: $10-24.9 Million
Software Services for Oil & Gas Production
Industry
N.A.I.C.S.: 513210

JMI Realty LLC   (1)
111 Congress Ave Ste 2600, Austin, TX
78701
Tel.: (512) 539-3600
Web Site: http://www.jmirealty.com
Sales Range: $50-74.9 Million
Emp.: 11
Real Estate Investment Trust
N.A.I.C.S.: 525990
John C. Kratzer *(Pres & CEO)*
Gregory W. Clay *(Chief Investment Officer)*
James A. Chatfield *(Mng Partner & Sr VP)*
Tim Jackson *(Controller)*

JMI Sports LLC   (1)
100 Park Blvd, San Diego, CA 92101
Tel.: (619) 756-6340
Web Site: http://www.jmisports.com
Sales Range: $100-124.9 Million
Emp.: 10
Sports, Entertainment & Public Assembly
Facility Planning, Development & Investment Services
N.A.I.C.S.: 523999
Erik Judson *(Co-CEO)*
Kate Dimitruk *(Mgr-Bus Ops)*

Zach Davis *(Project Mgr)*
Kacie Renc *(Pres-Dev)*
Tom Stultz *(Co-CEO)*

JMK AUTO SALES INC.
391 Rte 22 E, Springfield, NJ 07081
Tel.: (973) 379-7744
Web Site:
http://www.jmkbmwsaab.com
Year Founded: 1965
Sales Range: $125-149.9 Million
Emp.: 160
Owner & Operator of Car Dealerships
N.A.I.C.S.: 441110
Robert Schoenenman *(Gen Mgr-BMW)*
Cathi Maier *(Partner & Gen Mgr-Saab)*
Roger Kosempel *(Pres)*
Darell Redmond *(Controller)*

JMK INTERNATIONAL, INC.
1401 N Bowie Dr, Weatherford, TX
76086
Tel.: (817) 737-3703
Web Site: http://www.jmkint.com
Year Founded: 1983
Sales Range: $25-49.9 Million
Emp.: 300
Mfr of Mechanical Rubber Goods
N.A.I.C.S.: 326291
Mike Micallef *(Pres)*

Subsidiaries:

JMK Operations Inc.   (1)
1401 N Bowie Dr, Weatherford, TX 76086
Tel.: (817) 737-3703
Web Site: http://www.jamak.com
Sales Range: $25-49.9 Million
Emp.: 15
Investment Holding Companies, Except
Banks
N.A.I.C.S.: 551112
Alfred M. Micallef *(Chm)*

Jamak Fabrication-Tex Ltd.   (1)
1401 N Bowie Dr, Weatherford, TX 76086
Tel.: (817) 594-8771
Web Site: http://www.jamak.com
Rev.: $37,649,696
Emp.: 250
Mechanical Rubber Goods
N.A.I.C.S.: 326291
Alfred M. Micallef *(Owner)*

JML UNLIMITED
242 W 36th St 8th Fl, New York, NY
10018
Tel.: (212) 243-3620
Year Founded: 1976
Sales Range: Less than $1 Million
Emp.: 7
Lithographic Commercial Printing
N.A.I.C.S.: 323111
Joseph Litvack *(Pres)*
Karen Litvack *(Owner)*

JMP COAL HOLDINGS, LLC
3228 Summit Square Pl Ste 180,
Lexington, KY 40509
Tel.: (859) 543-0515
Web Site:
http://www.jmpholdingsllc.com
Year Founded: 2004
Holding Company
N.A.I.C.S.: 551112
Mitch Potter *(Co-Chm & CEO)*
Tom Potter *(Co-Chm & COO)*
Elbert Foley *(CFO)*
Debbie Smith *(Treas)*
Jeff Sands *(VP-Mining Ops)*

Subsidiaries:

Blackhawk Mining, LLC   (1)
3228 Summit Square Pl Ste 180, Lexington,
KY 40509
Tel.: (859) 543-0515
Web Site: http://blackhawkmining.com

Acquires & Operates Coal Reserves, Mines,
Preparation Plants & Loading Facilities
N.A.I.C.S.: 212115
Nicholas R. Glancy *(Pres)*

JMR ELECTRONICS INC.
8968 Fullbride Ave, Chatsworth, CA
91311-5372
Tel.: (818) 993-4801
Web Site: http://www.jmr.com
Year Founded: 1982
Rev.: $38,157,817
Emp.: 50
Metal Stamping
N.A.I.C.S.: 332119
Josef Rabinovitz *(Pres)*
Marie Rabinovitz *(Exec VP)*
Mitch Guzik *(COO)*
Judy Schoen *(Controller)*

JMR FINANCIAL GROUP, INC.
130 W Superior St Ste 645, Duluth,
MN 55802
Tel.: (218) 727-5565
Web Site: http://www.jmrfg.com
Sales Range: $1-9.9 Million
Accounting, Tax, Employee Benefits,
Financial Planning & Wealth Management Services
N.A.I.C.S.: 561499
Nathan A. Madill *(Pres & Sec)*
Robin L. Rosenbaum *(Treas & VP)*

JMX INTERNATIONAL CORPORATION
1877 Porter Lake Dr, Sarasota, FL
34240
Tel.: (941) 377-5112
Web Site:
http://www.jmxinternational.com
Year Founded: 2003
Sales Range: $1-9.9 Million
Emp.: 11
Internet Retailer
N.A.I.C.S.: 449110
James P. Miller *(CEO)*
Gwen Heaton *(Bus Mgr)*

JN CHEVROLET
2999 N Nimitz Hwy, Honolulu, HI
96819-1903
Tel.: (808) 831-2500
Web Site:
http://www.jnautomotive.com
Year Founded: 1961
Sales Range: $50-74.9 Million
Emp.: 207
New Car Dealer
N.A.I.C.S.: 441110
Brad M. Nicolai *(Pres & Gen Mgr)*
Gayle Awong *(Mgr-JN Parts)*
Carlton Hill *(Mgr-Used Vehicle)*
Wayne Hirata *(Mgr-Audi Parts)*
Joseph P. Nicolai *(Chm)*
Bryan Marino *(Dir-Parts & Svc)*
Marisa Miner *(Mgr-Audi Svc)*
Brian Muratsuka *(Mgr-JN Svc)*
Darrell Toma *(Asst Treas)*
Kirk Wong *(Treas)*

JN-INTERNATIONAL MEDICAL CORPORATION
2720 N 84th St, Omaha, NE 68134
Tel.: (402) 932-7931
Web Site: http://www.jn-vaccines.org
Year Founded: 1998
Sales Range: $1-9.9 Million
Emp.: 17
Health & Allied Services
N.A.I.C.S.: 621999
Jeeri R. Reddy *(CEO & Dir-Scientific)*
Noel Koumae *(COO-Africa & Dir-Medical)*
Peter Gotzinger *(Dir-Ops)*

JNJ EXPRESS INC.

3935 Old Getwell Rd, Memphis, TN
38118
Tel.: (901) 362-3444
Web Site: http://www.jnjexpress.com
Rev.: $11,000,000
Emp.: 70
Trucking Service
N.A.I.C.S.: 484110
John T. Ennis *(Pres)*
Don Tinker *(Bus Mgr)*
Joe Hilderbrand *(Gen Mgr)*

JNJ MOBILE INC.
186 South St, Boston, MA 02111
Web Site:
  http://www.mocospace.com
Year Founded: 2005
Sales Range: $10-24.9 Million
Emp.: 50
Mobile Web Applications
N.A.I.C.S.: 516210
Justin Siegel *(Co-Founder & CEO)*

**JNS MEDIA SPECIALISTS,
INC.**
78080 Calle Estado Ste 201, La
Quinta, CA 92253
Tel.: (760) 775-0000   CA
Web Site: http://www.jnsnext.com
Year Founded: 2008
Sales Range: $1-9.9 Million
Emp.: 11
Advertising Agency Services
N.A.I.C.S.: 541810
Garry Sage *(Pres & CEO)*
Judy Sage *(CFO & VP)*
Risseth Lora *(VP-Ops)*
David Wells *(VP-Comm)*
Jessica Walke *(Sr Mgr-Mktg)*

JNS-SMITHCHEM, LLC
90 6th St, Paterson, NJ 07524
Tel.: (973) 278-9050
Web Site: http://www.jns-
  smithchem.com
Professional, Scientific & Technical
Services
N.A.I.C.S.: 541990
Michael Smith *(Co-Pres)*

Subsidiaries:

CheMarCo, Inc.   (1)
63 Pelham Davis Cir, Greenville, SC 29615
Tel.: (864) 234-6735
Web Site: http://www.chemarco.com
Sales Range: $1-9.9 Million
Emp.: 12
Chemical & Allied Products Merchant Whslr
N.A.I.C.S.: 424690
Fred Tolerico *(VP)*
Martin Carter *(Pres)*

JO-DI'S INC.
530 New Park Ave, West Hartford,
CT 06106
Tel.: (860) 236-5443
Web Site: http://www.jo-dis.com
Year Founded: 1970
Sales Range: $10-24.9 Million
Emp.: 60
Retailer of Automotive Sound Equip-
ment
N.A.I.C.S.: 441330
Joseph DiFazio *(Pres)*

JO-KELL INCORPORATED
1716 Lambert Ct, Chesapeake, VA
23320
Tel.: (757) 523-2900
Web Site: http://www.jokell.com
Rev.: $16,452,822
Emp.: 50
Electrical Apparatus & Equipment
N.A.I.C.S.: 423610

Martin J. Kelly *(Pres)*
Adrian Marchi *(COO)*
Kim Harrison *(Mgr-HR)*
Tara Perrone *(Dir-Creative)*

**JOAN B. MARCUS COMMUNI-
CATIONS LLC**
1004 N 22nd St, Allentown, PA 18104
Tel.: (610) 437-3255
Web Site:
  http://www.joanbmarcus.com
Year Founded: 1979
Sales Range: $1-9.9 Million
Emp.: 1
Grant Writing, Marketing Communica-
tions, Marketing Strategy & Content
Development
N.A.I.C.S.: 541820
Joan B. Marcus *(Pres)*

**JOAN PEARCE RESEARCH
ASSOCIATES**
419 N Larchmont Blvd Ste 30, Los
Angeles, CA 90004
Tel.: (323) 655-5464
Web Site:
  https://www.joanpearceresearch
  associates.com
Year Founded: 1992
Marketing Research Service
N.A.I.C.S.: 541910

**JOAN SMITH ENTERPRISES
INC.**
4320 W Chandler Blvd Ste 1, Chan-
dler, AZ 85226
Tel.: (480) 345-0005
Web Site: http://www.calpool.com
Sales Range: $25-49.9 Million
Emp.: 40
Swimming Pool Construction
N.A.I.C.S.: 238990
Jeremy Smith *(Owner & Pres)*

JOB STORE INC.
7100 E Hampden Ave, Denver, CO
80224
Tel.: (303) 757-7686
Web Site:
  http://www.jobstorestaffing.com
Sales Range: $10-24.9 Million
Emp.: 12
Temporary & Job Placement Service
N.A.I.C.S.: 561320
Dorothy Grandbois *(Pres)*

JOBAR INC.
995 Wildlife Lodge Rd, Lower Burrell,
PA 15068-2731
Tel.: (724) 339-8275   PA
Year Founded: 1987
Sales Range: $50-74.9 Million
Emp.: 490
Grocery Stores
N.A.I.C.S.: 445110

**JOBBERS AUTOMOTIVE
WAREHOUSE**
801 E Zimmerly St, Wichita, KS
67211
Tel.: (316) 267-4393
Web Site: http://www.jawinc.com
Sales Range: $10-24.9 Million
Emp.: 97
Automotive Supplies & Parts
N.A.I.C.S.: 423120
Judy Schott *(Office Mgr-Ops)*
Barry Leabo *(VP-Sls & Mktg)*

JOBBOT, INC.
1730 62nd St, Brooklyn, NY 11204
Tel.: (646) 780-0992   NY
Web Site: http://www.jobbot.biz
Year Founded: 2011
Online Employment Services
N.A.I.C.S.: 561311

Patrick Giordano *(Pres, CEO, CFO &
Treas)*
Robert Denn *(Sec)*

JOBCASE, INC.
201 Broadway, Suite 7, Cambridge,
MA 02139
Tel.: (833) 439-2464
Web Site: https://www.jobcase.com
Emp.: 200
Software Publisher
N.A.I.C.S.: 513210
Beth Clymer *(CFO)*
Fred Goff *(Co-Founder & CEO)*
Tony Deigh *(CTO)*

Subsidiaries:

AfterCollege, Inc.   (1)
98 Battery St Ste 601, San Francisco, CA
94111
Tel.: (415) 263-1300
Web Site: http://www.aftercollege.com
Education Services
N.A.I.C.S.: 611710

JOBE & COMPANY INC.
7677 Canton Center Dr, Baltimore,
MD 21224
Tel.: (410) 288-0560
Web Site:
  http://www.jobeandcompany.com
Sales Range: $10-24.9 Million
Emp.: 15
Supplier of Measurement & Control
Products
N.A.I.C.S.: 423830
Leonard Guralnick *(Pres)*

JOBE MATERIALS, L.P.
1150 Southview Dr, El Paso, TX
79928
Tel.: (915) 218-9900
Web Site:
  http://www.jobeconcrete.com
Year Founded: 2005
Sales Range: $10-24.9 Million
Emp.: 430
Concrete Products Mfr
N.A.I.C.S.: 327390
Mike Saldana *(Mgr)*
Stanley P. Jobe *(Co-Founder)*
Irene Epperson *(Co-Founder)*

JOBELEPHANT.COM INC.
5443 Fremontia Ln, San Diego, CA
92115
Tel.: (619) 795-0837
Web Site:
  http://www.jobelephant.com
Year Founded: 2000
Sales Range: Less than $1 Million
Emp.: 8
Internet/Web Design, Newspaper,
Recruitment
N.A.I.C.S.: 541810
Evelyn Ang *(Co-Pres)*

JOBFOX, INC.
7926 Jones Branch Dr Ste 1100,
McLean, VA 22102
Tel.: (703) 748-0162
Web Site: http://www.jobfox.com
Year Founded: 2005
Sales Range: $10-24.9 Million
Emp.: 65
Custom Computer Programming Ser-
vices
N.A.I.C.S.: 541511
Michelle Slagle *(CFO)*

JOBING.COM, LLC
4747 N 22nd St, Phoenix, AZ 85016
Tel.: (602) 200-6813
Web Site: http://www.jobing.com
Sales Range: $10-24.9 Million
Emp.: 276
Staffing Services

N.A.I.C.S.: 541612
Aaron Matos *(Co-Founder)*

JOBREQ.COM, INC.
Research Park 244 Wall St, Princ-
eton, NJ 08540-1512
Tel.: (609) 921-8142
Year Founded: 1999
Sales Range: $10-24.9 Million
Emp.: 12
Staffing Services
N.A.I.C.S.: 561311

**JOBSOHIO BEVERAGE SYS-
TEM**
41 S High St, Columbus, OH 43215-
6104
Tel.: (614) 224-6446   OH
Year Founded: 2004
Sales Range: $350-399.9 Million
Emp.: 7
Labor Economic Development Ser-
vices
N.A.I.C.S.: 813930
Kristi Tanner *(Treas & Sec)*
Mark Kvamme *(Pres)*
John Minor *(CEO)*
James Boland *(Chm)*
Erika Pryor *(Mgr-Content)*

JOBTARGET LLC
15 Thames St, Groton, CT 06340
Tel.: (860) 440-0635   CT
Web Site: http://www.jobtarget.com
Year Founded: 2001
Sales Range: $25-49.9 Million
Emp.: 63
Employment Placement Agencies
N.A.I.C.S.: 561311
Susan P. Hobart *(VP)*
Jeanine M. Sterling *(VP)*
Terry White *(VP)*
Warren Williams *(VP)*

JOBWORKS, INC.
7832 Bluffton Rd, Fort Wayne, IN
46809
Tel.: (260) 745-2000   IN
Web Site: http://www.jobworksinc.org
Year Founded: 1983
Sales Range: $10-24.9 Million
Emp.: 826
Job Training Services
N.A.I.C.S.: 624310
Becky Springer *(Gen Mgr)*
Mark Terry *(Dir-IT)*
Rebecca Griffiths *(Reg VP)*

**JOCKEY INTERNATIONAL,
INC.**
2300 60th St, Kenosha, WI 53140
Tel.: (262) 658-8111   WI
Web Site: http://www.jockey.com
Year Founded: 1876
Sales Range: $1-4.9 Billion
Emp.: 5,000
Innerwear Mfr
N.A.I.C.S.: 315120
Debra S. Waller *(Chm & CEO)*
James E. Althaus *(VP-Sls)*
Anne T. Arbas *(VP-Corp Taxes)*
R.E. Kwasny *(Treas & VP)*
Tim McCue *(Dir-eCommerce & Inter-
active)*
Dustin Cohn *(CMO & Sr VP)*
Debi Auman *(Dir-Mktg Svcs)*

JODAT LAW GROUP, P.A.
2620 S Tamiami Trl, Sarasota, FL
34239
Tel.: (941) 355-6328
Web Site:
  http://www.jodatlawgroup.com
Sales Range: $1-9.9 Million
Law firm
N.A.I.C.S.: 541110

Jodat Law Group, P.A.—(Continued)

Gary R. Jodat *(Founder & Mng Atty)*

JODI KRISTOPHER INC.
6015 Bandini Blvd, Los Angeles, CA
90040-2904
Tel.: (323) 890-8000   **CA**
Year Founded: 1990
Sales Range: $25-49.9 Million
Emp.: 200
Women's, Junior's & Misses' Dresses
Mfr
N.A.I.C.S.: 315250
Ira Rosenberg *(Pres)*
Ira Fogelman *(CFO)*

**JOE BANKS DRYWALL &
ACOUSTICS INC.**
119 Broadway St, Mangham, LA
71259
Tel.: (318) 248-2191
Web Site:
  http://www.joebanksdrywall.com
Rev.: $13,100,000
Emp.: 75
Drywall & Insulation Contractors
N.A.I.C.S.: 238310
John Glass *(Exec VP)*
Joel H. Banks III *(Pres)*

JOE BASIL CHEVROLET INC.
5111 Transit Rd, Depew, NY 14043
Tel.: (716) 683-6800
Web Site:
  http://www.joebasilchevrolet.com
Year Founded: 1952
Sales Range: $100-124.9 Million
Emp.: 230
New Car Dealers
N.A.I.C.S.: 441110
Jim Basil *(Pres)*

**JOE BENBASSET INCORPO-
RATED**
213 W 35th St Fl 11, New York, NY
10001
Tel.: (212) 594-8440
Rev.: $15,000,607
Emp.: 27
Women's Sportswear
N.A.I.C.S.: 315250
Murray Benbasset *(Pres)*
Lori Steiner *(Mgr-Sls)*

**JOE BLAND CONSTRUCTION,
LP.**
13111 Dessau Rd, Austin, TX 78754
Tel.: (512) 821-2808
Web Site:
  http://www.joeblandconstruc
  tion.com
Sales Range: $25-49.9 Million
Emp.: 300
Highway & Street Construction Ser-
vices
N.A.I.C.S.: 237310
Joe Bland *(Pres)*

JOE BRAND INC.
5300 San Dario Ave Ste 260, Laredo,
TX 78041-3052
Tel.: (956) 722-0771
Web Site: http://www.joebrand.com
Sales Range: $10-24.9 Million
Emp.: 80
Mens & Womens Clothing Stores
N.A.I.C.S.: 458110
Seymon Deutsch *(Pres)*

JOE BROWN COMPANY INC.
20 3rd Ave NE, Ardmore, OK 73401
Tel.: (580) 223-4555
Web Site:
  http://www.joebrowncompany.com
Sales Range: $10-24.9 Million

Emp.: 100
Ready Mixed Concrete
N.A.I.C.S.: 327320
Teresa Brown *(Pres)*
Scott Brown *(VP)*

JOE COOPER FORD INC.
6601 SE 29th St, Midwest City, OK
73110
Tel.: (405) 733-1611
Web Site:
  http://www.joecooperford.com
Sales Range: $25-49.9 Million
Emp.: 250
Automobiles, New & Used
N.A.I.C.S.: 441110
Joe Cooper *(Pres)*

**JOE CORBI'S WHOLESALE
PIZZA INC.**
1430 Desoto Rd, Baltimore, MD
21230-1202
Tel.: (410) 525-3810   **MD**
Web Site: http://www.joecorbi.com
Year Founded: 1983
Sales Range: $25-49.9 Million
Emp.: 284
Provider of Food Preparation Ser-
vices
N.A.I.C.S.: 311991
Barbara Swanson *(Mgr-HR)*

**JOE DANIELS CONSTRUC-
TION COMPANY**
919 Applegate Rd, Madison, WI
53713
Tel.: (608) 271-4800
Web Site: http://www.danielsco.com
Sales Range: $10-24.9 Million
Emp.: 100
Highway & Street Construction Ser-
vices
N.A.I.C.S.: 237310
Joseph Daniels *(Pres)*

JOE DICKEY ELECTRIC INC.
180 W South Range Rd PO Box 158,
North Lima, OH 44452
Tel.: (330) 549-3976
Web Site:
  http://www.dickeyelectric.com
Rev.: $13,800,000
Emp.: 100
General Electrical Contractor
N.A.I.C.S.: 238210
Joseph H. Dickey *(CEO)*
Patrick Leonard *(Project Mgr)*
David A. Dickey *(Pres)*
Kenneth Clark *(Gen Mgr-Svc)*

JOE FISHER
2108 W Burnside, Portland, OR
97210
Tel.: (503) 295-5576
Sales Range: $10-24.9 Million
Emp.: 61
New Car Dealers
N.A.I.C.S.: 441110
Jane Fisher Graybeal *(Sec)*
Ruth J. Fisher *(Pres)*

**JOE GARRELL & ASSOCI-
ATES INC.**
1551 21st Ave N Ste 24, Myrtle
Beach, SC 29578-9000
Tel.: (843) 449-9000   **SC**
Web Site: http://www.litus.com
Provider of Real Estate Services
N.A.I.C.S.: 531210
Joe Garrell *(Pres)*

Subsidiaries:

LTL Inc.   (1)
1551 21st Ave N 24, Myrtle Beach, SC
29577-7496
Tel.: (843) 448-9000

Sales Range: $10-24.9 Million
Emp.: 12
Provider of Real Estate Services
N.A.I.C.S.: 531210

JOE GIBBS RACING INC.
13415 Reese Blvd W, Huntersville,
NC 28078
Tel.: (704) 944-5000
Web Site:
  http://www.joegibbsracing.com
Year Founded: 1991
Sales Range: $25-49.9 Million
Emp.: 450
Professional Motorsports Organiza-
tion
N.A.I.C.S.: 711211
Heath Cherry *(VP-Partner Rels)*
Jimmy Makar *(Sr VP-Racing Ops)*
Steve deSouza *(Exec VP)*
Dave Alpern *(Pres)*
Don Meredith *(Exec VP)*
Coy Gibbs *(Vice Chm & COO)*
Tim Carmichael *(CFO)*
Wally Brown *(Dir-Competition)*
Todd Bowland *(Dir-Technical)*
J. J. Damato *(VP-Mktg Svcs)*
Dave Rogers *(Dir-Technical-NASCAR
XFINITY Series Ops)*

**JOE HALL FORD LINCOLN
MERCURY NISSAN**
1617 - 21st, Lewiston, ID 83501
Tel.: (208) 746-2391
Web Site: http://www.joehallford.com
Year Founded: 1969
Sales Range: $25-49.9 Million
Emp.: 80
Car Whslr
N.A.I.C.S.: 441110
Scott Rokstad *(Gen Mgr)*
Stephen Cravens *(Treas, Sec &
Comptroller)*

JOE KIDD AUTOMOTIVE
1065 Ohio Pike, Cincinnati, OH
45245
Tel.: (513) 752-1804
Web Site: http://joekiddauto.com
Year Founded: 1978
Sales Range: $10-24.9 Million
Emp.: 39
Car Whslr
N.A.I.C.S.: 441110
Tom James *(Gen Mgr)*

**JOE KOCH CONSTRUCTION,
INC.**
7068 Mahoning Ave, Youngstown,
OH 44515
Tel.: (330) 793-7333   **OH**
Web Site:
  http://www.joekochconstruction.com
Year Founded: 1984
Sales Range: $10-24.9 Million
Emp.: 24
Housing Construction Services
N.A.I.C.S.: 236115
Joseph E. Koch *(Pres)*
Kathy Cheliras *(Sec)*
Patricia A. Koch *(VP)*

**JOE LUNGHAMER CHEVRO-
LET, INC.**
475 Summit Dr, Waterford, MI 48328
Tel.: (248) 683-7100
Web Site:
  http://www.lunghamerchevy.com
Year Founded: 1954
Sales Range: $50-74.9 Million
Emp.: 70
Car Whslr
N.A.I.C.S.: 441110
Joseph E. Lunghamer *(CEO)*

JOE MACHENS CAPITAL CITY

FORD LINCOLN
807 Southwest Blvd, Jefferson City,
MO 65109
Tel.: (573) 634-4444
Web Site:
  http://www.joemachenscapitalcity
  fordlincoln.com
Sales Range: $25-49.9 Million
Emp.: 100
Car Dealership
N.A.I.C.S.: 441110
Tom Stegeman *(Gen Mgr-Sls Dept)*
Chris Ehase *(Gen Mgr-Sls)*
Rick McDonald *(Mgr-Used Cars)*
Matt Wilde *(Mgr-Fin)*
Terry Bradshaw *(Mgr-Fin)*
Sarah Streeter *(Mgr-Bus Dev)*
Brian Gillmore *(Mgr-Body Shop)*
Lee Rummerfield *(Mgr-Parts)*
Heath Smith *(Mgr-Quicklane)*
Beau Landrum *(Mgr-Recon)*
Jeffery Holstein *(Mgr-Fin)*
Kevin Osborne *(Mgr-New Car)*

JOE MACHENS FORD INC.
1911 W Worley St, Columbia, MO
65203
Tel.: (573) 445-4411
Web Site:
  http://www.joemachensford.com
Year Founded: 1969
Sales Range: $10-24.9 Million
Emp.: 175
Car Dealership Owner & Operator
N.A.I.C.S.: 441110
Terry Sells *(Gen Mgr-Sls)*
Barry Garrett *(Mgr-Comml Accounts)*
Marc Weiner *(Mgr-Fin)*
Gene Buck *(Fin Mgr-Supercenter)*
Kevin West *(Sls Mgr-Supercenter)*

JOE MCCLELLAND INC.
107 Maysville Ave, Zanesville, OH
43701
Tel.: (740) 452-3036
Web Site:
  http://www.okcoalandconcrete.com
Rev.: $10,415,603
Emp.: 25
Ready Mixed Concrete
N.A.I.C.S.: 327320
Kevin Knapp *(Gen Mgr)*

**JOE MONEY MACHINERY CO.
INC.**
2550 Cone Dr, Fultondale, AL 35217
Tel.: (205) 841-7000
Web Site: http://www.joemoney.com
Sales Range: $75-99.9 Million
Emp.: 9
General Construction Machinery &
Equipment
N.A.I.C.S.: 423810
Charles S. Money *(Pres)*
Don Franklin *(Mgr)*
Ricky Newton *(Mgr-Svc)*

JOE MYERS FORD
16634 NW Freeway, Houston, TX
77040-1922
Tel.: (713) 896-8200   **DE**
Web Site:
  http://www.joemyersford.com
Year Founded: 1964
Sales Range: $125-149.9 Million
Emp.: 300
Automobile Dealership
N.A.I.C.S.: 441110
Michael Bean *(Mgr-Fleet)*

JOE PIPER INC.
123 Industrial Dr, Birmingham, AL
35219
Tel.: (205) 290-2211
Web Site: http://www.joepiperinc.com
Rev.: $17,100,000
Emp.: 78

Industrial & Personal Service Paper Merchant Whslr
N.A.I.C.S.: 424130
Ann Piper Carpenter (Owner)
Mims Cooper (VP)
Charles Hawkins (Mgr-Credit)
Bill Miller (VP)

JOE RIZZA FORD, INC.
2100 S Harlem Ave, North Riverside, IL 60546-1412
Tel.: (708) 442-7000
Web Site: http://fordnr.rizzacars.com
Year Founded: 1978
Sales Range: $25-49.9 Million
Emp.: 125
New Car Whslr
N.A.I.C.S.: 441110
Daniel McMillan (CFO)
Joe Rizza (Pres)
John Livigni (Gen Mgr)

JOE SELF CHEVROLET INC.
8801 E Kellogg Dr, Wichita, KS 67207
Tel.: (316) 684-6521
Web Site: http://www.joeselfinc.com
Year Founded: 1977
Sales Range: $25-49.9 Million
Emp.: 120
Car Dealership
N.A.I.C.S.: 441110
Brandon Steven (Pres)

JOE SWARTZ ELECTRIC COMPANY
7200 Roswell St, Houston, TX 77022
Tel.: (713) 695-5835
Web Site:
http://www.joeswartzelectric.com
Sales Range: $25-49.9 Million
Emp.: 200
General Electrical Contractor
N.A.I.C.S.: 238210
Joseph G. Swartz (Pres)

JOE VAN HORN CHEVROLET, INC.
3008 Eastern Ave, Plymouth, WI 53073
Tel.: (920) 893-6361
Web Site:
http://www.vanhornchev.com
Rev.: $17,200,000
Emp.: 40
New Car Dealers
N.A.I.C.S.: 441110
Theresa Vanhorn (Pres & CEO)
Rodney Steffen (Mgr-Sls)

JOE WHEELER ELECTRIC MEMBERSHIP
25700 Alabama Hwy 24, Trinity, AL 35673
Tel.: (256) 552-2353
Web Site: http://www.jwemc.org
Rev.: $75,341,106
Emp.: 90
Distribution, Electric Power
N.A.I.C.S.: 221122
Patrick Holmes (CFO)

JOE'S REFRIGERATION, INC.
W5496 County Rd X, Withee, WI 54498
Tel.: (715) 229-2321   WI
Web Site:
http://www.joesrefrigerationinc.com
Year Founded: 1958
Sales Range: $1-9.9 Million
Emp.: 25
Manufactures, Installs & Maintains Dairy Equipment, Commercial Refrigerators & Freezers
N.A.I.C.S.: 333415

Christine Frankewicz (Treas & Sec)
Shelly Frankewicz (Sec-Payroll)
Bill Devine (Controller)
Steve Frankewicz (Owner)
Ken Frankewicz (Mgr-Warehouse)
Todd Roshell (Project Mgr)

JOE-ANNE COMPANY INTERNATIONAL
147 W Cherry St, Hicksville, NY 11801
Tel.: (516) 939-0700
Web Site: http://www.joeanne.com
Sales Range: $10-24.9 Million
Emp.: 12
Trimmings, Apparel
N.A.I.C.S.: 424310
Neil Moganstern (Pres)

JOERNS HEALTHCARE, LLC
2430 Whitehall Park Dr Ste 100, Charlotte, NC 28273
Tel.: (818) 428-3880
Web Site: http://www.joerns.com
Nursing Products Mfr
N.A.I.C.S.: 339112
Mark Ludwig (Pres & CEO)
Lindy Plummer (Dir-Mktg Comm)
Julie Wilson (VP-HR)

Subsidiaries:

RecoverCare LLC   (1)
1920 Stanley Gault Pkwy Ste 100, Louisville, KY 40223
Tel.: (502) 489-9449
Web Site: http://www.recovercare.com
Sales Range: $25-49.9 Million
Emp.: 800
Medical Product Distr
N.A.I.C.S.: 423450
Cynthia Sysol McCauley (Gen Counsel)
Jeffrey E. Sadtler (CIO)

JOFCO INC.
402 E 13th St, Jasper, IN 47546-2422
Tel.: (812) 482-5154   IN
Web Site: http://www.jofco.com
Year Founded: 1922
Sales Range: $100-124.9 Million
Emp.: 270
Wooden Office Furniture & Seating Mfr
N.A.I.C.S.: 337211
Sandra Harder (Mgr-Inventory)
John Nicholson (Mgr-Logistics)
Michelle Harper (Supvr-Shipping)
Scott Sturm (Controller)
Steve Fleck (Mgr-Pur)
Adam Smith (Controller)

JOFFREY'S COFFEE & TEA CO.
3803 Corporex Park Dr Ste 400, Tampa, FL 33619
Tel.: (813) 250-0404
Web Site: http://www.joffreys.com
Sales Range: $10-24.9 Million
Emp.: 100
Coffee & Tea Importer & Distr
N.A.I.C.S.: 424490
Ted Abrams (CEO)

JOGAN, INC.
84 Inverness Circle E, Englewood, CO 80112
Web Site: https://joganinc.com
Year Founded: 2021
Venture Capital
N.A.I.C.S.: 523999
Dan Dietrich (CEO)

Subsidiaries:

Davislogic Inc   (1)
11101 Resort Rd Ste 125, Ellicott City, MD 21042
Tel.: (410) 988-8942

Web Site: https://allhandsconsulting.com
Rev.: $3,000,000
Emp.: 6
Administrative Management & General Management Consulting Service
N.A.I.C.S.: 541611
Steve Davis (Pres)

JOHANNA FOODS INC.
Johanna Farms Rd, Flemington, NJ 08822
Tel.: (908) 788-2200   NJ
Web Site:
http://www.johannafoods.com
Sales Range: $50-74.9 Million
Emp.: 500
Food Mfr & Distr
N.A.I.C.S.: 311421
Robert A. Facchina (Pres & CEO)
David Boerger (Mgr-Warehouse)
Eva Rodriguez (Dir-Food Safety & Food Security)
Hugh Snyder (Mgr-Sls-Aseptic Div)
Jerry Sternberg (Dir-Sls-Chilled Beverages)
Joe Brennan (Mgr-Sls)
Mary Hegarty (Mgr-Employee Rels)
Paul Gibson (VP-Pur)
Rich Mascolo (Supvr-Maintenance)
Dale Kinney (Dir-Maintenance)
Ramon Lopez (Dir-Mfg)
Jonathan Zimmerman (Supvr-Production)
Anne Black (Mgr-Acctg Ops)
Donna Serio (VP-Sls-Yogurt)
Kimberly Cox (Mgr-Pur)
Nicole Branstetter (Coord-Quality Sys)

JOHANNESON'S INC.
2301 Johanneson Ave NW, Bemidji, MN 56601
Tel.: (218) 751-9644
Web Site:
http://www.marketplacefoods.com
Sales Range: $25-49.9 Million
Emp.: 800
Independent Supermarket
N.A.I.C.S.: 445110
Keith Johanneson (Pres)
Rich Johanneson (VP)

JOHANSON DIELECTRICS, INC.
15191 Bledsoe St, Sylmar, CA 91342-2710
Tel.: (818) 364-9800
Web Site:
http://www.johansondielectrics.com
Year Founded: 1978
Sales Range: $25-49.9 Million
Emp.: 600
Electronic Capacitors Mfr
N.A.I.C.S.: 334416
Eric Johansen (Pres)
Steve Cole (Mgr-Bus Dev-X2Y Technology)
Richard Besu (Mgr-Mfg)

JOHANSON MANUFACTURING CORPORATION
301 Rockaway Vly Rd, Boonton, NJ 07005
Tel.: (973) 334-2676   NJ
Web Site:
http://www.johansonmfg.com
Year Founded: 1945
Sales Range: $25-49.9 Million
Emp.: 50
Trimmer Capacitors & Microwave Tuning Elements Mfr & Supplier
N.A.I.C.S.: 334416
Nancy Johanson (Owner)
Robert Corazza (Mgr-Tool Room)
Mark Imbimbo (Mgr-Engrg)

JOHANSON TRANSPORTATION SERVICE
5583 E Olive Ave, Fresno, CA 93727-2559
Tel.: (559) 458-2200
Web Site:
http://www.johansontrans.com
Year Founded: 1972
Sales Range: $10-24.9 Million
Emp.: 25
Freight Transportation Arrangement Services
N.A.I.C.S.: 488510
Dave Hiersche (VP-IT)
Danielle Negueloua (Dir-Intl Ops-Sacramento)
Craig Johanson (VP-Logistics)
Randy Gabardi (VP-Ops)
Janice Spicer (CFO)
Jeff Perry (Mgr-Sacramento)
Jerry Beckstead (COO)
Larry Johanson (Pres & CEO)
Kevin O'Neill (VP-Northeast Reg)
Richard Johanson (Chm)
Rick Rattazzi (Sr VP-Perishables)
Sven Sorensen (Mgr-Ops JTS Logistics)
Alicia Ruiz (Dir-Compliance & Legal Affairs)
Spencer Shelman (Mgr-Ops-Midwest)
Jeff Mosqueda (VP-Sls-Temperature-Controlled Div)

JOHN & PHIL'S TOYOTA-SUBARU INC.
800 NW 5th St, Corvallis, OR 97330
Tel.: (541) 754-1515
Web Site: http://www.johnphils.com
Sales Range: $25-49.9 Million
Emp.: 45
Car Dealership
N.A.I.C.S.: 441110
Steve Jackson (Pres)

JOHN A. BIEWER CO. INC.
812 S Riverside Ave, Saint Clair, MI 48079
Tel.: (810) 329-4789
Web Site:
http://www.biewerlumber.com
Sales Range: $10-24.9 Million
Emp.: 150
Structural Lumber, Timber & Treated Wood Mfr
N.A.I.C.S.: 321114
Richard N. Biewer (Pres)
Gary Olmstead (CFO)
Laura Harper (Mgr-Credit)

JOHN A. MARTIN & ASSOCIATES, INCORPORATED
950 S Grand Ave 4th Fl, Los Angeles, CA 90015-2123
Tel.: (213) 483-6490   CA
Web Site: http://www.johnmartin.com
Year Founded: 1953
Sales Range: $25-49.9 Million
Emp.: 350
Provider of Structural Engineering & Design Services
N.A.I.C.S.: 541330
Hossain Ghaffari (Project Mgr)
Jackie Vinkler (Partner)
Shane S. Fitzgerald (Partner)
Michael McCoy (Dir-Bus Dev)
Barry Schindler (Partner)
Kal Benuska (Partner)
Kurt Clandening (Mng Partner)
Steven C. Ball (Partner)
John A. Martin Jr. (Sr Partner)

Subsidiaries:

Holben, Martin & White, Inc.   (1)
3501 E Speedway Blvd Ste 225, Tucson, AZ 85716
Tel.: (520) 327-9491

John A. Martin & Associates,
Incorporated—(Continued)

Web Site: http://www.hmwstructural.com
Emp.: 9
Construction Engineering Services
N.A.I.C.S.: 541330
Melanie Ormsby (Mgr-Fin)
Thomas Griffis (Pres)

John A Martin and Associates of
Nevada   (1)
7730 W Sahara Ave Ste 115, Las Vegas,
NV 89117-2753
Tel.: (702) 248-7000
Web Site: http://www.jamanv.com
Sales Range: $10-24.9 Million
Emp.: 50
Provider of Engineering Services
N.A.I.C.S.: 541330

John A. Martin & Associates, Ltd.   (1)
No 19 JianGuoMenWaiDa Street Suite 10A,
Beijing, 100045, China
Tel.: (86) 8526 1800
Web Site: http://www.johnmartin.com
Construction Engineering Services
N.A.I.C.S.: 541330

Martin & Chock, Inc.   (1)
1132 Bishop St Ste 1550, Honolulu, HI
96813-2813
Tel.: (808) 521-4513
Web Site: http://www.martinchock.com
Sales Range: $10-24.9 Million
Emp.: 7
Engineering Services
N.A.I.C.S.: 541330
Gary Chock (Pres)

Martin / Martin Wyoming, Inc.   (1)
4020 Laramie St, Cheyenne, WY 82001
Tel.: (307) 637-8422
Web Site: http://www.mmwyo.com
Emp.: 7
Construction Engineering Services
N.A.I.C.S.: 541330
John Shaffer (Pres)
Patrick McManus (Principal)

Martin/Martin Inc.   (1)
12499 W Colfax Ave, Lakewood, CO
80215-2897   (100%)
Tel.: (303) 431-6100
Web Site: http://www.martinmartin.com
Sales Range: $25-49.9 Million
Emp.: 150
Engineering Services
N.A.I.C.S.: 541330
Jack Petersen (Pres)

JOHN A. PENNY CO. INC.
270 Sidney St, Cambridge, MA
02139-4833
Tel.: (617) 547-7744
Year Founded: 1973
Sales Range: $25-49.9 Million
Emp.: 260
Electrical Contracting Services
N.A.I.C.S.: 238210
John A. Penney (Chm & CEO)
Wendy Fariel (VP-HR)

JOHN A. VAN DEN BOSCH CO.
4511 Holland Ave, Holland, MI 49424
Tel.: (616) 772-2179   MI
Web Site: http://www.vbosch.com
Year Founded: 1932
Sales Range: $10-24.9 Million
Emp.: 40
Producer & Seller of Seed & Grain
Products
N.A.I.C.S.: 311119
David van den Bosch (Chm & Dir-
Strategic Plng)
Jim van den Bosch (VP)
Steven Vander Wal (Mgr-Ops)
Don Clark (Pres & CEO)
Joel DeBruin (CEO)

JOHN A. VASSILAROS & SON INC
29 05 120 St, Flushing, NY 11354

Tel.: (718) 886-4140
Web Site:
    http://www.vassilaroscoffee.com
Year Founded: 1919
Sales Range: $10-24.9 Million
Emp.: 45
Roasted Coffee Mfr
N.A.I.C.S.: 311920
John A. Vassilaros (Pres)
Maria Vassilaros Petersen (Mgr)

JOHN ABELL CORPORATION
10500 SW 186th St, Miami, FL 33157
Tel.: (305) 253-4440   FL
Web Site:
    http://www.johnabellcorp.com
Year Founded: 1975
Emp.: 100
Distr of Quality Building Materials &
Services
N.A.I.C.S.: 423320
John Abell (Pres & CEO)
Jeff Abell (Mgr)
Teresa Rinchiuso (Co-Sec)
Michelle Saenz (Co-Sec)
John W. Abell Jr. (Pres & CEO)
John Abell III (Mgr-Sls)

JOHN ADCOCK INSURANCE AGENCY, INC.
313 W Fletcher Ave, Tampa, FL
33612
Tel.: (813) 935-8795   FL
Web Site:
    http://www.adcockinsurance.com
Year Founded: 1980
Sales Range: $1-9.9 Million
Emp.: 20
Insurance Agents
N.A.I.C.S.: 524210
Michael Adcock (Pres)

JOHN ASCUAGA'S NUGGET
1100 Nugget Ave, Sparks, NV 89431-
5750
Tel.: (775) 356-3300   NV
Web Site: http://www.janugget.com
Year Founded: 1960
Sales Range: $75-99.9 Million
Emp.: 3,000
Casino Operator
N.A.I.C.S.: 721120
John J. Ascuaga (Owner)
Stephen Ascuaga (Sr Exec VP)
David Cook (Controller)

JOHN ATENCIO GOLDSMITH, LTD.
3000 E 1st Ave, Denver, CO 80206
Tel.: (303) 830-7733
Web Site:
    http://www.johnatencio.com
Year Founded: 1976
Rev.: $11,322,230
Emp.: 35
Designer Jewelry Mfr & Distr
N.A.I.C.S.: 339910
Elizabeth Edwards (VP-Fin & Acctg)

JOHN B. RUDY COMPANY INC.
1815 S Anderson Ave, Compton, CA
90220
Tel.: (310) 639-2424
Web Site: http://www.jbrudy.com
Sales Range: $25-49.9 Million
Emp.: 24
Connectors, Electronic
N.A.I.C.S.: 459999
John A. Rudy (Pres)
Jason Chun (Mgr-Las Vegas)
Walt Lyons (Mgr-Ops)

JOHN BLEAKLEY RV CENTER INC.

6200 Fairburn Rd, Douglasville, GA
30134
Tel.: (770) 949-4500
Web Site: http://www.bleakleyrv.com
Sales Range: $25-49.9 Million
Emp.: 100
Recreational Vehicle Dealers
N.A.I.C.S.: 441210
John Bleakley (Pres)
Renee Bleakley (VP)
Glen McCormick (Mgr-Svcs)
Russell Borders (Parts Mgr)
Bryan Hays (Gen Mgr)
Jeff Agans (Sls Mgr)
Russ Underberg (Mgr-Svc)
Chad Hudson (Mgr-Fin)

JOHN BOUCHARD & SONS COMPANY
1024 Harrison St, Nashville, TN
37203-3327
Tel.: (615) 256-0112   TN
Web Site: http://www.jbouchard.com
Year Founded: 1900
Sales Range: $75-99.9 Million
Emp.: 150
Mechanical Contracting Services
N.A.I.C.S.: 331511
Dale Denny (CFO)
William D. Morgan (Pres)
John E. Bouchard III (Chm)

Subsidiaries:

John Bouchard & Sons Company -
Foundry Division   (1)
804 18th Ave N, Nashville, TN 37203
Tel.: (615) 256-0112
Web Site: http://www.jbouchard.com
Emp.: 120
Foundry Product Distr
N.A.I.C.S.: 423510
Milton Miller (Gen Mgr)

JOHN BOYD ENTERPRISES INC.
8401 Specialty Cir, Sacramento, CA
95828
Tel.: (916) 381-4790
Web Site: http://www.jbradspec.com
Year Founded: 1975
Rev.: $26,602,828
Emp.: 156
Radiators & Radiator Parts Mfr
N.A.I.C.S.: 336390
John Boyd (Owner)
Rick Ellstrom (Pres)

Subsidiaries:

JB Auto Core Inc.   (1)
6880 Florin Perkins Rd, Sacramento, CA
95828
Tel.: (916) 381-3351
Web Site: http://www.jbradspec.com
Rev.: $1,400,000
Emp.: 12
Heating Equipment, Except Electric
N.A.I.C.S.: 423120
John Boyd (Owner & CEO)

JOHN BUCK COMPANY
1 N Wacker Dr Ste 2400, Chicago, IL
60606
Tel.: (312) 993-9800
Web Site: http://www.tjbc.com
Year Founded: 1981
Sales Range: $10-24.9 Million
Emp.: 108
Real Estate Agents & Managers
N.A.I.C.S.: 531120
Blake Johnson (Pres)
Richard Lindsay (CEO & Dir-Dev)
Charles Beaver (Principal)
Merredith Treaster (Sr VP-West
Coast)
Dirk Degenaars (COO)
Kevin Hites (Chief Investment Officer)
Sam Persico (CFO)
Sherri Davis (Chief Admin Officer)

JOHN BUNNING TRANSFER COMPANY
1600 Elk St, Rock Springs, WY
82901
Tel.: (307) 362-3791
Web Site:
    http://www.bunningtransfer.com
Sales Range: $10-24.9 Million
Emp.: 100
Contract Haulers
N.A.I.C.S.: 484121
Chris N. Bunning (Pres)

JOHN BURNS REAL ESTATE CONSULTING, INC.
9140 Irvine Ctr Dr Ste 200, Irvine, CA
92618
Tel.: (949) 870-1200
Web Site:
    http://www.realestateconsulting.com
Year Founded: 2001
Sales Range: $50-74.9 Million
Emp.: 45
Market Analysis & Research Services
N.A.I.C.S.: 541910
John Burns (CEO)
Mollie Carmichael (Principal)
Don Walker (Pres & CFO)
Jody Kahn (Sr VP-Res)
Lesley Deutch (Principal-Boca Raton)
Chris Porter (VP-Irvine)
Kellie Sanchez (Mgr-Database)
Lisa Marquis Jackson (Sr VP-Bus
Dev)
Dan Fulton (Sr VP-Consulting-
Washington)
David Jarvis (Sr VP)
Dean Wehrli (Sr VP-Consulting-
Sacramento)
Kathy Ayuyao (Mgr-HR & Special
Events-Irvine)
Ken Perlman (Principal)
Liz Rhee (Coord-Mktg)
Pete Reeb (Principal)
Richard Mones (Mgr-Mktg)
Steve Burch (Sr VP-Consulting)
Todd Tomalak (VP)
Rick Palacios Jr. (Sr VP & Dir-Res-
Irvine)

JOHN C. BERRY & SONS INC.
104 S Leigh, Tetonia, ID 83452
Tel.: (208) 456-2271
Web Site: http://www.berryoil.net
Sales Range: $25-49.9 Million
Emp.: 6
Petroleum Products
N.A.I.C.S.: 424720
Ronald L. Berry (CEO)

JOHN CANNON HOMES INC.
6710 Professional Pkwy W Ste 100,
Sarasota, FL 34240-8444
Tel.: (941) 924-5935
Web Site:
    http://www.johncannonhomes.com
Year Founded: 1987
Sales Range: $25-49.9 Million
Emp.: 50
Homebuilder, Renovations & Interior
Design Services
N.A.I.C.S.: 236115
Phillipa Cannon (Pres & VP)
Michael Finley (CFO)
Mark Grigoli (Dir-Mktg & Sls)
Timothy Knight (COO)

JOHN CHRISTNER TRUCKING INC.
19007 W Hwy 33, Sapulpa, OK
74066-7545

Tel.: (918) 227-1600
Web Site:
   http://www.johnchristner.com
Year Founded: 1986
Rev.: $45,011,503
Emp.: 350
Trucking Service
N.A.I.C.S.: 484121
John M. Christner (Founder)
Daniel Christner (COO)
Darryl Christner (CFO)

JOHN COLEMAN HAYES CONSTRUCTION CO.

7340 Cockrill Bend Blvd, Nashville, TN 37209-1043
Tel.: (615) 269-6397
Sales Range: $10-24.9 Million
Emp.: 15
Construction Services
N.A.I.C.S.: 236210

JOHN CONTI COFFEE CO.

4406 Ole Brickyard Cir, Louisville, KY 40218
Tel.: (502) 499-8600
Web Site: http://www.johnconti.com
Year Founded: 1962
Sales Range: $100-124.9 Million
Emp.: 100
Roasted Coffee Mfr
N.A.I.C.S.: 561990
John A. Conti (Chm)

JOHN D STEPHENS INC.

272 Hurricane Shoals Rd NE, Lawrenceville, GA 30045-4402
Tel.: (770) 972-8000
Web Site:
   http://www.johndstephens.com
Sales Range: $10-24.9 Million
Emp.: 70
Sewer Construction Services
N.A.I.C.S.: 237110
John Stephens (Owner)

JOHN DAUGHERTY REALTORS INC.

520 Post Oak Blvd 6th Floor, Houston, TX 77027-9414
Tel.: (713) 626-3930
Web Site:
   http://www.johndaugherty.com
Year Founded: 1967
Sales Range: $1-4.9 Billion
Emp.: 100
Luxury Real Estate Brokers & Services
N.A.I.C.S.: 531210
Alason Connell (Dir-Mktg)
Donald E. Willmon (CFO)
Cheri Fama (Pres & COO)
Anne Incorvia (Exec VP)
John A. Daugherty Jr. (Founder, Chm & CEO)

JOHN DAY COMPANY

6263 Abbott Dr, Omaha, NE 68110-2806
Tel.: (402) 455-8000
Web Site: http://www.johnday.com
Year Founded: 1905
Sales Range: $10-24.9 Million
Emp.: 80
Farm & Garden Machinery & Equipment Sales
N.A.I.C.S.: 423820
John Fonda (Owner)

JOHN DEERY MOTOR CO.

6823 University Ave, Cedar Falls, IA 50613
Tel.: (319) 277-6200
Web Site: http://www.deery.com
Year Founded: 1975
Sales Range: $10-24.9 Million

Emp.: 50
New Car Dealers
N.A.I.C.S.: 441110
Scott Grinstead (Gen Mgr)
Johnny Deery (Mgr-Internet)
Joel Berding (Mgr-Sls)
Terry Johnson (Mgr-Sls)
John Deery Jr. (Owner)

JOHN DI NASO & SONS INC.

520 Industrial Loop, Staten Island, NY 10309
Tel.: (718) 948-1929
Web Site:
   http://www.dinasoandsons.com
Rev.: $16,830,536
Emp.: 30
Lumber & Other Building Materials
N.A.I.C.S.: 423310
John Di Naso (Pres & CEO)

JOHN DONOGHUE AUTOMOTIVE, INC.

PO Box 527, Whiteville, NC 28472-0527
Tel.: (910) 642-2400
Sales Range: $10-24.9 Million
Emp.: 21
Car Whslr
N.A.I.C.S.: 441110
John Donoghue (Principal)

JOHN DRIGGS COMPANY, INC.

8700 Ashwood Dr, Capitol Heights, MD 20743
Tel.: (301) 350-4000
Web Site: http://www.driggs.net
Year Founded: 1969
Sales Range: $25-49.9 Million
Emp.: 200
Excavation & Grading Services
N.A.I.C.S.: 238910

JOHN E. GREEN CO.

220 Victor Ave, Highland Park, MI 48203-3116
Tel.: (313) 868-2400   MI
Web Site: http://www.johnegreen.com
Year Founded: 1909
Provider of Mechanical & Fire Protection Contracting Services
N.A.I.C.S.: 238220
John R. Green (Dir-HR & Sec)
Sue Haney (Coord- Estimating & Proposal)
Michael J. Green (Pres)
John R. Stelter (CFO & Treas)
Robert Martin (COO)
Kirk Fischer (CIO)
Dennis Quinn (Dir-Corp Safet)
Dave Jones (Dir- Corp Quality)

JOHN E. KELLY & SONS ELECTRICAL CONSTRUCTION, INC.

8431 Old Marlboro Pike Ste 201, Upper Marlboro, MD 20772
Tel.: (301) 736-2250
Web Site: http://www.kellycos.com
Sales Range: $10-24.9 Million
Emp.: 110
Electrical Wiring Services
N.A.I.C.S.: 238210
Steve Howard (Gen Mgr)

JOHN E. QUARLES CO.

1801 Park Pl Ave, Fort Worth, TX 76110
Tel.: (817) 926-2271
Web Site:
   http://www.quarleslumber.com
Sales Range: $10-24.9 Million
Emp.: 31
Lumber, Plywood & Millwork
N.A.I.C.S.: 423310

Lonnie Goolesby (Gen Mgr)
Paul Reuland (Controller)
Bart Graves (VP & Gen Mgr)

JOHN EAGLE A MANAGEMENT, LLC

1925 Cedar Springs Rd Ste 204, Dallas, TX 75201
Tel.: (214) 954-0164   TX
Web Site: http://www.johneagle.com
Sales Range: $150-199.9 Million
Emp.: 1,500
Holding Company; New & Used Car Dealerships Owner & Operator
N.A.I.C.S.: 551112
John R. Eagle (Pres & Mng Partner)

Subsidiaries:

Clear Lake Infiniti, LP   (1)
14705 Gulf Freeway, Houston, TX 77034
Tel.: (713) 589-4000
Web Site: http://www.clearlakeinfiniti.com
Sales Range: $1-9.9 Million
Emp.: 35
New & Used Car Dealer
N.A.I.C.S.: 441110

John Eagle Acura   (1)
16015 Katy Fwy, Houston, TX 77094
Tel.: (281) 589-0600
Web Site: http://www.johneagleacura.com
Rev.: $21,100,000
New & Used Car Dealer
N.A.I.C.S.: 441110
German Fuentes (Mgr-Sls)
Avery Barksdale (Mgr-Fleet)
Jamarr Carswell (Mgr-Fin)
T. J. Morin (Mgr-Pre-Owned Sls)
Valerian Kuznetsov (Mng Partner)
Johnnie Cantu (Mgr-Parts)
Derek Bennett (Dir-Svc)
Charles Reese (Sls Mgr)
Diana Norris (Mgr-Customer Relation)
Roger Reyna (Gen Mgr)

John Eagle Honda of Houston   (1)
18787 Northwest Fwy, Houston, TX 77065
Tel.: (281) 653-5278
Web Site: http://www.johneaglehonda.com
Sales Range: $50-74.9 Million
Emp.: 150
New & Used Car Distr
N.A.I.C.S.: 441110
Mac DeLaup (Pres & Mng Partner)
Carol Rainoshek (Comptroller)
Glen Holender (Gen Mgr)
Greg Cypher (Gen Mgr-Sls)
Adam Wiese (Dir-Fin)
Christine Clauder (Dir-Mktg-IT)
Shawn Smith (Dir-Svc)
Xavier Vargas (Dir-Internet)
Nicholas Herrin (Dir-New Car Sls)
Jeff Koch (Mgr-Used Car Sls)
Chris Lynn (Mgr-Parts)
Kristy Rainoshek (Office Mgr)

John Eagle Sport City Motors, LLP   (1)
12650 Lyndon B Johnson Fwy, Dallas, TX 75228
Tel.: (972) 681-3000
Web Site: http://www.sportcitytoyota.com
Sales Range: $100-124.9 Million
Emp.: 300
New & Used Car Dealer
N.A.I.C.S.: 441110
Corey Byrd (Gen Mgr)

JOHN EVANS' SONS, INC.

1 Spring Ave, Lansdale, PA 19446
Tel.: (215) 368-7700
Web Site:
   http://www.springcompany.com
Year Founded: 1850
Sales Range: $10-24.9 Million
Emp.: 80
Spring Mfr
N.A.I.C.S.: 332613
Allan Davey (Pres)
Frank Davey (Chm)

JOHN F BUCHAN HOMES

2821 Northup Way Ste 100, Bellevue, WA 98004-1447
Tel.: (425) 827-2266
Web Site: http://www.buchan.com
Year Founded: 1969
Sales Range: $10-24.9 Million
Emp.: 50
Housing Construction Services
N.A.I.C.S.: 236117
Heather Dosch (Owner)

JOHN F. KENNEDY CENTER FOR THE PERFORMING ARTS

2700 F St NW,, Washington, DC 20566
Tel.: (202) 416-8000
Web Site: http://www.kennedy-center.org
Year Founded: 1976
Sales Range: $300-349.9 Million
Emp.: 1,100
Performing Arts Services
N.A.I.C.S.: 711310
Maria C. Kersten (Gen Counsel)
Jeffrey Finn (VP-Theater Producing & Programming)
Robert Van Leer (Sr VP-Artistic Plng)
Deborah F. Rutter (Pres)
Simone Eccleston (Dir-Hip Hop Culture)
David M. Rubenstein (Chm)

JOHN FAYARD MOVING AND WAREHOUSING

13486 Fastway Ln, Gulfport, MS 39503-4609
Tel.: (228) 864-2262
Web Site: http://www.johnfayardwarehouse.com
Year Founded: 1982
Sales Range: $10-24.9 Million
Emp.: 75
Provider of Long Distance Trucking Services
N.A.I.C.S.: 484210
John Fayard Jr. (Pres)

JOHN FOGARTY CUSTOM BUILT HOMES

4550 Westbranch Hwy, Lewisburg, PA 17837
Tel.: (570) 523-3203
Web Site:
   http://www.fogartyhomes.com
Sales Range: $10-24.9 Million
Emp.: 20
New Construction, Single-Family Houses
N.A.I.C.S.: 236115
Perry L. Berger (Dir-Mktg)
Mary Switzer (Office Mgr)
Brad Haubert (Pres & CEO)

JOHN G. SHEDD AQUARIUM

1200 S Lk Shore Dr, Chicago, IL 60605
Tel.: (312) 939-2435   IL
Web Site:
   http://www.sheddaquarium.org
Year Founded: 1929
Sales Range: $75-99.9 Million
Emp.: 300
Public Aquarium
N.A.I.C.S.: 712130
Joyce M. Simon (CFO & Exec VP)
Jim Robinett (Sr VP-External & Regulatory Affairs)
Anna Pachl (Controller)
Tim Binder (Exec VP-Animal Care)
Jennifer Baryl (Sr VP)
Sandy Marek (Sr VP-Dev)

JOHN G. WEATHERFORD INC.

363 Front St, Forest, MS 39074

John G. Weatherford Inc.—(Continued)
Tel.: (601) 469-3931
Sales Range: $10-24.9 Million
Emp.: 5
Petroleum Bulk Stations
N.A.I.C.S.: 424710
Dale Weatherford *(Treas & Sec)*

JOHN H. BONER COMMUNITY CENTER
2236 E 10th St, Indianapolis, IN 46201
Tel.: (317) 633-8210   IN
Web Site: http://www.jhbcc.org
Year Founded: 1972
Sales Range: $10-24.9 Million
Emp.: 157
Community Development Services
N.A.I.C.S.: 624190
Charles Anderson *(VP)*
Valerie Davis *(Sec)*
Joe Whitsett *(Treas)*
Ryan McKeown *(Pres)*

JOHN H. BURROWS INC.
1925 Freeport Blvd, Sparks, NV 89531-5565
Tel.: (775) 358-2442   NV
Web Site: http://www.johnhburrow.com
Year Founded: 1968
Sales Range: $25-49.9 Million
Emp.: 150
Provider of Fresh Fruits & Vegetables
N.A.I.C.S.: 424480
John H. Burrows *(Pres)*
Tammy Price *(Controller)*

JOHN H. CARTER COMPANY INCORPORATED
2728 N Arnoult Rd, Metairie, LA 70002
Tel.: (504) 887-8550
Web Site: http://www.johnhcarter.com
Sales Range: $25-49.9 Million
Processing & Packaging Equipment
N.A.I.C.S.: 423830
Tony Vernace *(Mgr-IT)*

Subsidiaries:

Process Pumps & Equipment Inc.   (1)
9656 St. Vincent Ave, Shreveport, LA 71106
Tel.: (225) 677-9292
Web Site: http://www.ppe-corp.com
Industrial Machinery & Equipment Merchant Whslr
N.A.I.C.S.: 423830

JOHN H. DANIEL COMPANY INC.
120 W Jackson Ave, Knoxville, TN 37902
Tel.: (865) 637-6441
Web Site: http://www.johnhdaniel.com
Rev.: $17,339,581
Emp.: 20
Men's & Boys' Suits
N.A.I.C.S.: 315250
Richard Bryan *(Pres)*

JOHN H. FRISCHKORN, JR. INC.
1801 Roseneath Rd, Richmond, VA 23230-4330
Tel.: (757) 838-1700   VA
Web Site: http://www.frischkorn.com
Year Founded: 1996
Rev.: $50,000,000
Emp.: 200
Provider of Industrial Supplies
N.A.I.C.S.: 423840
Larry Pearsen *(Pres)*
Dwight Tayne *(CFO)*

JOHN HANCOCK STRATEGIC DIVERSIFIED INCOME FUND
30 Dan Rd, Canton, MA 02021
Web Site: http://www.jhfunds.com
Closed-End Investment Fund
N.A.I.C.S.: 525990
Charles A. Rizzo *(CFO)*

JOHN HARDY USA, INC.
330 Hudson St 13 Fl, New York, NY 10013
Tel.: (212) 219-4288
Web Site: http://www.johnhardy.com
Sales Range: $50-74.9 Million
Emp.: 70
Fine Jewelry Distr
N.A.I.C.S.: 423940
Damien Dernoncourt *(Chm)*
Robert Hansan *(Gen Mgr)*

JOHN HARVARD'S BREW-HOUSE LLC
33 Dunster St, Cambridge, MA 02138
Tel.: (617) 868-3585
Web Site: http://www.johnharvards.com
Sales Range: $10-24.9 Million
Emp.: 50
Eating Place
N.A.I.C.S.: 722511
Ashley Tart *(Gen Mgr)*

JOHN HENRY FOSTER COMPANY OF SAINT LOUIS INC.
4700 Le Bourget Dr, Saint Louis, MO 63134-3118
Tel.: (314) 427-0600   MO
Web Site: http://www.jhf.com
Year Founded: 1983
Sales Range: $10-24.9 Million
Emp.: 80
Distribution of Industrial Machinery & Equipment
N.A.I.C.S.: 423830
Adam Wilson *(Mgr-IT)*
Rich Lemp *(Mgr-Trng)*
Todd Meier *(Engr-Mechanical)*
Jill Sorcabal *(Mgr-HR)*

JOHN HINDERER HONDA
1515 Hebron Rd, Heath, OH 43056
Tel.: (740) 522-1106
Web Site: http://www.hindererhonda1.com
Year Founded: 1990
Sales Range: $10-24.9 Million
Emp.: 75
Car Whslr
N.A.I.C.S.: 441110
Joe Bertke *(Gen Mgr)*
John Hinderer *(Pres)*
John Durbin *(Mgr-Sls)*
Bobby J. Pagani *(Mgr-Body Shop)*

JOHN HINE AUTO & TRUCK CENTER
1545 Camino Del Rio S, San Diego, CA 92108
Tel.: (619) 297-4251
Web Site: http://www.johnhine.com
Year Founded: 1957
Sales Range: $50-74.9 Million
Emp.: 110
Car Whslr
N.A.I.C.S.: 441110
John Hine *(Pres)*
Dave Miller *(VP)*

JOHN HUBLER NISSAN-SUZUKI INC.
201 S Emerson Ave, Greenwood, IN 46143
Tel.: (317) 887-2500
Rev.: $11,100,000
Emp.: 33
New Car Dealers

N.A.I.C.S.: 441110
John Hubler *(Pres)*
Cindy France *(Controller)*

JOHN J. CAMPBELL CO., INC.
6012 Resources Dr, Memphis, TN 38134-7624
Tel.: (901) 372-8400   TN
Web Site: http://www.campbellroofing.com
Year Founded: 1971
Sales Range: $100-124.9 Million
Emp.: 150
Roofing Contracting Services
N.A.I.C.S.: 238160
Randy Fisher *(Pres)*
Greg Campbell *(Sr VP)*

JOHN J. DOODY & SON INC.
2461 E 17th St, Brooklyn, NY 11235
Tel.: (718) 648-6000
Web Site: http://www.doodyhomecenters.com
Sales Range: $10-24.9 Million
Emp.: 60
Hardware Stores
N.A.I.C.S.: 444140
Nina Strzelecki *(Sec & Mgr-HR)*
Peter Doody *(Chm)*

JOHN J. KIRLIN INC.
515 Dover Rd Ste 2100, Rockville, MD 20850
Tel.: (301) 424-3410
Web Site: http://www.jjkllc.net
Sales Range: $100-124.9 Million
Emp.: 800
Heating & Ventilating Contracting Services
N.A.I.C.S.: 238220
Kevin M. Walsh *(Pres & CEO)*

Subsidiaries:

John J. Kirlin Inc. Carolinas Div. (1)
8000 Brownleigh Dr, Raleigh, NC 27617
Tel.: (919) 787-4862
Sales Range: $10-24.9 Million
Emp.: 35
Plumbing Contractor
N.A.I.C.S.: 238220
Joseph Turner *(Pres)*

JOHN JACKSON MASONRY
5691 B Power Inn Rd, Sacramento, CA 95824
Tel.: (916) 381-8021
Web Site: http://www.johnjacksonmasonry.com
Sales Range: $10-24.9 Million
Emp.: 120
Masonry & Other Stonework
N.A.I.C.S.: 238140
Jeff Barber *(Pres)*
Wayne Mika *(Project Mgr)*

JOHN K. BURCH COMPANY INCORPORATED
4200 Brockton Dr SE, Grand Rapids, MI 49512
Tel.: (616) 698-2800
Web Site: http://www.burchfabrics.com
Sales Range: $10-24.9 Million
Emp.: 45
Upholstery Fabrics, Woven
N.A.I.C.S.: 424310
John B. Burch *(Pres)*

JOHN KNOX VILLAGE OF FLORIDA, INC.
651 SW 6th St, Pompano Beach, FL 33060
Tel.: (954) 783-4000   FL
Web Site: http://www.johnknoxvillage.com
Year Founded: 1978
Sales Range: $25-49.9 Million

Emp.: 650
Lifecare Retirement Community Operator
N.A.I.C.S.: 623311
Nanette Rudolf Olson *(Exec Dir)*
Jean Eccleston *(CFO)*
Gerald Stryker *(Pres & CEO)*
Jack Crissy *(Treas)*
Paul Simpson *(Vice Chm)*
Pauline Grant *(Sec)*
Verna Chisman *(Dir-Wellness)*
Kim Morgan-Vagnuolo *(Dir-Mktg)*
William G. Knibloe II *(Chm)*

JOHN KOHL AUTO CENTER INC.
3516 S Lincoln Ave, York, NE 68467
Tel.: (402) 362-5511
Web Site: http://www.johnkohlauto.com
Rev.: $14,272,854
Emp.: 35
New & Used Car Dealers
N.A.I.C.S.: 441110
John P. Kohl *(Owner, Pres & CEO)*
Ben Kohl *(Gen Mgr)*
Carol Kohl *(Office Mgr)*

JOHN L. CONLEY INC.
4344 Mission Blvd, Montclair, CA 91763
Tel.: (909) 627-0981
Rev.: $14,000,000
Emp.: 50
Prefabricated Greenhouse Mfr
N.A.I.C.S.: 332311
John L. Conley *(Chm)*

JOHN L. JERSEY & SON INC.
PO Box 1528, Scappoose, OR 97056
Tel.: (503) 543-3420
Sales Range: $25-49.9 Million
Emp.: 100
Excavation & Grading, Building Construction
N.A.I.C.S.: 238910
John L. Jersey II *(Pres)*

JOHN L. SCOTT INC.
11040 Main St Ste 200, Bellevue, WA 98004-1668
Tel.: (206) 230-7600
Web Site: http://www.johnlscott.com
Sales Range: $25-49.9 Million
Emp.: 55
Real Estate Services
N.A.I.C.S.: 531210
Phil McBride *(COO)*
J.Lennox Scott *(Chm & CEO)*
Howard Chung *(VP-Broker Excellence)*
Jeff Cohen *(VP-Professional Achievement)*
Jennifer Lind *(VP-Business Strategy)*
Barry Matheny *(VP-Relocation Svcs & eBusiness)*
Tim Wynne *(VP-John L. Scott Affiliates)*
Jon Hunter *(VP-Residential Success)*
Andrew Mathews *(Gen Counsel)*
Monty D. Smith *(Chief Growth Officer)*

JOHN LENORE & COMPANY, INC.
1250 Delevan Dr, San Diego, CA 92102-2437
Tel.: (619) 232-6136   CA
Web Site: http://www.johnlenore.com
Year Founded: 1966
Sales Range: $10-24.9 Million
Emp.: 75
Groceries & Related Products
N.A.I.C.S.: 424810

Subsidiaries:

JDL Motor Express (1)
1250 Delavan Dr, San Diego, CA 92102-2437
Tel.: (619) 232-6136
Sales Range: Less than $1 Million
Local Trucking without Storage
N.A.I.C.S.: 484110

Logret Import & Export Co. Inc. (1)
1250 Delavan Dr, San Diego, CA 92102-2437
Tel.: (626) 961-9800
Web Site: http://www.logret.com
Sales Range: $10-24.9 Million
Emp.: 20
Beer, Wine & Spirits Importer & Distr
N.A.I.C.S.: 424810

PJJ Enterprises Inc. (1)
1250 Delavan Dr, San Diego, CA 92102-2437
Tel.: (619) 232-6136
Sales Range: $10-24.9 Million
Emp.: 100
Equipment Rental & Leasing
N.A.I.C.S.: 532289

JOHN M. ELLSWORTH CO., INC.
8700 W Bradley Rd, Milwaukee, WI 53224
Tel.: (414) 354-1414
Web Site: http://www.jmesales.com
Year Founded: 1974
Sales Range: $10-24.9 Million
Emp.: 30
Industrial Machinery Equipment Whslr
N.A.I.C.S.: 423830
John Ellsworth (Pres)
Phillip Areddia (VP)
Rick Carey (Mgr-Sls)

JOHN M. HARTEL CO. INC.
144 N Kinderkamack Rd, Montvale, NJ 07645-1337
Tel.: (201) 391-5000
Web Site: http://www.jmhartel.com
Year Founded: 1947
Sales Range: $10-24.9 Million
Emp.: 40
Plumbing Fixtures, Equipment & Supplies
N.A.I.C.S.: 423720
Frederick Hartel (CEO)

JOHN M. HESS AUCTION SERVICE, INC.
1667 Cider Press Rd, Manheim, PA 17545
Tel.: (717) 664-5238 PA
Web Site: http://www.hess-auctiongroup.com
Year Founded: 1998
Sales Range: $25-49.9 Million
General Merchandise & Real Estate Auctioneer
N.A.I.C.S.: 561990
John M. Hess (Founder & Pres)

Subsidiaries:

Conestoga Auction Company, Inc. (1)
768 Graystone Rd, Manheim, PA 17545
Tel.: (717) 664-5238
Web Site: http://www.conestogaauction.com
Sales Range: $1-9.9 Million
Emp.: 25
General Merchandise & Real Estate Auctioneer
N.A.I.C.S.: 561990
Doris DeHart (Mgr)

JOHN M. OLSON CORPORATION
26210 Harper Ave, Saint Clair Shores, MI 48081-2203
Tel.: (586) 771-9330 MI
Web Site: http://www.jmolson.com

Year Founded: 1970
Sales Range: $200-249.9 Million
Emp.: 90
Contracting & Construction Services
N.A.I.C.S.: 541618
John M. Olson (Chm & CEO)
Robert Barry (VP-Fin)
Steven Braun (Pres)

JOHN MILLS DISTRIBUTING CO. INC
3360 N Benzing Rd, Orchard Park, NY 14127
Tel.: (716) 822-0854
Web Site:
http://www.johnmillsdistributing.com
Rev.: $14,000,000
Emp.: 32
Meats & Meat Products
N.A.I.C.S.: 424470
John Mills (Pres)
Douglas McLvor (Mgr-Shipping)

JOHN MORIARTY & ASSOCIATES INC.
3 Church St, Winchester, MA 01890-1804
Tel.: (781) 729-3900 MA
Web Site: http://www.jm-a.com
Year Founded: 1985
Sales Range: $100-124.9 Million
Emp.: 180
Nonresidential Construction Services
N.A.I.C.S.: 236220
John J. Moriarty (Founder, Pres & Principal)
Dean Aiguier (Mgr-Construction)
Jeffrey Loch (Project Mgr)
Jack MacKinnon (Superintendent)
Todd Newell (Mgr-Project Safety)
Bill Twomey (Superintendent-Construction)
Scott Yardley (Mgr-Safety)
Ray Galvin (Sr VP)
Brian Varney (Supvr-MEP)
Joel Walfish (Mgr-Construction)
Sean Lee (Superintendent)
Tim Kotsiopoulos (Superintendent)
Lou Dahan (CFO)

JOHN MOURIER CONSTRUCTION, INC.
1430 Blue Oaks Blvd Ste 190, Roseville, CA 95747-5157
Tel.: (916) 782-8879
Web Site: http://www.jmchomes.com
Sales Range: $200-249.9 Million
Emp.: 200
Construction Management Services
N.A.I.C.S.: 236115
John L. Mourier III (Pres)

JOHN MUIR HEALTH
1400 Treat Blvd, Walnut Creek, CA 94597
Tel.: (925) 941-2000
Web Site: http://www.jmmdhs.com
Year Founded: 1997
Sales Range: $650-699.9 Million
Emp.: 3,600
Health Care Srvices
N.A.I.C.S.: 541611

JOHN MULLEN & CO, INC.
677 Ala Moana Blvd, Honolulu, HI 96813-5419
Tel.: (808) 531-9733
Web Site: http://www.johnmullen.com
Year Founded: 1959
Sales Range: $10-24.9 Million
Emp.: 90
Claim Adjusting Services
N.A.I.C.S.: 524291
James A. Granata (Gen Mgr)
J. Terrence Mullen (Pres)
Sherry J. Hunt (VP)

Althea Fujio (Acct Mgr)
Stephen Nakao (Mgr-Workers Compensation)
Cyndy Knudson (Dir-Fin & Info Sys)
Laurie Hagedorn (Mgr-HR)

JOHN N. SAUDER AUTO COMPANY
875 W Main St, New Holland, PA 17557
Tel.: (717) 354-4381
Year Founded: 1947
Sales Range: $10-24.9 Million
Emp.: 45
Car Whslr
N.A.I.C.S.: 441110
John Sauder (Pres)

JOHN NEWCOMB ENTERPRISES INC.
910 Triangle St, Blacksburg, VA 24060-7716
Tel.: (540) 552-7718 VA
Year Founded: 1989
Sales Range: $25-49.9 Million
Emp.: 1,400
Eating Place
N.A.I.C.S.: 722513
John Newcomb (Owner)
Derwood Johnson (Mgr-Multi-Unit)

JOHN NORTH FORD
3002 W Us Hwy 50, Emporia, KS 66801-5198
Tel.: (620) 343-1700
Web Site: http://www.jnford.com
Year Founded: 1963
Sales Range: $10-24.9 Million
Emp.: 40
New Car Whslr
N.A.I.C.S.: 441110
Ron Carlson (Gen Mgr)
Justin Neuman (Mgr-Fin)
Tim North (Owner)
Jim Wright (Mgr-Svc)

JOHN PATON, INC.
73 E State St, Doylestown, PA 18901-4359
Tel.: (215) 348-7050 PA
Web Site: http://www.goldenblossom honey.com
Year Founded: 1921
Sales Range: $1-9.9 Million
Emp.: 7
Honey Mfr & Distr
N.A.I.C.S.: 424490
Joan Lucas (Dir-Sls)
Jon Paton (Pres)

JOHN PAUL MITCHELL SYSTEMS
20705 Center Pointe Pkwy, Santa Clarita, CA 91350
Tel.: (310) 248-3888 CA
Web Site:
http://www.paulmitchell.com
Year Founded: 1980
Sales Range: $800-899.9 Million
Emp.: 100
Hair Preparations Mfr & Distr
N.A.I.C.S.: 424210
John Paul DeJoria (Founder & Chm)
Stephanie Kocielski (VP-Education)
Michaeline DeJoria (CEO)
Jason Yates (Pres)
Sean Ansett (Sr Dir-Sustainability)

Subsidiaries:

John Paul Pet, L.L.C. (1)
PO Box 98437, Las Vegas, NV 89074
Web Site: http://www.johnpaulpet.com
Pet Care Services
N.A.I.C.S.: 812910
Saeed Rouhifar (Pres)
John Paul DeJoria (Founder & Chm)

JOHN PAUL RICHARD INC.
26800 Agoura Rd, Calabasas, CA 91301-5129
Tel.: (818) 871-1300
Web Site:
http://www.johnpaulrichard.com
Year Founded: 1996
Rev.: $12,000,000
Emp.: 65
Women's Apparel Mfr & Distr
N.A.I.C.S.: 315250
John Paul Beltran (Co-Founder & CEO)
Richard Hirsch (Co-Founder)
Bertan Kalatchi (Co-Founder)

JOHN Q. HAMMONS HOTELS INC.
300 S John Q Hammons Pkwy Ste 900, Springfield, MO 65806
Tel.: (417) 864-4300 DE
Web Site: http://www.jqhotels.com
Sales Range: $400-449.9 Million
Emp.: 5,800
Hotel Owner & Operator
N.A.I.C.S.: 721110
Jacqueline A. Dowdy (CEO)
Kent Foster (VP-HR)
Joe Morrissey (Sr VP-Ops)
Christopher Smith (Sr VP-Admin & Control)
Bill George (VP-Capital Plng & Asset Mgmt)
Phill Burgess (VP-Sls & Revenue Optimization)
Greggory D. Groves (Gen Counsel & Sr VP)
Patrick Blache (VP-IT)
Betsy Kinnear (Dir-Brand Revenue Optimization)
Jennifer Torsleff (Sr Dir-Revenue Optimization)
Rick Beran (VP-Food & Beverage)
Misty Wise (Dir-Digital Strategy & ECommerce)
Nick Larsen (Dir-Revenue Optimization)

JOHN R. MCKENZIE JOBBER, INC.
210 Tavernier St, Tavernier, FL 33070-2627
Tel.: (305) 852-2881 FL
Year Founded: 1969
Sales Range: $10-24.9 Million
Emp.: 23
Petroleum Products
N.A.I.C.S.: 424720
Gregory R. McKenzie (Pres)
Jessica McKenzie (CFO)
Lindsey Nelson (Mgr-Quality Control)

Subsidiaries:

Florida Country Stores Inc. (1)
PO Box 640, Tavernier, FL 33070-0640 (100%)
Tel.: (305) 852-2881
Web Site:
http://www.mckenziepetroleum.com
Sales Range: $10-24.9 Million
Emp.: 15
Operator of Convenience Stores & Gas Stations
N.A.I.C.S.: 459999
Gregory R. McKenzie (Pres)
Jessica McKenzie (VP)

Florida Keys Food Stores, Inc. (1)
PO Box 640, Tavernier, FL 33070-0640 (100%)
Tel.: (305) 852-2881
Web Site:
http://www.mckenziepetroleum.com
Sales Range: $10-24.9 Million
Emp.: 15
Provider of Convenience Stores

John R. McKenzie Jobber, Inc.—(Continued)
N.A.I.C.S.: 424720
Gregory R. McKenzie (Pres)
Jessica McKenzie (CFO)

JOHN R. MORREALE INCORPORATED
216 N Peoria St, Chicago, IL 60607
Tel.: (312) 421-3664
Web Site: http://www.jrmorreale.com
Rev.: $146,608,677
Emp.: 67
Meat Sales
N.A.I.C.S.: 424470
Jerry Schommer (Controller)

JOHN R. TURNER HOLDING COMPANY
720 Hwy 15 S, Jackson, KY 41339
Tel.: (606) 666-7575   KY
Year Founded: 1998
Sales Range: $10-24.9 Million
Emp.: 68
Multiple Bank Holding Company
N.A.I.C.S.: 551111
Lewis H. Warrix (Chm, Pres & CEO)
Marty Snowden (Pres/CEO-Citizens Bank & Trust Co of Jackson)

Subsidiaries:

Citizens Bank & Trust Co. of Jackson   (1)
720 Hwy 15 S, Jackson, KY 41339
Tel.: (606) 666-7575
Web Site:
http://www.citizensbankjackson.com
Sales Range: $1-9.9 Million
Emp.: 51
Commericial Banking
N.A.I.C.S.: 522110
Lewis H. Warrix (Chm)
Marty Snowden (Pres & CEO)
Diane Dunahoo (Exec VP)
J. B. Morgan (Exec VP)

Farmers Deposit Bank of Middleburg, Inc.   (1)
2959 Shorttown Rd, Middleburg, KY 42541
Tel.: (606) 536-0425
Web Site: http://www.farmersdeposit.com
Sales Range: $1-9.9 Million
Emp.: 17
Commericial Banking
N.A.I.C.S.: 522110
Anna Lou Tarter Smith (Chm)

JOHN R. WOOD, INC.
9130 Corsea Del Fontana Way, Naples, FL 34109
Tel.: (239) 592-1011   FL
Web Site: http://www.johnrwood.com
Year Founded: 1958
Sales Range: $1-4.9 Billion
Emp.: 400
Real Estate Broker
N.A.I.C.S.: 531210
Dottie Babcock (COO)
Ginny Alexander (Dir-Relocation & Referrals)
John R. Wood (Chm)
Gwen Vanloo (Mgr-Acctg)
Phil Wood (Exec VP)

JOHN R. YOUNG & CO. INC.
751 Lumber St, Green Lane, PA 18054
Tel.: (215) 234-4351   PA
Web Site:
http://www.johnryoungco.com
Year Founded: 1890
Sales Range: $10-24.9 Million
Emp.: 23
Fuel & Lubricant Distr
N.A.I.C.S.: 457210
Donald A. Young (Pres)
Bill Shaak (Mgr-PCMO Segment)
Jim Butler (Mgr-Transport & Industrial Segment)

JOHN REYER COMPANY
City Ctr, Sharon, PA 16146
Tel.: (724) 981-2200   PA
Web Site: http://www.reyers.com
Year Founded: 1879
Sales Range: $125-149.9 Million
Emp.: 200
Sales of Shoes & Accessories
N.A.I.C.S.: 458210
Mark B. Jubelirer (Pres)
Steven W. Jubelirer (VP)
Kim Jones (CIO)

JOHN RICHARD INCORPORATED
306 Eastman St, Greenwood, MS 38930
Tel.: (662) 453-5809
Web Site: http://www.johnrichard.com
Year Founded: 1980
Sales Range: $25-49.9 Million
Emp.: 450
Whslr of Furniture & Home Decorations
N.A.I.C.S.: 335131
Patrick Vaughn (Mgr-Engrg)
Alex J. Malouf Jr. (Owner)

JOHN ROBERTS COMPANY
9687 E River Rd, Minneapolis, MN 55433-5514
Tel.: (763) 755-5500   MN
Web Site: http://www.johnroberts.com
Year Founded: 1951
Sales Range: $50-74.9 Million
Emp.: 400
Provider of Commercial Printing & Lithography Services
N.A.I.C.S.: 323111
Michael R. Keene (Pres & CEO)
Michael V. Thews (CFO & VP)
Julie Petrangelo (Controller)
Marnie Janezich (Mgr-Pur)

JOHN ROHRER CONTRACTING CO.
2820 Roe Ln Bldg S, Kansas City, KS 66103
Tel.: (913) 236-5005
Web Site:
http://www.johnrohrercontracting.com
Sales Range: $10-24.9 Million
Emp.: 50
Concrete Construction & Repair
N.A.I.C.S.: 238110
Brandon D. McMullen (VP & Div Mgr)

JOHN S. FREY ENTERPRISES
1900 E 64th St, Los Angeles, CA 90001-2104
Tel.: (323) 583-4061   CA
Web Site:
http://www.madisonind.com
Year Founded: 1950
Sales Range: $300-349.9 Million
Emp.: 650
Holding Company
N.A.I.C.S.: 551112
John S. Frey Jr. (Chm & Pres)
Mike Eyestone (Gen Mgr)

Subsidiaries:

Finish Line Industries   (1)
705 S Springbrook Ste A-100, Newberg, OR 97132
Tel.: (503) 554-1574
Web Site: http://www.finishlineind.com
Painting Services
N.A.I.C.S.: 238320
Chris Thom (Pres)

Finishline Industries Inc. of Georgia   (1)
1275 S Main St NE, Conyers, GA 30012-4853   (100%)
Tel.: (770) 483-7293
Web Site: http://www.finishline-doors.com

Sales Range: $10-24.9 Million
Emp.: 6
Mfr of Overhead & Walk-In Doors
N.A.I.C.S.: 332321

Madison Industries Inc.   (1)
1900 E 64th St, Los Angeles, CA 90001-2104   (100%)
Tel.: (323) 583-4061
Web Site: http://www.madisonind.com
Sales Range: $25-49.9 Million
Emp.: 190
Fabrication & Erection of Modular Steel Buildings, Canopies & Doors
N.A.I.C.S.: 236220
Jacob Torres (Mgr-Engrg & Quality Control)

Subsidiary (Domestic):

Madison Industries Inc. of Arizona   (2)
2100 S 11th Ave, Phoenix, AZ 85007-4160   (100%)
Tel.: (602) 252-3083
Web Site: http://www.madisonind.com
Sales Range: $10-24.9 Million
Emp.: 12
Fabrication & Erection of Modular Steel Buildings, Canopies & Doors
N.A.I.C.S.: 332312

Madison Industries Inc. of Georgia   (2)
1035 Iris Dr, Conyers, GA 30094   (100%)
Tel.: (770) 483-4401
Web Site: http://www.madisonind.com
Sales Range: $25-49.9 Million
Fabrication & Erection of Modular Steel Buildings & Canopies
N.A.I.C.S.: 236210
Sam Frey (Gen Mgr)

Madison, Inc.   (2)
8500 New Sapulpa Rd, Tulsa, OK 74131-3829   (100%)
Tel.: (918) 224-6990
Web Site: http://www.madisonind.com
Sales Range: $25-49.9 Million
Emp.: 50
Fabrication And Erection of Modular Steel Buildings Canopies And Doors
N.A.I.C.S.: 236220
Jimmy Woods (Pur Asst)

Task Force Tips LLC   (2)
3701 Innovation Way, Valparaiso, IN 46383-8395
Tel.: (219) 462-6161
Web Site: http://www.tft.com
Fire Fighting Equipment Mfr
N.A.I.C.S.: 332919
Stewart McMillan (Chm & CEO)
Martin Sonnenberg (Pres &COO)
Jim Menke (VP-Domestic Sls)

Phoenix Metallics, Inc.   (2)
4500 Self Lexco Dr Ste 400, Phoenix, AZ 85282   (100%)
Tel.: (602) 254-6144
Sales Range: $10-24.9 Million
Emp.: 9
Miscellaneous Metal Items, School Lockers, Powder Paint Coatings
N.A.I.C.S.: 332322

JOHN S. JAMES CO.
6002 Commerce Blvd Ste 115, Garden City, GA 31408
Tel.: (912) 232-0211
Web Site:
http://www.johnsjames.com
Year Founded: 1941
Sales Range: $10-24.9 Million
Emp.: 60
Provider of Freight Forwarding, Customs Brokerage, Cargo Insurance & Other Related Transportation & Logistics Services
N.A.I.C.S.: 488510
Len James (CFO)
Richard Jones (Office Mgr)
Karen Pfau (Mgr-Export)

JOHN SNOW, INC.
44 Farnsworth St, Boston, MA 02210-1209

Tel.: (617) 482-9485   MA
Web Site: http://www.jsi.com
Year Founded: 1978
Sales Range: $25-49.9 Million
Emp.: 350
Health Care Management Consulting Services
N.A.I.C.S.: 541611
Joel Lamstein (Founder)
Patricia Fairchild (VP-Health Svcs-United States)
Alexander K. Baker (COO)
Carolyn Hart (Dir-Washington)
Debra Olesen (Dir-Health Svcs-Denver-United States)
Jonathan Stewart (Dir-Health Svcs-Northern New England & United States)
Ken Olivola (Dir-Intl Div-Boston)
Penelope Riseborough (Dir-Comm)
Stewart Landers (Dir-Health Svcs-Boston-United States)
Margaret M. Crotty (Pres & CEO)
Margaret Crotty (Pres & CEO)

Subsidiaries:

The Manoff Group, Inc.   (1)
4301 Connecticut Ave N W Ste 454, Washington, DC 20008-2304
Tel.: (202) 364-9680
Web Site: http://www.manoffgroup.com
Professional, Scientific & Technical Services
N.A.I.C.S.: 541990
Heather Davis (Mgr-Comm)

JOHN STAURULAKIS, LLC
7852 Walker Dr Ste 200, Greenbelt, MD 20770
Tel.: (301) 459-7590
Web Site: http://www.jsitel.com
Year Founded: 1962
Emp.: 100
Telecommunication Servicesb
N.A.I.C.S.: 517810
Steve Meltzer (Pres)
Leo Staurulakis (Exec VP)
Tasos Tsolakis (CEO)

Subsidiaries:

Mid-State Consultants, Inc.   (1)
1475 N 200 W, Nephi, UT 84648
Tel.: (435) 623-8601
Web Site: http://www.mscon.com
Business Consulting Services
N.A.I.C.S.: 541618
Mike Riley (VP-Engrg)
Vance Gadd (Treas, Sec & VP-Design & OSP)
Steve Carter (Dir-MSCSS)
Steve Kidd (Pres)
Brent Sherry (Reg VP)

JOHN STEWART CO. INC.
1388 Sutter St Fl 11, San Francisco, CA 94109
Tel.: (415) 345-4400   CA
Web Site: http://www.jsco.net
Year Founded: 1978
Sales Range: $100-124.9 Million
Emp.: 1,000
Real Estate Managers
N.A.I.C.S.: 531210
John K. Stewart (Chm)
Jack Gardner (Pres & CEO)
Dan Levine (Sr VP)
Mari Tustin (Sr VP)
Loren Sanborn (Sr VP)
Lori Horn (VP)
Steve McElroy (VP)
Sonya Rosenbach (Officer-Acctg)
Noah G. Schwartz (COO)

JOHN SULLIVAN AUTOMOTIVE GROUP
350 Automall Dr, Roseville, CA 95678
Tel.: (916) 782-1243   CA
Web Site: http://www.chevyworld.com
Year Founded: 1951

Sales Range: $125-149.9 Million
Emp.: 200
New & Used Auto Dealer
N.A.I.C.S.: 441110
John L. Sullivan (Pres)
Steve Ruckel (Controller)
Dave Rogers (VP & Gen Mgr)

Subsidiaries:

John L. Sullivan Investments Inc. (1)
350 Automall Dr, Roseville, CA 95661
Tel.: (916) 782-2163
Sales Range: $25-49.9 Million
Automobiles, New & Used
N.A.I.C.S.: 441110
John L. Sullivan (Owner & Pres)

JOHN T. DAVIS OIL CO. INC.
2615 W Jefferson St, Anniston, AL 36201
Tel.: (256) 231-1113
Rev.: $21,400,000
Emp.: 61
Convenience Store
N.A.I.C.S.: 424710
John Thomas Davis (Owner)
Holly Rowe (Controller)

JOHN T. HOWE INC.
1389 Lk Ariel Hwy, Lake Ariel, PA 18436
Tel.: (570) 698-5821
Web Site:
http://www.johnthoweinc.com
Rev.: $11,000,000
Emp.: 10
Gasoline
N.A.I.C.S.: 424720
Bruce D. Howe (Pres)

JOHN T. MATHER MEMORIAL HOSPITAL
75 N Country Rd, Port Jefferson, NY 11777
Tel.: (631) 473-1320   NY
Web Site:
http://www.matherhospital.org
Year Founded: 1928
Sales Range: $200-249.9 Million
Emp.: 2,691
Health Care Srvices
N.A.I.C.S.: 622110
Joseph Wisnoski (CFO & VP-Fin)
Joan Faro (Chief Medical Officer)
Diane Marotta (VP-Nursing)
Leo Sternlicht (Sec)
Thomas Heiman (VP-HR)
Kevin Murray (CFO & VP-Fin)
Marie Mulligan (VP-Pub Affairs)
Ann Lee (Dir-Matls Mgmt)
Michael Tofano (Dir-Internal Medicine Residency Program)
Imtiaz Khokhar (Dir-Hospital Medicine & Asst Dir-Internal Medicine Residency)
Craig Player (Dir-Admin-Imaging Svcs)
Christine Santini (Dir-Mktg & Comm)

JOHN T. VUCUREVICH FOUNDATION
2800 Jackson Blvd Ste 410, Rapid City, SD 57702
Tel.: (605) 343-3141
Web Site: http://www.jtvf.org
Year Founded: 1985
Charity Foundation
N.A.I.C.S.: 813211
Alan Solano (Pres & CEO)
Shelly Adams (Sec & Mgr-Grants)
Jessica Gromer (Program Officer)

JOHN V. SCHULTZ CO.
7200 Peach St Unit 300, Erie, PA 16509
Tel.: (814) 868-7125

Web Site:
http://www.johnvschultz.com
Sales Range: $10-24.9 Million
Emp.: 75
Furniture Retailer
N.A.I.C.S.: 449110
Jonathon DiPrinzio (Mgr-Sls)
Matt Schultz (Co-Pres)
John V. Schultz Jr. (Co-Pres)

JOHN VANCE MOTORS INC.
5322 S Division St, Guthrie, OK 73044
Tel.: (405) 282-2113
Web Site:
http://www.vanceautogroup.com
Sales Range: $25-49.9 Million
Emp.: 200
Automobiles, New & Used
N.A.I.C.S.: 441110
John T. Vance (Pres)
Warren Croket (VP-Special Fin)

JOHN VOLPI & CO., INC.
5263 Northrup Ave, Saint Louis, MO 63110
Tel.: (314) 772-8550
Web Site: http://www.volpifoods.com
Year Founded: 1902
Sales Range: $10-24.9 Million
Emp.: 115
Meat Product Production & Distribution Services
N.A.I.C.S.: 424470
Lorenza Pasetti (Pres)

JOHN W. DANFORTH CO.
300 Colvin Woods Pkwy, Tonawanda, NY 14150
Tel.: (716) 832-1940   NY
Web Site: http://www.jwdanforth.com
Year Founded: 1884
Sales Range: $125-149.9 Million
Emp.: 210
Provider of Contracting Services
N.A.I.C.S.: 237110
Nickolas Optis (VP)
Kevin G. Reilly (Chm & CEO)
Robert Beck (Pres)
Jason Rudich (VP-Estimating)
Brian Tubin (CFO & VP)
Patrick McParlane (Exec VP)
Steve DiRaimo (VP-Bus Dev & Acq)
John Samar (Exec VP-Western New York)
Tom Shannon (VP-Ops-Albany)

JOHN W. GLEIM, JR. INC.
625 Hamilton St, Carlisle, PA 17013
Tel.: (717) 766-6470
Web Site: http://www.jwgleim.com
Sales Range: $10-24.9 Million
Emp.: 120
Excavation & Grading, Building Construction
N.A.I.C.S.: 238910
Jim Gleim (Pres)

JOHN W. HENRY & COMPANY, INC.
301 Yamato Rd Ste 2200, Boca Raton, FL 33431
Tel.: (561) 241-0018
Web Site: http://www.jwh.com
Rev.: $12,400,000
Emp.: 5
Futures Advisory Service
N.A.I.C.S.: 523940
John W. Henry (Chm)
Kevin Koshi (Pres)
Keith Holmgren (Dir-Proprietary Sys)
Ken Mahes (CTO)

JOHN W. MCDOUGALL CO. INC.

3731 Amy Linn Dr, Nashville, TN 37218
Tel.: (615) 321-3900
Web Site: http://www.jwmcd.com
Rev.: $14,885,151
Emp.: 150
Sheet Metalwork
N.A.I.C.S.: 332322
Alec McDougall (Pres)
Darryl Skelton (Project Mgr)
George Holland (Project Mgr)

JOHN W. ROOKER & ASSOCIATES INC.
4920 N Royal Atlanta Dr, Tucker, GA 30084-3031
Tel.: (770) 491-7711   GA
Web Site: http://www.rookerco.com
Year Founded: 1955
Sales Range: $25-49.9 Million
Emp.: 40
Industrial Buildings & Warehouses
N.A.I.C.S.: 236220
John W. Rooker (Chm & CEO)
William J. Cole (Pres)
Daniel B. Pattillo (Pres-Rooker Real Estate)
J. Elbert Rivers (Pres-Properties)

JOHN W. STONE OIL DISTRIBUTORS LLC
87 First St, Gretna, LA 70053-4746
Tel.: (504) 366-3401   LA
Web Site: http://www.stoneoil.com
Year Founded: 1946
Rev.: $300,000,000
Emp.: 150
Petroleum Product Distr
N.A.I.C.S.: 424720
John W. Stone Jr. (Pres)

JOHN WAGNER ASSOCIATES, INC.
5255 W 11000 N, Highland, UT 84003
Tel.: (801) 492-3880
Web Site:
http://www.grabberman.com
Sales Range: $125-149.9 Million
Emp.: 400
Construction Products & Supplies Distr & Mfr
N.A.I.C.S.: 423710
Jack Kroll (Chm)
Tom Dorsey (Mgr-Sls-Southeast)
Barry Boatwright (Mgr-Product Category-Product Category Mgmt)
Rob Waterhouse (Pres & CEO)
Mike Toole (VP-Sls)
Darren Jones (Dir-Mktg)

Subsidiaries:

John Wagner Associates, Inc. - Pacific Division   (1)
205 Mason Cir, Concord, CA 94520
Tel.: (925) 687-6606
Web Site: http://www.grabberman.com
Construction Products & Supplies Distr & Mfr
N.A.I.C.S.: 332510
Steve Jenson (Sls Mgr-West)
Shane Hilt (Branch Mgr)

JOHN WIESNER INC.
1645 I 45 N, Conroe, TX 77304
Tel.: (936) 756-8161
Web Site:
http://www.wiesnerauto.com
Rev.: $92,193,924
Emp.: 250
Automobiles, New & Used
N.A.I.C.S.: 441110
Gary Bridges (Dir-Fin)
Amy Coopland (Mgr-Fin)
Annette Harris (Mgr-Fin)

JOHN XXIII HOME

2250 Shenago Valley Freeway, Hermitage, PA 16148
Tel.: (724) 981-3200   PA
Web Site:
http://www.johnxxiiihome.org
Year Founded: 1971
Sales Range: $10-24.9 Million
Emp.: 214
Nursing Care Services
N.A.I.C.S.: 621610
David D'Amore (Dir-Medical)
Celeste Muenz (Mgr-Bus)
John Matune (Chm)
Raymond Shaffer (Treas & Sec)
Joe McLaughlin (Vice Chm)
Jodi Shuchart (Dir-Nursing)
Lisa Maddy (Mgr-Bus Office)
John B. Rossi (Dir-HR & Dev)
Linny Harden (Mgr-Personal Care)
Sean Bayless (Coord-Admissions)
Ron Rodgers (Dir-Maintenance)
Barb Thompson (Mgr-Housekeeping & Laundry)
Sue Pisarcik (Mgr-Dietary)
Ruth Timko (Dir-Activities & Volunteer)

JOHN'S ISLAND CLUB, INC.
3 John's Is Dr, Vero Beach, FL 32963
Tel.: (772) 231-1700
Web Site:
http://www.johnsislandclub.org
Sales Range: $10-24.9 Million
Emp.: 300
Country Club
N.A.I.C.S.: 713910
Brian Kroh (Gen Mgr)
Debbie Gaw (Mgr-Mdse)
John Goheen (Mgr-Night & Enviromental Svcs)

JOHN-WILLIAM FINE FURNITURE & INTERIORS INC.
2805 Bee Caves Rd Ste 117, Austin, TX 78746
Tel.: (512) 323-2957
Web Site: http://www.jwinteriors.com
Sales Range: $10-24.9 Million
Emp.: 10
Furniture Retailer
N.A.I.C.S.: 449110
Michael Morrison (Sr VP)
Jerry Horhn (Mgr-Store)

JOHNCARLO WOODWORKING, INC.
30 Clifton St, Westfield, MA 01085
Tel.: (413) 562-4002
Web Site:
http://www.johncarloww.com
Year Founded: 1986
Sales Range: $1-9.9 Million
Emp.: 10
Millwork Services
N.A.I.C.S.: 321918
Giancarlo Fiordalice (Pres)

JOHNNIE-O
2712 Wilshire Blvd, Santa Monica, CA 90403
Tel.: (877) 787-4703
Web Site: http://www.johnnie-o.com
Year Founded: 2006
Sales Range: $1-9.9 Million
Emp.: 30
Clothing Retailer
N.A.I.C.S.: 458110
Dave Gatto (CEO)
Robert L. Berner III (Executives)

JOHNNY CUPCAKES
378 University Ave, Westwood, MA 02090
Tel.: (781) 331-3177
Web Site:
http://www.johnnycupcakes.com

Johnny Cupcakes—(Continued)

Year Founded: 2001
Sales Range: $1-9.9 Million
Emp.: 36
T-Shirts
N.A.I.C.S.: 458110
John Earle (Owner)
Katherine Bolger (Dir-Customer Svc)

JOHNNY JANOSIK INC.

11151 Trussum Pond Rd, Laurel, DE
19956
Tel.: (302) 875-5955   DE
Web Site:
    http://www.johnnyjanosik.com
Year Founded: 1953
Sales Range: $25-49.9 Million
Emp.: 400
Homefurnishings
N.A.I.C.S.: 449110
David Kohler (CEO)
Debi Quillen (Mgr-Sls)

**JOHNNY KETELSEN RECRE-
ATIONAL VEHICLES INC.**

1500 Ketelsen Dr, Hiawatha, IA
52233-2217
Tel.: (319) 377-8244
Web Site: http://www.ketelsenrv.com
Year Founded: 1962
Sales Range: $10-24.9 Million
Emp.: 35
Recreational Vehicle Dealers
N.A.I.C.S.: 441210
Gary S. Ketelsen (Pres)

**JOHNNY LONDOFF CHEVRO-
LET, INC.**

1375 Dunn Rd, Florissant, MO 63031
Tel.: (314) 262-4526
Web Site: http://www.londoff.com
Year Founded: 1958
Sales Range: $50-74.9 Million
Emp.: 80
New Car Dealers
N.A.I.C.S.: 441110
Johnny Londoff (Owner)
John Londoff Jr. (Pres)

**JOHNNY MACS' SPORTING
GOODS STORES**

10100 Watson Rd, Saint Louis, MO
63127
Tel.: (314) 966-5444
Web Site:
    http://www.johnnymacs.com
Sales Range: $10-24.9 Million
Emp.: 110
Sporting Goods & Bicycle Shops
N.A.I.C.S.: 459110
Jordan Spurlock (Mgr-Ballwin)
Paul Weiblen (Asst Mgr-Warehouse)
Candace Bingham (Dir-Pur)
Andy Busch (Mgr)
Adam Morse (Mgr)
Chuck Rolwes (Mgr)
Jenna Theismann (Mgr)
Phil Steele (Reg Mgr)

**JOHNNY RIBEIRO BUILDER
INC.**

195 E Reno Ave, Las Vegas, NV
89119-1123
Tel.: (702) 798-1133   NV
Web Site: http://www.ribeirocorp.com
Year Founded: 1962
Sales Range: $10-24.9 Million
Emp.: 100
Provider of Nonresidential Construc-
tion Services
N.A.I.C.S.: 236220
Ed Yuill (VP)
Johnny A. Ribeiro Jr. (Pres)

**JOHNS HOPKINS HEALTH
SYSTEM**

601 N Carolina St, Baltimore, MD
21205
Year Founded: 1986
Emp.: 28,000
Hospital
N.A.I.C.S.: 622110
Kevin Sowers (Pres)

**JOHNS HOPKINS REAL ES-
TATE**

3910 Keswick Rd Ste N3100, Balti-
more, MD 21211
Tel.: (443) 997-3737
Web Site: http://www.fm.jhu.edu
Real Estate Services
N.A.I.C.S.: 531210
David M. McDonough (Asst Dir)
William Makowy (Sr Project Mgr)
Bob McLean (VP)
Amy Mercurio (Dir-Plng, Design &
Construction)
David Ashwood (Dir-Plant Ops)
David Alexander (Dir-Fin)
Greg Smith (Dir-Parking & Transpor-
tation)
Lee Coyle (Dir-Plng & Architecture)
Mitch Bonanno (Chief Real Estate
Officer)
Andrew Mabry (Coord-Admin)
Sharon Mackey (Supvr-Housing Cus-
todial)
Jason Mathias (Coord-Sustainability)
Denise Mazzoni (Coord-Sr Admin)
Robert McLean (VP-Facilities & Real
Estate)
John Mitchell (Asst Dir-D&C Contrac-
tin)

JOHNS HOPKINS UNIVERSITY

3400 N Charles St, Baltimore, MD
21218
Tel.: (410) 516-8000
Web Site: http://www.jhu.edu
Year Founded: 1876
Emp.: 25,000
Colleges & Universities
N.A.I.C.S.: 611310
Stephanie Reel (CIO)
Helene Grady (VP-Plng & Budget)
Kerry A. Ates (VP)
Daniel G. Ennis (Sr VP-Fin & Admin)
Ralph D. Semmel (Dir-Applied Phys-
ics Lab)
Keith Hill (VP-Corp Security)
Fritz W. Schroeder (VP-Dev & Alumni
Rels)
Thomas S. Lewis (VP-Govt & Com-
munity Affairs)
Paul Pineau (Gen Counsel & VP)
Sunil Kumar (Sr VP-Academic Affairs
& Provost)
Jonathan Kindred (Asst Dir-Student
Athlete Success)
Jason Perlioni (Chief Investment Offi-
cer)
Susan Ridge (VP-Comm)
Maureen S. Marsh (Sec)
James Jarrell (Chief Audit Officer)
Brian Smith (Chief Procurement Offi-
cer)
Jonathan Links (Chief Risk & Compli-
ance Officer)
Robert A. McLean (VP-Facilities &
Real Estate)
Joanna Pratt (Mng Dir-Markets &
Risk)
Christopher Lenox (Mng Dir-
Investments)
Leonard Moss (Chief Security Officer-
Applied Physics Laboratory)
Ronald J. Daniels (Pres)

Subsidiaries:

BioVenture Centre Pte. Ltd.   (1)

11 Biopolis Way 04-08 Helios Building, Sin-
gapore, 138667, Singapore
Tel.: (65) 68740168
Sales Range: $1-9.9 Million
Emp.: 5
Life Science Incubation Services; Owned
92% by Becton Dickinson & Company &
8% by Johns Hopkins University
N.A.I.C.S.: 541715

The Johns Hopkins University
Press   (1)
2715 N Charles St, Baltimore, MD 21218
Tel.: (410) 516-6900
Web Site: http://www.press.jhu.edu
Emp.: 110
Scholarly Books & Journals Publisher
N.A.I.C.S.: 513130
Erik A. Smist (Sr Dir-Fin & Admin & Assoc
Dir)
Kelly Rogers (Mgr-Rights)

JOHNS-BYRNE CO.

6701 W Oakton St, Niles, IL 60714-
3032
Tel.: (847) 583-3100
Web Site: http://www.johnsbyrne.com
Year Founded: 1959
Packaging Services
N.A.I.C.S.: 561910
Corey Gustafson (Pres)

Subsidiaries:

Chicago Printing Company, Inc.   (1)
1067 N Old Rand Rd, Wauconda, IL 60084-
1239
Tel.: (847) 526-6440
Web Site: http://www.chicagoprintequip.com
Sales Range: $1-9.9 Million
Emp.: 4
Industrial Machinery & Equipment Merchant
Whslr
N.A.I.C.S.: 423830

JOHNSON & BLANTON

537 E Park Ave, Tallahassee, FL
32301
Tel.: (850) 224-1900
Web Site:
    http://www.johnsonblanton.com
Year Founded: 1995
Sales Range: $1-9.9 Million
Emp.: 4
Government Relations & Political
Consulting
N.A.I.C.S.: 541618
John Johnson (Founder, Principal &
Partner)
Melanie Brown (Dir-Govt Rels)
Cheryl Adams (Office Mgr)
Darrick D. McGhee (VP-Govt Rels)
Diane Carr (Gen Counsel)
Travis Blanton (Partner)

JOHNSON & HOFFMAN, LLC

40 Voice Rd, Carle Place, NY 11514
Tel.: (516) 742-3333
Web Site:
    http://www.johnsonhoffman.com
Year Founded: 1949
Metal Stamping
N.A.I.C.S.: 332119
Larry Zettwoch (VP-Sls & Mktg)

JOHNSON & QUIN, INC.

7460 N Lehigh Ave, Niles, IL 60714-
4099
Tel.: (847) 588-4800   IL
Web Site: http://www.j-quin.com
Year Founded: 1876
Sales Range: $75-99.9 Million
Emp.: 100
Direct Marketing Products & Services
N.A.I.C.S.: 541860
David Henkel (Pres)
Bob Arkema (Exec VP)
Bob Granat (VP-Ops)
Kay Wilt (Dir-Mktg)

Andrew Henkel (VP-Sls)
Robert Pullman (Dir-Natl Sls)
Manish Haria (VP-IT & Security)

JOHNSON & TOWERS, INC.

2021 Briggs Rd, Mount Laurel, NJ
08054-4608
Tel.: (856) 234-6990   PA
Web Site:
    http://www.johnsontowers.com
Year Founded: 1927
Sales Range: $75-99.9 Million
Emp.: 206
Diesel Engines & Transportation
Equipment & Supplies Sales
N.A.I.C.S.: 423830
David Johnson (Pres)
Bob Shomo (VP-Selected Products)
Walter F. Johnson III (Chm)

Subsidiaries:

Johnson Truck Center LLC   (1)
3801 Ironwood Pl, Hyattsville, MD 20785
Tel.: (301) 832-9100
Web Site:
    http://www.johnsontruckcenter.com
Emp.: 75
New Truck Dealer
N.A.I.C.S.: 441110

**JOHNSON ARCHITECTURAL
METAL COMPANY**

2160 Kingston Ct SE Ste I, Marietta,
GA 30067
Tel.: (770) 953-8485
Web Site: http://www.jamco-inc.com
Sales Range: $25-49.9 Million
Emp.: 150
Glass & Glazing Work
N.A.I.C.S.: 238150
Philip Greeves (Pres)
George F. Johnson Sr. (Treas)

JOHNSON AUTO PLAZA, INC.

12410 E 136th Ave, Brighton, CO
80601
Tel.: (303) 654-1940
Web Site:
    http://www.coloradododge.com
Year Founded: 1992
Sales Range: $10-24.9 Million
Emp.: 60
Car Whslr
N.A.I.C.S.: 441110
Richard Johnson (Pres)
Tom Mack (Dir-Svc)

**JOHNSON BROS RUBBER
CO.**

42 W Buckeye St, West Salem, OH
44287
Tel.: (419) 853-4122
Web Site:
    http://www.johnsonbrosrubbercom
    pany.com
Sales Range: $10-24.9 Million
Emp.: 100
Foams & Rubber
N.A.I.C.S.: 424990
Lawrence G. Cooke (Pres)
Eric Vail (Exec VP)

**JOHNSON BROS. CORPORA-
TION**

5476 Lithia-Pinecrest Rd, Lithia, FL
33547
Tel.: (813) 685-5101
Web Site: http://www.johnson-
    bros.com
Year Founded: 1929
Sales Range: $100-124.9 Million
Emp.: 200
Heavy Construction; Power Plants,
Materials Handling Facilities, High-
ways; Bridges, Underground Utilities;
Treatment Facilities
N.A.I.C.S.: 236210

Derek Fogt *(Exec VP)*
Kathy Ippolito *(Sec)*
Tim W. Winn *(Pres)*
Frank Renda *(Chm)*
Teressa Fields *(Treas & Sec)*

JOHNSON BROTHERS BAKERY SUPPLY

10731 Interstate Hwy 35 N, San Antonio, TX 78233
Tel.: (210) 590-2575
Web Site:
http://www.jbrosbakerysupply.com
Rev.: $20,000,000
Emp.: 40
Baking Supplies
N.A.I.C.S.: 424490
Kevin R. Johnson *(Pres)*
John Hawkins *(Mgr-Pur)*

JOHNSON BROTHERS LIQUOR COMPANY

1999 Shepard Rd, Saint Paul, MN 55116
Tel.: (651) 649-5800   MN
Web Site:
https://www.johnsonbrothers.com
Year Founded: 1953
Sales Range: $550-599.9 Million
Emp.: 3,500
Wine & Distilled Alcoholic Beverage Merchant Wholesalers
N.A.I.C.S.: 424820
Scott Belsaas *(CFO)*
Kevin Longering *(Controller)*
Christina Horner *(Dir-Mktg)*
Mark Hubler *(Pres)*

Subsidiaries:

Indiana Wholesale Wine & Liquor Co.   (1)
200 Lumber Ctr Rd, Michigan City, IN 46360
Tel.: (219) 879-8855
Sales Range: $10-24.9 Million
Emp.: 50
Wine & Liquor Whslr
N.A.I.C.S.: 424820
Randy Patterson *(Mgr-Ops)*

Johnson Brothers Carolina Distributing   (1)
712 Ellis Rd, Durham, NC 27703-6017
Tel.: (919) 596-1144
Web Site: http://www.johnsonbrothers.com
Sales Range: $25-49.9 Million
Emp.: 60
Wine & Distilled Beverages
N.A.I.C.S.: 424820
Jason Lemansky *(Chm & Pres)*
Steve Saltz *(Controller & Mgr-Ops)*

Johnson Brothers Liquor Company of Rhode Island   (1)
1 Compass Cir, North Kingstown, RI 02852-2606
Tel.: (401) 294-6610
Sales Range: $25-49.9 Million
Emp.: 35
Wholesale Liquor & Wine
N.A.I.C.S.: 424820

Northwest Beverages Inc.   (1)
1358 39th St N, Fargo, ND 58102-2808   (100%)
Tel.: (701) 282-4660
Web Site: http://www.johnsonbrothers.com
Sales Range: $10-24.9 Million
Emp.: 30
Manufacture & Retail Of Liquor
N.A.I.C.S.: 424810
Bob Nelson *(Plant Mgr)*

Western Wholesale Liquor Co.   (1)
401 7th St, Rapid City, SD 57701-2759
Tel.: (605) 343-1132
Sales Range: $25-49.9 Million
Emp.: 16
Distr of Wine And Spirits
N.A.I.C.S.: 445320

JOHNSON CARLIER INC.

738 S 52nd St, Tempe, AZ 85281-7211
Tel.: (602) 275-2222
Web Site:
http://www.johnsoncarlier.com
Year Founded: 1921
Emp.: 200
Building & Construction Services
N.A.I.C.S.: 236220
Helen Spencer *(CFO)*
Chris Johnson *(CEO)*
Tom Harrison *(Mng Dir & Sr VP)*
Laura Shivers *(Dir-Bus Strategy)*

Subsidiaries:

BEC Southwest, Inc.   (1)
2396 N Colter Dr, Flagstaff, AZ 86004   (100%)
Tel.: (928) 527-8317
Web Site: http://www.becsouthwest.com
Rev.: $1,800,000
Emp.: 12
Engineering & Construction Services
N.A.I.C.S.: 236220
Marc Daniels *(Pres & COO)*
Amy Valenzuela *(CFO & VP)*

JOHNSON CARPET INC.

4034 Chicago Dr SW, Grandville, MI 49418
Tel.: (616) 531-3100
Web Site:
http://www.johnsoncarpet.com
Rev.: $24,536,079
Emp.: 30
Floor Covering Stores
N.A.I.C.S.: 449121
Beth Johnson *(Pres & CEO)*

JOHNSON CITY CHEMICAL CO. INC.

402 Steel St, Johnson City, TN 37601
Tel.: (423) 926-2167
Web Site: http://www.railsiding.com
Year Founded: 1974
Sales Range: $10-24.9 Million
Emp.: 45
Fertilizers & Agricultural Chemicals
N.A.I.C.S.: 424910
W. Bennett Spratlin *(Pres)*
Larry Suite *(CFO)*

JOHNSON CONCRETE CO.

217 Klumac Rd, Salisbury, NC 28144
Tel.: (704) 636-5231
Web Site:
http://www.johnsoncmu.com
Sales Range: $10-24.9 Million
Emp.: 25
Concrete Products Mfr
N.A.I.C.S.: 327331
Frances H. Johnson *(Owner)*
Charles B. Newsome *(Exec VP & Gen Mgr)*
Jeff Earnhardt *(Gen Mgr)*
Sherry Beck *(Mgr-Hardscape Sls)*

JOHNSON CONTRACTING COMPANY

2750 Morton Dr, East Moline, IL 61244
Tel.: (309) 755-0601
Web Site: http://www.jccinc.com
Sales Range: $10-24.9 Million
Emp.: 130
Sheet Metalwork
N.A.I.C.S.: 238390
C. Douglas Johnson *(Pres)*
Cal Askeland *(Controller)*

JOHNSON CONTRACTORS INC.

3635 2nd St, Muscle Shoals, AL 35661
Tel.: (256) 383-0313

Web Site:
http://www.johnsoncont.com
Sales Range: $10-24.9 Million
Emp.: 106
Industrial Buildings New Construction
N.A.I.C.S.: 236210
Robert Staples *(Project Mgr)*
Thomas Counts *(Owner)*
Billy Davis *(Project Mgr)*
Mark Frederick *(Project Mgr)*

JOHNSON COUNTY WASTEWATER

11811 S Sunset Dr Ste 2500, Olathe, KS 66061-7061
Tel.: (913) 715-8500
Web Site: http://www.jcw.org
Year Founded: 1945
Sales Range: $75-99.9 Million
Emp.: 2,000
Sewerage Systems
N.A.I.C.S.: 221320
John P. O'Neil *(Gen Mgr-Wastewater)*
James Bills *(Mgr-GIS)*
Lori Sand *(Dir-Comm)*
Aaron Witt *(Mgr-Engrg)*
Curtis Norris *(Superintendent)*
Beth Brandel *(Dir-Bus Dev & Plng Div)*
Lisa Davis *(Dir-Customer Rels Div)*
Kurt Winters *(Dir-Ops & Maintenance Div)*
Tony Holt *(Dir-Water Quality Lab Div)*

JOHNSON DESIGN GROUP

550 River St SE, Ada, MI 49301-9524
Tel.: (616) 676-5557
Web Site:
http://www.johnsondesign.com
Year Founded: 1985
Sales Range: Less than $1 Million
Emp.: 3
Advertising Agencies, Business-To-Business, Consumer Marketing, Internet/Web Design, Logo & Package Design, Point of Purchase
N.A.I.C.S.: 541810
Karen Johnson *(Dir-Creative)*

JOHNSON DIRECT

250 N Sunnyslope Rd Ste 203, Brookfield, WI 53005
Tel.: (262) 782-2750
Web Site:
http://www.johnsondirect.com
Year Founded: 1999
Rev.: $21,000,000
Emp.: 13
Advetising Agency
N.A.I.C.S.: 541810
Grant A. Johnson *(Founder & CEO)*
Randy Jaroch *(Sr Copywriter)*
Robert Trecek *(Dir-Bus Dev)*
Denise B. Hearden *(Dir-eMktg)*
Mary B. Nygaard *(Art Dir)*
Mara Frier *(Mgr-Agency)*
Sandy Pagel *(Asst Acct Exec)*
Maria Johnson *(VP)*
Steve Gardener *(PR Exec)*
Lynn Nawrocki *(Creative Strategist)*
Lisa Robbins *(VP-Client Svcs)*
Stacey Smart *(Acct Exec-PR)*

JOHNSON DODGE CHRYSLER JEEP, INC.

481 Route 46, Budd Lake, NJ 07828
Tel.: (908) 850-8700
Web Site:
http://www.johnsondodge.com
Year Founded: 1981
Sales Range: $10-24.9 Million
Emp.: 45
Car Whslr
N.A.I.C.S.: 441110
Jhon Jhonson *(Principal)*

JOHNSON ELECTRIC SUPPLY CO.

1841 Riverside Dr, Cincinnati, OH 45202
Tel.: (513) 421-3700
Web Site: http://www.johnson-electric.com
Year Founded: 1907
Sales Range: $10-24.9 Million
Emp.: 50
Electrical Construction Material Distr
N.A.I.C.S.: 423610
Douglas N. Johnson *(Pres)*
Bobby Johnson *(VP-Sls)*
Larry Gilman *(Branch Mgr)*

JOHNSON EQUIPMENT COMPANY INC.

PO Box 802009, Dallas, TX 75380-2009
Tel.: (972) 661-9822   TX
Web Site: http://www.jequip.com
Year Founded: 1959
Sales Range: $25-49.9 Million
Emp.: 75
Sell & Install Loading Dock Equipment
N.A.I.C.S.: 423830
Randall L. Johnson *(Pres)*
Chris Hammons *(VP)*
David Orozco *(Dir-Strategic Accts)*

Subsidiaries:

Johnson Equipment Company S. de R. L. de C.V.   (1)
Luis Quintanar S 1930-A Col Progreso, 32340, Monterrey, Nuevo Leon, Mexico
Tel.: (52) 8183475773
Web Site:
http://www.johnsonequipment.com.mx
Door & Dock Products Mfr
N.A.I.C.S.: 332321

JOHNSON FEED INCORPORATED

305 W Industrial Rd, Canton, SD 57013
Tel.: (605) 987-4201
Web Site:
http://www.johnsonfeedinc.com
Rev.: $29,054,310
Emp.: 60
Trucking Service
N.A.I.C.S.: 484121
Mitch Johnson *(Dir-HR)*
Todd Johnson *(Pres)*

JOHNSON FINCH & MCCLURE CONSTRUCTION, INC.

9749 Cactus St, Lakeside, CA 92040
Tel.: (619) 938-9727
Web Site: http://www.jfmcon.com
Year Founded: 1977
Sales Range: $25-49.9 Million
Emp.: 200
Other Specialty Trade Contracting Services
N.A.I.C.S.: 238990
Mark Finch *(CEO)*
Scott McClure *(Pres)*
Lance McClure *(VP & Mgr-Ops)*
Joe LaRussa *(Mgr-Lath & Plaster Dept)*

JOHNSON FLOOR COMPANY, INC.

9690 W 55th St, La Grange, IL 60525
Tel.: (708) 354-5510
Web Site:
http://www.johnsonfloor.com
Rev.: $10,000,000
Emp.: 60
Flooring Contractors
N.A.I.C.S.: 238330

Johnson Floor Company, Inc.—(Continued)

Jeff Johnson *(Pres)*
Dan Noonan *(VP)*
Eric Dahlgren *(VP)*
Bob Cikanek *(Mgr-Technical)*

JOHNSON FOODS, INC.
336 Blaine Ave, Sunnyside, WA
98944
Tel.: (509) 837-4214
Web Site:
  http://www.johnsonfoods.com
Rev.: $55,600,000
Emp.: 300
Fruit & Vegetable Canning
N.A.I.C.S.: 311421
George E. Johnson *(CEO)*
Nyle J. Farmer *(CFO)*

JOHNSON GAS APPLIANCE CO.
520 E Ave NW, Cedar Rapids, IA
52405
Tel.: (319) 365-5267
Web Site:
  http://www.mendotahearth.com
Rev.: $11,843,656
Emp.: 50
Burners, Furnaces, Boilers & Stokers
N.A.I.C.S.: 333414
Steve O'Donnell *(Pres)*
Bill O'Donnell *(VP)*
Amy Woodward *(Controller)*

JOHNSON HARDWARE CO.
1201 Pacific St, Omaha, NE 68108
Tel.: (402) 444-1650
Web Site: http://www.jhcomaha.com
Sales Range: $10-24.9 Million
Emp.: 100
Construction & Commercial Hardware
Distr
N.A.I.C.S.: 423710
Rich Nicoll *(Owner)*
William Stock *(Pres)*
David Sullivan *(VP)*

JOHNSON HICKEY MURCHISON, PC
651 E 4th St Ste 200, Chattanooga,
TN 37403-1921
Tel.: (423) 267-5945
Web Site: http://www.jhmcpa.com
Offices of Certified Public Accountants
N.A.I.C.S.: 541211
Jeff Durham *(Partner)*

JOHNSON HOLDING CO.
3902 W Mt Pleasant St, West Burlington, IA 52655
Tel.: (319) 754-4747
Web Site: http://www.johnsonhc.com
Holding Company
N.A.I.C.S.: 551112
Mike Schmidt *(Pres)*

Subsidiaries:

Oskaloosa Concrete Products   **(1)**
1969 Hwy 92 W, Oskaloosa, IA 52577
Tel.: (641) 672-2457
Rev.: $330,000
Emp.: 2
Blocks, Concrete Or Cinder; Standard
N.A.I.C.S.: 327331
Ross Yoder *(Mgr)*

JOHNSON HOMES OF MERIDIAN
2310 Hwy 45 N, Meridian, MS 39301
Tel.: (601) 693-3356
Web Site:
  http://johnsonhomesmeridian.com
Rev.: $40,000,000
Emp.: 35
Investment Services
N.A.I.C.S.: 523999

Bill Johnson *(CEO)*

JOHNSON HYUNDAI OF CARY INC.
5000 Old Raleigh Rd, Cary, NC
27511-7933
Tel.: (919) 877-1829
Web Site:
  http://www.johnsonhyundai.com
Year Founded: 2004
Sales Range: $10-24.9 Million
Emp.: 35
Car Whslr
N.A.I.C.S.: 441110
Sherry Wilkinson *(Mgr-Guest Rels)*
C. David Johnson Jr. *(Pres)*

JOHNSON INTERNATIONAL CO.
20205 59th Pl S, Kent, WA 98032
Tel.: (253) 479-9900
Web Site:
  http://www.johnsoninternational.com
Year Founded: 1976
Sales Range: $10-24.9 Million
Emp.: 100
Hardwood & Softwood Products
Whslr
N.A.I.C.S.: 423310
Lisa M. Johnson *(Chm & CEO)*
Matthew Deines *(Pres)*

JOHNSON LUMBER COMPANY
600 Tennant Ave, Morgan Hill, CA
95037
Tel.: (408) 778-1550
Web Site: http://www.johnsonlumber.com
Year Founded: 1980
Sales Range: $1-9.9 Million
Emp.: 86
Lumber: Rough, Dressed & Finished
N.A.I.C.S.: 423310
Mike Johnson *(Pres)*
Joe McAvoy *(Mgr-Sls)*
Mike Seda *(CFO)*
Dan Goshay *(Mgr)*

JOHNSON MACHINE WORKS INC.
318 N 11th St, Chariton, IA 50049
Tel.: (641) 774-2191
Web Site: http://www.jmworks.com
Sales Range: $10-24.9 Million
Emp.: 100
Fabricated Structural Metal
N.A.I.C.S.: 332312
Jeffrey Johnson *(Pres)*
Shawn Garton *(VP)*
Brian Franks *(CFO)*

JOHNSON MACHINERY CO.
800 E La Cadena Dr, Riverside, CA
92507
Tel.: (951) 686-4560
Web Site: http://www.johnsonmachinery.com
Sales Range: $100-124.9 Million
Emp.: 220
General Construction Machinery &
Equipment
N.A.I.C.S.: 423810
Kevin M. Kelly *(CFO & VP)*
Albert Sanchez *(VP-Support Svcs)*
Bryn Glover *(Mgr-Mktg)*
Larry Boardman *(Mgr-Svc Ops)*
William R. Johnson Jr. *(Pres)*

JOHNSON MOTOR SALES INC.
620 Deere Dr, New Richmond, WI
54017
Tel.: (715) 246-2261

Web Site:
  http://www.johnsonmotorsales.com
Rev.: $28,000,000
Emp.: 85
New Car Dealers
N.A.I.C.S.: 441110
Mick Anderson *(Owner & Pres)*
Greg Anderson *(Gen Mgr)*
Chris Wheeler *(Gen Mgr-Sls)*
Marc McSorley *(Mgr-Body Shop)*
Missy Trautmiller *(Office Mgr)*
Sandy Bollom *(Controller)*
Luke Berends *(Mgr-Parts)*
Jim Mathews *(Mgr-Sls)*
Ashley Buhr *(Mgr-Fin)*
Brad Lutz *(Mgr-HR)*
David Koch *(Mgr-Sls)*
James Stabe *(Mgr-Fin)*
Rob Decker *(Dir-Fin)*
Steve Ritter *(Bus Mgr)*

JOHNSON MOTORS INC.
1891 Blinker Pkwy, Du Bois, PA
15801
Tel.: (814) 371-4444
Web Site:
  http://www.johnsonauto.com
Sales Range: $25-49.9 Million
Emp.: 80
Antique Automobiles
N.A.I.C.S.: 441120
Robert G. Johnson *(Pres)*
Jim Bair *(Gen Mgr)*

JOHNSON NEWSPAPER CORPORATION
260 Washington St, Watertown, NY
13601-3301
Tel.: (315) 782-1000
Web Site:
  http://www.watertowndailytimes.com
Year Founded: 1870
Sales Range: $100-124.9 Million
Emp.: 250
Newspaper Publishing
N.A.I.C.S.: 513110
Harold B. Johnson *(Pres)*
John B. Johnson Jr. *(Chm & CEO)*

Subsidiaries:

The Register Star   **(1)**
364 Warren St, Hudson, NY 12534-2419
Tel.: (518) 828-1616
Web Site: http://www.registerstar.com
Sales Range: $10-24.9 Million
Emp.: 83
Daily Newspaper Publishing Services Except Saturdays
N.A.I.C.S.: 513110

JOHNSON O'CONNOR FERON & CARUCCI, LLP
101 Edgewater Dr Ste 201, Wakefield, MA 01880
Tel.: (781) 914-3400
Web Site: http://www.jocllp.com
Year Founded: 1945
Accounting & Consulting Services
N.A.I.C.S.: 541211
John Carucci *(Partner)*

JOHNSON O'HARE CO. INC.
1 Progress Rd, Billerica, MA 01821
Tel.: (978) 663-9000
Web Site: http://www.johare.com
Sales Range: $10-24.9 Million
Emp.: 100
Bond Brokers
N.A.I.C.S.: 424410
John Saidnawey *(COO)*
Bobbie O'Hare *(VP-Bus Dev)*
Kevin Shea *(Exec VP-Confectionery)*
Carl Annese *(Exec VP-Corp Retail Ops)*
Gary Rosenthal *(Exec VP & Gen Mgr-NY & NJ)*
Harry O'Hare Jr. *(Pres)*

JOHNSON OIL CO. OF HALLOCK
1215 S Atlantic St, Hallock, MN
56728
Tel.: (218) 843-2681
Rev.: $29,417,602
Emp.: 9
Petroleum Products
N.A.I.C.S.: 424720

JOHNSON OIL COMPANY GAYLORD
502 S Otsego Ave, Gaylord, MI
49735
Tel.: (989) 732-2451
Web Site:
  http://www.johnsonspropane.com
Sales Range: $10-24.9 Million
Emp.: 115
Petroleum Gas Distr
N.A.I.C.S.: 424710
Kevin R. Johnson *(Pres)*

JOHNSON PARTNERS INC.
3146 Leeman Ferry Rd SW, Huntsville, AL 35801
Tel.: (256) 883-6364
Sales Range: $10-24.9 Million
Emp.: 500
Fast-Food Restaurants Owner & Operator
N.A.I.C.S.: 722513
Jack Johnson *(Pres)*

JOHNSON POWER LTD.
2530 Braga Dr, Broadview, IL 60155
Tel.: (708) 345-4300
Web Site:
  http://www.johnsonpower.com
Sales Range: $10-24.9 Million
Emp.: 40
Motor Vehicle Drive Shaft Mfr
N.A.I.C.S.: 336350
Lisa Johnson *(Pres)*

JOHNSON PUBLISHING COMPANY, INC.
200 S Michigan Ave, Chicago, IL
60605-2103
Tel.: (312) 322-9200
Web Site:
  http://www.johnsonpublishing.com
Year Founded: 1942
Sales Range: $100-124.9 Million
Emp.: 250
Publisher of Magazines/Books; Radio
Broadcasting; Television Production;
Mfr of Cosmetics
N.A.I.C.S.: 513120
Linda Johnson Rice *(CEO & CEO)*
Kierna Mayo *(Editor in Chief)*
Kathy Chaney *(Mng Editor-Ebony Magazine)*

Subsidiaries:

Fashion Fair Cosmetics, LLC   **(1)**
200 S Michigan Ave 9th Fl, Chicago, IL
60604
Tel.: (312) 322-9444
Web Site: http://www.fashionfair.com
Sales Range: $25-49.9 Million
Emp.: 150
Cosmetics Retailer
N.A.I.C.S.: 456120
Amy S. Hilliard *(Pres)*

JOHNSON REGIONAL MEDICAL CENTER
1100 E Poplar St, Clarksville, AR
72830
Tel.: (479) 754-5454
Web Site: http://www.jrmc.com
Year Founded: 1996
Sales Range: $25-49.9 Million
Emp.: 505
Community Health Care Services
N.A.I.C.S.: 621498

Freeman Wish *(Sec)*
Rickey Casey *(Vice Chm)*

JOHNSON SCANNELL & AS-SOCIATES
11400 SE 8th St Ste 445, Bellevue, WA 98004
Tel.: (425) 709-2345
Web Site:
    http://www.ameripriseadvisors.com
Year Founded: 1999
Sales Range: $1-9.9 Million
Emp.: 6
Financial Advisory Services
N.A.I.C.S.: 523940
Erin Scannell *(Principal)*

JOHNSON SERVICE GROUP INC.
1 E Oakhill Dr Ste 200, Westmont, IL 60559
Tel.: (630) 655-3500
Web Site: http://www.jsginc.com
Sales Range: $25-49.9 Million
Emp.: 1,000
Provider of Temporary Help Services
N.A.I.C.S.: 561320
Dale Slater *(Co-Owner)*
Susan Sproule *(Mgr-HR)*
Cynthia Rodriguez *(Supvr-Customer Acctg)*

JOHNSON SEWELL FORD LINCOLN MERCURY
3301 Hwy 281 N, Marble Falls, TX 78654
Tel.: (830) 693-5577
Web Site:
    http://www.johnsonsewell.com
Sales Range: $10-24.9 Million
Emp.: 100
Automobiles, New & Used
N.A.I.C.S.: 441110
Ross H. Johnson *(Owner)*
Sherry Drehobl *(Controller)*

JOHNSON SMITH COMPANY
4514 19th St Ct E, Bradenton, FL 34203
Tel.: (941) 747-5566   FL
Web Site:
    http://www.johnsonsmith.com
Year Founded: 1914
Sales Range: $75-99.9 Million
Emp.: 100
Mail Order Novelties & Gifts
N.A.I.C.S.: 334413
Kim Boyd *(VP-Mktg)*
Mark Morris *(Controller)*

JOHNSON STORAGE & MOVING COMPANY
221 N Broadway, Denver, CO 80203-3918
Tel.: (303) 778-6683   CO
Web Site:
    http://www.johnsonstorage.com
Year Founded: 1900
Sales Range: $10-24.9 Million
Emp.: 400
Moving & Storage Company
N.A.I.C.S.: 484210
Mark K. Johnson *(Owner)*
Bill Ebbert *(Dir-Legal Ops)*
Belinda Mikulski *(Coord-Move)*
Cody Tomlinson *(Mgr-Logistics Div)*
Joe Cavalcante *(Mgr-Long Haul Fleet)*

Subsidiaries:

Centennial, Colorado Storage & Moving   (1)
7009 S Jordan Rd, Centennial, CO 80112-6901   (100%)
Tel.: (303) 690-2600

Sales Range: $10-24.9 Million
Emp.: 35
Moving & Storage
N.A.I.C.S.: 484110

Century Moving & Storage Inc   (1)
951 N Main St, Lombard, IL 60148 **(100%)**
Web Site: http://www.dupagemoving.com
Household Goods Moving & Storage
N.A.I.C.S.: 484110

Security Van Lines   (1)
100 W Airline Dr, Kenner, LA 70062   (100%)
Tel.: (504) 466-4449
Web Site: http://www.securityvanlines.net
Household Goods Transport; Local Furniture Moving & Storage
N.A.I.C.S.: 484210

JOHNSON SUPPLY & EQUIPMENT CORP.
10151 Stella Link Rd, Houston, TX 77025
Tel.: (713) 661-6666   TX
Web Site:
    http://www.johnsonsupply.com
Year Founded: 1953
Sales Range: $10-24.9 Million
Emp.: 280
Compressors, Controls, Tubing, Fittings, Miscellaneous Parts & Supplies Whslr for Refrigeration, Air Conditioning & Heating
N.A.I.C.S.: 423730
Don Wile *(CFO)*
Darrell Simoneaux III *(VP)*

JOHNSON WESTERN GUNITE COMPANY
940 Doolittle Dr, San Leandro, CA 94577
Tel.: (510) 568-8112
Web Site: http://www.jwgunite.com
Rev.: $15,628,009
Emp.: 50
Structural Concrete Contractor
N.A.I.C.S.: 238990
David E. Bowers *(VP & Controller)*

JOHNSON'S GENERAL STORES INC.
1009 S Seneca St, Wichita, KS 67213
Tel.: (316) 942-6776
Sales Range: $10-24.9 Million
Emp.: 80
Convenience Store
N.A.I.C.S.: 445131
J. Johnson *(Pres)*

JOHNSON'S TIRE SERVICE
3330 Denali St, Anchorage, AK 99503-4033
Tel.: (907) 562-7090
Web Site: http://www.jtsalaska.com
Year Founded: 1982
Sales Range: $10-24.9 Million
Emp.: 95
Tire & Related Product Whslr
N.A.I.C.S.: 441340
Kelly Geade *(Pres)*
Mike Fox *(Mgr-Ops)*
Vatau Alenepi *(Gen Mgr-Retail Sls)*
Michelle Hogan *(VP)*
James Johnson *(Owner)*
Rich Lamar *(Gen Mgr)*

JOHNSON, MIRMIRAN & THOMPSON, INC.
40 Wight Ave, Hunt Valley, MD 21030
Tel.: (410) 329-3100
Web Site: http://www.jmt.com
Year Founded: 1971
Engineering & Architectural Services
N.A.I.C.S.: 541330
Bill Smith *(CIO & Sr VP)*

Subsidiaries:

Structural Engineering Associates, Inc.   (1)
3838 NW Loop 410, San Antonio, TX 78229
Tel.: (210) 735-9202
Web Site: http://www.seatx.com
Sales Range: $1-9.9 Million
Emp.: 44
Engineeering Services
N.A.I.C.S.: 541330
Charles Garza *(Treas)*
Allen G. Shiau *(Project Mgr)*
John C. Rojas *(Project Mgr)*

JOHNSON-LANCASTER & ASSOCIATES, INC.
13031 US Hwy 19 N, Clearwater, FL 33764
Tel.: (727) 796-5622   FL
Web Site: http://www.johnson-lancaster.com
Year Founded: 1980
Commercial Equipment Whslr
N.A.I.C.S.: 423440
Gerald Lancaster *(CEO)*

Subsidiaries:

Bezac Equipment Co.   (1)
3721 Mahoning Ave, Youngstown, OH 44515
Tel.: (330) 797-1550
Web Site: http://www.bezac.com
Commercial Equipment Whslr
N.A.I.C.S.: 423440

JOHNSON-MANLEY LUMBER COMPANY
1501 N 15th Ave, Tucson, AZ 85705
Tel.: (520) 882-0885
Year Founded: 1970
Sales Range: $10-24.9 Million
Emp.: 140
Framing Contractors
N.A.I.C.S.: 423310
Paul Patrick Manley *(Owner)*

JOHNSONRAUHOFF
2525 Lake Pines Dr, Saint Joseph, MI 49085
Tel.: (269) 428-9212   MI
Web Site: http://www.johnson-rauhoff.com
Year Founded: 1969
Rev.: $10,000,000
Emp.: 60
Advetising Agency
N.A.I.C.S.: 541810
Don Johnson *(Founder)*
Jackie Huie *(CEO)*
Mason Johnson *(Pres)*
Earl Peters *(VP-Production Svcs)*
Julie Marsh *(Controller)*
Chris Graham *(Dir-Acct & Mgr-Bus Unit)*
Jennifer O'Neill *(Acct Exec-Mktg-Harbor Shores)*
Jackie Forestieri *(Coord-Quality Assurance)*
Bob Keys *(Mdse Coord-Walmart-Image Studio)*
Roberta Pope *(Sr Acct Mgr-Walmart)*
Lyn Wilson *(Acct Mgr-Sur La Table)*
Brian Poole *(Dir-Art)*

Subsidiaries:

JohnsonRauhoff Marketing Communications   (1)
Appliance Park Bldg 4, Louisville, KY 40225
Tel.: (502) 452-5469
Emp.: 5
N.A.I.C.S.: 541810

JohnsonRauhoff Marketing Communications   (1)
300 W Britain Ave, Benton Harbor, MI 49022
Tel.: (269) 428-3377
Web Site: http://www.johnsonrauhoff.com

Emp.: 20
N.A.I.C.S.: 541810
Rob Regovich *(Studio Mgr)*

JOHNSONS OF CHICKASHA INC.
3121 S 4th St, Chickasha, OK 73018
Tel.: (405) 222-2062
Web Site: http://www.jocok.com
Sales Range: $10-24.9 Million
Emp.: 37
Automobiles New & Used
N.A.I.C.S.: 441110

JOHNSONVILLE, LLC
PO Box 906, Sheboygan Falls, WI 53085
Tel.: (920) 453-6900   WI
Web Site:
    http://www.johnsonville.com
Year Founded: 1945
Sales Range: $400-449.9 Million
Emp.: 1,000
Sausage Mfr
N.A.I.C.S.: 311612
Bill Morgan *(Pres)*
Tammy Strebe *(Mgr-Customer Insights)*
Michael Suprick *(Pres)*
Michael S. Stayer-Suprick *(CEO)*

Subsidiaries:

PrimaBaguz Sdn. Bhd.   (1)
Lot 16 18 Jalan P10 13, 43650, Bandar Baru Bangi, Malaysia   **(100%)**
Tel.: (60) 389253788
Web Site: http://www.primabaguz.com
Food Product Mfr & Distr
N.A.I.C.S.: 311412

Salm Partners, LLC.   (1)
590 Woodrow St, Denmark, WI 54208
Tel.: (920) 863-1438
Web Site: http://www.salmpartners.com
Sales Range: $25-49.9 Million
Emp.: 180
Meat Product Production Services
N.A.I.C.S.: 311612
Christopher P. Salm *(CEO)*
Ken Chappa *(Mgr-Maintenanace & Engrg)*
Mark Salm *(Mgr-Construction)*
Paul Hargarten *(Dir-Technical Svcs)*
Daniel Timm *(Coord-Warehouse)*
Bill Hagenow *(Coord-Safety)*
Michelle Linsmeier *(Mgr-Acctg)*

JOHNSTECH INTERNATIONAL CORP.
1210 New Brighton Blvd, Minneapolis, MN 55413
Tel.: (612) 378-2020
Web Site: http://www.johnstech.com
Sales Range: $50-74.9 Million
Emp.: 100
Electronic Connectors
N.A.I.C.S.: 334417
David G. Johnson *(Founder, Pres & CEO)*
Loren Hillukka *(Mgr-Midwest Reg)*

JOHNSTON BROTHERS FARM
518 CR 45, Bunnell, FL 32110
Tel.: (386) 437-3272
Vegetable Farming
N.A.I.C.S.: 445230

JOHNSTON ENTERPRISES INC.
411 W Chestnut Ave, Enid, OK 73701
Tel.: (580) 233-5800
Web Site: http://www.jeinc.com
Rev.: $109,300,000
Emp.: 400
Grain & Seed Sales
N.A.I.C.S.: 424510
Lew Meibergen *(Chm)*
Gary Tucker *(CFO)*
Lewis Cunningham *(Controller)*

Johnston Enterprises Inc.—(Continued)

JOHNSTON ENTERPRISES INC.
2819 Fire Rd, Egg Harbor Township, NJ 08234
Tel.: (609) 645-8135
Holding Company
N.A.I.C.S.: 551112
James E. Johnston Jr. (Chm & CEO)
James Johnston III (Pres)

Subsidiaries:

Agate Construction Company, Inc.   (1)
1030 Rte 83, Cape May Court House, NJ 08210
Tel.: (609) 624-9090
Web Site: http://www.agateconstruction.net
Sales Range: $25-49.9 Million
Emp.: 25
General Contractor, Highway & Street Construction
N.A.I.C.S.: 237310
James E. Johnston Jr. (Chm & CEO)
James Johnston III (Pres)
Larry Zoerb (Sr VP-Engrg)

Tuckahoe Sand & Gravel Co., Inc.   (1)
100 Sharp Rd, Tuckahoe, NJ 08270
Tel.: (609) 861-2082
Web Site: http://www.tuckahoesand-gravel.com
Sales Range: $25-49.9 Million
Emp.: 35
Construction Sand & Gravel Mining
N.A.I.C.S.: 212321
Ron Carusi (Mgr-Sls)

JOHNSTON INDUSTRIAL SUPPLY INC.
3121 E Cairo St, Springfield, MO 65802
Tel.: (417) 866-4141
Web Site:
http://www.johnstoncompanies.com
Sales Range: $25-49.9 Million
Emp.: 75
Industrial Supplies Distr
N.A.I.C.S.: 423840
Michael Smith (Dir-Ops)
Susie Johnston (CEO)
Michelle Holt (Controller)
Patricia Johnston Jr. (Pres)

Subsidiaries:

Johnston Integration Technology LLC   (1)
3121 E Cairo St, Springfield, MO 65802
Tel.: (417) 866-4141
Web Site:
http://www.johnstoncompanies.com
Rev.: $50,000,000
Emp.: 35
Broker Services
N.A.I.C.S.: 541990
Susie Johnston (Pres)

JOHNSTON INDUSTRIAL SUPPLY, INC.
2433 S Cherry Ave, Fresno, CA 93706
Tel.: (559) 233-1822   CA
Web Site: http://www.jiscodirect.com
Year Founded: 1962
Sales Range: $10-24.9 Million
Emp.: 40
Industrial Machinery & Equipment
N.A.I.C.S.: 423830
Leo Johnson (Gen Mgr)

JOHNSTON SUPPLY INC.
184 N Main St, Marion, OH 43302
Tel.: (740) 383-5291
Web Site:
http://www.johnstonsupply.net
Sales Range: $10-24.9 Million
Emp.: 45

Provider of Pumps & Pumping Equipment
N.A.I.C.S.: 423830
Steve Johnston (Owner)

JOHNSTON, LEMON & CO. INC.
1101 Vermont Ave NW Ste 800, Washington, DC 20005-3521
Tel.: (202) 842-5500   DC
Web Site:
http://www.johnstonlemon.com
Year Founded: 1920
Sales Range: $150-199.9 Million
Emp.: 40
Financial Services
N.A.I.C.S.: 523150
James H. Lemon Jr. (Chm)

JOHNSTONE FOODS INC.
2101 Northside Dr Ste 202, Panama City, FL 32405
Tel.: (850) 769-1397
Web Site: http://www.mcdjfi.com
Sales Range: $10-24.9 Million
Emp.: 6
Fast-Food Restaurant Owner & Operator
N.A.I.C.S.: 722513
Thomas T. Johnstone (Pres)

JOHNSTONE SUPPLY
4320 Pacific Hwy, San Diego, CA 92110
Tel.: (619) 298-7168
Web Site:
http://www.johnstonesupplysd.com
Rev.: $19,000,000
Emp.: 49
Industrial Supplies Merchant Whslr
N.A.I.C.S.: 423840
Karen Atwater Thomas (Sec)
Bill Byrne (Gen Mgr)
Carole Atwater (Pres)
Henry Atwater (Owner)

JOHNSTONE SUPPLY INC.
11632 NE Ainsworth Cir, Portland, OR 97220-9016
Tel.: (503) 256-3663   OR
Web Site:
http://www.johnstonesupply.com
Year Founded: 1953
Sales Range: $10-24.9 Million
Emp.: 60
Warm Air Heating & Air Conditioning Products Distr
N.A.I.C.S.: 423730
Pam Wines (Sec)
Ben Brasseur (VP)
John Tisera (Pres & CEO)

Subsidiaries:

Certified Supply Inc.   (1)
2701 W 7th Ave, Denver, CO 80204
Tel.: (303) 573-5626
Web Site: http://www.johnstonesupply.com
Sales Range: $10-24.9 Million
Emp.: 35
Electronic Parts & Equipment
N.A.I.C.S.: 423690
Carla Myers (Pres)

Johnstone Supply, Inc.   (1)
370 Market St, Kenilworth, NJ 07033
Tel.: (908) 298-1212
Web Site: http://www.johnstonesupply.com
Sales Range: $10-24.9 Million
Provider of Warm Air Heating & Air Conditioning Services
N.A.I.C.S.: 423730
Robert Zimmermann (Pres)

JOHNSTONWELLS PUBLIC RELATIONS
387 Corona St, Denver, CO 80218
Tel.: (303) 623-3366

Web Site:
http://www.johnstonwells.com
Year Founded: 1971
Sales Range: $1-9.9 Million
Emp.: 25
Public Relations & Brand Management
N.A.I.C.S.: 541820

JOHNSTOWN WELDING & FABRICATION
84 Iron St, Johnstown, PA 15906
Tel.: (814) 539-6922
Web Site: http://www.jwfi.com
Sales Range: $25-49.9 Million
Emp.: 500
Fabricated Structural Metal
N.A.I.C.S.: 332312
William Polacek (CEO)
Dan Dorian (Controller)

JOIN ENTERTAINMENT HOLDINGS, INC.
101 E Park Blvd 6th Fl, Plano, TX 75074   NV
Year Founded: 2006
RINO—(OTCIQ)
Sales Range: $150-199.9 Million
Emp.: 360
Holding Company; Television Network Developer
N.A.I.C.S.: 551112
Alain Logua (CEO)

JOINT HOLDINGS/BASIC METAL INDUSTRIES, INC.
11921 FM 529, Houston, TX 77041
Tel.: (713) 937-7474   DE
Web Site: http://www.lhshouston.com
Sales Range: $10-24.9 Million
Holding Company
N.A.I.C.S.: 551112
Gerald Hodge (Pres)
Ann Parr (Sec)

Subsidiaries:

Bi Metallurgical Specialties, Inc.   (1)
11921 Fm 529 Rd, Houston, TX 77041
Tel.: (713) 896-7989
Web Site: http://www.lhshouston.com
Sales Range: $10-24.9 Million
Emp.: 50
Steel
N.A.I.C.S.: 423510
Gerald Hodge (CEO)

Longhorn Steel & Flamecutting, Inc.   (1)
11921 FM 529 Rd, Houston, TX 77041
Tel.: (713) 896-7988
Web Site: http://www.lhshouston.com
Sales Range: $1-9.9 Million
Emp.: 70
Metals Service Centers & Offices
N.A.I.C.S.: 423510
William Hansberger (Gen Mgr)

JOINT VENTURE MARKETING & COMMUNICATIONS
10003 Derekwood Ln Ste 112, Lanham, MD 20706
Tel.: (301) 577-0887
Web Site: http://www.jointv.com
Year Founded: 1989
Sales Range: Less than $1 Million
Emp.: 8
N.A.I.C.S.: 541810
Chris Napolitano (Acct Mgr)

JOINT VENTURE PIPING INC.
4040 Red Bluff Rd, Pasadena, TX 77503
Tel.: (281) 842-9353
Web Site: http://www.jvic.com
Sales Range: $25-49.9 Million
Emp.: 3,000
Specialty Welding Turnaround Services

N.A.I.C.S.: 541611
Joe Vardell (Pres)

JOKAKE CONSTRUCTION COMPANY
5013 E Washington St Ste 100, Phoenix, AZ 85034
Tel.: (602) 224-4500
Web Site: http://www.jokake.com
Year Founded: 1983
Sales Range: $25-49.9 Million
Emp.: 100
Civil Engineering Services
N.A.I.C.S.: 237310
Casey Cartier (Pres & CEO)
Allison Black (Mgr-Mktg Project)

JOLIET AREA COMMUNITY HOSPICE
250 Water Stone Cir, Joliet, IL 60431
Tel.: (815) 740-4104   IL
Web Site:
http://www.joliethospice.org
Year Founded: 1982
Sales Range: $10-24.9 Million
Emp.: 166
Community Care Services
N.A.I.C.S.: 624229
George Rydman (Pres)
Cathy Schley (Sec)
Carolyn Dystrup (VP)
Jim Galligan (Treas)
Muhamad Krad (Dir-Medical)
Mary Sheehan (CEO)
Eileen Hooks Gutierrez (Sr Dir-Dev & Comm)

JOLLEY TROLLEY TRANSPORTATION OF CLEARWATER, INC.
483 Mandalay Ave Ste 213, Clearwater, FL 33767
Tel.: (727) 445-1200
Web Site:
http://www.clearwaterjolleytrolley.com
Sales Range: $1-9.9 Million
Emp.: 45
Trolley Transportation
N.A.I.C.S.: 485999
Rosemary Windsor Longenecker (Exec Dir)

JOLLY ROOFING & CONTRACTING CO., INC.
711 Chaney Cv, Collierville, TN 38017-2993
Tel.: (901) 854-5393
Web Site: http://www.jollyroofing.com
Sales Range: $10-24.9 Million
Emp.: 140
Roofing Installation Services
N.A.I.C.S.: 238390
Greg McOlgan (COO)
Trip Swords (Controller)
John Jolly Jr. (CEO)

JOMAR GROUP LTD.
7243 Miller Dr Ste 100, Warren, MI 48092
Tel.: (586) 268-1220   MI
Web Site: http://www.jomar.com
Year Founded: 1966
Rev.: $14,246,701
Emp.: 25
Industrial Plumbing & Valve Hydronic Components
N.A.I.C.S.: 423720
Paul Craig (Pres)
Dan Blake (VP & Mgr-Sls-Eastern Reg)

JOMAR INVESTMENTS LC
15 Lakeside Dr, Lake Saint Louis, MO 63367
Tel.: (636) 561-1885
Sales Range: $10-24.9 Million

Emp.: 250
Eating Place
N.A.I.C.S.: 722511
James Erkmann (Pres)
Paula Jackson (COO)
Pat Smith (Office Mgr)

JOMAR INVESTMENTS, INC.
400 Gordon Industrial Ct, Byron Center, MI 49315
Tel.: (616) 878-3633   MI
Web Site:
   http://www.newlifeparts.com
Year Founded: 1974
Commercial Truck & Trailer Parts Whslr
N.A.I.C.S.: 423120
Robert L. Hinton (Pres)
Daniel Woltjer (VP-Fin & Admin)

JOMAR TEXTILES INC.
5300 Whitaker Ave, Philadelphia, PA 19124
Tel.: (215) 634-5800
Web Site:
   http://www.jomartextiles.com
Year Founded: 1967
Sales Range: $10-24.9 Million
Emp.: 120
Operator of Family Clothing, Fabrics & Houseware Stores
N.A.I.C.S.: 458110
James Boligitz (Controller)
Veronica LaSerre (Mgr)

JOMAX CONSTRUCTION COMPANY
S Hwy 281, Great Bend, KS 67530
Tel.: (620) 792-3686
Web Site: http://www.jomaxgb.com
Sales Range: $25-49.9 Million
Emp.: 100
Oil & Gas Pipeline Construction
N.A.I.C.S.: 237120
M. E. Nichols (Pres)

JOMIRA/ADVANCE
470 3rd St Ste 211, San Francisco, CA 94107
Tel.: (415) 356-7801   CA
Web Site:
   http://www.jomirabooks.com
Year Founded: 1985
Sales Range: $10-24.9 Million
Emp.: 10
Book Publishers
N.A.I.C.S.: 513130
Gerardo Joffe (Owner)

Subsidiaries:

JOMIRA.COM   (1)
470 3rd St Ste 211, San Francisco, CA 94107
Tel.: (415) 356-7801
Web Site: http://www.jomira.com
Book Retailer
N.A.I.C.S.: 459210

JON BYK ADVERTISING, INC.
140 S Barrington Ave, Los Angeles, CA 90049-3309
Tel.: (310) 476-3012   CA
Web Site:
   http://www.bykadvertising.com
Year Founded: 1959
Sales Range: Less than $1 Million
Emp.: 10
Advertising, Medical, Outdoor
N.A.I.C.S.: 541810
Don Lauron (Art Dir)
Peter Vidalis (Dir-Admin)

JON F. SWIFT INC.
2221 8th St, Sarasota, FL 34237
Tel.: (941) 951-6100
Web Site: http://www.jonfswiftinc.com
Year Founded: 1979

Sales Range: $1-9.9 Million
Emp.: 15
General Construction Contractor
N.A.I.C.S.: 236220
Jon F. Swift (CEO)
Jason F. Swift (Pres)
Ross Russo (VP)

JON HALL CHEVROLET, INC.
551 N Nova Rd, Daytona Beach, FL 32114-1701
Tel.: (386) 255-4444
Web Site:
   http://www.jonhallchevrolet.com
Sales Range: $125-149.9 Million
New & Used Car Dealers
N.A.I.C.S.: 441110
Glenn S. Ritchey (Pres)
Ted W. Serbousck (VP)

JON HALL HONDA
330 N Nova Rd, Daytona Beach, FL 32114
Tel.: (386) 253-4478
Web Site:
   http://www.jonhallhonda.com
Sales Range: $10-24.9 Million
Emp.: 43
New Car Whslr
N.A.I.C.S.: 441110
Jon Hall (Owner)

JON HART DESIGN CO.
PO Box 8558, San Antonio, TX 78202
Tel.: (210) 226-8544
Web Site:
   http://www.jonhartdesign.com
Sales Range: $10-24.9 Million
Emp.: 50
Womens Handbag & Purse Mfr
N.A.I.C.S.: 316990
Douglas Smith (Pres)
Mark Risien (VP)
Beverly Rosen (VP)

JON MURDOCK, INC.
600 McCall Rd, Manhattan, KS 66502-5036
Tel.: (785) 776-1950
Web Site:
   http://www.murdockchevrolet
cadillac.com
Year Founded: 1982
Sales Range: $10-24.9 Million
Emp.: 40
Car Whslr
N.A.I.C.S.: 441110
Kevin Murdock (Gen Mgr)
Jon Murdock (Pres)
Randy Stelter (Mgr-Parts & Accessories)
Tracy Trout (Mgr-Sls)

JONAS PAUL EYEWEAR, LLC
401 Hall St SW Ste 134, Grand Rapids, MI 49503
Tel.: (616) 723-8039   MI
Web Site:
   http://www.jonaspauleyewear.com
Year Founded: 2013
Sales Range: $1-9.9 Million
Emp.: 12
Eyeglasses Product Distr
N.A.I.C.S.: 423460
Ben Harrison (Co-Founder)
Laura Harrison (Co-Founder)

JONATHAN GREEN & SONS
48 Squankum Yellowbrook Rd, Howell, NJ 07731
Tel.: (732) 938-7007
Web Site:
   http://www.jonathangreen.com
Sales Range: $10-24.9 Million
Emp.: 50

Farm Supplies
N.A.I.C.S.: 424910
Barry Green Sr. (CEO)
Barry Green Jr. (Pres)

JONATHAN'S LANDING, INC.
16823 Captain Kirle Dr, Jupiter, FL 33477-1299
Tel.: (561) 747-7600
Web Site:
   http://www.jonathanslanding.com
Resort
N.A.I.C.S.: 459110
Tim Richards (Gen Mgr)
Joe DiPasquantonio (Mgr-Clubhouse)
Wendy Seely (Dir-Membership Scvs)

JONATHAN'S PLACE
6065 Duck Creek Dr, Garland, TX 75043
Tel.: (972) 303-5303   TX
Web Site: http://www.jpkids.org
Year Founded: 1991
Sales Range: $1-9.9 Million
Child Care Services
N.A.I.C.S.: 624110
Lisa Matthews (Founder)
Allicia Frye (CEO)
Michael Strickland (Dir-Residential Programs)
Stacey Walker (Vice Chm)
Savannah Franklin (Asst Sec)

Subsidiaries:

Promise House, Inc.   (1)
224 W Page Ave, Dallas, TX 75208
Tel.: (214) 941-8578
Web Site: http://www.promisehouse.org
Sales Range: $1-9.9 Million
Community Development Services
N.A.I.C.S.: 813319
Judy Marshall (COO)
Eric Hood (Dir-Emergency Shelter Svcs)
Ellis Lee (Dir-Ops)
Regina Levine (Chief Program Officer)
Cobi Gray (Chief Philanthropy Officer)
Justin Scott (Pres)
Errika Flood-Moultrie (VP)
Sean Mhlanga (Treas)
Catherine Yates (Sec)
Charles M. Wolford II (CEO)

JONES & JONES INC.
110 E 9th St, Tifton, GA 31794
Tel.: (229) 382-6300
Web Site:
   http://www.jonesandjones.com
Sales Range: $25-49.9 Million
Emp.: 80
Provider of Construction Services
N.A.I.C.S.: 236220
Jonathan Jones (Pres)

JONES & LANIER ELECTRIC INC.
108 Parkwood Cir, Carrollton, GA 30117
Tel.: (770) 832-2902
Web Site:
   http://www.westgeorgiaelectric.com
Sales Range: $10-24.9 Million
Emp.: 100
General Electrical Contractor
N.A.I.C.S.: 238210
Dennis Jones (Pres & CEO)
Annette Jones (Treas & Sec)
Jared Jones (VP)
Joseph L. Dedman (VP)
Clyde West (VP)
David West (Project Mgr)
Tony Schultz (Project Mgr)
James D. Dedman (Project Mgr)
David Spivey (Project Mgr & Coord-BIM)
Steven R. Hopper (Coord-Industry Resources & Safety)
Charles Kin White III (CFO & VP)

JONES & VINING INC.
1115 W Chestnut St, Brockton, MA 02301-7501
Tel.: (508) 232-7470   DE
Web Site:
   http://www.jonesandvining.com
Year Founded: 1930
Sales Range: $10-24.9 Million
Emp.: 300
Mfr & Sales of Shoe Components
N.A.I.C.S.: 316990
Charlie Liberge (Pres)
Lee Goldberg (CEO)

Subsidiaries:

Jones & Vining Inc. - China
Factory   (1)
Niushan Industrial Park, Dongcheng District, Dongguan, 523128, Guangdong, China
Tel.: (86) 769 22669890
Footwear Mfr
N.A.I.C.S.: 316210

Jones & Vining Inc. - Lasts
Factory   (1)
1 Compu-Last Dr, Walnut Ridge, AR 72476
Tel.: (870) 886-6621
Footwear Mfr
N.A.I.C.S.: 316210

Jones & Vining Inc. - Maine
Factory   (1)
765 Webster St, Lewiston, ME 04241
Tel.: (207) 784-3547
Footwear Mfr
N.A.I.C.S.: 316210

Jones & Vining Inc. - Taiwan TBC
Factory   (1)
No 11 8th Road Industrial Park, Taichung, Taiwan
Tel.: (886) 4 2359 5940
Footwear Mfr
N.A.I.C.S.: 316210
Bella Tuan (Mgr)

Jones & Vining Inc. - Vietnam
Factory   (1)
Lot 11-15 Ho Nai Industrial Zone, Trang Bom, Dong Nai, Vietnam
Tel.: (84) 613 671206
Footwear Mfr
N.A.I.C.S.: 316210

JONES BROS. DIRT & PAVING CONTRACTORS, INC.
1401 S Grandview Ave, Odessa, TX 79761
Tel.: (432) 332-0721
Web Site:
   http://www.jonesbrosdirt.com
Sales Range: $10-24.9 Million
Emp.: 100
Highway & Street Construction Services
N.A.I.C.S.: 237310
R. E. Jones (Pres)

JONES BROTHERS COMPANY INC.
4100 Meadow Ln, Bossier City, LA 71111
Tel.: (318) 746-5735
Web Site:
   http://www.jonesbrothers.com
Year Founded: 1953
Sales Range: $10-24.9 Million
Emp.: 50
Petroleum Industry Machinery Distr
N.A.I.C.S.: 238990
Don Jones (Pres)
Tom Jones (Owner & Pres)

JONES CAPITAL, LLC
10000 Memorial Dr, Ste 700, Houston, TX 77024
Tel.: (713) 804-9430
Web Site: https://jones.com
Year Founded: 1949
Private Equity
N.A.I.C.S.: 523999

Jones Capital, LLC—(Continued)

Jonathan Jones *(CEO)*

Subsidiaries:

Jones Logistics, LLC (1)
6184 Highway 98 W Ste 210, Hattiesburg, MS 39402
Tel.: (800) 956-1151
Web Site: https://www.joneslogistics.com
Truck Transportation
N.A.I.C.S.: 484110

Subsidiary (Domestic):

Nationwide Express Inc. (2)
1211 E Ln St, Shelbyville, TN 37160
Tel.: (931) 680-2400
Web Site: http://www.nationwide-express.com
Sales Range: $25-49.9 Million
Emp.: 220
Trucking Except Local
N.A.I.C.S.: 484121
David Coffey *(Pres)*
Jerry Barber *(Dir-Bus Dev)*
Jeff Hurst *(VP-Ops)*
Ronny Boswell *(VP-IT)*
Tim Edelstein *(VP-Safety)*

JONES CHEVROLET INCOR-PORATED
21505 Rte 6, Warren, PA 16365
Tel.: (814) 723-7222 **PA**
Web Site:
http://www.joneschevrolet.com
Year Founded: 1920
Sales Range: $10-24.9 Million
Emp.: 30
Sales of New & Used Automobiles
N.A.I.C.S.: 441110
Brent Jones *(Owner)*

JONES COMPANIES LTD.
312 S 14th Ave, Humboldt, TN 38343-3312
Tel.: (731) 784-2832 **TN**
Web Site: http://www.jonesyarn.com
Year Founded: 1936
Sales Range: $25-49.9 Million
Emp.: 512
Provider of Yarn Spinning Services
N.A.I.C.S.: 313110
Richard Ayers *(CFO)*
Gena Simmons *(Controller)*
Jeremy Raines *(VP)*
Scott Butler *(COO)*
Ralph Jones III *(Chm)*

Subsidiaries:

Jones Fiber Products Inc. (1)
1184 Channel Ave, Memphis, TN 38106 (100%)
Tel.: (901) 948-4469
Web Site: http://www.jonesfiber.com
Sales Range: $10-24.9 Million
Emp.: 75
Mfr of Textile Goods
N.A.I.C.S.: 313230

JONES COMPANY, INC.
201 Pendleton St, Waycross, GA 31501-2906
Tel.: (912) 283-1661 **GA**
Year Founded: 1982
Sales Range: $500-549.9 Million
Emp.: 7
Gasoline Service Stations; Automobile Sales; Grocery & Convenience Store Operator
N.A.I.C.S.: 457120
Greg Higginson *(CFO)*
James C. Jones III *(Chm & CEO)*

Subsidiaries:

Bacon Grocery Co., Inc. (1)
1107 W 12th St, Alma, GA 31510-1815 (100%)
Tel.: (912) 632-5901
Web Site: http://www.slashfoods.com

Sales Range: $25-49.9 Million
Emp.: 75
Grocery Warehouse
N.A.I.C.S.: 445131
James A. Walker *(Pres)*
Robin Johnson *(Office Mgr)*
Chuck Overstreet *(Gen Mgr)*

Fuel South Inc. (1)
3020 Harris Rd, Waycross, GA 31503
Tel.: (912) 284-0264
Web Site: http://www.slashsoods.com
Sales Range: $10-24.9 Million
Emp.: 38
Petroleum & Petroleum Products; Convenience Food Stores
N.A.I.C.S.: 424710
Eric Gardner *(Gen Mgr)*

Kwickie/Flash Foods, Inc. (1)
215 Pendleton St, Waycross, GA 31501-2906 (100%)
Tel.: (912) 285-4011
Web Site: http://www.flashfoods.com
Sales Range: $125-149.9 Million
Retail Grocery Gasoline Service Station
Lessor of Real Estate Property Distr
N.A.I.C.S.: 445110

Walker-Jones Chevrolet-Buick (1)
2700 Memorial Dr, Waycross, GA 31503 (100%)
Tel.: (912) 283-4250
Web Site: http://www.walkerjones.com
Sales Range: $25-49.9 Million
Emp.: 150
Automobile Dealer Services
N.A.I.C.S.: 441110

JONES DAIRY FARM
800 Jones Ave, Fort Atkinson, WI 53538
Tel.: (920) 563-2431 **WI**
Web Site:
http://www.jonesdairyfarm.com
Year Founded: 1889
Sales Range: $200-249.9 Million
Emp.: 365
Meats Processor
N.A.I.C.S.: 424470

Subsidiaries:

Ralph & Paul Adams, Inc. (1)
103 Railroad Ave, Bridgeville, DE 19933
Tel.: (302) 337-8208
Web Site: http://www.rapascrapple.com
Sales Range: $10-24.9 Million
Emp.: 50
Processors of Scrapple
N.A.I.C.S.: 311612
Donna Seefried *(VP)*

JONES DAY
North Point 901 Lakeside Ave, Cleveland, OH 44114-1190
Tel.: (216) 586-3939 **OH**
Web Site: https://www.jonesday.com
Year Founded: 1893
Sales Range: Less than $1 Million
Emp.: 4,500
Law firm
N.A.I.C.S.: 541110
David G. Heiman *(Partner)*
David A. Kutik *(Partner)*
Rachel L. Rawson *(Partner)*
James A. Cox *(Partner-Dallas)*
Warren N. Nachlis *(Partner-New York & Boston)*
David F. Adler *(Partner)*
David B. Alden *(Partner)*
Mark J. Andreini *(Partner)*
Brett P. Barragate *(Partner)*
Mark A. Belasic *(Partner)*
John V. Biernacki *(Partner)*
Kevin D. Boyce *(Partner)*
Thomas A. Briggs *(Partner-San Diego)*
Denise A. Carkhuff *(Partner)*
David B. Cochran *(Partner)*
Thomas Demitrack *(Partner)*
Robert S. Faxon *(Partner)*
Michelle K. Fischer *(Partner)*

Timothy P. Fraelich *(Partner)*
Calvin P. Griffith *(Partner)*
Theodore M. Grossman *(Partner)*
Daniel C. Hagen *(Partner)*
Thomas A. Hamilton *(Partner)*
William A. Herzberger *(Partner)*
Stephen J. Kaczynski *(Partner)*
Sanjiv K. Kapur *(Partner)*
Christopher M. Kelly *(Partner-New York)*
Patrick J. Leddy *(Partner)*
Heather Lennox *(Partner-Cleveland & New York)*
David M. Maiorana *(Partner)*
Stephen C. Mixter *(Partner)*
Eric H. Mosier *(Partner-Chicago)*
Dennis L. Murphy *(Partner)*
John A. Rego *(Partner)*
Geoffrey J. Ritts *(Partner)*
Stephen G. Sozio *(Partner)*
Jeffery D. Ubersax *(Partner)*
Robert S. Walker *(Partner)*
Stanley Weiner *(Partner)*
Meredith M. Wilkes *(Partner)*
Paula Batt Wilson *(Partner)*
Henry Klehm III *(Partner)*
Bryan E. Davis *(Partner-Atlanta)*
J. Bruce McDonald *(Partner-Washington & Houston)*
Evan Miller *(Partner-Washington)*
Lyle G. Ganske *(Partner & Co-Chm-Acq & Merger-Global)*
Carl E. Black *(Partner)*
Joseph D. Hatina *(Partner)*
Peter E. Izanec *(Partner)*
Ryan B. McCrum *(Partner)*
Thomas A. Howley *(Partner-Houston)*
Terri L. Chase *(Partner-New York)*
Colleen E. Laduzinski *(Partner-New York)*
Veerle Roovers *(Partner-New York)*
Tracy V. Schaffer *(Partner-New York)*
Eric Barbier de La Serre *(Partner-Paris)*
Todd P. Kelly *(Partner)*
Michelle Taylor *(Partner-Hong Kong)*
Kenneth R. Boehner *(Partner)*
Omar Samji *(Partner)*
Kevin R. Noble *(Partner)*
Joanne Bush *(Partner-Labor & Employment Practice)*
Catherine Nasser *(Partner)*
Stephen J. Obie *(Partner)*
Johannes Perlitt *(Partner)*
Louis Mercedes *(Partner-Private Equity-Boston)*
Jack Williams *(Partner)*
Jessica Bradley *(Partner)*
Patricia A. Dunn *(Partner)*
Jan Wenning Egan *(Partner)*
J. Laurens Wilkes *(Partner)*
Elizabeth G. Myers *(Partner)*
Kenneth Field *(Partner)*
John Gore *(Partner)*
Rosanna K. McCalips *(Partner)*
Hashim M. Mooppan *(Partner)*
Danielle M. Varnell *(Partner)*
David Andrew Kern *(Partner)*
Louis J. Jenull *(Partner)*
Michael P. Considine *(Partner)*
Grayson D. Yeargin *(Partner)*
Laura Fraedrich *(Partner)*
Edgar J. Asebey *(Partner)*
Timothy P. FitzSimons *(Partner)*
Stephen Olson *(Partner-Energy Practice)*
William Axtman *(Partner-M&A Practice)*
Marcia Kelson *(Partner-Employee Benefits & Exec Compensation Practice)*
Andrew R. Stanton *(Partner-Bus & Tort Litigation Practice-Pittsburgh)*
Ryan Walsh *(Partner-Intellectual Property Practice)*

Julia McEvoy *(Partner-Antitrust & Competition Law Practice-Washington)*
Matthew Divelbiss *(Partner-Bus & Tort Litigation Practice-Pittsburgh)*
Edward Carter *(Partner-Bus & Tort Litigation Practice)*
Jason Grove *(Partner-Private Equity Practice)*
Miguel Eaton *(Partner-Employee Benefits & Exec Compensation Practice-Washington)*
Paul Lettow *(Partner-Govt Regulation Practice-Washington)*
Margaret Gleason *(Partner-Bus & Tort Litigation Practice)*
William Sultemeier *(Partner-Energy Practice)*
Daniel Michaels *(Partner-Private Equity Practice)*
Stephen Hibbard *(Partner-Fin Institutions Litigation & Regulation Practice)*
Jay Tambe *(Partner-New York)*
Eric Snyder *(Partner-Investigations & White Collar Defense Practice-Washington)*
Michael Conway *(Partner-Fin Institutions Litigation & Regulation Practice-Chicago)*
Tina Tabacchi *(Partner-Chicago)*
Ginger R. Burton *(Partner-Real Estate Practice-Atlanta)*
Tom Wearsch *(Partner-Bus Restructuring & Reorganization Practice)*
Jackie Hodes *(Partner-Mergers & Acq Practice)*
Michael Hazzard *(Partner-Govt Regulation Practice)*
Maxwell Fox *(Partner-Intellectual Property Practice-Tokyo)*
Roy Ginsburg *(Partner-Labor & Employment Practice-Minneapolis)*
Peter Ekberg *(Partner-Mergers & Acq Practice-Minneapolis)*
Annamarie Daley *(Partner-Bus & Tort Litigation Practice-Minneapolis)*
Erik Lundgren *(Partner-Employee Benefits & Executive Compensation Practice)*
Sergio Alvarez-Mena *(Partner-Fin Institutions Litigation & Regulation Practice)*
Cherie Owen *(Partner-Govt Regulation Practice-Washington)*
Lisa M. Ropple *(Partner-Cybersecurity, Privacy, Data Protection & Govt Regulation)*
David Vander Haar *(Partner-Minneapolis)*
Jeffrey Maddox *(Partner-Capital Markets Practice-Singapore)*
Thomas Bouvet *(Partner-Intellectual Property Practice-Paris)*
Marcus Quintanilla *(Partner)*
Michael Riess *(Partner)*
Kelly Turner *(Partner-Capital Markets Practice)*
Michael Gleason *(Partner-Antitrust & Competition Law Practice)*
Kristen Lejnieks *(Partner-Bus & Tort Litigation Practice)*
Dan Moss *(Partner-Bus Restructuring & Reorganization Practice)*
Paul Green *(Partner-Bus Restructuring & Reorganization Practice)*
Heith Rodman *(Partner-Fin Institutions Litigation & Regulation Practice)*
Daniel Merrett *(Partner-Bus Restructuring & Reorganization Practice)*
Craig Friedman *(Partner-Labor & Employment Practice)*
A. Patricia Campbell *(Partner-Intellectual Property Practice)*

Mark Rasmussen *(Partner-Securities Litigation & SEC Enforcement Practice)*
Lindsay Hedrick *(Partner-Labor & Employment Practice)*
Marjorie Duffy *(Partner-Securities Litigation & SEC Enforcement Practice)*
Andrew Luger *(Partner-Investigations & White Collar Defense Practice-Minneapoli)*
David P. Bergers *(Partner-Boston)*
Dean Bachus *(Partner-Chicago)*
Michael Lishman *(Partner-Merger & Acq Practice-Melbourne)*
Michael Hendershot *(Partner-Intellectual Property Practice)*
Patrick Belville *(Partner-M&A Practice-Detroit)*
Tamera Weisser *(Partner)*
Thomas M. Devaney *(Partner-Private Equity Practice-New York)*
Bryan K. Brown *(Partner)*
Jonn R. Beeson *(Partner)*
Robert A. Profusek *(Partner & Co-Chm-Acq & Merger-Global)*
Richard J. Bedell Jr. *(Partner)*
Charles W. Hardin Jr. *(Partner)*
John M. Newman Jr. *(Partner)*
John M. Saada Jr. *(Partner)*
Francis A. Muracca II *(Partner-Pittsburgh)*
Charles Kotuby Jr. *(Partner-Global Disputes Practice)*
Charles Hodges II *(Partner-Tax Practice)*
William Laxton Jr. *(Partner-Bus & Tort Litigation Practice)*

JONES DEALERSHIPS
1335 Manheim Pike, Lancaster, PA 17601
Tel.: (717) 394-0711
Web Site:
   http://www.joneshonda.com
Sales Range: $75-99.9 Million
Emp.: 500
Sales of New & Used Automobiles
N.A.I.C.S.: 441110
Donald L. Slavin *(Pres)*
Steven G. Jones *(Treas)*
Charles Bowman *(Comptroller)*

JONES EDMUNDS & ASSOCIATES, INC.
730 NE Waldo Rd, Gainesville, FL 32641
Tel.: (352) 377-5821
Web Site:
   http://www.jonesedmunds.com
Year Founded: 1974
Sales Range: $10-24.9 Million
Emp.: 140
Engineering & Environmental Services
N.A.I.C.S.: 541330
Rick Ferreira *(CEO)*
Doug Toth *(Sr VP)*
Chris Baggett *(VP-Tampa)*

JONES ENERGY, INC.
807 Las Cimas Pkwy Ste 350, Austin, TX 78746
Tel.: (512) 328-2953   DE
Web Site:
   http://www.jonesenergy.com
Year Founded: 1988
Rev.: $236,873,000
Assets: $405,575,000
Liabilities: $1,210,558,000
Net Worth: ($804,983,000)
Earnings: ($1,298,776,000)
Emp.: 83
Fiscal Year-end: 12/31/18
Oil Exploration & Production Services
N.A.I.C.S.: 211120
Kirk Goehring *(COO & Sr VP)*

Subsidiaries:

Jones Energy Finance Corp.   (1)
807 Las Cimas Pkwy Ste 350, Austin, TX 78746
Tel.: (512) 328-2953
Oil & Gas Field Services
N.A.I.C.S.: 213112

JONES ENTERPRISES INC.
210 Philadelphia St, La Porte, IN 46350
Tel.: (219) 362-9908
Web Site: http://www.nrpjones.com
Rev.: $11,058,403
Emp.: 200
Industrial Supplies
N.A.I.C.S.: 423840
Mary Jo Anderson *(Mgr-HR)*

JONES FORD, INC.
5757 Rivers Ave, North Charleston, SC 29406
Tel.: (843) 744-3311
Web Site: http://www.jonesford.com
Sales Range: $50-74.9 Million
Emp.: 150
Car Whslr
N.A.I.C.S.: 441110
Richard G. Cooper *(VP)*
David M. Walters Sr. *(Pres)*

JONES INTERNATIONAL UNIVERSITY
9697 E Mineral Ave, Englewood, CO 80112
Tel.: (303) 784-8904   CO
Web Site: http://www.jiu.edu
Year Founded: 1993
Colleges & Universities
N.A.I.C.S.: 611310
Christine Spath *(CFO)*

Subsidiaries:

Jones Cyber Solutions, Ltd.   (1)
9697 E Mineral Ave, Centennial, CO 80112
Tel.: (303) 784-3600
Web Site: http://www.jonescyber.com
Software Publisher
N.A.I.C.S.: 513210

Jones Interactive, Inc.   (1)
9697 E Mineral Ave, Englewood, CO 80112-3408   (100%)
Tel.: (303) 792-3111
Web Site: http://www.jones.edu
Sales Range: $25-49.9 Million
Emp.: 200
Information Management & Data Processing Services
N.A.I.C.S.: 518210
Glenn R. Jones *(Pres)*

Jones Knowledge Group, Inc.   (1)
9697 E Mineral Ave, Centennial, CO 80112
Tel.: (800) 350-6914
Web Site: http://www.jonesknowledge.com
Online Education Services
N.A.I.C.S.: 516210
Glenn R. Jones *(Founder & CEO)*

Jones Knowledge, Inc.   (1)
9697 E Mineral Ave, Englewood, CO 80112
Tel.: (303) 792-3111
Sales Range: $25-49.9 Million
Emp.: 50
Internet Educational Tools
N.A.I.C.S.: 519290
Tony Erdle *(Sr VP)*

Jones Programming Services, Inc.   (1)
9697 E Mineral Ave, Englewood, CO 80112-3408
Tel.: (303) 792-3111
Web Site: http://www.jones.com
Sales Range: $25-49.9 Million
Emp.: 300
General Media & Broadcasting Services
N.A.I.C.S.: 516120

Jones Properties, Inc.   (1)
9697 E Mineral Ave, Centennial, CO 80112-3408   (100%)

Tel.: (303) 792-3111
Web Site: http://www.jones.com
Sales Range: $25-49.9 Million
Emp.: 140
Management of Company Properties
N.A.I.C.S.: 531210
Stacey Slaughter *(CFO)*

Jones Spacelink, Ltd.   (1)
9697 E Mineral Ave, Englewood, CO 80112-3408   (93%)
Tel.: (303) 792-3111
Web Site: http://www.jonescorp.com
Sales Range: $25-49.9 Million
Emp.: 300
Cable Television Services
N.A.I.C.S.: 516210
Glenn R. Jones *(Chm & CEO)*
Gregory J. Liptak *(Pres)*

Jones e-global library, Inc.   (1)
9697 E Mineral Ave, Centennial, CO 80112
Tel.: (888) 235-6637
Web Site: http://www.eglobyllibrary.com
Online Library Development & Maintenance Services
N.A.I.C.S.: 519210
Glenn R. Jones *(Chm & CEO)*
Joseph Gregg *(Pres)*
John Goodwin *(Sr VP-Sls & Mktg)*
Stacey Slaughter *(CFO)*

JONES JUNCTION AUTO GROUP
1510 Bel Air Rd, Bel Air, MD 21014
Tel.: (410) 879-6400
Web Site:
   http://www.jonesjunction.com
Sales Range: $25-49.9 Million
Emp.: 700
New Car Retailer
N.A.I.C.S.: 441110
Chad Duke *(Mgr-Sls)*

JONES LANG LASALLE AMERICAS, INC
500 E Pratt St Ste 1250, Baltimore, MD 21202
Tel.: (443) 451-2600
Web Site: https://www.us.jll.com
Real Estate Investment Services
N.A.I.C.S.: 531190

JONES MEMORIAL HOSPITAL
191 N Main St, Wellsville, NY 14895-0072
Tel.: (585) 593-1100   NY
Web Site: http://www.jmhny.org
Year Founded: 1921
Sales Range: $25-49.9 Million
Emp.: 448
Health Care Srvices
N.A.I.C.S.: 622110
Eva Benedict *(CEO)*
Gary Balcom *(Treas)*
Kimberly Toot *(Sec)*
Samantha Gilkey *(Sec)*
Dan Johnson *(Treas)*
Karol Marciano *(Vice Chm)*
Rich Ewell *(Chm)*

JONES METAL PRODUCTS CO.
200 N Center St, West Lafayette, OH 43845
Tel.: (740) 545-6381   OH
Web Site: http://www.jmpforming.com
Year Founded: 1923
Rev.: $13,500,000
Emp.: 56
Surgical Appliances & Supplies
N.A.I.C.S.: 332322
Marion Setton *(Chm)*
Dan Erb *(Pres & CEO)*
Mike Baker *(Controller)*
Chris Barlow *(Mgr-Engrg)*

JONES MOTOR CO. INC.
545 Florence Rd, Savannah, TN 38372

Tel.: (731) 925-4923
Web Site:
   http://www.jonesmotorcompany.com
Sales Range: $25-49.9 Million
Emp.: 100
New & Used Car Sales
N.A.I.C.S.: 441110
Chad Jones *(Owner)*
Bill Williams *(Mgr-HR)*

JONES OIL CO. INC.
Hwy 50, Shoals, IN 47581
Tel.: (812) 247-3183
Rev.: $46,031,806
Emp.: 12
Petroleum Bulk Stations
N.A.I.C.S.: 424710

JONES PAINT & GLASS INC.
1250 W 100 N, Provo, UT 84601
Tel.: (801) 374-6711
Web Site: http://www.jonespg.com
Rev.: $21,953,178
Emp.: 140
Glass Windows, Shutters, Jalousies & Similar Items
N.A.I.C.S.: 332321
Kenneth H. Jones Jr. *(Pres)*

JONES PERINI JOINT VENTURE
PO Box 9160, Framingham, MA 01701
Tel.: (508) 628-2000
Sales Range: $10-24.9 Million
Civil Engineering Services
N.A.I.C.S.: 236220
Joanne Konz *(Asst VP)*

JONES PETROLEUM COMPANY, INC.
407 E 2nd St, Jackson, GA 30233
Tel.: (770) 775-2386
Web Site:
   http://www.jonespetroleum.com
Sales Range: $10-24.9 Million
Emp.: 54
Fuels Whslr, Distr & Retailer
N.A.I.C.S.: 424710
William B. Jones *(Pres)*
Ren Anderson *(VP)*

JONES PLASTIC & ENGINEERING COMPANY, LLC
2410 Plantside Dr, Jeffersontown, KY 40299-2528
Tel.: (502) 491-3785   KY
Web Site:
   http://www.jonesplastic.com
Year Founded: 1961
Emp.: 2,400
Custom Injection Molded Plastics Mfr
N.A.I.C.S.: 326199
Craig Jones *(CEO)*

Subsidiaries:

Jones Plastic & Engineering Company, LLC - Camden Division   (1)
470 Benton Industrial Rd, Camden, TN 38320
Tel.: (731) 584-1398
Emp.: 220
Molding & Stamping Services
N.A.I.C.S.: 333517

Jones Plastic & Engineering Company, LLC - Jeffersontown Division   (1)
2410 Plantside Dr, Jeffersontown, KY 40299
Tel.: (502) 491-3785
Sales Range: $50-74.9 Million
Stamping & Welding Services
N.A.I.C.S.: 333517

Jones Plastic & Engineering Company, LLC - Williamsburg Division   (1)

Jones Plastic & Engineering Company, LLC—(Continued)

40 Williamsburg Plastics Rd, Williamsburg, KY 40769
Tel.: (606) 549-0035
Sales Range: $50-74.9 Million
Stamping & Welding Services
N.A.I.C.S.: 333517

Jones Plastic & Engineering de Monterrey, S.A. de C.V.   **(1)**
Carr Miguel Aleman Km 16 13, 66600, Apodaca, Nuevo Leon, Mexico
Tel.: (52) 818 625 3500
Sales Range: $25-49.9 Million
Emp.: 200
Stamping & Welding Services
N.A.I.C.S.: 333517

Juarez Mexico Division   **(1)**
Parque Industrial Intermex Sur, Ciudad Juarez, 32720, Mexico
Tel.: (52) 656 295 3600
Web Site: http://www.jonesplastic.com
Emp.: 400
Plastics Product Mfr
N.A.I.C.S.: 326199
Manuel Rivera *(Mng Dir)*

Rev-A-Shelf LLC   **(1)**
12400 Rd Jones Way, Louisville, KY 40299-2527
Tel.: (502) 499-5835
Web Site: http://www.rev-a-shelf.com
Storage Organizing Products Mfr
N.A.I.C.S.: 332510
David P. Noe *(Gen Mgr)*
Rob Jenkins *(Dir-OEM Sls & Mktg)*
Eddie Chappel *(Mgr-Sls-Western)*
Mike Jones *(Mgr-Mid-West)*
Mike Marcum *(Mgr-Rocky Mountain)*
Pat Carrico *(Mgr-Sls-Eastern)*
Tom Evey *(Mgr-Great Lakes)*

Subsidiary (Domestic):

Sideline, Inc.   **(2)**
9332 E Raintree Rd Ste 100, Scottsdale, AZ 85260
Tel.: (480) 860-0444
Web Site: http://www.sidelinesinc.com
Sporting & Recreational Goods & Supplies Merchant Whslr
N.A.I.C.S.: 423910

JONES PRODUCE, INC.
903 A St SE, Quincy, WA 98848
Tel.: (509) 787-3537   **WA**
Web Site:
http://www.jonesofwashington.com
Year Founded: 1967
Rev.: $12,300,000
Emp.: 500
Vineyard & Wine Production; Fresh Fruit & Vegetable Farm
N.A.I.C.S.: 111332
Debbie Hassan *(Controller)*
Allan Williams *(Dir-Sls & Mktg-Wine)*

JONES PUBLIC AFFAIRS, INC.
1420 K St NW Ste 1050, Washington, DC 20005
Tel.: (202) 742-5254
Sales Range: Less than $1 Million
Emp.: 7
Communications, Crisis Communications, Event Planning & Marketing, Government/Political/Public Affairs, Health Care, Media Relations, Strategic Planning/Research
N.A.I.C.S.: 541810
Carrie Jones *(Mng Dir & Principal)*
Jennifer Weissblum *(Acct Dir)*
Deborah Danuser *(Acct Supvr)*
Tara Goodin *(Sr Acct Exec)*
Rhonda Slater *(Acct Coord)*
Berna Diehl *(Sr VP-Media Rels)*
Julie Lane *(Sr Acct Exec)*
Kathy Wahlbin *(Sr VP-Digital & Social Media)*
Jennifer Rodriguez *(VP-Advocacy Rels)*

Tracy Blinder-Gurrisi *(Acct Dir-Boston)*
Carly Whiteside *(Acct Dir)*

JONES SIGN CO., INC.
1711 Scheuring Rd, De Pere, WI 54115
Tel.: (920) 983-6700
Web Site: http://www.jonessign.com
Year Founded: 1975
Sales Range: $10-24.9 Million
Emp.: 300
Specialty Trade Contractors
N.A.I.C.S.: 238910
John Mortensen *(Pres)*
Evie Saharsky *(Dir-Svc & Permitting)*

Subsidiaries:

C A S Corp.   **(1)**
901 W Melinda Ln, Phoenix, AZ 85027
Tel.: (623) 412-2220
Web Site: http://www.nationalmallfront.com
Sales Range: $1-9.9 Million
Emp.: 60
Structural Steel Erection
N.A.I.C.S.: 238120
Cynthia Yoder *(Treas & Sec)*
Dave Thomas *(CFO)*
Doug VanRoekel *(Project Mgr)*
Levi Hancock *(Gen Mgr-Plant)*
John Mortensen *(Pres)*

JONES STORES INC.
250 N US Hwy 701 Byp, Tabor City, NC 28463-8378
Tel.: (910) 653-4001   **NC**
Year Founded: 1954
Sales Range: $25-49.9 Million
Emp.: 600
Variety Stores
N.A.I.C.S.: 455219
Michael K. Jones *(Pres & Treas)*

JONES TRACTOR & EQUIPMENT CO., INC.
12793 US Hwy 19 S, Thomasville, GA 31792
Tel.: (229) 226-4881
Web Site: http://www.greensouth.com
Year Founded: 1971
Sales Range: $25-49.9 Million
Emp.: 30
Sales of Farm & Garden Machinery
N.A.I.C.S.: 423820
Kim B. Jones *(Pres)*

JONES VENDING & OCS DISTRIBUTING INC.
5409 Bulwer Ave, Saint Louis, MO 63147-3011
Tel.: (314) 383-0222
Web Site: http://www.jonesvend.com
Year Founded: 1970
Rev.: $50,000,000
Emp.: 90
Confectionery Distr
N.A.I.C.S.: 424450
Larry E. Jones *(Pres & CEO)*

JONES, MARESCA & MCQUADE, P.A.
10500 Little Patuxent Pkwy Ste 770, Columbia, MD 21044-3544
Tel.: (410) 884-0220   **MD**
Web Site:
http://www.jmmcpafirm.com
Sales Range: $1-9.9 Million
Accounting & Consulting Services
N.A.I.C.S.: 541211
David Jones *(Mng Partner)*
Mario Maresca *(Partner)*
Aaron Bloom *(Partner)*

JONES-HAMILTON CO.
30354 Tracy Rd, Walbridge, OH 43465-9775
Tel.: (419) 666-5910   **CA**

Web Site: http://www.jones-hamilton.com
Year Founded: 1951
Chemicals & Compounds Producer, Packager & Distr
N.A.I.C.S.: 325180
Evert Talbot *(Mgr-Chemical Div)*
Carl Knueven *(Dir-Corp Res & Dev)*
Sam Perras *(Mgr-Environmental, Health & Safety)*
Gerry Danes *(Mgr-Regulatory Affairs)*
Brian Brooks *(CFO)*
Tim Poure *(Pres & CEO)*
Tim Villa Jr. *(Mgr-IT)*

JONES-ONSLOW ELECTRIC MEMBERSHIP CORPORATION
259 Western Blvd, Jacksonville, NC 28546
Tel.: (910) 353-1940   **NC**
Web Site: http://www.joemc.com
Year Founded: 1939
Sales Range: $125-149.9 Million
Emp.: 191
Electricity Provider Association
N.A.I.C.S.: 813910
John Pierce *(Chm)*
Thomas Waller *(Treas & Sec)*
Horace Phillips *(Vice Chm)*

JONESTOWN BANK & TRUST COMPANY
2 W Market St, Jonestown, PA 17038
Tel.: (717) 865-2112
Web Site: http://www.bankjbt.com
Sales Range: $10-24.9 Million
Emp.: 100
Banking Services
N.A.I.C.S.: 522180
C. Bill Roth *(CFO)*
Heather Via *(Mgr-Contact Center)*
Carrie Ehrgood *(Mgr-Quentin Road)*
Rick Rollman *(Acct Dir-Sls)*
Charles Neubauer *(Acct Dir-Sls)*
Susan Berresford *(Mgr-Ebenezer)*
Elizabeth Wine *(Mgr-Bowman Street)*
Mitzi Wingert *(Mgr-Palmyra)*

JONESTRADING INSTITUTIONAL SERVICES LLC
32133 Lindero Canyon Rd Ste 208, Westlake Village, CA 91361
Tel.: (818) 991-5500
Web Site:
http://www.jonestrading.com
Sales Range: $100-124.9 Million
Emp.: 50
Securities Brokerage
N.A.I.C.S.: 523150
William Jones *(Chm)*
Jack Garceau *(CTO)*
Steve Chmielewski *(Gen Counsel)*
Alan Hill *(CEO)*
Tim O'Neil *(Pres-Trading)*
David J. Mazzullo *(Pres-Sls)*
Tom Carter *(Mng Dir & Office Mgr)*
Steve Tullar *(Mng Dir & Office Mgr-Aspen)*
Andrew Tuthill *(Mng Dir)*
Moe Cohen *(Mng Dir & Head-Investment Banking Equities & Capital Markets)*
Michael Hock *(Mng Dir & Office Mgr-Morristown)*
Rick Andrews *(Mng Dir & Office Mgr-Dallas)*
David Lutz *(Mng Dir & Office Mgr-Annapolis)*
Paul Farrington *(Mng Dir & Office Mgr-Atlanta)*
Carol Castro *(Mng Dir & Office Mgr-Charleston)*
Kevin Horgan *(Mng Dir & Office Mgr-Hanalei)*
Andrew Volz *(COO)*
David Walrod *(Mng Dir)*

Scott Cooper *(VP & Office Mgr-Pittsford)*
Jeremiah Dickson *(Mng Dir & Head-Ops-Global)*
Phil Geha *(VP & Office Mgr-Lake Mary)*
Lawrence Harasym *(Chief Compliance Officer)*
John Martinelli *(Mng Dir & Office Mgr-Mill Valley)*
Trent McNair *(CFO)*
Chris Minor *(Mng Dir & Office Mgr-Westlake Village)*
Jeffrey Sloves *(Mng Dir & Office Mgr-New York)*
Brian Tafaro *(Mng Dir & Office Mgr-Princeville)*
Chris Wildman *(Mng Dir-Global Execution Svcs)*
David O'Shaughnessy *(Mng Dir-Derivatives Trading Svcs-New York)*
Jeff Micsky *(Head-Derivatives-Global)*
Timothy Baker *(Sr VP-Equity Sls Trading Grp)*
Peter Sellers *(Head-Outsourced Trading-Europe)*
Jon Jefferies *(Mng Dir-Equity Trading)*
Jeff Leveen Jr. *(Head-Outsourced Trading)*

JONI AND FRIENDS
30009 Ladyface Ct, Agoura Hills, CA 91301
Tel.: (818) 707-5664   **CA**
Web Site:
http://www.joniandfriends.org
Year Founded: 1979
Sales Range: $10-24.9 Million
Emp.: 153
Disability Assistance Services
N.A.I.C.S.: 624120
Doug Mazza *(Pres & COO)*
Marc Stein *(VP-Field Svcs)*
Lorraine Mazza *(VP-Dev)*
Joni Eareckson Tada *(Founder & CEO)*

JONQUIL STEEL & CONSTRUCTION CO.
140 Veterans Memorial Hwy, Mableton, GA 30126
Tel.: (770) 948-9876
Web Site: http://www.jonquilsteel.com
Rev.: $11,400,000
Emp.: 50
Steel Building Construction
N.A.I.C.S.: 236220
Thomas Aikens *(Chm)*

JOORNEY LLC
407 Lincoln Rd Ste 2K, Miami Beach, FL 33139
Web Site: http://www.joorney.com
Year Founded: 2013
Sales Range: $1-9.9 Million
Emp.: 45
Business Management Services
N.A.I.C.S.: 541611
Benjamin Jarmon *(Founder & CEO)*
Paul Monson *(Partner & Sls Dir)*
Ognjen Cvetkovic *(Partner & Dir-Ops)*
Matt Wolf *(Head-Advisory)*
Marianella Manzur *(VP-Bus Dev)*

JORBAN-RISCOE ASSOCIATES INC.
9808 Alden St, Lenexa, KS 66215
Tel.: (913) 438-1244
Web Site: http://www.jorban-riscoe.com
Sales Range: $10-24.9 Million
Emp.: 35
Warm Air Heating & Air Conditioning
N.A.I.C.S.: 423730
Mark Riscoe *(Pres)*
Joe Riscoe *(VP)*

Craig Zernickow (CTO)
Mike Lorenz (VP)
Kurt Harre (VP-Ops)
Kevin Harre (VP-Sls & Mktg)

JORDACHE ENTERPRISES
1400 Broadway 15th Fl, New York,
NY 10018
Tel.: (212) 643-8400   NY
Web Site:
http://www.jordachecorporate.com
Year Founded: 1978
Sales Range: $1-9.9 Million
Emp.: 5
In House Advertising Agency
N.A.I.C.S.: 541810
Joseph Nakash (Chm & CEO)
Liz Berlinger (Pres)
Joe Taylor (CFO)
Shaul Nakash (CMO)
Emzon Shung (Exec VP-Real Estate
& Aviation)
Robert Spiegelman (Gen Counsel)
Mansi Shah (Coord-Production)

JORDAN FORD INC.
13010 N Interstate Hwy 35, San An-
tonio, TX 78233
Tel.: (210) 653-3673
Web Site:
http://www.jordanfordsa.com
Rev.: $173,554,454
Emp.: 200
Automobiles; New & Used
N.A.I.C.S.: 441110
Jeff Coan (Dir-Fin)
Marc Cross (Gen Mgr)

JORDAN IMPLEMENTS CO.
1280 E Main St, Brawley, CA 92227
Tel.: (760) 344-3322
Web Site:
http://www.jordanimplement.com
Sales Range: $25-49.9 Million
Emp.: 50
Farm Equipment & Supplies
N.A.I.C.S.: 459999
Steven Ellison (Pres)
Robert Conway (Gen Mgr)
David Hoskins (Product Mgr)

JORDAN INDUSTRIES, INC.
Arbor Lake Ctr Ste 550 1751 Lake
Cook Rd, Deerfield, IL 60015
Tel.: (847) 945-5591   IL
Year Founded: 1988
Sales Range: $250-299.9 Million
Emp.: 1,393
Investment Holding Company
N.A.I.C.S.: 551112
Andrew Rice (Sr VP-Corp Dev)
David W. Zalaznick (Accountant)
Lisa M. Ondrula (VP & Controller)
Joseph C. Linnen (Sr VP-Bus Dev)
Jesse Clyde Nichols III (Accountant)
John W. Jordan II (Chm & CEO)

Subsidiaries:

Aromatech Holding Company   (1)
140 Centennial Ave Ste 100, Piscataway,
NJ 08854-3908   **(100%)**
Tel.: (908) 707-0707
Sales Range: $10-24.9 Million
Emp.: 50
Perfumes Natural Or Synthetic
N.A.I.C.S.: 325620

Beemak Plastics, Inc.   (1)
16711 Knott Ave, La Mirada, CA 90638-
6013
Tel.: (310) 886-5880
Web Site: http://www.beemak.com
Sales Range: $10-24.9 Million
Emp.: 74
Plastic Literature & Card Holders; Point of
Purchase Displays Mfr
N.A.I.C.S.: 326199
Isabel Banuelos (Mgr-Acct)

Subsidiary (Domestic):

Valmark Industries, Inc.   (2)
7900 National Dr, Livermore, CA
94550-6424   **(100%)**
Tel.: (925) 960-9900
Web Site: http://www.valmark.com
Printing & Manufacture of Specialty Pres-
sure Sensitive Labeling Products
N.A.I.C.S.: 323111

DRE Inc.   (1)
1800 Williamson Ct, Louisville, KY 40223
Tel.: (502) 244-4444
Web Site: http://www.dremed.com
Operating Room & Surgical Equipment Distr
N.A.I.C.S.: 423450
Antonio Scott (CEO)

Deflect-O Corp.   (1)
7035 E 86th St, Indianapolis, IN 46250-
1547
Tel.: (317) 849-9555
Web Site: http://www.deflecto.com
Sales Range: $25-49.9 Million
Emp.: 300
Plastics Hardware & Office Products
N.A.I.C.S.: 326199
Paul Thompson (Pres)

Subsidiary (Non-US):

Deflecto Canada Limited   (2)
221 Bunting Road, Saint Catharines, L2M
3Y2, ON, Canada   **(100%)**
Tel.: (905) 641-8872
Web Site: https://www.deflecto.com
Sales Range: $25-49.9 Million
Emp.: 100
Heating Equipment & Hvac Installation Ser-
vices
N.A.I.C.S.: 333415
John Williams (Pres)

Euclid Universal Corp.   (1)
30500 Bruce Industrial Pkwy Ste B, Solon,
OH 44139   **(100%)**
Tel.: (440) 349-4083
Web Site: http://www.imperialelectric.com
Sales Range: $10-24.9 Million
Emp.: 75
Mfr of Gears & Gear Boxes
N.A.I.C.S.: 333612
David Molnar (Pres)

Hoveround Corp.   (1)
6010 Cattleridge Dr, Sarasota, FL 34232
Tel.: (941) 739-6200
Web Site: http://www.hoveround.com
Sales Range: $100-124.9 Million
Emp.: 530
Wheelchair Mfr
N.A.I.C.S.: 339113
George Kruse (CFO)

Lakeshore Staffing Inc.   (1)
1 N Franklin St Ste 600, Chicago, IL 60606-
3456
Tel.: (847) 709-1700
Web Site: http://www.lakeshorestaffing.com
Sales Range: $10-24.9 Million
Emp.: 20
Temporary Help Service
N.A.I.C.S.: 561320
John Paller (Gen Mgr)

Nashville Transmission Parts   (1)
210 North First St, Nashville, TN 37213-
1104
Tel.: (615) 256-3346
Web Site: http://www.daccoinc.com
Sales Range: $1-9.9 Million
Emp.: 5
Motor Vehicle Supplies & New Parts
N.A.I.C.S.: 423120

Rolite Plastics Inc.   (1)
303 Oxford St, Dover, OH 44622   **(100%)**
Tel.: (740) 922-0696
Web Site: http://www.rolite.com
Sales Range: $10-24.9 Million
Emp.: 50
Extruded Finished Plastics Products
N.A.I.C.S.: 326199

The Scott Motors Company   (1)
1501 Lavelle Rd, Alamogordo, NM
88310-7633   **(100%)**
Tel.: (330) 734-3600
Sales Range: $10-24.9 Million
Emp.: 50

Electrical & Magnetic Motor Component
Parts Mfr
N.A.I.C.S.: 335312

JORDAN LUMBER & SUPPLY INC.
1939 Hwy 109, Mount Gilead, NC
27306
Tel.: (910) 439-6121
Web Site:
http://www.jordanlumber.com
Year Founded: 1939
Sales Range: $25-49.9 Million
Emp.: 320
Sawmills & Planing Mills
N.A.I.C.S.: 321113
Lewis Dorsett (Controller)
Justin Davey (Mgr-Sys)
Robert B. Jordan III (Pres)
Jack Jordan Sr. (VP)

JORDAN MOTORS, INC.
609 E Jefferson Blvd, Mishawaka, IN
46545-6524
Tel.: (574) 259-1981   IN
Web Site: http://www.jordanauto.com
Year Founded: 1947
Sales Range: $125-149.9 Million
Emp.: 140
Sales of New & Used Automobiles
N.A.I.C.S.: 441110
Joel Girten (Mgr-Bus)
Kevin Ball (Acct Exec-PreOwned)
Kara Mitchell (Mgr-Pre-Owned Sls)
Mike Banashak (Acct Exec-
PreOwned)
Mike Gaffney (Acct Exec-Toyota)
Ryan Liedtky (Acct Exec-Toyota)
Jeff Miller (Mgr-Fleet Ops)
Jessica Brandli (Mgr-Toyota Sls)
Terrie Hoefle (Coord-Ford Appoint-
ment)
Amy Haefner (Mgr-Collision Center)
Dennis Farrar (Mgr-Carwash & De-
tail)
Thomas Kaniewski (Mgr-Ford Leas-
ing)
Cory Hayden (Dir-Svc)
Todd Elgas (Dir-Pre-Owned)
Patty Thornberg (Dir-Toyota Svcs)

JORDAN-KITT MUSIC INC.
12303 Twinbrook Pkwy, Rockville,
MD 20852
Tel.: (301) 474-9500
Web Site: http://www.jordankitts.com
Year Founded: 1983
Sales Range: $25-49.9 Million
Emp.: 175
Musical Instrument Sales
N.A.I.C.S.: 459140
Rick Grant Jr. (Pres)

JORDAN-WILCOMB CON-STRUCTION, INC.
406 S 6th St, Boise, ID 83702
Tel.: (208) 344-2441
Web Site: http://www.jordan-
wilcomb.com
Sales Range: $10-24.9 Million
Emp.: 16
Nonresidential Construction Services
N.A.I.C.S.: 236220
Tim Wilcomb (Pres)

JORDAN/ZALAZNICK ADVIS-ERS, INC.
9 W 57th St 33rd Fl, New York, NY
10019
Tel.: (212) 485-9410   DE
Investment Advisory & Asset Man-
agement Services
N.A.I.C.S.: 523940
David W. Zalaznick (Co-Founder,
Chm & CEO)

Gordon Nelson (Chief Investment Of-
ficer & Sr Mng Dir)
Sang Lee (CFO & Chief Compliance
Officer)
Todd J. Lanscioni (Mng Dir)
Reagan P. Hogerty (Mng Dir)
Rhett Madison (Mng Dir)
Lee Grzesh (VP & Controller)
Jessica Clemence (VP & Dir-Bus
Dev)
Matthew DeLong (VP)
Eric Kieras (Mng Dir)
Grant Smith (VP)
John W. Jordan II (Co-Founder &
Principal)

Subsidiaries:

JZ Asset Management UK LLP   (1)
17A Curzon Street, London, W1J 5HS,
United Kingdom
Tel.: (44) 20 7491 3633
Investment Advisory & Asset Management
Services
N.A.I.C.S.: 523940
Jock Green-Armytage (Sr Partner)
Miguel Rueda (Sr Partner)
Martin Wright (Sr Partner)
Torben Luth (Partner)
Ole Groth (Partner)
Michael Schmitz (Partner)
Alvaro Mata Mayrand (Partner)
Carlos Artal (Partner)
Nicola Zaino (Principal)
Alvaro Videgain (Principal)

Holding (Domestic):

Godrej Consumer Products (UK)
Ltd   (2)
2nd Floor Central House Balfour Block
Balfour Road, Hounslow, TW3 1HY, United
Kingdom
Tel.: (44) 20 8538 1256
Web Site: http://www.godrejuk.com
Consumer Products Distr
N.A.I.C.S.: 424210
M. Alicia (Mgr-Product Dev)

JZ Partners, LLC   (1)
9 W 57th St 33rd Fl, New York, NY 10019
Tel.: (212) 485-9410
Web Site: http://www.jzpartners.com
Private Equity & Investment Management
Services
N.A.I.C.S.: 523999
David W. Zalaznick (Chm & CEO)
Gordon Nelson (Chief Investment Officer &
Sr Mng Dir)
Reagan P. Hogerty (Mng Dir)
Todd J. Lanscioni (Mng Dir)
Eric Kieras (Mng Dir)
Rhett Madison (Mng Dir)
Sang Lee (CFO & Chief Compliance Offi-
cer)
Jessica Clemence (VP & Dir-Bus Dev)
Matthew DeLong (VP)
Grant Smith (VP)
Lee Grzesh (VP & Controller)
Emmett Mosley IV (Mng Dir)

Jz International Ltd.   (1)
17A Curzon Street, London, W1J 5HS,
United Kingdom
Tel.: (44) 2074913633
Portfolio Mgmt
N.A.I.C.S.: 523940
David W. Zalaznick (Founder & Chm)
Miguel Rueda (Mng Partner)

JORDANO'S, INC.
550 S Patterson Ave, Santa Barbara,
CA 93111
Tel.: (805) 964-0611   CA
Web Site: http://www.jordanos.com
Year Founded: 1915
Sales Range: $50-74.9 Million
Emp.: 595
Marketer & Whslr of Food, Beverages
& Culinary Equipment
N.A.I.C.S.: 424810
Jeffrey S. Jordano (Exec VP-Pacific
Beverage)
Peter C. Jordano (Pres & CEO)
Bob McLean (Controller)
Michael Sieckowski (CFO)

Jordano's, Inc.—(Continued)

Subsidiaries:

Jordano's Food Service, Inc. (1)
550 S Patterson Ave, Santa Barbara, CA
93111
Tel.: (805) 964-0626
Web Site: http://www.jordanos.com
Food Product Retailer
N.A.I.C.S.: 445298
Mike Sagraves (VP-Sls)

Jorlease Inc. (1)
550 S Patterson Ave, Santa Barbara, CA
93111-2405
Tel.: (805) 964-0611
Sales Range: $10-24.9 Million
Emp.: 28
Provider of Food & Beverage Services
N.A.I.C.S.: 532490

Pacific Beverage Co. Inc. (1)
550 S Patterson Ave, Santa Barbara, CA
93111-2405 (100%)
Tel.: (805) 964-0611
Web Site: http://www.jordanos.com
Sales Range: $10-24.9 Million
Emp.: 28
Provider of Food & Beverage Services
N.A.I.C.S.: 424810
Jeffrey S. Jordano (Pres)

JORDY-CARTER INC.
1212 S Broadway Ste 100, Denver,
CO 80210
Tel.: (303) 744-6106
Web Site: http://www.jordycarter.com
Rev.: $13,518,657
Emp.: 40
Office Furniture
N.A.I.C.S.: 541310
Bill O'Meara (Acct Mgr)
Julia Owen (Coord-Sls & Mktg)
J. Charles Jordy Jr. (Pres)

JORGENSEN'S INC.
215 N State St, Stanton, MI 48888
Tel.: (989) 831-8345
Year Founded: 1986
Sales Range: $10-24.9 Million
Emp.: 35
Operator of Grocery Stores
N.A.I.C.S.: 445110
Chris Jorgensen (Pres)

JORMAC AEROSPACE, INC.
11221 69th St N, Largo, FL 33773
Tel.: (727) 549-9600 FL
Web Site: http://www.jormac.com
Year Founded: 2006
Sales Range: $1-9.9 Million
Emp.: 24
Airport Services
N.A.I.C.S.: 488190
Juan pablo camargo (CEO)

JORO FASHIONS INCORPORATED
8780 NW 102nd St, Medley, FL
33178
Tel.: (305) 888-8178
Sales Range: $25-49.9 Million
Emp.: 15
Women's & Misses' Outerwear
N.A.I.C.S.: 315250
Robert Rubenstein (Pres)
Dennis Banard (Controller)
Bertha Blauner (Mgr-Production)
Michele Hutra (Product Mgr)

JOSEPH A. NATOLI CONSTRUCTION CORP.
293 Changebridge Rd, Pine Brook,
NJ 07058-9513
Tel.: (973) 575-1500
Web Site: http://www.jnatoli.com
Year Founded: 1975
Nonresidential Construction Services
& Senior Living Facilities
N.A.I.C.S.: 236220

Joseph A. Natoli (Founder& Chm)
Paul R. Natoli (Pres & CEO)
Thomas G. Sutphen Jr. (CFO)

JOSEPH AUTO GROUP
9750 Montgomery Rd, Cincinnati, OH
45252
Tel.: (513) 891-7200
Web Site: http://www.josephauto.com
Sales Range: $600-649.9 Million
Emp.: 850
Automobile Dealership
N.A.I.C.S.: 441110
Gregory G. Joseph (Exec VP & Atty)

Subsidiaries:

Joseph Volkswagen of Cincinnati (1)
3813 Montgomery Rd, Cincinnati, OH
45212
Tel.: (513) 914-1785
Web Site: http://www.josephvw.com
Sales Range: $1-9.9 Million
Emp.: 40
New Car Dealer Distr
N.A.I.C.S.: 441110
Tim Marsh (Partner & VP)

JOSEPH BEHR & SONS INC.
1100 Seminary St, Rockford, IL
61104
Tel.: (815) 987-2600 IL
Web Site: http://www.behrim.com
Year Founded: 1906
Sales Range: $250-299.9 Million
Emp.: 300
Dealer & Broker of Scrap Iron & Steel
N.A.I.C.S.: 423930
Richard Behr (Chm)
April Potts (Controller)
Leland R. Foecking (CFO)

JOSEPH BETH BOOKSELLERS LLC
1727 Riverside Dr, Cincinnati, OH
45202
Tel.: (513) 412-5700
Web Site: http://www.josephbeth.com
Year Founded: 1986
Sales Range: $500-549.9 Million
Emp.: 500
Sales of Books
N.A.I.C.S.: 449210
Neil Van Uum (Founder & Pres)
Mark Wilson (COO)

JOSEPH C. SANSONE COMPANY
18040 Edison Ave, Chesterfield, MO
63005
Tel.: (636) 537-2700
Web Site: http://www.jcsco.com
Rev.: $15,000,000
Emp.: 65
Business & Tax Solution Services
N.A.I.C.S.: 561499
Michael Bauer (VP-Sls & Mktg)
Michael McDonald (VP-Real Estate)
Joseph C. Sansone (Pres)
Zeke J. Sansone (CEO)
Carlotta Sansone (COO)
Tammy Frost (Sr Dir-Property Tax)
Chuck Vogel (CFO)

JOSEPH CONSTRUCTION CO. INC.
203 Letterman Rd, Knoxville, TN
37919-6327
Tel.: (865) 584-3945 TN
Web Site:
http://www.josephconst.com
Year Founded: 1972
Sales Range: $10-24.9 Million
Emp.: 110
Nonresidential Construction Services
N.A.I.C.S.: 236220
Joe R. Zappa (Founder)

JOSEPH DAVIS, INC.
120 W Tupper St, Buffalo, NY 14201-2158
Tel.: (716) 842-1500 NY
Web Site:
http://www.josephdavis.com
Year Founded: 1948
Sales Range: $50-74.9 Million
Emp.: 650
General Mechanical Contractors; Fire
Protection
N.A.I.C.S.: 238220
Jeffrey J. Davis (Pres)

Subsidiaries:

Davis Fire Protection Co., Inc. (1)
120 W Tupper St, Buffalo, NY 14201-2158
Tel.: (716) 842-1500
Sales Range: $10-24.9 Million
Emp.: 13
Fire Protection
N.A.I.C.S.: 238220

JOSEPH ELETTO TRANSFER INCORPORATED
200 600 W John St, Hicksville, NY
11801-1040
Tel.: (516) 937-3950
Web Site:
http://www.josephelettotransfer.com
Rev.: $20,358,954
Emp.: 100
Trucking Service
N.A.I.C.S.: 484121
James Vaughan (Dir-Safety)

JOSEPH F. BOENTE SONS INC.
543 W Main St, Carlinville, IL 62626
Tel.: (217) 854-3164
Web Site:
http://www.jfboentesons.com
Sales Range: $10-24.9 Million
Emp.: 100
Convenience Store
N.A.I.C.S.: 445131
Lawrence Boente (Pres)

JOSEPH G. PULITANO INSURANCE AGENCY INC.
214 Lincoln St Ste 110, Allston, MA
02134
Tel.: (617) 783-2622
Web Site: http://www.armltc.com
Year Founded: 1986
Sales Range: $1-9.9 Million
Emp.: 20
Long Term Care Insurance Distr &
Marketer
N.A.I.C.S.: 524210
Henrik Larsen (CEO)
Mary DePalma-Nadler (Dir-Ops)
Derek Miele (Dir-Affinity Mktg)
Nate Pomeroy (Dir-Bus)
Jonathan Kondracki (Assoc Dir-Grp
Mktg)
Robert Cushing Jr. (Dir-Fin Svcs
Mktg)

JOSEPH HUGHES CONSTRUCTION
11125 SW Barbur Blvd, Portland, OR
97219-8629
Tel.: (503) 624-7100
Web Site: http://www.joehughes.com
Year Founded: 1981
Sales Range: $10-24.9 Million
Emp.: 20
Building Renovation & Repair Services
N.A.I.C.S.: 236220
Joseph Hughes (Pres)
Angel Benavidez (Dir-Bus Dev)
Travis Marshall (Coord-Bid)

JOSEPH J. BLAKE ASSOCIATES, INC.
425 Broad Hollow Rd Ste 429, Melville, NY 11747
Tel.: (516) 827-0222
Web Site:
http://www.josephjblake.com
Year Founded: 1946
Sales Range: $10-24.9 Million
Emp.: 95
Real Estate Appraisal Services
N.A.I.C.S.: 531320
Joseph W. Hatzell (Partner-Miami)
Peter Meyers (Mng Partner-Los Angeles)
Joel Pakula (Partner-Atlanta)
Ted Allen (Mng Partner)
Richard Klein (Partner-Miami)
Kevin J. Leprohon (Mng Partner)
Kevin T. Quinn (Mng Partner)
Michael J. Maglocci (Mng Partner)
Thomas J. Shields (Mng Partner)
Arturo Singer (Mng Partner)
Mary E. Jiritano (CFO)
Christophe Porsella (Partner)
Brian Rapela (Partner-San Francisco)
Joanna C. Trunnell (Partner-Washington)
Ken P. Wilson (Mng Dir-Client Rels &
Bus Dev)
Michael Maglocci (Mng Partner)
Ryosuke Fukusako (Mng Dir)
Ken P. Wilson (Mng Dir-Client Rels &
Bus Dev-Dallas & Mng Dir-Client
Rels & Bus Dev)
Matthew Smith (Partner-Washington)

Subsidiaries:

Blake & Sanyu (1)
Hirakawacho Daiichi Seimei Bldg 4th Floor
1-2-10 Hirakawacho, Chiyoda-ku, Tokyo,
102 0093, Japan
Tel.: (31) 352139750
Web Site: http://www.sanyu-appraisal.co.jp
Real Estate Debt & Equity Consultants
N.A.I.C.S.: 531390
Ryosuke Fukusako (Mng Dir)

JOSEPH J. HENDERSON & SON, INC.
4288 Old Grand Ave, Gurnee, IL
60031
Tel.: (847) 244-3222 IL
Web Site:
http://www.jjhenderson.com
Year Founded: 1928
Sales Range: $75-99.9 Million
Emp.: 50
Contracting & Construction Services
N.A.I.C.S.: 237110
David A. Henderson (Pres)
Peter Bjerning (Project Mgr)

JOSEPH JINGOLI & SON, INC.
100 Lenox Dr Ste 100, Lawrenceville,
NJ 08648
Tel.: (609) 896-3111
Web Site: http://www.jingoli.com
Year Founded: 1922
Sales Range: $500-549.9 Million
Emp.: 720
Construction & Renewable Energy
Developer
N.A.I.C.S.: 333120
Michael D. Jingoli (CFO & COO)
Frank E. DiCola (Chm)
Robert E. Reager (Pres)
Dennis T. Mockaitis (Sr VP-Gen Construction Div)
Michael Burdalski (Sr VP-Construction Mgmt Div)
Paul J. Ryan (Sr VP-Power, Civil &
Mechanical Div)
Patrick S. Reager (Sr VP-Estimating
& Project Mgmt Div)

Bobby McGee *(Dir-Safety)*
Jingoli Power *(CEO)*
Peggy Reager *(Dir-HR)*
Joseph R. Jingoli Jr. *(CEO)*

JOSEPH L. ERTL, INC.
502 5th St NW, Dyersville, IA 52040
Tel.: (563) 875-2436
Emp.: 200
Die Casting
N.A.I.C.S.: 331523
Jane Ertl *(VP)*

Subsidiaries:

Dyersville Die Cast   (1)
502 5th St NW, Dyersville, IA 52040-0327
Tel.: (563) 875-2436
Web Site: http://www.dyersvillediecast.com
Die Casting
N.A.I.C.S.: 331523
Bob Willits *(Gen Mgr)*

Division (Domestic):

Moultrie Die Cast   (2)
222 Industrial Dr, Moultrie, GA 31768
Tel.: (229) 985-3719
Sales Range: $25-49.9 Million
Emp.: 30
Die Casting
N.A.I.C.S.: 331523
Mike Hiers *(Plant Mgr)*
Bob Willits *(Gen Mgr)*

JOSEPH M. SMITH COMMU-NITY HEALTH CENTER, INC.
287 Western Ave, Allston, MA 02134
Tel.: (617) 783-0500   MA
Web Site: http://www.jmschc.org
Year Founded: 1970
Sales Range: $10-24.9 Million
Emp.: 194
Community Health Care Services
N.A.I.C.S.: 621498
Elizabeth Browne *(Exec Dir)*
Maria Celli *(Dir-Behavioral Health)*
Alin Pop *(Dir-IT)*
James S. Souza *(CFO)*
Pamela Burns *(Dir-HR)*
David Norton *(Chm)*
William J. Horgan *(Dir-Dental)*
Paola Ferrer *(Dir-Grants & Dev)*
Kamau Karanja *(Dir-Medical)*
Hieu Do *(Vice Chm)*
Peter Koutoujian Sr. *(Treas)*

JOSEPH M. ZIMMER INC.
8860 Citation Rd Ste C, Baltimore, MD 21221
Tel.: (410) 780-0600
Rev.: $25,000,000
Emp.: 65
Mechanical Contractor
N.A.I.C.S.: 238220
Rhonda Hughes *(VP & Controller)*
Joseph M. Zimmer Jr. *(Pres)*

JOSEPH MCCORMICK CON-STRUCTION CO. INC.
3340 Pearl Ave, Erie, PA 16510
Tel.: (814) 899-3111
Web Site:
http://www.jmccormickconstruc
tion.com
Sales Range: $10-24.9 Million
Emp.: 50
Highway & Street Paving Contractor
N.A.I.C.S.: 237310
Owen McCormick *(Owner)*

JOSEPH MCDONNELL ENTER-PRISES
2847 Southwestern Blvd, Orchard Park, NY 14127
Tel.: (716) 674-0678   NY
Web Site:
http://www.customcarpetcen
ters.com

Year Founded: 1993
Rev.: $10,000,000
Emp.: 40
Floor Covering Stores
N.A.I.C.S.: 449121
Tom McDonnell *(VP)*

JOSEPH MINTON INC.
2623 White Settlement Rd, Fort Worth, TX 76107
Tel.: (817) 332-3111
Web Site:
http://www.josephmintonanti
ques.com
Sales Range: $25-49.9 Million
Emp.: 10
Interior Designer
N.A.I.C.S.: 541410
Joseph Minton *(Pres)*

JOSEPH OAT CORPORATION
2500 Broadway Drawer 10, Camden, NJ 08104-0010
Tel.: (856) 541-2900
Web Site: http://www.josephoat.com
Year Founded: 1788
Sales Range: $10-24.9 Million
Emp.: 150
Designer & Fabricator of Pressure Vessels, Reactors, Columns & Heat Exchanges
N.A.I.C.S.: 332410
Ron Kaplan *(Pres)*
Cliff DeCoursey *(Mgr-Corp Sls)*
John T. McDonald *(Mgr-Mktg & Sls)*

JOSEPH P. ADDABBO FAMILY HEALTH CENTER, INC.
6200 Beach Channel Dr, Arverne, NY 11692
Tel.: (718) 945-7150   NY
Web Site: http://www.addabbo.org
Year Founded: 1987
Sales Range: $25-49.9 Million
Emp.: 417
Community Health Care Services
N.A.I.C.S.: 621498
Saywalah Kesselly *(Sec)*
Sandria Ackbersingh *(Treas)*
Sylvester Okonkwo *(Chm)*

JOSEPH P. CARRARA & SONS INC.
167 N Shrewsbury Rd, North Claren-don, VT 05759
Tel.: (802) 775-2301
Web Site: http://www.jpcarrara.com
Sales Range: $10-24.9 Million
Emp.: 45
Prestressed Concrete Products
N.A.I.C.S.: 327390
Paul J. Carrara Jr. *(Pres)*

JOSEPH PEDOTT ADVERTIS-ING & MARKETING, INC.
425 California St, San Francisco, CA 94104
Tel.: (415) 397-6992
Web Site: http://www.jeiusa.com
Year Founded: 1958
Sales Range: $1-9.9 Million
Emp.: 25
In House Advertising Agency
N.A.I.C.S.: 541810
Joseph Pedott *(Pres)*
Michael P. Hirsch *(VP)*
Alfred Lam *(Office Mgr & Media Buyer)*

JOSEPH VICTORI WINES, INC.
17 Prospect St, Huntington, NY 11743
Tel.: (631) 423-8500   NY
Web Site: http://www.jvwines.com
Year Founded: 1910
Sales Range: $250-299.9 Million

Emp.: 125
Importer & Distributor of Alcoholic Beverages
N.A.I.C.S.: 312130
John Umbach *(Pres)*

JOSEPH'S HOUSE OF CAMDEN
555 Atlantic Ave, Camden, NJ 08105
Tel.: (856) 246-1087   NJ
Web Site:
http://www.josephshouseofcam
den.org
Year Founded: 2010
Sales Range: $1-9.9 Million
Emp.: 10
Homeless People Assistance Ser-vices
N.A.I.C.S.: 624221
John Klein *(Exec Dir)*
Shawn Sheekey *(Exec Dir)*

JOSH & JOHN'S HOME MADE ICE CREAM, INC.
111 E Pike's Peak Ave, Colorado Springs, CO 80903
Tel.: (719) 632-0299   CO
Web Site:
http://www.joshandjohns.com
Sales Range: $10-24.9 Million
Emp.: 30
Ice Cream Mfr
N.A.I.C.S.: 311520
John Krakauer *(Pres)*

JOSHUA & CO.
300 S Hunter St, Aspen, CO 81611
Tel.: (970) 925-8810
Web Site: http://www.joshuaco.com
Sales Range: $1-9.9 Million
Emp.: 35
Real Estate Broker
N.A.I.C.S.: 531210
Joshua Saslove *(CEO)*

JOSHUA GREEN CORPORA-TION
1425 4th Ave Ste 420, Seattle, WA 98101
Tel.: (206) 622-0420
Web Site:
http://www.joshuagreencorp.com
Sales Range: $10-24.9 Million
Emp.: 6
Private Investment Firm; Holding Company
N.A.I.C.S.: 551112
Sandra L. Spurlock *(Office Mgr)*
Jay G. Campbell *(CFO & VP)*
Aaron W. Singleton *(Exec VP)*
Joshua Green III *(Chm)*
Stanley B. McCammon III *(Pres & CEO)*

Subsidiaries:

Clyde/West Inc.   (1)
13805 NE Sandy Blvd, Portland, OR 97230
Tel.: (503) 252-5933
Web Site: http://www.clydewest.com
Sales Range: $10-24.9 Million
Emp.: 80
General Construction Machinery & Equip-ment
N.A.I.C.S.: 423310
Patrick McConnell *(Pres)*
Gary Nadeau *(Mgr-Inventory)*
John Cushman *(Mgr-Washington)*
Rick Semke *(VP-Sls)*
Jake Zayas *(Mgr-Sls)*
Gary Labelle *(Mgr-Washington)*

Cuizina Food Company   (1)
18565 142nd Ave NE, Woodinville, WA 98072
Tel.: (425) 486-7000
Web Site: http://www.cuizina.com
Sales Range: $1-9.9 Million
Frozen Soups & Sauces Mfr
N.A.I.C.S.: 311412

Ric Ferrera *(Founder & Chm)*
Alan Mitchell *(COO & VP-Ops)*
Erik Bugge *(Pres)*
Jamie Colbourne *(CEO)*
Kent Roundhill *(Exec Dir-Sls)*

Far Bank Enterprises, Inc.   (1)
8500 NE Day Rd, Bainbridge Island, WA 98110
Tel.: (206) 780-8767
Web Site: http://www.farbank.com
Holding Company
N.A.I.C.S.: 551112
Marc A. Bale *(VP)*
Larry Barrett *(Pres & COO)*
Patrice Stankavich *(VP-HR)*
Glenn Simpson *(Mgr-E-Commerce)*
Tag Kleiner *(VP-Mktg)*
Kris Klein *(CEO)*

Holding (Domestic):

Rio Products Intl., Inc.   (2)
5050 S Yellowstone Hwy, Idaho Falls, ID 83402
Tel.: (208) 524-7760
Web Site: http://www.rioproducts.com
Emp.: 30
Fly Fishing Equipment Mfr
N.A.I.C.S.: 339920

Sage Manufacturing Corporation   (2)
8500 NE Day Rd, Bainbridge Island, WA 98110
Tel.: (206) 842-6608
Web Site: http://www.safeflyfish.com
Emp.: 175
Fly Fishing Equipment Mfr
N.A.I.C.S.: 339920
David Lantz *(Mgr-Mktg)*

JOSHUA PARTNERS, LLC
21 Vintage Farm Ln, Newtown, PA 18940
Tel.: (215) 497-9340
Web Site:
http://www.joshuapartners.com
Year Founded: 2007
Privater Equity Firm
N.A.I.C.S.: 523999
Charles Corpening *(Chm)*
Robert Henry *(Principal)*

Subsidiaries:

Medicia Holdings LLC   (1)
2351 US Route 130, Dayton, NJ 08810
Tel.: (732) 438-3200
Web Site: http://www.medicia.com
Sales Range: $25-49.9 Million
Emp.: 300
Pharmaceutical & Personal Care Product Contract Manufacturing Services
N.A.I.C.S.: 325412

Ray Industries, Inc.   (1)
515 Frederick St, Waukesha, WI 53186
Tel.: (262) 650-6650
Web Site: http://www.rayindustries.com
Sales Range: $10-24.9 Million
Emp.: 25
Parts & Components Mfr
N.A.I.C.S.: 332710
Raymond Fish *(Pres & Treas)*

JOSIE ACCESSORIES INC.
261 5th Ave Ste 1005, New York, NY 10016
Tel.: (212) 889-6376
Rev.: $45,000,000
Emp.: 50
Tablecloth Mfr
N.A.I.C.S.: 314120
Mark Siegel *(Pres)*

JOSINA LOTT RESIDENTIAL & COMMUNITY SERVICES
120 S Holland Sylvania Rd, Toledo, OH 43615
Tel.: (419) 866-9013   OH
Web Site: http://www.josinalott.org
Year Founded: 1979
Sales Range: $1-9.9 Million
Emp.: 86
Developmental Disability Assistance Services
N.A.I.C.S.: 623210

Josina Lott Residential & Community Services—(Continued)

Pat Baker (Dir-Ops)
Beth Baumert (Dir-Community Svcs)
Carol Parcell (Dir-IT)
Michael Malone (Exec Dir)
Marge Bollman (VP)
Jonathan Ashton (Pres)
Lynn Ritter (Sec)
Joseph A. Beham (Treas)
Diann Stretten (VP)

JOTO PR AGENCY
411 Cleveland St Ste 204, Clearwater, FL 33755
Tel.: (888) 202-4614
Web Site: http://www.jotopr.com
Year Founded: 2009
Sales Range: $1-9.9 Million
Public Relations Agency
N.A.I.C.S.: 541820
Karla Jo Helms (CEO)
Diane D. Stein (Pres)

JOTTAN INC.
16 Cathy Ln, Florence, NJ 08518
Tel.: (609) 291-8700
Web Site: http://www.jottan.com
Year Founded: 1980
Sales Range: $10-24.9 Million
Emp.: 85
Provider of Roofing Contracting Services
N.A.I.C.S.: 238160
Toby Chrostowski (Pres)
George Gulla (Project Mgr)

JOULE ASSETS, INC.
2 Depot Plz, Bedford Hills, NY 10507
Tel.: (914) 977-3444   DE
Web Site: http://www.jouleassets.com
Financial Solutions
N.A.I.C.S.: 523999
Mike Gordon (Founder & CEO)
Jessica Stromback (Chm/Sr VP-Europe)
Gregg Lerman (Chief Sls Officer)
Stephen Filler (Chief Legal Officer & VP-Bus Dev)
Sherry Rothenberg (VP-Mktg)
Glenn Weinberg (Dir-JouleCommunity Power)

Subsidiaries:

Joule Capital, LLC   (1)
19201 SW Teton Ave, Tualatin, OR 97062
Tel.: (866) 491-5854
Web Site: http://www.joulesmart.com
Financial Solutions
N.A.I.C.S.: 523999
Dennis Quinn (Pres)
Patrick O'Neill (Founder & COO)
Maria Fields (Sr VP-Bus Dev)

JOURNAL PUBLICATIONS, INC.
1500 Paxton St, Harrisburg, PA 17104
Tel.: (717) 236-4300
Web Site:
    http://www.journalmultimedia.com
Sales Range: $10-24.9 Million
Emp.: 60
Multi-Title Publishing & Events Management Company
N.A.I.C.S.: 513120
David Schankweiler (CEO)
Lawrence Kluger (Pres)
Beth Feltenberger (Dir-Events & Mktg)
Zander Gambill (VP-Audience Dev)

Subsidiaries:

Eastern Pennsylvania Business Journal   (1)
65 E Elizabeth Ave Ste 700, Bethlehem, PA 18018

Tel.: (610) 807-9619
Web Site: http://www.lvb.com
Sales Range: $10-24.9 Million
Emp.: 16
Commercial Printing & Newspaper Publishing Combined
N.A.I.C.S.: 513110
Donna Schankweiler (Mgr-HR)

NJBIZ   (1)
220 Davidson Ave Ste 302, Somerset, NJ 08873
Tel.: (732) 246-7677
Web Site: http://www.njbiz.com
Sales Range: $10-24.9 Million
Emp.: 35
Business Information Publisher Specific to New Jersey
N.A.I.C.S.: 513110
Susan Alexander (Acct Exec)
AnnMarie Karczmit (Gen Mgr)
Anjalee Khemlani (Deputy Mng Editor)
Ken Kiczales (Publr)
Howard Burns (Editor)

JOURNEY FORWARD
755 Dedham St, Canton, MA 02021
Tel.: (781) 828-3233   MA
Web Site: http://www.journey-forward.org
Year Founded: 2008
Sales Range: $1-9.9 Million
Emp.: 12
Patient Wellness Services
N.A.I.C.S.: 621498
John Walters (VP & Program Dir)
Ann Connors (Office Mgr)
Daniel Cummings (Pres)
Thomas Cummings (Chm)
James Cummings (Sec)
Mark Shays (Treas)

JOURNEY HOUSE, INC.
1232 N Los Robles Ave, Pasadena, CA 91104
Tel.: (626) 798-9478   CA
Web Site:
    http://www.journeyhouseyouth.org
Year Founded: 1983
Rev.: $1,454,457
Assets: $1,604,248
Liabilities: $1,699
Net Worth: $1,602,549
Earnings: $1,226,323
Emp.: 2
Fiscal Year-end: 12/31/14
Foster Care Services
N.A.I.C.S.: 624110
Ben Sarafi (Sec)
Fred Wong (Pres)
Jorge Camarena (Program Dir)
Tim Mayworm (Exec Dir)
Venise Williams (Treas)
Ben Sarafi (Sec)
Fred Wong (Pres)
Jorge Camarena (Program Dir)
Tim Mayworm (Exec Dir)
Venise Williams (Treas)

JOURNEY MENTAL HEALTH CENTER
625 W Washington Ave, Madison, WI 53703
Tel.: (608) 280-2700   WI
Web Site: http://www.journeymhc.org
Year Founded: 1948
Sales Range: $10-24.9 Million
Emp.: 378
Behavioral Healthcare Services
N.A.I.C.S.: 621420
Alan Zoellner (CFO)
Brian Miller (Chief Dev Officer)
Colleen Clark Buss (Chief HR Officer)
Karen Neitzel (COO)
Pamela Bean (Principal)
Robin Gates (Principal)

JOURNEY MEXICO

2163 Lima Loop 130-144, Laredo, TX 78045
Tel.: (619) 819-5111
Web Site:
    http://www.journeymexico.com
Year Founded: 2003
Sales Range: $1-9.9 Million
Emp.: 16
Luxury Travel Tours
N.A.I.C.S.: 561510
Zachary Rabinor (Founder, Pres & CEO)
Rebecca Scotti (CFO)
Matteo Luthi (COO)
Judit Elek (Mgr-Group Sls)
Karina Huet (Product Mgr)
Lillian Aviles (Dir-Mktg)
Miguel Moreno (Mgr-Fin)
Monika Zuber (Mgr-Groups)
Sean Emmerton (Dir-Villa Program)
Amberley Shermon (Mgr-Bus Dev-UK & Europe)
Alfonso Sumano (Dir-Bus Dev)

JOURNEYMAN CONSTRUCTION, INC.
7701 N Lamar Ste 100, Austin, TX 78752
Tel.: (512) 247-7000
Web Site:
    http://www.journeymanco.com
Year Founded: 1996
Sales Range: $75-99.9 Million
Emp.: 100
Commercial & Institutional Building Construction
N.A.I.C.S.: 236220
Sam Kumar (Pres)
Andrew Waterman (Reg VP)
Gary Willard (Reg VP)
Judy Fisher (VP & Controller)
Jason C. Spencer (Exec VP)
David Gregorcyk (VP-Risk Mgmt)

JOY CONE COMPANY
3435 Lamor Rd, Hermitage, PA 16148-3050
Tel.: (724) 962-5747   PA
Web Site: http://www.joycone.com
Year Founded: 1918
Sales Range: $100-124.9 Million
Emp.: 275
Ice Cream Cone Mfr
N.A.I.C.S.: 311821
Joseph A. George (CEO)
Joseph Marincic (COO)
Scott P. Kalmanek (Controller)
David George (Pres)

Subsidiaries:

Joy Cone Company - Western Facility   (1)
2843 W Shamrell Blvd, Flagstaff, AZ 86001
Tel.: (928) 774-0225
Web Site: http://www.joycone.com
Emp.: 100
Ice Cream Cone Mfr
N.A.I.C.S.: 311821

Novelty Co.ne Co.   (1)
807 Sherman Ave, Pennsauken, NJ 08110-2684
Tel.: (856) 665-9525
Web Site: http://www.noveltycone.com
Commercial Bakeries
N.A.I.C.S.: 311812
Steven Marinucci (Pres)

JOY FOR OUR YOUTH INC.
1805 Swarthmore Ave, Lakewood, NJ 08701
Tel.: (732) 730-2121   NJ
Web Site: http://www.kars4kids.org
Year Founded: 2001
Sales Range: $25-49.9 Million
Emp.: 74
Child & Youth Care Services
N.A.I.C.S.: 624110

Robert Moskovits (VP-Bus Dev)
David Kronglas (Controller)
Eli Mintz (CEO)
Esti Landau (CMO)
Wendy Kirwan (Dir-PR)
Ben Turin (Gen Counsel)

JOY MARK INC.
1407 Broadway Rm 903, New York, NY 10018
Tel.: (212) 695-7661
Rev.: $14,295,427
Emp.: 10
Sportswear, Women's & Children's
N.A.I.C.S.: 424350
Raymond Tsai (Pres)

JOY PIPE USA LLC
39850 IH 10 W, Boerne, TX 78006
Tel.: (830) 249-7400
Web Site: http://www.joypipe.com
Sales Range: $25-49.9 Million
Emp.: 11
Pipes Mfr
N.A.I.C.S.: 423510
William F. Thomas (Pres)

JOY! COMMUNICATIONS
3461 SE Willoughby Blvd, Stuart, FL 34994
Tel.: (772) 283-2000
Web Site: http://www.joycomm.com
Emp.: 15
Communication Technology Development Services
N.A.I.C.S.: 517112
Peter Engle (Owner)

Subsidiaries:

Joy! Communications-Ft. Lauderdale   (1)
3461 SE Willoughby Blvd, Stuart, FL 34994
Tel.: (954) 971-0066
Web Site: http://www.joycomm.com
Sales Range: $1-9.9 Million
Emp.: 12
Electronic Parts & Equipment Merchant Whslr
N.A.I.C.S.: 423690
Peter Engle (Owner & Pres)

JOYCE & ASSOCIATES CONSTRUCTION, INC.
6994 Highway 70 Bypass, Newport, NC 28570
Tel.: (252) 223-3171
Web Site:
    http://www.joyceandassoc.com
Year Founded: 2000
Sales Range: $25-49.9 Million
Emp.: 34
Commercial & Institutional Building Construction Services
N.A.I.C.S.: 236220
Patrick P. Joyce (Pres)
Dorothy Smith (Office Mgr)
Randy Dodge (Project Mgr & Coord-Metal Building)
William Styron (VP & Project Mgr)
Richard Hall (Project Mgr)
Robert E. Bittner Jr. (VP & Project Mgr)

JOYCE BROS STORAGE & VAN CO.
1915 Janice Ave, Melrose Park, IL 60160
Tel.: (708) 681-1700
Web Site: http://www.joycebros.com
Rev.: $13,036,840
Emp.: 50
Household Goods Transport
N.A.I.C.S.: 484210
Michael Mudd (Pres)
Dennis I. Mudd Sr. (Chm)

JOYCE FARMS, INC.

4787 Kinnamon Rd, Winston Salem, NC 27103
Tel.: (800) 755-6923
Web Site: http://www.joyce-farms.com
Year Founded: 1962
Poultry & Poultry Products Whslr & Distr
N.A.I.C.S.: 424440
Ronald A. Joyce *(Chm)*
Mark Parham *(Gen Mgr)*
Allen Williams *(Chief Ranching Officer)*
Chris Campbell *(Controller)*
Eric Ivey *(Ops Mgr)*
Stuart Joyce *(Exec VP)*
Ryan Joyce *(Pres & CEO)*
Tom Sprouse *(Dir-Maintenance)*
Jimmy Douglas Mitchell Jr. *(Mgr-Quality Assurance)*

JOYCE FOOD PRODUCTS INC.
80 Ave K, Newark, NJ 07105-3803
Tel.: (973) 491-9696 NJ
Year Founded: 1979
Sales Range: $25-49.9 Million
Emp.: 200
Food Production & Sales
N.A.I.C.S.: 311423
Howard Freundlich *(Pres)*

Subsidiaries:

Goodmans Matzoh Products Inc (1)
80 Ave K, Newark, NJ 07105-3803
Tel.: (973) 589-4900
Rev.: $490,000
Emp.: 4
Food Products Sales
N.A.I.C.S.: 424490

JOYCE LESLIE INC.
170 W Commercial Ave, Moonachie, NJ 07074
Tel.: (201) 804-7800
Web Site: http://www.joyceleslie.com
Sales Range: $50-74.9 Million
Emp.: 75
Ready-To-Wear Apparel, Women's
N.A.I.C.S.: 458110
Cheryl O'Reilly *(Mgr-HR)*
Janet Perretta *(Supvr-Accts Payable)*
Michelle Schneidereit *(Mgr-Store)*
Celia Clancy *(CEO)*

JOYCE MANUFACTURING CO.
1125 Berea Industrial Pkwy, Berea, OH 44017
Tel.: (440) 239-9100
Web Site: http://www.joycemfg.com
Year Founded: 1955
Sales Range: $10-24.9 Million
Emp.: 70
Prefabricated Metal Building & Component Mfr
N.A.I.C.S.: 332311
Russell Schmidt *(Pres)*
Tim Felker *(VP)*
Todd Schmidt *(Sec)*
Gary Winkler *(VP)*

JOYCE MOTORS CORP.
3166 State Rte 10, Denville, NJ 07834
Tel.: (973) 361-3000
Web Site:
http://www.joycehonda.com
Sales Range: $10-24.9 Million
Emp.: 100
New & Used Car Dealer
N.A.I.C.S.: 441110
Tom Stark *(VP)*

JOYVA CORPORATION
53 Varick Ave, Brooklyn, NY 11237
Tel.: (718) 497-0170 NY
Web Site: http://www.joyva.com

Year Founded: 1910
Sales Range: $75-99.9 Million
Emp.: 75
Halvah, Candies & Sesame Products Mfr
N.A.I.C.S.: 311340
Sanford Wiener *(Treas)*

JP CHEVROLET INC.
101 N Philadelphia Blvd, Aberdeen, MD 21001
Tel.: (410) 272-0300 MD
Web Site: http://www.jpchevrolet.com
Year Founded: 1937
Sales Range: $10-24.9 Million
Emp.: 29
Sales of New & Used Automobiles
N.A.I.C.S.: 441110
William Church *(Pres)*

JP LAWRENCE BIOMEDICAL, INC.
3890 131st Ave NE, Blaine, MN 55449
Tel.: (801) 709-3181 DE
Emp.: 100
Investment Services
N.A.I.C.S.: 523999
Joshua Packer *(Exec Dir)*

Subsidiaries:

IBEX Preclinical Research, Inc. (1)
1072 Rsi Dr, Logan, UT 84321-2201
Tel.: (435) 752-4448
Web Site: https://ibexresearch.com
Research & Development in the Physical, Engineering & Life Sciences
N.A.I.C.S.: 541715

JP LOGISTICS & MOTOR-SPORTS, INC.
11057 Penrose St, Sun Valley, CA 91352
Tel.: (818) 381-8313
Web Site: http://www.jplogistics.net
Year Founded: 1996
Sales Range: $1-9.9 Million
Emp.: 20
Nationwide Transportation, Global Shipping & Long & Short-Term Storage of Automobiles
N.A.I.C.S.: 488510
George Sukunyan *(Owner)*

JP MOTORS, INC.
3675 Frontage Rd, Peru, IL 61354
Tel.: (815) 223-7000 IL
Web Site: http://www.jpchevy.com
Rev.: $11,200,000
Emp.: 49
New Car Dealers
N.A.I.C.S.: 441110
Scott Ansteth *(Gen Mgr)*
Steve Cooke *(Mgr-Svc)*
Scott Passow *(Mgr-Fin)*
Joseph Leydon *(Pres)*
Josie Urbino *(Office Mgr)*

JP OIL COMPANY INC.
1604 W Pinhook Rd Ste 300, Lafayette, LA 70505
Tel.: (337) 234-1170
Web Site: http://www.jpoil.com
Year Founded: 1986
Sales Range: $100-124.9 Million
Emp.: 150
Oil & Gas Producer
N.A.I.C.S.: 211120
Chris M. Van Way *(Pres & CEO)*
Henry E. David *(Mgr-Production Engrg)*
Cal Seneca *(Dir-HR)*
Ernest Seneca *(Mgr-Land)*
Frank L. Walker *(CFO & Treas)*

JP ORIGINAL CORP.

19101 E Walnut Dr N, City of Industry, CA 91748
Tel.: (626) 839-4300
Web Site: http://www.jpo.com
Sales Range: $10-24.9 Million
Emp.: 50
Shoes Distr
N.A.I.C.S.: 424340
C. H. Hsueh *(CEO)*

JP RYAN ENTERPRISES INC.
26515 Interstate 45 N, Spring, TX 77380
Tel.: (281) 363-1106
Web Site: http://www.ryansales.net
Sales Range: $10-24.9 Million
Emp.: 4
Electrical Apparatus & Equipment
N.A.I.C.S.: 423610
Mary Ryan *(Pres)*

JPC GROUP, INC.
1309 S Harmony St, Philadelphia, PA 19146
Tel.: (215) 243-9660
Web Site:
http://www.jpcgroupinc.com
Rev.: $42,849,000
Emp.: 160
Engineering & Construction Services
N.A.I.C.S.: 541330
Jeffrey Petrongolo *(Treas)*
John Petrongolo *(Sec)*
Joseph Petrongolo Jr. *(Pres)*

JPI NATIONAL CONSTRUC-TION INC.
600 Las Colinas Blvd E Ste 1800, Irving, TX 75039-5625
Tel.: (972) 556-6970 TX
Year Founded: 1998
Sales Range: $25-49.9 Million
Emp.: 1,200
Real Estate
N.A.I.C.S.: 236116
Robert D. Page *(Pres & CIO)*
J. Frank Miller *(Chm)*
Karen Tepera *(VP-Bus Dev)*
Thomas O'Brien *(Mng Partner & Exec VP)*
Paul Crisalli *(Sr VP)*
James Duncan *(Partner & VP-Ops)*
David Flad *(VP & Sr Asset Mgr)*
Heidi Mather *(Sr VP-Dev Partner)*
Bob McCullough *(Mng Partner & Sr VP)*
Greg Lamb *(Mng Partner & Exec VP)*
Mollie Fadule *(CFO)*
Payton Mayes *(CEO)*

JPL INTEGRATED COMMUNIC-TIONS, INC.
471 JPL Wick Dr, Harrisburg, PA 17111
Tel.: (717) 558-8048
Web Site: http://www.jplcreative.com
Year Founded: 1989
Sales Range: $10-24.9 Million
Emp.: 100
Advetising Agency
N.A.I.C.S.: 541810
Luke Kempski *(Pres)*
Matt Daly *(VP-Client Solutions)*
Mary Pedersen *(Dir-Creative)*
Paul Grosso *(VP-Media Production)*
Susan Cort *(Dir-Comm)*
Bill Kobel *(VP-Strategy & Integrated Comm)*
Mary Boyer *(VP-Fin)*
Kelly Seipe *(Dir-Acct Mgmt)*
Ryan Pudloski *(Dir-Technical Solutions)*
Nick Lucente *(Mgr-Digital Mktg)*
Jenny Fedullo *(Mgr-Learning Solutions)*

Traci Gallagher *(Mgr-Media Production)*
Jill Sailer *(Sr Acct Mgr)*
Jason Menicheschi *(Sr Acct Mgr-Meetings & Events)*

JPL MANAGEMENT INC.
430 Commerce Dr, Elizabethtown, KY 42701
Tel.: (270) 769-2248
Rev.: $12,000,000
Emp.: 520
Franchise Owner of Fast-Food Restaurants
N.A.I.C.S.: 722513
James Schory *(Pres)*

JPR HOMES
1801C Park Court Pl, Santa Ana, CA 92701-5009
Tel.: (714) 972-9944 CA
Web Site: http://www.jprhomes.com
Year Founded: 1982
Sales Range: $75-99.9 Million
Emp.: 10
Housing Development Solutions
N.A.I.C.S.: 236115
Jeffrey P. Rhodes *(Pres)*
Kelly V. Hansen *(CFO & VP)*

JPS HEALTH NETWORK
1500 S Main St, Fort Worth, TX 76104
Tel.: (817) 921-3431
Web Site: http://www.jpshealthnet.org
Year Founded: 1906
Sales Range: $350-399.9 Million
Emp.: 3,200
Medical Health Network
N.A.I.C.S.: 622110
Robert Earley *(Pres & CEO)*
Bill Whitman *(COO)*
David Salsberry *(CFO)*
Merianne Roth *(Chief Strategy Officer & VP)*

JPW CONSULTING
332 Springfield Ave, Summit, NJ 07901
Tel.: (908) 219-4650
Web Site:
http://www.jpwconsulting.com
Year Founded: 1998
Sales Range: $1-9.9 Million
Emp.: 1
Training & Consulting
N.A.I.C.S.: 541618
John Wurch *(Founder & Pres)*

JR CONTROLS INC.
4663 E Guasti Rd, Ontario, CA 91761
Tel.: (909) 390-6017
Web Site:
http://www.westcoastent.com
Sales Range: $25-49.9 Million
Emp.: 150
Printed Circuit Boards
N.A.I.C.S.: 334412
James Savage *(Pres)*

JR INSULATION SALES & SERVICE
3 Sta 30085 KM 2 9, Penuelas, PR 00624
Tel.: (787) 836-1756
Web Site: http://www.caribe.net
Year Founded: 1984
Sales Range: $10-24.9 Million
Emp.: 200
Scaffolding, Drywall & Industrial Vacuums; Environmental Work & Asbestos Removal.
N.A.I.C.S.: 238310
Jose Ruiz *(Pres)*

JRC LOGISTICS

JRC Logistics—(Continued)

5870 Trinity Pky, Centreville, VA 20120
Tel.: (703) 378-0483
Year Founded: 2001
Rev.: $21,400,000
Emp.: 50
Logistic Services
N.A.I.C.S.: 488510
Dina Gerrald (Controller)

JRC PIZZA LLC
4937 E 5th St, Tucson, AZ 85711
Tel.: (520) 323-3500
Sales Range: $10-24.9 Million
Emp.: 10
Pizzeria Owner & Operator
N.A.I.C.S.: 722513
James Gerety (Owner)

JRD PACKAGING AND INDUS-TRIAL SUPPLY
1160 E Main St, Mount Joy, PA 17552
Tel.: (717) 653-2345
Web Site:
http://www.jrdpackaging.com
Year Founded: 2004
Rev.: $3,800,000
Emp.: 8
Corrugated & Solid Fiber Box Mfr
N.A.I.C.S.: 322211
William Davidson (Principal)

JRH ELECTRONICS L.L.C.
751 Rte 73 N Ste1, Marlton, NJ 08053
Tel.: (856) 988-8696
Web Site: http://www.jrhelec.com
Year Founded: 1992
Sales Range: $10-24.9 Million
Emp.: 8
Other Electronic Part & Equipment Whslr
N.A.I.C.S.: 423690
Mary Ann Todd (Pres)

JRH INDUSTRIES LLC
4481 Munson St NW Ste 302, Canton, OH 44718
Tel.: (330) 491-0167
Web Site:
http://www.jrhindustries.com
All Other Miscellaneous General Purpose Machinery Mfr
N.A.I.C.S.: 333998
Jeff Headlee (Pres)

Subsidiaries:

Premier Hydraulics, LLC (1)
10 Fruit Ave, Farrell, PA 16121
Tel.: (724) 342-6506
Web Site: http://www.premier-hydraulics.com
All Other Miscellaneous General Purpose Machinery Mfr
N.A.I.C.S.: 333998

JRJR33, INC.
2950 N Harwood St 22nd Fl, Dallas, TX 75201
Tel.: (469) 913-4115   FL
Web Site:
http://www.jrjrnetworks.com
Year Founded: 2007
Sales Range: $125-149.9 Million
Holding Company; Online & Mail Order Retailer
N.A.I.C.S.: 551112
John Rochon Jr. (Vice Chm, CFO & Treas)
John P. Rochon Sr. (Chm, Pres & CEO)

Subsidiaries:

Agel Enterprises, Inc. (1)

2174 W Grove Pkwy Ste 100, Pleasant Grove, UT 84062   (100%)
Tel.: (801) 642-3850
Web Site: http://www.agel.com
Health & Beauty Gel Products Mfr & Retailer
N.A.I.C.S.: 325620
Craig Bradley (Pres & Mng Dir-AgelCares)
Jeremiah Bradley (Co-CEO)
Jeff Higginson (Co-CEO)
Jeff Warwick (Gen Counsel)
Samuel Higginson (Reg VP-North America & Europe)
Zach Bradley (Reg VP-Latin America & South East Asia)
Scott Higginson (VP-Sls & Comm)
Joel Rockwood (VP-R&D)
Richard Holt (Controller-Intl)
Layne Argyle (VP-Ops)
Gary Hasson (VP-Intl)
Glen Jensen (Founder & Grp CEO)

Subsidiary (Non-US):

Agel Enterprises International Sdn. Bhd.   (2)
5-3 Medan Kelang Lama 28 No 419, Jalan Kelang Lama, 58000, Kuala Lumpur, Malaysia   (100%)
Tel.: (60) 12 568 2088
Holding Company; Regional Managing Office
N.A.I.C.S.: 551112
Zach Bradley (Reg VP)

Subsidiary (Domestic):

Agel Enterprises (Malaysia) Sdn. Bhd.   (3)
5-3 Medan Kelang Lama 28 No 419, Jalan Kelang Lama, 58000, Kuala Lumpur, Malaysia   (100%)
Tel.: (60) 12 568 2088
Health & Beauty Gel Products Mfr & Marketer
N.A.I.C.S.: 325620
Keith Ganesan (Gen Mgr)

Subsidiary (Non-US):

Agel Enterprises Pte. Ltd.   (3)
15 Enggor Street 10-02 Realty Centre, Singapore, 079716, Singapore   (100%)
Tel.: (65) 6238 0368
Health & Beauty Gel Products Mfr & Marketer
N.A.I.C.S.: 325620
Albert Lee (Gen Mgr)

Subsidiary (Non-US):

Agel Enterprises RS LLC   (2)
Rusakovskaya St 13, 107140, Moscow, Russia   (100%)
Tel.: (7) 499 554 0 554
Health & Beauty Gel Products Mfr & Retailer
N.A.I.C.S.: 325620

Agel International SRL   (2)
Lima 287 5 Piso Oficina A, C1073AAE, Buenos Aires, Argentina   (99%)
Tel.: (54) 11 6632 2063
Holding Company; Regional Managing Office
N.A.I.C.S.: 551112
Zach Bradley (Reg VP)

Subsidiary (Domestic):

Agel Enterprises Argentina SRL   (3)
Lima 287 5 Piso Oficina A, C1073AAE, Buenos Aires, Argentina
Tel.: (54) 11 6632 2063
Web Site: http://cl.agel.com
Health & Beauty Gel Products Mfr & Marketer
N.A.I.C.S.: 325620
Nestor Gola (Gen Mgr)

Happenings Communications Group, Inc.   (1)
115 N State St, Clarks Summit, PA 18411
Tel.: (570) 587-3532
Web Site:
http://www.happeningsmagazinepa.com
Emp.: 10
Regional Events & Advertising Magazine Publisher
N.A.I.C.S.: 513120

Paula Rochon Mackarey (Publr)
Barbara Toolan (Mng Editor)
Lisa Ragnacci (Dir-Art)
Peter Salerno (Assoc Dir-Art)

Kleeneze UK Limited   (1)
Express House Clayton Business Park
Clayton le Moors, Accrington, BB5 5JY, Lancashire, United Kingdom
Tel.: (44) 1 254 304171
Web Site: http://www.kleeneze.co.uk
Home Shopping Services
N.A.I.C.S.: 561990

My Secret Kitchen Ltd.   (1)
The Willows Kent End, Ashton Keynes, Swindon, SN6 6PF, United Kingdom
Tel.: (44) 1285689344
Web Site: http://www.mysecretkitchen.co.uk
Specialty Food & Beverage Online Retailer
N.A.I.C.S.: 445298
Clare Moran (Founder & CEO)

Paperly, Inc.   (1)
3629 N Halsted, Chicago, IL 60613
Tel.: (773) 661-1357
Web Site: http://www.paperly.com
Online & Mail Order Custom Stationery Retailer
N.A.I.C.S.: 322230
Jay Rudman (Co-Founder & CEO)
Cindy Rudman (Co-Founder)

Uppercase Living, LLC   (1)
1546 S 4650 W, Salt Lake City, UT 84104-5314
Tel.: (801) 619-5000
Web Site: http://www.uppercaseliving.com
Home Decor Products Online Retailer
N.A.I.C.S.: 449129
Wendy Lindahl (Dir-Sls)

Your Inspiration at Home Pty. Ltd.   (1)
3/2A Resources Court, Molendinar, Gold Coast, 4214, QLD, Australia
Tel.: (61) 755394229
Web Site:
http://www.yourinspirationathome.com.au
Spices, Herbs, Oils & Vinegars Online & Mail Order Retailer
N.A.I.C.S.: 445298
Colleen Walters (Founder, CEO & Spice Curator-Global)
Steve Magarry (Ops Mgr)

JRL ENTERPRISES INC.
3 Gtwy Ctr Ste 1580, Pittsburgh, PA 15222
Tel.: (412) 471-9315
Year Founded: 1987
Sales Range: $10-24.9 Million
Emp.: 60
Temporary Personnel Services
N.A.I.C.S.: 488210

JRL ENTERPRISES, INC.
1820 St. Charles Avenue Suite 203, New Orleans, LA 70130
Tel.: (601) 709-2860   LA
Web Site: http://www.icanlearn.com
Year Founded: 1990
Sales Range: $10-24.9 Million
Emp.: 150
Educational Software Development
N.A.I.C.S.: 541511
John R. Lee (Pres)
Randall O'Brien (Dir-Fin)
Lawrence Robinson (Dir-HR)

JRL VENTURES, INC.
2443 SW Pine Island Rd, Cape Coral, FL 33991
Tel.: (239) 283-0800   FL
Web Site:
http://www.jrlventuresinc.com
Year Founded: 1994
Sales Range: $10-24.9 Million
Emp.: 143
Composites Tooling, Molds & Other Products Mfr
N.A.I.C.S.: 333514
J. Robert Long (Owner & CEO)
Matt Chambers (Pres)

Todd Biddison (Project Mgr)
Kevin Long (Project Mgr)
Sidney L. Lanier (Dir-Product Dev)
John Long (Mgr-Mill Mfg & Facilities)
Dan Locke (Mgr-Design)
Steve Swarts (Mgr-Design)
Chris Hughes (Mgr-Ops)
Matt Workman (Project Mgr)

JRM CONSTRUCTION MANAGEMENT, LLC
242 W 36th St 9th Fl, New York, NY 10018
Tel.: (212) 545-0500   NY
Web Site: http://www.jrmcm.com
Year Founded: 2007
Sales Range: $200-249.9 Million
Emp.: 164
Retail & Commercial Construction
N.A.I.C.S.: 236210
David McWilliams (CEO)

JRS ADVERTISING
8350 N Central Expy Ste 1313, Dallas, TX 75206-1619
Tel.: (214) 871-2305
Year Founded: 1985
Sales Range: $25-49.9 Million
Emp.: 10
N.A.I.C.S.: 541810
Jay B. Serio (Principal & Agency Pres)
Robert Joiner (Exec VP & Creative Dir)
Chip Rowland (Treas & Media Dir)
Allen Weaver (Dir-Creative)
Karen Mosher (Office Mgr)
Ronda Wilson (Media Buyer)
Tom Schmitt (Dir-Strategic Plng)

JRS COUNTRY STORE INC.
710 W 4th St Ste J, Pueblo, CO 81003
Tel.: (719) 545-1923
Rev.: $15,157,000
Emp.: 120
Convenience Stores, Independent
N.A.I.C.S.: 445131
Rollie Leyh (Pres)
Dan Montoya (Controller)

JRS HOLDING, INC.
20445 W Capitol Dr, Brookfield, WI 53045-2745
Tel.: (262) 781-7711   WI
Web Site: http://www.safro.com
Year Founded: 1967
Sales Range: $75-99.9 Million
Emp.: 350
Holding Company; Automobile Dealerships
N.A.I.C.S.: 551112
Martin Thomas (Exec VP)
Jeanne M. Safro (VP)

JRS TRUCKING SERVICE, INC.
230-79 International Airport Center Blvd, Springfield Gardens, NY 11413
Tel.: (718) 553-2700
Web Site:
http://www.jrstruckingserviceinc.com
Rev.: $14,000,000
Emp.: 141
General Freight Trucking, Long-Distance, Truckload
N.A.I.C.S.: 484121
Anthony Ferone (Pres)
John Lampasone (VP)
Harry Gaither (Mgr-Ops)

JS CONSTRUCTION, S.E.
231 Zona Industrial Reparada 1, Ponce, PR 00716
Tel.: (787) 844-6169
Web Site:
http://www.jsconstructionse.com

Sales Range: $10-24.9 Million
Emp.: 25
Cable Television Installation; Utility Services
N.A.I.C.S.: 238210
Jose A. Santaella *(Pres)*
Alberto Rivera *(Mgr-Aerial Construction)*
Jorge Cedeno *(Mgr-Underground Construction)*

JS&A GROUP, INC.
3350 Palm Ctr Dr, Las Vegas, NV 89103
Tel.: (702) 597-2000   NV
Web Site: http://www.blublocker.com
Year Founded: 1971
Sales Range: $75-99.9 Million
Emp.: 10
Sunglasses Mfr
N.A.I.C.S.: 456130
Joseph Sugarman *(Founder & CEO)*

JS2 COMMUNICATIONS
661 N Harper Ave Ste 208, Los Angeles, CA 90048
Tel.: (323) 866-0880
Web Site: http://www.js2comm.com
Sales Range: $10-24.9 Million
Emp.: 10
Public Relations
N.A.I.C.S.: 541820
Jill Sandin *(Co-Founder & Pres)*
Jeff Smith *(Co-Founder, CEO & CFO)*
Pete Sanders *(VP)*

Subsidiaries:

JS2 Communications   (1)
41 E 11th St 11th Fl, New York, NY 10003
Tel.: (212) 905-6260
Web Site: http://www.js2comm.com
N.A.I.C.S.: 541810
Pete Sanders *(VP)*
Elizabeth Cahill *(Acct Dir)*
Josh Ferri *(Asst Acct Exec)*
Cynthia Patnode *(Acct Coord)*
Tom Freydl *(VP & Gen Mgr)*
Kris Zillo *(Acct Supvr)*

JSA HEALTHCARE CORPORATION
10051 5th St N Ste 200, Saint Petersburg, FL 33702
Tel.: (727) 824-0780
Web Site:
   http://www.jsahealthcare.com
Sales Range: $25-49.9 Million
Emp.: 450
Physicians Offices Owner & Operator
N.A.I.C.S.: 621111
Bob Trinh *(VP-Market)*
Barbara Allen *(Chief Medical Officer)*

JSB INDUSTRIES INC.
130 Crescent Ave, Chelsea, MA 02150
Tel.: (617) 846-1565   MA
Web Site: http://www.muffintown.com
Year Founded: 1978
Sales Range: $10-24.9 Million
Emp.: 45
Mfr of Bread, Cake & Related Products
N.A.I.C.S.: 311812
Brian Anderson *(VP-Pur)*
Scott Anderson *(VP)*
Russell Sbrizza *(Mgr-Sls)*

JSE, INC.
4575 23rd Ave S Ste 500, Fargo, ND 58104
Tel.: (701) 356-5003
Web Site:
   http://www.jsecompanies.com
Year Founded: 2006
Sales Range: $10-24.9 Million
Emp.: 33

Mortgage Brokerage Services
N.A.I.C.S.: 522310
Jeff Shipley *(Owner & Pres)*
Daryl Braham *(CFO & COO)*

JSI SHIPPING
1535-B Rollins Rd, Burlingame, CA 94010
Tel.: (650) 697-3963
Web Site: http://www.jsishipping.com
Year Founded: 1983
Sales Range: $25-49.9 Million
Emp.: 100
Freight Forwarding
N.A.I.C.S.: 488510
James Cullen *(Owner)*
Myla Nucum *(Mgr-Global Bus Dev)*
Rachel Bates *(Mgr-Intl Ops)*
Tony Tse *(Controller)*

JSJ CORPORATION
700 Robbins Rd, Grand Haven, MI 49417-2603
Tel.: (616) 842-6350   MI
Web Site: http://www.jsjcorp.com
Year Founded: 1970
Sales Range: $250-299.9 Million
Emp.: 2,500
Office Furniture Electromechanical & Specialized Product Mfr
N.A.I.C.S.: 336370
Erick P. Johnson *(Sec & Exec VP)*
Eric Boonstra *(Treas, VP-Fin & Controller)*
Jim D. Nutt *(VP-IT)*
Tomas J. Rizzi *(COO & Exec VP)*
Nelson Jacobson Jr. *(Chm & CEO)*

Subsidiaries:

Dake Corporation   (1)
724 Robbins Rd, Grand Haven, MI 49417
Tel.: (800) 937-3253
Web Site: http://www.dakecorp.com
Industrial Machinery Whslr
N.A.I.C.S.: 423830

Subsidiary (Domestic):

Dake Couplings   (2)
724 Robbins Rd, Grand Haven, MI 49417
Tel.: (800) 866-4423
Web Site: http://www.metercouplings.com
Meter Coupling Mfr
N.A.I.C.S.: 332996

Dake OEM Furniture   (2)
17237 Van Wagoner Rd, Spring Lake, MI 49456
Tel.: (855) 999-5055
Web Site: http://www.dakefurniture.com
Household Furniture Mfr
N.A.I.C.S.: 337126

GHSP, Inc.   (1)
1250 S Beechtree, Grand Haven, MI 49417-2840   (80%)
Tel.: (616) 842-5500
Web Site: http://www.ghsp.com
Sales Range: $25-49.9 Million
Metal Component Mfr
N.A.I.C.S.: 336370
Jeff Smith *(COO)*
Dan Dawiedczyk *(Pres)*
John Major *(Mktg Dir)*

Hudson Technologies   (1)
1327 N US Hwy 1, Ormond Beach, FL 32174-2900
Tel.: (386) 672-2000
Web Site: http://www.hudson-technologies.com
Sales Range: $25-49.9 Million
Emp.: 250
Deep Drawn Metal Enclosures, Cases & Stampings Mfr
N.A.I.C.S.: 332119
Paul Shacklady *(Dir-Mfg Engrg)*
Mike Prins *(Pres)*

JSJ Furniture Corporation   (1)
17237 Van Wagoner Rd, Spring Lake, MI 49456-9702
Tel.: (616) 847-7000
Web Site: http://www.izzyplus.com

Sales Range: $1-9.9 Million
Mfr & Distributor of Furniture
N.A.I.C.S.: 337211
Chuck Saylor *(Founder)*

Unit (Domestic):

ABCO Office Furniture   (2)
4121 Rushton St, Florence, AL 35630-6374   (100%)
Tel.: (256) 336-0070
Web Site: http://www.abcofurniture.com
Mfr of Office Furniture & Store Fixtures
N.A.I.C.S.: 337214

Fixtures Furniture   (2)
1642 Crystal Ave, Kansas City, MO 64126-2871   (100%)
Tel.: (816) 245-5800
Web Site: http://www.fixturesfurniture.com
Mfr of Institutional, Office & Hospitality Seating & Tables
N.A.I.C.S.: 337127

Harter   (2)
11451 Harter Dr, Middlebury, IN 46540-9663   (100%)
Tel.: (574) 825-5871
Web Site: http://www.izzyplus.com
Emp.: 100
Mfr of Custom Office Furniture; Office Chairs
N.A.I.C.S.: 337214
Scott Carpenter *(VP)*

McLoone Metal Graphics, Inc.   (1)
75 Sumner St, La Crosse, WI 54603-3132   (90%)
Tel.: (608) 784-1260
Web Site: http://www.mcloone.com
Sales Range: $25-49.9 Million
Commercial Printing
N.A.I.C.S.: 541430
Dave Deyoung *(Pres)*

Sparks Belting Company   (1)
3800 Stahl Dr SE, Grand Rapids, MI 49546
Tel.: (616) 949-2750
Web Site: http://www.sparksbelting.com
Conveyor Belts Mfr
N.A.I.C.S.: 333922

JSJ PHARMACEUTICALS
171 Church St Ste 140, Charleston, SC 29401
Tel.: (843) 965-8333   SC
Web Site: http://www.innocutis.com
Year Founded: 2003
Sales Range: $10-24.9 Million
Emp.: 10
Pharmaceutical Preparations
N.A.I.C.S.: 325412

JSL FOODS INC.
3550 Pasadena Ave, Los Angeles, CA 90031
Tel.: (323) 223-2484
Web Site: http://www.jslfoods.com
Rev.: $13,600,000
Emp.: 60
Pasta Products Mfr
N.A.I.C.S.: 311999
Marco Melgar *(Mgr-Safety)*
Miguel Angel Villanueva *(Mgr-Quality Control & Assurance)*
Uriel Celis *(Supvr-Warehouse)*

JSML MEDIA, LLC
11200 86th Ave N, Minneapolis, MN 55369
Tel.: (763) 657-2263
Web Site: http://www.jsml.com
Year Founded: 2006
Sales Range: $10-24.9 Million
Emp.: 5
Media Buying Services
N.A.I.C.S.: 541810
Michelle Leatherman *(Partner & Exec VP)*
Jill Sakin *(Pres)*

Subsidiaries:

JSML Media, LLC   (1)
11200 86th Ave N, Maple Grove, MN 55369

Tel.: (763) 657-2263
Web Site: http://www.jsml.com
Emp.: 10
N.A.I.C.S.: 541830
Jill Sakin *(Pres)*
Michelle Leatherman *(Partner & Exec VP)*

JSMN INTERNATIONAL INC.
591 Summit Ave Ste 522, Jersey City, NJ 07306
Tel.: (201) 792-6800
Web Site: http://www.jsmninc.com
Year Founded: 1998
Sales Range: $10-24.9 Million
Emp.: 275
Information Technology Staffing Services
N.A.I.C.S.: 561311
Ravinder Thota *(Pres)*

JSP INTERNATIONAL
1285 Drummers Ln Ste 301, Wayne, PA 19087
Tel.: (610) 651-8600   PA
Web Site: http://www.jsp.com
Year Founded: 1985
Sales Range: $100-124.9 Million
Emp.: 450
Mfr of Expanded Polypropylene Bead Foam
N.A.I.C.S.: 325211
Zachary Estrin *(Gen Counsel & VP)*
Richard Allaway *(Pres & CEO)*
Richard Bulley *(CFO)*

Subsidiaries:

JSP Mold LLC   (1)
404 E 4th St, Milledgeville, IL 61051   (100%)
Tel.: (815) 225-7110
Web Site: http://www.jspmold.com
Sales Range: $10-24.9 Million
Emp.: 50
Mfr of Rubber Products
N.A.I.C.S.: 333511
Mike McDaniels *(Plant Mgr)*
Bob Fredericks *(Plant Mgr)*

JT CONSTRUCTION CO. INC.
6800 Parktown Blvd Bldg E Ste 226, San Antonio, TX 78213
Tel.: (210) 641-1244
Rev.: $20,000,000
Emp.: 11
Industrial Building Construction
N.A.I.C.S.: 236210

JTD ENTERPRISES INC.
4446 Pet Ln Ste 103, Lutz, FL 33559
Tel.: (813) 991-7111
Web Site: http://www.jtdent.com
Sales Range: $10-24.9 Million
Emp.: 11
Tubular Assemblies Used In Golf Ball Accessories, Flagpoles & Defense Technologies
N.A.I.C.S.: 332996
Deni Nihra *(Pres)*

JTE MULTIMEDIA, LLC
18 Elizabeth St Ste 100, West Conshohocken, PA 19428
Tel.: (610) 889-3730
Web Site:
   http://www.jtemultimedia.com
Periodical Publishers
N.A.I.C.S.: 513120
John Elduff *(Mng Dir)*
Stacy Phillips *(Mng Editor)*
Dennis Lewis *(Mgr-Production)*

Subsidiaries:

Hospital Practice   (1)
1235 Westlakes Dr Ste 320, Berwyn, PA 19312
Tel.: (610) 889-3730
Web Site:
   http://www.hospitalpracticemed.com
Medical Periodical

JTE Multimedia, LLC—(Continued)
N.A.I.C.S.: 513120

Postgraduate Medicine (1)
1235 Westlakes Dr Ste 320, Berwyn, PA
19312
Tel.: (610) 889-3733
Web Site: http://www.postgradmed.com
Sales Range: $1-9.9 Million
Emp.: 10
Magazine for Primary Care Physicians
N.A.I.C.S.: 513120

The Physician & Sportsmedicine (1)
1235 Westlakes Dr Ste 320, Berwyn, PA
19312
Tel.: (610) 889-3732
Web Site: http://www.physssportsmed.com
Sales Range: $10-24.9 Million
Emp.: 5
Magazine for Sports Medicine
N.A.I.C.S.: 513120

JTF BUSINESS SYSTEMS
85 S Bragg St 601, Alexandria, VA
22312
Tel.: (703) 658-2000
Web Site: http://www.jtfbus.com
Year Founded: 1987
Sales Range: $1-9.9 Million
Copying Machinery Distr
N.A.I.C.S.: 423420
Matt Matini (Pres)

JTF CONSTRUCTION, INC.
4235 Muhlhauser Rd, Fairfield, OH
45014
Tel.: (513) 860-9835
Web Site:
    http://www.jtfconstruction.com
Sales Range: $10-24.9 Million
Emp.: 70
Nonresidential Construction Services
N.A.I.C.S.: 236220
Gregory W. Fisher (Pres)

JTL CAPITAL, LLC
4807 W Lovers Ln 2nd Fl, Dallas, TX
75209
Tel.: (214) 692-5085
Web Site: http://www.jtlcapital.com
Emp.: 3
Real Estate Investment & Develop-
ment
N.A.I.C.S.: 523999
David A. Lane (Mng Partner)

Subsidiaries:

Las Ventanas al Paraiso (1)
KM 19 5 Ctra Transpeninsular, San Jose
del Cabo, 23400, Baja California Sur,
Mexico (100%)
Tel.: (52) 6241442800
Web Site: http://www.rosewoodhotels.com
Sales Range: $50-74.9 Million
Emp.: 410
Hotel Operator
N.A.I.C.S.: 721110
Daniel Scott (Mng Dir)

JTO INC.
6011 Heisley Rd, Mentor, OH 44060
Tel.: (440) 352-1900
Web Site: http://www.jtoinc.com
Year Founded: 1978
Sales Range: $10-24.9 Million
Emp.: 38
Commercial & Office Building, New
Construction
N.A.I.C.S.: 236220
William Wickli (Branch Mgr)
Timothy Posar (CFO)
Leong Tan (VP)
Mark Clark (VP)

JTR & CO. INC.
1102 S 3rd St, San Jose, CA 95112
Tel.: (408) 293-3272
Web Site:
    http://www.areadistributing.com

Sales Range: $10-24.9 Million
Emp.: 80
Whslr of Industrial Paper & Packag-
ing Products
N.A.I.C.S.: 493110

JTS COMMUNITIES, INC.
401 Watt Ave Ste 2, Sacramento, CA
95864
Tel.: (916) 487-3434
Web Site:
    http://www.jtscommunities.com
Year Founded: 1973
Sales Range: $200-249.9 Million
Emp.: 500
General Contractor of Single-Family
Housing
N.A.I.C.S.: 236115
Jack T. Sweigart (Pres & CEO)
Corinne Mostad (Portfolio Mgr)
Ian Craig (Gen Counsel)

JTS CONSTRUCTION
7001 McDivitt Dr Ste B, Bakersfield,
CA 93313-2030
Tel.: (661) 835-9270
Web Site:
    http://www.jtsconstruction.com
Sales Range: $10-24.9 Million
Emp.: 80
Civil Engineering Services
N.A.I.C.S.: 237310
Lee Hawkins (Pres)

JUAREZ BROTHERS TRUCK-
ING INC.
1400 S Union Ave, Bakersfield, CA
93307
Tel.: (661) 833-6280
Rev.: $15,000,000
Emp.: 200
Trucking Service
N.A.I.C.S.: 484110
Cesar Juarez (Pres)

JUBA'S INC.
219 S Main St, Blue Earth, MN
56013
Tel.: (507) 526-2161
Web Site:
    http://www.jubassupervalu.com
Sales Range: $10-24.9 Million
Emp.: 123
Grocery Stores, Independent
N.A.I.C.S.: 445110
Thomas J. Juba (Pres)

JUBITZ CORPORATION
33 NE Middlefield Rd, Portland, OR
97211
Tel.: (503) 283-1111
Web Site: http://www.jubitz.com
Year Founded: 1952
Sales Range: $50-74.9 Million
Emp.: 300
Goods & Services to the Transporta-
tion Industry; Travel Centers
N.A.I.C.S.: 457120
Frederick D. Jubitz (Pres & CEO)
Gaylene Salvagno (VP-Fleet Svcs)

Subsidiaries:

Vancouver Oil Company Inc. (1)
1503 NE 136th St, Vancouver, WA 98685
Tel.: (360) 574-5440
Web Site: http://www.vancouveroil.com
Emp.: 20
Petroleum Bulk Stations & Terminals
N.A.I.C.S.: 424710
Todd Shaw (Gen Mgr)

JUDCO MANUFACTURING
INC.
1429 240th St, Harbor City, CA
90710
Tel.: (310) 534-0959

Web Site: http://www.judcomfg.com
Rev.: $17,500,000
Emp.: 500
Electric Switches
N.A.I.C.S.: 335931
Thomas Buttner (Pres)
Kurt George (Dir-Ops)

JUDDS BROTHERS CON-
STRUCTION COMPANY
3835 N 68th St, Lincoln, NE 68505
Tel.: (402) 467-4666
Web Site: http://www.juddsbros.com
Sales Range: $10-24.9 Million
Emp.: 55
Underground Utilities Contractor
N.A.I.C.S.: 237110
Raymond E. Judds (Founder & Chm)
John Judds (Pres & CEO)
Kevin Steele (VP)

JUDGE ROTENBERG EDUCA-
TIONAL CENTER
250 Tpke St, Canton, MA 02021
Tel.: (781) 828-2202 MA
Web Site: http://www.judgerc.org
Year Founded: 1971
Sales Range: $50-74.9 Million
Emp.: 1,249
Developmental Disability Assistance
Services
N.A.I.C.S.: 623210
Henry Slucki (Chm)

JUDICIAL CORRECTION SER-
VICES, INC.
34 Peachtree St Ste 1000, Atlanta,
GA 30303
Tel.: (404) 591-3180
Web Site:
    http://www.judicialservices.com
Year Founded: 2000
Rev.: $10,100,000
Emp.: 208
Detective & Armored Car Services
N.A.I.C.S.: 561611

JUDICIAL WATCH, INC.
425 3rd St SW Ste 800, Washington,
DC 20024
Tel.: (202) 646-5172 DC
Web Site:
    http://www.judicialwatch.org
Year Founded: 1994
Sales Range: $25-49.9 Million
Emp.: 46
Legal Aid Services
N.A.I.C.S.: 541199
Jill Farrell (Dir-Pub Affairs)
Ariana Azizkeya (Mgr-Direct Re-
sponse Mktg)
John Albertella (Dir-Direct Mktg)
John Britten (Dir-Digital Strategy)
Christopher J. Farrell (Dir-Res & In-
vestigation)
Paul J. Orfanedes (Treas, Sec & Dir-
Litigation)
Steve Andersen (Dir-Dev)
Thomas Fitton (Pres)

JUDITH RIPKA COMPANIES
INC.
200 Madison Ave, New York, NY
10016-3902
Tel.: (212) 391-2340
Web Site: http://www.judithripka.com
Year Founded: 1973
Sales Range: $50-74.9 Million
Emp.: 115
Jewelry Designer, Retailer & Whole-
saler
N.A.I.C.S.: 458310
Janice Winter (Pres)
David Ripka (COO)
Judith Ripka (CEO)
Beth Vogel (Sr VP-Sls & Mdsg)

Diana Brenna (COO)
Jessica A. Stark (VP-Comm)
Roza Golden (Dir-Sls-Intl)
Lance Jackowitz (Controller)
Lynda Smith (Product Dir-Dev)
Kendra Bridelle (VP-Sls)

JUDSON SERVICES, INC.
2181 Ambleside Dr, Cleveland, OH
44106
Tel.: (216) 791-2004 OH
Web Site:
    http://www.judsonsmartliving.org
Year Founded: 1906
Sales Range: $25-49.9 Million
Emp.: 527
Elder Care Services
N.A.I.C.S.: 624120
James J. Carnovale (CFO & Sr VP-
Fin)
Cynthia H. Dunn (Pres & CEO)
James D. Vail (Asst Sec)
Frank J. Ondus (VP-Community Well-
ness)
Heather L. Freemont (VP-Sls)
Nicole R. Thomas (VP-HR)
William F. Fehrenbach (VP)
Kristina M. Kupre (VP-Mktg)
Mary Lou Mihalek (Mgr-Corp Office)
Sally Moennich (VP-Community
Smart Lvng)

JUDSON'S INC.
1390 13th St SE, Salem, OR 97302-
2512
Tel.: (503) 363-4141
Web Site:
    http://www.judsonsplumbing.com
Sales Range: $10-24.9 Million
Emp.: 75
Air Conditioning System Installation
Services
N.A.I.C.S.: 238220
Rich Ackerman (Owner)

JUDY CONSTRUCTION COM-
PANY INC.
PO Box 457, Cynthiana, KY 41031-
1509
Tel.: (859) 234-6900 KY
Web Site:
    http://www.judyconstructionco.com
Year Founded: 1974
Sales Range: $25-49.9 Million
Emp.: 150
Provider of Construction Services
N.A.I.C.S.: 237990
Jim Cowley (Treas)
Dale Wilson (VP & Sr Project Mgr)

JUGGERNAUT MANAGEMENT,
LLC
4445 Willard Ave Ste 11, Chevy
Chase, MD 20815-3690
Tel.: (301) 215-7740
Web Site:
    http://www.juggernautcap.com
Intermediation
N.A.I.C.S.: 523910
John D. Shulman (Founder & Mng
Partner)
Craig Hille (Mng Partner)
Chuck Dieveney (Mng Dir)
Alex Deegan (Principal)
Benton Lee (Principal)
Kevin Kuntz (CFO)
Andrew Mueller (VP)
Ryan Osgood (VP)
Cheryl Snyder (Mgr-Bus)

Subsidiaries:

French Transit Ltd. (1)
398 Beach Rd, Burlingame, CA 94010-2004
Tel.: (800) 829-7825
Web Site: http://www.thecrystal.com

Drugs & Druggists' Sundries Merchant Whslr
N.A.I.C.S.: 424210

Mitchell & Ness Nostalgia Company (1)
121 S Broad St 4th Fl, Philadelphia, PA 19107
Tel.: (267) 765-0663
Web Site: http://www.mitchellandness.com
Vintage Sports Jerseys & Memorabilia Mfr
N.A.I.C.S.: 459110
Peter Capolino (Founder)

JUHL ENERGY, INC.
1502 17th St SE, Pipestone, MN 56164
Tel.: (507) 562-8090   DE
Web Site: http://www.juhlenergy.com
Year Founded: 2006
Sales Range: $10-24.9 Million
Emp.: 60
Renewable Energy & Wind Farm Development
N.A.I.C.S.: 237130
Daniel J. Juhl (Chm & CEO)
John P. Mitola (Pres)
Corey Juhl (VP-Project Dev)
Tyler Juhl (VP-Energy Svcs)
John J. Brand (CFO)
Clay Norrborm (Mng Dir-Juhl Renewable Assets, Inc.)
Aaron Thibert (VP-Juhl Renewable Energy Sys)

JUICE COMMUNICATIONS
1824 Lincoln St, Denver, CO 80203-1009
Tel.: (303) 629-0565
Year Founded: 1998
Sales Range: $10-24.9 Million
Emp.: 9
Advetising Agency
N.A.I.C.S.: 541810
Renee Doubleday (Acct Supvr)

JUICE TECHNOLOGIES, LLC
990 W Third Ave, Columbus, OH 43212
Tel.: (800) 518-5576
Web Site: http://www.plugsmart.com
Year Founded: 2008
Sales Range: $1-9.9 Million
Emp.: 25
Technology & Energy Solutions, Including Self-Funding Energy Efficiency, Renewable Energy & Power Generation
N.A.I.C.S.: 221122
David B. Zehala (Pres)

JUICEBLENDZ INTERNA-TIONAL INC.
2893 Executive Park Dr, Weston, FL 33331
Tel.: (954) 217-3014
Web Site: http://www.juiceblendz.com
Sales Range: $1-9.9 Million
Emp.: 90
Smoothie Mfr & Retailer; Retail Store Franchisor
N.A.I.C.S.: 311999
Adam Ogden (Founder & CEO)

JUJAMCYN THEATRES CORP.
246 W 44th St, New York, NY 10036
Tel.: (212) 840-8181
Web Site: http://www.jujamcyn.com
Rev.: $24,100,000
Emp.: 450
Theater Building, Ownership & Operation
N.A.I.C.S.: 531120
Jordan Roth (Pres)

JUKONSKI TRUCK SALES AND SERVICE
66 Thomas St, Middletown, CT 06457
Tel.: (860) 344-0341
Web Site: http://www.mitsutruck.com
Rev.: $13,000,000
Emp.: 77
General Truck Repair
N.A.I.C.S.: 811111
Richard Jukonski Sr. (Pres & CEO)

JULIA DYCKMAN ANDRUS MEMORIAL, INC.
1156 N Broadway, Yonkers, NY 10701
Tel.: (914) 965-3700   NY
Web Site:
    http://www.andruschildren.org
Year Founded: 1974
Sales Range: $25-49.9 Million
Emp.: 861
Child & Family Care Services
N.A.I.C.S.: 624190
Bryan R. Murphy (Pres & CEO)
Kerron D. Norman (Chief Program Officer & VP)
Deborah A. Clark (Sec)
John P. McLaughlin (Chm)
Steven J. Friedman (Treas)
Thomas J. Condon (Vice Chm)
Carter Kahle (Dir-Clinical Svcs-Day Program)
Christine Novak Micka (VP-Institutional Advancement)
Christine Monroe (CFO & VP)
Frances Clayton (Dir-Early Learning Center)
Leslie Zeller (Dir-Admissions & Campus Programs)
Pauline Del Rosario (Asst Dir-Residential Svcs)
Rosario Velez (Dir-Facilities)
Sandra Vilar-Ferreir (Dir-Clinical Svcs-Residential)
Siobhan Masterson (Sr Dir-Campus Programs)
Tito Del Pilar (VP-HR & Knowledge)

JULIAN ELECTRIC INC.
406 Plaza Dr, Westmont, IL 60559
Tel.: (630) 920-8951
Web Site:
    http://www.julianelectric.com
Year Founded: 1959
Sales Range: $10-24.9 Million
Emp.: 80
Battery Cable Wiring Sets For Internal Combustion Engines
N.A.I.C.S.: 336320
Kenneth A. Julian (Pres)

JULIAN FREIRICH CO. INC.
815 W Kerr St, Salisbury, NC 28144
Tel.: (704) 636-2621
Web Site: http://www.freirich.com
Sales Range: $10-24.9 Million
Emp.: 50
Prepared Beef Products Mfr
N.A.I.C.S.: 424470
Denais Arrasmith (Gen Mgr)

JULIAN GOLD INC.
4109 McCullough Ave, San Antonio, TX 78212
Tel.: (210) 824-2493
Web Site: http://www.juliangold.com
Sales Range: $50-74.9 Million
Emp.: 50
Dress Shops
N.A.I.C.S.: 458110
Robert E. Gurwitz (Pres)
Kathy Beaman (Controller)
Fran Stamper (VP & Mgr-Mdsg)

JULIAN LUMBER CO. INC.
Hwy 3 E, Antlers, OK 74523
Tel.: (580) 587-2735
Sales Range: $10-24.9 Million
Emp.: 60
Lumber Sales
N.A.I.C.S.: 321114
Derek Porter (Pres)

JULIANI KENNEY INVEST-MENT CAPITAL, LLC
61 N Beacon St 2nd Fl, Boston, MA 02134
Tel.: (781) 727-1015
Web Site: http://www.jkicorp.com
Sales Range: $1-9.9 Million
Real Estate Investment & Development Services
N.A.I.C.S.: 523999
Richard Juliani (Principal)

JULIE A. LAITIN ENTER-PRISES, INC.
708 3rd Ave 13th Fl, New York, NY 10017
Tel.: (212) 286-2424
Year Founded: 1982
Sales Range: $10-24.9 Million
Emp.: 5
N.A.I.C.S.: 541810
Julie A. Laitin (Pres)

JULIETTE FOWLER HOMES INC.
1234 Abrams Rd, Dallas, TX 75214
Tel.: (214) 827-0813   TX
Web Site:
    http://www.fowlerhomes.org
Year Founded: 1892
Sales Range: $10-24.9 Million
Emp.: 322
Child & Elderly People Assistance Services
N.A.I.C.S.: 624110
Ann McKinley (Exec Dir-Mission Advancement)
Nicole Gann (COO)
Sabrina R. Porter (Pres & CEO)
Billie Collins (Exec Dir-Affordable Housing)
Diana Patten (Exec Dir-Assisted Living & Healthcare Svcs)
Kristen Mazza (Exec Dir-Independent Living & Youth Svcs)
Roland T. Bandy Jr. (Chm)

JULISKA
465 Canal St, Stamford, CT 06902
Tel.: (203) 316-0212
Web Site: http://www.juliska.com
Sales Range: $10-24.9 Million
Emp.: 55
Home Furnishing Merchant Whslr
N.A.I.C.S.: 423220
David Gooding (Founder)
O. Virginia Smart (Mgr-Distr Center)
Cindy Fino (Mgr-HR)
Virginia Fournier (Mgr-Warehouse)
Rita Rosenblum (Dir-Sls)

JULIUS BRANSCOME INC.
7812 Bethlehem Rd, Manassas, VA 20109-2716
Tel.: (703) 590-3600
Sales Range: $10-24.9 Million
Emp.: 70
Highway & Street Construction Contracting Services
N.A.I.C.S.: 237310
Kevin Huddleston (Mgr-HR)

JULIUS SCHEPPS COMPANY, INC.
500 Montezuma Ave Ste 200 C, Santa Fe, NM 87501-2590
Tel.: (505) 983-9136   NM
Year Founded: 1934
Sales Range: $10-24.9 Million
Emp.: 54

Provider of Subdivision & Developing Services
N.A.I.C.S.: 237210
Joseph Schepps (Pres)

Subsidiaries:

Schepps New Mexico Development Corp. (1)
500 Montezuma Ave Ste 200C, Santa Fe, NM 87501-2590
Tel.: (505) 983-9136
Web Site: http://www.sanbusco.com
Sales Range: $10-24.9 Million
Emp.: 15
Provider of Real Estate Agent & Managing Services
N.A.I.C.S.: 531210

JUMBOSHRIMP ADVERTISING INC.
431 Bryant St, San Francisco, CA 94107
Tel.: (415) 369-0500
Web Site:
    http://www.jumboshrimp.com
Sales Range: $10-24.9 Million
Emp.: 15
Advetising Agency
N.A.I.C.S.: 541810
Steve Perham (Dir-Creative & Art)

JUMP DESIGN GROUP
1400 Broadway 2nd Floor, New York, NY 10118
Tel.: (212) 869-3300
Web Site:
    http://www.jumpdesigngroup.com
Apparels Retailer & Mfr
N.A.I.C.S.: 315990
Ashesh Amin (CEO)

Subsidiaries:

Cathy Daniels Ltd. (1)
1411 Broadway M, New York, NY 10018-3402
Tel.: (212) 354-1600
Women's Apparel Sales
N.A.I.C.S.: 315250

Marina, Inc. (1)
1400 Broadway Ste 201, New York, NY 10018
Tel.: (212) 869-3300
Sales Range: $1-9.9 Million
Emp.: 9
Apparel Whslr
N.A.I.C.S.: 424350

JUMP INC.
6725 Academy Rd NE, Albuquerque, NM 87109
Tel.: (505) 857-2276
Web Site:
    http://www.cblegacynm.com
Sales Range: $10-24.9 Million
Emp.: 150
Real Estate Leasing & Rentals
N.A.I.C.S.: 531210
Michael Carter (Co-Owner)

JUMP!
1417 Mayson St, Atlanta, GA 30324
Tel.: (404) 574-2910
Web Site: http://www.jumphi.com
Sales Range: Less than $1 Million
Emp.: 10
N.A.I.C.S.: 541810
Matt Thomason (Dir-Sls & Mktg)
Rob Jameson (Pres)
Trent Thurman (Dir-Creative)

JUMP2 GROUP
6620 Cypresswood Dr Ste 120, Spring, TX 77379
Tel.: (832) 717-4331
Web Site:
    http://www.jump2group.com
Year Founded: 2001

Jump2 Group—(Continued)

Sales Range: $1-9.9 Million
Emp.: 5
Advertising Agencies
N.A.I.C.S.: 541810
Mary Kuna (Owner)
Diana Jaques (Owner)

JUN CERAMIC, INC.

9001 Fullbright Ave, Chatsworth, CA 91311
Tel.: (747) 224-0600
CA
Web Site: http://www.cepactile.com
Year Founded: 1989
Sales Range: $1-9.9 Million
Porcelain Mosaic Tile Distr
N.A.I.C.S.: 423320
Katsura Watanabe (CEO)

JUNCO STEEL CORPORATION

Minillas Industrial Park 155 8th St, Bayamon, PR 00960
Tel.: (787) 798-1000
Web Site: http://www.juncosteel.com
Sales Range: $10-24.9 Million
Emp.: 45
Steel
N.A.I.C.S.: 332996
Miguel Torregrosa (Pres)

JUNCTION INTERNATIONAL, LLC

9760 Roche Place, West Palm Beach, FL 33414
Tel.: (646) 688-3048
Web Site:
    http://www.junctioninternational.com
Year Founded: 2008
Sales Range: $1-9.9 Million
Emp.: 20
Multilingual Translation Services
N.A.I.C.S.: 541930
Andres Volosin (Co-Founder, VP & CTO)
Claudia Waitman (Co-Founder, Pres & CEO)

JUNCTION SOLUTIONS, INC.

4643 S Ulster St Suite 400, Denver, CO 80237
Tel.: (888) 403-3533
CO
Web Site:
    http://www.junctionsolutions.com
Year Founded: 2002
Sales Range: $25-49.9 Million
Emp.: 191
Reseller of Microsoft Dynamics AX with Industry-Specific ERP Solutions & Services for Retail, Food, Beverage, CPG & Life Sciences Manufacturers
N.A.I.C.S.: 513210
Jeff Grell (Co-Founder, Pres & CEO)
Nick Bova (COO)
George Casey (CTO & CMO)
Jeff Allen (CFO)
Christian Hutter (Exec VP-Products & Strategy)
Shawn Conway (Chief Supply Chain Officer)
Jeff Verhagen (CIO)
Doug Bolen (Controller)
Greg Smith (Controller)
Jim Poulin (CTO)
Bill Heston (Dir-Info)
Bob McCullough (Grp VP-Mfg)
Kevin Krieger (Mgr-IT)
Nathan Hoffman (Sr VP)
Joe DeHaai (VP-Sls)
Paul Webb (VP-Tech)

JUNEAU BIOSCIENCES, LLC

2749 E Parleys Way Ste 300, Salt Lake City, UT 84109
Tel.: (801) 231-7147
UT

Web Site:
    http://www.juneaubiosciences.com
Year Founded: 2007
Medical Diagnostic Testing Services
N.A.I.C.S.: 621512
Kenneth Ward (Founder & CEO)
Hans Albertsen (Chief Scientific Officer)

JUNGCLAUS-CAMPBELL CO. INC.

825 Massachusetts Ave, Indianapolis, IN 46204
Tel.: (317) 264-6655
Web Site: http://www.jungclaus.com
Rev.: $20,856,343
Emp.: 15
Institutional Building Construction
N.A.I.C.S.: 236220
F. Timothy Nagler (Pres)
Allen Garrrett (CFO)

JUNGE FORD INC.

1001 Ford Ln, Center Point, IA 52213
Tel.: (319) 849-2022
Web Site: http://www.junge.com
Rev.: $11,300,000
Emp.: 40
New Car Dealers
N.A.I.C.S.: 441110
Gary L. Junge (Owner, Pres & Co-CEO)
Jason Junge (Owner, Co-CEO, Treas & Sec)

JUNGE LINCOLN MERCURY INC.

1510 Collins Rd NE, Cedar Rapids, IA 52402-2413
Tel.: (319) 393-6500
Year Founded: 1976
Sales Range: $10-24.9 Million
Emp.: 45
Car Whslr
N.A.I.C.S.: 441110
Jason Junge (Gen Mgr)

JUNGS TRUCKING, INC.

201 W Air Cargo Way, Milwaukee, WI 53207-6013
Tel.: (414) 747-0100
WI
Web Site:
    http://www.junglogistics.com
Year Founded: 1993
Sales Range: $1-9.9 Million
Emp.: 25
Trucking Service
N.A.I.C.S.: 484110
John Jung (Pres)

JUNIOR GALLERY LTD.

463 7th Ave, New York, NY 10018-7604
Tel.: (212) 273-8800
NY
Web Site: http://www.jgallery.com
Sales Range: $200-249.9 Million
Emp.: 350
Women's & Junior's Outerwear Mfr
N.A.I.C.S.: 424350

JUNIOR'S BUILDING MATERIALS, INC.

7574 Battlefield Pkwy, Ringgold, GA 30736
Tel.: (706) 937-3400
Web Site:
    http://www.juniorsmaterials.com
Sales Range: $10-24.9 Million
Emp.: 40
Building Materials Whslr
N.A.I.C.S.: 444180
Jason Boehm (CFO)
Otto Boehm III (Sec)
Otto W. Boehm Jr. (CEO)

JUNIPER ELBOW CO. INC.

7215 Metropolitan Ave, Middle Village, NY 11379
Tel.: (718) 326-2546
Web Site:
    http://www.juniperindustries.com
Rev.: $19,300,000
Emp.: 185
Elbows for Air Ducts, Stovepipes & Sheet Metal Mfr
N.A.I.C.S.: 332322
Elliot Wiener (VP)

JUNIPER GROUP, INC.

20283 State Rd Ste 400, Boca Raton, FL 33498
Tel.: (561) 829-4670
NV
Web Site:
    http://www.junipergroup.com
Year Founded: 1997
Sales Range: $1-9.9 Million
Emp.: 6
Broadband Installer & Wireless Infrastructure Construction Services
N.A.I.C.S.: 237130
Vlado P. Hreljanovic (Chm, CEO, CFO & Sec)

JUNIPER INVESTMENT COMPANY, LLC

555 Madison Ave 24th Fl, New York, NY 10022-3315
Tel.: (212) 339-8500
DE
Web Site:
    http://www.juniperfunds.com
Year Founded: 2007
Alternative Investment Funds, Private Equity & Merchant Banking Services
N.A.I.C.S.: 523999
Alexis P. Michas (Founder & Mng Partner)
John A. Bartholdson (Co-Founder & Partner)
Nassos Michas (Chm)
Edward C. Reeves (Principal)
George B. Moore (Partner)

Subsidiaries:

Newton Capital Partners, L.P.   (1)
555 Madison Ave 24th Fl, New York, NY 10022
Tel.: (212) 339-8555
Web Site: http://www.newtoncapital.net
Alternative Investment Fund
N.A.I.C.S.: 525910

Theragenics Corporation   (1)
5203 Bristol Industrial Way, Buford, GA 30518-1799
Tel.: (770) 831-5137
Web Site: http://www.theragenics.com
Sales Range: $75-99.9 Million
Emp.: 534
Radioactive Implants for Disease Treatment
N.A.I.C.S.: 334515
Francis J. Tarallo (CEO)

Subsidiary (Domestic):

CP Medical   (2)
803 NE 25th Ave, Portland, OR 97232
Tel.: (503) 232-1555
Web Site: http://www.cpmedical.com
Sales Range: $25-49.9 Million
Emp.: 100
Medical Supplies
N.A.I.C.S.: 339112
Janet Zeman (Pres)

Galt Medical Corp.   (2)
2220 Merritt Dr, Garland, TX 75041
Tel.: (972) 271-5177
Web Site: http://www.galtmedical.com
Sales Range: $100-124.9 Million
Emp.: 50
Develops, Manufactures & Markets Disposable Medical Devices Used for Vascular Access
N.A.I.C.S.: 339112
Mark Kesti (VP-Sls)

JUNIPER LANDSCAPING, INC.

5880 Staley Rd, Fort Myers, FL 33905
Tel.: (239) 561-5980
FL
Web Site: https://junipercares.com
Year Founded: 1981
Custom Home Landscape Services
N.A.I.C.S.: 541320
Michael Duke (Owner)
Dan DeMont (VP)
Jake Rubin (COO)
Jason Gilmore (CFO)
Stacie Trace (Chief HR Officer)

Subsidiaries:

Rips Professional Lawn Care, Inc.   (1)
511 N Arnold Hwy 79, Panama City Beach, FL 32413-2413
Tel.: (850) 233-6396
Web Site: http://www.ripsprolawncare.com
Landscaping Services
N.A.I.C.S.: 561730
Debra K. Thompson (VP)

JUNK MY CAR, LLC

4 Corporate Dr Ste 386, Shelton, CT 06484
Web Site: http://www.junkmycar.com
Year Founded: 2004
Sales Range: $10-24.9 Million
Emp.: 52
Vehicle Purchasing, Removal & Recycling Services
N.A.I.C.S.: 488410
Tim Yarosh (Owner & Pres)

JUNO INVESTMENTS LLC

950 3rd Ave Ste 2300, New York, NY 10022
Tel.: (212) 688-2700
Web Site:
    http://www.junoinvestments.com
Privater Equity Firm
N.A.I.C.S.: 523999
James Haber (Co-Founder & Mng Dir)
John Huber (Co-Founder & Mng Dir)
Philip L. Kampf Jr. (Mng Dir)

Subsidiaries:

AO Precision Manufacturing LLC   (1)
1870 Mason Ave, Daytona Beach, FL 32117
Tel.: (386) 274-5882
Web Site: http://www.aopmfg.com
Sales Range: $75-99.9 Million
Emp.: 220
Firearms, Defense, Aerospace & Other Industrial Products Mfr
N.A.I.C.S.: 332994
Steven C. Torma (CEO)

Optim Incorporated   (1)
64 Technology Park, Sturbridge, MA 01566
Tel.: (508) 347-5100
Web Site: http://www.optimnet.com
Sales Range: $50-74.9 Million
Emp.: 50
Medical & Industrial Fiber Optic Imaging Equipment Mfr
N.A.I.C.S.: 334310

Southeastern Metal Products LLC   (1)
1420 Metals Dr, Charlotte, NC 28206-1331
Tel.: (704) 596-4017
Web Site: http://www.semplic.com
Sales Range: $25-49.9 Million
Emp.: 100
Metal Component Stamping, Welding & Fabrication
N.A.I.C.S.: 332119
Tim Hagen (CFO)
Calvin Scercy (Coord-Safety)

JUNO TECHNOLOGY CORPORATION

154 Toledo St, Farmingdale, NY 11735
Tel.: (631) 300-1000
Sales Range: $10-24.9 Million

Telecommunications & Information Technology Systems Integration Services
N.A.I.C.S.: 541519
David Giangano *(Co-Founder & Pres)*
Joseph Fuccillo *(Pres & CTO)*
Edmond Baydian *(Chief Svc Officer)*
Anthony Fernandez *(CFO)*
Joseph Cassano *(Exec VP-Sls)*
Frances Vinci *(Co-Founder & Exec VP-Bus Dev)*

JUNONIA LTD.
1355 Mendota Heights Rd Ste 290, Saint Paul, MN 55120-1285
Tel.: (651) 365-1830
Web Site: http://www.junonia.com
Sales Range: $10-24.9 Million
Emp.: 20
Women's Clothing Retailer
N.A.I.C.S.: 315250
Anne Kelly *(Founder & Chm)*
Shanti Shah *(Owner)*

JUNTO DESIGN STUDIO, LLC
101 S Franklin St Ste 203, Tampa, FL 33602
Tel.: (813) 390-8125
Web Site: http://www.juntods.com
Sales Range: $1-9.9 Million
Architectural & Interior Design Services
N.A.I.C.S.: 541310
Bill Rapp *(Principal)*
John Mistretta *(Principal)*

JUNXURE
3651 Trust Dr, Raleigh, NC 27616
Web Site: http://www.junxure.com
Year Founded: 2000
Sales Range: $1-9.9 Million
Emp.: 46
Office Management Software
N.A.I.C.S.: 513210
Greg Friedman *(Pres)*
Ken Golding *(VP)*
John Shangler *(Exec VP)*

JUPE FEEDS, INC.
PO Box 40, Temple, TX 76503
Tel.: (254) 773-5211
Web Site:
http://www.windlandsfarmproducts.com
Sales Range: $10-24.9 Million
Emp.: 35
Animal Feed Mfr
N.A.I.C.S.: 311119
Dennis Jupe *(Dir-Engrg & Environmental Affairs)*
Darren Jupe *(Treas & VP)*

JUPE MILLS, INC.
107 S Roberts St, West, TX 76691
Tel.: (254) 826-5301   TX
Web Site: http://www.westfeeds.com
Year Founded: 1989
Mfr & Distribution of Livestock Feeds
N.A.I.C.S.: 311119
Donna Charanza *(Co-Owner)*
Jerry Charanza *(Co-Owner)*
Lisa Ray *(Mgr-Office/Wholesale)*
Michelle Hutyra *(Mgr-Acctg)*
Cindy Kalina *(Mgr-Retail)*
Callie Poteet *(Mgr-Retail/Wholesale)*
Clarence Talley *(Mgr-Grain)*

JUPITER ALUMINUM CORPORATION
1745 165th St, Hammond, IN 46320-2805
Tel.: (219) 932-3322   IN
Web Site:
http://www.jupiteraluminum.com
Year Founded: 1992
Sales Range: $10-24.9 Million
Emp.: 100
Mfr of Aluminum Extruded Products
N.A.I.C.S.: 331318
Dietrich M. Gross *(Founder)*

Subsidiaries:
Jupiter Aluminum Corporation - Jupiter Coil Coating Division   (1)
205 E Carey St, Fairland, IN 46126
Tel.: (317) 835-2247
Web Site: http://www.jupiteraluminum.com
Coil Coating Services
N.A.I.C.S.: 332812
Paul Henry Chevalier *(Pres)*

JUPITER CHEVROLET, LP.
116 11 OBJ Freeway, Garland, TX 75041
Tel.: (972) 271-9900
Web Site:
http://www.jupiterchevy.com
Sales Range: $25-49.9 Million
Emp.: 96
Car Whslr
N.A.I.C.S.: 441110
Michael Matetich Jr. *(Pres & CEO)*

JUPITER REALTY CORPORATION
401 N Michigan Ave, Chicago, IL 60611
Tel.: (312) 642-6000
Web Site:
http://www.jupiterrealty.com
Year Founded: 1985
Sales Range: $10-24.9 Million
Emp.: 7
Real Estate Development Services
N.A.I.C.S.: 237210
Donald A. Smith *(Chm & CEO)*
E. Michael Pompizzi *(Pres & CFO)*
Jerry J. Ong *(Exec VP)*

JURUPA COMMUNITY SERVICES DISTRICT
11201 Harrel St, Mira Loma, CA 91752
Tel.: (951) 685-7434
Web Site: http://www.jcsd.us
Emp.: 100
Water, Sewer & Street Lights Facilities
N.A.I.C.S.: 221310
Jane Anderson *(Chm)*
Chad Blais *(VP)*
Todd M. Corbin *(Gen Mgr)*
Chris Berch *(Gen Mgr)*

JUS BY JULIE LLC
1212 Ave M, Brooklyn, NY 11210
Tel.: (718) 375-1121   NY
Web Site: http://www.jusbyjulie.com
Year Founded: 2014
Sales Range: $10-24.9 Million
Emp.: 40
Food & Beverage Product Mfr
N.A.I.C.S.: 311412
Julie Maleh *(Founder)*

JUST ADD PLASTICS INC.
5322 Essex Farms Pl, Stone Mountain, GA 30088
Tel.: (770) 981-3244
Web Site:
http://www.justaddplastic.com
Year Founded: 1986
Sales Range: $10-24.9 Million
Emp.: 20
Industrial Machinery & Equipment Mfr
N.A.I.C.S.: 423830

JUST ANOTHER ACQUISITION CORP.
122 E 42nd St Unit 2105, New York, NY 10168
Tel.: (212) 277-5300   DE
Year Founded: 2021
Investment Services
N.A.I.C.S.: 523999
Philip Wagenheim *(Chm, CEO & CFO)*

JUST BORN, INC.
1300 Stefko Blvd, Bethlehem, PA 18017-6620
Tel.: (800) 445-5787
Web Site: http://www.justborn.com
Year Founded: 1923
Candy Mfr
N.A.I.C.S.: 311340
David L. Yale *(Pres & COO)*
Matthew Pye *(VP-Sls & Mktg)*

JUST FABULOUS, INC.
2301 Rosecrans Ave Ste 4100, El Segundo, CA 90245-4993
Tel.: (310) 683-0938
Web Site: http://www.justfab.com
Year Founded: 2010
Sales Range: $75-99.9 Million
Emp.: 375
Online Fashion Retailer
N.A.I.C.S.: 424340
Adam Goldenberg *(Co-CEO)*
Don Ressler *(Co-CEO)*
Nina Fuhrman *(Chief Merchant Officer)*
Laura Joukovski *(Pres)*

Subsidiaries:
ShoeDazzle.com, Inc.   (1)
800 Apollo St, El Segundo, CA 90245
Web Site: http://www.shoedazzle.com
Sales Range: $75-99.9 Million
Emp.: 200
Women's Shoes, Handbags & Jewelry Retailer
N.A.I.C.S.: 458210
Nina Fuhrman *(Chief Merchant Officer)*
Laura Joukovski *(Pres)*

JUST FOR WRAPS
5745 Ricken Backer Rd, Commerce, CA 90040-1605
Tel.: (213) 239-0503
Web Site: http://www.wrapper.com
Rev.: $30,204,905
Emp.: 400
Provider of Women's Sportswear
N.A.I.C.S.: 315250
Vrajesh Lal *(Pres)*
Carlos Villalobos *(Mgr-IT)*

JUST KID, INC.
27 Ann St, Norwalk, CT 06854
Tel.: (203) 358-2120
Web Site: http://www.justkidinc.com
Year Founded: 1993
Rev.: $10,000,000
Emp.: 20
Media Buying Services
N.A.I.C.S.: 541830
George Carey *(Founder & CEO)*
Laurie Klein *(VP)*
Bruce Miller *(Chief Creative Officer)*
Janet Oak *(Mng Partner-Strategy & Innovation)*
Tiina Salzberg *(Mng Dir-Strategy & Innovation)*

JUST LIKE FAMILY HOME CARE, LLC
3200 Bailey Ln Ste 117, Naples, FL 34105
Tel.: (239) 431-6661
Web Site:
http://www.justlikefamilyhomecare.com
Sales Range: $10-24.9 Million
Emp.: 15
Women Healthcare Services
N.A.I.C.S.: 621610

Jacob Nassberg *(Co-Owner)*
Elsabeth Nassberg *(Co-Owner)*
Lauren McKyton *(Dir-Nursing)*
Pat Erickson *(Mgr-Acct)*

JUST MEDIA, INC.
6001 Shellmound St Ste 700, Emeryville, CA 94608
Tel.: (510) 740-2300   CA
Web Site: http://www.justmedia.com
Year Founded: 1997
Sales Range: $25-49.9 Million
Emp.: 13
Media Buying Services
N.A.I.C.S.: 541810
Deborah Lauzardo *(Sr VP-Fin)*
Brandon Friesen *(CEO)*
Daniel Lorenze *(Head-Content Creation)*
Elizabeth Dawson *(Creative Dir)*
Joe Parente *(CFO)*
Alan Burgis *(COO)*
Heather Fitzgerald *(Sr VP-Strategy & Analytics-Global)*

Subsidiaries:
Just Media Ltd.   (1)
90 Whitfield St, London, W1T 4EZ, United Kingdom
Tel.: (44) 207 803 4400
Web Site: http://www.justmedia.co.uk
Media Buying Services, Strategic Planning/Research
N.A.I.C.S.: 541830
Andy Emptage *(Grp Acct Dir)*
Jacqui Seddon *(Mng Dir)*
Paul Hutt *(Acct Dir-Media)*
Simon Fung *(Dir-Accts)*

JUST MY SHOPPING INC.
2168 3rd Ave, New York, NY 10035
Tel.: (212) 996-6979
Web Site:
http://www.measuredup.com
Year Founded: 2000
Rev.: $2,000,000
Emp.: 7
Shopper's Reviewing Services
N.A.I.C.S.: 455219
David Oreily *(CEO)*
Ron Williams *(Mgr)*

JUST PLAY PRODUCTS, LLC
4850 T-Rex Ave, Ste 100,, Boca Raton, FL 33431
Tel.: (800) 317-3245
Web Site:
https://justplayproducts.com
Year Founded: 2010
Toy Product Mfr
N.A.I.C.S.: 339930
Geoffrey Greenberg *(Co-CEO)*

Subsidiaries:
Tara Toy Corp.   (1)
40 Adams Ave, Hauppauge, NY 11788
Tel.: (631) 273-8697
Web Site: http://taratoy.com
Sales Range: $1-9.9 Million
Emp.: 100
Luggage
N.A.I.C.S.: 316990
Bruce Pearl *(Pres)*
Brooke Rabinowitz *(Acct Mgr-Natl)*

JUST RITE ACOUSTICS INC.
1501 Estes Ave, Elk Grove Village, IL 60007
Tel.: (847) 357-8200
Web Site:
http://www.justriteacoustics.com
Rev.: $18,904,021
Emp.: 135
Provider of Acoustical & Ceiling Work
N.A.I.C.S.: 238310
Brad Swaback *(Pres)*
Bob Dixon *(Project Mgr-Specialty)*

Just Rite Acoustics Inc.—(Continued)

David Martin (Project Mgr & Acct Mgr)
Dennis Klich (Mgr-Pur)
Randy Benner (Project Mgr)
Jeff Harbeck (Mgr-Acct)
Jamie Harrison (VP & Mgr-Sls)

JUSTBETTERCARS.COM INC.
901 Riverside Ave, Roseville, CA 95678-4338
Tel.: (916) 782-4445
Web Site:
http://www.justbettercars.com
Sales Range: $10-24.9 Million
Emp.: 6
Car Whslr
N.A.I.C.S.: 441110
Eric Fischer (CEO)
Holly Fischer (Sec)
Brian Zambrano (COO)

JUSTICE FAMILY GROUP, LLC
PO Box 2170, Beaver, WV 25813
Tel.: (304) 252-1074
Sales Range: $10-24.9 Million
Emp.: 5
Resort Operator
N.A.I.C.S.: 721110
Jim Justice (Owner)

Subsidiaries:

The Greenbrier   (1)
101 Main St W, White Sulphur Springs, WV 24986-2414   (100%)
Tel.: (304) 536-1110
Web Site: http://www.greenbrier.com
Hotel Operator
N.A.I.C.S.: 721110
Cindi Napier (Dir-Grp Sls)
Greg Furlong (VP-Sls & Event Svcs)
Joyce Wood (Dir-Natl Sls)
Tom Gardinier (Reg Sls Mgr-All Golf & Sports Grp)
Tom McNeill (Dir-Natl Sls)

JUSTICE RESOURCE INSTITUTE INC
160 Gould St Ste 300, Needham, MA 02494-2300
Tel.: (781) 559-4900   MA
Web Site: http://www.jri.org
Year Founded: 1973
Sales Range: $100-124.9 Million
Emp.: 2,130
Community Health Care Services
N.A.I.C.S.: 624190
Mia DeMarco (COO)
Stephanie Ward (VP)
Jennifer L. Miguel (Exec VP)
Bisser Dokov (CFO)
John Gatto (Sr VP-Community Health)
Patti Maguire (Sr VP)
Mark Schueppert (Gen Counsel & VP-HR)
Joseph Spinazzola (VP-Behavioral Health & Trauma Svcs)
Andy Pond (Pres)
Kari E. Beserra (Exec VP)
Stacey Forrest (Asst Exec Dir-Connecticut)
Sean Rose (Exec Dir-Connecticut)

JUSTICEWORKS YOUTHCARE INC.
1500 Ardmore Blvd Ste 410, Pittsburgh, PA 15221
Tel.: (510) 418-2422
Web Site:
http://www.justiceworksyouth
care.com
Year Founded: 1999
Sales Range: $1-9.9 Million
Emp.: 206

In-Home & Community Service Care for Juvenile Offenders
N.A.I.C.S.: 624110
Dan Heit (Founder)
Errone Cody (Dir-Western PA)
Dipesh Chauhan (Program Dir-Dev)
Dana Malin (Dir-HR)
Renee Kresge (Program Dir-Northeast)
Marc A. Maddy (Program Dir-Evaluation & Quality Assurance)
Jeffrey Ralph (Dir-Southeast PA)
Theresa Fonaliedas (Program Dir-Pike County)
Hilary Maugham (Dir-Program-York County)
Lisa Snyder (Dir-Indiana County)
Jennifer Wingard (Program Dir-Jefferson & Clarion County)
Matthew Kurowsky (Program Dir-Washington County)
Emily Knauer (Program Dir-Dauphin County)
Sean Lazarus (Program Dir-Adams County)
Ian Nutt (Program Dir-Lycoming County)
Amber Stewart (Dir-Westmoreland & Amstrong Counties)

JUSTISS OIL COMPANY, INC.
1120 E Oak St, Jena, LA 71342-3904
Tel.: (318) 992-4111   LA
Web Site: http://www.justissoil.com
Year Founded: 1946
Sales Range: $300-349.9 Million
Emp.: 400
Extractor of Oil & Gas; Producer of Fabricated Metal Products
N.A.I.C.S.: 213111
Wayne Pritchard (Mgr-Drilling Ops)
W. B. McCartney (Exec VP)
Michael Joy (Mgr-HR & HSE)
Adam Williams (VP-Bus Dev)
Justin Brixey (Mgr-Drilling Ops)
Logan Raborn (Mgr-Production Ops)
James F. Justiss Jr. (Pres)

Subsidiaries:

Baker/Altech   (1)
100 Hwy 64 E, Arp, TX 75750
Tel.: (903) 859-2111
Web Site: http://www.bakeraltech.com
Sales Range: $10-24.9 Million
Emp.: 130
Repair of Storage Tanks Mfr
N.A.I.C.S.: 332420
Ernest E. Maddox (VP-Mfg)

JUUT HOLDINGS INC.
310 Groveland Ave, Minneapolis, MN 55403
Tel.: (612) 676-2250
Web Site: http://www.juut.com
Sales Range: $10-24.9 Million
Emp.: 400
Holding Company; Salon Operator
N.A.I.C.S.: 551112

JUVO TECHNOLOGIES, LLC
518 Main St, Hattiesburg, MS 39401
Tel.: (888) 300-1853
Web Site: http://www.juvotec.com
Year Founded: 2007
Telecom Expense Management & Other Telecommunications Services
N.A.I.C.S.: 517810

JV SMITH COMPANIES
701 W 16th St Ste 101, Yuma, AZ 85364
Tel.: (928) 783-4479
Web Site:
http://www.jvsmithcompanies.com
Sales Range: $50-74.9 Million
Emp.: 85

Other Vegetable & Melon Farming Services
N.A.I.C.S.: 111219
Terre Catanzaro (Chief Admin Officer)
Randy Bache (COO)
Austin Savage (CFO)

JVC BROADCASTING CORP.
3075 Veterans Memorial Hwy Ste 201, Ronkonkoma, NY 11779
Tel.: (631) 648-2500
Web Site:
http://www.jvcbroadcasting.com
Year Founded: 2008
Sales Range: $25-49.9 Million
Radio Broadcasting
N.A.I.C.S.: 516110
Vic Latino (COO & VP)
Steve Harper (Dir-Special Events)

JVC CORPORATION
305 Rte 73 N, Marlton, NJ 08053
Tel.: (856) 983-2222
Web Site:
http://www.marltonjoacanals.com
Rev.: $10,000,000
Emp.: 20
Liquor Stores
N.A.I.C.S.: 445320
Joseph Canal (CEO)

JVIS USA LLC
52048 Shelby Pkwy, Shelby, MI 48315
Tel.: (586) 884-5700
Web Site: http://www.jvisusallc.com
Year Founded: 2006
Sales Range: $25-49.9 Million
Emp.: 600
Engineering Design, Tooling Services & Automotive Components Mfr
N.A.I.C.S.: 336390
Jason Murar (Pres & CEO)

Subsidiaries:

JVIS Manufacturing   (1)
1285 N Crystal Ave, Benton Harbor, MI 49022-9215
Tel.: (269) 927-8200
Molded Auto Interior Components Mfr
N.A.I.C.S.: 336390

JVK CONSTRUCTORS LLC.
7127 Crossroads Blvd Ste 105, Brentwood, TN 37027
Tel.: (615) 309-4949
Web Site:
http://www.jvkconstructors.com
Sales Range: $10-24.9 Million
Emp.: 7
Nonresidential Construction Services
N.A.I.C.S.: 236220
Tom Ellis (VP)

JVKELLYGROUP, INC.
145 E Main St, Huntington, NY 11743
Tel.: (631) 427-2888   NY
Web Site: http://www.jvkg.com
Year Founded: 2002
Sales Range: $1-9.9 Million
Emp.: 65
Business Consulting Services
N.A.I.C.S.: 541618
James V. Kelly (CEO)
Lawrence Comella (Sr Dir)

JVPK INC.
11040 N 19th Ave, Phoenix, AZ 85029
Tel.: (602) 997-7283
Rev.: $27,200,000
Residential Painting
N.A.I.C.S.: 238320

Subsidiaries:

Pete King Corporation   (1)
11040 N 19th Ave, Phoenix, AZ 85029

Tel.: (602) 944-4441
Web Site: http://www.petekingaz.com
Painting & Paper Hanging
N.A.I.C.S.: 238320

JW ENTERPRISES LTD.
3521 N California Ave, Peoria, IL 61603
Tel.: (309) 681-1600
Sales Range: $75-99.9 Million
Emp.: 350
Magazines
N.A.I.C.S.: 424920

JW OPERATING COMPANY
PO Box 226406, Dallas, TX 75222-6406
Tel.: (972) 233-8191
Web Site: http://www.jwenergy.com
Sales Range: $150-199.9 Million
Emp.: 150
Crude Petroleum Production
N.A.I.C.S.: 211120
Don G. Bizzell (VP)
Jeffery M. Brown (VP-Engrg)

JWALCHER COMMUNICATIONS
2986 Ivy St, San Diego, CA 92104
Tel.: (619) 295-7140
Web Site: http://www.jwalcher.com
Sales Range: Less than $1 Million
Emp.: 5
Collateral, Email, Internet/Web Design, Local Marketing, Magazines, Media Planning, Media Relations, Newspaper, Publicity/Promotions, Radio, T.V.
N.A.I.C.S.: 541810
Laura Walcher (Principal-PR Counsel)
Jean Walcher (Pres)
Sandy Young (Acct Exec)

JWB REAL ESTATE CAPITAL LLC
7563 Philips Hwy Ste 109, Jacksonville, FL 32256
Tel.: (904) 677-6777
Web Site:
http://www.jwbrealestatecapital.com
Year Founded: 2006
Sales Range: $10-24.9 Million
Emp.: 35
Real Estate Development Services
N.A.I.C.S.: 531390
Gregg Cohen (CEO)
Alex Sifakis (Pres)
Adam Rigel (CFO)
Adam Eiseman (COO)
Josh Roberts (Acct Exec)

JWC CONSTRUCTION INC.
2580 Fortune Way, Vista, CA 92081
Tel.: (760) 727-2494
Web Site:
http://www.jwcconstruction.com
Rev.: $10,000,000
Emp.: 75
Residential Construction Services
N.A.I.C.S.: 236115
Jon Wayne (Pres & CEO)

JWCH INSTITUTE, INC.
1910 W Sunset Blvd Ste 650, Los Angeles, CA 90026
Tel.: (213) 484-1186   CA
Web Site: http://www.jwchinstitute.org
Year Founded: 1960
Sales Range: $25-49.9 Million
Emp.: 472
Healtcare Services
N.A.I.C.S.: 622110
Brenda Sandoval (Dir-Ops)
Jeanne Lam (CFO)
Kim Tran (Dir-Quality Improvement)
Paul Gregerson (Chief Medical Officer)
Kathleen J. House (Sec)

Alvaro Ballesteros *(CEO)*
Sergio Avina *(Dir-HIV Svcs & Sub-stance Abuse)*
Keith Terasaki *(Chm)*
Jon Dang *(Dir-IT)*
Mike Johnson *(COO)*
Brenda Wiewel *(VP-Mental Health Svcs)*
Lawrence Fernandez Jr. *(Vice Chm)*

JWD GROUP INC.

300 Colvin Woods Pkwy, Tonawanda, NY 14150
Tel.: (716) 832-1940
Web Site: http://www.jwdanforth.com
Year Founded: 1884
Sales Range: $50-74.9 Million
Emp.: 400
Heating, Ventilating, Air Conditioning, Process Piping, Plumbing, Sheet-metal & Fire Protection Systems Contractors
N.A.I.C.S.: 238220
Kevin G. Reilly *(Chm)*

Subsidiaries:

JWD Group Inc. - Danforth Albany Facility (1)
6 Fairchild Sq, Clifton Park, NY 12065
Tel.: (518) 406-5696
Plumbing, Heating & Air-Conditioning Installation Services
N.A.I.C.S.: 238220

JWD Group Inc. - Danforth Rochester Facility (1)
930 Old Dutch Rd, Victor, NY 14564
Tel.: (585) 924-7030
Plumbing, Heating & Air-Conditioning Installation Services
N.A.I.C.S.: 238220

John W. Danforth Service Co. (1)
300 Colvin Woods Pkwy, Tonawanda, NY 14150-6908
Tel.: (716) 832-1940
Web Site: http://www.jwdanforth.com
Sales Range: $10-24.9 Million
Emp.: 45
Plumbing, Heating, Air-Conditioning
N.A.I.C.S.: 238220
Kevin Reilly *(Chm)*
Robert Beck *(Pres & CEO)*
Steven DiRaimo *(VP-Bus Dev & Acq)*
Patrick McParlane *(Exec VP)*
Nickolas Optis *(Exec VP)*
Jason Rudich *(VP-Estimating)*
Tom Shannon *(VP-Albany Ops)*
Brian Tubin *(CFO & VP)*
Gerard Wilson *(VP-Client Solutions)*
Raymond Rudolph *(Exec VP)*

Subsidiary (Domestic):

Tougher Industries Enterprises, LLC (2)
47 Broadway, Albany, NY 12204
Tel.: (518) 465-3426
Web Site: http://www.tougher.net
HVAC Contractors
N.A.I.C.S.: 238220

JWIN ELECTRONICS CORP.

2 Harbor Park Dr, Port Washington, NY 11050
Tel.: (516) 626-7188
Web Site: http://www.jwin.com
Sales Range: $125-149.9 Million
Emp.: 100
Television Receiving Sets
N.A.I.C.S.: 334310
Julia Lee *(Supvr-HR)*
Peter Ma *(Coord-HR)*
Jose Penaflor *(Asst Mgr-Warehouse)*

JWK INTERNATIONAL CORP.

7617 Little River Tpke Ste 1000, Annandale, VA 22003-2618
Tel.: (703) 750-0500   VA
Year Founded: 1973
Sales Range: $100-124.9 Million

Emp.: 150
Provider of Systems Integration, Research & Development & Professional Services
N.A.I.C.S.: 541330
Jay W. Khim *(Chm & CEO)*

JWM MANAGEMENT, INC.

1229 S Tamiami Trl, Sarasota, FL 34239
Tel.: (941) 342-1754
Web Site: http://www.jwmmanagement.com
Year Founded: 1989
Sales Range: $25-49.9 Million
Emp.: 10
Real Estate Development & Management
N.A.I.C.S.: 237210
Gavin Meshad *(VP)*

JWM PRODUCTIONS, LLC

6930 Carroll Ave Ste 600, Takoma Park, MD 20912
Tel.: (301) 891-1769
Web Site: http://www.jwmprods.com
Year Founded: 1996
Sales Range: $1-9.9 Million
Emp.: 5
Television Production Services
N.A.I.C.S.: 512110
Jason Williams *(Co-Founder & Pres)*
Bill Morgan *(Co-Founder & Mng Dir)*

JWSIEG WINES

1180 Seminole Trl Ste 290, Charlottesville, VA 22901-5713
Tel.: (434) 244-5300
Web Site: http://www.jwsiegwines.com
Rev.: $18,100,000
Emp.: 50
Wine Distr
N.A.I.C.S.: 424820
Smith Williams *(Pres)*
Ashley Sieg Williams *(VP & Dir-Mktg & PR)*
Don Carlstrom *(Mgr-Sls-Greater Richmond)*
Geoff Hoffman *(Mgr-Chain Store Sls)*

JX ENTERPRISES INC.

820 Silvernail Rd Ste A, Pewaukee, WI 53072
Tel.: (262) 547-0001
Web Site: http://www.jxe.com
Year Founded: 1970
Rev.: $86,200,000
Emp.: 100
Commercial Trucks Dealer
N.A.I.C.S.: 423110
Eric Jorgensen *(Pres & CEO)*
Rick Smith *(Mgr-Corp Outreach)*
Marty Kleker *(VP-Sls, Lease & Rental)*

Subsidiaries:

JX Graphics (1)
4205 Anderson Rd Deforest, Madison, WI 53532
Tel.: (866) 593-9873
Emp.: 30
Painting Services
N.A.I.C.S.: 811121

JX PacLease (1)
4705 Rib Mountain Dr, Wausau, WI 54401
Tel.: (715) 359-4216
Truck Rental & Leasing Services
N.A.I.C.S.: 532120

Peterbilt Northern Illinois (1)
42400 Old Hwy 41, Wadsworth, IL 60083
Tel.: (847) 395-7222
Sales Range: $25-49.9 Million
Emp.: 50
Trucks, Tractors & Trailers: New & Used
N.A.I.C.S.: 441110
Kurt Jorgensen *(Pres & CEO)*

Peterbilt of Wisconsin Inc (1)
820 Silvernail Rd Ste A, Pewaukee, WI 53072
Tel.: (262) 547-0001
Web Site: http://www.jxe.com
Emp.: 60
Commercial Truck Dealer
N.A.I.C.S.: 423110
Erik Jorgensen *(Pres & CEO)*

JZZ TECHNOLOGIES, INC.

17 Sunny Line Dr Calverton, New York, NY 11933
Web Site: http://www.jzztech.com
Software Development Services
N.A.I.C.S.: 541511
Charles Cardona *(Pres & CEO)*
Deirdrea Renwick *(CFO)*

Jzz Technologies, Inc.—(Continued)